"Honoring Tomorrow's Leaders Today®"

WHO'S WHO
AMONG AMERICAN
HIGH SCHOOL STUDENTS

1974-1975

NINTH ANNUAL EDITION

VOLUME II

"*Who's Who Among American High School Students* is a publication of Educational Communications Inc. of Northfield, Illinois and has no connection with *Who's Who In America* and its publisher, Marquis—Who's Who, Inc." Students featured in this volume attended school in the following states: Illinois, Indiana, Iowa, Kansas, Michigan, Minnesota, Missouri, Nebraska, North Dakota, South Dakota and Wisconsin.

Northbrook, Illinois 60062
Printed in U.S.A.
ISBN 0-915130-01-7
Library of Congress Catalog Card Number 68-43796

TABLE OF CONTENTS

Paul C. Krouse, *Publisher*

FOREWORD

We wish to take this opportunity to congratulate the 240,000 students being recognized this year by WHO'S WHO AMONG AMERICAN HIGH SCHOOL STUDENTS, 1974-75. The students featured in this year's four-volume series represent approximately 4% of our nation's 6,000,000 junior and senior class high school students. The achievements and accomplishments of this group are a tribute to their own skills and desires as well as a reflection of the dedication and abilities of their parents and teachers.

At this time we would like to clarify the purpose and objectives of our program. WHO'S WHO was first published in 1967 in order to provide national recognition for the positive achievements of junior and senior class high school students throughout the country. Like other award programs at the adult as well as student levels, it is our intention to stimulate positive achievement and then to recognize and honor those who have attained uncommon levels of such achievement.

We believe the need for this program is due to the fact that not enough recognition is afforded to students who are committed to positive achievement in academics, athletics, extra-curricular activities and community service. Almost by definition, "good news" is rarely considered "newsworthy". WHO'S WHO AMONG AMERICAN HIGH SCHOOL STUDENTS attempts to bridge this gap by promoting the good news about good students.

It has been our happy experience since this program was first introduced to learn that there are literally hundreds of thousands of students attending our nation's 24,000 public, private and parochial high schools who are indeed involved in positive programs, committed to unusual levels of excellence and capable enough to achieve uncommon levels of performance. Many of these students reach their goals through natural abilities, others because of exceptional guidance and instruction and some through extraordinary dedication, devotion and drive. However they do it, they do it. With very few exceptions, the general public is not aware of these students or their accomplishments. We are hopeful that through the distribution of this book to libraries, colleges, etc., a greater awareness of these students and their accomplishments will be realized.

In conclusion, we wish to offer our thanks and gratitude to the many thousands of high school principals, guidance counselors, youth program sponsors, educational association administrators and scholarship agencies whose cooperation has made WHO'S WHO AMONG AMERICAN HIGH SCHOOL STUDENTS the largest publication in the field of student recognition programs.

Paul C. Krouse, *Publisher*

MESSAGE FROM THE PRESIDENT OF THE UNITED STATES

The letter reproduced on this page was sent by the President of the United States to graduating high school classes throughout the United States.

THE WHITE HOUSE

WASHINGTON

TO THE 1975 HIGH SCHOOL GRADUATES:

As high school graduates, you are passing an important milestone. You are about to enter into a society that is filled with challenge and opportunity. What you do with your lives from this point forward will determine not only your personal self-fulfillment, but the general well-being of our nation.

You carry with you the hopes of those who know and trust you. The future of America depends on your generation. You can make of America whatever you want. The opportunities before you are as great as the challenges.

Education is the greatest key to a better life. But to open the door of opportunity you need faith in yourselves, pride in what you have accomplished, and the idealism to persevere. If you add to this the awareness that learning never ceases, you will indeed bring to your lives the kind of meaning and satisfaction you seek.

I wish you every success on the road ahead.

Gerald R. Ford

MESSAGES FROM THE BOARD OF CONTRIBUTING EDITORS

THE HONORABLE
RICHARD B. HATCHER
Mayor
City of Gary, Indiana

R. G. HATCHER

In the Fifties classifiers dubbed students *"The Silent Generation."* In the Sixties it was *"The Violent Generation."* Now, in the mid-Seventies phrase-makers are looking at today's students and scratching their heads in perplexity. Those of you who have been listed in this volume are fortunate. Since the nation hasn't yet decided who you are, you can decide who you are going to be and what you are going to say and do.

By appearing in *Who's Who Among American High School Students* you have already given an indication of just who and what you are. You have shown that you have the ability to accomplish a task, that you take your responsibilities seriously and that you have the potential to become truly productive citizens. You rose to the challenge of your studies and you met that challenge successfully.

In today's turbulent world, we need, perhaps more than ever before, young men and women who welcome challenge at whatever level they confront it. We need citizens who are prepared to accept society's monumental problems and deal with them before they overwhelm us. The people who will be dealing with these problems are the people who are today preparing themselves for the future—you.

You who have been cited for excellence in this volume have shown that you are preparing yourselves to join the committed. You have shown, by your actions and accomplishments, that you are preparing to come to grips with the world.

This nation needs your critical abilities, your skills and your dedication, commitment and participation. We need you living in our communities, pressing for change, working in our unions and businesses and teaching in our schools. Without your help the struggle to achieve a new, more just and equitable society will go on; but, it will be harder and longer and the resolution more uncertain.

Generations of youth to come will be watching. And you know better than anyone else how critical and perceptive youth can be. How in years to come will you be judged? Will you succumb to indifference? Will you lose the vitality and commitment you now possess?

Inclusion in this volume signifies the beginning of the accomplishments and challenges that lay ahead of you. To successfully meet the challenge of the future you must greatly expand your knowledge and widen the scope of your experience. In so doing, you will better prepare yourselves for the day when tomorrow's youth will sit in judgement on your deeds.

THE HONORABLE
FRANK E. MOSS
Member of the United States Senate from Utah

FRANK MOSS

You are being honored for your accomplishments in scholarship, community service, and athletic competition. I am delighted to join in that recognition and to congratulate you.

I wish my message to you were a simple and optimistic one, that I could assure you a future of unlimited opportunities and satisfactions. Unfortunately, as you are aware from your studies and community activities, the country and the world are deeply troubled. We have just experienced a political upheaval without parallel in our two-hundred year history. The nation's pre-eminent wealth and power are no longer as secure. Economic opportunities for our citizens have been shrinking rather than growing. Other, particularly poorer, countries face worse prospects. Their populations are outstripping their food supplies; food production is dependent on energy; and energy costs are threatening to cripple their economies.

I do not believe that our difficulties are insurmountable. It must be a cooperative effort, however, not merely an attempt to preserve and enhance our own advantages. None of us, individual or country, has exclusive control of our fate. Your concern and desire to learn to excell are precisely the qualities we need to help solve our problems. I am confident that you will make an indispensible contribution.

MARJORIE S. CRAIG
Secretary
The American Association of Gifted Children, Inc.

M. L. CRAIG

The exciting accomplishments of the outstanding high school students cited in this book illustrate the tremendous potential of young people today. Their leadership capabilities are already in evidence. Everywhere, we see fine young people rising to the challenges inherent in all worthwhile fields of human endeavor and helping to thrust the world ahead. Since our knowledge has increased so rapidly, the opportunities for a satisfying and significant life were never greater than they are now.

Each individual decides the ingredients which will make for him the most successful and worthwhile life. He determines his particular goals and the path by which they will be reached. He is helped by taking advantage of the knowledge, experience and wisdom of his predecessors and of his family, friends and teachers. His ambitions and purposes are enhanced if he pursues the kind of bouyant good health which creates energy, drive, enthusiasm and perseverance, which assures the mental and emotional well-being required to cope with the tensions and stresses of a dynamic society, and which includes the spiritual substances needed for self-confidence, strong character and maturity.

The gifted, creative and talented individual has a special obligation to discover, evaluate and develop his particular abilities. As a contributing member of the human race, he is concerned with ascertaining ways of advancing the quality of life for everyman. He recognizes the interdependence of all persons and the variety of roles required as practitioners, facilitators or leaders. Respect for the dignity of the individual, courtesy, propriety, reason, civility, integrity—all have their place. Freedom to determine one's way of life embodies responsibility toward others.

The joy of living is most nearly reached by doing one's best in work that has significance, following sound personal and health values and cultivating warm and happy human relationships. Then, some vestige of one's voyage will remain forever.

DR. CECILY CANNAN SELBY
National Executive Director
Girl Scouts of the U.S.A.

C. C. SELBY

My warmest congratulations to all of you who are being cited for recognition in WHO'S WHO AMONG AMERICAN HIGH SCHOOL STUDENTS, 1974–75. Already you have demonstrated your potential for leadership by the contributions you have made to your respective schools and communities.

All of us who take pride with you in your achievements are aware of the day-by-day choices you have had to make in order to reach this coveted goal.

Life's greatest privilege is this ability to make choices. You who are being recognized know this, since, obviously, your choice has been to try to live up to your highest potential. In Girl Scouts, we say, "On my honor, I will try . . ."

To increase human potential, there is need for a higher expectation of self, a higher expectation for success, for achievement. It is my belief that only from this sense of potential can come hopeful, informed and intelligent choice. It has been said that the purpose of education is to help young people deal with moral issues or values. Education, then, is a preparation for decision-making. It takes "educated" values to make educated choices.

One of the products of choice which derives from a higher expectation of one's potential is the luxury of adopting and following an ethical code. If one does not have choice in one's actions or one's way of life, why need ethical guidelines? A human being without choice has only one law to follow—the law of others. A human being with choice participates with others and makes decisions based upon the system of values he develops in his youth, enriching and expanding them each year thereafter. Thus he gains the freedom to learn, rather than the constrainment to be taught.

As life increases the number of things between which we must choose, it also increases the need for the capacity to deal with choice. We need to develop not only the skill and background to deal with choice intelligently but also the ethical and spiritual framework within which to test and direct the choice.

PETER MacDONALD
Chairman
Navajo Tribal Council

PETER MacDONALD

One of the most sought for and yet an ever elusive element in our lives today is meaning. In our technological age where everything undergoes sudden changes, we often find ourselves wondering where we are and even what we are.

We live in a fast paced society where fashion changes, where values constantly undergoes transformation, we wonder whether we are coming or going.

We live in an age where social, political and economic institutions are in constant upheavals that we wonder if anything is for real.

So we look for security in keeping up with the fashion of the times and we look for happiness by trying to be accepted within our groups. We search for meanings in the best sellers list, in popular movies or in the arts.

In short we look for meanings to our lives beyond ourselves, in material things and through certain artificial mode of behavior. I declare that we are looking in the wrong place and I suggest that we look to ourselves for the meaning that has been eluding us.

Our environment changes, our mode of living changes, our beliefs and values are never the same; yet our basic need remains unchanged from generation to generation. Nor do these basic needs differ from person to person or is affected by economic or social status. This need is that of finding meaning to our lives. We are thinking beings, one who reasons and plans, we strive constantly for a new status or a new station.

We are never satisfied with the present nor with what we have. We thrive on challenge and difficulties.

Problems challenge our minds and our physical resources. What we don't have we create, making us creative and innovative.

Sadness and sufferings make us appreciative and we have respect for things we cannot control.

Our ideals gives us the inspirations and the motivation to perfect what is imperfect within ourselves and within our surroundings.

Our sense of justice gives us the courage and the determination to strive for that which is good and right in our society.

Our concept of a Supreme Being enables us to visualize and makes us understand the larger purpose of life, which is humanity and its purpose.

These are the instrinsic values of life that do not change with the time and each of us have to experience them in our life. And these are the values that give us meaning and purpose in life so we can have the will and the motivation to accept life, its problems and its rewards with understanding and tolerance.

It is not necessary that one must be knowledgeable in most literary work to understand life, but it is necessary that one must accept and appreciate the good, the bad and the ugly of life in order to find meaning in life.

Wealth and learning are the means to an end, but understanding, appreciation and respect are the end in themselves.

It is not so much that we do what is right as it is to know what it is that we are doing.

It is not how much control or influence we have over others as it is that we learn how to control ourselves.

It is much easier to manipulate things or others as it is much more difficult to overcome our prejudice, our enviness, our fears and our selfish motives.

Before we attack the problems of the world, we must first address the problems that exist within ourselves.

Thank you.

MARLO THOMAS
Entertainer, Actress, Businesswoman

MARLO THOMAS

There's an exhilarating feeling of change, a very positive kind of change, emanating from high schools today. It used to be that students were urged to exhibit school spirit. The greater the cheering and clapping, the more exemplary the student's behavior.

There were impenetrable lines separating boys sports from girls sports and boys courses from girls courses. While these stereotypes are still around, they are not longer flourishing. And this is to your credit. You have decided it was time for a change.

School spirit is still important, yet students now understand that individual spirit must come first. You have stopped to examine your own tastes and you've discovered that it's fun for a boy to take a course in cooking and it's invigorating for a girl to train with a team. In doing so, you—the boys and the girls—became the men and the women.

Now that high school is over, you must continue, not to struggle, but to be. The Class of '75 has excelled like no other class before it in ignoring boundaries and leaping beyond conventional limitations.

Your name appears in this volume because you tried. I'm sure there have been times when *each* of you fell short of a goal, but *all* of you possess that uncanny ability to bounce back, higher and stronger than before.

You are to be congratulated for not allowing yourself to stumble into ruts, even though ruts are secure and comfortable. YOU worked a little harder than required, YOU gave a little more of yourself than necessary. You are not "just" richer for your efforts, you are freer for them. You've freed yourself to be anything—to be everything—you want to be.

Now that you have graduated high school with an honor so rare as being invited into *WHO'S WHO,* take a quick look behind you. The years were good, but you've outgrown the corridors themselves. Stretch your muscles and your mind and your spirit, take that first step in *any* new direction and know how unlimited your possibilities really are.

THE HONORABLE
RICHARD G. LUGAR
Mayor
City of Indianapolis, Indiana

LUGAR

This Bicentennial year should challenge each of you as exceptional students and leaders to consider the remarkable opportunities provided by a Constitution that protects our freedoms rather than restricts them.

Unfortunately, life in this Country has often become a jumble of practices which have cast aside much competition, many market places, even basic equality of opportunity while suggesting that results based on race, ethnic origin, sex, and any other chosen characteristics should be imposed by government. Equality of opportunity should mean just that—an equal opportunity to work for a living, to work for a good education, to compete against others in an open system of competition for results. Equality of results means fixing the ball game, eliminating the competition handicapping all the citizen players, and dictating the results on the basis of enthusiasm of the moment with the judges being non-elective officials insulated from the votes of citizens in a democracy. Under the guise of taking politics out of government, our opposition has installed a non-elected "faceless bureaucracy." Government has become increasingly invisible, and attacks upon the strangling web of regulation and force which imposes "goodness" leads to frustration in trying to find invisible tyranny and to ridicule of the critic. The citizen critic is accused of lacking sophistication, compassion, and enthusiasm for equality, of somehow being allied with evil intent even as he or she fights for a modest restoration of personal freedom without harm to the freedom of any other citizen.

For these reasons, I urge each of you to become an advocate of freedom as you creatively share your view on how freedom can best be restored to the American citizen.

DR. DAVID PIERPONT GARDNER
President
University of Utah

DAVID GARDNER

In the old Thomas building on the University of Utah campus, the following quotation from Milton is inscribed in marble? *"What in me is dark, illumine, what is low, raise and support."* Thus expressed is education's essential purpose, starkly, beautifully simple, yet enduring and fixed as the marble in which it is inscribed. It is a motto, a means, an end, inclusive of a university's essence, tarnished in practice, but elevating in concept.

We hear much these days about a no-growth economy and zero growth in education, but there can be no moratorium on learning itself. Knowledge grows in the night while we sleep. We wake to find ourselves already behind. This is the anxiety, the deep inward drive I hope each of you feels as you move forward from the achievements recognized by this volume.

You are at the beginning now of life's adult journey. A first step from here lays down a direction, is an exertion of will, a commitment—to a future good or ill. A first step in the direction of a bad habit may be a long journey to a cure. On the other hand, a first step in the direction of a personal objective may be a long journey of satisfaction with rewards commensurate with the hard work.

Your achievements to this point have increased your options; and the essence of freedom is choice. The more options you have, the greater your freedom, the greater your implied opportunities, and, of course, the greater the risks.

Build well from here! The country will need your strengths, your clear sense of purpose and your willingness to be involved. Doors will open to you now according to your effort, commitment, and capability. Your journey will be not only a personal passage but a voyage of vital concern to us all.

MORTON TEMSKY
Chairman
Business Department
National Association of Management Educators

MORTON TEMSKY

Education for the 70's and 80's should be challenging and rewarding. For you, who are about to graduate high school, you will find that education is a continuing process and will not be a stop and go situation. Knowledge and the ability to put one's resources to work to better serve one's fellow man as well as to improve oneself to earn a livelihood are essential.

As an educator, I have one thought to have you think about—develop to your highest potential and capabilities. Make use of your abilities to be creative, solve problems, think in terms of people and human relations—communicate.

We need people of high ethical and moral standards who will overcome many of the social and economic ills that hinder progress. We need responsible leaders and outstanding people, like yourselves, to continue to create freedom and peace in the years to come.

WALLY WIKOFF
Executive Director
National Scholastic Press Association

WALLY WIKOFF

How important is a record of outstanding achievement in high school? Many of us who have interviewed more than our share of graduates in their first real effort to face a competitive world are impressed by such academic achievements.

And yet—this is important—it is not the whole picture. Scholastic leadership is not enough. A true leader is one who does it so subtly that one can scarcely identify the leader. That calls for a quality even greater than a straight A average. It calls for sensitivity to the ideas of your fellow man, a willingness to admit that you don't have all the answers, a respect for those who disagree with your point of view. Employers—the world for that matter—are looking for the WHOLE person. Such a person who is attuned to those around him not only has the makings of a true leader but has a moral obligation to himself and to society to become one. Look through the names in this book. Many of them will be such leaders in years to come.

REED J. IRVINE
Chairman of the Board
Accuracy in Media, Inc.

REED J. IRVINE

Probably the greatest difference between my generation and yours is that television has been an important factor in your education since your infancy. Some think that the tube is second only to parents in the strength of its influence on young people.

This has had its good effects and its bad effects. Today a young American sees more of the world by the time he finishes high school—via television—than the people of earlier generations saw in a lifetime. But the bad aspect of this is that most of what you see via television is selected, edited and arranged by a relatively limited number of people. What you see is not necessarily the whole story. It may not even be an accurate representation of part of the story.

For example, a few years ago one of our great television networks showed a touching scene of a mother polar bear being killed from an airplane by ruthless hunters who were violating the law. At least that is what the audience thought they saw. But it was not what actually happened. The mother bear was actually shot with a tranquilizer by the authorities so they could tag her. The tear-jerking scene had been created by misleading editing and dishonest narration.

Before television, we used to say that seeing was believing. Now an important part of the education of any young person should be to learn that what we see is not always to be believed. During the Vietnam War, one of the turning points was what was called the Tet Offensive by the Viet Cong. Militarily it was a great defeat for the Communists. Their all-out effort failed to attain its objectives, and they were badly crippled by the heavy casualties they suffered. But the news media, especially television, gave the viewer the opposite impression. The Tet Offensive was widely interpreted as an American defeat. Some think that this was a factor in President Lyndon Johnson's decision not to run for another term.

Months later, a senior producer for one of the television networks was approached by one of his employees who was concerned about the fact that a false image of the Tet Offensive had been conveyed to the public. It had become clear that the Communists had suffered a serious defeat, and the producer was asked if something should not be done to correct the widespread impression on the part of the public that it was the Americans who had been defeated. The producer thought a bit, and then uttered a classic judgment. Nothing should be done, he said. The public thought Tet had been a defeat, therefore it was a defeat.

This was the first battle in which America was defeated by its own television.

The great educational influence of television on your lives must be matched by education in the art of questioning, investigating and exposing error and misrepresentation in the mass media.

DR. S. NORMAN FEINGOLD
National Director
B'nai B'rith Career & Counseling Services

DR. FEINGOLD

In spite of the recession and high unemployment rate, particularly for minority youth, I remain an optimist by conviction and temperament. My recent tenure as President of the American Personnel and Guidance Association reinforced my conviction that youth is the most precious resource of any country. Ninety percent of the people 30 years and younger in the United States who are alive today will be here in the year 2,000. Youth of today will meet the challenges and changes of a technological society in new people-centered adaptations.

The number of people employed in manufacturing has not changed appreciably in the last decade. From now to the year 2,000, increasingly greater numbers of people must be employed in human services. Young people can visualize the pressing needs for human services in a new world of work. It is the young people who will help to see that new, creative and meaningful careers are available.

Some projected people-needs are:

- At least one million more people could be effectively employed in nursing homes. At present, few if any psychologists, counselors, or social workers are employed in such homes. My recommendation is to train a human services generalist who combines the talents and skills of psychologist, counselor and social worker.
- One million additional workers will be needed in each of the following areas: recreation centers, day care centers, apartments and hotels for the aging and handicapped, retirement villages, educational parks and leisure technology.
- Two million additional mental health technicians will be needed to help individuals cope with the increasing stress that results from rapid technological changes.
- Half a million more workers trained in human services with specialized health knowledge and skills will be needed in health spas.
- Approximately one thousand futuristic counselors and one hundred fifty thousand technological displacement counselors will be needed in a wide variety of work settings.

Four other areas where needs and opportunities are projected are:

- Ocean farming will be in greater demand as the scarcity of land food becomes more apparent. One hundred thousand workers can be employed in the search for and utilization of new sources of food.
- Inadequate housing and transportation are two of the greatest deterrents to employment of the physically disabled, the aging, and the poor. We need to train people to understand their needs and design and build suitable housing and transportation.
- We need more readable signs on our roads. There is no uniform code for traffic signs among our fifty states. Many accidents can be traced to poorly posted directions. Thousands and thousands of workers could be employed to improve highway communication.
- Five hundred thousand conservation technicians need to be trained in specialized ecological services.

The number of women in the work force probably will continue to rise. The percentage of women in professional, managerial, supervisory and executive positions will increase substantially by the year 2,000 and will not have peaked.

There are many other projections of the need for human service workers by the year 2,000. Obviously, it will be extremely difficult to meet these needs, professionally and financially. I fully recognize the hard, bottomline economic implications of these projections. Nevertheless, I believe this is the direction that we must take if society is to survive with dignity and respect for each person.

Only if we can perceive the future that we want, will we eventually be able to live it. My prediction is that we will ultimately make these changes in the world of work and the world of leisure. Only in this way can our society truly tap the tremendous potential of all people to make this world of ours a better place in which to live.

It is the youth of today who are the leaders of tomorrow. I have great hopes for our future because it is in the hands of youth who are our greatest potential and resource. Our futures can be bright ones.

Let these new careers, more than ever before, be people-oriented. Young people are creative, flexible, and adaptable to a new world. They can help change peoples' images and concepts of themselves throughout the changing world of work by stressing the approach, "I am I" and "I like me."

FRANK STANTON
Chairman
The American National Red Cross

FRANK STANTON

Most outstanding young people want to make their lives significant. Frequently this desire is translated into seeking the coveted rewards of success. In our society success is often measured in terms of material acquisitions. I am sure you realize that in tomorrow's world more significant challenges exist. Essential human needs and aspirations demand our urgent attention. I hope you will accept your share of the responsibility to make tomorrow's world a better place to live.

The 200th Anniversary of this nation occurs in 1976. We have survived and strengthened our society because of the willingness of our citizens to work together for the benefit of all. The Spirit of 1776 has been the foundation for achievement in the past; it must be maintained in the future.

You are on your way, you who have been honored through inclusion in *Who's Who Among American High School Students*. I salute you for the achievements that have brought about your selection. I look forward to your accomplishments in the years ahead. During your lives you will have the chance to respond to the needs of others, to give voluntarily of your talents and your skills. The voluntary service that you will give will be among your most cherished satisfactions. I would be pleased if you chose to give a measure of that service through the Red Cross. But, whatever avenue you select, the tangible expression of your humanitarian concern for others will be the hallmark of tomorrow's citizen leadership.

MICHAEL McCLOSKEY
Executive Director
Sierra Club

MICHAEL McCLOSKEY

Someone once is reputed to have sneered, "Why should I worry about posterity? What has it ever done for me?" Well *you* are posterity. You are to be the beneficiaries of all the intense work over the past five years for a better environment. "Saving the environment for posterity" should have special meaning for today's high school graduates. Many environmental improvement programs should be reaching their full potential in a decade from now as your lives and careers reach their full potential.

This nation has just experienced one of its great eras of environmental reform. Sweeping programs have been launched to clean up our waters by 1983, to bring back clean air by the end of this decade, to control noise, regulate pesticides and radiation, to prevent dumping of hazardous wastes in the ocean, to protect scenic coastlines and wetlands, and to defend species of animals and plants which are endangered. The nation has established a national policy to protect the environment and has brought a whole series of new agencies into existence to administer its environmental laws.

Is everything taken care of then? Can you sit back and wait to enjoy a better environment? By no means. More reform programs remain to be enacted—measures await enactment in 1975 to regulate toxic substances, to curb the abuse of strip mining, and to enforce energy conservation. Moreover, polluters and all-out developers are still working to undermine and repeal many of the basic environmental laws—all under the guise of relaxing restrictions and clean-up schedules, just a little. But the greatest enemy of progress is apathy. Further progress will only come if each generation keeps demanding it. You can't assume a better environment is your birthright—you can't take it for granted.

If you really want a clean and attractive environment, you have to get involved. You have to learn the issues—join an ecology club or environmental organization. Write your legislators and public officials. Tell them there is still too much pollution, too little open space, too much congestion. If they don't hear from you consistently, public officials and agencies have a way of becoming lax. They do hear from the other side. If they only hear from those who want to slow down environmental programs, they will start to go slower and slower with their programs. Environmental reform programs can come to a standstill if the public does not keep prodding those who run them.

Thus, if you want a better environment, you will have to earn it. The legal apparatus to produce it is there, but it will take your interest to keep it running. If you do, some day posterity may thank you, too.

DR. ARJAY MILLER
Dean
Stanford University
Graduate School of Business

ARJAY MILLER

In the years to come America and the world will require a quality of leadership surpassing anything we have ever known. The problems facing us are enormous; the difficulties involved in solving them are legion.

However, a crisis, as the Ancient Chinese defined it, is a "dangerous opportunity". The challenge of building a better world awaits those who are willing to prepare themselves and work diligently for its realization. Here at the Stanford Graduate School of Business we teach our students how to manage effectively in a constantly changing world, in both the public and private sectors. The acceleration of change will continue to increase over the years ahead.

Those of you who have achieved the honor which is noted in this volume are among those who will have the opportunity to lead future generations to fulfillment. You have an exciting time ahead of you, and I cannot but envy your position.

PAUL DE FRANCIS
National Director
Performing and Visual
Arts Society

PAUL DEFRANCIS

This message is for two types of students, the academic and the arts oriented.

For those of you who will pursue a career in math, science, psychology, business or some other "non-art" career you might consider broadening your horizons by developing your knowledge and appreciation for the arts such as music, jazz, literature, dance, theatre, design of everyday commodities and buildings, and art. There are too many people in the world who don't *hear* and *see* as much as they might because of narrow education, town facilities, peer value systems, or whatever. You will be a more interesting person and you will live a fuller, richer life if you would patronize art museums, hear good jazz and classics, attend the theatre, and perhaps even getting personally involved in one of the arts activities. Don't limit your non-working hours to "beer and T.V."; instead, treat your soul to man's greatest creations and give an occasional feast to your eyes and ears.

On the other hand, if you are headed for a career in the arts you should be thinking in terms of widening your academic knowledge and developing a respect for physical activities and skills. I see too many youngsters concentrating on their artistic skills while neglecting the areas of liberal arts and physical fitness. A knowledgeable and active artist makes for a richer, longer life and a more interesting person.

In summary, a fully educated person possesses saleable skills, sufficient awareness of the world's problems, and the ability to live a rich and full life by participating in a wide variety of leisure activities.

CLARENCE M. KELLEY
Director
Federal Bureau of Investigation

CLARENCE M. KELLY

"No man is free who cannot command himself."
Pythagoras 582–500 B.C.

It will not be possible to determine in my lifetime whether or not the education you have received thus far has implanted in you the concept of self-denial—that self-discipline which enables a man to "command himself." But, in years to come, the condition of this Nation will afford proof of the scope of education you have received. For you will be leaders, and your self-discipline—or lack of it—will be reflected in the future of the Republic whose two hundred years of existence we are so soon to celebrate.

This is an affluent Nation, and it is not easy to develop self-discipline when material things are readily available and when, in almost all areas of life, great emphasis is placed on material aggrandizement. Earlier generations—those indomitable colonists who believed themselves capable of self-government—were not troubled by overabundance. Their very survival required the strictest of self-discipline. And—according to the recorded observations of a French observer—they also subjected themselves to the disciplines inherent in the Christian religion. Alexis de Tocqueville expressed his total certainty that the Americans held religion "to be indispensable to the maintenance of republican institutions. This opinion is not peculiar to a class or citizens or to a party, but it belongs to the whole nation and to every rank of society." Their religion and their liberty, Tocqueville felt, were so combined in their minds that Americans could not conceive of one without the other.

But great changes have taken place since Tocqueville found an America in which religion, by universal consent, was a paramount, if indirect, ruling force. Then every principle of the moral world was fixed and determined. The political world was left to the debates and experiments of men—but the morality stemming from religion was the standard against which all debates and experiments were tested. Today, that standard is not as solidly fixed as it once was, and, in every area of life, egocentrics are practicing, endorsing, and promoting—particularly among young people—a variety of doctrines which add up to one thing—self-indulgence.

I believe that self-government can exist in any nation only as long as the citizens are self-disciplined. In my opinion, the challenge before you young leaders of the future is a simple one of choice: self-discipline—and the continuation of self-rule; or self-indulgence—and, ultimately, the death of individual freedom.

CLARENCE C. BARKSDALE
President
First National Bank in St. Louis

C. C. BARKSDALE

As our nation approaches its bicentennial, perhaps this is the time for all of us—young and old alike—to reaffirm our belief in the American System. Our nation was founded on the ideal that each of us is created as an equal and given the opportunity to reach our own level of achievement.

Your selection for *"Who's Who Among American High School Students"* evidences great belief in your achievements at this early period of your life and your potential. Hopefully, each of you will use this as a stepping stone to help make the future of America truly great.

Regardless of the field that interests you—whether it is in business, education, a profession or as a housewife—you have a contribution to make to your country and the significance of your contribution is the real challenge ahead for each of you. I feel that America's future is in good hands—the firm grasp of its youth.

DR. CYRIL O. HOULE
Professor of Education
University of Chicago

CYRIL O. HOULE

The young men and women honored in this book have all been chosen because they demonstrated leadership in one or more of their many activities. They can take pride in this accomplishment even as they may feel gratified by other less visible feelings of growth and achievement.

But what of the future? Will new honors and satisfactions come in the years ahead?

The blunt answer is that for some people they will and for others they will not. The difference between the fortunate and the unfortunate will be caused by many things. Among them are personal initiative, enough money and other resources to take advantage of opportunities, and just plain good luck. Among the most important causes, however, is one which is in the control of each person. Does he or she keep on learning: to be a better and broader person, to increase occupational skills, to know how to be an effective member of the community, and to be at peace with himself or herself ethically and religiously.

If the answer is "yes" rather than "no," there is a much greater chance that when new challenges must be met the person concerned will be able to cope with them. These challenges will continue throughout life, right to the very end. People are happy only if they feel that their lives are harmonious—within themselves, in their homes, at work and as citizens—and such harmony usually comes by making plans and carrying out programs of self improvement. At each stage of life we like to look back with satisfaction on what we have accomplished, even as the high school seniors mentioned in this book can view with pride all that they have achieved. They know that they prepared themselves to exert leadership and that the honor of inclusion in this book came as a result. So it will be throughout life. As someone once said, happy memories must be arranged for in advance.

WESLEY APKER
Executive Secretary
National Association of State Boards of Education

WESLEY APKER

Selection to appear in any reputable Who's Who publication is an event of distinction, an achievement of which you can be proud. It demonstrates that you possess both intellectual and leadership capabilities which are above the average. The test of your potential however, is yet to come. The test comes when you are confronted with choices, career choices, ethical choices, leadership choices, judgement choices, and so on.

We have seen too many examples of leaders who were not ethical, were not insightful or were not courageous. Too often judgemental errors have occurred because of intellectual softness and ethical expediency. Too many potential leaders fail to identify their core values and the limits beyond which they will not compromise. Effective leadership calls for a proper mix of wisdom and intellect, insight and courage, all firmly grounded on a thoughtfully conceived value system.

Your potential is great and I wish you well. But I also admonish you as a future leader not to remake the mistakes of the past. Should you do that you will have not only failed yourself but others as well.

THE HONORABLE
RICHARD F. KNEIP
Governor
State of South Dakota

RICHARD F. KNEIP

As I reflect upon your past accomplishments and the challenges all of you will be facing in the years to come, I am reminded of Janus, the Roman god of gates and beginnings represented with the two opposite faces.

You can look backward with a sense of pride, for you have been honored as scholars, leaders, musicians and athletes by those who have had the opportunity to observe your activities first hand, and in many instances to work directly with you on school and civic projects. But now you find yourselves on the threshold.

As you look toward the future, do you see yourselves basing all of your decisions and activities upon the successes of the past, daring not to involve yourselves in new projects or previously untraveled paths? Or do you see yourselves using those past achievements as a very personal reminder that you do possess the intelligence, ambition and creativity to attempt totally new projects whether they be in a chosen field of study, politics, religion or community affairs?

I sincerely hope that you will choose that second alternative. Utilize your past learning experiences as personal incentives to attempt and conquer new objectives. Then, when you are faced with a dilemma you can put yourselves in the position of Janus, with a firm knowledge of your past abilities and an optimistic view of your future capabilities.

SARA-ALYCE P. WRIGHT
Executive Director
National Board of the Young Women's Christian Association of the U.S.A.

SARA-ALYCE P. WRIGHT

Every period in history has special challenges, never quite the same as those of any previous time. Every generation of young people has unique opportunities to address or deny the challenges which face them.

Those who are graduating from high school now not only will be preparing for the future, but also will be moving into the future. I have been very impressed with the way in which today's students are dealing with this fact. Working with younger children, with their peers, with the aging, in community development projects, counseling efforts, educational activities, already they have an awareness of problems and issues which must be solved if truly there is to be "a new world comin' afterwhile."

Their intent is to work constructively to bring about needed change. Their concern is that democracy be made to work for all. Idealists! Realists! "Doers of the Word and not hearers only"! I am proud to salute them and join with them as they move into the future living, learning, doing, being.

DONALD J. HALL
President
Hallmark Cards

DONALD J. HALL

You will be told many times in the next few years that the hope of this nation rests with you. It has ever been thus. Each of us, at some point in our lives, has been charged with the responsibility of contributing to this nation's quality of life.

This responsibility is not an easy burden to bear at any age. Even recognized leaders, including young people such as yourselves, dwell laboriously on the question: "How can I make a difference?"

I can't answer that question with specifics, but I know that no one ever failed because he or she did the best job possible on any given task. You will derive great comfort and inner strength all your life if you can say to yourself at the end of each day: "I have done my best." But do not fall prey to comparing yourself with others; beyond a wholesome discipline, be kind to yourself as well as others. Your best is all you or anyone else can ask of your life, and if you meet this challenge with kindness, you will "make a difference."

CLIFF HUMPHREY

CLIFFORD C. HUMPHREY
Director
Ecology Action Educational Institute

I take this opportunity to make a special plea to all those watching your progress. I am asking them to give you enough room to grow. You can show us new insights into our problems and contribute to their solution.

While data and procedures are a necessary part of education, they remain only a part. Much more important to our welfare is the ability to analyze social situations and natural phenomena; to be able to choose or construct the proper devices to solve a problem if it needs solving, and then to apply a technique that will be successful. The erroneous defining of a problem is a special danger. We will never be able to teach someone how to solve a problem that has not been adequately observed.

As times and conditions change, the areas of our concern will have to be redefined, and the tools and techniques being utilized, as well as our goals, will have to be continually reevaluated. The full force of human imagination and creative power must come to our aid. Most valuable of all is the human resource of analytical skills, and creative response. It is individual effort that makes the difference between just another memorandum or experiment, and a major breakthrough.

It is obvious that societies the world over have been doing something wrong or we wouldn't be burdened with problems of hunger, fuel and resource shortages, dehumanized work, and overpopulation. Perhaps at this moment in human history, we are watching the development of a cultural consciousness that is future oriented. This we have never had before. The problems of managing such a cultural change to coincide with basic planetary conditions are not only monumental but also new to human experience. We do not know how to do this, only that it must be done. I do not mean to frighten people that are learning about the world we live in. But more is riding on your shoulders, and all of ours, than in past years. There is a transition to be made from doing to the environment what we believe to be beneficial to us, to doing what is beneficial to the environment. We must recognize that we are all part of the environment, and are dependent upon it.

I believe we should all try to bring this cultural transition into focus. It can be a time of academic challenge, scientific rigor, and human co-operation. It can be a time when many people are able to explore and realize their organizational and creative skills. Do not be afraid to walk out to the edge of our understanding and work there.

MAURICE B. MITCHELL

MAURICE B. MITCHELL
Chancellor
University of Denver

Contrary to opinions, so often expressed lately, that we have a sorry world to turn over to our young people, I believe we have an exciting and challenging world to offer them. This is particularly true for those represented in this book—the cream of America's schools—for no one can doubt that one day they will be in the forefront of our leadership.

Their natural curiosity has been stimulated and encouraged in asking "why" and (even more importantly) "why not?" They have learned to know and use the vast and ever more sophisticated resources of libraries and laboratories and yet are well aware that not all answers can come from there. They understand clearly that many answers will come from that marvelous resource, the human brain. Intellectually as well as physically, they have grown taller and stronger.

We live at that unhappy moment of our history when the beneficence of a surging technology has often disillusioned us with its side effects of an exploding population, contamination of earth, air and water and wasting of our natural resources. We have come to learn that the fate of the world rests not (as we may have hoped) with technology but with man, and through the humanities man learns to know himself.

These young people have diverse goals, individual values and personal visions of what they must find and do and be. In making their choices they can have no greater aides than the curiosity with which they are endowed and the discrimination they have learned.

Certainly today's world is rife with problems—and therein lies the challenge. The excitement lies in the search for answers.

LESTER G. BENZ

LESTER G. BENZ
Executive Secretary Emeritus
Quill & Scroll Society

It is an honor for a student to be selected for inclusion in *Who's Who Among American High School Students*. But any honor carries with it a certain measure of responsibility. Those who achieve recognition and success in their youth are looked to for leadership for tomorrow's world.

Today's high school graduate is tempted to assume a posture of pessimism. He or she may look to the future and think, "The World has short changed me. There is no future any more." Recent years of inflation, recession and economic uncertainty have contributed to this feeling of frustration. The future, indeed, too often seems to hold limited promise for today's youth.

But opportunity never comes to the defeatist. Opportunities are *made* by the spirited and the well prepared person. Never in the history of the World have there been more challenging opportunities for young people than exist today.

Regardless of economic conditions, there are always opportunities for the ambitious and well prepared man or woman who has the will and the determination to rise above adversity and take his place in a world that is crying for leadership. Unlimited opportunities lie on the horizon for today's youth.

So, as you look toward the future, plan with confidence and optimism. Limitless opportunities are there for men and women of ability who can muster the ambition and the initiative to take advantage of them. Tomorrow's positions of responsibility and leadership will be filled by today's youth with these qualities.

THE EDUCATIONAL COMMUNICATIONS SCHOLARSHIP FOUNDATION

During the 1974-75 academic year, approximately 3,000 students competed for scholarship awards sponsored by The Foundation by submitting their ACT or SAT examination scores. Semi-finalists were selected by performance on these tests. Each semi-finalist was then sent a Need-For-Financial-Aid Form and winners were selected based on performance, need and leadership qualifications.

Of the twenty-nine winners shown here twenty-one received grants of $1000.00 and eight received grants of $500.00. A total of $25,000.00 was awarded. Over $75,000.00 has been distributed through the foundation to date.

1974-75 SCHOLARSHIP WINNERS

Paul W. Baerman
New Hartford Senior High School
New Hartford, NY
University of Rochester
Rochester, NY

William M. Blazak
Irvington High School
Irvington, NJ
Seton Hall University
South Orange, NJ

Sheila K. Briss
Hatton Public High School
Hatton, ND
North Dakota State University
Fargo, ND

Eugenia B. Burrell
Xavier High School
Phoenix, AZ
University of Notre Dame
South Bend, IN

Anita Jo Fabian
Willoughby South High School
Willoughby, OH
Wittenberg University
Springfield, OH

Julie Ann Gorman
Trinity High School
River Forest, IL
Loyola University
Chicago, IL

Jeanne Haupert
Spalding High School
Granville, IA
Clarke College
Dubuque, IA

Sarah E. Hein
Sacred Heart
Salina, KS
University of Kansas
Lawrence, KS

Randall D. Hinrichs
Riceville Community High School
Riceville, IA
Massachusetts Institute of Technology
Cambridge, MA

Warren E. Hughes
Bishop Eustace Preparatory School
Pennsauken, NJ
University of Notre Dame/Engineering
South Bend, IN

Constance Ann Jennings
Washburn High School
Minneapolis, MN
Bob Jones University
Greenville, SC

Randall H. Kikukawa
Roosevelt High School
Honolulu, HI
Harvard
Cambridge, MA

Ann D. Kottwitz
Peabody High School
Peabody, KS
Kansas State University
Manhattan, KS

Sherry Maria Lane
Marian Catholic
Chicago Heights, IL
University of Illinois
Champaign-Urbana, IL

Ronald James Lardie
Raton High School
Raton, NM
United States Military Academy
West Point, NY

Robert Mauro
Ulysses S. Grant High School
Van Nuys, CA
Leland Stanford Jr. University
Stanford, CA

Sharon A. Miller
Riverside High School
Buffalo, NY
Columbia University/Engineering
New York, NY

Graceiela H. Miyares
Bennett High School
Buffalo, NY
State Univ. of New York at Buffalo
Buffalo, NY

Gerald L. Moody, Jr.
Brookstone School
Columbus, GA
Georgia Institute of Technology
Atlanta, GA

Timothy Morris
Rosemark Academy
Rosemark, TN
Christian Brothers College
Memphis, TN

Rodney Norder
Crescent-Iroquois Community High School
Crescent City, IL
Rose-Hulman Institute of Technology
Terre Haute, IN

Eve C. Pinsker
Mt. Lebanon High School
Pittsburgh, PA
University of Michigan
Ann Arbor, MI

Chad P. Premeau
Medford Senior High School
Medford, WI
Lawrence University
Appletown, WI

Terry L. Rusk
Cedar Lake Academy
Cedar Lake, MI
Andrews University
Berrien Springs, MI

Robert C. Smoot
Hampshire High School
Romney, WV
West Virginia University
Morgantown, WV

Laura Susan Todd
Fern Creek High School
Fern Creek, KY
Eastern Kentucky University
Richmond, KY

Andrew A. Wiener
Highland Park High School
Dallas, TX
Duke University
Durham, NC

Sharon F. Witherspoon
Oak Ridge High School
Oak Ridge, TN
Bryn Mawr College
Bryn Mawr, PA

Paul Edward Zilk
Blackfoot High School
Blackfoot, ID
Harvard College
Cambridge, MA

SIXTH ANNUAL NATIONAL OPINION SURVEY

While many people presume to speak for youth, not very many have the opportunity to listen to what youth is saying. Educational Communications, Inc. is in a unique position. Since we communicate with over 240,000 high achieving students, each year, we can listen. And, given the opportunity, these students are eager to speak. ECI believes that the attitudes and opinions of these outstanding young adults are at least as important as their impressive achievements. Consequently, we have conducted this "Annual Survey of High Achievers" since 1970.

In order to assure universal relevancy of the questions, our sample questionnaire was sent to our 25 student advisory panel for comments, suggestions and changes. Once the final survey instrument was approved, it was sent to WHO'S WHO students for completion on an anonymous basis. The responses received from the students were then tabulated by computer with the results published in booklet form and distributed to key government officials, educators, research groups and the press.

Each year the project receives wide interest and favorable response from the audience exposed to its entirety. It has been publicized by virtually every major newspaper in the country, reported on radio and TV network news broadcasts and featured in prestigious news magazines and special interest journals. Most importantly, however, it is widely used by university and private sector research organizations in their varied and important studies.

It is important to note that the purpose of this annual survey is educational and ECI is not attempting to promote or negate any political, moral or social philosophy. Furthermore, we are not supported or subsidized by any political or social organizations, firms or individuals.

Following is a statistical breakdown of the 1975 Survey of High Achievers.

STATISTICAL DEMOGRAPHIC ANALYSIS OF STUDENTS SURVEYED

STUDENT REPRESENTATION BY AGE

16 years old	5%
17 years old	40%
18 years old	52%
19 years old	1%

STUDENT REPRESENTATION BY SEX

Male	42%
Female	57%

STUDENT REPRESENTATION BY RACE

Caucasion	90%
Black	7%
Other	3%

STUDENT REPRESENTATION BY RELIGION

Protestant	52%
Catholic	29%
Jewish	2%
Other	14%

STUDENT REPRESENTATION BY TYPE OF SCHOOL:

Parochial	9%
Private	15%
Public	74%

STUDENT REPRESENTATION BY CLASS YEAR

Junior	31%
Senior	68%

STUDENT REPRESENTATION BY GRADE POINT AVERAGE

A	69%
B	28%
C	2%

STUDENT REPRESENTATION BY FUTURE PLANS

Going to College	96%
Work, Trade School, Military, Etc.	39%

STUDENT REPRESENTATION BY SCHOLARSHIP AWARDS:

Receiving some form of scholarship	44%
No scholarships	53%

STUDENT REPRESENTATION BY REGION

Northeast	14%
Midwest	35%
South	23%
Southwest	12%
West	15%

STUDENT REPRESENTATION BY TYPE OF COMMUNITY

Urban	19%
Suburban	34%
Rural/Small Town	46%
No Answer	1%

STUDENT REPRESENTATION BY FAMILY INCOME

Under $6,000 (Per Year)	5%
$6,000 to $9,999 (Per Year)	13%
$10,000 to $15,000 (Per Year)	29%
Over $15,000 (Per Year)	47%
No Answer	6%

The first three questions on the questionnaire called for write-in answers and the results are shown in order of response only. All other questions are tabulated by total response, sex, race, religion, region of country, type of school and type of community. Only the total response will be shown here.

QUESTIONS AND ANSWERS

1. List three things your nation has done in the past four years of which you are particularly proud.
1. Ending Vietnam war.
2. Cleaning up corruption in government/handling of Watergate.
3. Space Program — Moon Landing — Apollo — Soyuz Sky Lab

2. What do you think the nation's top three priorities should be during the coming year?
1. Strengthen Economy/Stop Inflation.
2. New Energy Plan
3. Unemployment

3. a. List the three individuals whom you feel have made the greatest contribution to the *world* during your lifetime.
1. Kissinger
2. Kennedy, J. F.
3. Nixon

b. List the three individuals whom you feel have made the greatest contribution to the *nation* during your lifetime.
1. Kissinger
2. Kennedy
3. Nixon

4. Your political views are most clearly associated with which political party:

Democrat	37%
Independent	25%
Republican	24%
Other	6%

5. Politically, do you consider yourself:

Far Left	3%
Left of Center	24%
Center	41%
Right of Center	16%
Far Right	2%

6. Most of your elected officials are: (check all that apply)

Persons of honor and integrity	18%
Voting the will of their constituents	15%
Doing a good job representing the people	22%
Living up to the standards you expect from them	16%
Influenced to too large a degree by the wishes of major corporations and/or interest groups	55%
Interested only in being elected, not dealing firmly with the nation's problems	33%

7. a. Will you be 18 in time to vote in the 1976 elections?

Yes	95%
No	4%

b. If yes, do you plan to register and vote?

Yes	92%
No	3%

8. a. If you are a Democrat (or an Independent who leans toward one of the following Democrats) which *one* of the following declared or potential candidates would you support for the Democratic Presidential nomination?

Sen. Lloyd Bensten (Texas)	2%
Jimmy Carter (former Gov. Ga.)	1%
Fred Harris (former Sen. Okla.)	1%
Sen. Hubert Humphrey (Minn.)	6%
Sen. Henry Jackson (Wash.)	6%
Sen. Edward Kennedy (Mass.)	15%
Sen. George McGovern (S.D.)	4%
Sen. Edmund Muskie (Maine)	4%
Terry Sanford (former Gov. N.C.)	1%
Rep. Morris Udall (Ariz.)	1%
Gov. George Wallace (Ala.)	8%

b. If you are a Republican (or an Independent who leans towards one of the following Republicans) which *one* of the following declared or potential candidates would you support for the Republican Presidential nomination?

Sen. Howard Baker (Tenn.)	3%
John Connally (former Gov., Texas)	2%
President Gerald Ford	20%
Sen. Charles Percy (Ill.)	2%
Ronald Reagan (former Gov., Calif.)	7%
Vice President Nelson Rockefeller	1%

c. Whether you're a Democrat, Republican or Independent, assume President Ford wins the Republican nomination. Would you then support and vote for a conservative third party headed by Ronald Reagan in 1976?

Yes	16%
No	76%

9. a. Please rate President Ford's overall performance in domestic policy:

Excellent	4%
Good	43%
Only Fair	39%
Poor	11%

b. Please rate President Ford's overall performance in foreign policy:

Excellent	10%
Good	49%
Only Fair	31%
Poor	7%

10. a. In regard to government subsidization of health care, do you believe health care should be:

Available to all regardless of age or income	42%
Available only to those in financial need	41%
Available to all elderly only	4%
The responsibility of each individual, not of government	10%

b. If you favor a government health care system of some type, should such a program be *administered* by:

Federal Government	36%
State Governments	25%
Local Governments	16%
Private Insurance Agencies	6%

11. a. When energy is in critically short supply, do you favor:

Enforced Government regulation	54%
Self-regulation	44%

b. Do you agree that environmental standards (such as auto exhaust emissions and reclamation of strip mined land) should be relaxed when energy is in short supply and the economy in recession?

Yes	29%
No	67%

12. Do you favor a Federal law requiring registration of:

Handguns only	12%
All guns	74%
No law	13%

13. In your opinion, government spending for the following programs should be: (This question is aimed at ascertaining your feelings about government priorities — not how much you know about exact dollar amounts the government is spending on the following)

	Increased	Kept Same	Decreased
Housing	36%	46%	14%
Education	76%	19%	3%
Welfare/relief here at home	27%	30%	40%
Social Security	39%	46%	11%
Highway construction	12%	54%	31%
Pollution research/control	65%	28%	5%
Farm subsidies	30%	44%	21%
Revenue sharing	15%	57%	17%
Jobs/job training programs	62%	29%	6%
Federal courts	23%	60%	13%
Local law enforcement assistance	46%	44%	6%
Military aid to other nations	3%	23%	71%
Foreign economic/social aid	8%	42%	47%
Defense budget	20%	43%	34%
Space	22%	33%	43%
Secret CIA operations	6%	31%	61%
Intelligence gathering by CIA	8%	41%	49%

14. Today a great many institutions are under attack. How much confidence do you have in the following:

	Great Deal	Some	Very Little
Presidency	31%	53%	14%
U.S. Senate	26%	56%	16%
U.S. House of Representatives	25%	56%	16%
U.S. Supreme Court	46%	41%	11%
Your State Government	22%	58%	18%
Your Local Government	18%	49%	30%
FBI	33%	46%	18%
CIA	11%	38%	48%
Your Local law enforcement	25%	44%	29%
Medical profession	58%	34%	6%
Legal profession	29%	51%	17%
Major U.S. corporations	6%	40%	52%
Banks/financial institutions	29%	56%	13%
Private charitable groups	30%	53%	15%
Organized labor	10%	50%	36%
The media	20%	52%	26%
Advertising	4%	30%	64%
U.S. military services	39%	44%	14%

15. a. Under the law, everyone has equal rights. In actuality:

The laws are applied equally to everyone	12%
The laws are not applied equally	87%

b. If you believe the laws are not equally applied to all, which of the following groups do you feel are adversely affected (check all that apply):

Blacks	28%
Spanish-speaking Americans	25%
American Indians	28%
All racial minorities	39%
Nationality groups	16%
Women	36%
People of lower socio-economic status	66%

c. Do you feel that laws have become too oriented in favor of minority groups?

Yes	42%
No	53%

16. a. Is your community or your high school experiencing serious racial problems?

Yes	9%
No	90%

b. Do you feel racial prejudice towards others?

Yes	20%
No	77%

c. Do you feel you have been racially discriminated against by (check all that apply):

School administrators	8%
Teachers	6%
Fellow students	9%
Police	6%
Potential/present employers	10%

17. Industrial labor unions should be allowed to strike:

With no restrictions	12%
Only if the national welfare/economy are not endangered	62%
Should not be allowed to strike and all disputes should be subject to binding arbitration	22%

18. a. Professionals, such as teachers and doctors, should:

Be allowed to strike	38%
Not be allowed to strike; disputes should be subject to binding arbitration	58%

b. Government workers, such as police, firemen, sanitation workers, postal workers, etc., should:

Be allowed to strike	31%
Not be allowed to strike; disputes should be subject to binding arbitration	65%

19. In regard to controlling pollution and preserving the environment, do you feel the government is doing:

Too much	5%
Correct amount	21%
Too little	71%

20. Again regarding pollution and environmental preservation, do you believe private industry, such as auto manufacturers, oil and steel companies, timber companies, etc.; (check all that apply)

Is making a sincere attempt to meet environmental standards	18%
Is not making a sincere attempt	59%
Should be allowed more leeway in meeting present standards	8%
Should be held strictly to present standards & fined if it does not meet them	72%
Should not be subject to any government regulation in this area	2%

21. a. The FBI/other federal, state and local law enforcement groups are justified in keeping private citizens under investigation by wire tapping, opening mail, personal surveillance, if the individuals are: (check all that apply)

Members of anti-war or other protest groups	15%
Members of community action groups	2%
Communist Party members	38%
Socialist Party members	23%
Newsmen who've received "leaked" information	10%
U.S. government employees	11%
Employees of foreign governments	20%
Only with a court order & Dept. of Justice approval	56%
Any time they feel it necessary	8%
In no cases	20%

b. Should American citizens be allowed access to government files on themselves?

Yes	82%
No	14%

22. What is your main source of information about current events?

Newspapers	46%
Newsmagazines	20%
Radio	28%
Television	47%
Other people	12%
School	7%

23. a. Do you think the media present a full, fair, accurate and unbiased view of the news:

Almost all of the time	12%
The majority of the time	56%
Less than half of the time	25%
Rarely or never	5%

b. Do you generally believe what you read in newspapers/magazines and what you hear or see on radio/TV news shows?

Yes	84%
No	13%

24. a. Do you think the government regulates news information by controlling the news it releases to the media?

Yes	73%
No	24%

b. Do you think the government regulates news information by putting pressure on the media to present news favorably?

Yes	45%
No	50%

25. a. Should the government make public all information except that related to national defense?

Yes	66%
No	31%

b. If yes, who should define "national defense" and, therefore, have control over what information is released? (Check all that apply)

The President	15%
A joint Congressional committee	27%
Each separate government agency or department	6%
A separate non-political agency that would respond to press, citizen or Congressional inquiries	31%

26. If a war developed in the following areas, would you favor U.S. military involvement if a communist country were the aggressor or a participant?

South/Central America	50%
Europe	52%
Middle East	33%
Southeast Asia	16%
Africa	21%
Korea	25%

27. With regard to U.S. foreign policy, we should (check all that apply):

Cease all foreign aid	6%
Give aid for domestic and social development only	46%
Give aid for military affairs	15%
Withdraw all troops outside U.S.	11%
Significantly reduce troop commitments to NATO	20%
Not get involved in wars where U.S. not directly threatened	47%
Not involve ourselves at all in internal affairs of other countries	31%
Support all anti-Communist governments	23%
Support only democratic governments	18%
Significantly reduce our financial support of U.N.	20%
Increase our financial support of U.N.	17%
Attempt to work as much as possible through multinational organizations, rather than bi-laterally	48%

28. In your opinion, those persons who refuse to serve when drafted for the Vietnam conflict should be:

Granted total amnesty	28%
Granted amnesty only if they serve in a domestic social program	53%
Brought to trial and punished	16%

29. a. U.S. policy in the Middle East should be predicated on:

Maintaining a balance of power	46%
Full support of Israeli position	10%
More critical support of Israeli position	9%
Full support of Arab position	None
Establishment of a nation for Palestinians	6%
U.S. needs for oil	19%
Strengthening detente with Russia	8%

b. Where would you place primary blame for the continuing Middle East stalemate?

With Israel	12%
With Egypt	9%
With Syria	5%
With all Arab-block countries	33%
With Palestinian groups	12%
With the USSR	14%
With the USA	7%

30. a. Do you feel the women's liberation movement generally has been:

Very effective	23%
Somewhat effective	71%
Ineffective	6%

b. Has the women's movement changed attitudes about women, their role in society, their rights, etc., on the part of (check all that apply):

Yourself	55%
Your friends	60%
Your mother	24%
Your father	17%

31. Are you in favor of the equal rights amendment for women?

Yes	63%
No	32%

32. a. Should men and women receive equal pay for equal work?

Yes	99%
No	1%

b. Should full-time housewives be granted a salary or salary equivalent that would allow them to qualify for social security and other benefits that accrue to workers?

Yes	35%
No	60%

33. a. Do you feel men are (check all that apply):

Less emotional than women	57%
More intelligent than women	5%
More capable in business than women	20%

b. If yes to any of the above, do you feel these differences are:

Innate	5%
Culturally derived	26%
A combination of both	32%

34. a. Do you believe there's been an actual increase in homosexuality over the past decade or that the percentage of homosexuals has remained about the same, but they've just become more visible?

Actual increase	28%
Increased visibility only	69%

b. If you believe there's been an actual increase, do you believe the role of the women's movement in the rise has been:

Very significant	3%
Somewhat significant	13%
Not significant	12%

35. Do you feel the impact of the women's movement or men's feelings about themselves (their societal role, their emotions, their masculinity, etc.) has been generally:

Favorable	31%
Unfavorable	39%
No effect	27%

36. When both marriage partners are working, should they:

Share household tasks equally	58%
The man take on more household tasks than are usually accepted in a traditional marriage	20%
The woman continue to do all traditional household tasks and the man all traditional maintenance and other duties	19%

37. Do you plan to marry?

Yes	89%
No	7%

38. Are you in favor of the traditional marriage contract or would you favor a legal trial marriage in which couples live together a year or more before finalizing a marriage contract?

Traditional	77%
Trial	20%

39. Today many couples live together without marrying:

This is dangerous and can lead to emotional crisis	17%
I would not condemn others, but I would not do so	53%
I would seriously consider it	18%
It's a good idea and may prevent future divorces	16%

40. a. If you married and found it not working, would you seek a divorce if all means of solving the problem failed?

Yes	75%
No	21%

b. Are your parents divorced?

Yes	8%
No	91%

41. a. When you marry, do you plan to practice some form of birth control?

Yes	85%
No	10%

b. If yes, will you use some form of artifical contraceptive?

Yes	66%
No	13%

42. What number of children do you think comprises the ideal family?

0	2%
1	3%
2	52%
3	22%
4	11%
5+	4%

43. Would you prefer your husband or wife to be a virgin when you marry?

Yes	56%
No	37%

44. Premarital sex is acceptable:

If couples are going steady	4%
If couples plan to marry	16%
Under any circumstances where there is mutual consent	42%
Under no circumstances	34%

45. a. Have you ever participated in sexual intercourse?

Yes	29%
No	69%

b. If yes, did you use some form of contraceptive?

Yes	15%
No	13%

c. If you have not, is this due to:

Your own moral standards	50%
Parental disapproval	5%
Fear of pregnancy	9%
Lack of opportunity	10%
Other	5%

46. If parental disapproval and the possibility of pregnancy were removed, would you engage in premarital sex with someone you cared for deeply?

Yes	53%
No	40%

47. a. If you were involved in an unwanted pregnancy, would you approve of (if male) or have (if female) an abortion?

Yes	41%
No	56%

b. In the case of an unwanted pregnancy while unmarried, abortion should be allowed:

If the woman desires it	45%
If the woman desires it and the father is unknown	6%
Only if the father gives his approval	4%
Only if a doctor says it is necessary to save the life of the mother	37%
In no cases	9%

48. Where have you learned most of your information about sex?

School	29%
Home	27%
Friends	32%
Physician	2%
Church	2%
Movies	5%
Books	38%

49. Please rate your school's sex education program:

Excellent	7%
Adequate	30%
Poor	26%
None exists	37%

50. Have you used:

	Never	Once or Twice	Several Times	Regularly
Marijuana	73%	9%	11%	5%
Cocaine	92%	1%	0%	7%
Heroin	93%	0%	7%	
LSD or other hallucinogenic drugs	91%	1%	1%	0%
Uppers such as Speed or amphetamines	88%	3%	2%	0%
Downers such as barbituates	90%	2%	2%	0%

51. If you wished, could you readily purchase most of the above drugs in or near your high school?

Yes	78%
No	20%

52. With regard to marijuana:

Penalties for use should be stricter	32%
Penalties for use should be less strict	22%
Penalties for use should remain as they are	21%
It should be legalized	23%

53. If marijuana were legalized would you use it?

Yes	19%
No	78%

54. a. Even if you are not a drug user, do you socialize with friends who are users and who carry drugs in their cars or on their persons?

Yes	47%
No	50%

b. If you discovered a friend was hooked on drugs, would you (check all that apply):

Suggest they seek counseling	70%
Advise them to talk to parents or other trusted adult	41%
Try to help them yourself	71%
Tell their parents	3%
Tell a counselor, clergyman or doctor	18%
Turn them in to police or school authorities	2%
Ignore the situation	5%
Break up the friendship	4%

55. a. Do you feel drug use in your high school over the past two or three years has:

Increased	60%
Remained about the same	28%
Decreased	11%

b. Do you feel drug use has become an accepted part of the "lifestyle" among teens in your community?

Yes	53%
No	44%

56. Have you used these alcoholic beverages:

	Never	Once or Twice	Several Times	Regularly
Beer	25%	25%	31%	16%
Wine	21%	32%	36%	8%
Hard liquor	35%	28%	27%	6%

57. a. If your school or community has a drug education program, does that program include alcohol use?

Yes	55%
No	25%

b. Please rate your school or community drug education program:

Excellent	7%
Adequate	35%
Poor	33%
None exists	22%

58. a. If you drink, is it (check all that apply):

With friends for enjoyment	57%
Just to be "part of the crowd"	8%
To help you cope with emotional problems	2%
To get high	12%
Alone, because you're often bored	2%
At parties because you feel inadequate, shy or "uptight" without alcohol	4%
At family get togethers	36%

b. Do your parents approve of your drinking:

Yes	36%
No	16%
They don't know	17%

59. If you are underage and wished to, could you purchase alcoholic beverages in your community?

Yes	74%
No	19%

60. Please indicate the words you feel best describe your high school by and large:

Challenging (or)	39%
Routine	58%
Relevant subjects (or)	73%
Irrelevant subjects	20%
Good teachers (or)	55%
Just adequate teachers (or)	38%
Poor teachers	3%
Important (or)	84%
Useless	8%
Dangerous (or)	7%
Safe	86%
Cares about you (or)	72%
Doesn't care about you	22%
Stimulating (or)	54%
Boring	37%

61. a. Has your high school curriculum adequately prepared you for the college of your choice (if you plan to attend college)?

Yes	72%
No	22%

b. If you attend a vocational high school, has it adequately prepared you for your chosen career (if you do not plan to attend college)?

Yes	1%
No	0%

c. Whether you plan or do not plan on attending college, how would you rate the career guidance program in your school?

Excellent	18%
Satisfactory	45%
Poor	31%
None exists	5%

62. a. In regard to college entrance exams, did you place:

Above your expectations	32%
Below your expectations	19%
Where you expected to qualify for the college of your choice	31%
Below the qualifying level of your chosen college	1%

b. If you placed below your expectations or below the qualifying level of the college of your choice, do you feel this was due to personal reasons (such as nervousness, physical illness or inadequate preparation on your part) or to the fact that you were not adequately prepared by your high school curriculum or counseling?

Inadequate preparation by high school	8%
Personal reasons	13%

63. College acceptance should be predicated upon which of the following?

Achievement test scores	9%
Recommendations	10%
High school performance record	21%
All of the above equally	75%
Other	6%

64. Do you feel high schools and colleges place too much emphasis on athletic excellence at the expense of academic excellence?

Yes	61%
No	37%

65. a. Students should have a voice in:

Planning the curriculum	47%
Firing/retaining of teachers	2%
Both	42%
Neither	9%

b Students at your high school *do* have a voice in:

Planning the curriculum	33%
Firing/retaining of teachers	1%
Both	2%
Neither	63%

66. Should teachers be tested at regular intervals to determine job retention?

Yes	86%
No	12%

67. a. Do you think the present public education system provides equal educational opportunities to all Americans?

Yes	33%
No	66%

b. If not, which groups do you feel are negatively affected (check all that apply):

Blacks	15%
Latinos	10%
American Indians	18%
Ethnic/linguistic minorities	17%
Rural area dwellers	10%
Inner city youth	20%
All of the above	18%
None of the above	3%
Other	8%

c. Do you favor the goal of equal education opportunity?

Yes	96%
No	2%

d. Should students be bussed to schools to achieve a greater equality of education?

Yes	25%
No	71%

68. If you oppose bussing, but approve of the goal of equal educational opportunity, which of the following programs would you support as a means of achieving the goal (check all that apply):

Expanded Head Start programs	29%
Bi-lingual education and testing	29%
More money for poor schools	53%
Bonus money for teachers who teach in poor schools	16%
More money for compensatory education programs at high school level	25%
Open-housing policy to increase racial integration	23%
Inter-racial high school exchange programs	19%
Transferable school vouchers	8%
None of the above	5%

69. Do you approve of the policy in effect in many undergraduate and graduate schools of admitting minority students who do not meet the academic requirements which are applied to non-minority students and who, therefore, are taking the places which could otherwise go to more academically-qualified candidates?

Yes	13%
No	82%

70. a. Do you think college scholarships are distributed fairly?

Yes	34%
No	63%

b. It not, which groups do you feel are adversely affected (check all that apply):

Blacks	6%
Latinos	4%
American Indians	6%
Persons of lower socio-economic status	10%
Middle class	51%
Other	10%

71. If you plan to acquire a college diploma, is it:

To get a good job	56%
To gain social status	3%
Because it is expected by your family	6%
To develop your mind and increase your awareness	55%
To bide time until you decide what you want to do	4%

72. Do you have a definite career goal in mind?

Yes	72%
No	27%

73. a. At present, which of the following curricula do you intend to pursue in college?

Physical Science	7%
Biological Science	10%
Engineering	12%
Social Science	7%
Humanities	9%
Medicine (pre-med)	15%
Law (pre-law)	9%
Business Administration	11%
Journalism	5%
Education	10%
Technical course	2%
Other	18%

b. At present, do you plan to do graduate work in your chosen field? (This would include law or medical school)

Yes	60%
No	28%

74. In achieving your career goal, do you think it is most important to:

Enjoy your job	84%
Earn lots of money	7%
Contribute to improving society	27%
Gain status in the community	2%
Have job security	12%

75. a. Has the economic situation affected:

Whether you will attend college	9%
Which college you will select	31%
Whether you will work while in college	41%

b. While at college will you work:

Full-time	2%
Part-time	63%
Not at all	27%

76. Would you describe your life at home with your parents and family as:

Happy and close most of the time	59%
Satisfactory	35%
Unhappy most of the time	5%

77. a. Can you communicate with your parents:

Easily	40%
About average	45%
With difficulty	13%

b. When you have a family problem, do you usually get together and work it out as a group?

Yes	44%
No	53%

78. Who has helped you the most when you've had a serious problem?

Mother	37%
Father	13%
Other relative	7%
Friend	41%
Teacher or counselor	6%
Religious leader	4%

79. a. When you have children, will you raise them the same way your parents raised you?

Yes	43%
No	55%

b. If not, will you (check all that apply):

Be a stricter disciplinarian	10%
Be a more liberal disciplinarian	24%
Be more conservative in your social & sexual outlook	4%
Be more liberal in your social & sexual outlook	38%
Provide a more home-centered life	30%
Provide a less home-centered life	7%
Raise your children in the traditional boy/girl roles	11%
Raise your children as people without regard to traditional sex roles	33%

80. a. Do you consider yourself a member of an organized religion?

Yes	80%
No	19%

b. If yes, is it the result of your parents' influence or a choice you made on your own?

Parental influence	46%
Own choice	36%

81. Do you plan to bring your own children up in your religion only, or will you expose them to a variety of religious beliefs?

Own religion only	44%
Variety of beliefs	50%

82. a. Do you attend religious services:

Regularly	59%
Occasionally	26%
On holidays only	5%
Never	10%

b. Do you participate in church or other religious institution activities (such as youth groups, charitable activities, etc.):

Regularly	35%
Occasionally	38%
Never	27%

83. Which of the following statements comes closest to your religious beliefs?

There is a personal God or Supreme Being	78%
There is some kind of vital force or spirit in the world	11%
I'm not sure there is a personal God or vital force	7%
There is no personal God or vital force	3%

84. a. Do you feel religion is relevant in today's society?

Yes	86%
No	11%

b. What role does religion play in your own moral standards and actions?

Very significant role	50%
Somewhat significant	36%
Not at all significant	14%

85. Do you believe an individual has the right to decide when to end his own life?

Yes	42%
No	54%

GLOSSARY OF ABBREVIATIONS

Complete Title/Word	Abbreviation
American Field Service	AFS
American Legion Award	AmLegAwd
American Legion Boys State	ALBoysSt
American Legion Auxiliary Girls State	ALAGirlsSt
Annual/Yearbook Editor In Chief	EdYrbk
Annual/Yearbook Fashion Editor	FshEdYrbk
Annaul/Yearbook Other	Yrbk
Annual/Yearbook Sports Editor	SptEdYrbk
Annual/Yearbook Staff/Reporter	RptrYrbk
Audio-Visual	Aud/Vis
Band	Band
Baseball	Bsbl
Basketball	Bsktbl
Bausch & Lomb Science Award	BauchLmbAwd
Betty Crocker Award	BttyCrckrAwd
Chamber of Commerce Award	ChmbCommrsAwd
Cheerleading	Chrldr
Choir	Chr
Chorale	Chrl
Chorus	Chrs
Church Worker	ChrhWkr
Citizenship Award	CitAwd
City Council	CtyCnl
Civic Club	CivCl
Civil Air Patrol	CAP
Coaching Activities	CchngActv
Community Worker	CmntyWkr
Concert Band	CncrtBnd
Danforth (I Dare You) Award	DanFAwd
Daughters Of The American Revolution Award	DARAwd
Drill Team	DrlTm
Drum & Bugle Corp.	DrmBgl
Drum Majorette	DrmMjrt
Elks Award	ElkAwd
English Club	EngCl
Football	Ftbl
4-H Award	4-HAwd
4-H Club	4-H
French Club	FrCl
Future Business Leader of America	FBLA
Future Doctors of America	FDA
Future Farmers of America	FFA
Future Homemakers of America	FHA
Future Nurses of America	FNA
Future Scientists of America	FSA
Future Teachers of America	FTA
German Club	GerCl
Girls Athletic Assn.	GAA
God & Country Award	GodCntryAwd
Golf	Glf
Governor's Honor Program Award	GovHonPrgAwd
Historian Freshman Class	HstFrshCls
Historian Junior Class	HstJrCls
Historian Senior Class	HstSrCls
Historian Sophomore Class	HstSophCls
Honor Roll	HonRl
Hospital Aide (Candy Striper)	HospAde
Interclub Council	IntrClCncl
Intramural Sports	IMSpt
Jaycees Award	JCAwd
Junior Achievement	JA
Junior Achievement Award	JAAwd
Jr. Chamber of Commerce	JCC
Jr. Nat'l. Honor Society	JrNHS
Junior Engineering Tech. Society Award	JETSAwd
Key Club	KeyCl
Kiwanis Award	KiwanAwd
Library Aide	LbryAde
Lions Club Award	LionAwd
Literary Magazine	LitMag
Madrigal	Mdrgl
Marching Band	MrchBnd
Math Club	MthCl
Masonic Award	MasAwd
Model UN	ModUN
Nat'l. Catholic Music Education Assn.	NatlCathMusEdAsoc
Nat'l. Council of Teachers of English	NCTE
Nat'l. Forensic League	NatlFornLg
Nat'l. Honor Society	NHS
Nat'l. Merit Finalist	NatlMeritFnl
Nat'l. Merit Letter of Commendation	NatlMeritCmnd
Nat'l. Merit Scholarship	NatlMeritSchl
Nat'l. Merit Semi-Finalist	NatlMeritSF
Nat'l. Science Foundation	NatlSciFnd
Nat'l. Thespian Society	NatlThespSoc
Newspaper Staff/Reporter	RptrSchPpr
Newspaper Editor In Chief	EdSchPpr

GLOSSARY OF ABBREVIATIONS

Complete Title/Word	Abbreviation
Newspaper Fashion Editor	FshEdSchPpr
Newspaper Sports Editor	SptEdSchPpr
Newspaper Other	SchPpr
Office Aide	OffAde
Optimist Club Award	OptClAwd
Orchestra	Orch
Pep Band	PepBnd
Pep Club	PpCl
Political Worker	PolWkr
Powder Puff Football	PPFtbl
President's Award	PresAwd
President Freshman Class	PresFrshCls
President Junior Class	PresJrCls
President Senior Class	PresSrCls
President Sophomore Class	PresSophCls
Quill & Scroll	Quill&Scroll
Red Cross Aide	RedCrAde
Rotary International Award	RotaryAwd
R.O.T.C.	ROTC
Russian Club	RusCl
Sacristan	Sacrstn
Sanctuary Society	SancSoc
School Aide	SchAde
School Musical	SchMus
School Play	SchPl
Science Club	SciCl
Scout Activities	SctActv
Secretary Freshman Class	SecFrshCls
Secretary Junior Class	SecJrCls
Secretary Senior Class	SecSrCls
Secretary Sophomore Class	SecSophCls
Secretary/Treasurer Freshman Class	SecTrsFrshCls
Secretary/Treasurer Junior Class	SecTrsJrCls
Secretary/Treasurer Senior Class	SecTrsSrCls
Secretary/Treasurer Sophomore Class	SecTrsSophCls
Soccer	Socr
Sodality	Sdlty
Sons Of American Revolution Award	SARAwd
Spanish Club	SpnCl
Student Council	StuCncl
Student Government	StuGov
Swimming	Swmmng
Teacher Aide	TchrAde
Teens	Teen
Tennis	Tennis
Time Mag. Current Events Award	TIMEAwd
Track	Trk
Treasurer Freshman Class	TrsFrshCls
Treasurer Junior Class	TrsJrCls
Treasurer Senior Class	TrsSrCls
Treasurer Sophomore Class	TrsSophCls
Twirler	Twrl
U.N. Youth Organ.	UNYO
VF.W. Award	VFWAwd
Vice President Freshman Class	VPFrshCls
Vice President Junior Class	VPJrCls
Vice President Senior Class	VPSrCls
Vice President Sophomore Class	VPSophCls
Voice of Democracy Award	VoiceDemAwd
Wrestling	Wrstlng
Youth Fellowship	YthFlsp
Youth Foundation	YthFnd
Youth Legislature	YthLg

EDITOR'S NOTE: The above abbreviations were compiled and utilized in order to conserve space and permit the listing of as much data per student as possible. Many biographies on the following pages contain abbreviations and symbols not listed here and for the most part were received from the students in that manner with no explanation given.

SAMPLE BIOGRAPHY

This sample is presented to familiarize the reader with the format of the biographical listings. Students are identified by name, school and location. Home addresses are not published in order to protect the privacy and integrity of all students.

Name
High School
Location ...... Wolk, Allan I.; Beach H.S.; Miami, FL.;
Class Year .... Sr.;
Rank in Class . 10-350 /PresStuCncl; VPSrCls; EdYrbk; UNYO;
(when given) Ftbl; 4-H; NHS; CitAwd; AmLegAwd; SctAwd;
Accomplishments NatlFornLg;
Future Plans .. Harvard College; Bio Chemist.

STUDENT BIOGRAPHIES

A

AADLAND, Lorne A; Veblen Public HS; Veblen, SD; 5/17 VPBand; VPChrs; HonRl; SchPl; PresStuCncl; SptEdSchPpr; Bsktbl; AmLegAwd; BttyCrckrAwd; 4-HAwd; Northern St College; Business Admin.

AAGAARD, James G; Audubon HS; Audubon, IA; 15/120 PresFrshCls; ALBoysSt; Band; ChrhWkr; CncrtBnd; HonRl; Bsktbl; CaptFtbl; CaptTrk; CaptAmLegAwd; Iowa State; Physical Therapy.

AAKER, Mark A; Eau Claire Memorial HS; Eau Claire, WI; 13/450 HonRl; LitMag; ModUN; NatlMeritCmnd; SchPl; RptrSchPpr; LatCl; BauchLmbAwd; College; Professional.

AALAND, David; Larimore HS; Larimore, ND; Band; Chr; CmntyWkr; CncrtBnd; MrchBnd; PepBnd; SctActv; YthFlsp; College; Professional.

AALUND, Lee A; Michigan Luth Seminary; Waukegan, IL; 2/85 SecSophCls; Chrs; HonRl; Twrl; RptrYrbk; EdYrBk; IMSpt; Clg Of Lake County; Psych And Pre Law.

AAMOTH, Robert J; H H Dow HS; Midland, MI; SecFrshCls; Band; CncrtBnd; HonRl; LitMag; LbryAde; MrchBnd; NHS; NatlMeritFnl; NatlMeritCmnd; Coll; Law.

AANENSEN, Joan E; Northern University HS; Cedar Falls, IA; Band; Chrs; Orch; PepBnd; PolWkr; SchMus; SchPl; Tennis; University; Professional.

AARON, Emily; Carroll HS; Wichita, KS; HonRl; NatlFornLg; RptrSchPpr;.

AARON, Helen; Immaculata HS; Leavenworth, KS; Chr; CmntyWkr; HospAde; SchMus; RptrSchPpr; PpCl; IMSpt; Univ Of Ks; Physical Educ.

AARON, La Vinnia J; Lennox HS; Lennox, SD; 36/117 Chrs; HonRl; MrchBnd; SchPl; Twrl; 4-H; FHA; 4-HAwd; Augustana Coll; Social Work.

AARON, Robert J; Niles North HS; Skokie, IL; 42/632 Band; CncrtBnd; HonRl; MrchBnd; NHS; NatlThespSoc; SchMus; SchPl; SctActv; PresMthCl; Univ Of Ill; Math.

AARRESTAD, Theodore; Brainerd HS; Brainerd, MN; 73/475 Chr; ChrhWkr; CncrtBnd; HonRl; MrchBnd; NHS; PepBnd; HstFrshCls; Trk; CitAwd; Concordia Coll.

AASEBY, Connie B; Lincoln HS; Thief River Falls, MN; Band; CmntyWkr; HonRl; MrchBnd; RptrYrbk; SchPpr; FHA; Bsktbl; PPFtbl; VoiceDemAwd; Vocational & Clge; Nursing.

AASEN, Elaine P; Northwood HS; Aneta, ND; ALAGirlsSt; Band; Chr; Chrs; CncrtBnd; HonRl; MrchBnd; PepBnd; FHA; Univ Of Nd; Physical Therapist.

AASEN, Linda M; Iola Scandinavia HS; Iola, WI; 2/57 Band; Chrs; CncrtBnd; HonRl; JrNHS; Mdrgl; MrchBnd; NatlFornLg; PepBnd; SchPl; FTA; College; Music.

AASTRUP, Sibyl A; Meservey Thornton HS; Thornton, IA; VPFrshCls; SecJrCls; Chr; DrmMjrt; HonRl; Mdrgl; MrchBnd; NHS; SchPl; Glf; Aib In Des Moines; Legal Secretary.

AAVANG, Cindy M; Mt Horeb HS; Mt Horeb, WI; Band; Chr; ChrhWkr; CncrtBnd; HonRl; MrchBnd; NHS; Orch; SchMus; Trk; Univ Of Mn; Environmental Biology.

ABAHAZY, Susan; Riverside HS; Dearborn Heights, MI; HonRl; NHS; RptrSchPpr; FrCl; GAA; IMSpt; Univ; Journ.

ABARAVICIUS, Alice A; St Augustine HS; Chicago, IL; SchPl; RptrSchPpr; IMSpt; PPFtbl; Nurse.

ABASCAL, Bryan K; Bishop Noll HS; E Chicago, IN; 168/370 Indiana Univ; Doctor.

ABBAS, Connie; Aplington Comm HS; Aplington, IA; TrsJrCls; Band; Chrs; CncrtBnd; HonRl; MrchBnd; PepBnd; RptrSchPpr; Secretary.

ABBAS, Kevin R; Ackley Geneva HS; Ackley, IA; VPSophCls; SecJrCls; HonRl; YthFlsp; Bsbl; CaptBsktbl; Ftbl; Glf;.

ABBEY, Barbara L; Corning Community; Hs; Bridgewater, IA; 7/75 Chrs; HonRl; SchPl; Teen; PpCl; LetterBsbl; Bsktbl; LetterTrk; CaptChrldr; PPFtbl; Northwest Missouri State Univ; Secretary.

ABBEY, Gentra L; Dodge City Sr HS; Dodge City, KS; PresFrshCls; HstSophCls; HstJrCls; Band; HonRl; PepBnd; SchMus; StuCncl; RptrSchPpr; CivCl; PPFtbl; Dodge City Comm Col; Lawyer.

ABBEY, Michael C; Trenton Sr HS; Trenton, MO; PresSrCls; NHS; StuCncl; FFA; LetterFtbl; Trade School.

ABBOTT, Anthony G; Humboldt HS; West St Paul, MN; LetterFtbl; LetterWrstlng; Trade; Pipefitter.

ABBOTT, Bruce D; J D Darnall HS; Geneseo, IL; HonRl; JA; StuGov; YthLg; SciCl; LetterGlf; LetterTrk; Univ Of Illinois; Computer Science.

ABBOTT, Deanna M; Harrison HS; Farmington Hills, MI; VPSrCls; Band; CncrtBnd; HonRl; JA; MrchBnd; NHS; NatlMeritCmnd; AmLegAwd; Cottey Clg; Child Psychologist.

ABBOTT, Debra A; Gardner HS; Gardner, KS; 12/92 HonRl; SctActv; YthFlsp; Yrbk; PresPpCl; Johnson Co Jr Co; Art.

ABBOTT, Donna; St Agnes Acad; Alliance, NE; SecJrCls; ChrhWkr; HonRl; NHS; Sdlty; StuCncl; Yrbk; FSA; SpnCl; SciCl; College; Dental Hygiene.

ABBOTT, Jeffery; R Nelson Shider HS; New Haven, IN; HonRl; JA; NHS; StuGov; JAAwd; Indiana Univ; Accounting.

ABBOTT, Joan L; Libertyville HS; Libertyville, IL; 74/458 HonRl; LbryAde; NatlMeritCmnd; College; Doctor.

ABBOTT, Katherine; Sault Area HS; Sault Ste Marie, MI; 39/346 HonRl; SchPpr; College; Professional Lawyer.

ABBOTT, Lori; So Soo City Sr HS; Dakota City, NE; 25/180 ALBoysSt; ChrhWkr; DrlTm; HonRl; JrNHS; StuCncl; Yrbk; SpnCl; MthCl; Chrldr; College; Interior Decortato.

ABBOTT, Mark R; John F Kennedy HS; Bloomington, MN; HonRl; NatlFornLg; NatlMeritSF; TchrAde; Univ Of Minn; Astronomer.

ABBOTT, Marta L; Hoopeston East Lynn HS; Hoopeston, IL; Band; Chr; Chrs; ChrhWkr; CncrtBnd; HonRl; MrchBnd; PepBnd; StuCncl; YthFlsp; LetterBsbl; LetterTrk; GAA; IMSpt; Lincoln Christian College; Christian Educ.

ABBOTT, Robert L; Blackford HS; Montpelier, IN; Aud/Vis; ChrhWkr; HonRl; YthFlsp; 4-H; FFA; PpCl; LetterWrstlng; 4-HAwd;.

ABBOTT, Susan C; Eisenhower HS; Decatur, IL; 1/300 HonRl; HospAde; PresJA; NHS; NatlMeritCmnd; SctActv; JAAwd; Univ Of Illinois; Chemistry.

ABBOTT, Thomas R; Hammond HS; Hammond, IN; CncrtBnd; MrchBnd; PepBnd; StuCncl; PresKeyCl; Trade School; Accounting.

ABDERHALDEN, Norman; Lockport Cen Hs; Lockport, IL; Band; HonRl; PepBnd; U ; Study Mathematics.

ABDO, Regina A; Cathedral HS; Omaha, NE; HstSrCls; Chr; Chrs; ChrhWkr; CmntyWkr; JA; NatlCathMusEdAsoc; NatlSciFnd; StuCncl; Bsktbl; Un Med Center; Nursing Gerontology.

ABEL, Bette J; Maries R Ii HS; Belle, MO; 8/53 Band; ChrhWkr; CncrtBnd; HonRl; MrchBnd; NHS; StuCncl; PresFHA; PpCl; Bsktbl; College.

ABEL, Christopher A; Southport HS; Indianapolis, IN; 19/450 ALBoysSt; Band; NatlFornLg; NHS; NatlMeritSF; NatlThespSoc; SctActv; LionAwd; NCTE; OptClAwd; Virginia Military Inst; Military.

ABEL, Robin R; Scottsbluff Sr HS; Scottsbluff, NE; HonRl; Bsbl; LetterFtbl; LetterTrk; CchngActv; IMSpt; College.

ABEL, Ronald; Granada Huntley HS; Granada, MN; CAP; CmntyWkr; NatlSciFnd; StuCncl; SciCl; College; Law Enforcement.

ABEL, Susan L; Maries County Rii HS; Belle, MO; PresSophCls; SecTrsSophCls; Band; ChrhWkr; CncrtBnd; HonRl; MrchBnd; NHS; PepBnd; StuCncl; FHA; Business School; Vocation.

ABELE, Mary K; Dearborn HS; Dearborn, MI; Chr; Chrs; ChrhWkr; College; Art.

ABELL, Carol A; Chester HS; Chester, IL; 22/120 HonRl; OffAde; SchAde; Mc Kendree College; Business Education.

ABELL, Dixie L; Romeoville HS; Lockport, IL; 20/293 Chrs; HonRl; JrNHS; NHS; StuGov; RptrSchPpr; Blackburn College; Teacher.

ABELL, Helene L; Lincoln HS; Barnard, KS; HospAde; JA; OffAde; StuCncl; EdYrBk; 4-H; Trk; CaptChrldr; 4-HAwd; JAAwd; Fort Hays State; Psychology.

ABELL, Wendy J; Abraham Lincoln HS; Bloomington, MN; Band; Chrs; ChrhWkr; DrmMjrt; MrchBnd; NatlFornLg; NatlThespSoc; SchMus; SchPl; TchrAde; Twrl; RptrSchPpr; Swmmng; Univ Of Wisconsin; Theatre.

ABELL, William R; South Hamilton Comm HS; Ellsworth, IA; Chr; Chrs; CncrtBnd; HonRl; MrchBnd; SchMus; StuCncl; TreasFFA; Bsbl; Bsktbl; Ftbl; LetterTrk; Iowa St Univ; Law.

ABELLA, Michael J; Girard HS; Girard, KS; PresJrCls; SchPl; YthFlsp; RptrYrbk; EdYrBk; Yrbk; VP4-H; SpnCl; SciCl; LetterTrk; Chrldr; 4-HAwd; University; Journalism.

ABELS, Phil J; Eagle Grove HS; Eagle Grove, IA; Band; Chrs; CncrtBnd; HonRl; PepBnd; LetterFtbl; Philosiphy.

ABENDROTH, Michael A; St Elmo HS; St Elmo, IL; 2/62 Band; Chrs; ChrhWkr; CncrtBnd; HonRl; JrNHS; NHS; Orch; SchMus; SchPl; LetterBsbl; LetterBsktbl; LetterFtbl; Univ Of Illinois; Anesthesiologist.

ABENDROTH, Paul H; St Elmo HS; St Elmo, IL; 5/54 Band; Chrs; HonRl; SchMus; SchPl; YthFlsp; Bsbl; Bsktbl; Ftbl; Trk; Clge; Eng.

ABERLE, David L; Tremont HS; Tremont, IL; 9/70 Band; ChrhWkr; HonRl; MrchBnd; NatlThespSoc; PepBnd; SchPl; SctActv; StuCncl; YthFlsp; Bsktbl; LetterCchngActv; College; Professional.

ABERLE, Jeanette S; Troy HS; Troy, KS; ALAGirlsSt; Band; Chr; Chrl; CncrtBnd; HonRl; MrchBnd; NHS; SchPl; EdSchPpr; K State; Interior Design.

ABERNATHY, Barbara J; Woodland HS; Glen Allen, MO; 12/63 ChrhWkr; HonRl; MrchBnd; YthFlsp; SptEdYrbk; SptEdSchPpr; FHA; PpCl; CaptChrldr; IMSpt; College Semo; Biology.

ABERNATHY, Carne M; John J Pershing HS; Detroit, MI; CmntyWkr; HonRl; TreasMrchBnd; NHS; OffAde; TchrAde; Yrbk; Wayne St Univ; Pediatric Nurse.

ABERNATHY, Katherine A; Carmel Girls HS; Mundelein, IL; 8/195 TrsFrshCls; Chrs; HonRl; JrNHS; NHS; StuCncl; StuGov; RptrYrbk; 4-H; College; Business Admin.

ABERNATHY, Nancy C; Buhler HS; Hutchinson, KS; Chr; Chrs; ChrhWkr; CmntyWkr; HonRl; SchPl; TchrAde; Bsktbl; Trk; College; Nursing.

ABLEMAN, Gail K; Craig Sr HS; Jonesville, WI; Chr; ChrhWkr; CmntyWkr; HonRl; SchMus; Teen; YthFlsp; SchPpr; 4-H; SpnCl; CchngActv; College; Professional.

ABLER, Julie; John F Kennedy HS; Romulus, MI; 4/435 Band; HonRl; MrchBnd; NHS; StuGov; 4-H; MthCl; Mercy College Of Det; Medical Technologist.

ABLES, John E; E G Edison HS; East Gary, IN; VPBand; CncrtBnd; HonRl; MrchBnd; PepBnd; LetterBsbl; Purdue Univ.

ABLES, Lynn M; Glenbard North HS; Glendale Hts, IL; 1/400 CncrtBnd; HonRl; MrchBnd; NatlThespSoc; SchPl; StuCncl; GerCl; PpCl; LetterTennis; LetterTrk; Univ; Science.

ABMAN, Tracey A; New Trier West HS; Wilmette, IL; 120/694 CmntyWkr; HonRl; HospAde; PolWkr; College; Sociology.

ABOLT, James C; Marist HS; Oak Lawn, IL; 12/393 HonRl; NHS; LetterBsktbl; CchngActv; IMSpt; College

ABOTOBIK, Alice M; Mercy HS; Maryland Hts, MO; Chrs; HonRl; HospAde; JrNHS; VPNatlMeritCmnd; SchAde; SchMus; TchrAde; RptrYrbk; SpnCl; VoiceDemAwd; Univ Of Mo St Louis; Teacher Spcl Edctn.

ABOUREZK, Susan R; Stevens HS; Rapid City, SD; 18/413 ALAGirlsSt; Band; HonRl; LbryAde; SchAde; SchPl; Twrl; 4-H; GAA; AmLegAwd; College; Major Study.

ABOUSSIE, Joyce A; St Josephs Academy; St Louis, MO; PresJrCls; PolWkr; StuCncl; SpnCl; PpCl; GAA; St Louis Univ; Political Science.

ABOWD, Marypat; Harrison HS; Farmington Hills, MI; 5/450 PresJrCls; PresSrCls; ALAGirlsSt; NHS; SchPl; JAAwd; CitAwd; Col; Statistician In Bus.

ABOYME, Gerry B; Normandy HS; Normandy, MO; TrsSrCls; Chr; HonRl; StuCncl; StuGov; RptrYrbk; EngCl; Bsbl; LetterFtbl; Wrstlng; Us Air Force Acad.

ABRAHAMS, Rex W; Hillsboro HS; Hillsboro, KS; PresStuCncl; YthFlsp; LetterFtbl; LetterTrk; Bethel Clg.

ABRAHAMSEN, Heidi L; Park Center HS; Brooklyn Pk, MN; 1/504 SecFrshCls; PresJrCls; Chr; HonRl; SchPl; StuCncl; RptrSchPpr; Glf; Swmmng; Univ Of Mn ; Psychology.

ABRAHAMSON, Cindy F; Cedarville HS; Cedarville, MI; VPFrshCls; Aud/Vis; Band; SctActv; TchrAde; College; Sec.

ABRAHAMSON, Karen J; Bloomer HS; Bloomer, WI; 2/122 AFS; SecBand; Chrs; HonRl; HospAde; NHS; SchPl; EdYrBk; PpCl; DARAwd; Univ Wi Eau Claire; Nursing.

ABRAHAMSON, Kevin J; Chisago Lakes HS; Lindstrom, MN; ChrhWkr; CncrtBnd; HonRl; MrchBnd; PepBnd; FFA; Bsbl; LetterBsktbl; College; Business.

ABRAHAMSON, Micheal P; Sevastopol HS; Sturgeon Bay, WI; 16/91 ChrhWkr; NHS; Quill&Scroll; StuCncl; SptEdSchPpr; LetterBsktbl; LetterTrk; IMSpt; U Of Wi Eau Claire; Cpa.

ABRAHAMSON, Nila J; Lyman HS; Kennebec, SD; ALAGirlsSt; HonRl; NatlFornLg; PolWkr; 4-H; GerCl; 4-HAwd; College; Para Legal.

ABRAMCZYK, Glenn A; S Milwaukee Sr HS; S Milwaukee, WI; 6/446 ALBoysSt; Aud/Vis; HonRl; JrNHS; NHS; CaptFtbl; Trk; IMSpt; College; Engineering.

ABRAMOFF, Monica M; Brookfield Central HS; Brookfield, WI; ChrhWkr; LitMag; NatlMeritSF; SpnCl; U Of Wi; Metalurgical Engineer.

ABRAMOVICH, Connie L; Manitowoc Lutheran HS; Manitowoc, WI; 3/81 TrsSrCls; Chr; NatlMeritCmnd; EdYrBk; SchPpr; Trk; Dr Martin Luther Col; Teacher.

ABRAMOWICZ, Gary R; Stanley Boyd HS; Stanley, WI; 4/110 ALBoysSt; PresBand; ChrhWkr; CncrtBnd; MrchBnd; PepBnd; SctActv; TchrAde; Univ; Accountant.

ABRAMS, Joe G; Arkansas City HS; Arkansas City, KS; Chr; SchMus; StuCncl; TchrAde; FTA; SciCl; Kansas State Univ; Engineering.

ABRAMS, Marshall D; Chicago Public HS; Chicago, IL; Band; NatlMeritCmnd; SchPl; StuGov; RptrSchPpr; FrCl; MthCl; Univ Of California; Physics.

ABRAMSON, Brian D; Toivola Meadowland HS; Meadowlands, MN; 2/30 Aud/Vis; HonRl; SchPl; StuCncl; StuGov; RptrYrbk; RptrSchPpr; FFA; Bsbl; Bsktbl; College; Agriculture.

ABRAMSON, David P; New Trier West HS; Wilmette, IL; 72/694 HonRl; Univ Of Michigan; Business.

ABRAMSON, Ellen J; Horace Mann HS; Gilbert, MN; Band; Chr; ChrhWkr; CncrtBnd; HonRl; MrchBnd; SchPl; StuCncl; University; Ecology.

ABRAMSON, Sandra S; Peoria HS; Peoria, IL; 15/481 HonRl; HospAde; JrNHS; NHS; NatlMeritCmnd; College; Business Adm.

ABRAMSON, Sharon K; Holdrege Senior HS; Holdredge, NE; Band; Chrs; CncrtBnd; HonRl; HospAde; MrchBnd; PepBnd; SchMus; Teen; PpCl; Possibly College; Professional Work.

ABROMITIS, Frank; Carl Sandburg HS; Palos Park, IL; College; Civil Engineer.

ABSHEAR, Mark W; Laurel HS; Oldenburg, IN; 1/48 HonRl; NHS; StuCncl; Yrbk; Eastern Kentucky Univ; Accountant.

ABSIL, Robert P; Arlington HS; Arlington Heights, IL; 4/580 HonRl; RptrSchPpr; SciCl; RotaryAwd; Il Institute Of Tech; Chemical Engineer.

ABTS, Anthony J; West De Pere HS; De Pere, WI; 2/200 Chrs; ChrhWkr; HonRl; NHS; Yrbk; RptrSchPpr; FTA; PresSciCl; IMSpt; CitAwd; St Norbert Clg; Educator.

ABTS, Joseph A; Creighton Prep HS; Omaha, NE; Bsbl; Bsktbl; Trk;.

ABTS, Julie A; Cochrane Fountain City HS; Fountain City, WI; DrlTm; NHS; RptrYrbk; PpCl; GAA; Minnesota Sch Of Bus; Court Reporting.

ABY, Steve J; Wethersfield HS; Kewanee, IL; PresJrCls; HonRl; SchMus; SchPl; StuCncl; StuGov; SptEdSchPpr; Bsktbl; CaptGlf; Univ Of Iowa; Lawyer.

ACCETTURA, Rosemarie; J F Kennedy Hs; Chicago, IL; HonRl; NHS; SecFBLA; MthCl; PpCl; GAA; Business School;secretarial.

ACCETTURO, Mary R; Lourdes HS; Chicago, IL; ChrhWkr; CmntyWkr; HonRl; JrNHS; NHS; SchAde; TchrAde; FBLA; PpCl; CchngActv; IMSpt; TIMEAwd; De Paul University; Cpa.

ACCOLA, Kevin D; Carbondale Comm HS; Carbondale, IL; CaptFtbl; CchngActv; Southern Ill U; Vet.

ACE, Dawn; Tigerton Hs; Tigerton, WI; Band; Chr; Chrs; ChrhWkr; HonRl; PepBnd; SchPl; SctActv; SchPpr; GAA; Colege Northland; Professional.

ACEVEDO, Anita M; Central HS; Omaha, NE; Chrs; ChrhWkr; CmntyWkr; HonRl; JA; OffAde; SchAde; SchMus; Bsktbl; College.

ACEVEDO, Leslie A; Cass Tech HS; Detroit, MI; CmntyWkr; HonRl; HospAde; OffAde; PolWkr; Univ Of Mi; Marine Biology.

ACEVEDO, Melvin; North Chicago HS; North Chicago, IL; HonRl; SpnCl; Coll; Language.

ACEY, Sherry J; Chaffee HS; Chaffee, MO; 15/64 Chr; CncrtBnd; HospAde; MrchBnd; NHS; SctActv; Twrl; Yrbk; FHA; Trade School; Bookeeping.

ACHEN, Catherine M; Frederick Public HS; Frederick, SD; 9/32 Band; Chrs; CmntyWkr; HonRl; SchPl; RptrYrbk; Yrbk; 4-H; Trk; 4-HAwd; Mount Marty; Home Ec.

ACHENBACH, Mark R; Collinsville HS; Collinsville, IL; Band; CncrtBnd; HonRl; MrchBnd; NHS; Orch; PepBnd; SctActv; YthFlsp; GerCl; SciCl; Univ Of Illinois; Civil Engineering.

ACHESON, Jane I; Chester Area HS; Chester, SD; 5/32 ALAGirlsSt; Band; Chrs; CncrtBnd; DrlTm; DrmMjrt; HonRl; Mdrgl; MrchBnd; NHS; Augustana College; Physical Therapy.

ACHEY, Mary K; Lisbon Community HS; Lisbon, IA; Band; Chrs; CncrtBnd; MrchBnd; PepBnd; SchMus; SchPl; Twrl; 4-H; St Lukes Nurses College; Nurse.

ACHMAN, Beverly M; Mt Iron HS; Iron, MN; AFS; Band; CncrtBnd; HospAde; MrchBnd; PepBnd; RptrYrbk; 4-H; FNA; GerCl; GAA; AmLegAwd; Eveleth Area Voc Tech; Accountant.

ACHTERHOF, David R; Hamilton HS; Holladn, MI; 14/125 Band; CncrtBnd; HonRl; MrchBnd; NHS; PepBnd; TchrAde; PresFFA; CaptBsbl; LetterBsktbl; Davenport Coll Bus; Accounting.

ACKATZ, Debra K; East Troy HS; East Troy, WI; 20/116 Band; HonRl; MrchBnd; PepBnd; TchrAde; PresFrshCls; Yrbk; FHA; PpCl; IMSpt; Uw Lacroose ;elem Ed.

ACKER, Barbara T; Rib Lake HS; Rib Lake, WI; 7/60 SecJrCls; SecSrCls; Chr; HonRl; SchPpr; University; Teacher.

ACKER, Roberta M; Zion Benton HS; Winthrop Harbor, IL; 5/430 HonRl; Bsbl; Tennis; College; Theraputics.

ACKERMAN, Cindy J; Patrick Henry HS; Mpls, MN; 17/423 Band; ChrhWkr; SecCncrtBnd; HonRl; SecMrchBnd; NHS; PepBnd; TchrAde; YthFlsp; U Of Mo; Sec Guidance Councelor.

ACKERMAN, Doris E; Chenoa HS; Chenoa, IL; 5/54 AFS; Chr; Chrs; ChrhWkr; HonRl; HospAde; Mdrgl; SchMus; SchPl; YthFlsp; 4-H; FHA; LatCl; Goshen College; Medical Lab Tech.

ACKERMAN, Faith; Central HS; Aberdeen, SD; ChrhWkr; HonRl; NHS; YthFlsp; SpnCl; Grace Bible College; Missionary.

ACKERMAN, John; Heelan HS; Sioux City, IA; 1/247 HonRl; NHS; IMSpt; Morningside Coll; Law.

ACKERMAN, Linda G; Willowbrook HS; Villa Park, IL; 94/814 AFS; Chrs; HonRl; NHS; SctActv; College; Art.

ACKERMAN, Mark S; Thornridge HS; So Holland, IL; 24/672 CmntyWkr; HonRl; JA; NHS; TchrAde; GerCl; Bsbl; LetterTennis; IMSpt; U Of Illnois; Architecture.

ACKERMAN, Marvin W; Irene HS; Irene, SD; HonRl; Bsbl; Bsktbl; Ftbl; Trk; Wrstlng;.

ACKERMAN, Michelle; St Stephen Area HS; Saginaw, MI; 2/105 HonRl; LbryAde; EdSchPpr; Mich St Univ; Engineering.

ACKERMAN, Michelle M; St Stephen Area HS; Saginaw, MI; 2/105 HonRl; LbryAde; PresNHS; EdSchPpr; Mi St Univ; Engineering.

ACKERMAN, Patrick P; English Valleys HS; N English, IA; PresSrCls; ALBoysSt; Chrs; CncrtBnd; HonRl; SchMus; StuCncl; SptEdSchPpr; CaptFtbl; CaptGlf; Northeast Missouri St; Teach.

ACKERMAN, Paula J; Lincoln HS; Lincoln, KS; 15/63 HonRl; LbryAde; OffAde; SchPl; TchrAde; FHA; GerCl; PpCl; Cloud County Comm College; Math.

ACKERMANN, Erich; Joliet Catholic HS; Lockport, IL; 28/178 CncrtBnd; HonRl; LitMag; NHS; SchMus; YthLg; RptrYrbk; RptrSchPpr; FSA; RusCl; Creighton Univ; Law.

ACKERMANN, James D; Lakefield HS; Lakefield, MN; HonRl; FFA; Worthington Comm College; Farmer.

ACKERMANN, John R; Gibraltar HS; Sister Bay, WI; 10/68 ALBoysSt; Aud/Vis; LitMag; NatlMeritSF; PolWkr; SchPl; StuCncl; Yrbk; EdSchPpr; Trk; Univ Of Dayton; Communications.

ACKERS, Mark A; Macomb HS; Macomb, IL; ALBoysSt; Chr; CncrtBnd; SchMus; SchPl; LetterBsktbl; LetterFtbl; Tennis; LetterTrk; Western Il Univ; Music.

ACKERSON, Audrey; Cornell HS; Cornell, WI; HonRl; College; Professional.

ACKERSON, Steven E; Ionia HS; Ionia, MI; 7/226 Band; CncrtBnd; HonRl; MrchBnd; NHS; PepBnd; SchMus; Ferris State Clg; Accounting.

ACKERSON, Tanya L; Bowdle Public HS; Bowdle, SD; Band; Chrs; ChrhWkr; DrlTm; HonRl; MrchBnd; SchPl; StuCncl; Yrbk; SchPpr; FTA; South Dakota State Univ.

ACKLEY, Cheryll L; Downers Grove North HS; Westmont, IL; 25/530 AFS; HonRl; NHS; Southern Illinois Univ; Mathematics.

ACKLIN, Sharyn M; Liberty HS; Mtn View, MO; 3/106 SecSrCls; Band; ChrhWkr; CncrtBnd; HonRl; MrchBnd; PepBnd; TchrAde; RptrYrbk; FHA; Sw Missouri State Univ.

ACKMAN, Philip W; Fort Atkinson HS; Fort Atkinson, WI; AFS; Chr; HonRl; NHS; NatlThespSoc; SchMus; SchPl; KeyCl; SpnCl; Univ; Mechanical Engineering.

ACKMAN, Sandi M; Greeley Public HS; Greenley, NE; 5/23 Chr; ChrhWkr; HonRl; LbryAde; PepBnd; SchPl; RptrYrbk; 4-H; 4-HAwd; Trade School; Accounting.

ACKS, Martin S; Stephen Decatur HS; Decatur, IL; Aud/Vis; JA; NHS; TreasRusCl; PresSciCl; Bsktbl; Univ Of Illinois.

ACORD, Robert E; Marion HS; Marion, IN; HonRl; CaptBsktbl; LetterFtbl; LetterTrk; Indiana Central College.

ACRI, Robert C; New Trier East HS; Wilmette, IL; ChrhWkr; CmntyWkr; HonRl; SctActv; StuGov; LetterFtbl; LetterWrstlng; GodCntryAwd; College; Medicine.

ACTON, Larry A; Turner HS; Kansas City, KS; CncrtBnd; HonRl; MrchBnd; NHS; SchMus; SchPl; FrCl; Ftbl; LetterWrstlng; OptClAwd; Air Force Academy.

ADAIR, Carolyn R; Platte Co R 3 HS; Platte City, MO; Chrs; HonRl; LitMag; OffAde; SchPl; StuCncl; TchrAde; RptrYrbk; RptrSchPpr; University; Business Management.

ADAIR, Chanda L; Laura Speed Elliot HS; Boonville, MO; VPSpnCl; LetterPpCl; SciCl; LetterBsktbl; LetterTrk; Chrldr; Vocational School; Business.

ADAIR, Edward G; Lockport Central HS; Lockport, IL; NHS; Bsbl; Ftbl; Wrstlng; Lewis Univ; Psychiatrist.

ADAIR, James D; Taylor HS; Kokomo, IN; 30/281 Band; CncrtBnd; HonRl; MrchBnd; YthFlsp; Wrstlng; CchngActv; College; Math.

ADAM, John F; Keota HS; Wellman, IA; 6/60 ALBoysSt; Band; CncrtBnd; HonRl; MrchBnd; VPNHS; NatlMeritCmnd; LetterBsbl; CaptBsktbl; LetterTrk; Univ Of Iowa; Architecture.

ADAMCZYK, Marianne; Ridgewood HS; Norridge, IL; SecChr; HonRl; PresNHS; SchMus; TchrAde; EdYrBk; GAA; College; Anthropology.

ADAMCZYK, Mary Kay M; Streator Twp HS; Streator, IL; 95/378 PresJrCls; VPSrCls; Band; ChrhWkr; YthFlsp; Illinois State Univ; Scientific Research.

ADAMCZYK, Stephen; Churchill HS; Livonia, MI; HonRl; NatlFornLg; PolWkr; SchPl; StuGov; LatCl; James Madison College; Pre Law.

ADAMCZYK, Ted D; Weber HS; Chicago, IL; 35/192 HonRl; IMSpt; U Of Il Urbana Champaign; Chem.

ADAMICH, Greg J; Robbinsdale Sr HS; Robbinsdale, MN; CtyCnl; HonRl; LbryAde; NHS; StuGov; Bsktbl; CaptTennis; Macalaster Clg; Business.

ADAMITIS, James; St Ignatius College Prep; Chicago, IL; 39 HonRl; NHS; NatlMeritCmnd; CaptSwmmng;.

ADAMKIEWICZ, Steven N; St Patrick HS; Chicago, IL; 14/450 ChrhWkr; HonRl; Loyola Univ; Optometry.

ADAMS, Ann E; Bishop Dwenger HS; Fort Wayne, IN; Chrs; CmntyWkr; DrlTm; LbryAde; OffAde; PolWkr; SchMus; SchPl; StuCncl; RptrYrbk; Chrldr; GAA; IMSpt; University; Business.

ADAMS, Brenda J; Hallsville HS; Columbia, MO; 5/48 TrsFrshCls; ChrhWkr; HonRl; HospAde; NHS; Univ Of Missouri; Cytotechnologist.

ADAMS, Brian; Chicago Vocational HS; Chicago, IL; 21/779 HonRl; NHS; CitAwd; Ill Inst Of Tech; Engr Tech.

ADAMS, Cathy; Polo HS; Polo, MO; SecJrCls; Chr; ChrhWkr; HonRl; StuCncl; EdYrBk; SchPpr; FHA; FrCl; PpCl; Chrldr; Business Schl; Vocation.

ADAMS, Charles D; Centerville HS; Centerville, IA; 5/152 VPJrCls; PresSrCls; ModUN; NHS; SchPl; PresYthFlsp; LetterFtbl; CaptTrk; CchngActv; Ia State Univ; Chemical Eng.

ADAMS, Charles E; South Knox HS; Wheatland, IN; Band; ChrhWkr; CmntyWkr; CncrtBnd; HonRl; MrchBnd; PepBnd; Bsbl; Bsktbl; Trk; CchngActv; University; Engineering.

ADAMS, Charles V; Spring Hill HS; Spring Hill, KS; 7/60 Band; Chrs; ChrhWkr; CncrtBnd; HonRl; Mdrgl; MrchBnd; NHS; PepBnd; SchMus; StuCncl; LetterBsktbl; LetterFtbl; LetterTrk; Ks State Univ; Architecture.

ADAMS, Cindy L; Pontiac HS; Pontiac, IL; 12/200 Band; Chr; Chrs; ChrhWkr; CncrtBnd; HonRl; MrchBnd; PepBnd; SchMus; YthFlsp; RptrYrbk; FrCl; College; Biology.

ADAMS, Constance J; Dwight D Eisenhower HS; Rochester, MI; 40/548 Chrs; ChrhWkr; CmntyWkr; HonRl; NHS; SchPl; TchrAde; YthFlsp; SpnCl; Oakland U; Law Enforcement.

ADAMS, Curtis R; Carl Sandburg HS; Palos Park, IL; 135/700 Chrs; HonRl; NatlMeritFnl; YthFlsp; SpnCl; MthCl; LetterBsbl; LetterFtbl; CaptSwmmng; Univ Of Il; Law.

ADAMS, Cynthia L; Hume HS; Hume, MO; ChrhWkr; HonRl; ModUN; NHS; PolWkr; StuCncl; StuGov; CivCl; FHA; PpCl; LetterBsktbl; DanFAwd; CitAwd; College; Professional.

ADAMS, Daniel R; Watertown Senior HS; Watertown, SD; College; Liberal Arts.

ADAMS, Daryl S; Harlan HS; Chicago, IL; 12/600 HonRl; NHS; NatlMeritCmnd; StuCncl; StuGov; TchrAde; YthLg; RptrYrbk; SptEdYrbk; Yrbk; IMSpt; JCAwd; JAAwd; Dartmouth College; Physical Ed.

ADAMS, David E; Metz HS; Rich Hill, MO; 1/12 PresFrshCls; Band; ChrhWkr; HonRl; SchPl; StuCncl; 4-H; PpCl; LetterBsbl; Bsktbl; LetterTrk; CchngActv; 4-HAwd; Univ Of Mo; Law.

ADAMS, Denise L; Plankinton HS; Plankington, SD; Band; CmntyWkr; HonRl; SchPl; EdSchPpr; 4-H; FHA; Bsktbl; 4-HAwd; CitAwd; College; Music Teacher.

ADAMS, Donald; Fremont Hs; Fremont, IN; 1/63 PresFrshCls; PresSophCls; HonRl; NHS; SchPl; StuCncl; FrCl; MthCl; LetterBsktbl; LetterTrk; Tri State College; Chemical Engineering.

ADAMS, Donna M; Stratford HS; Stratford, WI; 17/90 Band; CncrtBnd; HonRl; MrchBnd; PepBnd; Yrbk; FHA; FrCl;.

ADAMS, Doug D; Vandalia Comm HS; Vandalia, IL; Aud/Vis; HonRl; SchPl; SciCl; Bsbl; Bsktbl; Glf; College; Recreation.

ADAMS, Douglas M; Waukesha So HS; Waukesha, WI; Band; Chrs; MrchBnd; SchMus; SchPl; SctActv; RptrYrbk; EdYrBk; SptEdYrbk; Univ Of Wisconsin; Medical.

ADAMS, Elisabeth J; Culver Academy; Culver, IN; 14/169 StuGov; CaptLetterTennis; IMSpt; PPFtbl; Univ Of Nc; Law.

ADAMS, Gail B; Erskine HS; Erskine, MN; HospAde; Orch; SchPl; Wisconsin St Univ; Art.

ADAMS, Gregory M; Newton HS; Newton, IA; HonRl; Yrbk; College; Proffessional.

ADAMS, Janice J; Greenwood HS; Greenwood, IN; Band; CncrtBnd; HonRl; HospAde; MrchBnd; YthFlsp; LatCl; PpCl; Chrldr; Indiana Univ; Teaching.

ADAMS, Jeanne; Pacelli HS; Austin, MN; ChrhWkr; CmntyWkr; HonRl; EdSchPpr; 4-H; SpnCl; Tennis; IMSpt; 4-HAwd; CitAwd; Univ Of Minn; Professional.

ADAMS, Jerome R; Auburndale HS; Milladore, WI; Band; CncrtBnd; HonRl; LbryAde; MrchBnd; PepBnd; SchAde; FBLA; Ftbl; Trk; College.

ADAMS, Jerry R; Nishna Valley HS; Emerson, IA; ALBoysSt; Band; Chrs; ChrhWkr; CncrtBnd; HonRl; MrchBnd; PepBnd; Wrstlng; Coll; Mech/elec.

ADAMS, Joetta E; Frontenac HS; Frontenac, KS; TrsFrshCls; HonRl; SchPl; StuCncl; FHA; PpCl; Trk; Chrldr; PPFtbl; College; Business.

ADAMS, Joseph M; Ford Central HS; Roberts, IL; ALBoysSt; Band; Chrs; HonRl; Mdrgl; PepBnd; SchPl; Univ Of Illinois; Engineering.

ADAMS, Karen L; Littlefield HS; Brutus, MI; 1/32 LetterBand; Chr; CncrtBnd; HonRl; LbryAde; MrchBnd; OffAde; PepBnd; SchPl; LetterTrk; Col; Lawyer.

ADAMS, Karla B; Concordia Academy; St Paul, MN; 1/46 Band; CncrtBnd; DrlTm; HonRl; HospAde; ModUN; PepBnd; StuCncl; EdYrBk; EdSchPpr; Univ; Law.

ADAMS, Katherine A; Limestone Comm HS; Bartonville, IL; 3/326 HonRl; Mdrgl; StuGov; FrCl; GerCl; University; Teacher.

ADAMS, Kent L; Wichita East HS; Wichita, KS; HonRl; TchrAde; CaptTrk; Kansas St Univ; Economics.

ADAMS, Krista; Courtland HS; Courtland, KS; TrsFrshCls; Chrs; DrlTm; HonRl; MrchBnd; 4-H; Trk; Chrldr; 4-HAwd; PresAwd; Ft Hays St Coll; Teacher.

ADAMS, Lesli L; Eldora HS; Eldora, IA; 6/63 TrsSophCls; HonRl; JrNHS; StuCncl; SptEdYrbk; RptrSchPpr; FrCl; Bsktbl; Clge; Wildlife Biology.

ADAMS, Linda C; Trenton HS; Trenton, MI; 20/571 Chr; ChrhWkr; HonRl; NHS; YthFlsp; Wayne St Univ; Med Tech.

ADAMS, Lori B; Tipton Comm HS; Tipton, IA; HonRl; OffAde; YthFlsp; LetterBsbl; LetterBsktbl; LetterTrk; U Of Northern Ia; Phy Ed Teach.

ADAMS, Marcia L; Lyons Twp HS; Western Springs, IL; Chr; HonRl; FHA; Illinois State Univ; Elem Education.

ADAMS, Mark J; Metamora Township HS; Metamora, IL; 11/173 ALBoysSt; HonRl; College; Vocational.

ADAMS, Mary A; Seneca HS; Seneca, MO; ChrhWkr; PresFrshCls; PepBnd; TchrAde; 4-H; FHA; Chrldr; GAA; PPFtbl; 4-HAwd; Col; Professional.

ADAMS, Monika M; Fraser HS; Fraser, MI; 10/557 Chrs; CncrtBnd; HonRl; MrchBnd; NHS; NatlMeritSchl; PepBnd; TreasYthFlsp; 4-H; VoiceDemAwd; Wayne State Univ.

ADAMS, Nancy M; St Louise De Marillac HS; Park Ridge, IL; CmntyWkr; NatlMeritCmnd; SchMus; SchPl; StuGov; RptrSchPpr; Univ; Anthropology.

ADAMS, Patricia A; E Peoria Community HS; Morton, IL; 21/451 HonRl; NHS; StuCncl; RptrSchPpr; LatCl; MthCl; Bsbl; Bsktbl; Ftbl; Tennis; TreasGAA; Illinois State Univ; Pre Med.

ADAMS, Patricia A; Oskaloosa HS; Oskaloosa, KS; 9/37 Chr; HonRl; OffAde; SchAde; SchPl; 4-H; FBLA; FrCl; LetterPpCl; 4-HAwd; Business Sch; Secretary.

ADAMS, Raymond B; St Ignatius HS; Chicago, IL; 20/200 PresJrCls; HonRl; JrNHS; NatlMeritCmnd; SchMus; StuCncl; StuGov; Ftbl; Trk; Honard; Guitarist.

ADAMS, Rebecca A; Seperior HS; Superior, NE; 14/92 Band; Chrs; CncrtBnd; HonRl; MrchBnd; PepBnd; FBLA; PpCl; University; Music.

ADAMS, Richard; Clifton Central; Chebanse, IL; 12/154 JrNHS; NHS; Pres4-H; FFA; MthCl; Ftbl; LetterTrk; College; Agriculture Farming.

ADAMS, Robin G; Marquette HS; Alton, IL; HonRl; OffAde; Journalism.

ADAMS, Roger G; Wausau West HS; Wausau, WI; SchAde; StuCncl; Ftbl; College.

ADAMS, Ronald E; West Richland HS; Noble, IL; 10/302 ALBoysSt; CncrtBnd; HonRl; Orch; SchPl; Yrbk; LetterBsbl; LetterBsktbl; Trk; College; Electronics.

ADAMS, Sandra L; Mt Pleasant HS; Mt Pleasant, MI; 48/348 Chr; HonRl; LitMag; NatlMeritSchl; NHS; NatlThespSoc; SchMus; SchPl; YthFlsp; FrCl; Central Mi University; Science.

ADAMS, Sandy K; Shawnee HS; Mc Clure, IL; 13/70 ChrhWkr; HonRl; SchPl; YthFlsp; 4-H; FBLA; PpCl; Bsktbl; Trk; Shawnee Jr College; Art.

ADAMS, Sarah J; Norwell HS; Markle, IN; 2/203 ChrhWkr; HonRl; NHS; NatlMeritSF; NatlThespSoc; SchPl; TchrAde; YthFlsp; RptrSchPpr; LatCl; DARAwd; College; Professional.

ADAMS, Scott R; Robinson HS; Robinson, IL; 10/185 ChrhWkr; HonRl; IntrClCncl; Quill&Scroll; PresYthFlsp; Yrbk; SciCl; Rose Hulman Inst Tech; Elec Engineer.

ADAMS, Sharon K; Morton East HS; Cicero, IL; 25/771 ChrhWkr; JrNHS; LitMag; NHS; Bsktbl; CaptTennis; Trk; GAA; Augustana College; Mathematics.

ADAMS, Sherwood; Ralston HS; Omaha, NE; /250 Univ Of Nebr; Architecture.

ADAMS, Teresa A; New Palestine HS; New Palestine, IN; 21/155 Band; CncrtBnd; HonRl; HospAde; MrchBnd; NHS; PepBnd; SctActv; Yrbk; LatCl; LetterTrk; GAA; OptClAwd; College; Nursing.

ADAMS, Theresa A; Chicago Vocational HS; Chicago, IL; 21/783 ChrhWkr; DrlTm; HonRl; OffAde; TchrAde; Trk; Ill State Univ; Accounting.

ADAMS, Theresa M; Acadmey Of Our Lady HS; Chicago, IL; 10/178 HonRl; NHS; FNA; GAA; Univ Of Chicago; Medicine.

ADAMS, Thomas; Oskaloosa Sr HS; Oskaloosa, IA; Band; ChrhWkr; CncrtBnd; HonRl; MrchBnd; NHS; StuCncl; Bsktbl; Trk; College.

ADAMS, Vanessa M; Chicago Vocational HS; Chicago, IL; 15/697 HonRl; JrNHS; LbryAde; NHS; OffAde; PpCl; Bsktbl; Illinois Inst Of Tech; Photography.

ADAMS, Veva E; Hoxie HS; Grainfield, KS; 4/57 ALAGirlsSt; Band; ChrhWkr; CncrtBnd; HonRl; MrchBnd; PepBnd; FHA; Kansas State Univ; Accountant.

ADAMS, Warren P; Providence HS; Tinley Park, IL; 4/128 HonRl; FrCl; MthCl; SciCl; Trk; Lewis University.

ADAMS, Winalee; East Jackson HS; Jackson, MI; 5/125 Chr; PresJA; NHS; NatlMeritSF; OffAde; SchMus; StuCncl; Bsktbl; LetterGlf; U Of Mi; Engineering Computer Science.

ADAMSKI, Joan M; United Township HS; East Moline, IL; 122/589 HonRl; OffAde; Teen; SchPpr; 4-H; Trk; LetterChrldr; GAA; 4-HAwd; Black Hawk College; Business Administration.

ADAMSON, Cynthia K; Kearney HS; Kearney, NE; Band; DrlTm; HonRl; HospAde; NatlFornLg; NatlMeritCmnd; TchrAde; PpCl; Kearney State Coll; Med Tech.

ADAMSON, James A; Rantoul Township HS; Rantoul, IL; Aud/Vis; Band; CncrtBnd; HonRl; MrchBnd; OffAde; PepBnd; SchPl; SctActv; StuCncl; College; Psychology.

ADAMSON, Lois A; Brainerd Sr HS; Brainerd, MN; 5/460 VPAFS; ChrhWkr; CncrtBnd; MrchBnd; NHS; NatlMeritCmnd; StuCncl; LatCl; LetterBsktbl; EldAwd; Univ Of Minnesota; Engineering.

ADAMSON, Randy G; Geneseo HS; Geneseo, KS; PresFrshCls; ALBoysSt; Band; Chrs; HonRl; SchPl; YthFlsp; SptEdYrbk; Bsktbl; College; Education.

ADAMSON, Susan M; Moweaqua Unit 6a HS; Moweaqua, IL; Band; Chrs; HonRl; SchMus; FHA; SpnCl; LetterTennis; LetterTrk; LetterChrldr; GAA; Coll; Prof.

ADASHEK, Steven J; Wm Fremd HS; Palatine, IL; 62/650 Aud/Vis; VPChr; HonRl; Mdrgl; NatlThespSoc; SchMus; SchPl; StuCncl; VPTeen; SchPpr; LetterTennis; Washington Univ; Medicine.

ADCOCK, Carol A; Macon HS; Macon, IL; 9/56 SecJrCls; HonRl; NHS; Chrldr; GAA;.

ADCOCK, Patricia S; Malta Bend HS; Malta Bend, MO; Chrl; Chrs; HonRl; NatlThespSoc; SchPl; RptrSchPpr; FFA; FHA; Bsbl; Bsktbl;.

ADDANTE, Joseph C; Proviso West HS; Hillside, IL; 9/1086 College.

ADDERSPECK, Helga R; Taft HS; Chicago, IL; 65/780 Band; HonRl; Orch; TchrAde; Yrbk; GAA; College; Math Comp Science.

ADDINGTON, Philip J; Marias Des Cygnes HS; Seneca, MO; 4/13 ChrhWkr; CmntyWkr; HonRl; SchPl; SctActv; StuCncl; FFA; LetterBsktbl; LetterFtbl; LetterTrk; CitAwd; College; Biology.

ADDIS, Ann E; Toulon HS; Toulon, IL; 5/52 Band; Chr; HonRl; SchMus; SchPl; Yrbk; Pres4-H; GAA; DanFAwd; 4-HAwd; St Marys Coll; Music.

ADDISON, Karmen J; Hagerstown Jr Sr HS; Greens Fork, IN; 7/96 ALAGirlsSt; Band; NHS; TchrAde; YthFlsp; Yrbk; 4-H; FHA; PresSpnCl; Trk; Purdue Univ; Math.

ADDISON, Lori J; Monroe City HS; Monroe City, MO; EdYrBk; FHA; SpnCl; PpCl; College

ADDLEMAN, John A; Thornridge HS; Dolton, IL; 106/686 HonRl; LetterSwmmng; LetterTrk; AmLegAwd; Univ Of Chicago; History.

ADDUCCI, Michael C; Mendel Catholic HS; Chicago, IL; 24/160 HonRl; MthCl; LetterBsbl; College; Professional.

ADDY, Robert D; Farragut Comm School;; Imogene, IA; TrsJrCls; Band; CncrtBnd; HonRl; MrchBnd; PepBnd; YthFlsp; LetterTrk; Iowa State; Elec Eng.

ADDY, Ronda; Woodruff HS; Peoria, IL; JA; SchPl; TchrAde; SpnCl; IMSpt; College; Vocation.

ADE, Ellen; Huntington Catholic HS; Huntington, IN; HonRl; HospAde; RptrYrbk; PpCl; Lutheran Hosp Schl; Opertng Rm.

ADEE, Cristie A; Sycamore HS; Clare, IL; 7/200 Chr; CAP; CncrtBnd; HonRl; MrchBnd; NHS; PepBnd; SctActv; 4-H; 4-HAwd; Univ; Interpreter.

ADEE, Rex; North Central HS; Haddam, KS; Band; HonRl; MrchBnd; PepBnd; SchMus; SchPl; YthFlsp; FFA; Ftbl; Chrldr;.

ADELMANN, Mark M; Danube HS; Kiester, MN; 4/43 Band; Chr; ChrhWkr; SchMus; SchPl; StuCncl; Bsbl; Bsktbl; Ftbl; Trk; Oral Roberts Univ; Professional Baseball.

ADELMEYER, Patricia; St Marys Springs HS; Fond Du Lac, WI; 19/120 Chrs; CmntyWkr; NHS; SchPl; StuCncl; RptrYrbk; LatCl; Chrldr; College; Special Education.

ADELSTEIN, Douglas W; Parkway Central HS; Chesterfield, MO; 50/450 CmntyWkr; JCC; Tennis; ChmbCommrsAwd; JCAwd; KiwanAwd; RotaryAwd; Univ; Law.

ADEN, Donald L; Neillsville HS; Neillsville, WI; 41/114 ALBoysSt; ChrhWkr; CmntyWkr; HonRl; JCC; SancSoc; SchAde; TchrAde; 4-H; FFA; PpCl; LetterBsbl; LetterFtbl; Trade School; Electronics.

ADEN, Julie B; Illinois Valley Central HS; Chillicothe, IL; 1/225 Band; Chrs; CmntyWkr; MrchBnd; NHS; SctActv; YthFlsp; 4-H; CaptBsktbl; GAA; 4-HAwd; College; Med.

ADEN, Lona R; Palmer Cons HS; Palmer, IA; 1/22 PresFrshCls; HonRl; ModUN; RptrSchPpr; FHA; LetterBsktbl; Ia State Univ; Home Economics.

ADEN, Mary L; Farnam Public HS; Farnam, NE; SecFrshCls; SecJrCls; Band; Chrs; HonRl; MrchBnd; SchPl; TchrAde; RptrYrbk; EdSchPpr; 4-H; PpCl; Chrldr; College; Professional.

ADER, Jesse V; North Putnam Jr Sr HS; Greencastle, IN; 6/114 HonRl; 4-H; FFA; SpnCl; MthCl; 4-HAwd; College; Vocational Ag Teacher.

ADIX, Paul K; Ogden Community Sch; Ogden, IA; 19/56 CmntyWkr; 4-H; MthCl; SciCl; LetterBsktbl; LetterFtbl; LetterTrk; CchngActv; Iowa State University; Vet Med.

ADKINS, Jennie D; Liberty Sr HS; Liberty, MO; 3/306 Band; Chr; ChrhWkr; CncrtBnd; HonRl; JrNHS; MrchBnd; NHS; OffAde; GAA; IMSpt; Univ Of Mo Rolla; Petroleum Engr.

ADKINS, Karen L; Lindblom Tech HS; Chicago, IL; 139/637 JA; OffAde; TchrAde; FrCl; GAA; University Of Chicago; Professional.

ADKINS, Kathy D; Savannah HS; Savannah, MO; SecBand; TreasChr; HonRl; NHS; PresStuCncl; Pres4-H; PresFrCl; TreasPpCl; GAA; DARAwd; 4-HAwd; LionAwd; College.

ADKINS, Leona M; Huron Sr HS; Romulus, MI; ChrhWkr; HonRl; College; Lpn.

ADKINS, Lisa G; Excelsior Springs West HS; Excelsior Springs, MO; Chrs; HonRl; JrNHS; NHS; OffAde; StuCncl; FTA; PpCl; SciCl; College; Teaching.

ADKINS, Mark K; Charleston HS; Charleston, IL; RptrSchPpr; Siu; Ba In Photo.

ADKINS, Regina F; North Platte HS; Camden Point, MO; Band; ChrhWkr; HonRl; LbryAde; MrchBnd; SecFHA; PresPpCl; LetterBsktbl; Chrldr; CitAwd; College; Secretary.

ADKINS, Susan D; Savannah HS; Savannah, MO; ALAGirlsSt; Band; VPChr; HonRl; NHS; YthFlsp; 4-H; Chrldr; GAA; 4-HAwd; College.

ADKISON, Carol E; Whiting HS; Whiting, IN; 3/100 PresJrCls; ALAGirlsSt; HonRl; JA; NHS; RptrSchPpr; FTA; GerCl; GAA; AmLegAwd;.

ADKISSON, Timothy A; East Prairie HS; East Prairie, MO; Band; CtyCnl; HonRl; MrchBnd; SchPl; SctActv; StuCncl; FFA; SpnCl; Ftbl; Mo Univ; Veterinarian.

ADLAM, Bobbi J; Unionville Sebewaing Area HS; Unionville, MI; 416/125 SecTrsSrCls; HstSrCls; Chrs; ChrhWkr; HonRl; HospAde; NHS; OffAde; SecStuCncl; FHA; SecLatCl; 4-HAwd; Ferris St College; Medical Asst.

ADLER, Cynthia P; Gage Park HS; Chicago, IL; ChrhWkr; HonRl; ModUN; OffAde; StuCncl; Univ Of Illinois; German.

ADLER, Mary J; Milbank HS; Milbank, SD; SecSrCls; PresAFS; ALAGirlsSt; HonRl; NatlFornLg; NHS; VPStuCncl; RptrSchPpr; PpCl; VoiceDemAwd; College; Biology.

ADOLPH, Randy L; Farmington Sr HS; Farmington, MO; ALBoysSt; Chr; Chrl; Chrs; ChrhWkr; HonRl; Mdrgl; NHS; SchMus; TchrAde; College; Veterinarian.

ADOLPHSON, Karen D; Galesburg Sr HS; Galesburg, IL; 8/588 ALAGirlsSt; VPChr; HonRl; NHS; NatlThespSoc; SchMus; SchPl; StuCncl; Yrbk; DARAwd; Augustana College; Music.

ADOLPHUS, Kenneth; Ecorse HS; Ecorse, MI; HonRl; JA; NHS; Univ Of Mi; Architecture.

ADREON, Gary F; Eddyville Comm HS; Eddyville, IA; PresJrCls; HonRl; PolWkr; SchPl; TchrAde; RptrYrbk; LetterBsbl; LetterFtbl; Trk; Wrstlng; College; Vocational.

ADRIAN, Gary W; Helias HS; Jefferson City, MO; Aud/Vis; HonRl; LbryAde; OffAde; SpnCl; LetterFtbl; Mu Clge; Pro.

ADRIANCE, Lynna M; Paw Paw HS; Paw Paw, MI; PresSrCls; HonRl; JrNHS; NHS; NatlMeritFnl; NatlMeritSchl; NatlMeritSF; StuCncl; FHA; GAA; Grand Rapids Baptist College; Social Worker.

ADSIT, Jane E; Richland Center HS; Richland Center, WI; ChrhWkr; HonRl; LbryAde; ModUN; TchrAde; RptrYrbk; 4-H; FBLA; FHA; LatCl; College; Professional.

AEIKENS, Norine A; Raymond HS; Raymond, MN; 3/29 TrsJrCls; Band; Chr; ChrhWkr; CncrtBnd; HonRl; LbryAde; MrchBnd; NHS; OffAde; PepBnd; IMSpt; St Cloud Business College; Court Reptg.

AELMORE, John D; Greensburg HS; Greensburg, KS; 6/50 VPFrshCls; TrsSophCls; ALBoysSt; Band; Chr; Chrs; CncrtBnd; HonRl; Mdrgl; MrchBnd; LetterBsktbl; LetterFtbl; College; Business.

AERTS, Pam A; East De Pere HS; De Pere, WI; 46/198 CncrtBnd; MrchBnd; Orch; PepBnd; RptrYrbk; SptEdSchPpr; FTA; CaptTrk; PresGAA; IMSpt; Univ Of Wisconsin; Biology.

AERZS, Karen; Aquinas HS; David City, NE; 2/87 Chr; Chrs; HospAde; NHS; NatlThespSoc; Quill&Scroll; SchMus; TchrAde; RptrYrbk; SpnCl; Univ Of Nebraska; Nursing.

AESCHLIMAN, David J; Central Of Lee Co HS; Montrose, IA; HonRl; SchPl; SctActv; LetterFtbl; CaptTrk; College; Engineering Field.

AESCHLIMAN, Rick J; Perry Lecompton HS; Topeka, KS; 5/90 HonRl; LbryAde; SchPl; StuCncl; RptrSchPpr; LetterFtbl; LetterTrk; LetterWrstlng; Ottawa Univ.

AFABLE, Mark V; Clifton Central HS; Clifton, IL; Band; CncrtBnd; PepBnd; SchMus; SchPl; FrCl; LetterFtbl; LetterTrk; Marquette University; Liberal Arts.

AFFOLDER, Trenna R; Puxico HS; Kinder, MO; PresJrCls; Chrs; HonRl; MrchBnd; StuCncl; FHA; PpCl; IMSpt; PresAwd; Clge; Tech Training.

AFTONOMOS, Maria S; Benson HS; Omaha, NE; Chr; Chrs; ChrhWkr; HonRl; NHS; Orch; SchMus; PpCl; CaptChrldr; GAA; U Of Ne; Psychology.

AGAR, Timothy G; Browns Valley Public HS; Browns Valley, MN; PresSophCls; Band; Chr; Chrs; ChrhWkr; CmntyWkr; HonRl; LbryAde; MrchBnd; OffAde; SchMus; Swmmng; Tennis; Trk; Rockhurst College; Religion.

AGATSTEIN, Louis W; Clayton HS; Clayton, MO; 20/200 NHS; NatlThespSoc; SchMus; SchPl; SctActv; Yrbk; College; Engineer.

AGEE, Karl D; Bentley HS; Livonia, MI; HonRl; PolWkr; SctActv; Yrbk; SchPpr; Univ Of Mi; Pro Biologist.

AGEMA, Steven K; Calvin Christian HS; Wyoming, MI; Band; HonRl; TchrAde; SecTrsSophCls; IMSpt; Coll; Attng.

AGEN, Mark D; Wrightstown HS; Kaukauna, WI; TrsJrCls; TrsSrCls; HonRl; StuGov; 4-H; SpnCl; MthCl; Bsktbl; LetterFtbl; Trk; 4-HAwd; College; Professional.

AGERTER, Mark D; Munster HS; Munster, IN; Band; HonRl; TchrAde; YthFlsp; SchPpr; Ftbl; IMSpt; Purdue U Calumet; Engineering.

AGIN, James W; Harrisburg HS; Harrisburg, IL; HonRl; Pres4-H; PresFFA; 4-HAwd; College; Agriculture Mechanics.

AGLINSKAS, Peter R; St Laurence HS; Chicago, IL; CncrtBnd; HonRl; Univ; Herpetologist.

AGNEW, Ann L; Lawson HS; Rayville, MO; Band; Chrs; ChrhWkr; HonRl; NHS; SchMus; SchPl; RptrYrbk; RptrSchPpr; RotaryAwd; Nursing School; Registered Nurse.

AGNEW, Candace A; University City Sr HS; University City, MO; Chr; SecJA; NatlMeritCmnd; StuGov; Twrl; PresPpCl; Univ; Retailing.

AGNEW, Gerald P; St Mary HS; Burlington, WI; PresSophCls; PresJrCls; ALBoysSt; HonRl; SctActv; StuCncl; RptrYrbk; LetterBsbl; LetterBsktbl; CaptFtbl; La Crosse; Teacher.

AGNEW, Mari L; Greenfield HS; Greenfield, WI; Chrl; HonRl; ModUN; StuGov; LetterTrk; GAA; Redwoods Coll.

AGOSTINELLI, Maria; South Lake HS; East Detroit, MI; 27/500 HonRl; Univ Of Detroit; Business.

AGOSTO, Cheryle A; Neodesha HS; Altoona, KS; Band; Chr; ChrhWkr; CncrtBnd; LbryAde; MrchBnd; OffAde; PepBnd; Trk; IMSpt; Independence Community Junior College.

AGRAN, Raymond D; New Trier West HS; Wilmette, IL; 22/694 Aud/Vis; Chrs; HonRl; NatlFornLg; Univ; Law.

AGUILAR, Dawn M; Highland Park HS; St Paul, MN; Chrs; IntrClCncl; LbryAde; MrchBnd; OffAde; SchAde; SchPl; StuCncl; TchrAde; College; Dancing.

AHERN, Craig L; Truman Public HS; Lewisville, MN; TrsJrCls; Band; CncrtBnd; MrchBnd; FFA; LetterFtbl; LetterTrk; CaptWrstlng; St Cloud State.

AHERN, Ellen M; Notre Dame HS; Chicago, IL; 9/302 Chrl; HonRl; JrNHS; NatlFornLg; NHS; NatlMeritCmnd; RedCrAde; SchPpr; Univ; Special Education.

AHERN, Michael; Sacred Heart HS; Salina, KS; ALBoysSt; HonRl; NHS; TchrAde; FBLA; KeyCl; SpnCl; Bsktbl; Glf; Trk; Ks State Univ; Lawyer.

AHISTROM, Rhonda J; Sacred Heart HS; Salina, KS; Band; Chrs; CncrtBnd; HonRl; MrchBnd; NatlMeritCmnd; StuCncl; SchPpr; FHA; PpCl; Coll; Nurse.

AHL, Joanne M; J F K Prep HS; Green Bay, WI; Chrs; ChrhWkr; CmntyWkr; HonRl; LbryAde; SchPl; SctActv; Bsktbl; LetterTrk; GAA; IMSpt; PPFtbl; Uw Green Bay; Performing Arts.

AHLAND, Theresa N; Rolla HS; Rolla, MO; 13/307 ChrhWkr; CmntyWkr; HonRl; SctActv; Univ; Computer Science.

AHLBERG, Thomas L; Worthington Senior HS; Worthington, MN; 80/309 HonRl; NHS; TchrAde; FFA; SciCl; LetterFtbl; Univ Of Minnesota; Bio Teacher.

AHLBORN, Scott E; Bloom Township HS; Chicago Hts, IL; 161/865 HonRl; NHS; OffAde; RedCrAde; Michigan State University; Landscape.

AHLERS, Bonita; Pepin HS; Pepin, WI; 2/46 HonRl; SchPl; PpCl; Bsktbl; GAA; BttyCrckrAwd; Rochester Comm College; Airline Stewardess.

AHLERS, Bonnie R; Pepin HS; Pepin, WI; 2/45 VPChrhWkr; HonRl; LbryAde; NHS; Yrbk; VPFHA; PpCl; GAA; Trade School; Airline Stewardess.

AHLERS, Denise M; Sacred Heart Acad; Mt Pleasant, MI; SecSrCls; HonRl; OffAde; PpCl; Bsbl; Central Mich Univ; Elem Teach.

AHLERS, Gregor J; Granite City South HS; Granite City, IL; 17/630 HonRl; NHS; SctActv; Trk; University; Chemistry.

AHLGRIM, Ryan; Willowbrook Hs; Lombard, IL; HonRl; SctActv; TchrAde; UNYO; YthFlsp; EdSchPpr; Goshen College; Ministry.

AHLGRIM, Scott A; York Comm HS; Elmhurst, IL; 140/950 ChrhWkr; CncrtBnd; HonRl; Augustana College; Science.

AHLGRIMM, John R; Mineral Point HS; Mineral Point, WI; 14/95 Band; HonRl; MrchBnd; NHS; SchMus; SctActv; YthFlsp; LetterBsktbl; CaptGlf; University Of Wisconsin; Engineering.

AHLIN, Lori J; Escanaba Area Public HS; Escanaba, MI; 5/383 DrmMjrt; TreasJA; NHS; NatlMeritCmnd; RedCrAde; PresFTA; PresSpnCl; BttyCrckrAwd; JAAwd; RotaryAwd; Mi Tech U; Business Adm/acct.

AHLSTROM, Diane M; Sacred Heart HS; Salina, KS; Band; HonRl; MrchBnd; PepBnd; FBLA; College; Accounting.

AHLSTROM, Rhonda J; Sacred Heart HS; Salina, KS; 3/56 Band; Chrs; CncrtBnd; NatlFornLg; NHS; NatlMeritCmnd; StuCncl; SchPpr; FHA; PpCl; College; Nursing.

AHMANN, Donna M; Hempstead HS; Dubuque, IA; 22/509 Chr; HonRl; JA; JrNHS; NHS; SchMus; SchPl; IMSpt; Univ Of N Iowa.

AHOLT, Jane L; Glasgow R Ii HS; Glasgow, MO; 4/48 SecTrsFrshCls; SecJrCls; Chr; Chrs; HonRl; NHS; SchMus; SchPl; CaptBsbl; CaptBsktbl;.

AHRENS, Anita M; Rolla HS; Rolla, MO; 34/313 HonRl; HospAde; SchPl; SctActv; FHA; FrCl; LatCl; Coll; Teach.

AHRENS, Barbara; Irving Crown Hs; Algonquin, IL; 3/365 Chrs; HonRl; JrNHS; Mdrgl; NHS; StuCncl; TchrAde; RptrSchPpr; SciCl; Tennis; U; Professional.

AHRENS, Cheryl A; L D F HS; Marshalltown, IA; Chrs; Mdrgl; Marshalltown Comm College; Nursing.

AHRENS, Luanne M; Cal Comm HS; Latimer, IA; 6/34 CmntyWkr; HonRl; StuCncl; 4-H; Iowa State Univ; Child Development.

AHRENS, Rhonda L; Paynesville HS; Paynesville, MN; 8/123 Band; ChrhWkr; CmntyWkr; CncrtBnd; HonRl; MrchBnd; PepBnd; YthFlsp; RptrYrbk; Yrbk; FHA; College; Nursing.

AHRENS, Steven J; Proviso HS East; Maywood, IL; 6/1049 HonRl; Quill&Scroll; SptEdSchPpr; LetterGlf; College; Math/journalism.

AIELLO, Bart L; Mendel Catholic Prep HS; Chicago, IL; 6/191 ChrhWkr; HonRl; NatlMeritCmnd; StuCncl; RptrYrbk; RptrSchPpr; KeyCl; GerCl; PpCl; IMSpt; Univ Of Illinois; Accounting.

AIGNER, Margaret E; Brookfield East HS; Brookfield, WI; CmntyWkr; HonRl; HospAde; YthFlsp; Univ Of Wisc; Psychologist.

AIKIN, Michelle D; Auoha Community HS; Auoca, IA; 13/46 Band; HonRl; MrchBnd; PepBnd; Quill&Scroll; SchMus; SchPl; EdSchPpr; PresFTA; LetterTrk; College; Foreign Languages.

AILOR, Audrey D; Meadville R Iv HS; Meadville, MO; 7/36 HonRl; NHS; OffAde; StuCncl; EdYrBk; SchPpr; FHA; LetterBsbl; LetterTrk; IMSpt; Central Mo St Univ.

AILTS, Rolayne L; Flandreau Public HS; Flandreau, SD; SecSophCls; Chr; HonRl; NHS; StuCncl; College.

AIMEN, Julie B; New Trier East HS; Winnetka, IL; PresJrCls; CmntyWkr; HonRl; PolWkr; StuCncl; College; Social Work.

AIMERS, Lee T; Wauconda HS; Wauconda, IL; CncrtBnd; NHS; Orch; PepBnd; SchPl; StuCncl; TchrAde; Bsbl; Ftbl; LetterGlf; LetterWrstlng; Bemidji State College; Forestry.

AINGER, David A; Alden Hebron HS; Harvard, IL; 12/42 VPFrshCls; Aud/Vis; Band; Chr; Chrs; ChrhWkr; CmntyWkr; CncrtBnd; HonRl; MrchBnd; Orch; PepBnd; SchMus; SchPl; Univ Of Wisconsin; Farmer.

AIPPERSPACH, Audrey V; Golden Valley HS; Golden Valley, ND; 2/12 SecSrCls; Band; Chrs; CncrtBnd; HonRl; PepBnd; RptrYrbk; RptrSchPpr; LetterBsktbl; BttyCrckrAwd; Coll; Greenhouse Tech.

AIRGOOD, Kristopher C; Manchester HS; N Manchester, IN; Band; HonRl; NHS; 4-H; KeyCl; Bsbl; Bsktbl; LetterFtbl; LetterTrk; College; English.

AISTRUP, Cynthia; Hanston HS; Hanston, KS; 1/15 PresSophCls; SecJrCls; Band; Chrs; HonRl; NatlMeritCmnd; SchPl; PpCl; Chrldr; Ft Hayes Ks St Coll; Eng Teach.

AITCHISON, Neil J; Western Dubuque HS; Cascade, IA; 71/246 Aud/Vis; Chr; Chrl; Chrs; CmntyWkr; JA; SchMus; SchPl; 4-H; Bsktbl; LetterFtbl; Swmmng; Trk; 4-HAwd;.

AITKEN, Lyle W; Sparta HS; Sparta, IL; 40/165 PresSrCls; HonRl; StuGov; Bsbl; CaptFtbl; LetterTrk; Millakin Univ; Business Admin.

AKARD, Sarah A; Heritage Christian HS; Indianapolis, IN; Chr; ChrhWkr; HonRl; NatlSciFnd; SchMus; RptrSchPpr; Purdue Univ; Biology.

AKEMAN, Susan B; Slater HS; Slater, MO; 3/55 ALAGirlsSt; Band; Chrs; CncrtBnd; HonRl; LbryAde; MrchBnd; PepBnd; SchPl; Twrl; GAA; Mo Univ; Business Admin.

AKER, Nancy L; Truman HS; Independence, MO; Chr; ChrhWkr; CmntyWkr; HonRl; HospAde; SctActv; SpnCl; PpCl; College.

AKER, Sharon K; Slinger HS; Slinger, WI; Band; CncrtBnd; MrchBnd; PepBnd; LetterBsktbl; Trk; GAA; PresAwd; Marquette Univ; Medicine.

AKERLUND, Carol; Ashland HS; Ashland, IL; Band; Chrs; CncrtBnd; MrchBnd; NHS; SchPl; StuCncl; RptrSchPpr; PpCl; Chrldr; Coll.

AKERMAN, Beverly; Cherry HS; Iron, MN; HonRl; 4-H; PpCl; Trk; Technical School; Working.

AKERS, Cindy D; Valley R 6 HS; Belgrade, MO; VPFrshCls; PresSophCls; PresJrCls; Band; Chrs; ChrhWkr; HonRl; SchPl; StuCncl; SchPpr; GAA; DARAwd;.

AKERS, Jerry D; Central City Comm HS; Central City, IA; ChrhWkr; NatlThespSoc; Quill&Scroll; SchPl; YthFlsp; RptrSchPpr; Pres4-H; LetterBsbl; LetterBsktbl; LetterFtbl; Univ; Teach.

AKERS, Loree J; Dekalb Sr HS; Dekalb, IL; 10/350 Band; CncrtBnd; HonRl; JrNHS; MrchBnd; NHS; Orch; PepBnd; SchMus; StuCncl; DARAwd; Univ; Professional.

AKERS, Michael W; Crispus Attucks HS; Indianapolis, IN; ALBoysSt; Aud/Vis; LbryAde; Trk; IMSpt; Vincennes Univ; Vocation.

AKERS, Steve C; Paris HS; Holliday, MO; ALBoysSt; ChrhWkr; CmntyWkr; HonRl; NHS; SchPl; 4-H; LetterFtbl; IMSpt; AmLegAwd; 4-HAwd; GodCntryAwd; New Mexico St Univ; Journalism.

AKERS, Toni C; North Central HS; Shelburn, IN; Aud/Vis; Chr; Chrs; ChrhWkr; FBLA; FSA; PpCl; Trk; Chrldr; Vincennes Univ; English.

AKERSON, Dale A; Wahoo HS; Colon, NE; PresJrCls; ALBoysSt; HonRl; YthFlsp; SpnCl; CaptFtbl; LetterTrk; LetterWrstlng; CchngActv; GovHonPrgAwd; Trade Sch; Refrigeration.

AKERSON, Jeffrey D; Holdrege HS; Holdrege, NE; 1/120 ALBoysSt; Band; ChrhWkr; HonRl; MrchBnd; StuCncl; YthFlsp; Bsbl; LetterBsktbl; CaptFtbl; Kearney State College; Dr.

AKINS, Patricia L; Hastings Senior HS; Hastings, NE; 107/341 Chr; DrlTm; HonRl; LbryAde; Teen; PpCl; Bsktbl; LetterSwmmng; Trk; IMSpt; Univ Of Wyoming; Wildlife Conservation.

AKRE, Valerie L; Atwater Public HS; Atwater, MN; 7/52 ALAGirlsSt; ChrhWkr; HonRl; SchPl; TchrAde; EdYrBk; RptrSchPpr; FFA; Willmar Vocation Technical; Medical Sec.

ALADEEN, Becky L; Central HS; St Joseph, MO; 61/600 Chr; ChrhWkr; CmntyWkr; HonRl; SchMus; StuGov; Chrldr; College; Social Worker.

ALAMPRESE, Deborah L; Fenton HS; Wood Dale, IL; 15/367 VPSrCls; CncrtBnd; HonRl; MrchBnd; NHS; Quill&Scroll; StuCncl; Yrbk; LetterTennis; GAA; Clge; Environmental/sci.

ALANDER, Dirk H; Plainfield HS; Plainfield, IL; 41/297 Band; HonRl; NatlThespSoc; Quill&Scroll; SctActv; Yrbk; SchPpr; GerCl; Ftbl; LetterTrk; Univ Of Ill; Medical Profession.

ALARIE, Kathleen A; All Saints Central HS; Bay City, MI; 4/138 Band; ChrhWkr; HonRl; NHS; Orch; PepBnd; StuCncl; 4-H; Bsktbl; 4-HAwd; Delta Coll; Phy Therapy.

ALARIE, Peggy S; Kearsley HS; Flint, MI; Chr; ChrhWkr; CmntyWkr; MrchBnd; NHS; RedCrAde; SctActv; Twrl; FrCl; Swmmng; Trk; Univ Of Michigan; Medicine.

ALBAUGH, Kevin L; Hillsdale HS; Hillsdale, MI; 4/180 Band; CncrtBnd; HonRl; JrNHS; MrchBnd; NHS; Orch; PepBnd; StuCncl; StuGov; LetterBsbl; Bsktbl; Ftbl; LetterTrk; Univ Of Michigan; Music.

ALBEE, Dennis; Lakeshore HS; Stevensville, MI; 35/250 ChrhWkr; HonRl; SchAde; SchPl; KeyCl; MthCl; Michigan State U; Economics.

ALBEE, Neal E; Burlington HS; Burlington, WI; 27/289 Band; HonRl; PresNHS; NatlMeritSchl; StuGov; RptrSchPpr; SptEdSchPpr; PresLatCl; Ftbl; CchngActv; Luther College; Medicine.

ALBERG, Doris D; Armstrong Sr HS; Neenah, WI; 14/604 Chr; HonRl; NHS; SchMus; SchPl; College; Mathematics.

ALBERICO, Patrick; Carlinville HS; Carlingville, IL; Band; CncrtBnd; HonRl; SchPl; Univ Of Illinois; Engineering Physics.

ALBERS, Connie L; Central Comm HS; Germantown, IL; VPJrCls; HonRl; NHS; VPFHA; FrCl; DARAwd; Business Sch; Business.

ALBERS, David J; St Charles HS; St Charles, MI; CmntyWkr; HonRl; SchPl; Bsbl; Bsktbl; Glf; IMSpt; JCAwd; CitAwd; VoiceDemAwd;.

ALBERS, Denise A; Cedar Catholic HS; Hartington, NE; 6/69 TrsFrshCls; SecJrCls; Band; Chrs; CncrtBnd; HonRl; MrchBnd; NHS; PepBnd; Yrbk; GerCl; PpCl; Trk; Mt Marty College; Medicine.

ALBERS, James W; Bellevue Sr HS; Bellevue, NE; PresBand; ChrhWkr; CncrtBnd; JrNHS; MrchBnd; NHS; NatlMeritSF; PepBnd; SchMus; UNYO; EdYrBk; College; Political Science.

ALBERS, Leonna; Franklin Public HS; Bloomington, NE; Chrs; ChrhWkr; HonRl; SchPl; 4-H; FHA; EngCl; Trk; Trade School.

ALBERS, Le Rae A; Carpio HS; Foxholm, ND; SecSophCls; Band; Chrs; HonRl; SchAde; SchPl; EdSchPpr; PpCl; College; Nursing.

ALBERS, Rebecca J; Franklin Public HS; Bloomington, NE; 16/54 ALAGirlsSt; Band; Chrs; CncrtBnd; HonRl; PepBnd; SchPl; 4-H; PpCl; College; Vocation.

ALBERSON, Sharon K; Valley Center HS; Valley Center, KS; HonRl; LbryAde; SchAde; TchrAde; Friends Univ; Business.

ALBERT, Christian; Marysville HS; Marysville, MI; 21/176 PresFrshCls; CtyCnl; HonRl; NHS; SchPl; StuCncl; Bsktbl; Ftbl; Trk; Mich Tech Univ; Civil Eng.

ALBERT, Julie A; Caledonia HS; Calendonia, MN; Chrs; DrlTm; HonRl; MrchBnd; NHS; SchPl; SctActv; EdYrBk; SpnCl; College; Professnl.

ALBERT, Lorie C; Ladywood St Agnes HS; Indianapolis, IN; Chr; Chrs; CmntyWkr; HospAde; Mdrgl; SchMus; StuCncl; FrCl; College; Physical Therapists.

ALBERT, Mark T; Northridge HS; Middlebury, IN; Band; ChrhWkr; CncrtBnd; HonRl; MrchBnd; PpCl; LetterBsktbl; LetterFtbl; Glf; College; Civil Mech Engineer.

ALBERTS, Connie S; Marion HS; Marion, MI; 4/57 SecJrCls; SecSrCls; ChrhWkr; HonRl; LbryAde; NHS; StuGov; BttyCrckrAwd; Central Mi Univ.

ALBERTSEN, Steven L; Exira Comm HS; Exira, IA; 2/44 SecJrCls; Chrs; HonRl; NHS; SchPl; FFA; LetterBsbl; LetterBsktbl; LetterFtbl; Trk; Iowa State Univ; Computer.

ALBERTSEN, Steven L; Exira Community HS; Exira, IA; 1/43 SecJrCls; Chrs; HonRl; NHS; SchPl; RptrSchPpr; FFA; LetterBsbl; LetterBsktbl; LetterFtbl; LetterTrk; Iowa State Univ; Agribusiness.

ALBERTSON, Guy L; Sedgwick HS; Sedgwick, KS; PresJrCls; Chr; Chrs; HonRl; JA; Mdrgl; TchrAde; Bsbl; Bsktbl; Ftbl; College;.

ALBERTSON, Kerry T; Humboldt HS; Humboldt, IA; Band; CncrtBnd; HonRl; MrchBnd; NHS; PepBnd; SchMus; RptrSchPpr; LetterGlf; IMSpt; Ia State U; Engineer.

ALBERTSON, Ruth M; Hackett HS; Kalamazoo, MI; 13/143 HospAde; Bronson Methodist School Of Nursing; R N.

ALBIERO, Donna M; Forest Park HS; Crystal Falls, MI; Band; CncrtBnd; HonRl; MrchBnd; StuCncl; RptrYrbk; FNA; Trk; Chrldr; IMSpt; College; Professional.

ALBIN, Diane M; Hubbard HS; Chicago, IL; SecJrCls; SecSrCls; NHS; Quill&Scroll; SecStuGov; SecFTA; TreasSpnCl; MthCl; PpCl; GAA; U Of Il; Pharmacy.

ALBIN, Linda M; Central HS; Omaha, NE; Chr; HonRl; Yrbk; FrCl; National Col Of Bus; Dat Processing.

ALBIN, Rosanne A; Caro Comm HS; Caro, MI; 31/169 HonRl; LbryAde; NHS; SchPl; SecSctActv; TchrAde; 4-H; LetterBsbl; Trk; 4-HAwd; Saginaw Valley College; Veterinarian.

ALBOSTA, Bridget; Hemlock HS; Hemlock, MI; 2/170 SecFrshCls; VPSophCls; Band; ChrhWkr; SchPl; StuCncl; GAA; IMSpt; Delta Coll; Computer Program.

ALBRECHT, Carol D; Ponca HS; Jackson, NE; Chr; Chrs; HonRl; SchPl; 4-H; PpCl; LetterTrk; 4-HAwd; Col; Specialized Nurse.

ALBRECHT, Cynthia; Alsen Public HS; Alsen, ND; ALAGirlsSt; Band; LbryAde; PepBnd; SchPl; StuCncl; YthFlsp; SchPpr; Bsktbl; Chrldr; College; Optometry.

ALBRECHT, David K; Braymer C 4 HS; Braymer, MO; VPJrCls; HonRl; VPFFA; Ftbl; Trade School; Vocational.

ALBRECHT, Fred; Carrolton HS; Carrollton, IL; 28/85 HonRl; NHS; SchPl; StuCncl; FBLA; FTA; Wrstlng; AmLegAwd; Western Ill Univ; Conservation.

ALBRECHT, Fred J; Carrollton HS; Carrollton, IL; 28/84 HonRl; StuCncl; FBLA; FFA; FSA; FTA; LetterFtbl; LetterWrstlng; AmLegAwd; Western Illinois Univ; Conservation.

ALBRECHT, James T; Hillcrest HS; Hazel Crest, IL; 2/475 HonRl; JrNHS; NHS; SptEdSchPpr; MthCl; Glf; LetterTennis; U Of Notre Dame; Busi.

ALBRECHT, Joan M; Rushford HS; Rushford, MN; VPFrshCls; AFS; Chr; Chrs; HonRl; LbryAde; StuCncl; LetterTrk; Chrldr; CchngActv; Col; Vocation.

ALBRECHT, Karen; Wabasha Kellogg HS; Wabasha, MN; 20/98 Chr; Chrs; HonRl; NHS; SpnCl; PpCl; College Of St Theresa; Undecided.

ALBRECHT, Karl; Melrose Mindoro HS; Mindoro, WI; 2/84 AFS; HonRl; RptrSchPpr; EdSchPpr; Trk; AmLegAwd; CitAwd; College.

ALBRECHT, Kenneth J; Messmer HS; Milwaukee, WI; ChrhWkr; CmntyWkr; HonRl; SciCl; Marquette Univ; Biology.

ALBRECHT, Robert; Alsen Public HS; Alsen, ND; 2/6 PresSophCls; VPSrCls; Chrs; HonRl; SchPl; StuCncl; Bsbl; Bsktbl; Trk; College; Law.

ALBRECHT, Roxie M; Wapsie Valley HS; Readlyn, IA; 2/94 HonRl; NHS; SchPl; Yrbk; 4-H; Bsktbl; LetterGlf; University Of Iowa; Medicine.

ALBREGTS, Christine L; Frontier HS; Brookston, IN; HonRl; LbryAde; SchMus; SchPl; RptrYrbk; RptrSchPpr; 4-H; PpCl; GAA; 4-HAwd; Indiana University; Television.

ALBRIGHT, Cynthia A; Newton HS; Newton, KS; 8/308 HonRl; Orch; SchMus; SctActv; CivCl; Univ Of Ks.

ALBRIGHT, Eileen M; Black Hawk HS; Browntown, WI; Band; ChrhWkr; HonRl; SchPl; 4-H; FFA; LetterBsktbl; LetterTrk; GAA; IMSpt; 4-HAwd; College; Nursing.

ALBRIGHT, Maribeth; Atwood Hammond HS; Hammond, IL; Band; Chrs; DrlTm; HonRl; HospAde; MrchBnd; NHS; PepBnd; DARAwd; Loyola Univ; Psychology.

ALBRIGHT, Mike A; Monroe Sr HS; Monroe, WI; Aud/Vis; 4-H; FFA;.

ALBRIGHT, Richard J; St Edmond HS; Fort Dodge, IA; PresSophCls; ChrhWkr; SchPl; SctActv; StuCncl; EdSchPpr; SptEdSchPpr; KeyCl; Ftbl; Trk; Wrstlng; Iowa State Univ; Law.

ALBRIGHT, Susan; Champaign Central HS; Champaign, IL; Band; CncrtBnd; HonRl; JrNHS; MrchBnd; NHS; PepBnd; TchrAde; IMSpt; Eastern Il Univ;.

ALBRIGHT, Toni S; Van Buren HS; Kinghtsville, IN; 6/72 SecJrCls; Band; NHS; StuCncl; Yrbk; FTA; VPSpnCl; SciCl; Chrldr; IMSpt; College; Gymnastic.

ALBRITTON, Shawn J; St Pius X HS; Arnold, MO; 28/100 HonRl; SecTrsFrshCls; StuGov; SciCl; LetterBsbl; Bsktbl; Socr; IMSpt; Univ;.

ALBRITTON, Tammie J; Newman HS; Newman, IL; 3/36 SecSophCls; ALAGirlsSt; HonRl; NHS; Yrbk; RptrSchPpr; FHA; PpCl; GAA; Millikin Univ; Lawyer.

ALBY, Toni M; St Marys HS; Burlington, WI; Band; Chr; CncrtBnd; MrchBnd; PepBnd; SchPl; PpCl; IMSpt; College; Physical Education.

ALCALA, Jane M; Dondero HS; Royal Oak, MI; 32/535 Chr; HonRl; HospAde; Mdrgl; NHS; TchrAde; TreasYthFlsp; SpnCl; GAA; University Of Michigan; Nurse.

ALCOCK, Thomas W; Cheboygan Area HS; Cheboygan, MI; HonRl; TchrAde; Ftbl; N Central Mich College; Automotive Serv.

ALCORN, Kathy L; Beardstown HS; Beardstown, IL; 18/128 ChrhWkr; HonRl; Mdrgl; NHS; OffAde; SchMus; YthFlsp; RptrYrbk; RptrSchPpr; FTA; Il State Univ; Business.

ALDAY, Michael G; Shelbyville HS; Shelbyville, IL; Band; CncrtBnd; HonRl; MrchBnd; PepBnd; SchMus; SctActv; TchrAde; RptrSchPpr; College; Special Ed.

ALDEN, Belinda G; Central City Comm HS; Central City, IA; Band; Chr; HonRl; MrchBnd; Quill&Scroll; SchMus; YthFlsp; Bsbl; Chrldr; 4-HAwd; Coll; Nursing.

ALDEN, Johnie D; Penney HS; Hamilton, MO; PresSrCls; ALBoysSt; HonRl; SchMus; SctActv; StuGov; TreasFFA; Bsktbl; LetterFtbl; LetterGlf; Trade School; Draftsman.

ALDER, Janet L; Verdigre Public HS; Verdigre, NE; 9/38 HonRl; NHS; NatlMeritCmnd; SchPl; StuCncl; RptrYrbk; RptrSchPpr; SchPpr; SpnCl; PpCl; LetterTrk; IMSpt; College; Photography.

ALDERFER, Terri R; Tippecanoe Valley HS; Mentone, IN; HonRl; Yrbk; SchPpr; FTA; SpnCl; SciCl; Ics; Airline.

ALDERSON, Carol L; Shelby HS; Shelby, MI; Chr; Chrs; CmntyWkr; NatlFornLg; SchAde; TchrAde; SchPpr; SpnCl; Hope College; Child Psychology.

ALDERSON, Michael J; Delavan HS; Delavan, IL; 6/53 PresSrCls; ALBoysSt; Band; CncrtBnd; HonRl; Orch; SchPl; StuCncl; FrCl; SpnCl; MthCl; SciCl; LetterGlf; Univ Of Illinois; Accounting.

ALDRED, Jama L; Switzerland Co HS; Vevay, IN; SecBand; CncrtBnd; MrchBnd; NHS; OffAde; PepBnd; TchrAde; YthFlsp; 4-H; PresFHA; PpCl; 4-HAwd;.

ALDRICH, Dean P; Garwin HS; Garwin, IA; 10/33 CncrtBnd; HonRl; MrchBnd; SchPl; StuCncl; RptrSchPpr; FrCl; LetterBsbl; LetterBsktbl; LetterFtbl; College.

ALDRICH, Lori L; Chesaning HS; Oakley, MI; Aud/Vis; CmntyWkr; HonRl; TreasStuCncl; College; Secretary.

ALDRICH, Michael E; Cretin HS; St Paul, MN; DrlTm; HonRl; ROTC; EdYrBk; SptEdYrbk; Bsktbl; Ftbl; Socr; LetterTrk; IMSpt; St Thomas Clg; Accountant.

ALDRICH, Winifred M; Harper Creek HS; Battle Creek, MI; 28/231 TrsSophCls; TrsJrCls; PresSrCls; SecBand; ChrhWkr; HonRl; NHS; StuCncl; TchrAde; SpnCl; Kellogg Comm; Computer Programming.

ALDRIDGE, Dawn V; Rantool Township HS; Rantoul, IL; VPSophCls; VPJrCls; Chr; ChrhWkr; CncrtBnd; LitMag; MrchBnd; SchMus; SecStuCncl; SpnCl; Univ; Spec Educ.

ALEA, Peter M; Proviso West HS; Northlake, IL; 240/1150 HonRl; PolWkr; YthLg; SpnCl; Bsktbl; Swmmng; Tennis; College; Oceanography.

ALEJOS, Susan F; Washburn Rural HS; Topeka, KS; Band; CncrtBnd; HonRl; MrchBnd; PepBnd; University; Medicine.

ALEKSIAK, Mary; Meadow Heights HS; Patton, MO; HonRl; NHS; OffAde; SchAde; StuCncl; TchrAde; SchPpr; FHA; AmLegAwd; College; Med Lab Tech.

ALER, Denise C; Carl Sandburg HS; Palos Hts, IL; TrsSophCls; CncrtBnd; DrlTm; DrmMjrt; HonRl; MrchBnd; SctActv; StuCncl; Twrl; SchPpr; Univ Of Illinois.

ALESHIRE, Melisa G; Spokane HS; Highlandville, MO; TrsFrshCls; HstSophCls; HonRl; SchPl; Yrbk; 4-H; LetterBsbl; 4-HAwd; Burge School Of Nursing.

ALESSI, David M; Grosse Pointe South HS; Grosse Pointe Park, MI; ChrhWkr; HonRl; SchAde; StuGov; TchrAde; Michigan State Univ; Medicine.

ALEX, Barbara J; Stillman Valley HS; Davis Jct, IL; 7/120 Band; CncrtBnd; HonRl; NHS; TchrAde; YthFlsp; FHA; FTA; College; Architect.

ALEXANDER, Barbara J; Mark Twain HS; New London, MO; 16/69 Band; CncrtBnd; HonRl; LbryAde; MrchBnd; PepBnd; FHA;.

ALEXANDER, Carol A; Palatine HS; Palatine, IL; 14/440 ChrhWkr; HonRl; NatlMeritSF; SctActv; YthFlsp; RptrYrbk; FrCl; University.

ALEXANDER, Cheryl C; John Marshall Harlan HS; Chicago, IL; 4/800 CmntyWkr; HonRl; ModUN; StuCncl; StuGov; TchrAde; SpnCl; PpCl; GAA; Coll; Psychiatrist.

ALEXANDER, Craig M; Cleveland HS; St Louis, MO; HonRl; NHS; CaptFtbl; Univ; Law.

ALEXANDER, Curtis L; Hubbard Comm HS; Hubbard, IA; ChrhWkr; SchPl; Bsbl; Bsktbl; Ftbl; Glf; Ia Wesleyan; Marine Biology.

ALEXANDER, Donnie L; Holden R 3 HS; Holden, MO; 13/100 ALBoysSt; HonRl; NHS; StuGov; 4-H; SciCl; Uof Kansas; Architecture.

ALEXANDER, Douglas W; Stony Brook HS; Madison, WI; 8/69 Chr; ChrhWkr; CncrtBnd; HonRl; SchPl; StuGov; YthFlsp; Tennis;.

ALEXANDER, Harley R; Grand Rapids HS; Grand Rapids, MN; 13/374 HonRl; Staples Vo Tech Sch; Draftsman.

ALEXANDER, James E; Oak Park Sr HS; Gladstone, MO; 47/602 HonRl; VPNHS; TchrAde; RptrSchPpr; SpnCl; Trk; University Of Arizona; Biology.

ALEXANDER, Karen S; Sullivan HS; Sullivan, IN; 12/140 PresFrshCls; ALAGirlsSt; Chr; Chrs; HonRl; HospAde; JrNHS; NHS; PolWkr; SchMus; Teen; 4-H; LatCl; MthCl; St Mary Of The Woods College; Biology.

ALEXANDER, Laura L; Michigan Center HS; Jackson, MI; 14/149 ALAGirlsSt; ChrhWkr; HonRl; HospAde; NHS; OffAde; PolWkr; SchMus; StuCncl; FHA; Univ Mi; Bs/rn.

ALEXANDER, Lynett S; Rockridge HS; Il City, IL; 6/139# HonRl; NHS; 4-H; FrCl; College; Veterinarian.

ALEXANDER, Mary A; Resurrection HS; Chicago, IL; Chr; HonRl; Mdrgl; NatlThespSoc; SchMus; SchPl; Rosary College; Medicine.

ALEXANDER, Merle G; Blue Hill Community HS; Blue Hill, NE; 17/40 Band; Chr; Chrl; Chrs; ChrhWkr; CncrtBnd; DrlTm; JA; MrchBnd; PepBnd; Ftbl; Swmmng; Trk; Trade School; Vocation.

ALEXANDER, Norman C; Freeport Sr HS; Freeport, IL; 157/494 Band; CncrtBnd; HonRl; MrchBnd; Orch; PepBnd; Northern Ill Univ; Computer Science.

ALEXANDER, Pamela S; Monticello HS; White Heath, IL; 2/168 CncrtBnd; HonRl; HospAde; MrchBnd; NHS; RptrYrbk; RptrSchPpr; AmLegAwd; Univ Of Illinois; Nursing.

ALEXANDER, Robin L; William Bogan HS; Chicago, IL; 5/732 Chrs; ChrhWkr; HonRl; JrNHS; OffAde; SchMus; SctActv; SptEdSchPpr; FrCl; Chrldr; Augustana Coll; Elementary Ed.

ALEXANDER, Toni; Vestaburg HS; Vestaburg, MI; 3/62 SecJrCls; Band; CncrtBnd; HonRl; NHS; SchPl; TchrAde; YthLg; RptrSchPpr; SpnCl; Central Mi Univ; Forestry.

ALEXANDER, Vynessa; Chicago Vocational HS; Chicago, IL; HonRl; NHS; SchAde; StuCncl; StuGov; TchrAde; EdYrBk; PresFBLA; PpCl; GAA; College; Public Admin.

ALFARO, Jeffrey D; Augusta Sr HS; Augusta, KS; TrsSophCls; ALBoysSt; HonRl; NHS; StuGov; YthFlsp; SpnCl; Bsbl; LetterBsktbl; CaptFtbl; LetterTennis; CitAwd; College.

ALFIREVIC, Janine M; St Augustine HS; Chicago, IL; 8/90 SecFrshCls; Chrs; CmntyWkr; HonRl; HospAde; NHS; SchPl; StuCncl; RptrYrbk; RptrSchPpr; College; Health Field.

ALFORD, Jan; Naper Public HS; Bonesteel, SD; 1/19 Band; Chr; Chrs; ChrhWkr; CncrtBnd; HonRl; SchPl; Yrbk; Chrldr; Grace Bible Institute; Music.

ALFORD, Kamella A; Rantoul Township HS; Rantoul, IL; HonRl; OffAde; StuCncl; TreasYthFlsp; Yrbk; SpnCl; Swmmng; College; Psychology.

ALFRED, Michele D; St Marks HS; St Louis, MO; 23/36 Chr; Chrs; ChrhWkr; HonRl; SchPl; Sdlty; SchPpr; MthCl; IMSpt; Forest Park College; Medicine.

ALFREDSON, Carl I; Norway HS; Norway, MI; HonRl; SchPl; YthFlsp; 4-H; LetterFtbl; Trk; IMSpt; Trade School; Vocation.

ALFT, Karen K; Tigerton HS; Tigerton, WI; 3/36 SecJrCls; Chr; Chrs; HonRl; NatlFornLg; NHS; SchPl; SctActv; EdSchPpr; Trk; Technical Inst; Secretarial Science.

ALGEE, Tanya R; Cus HS; Chicago, IL; CmntyWkr; HonRl; HospAde; PolWkr; StuGov; Twrl; YthFnd; FDA; FNA; FTA; Coll; Doctor.

ALGER, Julie A; Wabash HS; Wabash, IN; 28/203 ChrhWkr; CmntyWkr; HonRl; NatlFornLg; NHS; PolWkr; Quill&Scroll; StuCncl; EdYrBk; RptrSchPpr; Purdue College; English.

ALGER, Michael D; Spencer HS; Spencer, IA; AFS; Aud/Vis; Band; CmntyWkr; CncrtBnd; HonRl; LitMag; MrchBnd; ModUN; IMSpt; Simpson Col; English Lit.

ALGIERS, Karen E; Hartford Union HS; Hartford, WI; Band; ChrhWkr; CmntyWkr; HonRl; JrNHS; NHS; NatlMeritFnl; PepBnd; StuCncl; Yrbk; GAA; Marquette Univ; Bio Medical.

ALI, Syed J; Shelbyville HS; Shelbyville, IN; 54/267 HonRl; NatlMeritCmnd; SciCl; LetterWrstlng; IMSpt; In Univ.

ALIBER, Jennifer; U Of C Labratory HS; Chicago, IL; SchPl; FrCl; IMSpt; College; Biol Psych.

ALIG, Dale M; Aol Spalding Institute; Metamora, IL; 25/99 ChrhWkr; Quill&Scroll; EdSchPpr; Isu; Pro.

ALJETS, Dawn R; Edwardsville HS; Dorsey, IL; Chrs; CncrtBnd; MrchBnd; PepBnd; YthFlsp; Sec4-H; SecFHA; GAA; PPFtbl; 4-HAwd; College; Medicine.

ALKE, Kathleen L; Osage Comm HS; Osage, IA; NHS; RptrYrbk; RptrSchPpr; FTA; PpCl; LetterBsktbl; LetterTennis; U Of Northern Iowa; Physical Education.

ALKEMA, Susan M; Brooklyn Center HS; Fridley, MN; Band; CncrtBnd; LitMag; Quill&Scroll; FBLA; SpnCl; DanFAwd; College; Professional.

ALLABEN, Elizabeth A; North Farmington HS; Farmington Hills, MI; 1/449 CmntyWkr; HonRl; SecNHS; TreasSctActv; FrCl; DARAwd; Univ Of Michigan; Engineer.

ALLAMAN, John; Southern 120 HS; Stronghurst, IL; ALBoysSt; Band; CncrtBnd; MrchBnd; PepBnd; SchPl; StuCncl; West Il Univ; Social Sci.

ALLAN, Steve D; Redwood Falls HS; Redwood Falls, MN; HonRl; 4-H; SpnCl; PpCl; LetterBsktbl; Ftbl; 4-HAwd; Southwest Mn St Coll.

ALLAR, Gerald; Milwaukee Lutheran HS; Milwaukee, WI; 16/224 Band; ChrhWkr; CncrtBnd; HonRl; MrchBnd; NHS; Orch; PepBnd; Wrstlng; IMSpt; Uw Mil;phys Ther.

ALLARD, Joyce K; Northwest Webster HS; Fort Dodge, IA; 4/22 PresJrCls; Chrs; ChrhWkr; HonRl; SchPl; TchrAde; EdYrBk; LetterBsktbl; LetterTrk; Northwest Mo State; Phy Ed.

ALLARD, Lauren J; Connersville HS; Connersville, IN; 19/371 HonRl; NHS; Business School; Secretary.

ALLARD, Lesley; Bennett County HS; Martin, SD; ALAGirlsSt; ChrhWkr; CmntyWkr; HonRl; NHS; PolWkr; SchPl; EdYrBk; AmLegAwd; College; Medicine.

ALLARDYCE, James D; Frankenmuth HS; Frankenmuth, MI; 2/158 PresFrshCls; PresSophCls; ALBoysSt; CncrtBnd; NHS; StuCncl; SptEdYrbk; Ftbl; CaptTrk; AmLegAwd; U Of Mi; Medicine.

ALLARIA, Vincent J; Edwardsville HS; Edwardsville, IL; HonRl; NHS; LetterBsbl; LetterBsktbl; LetterFtbl; CchngActv; Eastern Illinois Univ; Education.

ALLBRITTON, John M; South Pemiscot HS; Steele, MO; Band; ChrhWkr; CmntyWkr; CncrtBnd; HonRl; MrchBnd; NHS; PepBnd; SpnCl; Bsbl; College; Aviation.

ALLEBRANDI, Thomas M; Carmel HS; Indianapolis, IN; 38/525 Band; HonRl; MrchBnd; NHS; NatlMeritSF; PepBnd; SchMus; YthFlsp; IMSpt; Rhit; Professional Physics Or Mathematics.

ALLEE, Douglas L; Sheridan Rii HS; Sheridan, MO; HstFrshCls; SecSophCls; TrsSophCls; ALBoysSt; CmntyWkr; HonRl; LbryAde; StuCncl; FFA; Bsbl; Bsktbl; Trk; Trade School; Vocational.

ALLEGAR, Steve C; Maine South HS; Park Ridge, IL; HonRl; NHS; SctActv; Socr; Colorado School Of Mines; Chemical Engineer.

ALLEGER, Deon; Kickapoo HS; Springfield, MO; 99/385 Band; HonRl; HospAde; MrchBnd; OffAde; FBLA; FHA; Southwest Missouri St Univ; Business Adm.

ALLEGER, Richard P; Northrop HS; Fort Wayne, IN; 38/568 Band; ChrhWkr; CncrtBnd; HonRl; MrchBnd; Orch; PepBnd; SchMus; RptrYrbk; RptrSchPpr; Purdue University; Chemistry.

ALLEMAN, Janeen R; Putnam County HS; Magnola, IL; 7/80 Band; Chrs; HonRl; SchMus; RptrSchPpr; FHA; FrCl; PpCl; GAA; 4-HAwd; U Of Ill.

ALLEN, Al; Bremen Communtiy HS; Blue Island, IL; 9/425 Art Center College; Industrial Designer.

ALLEN, Anthony G; D C HS; Dallas City, IL; 1/30 PresSophCls; VPSrCls; HonRl; NHS; NatlMeritCmnd; StuCncl; EdSchPpr; Bsbl; Trk; Wrstlng; College.

ALLEN, Arcita; St Marys Center For Learning; Chicago, IL; CmntyWkr; LitMag; LbryAde; NatlFornLg; SchPl; StuCncl; StuGov; YthFlsp; YthLg; Yrbk; Univ Of Ill Circle Camp; Sp Andhearing Ther.

ALLEN, Arcita; St Marys Center For Learn Ing; Chicago, IL; CmntyWkr; LitMag; LbryAde; NatlFornLg; SchPl; StuCncl; StuGov; YthFlsp; YthLg; Yrbk; Univ Of Ill Circle Camp; Speech& Hear Ther.

ALLEN, Barbara; Deckerville HS; Deckerville, MI; 3/79 TrsSophCls; ALAGirlsSt; HonRl; NatlMeritSF; TchrAde; PresAwd; Alma College; Social Work.

ALLEN, Barbara A; Pardeeville HS; Pardeeville, WI; 10/104 TrsSrCls; ALAGirlsSt; HonRl; HospAde; NHS; Yrbk; 4-H; CaptBsktbl; LetterTrk; GAA; IMSpt; DARAwd; CitAwd; U W Oshkosh; Nurse.

ALLEN, Betty L; Paxton Cons HS; Paxton, NE; Chrs; HonRl; SchMus; SchPpr; PpCl; LetterTrk; LetterChrldr; LetterGAA; College.

ALLEN, Beverly M; Hillman HS; Hillman, MI; Band; HonRl; MrchBnd; SchPl; TchrAde; Yrbk; 4-H; FHA; Bsktbl; College; Secondary Teachig.

ALLEN, Billy; Lindblom HS; Chicago, IL; 59/700 TrsSophCls; Band; Chr; CmntyWkr; DrmBgl; HonRl; LitMag; LbryAde; NatlMeritSF; OffAde; SchAde; SchPl; TchrAde; Northwestern Univ; Medicine.

ALLEN, Billy; Lindblom Technical HS; Chicago, IL; 54/700 TrsJrCls; Band; Chr; ChrhWkr; HonRl; LbryAde; NatlMeritSF; OffAde; SchAde; TchrAde; GerCl; Northwestern Univ; Medicine.

ALLEN, Bradley C; Riverton Comm HS; Springfield, IL; 9/65 Band; MrchBnd; PepBnd; SctActv; StuCncl; StuGov; YthFlsp; Bsbl; LetterFtbl; IMSpt; Eastern Ill Univ; Industrial Technology.

ALLEN, Brian A; Ionia HS; Lonia, MI; 17/226 CncrtBnd; HonRl; MrchBnd; NHS; SchMus; SchPpr; PresSciCl; CaptBsktbl; LetterTrk; IMSpt; Mich State Univ; Zoology.

ALLEN, Brian G; Grand Rapids Sr HS; Grand Rapids, MN; 32/377 HonRl; KiwanAwd; RotaryAwd; Word Of Life Bible Inst; Elec.

ALLEN, Bruce C; Aledo HS; Aledo, IL; 1/101 HonRl; NatlMeritCmnd; SchMus; SchPl; SctActv; StuCncl; LetterBsktbl; LetterFtbl; LetterTrk; RotaryAwd; VoiceDemAwd; Univ Of Illinois; Agricultural Engineer.

ALLEN, Carolyn J; Pine River HS; Le Roy, MI; 2/86 HonRl; TreasNHS; 4-H; DanFAwd; Ferris State College; Pharmacy.

ALLEN, Cathy L; Windsor HS; Windsor, IL; 5/56 SecJrCls; HonRl; NHS; NatlThespSoc; SchPl; StuCncl; RptrYrbk; FHA; Chrldr; PresChrldr; Coll; Acct.

ALLEN, Charles C; Necedah HS; Necedah, WI; 2/42 TrsSophCls; HonRl; RptrYrbk; PpCl; LetterBsktbl; Ftbl; Trk; Uw Eau Claire; Med Tech.

ALLEN, Cheryl D; Normandy Sr HS; Vinita Park, MO; HonRl; NHS; PpCl; Businesss; Vocation.

ALLEN, Chester L; Springs Valley HS; French Lick, IN; 4/83 PresSophCls; ALBoysSt; ChrhWkr; HonRl; FrCl; PpCl; LetterBsktbl; LetterFtbl; LetterTrk; Circleville Bible College.

ALLEN, Craig D; Lincoln HS; Manitowoc, WI; 1/680 ChrhWkr; HonRl; NHS; StuCncl; StuGov; SpnCl; Ftbl; Tennis; Trk; LetterWrstlng; College; Res Scientist.

ALLEN, Cynthia L; Hopkins Eisenhower HS; Edina, MN; StuGov; TchrAde; YthFlsp; Yrbk; LetterTrk; Univ Of Kansas; Occupational Therapy.

ALLEN, Daniel P; Lewis Central HS; Council Bluffs, IA; 1/164 VPSrCls; Chr; HonRl; Mdrgl; NHS; SchMus; LetterBsktbl; Glf; Creighton University; Business Exec.

ALLEN, David; St Anne HS; Pembroke, IL; 14/155 ChrhWkr; HonRl; FTA; Bsbl; Bsktbl; Univ Of Il; Communications.

ALLEN, David; Atchison Jr Sr HS; Atchison, KS; 10/164 TrsSrCls; ALBoysSt; HonRl; ModUN;

NHS; SchPl; SctActv; RptrSchPpr; Ftbl; Service Acad; Military Officer.

ALLEN, Debra J; Plainfield HS; Mooresville, IN; 19/259 CncrtBnd; JrNHS; LbryAde; MrchBnd; NHS; PepBnd; RptrYrbk; GerCl; PpCl; Butler Univ; Business Admin.

ALLEN, Debra L; Adair County R Ii HS; Brashear, MO; SecSophCls; VPBand; Chrs; ChrhWkr; CncrtBnd; DrmMjrt; Sec4-H; TreasBsbl; Bsktbl; Trk; LetterChrldr; 4-HAwd; Ne Mo St Univ; Teaching.

ALLEN, Debra M; Chosen Valley HS; Chatfield, MN; 1/82 ALAGirlsSt; Band; Chr; ChrhWkr; CncrtBnd; HonRl; MrchBnd; NHS; NatlMeritSF; Univ; Physical Therapy.

ALLEN, Elizabeth A; Central Catholic HS; Grand Island, NE; ALAGirlsSt; PresBand; CmntyWkr; NHS; SchMus; SctActv; EdYrBk; SchPpr; PresPpCl; PPFtbl; Univ Of Nebraska; Finance.

ALLEN, Frederick L; Minot Senior HS; Minot, ND; 64/656 Band; Chr; Chrs; CncrtBnd; HonRl; JrNHS; LitMag; MrchBnd; NHS; NatlThespSoc; PepBnd; Trk;.

ALLEN, Garold R; St Rita HS; Oak Park, IL; 193/455 PresFrshCls; TrsJrCls; FrCl; Ftbl; Trk; CchngActv; College; Law Enforcement.

ALLEN, Gary; Ca HS; Indianapolis, IN; Band; Chr; DrlTm; HonRl; JA; MrchBnd; Orch; ROTC; StuCncl; Itt Tech; Electronics Engineer.

ALLEN, Gary E; Albert City Truesdale HS; Laurens, IA; PresSophCls; PresJrCls; HonRl; SchPl; SctActv; StuCncl; YthFlsp; 4-H; FFA; LetterBsbl; LetterBsktbl; LetterFtbl; LetterTrk; College.

ALLEN, Howard L; Powhattan HS; Horton, KS; 2/19 PresSophCls; HonRl; NHS; SchPl; StuCncl; VPFFA; LetterBsktbl; Ftbl; LetterTrk; Ks State U; Engr.

ALLEN, James F; Berkley HS; Huntington Woods, MI; Aud/Vis; CmntyWkr; ModUN; Tennis; Trk; IMSpt; Mich St U; Bus Admin.

ALLEN, James L; Eldorado HS; Eldorado, IL; 1/114 PresSrCls; HonRl; NHS; PresNatlThespSoc; SchMus; SchPl; PresGerCl; LetterFtbl; Univ Of Illinois; Physics.

ALLEN, Janel M; Rudyard HS; Kincheloe Afb, MI; ALAGirlsSt; Chrs; DrlTm; HonRl; StuCncl; RptrSchPpr; LetterBsbl; LetterTrk; IMSpt; AmLegAwd; College; Elementary School Teacher.

ALLEN, Janet K; Lutheran North HS; St Louis, MO; PresJrCls; HonRl; StuCncl; StuGov; EdYrBk; PpCl; Bsktbl; Socr; CchngActv; GAA; LetterIMSpt; Univ Of Missouri; Occupational Therapy.

ALLEN, Jeffery L; West Delaware HS; Greeley, IA; PresSophCls; ALBoysSt; NHS; NatlThespSoc; Ftbl; Glf; LetterWrstlng; AmLegAwd; JCAwd; USJCAwd; University Of Iowa; Medicine.

ALLEN, Jeffrey W; Sts Peter & Paul Seminary; Port Huron, MI; Chr; ChrhWkr; CmntyWkr; HonRl; SchPl; MthCl; LetterBsktbl; LetterSocr; IMSpt; Michigan St Univ; Dentistry.

ALLEN, Jennifer L; Purdy R Ii HS; Purdy, MO; 2/40 VPSophCls; Chrs; ChrhWkr; HonRl; VPNHS; SecStuCncl; RptrYrbk; RptrSchPpr; VPFHA; LetterBsktbl; Missouri S St College; Law Enforcement.

ALLEN, John J; University HS; Normal, IL; Chrs; HonRl; SchPl; StuCncl; StuGov; RptrSchPpr; Bsbl; Bsktbl; Ftbl; IMSpt; U Of Il; Architect.

ALLEN, John J; Evergreen Park Community HS; Evergreen Park, IL; CmntyWkr; HonRl; PolWkr; MthCl; IMSpt; U Of Southern Il; Mechanical Engineering.

ALLEN, Joni; Ofallon Township Hs; Bellville, IL; SecJrCls; HonRl;.

ALLEN, Kay; Chosen Valley HS; Eyota, MN; PresSrCls; Chr; HonRl; MrchBnd; NHS; SchMus; StuCncl; EdYrBk; 4-H; College; Professional.

ALLEN, Kelly A; Appleton HS; Appleton, WI; Chrs; CmntyWkr; NatlFornLg; NatlThespSoc; SchMus; SchPl; StuGov; RptrSchPpr; FrCl; College; Advertising.

ALLEN, Kenneth D; Rolfe Community HS; Rolfe, IA; TrsJrCls; ALBoysSt; Chrs; ChrhWkr; HonRl; SchAde; YthFlsp; EdYrBk; Bsktbl; Trk;.

ALLEN, Kevin; Granite City Hs; Granite City, IL; Band; ChrhWkr; Quill&Scroll; RptrSchPpr; SptEdSchPpr; CchngActv; Southern Illinois University; Journalism.

ALLEN, Kimberly I; Airport HS; Carleton, MI; HstSophCls; HstJrCls; HstSrCls; ALAGirlsSt; NHS; NatlSciFnd; RptrYrbk; PresFrCl; MthCl; LetterChrldr; College; Accounting.

ALLEN, Kimberly S; Jersey Community HS; Jerseyville, IL; Band; CncrtBnd; HonRl; MrchBnd; NHS; OffAde; PepBnd; StuCncl; 4-H; SpnCl; Drake; Business.

ALLEN, Kim R; Bishop Mc Namara HS; St Anne, IL; Band; CmntyWkr; CncrtBnd; HonRl; OffAde; SchPl; StuCncl; Yrbk; SpnCl; Chrldr; Univ; Medicine.

ALLEN, Larry D; Wawasee HS; Syracuse, IN; 1/270 ChrhWkr; HonRl; JrNHS; NHS; Orch; SchPl; StuCncl; YthFlsp; LetterBsktbl; LetterFtbl; Glf; College; Engineering.

ALLEN, Leslie S; Adel HS; Adel, IA; TrsJrCls; TrsSrCls; Chrs; CmntyWkr; CncrtBnd; HonRl; NHS; NatlThespSoc; SchMus; StuGov; PresYthFlsp; College; Music.

ALLEN, Lorene K; Minonk Dana Ruthland HS; Minonk, IL; Band; Chr; Chrs; CncrtBnd; HonRl; Mdrgl; MrchBnd; RptrYrbk; FrCl; SciCl;.

ALLEN, Louise H; University HS; Champaign, IL; 1/42 HospAde; LitMag; ModUN; NatlMeritSF; PepBnd; PolWkr; SchPl; StuGov; TchrAde; YthLg; Yrbk; GerCl; GAA; Univ Of Ill; Lawyer.

ALLEN, Mark B; Peoria Heights HS; Peoria Heights, IL; PresSrCls; HonRl; NatlThespSoc; SchPl; StuCncl; RptrYrbk; Yrbk; RptrSchPpr; LetterBsbl; LetterBsktbl; Il Central College; Police Sci.

ALLEN, Mark S; Midland HS; Midland, MI; NatlMeritSchl; Bsbl; Ftbl; Wrstlng; Mich Tech Univ; Eng.

ALLEN, Mary J; South Page HS; Bedford, IA; Chr; Chrs; LbryAde; SchAde; TchrAde; Teen; FFA; FHA; FNA; SpnCl; University; Professional.

ALLEN, Mary K; Cass Lake HS; Cass Lake, MN; 12/48 Band; Chrs; HonRl; LbryAde; OffAde; SchAde; SptEdSchPpr; FHA; Bsktbl; IMSpt; St Benedicts; Nurse.

ALLEN, Michael; Dixon Hs; Dixon, IL; 83/333 ChrhWkr; HonRl; SctActv;.

ALLEN, Nellie L; Meridian HS; Pulaski, IL; Chrs; CmntyWkr; HonRl; SchMus; SchPl; YthFlsp; IMSpt; Shawnee Jr Col.

ALLEN, Nicholas; Midland HS; Midland, MI; 89/443 Aud/Vis; HonRl; PolWkr; FrCl; Swmmng; University Of Michigan; Humanities.

ALLEN, Pamela R; Cambridge HS; Cambridge, NE; Chr; CmntyWkr; HospAde; SchPl; PpCl; Clge; Vocation.

ALLEN, Pamela S; Southern Boone County HS; Hartsburg, MO; PresSophCls; ALAGirlsSt; Chrs; CmntyWkr; HospAde; OffAde; SchPl; StuCncl; FHA; IMSpt; Advertising.

ALLEN, Patti; Rosedale HS; Rosedale, IN; 7;48 VPFrshCls; PresSrCls; ALAGirlsSt; Band; HonRl; MrchBnd; NHS; GAA; Business;secretary.

ALLEN, Paula M; Franklin HS; Franklin, IL; SecJrCls; Band; Chrs; OffAde; SchPl; SctActv; TchrAde; Yrbk; 4-H; FHA;.

ALLEN, Paul S; Sparland Unit #3 HS; Speer, IL; 3/21 VPFrshCls; NHS; StuCncl; College.

ALLEN, Randall R; Oregon Davis HS; Walkerton, IN; 19/65 Aud/Vis; ChrhWkr; HonRl; NHS; NatlMeritSchl; YthFlsp; Bsbl; Bsktbl; IMSpt; AmLegAwd; College; Professional.

ALLEN, Robert; Albany HS; Albany, WI; 3/34 ALBoysSt; Chr; Chrs; Mdrgl; NHS; SchMus; SchPpr; FFA; GerCl; Marquette Univ; Electrical Engineer.

ALLEN, Robin L; Larkin HS; Elgin, IL; 1/650 CncrtBnd; HonRl; MrchBnd; PepBnd; EdYrBk; EdSchPpr; JCAwd; U Of Il.

ALLEN, Ronald L; Lincoln HS; Wisconsin Rapids, WI; 8/650 ALBoysSt; HonRl; NHS; NatlMeritCmnd; KeyCl; Bsktbl; University; Medicine.

ALLEN, Ronnie L; Sabetha HS; Sabetha, KS; PresFrshCls; VPJrCls; PresSrCls; HonRl; PresStuCncl; Ftbl; LetterGlf; Swmmng; IMSpt; LionAwd; Univ; Law.

ALLEN, Sandra E; Dowagiac Union HS; Dowagiac, MI; 15/195 HonRl; NHS; Sec4-H; 4-HAwd; Southwestern Michigan College; Secretary.

ALLEN, Sandra J; Clinton HS; Clinton, MO; 4/167 ALAGirlsSt; Band; ChrhWkr; CncrtBnd; HonRl; MrchBnd; NatlFornLg; NatlThespSoc; SchPl; YthFlsp; Central Mo St Univ; Med Tech.

ALLEN, Sandra L; Morgan Park HS; Chicago, IL; 53/639 Band; Chr; ChrhWkr; CmntyWkr; HonRl; OffAde; SchAde; StuCncl; YthFlsp; FrCl; PpCl; CchngActv; George Williams College; Child Dvlpmt.

ALLEN, Scott D; Knoxville HS; Knoxville, IA; 50/180 ALBoysSt; HonRl; StuCncl; TchrAde; Bsktbl; Ftbl; Trk; College; Art.

ALLEN, Sheila M; Eastern School District HS; Koleen, IN; 1/60 TrsJrCls; HonRl; VPNHS; Quill&Scroll; SchPpr; FHA; PpCl; Chrldr; GAA; CitAwd; Business Schl; Business.

ALLEN, Sheree L; Chapman HS; Enterprise, KS; AFS; Chr; ChrhWkr; HonRl; SchPl; StuCncl; YthFlsp; PpCl; LetterBsktbl; Chrldr; University; Vocation.

ALLEN, Sherry L; Lindblom HS; Chicago, IL; 78/670 Chr; ChrhWkr; CmntyWkr; HonRl; JA; Mdrgl; SchAde; SchPl; StuCncl; TchrAde; SpnCl; Univ Of Ill; Nursing.

ALLEN, Steven R; Leavenworth HS; Leavenworth, IN; ChrhWkr; OffAde; SchAde; SchPl; TchrAde; Bsbl; Bsktbl; Trk; CchngActv; IMSpt; Coll.

ALLEN, Terressa E; Worthington Jefferson HS; Worthington, IN; HonRl; LbryAde; NHS;.

ALLEN, Thomas D; Ashland Community HS; Ashland, IL; Band; HonRl; MrchBnd; NHS; PepBnd; SchMus; StuCncl; RptrSchPpr; SciCl; IMSpt; College; Professional.

ALLEN, Thomas F; Poplar Bluff Senior HS; Poplar Bluff, MO; 59/350 Band; CncrtBnd; HonRl; MrchBnd; NHS; NatlMeritCmnd; PepBnd; SchPl; StuCncl; KeyCl; SciCl; Military Academy; Military.

ALLEN, Timothy; Nemaha Valley HS; Oneida, KS; Chrs; KeyCl; Trk; CchngActv; Ks Univ.

ALLEN, Valerie A; Pecatonica HS; Pecatonica, IL; 1/60 Chrs; DrlTm; HonRl; JrNHS; NHS; TchrAde; FHA; PpCl; Rock Valley Comm College; Mathematics.

ALLEN, Vicki S; Oregon Davis HS; Walkerton, IN; HonRl; LbryAde; SchMus; Teen; YthFlsp; 4-H; FHA; SecTrsSophCls; SciCl; GAA; College; Special Education.

ALLEN, Vicky L; West Ottawa HS; West Olive, MI; 15/265 Chr; Chrs; HonRl; NHS; OffAde; Davenport College; Legal Secretary.

ALLEN, Walter V; Southwest HS; St Louis, MO; 8/586 VPJrCls; PresSrCls; ALBoysSt; HonRl; LitMag; NatlMeritCmnd; NatlMeritSF; StuGov; TchrAde; SptEdYrbk; LetterBsktbl; Chrldr; Univ; Anestesiology.

ALLEN, Wayne C; Avoha Community HS; Avoca, IA; College.

ALLEN, William F; Sikeston HS; Sikeston, MO; 3/258 ALBoysSt; HonRl; YthFlsp; LetterTennis; U Of Ms; Engr.

ALLEN, William G; Trenton HS; Trenton, MI; HonRl; NHS; StuGov; Ftbl; Trk; College; Pre Law.

ALLEN, William J; Marceline HS; Maceline, MO; HonRl; SchPl; RptrYrbk; SciCl; LetterFtbl; LetterTrk; Work; Grocery Man.

ALLEN, William R; Cedar Lake Acad; Fruitport, MI; CaptBsktbl; Ftbl; IMSpt; Andrews Univ; Medical Field.

ALLENDER, Eric W; Mt Pleasant HS; Mt Pleasant, IA; 1/150 Chr; HonRl; MrchBnd; NatlFornLg; NHS; NatlMeritFnl; NatlMeritCmnd; NatlThespSoc; AmLegAwd; GodCntryAwd; Univ Of Iowa; Theatre Tech.

ALLENDER, Thomas D; Mt Pleasant HS; Mt Pleasant, IA; PresFFA; College.

ALLENSTEIN, Paul A; Marquette Sr HS; Marquette, MI; NatlMeritSF; Orch; Univ; Engineering.

ALLENSWORTH, Chelsea; Galesburg Senior HS; Galesburg, IL; 95/580 DrlTm; HonRl; LbryAde; NHS; RptrSchPpr; LatCl; PpCl; GAA; Drake Univ; Art Education.

ALLER, Karen K; Burlington HS; Burlington, IA; Chrs; ChrhWkr; PpCl; Iowa State; Computer Science.

ALLERS, Richard; Red Bud Cu HS; Red Bud, IL; Band; ChrhWkr; CmntyWkr; HospAde; PolWkr; SchMus; SchPl; YthFlsp; MthCl; Bsbl; Southeast Mo St Univ; Air Force.

ALLERS, Robin K; Red Bud C U HS; Red Bud, IL; Chr; Chrs; ChrhWkr; HonRl; HospAde; SchMus; YthFlsp; FHA; FTA;.

ALLES, Gail E; Proviso West HS; Westchester, IL; MrchBnd; NHS; NatlMeritCmnd; Orch; SchPl; SctActv; RptrSchPpr; TreasFrCl; Bsbl; Swmmng; Tennis; Chrldr; College; Physician.

ALLES, Mark; St Joseph HS; Chicago, IL; 1/102 VPFrshCls; ChrhWkr; HonRl; NHS; Quill&Scroll; StuGov; SptEdYrbk; SchPpr; MthCl; VoiceDemAwd; College; Priesthood.

ALLES, Patrick G; Hontington Catholic HS; Roanoke, IN; ChrhWkr; DrlTm; HonRl; JA; FrCl; JAAwd; College.

ALLES, William L; Glenbrook South HS; Glenview, IL; 5/579 Band; CncrtBnd; HonRl; MrchBnd; NatlFornLg; NHS; NatlMeritCmnd; Orch; PepBnd; Northwestern Univ; Music.

ALLEY, Margaret A; Isabel Public HS; Isabel, SD; 1/12 PresJrCls; SecSrCls; Band; Chrs; DrlTm; NHS; SchPl; EdYrBk; LetterTrk; DARAwd; Univ Of Sd; Doctor.

ALLEY, Pamela J; Chase County HS; Imperial, NE; Chr; CtyCnl; CmntyWkr; SchMus; SchPl; SctActv; TchrAde; SchPpr; 4-H; PpCl; Trk;.

ALLEY, Terry L; Chase County HS; Champion, NE; ChrhWkr; CmntyWkr; SctActv; 4-H; FFA; Ftbl; Wrstlng;.

ALLGAIER, Catherine F; Lawson Rxii HS; Lawson, MO; RptrYrbk; FHA; LetterPpCl; Trk; Chrldr;.

ALLING, Amelia; Green Lake Hs; Green Lake, WI; ALAGirlsSt; HonRl; NHS; NatlThespSoc; SchPl; RptrSchPpr; PpCl; Chrldr; Uw Madison ; Business.

ALLIS, William H; North Central HS; Indianapolis, IN; 107/1168 HonRl; NatlMeritSF; SchPl; Univ; Environmental Science.

ALLISON, Brian R; Phillipsburg HS; Phillipsburg, KS; VPSophCls; Chr; HonRl; VPStuCncl; TchrAde; Yrbk; FFA; LetterFtbl; LetterTrk; LetterWrstlng; College; Vocation.

ALLISON, James A; Northridge HS; Goshen, IN; 2/140 Chr; HonRl; SchMus; SecJrCls; KeyCl; PpCl; Bsbl; Bsktbl; Ftbl; Trk; Coll.

ALLISON, Jeanine; Northwestern HS; Blandinsville, IL; HonRl; OffAde; FHA; MthCl; SciCl; College; Professional.

ALLISON, John P; Northridge HS; Gosher, IN; Chr; Chrl; Chrs; HonRl; YthFlsp; RptrYrbk; KeyCl; PpCl; LetterBsbl; LetterFtbl; Ball St Coll; Architecture.

ALLISON, Joy E; Turner HS; Kansas City, KS; Band; Chr; ChrhWkr; HonRl; JrNHS; NHS; SchPl; StuCncl; EdYrBk; FrCl; College; Nursing.

ALLISON, Lorrie L; Sully Buttes HS; Onida, SD; Band; Chrs; CmntyWkr; HonRl; NHS; StuCncl; Bsktbl; Glf; Trk; Chrldr; College.

ALLISON, Lynette E; Pioneer HS; Ann Arbor, MI; 1/643 PresJrCls; HonRl; Orch; StuGov; Bsbl; Brown Univ; Lawyer.

ALLISON, Mark T; North Callawy HS; Kingdom City, MO; ChrhWkr; SctActv; PresStuCncl; PresStuGov; VPYthFlsp; LetterFtbl; Wrstlng; College; Prof.

ALLISON, Mona L; Albia Community HS; Albia, IA; Aud/Vis; Yrbk; RptrSchPpr; FTA; Photographer.

ALLISON, Patricia J; Basehor HS; Basehor, KS; SecTrsFrshCls; Band; Chrs; CncrtBnd; DrlTm; HonRl; PepBnd; SchPl; Twrl; Yrbk; Kansas State Univ; Elementary Education.

ALLISON, Rebecca S; East HS; Evansdale, IA; 5/330 Chrl; HonRl; NHS; SchMus; StuCncl; StuGov; RptrSchPpr; EdSchPpr; GerCl; PpCl; Univ; Accounting.

ALLISON, Sharon; Williamsville HS; Sherman, IL; 15/65 ChrhWkr; CmntyWkr; HonRl; JA; LbryAde; OffAde; SchPl; 4-H; PpCl; Coll; Teacher.

ALLISON, Terry D; Thornton Twp HS; Riverdale, IL; 9/750 Aud/Vis; ChrhWkr; HonRl; NHS; PresYthFlsp; PpCl; ChmbCommrsAwd; Wheaton College; Ministry.

ALLMAN, Cheryl; Central HS; Bay City, MI; 200/201 PresJrCls; PresSrCls; ALAGirlsSt; ChrhWkr; CAP; CmntyWkr; SptEdSchPpr; 4-H; Ftbl; Wrstlng;.

ALLMAN, Robert F; Duchesne HS; St Charles, MO; 73/137 ALBoysSt; CmntyWkr; StuCncl; RptrSchPpr; KeyCl; LatCl; CaptBsktbl; LetterFtbl; LetterGlf; IMSpt; Trade Sch; Mason.

ALLMARAS, Ronald C; New Rockford Central HS; New Rockford, ND; 12/67 ALBoysSt; Band; CncrtBnd; HonRl; MrchBnd; PepBnd; 4-H; FFA; MthCl; SciCl; Ndsu; Engi.

ALLMAYER, Mary J; Farmington Sr HS; Farmington Hls, MI; ChrhWkr; HonRl; NHS; StuCncl; PresYthFlsp; 4-H; LetterPpCl; 4-HAwd; JCAwd; RotaryAwd; Schoolcraft Comm College; Child Care Worker.

ALLORI, Raymond M; St Ignatius College Prep HS; Chicago, IL; 24/157 Chr; ChrhWkr; CmntyWkr; HonRl; JrNHS; NHS; SchAde; SctActv; TchrAde; LetterSocr; AmLegAwd; Univ Of Chicago; Lawyer.

ALLSOP, Gregory L; Bethany HS; Moweaqua, IL; 3/30 ALBoysSt; HonRl; NHS; StuCncl; Bsbl; Bsktbl; CaptFtbl; CaptTrk; College; Business Administration.

ALLSOPP, Lloyd R; Benton HS; Whittington, IL; 4-H; FFA; DanFAwd; Rend Lake Jr College; Auto Mechanic.

ALLSPACH, Jo E; Mt Pulaski HS; Mt Pulaski, IL; 5/100 ChrhWkr; NHS; TchrAde; RptrSchPpr; 4-H; FFA; GerCl; Tennis; GAA; 4-HAwd; PresAwd; Illinois St Univ; Physical Ed.

ALLSUP, Nancy L; Rushville HS; Rushville, IL; 14/121 Band; Chrs; CncrtBnd; HonRl; HospAde; MrchBnd; NHS; PepBnd; PpCl; Passavant School Of Nursing; Reg Nurse.

ALMENDINGER, Donna L; Indianola HS; Indianola, IA; 57/225 Band; CncrtBnd; DrlTm; DrmMjrt; HonRl; LbryAde; MrchBnd; Trk; GAA; PresAwd; Clge; Pro.

ALMERANTI, Lisa M; Dominican HS; East Detroit, MI; Chrl; ChrhWkr; HonRl; LbryAde; SchAde; SctActv; Wayne State Univ; Special Education.

ALMERAS, Mary J; North Knox HS; Bicknell, IN; 16/125 ALAGirlsSt; HonRl; LbryAde; NHS; FHA; FTA; LatCl; Indian State Univ; Elementary Education.

ALMS, Kent A; Steeleville Comm Unit HS; Steeleville, IL; 2/55 Band; Chr; Chrs; CncrtBnd; HonRl; MrchBnd; NHS; LetterBsbl; LetterGlf; University; Professional.

ALMS, Scot W; Steeleville HS; Steeleville, IL; 6/55 HonRl; NHS; Yrbk; LetterBsktbl; LetterGlf; Trade Schl; Vocation.

ALONGI, Barbara J; St Marys Acad; Rochelle, IL; ChrhWkr; HonRl; SchAde; StuGov; YthFlsp; Swmmng; Tennis; GAA; CitAwd; Coll; Major Study.

ALOOT, Darlene M; Bishop Foley HS; Madison Hts, MI; 8/187 HonRl; NHS; SchPl; RptrYrbk; Yrbk; Chrldr; PPFtbl; University Of Michigan; Architecture.

ALRICK, John J; Hutchinson HS; Hutchinson, MN; HstSrCls; Band; CncrtBnd; Teen; CaptFtbl; CaptGlf; MasAwd; Concordia College; Business.

ALSETH, Linnae M; Atwater HS; Atwater, MN; 3/63 Band; ChrhWkr; CncrtBnd; HonRl; LbryAde; MrchBnd; NHS; PepBnd; SchMus; SchPl; Bsktbl; College.

ALSLEBEN, Angela A; Glencoe Senior HS; Glencoe, MN; 3/154 Aud/Vis; Band; CncrtBnd; HonRl; MrchBnd; PepBnd; StuCncl; Vocational School; Interior Decorator.

ALSMAN, Pamela J; No Knox HS; Sandborn, IN; HonRl; NHS; Yrbk; FTA; FrCl; Bsktbl; University; Professional.

ALSOBROOK, Cheryl L; North Farmington HS; Farmington Hills, MI; HonRl; NHS; FrCl; Univ Mi; Math/sci.

ALSTERBERG, Karen; Neillsville HS; Neillsville, WI; HonRl; NHS; EdYrBk; FTA; SpnCl; PpCl; Univ; Psychology Major.

ALSTON, Sheryl A; Henry Ford Ii HS; Sterling Hts, MI; VPNHS; CaptChrldr; PPFtbl; Mi State Univ; Medical Tech.

ALSUP, Susan E; Willow Springs HS; Willow Springs, MO; 1/90 VPFrshCls; PresJrCls; ALAGirlsSt; ChrhWkr; HonRl; LbryAde; StuCncl; VPYthFlsp; FHA; PresSciCl; Univ; Med Sch.

ALT, Brian G; Motley HS; Motley, MN; ChrhWkr; HonRl; SchPl; YthFlsp; FFA; PpCl; Satples Voc Tech; Machinist.

ALT, Brian L; Robert S Tower HS; Warren, MI; HonRl; Teen; CaptSwmmng; Trk; Michigan St Univ; Horticulture.

ALT, Steve C; Aquinas HS; Shelby, NE; Chr; SchPl; SpnCl; MthCl; Ftbl; Trk; LetterWrstlng; College; Professional.

ALTEMEIER, Donna L; Grinnell HS; Grinnell, IA; HonRl; 4-H; 4-HAwd; American Inst Of Business; General Office.

ALTENBACH, Cynthia; Resurrection HS; Chicago, IL; 12/261 HonRl; NHS; Teen; Bsktbl; Univ Of Illinois; Computer Engineering.

ALTENHOFEN, Cynthia L; Newton HS; Kellogg, IA; 5/318 HonRl; NHS; NatlThespSoc; SchMus; SchPl; Ia State Univ; Computer Sciences.

ALTEPETER, Cynthia M; Carl Sandburg HS; Palos Heights, IL; Chr; Chrl; HonRl; LitMag; SctActv; Bsbl; Moraine Valley Coll;medicine.

ALTER, Jonathan H; Phillips Acad; Chicago, IL; 3/383 HstSophCls; PresSrCls; ALBoysSt; ModUN; ROTC; EdSchPpr; FDA; SecMthCl; Swmmng; Harvard; Biophysics.

ALTER, Karen S; Hale HS; Hale, MO; 8/20 Band; Chr; Chrl; Chrs; CmntyWkr; CncrtBnd; HonRl; Mdrgl; MrchBnd; StuCncl; Bsbl; CaptBsktbl; Trk; Chrldr; Missouri Western Univ; Law Enforcement.

ALTERGOTT, William H; William Fremd HS; Palatine, IL; HonRl; RptrSchPpr; LatCl; University; Chemical Engineering.

ALTGILBERS, Donald; Central Community HS; Aristan, IL; HonRl; Yrbk; SchPpr; Army, Coll.

ALTHOFF, Leann; Okawville HS; Nashville, IL; 14/60 TchrAde; YthFlsp; Kaskaskia College; Acounting.

ALTHOFF, Margaret; Thornwood HS; S Holland, IL; 135/852 ChrhWkr; HonRl; NHS; StuCncl; StuGov; Chrldr; IMSpt; 4-HAwd; Univ Of Il Circle Campus, Spanish.

ALTHOFF, Steven; Center Grove HS; Greenwood, IN; 33/235 ChrhWkr; HonRl; JrNHS; NHS; Bsbl; Bsktbl; Tennis; Purdue; Forestry.

ALTHOUSE, Debra; Melvin Sibley HS; Melvin, IL; ALAGirlsSt; Band; Chrs; HonRl; SchMus; StuCncl; RptrYrbk; RptrSchPpr; Chrldr; GAA; Parkland Jr College; Business.

ALTIER, John; Cretin HS; St Paul, MN; Aud/Vis; CmntyWkr; ROTC; SchPl; SctActv; Trade School; Professional.

ALTIER, Mary C; St Mary Of P H HS; Chicago, IL; Chrs; HonRl; LbryAde; SchPl; RptrYrbk; EdSchPpr; FTA; College; Veterinary.

ALTIMARI, Anthony F; Campion Jesuit HS; Chicagom, IL; 3/98 Band; HonRl; ModUN; PolWkr; StuGov; EdYrBk; RptrSchPpr; FTA; LetterBsbl; Ftbl; Northwestern Univ; Law.

ALTISER, Susan R; Newtown Harris HS; Newtown, MO; VPSophCls; PresJrCls; CncrtBnd; HonRl; NHS; Quill&Scroll; SchPl; StuCncl; Twrl; RptrYrbk; Bsbl; Bsktbl; Ne Missouri State Univ; Teach.

ALTMAIER, Ralph; West Sr HS; Riverside, IA; HonRl; Univ; Mathematics.

ALTMAN, Richard H; South Newton HS; Kentland, IN; 7/110 ChrhWkr; RptrSchPpr; LatCl; Purdue Univ; Science.

ALTMAN, Vicki L; East HS; Kansas City, MO; 4/289 ChrhWkr; HonRl; JrNHS; StuCncl; GAA; College; Pro.

ALTMANN, Debra M; Auburndale HS; Milladore, WI; Chrs; HonRl; FBLA; FHA; PpCl;.

ALTO, Nanette D; Nevis HS; Nevis, MN; Chr; HonRl; JCC; StuCncl; RptrYrbk; RptrSchPpr; 4-H; SciCl; LetterBsktbl; PresAwd; Col;.

ALTON, Debra; Northwest HS; Omaha, NE; Band; Chr; ChrhWkr; CncrtBnd; HonRl; MrchBnd; SchPpr; PpCl; GodCntryAwd; College; Medical Technician.

ALTON, Jeanine P; Mound Westonka HS; Wayzata, MN; AFS; Chr; ChrhWkr; HonRl; NHS; NatlMeritCmnd; SchMus; SchPl; GerCl; College.

ALTON, Leif E; North Adams HS; Jerome, MI; 2/52 Band; HonRl; NHS; SchPl; TchrAde; Yrbk; RptrSchPpr; SchPpr; FTA; Trk; Collge.

ALTSCHEFFEL, William R; Buena Vista HS; Saginaw, MI; HonRl; Quill&Scroll; SptEdYrbk; Bsbl; College; Architecture.

ALTSCHULER, Sheryl; West HS; Green Bay, WI; Band; ChrhWkr; HonRl; NHS; NatlMeritCmnd; StuCncl; YthLg; FrCl; MthCl; GAA; Uw Mad.

ALTSHULER, Barry A; Evanston Twp HS; Evanston, IL; 10/1100 CmntyWkr; HonRl; NatlFornLg; PolWkr; Quill&Scroll; SchPl; TchrAde; RptrSchPpr; College; Medicine.

ALUIA, Josephine A; Lake Shore HS; St Clair Shores, MI; HonRl; NHS; Clg; Data Processor.

ALUMBAUGH, Karen R; Herrin HS; Herrin, IL; 18/209 CmntyWkr; DrlTm; LbryAde; TchrAde; FHA; John A Logan; Secretary.

ALVAREZ, Flor S; Kirksville HS; Kirksville, MO; Chrs; HonRl; NHS; Orch; SchMus; StuCncl; FTA; FrCl; University.

ALVERSON, Timothy C; Hillsboro HS; Coffeen, IL; Band; CmntyWkr; CncrtBnd; HonRl; MrchBnd; PepBnd; College; Engineering.

ALVEY, Linda S; Whiteland Comm HS; New Whiteland, IN; Chr; ChrhWkr; CmntyWkr; OffAde; YthFlsp; 4-H; FBLA; FTA; MthCl; PpCl; College; Social Work.

ALVEY, Nora E; Brown County HS; Columbus, IN; 14/169 HonRl; NHS; TchrAde; U Of Evansville; Computer Science.

ALVIS, Keith E; Sherwood HS; Blairstown, MO; Bsktbl; Ftbl; Trk;.

ALWARD, Brenda J; Fountain Central HS; Wallace, IN; Band; CncrtBnd; HonRl; MrchBnd; NHS; OffAde; FBLA; Indiana Univ; Business.

ALWIN, David M; Baraboo HS; North Freedom, WI; 2/230 CncrtBnd; HonRl; MrchBnd; NatlMeritFnl; StuCncl; RptrSchPpr; Pres4-H; KeyCl; Trk; JCAwd; Harvard; Lawyer.

ALWIN, Steven L; Parker Senior HS; Janesville, WI; 3/387 HonRl; NHS; TchrAde; LatCl; LetterSwmmng; LetterTrk; U W Whitewater; Political Science.

AMACHER, Kathy M; Rich Central HS; Park Forest, IL; 9/400 DrlTm; HonRl; NHS; SptEdSchPpr; Univ Of Illinois; Medicine.

AMACHER, Lisa M; Fort Atkinson Senior HS; Fort Atkinson, WI; Band; CncrtBnd; HonRl; MrchBnd; PepBnd; Yrbk; SpnCl; LetterTennis; Music Sch Or Conservatory; Music Major.

AMADEI, Celeste M; Notre Dame HS; Chicago, IL; 36/302 ChrhWkr; HonRl; NHS; OffAde; Loyola Univ; Nurse.

AMAIMO, Jan E; Frank Cody HS; Detroit, MI; ChrhWkr; CmntyWkr; DrlTm; HonRl; OffAde; SctActv; TchrAde; YthFlsp; SchPpr; FTA; Alma College; Sociology.

AMAN, Bradley A; Fairfield Community HS; Fairfield, IL; VPFrshCls; Band; ChrhWkr; CmntyWkr; HonRl; FTA; LatCl; Ftbl; Trk; CchngActv; U Of Mo; Petroleum Engi.

AMANN, Bryan L; John Glenn HS; Westland, MI; VPSophCls; PresBand; CncrtBnd; HonRl; PresMrchBnd; PepBnd; PolWkr; StuCncl; TchrAde; FBLA; U Of Mi; Business Degree.

AMANN, Diane M; Carmel Girls HS; Libertyville, IL; 9/173 Chrs; HonRl; LitMag; LbryAde; NHS; NatlMeritCmnd; StuCncl; RptrSchPpr; LatCl; Trk; Univ Of Ill; Journalism.

AMANN, Susan M; Marissa HS; Marissa, IL; 9/74 SecFrshCls; Chrs; ChrhWkr; CmntyWkr; HonRl; OffAde; SchAde; SchMus; 4-H; FHA; GAA; Southeast Mo State; Nursing.

AMATI, Susan E; Rich East HS; Park Forest, IL; 48/326 TrsSophCls; TrsJrCls; VPAFS; HonRl; OffAde; Yrbk; CchngActv; College; Photography.

AMATO, Barb M; Palatine HS; Palatine, IL; 99/435 Chrl; Chrs; HonRl; GAA; Illinois State Univ; Interior Design.

AMAYO, Anna M; Turner HS; Kansas City, KS; Chrs; CmntyWkr; HonRl; HospAde; PolWkr; PresFNA; PpCl; Bsktbl; Chrldr; College; Nursing.

AMBERGER, Joann; Juneau HS; Milwaukee, WI; 30/229 Band; HonRl; LbryAde; MrchBnd; TchrAde; SpnCl; PpCl; Univ Of Wi At Milwaukee; Registered Nurse.

AMBLER, Donna L; Highland HS; Highland, IN; 179/538 Chrl; OffAde; SctActv; PresYthFlsp; FHA; Business School; Secretary.

AMBROSE, Bernard D; Martin Luther King HS; Detroit, MI; HonRl; FTA; FrCl; Bsktbl; Clg; Prof.

AMBROSELLI, Dominic; St John Cathedral HS; Milwaukee, WI; 1/154 VPFrshCls; ChrhWkr; HonRl; PresNHS; Sacrstn; SchAde; TchrAde; Yrbk; RptrSchPpr; SchPpr; SpnCl; IMSpt; Marquette Univ; Biomedical Engineering.

AMBROSO, Michael T; Lake Orion HS; Lake Orion, MI; CmntyWkr; HonRl; PolWkr; StuCncl; StuGov; LetterBsktbl; E Michigan Univ; Law.

AMBROSY, David J; Andrew Community HS; Zwingle, IA; Aud/Vis; Chrs; ChrhWkr; TchrAde; Pres4-H; DanFAwd; 4-HAwd; Trade School.

AMBROZ, Ann M; New Prague HS; New Prague, MN; 16/196 ALAGirlsSt; Chr; HonRl; NHS; SchPl; SecStuCncl; Yrbk; RptrSchPpr; PresGerCl; PpCl; College Of St Catherine; Business Mgmt.

AMBUEHL, Janeen R; Salem Comm HS; Salem, IL; 13/203 PresFrshCls; VPSophCls; Chr; Chrs; HonRl; JrNHS; NHS; SchPpr; PresFrCl; Texas Bible College; Religious Education.

AMDAHL, Debra K; Bay View HS; Milwaukee, WI; Chr; ChrhWkr; SchMus; TchrAde; MthCl; College; Chemical Engineering.

AMDAL, David G; North Greene HS; White Hall, IL; Band; HonRl; MrchBnd; Orch; PepBnd; St Louis College Of Pharmacy; Pharmacist.

AMEDEO, David M; Maine South HS; Park Ridge, IL; 30/849 Band; HonRl; JrNHS; NHS; TchrAde; TreasSpnCl; Socr; College; Medicine.

AMEDURI, Gina M; St Joseph HS; South Bend, IN; 33/277 HonRl; FDA; College; Medicine.

AMEN, Debbie; Hamlin HS; Lake Norden, SD; 1/66 VPFrshCls; SecSophCls; ALAGirlsSt; DrlTm; HonRl; RptrYrbk; FHA; PpCl; Trk; Chrldr; South Dakota State Univ; Secretarial Scienc.

AMENTA, Edwin L; Glenbrook South HS; Glenview, IL; 7/580 VPSrCls; HonRl; VPNHS; NatlMeritCmnd; StuGov; KeyCl; Bsbl; Ftbl; Wrstlng; IMSpt; In U.

AMERINE, Jane E; Platteview HS; Omaha, NE; HonRl; NHS; SchMus; PpCl; Bsbl; Chrldr; College.

AMERSON, Pamela; Beaumont HS; St Louis, MO; Chr; HonRl; JA; JAAwd; Univ; Professional.

AMES, Anthony I; Clarke Community HS; Weldon, IA; 11/104 Band; CncrtBnd; HonRl; MrchBnd; PepBnd; PolWkr; SctActv; TchrAde; 4-H; SciCl; Iowa State University.

AMES, Anthony I; Clarke Comm HS; Weldon, IA; 10/96 Band; CmntyWkr; CncrtBnd; HonRl; MrchBnd; PepBnd; PolWkr; TchrAde; 4-H; SciCl; IMSpt; Iowa State Univ; Engineer.

AMES, Carol J; Melvin Sibley HS; Sibley, IL; 6/32 SecFrshCls; SecSophCls; PresJrCls; ChrhWkr; VPNHS; SctActv; SecStuCncl; EdYrBk; EdSchPpr; Chrldr; University; Child Development.

AMES, Jeanette L; Minot HS; Minot, ND; Chr; CncrtBnd; HonRl; MrchBnd; NHS; PepBnd; SchMus; Univ Of Minnesota.

AMES, Karen L; Coldwater HS; Coldwater, MI; 4-H; PpCl; Trk; LetterChrldr; PPFtbl; 4-HAwd; College; Nursing.

AMES, Kerry L; South Putnam HS; Fillmore, IN; 3/100 TrsFrshCls; PresSophCls; PresJrCls; ALBoysSt; NHS; 4-H; FFA; LetterBsktbl; CaptTrk; Purdue U; Agricultural Economics & Educ.

AMETTIS, Barry J; Richmond Burton HS; Richmnd, IL; ALBoysSt; HonRl; StuCncl; FrCl; LetterBsbl; LetterFtbl; College; Accountant.

AMICK, Richard K; Lincoln HS; Cambridge City, IN; Aud/Vis; CmntyWkr; HonRl; OffAde; PolWkr; RptrYrbk; Indiana Univ; Optometry.

AMICK, Ruthanne I; Highland HS; Highland, IN; 101/587 Chr; ChrhWkr; Quill&Scroll; YthFlsp; RptrYrbk; VPSpnCl; Univ; Elec Engin.

AMMAN, Beth A; Fulton HS; Fulton, IL; 30/124 PresBand; Chrs; ChrhWkr; PresCncrtBnd; HonRl; NHS; NatlThespSoc; TchrAde; Yrbk; PresFTA; LetterBsktbl; LetterTrk; Coll; Teaching.

AMMAN, Beth M; Wahoo HS; Ithaca, NE; Chr; Chrs; ChrhWkr; HonRl; SchMus; YthFlsp; 4-H; College; Nurse.

AMMANN, John J; St Thomas Aquinas HS; Florissant, MO; 1/333 PresJrCls; Aud/Vis; ChrhWkr; HonRl; NHS; SchPl; College; Broadcasting.

AMMOND, James T; Ogemaw Heights HS; West Branch, MI; 44/175 Band; CncrtBnd; StuCncl; KeyCl; LetterFtbl; LetterTrk; Central Michigan University.

AMONETTE, George; Cloverdale HS; Cloverdale, IN; Band; DrlTm; MrchBnd; Orch; ROTC; SchPl; FrCl; SciCl; College; Career In The Service.

AMOROSO, Jean; Messmer HS; Milwaukee, WI; 4/209 HonRl; HospAde; NHS; OffAde; SchAde; StuGov; TchrAde; RptrSchPpr; EdSchPpr; FTA; Marquette Univ; Physical Therapist.

AMOS, Kathryn; Martensdale St Marys Hs; Prole, IA; 3/40 Band; ChrhWkr; HonRl; HospAde; MrchBnd; PepBnd; 4-H; PpCl; GAA; Chrldr; American Inst Of Business; Secretary.

AMOS, Linda M; East Union HS; Afton, IA; 1/61 HonRl; 4-H; Bsbl; Bsktbl; Trk; Col; Teach.

AMOS, Rosalee; Sargent Public HS; Sargent, NE; HonRl; NHS; NatlThespSoc; SchMus; SchPl; FBLA; FHA; PpCl; Bsktbl; Univ Of Nebr; Fashion Designing.

AMPTMANN, Wayne; St Dominic HS; Wentzville, MO; 2/138 VPSophCls; HonRl; NHS; Sdlty; StuCncl; StuGov; SchPpr; IMSpt; Univ Mo Columbia; Engineering.

AM RHEIN, Stephen; South Decatur HS; Greensburg, IN; 1/86 PresSophCls; HonRl; NHS; KeyCl; FrCl; PpCl; Bsbl; Ftbl; EldAwd; OptClAwd; Purdue Univ.

AMS, Susanna M; Bishop Mc Namara HS; Kankakee, IL; 18/161 HonRl; NatlMeritFnl; SchPl; RptrYrbk; SpnCl; Marquette Univ; Lawyer.

AMSBARY, Elizabeth C; University HS; Champaign, IL; SecTrsJrCls; Mdrgl; SchPl; StuCncl; StuGov; YthFlsp; RptrSchPpr; Pres4-H; SecLatCl; 4-HAwd; Univ; Vet.

AMSDEN, Connie L; Paxton HS; Ludlow, IL; 13/128 ChrhWkr; HonRl; NHS; Treas4-H; LatCl; GAA; IMSpt; Business School; Secretarial Work.

AMSTUTZ, Jerry L; Jackson County Western HS; Jackson, MI; 3/150 Chr; ChrhWkr; CncrtBnd; HonRl; NatlFornLg; NHS; TchrAde; LetterBsbl; CchngActv; Geneva College; Statistician.

AMTHOR, James R; Holt HS; Holt, MI; 55/325 HonRl; NHS; KeyCl; LetterBsktbl; LetterFtbl; LetterTrk; Us Air Force Academy; Pilot.

AMUNDSON, Donald R; Armstrong Sr HS; Plymouth, MN; 84/599 Band; ChrhWkr; HonRl; Univ Of Mn; Electrical Engineer.

AMUNDSON, Eric E; Valley Community HS; Postville, IA; ALBoysSt; Band; Chrs; ChrhWkr; HonRl; SchPl; StuCncl; 4-H; LetterFtbl; 4-HAwd; Trade; Vocation.

AMUNDSON, Julie M; Plattsmouth HS; Plattsmouth, NE; HonRl; TchrAde; RptrYrbk; RptrSchPpr; SchPpr; PpCl; Bsktbl; Swmmng; LetterTrk; Chrldr; GAA; College; Law.

AMUNDSON, Teresa G; Nesco HS; Zearing, IA; Band; Chrs; ChrhWkr; CncrtBnd; HonRl; SchMus; VPYthFlsp; Yrbk; Bsktbl; Trk; Coll; Bus.

AMUNDSON, Terry L; Holmen HS; Holmen, WI; 8/98 Band; CncrtBnd; HonRl; MrchBnd; NHS; PepBnd; StuCncl; LetterBsbl; Bsktbl; Ftbl; Viterbo College; Medical Tech.

AMY, Jan M; Harper Creek HS; Battle Creek, MI; 9/282 SecSophCls; HstJrCls; ALAGirlsSt; CncrtBnd; HonRl; ModUN; NHS; SchMus; StuCncl; PpCl; Mi State Univ; Law.

ANAN, Thomas J; St Agatha HS; Detroit, MI; 1/105 Chrs; CmntyWkr; HonRl; NHS; SctActv; RptrYrbk; RptrSchPpr; Kalamazoo Coll; Medicine.

ANAS, David J; Franklin HS; Livonia, MI; HonRl; Tennis; College; Professional.

ANASTASIA, Larry A; Bremen HS; Midlothian, IL; 50/475 HonRl; NHS; Swmmng; LetterTrk; IMSpt; College; Electrical Engineering.

ANAWIS, Mark A; Loyola Academy; Skokie, IL; 19/442 HonRl; NHS; NatlMeritFnl; NatlMeritCmnd; NatlMeritSchl; RedCrAde; SchPpr; Univ; Medicine.

ANCOG, Consuelo; Marian HS; Birmingham, MI; HonRl; ModUN; NatlMeritSF; Quill&Scroll; EdSchPpr; Univ Of Michigan.

ANCY, Annette R; North County HS; Bonne Terre, MO; HonRl; JrNHS; NHS; TchrAde; FHA; PpCl; Trk; Chrldr; College; Professional.

ANDA, Jon A; Prospect HS; Mt Prospect, IL; 48/614 HonRl; StuCncl; StuGov; Bsktbl; Univ Of Illinois; Business Administration.

ANDEJESKI, Yvonne M; Prospect HS; Arlington Hts, IL; 30/614 HonRl; HospAde; OffAde; PolWkr; Univ Of Iowa; Nursing.

ANDERBERG, Jo D; Arthur County HS; Arthur, NE; 1/12 SecSophCls; VPJrCls; VPSrCls; ALAGirlsSt; Chr; Chrs; HonRl; SchPl; StuCncl; CaptFtbl; College.

ANDEREGG, Dorothy; Hastings Sr HS; Hastings, MN; Band; Chrs; CncrtBnd; MrchBnd; NHS; PepBnd; SchMus; 4-H; Bsktbl; Trk; Wis Univ; Dance Teacher.

ANDEREGG, Linda; Hempstead HS; Dubuque, IA; 95/209 Chr; HospAde; SchMus; SchPl; SctActv; StuCncl; StuGov; YthFlsp; GerCl; IMSpt; College.

ANDERHOUS, Susan J; Homewood Flossmoor HS; Homewood, IL; ChrhWkr; CmntyWkr; SctActv; TchrAde; Teen; RptrSchPpr; EdSchPpr; SpnCl; PpCl; Swmmng; College; Special Ed.

ANDERS, Charles M; Albert Cty Truesdale Comm HS; Albert City, IA; 6/50 PresSophCls; VPJrCls; Chr; Chrs; ChrhWkr; HonRl; StuCncl; SptEdSchPpr; Bsbl; Ftbl; Iowa State U; Biology.

ANDERS, Lynn L; Wm L Brown HS; Union Center, SD; 24/204 HonRl; NHS; TchrAde; YthFlsp; RptrSchPpr; College; Law Enforcement.

ANDERS, Robyn S; Boone Jr Sr HS; Boone, IA; Chrs; LbryAde; NatlThespSoc; SchPl; SctActv; RptrSchPpr; FrCl; SpnCl; College; Theater Arts.

ANDERS, Sylvia S; Oskaloosa Senior HS; Oskaloosa, IA; 10/195 Band; Chr; Chrs; ChrhWkr; CncrtBnd; HonRl; MrchBnd; NHS; Orch; PepBnd; U Of Northern Ia; Music Major.

ANDERS, Terri L; Rockridge HS; Illinois City, IL; 15/147 Band; ChrhWkr; CncrtBnd; HonRl; MrchBnd; NHS; EdYrBk; FTA; LatCl; PresAwd; Black Hawk College; Secondary Music Teacher.

ANDERSAN, Crystal R; East Chas HS; Wagner, SD; PresSrCls; Chrs; DrlTm; HonRl; NHS; FHA; PpCl; DARAwd; Lake Area Vo Tech; Child Care.

ANDERSEN, Cynthia K; St Anthony HS; Effingham, IL; SecSophCls; SecJrCls; Chrl; ChrhWkr; DrlTm; HospAde; SchPl; StuCncl; FrCl; PpCl; University; Professional.

ANDERSEN, Daryl D; Verdigre Public HS; Winnetoon, NE; 3/39 PresSrCls; ALBoysSt; HonRl; NHS; StuCncl; RptrSchPpr; FFA; Bsbl; LetterBsktbl; IMSpt; U Of Ne; Agriculture.

ANDERSEN, David; Chaparral HS; Anthony, KS; CncrtBnd; HonRl; NHS; KeyCl; AmLegAwd; DanFAwd; Pratt Jr Coll; Enviorn Sci.

ANDERSEN, Donalyn M; Aurora HS; Aurora, NE; Chr; SchMus; Teen; YthFlsp; EdSchPpr; FBLA; FHA; Chrldr; 4-HAwd; VFWAwd; U Of Ne; Elementry Ed Or Business.

ANDERSEN, Donna R; Wilbur Clatonia HS; Clatonia, NE; ALAGirlsSt; Chrs; HonRl; SchPl; YthFlsp; RptrSchPpr; FBLA; FHA; PpCl; Chrldr; College.

ANDERSEN, John; Culver Military Academy; Calumet City, IL; 68/163 Band; CncrtBnd; HonRl; MrchBnd; ROTC; GerCl; Socr; IMSpt; CitAwd; Purdue U; Computer Technologist.

ANDERSEN, Julie M; Kimball Cty HS; Kimball, NE; PresJrCls; Band; Chr; CncrtBnd; DrmMjrt; HonRl; Mdrgl; MrchBnd; PepBnd; SchMus; StuCncl; TchrAde; FHA; PpCl; College; Stewardess.

ANDERSEN, Kenneth; Center Point Cons HS; Center Point, IA; 1/48 VPSophCls; ALBoysSt; Band; Chr; Chrs; CncrtBnd; HonRl; MrchBnd; NHS; NatlMeritFnl; College; Medical Doctor.

ANDERSEN, Lisa; Ashley HS; Bannister, MI; 18/42 Band; CncrtBnd; MrchBnd; PepBnd; SchPl; TchrAde; Yrbk; FHA; GAA; IMSpt; Coll; Lpn.

ANDERSEN, Lori B; Hurley HS; Hurley, SD; 4/24 SecJrCls; TrsJrCls; ALAGirlsSt; NHS; SchPl; RptrSchPpr; FHA; PpCl; LetterBsktbl; CaptChrldr; Univ Of Sd; Nursing.

ANDERSEN, Mary P; Holy Angels HS; Richfield, MN; 31/114 Chrs; HospAde; RedCrAde; StuCncl; EdYrBk; IMSpt; PPFtbl; College; Nursing.

ANDERSEN, Nancy J; North Linn HS; Walker, IA; Band; Chrs; CmntyWkr; HonRl; JrNHS; YthFlsp; FHA; SpnCl; LetterBsbl; LetterBsktbl; Univ; Elementary Education.

ANDERSEN, Ronee D; Treynor Community HS; Treynor, IA; 2/37 Band; DrlTm; HonRl; NHS; SchMus; TreasFHA; LetterBsbl; LetterBsktbl; LetterTrk; PPFtbl; College; Accounting.

ANDERSEN, Steven L; Plattsmouth HS; Plattsmouth, NE; Band; ChrhWkr; CncrtBnd; HonRl; MrchBnd; SctActv; StuCncl; PresYthFlsp; Ftbl; GodCntryAwd; College; Vet Med.

ANDERSEN, Steven S; East Grand Rapids HS; Grand Rapids, MI; Band; CncrtBnd; MrchBnd; NatlMeritSF; Orch; PepBnd; SchMus; AmLegAwd; Grand Rapids J C; Medicine.

ANDERSEN, Susan K; Spring Hill HS; Olathe, KS; 3/59 TrsJrCls; DrmMjrt; HonRl; Mdrgl; NHS; StuCncl; Twrl; Yrbk; FHA; Chrldr; Baker Univ; Psychology.

ANDERSEN, Walter R; Wilber Clatonia HS; Clatonia, NE; Chrs; ChrhWkr; CtyCnl; CmntyWkr; HonRl; SchPl; RptrSchPpr; Bsbl; LetterBsktbl; Trk; College; Business Admin.

ANDERSH, Christine; East Charles Mix HS; Wagner, SD; DrlTm; HospAde; LbryAde; SchPl; Yrbk; FHA; FNA; PpCl; Trk; VoiceDemAwd; College N State; Physical Ther.

ANDERSH, Debra; Wagner HS; Wagner, SD; Chrs; DrlTm; HonRl; HospAde; LbryAde; SctActv; 4-H; FHA; FNA; Trk; Coll; Nursing.

ANDERSON, Alma; Worthington Sr HS; Worthington, MN; 5/262 ChrhWkr; CmntyWkr; JrNHS; LitMag; NatlFornLg; NHS; Quill&Scroll; YthFlsp; RptrSchPpr; FTA; Worthington Community College; Spec Educ.

ANDERSON, Angela J; Roosevelt HS; Gary, IN; 7/624 HonRl; NHS; NatlMeritCmnd; SctActv; FTA; EngCl; FrCl; MthCl; Univ Of Calif; Medicine.

ANDERSON, Angela M; Pillager HS; Pillager, MN; SecTrsSophCls; Band; Chr; Chrs; ChrhWkr; CncrtBnd; HonRl; MrchBnd; Orch; PepBnd; Coll; Social Work.

ANDERSON, Arlene A; Decatur Public HS; Decatur, NE; 2/15 Band; Chr; Chrl; Chrs; ChrhWkr; HonRl; LbryAde; SchMus; SchPl; YthFlsp; College; Youth Ministry.

ANDERSON, Audrey A; Postville HS; Postville, IA; 3/95 PresJrCls; Chrs; HonRl; NHS; NatlMeritSF; NatlThespSoc; StuCncl; PresPpCl; AFS; PPFtbl; CitAwd; College; Journalism.

ANDERSON, Ava J; Wyaconda C 1 HS; Wyaconda, MO; 2/20 SecFrshCls; SecSophCls; Chrs; ChrhWkr; HonRl; NHS; StuCncl; SciCl; Bsbl; Bsktbl; IMSpt; Univ Of Mo; Nursing.

ANDERSON, Barbara; Glenwood Public HS; Lowry, MN; 17/132 PresSrCls; NHS; StuCncl; FNA; GerCl; GAA; St Cloud School Of Nursing; Rn.

ANDERSON, Barbara H; Grosse Pointe South HS; Grosse Point Park, MI; Chr; Chrs; HonRl; SchPl; StuGov; YthFlsp; Michigan St Univ; Math.

ANDERSON, Barbara J; Notre Dame HS; Burlington, IA; HonRl; HospAde; ModUN; RptrYrbk; SpnCl; LetterTrk; College; Education Field.

ANDERSON, Barbara M; Crawford HS; Crawford, NE; 15/40 HonRl; SchPl; SecStuCncl; PresPpCl; JAAwd; Lincoln Sch Of Commerce; Legal Secretary.

ANDERSON, Barbara R; Central HS; Aberdeen, SD; ChrhWkr; CmntyWkr; HonRl; LitMag; SchMus; SchPl; StuGov; YthFlsp; PresPpCl; Chrldr; Sdsu; Nursing.

ANDERSON, Beth L; Dawson Boyd HS; Dawson, MN; AFS; Chr; CncrtBnd; HonRl; Orch; PepBnd; SchPl; RptrSchPpr; FHA; Chrldr; U Of Minn; Registered Nurse.

ANDERSON, Betsy L; Echo Public HS; Echo, MN; SecJrCls; Band; Chrs; CncrtBnd; HonRl; MrchBnd; SchPl; StuCncl; RptrSchPpr; FFA; PpCl; Trk; LetterChrldr; GAA; College; Professional.

ANDERSON, Brenda M; South Holt R I HS; Oregon, MO; 2/40 PresSrCls; ALAGirlsSt; ChrhWkr; CmntyWkr; NHS; SchPl; PresYthFlsp; Chrldr; DARAwd; KiwanAwd; University; Professional.

ANDERSON, Brian; Grand Rapids Sr HS; Grand Rapids, MN; 10/385 Band; Chr; ChrhWkr; CncrtBnd; HonRl; Mdrgl; PepBnd; SchMus; YthFlsp; Tennis; Mo Inst Of The Bible; Bible Related.

ANDERSON, Calvin; Lincoln Way Hs; New Lenox, IL; 59/498 Band; HonRl; MrchBnd; NHS; PepBnd; SchMus; MthCl; Illinois State U; Music Teacher.

ANDERSON, Carletta E; Oelrichs HS; Oelrichs, SD; Band; Chrs; HonRl; SchPl; Yrbk; 4-H; Bsktbl; Trk; Chrldr; 4-HAwd; College; Major Study.

ANDERSON, Carl L; Oregon HS; Oregon, WI; HonRl; NHS; LetterFtbl; CaptTrk; IMSpt; Tech College; Electronic Tech.

ANDERSON, Carol A; Horace Mann HS; N Fond Du Lac, WI; VPSrCls; Chrs; HonRl; NatlFornLg; NHS; SchPl; RptrYrbk; KeyCl; FrCl; CaptBsktbl; GAA; IMSpt; DARAwd;.

ANDERSON, Carole; Dubois HS; Dubois, IN; Band; Chrs; HonRl; MrchBnd; SctActv; YthFlsp; Yrbk; 4-H; PpCl; 4-HAwd; College; Journalism.

ANDERSON, Carol J; Ishpeming Sr HS; Ishpeming, MI; 44/201 Chrl; Chrs; HonRl; SchPl; StuCncl; StuGov; UNYO; SchPpr; FrCl; BttyCrckrAwd; University.

ANDERSON, Carol M; Castlewood HS; Castlewood, SD; 1/30 Band; ChrhWkr; CmntyWkr; CncrtBnd; DrmMjrt; PresFrshCls; MrchBnd; YthFlsp; 4-H; FHA; Clg; Teacher.

ANDERSON, Carol R; Buffalo Grove HS; Buffalo Grove, IL; 28/290 AFS; ChrhWkr; HonRl; NHS; Yrbk; PpCl; College; Pediatrician.

ANDERSON, Carolyn; Northern Heights HS; Reading, KS; 5/35 HonRl; ModUN; NHS; PolWkr; Yrbk; RptrSchPpr; PPFtbl; DARAwd; CitAwd; Ks State Univ; Scientific.

ANDERSON, Carrol D; Winamac Community HS; Winamac, IN; HonRl; Ball St Univ; Architet.

ANDERSON, Catherine L; North Decatur HS; Greensburg, IN; 2/83 Band; CncrtBnd; HonRl; NHS; StuCncl; 4-H; FHA; PpCl; SciCl; GAA; In Purdue Univ; Nursing.

ANDERSON, Catherine; Hays HS; Hays, KS; CncrtBnd; HonRl; MrchBnd; ModUN; Orch; PepBnd; StuCncl; EdSchPpr; SpnCl; PpCl; Coll; Curriculum Major Study.

ANDERSON, Charles L; Blissfield HS; Blissfield, MI; 2/138 PresFrshCls; PresJrCls; VPJrCls; PresSrCls; Band; NHS; StuCncl; CaptTrk; AmLegAwd; BttyCrckrAwd; RotaryAwd; Univ Of Chicago; Medicine.

ANDERSON, Charles R; Braymer C 4 HS; Braymer, MO; TrsJrCls; Chr; Chrs; HonRl; Mdrgl; SchPl; YthFlsp; 4-H; FFA; MthCl; PpCl; CaptBsbl; CaptBsktbl; Nw Missouri State; Liberal Arts.

ANDERSON, Cheryl A; Monrovia HS; Mooresville, IN; 8/92 CncrtBnd; MrchBnd; NHS; OffAde; PepBnd; StuCncl; RptrYrbk; DARAwd; Undecided;.

ANDERSON, Cheryl L; Lindblom HS; Chicago, IL; 38/599 ChrhWkr; OffAde; TchrAde; SpnCl; GAA; Coll; Eng.

ANDERSON, Cindy R; Marinette Sr HS; Marinett, WI; 23/243 Chrs; HonRl; RptrYrbk; Yrbk; RptrSchPpr; LatCl; Bay De Nac Comm Clg; Nursing.

ANDERSON, Clark A; North HS; Sioux City, IA; 15/350 PresSrCls; Aud/Vis; Band; ChrhWkr; CmntyWkr; CncrtBnd; HonRl; MrchBnd; NatlFornLg; NatlMeritSF; Bsktbl; Ftbl; Tennis; Univ; Professional.

ANDERSON, Claude A; Highland Pk Sr HS; St Paul, MN; Band; Chr; ChrhWkr; CmntyWkr; DrlTm; DrmBgl; LbryAde; MrchBnd; SchAde; SchMus; SchPl; StuCncl; Yrbk; College; Professional.

ANDERSON, Cloette D; Potter Public HS; Potter, NE; ALAGirlsSt; Chrs; CncrtBnd; HonRl; SchPl; YthFlsp; Yrbk; SecPpCl; Trk; Nebraska Wesleyan Univ; Psychology.

ANDERSON, Colleen S; Crestland HS; Early, IA; Band; Chrs; CncrtBnd; MrchBnd; 4-H; FrCl; SpnCl; Glf; 4-HAwd; College; Major Study.

ANDERSON, Connie; Diamond R 4 HS; Diamond, MO; 1/54 HonRl; NHS; RptrYrbk; EdYrBk; RptrSchPpr; SchPpr; FHA; MthCl; GAA; IMSpt; Univ; Medical Techn.

ANDERSON, Cynthia; South Shore HS; Chicago, IL; 13/462 PresSrCls; HonRl; NHS; OffAde; StuCncl; StuGov; TchrAde; EdYrBk; Chrldr; Illinois State Univ; Special Ed.

ANDERSON, Cynthia D; Penney HS; Kingston, MO; SecSrCls; HonRl; SchPl; SecStuCncl; RptrSchPpr; VPSpnCl; CaptBsktbl; Chrldr; BttyCrckrAwd; DARAwd; Mo Univ; Registered Nurse.

ANDERSON, Cynthia J; Papillion HS; Papillion, NE; Chrs; ChrhWkr; HonRl; NHS; RedCrAde; StuCncl; TchrAde; RptrYrbk; RptrSchPpr; FHA; Chrldr; CchngActv; University Of Nebraska; German.

ANDERSON, Cynthia K; Southland HS; Adams, MN; 38/125 Chrs; ChrhWkr; HonRl; NHS; EdYrBk; GerCl; Dental Assist.

ANDERSON, Dale L; Goodland HS; Goodland, KS; 4-H; FFA; Wrstlng; Junior College; Livestock Industry.

ANDERSON, Daniel L; Hibbing HS; Hibbing, MN; 23/432 HonRl; NHS; NatlMeritCmnd; MthCl; Tennis; Gustavus Adolphus Coll.

ANDERSON, Daniel R; Harding County HS; Buffalo, SD; 1/27 ALBoysSt; PresBand; Chr; Chrl; Chrs; ChrhWkr; CmntyWkr; CncrtBnd; HonRl; Mdrgl; Tennis; LetterTrk; 4-HAwd; Pacific Lutheran Univ; Religion.

ANDERSON, Darla J; Rochester Comm HS; Rochester, IN; 5/163 Chr; HonRl; NHS; SctActv; FrCl; PpCl; Clg; Nursing.

ANDERSON, Darrel; Fairbury HS; Fairbury, NE; Aud/Vis; ChrhWkr; SctActv; YthFlsp; College; Veterinarian.

ANDERSON, David; Albia Comm HS; Albia, IA; 14/150 ALBoysSt; Band; HonRl; NHS; Trk; IMSpt; Iowa State U; Civil Engineering.

ANDERSON, David; Andrew Jackson HS; South Bend, IN; Band; CncrtBnd; HonRl; MrchBnd; Orch; PepBnd; IMSpt; Iusb; General Mgmt.

ANDERSON, David B; Alpena HS; Alpena, MI; Band; ChrhWkr; HonRl; LitMag; MrchBnd; PolWkr; RptrSchPpr; EdSchPpr; LetterBsktbl; College; Journalism.

ANDERSON, David G; Ogemaw Hts HS; West Branch, MI; HonRl; TchrAde; RptrYrbk; LetterBsbl; LetterBsktbl; LetterFtbl; LetterTrk; IMSpt; Alma College; Lawyer.

ANDERSON, David P; Falls HS; International Fls, MN; 61/285 HonRl; SctActv; LetterFtbl; LetterTrk; College.

ANDERSON, Dawn; Laurens Community HS; Laurens, IA; 11/52 Chr; Chrs; ChrhWkr; HonRl; NHS; SchMus; SchPl; SctActv; SchPpr; Morningside College; English.

ANDERSON, Dawn M; Wayzata HS; Wayzata, MN; 7/455 Chr; ChrhWkr; HonRl; HospAde; NHS; Clge; Vet.

ANDERSON, Debbie J; Willow Lake Public HS; Willow Lake, SD; 10/35 Band; HonRl; 4-H; FHA; Trk; Nettleton Clge In Sioux Falls; Secretarial.

ANDERSON, Debbie K; Sisseton HS; Sisseton, SD; 5/96 HonRl; NHS; SchPl; TreasStuCncl; Pres4-H; Trk; GAA; AmLegAwd; 4-HAwd; JCAwd; VFWAwd; University; Professional.

ANDERSON, Deborah J; Belleville HS; Belleville, MI; Aud/Vis; HonRl; LbryAde; Orch; TchrAde; Eastern Michigan University.

ANDERSON, Deborah J; Prairie Farm HS; Prairie Farm, WI; PresFrshCls; Band; Chr; CncrtBnd; HonRl; PepBnd; StuCncl; Twrl; TreasPpCl; Chrldr; College; Music.

ANDERSON, Deborah L; Lancaster HS; Lancaster, MN; ChrhWkr; HonRl; SchPl; TchrAde; Twrl; RptrSchPpr; FHA; PpCl; Univ Of Nd; Rn.

ANDERSON, Debra; Central HS; Rapid City, SD; 95/552 Band; CncrtBnd; DrlTm; MrchBnd; Orch; PepBnd; SchMus; StuCncl; PpCl; Sd State Univ; Music.

ANDERSON, Debra; Guilford HS; Rockford, IL; AFS; ChrhWkr; HonRl; NHS; SctActv; TchrAde; EngCl; Illinois State Univ; Languages.

ANDERSON, Debra J; Fremont HS; Fremont, NE; 67/418 ALAGirlsSt; Band; Chr; ChrhWkr; CaptDrlTm; NHS; SchMus; PresYthFlsp; PpCl; Ne Wesleyan Univ; Elem Ed.

ANDERSON, Debra S; Northwest HS; House Springs, MO; 16/370 ChrhWkr; HonRl; LbryAde; SchAde; Southwest Missouri State Univ; Argiculture.

ANDERSON, Denise R; Exira Comm HS; Brayton, IA; 7/48 SecTrsSrCls; ALAGirlsSt; HonRl; SchPpr; 4-H; PpCl; Bsktbl; PPFtbl; CitAwd; Community Col; Medical Secretary.

ANDERSON, Dennis R; West HS; Sioux City, IA; Chr; Chrs; SchMus; RptrSchPpr; SptEdSchPpr; ChmbCommrsAwd; Ia Univ; Zoology.

ANDERSON, Diana M; Starkweather Public HS; Starkweather, ND; 1/18 Chrs; ChrhWkr; CmntyWkr; CncrtBnd; HonRl; PepBnd; EdSchPpr; 4-H; LetterBsktbl; Trk; 4-HAwd; Williston Univ; Pre Med.

ANDERSON, Diane; West Aurora Hs; North Aurora, IL; 55/625 JrNHS; NHS; PpCl; Western Ill U; Math Major.

ANDERSON, Diane L; Arapahoe HS; Arapahoe, NE; 5/30 Band; Chr; CncrtBnd; DrmMjrt; HonRl; SctActv; FHA; PpCl; LetterBsktbl; LetterTrk; 4-HAwd; College;.

ANDERSON, Diane L; New York Mills HS; New York Mills, MN; PresSophCls; CncrtBnd; HonRl; PresNHS; RedCrAde; StuCncl; TchrAde; FHA; PresPpCl; Chrldr; Alexandria Voc Inst; Accountant.

ANDERSON, Dianna L; Churubusco HS; Churubusco, IN; 96/105 ChrhWkr; SchPl; YthFlsp; RptrSchPpr; 4-H; FHA; KeyCl; PpCl; GAA; DanFAwd; College; Social Work.

ANDERSON, Dinah L; Marion HS; Marion, IL; HonRl; HospAde; OffAde; PolWkr; FBLA; PpCl; South Ill Univ; Political Science.

ANDERSON, Donald; Waseca HS; Waseca, MN; 39/206 Band; Chr; ChrhWkr; CmntyWkr; CncrtBnd; HonRl; Mdrgl; MrchBnd; PepBnd; SchMus; Augustana Col; Science.

ANDERSON, Donald C; Holy Cross HS; Chicago, IL; 12c08 Band; CncrtBnd; HonRl; MrchBnd; NHS; PepBnd; VPStuCncl; RptrYrbk;.

ANDERSON, Donald D; Centennial HS; Champaign, IL; ChrhWkr; HonRl; JrNHS; NHS; SctActv; YthFlsp; University; Business Admin.

ANDERSON, Donna L; Genoa Public HS; Genoa, NE; 4/27 Chr; Chrs; HonRl; LbryAde; NHS; SchPl; YthFlsp; RptrSchPpr; FHA; VPPpCl; Kearney State College; Education.

ANDERSON, Douglas; Wauwatosa West HS; Wauwatosa, WI; 13/436 Band; CncrtBnd; HonRl; NatlThespSoc; SchMus; SctActv; MthCl; JAAwd; RotaryAwd; U Of Michigan; Corporate Law.

ANDERSON, Douglas D; Donovan HS; Donovan, IL; 1/51 Chr; HonRl; Mdrgl; NHS; SchPl; FTA; PpCl; CaptBsbl; CaptBsktbl; LetterGlf; College; Engineering.

ANDERSON, Duncan; Le Sueur HS; Le Sueur, MN; AFS; HonRl; NHS; Orch; PepBnd; SchMus; SchPl; Yrbk; 4-H; Trk; St Olaf; Medicine.

ANDERSON, Edmund P; Boyne City HS; Boyne City, MI; 1/130 PresSrCls; Band; SchMus; StuCncl; TchrAde; Col; Elect Engineer.

ANDERSON, Edna M; Deland Weldon HS; Weldon, IL; 7/40 SecSrCls; AFS; HonRl; TreasStuCncl; Yrbk; RptrSchPpr; SecFHA; Trk; LetterChrldr; PresGAA; Univ; Special Education.

ANDERSON, Edward A; Mooseheart HS; Mooseheart, IL; 2/17 PresJrCls; PresSrCls; Chr; Chrs; DrlTm; HonRl; ROTC; TchrAde; SchPpr; LetterFtbl; LetterTrk; LetterWrstlng; University; Law.

ANDERSON, Edwina D; Cambridge Senior HS; Cambridge, MN; Band; Chr; CncrtBnd; MrchBnd; PepBnd; YthFlsp; VP4-H; 4-HAwd; College; Curriculum Of Major Study.

ANDERSON, Elizabeth; Elizabeth Seton HS; South Holland, IL; 25/250 PresSrCls; Chrs; CmntyWkr; HonRl; IntrClCncl; NHS; SchMus; StuCncl; StuGov; LatCl; Loyola Univ; Pre Med.

ANDERSON, Elizabeth; Rock Island HS; Rock Island, IL; Band; Chrs; ChrhWkr; CncrtBnd; HonRl; NHS; PepBnd; SchMus; RptrSchPpr; FrCl; College; Botany.

ANDERSON, Ellen M; Plattsmouth HS; Plattsmouth, NE; 12/133 Band; CncrtBnd; HonRl; NHS; StuCncl; Yrbk; Treas4-H; VPPpCl; CaptBsktbl; LetterGlf; CaptTrk; PresGAA; College; Nursing.

ANDERSON, Eric A; Bradley Bourbonnais HS; Bourbonnais, IL; HonRl; NHS; College.

ANDERSON, Eric B; Roosevelt HS; Britt, MN; 14/284 Band; CncrtBnd; HonRl; MrchBnd; ModUN; NatlFornLg; NHS; NatlMeritSF; Orch; PepBnd; SchMus; IMSpt; Univ Of Minn; Research Computer Science.

ANDERSON, Eric D; Pine River HS; Tustin, MI; HonRl; NHS; FrCl; LetterTrk; College; Electrical Engineer.

ANDERSON, Eric P; Ash Grove HS; Bois D Arc, MO; HonRl; ModUN; 4-H; FFA; FSA; MthCl; SciCl; Ftbl; 4-HAwd; Univ Of Mo; Medical.

ANDERSON, Eugene L; Smithton Rvi HS; Smithton, MO; 15/41 PresSrCls; Band; Chrs; ChrhWkr; HonRl; MrchBnd; NHS; SchPl; StuCncl; 4-H; PpCl; LetterBsbl; CaptBsktbl; CchngActv; State Fair Community College.

ANDERSON, Gail J; Alton R Iv HS; Alton, MO; 4/87 Band; HonRl; LbryAde; StuCncl; TchrAde; PpCl; CaptBsktbl; LetterChrldr; Stephens College; Physical Ed.

ANDERSON, Gale T; Michigan Public HS; Michigan, ND; HstFrshCls; SecTrsSophCls; SecTrsJrCls; SecTrsSrCls; Band; Chr; Chrs; CncrtBnd; DrmMjrt; HonRl; MrchBnd; PepBnd; StuCncl; EdYrBk; Univ Of North Dakota; Chemical Engineering.

ANDERSON, Gayle C; Paynesville HS; Paynesville, MN; 2/115 ALAGirlsSt; Chr; HonRl; Mdrgl; NHS; SchMus; SctActv; StuGov; Yrbk; RptrSchPpr; Augsburg College; Speech Communictions.

ANDERSON, Gerald A; Swed City Comm HS; Swea City, IA; Band; ChrhWkr; CmntyWkr; CncrtBnd; HonRl; MrchBnd; SchMus; SchPl; SctActv; FFA; Coll; Agriculture.

ANDERSON, Gerald L; Mchenry Public HS; Mchenry, ND; Band; Chrs; CmntyWkr; CncrtBnd; PepBnd; SchPl; 4-H; PpCl; Bsktbl; Trk;.

ANDERSON, Glenda R; West Sioux Comm HS; Howarden, IA; Band; ChrhWkr; HonRl; SctActv; VPYthFlsp; PresFHA; LetterTrk; Chrldr; SecGAA; IMSpt; Wayne St Clg; Special Educ.

ANDERSON, Glenn A; Belview HS; Belview, MN; 2/20 CmntyWkr; HonRl; JrNHS; NHS; PolWkr; StuGov; YthLg; Bsktbl; Univ; Pro.

ANDERSON, Greg; Ditworth Public HS; Dilworth, MN; Band; ChrhWkr; CncrtBnd; HonRl; MrchBnd; Orch; PepBnd; SchPl; SctActv; College; Math.

ANDERSON, Greg B; Dist 911 HS; Isanti, MN; Chr; ChrhWkr; SctActv; Glf; Bethe College; Business Administration.

ANDERSON, Gregg A; Gothenburg HS; Gothenburg, NE; 13/84 SecFrshCls; HonRl; TchrAde; YthFlsp; PresFFA; Glf; IMSpt; AmLegAwd; University Of Nebraska; Eg Econ.

ANDERSON, Gwendolyn S; Morton HS; Morton, IL; 6/312 Chrs; HonRl; NHS; College; Accounting.

ANDERSON, Harlyn E; White Bear Sr HS; White Bear Lake, MN; CncrtBnd; PepBnd; SctActv; Bsbl; Bsktbl; University Of Minnesota.

ANDERSON, Helen M; Marion Public HS; Ogdensburg, WI; SecTrsFrshCls; Chrs; Mdrgl; NHS; StuCncl; RptrYrbk; 4-H; VPSpnCl; GAA; 4-HAwd; Univ Of Oshkosh; Music Therapy.

ANDERSON, Irene L; Jefferson Sr HS; Alexandria, MN; 28/340 ChrhWkr; CmntyWkr; HonRl; Orch; RedCrAde; SctActv; TchrAde; RptrYrbk; GodCntryAwd; Anoka Tec; Occupational Therapy.

ANDERSON, Iris J; Albert Lea Central HS; Albert Lea, MN; Chr; ChrhWkr; NatlThespSoc; Orch; College; Communications.

ANDERSON, Ivy I; Northwestern HS; Flint, MI; 12/540 HstSophCls; HonRl; NHS; StuGov; General Motors Inst; Eng.

ANDERSON, James A; Shabbona HS; Shabbona, IL; 2/44 HonRl; SchPl; SctActv; StuCncl; RptrYrbk; FFA; VPFrCl; SciCl; BauchLmbAwd; EldAwd; Northern Ill Univ; Doctor.

ANDERSON, James E; Haworth HS; Kokomo, IN; 45/403 Chr; Mdrgl; NHS; SchMus; StuGov; CivCl; PpCl; LetterFtbl; CaptWrstlng; RotaryAwd; Ball State; Law.

ANDERSON, James F; Platte City HS; Ferrelview, MO; 21/85 ChrhWkr; CncrtBnd; HonRl; JrNHS; MrchBnd; NHS; PepBnd; LetterFtbl; Trk; LetterWrstlng; U Of Mo Columbia; Md.

ANDERSON, James R; Cumberland HS; Cumberland, WI; 5/126 TrsJrCls; Chr; HonRl; SchPl; SctActv; StuCncl; YthFlsp; SpnCl; PpCl; LetterBsktbl; Glf; IMSpt; College; Engineering.

ANDERSON, Jana G; Grand Island Senior HS; Grand Island, NE; 1/432 ALAGirlsSt; CmntyWkr; HonRl; YthFlsp; SpnCl; CaptChrldr; IMSpt; KiwanAwd; MasAwd; PresAwd; Univ Of Nebr; Special Education.

ANDERSON, Jane E; Racine Lutheran HS; Racine, WI; ChrhWkr; HonRl; SchPl; TchrAde; YthFlsp; GerCl; PpCl; GAA; College; Professional.

ANDERSON, Janet; Coon Rapids HS; Coon Rapids, IA; Band; Chr; Chrs; CncrtBnd; HonRl; MrchBnd; NHS; SchMus; FHA; Glf; Univ Of Norther Ia; Business Education.

ANDERSON, Janet M; North County HS; Bonne Terre, MO; 1/170 Band; CncrtBnd; HonRl; HospAde; MrchBnd; NHS; PepBnd; SchPl; SctActv; 4-H; FrCl; GAA; Central Method; Dentist.

ANDERSON, Janet M; Becker Public HS; Becker, MN; Band; Chr; HonRl; VPStuCncl; College; Vocal Performing.

ANDERSON, Janice L; Thornton Fractional N HS; Calumet City, IL; 50/433 Band; CmntyWkr; HonRl; PepBnd; PolWkr; FTA; Northern Ill Univ; Accounting.

ANDERSON, Jean E; Prospect HS; Mt Prospect, IL; Chrs; HonRl; College; Accounting.

ANDERSON, Jeanie; Saginaw HS; Saginaw, MI; Chrs; ChrhWkr; HonRl; JrNHS; Swmmng; John Wesley College ;.

ANDERSON, Jeannine; Lincoln Sr HS; Bloomington, MN; Chr; Chrs; HonRl; JA; LbryAde; YthFlsp; 4-H; PpCl; 4-HAwd; JAAwd; Univ; Art.

ANDERSON, Jeffrey; Campbell Tintah HS; Campbell, MN; Band; Chr; HonRl; MrchBnd; PepBnd; SctActv; StuCncl; RptrSchPpr; SchPpr; FFA; Crookston Tech Col; Natural Resource Techni.

ANDERSON, Jill S; Maine Twp East HS; Park Ridge, IL; ChrhWkr; HonRl; HospAde; NHS; Quill&Scroll; SctActv; Yrbk; Valparaiso Univ; Nursing.

ANDERSON, Joel C; Hector HS; Hector, MN; 3/51 ChrhWkr; HonRl; StuCncl; StuGov; TchrAde; YthFlsp; FFA; Bsbl; Bsktbl; LetterFtbl; College; Psychologist.

ANDERSON, John J; Manistee HS; Manistee, MI; 19/169 ALBoysSt; ChrhWkr; CmntyWkr; CncrtBnd; HonRl; MrchBnd; NHS; PepBnd; Trk; Wrstlng; Mi Tech.

ANDERSON, Joseph S; New Monroe Comm HS; Monroe, IA; 1/65 PresFrshCls; VPJrCls; ALBoysSt; Chrs; NHS; StuCncl; PresYthFlsp; VPSciCl; CaptBskbtl; LetterTrk; Coll; Ministry.

ANDERSON, Judith; Mooseheart HS; Mooseheart, IL; 1/22 SecFrshCls; PresSophCls; SecJrCls; HstSrCls; Band; Chr; Chrs; Trk; GAA; IMSpt; Univ; Professional.

ANDERSON, Judith A; Eau Claire Memorial HS; Eau Claire, WI; 10/434 Chr; ChrhWkr; HonRl; PpCl; Chrldr; Vocational Schl; Bus.

ANDERSON, Judith R; Wahpeton HS; Wahpeton, ND; AFS; ChrhWkr; CmntyWkr; HonRl; JrNHS; RedCrAde; EdSchPpr; GerCl; LetterSocr; LetterTrk; DARAwd; University; Medical Tech.

ANDERSON, Julie A; J D Darnall HS; Geneseo, IL; 17/217 AFS; HonRl; JA; NatlThespSoc; Yrbk; SecFTA; Augustana College.

ANDERSON, Julie M; Cheteic HS; New Auburn, WI; Band; Chr; CncrtBnd; HonRl; HospAde; MrchBnd; PepBnd; RptrSchPpr; Pres4-H; FBLA; FHA; Bsbl; Trk; JAAwd; Trade School; Peace Corp.

ANDERSON, Julie N; Bethlehem Academy; Faribault, MN; 12/84 Chrs; HonRl; HospAde; NHS; SchPl; SctActv; StuCncl; TchrAde; RptrYrbk; College; Psychology.

ANDERSON, Karen F; R L Senior HS; Rice Lake, WI; 34/265 Band; CncrtBnd; PepBnd; Pres4-H; FHA; DARAwd; 4-HAwd; JAAwd; RotaryAwd; College; Professional.

ANDERSON, Karen J; Traverse City Sr HS; Traverse City, MI; 37/602 HonRl; NHS; Nw Mi Clg; Commercial Art.

ANDERSON, Karla R; Egan HS; Flandreau, SD; SecJrCls; Band; MrchBnd; SchMus; SchPl; RptrYrbk; RptrSchPpr; CaptBskbtl; LetterTrk; CaptChrldr; Dakota Weseylan Univ; Nursing.

ANDERSON, Karl C; Horton Watkins HS; St Louis, MO; 155/498 ChrhWkr; SchAde; SchMus; SctActv; TchrAde; LetterBsbl; LetterBskbtl; LetterFtbl; Valparaiso U; Bus Admin Compt Science.

ANDERSON, Kathi E; Shakamak HS; Jasonville, IN; 4/70 HstSophCls; HstJrCls; NHS; Quill&Scroll; StuCncl; TchrAde; SchPpr; MthCl; SciCl; BttyCrckrAwd; U Of In; Criminal Psycology.

ANDERSON, Kathy; Oakridge HS; Muskegon, MI; 2/120 HonRl; JrNHS; NHS; StuCncl; TchrAde; RptrSchPpr; FBLA; DanFAwd; Muskegon Comm Coll; Bus.

ANDERSON, Kathy A; Lasalle Peru Twp HS; Utica, IL; 3/460 LitMag; FrCl; University; Optometry.

ANDERSON, Kathy Jo; Pekin Community HS; Pekin, IL; 38/759 HonRl; SchAde; SchPl; StuCncl; RptrSchPpr; Il Cntrl Col; Elem Teacher.

ANDERSON, Kathy M; Edgemont HS; Edgemont, SD; 1/33 SecFrshCls; SecJrCls; Chrs; ChrhWkr; HonRl; NHS; SchPl; TchrAde; YthFlsp; Yrbk; College; Medical Technology.

ANDERSON, Kent J; Southwest HS; Green Bay, WI; HonRl; LetterFtbl; LetterTrk; LetterWrstlng; IMSpt; St Norbert College; Business Administration.

ANDERSON, Kent M; Hanson HS; Alexandria, SD; TrsSophCls; PresJrCls; HonRl; Quill&Scroll; SchPl; StuCncl; RptrYrbk; SchPpr; LetterTrk; College; Mathematics.

ANDERSON, Kerry G; Stratford Community HS; Stratford, IA; VPJrCls; Chrs; ChrhWkr; CmntyWkr; HonRl; SchMus; SchPl; SctActv; StuCncl; YthFlsp; PpCl; SciCl; Bsbl; University; Vocation.

ANDERSON, Kevin R; Oregon Davis HS; Walkerton, IN; Band; Chr; HonRl; SctActv; 4-H; Bsbl; Bskbtl; Trk; 4-HAwd;.

ANDERSON, Kim; Glenwood HS; Glenwood, MN; 19/140 HonRl; LbryAde; NatlFornLg; OffAde; SchMus; SchPl; StuCncl; Yrbk; EdSchPpr; Chrldr; Alexandria Tech; Business.

ANDERSON, Kim A; Hutchinson HS; Hutchinson, MN; SecJrCls; SecSrCls; AFS; SecChr; Chrl; Chrs; ChrhWkr; HonRl; NHS; NatlThespSoc; Gustarus Adolphus; Elem Teacher.

ANDERSON, Kimberly; Kennedy Public HS; Drayton, ND; TrsSophCls; Band; HonRl; MrchBnd; FHA; SpnCl; PpCl; Chrldr; 4-HAwd; Bus School; Vocation.

ANDERSON, Kimberly J; Velva Public HS; Bergen, ND; PresSophCls; Band; Chrs; PresChrhWkr; VPNHS; PresNatlThespSoc; StuCncl; SptEdYrbk; FHA; BttyCrckrAwd; College; Horticulture.

ANDERSON, Kristine; Comfrey Public HS; Comfrey, MN; VPFrshCls; Chrs; HonRl; SchPl; GAA; CitAwd; College; Professional.

ANDERSON, Kristine K; New Monroe HS; Monroe, IA; 4/48 Band; Chrs; HonRl; MrchBnd; NHS; StuCncl; YthFlsp; LetterBskbtl; LetterTrk; CitAwd; Cedarville Coll.

ANDERSON, Kristine L; Plymouth HS; Plymouth, IN; 6/216 Chr; Chrs; HonRl; NHS; SchMus; EngCl; VPSpnCl; MthCl; GAA; Indiana University; Spanish.

ANDERSON, Larry; Paxton Consolidated HS; Paxton, NE; PresFrshCls; PresSophCls; HstJrCls; HonRl; StuCncl; SptEdYrbk; CchngActv; Col; Bus.

ANDERSON, Laura E; Gothenburg Public HS; Brady, NE; Chrs; HonRl; NatlThespSoc; SchMus; SchPl; SecStuCncl; TchrAde; 4-H; FrCl; PpCl; College; Registered Nurse.

ANDERSON, Laura M; Salina HS; Salina, KS; VPSophCls; ChrhWkr; DrlTm; HonRl; LitMag; StuCncl; TchrAde; RptrYrbk; EdYrBk; PpCl; Kansas State University; Art.

ANDERSON, Laura M; Brandon HS; Ortonville, MI; CmntyWkr; HonRl; NHS; PolWkr; TchrAde; PpCl; CaptBskbtl; PPFtbl; CitAwd; Oakland Univ; Nursing.

ANDERSON, Lauren F; Sullivan HS; Chicago, IL; 37/276 Chr; HonRl; LbryAde; NHS; TchrAde; Yrbk; SchPpr; KeyCl; U Of Ill; Veterinarian.

ANDERSON, Laurie K; Norborne HS; Norborne, MO; 1/30 SecTrsFrshCls; ALAGirlsSt; CncrtBnd; HonRl; NHS; RptrSchPpr; FHA; FrCl; PpCl; College; Accounting.

ANDERSON, Lawrence M; Saint Francis HS; Wyoming, MN; 1/150 TrsSrCls; HonRl; NatlFornLg; NatlMeritCmnd; RptrSchPpr; VoiceDemAwd; Pillsbury Baptist Bible Coll.

ANDERSON, Leah J; Manual HS; Peoria, IL; 32/329 ChrhWkr; HonRl; LbryAde; StuCncl; YthFlsp; Western Illinois Univ; Sociology.

ANDERSON, Lee; Bowbells HS; Bowbells, ND; PresFrshCls; TrsSophCls; ChrhWkr; HonRl; MrchBnd; SchPl; Bsbl; Nd State Univ; Agriculture.

ANDERSON, Leeann; Harrisonville Sr HS; Harrisonville, MO; 3/165 Chrs; HonRl; SchPl; RptrYrbk; SpnCl; Bskbtl; Chrldr; PPFtbl; Stephens Col; Social Work.

ANDERSON, Lenae C; Willmar Sr HS; Blomkest, MN; 21/320 PresAFS; NatlFornLg; NHS; Orch; PolWkr; SchPl; PresStuCncl; Sec4-H; Trk; AmLegAwd; 4-HAwd; VFWAwd; CitAwd; Luther College; Political Science.

ANDERSON, Linda K; Arthur Hill HS; Saginaw, MI; HonRl; NHS; NatlMeritCmnd; Orch; SchMus; SctActv; YthFlsp; IMSpt; College; Biology.

ANDERSON, Linda M; Western HS; Bay City, MI; 2/448 SecFrshCls; SecSophCls; SecJrCls; SecSrCls; NHS; CaptBsbl; CaptTennis; Chrldr; DARAwd; JCAwd; Univ Of Michigan; Accountant.

ANDERSON, Linda S; Central HS; Hartland, MN; 11/526 Chrl; Chrs; ChrhWkr; TrsFrshCls; NatlMeritCmnd; NatlThespSoc; PolWkr; SchMus; Augsburg Col; English.

ANDERSON, Linda S; Pekin Community HS; Pekin, IL; 5/803 Chr; HonRl; NHS; NatlMeritSF; FrCl; Wheaton Coll; Elementary School Teacher.

ANDERSON, Lisa; Hudson Senior Hs; Hudson, WI; 22/220 SecTrsJrCls; Chrs; HonRl; HospAde; SchMus; SchPl; StuCncl; RptrSchPpr; Chrldr; College; Nursing.

ANDERSON, Lisa; Baxter HS; Baxter Springs, KS; ALBoysSt; CncrtBnd; HonRl; NatlFornLg; NHS; RptrYrbk; MthCl; VoiceDemAwd; Kansas State Univ; Pre Law.

ANDERSON, Lisa J; Tri Point HS; Kempton, IL; 12/33 VPBand; HonRl; SchPl; Yrbk; RptrSchPpr; FHA; SpnCl; GAA; AmLegAwd; Pres4-HAwd; Kankakee Community Clg; Clerical.

ANDERSON, Lisa R; Central Webster HS; Fort Dodge, IA; 10/45 Band; Chrs; DrmMjrt; HonRl; SchPl; Yrbk; EdSchPpr; 4-H; Chrldr; 4-HAwd; Iowa State Univ; Home Economics.

ANDERSON, Lisa S; Schuyler R I HS; Queen City, MO; 4/80 VPFrshCls; TrsJrCls; ChrhWkr; HonRl; NHS; StuCncl; TchrAde; FHA; LetterBskbtl; LetterTrk; Ne Missouri State Univ; Home Economics.

ANDERSON, Lorie S; Ashland Greenwood HS; Ashland, NE; 6/61 ALAGirlsSt; CncrtBnd; HonRl; JrNHS; NHS; NatlThespSoc; PepBnd; StuCncl; RptrYrbk; PPFtbl; Hastings Clg; Law.

ANDERSON, Lori J; Ogilvie HS; Ogilvie, MN; HonRl; TchrAde; RptrYrbk; 4-H; LetterTrk; LetterChrldr; GAA; IMSpt; PPFtbl; 4-HAwd; Beauty Culture.

ANDERSON, Lynn K; Cooley HS; Detroit, MI; HonRl; NHS; ROTC; RptrSchPpr; U Of Detroit; Journalism.

ANDERSON, Marcie E; Belfield HS; Belfield, ND; ALAGirlsSt; Band; ChrhWkr; CncrtBnd; HonRl; LbryAde; MrchBnd; ModUN; NHS; PepBnd; TchrAde; Trk; CaptChrldr; IMSpt; Univ.

ANDERSON, Mariette J; Stephen Public HS; Stephen, MN; 4/44 Band; HonRl; GerCl; Univ Of Mn; Child Care.

ANDERSON, Mari F; Tracy HS; Garvin, MN; 2/120 ALAGirlsSt; Chrs; CncrtBnd; HonRl; HospAde; MrchBnd; PepBnd; SchMus; FHA; Trk; College; Pharmacology.

ANDERSON, Mark D; New Hampton HS; New Hampton, IA; 2/170 VPJrCls; ALBoysSt; Band; NHS; StuCncl; RptrSchPpr; MthCl; Ftbl; College; Engineering.

ANDERSON, Mark J; Manistee Catholic Central HS; Manistee, MI; 3 ALBoysSt; HonRl; NHS; Bsbl; Bskbtl; CaptFtbl; VoiceDemAwd;.

ANDERSON, Mark L; West Central HS; Hartford, SD; 45/75 Chrs; LbryAde; SchMus; TreasStuCncl; RptrSchPpr; Pres4-H; LetterFtbl; LetterWrstlng; AmLegAwd; CitAwd; Univ Of So Dakota; Agriculture.

ANDERSON, Mark S; Hillsdale HS; Hillsdale, MI; 30/190 Band; HonRl; NHS; SchPl; RptrSchPpr; Bsktbl; Tennis; Trk; Univ Of Mi; Engineering.

ANDERSON, Mark S; Leeds Public HS; Leeds, ND; 1/31 TrsJrCls; PresSrCls; ALBoysSt; SctActv; EdYrBk; FFA; SciCl; Nd State U; Mechanical Engineer.

ANDERSON, Mark W; Fisher HS; Fisher, MN; Chr; HonRl; RptrYrbk; SptEdYrbk; U Of Nd; Math.

ANDERSON, Mary; Maplelake HS; Buffalo, MN; 2/60 CncrtBnd; JrNHS; MrchBnd; NHS; SchPl; TchrAde; RptrSchPpr; 4-H; FHA; PpCl; Rochester Comm Col; Rn.

ANDERSON, Mary E; Glenbard South HS; Glen Ellyn, IL; 56/313 CmntyWkr; HonRl; HospAde; StuGov; TchrAde; RptrYrbk; SpnCl; PpCl; Chrldr; GAA; College; Social Worker.

ANDERSON, Mary E; Mineral Point HS; Mineral Point, WI; 22/90 Band; Chr; Chrs; ChrhWkr; CncrtBnd; HonRl; MrchBnd; OffAde; Orch; PepBnd; W Wisconsin Tech Inst; Medical Records.

ANDERSON, Mary L; Clifford Galesburg HS; Clifford, ND; 2/21 VPSophCls; Band; ChrhWkr; DrlTm; HonRl; StuCncl; EdYrBk; RptrSchPpr; GAA; BttyCrckrAwd; St Lukes Sch Of Nursing.

ANDERSON, Mervin L; Eagle Grove HS; Woolstock, IA; Chr; ChrhWkr; CmntyWkr; HonRl; NHS; NatlThespSoc; SchMus; SchPl; SpnCl; LetterTrk; Ia State U; Marine Officer Career.

ANDERSON, Michael; Roosevelt HS; St Louis, MO; Chr; CmntyWkr; HonRl; NHS; OffAde; SchPl; StuCncl; YthFlsp; EdYrBk; Swmmng;.

ANDERSON, Michael E; Goldfield Comm HS; Goldfield, IA; HonRl; SchPl; StuGov; RptrYrbk; RptrSchPpr; LetterTrk; IMSpt; Army; Professnl.

ANDERSON, Myrna; Hay Springs Public HS; Hay Springs, NE; 1/40 NHS; SchPl; StuCncl; EdYrBk; 4-H; PpCl; GAA; EldAwd; 4-HAwd; CitAwd; Univ Of Ne; Law.

ANDERSON, Myrna J; Tri Mont Area HS; Trimont, MN; 3/27 TrsJrCls; Chr; HonRl; NHS; StuGov; RptrYrbk; RptrSchPpr; GAA; IMSpt; Mankato State Univ; Registered Nurse.

ANDERSON, Myrna J; Hay Springs Public HS; Hay Springs, NE; 1/40 HonRl; NHS; OffAde; SchPl; StuCncl; EdYrBk; Yrbk; RptrSchPpr; LetterPpCl; LetterTrk; 4-HAwd; College; Law.

ANDERSON, Nancy A; O Neill Public HS; Oneill, NE; SecSophCls; Chr; Chrs; ChrhWkr; HonRl; SchMus; PresSophCls; PpCl; Coll; Legal Secretary.

ANDERSON, Nancy A; Cadott HS; Cadott, WI; 10/95 Band; HonRl; OffAde; TchrAde; PpCl; LetterBskbtl; GAA; Col; Professional.

ANDERSON, Nancy F; Lidgerwood Public HS; Geneseo, ND; ChrhWkr; CncrtBnd; HonRl; PepBnd; SchPl; YthFlsp; Yrbk; SchPpr; FHA; College; Professional.

ANDERSON, Nancy J; Wahpeton HS; Wahpeton, ND; HonRl; JrNHS; Yrbk; PpCl; LetterSwmmng; GAA; IMSpt; PPFtbl; College; Dental Field.

ANDERSON, Nancy M; Taylors Falls HS; Shafer, MN; 1/27 PresJrCls; SecBand; SecChr; HonRl; NatlFornLg; PresStuCncl; RptrYrbk; Pres4-H; GerCl; CaptBsktbl; Mankato State; Geographer.

ANDERSON, Nina; Ashland Senior HS; Ashland, WI; 22/216 ChrhWkr; HonRl; NHS; Northland College; Commercial Art.

ANDERSON, Ovella S; R 1 North Callaway HS; Kingdom City, MO; HonRl; TchrAde; FTA; SpnCl; Bus Sch; Secretary.

ANDERSON, Pamela; North HS; Omaha, NE; Band; CncrtBnd; HonRl; HospAde; MrchBnd; NHS; PepBnd; EdSchPpr; LatCl; Univ Of Nebraska Medical Center;nursing.

ANDERSON, Patricia; Kalkaska HS; Kalkaska, MI; Chr; ChrhWkr; CmntyWkr; HonRl; PolWkr; SchPl; FHA; GAA; Bus School; Professional.

ANDERSON, Patricia A; Crivitz HS; Crivitz, WI; PresSophCls; HonRl; NHS; SchPl; StuCncl; RptrYrbk; RptrSchPpr; FrCl; Chrldr; Nursing.

ANDERSON, Patricia J; Whiteland Community HS; Whiteland, IN; 12/184 DrmMjrt; MrchBnd; NHS; Orch; SchMus; StuCncl; 4-H; FTA; In Central U; Music.

ANDERSON, Patricia J; Wentzville R Iv Jr/sr HS; Wentzville, MO; CmntyWkr; HonRl; SctActv; YthFlsp; PpCl; LetterBsbl; LetterBsktbl; GAA; IMSpt; Beauty Coll.

ANDERSON, Patrick; Marist HS; Oak Lawn, IL; 32/375 Chrs; HonRl; NatlMeritCmnd; SchMus; SciCl; Ftbl; Trk; IMSpt; Univ Il;engineering.

ANDERSON, Patsi E; Wisconsin Academy; Sturgeon, MO; 1/84 SecTrsFrshCls; TrsJrCls; HonRl; NHS; EdYrBk; Andrews Univ; Business.

ANDERSON, Paul A; Arsenal Technical HS; Indianapolis, IN; CmntyWkr; HonRl; StuCncl; CaptFtbl; IMSpt; Franklin Coll; Phy Ed.

ANDERSON, Paul B; St Croix Falls HS; Dresser, WI; VPFrshCls; PresSrCls; ALBoysSt; ChrhWkr; HonRl; SctActv; StuCncl; LetterBsktbl; LetterFtbl; LetterTrk; AmLegAwd; University; Professional.

ANDERSON, Peggy R; Sargent Central HS; Forman, ND; TrsSophCls; Aud/Vis; HonRl; HospAde; RptrSchPpr; Pres4-H; FHA; PpCl; 4-HAwd;.

ANDERSON, Perri L; Clay Central HS; Royal, IA; HonRl; SchPl; SpnCl; Bus Sch.

ANDERSON, Phillip A; Mooseheart HS; Mooseheart, IL; 4/22 VPFrshCls; VPChr; Chrs; CncrtBnd; HonRl; MrchBnd; ROTC; SctActv; SchPpr; BttyCrckrAwd; Univ; Lawyer.

ANDERSON, Polly; Michigan Public HS; Mapes, ND; 20/23 PresJrCls; ALAGirlsSt; HonRl; StuCncl; FHA; PpCl; Business College; Secretary.

ANDERSON, Rainell L; Macksville HS; Seward, KS; PresSophCls; HonRl; NHS; SchPl; StuCncl; TchrAde; PpCl; LetterBsktbl; Chrldr; College; Elementary Education.

ANDERSON, Ralph; Newark Hs; Newark, IL; PresBand; Chrs; CncrtBnd; NHS; PepBnd; SchPl; StuCncl; FTA; College; Music.

ANDERSON, Randi G; Rochester HS; Springfield, IL; 29/77 TrsFrshCls; Chrs; HonRl; SchAde; SchPl; College; Child Care.

ANDERSON, Randy E; Notre Dame HS; W Burlington, IA; 31/82 Trk; IMSpt; JETSAwd; College.

ANDERSON, Randy L; Midland HS; Center Junction, IA; 8/49 VPSrCls; Band; Chrs; ChrhWkr; CmntyWkr; HonRl; Mdrgl; MrchBnd; NHS; SchMus; Univ Of Iowa; Broadcat Journalism.

ANDERSON, Rebecca L; Carter H Harrison HS; Chicago, IL; 8/400 SecSrCls; Chrs; CaptChrldr; Howard Univ; Communications.

ANDERSON, Rebecca L; John Marshall HS; Indianapolis, IN; 8/534 Chr; Chrs; ChrhWkr; HonRl; NHS; SchMus; College; Nursing.

ANDERSON, Renae; Kennedy Public HS; Drayton, ND; Band; Chr; Chrs; ChrhWkr; CmntyWkr; HonRl; PepBnd; EdYrBk; FHA; GAA; Coll.

ANDERSON, Renee M; Towner HS; Denbigh, ND; SecSophCls; Chrs; CncrtBnd; HonRl; SchPl; Yrbk; 4-H; FHA; GAA; 4-HAwd; VoiceDemAwd; University; Professional.

ANDERSON, Rex E; Guide Rock Public HS; Guide Rock, NE; 1/15 PresFrshCls; Band; Chr; CncrtBnd; MrchBnd; PepBnd; SchPl; SctActv; StuCncl; SpnCl; Hsatings College; Teacher.

ANDERSON, Rhonda M; Avon HS; Avon, IL; 2/46 Band; NHS; NatlMeritCmnd; EdYrBk; VPFHA; KeyCl; Trk; GAA; DanFAwd; 4-HAwd; Ill State Univ; Teaching Math.

ANDERSON, Richard A; South Hamilton HS; Jewell, IA; 18/92 Band; Chrs; CncrtBnd; HonRl; NHS; StuCncl; Pres4-H; PresFFA; SecMthCl; Bsbl; Bsktbl; Ftbl; 4-HAwd; Iowa State Univ; Agriculture.

ANDERSON, Richard C; Chaminade HS; St Charles, MO; 8/107 HonRl; LitMag; Univ Of Missouri; Computer Science.

ANDERSON, Richard W; Maine Township HS; Park Ridge, IL; Bsktbl; LetterTennis; Univ Of Il; Pre Medicine.

ANDERSON, Rieta K; Pleasant Hill HS; Pleasant Hill, MO; 2/112 HonRl; NHS; SecStuCncl; Yrbk; SchPpr; VPFHA; LetterBsktbl; Business College; Legal Secretary.

ANDERSON, Robert D; Austin HS; Austin, IN; PresSrCls; ALBoysSt; ChrhWkr; NHS; SchPl; StuCncl; YthFlsp; SciCl; Trk; IMSpt; In St U; Teaching.

ANDERSON, Robert P; Elcho HS; Kempster, WI; 9/50 CncrtBnd; HonRl; MrchBnd; NHS; PepBnd; SchPl; SpnCl; SciCl; LetterBsktbl; IMSpt; Marathon County Center.

ANDERSON, Robert P; Forest View HS; Mt Prospect, IL; 77/650 HonRl; JrNHS; NHS; TchrAde; Iit; Engineer.

ANDERSON, Robert P; St Laurence HS; Justice, IL; HonRl; Bsbl; IMSpt; College; Cpa.

ANDERSON, Robin; Semeo Community HS; Gilman, IA; Band; Chrs; ChrhWkr; CncrtBnd; HonRl; MrchBnd; SchMus; SchPl; YthFlsp; FTA; Major In Music Education.

ANDERSON, Rodney; Paola HS; Paola, KS; PresSophCls; CncrtBnd; StuCncl; TchrAde; SchPpr; GerCl; HstSophCls; Bsktbl; Ftbl; Tennis; Ks Univ; Journ.

ANDERSON, Roy L; Hinsdale Central HS; Hinsdale, IL; 52/583 College; Chemistry.

ANDERSON, Ruth; Rozin Orr HS; Chicago, IL; 10/220 Chrs; HonRl; NHS; OffAde; MthCl; Clge; Nursing.

ANDERSON, Ruth A; Riverdale HS; Gotham, WI; Band; Chr; CncrtBnd; HonRl; MrchBnd; PepBnd; FHA; PpCl; SciCl;.

ANDERSON, Sandra K; Milaca Sr HS; Foreston, MN; 24/150 Band; Chr; HonRl; Mdrgl; NHS; SchMus; SchPl; 4-H; DanFAwd; 4-HAwd; Stout Univ; Home Economics.

ANDERSON, Sandra L; Tigerton HS; Tigerton, WI; 4/36 PresSophCls; Band; SecNHS; SchPl; YthLg; EdYrBk; TreasFHA; TreasPpCl; CaptChrldr; BttyCrckrAwd; Technical Inst; Secretarial Science.

ANDERSON, Sandra L; T F South HS; Lansing, IL; 28/552 HonRl; NHS; OffAde; PpCl; Tennis; Western Il Univ; Physical Ed.

ANDERSON, Sandra L; Tigerton HS; Tigerton, WI; 4/36 PresSophCls; VPSrCls; HonRl; NHS; PepBnd; StuCncl; EdYrBk; CaptChrldr; BttyCrckrAwd; DARAwd; Uw Platteville; Tech Communications.

ANDERSON, Sandy; Norwood R I HS; Norwood, MO; 4/20 PresFrshCls; CncrtBnd; HonRl; NHS; SchPl; StuCncl; RptrYrbk; FHA; PpCl; Chrldr;.

ANDERSON, Scott R; Moline Sr HS; Moline, IL; 105/846 Band; Chr; ChrhWkr; CmntyWkr; HonRl; JrNHS; Mdrgl; MrchBnd; NHS; NatlThespSoc; SchMus; SchPl; SchPpr; Augustana College; Music Ed.

ANDERSON, Scot W; Rock Island HS; Rock Island, IL; SctActv; KeyCl; Ftbl; IMSpt; Col; Forestry.

ANDERSON, Sharon; New Auburn HS; New Auburn, WI; /32 VPSrCls; ALAGirlsSt; HonRl; SecStuCncl; TchrAde; PresFHA; Bsbl; Swmmng; Trk; Chrldr; Univ;teach Or Sec.

ANDERSON, Sherrie; Rockwell City Comm HS; Rockwell City, IA; 10/62 JCC; PpCl; Nursing Sch; Rn.

ANDERSON, Stanley D; Hales Franciscan HS; Chicago, IL; 2/60 HstJrCls; HstSrCls; HonRl; StuCncl; StuGov; EdYrBk; PpCl; College; Engineer.

ANDERSON, Stephen H; Andover HS; Orchard Lake, MI; 8/450 JrNHS; NHS; NatlMeritFnl; RedCrAde; StuCncl; FrCl; SciCl; ChmnSwmmng; Univ Mi; Physician.

ANDERSON, Stephen J; West Waterloo HS; Waterloo, IA; 29/527 ALBoysSt; HonRl; JA; Natl-

MeritSF; PolWkr; AmLegAwd; JAAwd; NCTE; College; Law.

ANDERSON, Steven E; John F Kennedy HS; Bloomington, MN; HonRl; NatlMeritSF; U Of Mn; Comp Science.

ANDERSON, Steven J; Naperville Central HS; Naperville, IL; 33/844 HonRl; NHS; LetterTennis; U Of Il; Busi.

ANDERSON, Steven K; Pike HS; Indianapolis, IN; Band; CncrtBnd; HonRl; MrchBnd; SchMus; SctActv; YthFlsp; LatCl; Trk; LetterWrstlng; CchngActv; College; Medical Technology.

ANDERSON, Steven P; Boylan Catholic HS; Rockford, IL; 19/360 HonRl; NHS; IMSpt; Rock Valley Clg; Police Science.

ANDERSON, Steven S; Burlington HS; Burlington, IA; 100/450 LetterFtbl; IMSpt; Univ Of Iowa; Government.

ANDERSON, Susan; Morgan Public HS; Morgan, MN; Chrs; HonRl; SchPl; GAA; PPFtbl; Vocational School; Accounting.

ANDERSON, Susan C; Wolford HS; Pleasant Lake, ND; 2/7 Chr; ChrhWkr; HonRl; LbryAde; SchPl; RptrSchPpr; SchPpr; PpCl; Bsktbl; Chrldr; College; Social Work.

ANDERSON, Susan E; Mundelein HS; Mundelein, IL; 36/450 Chrs; ChrhWkr; HonRl; LitMag; NatlMeritFnl; Quill&Scroll; SchPl; Yrbk; Univ Of Il Champagne; Theater.

ANDERSON, Tamara; Huron Senior HS; Huron, SD; 1/311 Chrs; DrlTm; NHS; YthFlsp; RptrSchPpr; GerCl; PpCl; GAA; College;.

ANDERSON, Teresa J; Cottonwood Public HS; Cottonwood, MN; 1/40 Chr; Chrs; ChrhWkr; HonRl; NHS; NatlMeritCmnd; RptrYrbk; EdYrBk; RptrSchPpr; 4-H; FHA; PpCl; Trk; Sw Minnesota St College; Accounting.

ANDERSON, Terry J; Oskaloosa HS; Oskaloosa, IA; 87/190 HonRl; PresSctActv; Wrstlng; IMSpt; Trade School; Professional.

ANDERSON, Theodore A; Arcadia Valley HS; Pilot Knob, MO; 22/91 HonRl; LbryAde; NHS; TchrAde; FTA; SpnCl; Bsktbl; DARAwd; EldAwd; CitAwd; College; Electrical Eng.

ANDERSON, Theresa A; J D Darnall Sr HS; Geneseo, IL; ALAGirlsSt; CmntyWkr; NHS; NatlThespSoc; StuCncl; SchPpr; Northern Illinois Univ; Art.

ANDERSON, Timothy C; Laurel Public HS; Laurel, NE; 32/62 ChrhWkr; SctActv; YthFlsp; 4-H; Bsbl; LetterBsktbl; LetterFtbl; Glf; 4-HAwd; Univ Of Nebraska; Agriculture.

ANDERSON, Timothy M; Canton HS; Canton, SD; ALBoysSt; Band; ChrhWkr; CncrtBnd; HonRl; NHS; Bsbl; CaptBsktbl; CaptFtbl; LetterTrk; Sd State Univ; Math.

ANDERSON, Timothy P; Arapahoe Public HS; Elwood, NE; 2/30 Band; ChrhWkr; CmntyWkr; DrmMjrt; HonRl; SchPl; YthLg; EdSchPpr; 4-H; College; Accountant.

ANDERSON, Tod D; Big Rapids HS; Big Rapids, MI; HonRl; MthCl; LetterFtbl; Ferris State College; Optometry.

ANDERSON, Valerie J; Roosevelt HS; Des Moines, IA; Chr; PresNatlMeritCmnd; NatlThespSoc; Orch; PolWkr; SchMus; SchPl; StuCncl; FrCl; GerCl; Univ; Music.

ANDERSON, Valerie K; Forest Lake Sr HS; Marine On St Croix, MN; 52/353 TrsFrshCls; Chr; HonRl; StuCncl; PpCl; GAA; Trade Schl; Cosmetology.

ANDERSON, Wanda J; Chicago Vocational HS; Chicago, IL; CmntyWkr; HonRl; JA; JrNHS; NHS; NatlMeritCmnd; SchPl; TchrAde; Loyola Nursing Campus; Nursing.

ANDERSON, Wanda J; Cvs HS; Chicago, IL; 21/674 HonRl; JA; JrNHS; LbryAde; NHS; OffAde; TchrAde; MthCl; Loyola Univ; Nursing.

ANDERSON, William W; Elgin Public HS; Elgin, NE; 9/26 CmntyWkr; HonRl; YthFlsp; FFA; Bsktbl; Ftbl; U Of Ne Lincoln; Agriculture Major.

ANDERSON, Yvette; St Thomas Apostle Hs; Chicago, IL; 1/38 Chr; CmntyWkr; HonRl; HospAde; NHS; StuCncl; TchrAde; Bsktbl; GAA; JCAwd; Eastern Illinois U; Medical Technology.

ANDING, Mary Jo; Acad Of The Holy Angels; Minneapolis, MN; HonRl; RptrYrbk; Yrbk; RptrSchPpr; Bsktbl; Trk; IMSpt; PPFtbl; Univ Of Mn; Physical Therapist.

ANDRACKI, Julie A; Schlarman HS; Westville, IL; 13/68 PresFrshCls; PresJrCls; NHS; SchMus; SchPl; PresStuCncl; EdYrBk; 4-H; BttyCrckrAwd; DARAwd; 4-HAwd; Univ Of Illinois; Physician.

ANDRAE, David; Meramec Valley HS; Pacific, MO; Bsktbl; Trk;.

ANDREAS, Paul A; Mitchell HS; Mitchell, NE; PresFrshCls; Chrl; Mdrgl; SchPl; YthFlsp; PresFFA; KeyCl; LetterBsktbl; LetterFtbl; LetterTrk; CchngActv; College.

ANDREASEN, Bethany J; Owen Withee HS; Withee, WI; 3/98 Chr; Chrs; ChrhWkr; HonRl; NHS; SchPl; TchrAde; Pres4-H; LetterTrk; 4-HAwd; Clge; Music.

ANDREASEN, Jim D; Superior HS; Hardy, NE; HonRl; Pres4-H; FFA; LetterFtbl; LetterTrk; 4-HAwd; Trade School; Agriculture.

ANDREE, Susan; Genoa Kingston HS; Genoa, IL; /99 Chrs; HonRl; SchPl; Yrbk; FrCl; LetterBsktbl; GAA; Armed Forces;rn.

ANDREESEN, John L; Anamosa Community HS; Anamosa, IA; 6/138 SecTrsSophCls; Band; CncrtBnd; NHS; Orch; PepBnd; RptrYrbk; GovHonPrgAwd; Univ Of N Iowa; Music.

ANDREINI, Jay P; Jeffers HS; South Range, MI; 5/48 PresFrshCls; HonRl; HospAde; JrNHS; NHS; NatlMeritCmnd; Sacrstn; PpCl; LetterBsktbl; LetterTrk; Mi Tech Univ; Medicine.

ANDREJASICH, Mary C; Mount Assisi HS; Summit, IL; 14/145 HonRl; JrNHS; NHS; SchPl; College; Professional.

ANDRES, Bob; Crete HS; Crete, NE; 18/115 Band; Chr; Chrl; CncrtBnd; HonRl; MrchBnd; NHS; Bsbl; Bsktbl; Ftbl; St Olaf Or Voc Ne; Pre Med Music Minor.

ANDRES, Stacy R; Union HS; Grand Rapids, MI; HonRl; HospAde; JA; MrchBnd; SchMus; SchPl; YthFlsp; LetterTennis; IMSpt; GovHonPrgAwd; Michigan St Univ; Nursing.

ANDRESS, Howard J; Waterford Kettering HS; Drayton Plains, MI; 5/450 PresFrshCls; PresSrCls; Chr; CmntyWkr; NHS; NatlThespSoc; StuCncl; StuGov; IMSpt; Univ Of Mi; Law.

ANDREW, Cheryl S; Blue River Valley HS; Mooreland, IN; Band; Chr; CncrtBnd; MrchBnd; PepBnd; YthFlsp; VP4-H; LatCl; GAA; IMSpt; 4-HAwd; Ball St Univ; History Teacher.

ANDREW, Dean R; Theodore Roosevelt HS; Des Moines, IA; 39/441 HonRl; NatlMeritSF; YthFlsp; SpnCl; Bsbl; Bsktbl; Ftbl; Trk; CchngActv; Univ Of Ks; Geography.

ANDREW, Debra L; Wauneta Public HS; Wauneta, NE; ChrhWkr; CmntyWkr; HonRl; HospAde; NHS; NatlMeritSchl; OffAde; StuGov; TchrAde; FNA;.

ANDREW, John A; Maine Twp So HS; Park Ridge, IL; 10/850 HonRl; JrNHS; NHS; SchMus; LetterSwmmng; College; Pre Medicine.

ANDREW, Kerin K; Lincoln Comm HS; Mechanicsville, IA; SecBand; CncrtBnd; MrchBnd; NHS; StuCncl; TreasYthFlsp; RptrYrbk; RptrSchPpr; LetterTrk; LetterChrldr; Coe College; Sociology.

ANDREWS, Carolyn M; Marcus Community HS; Marcus, IA; Chr; Chrs; ChrhWkr; SchMus; YthFlsp; FHA; PpCl; Bsktbl; IMSpt; College; Vocation.

ANDREWS, Clark E; Holbrook Public HS; Cambridge, NE; PresFrshCls; PresJrCls; Band; Chrs; SchMus; SchPl; PresStuCncl; VPFFA; Bsbl; LetterBsktbl; LetterFtbl; LetterTrk; 4-HAwd; College; Farming.

ANDREWS, Darlene M; Clio Area HS; Clio, MI; HonRl; ROTC; FHA; College; Professional.

ANDREWS, David L; Ithaca HS; Ithaca, MI; 8/144 HonRl; SptEdYrbk; Ftbl; Wrstlng; RotaryAwd; College; Cpa.

ANDREWS, Diana L; Union County HS; Liberty, IN; Chrs; HonRl; TchrAde; RptrSchPpr;.

ANDREWS, Gary E; Lakeview HS; Battle Creek, MI; HonRl; SchMus; Bsbl; Bsktbl; LetterFtbl; IMSpt; College; Accounting.

ANDREWS, Gregory R; Bloomington HS; Bloomington, IL; 13/391 HonRl; NHS; NatlMeritCmnd; NatlMeritSchl; TchrAde; FrCl; MthCl; Ill St Univ; Physician.

ANDREWS, Janet L; Richards HS; Oak Lawn, IL; 32/1023 Chrs; HonRl; NHS; OffAde; StuCncl; RusCl; MthCl; Illinois St Univ; Special Educ.

ANDREWS, Joel C; Floodwood HS; Floodwood, MN; 9/47 ChrhWkr; CmntyWkr; HonRl; JA; NHS; SchPl; SctActv; EdSchPpr; FFA; Ftbl; Bible School; Missionary.

ANDREWS, John; Downers Grove North Hs; Downers Grove, IL; CncrtBnd; MrchBnd; NHS; Quill&Scroll; RptrYrbk; Ftbl; Glf; Swmmng; Purdue University; Industrial Management.

ANDREWS, Laurie; Fargo North HS; Fargo, ND; Band; ChrhWkr; CncrtBnd; HonRl; HospAde; Orch; PepBnd; Brigham Young Univ; Medicine.

ANDREWS, Lynette M; Harold L Richards HS; Oak Lawn, IL; Chrs; HonRl; OffAde;.

ANDREWS, Mark D; Rochester HS; Rochester, MI; Band; Chr; CncrtBnd; HonRl; Mdrgl; MrchBnd; SchMus; LatCl; SpnCl; Ftbl; U Of Mi; Music Education.

ANDREWS, Mark W; Union Star R 2 HS; Union Star, MO; VPFrshCls; PresSophCls; Band; CncrtBnd; HonRl; MrchBnd; SchPl; StuCncl; 4-H; College; Professional.

ANDREWS, Pamela K; Graceville Public HS; Johnson, MN; Chrs; HonRl; NHS; Yrbk; SchPpr; 4-H; FHA; Chrldr; GAA; PPFtbl; Trade Schl; Secretary.

ANDREWS, Peggy L; Pepin Public HS; Pepin, WI; 1/45 TrsFrshCls; TrsSophCls; TrsJrCls; Chrs; CncrtBnd; HonRl; HospAde; MrchBnd; NHS; PepBnd; Chrldr; City Col Of Cosmatology; Reservationist.

ANDREWS, Rick J; Lake Central HS; Dyer, IN; 1/453 ALBoysSt; NHS; NatlSciFnd; NatlThespSoc; SchMus; SchPl; StuCncl; StuGov; TreasFDA; PresSciCl; Medical Research.

ANDREWS, Roberta S; South Haven HS; South Haven, MI; Yrbk; RptrSchPpr; LetterTrk; College.

ANDREWS, Shawnna L; Neoga HS; Neoga, IL; 8/73 AFS; Band; Chrs; HonRl; PresStuCncl; TchrAde; EdSchPpr; PpCl; SciCl; GAA; Lakeland Jr Clg; Dr.

ANDREWS, Thomas G; Holbrook Public HS; Holbrook, NE; 2/13 PresFrshCls; HstSophCls; PresJrCls; SecTrsSrCls; ALBoysSt; Band; Chr; ChrhWkr; CmntyWkr; CncrtBnd; Bsbl; CaptBsktbl; CaptFtbl; Trk; College; Education.

ANDREWS, Thomas G; St Laurence HS; Chicago, IL; 11/372 HonRl; SpnCl; Univ Of Notre Dame; Environmentalist.

ANDREWS, Victoria L; Kirksville Sr HS; Kirksville, MO; 12/188 Band; CncrtBnd; DrlTm; HonRl; MrchBnd; PepBnd; SchMus; 4-H; FrCl; SpnCl; College.

ANDREWS, Wesley C; Kirksville Sr HS; Novinger, MO; PresSophCls; ALBoysSt; Chrs; StuCncl; SptEdSchPpr; 4-H; Bsbl; LetterBsktbl; DanFAwd; Univ Of Missouri; Journalism.

ANDREWS, William J; Weber HS; Chicago, IL; 28/192 HonRl; TreasSctActv; RptrSchPpr; LatCl; Loyola U; Accounting.

ANDRIES, Kristine M; Lynd Public HS; Marshall, MN; 7/17 PresJrCls; Chrs; HonRl; SchPl; StuCncl; Yrbk; SchPpr; 4-H; FHA; Trade School.

ANDRIJAUSKAS, Loretta R; Maria HS; Chicago, IL; CmntyWkr; NatlMeritSchl; RedCrAde; SctActv; StuCncl; EdYrBk; FDA; FSA; Bsktbl; Swmmng; U Of Il Chicago; X Ray Technologist.

ANDRIOTIS, Susan K; Tiskilwa HS; Tiskilwa, IL; TrsJrCls; TrsSrCls; Band; HonRl; MrchBnd; PepBnd; 4-H; FHA; Chrldr; GAA; College; Child Care.

ANDRITSOS, Mary; Greenfield Sr HS; Greenfield, WI; HonRl; SchAde; StuGov; TchrAde; Twrl; Swmmng; GAA; Marquett Univ; Nursing.

ANDROS, Julie E; Olivia Public HS; Olivia, MN; VPJrCls; Band; Chr; ChrhWkr; CncrtBnd; HonRl; Mdrgl; SchMus; StuCncl; YthFlsp; Concordia Clg; Home Economics.

ANDRUS, Julie D; De Witt HS; Lansing, MI; 4/126 ChrhWkr; HonRl; JrNHS; NHS; NatlThespSoc; SchPl; FrCl; PpCl; LetterBttyCrckrAwd; GAA;.

ANDRYS, David; Sacred Heart HS; East Grand Forks, MN; SecTrsJrCls; SecSophCls; ChrhWkr; ModUN; StuCncl; Yrbk; SchPpr; U Of Nd; History Pol Science.

ANDVICK, Judith M; Bloomington HS; Bloomington, IL; Chr; ChrhWkr; HonRl; HospAde; SctActv; FrCl; PpCl; CaptBsktbl; GAA; IMSpt; S Illinois Univ; Nursing.

ANEGON, Anthony C; Bridgeport HS; Aginaw, MI; 13/330 HonRl; JrNHS; NHS; StuCncl; Bsktbl; Ftbl; LetterGlf; LetterTennis; Univ Of Mi; Pre Law.

ANENSON, Kenneth J; Cavalier HS; Cavalier, ND; TrsFrshCls; Chr; Chrs; HonRl; SchPl; PpCl; Bsbl; LetterBsktbl; Ftbl; Glf;.

ANEST, Paula M; Bayard HS; Bridgeport, NE; Chrs; OffAde; SchMus; SchPl; FHA; SpnCl; PpCl; University Of Nebraska; Food & Nutrition.

ANGEL, Cathy S; Memphis HS; Goodells, MI; 10/90 ChrhWkr; HonRl; SctActv; TchrAde; 4-H; Oakland Univ; Nursing.

ANGEL, Michele A; Saint Mary Academy; Newport, MI; ChrhWkr; CmntyWkr; LbryAde; OffAde; PolWkr; TchrAde; RptrYrbk; FrCl; VFWAwd; VoiceDemAwd; College; Chiropractic.

ANGELI, Penny M; West Iron County HS; Iron River, MI; Band; Chrs; CmntyWkr; RptrYrbk; Yrbk; LetterBsktbl; LetterTennis; LetterTrk; GAA; IMSpt; Central Mi U; Phy Ed.

ANGELICA, Thomas J; Hillcrest HS; Country Club Hls, IL; 29/446 JrNHS; NHS; MthCl; Univ Of Illinois; Psychology.

ANGELILLI, Jeanette M; Maine North HS; Des Plaines, IL; Chr; ChrhWkr; HonRl; SchAde; SchMus; TchrAde; College; Child Care.

ANGELO, Nanette; South Lake HS; East Detroit, MI; 9/515 CtyCnl; HonRl; NHS; NatlMeritSchl; PpCl; Chrldr; Mich St U; Pre Lw.

ANGELOFF, Veronica; West Iron County HS; Iron River, MI; 9/179 ChrhWkr; HonRl; PolWkr; Teen; SchPpr; 4-H; FrCl; Northern Michigan Univ; Law.

ANGELOUSIS, Anastasia; Chadsey HS; Detroit, MI; 4/352 HonRl; LbryAde; NHS; NatlMeritSchl; OffAde; SchAde; SchPl; StuCncl; TchrAde; BauchLmbAwd; Wayne State Univ; Medicine.

ANGER, Mary L; Kingston HS; Kingston, MI; SecSophCls; TrsJrCls; Band; CncrtBnd; HonRl; NHS; StuCncl; TchrAde; FrCl; CaptBsktbl; Cosmetology Sch; Beautician.

ANGERMEIER, Glenn V; Mt Vernon HS; Mt Vernon, IN; ALBoysSt; NHS; NatlThespSoc; VP4-H; SecKeyCl; PresFrCl; Univ Of Evansville; Engineer.

ANGILELLO, Peter M; Parker Sr HS; Janesville, WI; VPJrCls; TreasAFS; ALBoysSt; Chr; ChrhWkr; HonRl; NatlThespSoc; SchMus; SchPl; Yrbk; FFA; College; Elem Education.

ANGLE, Theresa L; Woodland R 4 HS; Marble Hill, MO; 7/63 HonRl; StuCncl; FHA; PresPpCl; Se Missouri St Univ; Nursing.

ANGLEN, Jeff O; Rockbridge Sr HS; Columbia, MO; VPFrshCls; NHS; NatlMeritFnl; NatlMeritSF; Univ Of Mo; Medicine.

ANGLETON, Eddie L; Brazil HS; Brazil, IN; 22/198 Band; CncrtBnd; HonRl; MrchBnd; NHS; NatlMeritCmnd; Indiana State University; Medicine.

ANGLIM, Van M; Gladstone HS; Gladstone, MI; 47/179 CmntyWkr; HonRl; SctActv; RptrYrbk; SptEdYrbk; MthCl; SciCl; Bsktbl; Ftbl; University; Professional.

ANGLIN, Ann J; Tippycanoe Valley HS; Warsaw, IN; TrsSophCls; Band; Chrs; ChrhWkr; CmntyWkr; CncrtBnd; DrmMjrt; HonRl; HospAde; JrNHS; MrchBnd; Chrldr; GAA;.

ANGLIN, James P; Wahlert HS; Dubuque, IA; HonRl; StuGov; Bsbl; Bsktbl; Ftbl; Trk; College.

ANGLIN, Kevin D; Western HS; Sheffield, IL; 4/50 ALBoysSt; HonRl; NHS; StuCncl; LetterBsktbl; LetterFtbl; LetterTrk; College; Sports.

ANGOTTI, Nora D; El Paso HS; El Paso, IL; 20/98 AFS; ChrhWkr; CmntyWkr; CncrtBnd; MrchBnd; NHS; TchrAde; SchPpr; 4-H; MthCl; 4-HAwd;.

ANGSTEN, Daniel J; Crystal Lake HS; Crystal Lake, IL; PresJrCls; ChrhWkr; CmntyWkr; PolWkr; SctActv; TchrAde; Yrbk; College; Photography.

ANGSTEN, Joan L; Carl Schurz HS; Chicago, IL; 24/804 Chr; Chrs; ChrhWkr; CmntyWkr; HonRl; JA; NHS; StuCncl; YthFlsp; GAA; Trinity Clge; Psychology & Sociology.

ANGSTMANN, Ann; Bennett HS; Marion, IN; 6/15 ALAGirlsSt; Chr; ChrhWkr; HonRl; NHS; Quill&Scroll; SchPl; TchrAde; Teen; Twrl; YthFlsp; RptrYrbk; Yrbk; EdSchPpr; FBLA; Coll; Nursing.

ANGULSKI, Gail L; Albany HS; Avon, MN; 21/130 PresFrshCls; Band; Chrs; CncrtBnd; DrmMjrt; HonRl; PepBnd; SchPl; StuGov; FHA; College; Psychology.

ANGUS, Tom M; Burt Comm HS; Burt, IA; Band; ChrhWkr; CncrtBnd; HonRl; MrchBnd; NHS; PepBnd; 4-H; LetterBsbl; Bsktbl; Univ; Ag.

ANGUS, Warren L; Mount Ayr Comm HS; Mount Ayr, IA; 2/75 PresSrCls; Band; HonRl; NHS; NatlMeritSF; StuCncl; 4-H; PresFFA; LetterFtbl; 4-HAwd; Iowa State U; Farm Operation.

ANHALT, Kathleen M; Niles North HS; Morton Grove, IL; 28/641 HonRl; JrNHS; NHS; OffAde; TchrAde; CaptChrldr; Northwestern University; Speech.

ANHALT, Tammy M; Grayslake HS; Grayslake, IL; 49/281 HonRl; 4-H; SpnCl; GAA; IMSpt; Bel Rea Inst; Animal Technologist.

ANKENBRANDT, Paul S; Mt Carmel HS; Mt Carmel, IL; 6/183 NHS; KeyCl; Bsktbl; College.

ANKENY, Sue M; Cedar Catholic HS; Hartington, NE; 1/68 VPFrshCls; VPSophCls; VPSrCls; Chrs; HonRl; VPStuCncl; RptrYrbk; College; Teacher.

ANKERHOLZ, Rian; Lyons HS; Lyons, KS; PresSrCls; Chr; ModUN; RptrSchPpr; KeyCl; Bsktbl; CitAwd; Kansas University.

ANKROM, Gayle L; Falls City Senior HS; Falls City, NE; TrsFrshCls; SecJrCls; Chrs; DrlTm; NHS; SchMus; StuCncl; YthFlsp; 4-H; 4-HAwd; College; Art.

ANKROM, Jeffrey S; W P Chrysler Memorial HS; New Castle, IN; Chrl; HonRl; Mdrgl; In Univ; Music.

ANLIKER, Jeffrey; Forbes Public HS; Forbes, ND; PresSophCls; PresJrCls; ChrhWkr; HonRl; SchPl; StuCncl; Bsktbl; Trk; Wrstlng; IMSpt;.

ANLSTROM, Christopher J; Lockport Central HS; Lockport, IL; HonRl; NatlFornLg; NHS; SchPpr; 4-H;.

ANNABLE, Rose M; Vienna HS; Cypress, IL; 6/104 Chrs; HonRl; HospAde; RedCrAde; TchrAde; FHA; TreasFNA; FTA; SpnCl; PpCl; Shawnee Coll; Reg Nurse.

ANNALA, Jeffrey R; Oswego HS; Oswego, IL; 9/239 HonRl; NHS; LetterBsktbl; LetterTrk; College.

ANNAN, Alyssa L; Onaga HS; Onaga, KS; TrsSrCls; CmntyWkr; HonRl; OffAde; SchMus; SchPl; Yrbk; SpnCl; PpCl; CitAwd; Ks St U; Med Tech.

ANNEGERS, Andy J; Southern HS; Stronghurst, IL; FFA; Bsbl; LetterBsktbl; Ftbl; Trk; Spoon River Trade Schl; Farming.

ANNERINO, Maureen F; St Mary Of Perpetual Help HS; Chicago, IL; 4/96 TrsFrshCls; VPJrCls; Chrs; HonRl; SchPl; Business School; Legal Secretary.

ANNETT, Roy F; Waterford Mott HS; Pontiac, MI; 37/410 PresSophCls; PresJrCls; PresSrCls; SctActv; Bsktbl; Albion College; Real Estate.

ANNIS, Lynn F; Spencer HS; Spencer, IA; HonRl; HospAde; NatlThespSoc; SchMus; SchPl; SpnCl; PpCl; Trk; Sw Minnesota St College; Psychology.

ANSCHUTZ, Mona; Tina Avalon HS; Bogard, MO; PresSophCls; Band; NHS; Yrbk; 4-H; FHA; PpCl; Bsbl; Bsktbl; 4-HAwd; Trade School; Practical Nursing.

ANSELL, Kathryn L; Cooks Jr Sr HS; Garden, MI; Band; ChrhWkr; CncrtBnd; HonRl; PepBnd; SchPl; 4-H; FrCl; Bsktbl; Chrldr; Airline Stewardess.

ANSELMENT, Sharon E; Mc Leansboro HS; Dahlgren, IL; ChrhWkr; CmntyWkr; NHS; NatlMeritSchl; RedCrAde; Sdlty; CivCl; 4-H; Bsktbl; Tennis; Trk; GodCntryAwd;.

ANSHUTZ, Marlene K; Macksville HS; Great Bend, KS; Band; Chrs; HonRl; HospAde; LbryAde; MrchBnd; NHS; PepBnd; PpCl; Nursing.

ANSPACH, William J; Buena Vista HS; Saginaw, MI; 2/259 HonRl; MthCl; Tennis; Coll; Math.

ANSTINE, Ricky D; Chilhowee HS; Blairstown, MO; 2/19 PresFrshCls; VPSophCls; PresJrCls; HonRl; StuCncl; StuGov; Yrbk; SchPpr; LetterBsktbl; Trk; Trade Sch; Auctioneer.

ANSTROM, Nanette K; Bradley Bourbonnais HS; Bradley, IL; 56/348 HonRl; HospAde; NHS; SchMus; StuCncl; College; Nursing.

ANTHONY, James E; North Sr HS; Eau Claire, WI; 40/352 Band; CncrtBnd; HonRl; MrchBnd; PepBnd; SctActv; LetterSwmmng; Tennis; University.

ANTHONY, Karen L; Harrisonville HS; Harrisonville, MO; 5/153 AFS; HonRl; College; Accounting.

ANTHROP, Joseph; Southwestern HS; West Point, IN; HonRl; Univ Of Purdue; Drafting.

ANTICOLI, Tracy L; Bellevue HS; Bellevue, NE; 85/616 ChrhWkr; HonRl; NHS; StuCncl; TreasFHA; VPFrCl; Tennis; PPFtbl; Ia St Univ; Home Economics Ed.

ANTILLA, Julie M; Osseo HS; Brooklyn Park, MN; 119/383 Chr; ChrhWkr; HonRl; OffAde; Orch; YthFlsp; RptrYrbk; College; Secretary.

ANTILLA, Karen A; Calumet HS; Laurium, MI; 10/167 DrlTm; HonRl; NHS; NatlMeritCmnd; ROTC; SchPl; PpCl; GovHonPrgAwd; VFWAwd; College; Professional.

ANTKOWIAK, Stacy A; Taft HS; Chicago, IL; 11/817 Band; CncrtBnd; HonRl; NHS; Orch; PepBnd; Yrbk; KeyCl; CaptTennis; LetterGAA; Univ Of Notre Dame; Architecture.

ANTKOWICZ, Phillip; Shawnee Mission South HS; Overland Park, KS; Band; DrlTm; DrmBgl; HonRl; MrchBnd; Orch; PepBnd; PpCl; College; Musician.

ANTOGNOZZI, Lisa M; Martin Hughes HS; Buhl, MN; ALAGirlsSt; Band; Chr; HonRl; HospAde; NHS; SctActv; RptrYrbk; RptrSchPpr; LetterBsktbl; College; Science.

ANTOINE, Marianne E; Prairie Du Chien Senior HS; Prairie Du Chien, WI; 1/133 Band; Chrs; HonRl; ModUN; NHS; NatlMeritCmnd; SctActv; Bsktbl; Swmmng; SecGAA; Marquette Univ; Medical Field.

ANTOLIK, John G; Fort Dodge Sr HS; Ft Dodge, IA; ALBoysSt; HonRl; NatlFornLg; NHS; LatCl; Bsktbl; Ftbl; Trk; IMSpt; Univ Of Iowa; Law.

ANTON, Nancy J; Centennial Sr HS; Lexington, MN; 44/219 Chr; ChrhWkr; Mdrgl; NHS; LetterTrk; GAA; College; Physical Therapy.

ANTON, William G; South Field Lathrup HS; South Field, MI; HonRl; LbryAde; OffAde; TchrAde; Bsbl; Bsktbl; LetterFtbl; IMSpt; Oakland Univ; Dentist.

ANTONACCI, Diana J; Riverton HS; Riverton, IL; 1 60 PresSrCls; Aud/Vis; Chrs; ChrhWkr; NatlFornLg; NHS; SchMus; StuCncl; GAA; IMSpt; U Of Il; Pre Med.

ANTONELLI, Laura C; Sault Area HS; Sault Ste Marie, MI; CncrtBnd; HonRl; MrchBnd; Western Mi Univ; Fashion Merchandising.

ANTONINI, Richard H; Benet Academy; Lisle, IL; 33/230 HonRl; NHS; SctActv; StuGov; TchrAde; GerCl; College; Marine Biology.

ANTONISSEN, David A; Niagara HS; Niagara, WI; Band; ChrhWkr; U Of River Falls; Agriculture.

ANTONS, Randy G; Midland Community HS; Center Junction, IA; HonRl; LetterBsbl; LetterBsktbl; Trade; Vocational.

ANTONSON, Peter; Northwood HS; Northwood, ND; ALBoysSt; HonRl; StuCncl; YthFlsp; Bsbl; Bsktbl; Ftbl; Glf; Univ Of Nd; Teacher.

ANTOR, Sharon M; Sparta Sr HS; Sparta, MI; 66/214 HonRl; OffAde; FHA; College; Practical Nurse.

ANTROBUS, Peggy H; Jennings HS; Jennings, MO; TrsFrshCls; JA; SchPl; StuCncl; FHA; EngCl; GAA; IMSpt; Se Mo State; Bs In Nursing.

ANUNDSON, Christine; Lake Of The Woods HS; Pitt, MN; 7/53 HonRl; NHS; 4-H; FHA; IMSpt; 4-HAwd; Bemidji Avti.

ANZALONE, Angela M; Joliet West HS; Joliet, IL; SecTrsJrCls; StuCncl; Bsktbl; GAA; College; Professional.

APATOFF, Brian R; New Trier Township East HS; Winnetka, IL; AFS; CmntyWkr; HonRl; LitMag; SciCl; Reed Coll; Medical Research.

APLEY, Brenda; Geneva Public HS; Geneva, NE; 16/64 Band; Chr; HonRl; JrNHS; NHS; SchMus; StuCncl; YthFlsp; RptrYrbk; FBLA; College Or U; Professional Secretary.

APOL, David; Waverly HS; Lansing, MI; NHS; SctActv; YthLg; Wrstlng; KiwanAwd; VoiceDemAwd; Wheaton College; Law.

APPEL, Dale R; Okabena HS; Heron Lake, MN; TrsFrshCls; NHS; FFA; Trade School; Agriculture.

APPEL, Joylene; Redfield Public HS; Redfield, SD; Band; ChrhWkr; CncrtBnd; HonRl; MrchBnd; PepBnd; SchAde; SchMus; FNA; IMSpt; Dakota State College; Secretarial.

APPELBAUM, Jo; William Chrisman HS; Sugar Creek, MO; Chr; ChrhWkr; HonRl; SchMus; Sdlty; StuCncl; RptrSchPpr; College; Dental Hygiene.

APPELBAUM, Steven; Evanston Township HS; Evanston, IL; 33/1100 HonRl; Univ Of Ill; Architecture.

APPELGATE, Thomas; South Tama County HS; Toledo, IA; 29/200 PresFrshCls; Band; ChrhWkr; HonRl; NatlThespSoc; SchMus; SchPl; KiwanAwd; Wartburg Coll; Music Therapy.

APPELHOF, Mark A; Clear Lake HS; Goodwin, SD; 3/57 HonRl; 4-H; FFA; College; Vet.

APPELL, Dennis A; R O V A Sr HS; Altona, IL; 11/72 Band; CncrtBnd; HonRl; MrchBnd; NHS; SchPl; YthFlsp; 4-H; SciCl; Carl Sandburg Comm College; Physics.

APPELT, Marian R; Libertyville HS; Libertyville, IL; 3/431 AFS; HonRl; JrNHS; NHS; Orch; RedCrAde; SchAde; SchMus; YthFlsp; RptrSchPpr; North Dakota State Univ; Chemistry.

APPERT, Sharon M; Hazelton HS; Hazelton, ND; 7/29 Band; ChrhWkr; HonRl; HospAde; MrchBnd; PepBnd; SchPl; 4-H; PpCl; CncrtBnd; Trade School; Secretarial.

APPICELLI, Steven J; Barnum HS; Barnum, MN; 7/69 HstFrshCls; HonRl; LbryAde; PepBnd; StuGov; SptEdSchPpr; FrCl; Bsktbl; Ftbl; Glf; Trade School; Vocation.

APPLE, Cathy L; Oakland HS; Oakland, IL; 1/44 PresSophCls; VPJrCls; Band; CncrtBnd; HonRl; MrchBnd; NHS; StuCncl; Yrbk; MthCl; Univ Of Il; Bus.

APPLE, Stephen M; New Buffalo HS; New Buffalo, MI; Band; CncrtBnd; HonRl; MrchBnd; StuCncl; CaptTrk; IMSpt; Michigan Tech Univ; Mechanical Engineer.

APPLE, Thomas W; St Thomas Aquinas HS; Florissant, MO; Band; Univ; Phsych.

APPLEBY, Darlene J; Chisago Lakes Area Sr HS; Center City, MN; HonRl; YthFlsp; Yrbk; PpCl; College; Accounting.

APPLEBY, Lori E; Roxana Sr HS; East Alton, IL; 11/290 Chr; HonRl; NHS; NatlMeritCmnd; OffAde; YthFlsp; FrCl; PpCl; Univ; French.

APPLEDORN, Bonnie M; Unity HS; Mendon, IL; HonRl; LbryAde; 4-H; FHA; Bsbl; GAA; Receptionist.

APPLEDORN, Roxanne L; Mason County Central HS; Ludington, MI; 6/135 Chr; ChrhWkr; CmntyWkr; HonRl; OffAde; SchMus; SchPl; TchrAde; EdSchPpr; SpnCl; West Shore Comm Clg; Medicine.

APPLEGATE, Greg L; Whitmore Lake HS; Whitmore Lake, MI; ALBoysSt; HonRl; NHS; SchMus; SchPl; StuCncl; FrCl; Bsktbl; CchngActv; KiwanAwd; Michigan State Univ; Journalism.

APPLEGATE, Julia D; Monroe Central HS; Parker City, IN; AFS; DrlTm; DrmMjrt; MrchBnd; RptrSchPpr; FHA; LatCl; LetterBsktbl; Trk; IMSpt; College; Professional Actress.

APPLEGATE, Kristine K; Osborne HS; Luray, KS; Band; Chrs; CncrtBnd; HonRl; MrchBnd; PepBnd; SchPl; TchrAde; Twrl; Chrldr; Goodland Vo Tech; Secretary.

APPLEGATE, Mark W; Springfield Se HS; Springfield, IL; 26/596 Band; Chr; ChrhWkr; CmntyWkr; CncrtBnd; MrchBnd; StuCncl; TchrAde; MthCl; Glf;.

APPLEGATE, Stacy E; Louisville HS; Louisville, NE; 2/40 TrsSrCls; HonRl; NHS; StuCncl; FrCl; LetterBsktbl; LetterFtbl; LetterTrk; Yankton Clg; Law.

APPLEGATE, Susan R; Newton HS; Willow Hill, IL; 2/187 SecJrCls; Band; SecChrhWkr; CncrtBnd; HonRl; MrchBnd; PresNHS; SchMus; Pres4-H; LatCl; Lincoln Trl Clge; Animal Indus.

APPLEOFF, Douglas R; Falls City Sr HS; Falls City, NE; VPFrshCls; VPJrCls; Band; Chrs; HonRl; NHS; NatlThespSoc; SchMus; StuCncl; Yrbk; College.

APPLEQUIST, Susan M; Wheeling HS; Wheeling, IL; 46/449 Band; CncrtBnd; HonRl; MrchBnd; NHS; PepBnd;.

APPLETON, Donald R; Dayton HS; Dayton, IA; 5/32 SecFrshCls; HonRl; NHS; EdYrBk; LetterBsbl; LetterBsktbl; LetterGlf; LetterTrk; CchngActv; IMSpt; Buena Vista College; Accounting.

APPS, Kim; Wild Rose Public HS; Wild Rose, WI; Band; HonRl; PepBnd; FBLA; FHA; PpCl; Trk; GAA; IMSpt; Coll; Professional.

APPS, Leslie H; Lincolnwood HS; Waggoner, IL; Band; ChrhWkr; CncrtBnd; HonRl; MrchBnd; PepBnd; SctActv; SpnCl; SciCl; LetterTrk; Univ; Usaf.

AQUILANI, Laureen K; Ogden HS; Ogden, IA; 15/60 ChrhWkr; HonRl; MrchBnd; NHS; NatlThespSoc; FHA; FrCl; PpCl; CaptBsktbl; Glf; Comm College; Executive Secretary.

AQUILINA, Rosemarie E; Sts Peter & Paul Area HS; Saginaw, MI; Chrs; ChrhWkr; DrlTm; HonRl; JrNHS; SchMus; GerCl; PpCl; Bsktbl; IMSpt; University; Medical Doctor.

ARAI, Makoto R; Hinsdale Central HS; Oak Brook, IL; NHS; NatlMeritSF; MthCl; Mass Inst Of Tech; Biochemistry.

ARAND, Carolyn R; St Marys HS; Belvue, KS; 2/60 HonRl; NHS; TchrAde; 4-H; EngCl; SpnCl; MthCl; PpCl; SciCl; 4-HAwd; Kansas State University; Veterinary Med.

ARAND, Corliss J; Union HS; Union, MO; SecJrCls; CmntyWkr; HonRl; JA; OffAde; StuCncl; 4-H; GerCl; PpCl; Bsktbl; Chrldr; PPFtbl; X Ray School; Radiologist Tech.

ARAND, Walter A; St Joseph HS; Lagrange Pk, IL; 1/229 HonRl; GerCl; Socr; IMSpt; Pre Med; Medical.

ARANDA, Leon P; Boystown HS; Boystown, NE; ChrhWkr; CmntyWkr; JA; LetterFtbl; Trk; CaptWrstlng; IMSpt; JAAwd; College; Professional.

ARANDA, Parfacto; Boystown HS; Boystown, NE; VPFrshCls; VPJrCls; Band; Chr; CmntyWkr; JA; Ftbl; Wrstlng; IMSpt; College; Chef.

ARANGO, Ivette M; St Pius X HS; Kansas City, MO; 31/129 Chrs; DrlTm; HonRl; SchMus; SpnCl; PpCl; GAA; College.

ARAUJO, Dennis D; Streator HS; Streator, IL; 39/400 PresSrCls; HonRl; StuGov; PpCl; LetterBsktbl; LetterFtbl; LetterTrk; Bradley Univ; Architectural Engineering.

ARBAUGH, Scott J; Chaminade HS; St Louis, MO; CmntyWkr; HonRl; NatlFornLg; CivCl; OptClAwd; University; Professional.

ARBEGUST, Pamela S; Riverdale HS; Muscoda, WI; HonRl; College; Art Teacher.

ARBOGAST, Rebecca A; Lewis Central HS; Council Bluffs, IA; 6/172 TrsSrCls; HonRl; NatlMeritCmnd; StuCncl; Yrbk; Univ; Lawyer.

ARBUCKIE, Rhonda L; Normal Comm HS; Normal, IL; Chr; ChrhWkr; SchMus; Bob Jones Univ; Music.

ARBUCKLE, David C; Buhler HS; Hutchinson, KS; 20/160 Chrs; HonRl; NHS; Quill&Scroll; StuCncl; RptrSchPpr; EdSchPpr; Bsktbl; Ftbl; Trk; Kansas Univ; Eng.

ARBUCKLE, Mark A; South Newton HS; Kentland, IN; HonRl; Yrbk; PresFBLA; LatCl; Bsbl; CchngActv; Int Jr Coll;accountant.

ARCARI, Betsy; Acad Of The Sacred Heart; Pontiac, MI; VPJrCls; CmntyWkr; HonRl; StuGov; RptrYrbk; 4-H; PresAwd; Depauw Univ; Liberal Arts.

ARCERI, Donald L; Chaminade College Prep; Lake St Louis, MO; 14/107 HstFrshCls; HstSophCls; HstJrCls; HstSrCls; HonRl; HospAde; JrNHS; NHS; StuCncl; StuGov; RptrSchPpr; LetterBsbl; LetterBsktbl; LetterFtbl; University; Professional.

ARCHAMBAULT, Paula; Fenton Senior HS; Fenton, MI; HonRl; JA; NHS; SchPl; LatCl; JAAwd; Coll; Pro.

ARCHER, Anne C; Downers North HS; Downers Grove, IL; 89/587 Chr; Chrs; NHS; Quill&Scroll; SchMus;.

ARCHER, Brian D; Gull Lake HS; Battle Creek, MI; 14/245 CncrtBnd; HonRl; MrchBnd; PepBnd; SchMus; SchPl; SctActv; StuGov; RptrYrbk; SciCl; College; Engineering.

ARCHER, Deborah M; Beaumont HS; St Louis, MO; 1/700 ChrhWkr; HonRl; NHS; TchrAde; LatCl; College; Law.

ARCHER, Denise D; Switz City Central HS; Linton, IN; HonRl; OffAde; StuCncl; TchrAde; Yrbk; FHA; PpCl; LetterBsbl; LetterBsktbl; LetterGAA; College; Vocation.

ARCHER, Jan G; Roosevelt HS; Des Moines, IA; Aud/Vis; Band; Chrs; ChrhWkr; DrlTm; NatlMeritCmnd; RptrYrbk; Yrbk; RptrSchPpr; Univ Of Ia; Health.

ARCHER, Jerry W; South Pemiscot HS; Steele, MO; TrsFrshCls; ChrhWkr; HonRl; JrNHS; NHS; SchPl; StuCncl; FFA; KeyCl; CaptBsbl; LetterBsktbl; CaptFtbl; College; Coach.

ARCHER, John M; Switz Co HS; Veray, IN; NHS; 4-H; FFA; SpnCl; LetterBsbl; LetterBsktbl; LetterGlf; DanFAwd; Indiana Inst Of Tech; Coach.

ARCHER, Kathy L; Linden HS; Linden, MI; Band; CncrtBnd; HonRl; MrchBnd; NatlMeritSF; PepBnd; SctActv; SpnCl; LetterTrk; IMSpt; PPFtbl; University; Botanist.

ARCHER, Ronnie D; Davis Co Comm HS; Moulton, IA; HonRl; VP4-H; LetterFtbl; Trk; Navy; Electronic Field.

ARCHIBALD, Geri M; Acad Of Our Lady; Chicago, IL; HonRl; NHS; SchMus; SchPl; GAA; Medicine.

ARCHIBALD, Roger L; Nokomis HS; Nokomis, IL; 6/98 ChrhWkr; HonRl; StuCncl; Pres4-H; PresFFA; Bsbl; LetterBsktbl; Ftbl; LetterTrk; DanFAwd; 4-HAwd; Eastern Ill Univ; Accounting.

ARCHIBALD, Tracy A; East HS; Wichita, KS; 10/657 Chr; HonRl; Quill&Scroll; StuGov; RptrSchPpr; SchPpr; DARAwd; Drake Univ; Journalism.

ARCHIE, Carol L; Cass Tech HS; Detroit, MI; HospAde; NHS; NatlMeritCmnd; OffAde; PolWkr; RptrSchPpr; EdSchPpr; SciCl; Univ Of Mi; Med Doctor.

ARCUS, Amy P; Proviso West HS; Hillside, IL; 18/948 Chrs; HonRl; JrNHS; SchPl; StuGov; RptrSchPpr; Univ Of Illinois; Veterinarian.

ARDT, Thomas E; Ardt HS; Downers Grove, IL; 2/14 Band; Chr; Chrl; Chrs; ChrhWkr; CncrtBnd; HonRl; NatlSciFnd; MrchBnd; OffAde; College; Accounting.

ARDYS, Rasa M; Bloomington HS; Bloomington, IL; HonRl; Isu; Educational Psych.

AREHART, Kim L; Western HS; Jackson, MI; SecSophCls; SecJrCls; Band; Chr; DrmMjrt; NHS; OffAde; TchrAde; RptrYrbk; Yrbk; SpnCl; College; Nursing.

ARENDS, Barbara J; Melvin Sibley HS; Melvin, IL; SecJrCls; ALAGirlsSt; HonRl; SchPl; VPStuCncl; SchPpr; VPFTA; SecPpCl; Chrldr; PresGAA; U Of Il; Elementary Ed Major.

ARENDS, Mary K; Oak Park River Forest HS; River Forest, IL; Chr; ChrhWkr; CmntyWkr; HonRl; LbryAde; NatlFornLg; SchMus; SchPl; Tennis; Ill State Univ; History.

ARENDS, Roderick J; Melvin Sibley HS; Melvin, IL; 5/25 ALBoysSt; HonRl; SctActv; YthFlsp; Yrbk; LetterBsbl; LetterBsktbl; Ill St Univ; Agric.

ARENDS, Ronda; Bayard HS; Bayard, NE; Chr; HonRl; LitMag; RptrYrbk; Yrbk; RptrSchPpr; SchPpr;.

ARENDT, Sharon C; Armstrong HS; Neenah, WI; Band; SecChrhWkr; HonRl; HospAde; NHS; SchMus; RptrYrbk; Yrbk; RptrSchPpr; EdSchPpr; Uw Mad; Journalism.

ARENS, Debbie K; Sacred Heart HS; Sedalia, MO; 6/29 TrsFrshCls; SecSophCls; Chr; HonRl; JrNHS; NHS; SchMus; PpCl; Chrldr; Coll; Business Teacher.

ARENS, Keith A; St Marys HS; Remsen, IA; Chrs; HonRl; SptEdSchPpr; SchPpr; Bsbl; Bsktbl; Trade School.

ARENS, Patrick D; Fowler HS; Fowler, MI; Band; Chr; CncrtBnd; HonRl; NHS; TchrAde; 4-H; College.

ARENS, Robert J; St Marys HS; Remsen, IA; Band; CmntyWkr; HonRl; JA; JCC; JrNHS; RedCrAde; DanFAwd; PresAwd; VoiceDemAwd; Trade School; Agriculture.

ARENSDORF, Gerald D; Mc Pherson County HS; Tryon, NE; HonRl; SchPl; Yrbk; 4-H; LetterBsktbl; LetterFtbl; CaptTrk;.

ARENT, Cynthia M; Coloma HS; Coloma, MI; CncrtBnd; HonRl; MrchBnd; PresNHS; NatlMeritCmnd; PepBnd; TreasYthFlsp; 4-H; FTA; SecLatCl; Mich State Univ; Medical Technology.

ARENT, Dawn M; St Joseph HS; St Joseph, MI; Chr; Chrl; HonRl; NatlThespSoc; SchMus; SchPl; YthFlsp; Yrbk; FrCl; PpCl; Col; Professional.

ARENTSEN, Teresa L; Wesclin Jr Sr HS; New Baden, IL; 3/100 TrsSrCls; HonRl; IntrClCncl; PresNHS; EdSchPpr; FHA; PresGerCl; PpCl; LetterChrldr; GAA; College; Liberal Arts.

ARENTSEN, Teresa L; Wesclin HS; New Baden, IL; 3/100 TrsSrCls; HonRl; IntrClCncl; PresNHS; EdSchPpr; FHA; PresGerCl; PpCl; Chrldr; PresAwd; Il St U; Business Admin.

ARENTSEN, Teresa L; Wesolin HS; New Baden, IL; 3/100 TrsSrCls; HonRl; IntrClCncl; PresNHS; EdSchPpr; FHA; PresGerCl; PpCl; LetterChrldr; GAA; Coll; Curr Of Maj Stud.

ARENTSON, Bruce; Harlan Comm HS; Harlan, IA; 15/259 ChrhWkr; HonRl; NHS; 4-H; FFA; CchngActv; DanFAwd; 4-HAwd; KiwanAwd; Ia State Univ; Vet.

ARFT, Joleen L; Lamar R 1 HS; Lamar, MO; Band; ChrhWkr; CncrtBnd; DrmMjrt; HonRl; HospAde; NatlFornLg; NHS; PepBnd; PpCl; Clge; Teaching.

ARGABRIGHT, Ann L; Archie HS; Archie, MO; Band; Chrs; CncrtBnd; HonRl; MrchBnd; NatlMeritSchl; SchPl; FHA; PpCl; Bsktbl;.

ARGANBRIGHT, Dave E; Panora Linden HS; Guthrie Center, IA; 8/36 VPFrshCls; PresSrCls; Bsbl; CaptFtbl; Ia St U; Bs In Agronomy.

ARGANBRIGHT, Lynette A; Valentine HS; Valentine, NE; Band; HonRl; HospAde; LbryAde; NHS; SctActv; FTA; PpCl; Chrldr; MasAwd; Univ Of Nebraska; Business.

ARGENTO, Nina; Marian Catholic HS; Chicago Heights, IL; 1/328 HonRl; NHS; NatlMeritCmnd; Sdlty; SpnCl; AmLegAwd; VoiceDemAwd; Col Of St Francis; Medical Technologist.

ARGO, Carlene C; Naperville Central HS; Naperville, IL; Chrs; ChrhWkr; HonRl; HospAde; SchPl; Univ Of Illinois.

ARGO, Michael A; Lawrenceville HS; Lawrenceville, IL; 1/186 HonRl; PresNHS; NatlMeritSchl; LatCl; LetterBsktbl; Ftbl; DanFAwd; SARAwd; Rose Hulman Inst Of Tech; Elec Engineer.

ARGUE, Michael J; Belleville HS; Belleville, WI; PresSophCls; CncrtBnd; HonRl; MrchBnd; PepBnd; StuCncl; YthFlsp; Sec4-H; LetterTrk; LetterWrstlng; U Of Wi River Falls; Musician.

ARHART, Randal D; Masn City HS; Mason City, IA; HonRl; SctActv; LetterBsbl; IMSpt; N Iowa Area Comm Clg; Accounting.

ARIAS, Teresa L; St Augustine HS; Chicago, IL; TrsSophCls; Chr; Chrs; DrlTm; JA; SchMus; SchPl; RptrSchPpr; Moser Business Schl; Secretary.

ARIE, Diane M; Marquette HS; West Point, IA; 8/51 TrsJrCls; Band; CncrtBnd; MrchBnd; PepBnd; SchPl; RptrYrbk; SchPpr; PpCl; Amer Inst Of Business; Executive Sec.

ARIN, Merle A; Lancaster Public HS; Lancaster, MN; Aud/Vis; ChrhWkr; SchPl; YthFlsp; Yrbk; SciCl; LetterBsktbl; Clge; Pro Roman Catholic Preist.

ARKIN, Andrew J; Oak Park & River Forest HS; River Forest, IL; PresFrshCls; StuCncl; StuGov; CaptFtbl; CaptTennis; CaptWrstlng; Univ; Business.

ARKIN, Charles A; Lake Park HS; Roselle, IL; 100/536 Aud/Vis; Band; CncrtBnd; HonRl; MrchBnd; PepBnd; Univ Of Illinois; Accountant.

ARKUS, Constance A; Maine West HS; Des Plaines, IL; HonRl; NatlMeritSchl; Marquett Univ; Journalism.

ARLOW, Donald; Prospect Hs; Mt Prospect, IL; 46 HonRl; SctActv; U Od Illinios;general Cirriculum Las.

ARMAGOST, Lesa A; North Andrew HS; Rea, MO; 1/18 Chr; Chrs; HonRl; ModUN; SchPl; StuGov; EdYrBk; Pres4-H; VPFHA; PpCl; Chrldr; BttyCrckrAwd; DanFAwd; William Sewell College.

ARMBRIGHT, Twila E; Homer Community HS; Dakota City, NE; Chrs; HonRl; LbryAde; SchPl; SctActv; RptrYrbk; RptrSchPpr; 4-H; SpnCl; PpCl; College Of St Mary; Medicine.

ARMBRISTER, Donna M; Palco HS; Zurich, KS; 8/26 Band; Chrs; CncrtBnd; HonRl; MrchBnd; PepBnd; SchPl; StuCncl; Trade School; Secretarial.

ARMBRUST, Scott F; Crown Point HS; Crown Point, IN; TrsJrCls; HonRl; StuCncl; StuGov; LetterTennis; RotaryAwd; Valparaiso Univ; Engineering.

ARMBRUSTER, Barbara J; Unionville Sebewaing Sr HS; Sebewaing, MI; Band; HonRl; HospAde; NHS; YthFlsp; Yrbk; 4-H; FHA; LatCl; College; Special Ed.

ARMBRUSTER, Beverly; Irego Community HS; Ellis, KS; 14/78 TrsSophCls; Band; PresSophCls; HonRl; MrchBnd; SchPl; 4-H; FHA; PpCl; Business School; Secretary.

ARMBRUSTER, Janet M; Ellsworth Sr HS; Hager City, WI; HonRl; Mdrgl; NHS; StuCncl; PpCl; Chrldr; GAA; College; Professional.

ARMENTROUT, Steven J; Reavis HS; Burbank, IL; 6/670 CmntyWkr; HonRl; NHS; SchAde; YthFlsp; GerCl; LetterGlf; College.

ARMFIELD, Avis A; Clinton HS; Janesville, WI; 2/92 Chr; CncrtBnd; NHS; NatlMeritFnl; NatlMeritSchl; NatlThespSoc; SchMus; 4-H; GovHonPrgAwd; KiwanAwd; Lawrence University; Science.

ARMITAGE, Terry J; Smith Center HS; Smith Center, KS; 5/70 HonRl; Col; Solar Scientist.

ARM KNECHT, Bonnie A; Nemaha Valley HS; Talmage, NE; Chrs; ChrhWkr; CmntyWkr; HonRl; SchAde; SchPl; YthFlsp; PpCl; IMSpt;.

ARMOCK, David A; Sparta HS; Conklin, MI; Band; CncrtBnd; HonRl; MrchBnd; NHS; PepBnd; SctActv; LetterBsktbl; LetterFtbl; College; Avionics.

ARMONTROUT, Jeffrey P; Boone County R Vi HS; Centralia, MO; 46/86 YthFlsp; FFA; Bsktbl; CaptFtbl; CchngActv; College.

ARMOVIT, Jackie Z; Onsted Community HS; Onsted, MI; TrsSophCls; Band; Chr; CncrtBnd; HonRl; MrchBnd; OffAde; PepBnd; SchPl; TchrAde; University; Medical Technologist.

ARMS, Juanita; Martin Public HS; Shelbyville, MI; HonRl; LbryAde; TchrAde; RptrYrbk; Yrbk; RptrSchPpr; SchPpr; 4-H; College; Liberal Arts.

ARMSTRONG, Alfonzo; Soldan HS; St Louis, MO; 1/783 HonRl; SchAde; SctActv; Amer Col Of Paris; Data Processor.

ARMSTRONG, Brent D; Creighton Preparatory HS; Omaha, NE; ChrhWkr; Sdlty; LetterBsktbl; LetterFtbl; College; Management.

ARMSTRONG, Bruce A; Decatur Central HS; Indianapolis, IN; 14/343 ALBoysSt; HonRl; NHS; PolWkr; SctActv; StuCncl; LetterSwmmng; Gen Motors Inst; Mech Engr.

ARMSTRONG, David S; Lyons Township HS; Lagrange Park, IL; Aud/Vis; MthCl; Univ Of Illinois; Engineering.

ARMSTRONG, Dianne K; Big Springs HS; Brule, NE; TrsSophCls; SecJrCls; Band; ChrhWkr; CncrtBnd; MrchBnd; PepBnd; FHA; PpCl; Chrldr; Bus Sch; Secretary.

ARMSTRONG, Donna R; Wichita S HS; Wichita, KS; NHS; Orch; SchPl; StuGov; PpCl; LetterTrk; University; Professional.

ARMSTRONG, Douglas B; Hemingford HS; Hemingford, NE; VPJrCls; ALBoysSt; Band; Chrs; CncrtBnd; HonRl; MrchBnd; NHS; PepBnd; SchPl; StuGov; TchrAde; 4-H; SciCl; LetterBsktbl; College; Agriculture.

ARMSTRONG, James G; Guilford HS; Rockford, IL; College; Psychology.

ARMSTRONG, James W; Portage Northern HS; Portage, MI; ChrhWkr; CmntyWkr; HonRl; LitMag; NHS; NatlMeritSF; SchMus; SchPl; SctActv; YthFlsp; Coll; Earth Science.

ARMSTRONG, Jennifer H; St Marys Academy; Chicago, IL; Chrs; JA; OffAde; SchMus; StuCncl; TchrAde; RptrYrbk; Glf; GAA; IMSpt; Duke Univ; Law.

ARMSTRONG, Jennifer J; Mattoon Sr HS; Mattoon, IL; 88/391 SecJrCls; AFS; CncrtBnd; HonRl; MrchBnd; StuCncl; PpCl; Ill State Univ; Special Education.

ARMSTRONG, Joyce; Evanston Township; Evanston, IL; Band; Chr; Chrs; HonRl; LetterTennis; LetterTrk; U Of Ill; Biological Science.

ARMSTRONG, Karen E; Sycamore HS; Sycamore, IL; 9/220 VPSophCls; Band; Chr; HonRl; MrchBnd; Treas4-H; PresPpCl; LetterTrk; Chrldr; GAA; University.

ARMSTRONG, Karl W; Lindblom HS; Chicago, IL; 12/599 HonRl; JA; Quill&Scroll; StuCncl; TchrAde; RptrSchPpr; GerCl; SciCl; Northwestern; Biochemistry.

ARMSTRONG, Keith; Eldora HS; Eldora, IA; ALBoysSt; HonRl; NHS; NatlMeritCmnd; RptrYrbk; SpnCl; SciCl; LetterFtbl; LetterTrk; Coll Iowa State; Chem Enginer.

ARMSTRONG, Laura K; Thayer HS; Thayer, MO; 9/49 Band; Chr; ChrhWkr; Mdrgl; MrchBnd; PepBnd; Harding; English.

ARMSTRONG, Lori J; Rockridge HS; Reynolds, IL; Band; CncrtBnd; HonRl; StuCncl; SecYthFlsp; 4-H; FNA; LatCl; Chrldr; 4-HAwd; College.

ARMSTRONG, Lynn; Mahomet Seymour HS; Mahomet, IL; TrsFrshCls; HonRl; College; Medical.

ARMSTRONG, Lynn A; Tri County HS; What Cheer, IA; SecSophCls; SecJrCls; Band; ChrhWkr; HonRl; Yrbk;.

ARMSTRONG, Marc C; Holland HS; Holland, MI; ALBoysSt; CmntyWkr; TchrAde; LetterBsbl; LetterFtbl; IMSpt; Saginaw Vly St Clg; Business.

ARMSTRONG, Mark A; Warren HS; Sterling Heights, MI; 1/374 PresFrshCls; Chrs; HonRl; NHS; StuCncl; StuGov; Bsktbl; LetterFtbl; Trk; IMSpt; Wayne State Univ; Corporate Lawyer.

ARMSTRONG, Mary R; Winamac Comm HS; Winamac, IN; Aud/Vis; CmntyWkr; LbryAde; SchPpr; 4-H; FHA; SciCl; IMSpt; Trade School; Vocation.

ARMSTRONG, Patricia W; Northwest HS; High Ridge, MO; College; Acctng.

ARMSTRONG, Rebecca D; Sycamore HS; Sycamore, IL; 13/200 PresSophCls; AFS; SecCncrtBnd; HonRl; MrchBnd; NHS; NatlThespSoc; PepBnd; SchPl; VPStuCncl; LetterBsktbl; LetterTrk; Chrldr; Univ; Chemical.

ARMSTRONG, Robert N; Ecorse HS; Ecorse, MI; 7/209 Band; Chr; ChrhWkr; HonRl; JA; MrchBnd; NHS; StuCncl; LetterBsbl; LetterFtbl; Col; Law.

ARMSTRONG, Shelley D; No Decatur HS; Greensburg, IN; 5/83 ALAGirlsSt; Chr; ChrhWkr; CmntyWkr; HonRl; NHS; OffAde; SchPl; YthFlsp; RptrSchPpr; SchPpr; FHA; GAA; 4-HAwd; Indiana Purdue Univ; Nursing.

ARMSTRONG, Vanessa L; Bourbon HS; Bourbon, MO; Band; HonRl; StuCncl; Twrl; YthFlsp; FHA; SpnCl; PpCl; Trk; College; Nurse.

ARMSTRONG, Vesta S; Rushville HS; Rushville, NE; HstJrCls; Chrs; ChrhWkr; HonRl; Mdrgl; College; Director Of Christian Education.

ARMUTH, Kent W; Columbus North HS; Edinburg, IN; ChrhWkr; CmntyWkr; HonRl; PolWkr; YthFlsp; 4-H; FFA; IMSpt; 4-HAwd; Purdue; Pro.

ARN, Lori I; Jayhawk Linn HS; Kincaid, KS; SecTrsFrshCls; Chrs; ChrhWkr; CmntyWkr; VPYthFlsp; RptrYrbk; RptrSchPpr; VP4-H; SecSpnCl; 4-HAwd; Armed Services; Data Processing.

ARNDT, Beverly B; Northwestern Lutheran Acad; Glenham, SD; Band; CncrtBnd; DrmBgl; HonRl; MrchBnd; SchPl; StuCncl; Bsktbl; IMSpt; PPFtbl; U Of Sd.

ARNDT, Janet M; La Moure Public HS; Fullerton, ND; 5/47 Band; Chrs; CncrtBnd; HonRl; PepBnd; Yrbk; PpCl; Bsktbl; Trk; GAA; Nd U; Accntg.

ARNDT, Jennifer S; Webb HS; Reedsburg, WI; AFS; CncrtBnd; HonRl; NatlThespSoc; Orch; SchMus; SctActv; PpCl; LetterTrk; Chrldr; Northwestern University; Medicine.

ARNDT, Karen; Queen Of Peace Hs; Chicago, IL; 3/430 HonRl; LitMag; LbryAde; NHS; StuCncl; EdYrBk; SpnCl; GAA; University Of Ill; Pre Pharmacy.

ARNDT, Katherine W; Antigo HS; Antigo, WI; NatlFornLg; FBLA; PresSpnCl; Ncti; Advertise.

ARNDT, Robin L; Carson HS; Carson, ND; VPFrshCls; PresJrCls; ALBoysSt; HonRl; StuCncl; FFA; SciCl; LetterBsktbl; LetterFtbl; LetterTrk; College.

ARNDT, Roxi; Whittemore Prescott HS; Prescott, MI; 2/74 VPJrCls; ChrhWkr; NHS; SchPl; StuCncl; EdYrBk; 4-H; GerCl; Bsktbl; CitAwd; College Delta; Secretarial Associates Degre.

ARNDT, Steven J; Valders HS; Whitelaw, WI; HonRl; OffAde; Bsktbl; LetterFtbl; LetterTrk; Wrstlng; Univ Of Wis; Conservation.

ARNESON, Cheryl; Clark HS; Clark, SD; AFS; HonRl; RptrSchPpr; Univ; Veterinary Med.

ARNESON, Dean L; Niobrara HS; Niobrara, NE; Band; Chr; Chrl; Chrs; HonRl; SchMus; Bsktbl; Ftbl; Trk; PresAwd; U Of Nebraska.

ARNESON, Mary; Hamlin HS; Hayti, SD; 8/66 SecFrshCls; Band; Chrs; CmntyWkr; HonRl; MrchBnd; PolWkr; RptrYrbk; IMSpt; 4-HAwd; Coll.

ARNETT, Jan M; Pacific HS; Pacific, MO; HonRl; SchMus; YthFlsp; PpCl; Socr; LetterChrldr; College; Professional.

ARNETT, Kathy; Warsaw Comm HS; Claypool, IN; ChrhWkr; SchPl; College; Physician.

ARNETT, Kathy J; Salem HS; Salem, MO; HonRl; PpCl; SciCl; College; Professional.

ARNETTE, Walter G; Meramec Valley HS; Pacific, MO; Band; CncrtBnd; HonRl; MrchBnd; SciCl; Clge; Prof.

ARNEY, Thomas; Oak Creek HS; Oak Creek, WI; HonRl; SctActv; GerCl; Wrstlng; College; Psychology.

ARNING, Rose; Sheldon Senior HS; Ashton, IA; HonRl; LbryAde; NHS; Quill&Scroll; Yrbk; RptrSchPpr; FTA; Coll; Broadcasting.

ARNOLD, Bobette L; Belton HS; Belton, MO; SecTrsSrCls; Band; CncrtBnd; HonRl; MrchBnd; NHS; SchMus; StuCncl; SpnCl; Trk; Central Mo St; Business Education.

ARNOLD, Bradley W; Avon HS; Plainfield, IN; 25/155 CmntyWkr; HonRl; ModUN; StuGov; TchrAde; YthFlsp; MthCl; SciCl; Bsktbl; Trk; Iupui; Dentistry.

ARNOLD, Cheryl L; Falls City Sr HS; Salem, NE; HonRl; Business; Secretary.

ARNOLD, Christine K; Turner HS; Kansas City, KS; 9/290 ChrhWkr; HonRl; JrNHS; LitMag; NHS; TchrAde; SpnCl; College; Business.

ARNOLD, David; Malden HS; Malden, MO; 2/125 NatlMeritFnl; PolWkr; RptrYrbk; EdSchPpr; Ftbl; Glf; Trk; RotaryAwd; U Of Chicago; Political Science.

ARNOLD, David C; N Greene Unit #3 HS; Hillview, IL; 13/121 ChrhWkr; HonRl; NHS; LetterBsbl; LetterFtbl; Trk; College.

ARNOLD, David N; Malden HS; Malden, MO; 1/125 HonRl; NatlMeritSF; PolWkr; StuCncl; RptrYrbk; EdSchPpr; Ftbl; Glf; Trk; RotaryAwd; Univ; Humanities.

ARNOLD, Deborah A; Lincolnwood HS; Waggoner, IL; 5/61 ALAGirlsSt; VPBand; HonRl; VPStuCncl; VPFTA; SpnCl; PpCl; Chrldr; Eastern Illinois Univ; Medical Tech.

ARNOLD, Delena M; Rushford HS; Rushford, MN; HonRl; LbryAde; Junior College; Key Punch Computers.

ARNOLD, Duane K; Muskegon HS; Muskegon, MI; HonRl; JA; YthFlsp; Wrstlng; IMSpt; Univ Of Michigan; Aerospace Engineering.

ARNOLD, Georgette; Holy Redeemer HS; Detroit, MI; 35/190 ChrhWkr; CmntyWkr; HonRl; LbryAde; NatlThespSoc; PolWkr; RedCrAde; StuGov; UNYO; RptrYrbk; Univ Of Detroit; Political Science.

ARNOLD, Ginger R; Mark Twain HS; New London, MO; Band; HospAde; Sdlty; StuCncl; YthFlsp; Pres4-H; PpCl; Bsktbl; Chrldr; PPFtbl; 4-HAwd; MasAwd; Trade School; Nursing.

ARNOLD, Jacqueline; Ford Central HS; Roberts, IL; HonRl; SchPl; EdYrBk; FTA; PpCl; Chrldr; Parkland Jr College; Prof Of Psychology.

ARNOLD, Janet; Orrick HS; Orrick, MO; SecTrsFrshCls; Chrs; ChrhWkr; HonRl; NHS; YthFlsp; Yrbk; 4-H; FHA; PPFtbl;.

ARNOLD, Jerry W; Ashland HS; Ashland, KS; 1/30 PresJrCls; Band; CncrtBnd; NHS; NatlMeritFnl; SctActv; StuCncl; Bsktbl; Ftbl; Trk; Univ; Veterinary Med.

ARNOLD, Jim; Urbana Senior HS; Urbana, IL; PresJrCls; StuGov; Ftbl; Trk; Wrstlng; PresAwd; College; Professional.

ARNOLD, Joyce M; Orrick HS; Richmond, MO; 3/42 SecFrshCls; Band; ChrhWkr; HonRl; NHS; TchrAde; Yrbk; FHA; PpCl; PPFtbl;.

ARNOLD, June; Marian HS; Hays, KS; VPJrCls; ChrhWkr; HonRl; NatlFornLg; NatlThespSoc; SchPl; StuCncl; RptrSchPpr; EdSchPpr; SchPpr; College; Music Or Drama Teacher.

ARNOLD, Kathy L; Cardinal Ritter HS; Indianapolis, IN; Band; Chrs; HonRl; MrchBnd; SchMus; SchPl; Twrl; SpnCl; Trk; PPFtbl; Indiana School Of Practical Nursing; Nurse.

ARNOLD, Kim D; Greenville HS; Greenville, MI; Band; MrchBnd; PepBnd; FrCl; Bsktbl; LetterFtbl; LetterTrk; IMSpt; Ferris State; Drafting.

ARNOLD, Laurie L; Brimfield HS; Brimfield, IL; 1/55 SecFrshCls; SecSophCls; ChrhWkr; HonRl; NHS; SecStuCncl; PresYthFlsp; PresSpnCl; VPPpCl; CaptChrldr; C; Law Engineering.

ARNOLD, Mary; Aurora HS; Aurora, NE; 23/90 Chrs; ChrhWkr; HonRl; TchrAde; YthFlsp; PpCl; BttyCrckrAwd; Neb Wesleyan Univ; Spec Ed.

ARNOLD, Mary I; Rushford HS; Rushford, MN; Chrs; CmntyWkr; DrlTm; HonRl; TchrAde; Yrbk; FHA; FTA; PpCl; College; Home Economics.

ARNOLD, Mary L; Mayo HS; Rochester, MN; 41/456 DrlTm; NHS; EdYrBk; Augustana College; Nursing.

ARNOLD, Myla B; Milbank HS; Twin Brooks, SD; Chr; Chrs; ChrhWkr; HonRl; HospAde; YthFlsp; 4-H; 4-HAwd; Sw Minnesota St College; Medical Tech.

ARNOLD, Nathan G; Alton R 4 HS; Alton, MO; 7/56 Band; Chrs; ChrhWkr; CncrtBnd; HonRl; MrchBnd; PepBnd; SchMus; RptrSchPpr; SptEdSchPpr; SchPpr; College; Music.

ARNOLD, Neal E; Northrop HS; Ft Wane, IN; HonRl; NatlMeritSF; LetterBsktbl; LetterFtbl; Ball State U; Architecture.

ARNOLD, Penny J; Clare HS; Clare, MI; Band; CncrtBnd; HonRl; MrchBnd; NHS; TchrAde; 4-H; Central Mi Univ; Elem Or Special Ed.

ARNOLD, Robert M; Parkway North Sr HS; St Louis County, MO; 1/500 PresSrCls; CmntyWkr; JrNHS; NatlFornLg; NHS; PolWkr; StuCncl; StuGov; Ftbl; Medical Schl; Medicine.

ARNOLD, Scott R; Glenbrook South HS; Glenview, IL; 40/600 JrNHS; NHS; NatlMeritSF; KeyCl; Ftbl; LetterSocr; Trk; Med Schl; Physician.

ARNOLD, Sheri S; Milton Senior HS; Milton Jct, WI; AFS; Chr; ChrhWkr; HonRl; SchMus; FrCl; LetterTrk; College.

ARNOLD, Steven; Orchard View HS; Muskegon, MI; 10/250 Band; ChrhWkr; HonRl; MrchBnd; Orch; YthFlsp; Yrbk; SchPpr; Tennis; Muskegon Community Coll; Engineering.

ARNOLD, Steven D; Marion HS; Marion, IA; Aud/Vis; Band; CncrtBnd; LbryAde; MrchBnd; PepBnd; PolWkr; SchPpr; Eastern Ky Univ; Law Enforcement.

ARNOLD, Timothy J; Ritenour Sr HS; Overland, MO; HonRl; JA; Arizona St Univ; Architect.

ARNOLD, Tina M; Marine City HS; Marine City, MI; Chrl; JrNHS; NHS; SpnCl; IMSpt; Univ; Foreign Lang.

ARNOLD, Todd W; Roxana HS; East Alton, IL; 4/290 Band; HonRl; MrchBnd; NHS; PresStuCncl; MthCl; Bsbl; LetterBsktbl; LetterTrk; College; Medicine.

ARNOLD, Tom; Richardton HS; Richardton, ND; 2/40 VPFrshCls; PresJrCls; ALBoysSt; Band; Chr; HonRl; StuCncl; Bsktbl; Ftbl; Trk; Army; Veterinary Science.

ARNOLD, Virginia M; Milton Sr HS; Avalon, WI; Band; Chrs; HonRl; MrchBnd; OffAde; YthFlsp; 4-H; FFA; FHA; CaptTennis; 4-HAwd; Univ Of Madison.

ARNOLD, Walter T; Alpena Sr HS; Alpena, MI; HonRl; TchrAde; Alpena Comm College; Biology.

ARNOLD, William C; Edina East HS; Edina, MN; ChrhWkr; OffAde; TchrAde; LatCl; Univ Of Minnesota.

ARNOLDY, Diane K; Tipton HS; Tipton, KS; 1/22 PresFrshCls; TrsSophCls; Chrs; ChrhWkr; NatlMeritSF; PresStuCncl; EdYrBk; EdSchPpr; CaptTrk; Chrldr; Ks St Univ; Arcitecture.

ARNOLDY, Jocile; Tipton HS; Tipton, KS; PresSrCls; ALAGirlsSt; HonRl; ModUN; StuCncl; Yrbk; 4-H; PpCl; Trk; 4-HAwd; Hutchinson Jr Coll; Medical.

ARNOLDY, Lucy; Tipton HS; Tipton, KS; 2/22 SecJrCls; HonRl; NatlMeritCmnd; Yrbk; BttyCrckrAwd; Fort Hays Kans St Coll; Dietetics.

ARNOSTI, Donald A; Whitefish Bay HS; Milwaukee, WI; 25/300 Band; Chrs; CmntyWkr; CncrtBnd; HonRl; MrchBnd; NatlMeritFnl; NatlMeritSF; PepBnd; Sacrstn; Lawrence; Forestry.

ARNOTT, Kimberly J; Dearborn HS; Dearborn, MI; Chrs; HonRl; SctActv; FrCl; Mi St U; Child Deve.

AROCHA, Priscilla A; Bay City Central HS; Bay City, MI; HonRl; NatlMeritFnl; NatlMeritSchl; OffAde; PolWkr; TchrAde; SpnCl; Univ Of Michigan; Lawyer.

ARONSON, Kenneth S; Evanston Twp HS; Skokie, IL; 27/1200 HonRl; NatlFornLg; NatlMeritCmnd; PolWkr; UNYO; MthCl; Northwestern Univ; Bio Med Engineering.

ARONSON, Miriam J; Albert City Truesdale HS; Albert City, IA; Band; Chr; CncrtBnd; HonRl; Mdrgl; MrchBnd; PepBnd; SchPl; StuCncl; RptrSchPpr; FHA; Bsbl; Bsktbl; College.

ARONSON, Paul S; Glenbard South HS; Glen Ellyn, IL; HonRl; NatlMeritCmnd;.

ARORA, Vandna; Menomonie HS; Menomonie, WI; 3/238 HonRl; NHS; SctActv; VPStuCncl; RptrSchPpr; PresFDA; Tennis; GAA; KiwanAwd; U Minn Minneapolis; Medicine.

ARP, Brent W; Blair HS; Blair, NE; 2/135 VPSophCls; ALBoysSt; Chrs; CmntyWkr; HonRl; StuCncl; 4-H; FFA; Bsktbl; Trk; 4-HAwd; College; Agriculture.

ARP, Catherine E; Normandy HS; St Louis, MO; Band; CncrtBnd; HonRl; MrchBnd; Orch; StuCncl; Swmmng; College; Music.

ARP, John W; Cumberland Massena HS; Massena, IA; 1/30 VPFrshCls; PresJrCls; ALBoysSt; CncrtBnd; HonRl; NHS; Pres4-H; LetterBsbl; LetterBsktbl; CaptFtbl; Ia State U; Engineering.

ARP, Lori R; Edgerton Public HS; Edgerton, MN; StuCncl; TchrAde; FTA; CaptBsktbl; Trk; IMSpt; College; Coach & Teacher.

ARQUILLA, Carmela; Charles P Steinmetz HS; Chicago, IL; 1/617 Band; HonRl; NHS; NatlMeritCmnd; RedCrAde; TchrAde; Univ Of Ill; Math.

ARQUILLA, Marianne; Ridgewood HS; Norridge, IL; 9/360 TrsSrCls; Chr; HonRl; NHS; PolWkr; StuCncl; StuGov; TchrAde; RptrSchPpr; De Paul Univ; Business Management.

ARRENHOLZ, Daniel A; Peoria HS; Peoria, IL; 85/480 HonRl; NatlMeritCmnd; GerCl; LetterSocr; Blackburn College; Biology.

ARRIGO, Barbara D; Roger C Sullivan HS; Chicago, IL; 20/276 Chr; HonRl; NHS; EdSchPpr; KeyCl; E Illinois Univ; Education.

ARROWOOD, Larry; Muskego HS; Muskego, WI; HonRl; NHS; Bsbl; IMSpt; Coll; Art.

ARSENAULT, Susan M; Crestwood HS; Dearborn Heights, MI; NHS; FrCl; Madonna College; Nursing.

ARSHT, Michelle; Berkley HS; Oak Park, MI; Chr; Chrl; MrchBnd; SchPl; StuGov; College.

ARSZMAN, Magdalene M; Our Lady Of Grace Academy; Indianapolis, IN; 8/60 Chrs; HonRl; JA; SchMus; SchPl; StuCncl; FrCl; Marian College; Language.

ARTEMAN, Nancy M; Wapella HS; Wapella, IL; VPJrCls; HonRl; SchPl; Yrbk; College; Medical Technology.

ARTER, Kevin C; Anderson HS; Anderson, IN; HonRl; NHS; IMSpt; University; Science.

ARTER, Thomas C; Crown Point HS; Crown Point, IN; 49/493 Band; CncrtBnd; HonRl; MrchBnd; NatlMeritFnl; NatlMeritSF; PolWkr; SpnCl; SciCl; IMSpt; Purdue Univ; Science.

ARTERBURY, Allan; New Underwood HS; Formingdale, SD; 7/26 HonRl; College; Curriculum Of Major Study.

ARTHUR, Donna J; Edgewood HS; Stinesville, IN; 7/175 SecFrshCls; TrsSophCls; VPJrCls; ChrhWkr; HonRl; NHS; StuCncl; RptrSchPpr; FHA; PpCl; In Univ; Journalism.

ARTHUR, Jacquelyn L; Marshall HS; Dennison, IL; 1/124 Band; Chr; Chrs; CncrtBnd; HonRl; MrchBnd; NHS; PepBnd; YthFlsp; EdYrBk; LatCl; SciCl; GAA; College; Computer Science.

ARTHUR, Steven J; Edgewood HS; Edgewood, IA; Band; Chr; NHS; SchMus; SchPl; MthCl; LetterBsbl; Bsktbl; LetterFtbl; LetterGlf; College; Business.

ARTHUR, Steve T; Randolph Southern HS; Lynn, IN; 1/64 VPSrCls; HonRl; NHS; NatlMeritSF; StuCncl; 4-H; ChmnBsktbl; Coll; Pre Med.

ARTING, George; Dundee HS; Dundee, MI; 6/128 Aud/Vis; Band; CncrtBnd; HonRl; MrchBnd; PepBnd; TchrAde; 4-H; SciCl; 4-HAwd; Trade School; Data Processing.

ARTIS, Tamara C; Lindblom Tech HS; Chicago, IL; 50/599 Chr; Chrs; ChrhWkr; HonRl; IntrClCncl; JA; Mdrgl; StuCncl; TchrAde; Loyola Univ; Medicine.

ARTMAN, Rosemary A; Duchesne HS; St Ann, MO; 16/183 Chrs; HonRl; NHS; SchMus; YthFlsp; Yrbk; FrCl; PpCl; CitAwd; College; Accounting.

ARTWEIN, Joanne M; St Agnes HS; Springfield, MO; Band; Chrs; CncrtBnd; HonRl; SpnCl;.

ARTZ, Carol A; Alma HS; Alma, NE; Chrs; CmntyWkr; CncrtBnd; MrchBnd; PepBnd; SchPl; Yrbk; 4-H; PpCl; School Of Nursing; Nurse.

ARTZ, Catherine F; Marceline HS; Marceline, MO; 6/62 HonRl; NHS; StuCncl; 4-H; PresSciCl; CaptBsktbl; Trk; IMSpt; DARAwd; Sec4-HAwd; Univ Of Mo Colombia; Agricultural Engineer.

ARTZ, Monte L; Wilcox HS; Republican City, NE; VPSrCls; Band; ChrhWkr; CncrtBnd; HonRl; PresNHS; PepBnd; SchMus; SecFFA; Bsktbl; U Of Ne; Agriculture.

ARUNDEL, William J; St Ritas HS; Chicago, IL; HonRl; StuCncl; LetterBsbl; Bsktbl; CchngActv; Lewis Univ; Accounting.

ARUNSKI, Joyce I; Bishop Dubourg HS; St Louis, MO; ALAGirlsSt; NHS; RedCrAde; SptEdYrbk; RptrSchPpr; PepBnd; FTA; Trk; PPFtbl; University; Psychology.

ARVIN, Alan T; North HS; Omaha, NE; HonRl; OffAde; TchrAde; Bsktbl; University; Business.

ARVOY, Deb M; Durand HS; Durand, MI; VPSrCls; Chrs; HonRl; SctActv; TchrAde; PpCl; Bus Clge; Secretarial.

ARY, Sally; Tiskilwa HS; Tiskilwa, IL; Band; HonRl; HospAde; YthFlsp; FHA; Chrldr; GAA; IMSpt; College; Vocational Nursing.

ASAL, Debra L; Eureka HS; Eureka, IL; 18/102 SecFrshCls; Band; Chr; HonRl; MrchBnd; SchMus; TchrAde; RptrYrbk; FrCl; Chrldr; Undecided.

ASAY, Susan L; Bayard HS; Bayard, NE; 11/43 Chrs; HonRl; SchMus; Yrbk; RptrSchPpr; FHA; PresPpCl; LetterTrk; Chrldr; BttyCrckrAwd; Glen E Clark Business Schl; Secretary.

ASBURY, Merrianne; Brown County HS; Morgantown, IN; 6/206 DrlTm; Yrbk; 4-H; FHA; FrCl; PpCl; Trk; GAA; 4-HAwd; Coll.

ASCH, Thomas F; Evanston Twp HS; Evanston, IL; HonRl; NatlFornLg; NatlMeritSF; PolWkr; StuGov; YthLg; Univ Of Chicago; Law.

ASCHE, Darci L; North Sargent HS; Gwinner, ND; 4/15 VPFrshCls; PresSophCls; Band; Chr; HonRl; StuCncl; Bsktbl; Chrldr; CchngActv; GAA; College; Home Economics.

ASCHENBRENNER, Joan L; Auburndale HS; Milladore, WI; Band; CncrtBnd; HonRl; MrchBnd; PepBnd; FBLA;.

ASCHENBRENNER, Sharolyn; Pinckney HS; Pinckney, MI; 1/180 PresSophCls; Band; CncrtBnd; HonRl; MrchBnd; VPNHS; NatlMeritCmnd; PepBnd; SchPpr; GodCntryAwd; College.

ASCHER, Adeena; Oak Park HS; Oak Park, MI; 30/500 Chr; Chrs; CmntyWkr; HonRl; JrNHS; LitMag; NatlMeritSF; NCTE; Univ; English.

ASELTINE, Karen; Dexter HS; Dexter, MI; HonRl; NHS; RedCrAde; Yrbk; 4-H; DARAwd; Mi St Univ.

ASENBRENNER, David L; Marion HS; Caroline, WI; Band; CncrtBnd; HonRl; MrchBnd; PepBnd; TchrAde; SchPpr; Bsbl; Bsktbl; College; Business Adminstration.

ASH, Cathey D; Puxico R 8 HS; Puxico, MO; Band; Chr; ChrhWkr; HonRl; NHS; SchPl; StuCncl; TchrAde; FTA; SciCl; Univ Of Mo Columbia; Computer Programmer.

ASH, Darryl; Humboldt St Vincent HS; St Vincent, MN; 1/11 PresSophCls; Band; Chr; ChrhWkr; CncrtBnd; HonRl; PepBnd; SchMus; RptrYrbk; FFA; Univ Of Mn; Political Science.

ASH, Linda F; California HS; California, MO; 44/88 Chr; HonRl; FHA; SpnCl; College; Medical Tech.

ASH, Marlyn; Jamestown C 1 HS; Pittsburg, KS; Chr; HonRl; TchrAde; YthFlsp; EdYrBk; PpCl; Trk; Chrldr; Kansas State Col; Lawyer.

ASH, Maureen M; Milaca HS; Milaca, MN; Mdrgl; SchMus; SchPl; StuCncl; RptrYrbk; 4-H; Bsktbl; Trk; 4-HAwd; Univ; Medicine.

ASH, Nancy L; Three Rivers HS; Three Rivers, MI; 66/210 Band; ChrhWkr; CncrtBnd; HonRl; MrchBnd; PepBnd; YthFlsp; 4-H; SpnCl; 4-HAwd; Us Army Reserve; Business.

ASHAUER, Rita K; Worden HS; Worden, IL; 1/21 TrsJrCls; Chrs; HonRl; SchPl; VPStuCncl; EdYrBk; RptrSchPpr; FHA; GerCl; GAA; Southern Illinois Univ; Medicine.

ASHBACHER, Cherie A; Waukon Sr HS; Lansing, IA; 15/155 CmntyWkr; HonRl; HospAde; LbryAde; NHS; Quill&Scroll; YthFlsp; EdYrBk; GerCl; Bsktbl; Womens Army Corp Univ; Pro.

ASHBACHER, Emma L; Northeast HS; Arma, KS; ALAGirlsSt; Chr; Chrs; ChrhWkr; DrmBgl; HonRl; NatlThespSoc; Quill&Scroll; RptrSchPpr; SchPpr; SpnCl; College; Vocation.

ASHBACHER, John J; Northeast HS; Arma, KS; Chrs; RptrSchPpr; Bsbl; Bsktbl; Ftbl; Trade School; Vocation.

ASHBECK, Joyce L; Auburndale HS; Auburndale, WI; 1/94 HonRl; VPNHS; StuCncl; EdYrBk; SecFBLA; PresGerCl; PpCl; LetterBsktbl; LetterTrk; St Josephs School; X Ray Tech.

ASHBECK, Richard T; Gordon Technical HS; Chicago, IL; HonRl; Tennis; IMSpt; De Paul Univ; Accountant.

ASHBURN, Sharell A; Salem Senior HS; Salem, MO; Band; ChrhWkr; CmntyWkr; CncrtBnd; HonRl; MrchBnd; PepBnd; EdYrBk; SptEdYrbk; SciCl; Univ Of Mo Columbia; Park Ranger.

ASHCRAFT, Mike L; Newton HS; Newton, KS; NatlMeritFnl; NatlMeritSchl; TchrAde; Ks St Univ;.

ASHCRAFT, Pamela S; Maroa Forsyth HS; Maroa, IL; 2/70 SecSrCls; Band; Chrs; CncrtBnd; HonRl; MrchBnd; NHS; StuCncl; TreasYthFlsp; EdYrBk; FHA; TreasGAA; Decatur Comm College; Secretary.

ASHE, Daniel; Marion HS; Marion, IL; 43/274 ChrhWkr; NHS; SctActv; PpCl; John A Logan Col; Engineering.

ASHELIN, Cynthia A; Cotter HS; Winona, MN; 11/104 ALAGirlsSt; Chrs; HonRl; NatlFornLg; NHS; StuCncl; 4-H; SpnCl; 4-HAwd; St Teresa College; Spanish & Speech Therapy.

ASHENBRENNER, Susan G; Bishop Borgess HS; Detroit, MI; 4/365 HonRl; NHS; NatlMeritSF; SchMus; SchPl; RptrSchPpr; FNA; FrCl; Chrldr; Mercy College Of Detroit; Nursing.

ASHENDORF, Arthur D; North Muskegon HS; N Muskegon, MI; 2/87 SecSophCls; ChrhWkr; CmntyWkr; NHS; NatlMeritFnl; SciCl; Ftbl; Tennis; Trk; Stanford Univ.

ASHENDORF, Arthur D; North Muskegon HS; North Muskegon, MI; 2/86 SecSophCls; ChrhWkr; HonRl; NHS; NatlMeritSF; PolWkr; RptrSchPpr; Ftbl; Trk; IMSpt; Northwestern Univ; Engineering.

ASHER, Deborah K; Waldron HS; Waldron, IN; 5/76 Band; Chr; Chrs; ChrhWkr; CncrtBnd; HonRl; MrchBnd; PepBnd; RptrSchPpr; GAA; Univ; Music.

ASHER, Dennis A; Winona HS; Winona, MO; VPBand; CncrtBnd; HonRl; MrchBnd; NHS; Bsbl; Bsktbl; College; Liberal Arts.

ASHER, Jeffrey W; Niles North HS; Evanston, IL; Aud/Vis; CmntyWkr; HonRl; OffAde; SchAde; SctActv; University; Nuclear Engineering.

ASHER, Kathryn A; Brown County HS; Nashville, IN; ChrhWkr; CmntyWkr; DrlTm; HonRl; SctActv; TchrAde; PpCl; Indiana Univ; Nursing.

ASHER, Leslie J; Aberdeen Central HS; Aberdeen, SD; ALAGirlsSt; Band; DrlTm; HonRl; Orch; Swmmng; CitAwd; Univ; Pharmacy.

ASHER, Mardell A; Aurora HS; Aurora, NE; SecTrsSophCls; Band; Chrs; CncrtBnd; HonRl; HospAde; MrchBnd; SchPl; TchrAde; Chrldr; Col; Forestry.

ASHER, Marian S; Clare HS; Clare, MI; ChrhWkr; HonRl; NHS; SctActv; TchrAde; YthFlsp; MasAwd; VoiceDemAwd; Central Mich Clg; Elementary Teaching.

ASHFORT, Cathy S; Bloom Township HS; Chicago Hts, IL; 103/1108 SecFrshCls; TrsSophCls; Chr; HonRl; JrNHS; NHS; SchMus; StuCncl; RptrSchPpr; College.

ASHKANAZI, Judith D; Parkway North Sr HS; Creve Coeur, MO; 25/563 Band; ChrhWkr; CncrtBnd; JrNHS; MrchBnd; NHS; Orch; SchMus; Bsbl; University; Medicine.

ASHLEY, Carl; Marquette Univ HS; Milwaukee, WI; HonRl; HospAde; NatlMeritCmnd; Orch; SchAde; SctActv; TchrAde; Wrstlng; IMSpt; KiwanAwd; Georgetown Or Marquette; Economic, Law.

ASHLEY, David W; Velva Public HS; Velva, ND; 5/48 Band; Chr; Chrs; CncrtBnd; HonRl; MrchBnd; PresNHS; SptEdYrbk; LetterBsktbl; LetterFtbl; No Dakota State Univ; Agriculture.

ASHLEY, Deborah R; Stafford HS; Stafford, KS; Chr; Chrs; NatlFornLg; SctActv; PpCl; Bsbl; LetterBsktbl; Trade Or Bus Sch.

ASHLEY, Diane M; Lyle Public HS; Lyle, MN; TrsSophCls; Band; Chr; Chrs; ChrhWkr; HonRl; JrNHS; FHA; FTA; GAA; College; Vocation.

ASHLEY, Julie A; Casey HS; Casey, IL; 1/100 Chr; ChrhWkr; CmntyWkr; CncrtBnd; HonRl; RedCrAde; SchMus; StuCncl; Bsktbl; Trk; Chrldr; GAA; IMSpt; University; Math.

ASHLEY, Karen R; Gull Lake HS; Richland, MI; 17/245 Band; Chr; CncrtBnd; HonRl; IntrClCncl; JA; MrchBnd; SchMus; SchPl; StuCncl; College; Psychology.

ASHLEY, Richard E; Charles Sumner HS; St Louis, MO; 46/400 ChrhWkr; CmntyWkr; LitMag; NatlMeritCmnd; PolWkr; Quill&Scroll; SchAde; StuCncl; StuGov; TchrAde; YthFlsp; RptrSchPpr; EdSchPpr; SchPpr; University Of Kansas; Journalism.

ASHLEY, Tammy J; Vanderbilt Area HS; Vanderbilt, MI; SecFrshCls; SecSophCls; PresJrCls; HonRl; TreasStuCncl; EdYrBk; Bsktbl; LetterTrk; Msu; Biology.

ASHMORE, Barbara; Herbert H Dow HS; Midland, MI; ChrhWkr; HonRl; HospAde; NHS; PolWkr; Yrbk; EngCl; Delta; Registered Physical Therapist.

ASHMORE, Bonita J; Bloomingdale HS; Grand Junction, MI; 25/95 Chr; SchPl; StuGov; TchrAde; YthFlsp; CivCl; College; Lawyer.

ASHTON, Annette M; Neligh HS; Neligh, NE; 20/60 ChrhWkr; CmntyWkr; HonRl; NHS; OffAde; StuCncl; 4-H; FHA; SpnCl; PpCl; Norfolk Beauty College; Beautician.

ASHTON, Craig A; Coldwater HS; Coldwater, MI; Band; MrchBnd; PolWkr; 4-H; FFA; 4-HAwd; KiwanAwd; Michigan State Univ; Veterinary Medicine.

ASHTON, Cynthia R; Jeffersonville HS; Jeffersonville, IN; AFS; Chr; HonRl; HospAde; JA; OffAde; Yrbk; FNA; PpCl; PPFtbl; Nurse.

ASHTON, Timothy G; Neligh Public HS; Neligh, NE; 3/45 ALBoysSt; Band; HonRl; MrchBnd; NHS; PepBnd; StuCncl; Yrbk; SchPpr; Ftbl; LetterTrk; Trade School.

ASKEW, David J; Harry S Truman HS; Taylor, MI; 54/460 Aud/Vis; ChrhWkr; CmntyWkr; HonRl; JA; OffAde; SchPl; StuGov; Ftbl; Trk; Univ; Professional.

ASKUIG, Linda L; Goldfield Comm HS; Goldfield, IA; LetterCncrtBnd; HonRl; PepBnd; SchMus; SchPl; Twrl; Yrbk; LetterBsbl; Coll; Stewardess.

ASLESON, Debbie D; Mapleton HS; Mapleton, ND; 1/10 PresSophCls; ALAGirlsSt; Band; Chrs; ChrhWkr; CmntyWkr; HonRl; SchMus; SchPl; StuCncl; Medical Institute Of Minnesota; Med Assist.

ASLIN, Richard D; Clio HS; Clio, MI; RptrYrbk; Bsbl; Bsktbl; LetterFtbl; IMSpt; Univ; Psychologyor Law.

ASMUS, Robert E; Clarke Comm HS; Osceola, IA; Pres4-H; VPFFA; LetterWrstlng; College; Agriculture.

ASMUS, Ronald D; Homestead HS; Mequon, WI; 23/410 HonRl; JrNHS; NHS; PolWkr; SctActv; TchrAde; Bsktbl; LetterFtbl; IMSpt; College; Law.

ASMUSSEN, Melanie K; Savannah R Iii HS; St Joseph, MO; HonRl; NHS; PolWkr; StuCncl; TchrAde; 4-H; PpCl; VPSciCl; GAA; CitAwd; Univ; Med.

ASPAN, Joyce V; Bogan HS; Chicago, IL; 13/704 HonRl; NHS; NatlMeritCmnd; SchMus; SchPl; EdYrBk; RptrSchPpr; GAA; Univ Of Illinois; English.

ASPENSON, Jeffrey T; Seneca HS; Ferryville, WI; VPSrCls; ALBoysSt; Band; HonRl; SchPl; SctActv; StuCncl; RptrYrbk; LetterBsktbl; LetterTrk; Univ; Professional.

ASPER, Bradley J; Luck HS; Luck, WI; 4-H; FFA; LetterFtbl; LetterTrk; LetterWrstlng; 4-HAwd; Trade Sch; Vocation.

ASPERHEIM, Scott M; Shawnee Mission Nw HS; Shawnee, KS; ChrhWkr; CmntyWkr; HonRl; Orch; SctActv; TchrAde; YthFlsp; Bsbl; Tennis; College; Architecture.

ASPHOLM, Rona L; Manson HS; Manson, IA; Band; ChrhWkr; HonRl; NHS; Orch; RptrSchPpr; 4-H; PpCl; Chrldr; 4-HAwd; College; Health.

ASPLUND, Twila; Wilton HS; Wilton, ND; 6/36 ALAGirlsSt; Chrl; Chrs; DrlTm; NHS; SchPl; EdYrBk; PpCl; BttyCrckrAwd; MasAwd; Mary College; Pre Med.

ASPROOTH, Jody A; Washington HS; Cedar Rapids, IA; 49/476 VPChr; Chrl; PresChrs; ChrhWkr; NHS; NatlMeritCmnd; Orch; SchMus; PresSctActv; TreasYthFlsp; Augsburg Coll; Music Ed.

ASQUITH, Grace A; Stockbridge HS; Stockbridge, MI; Chrs; ChrhWkr; CncrtBnd; LbryAde; MrchBnd; NHS; MthCl; SciCl; DARAwd; 4-HAwd; Mi State Univ.

ASSAD, Peter D; St Thomas Academy; Edina, MN; 1/96 TrsJrCls; TrsSrCls; DrlTm; NHS; NatlMeritFnl; NatlMeritSF; ROTC; SchPl; StuCncl; RptrYrbk; LetterBsbl; CaptFtbl; IMSpt; OptClAwd; College; Medicine.

ASSEL, Julia L; Penney HS; Hamilton, MO; Band; Chr; Chrs; CncrtBnd; HonRl; MrchBnd; PepBnd; SecSpnCl; PpCl; College; Music.

ASSELIN, Anne M; Kingsford HS; Kingsford, MI; Chrs; ChrhWkr; HonRl; HospAde; OffAde; StuCncl; SchPpr; SecFNA; PpCl; Chrldr; Coll; Spec Educ.

ASSMANN, Andrew W; Dunlap Community HS; Earling, IA; TrsJrCls; ALBoysSt; HonRl; JrNHS; SchPl; PresPpCl; LetterBsktbl; Trade School; Professional.

ASSMANN, Michael G; Dunlap Community HS; Dunlap, IA; HonRl; SchPl; 4-H; Ftbl; 4-HAwd; College.

AST, Robin; Maynard Public HS; Maynard, MN; PresSophCls; ALAGirlsSt; Band; HospAde; NHS; SchPl; SchPpr; Gustavus Adolphus College; Reg Nurse.

ASTLING, Donna; Dekalb Hs; Dekalb, IL; Aud/Vis; HonRl; NHS; Teen; College;vocation.

ASTOR, Susan B; Theodore Roosevelt HS; Wyandotte, MI; HonRl; LitMag; NHS; TchrAde; RptrSchPpr; EdSchPpr; Wayne St Univ; Journalism.

ASTRAUSKAS, Leonard J; Mundelein HS; Mundelein, IL; 25/377 HonRl; NHS; LetterBsbl; LetterFtbl; CaptTrk; College; Natural Science.

ASTROM, John; Guinn HS; Mackinaw City, MI; NHS; NatlMeritSchl; ROTC; SchAde; TchrAde; Yrbk; Swmmng; IMSpt; JAAwd; JETSAwd; College; Professional.

ASTROTH, Karen M; Central Community HS; Breese, IL; 1/136 Chrs; HonRl; HospAde; JrNHS; SchPl; StuCncl; Yrbk; FHA; Chrldr; 4-HAwd; College; Medical Field.

ASTRUP, Karen L; Drayton Public HS; Drayton, ND; VPFrshCls; ALAGirlsSt; Band; Chrs; ChrhWkr; CmntyWkr; CncrtBnd; HonRl; RptrSchPpr; 4-H; Chrldr; Univ.

ATCHISON, Dave A; Gibson Southern HS; Fort Branch, IN; 15/229 ChrhWkr; HonRl; NHS; SctActv; KeyCl; LatCl; LetterFtbl; LetterTrk; LetterWrstlng; Indiana U; Math.

ATCHISON, Dave T; Hays HS; Hays, KS; ALBoysSt; Chr; HonRl; NatlFornLg; Orch; SchMus; SchPl; StuGov; PpCl; LetterTennis; Ks State U; Music Education.

ATCHISON, Robert L; Hays HS; Hays, KS; VPSrCls; Chr; HonRl; NatlFornLg; Orch; SchMus; SchPl; Bsktbl; LetterFtbl; Tennis; Professional.

ATEN, Cindy J; Newton HS; Hidalgo, IL; HonRl; Mdrgl; PolWkr; SchMus; RptrYrbk; 4-H; PpCl; GAA; University; Vocation.

ATHEN, Michael D; Farragut HS; Riverton, IA; HonRl; 4-H; FFA; LetterFtbl; 4-HAwd; Iowa Western Comm Clg; Mechanical Tech.

ATHENS, Laura A; Trenton HS; Trenton, MI; 13/575 TrsFrshCls; HonRl; HospAde; JrNHS; LitMag; NHS; SchPl; StuCncl; TchrAde; PPFtbl; U Of Mi; Psychology.

ATHERLY, Randall B; Topeka West HS; Topeka, KS; HonRl; ModUN; Kansas State Univ;architect.

ATHERTON, Dorrance E; Bloomfield Comm HS; Bloomfield, NE; ChrhWkr; RedCrAde; SchPl; SctActv; SptEdSchPpr; CaptFtbl; Swmmng; LetterTrk; IMSpt; PresAwd; Technical School.

ATHEY, Cynthia L; Casey Jr Sr HS; Casey, IL; Band; HonRl; MrchBnd; PepBnd; TchrAde; FHA; FTA; SpnCl; PpCl; College; Liberal Arts.

ATKINS, Danette S; Chillicothe HS; Chillicothe, MO; 4/185 Band; CncrtBnd; HonRl; MrchBnd; PepBnd; TchrAde; EdSchPpr; FTA; FrCl; Southwest Missouri St Univ; Accounting.

ATKINS, Deidre A; Northeastern HS; Richmond, IN; 64/122 HonRl; HospAde; SctActv; FHA; SecLatCl; PpCl; Nursing Sch; Nursing.

ATKINS, Janice E; Pomeroy Community HS; Pomeroy, IA; TrsFrshCls; VPJrCls; HonRl; StuCncl; Twrl; EdSchPpr; LetterBsktbl; LetterTrk; Chrldr; IMSpt; CitAwd; Iowa Central Comm Clg; Executive Secretary.

ATKINS, Susan C; Western HS; Parma, MI; 7/157 SecFrshCls; HonRl; VPNHS; SctActv; StuCncl; TchrAde; SpnCl; GAA; College; Social Sci.

ATKINS, Zivit; Metro Hs; Chicago, IL; TchrAde; College; Psychologist.

ATKINSON, Charlene C; Turner HS; Kansas City, KS; 8/295 SecChr; HonRl; NatlFornLg; NHS; PresNatlThespSoc; SchMus; SchPl; StuCncl; FrCl; College; Professional English.

ATKINSON, Dana L; Fairfield Community HS; Geff, IL; 1/170 HonRl; YthFlsp; 4-H; FFA; FTA; KeyCl; MthCl; SciCl; Trk; DanFAwd; U Of Ill; Math.

ATKINSON, Dana L; Fairfield Comm HS; Geff, IL; ALBoysSt; NHS; Pres4-H; TreasFFA; FTA; KeyCl; MthCl; SciCl; Bsktbl; Trk; DanFAwd; 4-HAwd; Mit; Mathematician.

ATKINSON, David L; Colon HS; Leonides, MI; 2/65 PresSrCls; HonRl; NatlMeritCmnd; Yrbk; SchPpr; Bsktbl; BauchLmbAwd; Stanford; Chemistry.

ATKINSON, Joanne M; Prospect HS; Arlington Hts, IL; 75/614 CmntyWkr; HonRl; NatlMeritCmnd; Univ Of Illinois; Sociology.

ATKINSON, Julia A; Rock Island Sr HS; Rock Island, IL; PresBand; Chr; ChrhWkr; CncrtBnd; HonRl; JrNHS; MrchBnd; PepBnd; YthFlsp; 4-H; 4-HAwd; College; Christian Ed.

ATKINSON, Melinda A; North Callaway HS; Kingdom City, MO; 16/77 TrsFrshCls; Chrs; HonRl; MrchBnd; NHS; SchMus; SchPl; StuCncl; TchrAde; Yrbk; FHA; VPFTA; VPFrCl; CaptChrldr; College; Social Work.

ATKINSON, Robert; Junction City HS; Fort Ricey, KS; /303 Univ; Of Kansas; Engineering.

ATKINSON, Ruth A; St Francis HS; Little Falls, MN; 10/25 Band; Chr; HospAde; SchPl; StuCncl; RptrSchPpr; GAA; St Cloud St College ;speech Therapist.

ATKINSON, Sallie M; Brazil HS; Brazil, IN; ChrhWkr; HonRl; LbryAde; SchPl; TchrAde; Yrbk; 4-H; FHA; KiwanAwd; PresAwd; Bus School; Vocation.

ATON, Susan F; Marion HS; Marion, WI; 1/84 ALAGirlsSt; SecChrhWkr; HonRl; PresNHS; SpnCl; PresPpCl; Bsbl; Chrldr; GAA; DARAwd; Coll; Physical Education.

ATOR, Bona J; Pittsfield HS; Pittsfield, IL; CmntyWkr; HonRl; SchPl; RptrSchPpr; SptEdSchPpr; MthCl; SecTrsSophCls; Trk; IMSpt; John Wood Comm Coll; Accounting.

ATTEBERRY, Bette J; Russell Comm HS; Russell, IA; 2/28 Chrs; SchPl; Yrbk; RptrSchPpr; FTA; Bsktbl; Ia West Comm Coll; Physicians Asst.

ATTEBERRY, John B; Guthrie Center HS; Guthrie Center, IA; PresFrshCls; Chr; CncrtBnd; PolWkr; SchMus; FrCl; LetterFtbl; LetterTrk; LetterWrstlng;.

ATTEBERRY, Kathryn; Riverview Gardens HS; St Louis, MO; 4/800 IntrClCncl; NHS; NatlMeritCmnd; SchMus; SchPl; JAAwd; Univ Of Mo; Engineering.

ATTEBERRY, Rebecca A; Colome HS; Colome, SD; 2/34 Band; Chrs; ChrhWkr; HonRl; LbryAde; OffAde; SchPl; RptrYrbk; RptrSchPpr; PresPpCl; Chrldr; College; Guidance Counseling.

ATTERMEIER, Kurt; Thomas More HS; Cudahy, WI; HonRl; NHS; SctActv; StuGov; EdYrBk; PpCl; College; Prof Engineering.

ATTIE, Desiree M; Fordson HS; Dearborn, MI; CmntyWkr; HonRl; NHS; SchAde; TchrAde; Tennis; Trk; GAA; Univ Of Michigan; Pharmacist.

ATTUTIS, Matthew; Westville HS; Westville, IL; 36/105 ALBoysSt; HonRl; SchPl; SctActv; StuCncl; SptEdYrbk; SpnCl; Bsbl; Ftbl; IMSpt;.

ATTWOOD, Leann; Smith Center HS; Smith Center, KS; CncrtBnd; HonRl; MrchBnd; PepBnd; TchrAde; 4-H; Bsktbl; Trk; IMSpt; PPFtbl; College; Prof.

ATWELL, Debra G; Neelyville HS; Nellyville, MO; Band; TreasChrhWkr; CncrtBnd; HonRl; MrchBnd; Twrl; PresFHA; TreasFTA; PpCl; Chrldr; College; Vocation.

ATWELL, Karen A; J D Darnall HS; Geneseo, IL; 9/220 ChrhWkr; CmntyWkr; HonRl; JA; PresLbryAde; NHS; NatlThespSoc; SchMus; SchPl; RptrYrbk; 4-H; Chrldr; GAA; PPFtbl; Northwestern University; Archeology.

ATWELL, Shirley A; Charleston Sr HS; Lerna, IL; HonRl; Eastern Ill Univ; Business Management.

ATWELL, Todd; Atkinson HS; Atkinson, IL; 14/41 ALBoysSt; HonRl; NHS; SchPl; StuCncl; RptrSchPpr; FFA; Bsbl; Trk; AmLegAwd; Ill Coll.

ATWELL, Valorie R; Minneapolis HS; Delphos, KS; VPSophCls; TrsJrCls; ChrhWkr; HonRl; SchMus; SchPl; Yrbk; 4-H; FHA; PpCl; College Or Bus Sch; Stenographer.

ATWOOD, Ann M; Bloomington HS; Bloomington, IL; VPFrshCls; ChrhWkr; CmntyWkr; VPStuCncl; YthFlsp; SpnCl; PpCl; Glf; GAA; PresAwd; Univ; Social Wrk.

ATWOOD, Julie A; Springfield HS; Springfield, IL; 16/585 Chr; ChrhWkr; CmntyWkr; NHS; PolWkr; SchPl; FrCl; Univ Of Ill; Law.

ATWOOD, Lindy L; Norfolk Sr HS; Norfolk, NE; HonRl; HospAde; SchPl; StuCncl; TchrAde; 4-H; PpCl; Trk; Chrldr; IMSpt; College; Professional.

ATZ, Rockney J; Okabena HS; Lakefield, MN; 11/24 SecSophCls; Band; CncrtBnd; HonRl; MrchBnd; SchPpr; 4-H; FFA; LetterBsktbl; 4-HAwd; University Of Minnesota; Horticultural.

ATZENHOFER, Kim; Dominican HS; St Clair Shores, MI; TrsJrCls; HonRl; JrNHS; NHS; StuCncl; StuGov; Ftbl; PPFtbl; Univ Of Mich; Nursing.

AUBERRY, Karen M; Valle HS; St Genevieve, MO; Chrs; HonRl; NHS; SchMus; StuCncl; SchPl; Twrl; PpCl; LetterTrk; PPFtbl; College; Social Work.

AUBRY, Kenton P; Lincoln HS; Manitowoc, WI; Ftbl; Coll; Accounting.

AUBUCHON, Frank G; Sullivan HS; Sullivan, MO; 68/159 Band; Chr; Chrs; CAP; CncrtBnd; Mdrgl; NatlThespSoc; PepBnd; Se Missouri St Univ; Law Enforcement.

AUCH, Noreen J; Dickinson HS; Dickinson, ND; Chrl; ChrhWkr; HonRl; HospAde; LbryAde; YthFlsp; RptrSchPpr; SecFBLA; GerCl; PresAwd; Business School; Secretary.

AUCHAMPACH, Lori J; Garner Hayfield HS; Garner, IA; 14/85 Chr; Band; Chrs; HonRl; HospAde; Mdrgl; MrchBnd; NHS; PepBnd; FNA; Iowa Central Comm Coll; Nursing.

AUCUTT, Robert L; Yorkville HS; Yorkville, IL; 28/150 SchPl; TchrAde; SchPpr; MthCl; Bsbl; Bsktbl; Trk; PresAwd; University; Professional.

AUDE, Jane E; Chadwick HS; Chadwick, IL; Band; Chr; CncrtBnd; HonRl; MrchBnd; SchMus; StuCncl; SptEdYrbk; Glf; GAA; College;.

AUDSLEY, Robert E; Chilhowee Riv HS; Chilhowee, MO; 5/14 ALBoysSt; HonRl; SptEdSchPpr; SchPpr; LetterBsktbl; LetterTrk; Centra Missouri State Univ; Industrial Arts.

AUEN, Kathleen L; Wall Lake Comm HS; Wall Lake, IA; 1/27 NatlFornLg; NHS; NatlMeritCmnd; SchPl; EdSchPpr; PresFrCl; LetterBsktbl; LetterTrk; AmLegAwd; 4-HAwd; Iowa State U; Biological Research.

AUER, Elaine S; Bogard R Iv HS; Bogard, MO; 1/9 SecJrCls; TrsSrCls; HonRl; OffAde; EdSchPpr; CaptBsbl; CaptBsktbl; CaptTrk; Chrldr; TIMEAwd; Central Mo St Univ; Business Administration.

AUERNHEIMER, Darlene M; Halstead HS; Halstead, KS; 15/66 Band; Chr; CncrtBnd; HonRl; MrchBnd; PepBnd; SchPl; SecYthFlsp; PpCl; CitAwd; Bethel Clg.

AUESTAD, Andrea K; South Hamilton HS; Randall, IA; Band; Chrs; CncrtBnd; HonRl; MrchBnd; Orch; SchMus; StuCncl; RptrYrbk; MthCl; Des Moines Coll; Acct.

AUFDERHAR, Kenneth G; Wisconsin Academy; Mcfarland, WI; Architect.

AUFDERHEIDE, William R; New Ulm HS; New Ulm, MN; Chr; HonRl; GerCl; Ftbl; LetterTrk; IMSpt; College.

AUGHE, Robin; Centerville Sr HS; Centerville, IN; 14/119 StuCncl; StuGov; TchrAde; EdSchPpr; 4-H; FNA; SpnCl; AmLegAwd; 4-HAwd; JCAwd; Univ; Journalist.

AUGHENBAUGH, Vince J; Watertown Sr HS; Watertown, SD; Band; Chr; Chrs; CncrtBnd; DrmMjrt; Mdrgl; MrchBnd; NatlFornLg; NatlThespSoc; PepBnd; SchMus; SchPl; South Dakota St Univ; Music.

AUGSBURGER, Constance; Dekalb Senior Hs; Dekalb, IL; 13 Chr; CtyCnl; SecCncrtBnd; MrchBnd; NHS; SchMus; SchPl; SecTeen; FrCl; AmLegAwd; U;foreign Language Or Biology.

AUGST, Linda R; Menahga Public HS; Menahga, MN; 5/53 ALAGirlsSt; Band; Chr; ChrhWkr; DrmMjrt; HonRl; HospAde; SchPl; StuCncl; SchPpr; Clge; Nursing.

AUGUST, Deborah A; St Joseph Acad; Green Bay, WI; CmntyWkr; VPJA; NHS; PolWkr; ROTC; SchMus; SctActv; StuCncl; UNYO; YthLg; University; Law Field.

AUGUSTINE, James B; Frederick Remington HS; Potwin, KS; SecTrsSophCls; HonRl; NHS; PepBnd; SchMus; Yrbk; Bsbl; LetterBsktbl; LetterFtbl; LetterGlf; Univ Of Kansas; Medicine.

AUGUSTINE, Mary E; Mt Assisi Acad; Evergreen Park, IL; 2/192 Chr; HonRl; ModUN; NatlFornLg; NHS; SchMus; StuCncl; YthLg; Yrbk; SpnCl; U Of Il; English.

AUGUSTYNIAK, Michael E; Leo HS; Grabill, IN; Chr; ChrhWkr; SctActv; Bsktbl; Ftbl; Trk; Purdue Univ.

AUKAMP, Michael J; Macon HS; Macon, IL; CmntyWkr; HonRl; SchPl; SptEdSchPpr; SpnCl; PpCl; LetterBsbl; LetterBsktbl; Lincoln Jr Col; Bus Admin.

AUKEE, Anita; Wayne Memorial HS; Wayne, MI; 5/650 Chr; ChrhWkr; NHS; NatlMeritCmnd; NatlThespSoc; Orch; SchMus; DARAwd; St Olaf College.

AUKES, Terry A; Elmore Public HS; Elmore, MN; 1/26 PresFrshCls; Band; CncrtBnd; HonRl; MrchBnd; NHS; SchPl; SctActv; StuCncl; RptrYrbk; U Of Minn; Doctor Of Medicine.

AUL, Diana L; Sabetha HS; Sabetha, KS; Band; Chrs; CncrtBnd; HonRl; MrchBnd; PepBnd; FHA; Washburn Univ; Elementary.

AULBACH, Linda S; Mehlville HS; St Louis, MO; Tennis; Se Mo St; Botany.

AULBUR, Carl A; Community R 6 HS; Laddonia, MO; 22/70 HonRl; JA; NHS; SchPl; PresFFA; PpCl; IMSpt; Linn Technical College; Machinist.

AULD, Jeffrey M; Oskaloosa Senior HS; Oskaloosa, IA; PresSrCls; ALBoysSt; Chr; CncrtBnd; HonRl; NHS; NatlThespSoc; Orch; SchMus; SchPl; Brookes Institute Of Photography; Photograp.

AULERT, Michael; Maine Township Hs; Des Plaines, IL; 140/748 HonRl; LetterBsktbl; College; Field Of Science.

AULL, Lennis M; Muscatine HS; Muscatine, IA; ALBoysSt; NHS; LetterBsktbl; College.

AULT, Brian J; Northrop HS; Ft Wayne, IN; 154/643 Band; CncrtBnd; JA; MrchBnd; Orch; PepBnd; JAAwd; College; Professional Cpa.

AULT, Stacey C; P A Allen HS; Bluffton, IN; 6/139 HonRl; NHS; StuCncl; PresSpnCl; CaptTrk; RotaryAwd; Univ; Forestry.

AUMAN, Carol A; Aurora HS; Marquette, NE; Band; Chr; Chrs; CncrtBnd; HonRl; MrchBnd; TchrAde; RptrYrbk; RptrSchPpr; 4-H; PpCl; Mount Marty College; Journalism.

AUMAN, Daniel T; Bs HS; Baxter Springs, KS; ALBoysSt; Band; Chr; Chrl; Chrs; ChrhWkr; CmntyWkr; HonRl; LbryAde; MrchBnd; College; Professional.

AUMEN, Carl; Fairview HS; Fairview, MI; 3/44 PresSrCls; HonRl; NHS; SctActv; Yrbk; RptrSchPpr; EdSchPpr; Univ Of Notre Dame Us Air Force.

AUMEN, Ulrica L; Fairview HS; Fairview, MI; ALAGirlsSt; HonRl; NatlFornLg; SchMus; SchPl; 4-H; Bsktbl; Swmmng; Tennis; LetterChrldr; College.

AUMILLER, Sharon E; Auburn HS; Auburn, IL; 9/59 Chr; Chrl; Chrs; ChrhWkr; HonRl; JA; NHS; OffAde; YthFlsp; VFWAwd; Clge; Rn.

AUNE, David R; Hendrum Perley HS; Hendrum, MN; 1/25 TrsFrshCls; TrsJrCls; PresSrCls; Band; Chr; HonRl; NatlMeritCmnd; NatlThespSoc; StuCncl; CitAwd; Brown Inst; Radio/tv Broadcasting.

AUNE, James E; Holy Trinity HS; Winsted, MN; 1/49 Aud/Vis; ChrhWkr; HonRl; ModUN; NatlMeritSchl; College; Nuclear Engineering.

AUNE, Teresa L; North Central Of Barne HS; Sanborn, ND; VPSophCls; VPJrCls; CncrtBnd; HonRl; MrchBnd; PepBnd; SptEdSchPpr; 4-H; LetterBsktbl; LetterTrk; College; Phy Ed Major.

AUNER, Robert J; Antigo HS; Antigo, WI; 2/376 PresFrshCls; PresCncrtBnd; StuCncl; SptEdYrbk; 4-H; GerCl; MthCl; LetterTrk; DARAwd; 4-HAwd; U Of Wi Madison; Engineering.

AUPPERLE, Daniel C; Lancaster HS; Lancaster, WI; 20/159 HonRl; NHS; StuCncl; FFA; Trk; Wrstlng; CchngActv; IMSpt; 4-HAwd; PresAwd; U Of Wis Mdsn; Veterinary.

AUPPERLE, Mark; Anita HS; Anita, IA; 19/64 Band; CmntyWkr; HonRl; NatlFornLg; NHS; PresYthFlsp; LetterFtbl; LetterGlf; LetterTrk; LetterWrstlng; Morningside College; Lawyer.

AURAND, Dianna E; Stockton HS; Stockton, IL; 13/86 TrsSophCls; HonRl; PresLbryAde; RptrYrbk; FHA; SecGAA; Business School; Accounting.

AURAND, Tim W; Lena Winslow HS; Eleroy, IL; HonRl; NHS; SchPl; StuCncl; TchrAde; RptrYrbk; FTA; LetterFtbl; LetterTrk; Highland Comm College; Mathematics.

AURELIUS, Susan L; Hastings Senior HS; Hastings, MN; 1/434 HonRl; NHS; SchPl; College; Accountant.

AURON, Michelle M; Marian Catholic HS; Glenwood, IL; 41/335 Band; CncrtBnd; HonRl; MrchBnd; NHS; PepBnd; SchMus; College; Special Ed.

AUSBORN, Kris M; Lake City HS; Lake City, IA; 6/67 TrsSophCls; ALBoysSt; HonRl; NHS; RptrSchPpr; LetterFtbl; LetterTrk; KiwanAwd; Iowa State; Business Ad.

AUSMAN, Charles J; Elkmound HS; Elk Mound, WI; TrsFrshCls; TrsSophCls; TrsJrCls; Band; HonRl; TchrAde; 4-H; Bsbl; CaptBsktbl; CitAwd;.

AUSMAN, Jeffrey P; Eastbrook HS; Marion, IN; 8/169 Band; ChrhWkr; CncrtBnd; HonRl; MrchBnd; PepBnd; YthFlsp; SpnCl; Univ; Electronics.

AUSMUS, Debbie; Webber Twp HS; Mt Vernon, IL; 9/32 HonRl; LbryAde; Yrbk; PpCl; Chrldr; GAA; Rend Lake Jr College; Vocation.

AUST, Jane A; East Central HS; Guilford, IN; 18/180 Band; HonRl; MrchBnd; NHS; Twrl; PpCl; LetterBsktbl; GAA; Marian Coll.

AUSTEN, Janice; Milford HS; Pleasant Dale, NE; 1/47 PresFrshCls; PresSophCls; Band; Chrs; NHS; PepBnd; SchMus; StuGov; FHA; PpCl; College; Deaf Education.

AUSTIN, Angela; North White HS; Monon, IN; 8/120 Chr; DrmMjrt; HonRl; MrchBnd; TchrAde; 4-H; FTA; GerCl; PpCl; 4-HAwd; Univ; Elementary Education.

AUSTIN, Anna; Ofallow Township HS; Ofallon, IL; 11/285 HonRl; HospAde; JrNHS; ModUN; NHS; SchPl; StuCncl; SciCl; IMSpt; AmLegAwd; Illinois Su; Med Tech.

AUSTIN, Anna M; O Fallon Twp HS; O Fallon, IL; 11/296 HonRl; HospAde; JrNHS; ModUN; NHS; OffAde; SchPl; StuCncl; SpnCl; SciCl; University; Medicine.

AUSTIN, Ariel T; Rio HS; Rio, WI; 1/52 VPSophCls; VPJrCls; HonRl; SctActv; StuCncl; TchrAde; Bsktbl; Ftbl; Trk; JCAwd; College; Vocation.

AUSTIN, Beth A; Douglas Mac Arthur HS; Saginaw, MI; HonRl; LitMag; OffAde; Justin Morrill College; Psychology.

AUSTIN, Christopher L; B C Central HS; Battle Creek, MI; 18/514 HonRl; NHS; NatlMeritCmnd; StuGov; Bsbl; Air Force Academy; Officer Usaf.

AUSTIN, Darrel L; Niles HS; Niles, MI; Chr; Chrs; JA; SchMus; SchPl; StuCncl; StuGov; SchPpr; Tennis; IMSpt; Suomi Coll; Lawyer.

AUSTIN, Debbi J; Cobden Unit HS; Cobden, IL; TrsSophCls; Band; HonRl; SchPl; RptrYrbk; FHA; PpCl; SciCl; College; Horticulture.

AUSTIN, Deborah F; Rock County HS; Bassett, NE; Band; CncrtBnd; MrchBnd; PepBnd; SchMus; SchPl; StuCncl; Twrl; PpCl; Trk; Coll; Medicine.

AUSTIN, Donna A; Circle HS; Towanda, KS; Band; Chrs; CncrtBnd; HonRl; MrchBnd; PpCl; Trade School; Professional.

AUSTIN, Elizabeth A; Blue Mound HS; Blue Mound, IL; 9/38 AFS; Chrs; ChrhWkr; HonRl; YthFlsp; Yrbk; SchPpr; FHA; FTA; Jr College; Medical Secretary.

AUSTIN, Mark W; Frankton HS; Anderson, IN; 46/168 Yrbk; SchPpr; 4-H; Iupui; Art Teacher.

AUSTIN, Patty K; Rushford Public HS; Rushford, MN; PresSrCls; Band; CmntyWkr; HonRl; NHS; StuCncl; PresFHA; CaptBsktbl; Trk; Chrldr; GAA; IMSpt; PresAwd; College; Veterinarian.

AUSTIN, Randy S; Laingsburg HS; Laingsburg, MI; PresSophCls; HonRl; SchAde; StuCncl; StuGov; TchrAde; Bsbl; Bsktbl; LetterGlf; IMSpt; Coll; Prof.

AUSTIN, Rhonda J; Mosinee HS; Mosinee, WI; Chr; Chrs; ChrhWkr; PolWkr; RptrSchPpr; FBLA; FHA; North Central Tech Instit; Arts.

AUSTIN, Richard L; Eastern HS; Lansing, MI; Chrs; HonRl; Mdrgl; NHS; SchMus; TchrAde; College; Grafting.

AUSTIN, Rita S; Highland HS; Lewistown, MO; Chr; HonRl; YthFlsp; Yrbk; SptEdSchPpr; SchPpr; PresAwd;.

AUSTIN, Susan L; Harlem HS; Rockford, IL; 20/500 SecSophCls; SecJrCls; SecSrCls; Band; HonRl; NHS; NatlThespSoc; SctActv; StuCncl; SecGAA; Augustana College; Pre Law.

AUSTIN, Victoria L; Evanston Township HS; Evanston, IL; Band; HonRl; MrchBnd; NHS; NatlMeritFnl; Orch; StuCncl; PresPpCl; Wellesley University.

AUSTINSON, Jane M; Ada HS; Ada, MN; Band; Chr; HonRl; NatlThespSoc; PepBnd; SchPl; FHA; Chrldr; GAA; IMSpt; College; Physical Therapy.

AUSTON, Margie C; St Thomas Apostle HS; Chicago, IL; PresJrCls; Chr; Chrs; ChrhWkr; HospAde; SchPl; StuCncl; RptrSchPpr; Chrldr; College; Psychology.

AUSTRENG, Jolayne; Raori HS; Cold Spring, MN; Band; Chr; ChrhWkr; PresSophCls; HonRl; MrchBnd; NatlThespSoc; SchMus; TchrAde; GAA; Vocational; Dental Hygienist.

AUVIL, Janet L; Cass City HS; Snover, MI; 4/130 TrsFrshCls; HonRl; HospAde; JrNHS; NHS; OffAde; SchPl; PresStuCncl; 4-H; PPFtbl; Mich State U; Math.

AUVINEN, Laura M; Freeport HS; Freeport, IL; Band; CncrtBnd; HonRl; MrchBnd; Orch; SchMus; GerCl; Highland Comm College; Pharmacy.

AUXIER, Denise J; Pawnee City HS; Pawnee City, NE; Band; Chr; Chrs; HonRl; PepBnd; SchPl; Twrl; RptrYrbk; Univ Of Nebr; Social Worker.

AUXIER, Karen J; Lew Wallace HS; Gary, IN; 6/513 HonRl; JrNHS; LbryAde; NHS; TchrAde; PresEngCl; FrCl; VPSciCl; Purdue U; Pharmacy.

AVADIAN, Arlene; Hamilton Senior HS; Milwaukee, WI; 60/786 Chr; Chrl; CncrtBnd; HospAde; MrchBnd; NHS; Orch; SchMus; Lawrence University; Music.

AVANTS, Connie S; Sarcoxie HS; Sarcoxie, MO; SecFrshCls; TrsJrCls; Band; Chr; DrlTm; HonRl; MrchBnd; SchPl; 4-H; FHA; FTA; MthCl; PpCl; College; Accounting.

AVEN, Louann; Reese HS; Saginaw, MI; 2/127 Band; CncrtBnd; HonRl; MrchBnd; NatlMeritCmnd; NatlMeritSchl; SptEdYrbk; PpCl; LetterGAA; CitAwd;.

AVEN, Peggy; Akron Fairgrove HS; Fairgrove, MI; 5/80 Band; CncrtBnd; HonRl; MrchBnd; PepBnd; SchPl; Chrldr; CitAwd; Central Mich Univ;.

AVENIA, Veronica C; L Anse Creuse HS; Mt Clemens, MI; 70/564 Chr; HonRl; JrNHS; NHS; NatlMeritSF; FrCl; GerCl; PPFtbl; Oakland Univ; Nursing.

AVENT, Gary L; Cumberland HS; Maben, MO; Chr; ChrhWkr; SchPl; FFA; College; Professional.

AVERBECK, Cindy M; Cochrane Fountain City HS; Cochrane, WI; 1/89 Band; ChrhWkr; CncrtBnd; MrchBnd; NHS; PepBnd; SchMus; VPFBLA; LetterTrk; DARAwd; Univ; Pro Law.

AVERBECK, Roxanne P; Cochrane Fountain City HS; Cochrane, WI; Band; ChrhWkr; CncrtBnd; MrchBnd; PepBnd; SchMus; FBLA; FHA;.

AVERILL, Daniel P; Shrine HS; Royal Oak, MI; HonRl; JA; NatlMeritSF; SctActv; RptrSchPpr; Univ; Computer Engineering.

AVERS, Victoria A; Notre Dame HS; Chicago, IL; TrsSrCls; IntrClCncl; SchPl; PpCl; Bsbl; LetterBsktbl; GAA; Coll; Phys Teacher.

AVERY, Becky A; Plainfield HS; Plainfield, IL; 64/315 Band; ChrhWkr; CmntyWkr; CncrtBnd; DrlTm; HonRl; HospAde; MrchBnd; NHS; FNA; St Xavier Clg; R N Bs.

AVERY, Dean R; Gresham Public HS; Gresham, NE; VPJrCls; ALBoysSt; HonRl; YthFlsp; 4-H; SpnCl; LetterFtbl; CchngActv; AmLegAwd; 4-HAwd; Milford Neb Trade; Construction.

AVERY, Denis T; Meservey Thornton HS; Meservey, IA; Chr; Chrs; ChrhWkr; PolWkr; SchPl; RptrSchPpr; 4-H; Bsbl; Ftbl; 4-HAwd; Westmar HS Coaching.

AVERY, George E; Wheaton Central HS; Wheaton, IL; 28/345 Band; CncrtBnd; HonRl; MrchBnd; NHS; PepBnd; LetterSocr; Marquette Univ; Anthropology.

AVERY, Kevin B; Grand Rapids HS; Bovey, MN; 80/377 LetterBsbl; Trk; IMSpt; College; Engineering.

AVERY, Pamela L; Harper Creek HS; Battle Creek, MI; 2/282 ALAGirlsSt; TreasBand; CncrtBnd; HonRl; MrchBnd; NHS; PepBnd; FrCl; Trk; OptClAwd; Education.

AVERY, Paul C; Harper Creek HS; Battle Creek, MI; PresBand; PresCncrtBnd; PresMrchBnd; PepBnd; RedCrAde; SchPl; Bsktbl; Junior Coll; Policeman.

AVGERINOS, Nickolas; George Rogers Clark HS; Hammond, IN; ALBoysSt; HonRl; GerCl; SciCl; College; Professional.

AVILA, John; St Francis De Sales HS; Lansing, IL; ChrhWkr; CmntyWkr; Bsbl; College; Data Processing.

AVILA, Thomas D; Northside HS; Muncie, IN; 53/312 PresSrCls; ChrhWkr; HonRl; StuCncl; StuGov; TchrAde; YthFlsp; Bsbl; Wrstlng; IMSpt; Ball State Univ; Pre Med.

AVINGTON, Arthur L; Horace Mann HS; Gary, IN; ALBoysSt; HonRl; JrNHS; NHS; SchPpr; Bsktbl; Tennis; EldAwd; KiwanAwd; University; Basketball.

AVIS, James D; Stephen Decatur HS; Decatur, IL; HonRl; NHS; NatlMeritSF; Orch; Millikin U; Chem/physics.

AVISCHIOUS, Thomas S; Prospect HS; Arlington Hgts, IL; 4/600 HonRl; NHS; LetterSwmmng; Coll; Engi.

AVIZA, Anna V; Carmel Girls HS; Downey, IL; 16/173 Chr; HonRl; LitMag; Loyola Univ; Law.

AVRAM, Sherry L; Plainfield HS; Joliet, IL; Chr; SchMus; SctActv; RptrYrbk; North Park College; Psychology.

AWALD, Terri; Oregon Davis HS; Walkerton, IN; 1/65 Band; CncrtBnd; HonRl; NHS; PepBnd; 4-H; PpCl; SciCl; AmLegAwd; 4-HAwd; Purdue Univ; Veterinarian.

AWALD, Terri L; Oregon Davis HS; Walkerton, IN; 1/63 Band; CncrtBnd; HonRl; NHS; PepBnd; SchPl; 4-H; PpCl; SciCl; 4-HAwd; Purdue U; Vet Med.

AWALT, Kathryn A; Sycamore HS; Sycamore, IL; 3/240 HonRl; NHS; SctActv; SpnCl; PpCl; College; Spanish.

AXELROD, Julie S; Niles Township West HS; Lincolnwood, IL; 9/630 AFS; HonRl; NHS; SchPl; TchrAde; Stanford University; Psychology.

AXELSON, Joseph C; Mahtomedi Senior HS; Whte Bear Lake, MN; Band; Chr; HonRl; 4-H; GerCl; Bsktbl; LetterFtbl; LetterTrk; 4-HAwd; College; Health.

AXELSON, Julianne K; Mcpherson HS; Mcpherson, KS; ALAGirlsSt; Band; Chr; CncrtBnd; DrlTm; HonRl; MrchBnd; PepBnd; SchMus; RptrSchPpr; SchPpr; College.

AXLINE, James R; Thomas Jefferson HS; Cedar Rapids, IA; 48/421 Band; CmntyWkr; CncrtBnd; HonRl; MrchBnd; Orch; PepBnd; PolWkr; SctActv; SciCl; Coe Clge; Biology.

AXLINE, Nancy J; Crispus Attucks HS; Indianapolis, IN; 2/250 Chrl; ChrhWkr; HonRl; NHS; NatlMeritSF; SchPl; FrCl; Chrldr; In U; Medicine.

AXOTIS, Antonia E; Lake Forest Academy; Waukegan, IL; ChrhWkr; HonRl; StuGov; SecYthFlsp; RptrYrbk; RptrSchPpr; College; Science.

AXT, Faye L; Mc Clusky HS; Mc Clusky, ND; HonRl; FHA; LetterTrk; Trinity Bible College.

AXTELL, Steven C; Callaway HS; Callaway, NE; 3/25 Band; Chr; CncrtBnd; HonRl; MrchBnd; NHS; SchPl; RptrYrbk; Bsktbl; LetterFtbl; Univ Of Nebr; Mechanical Engr.

AXUP, Peter R; Rock Island HS; Rock Island, IL; 9/624 Band; CncrtBnd; MrchBnd; NHS; PepBnd; College; Engineering.

AYERS, Cheri; Fairbury Senoir HS; Fairbury, NE; 32/172 Band; Chrs; ChrhWkr; CncrtBnd; MrchBnd; SchMus; YthFlsp; FBLA; GerCl; Swmmng; IMSpt; College; Accounting.

AYERS, Gary L; Penney HS; Hamilton, MO; 3/76 HonRl; StuCncl; YthFlsp; RptrSchPpr; PresFFA; Bsktbl; U Of Mo; Agriculture.

AYERS, Janice L; Ludington HS; Ludington, MI; ChrhWkr; CmntyWkr; HonRl; NHS; YthFlsp; CaptBsktbl; CchngActv; IMSpt; EldAwd; JCAwd; Central Mi Univ; Accntg.

AYERS, Kristy L; Green City Ri HS; Green City, MO; HstFrshCls; TrsJrCls; ALAGirlsSt; ChrhWkr; CmntyWkr; CncrtBnd; HonRl; MrchBnd; NHS; PepBnd; SchPl; StuCncl; Bsbl; Bsktbl; Univ Of Missouri; Med Technician.

AYERS, Linda J; Quincy Sr HS; Quincy, IL; 19/816 ChrhWkr; HonRl; HospAde; NHS; YthFlsp; LetterSwmmng; DARAwd; Iowa St Univ; Biology.

AYERS, Rodney D; Green City R 1 HS; Green Castle, MO; 1/36 ChrhWkr; HonRl; NHS; StuCncl; FBLA; LetterBsktbl; LetterTrk; College.

AYESH, Kevin B; Wichita North HS; Wichita, KS; 7/549 ChrhWkr; HonRl; NHS; Orch; SchMus; FrCl; GerCl; Univ Of Texas Austin; Music.

AYLMER, Jane; Salisbury R 4 HS; Salisbury, MO; 2/89 VPSophCls; PresJrCls; VPSrCls; ALAGirlsSt; HonRl; StuCncl; CitAwd; Univ Of Mo; Dental Hygiene.

AYLSTOCK, Cathy A; Brookville HS; Brookville, IN; 18/173 VPBand; HonRl; MrchBnd; NHS; StuCncl; VP4-H; SecFTA; LetterBsktbl; LetterTrk; LetterGAA; University; Law Enforcement.

AYLWARD, Mary A; Hoisington HS; Hoisington, KS; ALAGirlsSt; Chr; ChrhWkr; HonRl; JrNHS; PresNHS; SchPl; SpnCl; PpCl; Chrldr; Ft Hays Ks State Col; Medical Technition.

AYOTTE, Janice C; Walled Lake Central HS; Union Lake, MI; 12/370 CmntyWkr; HonRl; JrNHS; NHS; Michigan State University; Veterinarian.

AYRE, Cynthia S; Salina HS; Salina, KS; 16/364 LitMag; NHS; StuGov; EdYrBk; EdSchPpr; FTA; SpnCl; HstJrCls; LetterTennis; GAA; Fort Hays Ks State Coll; Psych.

AYRES, Dean; North Chicago Community HS; Great Lakes, IL; PresSrCls; HonRl; JrNHS; NHS; NatlMeritCmnd; NatlMeritSchl; SctActv; SpnCl; SciCl; College; Math.

AYRES, Lea C; Central Salem HS; Burlington, WI; Chr; Chrl; Chrs; LbryAde; SchMus; SchPl; SctActv; FTA;.

AYRES, Lea D; Yorktown HS; Yorktown, IN; NHS; RptrYrbk; FrCl; Indiana Univ; English.

AYRES, Sandra K; Superior HS; Superior, NE; Band; ChrhWkr; CncrtBnd; HonRl; MrchBnd; PepBnd; SchPl; FBLA; FHA; College; Foreign Language Teacher.

AZBELL, Kristy L; V I T HS; Table Grove, IL; 1/58 PresSophCls; Band; Chr; CncrtBnd; HonRl; JrNHS; MrchBnd; NHS; PepBnd; SchPl; StuCncl; TchrAde; EdYrBk; FrCl; College; Professional.

AZELTINE, Leroy E; Smith Center HS; Smith Center, KS; 26/61 ALBoysSt; Chr; Chrs; HonRl; SchPl; TchrAde; Bsbl; Ftbl; Ft Hays Kansas St College; Architecture.

B

BAACK, Karla A; Williamsburg Comm HS; Homestead, IA; 1/100 PresSophCls; Chrs; HonRl; NHS; StuCncl; EdSchPpr; GerCl; LetterBsktbl; LetterTrk; Chrldr; Coll; Physical Therapy.

BAADE, Cynthia A; Titonka Consolidated HS; Titonka, IA; 3/48 VPJrCls; Chr; HonRl; NHS; SchMus; YthFlsp; EdYrBk; EdSchPpr; Bsktbl; PPFtbl; Ia Central Comm Clge; Rn.

BAADE, Ryan D; Titonka HS; Titonka, IA; Chr; Chrs; ChrhWkr; SchMus; SchPl; YthFlsp; FFA; Iowa Lakes Comm Coll; Auto Mech.

BAALMANN, Bernice L; Grinnell HS; Grinnell, KS; LetterBand; LetterChrs; DrlTm; HonRl; MrchBnd; PepBnd; PpCl; CitAwd; College.

BAALRUD, Peggy S; New Auburn HS; New Auburn, WI; SecFrshCls; Band; Chr; HonRl; LbryAde; NatlFornLg; RptrYrbk; EdSchPpr; FHA; Trk; College; Teaching.

BAAS, Richard; Kalamazoo Christian HS; Kalamazoo, MI; HonRl; NHS; Glf; Calvin College; Biology Major.

BAASKE, Walter; Downers Grove Comm HS; Woodridge, IL; 140/830 Aud/Vis; ChrhWkr; CAP; HonRl; LbryAde; SctActv; TchrAde; LetterSwmmng; Ill Inst Of Tech; Architect.

BAATZ, Deborah K; Edwardsburg HS; Edwardsburg, MI; Band; Chr; Chrl; Chrs; CncrtBnd; HonRl; MrchBnd; NHS; PepBnd; TchrAde; Olivet College; Music.

BAATZ, Eric C; Edwardsburg HS; Edwardsburg, MI; Band; Chr; ChrhWkr; CncrtBnd; DrmMjrt; HonRl; MrchBnd; PepBnd; SctActv; YthFlsp; GerCl; Bsktbl; LetterTrk; LetterWrstlng; Us Navy; Nuclear Training.

BABB, Susan C; Mercy HS; Omaha, NE; 14/75 HonRl; JA; NatlFornLg; NHS; SchMus; SchPl; Sdlty; Yrbk; RptrSchPpr; EngCl; Univ Of Neb; Journalism.

BABB, Timothy J; Pioneer HS; Lucerne, IN; ALBoysSt; Band; CncrtBnd; HonRl; MrchBnd; PepBnd; StuCncl; YthFlsp; 4-H; Trk; IMSpt; Nashville Auto D College; Mechanic.

BABBITT, Jeff; Sibley HS; Sibley, IA; 12/105 ALBoysSt; HonRl; MrchBnd; NHS; PepBnd; StuCncl; GerCl; Ftbl; Glf; Wrstlng; Univ; Professional.

BABBITT, Lyle C; Boone HS; Boone, IA; Band; ChrhWkr; CncrtBnd; MrchBnd; PepBnd; Technical School; Farm.

BABBITT, Vicki M; Rudyard Area HS; Kinross, MI; 33#41#72 SctActv; YthFlsp; 4-H; FFA; Trk; IMSpt; RotaryAwd; College; Veterinarian.

BABCOCK, Deborah; Arthur Hill HS; Saginaw, MI; Band; CncrtBnd; DrlTm; MrchBnd; PepBnd; YthFlsp; Swmmng; Trk; GAA; IMSpt; W Mich Univ; Field Of Biology.

BABCOCK, Del M; Hammond Baptist HS; Hammond, IN; ChrhWkr; DrlTm; HonRl; JrNHS; NHS; Orch; SchMus; SctActv; TchrAde; RptrYrbk; RptrSchPpr; PpCl; Trk; Hyles Anderson College; Elementary Educ.

BABCOCK, Glen A; Kimball HS; Royal Oak, MI; Band; CncrtBnd; HonRl; MrchBnd; Orch; PepBnd; StuCncl; TreasYthFlsp; Bsbl; Grand Valley State College; Public Service.

BABCOCK, Lona J; Monett HS; Monett, MO; Chr; ChrhWkr; CmntyWkr; HonRl; OffAde; YthFlsp; FTA; PpCl; Bus Schl; Vocation.

BABCOCK, Lyndon R; Kenwood HS; Chicago, IL; PresSrCls; VPSrCls; SecSrCls; TrsSrCls; HonRl; NHS; NatlMeritFnl; NatlMeritSchl; LetterSocr; LetterSwmmng; JAAwd; College; Engr.

BABCOCK, Patricia M; Chaparral HS; Attica, KS; ChrhWkr; CmntyWkr; HonRl; TchrAde; SchPpr; FTA; LetterBsktbl; College; Pro Softball.

BABECKI, Susan E; The Immaculata HS; Chicago, IL; 72/198 HonRl; Chrldr; Commercial Art.

BABEL, Wayne A; St Francis HS; Lindsay, NE; 8/33 VPJrCls; HonRl; StuCncl; FFA; SciCl; Ftbl; IMSpt; Northeast Ne Tech Coll; Auto Mechanic.

BABER, James J; Barrington HS; Barrington, IL; HonRl; JA; StuCncl; FBLA; SpnCl; Northwood Institute Univ; Auto Dealer.

BABETCH, Phyllis D; William Fremd HS; Palatine, IL; 45/620 HonRl; Knox College; Law.

BABI, Jeanette L; West Holt HS; Atkinson, NE; Chrs; DrlTm; LbryAde; SchPl; SctActv; RptrYrbk; 4-H; PpCl; College; Elementary Teacher.

BABIAK, Joseph J; Mosinee Sr HS; Mosinee, WI; ChrhWkr; HonRl; NatlFornLg; TchrAde; RptrSchPpr; Uw College; Business Admin.

BABICH, Patricia; Taylorville HS; Taylorville, IL; Chr; HonRl; LbryAde; NatlThespSoc; SchMus; SchPl; SctActv; SpnCl; PpCl; Tennis; Western Ill Univ; Teaching.

BABICKI, Raymond J; Joliet Central HS; Joliet, IL; 43/491 HonRl; NHS; College; Mechanics.

BABLER, Bryan C; Monticello HS; Monticello, WI; 1/27 Band; CncrtBnd; HonRl; MrchBnd; PepBnd; SchPl; StuCncl; SpnCl; LetterBsbl; LetterBsktbl; LetterGlf; Univ Of Wisconsin; Pharmacy.

BABLER, Glenda J; New Glarus HS; Belleville, WI; 1/60 ALAGirlsSt; Band; ChrhWkr; CncrtBnd; HonRl; LbryAde; MrchBnd; VPNHS; PepBnd; StuCncl; YthFlsp; RptrSchPpr; FBLA; FHA; Technical College; Accounting.

BABLER, Gwendolyn J; New Glarus HS; Belleville, WI; 1/60 ALAGirlsSt; Band; ChrhWkr; NHS; PepBnd; RptrSchPpr; SecFBLA; FHA; FTA;.

BAC, James A; William Jennings Bryan HS; Omaha, NE; 27/418 DrlTm; HonRl; JrNHS; ModUN; ROTC; Tennis; College; Air Force.

BACA, Annamarie A; St Augustine HS; Chicago, IL; Chrs; HonRl; NHS; SchMus; Yrbk; RptrSchPpr; VoiceDemAwd; College; Nursing.

BACCI, Kenneth B; Romeo Sr HS; Washington, MI; 7/320 Chr; ChrhWkr; HonRl; NHS; TchrAde; EdYrBk; Yrbk; Trk; Wrstlng; Michigan St Univ; Engineer.

BACEVICH, Thomas J; Bishop Noll Institute; Highland, IN; 24/342 HonRl; NHS; MthCl; LetterBsbl; IMSpt; St Louis U; Physician.

BACH, Janet M; Douglas Mac Arthur HS; Saginaw, MI; 20/300 HonRl; HospAde; NHS; PolWkr; FrCl; PresPpCl; LetterTennis; Albion College; Medicine.

BACH, Kevin J; Austin Catholic Prep; St Clair Shores, MI; 8/148 CncrtBnd; HonRl; NHS; SctActv; SciCl; IMSpt; Univ; Math.

BACH, Roberta L; Roosevelt HS; East Chicago, IN; 3/219 HonRl; NHS; TreasSctActv; StuGov; FHA; LatCl; VPMthCl; PresPpCl; VPSciCl; GAA; Purdue Univ; Pharmacy.

BACHARA, Celinda C; Westfield HS; Coloma, WI; 14/102 Band; Chrs; ChrhWkr; CncrtBnd; DrmMjrt; HonRl; MrchBnd; NHS; PepBnd; SpnCl;.

BACHELLER, Cheryl D; Armada HS; Allenton, MI; 6/95 Band; Chrs; HonRl; NHS; SchMus; StuCncl; SpnCl; PpCl; IMSpt; Univ Of Michigan.

BACHENBERG, Phillip S; Bryan HS; Omaha, NE; Chr; CmntyWkr; HonRl; NHS; SchMus; PresYthFlsp;.

BACHENBERG, Rachel S; Osceola HS; Osceola, NE; 1/50 ALAGirlsSt; Band; Chrs; ChrhWkr; NHS; PpCl; LetterTrk; Chrldr; U Of Ks; Music Therap.

BACHKORA, Mary T; Marian HS; Hays, KS; DrlTm; NatlThespSoc; SchPl; StuCncl; RptrSchPpr; SchPpr; PresPpCl; College; Professional.

BACHLEDA, Paul E; A E Stevenson HS; Prairie View, IL; 74/231 Univ Of Illinois; Agriculture.

BACHLER, Kevin L; Zion Benton Township HS; Zion, IL; 73/405 HonRl; LitMag; PresGerCl; Ftbl; Ill State Univ; High School Teacher.

BACHMAN, Daniel L; Claflin HS; Claflin, KS; Chrs; SchPl; FFA; PpCl; Col;.

BACHMAN, Debbie J; Knoxville HS; Knoxville, IA; 21/274 SecFrshCls; HonRl; NHS; StuCncl; 4-H; Bsktbl; Trk; PPFtbl; 4-HAwd; Univ Of Northern Iowa; Physical Educ.

BACHMAN, Debbi J; Bowdle HS; Bowdle, SD; 8/29 Band; Chrs; CncrtBnd; DrlTm; HonRl; MrchBnd; PepBnd; SchPl; EdSchPpr; Trade School; Professional.

BACHMAN, Elizabeth; South Newton HS; Brook, IN; 25/105 Band; ChrhWkr; CmntyWkr; CncrtBnd; HonRl; MrchBnd; OffAde; PepBnd; SchMus; PPFtbl; Col; Professional.

BACHMAN, James; Eastridge HS; Kankakee, IL; 16/269 SecJrCls; PresSrCls; HonRl; NHS; StuCncl; Yrbk; RptrSchPpr; Tennis; RotaryAwd; Univ Of Il; Law.

BACHMAN, Lucinda E; Salem Comm HS; Salem, IL; 8/219 HospAde; JrNHS; NHS; SecStuCncl; RptrSchPpr; PpCl; South Ill Univ; Liberal Arts.

BACHMAN, Marjorie S; Lowpoint Washburn HS; Lowpoint, IL; AFS; Chr; Chrs; ChrhWkr; HonRl; SchPl; YthFlsp; Sec4-H; FHA; 4-HAwd; Secretarial.

BACHMANN, Randy N; Gorham HS; Gorham, IL; 6/30 HonRl; StuCncl; StuGov; 4-H; FFA; Bsktbl; 4-HAwd; College.

BACHMEIER, Beth E; Esmond HS; Esmond, ND; 3/22 SecTrsSophCls; SecJrCls; PresSrCls; ALAGirlsSt; Band; PresFrshCls; SchPl; RptrSchPpr; PpCl; Chrldr; U Fo Nd; Law.

BACHMEIER, Kevin M; Emmons Central HS; Strasburg, ND; 21/36 VPSophCls; NHS; SptEdSchPpr; Bsktbl; Ftbl; Mary College;.

BACHMEIER, Lawrence W; Cardinal Muench Seminary; Walhalla, ND; ChrhWkr; CmntyWkr; PolWkr; RedCrAde; SctActv; StuCncl; CivCl; CchngActv; DanFAwd; GodCntryAwd; Ndsu; Social Work, Priesthood.

BACHNER, Gretchen M; St Louise De Marillac HS; Niles, IL; 9/254 U Of Notre Dame; Interpreter.

BACHTEL, Edward; Penney HS; Hamilton, MO; Band; MrchBnd; SchPl; StuCncl; SchPpr; FFA; SpnCl; Mo Univ; Journalism.

BACHTELL, Paula J; Starmont HS; Wadena, IA; ChrhWkr; HonRl; StuCncl; RptrYrbk; RptrSchPpr; PresFHA; VPFTA; GAA; IMSpt; PPFtbl; Business School; Professional.

BACK, Barbara J; Oak Grove HS; Goodhue, MN; 12/50 SecBand; Chr; HonRl; Mdrgl; SecNHS; OffAde; 4-H; FHA; PresPpCl; 4-HAwd; College; Home Ec Major.

BACK, Michael H; Brookville HS; Brookville, IN; 65/179 ALBoysSt; SpnCl; LetterBsktbl; LetterGlf; LetterTennis; Bus Sch; Prof.

BACK, Patricia E; Immaculate Conception Academy; Brookville, IN; Chrs; HonRl; LitMag; NHS; Orch; Quill&Scroll; SchPl; SpnCl; Tennis; GAA; Marian College; Nursing.

BACKA, Carolyn; Grand Blanc HS; Flint, MI; 210/640 NatlFornLg; VPNatlThespSoc; SchMus; SchPl; Teen; PPFtbl; Mott W Mi Flint Bishop Airport;air Traf Con.

BACKAS, Paul N; Hinsdale Central HS; Clarenoon Hills, IL; 14/608 Band; CncrtBnd; HonRl; MrchBnd; NHS; Orch; SchMus; SctActv; IMSpt; Univ Il; Sci.

BACKES, Daryl L; Fatima HS; Bonnots Mill, MO; 27/126 ChrhWkr; CmntyWkr; HonRl; NHS; SptEdSchPpr; 4-H; FBLA; SciCl; LetterBsktbl; LetterTrk; Lincoln Univ; Business Adm.

BACKFISCH, Joan; Zalma HS; Zalma, MO; 8/28 VPJrCls; Chrl; ChrhWkr; CmntyWkr; HonRl; Teen; FHA; SpnCl; Tennis; Chrldr; College; Accountant.

BACKHAUS, Stan E; Bismarck HS; Bismarck, ND; 79/600 Chr; ChrhWkr; HonRl; SchMus; Bible Schl; Christian Service.

BACKLIN, William W; Mason City Sr HS; Mason City, IA; 19/472 Chr; Chrl; Chrs; ChrhWkr; HonRl; Mdrgl; NHS; NatlThespSoc; SchPl; Univ Of No Iowa; Music.

BACKLUND, David B; Velva Public HS; Velva, ND; ChrhWkr; CmntyWkr; HonRl; SchPl; TchrAde; LetterBsbl; LetterBsktbl; Swmmng; Trk; IMSpt; Business Schl; Liberal Arts.

BACKS, Janet L; Okawville HS; Okawville, IL; 3/69 Chr; Chrs; ChrhWkr; HonRl; Mdrgl; NHS; SchPl; YthFlsp; RptrYrbk; PpCl;.

BACKS, Sandra K; Okawville HS; Venedy, IL; 1/69 HonRl; LbryAde; NHS; Teen; YthFlsp; RptrYrbk; PpCl; IMSpt;.

BACKSEN, Susan K; Mandan HS; Mandan, ND; 125/293 Chrs; ChrhWkr; CmntyWkr; HonRl; NHS; PolWkr; Yrbk; LatCl; PpCl; LetterTennis; College; Nursing.

BACKSMEIER, Susan L; Normal Comm HS; Normal, IL; 47/441 HonRl; SecNHS; OffAde; TchrAde; RptrYrbk; PpCl; Bsktbl; Trk; Chrldr; GAA; Concordia College; Teacher.

BACKSTRAND, Ken W; Lakeview HS; St Clair Shores, MI; ChrhWkr; CmntyWkr; HonRl; JA; StuCncl; TchrAde; Wrstlng; IMSpt; Coll; Lawyer.

BACKSTROM, Anita C; Pelican Rapids HS; Erhard, MN; Chr; HonRl; OffAde; 4-H;.

BACKSTROM, Orn U; Highland Park HS; Highland Park, IL; ALBoysSt; Orch; College.

BACON, Barry J; Maplewood Academy; Two Harbors, MN; PresSophCls; Band; Chr; Chrl; HonRl; Bsktbl; College; Professional.

BACON, Chris N; Marshalltown HS; Marshalltown, IA; ALBoysSt; Band; HonRl; MrchBnd; ModUN; PresJrCls; Tennis; IMSpt; University; Private Business.

BACON, Curtis; Bishop Ryan HS; Minot, ND; 3/77 VPSrCls; HonRl; NHS; NatlMeritSchl; StuCncl; Yrbk; KeyCl; Bsktbl; Ndsu; Physics.

BACON, Curtis J; Bishop Ryan HS; Minot, ND; 3/75 PresFrshCls; VPJrCls; VPSrCls; HonRl; NHS; NatlMeritSchl; StuCncl; RptrYrbk; Yrbk; KeyCl; LetterBsktbl; CaptFtbl; LetterTrk; College; Professional.

BACON, Duane; Millington HS; Millington, MI; 3/178 HonRl; LitMag; Quill&Scroll; SchPl; TchrAde; RptrYrbk; Yrbk; Bsbl; Glf; Us Naval Acad; Professional Officer.

BACON, Gail R; Walther Lutheran HS; Forest Park, IL; VPSophCls; VPSrCls; Chr; ChrhWkr; HonRl; NHS; NatlThespSoc; OffAde; StuCncl; RptrYrbk; RptrSchPpr; Chrldr; GAA; So Illinois Univ; Nursing.

BACON, James R; North Miami HS; Mexico, IN; ALBoysSt; ChrhWkr; HonRl; StuCncl; FrCl; LetterBsbl; LetterBsktbl; LetterFtbl; LetterTrk; College; Vocation.

BACON, Kelly W; Lyons Public HS; Lyons, NE; VPFrshCls; PresJrCls; HonRl; JrNHS; NHS; StuCncl; SecFFA; Bsktbl; LetterFtbl; Trade School.

BACON, Terri L; Fenton HS; Fenton, MI; DrmMjrt; HonRl; MrchBnd; NHS; NatlThespSoc; SchMus; SchPl; Twrl; College; Vocation.

BADANEK, Katherine E; Godwin Heights HS; Wyoming, MI; 1/186 HonRl; NHS; RptrSchPpr; PpCl; Trk; GAA; PPFtbl; BttyCrckrAwd; CitAwd; College.

BADE, Cynthia F; Cochrane Fountain City HS; Cochrane, WI; 9/93 Band; Chrs; CncrtBnd; MrchBnd; NHS; PepBnd; SchMus; SecFBLA; TreasFHA; Coll; Sci.

BADE, John W; Mid County Jr Sr HS; Varna, IL; 6/60 Band; ChrhWkr; HonRl; SchPl; Trk; U Of Ill; Aeronautical Eng.

BADE, Ladonna R; Fair Grove HS; Fair Grove, MO; 8/46 Band; MrchBnd; FHA; SpnCl; PresPpCl; SciCl; PresBsbl; PPFtbl; Drury U; Nursing.

BADEAU, Terri L; Case HS; Racine, WI; 27/650 PresSrCls; ChrhWkr; HonRl; SctActv; StuCncl; PresStuGov; FBLA; FrCl; LetterSwmmng; DARAwd; OptClAwd; Marquette Univ; Bio Medical Engineer.

BADEN, Cynthia A; Benson HS; Omaha, NE; Chr; Chrs; ChrhWkr; HonRl; NHS; SctActv; StuCncl; MthCl; GAA; Univ Of Nebraska At Lincoln; Accounting.

BADER, Barbara I; East Kentwood HS; Kentwood, MI; Chr; HonRl; NHS; SchPpr; College; Occupational Therapist.

BADER, John L; Lemars Comm HS; Lemars, IA; 7/183 ALBoysSt; Band; CncrtBnd; HonRl; NHS; NatlThespSoc; SchMus; SchPl; StuCncl; College; Theater.

BADGER, Suzanne R; Ryan HS; Omaha, NE; Chr; Chrl; Chrs; HonRl; NatlFornLg; NHS; SchMus; EdSchPpr; SpnCl; PpCl; IMSpt; AmLegAwd; OptClAwd; Univ Of Nebraska; Law.

BADILLO, Margaret C; Josephinum HS; Chicago, IL; SecFrshCls; TrsSophCls; NHS; StuCncl; StuGov; Yrbk; Mac Cormac Jr College; Accounting.

BA DOUR, Diana; Memorial HS; Eau Claire, WI; HospAde; PpCl; Eau Claire Voc Inst; Lab Technologist.

BADYNSKI, Kurt A; Glenbard East HS; Lombard, IL; Band; Chr; CncrtBnd; HonRl; MrchBnd; NHS; Orch; PepBnd; University Of Denver; Vet.

BAECKER, Bruce P; Cochrane Fountain City HS; Independence, WI; Aud/Vis; ChrhWkr; CmntyWkr; TchrAde; 4-H; FFA; SciCl; Ftbl; Wrstlng; Farmer.

BAEDKE, Russell; Turtle Lake HS; Turtle Lake, WI; Chrs; Ftbl; Glf; Wrstlng; Trade School.

BAEHR, Peter H; Thorp HS; Withee, WI; 1/95 HonRl; JA; NHS; StuCncl; LetterFtbl; LetterTrk; LetterWrstlng; JAAwd; Navy; Electronics.

BAELE, Lori; Annawan HS; Annawan, IL; SecSophCls; NHS; SchPl; StuCncl; FHA; Bsbl; Chrldr; GAA;.

BAELE, Roger; Marian HS; South Bend, IN; 18/170 ChrhWkr; HonRl; Mdrgl; SchAde; SchPl; SctActv; SptEdYrbk; Yrbk; Trk; IMSpt; College.

BAENEN, Jeanne K; West HS; Green Bay, WI; 6/390 Chrs; HonRl; RptrSchPpr; FrCl; GAA; Col ; Int Decor.

BAER, Christine M; Lebanon HS; Trenton, IL; 12/93 PresBand; Chrs; HonRl; NHS; SchMus; SecStuCncl; TchrAde; SptEdYrbk; Yrbk; RptrSchPpr; VP4-H; FHA; 4-HAwd; College.

BAER, Kaye D; Niantic Harristown HS; Decatur, IL; VPFrshCls; Band; Chrs; ChrhWkr; CncrtBnd; HonRl; MrchBnd; PepBnd; Quill&Scroll; SchPl; StuCncl; RptrYrbk; Yrbk; RptrSchPpr; College.

BAER, Ruth A; Lawrence HS; Lawrence, KS; 14/548 Chr; HonRl; NatlMeritSF; Orch; PolWkr; SchMus; SctActv; TchrAde; SpnCl; Univ; Science.

BAERENWALD, Vicki; Brewster Public HS; Brewster, MN; 4/25 Band; Chrs; ChrhWkr; HonRl; NHS; SchPl; StuCncl; RptrYrbk; EdSchPpr; Mankato St Coll; Mass Comm.

BAERTSCH, Sandra F; Beach HS; Beach, ND; 6/39 TrsFrshCls; VPJrCls; HonRl; StuCncl; FHA; GerCl; LetterBsktbl; PPFtbl; College; Veterinarian.

BAERTSCHI, Steven W; Illinois Valley Cntrl HS; Chillicothe, IL; Band; CncrtBnd; HonRl; MrchBnd; NatlMeritSchl; PepBnd; SctActv; LetterBsbl; Bradley University.

BAETEN, Deborah L; West De Pere HS; De Pere, WI; 5/194 SecSrCls; ALAGirlsSt; Band; NatlFornLg; NatlMeritSchl; SchMus; LetterTrk; Chrldr; GAA; DanFAwd; Uw Whitewater; Acct.

BAETEN, Edwin; Oakfield HS; Oakfield, WI; 9/56 PresFrshCls; HonRl; Ftbl; Glf; DanFAwd; EldAwd; VFWAwd; CitAwd; College; Computer Science.

BAETEN, Patricia J; Wrightstown HS; Wrightstown, WI; PresJrCls; Chr; SchPl; StuCncl; StuGov; RptrYrbk; EdYrBk; RptrSchPpr; Chrldr; GAA; Clge;.

BAETZ, Bruce A; Oxford HS; Oxford, MI; Oakland Univ; Economics.

BAGBY, Barbara A; Southwest HS; Kansas City, MO; 47/503 NHS; SchMus; SchPl; RptrSchPpr; EngCl; VPSciCl; Swmmng; IMSpt; College; Elem Education.

BAGBY, Brian; Alton HS; Alton, IL; 36/858 Band; HonRl; MrchBnd; NHS; NatlMeritFnl; NatlMeritSF; Orch; SchMus; MthCl; SciCl; Siu;chemistry Research.

BAGBY, Cindy J; Wausau West HS; Wausau, WI; 61/450 Chr; NHS; SchMus; SecStuCncl; SecTeen; RptrYrbk; SciCl; LetterSwmmng; College; Stewardess.

BAGBY, Linda K; Big Springs HS; Big Springs, NE; 1/21 PresFrshCls; TrsJrCls; CncrtBnd; HonRl; MrchBnd; NHS; StuCncl; FHA; PpCl; IMSpt; Business Sch; Vocation.

BAGBY, Lorrie J; Porta HS; Petersburg, IL; 8/131 TrsFrshCls; HonRl; MrchBnd; NHS; NatlThespSoc; SchMus; StuCncl; Yrbk; 4-H; 4-HAwd; College; Optometrist.

BAGIENSKI, Richard D; Anderson HS; Anderson, IN; 89/600 HonRl; Trk; Univ; Teacher.

BAGINSKI, Michael R; Paul K Cousino HS; Warren, MI; 10/600 Chrs; HonRl; IntrClCncl; LitMag;

NHS; SctActv; LetterTrk; Albion Col; Oceanography.

BAGINSKI, Regina B; Lourdes HS; Chicago, IL; 65/299 HonRl; College; Professional.

BAGINSKI, Stephen P; Springfield Se HS; Springfield, IL; 7/507 ChrhWkr; HonRl; NHS; NatlMeritFnl; YthFlsp; MthCl; Bsktbl; LetterGlf; Illinois St Univ; Accounting.

BAGLEY, Dennis W; Marion Adams HS; Atlanta, IN; 5/105 PresJrCls; Band; CncrtBnd; MrchBnd; PresNHS; Orch; PepBnd; PresStuCncl; FTA; LatCl; Ball St U; Math.

BAGLEY, Janice A; Niles West HS; Morton Grove, IL; ChrhWkr; HonRl; NatlMeritSchl; Illinois State Univ; Teaching.

BAGLEY, Katrina L; Marion Adams HS; Atlanta, IN; TreasBand; CncrtBnd; TreasJrNHS; NHS; FFA; FHA; TreasFTA; PpCl; Trk; Chrldr; GAA; PPFtbl; Univ; Teaching.

BAGSBY, Margaret; Gibault Catholic Hs; Redbud, IL; PresJrCls; Chrl; Chrs; HonRl; NHS; SchMus; SctActv; StuCncl; YthFlsp; EdSchPpr;.

BAHLER, Elizabeth R; Monroe Senior HS; Monroe, WI; Chr; ChrhWkr; HonRl; HospAde; SchMus; YthFlsp; GerCl; PpCl; Swmmng; Tennis; College; Study In Music.

BAHLEY, Roberta; South Heart HS; South Heart, ND; 1/25 HonRl; LbryAde; ModUN; SchPl; StuCncl; FHA; Bsktbl; Chrldr; DanFAwd; PresAwd; Dickinson St Col; Accounting.

BAHLMANN, Glenna; Sumner Community HS; Waterloo, IA; Chr; Chrs; ChrhWkr; HonRl; HospAde; YthFlsp; FHA; PpCl; Chrldr; PresAwd; Technical School; Nursing.

BAHNKE, Richard W; Central HS; Omaha, NE; HonRl; NatlMeritFnl; NatlMeritSF; Orch; PepBnd; SchMus; TchrAde;.

BAHR, Alan J; Antigo HS; Antigo, WI; U Of Wi; Business Management.

BAHR, Cindy M; Northeast HS; Lincoln, NE; ChrhWkr; HonRl; OffAde; PolWkr; TchrAde; YthFlsp; Univ Of Nebraska; Elementary Education.

BAHR, Diane; Litchfield Sr HS; Litchfield, MN; Chr; HonRl; SchMus; RptrSchPpr; PpCl; GAA; IMSpt; JCAwd; PresAwd; Trade School; Prof.

BAHR, Donna L; Lincoln City Rii; Elsberry, MO; 10/69 HonRl; NHS; ROTC; YthFlsp; SptEdSchPpr; FHA; Bsktbl; Chrldr; GAA;.

BAHR, John A; Otis Bison HS; Olmitz, KS; PresJrCls; ALBoysSt; NHS; Bsktbl; Ftbl; Trk; Barton County Comm Clg; Electronics.

BAHR, Julie A; Humboldt St Vincent HS; Humboldt, MN; SecTrsJrCls; Band; Chrs; HonRl; Orch; PepBnd; PresStuCncl; YthFlsp; EdYrBk; LetterBsktbl; University; Special Ed.

BAHR, Laurence D; Palatine HS; Palatine, IL; 21/440 Aud/Vis; Band; HonRl; TreasJA; NHS; NatlMeritSF; PolWkr; Quill&Scroll; EdSchPpr; JAAwd; Coll; Environmental Science.

BAHR, Susan K; Kirksville HS; Kirksville, MO; 50/180 ChrhWkr; HonRl; SchPl; StuCncl; TchrAde; TreasPpCl; Tennis; Chrldr; GAA; Univ; Business Adm.

BAHR, William; Madison HS; Milwaukee, WI; PresSrCls; Band; CncrtBnd; HonRl; MrchBnd; NHS; NatlMeritSchl; Bsbl; Bsktbl; Concordia College; Business.

BAHRE, Nancy J; Springfield HS; Springfield, IL; 40/625 Chrl; Chrs; NHS; SchPl; YthFlsp; GerCl; Illinois St Univ; Accounting.

BAIER, Barbara A; Bloomfield HS; Wausau, NE; 6/48 Chrs; HonRl; NatlThespSoc; SchPl; TchrAde; SchPpr; FHA; GerCl; 4-HAwd; College.

BAIER, Mark J; La Crosse HS; La Crosse, KS; PresJrCls; ChrhWkr; HonRl; NatlMeritSchl; SchPl; SctActv; PpCl; Bsbl; LetterBsktbl; LetterFtbl; Swmmng; LetterTrk; College; Professional.

BAIER, Philip; Beaver Dam HS; Beaver Dam, WI; 14/310 ALBoysSt; HonRl; PpCl; Bsktbl; Wrstlng; Univ Of Mn; Architecture.

BAIER, Timothy L; West Liberty HS; W Liberty, IA; Band; Chrs; ChrhWkr; HonRl; NHS; Sacrstn; SchMus; StuCncl; StuGov; SciCl; College; Science.

BAIETTO, Marie; West Leyden HS; Franklin Pk, IL; 8/410 HonRl; LitMag; TreasSpnCl; LetterBsktbl; GAA; Loyola Univ; Rn.

BAILAR, Rodney B; North Platte HS; North Platte, NE; 25/393 HonRl; NatlMeritSF; SchAde; PresStuCncl; KeyCl; LatCl; Bsktbl; LetterFtbl; LetterTrk; IMSpt; RotaryAwd; Univ; Medicine.

BAILEY, Alan D; Sioux Rapids Comm HS; Sioux Rapids, IA; 3/19 VPSophCls; Aud/Vis; HonRl; NHS; SchPl; RptrYrbk; Bsktbl; Ftbl; GovHonPrgAwd; U Of Ia; Engi.

BAILEY, Alisa A; United Township HS; East Moline, IL; 5/514 ChrhWkr; CncrtBnd; HonRl; MrchBnd; NHS; PepBnd; StuCncl; FrCl; PpCl; GAA; College; Special Education.

BAILEY, Anita Y; Purdy HS; Purdy, MO; TrsSophCls; Chrs; HonRl; NHS; Yrbk; EdSchPpr; FHA; PpCl;.

BAILEY, B James; Hononegah HS; Rockton, IL; 10/188 Band; CncrtBnd; HonRl; JA; MrchBnd; PepBnd; SchMus; StuCncl; RptrYrbk; Univ Of Illinois; Landscape Architect.

BAILEY, Cheryl; Ionia HS; Ionia, MI; 12/226 TrsSophCls; TrsJrCls; TrsSrCls; HonRl; NHS; OffAde; Trk; IMSpt; Lansing Community College; Accounting.

BAILEY, Cindy K; N Clay HS; Louisville, IL; 3/67 PresSophCls; Band; Chrs; ChrhWkr; DrmMjrt; HonRl; JrNHS; MrchBnd; NHS; NatlThespSoc; PepBnd; Trk; Chrldr; Univ Of Il; Medical Technologist.

BAILEY, Cynthia J; Sabetha HS; Sabetha, KS; Band; Chr; Chrl; Chrs; ChrhWkr; CmntyWkr; CncrtBnd; HonRl; Mdrgl; MrchBnd; NHS; Kansas State Univ; Horticulture.

BAILEY, Daryl W; Coloma HS; Coloma, MI; PresSrCls; Band; ChrhWkr; HonRl; StuCncl; StuGov; TchrAde; SptEdSchPpr; Bsktbl; CaptFtbl; Trk; IMSpt; Michigan State Univ; Political Science.

BAILEY, David L; Mills Prairie HS; Mill Shoals, IL; 5/18 HonRl; PolWkr; StuCncl; RptrYrbk; SptEdYrbk; 4-H; FFA; Bsbl; Bsktbl; LetterTrk; Trade School; Auto Mechanic.

BAILEY, Debra E; Fowlerville HS; Fowlerville, MI; Chr; CmntyWkr; HonRl; LbryAde; OffAde; TchrAde; RptrYrbk; 4-H; PpCl; 4-HAwd; College; Vocation.

BAILEY, Debra K; St Charles HS; St Charles, MI; TrsSophCls; HonRl; NHS; StuCncl; RptrYrbk; LetterBsktbl; LetterTrk; GAA; IMSpt; Coll; Coach.

BAILEY, Debra K; Sumner HS; Kansas City, KS; Band; CncrtBnd; HonRl; IntrClCncl; JrNHS; MrchBnd; NHS; Orch; PepBnd; SchMus; TchrAde; Teen; PpCl; SciCl; Purdue Univ; Medicine.

BAILEY, Debra K; Howell HS; Howell, MI; 97/377 Band; ChrhWkr; CncrtBnd; HonRl; MrchBnd; OffAde; SchMus; SctActv; TchrAde; 4-H;.

BAILEY, Dennis C; Oak Park Academy; Sioux City, IA; PresSrCls; Band; Chr; Chrl; HonRl; RptrYrbk; Union College; Elec Engineer.

BAILEY, Judith A; Triton HS; Argos, IN; CncrtBnd; HonRl; MrchBnd; PepBnd; PolWkr; Yrbk; 4-H; FTA; GAA; 4-HAwd; Indiana Univ; Special Education.

BAILEY, Judith A; Marian HS; Omaha, NE; 9/165 HonRl; NHS; FrCl; LetterTrk; College; Science.

BAILEY, Julia C; Oakville Senior HS; St Louis, MO; Chrs; HonRl; NHS; FTA; FrCl; PpCl; LetterBsktbl; LetterTrk; GAA; IMSpt; Southeast Missouri State Univ; Physical Edu.

BAILEY, Kathryn; Eisenhower Hs; Decatur, IL; 27/303 AFS; Chr; ChrhWkr; HonRl; NHS; Yrbk; Tennessee Temple College; Music.

BAILEY, Kathy L; Okemos HS; East Lansing, MI; Chr; Chrl; NHS; PolWkr; YthFlsp; College.

BAILEY, Linda L; Ashland HS; Ashland, WI; 15/225 Chr; HonRl; NHS; SchMus; SpnCl; PpCl; LetterTrk; GAA; U Of Wis Eau Claire; Social Wkr.

BAILEY, Lloyd M; N Decatur HS; St Paul, IN; PresFrshCls; PresSophCls; PresJrCls; ALBoysSt; Band; CncrtBnd; MrchBnd; RptrSchPpr; EdSchPpr; Bsktbl; Ftbl; Indiana Central Col; Law.

BAILEY, Lyndon L; Argos Comm HS; Tippecanoe, IN; ChrhWkr; 4-H; FFA; Bsktbl; Socr; Trk; IMSpt; AmLegAwd; 4-HAwd; Farming.

BAILEY, Marguerite E; Immaculata HS; Ft Laenworth, KS; 2/65 Chr; Chrs; ChrhWkr; HonRl; ModUN; SchMus; StuCncl; PresFrCl; SpnCl; PpCl; Manhattanville Col; Foreighn Service.

BAILEY, Michael J; Ofallon Twp HS; Ofallon, IL; Chr; Chrs; HonRl; Mdrgl; SchMus; SchPl; GerCl; Southern Illinois Univ; Politics.

BAILEY, Mickey E; West Vigo HS; St Mary Of Woods, IN; HonRl; YthFlsp; 4-H; FTA; MthCl; 4-HAwd; In State Univ; Veterinary.

BAILEY, Pamela; Rolling Meadows HS; Rolling Meadows, IL; 12/546 Band; HonRl; NHS; Quill&Scroll; SchPpr; Carbondale Univ; Journalism.

BAILEY, Ralph E; Shenandoah HS; New Castle, IN; 3/139 LbryAde; NHS; NatlMeritCmnd; SpnCl; MthCl; Ftbl; Purdue Univ; Pharmacy.

BAILEY, Raymond L; Central City Comm HS; Central City, IA; LetterBsktbl; Trade School; Auto Mechanic.

BAILEY, Renee M; Hannibal HS; Hannibal, MO; ALAGirlsSt; ChrhWkr; CmntyWkr; HonRl; PolWkr; SctActv; UNYO; FBLA; FTA; GAA; Hannibal La Grange Coll; Medical Field.

BAILEY, Rick D; West Aurora HS; North Aurora, IL; 20/750 PresSrCls; Band; ChrhWkr; HonRl; NHS; NatlMeritCmnd; PepBnd; StuCncl; StuGov; Illinois St Univ; Psychology.

BAILEY, Sandra L; Kimball HS; Royal Oak, MI; Band; ChrhWkr; CncrtBnd; MrchBnd; NHS; NatlMeritFnl; Orch; Mich State U; Music Therapy.

BAILEY, Sharon A; Freeland HS; Freeland, MI; TrsSophCls; Chr; CncrtBnd; HonRl; MrchBnd; NHS; NatlThespSoc; SchMus; SctActv; Yrbk; Univ.

BAILEY, Steven R; Adams Central HS; Decatur, IN; 15/120 PresSophCls; SecJrCls; VPSrCls; HonRl; NHS; RptrSchPpr; FrCl; Wrstlng; U Of In; Accounting.

BAILEY, Stuart J; Apollo HS; St Cloud, MN; PresJrCls; Chrs; HonRl; SchPl; StuCncl; RptrSchPpr; LetterBsbl; LetterFtbl; LetterWrstlng; AmLegAwd; College North Dakota State; Architecture.

BAILEY, Walter D; Mills Prairie HS; Mill Shoals, IL; SecSophCls; HonRl; EngCl; Bsbl; S Illinois Univ; Forestry.

BAILEY, Wesley A; Smith Cotton HS; Sedalia, MO; HonRl; NatlFornLg; SchPl; FrCl; LetterBsbl; IMSpt; Col Usaf Acad; Computer Program.

BAILEY DAVIS, Connie A; Greenville Senior HS; Greenville, MI; HonRl; TchrAde; SchPpr; GAA; ChmnPPFtbl; Business School; Carpentry Sec.

BAILEYS, Marsha L; Portland HS; Portland, MI; 9/126 SecFrshCls; Band; CncrtBnd; HonRl; MrchBnd; PepBnd; StuCncl; TchrAde; Chrldr; PPFtbl; College; Dental Hygiene.

BAILLARGEON, Debra J; Ralston HS; Ralston, NE; 8/251 ALAGirlsSt; HonRl; NHS; SctActv; College; Commercial Art.

BAILLIE, Jonathan J; Loup City HS; Loup City, NE; 10/60 Band; Chr; Chrs; CncrtBnd; HonRl; MrchBnd; 4-H; FFA; Ftbl; DARAwd;.

BAILO, Clark; South Lyon HS; Northville, MI; 3/270 Band; HonRl; MrchBnd; NHS; StuCncl; StuGov; LatCl; PresAwd; Notre Dame; Doctor.

BAIN, Elizabeth; Gaylord HS; Gaylord, MI; HonRl; JrNHS; NHS; OffAde; SchAde; StuCncl; TchrAde; SchPpr; FHA; CitAwd; College; Pre Med.

BAIN, Vicky S; O Fallon Township HS; O Fallon, IL; ChrhWkr; HonRl; Clge; Pro Rn.

BAINBRIDGE, Jay M; Avon HS; St Augustine, IL; TrsJrCls; Chrs; HonRl; Mdrgl; NHS; SchMus; SchPl; StuCncl; RptrYrbk; FrCl; University; Medicine.

BAINE, Robert P; Chaminado Coll Prep; Creve Coeur, MO; CmntyWkr; HonRl; LitMag; PolWkr; SctActv; StuGov; Ftbl; Trk; IMSpt; CitAwd; Air Force Academy.

BAINES, Corliss A; Queen Of Peace HS; Chicago, IL; Chrs; HonRl; LbryAde; NHS; NatlMeritFnl; NatlMeritCmnd; SpnCl; Univ Of Ill; Cpa.

BAINTER, Bradley L; Northwestern HS; Sciota, IL; 7/55 PresSrCls; VPAFS; HonRl; NHS; StuCncl; VPSpnCl; MthCl; SciCl; LetterBsktbl; LetterFtbl; LetterGlf; College; Coaching.

BAIR, Cherylyn; Swartz Creek HS; Goodrich, MI; 1/400 Band; HonRl; JrNHS; MrchBnd; NHS; NatlMeritSF; College; Medical Technology.

BAIR, Darla F; Dubois HS; Dubois, IN; Band; Chrs; ChrhWkr; CncrtBnd; HonRl; MrchBnd; NHS; PolWkr; SecStuCncl; 4-H; Indiana Univ; Muic Therapist.

BAIR, Paula L; Churubusco HS; Churubusco, IN; ChrhWkr; HonRl; TchrAde; YthFlsp; PresFHA; PresFTA; LatCl; PpCl; Ftbl; IMSpt; Indiana U; Accounting.

BAIRD, Debra A; Eastbrook HS; Upland, IN; HonRl; NatlThespSoc; SchPl; Yrbk; 4-H; PpCl; GAA; College; Computer Programming.

BAIRD, Joy A; Bayard HS; Bayard, NE; SecFrshCls; ALAGirlsSt; Chr; Chrs; ChrhWkr; HonRl; SchMus; SchPl; StuGov; FHA; Bus Sch; Private Secretary.

BAIRD, Karla J; Waterford Mott HS; Pontiac, MI; 27/395 ChrhWkr; HonRl; HospAde; SchMus; Ferris State College; Radiologist.

BAIRD, Madison W; Hillsboro HS; Fletcher, MO; 17/178 HonRl; NHS; MthCl; College; Vocation.

BAIRD, Marianne J; Benet Academy; Naperville, IL; HonRl; PpCl; College; Nursing.

BAIRD, Penny S; Yorkville HS; Yorkville, IL; 9/128 OffAde; SchMus; SchPl; RptrYrbk; RptrSchPpr; VPSpnCl; GAA; 4-HAwd; Northern Illinois Univ; Finance.

BAISCH, Susan P; Adlai E Stevenson HS; Livonia, MI; 26/750 ALAGirlsSt; ChrhWkr; CmntyWkr; HonRl; NatlMeritSF; OffAde; StuGov; LetterSwmmng; GAA; IMSpt; Univ; Engineering.

BAISCH, Tim; Kaukauna HS; Kaukauna, WI; 1/350 HospAde; JrNHS; SchPl; LatCl; MthCl; Ftbl; Trk; Wrstlng; IMSpt; EldAwd; GovHonPrgAwd; Uw Madison; Med.

BAITMAN, Candy L; Oak Lawn Comm HS; Oak Lawn, IL; 20/600 Band; CncrtBnd; HonRl; MrchBnd; NHS; StuCncl; Northern Illinois University; Social Work.

BAITS, Paul; Rockford East Sr Hs; Rockford, IL; 3/665 ALBoysSt; DrlTm; HonRl; JrNHS; NHS; NatlMeritFnl; NatlMeritSF; ROTC; SchMus; SctActv; Univ Of Ill; Electrical Engineer.

BAITS, Paul G; Rockford East HS; Rockford, IL; 3/665 ALBoysSt; DrlTm; HonRl; JrNHS; NHS; NatlMeritSF; ROTC; SchMus; Univ Of Ill; Electrical Engineer.

BAIZE, Jennifer A; Farmington HS; Farmington Hills, MI; Band; CncrtBnd; HonRl; MrchBnd; PepBnd; SecTrsFrshCls; LatCl; Work With Animals.

BAJT, Mary Lynn S; St Francis Academy; Lockport, IL; HonRl; SchMus; StuCncl; SpnCl; GAA; College.

BAKAL, Ardis H; Rich Central HS; Olympia Fields, IL; 14/400 HonRl; NatlFornLg; NHS; Quill&Scroll; SchPpr; Univ Of Illinois; Biology.

BAKENHUS, Diane; Lakeview HS; Leigh, NE; Chr; ChrhWkr; HonRl; SchPl; PpCl; College; Teacher Of Elementary Education.

BAKENHUS, Ivy D; Lakeview HS; Columbus, NE; 1/79 VPFrshCls; Band; CncrtBnd; HonRl; NHS; YthFlsp; Bsktbl; Chrldr; 4-HAwd; PresAwd; College; Teacher.

BAKENHUS, Spring M; Lakeview HS; Columbus, NE; SecSrCls; VPBand; ChrhWkr; HonRl; StuCncl; YthFlsp; RptrSchPpr; 4-H; PresPpCl; LetterBsktbl; LetterTrk; GAA; 4-HAwd; Nebraska Methodist Hosp Schl; Nursing.

BAKER, Alania M; Laingsburg HS; Laingsburg, MI; 6/86 PresSrCls; HonRl; NHS; SchMus; SchPl; StuCncl; StuGov; EdYrBk; 4-H; SpnCl; Bus Sch; Pro.

BAKER, Annette; Lawrence Central HS; Indianapolis, IN; PresJrCls; CmntyWkr; JrNHS; RedCrAde; StuCncl; EdSchPpr; FFA; Bsktbl; Socr; Swmmng; Sec.

BAKER, Barbara S; Warren Township HS; Gurnee, IL; Chr; Chrl; Chrs; ChrhWkr; HonRl; SchMus; SchPpr; 4-H; Chrldr; GAA; Univ; German.

BAKER, Bart R; Southwestern HS; Shipman, IL; 11/165 HonRl; NHS; StuCncl; SchPpr; FFA; PpCl; Bsktbl; U Of Il; Farm Management.

BAKER, Becky M; Springfield Catholic HS; Springfield, MO; SecJrCls; Chrs; ChrhWkr; HonRl; LitMag; StuGov; YthLg; SpnCl; GAA; IMSpt; St Marys Col; Counceler.

BAKER, Betsy J; Summerfield HS; Petersbug, MI; 5/70 Band; CncrtBnd; HonRl; MrchBnd; NHS; SchPl; TchrAde; Yrbk; SchPpr; Chrldr; Col; Elem Ed..

BAKER, Betty J; Atlanta HS; Atlanta, MO; 6/12 TrsSrCls; Band; Chr; Chrs; ChrhWkr; CmntyWkr; HonRl; PepBnd; EdYrBk; Bsktbl; Civil Service.

BAKER, Bonnie M; Monticello HS; Monticello, WI; TrsFrshCls; TrsSophCls; Band; CmntyWkr; HonRl; ModUN; NatlFornLg; PepBnd; TchrAde; RptrSchPpr; Business School; Vocational.

BAKER, Brenda I; Lawson HS; Lawson, MO; PresSophCls; Chrs; HonRl; NHS; SchPpr; FHA; PpCl; Trk; Chrldr; RotaryAwd; School; Airline Stewardess.

BAKER, Brenda S; Topeka HS; Topeka, KS; AFS; Chrs; CmntyWkr; HonRl; HospAde; OffAde; StuCncl; TchrAde; SchPpr; PpCl; Washburn Univ; Md.

BAKER, Brenda S; Harrisonville HS; Jarrisonville, MO; 2/152 HonRl; YthFlsp; Sec4-H; MthCl; PpCl; SciCl; ChmnBsktbl; LetterTrk; IMSpt; PPFtbl; College; Physical Education.

BAKER, Carla R; Redford Union HS; Detroit, MI; ChrhWkr; HonRl; LbryAde; YthFlsp; Mercy Clg Of Detroit; Medical Records Adm.

BAKER, Carol E; Lakeview HS; Battle Creek, MI; HonRl; NHS; NatlMeritSF; Quill&Scroll; StuGov; YthFlsp; SchPpr; PpCl; Michigan St; Bus Management.

BAKER, Charles S; Dixon HS; Dixon, MO; Band; Chrs; ChrhWkr; HonRl; MrchBnd; FTA; LetterBsbl; LetterBsktbl; LetterTrk; Univ; Bus Adm.

BAKER, Cheryl L; Reitz Memorial HS; Newburgh, IN; 1/224 CmntyWkr; HonRl; TchrAde; SecFrCl; OptClAwd; Univ; Mathematics.

BAKER, Cynthia; Coon Rapids Community HS; Coon Rapids, IA; 9/49 Band; Chr; ChrhWkr; HonRl; MrchBnd; TchrAde; RptrYrbk; 4-H; FHA; Univ; Professional.

BAKER, Cynthia A; O Fallon Township HS; O Fallon, IL; ChrhWkr; HonRl; RptrSchPpr; FHA; FrCl; PpCl; SciCl; Chrldr; IMSpt; Missouri U; Interior Desgin.

BAKER, Cynthia A; Laona HS; Laona, WI; Chrs; ChrhWkr; HonRl; LbryAde; NatlFornLg; OffAde; TchrAde; RptrSchPpr; SchPpr; 4-H; IMSpt; College; Journalism.

BAKER, Daniel M; St Marys HS; Independence, MO; TrsFrshCls; Chrs; HonRl; SctActv; StuCncl; SptEdYrbk; LatCl; LetterFtbl; CaptTrk; Clge; Forest Ranger.

BAKER, David K; Carroll HS; Ft Wayne, IN; 12/206 VPJrCls; PresSrCls; ALBoysSt; HonRl; JrNHS; NatlFornLg; NHS; SchMus; StuCncl; StuGov; College; Business Law.

BAKER, Debbie A; Toluca HS; Toluca, IL; Band; HonRl; LbryAde; SchPl; FHA; FSA; SpnCl; PpCl; SciCl; GAA;.

BAKER, Deborah; Rogers City HS; Rogers City, MI; 26/156 Band; CncrtBnd; HonRl; MrchBnd; NHS; PepBnd; RptrYrbk; Yrbk; PpCl; Trk; Michigan Tech Univ, Cpa.

BAKER, Debra; West Noble HS; Wawaka, IN; 8/123 NHS; PpCl; St Josephs Hosp; Nursing.

BAKER, Diana L; Baldwin HS; Wellsville, KS; ChrhWkr; DrlTm; LbryAde; OffAde; FHA; SpnCl; PpCl;.

BAKER, Donna M; St Charles HS; St Charles, MO; ChrhWkr; HonRl; NHS; NatlMeritCmnd; Orch; KeyCl; PpCl; Drake Univ; Business Admin.

BAKER, Don R; Roxana HS; East Alton, IL; 14/290 Band; CncrtBnd; HonRl; JA; MrchBnd; NatlMeritSF; PepBnd; Quill&Scroll; SchMus; SctActv; Coll; Geophysicist.

BAKER, Elizabeth S; Fulton HS; Fulton, MO; Chrs; HospAde; MrchBnd; RedCrAde; SctActv; TchrAde; FrCl; Bsbl; Bsktbl; LetterTrk; College; Mathematics.

BAKER, Grace; Shrine HS; Royal Oak, MI; 26/163 NHS; PpCl; Bsbl; Bsktbl; IMSpt; Wane St Univ;biology.

BAKER, Ivan L H; Hays HS; Hays, KS; 8/251 ALBoysSt; Chr; HonRl; NatlFornLg; PolWkr; SchMus; StuGov; EdSchPpr; OptClAwd; Univ Of Missouri; Journalism.

BAKER, Jack R; Augusta HS; Augusta, KS; ALBoysSt; NHS; NatlMeritSF; StuCncl; EdYrBk; College; Engineering.

BAKER, James C; Normal Comm HS; Normal, IL; 4-H; MthCl; LetterSwmmng; Univ Of Illinois; Engineering.

BAKER, James F; Switzerland Cnty HS; Vevay, IN; 1/105 HonRl; LbryAde; Indiana Univ; Chemistry.

BAKER, James M; Chase County HS; Cottonwood Falls, KS; Chrs; ChrhWkr; HonRl; SctActv; TchrAde; 4-H; Ftbl; Wrstlng; 4-HAwd; Coll; Vocation.

BAKER, Janice L; Dominican HS; Detroit, MI; TrsSophCls; HonRl; LbryAde; TchrAde; College; Eng.

BAKER, Jeffrey R; Ford Central HS; Roberts, IL; 2/65 SecAFS; ALBoysSt; Band; ChrhWkr; HonRl; PepBnd; StuCncl; LetterBsktbl; LetterTrk; U Of Il; Eng.

BAKER, Joan M; Eddyville Comm HS; Eddyville, IA; PresJrCls; Band; SecChr; Chrs; CncrtBnd; DrmMjrt; HonRl; MrchBnd; Quill&Scroll; SchPl; StuCncl; Teen; RptrSchPpr; 4-H; CaptChrldr; Iowa St Univ; Journalism.

BAKER, John; Goodland HS; Goodland, KS; 12/133 Chrs; HonRl; NHS; SchMus; Ftbl; Univ Of Kansas-;architecture.

BAKER, John G; Valley HS; Bismarck, MO; SecSophCls; HonRl; College.

BAKER, John M; West Washington HS; Salem, IN; 3/90 CncrtBnd; HonRl; MrchBnd; PepBnd; SchPl; 4-H; Trk; DARAwd; 4-HAwd; Purdue Univ; Mechanical Engineering.

BAKER, Judith L; Neoga HS; Sigel, IL; 6/73 HonRl; StuCncl; FHA; PpCl; GAA; U Of Southern Il; Registered Nurse.

BAKER, Karen E; North Central HS; Perth, ND; Band; ChrhWkr; CncrtBnd; HonRl; JA; StuCncl; StuGov; FHA; SciCl; IMSpt; Clge; Pro.

BAKER, Karen M; Warner Independent HS; Aberdeen, SD; 4/21 Chrl; Chrs; HonRl; LbryAde; RptrSchPpr; SchPpr; PpCl; Coll; Med Tech.

BAKER, Kathryn L; Charleston HS; Charleston, MO; 7/168 TrsSophCls; ALAGirlsSt; Band; HonRl; NHS; Southeast Missouri St Univ; Art.

BAKER, Keith D; Whiteland Comm HS; New Whiteland, IN; 3/174 ChrhWkr; NHS; SptEdSchPpr; 4-H; FTA; SpnCl; LetterBsbl; LetterBsktbl; 4-HAwd; Purdue U; Pharmacy.

BAKER, Kelly D; Mitchell HS; Mitchell, IN; ChrhWkr; DrlTm; SchPl; SecStuCncl; YthFlsp; Yrbk; SchPpr; 4-H; Chrldr; CitAwd; College.

BAKER, Kennie J; Maysville R I HS; Maysville, MO; Chrs; HonRl; SctActv; FHA; Trk; PresAwd; College; Psychology.

BAKER, Larry; Octavia HS; Colfax, IL; 12/44 ChrhWkr; CmntyWkr; HonRl; NHS; Yrbk; FFA; SARAwd; Joliet Junior College; Farm.

BAKER, Laura M; Satanta HS; Satanta, KS; ALAGirlsSt; Band; ChrhWkr; CmntyWkr; CncrtBnd; HonRl; HospAde; JrNHS; NatlFornLg; NHS; PepBnd; SctActv; TchrAde; PpCl; College; Psychology.

BAKER, Laurie J; Blue Earth HS; Blue Earth, MN; 19/105 VPJrCls; SecSrCls; Band; Chr; HonRl; NHS; PepBnd; YthFlsp; GerCl; IMSpt; Mankato St Coll; Nurse.

BAKER, Leslie E; New Trier West HS; Glenview, IL; 145/675 CmntyWkr; HonRl; HospAde; LitMag; NatlFornLg; PolWkr; SchMus; SchPl; TchrAde; Antioch College.

BAKER, Linda M; Brown County HS; Nineveh, IN; 2/165 ChrhWkr; CmntyWkr; HonRl; NHS; NatlMeritSF; OffAde; SchAde; TchrAde; RptrSchPpr; PresFrCl; LionAwd; Indiana Univ; Business.

BAKER, Linda M; Green Valley HS; Green Valley, IL; 2/29 PresBand; ChrhWkr; DrlTm; HonRl; NHS; SchPl; StuCncl; EdYrBk; RptrSchPpr; GAA; Il Central Coll; Dental Hygiene.

BAKER, Lynda M; Turtle Mtn Comm HS; Belcourt, ND; HonRl; HospAde; NHS; SchPpr; PpCl; Chrldr; N Dakota St Univ.

BAKER, Marie E; Winnebago HS; Winnebago, IL; 3/108 Band; Chrs; ChrhWkr; CncrtBnd; HonRl; PepBnd; GerCl; College; Nursing.

BAKER, Martha K; Trico HS; Willisville, IL; 3/90 HonRl; NHS; SchMus; SchPl; Yrbk; SecFBLA; FHA; PpCl; College; Biology.

BAKER, Mary A; Marissa HS; Marissa, IL; Aud/Vis; HonRl; LbryAde; NHS; SctActv; RptrSchPpr; FHA; MthCl; Bus Sch; Actng. .

BAKER, Melynda K; Dekalb HS; Dekalb, IL; Chr; CncrtBnd; HonRl; HospAde; MrchBnd; SchMus; StuCncl; 4-H; FrCl; 4-HAwd; Univ; Pro.

BAKER, Michael; Grayville Comm HS; Grayville, IL; Band; ChrhWkr; CncrtBnd; HonRl; MrchBnd; PepBnd; SchPpr;.

BAKER, Michael F; Rushford HS; Rushford, MN; HonRl; NHS; StuCncl; SchPpr; LetterFtbl; LetterTrk;.

BAKER, Michelle M; Wyandotte HS; Kansas City, KS; HonRl; HospAde; SctActv; Junior College; Architecture.

BAKER, Mike S; Bradley Bourbonnais HS; Bourbonnais, IL; PresFrshCls; HonRl; NHS; StuCncl; RptrSchPpr; SptEdSchPpr; Bsbl; Bsktbl; Ftbl; Ill St Univ; Indus Tech.

BAKER, Nancy A; Arlington HS; Indianapolis, IN; 21/398 CncrtBnd; HonRl; MrchBnd; NHS; Orch; PepBnd; SchAde; FrCl; GAA; DARAwd; Indiana U; Pre Med.

BAKER, Nancy D; Benton Harbor HS; Sodus, MI; 67/435 Chr; HonRl; NHS; 4-H; SpnCl; 4-HAwd; Lake Michigan Clg; Science.

BAKER, Nicholas; De Smet HS; St Louis, MO; 47/178 Chr; ChrhWkr; HonRl; NHS; LetterFtbl; Trk; LetterWrstlng; IMSpt; OptClAwd; Univ; Vetrinarian.

BAKER, Paula J; Swan Valley HS; Saginaw, MI; 22/165 ChrhWkr; HospAde; NHS; TchrAde; 4-H; SpnCl; SciCl; Michigan St Univ; Nursing.

BAKER, Paul D; Andes Central HS; Pickstown, SD; 4/46 ALBoysSt; Chrs; HonRl; VPNHS; SchPl; PresStuCncl; SptEdYrbk; Ftbl; Trk; CaptWrstlng; South Dakota St Univ; Zoology.

BAKER, Randal L; La Plata Rii HS; La Plata, MO; SecSophCls; ChrhWkr; CmntyWkr; HonRl; NHS; RedCrAde; SchPl; 4-H; FFA; FrCl; PpCl; Bsbl; Bsktbl; College; Agriculture.

BAKER, Randy E; Sycamore HS; Sycamore, IL; 45/236 AFS; HonRl; StuCncl; RptrYrbk; RptrSchPpr; Bsktbl; LetterFtbl; LetterTrk; Wrstlng; IMSpt; University; Journalism.

BAKER, Randy L; Eldora Comm HS; Eldroa, IA; PresSrCls; ChrhWkr; HonRl; LetterBsbl; CaptFtbl; LetterTrk; LetterWrstlng; Coll.

BAKER, Robert J; Hill Community HS; Lansing, MI; 8/350 Chr; HonRl; JrNHS; NHS; Orch; SchMus; StuCncl; StuGov; RptrSchPpr; Hope College; Medicine.

BAKER, Sabrina; Flushing HS; Flushing, MI; Band; CncrtBnd; HonRl; MrchBnd; NHS; NatlSciFnd; RedCrAde; SctActv; StuGov; RptrYrbk; Alma College; Medical Tech.

BAKER, Sam M; Knoxville HS; Knoxville, IA; HonRl; StuCncl; Bsbl; Bsktbl; Ftbl; Simpson College; Business.

BAKER, Sarah J; Stromsburg Public HS; Stromsburg, NE; SecFrshCls; Chrs; ChrhWkr; HonRl; NHS; SchMus; YthFlsp; SchPpr; PpCl; AmLegAwd; Bus School; Vocational.

BAKER, Sharon K; Prairie Home HS; Jamestown, MO; 1/16 PresFrshCls; SecSophCls; ALAGirlsSt; Chrs; HonRl; SchPl; EdYrBk; FHA; Bsktbl; DARAwd; Technical Sch; Technician.

BAKER, Susan; Fairfield Community HS; Fairfield, IL; Band; CncrtBnd; HonRl; MrchBnd; StuCncl; FTA; Chrldr; Illinois State; Special Ed.

BAKER, Terri L; Glidden Public HS; Glidden, WI; 4/30 Chrs; ChrhWkr; CmntyWkr; HonRl; StuCncl; TchrAde; EdYrBk; RptrSchPpr; EdSchPpr; PpCl; Univ Or Tech School; Journalism Art.

BAKER, Timothy B; Ouid Elsie HS; Elsie, MI; 3/165 ALBoysSt; Band; Chr; CncrtBnd; MrchBnd; PepBnd; SchPl; YthFlsp; RptrSchPpr; SchPpr;.

BAKER, Tracy A; Frankfort Sr HS; Frankfort, IN; Band; CncrtBnd; IntrClCncl; MrchBnd; PepBnd; SchMus; SctActv; FrCl; MthCl; SciCl; Bsktbl; Ftbl; Purdue Univ; Pharmacy.

BAKER, Vickie L; Woodland HS; Marble Hill, MO; Band; ChrhWkr; CncrtBnd; HonRl; MrchBnd; NHS; PepBnd; FHA; SecPpCl; Chrldr; College; Physical Therapist.

BAKER, William R; Grand Rapids Sr HS; Grand Rapids, MN; 16/377 PresSophCls; ChrhWkr; HonRl; StuGov; LetterBsbl; CaptFtbl; LionAwd; CitAwd; Univ Of Minnesota; Dentist.

BAKET, Linda G; Sioux Valley Comm HS; Linn Grove, IA; Band; Chr; CncrtBnd; Mdrgl; MrchBnd; NHS; PepBnd; SchMus; SchPl; LetterTrk; College; Musician.

BAKKE, Derk A; Burke Central HS; Lignite, ND; Chr; ChrhWkr; CmntyWkr; SchPl; Bsktbl; Trade.

BAKKE, Larry J; Binford HS; Binford, ND; Band; 4-H; FFA; LetterBsktbl; LetterFtbl; CaptTrk; IMSpt; 4-HAwd; PresAwd; Ndsu; Veterinary Medicine.

BAKKE, Randall W; Midway Jr Sr HS; Inkster, ND; Aud/Vis; HonRl; SchPl; FFA; LetterBsktbl; LetterFtbl; Tennis; LetterTrk; Concordia College; Speech.

BAKKEN, Jeanette A; Central HS; Aberdeen, SD; SecSophCls; Band; Chrs; CncrtBnd; HonRl; MrchBnd; PepBnd; PpCl; Business School; Professional.

BAKKEN, Peter; North HS; Fargo, ND; LitMag; NatlFornLg; NHS; NatlMeritSchl; Orch; GodCntryAwd;.

BAKKEN, Roxane R; Goodridge HS; Grygla, MN; TrsSrCls; HonRl; JrNHS; NHS; OffAde; SchMus; Yrbk; FTA; PpCl; Bsktbl; Vocational Schl; Med Secretary.

BAKKEN, Wendy J; Mt St Benidict HS; Crookston, MN; Chrs; DrmBgl; HospAde; ModUN; Sdlty; TchrAde; GerCl; PpCl; Trk; Voc Sch; Med Secretary.

BAKKER, Jon; Wellsburg Comm HS; Wellsburg, IA; 2/33 TrsJrCls; Chrs; HonRl; SchMus; YthFlsp; RptrSchPpr; PpCl; Dordt College; Engineering.

BAKKESTUEN, Cheryl L; Westby HS; Westby, WI; Band; ChrhWkr; CncrtBnd; HonRl; NHS; SchPl; RptrSchPpr; 4-H; FHA; 4-HAwd; Lacross Univ; Major Biology Minor Math.

BAKOS, Sharon J; Morton Sr HS; Hammond, IN; 46/499 HonRl; TchrAde; RptrSchPpr; SecSciCl; Tennis; University; Journalism.

BAKSYS, Sandra; Sacred Heart Academy; Springfield, IL; 3/149 Chr; ChrhWkr; HonRl; NHS; NatlMeritCmnd; SchMus; SchPl; EdSchPpr; SpnCl; GAA; Northwestern U; Ma In Journalism.

BAKULA, Paul; De Smet HS; St Louis, MO; 15/188 HonRl; IMSpt; Rockhurst Coll; Education.

BALABAN, George T; Mauston HS; Mauston, WI; CmntyWkr; HonRl; JrNHS; NHS; PolWkr; LatCl; MthCl; Bsbl; Ftbl; College; Professional.

BALABAN, Pat A; Lourdes HS; Chicago, IL; 18/277 CmntyWkr; HonRl; NHS; NatlMeritCmnd; College; Special Education.

BALAGNA, Crystal A; Farmington East HS; Farmington, IL; 1/130 Band; CmntyWkr; HonRl; LbryAde; NHS; SchMus; EdYrBk; PresFrCl; AmLegAwd; Illinois State Univ; Elem Education.

BALAJA, Pamela G; Addison Trail HS; Addison, IL; 99/596 Chr; Chrl; HonRl; HospAde; LbryAde; College; Hs Counseling Political Science.

BALAS, Thomas L; Hazen HS; Hazen, ND; ALBoysSt; HonRl; SctActv; TchrAde; PresYthFlsp; Bsbl; Bsktbl; CaptFtbl; LetterTrk; AmLegAwd; Univ; Athletic Trainer.

BALASA, Cindy A; Naperville Central HS; Naperville, IL; ChrhWkr; CmntyWkr; HonRl; OffAde; Teen; College; Professional.

BALASH, Terence J; John Glenn HS; Bay City, MI; 12/360 HonRl; JrNHS; NHS; SchMus; LetterTennis; LetterWrstlng; Saginaw Vly St Clg; Math.

BALCER, Carolyn S; Millington HS; Millington, MI; NHS; VPFHA; College; Professional.

BALCER, Debb E; Olivia Public HS; Olivia, MN; 9/104 Chrs; CmntyWkr; HonRl; MrchBnd; SctActv; Twrl; YthFlsp; FHA; GerCl; PpCl; LetterTrk; Chrldr; VPGAA; Augsburg College; Accounting.

BALCER, Marjorie H; Duluth Cathedral HS; Duluth, MN; 6/146 CmntyWkr; HonRl; ModUN; NHS; NatlThespSoc; SchPl; Univ Mn Duluth; Botany.

BALCEROWSKI, Beverly; St Francis HS; St Francis, WI; AFS; Band; HonRl; NHS; PresSpnCl; GAA; Bi Lingual Ed.

BALCHIK, Mark A; Lumen Christi HS; Jackson, MI; Band; CncrtBnd; MrchBnd; PepBnd; Sacrstn; LetterTrk; IMSpt; College; Math.

BALCIUNAS, Regina K; Maria HS; Chicago, IL; 9/301 HonRl; HospAde; PresNHS; Orch; GerCl; Univ Of Ill; Medical Technology.

BALCIUNAS, Rudolf M; Lindblom HS; Chicago, IL; Illinois Inst Of Tech; Mechanic.

BALCOM, Jennie L; Marion HS; Marion, IA; VPSrCls; Band; Chr; Chrs; ChrhWkr; CncrtBnd; HonRl; LbryAde; MrchBnd; ModUN; NatlFornLg; NHS; NatlMeritSF; Quill&Scroll; SchMus; Drake Univ; Journalism.

BALD, Timothy; Aquin Central Catholic HS; Freeport, IL; VPFrshCls; PresSophCls; Band; Chrs; HonRl; NHS; NatlThespSoc; SchMus; StuCncl; College; Theatre Education.

BALDAUF, Roseann; St Louise De Marillac HS; Morton Grove, IL; NHS; Moser Business Sch; Accounting.

BALDNER, Curtis D; Dallas Comm HS; Dallas Center, IA; ChrhWkr; HonRl; SctActv; YthFlsp; RptrSchPpr; 4-H; PpCl; LetterBsbl; Bsktbl; IMSpt; College; Industrial Arts.

BALDRIDGE, Thomas F; Carmel HS; Carmel, IN; 4/523 ALBoysSt; Band; Chr; CncrtBnd; HonRl; NHS; NatlMeritSF; NatlThespSoc; StuGov; RptrSchPpr; Coll; Engr.

BALDRY, Dean K; Wheaton HS; Dumont, MN; 28/89 VPJrCls; ALBoysSt; PepBnd; SchAde; Teen; Yrbk; 4-H; Bsbl; CaptFtbl; Trk; College; Professional.

BALDUS, Joan C; Coopersville HS; Coopersville, MI; 6/173 Chr; HonRl; NHS; LatCl; PpCl; Butterworth Sch Of Nursing; Rn.

BALDWIN, Ann C; Elgin HS; Bartlett, IL; 23/749 Band; HonRl; HospAde; NHS; NatlMeritCmnd; FNA; GerCl; Swmmng; College; Vocation.

BALDWIN, Brian; Logan HS; Lacrosse, WI; 6/220 ALBoysSt; HonRl; NatlMeritCmnd; SctActv; StuCncl; Ftbl; Wrstlng; VoiceDemAwd; Air Force Acad.

BALDWIN, Cathy L; Norris City Omaha HS; Broughton, IL; Aud/Vis; Chrs; HonRl; LbryAde; OffAde; GAA; IMSpt; College; Professional.

BALDWIN, Deborah; Oakville Senior HS; St Louis, MO; 4/340 HonRl; NHS; NatlMeritCmnd; StuCncl; MthCl; PpCl; GAA; IMSpt; LionAwd; Se Mo State Univ; Physical Educ.

BALDWIN, Donald E; Roncalli HS; Omaha, NE; HonRl; NHS; LetterFtbl; Socr; LetterTrk; CaptWrstlng; Univ; Busi.

BALDWIN, Doreen L; Morley Stanwood HS; Big Rapids, MI; 1/74 Band; CncrtBnd; HonRl; MrchBnd; NHS; PepBnd; SchPl; Yrbk; SchPpr; GerCl; Bsktbl; Tennis; GAA; Central Michigan Univ; Chemistry.

BALDWIN, Eric; Tecumseh HS; Tecumseh, MI; 4-H; Trk; College; Turf Grass Management.

BALDWIN, Gregory A; Norris City Omaha HS; Broughton, IL; Aud/Vis; Band; Chrs; CncrtBnd; LbryAde; MrchBnd; Bsktbl; Trk; IMSpt; Trade Schl; Vocation.

BALDWIN, James; Shilah Hs; Chrisman, IL; 1/44 TrsFrshCls; Aud/Vis; CmntyWkr; HonRl; SchPl; TchrAde; FFA; Bsktbl; Trk; Collge;teacher.

BALDWIN, Janice E; Eisenhower HS; Chicago, IL; 8/654 Band; ChrhWkr; CncrtBnd; HonRl; MrchBnd; NHS; Orch; PepBnd; SchAde; TchrAde; U Of Il; Accounting.

BALDWIN, Jo Ann; Our Lady Of Grace Ac HS; West Newton, IN; Chrs; CmntyWkr; HonRl; PolWkr; SchMus; TchrAde; SchPpr; FrCl; Swmmng; IMSpt; Butler Univ; Dance.

BALDWIN, Julie; Olin Consolidated HS; Hale, IA; /23 Band; Chr; Chrs; CncrtBnd; HonRl; LbryAde; MrchBnd; SchMus; Trk; Chrldr; Correspondence Course; Conservation.

BALDWIN, Julie L; Northeast Nodaway HS; Ravenwood, MO; TrsFrshCls; PresSophCls; ChrhWkr; DrmMjrt; RptrSchPpr; PpCl; Chrldr; Univ; Professnl.

BALDWIN, Katherin M; Hillsboro HS; Hillsboro, WI; ChrhWkr; CmntyWkr; HonRl; LbryAde; NatlFornLg; SchPl; TchrAde; YthFlsp; FHA; IMSpt;.

BALDWIN, Mark F; Glenbrook South HS; Glenview, IL; Band; ChrhWkr; HonRl; MrchBnd; NatlFornLg; NHS; PepBnd; PolWkr; Univ; Law.

BALDWIN, Mary M; Washington HS; Germantown, WI; 2/210 Band; NHS; PepBnd; SchPl; ChmnTwrl; ChmnMthCl; LetterBsktbl; Chrldr; PresGAA; Uw Eau Claire; Teacher.

BALDWIN, Nancy; Muskegon Heights Senior HS; Muskegon Heights, MI; 3/214 Band; ChrhWkr; HonRl; MrchBnd; NHS; SchPpr; FTA; DARAwd; Central Michigan U; Special Education.

BALDWIN, Ronald; Adrian HS; Adrian, MI; 74/700 4-H; IMSpt; Coll.

BALDWIN, Sharon L; Alma HS; Alma, WI; Band; SecChrs; HonRl; PresNHS; SchMus; SchPl; RptrSchPpr; Pres4-H; VPFBLA; Chrldr; GAA; 4-HAwd; Univ Of Wis; Youth Development.

BALDWIN, Starleen G; West Harrison HS; Little Sioux, IA; Chrs; ChrhWkr; HonRl; SchPl; Bsktbl; Swmmng; LetterTrk; IMSpt; Business Schl; Professional.

BALDWIN, Tammy K; Richland HS; Catron, MO; 5/33 SecFrshCls; SecSophCls; SecSrCls; HonRl; SchPl; VPStuCncl; RptrYrbk; FHA; Se Mo State U; Speech Or Journalism.

BALDWIN, William L; Carl Sandburg HS; Palos Park, IL; 151/700 Illinois State Col; Business.

BALDY, Brian R; Hartford HS; Hartford, WI; PresSrCls; ALBoysSt; HonRl; NHS; SctActv; StuCncl; Glf; LetterSwmmng; LetterTrk; The Citadel.

BALDYS, Mariola; St Joseph HS; Chicago, IL; 6/150 Chrs; HonRl; PresNHS; NatlMeritCmnd; StuCncl; FSA; FrCl; MthCl; SciCl; JAAwd; CitAwd; VoiceDemAwd; Loyola Univ; Medicine.

BALE, Debbie L; Delavan HS; Delavan, IL; 9/54 Band; DrlTm; HonRl; HospAde; NatlThespSoc; SchPl; PresStuCncl; RptrSchPpr; FNA; SecSciCl; Trk; Methodist Schl Of Nursing; R Nurse.

BALE, Marsha D; Tecumseh HS; Tipton, MI; 1/242 SecJrCls; Band; IntrClCncl; LitMag; NHS; NatlMeritCmnd; SchMus; SchPl; YthFlsp; SpnCl; Western Mich Univ; Paper Science.

BALEJ, Diana L; Riverside Brookfield HS; Brookfield, IL; 31/471 Chrl; HonRl; YthFlsp; Univ Of Illinois; Biological Sciences.

BALENTINE, Audrey M; St Thomas Apostle HS; Chicago, IL; 9/45 HonRl; HospAde; TchrAde; College; Nursing.

BALER, Claudia M; Ann Arbor Huron HS; Ann Arbor, MI; 19/572 PresFrshCls; Chr; HonRl; NatlFornLg; PolWkr; SchMus; StuGov; Yrbk; DARAwd; OptClAwd; Pol Sci/law.

BALERUD, Lee J; Magic City Campus HS; Minot, ND; HstJrCls; ALBoysSt; Band; CncrtBnd; HonRl; NHS; Orch; PepBnd; StuCncl; LetterTrk; Attorney.

BALES, Mary; Hardin Central C 2 HS; Hardin, MO; Chrs; ChrhWkr; CmntyWkr; HonRl; LbryAde; SecTrsFrshCls; 4-HAwd; Trade School.

BALES, Thomas A; Baraboo HS; Baraboo, WI; ALBoysSt; Band; ChrhWkr; HonRl; StuCncl; PresKeyCl; Bsbl; Ftbl; Univ Of Wis Madison; Medicine.

BALEY, Richard M; Argo Community HS; Hickory Hills, IL; 22/512 HonRl; NHS; LetterBsbl; Bsktbl; LetterFtbl; University Of Illinois; Medicine.

BALGE, Daniel N; Northwestern Prep School; Mequon, WI; PresSophCls; Chrs; SchMus; StuCncl; EdSchPpr; Bsktbl; Ftbl; Trk; IMSpt; College; Ministry.

BALGEMAN, Robert E; Westview HS; Kankakee, IL; 6/270 SecJrCls; NHS; StuCncl; LetterSwmmng; CaptTrk; University; Civil Engineering.

BALHORN, Jaclyn J; Northland HS; Remer, MN; 6/57 Chrs; HonRl; NHS; SchPl; RptrSchPpr; PpCl; Chrldr; PPFtbl; St Cloud State U; Psychology.

BALICH, Robert P; St Laurence HS; Chicago, IL; 126/380 Band; ChrhWkr; CmntyWkr; CncrtBnd; HonRl; SctActv; LetterBsbl; LetterBsktbl; LetterFtbl; LetterWrstlng; University; Physical Therapy.

BALISTRERI, Carol A; Pewaukee HS; Pewaukee, WI; 14/125 Band; Chr; ChrhWkr; CncrtBnd; HonRl; LbryAde; MrchBnd; NatlMeritSF; PepBnd; SpnCl; LetterBsktbl; Trk; GAA; IMSpt; Carroll College; Music.

BALK, Nancy A; Sr HS; Charles City, IA; Chrl; Chrs; HonRl; NHS; MthCl; PpCl; College; Medicine.

BALK, Timothy T; Centreville HS; Centreville, MI; 12/54 ChrhWkr; CmntyWkr; HonRl; SchPl; TchrAde; EdSchPpr; SptEdSchPpr; LetterBsbl; LetterBsktbl; LetterFtbl; Glen Oaks Community College; Accounting.

BALKE, Gary D; Benton County HS; Cole Camp, MO; SecJrCls; ALBoysSt; Chr; HonRl; NHS; NatlThespSoc; LetterBsbl; LetterBsktbl; College; Vocation.

BALL, Carolyn J; West Pike HS; New Canton, IL; 2/32 Band; DrmMjrt; HonRl; SecNHS; EdYrBk; FHA; Chrldr; GAA; BttyCrckrAwd; 4-HAwd; Western Illinois Univ; English.

BALL, Carolyn M; Hermitage HS; Hermitage, MO; 3/23 SecSophCls; SecSrCls; Chrs; ChrhWkr; CmntyWkr; HonRl; TchrAde; RptrYrbk; RptrSchPpr; PresPpCl; LetterBsktbl; Chrldr; CchngActv; Southwest Baptist College; Music.

BALL, David L; Koshkonong HS; Koshkonong, MO; Chr; Chrl; Chrs; ChrhWkr; HonRl; LitMag; OffAde; SchPl; EdYrBk; RptrSchPpr; College; Professional.

BALL, Debra A; Brighton HS; Brighton, MI; 6/300 TrsSophCls; Band; HonRl; MrchBnd; NatlFornLg; PresNHS; TreasNatlThespSoc; LetterBsktbl; Tennis; GAA; U Of Mich; Architecture.

BALL, Debra A; Rushville HS; Rushville, IL; 7/127 Band; Chrs; CncrtBnd; HonRl; HospAde; MrchBnd; NHS; PepBnd; 4-H; PpCl; Western Ill Univ.

BALL, Douglas J; Saints Peter & Paul HS; Saginaw, MI; 6/105 HstSophCls; HstJrCls; HstSrCls; NHS;

SchPl; StuGov; GerCl; Bsktbl; Ftbl; Jr College; Chemical Engineer.

BALL, Jane E; Carman Sr HS; Flint, MI; Chr; HonRl; LbryAde; NatlThespSoc; SchMus; SchPl; SctActv; TchrAde; RptrYrbk; Yrbk; Mich St Univ.

BALL, Jeffrey C; St Ignatius College Prep; Chicago, IL; 55/155 Chr; HonRl; NatlMeritSF; SctActv; YthFlsp; IMSpt; Univ Of Il; Accounting.

BALL, Kathy L; Ashton HS; Ashton, IL; 4/41 Band; Chr; ChrhWkr; HonRl; Mdrgl; NHS; StuCncl; Yrbk; VPFHA; GAA; G Williams Clge; Behavioral Sci.

BALL, Kenneth A; Boone County R 6 HS; Centralia, MO; Chrs; HonRl; FBLA; RotaryAwd; Linn Tech Coll; Auto Mech.

BALL, Kenny L; Girard HS; Girard, IL; Band; CncrtBnd; HonRl; MrchBnd; SctActv; YthFlsp; FrCl; SciCl; Bsktbl; Florida State; Marine Biology.

BALL, Kirk; John F Kennedy HS; Cedar Rapids, IA; 20/578 NHS; SctActv; FrCl; MthCl; IMSpt; College; Oceanographer.

BALL, Lee Anna; Central HS; Switz City, IN; 2/47 TrsJrCls; SecSrCls; ChrhWkr; HonRl; VPNHS; OffAde; TchrAde; YthFlsp; 4-H; 4-HAwd; Indiana Voc Tech College; Medical Asst.

BALL, Patrick J; Springville Comm HS; Springville, IA; 8/59 HonRl; StuGov; TchrAde; 4-H; FSA; SciCl; Bsktbl; Ftbl; AmLegAwd; 4-HAwd; Mount Mercy Coll; Med Tech Or Marine Biolog.

BALL, Phebe A; Hermitage HS; Hermitage, MO; 1/16 VPSophCls; VPJrCls; Chrs; ChrhWkr; HonRl; SchPl; StuCncl; RptrYrbk; RptrSchPpr; Chrldr; Baylor Univ; Pre Med.

BALL, Phillip; Atchison HS; Atchison, KS; 6/166 VPSophCls; ALBoysSt; HonRl; ModUN; NHS; SchMus; EdYrBk; SchPpr; Ftbl; Glf; Kansas Univ Coll; Cpa.

BALL, Phyllis; Glenbrook North Hs; Northbrook, IL; 79/650 Band; ChrhWkr; CncrtBnd; HonRl; MrchBnd; TchrAde; YthFlsp; GAA; U Of Illinois; Elementary Education.

BALL, Roger D; Centralia HS; Centralia, MO; HonRl; StuCncl; SchPpr; 4-H; FFA; 4-HAwd; College; Livestock Auctioneer.

BALL, Sandra B; Arlington HS; Indianapolis, IN; HonRl; NHS; NatlThespSoc; Orch; SchMus; SchPl; StuCncl; Yrbk; GerCl; University; Rehabilitation.

BALL, Steven C; Blair HS; Blair, NE; ChrhWkr; HonRl; SctActv; StuCncl; YthFlsp; Bsktbl; Trk;.

BALL, Tamara J; East HS; Kansas City, MO; 5/289 TrsJrCls; Band; HonRl; IntrClCncl; JrNHS; MrchBnd; StuCncl; RptrSchPpr; SpnCl; Coll.

BALL, Timothy S; West Lafayette Sr HS; W Lafayette, IN; SchMus; TchrAde; Ftbl; LetterTrk; CaptIMSpt; Purdue University; Landscape Architecture.

BALL, Warren W; Edwardsburg HS; Edwardsburg, MI; 32/175 HonRl; NHS; NatlMeritCmnd; TchrAde; College; Electical Engineer.

BALLA, Daniel; Elk Grove Hs; Elk Grove Vill, IL; 51/505 HonRl; LetterTrk; University Of Illinois; Architecture.

BALLANCE, Anya R; Bishop Ward HS; Kansas City, KS; Band; HonRl; JA; NHS; StuGov; VPMthCl; JAAwd; VFWAwd; VoiceDemAwd; University; Political Science.

BALLARD, Cathy J; Beardstown HS; Beardstown, IL; 38/140 PresFrshCls; CmntyWkr; HonRl; LbryAde; OffAde; SchAde; TchrAde; FFA; Chrldr; 4-HAwd; Western Il U; Business.

BALLARD, David L; Chadsey HS; Detroit, MI; Band; HonRl; SchAde; Univ; Pathologist.

BALLARD, Janet L; Roxana HS; East Alton, IL; Chrs; HonRl; JA; NatlMeritCmnd; OffAde; SchMus; FrCl; PpCl; SciCl; Bsktbl; Univ Of Illinois; Veterinarian.

BALLARD, Jo Ellen; Jersey Comm HS; Jerseyville, IL; Band; HonRl; MrchBnd; 4-H; SciCl; GAA; Lewis & Clark Comm College; Nursing.

BALLARD, Keith; Spalding HS; Granville, IA; Bsktbl; CchngActv; IMSpt; Trade School; Vocation.

BALLARD, Mary J; North Greene HS; White Hall, IL; Band; LbryAde; MrchBnd; SchPl; StuCncl; Twrl; 4-H; PpCl; GAA; 4-HAwd; College; Physical Therapist.

BALLARD, Roxanne; Morton East HS; Berwyn, IL; 33/710 HonRl; NHS; NatlMeritFnl; NatlMeritCmnd; Quill&Scroll; RptrYrbk; Yrbk; College; Business Adm.

BALLARD, Roy W; Mooresville HS; Mooresville, IN; 14/269 HonRl; JrNHS; NHS; PresFFA; FrCl; SciCl; Purdue Univ; Agriculture.

BALLARD, Troy L; High School; Portland, IN; 1/187 VPJrCls; HonRl; NHS; StuCncl; MthCl; SciCl; LetterBsbl; Ball State U.

BALLER, Karen; Beloit Memorial HS; Beloit, WI; 1/600 Band; ChrhWkr; CncrtBnd; HonRl; MrchBnd; NHS; Orch; SctActv; EdSchPpr; College; Medicine.

BALLEW, Brian E; Davis County Comm HS; Bloomfield, IA; SecFrshCls; Band; Chrs; ChrhWkr; HonRl; PolWkr; FrCl; LetterBsbl; LetterBsktbl; LetterTrk; Trade Or Business; Professional.

BALLINGER, Barb M; Illiopolis HS; Illiopolis, IL; HonRl; LbryAde; NHS; TchrAde; LetterTrk; Chrldr; College.

BALLINGER, Janet; Hamburg HS; Hamburg, IA; SecJrCls; Band; Chrs; CncrtBnd; HonRl; NHS; SchMus; Yrbk; SchPpr; Chrldr; College.

BALLINGER, Virginia A; Fairfield HS; Sylvia, KS; HonRl; NatlMeritCmnd; TchrAde; College; Nursing.

BALLOM, Adrian D; Paseo HS; Kansas City, MO; Chr; ChrhWkr; CmntyWkr; NatlMeritCmnd; PolWkr; ROTC; SchMus; SctActv; 4-H; College; Liberal Arts.

BALLOR, Kimberly; Bay City Central HS; Bay City, MI; 16/ HonRl; NHS; NatlMeritCmnd; EngCl; IMSpt; PPFtbl; Saginaw Valley St Coll; Medical-technology.

BALLOW, Valerie M; Park Tudor HS; Indianapolis, IN; TreasJA; NatlMeritCmnd; PolWkr; StuCncl; RptrYrbk; PresCivCl; Bsktbl; CchngActv; IMSpt; PPFtbl; In Univ; Law.

BALLS, Leisa J; Sarcoxie HS; Sarcoxie, MO; 8/65 Band; Chr; CncrtBnd; HonRl; Mdrgl; PepBnd; SchPl; YthFlsp; 4-H; FHA; FTA; PpCl; GAA; College; Music.

BALLSRUD, David E; Charleston HS; Charleston, IL; Band; HonRl; LetterBsbl; LetterBsktbl; CaptFtbl; Eastern Il Univ; Business.

BALMA, Michael J; Lake Forest HS; Lake Bluff, IL; 13/435 HonRl; JrNHS; NHS; LetterTennis; U Of Penn; Patent Law.

BALMER, Jean; North Miami HS; Akron, IN; 20/112 ChrhWkr; CmntyWkr; HonRl; NHS; 4-H; Bsktbl; Swmmng; GodCntryAwd; CitAwd; Kokomo Business; Secretarial.

BALMER, Joseph W; Bishop Du Bourg HS; St Louis, MO; Chrs; StuGov; LetterBsbl; LetterFtbl; LetterSocr; College; Professional.

BALODIS, Ingrida R; North HS; Omaha, NE; University; Vocationl.

BALOGA, Lynn M; New Ulm Sr HS; New Ulm, MN; 14/250 Chr; Chrl; HonRl; SchPpr; 4-H; SpnCl; Chrldr; GAA; St Olaf College; Psychology.

BALOW, Christopher E; Eau Claire Memorial HS; Eau Claire, WI; 41/420 HonRl; JrNHS; NHS; Bsbl; Bsktbl; Embry Riddle Aeronautic; Commercial Pilot.

BALS, Diane K; Crete HS; Crete, NE; 43/115 SecSophCls; SecTrsJrCls; SecTrsSrCls; ALAGirlsSt; Band; CncrtBnd; HospAde; PepBnd; SctActv; LetterGlf; Clge; Nursing Career.

BALS, Pamela S; Loup City Public HS; Loup City, NE; ALAGirlsSt; Band; CncrtBnd; DrlTm; HonRl; NHS; SchPl; StuGov; RptrSchPpr; Chrldr; College; Nursing.

BALSER, Douglas; Bishop Dwenger HS; Fort Wayne, IN; HonRl; JA; PolWkr; SchMus; SchPl; StuCncl; StuGov; GerCl; IMSpt; JAAwd; Purdur Univ; Engrg.

BALSEWICH, Ronald J; Brother Rice HS; Chicago, IL; 17/416 HonRl; NHS; NatlMeritCmnd; Loyola University; Psychology.

BALSKUS, Michael J; De La Salle HS; Chicago, IL; Band; HonRl; NHS; StuGov; Yrbk; Tennis; Clg; Accounting.

BALTAZOR, Gerald; Sacred Heart HS; Salina, KS; VPSrCls; Chr; Chrl; Chrs; LetterTrk; Coll; Electricity.

BALTHAZOR, Marty J; Palco HS; Palco, KS; VPFrshCls; TrsSophCls; HonRl; SchPl; StuCncl; TchrAde; Bsktbl; Ftbl; Glf; Colby Comm Clg; Professional.

BALTIMORE, Andre J; Berkeley Sr HS; Berkeley, MO; 5/300 HonRl; JA; NHS; FTA; Tennis;.

BALTRUS, Dale R; Lakeforest HS; Lake Bluff, IL; 88/443 Iowa St Univ; Doctor.

BALTZELL, Pierre E; Sully Buttes HS; Onida, SD; TrsJrCls; PresSrCls; ALBoysSt; Band; CncrtBnd; HonRl; MrchBnd; NHS; PepBnd; Coll; Prof.

BALUANZ, Patricia A; Tripoli Comm HS; Waverly, IA; Chr; Chrl; Chrs; HonRl; Mdrgl; SchMus; YthFlsp; 4-H; 4-HAwd; American Inst Of Business; Computer Prog.

BALWINSKI, Paula A; All Saints HS; Bay City, MI; 9/140 ChrhWkr; CmntyWkr; HonRl; NHS; OffAde; SchAde; TchrAde; KeyCl; Saginaw Valley St Coll; Comp Sci.

BALZ, Linda K; Athens HS; Athens, WI; 4/69 Band; ChrhWkr; HonRl; NatlFornLg; NHS; StuCncl; FBLA; FHA; PpCl; LetterTrk; Job.

BALZER, Diane; Unionville Sebewarig HS; Unionville, MI; Band; ChrhWkr; CncrtBnd; HonRl; LbryAde; MrchBnd; StuCncl; FHA; PpCl; Chrldr; Beauty.

BALZER, Kay M; Liberty HS; Liberty, IL; PresFrshCls; PresSophCls; Band; HonRl; SchPl; VPStuCncl; Yrbk; TreasFHA; Trk; Chrldr; Univ; Phy Ther.

BALZUM, Elise M; Ada HS; Ada, MN; 14/61 HonRl; JrNHS; NHS; SchPl; RptrSchPpr; EdSchPpr; FHA; PpCl; VoiceDemAwd;.

BAME, Kevin D; Trico HS; Ava, IL; 11/76 TrsSophCls; HonRl; StuCncl; RptrYrbk; Yrbk; 4-H; PpCl; SciCl; DanFAwd; Southern Il U; Engineer.

BAME, Pamela; Milan HS; Maybee, MI; Aud/Vis; HonRl; OffAde; 4-H; SpnCl;.

BAMESBERGER, Joanne K; Bartley HS; Indianola, NE; 1/15 VPSophCls; SecSrCls; Band; Chrs; ChrhWkr; HonRl; YthFlsp; PpCl; PresGAA; 4-HAwd; College; Child Development.

BAMESBERGER, Keith; Bartley HS; Indianola, NE; PresFrshCls; Chr; HonRl; MrchBnd; PepBnd; SchMus; SchPl; YthFlsp; Bsktbl; Trk; College; Vocation.

BAMMAN, Jeffrey; Rock Island Senior HS; Rock Island, IL; HonRl; JrNHS; SctActv; KeyCl; Univ Of Il; Engineering.

BAMMERLIN, Karen L; High School; Roann, IN; Band; CncrtBnd; MrchBnd; PepBnd; 4-H; FHA; CaptBsktbl; GAA; 4-HAwd; College; Secretary.

BANACH, Jo Ann; Aquinas HS; Lincoln Park, MI; PresSrCls; Chrl; HonRl; JA; LbryAde; OffAde; SchPl; RptrSchPpr; Tennis; JAAwd; Coll; Sec Sci.

BANAS, Daniel E; Wilmot Union HS; Genoa City, WI; ALBoysSt; HonRl; NHS; Quill&Scroll; StuCncl; RptrSchPpr; LetterBsbl; LetterFtbl; CaptIMSpt; U Of Wis; Bus.

BANAS, Sharon K; George Rogers Clark HS; Whiting, IN; 30/245 Chr; SctActv; StuCncl; TchrAde; Yrbk; SpnCl; PpCl; IMSpt; Secretarial Employment.

BANCZAK, Robert K; Mundelein HS; Mundelein, IL; 18/415 Band; College; Chemical Engineering.

BANDELIER, Pamela L; Gallatin R V HS; Gallatin, MO; SecSrCls; Band; Chr; CncrtBnd; HonRl; MrchBnd; PepBnd; SchPl; RptrYrbk; Yrbk; Bsbl; LetterBsktbl; LetterTrk; PPFtbl; Sw Baptist College; Home Economics.

BANDELIER, Pamela L; Gallatin HS; Gallatin, MO; SecTrsSrCls; Band; Chr; ChrhWkr; CncrtBnd; HonRl; MrchBnd; PepBnd; SchPl; SctActv; RptrYrbk; Yrbk; SchPpr; FHA; PresPpCl; Southwest Baptist College; Home Economics.

BANDJASKI, Jeffrey; St Laurence Hs; Chicago, IL; HonRl; Bsbl; De Paul U; Accountancy.

BANDROWSKY, Timothy; St Laurence HS; Hickory Hills, IL; 12/385 HonRl; NatlMeritCmnd; Case Western Reserve Univ; Dentistry.

BANDT, Jane S; Ripon Senior HS; Ripon, WI; ChrhWkr; HonRl; SchPl; 4-H; FHA; GerCl; 4-HAwd; JAAwd; PresAwd; CitAwd; College; Professional.

BANDURSKI, Jeffrey J; Homestead HS; Mequon, WI; 20/402 HonRl; Quill&Scroll; RptrSchPpr; SptEdSchPpr; LetterGlf; IMSpt; Marquette U; Journalism.

BANDY, Kimberly S; Tri Valley HS; Downs, IL; Band; Chrs; ChrhWkr; HonRl; OffAde; SchPl; YthFlsp; RptrYrbk; SchPpr; IMSpt; Clg; Legal Sec.

BANDY, William F; Illinois Valley Central HS; Chillicothe, IL; 5/230 Band; CncrtBnd; HonRl; MrchBnd; PresNHS; PepBnd; SctActv; CaptTrk; College; Liberal Arts.

BANE, Connie M; Oakland Comm HS; Oakland, IA; 5/39 TrsJrCls; RptrSchPpr; SptEdSchPpr; SchPpr; 4-H; FNA; PpCl; LetterBsktbl; LetterTrk; 4-HAwd; College; Industrial Arts.

BANERIAN, Steven P; Thomas More HS; West Allis, WI; 6/155 HonRl; NHS; NatlMeritFnl; NatlSciFnd; Quill&Scroll; Yrbk; RptrSchPpr; SchPpr; BauchLmbAwd;.

BANGASSER, Kathleen; Ogorman Hs; Sioux Falls, SD; Chrs; ChrhWkr; CncrtBnd; MrchBnd; PepBnd; College; Music Ed.

BANGEL, Linda L; Kewanna HS; Kewanna, IN; 1/25 Band; Chr; Chrs; ChrhWkr; CncrtBnd; HonRl; LbryAde; GAA; DARAwd; 4-HAwd; Valparaiso Univ; Nursing.

BANGERT, Barbara E; Concordia Acad; St Paul, MN; 4/51 PresFrshCls; SecJrCls; Chr; HonRl; NHS; SchMus; GerCl; CaptBsktbl; Tennis; Chrldr; Lakewood Jr Coll; Nursing.

BANGS, Wayne K; Westhope Public HS; Landa, ND; Chrs; HonRl; SchPl; TchrAde; SptEdSchPpr; SchPpr; VPFFA; Bsktbl; Ftbl; LetterTrk; U Of Nd; Economics.

BANIK, Michael K; Technical Vocational HS; Hammond, IN; 5/300 PresSophCls; VPSrCls; ALBoysSt; HonRl; NHS; NatlMeritSF; StuCncl; LetterSocr; LetterTrk; LetterWrstlng; College; Engineering.

BANKEN, Robert E; White Bear HS; White Bear Lake, MN; Chr; ChrhWkr; CmntyWkr; GerCl; PpCl; Bsbl; Socr; Tennis; IMSpt; College; Politician.

BANKER, Jeneen A; Richland Center HS; Richland Center, WI; 29/183 Band; Chr; ChrhWkr; CncrtBnd; HonRl; Mdrgl; NHS; PepBnd; SchPl; SecYthFlsp; College; Music Education.

BANKER, Tracy C; North Greene HS; Roodhouse, IL; ChrhWkr; CmntyWkr; HonRl; NHS; RedCrAde; StuCncl; StuGov; TchrAde; 4-H; College.

BANKS, Carla J; Mt Vernon HS; Greenfield, IN; 1/143 HonRl; NHS; OffAde; TchrAde; PpCl; University; Physical Therapist.

BANKS, Cathie I; Monett HS; Monett, MO; Band; ChrhWkr; CncrtBnd; MrchBnd; NatlFornLg; PepBnd; FTA; PpCl;.

BANKS, David M; Lanphier HS; Springfield, IL; 39/473 ChrhWkr; NHS; PolWkr; Sacrstn; Lincolnland College; Anesthetist.

BANKS, Fred; Lindblom Tech HS; Chicago, IL; 32/750 ChrhWkr; CmntyWkr; HonRl; NHS; NatlMeritCmnd; SchAde; SctActv; TchrAde; SpnCl; MthCl; LetterBsktbl; Swmmng; CchngActv; Univ; Doctor.

BANKS, Gregory A; St Francis HS; Glen Ellyn, IL; PresBand; HonRl; Sacrstn; SchMus; SctActv; Trk; AmLegAwd; Univ Of Ill; Electrical Engineer.

BANKS, Kendall L; Maine South HS; Park Ridge, IL; HonRl; Orch; PolWkr; SctActv; CaptSwmmng; Univ; Forestry.

BANKS, Michael A; Princeton HS; Princeton, MO; ChrhWkr; CmntyWkr; HonRl; SchPl; CaptBsktbl; CaptFtbl; LetterGlf; Swmmng; Trk; College.

BANKS, Sherri R; Highland Senior HS; Highland, IN; 92/538 Chr; Chrs; HonRl; HospAde; NHS; NatlMeritSchl; NatlThespSoc; OffAde; SchMus; TchrAde; College; Professional.

BANKSTON, Angelia D; Rosary HS; Detroit, MI; 12/144 SecFrshCls; HonRl; OffAde; College; Medicine.

BANN, Jennifer M; Fridley Sr HS; Fridley, MN; 64/432 Chr; HonRl; NHS; 4-H; FFA; Bsktbl; DanFAwd; Univ Of Minn; Home Ec.

BANNER, Margaret H; Hackett HS; Kalamazoo, MI; 9/143 ChrhWkr; CmntyWkr; HonRl; NHS; FrCl; LetterBsktbl; IMSpt; Western Michigan Univ; Occupational Therapy.

BANNES, Karen E; Carl Sandburg HS; Tinley Park, IL; 75/700 HonRl; NHS; GerCl; MthCl; PpCl; Univ; Nurse.

BANNICK, Randy L; Lake Benton Public #404 HS; Lake Benton, MN; Band; Chr; CncrtBnd; HonRl; MrchBnd; NHS; PepBnd; SchPl; FFA; Trade School; Radio Tv Broadcasting.

BANNING, Bruce A; Calumet HS; Gary, IN; 2/370 VPSophCls; HonRl; NHS; StuCncl; TchrAde; SpnCl; LetterBsktbl; LetterFtbl; AmLegAwd; College; Business.

BANNING, John C; Brookfield HS; Brookfield, MO; VPSophCls; VPJrCls; HonRl; NHS; PresStuCncl; RptrYrbk; RptrSchPpr; LetterBsktbl; LetterFtbl; IMSpt; College; Law.

BANNING, Robert D; Smith Cotton HS; Sedalia, MO; 7/342 ALBoysSt; NHS; MthCl; Univ Of Missouri; Mechanical Eng.

BANNON, Laura M; Pattonville HS; Bridgeton, MO; Chrs; ChrhWkr; HonRl; LbryAde; NHS; OffAde; SchAde; SchMus; StuCncl; TchrAde; FrCl; MthCl; PpCl; CaptChrldr; College.

BANNON, Lisa K; Pattonville Sr HS; Bridgeton, MO; Chrs; CmntyWkr; HonRl; NatlMeritCmnd; SchAde; PpCl; Chrldr; IMSpt; PPFtbl; College; Vocation.

BANNOS, Thomas S; Proviso West HS; Westchester, IL; 20/1100 Chr; Chrs; HonRl; NHS; NatlThespSoc; SchMus; SchPl; TchrAde; CaptSocr; Univ; Chemical Engineer.

BANSE, Perry R; Benton Community HS; Van Horne, IA; 27/142 ChrhWkr; HonRl; Mdrgl; NatlThespSoc; RedCrAde; RptrSchPpr; LetterFtbl; Trk; Wrstlng;.

BANTA, David; Forest Lake Sr HS; Wyoming, MN; Band; CncrtBnd; HonRl; MrchBnd; Orch; PepBnd; SchMus; SctActv; StuCncl; TreasFFA; GodCntryAwd; College; Civil Engineer.

BANTA, Stephanie A; Deerfield HS; Deerfield, IL; PresAFS; HonRl; ModUN; NHS; NatlMeritFnl; FrCl; Georgetown Univ; International Affairs.

BANTER, Cinda D; Eastbrook HS; Upland, IN; 60/170 SchPl; 4-H; FHA; Fort Wayne Jr Bus Col; Fashion Merch.

BANTISTA, Teresa; Depue HS; Depue, IL; Band; Chrs; HonRl; PepBnd; SchMus; FHA; CchngActv; GAA; Comm.coll.

BANTLE, Wendy M; Marinette Sr HS; Marinette, WI; 3/439 Band; ChrhWkr; CmntyWkr; CncrtBnd; HonRl; MrchBnd; NHS; NatlMeritSchl; PepBnd; SchMus; YthFlsp; PpCl; GAA; Marquette Univ; Bio Medical Engineer.

BANTZ, Kyle E; Delta HS; Albany, IN; SecTrsFrshCls; TchrAde; SchPpr; 4-H; FFA; FrCl; SciCl; Trade; Vocation.

BANWART, Sandra K; West Bend Community HS; West Bend, IA; 2/46 SecSophCls; VPSrCls; PresChr; HonRl; NHS; SecSciCl; LetterBsktbl; LetterTrk; IMSpt; 4-HAwd; Wartburg College; Physical Therapy.

BANYARD, Richard A; West HS; Minneapolis, MN; 22/303 HonRl; NatlFornLg; NHS; NatlMeritSF; Lib Arts Col; Political Science.

BAPTIST, Michael R; Andrews Academy; Berrien Springs, MI; VPFrshCls; PresSophCls; Aud/Vis; JA; NHS; StuCncl; StuGov; EdYrBk; Yrbk; RptrSchPpr; Andrews Univ Mi; Communications.

BARA, Anita M; Lourdes HS; Chicago, IL; 25/283 SecTrsJrCls; SecTrsSrCls; Chrl; Chrs; HonRl; LbryAde; NHS; Univ Of Illinois; Biology.

BARA, Jeff W; Dearborn HS; Pearborn, MI; HonRl; NHS; NatlMeritSF; SchPpr; Coll; Elec Tech.

BARAGA, Katherine L; Nathan Hale HS; West Allis, WI; Chrl; HonRl; OffAde; Orch; StuCncl; Swmmng; IMSpt; College; Professional Nursing.

BARAKS, Marcus J; Sherrard HS; Milan, IL; 10/90 Band; HonRl; MrchBnd; NHS; PepBnd; RptrSchPpr; FrCl; Bsktbl; Coll; Acct.

BARAN, Nancy L; T F South HS; Lansing, IL; 10/552 PresNHS; LatCl; PpCl; Swmmng; GAA; Eastern Ill Univ; Secondary Ed.

BARANOUSKI, Marc L; Quincy HS; Quincy, MI; ChrhWkr; HonRl; SchPl; YthFlsp; 4-H; SciCl; Bsbl; Bsktbl; 4-HAwd; CitAwd; Tri State; Mechanical Engineer.

BARANOWSKI, Anne M; Cabrini HS; Allen Park, MI; 36/167 HonRl; RptrSchPpr; PresAwd; College; Physical Therapist With Children.

BARANOWSKI, Daniel F; Carmel HS; Mundelein, IL; 5/166 PresSophCls; JrNHS; NHS; SchMus; LetterGlf; Univ Of Illinois; Law.

BARANOWSKI, John M; Lake Central HS; Dyer, IN; 42/453 Chr; CmntyWkr; HonRl; NHS; NatlThespSoc; SchPl; SctActv; TchrAde; SpnCl; VFWAwd; Ball State; Theatre.

BARANOWSKI, Lisa M; Green Lake Public HS; Green Lk, WI; 1/36 PresFrshCls; Band; HonRl; NHS; StuCncl; Yrbk; SpnCl; Bsktbl; Chrldr; GAA; College.

BARANY, Ernest J; Penn HS; Mishawaka, IN; HonRl; JA; ModUN; NatlMeritSF; Clg; Physics.

BARAVETTO, Lori A; Iron Mountain HS; Iron Mountain, MI; 10/157 Band; Chrs; CncrtBnd; DrmMjrt; HonRl; HospAde; Mdrgl; NatlFornLg; PresFTA; TreasFrCl; Coll; Journalism.

BARB, Cheryl; Council Grove HS; Alta Vista, KS; ChrhWkr; CmntyWkr; NHS; NatlMeritSchl; NatlMeritSF; TchrAde; FFA; FHA; Kansas State Univ; Pre Vetinary.

BARBEE, John S; Mt Vernon Township HS; Mt Vernon, IL; HonRl; Orch; SchMus; SctActv; College; Physician.

BARBEE, Lori; Harrold HS; Harrold, SD; 1/12 ALAGirlsSt; Band; Chrs; HonRl; LbryAde; StuCncl; EdYrBk; FTA; DARAwd; VoiceDemAwd; Northern St Coll; Elementary Teaching.

BARBEE, Mark D; Macarthur HS; Decatur, IL; 15/450 PresSrCls; HonRl; JrNHS; StuCncl; StuGov; GerCl; Univ Of Illinois; Dentist.

BARBEE, Michelle E; Porta HS; Petersburg, IL; 19/122 Chrs; ChrhWkr; Mdrgl; SchMus; RptrYrbk; 4-H; SpnCl; GAA; College; Social Worker.

BARBEE, Rustam A; Riverside HS; Milw, WI; PresSophCls; Chrs; CmntyWkr; HonRl; NatlMeritFnl; NatlMeritSF; StuGov; SchPpr; SpnCl; Bsbl; Univ.

BARBEE, Will J; Sutton Public HS; Sutton, NE; Chrs; SchAde; StuCncl; FFA; Wrstlng; Trade School; Vocational.

BARBER, Christine; Richland HS; Essex, MO; SecFrshCls; TrsJrCls; HonRl; StuCncl; EdSchPpr; FHA; College; Vocation.

BARBER, Deirdre; Mishicot HS; Maribel, WI; Band; Chrs; CncrtBnd; HonRl; MrchBnd; NatlFornLg; SchMus; SchPl; StuCncl; RptrSchPpr; Univ; Professional.

BARBER, Glen R; Pana Sr HS; Pana, IL; 14/149 PresBand; CncrtBnd; HonRl; MrchBnd; NHS; YthFlsp; 4-H; Bsktbl; LetterTennis; Trk; So Il Univ; Aviation Tech.

BARBER, James L; East Buchanan HS; Gower, MO; 12/65 VPFrshCls; PresSophCls; Band; HonRl; MrchBnd; PepBnd; SchPl; SptEdYrbk; LetterBsktbl; LetterFtbl; Missouri Western Clg; Business Adm.

BARBER, Kay; Echo Public HS; Vesta, MN; SecSophCls; Band; Chr; HonRl; MrchBnd; SchPl; StuCncl; RptrSchPpr; 4-H; PpCl; College; Handicaps.

BARBER, Marvin S; West Side HS; Gary, IN; Band; ChrhWkr; CmntyWkr; HonRl; PolWkr; SchMus; YthFlsp; CivCl; FrCl; Glf; Tennis; Talladega College; Law.

BARBER, Steven C; Western Comm Unit HS; Wyanet, IL; 5/57 TrsJrCls; Band; Chrs; CncrtBnd; MrchBnd; PepBnd; SchPl; RptrYrbk; RptrSchPpr; 4-H; College; Business.

BARBER, Suzanne K; Brandywine HS; Niles, MI; 4/150 AFS; Band; Chr; HonRl; Mdrgl; NHS; Orch; SchMus; AmLegAwd; College; Prof Musician.

BARBER, Troy D; Holcomb HS; Garden City, KS; TrsFrshCls; VPSophCls; CncrtBnd; HonRl; MrchBnd; RptrYrbk; Bsbl; Bsktbl; LetterFtbl; Trk; College; Vocation.

BARBERRA, Michael G; Iowa Falls HS; Iowa Falls, IA; VPFrshCls; PresSophCls; Chrs; HonRl; SchMus; PresStuGov; TchrAde; SptEdYrbk; PresFTA; LetterBsktbl; CaptTrk; Univ Of Northern Iowa; English.

BARBIER, Michele; Nerinx Hall HS; St Louis, MO; StuCncl; RptrSchPpr; PpCl; GAA; St Louis Coll; Pharmacist.

BARBOUR, Koelle G; Senior HS; Jefferson City, MO; HonRl; JrNHS; NHS; NatlMeritCmnd; StuCncl; VPMthCl; TreasSciCl; IMSpt; Univ Of Rolla; Engineering.

BARCE, Holly; Benton Central HS; Fowler, IN; 6/263 ChrhWkr; HonRl; NHS; SchPl; StuCncl; RptrSchPpr; 4-H; VoiceDemAwd; Lib Arts College; Law.

BARCHAK, Jim M; Pierce City HS; Wentworth, MO; ALBoysSt; HonRl; ModUN; NHS; TreasKeyCl; MthCl; SciCl; LetterFtbl; College; Professional.

BARCLAY, Ruth A; Chippewa Valley HS; Mt Clemens, MI; ChrhWkr; HonRl; HospAde; NatlMeritSF; OffAde; TchrAde; Yrbk; FTA; Taylor Univ; Nursing.

BARCLAY, Steven C; Olympia HS; Mclean, IL; TrsFrshCls; PresJrCls; VPChrhWkr; HonRl; SchPl; StuGov; SpnCl; PpCl; Bsbl; Ftbl; Glf; Trk; Wrstlng; College; Law.

BARCZAK, Patricia; St Marys Acad; Milwaukee, WI; PresSophCls; Chrs; HospAde; NHS; StuCncl; StuGov; PpCl; Chrldr; IMSpt; Univ; Language.

BARCZYK, Joanne; Palatine Hs; Palatine, IL; Chr; HonRl; Mdrgl; NHS; NatlThespSoc; SchMus; 4-H; University;medicine Md.

BARDEN, Samuel C; Carroll HS; Fort Wayne, IN; 6/210 Band; CncrtBnd; HonRl; MrchBnd; NHS; YthFlsp; 4-H; ChmbCommrsAwd; Univ Of Indiana; Astronomy.

BARDEN, Walter M; St Francis HS; Wheaton, IL; 8/88 Chr; Chrl; Chrs; CmntyWkr; HonRl; RedCrAde; SchMus; SchPl; FDA; FSA; SciCl; LetterBsktbl; LetterTennis; College; Doctor.

BARDGETT, James F; Marquette HS; Ottawa, IL; 8/100 VPFrshCls; TrsJrCls; HonRl; LetterBsktbl; CaptFtbl; CaptTrk; CchngActv; Colorado School Of Mines; Engineering.

BARDOL, Michele; Riverview Gardens HS; St Louis, MO; 136/750 ChrhWkr; HonRl; IntrClCncl; JrNHS; PpCl; GAA; Forest Park College; Clinical Lab Tech.

BARDOLE, Mary A; East Greene Comm HS; Rippey, IA; PresSophCls; Chrs; ChrhWkr; CncrtBnd; NHS; SchMus; SchPl; RptrSchPpr; 4-H; College; Nursing.

BARDON, Julia M; Potosi HS; Potosi, WI; Band; CncrtBnd; HonRl; HospAde; MrchBnd; PepBnd; TchrAde; FHA; PpCl; Univ; Nursing.

BARDOS, Krisztina M; Warsaw Comm HS; Warsaw, IN; TrsJrCls; Band; CncrtBnd; DrmMjrt; HonRl; MrchBnd; PepBnd; SchMus; College.

BARDUSK, Susan J; John F Kennedy HS; Chicago, IL; 80/544 Chrs; HonRl; LbryAde; FNA; SpnCl; GAA; Niu; Physical Therapist.

BARDWELL, Cindy M; Tyndall HS; Springfield, SD; SecSophCls; Chr; Chrs; HonRl; Bsktbl; College; Professional.

BARELLO, Joseph J; Joliet East HS; Joliet, IL; 71/387 PresFrshCls; IMSpt; JAAwd; PresAwd; Maharishi International Univ; Shalon Priest.

BARENT, Debra J; Lewellen HS; Lewellen, NE; ALAGirlsSt; Chrl; Chrs; HonRl; LbryAde; NatlMeritCmnd; SchMus; SchPl; StuGov; LetterTrk; College; Secretarial.

BARENTHSEN, Roger S; Powers Lake HS; Powers Lake, ND; Band; Chr; Chrs; ChrhWkr; CncrtBnd; MrchBnd; PepBnd; SchPl; StuCncl; 4-H; FFA; Bsktbl; Ftbl; University; Vocation.

BARES, Bonnie E; Ozaukee HS; Belgium, WI; 7/81 HonRl; NHS; PresStuCncl; TchrAde; EdSchPpr; VPPpCl;.

BARES, Carol A; Tyndall HS; Tyndall, SD; ALAGirlsSt; Chrs; ChrhWkr; HonRl; TreasStuCncl; StuGov; RptrYrbk; 4-H; FHA; Bsbl; CaptBsktbl; DARAwd; 4-HAwd; Nettleton Business College; Accounting.

BARFKNECHT, Andrew T; Ofallon Township HS; Ofallon, IL; 1/328 ChrhWkr; HonRl; PresNHS; NatlMeritSF; SctActv; LetterWrstlng; Purdue Univ; Chemistry.

BARGAS, Connie; Joliet East Hs; Joliet, IL; 5/381 ALAGirlsSt; HonRl; NHS; MthCl; CaptBsktbl; LetterTennis; Trk; CchngActv; PresGAA; AmLegAwd; College; Chemistry.

BARGEN, Cheryl D; Superior HS; Superior, NE; 11/83 ChrhWkr; CmntyWkr; DrlTm; HonRl; StuCncl; YthFlsp; 4-H; FBLA; FFA; PpCl; Lincoln School Of Commerce; Bookkeeper.

BARGEN, Linda; Superior HS; Superior, NE; 6/78 SecSrCls; Band; CncrtBnd; HonRl; MrchBnd; NHS; StuCncl; Teen; YthFlsp; FBLA; Lincoln School Of Commerce; Business Manage.

BARGER, Floyd E; Crothersville HS; Crothersville, IN; 10/54 Vincennes University; Mechanic.

BARGER, Regina L; Scottsburg HS; Lexington, IN; 5/174 ChrhWkr; CncrtBnd; HonRl; MrchBnd; NHS; FSA; FTA; FrCl; PpCl; BttyCrckrAwd; Ball State Univ; Music.

BARGER, Tony A; Springfield HS; Battle Creek, MI; 8/84 Band; ChrhWkr; CncrtBnd; HonRl; JrNHS; MrchBnd; NHS; PepBnd; StuGov; Kellogg Com College; Pharmacy.

BARGFREDE, Cheryl L; Jackson HS; Estherville, IA; 8/108 SecSophCls; SecJrCls; Band; CncrtBnd; MrchBnd; OffAde; PepBnd; StuCncl; TchrAde; Chrldr; Coll; Med Asst.

BARGSTADT, Julie J; Randolph Public HS; Randolph, NE; 11/60 Chrs; ChrhWkr; HonRl; SchPl; StuCncl; EdYrBk; PpCl; Chrldr; College; Professional.

BARGSTEN, Joey; Northwest Webster Com HS; Clare, IA; PresFrshCls; TrsJrCls; SecBand; Chrs; CncrtBnd; NHS; Yrbk; SchPpr; Clge.

BARHAM, Joyce M; R U C E HS; Reddick, IL; Chrs; CncrtBnd; MrchBnd; NHS; PepBnd; SchPl; Yrbk; EdSchPpr; PresFrCl; GAA; Il State U.

BARICKMAN, Paul H; Streator Twp HS; Streator, IL; 8/400 HonRl; IntrClCncl; NHS; Quill&Scroll; StuGov; EdSchPpr; Univ Of Notre Dame; Law.

BARIL, Debra; Lake Linden Hubbell HS; Lake Linden, MI; Band; HonRl; NatlFornLg; OffAde; SchPl; StuCncl; SchPpr; PpCl; Chrldr; EldAwd; Col; Nursing.

BARINGHAUS, James M; Churchill HS; Westland, MI; ALBoysSt; CtyCnl; PolWkr; StuCncl; StuGov; Univ; Bus Admin.

BARK, Dale R; Desoto HS; Desoto, WI; VPFrshCls; VPSophCls; ALBoysSt; PresBand; CncrtBnd; HonRl; MrchBnd; PepBnd; StuCncl; RptrYrbk; SptEdYrbk; LetterBsktbl; 4-HAwd; Univ Of Wisc; Journalism.

BARKDULL, Nancy; James Whitcomb Riley HS; South Ben, IN; Band; CncrtBnd; MrchBnd; Yrbk; College Or Art School; Art And Writing.

BARKE, Bradley J; Fargo North HS; Fargo, ND; Band; ChrhWkr; CmntyWkr; SchMus; YthFlsp; RptrSchPpr; SptEdSchPpr; University; Liberal Arts.

BARKE, Gary W; East Chain HS; East Chain, MN; 11/27 HstSrCls; Chrs; ChrhWkr; CmntyWkr; HonRl; SchPl; 4-H; Bsktbl; LetterFtbl; LetterTrk; Vocatonal School; Electronics.

BARKEMA, Ronald E; South Hamilton HS; Kamrar, IA; Band; CncrtBnd; HonRl; MrchBnd; Orch; PepBnd; SchPl; 4-H; FFA; College; Agriculture.

BARKER, Bonita A; Cascade HS; Clayton, IN; 12/134 ChrhWkr; HonRl; PresLbryAde; NHS; TchrAde; Pres4-H; VPLatCl; 4-HAwd; Indiana Central Bus; Secretary.

BARKER, Charlotte A; Pecatonica HS; Pecatonia, IL; Band; Chrs; ChrhWkr; Quill&Scroll; SchMus; SchPl; VPStuCncl; TchrAde; RptrYrbk; FTA; Ill State Univ; Special Education.

BARKER, Darlene J; Conway HS; Conway, MO; DrlTm; 4-H; FHA; PpCl; DanFAwd; 4-HAwd;.

BARKER, Denise J; North Linn; Ryan, IA; 11/68 Chrs; HonRl; Ia State Univ; Botany.

BARKER, Gary N; Salem Community HS; Salem, IL; 2/213 HonRl; NHS; SchMus; PresStuCncl; Yrbk; MthCl; LetterBsktbl; LetterFtbl; LetterTrk; EldAwd; GovHonPrgAwd; Southern Ill Univ; Medicine.

BARKER, James; West Delaware HS; Dundee, IA; HonRl; NHS; Ftbl; Wartburg College, Math And Com Puter Scienc.

BARKER, James B; Oak Park River Forest HS; River Forest, IL; 48/1025 Aud/Vis; Chr; Chrl; ChrhWkr; HonRl; Mdrgl; Univ Of Illinois; Engineering.

BARKER, Jill A; Aurora HS; Aurora, MO; Band; CmntyWkr; DrlTm; HonRl; NHS; PolWkr; StuGov; CaptChrldr; PPFtbl; CitAwd; Univ; Professional.

BARKER, John L; Waldron HS; Waldron, IN; 10/78 VPSophCls; Band; CncrtBnd; HonRl; JA; MrchBnd; PepBnd; Pres4-H; VPFFA; SecKeyCl; 4-HAwd; Indiana University.

BARKER, John M; Reddick HS; Essex, IL; 1/45 PresFrshCls; PresSophCls; PresJrCls; Band; CncrtBnd; HonRl; SchPl; SecTrsSophCls; Trk; AmLegAwd; Usaf Acad; Pro.

BARKER, Joni; Wapello Comm HS; Wapello, IA; Band; Chrs; CncrtBnd; HonRl; MrchBnd; PepBnd; SchMus; Yrbk; Bsktbl; IMSpt; Business School.

BARKER, Judith L; Hannibal HS; Hannibal, MO; 6/266 Band; HonRl; HospAde; NHS; PresSctActv; TchrAde; YthFlsp; EdSchPpr; SecPpCl; Tennis; U Of Mo; Medical Tech.

BARKER, Kay V; Conway HS; Conway, MO; 30/64 ChrhWkr; TchrAde; 4-H; FHA; FNA; FTA; PpCl; Bsbl; College.

BARKER, Lauren M; Oak Park HS; Kansas City, MO; Chr; HonRl; StuCncl; TchrAde; PpCl; LetterTrk; Chrldr; IMSpt; PresAwd; Univ Of Missouri; Forestry.

BARKER, Lori A; Covington Community HS; Covington, IN; 11/90 HonRl; NHS; Quill&Scroll; SchPl; RptrSchPpr; FHA; LatCl; BttyCrckrAwd; Vincinnes Univ; Nursing.

BARKER, Mark B; Burris HS; Muncie, IN; PresSrCls; StuCncl; SchPpr; Bsbl; Bsktbl; Trk; College; Law.

BARKER, Norman G; Du Bois HS; French Lick, IN; 17/81 PresJrCls; Band; NHS; SchMus; PresStuCncl; YthFlsp; Bsbl; LetterBsktbl; DanFAwd; DARAwd; Indiania St Univ; Math.

BARKER, Stephen; King City Ri HS; King City, MO; 3 PresFrshCls; ChrhWkr; CmntyWkr; HonRl; NHS; SchPl; Bsbl; Bsktbl; Ftbl; Trk; William Jewell College; Undecided.

BARKER, Sue E; Dekalb HS; Dekalb, IL; HonRl; StuCncl; 4-H; SpnCl; SciCl; College.

BARKER, Susan; Holdrege Sr HS; Holdrege, NE; Band; ChrhWkr; CncrtBnd; HonRl; MrchBnd; PepBnd; 4-H; PpCl; Trk; Univ; Professional.

BARKER, Susan C; North Decatur HS; St Paul, IN; 17/92 Chr; DrlTm; HonRl; NHS; SchMus; YthFlsp; RptrSchPpr; 4-H; GAA; 4-HAwd; College; Vocation.

BARKER, William K; Staunton HS; Staunton, IL; 17/105 HonRl; College; Business.

BARKHAUS, Rodney L; Bonduel HS; Bonduel, WI; VPSophCls; PresSrCls; ALBoysSt; HonRl; SchPl; StuCncl; YthFnd; Yrbk; 4-H; PpCl; Trade School; Dnr Foresty Work.

BARKLEY, Mary; Annandale HS; Annandale, MN; 4/120 PresJrCls; PresSrCls; MrchBnd; NHS; SchMus; StuCncl; College; Profesional.

BARKOFSKE, Mark S; Rockhurst HS; Prairie Village, KS; RptrYrbk; SchPpr; SpnCl; CaptTrk; Chrldr; IMSpt; Johnson Co Comm Clg; Business.

BARKS, Duncan R; R 1 North Callaway HS; Kingdom City, MO; 10/76 ALBoysSt; HonRl; NHS; SchPl; SptEdYrbk; 4-H; SecFFA; FTA; PresFrCl; CaptBsktbl; Ftbl; Trk; College; Business.

BARKS, Rita B; Neodesha HS; Neodesha, KS; TrsJrCls; HonRl; LbryAde; StuCncl; Yrbk; FHA; MthCl; PpCl; PPFtbl; ChmbCommrsAwd; Acct.

BARKSDALE, Kimberly A; Lutheran West HS; Detroit, MI; ChrhWkr; CmntyWkr; DrlTm; HonRl; NatlMeritSF; StuCncl; GerCl; TreasPpCl; College; Pre Med.

BARLAGE, Deann L; Campbell Tintah HS; Tenney, MN; VPFrshCls; Chr; RptrSchPpr; FHA; Bsktbl; Trk; Chrldr; PresAwd; Trade Sch; Vocation.

BARLAMENT, Richard S; West De Pere HS; De Pere, WI; HonRl; SchPl; FrCl; LetterFtbl; LetterGlf; Western Il U; Athletic Training.

BARLAR, Mary E; Valley Park HS; Valley Park, MO; HonRl; NHS; Yrbk; TreasFHA; VPFrCl; PpCl; CchngActv; Univ; Accountant.

BARLASS, Carol A; Milton Sr HS; Janesville, WI; Band; Chr; CncrtBnd; HonRl; MrchBnd; SchMus; TreasStuCncl; TchrAde; Yrbk; 4-H; SpnCl; PpCl; LetterNe Oklahoma A&m College; Research.

BARLEY, Angela E; Lindbloom HS; Chicago, IL; HonRl; OffAde; TchrAde; Univ Of Chicago; Sociology.

BARLOW, Cindy A; Waldron HS; Shelbyville, IN; Band; Chr; Chrs; CncrtBnd; MrchBnd; RptrSchPpr; 4-H; LatCl; CaptChrldr; GAA; Ball State; Secretarial.

BARLOW, Mary A; Springfield Southeast HS; Springfield, IL; Chr; ChrhWkr; CmntyWkr; HonRl; OffAde; TchrAde; CchngActv; GAA; Lincoln Land Comm Clg; Data Processing.

BARLOW, Patricia; Clarkston HS; Clarkston, MI; 4/420 Chr; HonRl; Mdrgl; NHS; NatlThespSoc; SchMus; StuCncl; StuGov; CitAwd; Olivet Nazarene Coll; Social Welfare.

BARLOW, Terry J; Mt Carroll HS; Mt Carroll, IL; 4/75 ALBoysSt; HonRl; JrNHS; LitMag; NHS; NatlMeritCmnd; SchMus; SchPl; StuCncl; StuGov; YthFnd; LetterBsktbl; LetterFtbl; LetterTrk; Texas Christian Univ; Computer Programmer.

BARLOW, Timothy H; Galva HS; Glva, IL; 7/69 HonRl; NHS; YthFlsp; PpCl; Bsktbl; Ftbl; Univ; Marketing.

BARMANN, Carolyn S; Maryville R 2 HS; Maryville, MO; HospAde; NHS; PresYthFlsp; EdSchPpr; FHA; SpnCl; PpCl; Tennis; IMSpt; BttyCrckrAwd; Northwest Missouri State Univ; Journalism.

BARMANN, Carolyn S; Maryville R Ii HS; Maryville, MO; ALAGirlsSt; HospAde; EdSchPpr; FHA; PpCl; Tennis; Nw Missouri St Univ; Journalism.

BARMORE, Angela K; Orangeville HS; Freeport, IL; 4/58 SecJrCls; Band; HonRl; SctActv; YthFlsp; FHA; Bsbl; Bsktbl; Chrldr; College; Liberal Arts.

BARNA, Debra J; Ralston HS; Omaha, NE; 35/260 AFS; Chr; Chrs; HonRl; HospAde; SchPl; SctActv; PpCl; Navy; Nursing.

BARNACK, Mark J; Lew Wallace HS; Gary, IN; 11/513 HonRl; JrNHS; NHS; TchrAde; Ftbl; Purdue Univ.

BARNARD, Gregory L; Wayne City HS; Wayne City, IL; 11/54 VPSophCls; HonRl; PresNHS; RptrSchPpr; FFA; MthCl; PpCl; Rend Lake Jr College; Vocational.

BARNARD, Michael P; Pinckney HS; Lakeland, MI; Aud/Vis; Band; Chr; ChrhWkr; CmntyWkr; HonRl; SctActv; StuCncl; StuGov; YthFlsp; LetterFtbl; Swmmng; LetterTrk; University; Architectural Engineer.

BARNARD, Vicki A; Crete HS; Pleasant Dale, NE; Chr; CmntyWkr; HonRl; NatlThespSoc; SchMus; SchPl; TchrAde; YthFlsp; LetterTrk; GAA; Special Education.

BARNARD, Victoria A; Berkeley HS; Berkeley, MO; 9/287 Band; CncrtBnd; HonRl; MrchBnd; NHS; VPSophCls; SchMus; VPSctActv; PresFTA; FrCl; College; English.

BARNAS, Barbara J; Wilber Clatonia Public HS; Wilber, NE; 2/42 Band; Chr; HonRl; StuCncl; StuGov; 4-H; FHA; PpCl; LetterTrk; Chrldr; Coll.

BARNBY, Shelley; Central Cass HS; Casselton, ND; Band; Chr; CncrtBnd; HonRl; HospAde; MrchBnd; PepBnd; FHA; North Dakota School/science; Social Work.

BARNES, Anita J; King City R 1 HS; King City, MO; Chrs; ChrhWkr; HonRl; MrchBnd; NHS; SchPl; Twrl; SecYthFlsp; EdYrBk; LetterBsktbl; Northwest Mo State U.

BARNES, Ann M; Spencer HS; Spencer, IA; SecTrsSrCls; AFS; ChrhWkr; CncrtBnd; HonRl; HospAde; NatlFornLg; NHS; NatlThespSoc; StuCncl; U Of S D; Med Tech.

BARNES, Barbara J; Sandusky HS; Sandusky, MI; Band; SchPl; 4-H; GerCl; SpnCl; PpCl; Ablion College; Medical Field.

BARNES, Beverly L; Batavia HS; Batavia, IL; 13/206 TrsSrCls; AFS; Chr; NHS; SchMus; StuCncl; RptrYrbk; EdSchPpr; PPFtbl; DARAwd; U; Elem Ed.

BARNES, Billy J; Walker R Iv HS; Walker, MO; 1/21 HonRl; SchPl; StuCncl; StuGov; PpCl; LetterBsktbl; LetterTrk; DARAwd; PresAwd; CitAwd; College; Pro Or Vocation.

BARNES, Brenda L; North Branch HS; North Branch, MI; 5/141 Band; CncrtBnd; HonRl; HospAde; LbryAde; PresNHS; RedCrAde; Yrbk; 4-H; PpCl; College; Medical Lab Tech.

BARNES, Charlene; Montabella HS; Edmore, MI; 19/94 Chr; CmntyWkr; HonRl; NHS; SchPl; RptrYrbk; SpnCl; PPFtbl; Michigan State Univ; Fisheris And Wildlife.

BARNES, Constance M; Valders HS; Newton, WI; PresSrCls; HonRl; NatlMeritCmnd; SchPl; StuCncl; PpCl; Bsktbl; Chrldr; IMSpt; AmLegAwd; Business School.

BARNES, Cynthia L; Northridge HS; Middlebury, IN; 11/117 HonRl; NHS; SctActv; TchrAde; YthFlsp; RptrSchPpr; FTA; SpnCl; Indiana State Univ; Governmental Service.

BARNES, Daniel B; St Pius X HS; Arnold, MO; 7/137 PresJrCls; PresSrCls; ALBoysSt; HonRl; JrNHS; NHS; StuCncl; Yrbk; SptEdSchPpr; MthCl; LetterBsbl; LetterFtbl; Socr; College; Zoology.

BARNES, Donald; Springfield Southeast HS; Springfield, IL; DrmBgl; NatlMeritFnl; StuGov; LetterTennis;.

BARNES, Ettienne A; Saginaw HS; Saginaw, MI; 20/435 SecTrsSrCls; ChrhWkr; NHS; StuCncl; PpCl; Bsktbl; DARAwd; E Mich U; Special Education.

BARNES, Gary C; Lamar HS; Lamar, MO; AFS; HonRl; OffAde; PresStuCncl; SecKeyCl; CaptFtbl; LetterTrk; CchngActv; Southwest Mo State; Teach Phy Ed.

BARNES, Ginger M; Lawrence HS; Lawrence, MI; VPFrshCls; VPSophCls; Band; ChrhWkr; MrchBnd; SchMus; Teen; YthFlsp; SchPpr; 4-H; SpnCl; PpCl; Bsktbl; Ftbl; Jr College; Business.

BARNES, James E; Hiawatha HS; Esmond, IL; 4/50 VPFrshCls; TrsSophCls; HonRl; NHS; RptrYrbk; SchPpr; VPFFA; LetterTrk; DanFAwd; 4-HAwd; Iowa St U; Agriculture.

BARNES, Jill; Claffin HS; Ellinwood, KS; 10/50 VPFrshCls; CncrtBnd; DrlTm; HonRl; MrchBnd; SchPl; TchrAde; SchPpr; FHA; IMSpt; Coll; Airline Car.

BARNES, Joyce L; Highland HS; Highland, IN; 38/538 Bsktbl; Trk; SecGAA; PPFtbl; University; Physical Therapy.

BARNES, Keith H; Watertown Sr HS; Watertown, MN; Band; Chr; ChrhWkr; HonRl; SchMus; SchPl; YthFlsp; LetterBsbl; LetterBsktbl; LetterFtbl; College; Physical Education.

BARNES, Kelly A; Missouri Valley Public HS; Missouri Valley, IA; Chr; Chrs; ChrhWkr; RptrYrbk;

PpCl; SciCl; Bsbl; Bsktbl; GAA; IMSpt; College; Curriculum Of Major Study.

BARNES, Kenneth A; Maryville R Ii HS; Maryville, MO; 24/129 ALBoysSt; Band; MrchBnd; ModUN; NHS; YthFlsp; FFA; KeyCl; Nw Missouri State Univ; Agriculture.

BARNES, Kenneth W; Rogers HS; Michigan City, IN; CncrtBnd; HonRl; JrNHS; NHS; NatlMeritCmnd; Orch; SchMus; 4-H; 4-HAwd; Us Naval Acad.

BARNES, Lawrence E; Lilbourn HS; Lilbourn, MO; 33/71 Chr; Chrs; ChrhWkr; HonRl; SchPl; RptrYrbk; RptrSchPpr; MasAwd; College; Professional.

BARNES, Linda L; Clarkton HS; Clarkton, MO; 2/33 Band; Chrs; CncrtBnd; HonRl; LbryAde; MrchBnd; NHS; PepBnd; StuCncl; Chrldr; Ozarko; Social Worker.

BARNES, Mark J; Elk Rapids HS; Kewadin, MI; 6/67 HonRl; JrNHS; NHS; Tennis; Northwestern Mich College; Communications.

BARNES, Mary C; Hinsdale Central HS; Oak Brook, IL; 16/608 HonRl; NHS; NatlMeritSF; StuCncl; Univ Of Missouri; Journalism.

BARNES, Mary E; Niantic Harristown HS; Decatur, IL; Band; CncrtBnd; HonRl; MrchBnd; NHS; Quill&Scroll; SecStuCncl; EdYrBk; SpnCl; GAA;.

BARNES, Patrick; Northridge HS; Middleburg, IN; HonRl; SchPl; PpCl; Trk; College; Forestry.

BARNES, Patrick W; Lourdes HS; Rochester, MN; Univ; Business Admin.

BARNES, Rebecca K; Leadwood HS; Elvins, MO; 5/59 PresChrhWkr; HonRl; TreasNHS; StuCncl; Yrbk; VPFHA; Chrldr; IMSpt; College; Home Economics.

BARNES, Roxie A; Smith Center HS; Smith Center, KS; 1/61 HonRl; NatlMeritCmnd; FHA; PpCl; BauchLmbAwd; Kansas State Univ; Chemical Engineer.

BARNES, Ruth L; Sunshine Bible Academy; Lemmon, SD; 1/30 SecJrCls; PresSrCls; ChrhWkr; HonRl; SchAde; SchPl; StuCncl; TchrAde; EdYrBk; 4-H; PpCl; LetterBsktbl; LetterTrk; 4-HAwd; No Dakota St Univ; Business.

BARNES, Sheryl L; Washburn Rural HS; Wakarusa, KS; 1/185 SecSrCls; TrsSrCls; Band; HonRl; OffAde; SctActv; StuCncl; PpCl; Bsbl; Chrldr; Wichita State Univ; Phys Therapist.

BARNES, Teresa A; E Lansing HS; E Lansing, MI; Chr; Chrl; NatlMeritSF; Orch; College; Music.

BARNES, Terrance D; East Detroit HS; Warren, MI; 45/875 ChrhWkr; HonRl; NatlFornLg; NHS; NatlMeritSF; YthLg; GerCl; MthCl; LetterTrk; Tennessee Temple College; Theology.

BARNES, Terry S; Eaton Rapids HS; Eaton Rapids, MI; 42/162 HonRl; NHS; 4-H; LetterTrk; VPPPFtbl; College; Medical Field.

BARNES, Theresa A; Winola HS; Viola, IL; Band; ChrhWkr; CncrtBnd; MrchBnd; Orch; PepBnd; 4-H; SpnCl; Bsbl; LetterBsktbl; College.

BARNES, Thomas; Conde Public HS; Conde, SD; TrsJrCls; Band; Chrs; CncrtBnd; HonRl; MrchBnd; SchPl; RptrYrbk; RptrSchPpr; College; Professional Wildlife.

BARNES, Tony N; S Sioux HS; S Sioux City, NE; 28/196 HonRl; JA; JrNHS; Bsktbl; LetterFtbl; LetterTrk; College.

BARNES, Vickey J; Clarkton HS; Clarkton, MO; 5/40 SecTrsSophCls; Band; Chrs; CncrtBnd; HonRl; MrchBnd; PepBnd; PpCl; Chrldr;.

BARNES, William J; St Viator HS; Arlington Hts, IL; 17/245 CmntyWkr; HonRl; SchPl; RptrSchPpr; Glf; College; Journalism.

BARNES, William P; Assumption Jr Sr HS; Assumption, IL; Chrs; HonRl; NHS; NatlThespSoc; SchPl; StuCncl; EdYrBk; N Il Univ; Professional.

BARNES, William V; Saline HS; Saline, MI; HonRl; FDA; GerCl; Michigan Tech Univ; Engineer.

BARNET, Mary; Sterling Hs; Sterling, IL; 71/450 Band; CncrtBnd; MrchBnd; PepBnd; Sauk Valley College; X Ray Technician.

BARNETT, Ann; Brookings HS; Brookings, SD; 61/191 Quill&Scroll; SchMus; SchPl; RptrSchPpr; SptEdSchPpr; 4-H; FHA; IMSpt; 4-HAwd; Univ; Fashion Design.

BARNETT, Barb; Newton Community HS; Newton, IA; 1/310 Chr; Chrl; HonRl; NHS; SchMus; SchPl; Cpa.

BARNETT, Cheryl; Danville HS; Danville, IL; VPSrCls; CncrtBnd; HonRl; MrchBnd; JA; PepBnd; IMSpt; RotaryAwd; Danville Jr College; Computer Programming.

BARNETT, Deann R; Underwood HS; Underwood, IA; 1/41 PresJrCls; Band; CncrtBnd; HonRl; NHS; PepBnd; SchMus; SchPl; StuCncl; LetterBsbl; College; Professional.

BARNETT, Debra K; Fredericktown Sr HS; Fredericktown, MO; 33/130 Chr; HonRl; SpnCl; PpCl; CitAwd; Mineral Area Coll; Secretary.

BARNETT, Jeffrey M; Warsaw Comm HS; Warsaw, IN; Band; ChrhWkr; CncrtBnd; MrchBnd; NatlMeritSF; College; Minister.

BARNETT, John B; Fort Zumwalt HS; St Peters, MO; 141/375 ChrhWkr; HonRl; NHS; ROTC; SctActv; LetterBsktbl; LetterFtbl; LetterTrk; LetterWrstlng; GodCntryAwd; Sw Missouri State Univ; Forester.

BARNETT, Kevin L; North Nodaway R Vi HS; Hopkins, MO; 3/27 SecSophCls; TrsJrCls; Band; CncrtBnd; HonRl; MrchBnd; PepBnd; SchMus; YthFlsp; 4-H; SciCl; IMSpt; Northwest State Univ; Professional.

BARNETT, Patricia; Sherwood HS; Garden City, MO; 8/63 PresSrCls; HonRl; NHS; OffAde; EdSchPpr; Bsbl; Southwest Missouri State.

BARNETT, Patricia A; Sherwood Jr Sr HS; Garden City, MO; 8/63 PresSrCls; HonRl; NHS; OffAde; EdSchPpr; Univ; Teacher.

BARNETT, Regina K; Seneca HS; Seneca, MO; Chr; HonRl; SchPl; TchrAde; SchPpr; FTA; MthCl; Chrldr; Missouri Southern State College; Business.

BARNETT, Richard L; Baxter Springs HS; Baxter Springs, KS; VPJrCls; ALBoysSt; Band; HonRl; ModUN; NatlThespSoc; RptrYrbk; KeyCl; Glf; 4-HAwd; College.

BARNETT, Sherry K; Arlington HS; Indianapolis, IN; 34/427 CmntyWkr; HonRl; NHS; SchMus; CivCl; Socr; Swmmng; Indiana University; Medicine.

BARNETT, Steve L; Lake Crystal Public HS; Lake Crystal, MN; 7/60 PresFrshCls; HonRl; SchPl; StuCncl; YthFlsp; PresFFA; LetterBsbl; LetterBsktbl; LetterFtbl; LetterTrk; PresAwd; College; Business Mgmt.

BARNETT, Terri L; Adlai E Stevenson HS; Deerfield, IL; 19/235 HonRl; NHS; StuCncl; StuGov; FrCl; PpCl; LetterBsktbl; Univ Of Illinois; Psychology.

BARNETT, Terry; Marion Adams HS; Sheridan, IN; JrNHS; NHS; 4-H; SciCl; 4-HAwd; Purde Univ;.

BARNETT, Terry L; Atwood Hammond HS; Hammond, IL; 1/54 VPJrCls; ALBoysSt; Band; Chr; Chrs; ChrhWkr; HonRl; Mdrgl; NHS; StuCncl; YthFlsp; Bsbl; Bsktbl; Univ Of Illinois; Civil Engineer.

BARNEY, James J; Mc Donell HS; Chippewa Falls, WI; 24/93 HonRl; RptrYrbk; RptrSchPpr; Univ Of Wis; Dentist.

BARNEY, Kevin L; Dekalb HS; Dekalb, IL; 28/375 ChrhWkr; HonRl; SctActv; TchrAde; RptrSchPpr; Brigham Young Univ; Lawyer.

BARNEY, Paul M; Michigan Public HS; Michigan, ND; Band; CncrtBnd; HonRl; MrchBnd; PepBnd; FFA; LetterBsktbl; LetterFtbl; College.

BARNEY, Rodney L; Peoria Heights HS; Peoria Hts, IL; 6/93 Band; CncrtBnd; HonRl; MrchBnd; SecTrsFrshCls; PepBnd; GerCl; IMSpt; Coll; Med Tech.

BARNEY, Sally D; Highland HS; Highland, IN; 5/537 ALAGirlsSt; Chr; Mdrgl; NatlFornLg; NatlThespSoc; SchMus; SchPl; GerCl; PPFtbl; CitAwd; Brigham Young Univ.

BARNHARST, Susan M; New Lisbon HS; Camp Douglas, WI; 8/57 SecSophCls; ALAGirlsSt; Band; Chrs; HonRl; NHS; SchMus; Bsktbl; Trk; GAA; IMSpt; Trade School; Accounting.

BARNHART, Joni A; Rock Port R Ii HS; Rock Port, MO; 8/43 ChrhWkr; HonRl; StuCncl; Univ Mo; Veterinary Medicine.

BARNHART, Terri L; Oak Park HS; Kansas City, MO; CmntyWkr; HonRl; HospAde; PolWkr; SchPl; SctActv; StuCncl; TchrAde; GerCl; SpnCl;.

BARNHART, Victor A; Assumption HS; Madison, IL; Band; HonRl; NatlMeritCmnd; SchMus; Southern Ill; Music.

BARNHILL, Elizabeth; Roncalli HS; Indianapolis, IN; HonRl; Chrldr; PPFtbl; College.

BARNHILL, Jessie M; Matthews HS; Matthews, MO; Chr; Chrs; ChrhWkr; CmntyWkr; HonRl; JA; JrNHS; SchMus; SchPl; StuCncl; Yrbk; 4-H; FHA; PpCl; Business School.

BARNHOUSE, Ricky D; Nixa HS; Nixa, MO; 5/86 HonRl; SpnCl; MthCl; PpCl; SciCl;.

BARNI, Pamela K; Cor Jesu Academy; St Louis, MO; Chrl; HospAde; SchMus; EdYrBk; Southeast Mo State Univ; Bach /f Science.

BARNICK, Carol L; Jud Public HS; Jud, ND; 1/11 TrsSophCls; SecTrsJrCls; SecTrsSrCls; ChrhWkr; HonRl; LbryAde; Bsktbl; LetterTrk; LetterChrldr; PresAwd; Concordia Clg; Curriculum.

BARNSTEAD, Patricia A; Brazil HS; Brazil, IN; 1/165 Band; CncrtBnd; HospAde; MrchBnd; NHS; OffAde; PepBnd; FHA; SpnCl; SciCl; Indiana State U; Secretarial Thechnology.

BARNUM, Fawn D; Lasalle Peru Township HS; Peru, IL; Band; CncrtBnd; HonRl; MrchBnd; PepBnd; SctActv; SpnCl; PpCl; Coll; Med Lab Tech.

BARNUM, Kathleen J; Waterford Mott HS; Drayton Plains, MI; 11/400 Chrs; ChrhWkr; HonRl; Yrbk; Mi Christian Col; Math Or Art.

BARNUM, Ruth M; H H Dow HS; Midland, MI; 34/410 Chrs; ChrhWkr; HonRl; NHS; EngCl; Delta College; Interior Design.

BARO, Steven M; Central Comm HS; Albers, IL; HonRl; NHS; SchPl; SchPpr; Bsktbl; LetterFtbl; Socr; IMSpt; S Il U; Civil Engineering.

BAROHN, Gary A; Parkway North Sr HS; Creve Coeur, MO; 131/492 Tennis; Trk; Wrstlng; Embry Riddle Aero U; Aero Engineering.

BARON, Barry; Hesperia HS; Hesperia, MI; 1/85 HonRl; NHS; NatlMeritCmnd; 4-H; SpnCl; Univ; Chemical Engr.

BARON, Dean; Osborn HS; Detroit, MI; PresSrCls; HonRl; SpnCl; Univ; Oceanography.

BARON, Frank D; Zeeland HS; Zeeland, MI; 2/170 ALBoysSt; Band; ChrhWkr; HonRl; JrNHS; NHS; NatlMeritCmnd; LetterGlf; Western Mi U; Mechanical Eng.

BARON, Greg; Calumet HS; Gary, IN; JrNHS; NHS; Quill&Scroll; StuCncl; SptEdSchPpr; LatCl; Bsktbl;.

BARON, Joanne L; Joliet West HS; Joliet, IL; 54/495 Chr; CmntyWkr; HonRl; NHS; OffAde; SchAde; SchMus; TchrAde; Loyola Univ; Biology.

BARON, Joseph F; Calumet HS; Laurium, MI; Band; Chr; Chrl; CncrtBnd; HonRl; MrchBnd; PepBnd; SchMus; StuCncl;.

BARON, Stephanie B; Deerfield HS; Highland Park, IL; HonRl; NatlMeritCmnd; Univ Of Wisconsin.

BARONE, Deana L; Lockport Central HS; Crest Hill, IL; PresChr; PresChrhWkr; HonRl; HospAde; JA; Mdrgl; NatlThespSoc; SchAde; EdSchPpr; Chrldr; Ill State U; Elem Ed.

BARONE, Robert A; Holy Trinity HS; Chicago, IL; 4/170 HonRl; Coll; Curriculum Of Major Study.

BARONE, Thomas; Sycamore HS; Sycamore, IL; 19/201 HonRl; NHS; NatlMeritSF; SctActv; SpnCl; Ftbl; U Of Illinois; Professional.

BARONOVIC, Marcia L; Duchesne HS; St Charles, MO; 28/187 TrsSrCls; SecTrsSrCls; HonRl; NHS; SchMus; TreasStuCncl; EdYrBk; PpCl; Missouri Uni At Columbia; Physicl Therapist.

BAROTT, Brian R; Centennial HS; Lino Lakes, MN; Chr; CncrtBnd; HonRl; JrNHS; Mdrgl; MrchBnd; NHS; StuCncl; Bsktbl; Trk; College.

BAROWSKY, Teri; Bryan Sr HS; Omaha, NE; DrlTm; HonRl; RptrSchPpr; SchPpr; SpnCl; PpCl; Glf; Trk; GAA; IMSpt; College; Tv Or Newspaper Reporter.

BARR, Carla; Montezuma HS; Montezuma, IN; 2/55 Chr; HonRl; MrchBnd; YthFlsp; Yrbk; 4-H; FrCl; LatCl; PpCl; GAA; Liberal Arts Coll; Music Minister.

BARR, Daniel; Anderson Senior HS; Anderson, IN; 30/730 VPJrCls; PresSrCls; ALBoysSt; HonRl; NHS; FrCl; GerCl; Swmmng; DARAwd; CitAwd; Purdue Univ; Pharmacy.

BARR, David P; Bloomington HS; Bloomington, WI; VPJrCls; ALBoysSt; Chr; Chrs; ChrhWkr; HonRl; JrNHS; Mdrgl; NatlFornLg; NHS; Marquette Dental School; Dentist.

BARR, Paula J; O Fallon Township HS; O Fallon, IL; Chr; Chrs; ChrhWkr; HonRl; HospAde; LbryAde; NHS; RedCrAde; YthFlsp; Col; Nursing Us Air Force.

BARR, Ronald P; Aurora Central HS; Aurora, IL; 24/130 VPSophCls; HonRl; NHS; NatlMeritSF; StuCncl; Trk; IMSpt; GovHonPrgAwd; Univ; Computer Sci.

BARR, Terri J; Rushford HS; Lewiston, MN; Chrs; HonRl; LbryAde; 4-H; Winona Area Tech Institute; Secretary.

BARRAGER, Dana E; J C Harmon HS; Kansas City, KS; ALBoysSt; HonRl; LitMag; NatlFornLg; NHS; NatlMeritCmnd; StuCncl; SchPpr; FrCl; SciCl; U Of Ks; Social Sci.

BARRAND, Linda M; Cadillac HS; Cadillac, MI; 13/286 Band; ChrhWkr; CncrtBnd; HonRl; MrchBnd; NatlFornLg; NHS; NatlMeritCmnd; Central Michigan Univ; Spec Education.

BARRENTINE, Sarah G; Calumet HS; Gary, IN; Chr; HonRl; LbryAde; NHS; OffAde; SctActv; TchrAde; Trade School.

BARRETT, Holly A; Essex Comm HS; Essex, IA; 2/37 ChrhWkr; HonRl; HospAde; NHS; Orch; StuCncl; SpnCl; SciCl; LetterBsktbl; LetterTrk; Graceland College; Psychology.

BARRETT, Jacqueline S; Lawrence Central HS; Indianapolis, IN; Chr; NatlFornLg; NHS; SecNatlThespSoc; PresQuill&Scroll; SchMus; SchPl; Yrbk; Indiana Univ; Journalism.

BARRETT, James D; Kirksville HS; Kirksville, MO; VPSrCls; ALBoysSt; Band; HonRl; SchMus; SchPl; Yrbk; SptEdSchPpr; Bsbl; LetterWrstlng; AmLegAwd; Southwest Missouri Univ; Drama.

BARRETT, Kathleen M; Slayton HS; Avoca, MN; 19/102 Band; Chr; ChrhWkr; CncrtBnd; LetterTennis; Trk; Chrldr; GAA; PPFtbl; 4-HAwd; College; Professional.

BARRETT, Kathy M; St Louise De Marillac HS; Niles, IL; HstFrshCls; HstSophCls; HstJrCls; HospAde; Bsbl; Bsktbl; Swmmng; CchngActv; IMSpt; CitAwd; Loyola U; Nursng.

BARRETT, Kim K; North Platte HS; North Platte, NE; 39/397 HonRl; Quill&Scroll; StuCncl; SchPpr; 4-H; PpCl; College; Vacation.

BARRETT, Linda; Willmar Senior HS; Willmar, MN; /365 ChrhWkr; SchPl; TchrAde; YthFlsp; FrCl; PpCl; Willmar Jr Coll; Pre School Teacher.

BARRETT, Mary Beth; Forest View HS; Mt Prospect, IL; ChrhWkr; DrlTm; HonRl; NHS; PolWkr; FrCl; Carroll College; Accounting.

BARRETT, Matthew B; Waterford Mott HS; Pontiac, MI; 5/336 Chr; Chrl; Chrs; HonRl; IntrClCncl; SchAde; StuCncl; StuGov; TchrAde; LetterTrk; Olivet Clge; Radio Broadcaster.

BARRETT, Michael J; Assumption HS; Wisconsin Rapids, WI; 2/120 ALBoysSt; Band; HonRl; NHS; NatlMeritSF; PresKeyCl; MthCl; Bsktbl; IMSpt; U Of Wi; Actuary.

BARRETT, Nancy A; St Barbara HS; Chicago, IL; 16/88 HonRl; SchPl; StuCncl; EdYrBk; RptrSchPpr; SecFSA; University; Pharmacology.

BARRETT, Nancy R; Rockford East HS; Rockford, IL; 31/665 Chr; CmntyWkr; HonRl; NHS; NatlThespSoc; Quill&Scroll; SchMus; SchPl; Luther College; Computer Science.

BARRETT, Peggy J; Zalma HS; Grassy, MO; SecFrshCls; VPSophCls; HstJrCls; TrsSrCls; Chrs; HonRl; SchPl; StuCncl; TchrAde; LetterChrldr; Secretarial.

BARRETT, Sandee G; Triplains HS; Winona, KS; SecTrsFrshCls; SecTrsSophCls; Band; HonRl; MrchBnd; PpCl; LetterBsktbl; Ricks College; Forestry.

BARRETT, Tammara D; W Aurora HS; Aurora, IL; 10/742 Chr; Chrs; HonRl; JrNHS; Mdrgl; NHS; Univ Of Illinois; Professional.

BARRETT, Tammy J; Mauston Area HS; Mauston, WI; ALAGirlsSt; HonRl; SchPl; StuCncl; Yrbk; PpCl; Bsktbl; Chrldr; PPFtbl; PresAwd; College; Business.

BARRETT, Tammy K; Baraga HS; Baraga, MI; TrsSophCls; TrsJrCls; HonRl; PpCl; Bsktbl; LetterTrk; Mich Tech U; Medical Tech.

BARRETT, Theresa; Morgan Public HS; Morgan, MN; Chr; Chrs; HonRl; TchrAde; RptrSchPpr; FTA; GAA; Trade School; Professional.

BARRETT, Toni L; Arlington HS; Indianapolis, IN; 25/400 PresSrCls; CmntyWkr; MrchBnd; NHS; Quill&Scroll; StuCncl; TchrAde; SchPpr; PpCl; PPFtbl; Indiana Univ; Radio & Broadcasting.

BARRETT, William A; Hamburg HS; Hamburg, IA; HonRl; FFA; Trk; Wrstlng; College; Agriculture.

BARRETT, William R; Birch Run Area HS; Clio, MI; 5/150 Aud/Vis; HonRl; NHS; TchrAde; SpnCl; SciCl; B S Mi Tech Univ; Med Doctor.

BARRICK, Murray R; Clarion Public HS; Woolstock, IA; Chrs; HonRl; RptrSchPpr; 4-H; FFA; FrCl; Bsktbl; LetterTrk; 4-HAwd;.

BARRICK, Roger A; Madison HS; Winfred, SD; HonRl; 4-H; FFA; Bsktbl; Ftbl; Trade School.

BARRICK, Scott D; Northeast Hamilton HS; Blairsburg, IA; Band; Chr; Chrs; CncrtBnd; MrchBnd; SchMus; 4-H; LetterBsktbl; LetterFtbl; CaptTrk; Iccc At Webster City; Livestock Marketing.

BARRICK, Toni A; Marion Adams HS; Sheridan, IN; 3/99 HstJrCls; HonRl; NatlMeritCmnd; StuCncl; SpnCl; SciCl; Bsbl; Ftbl; CaptSwmmng; Trk; College; C P A.

BARRINGER, Pamela J; Mulberry Grove HS; Mulberry Grove, IL; Chrs; HonRl; MrchBnd; RptrYrbk; RptrSchPpr; SciCl; Bsbl; Trk; Chrldr; IMSpt;.

BARRIO, Caroline E; South HS; Omaha, NE; Chr; HonRl; JA; NHS; RptrSchPpr; SchPpr; EngCl; SpnCl; SecMthCl; Creighton Univ; Pharmacy.

BARRIS, Marty A; Chaska Sr HS; Chaska, MN; 1/215 Band; CncrtBnd; HonRl; JrNHS; MrchBnd; NHS; Orch; StuCncl; TchrAde; Trk; U Of Minn; Mech Eng.

BARRO, Margaret A; Southwest HS; St Louis, MO; 51/597 HonRl; HospAde; TreasStuCncl; CivCl; FrCl; PpCl; GAA; IMSpt; Univ; Law.

BARROH, Kathleen M; Immaculate Heart Of Mary HS; Westchester, IL; 15/213 HonRl; SchPl; TchrAde; PpCl; Swmmng; CaptChrldr; CchngActv; GAA; Coll; Pro.

BARRON, Cindy; Tri County Area HS; Pierson, MI; 15/94 VPFrshCls; ChrhWkr; HonRl; NHS; StuCncl; TchrAde; RptrYrbk; RptrSchPpr; Trk; GAA; College; Curriculum Of Major Study.

BARRON, Martin R; Beardstown HS; Beardstown, IL; 16/121 PresSrCls; Band; CncrtBnd; HonRl; MrchBnd; NHS; PepBnd; StuGov; TchrAde; PresSciCl; College; Teacher.

BARRON, Maureen P; Immaculate Heart Of Mary HS; Westchester, IL; 25/246 Chrl; CmntyWkr; HonRl; OffAde; Swmmng; Chrldr; GAA; IMSpt; College; Nursing.

BARRON, Scherri; Windsor HS; Barnhart, MO; ChrhWkr; HonRl; LbryAde; OffAde; SchPl; TchrAde; SpnCl; Tennis; Chrldr; Missoui State; Doctors Assistant Tech.

BARROW, Michelle R; Lutheran West HS; Detroit, MI; ChrhWkr; HonRl; LbryAde; OffAde; Detroit Clg Of Bus; Executive Secretary.

BARROWS, Cindy E; Inland Lakes HS; Indian River, MI; 3/86 SecFrshCls; PresJrCls; Band; Chr; Chrs; ChrhWkr; DrmMjrt; HonRl; LbryAde; MrchBnd; NHS; Trk; LetterChrldr; VFWAwd; College; Journalism.

BARROWS, Thomas E; Dundee Community HS; Carpentersville, IL; 35/364 Illinois State University; Accounting.

BARRUS, Janet M; Lake Forest HS; Lake Forest, IL; 7/450 CmntyWkr; HonRl; HospAde; JrNHS; NHS; NatlMeritFnl; NatlMeritSF; SchPl; Purdue Univ; Vet.

BARRY, Anne; Seneca HS; Joplin, MO; Aud/Vis; HonRl; TchrAde; FTA; College; Professional.

BARRY, Anthony L; Lapeer HS; North Branch, MI; Band; CncrtBnd; MrchBnd; PepBnd; SchMus; SctActv; Yrbk; 4-H; KeyCl; 4-HAwd; Eastern Mi U; Industrial Tech.

BARRY, Diane B; Liberty Comm Unit 2 HS; Liberty, IL; 6/60 VPSrCls; Chr; Chrs; HonRl; NHS; SchPl; PresSdlty; StuCncl; Yrbk; SptEdSchPpr; SecFBLA; PresFHA; SpnCl; TreasGAA; Quincy College; Business Mgmt.

BARRY, John E; Mahtomedi HS; Mahtomedi, MN; PresJrCls; ChrhWkr; CmntyWkr; HonRl; Sacrstn; PresStuCncl; TchrAde; SptEdSchPpr; Bsktbl; CchngActv; St Johns Collegeville Mn; Law.

BARRY, John T; Marist HS; Chicago, IL; 29/365 Chr; CmntyWkr; HonRl; NHS; StuCncl; SptEdSchPpr; SciCl; CaptBsktbl; Northern Ill Univ.

BARRY, Julie A; Marquette HS; Michigan City, IN; Chrs; ChrhWkr; HonRl; SchMus; SchPl; SchPpr; SpnCl; Swmmng; College; Professional.

BARRY, Julie M; Lincoln HS; Vincennes, IN; Chrs; ChrhWkr; CmntyWkr; TchrAde; FshEdYrbk; LetterBsbl; Tennis; IMSpt; Univ; Md.

BARRY, Kathleen A; Shorewood HS; Shorewood, WI; HonRl; SchMus; SchPl; PpCl; Chrldr; IMSpt; Col; Pro.

BARRY, Kathleen S; Liberty Unit 2 HS; Liberty, IL; 1/64 SecFrshCls; Chrs; HonRl; NHS; SchPl; Sdlty; RptrYrbk; PresFHA; PresFNA; PpCl; SciCl; GAA; Blessing Hosp School; Nursing.

BARRY, Kathy S; Liberty HS; Liberty, IL; 1/62 SecFrshCls; HonRl; LbryAde; NHS; RptrYrbk; VPFHA; PresFNA; PpCl; TreasSciCl; GAA; Blessing Hosp; Nurse.

BARRY, Stephen M; Harper Creek Sr HS; Battle Creek, MI; ALBoysSt; HonRl; NHS; Orch; SctActv; SchPpr; SpnCl; Bsktbl; Ftbl; AmLegAwd; Mi State U; Oceanography.

BARRY, Stephen M; Harper Creek HS; Battle Creek, MI; ALBoysSt; HonRl; NHS; Orch; SctActv; SpnCl; Bsktbl; College; Oceanography.

BARRY, Susan E; Carrollton HS; Carrollton, MO; Band; Chrs; HonRl; HospAde; NHS; PepBnd; SchMus; GerCl; SciCl; Bsktbl; Cmsu; Phy Ed.

BARRY, Thomas J; Adams Central HS; Hastings, NE; 9/54 VPSrCls; Band; Chr; HonRl; Mdrgl; NHS; SchMus; SchPpr; CaptBsktbl; CaptFtbl; LetterTrk; ChmbCommrsAwd; PresAwd; College; Science.

BARSEMA, Arthur R; Glenbard West HS; Wheaton, IL; 37/508 HonRl; NHS; LetterTrk; College; Mech Engineering.

BARSKETIS, Ophelia L; Maria HS; Chicago, IL; HonRl; LitMag; NHS; SctActv; SchPpr; FrCl; PresGerCl; Univ Of Chicago; Law.

BARSKI, Linda S; William Fremd HS; Palatine, IL; Chrs; HonRl; YthFlsp; Yrbk; SchPpr; Harper College; Business.

BARSKI, Ramona M; Good Counsel HS; Chicago, IL; 7/270 Chr; HonRl; JA; NHS; StuCncl; FNA; Univ Of Illinois; Occupational Therapy.

BARSTOW, Jonathan; Central HS; Hancock, MI; Band; CncrtBnd; HonRl; MrchBnd; Orch; SchPl; Bsbl; Chrldr; Mi Tech Univ; Computer Sciences.

BART, Stephen T; St Patrick HS; Chicago, IL; HonRl; SpnCl; College; Business.

BARTA, Barbara A; Nazareth Academy; Westchester, IL; StuGov; TchrAde; University; Special Education.

BARTA, Julie; Ellsworth HS; Ellsworth, KS; 1/69 ALAGirlsSt; HonRl; Quill&Scroll; Yrbk; RptrSchPpr; GerCl; PpCl; Kansas State Univ; Accounting.

BARTA, Kent; Niobrara Public HS; Niobrara, NE; Chr; HonRl; Sacrstn; StuGov; 4-H; Bsbl; IMSpt; 4-HAwd; Nebraska Univ; Agriculture.

BARTA, Lynn M; La Salle HS; Cedar Rapids, IA; 1/147 Chr; Chrs; HonRl; HospAde; ModUN; NatlFornLg; NHS; SctActv; Creighton Univ; Nursing.

BARTA, Millie C; Ellsworth HS; Ellsworth, KS; Band; Chrl; Chrs; CncrtBnd; HonRl; MrchBnd; PepBnd; Quill&Scroll; SchMus; YthFlsp; Yrbk; PpCl; LetterTennis; LetterTrk; College; Professional.

BARTA, Rick W; Hackett HS; Portage, MI; LbryAde; Bsbl; CaptBsktbl; Trk; CchngActv; IMSpt; Western Mich U; Cpa.

BARTA, Thomas D; New Prague HS; Jordan, MN; 25/196 HonRl; NHS; Sec4-H; FFA; 4-HAwd; Univ Of Minnesota; Medicine.

BARTA, Wayne A; Premontre HS; Green Bay, WI; 20/156 Band; ChrhWkr; CncrtBnd; HonRl; MrchBnd; PepBnd; ROTC; LetterTennis; CaptIMSpt; OptClAwd; College; Medicine.

BARTEL, Anne K; Lyons Township HS; Western Springs, IL; AFS; Chrs; HonRl; HospAde; NHS; Augustana College; Foreign Language.

BARTEL, Bonnie; Hilbert HS; Chilton, WI; 2/66 TrsJrCls; HonRl; NHS; StuGov; TchrAde; YthFlsp; RptrYrbk; PpCl; GAA; IMSpt; Fox Valley Tech; Vocation.

BARTEL, Cheryl R; Enterprise Academy; Durham, KS; SecFrshCls; SecSrCls; Band; Chr; HonRl; SecFrshCls; OffAde; Yrbk; FFA; IMSpt; College; Dietetics.

BARTEL, Cindy S; Valders HS; Valders, WI; Chrs; HonRl; NatlFornLg; NHS; SchPl; StuGov; FshEdYrbk; FHA; PpCl; VoiceDemAwd; Coll; Psychology.

BARTEL, Gary A; Omro Senior HS; Omro, WI; AFS; Band; ChrhWkr; CncrtBnd; HonRl; MrchBnd; SptEdSchPpr; FFA; LetterBsktbl; LetterFtbl; KiwanAwd; University Of Wisconsin; Forestry.

BARTEL, Kathy L; Frazee HS; Frazee, MN; ChrhWkr; HonRl; LbryAde; SchMus; Yrbk; FHA; Trk; PPFtbl; Col; Nursing.

BARTELDS, Dawn R; New Prague HS; Elko, MN; Band; Chrs; ChrhWkr; SchPl; RptrSchPpr; VP4-H; SpnCl; PpCl; IMSpt; PresAwd; Canby Vocational; Dental Asst.

BARTELL, James M; William G Mather HS; Munising, MI; 1/142 ALBoysSt; Aud/Vis; ChrhWkr; HonRl; NHS; NatlMeritSF; SchPl; StuCncl; College; Computer Technician.

BARTELL, Karen; Bristol HS; Conde, SD; VPFrshCls; ALAGirlsSt; SecTrsSrCls; PolWkr; YthFnd; Yrbk; 4-H; 4-HAwd; College; Art.

BARTELL, Monica M; Beaver Dam Sr HS; Beaver Dam, WI; 1/314 AFS; ALAGirlsSt; Chrs; HonRl; Mdrgl; NatlMeritCmnd; SchMus; SchPpr; SpnCl; GAA; Uw Eau Claire; Business.

BARTELL, Thad E; West HS; Madison, WI; 22/650 Aud/Vis; Chr; HonRl; Mdrgl; NHS; NatlMeritSF; NatlThespSoc; SchMus; SchPl; StuGov; Univ.

BARTELLI, Denise J; Colgan HS; Pittsburg, KS; 6/34 SecFrshCls; SecSrCls; ChrhWkr; CmntyWkr; HonRl; HospAde; VPNHS; StuCncl; EdYrBk; PpCl; U Of Ks.

BARTELS, Bill J; Eastern Allamakee HS; Lansing, IA; ALBoysSt; Band; CmntyWkr; CncrtBnd; HonRl; PepBnd; YthFlsp; PpCl; Bsktbl; AmLegAwd; Trade School ;pro.

BARTELS, Cindy L; Homer Community HS; Hubbard, NE; 2/22 Chrs; ChrhWkr; CmntyWkr; HonRl; NHS; Yrbk; 4-H; Chrldr; MasAwd; CitAwd; Univ; Curr Of Major Study.

BARTELS, Cynthia K; Washington Sr HS; Sioux Falls, SD; ALAGirlsSt; Chrs; ChrhWkr; HonRl; NHS; Teen; GerCl; Trk; IMSpt; Bethel College; Elem Educ.

BARTELS, David G; Lead HS; Lead, SD; 21/168 ALBoysSt; Band; CncrtBnd; HonRl; MrchBnd; Quill&Scroll; SctActv; RptrYrbk; EdSchPpr; Wrstlng; College; Professional.

BARTELS, Dawn R; New Haven HS; Fort Wayne, IN; VPChr; HonRl; NHS; PolWkr; GerCl; Indiana Univeristy; Medical.

BARTELS, Debbie S; Tecumseh Public HS; Elk Creek, NE; Chr; VPChrhWkr; HonRl; Pres4-H; PpCl; Chrldr; 4-HAwd; College; Medicine.

BARTELS, James M; Bay View HS; Milwaukee, WI; 3/569 HonRl; Quill&Scroll; SchAde; SctActv; Yrbk; SchPpr; MthCl; SciCl; BauchLmbAwd; Marquette Univ; Biomedical Eng.

BARTELS, Joy; Meridian HS; Tobias, NE; Band; HonRl; LbryAde; PepBnd; SchPl; StuCncl; RptrSchPpr; SchPpr; PPFtbl; 4-HAwd; Univ Of Ne; Vocal Mus.

BARTELS, Melanie L; Newell HS; Nisland, SD; Chrs; HonRl; LbryAde; NHS; SctActv; SchPpr; 4-H; FHA; SpnCl; PpCl; Bsktbl;.

BARTELS, Rebecca A; St Marys HS; Independence, MO; Chrs; DrlTm; HospAde; RedCrAde; SchMus; Yrbk; PpCl; Avila Clg; Nursing.

BARTELS, Teresa M; Meridian HS; Tobias, NE; 3/34 PresSophCls; ALAGirlsSt; ChrhWkr; HonRl; NHS; SchPl; EdYrBk; 4-H; LetterTrk; Chrldr; PPFtbl; 4-HAwd; College; English.

BARTELS, Thomas G; Meridian Public HS; Tobias, NE; 1/29 PresSophCls; ALBoysSt; Chrs; ChrhWkr; HonRl; NHS; NatlMeritCmnd; SchAde; SchPl; YthFlsp; Yrbk; Bsktbl; LetterFtbl; LetterTrk; College; Ministry.

BARTELS, William O; Interlochen Arts Academy; Stevensville, MI; Chr; CmntyWkr; Mdrgl; SchMus; SchPl; SctActv; StuCncl; LetterWrstlng; IMSpt; OptClAwd; VoiceDemAwd; St Edwards Univ; Theater.

BARTELSON, Kimberly; Winona Senior HS; Winona, MN; HonRl; FFA; Winona Area Tech Inst; Power Mechanics.

BARTELT, Susan J; Lyons Township HS; Western Springs, IL; AFS; Chr; Chrs; ChrhWkr; Elmhurst College; Business.

BARTELT, Thomas L; Southridge HS; Huntingburg, IN; 15/175 ChrhWkr; HonRl; YthFlsp; CchngActv; Engineering.

BARTENES, Marcy L; Highland Park HS; Highland Park, IL; CmntyWkr; HonRl; HospAde; FHA; College.

BARTH, Ellen J; Pardeeville HS; Pardeeville, WI; PresJrCls; Band; HonRl; NHS; StuCncl; Trk; Chrldr; GAA; IMSpt; PresAwd; College.

BARTH, Lori; Fairbury HS; Fairbury, NE; 57/132 Band; Chrs; ChrhWkr; HospAde; OffAde; SctActv; YthFlsp; 4-H; SpnCl; PpCl; Southeast Community College; Surgical Tech.

BARTH, William A; Minonk Dana Rutland HS; Minonk, IL; 1/59 PresBand; Chrs; Mdrgl; NHS; NatlMeritCmnd; PresStuCncl; PresYthFlsp; VP4-H; CaptBsktbl; 4-HAwd; Cornell Univ; Law.

BARTHEL, K; Nebraska Christian HS; Emelia, NE; PresFrshCls; VPSophCls; StuGov; YthFlsp; 4-H; Trk; IMSpt; 4-HAwd; College.

BARTHEL, Weston W; Nebraska Christian HS; Amelia, NE; PresSrCls; SchPl; RptrYrbk; RptrSchPpr; 4-H; CaptFtbl; 4-HAwd; Bible College; Rancher.

BARTHELL, Edward N; Armstrong Sr HS; Neenah, WI; 10/604 Aud/Vis; ChrhWkr; CmntyWkr; HonRl; JA; NHS; NatlMeritFnl; NatlMeritSF; SctActv; StuCncl; CchngActv; IMSpt; JAAwd; Univ Of Wis; Physician.

BARTHOLOMEW, Kim; West Concord HS; West Concord, MN; 8/44 SecSrCls; Chr; DrmMjrt; HonRl; NHS; SchPl; EdSchPpr; Chrldr; GAA; BttyCrckrAwd; College; Marketing Program.

BARTHOLOMEW, Linda M; New Haven HS; New Haven, IN; 9/239 TrsJrCls; Chr; ChrhWkr; HonRl; TreasJA; NatlMeritCmnd; NatlThespSoc; SecStuGov; GerCl; SciCl; Univ; Teach.

BARTHOLOMEW, Michael E; John Marshall HS; Rochester, MN; 24/608 Band; CncrtBnd; JrNHS; MrchBnd; PresNHS; PepBnd; SchMus; FrCl; GerCl; LetterBsbl; IMSpt; Luther Clg; German & Accounting.

BARTHOLOMEW, Ruth E; Erie HS; Erie, KS; TrsSophCls; SecJrCls; Band; DrlTm; HonRl; PepBnd; SchPl; YthFlsp; Yrbk; SchPpr; Sec4-H; BttyCrckrAwd; DanFAwd; 4-HAwd; Baker Univ; Radio Broadcasting.

BARTHOLOMEW, Timothy R; Triopia HS; Arenzville, IL; Band; CncrtBnd; MrchBnd; PepBnd; SchMus; SctActv; University; Music.

BARTHULY, Jane L; St Marys HS; St Marys, KS; Chrs; HonRl; LbryAde; RptrYrbk; Yrbk; RptrSchPpr; SchPpr; FHA; PpCl; Trk; Kansas State Univ; Architecture Inter Desgn.

BARTIMOCCIA, Robert; Evanston Township HS; Evanston, IL; HonRl; Trk; Univ Of Wis;forestry.

BARTKUS, Vida J; Crestwood HS; Dearborn Heights, MI; RusCl; College; Accountant.

BARTLE, John R; Univ High Of Urbana; Champaign, IL; 14/38 VPFrshCls; SecJrCls; SecTrsSrCls; ModUN; StuCncl; YthLg; SptEdSchPpr; Bsbl; CaptBsktbl; LetterTrk; Swarthmore Clg; Us Senator.

BARTLE, Mark F; Enderlin Public HS; Enderlin, ND; Band; CncrtBnd; HonRl; MrchBnd; PepBnd; TchrAde; 4-H; FFA; HstSophCls; 4-HAwd;.

BARTLE, Raymond L; Union HS; Union, MO; 33/174 ALBoysSt; HonRl; JA; SchPl; StuCncl; LetterBsbl; LetterBsktbl; CchngActv; IMSpt; PresAwd; University; Liberal Arts.

BARTLETT, Brian R; Frankenmuth HS; Frankenmuth, MI; Band; HonRl; PresJA; NatlFornLg; PepBnd; TchrAde; Ftbl; Glf; IMSpt; JAAwd; University Of Michigan; Computer Engineer.

BARTLETT, Bruce A; Cozad HS; Cozad, NE; Band; CncrtBnd; MrchBnd; Ftbl; Trk; College.

BARTLETT, Marilyn K; Waverly HS; Waverly, KS; 2/24 SecJrCls; SecSrCls; HonRl; OffAde; SchPl; StuCncl; Yrbk; PpCl; Trk; College; Elementary Education.

BARTLETT, Mary; Iowa Falls HS; Iowa Falls, IA; Chr; ChrhWkr; CncrtBnd; DrmMjrt; MrchBnd; NHS; SchMus; SchPl; University; Communications.

BARTLETT, Phyllis D; Public HS; Mc Henry, ND; Chrs; ChrhWkr; CmntyWkr; HonRl; HospAde; LbryAde; OffAde; SchAde; SchMus; TchrAde; RptrYrbk; Yrbk; RptrSchPpr; SchPpr; 4-H; College; Commercial Artist.

BARTLETT, Randy L; United Township HS; Moline, IL; PresJrCls; ALBoysSt; Chr; ChrhWkr; CmntyWkr; HonRl; NHS; VPStuCncl; YthFlsp; Black Hawk College; Psychology.

BARTLEY, Beverly L; Rolling Meadows HS; Mt Prospect, IL; HonRl; NatlThespSoc; SchMus; SchPl; College; Business Admin.

BARTLEY, Bruce A; Taylors Falls HS; Taylor Falls, MN; TrsFrshCls; StuCncl; LetterBsktbl; LetterFtbl; LetterTrk; CchngActv; IMSpt; College.

BARTLEY, David W; West Bend East HS; West Bend, WI; 77/240 4-H; CaptFtbl; LetterTrk; CaptWrstlng; Univ Of Wisconsin; Engineering.

BARTLEY, Dorian A; Loy Norrix HS; Kalamazoo, MI; Aud/Vis; TreasChr; CmntyWkr; NatlMeritSF; SchMus; GerCl; IMSpt; PPFtbl; Coll; Trial Lawyer.

BARTLEY, Julie M; Acad Of Our Lady Spalding Ins; Peoria, IL; SchMus; SchPl; GerCl; PpCl; Chrldr; PPFtbl; Coll; Phy Therapy.

BARTLEY, Valerie A; Mc Donald County HS; Anderson, MO; 2/175 PresJrCls; ChrhWkr; HonRl; JrNHS; NHS; StuCncl; SchPpr; FHA; PresFTA; PpCl; College; Medical Career.

BARTLING, Jackie J; Southside HS; Muncie, IN; I V Tech; Secretarial.

BARTLING, Linda M; Batesville HS; Morris, IN; 4/150 SecFrshCls; PresSophCls; ALAGirlsSt; CncrtBnd; HonRl; JrNHS; MrchBnd; StuCncl; LionAwd; VFWAwd; Nursing.

BARTLOW, Michael D; Washburn Rural HS; Topeka, KS; 14/199 HonRl; FBLA; Bsktbl; LetterTennis; IMSpt; Col; Acct.

BARTMAN, Laura B; New Holland Middletown HS; New Holland, IL; 3/28 PresSophCls; Band; PresChrs; HonRl; NHS; PresStuCncl; EdSchPpr; Chrldr; GAA; BttyCrckrAwd; DARAwd; 4-HAwd; Univ Of Ill.

BARTMAN, Susan K; Clio Area HS; Clio, MI; 4/364 HonRl; NHS; LatCl; DARAwd; EldAwd; Mich Tech; Med Tech.

BARTOK, Patty J; Eldorado HS; Eldorado, IL; 2/110 SecFrshCls; HonRl; NHS; SctActv; EdYrBk; Yrbk; 4-H; SpnCl; Bsktbl; Trk; GAA; DARAwd; Memphis State Univ; Business.

BARTOLAC, Linda L; Calumet HS; Gary, IN; 2/308 ALAGirlsSt; HonRl; JrNHS; PresNHS; SctActv; FrCl; PpCl; SciCl; GAA; PPFtbl; Purdue U; Medicine.

BARTOLI, Gloria; Lostant Hs; Lostant, IL; 3/16 SecSrCls; TrsSrCls; Band; Chrs; HonRl; NHS; SchPl; StuCncl; Yrbk; GAA;.

BARTOLOMEI, Frederick J; De La Salle HS; Roseville, MI; 12/125 NatlFornLg; NatlThespSoc; SchMus; SchPl; StuCncl; EdSchPpr; PpCl; Ftbl; LetterSwmmng; Trk; LetterChrldr; Univ Of Michigan; Medicine.

BARTOLONE, Christine M; St Scholastica HS; Park Ridge, IL; 50/243 Chrs; ChrhWkr; NatlMeritCmnd; PpCl; Bsktbl; Univ; Dental Hygienist.

BARTOLOTTA, Bernadette M; Edward Tilden HS; Dubuque, IA; 4/300 HonRl; HospAde; NHS; ROTC; StuCncl; TchrAde; EdYrBk; EdSchPpr; DARAwd; Loyola University.

BARTON, Jacqueline J; Creston HS; Creston, IA; Chrs; NatlMeritSF; GAA; GovHonPrgAwd; Coll; Veterinary.

BARTON, John E; Morton HS; Morton, IL; 50/285 ChrhWkr; HonRl; JA; SctActv; YthFlsp; RptrSchPpr; SchPpr; FFA; Swmmng; LetterTrk; JAAwd; Univ Of Illinois.

BARTON, Lisa A; North Newton HS; Fair Oaks, IN; SecFrshCls; SecJrCls; DrlTm; HonRl; HospAde; StuCncl; 4-H; FBLA; MthCl; PpCl; College; Lpn.

BARTON, Mark S; St Charles HS; St Charles, MO; 3/547 HonRl; JrNHS; NHS; SctActv; GerCl; SciCl; Wrstlng; AmLegAwd; DARAwd; GodCntryAwd; Univ Of Mo; Physics.

BARTON, Melissa J; Grafton HS; Grafton, WI; 6/220 SecSrCls; Band; CncrtBnd; HonRl; MrchBnd; NHS; SchMus; StuCncl; SciCl; GAA; College; Business Administration.

BARTON, Raymond J; Grosse Pointe North HS; Grosse Pointe, MI; HonRl; JrNHS; NHS; FBLA; GerCl; Trk; U Of Mi; Business Administration Law.

BARTON, Ronald A; Ozark HS; Ozark, MO; 7/92 PresSrCls; PresBand; ChrhWkr; CncrtBnd; HonRl; PepBnd; SchPl; StuCncl; StuGov; MthCl; PpCl; Bsbl; Bsktbl; College; Engineering.

BARTON, Russell; South Beloit HS; So Beloit, IL; 4/81 PresFrshCls; PresSophCls; PresJrCls; ALBoysSt; HonRl; NHS; StuCncl; LetterBsktbl; LetterFtbl; Trk; AmLegAwd; Univ; Medicine.

BARTON, Sharon K; Luverne Comm School; Livermore, IA; 7/17 Band; Chrs; CncrtBnd; HonRl; PepBnd; TchrAde; RptrYrbk; PpCl; Trk; Chrldr; Trade School; Vocation.

BARTON, Victoria M; Mayville HS; Mayville, MI; 10/121 Band; CncrtBnd; HonRl; MrchBnd; NHS; NatlMeritCmnd; PepBnd; SchPl; TchrAde; Yrbk; College; Physical Therapy.

BARTOS, Emily J; Verdigre Public HS; Verdigre, NE; 1/38 PresJrCls; HonRl; SecNHS; StuCncl; Twrl; TreasYthFlsp; RptrYrbk; RptrSchPpr; Pres4-H; SecFFA; Univ Of Nebr Rotc; Medical Science Research.

BARTOS, Janice K; Verdigre HS; Verdigre, NE; 3/44 Band; Chr; Chrs; ChrhWkr; CmntyWkr; CncrtBnd; HonRl; HospAde; MrchBnd; NHS; Trk; Chrldr; IMSpt; Nebraska Wesleyan Univ; Nursing.

BARTOSCH, Michael; Ridgewood HS; Norridge, IL; HonRl; Bsktbl; LetterFtbl; LetterTennis; U Of Notre Dame; Business Administration.

BARTOSZEK, Joan; St Andrew HS; Detroit, MI; 26/84 VPFrshCls; ChrhWkr; SchPl; RptrYrbk; Yrbk; PpCl; Trk; Chrldr; Univ Of Michigan; Physical Therapy.

BARTOW, Gary J; Tekonsha HS; Homer, MI; PresFrshCls; HonRl; OffAde; SctActv; StuCncl; StuGov; Bsbl; Bsktbl; Ftbl; Trk; College; Major Study.

BARTSCH, Dawn M; Chosen Valley HS; Chatfield, MN; ALAGirlsSt; ChrhWkr; HonRl; TchrAde; SchPpr; 4-H; FHA; FTA; SpnCl; GAA; College; Social Work.

BARTSCH, Kay; Granton Public HS; Granton, WI; Band; Chr; HonRl; NHS; YthFlsp; 4-H; FHA; Trk; Chrldr; GAA; 4-HAwd; College; Social Work.

BARTSCH, Kay J; Granton Public HS; Granton, WI; 3/25 Band; Chrs; ChrhWkr; HonRl; NHS; StuCncl; 4-H; FHA; LetterTrk; Chrldr; GAA; 4-HAwd; College; Elem Teacher.

BARTSCH, Mary; Esmond Public HS; Esmond, ND; ALAGirlsSt; Chrs; HonRl; SchPl; TchrAde; RptrYrbk; RptrSchPpr; Bsktbl; Trk; Chrldr; Coll; Medical Tech.

BARTSCH, Ronald A; Esmond Public HS; Harvey, ND; VPJrCls; TrsSrCls; HonRl; SchPl; LetterBsbl; LetterBsktbl; LetterFtbl; LetterTrk; Trade School; Vocation.

BARTUSKA, Holly A; Midway HS; Forest River, ND; 1/40 ALAGirlsSt; HonRl; NHS; SchPl; StuCncl; Yrbk; PresFHA; 4-HAwd; Trade School; Vocation.

BARTZ, Carol L; Appleton West HS; Appleton, WI; ChrhWkr; FrCl; PpCl; Bsktbl; College; Occupational Therapy.

BARTZ, Christine A; Allegan HS; Allegan, MI; TreasBand; HonRl; MrchBnd; NHS; PepBnd; SchPl; 4-H; SpnCl; LetterBsbl; LetterTennis; 4-HAwd; Ferris St College; Surgical Tech.

BARTZ, Lynne; Carmel Hs; Mundelein, IL; 29 Chrs; HonRl; NHS; SchMus; SchPl; StuCncl; 4-H; GerCl; 4-HAwd; College;dental Hygiene.

BARTZ, Nancy E; Paynesville Sr HS; Paynesville, MN; 1/135 Band; Chr; ChrhWkr; CncrtBnd; HonRl; NHS; SctActv; StuCncl; StuGov; PresAwd; College; Law.

BARTZ, Steven M; Saint Rita HS; Chicago, IL; 30/449 TrsJrCls; HonRl; NHS; TreasStuCncl; LetterFtbl; Univ Of Illinois; Physician.

BARWICK, James F; G S Parker Sr HS; Janesville, WI; 90/387 HonRl; Quill&Scroll; RptrYrbk; Yrbk; Univ Of Wis Whitewater; Marketing Adv.

BARZ, Danny A; Meservey Thornton HS; Thornton, IA; HonRl; SchPl; Bsbl; Bsktbl; Ftbl; Glf; College; Professional.

BARZANO, Lorie J; Amos Alonzo Stagg HS; Hickory Hills, IL; 6/500 HonRl; JrNHS; NHS; Quill&Scroll; StuCncl; StuGov; YthLg; RptrYrbk; SchPpr; PpCl; Tennis; Knox College; Law.

BASACCHI, Cynthia L; Regina HS; Detroit, MI; HonRl; LbryAde; SchPl; FNA; College; Professional.

BASAK, Kimberly J; Morton West HS; Lyons, IL; HonRl; NHS; SctActv; TchrAde; FrCl; College; Accounting.

BASAK, Lescek S; Hackett HS; Kalamazoo, MI; HonRl; IMSpt; W Mich Univ; Elec Engr.

BASAK, Leszek S; Hackett HS; Kalamazoo, MI; 14/144 HonRl; Western Michigan Univ; Elec Engineer.

BASCHULT, Mark T; Fremont Sr HS; Fremont, NE; 40/425 Chr; HonRl; JrNHS; StuCncl; Treas4-H; MthCl; LetterFtbl; CaptSwmmng; IMSpt; Iowa St Univ; Construction Engineer.

BASGALL, Joyce A; La Crosse HS; La Crosse, KS; Band; CncrtBnd; HonRl; MrchBnd; Orch; SchAde;

StuGov; RptrYrbk; Yrbk; SecTrsSophCls; IMSpt; College; Major In Psychology.

BASGOZ, Nesli O; Bloomington North HS; Bloomington, IN; 7/516 HonRl; HospAde; NHS; NatlMeritSF; PresFrCl; College; International Relations.

BASHAM, Cynthia M; Riverton HS; Nevada, MO; Band; Chr; HonRl; NHS; StuCncl; FHA; PresSpnCl; PpCl; Trk; PPFtbl; Fort Scott Jr College; Nursing.

BASHAW, John R; Lake Linden Hubbell HS; Lake Linden, MI; 17/63 PresFrshCls; CmntyWkr; HonRl; SchPl; StuCncl; StuGov; Bsbl; Gogebic Comm College; Tool & Die Maker.

BASHORE, Tanya L; F C HS; Fairfield, IL; Chrs; ChrhWkr; HonRl; SchPl; SctActv; 4-H; FHA; SciCl; Tennis; Business School; Automotive Mechanic.

BASILE, Paul M; Notre Dame Boys HS; Park Ridge, IL; 2/276 Band; CncrtBnd; HonRl; MrchBnd; NHS; NatlMeritFnl; NatlMeritSF; PepBnd; SchMus; Yrbk; U Of Ill; Music.

BASILE, Paul M; Notre Dame HS For Boys; Park Ridge, IL; 2/276 Band; CncrtBnd; MrchBnd; NHS; NatlMeritSF; PepBnd; SchMus; RptrYrbk; U Of Il; Teacher.

BASINGER, Karen A; Enfield HS; Enfield, IL; ALAGirlsSt; Band; Chrs; ChrhWkr; CncrtBnd; HonRl; MrchBnd; Pres4-H; FHA; DanFAwd; Belleville Area Jr C; Med Lab Technician.

BASINGER, Monte R; Van Far HS; Farber, MO; ALBoysSt; Band; CmntyWkr; CncrtBnd; MrchBnd; TchrAde; 4-H; FFA; LetterBsktbl; CaptFtbl; LetterTrk; PresAwd; College.

BASINSKI, William S; Lockport Central HS; Lockport, IL; 6/550 HonRl; NHS; Lewis Univ; Chemistry.

BASKE, Christine A; Holly HS; Holly, MI; CmntyWkr; HonRl; FTA; SpnCl; Tennis; E Mich U; Fashion Design.

BASKETT, Martha; Riverton HS; Riverton, KS; Band; Chr; ChrhWkr; HonRl; Mdrgl; NHS; SctActv; TchrAde; FHA; MthCl;.

BASLER, Diann; Cobden Unit HS; Cobden, IL; 3/50 PresSophCls; Band; Chrs; CncrtBnd; HonRl; Mdrgl; MrchBnd; PepBnd; SchMus; DanFAwd; Univ; Lawyer.

BASLER, Michelle L; Boone Valley Comm HS; Renwick, IA; 10/26 ChrhWkr; CmntyWkr; CncrtBnd; HonRl; TchrAde; EdYrBk; SecFHA; PpCl; LetterBsktbl; IMSpt; Unif Of Ia ;elem Ed.

BASLER, Sandy; Ste Cen Senior HS; Genevieve, MO; SecFrshCls; HstJrCls; CmntyWkr; HonRl; SchAde; SchMus; SchPl; SctActv; TchrAde; FrCl; South East Mo State Univ; Teacher.

BASNER, Barbara A; Arthur Hill HS; Saginaw, MI; NHS; College; Prof.

BASS, Denise K; Branson HS; Branson, MO; Band; HonRl; LbryAde; MrchBnd; TchrAde; YthFlsp; RptrYrbk; Yrbk; SchPpr; FFA; SpnCl; PpCl; Bsbl; Trade; Dental Technician.

BASS, John W; Salem Sr HS; Salem, MO; 4/180 Band; CncrtBnd; HonRl; MrchBnd; StuCncl; PpCl; SciCl; Bsktbl; LetterFtbl; Trk; CitAwd; Medical School; Doctor.

BASS, Lori J; University HS; Normal, IL; SecJrCls; Chrs; HonRl; NatlFornLg; NatlThespSoc; SchMus; SchPl; StuCncl; College.

BASS, Marcia L; South Decatur HS; Westport, IN; 1/121 PresFrshCls; Band; ChrhWkr; NHS; StuCncl; FrCl; PpCl; LetterChrldr; GAA; Univ; Professional.

BASS, Mary L; Glendale HS; Springfield, MO; HonRl; TchrAde; MthCl; GAA; College; Math.

BASS, Maurice L; Anna Jonesboro Comm HS; Anna, IL; FTA; PresKeyCl; LatCl; Bsktbl; Trk; Univ; Teacher.

BASS, Patricia A; Macarthur HS; Decatur, IL; AFS; CncrtBnd; HonRl; HospAde; JrNHS; LitMag; MrchBnd; RedCrAde; SctActv; GerCl; St Johns School Of Nur; Nursing.

BASS, Richard; Doniphan HS; Doniphan, NE; ChrhWkr; HonRl; StuCncl; StuGov; YthFlsp; Bsbl; Glf; Ftbl; Trk; IMSpt;.

BASSEL, Kathy A; Marillac HS; Northbrook, IL; 64/256 PresJrCls; NHS; StuCncl; StuGov; PpCl; AmLegAwd; Western Il U; Spec Ed.

BASSETT, Brian M; Lakeshore HS; Stevensville, MI; HonRl; SchAde; SctActv; College; Chem Engineering.

BASSETT, Catherine L; Corwith Wesley Comm HS; Corwith, IA; Chr; Chrs; HonRl; Mdrgl; SchMus; YthFlsp; SchPpr; Bsktbl; Trk; Ia St Clge; Fashion Merchandizing.

BASSETT, Elizabeth A; Highland Park HS; Highland Park, IL; 120/643 NatlMeritCmnd; Univ Of Illinois.

BASSETT, Roberta R; Mullen Public HS; Mullen, NE; Chrs; ChrhWkr; HonRl; StuCncl;.

BASSING, Roberta L; Sycamore HS; Sycamore, IL; 29/201 Band; CAP; CncrtBnd; HonRl; MrchBnd; NHS; RptrYrbk; SpnCl; Augustana Col; Business Ed.

BAST, Joseph L; Kimberly HS; Kimberly, WI; TrsJrCls; Aud/Vis; Band; ChrhWkr; HonRl; NatlFornLg; StuCncl; RptrSchPpr; CaptWrstlng; Clge; Law.

BASTERT, Bruce L; Unity HS; Loraine, IL; Band; CncrtBnd; MrchBnd; PepBnd; SchMus; SchPl; SpnCl; LetterFtbl;.

BASTIAN, Cindy L; Wrightstown HS; Kaukauna, WI; Band; CncrtBnd; HonRl; StuCncl; RptrSchPpr; SchPpr; Chrldr; GAA; IMSpt; 4-HAwd; Trade Schl; Public Relations.

BASTIAN, Debra; Slinger Community HS; Richfield, WI; HonRl; SctActv; StuCncl; 4-H; FHA; SpnCl; PpCl; GAA; Lacrosse Univ; School Of Business.

BASTIAN, Sue E; R Nelson Snider HS; Fort Wayne, IN; 35/498 Chr; HonRl; StuCncl; LatCl; Indiana Univ; Med Tech.

BASTIAN, Tammy L; Holmen HS; Holmen, WI; 3/115 HonRl; NHS; SchPl; VPFrCl; PpCl; LetterTrk; VFWAwd; VoiceDemAwd; Coll.

BASTIANELLI, Cynthia A; St Agatha HS; Detroit, MI; SchPl; TchrAde; FHA; SpnCl; PpCl; Bsktbl; PPFtbl; College; Professional.

BASTIANELLI, Linda M; St Agatha HS; Detroit, MI; CmntyWkr; HonRl; NHS; NatlMeritSchl; RedCrAde; StuGov; DanFAwd; GovHonPrgAwd; CitAwd; VoiceDemAwd; College; Business World.

BASTIEN, Patricia; North Adams HS; North Adams, MI; Band; CncrtBnd; HonRl; MrchBnd; PepBnd; SchPl; StuCncl; TchrAde; RptrSchPpr; GAA; College; Social Worker.

BASTIEN, Randall; Elverado HS; Vergennes, IL; 2/42 PresFrshCls; SecSophCls; SchPpr; PpCl; Bsbl; Ftbl; Trk; IMSpt; College; Physical Education.

BASTIN, Dale L; Golden Plains HS; Selden, KS; PresSophCls; VPJrCls; ALBoysSt; DrmBgl; HonRl; StuCncl; SchPpr; Bsbl; Bsktbl; Trk; College; Agri Worker.

BASYDLO, Terry L; Pinckney Community HS; Pinckney, MI; Bsbl; Bsktbl; Ftbl; College; Architecture.

BASYE, Kim; Stafford HS; Stafford, KS; SecTrsFrshCls; Band; Chr; Chrs; CncrtBnd; HonRl; MrchBnd; TchrAde; EdSchPpr; PpCl; Business School; Cpa.

BATA, Jeff C; Kensal Public HS; Kensal, ND; 1/20 PresSophCls; ALBoysSt; ChrhWkr; HonRl; SchPl; StuCncl; EdSchPpr; LetterBsbl; LetterBsktbl; LetterTrk; Clg; Major Study.

BATCHELDER, Irene M; Fort Zumwalt HS; St Peters, MO; 9/353 Chrs; ChrhWkr; HonRl; JrNHS; NHS; SchPl; StuCncl; RptrYrbk; PpCl; GAA; PPFtbl; College; Psychology.

BATCHELDER, Patricia R; Highland HS; Highland, KS; VPJrCls; ChrhWkr; CmntyWkr; HonRl; LbryAde; RptrSchPpr; SchPpr; PpCl; College; Home Ec.

BATCHELOR, Gary E; Centerville HS; Richmond, IN; ChrhWkr; CncrtBnd; HonRl; MrchBnd; NHS; PepBnd; YthFlsp; SciCl; PresAwd; Indiana U; Social Science.

BATCHMAN, Richard K; Otis Bison Sr HS; Great Bend, KS; Band; Chr; CncrtBnd; HonRl; MrchBnd; PepBnd; SchPl; StuCncl; StuGov; 4-H; Ftbl; Barton County Comm College.

BATDORF, Tyler M; Pawhuska HS; Sedan, KS; 2/96 ALBoysSt; HonRl; NHS; StuCncl; Bsbl; LetterBsktbl; AmLegAwd; 4-HAwd; GovHonPrgAwd; LionAwd; CitAwd; Oklahoma St Univ; Veterinarian.

BATEMAN, Carol S; Washington Cath HS; Washington, IN; 3/40 SecSrCls; Chrs; HonRl; YthFlsp; RptrYrbk; 4-H; PpCl; Indiana Univ; Social Worker.

BATEMAN, Joseph D; Atwood Hammond HS; Hammond, IL; PresJrCls; PresSrCls; Band; Chrs; ChrhWkr; CncrtBnd; HonRl; NHS; SctActv; CaptBsktbl; CaptFtbl; Trk; AmLegAwd; So Illinois Univ; Medicine.

BATEMAN, Julie L; Porta HS; Petersburg, IL; Chr; Chrl; LbryAde; SchMus; TchrAde; RptrSchPpr; FHA; Trk; GAA; IMSpt;.

BATEMAN, Linda K; Tuscola Comm HS; Tuscola, IL; 1/126 ChrhWkr; HonRl; LbryAde; YthFlsp; 4-H; FHA; KeyCl; BttyCrckrAwd; DanFAwd; Univ Of Illinois; Accounting.

BATEMAN, Mark D; Manual HS; Indianapolis, IN; CAP; CmntyWkr; HonRl; NHS; StuGov; YthFlsp; LetterBsbl; LetterFtbl; CchngActv; 4-HAwd; In Univ; Athletic Career.

BATEMAN, Nancy A; Farmer City Mansfield HS; Mansfield, IL; AFS; ChrhWkr; CmntyWkr; OffAde; YthFlsp; VP4-H; GAA; IMSpt; 4-HAwd; Parkland College; Biology.

BATENHORST, Mary; Central Catholic HS; West Point, NE; 16/76 TrsJrCls; Band; Chrs; HonRl; HospAde; NHS; RedCrAde; SpnCl; PpCl; Chrldr; Coll; Elementary Education.

BATES, Cathleen M; Roncalli HS; Indianapolis, IN; Chrl; HonRl; OffAde; SchMus; SchPl; StuCncl; SpnCl; PpCl; Chrldr; PPFtbl; St Joseph College; Major Bus Marketing.

BATES, Cheryl L; Wentzville HS; O Fallon, MO; Band; CncrtBnd; HonRl; MrchBnd; SchPl; TchrAde; PpCl; LetterTrk; Chrldr; GAA; Clge; Vocation.

BATES, Debra J; Glenbrook South HS; Wheeling, IL; 109/600 HonRl; LitMag; StuCncl; StuGov; Western Illinois Univ; Fashion Merch.

BATES, Donald P; Webb HS; Reedsburg, WI; PresSophCls; HonRl; JrNHS; NHS; StuCncl; StuGov; EdSchPpr; KeyCl; SpnCl; CaptTrk; Col U W; Journalism.

BATES, Elizabeth A; Oneill Public HS; Emmet, NE; Chr; Chrs; ChrhWkr; HonRl; SchMus; YthFlsp; MasAwd; Omaha Methodist Sch Nursing; Rn.

BATES, James E; Pennfield HS; Battle Creek, MI; 11/175 Band; CncrtBnd; HonRl; JA; MrchBnd; PepBnd; TchrAde; SciCl; Wrstlng; University Of Michigan; Engineering.

BATES, Jeffrey S; Kewanee HS; Kewanee, IL; 23/217 ChrhWkr; HonRl; StuCncl; 4-H; FFA; LetterWrstlng; 4-HAwd;.

BATES, Julie A; Twin Valley HS; Boyne City, MI; Band; TchrAde; 4-H; Michigan Tech; Geophysics.

BATES, Leslie C; Port Huron HS; Port Huron, MI; ChrhWkr; HonRl; NHS; TchrAde; SchPpr; SpnCl; Bsktbl; Ftbl; Trk; U Of Mi; Law Or Medicine.

BATES, Michele J; Great Bend Sr HS; Great Bend, KS; HonRl; LitMag; NHS; NatlThespSoc; SchPl; RptrSchPpr; EdSchPpr; SecSpnCl; NCTE; University Of Kansas.

BATES, Robert; Remsen St Marys HS; Rensen, IA; 5/47 VPJrCls; TrsSrCls; HonRl; StuCncl; StuGov; Bsktbl; Glf; CitAwd; Purdue Univ; Indust Manage.

BATES, Sharon J; Winchester Comm HS; Winchester, IN; ALAGirlsSt; HonRl; NHS; SchPl; College; Secretary.

BATES, Sherri; Pender Public HS; Pender, NE; Band; HonRl; Mdrgl; SchPl; StuCncl; Twrl; SchPpr; Glf; Chrldr; Coll; Medical.

BATES, William B; Southwest HS; Kansas City, MO; 33/510 Chr; Chrl; HonRl; Mdrgl; NHS; OffAde; SchAde; SchMus; SchPl; StuGov; S M U; Actor.

BATESON, Cindy L; North Clay Comm HS; Louisville, IL; ChrhWkr; SctActv; Pres4-H; SpnCl; PpCl; GAA; 4-HAwd; St Louis Christian Col; Teach.

BATEY, Diane R; Swartz Creek HS; Swartz Creek, MI; HonRl; College; English.

BATEY, Karen; Maine Twp Hs West; Des Plaines, IL; Chrs; HonRl; HospAde; NatlMeritCmnd; Tennis; Trk; Illinois State U; Wildlife Biology.

BATH, Jennifer L; Midland HS; Midland, MI; 84/433 CncrtBnd; HonRl; MrchBnd; NHS; Orch; Trk; Chrldr; GAA; Univ Of Mi; Dental Hygienist.

BATHAUER, Donna D; Alexandria Monroe HS; Alexandria, IN; 9/225 Chr; ChrhWkr; HonRl; HospAde; StuCncl; Twrl; YthFlsp; 4-H; Chrldr; IMSpt; College; Professional.

BATHE, David A; Lincoln HS; Vincennes, IN; Chrl; ChrhWkr; CmntyWkr; HonRl; NatlFornLg; OffAde; PolWkr; SchAde; SchPl; SctActv; Teen; YthFlsp; College; Education.

BATHON, Dale A; Marion Senior HS; Marion, IL; 5/270 HonRl; NHS; TchrAde; MthCl; PresSciCl; U Of Ill; Engineering.

BATHON, Wayne; Nashville Community HS; Oakdale, IL; 69/138 LetterBsbl; LetterFtbl;.

BATHRICK, Cynthia A; Union City HS; Union City, MI; 3/81 HonRl; ModUN; NHS; NatlMeritSF; StuCncl; TchrAde; RptrYrbk; PresFTA; TreasSpnCl; PpCl; Kellogg Comm Col; Bus Admin.

BATIE, Cheryl E; Lexington HS; Lexington, NE; 14/142 ALAGirlsSt; Band; CncrtBnd; DrlTm; HonRl; MrchBnd; NHS; PepBnd; 4-H; PpCl; Univ Of Ne; Food Science.

BATKE, Therese A; Palatine HS; Palatine, IL; 5/441 HonRl; JrNHS; Harper Jr College; Med Technology.

BATT, Christeen; Burt Community HS; Burt, IA; HonRl; SchPl; StuCncl; TchrAde; RptrYrbk; Yrbk; RptrSchPpr; SchPpr; FTA; VoiceDemAwd; Hamilton College; Office Receptionist.

BATTAGLIA, Nicholas O; Griffin HS; Springfield, IL; 39/192 HonRl; StuCncl; StuGov; SchPpr; PpCl; Bsbl; Ftbl; LetterTrk; IMSpt; Univ Of Eastern Ill; Law.

BATTEN, Colleen F; Tomah Sr HS; Camp Douglas, WI; 14/283 Band; ChrhWkr; CncrtBnd; HonRl; MrchBnd; NHS; RptrSchPpr; College; Vocation.

BATTEN, Karen S; Chatard HS; Indianapolis, IN; 1/200 Chrs; HonRl; NatlFornLg; NHS; SchPl; StuCncl; FrCl; PpCl; IMSpt; PPFtbl; Butler U; Elem Ed.

BATTERSON, Pamela R; Vandercook Lake HS; Jackson, MI; 2/99 HonRl; OffAde; StuCncl; TchrAde; Chrldr;.

BATTERSON, Timothy J; St Louis Univ HS; Granite City, IL; 12/210 HonRl; NatlMeritFnl; NatlMeritSF; SptEdSchPpr; LetterFtbl; IMSpt; Univ; Medicine.

BATTERTON, Debra J; Astoria HS; Astoria, IL; ChrhWkr; HonRl; NHS; OffAde; TchrAde; Trk; GAA; Spoon River College; Data Processing.

BATTIATO, Patricia A; Driscoll HS; Addison, IL; Chrs; HonRl; Univ Of Illinois; Pediatrician.

BATTIOLA, Richard J; Premontre Sr HS; Green Bay, WI; 10/160 HonRl; SctActv; KeyCl; SpnCl; PpCl; Bsktbl; Ftbl; Trk; Univ; Prof.

BATTISTA, Robert J; St Joseph HS; Cicero, IL; 10/176 ChrhWkr; HonRl; NHS; SctActv; StuCncl; StuGov; SpnCl; PpCl; College; Business.

BATTISTELLA, Beverly G; Forest Park HS; Crystal Falls, MI; ChrhWkr; HospAde; OffAde; SchAde; YthFlsp; Yrbk; SchPpr; FNA; Trk; Trade School; Cosmetology.

BATTLE, Debra L; R Nelson Snider HS; Fort Wayne, IN; 14/506 ALAGirlsSt; HonRl; PolWkr; Purdue U; Accounting.

BATTLE, Mary P; Regina HS; Detroit, MI; ChrhWkr; HonRl; HospAde; NHS; PolWkr; TchrAde; FHA; College; Social Studies.

BATTLES, Ann M; Genoa Public HS; Genoa, NE; 4/45 Band; CncrtBnd; HonRl; MrchBnd; PepBnd;.

BATTLES, Kathleen M; Waukesha North HS; Waukesha, WI; 28/305 AFS; HonRl; NHS; SctActv; FBLA; PpCl; Trk; Univ Of Wisconsin; Business.

BATTY, Cheryl A; Arthur HS; Arthur, IL; 5/47 SecFrshCls; ALAGirlsSt; Chrs; HonRl; SchPl; StuCncl; FHA; Trk; Chrldr; PresAwd; Illinois State Univ; Special Ed.

BAUCH, Lillian K; Wittenberg Birnamwood HS; Birnamwood, WI; ChrhWkr; HonRl; NatlFornLg; NHS; 4-H; FBLA; FHA; GAA; BttyCrckrAwd; Social Work.

BAUCH, Richard E; Max Public HS; Benedict, ND; VPJrCls; ALBoysSt; Band; HonRl; 4-H; PpCl; Bsktbl; Glf; IMSpt; Trade School; Professional.

BAUCH, Thomas C; Aquin Central Catholic HS; Freeport, IL; HonRl; NatlThespSoc; SchMus; Yrbk; CaptBsktbl; LetterFtbl; LetterTrk; College.

BAUCHE, Kurt D; Union HS; Union, MO; 44/174 ALBoysSt; Band; ChrhWkr; CncrtBnd; PolWkr; StuCncl; YthFlsp; 4-H; LetterBsktbl; Ftbl; Glf; 4-HAwd; College; Instrumental Music Instructor.

BAUCOM, Barbara; Campbellsport HS; Campbellsport, WI; 35/147 HonRl; LbryAde; SpnCl; Uw Of Madison; Vet Or Wildlife Ecologist.

BAUD, Teresa; Hutsonville HS; Hutsonville, IL; 4/40 ChrhWkr; HospAde; NHS; RptrYrbk; Yrbk; 4-H; FHA; FNA; 4-HAwd; JAAwd; Coll; Nursing.

BAUDHUIN, Theresa; Sturgeon Bay Senior HS; Sturgeon Bay, WI; HonRl; PpCl; GAA; IMSpt; College; Professional.

BAUDLER, Joan M; Bridgewater Fontanelle HS; Fontanelle, IA; 2/43 Band; Chrs; CncrtBnd; HonRl; NHS; SchPl; 4-H; LetterBsktbl; LetterGlf; LetterTrk; 4-HAwd; Iowa St Univ; Medical Technology.

BAUDOIN, Kathleen M; Grand Meadow Public HS; Grand Meadow, MN; 5/42 PresSophCls; ALAGirlsSt; Band; Chr; Chrs; ChrhWkr; CncrtBnd; HonRl; MrchBnd; NHS; Bsktbl; Chrldr; GAA; Minnesota Schl Of Business; Secretary.

BAUDOUX, Cynthia L; Buena Vista HS; Saginaw, MI; HonRl; JA; NHS; OffAde; SchAde; Saginaw Valley College; Medical Tech.

BAUER, Amanda; Bemidji HS; Bemidji, MN; Band; CncrtBnd; MrchBnd; NHS; TchrAde; Yrbk; 4-H;.

BAUER, Angela M; Lincoln HS; Vincennes, IN; 28/328 CmntyWkr; VPDrlTm; HonRl; OffAde; SchMus; SctActv; TchrAde; RptrYrbk; RptrSchPpr; VPFTA; GAA; Indiana St Univ; German.

BAUER, Betty L; Paxton HS; Paxton, IL; TrsFrshCls; HonRl; Mdrgl; NHS; RptrSchPpr; SecSciCl; LetterBsbl; Bsktbl; Chrldr; TreasGAA; College; Health Fields.

BAUER, Carol A; Jeffersonville HS; Jeffersonville, IN; 3/635 HonRl; NHS; SctActv; FTA; PpCl; SciCl; EldAwd; Berea College; Natural Resources.

BAUER, Cheryl K; Bayard HS; Bayard, NE; 3/46 Band; Chrs; HonRl; MrchBnd; NHS; PepBnd; SchMus; FHA; SpnCl; PpCl; College; Professional.

BAUER, Craig A; Hildreth HS; Hildreth, NE; 6/22 VPFrshCls; TrsSophCls; VPJrCls; Bsbl; Bsktbl; Ftbl; Trk; EldAwd; 4-HAwd; CitAwd; College, Farming;.

BAUER, Diane R; Mulberry Grove HS; Smithboro, IL; 1/51 Band; Chrs; ChrhWkr; CncrtBnd; HonRl; MrchBnd; NHS; OffAde; PepBnd; StuCncl; YthFlsp; Chrldr; GAA; College.

BAUER, Francis; Lincoln County Hs; Sinex, MO; HonRl; JA; NHS; SchPl; 4-H; FFA; Trk; 4-HAwd; College;farming.

BAUER, Francis G; Lincoln County R 1 HS; Silex, MO; HonRl; NHS; RptrSchPpr; 4-H; FFA; LetterTrk; College.

BAUER, Gerolynn H; Riverside HS; Dearborn Heights, MI; Band; CncrtBnd; HonRl; MrchBnd; NHS; PepBnd; FrCl; LetterGAA; College; Medical Technologist.

BAUER, Helmuth; Greenfield HS; Greenfield, WI; 12/386 HonRl; GerCl; Bsktbl; Socr; Tennis; Univ; Engineer.

BAUER, Jan; Nesco HS; Zearing, IA; 2/36 Band; Chrs; CncrtBnd; HonRl; PepBnd; AmLegAwd; College.

BAUER, Janet W; University City HS; St Louis, MO; 15/553 AFS; Chr; ChrhWkr; HonRl; Quill&Scroll; SchAde; Twrl; Yrbk; College.

BAUER, Jeffrey A; Durand Unified HS; Durand, WI; HonRl; NHS; StuCncl; Tech School; Vocational.

BAUER, Joanne; Portland HS; Lyons, MI; 19/124 HonRl; LbryAde; FTA; SpnCl; IMSpt; PPFtbl; Grand Rapids Jr Coll; Bolgett Sch Of Nurse.

BAUER, John A; East Pike HS; Pearl, IL; Chrs; ChrhWkr; HonRl; SchPl; Yrbk; FFA; Bsbl; Bsktbl; Coll; Agri.

BAUER, Lynn; Ida Public HS; Ida, MI; 14/154 ALAGirlsSt; CncrtBnd; HonRl; MrchBnd; NHS; PepBnd; SchMus; PpCl; AmLegAwd; Mich St Univ;doctor.

BAUER, Marie C; Maplewood Richmond HS; Richmond Heights, MO; 4/160 HonRl; HospAde; NHS; SchPl; GerCl; Bsktbl; GAA; IMSpt; College; Curriculum Of Major Study.

BAUER, Mary E; Mt Assisi Academy; Chicago, IL; 32/189 HonRl; SchMus; SchPl; GAA; IMSpt; U Of Ill; Professional Vet Med.

BAUER, Mary K; Harrisonville HS; Harrisonille, MO; 22/153 AFS; ChrhWkr; HonRl; Quill&Scroll; StuCncl; EdYrBk; 4-H; FrCl; PpCl; 4-HAwd; College; Home Econ.

BAUER, Mary L; Resurrection HS; Chicago, IL; 7/294 CmntyWkr; HonRl; NHS; SchPl; FrCl; SciCl; College; Professional.

BAUER, Matthew P; De Smet Jesuit HS; St Louis, MO; 60/182 PresSophCls; VPJrCls; ChrhWkr; HonRl; JrNHS; NHS; NatlThespSoc; LetterFtbl; Chrldr; IMSpt; Univ; Communications.

BAUER, Michael D; Holstein Comm HS; Holstein, IA; 14/36 ALBoysSt; Band; Chr; Chrs; ChrhWkr; CncrtBnd; Mdrgl; MrchBnd; PepBnd; SchPl; Univ; Coll Music Prof.

BAUER, Nancy A; Center Sr HS; Kansas City, MO; 4/431 NHS; SchMus; SchPl; SctActv; PresSpnCl; PpCl; College.

BAUER, Patricia; Columbia HS; Columbia, IL; TchrAde; FshEdYrbk; Yrbk; RptrSchPpr; EdSchPpr; FHA; FTA; FrCl; PpCl; GAA; Belleville Area Jr Coll; Med Lab Tech.

BAUER, Paul M; Richmond HS; Richmond, MI; Chr; College.

BAUER, Randall; Union HS; Grand Rapids, MI; HonRl; JA; NHS; Orch; SchMus; YthFlsp; JAAwd; Coll; Architecture.

BAUER, Rhonda E; Bryant HS; Appleton City, MO; 6/45 ChrhWkr; HonRl; PresQuill&Scroll; SecSchAde; SchPl; TchrAde; YthFlsp; 4-H; FBLA; FHA; PPFtbl; 4-HAwd; St Pauls College; Elementary Ed.

BAUER, Rita L; Elkhorn Valley HS; Tilden, NE; Band; CncrtBnd; HonRl; LbryAde; MrchBnd; PepBnd; FHA; PpCl; Nursing Sch; Nursing.

BAUER, Sam M; Concorda HS; Concordia, KS; 7/165 HonRl; StuGov; PresSciCl; Ftbl; Trk; IMSpt; University; Science.

BAUER, Sheryl A; Lomira Community HS; Brownsville, WI; HonRl; TreasNHS; TreasStuCncl; Yrbk; EdSchPpr; 4-H; GAA; Exec Secretary; Secretarial Work.

BAUER, Susan C; Laville Jr Sr HS; Lakeville, IN; NHS; TchrAde; 4-H; Bsbl; LetterBsktbl; LetterTrk; GAA; PresAwd; Business School.

BAUERKEMPER, Janis A; Walnut Community HS; Walnut, IA; ALAGirlsSt; HonRl; JrNHS; SchPl; StuCncl; YthFlsp; RptrSchPpr; FHA; LetterBsbl; LetterBsktbl; LetterWrstlng; CchngActv; Business School.

BAUERLE, Rhonda L; Chase Co HS; Imperial, NE; Band; Chrs; ChrhWkr; CncrtBnd; HonRl; MrchBnd; PepBnd; YthFlsp; 4-H; PpCl; Bsbl; LetterTrk; 4-HAwd; College; Home Economics.

BAUERNFEIND, Mary J; Hudson HS; Hudson, WI; 17/250 Aud/Vis; Band; Chrs; ChrhWkr; CncrtBnd; HonRl; MrchBnd; PepBnd; University Of Minnesota; Music Therapy.

BAUGH, Mary; Turner HS; Kansas City, KS; 3/410 Band; ChrhWkr; HonRl; NHS; PepBnd; SchPl; FrCl; Bsktbl; Soc.

BAUGHER, Cynthia A; Keokuk Senior HS; Keokuk, IA; LetterBand; LetterChr; HonRl; Mdrgl; NHS; StuCncl; LetterTennis; KiwanAwd; SchPpr; PpCl; Univ Of Northern Iowa; Business.

BAUGHMAN, Jeffery M; Davis County Comm HS; Pulaski, IA; ChrhWkr; HonRl; PolWkr; StuCncl; YthFlsp; FFA; LetterBsktbl; LetterFtbl; IMSpt; Trade School; Diesel Engine Mechanic.

BAUGHMAN, Michelle; Mason Senior HS; Mason, MI; Chr; Chrs; SchMus; PpCl; Bsbl; PPFtbl; 4-HAwd; Ingham Intermediate School; Cosmetology.

BAUGHMAN, William J; Thornridge HS; South Holland, IL; HonRl; LetterTrk; PresAwd; Univ Of Illinois; Electrical Engineering.

BAUHS, Terri; Salem HS; Salem, SD; 2/54 TrsSrCls; Band; Chrs; CncrtBnd; HonRl; MrchBnd; OffAde; Orch; RptrYrbk; RptrSchPpr; Sd St Univ; Rn.

BAUKOL, Mary L; Webster HS; Webster, SD; 10/75 ALAGirlsSt; CncrtBnd; HonRl; NatlMeritFnl; RptrYrbk; SchPpr; Swmmng; Trk; Chrldr; GAA; College; Nursing.

BAULT, Deborah S; Cloverdale HS; Cloverdale, IN; Chrs; LbryAde; NatlThespSoc; SchMus; SchPl; SpnCl; PpCl; Bsbl; CchngActv; Business School; Secretary.

BAUM, Karen Y; Hastings HS; Hastings, MI; VPSophCls; LetterChr; ChrhWkr; HonRl; OffAde; StuCncl; StuGov; SchPpr; College; Writing.

BAUMAN, Ann M; Reese HS; Reese, MI; HonRl; OffAde; 4-H; GerCl; Saginaw Valley Clg; Nursing Science.

BAUMAN, Brenda R; Bern Rural HS; Bern, KS; 1/11 PresJrCls; VPBand; HonRl; Mdrgl; NHS; StuCncl; SecYthFlsp; RptrSchPpr; Pres4-H; Chrldr; Univ; Vocation.

BAUMAN, Carolyn; Okabena HS; Okabena, MN; 1/20 SecFrshCls; Band; Chrs; ChrhWkr; HonRl; MrchBnd; NHS; RptrYrbk; 4-H; GAA; Sw Mn State; Music.

BAUMAN, Christine; Delano HS; Delano, MN; 1/114 DrlTm; HonRl; MrchBnd; NatlThespSoc; SchMus; RptrYrbk; RptrSchPpr; EdSchPpr; PpCl; AmLegAwd; College; Accounting.

BAUMAN, Cynthia L; Mukwonago HS; Big Bend, WI; 1/238 Chrs; HonRl; SecNHS; YthFlsp; SpnCl; IMSpt; LionAwd; Nursing School; Registered Nurse.

BAUMAN, Daniel L; Usd #406 HS; Wathena, KS; 4/33 ALBoysSt; SecSophCls; Chrs; CncrtBnd; HonRl; PepBnd; SchPl; PresStuCncl; EdSchPpr; Trk; Missouri Western St Col.

BAUMAN, David M; Indian Creek HS; Franklin, IN; 2/115 HonRl; NHS; OffAde; Quill&Scroll; StuCncl; RptrSchPpr; FTA; SpnCl; IMSpt; AmLegAwd; Purdue U; Math.

BAUMAN, Donna L; East HS; Waterloo, IA; 6/330 Band; SecFrshCls; CncrtBnd; JrNHS; MrchBnd; NHS; StuGov; LetterSwmmng; U Of Northern Iowa; Elem Teach.

BAUMAN, James; Battle Creek Central HS; Battle Creek, MI; ChrhWkr; HonRl; NHS; NatlMeritSchl; NatlThespSoc; SctActv; YthFlsp; Bsktbl; Ftbl; Trk; Albion Coll.

BAUMAN, Kenneth A; Holland HS; Holland, MI; YthFlsp; GerCl; LetterBsktbl; CaptFtbl; CchngActv; Hope College; Economics Major.

BAUMAN, Kim L; Rock Valley Comm HS; Rock Valley, IA; 1/63 Band; Chrs; ChrhWkr; HonRl; MrchBnd; NHS; PepBnd; SchPl; RptrYrbk; PpCl; Glf; Chrldr; Creighton Univ; Social Work.

BAUMAN, Kim L; Lancaster HS; Lancaster, WI; TrsJrCls; ALAGirlsSt; Band; ChrhWkr; CncrtBnd; DrmMjrt; LetterTrk; ChmnChrldr; GAA; IMSpt; Univ; Medical Field.

BAUMAN, Mary M; Divine Savior Holy Angels HS; Milwaukee, WI; AFS; Chrs; ChrhWkr; CmntyWkr; DrmBgl; JA; JrNHS; NHS; RedCrAde; SchPl; College; Medicine Cancer Research.

BAUMAN, Pamela E; St Marys HS; Burlington, WI; 2/76 Band; CmntyWkr; HonRl; LbryAde; NatlMeritSF; PpCl; Univ Of Wisc; Education.

BAUMAN, Sandy K; Morton HS; Morton, IL; Chrs; HonRl; HospAde; RptrSchPpr; 4-H; FFA;.

BAUMAN, Steven J; William J Brown HS; Sturgis, SD; 51/208 ALBoysSt; HonRl; NatlFornLg; NHS; LetterBsktbl; LetterFtbl; LetterTrk; College; Professional Engineer.

BAUMAN, Tony J; Madison HS; Madison, SD; HonRl; NHS; KeyCl; LetterTrk; College.

BAUMANN, Catherine C; Benet Academy; Naperville, IL; Band; CncrtBnd; HonRl; MrchBnd; NatlMeritCmnd; Yrbk; College; Elem Education.

BAUMANN, Charles W; Westview HS; Lake City, IA; PresSophCls; PresJrCls; PresSrCls; PresAFS; ALBoysSt; Aud/Vis; Band; Chrs; ChrhWkr; CncrtBnd; MrchBnd; College; Professional.

BAUMANN, Debbie; Savannah R Iii Sr HS; Savannah, MO; ALAGirlsSt; Band; Chr; HonRl; OffAde; PepBnd; SchMus; 4-H; FFA; GAA; Univ; Agriculture.

BAUMANN, Georgine M; Mosinee HS; Edgar, WI; 15/163 Chr; Chrl; Chrs; HonRl; NHS; RptrSchPpr; PresFHA; BttyCrckrAwd; Technical Sch; Mech Design.

BAUMANN, Keith; Marshfield Senior HS; Marshfield, WI; ChrhWkr; HonRl; LitMag; SchPpr; IMSpt; Univ Of Wi; Business.

BAUMANN, Lori A; Central Catholic HS; W Point, NE; HonRl; NHS; SchPl; SpnCl; MthCl; PpCl; SciCl; Chrldr; Col; Pro.

BAUMANN, Margaret; Park River HS; Park River, ND; /63 VPJrCls; ALAGirlsSt; Band; HospAde; NHS; SchPl; StuCncl; RptrYrbk; 4-H; FHA; Univer Of Nd; Curr Of Major St.

BAUMANN, Mark D; Riverton HS; Galena, KS; ALBoysSt; ChrhWkr; HonRl; NHS; StuCncl; SciCl; Bsbl; Bsktbl; Ftbl; Trk; CitAwd; College.

BAUMANN, Patrick; Custer HS; Custer, SD; 8/56 Chr; ChrhWkr; HonRl; LbryAde; SchMus; SptEdSchPpr; 4-H; Usd Vermillion; Biology.

BAUMANN, Patrick J; Newman HS; Wausau, WI; Band; Chrs; ChrhWkr; CncrtBnd; HonRl; MrchBnd; OffAde; PepBnd; SctActv; TchrAde; LatCl; Bsbl; LetterFtbl; CchngActv; University Of Wisconsin; Vet.

BAUMANN, Patti S; Pekin Eastern HS; Pekin, IN; ChrhWkr; HonRl; NHS; StuCncl; 4-H; PpCl; SciCl; LetterTrk; GAA; 4-HAwd; JCAwd; College; Medicine.

BAUMANN, Sharon G; Nathan Hale HS; West Allis, WI; CncrtBnd; DrlTm; YthFlsp; YthLg; Uw Waukesha; Rn.

BAUMEISTER, Andrew J; Burr Oak Community HS; Burr Oak, MI; 16/34 Band; Chrs; ChrhWkr; HonRl; PolWkr; SchMus; SchPl; YthFlsp; 4-H; Ftbl; Auto And Motorcylce Mechanic.

BAUMEISTER, Carol A; St Marys HS; Burlington, WI; Chrs; HonRl; SchPl; SctActv; RptrYrbk; LetterTrk; Chrldr; GAA; IMSpt; PPFtbl; Whitewater Univ; Cpa.

BAUMEISTER, Carol A; River Valley HS; Sawyer, MI; TreasChrhWkr; HonRl; MrchBnd; TreasNHS; Orch; PepBnd; TchrAde; VP4-H; GerCl; 4-HAwd; College.

BAUMEISTER, Judith M; Burr Oak Comm HS; Burr Oak, MI; 7/34 SecSophCls; PresSrCls; Chrs; NHS; SchMus; Yrbk; FrCl; PPFtbl; DARAwd; 4-HAwd; Ferris State Col; Library Techn.

BAUMER, Jodell K; Little Wolf HS; Manawa, WI; SecJrCls; Band; HonRl; StuCncl; RptrSchPpr; 4-H; FHA; Bsktbl; GAA; IMSpt; U; Professional.

BAUMERT, Brian A; Howells Public HS; Howells, NE; 6/42 TrsJrCls; Band; Chrs; HonRl; MrchBnd; PepBnd; Bsktbl; Ftbl; Trk; DanFAwd; U Of Ne Wesleyan; Business Adm.

BAUMERT, Marcia B; Central Catholic HS; West Point, NE; 12/77 Chrs; HonRl; NHS; SchPl; 4-H; SpnCl; MthCl; PpCl; 4-HAwd; VoiceDemAwd; U Of Ne; Fashion Const & Design.

BAUMERT, Michael J; Howells Public HS; Howells, NE; Band; Chrs; CncrtBnd; MrchBnd; PepBnd; StuCncl; Ftbl; Trk; 4-HAwd; College; Agri Business.

BAUMGARDNER, Dennis J; Springfield Se HS; Springfield, IL; 12/505 PresBand; MrchBnd; NHS; SchMus; StuCncl; Tennis; College; Medicine.

BAUMGART, Paul D; Pulaski HS; Pulaski, WI; HonRl; NHS; FFA; LetterTrk; IMSpt; U W Green Bay; Meteorology.

BAUMGARTEN, Kathy L; Stewardson Strasburg HS; Stewardson, IL; Chr; Chrs; SchPl; Yrbk; FHA; PpCl; Bsktbl; LetterChrldr; Patricia Stevens; Public Relations.

BAUMGARTEN, Marsha L; Arthur Hill HS; Saginaw, MI; Band; MrchBnd; Orch; PepBnd; SchMus; FrCl; Bsktbl; Trk; University; Music.

BAUMGARTNER, Cynthia A; Sabetha HS; Sabetha, KS; ChrhWkr; HonRl; OffAde; SchAde; TchrAde; SecFBLA; FHA; SpnCl; Trk; IMSpt; Business School; Medical Secretary.

BAUMGARTNER, Jane M; Don Bosco HS; Laporte, IA; Chr; Chrs; HonRl; JA; JrNHS; NHS; SchMus; 4-H; PpCl; Chrldr; Hawkeye Tech; Major Study.

BAUMGARTNER, Jeffrey M; Morton East HS; Cicero, IL; 11/775 HonRl; JrNHS; NHS; Univ Of Illinois; Accounting.

BAUMGARTNER, Julie A; Rothsay Public HS; Rothsay, MN; SecJrCls; ALAGirlsSt; ChrhWkr; CncrtBnd; HonRl; Mdrgl; NHS; RptrYrbk; RptrSchPpr; LetterTrk; College.

BAUMGARTNER, Raymond J; Argyle HS; Monroe, WI; HonRl; VP4-H; FFA; 4-HAwd; U Of Wi Madison; Dairy Farmer.

BAUMGRAS, Edward L; Mio Au Sable HS; Luzerne, MI; 1/48 HonRl; NHS; TchrAde; Lake Superior St Coll; Chemistry.

BAUMGRAS, Shelley L; Portland HS; Portland, MI; Band; HonRl; JrNHS; LbryAde; MrchBnd; NHS; TchrAde; SpnCl; PPFtbl; VoiceDemAwd;.

BAUMHARDT, Kathleen K; Kewaskum HS; Adell, WI; 11/175 ALAGirlsSt; CncrtBnd; HonRl; NatlFornLg; NHS; SchMus; SchPl; PresStuGov; DARAwd; KiwanAwd; College; Professnl.

BAUMHOVER, David J; Fonda Comm HS; Fonda, IA; 1/30 ChrhWkr; HonRl; JrNHS; ModUN; NHS; SchPl; RptrYrbk; RptrSchPpr; GerCl; PpCl; LetterBsbl; LetterBsktbl; LetterFtbl; Univ; Criminal Justice.

BAUMLE, Steve R; Forest View HS; Mt Prospect, IL; 140/650 HonRl; GerCl; LetterTennis; North Ill Univ; Doctor.

BAUMLER, Karen M; Central Cass HS; Wheatland, ND; VPSophCls; TrsJrCls; HonRl; NHS; TreasCivCl; LetterBsktbl; LetterTrk; LetterChrldr; GAA; 4-HAwd; Coll; Vocation.

BAUMSTARK, Mary L; Harry A Burke HS; Omaha, NE; 4/600 AFS; ChrhWkr; HonRl; VPJA; NHS; NatlMeritSF; NatlThespSoc; SchPl; SpnCl; College; Astronomy.

BAUNE, Joyce; Pershing HS; Plummer, MN; Band; CncrtBnd; HonRl; MrchBnd; PepBnd; RptrSchPpr; FHA; Chrldr; IMSpt; College; Professional Nursing.

BAUR, Pamela; St Pius HS; Festus, MO; Band; CncrtBnd; MrchBnd; PepBnd; PpCl; College; Nursing.

BAUSERMAN, Joyce R; Churubusco HS; Churubusco, IN; 3/103 ChrhWkr; HonRl; HospAde; JA; NHS; Quill&Scroll; SchPl; SctActv; TchrAde; SchPpr; 4-H; FTA; LatCl; Purdue Univ; Forestry.

BAUSONE, Terese A; Maria HS; Chicago, IL; 7/301 ChrhWkr; HonRl; NHS; Sdlty; SpnCl; GAA; University Of Ill; Nursing.

BAUTCH, Marlene R; Whitehall Memorial HS; Whitehall, WI; SecSophCls; Band; HonRl; JrNHS; NatlFornLg; SchPl; Yrbk; SpnCl; GAA; ChmbCommrsAwd; Uw Eau Claire; Music Therapy.

BAUTERS, Jeanine; Marian HS; Mishawaka, IN; 5/129 HonRl; NHS; SchPl; SchPpr; 4-H; Tennis; IMSpt; Coll; Med.

BAUTISTA, Roberto; Proviso East HS; Melrose Pk, IL; 72/1001 HonRl; NHS; Orch; Tennis; Trk; Univ Of Illinois; Physicist.

BAUTISTA, Steven J; Mendel Catholic Prep HS; Chicago Ridge, IL; 4/170 HonRl; LbryAde; OffAde; Yrbk; Southern Calif Univ; Architecture.

BAUTZ, Gregory F; Waukesha North HS; Waukesha, WI; Univ; Wildlife Management.

BAUWENS, Jonathan E; Marian HS; South Bend, IN; 5/118 Chr; ChrhWkr; CmntyWkr; HonRl; NHS; SchPl; SctActv; Bsktbl; LetterGlf; University; Medicine.

BAVLER, Mark; Rosemount HS; Rosemount, MN; 450 HstJrCls; Band; CncrtBnd; MrchBnd; PepBnd; SchMus; StuGov; SptEdYrbk; RptrSchPpr; CchngActv; College;professional.

BAWDEN, Vicki; Richmond Burton HS; Spring Grove, IL; 5/75 HonRl; JA; JrNHS; NHS; SchPl; EdYrBk; GAA; AmLegAwd; College; Nursing.

BAWOL, Sharon L; St Andrew HS; Detroit, MI; Chr; ChrhWkr; CmntyWkr; HonRl; LitMag; Sdlty; StuGov; RptrSchPpr; SchPpr; PpCl; Mary Grove; Fashion Designer.

BAX, Rita A; Jc HS; Jefferson, MO; 3/486 Chr; HonRl; JrNHS; NHS; Quill&Scroll; StuCncl; RptrSchPpr; SchPpr; MthCl; SciCl; Northeast Mo State; Mathamatics.

BAX, Rita A; Jefferson City Sr HS; Jefferson, MO; 3/486 HonRl; JrNHS; NHS; NatlMeritCmnd; Quill&Scroll; StuCncl; RptrSchPpr; SchPpr; MthCl; Northeast Ms Univ; Mathematics.

BAXA, Patti A; Sacred Heart Academy; Springfield, IL; 5/143 Chr; HonRl; NHS; SchMus; RptrSchPpr; SchPpr; MthCl; Illinois State; Commercial Art.

BAXA, Ronald J; Meridian Public HS; Tobias, NE; Band; Chr; ChrhWkr; CmntyWkr; CncrtBnd; HonRl; MrchBnd; NHS; OffAde; PepBnd; Trade School; Vocation.

BAXA, William J; Waukesha South Campus HS; Waukesha, WI; 22/583 HonRl; NHS; PresSctActv; SpnCl; MthCl; IMSpt; Marquette Univ; Dentistry.

BAXLEY, Alice G; Whiting HS; Whiting, IN; 7/102 ChrhWkr; HonRl; NHS; Yrbk; FTA; SpnCl; Lincoln Christian College.

BAXTER, Cheryl L; Riverdale HS; Avoca, WI; 10/90 AFS; ALAGirlsSt; Band; Chr; Chrs; ChrhWkr; CncrtBnd; HonRl; Mdrgl; NHS; PepBnd; SchMus; SchPl; Twrl;.

BAXTER, Darrel L; St Louis HS; St Louis, MI; CmntyWkr; 4-H; FFA; Bsktbl; Ftbl; DanFAwd;.

BAXTER, Dawn M; Ralston HS; Omaha, NE; 25/252 Chr; HonRl; NHS; Quill&Scroll; TchrAde; EdSchPpr; FrCl; U Of Ne Lincoln; English Major & Lawyer.

BAXTER, Janice A; Rudyard Area HS; Rudyard, MI; 25/116 Aud/Vis; Band; Chr; ChrhWkr; HonRl; LbryAde; SecYthFlsp; 4-H; 4-HAwd; Bible School; Medicine.

BAXTER, Rex; Hauser HS; Columbus, IN; TchrAde; FFA; PpCl; College.

BAXTER, Wade E; Harlem North HS; Loves Park, IL; Band; CncrtBnd; HonRl; JA; MrchBnd; PepBnd; SchPl; Yrbk; 4-H; Bsktbl; Ftbl; Trk; College; Social Service.

BAXTER, William J; Gordon Tech HS; Chicago, IL; 35/618 Band; ChrhWkr; HonRl; LbryAde; StuCncl; SchPpr; SpnCl; MthCl; SciCl; College; Engineer.

BAY, Janet L; Salem Sr HS; Salem, MO; HonRl; StuCncl; PresSpnCl; PresPpCl; Drury Col; Home Economics.

BAY, Russell D; Wayne Comm HS; Corydon, IA; TrsSophCls; Band; CncrtBnd; HonRl; JrNHS; MrchBnd; NHS; PepBnd; Bsktbl; Iowa University; Medicine.

BAYER, Annette L; Roanoke Benson HS; Roanoke, IL; AFS; Band; Chrs; CncrtBnd; Mdrgl; MrchBnd; PepBnd; SctActv; FHA; College; Music.

BAYER, David G; Lake Zurich HS; Kildeer, IL; HonRl; LetterGlf; Univ Of Illinois; Lawyer.

BAYER, Janet C; Horton Watkins HS; St Louis, MO; 14/434 Chrl; SecCncrtBnd; LitMag; SecMrchBnd; NatlFornLg; SecNHS; NatlMeritFnl; NatlThespSoc; Quill&Scroll; SchMus; Univ Of Ia; Communications.

BAYLOM, Blaire V; Kenwood HS; Chicago, IL; Chr; ChrhWkr; SchPl; YthFlsp; FrCl; GAA; JAAwd; College; Biological Sciences.

BAYLOR, Barbara W; New Trier West HS; Northfield, IL; 127/698 Chr; HonRl; HospAde; SchMus; SchPl; SctActv; StuGov; RptrYrbk; RptrSchPpr; Northwestern University; Communications.

BAYLOR, Mark C; Farmington East HS; Farmington, IL; 9/141 Band; CncrtBnd; HonRl; MrchBnd; NHS; PepBnd; SpnCl; College; Professional.

BAYNE, Vicki L; Tri County R 7 HS; Jamesport, MO; PresFrshCls; TrsJrCls; ChrhWkr; HonRl; Yrbk; Pres4-H; PresFHA; VPSciCl; CaptChrldr; 4-HAwd; College; Reg Nurse.

BAYS, Donna J; Zionsville Comm HS; Zionsville, IN; ALAGirlsSt; CncrtBnd; DrlTm; HonRl; MrchBnd; NHS; Quill&Scroll; SctActv; VPYthFlsp; EdSchPpr; College; Political Journalism.

BAYS, Sharon E; Wheaton North HS; Wheaton, IL; PresAFS; HonRl; HospAde; NatlFornLg; NHS; PolWkr; StuCncl; StuGov; TchrAde; RptrYrbk; Cornell University; Food Science.

BAYSINGER, Linda K; Brazil Sr HS; Brazil, IN; 3/202 HonRl; NHS; TchrAde; YthFlsp; CivCl; Pres4-H; PresFHA; PpCl; IMSpt; 4-HAwd; Trade Sch; Cashier.

BAZEY, John D; Luck HS; Cumberland, WI; 1/53 Band; ChrhWkr; CncrtBnd; HonRl; MrchBnd; NHS; PepBnd; SchPl; Treas4-H; 4-HAwd; University; Vocation.

BAZINET, Michael J; Rock Public HS; Rock, MI; 16/30 CmntyWkr; SchPl; SctActv; SchPpr; PpCl; Bsbl; Bsktbl; Tennis; Trk; Trade School; Field Of Electronics.

BAZY, Mary J; Springfield Gardens HS; Sterling Hts, MI; 45/900 JrNHS; TchrAde; Univ Of Michigan; Medicine.

BAZZELL, Sheryl; Riverside HS; Drbn Hgts, MI; Chrs; HonRl; GAA; Trade School; Beauty School.

BAZZETTA, Thomas G; Woodruff HS; Peoria, IL; 25/270 VPFrshCls; HonRl; StuCncl; KeyCl; GerCl; LatCl; Bsbl; Ftbl; Southern Ill Univ; Agriculture.

BEACH, Cheryl D; Howell HS; Howell, MI; 76/368 TrsFrshCls; Band; CncrtBnd; DrmBgl; HonRl; MrchBnd; NHS; PepBnd; StuGov; Trk; GAA; Ferris State College; Pharmacology.

BEACH, Jane L; Greenwood HS; Springfield, MO; TrsFrshCls; Chrs; ChrhWkr; DrmBgl; DrmMjrt; HonRl; SchMus; StuCncl; SchPpr; Glf; Clge; Prof.

BEACH, Jeffery S; Vestaburg HS; Edmore, MI; Band; CncrtBnd; HonRl; MrchBnd; PepBnd; TchrAde; Bsktbl; Ftbl; Trk; Arm Services.

BEACH, Joan M; Floyd Central HS; Pekin, IN; 1/287 ChrhWkr; HonRl; JrNHS; NHS; PolWkr; TchrAde; Pres4-H; FTA; SpnCl; PpCl; Trk; GAA; KiwanAwd; Purdue Univ; Nuclear Engineer.

BEACH, Kevin J; Grand Ledge HS; Eagle, MI; HonRl; JrNHS; NHS; NatlMeritSF; StuCncl; FrCl; RotaryAwd; U Of Mi; Lawyer Political Scien.

BEACH, Robert L; Homewood Flossmoor HS; Homewood, IL; 63/940 Chr; HonRl; NHS; NatlMeritCmnd; RusCl; Univ Of Illinois; Medicine.

BEACHAM, Andrea; Bernie HS; Bernie, MO; 4/55 Chr; Chrs; ChrhWkr; HonRl; JrNHS; SchMus; SchPl; TchrAde; FHA; Chrldr; Southeast Mo St Univ; Music.

BEACHY, Annet K; Northwestern HS; Kokomo, IN; Chr; HonRl; LbryAde; NHS; OffAde; VPYthFlsp; College.

BEACHY, Jill M; Laker HS; Pigeon, MI; 54/146 PresSophCls; HonRl; HospAde; LbryAde; StuCncl; TchrAde; TreasYthFlsp; FHA; GerCl; IMSpt; Central Michigan Univ; Social Worker.

BEACHY, Lois E; Northridge HS; Middlebury, IN; SecJrCls; PresStuCncl; PresFHA; Col ;home Ec.

BEACHY, Philip; Goshen HS; Goshen, IN; NHS; NatlMeritFnl; Orch; SchMus; StuGov; SciCl; Wrstlng; BauchLmbAwd; RotaryAwd; Goshen College; Pre Medical.

BEACHY, Philip A; Goshen HS; Goshen, IN; 3/750 NHS; NatlMeritSF; Orch; SchMus; StuGov; GerCl; PpCl; SciCl; LetterWrstlng; RotaryAwd; Goshen College; Medicine.

BEACOM, Connie J; O Gorman HS; Sioux Falls, SD; PresChrhWkr; HospAde; VPJA; PolWkr; SchPl; SctActv; TchrAde; Bsbl; College; Secretary.

BEADIE, Nancy; Elmhurst HS; Fort Wayne, IN; 7/342 CmntyWkr; HonRl; JA; NatlFornLg; Quill&Scroll; StuCncl; RptrSchPpr; Chrldr; Univ; Writer.

BEADLE, Albert; Noblesville HS; Noblesville, IN; 10/256 VPFrshCls; VPSophCls; VPJrCls; VPSrCls; HonRl; NHS; Yrbk; GerCl; SpnCl; MthCl; De Pauw Univ; Medicine.

BEADLE, Jolleen K; Swea City Comm HS; Swea City, IA; 1/32 PresFrshCls; Band; ChrhWkr; CncrtBnd; HonRl; MrchBnd; NHS; PepBnd; StuCncl; FFA; LetterBsbl; CaptBsktbl; LetterTrk; College; Vet Asst.

BEADLES, Margaret D; Bloomington HS; Bloomington, IL; HonRl; NatlFornLg; PolWkr; GerCl; MthCl; SciCl; Trk; Illinois Wesleyan Univ; Dentist.

BEAGLE, Deanna L; Pine River HS; Tustin, MI; 4/80 ChrhWkr; HonRl; LbryAde; NHS; OffAde; SchPl; Yrbk; 4-H; FHA; DARAwd; College; Recreation Techonologist.

BEAGLE, Jay R; Greensburg HS; Greensburg, IN; 20/200 ALBoysSt; DrmBgl; HonRl; NHS; SchMus; YthFlsp; LatCl; SciCl; CaptTrk; CchngActv; Indinan Univ; Dentrist.

BEAH, Debbie D; Marmaton Valley HS; Kincaid, KS; CmntyWkr; HonRl; MrchBnd; Twrl; 4-H; FHA; PpCl; Chrldr; JAAwd;.

BEAKUP, Joellen M; St Johns HS; Elsie, MI; 14/333 HonRl; NHS; YthFlsp; 4-H; Ferris St College; Legal Assistance.

BEAL, Cynthia S; Albia Comm HS; Albia, IA; ChrhWkr; CmntyWkr; HonRl; NHS; StuCncl; YthFlsp; FHA; College; Cosmetology.

BEAL, Paula D; Round Lake Sr HS; Round Lake, IL; PresJrCls; ALAGirlsSt; JA; EdYrBk; 4-H; SpnCl; GAA; AmLegAwd; 4-HAwd; JAAwd; Mosers Business Clg; Public Relations.

BEAL, Ron D; Sedgwick HS; Sedgwick, KS; HonRl; RptrSchPpr; SptEdSchPpr; Bsbl; LetterBsktbl; LetterFtbl; Glf; Tennis; LetterTrk; TIMEAwd; PresAwd; College; Professional.

BEAL, Vicki A; Zalma HS; Arab, MO; 6/23 VPFrshCls; ChrhWkr; StuCncl; FHA; Se Missouri University; Law.

BEAL, Vicki L; Blackford HS; Hartford City, IN; 17/252 Band; CncrtBnd; HonRl; MrchBnd; PepBnd; TchrAde; SpnCl; Purdue Univ; Optometry.

BEALL, Cheryl L; Crown Point HS; Crown Point, IN; HonRl; NHS; Quill&Scroll; TchrAde; RptrSchPpr; SchPpr; 4-H; FTA; FrCl; Indiana University; Nurse.

BEALS, Bradley; Stewardson Strasburg HS; Effingham, IL; Band; CncrtBnd; HonRl; LbryAde; MrchBnd; SchPl; RptrYrbk; RptrSchPpr;.

BEALS, Cynthia L; Brown City HS; Brown City, MI; HonRl; LbryAde; NHS; TchrAde; Pres4-H; FTA; 4-HAwd; Olivet Clge; English.

BEALS, Melissa M; Mendota Township HS; Mendota, IL; Band; CncrtBnd; HonRl; MrchBnd; NHS; NatlSciFnd; PepBnd; SciCl; CaptBsktbl; GAA; Univ; Major Study.

BEALS, Robin S; Belle Fourche HS; Belle Fourche, SD; 7/112 Chrs; ChrhWkr; HonRl; LbryAde; NHS; SchMus; PpCl; College; Legal Secreterial.

BEALS, Susan L; Fairfax Independent HS; Fairfax, SD; SecTrsJrCls; Band; Chr; Chrs; HonRl; LbryAde; MrchBnd; SchPl; StuCncl; RptrYrbk; CaptBsktbl; CaptGAA; College.

BEAM, Linda J; Hillsboro HS; Taylor Springs, IL; HonRl; NHS; Yrbk; PresFHA; MthCl; Southern Ill Univ.

BEAM, Michael K; La Ville HS; Plymouth, IN; ChrhWkr; CncrtBnd; MrchBnd; Orch; AmLegAwd; Coll; Architecture.

BEAM, Tracy M; Taylors Falls HS; Stacy, MN; PresSrCls; Chr; HonRl; NatlFornLg; SchPl; StuGov; RptrYrbk; SciCl; LetterBsbl; LetterBsktbl; IMSpt; Luther College; Veterinarian.

BEAMER, Robyn D; Mexico HS; Mexico, MO; CncrtBnd; JrNHS; Mdrgl; PresNHS; NatlMeritSF; StuCncl; YthFnd; LatCl; JETSAwd; RotaryAwd; Univ Of Mo Columbia; Medicine.

BEAMS, Valerie L; Fremont HS; Fremont, IN; 1/73 TrsFrshCls; SecSophCls; Band; Chr; CncrtBnd; HonRl; MrchBnd; SchMus; SchPl; TchrAde; LetterTrk; LetterChrldr; GAA; PPFtbl; College; Math.

BEAMSLEY, Nancy A; Dundee HS; Carpentersville, IL; 33/362 TrsJrCls; SecSrCls; MrchBnd; SchMus; StuCncl; StuGov; PpCl; Univ Of Illinois; Occupational Therapy.

BEAN, Debbie; Arnold HS; Arnold, NE; 3/31 PresSrCls; HonRl; Mdrgl; SchMus; SctActv; EdYrBk; FFA; Bsktbl; Glf; BttyCrckrAwd; North Platte Beauty Acad; Beatician.

BEAN, James D; Reavis HS; Burbank, IL; 57/676 HonRl; NHS; LetterTrk; Chicago State Univ; Teacher.

BEAN, Karen M; Carl Sandburg HS; Orland Pk, IL; NHS; PresSpnCl; PpCl;.

BEAN, Randy T; Battle Creek Comm HS; Battle Creek, IA; 8/23& Band; CmntyWkr; HonRl; MrchBnd; Orch; PepBnd; LetterBsbl; LetterFtbl; Glf; Trk; Iowa U; Major Study.

BEAN, Telitha F; Waco Comm HS; Wayland, IA; AFS; Band; Chrs; CncrtBnd; HonRl; MrchBnd; NHS; PepBnd; SchMus; SchPl; 4-H; SpnCl; PpCl; College; Computer Science.

BEANE, James D; Virden HS; Virden, IL; TrsSophCls; ChrhWkr; HonRl; Yrbk; 4-H; FrCl; Bsbl; Bsktbl; LetterFtbl; LetterTrk; College; Business Mgmt.

BEARD, Bill; Blue Valley HS; Stilwell, KS; CmntyWkr; HonRl; NHS; SctActv; StuCncl; 4-H; Bsbl; Bsktbl; Ftbl; College; Professional.

BEARD, Cheryl R; Salem Comm HS; Salem, IL; 6/203 Band; Chrs; ChrhWkr; CncrtBnd; HonRl; LbryAde; MrchBnd; NHS; PepBnd; Yrbk; Hardeman College; Business.

BEARD, Cynthia; Corning Community HS; Corning, IA; 13/75 Chrs; HonRl; SchMus; SchPl; Teen; Yrbk; Glf; Trk; Chrldr; PPFtbl; Patricia Stevens; Fashion Merchandising.

BEARD, Daniel L; Holden Sr HS; Holden, MO; Chr; Chrs; HonRl; LbryAde; TchrAde; FFA;.

BEARD, Janet E; Hot Springs HS; Hot Springs, SD; DrlTm; HonRl; LbryAde; OffAde; YthFlsp; FrCl; PpCl; Chrldr; College; Legal Secretary.

BEARD, Jill E; Greenview HS; Greenview, IL; 1/49 Band; Chrs; CncrtBnd; HonRl; MrchBnd; NHS; PepBnd; SchMus; VPStuCncl; FHA; FSA; Univ; Doctor.

BEARD, Karen D; Centerville HS; Moulton, IA; 4/130 Band; ChrhWkr; CmntyWkr; HonRl; YthFlsp; 4-H; FHA; PpCl; 4-HAwd; CitAwd;.

BEARD, Mary A; Ozark HS; Ozark, MO; 9/90 HonRl; StuCncl; FBLA; VPFHA; PpCl; Chrldr; Sw Missouri St Univ; Secretarial.

BEARD, Randal G; Colfax Comm HS; Colfax, IA; VPSophCls; HonRl; StuGov; 4-H; SpnCl; IMSpt; 4-HAwd; College; Wildlife Biologist.

BEARD, Randy H; Gibraltar HS; Ellison Bay, WI; 2/70 HonRl; NHS; TchrAde; Bsktbl; IMSpt; BttyCrckrAwd; U Of Eal Claire; Professional.

BEARD, Sheila A; Centralia HS; Centralia, KS; PresSrCls; ALAGirlsSt; HonRl; SecStuCncl; Yrbk; 4-H; Chrldr; DARAwd; 4-HAwd; Kansas State University; Home Economics.

BEARD, William J; South Decatur HS; Greensburg, IN; Band; ChrhWkr; SctActv; YthFlsp; 4-H; MthCl; SciCl; LetterBsbl; LetterFtbl; LetterGlf; Wrstlng; 4-HAwd; Rose Hulman Inst; Elec Engineer.

BEARDEN, Lisa A; George Rogers Clark HS; Whiting, IN; TrsJrCls; OffAde; FrCl; CchngActv; College; Business Admin.

BEARDEN, Michael C; Gladbrook Community HS; Gladbrook, IA; Band; Chrs; CncrtBnd; HonRl; MrchBnd; ModUN; PepBnd; SchPl; YthFlsp; EdYrBk; Math.

BEARE, Terri L; Herrin HS; Herrin, IL; 1/211 VPFrshCls; VPSophCls; Chrs; CncrtBnd; HonRl; NHS; NatlMeritCmnd; StuCncl; Chrldr; AmLegAwd; Southern Il Univ; Music Major (vocal).

BEARINGER, Joyce E; Midland Community HS; Onslow, IA; 5/49 Band; Chr; HonRl; NHS; SchMus; Twrl; YthFlsp; RptrYrbk; RptrSchPpr; LetterChrldr; College; Occupational Therapy.

BEARROWS, Thomas R; Rochelle Twp HS; Rochelle, IL; 3/225 VPSrCls; ChrhWkr; HonRl; NHS; NatlMeritCmnd; SchPl; LatCl; Trk; BauchLmbAwd; Univ Of Ill; Medicine.

BEARY, Christine; Twin Cedars Hs; Lovilia, IA; 2/42 VPFrshCls; SecSophCls; Band; SchPl; Pres4-H; PresFTA; TreasPpCl; PresSciCl; LetterTrk; 4-HAwd; U Of Northern Iowa; Education.

BEARY, Patrick A; Knoxville HS; Knoxville, IA; VPSophCls; PresJrCls; ALBoysSt; HonRl; RptrYrbk; RptrSchPpr; SciCl; LetterBsbl; Bsktbl; LetterTrk; CchngActv; College; Art.

BEASING, Kevin S; Falls City HS; Falls City, NE; Band; CncrtBnd; HonRl; MrchBnd; NHS; PepBnd; SecSpnCl; LetterGlf; Univ.

BEASLEY, Lori; Benton Consolidated HS; Thompsonville, IL; 65/185 HstJrCls; HstSrCls; ChrhWkr; HonRl; SchMus; RptrYrbk; RptrSchPpr; 4-H; Glf; GAA; Rend Lake Jr Coll.

BEASON, Karen D; Taylor HS; Kokomo, IN; HonRl; NHS; SchPl; Yrbk; Tennis; Chrldr; GAA; PPFtbl;.

BEASON, Susan K; Lakefield HS; Lakefield, MN; 5/65 Chrs; ChrhWkr; CncrtBnd; HonRl; SchMus; EdSchPpr; PresSciCl; Minneapolis College; Commercial Art.

BEATTIE, Byron J; Trenton HS; Trenton, MI; PresJrCls; ChrhWkr; CmntyWkr; HonRl; NHS; StuCncl; StuGov; Bsktbl; LetterFtbl; CchngActv; Eastern Mich Univ; Pre Medicine.

BEATTIE, Christine A; L C HS; La Moille, IL; Chrs; HonRl; SchPpr; GAA; Trade Sch; Prof.

BEATTIE, Jayne M; So Nodaway HS; Barnard, MO; 1/28 ALAGirlsSt; Band; HonRl; NHS; SchPl; VPStuCncl; EdYrBk; 4-H; LetterBsktbl; LetterTrk; CchngActv; 4-HAwd; Univ; Professional.

BEATTIE, Sally A; Amboy HS; Harmon, IL; Band; CncrtBnd; HonRl; MrchBnd; SecNHS; PepBnd; 4-H; PresPpCl; GAA; College.

BEATTIE, Susan K; Minden HS; Minden, NE; 25/106 Band; Chr; Chrs; CncrtBnd; HonRl; HospAde; MrchBnd; NHS; PepBnd; Wesleyan Univ; Nursing.

BEATTIE, Timothy J; Marshall HS; Marshall, MI; HonRl; LetterFtbl; Tennis; Adrian Coll; Bus.

BEATTY, Dawn H; Marshal HS; Marshall, MI; HonRl; JA; PolWkr; Bsbl; Kellogg Comm Clg; Education.

BEATTY, Gary; West Platte HS; Rushville, MO; HonRl; ModUN; SchPl; RptrYrbk; Yrbk; RptrSchPpr; Trade School.

BEATTY, Leslie A; Kirksville R Iii HS; Kirksville, MO; CmntyWkr; CncrtBnd; HonRl; MrchBnd; PepBnd; SchMus; FBLA; FrCl; PpCl; Nmsu Univ; Special Ed Or Medical.

BEATTY, Marie A; Lourdes HS; Chicago, IL; 75/299 ChrhWkr; HonRl; JA; NHS; StuCncl; SpnCl; College; History.

BEATTY, Mary; Granite City South HS; Granite City, IL; PresJrCls; NHS; PolWkr; StuGov; Bsbl; Socr; Swmmng; Tennis; CchngActv; IMSpt; Univ; Chem Engin.

BEATTY, Michael; Wabaunsee HS; Maple Hill, KS; ALBoysSt; Chr; SchPl; StuCncl; SptEdYrbk; CchngActv; Eksc College; Pre Dental.

BEATTY, Theresa J; Menasha HS; Menasha, WI; 75/304 PresSrCls; DrlTm; HonRl; HospAde; JA; LitMag; NHS; OffAde; SchMus; StuGov;.

BEATY, Elizabeth A; Benton Consolidated HS; Ewing, IL; 11/185 HonRl; NHS; 4-H; FHA; Trk; GAA; IMSpt; AmLegAwd; 4-HAwd; College; Accounting.

BEAUBIEN, Kathleen A; Cabrini HS; Allen Park, MI; 1/167 ALAGirlsSt; HonRl; HospAde; NHS; OffAde; RedCrAde; SchPpr; LatCl; SciCl; VoiceDemAwd; University; Physician.

BEAUCHAMP, Brian L; Crown Point HS; Crown Point, IN; HonRl; NHS; StuCncl; LatCl; Bsktbl; Tennis; LetterTrk; Indiana St University.

BEAUCHAMP, Gail S; Iron Mountain HS; Iron Mountain, MI; 36/158 Chrs; CmntyWkr; HospAde; LbryAde; RedCrAde; 4-H; FrCl; Northern Michigan Univ; History.

BEAUCHAMP, Lissa M; Central HS; St Joseph, MO; SecJrCls; HonRl; SchMus; StuGov; RptrYrbk; FrCl; PpCl; SciCl; Swmmng; Chrldr; College; Speech Therapy.

BEAUCHESNE, Sharon; Carman HS; Flint, MI; PresSrCls; NatlMeritCmnd; StuGov; TchrAde; FTA; Trk; PPFtbl; College; Teaching.

BEAUCHINE, Michael D; William G Mather HS; Munising, MI; 5/127 ALBoysSt; ChrhWkr; HonRl; NHS; SchPl; SctActv; StuCncl; Michigan Tech Univ; Chemical Engineer.

BEAUDETTE, Debbie A; Holy Redeemer HS; Detroit, MI; 17/168 HonRl; SecNHS; StuGov; RptrYrbk; Yrbk; Bsktbl; DARAwd; Eastern Mi U; Special Education.

BEAUMARCHAIS, Diane M; Milford HS; Highland, MI; 140/553 IMSpt; Western Mi Univ; Social Work.

BEAUMONT, Christine A; Little Falls Comm HS; Little Falls, MN; Chr; ChrhWkr; SchMus; FrCl; PpCl; LetterBsktbl; Trk; Chrldr; GAA; College; Professional.

BEAUPRE, Karen A; Al Brook HS; Saginaw, MN; Chr; HonRl; TchrAde; RptrSchPpr; FHA; PpCl; Social Work.

BEAUSOLEIL, Laurie L; Waukegan East HS; Waukegan, IL; HonRl; OffAde; SchMus; Chrldr; State School.

BEAUVAIS, Bernard J; Somerset HS; Somerset, WI; HonRl; CaptFtbl; CaptWrstlng; CchngActv; Trade School; Construction.

BEAUVAIS, Judith A; Mundelein HS; Mundelein, IL; ChrhWkr; HonRl; SctActv; TchrAde; PresKeyCl; TreasFrCl; IMSpt; U Of Il; Social Work.

BEAVERS, Dennis G; Covington HS; Covington, IN; 1/100 Chrs; HonRl; NHS; SchPl; StuCncl; LetterBsbl; LetterBsktbl; LetterFtbl; LetterTrk; College.

BEBB, Leslie A; Herbert Henry Dow HS; Midland, MI; 108/450 Chr; HonRl; NHS; EngCl; Michigan St University.

BEBEAU, Brian K; Buffalo Grove HS; Buffalo Grove, IL; 11/290 Band; CncrtBnd; HonRl; MrchBnd; NHS; NatlMeritCmnd; Orch; PepBnd; SchMus; Beloit College; Electronic Music.

BEBEE, Roxanne; Mc Auley Regional HS; Carthage, MO; 1/34 ALAGirlsSt; Chrs; ChrhWkr; HonRl; ModUN; NHS; SchPl; TchrAde; PpCl; IMSpt; U Of Mo; Engineering.

BEBEL, Mitchell R; St Thomas Academy; Mendota Hts, MN; HonRl; NatlMeritSF; RptrYrbk; RptrSchPpr; College; Law.

BEBENEK, Linda J; George Rogers Clark HS; Hammond, IN; 11/260 Chrs; LbryAde; NHS; OffAde; Sdlty; EdYrBk; FrCl; PpCl; GAA; College; Accountant.

BECHARD, Richard B; Grinnell HS; Grinnell, KS; PresFrshCls; TrsSrCls; Band; PepBnd; Sacrstn; SctActv; Bsktbl; Ftbl; Trk; College; Ecology.

BECHER, Anita R; Fremont HS; Fremont, IN; 2/62 ChrhWkr; HonRl; NHS; SchPl; StuCncl; Teen; YthFlsp; FHA; FrCl; MthCl; Clge; Secretarial Science.

BECHER, Anne E; Chatard HS; Indianapolis, IN; 3/190 HonRl; NHS; FrCl; PpCl; LetterTennis; CchngActv; IMSpt; Indiana U; Nursing.

BECHER, Gregory J; Lancaster Sr HS; Lancaster, WI; PresAFS; Aud/Vis; Band; Chr; ChrhWkr; CncrtBnd; HonRl; HospAde; NHS; Orch; SctActv; YthFlsp; TreasSpnCl; Trk; College; Chemical Engineering.

BECHER, Margaret M; Incarnate Word HS; Cool Valley, MO; 29/111 HonRl; Quill&Scroll; StuCncl; RptrSchPpr; Socr; PPFtbl; College; Engineering.

BECHER, Michael D; Forest Park HS; Ferdinand, IN; HonRl; NHS; StuCncl; Yrbk; Bsbl; College; Business.

BECHER, Robert G; Stratford Sr HS; Stratford, WI; 4/90 VPFrshCls; Band; Chr; NHS; PepBnd; SchMus; SctActv; StuCncl; LetterFtbl; LetterTrk; Univ Of Wis Milwaukee; Engineering.

BECHER, Susan M; Hinsdale Central HS; Hinsdale, IL; 71/583 HonRl; HospAde; LitMag; NatlMeritCmnd; Univ Of Illinois; Law.

BECHERER, Luan; Northwood HS; Minong, WI; HonRl; RptrYrbk; College; X Ray Technician.

BECHMANN, Mary C; University HS; Milwaukee, WI; AFS; CmntyWkr; HonRl; ModUN; NatlMeritFnl; OffAde; RedCrAde; EdSchPpr; LatCl; College; Physician.

BECHTEL, Stephen E; Donald E Gavic HS; Hammond, IN; 3/329 CncrtBnd; HonRl; JrNHS; NHS; NatlMeritSF; Orch; StuCncl; LetterTennis; LetterTrk; IMSpt; U Of Mi; Engineering.

BECHTOLD, Carl; Naper Public HS; Naper, NE; ChrhWkr; HonRl; SchPl; Yrbk; RptrSchPpr; College.

BECHTOLD, James L; Roncalli HS; Martinsville, IN; HonRl; College; Math.

BECHTOLD, Kathy; Atchison HS; Atchison, KS; HonRl; NHS; RedCrAde; SchPl; RptrSchPpr; SchPpr; PpCl; Bsbl; Kansas Univ; Physical Therapy.

BECK, Barbara J; Elk Grove HS; Elk Grove, IL; HonRl; NHS; Quill&Scroll; StuCncl; RptrYrbk; Yrbk; College; Elem Education.

BECK, Brenda J; Lennox HS; Worthing, SD; 2/95 ALAGirlsSt; Chr; Chrs; ChrhWkr; HonRl; Mdrgl; SchPl; FHA; Business School; Vocation.

BECK, Brian; Carroll Community HS; Carroll, IA; 28/104 Aud/Vis; Chr; Chrl; Chrs; SchMus; SchPl; StuCncl; YthFlsp; RptrYrbk; Bsktbl; College; Professional.

BECK, Catherine M; Ottawa HS; Ottawa, KS; 28/186 Chrs; ChrhWkr; HonRl; Sec4-H; SpnCl; PpCl; 4-HAwd; Ottawa Univ; Elem Ed.

BECK, Cheryl A; Andrew Comm HS; Bellevue, IA; 11/39 Chrs; PresChrhWkr; HonRl; LbryAde; NatlThespSoc; SchPl; 4-H; GerCl; 4-HAwd; Kirkwood Comm College; Interl Trade.

BECK, Constance; Greenfield HS; Greenfield, IL; 7/75 Band; HonRl; NatlMeritCmnd; PepBnd; SctActv; RptrYrbk; FrCl; Trk; GAA; IMSpt; Univ Il;engineering.

BECK, Debbie K; Lennox HS; Worthing, SD; 25/117 Chr; Chrs; ChrhWkr; HonRl; LbryAde; OffAde; SchPl; FHA; DARAwd; Business School; Vocation.

BECK, Deborah S; Pecatonica HS; Pecatonica, IL; 4/61 SecSrCls; Chrs; DrlTm; HonRl; NHS; Quill&Scroll; TchrAde; EdYrBk; Trk; Univ; Business Education.

BECK, Debra L; Mobridge HS; Mobridge, SD; 2/75 Chrs; ChrhWkr; HonRl; NatlMeritFnl; StuGov; RptrYrbk; RptrSchPpr; EdSchPpr; SptEdSchPpr; Sd State U; Nursing.

BECK, Diann J; Drayton Public HS; Drayton, ND; 6/35 Band; Chr; Chrs; ChrhWkr; CncrtBnd; HonRl; PepBnd; YthFlsp; EdYrBk; RptrSchPpr; College; Nursing.

BECK, Donna J; Cochrane Fountain City HS; Fountain City, WI; Aud/Vis; ChrhWkr; DrlTm; LbryAde; SchMus; TchrAde; 4-H; FDA; FHA; College; History.

BECK, George A; Natoma HS; Natoma, KS; CmntyWkr; JA; SchPl; StuCncl; 4-H; FFA; Ftbl; Trk; 4-HAwd; CitAwd; Army.

BECK, Glori J; Clarks Public HS; Clarks, NE; 1/25 PresJrCls; Band; CncrtBnd; HonRl; NHS; PepBnd; SchAde; SchPl; StuCncl; StuGov; TchrAde; Chrldr; Univ Of Nebraska; Medical Tech.

BECK, Jan M; Duchesne HS; St Charles, MO; TreasBand; Chrs; DrlTm; HonRl; NHS; SchMus; StuCncl; ChmnTwrl; LatCl; PresPpCl; Univ Of Mo At Columbia; Physical Therapy.

BECK, Julie C; Sunset Hill HS; Shawnee Mission, KS; SecTrsJrCls; SecAFS; HospAde; Mdrgl; SancSoc; SchMus; SchPl; StuCncl; YthFlsp; RptrYrbk; University; Professional.

BECK, Kip; Neillsville HS; Neillsville, WI; Band; CncrtBnd; HonRl; MrchBnd; PepBnd; 4-H; Socr; Trk; Wrstlng; College; Professional.

BECK, Lee D; Taylor HS; Taylor, WI; 3/25 VPSrCls; HonRl; SchPl; RptrYrbk; RptrSchPpr; 4-H; FHA; GAA; CitAwd;.

BECK, Leslie M; Bremen HS; Midlothian, IL; 14/468 HonRl; NHS; OffAde; PepBnd; SecStuCncl; TchrAde;.

BECK, Linnea M; St James HS; St James, MN; Chr; HonRl; Mdrgl; NHS; SchPl; StuCncl; RptrSchPpr; Trk; RotaryAwd; Coll; Education.

BECK, Louis R; Dysart Geneseo HS; Buckingham, IA; 1/53 PresSophCls; PresJrCls; Band; Chr; Chrl; Chrs; ChrhWkr; CmntyWkr; CncrtBnd; HonRl; Bsbl; LetterFtbl; LetterGlf; LetterWrstlng; Iowa State Univ; Agriculture.

BECK, Mary; Sheffield Chapin Community; Sheffield, IA; 16/50 ChrhWkr; CncrtBnd; HonRl; SchPl; YthFlsp; 4-H; LetterBsbl; LetterBsktbl; LetterPPFtbl; 4-HAwd; Wartburg; Math Teacher.

BECK, Ronald L; Lutheran HS; Florissant, MO; 4/103 HonRl; NHS; SctActv; TchrAde; LatCl; Bsbl; Ftbl; CchngActv; College; Doctor.

BECK, Scottie R; Avon HS; Danville, IN; HonRl; SchPl; SctActv; TchrAde; 4-H; FHA; LatCl; Purdue Univ; Nursing.

BECK, Sherree J; Copeland HS; Copeland, KS; DrlTm; HonRl; SchPl; StuGov; EdSchPpr; PpCl; Bsktbl; Univ Of Kansas; Broadcasting.

BECK, Sylvia; Menomonee Falls East HS; Menomonee Falls, WI; 6/346 ALAGirlsSt; HonRl; TreasNHS; GerCl; GovHonPrgAwd; KiwanAwd; Marquette Univ; Business.

BECK, Thomas A; Hastings HS; Hastings, NE; 35/384 ChrhWkr; CmntyWkr; HonRl; NatlMeritSF; SctActv; RptrSchPpr; Ftbl; Unif Of Ne ; Chemical Eng.

BECKEMEIER, William M; Naperville Central HS; Naperville, IL; 44/844 LetterSocr; Univ Of Ill; Veterinarian.

BECKEMEYER, Brenda S; Carlyle HS; Carlyle, IL; 5/138 Chr; ChrhWkr; HonRl; HospAde; NHS; TchrAde; YthFlsp; 4-H; FTA; FrCl; Deaconess Hosp Schl; Nurse.

BECKENBACH, Lerae A; Hyannis HS; Hyannis, NE; 10/24 Band; Chr; ChrhWkr; CmntyWkr; CncrtBnd; LbryAde; MrchBnd; PepBnd; SchMus; StuGov; YthFlsp; RptrYrbk; RptrSchPpr; Univ Of Nebr; Professional.

BECKER, Alan L; Pomeroy Community HS; Pomeroy, IA; Chr; Chrs; CncrtBnd; HonRl; LbryAde; MrchBnd; YthFlsp; RptrYrbk; RptrSchPpr; FrCl; Ia Central Com Col; Horticlutur.

BECKER, Chris S; Parkside HS; Jackson, MI; 160/416 Band; HonRl; SctActv; YthFlsp; GerCl; PpCl; LetterFtbl; Socr; LetterWrstlng; IMSpt; MasAwd; Michigan Tech Univ; Civil Engineer.

BECKER, Connie L; Nauvoo Colusa HS; Niota, IL; LbryAde; FHA; Bsktbl; Trk; Chrldr; College; Medicine.

BECKER, Cynthia; St Pius X HS; Arnold, MO; Chr; Chrs; ChrhWkr; HonRl; StuCncl; College.

BECKER, Daniel P; Hinsdale Central HS; Oakbrook, IL; HonRl; Sacrstn; University; Veterinarian.

BECKER, Dave L; Parkersburg HS; Parkersburg, IA; TrsJrCls; ChrhWkr; HonRl; NHS; StuCncl; 4-H; FFA; PpCl; CaptFtbl; CaptWrstlng; Trade School.

BECKER, David P; Montini HS; Lombard, IL; 7/154 HonRl; NHS; LetterBsktbl; LetterFtbl; College; Science.

BECKER, Debra; Freeman Public HS; Freeman, SD; 6/63 DrlTm; HonRl; SchMus; SchPl; TchrAde; YthFlsp; Yrbk; FHA; GerCl; Grace Bible Institute; Physical Therapy.

BECKER, Debra J; Von Steuben HS; Chicago, IL; 5/231 Band; Chr; HonRl; NHS; TchrAde; Yrbk; RptrSchPpr; FrCl; PpCl; Univ Of Illinois; Accounting.

BECKER, Debra K; Hillsboro HS; Hillsboro, IL; 18/190 ChrhWkr; HonRl; FHA; College; Professional.

BECKER, Denise E; Redfield Public HS; Redfield, SD; 1/97 HonRl; NHS; PolWkr; SchPl; TchrAde; Yrbk; 4-H; FHA; FTA; Trk; College; Mathematics.

BECKER, Elaine L; Carroll HS; Wichita, KS; PresFrshCls; VPFrshCls; PresSophCls; VPSophCls; PresJrCls; VPJrCls; PresSrCls; VPSrCls; CmntyWkr; HonRl; HospAde; College; Professional Med.

BECKER, Elizabeth A; Holy Angels HS; Bloomington, MN; 44/122 MrchBnd; SctActv; TchrAde; Yrbk; LetterBsktbl; CaptTrk; LetterChrldr; CaptGAA; LetterIMSpt; PPFtbl; College; Physical Ed.

BECKER, Gregory M; Ben Davis HS; Indianapolis, IN; 11/650 ALBoysSt; Band; CncrtBnd; HonRl; MrchBnd; NHS; StuCncl; FrCl; General Motors Institute; Engineering.

BECKER, Jean; Cathedral HS; New Ulm, MN; 27/93 LbryAde; SctActv; Sdlty; PpCl; Jr Coll; Fashion Merchandising.

BECKER, Jean M; Highland Park HS; Highland Park, IL; 20/643 SecSophCls; HonRl; JrNHS; NHS; NatlMeritCmnd; SchMus; TchrAde; PpCl; Chrldr; University; Art.

BECKER, Joann M; St Anthony HS; St Louis, MO; 2/72 Chrs; DrlTm; HonRl; NHS; PolWkr; SchMus; RptrSchPpr; LatCl; Univ Of Mo St Louis; Business Advertising.

BECKER, Joann M; St Joseph HS; Kenosha, WI; Chr; Chrs; LbryAde; Yrbk; GerCl; Tennis; College.

BECKER, John G; Lenora HS; Lenora, KS; ALBoysSt; ChrhWkr; CmntyWkr; HonRl; SchAde; TchrAde; PpCl; Farming.

BECKER, John J; Benton Community HS; Watkins, IA; Aud/Vis; Chrs; ChrhWkr; HonRl; NHS; NatlThespSoc; SchMus; SchPl; StuGov; RptrYrbk; FFA; 4-HAwd; College; Farming.

BECKER, Judy; St Francis HS; Cedar, MN; Band; HospAde; RptrYrbk; RptrSchPpr; Chrldr; Coll; Psychology.

BECKER, Julia K; Paul Harding HS; Ft Wayne, IN; SecJrCls; HonRl; StuCncl; StuGov; RptrYrbk; RptrSchPpr; SpnCl; Chrldr; University; Biochemistry.

BECKER, Kallie A; Arthur Hill HS; Saginaw, MI; Band; CmntyWkr; Band; HonRl; MrchBnd; NHS; NatlMeritSF; Twrl; FrCl; GAA; Ferris St Col; Pharmacy.

BECKER, Karen; Platte Valley Acad; Shelton, NE; VPFrshCls; PresSophCls; SecJrCls; Chr; ChrhWkr; HonRl; NHS; StuCncl; TchrAde; RptrSchPpr; Bsktbl; Union College; Elementary Education.

BECKER, Karl R; Greenview HS; Greenview, IL; 2/52 Chrs; CncrtBnd; NHS; Orch; SchMus; StuGov; RptrSchPpr; 4-H; Bsktbl; Glf; College; Social Work.

BECKER, Kevin A; Bishop Luers HS; Ft Wayne, IN; 44/230 ALBoysSt; HonRl; NHS; StuCncl; RptrSchPpr; EdSchPpr; SptEdSchPpr; PresKeyCl; Ftbl; CaptTrk; RotaryAwd; College.

BECKER, Kimberly A; Burt Township HS; Grand Marais, MI; VPFrshCls; SecTrsJrCls; Chr; HonRl; SchPl; StuCncl; Yrbk; 4-H; Bsbl; Chrldr; Psychology.

BECKER, Laurie; Don Bosco HS; Jesup, IA; Chrs; HonRl; IntrClCncl; JrNHS; NHS; NatlThespSoc; SchPl; PpCl; Socr; IMSpt; Hawkeye Tech; Secretary.

BECKER, Laurie A; Morgan Public HS; Morgan, MN; SecSrCls; ALAGirlsSt; Band; Chr; ChrhWkr; HonRl; MrchBnd; SchPl; RptrYrbk; EdSchPpr; Univ; Journalism.

BECKER, Lois; Zap Public HS; Zap, ND; PresFrshCls; PresSrCls; SchAde; SchPl; StuCncl; TchrAde; 4-H; GerCl; 4-HAwd; Minot State College; Elementaryteaching.

BECKER, Lois A; New Ulm Sr HS; New Ulm, MN; 5/241 ChrhWkr; HospAde; NatlFornLg; Yrbk; College; Mathematics.

BECKER, Luanne P; Hyannis HS; Ashby, NE; 19/24 Chrs; NHS; StuCncl; PpCl; Trk; 4-HAwd; Univ Of Wyoming; Bus.

BECKER, Mark E; Mendota Township HS; Sublette, IL; HonRl; SctActv; FFA; Sauk Valley Jr College; Agriculture.

BECKER, Mark H; Bishop Luers HS; Fort Wayne, IN; Chr; SctActv; SchPpr; KeyCl; Ftbl; Trk; College; Conservation.

BECKER, Mary C; New Prague HS; Jordan, MN; 25/200 HonRl; NHS; Sec4-H; SpnCl; Univ; Horticulture Field.

BECKER, Mary E; Mater Dei HS; Bartelso, IL; 22/198 Chrs; HonRl; Sacrstn; SchPl; TchrAde; Kaskaskia Jr College; Accounting.

BECKER, Norman E; Burt Community HS; Burt, IA; 2/18 PresSrCls; Band; Chrs; HonRl; NHS; SptEdSchPpr; LetterBsbl; LetterBsktbl; Iowa State Univ; Agricultural Bus.

BECKER, Robert C; Greenville HS; Williamsville, MO; 1/61 PresBand; VPChrs; SchPl; SctActv; StuCncl; PresYthFlsp; LetterBsbl; CaptBsktbl; LetterTrk; U Of Mo Columbia; Gen Agriculture.

BECKER, Ronald A; Aurora HS; Phillips, NE; 12/95 Band; ChrhWkr; CmntyWkr; CncrtBnd; HonRl; MrchBnd; NHS; SchAde; TchrAde; YthFlsp; Wesleyan University; Business.

BECKER, Stanley J; Wynot Public HS; Wynot, NE; LetterBsktbl; LetterGlf; College.

BECKER, Stephan E; New Trier East HS; Kenilworth, IL; 8/847 CncrtBnd; HonRl; NatlMeritFnl; College; Law.

BECKER, Steven; East Wayne HS; Williamsville, MO; HonRl; SchPl; StuCncl; Bsktbl; Trk; IMSpt; Columbia Ga Coll.

BECKER, Steven L; Wyndmere Public HS; Wyndmere, ND; 3/55 VPSophCls; ALBoysSt; Band; CmntyWkr; CncrtBnd; HonRl; NHS; LetterBsktbl; LetterFtbl; LetterTrk; U Of North Dakota; Engineering.

BECKER, Susan E; Garden City Sr HS; Garden City, KS; HonRl; NatlMeritSF; TchrAde; FSA; PpCl; SecSciCl; IMSpt; College; Liberal Arts.

BECKER, Susan M; St Louise De Marillac HS; Wilmette, IL; 5/248 NatlMeritSF; Orch; SchPl; StuGov; RptrYrbk; Yrbk; College; Chemical Engineering.

BECKER, Susan M; Marillac HS; Wilmette, IL; 3/263 NatlMeritFnl; Orch; SchPl; StuGov; RptrYrbk; Oberlin College; Chemical Engineer.

BECKER, Susan R; Prairie Heights HS; Pleasant Lak, IN; 36/118 SecSrCls; HospAde; SchPl; StuCncl; YthFlsp; Yrbk; Lutheran School Of Nursing; Registered Nurs.

BECKER, Tasha D; Platteview Jr Sr HS; Papillion, NE; Band; CncrtBnd; DrmMjrt; MrchBnd; TchrAde; LetterBsktbl; LetterTrk; Chrldr; GAA; Radiation Therapy Technology.

BECKER, Todd A; Holmen HS; Holmen, WI; 12/115 VPSophCls; Band; CncrtBnd; HonRl; MrchBnd; PepBnd; StuCncl; 4-H; LetterBsbl; LetterBsktbl; LetterGlf; IMSpt; 4-HAwd; Univ Of Wisconsin.

BECKER, William J; Wichita North HS; Wichita, KS; 15/600 VPJrCls; HonRl; ModUN; NHS; Orch; StuCncl; SpnCl; MthCl; Ftbl; OptClAwd; Wichita State U; Computer Tech.

BECKETT, Cheryl A; Okemos HS; Okemos, MI; 14/270 CncrtBnd; HospAde; MrchBnd; PolWkr; SctActv; TchrAde; Twrl; Mich St Univ; Med.

BECKETT, Linda L; Madison HS; Madiosn Hts, MI; ChrhWkr; CmntyWkr; Quill&Scroll; SchPl; TchrAde; RptrYrbk; RptrSchPpr; SchPpr; SciCl; EdSchPpr; Central Mi Univ; Social Work.

BECKEY, David; Lakeview Sr HS; St Clair Shores, MI; Chr; ChrhWkr; CncrtBnd; HonRl; SchPl; StuCncl; YthFlsp; Bsbl; Bsktbl; Ftbl; College; Medicine.

BECKHAM, Tonchita S; Central Usd #462 HS; Burden, KS; HstJrCls; Band; Chr; HonRl; MrchBnd; OffAde; PepBnd; SchPl; Yrbk; PpCl; Cowley Co Jr Col; Elementary Teacher Or Sec.

BECKHAM, Tonchita S; Central HS; Burden, KS; HstJrCls; Band; Chrs; ChrhWkr; CmntyWkr; HonRl; OffAde; SchPl; Yrbk; PpCl; Cowley County Comm College; Business.

BECKLER, Cindy M; Faulkton HS; Seneca, SD; Band; Chrs; DrlTm; HonRl; MrchBnd; SchPl; 4-H; FHA; PpCl; Coll; Prof Biology.

BECKLEY, Thomas P; Pontiac Northern HS; Pontiac, MI; 2/500 Band; CncrtBnd; HonRl; MrchBnd; Orch; CaptTennis; VoiceDemAwd; Kalamazoo Coll; Engi.

BECKLIN, Shari J; Cambridge Senior HS; Cambridge, MN; TrsJrCls; ALAGirlsSt; Band; Chrs; ChrhWkr; StuCncl; StuGov; YthLg; LetterTrk; ChmnChrldr; College; Elem Education.

BECKMAN, Angela M; Newaygo HS; Newaygo, MI; PresJrCls; ChrhWkr; HonRl; NHS; SchPl; StuCncl; TchrAde; FTA; LetterBsktbl; LetterTrk; University; Teacher For The Handicap.

BECKMAN, Brenda J; Notre Dame HS; Burlington, IA; 30/70 PresSophCls; HonRl; HospAde; NHS; SctActv; StuCncl; RptrSchPpr; Tennis; Chrldr; IMSpt; College; Nursing.

BECKMAN, Carrie; Appleton East HS; Appleton, WI; Aud/Vis; ChrhWkr; CmntyWkr; HospAde; NatlFornLg; YthFlsp; SecTrsFrshCls; Yrbk; RptrSchPpr; LatCl; Uw Lacrosse; Recreational Therapy.

BECKMAN, Denise; Wakefield HS; Wakefield, MI; 7/63 Band; Chr; ChrhWkr; HonRl; HospAde; Yrbk; RptrSchPpr; Chrldr; Northern Mich Univ; Nursing.

BECKMAN, Elaine K; Newton HS; Wheeler, IL; HonRl; NHS; FNA; GAA; IMSpt; Univ; Nure.

BECKMAN, Gregory B; Huntington North HS; Huntington, IN; TrsFrshCls; Chrs; ChrhWkr; CmntyWkr; YthFlsp; Bsbl; Bsktbl; Ftbl; College.

BECKMAN, June; Petersburg Public HS; Petersburg, NE; 4/15 HstSophCls; HstJrCls; Chr; Chrs; HonRl; JrNHS; NHS; SchPl; RptrYrbk; Grand Island Business School; Secretary.

BECKMAN, Kenneth G; Dubois HS; Dubois, IN; 9/90 ALBoysSt; Band; HonRl; JrNHS; MrchBnd; PepBnd; 4-H; FFA; PpCl; College; Farming.

BECKMAN, Lori S; Westview HS; Lake City, IA; SecFrshCls; AFS; Chrs; CmntyWkr; HonRl; MrchBnd; SctActv; YthFlsp; PpCl; Chrldr; Business School; Airline Stewardess.

BECKMAN, Nancy; Hoxie HS; Menlo, KS; Chr; HonRl; StuCncl; TchrAde; Yrbk; FHA; Fort.

BECKMAN, Nancy J; Portage Central HS; Portage, MI; Band; CncrtBnd; HonRl; MrchBnd; PepBnd; SctActv; TchrAde; PresAwd; College; Occupational Therapist.

BECKMAN, Philip M; Creston HS; Grand Rapids, MI; 1/454 ALBoysSt; ChrhWkr; HonRl; JrNHS; NHS; NatlMeritFnl; NatlMeritCmnd; NatlMeritSchl; NatlMeritSF; IMSpt; Wheaton Col; Doctor.

BECKMANN, Beverly J; West Smith Co U D 235 HS; Athol, KS; Chr; ChrhWkr; HonRl; SchMus; StuCncl; YthFlsp; PpCl; Nursing.

BECKMANN, Charles E; Rosalie Public HS; Rosalie, NE; 2/11 PresFrshCls; ALBoysSt; HonRl; SchPl; 4-H; Bsktbl; Ftbl; Trk; AmLegAwd; 4-HAwd; U Of Nebraska; Architectur.

BECKMANN, Denise M; Muskegon Catholic Central HS; Muskegon, MI; 19/209 ChrhWkr; CmntyWkr; HonRl; NHS; VPSctActv; StuCncl; PpCl; LetterBsktbl; Tennis; BttyCrckrAwd; Wayne State Univ; Pharmacy.

BECKMANN, Karen M; Mater Dei HS; Breese, IL; 10/182 Chrs; DrlTm; HonRl; HospAde; NHS; SchMus; SchPl; 4-H; FrCl; AmLegAwd; Univ; Prof.

BECKMANN, Kathryn; Duchesne HS; St Charles, MO; 71/187 ChrhWkr; HonRl; PolWkr; Univ; Professional.

BECKMANN, Lois A; Rock Island HS; Milan, IL; Chr; Chrs; ChrhWkr; DrlTm; HonRl; JrNHS; SchMus; SchPl; StuGov; 4-H; Bsktbl; CchngActv; College; Engineering.

BECKMEIER, Carolyn S; Patoka Comm Unit 100 HS; Vernon, IL; ChrhWkr; CmntyWkr; HonRl; LbryAde; SchPl; TchrAde; YthFlsp; RptrYrbk; Millikin University.

BECKNER, Linda S; Rossville Alvin HS; Rossville, IL; Chrs; HonRl; OffAde; SchAde; TchrAde; RptrYrbk; RptrSchPpr; PresFHA; Bsktbl; Socr; Trk; Chrldr; GAA; Junior College; Vocation.

BECKNER, Richard R; Neosho HS; Goodman, MO; HonRl; SctActv; Professional.

BECKWITH, Paula S; Boone HS; Boone, IA; 1/215 HonRl; LetterBsbl; LetterBsktbl; LetterTennis; LetterTrk; U Of Ia; Medical Field.

BECKWITH, Scott A; East Troy HS; East Troy, WI; Aud/Vis; HonRl; StuCncl; Bsbl; Bsktbl; Ftbl; Trk; Coll; Pro.

BECUE, Michael A; Western HS; Sheffield, IL; 4/52 Band; CmntyWkr; HonRl; MrchBnd; PepBnd; Trade School; Law Enforcement.

BECVAR, Jean M; Scotland HS; Scotland, SD; 1/45 Chr; Chrs; HonRl; HospAde; StuCncl; Yrbk; SecFHA; PpCl; Chrldr; Mitchell Area Vocational Tech Schl; Nursing.

BECVAR, Laura A; St Johns HS; St Louis, MO; 1/90 Chr; Chrs; HonRl; PresNHS; SchMus; SchPl; PpCl; Univ; Accounting.

BEDAN, Richard C; Jeffersonville HS; Jeffersonville, IN; PresSophCls; VPSophCls; HstJrCls; HonRl; JrNHS; NHS; KeyCl; PpCl; Bsktbl; Trk; Wrstlng; Purdue Univ; Pharmacist.

BEDARD, Cynthia; Lincoln HS; Thief River Falls, MN; 22/256 SecTrsJrCls; NHS; NatlThespSoc; SchMus; SchPl; FFA; GAA; IMSpt; PPFtbl; 4-HAwd; College Of St Benedict; Music Major.

BEDARD, Debra; Berkley HS; Berkley, MI; Band; Chrs; CmntyWkr; DrlTm; Mdrgl; MrchBnd; PolWkr; TchrAde; FDA; GAA; Oakland Univ; Rn.

BE DELL, Cynthia S; Bradley Bourbonnais Comm HS; Bourbonnais, IL; 25/360 HonRl; College Of St Francis; Occupational Therapy.

BEDELL, Denise; Regina HS; Detroit, MI; StuCncl; Bsbl; Bsktbl; Trk; GAA; PPFtbl; East Mich Univ;psychology.

BEDELL, Roberta J; Corunna HS; Durand, MI; 24/210 HonRl; SchPl; RptrYrbk; 4-H; PpCl; Chrldr; GAA; 4-HAwd; Michigan State Univ.

BEDIENT, Brian L; Polk Public HS; Bradshaw, NE; 2/21 ALBoysSt; CncrtBnd; HonRl; SchPl; StuCncl; YthFlsp; RptrYrbk; 4-H; LetterBsktbl; LetterFtbl; LetterTrk; 4-HAwd; Univ Of Nebraska.

BEDMAN, Connie K; E J Cooper Sr HS; Crystal, MN; 19/635 CncrtBnd; HonRl; MrchBnd; NHS; Orch; PepBnd; SecGerCl; GAA; College.

BEDNAR, Mark F; St Edmond HS; Fort Dodge, IA; ChrhWkr; StuCncl; LatCl; Bell & Howell Inst; Electronics.

BEDNARCZYK, Diane D; Morton West HS; Berwyn, IL; 89/750 Chrs; HonRl; Quill&Scroll; SctActv; SchPpr; 4-H; FrCl; Univ Of Ill; Medicine.

BEDNAREK, James M; Greendale HS; Greendale, WI; 51/335 ChrhWkr; HonRl; NatlFornLg; Sdlty; SptEdSchPpr; GerCl; LetterTennis; IMSpt; University Green Bay; Environmental Engr.

BEDNAREK, Mary Ellen; St Catherines HS; Racine, WI; CmntyWkr; HonRl; LbryAde; OffAde; RedCrAde; SctActv; TchrAde; SpnCl; Chrldr; College; Law.

BEDNARZ, Karen A; Proviso West HS; Hillside, IL; 31/1117 HonRl; VPNHS; StuGov; Triton Jr College; Science.

BEDNARZ, Robin E; Richmond HS; Richmond, MI; Chr; CmntyWkr; HonRl; Mdrgl; NatlMeritSF; SchMus; SchPl; StuGov; RptrYrbk; Yrbk; SchPpr; DanFAwd; Mich State Univ; Veterinarian.

BEDORE, Gary M; Benet Academy; Lisle, IL; 6/250 HonRl; NHS; EdSchPpr; LetterTrk; Kansas Univ; Journalism.

BEDROSIAN, Daniel; Manchester HS; Manchester, MI; 8/100 HonRl; OffAde; SchPpr; FrCl; GerCl; Ftbl; Univ Of Mi; Math Or Science.

BEDWELL, Lee A; Northrop HS; Fort Wayne, IN; Chr; Chrs; ChrhWkr; HonRl; Mdrgl; SchMus; SchPl; College; Missionary Work.

BEE, Debra L; Josephinum HS; Chicago, IL; ChrhWkr; HonRl; RedCrAde; SchPl; StuGov; YthFlsp; RptrYrbk; College; Professional.

BEEAN, Lillian K; Ithaca HS; Ithaca, MI; TrsSophCls; Band; Chr; ChrhWkr; HonRl; Mdrgl; MrchBnd; NHS; PepBnd; SchMus; YthFlsp; FTA; Michigan Tech Univ; Computer Science.

BEEBE, Bruce D; Glenbrook So HS; Glenview, IL; 90/600 ChrhWkr; HonRl; LbryAde; NatlFornLg; PolWkr; College; Naval Architecture.

BEEBE, Deborah; Schell City R 1 HS; Harwood, MO; Chrs; HonRl; SchPl; TchrAde; EdYrBk; RptrSchPpr; PpCl; Chrldr;.

BEEBE, Kimberly R; West HS; Green Bay, WI; 19/390 Chrs; HonRl; NHS; SchMus; EdYrBk; Bsktbl; Glf; LetterTrk; LetterChrldr; GAA; Univ; Business Major.

BEEBE, Michael J; Hartland HS; Brighton, MI; StuCncl; Bsbl; Ftbl; Mich St Univ; Engineer.

BEEBE, Michael L; Kalkaska HS; Kalkaska, MI; CAP; HonRl; MrchBnd; RedCrAde; StuGov; CivCl; Bsktbl; Ftbl; Glf; Wrstlng; Rets Elec Schl; Elec Technology.

BEEBE, Robin R; Lincoln Sr HS; Bloomington, MN; VPFrshCls; AFS; ChrhWkr; HonRl; NHS; CaptChrldr; CchngActv; GAA; IMSpt; University; Counselor.

BEEBE, Teri L; Ellsworth Sr HS; Ellsworth, WI; ChrhWkr; HonRl; NatlMeritSF; FHA; College.

BEECHER, Timothy M; St Philip HS; Battle Creek, MI; 18/88 HonRl; MrchBnd; PepBnd; TchrAde; 4-H; LetterBsbl; LetterBsktbl; IMSpt; 4-HAwd; CitAwd; College; Broadcasting.

BEED, Vaughn K; West Point HS; West Point, NE; Chr; Chrs; HonRl; SchAde; TchrAde; RptrSchPpr; LetterFtbl; LetterTrk; Univ; Cpa.

BEEDLE, Patricia A; Mitchell HS; Mitchell, SD; /290 HonRl; SchPl; SpnCl; PpCl; College; Teaching.

BEEG, Gregg M; Arthur Hill HS; Saginaw, MI; HonRl; Bsbl; Bsktbl; Ftbl; IMSpt; PresAwd; College; Accounting.

BEEGHLY, Kathleen A; Ryan HS; Omaha, NE; Chrs; NHS; SchMus; StuCncl; FshEdYrbk; PpCl; Chrldr; College Of St Marys; Medicine.

BEEGLE, Bret; Reitz Memorial HS; Evansville, IN; VPFrshCls; PresSophCls; PresJrCls; PresSrCls; HonRl; SchAde; StuCncl; Bsktbl; Ftbl; Univ; Law.

BEEHLER, David W; Foley HS; Foley, MN; ALBoysSt; Band; ChrhWkr; CmntyWkr; CncrtBnd; HonRl; MrchBnd; PepBnd; StuCncl; IMSpt; Clge; Medicine.

BEEKMAN, Sandra K; Buffalo Center HS; Buffalo Center, IA; Band; Chr; SecChrhWkr; HonRl; YthFlsp; CivCl; FFA; Trk; GAA; 4-HAwd; Collge; Foreign Agriculturist.

BEELEN, Patricia S; Holland Christian HS; Holland, MI; 13/261 Chr; ChrhWkr; CmntyWkr; HonRl; LitMag; SchPl; SchPpr; FDA; GerCl; IMSpt; Calvin Clg; Medical Field.

BEELER, David B; Sterling HS; Sterling, IL; 3/425 ChrhWkr; NHS; NatlMeritSF; LatCl; Tennis; Wrstlng; College; Engr.

BEELER, James C; Beloit HS; Beloit, KS; 1/76 ALBoysSt; NatlMeritSchl; SchPl; PresStuCncl; Yrbk; SciCl; LetterBsktbl; LetterFtbl; LetterGlf; EldAwd; Univ Of Kansas; Physical Science.

BEELER, Jonathan C; Beloit HS; Beloit, KS; 1/76 PresJrCls; NatlMeritFnl; NatlMeritSchl; SchPl; StuCncl; RptrYrbk; SciCl; LetterBsktbl; LetterFtbl; LetterGlf; Univ Of Kansas; Professional.

BEELER, Michael A; High School; Truro, IA; PresFrshCls; SecSophCls; Band; HonRl; NHS; PresStuCncl; VP4-H; Ftbl; Wrstlng; 4-HAwd; College.

BEELER, Rodney C; Morton HS; Morton, IL; 75/300 ChrhWkr; HonRl; SctActv; StuCncl; LatCl; PpCl; IMSpt; AmLegAwd; U Of Ks; Architectural Engineering.

BEELER, Viola L; M L King HS; Detroit, MI; Chrs; HonRl; LbryAde; OffAde; SchAde; TchrAde; RptrSchPpr; SchPpr; FTA; CitAwd; Coll; Pro.

BEELER, Wayne F; South Spencer HS; Richland, IN; ALBoysSt; ChrhWkr; CmntyWkr; NHS; ROTC; SctActv; StuGov; FBLA; LetterFtbl; GodCntryAwd; Trade Sch.

BEEM, Diane M; Godwin Heights HS; Wyoming, MI; 5/186 LbryAde; PresNHS; SchMus; RptrSchPpr; SecFHA; PpCl; CaptGlf; CaptTennis; GAA; DARAwd; Kendall Sch; Advertising Design.

BEEM, Susan R; Oregon Davis HS; Walkerton, IN; ALAGirlsSt; ChrhWkr; CmntyWkr; HonRl; OffAde; YthFlsp; PpCl; College; Political Science.

BEEMAN, Kenneth E; Pinkey HS; Hamburg, MI; NHS; SctActv; LetterFtbl; Trk; LetterWrstlng; PresAwd; College.

BEEMER, Beth J; Eldora HS; Eldora, IA; 7/64 SecJrCls; TrsSrCls; HonRl; StuCncl; FrCl; PpCl; LetterTrk; LetterChrldr; PPFtbl; Univ Of Iowa; Art.

BEEMER, Chad; Bedford Community HS; Bedford, IA; 20/70 ChrhWkr; CmntyWkr; HonRl; PepBnd; Glf; N W Missouri S U.

BEEMER, Molly; Concord HS; Concord, MI; 17/69 ChrhWkr; HonRl; LbryAde; NHS; SchPl; TchrAde; YthFlsp; Yrbk; SpnCl; CitAwd; Jackson Comm Col; Medical Assistant.

BEEMER, Randy D; Bedford Comm HS; Gravity, IA; CmntyWkr; HonRl; Teen; FFA; Bsktbl; CaptFtbl; Tennis; Trk; CchngActv; Trade School; Vocation.

BEEMER, W H; River Valley HS; Sawyer, MI; 1/147 VPFrshCls; HonRl; NHS; NatlMeritFnl; NatlMeritSF; VPStuCncl; PresGerCl; Glf; Wrstlng; AmLegAwd; Kalamazoo Clg; Pre Med.

BEEMER, W Howard; River Valley HS; Sawyer, MI; 1/160 VPFrshCls; ChrhWkr; HonRl; NHS; NatlMeritSF; VPStuCncl; TchrAde; PresGerCl; LetterGlf; Wrstlng; IMSpt; College; Medicine.

BEENES, David A; Marist HS; Chicago, IL; 36/393 ChrhWkr; CmntyWkr; HonRl; NHS; Bsbl; Lewis Univ; Accounting.

BEENINGA, Barry L; Washington Sr HS; Sioux Falls, SD; Chrs; HonRl; SecNHS; Arizona St Univ; Communications.

BEENKEN, Debra D; Grundy Center Comm HS; Grundy Center, IA; LetterBand; CncrtBnd; HonRl; MrchBnd; PepBnd; RptrSchPpr; SchPpr; 4-H; SecFBLA; LetterBsktbl; 4-HAwd; PresAwd;.

BEER, Kim R; Fairfield Jr Sr HS; New Paris, IN; 14/104 Chr; SchMus; VP4-H; FHA; TreasFNA; 4-HAwd; Moody Bible Inst; Physical Therapist.

BEER, Michael S; University HS; Normal, IL; 15/158 PresFrshCls; PresJrCls; Band; Chrs; ChrhWkr; CmntyWkr; CncrtBnd; HonRl; MrchBnd; NatlFornLg; NatlThespSoc; Orch; PepBnd; PolWkr; SchMus; Harvard Duke Univ; Law.

BEER, Robert A; Bergan HS; Peoria, IL; Chrs; ChrhWkr; HonRl; SctActv; SciCl; LetterFtbl; LetterSwmmng; Univ; Vet Medicine.

BEERMANN, Deborah S; Concordia R2 HS; Concordia, MO; 3/47 SecFrshCls; Chr; Chrs; HonRl; ModUN; RedCrAde; SchPl; StuCncl; YthFlsp; College.

BEERS, Timothy C; Wm H Harrison HS; W Lafayette, IN; 5/300 ALBoysSt; Band; HonRl; MrchBnd; NatlFornLg; NHS; NatlMeritSF; StuCncl; MthCl; SciCl; Purdue U; Mechanical Engr.

BEERT, Michael C; Rockford West HS; Rockford, IL; VPJrCls; PresSrCls; PresChr; Mdrgl; NHS; NatlThespSoc; Orch; StuCncl; Trk; Roosevelt Univ; Music.

BEERY, Monte; East HS; Des Moines, IA; 1/488 Band; CncrtBnd; MrchBnd; StuGov; RptrYrbk; FrCl; Ia Univ; Civil Engineer.

BEESE, Rudolf H; Beloit Memorial HS; Beloit, WI; 41/600 HonRl; NHS; Orch; SchMus; StuGov; YthLg; Swmmng; Valparaiso Univ; Medicine.

BEESLEY, Joan E; Taylor Center HS; Taylor, MI; 3/400 ALAGirlsSt; HonRl; NHS; OffAde; TchrAde; RptrYrbk; SchPpr; FDA; LatCl; Henry Ford Comm College; Physical Therapy.

BEESON, James W; Greenfield Central HS; Greenfield, IN; 1/275 VPSrCls; Chr; ChrhWkr; HonRl; PresNHS; NatlThespSoc; SchPl; StuCncl; PresSciCl; Tennis; Univ Of Butler; Medical Doctor.

BEESON, Judith; Wagner HS; Wagner, SD; ChrhWkr; DrlTm; HonRl; HospAde; NatlFornLg; OffAde; StuCncl; RptrSchPpr; FHA; FNA;.

BEETHAM, Marnie A; Bay City Central HS; Bay City, MI; Chr; HonRl; MrchBnd; StuCncl; GAA; PPFtbl; Northern Mi Univ; Nursing.

BEETHE, Kathleen J; Elk Creek HS; Steinauer, NE; 2/13 Chrs; HonRl; Mdrgl; TchrAde; Yrbk; PpCl; Bsktbl; U Of Nebraska; Teacher.

BEEZLEY, Dana A; Memorial HS; Joplin, MO; 2/221 HonRl; JrNHS; NatlFornLg; NatlThespSoc; Orch; SchMus; SchPl; StuCncl; YthFlsp; Missouri So State College; Law.

BEFORT, Warren L; Wichita HS East; Wichita, KS; 49/657 ALBoysSt; Chrs; HonRl; NatlMeritSF; TchrAde; RptrSchPpr; LetterBsbl; Coll; Vet Med Or Agronomy.

BEGALKA, Dorothy; Clear Lake HS; Clear Lake, SD; 2/5 SecSophCls; SecTrsSrCls; HonRl; NatlFornLg; SchPl; AmLegAwd; 4-HAwd; KiwanAwd; VFWAwd; VoiceDemAwd; Coll.

BEGGIN, Mary C; Freeport Sr HS; Freeport, IL; 1/507 VPAFS; Chrs; ChrhWkr; HonRl; NatlThespSoc; SctActv; TchrAde; VPFrCl; TreasPpCl; Northern Ill Univ; Special Ed.

BEGLE, Doris A; Marian Hts HS; Ferdinand, IN; 2/28 VPJrCls; ALAGirlsSt; HonRl; JrNHS; VPNHS; VPSdlty; RptrSchPpr; GAA; BauchLmbAwd; University Of Evansville; Medical Tech.

BEGROW, Susan J; Tigerton HS; Tigerton, WI; 1/36 SecFrshCls; ALAGirlsSt; Band; Chr; Chrs; ChrhWkr; HonRl; JA; LitMag; MrchBnd; NatlFornLg; NHS; Trk; Univ Of Wisconsin; Music.

BEGUHN, Steven G; Oconomowoc Sr HS; Oconomowoc, WI; 11/324 AFS; Aud/Vis; CmntyWkr; HonRl; JrNHS; LbryAde; NHS; OffAde; SctActv; College; Accountant.

BEGUIN, Roxane C; Rushville HS; Rushville, NE; 3/40 VPFrshCls; Chr; Chrs; CmntyWkr; HonRl; YthFnd; 4-H; PpCl; LetterTrk; Chrldr; GAA; 4-HAwd; College; Vocation.

BEGUIN, Theresa L; Rushville HS; Rushville, NE; 3/39 Chr; Chrs; ChrhWkr; HonRl; JrNHS; NHS; SchPl; StuCncl; StuGov; FTA; PpCl; College; Veterinarian.

BEHL, Steven M; Watertown HS; Watertown, WI; 33/330 ALBoysSt; 4-H; Ftbl; LetterTrk; LetterWrstlng; IMSpt; U Of Wi; Engineering.

BEHLE, Mark H; Baxter Community HS; Baxter, IA; 2/32 Band; Chr; HonRl; NHS; PepBnd; SchPl; YthFlsp; LetterBsbl; LetterBsktbl; CaptTrk; Wartburg Clg; Mathematics.

BEHLING, Joy E; Crystal Lake HS; Crystal Lake, IL; 30/480 Chr; ChrhWkr; DrlTm; HonRl; MrchBnd; NHS; FrCl; PpCl; IMSpt; PPFtbl; Univ Of Il; Lawyer.

BEHLMANN, Diane; Mercy HS; St Louis, MO; SchMus; RptrYrbk; PpCl; Bsktbl; Trk; GAA; IMSpt; PPFtbl; College.

BEHM, Randolph P; Joseph A Craig HS; Janesville, WI; 21/474 PresCncrtBnd; HonRl; MrchBnd; NHS; NatlMeritCmnd; Orch; PepBnd; Quill&Scroll; SptEdYrbk; EldAwd; Univ Of Wisconsin; Mathematics.

BEHM, Suzanne R; Beaver Dam Sr HS; Beaver Dam, WI; HonRl; TchrAde; Bsktbl; CaptIMSpt; Bookkeeper.

BEHME, Keith D; Flushing HS; Flushing, MI; 105/452 Band; CncrtBnd; HonRl; MrchBnd; NHS; NatlMeritSchl; PolWkr; RedCrAde; SchMus; SptEdSchPpr; College; Teaching.

BEHME, Sharon L; Carlinville HS; Carlinville, IL; 13/156 Chr; Chrs; HonRl; JrNHS; LbryAde; NHS; SchPl; TchrAde; 4-H; KeyCl; GAA; AmLegAwd; BttyCrckrAwd; E Illinois Univ; Home Economics.

BEHME, Teri L; Morton HS; Morton, IL; HonRl; OffAde; YthFlsp; PpCl; Bsbl; Bsktbl; Tennis; GAA; IMSpt; PresAwd; Ill St Univ; Spe Educ.

BEHN, Carolyn R; Webb HS; Rock Springs, WI; PresSophCls; AFS; HonRl; NatlMeritSchl; StuCncl; LatCl; PpCl; Trade Sch; Voc.

BEHNCKE, Julee R; Fennimore HS; Fennimore, WI; Band; Chrs; HonRl; HospAde; NHS; StuCncl; EdYrBk; RptrSchPpr; LetterTrk; Chrldr; Coll.

BEHNKE, Craig A; Horace Mann HS; N Fond Du Lac, WI; 4/100 ALBoysSt; NHS; LetterFtbl; LetterTrk; Wrstlng;.

BEHNKE, Jeffery J; Horace Mann HS; N Fond Du Lac, WI; ALBoysSt; HonRl; NHS; LetterBsbl; LetterBsktbl; Ftbl; Trk; EldAwd; KiwanAwd; U Of Wi Madison; Engineering.

BEHNKE, Suzanna K; St Philip Catholic Cntrl HS; Battle Creek, MI; 3/100 VPFrshCls; ALAGirlsSt; HonRl; StuCncl; StuGov; LatCl; LetterBsktbl; CaptTrk; Chrldr; PPFtbl; U Of Notre Dame; Mech & Elec Engr.

BEHNKEN, Nancy J; R O V A Comm HS; Altona, IL; 5/100 Band; Chr; Chrl; Chrs; ChrhWkr; CncrtBnd; DrmMjrt; HonRl; JrNHS; Mdrgl; LetterChrldr; LetterGAA; 4-HAwd; Univ Of Ill; Business.

BEHRENDS, Debra K; Brownstown HS; Brownstown, IL; 4/32 HonRl; SchPl; TchrAde; FHA; PpCl; Chrldr; GAA; Secretary.

BEHRENDS, Gary A; Johnson Brock HS; Elk Creek, NE; Band; Chr; PepBnd; SctActv; 4-H; LetterFtbl; USJCAwd; Trade School.

BEHRENDS, Glenn A; Wellsburg Community HS; Wellsburg, IA; 13/34 PresJrCls; PresSrCls; ALBoysSt; Band; Chr; Bsktbl; Ftbl; Trk; DanFAwd; CitAwd; College.

BEHRENDS, Mary K; Woodruff HS; Peoria, IL; 68/335 Chr; Chrs; CmntyWkr; SchMus; SctActv; KeyCl; SpnCl; Chrldr; Ill Central Clg; Airline Reservationist.

BEHRENDS, Scott C; Mountain Lake HS; Mountain Lake, MN; HonRl; SctActv; StuCncl; YthFlsp; LetterBsbl; LetterBsktbl; LetterFtbl; LetterGlf; IMSpt; College; Professional.

BEHRENDT, Linda S; Ferndale HS; Pleasant Ridge, MI; 32/520 ChrhWkr; NHS; GerCl; Concordia Lutheran Col; Deaconess.

BEHRENS, Barbara J; Brookfield East HS; Brookfield, WI; 66/514 Band; HonRl; OffAde; MthCl; University Of Wisconsin; Music.

BEHRENS, Kelly D; Albert City Truesdale HS; Albert City, IA; PresFrshCls; Band; Chr; CncrtBnd; HonRl; MrchBnd; PepBnd; SchPl; StuCncl; FFA; Ia St Univ; Engr.

BEHRENS, Melissa E; Mead Public HS; Mead, NE; TrsFrshCls; SecSophCls; VPJrCls; Band; Chrs; CncrtBnd; HonRl; NHS; NatlThespSoc; PepBnd; Bsktbl; LetterTrk; 4-HAwd; College.

BEHRENS, Miriam L; Lincoln HS; Lincoln, KS; 1/69 PresFrshCls; Band; Chr; Chrs; HonRl; LbryAde; TchrAde; SchPpr; FHA; Trade School; Professional.

BEHRENS, Rhonda L; Kirksville Sr HS; Kirksville, MO; Chrs; HonRl; SpnCl; PpCl; University.

BEHRER, Barbara L; Rockridge HS; Taylor Ridge, IL; 9/120 PresSrCls; AFS; ChrhWkr; CmntyWkr; NHS; StuCncl; StuGov; YthFlsp; 4-H; FNA; Coll; Prof.

BEHRINGER, Randall L; Winneconne HS; Oshkosh, WI; ALBoysSt; Chrs; HonRl; Mdrgl; NHS; SchPl; Yrbk; RptrSchPpr; FFA; Bsktbl; Ftbl; LetterTrk; Brown Institute; Broadcasting.

BEHRMAN, Cynthia R; Bucklin R 2 HS; Bucklin, MO; SecSophCls; DrmMjrt; PresNHS; PresStuCncl; EdYrBk; EdSchPpr; PresFHA; Bsbl; Bsktbl; Trk; Chrldr; 4-HAwd; Univ Of Missouri; Accounting.

BEHRNS, Nancy K; Dieterich HS; Dieterich, IL; 3/38 SecJrCls; PresSrCls; TreasBand; HonRl; StuCncl; RptrYrbk; RptrSchPpr; PresFHA; PresSpnCl; SciCl; CaptChrldr; GAA; 4-HAwd; Southern Ill Univ; Journalism.

BEICOS, Rose S; Rich South HS; Park Forest, IL; Band; CncrtBnd; DrmMjrt; HonRl; MrchBnd; PepBnd; SchPl; GerCl; LetterTennis; Trk; Univ; Dentist.

BEIDECK, Jennifer; Mccook Senior HS; Mccook, NE; 24/170 AFS; Band; HonRl; MrchBnd; NHS; PpCl; Chrldr; PPFtbl; University.

BEIDER, Perry C; Oak Park HS; Oak Park, MI; Band; Chr; CncrtBnd; LitMag; NatlMeritSF; SchMus; RptrSchPpr; College; Writer.

BEIDLE, Kim; South Shore HS; Cornucopia, WI; RptrYrbk; SptEdYrbk; Yrbk; RptrSchPpr; SptEdSchPpr; SchPpr; 4-H; FHA; LetterTrk; PresAwd; Duluth Area Voc Tech; Occupational Therapy.

BEIERMANN, Susan G; Lakeview HS; Platte Center, NE; 3/68 ALAGirlsSt; Band; HonRl; NHS; EdYrBk; 4-H; LetterBsktbl; Chrldr; OptClAwd; PresAwd; Platte College; Prof.

BEIGET, John W; Black Hawk HS; South Wayne, WI; VPSophCls; PresJrCls; ChrhWkr; CmntyWkr; HonRl; HospAde; NHS; LetterBsbl; LetterFtbl; LetterWrstlng; Stevens Point Uw; Conservationist.

BEIGHLEY, Bradley; Platteville HS; Platteville, WI; Chr; ChrhWkr; HonRl; SchMus; SchPl; StuCncl; FrCl; Trk; College; Pre Law.

BEIGHLEY, Karla J; Holcombe HS; Holcombe, WI; 1/42 VPFrshCls; PresSophCls; VPJrCls; HonRl; SptEdYrbk; LetterTrk; GAA; DanFAwd; Coll; Teacher.

BEIL, Gerhard; Truman HS; Independence, MO; ChrhWkr; CtyCnl; CmntyWkr; JA; NHS; NatlMeritSchl; PolWkr; SctActv; TchrAde; YthFlsp; College; Electronics.

BEILMANN, Karen; North Kansas City HS; Kansas City, MO; 1/437 Chr; CmntyWkr; HonRl; JrNHS; NHS; SchMus; TchrAde; 4-H; 4-HAwd; Coll; Secretarial.

BEIMAL, Barbara E; Glenbard East HS; Lombard, IL; 73/656 HonRl; OffAde; TchrAde; Bsbl; Bsktbl; Ftbl; CchngActv; PresGAA; North Ill Univ; Teacher.

BEINE, Beth A L; Slinger HS; Slinger, WI; Band; Chr; CncrtBnd; HonRl; MrchBnd; PepBnd; Yrbk; LetterBsktbl; LetterTrk; GAA; RotaryAwd; Madison Tech Schl; Occupatinal Therapy.

BEINING, Daniel G; Wrightstown HS; Greenleaf, WI; HonRl; Bsktbl; Ftbl; VFWAwd; VoiceDemAwd; College; Univ.

BEIRNE, Mary E; Morgan Park HS; Chicago, IL; 6/550 HonRl; NHS; LatCl; MthCl; Bsktbl; Tennis; Knox College; Bio Chemist.

BEISIEGEL, Sharon; Althoff Catholic Hs; Freeburg, IL; 30 Chrs; HonRl; LbryAde; NHS; RedCrAde; LatCl; College;horticulture.

BEISSEL, Tammy J; Brown County HS; Nineveh, IN; 19/200 ALAGirlsSt; HonRl; ModUN; 4-H; FrCl; PpCl; Trk; CchngActv; 4-HAwd; OptClAwd; College; Social Sciences.

BEISWANGER, Lee; Prairie Heights HS; Wolcottvlle, IN; 12/108 PresSrCls; PepBnd; StuCncl; SciCl; Bsktbl; 4-HAwd; Purdue Univ; Agriculture Economics.

BEISWENGER, Gloria J; Fisher HS; Fisher, MN; 1/30 SecJrCls; Band; Chrs; HonRl; MrchBnd; PepBnd; FHA; LetterBsktbl; Univ; Prof.

BEITZ, Robert J; Waukesha South HS; Waukesha, WI; VPFrshCls; PresSrCls; HonRl; NHS; StuCncl; StuGov; MthCl; SciCl; Carroll College; Law.

BEJOT, Terry W; Ainsworth HS; Ainsworth, NE; 4/69 Band; CncrtBnd; HonRl; NHS; TchrAde; Yrbk; SciCl; LetterBsktbl; LetterFtbl; LetterTrk; CchngActv; IMSpt; University Of Nebraska; Doctor.

BEJOT, Thomas A; Ainsworth HS; Ainsworth, NE; HonRl; NHS; TchrAde; CivCl; FrCl; SciCl; LetterFtbl; Glf; LetterTrk; LetterWrstlng; EldAwd; VoiceDemAwd; University Of Nebraska Lincoln; Engineering.

BEKEMEIER, Daniel E; Reese HS; Reese, MI; 5/120 ChrhWkr; HonRl; NHS; Bsktbl; Trk; AmLegAwd; PresAwd; College; Accounting.

BEKINS, Randell L; Grand Haven HS; Grand Haven, MI; PresFrshCls; Band; ChrhWkr; CncrtBnd; HonRl; JrNHS; MrchBnd; NHS; PepBnd; StuCncl; PresYthFlsp; LetterFtbl; LetterWrstlng; Michigan Tech Univ; Engineering.

BELAND, Jane; Summerfield HS; Dundee, MI; 1/69 PresFrshCls; ALAGirlsSt; Chrs; HonRl; LbryAde; 4-H; SpnCl; Univ Of Michigan.

BELAND, Jane M; Summerfield HS; Dundee, MI; 1/69 PresFrshCls; ALAGirlsSt; Chrl; HonRl; NHS; SchAde; TreasStuCncl; TchrAde; LetterBsktbl; LetterTrk; U Of Mich; Doctor.

BELANGER, Melissa A; Catholic Memorial HS; Waukesha, WI; College; Art.

BELANGER, Patrick S; Novi HS; Northville, MI; HonRl; NHS; RptrSchPpr; LetterTennis; Univ.

BELANGER, Rebecca E; Bayfield HS; Bayfield, WI; 3/50 Band; Chr; CncrtBnd; HonRl; MrchBnd; NHS; PepBnd; Univ; Physical Therapy.

BELANGER, Sherry L; Harold L Richards HS; Worth, IL; HonRl; NHS; SchAde; SecFrCl; GAA; Univ Of Illinois; Veterinary Medicine.

BELANGER, Vicky L; Thorp HS; Thorp, WI; 5/74 ALAGirlsSt; HonRl; NHS; SchMus; EdYrBk; FBLA; MthCl; Tennis; AmLegAwd; CitAwd; Univ Of Wi Eu Claire; Nursing.

BELCHER, David; Parkway Central HS; Creve Coeur, MO; 24/450 JrNHS; NatlMeritCmnd; Ftbl; Socr; Univ;law.

BELCHER, Johnita C; Mexico Sr HS; Mexico, MO; Band; ChrhWkr; CmntyWkr; CncrtBnd; MrchBnd; PepBnd; StuCncl; Yrbk; Trk; GAA; IMSpt; University; Child Psychology.

BELCHER, Mickey J; Kinsley HS; Kinsley, KS; 5/74 ALBoysSt; Chr; HonRl; StuCncl; SpnCl; Trk; LetterWrstlng; Technical School; Computer Science.

BELDEN, Paula D; Alliance HS; Alliance, NE; 12/150 VPFrshCls; TrsSophCls; TreasBand; TreasCncrtBnd; HonRl; TreasMrchBnd; TreasPepBnd; SctActv; GerCl; MasAwd; Clge; Curr Of Major Study.

BELEKEVICH, James W; West HS; Green Bay, WI; HonRl; SchPpr; GerCl; Univ Of Wi; Professional.

BELGARDE, Bernida J; Dunseith Public HS; Dunseith, ND; 1/37 SecSrCls; TrsSrCls; HonRl; SchPl; StuCncl; RptrYrbk; RptrSchPpr; CaptBsktbl; Trk; BttyCrckrAwd; Ndsu.

BELKNAP, David C; South County Tech HS; St Louis, MO; Band; HonRl; JA; MrchBnd; SctActv; YthFlsp; SchPpr; Glf; Swmmng; Wrstlng; CchngActv;.

BELL, Bob; Garber HS; Essexvilee, MI; CncrtBnd; HonRl; SchPl; TchrAde; Teen; GodCntryAwd; Coll;.

BELL, Bruce E; Evanston Township HS; Evanston, IL; 128/1100 HonRl; NatlFornLg; SctActv; StuCncl; StuGov; University Of Illinois; Criminal Law.

BELL, Cathy L; Muncie Southside HS; Muncie, IN; 3/327 ALAGirlsSt; ChrhWkr; HonRl; PresNHS; OffAde; VPFrCl; VPPpCl; Ball State University; Cert Public Account.

BELL, Claire M; Lincoln Senior HS; Rudolph, WI; PresChrhWkr; CmntyWkr; HonRl; Orch; University; Special Ed Teacher.

BELL, Dan K; Marion Adams HS; Sheridan, IN; 1/109 Band; ChrhWkr; CncrtBnd; HonRl; JrNHS; MrchBnd; NHS; NatlMeritSF; PepBnd; Teen; YthFlsp; 4-H; LatCl; Earlham Col; Computer Science.

BELL, David; United Township Hs; East Moline, IL; 26/700 HonRl; PpCl; College; Chemistry.

BELL, Debra L; Allegan HS; Allegan, MI; Band; DrmMjrt; HonRl; HospAde; PepBnd; StuCncl; Twrl; YthLg; SpnCl; College.

BELL, Douglas N; Rock Island Senior HS; Rock Island, IL; 21/661 HonRl; NHS; NatlMeritCmnd; SpnCl;.

BELL, Janice L; Avon HS; Plainfield, IN; TrsJrCls; HonRl; Yrbk; PpCl; Chrldr; PPFtbl; College; Teaching.

BELL, Jeff P; Plattsmouth HS; Plattsmouth, NE; Band; CncrtBnd; MrchBnd; PepBnd; TchrAde; FBLA; FrCl; U Of Nebraska; Business Administration.

BELL, Joni; Atlantic HS; Atlantic, IA; Band; Chrs; CncrtBnd; PresFrshCls; NHS; Quill&Scroll; RptrYrbk; 4-H; FNA; GAA; Drake Univ; Med Tech.

BELL, Judy E; Beaver Dam Sr HS; Beaver Dam, WI; 13/349 AFS; Band; CncrtBnd; MrchBnd; PepBnd; SchMus; SctActv; SecSpnCl; GAA; IMSpt; College.

BELL, Judy F; Valley HS; Belgrade, MO; 2/50 SecSophCls; Band; Chrs; CncrtBnd; HonRl; NHS; SchPl; StuCncl; FHA; PpCl;.

BELL, Karen; Boone Senior HS; Boone, IA; Band; Chrs; CncrtBnd; MrchBnd; NHS; NatlThespSoc; SchMus; SchPl; YthFlsp; Coll; Comercial Art.

BELL, Katherine P; Brf HS; Black River Falls, WI; 16/137 DrmMjrt; HonRl; NHS; SchAde; SchMus; LetterBsktbl; Chrldr; GAA; MasAwd; PresAwd; Wi Univ Madison; Womens Phy Ed.

BELL, Kent D; Schell City Public HS; Schell City, MO; PresFrshCls; ChrhWkr; HonRl; SchPl; LetterBsktbl; Trk; Trade Sch; Farmer.

BELL, Kerry A; Watseka HS; Watseka, IL; 56/142 ALBoysSt; Aud/Vis; ChrhWkr; HonRl; StuCncl; Yrbk; CaptBsbl; CaptBsktbl; LetterFtbl; CaptTrk; Eastern Illinois Univ; Accounting.

BELL, Lawrence W; Smithton HS; Sedalia, MO; 2/41 Band; CncrtBnd; HonRl; MrchBnd; PepBnd; SchPl; StuCncl; RptrSchPpr; Univ Of Missouri; Mechanical Engineering.

BELL, Luann Y; U D 237 HS; Gaylord, KS; ALAGirlsSt; ChrhWkr; CmntyWkr; DrlTm; HonRl; OffAde; Twrl; Bsktbl; Chrldr; 4-HAwd; Clge; Secretary.

BELL, Mary E; Sparta HS; Sparta, WI; 7/200 HonRl;

NHS; SchMus; RptrYrbk; 4-H; SpnCl; U Of Wis; Pharmacy.

BELL, Melvin R; Schulte HS; Terre Haute, IN; 61/88 Chr; HonRl; Bsbl; CaptBsktbl; CaptFtbl; CaptTrk; AFS; EldAwd; PresAwd; Coll; Psychology.

BELL, Nancy J; Rossville Alvin HS; Hoopeston, IL; 10/39 TrsJrCls; TrsSrCls; Chrs; HonRl; SptEdYrbk; RptrSchPpr; SpnCl; Trk; GAA; IMSpt; Coll.

BELL, Patrick J; Hemlock HS; Saginaw, MI; 1/165 NatlMeritSchl; NatlMeritSF; Quill&Scroll; TchrAde; 4-H; FrCl; Bsktbl; LetterFtbl; LetterTrk; VoiceDemAwd; Ferris State Clge; Optomitrist.

BELL, Robert C; Chesaning HS; Chesaning, MI; SecSophCls; ALBoysSt; Band; HonRl; MrchBnd; NHS; PresStuCncl; LetterFtbl; LetterTrk; IMSpt; Central Mi Univ.

BELL, Stephanie D; Alpena HS; Alpena, MI; LetterBsktbl; U Of Mi ;med Illustrator.

BELL, Steven A; North Mahaska HS; New Sharon, IA; PresFrshCls; TrsSophCls; HonRl; StuCncl; YthFlsp; SchPpr; FFA; CaptFtbl; LetterGlf; CaptWrstlng;.

BELL, Thomas G; Burlington Community HS; Burlington, IA; 6/501 ChrhWkr; CncrtBnd; HonRl; MrchBnd; PresNHS; NatlMeritSF; PepBnd; StuCncl; YthFlsp; LetterTrk; U Of Iowa; Pre Medicine.

BELL, Wanda R; Christian Fenger HS; Chicago, IL; 42/708 HonRl; HospAde; NatlSciFnd; SctActv; RptrSchPpr; SpnCl; GAA; Babson College; Cpa.

BELL, William; Shepherd HS; Shepherd, MI; 24/150 Chr; HonRl; NHS; SchPl; LatCl; Bsktbl; Tennis; Trk; CchngActv; Ferris State College; Commercial Art.

BELLAR, Marcene L; West Elk HS; Howard, KS; 5/48 ALAGirlsSt; DrlTm; HonRl; NHS; OffAde; StuCncl; YthFlsp; 4-H; PpCl; Bsktbl; Trk; Kansas State Univ; Dental Asst.

BELLAS, Kathleen A; Oak Lawn Comm HS; Oak Lawn, IL; Chr; HonRl; Mdrgl; NHS; TchrAde; Univ Of Illinois; Engineering.

BELLAS, Robert E; Joliet East HS; Joliet, IL; 1/426 Chr; HonRl; Mdrgl; NHS; NatlMeritCmnd; Orch; SchMus; MthCl; SciCl; AmLegAwd; Univ Chicago; Medical Research.

BELLATTI, John; Jacksonville Hs; Jacksonville, IL; ALBoysSt; ChrhWkr; HonRl; MrchBnd; NHS; KeyCl; LatCl; LetterBsbl; LetterBsktbl; LetterGlf; Liberal Arts College; Math Or Science.

BELLER, Gary L; St Francis HS; Humphrey, NE; TrsFrshCls; Chr; ChrhWkr; CmntyWkr; HonRl; Sacrstn; GerCl; PpCl; Bsktbl; Ftbl; College.

BELLEW, Connie; Fredericktown Sr HS; Saco, MO; 3/124 ChrhWkr; CmntyWkr; HonRl; NHS; TchrAde; SpnCl; Mineral Area Col; American History Teacher.

BELLEW, Pamela; North P Senior HS; North Platte, NE; SecTrsFrshCls; OffAde; StuCncl; PpCl; Chrldr; GAA; IMSpt; PPFtbl; Coll; Teaching.

BELLICH, Joseph J; Thomson HS; Thomson, IL; 4/44 Band; Chr; Chrs; CmntyWkr; CncrtBnd; HonRl; JrNHS; Mdrgl; MrchBnd; NHS; NatlMeritCmnd; Bsbl; Bsktbl; College; Forest Conservation.

BELLIGAN, Brenda J; Oak Creek HS; Oak Creek, WI; 4/348 AFS; HonRl; JrNHS; NHS; NatlMeritFnl; Bsktbl; ChmnTrk; GAA; IMSpt; AmLegAwd; Matc; Acct.

BELLINGER, Cathy A; Clio HS; Clio, MI; ChrhWkr; CmntyWkr; NHS; RedCrAde; ROTC; SchPl; StuGov; YthFlsp; IMSpt; LionAwd; College; Professional.

BELLINGER, Karen; Lakeshore HS; Stevensville, MI; Band; CncrtBnd; HonRl; JA; MrchBnd; YthFlsp; College; Vocation.

BELLINGER, Kathy A; Kalkasva HS; Kalkaska, MI; HonRl; NHS; 4-H; PresAwd; Business School; Professional.

BELLINGHAUSEN, Randy; Lake City Community HS; Yetter, IA; 5/62 Aud/Vis; HonRl; NatlFornLg; SctActv; KiwanAwd; Univ Of Iowa; Law.

BELLOTT, Barry J; Streator HS; Streator, IL; ALBoysSt; HonRl; Ftbl; LetterTrk; LetterWrstlng; JCAwd; College; Accountant.

BELLOWS, Cindy J; Cameron HS; Cameron, WI; 6/51 TrsJrCls; Band; ChrhWkr; CncrtBnd; HonRl; MrchBnd; NHS; PepBnd; SchPl; StuCncl; TchrAde; AmLegAwd; Univ Of Eau Claire; Accounting.

BELLUOMINI, Karen L; Notre Dame HS; Chicago, IL; 31/302 HonRl; NHS; PolWkr; SchAde; TchrAde; SchPpr; Tennis; IMSpt; Ne Illinois Univ; Special Education.

BELLVILLE, Arlen T; Whittemore Prescott Area HS; Prescott, MI; 21/73 Band; Chr; MrchBnd; PepBnd; TchrAde; Yrbk; Trk; Air Force; Admn & Business.

BELLVILLE, Dennis J; Southgate HS; Southgate, MI; 2/366 PresJrCls; CmntyWkr; HonRl; JrNHS; LitMag; PresNHS; NatlMeritCmnd; StuGov; SchPpr; VPSpnCl; CaptSwmmng; CaptTrk; EldAwd; Univ Of Michigan; Dentistry.

BELLVILLE, James M; Hale HS; Hale, MI; 8/75 PresSrCls; ALBoysSt; Band; Chr; HonRl; 4-H; Bsbl; Bsktbl; Ftbl; Lake Superior State Clge; Natural Resources.

BELOBRADIC, Brian C; St Thomas Aquinas HS; Florissant, MO; 130/389 CmntyWkr; Socr; IMSpt; College; Business.

BELOFSKY, David A; Deerfield HS; Deerfield, IL; HonRl; ModUN; PolWkr; StuCncl; RptrSchPpr; SchPpr; Coll; Professional.

BELONGER, Paul J; Washington HS; Two Rivers, WI; 21/219 HonRl; NHS; LetterBsktbl; LetterFtbl; CaptTrk; Uw Milwaukee; Geologist.

BELOW, Scott D; Watertown HS; Watertown, SD; Chrs; ChrhWkr; NatlFornLg; SchMus; 4-H; IMSpt; 4-HAwd; Clg; Dentistry.

BELOY, Mary Jo; Aurora Hoyt Lakes HS; Aurora, MN; Chr; HonRl; HospAde; FrCl; MthCl; SecPpCl; LetterTrk; AmLegAwd; College; Biology.

BELSETH, Marilyn J; Milan HS; Milan, MN; Band; Chrl; ChrhWkr; HonRl; SchPl; RptrSchPpr; FshEdSchPpr; FHA; Trk; LetterChrldr; Augustana Col; Nursing.

BELSLEY, Donald A; Mediapolis HS; Oakville, IA; 13/86 Chr; Chrs; HonRl; RptrYrbk; 4-H; SpnCl; SciCl; College; Computer Programmer.

BELTH, Ann; Edgewood HS; Bloomington, IN; 1/161 ALAGirlsSt; HonRl; NHS; 4-H; FrCl; In Univ.

BELTMAN, Brenda; Platte HS; Platte, SD; ChrhWkr; CmntyWkr; HonRl; RptrYrbk; EdYrBk; RptrSchPpr; 4-H; GerCl; PpCl; 4-HAwd; College; Vocation.

BELTMAN, Daryl J; Maurice Orange City HS; Orange City, IA; ALBoysSt; Chr; HonRl; JrNHS; StuCncl; TchrAde; FTA; LetterBsbl; LetterBsktbl; LetterFtbl; College.

BELTRAN, Louis J; St Ignatius College Prep; Chicago, IL; 52/200 HonRl; SchPpr; SpnCl; College; Professional.

BELTZ, Dwight K; Haven HS; Haven, KS; 7/90 Aud/Vis; ChrhWkr; HonRl; SchPl; TchrAde; Glf; Univ Of Kansas; Economics.

BELTZ, Gary A; Randolph Public HS; Randolph, NE; PresJrCls; PresBand; NatlThespSoc; SchMus; PresStuCncl; SpnCl; College; Liberal Arts.

BELTZ, Jennifer B; Washington HS; Cedar Rapids, IA; 16/470 Chr; NHS; Quill&Scroll; SchPpr; GerCl; Wake Forest University.

BELYEU, Stacia A; Inkster HS; Inkster, MI; NHS; StuCncl; Yrbk; MthCl; College; Nursing.

BELZER, Barbara L; Appleton West HS; Appleton, WI; 24/640 AFS; JA; LitMag; NHS; NatlThespSoc; SctActv; EdSchPpr; SecSpnCl; PpCl; IMSpt; NCTE; University; Journalism.

BELZER, Barbara L; Ahs West HS; Appleton, WI; 20/640 LitMag; NatlMeritCmnd; NatlThespSoc; Quill&Scroll; SctActv; EdSchPpr; SecSpnCl; PpCl; IMSpt; NCTE; Uni ;journalist.

BEMBENEK, Cathy E; Rockridge HS; Reynolds, IL; Chrs; SchMus; StuGov; Twrl; YthFlsp; 4-H; LatCl; DanFAwd; 4-HAwd; JAAwd; College; Legal.

BEMBENICK, Linda; Downers Grove Community Hs N; Downers Rove, IL; 55/524 Band; Chr; CncrtBnd; HonRl; NHS; Orch; SchMus; 4-H; GAA; 4-HAwd; U Of Illinois; Accounting.

BEMBNISTER, Thomas E; Mc Donell Central HS; Chippewa Falls, WI; ALBoysSt; Band; HonRl; ModUN; SchMus; SchPl; SctActv; Yrbk; SptEdSchPpr; College.

BEMENT, Sheryl; Cahokia HS; Cahokia, IL; Band; HonRl; HospAde; MrchBnd; StuGov; YthFlsp; GerCl; PpCl; LetterTrk; Coll; Legal Sec.

BEMIS, Jeffrey B; Winchester Comm HS; Winchester, IN; ChrhWkr; HonRl; 4-H; Business School.

BEMIS, Roger S; Joliet Twp West HS; Joliet, IL; 67/495 Band; Chr; CncrtBnd; HonRl; Mdrgl; MrchBnd; NHS; Orch; PepBnd; ROTC; University.

BENAMOU, Marc; Huron HS; Annarbor, MI; Band; CncrtBnd; HonRl; MrchBnd; Orch; PepBnd; SchMus; LatCl; Oberliu College; Music.

BENARD, Linda; Pope County HS; Simpson, IL; ChrhWkr; SchPl; FHA; FTA; SpnCl; PpCl; GAA; 4-HAwd; JAAwd; College; Professional.

BENASH, Violet G; Our Lady Of Mt Carmel HS; Wyandotte, MI; 1/61 HonRl; NHS; SchMus; TchrAde;.

BENAVIDEZ, Jackie L; La Moille Comm HS; Ohio, IL; SecJrCls; HonRl; SecLbryAde; Sec4-H; SecFHA; PpCl; Trk; Chrldr; GAA; College; Nursing.

BENBENEK, Joseph; Lakeland Union HS; Hzaelhurst, WI; ALBoysSt; DanFAwd; Army; Surveyor.

BENBOW, Cheryl; Laboure HS; St Louis, MO; PresFrshCls; VPJrCls; Chr; CmntyWkr; HonRl; JrNHS; NHS; SchMus; SchPl; StuCncl; Coll; Psychologist.

BENCE, Vickie L; Oconomowoc Senior HS; Oconomowoc, WI; 31/223 AFS; HonRl; JrNHS; NHS; OffAde; FHA; PresGerCl; PpCl; GAA; Whitewater Univ; Accounting.

BENCKENDORF, Mary; Morton HS; Morton, IL; Chrs; ChrhWkr; SchPpr; Trk; GAA; IMSpt; PPFtbl; College; Teacher.

BENCO, Robert J; Joliet Catholic HS; Crest Hill, IL; 1/176 HonRl; NHS; NatlMeritCmnd; OffAde; TchrAde; RptrSchPpr; LatCl; RusCl; LetterBsbl; EldAwd; Northwestern Univ; Medicine.

BENCZIK, Stephen J; Plymouth HS; Plymouth, IN; 21/224 HonRl; 4-H; PresFFA; KeyCl; SpnCl; MthCl; PpCl; LetterFtbl; LetterTrk; 4-HAwd; Purdue Univ; Engineering.

BENDA, David C; Bath HS; Bath, MI; Band; CncrtBnd; HonRl; MrchBnd; PepBnd; SctActv; TchrAde; University; Professional.

BENDALL, Joellen M; Rochester HS; Rochester, IN; 15/162 Band; ChrhWkr; HonRl; NatlFornLg; NHS; RptrYrbk; EdSchPpr; 4-H; FrCl; PpCl; University; Journalism.

BENDER, Allen K; Northwood HS; Minong, WI; 3/33 PresJrCls; ALBoysSt; HonRl; StuCncl; RptrYrbk; EdSchPpr; GerCl; College; Architect.

BENDER, Barbara A; Assumption HS; Wi Rapids, WI; 3/117 HonRl; NHS; NatlMeritCmnd; TchrAde; RptrYrbk; PresFTA; VPFrCl; U Of Wi; Pre Law.

BENDER, Betty A; Forest Lake HS; Forest Lake, MN; 10/353 Chr; ChrhWkr; HonRl; JrNHS; LitMag; NatlFornLg; NHS; StuCncl; RptrYrbk; Yrbk; Gustavus Adolphus.

BENDER, Bruce M; Evanston Twp HS; Evanston, IL; Aud/Vis; Chr; HonRl; SchMus; SctActv; StuCncl; RptrYrbk; University.

BENDER, Deborah; Sturgis HS; Sturgis, MI; HonRl; HospAde; LitMag; NHS; OffAde; RedCrAde; SctActv; 4-H; PPFtbl; Bronson Meth Hosp; Nursing.

BENDER, Janet L; Belleville East HS; Belleville, IL; AFS; Chrs; CmntyWkr; HonRl; NHS; OffAde; SchMus; SchPl; StuCncl; RptrSchPpr; SchPpr; PresFHA; VFWAwd; College.

BENDER, Judy M; Appleton HS West; Appleton, WI; 91/633 CmntyWkr; HospAde; FBLA; CchngActv; Nursing School; Registered Nurse.

BENDER, Karlan J; Augres Sims HS; Augres, MI; CmntyWkr; HonRl; PresSptEdYrbk; RptrSchPpr; EdSchPpr; Univ Of Michigan; Pharmacy.

BENDER, Kenneth E; Forman HS; Manito, IL; TrsSophCls; LetterBsbl; LetterGlf; College; Vocation.

BENDER, Laurie A; W J Brown HS; Ft Meade, SD; 22/203 SecSrCls; ALAGirlsSt; Band; Chr; Chrs; ChrhWkr; CncrtBnd; HonRl; Mdrgl; MrchBnd; NHS; SecNatlThespSoc; PepBnd; SchMus; Chrldr; College; Special Education.

BENDER, Marilyn K; Hanson Ind #40 HS; Fulton, SD; 17/45 VPJrCls; VPSrCls; Chrs; HonRl; HospAde; JA; Quill&Scroll; SchPl; Trk; Chrldr; Vocational Tech; Lpn Training.

BENDER, Roger D; Carthage Ind HS; Carthage, SD; Chrs; ChrhWkr; HonRl; SchPl; StuCncl; Bsktbl; LetterFtbl; Trk; AmLegAwd; Trade Schl; Vocation.

BENDER, Sharon; Southside HS; Ft Wayne, IN; 40/438 Chr; ChrhWkr; HonRl; OffAde; YthFlsp; EngCl; SpnCl; PpCl; IMSpt; Univ; Social Work.

BENDER, Sherieda K; Tomah Sr HS; Tomah, WI; 2/264 Chr; ChrhWkr; HonRl; IntrClCncl; Mdrgl; NatlFornLg; NatlMeritSF; SchMus; SpnCl; PpCl; SciCl; GAA; IMSpt; Iowa State Univ; Veterinary Med.

BENDER, Terry L; Tri County Comm HS; Keswick, IA; 5 .48 PresFrshCls; TrsSophCls; SecJrCls; PresSrCls; Band; Chr; HonRl; Bsbl; CaptBsktbl; Trk; Wm Penn Clg; Math.

BENDER, Tony; Frederick Public HS; Frederick, SD; ChrhWkr; CmntyWkr; HonRl; LbryAde; SctActv; IMSpt; College.

BENDON, Kathleen; Ryan HS; Omaha, NE; NHS; SchMus; StuCncl; PpCl; Trk; Chrldr; Univ Of Nebr Medical Center; Nursing.

BENDORF, Susan; Westside HS; Omaha, NE; Band; Chr; CncrtBnd; HonRl; HospAde; MrchBnd; SchMus; Trk; Univ Of Ne; Engr.

BENECKI, Jean M; Ladywood HS; Livonia, MI; HonRl; NHS; NatlMeritFnl; NatlMeritCmnd; OffAde; Quill&Scroll; StuCncl; RptrSchPpr; SecFHA; College; Secretarial.

BENEDA, Diane M; Lankin Public HS; Lankin, ND; ALAGirlsSt; Chrs; ChrhWkr; HonRl; SchPl; StuCncl; RptrYrbk; RptrSchPpr; 4-H; LetterBsktbl; LetterTrk; LetterChrldr; 4-HAwd; Und.

BENEDA, Philip J; St Vincent De Paul Sem HS; Chicago, IL; 3/9 Chr; HonRl; LbryAde; Sacrstn; SchMus; SchPl; EdYrBk; RptrSchPpr; Loyola Univ; Accounting.

BENEDETTO, Lisa B; Metamara Township HS; E Peoria, IL; 1/172 VPJrCls; ChrhWkr; HonRl; NHS; StuGov; FrCl; PpCl; Eastern Il Univ; Accounting.

BENEDICT, Cindy; Hermitage HS; Hermitage, MO; VPSophCls; Chrs; HonRl; TchrAde; Yrbk; 4-H; PpCl; GAA; GodCntryAwd; CitAwd; College; Physical Therapist.

BENEDICT, Kimberly M; Frontenac HS; Frontenac, KS; 3/41 HonRl; HospAde; MrchBnd; PepBnd; EdYrBk; RptrSchPpr; FHA; SpnCl; MthCl; College; Law.

BENEDICT, Sharon; Eleva Strum Central HS; Eleva, WI; 13/72 HonRl; OffAde; SchAde; StuCncl; StuGov; RptrSchPpr; SptEdSchPpr; SchPpr; GAA;.

BENEDICT, Teresa; Manchester Hs; Manchester, MI; Chrs; HonRl; StuCncl; TchrAde; GerCl; PpCl; Trk; Chrldr; GAA; Michigan State U;interior Design.

BENEFIEL, Jane A; Gibson City HS; Gibson City, IL; 5/87 AFS; Chrs; CncrtBnd; HonRl; MrchBnd; NHS; SchMus; StuCncl; VPFTA; GAA; Eastern Illinois Univ; Elem Education.

BENEKER, Lowell; Brookville HS; Brookville, IN; 20/180 ChrhWkr; CmntyWkr; HonRl; 4-H; SpnCl; SciCl; 4-HAwd; Univ; Math.

BENES, Elisabeth A; Muskegon HS; Sheldon, IA; HonRl; FrCl; Northwestern Coll; Elem Ed.

BENESH, Joann L; West Chicago Community HS; West Chicago, IL; 2/312 AFS; Chr; HonRl; NHS; NatlThespSoc; SchMus; SchPl; TchrAde; LatCl; MthCl; Il Univ; Vet/medicine.

BENEVENTI, Robert A; Carl Sandburg HS; Oak Forest, IL; 19/700 HonRl; SpnCl; Univ; Accountant.

BENGE, La Donna; Flaxton HS; Flaxton, ND; 1/15 SecSophCls; TrsSophCls; PresJrCls; Chr; Chrs; ChrhWkr; DrlTm; HonRl; StuCncl; Yrbk; CaptBsktbl; LetterTrk; LetterChrldr; 4-HAwd; Minot St College; Music.

BENGE, Vicki L; Gibbon Public HS; Gibbon, NE; Chrs; HonRl; StuCncl; YthFlsp; 4-H; FBLA; LetterBsktbl; Trk; College; Social Worker.

BENGELSDORF, Steven; Dundee HS; Dundee, MI; 4/124 HonRl; NHS; StuCncl; Michigan Tech Univ; Geology.

BENGTSON, Bruce H; Dassel Cokato HS; Dassel, MN; 3/120 Chr; ChrhWkr; HonRl; LbryAde; Mdrgl; NatlFornLg; NHS; NatlMeritCmnd; SchMus; SchPl; Glf; North Park College.

BENGTSON, Melanie L; Breckenridge HS; Breckenridge, MN; Band; Chr; ChrhWkr; CncrtBnd; HonRl; MrchBnd; NatlMeritSF; PepBnd; SchPl; 4-H; FrCl; GAA; College; Mathematics.

BENGTSON, Peter S; E Rockford HS; Rockford, IL; 145/665 ChrhWkr; Univ Of Il; Pharmacy.

BENGTSON, Sheldon J; Westview Sr HS; Braham, MN; 3/100 Chr; PresChrhWkr; HonRl; NatlFornLg; NHS; SchPl; Pres4-H; VPFFA; LetterWrstlng; 4-HAwd; College; Business Admin.

BENGTSON, Sue; Mankato West HS; Mankato, MN; CmntyWkr; HonRl; College; Child Psychologist Or Peditrician.

BENGTSON, Vrenda L; Marshall County Central HS; Newfolden, MN; Chr; Chrs; ChrhWkr; HonRl; LbryAde; RptrYrbk; SchPpr; 4-H; FHA; PpCl; College; Police Work.

BENHAM, Amber; Fremont HS; Fremont, NE; Chr; ChrhWkr; DrlTm; NHS; NatlThespSoc; SchMus; SchPl; FNA; SpnCl; Nursing School; Rn.

BENHAM, Gary A; Galena HS; Galena, MO; CmntyWkr; SchPl; 4-H; PresFFA; Bsbl; Bsktbl; Trk; 4-HAwd; JAAwd;.

BENIK, Michael; Bolingbrook Hs; Bolingbrook, IL; 2/250 CmntyWkr; HonRl; NHS; RptrSchPpr; CaptSocr; College; Politics.

BENINATO, Gloria L; Carl Sandburg HS; Orland Park, IL; 69/680 HonRl; NatlMeritCmnd; EdYrBk; SptEdYrbk; MthCl; Loyola Univ; Dental Hygiene.

BENINCOSA, Kelly R; Galena HS; Galena, IL; 45/114 AFS; Chrs; MrchBnd; SchMus; SctActv; FFA; SpnCl; LetterGlf; William Woods College; Horse Trainer.

BENING, Stephen; Carbondale Community Hs; Carbondale, IL; 29 ChrhWkr; HonRl; LitMag; ModUN; EdYrBk; SpnCl; PpCl; SciCl; Ftbl; Trk; So Illinois U;business.

BENISHEK, Anne E; Whitnall HS; Franklin, WI; SecAFS; ChrhWkr; HonRl; HospAde; NHS; NatlMeritCmnd; SchPl; SctActv; GerCl; CaptSwmmng; College; Biology.

BENISHEK, Bobbi A; Antigo HS; Antigo, WI; 4-H; FBLA; LetterChrldr; Technical School; Dental Hygeienist.

BENJAMIN, Dawn G; Hudson Area HS; Hudson, MI; 13/127 Chr; CncrtBnd; HonRl; MrchBnd; NHS; PepBnd; SchAde; TchrAde; LetterBsktbl; GAA; Undecided;.

BENJAMIN, George R; Tri Valley HS; Ellsworth, IL; SecFrshCls; Band; Chrs; ChrhWkr; HonRl; TreasStuCncl; TchrAde; VP4-H; PresFFA; 4-HAwd; Univ Of Illinois; Agriculture.

BENJAMIN, Judy; Cosmos HS; Litchfield, MN; SchMus; SchPl; YthFlsp; RptrSchPpr; SchPpr; FHA; Chrldr; GAA;.

BENJAMIN, Marsha; Morton HS; Morton, IL; 59/286 HonRl; StuCncl; TchrAde; Chrldr; GAA; Univ; Elementary School Teacher.

BENJAMIN, Miriam B; Niles Twp East HS; Skokie, IL; 55/503 Band; CncrtBnd; HonRl; JrNHS; MrchBnd; NHS; Orch; PepBnd; College; Music.

BENJAMIN, Shelley A; Western Mich Christian HS; Muskegon Hts, MI; Band; ChrhWkr; HonRl; MrchBnd; NHS; OffAde; SchPl; Teen; YthFlsp; IMSpt; College; Music.

BENKE, Michael G; Thornton Fractional HS; Lansing, IL; 23/563 PresSophCls; PresChr; HonRl; TreasJrNHS; SchMus; SchPl; StuCncl; CaptSwmmng; Univ Of Illinois; Music.

BENKE, Patti R; Oak Park HS; Kansas City, MO; Chr; HonRl; MrchBnd; RedCrAde; StuCncl; Twrl; Treas4-H; GerCl; Swmmng; LetterTennis; GAA; IMSpt; OptClAwd; College.

BENKER, Nancy J; Madonna HS; Chicago, IL; Chr; Chrs; HonRl; OffAde; StuCncl; CivCl; SciCl; Northern Il Univ; Medical Tech.

BENKERT, David E; Monroe HS; Monroe, WI; ALBoysSt; Band; CncrtBnd; HonRl; MrchBnd; SctActv; Bsktbl; Notre Dame College; Business Admin.

BENKO, Edward A; Granite City HS; Granit City, IL; LetterFtbl; LetterTrk; Trade; Vocational.

BENKSE, Jean; Depue HS; Depue, IL; 4/28 PresFrshCls; Chrs; ChrhWkr; HonRl; NHS; PepBnd; RptrYrbk; RptrSchPpr; GAA; College; Music Major.

BENLING, Joy E; Crystal Lake Comm HS; Crystal Lake, IL; 36/473 Band; ChrhWkr; CncrtBnd; DrlTm; HonRl; MrchBnd; NHS; SchAde; SctActv; StuCncl; YthFlsp; Univ Of Illinois; Lawyer.

BENNER, Colleen L; Edina East HS; Edina, MN; 74/449 Chr; HospAde; SchMus; YthFlsp; SpnCl; Tennis; IMSpt; College; Biochem Engineer.

BENNER, Kenneth E; Shabbona HS; Lee, IL; 10/44 PresSrCls; Chrs; HonRl; OffAde; StuCncl; YthFlsp; Yrbk; SptEdSchPpr; LetterBsbl; LetterBsktbl; LetterTrk; 4-HAwd; Western Ill Univ; Business.

BENNER, Steven L; Milford Township HS; Milford, IL; SecFrshCls; VPSophCls; PresJrCls; HonRl; SchPpr; GerCl; LetterBsbl; LetterFtbl; LetterGlf; Trk; IMSpt; Eastern Illinois Univ; Physical Education.

BENNER, Sue L; Bloomingdale HS; Bloomingdale, MI; 22/87 Band; CmntyWkr; CncrtBnd; HonRl; OffAde; PepBnd; SchPl; StuCncl; Yrbk; FrCl; Business College; Medical Secretary.

BENNETT, Aimee; Thornton HS; Harvey, IL; 37/750 HonRl; NHS; GerCl; PpCl; Stephens Clge.

BENNETT, Alan M; Potosi HS; Potosi, WI; 20/70 VPSophCls; HonRl; SchPpr; Bsbl; Bsktbl; CaptFtbl; CaptTrk; IMSpt; PPFtbl; Vocational School; Machinery Partsman.

BENNETT, Athena; Northwest HS; Indianapolis, IN; 25/432 Aud/Vis; HonRl; JrNHS; Mdrgl; NHS; SchMus; StuCncl; YthFlsp; IMSpt; In Voc Tech Coll; Operating Rm Tech.

BENNETT, Barbara E; Bloomington HS; Bloomington, IL; 68/390 Band; Chr; HonRl; Mdrgl; NatlThespSoc; Orch; PepBnd; SchMus; SchPl; Eastern Illinois Univ; Archeology.

BENNETT, Bruce L; United Twp HS; Green Rock, IL; 31/950 ChrhWkr; CmntyWkr; HonRl; LitMag; SctActv; RptrYrbk; Yrbk; RptrSchPpr; SchPpr; KeyCl; GerCl; LetterFtbl; LetterTrk; Black Hawk College; Doctor.

BENNETT, Carol S; Westfield HS; Westfield, IL; 2/21 SecJrCls; HonRl; NHS; SchMus; SchPl; StuCncl; YthFlsp;,FHA; Trk; Chrldr; College; Medical Asst.

BENNETT, Cassanra J; Adrian Sr HS; Adrian, MI; Chr; ChrhWkr; YthFlsp; YthLg; College; Nursing.

BENNETT, Christopher M; Evanston Township HS; Evanston, IL; 243/1100 HonRl; Univ Of Ill; Psychology.

BENNETT, Cindy K; Cowan HS; Muncie, IN; HonRl; Yrbk; SpnCl; Bus School.

BENNETT, Darcy; Walker HS; Walker, MN; Chr; NatlFornLg; SchAde; TchrAde; RptrSchPpr; SpnCl;.

BENNETT, David; North Side HS; Fort Wayne, IN; 24/476 PresJrCls; ALBoysSt; HonRl; NatlFornLg; NHS; PolWkr; StuCncl; YthLg; SchPpr; ChmbCommrsAwd; Williams; History.

BENNETT, David M; Wood HS; Wood, SD; 1/16 ALBoysSt; Band; Chr; ChrhWkr; HonRl; SchPl; TchrAde; Yrbk; RptrSchPpr; Pres4-H; CaptTrk; Trinity Bible Inst;.

BENNETT, Debbie L; Shelby HS; New Era, MI; Band; CncrtBnd; HonRl; JrNHS; MrchBnd; PepBnd; SchPl; StuGov; 4-H; College; Teaching.

BENNETT, Debbie S; West Vigo HS; West Terre Haute, IN; HonRl; Purdue Univ; Nursing.

BENNETT, Debra; Cheboygan Area HS; Cheboygan, MI; CmntyWkr; NHS; StuGov; YthFnd; JAAwd; JETSAwd; KiwanAwd; LionAwd; CitAwd; VoiceDemAwd; Trade Sch; Prof.

BENNETT, Debra J; Benton Cons HS; Thompsonville, IL; 16/168 ChrhWkr; HonRl; RptrSchPpr; 4-H; FHA; SpnCl; Rend Lake Jr College; Nursing.

BENNETT, Dennis W; Yorktown HS; Muncie, IN; Aud/Vis; SctActv; StuCncl; YthFlsp; FBLA; LetterTrk; College; Business.

BENNETT, Denver; Madison HS; Madison Heights, MI; Band; CAP; CncrtBnd; HonRl; MrchBnd; NHS; YthFnd; FSA; Bsktbl; Tenn Tech U; Engineering.

BENNETT, Diane E; Lincoln HS; Ypsilanti, MI; SecSrCls; HonRl; MrchBnd; NatlMeritFnl; Orch; SchMus; StuCncl; 4-H; FrCl; 4-HAwd; Eastern Mi Univ; Medical Technologist.

BENNETT, Garry D; Chicago Voc HS; Chicago, IL; CmntyWkr; HonRl; Illinois Inst Of Tech; Electrical Eng.

BENNETT, Jerilee; Fredericktown HS; Fredericktown, MO; 16/150 ALAGirlsSt; Band; CncrtBnd; HonRl; MrchBnd; PpCl; College; Journalism.

BENNETT, Joanne E; Moberly Senior HS; Moberly, MO; 22/210 SecJrCls; VPSrCls; HonRl; NHS; Quill&Scroll; Yrbk; SchPpr; SecMthCl; PpCl; Trk; Univ Of Missouri Columbia; Journalism.

BENNETT, Joy T; Aquinas HS; Chicago, IL; 28/152 Chrs; HonRl; HospAde; LbryAde; NHS; NatlMeritCmnd; StuGov; Univ; Journalism.

BENNETT, Judi A; Calhoun HS; Kampsville, IL; 17/77 HonRl; Yrbk; 4-H; PpCl; Bsbl; Trk; Chrldr; GAA; DanFAwd; 4-HAwd; College; Bank Clerk.

BENNETT, Judith A; Lockport Central HS; Lockport, IL; 9/550 HonRl; NHS; OffAde; Quill&Scroll; StuCncl; StuGov; RptrSchPpr; FrCl; SciCl; St Louis College; Pharmacist.

BENNETT, Kenn L; North Platte Senior HS; North Platte, NE; ALBoysSt; CmntyWkr; HonRl; NatlFornLg; SchPl; SctActv; 4-H; KeyCl; LetterFtbl; GodCntryAwd; U Of Ne; Attorney.

BENNETT, Lawrence N; Gordon Technical HS; Chicago, IL; 17/618 HonRl; U Of Ill; Biological Science.

BENNETT, Liane M; Petersburg Porta HS; Petersburg, IL; 2/97 Band; TreasJA; NHS; NatlMeritFnl; YthFlsp; RptrYrbk; Sec4-H; FFA; GAA; 4-HAwd; JAAwd; Univ Of Ill; Forestry.

BENNETT, Lou Ann; Decatur Central HS; Indianapolis, IN; 15/319 HonRl; NHS; 4-H; LatCl; Purdue Univ; Mathematics.

BENNETT, Mary J; Patrick Henry HS; Minneapolis, MN; Chr; HonRl; Mdrgl; NHS; OffAde; StuGov; TchrAde; Teen; Swmmng; IMSpt; Jah; Receptionist.

BENNETT, Michael E; Cairo HS; Cairo, IL; 2/100 ALBoysSt; Aud/Vis; HonRl; StuCncl; SptEdSchPpr; FBLA; FrCl; MthCl; SciCl; IMSpt; Clge.

BENNETT, Mike E; Cairo HS; Cairo, IL; 2/100 ALBoysSt; Aud/Vis; HonRl; StuCncl; SptEdSchPpr; FBLA; FrCl; MthCl; Bsbl; Bsktbl; Coll; Pro.

BENNETT, Mike T; Laurel HS; Laurel, IN; HonRl; LetterBsbl; LetterBsktbl; LetterTrk; Factory Work.

BENNETT, Patricia A; R Nelson Snider HS; Fort Wayne, IN; 40/515 Chr; HonRl; SchAde; 4-H; SpnCl; PpCl; Swmmng; Trk; SecGAA; IMSpt; In U; Medical Technology.

BENNETT, Patricia L; Christopher Comm HS; Mulkeytown, IL; SecFrshCls; TrsJrCls; HonRl; NHS; TchrAde; FHA; Chrldr; AmLegAwd; College; Home Ec.

BENNETT, Randall; Williamsburg HS; Williamsburg, KS; 3/28 Chr; Chrs; HonRl; Mdrgl; NHS; TchrAde; YthFlsp; EdSchPpr; FFA; College.

BENNETT, Richard L; Jackson HS; Jackson, MI; 44/386 CmntyWkr; HonRl; NHS; SchAde; TchrAde; LetterTrk; JCAwd; PresAwd; VoiceDemAwd; College.

BENNETT, Rick E; Oregon Davis HS; Grovertown, IN; 7/72 HonRl; NHS; 4-H; FFA; Bsbl; Bsktbl;.

BENNETT, Robin; Mason County Central HS; Scottville, MI; 32/133 Band; ChrhWkr; CncrtBnd; HonRl; MrchBnd; Orch; PepBnd; SchMus; TchrAde; RptrYrbk; Aquinas College.

BENNETT, Sandra A; Luke M Powers HS; Flint, MI; Band; CmntyWkr; HonRl; MrchBnd; NHS; SchMus; RptrSchPpr; SchPpr; CaptBsktbl; U Of Mi Flint; Social Worker.

BENNETT, Sarah L; Pennfield HS; Battle Creek, MI; 4/170 Chr; CmntyWkr; HonRl; Mdrgl; NHS; SctActv; TchrAde; YthFlsp; SciCl; PresSrCls; Coll; Pro.

BENNETT, Scott A; River Valley HS; Buchanan, MI; Band; ChrhWkr; HonRl; Col; Aviation Tech.

BENNETT, Stephen D; Larkin HS; Elgin, IL; 4/573 VPSrCls; Chrs; HonRl; NatlMeritCmnd; PolWkr; Northern Ill Univ; Lawyer.

BENNETT, Steven C; Columbia Hgts HS; Columbia Heights, MN; HonRl; LitMag; NatlFornLg; NHS; NatlMeritSF; SchMus; SchPl; StuCncl; RptrSchPpr; LetterTennis; College; Criminal Law.

BENNETT, Steven D; Chelsea HS; Chelsea, MI; 3/210 HonRl; PresNHS; NatlMeritCmnd; RptrYrbk; W Mich Univ; Scientific Research.

BENNETT, Susan R; Niles Sr HS; Niles, MI; Band; CncrtBnd; HonRl; MrchBnd; PepBnd; StuGov; LatCl; LetterBsktbl; CchngActv; GAA; Univ Of Michigan; Political Science.

BENNETT, Tarryll J; Glenburn HS; Deering, ND; 3/28 Chrs; ChrhWkr; CncrtBnd; DrlTm; HonRl; StuCncl; PpCl; LetterChrldr; CchngActv; GAA; Univ Of North Dak; Social Worker.

BENNETT, Terry L; Chesaning Union HS; Chesaning, MI; 16/241 Chr; Chrl; ChrhWkr; Calvin College; Medicine.

BENNETT, Toni J; Magic City Campus HS; Minot, ND; Band; ChrhWkr; CncrtBnd; HonRl; HospAde; MrchBnd; Orch; SpnCl; College; Social Work.

BENNIN, Joy M; Waterloo Community HS; Waterloo, WI; 1/78 AFS; Band; Chr; HonRl; NatlFornLg; SchMus; StuCncl; Yrbk; RptrSchPpr; LionAwd; New Mexico State Univ; Pre Med Program.

BENNINGER, Arlene J; Dodgeland HS; Reeseville, WI; 7/77 ALAGirlsSt; Chrs; ChrhWkr; HonRl; NatlFornLg; NHS; TchrAde; PresYthFlsp; LetterChrldr; JCAwd; Univ Of Wi; Communications Arts.

BENO, Janice M; St Francis De Sales HS; Chicago, IL; 7/292 Chrs; HonRl; NHS; SchMus; SctActv; TchrAde; SchPpr; PpCl; Chrldr; GAA; Western Il Univ; Special Ed Teacher.

BENOIST, Terence J; Arcadia Valley HS; Ironton, MO; 5/87 Aud/Vis; HonRl; NHS; TchrAde; Yrbk; FBLA; FrCl; SpnCl; LetterBsbl; IMSpt; U Of Missouri.

BENOY, Nathan R; Forest Lake HS; Forest Lake, MN; Band; CncrtBnd; HonRl; LitMag; MrchBnd; PepBnd; SctActv; Yrbk; RptrSchPpr; College; Pre Med.

BENOY, Victoria L; Mentor Public HS; Mentor, MN; 4/15 VPJrCls; Band; ChrhWkr; HonRl; LbryAde; RptrSchPpr; FHA; Bsktbl; Chrldr; GAA; Univ; Counselor.

BENRUD, Peggy M; Melrose Mindora HS; Melrose, WI; Band; Chr; Chrl; PresChrs; ChrhWkr; CncrtBnd; HonRl; MrchBnd; PepBnd; SctActv; PresFHA; Tennis; GAA; Stout St Univ; Child Development.

BENRUD, Peggy M; Melrose Mindoro HS; Melrose, WI; Band; Chr; PresChrs; CncrtBnd; MrchBnd; PepBnd; SctActv; PresFHA; Trk; GAA; Stout State Univ; Home Ec.

BENSCHEIDT, Michael A; Hutchinson HS; Hutchinson, KS; HonRl; NatlFornLg; Glf; Coll.

BENSCHOTER, Ronald J; Sand Creek HS; Sand Creek, MI; VPJrCls; ALBoysSt; HonRl; NHS; NatlThespSoc; SchMus; SchPl; StuGov; Ftbl; AmLegAwd; U Of Western Mi; Professional.

BENSEMA, Gary; Harold L Richards Hs; Oak Lawn, IL; HonRl; JrNHS; LitMag; NHS; NatlMeritCmnd; Quill&Scroll; YthFlsp; LetterTrk;.

BENSEN, Mabel; Neillsville Hs; Neillville, WI; 6/115 ALAGirlsSt; Chrs; NHS; SchPl; TchrAde; Pres4-H; VPFTA; Bsktbl; Trk; Chrldr; U Wi River Falls; Veterinary Medicine.

BENSEND, Andy F; Barron Sr HS; Dallas, WI; 8/138 ALBoysSt; Band; Chr; ChrhWkr; CncrtBnd; HonRl; Mdrgl; MrchBnd; NHS; PepBnd; SchMus; LetterWrstlng; EldAwd; 4-HAwd; College; Agriculture.

BENSLEY, Terry L; Westfield HS; Westfield, IL; SecSophCls; VPSrCls; HonRl; NHS; SchPl; EdYrBk; FHA; SecSpnCl; Chrldr; BauchLmbAwd; E Il U.

BENSON, Blake P; Forest Lake Senior HS; Forest Lake, MN; 14/350 Band; CncrtBnd; HonRl; MrchBnd; NHS; PepBnd; RptrYrbk; CaptBsktbl; LetterFtbl; Univ Of Minnesota; Engineering.

BENSON, Bonnie L; Westfield HS; Noblesville, IN; 8/87 SecFrshCls; ALAGirlsSt; SecChr; HonRl; SecNHS; NatlThespSoc; SchMus; SchPl; SecStuCncl; YthFlsp; Chrldr; GAA; IMSpt; PPFtbl; Indiana Central Univ; Elem Ed.

BENSON, Carolee R; Holdrege HS; Lindsborg, KS; 1/131 SecAFS; Band; Chr; Chrl; Chrs; CncrtBnd; HonRl; HospAde; MrchBnd; PepBnd; SchMus; StuCncl; Yrbk; PresPpCl; Bethany College; History.

BENSON, Charles E; Booker T Washington HS; Chicago, IL; PresJrCls; CmntyWkr; HonRl; JA; NatlCathMusEdAsoc; ROTC; StuGov; YthFlsp; RptrYrbk; FSA; Loyola Coll; Music.

BENSON, Charles N; Mahomet Seymour HS; Champaign, IL; 9/130 HonRl; NHS; SchMus; SchPl; SctActv; StuCncl; LetterBsktbl; LetterFtbl; LetterTrk; LionAwd; College.

BENSON, Charles R; Hanson HS; Fulton, SD; SecFrshCls; VPSophCls; SecTrsJrCls; Band; Bsbl; Bsktbl; Ftbl; Trk; CchngActv; IMSpt; Col ; Educ.

BENSON, Debbie K; Rushford HS; Rushford, MN; AFS; Chrs; DrlTm; HonRl; MrchBnd; OffAde; TchrAde; EdSchPpr; SchPpr; FHA; College Of St Teresa; Edical Study.

BENSON, Elizabeth G; Humboldt HS; St Paul, MN; Chr; ChrhWkr; HospAde; SchAde; SctActv; Armed Services; Medical Field.

BENSON, Ellsworth J; Sheyenne Public HS; Sheyenne, ND; 1/16 PresJrCls; PresSrCls; Chr; ChrhWkr; CmntyWkr; HonRl; EdYrBk; LetterBsbl; LetterBsktbl; AmLegAwd; EldAwd; Univ Of North Dakota; Doctor.

BENSON, James P; Edwardsville HS; Edwardsville, IL; 37/461 HonRl; SchMus; SchPl; Westminster College; Economics.

BENSON, Jane D; Monroe City R 1 HS; Monreo City, MO; ChrhWkr; HonRl; TchrAde; Yrbk; FHA; 4-HAwd; Collge; Vocation.

BENSON, Jill M; Lake Zurich Senior HS; Lake Zurich, IL; 2/195 AFS; Band; ChrhWkr; CncrtBnd; JrNHS; LbryAde; MrchBnd; Univ Of Illinois; Doctor.

BENSON, Jodi S; Mankato West HS; North Mankato, MN; HonRl; StuCncl; StuGov; PpCl; Rochester Comm College; Register Nurse.

BENSON, John H; Thornridge HS; Calumet City, IL; Chrl; ChrhWkr; HonRl; LitMag; Mdrgl; NHS; NatlThespSoc; SchPl; Gustavus Adolphus; Theology.

BENSON, Johnny J; Ashby Public HS; Ashby, MN; PresChrhWkr; CmntyWkr; HonRl; JA; NHS; SchAde; TchrAde; AmLegAwd; JAAwd; CitAwd; College; Professional.

BENSON, Julie A; Kenyon HS; Kenyon, MN; 3/7 AFS; Chr; HonRl; NHS; SchMus; SchPl; YthFlsp; Yrbk; PresFHA; LetterBsktbl; Col; Rn.

BENSON, Kathy; Flasher Public HS; Flasher, ND; MrchBnd; PepBnd; SchPl; StuCncl; SchPpr; 4-H; 4-HAwd; Teachers Aid.

BENSON, Lorie; Wabash HS; Wabash, IN; ChrhWkr; HonRl; NHS; OffAde; SchAde; SctActv; FHA; FrCl; PpCl; SciCl; Okla Baptist Univ; Physical Therapy.

BENSON, Marc S; Worthington Senior HS; Worthington, MN; College.

BENSON, Nancy L; Sterling HS; Sterling, IL; 19/374 ALAGirlsSt; Chr; HonRl; NHS; StuCncl; RptrSchPpr; GerCl; GAA; College; Public Relations.

BENSON, Nicholas J; Vocational HS; Minneapolis, MN; Band; ChrhWkr; TchrAde; Bsktbl; IMSpt; Trade; Computer Tech.

BENSON, Paul H; Larkin HS; Elmhurst, IL; 1/575 Chr; ChrhWkr; HonRl; NatlFornLg; NatlMeritFnl; NatlMeritSchl; PresYthFlsp; SpnCl; LetterTennis; RotaryAwd; St Olaf Coll; Math Or Philosophy.

BENSON, Ramona J; Columbia Heights HS; Columbia Heights, MN; 49/532 Chr; Chrs; HonRl; MrchBnd; NHS; NatlMeritSF; Swmmng; LetterTrk; PresGAA; PresAwd; Clge; Prof.

BENSON, Rebecca E; Hector Comm HS; Hector, MN; 11/49 SecBand; Chr; ChrhWkr; CncrtBnd; HonRl; MrchBnd; SchPl; SecStuCncl; PresFHA; LetterTrk; Golden Valley Lutheran.

BENSON, Rebecca R; West Marshall HS; State Center, IA; 8/90 ChrhWkr; HonRl; MrchBnd; NHS; StuCncl; Twrl; YthFlsp; CaptBsktbl; Trk; GAA; Iowa St Univ; Applied Arts.

BENSON, Rita D; Lawrenceville HS; Lawrenceville, IL; 16/176 ChrhWkr; CmntyWkr; HonRl; HospAde; YthFlsp; 4-H; FHA; FNA; LatCl; 4-HAwd; Vincennes Univ; Nursing.

BENSON, Rossy L; Mabel Canton HS; Spring Grove, MN; Band; Chr; ChrhWkr; HonRl; SctActv; StuCncl; RptrSchPpr; 4-H; FHA; PpCl; College; Physical Therapist.

BENSON, Sandra L; Drummond HS; Drummond, WI; 1/42 ChrhWkr; HonRl; LbryAde; NHS; TchrAde; EdYrBk; GerCl; LetterBsbl; BttyCrckrAwd; Uw Eau Claire; Nursing.

BENSON, Sheryl A; West Richland HS; Noble, IL; ALAGirlsSt; HonRl; StuCncl; Yrbk; FDA; FFA; FSA; Chrldr; GAA; AmLegAwd; College; Veterinarian.

BENSON, Susan E; Burlington Comm HS; Burlington, IA; Chr; Chrs; HonRl; HospAde; NHS; StuCncl; Teen; PpCl; Glf; Swmmng; Chrldr; College; Fine Arts.

BENSON, Susan M; Rutllnd HS; Rutland, SD; 2/22 Band; Chr; ChrhWkr; CmntyWkr; HonRl; NHS; RptrYrbk; EdSchPpr; 4-H; Bsktbl; AmLegAwd; Augustana College; Medicine.

BENSON, Victoria M; Central HS; Burlington, IL; 12/75 HonRl; NHS; StuCncl; Yrbk; FTA; PpCl; Elgin Community College; Elementary Teacher.

BENSTEAD, Steven E; Kimball County HS; Kimball, NE; 10/105 VPFrshCls; PresSophCls; ALBoysSt; HonRl; NHS; EdYrBk; SptEdYrbk; SptEdSchPpr; Ftbl; U Of Ne; Journalism.

BENT, Bonita L; Oregon Davis HS; Hamlet, IN; Aud/Vis; Band; ChrhWkr; DrlTm; HonRl; PepBnd; PresYthFlsp; 4-H; GAA; 4-HAwd; Purdue; Veterinary.

BENT, Linda; Liberty Hs; Liberty, IL; 7/63 Band; CncrtBnd; HonRl; MrchBnd; PepBnd; SchPl; SecFHA; FNA; PpCl; GAA; St Louis Christian College; Nursing.

BENTE, Chet M; De Soto HS; Genoa, WI; 9/75 HonRl; OffAde; SctActv; LetterBsbl; LetterCchngActv; College; Lawyer.

BENTELE, Steven G; Truman Public HS; Truman, MN; 11/72 AFS; ChrhWkr; HonRl; TreasNHS; TchrAde; FFA; LetterBsbl; Bsktbl; Ftbl;.

BENTER, Bobbi; Horicon HS; Horicon, WI; 9/93 PresJrCls; HonRl; NHS; Quill&Scroll; SchMus; SchPl; StuCncl; RptrSchPpr; Trk; Univ Of Oshkosh; Journalism.

BENTERS, Kim A; Lanphier HS; Springfield, IL; 74/462 SecChr; Chrs; NHS; SchPl; PpCl; CaptChrldr; Springfield College.

BENTIVENGA, Michael G; Homewood Flossmoor HS; Homewood, IL; 61/940 Band; CmntyWkr; CncrtBnd; DrmMjrt; HonRl; MrchBnd; NHS; OffAde; Orch; PepBnd; SchMus; YthFlsp; Chrldr; IMSpt; Univ Of Illinois; Architecture.

BENTJEN, Chuck J; Pender Public HS; Thurston, NE; ChrhWkr; HonRl; LbryAde; FFA; College; History Teacher.

BENTLER, Mary L; Notre Dame HS; Burlington, IA; CmntyWkr; HonRl; PpCl; College; Vocation.

BENTLEY, Cindy L; Divernon HS; Springfield, IL; 11/28 AFS; CmntyWkr; HospAde; JrNHS; LbryAde; OffAde; RedCrAde; SchAde; FshEdYrbk; FshEdSchPpr; College; Artist.

BENTLEY, Cindy L; Muskego HS; Muskego, WI; HonRl; NHS; StuCncl; TchrAde; RptrSchPpr; Chrldr; GAA; IMSpt; Coll; Social Or Med Field.

BENTLEY, Deborah; Capac HS; Capac, MI; 1/111 TrsFrshCls; PresSophCls; Band; ChrhWkr; DrlTm; NHS; 4-H; FTA; Chrldr; DARAwd; Bob Jones Univ; Ed.

BENTLEY, Mary; Forest Park HS; Crystal Falls, MI; 12/88 Band; Chrs; CncrtBnd; HonRl; MrchBnd; RptrYrbk; 4-H; Colege; Child Care Services.

BENTLEY, Mary D; Broad Ripple HS; Indianapolis, IN; Chr; CmntyWkr; Mdrgl; NatlMeritFnl; PolWkr; SchMus; StuCncl; Indiana Univ; Communications.

BENTLEY, Melodie D; Alden Hebron HS; Hebron, IL; 1/42 SecSophCls; ALAGirlsSt; HonRl; NHS; SchPl; VPStuCncl; SptEdYrbk; LetterTrk; CaptChrldr; GAA; College; Business Administration.

BENTLEY, Thomas J; Notre Dame HS; St Clair Shores, MI; 13/250 HonRl; JrNHS; NHS; FrCl; LetterFtbl; LetterTrk; CaptWrstlng; IMSpt; Kenyon College; Law.

BENTLEY, William; Wayland Academy; Kokomo, IN; SecTrsJrCls; Band; Chr; LitMag; NatlMeritFnl; NatlMeritSF; Quill&Scroll; SctActv; StuCncl; PresSciCl; Univ Of Virginia; Astro Physics.

BENTLING, John R; Kelloggsville HS; Kentwood, MI; HonRl; SctActv; SchPpr; Trk; Jr College; Science.

BENTMANN, Karen; Incarnate Word Acad; Florissant, MO; VPSrCls; JA; TchrAde; GAA; IMSpt; JAAwd; CitAwd; Forest Park Comm Coll; Dent Hyg.

BENTON, Cindy D; Madison C 3 HS; Madison, MO; 1/15 TrsJrCls; PresSrCls; HonRl; NHS; SchPl; RptrSchPpr; FBLA; MasAwd;.

BENTON, Craig H; Evanston Township HS; Evanston, IL; StuCncl; Yrbk; SchPpr; LetterSwmmng; College.

BENTON, Daniel H; Plano HS; Plano, IL; HonRl;.

BENTON, Kimberly J; Guthrie Center Comm HS; Guthrie Center, IA; 14/55 Band; Chr; Chrs; ChrhWkr; CncrtBnd; HonRl; MrchBnd; PepBnd; RedCrAde; SchMus; LetterBsktbl; LetterGlf; Swmmng; Iowa St Univ; Professional.

BENTS, Lori L; Cumberland HS; Cumberland, WI; Chr; HonRl; LbryAde; Mdrgl; SchPl; StuCncl; Twrl; Trk; College; Pharmacy.

BENTSEN, Randy; Odebolt Arthur HS; Odebolt, IA; Chr; ChrhWkr; HonRl; SchMus; YthFlsp; Bsbl; Ftbl; Swmmng;.

BENTSON, Douglas W; Kaneland HS; Sugar Grove, IL; 17/160 CmntyWkr; HonRl; NHS; SchMus; SchPl; StuCncl; StuGov; TchrAde; 4-H; FSA; Trk; CaptWrstlng; 4-HAwd; Joliet Jr College; Agriculture.

BENTTINE, Elizabeth A; Riceville Community HS; Riceville, IA; ChrhWkr; HonRl; LbryAde; OffAde; 4-H; GAA; Trade Sch; Vet Asst.

BENTZ, Cynthia A; Cumberland HS; Almena, WI; 4/107 VPSrCls; HonRl; NHS; StuCncl; Yrbk; FNA; SpnCl; PpCl; Nursing.

BENWARE, Ricky E; Pleasant Hill HS; Pleasant Hill, MO; 4/111 Chrs; ChrhWkr; HonRl; NHS; SchMus; PresStuGov; PresSpnCl; SciCl; LetterBsktbl; Ftbl; LetterTrk; Wrstlng; College; Math.

BENYSHEK, Barbara D; Lisbon Community HS; Mt Vernon, IA; 2/43 ChrhWkr; HonRl; NHS; NatlMeritCmnd; NatlMeritSF; SchAde; TchrAde; RptrSchPpr; 4-H; FHA; GerCl;.

BENZ, Alice M; Seymour HS; Quincy, IL; 2/66 VPSophCls; Chr; HonRl; MrchBnd; NHS; OffAde; SchAde; StuCncl; RptrSchPpr; FHA; PpCl; IMSpt; College; Business Admin.

BENZ, Daniel A; Calhoun HS; Hamburg, IL; 3/62 HonRl; NHS; 4-H; FFA; DanFAwd; Univ Of Illinois; Veterinarian.

BENZ, Kay A; Arthur Hill HS; Saginaw, MI; ChrhWkr; HonRl; StuCncl; StuGov; GerCl; PpCl; College; Pharmacy.

BENZ, Matthew D; Beulah HS; Beulah, ND; Band; PepBnd; SchPl; SctActv; 4-H; FFA; PpCl; LetterFtbl; IMSpt; 4-HAwd; North Dakota State Univ; Animal Science.

BENZEL, Steven D; Alliance HS; Alliance, NE; HonRl; Yrbk; 4-H; College; Physical Science.

BENZINE, Sharon; Rio Public HS; Columbus, WI; Band; ChrhWkr; CncrtBnd; HonRl; MrchBnd; Orch; PepBnd; College; Nurse.

BERAHA, Paula; Rich Central Hs; Park Forest, IL; 4/374 CmntyWkr; HonRl; JrNHS; SecNHS; SchPl; TchrAde; RptrSchPpr; SchPpr; SpnCl; GAA; Northwestern U; Medicine.

BERAM, Daniel; St Agnes HS; St Paul, MN; Band; HonRl; SchPl; Glf; St Thomas College; Dentist.

BERAN, Anne E; Ames HS; Ames, IA; Chr; ModUN; NatlMeritSF; Orch; SchPl; YthFlsp; SpnCl; LetterSwmmng; LetterTrk; IMSpt; Coll; Languages.

BERAN, Holly J; Odell HS; Odell, NE; 1/20 ALAGirlsSt; Band; Chrs; CncrtBnd; HonRl; HospAde; Mdrgl; MrchBnd; Trk; DARAwd; Southeast Coll; Lpn.

BERANEK, George; Fenwick HS; Berwyn, IL; 35/223 HonRl; LatCl; GovHonPrgAwd; Wabash College; Pre Medical.

BERANEK, Linda J; Rice Lake HS; Rice Lake, WI; Chr; ChrhWkr; HonRl; LitMag; SchMus; SchPl; RptrSchPpr; 4-H; FHA; Univ Of Wis; Drama.

BERANEK, Margaret M; Hubbard HS; Chicago, IL; HonRl; GAA; Clge.

BERANEK, William M; Aquinas HS; Lacrosse, WI; Bsbl; Bsktbl; Ftbl; IMSpt; Valley City State College; Business.

BERANS, Basil; Canton R V HS; Williamstown, MO; 10/67 Chr; Chrs; ChrhWkr; CmntyWkr; CncrtBnd; MrchBnd; NHS; SchMus; SciCl; IMSpt; Univ Of Missouri; Major In Physics.

BERBERICH, Connie L; Oklee Public HS; Oklee, MN; 10/37 SecFrshCls; Chrs; HonRl; TchrAde; SchPpr; FHA; Bsktbl; GAA; IMSpt; Bemidji St College; Physical Education.

BERCHILD, Daniel P; Superior HS; Superior, WI; 20/547 Univ Of Wisconsin; Mathematics.

BERENDS, James O; Pennfield HS; Battle Creek, MI; 70/175 ALBoysSt; ChrhWkr; CmntyWkr; TchrAde; YthFlsp; RptrYrbk; SptEdYrbk; RptrSchPpr; SchPpr; LetterBsktbl; Wheaton Col; Phys Ed & History Teacher.

BERENDT, Karol A; Bishop Gallagher HS; Harper Woods, MI; 20/360 HonRl; NHS; OffAde; SchMus; SchPl; StuGov; TchrAde; Yrbk; LetterSwmmng; LetterTrk; College; Secretary.

BERENS, Karl A; Victoria HS; Victoria, KS; HonRl; NHS; SchPl; LetterFtbl; College; Professional.

BERENS, Thomas A; Newman HS; Wausau, WI; 54/129 Chrl; Chrs; HonRl; MrchBnd; PolWkr; SchMus; StuCncl; StuGov; Bsktbl; Tennis; College; Optometry.

BERES, Dianne J; Edison HS; E Gary, IN; 3/132 TrsSrCls; ALAGirlsSt; HonRl; NHS; OffAde; StuCncl; FrCl; SecTrsSophCls; GAA; Univ; Pol Sci.

BERES, Melody A; Lyons Township HS; Brookfield, IL; 21/1250 SecJrCls; AFS; CncrtBnd; HonRl; NHS; Orch; SchMus; Butler Univ; Elem Teacher.

BERESFORD, Barbara S; Wylie E Groves HS; Birmingham, MI; 31/683 TrsSophCls; ChrhWkr; CncrtBnd; HonRl; JrNHS; MrchBnd; NHS; StuGov; FrCl; LetterSwmmng; Central Mich U; Park & Recreation Admin.

BERG, Carol S; Warsaw Community HS; Warsaw, IN; HonRl; Business School; Secretary.

BERG, Cheryl J; Oregod Davis HS; Knox, IN; Band; Chr; HonRl; NHS; PepBnd; 4-H; PpCl; University; Nursing.

BERG, Chris M; Minnehaha Academy; Edina, MN; VPSophCls; PresSrCls; HonRl; NatlFornLg; SchPl; StuGov; Yrbk; RusCl; IMSpt; PPFtbl; Bethel College; Dental Hygiene.

BERG, Claudia L; Pioneer HS; Ann Arbor, MI; Chr; LitMag; U Of Mi; Fine Arts.

BERG, Corinne L; Valders HS; Manitowoc, WI; Band; CncrtBnd; HonRl; MrchBnd; PepBnd; Yrbk; Pres4-H; TreasFHA; PPFtbl; 4-HAwd;.

BERG, Cynthia; Homer HS; Dakota City, NE; 4/16 SecSrCls; Band; Chrs; ChrhWkr; LbryAde; NHS; SchPl; RptrSchPpr; PpCl; Hastings College; Pre Law.

BERG, David E; Minnehaha Acad; Bloomington, MN; PresFrshCls; HstSrCls; Chr; ChrhWkr; HonRl; NatlThespSoc; StuGov; YthFlsp; CaptBsbl; CaptSocr; U Of Denver; Professional.

BERG, Dawn; Custer HS; Milwaukee, WI; ChrhWkr; HonRl; JA; NHS; Orch; SchMus; FrCl; Trk; GAA; JAAwd; Marquette U; Librarian.

BERG, Dennis D; Sterling Public HS; Sterling, NE; CmntyWkr; CncrtBnd; LbryAde; MrchBnd; PepBnd; SchPl; Yrbk; 4-H; Bsktbl; LetterFtbl; Agriculture.

BERG, Donald A; Frederic Remington HS; Valley Center, KS; 12/53 ALBoysSt; Band; 4-H; LetterFtbl; LetterGlf; College; Professional.

BERG, Eric R; George S Parker Senior HS; Janesville, WI; 15/400 ALBoysSt; HonRl; NHS; LatCl; LetterTrk; Univ Of Wi Eau Claire; Dentistry.

BERG, Georgia L; Wahpeton Senior HS; Wahpeton, ND; ALAGirlsSt; Band; Chrs; CncrtBnd; HonRl; MrchBnd; Yrbk; SchPpr; PpCl; LetterGAA; State School Of Sci Wahpeton; Liveral Arts.

BERG, Gina J; Oregon Davis HS; Hamlet, IN; TrsJrCls; HonRl; YthFlsp; Yrbk; PpCl; GAA; DARAwd; Indiana U; Dentistry.

BERG, James; Starkweather Public HS; Starkweather, ND; 3/18 HonRl; PepBnd; SchPl; SctActv; StuCncl; 4-H; Bsktbl; Ftbl; Trk; 4-HAwd; College;agriculture.

BERG, James B; Starkweather HS; Starkweather, ND; PresFrshCls; ALBoysSt; Band; Chr; Chrs; HonRl; VPStuCncl; 4-H; Ftbl; 4-HAwd; Col; Agriculture.

BERG, John E; St Thomas Academy; St Paul, MN; 1/96 NatlFornLg; NatlMeritSF; ROTC; SchMus; SchPl; SctActv; RptrYrbk; SptEdYrbk; RptrSchPpr; GerCl; LetterFtbl; IMSpt; Harvard Univ; Physics.

BERG, Julie A; Fairmount Public HS; Fairmount, ND; 2/19 SecTrsFrshCls; SecTrsSophCls; SecTrsJrCls; SecTrsSrCls; ALAGirlsSt; HonRl; JrNHS; NHS; EdSchPpr; Bsbl; Trade Schl; Stenographic Course.

BERG, Kenneth E; Oskaloosa Sr HS; Oskaloosa, IA; HonRl; PolWkr; CaptFtbl; Trade School; Computer Programming.

BERG, Kevin A; St Thomas Academy; St Paul, MN; 1/100 PresJrCls; LitMag; StuCncl; Bsbl; Bsktbl; Ftbl; IMSpt; College; Law.

BERG, Kevin L; Dassel Cokato HS; Howard Lk, MN; HonRl; Yrbk; SchPpr; IMSpt; Vocational Sch; Photographer.

BERG, Kurt A; Riverside Brookfield HS; Brookfield, IL; 101/489 Band; CncrtBnd; HonRl; MrchBnd; PepBnd; SchMus; SchPl; University; Music.

BERG, La Verne; Roosevelt HS; Chicago, IL; ALAGirlsSt; ChrhWkr; HonRl; TrsFrshCls; LbryAde; Orch; PPFtbl; Coll Nursing.

BERG, La Vonne C; Pelican Rapids HS; Pelican Rapids, MN; HonRl; FrCl; Coll; Pro.

BERG, Lola A; St Francis HS; Humphrey, NE; Chrs; ChrhWkr; CncrtBnd; HonRl; MrchBnd; PepBnd; TchrAde; Yrbk; PpCl; Trk; Coll; Prof.

BERG, Mark E; Carmel Boys HS; Mundelein, IL; 1/186 CmntyWkr; HonRl; JrNHS; LitMag; NHS; NatlMeritCmnd; TchrAde; GerCl; Glf; Ivy League College; International Law.

BERG, Marlys A; Pecatonica HS; Blanchardville, WI; 3/58 SecSophCls; SecJrCls; Band; HonRl; MrchBnd; PepBnd; SchPl; RptrYrbk; FHA; JCAwd; Nurses Assistant.

BERG, Marsha L; Duluth Central HS; Duluth, MN; 1/485 PresJrCls; ALAGirlsSt; Chr; ChrhWkr; HonRl; Mdrgl; ModUN; NHS; SchMus; SchPl; StuCncl; RptrYrbk; PpCl; AmLegAwd; Carleton College; Life Science.

BERG, Nancy; Rhinelander HS; Rhinelander, WI; ChrhWkr; HonRl; TchrAde; SpnCl; PpCl; Swmmng; Tech School; Animal Tech.

BERG, Pamela; Fremont Sr HS; Fremont, NE; 73/422 HospAde; NHS; NatlThespSoc; SchMus; StuCncl; YthFlsp; 4-H; GerCl; PpCl; 4-HAwd; Ne Wesleyan Univ; Med.

BERG, Richard C; Streator Twp HS; Streator, IL; HonRl; NHS; GerCl; Augustana College; Dentist.

BERG, Robert A; Starkweather HS; Starkweather, ND; 4/17 PresFrshCls; TrsSophCls; Chrs; HonRl; SchPl; StuCncl; EdSchPpr; 4-H; Ftbl; Trk; 4-HAwd; College; Agriculture.

BERG, Susan H; Nazareth Academy; Western Springs, IL; TrsJrCls; Chrs; HonRl; SchMus; SchPl; StuGov; TchrAde; Teen; SchPpr; SpnCl; Bsktbl; Swmmng; Trk; CaptChrldr; College; Accounting.

BERG, Tammy J; Flaxton HS; Flaxton, ND; VPJrCls; Chrs; HonRl; SchPl; EdYrBk; Yrbk; PpCl; LetterBsktbl; College; Physical Therapist.

BERG, Thomas A; St Thomas Academy; Saint Paul, MN; 1/120 Chrs; HonRl; NatlFornLg; ROTC; SchPl; SctActv; EdYrBk; SciCl; Bsktbl; Ftbl; Wrstlng; College; Medicine.

BERGAN, Cynthia J; Mt St Benedict HS; Crookston, MN; ALAGirlsSt; Chr; Chrl; SchMus; SchPl; StuCncl; SchPpr; PpCl; Chrldr; IMSpt; Clg; Lawyer.

BERGAN, David L; Lake Mills Community HS; Lake Mills, IA; Chr; Chrs; HonRl; 4-H; FFA; SciCl; LetterBsbl; LetterBsktbl; LetterFtbl; LetterGlf; College; Agriculture.

BERGANT, Eva M; Good Counsel HS; Chicago, IL; 29/245 HonRl; JA; NHS; NatlMeritCmnd; NatlSciFnd; SchMus; SchPl; StuCncl; RptrYrbk; FrCl; TreasSciCl; Loyola Univ; Industrial Chemistry.

BERGANTINE, Ronald; Fergus Falls Sr HS; Fergus Falls, MN; PresFrshCls; PresSophCls; Chr; HonRl; NHS; NatlThespSoc; StuCncl; RptrYrbk; GerCl; Trk; Coll; Pro.

BERGDOLL, Douglas; Delta HS; Albany, IN; 67/225 PresFrshCls; PresSophCls; PresJrCls; NHS; SchAde; SchPl; StuGov; TchrAde; FrCl; Bsbl; Ball St Univ; Prof.

BERGDOLL, Sharon D; Delta HS; Albany, IN; 30/270 Chr; Chrs; HonRl; JrNHS; SchMus; RptrSchPpr; FrCl; Chrldr; University; Technology.

BERGE, Beth E; Aurelia Comm HS; Aurelia, IA; ALAGirlsSt; Band; Chr; Chrl; Chrs; ChrhWkr; CncrtBnd; DrlTm; HonRl; HospAde; Mdrgl; LetterGlf; GAA; AmLegAwd; College; Professional.

BERGE, Michael J; Prospect HS; Arlington Hts, IL; HonRl; NatlMeritSF; Northern Ill Univ; Geography.

BERGEMAN, Tim L; Madelia HS; Madelia, MN; 25/92 Aud/Vis; Band; ChrhWkr; HonRl; SctActv; YthFlsp; FFA; LetterBsktbl; CaptFtbl; LetterTrk; U M Waseca; Professional.

BERGER, Ann E; Spalding Acad; Spalding, NE; VPJrCls; Chrs; HonRl; NHS; StuCncl; TchrAde; 4-H; PpCl; St Mary's Omaha; Elem Ed.

BERGER, Christine M; Mount Assisi Acad; Hickory Hills, IL; Chrs; HonRl; ModUN; NHS; SchMus; StuCncl; RptrYrbk; LatCl; SpnCl; GAA; Loyola Univ Of Chicago; Medicine.

BERGER, Cindy S; Lansing HS; Leavenworth, KS; 5/98 ALAGirlsSt; Band; HonRl; NHS; NatlThespSoc; Twrl; LetterTrk; IMSpt; PPFtbl; AmLegAwd; College; Professional.

BERGER, Debbie M; Oakville Sr HS; St Louis, MO; CaptDrlTm; HonRl; JrNHS; NHS; SchMus; YthFlsp; YthLg; RptrSchPpr; SchPpr; CaptChrldr; IMSpt; University; Business.

BERGER, Deborah L; Wesclin Jr Sr HS; Trenton, IL; 2/100 TrsSophCls; Chrl; Chrs; HonRl; NHS; SecStuCncl; PresYthFlsp; FBLA; FrCl; GerCl; Chrldr; GAA; 4-HAwd; Illinois State Univ; Accounting.

BERGER, Gary L; Heelan HS; Sioux City, IA; 70/260 Chrl; ChrhWkr; SchMus; SctActv; FrCl; College; Elec Engineering.

BERGER, Gregory A; Auburn HS; Auburn, NE; 7/86 TrsJrCls; PresSrCls; CncrtBnd; HonRl; Mdrgl; MrchBnd; PepBnd; PresYthFlsp; VPMthCl; Ftbl; Univ On Ne; Agri.

BERGER, Jan E; New Trier West HS; Winnetka, IL; 88/698 Chr; HonRl; HospAde; PolWkr; Swmmng; Tennis; IMSpt; Skidmore College; Medicine.

BERGER, John D; Princeton HS; Princeton, MO; 12/52 PresSophCls; CncrtBnd; HonRl; MrchBnd; NHS; SchPl; StuCncl; 4-H; PresFFA; LetterFtbl; Northeast Mo State Univ; Agriculture.

BERGER, Kristine; St Elizabeth Acad; Saint Louis, MO; Band; CmntyWkr; CncrtBnd; HonRl; JA; OffAde; Orch; TchrAde; GAA; PPFtbl; Business; Travel Career.

BERGER, Robert D; Columbia Heights HS; Fridley, MN; HonRl; NatlFornLg; NatlMeritSF; SchMus; SchPl; SchPpr; Bsbl; Tennis; U Of M; Medical Field.

BERGER, Sandra A; Larimore HS; Emerado, ND; Band; Chrs; CncrtBnd; HonRl; 4-H; SpnCl; PpCl; 4-HAwd; PresAwd; Mayville St Coll; Home Ec.

BERGER, Steven J; Glenbrook N HS; Northbrook, IL; 1/650 HstFrshCls; TrsSophCls; PresSrCls; Aud/Vis; HonRl; NHS; NatlMeritFnl; FFA; CaptFtbl; CaptSocr; Univ Of Il; Farming.

BERGER, Susan I; Waubay Public HS; Waubay, SD; 4/53 HonRl; MrchBnd; PepBnd; SchPl; StuCncl; RptrYrbk; RptrSchPpr; FHA; PpCl; Chrldr; Northern State; Bus Educ.

BERGER, Vicki L; Regina HS; Mt Clemens, MI; Chrl; CmntyWkr; JrNHS; SchMus; College.

BERGER, Virginia M; Anita HS; Anita, IA; 4/61 ALAGirlsSt; Band; Chrs; HonRl; NHS; SptEdYrbk; Pres4-H; LetterBsktbl; BttyCrckrAwd; 4-HAwd; Univ Of Mn; Animal Health.

BERGER, William B; Granite HS; Granite City, IL; .

BERGERON, Barbara N; Madison Cons HS; Madison, IN; 22/360 VPSrCls; HonRl; NHS; NatlThespSoc; Quill&Scroll; StuCncl; RptrYrbk; SchPpr; SciCl; Trk; Coll; Nurse.

BERGERSEN, William M; Brainerd HS; Brainero, MN; ChrhWkr; HonRl; SchAde; StuCncl; TchrAde; YthFlsp; Swmmng; Trk; IMSpt; Voc Tech; Natural Resources.

BERGES, Patricia L; Newman Central Catholic HS; Sterling, IL; Chrs; NHS; SchMus; SchPl; StuCncl; EdSchPpr; CaptTrk; GAA; St Marys College; Special Educ.

BERGESON, Douglas M; Maine South HS; Park Ridge, IL; HonRl; NHS; PpCl; LetterTennis; Univ Of Illinois; Veterinarian.

BERGESON, Jean A; Joliet East HS; Elwood, IL; 17/407 VPChr; ChrhWkr; HonRl; Mdrgl; NHS; OffAde; SchMus; VPFrshCls; SciCl; Jolie Jr Col; Special Ed.

BERGESON, Susan R; St Charles HS; St Charles, IL; Chr; Chrl; ChrhWkr; Valparaiso University.

BERGET, Crystal J; Black Hawk HS; South Wayne, WI; Band; Chrs; ChrhWkr; CncrtBnd; HonRl; FHA; PpCl; LetterBsktbl; LetterTrk; Chrldr; GAA; Univ Of Wisconsin; Clothing Design.

BERGET, Kyle W; Hancock Public HS; Hancock, MN; PresSophCls; Chrs; CmntyWkr; SchPl; StuCncl; LetterBsbl; LetterBsktbl; LetterFtbl; Trk; Jr College.

BERGFALK, Joy; Rush City HS; Rush City, MN; 4/60 Band; Chr; ChrhWkr; CncrtBnd; HonRl; MrchBnd; NHS; PepBnd; IMSpt; VoiceDemAwd; Wheaton College; Youth Work Music.

BERGFIELD, Donald D; Arcola Community HS; Arcola, IL; ChrhWkr; HonRl; FFA; SpnCl; Farming.

BERGHORN, Kathie A; Cary Grove Comm HS; Cary, IL; 8/280 ChrhWkr; HonRl; NHS; StuCncl; YthFlsp; RptrYrbk; SpnCl; Chrldr; Univ Of Ill; Veterinarian.

BERGHS, Catherine L; Wabasso Public HS; Wabasso, MN; Chr; TreasChrs; ChrhWkr; HonRl; HospAde; LbryAde; PolWkr; SchPl; YthLg; RptrYrbk; RptrSchPpr; SchPpr; IMSpt; CaptPPFtbl; Jr College; Exec Secretary.

BERGIN, Julie; South Lyon HS; South Lyon, MI; 12/237 Chrs; CncrtBnd; HonRl; MrchBnd; NHS; NatlMeritCmnd; SchMus; YthFlsp; GAA; IMSpt; College; Psychology.

BERGIN, Mary M; Elizabeth Seton HS; Harvey, IL; 67/250 VPSrCls; Chrs; DrmMjrt; HonRl; HospAde; StuCncl; TchrAde; Twrl; Northern Ill University; Physical Therapy.

BERGIN, Sharon M; Mother Mcauley HS; Oak Forest, IL; 8/485 Chrs; HonRl; NatlMeritSF; Quill&Scroll; SchMus; RptrSchPpr; SchPpr; Univ Of Ill; Marine Biologist.

BERGLAND, Deborah L; Osseo HS; Osseo, WI; 2/40 ALAGirlsSt; Chr; HonRl; HospAde; MrchBnd; StuCncl; Yrbk; SchPpr; VPFHA; LetterBsktbl; Trade Sch.

BERGLEY, Fay P; Bismarck HS; Bismarck, ND; 244/591 Chr; ChrhWkr; JrNHS; OffAde; SchMus; SchPl; LatCl; College; Elementary Teacher.

BERGLIND, Catherine R; Mother Of Sorrows HS; Chicago, IL; HonRl; StuCncl; StuGov; SpnCl; MthCl; SciCl; College; Math Teacher.

BERGLINO, Veronica F; Evergreen Park HS; Evergreen Park, IL; Chrs; LitMag; NatlMeritCmnd; TchrAde; FTA; VPMthCl; St Xavier College; Historical Research.

BERGLUND, Chris A; Dundee Community HS; Dundee, IL; HonRl; GerCl; LetterBsbl; LetterBsktbl; LetterTennis; GAA; College; Science.

BERGLUND, Eric J; Dundee Comm HS; Dundee, IL; 1/362 TrsSrCls; Chr; Chrl; VPChrs; HonRl; NatlFornLg; NHS; NatlMeritFnl; NatlMeritSF; NatlThespSoc; SchMus; SchPl; StuGov; SciCl; Tennis; University; Computer Programmer.

BERGLUND, Eric J; Dundee Community HS; Dundee, IL; 1/369 TrsSrCls; HonRl; NatlFornLg; NHS; NatlMeritSF; NatlThespSoc; SchMus; SchPl; StuGov; Socr; Univ; Computer Sci.

BERGLUND, Mary; Nerinx Hall HS; St Louis, MO; 2/99 SecFrshCls; HonRl; EdSchPpr; Bsktbl; Swmmng; Dayton Univ.

BERGMAN, Anita J; Lincolnwood HS; Raymond, IL; VPFrshCls; PresSophCls; Band; ChrhWkr; CncrtBnd; HonRl; MrchBnd; NHS; Sdlty; 4-H; College; Professional.

BERGMAN, Cheryl A; Holdrege HS; Holdrege, NE; Chr; Chrs; ChrhWkr; HonRl; SchMus; SchPl; StuGov; YthFlsp; 4-H; PpCl; Trinit Western College.

BERGMAN, Cynthia K; Loomis HS; Loomis, NE; 1/21 VPBand; Chrs; VPNHS; PresTeen; Yrbk; SchPpr; VPPpCl; LetterTrk; GAA; EldAwd; Trinity College.

BERGMAN, David A; Ashland HS; Ashland, IL; 13/36 HonRl; TchrAde; RptrSchPpr; College; Special Ed Teacher.

BERGMAN, Jack C; Baxter Comm HS; Newton, IA; SecSrCls; LetterFtbl; Trk; Des Moines Area Comm College; Vocation.

BERGMAN, Lance J; Wm Fremd HS; Palatine, IL; 109/629 RptrSchPpr; SchPpr; LetterBsktbl; LetterFtbl; IMSpt; University Of Illinois; Engineering.

BERGMAN, Leah R; Marshall HS; Marshall, MO; 7/200 Band; Chrs; CncrtBnd; HonRl; MrchBnd; SchMus; StuCncl; StuCncl; PpCl; College; Medical Tech.

BERGMAN, Roxann K; Mead Public HS; Ithaca, NE; 8#29#41# NHS; 4-H; FHA; MthCl; LetterBsktbl; LetterTrk; Chrldr; Coll; Phy Ed.

BERGMANN, Glenn L; Pleasant Hill HS; Pleasant Hill, MO; ChrhWkr; HonRl; SpnCl; Ftbl; Trk; Air Force Academy.

BERGMANN, Kathryn L; Southwest HS; Minneapolis, MN; Chr; ChrhWkr; SchMus; SchPl; University; Liberal Arts.

BERGMANN, William G; Pleasant Hill HS; Pleasant Hill, MO; 54/104 ChrhWkr; Ftbl; Trk; College; Forestry.

BERGMEIER, Jay M; Tri County HS; De Witt, NE; TrsSophCls; Band; Chrs; HonRl; TchrAde; TreasFFA; Bsbl; LetterBsktbl; LetterFtbl; LetterTrk; PresAwd; College; Physical Therapy.

BERGNER, Jodi; New Richland HS; New Richland, MN; 30#41#50 SchPl; FHA; Chrldr; St Cloud State U; Physical Education.

BERGNER, John F; Pratt HS; Pratt, KS; Chrs; HonRl; PolWkr; SchMus; UNYO; Yrbk; 4-H; SciCl; OptClAwd;.

BERGQUIST, Brian J; Abraham Lincoln HS; Council Bluffs, IA; ALBoysSt; Band; HonRl; NatlFornLg; PresNHS; NatlThespSoc; PresStuCncl; PresEngCl; SciCl; VoiceDemAwd;.

BERGQUIST, Christiann; Maine South HS; Park Ridge, IL; Chr; HospAde; NHS; SctActv; StuCncl; TchrAde; PpCl; Millikin Univ; Biology.

BERGQUIST, Gloria; St Croix Lutheran HS; Inver Grove Height, MN; Band; Chr; CncrtBnd; HonRl; LbryAde; MrchBnd; PepBnd; IMSpt; PPFtbl; Carleton College; Professional.

BERGQUIST, Lynn; St James Senior HS; St James, MN; Chr; HonRl; SchPl; SchPpr; FHA; Trk; PPFtbl; PresAwd; College; Professional.

BERGQUOIST, Robert E; Logan View HS; Hooper, NE; ALBoysSt; Chrs; HonRl; SchPl; Yrbk; FFA; Letter Bsbl; LetterBsktbl; LetterFtbl; LetterTrk; U Of Nebr; Agriculture.

BERGREN, Joni L; South Barber HS; Kiowa, KS; Chr; HonRl; Mdrgl; OffAde; SchPl; StuCncl; PpCl;

Chrldr; IMSpt; PPFtbl; Kansas State; Managerial Bus.

BERGSCHNEIDER, Beverly A; Franklin HS; Franklin, IL; 4/42 Chrs; HonRl; MrchBnd; NHS; SchPl; TchrAde; RptrYrbk; SptEdSchPpr; 4-H; FFA; TreasFHA; SpnCl; PpCl; GAA; College.

BERGSRUD, Randy S; River Falls HS; River Falls, WI; Chr; Chrl; ChrhWkr; StuCncl; YthFlsp; Bsbl; Bsktbl; Ftbl; Trk; College; Professional.

BERGSTAD, Peggy; Appleton Public HS; Appleton, MN; 22/75 SecAFS; Chrs; CncrtBnd; HonRl; MrchBnd; PepBnd; SchPl; StuCncl; LetterBsktbl; Chrldr; Coll;soc Work.

BERGSTEIN, Mark F; Marshall Univ HS; Minneapolis, MN; NatlFornLg; NatlMeritSF; StuGov; TchrAde; Univ Of Minn.

BERGSTROM, Carl P; Taft HS; Chicago, IL; 148/850 Chr; ChrhWkr; HonRl; LitMag; LbryAde; SchAde; No Central College; Science.

BERGSTROM, Charles A; Rockford East HS; Rockford, IL; 28/660 Chr; ChrhWkr; HonRl; NHS; SchMus; Northern Il U; Biology.

BERGSTROM, Dean; Watertown HS; Maple Plain, MN; ALBoysSt; HonRl; JA; NHS; Bsbl; Univ Of Mn; Math.

BERGSTROM, Denis E; Ewing Public HS; Ewing, NE; 7/28 ALBoysSt; Chrs; HonRl; SchPl; StuCncl; YthFlsp; RptrSchPpr; FFA; LetterFtbl; LetterTrk; Trade Schl; Vocation.

BERGSTROM, Janice K; Nashwauk Keewatin Sr HS; Nashwauk, MN; Band; ChrhWkr; HonRl; SchPl; RptrYrbk; RptrSchPpr; FHA; PresFTA; FrCl; GAA; Coll.

BERGSTROM, Lita L; Oregon Davis HS; Grovertown, IN; SecSophCls; Band; Chr; HonRl; NHS; PepBnd; PpCl; Univ; Secretary.

BERGSTROM, Nancy K; Anselmo Merna HS; Merna, NE; 30/76 Band; Chrs; CncrtBnd; HonRl; MrchBnd; PepBnd; StuCncl; LetterTrk; LetterChrldr; College; Professional.

BERGSTROM, Pamela J; Clyde HS; Clyde, KS; TrsFrshCls; SecSophCls; Chr; Chrs; HonRl; Mdrgl; StuCncl; PpCl; Trk; GAA; Beloit Vo Tech Schl; Business.

BERGT, Linnea; Amherst HS; Amherst, NE; 5/26 HstSophCls; Band; HonRl; NHS; StuCncl; RptrYrbk; RptrSchPpr; Bsktbl; Trk; Chrldr; Grand Island Beauty College; Cosmetology.

BERGTHOLD, Tammy L; Paris Rii HS; Perry, MO; Chr; ChrhWkr; HonRl; SchMus; SchPl; SpnCl; PpCl; Bsbl; Trk; Chrldr; Blessing Sch Of Nursing; Nurse.

BERGTHOLDT, Christine D; Valle HS; Ste Genevieve, MO; 7/81 HonRl; NHS; SchPl; StuCncl; RptrYrbk; FHA; PpCl; Trk; PPFtbl; OptClAwd; College.

BERGUM, Carole J; Eveleth HS; Eveleth, MN; 1/164 Chrs; ChrhWkr; DrlTm; NHS; RptrSchPpr; PpCl; LetterTrk; Chrldr; BttyCrckrAwd; MasAwd; Univ Of Minn; Med Tech.

BERGUM, Van E; Lafarge HS; Lafarge, WI; HonRl; EngCl; MthCl; PpCl; SciCl; Bsbl; Bsktbl; Ftbl; University.

BERGWIN, Greg G; South Milwaukee HS; South Milwaukee, WI; Bsktbl; ChmnFtbl; DanFAwd; U Of Wi Lacrosse; Wild Life Man.

BERGY, John; Lowell Sr HS; Alto, MI; 2/197 HonRl; NHS; Electrical Engineering.

BERKE, Miriam R; Eustis Public HS; Eustis, NE; 3/27 PresFrshCls; HonRl; VPStuCncl; TchrAde; VPYthFlsp; 4-H; PpCl; CaptBsktbl; LetterTrk; Univ Of Nebraska; Veterinarian.

BERKE, Miriam R; Eustis HS; Cozad, NE; 3/28 PresFrshCls; Chrs; HonRl; VPStuCncl; TchrAde; VPYthFlsp; 4-H; PpCl; Bsktbl; U Of Ne; Veterinarians.

BERKEL, Susan C; Woodruff HS; Peoria, IL; 8/232 Chr; HonRl; JrNHS; NHS; SchMus; SchPl; College; Horticulture.

BERKENBOSLH, Heidi M; Prairie City Comm HS; Prairie City, IA; 6/50 Band; HonRl; LbryAde; NatlMeritFnl; PepBnd; SchPl; YthFlsp; 4-H; 4-HAwd; CitAwd; Ia State U.

BERKENKAMP, Thomas A; Eastridge HS; Kankakee, IL; 8/225 HonRl; NHS; SchMus; Bsktbl; Univ Of Ill; Architecture.

BERKES, Carol A; Dekalb Senior HS; Dekalb, IL; 23/350 ALAGirlsSt; Band; Chr; CncrtBnd; HonRl; MrchBnd; PepBnd; SchMus; SctActv; College; Nursing.

BERKHAHN, Jean; Mosinee Sr HS; Mosinee, WI; Chrs; CncrtBnd; HonRl; MrchBnd; NHS; SchMus; StuCncl; GAA; Madison Tech;medical Asst.

BERKICH, Daniel J; Middleton HS; Middleton, WI; Wrstlng; Univ Of Wisconsin; Engineering.

BERKLAND, Jeffrey L; Sentral Community HS; Fenton, IA; ALBoysSt; Band; HonRl; MrchBnd; PepBnd; SchMus; FFA; Bsktbl; Ftbl; Trk; Ia Coll; Music.

BERKOWITZ, Richard A; Niles East HS; Skokie, IL; 76/581 ALBoysSt; Aud/Vis; HonRl; NHS; KeyCl; PpCl; CaptBsbl; CaptSwmmng; U Of Il; Medicine.

BERKSHIRE, Brian; Pioneer HS; Royal Center, IN; 4/125 Band; CncrtBnd; MrchBnd; SchMus; SpnCl; Glf; Purdue; Lawyer.

BERKSHIRE, Cynthia; Hudson Area HS; Hudson, MI; 7/124 SecFrshCls; SecSophCls; SecSrCls; Chrs; HonRl; NHS; StuCncl; StuGov; Yrbk; Toledo Medical Educ Center; Dental Asst.

BERKSHIRE, Lori A; Boone Grove HS; Valparaiso, IN; 3/68 PresSophCls; ALAGirlsSt; HonRl; NHS; OffAde; EdYrBk; RptrSchPpr; Chrldr; GAA; Butler U; Math.

BERLAGE, James S; Charlevoix HS; Charlevoix, MI; PresSophCls; ALBoysSt; Band; CncrtBnd; MrchBnd; PepBnd; SchPl; SctActv; StuCncl; StuGov; RptrYrbk; Yrbk; RptrSchPpr; EdSchPpr; SptEdSchPpr; Michigan State Univ; Law.

BERLANGA, Victoria; St Francis Desales HS; Chicago, IL; 40/290 Band; CncrtBnd; HonRl; MrchBnd; Us Air Force; Medical Field.

BERLEKAMP, Jill D; Lees Summit HS; Lees Summit, MO; 212/373 Chr; DrlTm; HonRl; RedCrAde; TchrAde; PpCl; LetterTrk; Chrldr; GAA; IMSpt; Smsu At Springfield; Interior Design.

BERLETT, Dianne L; Woodruff HS; Peoria, IL; 44/281 TrsSophCls; HstJrCls; OffAde; SecStuCncl; KeyCl; PpCl; Illinois Central Coll; Secretarial.

BERLIN, Laureen; St Catherines HS; Racine, WI; Chrs; RedCrAde; StuCncl; IMSpt; PPFtbl; College.

BERLIN, Margaret A; Bonner Springs HS; Bonner Springs, KS; ChrhWkr; HonRl; SchPl; StuCncl; College; Science.

BERLIN, Robert T; Millington HS; Millington, MI; SecFrshCls; TrsSrCls; ALBoysSt; ChrhWkr; SchPl; CivCl; LetterBsbl; Bsktbl; LetterFtbl; Central Michigan University.

BERLO, Maryellen; University HS; E Jordan, MI; PresAFS; HonRl; RptrYrbk; TreasFHA; SpnCl; PpCl; GAA; IMSpt; U Of Mi; Special Ed & Psychology.

BERMAN, Beth; Clarenceville HS; Livonia, MI; 6/260 Band; CncrtBnd; HonRl; MrchBnd; NatlMeritCmnd; NatlMeritSF; SchPl; FrCl; Ferris St Col; Dental Hyg.

BERMAN, Christopher M; Crown Point HS; Crown Point, IN; 10/493 ALBoysSt; Chr; HonRl; LitMag; NHS; NatlMeritSF; PresNatlThespSoc; SchMus; SchPl; RptrSchPpr; KiwanAwd; College; Lawyer.

BERMAN, Susan J; New Trier West HS; Glenview, IL; 9/698 CmntyWkr; HonRl; IntrClCncl; NatlMeritCmnd; Univ Of Illinois; Professional.

BERMELE, Beth M; Saint Barbara HS; Chicago, IL; 19/88 SecJrCls; SecSrCls; HonRl; NatlSciFnd; StuCncl; StuGov; RptrSchPpr; FSA; SciCl; GAA; St Xavier College; Counselor.

BERNARD, Cynthia A; Wahpeton Senior HS; Mooreton, ND; Chrs; ChrhWkr; HonRl; LbryAde; StuCncl; SchPpr; PPFtbl; College; Professional.

BERNARD, Debra; Hall Hs; Spring Valley, IL; 11/127 PresBand; CncrtBnd; HonRl; NatlMeritCmnd; SchPl; RptrYrbk; SecFTA; SciCl; Trk; GAA; Ill Valley Comm College; Library Science.

BERNARD, Nancy J; Anthon Oto HS; Correctionville, IA; 1/33 SecFrshCls; DrlTm; HonRl; SecNHS; SchPl; StuCncl; Sec4-H; FHA; FTA; Bsktbl; Ftbl; Trk; Wrstlng; Univ Of Iowa.

BERNARD, Rebecca J; F J Reitz HS; Evansville, IN; 7/439 HonRl; JrNHS; NHS; RptrYrbk; RptrSchPpr; PpCl; CaptChrldr; MasAwd; Ball State Univ; Legal Secretary.

BERNARD, Robert C; Lakeville HS; Prior Lake, MN; 18/196 Band; PresCncrtBnd; HonRl; MrchBnd; NHS; PepBnd; SchMus; VPStuCncl; College; Forestry.

BERNARD, Suzetta R; Lakeland Union HS; Minocqua, WI; CncrtBnd; HonRl; MrchBnd; NHS; PepBnd; SchPpr; SpnCl; PpCl; LetterTrk; GAA; University; Spanish.

BERNARDI, Rose M; Pawnee HS; Pawnee, IL; 2/47 SecSophCls; Band; CncrtBnd; HonRl; JrNHS; LbryAde; MrchBnd; NHS; StuCncl; YthFlsp; RptrYrbk; FHA; FrCl; PpCl; Univ Of Illinois; Accounting.

BERNARDO, Domingo M; Proviso West HS; North Lake, IL; 50/1120 HonRl; NHS; Univ Of De Paul; Law.

BERNARDY, Kim L; Community HS; Detroit Lakes, MN; 10/270 AFS; Band; CncrtBnd; HonRl; MrchBnd; SecNHS; PepBnd; TreasYthFlsp; 4-H; SpnCl; Univ Of Mn; Botany.

BERNARDY, Susan T; Wabasso Public HS; Lucan, MN; CmntyWkr; HospAde; JrNHS; LbryAde; NHS; RedCrAde; TchrAde; RptrSchPpr; FHA; GAA; Trade; Vocation.

BERNASEK, Holly E; Chester HS; Chester, IL; 1/122 Band; Chrl; Chrs; HonRl; LbryAde; PresNHS; SchMus; SecStuCncl; EdYrBk; SecGAA; AmLegAwd; DARAwd; EldAwd;.

BERNAUER, Richard M; Southwest HS; Kansas City, MO; 25/500 Chr; HonRl; NHS; NatlMeritSF; StuCncl; SpnCl; Swmmng; IMSpt; KiwanAwd; CitAwd;.

BERNDT, Beth E; Brookfield East HS; Brookfield, WI; HonRl; NHS; OffAde; PpCl; Univ Of Wisconsin; Physical Therapy.

BERNDT, Caroll A; Bloom Township HS; Chicago Heights, IL; 5/1075 HonRl; LitMag; NHS; OffAde; Quill&Scroll; SchPpr; SecSpnCl; Winona State College; Elementary Education.

BERNDT, Cynthia; Hustisford HS; Hustisford, WI; 1/30 SecTrsSrCls; HonRl; NHS; TchrAde; EdYrBk; RptrSchPpr; Carroll College.

BERNDT, Darlene D; Merrill HS; Merrill, WI; 2/334 ChrhWkr; HonRl; GovHonPrgAwd; North Centrl Tech Inst; Radiologic Tech.

BERNDT, Deborah S; River Valley HS; Sawyer, MI; SecFrshCls; TrsSophCls; TrsJrCls; TrsSrCls; Band; CncrtBnd; HonRl; NHS; ChmnChrldr; PresAwd; Secretarial College; Sec Studies.

BERNDT, Jody L; Blue Earth HS; Blue Earth, MN; Chr; Mdrgl; Orch; PepBnd; SchMus; SchPl; YthFlsp; 4-H; GerCl; Chrldr; GAA; Sw Minnesota St College; Music.

BERNDT, Sandra J; North HS; Eau Claire, WI; PresSrCls; Chr; ChrhWkr; HonRl; SecNHS; SecNatlThespSoc; SchMus; SchPl; StuCncl; OptClAwd; Saint Olaf College; Music Education.

BERNDT, Sandra J; North Sr HS; Eau Claire, WI; PresSrCls; Chr; ChrhWkr; HonRl; Mdrgl; SecNHS; VPNatlThespSoc; SchMus; SchPl; StuCncl; Univ Of Wisconsin; Music Therapy.

BERNERT, Cynthia M; Elgin HS; Bartlett, IL; Band; Chr; OffAde; SchPl; StuCncl; FrCl; PpCl; Chrldr; GAA; Coll; Rectnal Director.

BERNEY, Susan D; Griswold HS; Griswold, IA; Band; CmntyWkr; HonRl; NHS; Orch; SchMus; RptrSchPpr; FHA; LetterGlf; MasAwd; Univ; Biology.

BERNHARDSON, Pamela L; Halstad Public HS; Lockhart, MN; SecSophCls; Chrs; HonRl; LbryAde; NatlThespSoc; OffAde; SchPl; 4-H; FFA; FHA; Bsktbl; Socr; CaptTrk; Chrldr; Moorhead St Univ; Physical Education.

BERNHARDT, Debra J; Martin Luther HS; Milwaukee, WI; 7/87 Chr; HonRl; Mdrgl; NHS; SchMus; Trk; CaptChrldr; IMSpt; Univ Of Wi Milw; Special Ed.

BERNHARDT, Mark; Lawrence HS; Lawrence, KS; 9/548 HonRl; PolWkr; StuCncl; YthFlsp; SpnCl; PpCl; LetterFtbl; LetterGlf; CaptWrstlng; IMSpt; Univ Of Ks; Pre Med.

BERNHART, Bruce J; Wichita HS; Wichita, KS; 64/465 Band; HonRl; NatlFornLg; NatlMeritCmnd; SchMus; SchPl; FrCl; VPSpnCl; MthCl; IMSpt; Wichita St Univ; Computer Science.

BERNI, Cynthia M; Hubbard HS; Chicago, IL; Chrs; HonRl; NHS; OffAde; Quill&Scroll; StuGov; VPFTA; VPPpCl; LetterTennis; GAA; Univ;.

BERNICA, Robert G; Hayden HS; Topeka, KS; 2/215 HonRl; JrNHS; NHS; LetterFtbl; LetterTrk; IMSpt; Univ; Prof.

BERNICKY, Lawrence J; Kennedy HS; Chicago, IL; 30/610 PresChrs; HonRl; NHS; PresStuCncl; Yrbk; IMSpt; JETSAwd; Univ Of Illinois; Journalism.

BERNING, Elizabeth M; Springfield HS; Springfield, IL; 52/585 Chr; OffAde; FrCl; College; Business Adm.

BERNING, Mark D; Shenandoah Community HS; Shenandoah, IA; ChrhWkr; HonRl; VPNatlThespSoc; SchPl; UNYO; RptrSchPpr; FTA; FrCl; IMSpt; RotaryAwd; University Of Northern Iowa; Psychology.

BERNING, Mary E; Huntington North HS; Huntington, IN; NatlThespSoc; Quill&Scroll; SchPl; TchrAde; SchPpr; College; Political Science.

BERNING, Sandy K; J C N HS; Nortonville, KS; Chrs; DrlTm; HonRl; CivCl; 4-H; MthCl; PpCl; Bsktbl; Trk; GAA; College; Secretary.

BERNING, William J; New Richmond Senior HS; New Richmond, WI; 1/155 PresSophCls; ALBoysSt; Yrbk; RptrSchPpr; Bsktbl; Trk; College; Major Study.

BERNS, Kathy; Brainerd HS; Brainerd, MN; Band; CncrtBnd; HonRl; MrchBnd; PepBnd; College; Professional Nursing.

BERNS, Kelly A; Gibraltar HS; Sister Bay, WI; PresJrCls; Band; Chr; Chrl; Chrs; CncrtBnd; MrchBnd; SchPl; StuGov; LetterTrk; CaptChrldr; IMSpt; College; Professional.

BERNS, Lucy A; Nokomis HS; Nokomis, IL; 5/89 VPBand; Chr; CmntyWkr; DrmMjrt; HonRl; SchMus; Yrbk; GAA; AmLegAwd; Eastern Illinois Univ; Business.

BERNS, Maralee R; Clay City HS; Clay City, IL; ChrhWkr; CncrtBnd; HonRl; Yrbk; RptrSchPpr; GAA; Olney Cntrl Coll; Fashion Merchandising.

BERNSTEIN, Louis; Highland Park HS; Highland Park, IL; HonRl; PolWkr; RptrSchPpr; SchPpr;.

BERNT, Kevin J; Scotus Central Catholic HS; Columbus, NE; 7/60 HonRl; NHS; 4-H; SciCl; Ftbl; Trk; IMSpt; 4-HAwd; OptClAwd; U Of Fl; Math.

BERNTSON, Randy L; Oakes Public HS; Guelph, ND; 25/61 Band; Chrs; ChrhWkr; HonRl; NHS; MthCl; LetterBsktbl; LetterFtbl; College.

BEROW, Mark A; Peoria HS; Peoria, IL; NatlMeritSF; Orch; Yeshiva Univ; Political Science.

BERRECKMAN, Claude E; Cozad HS; Cozad, NE; 1/106 PresSophCls; PresJrCls; HonRl; NHS; StuCncl; PresStuGov; YthFlsp; LetterBsktbl; LetterFtbl; LetterTrk; University; Law.

BERROND, Jan; Neponset HS; Neponset, IL; Chr; CmntyWkr; HonRl; SchPl; StuCncl; Yrbk; SchPpr; FHA; FrCl; Chrldr; Coll; Vocation.

BERRONG, Jacquelin; Madison HS; Madison, IL; ChrhWkr; HonRl; JCC; College; Special Education Teacher.

BERRY, Andrea; Northwest HS; Fenton, MO; Chr; HonRl; EdSchPpr; FBLA; FTA;.

BERRY, Beth A; Triplains HS; Monument, KS; Band; Chrs; HonRl; VPStuCncl; Yrbk; Pres4-H; PpCl; LetterBsktbl; Chrldr; 4-HAwd; College; Professional.

BERRY, Brenda L; Neelyville HS; Neelyville, MO; 2/51 Band; ChrhWkr; CmntyWkr; HonRl; JrNHS; NHS; EdSchPpr; FHA; FTA; CaptChrldr; Three Rivers Community College; Psychology.

BERRY, Calene S; Akron Fairgrove HS; Akron, MI; 12/80 HstSrCls; Band; Chr; ChrhWkr; CncrtBnd; HonRl; MrchBnd; NHS; PepBnd; SctActv; TchrAde; 4-H; Central Michigan Univ; Elem Schl Teacher.

BERRY, Carol A; Cuba HS; Ellisville, IL; HonRl; SctActv;.

BERRY, David W; Sidney Comm HS; Percival, IA; ALBoysSt; SchMus; SchPl; StuCncl; FHA; Bsbl; Bsktbl; Ftbl; Trk; College; Professional.

BERRY, Doug; Rockville HS; Rockville, IN; SptEdSchPpr; 4-H; PresFFA; Bsktbl; CaptFtbl; IMSpt; 4-HAwd;.

BERRY, Dwayne; Rockville HS; Rockville, IN; 4-H; VPFFA; LetterFtbl; IMSpt; 4-HAwd;.

BERRY, Elizabeth M; St Joseph HS; S Bend, IN; 1/243 HonRl; LbryAde; NHS; NatlMeritCmnd; SctActv; Trk; IMSpt; Univ; Prof.

BERRY, James M; Lyons Township HS; Western Springs, IL; Chr; Chrs; ChrhWkr; HonRl; NHS; SchMus; SctActv; YthFlsp; RptrYrbk; College; Law.

BERRY, Janet; Goodridge HS; Grygla, MN; 9/33 Chrs; ChrhWkr; HonRl; OffAde; SchPl; StuCncl; Yrbk; EdSchPpr; FHA; GAA; Neb Methodist Hosp Sch Of Nrsng; Rn.

BERRY, Jerilyn; Cobden Unit HS; Cobden, IL; 3/50 TrsJrCls; HonRl; MrchBnd; NHS; SchPl; Twrl; SptEdYrbk; PpCl; Chrldr; Univ.

BERRY, Jovanna S; Leadwood HS; Irondale, MO; PresFrshCls; VPSophCls; SecJrCls; Band; Chr; Chrs; ChrhWkr; CmntyWkr; CncrtBnd; HonRl; LitMag; MrchBnd; NHS; PepBnd; SctActv; College; Elementary Education.

BERRY, Karin D; University City Sr HS; University City, MO; 52/505 HonRl; Quill&Scroll; SchPpr; Univ; Journalism.

BERRY, Kathryn L; Seeger HS; Williamsport, IN; 1/120 PresSophCls; SecSrCls; Band; NHS; StuCncl; Yrbk; Trk; DARAwd; EldAwd; Purdue Univ.

BERRY, Kim A; Holdrege HS; Holdrege, NE; V29#32#3 PresSophCls; MrchBnd; PepBnd; SchMus; YthFlsp; Bsbl; Bsktbl; LetterFtbl; College;.

BERRY, Laura A; Southfield Lathrup HS; Lathrup, MI; Chrl; Chrs; HonRl; NatlMeritSF; PolWkr; SchMus; SchPl; TchrAde; FrCl; College; Law.

BERRY, Loni S; Everett HS; Lansing, MI; 1/496 ChrhWkr; HonRl; PolWkr; Calvin College; Professional.

BERRY, Mark S; Washington HS; Cedar Rapids, IA; TrsSophCls; ALBoysSt; Band; NHS; SctActv; PresStuGov; PresYthFlsp; Bsktbl; GodCntryAwd; Univ; Med.

BERRY, Michael B; Gladwin HS; Gladwin, MI; Aud/Vis; ChrhWkr; CmntyWkr; HonRl; NatlMeritFnl; PolWkr; StuCncl; TchrAde; FTA; Glf; Mid Mi Comm Clge; Teacher.

BERRY, Michael W; Turner HS; Kansas City, KS; 7/363 CncrtBnd; HonRl; NHS; StuCncl; SpnCl; College; Engineering.

BERRY, Pamela L; Avon HS; Indianapolis, IN; DrlTm; HonRl; LbryAde; ModUN; StuCncl; YthFlsp; RptrYrbk; FrCl; GerCl; GAA; Col; Gym Teacher.

BERRY, Susie M; Turkey Run HS; Bloomingdale, IN; Band; CncrtBnd; HonRl; NHS; Quill&Scroll; RptrSchPpr; SchPpr; 4-H; PresFHA; PpCl; Chrldr; Pres4-HAwd; Purdue Univ; Interior Designing.

BERRY, Vera L; Chicago Vocational HS; Chicago, IL; 51/954 Chr; ChrhWkr; HonRl; TchrAde; Loyola; Communication Arts.

BERRYHILL, Robert K; Zionsville Comm HS; Zionsville, IN; Chrs; ChrhWkr; HonRl; SchAde; TchrAde; YthFlsp; Bsktbl; Ftbl; CchngActv; IMSpt; PPFtbl; MasAwd; College; Professional.

BERSCHBACK, Charles T; Austin Catholic Prep; Grosse Pointe, MI; 24/115 PresSrCls; ChrhWkr; HonRl; NHS; StuCncl; StuGov; Univ Of Michigan; Law.

BERSCHE, Timothy; Farmington HS; Farmington, MI; ChrhWkr; HonRl; StuCncl; Ftbl; Trk; IMSpt; Um Dearborn; Business Mgmt.

BERSETH, Shelly R; St Marys Central HS; Bismarck, ND; Band; Chr; Chrs; CncrtBnd; HonRl; MrchBnd; NHS; RptrSchPpr; Chrldr; IMSpt; U Of Nd; Occupational Therapist.

BERT, Angela R; Chester HS; Chester, IL; 3/127 VPSophCls; ChrhWkr; HonRl; JA; NatlMeritCmnd; SchPl; StuCncl; RptrYrbk; 4-H; Bsbl; GAA; College; Psychology.

BERT, Sharon S; Chester HS; Chester, IL; 2/120 SecSrCls; Chrs; SecSrCls; SecJA; NHS; FHA; PpCl; EldAwd;.

BERTA, Susan M; Holy Rosary HS; Flint, MI; 14/58 HonRl; SchPl; SctActv; StuCncl; RptrYrbk; EdSchPpr; PpCl; Bsbl; Bsktbl; College; Elementary Education.

BERTA, Vince A; Bishop Noll HS; Lansing, IL; 86/360 HonRl; RusCl; SpnCl; MthCl; Ftbl; CaptWrstlng; IMSpt; College; Teaching & Coaching.

BERTANI, Mary; St Francis Acad; Jolliet, IL; 10/172 HonRl; NHS; SchMus; StuCncl; FrCl; CchngActv; GAA; IMSpt; PPFtbl; College; General.

BERTE, Marilyn A; Garrigan HS; Bode, IA; ChrhWkr; HonRl; 4-H; PpCl; IMSpt; Business School; Secretary.

BERTELSEN, Terri A; Meservey Thornton HS; Thornton, IA; VPJrCls; TrsSrCls; Band; Chrs; CncrtBnd; HonRl; MrchBnd; PepBnd; SchPl; Bsktbl; College; Secretary.

BERTELSON, Tammie; Mo Valley HS; Missouri Valley, IA; TrsJrCls; Chr; Chrs; HonRl; RptrYrbk; EdYrBk; 4-H; Trk; GAA; College; Vocation.

BERTHA, Marla P; Academy Of Our Lady; Chicago, IL; Chr; ChrhWkr; CmntyWkr; HonRl; Sdlty; StuGov; YthLg; CivCl; Trk; Chrldr; Bradley Univ; Medicine.

BERTHEL, Mark A; Delwood HS; Delmar, IA; SecFrshCls; Band; Chr; CncrtBnd; Mdrgl; MrchBnd; PepBnd; SchMus; SchPl; SctActv; StuCncl; Bsbl; Bsktbl; Tennis; University; Professional.

BERTHELSEN, Joel J; Clear Lake HS; Clearlake, IA; AFS; Band; HonRl; NHS; PepBnd; SchPl; 4-H; LetterBsktbl; LetterFtbl; LetterTrk; Clge; Lutheran Minister.

BERTHEUSON, Julie M; Thompson HS; Grand Forks, ND; ALAGirlsSt; Band; Chrs; SchPl; 4-H; PpCl; AmLegAwd; 4-HAwd; College; Professional.

BERTICH, John; Madison HS; Madison Heights, MI; VPFrshCls; HonRl; TchrAde; RptrYrbk; SchPpr; Oakland Comm Coll; Banking.

BERTLING, Karen; Mother Of Sorrow HS; Chicago, IL; 38/143 HonRl; FrCl; PpCl; Chrldr; GAA; Business School; Secretary.

BERTLING, Roger; Regina HS; Iowa City, IA; 14/50 RptrSchPpr; LetterFtbl; Buena Vista Coll;account.

BERTOLASI, Patricia A; Boylan Central Catholic HS; Rockford, IL; 12/350 HonRl; NHS; SecSdlty; RptrSchPpr; SpnCl; PpCl; Ftbl; College; Art.

BERTOLINO, Jane; Nokomis HS; Witt, IL; Band; Chr; HonRl; StuCncl; Yrbk; IMSpt; 4-HAwd; JCAwd; Eastern Il Univ; Phy Ed.

BERTOLONE, Richard G; Pershing HS; Detroit, MI; 2/483 HonRl; NHS; RptrYrbk; RptrSchPpr; SciCl; Wayne State University; Medicine.

BERTRAM, Kenneth W; St Laurence HS; Chicago, IL; 13/400 ChrhWkr; HonRl; IMSpt; KiwanAwd; Coll; Engin.

BERTRAM, Mark; St Marys Springs HS; Mount Calvary, WI; SciCl; KiwanAwd; Usaf; Electronics.

BERTRAND, Joseph G; Campion Jesuit HS; Chicago, IL; StuGov; Bsktbl; CaptFtbl; CaptTrk; University; Business Admin.

BERTRANG, Edward P; Oswego Sr HS; Oswego, IL; ChrhWkr; PresFFA; A&m College; Farmer.

BERTSCH, Ann R; Boone Jr Sr HS; Boone, IA; AFS; HonRl; LbryAde; OffAde; StuCncl; SecPpCl; IMSpt; Junior College; Dental Assistant.

BERTSCH, Brenda L; Eureka HS; Ashley, ND; Chr; Chrs; HonRl; Mdrgl; SchMus; SchPl; YthFlsp; PpCl; Col; General.

BERTSCH, Douglas; East Charles Mix HS; Wagner, SD; ALBoysSt; HonRl; StuCncl; StuGov; RptrSchPpr; SchPpr; Glf; College;.

BERTSCH, Kenneth; Starkweather Public HS; Stark Weather, ND; 4/17 PresFrshCls; PresJrCls; Band; HonRl; PepBnd; SchPl; StuCncl; 4-H; Bsktbl; Ftbl; College; Professional.

BERTSCH, Michael; Adams Central HS; Decatur, IN; 14/122 TrsFrshCls; VPSophCls; PresSrCls; Band; HonRl; NHS; SchPl; RptrSchPpr; Ftbl; Trk; Indiana Univ; Accountant.

BERTSCHE, Larry E; Flanagan HS; Flanagan, IL; Band; CncrtBnd; HonRl; MrchBnd; 4-H; FFA; SciCl; CaptBsbl; Ftbl; Wrstlng; College; Agriculture.

BERTSCHINGER, Terese L; St Martins Academy; Hill City, SD; HonRl; ModUN; NHS; NatlMeritCmnd; NatlMeritSF; StuCncl; 4-H; FSA; DanFAwd; 4-HAwd; South Dakota School; Engineering.

BERTUCCI, Mary T; Ishpeming HS; Rapid River, MI; 20/201 CmntyWkr; HonRl; NatlFornLg; NHS; StuGov; UNYO; FNA; FrCl; Northern Michigan Univ; Nursing.

BERTUZIS, Lina B; Maria HS; Chicago, IL; 8/303 Chrs; HonRl; NHS; SctActv; GerCl; Univ Il; Pharmacy.

BERTUZIS, Rasa L; Maria HS; Chicago, IL; 18/303 Chrs; HonRl; NHS; SctActv; SecGerCl; U Of Il; Med Tech.

BERUDTSON, Joel R; Rhinelander HS; Rhinelander, WI; 10/375 Band; ChrhWkr; CncrtBnd; HonRl; NHS; PepBnd; Carthage College.

BERULDSEN, Per J; Glenbrook North HS; Northbrook, IL; 197/600 CAP; LetterTrk; Purdue University; Mech Engineer.

BESCH, Greta J; Superior HS; Superior, WI; 5/540 Chr; ChrhWkr; HonRl; Mdrgl; TreasNHS; CaptTwrl; VPFrCl; GAA; BauchLmbAwd; PresAwd; University; Biology.

BESCH, John D; Garrigan HS; Whittemore, IA; 14/103 PresFrshCls; ALBoysSt; Chrs; ChrhWkr; HonRl; StuCncl; SchPpr; VP4-H; LatCl; VPMthCl; Ftbl; 4-HAwd; Iowa State Univ; Computer Science.

BESHEARS, Paula L; Fenton HS; Fenton, MI; 6/200 Chr; Chrl; HonRl; NHS; TreasNatlThespSoc; SchMus; SchPl; StuCncl; YthFlsp; FrCl; Clge; Piano.

BESHER, Debbie J; Meadow Heights HS; Patton, MO; 4/55 ChrhWkr; HonRl; PpCl; SciCl;.

BESING, Jan L; Tecumseh HS; Elberfeld, IN; Band; Chrs; NHS; NatlThespSoc; SchMus; SchPl; YthFlsp; PpCl; Trk; Chrldr; Indiana State; Dental Hygienist.

BESKE, Laurel L; Lake Park HS; Lake Park, MN; 1/41 Chr; HonRl; JrNHS; Twrl; YthFlsp; Yrbk; SptEdSchPpr; Bsktbl; Trk; Chrldr; College; Nursing.

BESON, Denise A; Freeland HS; Freeland, MI; 1/115 VPSophCls; SecSrCls; Band; HonRl; NHS; NatlThespSoc; PolWkr; SchMus; SchPl; 4-H; PpCl; Delta College; Broadcasting.

BESONEN, Rosena J; Ewen Trout Creek Consol HS; Ewen, MI; 7/70 VPSrCls; Band; CmntyWkr; HonRl; NHS; PolWkr; StuGov; YthFlsp; FBLA; Chrldr; Northern Mi Univ; Medical Curriculum.

BESORE, Nancy J; Glenbard West HS; Glen Ellyn, IL; 57/522 Chrs; HonRl; OffAde; Yrbk; PpCl; Arizona State Univ; Recreation.

BESS, Cathy L; Negaunee HS; Negaunee, MI; 16/149 Band; Chrs; CncrtBnd; HonRl; HospAde; MrchBnd; NHS; Orch; PepBnd; FNA; Univ; Social Work.

BESS, Juliette M; Peru HS; Peru, IN; 13/191 Band; Chr; CncrtBnd; HonRl; MrchBnd; NHS; PepBnd; 4-H; SpnCl; GAA; Indiana Univ; Elementary Education.

BESSAC, Kimberley A; Pardeeville Sr HS; Portage, WI; 22/91 Band; Chrs; HonRl; PepBnd; SchAde; SchMus; Yrbk; RptrSchPpr; 4-H; Alverno College; Nurse.

BESSETTE, Cynthia L; Crandon HS; Crandon, WI; DrlTm; HonRl; LbryAde; SchAde; RptrSchPpr; SpnCl; University.

BESSETTE, Paul A; Marist HS; Chicago, IL; HonRl; College; Engineering.

BESSEY, Jeffrey L; Paw Paw HS; Paw Paw, MI; 23/169 Band; HonRl; NHS; NatlMeritSchl; SctActv; StuCncl; TchrAde; 4-H; Bsktbl; LetterFtbl; LetterTennis; LetterTrk; IMSpt; Kalamazoo College; Psychology.

BESSLER, Eileen M; Our Lady Of Grace HS; Indianapolis, IN; Chrs; HonRl; ModUN; SchMus; PpCl; IMSpt; Ind Vo Tec College; Computer Technology.

BESSOLO, Lori A; Negaunee HS; Negaunee, MI; 4/143 Chr; Chrl; Chrs; ChrhWkr; CmntyWkr; HonRl; HospAde; JrNHS; NHS; Orch; RptrYrbk; Yrbk; University Of Michigan; Physical Therapy.

BEST, Dale R; Rockwell Swaledale HS; Rockwell, IA; 3/41 Band; CncrtBnd; HonRl; MrchBnd; NHS; PepBnd; RptrSchPpr; FFA; LionAwd; Niacc; Farm Operation.

BEST, Larry D; Fairfield Community HS; Fairfield, IL; LatCl; SciCl; Ftbl; Wrstlng;.

BEST, Sharon K; Mc Cook HS; Mccook, NE; 39/167 AFS; Band; Chr; CncrtBnd; HonRl; MrchBnd; NHS; PepBnd; SchPpr; FBLA; College; Professional.

BEST, Wronald S; Floyd Central HS; New Albany, IN; 56/275 Aud/Vis; HonRl; NHS; EdYrBk; U Of Louisville; Electrical Engin.

BESTUL, Daniel P; Lancaster Sr HS; Lancaster, WI; PresFrshCls; AFS; Aud/Vis; Band; CncrtBnd; HonRl; MrchBnd; Orch; PepBnd; SctActv; TchrAde; SpnCl; College; Attorney.

BESTUL, Daniel P; Lancaster HS; Lancaster, WI; PresFrshCls; AFS; Band; ChrhWkr; CmntyWkr; HonRl; NHS; PresSctActv; PresStuCncl; SpnCl; LetterTrk; College; Law.

BESWICK, Ralph W; Rock Island Sr HS; Rock Island, IL; 54/661 VPSrCls; ChrhWkr; HonRl; NHS; SchPl; StuCncl; StuGov; TchrAde; UNYO; YthFlsp; SpnCl; CaptFtbl; Trk; Central College; Psychology.

BETCHKAL, Janet A; New Trier East HS; Wilmette, IL; HonRl; OffAde; PolWkr; SchMus; RptrYrbk; Yrbk; MthCl; Vassar College; Chemistry.

BETHEL, Courtney A; Luther South HS; Chicago, IL; 3/204 Chr; CncrtBnd; HonRl; HospAde; NatlFornLg; NHS; NatlMeritSF; YthLg; EdYrBk; LetterTrk; GAA; IMSpt; Notre Dame Col; Medicine.

BETHEL, Lynette I; Menahga Public HS; Menahga, MN; 4/53 VPJrCls; HonRl; SchPl; Yrbk; SptEdSchPpr; SchPpr; 4-H; ChmnBsktbl; LetterTrk; 4-HAwd; Univ Of Mn Crookston; Light Horse Managemen.

BETHEL, Tami R; Washburn Rural HS; Topeka, KS; SecTrsJrCls; Chrs; HonRl; SchMus; StuCncl; Yrbk; SchPpr; PpCl; Bsbl; Chrldr; College; Spanish Teacher.

BETLACH, Scott; Hallock HS; Hallock, MN; 4/48 Band; HonRl; NHS; PepBnd; SchPl; SciCl; University Of Mn; Veterinary Medicine.

BETLEY, Anne M; Green Bay West HS; Green Bay, WI; 13/400 Chrs; HonRl; JA; SchMus; TreasFTA; PresFrCl; Col ; Med Tech.

BETOURNE, Phillip M; Centralia HS; Centralia, IL; 10/364 HonRl; NHS; LatCl; Ftbl; Wrstlng; Univ Of Illinois; Computer Technology.

BETTELYOUN, Cynthia J; East Chas Mix HS; Wagner, SD; SecJrCls; CmntyWkr; HonRl; HospAde; SchPl; RptrYrbk; FHA; FNA; Bsbl; Bsktbl; College.

BETTEN, Sonette L; Kanawha Community HS; Kanawha, IA; VPSophCls; Chr; HonRl; HospAde; LbryAde; Mdrgl; SchPl; YthFlsp; Yrbk; Bsktbl; Ia Cent Comm Coll; Accounting.

BETTENHAUSEN, Kathryn A; Peotone HS; Frankfort, IL; 11/104 SchMus; Yrbk; 4-H; PresFHA; Tennis; CchngActv; TreasGAA; DanFAwd; 4-HAwd; Univ Of Illinois; Communications.

BETTERMAN, James B; Creighton Prep; Omaha, NE; 10/249 PresSophCls; Aud/Vis; HonRl; NHS; SancSoc; Sdlty; StuCncl; StuGov; TchrAde; LatCl; Marquette; Dentistry.

BETTERMAN, Lyle; Jefferson Sr HS; Garfield, MN; HonRl; NHS; SchPpr; MthCl; Alexandria Tech School; Fluid Power Course.

BETTESWORTH, Daniel G; Dwight D Eisenhower HS; Saginaw, MI; 16/365 Aud/Vis; CmntyWkr; HonRl; JrNHS; NHS; SctActv; TchrAde; Univ Of Michigan; Nuclear Physicist.

BETTHAUSER, Elizabeth R; Tomah HS; Tomah, WI; Chr; CmntyWkr; IntrClCncl; RptrYrbk; Yrbk; EdSchPpr; SpnCl;.

BETTICE, Danine M; Immaculate Conception Acad; Batesville, IN; 14/67 Chrs; CAP; HonRl; NHS; Orch; SchPl; StuGov; RptrYrbk; GerCl;.

BETTING, Michael R; Ellendale HS; Ellendale, ND; Chr; NatlMeritFnl; NatlMeritCmnd; NatlMeritSF; Bsktbl; LetterFtbl; Glf; LetterTrk; Wrstlng; IMSpt; Univ Nd; Accounting & Computer Sciences.

BETTINGER, Donald W; Warsaw Community HS; Warsaw, IN; LetterBsktbl; LetterFtbl;.

BETTIS, Tammy L; Franklin HS; Franklin, IL; SecSrCls; HospAde; SchPl; Yrbk; FHA; SpnCl; PpCl; GAA;.

BETTIS, Vern W; Wayne Community HS; Allerton, IA; 12/74 Band; Chr; Chrs; CncrtBnd; HonRl; MrchBnd; NHS; PepBnd; SchMus; SchPl; LetterBsktbl; Glf; LetterTrk; College; Mathematics.

BETTMENG, Lois L; Hanson Ind #40 HS; Alexandria, SD; VPJrCls; Band; CmntyWkr; HonRl; Quill&Scroll; SchPl; Yrbk; SchPpr; FHA; Chrldr;.

BETTS, Dawn L; Rich East HS; Park Forest, IL; 21/350 HonRl; NatlFornLg; NHS; NatlThespSoc; PolWkr; SchPl; SecStuCncl; Yrbk; RptrSchPpr; Pres4-H; University Of Virginia; Law.

BETTS, Jane E; Southwest HS; Green Bay, WI; 126/420 AFS; Chr; Chrs; ChrhWkr; HonRl; Mdrgl; Orch; SchMus; LatCl; PpCl; LetterGlf; GAA; University Of Wisconsin; Nursing.

BETTS, Jeffery; Davison HS; Davison, MI; HonRl; NHS; TchrAde; Trk; IMSpt; Central Mich Univ; Professional Athletics.

BETTS, Kathryn C; Highland Park Sr HS; St Paul, MN; Chr; LitMag; Mdrgl; NatlMeritSF; SchMus; RptrYrbk; Macalester College; Music.

BETZ, Cheryl M; Larkin HS; Elgin, IL; University.

BETZ, Julia M; Benton Harbor S; Benton Harbor, MI; 59/413 SecFrshCls; ChrhWkr; HonRl; NHS; OffAde; StuCncl; UNYO; YthFlsp; GodCntryAwd; KiwanAwd; John Wesley Coll; Liberal Arts.

BETZ, Walter O; Lake Michigan Catholic HS; Benton Harbor, MI; VPJrCls; YthFlsp; CaptTrk; Grand Valley St Coll; Philosphy/theology.

BETZELBERGER, Kathy L; Delavan HS; Delavan, IL; 11/56 Band; HonRl; NHS; SchAde; SchMus; StuCncl; TchrAde; PpCl; SciCl; Western Il Univ; Elem Educ.

BETZEN, Nicholas M; Carroll HS; Colwich, KS; 9/220 HonRl; NatlMeritSF; CaptFtbl; College.

BETZINGER, Peggy M; Menominee HS; Menominee, MI; 11/275 SecFrshCls; SecSophCls; TrsSrCls; HonRl; NHS; StuCncl; RptrYrbk; PpCl; Tennis; IMSpt; Marquette U; Nursing Rn.

BETZINGER, Steve M; Menominee HS; Menominee, MI; 51/273 ChrhWkr; DrmBgl; NHS; SctActv; TchrAde; PpCl; LetterFtbl; LetterTrk; IMSpt; College.

BETZLER, Barbara J; Martin Hughes HS; Buhl, MN; Band; Chr; CncrtBnd; HonRl; MrchBnd; NHS; PepBnd; SecYthFlsp; RptrYrbk; LetterChrldr; Clge; Nursing.

BETZLER, Rose R; Sullivan HS; Sullivan, IL; Chrs; ChrhWkr; HonRl; YthFlsp; FHA; GerCl; Trade School; Vocation.

BETZOLD, Deborah J; Chisholm Senior HS; Chisholm, MN; PresSrCls; ALAGirlsSt; Band; CncrtBnd; HonRl; MrchBnd; OffAde; PepBnd; SctActv; RptrYrbk; PpCl; GAA; College; Professional.

BEUERLEIN, Robert M; Hayden HS; Topeka, KS; 1/201 ALBoysSt; Band; ChrhWkr; HonRl; NHS; NatlMeritCmnd; SchMus; StuCncl; LetterGlf; IMSpt; U Of Nebraska.

BEUKE, Arthur J; Leo HS; Chicago Ridge, IL; 41/200 HonRl; IMSpt; Col; Professional.

BEUKEMA, Karen L; Hinsdale Central HS; Hinsdale, IL; 68/583 ChrhWkr; HospAde; Northern Illinois Univ; Nursing.

BEULIGMANN, Richard; Mt Carmel Hs; Mt Carmel, IL; Chr; NHS; StuCncl; KeyCl; Bsktbl; LetterFtbl; Trk; Wrstlng; College; Science.

BEULIGMANN, Richard E; Mt Carmel HS; Mt Carmel, IL; Chrs; NHS; StuCncl; KeyCl; Bsktbl; LetterFtbl; Trk; Wrstlng; AmLegAwd; Univ Of Illinois; Science.

BEUMER, Christine M; Portland HS; Portland, IN; 17/187 HonRl; NHS; FrCl; PpCl; Clge; Pro Designer.

BEUMLER, James; Franklin HS; Livonia, MI; Chr; Chrl; ChrhWkr; HonRl; Mdrgl; CitAwd; College; History.

BEUSE, Linda A; Thornton Fractional South HS; Lansing, IL; 35/563 Band; HonRl; HospAde; NatlMeritCmnd; OffAde; 4-H; FNA; SciCl; Sec Of Executive.

BEUSSINK, Mark; Notre Dame HS; Jackson, MO; VPJrCls; VPSrCls; Chrs; HonRl; NatlMeritCmnd; Semo State; Conservation.

BEUTEL, Kathy S; Bremen Senior HS; Bremen, IN; 8/116 HonRl; JrNHS; NHS; SchPl; StuGov; TchrAde; 4-H; FTA; FrCl; PpCl; College; Medicine.

BEUTKE, William K; Woodland HS; Long Point, IL; 24/98 PresJrCls; CmntyWkr; HonRl; StuCncl; 4-H; FFA; PpCl; LetterBsktbl; CaptFtbl; 4-HAwd; Joliet Jr Clg; Ag.

BEUTLER, Patricia; Bancroft Public HS; Bancroft, NE; VPFrshCls; PresSrCls; ALAGirlsSt; Chrs; CncrtBnd; HonRl; NHS; StuCncl; Yrbk; Univ Nebr; Special Education.

BEUTNER, Janet M; Marquette HS; Michigan City, IN; HonRl; JA; SchMus; TchrAde; RptrYrbk; Tennis; GAA; JAAwd; College; Professional.

BEVARS, Robert P; Brodhead HS; Broadhead, WI; VPFrshCls; HonRl; StuCncl; FFA; LetterFtbl; Farming.

BEVER, Dennis W; Sedan HS; Sedan, KS; 3/39 PresSrCls; Band; CncrtBnd; NHS; SchPl; RptrYrbk; FSA; Bsktbl; Ftbl; Kansas State Univ; Engineering.

BEVER, Janet A; Sedan HS; Peru, KS; SecJrCls; Chrs; ChrhWkr; HonRl; NHS; TchrAde; FHA; FSA; BttyCrckrAwd; CitAwd; Kansas St Coll Pittsburgh; Nursing.

BEVERLY, Nancy; Pike HS; Indianapolis, IN; 9/259 ChrhWkr; NatlFornLg; NHS; NatlThespSoc; SchMus; SchPl; Yrbk; RptrSchPpr; FrCl; PpCl; Univ Of Evansville; Theatre.

BEVEROTH, Rebecca L; Salem Central HS; Salem, WI; ALAGirlsSt; Band; NatlFornLg; TreasNHS; NatlSciFnd; SchPl; YthFnd; RptrSchPpr; PresFrCl; LionAwd; College; English.

BEVIER, Mary C; Nauvoo Colusa HS; Nauvoo, IL; TrsSophCls; HonRl; SchPl; StuCncl; Chrldr;.

BEVIGNANI, Lawrence C; Downers Grove South HS; Woodridge, IL; HonRl; SctActv; College Of Dupage; Biology.

BEVILL, Robert S; Lowpoint Washburn HS; Washburn, IL; 4/68 ALBoysSt; SchMus; SctActv; PresStuCncl; SptEdSchPpr; LetterBsbl; LetterBsktbl; LetterGlf; LetterTrk; DARAwd; Eastern Illinois Univ; Medical Technology.

BEVILL, Robert S; Low Point Washburn HS; Washburn, IL; 3/68 SecTrsFrshCls; PresSophCls; AFS; ALBoysSt; Chrs; HonRl; LbryAde; SchMus; SchPl; SctActv; PresStuCncl; LetterBsbl; LetterBsktbl; LetterGlf; Eastern Ill Univ; Medical Technology.

BEVILL, Susan L; S Newton HS; Goodland, IN; CncrtBnd; DrlTm; MrchBnd; SchPl; TchrAde; Yrbk; SchPpr; FTA; PpCl; GAA; Purdue Univ; Child Study.

BEXELL, Candy; Brainerd Senior HS; Brainerd, MN; CmntyWkr; JA; NHS; NatlMeritSchl; RedCrAde; StuGov; RptrSchPpr; FFA; FSA; VoiceDemAwd; Menneapolis Coll; Art.

BEY, Claudette; Chicago Vocational HS; Chicago, IL; Chrs; DrlTm; HonRl; Orch; ROTC; SchMus; SchPl; StuCncl; TchrAde; Ia State Univ; Music.

BEYEA, Louise M; Keya Paha Co HS; Springview, NE; 1/26 VPFrshCls; SecSophCls; Band; Chrs; HonRl; StuGov; LetterBsktbl; LetterTrk; Chrldr; GAA; Kansas St.

BEYER, Alice M; Riverton HS; Galena, KS; 3/51 ALAGirlsSt; Band; Chr; Chrs; ChrhWkr; VPNHS; SecStuCncl; PresYthFlsp; PPFtbl; DanFAwd; Friends Bible Col; Christian Ed.

BEYER, Ann; Ladywood St Agnes HS; Indianapolis, IN; RedCrAde; SchMus; Trk; College; Physical Therapy.

BEYER, Betty L; Hitchcock Public HS; Wolsey, SD; 1/21 Band; Chr; ChrhWkr; HonRl; NHS; SchPl; StuCncl; EdYrBk; PresFHA; DARAwd; Augustana College; Social Services.

BEYER, Carol; Richland HS; Wahpeton, ND; 4/28 ALAGirlsSt; CmntyWkr; HonRl; HospAde; Yrbk; SptEdSchPpr; FHA; PpCl; IMSpt; Jamestown College; Registered Nurse.

BEYER, Catherine A; Topeka HS; Topeka, KS; AFS; Chr; Chrl; Chrs; ChrhWkr; HonRl; JA; NatlThespSoc; PolWkr; SchMus; SchPl; SctActv; StuGov; YthFlsp; Baylor Univ; Music.

BEYER, Curtis E; Bottineau HS; Bottineau, ND; 16/70 ALBoysSt; Band; DrmMjrt; HonRl; SctActv; SptEdSchPpr; SciCl; CaptBsktbl; LetterFtbl; VoiceDemAwd; Clg; Pro.

BEYER, Douglas H; Maplewood Academy; Ellsworth, WI; Band; ChrhWkr; CncrtBnd; HonRl; MrchBnd; College; Theology.

BEYER, Elizabeth K; Evanston Twp HS; Evanston, IL; Chr; Chrl; HonRl; College; Mathematics.

BEYER, Keith C; Athens HS; Athens, WI; 33/79 Chr; Chrs; HonRl; SctActv; PpCl; LetterFtbl; LetterWrstlng; CchngActv; College.

BEYER, Robert W; Northwood HS; Gordon, WI; Chrs; HonRl; StuGov; RptrYrbk; Yrbk; RptrSchPpr; SchPpr; Rice Lake Indianhead Tech ; Cpa.

BEYER, Ronald E; Lyons Twp HS; Western Springs, IL; 233/1250 HonRl; LetterBsktbl; CaptUniv Of Arizona; Special Education.

BEYER, Steven; T L Handy HS; Bay City, MI; 23/400 DrmMjrt; NHS; SchPl; SctActv; Yrbk; SciCl; EldAwd; Univ; Professional.

BEYER, Vicki L; Gretna Jr Sr HS; Gretna, NE; 8/87 ChrhWkr; CncrtBnd; HonRl; MrchBnd; NHS; LetterTrk; College; Sociology.

BEYER, Virginia M; Waldron HS; Waldron, IN; HonRl; OffAde; TchrAde; RptrYrbk; FHA; PpCl; IMSpt; Business.

BEYER, Wanda L; Oconto Falls HS; Oconto Falls, WI; 13/151 Band; HonRl; MrchBnd; SchPl; SecStuCncl; Yrbk; RptrSchPpr; SecFTA; SecPpCl; Trk; CaptChrldr; University; Nursing.

BEYERS, Annette M; Pana HS; Oconee, IL; 4/144 TrsJrCls; VPSrCls; Chrs; JrNHS; NHS; OffAde; TchrAde; Yrbk; RptrSchPpr; Pres4-H; FBLA; PresFTA; KeyCl; LetterTrk; Jr College; Accounting.

BEYERS, Kent G; Pana Sr HS; Pana, IL; 8/185 AFS; HonRl; NHS; 4-H; FFA; LetterBsktbl; LetterTennis; W Illinois Univ; Agribusiness.

BEYERS, Scott; Central HS; Pipestone, MN; Chr; Chrs; CAP; HonRl; SctActv; 4-H; Ftbl; Southwest Mn State U; Music Electronic.

BEZ, Donna J; Benet Academy; Naperville, IL; 19/242 Illinois State Univ; Elementary Education.

BEZANSON, Ralph D; Mariner HS; White Bear Lake, MN; NatlMeritSF; Univ; Vet.

BEZY, Karen L; Floyd Central HS; New Albany, IN; Chr; CmntyWkr; CncrtBnd; HonRl; JA; NHS; Natl-

MeritFnl; PolWkr; TchrAde; RotaryAwd; Indiana U Southeast; Nursing.

BHATTACHARYA, Atanu; Lapeer HS; Lapeer, MI; 2/426 ALBoysSt; HonRl; RedCrAde; SctActv; AmLegAwd; EldAwd; U Of Mich; Medicine.

BIAGGIO, Robert W; Roncalli HS; Manitowoc, WI; 12/141 PresJrCls; NHS; PolWkr; PresStuCncl; StuGov; TchrAde; Yrbk; KeyCl; College; Professional.

BIALAS, Kathleen M; Creston HS; Grand Rapids, MI; ALAGirlsSt; HonRl; JrNHS; NHS; NatlMeritCmnd; SpnCl; IMSpt; Coll; Pol Sci.

BIALEK, Richard W; Reavis HS; Burbank, IL; 1/705 Band; PresNHS; NatlMeritSF; SchMus; YthLg; RptrSchPpr; MthCl; LetterBsbl; CaptFtbl; Trk; IMSpt; College; Law.

BIALEK, Sandra M; Schurz HS; Chicago, IL; 5/800 Chrs; HonRl; NHS; NatlMeritCmnd; OffAde; SchMus; PresStuCncl; PpCl; LetterTennis; AmLegAwd; Northern Ill Univ; Bacteriologist.

BIANCO, Frederick J; Macon County Ri HS; Macon, MO; 26/117 ChrhWkr; CncrtBnd; HonRl; MrchBnd; PepBnd; SchMus; SpnCl; CaptBsktbl; LetterFtbl; LetterTrk; U Of Mo; Mechanical Engineering.

BIBA, Diane M; Regina Dominican HS; Chicago, IL; HonRl; HospAde; SchMus; SchPl; FrCl; GAA; Univ Of Ill; Biology.

BIBB, Julia A; Jeffersonville HS; Jeffersonville, IN; AFS; Chr; HonRl; JrNHS; NHS; SchMus; 4-H; FrCl; Bsktbl; Univ Of Kentucky; Zoology.

BIBBINS, Keith A; M L King HS; Detroit, MI; 1/200 Chrs; HonRl; JA; NHS; NatlMeritCmnd; NatlMeritSchl; NatlMeritSF; NatlSciFnd; StuCncl; StuGov; FDA; SpnCl; Trk; Howard Univ; Pharmacist.

BIBBS, Ricky G; Senath Hornersviller HS; Hornersville, MO; Chrs; TchrAde; LetterBsbl; CaptBsktbl; IMSpt; Business School;.

BIBLE, Kevin J; Sullivan HS; Sullivan, MO; 8/166 PresSrCls; CncrtBnd; HonRl; NHS; StuCncl; PresSpnCl; Bsbl; LetterFtbl; LetterTrk; Mo Univ; Engineering.

BIBLER, Jennifer B; Arlington HS; Indianapolis, IN; CncrtBnd; HonRl; HospAde; MrchBnd; NHS; NatlMeritCmnd; Orch; SchMus; StuCncl; Chrldr; Indiana U; Medicine.

BIBOW, Kim L; Magic City Campus HS; Minot, ND; Chr; Chrl; Chrs; HonRl; NHS; SctActv; StuCncl; SciCl; Trk; Chrldr; College Or Univ; Professional, Vocation.

BIBY, Brian G; Christopher Comm HS; Mulkeytown, IL; 1/62 Aud/Vis; ModUN; NHS; SchAde; EdYrBk; College; Engineer.

BICAK, Barbara A; Kearney Catholic HS; Kearney, NE; SecSophCls; SecTrsJrCls; Chrs; ChrhWkr; HospAde; Mdrgl; SchMus; SchPl; RptrYrbk; 4-H; Trk; DARAwd;.

BICAK, James S; Kearney Catholic HS; Kearney, NE; Chrs; HonRl; Mdrgl; NatlMeritCmnd; SchMus; SchPl; SctActv; PresStuCncl; RptrYrbk; Yrbk; LetterBsktbl; LetterFtbl; LetterTrk; Univ Of Nebraska; Architecture.

BICAN, Debbie A; Morton West HS; Stickney, IL; HonRl; College; Secretary.

BICCHINELLA, Cindy L; West Chicago Community HS; West Chicago, IL; SecJrCls; Chr; HonRl; StuCncl; PpCl; College; Zoology Or Dentistry.

BICCHINELLA, Shelly M; West Chicago HS; West Chicago, IL; SecFrshCls; Chrs; HonRl; SchMus; StuCncl; E Il Univ; Accounting.

BICE, Cindra S; Reddick HS; Essex, IL; 6/43 HstFrshCls; HstSrCls; HonRl; LbryAde; NHS; OffAde; SchPl; StuCncl; EdYrBk; FrCl; Chrldr; Kankakee Community College; Nursing.

BICE, Donald A; Coleman HS; Pound, WI; PresBand; ChrhWkr; CncrtBnd; HonRl; MrchBnd; PepBnd; SchMus; YthFlsp; Pres4-H; SecFFA; Trade School; Vocation.

BICE, Kevin L; Flora HS; Flora, IL; 4/143 ALBoysSt; Band; HonRl; NHS; PepBnd; SchMus; SpnCl; MthCl; Ftbl; Trk; U Of Ill; Medicine.

BICE, Michael L; Woodward Granger HS; Wooward, IA; 23/60 4-H; Bsktbl; Ftbl; Trk; 4-HAwd; College.

BICEK, Diane P; Bogan HS; Chicago, IL; 5/732 Band; ChrhWkr; CmntyWkr; CncrtBnd; HonRl; LbryAde; NHS; SchAde; SchPl; SctActv; TchrAde; FNA; FTA; College; Special Education.

BICEK, Paul D; Benet Academy; Downers Grove, IL; 4/230 HonRl; College Of St Thomas; Professional.

BICHLMEIER, Kathy M; Madison HS; Madison, NE; 3/66 ALAGirlsSt; ChrhWkr; CncrtBnd; HonRl; LbryAde; MrchBnd; NHS; PepBnd; 4-H; SpnCl; College.

BICHLMEIER, Stephen; Madison HS; Madison, NE; Band; Chr; CncrtBnd; MrchBnd; PepBnd; Bsktbl; Ftbl; Trk;.

BICIUNAS, Giedre O; Maria HS; Chicago, IL; 27/303 HonRl; De Paul University; Semantics.

BICK, Karen H; Oak Park HS; Oak Park, MI; TrsSrCls; SchAde; TreasStuCncl; FDA; U Of Mi; L S & A Honors Program.

BICKEL, Michael; Willow City Public HS; Willow City, ND; PresFrshCls; FFA; Trade Or Bus School; Curriculum Of Maj Stud.

BICKEL, Rob D; William A Wirt HS; Gary, IN; ChrhWkr; CmntyWkr; HonRl; NHS; TchrAde; RptrSchPpr; CaptBsktbl; IMSpt; PresAwd; Business Sch; Bus Mgmnt.

BICKEL, Shaun M; Huntington Catholic HS; Huntington, IN; ChrhWkr; HonRl; OffAde; SchPl; SctActv; VPStuCncl; TchrAde; Bsktbl; Glf; IMSpt; College; Pharmacy.

BICKERSTAFF, Cynthia S; Eudora HS; Eudora, KS; 14/40 DrlTm; HonRl; HospAde; BttyCrckrAwd; Navy; Medical Techician.

BICKET, Chris R; Benton Consolidated HS; Benton, IL; TrsFrshCls; VPSophCls; Chrs; HonRl; NHS; StuCncl; 4-H; VPSpnCl; SecMthCl; Univ Of Ill; Education.

BICKET, Danny J; Glendale HS; Springfield, MO; Aud/Vis; Band; Chr; ChrhWkr; HonRl; MrchBnd; PepBnd; TchrAde; MthCl; Tennis; U Of Ma At Rolla; Professional.

BICKETT, Kim T; Malden Comm HS; Princeton, IL; HstFrshCls; PresSrCls; SchPl; StuCncl; FFA; FrCl; PpCl; Bsbl; Bsktbl; Jr College; Agriculture.

BICKFORD, Cecilia L; Decatur Community HS; Oberlin, KS; 7/84 Band; Chr; HonRl; NatlFornLg; SecNHS; PepBnd; SchMus; University Of Kansas; Medicine.

BICKFORD, Julie R; Chisago Lakes HS; Chisago, MN; Chr; Chrs; HonRl; StuCncl; RptrYrbk; RptrSchPpr; FHA; Trk; CaptChrldr; GAA; AmLegAwd; PresAwd; College; Medical.

BICSOK, Sheryl A; Bentley HS; Burton, MI; HonRl; NHS; SchAde; StuCncl; FHA; PpCl; Mott Comm Clge; Education Teacher.

BIDDIX, Steven C; Adrian HS; Adrian, MI; 87/390 Band; CncrtBnd; HonRl; MrchBnd; PepBnd; TchrAde; RptrSchPpr; SchPpr; FrCl; Adrian Col; Journalism Newspaper.

BIDDLE, Vickie L; Yorkwood HS; Little York, IL; VPFrshCls; Chrs; DrlTm; HonRl; MrchBnd; SchPl; StuCncl; Yrbk; FBLA; FTA; Airline School.

BIDDLECOM, Charles A; Waukegan East HS; Waukegan, IL; 1/500 ALBoysSt; CmntyWkr; HonRl; JrNHS; NHS; GerCl; LatCl; Swmmng; AmLegAwd; VFWAwd; Us Air Force Acad; Astronautical Engineer.

BIDINGER, Michelle M; Morton Public HS; Morton, MN; Chrs; SptEdYrbk; SptEdSchPpr; PpCl; SciCl; CaptBsktbl; LetterTrk; LetterChrldr; AmLegAwd; Univ Of Morris; Physical Education.

BIDWELL, Kay M; Oshkosh North HS; Oshkosh, WI; 1/370 TreasLitMag; Mdrgl; NHS; NatlMeritCmnd; Orch; StuGov; VPFrCl; MthCl; LetterTrk; Univ Of Wisconsin.

BIEBER, Cindy L; Frederick HS; Barnard, SD; DrmMjrt; HonRl; MrchBnd; SchPl; YthFlsp; College; Vocation.

BIEBER, Debra L; Wells Easton HS; Wells, MN; 11/111 PresBand; Chrs; CncrtBnd; HonRl; LbryAde; MrchBnd; OffAde; StuCncl; RptrYrbk; Trk; Mankato State Clge; Chemistry.

BIEBER, Scott B; Bowdle HS; Bowdle, SD; PresSophCls; Band; Chrs; CncrtBnd; HonRl; MrchBnd; PepBnd; StuCncl; 4-H; LetterBsktbl; 4-HAwd; College; Accounting.

BIEDENBACH, Kay E; Belleville Township HS West; Belleville, IL; 44/800 HonRl; NatlFornLg; NHS; NatlMeritSF; NatlThespSoc; SchAde; SchMus; SchPl; CitAwd; U Of Il; Vet Med.

BIEGANEK, Julie A; Sauk Centre HS; Sauk Centre, MN; Band; Chr; CncrtBnd; HonRl; Mdrgl; MrchBnd; PepBnd; Swmmng; StuCncl; TchrAde; Brainerd Jr ;pro.

BIEGERT, Diane J; Lyons Twp HS; La Grange, IL; 118/1226 ChrhWkr; CncrtBnd; HonRl; NHS; SchMus; Tennis; Miami Univ; Elem Education.

BIEGLER, Todd; West Bend East HS; West Bend, WI; 22/237 Band; CncrtBnd; HonRl; MrchBnd; NHS; PepBnd; LetterFtbl; LetterTrk; LetterWrstlng; Uw Madison; Engin.

BIEHLER, Randy K; Shelbyville HS; Shelbyville, IL; 16/133 HonRl; NHS; TchrAde; SptEdSchPpr; SchPpr; 4-H; LetterBsbl; Bsktbl; LetterFtbl; LetterTrk; 4-HAwd;.

BIEHN, Debra; Cleveland Public HS; Madison Lake, MN; 12/41 SecTrsFrshCls; TrsSophCls; HstJrCls; SecTrsSrCls; Chr; HonRl; NatlThespSoc; SchPl; StuCncl; RptrYrbk; Vocational.

BIEHN, Julie A; Cleveland Public HS; Madison Lake, MN; Chr; ChrhWkr; HonRl; LbryAde; SchPpr; Mankato Vocational Tech; Secretarial Work.

BIEL, Brenda; Lefor HS; Dickinson, ND; 3/8 SecTrsFrshCls; SecJrCls; HonRl; LbryAde; TchrAde; RptrSchPpr; Bsktbl; Trk; GAA; Coll;.

BIEL, Chad J; Lefor Public HS; Dickinson, ND; PresJrCls; SchPl; StuCncl; RptrYrbk; EdYrBk; RptrSchPpr; 4-H; Bsktbl; Trk; IMSpt; 4-HAwd; College; Vocation.

BIEL, James A; George Rogers Clark HS; Whiting, IN; Band; ChrhWkr; CncrtBnd; Quill&Scroll; RptrSchPpr; GerCl; LetterTrk; University; Business Management.

BIEL, Mary E; Sparta Sr HS; Sparta, WI; 4/189 VPJrCls; HonRl; NHS; Linfield Coll.

BIELAWA, Donna M; Mc Henry HS; Mchenry, IL; 50/449 AFS; HonRl; TchrAde; RptrYrbk; EdYrBk; FTA; Trk; College; Nursing.

BIELAWSKI, Melanie; Jones Commercial HS; Chicago, IL; 149/437 HonRl; SchMus; TchrAde; Trk; GAA; KiwanAwd; LionAwd; Go To Work Secretary.

BIELEMA, Brenda J; Thomson HS; Thomson, IL; 5/39 Band; Chrs; ChrhWkr; HonRl; JrNHS; Mdrgl; SctActv; StuCncl; FHA; College; Teacher.

BIELEMA, Keith; Timothy Christian HS; Benwyn, IL; 18/90 Band; CncrtBnd; HonRl; MrchBnd; PepBnd; StuCncl; RptrSchPpr; IMSpt; Coll.

BIELEMA, Lori L; Fulton HS; Fulton, IL; Chr; Chrs; ChrhWkr; HonRl;.

BIELER, Thea; Kapaun Mt Carmel HS; Wichita, KS; 12/160 Chrs; HonRl; LbryAde; FrCl; Coll; Librarian.

BIELFELDT, Diane; Octavia HS; Anchor, IL; 1/45 PresFrshCls; Chrs; DrmMjrt; NHS; SchMus; SchPl; EdYrBk; RptrSchPpr; SciCl; Chrldr; College; Medical Secretary.

BIELKUS, Virginia; Boylan Central HS; Rockford, IL; 5/375 HonRl; JrNHS; NHS; Yrbk; SchPpr; FrCl; PpCl; Univ; Pharmacy.

BIELKUS, Virginia D; Boylan HS; Rockford, IL; 5/358 HonRl; JrNHS; NHS; Yrbk; SchPpr; University; Pharmacist.

BIEN, Richard N; Harrisonville Sr HS; Harrisonville, MO; 10/155 ALBoysSt; Band; ChrhWkr; HonRl; PresNatlFornLg; Quill&Scroll; PresStuCncl; PresYthFlsp; VPSciCl; LetterFtbl; LetterWrstlng; GodCntryAwd; Univ Of Missouri; Law.

BIENEK, Paul F; Harvey HS; Harvey, ND; TrsFrshCls; VPSrCls; ALBoysSt; HonRl; YthFlsp; Bsbl; Bsktbl; Glf; Trk; Univ Of Nd; Medicine.

BIENEMAN, Keith A; Washington Park HS; Racine, WI; 140/513 Band; CncrtBnd; Orch; Univ; Electrical Engineering.

BIENIEK, Nona R; Rib Lake HS; Rib Lake, WI; CncrtBnd; HonRl; MrchBnd; NatlFornLg; SchPl; SctActv; Yrbk; RptrSchPpr; SchPpr; PpCl; College; Professional.

BIENIEWSKI, Barbara D; Mother Guerin HS; Chicago, IL; 9/408 Aud/Vis; Chrs; HonRl; NHS; NatlMeritCmnd; TchrAde; VPMthCl; Depaul University; Teaching.

BIENKOWSKI, Marie; St Clement HS; Detroit, MI; VPSrCls; HonRl; SchMus; SchPl; TchrAde; RptrYrbk; SciCl; Wayne St Univ; Lawyer.

BIER, James V; Craig Sr HS; Janesville, WI; 7/500 HonRl; NatlFornLg; NHS; NatlMeritCmnd; TchrAde; MthCl; LetterBsbl; LetterFtbl; CchngActv; U Of Wi Madison; Engineering.

BIER, Thomas; Orchard View HS; Muskegon, MI; 6/252 PresFrshCls; CncrtBnd; MrchBnd; NHS; Yrbk; FrCl; IMSpt; Univ Of Michigan; Md.

BIERBAUM, Sharon; Washington Hs; Washington, MO; 9/276 Band; CncrtBnd; HonRl; JA; MrchBnd; PepBnd; StuCncl; Twrl; PpCl; Chrldr; College;accounting.

BIERBAUM, Steven M; Union HS; Union, MO; PresFrshCls; PresSophCls; ChrhWkr; CmntyWkr; HonRl; HospAde; Sacrstn; SctActv; LatCl; Bsbl; Bsktbl; College; Professional.

BIERBRAUER, Norma J; Plum City HS; Plum City, WI; 2/37 PresSrCls; ALAGirlsSt; Aud/Vis; HonRl; RptrYrbk; RptrSchPpr; FHA; SpnCl; PpCl;.

BIERCE, Douglas L; Murray Community HS; Murrya, IA; ChrhWkr; CmntyWkr; HonRl; SchPl; YthFlsp; Pres4-H; PresFBLA; Bsbl; LetterFtbl; Col; Social Sci.

BIERE, Lora L; Nemaha Valley HS; Dunbar, NE; ALAGirlsSt; Band; Chrs; ChrhWkr; HonRl; SchPl; YthFlsp; Yrbk; EngCl; College; Social Work.

BIERER, Jackie B; Warren County Rii HS; Wright City, MO; 7/51 HstSophCls; HonRl; StuCncl; YthFlsp; Yrbk; RptrSchPpr; FHA; PpCl; GAA; IMSpt; Business Sch; Secretarial.

BIERL, Sandra E; Louisa Muscatine HS; Letts, IA; 4/51 Band; CncrtBnd; HonRl; MrchBnd; PepBnd; Pres4-H; PpCl; Bsktbl; BttyCrckrAwd; 4-HAwd; College.

BIERLEIN, Louann A; Reese HS; Vassar, MI; 10/130 Chr; ChrhWkr; HonRl; LbryAde; ModUN; NatlMeritSF; YthFlsp; RptrSchPpr; GerCl; Bsbl; GAA; Michigan State Univ; Medical Tech.

BIERMA, Mike R; Maurice Orange City HS; Orange City, IA; Band; CncrtBnd; HonRl; MrchBnd; NHS; NatlMeritCmnd; Orch; PepBnd; MthCl; Ftbl; Iowa State University; Materials Engineer.

BIERMAN, Laura L; Holy Family HS; Lindsay, NE; 15/34 Chrs; HonRl; NHS; SchPl; TchrAde; 4-H; PpCl; Chrldr; College.

BIERMANN, Lou Ann; Washington Senior Hs; Washington, MO; 10/276 Chrs; HonRl; JA; Mdrgl; NHS; SchMus; 4-HAwd; Southwest State U; Bs In Nursing.

BIERNADSKI, George A; St Ignatius Coll Prep; Chicago, IL; 19/160 HonRl; SctActv; EdSchPpr; Glf; Trk; Univ; Prof.

BIERNOT, Marilyn S; Port Huron Northern HS; Port Huron, MI; 70/461 TrsSophCls; Aud/Vis; Band; HonRl; HospAde; NHS; StuCncl; College; All Arts.

BIERSCHENK, Mark; Benton Community HS; Van Horne, IA; HonRl; 4-H; FFA; Ftbl; Wrstlng; 4-HAwd; College; Farming.

BIERY, Edgar E; Pinckney HS; Pinckney, MI; PresSophCls; HonRl; NHS; SchPl; StuCncl; StuGov; YthLg; FBLA; GovHonPrgAwd; JAAwd; Univ; Business Admin.

BIES, Douglas A; Jasper HS; Jasper, IN; 1/280 PresFrshCls; SecTrsJrCls; ALBoysSt; CmntyWkr; HonRl; NHS; NatlMeritCmnd; StuGov; KeyCl; LetterTennis; Wabash College; Biology Major.

BIES, Michael L; Marcus Community HS; Marcus, IA; PresFrshCls; TrsJrCls; ALBoysSt; Chr; ChrhWkr; HospAde; Mdrgl; PresNHS; SchMus; StuCncl; LetterBsbl; CaptBsktbl; CaptMount Marty Col; Anesthesiologist.

BIESENTHAL, Cindy A; Markesan; Markesan, WI; Chrs; HonRl; MrchBnd; NHS; PepBnd; SchMus; EdYrBk; 4-H; PpCl; GAA; College; Secondary Education.

BIESTEK, Patricia J; George Rogers Clark HS; Hammond, IN; 9/260 Chr; NHS; Quill&Scroll; Sdlty; Yrbk; FrCl; KiwanAwd; St Francis Coll; Theology.

BIESTER, Cynthia L; Valley Falls HS; Valley Falls, KS; Band; DrlTm; HonRl; MrchBnd; NHS; PepBnd; YthFlsp; SecFHA; PpCl; College; Airline Hostess.

BIESTERFELD, Elaine J; Grant Park HS; Grant Park, IL; 7/57 HonRl; NHS; Yrbk;.

BIESTERFELD, Janelle; Russell HS; Russell, KS; Chrl; HonRl; LbryAde; OffAde; SchAde; RptrYrbk; 4-H; SpnCl; 4-HAwd; JAAwd;.

BIETZ, Cynthia A; Tripp HS; Tripp, SD; SecTrsSrCls; Chrs; DrlTm; OffAde; StuCncl; EdYrBk; RptrSchPpr; 4-H; CaptBsktbl; LetterTrk; Bus Coll; Med Asst.

BIEVENUE, Diane L; Red Bud HS; Pr Du Rocher, IL; CncrtBnd; HonRl; MrchBnd; PepBnd; Twrl; Yrbk; SchPpr; FBLA; PpCl; Belleville Area College; Commercial Art.

BIGA, Cynthia J; Lincoln Way HS; Frankfort, IL; 120/566 ChrhWkr; HonRl; SchAde; SctActv; Sec4-H; IMSpt; 4-HAwd; College; Commercial Art.

BIGA, Mary A; Daniel J Gross HS; Omaha, NE; 25/168 HonRl; OffAde; 4-H; 4-HAwd; Univ Of Nebraska; Early Childhood Educator.

BIGARD, Jeana F; Sacred Heart Academy; Mt Pleasant, MI; 4/53 VPSrCls; HonRl; NHS; StuGov; FrCl; PpCl; LetterBsktbl; Trk; Central Michigan Univ; Office Admin.

BIGBY, John W; Carrollton HS; Carrollton, MO; ChrhWkr; HonRl; NatlThespSoc; SchMus; StuCncl; YthFlsp; Bsbl; Bsktbl; Ftbl; Central Mo State; Undecided.

BIGELOW, Bradley D; Traverse Cy HS; Williamsburg, MI; 10/650 TrsFrshCls; VPBand; HonRl; MrchBnd; NHS; NatlMeritSF; Orch; PepBnd; SchMus; StuGov; U Of Mi; Medical.

BIGELOW, Clifford E; Engadine HS; Epoufette, MI; LetterFtbl; Trk;.

BIGELOW, Douglas L; Nashua HS; Nashua, IA; Band; Chr; CncrtBnd; HonRl; MrchBnd; PepBnd; SciCl; Coll; Brodcasting.

BIGELOW, Lynne A; Hale HS; Hale, MI; Band; HonRl; MrchBnd; NHS; PepBnd; SchPl; SctActv; TchrAde; RptrYrbk; Bsktbl; Coll; Library Sci.

BIGGS, Amy J; Murphysboro Twp HS; Murphysboro, IL; Band; Chrs; ChrhWkr; CncrtBnd; HonRl; MrchBnd; NHS; SchMus; SctActv; StuCncl; 4-H; SpnCl; LetterTrk; Chrldr; College.

BIGGS, David H; Concordia Lutheran HS; Fort Wayne, IN; VPJrCls; TrsSrCls; Band; HonRl; NHS; NatlMeritSF; PolWkr; StuCncl; StuGov; PresLatCl; College; Law.

BIGGS, Jason B; Collinsville HS; Fairmont City, IL; Band; Chrl; Chrs; CncrtBnd; HonRl; MrchBnd; Orch; ROTC; SchMus; FrCl; Siu E; Professional Musician.

BIGGS, Julie M; Mercy HS; St Louis, MO; 3/190 HonRl; JrNHS; StuCncl; TchrAde; RptrYrbk; PpCl; GAA; IMSpt; College; Mathematics.

BIGGS, Mark A; South Spencer HS; Richland, IN; 4/127 ChrhWkr; HonRl; Purdue University; Forestry.

BIGGS, Stephen; Brookfield HS; Brookfield, MO; HonRl; JrNHS; NHS; IMSpt; CitAwd; Vocational; Carpentry.

BIGGS, Tamara K; Ritenour Sr HS; St Louis, MO; 45/900 AFS; HonRl; JrNHS; NHS; College; Professional.

BIGHAM, Cheryl A; Sparta HS; Sparta, IL; Band; ChrhWkr; CncrtBnd; HonRl; HospAde; MrchBnd; Orch; PepBnd; RptrSchPpr; College; Medicine.

BIGHAM, Jean; Elverado HS; Vergeannes, IL; 1/46 PresFrshCls; VPSophCls; ChrhWkr; CmntyWkr; HonRl; PresStuCncl; EdYrBk; 4-H; PresFHA; FrCl; PpCl; Chrldr; DanFAwd; 4-HAwd; College.

BIGHAM, Larry D; Pinckneyville HS; Pinckneyville, IL; FrCl; PpCl; LetterBsktbl; So Illinois Univ; Chemistry.

BIGHAM, Rodney B; Perry Lecompton HS; Grantville, KS; 15/65 TrsJrCls; HonRl; OffAde; StuCncl; StuGov; 4-H; Bsbl; LetterBsktbl; LetterTrk; Wrstlng; 4-HAwd; Kansas State Univ; Agriculture Engineering.

BIGLER, Greg; Northwood HS; Nappanee, IN; 13/194 ChrhWkr; HonRl; NHS; PpCl; AmLegAwd; Purdue Univ; Mech Engineering.

BIGLER, Mary J; Anna Jonesboro HS; Anna, IL; 11/132 HonRl; Yrbk; FFA; William Woods College; Science.

BIGLEY, Denise A; Eldora Comm HS; Eldora, IA; Chr; Chrs; ChrhWkr; CmntyWkr; HonRl; SchMus; SctActv; YthFlsp; RptrSchPpr; SchPpr; Bsbl; Bsktbl; Univ Of North Iowa; Elem Educ.

BIGLEY, Teresa D; Culver Comm HS; Culver, IN; 24/99 VPSophCls; Chrl; HonRl; IntrClCncl; SchPl; TchrAde; YthFlsp; RptrYrbk; RptrSchPpr; FTA; Idaho State; Clinical Psychology.

BIGLOW, Jennifer A; St Louis Park HS; St Louis Park, MN; 99/700 AFS; ALAGirlsSt; CmntyWkr; NHS; GAA; IMSpt; Univ Of Minnesota; Doctor.

BIGMAN, Joel; Berkley HS; Oak Park, MI; NHS; NatlMeritSF; SciCl; Univ; Science Engineering.

BIGWOOD, Lori K; Bottineau HS; Bottineau, ND; 1/67 ALAGirlsSt; Band; Chr; ChrhWkr; CmntyWkr; CncrtBnd; HonRl; HospAde; MrchBnd; PepBnd; PolWkr; Chrldr; College; Professional.

BIKE, William S; Gordon Tech; Chicago, IL; 4/655 CmntyWkr; HonRl; NHS; NatlMeritSF; MthCl; IMSpt; GovHonPrgAwd; Coll; Professional.

BILDERBACK, Gwenith L; Trico HS; Percy, IL; 3/115 PresSrCls; Band; HonRl; NHS; NatlMeritSchl; SchMus; StuCncl; RptrYrbk; RptrSchPpr; Bsktbl; College; Medical Technology.

BILDERBACK, Michael R; Southridge HS; Huntingburg, IN; 1/142 ALBoysSt; Band; HonRl; NatlMeritSchl; PepBnd; LetterBsktbl; LetterFtbl; LetterTrk; OptClAwd; Depauw U; Biochemistry.

BILEK, Sharon L; West Ottawa 'S; Holland, MI; Chr; HonRl; NHS; SchAde; TchrAde; Aquinas College; Elementary Ed Teacher.

BILGER, Donald; Brookfield East HS; Brookfield, WI; 1/523 Aud/Vis; CncrtBnd; HonRl; LitMag; NHS; NatlMeritFnl; NatlMeritSchl; StuCncl; KeyCl;.

BILGER, Donald P; Brookfield East HS; Brookfield, WI; 1/519 Band; ChrhWkr; CncrtBnd; HonRl; NHS; NatlMeritSF; PepBnd; StuCncl; KeyCl; VPMthCl; Univ; Physical Science.

BILGRAM, Barbara R; Northwest HS; High Ridge, MO; Chr; ChrhWkr; CmntyWkr; SctActv; YthFlsp; SchPpr; CivCl; FHA; GerCl; LetterTrk; Bus Sch.

BILL, David C; Normal Community HS; Normal, IL; PresJrCls; CmntyWkr; HonRl; NHS; SchPl; PresStuCncl; EdSchPpr; MthCl; Illinois State Univ; English.

BILLARD, Brian; La Salle Peru Hs; Oglesby, IL; ALBoysSt; HonRl; Bsktbl; University Of Iowa; Dentist.

BILLBERG, Greg L; Roseau HS; Roseau, MN; 24/130 PresChrs; CncrtBnd; HonRl; Mdrgl; SchAde; RptrYrbk; Pres4-H; LetterBsktbl; AmLegAwd; 4-HAwd; College; Mass Communications.

BILLESBACH, Marjorie S; Blair HS; Blair, NE; HonRl; HospAde; StuCncl; FBLA; FHA; PpCl; Bsktbl; Trk; Chrldr; GAA; JAAwd; PresAwd; University; Major Study.

BILLINGER, Lora; Marian HS; Hays, KS; 4/61 ModUN; NHS; LatCl; PpCl; GAA; IMSpt; Ks St Univ; Computer Programmer.

BILLINGS, Dave G; Northrop HS; Fort Wayne, IN; Band; Chr; CncrtBnd; HonRl; MrchBnd; Orch; PepBnd; SchMus; YthFlsp; RptrSchPpr; College; Music.

BILLINGS, David D; Keya Paha County HS; Sptrinview, NE; 3/23 ALBoysSt; Chr; Chrs; HonRl; JrNHS; StuCncl; StuGov; Yrbk; Bsktbl; Ftbl;.

BILLINGS, Deborah A; Willowbrook HS; Villa Park, IL; CmntyWkr; HonRl; JrNHS; NHS; Orch; SchMus; College; Anthropology.

BILLINGS, George J; Pontiac Catholic HS; Troy, MI; 11/145 HonRl; NHS; SchPl; StuCncl; Bsktbl; Ftbl; Trk; Wrstlng; U Of Detroit; Mechanical Engr.

BILLINGS, Larry G; Clear Lake Community HS; Clear Lake, IA; Chr; Chrs; ChrhWkr; YthFlsp; 4-H; IMSpt; University; Engineering.

BILLINGS, Leslie A; Blue Valley HS; Olathe, KS; 10/92 Chrs; DrlTm; HonRl; NatlFornLg; NHS; SchPl; Yrbk; SchPpr; 4-H; Univ Of Kansas; Med Tech.

BILLINGS, William A; Kirkwood HS; Kirkwood, MO; 41/660 HonRl; IntrClCncl; NatlMeritSF; StuGov; YthFlsp; PpCl; Ftbl; LetterTrk; IMSpt; Univ;-sci.

BILLINGSLEY, Bruce A; Galesburg Senior HS; Galesburg, IL; 84/588 HonRl; NHS; SctActv; StuCncl; RptrYrbk; Yrbk; Trk;.

BILLINGTON, Jayne M; Benkelman HS; Benkelman, NE; 6/39 TrsFrshCls; VPSophCls; Band; Chrs; DrlTm; HonRl; NHS; SchPl; StuCncl; Yrbk; FHA; College; Music.

BILLINGTON, Michael R; Cisne HS; Cisne, IL; 5/61 ChrhWkr; HonRl; NHS; NatlMeritCmnd; SctActv; StuCncl; RptrYrbk; SptEdYrbk; RptrSchPpr; EdSchPpr; LatCl; MthCl; South Ill Univ; Psychiatrist.

BILLMEIER, Ronald F; Reese HS; Saginaw, MI; ChrhWkr; CmntyWkr; HonRl; SchAde; TchrAde; GerCl; LetterTrk; IMSpt; CitAwd; College; Professional.

BILLS, Julie J; Cass City HS; Cass City, MI; 20/130 Band; ChrhWkr; DrmMjrt; HonRl; MrchBnd; NHS; SchPl; TchrAde; EdYrBk; PPFtbl; Coll;.

BILLS, Kimberly S; Hanover Horton HS; Horton, MI; TrsFrshCls; PresJrCls; Band; Chr; CncrtBnd; HonRl; StuCncl; YthFlsp; RptrSchPpr; CaptBsktbl; Chrldr; Michigan St Univ; Medicine.

BILLS, Luann R; Polk Public HS; Polk, NE; 2/18 ALAGirlsSt; Chrs; CncrtBnd; HonRl; SchPl; TchrAde; RptrYrbk; EdSchPpr; LetterTrk; Chrldr; Business School; Vocation.

BILLUPS, Dennis R; Cainsville R I HS; Blythedale, MO; 1/12 TrsSophCls; Band; ChrhWkr; HonRl; MrchBnd; SchPl; Yrbk; FFA; Bsktbl; Trk; Trenton Jr Coll; Agri Business.

BILOZ, David; Jacksonville Hs; Jacksonville, IL; 25 CncrtBnd; HonRl; MrchBnd; PepBnd; KeyCl; LetterSoc; LetterTennis; U ; Aviation.

BILSBOROUGH, Michele E; Huntley HS; Huntley, IL; 10/48 TrsJrCls; Chrs; HonRl; NHS; StuGov; LatCl; GAA; Nursing School; Nurse.

BILTER, Carl; St Charles Hs; St Charles, IL; 14/450 Aud/Vis; Chr; HonRl; NHS; TchrAde; SpnCl; MthCl; Bradley U; Electrical Engineering.

BILTZ, Timothy G; Whitko HS; Pierceton, IN; VPChrhWkr; HonRl; SctActv; SecYthFlsp; YthFnd; Bsktbl; Glf; IMSpt; College; Business.

BILY, Cynthia; Wichita HS Southeast; Wichita, KS; 7/671 Chrs; HonRl; NatlMeritFnl; PpCl; BttyCrckrAwd; Ks St Univ; Chemical Engineer.

BILY, Cynthia A; Wichita Southeast HS; Wichita, KS; 8/671 Chrs; HonRl; NatlMeritSF; PresSpnCl; PpCl; Ksu; Chem Engineering.

BILYEU, Chuck F; Spfld Southeast HS; Springfield, IL; 41/464 HonRl; OffAde; MthCl; Bsbl; CaptFtbl; College; Computer Science.

BILYEU, Donna R; Spokane HS; Chestnutridge, MO; VPJrCls; Chrs; HonRl; StuCncl; Yrbk; FHA; Trade Sch; Professional.

BILYEU, Julianne; Lanphier HS; Springfield, IL; 21/473 CmntyWkr; CncrtBnd; HonRl; HospAde; JA; SecNHS; NatlMeritCmnd; YthFlsp; SptEdYrbk; DARAwd; Il Wesleyan; Rn.

BILYK, Marion; St Alphonsus HS; Detroit, MI; 9/108 ChrhWkr; CmntyWkr; HonRl; JA; NatlFornLg; NHS; SchPl; TchrAde; EdYrBk; LatCl; Univ Of Detroit; English.

BINDE, Cherlyn K; Ray HS; Ray, ND; 2/28 PresSrCls; Band; Chr; Chrs; CncrtBnd; HonRl; MrchBnd; PepBnd; SchMus; SchPl; Minot State College; Secretarial.

BINDE, Julie A; Milbank HS; Milbank, SD; HonRl; FHA; PpCl; PPFtbl; Col; Voc.

BINDER, Barbara S; Marian HS; Hays, KS; Chr; HonRl; IntrClCncl; NHS; StuCncl; TchrAde; 4-H; PpCl; ChmbCommrsAwd; 4-HAwd; Fort Hays College; Secretary.

BINDER, Ellen; Sullivan HS; Sullivan, MO; 24/166 HonRl; NHS; SchMus; SchPl; StuCncl; RptrYrbk; FHA; FTA; SpnCl; RotaryAwd; Univ Of Columbia Mo; Science.

BINDER, Rebecca; Table Rock HS; Table Rock, NE; 4/25 Band; Chrs; ChrhWkr; CmntyWkr; CncrtBnd; HonRl; MrchBnd; SchPl; Yrbk; 4-H; Coll; Elem Teacher.

BINDER, Sandi L; Bishop Noll Institute; Highland, IN; 156/360 SecSophCls; HonRl; SchPl; StuCncl; PpCl; College; Professnl.

BINDER, William D; Tecumseh HS; Teumsch, MI; Band; ChrhWkr; CncrtBnd; MrchBnd; NatlMeritFnl; NatlMeritSF; PepBnd; YthFlsp; Trk; IMSpt; Mi St U; Radio Sta Mgr.

BINDOKAS, Antanas; St Rita HS; Chicago, IL; RptrYrbk; RptrSchPpr; Univ Of Illinois; Veterinarian.

BINDSCHATEL, Brenda J; Clio HS; Clio, MI; 15/356 ChrhWkr; JrNHS; LitMag; NHS; SchPl; StuCncl; Spring Arbor College.

BINFORD, Karen; Haviland HS; Haviland, KS; TrsSophCls; SecSrCls; Chrs; HonRl; StuCncl; Yrbk; FHA; Univ; Registered Nurse.

BINGAMAN, Sandra K; Rock Island HS; Rock Island, IL; 52/652 NHS; GerCl; GAA; Texas Luth Coll; Medical Lab Tech.

BINGAMAN, Timothy A; Benton HS; St Joseph, MO; Aud/Vis; Chr; CtyCnl; LbryAde; NHS; RedCrAde; SchMus; SchPl; TchrAde; SciCl; College.

BINGEN, Linda M; Lyman HS; Presho, SD; Chr; DrlTm; HonRl; NHS; 4-H; PpCl; Trade Sch; Vocational Florist.

BINGERT, Chuck; Hebron HS; Hebron, ND; PresSophCls; PresJrCls; PresSrCls; SptEdYrbk; EdSchPpr; FFA; GerCl; Bsktbl; Ftbl; Trk; Nd State School Of Science;refrig Tech.

BINGHAM, Carolyn K; Bloomfield HS; Bloomfield, NE; 4/43 Chrs; HonRl; PpCl; College; Registered Nurse.

BINGHAM, Cynthia L; Mexico Sr HS; Mexico, MO; JA; SchMus; SctActv; StuCncl; TchrAde; LatCl; PpCl; University; Pediatrics.

BINGHAM, Dawn Y; South Newton HS; Brook, IN; 42/105 SchPl; SctActv; 4-H; FBLA; FHA; FTA; LatCl; PpCl; PPFtbl; 4-HAwd; Business School.

BINGHAM, Karen L; Rolling Meadows HS; Arlington Hts, IL; 18/546 Chr; Chrs; HonRl; JrNHS; NHS; SctActv; FrCl; Eastern Illinois Univ; Mathematics.

BINGHAM, Tammy S; Mulberry Grove HS; Greenville, IL; HonRl; FHA; PpCl; Hickey Sch; Sec.

BINGHEIM, Dennis; Centralia Hs; Centralia, IL; Band; CncrtBnd; MrchBnd; PepBnd; SchMus; SchPl; SctActv; KeyCl; GodCntryAwd; College; Music Major.

BINGLEY, Joan M; Reavis HS; Burbank, IL; 6/700 HonRl; SecJrNHS; NatlMeritSF; VPNatlThespSoc; SchPl; RptrSchPpr; College; Mathematics.

BINHHAM, Thomas D; Brown Co HS; Nashville, IN; 11/270 HonRl; SctActv; CaptFtbl; LetterWrstlng; Purdue Univ.

BINKLEY, Kathy; Madison HS; Madison Heights, MI; 2/242 HonRl; NHS; NatlMeritCmnd; NatlThespSoc; SchPl; TchrAde; RptrYrbk; SciCl; VoiceDemAwd; Univ Of Michigan; Geology.

BINKO, Julie M; Riverside Brookfield HS; Brookfield, IL; 35/489 AFS; HonRl; JrNHS; NHS; StuCncl; StuGov; SchPpr; FrCl; GerCl; CchngActv; Univ Of Illinois; Commercial Art.

BINNEBOSE, Debra A; Glenbrook South HS; Glenview, IL; AFS; HonRl; NHS; StuCncl; TchrAde; GAA; Univ; Food Service.

BINNEY, Lora L; Gallatin R V HS; Gallatin, MO; 1/52 Band; HonRl; NHS; SecStuCncl; PresFHA; LetterGlf; University Of Missouri; Computer Science.

BINSTOCK, Carla; St Marys HS; New England, ND; CncrtBnd; HonRl; MrchBnd; PepBnd; Lake Region Jr College; Nursing.

BINTZ, Marilu; Ladywood St Agnes HS; Indianapolis, IN; 1/116 VPJrCls; NatlMeritCmnd; SchMus; StuCncl; FrCl; CaptBsktbl; Glf; Tennis; GAA; IMSpt; Creighton U; Med.

BINTZ, Mary J; Tri Center HS; Neola, IA; Chrs; SchPl; Yrbk; 4-H; PpCl; LetterBsbl; CaptBsktbl; LetterTrk; College; Secretary.

BIPES, Mark E; Onamia Public HS; Onamia, MN; CncrtBnd; HonRl; MrchBnd; PepBnd; Trk; College; Professional.

BIRCH, Carol A; North Clay HS; Bible Grove, IL; HonRl; NHS; SchPl; TreasStuCncl; YthFlsp; 4-H; SpnCl; PpCl; 4-HAwd; PresAwd;.

BIRCH, Dennis L; Colon HS; Leonidas, MI; 5/58 TrsSrCls; ALBoysSt; NHS; TchrAde; SptEdSchPpr; LetterBsktbl; LetterFtbl; LetterTrk; Western Mich Univ; Political Science.

BIRCHER, Ronnie L; Pecatonica Area HS; Blanchardville, WI; 18/58 HonRl; YthFlsp; FFA; PpCl; Trk; Voc Sch; Tech Agriculture.

BIRCHLER, Mark A; Central HS; La Crosse, WI; ChrhWkr; HonRl; NHS; SctActv; StuCncl; TchrAde; YthFlsp; Ftbl; Wrstlng; PresAwd; Univ; Pro.

BIRD, Connie J; Hoopeston East Lynn HS; Hoopeston, IL; 1/128 TrsJrCls; NHS; NatlMeritCmnd; SecNatlThespSoc; TreasStuCncl; RptrYrbk; 4-H; Bsktbl; CaptChrldr; GAA; AmLegAwd; DARAwd; 4-HAwd; Univ Of Illinois.

BIRD, Karen; Lawrence Central HS; Indianapolis, IN; DrlTm; Quill&Scroll; SchPl; StuGov; SchPpr; SciCl; IMSpt; Univ; Home Econ.

BIRD, Marsha L; Oak Park HS; Kansas City, MO; Chr; HonRl; SchMus; PpCl; Chrldr; College; Clerical.

BIRD, Melony; Quinter HS; Quinter, KS; Band; ChrhWkr; CncrtBnd; HonRl; NHS; StuCncl; Twrl; YthFlsp; CivCl; FHA; Col; Bus Educator.

BIRD, Patricia A; Vienna HS; Vienna, IL; FHA; SpnCl; PpCl; Business School; Secretary.

BIRD, Richard A; Watseka Community HS; Watseka, IL; Band; CncrtBnd; HonRl; MrchBnd; SchPl; SctActv; LetterBsktbl; Air Force Academy; Test Pilot.

BIRD, Tony L; Dora R 3 HS; Dora, MO; VPSrCls; HonRl; NHS; SchPl; RptrYrbk; FFA; Bsbl; CaptBsktbl; Trade School; Vocation.

BIRK, Ramona J; Jasper HS; Jasper, IN; TreasChr; Chrs; ChrhWkr; HonRl; Orch; PolWkr; SchMus; SchPl; Sdlty; Pres4-H; Ball State University; Music.

BIRKETT, Nancy C; Southwest HS; Kansas City, MO; AFS; Chr; RedCrAde; SchMus; FrCl; CaptPpCl; Chrs; College; Professional.

BIRKEY, Marlin K; Manson HS; Manson, IA; 4/82 Band; HonRl; NHS; Orch; Sacrstn; SchMus; StuCncl; LetterFtbl; LetterWrstlng; College.

BIRKEY, Michele A; Olympia HS; Hopedale, IL; 13/276 Band; Chrs; HonRl; Mdrgl; NHS; SchMus; GerCl; PpCl; Wheaton College; Psychology.

BIRKEY, Vicki S; Morton HS; Pekin, IL; 2/293 Chrl; Chrs; ChrhWkr; HonRl; Mdrgl; NHS;.

BIRKHEIMER, Ricky J; Fairfield Comm HS; Fairfield, IL; Band; CmntyWkr; CncrtBnd; MrchBnd; PepBnd; Ftbl;.

BIRKNER, Michele D; Morton HS; Morton, IL; Chr; HonRl; ModUN; SchMus; SctActv; SchPpr; 4-H; FFA; GAA; 4-HAwd; Univ Of Illinois; Vo Agriculture Instructor.

BIRKY, Charlene K; Kouts HS; Kouts, IN; PresSophCls; Chr; HonRl; NHS; OffAde; SchPl; PresStuCncl; VPYthFlsp; FTA; SecPpCl; Bsktbl; GAA; College;.

BIRKY, Cliff L; Delavan HS; Delavan, IL; VPSophCls; HonRl; StuCncl; YthFlsp; FFA; Bsbl; Bsktbl; College.

BIRKY, Jane; Olympia HS; Hopendale, IL; 11/230 AFS; Chrs; SecChrhWkr; NHS; SecYthFlsp; GerCl; GAA; Colle; Sociology.

BIRMAN, Judith L; Gull Lake HS; Battle Creek, MI; 1/220 Band; Chr; ChrhWkr; HonRl; NHS; NatlMeritCmnd; Moody Bible Inst; Counseling.

BIRNBAUM, Jerome C; Browns Valley HS; Browns Valley, MN; Band; Chr; HonRl; NHS; StuCncl; RptrYrbk; Yrbk; AmLegAwd; College.

BIRNBAUM, Joan H; Browns Valley HS; Browns Valley, MN; TrsSophCls; ALAGirlsSt; Band; CncrtBnd; HonRl; MrchBnd; PepBnd; SchPl; RptrSchPpr; GAA; Coll; Speech Therapist.

BIROS, Patricia R; Evergreen Pk Comm HS; Evergreen Pk, IL; 90/439 CmntyWkr; HonRl; SchAde; SchPl; StuCncl; Twrl; SchPpr; PpCl; Little Comp Of Mary Hosp; Nursing.

BIRR, Frank H; Roncalli HS; Two Rivers, WI; Chr; Chrs; SchPl; YthFlsp; St Norberts Clg; Music.

BIRR, Sarah M; Horicon HS; Horicon, WI; VPBand; Chrs; ChrhWkr; DrmBgl; MrchBnd; Orch; PepBnd; SchMus; SchPl; StuCncl; Univ Of Wisconsin; Music.

BIRSCHBACH, Laurie R; Wayland Academy; Beaver Dam, WI; Chr; HonRl; SecNatlThespSoc; Quill&Scroll; SchPl; RptrYrbk; LetterBsbl; University; Film.

BIRSCHBACH, Mary J; St Marys Spring HS; Mt Calvary, WI; NHS; Yrbk; 4-H; LatCl; 4-HAwd; KiwanAwd; Tech School.

BIRUKOFF, Kristy S; Omro HS; Omro, WI; ChrhWkr; HonRl; JrNHS; LbryAde; Univ Of Wisconsin; Physics.

BISAILLON, David W; Bradley Bourbonnais HS; Bourbnnais, IL; 34/316 HonRl; Northern Illinois Univ; Elec Engineering.

BISCH, Kevin; Le Sueur Public HS; Le Sueur, MN; ChrhWkr; CmntyWkr; HonRl; JA; ROTC; SctActv; 4-H; College.

BISCHOFF, Gloria J; Beaver Dam Sr HS; Beaver Dam, WI; 4/350 Chrs; ChrhWkr; HonRl; SchMus; SptEdYrbk; Yrbk; 4-H; Univ Of Wi; Accountant.

BISCHOFF, Lon R; S Milwaukee Sr HS; South Milwaukee, WI; Aud/Vis; Band; CncrtBnd; MrchBnd; Orch; PepBnd; SchMus; SctActv; Milw Sch Of Engineering; Electrical Eng.

BISCHOFF, Pamela J; Stillman Valley HS; Stillman Valley, IL; 1/130 TrsSophCls; Band; ChrhWkr; HonRl; NHS; Pres4-H; VPFHA; FTA; PresPpCl; PPFtbl; 4-HAwd; CitAwd; Illinois State Univ; Math Teacher.

BISCHOFF, Paul N; Brookville HS; Cedar Grove, IN; 7/190 VPFrshCls; Aud/Vis; HonRl; NHS; PresStuCncl; KeyCl; GerCl; Glf; Tennis; LetterWrstlng; Rose Hulman Inst; Computer Sci.

BISCHOFF, Roger E; Tawas Area HS; Tawas City, MI; ChrhWkr; HonRl; NHS; College; Biology.

BISCHOPINK, Gail A; Homewood Flossmoor HS; Homewood, IL; Band; CncrtBnd; HonRl; HospAde; MrchBnd; Orch; SchPl; YthFlsp; Univ; Nursing.

BISEK, Ray A; Mahnomen Public HS; Mahnomen, MN; HonRl; 4-H; PresFFA; Ftbl; LetterTrk; LetterWrstlng; U Of Minn; Professional.

BISEL, Clark C; Mayo HS; Rochester, MN; SecTrsSophCls; Band; CncrtBnd; NHS; NatlMeritCmnd; SchPl; StuCncl; SciCl; LetterTennis; IMSpt; Mit; Engineer.

BISGES, Bonnie J; Fatima HS; Westphalia, MO; SecTrsJrCls; Chr; HonRl; RptrSchPpr; FBLA; FHA; FrCl;.

BISH, Theresa G; Giltner Public HS; Giltner, NE; Chr; Chrs; ChrhWkr; SchMus; YthFlsp; Yrbk; 4-H; PpCl; Trk; University; Psychology.

BISHOFF, Robert C; West HS; Green Bay, WI; ChrhWkr; HonRl; NHS; KeyCl; Bsktbl; Coll; Drafting.

BISHOP, Brenda L; Puxico HS; Puxico, MO; 6/41 ChrhWkr; HonRl; LbryAde; College.

BISHOP, Carla; Axtell HS; Axtell, KS; 1/26 Chr; HonRl; SchPl; PpCl; AmLegAwd; College Eksc; Biology.

BISHOP, David; Grosse Ile HS; Grossile, MI; Band; CncrtBnd; HonRl; MrchBnd; NHS; NatlMeritSF; PepBnd; SchMus; SchPl; Adrian College; Law.

BISHOP, Debbie J; Vienna HS; Simpson, IL; 6/102 VPJrCls; HonRl; PresNatlThespSoc; SchPl; TchrAde; RptrSchPpr; FHA; FTA; SpnCl; MthCl; VPPpCl; College.

BISHOP, Earl D; Rushville HS; Rushville, NE; CmntyWkr; HonRl; SctActv; TchrAde; YthFlsp; FFA; Ftbl; Trk; GodCntryAwd; CitAwd; Ranching.

BISHOP, John F; Our Lady Of The Lakes HS; Pontiac, MI; ChrhWkr; LetterBsbl; Bsktbl; Ftbl; CchngActv; IMSpt; College.

BISHOP, Kim R; Whitko HS; South Whitley, IN; HonRl; NatlThespSoc; SchMus; SchPl; RptrYrbk; FTA; In U; Business.

BISHOP, Larry J; North Decatur HS; Greensburg, IN; ALBoysSt; CncrtBnd; HonRl; MrchBnd; NHS; PepBnd; RptrYrbk; LetterBsbl; LetterBsktbl; LetterTrk; College; Electrical Eng.

BISHOP, Leslie A; Fremont HS; Fremont, NE; 57/412 Chr; ChrhWkr; HospAde; Quill&Scroll; SchMus; RptrSchPpr; 4-H; FrCl; PpCl; NCTE; Christian Education.

BISHOP, Libby E; Ogallala Sr HS; Ogallala, NE; NatlThespSoc; SchMus; SchPl; PpCl; Chrldr; IMSpt; Business School; Vocation.

BISHOP, Linda S; Puxico HS; Puxico, MO; 3/41 ChrhWkr; HonRl; College.

BISHOP, Linda S; Rock Island HS; Rock Island, IL; 39/685 CmntyWkr; NHS; StuGov; VPSpnCl; CaptSwmmng; Trk; GAA; EldAwd; Az St Univ; Home Economics.

BISHOP, Mark A; Indianola HS; Indianola, IA; 29/212 ALBoysSt; ChrhWkr; CmntyWkr; HonRl; NHS; PepBnd; PpCl; LetterBsktbl; CaptTrk; Wrstlng; IMSpt; 4-HAwd; Univ Of Oklahoma; Pharmacy.

BISHOP, Nancy A; Cheney HS; Cheney, KS; 7/38 Band; Chr; ChrhWkr; CmntyWkr; HonRl; SchMus; SctActv; TchrAde; EdYrBk; PresPpCl; 4-HAwd; Butler Cnty Comm Jr College; Phys Therapy.

BISHOP, Ruth; Bishop Dwenger HS; Fort Wayne, IN; Chrs; CmntyWkr; SctActv; 4-H; FTA; GerCl; 4-HAwd; CitAwd; College; Medicine.

BISHOP, Timothy C; Chesaning Union HS; Oakley, MI; HonRl; ROTC; SctActv; 4-H; Bsktbl; Ftbl; LetterTrk; IMSpt; 4-HAwd; College; Aerospace Engineering.

BISHOPP, James A; Sheldon HS; Sheldon, IL; 4/30 PresSophCls; PresJrCls; Band; Chrs; CncrtBnd; HonRl; PepBnd; Bsktbl; Trk; VoiceDemAwd; University; Business Administration.

BISHTON, D E; Northrop HS; Fort Wayne, IN; 54/560 CmntyWkr; HonRl; LitMag; NatlMeritSF; PolWkr; SchMus; Indiana Univ; Jeweler.

BISHTON, D Emalee; Northrop HS; Ft Wayne, IN; 63/587 HonRl; LitMag; NatlMeritSF; PolWkr; Art School; Artist.

BISS, Douglas D; Bridgeport HS; Bridgeport, NE; HonRl; SchPl; YthFlsp; KeyCl; CaptFtbl; LetterTrk; CaptWrstlng; College; Engineering.

BISS, Richard A; Stephen Tyng Mather HS; Chicago, IL; 11/438 Band; LetterCncrtBnd; HonRl; JrNHS; NHS; SchPl; MthCl; LetterSwmmng; Chicago Circle Clg; Veterinarian.

BISSELL, Leisa E; St Johns HS; St Johns, MI; 1/335 ChrhWkr; HonRl; NHS; OffAde; StuCncl; YthFlsp; Bsktbl; GAA; IMSpt; Lansing Comm Clge; Court Reporter.

BISSELL, Theodore R; Boyceville HS; Boyceville, WI; 2/65 VPSophCls; SecSrCls; Band; HonRl; NHS; TreasFBLA; SciCl; LetterBsktbl; LetterFtbl; ChmbCommrsAwd; Viterbo College; Pre Medicine.

BISSELL, Will B; Fort Calhoun HS; Fort Calhoun,

NE; VPSrCls; HonRl; LitMag; SchPl; SpnCl; Ftbl; CchngActv;.

BISSONNETTE, Gail M; Hale HS; Hale, MI; VPFrshCls; CncrtBnd; HonRl; MrchBnd; NHS; PepBnd; TchrAde; LetterBsktbl; LetterTrk; IMSpt; College; Physical Therapist.

BISTANY, John E; Maine West Township HS; Des Plaines, IL; ChrhWkr; HonRl; JrNHS; NHS; LetterWrstlng; Arizona State Univ; Civil Engineer.

BITNER, Dee A; Farmington East HS; Farmington, IL; 31/131 Band; CncrtBnd; HonRl; LbryAde; MrchBnd; SchMus; Twrl; FrCl; Western Ill Univ; Special Education.

BITNEY, Cheryl A; Bloomer HS; Bloomer, WI; 8/114 AFS; CmntyWkr; HonRl; NHS; SchPl; College; Professional.

BITTEL, James M; Thomas More Prep; Quinter, KS; 17/75 HonRl; ChmnModUN; NatlFornLg; NatlMeritCmnd; TrsFrshCls; RptrSchPpr; LetterTrk; AmLegAwd; MrchBnd; VoiceDemAwd; Ft Hays Ks St Coll;forestry & Ecol.

BITTEL, James M; Thomas More Prep HS; Quinter, KS; 30/90 HonRl; ModUN; NatlFornLg; NatlMeritCmnd; SchPl; RptrYrbk; RptrSchPpr; LetterTrk; AmLegAwd; VoiceDemAwd; Kansas Univ; Public Relations.

BITTEL, Kevin D; Quinter HS; Quinter, KS; VPSrCls; ChrhWkr; CmntyWkr; HonRl; JA; NHS; Sdlty; StuCncl; StuGov; Glf; College.

BITTER, Jerry B; St Piux HS; Arnold, MO; CncrtBnd; MrchBnd; PepBnd; SctActv; SciCl; LetterFtbl; College; Computer Tech.

BITTICK, Karen J; Sarcoxie HS; Stotts City, MO; Chr; HonRl; MrchBnd; 4-H; FHA; FTA; MthCl; Mssc; Elementary School Teacher.

BITTING, Robin D; Whitko HS; South Whitley, IN; 38/153 ChrhWkr; HonRl; NatlFornLg; NatlThespSoc; SchMus; SchPl; 4-H; 4-HAwd; Univ Of Evansville; Accounting.

BITTINGER, Laura L; Paxton HS; Paxton, IL; 9/137 HonRl; NHS; NatlThespSoc; SchPl; TchrAde; College; Lab Technician.

BITTLES, Michael; West Lafayette HS; West Lafayette, IN; NHS; Ftbl; Swmmng; Trk; Depauw Univ; Medicine.

BITTNER, Debra K; Hoisington HS; Hoisington, KS; HonRl; LbryAde; ModUN; NHS; TchrAde; FrCl; SpnCl; Barton County Comm Jr College; Medicine.

BITTNER, Diane M; Andrean HS; Merrillville, IN; 10/300 HonRl; NHS; SchMus; StuCncl; TchrAde; YthFlsp; FBLA; FHA; GAA; IMSpt; Ball State Univ; Cpa.

BITTNER, Gail A; Hanson HS; Alexandria, SD; 3/45 ALAGirlsSt; Chrs; HonRl; Quill&Scroll; SchPl; Yrbk; EdSchPpr; PpCl; Trk; AmLegAwd;.

BITTNER, John C; Paw Paw HS; Paw Paw, IL; TrsFrshCls; Band; Chrs; HonRl; LbryAde; NHS; SchPl; College; Elem Education.

BITZER, Denise K; Cambridge HS; Grandy, MN; JrNHS; NHS; SchMus; SchPpr; U Of Mn; English.

BIVENS, Christopher W; Griffin HS; Riverton, IL; HonRl; NHS; SchPl; KeyCl; PpCl; Bsktbl; LetterGlf; LetterTrk; College; Math.

BIVENS, Leslee D; Holdrege Sr HS; Holdrege, NE; Chrl; Chrs; SchMus; College; Medical Field.

BIVENS, Nancy J; Galesburg Sr HS; Galesburg, IL; 9/588 SecBand; Chr; CncrtBnd; HonRl; SecNHS; SctActv; GerCl; College; Music.

BIVINS, Joel W; South Pemiscot HS; Steele, MO; Band; ChrhWkr; CncrtBnd; HonRl; JrNHS; MrchBnd; NHS; SctActv; KeyCl; Bsbl; Bsktbl; Ftbl; College.

BIXEL, Barbara; Atlanta Community HS; Comins, MI; 3/59 ChrhWkr; HonRl; NHS; OffAde; EdYrBk; 4-HAwd; CitAwd; Col; Med Secretary.

BIXLER, Dorinda S; Hayes Center Public HS; Hayes Center, NE; 3/24 Band; Chr; Chrs; ChrhWkr; CncrtBnd; DrmMjrt; HonRl; MrchBnd; NHS; PepBnd; LetterTrk; Chrldr; IMSpt; DanFAwd; College.

BIXLER, Judith E; Elkhart Central HS; Elkhart, IN; 1/447 NHS; Orch; SchMus; College; Music.

BIZER, Dawn R; Northside HS; Fort Wayne, IN; Chr; ChrhWkr; HospAde; OffAde; Parkview School Of Nursing; Nursing.

BJELLAND, Ellen; Berthold Public HS; Berthold, ND; 1/15 SecSrCls; Chr; HonRl; YthFlsp; EdYrBk; GAA; North Dakota State Univ; Home Ec Education.

BJERKE, David A; Spring Grove Public HS; Spring Grove, MN; Chr; HonRl; SctActv; PpCl; LetterBsktbl; LetterFtbl; LetterTrk; Trade; Professional Welder.

BJERKE, Patricia L; Clifford Galesburg HS; Clifford, ND; 1/21 PresSrCls; Chr; HospAde; SchPl; SecStuCncl; RptrYrbk; EdSchPpr; PpCl; GAA; Pres4-HAwd; U Of Nd; Nursing.

BJORDAL, Linda L; Centerville Public HS; Centerville, SD; Band; Chrs; CncrtBnd; HonRl; MrchBnd; SchPl; 4-H; FHA; Trk; College; Vet Med.

BJORGAARD, Lori L; Marshall County Central HS; Newfolden, MN; 3/39 Band; Chrs; ChrhWkr; HonRl; StuCncl; 4-H; FHA; PpCl; Chrldr; GAA; Univ Of Minnesota; Secretary.

BJORK, Thomas; West Liberty Community HS; West Liberty, IA; 17/87 ALBoysSt; Band; ChrhWkr; CmntyWkr; HonRl; MrchBnd; SchMus; Bsktbl; College; Accounting.

BJORKLUND, Beverly R; Madison HS; Madison, SD; 4/159 HonRl; NHS; SchPl; 4-H; FHA; FNA; GAA; 4-HAwd; Dakota State College; Mathematics.

BJORKLUND, Gary W; Underwood HS; Underwood, MN; 1/47 PresFrshCls; PresSophCls; PresJrCls; PresSrCls; PresStuCncl; LetterBsbl; LetterBsktbl; LetterTrk; AmLegAwd; BttyCrckrAwd; College; Professional.

BJORNEBERG, Timothy K; Canton HS; Canton, SD; PresSophCls; PresJrCls; ALBoysSt; Chrs; HonRl; StuCncl; FFA; Bsktbl; LetterFtbl; LetterTrk; LetterWrstlng; IMSpt; 4-HAwd; So Dakota State Univ; Agricultural Engineer.

BJORNSON, Marilyn; Cavalier Public HS; Cavalier, ND; ALAGirlsSt; Band; Chrs; ChrhWkr; DrlTm; HonRl; HospAde; SchPl; EdYrBk; GAA; AmLegAwd; Univ Nd; Rn.

BJORNSON, Marilyn; Lincoln Sr HS; Bloomington, MN; Chr; NatlThespSoc; SchPl; PpCl; College.

BJORNSON, Pat A; Central HS; New Rockford, ND; 6/67 SecFrshCls; ALAGirlsSt; Band; HonRl; OffAde; SchPl; Yrbk; PpCl; Chrldr; GAA; IMSpt; Business School; Dental Asst.

BLACET, Robert W; Eisenhower HS; Decatur, IL; 23/301 HonRl; NHS; RptrSchPpr; Bradley Univ; Mech Engineering.

BLACHLY, David; Andrean HS; Valparaiso, IN; 58/250 HonRl; NHS; PolWkr; StuCncl; MthCl; Bsktbl; Univ; Acc.

BLACHLY, Robert K; Washington Comm HS; Washington, IL; 15/345 HonRl; Univ Of Illinois; Electrical Engineering.

BLACK, Alma B; Bethany HS; Moweaqua, IL; HstSophCls; Band; ChrhWkr; HonRl; NHS; SchPpr; FHA; Trk; GAA; BttyCrckrAwd; Undecided.

BLACK, Anita D; Madison Sr HS; Madison, IL; Band; HonRl; MrchBnd; NHS; PepBnd; LatCl; MthCl; Business Sch Or College; Secretary.

BLACK, Anita M; Fenton HS; Wood Dale, IL; Chr; ChrhWkr; NHS; Quill&Scroll; SchAde; StuGov; EdYrBk; Northern Illinois University; Journalism.

BLACK, Barbara L; Norris City Omaha HS; Norris City, IL; VPBand; Chr; ChrhWkr; HonRl; LbryAde; SchPl; TreasStuCncl; YthFlsp; FHA; VPGAA; Jr College; Physical Education Teacher.

BLACK, Cheryl A; Wayne Comm HS; Corydon, IA; 6/74 TrsJrCls; Chr; HonRl; StuCncl; TchrAde; Teen; YthFlsp; FBLA; PresFHA; SpnCl; Business School; Vocation.

BLACK, Cindy L; Atwood Hammond HS; Atwood, IL; SecTrsSrCls; ALAGirlsSt; Chrs; HonRl; Mdrgl; SchPpr; PpCl; GAA;.

BLACK, David J; Downers Grove North HS; Downers Grove, IL; Ftbl; Ok St Univ; Business.

BLACK, Dianne; Esmond Public HS; Esmond, ND; VPJrCls; HonRl; StuCncl; Yrbk; SchPpr; Chrldr; BttyCrckrAwd; CitAwd; VoiceDemAwd; Univ; Bs In Occupational Therapy.

BLACK, Elizabeth; Bishop Ryan HS; Minot, ND; 13/85 Chrs; HonRl; JrNHS; NHS; GerCl; Bsktbl; GAA; PPFtbl; Business School.

BLACK, Gale; Mississinewa HS; Marion, IN; ALAGirlsSt; Band; HonRl; MrchBnd; NHS; StuCncl; SpnCl; PpCl; Purdue Univ; Comp Sci.

BLACK, Joetta A; Van Buren HS; Carbon, IN; 3/71 TrsSophCls; NHS; PpCl; U Of In; History.

BLACK, Judy L; Ventura Community HS; Ventura, IA; SecSophCls; Chrs; HonRl; SchPl; TchrAde; YthFlsp; FTA; Bsktbl; Tennis; Sch Of Cosmetology; Cosmetologist.

BLACK, Karen J; Ashwaubenon HS; Green Bay, WI; 6/220 Band; CncrtBnd; DrlTm; HonRl; HospAde; MrchBnd; NHS; PepBnd; StuCncl; College; Nursing.

BLACK, Kerry L; Maine Twp Hs N HS; Des Plaines, IL; HonRl; LbryAde; NHS; NatlMeritFnl; SctActv; StuGov; SpnCl; LetterSwmmng; College; Engineering Or Math.

BLACK, Nancy M; Marillac HS; Morton Grove, IL; Chrs; LitMag; SchAde; SchMus; SchPl; SchPpr; Bsbl; GAA; Art School.

BLACK, Pamela J; Casey Jr Sr HS; Casey, IL; HonRl; RptrYrbk; RptrSchPpr; Lake Lano Jr Clg; Computer Programng.

BLACK, Robert M; Senior HS; Poplar Bluff, MO; SctActv; SpnCl; Ftbl; GodCntryAwd; Univ; Law.

BLACK, Ronald L; Rock Island HS; Rock Island, IL; HonRl; PresJA; LitMag; PresKeyCl; PpCl; IMSpt; JAAwd; Western Il Univ; Writing & Recreation.

BLACK, Ryan L; Lynch Public HS; Lynch, NE; ALBoysSt; 4-H; LetterBsbl; LetterBsktbl; LetterFtbl; Business School; Accounting.

BLACK, Susan; Tipton HS; Otterville, MO; LbryAde; SchPl; RptrYrbk; RptrSchPpr; Business School; Physical Therapist.

BLACK, Theresa A; Lesterville HS; Lesterville, MO; Chrs; CmntyWkr; HonRl; RedCrAde; ROTC; UNYO; FBLA; FHA; GAA; DARAwd; Business School; Vocation.

BLACK, Tracey A; Downers Grove South HS; Woodridge, IL; HonRl; LbryAde; SctActv; SpnCl; College; Biology.

BLACKABY, Patricia L; New Bloomfield R Iii HS; New Bloomfield, MO; HonRl; NHS; 4-H; FrCl; DARAwd;.

BLACKBURN, David A; Churchill HS; Westland, MI; 43/853 HonRl; StuCncl; FrCl; Bsbl; Bsktbl; SecJrCls; PresSrCls; Trk; CchngActv; Kalamazoo Col; Pre Med.

BLACKBURN, Julie M; St Francis Academy; Joliet, IL; CmntyWkr; HonRl; OffAde; SchMus; StuGov; LatCl; IMSpt; University; Professional.

BLACKBURN, Linda C; Taylorville HS; Taylorville, IL; 80/259 SecChr; Chrl; Chrs; DrlTm; HonRl; HospAde; LbryAde; Mdrgl; SchMus; SpnCl; PpCl;.

BLACKBURN, Nancy; Courtland HS; Courtland, KS; 3/22 VPSrCls; Band; Chrs; HonRl; SchPl; StuGov; EdYrBk; Chrldr; Cloud County Commumity College; Business.

BLACKBURN, Peggy; Prairie Hgts HS; Hudson, IN; 25/114 Chr; ChrhWkr; NHS; StuCncl; RptrYrbk; Bsktbl; Trk; Chrldr; CchngActv; GAA; IMSpt; DARAwd; Olivet Nazarene College; Nursing.

BLACKBURN, Timothy W; Guilford HS; Rockford, IL; 10/650 HonRl; College; Science.

BLACKER, Karen J; West Leyden HS; Northlake, IL; HonRl; NatlFornLg; NHS; PresNatlThespSoc; SchPl; TchrAde; FTA; Centenary Clg Of La; Civil Engineering.

BLACKFORD, Bill H; Triton HS; Tippecanoe, IN; VPFrshCls; ALBoysSt; HonRl; StuCncl; YthFlsp; 4-H; FFA; PpCl; LetterFtbl; LetterTrk; College; Agr.

BLACKFORD, Donna M; Bismarck Henning HS; Donville, IL; 12/74 HstJrCls; Band; Chrs; ChrhWkr; CncrtBnd; LbryAde; MrchBnd; PepBnd; StuCncl; YthFlsp; Danville Jr Coll; Library Arts.

BLACKFORD, Donna M; Bismarck Henning HS; Danville, IL; 12/76 HstJrCls; Band; Chrs; HonRl; NHS; StuCncl; PresYthFlsp; SchPpr; FTA; MthCl; Danville Jr College; Librarian.

BLACKFORD, James C; Yorkville HS; Yorkville, IL; NHS; StuCncl; Ftbl; Glf; Wrstlng; Univ; Pro.

BLACKHALL, Steven; Kingsford HS; Kingsfoed, MI; CmntyWkr; HonRl; SctActv; Bsbl; Wrstlng; IMSpt; Vocational; Auto Mechanic.

BLACKLAW, Susan L; Hubbard HS; Chicago, IL; 12/346 HonRl; PresJA; NHS; Quill&Scroll; TchrAde; EdSchPpr; PpCl; GAA; VFWAwd; VoiceDemAwd; Northwestern Univ; Law.

BLACKLOCK, Barbara M; Roxana HS; East Alton, IL; 3/275 SecTrsSophCls; SecTrsJrCls; SecTrsSrCls; SecChrs; ChrhWkr; DrlTm; HonRl; JrNHS; NHS; OffAde; SchMus; SctActv; DARAwd; South Ill Univ; Home Economics.

BLACKMAN, Lisa A; East Prairie HS; East Prairie, MO; 12/90 PresJrCls; Band; Chr; HonRl; Mdrgl; NHS; PepBnd; SchMus; SchPl; StuCncl; U Of Ms; Journalism.

BLACKMAN, Mark P; Marion Sr HS; Marion, IL; Band; ChrhWkr; CmntyWkr; HonRl; MrchBnd; SctActv; 4-H; PpCl; SciCl; Wrstlng; Univ; Mining Engineering.

BLACKMAN, Tamara K; Campbell HS; Campbell, MO; Band; SchPl; Pres4-H; VPFHA; CchngActv; IMSpt; 4-HAwd; College; Vet.

BLACKMER, Mark; Chippewa Hills HS; Remus, MI; 23/150 HonRl; SchPl; College.

BLACKMORE, Max L; North Putnam HS; Coatesville, IN; 5/136 TrsJrCls; TrsSrCls; ALBoysSt; NHS; 4-H; PresFFA; VPLatCl; PresMthCl; Trk; IMSpt; SARAwd; Rose Hulman Inst Of Tech; Law.

BLACKMORE, Michael D; North Putnam HS; Coatesville, IN; PresJrCls; ALBoysSt; HonRl; PresNHS; 4-H; PresFFA; LatCl; MthCl; Trk; College; Professional.

BLACKSMITH, Debra K; Central Community HS; West Point, IA; HonRl; SchPl; PpCl; Iowa St U.

BLACKWELL, Jeffrey L; Mc Cluer HS; Ferguson, MO; Aud/Vis; CncrtBnd; HonRl; MrchBnd; SctActv; Yrbk; SciCl; MasAwd; Univ Of Missouri; Optometry.

BLACKWELL, Linda K; Excelsior Springs W HS; Excelsior Springs, MO; 27/240 Band; CncrtBnd; DrmMjrt; HonRl; JrNHS; PepBnd; StuCncl; Twrl; RptrSchPpr; College.

BLACKWELL, Melanie; Cosmos HS; Cosmos, MN; Band; Chrs; MrchBnd; NHS; SchPl; EdSchPpr; FHA; Bsktbl; Trk; Chrldr; GAA; Voc Sch; Gen Sec.

BLACKWELL, Regina M; Neenah HS; Neenah, WI; AFS; CmntyWkr; HonRl; HospAde; NHS; RedCrAde; Yrbk; RptrSchPpr; PpCl; SciCl; Un Of Wi; Veterinarian.

BLACKWOOD, Cheryl J; Heritage Christian HS; Indianapolis, IN; 4/24 Chr; HonRl; NHS; NatlMeritCmnd; SchMus; TchrAde; LetterTrk; Chrldr; Milligan College; Doctor.

BLACKWOOD, Robert R; Heritage Christian HS; Indianapolis, IN; 1/38 HonRl; NatlMeritSF; YthFlsp; Bsktbl; Butler Univ; Business Admin.

BLADECKI, Barbara; T L Handy HS; Bay City, MI; 13/364 HonRl; NHS; StuCncl; CivCl; GAA; IMSpt; Saginaw Valley St Coll;med Tech.

BLAHA, Cynthia T; East Charles Mix HS; Wagner, SD; Chr; Chrs; ChrhWkr; HonRl; HospAde; FNA; VoiceDemAwd; Coll; Prof.

BLAHA, John W; Prairie HS; Amana, IA; PresFrshCls; PresJrCls; Chr; HonRl; Mdrgl; StuCncl; SchPpr; 4-H; PpCl; LetterBsbl; Ftbl; Trk; CaptWrstlng; College; Profession.

BLAHA, Paul; Marist HS; Chicago Ridge, IL; HonRl; JrNHS; NatlMeritCmnd; NatlSciFnd; LatCl; IMSpt; AmLegAwd; I I T; Elec Eng.

BLAHNIK, Barbara; Spring Valley HS; Spring Valley, MN; Band; HonRl; RptrYrbk; RptrSchPpr; 4-H; FFA; FHA; SpnCl; Trk; Rochester Comm College; Newspaper Reporter.

BLAHNIK, Bonita; Spring Valley HS; Spring Valley, MN; Band; ChrhWkr; NHS; 4-H; FHA; SpnCl; AmLegAwd; KiwanAwd; PresAwd; Rochester Comm College; English Teacher.

BLAHNIK, Jeffrey M; Union HS; Grand Rapids, MI; PolWkr; SchMus; SchPl; StuCncl; StuGov; Grand Rapids Jr College; Lawyer.

BLAHUNKA, Paul C; Providence HS; Lockport, IL; 32/128 HonRl; JrNHS; PresNHS; StuCncl; RptrSchPpr; SchPpr; MthCl; SciCl; LetterBsktbl; LetterTennis; College; Professional.

BLAIN, Amy L; Walkerville HS; Walkerville, MI; 2/28 HonRl; LitMag; PepBnd; SchPl; StuCncl; SptEdYrbk; RptrSchPpr; Bsbl; LetterBsktbl; IMSpt; EldAwd; 4-HAwd; Bob Jones Univ; Administration.

BLAIN, Mark; North Central HS; Indianapolis, IN; 159/1163 CmntyWkr; HonRl; IntrClCncl; NatlFornLg; PolWkr; SchPl; StuCncl; TchrAde; GerCl; Columbia Univ; Rabbinate.

BLAIN, Shirley; Roanoke Benson HS; Roanoke, IL; 2,98 PresFrshCls; PresSophCls; VPJrCls; PresSrCls; HonRl; ModUN; NHS; SchPl; TchrAde; FTA; College; Professional.

BLAIN, Teresa; Whitko HS; Columbia City, IN; HonRl; NHS; 4-H; Bsktbl; Tennis; GAA; 4-HAwd; MasAwd; Ball St Univ; Account.

BLAINE, Christy A; Donald E Gavit HS; Hammond, IN; 26/350 TrsJrCls; HonRl; JrNHS; TreasNHS; NatlThespSoc; OffAde; StuCncl; TchrAde; Yrbk; GerCl; Univ; Dental Hygienist.

BLAINE, Diane K; Swan Valley HS; Saginaw, MI; 6/160 HonRl; JrNHS; NHS; SchPl; PpCl; Delta Coll; Dental Asst.

BLAINE, Julie A; St Francis HS; Little Falls, MN; CncrtBnd; HospAde; SchMus; StuCncl; StuGov; TchrAde; EdYrBk; Yrbk; Bsktbl; IMSpt; College; Biology Physical Therapy.

BLAIR, Barbara J; Orient Macksburg HS; Lorimor, IA; 6/38 Band; Chrs; ChrhWkr; HonRl; SchPl; StuCncl; VPTeen; PresYthFlsp; 4-H; Bsktbl; Swmmng; 4-HAwd; College; Vocation.

BLAIR, Brian R; Octavia HS; Colfax, IL; 3/50 HonRl; NHS; SchMus; SchPl; RptrYrbk; RptrSchPpr; SciCl; Bsktbl; Ftbl; Trk; University; Engineering.

BLAIR, Janet L; Benkelman HS; Benkelman, NE; 4/30 Band; Chrs; ChrhWkr; HonRl; NHS; Orch; StuCncl; YthFlsp; Yrbk; 4-H; LetterTrk; 4-HAwd; Kearny St Col; Professional.

BLAIR, Julie; Lafayette HS; St Joseph, MO; 1/287 Chr; HonRl; RedCrAde; StuCncl; RptrYrbk; LatCl; PpCl; Chrldr; Coll; Architecture.

BLAIR, Kenneth L; Ashland HS; Ashland, IL; 3/30 Band; Chr; HonRl; NHS; SchMus; SchPl; StuCncl; RptrYrbk; SchPpr; PpCl; VPSciCl; AmLegAwd; Western Ill Univ; Accounting.

BLAIR, Laurie E; Highland Park HS; Highland Pk, IL; Chr; NHS; SchMus; SchPl; PpCl; Swmmng; Chrldr; College.

BLAIR, Laurie R; Glenwood Central HS; Glenwood, MN; 1/133 Chr; HonRl; NHS; YthFlsp; Yrbk; FHA; GerCl; MthCl; Chrldr; ALBoysSt; Col; Math.

BLAIR, Pamela J; Napoleon HS; Jackson, MI; 1/101 TrsJrCls; Band; CncrtBnd; HonRl; MrchBnd; NHS; NatlMeritSF; StuGov; TchrAde; EdYrBk; Central Mi U; Math.

BLAIR, Terence C; Wrightstown HS; Kaukauna, WI; 4/74 ALBoysSt; HonRl; NHS; PresStuCncl; SpnCl; PpCl; LetterBsktbl; LetterFtbl; CaptTrk; AmLegAwd; University Of Wisconsin; Geology.

BLAIR, Thomas D; Larkin HS; Elgin, IL; HonRl; NatlMeritSF; TchrAde; FrCl; RotaryAwd; Drake U Of Ia; Pharmacy.

BLAIS, William; Rock Island HS; Rock Island, IL; Aud/Vis; Band; Chrs; ChrhWkr; HonRl; NHS; SchMus; SchPl; Coll; Psychiatry.

BLAISDELL, Debbie L; Kalkaska HS; Kalkaska, MI; 4/180 PresFrshCls; PresSophCls; PresJrCls; HonRl; NHS; SchPl; StuCncl; FHA; Chrldr; GAA; College.

BLAISDELL, Mont; Hazen Public HS; Hazen, ND; PresFrshCls; ALBoysSt; CncrtBnd; HonRl; MrchBnd; SchPl; StuCncl; Bsktbl; Und; Go Into Law.

BLAJESKI, David S; Kimberly HS; Kimberly, WI; ChrhWkr; CmntyWkr; KeyCl; Bsbl; CaptFtbl; Trk; Trk; IMSpt; Univ; History.

BLAKE, Andrea L; Ottawa Hills HS; Grand Rapids, MI; 14/520 SecFrshCls; Chr; HonRl; JrNHS; NHS; OffAde; StuCncl;.

BLAKE, Charles D; Liberty Sr HS; Liberty, MO; Band; ChrhWkr; RedCrAde; SctActv; TchrAde; Swmmng; Wm Jewell College; Business.

BLAKE, Charmeann M; Egehand Public HS; Egehand, ND; 3/12 CmntyWkr; HonRl; JA; ModUN; NatlMeritCmnd; NatlMeritSF; SchPl; 4-HAwd; JAAwd; CitAwd; Trade College.

BLAKE, Jim D; Frontier HS; Brookston, IN; CmntyWkr; HonRl; StuCncl; TchrAde; FFA; SpnCl; LetterBsbl; LetterBsktbl; LetterFtbl; Farm.

BLAKE, Joseph; Ottawa Hs; Ottawa, KS; CmntyWkr; HonRl; LbryAde; SchPl; SctActv; RptrSchPpr; Pres4-H; SpnCl; LetterFtbl; 4-HAwd;.

BLAKE, Rodney S; Millington HS; Millington, MI; HonRl; NHS; NatlMeritCmnd; SctActv; LetterBsbl; LetterFtbl; Kirkland College; Conservation.

BLAKELY, Helen R; Ovid Elsie HS; Elsie, MI; Chrl; ChrhWkr; HonRl; NatlMeritSchl; SchMus; 4-H; 4-HAwd; CitAwd; Mi State Univ; Florist.

BLAKELY, Joan L; Elkton Pigeon Bay Port HS; Bay Port, MI; HonRl; NatlFornLg; NHS; SchPl; StuCncl; YthFlsp; College; Music Therapy.

BLAKELY, Kathleen A; Lansing Eastern HS; Lansing, MI; ChrhWkr; CncrtBnd; HonRl; MrchBnd; NHS; NatlMeritSF; SchMus; Great Lakes Bible College; Music.

BLAKELY, Linda K; Winfield HS; Winfield, KS; DrlTm; HonRl; NatlFornLg; College; Accounting.

BLAKELY, Lori; Maple Valley HS; Hornick, IA; 15/99 HonRl; ModUN; NHS; PolWkr; StuGov; Trk; 4-HAwd; JAAwd; MasAwd; PresAwd; Neb Meth Sch Of Nursing; Rn Degree.

BLAKELY, Todd P; Wheaton North HS; Wheaton, IL; CncrtBnd; HonRl; JrNHS; MrchBnd; NHS; Quill&Scroll; RptrSchPpr; Bsktbl; Socr; LetterTrk; College; Law.

BLAKEMORE, Denice A; Streator Twp HS; Streator, IL; Chrs; HonRl; StuCncl; FFA; PpCl; VFWAwd; College; Professional.

BLAKESLEE, Kent G; Great Bend Senior HS; Great Bend, KS; Band; CncrtBnd; HonRl; MrchBnd; PepBnd; SchMus; YthFlsp; 4-H; FFA; Bsktbl; Barton County Comm Jr College; Agriculture.

BLAKEY, David L; Toulon HS; Toulon, IL; 12/52 TrsSophCls; TrsJrCls; Band; Chr; HonRl; SchMus; StuCncl; Yrbk; LionAwd; Illinois Wesleyan Univ; Music.

BLAKLEY, Kathleen A; Moline HS; Moline, IL; Band; CmntyWkr; HonRl; JA; SctActv; Yrbk; LatCl; PpCl; SciCl; Blackhawk College; Veterinarian.

BLAKLEY, Keith E; Chicago Vocational HS; Chicago, IL; 250/1178 Il Inst Of Tech; Electronic Engineer.

BLAKLEY, Krista L; West Platte R Ii HS; Weston, MO; 3/75 AFS; ChrhWkr; HonRl; LbryAde; NHS; StuCncl; TchrAde; YthFlsp; 4-H; FrCl; PpCl; SciCl; College.

BLAKLEY, Lee A; Rochester HS; Rochester, MI; LbryAde; NatlMeritSF; SchPl; Michigan State Univ; Librarian.

BLAKLEY, Linda C; Mt Vernon HS; Mt Vernon, IN; ChrhWkr; CmntyWkr; DrlTm; HonRl; YthFlsp; CivCl; 4-H; SpnCl; GAA; Purdue Univ; Psychology.

BLANC, Caryn; Berlin HS; Berlin, WI; 1/265 Chrs; CncrtBnd; DrmMjrt; HonRl; Mdrgl; NatlFornLg; NatlMeritCmnd; EdYrBk; VFWAwd; Stevens Point Univ; Professional Musician.

BLANC, Nadia; Holy Family Academy; Chicago, IL; PresFrshCls; SecSophCls; PresJrCls; Band; Chrs; ChrhWkr; HonRl; NHS; OffAde; Sdlty; College; Pediatrician.

BLANCETT, Virgil L; Senath Hornesville HS; Senath, MO; 2/86 ALBoysSt; ChrhWkr; CmntyWkr; HonRl; NHS; SchMus; SchPl; ChrhWkr; StuGov; FrCl; South East Mi State Univ; Teacher.

BLANCHARD, Donita M; Polo Comm HS; Polo, IL; 19/92 Chr; Chrs; HonRl; SchPl; SecSctActv; FHA; GAA; Col; Nurses Training.

BLANCHARD, Douglas A; Oak Park & River Forest HS; Oak Part, IL; 290/1100 CmntyWkr; HonRl; PresStuCncl; StuGov; Ftbl; CchngActv; Eastern Ill; Psychology.

BLANCHARD, Kim; Gideon HS; Gideon, MO; Band; CncrtBnd; HonRl; MrchBnd; OffAde; PepBnd; SctActv; StuCncl; FHA; Chrldr;.

BLANCHARD, Kim Y; Charlevoix HS; Charlevoix, MI; 4/147 Band; CncrtBnd; MrchBnd; StuCncl; TchrAde; EdYrBk; LatCl; Univ Of Michigan; Occup Therapy.

BLANCHARD, Vicki L; West Marshall Comm HS; Clemons, IA; 15/88 Chr; Chrs; ChrhWkr; HonRl; HospAde; MrchBnd; NHS; SchPl; YthFlsp; BttyCrckrAwd; Northeast Missouri State Univ; Nursing.

BLANCHET, Gale E; St Michael Central HS; Chicago, IL; HonRl; StuCncl; PpCl; Loyola Univ; Elementary Ed.

BLANCHETT, Clare; Le Sueur HS; Le Sueur, MN; TrsJrCls; CncrtBnd; HonRl; NHS; StuCncl; RptrYrbk; RptrSchPpr; SpnCl; Univ Of Minn.

BLANCHETTE, Jill A; Bishop Mc Namara HS; Bourbonnais, IL; 59/172 HonRl; LitMag; PolWkr; SchPpr; FrCl; GAA; Coll; Law.

BLANCO, Orlando L; Monsignor Hackett HS; Kalamazoo, MI; 23/143 HonRl; SpnCl; CaptBsbl; CaptBsktbl; CaptFtbl; AmLegAwd; University Of Michigan; Law.

BLAND, Barbara J; Bethany HS; Bethany, IL; ALAGirlsSt; HonRl; StuCncl; 4-H; FHA; FTA; GerCl; Bsbl; Swmmng; Trk; CaptChrldr; GAA; 4-HAwd; College.

BLAND, Darrel F; Westhope Public HS; Westhope, ND; 3/17 PresFrshCls; VPSophCls; ALBoysSt; Chr; HonRl; SchPl; SchPpr; 4-H; CaptBsktbl; Ftbl; Trade Sch; Data Processing.

BLAND, Susan D; Sunnydale HS; Fairview, MO; Chr; Chrl; Chrs; HonRl; NHS; OffAde; StuCncl; GAA; IMSpt; Union College; Nurse.

BLAND, Susan K; Flint Northern HS; Flint, MI; 1/616 ChrhWkr; CncrtBnd; HonRl; MrchBnd; NHS; FrCl; MthCl; LetterTennis; VoiceDemAwd; Univ Of Mi; Med Pediatrics.

BLANE, Joy D; Woodruff HS; Peoria, IL; 17/288 AFS; Chr; ChrhWkr; HonRl; SchMus; GerCl; Mid American Nazavene Coll; Special Educ.

BLANEY, Larry C; St Charles Borromeo HS; Villa Park, IL; 5/20 VPJrCls; ChrhWkr; HonRl; StuCncl; SchPpr; FrCl; CaptBsktbl; CaptSocr; IMSpt; University Of Illinois; Engineering.

BLANK, Bonnie; Cochrane Fountain City Hs; Cochrane, WI; 5/96 4-H; FHA; PpCl; LetterTrk; LetterChrldr; 4-HAwd; JAAwd;.

BLANK, Diane L; Columbia HS; Columbia, IL; Band; HonRl; HospAde; LbryAde; SctActv; StuCncl; PresGAA; GodCntryAwd; Nursing School; Nurse.

BLANK, Frances M; Harvard HS; Harvard, IL; 14/156 AFS; Chr; HonRl; NHS; RptrYrbk; RptrSchPpr; FrCl; Eastern Illinois Univ; Commercial Artist.

BLANK, Jody G; West Bloomfield HS; West Bloomfield, MI; 10/450 HonRl; ModUN; NHS; NatlMeritCmnd; StuGov; KeyCl; LetterBsbl; LetterTennis; Univ Of Mi; Eng.

BLANKENAU, Thomas G; Bloomfield HS; Bloomfield, NE; 5/43 PresSophCls; PresJrCls; PresSrCls; Chr; Chrl; Chrs; HonRl; GerCl; Bsktbl; LetterGlf; University.

BLANKENBEKER, Marty L; Robinson HS; Robinson, IL; ChrhWkr; HonRl; SchPl; YthFlsp; 4-H; KeyCl; Ftbl; Trk; 4-HAwd; JAAwd; College; Agric Engineer.

BLANKENBURG, Rita K; Greenfield R 4 HS; Greenfield, MO; 3/38 Band; Chrs; ChrhWkr; HonRl; SecStuCncl; StuGov; SecFHA; PPFtbl; ChmbCommrsAwd; 4-HAwd; JCAwd; College; Professional.

BLANKENSHIP, Debra G; Limestone Comm HS; Peoria, IL; 42/390 Chr; Chrl; HonRl; Mdrgl; NHS; SchMus; SchPl; YthFlsp; FrCl; College; Prof Secretary.

BLANKENSHIP, Diniece; Moberly HS; Moberly, MO; 1/219 ChrhWkr; DrlTm; HonRl; NHS; StuCncl; MthCl; PPFtbl; DARAwd; Northeast Mo State Univ; Medicine.

BLANKENSHIP, Laura E; Winchester Community HS; Winchester, IN; Chrs; HonRl; StuCncl; TreasFBLA; FHA; SpnCl;.

BLANKENSHIP, Linda J; Mt Zion HS; Decatur, IL; Chr; Chrs; ChrhWkr; HonRl; Mdrgl; NHS; SchPpr; Eastern Illinois Univ; Special Education.

BLANKENSHIP, Marcia R; Columbus Unified HS; Columbus, KS; Chrs; ChrhWkr; HonRl; IntrClCncl; NHS; FHA; PpCl; BauchLmbAwd; DARAwd; 4-HAwd; NCTE; VFWAwd; College; Pediatrics.

BLANKENSHIP, Robert J; Salina S HS; Salina, KS; 71/365 VPSophCls; CmntyWkr; HonRl; IntrClCncl; ROTC; SchAde; StuCncl; TchrAde; YthFlsp; YthFnd; SchPpr; CaptSwmmng; CaptTrk; CchngActv; Kansas Univ; Professional.

BLANKENSHIP, Shari A; Carrollton HS; Carrollton, MO; 4/100 Band; DrlTm; SecHospAde; Mdrgl; NHS; NatlThespSoc; SchMus; SchPl; TchrAde; 4-HAwd; University; Medicine.

BLANKMAN, Diane M; Benton Central HS; Fowler, IN; 17/260 ChrhWkr; HonRl; NHS; PresFTA; FrCl; GAA; IMSpt; ALBoysSt; Purdue Univ; Pharmacy.

BLANKSCHIEN, Terry A; Marion HS; Caroline, WI; HonRl; 4-H; FFA; 4-HAwd; Vocational School; Automotive Technician.

BLANN, Cindy J; North Newton HS; Morocco, IN; Band; CncrtBnd; HonRl; MrchBnd; NHS; PepBnd; 4-H; College; Teacher.

BLANTON, Juanita M; Lyman HS; Lyman, NE; 6/19 Chrs; HonRl; NHS; NatlMeritSchl; SchMus; SchPl; YthFlsp; TreasFHA; PpCl; PPFtbl; Hairdressers License; Hairdresser.

BLASE, Donna M; St Johns HS; St Louis, MO; 11/88 Chr; CmntyWkr; HonRl; SchMus; SchPl; SctActv; RptrYrbk; PpCl; IMSpt; CitAwd; Fontbonne College; Special Education.

BLASE, Jim G; St Louis Univ HS; St Louis, MO; 25/210 Chr; HonRl; SchPl; RptrSchPpr; LetterFtbl; LetterTrk; LetterWrstlng; Chrldr; IMSpt; John Carroll Univ; Lawyer.

BLASE, Richard M; Christian Brothers College; St Louis, MO; 1/178 VPFrshCls; TrsSrCls; HonRl; LitMag; NHS; Quill&Scroll; StuCncl; RptrYrbk; EdSchPpr; Trk; St Louis Univ; Doctor.

BLASE, Steven; Hordville HS; Hordville, NE; 4/14 TrsSophCls; ChrhWkr; SchPl; RptrYrbk; RptrSchPpr; 4-H; Bsktbl; Ftbl; Trk; Univ Of Nebraska; Architecture.

BLASER, Kelly L; Norfolk HS; Norfolk, NE; 51/300 Chrs; ChrhWkr; HonRl; OffAde; TchrAde; Wayne State College; Physical Education.

BLASER, Melvin A; Rockridge HS; Milan, IL; 10/138 ALBoysSt; HonRl; NHS; LatCl; LetterBsktbl; LetterFtbl; LetterTrk; IMSpt; Univ Of Iowa; Forestry.

BLASINEY, Wanda M; St Vincent HS; Perryville, MO; HonRl; LbryAde; NHS; SchPl; 4-H; 4-HAwd; Se Mo State U.

BLASIUS, James F; Proviso West HS; Berkeley, IL; Band; CncrtBnd; HonRl; Illinois State University; Musician.

BLASKE, Christine L; Princeton HS; Princeton, MN; 7/183 Chr; HonRl; NHS; RptrSchPpr; 4-H; LetterTrk; Chrldr; 4-HAwd; U Of Nd; Library Science.

BLASKO, Kimberly A; St Peter & Paul HS; Saginaw, MI; CncrtBnd; HonRl; NHS; 4-H; FDA; SpnCl; PpCl; LetterChrldr; 4-HAwd; University; Veterinarian.

BLASS, Jolene; Jackson HS; Lake View, IA; 2/43 DrmMjrt; HonRl; NHS; SchMus; SchPl; StuCncl; RptrSchPpr; 4-H; Bsktbl; Trk; Uno; Pre Med.

BLASTIC, Sharon L; Lakeland Union HS; Woodruff, WI; 2/182 ChrhWkr; HonRl; HospAde; NHS; StuCncl; SchPpr; SpnCl; GAA; CitAwd; U Of Wi Madison; Occupational Therapy.

BLATCHFORD, Timothy P; Parchment HS; Parchment, MI; 6/180 HonRl; NHS; SchMus; StuCncl; StuGov; FrCl; LatCl; PpCl; LetterBsktbl; Ftbl; LetterTrk; Kalamazoo College; Chemistry.

BLATT, Beth A; New Trier East HS; Wilmette, IL; 33/860 Chrl; HonRl; LitMag; NatlMeritFnl; SchMus; SchPl; FrCl; LatCl; College; Foreign Service.

BLATTLER, Wendy; Columbus HS; Marshfield, WI; Chr; Chrs; ChrhWkr; JA; Mdrgl; NatlCathMusEdAsoc; SchMus; SchPl; Teen; Tennis; ;professional Singer.

BLATTNER, Joan E; St Charles HS; S Tcharles, MO; PresJrCls; ALAGirlsSt; Chr; HonRl; NHS; StuCncl; Yrbk; PpCl; CaptChrldr; In U; Fine Arts.

BLATTNER, Joanne L; Maria HS; Chicago, IL; 22/338 Aud/Vis; ChrhWkr; HonRl; LitMag; StuCncl; StuGov; TchrAde; Teen; SchPpr; GerCl; Business College; Certified Public Accounta.

BLATTNER, Stacey; Turner HS; Kansas City, KS; ChrhWkr; HonRl; LbryAde; PpCl; Rockhurst; Veterinary.

BLAUERT, Verlene J; Frazee HS; Frazee, MN; Band; ChrhWkr; CncrtBnd; HonRl; JA; Twrl; 4-H; FHA; JAAwd; Business School; Vocation.

BLAUVELT, Richard A; Berkley HS; Berkley, MI; ALBoysSt; Band; Chr; ChrhWkr; CmntyWkr; IntrClCncl; NatlMeritCmnd; PolWkr; StuGov; YthFlsp; Wayne St Univ; Medical Field.

BLAUW, Ellen J; Thornwood HS; South Holland, IL; 4/852 ChrhWkr; HonRl; JrNHS; Hope College.

BLAZEK, Cynthia J; Prescott Comm HS; Prescott, IA; ALAGirlsSt; ChrhWkr; HonRl; NHS; SchMus; SchPl; Yrbk; Pres4-H; Bsktbl; Tennis; Chrldr; 4-HAwd; College; Professional.

BLAZEK, Don E; Bennington HS; Omaha, NE; VPSrCls; PresBand; Chr; Chrs; HonRl; NHS; StuCncl; EdYrBk; MthCl; SciCl; College; Professional.

BLAZEK, Gerold J; Culver Military Academy; Chicago, IL; 2/169 Band; CncrtBnd; MrchBnd; PepBnd; StuGov; KeyCl; GerCl; Socr; Trk; IMSpt; College; Dentistry.

BLAZEK, Mary; Shrine HS; Royal Oak, MI; 10/163 AFS; HonRl; IMSpt; College; Chemistry Major.

BLAZEK, Thomas J; Morton East HS; Cicero, IL; HonRl; NatlFornLg; NHS; Quill&Scroll; SchPl; SchPpr; TreasFrCl; College.

BLAZEK, William; Wahpeton Sr HS; Wahpeton, ND; 10/140 TrsJrCls; Chr; HonRl; JrNHS; NHS; RptrSchPpr; IMSpt; N.i. S.s.s. Jr Col U.n.d. Univ;law.

BLAZEY, Gerald C; Brookings HS; Brookings, SD; 7/191 Chr; NHS; NatlMeritFnl; NatlThespSoc; ROTC; SchMus; SchPl; SctActv; LetterTrk; LetterWrstlng; Us Coast Guard Acad; Marine Sci.

BLAZEY, Jerry C; Brookings HS; Brookings, SD; 7/193 Chr; JrNHS; NHS; NatlMeritSF; VPNatlThespSoc; SchMus; SchPl; LetterTrk; Wrstlng; KiwanAwd; University; Professional.

BLEAM, Jill A; Wichita Heights HS; Wichita, KS; Chr; ChrhWkr; DrlTm; HonRl; Mdrgl; SchMus; SchPl; RptrYrbk; Yrbk; RptrSchPpr; Sterling College; Christian Youth Leadershp.

BLEASDALE, Earlette I; Bismark Henning HS; Henning, IL; 6/74 ChrhWkr; CmntyWkr; StuCncl; SchPpr; 4-H; PpCl; University Of Illinois; Artist.

BLEAZARD, George R; Marshall HS; Marshall, MO; Aud/Vis; Chrs; HonRl; OffAde; SchPl; StuCncl; StuGov; TchrAde; 4-H; Bsktbl; LetterFtbl; LetterTrk; LetterWrstlng; University Of Mo; Oral Surgeon.

BLECKMAN, Debra; Washington Hs; Washington, MO; 27/272 Chrs; HonRl; SchPl; 4-H; GerCl; GAA; 4-HAwd; Southeast Mo State; Computer Science.

BLEDSOE, Bradford S; Springs Valley HS; West Baden, IN; 6/75 ALBoysSt; HonRl; NHS; RptrYrbk; RptrSchPpr; LetterBsbl; CaptBsktbl; LetterFtbl; LetterGlf; LetterTrk; Indiana State Univ; Radio Tv.

BLEDSOE, Bryan A; Springs Valley HS; West Baden, IN; 5/85 Aud/Vis; HonRl; LbryAde; LatCl; PpCl; College; Law Enforcement.

BLEDSOE, Clayton N; Brazil HS; Brazil, IN; 50/165 Band; CncrtBnd; HonRl; MrchBnd; PepBnd; SchMus; SchPl; YthFlsp; RptrYrbk; Univ; History Teacher.

BLEDSOE, Diana I; Washington HS; Washington, IN; 14/217 Band; ChrhWkr; CncrtBnd; HonRl; MrchBnd; NHS; NatlThespSoc; PepBnd; SchMus; SchPl; In Univ; Lawyer.

BLEE, Michael T; Bishop Dwenger HS; Fort Wayne, IN; HonRl; FrCl; Swmmng; College.

BLEEKE, Anne M; Racine Lutheran HS; Racine, WI; 11/85 ChrhWkr; HonRl; JrNHS; NHS; RedCrAde; SchPpr; SciCl; LetterBsktbl; LetterTrk; LetterChrldr; College; Nursing.

BLEEKE, Richard R; Wayne HS; Ft Wayne, IN; 5/303 HonRl; TchrAde; KeyCl; Bsbl; Bsktbl; IMSpt; Indiana Univ; Political Science.

BLEEKER, Gregg; Pipestone HS; Pipestone, MN; Chr; ChrhWkr; CncrtBnd; MrchBnd; NHS; PepBnd; EdYrBk; Dordt College; Pre Med Music.

BLEHM, Mark A; Russell HS; Russell, KS; HonRl; RptrSchPpr; GerCl; LetterTrk; Kansas Univ; Medicine.

BLEHM, Sharon K; Gering HS; Gering, NE; Chrs; PpCl; Nebraska Western College; Accounting.

BLEICEFFER, Janice L; Maine South HS; Park Ridge, IL; HonRl; LitMag; LbryAde; PolWkr; SchMus; Univ Of Illinois; Pharmacy.

BLEICH, Arlin E; Diller HS; Steele City, NE; 5/19 PresSophCls; HonRl; StuCncl; YthFlsp; LetterBsktbl; DanFAwd; Milford Trade Sch; Computer Operator.

BLEICH, Marjorie A; California R 1 HS; California, MO; 7/98 Chr; Chrs; ChrhWkr; HonRl; NHS; PepBnd; Yrbk; 4-H; 4-HAwd; Central Missouri State Univ; Study Music.

BLEISCH, Kori L; O Fallon Twp HS; O Fallon, IL; HonRl; Business School; Professional.

BLEMKER, Carole S; Southridge HS; Huntingburg, IN; 26/136 Band; Chr; HonRl; SchMus; YthFlsp; RptrYrbk; 4-H; FrCl; PpCl; GovHonPrgAwd; In U; Journalism.

BLEND, Bruce W; New Salem HS; New Salem, ND; 1/53 VPFrshCls; HonRl; NatlMeritSchl; 4-H; FFA; LetterWrstlng; 4-HAwd; Ndsu; Agric Engr.

BLESI, Betsy; Sullivan HS; Sullivan, MO; DrlTm; HonRl; SchMus; StuCncl; RptrYrbk; SecSpnCl; Washington Univ St Louis; Business Admin.

BLESI, Joycelyn K; Sullivan HS; Sullivan, MO; 10/159 PresChrhWkr; HonRl; HospAde; NHS; FHA; VPSpnCl; Olivet Nazarene College; Missionary Nurse.

BLESS, Janet L; Greenview HS; Greenview, IL; 1/25 Band; PresChrs; HonRl; PresNHS; SchMus; SecStuCncl; VPYthFlsp; SptEdYrbk; CaptChrldr; IMSpt; College.

BLESS, Michael C; Lanphier HS; Springfield, IL; College; Computer Science.

BLESSED, Walter C; Seaholm HS; Birmingham, MI; 18/710 Albion College; Business Admin.

BLESSING, Deidra A; South Harrison HS; Bethany, MO; Band; Chr; CncrtBnd; DrmMjrt; HonRl; NatlThespSoc; SchPl; PpCl; LetterGlf; Chrldr; Univ; Vocation.

BLESSING, Martin G; Warsaw Comm HS; Warsaw, IN; Aud/Vis; Chr; Chrs; ChrhWkr; HonRl; NatlMeritFnl; SchMus; SchPl; SctActv; YthFlsp; IMSpt; Univ; Engineering.

BLESSINGTON, Maureen; West Bloomfield HS; West Bloomfield, MI; PresFrshCls; VPSophCls; PresJrCls; CmntyWkr; RedCrAde; StuCncl; StuGov; TchrAde; Clg.

BLEVINS, Dixon W; Bryant HS; Rich Hill, MO; 10/55 ChrhWkr; SchPl; StuCncl; Yrbk; RptrSchPpr; PresFBLA; SecFFA; PpCl; Bsbl; LetterFtbl; College; Mj Journalism.

BLEVINS, Jennifer; Grosse Pointe South HS; Grosse Pointe, MI; Chrs; ChrhWkr; CmntyWkr; HonRl; NHS; SchPl; StuCncl; StuGov; YthFlsp; Ohio Wesleyan Univ.

BLEVINS, Karen L; Emerson HS; Gary, IN; PresJrCls; ChrhWkr; HonRl; NatlThespSoc; SchPl; StuCncl; RptrYrbk; SptEdYrbk; PpCl; U Of Mich; Pharmacy.

BLEVINS, Vanetta J; Highland HS; Highland, KS; SecFrshCls; VPSophCls; Chrs; ChrhWkr; HonRl; SchPl; 4-H; PpCl; Bsbl; LetterBsktbl; Swmmng; Chrldr; 4-HAwd; JAAwd; Kansas State Univ; Designer.

BLEVINS, Vicki L; Reeds Spring HS; Reeds Spring, MO; HstFrshCls; VPSophCls; SecJrCls; HospAde; LbryAde; Twrl; RptrSchPpr; 4-H; FHA; FNA;.

BLEY, Allen; Browough HS; Moundville, MO; 7/24 PresSophCls; ALBoysSt; HonRl; StuCncl; TchrAde; Bsbl; Bsktbl; Trk;.

BLEY, John L; White Pine HS; White Pine, MI; 1/45 ALBoysSt; CncrtBnd; HonRl; NHS; PresStuCncl; PresTeen; LetterBsktbl; CaptFtbl; LetterTrk; IMSpt; Wash St U; Pre Law.

BLEYENBURG, Debbie S; Edgerton Public HS; Edgerton, MN; 5/35 PresFrshCls; Band; Chrs; ChrhWkr; HonRl; NHS; TchrAde; RptrYrbk; FTA; BttyCrckrAwd; Worthington Community Col; Secondary Educat.

BLICK, David R; Trinity HS; Hutchinson, KS; 1/17 ALBoysSt; HonRl; NHS; StuCncl; EdYrBk; LetterBsktbl; Ftbl; LetterTennis; College; Medicine.

BLICKENSDERFER, Michael D; Cerro Gordo HS; Cerro Gordo, IL; 3/75 PresSophCls; Band; HonRl; NHS; NatlMeritCmnd; VPNatlThespSoc; PresStuCncl; SptEdYrbk; AmLegAwd; Southern Illinois Univ; Business Admin.

BLICKENSDERFER, Owen E; Mott Lincoln HS; Mott, ND; ALBoysSt; Band; ChrhWkr; CncrtBnd; MrchBnd; PepBnd; SctActv; SciCl;.

BLICKENSDERFER, Peggy S; Cerro Gordo HS; Cerro Gordo, IL; 10/75 TrsJrCls; VPSrCls; Band; HonRl; NHS; TreasOffAde; TreasStuCncl; RptrYrbk; PresSpnCl; Chrldr; Bradley University; Nursing.

BLICKHAN, William P; Bement HS; Ivesdale, IL; 10/55 PresSrCls; Band; HonRl; StuCncl; LetterBsbl; CaptBsktbl; AmLegAwd; Univ Of Illinois; Agriculture.

BLIEFERNICH, Marcia L; Geneva Public HS; Geneva, NE; 5/57 Band; Chr; Chrs; CncrtBnd; DrmMjrt; HonRl; MrchBnd; NHS; PepBnd; Trk; Univ Of Neb; Bus Educ.

BLIEMEISTER, Michelle K; Central Catholic HS; West Point, NE; 11/79 HonRl; NHS; SchPl; EdSchPpr; SpnCl; MthCl; PresPpCl; SciCl; Trk; GAA; Coll; Biology.

BLIESNER, Peggy A; Appleton West HS; Appleton, WI; ChrhWkr; HonRl; Orch; Clge; Medical Tech.

BLIGHTON, Leslie A; Eau Claire HS; Eau Claire, MI; ALAGirlsSt; HonRl; NHS; SchPl; TchrAde; 4-H; PpCl; BttyCrckrAwd; College; Law.

BLILIE, Larry; Kindred Public HS; Kindred, ND; 24/48 CncrtBnd; HonRl; SctActv; SchPpr; FFA; Bsbl; Bsktbl; Ftbl; Glf; Tennis; Bismarck Jr College; Mechanical Eng.

BLINK, Jeffrey A; Antigo HS; Antigo, WI; College; Doctor.

BLINSKY, Terry L; Wishek Public HS; Wishek, ND; PresSrCls; ALBoysSt; ChrhWkr; CmntyWkr; HonRl; NHS; NatlMeritSchl; StuCncl; StuGov; LetterBsktbl; Trk; AmLegAwd; GovHonPrgAwd; College; Professional.

BLINSTRUB, David S; Pulaski HS; Pulaski, WI; 40/194 Aud/Vis; ChrhWkr; HonRl; MthCl; Bsktbl; Ftbl; U W.

BLINZLER, Barbara J; Sarcoxie HS; Sarcoxie, MO; Band; Chr; CmntyWkr; LetterDrlTm; HonRl; HospAde; FHA; PresBsktbl; Chrldr; IMSpt; Trade Sch; Nurse.

BLISS, Daniel J; Randolph HS; Randolph, MN; 7/43 CmntyWkr; HonRl; LbryAde; NHS; SchPl; SptEdSchPpr; 4-H; SciCl; Bsktbl; CaptTrk; College; Geology.

BLISS, Diane L; Bonner Spgs HS; Bonner Springs, KS; Chr; HonRl; SchPl; StuCncl; PpCl; U Of Ks; Business & Marketing.

BLISS, Leslie J; Norfolk Sr HS; Norfolk, NE; Chr; ChrhWkr; HonRl; SchPl; SchPpr; FrCl; College; Liberal Arts.

BLIXRUD, Mary E; Barrett Public HS; Barrett, MN; 1/19 Band; Chr; ChrhWkr; HonRl; MrchBnd; NHS; Pres4-H; FHA; 4-HAwd; College; Music.

BLIZZARD, Diane E; Harold L Richards HS; Oak Lawn, IL; ChrhWkr; HonRl; OffAde; Orch; TchrAde; Trk; College; Physical Education.

BLOBAUM, David E; Blair HS; Blair, NE; TrsJrCls; ALBoysSt; Chr; HonRl; NHS; SchMus; SchPl; StuCncl; Ftbl; Trk; College; Environmental Or Social Sciences.

BLOBAUM, Dawn A; Ft Dodge Sr HS; Ft Dodge, IA; 10/422 ChrhWkr; CmntyWkr; DrlTm; HonRl; JrNHS; MrchBnd; ModUN; NatlMeritCmnd; PolWkr; StuCncl; EdYrBk; PpCl; Univ; Architecture.

BLOBAUM, Diana; Leaf River HS; Leaf River, IL; Band; Chrs; ChrhWkr; CncrtBnd; DrlTm; HonRl; MrchBnd; PepBnd; GAA; 4-HAwd; Univ; Accounting.

BLOBAUM, Jeffrey D; Fairbury HS; Fairbury, NE; SecJrCls; ALBoysSt; HonRl; SchMus; SchPl; StuCncl; 4-H; GerCl; LetterWrstlng; IMSpt; U Of Ne; Math Sci.

BLOCH, Theodore M; Oak Lawn Community HS; Oak Lawn, IL; 13/667 HonRl; NHS; NatlMeritCmnd; Univ Il; Vet/medicine.

BLOCH, Timothy A; Austin Catholic Prep; St Clair Shores, MI; 52/115 HonRl; SchMus; SchPl; FrCl; Coll.

BLOCH, William F; St Clair HS; St Clair, MI; SchPl; TchrAde; RptrYrbk; Yrbk; RptrSchPpr; Lawrence Inst Of Tech; Architecture.

BLOCK, James R; Random Lake HS; Random Lake, WI; 16/97 Chrs; HonRl; IntrClCncl; Mdrgl; SchMus; StuGov; YthFlsp; LetterBsbl; LetterBsktbl; LetterFtbl; Professional Singer.

BLOCK, Joann C; Harvard HS; Harvard, IL; 41/160 AFS; ChrhWkr; HonRl; OffAde; Mc Henry County College; Accounting.

BLOCK, Joseph; Gurley Public HS; Lodgepole, NE; VPSophCls; Band; Chr; ChrhWkr; Mdrgl; SchMus; StuCncl; College; Business.

BLOCK, Joseph E; Romeoville HS; Romeoville, IL; 58/296 PresSrCls; CtyCnl; HonRl; IntrClCncl; PolWkr; VPStuGov; TchrAde; RptrSchPpr; Trk; Lewis University; Law.

BLOCK, Joyce L; Mount Acad; Atchison, KS; 3/50 SecSophCls; VPJrCls; ALAGirlsSt; HonRl; NHS; StuCncl; CivCl; MthCl; Chrldr; GAA; Ia St U; Interior Design.

BLOCK, Julie J; Onamia HS; Hillman, MN; 2/75 Chr; CncrtBnd; HonRl; MrchBnd; NHS; PepBnd; RptrYrbk; PPFtbl; JAAwd; RotaryAwd; Computer Tech.

BLOCK, Karen M; Maria HS; Chicago, IL; 124/368 Chr; Chrl; Chrs; ChrhWkr; IntrClCncl; SchMus; SpnCl; GAA; IMSpt; Univ; Nursing Rn Prog.

BLOCK, Laurie S; Thompson Comm HS; Thompson, IA; 7/33 SecJrCls; Band; CncrtBnd; HonRl; NHS; PepBnd; SecStuCncl; Twrl; RptrSchPpr; Trk; North Iowa Area Comm Coll; Nurse.

BLOCK, Patti S; Newcastle Public HS; Newcastle, NE; 6/24 VPJrCls; Chrs; CncrtBnd; HonRl; PepBnd; SchPl; TchrAde; RptrSchPpr; PpCl; Bsktbl; Trk; IMSpt; College; Professional.

BLOCK, Randall P; Aurora HS; Aurora, IN; CncrtBnd; HonRl; MrchBnd; NHS; PepBnd; Yrbk; IMSpt; Florida Tech; Oceanography.

BLOCK, Susan L; Dow City Arion Comm HS; Dunlap, IA; SecBand; CncrtBnd; MrchBnd; PepBnd; SchAde; TchrAde; PresFTA; PpCl; CaptPPFtbl;.

BLOCK, Timothy N; Bishop Noll HS; Calumet City, IL; HonRl; Bsbl; College; Professional.

BLOCK, Vicki A; Black Hawk HS; South Wayne, WI; HonRl; SchPpr; Business Schl; Business Machines.

BLOCKER, Bruce W; West HS; Davenport, IA; 54/807 Aud/Vis; ChrhWkr; HonRl; NatlThespSoc; SchPl; StuCncl; SciCl; Ftbl; LetterWrstlng; IMSpt; Col; Body And Fender.

BLOCKSTEIN, Susan; West Senior HS; Madison, WI; 41/580 AFS; ChrhWkr; CmntyWkr; NatlMeritCmnd; PolWkr; RedCrAde; SchMus; SchPl; StuCncl; StuGov; Univ; Engineering.

BLODGETT, Brian J; E Dubuque HS; E Dubuque, IL; 5/57 HonRl; SchPl; StuCncl; SptEdYrbk; RptrSchPpr; CaptBsbl; CaptBsktbl; LetterFtbl; AmLegAwd; Coll; Med.

BLODGETT, Gary; Kewanee Hs; Kewanee, IL; 5 Band; CncrtBnd; HonRl; MrchBnd; OffAde; PepBnd; SchAde; RptrSchPpr; GerCl; Glf; U Illinois ; Veterinary Medicine.

BLODGETT, Kelly J; Harlem HS; Rockford, IL; TrsFrshCls; HonRl; Quill&Scroll; Yrbk; PpCl; GAA; Trade; Sec/acct.

BLODGETT, Le Ann C; Ontonagon Area HS; Ontonagon, MI; Chrs; ChrhWkr; HonRl; HospAde; PolWkr; Twrl; PpCl; Trk; GAA; 4-HAwd; College; Professional.

BLOEBAUM, Heidi J; Waynesville HS; Ft Leonard Wood, MO; HonRl; NHS; StuGov; Univ; Physical Therapy.

BLOECHL, Timothy D; Oshkosh No HS; Oshkosh, WI; 45/368 Chr; VPCncrtBnd; NHS; PepBnd; SctActv; StuGov; RptrSchPpr; KeyCl; PpCl; LetterBsktbl; LetterTrk; Us Military Academy; Law.

BLOEMENDAAL, Ruth D; Chandler Lake Wilson HS; Lake Wilson, MN; Chr; ChrhWkr; CncrtBnd; HonRl; SchPl; PresYthFlsp; Sec4-H; FHA; GAA; 4-HAwd; College; Home Economics.

BLOEMER, Shirley; St Anthony Hs; Effingham, IL; 7/80 VPSophCls; Chrs; HonRl; NHS; SchMus; SchPl; StuCncl; RptrSchPpr; FTA; PpCl; Lakeland Junior College; Accountant.

BLOGIN, Monica A; St Piux X HS; Parkville, MO; Band; Chrs; ChrhWkr; HonRl; OffAde; PepBnd; SchMus; SctActv; PpCl; GAA; College; Medical Field.

BLOHOWIAK, Mary; Pulaski HS; Green Bay, WI; Band; Chr; ChrhWkr; HonRl; JrNHS; NHS; StuCncl; 4-H; PpCl; Chrldr; Patricia Stevens; Public Relations.

BLOK, Gilbert J; Rogers HS; Wyoming, MI; HonRl; JrNHS; ModUN; NHS; IMSpt; College; Engineering.

BLOK, Thomas M; Loy Norrix HS; Kalamazoo, MI; 1/350 ChrhWkr; CmntyWkr; NatlFornLg; NatlMeritFnl; NatlMeritSF; TchrAde; Kalamazoo Coll; Med.

BLOM, Joel W; Pella Comm HS; Pella, IA; 40/124 AFS; HonRl; SchMus; YthFlsp; Pres4-H; FFA; Bsbl; Bsktbl; LetterFtbl; 4-HAwd; Iowa State Univ; Agronomy.

BLOM, Shirley A; Pella Christian HS; Pella, IA; Band; SecChr; SecChrhWkr; CncrtBnd; LbryAde; MrchBnd; NatlMeritFnl; SecOffAde; PepBnd; StuCncl; SchPpr; Pres4-H; PpCl; 4-HAwd; Trade School; Secretary.

BLOM, Susan E; Louisville HS; Louisville, NE; Chr; ChrhWkr; HonRl; NHS; TreasFHA; FrCl; SecPpCl; CaptBsktbl; Chrldr; PresGAA; Wayne St College.

BLOMBERG, Connie I; Akron Community HS; Chatsworth, IA; HonRl; HospAde; LbryAde; FHA; Bsktbl; Univ; Professional Artist.

BLOMBERG, James; West Sioux HS; Hawarden, IA; HonRl; FFA; Voc Sch; Agric.

BLOMBERG, Koreen K; Bison HS; Faith, SD; 2/26 TrsSophCls; Band; HonRl; MrchBnd; Orch; PepBnd; SchPl; Pres4-H; ChmnPpCl; AmLegAwd; Voc Tech; Secretarial.

BLOMER, Georgia E; Barrett Public HS; Barrett, MN; SecJrCls; Chr; HonRl; SchPl; StuCncl; EdSchPpr; PresFHA; IMSpt; BttyCrckrAwd; College.

BLOMMERS, Joan D; Marion HS; Marion, IA; 40/200 HonRl; PolWkr; StuGov; LetterTrk; PPFtbl; Univ Of Missouri; Psychology.

BLOMQUIST, Barry D; Jefferson HS; Rockford, IL; AFS; Band; CAP; CncrtBnd; HonRl; Orch; SchMus; SchPl; SctActv; Socr; Illinois St Univ; Chemistry.

BLOMQUIST, William A; Rockford Guilford HS; Rockford, IL; 28/650 HonRl; NatlMeritCmnd; PolWkr; StuGov; TchrAde; Trk; College; Law.

BLOMS, Jeffrey J; Carpio HS; Foxholm, ND; PresFrshCls; HstSrCls; StuCncl; CaptBsktbl; CaptFtbl; Trk; Trade School; Recr Engineer.

BLOMSTROM, James P; Winner HS; Winner, SD; Band; CncrtBnd; NatlFornLg; PolWkr; SchPl; CivCl; SciCl; Ftbl; Wrstlng;.

BLONSKI, Julia; Notre Dame HS; Quincy, IL; 13/107 SecJrCls; Band; CncrtBnd; DrmMjrt; HonRl; MrchBnd; NHS; PepBnd; StuCncl; FrCl; Bradley Univ; Nursing.

BLOOD, Dearliss A; West Marshall HS; State Center, IA; 44/85 Band; Chr; Chrl; Chrs; ChrhWkr; CncrtBnd; Mdrgl; StuCncl; FrCl; 4-HAwd; American Inst Of Bus; Secretarial.

BLOOD, Terry R; Sacred Heart HS; Salina, KS; HonRl; NHS; Quill&Scroll; RptrSchPpr; College; Professional.

BLOOD, Wendi E; Springfield HS; Springfield, IL; ChrhWkr; HospAde; StuGov; RptrYrbk; SchPpr; Trk; Nursing.

BLOODWORTH, Darlyne K; Hamilton J Robichaud HS; Inkster, MI; 18/288 SecSrCls; HonRl; JrNHS; SchPl; SctActv; SchPpr; FNA; LetterBsbl; LetterBsktbl; Swmmng; GAA; IMSpt; Michigan State Univ; Hematologist.

BLOOM, Allen; Niles North Hs; Skokie, IL; 41/641 HonRl; HospAde; NHS; University; Medicine.

BLOOM, Richard S; Horton Watkins HS; Creve Coeur, MO; 91/499 Chrs; LitMag; ModUN; NatlMeritCmnd; NatlThespSoc; Quill&Scroll; SchMus; SchPl; StuCncl; StuGov; Dickinson College; Writer.

BLOOM, Sheila A; Odin HS; Odin, IL; 2 28 SecJrCls; HonRl; Yrbk; SchPpr; 4-H; SecFHA; PpCl; DanFAwd; 4-HAwd; CitAwd; Kaskaskia Jr Clg; Acct.

BLOOM, Shirley J; South Page HS; Braddyville, IA; VPSophCls; ChrhWkr; HonRl; Teen; FHA; FNA; LetterTrk; Trade; Vet Assistant.

BLOOMBURG, Lynda L; Kingsford HS; Iron Mountain, MI; CmntyWkr; Michigan St Univ; Animal Technology.

BLOOMER, Craig D; Farmington HS; Farmington, MI; HonRl; NHS; Trk; Michigan; Bus Admin.

BLOOMFIELD, John; Forest View Hs; Des Plaines, IL; 17 HonRl; NHS; NatlMeritCmnd; KeyCl; Tennis; College U Of Illinois;business Lawyer.

BLOOMFIELD, John A; Forest View HS; Des Plaines, IL; 17/620 HonRl; NHS; JrNHS; University Of Illinois; Business And Prelaw.

BLOOMFIELD, Patricia A; Ashland HS; Ashland, IL; 9/35 PresJrCls; Band; Chrs; CncrtBnd; NHS; StuCncl; RptrSchPpr; 4-H; SciCl; Chrldr; Univ Of Colorado; Biology.

BLOOMINGDALE, Sandy; Leaf River HS; Egan, IL; TrsFrshCls; TrsSophCls; Band; Chrs; CncrtBnd; HonRl; MrchBnd; PepBnd; FHA; GAA;.

BLOSS, Marcia L; Goshen HS; Goshen, IN; Chr; ChrhWkr; HonRl; LbryAde; SchAde; SchPl; StuCncl; StuGov; Twrl; YthFlsp; College; Airline Stewardess.

BLOSSOM, George W; Lake Forest HS; Lake Forest, IL; Band; CncrtBnd; HonRl; MrchBnd; NHS; NatlMeritFnl; Orch; PepBnd; College; Engineering.

BLOUGH, Karen A; Acad Of Our Lady; Chicago, IL; 15/160 HonRl; JrNHS; LitMag; NHS; SpnCl; PpCl; CaptChrldr; GAA; IMSpt; PPFtbl; College Of Bus; Accounting.

BLOUGH, Philip R; Hastings HS; Hastings, MI; Chr; Chrs; ChrhWkr; HonRl; SchMus; StuCncl; PresYthFlsp; 4-H; FrCl; 4-HAwd; N Mich Univ; Biology.

BLOUGH, Rory J; Jefferson HS; Rockford, IL; 18/335 HonRl; JrNHS; NHS; SchPl; CaptGlf; College; Forestry.

BLOUGH, Tim L; Hastings Sr HS; Hastings, MN; Band; Chr; MrchBnd; NHS; NatlThespSoc; PepBnd; SchMus; SchPpr; College; Illustrator.

BLOUNT, Susan M; Appleton West HS; Appleton, WI; 13/640 AFS; Band; CncrtBnd; MrchBnd; PepBnd; VPFrCl; PpCl; Uw Eau Claire; Pre Med.

BLOW, Michael A; Hamtramck HS; Hamtramck, MI; 17/150 PresJrCls; HonRl; StuCncl; PresStuGov; TchrAde; MthCl; SciCl; CaptBsktbl; CchngActv; New Mexico Military; Dentist.

BLOXAM, Mary J; Community HS; West Chicago, IL; 1/311 Chr; HonRl; NHS; NatlMeritSF; PresSciCl; College; Piano.

BLOYD, Laura D; Warsaw HS; Warsaw, IL; CmntyWkr; SchPl; SctActv; TreasFHA; GerCl; GAA; Trade Sch; Professional.

BLUCHER, Patti S; Lincoln HS; Park Falls, WI; LbryAde; Coll; Sub Teacher.

BLUE, Donna J; Eagle Grove HS; Eagle Grove, IA; Band; CncrtBnd; HonRl; NHS; PepBnd; SchMus; RptrYrbk; 4-H; SpnCl; College; Spanish Teacher.

BLUE, Janice E; Ottawa Twp HS; Utica, IL; 1/420 HonRl; NHS; 4-H; SciCl; GAA; Ill State Univ; Medicine.

BLUE, Larry A; Glenbrook South HS; Glenview, IL; 4/624 VPFrshCls; HstSrCls; Band; ChrhWkr; HonRl; JA; JrNHS; NatlFornLg; NHS; NatlMeritFnl; Bsbl; Bsktbl; Ftbl; Glf; Stanford Univ; Lawyer.

BLUE, Norma E; Heritage Christian HS; Noblesville, IN; 1/56 SecBand; SecChr; ChrhWkr; CncrtBnd; HonRl; Orch; PepBnd; 4-H; FrCl; Bsktbl; 4-HAwd; GovHonPrgAwd; Univ; Math.

BLUE, Peggy J; St Joseph Ogden HS; Urbana, IL; HonRl; YthFlsp; RptrSchPpr; FHA; FrCl; PpCl; GAA; Bus School ; Acct.

BLUE BIRD, Debbie A; Bennett Co HS; Batesland, SD; HonRl; IMSpt; Augustana.

BLUM, Daniel F; Monroe HS; Monroe, WI; HonRl; Bsbl; Ftbl; IMSpt; College; Professnl.

BLUM, David; Sauk Prairie HS; Sauk City, WI; HonRl; NatlFornLg; NHS; SchPl; RptrSchPpr; CaptTennis; IMSpt; AmLegAwd; EldAwd; OptClAwd; Univ Of Wi Eau Claire; Prof.

BLUM, David J; Millard HS; Omaha, NE; 13/330 Chr; ChrhWkr; HonRl; NHS; SchMus; VPStuCncl; SptEdYrbk; LetterBsbl; CaptBsktbl; U Of Ne; Pre Medical.

BLUM, Gale; New Glarus Hs; Monticello, WI; Band; Chrl; CncrtBnd; MrchBnd; PepBnd; RptrSchPpr; SchPpr; University; Small Business.

BLUM, Joanne T; Grosse Pointe North HS; Harper Woods, MI; CmntyWkr; HonRl; LbryAde; NHS; NatlMeritCmnd; Mi State Univ; Social Work.

BLUM, Neil J; Evanston Township HS; Evanston, IL; Band; HonRl; College; Medicine.

BLUM, Randee E; Parkway Central Sr HS; Creve Coeur, MO; HonRl; RptrYrbk; Indiana Univ.

BLUM, Randy L; Jefferson HS; Monroe, MI; 6/160 Band; CncrtBnd; JrNHS; MrchBnd; NHS; PepBnd; StuCncl; Michigan Tech; Bio Chemist.

BLUME, Curtis L; Clarinda Comm HS; Clarinda, IA; Chr; HonRl; SchMus; SchPl; 4-H; FFA; LetterBsbl; LetterBsktbl; LetterFtbl; IMSpt; 4-HAwd; Univ Of Northern Iowa; Physical Therapy.

BLUME, Joseph A; Marathon 'S; Marathon, WI; 6/98 PresFrshCls; PresJrCls; PresSrCls; StuCncl; StuGov; LetterTrk; North Central Tech Inst; Mechanical Design.

BLUMENAU, Michelle D; Our Lady Of Lakes HS; Clarkston, MI; 2/53 HonRl; HospAde; NatlMeritSchl; FrCl; Bsbl; PPFtbl; University; Medical Professional.

BLUMENBERG, Anthony N; East Prairie HS; East Prairie, MO; 25/80 ALBoysSt; Chr; Mdrgl; SchMus; SchPl; PresStuCncl; PresYthFlsp; RptrSchPpr; FFA; LetterBsktbl; Gulf Coast Bible Clg; Ministry.

BLUMENFELD, Stephen B; Rolling Meadows HS; Arlington Hts, IL; 50/546 ChrhWkr; CmntyWkr; HonRl; Carroll College; Psychology.

BLUMENKAMP, Lisa K; Glencoe HS; Glencoe, MN; Chr; DrlTm; HonRl; FHA; GerCl; Junior Coll; Child Day Care Work.

BLUMENSTOCK, Cheryl A; Crab Orchard HS; Marion, IL; 3/27 PresJrCls; Chr; ChrhWkr; HonRl; SchPl; RptrYrbk; SchPpr; FHA; PpCl; College; Music.

BLUMENSTOCK, Elvis E; Marion Sr HS; Creal Spgs, IL; 15/277 Band; ChrhWkr; HonRl; MrchBnd; Univ Of Ill; Civil Eng.

BLUMER, Bruce L; Aberdeen Central HS; Aberdeen, SD; AFS; ALBoysSt; Band; ChrhWkr; HonRl; NatlFornLg; PolWkr; SchPl; SctActv; Ftbl; College; Teaching.

BLUMER, Deanne K; Harry A Burke HS; Omaha, NE; ChrhWkr; HonRl; NHS; NatlMeritSF; YthFlsp; SpnCl; PpCl; LetterSwmmng; CaptTennis; GAA; College; Art.

BLUMER, Robert L; Monroe HS; Monroe, WI; Band; CncrtBnd; MrchBnd; 4-H; FFA; Wrstlng; IMSpt; Univ Of Wisconsin.

BLUMREICH, Karen E; Waterford Mott HS; Pontiac, MI; Chr; ChrhWkr; HonRl; HospAde; JA; SchAde; CchngActv; Mi State Univ Or Li Univ; Biological Scienc.

BLUNCK, Kimberly K; Pella Community HS; Pella, IA; AFS; HonRl; StuCncl; FrCl; RptrYrbk; YthFlsp; PpCl; Bsktbl; Iowa State Univ.

BLUNCK, Norma Jean; Osmond Community HS; Osmond, NE; 2/42 SecFrshCls; Band; HonRl; NHS; StuCncl; SecFBLA; PresPpCl; CaptTrk; AmLegAwd; 4-HAwd; U Of Ne At Lincoln; Pre Med.

BLUNDY, Patricia A; Brimfield HS; Brimfield, IL; 5 60 Chrs; HonRl; NHS; SchAde; TchrAde; RptrYrbk; SpnCl; Nursing.

BLUNK, Joseph W; Providence HS; New Albany, IN; HonRl; SchPl; YthFnd; LetterBsktbl; Trk; Campbells Comm College; Court Reporting.

BLUNK, Scott D; Elm Creek HS; Elm Creek, NE; 3/27 PresSophCls; Band; ChrhWkr; HonRl; NHS; SchPl; TchrAde; RptrSchPpr; Bsktbl; Col; Mathematics.

BLUNK, William E; Brunswick Jr&sr HS; Brunswick, MO; PresJrCls; TrsSrCls; ALBoysSt; NHS; FFA; DanFAwd; Univ Of Missouri; Ag Econ.

BLUST, Maryann; Our Lady Of The Lakes HS; Drayton Plains, MI; 6/53 PresJrCls; PresSrCls; HonRl; LbryAde; NHS; SchAde; StuCncl; TchrAde; EdYrBk; RptrSchPpr; SpnCl; Oakland Univ; Nursing.

BLUSTEIN, Sheryl J; Roosevelt HS; Chicago, IL; 10/293 Chr; HonRl; NHS; StuGov; PresSpnCl; Univ; Major Dramatics.

BLY, Brenda J; Drayton Public HS; Drayton, ND; Band; Chrs; CncrtBnd; HonRl; MrchBnd; PepBnd; SctActv; PpCl; University; Vocation.

BLYTHE, Benda R; Andover HS; Wichita, KS; Band; ChrhWkr; CncrtBnd; HonRl; HospAde; MrchBnd; NHS; RptrSchPpr; SpnCl; College; Law.

BLYTHE, Sally S; Cassville HS; Cassville, MO; 6/105 Band; Chr; ChrhWkr; CmntyWkr; CncrtBnd; DrmMjrt; HonRl; JrNHS; MrchBnd; NHS; College; Law.

BOADWAY, Brenda L; Western HS; Spring Arbor, MI; HonRl; OffAde; SchPl; TchrAde; YthFlsp; Trk; GAA; IMSpt; VFWAwd; Jackson Comm Coll; Nursing.

BOAL, Kimberly K; Waco Comm HS; Mt Pleasant, IA; 6/61 ALAGirlsSt; Band; Chr; ChrhWkr; HonRl; Mdrgl; PresNHS; SchMus; TreasStuCncl; Pres4-H; 4-HAwd; College; Music.

BOARD, Rosemary L; Harlem HS; Loves Park, IL; 120/523 Chr; ChrhWkr; CmntyWkr; HonRl; Mdrgl; SchMus; YthFlsp; Bsbl; Bsktbl; Ftbl; Rock Valley College; Nursing.

BOARDMAN, Susan E; Neb City HS; Union, NE; 33/127 HonRl; OffAde; FBLA; PpCl; Marriage.

BOATRIGHT, Cynthia D; Shortridge HS; Indianapolis, IN; HonRl; NHS; Orch; MthCl; Purdue U; Pharmacy.

BOATRIGHT, Dana D; Remington HS; Newton, KS; Chrs; CmntyWkr; MrchBnd; PepBnd; SchMus; SctActv; FHA; VPSpnCl; GAA; 4-HAwd; Oklahoma St Univ; Orthodontist.

BOATRIGHT, Leslie S; Brookfield Riii HS; Brookfield, MO; Band; Chr; CncrtBnd; HonRl; MrchBnd; SctActv; LetterTrk;.

BOAZ, Jennifer R; Wabash HS; Wabash, IN; 3/210 HonRl; JrNHS; NHS; Yrbk; College; Medicine.

BOBBE, Laurie E; Ellendale HS; Forbes, ND; SecFrshCls; SecJrCls; Band; Chrs; ChrhWkr; CncrtBnd; DrlTm; MrchBnd; PepBnd; Twrl; YthFlsp; FHA; PpCl; College; Nurse.

BOBBE, Ross Roger; Ellendale HS; Forbes, ND; 4-H; LetterWrstlng; Ndsu; Agric Eng.

BOBERG, Eric J; Brainerd HS; Lake Hubert, MN; PresNatlFornLg; SctActv; College.

BOBICK, Cheryl L; Rochester Adams HS; Rochester, MI; ChrhWkr; HonRl; NHS; NatlMeritSF; Orch; PolWkr; SchMus; TchrAde; YthFlsp; Swmmng; Alma Coll; Engineering.

BOBICZ, Margaret P; Ypsilanti Lincoln Cons HS; Ypsilanti, MI; 9/150 CncrtBnd; HonRl; MrchBnd; NHS; OffAde; Orch; PepBnd; SchMus; Twrl; GAA; Eastern Mich Univ.

BOBILLO, Diane C; Marquette HS; Michigan City, IN; SecFrshCls; PresSrCls; Chrl; CmntyWkr;

HonRl; SchMus; SchPl; RptrYrbk; SpnCl; Glf; Swmmng; Chrldr; Purdue Univ; Special Ed.

BOBKA, Thomas E; Maine South HS; Norridge, IL; HonRl; JA; NHS; NatlMeritCmnd; De Paul Univ; Optometrist.

BOBOLZ, Rita K; Hartley HS; Hartley, IA; VPBand; Chrs; ChrhWkr; NHS; SchPpr; Sec4-H; PresFHA; PpCl; LetterBsktbl; LetterTrk; 4-HAwd; PresAwd; College; Music.

BOBOWSKI, John M; Fordson HS; Dearborn, MI; TrsJrCls; Band; ChrhWkr; HonRl; JA; MrchBnd; NHS; StuCncl; StuGov; Bsbl; LetterBsktbl; IMSpt; JAAwd; Wayne State College; Law.

BOBOWSKI, Laura M; John Hersey HS; Arlington Hts, IL; Chr; HonRl; Mdrgl; NatlFornLg; NHS; NatlMeritSF; SchMus; SchPl; TchrAde; AmLegAwd; Nat Coll Of Ed; Spec Ed.

BOBULA, Thomas G; Gordon Tech HS; Chicago, IL; 21/618 HonRl; JA; PolWkr; StuCncl; Northern Ill Univ; Meteorology.

BOCCHIARDI, Mariann; Mt Vernon Township HS; Mt Vernon, IL; 1/436 ChrhWkr; HonRl; HospAde; VPNHS; PresYthFlsp; RptrYrbk; EdYrBk; FTA; SpnCl; Univ Of Illinois; Elementary Education.

BOCEK, Nancy R; Rich East HS; Park Forest, IL; 25/360 Chr; HonRl; JrNHS; NHS; SchMus; TchrAde; College; Dancer.

BOCHENEK, Sheree L; Deer River HS; Deer River, MN; CncrtBnd; MrchBnd; PepBnd; Quill&Scroll; SctActv; StuCncl; Twrl; RptrSchPpr; GerCl; PpCl; Univ Of Mn; Journalism.

BOCHMAN, David; Menomonie HS; Menomonie, WI; HonRl; ModUN; NHS; StuCncl; StuGov; YthFlsp; 4-H; Wrstlng; IMSpt; KiwanAwd; St Paul Bible College; Missions.

BOCHTLER, James F; St Bede HS; Dalzell, IL; 17/120 HonRl; LetterGlf; Ill Valley Comm College.

BOCK, Carrie M; Carpio Public HS; Foxholm, ND; SecFrshCls; SecTrsJrCls; Chrs; ChrhWkr; HonRl; SchPl; StuCncl; PpCl; Chrldr; IMSpt; Trade School; Vocation.

BOCK, Kimberly A; Wabasso Public HS; Wabasso, MN; Band; Chr; CncrtBnd; HonRl; MrchBnd; NHS; PepBnd; 4-H; FFA; 4-HAwd; Univ Of Mn Waseca; Vet Assistant.

BOCK, Loron K; Winnebago Lutheran Academy; Malone, WI; Chrs; ChrhWkr; 4-H; Bsbl; LetterFtbl; 4-HAwd; Trade Schl; Agriculture.

BOCK, Melissa; Leroy HS; Leroy, IL; HstSrCls; Band; Chr; Chrl; Chrs; ChrhWkr; HonRl; Mdrgl; MrchBnd; PPFtbl; Ill Weselyan Univ; Major In Psychology.

BOCK, Paul; Delta R 5 HS; Advance, MO; PresSrCls; HonRl; NHS; RptrYrbk; SptEdYrbk; SptEdSchPpr; FFA; CitAwd; College; Engineering.

BOCK, Tom; Charles City Comm HS; Charles City, IA; 15/250 Chr; Chrl; Chrs; ChrhWkr; CmntyWkr; HonRl; JA; NatlMeritCmnd; SctActv; YthFlsp; Trade; Professional.

BOCKELMANN, Janet L; Rich Central HS; Country Club Hills, IL; 11/413 SecAFS; Chr; Chrs; HonRl; IntrClCncl; Mdrgl; SchMus; PresGerCl; LetterMthCl; VPSciCl; College; Pharmacy.

BOCKERMAN, Jane A; Arapahoe Public HS; Arapahoe, NE; Chrs; LbryAde; SchPl; SchPpr; PpCl; College.

BOCKLAGE, Bradley E; St Thomas Aquinas Seminary; West Phalia, MO; 1/9 PresFrshCls; HonRl; LbryAde; SchPl; StuCncl; RptrYrbk; Bsktbl; LetterSocr; Chrldr; College; Priest.

BOCKSTAHLER, Karen F; Lowell HS; Lowell, IN; Band; Chr; HonRl; LbryAde; 4-H; FTA; Swmmng; GAA; IMSpt; College; History Teacher.

BOCKUS, Freddie J; North Platte Sr HS; North Platte, NE; 9/393 Band; CncrtBnd; HonRl; MrchBnd; NatlMeritSF; PepBnd; Univ Of Nebraska; Pharmacy.

BOCZKUR, Jean; Horace Mann HS; Biwabik, MN; PresJrCls; ALAGirlsSt; CmntyWkr; NHS; NatlMeritFnl; AmLegAwd; DARAwd; St Marys; Occupational Therapist.

BODDICKER, Stephanie; Benton Community HS; Newhall, IA; Band; HonRl; NHS; RptrYrbk; RptrSchPpr; SchPpr; FTA; SpnCl; Marquette Univ; Professional.

BODE, Alan J; Aplington Community HS; Austinville, IA; SecFrshCls; ALBoysSt; HonRl; SchPl; RptrYrbk; Mercy Hospital Schl; X Ray Tech.

BODE, Bradford C; Lyman HS; Lyman, NE; 1/19 PresSrCls; Chr; HonRl; NHS; NatlMeritCmnd; SchMus; StuCncl; Bsbl; Bsktbl; Ftbl; Kearney State Coll; Banking & Finance.

BODE, Cathy; Seymour HS; Seymour, IN; 71/334 HonRl; OffAde; SpnCl; PpCl; SciCl; Chrldr; AmLegAwd; Iupui In Indianapolis; Registered Nursing.

BODE, Cindy; Wisner Pilger HS; Wisner, NE; Chr; ChrhWkr; CncrtBnd; HonRl; MrchBnd; NHS; PepBnd; SchMus; Yrbk; FHA; Trade School; Vocational.

BODE, Sharon E; Helias HS; Jefferson City, MO; ALAGirlsSt; Chrs; ChrhWkr; CmntyWkr; HonRl; SchMus; College; Art.

BODEN, Cindy E; Bloomington HS; Bloomington, IL; 41/391 HonRl; TreasSpnCl; PpCl; LetterTennis; GAA; Illinois State Univ; Accounting.

BODEN, Edgar G; Brady HS; Brady, NE; 5/16 SecSophCls; Chrs; SecFrshCls; HonRl; SchMus; SchPl; StuGov; RptrYrbk; SchPpr; 4-H; Univ Of Nebraska; Agri Business.

BODEN, Janet L; Luther South HS; Burbank, IL; 13/217 Chr; HonRl; NHS; OffAde; SchMus; TchrAde; RptrSchPpr; SchPpr; Coll; English.

BODEN, Julie A; Rockford East HS; Rockford, IL; 30/665 Chr; ChrhWkr; CmntyWkr; HonRl; NatlMeritCmnd; Orch; SchMus; SchPpr; N Ill Univ; Interior Design.

BODENBENDER, Beverly E; Boscobel HS; Boscobel, WI; CncrtBnd; HonRl; MrchBnd; PepBnd; SchMus; PresFHA; LetterBsktbl; LetterTrk; GAA; Vocational School; Vocation.

BODENSTEINER, Jacinta; Walhalla Public HS; Walhalla, ND; 13/57 ALAGirlsSt; Band; Chrs; CncrtBnd; HonRl; PepBnd; GerCl; Bsktbl; GAA; Ndsss; Occupational Therapist.

BODENSTEINER, Leo R; Redwood Falls HS; Redwood Falls, MN; 1/126 TrsSophCls; Band; ChrhWkr; CncrtBnd; MrchBnd; NHS; SctActv; SpnCl; SciCl; IMSpt; Coll; Marine Biologist.

BODINE, Paul A; Glenbrook North HS; Northbrook, IL; HonRl; CchngActv; GovHonPrgAwd; Univ; Architecture.

BODINE, Randy L; Mt Zion HS; Decatur, IL; PresChrhWkr; NHS; SctActv; TchrAde; Bsktbl; Ftbl; LetterTrk;.

BODNER, Steven C; Park Tudor HS; Indianapolis, IN; VPSrCls; HonRl; NatlFornLg; ROTC; SchAde; StuCncl; TchrAde; SchPpr; KeyCl; Bsktbl; Ftbl; LetterGlf; LetterSocr; Vanderbilt College; Medicine.

BODSHAUG, Karen M; St Francis HS; St Francis, WI; 6/200 PresAFS; HonRl; NatlFornLg; SecSpnCl; PpCl; LetterGAA; Whitewater Clge; Soc Wrkr.

BODTKE, Dennis R; Beatrice HS; Beatrice, NE; 51/218 ChrhWkr; OffAde; StuGov; RptrYrbk; RptrSchPpr; SchPpr; GerCl; Bsbl; Bsktbl; LetterFtbl; College; Accounting.

BODTKE, Jean M; Bloom Twp HS; Chicago Hgts, IL; 1/903 Chr; Chrs; ChrhWkr; HonRl; NHS; NatlThespSoc; SchMus; SchPl; StuCncl; IMSpt; Valparaiso Univ; Nursing.

BOE, Debra R; Turtle Lake Public HS; Turtle Lake, ND; 12/44 SecFrshCls; SecSophCls; SecJrCls; ALAGirlsSt; ChrhWkr; HonRl; 4-H; FHA; CaptBsktbl; Trk; Nd St Sch Of Science; Nursng.

BOE, Jodi; Blair HS; Blair, NE; Chr; ChrhWkr; SchMus; SchPl; SecSophCls; 4-H; FHA; PpCl; Univ Or Trade; Cirriculum Of Major Study.

BOE, Tammie T; Ashby Public HS; Ashby, MN; Band; Chr; CncrtBnd; HonRl; MrchBnd; PepBnd; TchrAde; LetterBsktbl; LetterChrldr; GAA; Trade Or Bus School; Vocation.

BOEBINGER, Richard A; North Central HS; Indianapolis, IN; 91/1461 Chr; ChrhWkr; HonRl; NHS; NatlMeritSF; SchMus; SctActv; StuCncl; YthFlsp; Purdue Univ; Electrical Engineering.

BOECK, Brian C; Shelby Tennant HS; Portsmouth, IA; ALBoysSt; Band; MrchBnd; PepBnd; StuCncl; LetterBsbl; LetterBsktbl; LetterFtbl; LetterTrk; 4-HAwd; Clge; Teaching.

BOEDECKER, Sandra K; Rockwell City Comm HS; Rockwell City, IA; Band; ChrhWkr; CncrtBnd; HonRl; MrchBnd; SchMus; SchPl; YthFlsp; RptrSchPpr; FHA; PpCl; Bsktbl; Trade School; Interior Design.

BOEDEKER, Karla J; Clarence Lowden HS; Lowden, IA; PresSophCls; SecJrCls; SecSrCls; ALAGirlsSt; Band; Chrs; DrmMjrt; NHS; YthFlsp; EdSchPpr; St Lukes Sch Of Nursing; Reg Nurse.

BOEDER, Don E; Gibbon Public HS; Gibbon, MN; 10/52 SecSophCls; PresJrCls; FFA; LetterBsbl; LetterBsktbl; LetterFtbl; LetterTrk; PresAwd; Trade School; Professional.

BOEDER, Laurie; Hamilton HS; Menomonee Falls, WI; 12/256 Chr; ChrhWkr; CmntyWkr; NatlFornLg; NHS; NatlMeritCmnd; SchMus; SchPl; GerCl; College; Theatre & Journalism.

BOEDER, Steven; Watertown Senior HS; Watertown, WI; Chr; HonRl; JA; Ftbl; Swmmng; IMSpt; RotaryAwd; Univ Of Wi Eau Claire; Business Management.

BOEDER, Terry K; Cosmos HS; Cosmos, MN; SecSophCls; Band; Chr; CncrtBnd; DrmMjrt; MrchBnd; PepBnd; SchPl; Bsbl; Bsktbl; Ftbl; Glf; Vocational Tech School; Professional.

BOEDICKER, Terry A; Berkeley Sr HS; Berkeley, MO; 11/262 HonRl; College; Nursing.

BOEDING, Karen S; Marquette HS; West Point, IA; 1/49 Chr; Chrs; HonRl; LbryAde; NHS; OffAde; TreasStuCncl; SchPpr; FTA; LetterTrk; Bus Sch; Accounting.

BOEGEL, Catherine T; Campbellsport HS; Campbellsport, WI; 16/147 VPFrshCls; ALAGirlsSt; HonRl; JrNHS; NatlFornLg; NHS; StuCncl; FHA; Trk; IMSpt; U Of Wi Fond Du Lac; Special Ed.

BOEGLIN, Richard J; Forest Park HS; Ferdinand, IN; 30/130 ALBoysSt; Band; StuCncl; RptrYrbk; RptrSchPpr; LetterBsktbl; LetterTrk; In Univ; Forensics.

BOEHLER, Dennis J; Sutton HS; Sutten, NE; 13/55 CmntyWkr; HonRl; SchAde; SchMus; TchrAde; Ftbl; Wrstlng; AmLegAwd; PresAwd; Trade Sch; Draftig.

BOEHM, Thomas; Muskego HS; Hales Corners, WI; 5/346 ALBoysSt; ChrhWkr; HonRl; NHS; StuCncl; Trk; Wrstlng; Coll; Clergyman.

BOEHMER, Marcia A; St Charles HS; St Charles, MO; Band; ChrhWkr; CncrtBnd; HonRl; MrchBnd; NHS; OffAde; PepBnd; YthFlsp; MthCl; 4-HAwd; William Jewell College; Mathematics.

BOEHMER, Rita; Parkston HS; Parkston, SD; 9/96 ALAGirlsSt; HonRl; LbryAde; NatlFornLg; StuCncl; TchrAde; RptrYrbk; SciCl; 4-HAwd; Sd State Univ; Physical Ed Teacher.

BOEHMKE, Jeffrey; Rushford HS; Rushford, MN; Chr; HonRl; StuCncl; RptrSchPpr; FFA; Trk; Wrstlng; 4-HAwd; College; Aviation.

BOEHNE, Thomas T; Parkers Prairie HS; Parkers Prairie, MN; VPSrCls; Band; CncrtBnd; HonRl; MrchBnd; PepBnd; GerCl; Bsktbl; LetterFtbl; Moorhead State; Ed.

BOEHNKE, Rebecca S; Ventura HS; Garner, IA; CncrtBnd; HonRl; MrchBnd; NHS; NatlThespSoc; SchPl; RptrSchPpr; SecFTA; Bsktbl; Tennis; LetterChrldr; PPFtbl; Niacc Jr College; Nursing.

BOEHS, Kenneth P; Triopia HS; Bluffs, IL; ChrhWkr; HonRl; SpnCl; SciCl; Bsbl; Coll; Sci.

BOEKHOFF, Patti M; Wellsburg HS; Wellsburg, IA; Chrs; CncrtBnd; HonRl; NHS; SchMus; SchPl; PresTeen; VPYthFlsp; Yrbk; SchPpr; Cornell College; Visual Fine Arts.

BOEKHOUT, Barbara A; Laboure HS; St Louis, MO; 7/89 CAP; HonRl; JA; OffAde; SctActv; College; Business Admin.

BOELENS, Cynthia A; Atkinson HS; Atkinson, IL; 1/33 TrsSophCls; HonRl; NHS; SchPl; StuCncl; EdYrBk; 4-H; LetterBsktbl; Chrldr; 4-HAwd; Western Illinois Univ; Lawyer.

BOELMAN, Dara J; Boone Jr Sr HS; Boone, IA; Band; CncrtBnd; HonRl; MrchBnd; NHS; Orch; PepBnd; YthFlsp; 4-H; 4-HAwd; Univ; Professional.

BOENS, Dorrie; Sherrard; Coal Valley, IL; 3/90 VPSophCls; VPJrCls; ChrhWkr; CmntyWkr; HonRl; Yrbk; Ill College; Law Enforcement.

BOENSCH, Maureen E; Augres Sims HS; Augres, MI; 2/54 CncrtBnd; HonRl; MrchBnd; PepBnd; SchPl; TchrAde; 4-H; Bsktbl; Univ; Elem Teaching.

BOENSNECKER, Candice; Frankenmuth HS; Frankenmuth, MI; 23/158 ALAGirlsSt; ChrhWkr; CmntyWkr; HonRl; JA; NHS; TchrAde; Concordia Luth Jr Col; Teacher.

BOER, Kimberlee; East Grand Rapids HS; E Grand Rapids, MI; Chr; HospAde; FrCl; Michigan State Univ; Midical Technology.

BOERDING, Judith A; Duchesne HS; St Charles, MO; 25/136 HonRl; LatCl; PpCl; Chrldr; IMSpt; Northeast Missouri; Nursing.

BOERMAN, Twyla R; Byron Center HS; Byron Center, MI; 2/123 Band; HonRl; NatlMeritCmnd; Hope College; Mathematics.

BOERSEMA, Judy B; Unity Christian HS; Jenison, MI; Chr; ChrhWkr; HonRl; SchPl; EdYrBk; EdSchPpr; LetterBsktbl; LetterTrk; CchngActv; IMSpt; College; B S In Nursing.

BOERSEN, Nancy; Zeeland HS; Zeeland, MI; VPJrCls; VPSrCls; JrNHS; PPFtbl; Business School; Secretary.

BOERSMA, Eugene J; Central HS; Pipestone, MN; ChrhWkr; HonRl; NHS; IMSpt; Vocation Sch; Farm Equip Mechanics.

BOERSMA, Kathy; Sheldon HS; Sheldon, IA; Band; CncrtBnd; HonRl; MrchBnd; OffAde; PepBnd; SchMus; YthFlsp; FHA; PpCl; Business School; Vocation.

BOERSMA, Kenneth A; Chicago Christian HS; Palos Heights, IL; 3/170 Chr; ChrhWkr; HonRl; Mdrgl; SchPl; StuCncl; Yrbk; RptrSchPpr; GerCl; IMSpt; Calvin Col; Eduction Major.

BOERSMA, Marlene K; Central Christian HS; Raymond, MN; Chr; HonRl; JrNHS; NHS; SchMus; TchrAde; RptrSchPpr; EdSchPpr; FTA; PpCl; Dordt Coll; Elementary Teacher.

BOERSMA, Sandra K; Springfield Southeast HS; Springfield, IL; SchPl; StuGov; College.

BOERTMANN, Karin; Lawrence Central HS; Indianapolis, IN; MrchBnd; NHS; Swmmng; JAAwd; Indiana Univ; Certified Public Accountant.

BOERUP, Rebecca A; Gwinn HS; Gwinn, MI; Band; CncrtBnd; HonRl; MrchBnd; NHS; RptrYrbk; Yrbk; Bsktbl; IMSpt; Col N Mi U ;te Bio.

BOESCH, Maureen; St Francis HS; Humphrey, NE; Chr; Chrs; HonRl; SchPl; EdYrBk; 4-H; Trk; Chrldr; GAA; IMSpt; College; X Ray Tech.

BOESDORFER, Marcia L; Pleasant Plains HS; Pleasant Plains, IL; 8/57 SecBand; Chr; Mdrgl; NHS; SchMus; SchPl; SecStuCncl; SecYthFlsp; RptrYrbk; FTA; GAA; 4-HAwd; Illinois State Univ; Music.

BOESE, Suzanne K; Eastern Hancock HS; Wilkinson, IN; 1/95 ALAGirlsSt; HonRl; NHS; EdYrBk; Chrldr; EldAwd; LbryAde; PpCl; College; Professional.

BOESELAGER, Patrick J; Washington HS; Two Rivers, WI; RptrSchPpr; SchPpr; KeyCl; PpCl; LetterBsktbl; U W Lacrosse; Physical Edu.

BOESEN, Diana; Reavis; Burbank, IL; JrNHS; NHS; Moraine Valley Cc;accounting.

BOESPFLUG, Paul; St Gertrudes HS; Raleigh, ND; 7/20 ChrhWkr; HonRl; LbryAde; NHS; Sacrstn; SchMus; RptrSchPpr; SpnCl; Trk; College; Prof.

BOETCHER, Renee M; St Charles HS; St Charles, MI; HonRl; 4-H; LetterBsktbl; IMSpt; Col; Detal Asst.

BOETEL, Rodney L; Hartley Comm HS; Hartley, IA; ALBoysSt; Band; Chr; Chrs; CncrtBnd; HonRl; MrchBnd; SchPl; SctActv; LetterBsktbl; LetterFtbl; LetterTrk; University; Professional.

BOETSMA, Debra L; Culver Comm HS; Culver, IN; 7/101 Chrl; ChrhWkr; HonRl; IntrClCncl; NHS; TchrAde; YthFlsp; FTA; VPSpnCl; PpCl; College; Elementary Educ.

BOETTCHER, Carl S; Bonduel HS; Bonduel, WI; 6/122 PresSrCls; ALBoysSt; Band; Chr; Chrs; ChrhWkr; CncrtBnd; HonRl; MrchBnd; Orch; PepBnd; LetterBsktbl; Ftbl; Chrldr; Us Navy; Nuclear Physics.

BOETTCHER, Connie; West Holt HS; Atkinson, NE; 16/71 VPJrCls; HonRl; NHS; SchPl; StuCncl; Yrbk; 4-H; Chrldr; 4-HAwd; Chadron State Coll; Business.

BOETTCHER, Jane M; Elmore Public HS; Blue Earth, MN; Band; Chrs; ChrhWkr; HonRl; LbryAde; NHS; SchPl; TchrAde; FTA; PpCl; Coll; Med Lab Tech.

BOETTCHER, Paul E; Emmons HS; Emmons, MN; 4/21 PresFrshCls; PresSophCls; PresJrCls; Chrs; HonRl; SchPl; LetterBsbl; LetterBsktbl; LetterFtbl; PresAwd; College.

BOETTCHER, Uwe; Pinckney HS; Pinckey, MI; HonRl; Bsktbl; Ftbl; CaptSocr; Univ; Technical Electrician.

BOEVE, Jane; Holland HS; Holland, MI; 39/310 Chr; ChrhWkr; HonRl; HospAde; NHS; TchrAde; YthFlsp; FrCl; Hope College; Teaching Or Medicine.

BOGAARD, Jonathan H; Humboldt Comm HS; Humboldt, IA; 7/150 VPSophCls; ALBoysSt; HonRl; PresNHS; PresStuCncl; LetterFtbl; LetterTrk; Ia Central Comm College; Law Or Physics.

BOGANEY, Stanley H; Quigley South HS; Chicago, IL; Chr; Chrs; CncrtBnd; HonRl; NHS; SchMus; RptrYrbk; Yrbk; SchPpr; Bsktbl; Clge; Pro.

BOGARD, Dennis L; Mc Bain Rural Agrl HS; Mc Bain, MI; 3/64 TrsSrCls; HonRl; NHS; NatlMeritSchl; NatlMeritSF; StuCncl; LetterBsbl; LetterBsktbl; LetterFtbl; LetterTrk; Mi Univ; Engrin.

BOGART, Claire A; Sturgis HS; Sturgis, MI; JA; LbryAde; KeyCl; LatCl; Tennis; PPFtbl; EldAwd; JAAwd; Grand Valley State Clg; Nursing.

BOGART, Gene H; North Pemiscot HS; Wardell, MO; 2/60 ALBoysSt; Band; CncrtBnd; HonRl; MrchBnd; NHS; PepBnd; StuCncl; LetterBsbl; IMSpt; Trade School; Vocation.

BOGART, Susan D; Kearney HS; Kearney, MO; 4/77 Chr; ChrhWkr; HonRl; LbryAde; NHS; RptrYrbk; PpCl; Bsktbl; Trk; CitAwd; William Jewell Clg.

BOGDAN, Charles; Fenwick Hs; Berwyn, IL; 2/220 Band; Chr; CncrtBnd; HonRl; MrchBnd; NHS; NatlMeritFnl; SchMus; GerCl; MthCl;.

BOGDAN, Elizabeth M; Fitzgerald HS; Warren, MI; 7/412 NHS; PpCl; CaptSwmmng; GAA; PPFtbl; Wayne St; Busi Admin.

BOGDON, Sandra L; Oak Forest HS; Oak Forest, IL; 3/256 HonRl; HospAde; LitMag; SecNHS; Pres4-H; Clge; Pro.

BOGE, Michael D; Bloomington HS; Bloomington, IL; Chr; ChrhWkr; HonRl; NHS; StuCncl; StuGov; TchrAde; YthFlsp; GerCl; MthCl; PpCl; College; Medicine.

BOGENHAGEN, Nancy; White Lake HS; White Lake, SD; 5/27 Chr; Chrs; ChrhWkr; HonRl; Quill&Scroll; SchPl; RptrYrbk; RptrSchPpr; SchPpr; Bsktbl; Sd State Univ; General Registration.

BOGENRIEF, Bonnie B; Rockford West Sr HS; Rockford, IL; 24/335 TrsFrshCls; PresSophCls; VPAFS; Band; CncrtBnd; HonRl; JA; JrNHS; PresNHS; TreasGerCl; South Ill; Medical Tech.

BOGENSCHUTZ, Michael F; Batesville HS; Oldenburg, IN; 13/150 HonRl; NHS; Trk; CchngActv; Col; Engineering.

BOGER, Lee C; Shelbyville HS; Shelbyville, IN; 3/233 ChrhWkr; HonRl; NHS; TchrAde; SpnCl; SciCl; LetterFtbl; IMSpt; GovHonPrgAwd; General Motors Inst; Engineer.

BOGERT, Sue E; Park River HS; Park River, ND; ALAGirlsSt; HonRl; NHS; NatlMeritSchl; SchPl; FHA; PpCl; Bsktbl; GAA; IMSpt; Vocational Sch; Vocation.

BOGGESS, Jacquelyn; Freeport Senior Hs; Freeport, IL; 47/512 HonRl; StuCncl;.

BOGGIO, Massimo J; Carl Sandburg HS; Oak Forest, IL; 20/750 HonRl; JrNHS; NHS; SpnCl; LetterFtbl; LetterTrk; Univ Of Ill; Eng.

BOGGS, Debra D; River Rouge HS; River Rouge, MI; Band; CncrtBnd; HonRl; MrchBnd; SchMus; SctActv; FHA; PpCl; SciCl; CaptChrldr; Mcc Jr College; Special Education.

BOGGS, Janilee K; Mormon Trail HS; Weldon, IA; 1/38 PresJrCls; CncrtBnd; HonRl; SchPl; 4-H; FHA; PpCl; LetterBsktbl; LetterTrk; 4-HAwd;.

BOGGS, Jean M; Divernon HS; Divernon, IL; 6/28 ALAGirlsSt; HonRl; StuGov; GerCl; LetterTrk; GAA; College; Math.

BOGGS, Jo E; Tippecanoe Valley HS; Warsaw, IN; Band; Chrs; CncrtBnd; HonRl; MrchBnd; OffAde; PepBnd; StuCncl; FHA; Trade School; Beautician.

BOGGS, Judie C; Verdigre Public HS; Winnetoon, NE; Chr; Chrs; ChrhWkr; HonRl; NHS; StuCncl; TchrAde; YthFlsp;.

BOGGS, Lisa A; Tippecanoe Valley HS; Warsaw, IN; 12/131 Band; Chrs; CncrtBnd; DrmMjrt; HonRl; MrchBnd; NHS; Twrl; PpCl; Chrldr; Grace College; Physical Ed.

BOGGS, William J; Tippecanoe Valley HS; Mentone, IN; 33/133 Aud/Vis; HonRl; NHS; SchPl; SptEdYrbk; SchPpr; FTA; SpnCl; Bsbl; Bsktbl; Glf; Indiana University.

BOGGY, Pamela; Archbishop Bergan HS; Fremont, NE; 6/49 SecSophCls; PresSrCls; HonRl; LbryAde; NHS; RptrSchPpr; IMSpt; 4-HAwd; OptClAwd; VoiceDemAwd; Univ Of Neb; Journ Eng.

BOGI, John P; Dundee HS; Monroe, MI; TchrAde; YthFlsp; 4-H; FTA; LetterTrk; College; Chiropractor.

BOGLE, Grant C; De Kalb Sr HS; De Kalb, IL; PresFrshCls; PresSophCls; HonRl; StuCncl; Ftbl; AmLegAwd; College; Lawyer.

BOGLE, Marian D; Norwich HS; Norwich, KS; VPFrshCls; Chrs; HonRl; SecStuCncl; PpCl; Chrldr; PPFtbl; Hutchinson Comm Jr College; Nursing.

BOGNER, Eileen; Oelrichs Ind HS; Chadron, NE; VPSophCls; Band; HonRl; SchPl; SptEdYrbk; Trk; Chrldr; AmLegAwd; CitAwd; College; Secretarial.

BOGOLIN, Josephine M; Lourdes HS; Chicago, IL; NHS; NatlMeritFnl; FDA; JAAwd; Univ; Pre Med.

BOGUE, Barbara; Mark Twain HS; New London, MO; 6/60 PresFrshCls; PresSophCls; VPJrCls; ModUN; HonRl; SchPl; StuCncl; FTA; Central Methodist College, Sociology.

BOGUE, Elizabeth A; Gull Lake HS; Augusta, MI; 25/280 Band; HonRl; PepBnd; 4-H; LetterBsktbl; CchngActv; GAA; IMSpt; CaptPPFtbl; 4-HAwd; University; Forestry Conservation.

BOGUE, Russell G; Hays HS; Hays, KS; Chrs; ChrhWkr; HonRl; SchMus; SctActv; Kansas State Univ; Landscape Architecture.

BOGUE, Timothy J; Crete Monee HS; Crete, IL; 48/359 CncrtBnd; HonRl; MrchBnd; NHS; PepBnd; YthFlsp; MthCl; LetterTrk; IMSpt; De Pauw Univ; Math.

BOGUSZEWSKI, Michael J; Bradley Bourbonnais HS; Bradley, IL; 7/369 HonRl; NHS; NatlMeritSF; PresGerCl; VoiceDemAwd; Univ Of Chicago; Biological Science.

BOHABOJ, Victoria L; Dodge Public HS; West Point, NE; /38 Band; HonRl; MrchBnd; SchMus; SchPl; TchrAde; Yrbk; SchPpr; PpCl; LetterTrk; Technical Trade; Vocation.

BOHACZ, Christine A; Carl Schurz Public HS; Chicago, IL; 4/750 Chr; HonRl; NHS; OffAde; SchMus; SctActv; StuCncl; CaptTwrl; FrCl; GAA; Loyola Univ; Biology.

BOHAN, Jack A; St Joseph HS; Chicago, IL; SecJrCls; VPSrCls; HonRl; StuGov; SpnCl; MthCl; College; Data Processing.

BOHL, Lloyd L; Grant Park HS; Grant Park, IL; 8/59 Band; CncrtBnd; HonRl; NHS; PepBnd; PresFFA; Junior College; Farming.

BOHLAND, Cindy L; Catholic Central HS; Muskegon, MI; CmntyWkr; HospAde; JA; College; Professional.

BOHLAND, Michelle L; De Soto HS; De Soto, WI; ChrhWkr; CmntyWkr; HonRl; LbryAde; TchrAde; Yrbk; RptrSchPpr; PpCl; LetterGAA; University; Physical Therapist.

BOHLEBER, Michael L; Carmi Comm HS; Carmi, IL; 5/148 JrNHS; NHS; SchPl; LatCl; Swmmng; West Point Academy.

BOHLEN, Earl D; Milbank HS; Milbank, SD; Chr; Chrs; ChrhWkr; Mdrgl; RptrSchPpr; KeyCl; PpCl; LetterBsktbl; LetterFtbl; CchngActv; Univ Of South Dakota; Business.

BOHLEN, Kathy A; Lawrenceville HS; Lawrenceville, IL; 18/180 Band; HonRl; Yrbk; LatCl; Univ Of Illinois; Social Work.

BOHLEN, Pamela J; Armstrong Township HS; Fithian, IL; 6/42 Band; Chrs; HonRl; NHS; SchPl; 4-H; SpnCl; DanFAwd; 4-HAwd; Bowling Green College; Childhood Ed.

BOHLER, William J; Batavia Sr HS; Batavia, IL; AFS; HonRl; Quill&Scroll; SptEdYrbk; SptEdSchPpr; LatCl; LetterBsbl; LetterFtbl; LetterWrstlng; Purdue Univ; Electrical Engineering.

BOHLEY, Mary B; St Elizabeth Acad; St Louis, MO; HonRl; HospAde; NHS; PolWkr; SpnCl; PresSciCl; St Louis Univ; Nursing.

BOHLIN, Cynthia A; Hector Community HS; Hector, MN; Band; ChrhWkr; CncrtBnd; HonRl; MrchBnd; PepBnd; SpnCl; Chrldr; GAA; Bus Sch; Cur Of Maj Stud.

BOHLING, Grace K; St Pauls College HS; Concordia, MO; SecSrCls; Chr; CmntyWkr; CncrtBnd; HonRl; NHS; PepBnd; RptrSchPpr; 4-H; College; German.

BOHLING, Veronica J; Les Cheneaux HS; Cedarville, MI; HonRl; Chrldr; GAA; Business Sch.

BOHLKE, Susan K; Heelan HS; Sioux City, IA; 24/249 Band; Chrs; DrlTm; HonRl; JA; NHS; FrCl; PpCl; College; Botany.

BOHLMANN, Gretchen A; Watseka Comm HS; Watseka, IL; 5/138 HonRl; TreasNHS; SpnCl; Tennis; Trk; GAA; East Il Univ; Biology.

BOHLS, Roger A; Castlewood Independent HS; Castlewood, SD; 3/30 ALBoysSt; ChrhWkr; SchPl; PresStuCncl; Bsbl; CaptBsktbl; CaptFtbl; AmLegAwd; South Dakota St Univ; Science.

BOHM, Bonnie J; Bi Public HS; Bird Island, MN; 6/60 PresJrCls; ALAGirlsSt; NatlFornLg; NHS; SchMus; RptrYrbk; Chrldr; PPFtbl; AmLegAwd; DARAwd; St Benedict Coll.

BOHM, Raymond A; Seymour HS; Seymour, IN; StuCncl; RptrSchPpr; SptEdSchPpr; College; Pre Law.

BOHM, Rhondalyn H; Concordia HS; Concordia, KS; 25/140 Chr; ChrhWkr; HonRl; MrchBnd; NatlFornLg; SchPl; FrCl; PpCl; VFWAwd; VoiceDemAwd; Cloud County Comm College; Drama.

BOHM, Richard; Centreville HS; Centreville, MI; HonRl; Bsbl; Bsktbl; Ftbl; Wrstlng; Grand Valley State Coll; Science Field.

BOHMANN, Karen K; Mundelein HS; Mundelein, IL; 28/346 HonRl; Bsbl; Bsktbl; Tennis; GAA; College; Medical Technologist.

BOHN, Alissa; Marshall HS; Marshall, IL; 9/115 Band; Chr; Chrs; CncrtBnd; MrchBnd; NHS; PepBnd; 4-H; SpnCl; 4-HAwd; Eastern Ill Univ; Music.

BOHN, Carole L; St Anthony HS; St Louis, MO; ALAGirlsSt; HonRl; OffAde; SchPl; StuCncl; TchrAde; LatCl; Bsktbl; IMSpt; PresAwd; Accountant.

BOHN, Juliana K; Manchester HS; North Manchester, IN; DrmMjrt; HonRl; MrchBnd; NatlFornLg; NatlThespSoc; SctActv; Swmmng; Tennis; GAA; College; Physical Therapist.

BOHN, Margaret A; Kearney Catholic HS; Kearney, NE; VPSophCls; Chr; Chrs; ChrhWkr; Mdrgl; SchMus; SchPl; RptrYrbk; SptEdYrbk; LetterBsktbl; Ftbl; LetterTrk; IMSpt; Kearney St College; Art.

BOHN, Mary; St Anthony Of Paoua; St Louis, MO; 11/76 Chrs; CmntyWkr; HonRl; JA; SchMus; SctActv; StuCncl; LatCl; Bsktbl; IMSpt;.

BOHN, Robert F; Maconaquah HS; No Manchester, IN; Band; CncrtBnd; HonRl; JrNHS; MrchBnd; PepBnd; SctActv; YthFlsp; SchPpr; LatCl; SciCl; Purdue Univ; Computer Science.

BOHN, Susan L; Kewaskum HS; Kewaskum, WI; 4/156 AFS; ALAGirlsSt; HonRl; NHS; RptrSchPpr; FTA; SpnCl; Bsbl; Bsktbl; Glf; Univ Of Wisconsin; Foreign Language.

BOHNER, Sara L; Hillsdale HS; Osseo, MI; HospAde; Orch; TchrAde; 4-H; IMSpt; Ferris St College; Nurse.

BOHO, Bonnie A; Elizabeth Seton HS; South Holland, IL; 25/255 HonRl; NHS; SchMus; SchPl; StuCncl; RptrYrbk; RptrSchPpr; SpnCl; Loyola Univ; Nursing.

BOHR, Allen E; Clay Cenral HS; Royal, IA; HonRl; Bsktbl; Trade School.

BOHR, Marjorie; Notre Dame HS; Cresco, IA; 1/26 SecSrCls; Chrs; HonRl; Quill&Scroll; RptrYrbk; RptrSchPpr; EdSchPpr; BauchLmbAwd; Hamilton Business Col; Accounting.

BOHR, Mary E; Aurora Central Catholic HS; Aurora, IL; HonRl; TchrAde; RptrYrbk; 4-H; PpCl; LetterBsktbl; LetterTrk; Col; Pro.

BOHRER, Ardyth G; Shenandoah Community HS; Shenandoah, IA; Chr; HonRl; SchPl; Twrl; FNA; PpCl; LetterBsktbl; Chrldr; DARAwd; MasAwd; Bus Trade Sch; Legal Work.

BOHY, Tami; Broken Bow HS; Brokenbow, NE; ALAGirlsSt; Band; HonRl; RedCrAde; StuCncl; PpCl; GAA; IMSpt; PresAwd; Univ.

BOIES, Jim P; Estherville HS; Estherville, IA; Band; CncrtBnd; DrmBgl; HonRl; NatlFornLg; PepBnd; SchMus; SpnCl; Bsktbl; Ftbl; Univ; Engi.

BOIK, Lou Ann F; Cavalier HS; Cavalier, ND; DrlTm; HonRl; SchPl; FrCl; PpCl; SciCl; Coll.

BOIKE, Candice A; Nazareth Academy; Brookfield, IL; TrsJrCls; PresSrCls; HonRl; SchAde; StuGov; TchrAde; EngCl; PpCl; GAA; College.

BOILEK, Raymond E; Morton Sr HS; Hammond, IN; HonRl; NHS; TchrAde; Purdue Univ; Chemical Engineering.

BOILY, Alesandra J; Wrenshall HS; Wrenshall, MN; 9/30 Band; Chrs; HonRl; JA; NHS; SchPl; StuGov; Yrbk; LetterTrk; DanFAwd; Col; Professional.

BOIN, Michael G; St Benedict HS; Chicago, IL; 15/178 Chrs; HonRl; NHS; SchPl; SctActv; Ne Illinois Univ; Veterinarian.

BOING, Lawrence E; Greensburg HS; Greensburg, IN; 75/191 LatCl; PpCl; Purdue U; Pharmacy.

BOIVIN, Daniel S; Marinette HS; Marinette, WI; RedCrAde; SchPl; StuCncl; 4-H; PpCl; LetterBsktbl; LetterTrk; LetterWrstlng; College; Recreation Major.

BOJANOWSKI, Janice A; Elizabeth Seton HS; Chicago, IL; 15/252 HonRl; NHS; Orch; Univ Of Illinois; Pharmacy.

BOJANOWSKI, Maryellen B; Argo Community HS; Summit, IL; 7/432 TreasChr; HonRl; LitMag; TreasNHS; OffAde; SchMus; SciCl; Arizona State Univ; Medicine.

BOJAR, Pamela; Holy Family Acad; Chicago, IL; TrsFrshCls; Chrs; HonRl; LbryAde; SchPl; Yrbk; SpnCl; IMSpt; College; Lab Tech.

BOK, Robert A; Nashville Community HS; New Minden, IL; Band; ChrhWkr; CncrtBnd; HonRl; MrchBnd; PepBnd; GerCl; Bsktbl; LetterTennis; CchngActv; Univ; Biochemistry.

BOKA, Silvia D; Roger C Sullivan HS; Chicago, IL; 10/263 ChrhWkr; HonRl; HospAde; NHS; Loyola Univ; Biology.

BOKERMANN, Keith; Vianney HS; St Louis, MO; Band; Unkc; Pre Dental.

BOKHART, Judith E; Lake Michigan Catholic HS; Benton Harbor, MI; 8/87 Band; ChrhWkr; CmntyWkr; CncrtBnd; HonRl; JA; PepBnd; TchrAde; LatCl; University; Elementary Education.

BOKHOVEN, Nancy B; Pella Christian HS; New Sharon, IA; ChrhWkr; CmntyWkr; HonRl; HospAde; LbryAde; SchPl; YthFlsp; PpCl; LetterTrk; IMSpt; Grand View College; Nursing.

BOLAM, Leslie J; Pekin Community HS; Pekin, IL; CncrtBnd; HonRl; MrchBnd; NHS; Orch; SctActv; YthFlsp; College; Business.

BOLAN, Robin K; Norway HS; Norway, MI; HonRl; HospAde; NatlMeritFnl; SchPl; RptrYrbk; RptrSchPpr; 4-H; FHA; FNA; FrCl; University; Professional.

BOLAND, Barbara; Monticello Hs; Ivesdale, IL; 6/168 Band; HonRl; NHS; NatlMeritCmnd; SchPl; RptrYrbk; 4-H; PpCl; GAA; 4-HAwd; University Of Ill; Accounting.

BOLAND, Debbie K; West HS; Sioux City, IA; 24/265 Band; Chr; CncrtBnd; HonRl; MrchBnd; PpCl; Bsktbl; Chrldr; PPFtbl; AmLegAwd; College; Professional.

BOLAND, Kevin; Catholic Central HS; Detroit, MI; 4 HonRl; FrCl; Ftbl; IMSpt; Western Mich U; Bus Admin.

BOLANDER, Sandra J; Sacred Heart Academy; Newton, IL; 18/143 Chr; Chrs; CmntyWkr; HonRl; NHS; Sdlty; MthCl; PpCl; GAA;.

BOLDAN, Kelly J; Motley HS; Leader, MN; 4/32 HonRl; EdYrBk; EdSchPpr; FFA; FTA; PpCl; Bsbl; CaptBsktbl; CaptFtbl; LetterTrk; Univ Of Minnesota; Rural Communication.

BOLDEN, Mary L; Earle HS; St Louis, MO; ChrhWkr; HonRl; LbryAde; TchrAde; YthFlsp; Yrbk; FTA; SpnCl; Chrldr; St Louis U; Prof.

BOLDT, Cindy S; Harbor Beach Comm HS; Harbor Beach, MI; 28/135 Chr; ChrhWkr; HonRl; OffAde; SpnCl; PpCl; IMSpt; Bus School; Seretarial.

BOLDT, Debbie J; Harbor Beach Comm HS; Harbor Beach, MI; 29/136 Chr; ChrhWkr; HonRl; HospAde; NHS; FHA; FNA; PpCl; Trk; CitAwd; St Clair County Comm; Rn.

BOLDT, Julie; Border Central HS; Calvin, ND; Band; HonRl; PepBnd; SchPl; StuCncl; RptrYrbk; PpCl; Univ Of Niorth Dakato; Professional.

BOLE, Adrienne S; Good Counsel HS; Chicago, IL; 62/285 HonRl; SpnCl; College.

BOLE, Cathy; Wm A Wirt HS; Gary, IN; 84/240 Orch; PolWkr; RptrYrbk; Yrbk; PpCl; Bsbl; LetterBsktbl; CaptFtbl; Glf; GAA; De Pauw Univ; Nursing.

BOLE, Christy L; Athens HS; Battle Creek, MI; 1/100 PresJrCls; NHS; NatlMeritSchl; RedCrAde; VPStuCncl; Pres4-H; PpCl; Trk; VPGAA; 4-HAwd; Kellogg Comm College; Public Relations.

BOLEN, William; Bishop Mcnamara HS; Bradley, IL; HonRl; NHS; PolWkr; Glf; Swmmng; Trk; IMSpt; Illinois State Univ; Geophnsicist.

BOLES, Charles L; Savannah R 3 HS; Savannah, MO; 25/160 HonRl; Treas4-H; PresFFA; LetterFtbl; Univ Of Missouri; Vet.

BOLEY, Kim M; Hanover Horton HS; Jackson, MI; HonRl; PpCl; Jackson Com Col; Commerical Art.

BOLEY, Rodney J; Mt Horeb HS; Belleville, WI; Band; CncrtBnd; MrchBnd; PepBnd; 4-H; FFA; Trk; IMSpt;.

BOLGER, David P; Marian Central HS; Mc Henry, IL; 1/116 TrsSophCls; PresJrCls; HonRl; PresNHS; NatlMeritCmnd; StuGov; SchPpr; LetterGlf; Harvard Univ; Banking.

BOLHOUSE, Shirley L; Chicago Christian HS; Crestwood, IL; Chr; Chrs; HonRl; NHS; SchPl; PpCl; Hope College; Political Science.

BOLIN, Jane K; St James HS; St James, MN; 3/140 TrsJrCls; TrsSrCls; Chr; ChrhWkr; CncrtBnd; DrmMjrt; HonRl; NHS; RptrSchPpr; Swmmng; College; Professional.

BOLIN, Patricia K; Stephen Decatur HS; Decatur, IL; 16/476 Univ Of Illinois; Accounting.

BOLIN, Paul K; Carmel HS; Carmel, IN; 100/522 VPSrCls; NHS; SchMus; StuGov; SptEdYrbk; FDA; LetterTrk; Indiana Univ; Dentistry.

BOLINGER, Candice; North Central HS; Shelbury, IN; SecSrCls; StuCncl; Yrbk; Chrldr; Traingin Sch For Stewardess; Stewardess.

BOLINGER, Donald J; Haworth HS; Kokomo, IN; 25/456 HonRl; PresIntrClCncl; LitMag; PresNHS; OffAde; PolWkr; PresStuCncl; YthLg; PpCl; Ftbl; Swmmng; CchngActv; DARAwd; Indiana Univ; Law.

BOLINGER, John F; Shelbyville HS; Shelbyville, IL; 10/140 PresJrCls; ChrhWkr; HonRl; SchPl; StuCncl; YthFlsp; RptrSchPpr; 4-H; FrCl; Ftbl; Coll; Doctor.

BOLITHO, Todd; Albion HS; Albion, MI; Aud/Vis; Band; Chr; HonRl; SchMus; SchPl; SctActv; YthFlsp; FrCl; IMSpt; Albion Coll; Music, Psych, Minister.

BOLL, Julie; Black Hawk HS; Browntown, WI; Band; Chrs; HonRl; Mdrgl; YthFlsp; RptrYrbk; RptrSchPpr; FHA; PpCl; Chrldr; Fennimore; Business Machines.

BOLLARD, Paul W; Pocahontas Community HS; Pocahontas, IA; 10/75 VPFrshCls; VPSophCls; HonRl; NHS; PresStuCncl; PpCl; SciCl; Bsbl; Bsktbl; Ftbl; Trk; College; Elementary Administrator.

BOLLEN, Christie S; Stillman Valley HS; Byron, IL; ChrhWkr; HonRl; JrNHS; NHS; NatlMeritCmnd; College; Mental Health.

BOLLENBECK, Richard; Appleton West HS; Appleton, WI; 71/700 ChrhWkr; JA; MrchBnd; NHS; PepBnd; SctActv; JAAwd; St Olaf College; Economics.

BOLLENGIER, Gary R; Annawan HS; Atkinson, IL; 2/85 HonRl; 4-H; FFA; SpnCl; LetterFtbl; 4-HAwd; Coll Il; Computer Processing.

BOLLER, Sheryl A; Washington HS; Red Cloud, NE; 4/41 Chr; Chrs; ChrhWkr; HonRl; StuCncl; StuGov; YthFlsp; 4-H; FHA; PpCl; College; Music Therapy.

BOLLES, Bruce; Hesperia HS; Hesperia, MI; PresFrshCls; ALBoysSt; HonRl; NHS; StuCncl; StuGov; Ftbl; DanFAwd; Business College; Data Processing.

BOLLES, James A; Eau Claire N HS; Eau Claire, WI; 18/357 NHS; RptrSchPpr; SptEdSchPpr; LetterFtbl; U Of Wi; Journalism.

BOLLI, Terri L; Mexico HS; Mexico, MO; Band; CncrtBnd; JA; MrchBnd; PepBnd; PpCl; Trk; Chrldr; Smsu; Rn Or Art Sch.

BOLLIER, Philip A; Leo HS; Grabill, IN; 10/130 ALBoysSt; NHS; StuCncl; SptEdYrbk; LetterBsbl; LetterBsktbl; LetterFtbl; College.

BOLLIG, Coleen M; Hays HS; Hays, KS; ChrhWkr; HonRl; SchMus; College.

BOLLIG, Mark; Sentrol HS; Fenton, IA; ChrhWkr; SchPl; 4-H; FFA; Ftbl; Trk; IMSpt; AmLegAwd; ChmbCommrsAwd; 4-HAwd; College; Veterinarian.

BOLLIN, Cynthia; Nauvoo Colusa HS; Nauvoo, IL; 11/53 HonRl; NatlThespSoc; SchPl; SptEdYrbk; FBLA; Glf; College; Professional.

BOLLING, Charlotte A; Palo HS; Cowgill, MO; ChrhWkr; HonRl; LbryAde; YthFlsp; FFA; Excelsior Spg Voc Sch; Occupational Therapy.

BOLLING, Kevin D; Lawson HS; Lawson, MO; PresSrCls; Band; CmntyWkr; HonRl; NHS; PepBnd; Pres4-H; CaptBsktbl; CaptFtbl; LetterTrk; Mo Western State; Phy Ed.

BOLLINGER, Clarice F; Bowdle Public HS; Bowdle, SD; ChrhWkr; DrlTm; HonRl; PolWkr; YthFlsp; EdYrBk; PpCl; LetterBsktbl; LetterTrk; Chrldr; GAA; 4-HAwd;.

BOLLINGER, David; Lafayette HS; St Joseph, MO; 2/260 ALBoysSt; Band; ChrhWkr; HonRl; ModUN; PepBnd; ROTC; SchMus; StuCncl; OptClAwd; Harlaxton Stdy Centre England; Religion.

BOLLINGER, David A; Ashley HS; Lehr, ND; SecSophCls; TrsSrCls; Band; Chr; Chrs; CncrtBnd; HonRl; PepBnd; Ftbl; College; Professional.

BOLLINGER, Diana L; Malden HS; Malden, MO; Band; CncrtBnd; HonRl; MrchBnd; OffAde; PepBnd; TchrAde; PpCl; Trade School.

BOLLINGER, Kathy J; Northridge HS; Middlebury, IN; 16/117 Chr; Chrs; HonRl; OffAde; FrCl; PpCl; Manchester Coll; Elem Ed.

BOLLINGER, Kim R; Astoria HS; Browning, IL; 8/44 Chrs; CncrtBnd; HonRl; NHS; OffAde; SchPl; TchrAde; PresFHA; SpnCl; PpCl;.

BOLLINGER, Kristin R; Downers Grove North HS; Downers Grove, IL; 2/509 Chrs; HonRl; NatlMeritCmnd; U Of Il; Business Admn Major.

BOLLINGER, Patricia K; Mitchell Sr HS; Mitchell, SD; Band; Chr; CncrtBnd; HonRl; MrchBnd; SchPl; GAA; Univ Of Vermillion; Criminal Law.

BOLLINGER, Rebecca G; St Charles HS; St Charles, MO; CmntyWkr; HonRl; NHS; SctActv; College.

BOLLINGER, Sheri L; Bremen Public HS; Bremen, IN; HonRl; LbryAde; SchMus; StuCncl; 4-H; FrCl; PpCl; 4-HAwd; MasAwd; Iu; Art Teacher.

BOLLIVAR, Johnna L; Prophetstown HS; Prophetstown, IL; 6/100 AFS; Band; ChrhWkr; CncrtBnd; HonRl; JA; MrchBnd; NHS; PepBnd; SctActv; GAA; Sauk Valley College; Criminal Justice.

BOLLMANN, Julie K; Central HS; Norwood, MN; 10/94 HonRl; LbryAde; YthFlsp; FHA; EngCl; PPFtbl; VFWAwd; College; Acctg.

BOLLMANN, Mark A; Trico HS; Ava, IL; Chrs; ChrhWkr; CmntyWkr; HonRl; PepBnd; SchMus; SchPl; 4-H; LetterBsbl; IMSpt; Jr Clge.

BOLLUM, Mark; Goodhue HS; Goodhue, MN; ChrhWkr; CmntyWkr; HonRl; NHS; NatlMeritSchl; NatlThespSoc; StuCncl; YthFlsp; 4-H; Red Wing Vo Tech; Farm.

BOLLWERK, Victoria L; Edgemont HS; Edgemont, SD; AFS; Chrs; DrlTm; HonRl; NatlThespSoc; SchPl; StuCncl; FTA; FrCl; SciCl;.

BOLOTIN, Patricia A; Mother Mcauley Lib Arts HS; Oak Lawn, IL; CmntyWkr; HonRl; OffAde; SchAde; SchPl; SctActv; Marquette Univ; Personnel Management.

BOLOTIN, William J; Marist HS; Oak Lawn, IL; 39/393 ChrhWkr; CmntyWkr; HonRl; NHS; SchPl; SctActv; Teen; RptrYrbk; Glf; IMSpt; U Of Notre Dame; Lawyer.

BOLT, Burt E; Rockridge HS; Milan, IL; 50/140 SecSophCls; PresJrCls; ALBoysSt; PolWkr; SchMus; Yrbk; FNA; SpnCl; Trk; PresAwd; Vocational; Photography.

BOLT, Carrie S; Southeast Polk HS; Altoona, IA; 20/218 Chrs; DrlTm; HonRl; NHS; SctActv; TchrAde; PPFtbl; Area Xi Clge; Cpa.

BOLT, Kelly; Rockridge HS; Milan, IL; HonRl; Yrbk; FNA; FTA; GAA; 4-HAwd; JAAwd; Trade Sch.

BOLTE, Eric S; Nokomis HS; Nokomis, IL; HonRl; SctActv;.

BOLTON, Bradley J; Lauton HS; Lauton, MI; VPJrCls; ALBoysSt; HonRl; TreasStuCncl; StuGov; TchrAde; RptrSchPpr; LetterBsbl; LetterTrk; IMSpt; College; Business.

BOLTON, Janice E; Underwood HS; Neola, IA; SecSrCls; Band; ChrhWkr; CncrtBnd; HonRl; HospAde; MrchBnd; PepBnd; 4-H; Chrldr; College; Vocational.

BOLTON, Katherine; Heritage Hills HS; Gentryville, IN; 7/144 HonRl; TrsFrshCls; FrCl; PpCl; Univ Of Evansville; Accounting.

BOLTON, Kimberly A; Green Lake Public HS; Green Lake, WI; Band; Chrs; HonRl; LbryAde; SchMus; SchPl; TchrAde; SchPpr; 4-H; LetterWrstlng; Technical School; Science Technology.

BOLTON, Mary E; Glenbard East HS; Lombard, IL; HonRl; IntrClCncl; NatlMeritCmnd; Orch; SchMus; SchPl; Univ Of Ill; C P A.

BOLTON, Tim L; Ovid Elsie HS; Ovid, MI; HonRl; SchAde; SchMus; StuCncl; TchrAde; RptrSchPpr; EdSchPpr; Bsbl; Bsktbl; PPFtbl; College; Pofessional.

BOLTZ, Eric B; Delta HS; Albany, IN; 12/275 CncrtBnd; HonRl; JA; JrNHS; MrchBnd; NHS; 4-H; SciCl; Glf; Trk; Coll.

BOLTZ, James K; Big Springs HS; Big Springs, NE; 2/20 Chrs; HonRl; SchPl; StuCncl; Bsktbl; LetterFtbl; LetterTrk; University Of Nebr.

BOLTZ, Jeannie R; Warren County R 3 HS; Warrenton, MO; HonRl; NHS; RptrYrbk; Trk; Univ; Accounting.

BOLTZ, Lisa K; Earlville HS; Earlville, IL; 3/41 Chrs; CncrtBnd; HonRl; Mdrgl; NHS; SecStuCncl; EdYrBk; SecPpCl; Socr; TreasGAA;.

BOMA, James W; Morris Comm HS; Morris, IL; 17/250 Chr; HonRl; NHS; NatlThespSoc; Quill&Scroll; SchPl; SctActv; SptEdSchPpr; GerCl; Univ Of Illinois; Chemistry.

BOMA, Joseph G; Morris Comm HS; Morris, IL; 27/250 Band; CncrtBnd; HonRl; MrchBnd; SpnCl; MthCl; Illinois State Univ; Accounting.

BOMA, Robert D; Ford Central HS; Piper City, IL; Band; CncrtBnd; HonRl; MrchBnd; PepBnd; Illinois State Univ; Veterinarian.

BOMBACH, Daniel B; Bourbon HS; Cuba, MO; ChrhWkr; HonRl; Bsbl; College; Law Enforcement.

BOMBERG, Cheryl L; Plattsmouth HS; Plattsmouth, NE; 8/163 Chrs; HonRl; SchMus; FBLA; SecFHA; MthCl; PpCl; College; Dental Technician.

BOMBERGER, Mary L; Lincoln Southeast HS; Lincoln, NE; 39/498 Chr; ChrhWkr; HonRl; LitMag; NHS; SctActv; GerCl; Swmmng; Tennis; CchngActv; U Of Ne; Pre Pharmacy Or Language.

BOMBINSKI, Carolyn; Antigo HS; Antigo, WI; 6/373 Band; CncrtBnd; HonRl; LitMag; MrchBnd; PepBnd; FBLA; EldAwd; Univ Of Wi Oshkosh; Med Tech.

BOMER, Michael O; Mendel Catholic Prep; Chicago, IL; 15/191 CmntyWkr; HonRl; MthCl; Univ Of Louisville; Physician.

BOMGARDNER, Joan A; Unionville HS; Lucerne, MO; 8/82 ChrhWkr; CmntyWkr; HonRl; NHS; PepBnd; StuCncl; 4-H; FFA; PpCl; CaptBsktbl; Nw Mo State U; Spec Educ.

BOMMERSCHEIM, Judith A; Plainwell HS; Kalamazoo, MI; 7/224 Chrs; HonRl; LitMag; LbryAde; NHS; SchMus; SchPl; StuCncl; StuGov; RptrSchPpr; 4-H; W Mi Univ; English.

BONA, Kathleen A; Thorton Fractional North HS; Calumet City, IL; 47/480 SecSrCls; HonRl; OffAde; SchAde; StuCncl; TchrAde; FTA; College; Court Reporter.

BONACK, Jeannette M; Three Lakes HS; Three Lakes, WI; PresJrCls; Band; Chr; ChrhWkr; HonRl; StuCncl; SpnCl; Chrldr;.

BONAGURA, Karen; St Louise De Marillac Hs; Morton Grove, IL; 54/252 NHS; RptrYrbk; SpnCl; U; Professional.

BONAGURO, Susan M; Amos Alonzo Stagg HS; Palos Hills, IL; VPFrshCls; VPSophCls; HonRl; NatlMeritCmnd; FrCl; PpCl; SciCl; Chrldr; Northern Ill Univ; Nursing.

BONAM, Douglas A; Huntington North HS; Huntington, IN; ALBoysSt; HonRl; StuCncl; Swmmng; Ball State Univ; Architect.

BONAR, Kim E; Garrett HS; Auburn, IN; Band; Chr; HonRl; NHS; PepBnd; SchPpr; PpCl; LetterBsktbl; GAA; IMSpt; Ball State; Business Admin.

BONARDI, Gregory A; Harper Creek HS; Ceresco, MI; 29/230 HonRl; JA; NHS; NatlMeritSF; SctActv; 4-H; LetterBsbl; LetterFtbl; LetterWrstlng; 4-HAwd; JAAwd; Col; Architect.

BONAREK, Patricia A; St Augustine HS; Chicago, IL; NHS; FrCl; College; Oceanographer.

BONAWITZ, Jana M; Rosemount HS; Apple Valley, MN; Chr; HonRl; Mdrgl; NHS; RedCrAde; Yrbk; PpCl; Coll.

BONCZYK, Cynthia L; St Clement HS; Detroit, MI; SchPl; RptrYrbk; PpCl; LetterBsbl; CaptBsktbl; Chrldr; GAA; IMSpt; Coll; Psychology Or Phy Ed.

BOND, Gregory W; Hugoton Secondary HS; Hugoton, KS; VPFrshCls; PresSophCls; ALBoysSt; ChrhWkr; HonRl; NHS; Bsbl; Bsktbl; Ftbl; Trk; Garden City Juco; Bus.

BOND, Jan A; Castle HS; Boonville, IN; 38/283 Chr; ChrhWkr; HonRl; LbryAde; NatlThespSoc; SchMus; TchrAde; FTA; PpCl; SciCl; Indiana State Univ; Biology.

BOND, Kathleen E; Thomas Jefferson HS; Rockford, IL; 27/335 VPSophCls; VPJrCls; PresSrCls; HonRl; JrNHS; Augustana College; Religion.

BOND, Penny S; Milford Twp HS; Milford, IL; 8/68 TrsFrshCls; Band; HonRl; NHS; Quill&Scroll; FshEdYrbk; RptrSchPpr; GerCl; GAA; E Illinois University; Business.

BOND, Richard J; North Knox HS; Oaktown, IN; 1/125 ALBoysSt; Aud/Vis; HonRl; PresNHS; YthFlsp; 4-H; FrCl; MthCl; LetterBsbl; CaptBsktbl; LetterFtbl; College.

BOND, Vicki L; Wilsonville HS; Wilsonville, NE; TrsJrCls; Chrs; HonRl; LbryAde; SchPl; PresYthFlsp; Yrbk; RptrSchPpr; Sec4-H; SecPpCl; College; Nursing.

BONDE, Connie E; Kiel HS; Kiel, WI; AFS; Aud/Vis; Chrs; HonRl; NHS; SchMus; StuGov; TchrAde; GAA; IMSpt;.

BONDE, Karen; Kiel HS; Newton, WI; SecSophCls; Chr; HonRl; SchMus; SchPl; FHA; GAA; IMSpt; PresAwd; Secretary.

BONDE, Kevin; Kiel HS; Kiel, WI; 4/164 TrsSrCls; ALBoysSt; Band; CncrtBnd; HonRl; MrchBnd; NHS; StuCncl; 4-H; LetterTrk; College; Engineering.

BONDRA, Joseph A; Immaculate Conception HS; Warren, MI; PresFrshCls; PresSrCls; SchPl; StuCncl; RptrSchPpr; CaptBsbl; Bsktbl; Ftbl; College.

BONDS, Bruce; Stephen Decatur Hs; Decatur, IL; PresSophCls; PresStuCncl; StuGov; SptEdSchPpr; GerCl; SARAwd; U Of Illinois; Lawyer.

BONDS, Carolyn G; Gering HS; Gering, NE; 13/139 SecAFS; Band; Chr; Chrs; ChrhWkr; CncrtBnd; HonRl; MrchBnd; NHS; PepBnd; Dallas Bible Clge; Missions.

BONDS, Robert H; Providence St Mel HS; Chicago, IL; HonRl; NHS; Bsktbl; CaptTrk; College; Sports Broadcaster.

BONDY, Barbara A; Marian HS; Birmingham, MI; VPSrCls; CmntyWkr; HonRl; SecNHS; OffAde; SchAde; StuGov; RptrSchPpr; Chrldr; DanFAwd; Mi St Univ; Curriculum Of Major Study.

BONDY, Janet L; Brunswick HS; Brunswick, MO; Band; ChrhWkr; CncrtBnd; HonRl; LbryAde; NHS; RptrYrbk; RptrSchPpr; 4-H; 4-HAwd; Home Ec Related Career.

BONDY, Karin A; Ida HS; Monroe, MI; NHS; PpCl; Bsktbl; Trk; GAA; IMSpt; Professional.

BONDY, Maureen; Dunpee HS; Maybee, MI; Chr; Chrs; HonRl; LbryAde; NHS; OptClAwd; Univ Mich; Oceanographer.

BONE, Donna L; Mc Donald County R 1 HS; Pineville, MO; 13/166 Band; ChrhWkr; CmntyWkr; CncrtBnd; HonRl; HospAde; JrNHS; MrchBnd; PepBnd; SchMus; SchPpr; SpnCl; Crower College; Medicine.

BONE, Glenda S; Potosi HS; Mineral Point, MO; 35/275 Chr; HonRl; StuCncl; FBLA; Trk; Chrldr; IMSpt; 4-HAwd; Coll; Teach.

BONE, Sheree R; R 3 Senior HS; Mineral Point, MO; Band; CncrtBnd; HonRl; MrchBnd; NHS; SchAde; TchrAde; Twrl;.

BONER, Martha A; Williamsville HS; Williamsville, IL; ChrhWkr; HonRl; OffAde; SchPl; SctActv; TchrAde; YthFlsp; FHA; Tennis; GAA; Il State Univ; Social Worker.

BONER, Ronald L; Lohrville Comm HS; Lohrville, IA; 10/28 VPFrshCls; PresSophCls; VPSrCls; StuCncl; Yrbk; SptEdSchPpr; Bsbl; Bsktbl; Ftbl; Trk; College; Pre Med.

BONESS, Doreen; Mil Lutheran HS; Milwaukee, WI; 11/231 ChrhWkr; CmntyWkr; LbryAde; NHS; College.

BONESTELL, Michelle D; Lyman HS; Presho, SD; CncrtBnd; HonRl; NHS; StuCncl; YthFlsp; RptrSchPpr; 4-H; Bsktbl; Chrldr; CitAwd; Univ; Biological Research.

BONEY, Barbara L; Bishop Noll Institute HS; Calumet City, IL; ChrhWkr; DrlTm; HonRl; StuCncl; RptrYrbk; RptrSchPpr; MthCl; PpCl; GAA; College; Professional.

BONFER, Debra L; Milan HS; Milan, IN; 5/70 Band; CmntyWkr; CncrtBnd; HonRl; NHS; SchPl; Yrbk; LatCl; Bsktbl; IMSpt; Morehead St Univ; Music.

BONGLE, Cheryl A; Sevastopol HS; Sturgeon Bay, WI; Quill&Scroll; SchPl; SecStuCncl; RptrSchPpr; Univ Wi Stevens Point; Sociology.

BONHAM, David L; Malden HS; Malden, MO; 34/110 ChrhWkr; CmntyWkr; HonRl; NatlThespSoc; StuCncl; YthFlsp; EdYrBk; MthCl; LetterFtbl; LetterTrk; Bs Col; Electronics.

BONICATTO, David J; Hibbing HS; Hibbing, MN; 213/380 Chr; JA; SctActv; RptrSchPpr; PpCl; Bsbl; LetterBsktbl; Ftbl; Glf; JAAwd; College; Vocation.

BONIFAS, Steven J; Aurora Central Catholic HS; Aurora, IL; 7/165 PresFrshCls; HonRl; SctActv; StuCncl; EdSchPpr; Wrstlng; Creighton Univ; Physics.

BONIFIELD, Von L; Hannibal HS; Hull, IL; CaptFtbl; LetterTrk; CaptWrstlng; Ne Mo State Univ; Law Enforcement.

BONIKOWSKE, Randal R; Little Wolf HS; Ogdensburg, WI; PresSophCls; HonRl; TchrAde; FFA; LetterFtbl; LetterCchngActv;.

BONINI, Bruce E; Lake Linden HS; Lake Linden, MI; 1/60 VPSrCls; Band; HonRl; SchPl; StuCncl; RptrYrbk; Ftbl; Michigan Tech Univ; Business Admin.

BONISA, Robin M; Heritage Christian HS; New Palestine, IN; Chr; Chrl; ChrhWkr; Orch; SchMus; TchrAde; YthFlsp; SchPpr; Trk; Greenville Tech; Nursing.

BONITZER, Patricia A; Grover Cleveland HS; Mehlville, MO; 69/629 ChrhWkr; HonRl; JA; OffAde; SctActv; JAAwd; Junior College.

BONJOUR, Karen J; Warren HS; Apple River, IL; 6/60 PresSophCls; Band; CncrtBnd; HonRl; MrchBnd; PepBnd; StuCncl; Glf; PresGAA; College; Zoology.

BONK, Joseph J; Bridgeport HS; Saginaw, MI; 23/330 PresFrshCls; PresSophCls; PresSrCls; Band; CncrtBnd; HonRl; JrNHS; MrchBnd; NHS; NatlMeritCmnd; Michigan State; Law.

BONKIEWICZ, Ann J; Saint Patricks HS; Lodgepole, NE; Chr; Chrs; HonRl; NHS; SchPl; RptrYrbk; Tennis; Chrldr; Kearney State Coll; Psych.

BONKOWSKI, Jerome L; St Willibrord HS; Chicago, IL; 16/69 HonRl; NHS; SptEdYrbk; SptEdSchPpr; Bsbl; Bsktbl; CchngActv; IMSpt; CitAwd; VoiceDemAwd; Columbia Clg; Journalism.

BONNELL, Sandra L; Echo Public HS; Echo, MN; CmntyWkr; CncrtBnd; HonRl; JA; SchPl; StuCncl; TchrAde; FFA; MthCl; PresAwd; Clge; Prof.

BONNEMA, Craig L; Storm Lake Sr HS; Storm Lake, IA; 8/159 ALBoysSt; Chr; Chrs; SchPl; StuCncl; LetterFtbl; LetterTrk; LetterWrstlng; College.

BONNER, Connie M; Crystal Lake Community HS; Crystal Lake, IL; 1/470 Band; PresChrhWkr; HonRl; NHS; NatlMeritCmnd; RptrYrbk; FTA; FrCl; GAA; Coe College; Chemistry.

BONNER, Dianna L; Crispus Attucks HS; Indianapolis, IN; 3/250 Chr; Chrl; Chrs; ChrhWkr; HonRl; NHS; Butler Univ; Music.

BONNER, Kathy; Rockwell Swaledoale HS; Swaledale, IA; Chr; HonRl; SchMus; YthFlsp; FTA; PpCl; Chrldr; 4-HAwd; Niacc; Medical Secretary.

BONNER, Timothy A; Tinley Park HS; Tinley Park, IL; 30/289 NHS; MthCl; Univ Of Illinois; Chemical Engineering.

BONNEY, Bret C; Fredericktown HS; Fredericktown, MO; HonRl; FFA; GerCl;.

BONNEY, Robert A; St Charles HS; St Charles, MO; ALBoysSt; HonRl; YthFlsp; KeyCl; LetterBsbl; LetterBsktbl; IMSpt; Univ Of Missouri; Law.

BONO, Barbara A; Morton West HS; Berwyn, IL; AFS; SchAde; StuCncl; Upper Iowa University; Accounting.

BONOW, Kimberlee; Wahoo HS; Ithaca, NE; 12/75 Chr; ChrhWkr; RptrYrbk; Yrbk; 4-H; PpCl; Chrldr; IMSpt; College; Nursing.

BONSELL, Lynda C; White Bear HS; White Bear Lake, MN; Chr; Chrs; JrNHS; StuCncl; Yrbk; Coll; Psych.

BONTE, Janette A; Washburn Rural HS; Wakarusa, KS; 12/193 Band; Chr; Chrs; CncrtBnd; HonRl; JA; MrchBnd; PepBnd; SchMus; PpCl; Univ; Music.

BONTEKOE, Jane E; Linden HS; Linden, MI; SecJrCls; Band; HospAde; MrchBnd; Orch; PepBnd; 4-H; SpnCl; Bsktbl; Trk; Ferris State College; Nursing.

BONTER, Rebecca; Mackinaw City HS; Mackinaw City, MI; Chrs; SchPl; RptrYrbk; SchPpr; PpCl; Central Mich Univ; Health.

BONTRAGER, Daryl E; Blackduck HS; Blackduck, MN; 3/60 Chrs; HonRl; PresNHS; SchPl; VPStuCncl; Yrbk; AmLegAwd; Coll; Social Work.

BONTRAGER, Rodney L; Westview HS; Topeka, IN; Chr; Chrl; HonRl; Mdrgl; 4-H; FFA; LetterBsbl; LetterBsktbl; LetterSoccr; LetterTrk; College.

BONTREGER, Dean J; Westview HS; Shipshewana, IN; 24/65 YthFlsp; VPSophCls; 4-H; FFA; EngCl; GerCl; LetterBsbl; IMSpt; 4-HAwd; Agriculture.

BONUS, Janel A; Eisenhower HS; Utica, MI; 2/545 HonRl; NHS; FrCl; Wayne State Univ; Liberal Arts.

BOOE, Cindy L; Parkwood HS; Joplin, MO; Chr; HonRl; SchMus; PpCl; CaptChrldr; MasAwd; College; Music.

BOOE, Julie A; Atchison HS; Atchison, KS; HonRl; NatlMeritCmnd; RptrSchPpr; SchPpr; College; Secretary.

BOOHER, Frandora; Bluffton HS; Bluffton, IN; 24/139 DrlTm; MrchBnd; NHS; StuCncl; TreasTeen; RptrYrbk; RptrSchPpr; SpnCl; Chrldr; PresGAA; Purdue University; Psychology.

BOOK, Marcella J; Allen HS; Ponca, NE; 11/36 Band; ChrhWkr; HonRl; YthFlsp; Yrbk; FshEdSchPpr; FHA; PpCl; Bsbl; Bsktbl; Univ.

BOOK, Rose M; Borden HS; Borden, IN; 8/64 SecJrCls; HonRl; NHS; OffAde; SchAde; TchrAde; SptEdSchPpr; FHA; DARAwd; PresAwd; Bus Clge; Medical Secretary.

BOOKER, Karen S; North Salem HS; North Salem, IN; 5/36 TrsSrCls; Band; Chr; NHS; Quill&Scroll; SchPl; EdYrBk; RptrSchPpr; 4-H; VPPpCl; Purdue Univ; Fashion Merchandising.

BOOKER, Vicki J; Lovington HS; Lovington, IL; Band; Chrs; ChrhWkr; CncrtBnd; HonRl; MrchBnd; PepBnd; SchPpr; FHA; PpCl; Bsktbl; College; Medicine.

BOOKOUT, Janet L; Logan Rogersville HS; Rogersville, MO; SecTrsJrCls; Chrs; HonRl; OffAde; SchPl; StuCncl; YthFlsp; FHA; PpCl;.

BOOKS, Cathy L; Hillsdale HS; Hillsdale, MI; Chr; Chrs; ChrhWkr; HonRl; JA; LbryAde; YthFlsp; 4-H; PpCl; Bsktbl; Trk; GAA; College; Music.

BOOKWALTER, Dwayne R; Grayslake Community HS; Grayslake, IL; HonRl; LbryAde; NHS; 4-H; LetterGlf; 4-HAwd; College Of Lake County; Accounting.

BOOKWALTER, Ruth M; Caston HS; Twelve Mile, IN; 5/85 ChrhWkr; HonRl; NHS; YthFlsp; Yrbk; PpCl; BttyCrckrAwd; Ball State University.

BOOMER, Julie A; Perry Meridian HS; Indianapolis, IN; 14/550 Chr; HonRl; JrNHS; NHS; OffAde; SchAde; SchMus; StuCncl; RptrYrbk; Yrbk; Iupui; Med Tech.

BOOMGAARDEN, Mark L; West Sioux HS; Hawanden, IA; SchPl; StuCncl; YthFlsp; Yrbk; FFA; LetterBsbl; LetterBsktbl; LetterFtbl; LetterTrk; Wrstlng; IMSpt; GovHonPrgAwd; College; Physical Education.

BOOMSMA, Barbara L; Pella Christian HS; Pella, IA; VPFrshCls; TrsJrCls; SecChrhWkr; HonRl; LbryAde; SchPl; Bsbl; Bsktbl; LetterTrk; IMSpt; Nurse.

BOONE, Anthony G; Seymour HS; Plainville, IL; 15/66 Band; ChrhWkr; CncrtBnd; HonRl; MrchBnd; PepBnd; SchMus; SchPl; RptrSchPpr; EdSchPpr; Trk; IMSpt; Western Univ; Professional.

BOONE, Carolyn; Algona HS; Algona, IA; 7/119 CmntyWkr; Tennis; Trk; CitAwd; Ia St Univ; Pro.

BOONE, Mary A; Sheldon Community HS; Sheldon, IA; 13/112 Band; Chr; HonRl; NHS; Quill&Scroll; SchMus; VPYthFlsp; RptrYrbk; PpCl; LetterBsktbl; Ft Dodge Comm College; Nursing.

BOONE, Paul; Hamilton Se HS; Noblesville, IN; 32/134 ChrhWkr; HonRl; JA; 4-H; SpnCl; SciCl; Swmmng; Tennis; 4-HAwd; Vincennes Univ; Inhalation Therapy.

BOONSTRA, Mark T; Western Michigan ChristianHS; Muskegon, MI; PresBand; HonRl; MrchBnd; NatlFornLg; PepBnd; SchPl; VPStuCncl; MthCl; Bsktbl; Mi State U; Math Computer Science.

BOONSTRA, Patti L; Willmar HS; Willmar, MN; AFS; Chr; ChrhWkr; YthFlsp; RptrYrbk; PpCl; Trk; GAA; Coll;.

BOOREN, Julie A; Forest Lake Sr HS; Marine, MN; 19/353 HonRl; NHS; OffAde; RptrSchPpr; 4-H; KeyCl; GAA; 4-HAwd; Univ Of Minnesota; Nursing.

BOORSMA, Roxann P; Mona Shores HS; Muskegon, MI; Band; HonRl; MrchBnd; NHS; NatlMeritSF; NatlThespSoc; OffAde; RptrYrbk; FrCl; LetterTennis; Michigan St Univ; Law.

BOOS, Craig; Loyola Academy; Glenview, IL; 49 SecSophCls; Band; CncrtBnd; HonRl; NHS; NatlMeritCmnd; StuCncl; SchPpr; LetterFtbl; LetterWrstlng; U Notre Dame ;.

BOOSE, Diane C; Niles HS; Niles, MI; 8/364 Band; JA; MrchBnd; NatlMeritCmnd; PepBnd; SchMus; Univ Of Michigan; Engineering.

BOOT, Mike A; Kalamozoo Christian HS; Kalomazoo, MI; 1/136 ChrhWkr; HonRl; VPNHS; NatlMeritSF; SchMus; RptrYrbk; RptrSchPpr; Bsktbl; LetterTennis; IMSpt; Calvin Coll; Actuary.

BOOTEN, Cynthia L; Equality HS; Vardaman, IL; SecSophCls; PresJrCls; SecTrsSrCls; ChrhWkr; HonRl; Yrbk; FHA; PpCl; Bsbl; Bsktbl; GAA; IMSpt; DARAwd; Southeastern Il Univ; Business.

BOOTH, Barbara J; Centennial HS; Beaver Crossing, NE; 1/65 Band; Chrs; ChrhWkr; CncrtBnd; HonRl; MrchBnd; NHS; SchPl; RptrYrbk; PpCl; College; Teaching.

BOOTH, Carlye A; Stephen Decatur HS; Decatur, IL; Chr; PresChrhWkr; PresNHS; PolWkr; RptrYrbk; RptrSchPpr; Wrstlng; Brown Univ; Chemist.

BOOTH, Carrin V; Concordia Acad; St Paul, MN; PresSrCls; Chr; ChrhWkr; HospAde; SchPl; StuCncl; RptrYrbk; SchPpr; PpCl; Socr; Phy Ed Teacher.

BOOTH, Cynthia L; Washington HS; Brighton, IA; ChrhWkr; HonRl; HospAde; TchrAde; YthFlsp; 4-H; FBLA; CaptBsktbl; CaptTrk; CchngActv; PPFtbl; 4-HAwd; CitAwd; Mount Mercy College; Nursing.

BOOTH, Emily J; Ladywood St Agnes HS; Indianapolis, IN; ChrhWkr; StuCncl; StuGov; SpnCl; Chrldr; Univ; Spanish.

BOOTH, Mary L; Marion Co R Ii HS; Maywood, MO; VPJrCls; ChrhWkr; HonRl; SchPl; 4-H; FHA; PpCl; LetterBsbl; CaptBsktbl; Trk;.

BOOTH, Sandy A; Oak Park Academy; Cedar Rapids, IA; Chr; CmntyWkr; HonRl; HospAde; Swmmng; Union College; Nursing.

BOOTH, Teddie L; Beach HS; Beach, ND; Band; Chrs; ChrhWkr; CmntyWkr; HonRl; LbryAde; SchPl; YthFlsp; FHA; North Dakota S Univ; Lawyer.

BOOTH, Teresa; Lindblom Tech Hs; Chicago, IL; 66/657 ChrhWkr; CmntyWkr; HonRl; OffAde; SchAde; SctActv; TchrAde; LetterGAA; Illinois Inst Of Tech; Architecture.

BOOTTER, Ronald A; Evart HS; Evart, MI; HonRl; NHS; TchrAde; College; Professional.

BOOTZ, Dennis; Pinconning HS; Linwood, MI; 4/250 HonRl; NHS; Sacrstn; SctActv; Ftbl; Mich Tech; Forestry.

BOOZELL, Marcia A; Central Catholic HS; Bloomington, IL; PresSophCls; HonRl; NHS; StuCncl; StuGov; EdYrBk; FrCl; PpCl; College; Political Science.

BORAGE, Karen M; Hancock Pl HS; St Louis, MO; 9/150 DrlTm; HonRl; LbryAde; NHS; OffAde; StuCncl; TchrAde; PpCl; Chrldr; GAA; Missouri Bap Hosp; Nursing.

BORCHARD, Greg A; Redfield HS; Redfield, SD; Band; Chr; HonRl; SchMus; SchPl; PresKeyCl; LetterBsktbl; LetterFtbl; LetterGlf; LetterTrk; Coll.

BORCHARD, Nancy L; Concordia Academy; St Paul, MN; Chr; Chrs; HonRl; HospAde; NatlMeritCmnd; SchMus; Gustavus Adolphus College; Nursing.

BORCHARD, Rod A; Frankenmuth HS; Frankenmuth, MI; HonRl; NatlFornLg; SchPl; YthFlsp; LetterBsktbl; CaptGlf; Trk; Delta Clg.

BORCHARDT, Adina G; Berkley HS; Oak Park, MI; 89/580 Chr; RptrYrbk; Adrian Col; Mass Communication.

BORCHARDT, Debra A; Providence HS; Manhattan, IL; 4/121 VPJrCls; HonRl; NHS; StuCncl; Yrbk; SchPpr; MthCl; PpCl; SciCl; Tennis; St Joseph School; Nursing.

BORCHARDT, Eileen M; Lansing HS; Leavenworth, KS; HonRl; NHS; NatlThespSoc; RedCrAde; SchMus; SchPl; StuCncl; Yrbk; 4-H; SciCl; College; Library Science Drama.

BORCHARDT, Vicky; Charles City Comm HS; Charles City, IA; HonRl; NHS; 4-H; GerCl; PpCl; IMSpt; PPFtbl; 4-HAwd; No Ia Area Comm Coll; Assoc Nursing.

BORCHELT, Beverly A; Batesville HS; Batesville, IN; 14/150 Band; ChrhWkr; CncrtBnd; HonRl; NHS; NatlThespSoc; PepBnd; PresYthFlsp; Yrbk; MasAwd; Ball St U; Nurse.

BORCHERDING, Donna R; Cal Community HS; Latimer, IA; ChrhWkr; HonRl; SchMus; SchPl;

StuCncl; YthFlsp; SchPpr; LetterBsbl; ChmnBsktbl; CchngActv; Coll; Accnt.

BORCHERS, Kevin L; Edwardsville Sr HS; Edwardsville, IL; 118/463 Band; ChrhWkr; CncrtBnd; MrchBnd; PepBnd; PresYthFlsp; PpCl; LetterFtbl; IMSpt; Illinois State Univ; Education.

BORCHERT, Eddy C; West Vigo HS; West Terre Haute, IN; 27/194 HonRl; SctActv; TchrAde; FTA; KeyCl; FrCl; Ftbl; Trk; Purdue U; Chemists.

BORCZON, Robin L; Columbus North HS; Columbus, IN; PresAFS; HonRl; ModUN; NatlMeritCmnd; NatlThespSoc; SchMus; PresMthCl; Ind Univ.

BORDEN, Kathleen; Coldwater HS; Coldwater, MI; Chrs; YthFlsp; Business School; Secretarial.

BORDERS, Michela K; St Anne HS; Hopkins Park, IL; CAP; CmntyWkr; Bsktbl; Tech Sch; Computer Tech.

BORDOSHUK, Audrey M; Lourdes HS; Chicago, IL; 34/276 ChrhWkr; CmntyWkr; HonRl; NHS; NatlMeritCmnd; StuCncl; FrCl; IMSpt; Northern Il Univ.

BORDWELL, Richard E; Pocahontas Comm HS; Pocahontas, IA; PresFrshCls; PresSrCls; Band; HonRl; StuCncl; StuGov; PpCl; Bsktbl; Ftbl; Creighton University; Business.

BORDY, Gail A; William J Bogan HS; Chicago, IL; CncrtBnd; HonRl; NHS; 4-H; PresFrCl; Tennis; GAA; 4-HAwd; Michigan State Univ; Communications.

BOREEN, Daniel; Southwest HS; Green Bay, WI; 21/436 Chrs; HonRl; NHS; RptrYrbk; FBLA; FrCl; PpCl; Uw Green Bay; Business Fiele.

BORER, Nancy S; Pleasant Hill HS; Pleasant Hill, MO; SecBand; HonRl; StuCncl; EdSchPpr; Pres4-H; SecFTA; SpnCl; PpCl; SecSciCl; LetterTrk; College.

BORG, Gerald E; Proctor HS; Proctor, MN; Band; ChrhWkr; CncrtBnd; HonRl; MrchBnd; SchMus; StuCncl; Ftbl; Trk; CchngActv; College.

BORGARD, Leann R; Rutland Independent HS; Nunda, SD; SecSophCls; Band; Chrs; ChrhWkr; CncrtBnd; HonRl; MrchBnd; PepBnd; StuCncl; 4-H; College.

BORGARD, Leann R; Rutland HS; Nunda, SD; Band; ChrhWkr; HonRl; MrchBnd; StuCncl; 4-H; FHA; PpCl; LetterBsktbl; Chrldr; Clge.

BORGARDT, Traci L; Racine Lutheran HS; Racine, WI; Chr; HonRl; NHS; StuCncl; TchrAde; PpCl; Bsbl; LetterBsktbl; LetterFtbl; PresGAA; College; Law.

BORGELT, Steven C; R 1 North Callaway HS; Kingdom City, MO; 1/70 Band; Chrs; ChrhWkr; HonRl; PresNHS; SchMus; VPStuCncl; Pres4-H; SecFFA; FTA; College; Engineering.

BORGENDALE, Gary C; Dawson Boyd HS; Dawson, MN; 5/77 TrsSophCls; SecTrsJrCls; AFS; ALBoysSt; Aud/Vis; Chr; ChrhWkr; HonRl; LbryAde; SchMus; SchPl; Bsktbl; Ftbl; Univ Of Mn Crookston; Agri Bus Admin.

BORGERS, Frederick J; Chamiande College Prep School; Ballwin, MO; Aud/Vis; CmntyWkr; HonRl; JA; NatlFornLg; PolWkr; SchPl; SctActv; RptrYrbk; RptrSchPpr; University; Prof Pure Science.

BORGES, Jerome F; Glasgow R Ii HS; Glasgow, MO; 3/45 ALBoysSt; HonRl; SecNHS; VPStuCncl; Bsktbl; IMSpt; JAAwd; College; Architecture.

BORGETTI, Lucille I; Gavit HS; Hammond, IN; 18/350 HonRl; NHS; SctActv; TchrAde;.

BORGETTI, Richard J; Whiting HS; Whiting, IN; 5/102 ALBoysSt; Band; CncrtBnd; HonRl; MrchBnd; NHS; PepBnd; StuCncl; SpnCl; KiwanAwd; College; Professional.

BORGGREN, Carole J; Morgan Park HS; Chicago, IL; 2/550 Chr; ChrhWkr; HonRl; ModUN; NHS; NatlMeritCmnd; Quill&Scroll; SchAde; StuCncl; TchrAde; Chrldr; GAA; Northwestern Univ; Journalism.

BORGH, Julie A; Northwestern HS; Lk Nebagamon, WI; Chr; ChrhWkr; HonRl; HospAde; YthFlsp; Yrbk; RptrSchPpr; PresFBLA; CaptChrldr; GAA; Univ Of Wisc; Liveral Arts.

BORGLUM, Anne F; Wells Easton HS; Wells, MN; 10/111 Chrs; ChrhWkr; CmntyWkr; HonRl; NatlMeritCmnd; SchMus; StuCncl; SchPpr; FHA; LetterChrldr; St Teresas Coll; Physical Therapy.

BORGMAN, Beverly A; Slater HS; Slater, MO; Chr; Chrs; ChrhWkr; HonRl; OffAde; TchrAde; Yrbk; 4-H; FHA; Chrldr; Beauty School; Beautician.

BORGMANN, Barbara L; Osmond Community HS; Osmond, NE; 17/43 Chr; Chrs; HonRl; SchPl; TchrAde; PpCl;.

BORGMEYER, Ellen J; Duchesne HS; St Charles, MO; 40/190 HonRl; HospAde; SctActv; PpCl; LetterBsktbl; CchngActv; IMSpt; PPFtbl; College; Mathematics.

BORGWARDT, David W; Immanuel Lutheran HS; Eau Claire, WI; Chr; Chrs; ChrhWkr; LitMag; SchPl; RptrYrbk; College; Teaching.

BORHART, Sue M; Huntley HS; Huntley, IL; Band; Chrs; Mdrgl; 4-H; FFA; DanFAwd; College; Veterinarian.

BORIK, Frank C; Pinckney HS; Whitmore Lk, MI; 2/170 Band; CAP; CncrtBnd; HonRl; LbryAde; MrchBnd; NHS; PepBnd; SchPl; Wrstlng; U Of Mich; Doctor.

BORINO, Sheryl A; St Cecilia HS; Hastings, NE; 12/65 Band; Chr; Chrs; CncrtBnd; HonRl; HospAde; Mdrgl; MrchBnd; PepBnd; SchMus; SchPl; Mt Marty College; Nursing.

BORIO, Diane; St Francis Academy; Joliet, IL; 1/186 ALAGirlsSt; Chrs; HonRl; LitMag; NHS; NatlMeritSF; SchMus; VPStuCncl; FrCl; IMSpt; AmLegAwd; DARAwd; College Of St Catherine; French.

BORIS, Denise A; Davison HS; Davison, MI; Chr; HonRl; NatlFornLg; NHS; NatlThespSoc; SchMus; SchPl; PpCl; Univ Of Mich; Theatre & Speech Comm.

BORISON, Nancy J; Berkley HS; Huntington Woods, MI; ChrhWkr; TchrAde; Yrbk; SchPpr; SpnCl; Swmmng; College; Professional.

BORK, Michael D; Bishop Borgess HS; Dearborn Hts, MI; CmntyWkr; HonRl; NHS; SchMus; SchPl; PresStuCncl; StuGov; LetterBsktbl; CchngActv; IMSpt; Wayne State U; Pre Med.

BORK, Robert; Ford Central HS; Thawville, IL; ChrhWkr; HonRl; SchPl; EngCl; SpnCl; MthCl; SciCl; IMSpt; Collge; Accountant.

BORK, Wayne A; Ford Central HS; Piper City, IL; 2/65 ALBoysSt; HonRl; NHS; NatlMeritSchl; YthFlsp; FFA; LetterBsktbl; LetterFtbl; LetterTrk; SARAwd; Univ Of Illinois; Agriculture.

BORKOVEC, Lorre A; Greendale HS; Greendale, WI; AFS; Band; CncrtBnd; HonRl; HospAde; MrchBnd; ModUN; NatlFornLg; NHS; College.

BORKOVICH, Sandra D; Bogan HS; Chicago, IL; 24/704 HonRl; NHS; OffAde; SchAde; TchrAde; Yrbk; MthCl; PpCl; Bsktbl; Tennis; Univ Of Il; Mathematics.

BORKOWSKI, Sheryl K; Irwin Community HS; Irwin, IA; SecSrCls; Band; Chr; Chrs; CncrtBnd; HonRl; MrchBnd; PepBnd; Bsktbl; Trk; Trade School; Lpn.

BORLAND, Michael A; Humboldt HS; Humboldt, IA; 16/140 SecSrCls; Band; Chr; Chrl; ChrhWkr; HonRl; NatlMeritCmnd; SchMus; RptrSchPpr; SchPpr; LetterBsktbl; LetterFtbl; LetterTrk; Drake Univ; Journalism.

BORMAN, Gerald D; Broad Ripple HS; Indianapolis, IN; HonRl; Indiana University; Professional.

BORMAN, Julie A; Evansville Central HS; Evansville, IN; 45/630 HonRl; NHS; SchAde; SctActv; StuCncl; TreasYthFlsp; LatCl; Univ Evans; Nursng.

BORMANN, Dwight J; Garrigan HS; Bode, IA; ALBoysSt; HonRl; Iowa State U; Vet.

BORN, Douglas E; West HS; Sioux City, IA; ALBoysSt; HonRl; YthFlsp; FrCl; LetterBsktbl; LetterFtbl; Coll; Med.

BORN, Keith J; Lutheran HS Of Minneapolis; St Louis Park, MN; Band; HonRl; NHS; PepBnd; YthFlsp; Bsbl; Bsktbl; Ftbl;.

BORN, Ronald D; Cerro Gordo HS; Cerro Gordo, IL; 19/78 Band; CncrtBnd; HonRl; MrchBnd; PepBnd; SpnCl; U Of Ill; Engineer.

BORN, Roy A; Markesan HS; Fairwater, WI; 23/114 TrsFrshCls; ALBoysSt; CmntyWkr; HonRl; NHS; LetterBsbl; CaptBsktbl; LetterFtbl; College; Mechincal Engineer.

BORN, Tammara D; Cerro Gordo HS; Hammond, IL; 2/69 Band; HonRl; MrchBnd; NHS; PresOffAde; PepBnd; EdYrBk; FHA; SpnCl; GAA; Isu; Special Education.

BORNBACH, Keith R; Stratford HS; Stratford, WI; 22/118 Band; CncrtBnd; HonRl; MrchBnd; NHS; PepBnd; FFA; Trk; College; Mathematics.

BORNEMANN, Anita R; Center HS; Center, ND; Band; Chrs; ChrhWkr; HonRl; SchPpr; GerCl; LetterBsktbl; Chrldr; CchngActv; 4-HAwd; Minat State Col; Secretarial.

BORNEMANN, Susan H; Center HS; Hannover, ND; HstSophCls; PresJrCls; Band; Chrs; HonRl; StuCncl; RptrYrbk; EdYrBk; RptrSchPpr; PresFHA; LetterChrldr; Minot State; Med Secretary.

BORNEMEIER, Debra J; Elmwood Public HS; Elmwood, NE; SecTrsFrshCls; VPJrCls; SecSrCls; Band; Chrs; HonRl; PepBnd; SctActv; TchrAde; EdSchPpr; Marriage; Secretarial.

BORNER, Kevin N; Stanton Public HS; Stanton, ND; ALBoysSt; JA; NatlSciFnd; PolWkr; RedCrAde; SctActv; StuGov; UNYO; YthFnd; FBLA; Bsktbl; Ftbl; Trk; College; Vocation.

BORNHOEFT, Ralph; New Trier West Hs; Wilmette, IL; 103 HonRl; StuCncl; TchrAde; GerCl; MthCl; Bsktbl; LetterSocr; LetterTennis; Lawrence U;mathematics Science.

BORNITZKE, Joel R; Marshall HS; Marshall, WI; Band; Chrs; CncrtBnd; HonRl; MrchBnd; NHS; PepBnd; SchPl; StuCncl; SchPpr; FFA; College.

BORNMANN, Patricia L; St Charles HS; St Charles, MO; HonRl; NHS; Orch; GerCl; MthCl; PresSciCl; Ca Inst Of Tech ;physics &stro.

BORNOR, Sally A; Athens HS; Athens, MI; 3/90 NHS; SchPl; StuCncl; PpCl; College; Drafting.

BOROUGHF, Diane K; Breckenridge HS; Wheeler, MI; 14/91 HonRl; VPFHA; SpnCl;.

BOROVICH, Deana A; Lew Wallace HS; Gary, IN; 10/514 HonRl; JrNHS; NHS; RusCl; LetterBsktbl; GAA; PPFtbl; Purdue Calumet; Computer Sci.

BOROWCZYK, Janet J; Antigo Senior HS; Antino, WI; 35/365 HonRl; RptrYrbk; RptrSchPpr; LatCl; College; Nursing.

BOROWIAK, Steven; Lockport Central HS; Lockport, IL; HonRl; NHS; Lewis Univ; Professional.

BOROWIAK, Tami K; Charlevoix HS; Charlevoix, MI; Band; CncrtBnd; HonRl; Work; Nurses Aid.

BOROWIAK, Timothy R; Charlevoix HS; Charlevoix, MI; 13/147 4-H; Col; Vet Med.

BOROWIECKI, Fabian A; Marist HS; Chicago, IL; Band; CncrtBnd; DrlTm; HonRl; MrchBnd; NatlMeritFnl; NatlMeritSF; Orch; PepBnd; IMSpt; I I T; Architecture.

BORR, David W; Mandan HS; Mandan, ND; ALBoysSt; Chr; CncrtBnd; HonRl; MrchBnd; PepBnd; LetterBsktbl; College; Humanities.

BORRELLO, Joseph A; Fordson HS; Dearborn, MI; HonRl; LitMag; LbryAde; NHS; SchMus; TchrAde; IMSpt; U Of Mich; Dr Of Med Research.

BORROWMAN, Steven W; Monroe City HS; Monroe City, MO; VPSophCls; Band; Chr; Chrs; ChrhWkr; CmntyWkr; CncrtBnd; HonRl; MrchBnd; PepBnd; SchMus; Bsbl; CaptBsktbl; CaptFtbl; Univ Of Kirksville; Physical Ed.

BORST, Catherine J; Kingman HS; Kingman, KS; 5/114 Band; Chr; ChrhWkr; CmntyWkr; HonRl; MrchBnd; SchMus; TchrAde; Pres4-H; 4-HAwd; Sterling Col; Extension Agent.

BORST, Denise L; Durand Area HS; Lennon, MI; 17/202 Band; CmntyWkr; CncrtBnd; HonRl; NatlFornLg; SctActv; College; Professional.

BORST, Mark R; Kingman HS; Kingman, KS; 8/114 ALBoysSt; Chr; CmntyWkr; HonRl; SchAde; SptEdYrbk; 4-H; Bsbl; CaptBsktbl; LetterTrk; Emporia Kansas State Clg; Math.

BORST, Peggy J; Alba Public HS; Alba, MI; 4/14 TrsSophCls; HonRl; SchMus; SchPl; SctActv; StuCncl; YthFlsp; 4-H; Bsktbl; Chrldr; 4-HAwd;.

BORST, Sonja K; Alba Public HS; Alba, MI; PresFrshCls; TrsSophCls; PresJrCls; ChrhWkr; HonRl; OffAde; SchAde; SchPl; StuCncl; TchrAde; YthFlsp; SchPpr; 4-H; Bsktbl; Northwestern Mich College; Sec Science.

BORSUM, James; Pennfielo HS; Battle Creek, MI; 3/200 PresSrCls; ALBoysSt; NHS; StuCncl; StuGov; Trk; AmLegAwd; PresAwd; College; Engineering.

BORTELL, Russell D; Jonesville HS; Jonesville, MI; 17/90 ALBoysSt; HonRl; TchrAde; LetterBsbl; LetterBsktbl; LetterGlf; Trk; CchngActv; IMSpt; CitAwd; College.

BORTH, Brenda; Belview Public HS; Redwood Falls, MN; 6/21 PresSrCls; Band; Chr; HonRl; LbryAde; SchMus; SchPl; StuCncl; Trk; GAA; Willmar Vocational; Nurses Aid.

BORTH, Jerry O; Meade HS; Meade, KS; ALBoysSt; Aud/Vis; HonRl; LbryAde; TchrAde; RptrYrbk; Yrbk; Bsktbl; Tennis; Trk; Jr College; Agronomics.

BORTON, Allen L; Interlochen Arts Academy; Manitou Beach, MI; 1/136 Chr; Chrl; Chrs; ChrhWkr; HonRl; NHS; NatlMeritSF; Bible Col; Musical.

BORTON, Brenda L; Pennville HS; Pennville, IN; 4/39 ALAGirlsSt; HonRl; NHS; OffAde; SchPl; TchrAde; EdYrBk; EdSchPpr; 4-H; GAA; Ball State Univ; Accounting.

BORTON, Jay C; Pennville HS; Pennville, IN; PresFrshCls; PresSophCls; PresJrCls; Aud/Vis; Chr; HonRl; SecNHS; OffAde; SchMus; SctActv; PresStuCncl; FFA; LetterBsbl; LetterTrk; University; Law Enforcement.

BORTON, Loretta K; Nesco HS; Zearing, IA; Band; Chr; Chrs; ChrhWkr; CmntyWkr; HonRl; SchMus; SchPl; StuCncl; IMSpt; Mt St Claire Jr College; Music.

BORTSCHELLER, Kathy; St Marys HS; Remsen, IA; 15/60 Band; Chrs; CncrtBnd; HonRl; PepBnd; SchMus; RptrSchPpr; 4-H; PpCl; 4-HAwd; College; Prof Major Study.

BORUCKI, Lawrence R; St Edward HS; Carpentersville, IL; 12/123 ALBoysSt; Band; CncrtBnd; DrmBgl; HonRl; MrchBnd; PepBnd; Milwaukee Sch Of Eng; Mechanical Engineer.

BORUCKI, Lynda S; 6801 Southway HS; Greendale, WI; 4/343 Chr; HonRl; Mdrgl; ModUN; NHS; SchMus; PpCl; CaptChrldr; GAA; Clge; Pro Doctor Or Lawyer.

BORUFF, Paul; Aledo Hs; Aledo, IL; 26/101 ALBoysSt; Band; CncrtBnd; HonRl; MrchBnd; SchPl; Yrbk; LetterFtbl; LetterTrk; CaptWrstlng; U Of Illinois; Veterinarian.

BORUSZAK, Bruce L; Deerfield HS; Highland Park, IL; PresChrhWkr; CmntyWkr; HonRl; NatlMeritCmnd; EdSchPpr; LetterSwmmng; University Of Illinois; Cpa.

BORYSIAK, Joseph; Cabrini HS; Allen Park, MI; 21/167 ChrhWkr; CmntyWkr; HonRl; PolWkr; SctActv; SciCl; Glf; IMSpt; Univ; Dentistry.

BORZICK, Donna J; United Twp HS; E Moline, IL; ChrhWkr; Augustana College.

BOS, Julane; Central Wisc Christian HS; Waupun, WI; CncrtBnd; HonRl; NHS; StuCncl; RptrYrbk; Bsktbl; IMSpt; 4-HAwd; CitAwd; Univ; Nurse.

BOS, Lester D; Tri County Comm HS; What Cheer, IA; 3/46 StuCncl; FFA; Iowa State Univ; Agricultural Engineering.

BOS, Timothy; Zeeland Public HS; Zeeland, MI; 8/175 Band; CncrtBnd; HonRl; MrchBnd; ModUN; PepBnd; SctActv; YthFlsp; LatCl; Ftbl; Glf; CaptTrk; Wrstlng; College; Pharmacy.

BOSARD, Mary K; Stamford Public HS; Stamford, NE; ALAGirlsSt; Chr; HonRl; College; Accounting.

BOSCH, Barbara D; Pella Comm HS; Pella, IA; AFS; Band; Chrs; ChrhWkr; CncrtBnd; HonRl; TreasNHS; Orch; SchMus; TreasYthFlsp; College; Math.

BOSCH, Christopher; St Pius X HS; Kansan City, MO; Chrs; ROTC; SchPl; TchrAde; Bsktbl; Ftbl; Tennis; Trk; CchngActv; JCAwd; Univ Of Kan; Phys Ther.

BOSCH, Janet S; Mayville HS; Mayville, WI; 1/125 VPSrCls; ALAGirlsSt; Band; HonRl; VPNHS; PresStuCncl; EdYrBk; CaptBsktbl; CaptTennis; Trk; GAA; PPFtbl; Univ Of Wisconsin; Med Tech.

BOSCH, Jeffrey; Unity Christian HS; Hudsonville, MI; 17/198 CncrtBnd; HonRl; MrchBnd; StuCncl; College; Professioanl.

BOSCH, Kathryn S; Ogden HS; Ogden, IA; 9/56 HonRl; NHS; Twrl; EdSchPpr; 4-H; FHA; VPFrCl; PpCl; Bsbl; Iowa State Univ; Interior Designer.

BOSCH, Mary; Zeeland Public Hs; Holland, MI; Chr; ChrhWkr; HonRl; OffAde; College; Business.

BOSCH, Patsy A; Linton HS; Linton, ND; 3/60 PresFrshCls; SecTrsJrCls; Chrs; HonRl; PresNHS; StuCncl; TreasYrbk; SchPpr; Trk; Chrldr; Ndsss; Legal Sec.

BOSCH, Richard; Holland HS; Holland, MI; HonRl; SciCl; Hope College; Chemistry.

BOSCH, Thomas N; Finney HS; Detroit, MI; 11/380 HonRl; Trk; U Of Mi; Engineering.

BOSCHERT, Julie R; Duchesne HS; St Charles, MO; 42/180 Chrs; HonRl; FrCl; PpCl; Bsktbl; GAA; College; Secretary.

BOSCHERT, Victoria C; Duchesne HS; St Charles, MO; PresCmntyWkr; DrlTm; HonRl; Twrl; LetterSpnCl; Univ; Nursing.

BOSE, Richard P; Estherville HS; Estherville, IA; HonRl; Mdrgl; NHS; NatlMeritFnl; NatlMeritSchl; SchMus; Bsktbl; LetterTrk; IMSpt; 4-HAwd; Coll; Md.

BOSE, Theresa M; Estherville HS; Estherville, IA; 1/200 Band; Chrs; ChrhWkr; CncrtBnd; HonRl; MrchBnd; StuCncl; Teen; Sec4-H; SpnCl; LetterTrk; Chrldr; PresAwd; College; Art Teacher.

BOSECKER, Edward A; Edward Co Sr HS; W Salem, IL; VPFrshCls; PresJrCls; PresSrCls; Band; CncrtBnd; MrchBnd; SchMus; RptrSchPpr; LetterBsbl; LetterBsktbl; LetterTrk; Univ; Professional.

BOSECKER, Marcia B; Stillman Valley HS; Stillman Valley, IL; ChrhWkr; HonRl; HospAde; SchMus; StuCncl; RptrYrbk; VPFHA; PpCl; Trk; SecGAA; Southern Il U; Physical Therapist.

BOSER, Gary L; Lf Community HS; Little Falls, MN; VPSrCls; JrNHS; TchrAde; FSA; FTA; Bsktbl; Ftbl; Socr; Trk; CchngActv; Coll; Teacher.

BOSERUP, Rita; Elmwood Park HS; Elmwood Park, IL; 11/330 HonRl; LbryAde; NatlMeritCmnd; RptrSchPpr; SchPpr; FrCl; GerCl; Bsktbl; Tennis; Trk; Triton College; Accounting.

BOSHART, Ricky; Iowa Mennonite HS; Kalona, IA; 6/37 Band; Chr; ChrhWkr; CmntyWkr; HonRl; SchPl; StuCncl; 4-H; Bsktbl; Socr; Hesston Jr Coll; Bus Or Minist.

BOSI, Suzanne M; Reavis HS; Burbank, IL; 33/708 TrsSophCls; SecSrCls; Chr; HonRl; JrNHS; NHS; SchMus; StuGov; SecPpCl; GAA; IMSpt; Illinois State University; French Teacher.

BOSIO, John P; Houghton HS; Chassell, MI; 22/111 NatlMeritCmnd; StuCncl; EdSchPpr; LetterGlf; LetterSwmmng; Mich Tech Univ; Technical Writing.

BOSKO, Margaret A; Catholic Memorial HS; Waukesha, WI; PpCl; College; Accounting.

BOSLEY, James R; William Horlick HS; Racine, WI; ChrhWkr; NatlMeritFnl; NatlMeritSF; RptrYrbk; Yrbk; LetterFtbl; LetterSwmmng; Wrstlng; Northwestern U; Lawyer.

BOSMAN, Cindy L; Holland HS; Holland, MI; 6/317 HonRl; HospAde; RptrYrbk; GerCl; Bsbl; Coll; Med Tech.

BOSS, Gayle; Charlevoix HS; Charlevoix, MI; 1/147 VPFrshCls; Band; HonRl; MrchBnd; PolWkr; SchMus; YthFlsp; EdYrBk; RptrSchPpr; LatCl; Hope College; Communications Major.

BOSS, Jack; Allen Consolidated HS; Bellwood, NE; Chrs; SchAde; Bsbl; Bsktbl; Ftbl; Trk;.

BOSS, Janet; Davenport Community HS; Davenport, NE; ALAGirlsSt; HonRl; LbryAde; MrchBnd; OffAde; SchPl; SctActv; Teen; Twrl; AmLegAwd; 4-HAwd; Bus Sch; Acc.

BOSS, Kellen L; Monroe Senior HS; Monroe, WI; Band; CncrtBnd; DrmMjrt; HonRl; MrchBnd; Uw Madison; Law.

BOSS, Michael S; Shelby Public HS; Shelby, NE; PresJrCls; Band; Chr; HonRl; MrchBnd; SptEdSchPpr; Bsbl; Bsktbl; CaptFtbl; LetterTrk; PresAwd; CitAwd;.

BOSSARTE, Cheryl L; Seymour HS; Payson, IL; 6/68 Band; CncrtBnd; HonRl; MrchBnd; Orch; SchMus; YthFlsp; Pres4-H; TreasFrCl; Trk; Chrldr; GAA; IMSpt; College; Teacher.

BOSSE, Nadalie S; Onaga HS; Onaga, KS; 1/49 PresJrCls; TrsSrCls; HonRl; NatlSciFnd; SchMus; SchPl; RptrYrbk; EdYrBk; SpnCl; Chrldr; Ks Univ; Engineer.

BOSSEN, Karen K; Ogilvie HS; Mora, MN; 10/54 ALAGirlsSt; PresCncrtBnd; Mdrgl; NHS; SchMus; SchPl; EdYrBk; 4-H; CaptBsktbl; Glf; Chrldr; PPFtbl; 4-HAwd; University Of Minnesota; English.

BOSSERD, Joan L; Marshall HS; Marshall, MI; 3/257 Band; Chr; HonRl; Mdrgl; MrchBnd; Orch; SchMus; 4-H; 4-HAwd; RotaryAwd;.

BOSSERD, Thomas L; Marshall HS; Marshall, MI; Band; CncrtBnd; HonRl; MrchBnd; NHS; PepBnd; FFA; IMSpt; College.

BOSSERT, Peter T; Hartford Union HS; Hartford, WI; CmntyWkr; HonRl; NHS; RedCrAde; LatCl; LetterBsktbl; LetterFtbl; CaptSwmmng; Trk; Univ; Cpa.

BOSSHART, Daniel D; Jackson Public HS; Jackson, MN; Aud/Vis; Band; ChrhWkr; CncrtBnd; MrchBnd; PepBnd; SctActv; YthFlsp; Yrbk; FFA; LetterBsbl; LetterFtbl; LetterWrstlng; College; Ag Subject.

BOSSLER, Judith C; King City Ri HS; St Joseph, MO; TrsFrshCls; Chr; HonRl; JrNHS; VPNHS; SchPl; YthFlsp; FHA; PresPpCl; PPFtbl;.

BOSSMAN, Paul R; Lennox Public HS; Lennox, SD; 17/120 Chr; Chrs; ChrhWkr; SchPl; YthFlsp; IMSpt; U Of S D; Carpentry.

BOSSUYT, Ruth A; Milroy HS; Milroy, MN; SecSrCls; Chr; HonRl; Twrl; RptrSchPpr; EdSchPpr; FHA; Graite Falls Vo Tech; Accounting.

BOST, Kevin W; Murphysboro Township HS; Murphysboro, IL; 2/225 Band; HonRl; NHS; StuCncl; EdSchPpr; PresKeyCl; CaptBsbl; CaptFtbl; Wrstlng; University; Communications.

BOSTEL, Suellyn; Huntington North HS; Huntington, IN; Band; HonRl; MrchBnd; SchMus; GerCl; College.

BOSTETTER, Jeffrey L; Sturgis HS; Sturgis, MI; Band; ChrhWkr; HonRl; SchPl; Tennis; IMSpt; Albion College; Business.

BOSTICK, Charles; Mt Vernon S HS; Mount Vernon, IN; 1/260 PresJrCls; Band; CncrtBnd; HonRl; NHS; SchMus; StuGov; KeyCl; IMSpt; DARAwd; Coll; Arch.

BOSTICK, Dave; R N Snider HS; Fort Wayne, IN; 2/515 HonRl; NatlMeritSF; SctActv; IMSpt; Depauw U; Med.

BOSTICK, David A; Joliet Central HS; Joliet, IL; 51/491 Band; CncrtBnd; HonRl; MrchBnd; NHS; Orch; SchMus; GerCl; Glf; LetterTennis; Univ Of Il; Business.

BOSTON, Elizabeth A; Centennial Senior HS; Champaign, IL; Chr; NHS; SchMus; College.

BOSTON, Gary E; Lanphier HS; Springfield, IL; SecSophCls; Chr; Chrs; ChrhWkr; NHS; TreasStuCncl; PpCl; Bsktbl; Ftbl; Tennis;.

BOSTON, Melanie; Hillsboro HS; Hillsboro, WI; 5/68 Band; Chr; HonRl; MrchBnd; SchPl; YthFlsp; LetterTrk; Chrldr; IMSpt; AmLegAwd; College; Elementary Ed.

BOSTON, Mike D; Dowling HS; Des Moines, IA; 33/381 HonRl; LetterBsktbl; ChmnFtbl; LetterTrk; IMSpt; College; Law.

BOSTON, Robert; Delavan HS; Delavan, IL; ChrhWkr; HonRl; IMSpt; Ill Central College; Architecture.

BOSTON, Rory R; Alma Public HS; Alma, NE; Band; Chrs; MrchBnd; PepBnd; SchPl; SctActv; Bsbl; LetterBsktbl; LetterTrk; Central Tech Community Col; Electrical Sequ.

BOSTON, Sandra A; Elizabeth Seton HS; Calumet City, IL; 11/252 HonRl; NHS; TreasLatCl; AmLegAwd; Valparaiso Univ; Pre Medicine.

BOSTROM, Greg R; Wheaton Central HS; Wheaton, IL; 4/324 Chr; ChrhWkr; HonRl; NHS; NatlMeritSF; SchPpr; LatCl; LetterBsbl; LetterBsktbl;.

BOSWEIN, Douglas M; Hamilton HS; Milwaukee, WI; 29/786 HonRl; NHS; U Of Wisc; Accounting.

BOSWELL, Debra S; Jennings Co HS; Nebraska, IN; Band; ChrhWkr; CncrtBnd; MrchBnd; NHS; PepBnd; 4-H; Bsktbl; 4-HAwd; MasAwd; Purdue Univ; Math Teacher.

BOSWELL, Kaye L; Wethersfield HS; Kewanee, IL; 8/64 AFS; Band; CncrtBnd; HonRl; MrchBnd; PepBnd; SchPl; YthFlsp; RptrSchPpr; FrCl; PpCl; Drake Univ; Pharmacy.

BOSWELL, Mary J; Rich Central HS; Olympia Fields, IL; 9/400 Chr; ChrhWkr; HonRl; Mdrgl; NHS; SchMus; RptrSchPpr; SecSciCl; GAA; AmLegAwd; Vanderbilt; Chemistry.

BOTH, Benjamin A; Watseka Comm HS; Watseka, IL; 24/125 Band; CncrtBnd; HonRl; MrchBnd; Univ Of Ill; Pilot.

BOTHUN, Kathleen A; Dawson HS; Dawson, MN; AFS; Band; Chr; ChrhWkr; HonRl; HospAde; PepBnd; StuCncl; RptrYrbk; RptrSchPpr; FHA; Homemaker.

BOTHWELL, Brent S; Parkview HS; Springfield, MO; HonRl; GerCl; SpnCl; LetterSwmmng; LetterTrk; Kalamazoo College; Science.

BOTSFORD, Marcia D; Centerville Senior HS; Centerville, IN; 7/130 HonRl; JrNHS; NHS; Yrbk; GAA; College; Business.

BOTTGER, Lynne M; Mt Assisi Acad; Chicago, IL; 26/189 Chrs; HonRl; LbryAde; NHS; SchMus; SchPl; TchrAde; Glf; GAA; Il State Univ; Math.

BOTTOLFSON, Bill E; Hastings Senior HS; Hastings, NE; Denver City Clg; Business.

BOTTOMLEY, Bruce J; B Carroll HS; Wichita, KS; Band; HonRl; Mdrgl; PepBnd; SchMus; SptEdYrbk; SchPpr; SpnCl; Bsktbl; College; Professional.

BOTTOMLEY, Jeffery; Hononegah Hs; Rockton, IL; 22/188 Band; CncrtBnd; MrchBnd; PepBnd; LetterFtbl; Glf; LetterWrstlng; Rock Valley College;biology.

BOTTOMS, James D; Treynor Comm HS; Treynor, IA; PresSophCls; PresJrCls; ALBoysSt; HonRl; NHS; StuCncl; Bsktbl; Ftbl; Glf; AmLegAwd; Iowa State Univ; Agriculture.

BOTTORFF, Mary; Madison HS; Madison, IN; Band; HonRl; LbryAde; MrchBnd; NatlSciFnd; NatlThespSoc; SchMus; SchPl; SctActv; SchPpr; Prosser Voc School; Lpn.

BOTTORFF, Vanya; Williamsville HS; Williamsville, IL; 32#41#46 NHS; StuCncl; YthFlsp; Yrbk; PpCl; Univ Of Illinois; Physical Therapist.

BOTTRELL, H Arlene; Niantic Harristown HS; Blue Mound, IL; SecFrshCls; SecSophCls; Band; Chr; Chrs; ChrhWkr; CncrtBnd; HonRl; MrchBnd; PepBnd; Quill&Scroll; SchPl; SctActv; GAA; College; Music.

BOTTRELL, Helen A; Niantic Harristown HS; Blue Mound, IL; SecFrshCls; SecSophCls; Band; HonRl; Quill&Scroll; SctActv; StuCncl; EdYrBk; PresFBLA; GAA; Clg; Music Major.

BOTWINSKI, Christopher M; Herrin HS; Herrin, IL; 4/219 Chr; Chrs; CncrtBnd; HonRl; NatlMeritSF; SchMus; SctActv; Univ Of Ill; Computer Systems.

BOTZ, Lori J; Sts Peter & Paul HS; Saginaw, MI; 1/106 Chrs; HonRl; Mdrgl; NatlFornLg; NHS; SchMus; SchPl; YthFlsp; RptrYrbk; Chrldr; College; Math Or Science.

BOTZEK, Bonnie K; Foley HS; Foley, MN; VPJrCls; PresSrCls; VPChrs; PresChrhWkr; CmntyWkr; HonRl; OffAde; SchPl; StuCncl; RptrYrbk; St Cloud St Col; Counseling.

BOUC, Greg; Raymond Central HS; Ceresco, NE; TrsSophCls; TrsJrCls; TrsSrCls; Chrs; ChrhWkr; CmntyWkr; HonRl; JrNHS;.

BOUCHER, Dennis T; Lawton Bronson Comm HS; Bronson, IA; LbryAde; NatlThespSoc; SchPl; SctActv; SchPpr; 4-H; Trk; Wrstlng; IMSpt; Collge; Teacher History.

BOUCHER, Douglas W; Morgan Park HS; Chicago, IL; 20/550 JrNHS; ModUN; NHS; NatlMeritCmnd; University Of Illinois; Accounting.

BOUCHER, Marvin J; Magic City Campus HS; Minot, ND; Chr; HonRl; NatlThespSoc; SchMus; SchPl; StuCncl; GerCl; Wrstlng; Univ; Professional.

BOUCHER, Patrick J; Algoma HS; Algoma, WI; 19/110 VPFrshCls; CmntyWkr; SchAde; SctActv; StuCncl; StuGov; TchrAde; SchPpr; FrCl; LetterBsktbl; Coll; Biologist.

BOUCHIE, Donna K; Le Roy HS; Le Roy, IL; HonRl; SchMus; SchPl; SctActv; PpCl; GAA; College; Secretary Or Commercial Art.

BOUDOURIS, William; Bond County Community Unit 2; Greenville, IL; 15/183 Chr; HonRl; StuCncl; LatCl; Millikin U; Pharmacist.

BOUDREAU, Christopher R; Rich Central HS; Park Forest, IL; VPSrCls; HonRl; NatlMeritCmnd; KeyCl; MthCl; LetterBsbl; Univ; Engineering.

BOUDREAU, Deborah M; Richwoods HS; Peoria, IL; 9 495 HonRl; NatlMeritSF; TchrAde; MthCl; SciCl; GAA; IMSpt; College.

BOUDREAU, Marc A; Bradley Bourbonnais HS; Bourbonnais, IL; LetterBsbl; LetterBsktbl; University; Pilot.

BOUDREAU, Patricia M; Bradley Bourbonnais Comm HS; Bourbonnais, IL; HonRl; NHS; SpnCl; PpCl; LetterTrk; LetterChrldr; Junior College; Medical Lab Technician.

BOUGHAN, Patricia A; Three Rivers HS; Three Rivers, MI; 12/209 HonRl; JrNHS; NHS; TchrAde; VPYthFlsp; Yrbk; TreasLatCl; Bsktbl; Tennis; Trk; College; Computer Programming.

BOUGIE, Mary; St Joseph Acad; De Pete, WI; ChrhWkr; HospAde; OffAde; Orch; Yrbk; FDA; FrCl; Coll; Pre Med.

BOULANGER, Cindi L; Maize HS; Wichita, KS; Chr; HonRl; JrNHS; Mdrgl; NHS; SchMus; TchrAde; Bsbl; LetterTrk; 4-HAwd; Vernons Sch Cosmotology; Cosmotologist.

BOULAY, Yvonne M; St Johns HS; St Louis, MO; HonRl; SchMus; SchPl; RptrYrbk; EdYrBk; PpCl; IMSpt; Professional.

BOULWARE, William T; South Shelby HS; Shelbina, MO; VPFrshCls; ChrhWkr; CncrtBnd; HonRl; NHS; SctActv; StuCncl; FSA; LetterBsktbl; LetterFtbl; LetterTrk; College; Medicine.

BOUMA, Bonnie R; Hancock Public HS; Hancock, MN; 4/27 VPJrCls; PresSrCls; VPBand; HonRl; SchPl; VPStuCncl; RptrYrbk; PresFHA; Bsktbl; LetterChrldr;.

BOUNDY, David E; Holland HS; Holland, MI; 10/317 TrsFrshCls; Band; Chr; HonRl; Mdrgl; NHS; NatlMeritCmnd; Orch; PepBnd; SctActv; StuCncl; LetterTrk; Mit; Math.

BOURBEAU, Judy M; Drummond HS; Mason, WI; 2/44 SecSophCls; SecJrCls; SecSrCls; HonRl; LbryAde; NHS; TchrAde; EdYrBk; 4-H; GerCl; Uw La Crosse; Physical Therap.

BOUREK, Virgil A; Howells Public HS; Howells, NE; TrsSophCls; TrsSrCls; Band; ChrhWkr; CncrtBnd; HonRl; SchPl; 4-H; FFA; Trk; Wrstlng; Univ Of Nebr; Veterinary Medicine.

BOURGEOIS, Deborah; Menominee HS; Wallace, MI; 3/275 HonRl; JrNHS; NHS; Yrbk; FrCl; Univ Of Mich; Physical Therapy.

BOURGEOIS, Jean C; Superior Sr HS; Superior, WI; ChrhWkr; HonRl; JrNHS; NHS; StuCncl; PpCl; LetterTrk; Chrldr; GAA; College; Professional.

BOURGET, Lawrence P; Stanley Boyd HS; Boyd, WI; 2/100 PresSrCls; HonRl; SchPl; StuCncl; EdYrBk; Pres4-H; LetterTrk; Military; Engineer.

BOURISAW, Michael M; Blue Mound HS; Blue Mound, IL; 6/50 SecSrCls; ChrhWkr; HonRl; SchPl; StuCncl; TchrAde; FTA; Bsbl; Bsktbl; Millikin Univ; Business Admin.

BOURN, Cindy L; Gorin R Iii HS; Gorin, MO; 3/10 SecFrshCls; VPSophCls; TrsJrCls; Chrs; ChrhWkr; HonRl; OffAde; PolWkr; SchPl; StuCncl; YthFlsp; Bsbl; Bsktbl; College; Secretary.

BOURNE, Robert O; Octavia HS; Coulfax, IL; CmntyWkr; SchPpr; 4-H; FFA; Farming;.

BOURNEUF, Stephen; St Louis Univ HS; Ballwin, MO; Chr; CmntyWkr; HonRl; SchMus; SchPl; Socr; IMSpt; Coll; Pschology, Theatre.

BOURQUE, Joan; Willow Brook HS; Lombard, IL; HonRl; SchMus; SchPl; E Illinois Univ.

BOURQUE, Pamela K; Porta HS; Petersburg, IL; 5/97 ALAGirlsSt; HonRl; MrchBnd; NHS; RptrYrbk; RptrSchPpr;.

BOURQUIN, Julie A; Manlius HS; Manlius, IL; 2/32 HstFrshCls; TrsJrCls; TrsSrCls; PresBand; Chrs; ChrhWkr; CncrtBnd; HonRl; MrchBnd; NHS; PepBnd; GAA; BttyCrckrAwd; 4-HAwd; St Francis School Of Nursing; Nurse.

BOUSE, Kim Y; Perry HS; Haslett, MI; 10/120 HonRl; SctActv; TchrAde; FHA; FrCl; 1st Lansing Comm College.

BOUSFIELD, David M; Midland HS; Midland, MI; HonRl; NHS; PolWkr; StuCncl; LetterFtbl; CaptTrk; Mich Tech Univ; Creological Engr.

BOUSHEK, David R; Echo Public HS; Belview, MN; 4/27 Band; Pres4-H; FFA; LetterBsbl; LetterBsktbl; Bethany Lutheran; Engineering.

BOUSHO, David L; Chippewa Valley HS; Mt Clemens, MI; Band; CncrtBnd; Lawrence Institute Of Tech; Electrical Engi.

BOUSKA, Bradley J; Hillsboro HS; Hillsboro, MO; 10/184 SecJrCls; VPSrCls; ALBoysSt; Chr; Chrs; NHS; NatlMeritCmnd; SchMus; SchPl; LetterBsktbl;.

BOUSKA, Dorothy D; Stromsburg HS; Stromsburg, NE; 3/36 SecSophCls; Chrs; ChrhWkr; HonRl; NHS; OffAde; SchMus; 4-H; FHA; PpCl; College; Teacher.

BOUSSELOT, Linda J; Calamus Community HS; Calamus, IA; 6/28 Band; Chrs; HonRl; PepBnd; SchMus; SchPl; StuCncl; TchrAde; Bsktbl; Trk; Housewife; Professional.

BOUTCHER, Charles; Thornton Township HS; Dolton, IL; HonRl; NHS; StuGov; Wrstlng; Us Navy; Data Systems.

BOUWENS, Eric C; Loy Norris HS; Kalamazoo, MI; Band; CncrtBnd; MrchBnd; NatlMeritSF; PepBnd; YthFlsp; Kalamazoo College; Biological Science.

BOUXSEIN, Bruce D; Putnam County HS; Granville, IL; Band; Chr; Chrs; CncrtBnd; HonRl; SctActv; SpnCl; Bsktbl; Glf; Swmmng; College; Meteorologist.

BOVA, Paul J; St Pius X HS; Crystal City, MO; 17/116 HonRl; NHS; SciCl; College; Accountant.

BOVEN, Cindy L; Mattawan HS; Mattawan, MI; 28/105 SecFrshCls; HonRl; JrNHS; NatlFornLg; NHS; OffAde; Bsbl; CaptChrldr; CchngActv; GAA; Kalamazoo Comm Clg; Phy Educ.

BOVILL, Debbie; Egan HS; Egan, SD; 20 VPJrCls; TrsSrCls; Band; Chr; HonRl; OffAde; StuCncl; TchrAde; FHA; SpnCl; Business; Secre And Ibm.

BOWDEN, Diana L; Terre Haute North Vigo HS; Brazil, IN; 30/640 Band; ChrhWkr; CncrtBnd; HonRl; TreasJA; MrchBnd; NHS; PepBnd; PresYthFlsp; MthCl; Indiana St Univ; Special Education.

BOWDEN, Elizabeth A; Mtn View Birch Tree R3 HS; Birch Tree, MO; ALAGirlsSt; ChrhWkr; CncrtBnd; DrmMjrt; HonRl; TreasHospAde; NHS; SchMus; SecStuCncl; VPSpnCl; Wake Forest University; Medicine.

BOWDEN, Mark S; Highland Park HS; Highland Park, IL; Columbia College; Communications.

BOWDISH, Douglas P; Sturgis HS; Sturgis, MI; Band; ChrhWkr; MrchBnd; PepBnd; YthFlsp; PpCl; LetterTennis; IMSpt; Glen Oaks Cc; Civil Engr.

BOWDISH, Randall G; Papillion HS; Papillion, NE; 37/315 HonRl; SchAde; StuCncl; SptEdYrbk; SpnCl; LetterFtbl; IMSpt; Navy; Electronics.

BOWDITCH, Tamara A; Pittsford HS; Osseo, MI; 3/50 HonRl; OffAde; SchAde; SctActv; StuCncl; TchrAde; RptrYrbk; SchPpr; Swmmng; Chrldr; Clge; Pro.

BOWEN, Carla J; Highland HS; Troy, KS; ChrhWkr; HonRl; LbryAde; NHS; NatlThespSoc; SchAde; TchrAde; Yrbk; FHA; PpCl; Bsktbl; College; Professional.

BOWEN, Cary J; Riverdale HS; Riverdale, ND; 2/13 SecSophCls; ALAGirlsSt; SchPl; EdYrBk; PpCl; Chrldr; GAA; AmLegAwd; BttyCrckrAwd; DanFAwd; Nd St Univ; Interior Design.

BOWEN, Charles T; Jacksonville HS; Jacksonville, IL; 106/352 Chr; ChrhWkr; ModUN; NatlThespSoc; SchMus; SchPl; LetterSocr; Tennis; MasAwd; Nmsu Kirksville; Industrial Technology.

BOWEN, Cheryl R; Durand Unified HS; Durand, WI; Chr; CmntyWkr; DrlTm; Sacrstn; Sdlty; RptrYrbk; RptrSchPpr; FrCl; PpCl; College; Professional.

BOWEN, Donald D; Henry Senachwine HS; Henry, IL; 7/73 VPSrCls; HonRl; NHS; SchPl; PpCl; Bsbl; LetterBsktbl; Illinois Central Jr College; Elec Engineer.

BOWEN, Douglas S; Portland HS; Portland, IN; AFS; Band; Chr; ChrhWkr; Mdrgl; NHS; SchPl; StuCncl; PresFrCl; CitAwd; Taylor U; Music.

BOWEN, Eric L; Clinton Prairie HS; Colfax, IN; 30/103 Band; ChrhWkr; CmntyWkr; CncrtBnd; HonRl; MrchBnd; Orch; PepBnd; SchMus; SchPl; PresYthFlsp; 4-H; SecFFA; Ftbl; Purdue Univ; Ag Teacher.

BOWEN, Jay R; West HS; Green Bay, WI; HonRl; Northwest Tech Inst; Electrician.

BOWEN, Jon A; Lees Summit HS; Lees Summit, MO; 7/400 ALBoysSt; CncrtBnd; HonRl; MrchBnd; PresNHS; PepBnd; StuCncl; TchrAde; SciCl; LetterTrk; Univ Mo; Chemist.

BOWEN, Joseph R; Elkhart Central HS; Elkhort, IN; 30/470 HonRl; NHS; Bsbl; Bsktbl; LetterTrk; Purdue Univ; Banking.

BOWEN, Karen A; Durand Unified HS; Durand, WI; Band; ChrhWkr; CncrtBnd; MrchBnd; PepBnd; Sacrstn; Sdlty; PpCl; Chrldr; Trade School.

BOWEN, Mark K; Hillsboro HS; Hillsboro, IL; VPJrCls; Chr; StuGov; RptrSchPpr; SptEdSchPpr; LetterBsktbl; LetterTrk; College; Pharmacy.

BOWEN, Mary M; East HS; Waterloo, IA; Chr; ChrhWkr; HonRl; JrNHS;.

BOWEN, Melanie; Noble Hs; Olney, IL; SecTrsSrCls; Band; PresChrs; ChrhWkr; HonRl; SchMus; StuCncl; Yrbk; VPFHA; FrCl; College; Special Education.

BOWEN, Michael G; Ithaca HS; Ithaca, MI; ALBoysSt; Band; PresChr; CncrtBnd; Mdrgl; MrchBnd; PepBnd; SchMus; RptrSchPpr; Ftbl; Central Mi Univ; Music.

BOWEN, Michael J; Glenbard East HS; Lombard, IL; Wyoming Tech University.

BOWEN, Michael L; Flint Northern HS; Flint, MI; JA; LbryAde; OffAde; LetterTrk; Univ Of Toledo; Business Admin.

BOWEN, Pamela J; Buhler HS; Hutchinson, KS; Chrs; HonRl; NHS; TchrAde; RptrSchPpr; FHA; SpnCl; PpCl; Chrldr; GodCntryAwd; Coll; Sociology.

BOWEN, Pamela R; Nevada HS; Nevada, MO; 48/190 Chr; Chrl; Chrs; ChrhWkr; HospAde; LitMag; LbryAde; Mdrgl; SchMus; SchPl; Smsu; Social Work.

BOWEN, Ronald J; Fruitport HS; Muskegon, MI; 22/250 Chr; HonRl; HospAde; NHS; SchMus; SchPl; TchrAde; Muskegon Comm Col; Doctor.

BOWEN, William R; Waukegan HS; Waukegan, IL; 161/1000 Band; Chr; CncrtBnd; HonRl; LitMag; MrchBnd; StuGov; FTA; LatCl; SciCl;.

BOWENS, Brenda D; Robert Lindblom Tech; Chicago, IL; 268/637 Band; Chr; ChrhWkr; CncrtBnd; MrchBnd; ROTC; StuCncl; EdYrBk; Occupational Therapist.

BOWER, Christopher J; Rock Falls Township HS; Rock Falls, IL; 16/210 HonRl; NatlMeritCmnd; LatCl; CaptFtbl; Glf; Trk; CaptWrstlng; University Of Wisconsin; Business.

BOWER, Laurie A; Ottawa Twp HS; Ottawa, IL; Chr; Chrs; HonRl; PpCl; Eastern Illinois Univ; Music.

BOWERMAN, Dale W; Miller HS; Miller, MO; PresSophCls; NHS; StuCncl; PresFFA; LetterBsbl; LetterBsktbl; College; Agriculture.

BOWERMAN, Richard A; Trico HS; Willisville, IL; HonRl; StuCncl; FBLA; PpCl; SciCl; LetterBsbl; Bsktbl; IMSpt; PresAwd; Jr College; Vocation.

BOWERS, Carol; Rochester HS; Rochester, IN; 10/154 ALAGirlsSt; Band; NHS; SchPl; StuCncl; PpCl; AmLegAwd; Ball State University; Accounting.

BOWERS, Catherine A; Gaylord HS; Gaylord, MI; Band; DrmMjrt; NHS; RedCrAde; LetterBsktbl; LetterTrk; Chrldr; PresAwd; College; Engineer.

BOWERS, David B; Oregon Davis HS; Hamlet, IN; 4/65 PresSrCls; ALBoysSt; Chrs; HonRl; NHS; NatlThespSoc; SchMus; SctActv; Yrbk; EdSchPpr; LetterTrk; IMSpt; Indiana Univ; Criminal Law.

BOWERS, Frankie L; Greenwood HS; Springfield, MO; AFS; Band; DrmBgl; HonRl; ModUN; RptrSchPpr; SchPpr; LatCl; SpnCl; LetterGlf; Drury Coll; Vet Med.

BOWERS, Kimberly A; Harlem HS; Rockford, IL; 34/538 Band; Chrs; CncrtBnd; HonRl; MrchBnd; NHS; NatlThespSoc; PepBnd; SchMus; SchPl; Clge; Music Tchr.

BOWERS, Linda; Kirksville Senior HS; Kirksville, MO; ChrhWkr; HonRl; Yrbk; FBLA; PpCl; Tennis; Nmsu Univ; Fine Arts.

BOWERS, Melissa A; Beech Grove HS; Beech Grove, IN; 12/270 HonRl; LbryAde; NHS; OffAde; PolWkr; TchrAde; 4-H; FrCl; SciCl; Indiana Univ; Law.

BOWERS, Phillip C; Hordville HS; Hordville, NE; VPFrshCls; Chr; Chrs; ChrhWkr; SchPl; YthFlsp; 4-H; LetterBsktbl; LetterFtbl; LetterTrk;.

BOWERS, Rachel A; Edinburg Comm HS; Edinburg, IN; Band; MrchBnd; OffAde; PepBnd; RptrSchPpr; Bsktbl; Swmmng; Trk; GAA; 4-HAwd; College; Professional.

BOWERS, Rebecca; Dundee HS; Dundee, MI; 49/140 Chr; Chrs; HonRl; SchPl; 4-H; SpnCl; SciCl; Trk; 4-HAwd; Work At Univ Of Michigan.

BOWERS, Shawn; Sturgeon Bay HS; Sturgeon Bay, WI; ChrhWkr; DrmMjrt; NHS; Bsbl; IMSpt; Coll.

BOWERS, Steven; Gchs South HS; Granite City, IL; 39/550 ChrhWkr; SctActv; Socr; Trk; EldAwd; College Med School; Med Career.

BOWERSOX, Sue A; Maine Twp West HS; Des Plaines, IL; TrsFrshCls; PresSophCls; HonRl; Quill&Scroll; RptrYrbk; SptEdYrbk; PpCl; LetterSwmmng; Chrldr; College; Physical Education.

BOWES, William E; Roncalli HS; Omaha, NE; Chrs; HonRl; LetterBsktbl; Ftbl; Socr; Tennis; Us Air Force Academy; Aircraft Pilot.

BOWIE, Anthony L; Central HS; Kansas City, MO; NatlMeritCmnd; Bsktbl; Ftbl; Trk; Coll; Veterinary Med.

BOWIE, Arvelia M; Malden HS; Malden, MO; HonRl; FHA; PpCl; Chrldr;.

BOWIE, Lisa; Ritenour Senior HS; St Louis, MO; JA; StuCncl; Trk; Wrstlng; GAA; IMSpt; College; Professional.

BOWLDS, Thomas R; Tinley Park HS; Tinley Park, IL; NHS; PresFBLA; LetterFtbl; Northern Il Univ; Business.

BOWLES, John G; Rosholt HS; Custer, WI; 2/69 VPSrCls; ALBoysSt; Band; HonRl; NHS; NatlMeritCmnd; SchPl; StuCncl; Pres4-H; LetterWrstlng; College; Electrical Engineering.

BOWLES, Karen; Christopher HS; Christopher, IL; ChrhWkr; HonRl; LbryAde; SchPl; Univ; Professional.

BOWLEY, William L; Holdrege HS; Holdrege, NE; Band; Chrs; CncrtBnd; MrchBnd; OffAde; PepBnd; Ftbl; College; Law.

BOWLING, Chris E; Covington Community HS; Covington, IN; Quill&Scroll; StuCncl; YthFlsp; RptrSchPpr; SptEdSchPpr; SecLatCl; LetterBsbl; LetterBsktbl; LetterFtbl; LetterTrk;.

BOWLING, Kent A; Madison Cons HS; Madison, IN; 16/285 Band; ChrhWkr; CncrtBnd; HonRl; NHS; SchMus; LatCl; LetterTennis; LetterWrstlng; NCTE; University.

BOWLING, Marla L; Parkwood HS; Joplin, MO; HonRl; SctActv; Coll; Nuclear Physicist.

BOWLING, Shelbie K; Delta C 7 HS; Deering, MO; 5/21 Band; VPNHS; StuCncl; TchrAde; Twrl; FHA; FTA; PpCl; Business School.

BOWLYOW, Jill R; Southern HS; Lomax, IL; VPFrshCls; Chrs; CncrtBnd; HonRl; MrchBnd; PepBnd; TchrAde; FTA; FrCl; GAA; Vocational Business.

BOWMAN, Carolyn S; Forest Lake HS; Hugo, MN; Chr; CncrtBnd; OffAde; StuCncl; College.

BOWMAN, Christopher J; Grinnell HS; Grinnell, IA; 4/200 HonRl; NHS; NatlMeritFnl; PresSpnCl; LetterFtbl; LetterTrk; College.

BOWMAN, Dannette D; Worthington Sr HS; Worthington, MN; 276/302 ChrhWkr; HonRl; LbryAde; TchrAde; FTA; GerCl; Swmmng; PPFtbl; Vocation Sch; Marriage.

BOWMAN, Diane M; Preston Comm HS; Preston, IA; 1/26 TrsSophCls; PresSrCls; Chrs; CncrtBnd; HonRl; MrchBnd; NHS; PepBnd; SchMus; SchPl; 4-H; AmLegAwd; DARAwd; Comm College; Nursing.

BOWMAN, Frank; Waterford Twp HS; Pontiac, MI; Chr; HonRl; PolWkr; 4-H; FFA; FTA; Glf; Socr; CitAwd; VoiceDemAwd; Oakland U; History.

BOWMAN, Gina M; Savannah HS; Savannah, MO; Chr; ChrhWkr; CmntyWkr; HonRl; NHS; StuCncl; YthFlsp; SpnCl; CaptChrldr; GAA; William Jewell Coll.

BOWMAN, Grace E; St Johns HS; St Louis, MO; 18/95 Chr; Chrs; ChrhWkr; HonRl; NHS; SchMus; SchPl; SctActv; StuCncl; PpCl; LetterChrldr; IMSpt; College; Theater.

BOWMAN, James R; York Comm HS; Elmhurst, IL; 80/950 HonRl; NHS; Glf; College; Banking.

BOWMAN, James R; Lakeland Union HS; Minocqua, WI; Band; CncrtBnd; MrchBnd; PepBnd; SchMus; LetterBsktbl; Tech School; Fluid Power Tech.

BOWMAN, Jenise S; Stephen Decatur HS; Decatur, IL; 62/476 HonRl; RptrYrbk; FrCl; Univ Of Illinois; Psychology.

BOWMAN, Jo E; Pike HS; Indianapolis, IN; HonRl; JA; JrNHS; NHS; NatlMeritSchl; SchAde; StuCncl; StuGov; YthFlsp; FBLA; Bus Sch; Secretarial.

BOWMAN, Kathy S; Kewanee HS; Kewanee, IL; AFS; ALAGirlsSt; ChrhWkr; HonRl; SchMus; SchPl; StuCncl; StuGov; TchrAde; YthFlsp; EdSchPpr; FTA; FrCl; Knox College; Foreign Language.

BOWMAN, Kim; Glenbard West Hs; Glen Ellyn, IL; Band; CncrtBnd; HonRl; MrchBnd; NatlThespSoc; PepBnd; U Of Illinois; Accounting.

BOWMAN, Lea C; Hamilton Hts HS; Cicero, IN; ChrhWkr; HonRl; JrNHS; LbryAde; NHS; PresYthFlsp; FHA; FTA; SecFrCl; Central Business College; Secretary.

BOWMAN, Merry T; Deland Weldon HS; Weldon, IL; 4/38 Band; HonRl; SchMus; SchPl; StuCncl; EdYrBk; FrCl; LetterTrk; LetterChrldr; PresGAA; Univ Illinois; Physical Ed.

BOWMAN, Norman D; Carlinville HS; Carlinville, IL; Band; CncrtBnd; MrchBnd; PepBnd; Pres4-H; SpnCl; DanFAwd; 4-HAwd; Univ Of Illinois; Elec Engineer.

BOWMAN, Patricia A; Northwest HS; House Springs, MO; ChrhWkr; CmntyWkr; Sdlty; TchrAde; College; Counselor.

BOWMAN, Robert L; Norris HS; Cortland, NE; FFA; LetterBsbl; LetterFtbl; LetterTrk; LetterWrstlng; IMSpt; University; Vocation.

BOWMAN, Robert W; Macksville HS; Pawnee Rock, KS; 6/42 VPSophCls; VPJrCls; ChrhWkr; CmntyWkr; YthFlsp; Bsktbl; Ftbl; Trk; IMSpt; PresAwd; Clge; Pro.

BOWMAN, Rodney L; Polo Comm HS; Polo, IL; Band; ChrhWkr; CncrtBnd; DrmMjrt; HonRl; MrchBnd; Orch; PepBnd; West Ill Univ; Physics.

BOWMAN, Sandra; Capac HS; Emmett, MI; 7/109 HonRl; HospAde; LbryAde; NHS; OffAde; RedCrAde; SchAde; StuCncl; TchrAde; RptrSchPpr; College; Legal Secretarial Wk.

BOWMAN, Timothy M; Hagerstown Jr Sr HS; Hagerstown, IN; 11/100 Band; ChrhWkr; CncrtBnd; HonRl; MrchBnd; NHS; PepBnd; YthFlsp; IMSpt; College; Industrial Arts.

BOWN, Kim M; Sully Buttes HS; Onida, SD; Chr; Chrs; CmntyWkr; LitMag; PolWkr; RptrYrbk; Yrbk; RptrSchPpr; SchPpr; EngCl; PpCl; Bsktbl; College; Professional.

BOWSER, Nancy F; Eastridge HS; Kankakee, IL; 18/250 Chr; Chrs; CmntyWkr; HonRl; NHS; SchMus; StuCncl; 4-H; SpnCl; 4-HAwd; Univ; Biology.

BOWSFIELD, Cheryl; Hibbing HS; Hibbing, MN; 33/432 Band; CncrtBnd; HonRl; LbryAde; MrchBnd; NHS; Orch; PepBnd; SchMus; PpCl; Hibbing Comm Col Or U Of Mn; Medical Tech.

BOWYER, Paula; Worthington Senior HS; Worthington, MN; Band; Chr; CncrtBnd; MrchBnd; Sacrstn; SctActv; PpCl; IMSpt; PPFtbl; Worthington Community College.

BOXBERGER, Harold G; Hoisington HS; Hoisington, KS; HstSophCls; Chr; LbryAde; NatlMeritCmnd; StuCncl; TchrAde; SchPpr; LetterBsbl; LetterBsktbl; IMSpt; Clg; Computer Prog.

BOXELL, Laura; Winchester Community HS; Winchester, IN; Chr; ChrhWkr; HonRl; NHS; YthFlsp; RptrSchPpr; FHA; SpnCl; DARAwd; Ball State Univ; Elementary Ed.

BOYCE, Allan V; Coon Rapids HS; Blaine, MN; Chrs; ChrhWkr; HonRl; JrNHS; LbryAde; NHS; OffAde; SchMus; LetterSwmmng; IMSpt; Univ Of Mn; Communications.

BOYCE, Carol L; Lincoln Way HS; Mokena, IL; HonRl; NHS; OffAde; PolWkr; MthCl; Augustana College; Physical Therapy.

BOYCE, Dean A; East Waterloo HS; Waterloo, IA; 5/330 Band; ChrhWkr; CncrtBnd; HonRl; JrNHS; MrchBnd; Orch; PepBnd; Iowa State Univ; Architect.

BOYCE, Jeffrey W; Durand HS; Durand, MI; 23/180 Chr; ChrhWkr; HonRl; NatlFornLg; NHS; Quill&Scroll; SchPl; SptEdYrbk; SptEdSchPpr; VoiceDemAwd; Univ Of Michigan; Mathematics.

BOYCE, Jerry L; Spoon River Valley HS; Canton, IL; 4/52 ALBoysSt; ChrhWkr; HonRl; MrchBnd; NatlMeritFnl; RptrYrbk; RptrSchPpr; FFA; DanFAwd; 4-HAwd; Spoon Rvr Jr Clg; Farm Mgmnt.

BOYCE, John P; Kingsford HS; Kingsford, MI; HonRl; NHS; StuCncl; RptrSchPpr; SptEdSchPpr; LetterBsktbl; LetterSocr; College;.

BOYCE, Randall L; Fairfield Community HS; Fairfield, IA; 10/180 Band; CncrtBnd; HonRl; MrchBnd; NHS; NatlThespSoc; PepBnd; PolWkr; SchPl; SctActv; Iowa State University; Industrial Admini.

BOYCE, Theresa; Niangua HS; Point Lookout, MO; 1/24 Band; Chrs; HonRl; Yrbk; SchPpr; FBLA; FHA; PpCl; SciCl; BttyCrckrAwd; College; Business Education.

BOYCE, Warren E; Hope HS; Hope, KS; Band; ChrhWkr; HonRl; SchPl; Trade Schl; Auto Mechanics.

BOYD, Archie; Lilbourn HS; Lilbourn, MO; 24/77 ChrhWkr; SptEdYrbk; SchPpr; FFA; Univ; Agr Eng.

BOYD, Brenda K; Streator Twp HS; Streator, IL; CmntyWkr; HonRl; StuCncl; N Illinois Univ; Librarian.

BOYD, Carolyn; Centralia HS; Cintralia, KS; ChrhWkr; HonRl; YthFlsp; FHA; Business School; Secretarial Training.

BOYD, Craig A; Memorial HS; Joplin, MO; Chr; HonRl; College; Professional.

BOYD, Daniel R; Colfax Comm HS; Colfax, IA; YthFlsp; SchPpr; FTA; PpCl; LetterBsktbl; LetterTrk; CchngActv; IMSpt; University; Dentistry.

BOYD, David P; New Trier East HS; Kenilworth, IL; 9/850 Chrs; ChrhWkr; HonRl; NatlFornLg; NatlMeritCmnd; RedCrAde; StuGov; RptrSchPpr; SciCl; Duke Univ; Law.

BOYD, Davis M; New Trier East HS; Kenilworth, IL; Chrs; ChrhWkr; HonRl; NatlFornLg; NatlMeritCmnd; RedCrAde; FshEdYrbk; RptrSchPpr; Trk; Duke University; Law.

BOYD, Debbie A; Charleston HS; Westfield, IL; HospAde; RptrSchPpr; GAA; Jr Col; Registered Nurse.

BOYD, Debra S; Reading HS; Reading, MI; TrsFrshCls; HonRl; NHS; StuCncl; YthFlsp; EdSchPpr; Business School; Secretary.

BOYD, Dena; Mills Prairie HS; Mill Shoals, IL; VPSrCls; Chrs; HonRl; RptrYrbk; EdSchPpr; FHA; PpCl; Bsktbl; Chrldr;.

BOYD, Diane A; Ida HS; Petersburg, MI; Band; CncrtBnd; HonRl; MrchBnd; TchrAde; PpCl; Chrldr; IMSpt;.

BOYD, Elizabeth; Henry Ford HS; Detroit, MI; 18/500 Chrs; ChrhWkr; HonRl; NHS; OffAde; David Lipscomb Coll; Psych.

BOYD, Fred G; Calumet HS; Gary, IN; HonRl; NHS; 4-H; U Of In; Pre Med.

BOYD, Inman W; South HS; Wichita, KS; 18/510 PresFrshCls; PresSophCls; Chr; HonRl; LbryAde; ModUN; NatlFornLg; TchrAde; EdSchPpr; Wichita State Univ; Lawyer.

BOYD, Jamie M; St Joseph Academy; Adrian, MI; 1/33 HonRl; NHS; SchPl; RptrYrbk; Yrbk; FNA; E Michigan Univ; Occupational Therapist.

BOYD, Janis; Sparta HS; Sparta, IL; PresSophCls; PresJrCls; TrsSrCls; CmntyWkr; HospAde; StuCncl; RptrYrbk; FrCl; GAA; Belleville Area College; Executive Secretar.

BOYD, Jeffrey T; Charleston HS; Charleston, IL; 17/256 ChrhWkr; HonRl; NHS; NatlMeritCmnd; NatlMeritSF; College; Physics.

BOYD, Jim R; Avon HS; Avon, IL; 1/42 PresJrCls; HonRl; NHS; SchPl; StuCncl; StuGov; FFA; LetterBsktbl; LetterFtbl; LetterTrk; IMSpt; College; Mathematics.

BOYD, Katie L; Mormon Trail HS; Indianola, IA; 8/35 HonRl; Yrbk; FHA; PpCl; PPFtbl; Work;.

BOYD, Kent A; Mora HS; Mora, MN; 10/137 TrsJrCls; VPSrCls; Band; Chr; Chrl; Chrs; ChrhWkr; CmntyWkr; CncrtBnd; HonRl; Mdrgl; Bsbl; Wrstlng; Southwest St Univ; Biology.

BOYD, Kevin A; Hutsonville HS; Hutsonville, IL; HonRl; SchPl; TreasFFA; MthCl; PpCl; SciCl; University; Farming.

BOYD, Mark L; Forest Lake Sr HS; Forest Lake, MN; SchMus; StuCncl; RptrSchPpr; SchPpr; FFA; KeyCl; LetterBsbl; Ftbl; Trk; College; Sociology.

BOYD, Teresa S; Tri Jr Sr HS; Cambridge City, IN; 20/90 ALAGirlsSt; JA; NHS; NatlMeritSchl; PolWkr; StuGov; YthFlsp; FBLA; GAA; MasAwd; College; Professional.

BOYD, Thomas C; Riverside Brookfield HS; Brookfield, IL; 76/500 ChrhWkr; HonRl; SctActv; SciCl; Univ Of Wisc; Pre Med.

BOYDSTON, James D; Smithville HS; Smithvlle, MO; JrNHS; LetterFtbl; Coll ; Pro.

BOYDSTON, James D; Smithville R2 HS; Smithville, MO; Ftbl; Wrstlng; College.

BOYDSTON, Steven; Belton HS; Belton, MO; 53/282 ALBoysSt; Band; HonRl; NHS;.

BOYDUY, Theresa M; Riverside HS; Dearborn Heights, MI; SecFrshCls; SecSophCls; SecJrCls; SecSrCls; Chr; HonRl; JrNHS; ModUN; LetterGAA; IMSpt; College; Sciences Nursing.

BOYER, Bernard R; Potosi HS; Potosi, MO; 63/198 HonRl; LbryAde; SchPl; Ftbl; Trk; CchngActv; IMSpt; Navy; Electronic.

BOYER, Carla; St Pius X HS; Festus, MO; 22/116 SecFrshCls; Chrs; ChrhWkr; HonRl; Teen; PpCl; SciCl; Chrldr; College; Business.

BOYER. Cindy; Gibbon Public HS; Gibbon, NE; PresJrCls; ALAGirlsSt; Chrs; DrmMjrt; HonRl; MrchBnd; PpCl; Coll; Med.

BOYER, Debra M; Eagle Bend HS; Eagle Bend, MN; 9/36 SecSophCls; Chr; HonRl; SchPl; StuCncl; TchrAde; FTA; PpCl; CaptTrk; LetterChrldr; Bemidti St Coll; Tchr.

BOYER, Diane; Houghton Lake HS; Roscommon, MI; 1/115 VPJrCls; PresSrCls; HonRl; NHS; StuGov; TchrAde; FTA; Mich Tech Univ; Medicine.

BOYER, Evan D; North Vigo HS; Terre Haute, IN; NatlMeritCmnd; GerCl; LetterSwmmng;.

BOYER, Janet; Marshall Jr Sr HS; Marshall, MO; 13/156 SecJrCls; Band; Chrl; Chrs; CncrtBnd; HonRl; MrchBnd; NatlFornLg; SchMus; SchPl; Univ Of Mo; Medicine.

BOYER, Jeffrey L; Wabash HS; Wabash, IN; 7/216 HonRl; NHS; StuCncl; Bsktbl; LetterFtbl; IMSpt; College; Science.

BOYER, Joann M; Pontiac Catholic HS; Lake Orion, MI; HonRl; LetterBsbl; CaptBsktbl; Michigan St.

BOYER, Judy A; Sutherland Public HS; Sutherland, NE; TrsFrshCls; Band; Chr; CncrtBnd; DrlTm; HonRl; MrchBnd; PepBnd; SctActv; StuGov; Trk; Chrldr; Business School; Legal Secretary.

BOYER, Kevin P; C 4 Iron County HS; Uiburnum, MO; 14/50 TrsFrshCls; Band; HonRl; SchMus; RptrSchPpr; PpCl; LetterBsbl; LetterBsktbl; LetterFtbl; LetterTrk; Univ; Computer Science.

BOYER, Kristi A; Bremen HS; Bremen, IN; 4/120 ChrhWkr; HonRl; NHS; TchrAde; YthFlsp; FTA; FrCl; PpCl; College; Math.

BOYER, Martin W; Wyndmere Public HS; Barney, ND; HonRl; NHS; SchPl; StuCncl; FFA; Bsktbl; Ftbl; Trk; CchngActv; Trade Sch; Auto Mechanics.

BOYER, Nancy A; Morton HS; Morton, IL; CmntyWkr; ChrhWkr; HonRl; SchMus; YthFlsp; GerCl; Il Central College; Minister.

BOYER, Rick; Moravia Community HS; Unionville, IA; 1/42 TrsJrCls; HonRl; NHS; StuCncl; FFA; Ftbl; Indian Hills Com College; Ag Education Fiel.

BOYER, Steven D; Beaverton HS; Beaverton, MI; 2/128 Band; CncrtBnd; HonRl; MrchBnd; PresNHS; PepBnd; SchMus; SchPl; Bsbl; Ftbl; 4-HAwd; Cntrl Michigan Univ; Medicine.

BOYER, Terry R; Yates City HS; Yates City, IL; PresJrCls; TrsSrCls; ALBoysSt; Band; TchrAde; TchrAde; LetterBsktbl; LetterTrk; SARAwd; CitAwd; College; Art.

BOYER, Timothy A; Potosi R 3 HS; Potosi, MO; Chr; Chrs; ChrhWkr; HonRl; NHS; PolWkr; StuCncl; FNA; FTA; SciCl; Ftbl; College; Professional.

BOYERS, Grace A; Keelyville R 4 HS; Poplar Bluff, MO; 1/51 TrsFrshCls; TrsJrCls; Band; HonRl; NHS; EdYrBk; RptrSchPpr; FHA; PpCl; Chrldr; Three Rivers Community Clg; Secretarial Sci.

BOYKEN, Janine B; Titonka Cons HS; Titonka, IA; SecTrsJrCls; Chrs; HonRl; NHS; PolWkr; EdYrBk; EdSchPpr; PresPpCl; Chrldr; PPFtbl; OptClAwd; Business College; Public Relations.

BOYKIN, Karen M; St Thomas Apostle HS; Chicago, IL; 2/38 Chr; HonRl; HospAde; NatlMeritCmnd; SchPl; VoiceDemAwd; Coll; Business Administration.

BOYKO, Mary A; St Paul Kennedy HS; Chicago, IL; Aud/Vis; Chrs; HonRl; SchAde; SchPl; StuCncl; Yrbk; Chrldr; GAA; College; Nursing.

BOYLAN, Caprice M; St Louise De Marillac HS; Glenview, IL; CmntyWkr; HospAde; NatlMeritCmnd; Orch; SchAde; SctActv; Univ Of Ill; Chemical Engineering.

BOYLAN, Patrick J; Weber HS; Chicago, IL; Band; CncrtBnd; MrchBnd; LetterSwmmng; Eastern Illinois University; Business.

BOYLE, Brian H; Austin Catholic Prep; Detroit, MI; 10/135 HonRl; NHS; Quill&Scroll; SchPl; StuCncl; StuGov; University; Law.

BOYLE, Brian L; Grosse Pte South HS; Grosse Pte Park, MI; HonRl; IMSpt; Univ; Mechanical Engineering.

BOYLE, Cheryl L; Moline Sr HS; Moline, IL; 1/875 HonRl; JrNHS; NHS; StuCncl; SptEdSchPpr; 4-H; LatCl; SpnCl; Wrstlng; GAA; Montana State; Ele Education.

BOYLE, Christy L; Moline HS; Moline, IL; 31/826 HonRl; NHS; NatlThespSoc; SchMus; SchPl; SpnCl; LetterTennis; Western Il; Elem Ed.

BOYLE, Colleen N; Academy Of Our Lady; Chicago, IL; HonRl; NHS; RedCrAde; PresSdlty; TchrAde; FNA; PpCl; St Francis College; Accounting.

BOYLE, Doloros C; So Sioux City HS; So Sioux City, NE; 3/168 DrmMjrt; HonRl; JA; NHS; NatlThespSoc; RptrSchPpr; EdSchPpr; College; Accounting.

BOYLE, James A; Detroit Country Day HS; Oak Park, MI; VPSrCls; Chrs; HonRl; NatlMeritFnl; NatlMeritSF; EdYrBk; Bsbl; Dartmouth College; Law.

BOYLE, Jerome E; Quigley So HS; Chicago, IL; PolWkr; SctActv; StuGov; TchrAde; Yrbk; LetterSocr; LetterTrk; College; Attorney.

BOYLE, John C; Lawrence Central HS; Indianapolis, IN; 4/800 PresFrshCls; PresSophCls; PresJrCls; ALBoysSt; HonRl; StuGov; RptrYrbk; Yrbk; Ftbl; Wrstlng; Engineering.

BOYLE, Julie J; Sycamore Sr HS; Sycamore, IL; HonRl; SctActv; TchrAde; FrCl; College; Teacher.

BOYLE, Margaret M; Notre Dame HS; Burlington, IA; 26/80 LbryAde; Yrbk; SchPpr; Glf; Secretarial.

BOYLE, Mary K; Wauwatosa East HS; Wauwatosa, WI; Chrs; FTA; MthCl; IMSpt; Coll; Elementary Teacher.

BOYLE, Patricia L; Dexter HS; Whitmore Lake, MI; Band; CncrtBnd; HonRl; MrchBnd; OffAde; Cleary Coll; Legal Sec.

BOYLE, Thomas E; Oregon Davis HS; Hamlet, IN; SecFrshCls; TrsSophCls; PresJrCls; Aud/Vis; HonRl; StuGov; LetterBsbl; Bsktbl; Trk; IMSpt;.

BOYLE, Vivian; St Scholastica HS; Chicago, IL; 3/250 HonRl; Il Univ Champayne; Veterinarian Medicine.

BOYLES, Dawne Marie T; Kapaun Mt Carmel HS; Wichita, KS; Chr; Chrs; ChrhWkr; CmntyWkr; OffAde; RedCrAde; SchAde; SchPl; SctActv; CitAwd; College; Comm In Radio Or Tv.

BOYLES, Gary D; Rich Hill HS; Foster, MO; HonRl; JA; SchPl; Pres4-H; FBLA; FFA; LetterBsktbl; LetterFtbl; LetterTrk; CchngActv; C Ms U; Law Enforcement.

BOYLES, Gayla M; Burr Oak HS; Burr Oak, KS; 2/13 PresSophCls; PresSrCls; DrmMjrt; HonRl; SchPl; EdSchPpr; VPPpCl; Cloud Co Comm College; Business Mgmt.

BOYLES, Melissa; Glenbrook South Hs; Glenview, IL; Chrs; LitMag; NatlFornLg; SctActv; StuCncl; StuGov; TchrAde; KeyCl; FrCl; Swmmng; Wheaton College;writer English.

BOYNE, Marla J; Cary Grove HS; Cary, IL; 5/300 Chrs; ChrhWkr; HonRl; NHS; NatlMeritCmnd; FrCl; College; Home Economics.

BOYNE, Norman F; Ferndale HS; Ferndale, MI; HonRl; SchAde; SchPl; TchrAde; Ftbl; Col; Professional Electrician.

BOYOM, Carol J; Custer HS; Custer, SD; PresSophCls; ALAGirlsSt; Band; Chr; PepBnd; PolWkr; SchPl; StuCncl; Bsktbl; Chrldr; College; Professeional.

BOYS, Cheryl A; John Adams HS; South Bend, IN; 33/440 Chr; HonRl; SchMus; StuCncl; In Central U; Nurse.

BOYSEN, Christie A; Anita HS; Wiota, IA; 16/43 Chrs; HonRl; HospAde; NatlFornLg; RptrSchPpr; FHA; PpCl; Glf; Trk; GAA; Univ Of Iowa; Pharmacy.

BOYSEN, Denise J; Bowdle HS; Bowdle, SD; Band; Chr; Chrs; ChrhWkr; CncrtBnd; CaptDrlTm; HonRl; MrchBnd; PepBnd; LetterBsktbl; Trade; Vocation.

BOYSEN, Donna M; Bowdle HS; Bowdle, SD; ALAGirlsSt; Chrs; ChrhWkr; CaptDrlTm; HonRl; NHS; SecStuCncl; YthFlsp; EdYrBk; FHA; LetterBsktbl; Nettleton College; Administrative Asst.

BOYSEN, Mary; Roncalli HS; Omaha, NE; HonRl; NHS; StuCncl; SpnCl; Univ Ne; Management Law.

BOYSEN, Walter H; Omaha North HS; Omaha, NE; ALBoysSt; HonRl; JA; JrNHS; NatlMeritSF; StuGov; PresFrCl; MthCl; IMSpt; AmLegAwd; JAAwd; RotaryAwd; University; Civil Engineering.

BOYTS, Jerry D; Central HS; Springfield, MO; Band; Chr; HonRl; Mdrgl; MrchBnd; Orch; YthFlsp; YthLg; KeyCl; Glf; Drury College; Medicine.

BOYUM, Ronda E; Fairfax Public HS; Fairfax, MN; 13/53 Chr; Chrl; ChrhWkr; CmntyWkr; HonRl; HospAde; SchPl; RptrSchPpr; SchPpr; 4-H; FHA; PpCl; GAA; Vocational School; Vocation.

BOYUM, Thomas K; Kasson Mantorville HS; Kasson, MN; 14/88 Aud/Vis; HonRl; NHS; Wrstlng; Minn School Of Business; Accounting.

BOZARD, Sherrie; Industry HS; Industry, IL; 12/33 ChrhWkr; CmntyWkr; HonRl; LbryAde; Twrl; YthFlsp; RptrYrbk; RptrSchPpr; EdSchPpr; FHA; Northeast Missour St U; Social Worker.

BOZEK, Theresa H; Benet Academy; Lisle, IL; 7/230 HonRl; RptrYrbk; EdYrBk; Yrbk; University; Business.

BOZEKOWSKI, Kim; Trinity HS; Dickinson, ND; 4/136 Chr; Chrl; Chrs; ChrhWkr; HonRl; Mdrgl; PepBnd; SchMus; College; Engineer.

BOZELL, Jerry M; Columbus North HS; Columbus, IN; NatlFornLg; StuGov; Indiana Univ ;psychology.

BOZEMAN, Darrell G; Tecumseh HS; Tecumseh, MI; 37/240 PresSrCls; ALBoysSt; NatlMeritSchl; SchPl; StuCncl; YthFlsp; LetterBsbl; CaptBsktbl; Ftbl; AmLegAwd; Monroe Comm College; Industrualarts.

BOZEMAN, Jamilla T; Lindblom HS; Chicago, IL; 67/720 NHS; Quill&Scroll; RedCrAde; StuCncl; TchrAde; RptrSchPpr; SchPpr; MthCl; College; Special Ed.

BOZICH, Mark P; Hillcrest HS; Country Club Hills, IL; 40/482 JrNHS; NHS; CaptBsbl; Bsktbl; CaptFtbl; New Mexico State; Science.

BOZUNG, Patricia; St Patricks HS; Portland, MI; 2/47 PresFrshCls; ChrhWkr; NatlMeritCmnd; SchPl; RptrYrbk; EdYrBk; MthCl; SciCl; PPFtbl; Um Med Program; Prof Doctor.

BOZZI, Lynn M; Homewood Flossmoor HS; Glenwood, IL; 14/920 AFS; ChrhWkr; HonRl; NHS; Swmmng; Univ Of Illinois; Accounting.

BRAA, Cynthia K; Patrick Henry HS; Minneapolis, MN; 1/442 Chr; HonRl; Mdrgl; NHS; SchMus; StuGov; RptrYrbk; GerCl; KiwanAwd; RotaryAwd; Univ Of Minnesota.

BRAASCH, Paula J; Carl Sandburg HS; Orland Park, IL; 194/815 HonRl; PpCl; LetterTrk; LetterChrldr; LetterGAA; IMSpt; University; Physical Education.

BRAATELIEN, Richard B; Moline Sr HS; Moline, IL; PolWkr; Western Illinois Univ; Astronomy.

BRAATEN, Colleen R; Naperville Central HS; Naperville, IL; 16/844 Chr; HonRl; Ill State Univ; Accounting.

BRAATEN, David A; Oslo HS; Manvel, ND; 3/52 Band; HonRl; MrchBnd; StuCncl; 4-H; Bsktbl; IMSpt; College; Farming.

BRAATEN, Dennis; Wyndmere HS; Mc Leod, ND; 3/45 HonRl; StuCncl; 4-H; Ftbl; Trk; St Sch Of Sci; Geoligical Engrg.

BRAATEN, Dennis A; Wyndmere Public HS; Mc Leod, ND; ChrhWkr; HonRl; TreasNHS; StuCncl; 4-H; VPFFA; MthCl; LetterFtbl; LetterTrk; State Sch Of Science; Engineering.

BRAATZ, Lori K; Little Wolf HS; Manawa, WI; VPFrshCls; SecSophCls; Chr; Chrs; ChrhWkr; HonRl; RptrYrbk; PpCl; Clge; Prof.

BRABEC, Bruce E; Braham HS; Braham, MN; PresSrCls; Chr; HonRl; NHS; SchPl; StuCncl; EdYrBk; LetterBsbl; LetterFtbl; LetterWrstlng; College; Accounting.

BRABEC, Cindy S; Howells Public HS; Howells, NE; 3/44 StuGov; 4-H; PpCl; Business Schl; Professional.

BRABEC, Trudy J; Clarkson HS; Clarkson, NE; 1/39 PresSophCls; PresJrCls; Band; Chrs; CncrtBnd; HonRl; StuCncl; FHA; LetterTrk; Chrldr; Wayne State Coll; Math.

BRABY, Don E; Mormon Trail Comm HS; Garden Grove, IA; ChrhWkr; HonRl; PpCl; CaptFtbl; Trk; Trade School; Professional.

BRACH, John C; Lincoln Way HS; Frankfort, IL; HonRl; NHS; OffAde; LetterTrk; Schriener Jr College; Engineering.

BRACH, Kenneth J; St Willibrord HS; Dolton, IL; 12/69 Chrs; HonRl; NHS; SchPl; StuCncl; Yrbk; SchPpr; LatCl; MthCl; SciCl; DanFAwd; Northern Illinois Univ; Accounting.

BRACH, Nanci M; Montini HS; Lombard, IL; 4/153 Chrs; ChrhWkr; HonRl; NHS; Bsktbl; De Paul Univ; Music.

BRACHEAR, Dan E; Rochester HS; Rochester, IL; 1/82 HonRl; SctActv; Univ; Engineering.

BRACHEAR, Deborah K; Rochester HS; Rochester, IL; 4/80 Chr; HonRl; NHS; YthFlsp; 4-H; GerCl; Eastern Illinois Univ; Engineering.

BRACHER, Jeffrey L; Carmel For Boys HS; Mundelein, IL; 12/172 HonRl; Loyola Univ Of Chicago; Law Enforcement.

BRACHLE, Danny R; Petersburg HS; Albion, NE; PresFrshCls; Band; Chr; CncrtBnd; MrchBnd; PepBnd; SchPl; SctActv; Bsktbl; Ftbl; College; Auto Mechanic.

BRACHMANSKI, Elizabeth H; Good Counsel HS; Lincolnshire, IL; NHS; NatlSciFnd; RptrYrbk; RptrSchPpr; TreasGerCl; VPSciCl; GAA; Loyola University; Biology.

BRACHMANSKY, Heidi J; Cathedral HS; Chicago, IL; 2/127 HonRl; NHS; College; Law.

BRACHT, Cynthia; Milbank HS; Milbank, SD; Chr; Chrs; ChrhWkr; SctActv; YthFlsp; Yrbk; FBLA; GerCl; PpCl; Presentation Aberdee; Child Dev.

BRACISZESKI, Pam K; Manistee HS; Manistee, MI; 5/172 Band; CncrtBnd; HonRl; JrNHS; MrchBnd; NHS; NatlMeritCmnd; PepBnd; SchPl; LatCl; Michigan State.

BRACKEN, Lee; Plano HS; Plano, IL; 2/112 TrsFrshCls; HonRl; NHS; CaptLetterFtbl; LetterGlf; AmLegAwd;.

BRACKEN, Willa G; Covington HS; Kingman, IN; HonRl; YthFlsp; 4-H; FHA; FrCl; 4-HAwd; College; Professional.

BRACKEY, Alan C; Lake Mills Community HS; Lake Mills, IA; 5/84 ALBoysSt; Band; CmntyWkr; CncrtBnd; HonRl; MrchBnd; PepBnd; Bsktbl; Glf; IMSpt; Iowa State Univ; Chemical Eng.

BRACKMANN, Steven J; Wm Henry Harrison HS; Evansville, IN; 15/458 ChrhWkr; PresJA; NatlMeritSF; YthFlsp; GerCl; PpCl; SciCl; JAAwd; OptClAwd; Univ Of Evansville; Accounting.

BRACKNEY, Jo L; U S D 303 HS; Ness City, KS; HonRl; NHS; FHA; PpCl; LetterTrk; Clg; Vocation.

BRADACH, Patricia A; Custer HS; Milwaukee, WI; HonRl; JA; SctActv; Twrl; PpCl; U Of Wi; Registered Nurse.

BRADBURN, Theresa A; Lawrence Central HS; Indianapolis, IN; 33/709 TreasDrlTm; NHS; Quill&Scroll; SchAde; TchrAde; RptrYrbk; EdYrBk; SecPpCl; LetterSwmmng; PPFtbl; In Univ; Pre Med.

BRADBURY, Linda S; Warsaw Comm HS; Warsaw, IN; CmntyWkr; CaptDrlTm; StuCncl; University; Law.

BRADEMEYER, Debbie K; Verona Public HS; Verona, ND; SecFrshCls; VPSophCls; Band; Chrs; CncrtBnd; PepBnd; SchPl; PpCl; LetterTrk; Chrldr; Patricia Stevens Clg; Public Relations.

BRADEN, Barbara K; Geneva Public HS; Geneva, NE; Band; Chrs; HonRl; RptrYrbk; RptrSchPpr; CivCl; 4-H; FHA; PpCl; LetterTrk; Medical Technician.

BRADEN, Charlene C; Centralia HS; Goff, KS; Band; Chrs; HonRl; OffAde; SchMus; SchPl; TchrAde; CivCl; Bsbl; LetterTrk; Trade; Voc.

BRADEN, Denise M; Saline HS; Milan, MI; HonRl; LbryAde; StuCncl; 4-H; FHA; Chrldr; LetterBsktbl; CchngActv; GAA; DARAwd; Michigan State U.

BRADEN, James R; Marysville HS; Marysville, MI; CmntyWkr; HonRl; NHS; NatlMeritCmnd; StuCncl; FrCl; Swmmng; Tennis; Michigan St Univ; Chemistry.

BRADEN, Joy A; Waldron HS; Greensburg, IN; 2/76 ALAGirlsSt; Band; Chr; Chrs; ChrhWkr; HonRl; MrchBnd; NHS; LatCl; GAA; Business School; Vocation.

BRADEN, Shirley A; Geneva HS; Geneva, NE; 6/57 Band; Chr; Chrs; CncrtBnd; HonRl; MrchBnd; PepBnd; SchPl; RptrYrbk; Yrbk; Kearney State Clg; Biology Teacher.

BRADFIELD, Robin E; Elk Rapids HS; Elk Rapids, MI; HonRl; BttyCrckrAwd; Coll; Cpa.

BRADFORD, Bernadine; Calumet HS; Chicago, IL; 16/375 HonRl; JrNHS; NHS; OffAde; SchPl; SchAde; RptrYrbk; EdSchPpr; SciCl; GAA; Loyala Univ; Nursing.

BRADFORD, Blythe; Metro HS; St Louis, MO; 10/36 CmntyWkr; HonRl; JA; FrCl; Columbia Univ; Soc.

BRADFORD, David B; Glenbrook South HS; Glenview, IL; 18/600 HonRl; NHS; LetterSocr; LetterTennis; Ohio St Univ; Architecture.

BRADFORD, Marcia M; Schoolcraft HS; Schoolcraft, MI; 11/59 Band; CncrtBnd; HonRl; NHS; SchPl; YthFlsp; 4-H; KeyCl; CaptBsktbl; Trk; Mich St Univ; Psychology.

BRADFORD, Mary A; Richland Center HS; Richland Center, WI; 25/185 SecSrCls; Band; Chr; CncrtBnd; Mdrgl; NHS; RptrSchPpr; SpnCl; Trk; 4-HAwd; College; Animal Science.

BRADFORD, Michael J; Parchment HS; Parchment, MI; 10/168 Chr; Chrl; ChrhWkr; HonRl; JrNHS; NHS; NatlMeritCmnd; SchMus; SchPl; RptrYrbk; Yrbk; SchPpr; LatCl; LetterTrk; Western Mich Univ.

BRADFORD, Sandra L; Osborn Public HS; Osborn, MO; 1/15 VPFrshCls; SecTrsSophCls; PresJrCls; ALAGirlsSt; Band; ChrhWkr; HonRl; StuCncl; Bsbl; LetterBsktbl; Univ Mo Columbia; Medical Field.

BRADFORD, Sharon K; Oakland HS; Hindsboro, IL; 3/45 PresFrshCls; Chr; Chrs; HonRl; MrchBnd; NHS; SchMus; YthFlsp; Yrbk; 4-H; FHA; MthCl; PpCl; Chrldr; Barnes School Of Nursing; Nursing.

BRADFORD, William C; Cloquet Senior HS; Cloquet, MN; HonRl; NHS; LetterTrk; Univ Of Utah; Geological Engr.

BRADLEY, Alfred M; Sheldon Comm HS; Sheldon, IA; 6/146 Chrs; HonRl; NatlMeritCmnd; SchPl; VPSciCl; Glf; BauchLmbAwd; Sd State Univ; Electrical Engineering.

BRADLEY, Barbara L; Addison Trail HS; Addison, IL; Chr; HonRl; SctActv; 4-H; GerCl; University; Accounting.

BRADLEY, Brett R; Avon HS; Avon, IL; 5/40 VPJrCls; Chrs; HonRl; NHS; SchPl; StuCncl; FrCl; LetterBsktbl; LetterFtbl; LetterTrk; IMSpt; 4-HAwd; College; Professional.

BRADLEY, Cathy J; New Providence Comm HS; Union, IA; Band; Chr; Chrs; ChrhWkr; CncrtBnd; HonRl; LbryAde; MrchBnd; PepBnd; SchMus; SchPl; 4-H; Bsktbl; LetterTrk; College; Nursing.

BRADLEY, Con M; Mullen Public HS; Mullen, NE; 2/38 VPFrshCls; HonRl; TchrAde; YthFlsp; 4-H; Wrstlng; Doane Coll; Phsycology.

BRADLEY, Cynthia; Norris City Omaha HS; Norris City, IL; 17/53 Band; Chr; ChrhWkr; HonRl; MrchBnd; PepBnd; SchPl; GAA; IMSpt; Union Univ Jackson; Foreing Missionary.

BRADLEY, Dawn E; Normal Community HS; Normal, IL; Band; CncrtBnd; HonRl; MrchBnd; NatlMeritCmnd; SecYthFlsp; PpCl; Chrldr; Illinois State University; Dance.

BRADLEY, Debra A; Western Dubuque HS; Epworth, IA; 1/246 SecSrCls; Band; Chrs; HonRl; MrchBnd; NHS; SchMus; StuCncl; EdSchPpr; 4-H; U Of Northern Ia; Music Teacher.

BRADLEY, Gary L; Wyanet HS; Princeton, IL; 11/29 SecTrsSrCls; HonRl; NatlThespSoc; OffAde; SchPl; EdSchPpr; Pres4-H; SpnCl; 4-HAwd; Ivcc; Ag.

BRADLEY, James E; Redfield HS; Redfield, SD; 2/94 ALBoysSt; Band; HonRl; NHS; StuCncl; RptrSchPpr; PresKeyCl; LetterBsktbl; LetterFtbl; KiwanAwd; College; Business Admin.

BRADLEY, Janice M; Streator Twp HS; Streator, IL; SecTrsFrshCls; HonRl; SpnCl; No Illinois Univ; Nursing.

BRADLEY, Jill M; Fowlerville HS; Fowlerville, MI; HonRl; JrNHS; NHS; PolWkr; StuCncl; YthFlsp; Bsbl; CaptFtbl; Trk; CaptPPFtbl; Central Mi Univ; Pro Psychology.

BRADLEY, John T; Prairie Heights HS; Angola, IN; HstJrCls; Aud/Vis; HonRl; IntrClCncl; JrNHS; NHS; StuGov; SciCl; Glf; IMSpt; Col; Physician.

BRADLEY, Karen; Monrovia HS; Monrovia, IN; 5/94 Band; Chrs; HonRl; NatlMeritCmnd; PepBnd; RptrYrbk; RptrSchPpr; 4-H; FrCl; BttyCrckrAwd; Franklin Col; French Teacher.

BRADLEY, Lois; Boone County R6 HS; Centralia, MO; HonRl; SchPl; RptrYrbk; RptrSchPpr; SchPpr; SpnCl; PpCl; Ne Mo St Univ.

BRADLEY, Lynn; Normandy Senior HS; St Louis, MO; HonRl; JrNHS; NHS; StuCncl; TchrAde; FrCl; Tennis; IMSpt; College; Psychologist.

BRADLEY, Patricia L; Dodge City Sr HS; Dodge City, KS; Band; CncrtBnd; DrlTm; HonRl; MrchBnd; OffAde; Yrbk; FHA; FrCl; PpCl; IMSpt; St Lukes Sch; Nurse.

BRADLEY, Rhonda; Northwestern HS; Ashton, SD; Chrs; Mdrgl; SchPl; RptrYrbk; PpCl; Bsktbl; Trk; GAA; IMSpt; College.

BRADLEY, Robert S; Redfield HS; Redfield, SD; 1/88 Band; Chrs; HonRl; NatlFornLg; SchPl; StuCncl; RptrSchPpr; KeyCl; Ftbl; KiwanAwd; Collge; Curriculum Of Major Study.

BRADLEY, Shelley D; Ulysses HS; Ulysses, KS; ChrhWkr; DrlTm; HonRl; TchrAde; Teen; 4-H; FHA; PpCl; Bsktbl; Trk; Sw Kansas Voc Tech; Cosmotology.

BRADLEY, Stephanie O; Immaculata HS; Detroit, MI; PresJrCls; CmntyWkr; HonRl; HospAde; NHS; VPStuGov; Yrbk; SchPpr; LatCl; AmLegAwd; Northwestern Univ; Journalism.

BRADLEY, Susan; Glenbrook South Hs; Glenview, IL; ChrhWkr; HonRl; NHS; SchPl; RptrSchPpr; Northwestern; Journalism.

BRADLEY, Ted A; Hooker County HS; Mullen, NE; 3/30 CmntyWkr; HonRl; SchPl; SctActv; StuGov; 4-H; LetterTrk; CaptWrstlng; AmLegAwd; 4-HAwd; College.

BRADLEY, William M; Peoria Hts HS; Peoria Hts, IL; 5/100 PresFrshCls; CmntyWkr; JrNHS; NHS; PolWkr; StuCncl; StuGov; Yrbk; SpnCl; Univ Of Wisconsin; Law.

BRADNEY, William E; Elgin HS; Hanover Park, IL; 115/878 ChrhWkr; CncrtBnd; SctActv; YthFlsp; SciCl; LetterFtbl; Trk; Wrstlng; Southern Il Univ; Forestry.

BRADSHAW, Dawn; Ralston HS; Ralston, NE; 1 Chr; HonRl; ModUN; SecNatlFornLg; NHS; NatlMeritCmnd; SchMus; Bsktbl; Trk; Univ Of Ne;.

BRADSHAW, James R; Marine City HS; Marine City, MI; 7/161 PresJrCls; HonRl; JrNHS; NHS; NatlMeritCmnd; StuGov; RptrYrbk; RptrSchPpr; CaptBsktbl; CaptFtbl; Brown Univ; Acct.

BRADSHAW, Robert B; Boonville HS; Boonville, MO; ALBoysSt; VPNHS; NatlMeritSF; StuCncl; PresYthFlsp; Yrbk; Bsktbl; Glf; IMSpt; GodCntryAwd; Univ Of Mo; Bus Admini.

BRADSHAW, Steven E; Griggsville Comm HS; Griggsville, IL; 1/28 HonRl; PresNHS; NatlThespSoc; StuCncl; FFA; SpnCl; SciCl; Bsktbl; BauchLmbAwd; DanFAwd; Univ Of Ill; Elec Engineer.

BRADWAY, Becky J; Rochester HS; Springfield, IL; 10/77 Chr; NHS; SchPl; RptrYrbk; RptrSchPpr; Eastern Illinois Univ; Journalism.

BRADWAY, Carol J; Hillsboro HS; Hillsboro, MO; Chr; ChrhWkr; HonRl; NHS; SctActv; StuCncl; MthCl; PpCl; SciCl; PPFtbl; Univ.

BRADY, Anne M; Marian HS; Mishawaka, IN; 17/117 HonRl; MrchBnd; NHS; SchPpr; IMSpt; Nursing Sch; Nurse.

BRADY, Barbara; Marquette HS; Michigan City, IN; TrsFrshCls; HonRl; JA; RptrYrbk; SpnCl; Purdue Univ, Psychology.

BRADY, Barbara A; Mt Clemens HS; Mt Clemens, MI; 3/540 SecChr; HonRl; HospAde; NHS; NatlMeritSF; SchMus; TchrAde; FrCl; Swmmng; GAA; Mich St Univ; Psychology.

BRADY, Daniel M; Sault Area HS; Sault Ste Marie, MI; ChrhWkr; HonRl; NHS; SchAde; IMSpt; College; Data Process.

BRADY, David; Midland HS; Midland, MI; 100/500 HonRl; NatlMeritFnl; FrCl; Bsktbl; Fl Inst Of Tech; Ocean Tech.

BRADY, Deborah J; Ohawa HS; Ohawa, IL; 54/415 HonRl; HospAde; NHS; Yrbk; Bsbl; Chrldr; GAA; College.

BRADY, Gerald L; Galena R2 HS; Galena, MO; Band; Chr; Chrs; ChrhWkr; CncrtBnd; HonRl; PepBnd; StuCncl; PpCl; College; Math.

BRADY, John; St John Cathedral HS; Milwaukee, WI; Bsktbl; IMSpt; College; Accounting.

BRADY, John D; Christian Brothers College; St Louis, MO; 6/155 SecSophCls; VPJrCls; SecSrCls; HonRl; NHS; ROTC; Bsbl; Socr; CaptTrk; IMSpt; Univ; Professional.

BRADY, Lori A; Eastern Heights HS; Agra, KS; 1/21 PresSophCls; ALAGirlsSt; Chrs; HonRl; SchMus; SchPl; PresStuCncl; SecPpCl; Trk; AmLegAwd; Ks U; Lab Tech.

BRADY, Mary P; Central Catholic HS; Bloomington, IL; VPSophCls; VPJrCls; CmntyWkr; HonRl; StuGov; TchrAde; Teen; FrCl; PpCl; Glf; Clge; Pro.

BRADY, Patricia K; Rochelle Twp HS; Rochelle, IL; 20/212 SecJrCls; Chr; HonRl; Swmmng; PresGAA; Univ Of Illinois; Engineering.

BRADY, Patty M; Dekalb HS; Auburn, IN; College; Legal Secretary.

BRADY, Robert M; St Lawrence Sem; Mt Clemens, MI; 6/37 PresJrCls; CmntyWkr; HonRl; NatlFornLg; PolWkr; StuCncl; StuGov; SchPpr; CaptFtbl; CaptTrk; St Johns U; Law,

BRADY, Rosanne K; Park Hill HS; Kansas City, MO; HonRl; RedCrAde; SctActv; StuCncl; TchrAde; FHA; FTA; PpCl; Swmmng; Sms; Home Economics.

BRADY, Sharon A; Gladstone Area HS; Gladstone, MI; 9/171 ChrhWkr; CmntyWkr; CncrtBnd; MrchBnd; NHS; RptrYrbk; Yrbk; RptrSchPpr; SchPpr; FTA; PpCl; Northern Michigan Univ; Teacher.

BRADY, Terri A; Aquin HS; Cascade, IA; 1/67 HonRl; SchMus; StuCncl; RptrYrbk; RptrSchPpr; FrCl; PpCl; LetterBsktbl; LetterTrk; Chrldr; Grinnell College; Study Economics.

BRADY, Truman O; Seneca HS; Seneca, MO; CncrtBnd; HonRl; FTA; MthCl; Bsktbl; Ftbl; Tennis; Trk; IMSpt; PPFtbl; Clg; Pro.

BRAEM, Robert; Marquette Senior HS; Marwquette, MI; 76/384 HonRl; Glf; N Mch Univ.

BRAENDLE, Michael; Bangor John Glenn HS; Bay City, MI; Band; CncrtBnd; HonRl; MrchBnd; NHS; PepBnd; SchMus; SctActv; Bsbl; Ftbl; Ferris State; Offset Pressman.

BRAEUTIGAM, Barbara J; Frankenmuth HS; Birch Run, MI; HonRl; Univ; Professional.

BRAEUTIGAM, Kent T; Frankenmuth HS; Frankenmuth, MI; Band; CncrtBnd; HonRl; MrchBnd; StuCncl; IMSpt; State; Vet.

BRAGALONE, Andrew F; Hillsdale HS; Hillsdale, MI; HonRl; ModUN; SpnCl; CaptTennis; Pahrmacy College; Pharmacist.

BRAGALONE, Phyllis A; North Side HS; Fort Wayne, IN; HonRl; NHS; Indiana University; Biology.

BRAGG, Donna R; Mundelein HS; Mundelein, IL; 17/342 HonRl; TchrAde; SpnCl; IMSpt; University.

BRAGG, Larry M; Northwestern HS; Sumner, MO; SecFrshCls; SecJrCls; ALBoysSt; NHS; 4-H; LetterBsbl; LetterBsktbl; LetterTrk; DanFAwd; CitAwd; Usaf Acad; Usaf Officer.

BRAGG, Stephen W; W Nodaway R1 HS; Burlington Jct, MO; SecSrCls; ALBoysSt; Chr; Chrs; HonRl; ModUN; NHS; SchPl; StuCncl; N W M S U.

BRAHAM, Jean; Mother Guerin Hs; Chicago, IL; 6 Chrs; HonRl; NHS; StuCncl; StuGov; Bsktbl; Northwestern U;music.

BRAINARD, David A; Bishop Noll Institute; Highland, IN; ChrhWkr; SctActv; MthCl; LetterFtbl; LetterTrk; LetterWrstlng; College.

BRAINERD, Stuart W; New Trier East HS; Winnetka, IL; HonRl; NatlMeritFnl; NatlMeritSF; StuGov; TchrAde; MthCl; SciCl; IMSpt; Univ;computer Sci.

BRAKE, Linda J; Glendale HS; Springfield, MO; College.

BRAKEFIELD, Birdie M; Valley HS; Potosi, MO; HonRl; LbryAde; NHS; SchPl; Yrbk; Army; Clerical Work.

BRAKER, William P; Rich Central HS; Matteson, IL; Band; MrchBnd; Northern Illinois; Music.

BRALEY, Karma J; Northwestern HS; Modesto, IL; 10/55 Chrs; ChrhWkr; HonRl; SchMus; SchPl; TchrAde; Twrl; Yrbk; FHA; FTA;.

BRALICK, Andrew E; Sargent Public HS; Sargent, NE; Trade School; Auto Technician.

BRAMAN, Corrie E; Tomahawk HS; Tomahawk, WI; Band; CncrtBnd; MrchBnd; PepBnd; Yrbk; RptrSchPpr; SchPpr; Bsktbl; LetterSocr; LetterTrk; GAA; IMSpt; PresAwd; College; Professional.

BRAMAN, Dave E; Tomahawk HS; Tomahawk, WI; 4/170 ALBoysSt; CncrtBnd; HonRl; MrchBnd; NHS; NatlMeritCmnd; NatlSciFnd; SchMus; SchPl; TreasMthCl; Trk; Wrstlng; OptClAwd; Univ; Oceanography.

BRAMAN, Kerry A; Fulton HS; Ashley, MI; 16/65 VPSrCls; Chrs; CmntyWkr; HonRl; JA; OffAde; SchPl; VPStuCncl; TchrAde; Yrbk; Bsktbl; DanFAwd; 4-HAwd; CitAwd; College; Vocation.

BRAMAN, Nancy L; Central Montcalm HS; Stanton, MI; 17/128 TrsJrCls; PresSrCls; SchPl; StuCncl; StuGov; RptrYrbk; FDA; FNA; SpnCl; VoiceDemAwd; Western Mi Univ; Physicians Assistant.

BRAME, Mark A; Lakeshore HS; Saint Joseph, MI; OffAde; Adrian College.

BRAMER, Diane S; Yankton HS; Yankton, SD; HonRl; NHS; 4-H; LetterGlf; Chrldr; IMSpt; 4-HAwd; Univ Sd Vermillion; Dental Hygiene.

BRAMLET, John S; Naperville Central HS; Naperville, IL; HonRl; Eastern Ill Univ; Science.

BRAMLET, Timothy S; Griffin HS; Springfield, IL; 28/192 SecSophCls; StuCncl; StuGov; SptEdYrbk; EdSchPpr; Bsbl; Bsktbl; Glf; IMSpt; OptClAwd; Univ Of Illinois; Journalism.

BRAMMEIER, Sharon F; Okawville HS; Okawville, IL; 11/60 TrsSrCls; Chrs; NHS; NatlThespSoc; SchPl; EdYrBk; GerCl; Chrs; Eastern Ill U; Med Tech.

BRANAM, Brent; Finney HS; Detroit, MI; PresSrCls; CncrtBnd; NHS; LetterTennis; University; Pharmacy.

BRANCH, Leeann; Hononegah HS; Rockton, IL; 32/185 HonRl; RptrSchPpr; 4-H; SpnCl; GAA; College; Professional.

BRANCH, Lori A; Hackett HS; Kalamazoo, MI; 36/168 Nazareth Coll; Nursing.

BRANCH, Pamela D; Meridian HS; Edenville, MI; 10/125 PresSophCls; Chr; HonRl; NHS; StuCncl;

YthFlsp; 4-H; SecFrCl; Cntrl Michigan Univ; Marketing.

BRANCH, Roxanne J; Pine River HS; Leroy, MI; Chr; HonRl; SchPl; Yrbk; PresFHA; PpCl; Mich State Police Acad; State Trooper.

BRANCH, Stephen C; Harlem HS; Loves Park, IL; 33/520 Aud/Vis; Band; CncrtBnd; HonRl; MrchBnd; SctActv; StuCncl; TchrAde; Bsktbl; Rockford College; Law.

BRANCH, Thomas; Warren Woods HS; Warren, MI; 57/300 ChrhWkr; HonRl; Bsbl; Bsktbl; Ftbl; Tennis; Mccc; Vocational.

BRANCHAUD, James A; Winnebago Public HS; Winnebago, NE; 1/18 PresBand; Chr; NHS; SchMus; SchPl; PresStuCncl; ChmnBsktbl; LetterTrk; BttyCrckrAwd; PresAwd; U Of Neb.

BRANCHEAU, Anne M; St Mary Academy; Monroe, MI; 3/142 Chrl; ChrhWkr; HonRl; VPNHS; SchPl; StuGov; PresFNA; Trk; Nursing School; Nurse.

BRAND, Christy; Paoli HS; Paoli, IN; 20/114 Band; CncrtBnd; DrlTm; HonRl; MrchBnd; PepBnd; 4-H; SciCl; GAA; College; Dental Hygienist.

BRAND, Jean M; Cathedral HS; New Ulm, MN; ALAGirlsSt; Band; NHS; SchMus; SchPl; StuCncl; 4-H; PpCl; IMSpt;.

BRAND, Jefferson C; Warren County Riii HS; Warrenton, MO; 22/98 PresSrCls; HonRl; StuCncl; StuGov; FTA; LetterBsktbl; LetterFtbl; LetterGlf; LetterTrk; Univ; Mgmr.

BRAND, Jennifer A; Brown County HS; Nashville, IN; 8/206 Band; ChrhWkr; CncrtBnd; HonRl; MrchBnd; PepBnd; 4-H; FrCl; PpCl; Trk; Chrldr; GAA; College; Business Admin.

BRAND, John D; Batavia HS; Batavia, IL; 21/212 HonRl; Indiana Univ; Optometry.

BRAND, John S; Monroe Sr HS; Monroe, WI; 1/225 Chrl; Chrs; HonRl; NatlMeritSF; SchMus; SchPl; LetterTennis; LetterTrk; Univ Of Wi; Elec Engineering.

BRAND, Jonathan E; Berkley HS; Huntington Woods, MI; VPSophCls; ALBoysSt; NatlFornLg; PolWkr; StuGov; Yrbk; SciCl; Bsbl; SecJrCls; Political Science.

BRAND, Kathleen; Cathedral HS; New Ulm, MN; 6/86 Chrs; HonRl; JrNHS; JrNHS; NHS; SchMus; SctActv; Sdlty; PpCl; IMSpt; College.

BRAND, Kim; Northwest HS; Saint Louis, MO; HonRl; ModUN; NatlSciFnd; RedCrAde; StuCncl; StuGov; FFA; FHA; FSA; CitAwd; Coll; Prof.

BRANDAU, Robert E; Green Mountain HS; Marshalltown, IA; 1/24 PresFrshCls; VPSrCls; Chrs; HonRl; Mdrgl; SchMus; SchPl; SciCl; Bsktbl; Trk; Univ; Forestry.

BRANDEBERRY, Patty; Waldron HS; Waldron, MI; 8/53 OffAde; SchPl; TchrAde; Yrbk; FBLA; 4-H; 4-HAwd; Trade School; Professional.

BRANDEMUEHL, Catherine J; Lancaster HS; Lancaster, WI; Band; Chrs; CncrtBnd; Orch; SchMus; Bsktbl; LetterTrk; IMSpt; Bus Schl; Accounting.

BRANDENBURG, Katherine M; Cerro Gordo HS; Milmine, IL; 5/69 VPFrshCls; PresSrCls; Band; ChrhWkr; HonRl; HospAde; NHS; OffAde; SchMus; StuCncl; Col; Automated Inf Systems.

BRANDENBURG, Rachel J; Arlington HS; Arlington Hts, IL; 80/600 ChrhWkr; CmntyWkr; HonRl; NatlMeritSF; NatlThespSoc; PolWkr; SchMus; SchPl; SctActv; StuGov; TchrAde; Swmmng; Trk; Univ; Anthropology.

BRANDENBURGER, Daniel L; Clarks Public HS; Silver Creek, NE; ChrhWkr; CmntyWkr; HonRl; JA; NHS; RedCrAde; SchPl; 4-H; FFA; FHA; Trade Schl; Vocation.

BRANDES, Karen A; Southwest HS; St Louis, MO; 51/540 HospAde; FrCl; GAA; College; Nursing.

BRANDIBUR, Karen A; Kingston HS; Kingston, MI; HonRl; OffAde; TchrAde; Yrbk; FrCl; PpCl; LetterBsktbl; Trk; Chrldr; GAA; College.

BRANDIS, Marion J; Evanston Twp HS; Evanston, IL; Band; Chrs; CncrtBnd; HonRl; MrchBnd; Orch; PolWkr; Univ Of Michigan; Orchestral Conductor.

BRANDL, Cindy; Auburndale Hs; Auburndale, WI; HonRl; LbryAde; NatlFornLg; FBLA; GerCl; PpCl; Trk;.

BRANDL, Deborah A; C P Steinmetz HS; Chicago, IL; HonRl; SchAde; TchrAde; College; Data Processing.

BRANDL, Joseph P; Brainerd HS; Brainerd, MN; Aud/Vis; HonRl; NHS; SctActv; Clge Of St Thomas; Health Field.

BRANDL, Lynne L; Regis HS; Eau Claire, WI; TrsFrshCls; DrlTm; HonRl; HospAde; StuGov; SecFrCl; Chrldr; GAA; Eau Claire Univ.

BRANDLEY, Kim S; Northeastern HS; Foutain City, IN; Band; DrmMjrt; HonRl; HospAde; LbryAde; OffAde; SchAde; SchMus; TchrAde; 4-HAwd; Ball St Univ; Home Ec.

BRANDNER, Debra; Medford Senior HS; Medford, WI; Band; CncrtBnd; HonRl; MrchBnd; NHS; FFA; FHA; Swmmng; Trk; GAA; Col; Veterinary Med.

BRANDNER, Randall J; Medford HS; Medford, WI; 46/254 ALBoysSt; ChrhWkr; HonRl; NatlFornLg; NHS; SctActv; StuCncl; RptrYrbk; Bsbl; Bsktbl; U W Lacrosse; Psychology.

BRANDON, Donald; Mt Vernon Twp Hs; Mt Vernon, IL; 6 Chr; ChrhWkr; CncrtBnd; HonRl; MrchBnd; NHS; NatlThespSoc; Orch; KeyCl; College;music Teacher.

BRANDON, Mark R; Racine Lutheran HS; Racine, WI; 3/81 HonRl; NHS; RptrSchPpr; PpCl; Bsktbl; LetterFtbl; LetterTrk; College; Pre Medicine.

BRANDON, Rick A; Anderson HS; Anderson, IN; TchrAde; Bsbl; Univ; Elementary Teacher.

BRANDON, Thomas K; Lutheran HS; Racine, WI; PresJrCls; Chrl; HonRl; NHS; SctActv; StuCncl; SptEdYrbk; RptrSchPpr; LetterFtbl; LetterTennis; Concordia College; Drtr Christian Ed.

BRANDOW, Patsy; Kent City HS; Kent City, MI; 17/90 HonRl; NHS; TchrAde; RptrYrbk; RptrSchPpr; SchPpr; Trade School.

BRANDSTETTER, Brian J; Grayslake Comm HS; Grayslake, IL; 26/219 ChrhWkr; HonRl; NHS; RptrSchPpr; LetterBsktbl; College; Law.

BRANDT, Calvin V; New Haven HS; New Haven, MO; TrsFrshCls; TrsSophCls; TrsJrCls; TrsSrCls; HonRl; NHS; YthFlsp; E Central Jr College; Agriculture.

BRANDT, Caroline; Manteno Hs; Peotone, IL; 3/85 HonRl; NHS; OffAde; TchrAde; Yrbk; SchPpr; TreasSpnCl; TreasSciCl; Bsktbl; DARAwd; Illinois State U; Teacher Special Ed.

BRANDT, Carrie; Bonduel HS; Bonduel, WI; 19/122 SchPl; StuCncl; RptrYrbk; RptrSchPpr; FBLA; GerCl; Chrldr; GAA; DanFAwd; Technical Sch; Medical Assist.

BRANDT, Cheryl A; Clear Lake HS; Clear Lake, SD; 6/54 ALAGirlsSt; CncrtBnd; HonRl; SecNHS; SecNatlThespSoc; YthFlsp; AmLegAwd; DARAwd; 4-HAwd; CitAwd; Sd St Univ; Home Ec.

BRANDT, Christine A; Oak Lawn HS; Oak Lawn, IL; 169/630 HonRl; StuGov; 4-H; 4-HAwd; College; Nursing.

BRANDT, Cindy E; Weston HS; Hillpoint, WI; Band; Chr; ChrhWkr; CncrtBnd; PepBnd; YthFlsp; FHA; PpCl; Chrldr; IMSpt; Madison Area Tech Coll; Rehabilitation Ther.

BRANDT, Donna G; Sweet Springs R 7 HS; La Monte, MO; Chrs; HonRl; OffAde; YthFlsp; Yrbk; Sec4-H; FHA; VPPpCl; Chrldr; IMSpt; 4-HAwd; PresAwd; College; Secretary.

BRANDT, Kent; Grand Blanc Sr HS; Grand Blanc, MI; ALBoysSt; Chr; NHS; CchngActv; Univ Of Mi; Engineering.

BRANDT, Kristin M; Bishop Foley HS; W Bloomfield, MI; Aud/Vis; ChrhWkr; HonRl; Yrbk; LatCl; Trade Sch; Dental Assit.

BRANDT, Laurie A; Hillsboro HS; Hillsboro, KS; ChrhWkr; HonRl; OffAde; PolWkr; TchrAde; YthFlsp; PpCl; Bethel College; Business.

BRANDT, Lauri L; Onamia HS; Onamia, MN; Band; DrlTm; HonRl; MrchBnd; LetterTrk; CaptChrldr; PPFtbl; PresAwd; College; Professional.

BRANDT, Peter D; Crystal Lake HS; Crystal Lake, IL; 89/499 HonRl; NHS; RptrSchPpr; LetterFtbl; LetterWrstlng; Univ Of Wisconsin; Agriculture.

BRANDT, Rebecca M; Winamac Comm HS; Winamac, IN; DrlTm; HonRl; NHS; RptrSchPpr; SpnCl; SecPpCl; SecSciCl; Univ; Physical Therapist.

BRANDT, Samuel J; Garretson HS; Sherman, SD; 1/50 TrsSrCls; Chrs; HonRl; NHS; SchMus; SchPl; LetterFtbl; LetterTrk; LetterWrstlng; Us Naval Acad; Engineering.

BRANDT, Sandra K; Bishop Dwenger HS; Ft Wayne, IN; Chrs; HonRl; JA; NHS; SchPl; TchrAde; RptrYrbk; FrCl; GAA; JAAwd; Univ; Professional.

BRANDT, Tim J; Regina HS; Iowa City, IA; HstFrshCls; TrsSophCls; PresJrCls; HstSrCls; ALBoysSt; SchMus; SctActv; StuCncl; StuGov; SchPpr; College; Mechanical Eng.

BRANDTS, Larry J; St James Senior HS; St James, MN; 8/140 SecSrCls; Chr; Chrs; HonRl; Mdrgl; SchMus; SchPl; RptrSchPpr; College; Clinical Psychologist Phd.

BRANDVOLD, Katharine G; North Shore HS; Ryder, ND; ALAGirlsSt; Chrl; DrlTm; HonRl; Mdrgl; SecPepBnd; SchMus; VP4-H; LetterBsktbl; LetterTrk; LetterChrldr; 4-HAwd; College; Business.

BRANDYS, Michael F; Dixon HS; Dixon, IL; 4/327 CmntyWkr; HonRl; JrNHS; NHS; NatlMeritCmnd; RptrSchPpr; Univ Il; Architect.

BRANEKY, Donna K; Okawville HS; Okawville, IL; Chrs; DrmMjrt; LbryAde; FHA; PpCl; Trk; Business School; Professional.

BRANHAM, David; Camderton HS; Camdenton, MO; 9/160 VPJrCls; ALBoysSt; HonRl; NHS; SchPl; StuCncl; SpnCl; MthCl; Trk; Missouri Univ; Engineering.

BRANHAM, Kerry I; Northland Pines HS; Eagle River, WI; Band; Chrs; ChrhWkr; CAP; CncrtBnd; HonRl; MrchBnd; PepBnd; Quill&Scroll; SchPl; RptrSchPpr; FrCl; Ftbl;.

BRANIFF, Kathleen A; Luke M Powers HS; Flint, MI; HonRl; NHS; SchPl; TchrAde; CaptChrldr; Coll; Elem Ed.

BRANINE, Shirley A; Winfield HS; Winfield, KS; 59/181 Band; ChrhWkr; MrchBnd; PepBnd; StuCncl; TchrAde; FHA; FrCl; PpCl; LetterGlf; College; Home Ec.

BRANKIN, John P; Marist HS; Chicago, IL; 26/393 CmntyWkr; HonRl; PolWkr; Yrbk; SpnCl; IMSpt; University; Professional.

BRANKIN, Kevin M; Brother Rice HS; Hometown, IL; 63/416 HonRl; NatlMeritCmnd; SctActv; St Xavier College.

BRANLUND, Ruby J; South Shore HS; Iron River, WI; 4/39 ChrhWkr; HonRl; Yrbk; SchPpr; 4-H; Univ Of Wi; Art.

BRANNAMAN, Marie L; Lincoln Comm HS; Mechanicsville, IA; 3/63 HonRl; NHS; StuCncl;.

BRANNIAN, Allen R; Bgm HS; Malcom, IA; 26#29#32 HonRl; Mdrgl; SchMus; FFA; LetterBsbl; LetterWrstlng; 4-HAwd; College Or Business School; Business.

BRANNICK, Kathy M; Minooka HS; Minooka, IL; 22/103 HstJrCls; SecSrCls; Chr; Chrs; HonRl; SchPl; TchrAde; RptrYrbk; RptrSchPpr; FTA; GAA; Joliet Junior College; Teaching.

BRANNON, Michael J; Center Grove HS; Greenwood, IN; Band; MrchBnd; SchPl; 4-H; SpnCl; SciCl; BttyCrckrAwd; College; Veterinarian.

BRANSON, Janelle; Hays HS; Hays, KS; Band; HonRl; HospAde; NatlFornLg; PepBnd; TchrAde; PpCl; IMSpt; OptClAwd; College; Broadcasting.

BRANSON, Philip J; Taft HS; Chicago, IL; 4/900 HonRl; IntrClCncl; JrNHS; NHS; OffAde; RptrYrbk; Yrbk; MthCl; LetterSwmmng; IMSpt; Northwestern Univ; Medicine.

BRANSON, Suzanne M; Sullivan HS; Sullivan, MO; 16/150 Chr; CncrtBnd; HonRl; SchMus; StuCncl; RptrSchPpr; EdSchPpr; FrCl; CchngActv; Sw Missouri St University.

BRANSON, Wayne E; Genoa Kingston HS; Genoa, IL; 12/98 College; Engineering.

BRANSTAD, Mary E; Grantsburg HS; Grantsburg, WI; Chr; HstFrshCls; JrNHS; ROTC; StuCncl; UNYO; FBLA; FDA; PpCl; Univ.

BRANT, Kristen M; Larkin HS; Elgin, IL; CmntyWkr; HonRl; TchrAde; Trk; De Paul Univ; Science.

BRANTING, Darryl L; North Platte Senior HS; North Platte, NE; 1/400 HonRl; TchrAde; LatCl; New Mexico Tech; Geologist.

BRANTING, Tina M; North Platte HS; North Platte, NE; 256/397 SecSophCls; DrlTm; HonRl; Sec4-H; PpCl; Tennis; GAA; IMSpt; PPFtbl; Clge; Fashion Design Or Horse Production.

BRANTLEY, Denise M; Chicago Vocational HS; Chicago, IL; Band; ChrhWkr; HonRl; JA; OffAde; FTA; Business Schl; Legal Secretary.

BRANTNER, Becky S; Mendota Township HS; Mendota, IL; 21/189 PresSophCls; Band; PresChr; ChrhWkr; CncrtBnd; CaptDrlTm; HonRl; IntrClCncl; Mdrgl; MrchBnd; PepBnd; SchPl; StuCncl; GAA; Univ Of Ill; Music Ed.

BRANTON, Robert A; Pembine HS; Pembine, WI; 2/32 PresJrCls; ALBoysSt; HonRl; SchPl; StuGov; RptrYrbk; RptrSchPpr; LetterBsktbl; LetterFtbl; LetterGlf; LetterTrk; College.

BRANZ, Gary; E A Johnson HS; Clio, MI; 10/250 HonRl; SchAde; Michigan Tech Univ; Forest Engineering.

BRASCH, Kathleen A; Mooseheart HS; Mooseheart, IL; 3/23 Chr; Chrs; HonRl; NHS; ROTC; Yrbk; RptrSchPpr; Trk; CaptChrldr; GAA; College; Nursing.

BRASCHLER, Cheryl L; South Haven HS; South Haven, MI; 1/257 Band; Chrs; CncrtBnd; HonRl; MrchBnd; NHS; SchMus; SchPl; StuGov; TchrAde; 4-H; LetterSwmmng; College; Math.

BRASE, James M; North Central HS; Hanlontown, IA; 3/65 Band; HonRl; NHS; NatlMeritSF; SchMus; SchPl; RptrYrbk; Yrbk; FrCl; SciCl; U Of Ia; Engineering.

BRASEL, Deborah; Beardstown Hs; Beardstown, IL; HonRl; MrchBnd; OffAde; RedCrAde; TchrAde; RptrYrbk; FTA; SpnCl; LetterTrk;.

BRASEL, Marilyn J; Anna Jonesboro Comm HS; Anna, IL; 1/139 SecFrshCls; SecSophCls; SecJrCls; Band; CncrtBnd; HonRl; LbryAde; MrchBnd; PepBnd; RptrSchPpr; SchPpr; FTA; FrCl; Univ; Mathematics.

BRASEL, Marsha F; Effingham HS; Effingham, IL; ChrhWkr; HonRl; OffAde; SchMus; SchPl; SctActv; VPFTA; LatCl; PpCl; GAA; Mc Kendree Col; Art.

BRASEL, Timothy J; Dow City Arion HS; Dow City, IA; ALBoysSt; Band; Chr; Chrl; ChrhWkr; HonRl; PolWkr; StuCncl; RptrSchPpr; 4-H; 4-HAwd; College; Professional.

BRASEWICZ, Lynda M; Elizabeth Seton HS; Chicago, IL; 8/252 ChrhWkr; HonRl; NHS; RptrYrbk; FSA; MthCl; De Paul Univ; Mathematics.

BRASHAW, Paul W; Bridgeport HS; Saginaw, MI; Band; ChrhWkr; CmntyWkr; CncrtBnd; HonRl; Bsktbl; CchngActv; IMSpt; College; Professional.

BRASHEAR, Janice F; Southern Boone County R 1 HS; Hartsburg, MO; Band; ChrhWkr; HonRl; NHS; PepBnd; SchPl; TchrAde; FHA; LetterBsktbl; Trk; College; Social Work.

BRASK, Diane M; Grantsburg HS; Frederic, WI; PresSrCls; Band; ChrhWkr; CmntyWkr; CncrtBnd; HonRl; JA; LbryAde; MrchBnd; PepBnd; Bsbl; CaptBsktbl; Trk; GAA; College; Nursing.

BRASKET, Carol L; Sandoval HS; Sandoval, IL; HstFrshCls; HstSophCls; HstJrCls; Band; CncrtBnd; MrchBnd; PepBnd; SpnCl; Coll;.

BRASMER, Susan E; Moline Sr HS; Moline, IL; 13/822 Chr; HonRl; LitMag; NHS; NatlMeritCmnd; Quill&Scroll; SchMus; Yrbk; GerCl; University Of Illinois;engineering.

BRASS, Frances; Niles North HS; Skokie, IL; HonRl; JrNHS; NHS; StuCncl; StuGov; Bsbl; University; Law.

BRASS, Karen J; Platte Valley Acad; Jamestown, ND; SecJrCls; Chr; CmntyWkr; HonRl; LbryAde; SchPl; SpnCl; IMSpt; Coll; Social Worker.

BRASS, Lois A; Pella Christian HS; Pella, IA; Chr; ChrhWkr; HonRl; SchPl; StuCncl; RptrYrbk; RptrSchPpr; LetterBsktbl; University; Pharmacy.

BRASSIL, Mary T; Immaculate Heart Of Mary HS; Westchester, IL; 10/275 Chrl; HospAde; FrCl; SciCl; GAA; College; Medicine.

BRASWELL, Ruth M; Cvs HS; Chicago, IL; 31/1100 ChrhWkr; CmntyWkr; HonRl; JA; OffAde; SchPl; TchrAde; Univ; Law.

BRATCHER, Cheryl A; Seymour HS; Seymour, IN; 56/360 Band; CmntyWkr; HonRl; OffAde; SchPl; TchrAde; 4-H; FTA; Trk; CchngActv; Ind State U; Dental Hygiene.

BRATLAND, Bruce L; Twin Rivers HS; Bade, IA; PresFrshCls; Chrs; SchPl; StuCncl; VPYthFlsp; LetterFtbl; LetterTrk; LetterWrstlng; Jr College.

BRATLIE, Roberta L; Drayton Public HS; Drayton, ND; 5/35 Band; ChrhWkr; CncrtBnd; HonRl; PepBnd; EdYrBk; VPFHA; PpCl; College; Curriculum Of Major Study.

BRATON, Brenda S; Barnesville HS; Hawley, MN; 15/89 HonRl; SchPl; YthFlsp; RptrYrbk; RptrSchPpr; 4-H; FHA; PpCl; LetterTrk; 4-HAwd; Lakeland Med Den Acad; Medical Assistant.

BRATT, Kenneth E; Crispus Attucks HS; Indianapolis, IN; 14/265 HonRl; JrNHS; NHS; SchPl; StuGov; TchrAde; IMSpt; CitAwd; U Of Cinn; Architect.

BRATTEN, Steven J; Senior HS; Jefferson City, MO; 10/526 Chr; HonRl; JrNHS; NHS; NatlMeritSF; PolWkr; SctActv; StuCncl; YthLg; Univ Of Missouri; Law.

BRATTON, Ronald R; North Davitss HS; Plainville, IN; VPSrCls; Chr; ChrhWkr; SchMus; YthFlsp; PpCl; Ftbl; Vincennes Univ; Psychologist.

BRATTSTROM, Candice M; Tinley Park HS; Tinley Park, IL; 30/314 ChrhWkr; CncrtBnd; HospAde; MrchBnd; NHS; SchAde; 4-H; PpCl; College; Social Worker.

BRAUCH, William L; Waukesha North HS; Waukesha, WI; 57/327 NHS; SpnCl; MthCl; IMSpt; U Of Wi; Law.

BRAUER, Martin J; Concordia Academy; St Paul, MN; Chr; Chrl; ChrhWkr; HonRl; SchMus; SchPl; StuCncl; GerCl; Bsktbl; Ftbl; Tennis; Concordia Col; Psychology.

BRAUER, Melanie J; Sevastopol HS; Sturgeon Bay, WI; Chrs; RptrSchPpr; SchPpr; GAA; IMSpt; Tech; Dental Hygiene.

BRAUER, Pamela; Ellendale Hs; Ellendale, ND; PresSophCls; PresJrCls; PresSrCls; HonRl; HospAde; SchPl; YthFlsp; EdSchPpr; Pres4-H; PresFHA; VP.

BRAUER, Pamela K; Ellendale HS; Ellendale, ND; 2/46 PresSophCls; PresJrCls; PresSrCls; ALAGirlsSt; Chr; HonRl; SchPl; YthFlsp; EdSchPpr; Pres4-H; College; Nursing.

BRAUHER, Sheree L; Waterford Twnshp HS; Pontiac, MI; DrlTm; HonRl; NHS; SchPl; VPStuCncl; StuGov; SchPpr; Western Michigan University; Home Ec.

BRAUKER, John K; Franklin HS; Livonia, MI; Coll.

BRAUKER, Joyce D; Union City HS; Union City, MI; HonRl; ModUN; PolWkr; StuGov; YthFlsp; FTA; 4-HAwd; GovHonPrgAwd; PresAwd; Clge; Nursing.

BRAULT, Kathleen M; Crivitz HS; Crivitz, WI; TrsFrshCls; TrsSophCls; VPJrCls; TrsSrCls; HonRl; NHS; Bsbl; Bsktbl; Glf; Chrldr; Univ; Med Asst.

BRAUN, Carol I; Watseka Community HS; Watseka, IL; HonRl; NHS; TchrAde; GerCl; Chrldr; Illinois State Univ; Pharmacist.

BRAUN, Christina M; Holy Family Acad; Whitelaw, WI; 2/11 VPSophCls; PresJrCls; Chr; Chrl; Chrs; HonRl; Quill&Scroll; RptrYrbk; EdSchPpr; Lakeshore Tech; Med Asst.

BRAUN, Corinne; Neil Armstrong HS; Minneapolis, MN; 3/603 Chr; HonRl; LitMag; NHS; SchPl; StuCncl; StuGov; RptrSchPpr; Carleton Univ; Foreign Languages.

BRAUN, David; Valle HS; Ste Genevieve, MO; 2/80 HonRl; NHS; SctActv; SptEdSchPpr; MthCl; Tennis; IMSpt; Univ Of Mo Rolla.

BRAUN, Debra; Northwestern HS; Mellette, SD; 6/35 Band; Chrs; CncrtBnd; HonRl; PepBnd; SchPl; StuCncl; Sioux Valley School Of Nursing; Nursing.

BRAUN, Doris E; Hastings Senior HS; Vermillion, MN; HonRl; Trade School; Vocation.

BRAUN, Edward A; Princeton HS; Princeton, MN; 16/160 Band; CncrtBnd; HonRl; MrchBnd; NHS; PepBnd; 4-H; FFA; Glf; Wrstlng; Vocational Tech School; Marketing.

BRAUN, Geoffrey A; Berkeley Sr HS; Berkeley, MO; HonRl; LbryAde; NHS; RptrYrbk;.

BRAUN, Geri K; Valle HS; Ste Genevieve, MO; 4/82 Chrs; DrlTm; HonRl; NHS; SchMus; StuCncl; PpCl; LetterTrk; CaptChrldr; IMSpt; College; Med Therapy.

BRAUN, Gregory; Osceola HS; Osceola, WI; TrsJrCls; CncrtBnd; MrchBnd; NatlMeritSchl; PepBnd; StuGov; Yrbk; FrCl; Bsbl; Glf; College; Professional.

BRAUN, Jeffrey L; Seymour HS; Seymour, WI; 31/189 ALBoysSt; Band; ChrhWkr; HonRl; Ftbl; Trk; Wrstlng; IMSpt; Univ Of Wis Madison; Phy Ed Major.

BRAUN, Joseph A; Hibbing HS; Hibbing, MN; HonRl; JrNHS; ModUN; SpnCl; MthCl; Engineer.

BRAUN, Kathryn; Beatrice Senior HS; Beatrice, NE; 35/219 DrlTm; HonRl; HospAde; ModUN; OffAde; SchPl; StuCncl; 4-H; PpCl; Chrldr; Coll; Rn.

BRAUN, Kenneth J; Freeland HS; Freeland, MI; HonRl; Ftbl; Trk; Coll; Mech Engr.

BRAUN, Mark; Lutheran North HS; St Louis, MO; VPSophCls; Chr; ChrhWkr; HonRl; SchMus; StuCncl; YthLg; Trk; CchngActv; College; Journalism.

BRAUN, Michael R; Vianney HS; St Louis, MO; 41/170 StuGov; TchrAde; LetterFtbl; IMSpt; Univ Of Mo; Accountant.

BRAUN, Nancy S; Saline HS; Saline, MI; 30#41#48 NHS; SchMus; SchPpr; FHA; LetterBsbl; CchngActv; GAA; Mich State Univ; Phy Ed.

BRAUN, Sandy R; Jefferson City Senior HS; Jefferson, MO; HstFrshCls; ALAGirlsSt; NHS; VPNatlThespSoc; SchPl; StuCncl; SecLatCl; SecPpCl; Chrldr; College; Drama Studies.

BRAUN, Shirley A; Southland HS; Adams, MN; Band; ChrhWkr; HonRl; NHS; 4-H; FTA; College Of St Teresa; Social Work.

BRAUN, Stanley D; Baldwin HS; Baldwin City, KS; TrsSophCls; ALBoysSt; HonRl; OffAde; SchMus; SchPl; StuCncl; YthFlsp; FrCl; Tennis; College; Dental.

BRAUN, Stephen G; Athens HS; Athens, WI; 1/95 PresFrshCls; ALBoysSt; VPBand; NatlFornLg; NHS; StuCncl; RptrSchPpr; MthCl; CaptBsktbl; LetterFtbl; University; Chemistry.

BRAUN, Steven D; Nathan Hale HS; New Berlin, WI; HonRl; NatlMeritSF; Orch; SctActv; Bsktbl; LetterTennis; IMSpt; Clge; Biology.

BRAUN, Teresa A; Our Lady Star Of The Sea HS; Grosse Pte Wds, MI; TrsFrshCls; HonRl; HospAde; LbryAde; PresNHS; NatlThespSoc; SchMus; SchPl; GAA; IMSpt; Coll; Rn.

BRAUN, Tim D; Albert Lea HS; Albert Lea, MN; CmntyWkr; HonRl; OffAde; SctActv; StuCncl; EngCl; GerCl; Winona Clg; Surveyor Engineer.

BRAUN, Vickie; Mcclusky HS; Mcclusky, ND; Chr; Chrs; ChrhWkr; CmntyWkr; SchMus; SchPl; FHA; PpCl; Trk; GAA;.

BRAUNAGEL, Darwin D; Harvey HS; Harvey, ND; ALBoysSt; Chrs; HonRl; NatlMeritSchl; SchMus; SchPl; StuCncl; StuGov; GerCl; LetterBsbl; Bsktbl; CaptFtbl; LetterTrk; Univ Of N Dakota; Professional.

BRAUNER, Brenda R; Highland HS; Anderson, IN; 5/265 CmntyWkr; HonRl; NHS; StuCncl; LetterTrk; College; Nursing.

BRAUNS, Lora L; Crystal Lake HS; Crystal Lake, IL; 15/500 Band; ChrhWkr; CncrtBnd; HonRl; JrNHS; LitMag; NHS; NatlMeritFnl; NatlMeritCmnd; NatlMeritSchl; NatlMeritSF; Carleton College; Medicine.

BRAUNSCHEIDEL, Jeffrey J; Plymouth Salem HS; Plymouth, MI; HonRl; JA; NatlMeritSF; 4-H; 4-HAwd; College; Mathematics.

BRAUNSCHWEIG, Gail D; Pocahontas Community HS; Pocahontas, IA; 5/70 ALAGirlsSt; Band; Chrs; HonRl; NHS; TchrAde; EdSchPpr; PpCl; Chrldr; University Of So Dakota; Mass Communication.

BRAUNSCHWEIG, Kay M; Beaver Dam Sr HS; Beaver Dam, WI; 5/349 AFS; OffAde; SctActv; College; Nursing.

BRAUNSKY, Jane; Auburndale HS; Milladore, WI; Band; CncrtBnd; HonRl; MrchBnd; SchPpr; GerCl; PpCl; AmLegAwd; College; Nurse.

BRAUNSKY, Jane M; Auburndale HS; Milladore, WI; Band; CncrtBnd; HonRl; MrchBnd; PepBnd; GerCl; PpCl; AmLegAwd; Coll; Nursing.

BRAUNSROTH, Gail M; Milford HS; Pleasant Dale, NE; SecJrCls; Band; Chrs; HonRl; NHS; TchrAde; 4-H; FHA; GerCl; Chrldr; Kearney St College; Phy Ed Teacher.

BRAUNZ, Diana L; L C Mohr HS; South Haven, MI; HonRl; OffAde; TchrAde; SchPpr; PpCl; Tennis;.

BRAUS, Cathy J; North Kansas City HS; N Kansas City, MO; Chr; Chrs; CmntyWkr; DrlTm; HonRl; RedCrAde; SchMus; StuCncl; PpCl; Swmmng; Umkc; Teach Vocal Music.

BRAVERMAN, Sheleen C; Brainerd HS; Brainerd, MN; 11/440 CncrtBnd; HonRl; NHS; NatlMeritCmnd; TchrAde; YthFlsp; 4-H; FHA; FrCl; SpnCl; Hamline Univ; Psychology.

BRAWLEY, Brenda K; Summersville HS; Summersville, MO; TrsJrCls; Chrs; HonRl; LbryAde; SchPl; StuCncl; RptrYrbk; RptrSchPpr; FHA; PpCl;.

BRAWLEY, Georgia D; Jennings HS; Jennings, MO; 6/277 HonRl; Bsktbl; Tennis; GAA; Washington University; Architecture.

BRAWLEY, Mary L; Southern Reynolds R 2 HS; Ellington, MO; Chrs; ChrhWkr; HonRl; LbryAde; SchPl; Yrbk; EdSchPpr; FHA; PresPpCl; Chrldr; IMSpt; College; Teaching.

BRAWNER, James S; Kirksville Senior HS; Kirksville, MO; HonRl; NHS; StuCncl; FrCl; SciCl; CaptFtbl; Northeast Missouri State Univ; Medicine.

BRAWNER, Jeff M; Kirksville Sr HS; Kirksville, MO; ALBoysSt; HonRl; StuCncl; PresFFA; Ftbl; College; Agriculture.

BRAY, Arthur C; Bellflower Township HS; Bellflower, IL; 5/21 TrsJrCls; HonRl; Yrbk; FFA; SciCl; LetterBsktbl; Parkland College; Law Enforcement.

BRAY, Debbie S; Saybrook Arrowsmith HS; Arrowsmith, IL; VPFrshCls; TrsSophCls; TrsJrCls; ChrhWkr; SchMus; EdYrBk; RptrSchPpr; 4-H; FHA; Chrldr; Il State U; Elementary School Teacher.

BRAY, Dennis D; Clinton HS; Clinton, MO; HonRl; SctActv; SchPpr; LetterTrk; IMSpt; 4-HAwd; OptClAwd; Univ Of Mo Columbia; Medicine.

BRAY, Donna K; Maries Co Rii HS; Belle, MO; 2/56 HstSophCls; ChrhWkr; HonRl; NHS; PresYthFlsp; Pres4-H; FHA; PpCl; 4-HAwd; Sms; Fashin Merchandising.

BRAY, Gary L; Mt Zion HS; Decatur, IL; 6/195 ChrhWkr; HonRl; PresNHS; YthFlsp; SchPpr; LetterBsbl; College; Civil Engineer.

BRAY, George W; Ogemaw Heights HS; West Branch, MI; PresFrshCls; ALBoysSt; ChrhWkr; LetterBsktbl; CaptFtbl; LetterTrk; University; Dentistry.

BRAY, Jack; Bath HS; E Lansing, MI; 20/100 PresSrCls; ALBoysSt; HonRl; NatlMeritFnl; StuCncl; StuGov; Bsktbl; AmLegAwd; Central Mi Col; Biology Major.

BRAY, Jeff; Stafford Rd HS; Plainfield, IN; 22/265 ChrhWkr; HonRl; NHS; PolWkr; Purdue Univ; Chem Engineer.

BRAY, Lorna J; Lincolnwood HS; Farmersville, IL; 11/63 Band; CncrtBnd; HonRl; MrchBnd; PepBnd; StuGov; Yrbk; FTA; SpnCl; PpCl; University Of Illinois; Veterinarian.

BRAY, Marlita J; Central HS; Switz City, IN; HonRl; TchrAde; RptrYrbk; Marriage.

BRAY, Paula D; Lakeland R Iii HS; Lowry City, MO; PresSophCls; ALAGirlsSt; Band; HonRl; ModUN; StuCncl; Yrbk; EdSchPpr; Bsktbl; University Of Missouri; Oceanography.

BRAY, Robert M; St Bede Academy; Tonica, IL; VPSophCls; HonRl; LitMag; SchMus; SchPl; SchPpr; 4-H; LetterTennis; LetterTrk; IMSpt; U S Marines; Aviater.

BRAY, Roger A; Blair HS; Ft Calhoun, NE; SchPl; Pres4-H; FFA; SpnCl; IMSpt;.

BRAY, Russell D; Elkhorn HS; Elkhorn, WI; PresFrshCls; Band; ChrhWkr; HonRl; StuCncl; YthFlsp; 4-H; VPFFA; Bsktbl; LetterFtbl; 4-HAwd; Trade School; Agriculture.

BRAYE, Pamela G; Nokomis HS; Nokomis, IL; PresJrCls; HonRl; OffAde; StuCncl; Treas4-H; FHA; TreasGAA; Jr Col;.

BRAYER, Steve J; Columbus HS; Marshfield, WI; Chr; Chrs; HonRl; TreasStuCncl; RptrYrbk; RptrSchPpr; FrCl; Bsktbl; Glf; IMSpt; Clg; Prof.

BRAYSHAW, Bonnie L; Du Quoin HS; Du Quoin, IL; 11/147 PresBand; Chr; Chrs; ChrhWkr; CncrtBnd; LbryAde; MrchBnd; PepBnd; RptrSchPpr; SchPpr; Southern Illinois Univ; Music.

BRAZELL, Debbie; Mc Donald County HS; Anderson, MO; Chr; Chrs; HonRl; LbryAde; SchPl; SctActv; TchrAde; FHA; FTA; Coll; Policewoman.

BRAZELTON, Lynn; Lathrop HS; Lathrop, MO; 1/40 TrsJrCls; Chrs; DrlTm; HonRl; ModUN; SchPl; VPStuCncl; TchrAde; RptrYrbk; 4-H; VPFHA; FTA; Chrldr; IMSpt; Nw Mo St Univ; English Teacher.

BRAZILL, Paula L; Wichita North HS; Wichita, KS; Chrs; HonRl; JCC; FrCl; PpCl; Chrldr; IMSpt; College.

BRAZINSKI, Jeanne E; Marissa HS; Coulterville, IL; 1/63 ChrhWkr; DrlTm; HonRl; NHS; 4-H; FBLA; FHA; University; Accounting.

BRAZLEY, Venicia; Fenger HS; Chicago, IL; 15/593 HonRl; HospAde; NHS; OffAde; Ill Inst Of Tech; Chem Engrg.

BRCKA, Robert J; Garner Mayfield HS; Garner, IA; 12/84 CncrtBnd; HonRl; MrchBnd; NHS; SchPl; 4-H; Ftbl; Trk; CchngActv; CitAwd; Ia State Univ; Journalism.

BREACH, Susan D; Norfolk HS; Norflok, NE; HonRl; PpCl; Trade Sch; Secretary.

BREAULT, Rick A; Evergreen Park Comm HS; Evergreen Park, IL; 75/439 PresBand; Chr; CmntyWkr; CncrtBnd; Mdrgl; MrchBnd; NHS; Orch; PolWkr; PresStuCncl; CaptTrk; Wrstlng; College; Professional.

BRECHIN, Monica A; Addison Trail HS; Addison, IL; 25/586 Chrl; HonRl; NHS; OffAde; GerCl; PpCl; LetterTennis; Trk; GAA; Illinois State University; Mathematics.

BRECHLER, Lisa A; Fennimore HS; Fennimore, WI; 8/112 HonRl; LbryAde; NHS; SchPl; GAA; Clge; Bus.

BRECHT, Ann M; Pt Austin Public HS; Port Austin, MI; 5/39 Chrs; ChrhWkr; HonRl; LbryAde; SecNatlThespSoc; OffAde; SchAde; SchMus; SchPl; SctActv; Marygrove College; Pre Law.

BRECHT, Mary J; Leo HS; Holy Cross, IA; HonRl; LbryAde; SchMus; RptrYrbk; SchPpr; SpnCl; PpCl; SciCl; IMSpt; College; Study Math.

BRECHTING, Maureen; West Catholic HS; Comstock Park, MI; 31/329 Chrs; CmntyWkr; HonRl; NHS; StuCncl; CivCl; 4-H; SpnCl; IMSpt; 4-HAwd; Michigan State Univ; Dietetics.

BRECHWALD, Richard H; Mound Westonka HS; Wayzata, MN; Chr; HonRl; LetterTrk; Univ; Engineering.

BRECKMAN, David J; St Thomas HS; St Paul, MN; 68/96 4-H; LetterBsbl; Bsktbl; Ftbl; LetterWrstlng; IMSpt; St Cloud Coll; Business.

BRECKNER, Donald; Marysville HS; Smiths Creek, MI; 7/175 PresSrCls; NHS; Quill&Scroll; SchPl; StuCncl; RptrYrbk; EdSchPpr; FrCl; SciCl; Oakland Univ; Art History Major.

BRECKON, Ellen S; North Greene HS; Hillview, IL; 8/112 ALAGirlsSt; Band; ChrhWkr; HonRl; NHS; Orch; SchMus; Yrbk; VPFFA; IMSpt; College.

BREDBERG, Donald; Greendale HS; Greendale, WI; 38/390 ChrhWkr; HonRl; JrNHS; ModUN; NHS; SctActv; SciCl; Bsktbl; Trk; IMSpt; U Wi; Actuarial Science.

BREDEMANN, Joyce M; Brainerd HS; Brainerd, MN; Band; CncrtBnd; HonRl; JrNHS; MrchBnd; OffAde; Orch; SchPl; Trk; PresAwd; Trade Sch; Vocation.

BREDENSTEINER, Carl J; Thomas Carr Howe HS; Indianapolis, IN; 6/616 HonRl; NHS; NatlMeritSF; StuCncl; LatCl; Trk;.

BREDENSTEINER, Janet L; Farragut Comm HS; Farragut, IA; 2/35 PresJrCls; Band; Chr; Chrl; ChrhWkr; HonRl; NatlMeritCmnd; PepBnd; FrCl; CaptChrldr; College; Vocation.

BREDER, Dennis C; Mediapolis Comm HS; Mediapolis, IA; 5/90 HonRl; NatlMeritSchl; SchMus; Yrbk; LetterBsktbl; LetterGlf; U Of Ia; Doctor Or Accounting.

BREDESON, Daniel V; Argyle HS; Blanchardville, WI; 10/44 PresSophCls; Band; Chrs; ChrhWkr; HonRl; Mdrgl; SchMus; StuCncl; 4-H; CaptFtbl; Univ Wi; Teacher.

BREDESON, Mick V; North Central HS; Dazey, ND; 10/30 Band; CncrtBnd; HonRl; MrchBnd; PepBnd; StuCncl; LetterBsktbl; LetterTrk; CchngActv;.

BREDEWEG, Deborah J; L And M HS; Lyons, IN; 4/37 SecSrCls; ChrhWkr; DrlTm; HonRl; NHS; RptrYrbk; Pres4-H; FHA; FTA; 4-HAwd; JAAwd; Indiana State Univ; Elementary Education.

BREDEWEG, Reita J; Central HS; Worthington, IN; 8/43 HonRl; NHS; YthFlsp; Treas4-H; SecFHA; 4-HAwd; College; Secretary.

BREDLAU, Brian; O W Sr HS; Owen, WI; PresFrshCls; HonRl; SctActv; StuCncl; StuGov; FrCl; PpCl; Bsktbl; Ftbl; Glf; Moraine Park Tech Sch; Supermarket Manage.

BREED, Pat A; Nathan Hale HS; West Allis, WI; 53/543 Band; Chrs; ChrhWkr; HonRl; NatlThespSoc; Orch; PepBnd; LetterBsktbl; LetterTennis; Trk; Univ Of Wisconsin; Music.

BREEDEN, David M; Norris City Omaha HS; Broughton, IL; PresSophCls; PresJrCls; HonRl; SchPl; StuGov; FFA; Bsbl; Bsktbl; So Illinois Univ; Law.

BREEDEN, Jamie J; Covington HS; Covington, IN; Band; Chr; ChrhWkr; CmntyWkr; CncrtBnd; HospAde; MrchBnd; Orch; Trk; GAA; College; Registered Nurse.

BREEDEN, Sandra L; Chillicothe Rii HS; Chillicothe, MO; VPFrshCls; ALAGirlsSt; ChrhWkr; CncrtBnd; HonRl; MrchBnd; SchPl; StuCncl; Twrl; Univ Of Missouri; Business.

BREEDEN, Vickie L; Delwood HS; Elwood, IA; 1/28 ChrhWkr; CmntyWkr; HonRl; NHS; SchAde; YthFlsp; 4-H; FTA; MthCl; 4-HAwd; Univ; Prof.

BREEDING, Lyle A; Plymouth HS; Plymouth, IN; 72/212 PresBand; CncrtBnd; MrchBnd; Orch; PepBnd; SchMus; Yrbk; VPFFA; PpCl; Trk; Indiana St Univ; Music.

BREEDLOVE, Frances L; Maconaquah HS; Amboy, IN; 9/200 ALAGirlsSt; Band; CncrtBnd; HonRl; MrchBnd; NHS; PepBnd; SchPl; TchrAde; Yrbk; SchPpr; FHA; FTA; Ball St Univ; Teaching.

BREEDLOVE, John D; Forman HS; Manito, IL; 11/86 PresFrshCls; Band; HonRl; NHS; SchPl; SctActv; StuCncl; YthFlsp; FFA; Bsbl; Bsktbl; Trk; IMSpt; College; Engineer.

BREEN, Jill M; North Platte HS; North Platte, NE; Band; StuCncl; TchrAde; PpCl; Trk; Chrldr; GAA; IMSpt; PPFtbl; DARAwd; Univ; Major Study.

BREEN, Sarah R; St Pius X HS; Kansas City, MO; 7/132 VPBand; CncrtBnd; HonRl; ModUN; NHS; NatlMeritCmnd; OffAde; PepBnd; SchMus; SchPl; Univ Of Mo;.

BREEN, Susan L; Clinton HS; Clinton, IA; 4/516 Chr; Chrs; DrmBgl; HonRl; PresNatlFornLg; NHS; NatlMeritSF; PolWkr; SchMus; StuCncl; RptrSchPpr; Ftbl; PPFtbl; College; Business.

BREES, Patricia A; Girard HS; Girard, KS; 9/96 TrsFrshCls; DrlTm; HonRl; NHS; StuCncl; Teen; RptrYrbk; EdYrBk; FHA; PpCl; Bsbl; Bsktbl; Ftbl; Kscp; Business Admin.

BREESCHOTEN, Darryl J; Sioux Valley HS; Valga, SD; 15/66 ALBoysSt; Band; Chrs; PresSophCls; HonRl; MrchBnd; YthFlsp; LetterFtbl; LetterWrstlng; IMSpt; Farming.

BREESE, Vicki L; Sentral Community HS; Bancroft, IA; 13/37 ModUN; NHS; NatlMeritFnl; NatlMeritSchl; PolWkr; IMSpt; BauchLmbAwd; GovHonPrgAwd; PresAwd; CitAwd; Iowa State Univ.

BREGAR, Joann M; St Joseph HS; Chicago, IL; HonRl; NHS; College.

BREHMER, Betty J; Grant Deuel HS; Revillo, SD; Band; ChrhWkr; CncrtBnd; DrlTm; HonRl; MrchBnd; PepBnd; Yrbk; FHA; Vo Tech; Secretary.

BREHMER, Danny W; Litchfield Sr HS; Litchfield, MN; 5/182 PresSrCls; ALBoysSt; Band; CncrtBnd; HonRl; JrNHS; MrchBnd; NHS; PepBnd; Ftbl; Trk; LetterWrstlng; IMSpt;.

BREHMER, Kenneth A; Wausau East HS; Wausau, WI; 29/354 NHS; MthCl; Univ Of Wisconsin; Physical Engineer.

BREHMER, William G; Hoven HS; Hoven, SD; PresFrshCls; Band; Chr; Chrs; CncrtBnd; Mdrgl; MrchBnd; PepBnd; StuCncl; FFA; LetterBsktbl; Ftbl; College; Vocation.

BREID, Cynthia K; Logan Rogersville HS; Rogersville, MO; LbryAde; SchPl; StuCncl; TchrAde; 4-H; FrCl; PpCl; PPFtbl; DARAwd; 4-HAwd; College; Professional.

BREIDEL, Gary L; La Farge HS; La Farge, WI; CmntyWkr; HonRl; FFA; LetterBsbl; LetterBsktbl; LetterFtbl; Navy; Career Navy.

BREILAND, Keith; Lincoln Senior HS; Thief River Falls, MN; 36/254 HonRl; NHS; Coll; Dr Of Osteopathy.

BREIMEIER, Curtis L; New Salem HS; Hannover, ND; 3/50 VPSophCls; Chrs; HonRl; NatlMeritSchl; SchPl; StuCncl; FFA; MthCl; SciCl; College.

BREINIG, Dennis J; Acapahoe HS; Arapahoe, NE; 12/32 Chrs; SchPl; StuCncl; 4-H; Bsktbl; Ftbl; Trk; 4-HAwd; Trade School; Vocation.

BREINMER, Randolph H; Herbert Henry Dow HS; Midland, MI; Chr; HonRl; NHS; StuCncl; Bsktbl; Ftbl; Calvin College; Business Admin.

BREISTER, Susan M; Southwest HS; Green Bay, WI; 51/420 HonRl; SchMus; PpCl; LetterTrk; SecGAA; College; Science.

BREIT, Daniel L; Kapaum Mt Carmel HS; Wichita, KS; HonRl; JrNHS; NHS; PolWkr; SchPl; StuCncl; YthFlsp; SpnCl; Ftbl; IMSpt; JAAwd; College; Major Study.

BREITENFELDT, Bonita J; Giltner Public HS; Giltner, NE; Band; Chrs; ChrhWkr; CncrtBnd; HonRl; MrchBnd; PepBnd; Yrbk; PpCl; LetterTrk; College.

BREITENFELDT, Karen; Tigerton Hs; Tigerton, WI; 1/53 VPJrCls; Band; CncrtBnd; HonRl; LitMag; MrchBnd; NatlFornLg; NHS; PepBnd; SchPpr; Vocational School; Accounting.

BREITENSTEIN, Colleen C; St Charles HS; St Charles, MO; 29/540 Band; HonRl; Kansas Univ; Architecture.

BREITLING, Robert J; Mascoutah HS; Mascoutah, IL; 30/261 HonRl; College; Computer Science.

BREITUNG, Terry L; Cochrane Fountain City HS; Fountain City, WI; VPJrCls; StuCncl; LetterBsktbl; LetterFtbl; LetterTrk; College; Physical Ed.

BREITWEISER, Karen J; Homestead HS; Mequon, WI; 48/402 Band; HonRl; JrNHS; NHS; Univ Of Wisconsin; Veterinarian.

BREITWIESER, Danilee; Mt Vernon Sr HS; Mt Vernon, IN; 23;224 AFS; HospAde; NHS; SchMus; LatCl; Indiana University;medical Technology.

BREKKE, Kevin A; Rosholt HS; Rosholt, WI; 17/58 Band; ChrhWkr; CmntyWkr; CncrtBnd; HonRl; MrchBnd; PepBnd; SchMus; SchPl; SchPpr; Tech Sch; Computer Prog.

BREKKEN, Christine J; Mt St Benedict HS; Crookston, MN; PresFrshCls; PresSophCls; Chrs; ChrhWkr; SchMus; SchPl; StuCncl; 4-H; PpCl; Chrldr; St Catherines Clg; Professional.

BRELIE, Galen D; Sacred Heart Public HS; Sacred Heart, MN; 3/33 TrsFrshCls; Band; ChrhWkr; CncrtBnd; HonRl; MrchBnd; NatlMeritSchl; PepBnd; SchAde; SchMus; Univ Of Mn; Veterinarian.

BRELJE, Lori; Lutheran HS; Glencoe, MN; Band; Chr; HonRl; OffAde; SchPl; TchrAde; SchPpr; FTA; Concordia Teachers Coll; Communications.

BREMANIS, Astra; Battle Creek Central HS; Battle Creek, MI; 1/505 ChrhWkr; HonRl; NatlFornLg; NHS; RedCrAde; RptrYrbk; RptrSchPpr; OptClAwd; College; Law.

BREMANIS, Dace; Battle Creek Central HS; Battle Creek, MI; 5/505 ChrhWkr; HonRl; NatlFornLg; NHS; RedCrAde; RptrYrbk; RptrSchPpr; College; Law.

BREMER, Barbara J; La Ville HS; Bremen, IN; VPSophCls; VPJrCls; VPSpnCl; College; Special Educ.

BREMER, Jill A; Abbotsford HS; Abbotsford, WI; 4/70 AFS; Band; Chrs; ChrhWkr; CncrtBnd; HonRl; HonRl; Mdrgl; MrchBnd; NHS; EldAwd; Bellin Memorial Hosp Sch Of Nursing; Nurse.

BREMER, Marilyn L; Fingal Public HS; Fingal, ND; 2/21 SecSophCls; HonRl; SchPl; RptrSchPpr; LetterBsktbl; Nd State U; Professional.

BREMER, Renee E; Reese HS; Reese, MI; 15/127 CncrtBnd; HonRl; MrchBnd; NHS; SchAde; SchPl; MthCl; PpCl; Bsbl; Glf; Central Mi Univ; Math Teacher.

BREMMER, Martin L; Lockport Central HS; Lockport, IL; CncrtBnd; HonRl; MrchBnd; Lewis Univ; Chemistry.

BREMS, Laura A; Marian HS; Birmingham, MI; HonRl; HospAde; ModUN; NHS; StuGov; TchrAde; FTA; LetterSwmmng; St Marys Coll; Dr Or Nurse.

BREMS, Thomas J; Regis HS; Cedar Rapids, IA; SctActv; LetterBsbl; LetterFtbl; Wrstlng; IMSpt; Loras College; Accounting.

BREMSETH, Dawn L; High School; Rushford, MN; PresBand; Chrs; CncrtBnd; HonRl; MrchBnd; NHS; PepBnd; EdYrBk; SchPpr; 4-H; College Or Univ; Medical Health Field.

BREND, Jeffrey; Willowbrook Hs; Lombard, IL; HonRl; ModUN; SctActv; SchPpr; LetterFtbl; LetterTennis; Northern Illinois Univ; Accountant & Lawyer.

BRENDE, Timothy A; So Sioux HS; S Sioux City, NE; 10/200 HonRl; JA; JrNHS; MthCl; Bsktbl; Glf; College.

BRENDEMUEHL, Carol J; Oconomowoc Sr HS; Oconomowoc, WI; 15/223 TrsFrshCls; HonRl; NHS; StuCncl; TchrAde; SchPpr; FrCl; PpCl; College; Education.

BRENDEN, Jan R; Rothsay HS; Rothsay, MN; VPSrCls; Band; Chrs; ChrhWkr; CncrtBnd; HonRl; MrchBnd; NHS; PepBnd; SchMus; College; Teaching.

BRENDLEY, Keith W; Clinton Community HS; Clinton, IL; 13/180 Band; CncrtBnd; HonRl; MrchBnd; SchMus; SchPl; Ftbl; Glf; Wrstlng; IMSpt; College; Professional.

BRENNAN, Cheryl A; St Agnes Academy; Ellsworth, NE; TrsJrCls; Chr; HonRl; StuGov; 4-H; FSA; PpCl; LetterTrk; GAA; IMSpt; 4-HAwd; University Of Nebraska; Vocation.

BRENNAN, Dennis P; Benton Central Jr Sr HS; Fowler, IN; PresJrCls; HonRl; NatlThespSoc; SchPl; SctActv; StuCncl; SchPpr; Rose Hulman Institute Of Tech; Elect Eng.

BRENNAN, Diane; St Mary Acad; Monroe, MI; 20/139 CmntyWkr; HonRl; NHS; TchrAde; RptrSchPpr; Eastern Michigan Univ; Education.

BRENNAN, Diane M; Bryan HS; Omaha, NE; Chr; Chrs; ChrhWkr; DrlTm; HonRl; NHS; SchMus; PpCl; Trk; Clarkson Nursing School; Nurse.

BRENNAN, Gina R; St Bede Academy; Ladd, IL; 1/125 Chrs; HonRl; SchMus; SchPl; FrCl; Chrldr; GAA; Notre Dame; Psychology.

BRENNAN, Glenn A; Morton Sr HS; Hammond, IN; Chr; Chrs; StuGov; LetterBsbl; Bsktbl; LetterFtbl; Trk; College.

BRENNAN, John P; Wheeling HS; Buffalo Grove, IL; 29/449 ChrhWkr; HonRl; NHS; StuCncl; LetterFtbl; CaptTennis; Univ Of Notre Dame; Accountant.

BRENNAN, Kathleen A; Sacred Heart HS; Dearborn, MI; CmntyWkr; HonRl; HospAde; JA; LetterTrk; Clge; Tech Studies.

BRENNAN, Mark E; Columbia City Joint HS; Columbia City, IN; HonRl; ModUN; NatlFornLg; NatlMeritSF; NatlThespSoc; SchMus; SchPl; PresStuCncl; StuGov; SpnCl; Tennis; IMSpt; NCTE; OptClAwd;.

BRENNAN, Martin J; St Louis Univ HS; St Louis, MO; Band; ChrhWkr; OffAde; PolWkr; StuGov; RptrSchPpr; Ftbl; IMSpt; PresAwd; CitAwd; Business School; Prof Bus Admin.

BRENNAN, Mary F; Our Lady Of Mercy HS; Farmington Hills, MI; 18/283 Band; ModUN; NatlFornLg; NHS; NatlMeritFnl; NatlMeritSF; SchMus; SctActv; RptrYrbk; GerCl; Mi State U; Lingistics.

BRENNAN, Mary G; St John The Baptist HS; St Louis, MO; SecFrshCls; VPSophCls; PresJrCls; SecSrCls; Chrs; HonRl; NHS; SchMus; StuCncl; RptrYrbk; College.

BRENNAN, Mary J; Mason County Central HS; Ludington, MI; 23/131 Band; CncrtBnd; HonRl; PepBnd; TchrAde; 4-H; 4-HAwd; Westshore Comm Coll; Teaching.

BRENNAN, Mary K; James Whitcomb Riley HS; South Bend, IN; 8/260 SecSrCls; HonRl; NHS; RptrYrbk; Trk; GAA; 4-HAwd; Ball State Univ; Architecture.

BRENNAN, Michael A; St Patrick HS; Chicago, IL; 48/427 Chrs; HonRl; JrNHS; NHS; PolWkr; Quill&Scroll; StuCncl; RptrSchPpr; EdSchPpr; FTA; U Of San Diego; Teacher.

BRENNAN, Michael W; Campion Jesuit HS; Alsip, IL; 5/98 CmntyWkr; HonRl; LitMag; PolWkr; SchMus; StuGov; RptrSchPpr; LetterTennis; John Hopkins; Doctor.

BRENNAN, Sheila M; Lane Tech HS; Chicago, IL; PolWkr; SchAde; SchPl; VPStuCncl; StuGov; RptrYrbk; EdSchPpr; RusCl; JAAwd; University; Law.

BRENNAN, Terence P; Beloit Catholic HS; Beloit, WI; 4/90 Aud/Vis; HonRl; NHS; PresStuCncl; YthLg; CaptBsktbl; Socr; LetterTennis; Uw;law.

BRENNAN, Terri A; Cary Grove HS; Cary, IL; Chrs; HonRl; NHS; RptrYrbk; Illinois State University; Biology.

BRENNAN, Veronica R; Naperville Central HS; Naperville, IL; 23/844 Chr; Chrl; Chrs; HonRl; Mdrgl; NHS; SchMus; Yrbk; SchPpr; Univ Of Ill; Translator.

BRENNEKE, Mary C; Jefferson City Sr HS; Jefferson City, MO; 11/502 HonRl; JrNHS; NHS; 4-H; TreasFBLA;.

BRENNEMAN, John T; Warsaw Comm HS; Winona Lake, IN; OffAde; LetterFtbl; LetterTrk; Wrstlng; Ball State Univ; Architecht.

BRENNEMAN, Steven T; Delavan HS; Delavan, IL; 6/66 VPFrshCls; TrsJrCls; PresSrCls; ChrhWkr; HonRl; NHS; StuCncl; YthFlsp; Bsktbl; Univ Of Missouri; Engineering.

BRENNER, Barbara K; Marine City HS; Marine City, MI; 1/16 PresBand; PresChr; ChrhWkr; CncrtBnd; HonRl; MrchBnd; NHS; SchPl; TchrAde; EdYrBk; College; Music Ed/music Ther.

BRENNER, Barbara L; Michigan Lutheran Seminary; Bay City, MI; 9/81 Chr; Chrs; HonRl; Mdrgl; SchMus; RptrSchPpr; PpCl; Trk; IMSpt; Dr Martin Luther Coll; English.

BRENNER, Faye M; Durand Unified HS; Durand, WI; Chr; ChrhWkr; HonRl; VPNatlFornLg; NHS; Sacrstn; SchAde; PresSdlty; SchPpr; Pres4-H; GerCl; PpCl; Chrldr; Eau Claire Voc Tech Schl; Medical Clerical.

BRENNER, Joseph K; New Trier West HS; Wilmette, IL; 19/694 HonRl; NatlMeritFnl; NatlMeritSF; TchrAde; LetterBsbl; LetterBsktbl; IMSpt; Univ; Prof Pre Law.

BRENNER, Loretta K; Lake Mich Catholic HS; Benton Harbor, MI; 18/109 CmntyWkr; ModUN; NatlThespSoc; SchPl; Mich State Univ; Natural Resources.

BRENNER, Neal J; Highland HS; Lewistown, MO; 3/120 VPJrCls; HonRl; LbryAde; NHS; StuCncl; Yrbk; SchPpr; FSA; SciCl; Northeast Mo St; Enviromental Research.

BRENON, Connie S; North County R I HS; Bonne Terre, MO; 9/170 PresJrCls; CncrtBnd; DrlTm; HonRl; JrNHS; SecNHS; VPFHA; Trk; CaptChrldr; PPFtbl; 4-HAwd; PresAwd; College; Home Economics.

BRENT, George M; Heyworth HS; Heyworth, IL; 3/52 TrsFrshCls; Chrs; HonRl; NHS; SchMus; StuCncl; 4-H; LetterBsbl; LetterFtbl; Trk; Il State U; Civil Engineer.

BRENTON, Wyndy G; Hersey HS; Wheeling, IL; 41/731 Chr; Chrs; HonRl; JrNHS; NHS; SchMus; Harper Jr College; Nursing.

BRENZA, Dawn M; Maria HS; Chicago, IL; 21/301 Aud/Vis; Chrs; HonRl; NHS; NatlThespSoc; SecSdlty; Teen; Univ Of Illinois; Medical Tech.

BRESETTE, Carl M; Bayfield HS; Bayfield, WI; Band; RptrYrbk; 4-H; Bsbl; Bsktbl; Trk; Air Force.

BRESETTE, Edward A; Papillion HS; La Vista, NE; 72/342 Aud/Vis; TchrAde; Univ; Professnl.

BRESINA, Lynn M; St Croix HS; Solon Springs, WI; TrsJrCls; Band; Chrs; CncrtBnd; HonRl; NatlFornLg; SchPl; SchPpr; LetterBsbl; LetterBsktbl; College; Commercial Art.

BRESLIN, Debra; Dansville Agricultural HS; Dansville, MI; 14/74 SecSrCls; Chrs; HonRl; LbryAde; NHS; TchrAde; FHA; Eastern Mich Univ; Bs In Nursing.

BRESNAHAN, Katherine J; Central Cass HS; Casselton, ND; HonRl; NHS; SchPl; StuCncl; LetterBsktbl; LetterTrk; Chrldr; GAA; College.

BRESNAN, Marcia A; Moweagua HS; Moweagua, IL; SecTrsSrCls; Band; CncrtBnd; HonRl; NHS; PepBnd; SchMus; FHA; LetterTennis; GAA; Il State U; Accounting.

BRESNIK, Patti Jo; Chisholm Sr HS; Chisholm, MN; 30/136 HonRl; HospAde; LbryAde; OffAde; Orch; PepBnd; FNA; LetterTrk; GAA; IMSpt; Coll; Nursing.

BRESTER, Ann M; Howells Public HS; Howells, NE; 13/44 SchPl; StuGov; TchrAde; PpCl; Bus Schl; Accounting.

BRETT, James A; Marist HS; Chicago, IL; 16/374 HonRl; JA; NatlMeritSF; PolWkr; YthLg; SchPpr; IMSpt; Univ; English.

BRETTHAUER, Julie A; Plano HS; Plano, IL; 11/108 VPJrCls; Band; HonRl; JrNHS; MrchBnd; NHS; StuCncl; RptrYrbk; College; Teaching Business Courses.

BRETZ, Michelle D; Morris Sr HS; Morris, MN; PresFrshCls; HonRl; NHS; SchPl; TchrAde; RptrSchPpr; FHA; PpCl; Chrldr; College; Professional.

BREU, Susan M; Marshfield HS; Marshfield, WI; 47/363 Chrs; HonRl; HospAde; NatlFornLg; NHS; StuCncl; TchrAde; GerCl; PpCl; RotaryAwd; U Of Wis Eau Claire; Nursing.

BREUCKMAN, Tad M; St Marys HS; Burlington, WI; NHS; NatlMeritFnl; NatlMeritCmnd; NatlMeritSchl; NatlMeritSF; SctActv; LetterTrk; IMSpt; BttyCrckrAwd; KiwanAwd; Marquette Univ; Bio Physics.

BREUER, Martha J; Notre Dame HS; Burlington, IA; 6/75 ALAGirlsSt; HonRl; NHS; Yrbk; 4-H; PpCl; Trk; Chrldr; Jr College; Vocational.

BREUER, Monica J; Slinger HS; Allenton, WI; ALAGirlsSt; Band; Chrs; CncrtBnd; MrchBnd; OffAde; PepBnd; RptrYrbk; FBLA; FHA; Technical School.

BREUER, Patricia L; Wyndmere Public HS; Wundmere, ND; Chr; HonRl; LbryAde; NHS; TchrAde; RptrSchPpr; FHA; Ndsss; Dental Assisting.

BREUER, Theresa L; Sheldon Community HS; Sheldon, IA; SecJrCls; Chr; HonRl;.

BREUNIG, Carla J; Sandwich Comm HS; Sandwich, IL; 1/139 SecAFS; Chr; ChrhWkr; HonRl; NHS; SchPl; StuCncl; YthFlsp; EdYrBk; GerCl; LatCl; Chrldr; GAA; College; Russian Interpreter.

BREUNIG, Karen M; 9th Street HS; Sauk City, WI; 2/223 HonRl; NHS; SchPpr; FrCl; MthCl; PpCl; Univ Of Wis Baraboo; Business Major.

BREWCZAK, Susan C; Mt Clemens HS; Mt Clemens, MI; VPSophCls; TrsJrCls; Chr; HonRl; NHS; RedCrAde; SchMus; FrCl; Chrldr; GAA; IMSpt; PresAwd; Mi State U; Spec Ed.

BREWED, D S; Richland Center HS; Bloom City, WI; HonRl; LitMag; ModUN; 4-H; FFA; LatCl; SpnCl; Trk; IMSpt; 4-HAwd; Uw River Falls; Pre Vet.

BREWER, Brett L; C Cr 1 HS; Kahoka, MO; 16/91 PresFrshCls; HonRl; NHS; LetterBsktbl; CaptFtbl; Glf; Trk; College; Major In Business.

BREWER, Delora K; Melvern HS; Melvern, KS; 4/24 SecFrshCls; SecSophCls; Band; HonRl; MrchBnd; PepBnd; SchAde; PpCl; Bsbl; LetterBsktbl; College; Special Education.

BREWER, Denise M; Richland Center HS; Richland Center, WI; DrmBgl; SctActv; TchrAde; RptrYrbk; RptrSchPpr; 4-H; Trk; Chrldr; PresGAA; IMSpt; U W At Madison; Medical Technologist.

BREWER, Diane S; Richland Center HS; Bloom City, WI; HonRl; LitMag; ModUN; 4-H; FFA; LatCl; Trk; IMSpt; 4-HAwd; Uw River Falls; Pre Vet.

BREWER, D S; Richland Center HS; Bloom City, WI; HonRl; LitMag; ModUN; 4-H; LatCl; SpnCl; Trk; IMSpt; 4-HAwd; U W River Falls; Pre Vet.

BREWER, Gregory M; Naperville Central HS; Naperville, IL; CmntyWkr; HonRl; IntrClCncl; NatlMeritFnl; NatlMeritSF; StuCncl; PresStuGov; Illinois Inst Of Tech; Architect.

BREWER, Jane; Notre Dame HS; Cape Girardeau, MO; 2/79 CncrtBnd; HonRl; MrchBnd; NHS; PepBnd; EdSchPpr; FBLA; PpCl; RotaryAwd; Transcriptimist.

BREWER, Jennifer A; Mona Shores HS; Muskegon, MI; HonRl; NHS; NatlMeritSF; Muskegon Comm College; Accounting.

BREWER, John M; Maplewood Richmond Hts HS; Maplewood, MO; ALBoysSt; HonRl; GerCl; Bsktbl; AmLegAwd; Washington U.

BREWER, John R; North Clay Comm HS; Edgewood, IL; HonRl; LbryAde; PresFFA;.

BREWER, Joyce E; Bethany HS; Moweaqua, IL; 6/31 SecFrshCls; SecSophCls; SecJrCls; SecSrCls; Band; Chrs; ChrhWkr; CncrtBnd; HonRl; MrchBnd; NHS; Chrldr; 4-HAwd; College; Special Educ.

BREWER, Molana; Platteville 'S; Platteville, WI; AFS; Aud/Vis; Chr; LitMag; NatlFornLg; SchPl; SctActv; TchrAde; RptrSchPpr; EngCl; Uw Platteville; Secondary Teacher.

BREWER, Pamela L; Blue Valley HS; Stanley, KS; Band; CncrtBnd; HonRl; OffAde; PepBnd; TchrAde; RptrSchPpr; LetterBsktbl; GAA; Kansas City Vo Tech; Computers.

BREWER, Rita K; St Anns HS; Lexington, NE; TrsFrshCls; PresSophCls; VPJrCls; Chrs; HonRl; NHS; SchMus; SchPl; Yrbk; RptrSchPpr; PpCl; Kearney State; Social Work.

BREWER, Scot E; Tuscola HS; Tuscola, IL; 22/130 VPSophCls; Aud/Vis; SchPl; StuCncl; FrCl; SciCl; LetterTrk; GovHonPrgAwd; East Ill Univ; Dentistry.

BREWER, Shannon; Peoria Heights HS; Peoria Heights, IL; 8 Band; Chrs; ChrhWkr; CncrtBnd; HonRl; MrchBnd; NatlThespSoc; SchPl; StuCncl; LetterWrstlng; College Or Univ; Teaching Music.

BREWER, Vicki L; Gladwin HS; Gladwin, MI; 21/150 Chrs; ChrhWkr; HonRl; LbryAde; YthFlsp; PpCl; Bsbl; Missionary Work.

BREWER, Wes; Memorial HS; Joplin, MO; HonRl; LatCl; LetterBsktbl; LetterFtbl; LetterTrk; Technical School; Mechanic.

BREWNER, Sherri D; Carlyle HS; Shattuc, IL; HospAde; JA; SchPpr; PpCl; GAA; JAAwd; College; Certified Accountant.

BREWNER, Todd W; J B Conant HS; Hoffman Ests, IL; 22/629 HonRl; NHS; TchrAde; SciCl; Glf; U S M A; Nuclear Physics.

BREWSTER, Bethany; Blue Valley HS; Stilwell, KS; PresSrCls; HonRl; NatlCathMusEdAsoc; NHS; OffAde; TchrAde; RptrYrbk; Yrbk; PpCl; Chrldr; Univ; Speech.

BREWSTER, Bradley W; Sanborn Public HS; Sanborn, MN; Chr; HonRl; StuCncl; StuGov; FFA; Bsktbl; Ftbl; Trk; College.

BREWSTER, Pat E; Silver Lake HS; Silver Lake, KS; StuCncl; SptEdYrbk; Bsbl; Bsktbl; College.

BREY, Ann M; Saint Agatha HS; Detroit, MI; Chr; Chrs; ChrhWkr; HonRl; NHS; JETSAwd; U Of Michigan.

BREY, Carol A; Lanphier HS; Springfield, IL; 10/473 AFS; ChrhWkr; CncrtBnd; HonRl; JA; MrchBnd; NHS; Orch; StuCncl; SpnCl; Univ; Library Science.

BREY, Thomas E; Assumption HS; Wisconsin Rapids, WI; 20/120 PresSrCls; HonRl; NHS; StuCncl; TrsSophCls; CaptFtbl; LetterTrk; Univ; Economics.

BREYNE, Matthew M; Joliet Catholic HS; Romeoville, IL; 46/170 Band; ChrhWkr; CmntyWkr; HonRl; NHS; PolWkr; TchrAde; RptrYrbk; RptrSchPpr; RusCl; Ftbl; Tennis; Univ Of Ill; English Education.

BRICKEL, Diane L; Buena Vista HS; Saginaw, MI; HonRl; OffAde; SchPl; PpCl; VPSciCl;.

BRICKER, Elizabeth; Richmond HS; Richmond, IN; 43/700 Chr; ChrhWkr; HonRl; JrNHS; NHS; Orch; SchMus; YthFlsp; RptrYrbk; RptrSchPpr; College; Music Or Journalism.

BRICKLER, Mary E; S Milwaukee HS; South Milwaukee, WI; 10/432 HonRl; Univ; Pharmacist.

BRICKNER, Joetta J; Garrison HS; Douglas, ND; 26/58 Chrs; ChrhWkr; HonRl; LbryAde; RptrYrbk; RptrSchPpr; 4-H; PpCl; LetterBsktbl; 4-HAwd; U Of Nd Williston; Nursing.

BRICKNER, Timothy; Oregon Senior HS; Brooklyn, WI; 6/192 HonRl; NHS; StuCncl; EdYrBk; EdSchPpr; MthCl; Univ Wi Madison; Journalism.

BRIDE, Karen J; Pomeroy HS; Manson, IA; HonRl; MrchBnd; NHS; Twrl; RptrYrbk; RptrSchPpr; FHA; PpCl; Glf; DARAwd; College; Home Ec.

BRIDENSTINE, Colleen H; St Charles HS; St Charles, IL; Chr; Chrl; ChrhWkr; HonRl; MrchBnd; NatlMeritCmnd; College; Dental Hygiene.

BRIDESON, Marcia; Dallas Community HS; Dallas Center, IA; Chr; Chrs; ChrhWkr; DrlTm; HonRl; SchMus; YthFlsp; RptrSchPpr; PpCl; Bsktbl; College; Secretarial.

BRIDGE, Deborah L; Faulkton HS; Faulkton, SD; PresFrshCls; ALAGirlsSt; ChrhWkr; CncrtBnd; HonRl; PolWkr; StuCncl; RptrYrbk; LetterBsktbl; Chrldr; Univ; Pro.

BRIDGE, Janey A; Norfolk SeniorHS; Norfolk, NE; ChrhWkr; DrlTm; HonRl; HospAde; SchPl; FrCl; PpCl; LetterGlf; Chrldr; PPFtbl; College; Vetinary Asst.

BRIDGE, Jeanine L; Hononegah HS; Roscoe, IL; 21/199 HonRl; Bsktbl; Trk; GAA; Augustana Clge; Psychology.

BRIDGE, Jody L; Neligh Public HS; Neligh, NE; Aud/Vis; ChrhWkr; CmntyWkr; HonRl; NHS; 4-H; PpCl; LetterTrk; 4-HAwd; Norfolk Tech College; Nurse.

BRIDGE, Loretta S; Frontier HS; Monticello, IN; 8/71 VPFrshCls; TrsSophCls; Chr; HonRl; NHS; OffAde; SchPl; YthFlsp; 4-H; SpnCl; College; Commercial Art.

BRIDGES, Alan J; Annawan HS; Annawan, IL; 2/51 Chr; ChrhWkr; HonRl; Mdrgl; PresNHS; PresYthFlsp; SptEdYrbk; Bsktbl; Ftbl; Trk; Univ; Prof.

BRIDGES, Alice M; Southwest HS; St Louis, MO; OffAde; PolWkr; StuCncl; StuGov; RptrSchPpr; SchPpr; PpCl; GAA; PPFtbl; Univ Of Southern Calif; Psychologist.

BRIDGES, Catherine J; Broken Bow HS; Broken Bow, NE; ChrhWkr; HonRl; OffAde; YthFlsp; FBLA; PresFrshCls; 4-H; FHA; SpnCl; PpCl; Swmmng; Tennis; IMSpt; PresAwd; University.

BRIDGES, Cindy E; Windsor HS; Windsor, IL; 6/60 VPSrCls; Band; Chr; Chrs; ChrhWkr; CncrtBnd; HonRl; MrchBnd; NHS; NatlThespSoc; SchPl; LetterTrk; GAA; College; Music.

BRIDGES, Debra J; Hammond Baptist HS; Flossmoor, IL; Chr; Chrs; ChrhWkr; HonRl; SchAde; SchPl; StuCncl; Yrbk; CivCl; PpCl; CaptChrldr; Hyles Anderson College; Nursing.

BRIDGES, Donna S; Woodland R 4 HS; Lutesville, MO; 1/61 VPFrshCls; TrsSophCls; VPJrCls; PresBand; CncrtBnd; HonRl; MrchBnd; PepBnd; StuCncl; EdYrBk; IMSpt; DARAwd; RotaryAwd; CitAwd; Semd Univ; Music.

BRIDGES, Gladys L; Egyptian HS; Elco, IL; 3/67 Chrs; HonRl; NatlMeritSchl; RptrYrbk; PpCl; Shawnee College; Conservation.

BRIDGES, Gloria; Soldan HS; St Louis, MO; 12/635 ChrhWkr; CmntyWkr; HonRl; JA; NatlMeritSF; SchAde; StuCncl; StuGov; PpCl; Trk; Nursing School; Rn.

BRIDGES, Josephine; Soldan HS; St Louis, MO; Chr; ChrhWkr; HonRl; JA; StuCncl; Trk; Coll; Major Study.

BRIDGES, Joyce; Bishop Hogan HS; Kansas City, MO; 41/169 Chr; HonRl; JA; FBLA; FrCl; PpCl; GAA; IMSpt; JAAwd; College; Business Admin.

BRIDGES, Larry W; Harrisonville Sr HS; Harrisonville, MO; Band; Chrs; CncrtBnd; HonRl; NatlFornLg; Quill&Scroll; SchMus; SchPl; RptrSchPpr; SciCl; College; Professional.

BRIDGES, Lenderrick; Southeastern HS; Detroit, MI; 33/210 HstSrCls; Aud/Vis; Chr; HonRl; LbryAde; NatlFornLg; SchAde; SchPl; Tennis; CitAwd; E Mi Univ; Psychology.

BRIDGES, Stephen J; Coldwater HS; Coldwater, MI; 1/280 HonRl; NHS; GerCl; LetterTennis; IMSpt; DARAwd; KiwanAwd; Massachusetts Inst Of Tech; Engineer.

BRIDGES, Teresa P; Henryville Cons Jr Sr HS; Henryville, IN; 1/55 SecFrshCls; PresSophCls; PresJrCls; TrsSrCls; ALAGirlsSt; VPBand; VPChrs; CncrtBnd; HonRl; MrchBnd; SecNHS; IMSpt; AmLegAwd; BttyCrckrAwd; College; Doctor.

BRIDGFORD, Candy E; Hamburg Comm HS; Hamburg, IA; Chrs; DrmMjrt; MrchBnd; SctActv; Twrl; RptrYrbk; RptrSchPpr; SchPpr; PpCl; Chrldr; Iowa State U; Elementary Education.

BRIDGMAN, Jeanne; Coloma HS; Coloma, MI; Chr; ChrhWkr; CmntyWkr; HonRl; HospAde; SchMus; SchPl; TchrAde; SchPpr; FTA; Grand Valley College; Law Enforcement.

BRIDSON, Theresa L; Keith Country Day HS; Belvidere, IL; Chr; HonRl; SchPl; StuGov; TchrAde; RptrYrbk; PpCl; Glf; Swmmng; Chrldr; University; Veterinarian.

BRIEF, Geraldine; High School; Chicago, IL; Chrs; HonRl; HospAde; LbryAde; NHS; OffAde; SchPl; RptrYrbk; RptrSchPpr; FTA; Univ Of Ill; Occupational Therapist.

BRIEL, Bonnie L; West HS; Green Bay, WI; Aud/Vis; Chr; ChrhWkr; CmntyWkr; HonRl; College; Pharmacy.

BRIER, James W; Cardinal Ritter HS; Indianapolis, IN; HonRl; KeyCl; FrCl; LetterBsbl; LetterBsktbl; CaptFtbl; Wrstlng; IMSpt; Us Air Force Acad; Military Pilot.

BRIER, Linda A; Union County HS; Liberty, IN; ChrhWkr; CncrtBnd; HonRl; NHS; Orch; PresYthFlsp; Pres4-H; SpnCl; 4-HAwd; MasAwd; Health.

BRIERLEY, Heather C; Oak Park River Forest HS; Oak Park, IL; 110/1012 SecFrshCls; Chrs; ChrhWkr; CmntyWkr; Purdue Univ; Special Ed.

BRIETZMAN, Suanne J; Stoughton HS; Stoughton, WI; 2/228 Band; HonRl; JrNHS; NHS; GerCl; GAA; PPFtbl; Madison Bus Clge; Med Sec.

BRIGEL, Barbara K; Mount Assisi Academy; Chicago, IL; HonRl; ModUN; Business School; Accountant.

BRIGGIN, Leigh C; Horton Watkins HS; Creve Coeur, MO; 65/434 Univ Of Mo; Accounting.

BRIGGS, Abraham; St Ignatius College Prep; Chicago, IL; 71/200 CmntyWkr; NHS; PolWkr; CivCl; 4-H; LetterBsktbl; IMSpt; 4-HAwd; JETSAwd; Univ Of Illinois; Engineering.

BRIGGS, Debra R; Brown Cnty HS; Mt Sterling, IL; PresSrCls; ChrhWkr; HonRl; NHS; SchPl; YthFlsp; FTA; LetterBsbl; LetterBsktbl; LetterTrk; Chrldr; GAA; Western Illinois Univ; Accounting.

BRIGGS, Hazen S; Oakland Christian HS; Pontiac, MI; 1/20 Band; Chr; ChrhWkr; CncrtBnd; HonRl; LbryAde; MrchBnd; PepBnd; College; Minister.

BRIGGS, Janice R; Constantine HS; Constantine, MI; 6/106 Band; CncrtBnd; HonRl; MrchBnd; NHS; PepBnd; PolWkr; FrCl; PpCl; College; Political Science.

BRIGGS, Kristi F; Pardeeville HS; Pardeeville, WI; Band; CncrtBnd; HonRl; LbryAde; MrchBnd; SchMus; SchPl; TchrAde; Chrldr; Service; Truck Driver.

BRIGGS, Loretta A; North Maimi HS; Macy, IN; 9/125 Band; Chr; NHS; OffAde; PresStuCncl; TreasYthFlsp; RptrYrbk; SpnCl; SciCl; Trk; Univ; Music & Science.

BRIGGS, Mikel S; Naperville Central HS; Naperville, IL; 92/864 CaptBsbl; CaptFtbl; Millikin University.

BRIGGS, Pamela J; Virginia HS; Virginia, IL; ChrhWkr; HonRl; StuCncl; RptrSchPpr; FHA;

PpCl; Bsbl; Ftbl; GAA; IMSpt; Bus Sch; Legal Secretary.

BRIGGS, Tracy G; Bucklin Rii HS; Bucklin, MO; ALBoysSt; ChrhWkr; MrchBnd; SchPl; StuCncl; RptrYrbk; 4-H; SciCl; Northeast Missouri University; Business.

BRIGHAM, Pamela S; Shelby Public HS; Shelby, NE; 1/21 VPSophCls; VPJrCls; ALAGirlsSt; PresBand; Chrs; ChrhWkr; CncrtBnd; HonRl; MrchBnd; Orch; PepBnd; CaptChrldr; CitAwd; Univ Of Nebr.

BRIGHAM, Patricia J; Centennial HS; Utica, NE; 4/58 Band; Chrs; ChrhWkr; HonRl; NHS; YthFlsp; FHA; Bsktbl; LetterTrk; BttyCrckrAwd; Wesleyan U; Respiratory Therapy.

BRIGHT, Debra L; Fairmount Public HS; Fairmont, NE; 4/25 SecTrsSophCls; Chr; ChrhWkr; HonRl; LbryAde; NHS; SchAde; PpCl; LetterTrk; CitAwd; College.

BRIGHT, Julie R; Sully Buttes HS; Onida, SD; 3/59 ALAGirlsSt; NHS; Quill&Scroll; TchrAde; EdYrBk; EdSchPpr; Bsktbl; CaptTrk; CchngActv; IMSpt;.

BRIGHT, Lois A; O Neill Public HS; O Neill, NE; SecJrCls; Band; CncrtBnd; HonRl; MrchBnd; NHS; PepBnd; RptrYrbk; 4-H; PpCl; LetterBsktbl; LetterTrk; IMSpt; College; Accounting.

BRIGHT, Mimi L; Monrovia HS; Mooresville, IN; 3/128 Band; Chr; ChrhWkr; CncrtBnd; HonRl; MrchBnd; NHS; PepBnd; StuCncl; TchrAde; YthFlsp; Univ; Child Psychology.

BRIGHT, Pamela S; Atwood Hammond HS; Atwood, IL; 8/56 Chrs; HonRl; NHS; PresStuCncl; 4-H; CaptChrldr; GAA; Bradley Univ; Accounting.

BRIGHT, Tamara L; Macon Sr HS; Macon, IL; 21/64 RptrYrbk; FHA; PpCl; GAA; Richland Jr College; Accounting.

BRIGHUM, Debra J; Kimberly HS; Combined Locks, WI; 6/287 Band; Chr; HonRl; JrNHS; NHS; PepBnd; FNA; GovHonPrgAwd; U Wis Oshkosh; Registered Nurse.

BRILES, Cathy E; North Daviess HS; Plainville, IN; 5/113 Chrs; HonRl; OffAde; TchrAde; FHA; PpCl; IMSpt; Business College; Secetary.

BRILL, Janet A; New Holstein Sr HS; Malone, WI; PresSophCls; VPJrCls; PresSrCls; AFS; ChrhWkr; HonRl; NHS; Sdlty; TchrAde; LetterBsktbl; CaptTrk; GAA; IMSpt;.

BRILL, John W; Brandon HS; Ortonville, MI; 39/168 ChrhWkr; HonRl; PolWkr; SchAde; TchrAde; YthFlsp; SptEdYrbk; SptEdSchPpr; CaptFtbl; Wrstlng; Farmer.

BRILL, Josephine L; Mss Academy; Agency, MO; Band; CncrtBnd; HonRl; MrchBnd; PepBnd; SchMus; SchPl; RptrYrbk; 4-H; FrCl; College; Mathematics.

BRILL, Kevin M; Marist HS; Chicago, IL; 7/365 HonRl; NatlFornLg; SchPl; SctActv; LatCl; Ftbl; CchngActv; Loyola Univ; Lawyer.

BRILL, Lori J; Cabool HS; Cabool, MO; Chrl; Chrs; HonRl; Mdrgl; NHS; RptrYrbk; RptrSchPpr; FBLA; PpCl; CaptChrldr; Southwest Mo State Univ; Elem Teaching.

BRILL, Lynda L; U HS; Bloomington, IL; 18/125 TrsSophCls; Chr; Chrs; HonRl; NatlFornLg; NatlThespSoc; SchMus; SchPl; StuCncl; StuGov; Oberlin Col; Psychology, Art, Drama.

BRILL, Peggy S; Manual HS; Peoria, IL; JA; StuCncl; StuGov; UNYO; YthLg; GAA;.

BRILLEY, Donald E; St Teresa HS; Decatur, IL; 15/120 HonRl; NHS; Millikin Univ; Lawyer.

BRILLHART, Cheryl A; E Kentwood HS; Grand Rapids, MI; 27/428 CncrtBnd; HonRl; MrchBnd; NHS; GerCl; Olivet Nazarene Clg.

BRIM, Susan; Wabash HS; Wabash, IN; 15/210 DrlTm; HonRl; MrchBnd; NHS; OffAde; StuCncl; 4-H; FrCl; Tri State College; Accounting.

BRIMEYER, Barb A; Wahlert HS; Dubuque, IA; CmntyWkr; HonRl; LbryAde; PolWkr; StuGov; TchrAde; 4-H; FrCl; IMSpt; College; Business Admin.

BRIMMER, Burnell R; Lindblom HS; Chicago, IL; Chr; CmntyWkr; HonRl; SchAde; TchrAde; GerCl; SciCl; LetterTrk; Bradley Univ; Computer Science.

BRIN, Glen A; Niles North HS; Skokie, IL; Band; CncrtBnd; HonRl; MrchBnd; StuCncl; Socr; CaptWrstlng; IMSpt; Northern Illinois Univ; Business.

BRINCKS, Donna L; Kuemper HS; Carroll, IA; 15/281 Chrs; HonRl; SchMus; SchPl; SpnCl; IMSpt; PPFtbl; GovHonPrgAwd; College; Math Councelling.

BRINDA, John R; Boystown HS; Omaha, NE; 9/50 CmntyWkr; HonRl; JA; NHS; Quill&Scroll; Yrbk; SchPpr; LetterTennis; College; Professional.

BRINDEL, Sari; Marquette Senior HS; Marquette, MI; 64/450 HonRl; HospAde; NatlMeritCmnd; FNA; LatCl; Bsktbl; IMSpt; North Michigan University; X Ray Technican.

BRINEGAR, Lyle E; Moulton Udell Comm HS; Moulton, IA; VPJrCls; HonRl; SchPl; StuCncl; MthCl; College; Vocational.

BRINER, Timothy M; Savannah HS; Savannah, MO; Band; CncrtBnd; HonRl; MrchBnd; PepBnd; LatCl; College; Medicine.

BRING, Elizabeth M; Bancroft HS; Bancroft, NE; 15/32 DrlTm; HonRl; LbryAde; MrchBnd; OffAde; SchPpr; PpCl; Busi Sch; Sec Career.

BRINGGOLD, Rhonda L; Harvey HS; Harvey, ND; ALAGirlsSt; HonRl; HospAde; StuCncl; PpCl; LetterTrk; GAA; College; Science.

BRINGOLD, Michael W; Reese HS; Reese, MI; 6/127 HonRl; LbryAde; ModUN; NHS; NatlMeritCmnd; SchPl; SctActv; Tennis; LetterTrk; IMSpt; Ferris State Clge; Pharmacy.

BRINK, Brenda; Farragut HS; Farragut, IA; 1/44 PresFrshCls; Band; Chr; MrchBnd; NatlMeritCmnd; EdYrBk; BttyCrckrAwd; DARAwd; Ia State Univ; Home Ec Journalist.

BRINK, Catherine T; Notre Dame HS; Quincy, IL; Chrs; SchPl; StuCncl; StuGov; PpCl; Quincy Clge;.

BRINK, Debra L; Benton Harbor HS; Benton Harbor, MI; Band; HonRl; HospAde; JrNHS; LitMag; MrchBnd; ModUN; NHS; YthFlsp; Kalamazoo Coll; Eng.

BRINK, Edward E; Plattsmouth HS; Plattsmouth, NE; 24/163 TrsSophCls; PresJrCls; Band; CncrtBnd; MrchBnd; StuCncl; FrCl; Ftbl; Wrstlng; College; Pre La.

BRINK, Janet L; Dow City Arion Comm HS; Dow City, IA; Chrs; DrlTm; HonRl; SchMus; YthFlsp; RptrSchPpr; VPFrshCls; PpCl; Chrldr; IMSpt; Bus Sch.

BRINK, Lora L; Taylor HS; Kokomo, IN; 7/189 ALAGirlsSt; NHS; StuCncl; TchrAde; PresFrCl; LetterBsktbl; LetterTrk; PresGAA; IMSpt; PPFtbl; College; Guidance Counselor.

BRINK, Mary A; Graceville Public HS; Dumont, MN; Chrs; HonRl; PolWkr; SchMus; CtyCnl; RptrSchPpr; College; Vocal Music.

BRINK, William A; Deer River HS; Deer River, MN; PresSophCls; Band; CncrtBnd; HonRl; MrchBnd; PepBnd; Quill&Scroll; StuCncl; StuGov; SptEdSchPpr; CaptBsktbl; CchngActv; Community College; Agri Business.

BRINKER, Jane M; Washington HS; Washington, MO; 6/346 HonRl; NHS; StuCncl; Yrbk; 4-H; PresFBLA; FHA; PpCl; SciCl; East Central Jr College; Professional Bus.

BRINKER, John P; Axtell HS; Axtell, KS; 3/26 PresFrshCls; Chr; Chrl; Chrs; ChrhWkr; CmntyWkr; HonRl; Bsbl; CaptBsktbl; Ftbl; LetterTrk; AmLegAwd; DARAwd; Emporia Kansas State College; Business.

BRINKLEY, Jerry L; East Richland HS; Olney, IL; 25/253 Band; CncrtBnd; MrchBnd; PepBnd; College; Mathematics.

BRINKLEY, Lyla M; Neodesha HS; Neodesha, KS; 3/56 SecBand; HonRl; RptrYrbk; RptrSchPpr; FHA; PresMthCl; Trk; PPFtbl; CitAwd; Ks St Coll; Math.

BRINKMAN, Kenneth F; York Community HS; Elmhurst, IL; 116/957 HonRl; NHS; NatlMeritCmnd; NatlThespSoc; SchMus; MthCl; College; Architecture.

BRINKMAN, Laurel L; Garner Hayfield Comm HS; Garner, IA; 19/75 Band; Chrs; CncrtBnd; HonRl; MrchBnd; SchPl; YthFlsp; LetterBsbl; LetterFtbl; LetterChrldr; Mankato St Col; Theater Arts.

BRINKMAN, Randy J; Nemaha Valley HS; Cook, NE; TrsFrshCls; Band; Chrs; CncrtBnd; HonRl; MrchBnd; PepBnd; SchPl; CaptFtbl; LetterTrk; Us Army Reserve; Diesel Technician.

BRINKMANN, Gregory; St Joseph Franciscan Seminary; Morton Grove, IL; 3/18 PresJrCls; PresSrCls; Chr; ChrhWkr; HonRl; Sacrstn; SchPl; StuCncl; RptrSchPpr; Oakton; Theatretor Speech Major.

BRINKMANN, Lois J; Momence HS; Momence, IL; 1/118 PresFrshCls; Chrs; CncrtBnd; HonRl; MrchBnd; NHS; SchPl; SecStuCncl; PpCl; BttyCrckrAwd; Park Ridge Lutheran School Of Nursing; Nurs.

BRINKMEYER, Catherine M; Yankton HS; Yankton, SD; 9/239 ChrhWkr; NHS; StuGov; Pres4-H; LetterBsktbl; LetterTrk; Chrldr; AmLegAwd; VoiceDemAwd; Yankton College.

BRINKMEYER, Kristin L; Hubbard Comm HS; Radcliffe, IA; 3/43 PresSrCls; Chr; HonRl; SchMus; StuCncl; EdYrBk; FBLA; FHA; Chrldr; DanFAwd; Medical Field.

BRINKS, Junell; Balaton HS; Slayton, MN; 4/33 Chr; ChrhWkr; HonRl; LbryAde; NHS; SchPl; FHA; St Cloud State College; Medicine.

BRINKS, Kristi L; Hamilton HS; Holland, MI; 12/125 HonRl; TchrAde; 4-H; FTA; SpnCl; LetterBsktbl; Grand Vly State Col; Teaching Or Recreation.

BRINKS, Sheri B; Northern Mich Christian HS; Mc Bain, MI; 20/40 Chr; ChrhWkr; HonRl; RptrYrbk; 4-H; IMSpt; 4-HAwd; College; Elem Tchr.

BRINKS, William J; Hudsonville HS; Hudsonville, MI; Aud/Vis; ChrhWkr; HonRl; YthFlsp; Bsbl; Bsktbl; Ftbl; Wrstlng; IMSpt; AmLegAwd; Hope Pe Major.

BRINNEMAN, Susan E; Huntington North HS; Warren, IN; PresJrCls; PresSrCls; Band; CncrtBnd; MrchBnd; YthFlsp; Pres4-H; GAA; DARAwd; CitAwd; Bus Schl.

BRINSKELLE, Mark A; St Patrick HS; Chicago, IL; 80/372 Chrs; CmntyWkr; HonRl; JrNHS; NHS; YthFnd; PpCl; CaptSwmmng; CchngActv; IMSpt; College; Accounting.

BRINSON, Margie E; Springs Valley HS; French Lick, IN; 13/73 ALAGirlsSt; Band; HonRl; MrchBnd; PepBnd; TchrAde; PpCl; LetterTrk; CchngActv; IMSpt; College.

BRINTNALL, James W; Lake Mich Catholic HS; St Joseph, MI; 5/85 ChrhWkr; HonRl; JrNHS; NHS; SchMus; SctActv; Bsbl; Bsktbl; Ftbl; Univ; Professional Businessman.

BRINZA, James; Cudahy Sr HS; Cudahy, WI; Aud/Vis; Band; CncrtBnd; HonRl; MrchBnd; PepBnd; Yrbk; Ftbl; Trk; IMSpt; Tech School; Professional.

BRISCOE, Frank R; D C Everest HS; Ringle, WI; ChrhWkr; StuCncl; YthLg; RptrSchPpr; SchPpr; Bsktbl; LetterTrk; IMSpt; RotaryAwd; College; Law.

BRISCOE, James L; Canton R U HS; Williamstown, MO; 5/69 PresFrshCls; PresSophCls; HonRl; NHS; FSA; KeyCl; Bsbl; Tennis; College.

BRISCOE, Kelly A; South Beloit HS; South Beloit, IL; VPFrshCls; PresBand; HonRl; VPNHS; PepBnd; TreasStuCncl; RptrYrbk; PpCl; LetterBsbl; Illinois Wesleyan University; Nurse.

BRISCOE, Mark; Hume HS; Foster, MO; PresJrCls; HonRl; ModUN; Yrbk; 4-H; Work Study; Public Service.

BRISCOE, Thomas W; West Plains HS; West Plains, MO; 2/245 ALBoysSt; ChrhWkr; HonRl; NHS; NatlMeritFnl; StuCncl; RptrSchPpr; SecFFA; MthCl; EldAwd; Univ Of Missouri; Computer Science.

BRISKEY, Susan P; Waldron Area HS; Waldron, MI; 10/52 TchrAde; Eklhart Inst Of Tech; Medical Assistant.

BRISS, Sheila K; Hatton Public HS; Hatton, ND; SecSrCls; CmntyWkr; HonRl; SchPl; StuCncl; TchrAde; Yrbk; FHA; PpCl; Chrldr; N Dakota St Univ; Nurse.

BRISSON, Debbie L; Forest Lake HS; Forest Lake, MN; ChrhWkr; HonRl; RptrSchPpr; FrCl; College; French.

BRISSON, Marlene E; Larimore HS; Larimore, ND; SecJrCls; ALAGirlsSt; Chr; Chrs; CncrtBnd; HonRl; LitMag; MrchBnd; PepBnd; SchMus; FBLA; Chrldr; AmLegAwd; Univ; Business Adm.

BRISSON, Mary; Hamilton HS; Kingsford, MI; 25/167 Band; CncrtBnd; HonRl; HospAde; MrchBnd; PepBnd; FNA; CitAwd; Mich Tech Univ; Medical Technologist.

BRISTOL, Kevin C; Lutheran North HS; Bridgeton, MO; Chr; GerCl; Bsbl; Ftbl; IMSpt; College; Marine Biology.

BRISTOW, Denny N; Burt Comm HS; Bancroft, IA; HonRl; SchPl; StuCncl; RptrYrbk; SchPpr; LetterBsbl; Bsktbl; Trade School; Commercial Artist.

BRITAIN, Alexander H; South Shore HS; Herbster, WI; 9/37 HonRl; RptrYrbk; Yrbk; SciCl; Ftbl; Trk; College; Law.

BRITT, Anne M; O Fallon Township HS; O Fallon, IL; 13/294 Band; CncrtBnd; HonRl; MrchBnd; ModUN; NHS; SchMus; RptrSchPpr; SchPpr; FrCl; PpCl; Chrldr; GAA; Eastern Ill Univ; Education.

BRITT, Janis M; Century HS; Ullin, IL; SecFrshCls; SecSophCls; SecJrCls; SecSrCls; HonRl; OffAde; EdSchPpr; PresFHA; PpCl; GAA; Southern Ill Univ; Social Work.

BRITT, Lori; Lindblom Tech Hs; Chicago, IL; 51 TrsSophCls; TrsJrCls; Chr; HonRl; SchPl; StuGov; FDA; GerCl; SciCl; GAA; Northwestern U ; Dermatology.

BRITT, Sandra J; Patoka Comm Unit 100 HS; Vernon, IL; ChrhWkr; CmntyWkr; HonRl; SchPl; Yrbk; EdSchPpr; SchPpr; Sec4-H; DanFAwd; 4-HAwd;.

BRITT, Vicky L; Summersville HS; Hartshorn, MO; SecTrsFrshCls; SecSophCls; Chrs; HonRl; SchPl; StuCncl; RptrYrbk; EdSchPpr; FHA; PpCl; CaptChrldr; School Of The Ozarks; Lawyer.

BRITT, William S; Watwatosa East HS; Wauwatosa, WI; PresBand; ChrhWkr; CncrtBnd; MrchBnd; PepBnd; SctActv; MthCl; GodCntryAwd; Uw Madison; Industrial Management.

BRITTAN, William C; St Agnes HS; Alliance, NE; 3/19 VPFrshCls; ALBoysSt; RptrYrbk; FSA; SpnCl; SciCl; CaptBsktbl; CaptFtbl; CaptGlf; EldAwd; U Of Notre Dame; Lawyer.

BRITTEN, Garry L; St Ignatiws College Prep; Chicago, IL; CmntyWkr; NatlMeritCmnd; SchPl; SctActv; IMSpt; Univ; Communications.

BRITTEN, Jolene M; Weyerhaeuser HS; New Auburn, WI; CmntyWkr; HonRl; JA; JrNHS; SchPl; 4-H; Bsktbl; Trk; GAA; 4-HAwd; College; Business.

BRITTEN, Linda M; Orient Macksburg HS; Creston, IA; 12/42 PresSophCls; Chr; Chrs; ChrhWkr; HonRl; MrchBnd; SchMus; StuCncl; DARAwd; CitAwd; Southwestern Comm Coll; Teaching.

BRITTINGHAM, Mary A; Plainfield Jr Sr HS; Plainfield, IN; 38/260 HonRl; VPFBLA; College; Professional.

BRITTON, Debra A; Brazil HS; Brazil, IN; ChrhWkr; HonRl; LbryAde; NHS; YthFlsp; FHA; Bsktbl; Trk; Indiana State University; Business.

BRITTON, Donald O; Ypsilanti HS; Ypsilanti, MI; HonRl; PpCl; Bsbl; Bsktbl; Ftbl; Trk; CchngActv; College; Professional.

BRITTON, Kathy A; Eastern HS; Solsberry, IN; 6/72 SecJrCls; ChrhWkr; HonRl; NHS; Quill&Scroll; EdYrBk; EdSchPpr; Bsktbl; GAA; U In Bloomington; Nursng.

BRITTON, Steven R; Wauwatosa West HS; Wauwatosa, WI; 16/425 ChrhWkr; HonRl; NHS; Orch; MthCl; Univ Of Madison; Astronomy.

BRITZMAN, Linda; Richland R 4 HS; Richland, MO; FHA; Business School; Business Managing.

BRIZGYS, Vida E; Maria HS; Chicago, IL; 1/335 HonRl; NHS; NatlMeritCmnd; SctActv; University; Medicine.

BRO, Bruce; Exira HS; Exira, IA; 15/48 Band; Chr; HonRl; SchMus; RptrSchPpr; SchPpr; 4-H; FFA; College; Music Instructor.

BROADFOOT, John C; St Charles HS; St Charles, MO; 18/556 Band; CncrtBnd; DrmBgl; HonRl; JrNHS; MrchBnd; NHS; Orch; PepBnd; ROTC; SchMus; SctActv; YthFlsp; Univ Of Missouri; Music.

BROADHEAD, Sherrie; North Posey HS; Poseyville, IN; 15/173 SecTrsSrCls; Band; HonRl; NHS; OffAde; StuCncl; Yrbk; 4-H; IMSpt; KiwanAwd; Univ Of Evansville; Accounting.

BROADSTREET, Ned; Muncie Northside HS; Muncie, IN; 110/390 CmntyWkr; HonRl; StuGov; YthFlsp; SpnCl; Bsbl; Bsktbl; Ftbl; Air Force Acad; Pilot.

BROADWAY, Cheryl; Pope County HS; Golconda, IL; HonRl; RptrYrbk; FHA; FTA; SpnCl; PpCl; LetterBsbl; VPGAA; College; Teacher.

BROBECK, Laurie; Northeastern HS; Richmond, IN; 4/120 ALAGirlsSt; HonRl; NHS; TchrAde; LatCl; SpnCl; GAA; AmLegAwd; DanFAwd; Indiana Univ; Physical Therapy.

BROBERG, Loren D; Elkhorn Valley HS; Newman Grove, NE; PresJrCls; ALBoysSt; HonRl; StuCncl; LetterBsktbl; LetterFtbl; LetterTrk; AmLegAwd; LionAwd;.

BROBJORG, Shavonne H; Baltic HS; Baltic, SD; 2/25 TrsJrCls; Chrs; HonRl; NHS; OffAde; SchPl; TchrAde; EdYrBk; FHA; Trk; Univ.

BROCHIN, Bill; Connersville Senior HS; Connersville, IN; ChrhWkr; HonRl; GerCl; IMSpt; Purdue Univ; Vetrinarian.

BROCK, Arthur; Assumption Hs; E St Louis, IL; 12/123 ChrhWkr; HonRl; ModUN; SchPl; SctActv; LetterFtbl; LetterTrk;.

BROCK, Brenda E; Eminence HS; Monrovia, IN; Band; Chr; CncrtBnd; HonRl; MrchBnd; SecNHS; Yrbk; PpCl; GAA; Business School; Secretary.

BROCK, Bryan C; Wichita North HS; Wichita, KS; Chrs; HonRl; ModUN; NatlFornLg; NatlMeritSF; PolWkr; SchPl; YthLg; SchPpr; SpnCl; U Of Kansas; Mech Engineer.

BROCK, Freda A; Fountain Central HS; Veedersburg, IN; 25/140 Band; CncrtBnd; HonRl; PresLbryAde; MrchBnd; NHS; PepBnd; SchAde; FSA; SecSciCl; In St Univ; Special Education Teacher.

BROCK, Gregory A; South HS; Sheboygan, WI; Band; CncrtBnd; HonRl; NHS; Orch; PepBnd; KiwanAwd; College; Architecture.

BROCK, Kim S; Mc Donald Co HS; Anderson, MO; NHS; StuCncl; 4-H; PresFFA; 4-HAwd; Ne Oklahoma A&m; Animal Science.

BROCK, Linda; Humphrey HS; Humphrey, NE; 2/22 TrsSrCls; Chrs; ChrhWkr; HonRl; StuCncl; TchrAde; Yrbk; RptrSchPpr; PpCl; College; Math.

BROCK, Tammy S; Eastridge HS; Kankakee, IL; Chr; ChrhWkr; HonRl; SchMus; StuCncl; Yrbk; RptrSchPpr; 4-H; SciCl; Swmmng; College.

BROCK, Valerie; Cass Technical HS; Detroit, MI; CmntyWkr; HonRl; JrNHS; SchAde; SchMus; TchrAde; AmLegAwd; CitAwd; Psych.

BROCKA, Randall H; Parkersburg Comm HS; Parkersburg, IA; ChrhWkr; CncrtBnd; HonRl; MrchBnd; PepBnd; SctActv; 4-H; Ftbl; Swmmng; Trk; Coll; Voc.

BROCKEL, Brad A; Benthold HS; Burlington, ND; 5/15 Bsktbl; Ndsss; Computor Progammer.

BROCKEMEIER, Grant J; Wisner Pilger HS; Wisner, NE; VPJrCls; NHS; FFA; LetterFtbl; LetterTrk; LetterWrstlng;.

BROCKER, Richard A; Winnebago HS; Pecatonica, IL; 13/117 PresSrCls; ChrhWkr; NHS; StuCncl; YthFlsp; 4-H; GerCl; Ftbl; Purdue Univ; Agriculture.

BROCKGREITENS, Michael J; Duchesne HS; St Charles, MO; VPSrCls; PolWkr; StuGov; Socr; College; Political Science.

BROCKHAUS, Amy L; Wausau East HS; Wausau, WI; AFS; ChrhWkr; HospAde; SpnCl; Chrldr; GAA; IMSpt; Coll; Oceanography.

BROCKHAUS, Lynn M; St Francis HS; Madison, NE; 4/35 ALAGirlsSt; Chr; Chrs; HonRl; SchAde; RptrSchPpr; 4-H; PpCl; Chrldr; 4-HAwd; Coll; Journalism.

BROCKMAN, Barbara L; Marinette HS; Marinette, WI; SecFrshCls; TrsSophCls; CncrtBnd; MrchBnd; NHS; PepBnd; Twrl; EdYrBk; EdSchPpr; Chrldr; U Of Wis Madison; Respitory Therapy.

BROCKMAN, Fred; Eureka Hs; Congerville, IL; 11/106 Band; HonRl; NHS; PolWkr; SchMus; SptEdYrbk; SptEdSchPpr; 4-H; SecFFA; LetterTrk; Illinois State U; Agriculture.

BROCKMAN, Kirk E; Vianney HS; St Louis, MO; 1/195 HonRl; NHS; SchPl; LetterBsktbl; LetterFtbl; LetterTrk; College; Medicine.

BROCKMAN, Paul G; Batesville HS; Oldenburg, IN; TrsJrCls; ChrhWkr; HonRl; NHS; StuCncl; TchrAde; SpnCl; LetterBsbl; Ftbl; PresAwd; College; Business Management.

BROCKMAN, Steven M; Lake Central HS; Schereville, IN; 4/430 HonRl; NHS; EngCl; GerCl; Rose Hulman Inst Of Tech; Medicine.

BROCKMANN, Michael T; West Point HS; West Point, NE; ChrhWkr; CmntyWkr; HonRl; Quill&Scroll; TchrAde; YthFlsp; RptrSchPpr; SptEdSchPpr; 4-H; Bsbl; Bsktbl; Ftbl; Glf; Concordia Teachers College; Teaching.

BROCKMEYER, Jane; Steeleville HS; Steeleville, IL; SecFrshCls; SecSophCls; SecJrCls; SecSrCls; Chrs; ChrhWkr; CtyCnl; HospAde; Eastern Illinois; Elementary Ed.

BROCKMEYER, Tracy L; Lincolnwood HS; Harvel, IL; 12/61 HonRl; LbryAde; StuCncl; TchrAde; EdYrBk; FFA; E Illinois Univ; Business Educ.

BROCKSCHINK, John C; Norway Community HS; Norway, IA; PresSophCls; Aud/Vis; Band; Chr;

ChrhWkr; HonRl; SchPl; 4-H; LetterTrk; Trade School; Agricultural.

BROCKSCHMIDT, Celeste M; Andrean HS; Hobart, IN; 47/301 HonRl; NHS; Quill&Scroll; Sdlty; Yrbk; FHA; St Francis College.

BROCKSMITH, Mike P; South Knox HS; Vincennes, IN; HonRl; 4-H; FFA; IMSpt; College; Vocation Agriculture.

BROCKSTEIN, Sharon F; Maine Twp East HS; Des Plaines, IL; HonRl; HospAde; LitMag; College; Liberal Arts.

BROCKUS, Burl F; Moulton Udell HS; Moulton, IA; ChrhWkr; CmntyWkr; HonRl; JA; PolWkr; SctActv; Yrbk; Pres4-H; FHA;.

BROCKWAY, Robert M; Elk Grove HS; Elk Grove Vlg, IL; 150/505 YthFlsp; Bsbl; Ftbl; Illinois State University.

BROD, Craig D; Berkley HS; Oak Park, MI; HonRl; TchrAde; RptrYrbk; RptrSchPpr; College.

BROD, Kathryn L; Murphysboro Township HS; Mruphysboro, IL; Chr; Chrs; ChrhWkr; CmntyWkr; HonRl; HospAde; OffAde; SchAde; SpnCl; PPFtbl; J A Logan Jr Col; Nurse.

BRODACK, James W; West Leyden HS; Melrose Park, IL; 2/417 HonRl; Orch; SchMus; SctActv; StuCncl; RptrSchPpr; PresSciCl; Trk; College; Research Chemist.

BRODBECK, Debora; Mineral Point HS; Mineral Point, WI; 13#29#37 HonRl; MrchBnd; PepBnd; SchMus; EdSchPpr; FHA; GAA; Anoka Voc Sch, Fashion Buyer.

BRODBECK, Thomas M; Eastbrook HS; Van Buren, IN; 20/169 ALBoysSt; ChrhWkr; HonRl; NHS; SchMus; SchPl; RptrSchPpr; LatCl; LetterWrstlng; Huntington College; Ministry.

BRODBERG, Cheryl M; Mason HS; Mason, MI; 8/233 Band; ChrhWkr; HonRl; JrNHS; NHS; NatlThespSoc; SchMus; PresYthFlsp; Sec4-H; LetterBsktbl; John Wesley Coll; Social Work.

BRODECKY, Ernie F; Howells HS; Howells, NE; Aud/Vis; Chrl; ChrhWkr; LbryAde; SchPl; SctActv; RptrYrbk; RptrSchPpr; SchPpr; FFA; Bsbl; Bsktbl; LetterFtbl; Wrstlng; Trade School; Vocation.

BRODEN, Judy M; West Side HS; Gary, IN; CmntyWkr; HonRl; JrNHS; NHS; College; Data Processing.

BRODERICK, George R; Whiting HS; Whiting, IN; 3/100 HonRl; NHS; NatlMeritCmnd; RptrSchPpr; SpnCl; LetterFtbl; LetterGlf; Wrstlng; AmLegAwd; KiwanAwd; Indiana St Univ; Acct.

BRODERICK, Kelli S; North Central #28 HS; Rock Lake, ND; 5/26 Band; PepBnd; SchPl; TchrAde; LetterBsktbl; Chrldr; CchngActv; GAA; IMSpt; 4-HAwd; Ndsu; Parks & Recreation.

BRODERICK, Michael J; Brother Rice HS; Oak Lawn, IL; 92/416 HonRl; U Of Ill; Lawyer.

BRODERICK, Myron; Rock Lake Public HS; Rock Lake, ND; HonRl; SchAde; SchPl; SctActv; TchrAde; CchngActv; College; Electro Mechanical Technology.

BRODERICK, Patti A; New Trier East HS; Wilmette, IL; AFS; CAP; CmntyWkr; HonRl; HospAde; JA; LbryAde; OffAde; RedCrAde; Northwestern University.

BRODERICK, William R; George Rogers Clark HS; Whiting, IN; Aud/Vis; Band; ChrhWkr; CncrtBnd; HonRl; MrchBnd; StuCncl; SpnCl; Ftbl; Wrstlng; College; Professional.

BRODERIUS, Kimberly A; Hector Community HS; Hector, MN; 3/50 Band; Chr; HonRl; SecNHS; SchPl; Pres4-H; SecFHA; PresSpnCl; LetterTrk; 4-HAwd; University Of Minnesota; English.

BRODERIUS, Rebecca J; Hector HS; Hector, MN; 8/50 Band; Chr; CncrtBnd; HonRl; MrchBnd; NHS; SchPl; SctActv; RptrYrbk; LetterBsktbl; LetterTrk; Chrldr; GAA; Univ Of Minnesota; Health.

BRODERS, Lynette J; Durant Comm HS; Stockton, IA; 2/68 Chr; Chrs; ChrhWkr; HonRl; JrNHS; Mdrgl; NHS; OffAde; SchMus; StuCncl; IMSpt; DanFAwd; EldAwd; Iowa State Univ; Special Education.

BRODERSEN, Jacob K; Wm G Mather HS; Munising, MI; 7/127 Aud/Vis; Band; ChrhWkr; CmntyWkr; CncrtBnd; HonRl; MrchBnd; NHS; NatlMeritCmnd; PepBnd; SchPl; SctActv; StuGov; SciCl; LetterTrk; Air Force Academy; Communications Engineer.

BRODIE, Peggy A; Southport HS; Indianapolis, IN; 6/419 Chrs; HonRl; PresJA; Mdrgl; NHS; SchMus; VPMthCl; PresSciCl; JAAwd; VoiceDemAwd; Indiana Central University; Business Admin.

BRODY, Deborah A; New Trier Twp West HS; Glencoe, IL; 93/693 NatlMeritFnl; Orch; SchMus; SchPl; Hampshire Coll; Religion.

BRODZIK, Thomas; George Washington HS; Chicago, IL; 20/581 VPSrCls; HonRl; NHS; StuCncl; TchrAde; LatCl; SciCl; CaptBsbl; CaptBsktbl; AmLegAwd; College; Accounting.

BROEDER, Connie S; Maywood HS; North Platte, NE; 4/26 Band; Chrs; ChrhWkr; DrlTm; HonRl; JrNHS; SchPl; 4-H; PpCl; Trk; IMSpt; College; Vocation.

BROEK, Curtis A; Sioux Center Comm HS; Sioux Center, IA; 4/78 NHS; PresStuCncl; Pres4-H; VPFFA; LetterFtbl; Swmmng; Tennis; LetterTrk; 4-HAwd; GovHonPrgAwd; Univ Of Ia; Optometry.

BROEKER, Elaine E; Gasconade County Rii HS; Mt Sterling, MO; SecALAGirlsSt; TreasChrhWkr; HonRl; NHS; YthFlsp; 4-H; FHA; LatCl; DanFAwd; College; Home Economics.

BROER, Becky L; Hubbard Comm HS; Hubbard, IA; 2/31 PresJrCls; Chr; HonRl; SchMus; StuCncl; Yrbk; FHA; FrCl; Glf; Swmmng;.

BROEREN, James R; Premontre HS; Green Bay, WI; 37/157 HonRl; NHS; KeyCl; LetterBsktbl; ChmnFtbl; LetterTrk; College.

BROERS, Charles M; Tampico HS; Deer Grove, IL; 4/36 TrsJrCls; PresSrCls; HonRl; SchPl; Yrbk; 4-H; FFA; College; Civil Engineering.

BROGAN, Terence J; Proviso West HS; Berkeley, IL; Aud/Vis; HonRl; SptEdYrbk; Univ Of Illinois; Professional.

BROGE, Thomas S; Black Hawk HS; South Wayne, WI; PresFrshCls; PresSrCls; ChrhWkr; HonRl; RptrYrbk; SptEdYrbk; RptrSchPpr; Bsktbl; Ftbl; LetterTrk; College; Computar Science.

BROGHAMMER, Thomas J; West Delaware HS; Ryan, IA; Aud/Vis; Band; CncrtBnd; MrchBnd; PepBnd; SchMus; SchPl; Iowa State Univ; Farming.

BROIHIER, Elisa; St Joseph Senior HS; St Joseph, MI; Band; CncrtBnd; HonRl; MrchBnd; Orch; PepBnd; SchMus; StuCncl; StuGov; FrCl; Univ; Fine Arts.

BROKAW, Dave S; Zionsville Comm HS; Zionsville, IN; VPSophCls; PresJrCls; HonRl; StuCncl; StuGov; TchrAde; SpnCl; Ftbl; Trk; IMSpt; In U; Forensics.

BROKAW, Gail; Lenox Community HS; Lenox, IA; ChrhWkr; CncrtBnd; HonRl; Mdrgl; MrchBnd; SchMus; TchrAde; YthFlsp; Trk; University; Professional.

BROKAW, Joseph R; Southern Unit 120 HS; Stronghurst, IL; 5/56 VPSophCls; PresJrCls; VPSrCls; 4-H; PresFFA; Trk; Western Ill U; Agriculture.

BROKAW, Linda S; Raymore Peculiar HS; Raymore, MO; SecFrshCls; HonRl; StuCncl; FHA; SecFrCl; PpCl; Bsktbl; LetterTrk; LetterChrldr; GAA; Col; Vocation.

BROKAW, Patricia A; Gchs South HS; Granite City, IL; 42/630 Chrs; HonRl; NHS; TreasGAA; University.

BROKAW, Paula J; Lenox Community HS; Lenox, IA; 4/33 TrsFrshCls; Band; CmntyWkr; HonRl; SchPl; RptrYrbk; 4-H; LetterBsbl; Bsktbl; CaptTrk; College; Professional.

BROKHAUSEN, Janis D; Boylan Central HS; Rockford, IL; Band; ChrhWkr; HonRl; NHS; EdYrBk; Chrldr; BttyCrckrAwd; Ill State Univ; Sociology Psychology.

BROLLEY, John D; Evanston Township HS; Evantson, IL; Band; CncrtBnd; HonRl; MrchBnd; NatlMeritSF; PepBnd; Connecticut Clg; Music Comp.

BROMAN, Carol; Rosemount HS; Eagan, MN; Band; HonRl; Vocational School; Accounting.

BROMANDER, Theo M; Westwood HS; Smithland, IA; CncrtBnd; HonRl; NatlMeritSF; StuCncl; YthFlsp; 4-H; LetterBsktbl; LetterTrk; CchngActv; PPFtbl; College; X Ray Tech.

BROMANN, Dean A; Glenbard West HS; Glen Ellyn, IL; Chrs; HonRl; LatCl; Bsbl; CaptBsktbl; Wesleyan Univ.

BROMER, Susan J; Lemont Township HS; Lemont, IL; 12/140 TrsSophCls; HonRl; NHS; OffAde; SctActv; StuCncl; EdYrBk; FrCl; Univ Of Illinois; Psychology.

BROMLEY, Sue E; Sterling HS; Sterling, IL; 41/407 AFS; Chr; HonRl; NHS; YthFlsp; Yrbk; FrCl; CaptTennis; GAA; Illinois State Univ; Teacher.

BROMMER, Debra; Sioux Center Comm HS; Sioux Center, IA; SecTrsSrCls; Band; ChrhWkr; CmntyWkr; HonRl; YthFlsp; FHA; Glf; Swmmng; IMSpt; Northwestern Col; Curriculum Of Major Study.

BRONDYKE, Diane K; Fulton HS; Fulton, IL; 42/123 SecSophCls; Chr; VPChrs; HonRl; NatlThespSoc; SchPl; StuCncl; Yrbk; RptrSchPpr; Chrldr; GAA; Central College.

BRONDYKE, Russell; Fulton HS; Fulton, IL; DrmMjrt; JA; NatlThespSoc; SchPl; YthFlsp; SpnCl; Trinity Christian College; Business Adm.

BRONFENBRENNER, Martha; St Joseph HS; St Joseph, MI; 7/347 VPJrCls; HonRl; NHS; NatlMeritFnl; VPStuCncl; TchrAde; MthCl; LetterBsbl; LetterSwmmng; BauchLmbAwd; Coloado State U; Veterianarian.

BRONIAK, Christopher J; St Josephs Prep Col; Detriot, MI; 1/11 Band; CncrtBnd; HonRl; NHS; NatlMeritCmnd; SchPl; Yrbk; EdSchPpr; LetterTennis; IMSpt; Holy Redeemer Col ; Priest.

BRONKE, Cheryl; Maria HS; Chicago, IL; Chrs; HonRl; GAA; Coll; Education Of Sp Children.

BRONOW, Patricia; Washington Hs; Washington, MO; Chrl; HonRl; Yrbk; FrCl; College ; Accounting.

BRONSON, Aaron C; Woodruff HS; Peoria, IL; HonRl; OffAde; RptrSchPpr; LetterBsbl; Bsktbl; Coll; Engineering.

BRONSON, Eric E; Union City HS; Sherwood, MI; 1/112 NHS; YthFlsp; 4-H; LetterBsktbl; LetterFtbl; CaptTrk; Michigan State Univ; Agriculture.

BRONSTED, Sara; Lutheran West HS; Detroit, MI; SecSrCls; Chr; HonRl; NHS; SchMus; StuCncl; GerCl; PpCl; Chrldr; PPFtbl; Coll; Ed.

BROOK, Natalie J; Bath HS; East Lansing, MI; 3/90 PresJrCls; Band; ChrhWkr; CncrtBnd; PresFrshCls; NHS; StuCncl; 4-H; LetterChrldr; 4-HAwd;.

BROOKE, James L; Taylor HS; Hemlock, IN; Band; Chr; CncrtBnd; MrchBnd; PepBnd; TchrAde; PpCl; Trk; Wrstlng; IMSpt; LionAwd; Indiana Univ; Nuclear Engr.

BROOKE, Kathy L; South Harrison HS; Bethany, MO; Chrs; 4-H; PpCl; JCAwd; Univ.

BROOKER, Annette L; Pittsburg Sr HS; Pittsburg, KS; Chr; ChrhWkr; CmntyWkr; CncrtBnd; HonRl; IntrClCncl; MrchBnd; NatlFornLg; Pres4-H; FrCl; PresRusCl; 4-HAwd; University Of Kansas; Russian.

BROOKHOUSER, Gregory J; Plattsmouth HS; Plattsmouth, NE; 15/165 NHS; Ftbl; Wrstlng; Univ; Veterinary Medicine.

BROOKHYSER, Gretchen K; Athen Public HS; Athens, WI; Band; Chr; Chrl; Chrs; CmntyWkr; LbryAde; MrchBnd; PepBnd; FHA; SpnCl; Coll.

BROOKINS, Deborah A; George S Parker HS; Janesville, WI; 7/387 HonRl; NHS; TchrAde; GAA; University Of Wisconsin; Accounting.

BROOKS, Barbara; Richland Center HS; Cazinovia, WI; 46/187 Band; Chrs; CmntyWkr; HonRl; ModUN; NatlFornLg; SchPl; 4-H; GAA; 4-HAwd; Uw Madison; Horiculturist.

BROOKS, Barbara A; Reddick HS; Reddick, IL; 2/40 Band; HonRl; SchPl; FHA; Trk; GAA; Northern Illinois Univ; Computer Service.

BROOKS, Barbara J; Washington HS; Chicago, IL; 75/495 Chrs; HonRl; OffAde; SchAde; SchMus; SctActv; TchrAde; Teen; FNA; GerCl; RusCl; Michael Reese Hospital; Radiologist.

BROOKS, Barry H; Oak Park River Forest HS; Oak Park, IL; 79/1070 Band; StuCncl; Trk; AmLegAwd; Univ Of Il; Electronics Engineering.

BROOKS, Cathy E; Delta HS; Dunkirk, IN; 48/250 SecSophCls; Chr; JrNHS; SchMus; TchrAde; RptrSchPpr; FrCl; PpCl; Chrldr; ;social Work.

BROOKS, Christopher W; North Vigo HS; Terre Haute, IN; Aud/Vis; HonRl; PolWkr; SciCl; Rose Hulman Inst; Electrical Engineer.

BROOKS, Deania R; Newton Comm HS; Newton, IL; 19/199 Band; CncrtBnd; HonRl; MrchBnd; NHS; PepBnd; College; Business.

BROOKS, Denise L; Frederic Remington HS; Potwin, KS; SecSrCls; Band; DrmMjrt; HonRl; MrchBnd; NatlFornLg; NatlThespSoc; FHA; PpCl; Chrldr; College; Physical Therapy.

BROOKS, Dianne M; Rhame HS; Rhame, ND; 1/7 PresSophCls; SecJrCls; ALAGirlsSt; Chrs; HonRl; SchPl; EdYrBk; Trk; Chrldr; 4-HAwd; Nd Univ; Engr.

BROOKS, Douglas S; Ludington HS; Ludington, MI; HonRl; Bsbl; LetterFtbl; CchngActv; Central Mich Univ; Playng/teach Baseball.

BROOKS, Edward K; Port Huron Northern HS; Port Huron, MI; 59/450 Band; CmntyWkr; CncrtBnd; HonRl; MrchBnd; NatlMeritSF; PepBnd; Mich St Univ.

BROOKS, Gary; Abilene HS; Abilene, KS; 6/129 ALBoysSt; Chr; ChrhWkr; HonRl; Orch; SchMus; SchPl; StuCncl; Friends Univ; United Methodist Ministry.

BROOKS, Janet W; North Clay HS; Louisville, IL; Band; HonRl; StuCncl; 4-H; FHA; PpCl; GAA; Univ; Professional.

BROOKS, Janice K; Lenora HS; Edmond, KS; 1/15 SecTrsFrshCls; SecTrsSophCls; PresJrCls; HonRl; SchAde; SchPl; EdYrBk; RptrSchPpr; Colby Comm College; Physical Therapy.

BROOKS, Jeffrey; Bloomfield Community HS; Bloomfield, NE; 5/66 ALBoysSt; LbryAde; NHS; SchPl; EdYrBk; SpnCl; CitAwd; Univ Of Sd Vecmillion; Computer Science.

BROOKS, Jon R; Crawfordsville HS; Crawfordsville, IN; 30/230 VPSrCls; HonRl; NatlFornLg; SchPl; SchPpr; PresFrCl; NCTE; Butler Univ; Writer.

BROOKS, Joseph D; Carthage Comm HS; Carthage, IL; 4/90 PresFrshCls; HonRl; StuCncl; Ftbl; Trk; College; Professional.

BROOKS, Karen M; Pinckney HS; Pinckney, MI; Chr; HonRl; LbryAde; OffAde; SchAde; TchrAde; Trade School; Model.

BROOKS, Kelly E; Edwardsville Sr HS; Glen Carbon, IL; Aud/Vis; Chr; Chrs; HonRl; PolWkr; SchAde; StuCncl; TchrAde; RptrSchPpr; SpnCl; Southern Il Univ Edwardsville.

BROOKS, Kemarie; South Haven HS; South Haven, MI; Chrs; ChrhWkr; HonRl; Orch; SchMus; TchrAde; YthFlsp; SecTrsSophCls; LetterTrk; Jr College; Physical Therapy.

BROOKS, Kimberly S; Irving Crown HS; Algonquin, IL; 7/425 AFS; Band; ChrhWkr; CmntyWkr; CncrtBnd; DrlTm; HonRl; MrchBnd; NHS; Orch; PepBnd; SchMus; SciCl; GAA; College.

BROOKS, Larry J; Roncalli HS; Indpls, IN; ChrhWkr; HonRl; TchrAde; FrCl; Col; Lawyer.

BROOKS, Laurie R; Marquette HS; Alton, IL; 16/116 Chrs; HonRl; JA; NHS; NatlMeritSchl; SctActv; RptrYrbk; RptrSchPpr; Jr College; Business.

BROOKS, Lisa G; Ann Arbor Huron HS; Ann Arbor, MI; Chr; ChrhWkr; CmntyWkr; NatlMeritCmnd; SchAde; SctActv; FNA; FrCl; Bsktbl; Trk; Chrldr; Michigan St Univ; Model.

BROOKS, Lorraine K; John Marshall HS; Indianapolis, IN; 21/444 Chr; HonRl; NHS; Orch; SchMus; TchrAde; IMSpt; PPFtbl; Iupui Univ; Science.

BROOKS, Margie L; Stephen Decatur HS; Decatur, IL; 23/476 AFS; HonRl; NHS; OffAde; RptrYrbk; GerCl; Ill State Univ; German.

BROOKS, Rhonda; Capac HS; Capac, MI; 4/108 PresSrCls; Band; ChrhWkr; NHS; Chrldr; GAA; BttyCrckrAwd; 4-HAwd; College; At.

BROOKS, Richard; West Vigo HS; West Terre Haute, IN; Band; HonRl; MrchBnd; PepBnd; SchPl; Coll.

BROOKS, Robert L; Quincy Sr HS; Quincy, IL; 35/816 ChrhWkr; CncrtBnd; HonRl; MrchBnd; Orch; PepBnd; SchMus; SctActv; Univ Of Illinois; Chemistry.

BROOKS, Ronald J; O Gorman HS; Sioux Falls, SD; Chrs; NatlFornLg; NHS; StuCncl; StuGov; SptEdSchPpr; LetterFtbl; CchngActv; Univ; Professional.

BROOKS, Sandra L; Hastings HS; Hastings, MI; Chr; Chrl; Chrs; ChrhWkr; HonRl; SchMus; YthFlsp; Yrbk; Davenport Business School; Legal Secretary.

BROOKS, Stephen R; Zion Benton HS; Zion, IL; HonRl; LitMag; NatlMeritCmnd; StuCncl; University; Computer Science.

BROOKS, Steven E; Heritage Christian HS; Anderson, IN; PresSophCls; ChrhWkr; LetterSocr; IMSpt; College; Pastoral Ministry.

BROOKS, Sue K; Coldwater HS; Coldwater, MI; HonRl; OffAde; PolWkr; TchrAde; 4-H; SpnCl; DARAwd;.

BROOKS, Susan L; Ottawa HS; Ottawa, IL; 20/425 Chr; ChrhWkr; HonRl; HospAde; NHS; College; Veterinarian.

BROOKS, Suzette; East St Louis Sr HS; East St Louis, IL; PresFrshCls; Band; HonRl; JA; JrNHS; NHS; Sacrstn; SctActv; StuCncl; StuGov; TchrAde; FrCl; MthCl; Western Illinois Univ; Dentist.

BROOKS, Virgil; Winfield Sr HS; Winfield, KS; ALBoysSt; Orch; PepBnd; StuGov; TchrAde; Bsktbl; Wichita State Univ; American History.

BROOKS, William E; Cooter HS; Cooter, MO; PresFrshCls; PresJrCls; CncrtBnd; HonRl; PepBnd; SchPl; StuCncl; MthCl; CaptBsktbl; CaptIMSpt; Arkansas State Univ; Engineer.

BROOKS, William R; Winfield HS; Winfield, KS; VPFrshCls; PresSrCls; ALBoysSt; HonRl; NatlMeritCmnd; StuCncl; StuGov; KeyCl; LetterBsbl; Bsktbl; CaptFtbl; LetterTrk; IMSpt; Univ; Science.

BROOM, Cathryn; St Joseph Ogden HS; St Joseph, IL; 7/103 PresJrCls; Band; ChrhWkr; CmntyWkr; CncrtBnd; HonRl; TrsFrshCls; StuCncl; Yrbk; Trk; Univ Of Il; Secondary Education.

BROOM, Gerald E; Salem Comm HS; Salem, IL; ChrhWkr; HonRl; SctActv; StuCncl; SpnCl; PpCl; Bsbl; Bsktbl; LetterFtbl; Trk; Univ; Archit Engin.

BROOM, Tina M; Rantoul Twp HS; Rantoul, IL; 22/354 ALAGirlsSt; ChrhWkr; CmntyWkr; HonRl; JrNHS; NHS; StuCncl; TchrAde; YthFlsp; 4-H; FBLA; FrCl; PpCl; Parkland Jr College; Bookkeeping.

BROPHY, James R; Marist HS; Chicago, IL; 43/365 PresAud/Vis; CmntyWkr; NHS; SchMus; SchPl; RptrYrbk; LetterSwmmng; U S Air Force; Computer Technician.

BROPHY, William; East HS; Sioux City, IA; IMSpt; College.

BROSH, Donald L; Madison HS; Madison, NE; Trk; Wrstlng; IMSpt; College; Zoology.

BROSIO, Patricia K; Wheeling HS; Arlington Hts, IL; DrlTm; HonRl; JrNHS; NHS; De Paul Univ; Business.

BROSMER, Mary; Dubois HS; Celestine, IN; 16/81 Band; YthFlsp; RptrSchPpr; FHA; PpCl; Indiana Univ; Acc.

BROSSART, John J; Sacred Heart HS; E Grand Forks, MN; Chrl; HonRl; NatlFornLg; NatlMeritCmnd; PresStuCncl; SciCl; LetterBsktbl; LetterFtbl; LetterTrk; PresAwd; St Johns U; Law.

BROSSEAU, Johnny K; Crane HS; Crane, MO; 10/35 Band; Chr; Chrs; ChrhWkr; CncrtBnd; HonRl; NHS; SctActv; StuCncl; FFA; Plumbing Trade.

BROST, Carolyn M; Brown HS; Sturgis, SD; 11/205 Band; CncrtBnd; DrmMjrt; HonRl; MrchBnd; NHS; PepBnd; PolWkr; TchrAde; Business School; Secretary.

BROST, David L; Regis HS; Cedar Rapids, IA; Bsbl; Bsktbl; Ftbl; Iowa State Univ; Architecture.

BROSTE, Noel; Wilton HS; Wilton, ND; ALBoysSt; HonRl; SchPl; Bsbl; College; Farming.

BROSTER, Thomas L; Grayville HS; Grayville, IL; HonRl; NHS; Bsbl; Bsktbl; Trk; IMSpt; Ill Wesleyan Univ; Medicine.

BROSTOWITZ, David R; Greenfield HS; Greenfield, WI; 3/420 PresSrCls; HonRl; NHS; StuGov; PpCl; LetterFtbl; Trk; LetterWrstlng; IMSpt; Marquette Univ; Pro Med.

BROSZEIT, Rosemarie; Napoleon HS; Jackson, MI; 28/106 HonRl; Jackson Comm Col; Teach The Blind.

BROTEN, Jayne A; Warren HS; Viking, MN; Band; Chrs; CncrtBnd; HonRl; MrchBnd; PepBnd; Pres4-H; FHA; Trk; 4-HAwd; Univ Of Minn Crookston; Fashion Merchandsng.

BROTEN, Martha R; Minnehaha Academy; St Paul, MN; 1/125 Chr; ChrhWkr; HonRl; NHS; NatlMeritSchl; Orch; YthFlsp; GerCl; St Olaf Clg; Music.

BROTEN, Peggy A; Roseau HS; Roseau, MN; Chr; ChrhWkr; HonRl; LbryAde; Mdrgl; SchMus; SchPl; YthFlsp; Yrbk; 4-H; FFA; KeyCl; Bible School; Asst Veterinarian.

BROTHERSEN, Alyce; Bgm HS; Guernsey, IA; AFS; Chrs; HonRl; StuCncl; PpCl; Ftbl; CchngActv; PPFtbl; Drake Univ; Pe Major.

BROTHERTON, Orville L; Clayton HS; Clayton, MO; PresJrCls; ModUN; NatlThespSoc; PolWkr; SchMus; SchPl; StuGov; PpCl; LetterFtbl; LetterTrk; College; Political Science.

BROTMAN, Mark D; Newtrier West Township HS; Wilmette, IL; Band; CncrtBnd; HonRl; Orch; SchMus; IMSpt; U Of Wi; Business Administration.

BROTON, Ilene R; High School; Holton, MI; 15/65 PresSophCls; Chr; SpnCl; PpCl; Bsktbl; Glf; Trk; Wrstlng; PPFtbl; 4-HAwd; Michigan St Univ; Civil Engineer.

BROTT, Elizabeth; Winfield HS; Winfield, KS; 6/156 VPJrCls; Chrs; HonRl; HospAde; StuCncl; TchrAde; Yrbk; 4-H; College; Professional.

BROUGHTON, Clifford M; Lincoln Park HS; Lincoln Park, MI; 71/576 Aud/Vis; CtyCnl; LbryAde; ModUN; OffAde; PolWkr; SchAde; StuCncl; TchrAde; RptrYrbk; Wayne State Univ; Electrical Engineering.

BROUGHTON, La Danta S; El Dorado Spgs R 2 HS; El Dorado Springs, MO; 16/109 TrsFrshCls; ALAGirlsSt; Band; ChrhWkr; HonRl; NHS; NatlMeritCmnd; Twrl; CivCl; IMSpt; PPFtbl; Sw Missouri St Univ; Psychology.

BROUGHTON, Pamela D; Marengo HS; Marengo, IN; SecSophCls; VPJrCls; ALAGirlsSt; Band; HonRl; EdSchPpr; 4-H; FHA; Bsktbl; CaptChrldr; Univ; Educ.

BROUHARD, Robert E; Greenfield Central HS; Greenfield, IN; 50/293 HonRl; NHS; SciCl; Purdue Univ; Physician.

BROULIK, Dale A; Lincoln Comm HS; Mechanicsville, IA; PresJrCls; Band; Chr; Chrs; CncrtBnd; HonRl; Mdrgl; NHS; PepBnd; SchMus; SchPl; Ftbl;.

BROUSE, Mark A; Lakeshore HS; Stevensville, MI; HonRl; SctActv; College; Advertising.

BROUSSARD, Kerry L; Heritage Christian HS; Indianapolis, IN; Chr; ChrhWkr; LbryAde; SchAde; TchrAde; RptrSchPpr; SchPpr;.

BROUSSEAU, Jane E; Alpena Senior HS; Alpena, MI; TchrAde; Yrbk; College; Dental Field.

BROUWER, Becky A; Central Minn Christian HS; Raymond, MN; PresSophCls; Chr; HonRl; SchMus; TchrAde; RptrSchPpr; SchPpr; FTA; PpCl; LetterBsktbl; Dordt College; Secretary.

BROUWER, Susan J; East Kentwood HS; Kentwood, MI; ChrhWkr; HonRl; JrNHS; Teen; YthFlsp; SpnCl; PpCl; Bsktbl; GAA; Hope College; Teacher.

BROW, Theresa M; Sacred Heart HS; Dearborn, MI; Chrl; HonRl; SchAde; SchMus; TchrAde; PresSpnCl; College Aquinas.

BROWER, Cindy J; Holland HS; Holland, MI; Band; LbryAde; MrchBnd; FrCl; Bsbl; Bsktbl; IMSpt; Wmu.

BROWER, David R; Hamilton HS; Hamilton, IL; 1/70 HonRl; StuCncl; StuGov; LetterBsbl; Bsktbl; LetterFtbl; Bradley Univ; Elec Engineer.

BROWER, Eugenie M; St Clement HS; Center Line, MI; HonRl; JrNHS; VPNHS; YthFlsp; SecCivCl; U Of Mi; Bus Admin.

BROWER, Gerry L; North Side HS; Fort Wayne, IN; ChrhWkr; HonRl; NHS; SecKeyCl; IMSpt; ChmbCommrsAwd; Purdue Univ; Pre Med.

BROWER, Kenneth B; Barrington HS; Barrington, IL; 63/638 HonRl; NHS; College; Liberal Arts.

BROWER, Leah C; Zeeland Public HS; Zeeland, MI; Band; ChrhWkr; CncrtBnd; JrNHS; MrchBnd; NHS; PepBnd; PpCl; LetterGlf; Hope College; Medical Doctor.

BROWERS, Marcia A; Marquette Sr HS; Marquette, MI; 8/385 Chrs; ChrhWkr; 4-H; Michigan State Univ; Horticulture.

BROWN, Al C; North Chicago Community HS; North Chicago, IL; 36/267 Band; ChrhWkr; HonRl; NHS; SctActv; LetterFtbl; LetterTrk; LetterWrstlng; Air Force Academy;.

BROWN, Andrea D; Century HS; Olmsted, IL; 4/56 PresSophCls; Band; CncrtBnd; HonRl; MrchBnd; SptEdYrbk; FHA; ChmnChrldr; GAA; IMSpt; Shawnee Jr Coll.

BROWN, Andrea I; West Side HS; Gary, IN; ALAGirlsSt; HonRl; JrNHS; NHS; Orch; TreasStuCncl; StuGov; LatCl; PpCl; College; Biochemistry.

BROWN, Andrew; North Shore Country Day HS; Highland Park, IL; Chrs; LitMag; SchMus; SchPl; StuGov; SchPpr; CchngActv; NCTE; University; Professional.

BROWN, Anne E; Fayette HS; Fayette, MO; Band; Chrs; HonRl; LbryAde; NHS; PepBnd; FHA; Bsktbl; Chrldr; Univ Mo Columbia.

BROWN, Anne E; Memorial HS; Eau Claire, WI; HospAde; NHS; Orch; SchMus; TchrAde; FrCl; Swmmng; CchngActv; University; Lawyer.

BROWN, Barbara A; Lakeview HS; St Clair Shores, MI; 22/676 TrsJrCls; ChrhWkr; LbryAde; NHS; TchrAde; YthLg; Yrbk; PresFrCl; PpCl; Chrldr; Mc Comb Cty Comm College; Accounting.

BROWN, Barbara D; United Township HS; E Moline, IL; ChrhWkr; CncrtBnd; HonRl; MrchBnd; NatlMeritCmnd; Fort Wayne Bible Clg; Missionary Nurse.

BROWN, Becky; Gothenburg HS; Gothenburg, NE; CmntyWkr; HonRl; NatlThespSoc; SchPl; TchrAde; 4-H; PpCl; Univ.

BROWN, Becky A; Jamaica HS; Sidell, IL; SecSrCls; Band; HonRl; MrchBnd; OffAde; PolWkr; StuCncl; Bsktbl; Chrldr; GAA; College; Professnl.

BROWN, Betsy L; Cheboygan Area HS; Cheboygan, MI; ChrhWkr; CmntyWkr; SctActv; TchrAde; RptrSchPpr; College; Anesthetist.

BROWN, Beverly D; Great Bend Sr HS; Great Bend, KS; TrsSophCls; ChrhWkr; CmntyWkr; HonRl; NatlFornLg; NatlMeritSF; StuCncl; YthFlsp; FHA; FTA; FrCl; SpnCl; PpCl; Univ Of Ks; Juvenile Corrections.

BROWN, Bill G; Beaman Conrad Liscomb HS; Conrad, IA; ALBoysSt; Band; ChrhWkr; CncrtBnd; SctActv; LetterBsbl; Ftbl; LetterTrk; Wrstlng; Iowa State; Forestry.

BROWN, Brenda L; Columbus North HS; Columbus, IN; 104/500 Band; HonRl; OffAde; PepBnd; Sec4-H; FTA; GerCl; Bsktbl; IMSpt; Ball State Univ; Nursing.

BROWN, Brenda S; Butler HS; Butler, MO; SecAFS; ALAGirlsSt; ChrhWkr; DrlTm; HonRl; SchPl; StuCncl; Yrbk; TreasFHA; FrCl; Chrldr; IMSpt; PPFtbl; Nursing Sch; Nurse.

BROWN, Brent L; Huntington North HS; Warren, IN; Band; CncrtBnd; MrchBnd; PepBnd; VPSctActv; TchrAde; Sec4-H; TreasFFA; LetterFtbl; 4-HAwd; College; Professional.

BROWN, Brian K; North Side HS; Fort Wayne, IN; 36/499 Indiana Univ; Photography.

BROWN, Bruce A; Airport HS; Carleton, MI; 13/180 PresBand; HonRl; NHS; SchMus; SchPl; StuCncl; TchrAde; MthCl; PpCl; CaptTrk; U Of Mi; Computer Engineer.

BROWN, Bruce B; Smithville HS; Smithville, MO; 4/75 VPSophCls; PresJrCls; HonRl; JrNHS; NHS; StuCncl; SciCl; LetterFtbl; CaptWrstlng; College.

BROWN, Bruce E; Griffin HS; Springfield, IL; 50/200 HonRl; LbryAde; SctActv; YthFlsp; PpCl; SciCl; College; Insurance.

BROWN, Bryan L; Harper Creek HS; Battle Creek, MI; HonRl; NHS; 4-H; SpnCl; 4-HAwd; U Of Mi; Elec Engr.

BROWN, Bryan L; Haper Creek HS; Battle Creek, MI; HonRl; NHS; SchPpr; 4-H; Ferris College; Elec Engineer.

BROWN, Candice C; Warren HS; Warren, IL; 1/58 Band; CncrtBnd; HonRl; MrchBnd; NatlMeritCmnd; Orch; PepBnd; SchMus; PresFTA; GAA; College; Mathematics.

BROWN, Carmen E; Parkersburg HS; Parkersburg, IA; 2/48 Band; Chrs; CncrtBnd; HonRl; NHS; OffAde; StuCncl; SpnCl; LetterBsbl; LetterGlf; Univ.

BROWN, Carol J; Sheboygan North HS; Sheboygan, WI; 14/500 TrsSrCls; Chrl; HonRl; NatlFornLg; VPNHS; StuCncl; SchPpr; PresPpCl; DARAwd; Purdue University; Engineering.

BROWN, Carolyn F; St Thomas Apostle HS; Chicago, IL; 3/38 Chr; ChrhWkr; HonRl; NHS; OffAde; SchAde; Mundelein College; Physician.

BROWN, Cathryn; Manteno HS; Manteno, IL; 9/79 TrsSophCls; TrsJrCls; HonRl; Mdrgl; NHS; StuCncl; EdYrBk; FTA; Chrldr; AmLegAwd; Eastern Il Univ; Teacher Or Secretary.

BROWN, Cathy; Hershey Public HS; Hershey, NE; Chrs; HonRl; NHS; SchMus; StuCncl; TchrAde; Yrbk; 4-H; PpCl; Chrldr; Chadron St Coll; Basic Secty.

BROWN, Cecil; Carbondale Comm HS; Carbondale, IL; ALBoysSt; HonRl; PpCl; Bsbl; Bsktbl; IMSpt; AmLegAwd; College; Structrual Engineering.

BROWN, Cecil; Sunnydale Acad; Universuty, MO; Chr; PolWkr; Bsktbl; Ftbl; Trk; IMSpt; College; Professional.

BROWN, Charles B; New Trier East HS; Kenilworth, IL; 195/847 ChrhWkr; CmntyWkr; HonRl; SctActv; StuCncl; StuGov; MthCl; PresSciCl; Bsbl; Ftbl; Tennis; University; Engineer.

BROWN, Charles L; Lakeview HS; Decatur, IL; LetterAud/Vis; ChrhWkr; SchMus; SchPl; StuCncl; YthFlsp; Bsktbl; Ftbl; Trk; CchngActv; Eastern Ill Univ; Physical Education.

BROWN, Charles R; Griggsville HS; Griggsville, IL; 4/25 TrsFrshCls; Band; Chr; Chrs; CncrtBnd; HonRl; PepBnd; SpnCl; LetterBsbl; LetterBsktbl; College; Electronics.

BROWN, Cherry L; Century HS; Olmsted, IL; 5/60 TrsSophCls; TrsJrCls; TrsSrCls; HonRl; MrchBnd; Yrbk; 4-H; Chrldr; GAA; IMSpt; Murray St Univ; Med Tech.

BROWN, Cheryl L; North Central HS; Haddam, KS; 4/26 VPFrshCls; PresSophCls; SecSrCls; Band; HonRl; SchPl; StuCncl; EdYrBk; 4-H; PpCl; College; Vocation.

BROWN, Christy L; Southwestern HS; Shelbyville, IN; SecBand; CncrtBnd; MrchBnd; PepBnd; SecStuCncl; Treas4-H; SpnCl; PpCl; CaptChrldr; 4-HAwd; College; Nursing.

BROWN, Clifford W; Manual HS; Kansas, MO; LetterBsktbl; LetterFtbl;.

BROWN, Connie; Corunna HS; Vernon, MI; HonRl; JA; SchPl; SctActv; RptrSchPpr; PpCl; Mi St Univ; Floriculture.

BROWN, Connie; Aron HS; Plainfield, IN; 8/150 TrsSophCls; Chr; HonRl; ModUN; NHS; SchMus; StuCncl; Yrbk; PpCl; GAA; Iupui Indianapolis; Physical Therapist.

BROWN, Constance L; Alexandria Monroe HS; Alexandria, IN; 24/191 PresFrshCls; Chr; HonRl; NHS; StuCncl; 4-H; SecSpnCl; SecPpCl; CaptChrldr; IMSpt; Purdue Univ; Phy Ed.

BROWN, Cynthia B; North Callaway HS; Auxvasse, MO; 12/79 SecSophCls; HstJrCls; SecSrCls; PresBand; Chr; ChrhWkr; HonRl; NHS; SecStuCncl; SecPpCl; Trk; CitAwd; College; Professional.

BROWN, Cynthia E; Lebanon HS; Inauzle, NE; VPBand; DrlTm; DrmMjrt; HonRl; ModUN; SchPl; SptEdYrbk; FFA; PresPpCl; LetterBsktbl; Military Service.

BROWN, Cynthia J; Homestead HS; Fort Wayne, IN; 58/225 Band; CncrtBnd; HonRl; MrchBnd; PepBnd; LetterTrk; GAA; Parkview Sch Of Nursing; Rn.

BROWN, Daniel; Delavan Hs; Delavan, IL; 2/52 VPJrCls; Chrs; HonRl; Mdrgl; NatlMeritCmnd; StuCncl; Pres4-H; Trk; IMSpt; SARAwd; Icc Transfer To Ui; Farming.

BROWN, Daniel E; Delavan HS; Delavan, IL; 2/53 VPJrCls; Chrs; HonRl; NatlMeritCmnd; StuCncl; PresFFA; Trk; IMSpt; SARAwd; U Of I; Agriculture.

BROWN, Daniel L; Estherville Senior HS; Estherville, IA; Band; Chr; HonRl; PepBnd; SchMus; Ftbl; IMSpt; U S Air Force Academy; Law Major.

BROWN, Daniel L; Estherville Sr HS; Estherville, IA; Band; Chrs; CncrtBnd; HonRl; MrchBnd; PepBnd; SchMus; SchPl; SctActv; LetterFtbl; Swmmng; Tennis; Wrstlng; Us Air Force Academy; Law.

BROWN, Daryl L; Hillsdale HS; Hillsdale, MI; SctActv; LetterTrk;.

BROWN, David E; Gull Lake HS; Richland, MI; 34/234 CmntyWkr; HonRl; PresJA; NHS; PolWkr; RptrYrbk; SciCl; IMSpt; JAAwd; U Of Mi.

BROWN, Dawn E; Mattawan HS; Mattawan, MI; 3/105 HonRl; LbryAde; NHS; SchPl; TchrAde; Yrbk; SchPpr; PpCl; GAA; College; Police Science.

BROWN, Deborah K; Albion HS; Albion, MI; 3/204 ChrhWkr; HonRl; NHS; Univ Of Michigan; Clinical Psychology.

BROWN, Debra C; Lebanon HS; Lebanon, MO; Chr; HonRl; SchAde; TchrAde; SpnCl;.

BROWN, Debra J; Sault Area HS; Dafter, MI; Chr; ChrhWkr; CncrtBnd; HonRl; MrchBnd; PepBnd; SchMus; SchPl; TchrAde; YthFlsp; College; Professional Medicine.

BROWN, Debra S; Twin Lakes HS; Burnettsville, IN; 63/206 SecSophCls; ALAGirlsSt; Band; ChrhWkr; CmntyWkr; CncrtBnd; DrlTm; HonRl; JrNHS; LbryAde; MrchBnd; GAA; IMSpt; DARAwd; Purdue Univ; Animal Sciences.

BROWN, Deena M; Quincy Ii HS; Quincy, IL; SecFrshCls; SecSophCls; PresJrCls; PresSrCls; AFS; Chr; HonRl; IntrClCncl; JrNHS; NHS; NatlMeritFnl; NatlMeritCmnd; Trk; HstSophCls; Western Il Univ.

BROWN, Denise E; Andover HS; Birmingham, MI; 1/500 HonRl; NHS; NatlMeritSF; FrCl; PpCl; Miami Univ; Law.

BROWN, Dennis D; Willowbrook HS; Lombard, IL; 18/850 HonRl; TreasNHS; NatlMeritCmnd; Orch; LetterSocr; Earlham College; Biology.

BROWN, Denola M; Thomas Carr Howe HS; Indianapolis, IN; 49/717 HonRl; JA; ROTC; FrCl; Trk; Chrldr; AmLegAwd; College; Nurse.

BROWN, Diana S; Diamond Riv HS; Joplin, MO; 6/57 TrsSophCls; SecJrCls; Band; Chr; CncrtBnd; HonRl; Mdrgl; NHS; PepBnd; StuCncl; Pres4-H; FHA; MthCl; PpCl; Mssc College; Liberal Arts.

BROWN, Diane E; Dexter Sr HS; Dexter, MO; Band; CncrtBnd; HonRl; PepBnd; TchrAde; College; Art.

BROWN, Donald R; Plato HS; Falcon, MO; 2/36 HstFrshCls; TrsSophCls; TrsSrCls; HonRl; StuCncl; RptrSchPpr; 4-H; Bsbl; LetterBsktbl; LetterTrk; Univ Of Missouri; Veterinarian.

BROWN, Donald W; Whitnall HS; Greenfield, WI; Band; CncrtBnd; HonRl; MrchBnd; NHS; PepBnd;.

BROWN, Donna; Enterprise Acad; Meade, KS; VPFrshCls; VPSophCls; Chr; ChrhWkr; HonRl; SchAde; SchMus; SchPl; SctActv; RptrYrbk; RptrSchPpr; Southwestern Union College; Behavioral Sci.

BROWN, Donna J; South Haven HS; South Haven, KS; TrsSophCls; PresJrCls; TrsSrCls; Chrs; HonRl; SecNHS; RptrYrbk; Yrbk; Chrldr; Wichita State Univ; Theatre.

BROWN, Donnie L; Fenger HS; Chicago, IL; 58/716 HonRl; LitMag; NHS; NatlMeritSF; Quill&Scroll; ROTC; SptEdYrbk; EdSchPpr; FrCl; DARAwd; U Of Il; Biologist.

BROWN, Edwin T; Rockhurst HS; Kansas City, MO; HonRl; Rockhurst Col; Astronomy.

BROWN, Elaine G; Springfield HS; Springfield, IL; 26/585 Band; NHS; EdYrBk; PresFrCl; GAA; Indiana Univ; Business Advertising.

BROWN, Elizabeth A; St Agatha HS; Detroit, MI; Chr; Chrs; HonRl; SchMus; SctActv; SpnCl; PpCl; Univ Of Michigan; Mathematics.

BROWN, Ernest J; Shawnee Mission South HS; Overland Park, KS; ChrhWkr; HonRl; StuCncl; Trk; College; Landscape Designer.

BROWN, Eugene R; Athens HS; Athens, WI; CncrtBnd; NHS; PepBnd; FFA; PpCl; Ftbl; College; Music.

BROWN, Franklin K; Clarkton HS; Malden, MO; PresJrCls; Band; CncrtBnd; MrchBnd; PepBnd; PpCl; Bsbl; College; Law Inforcement.

BROWN, Freezell; Park Tudor HS; Indianapolis, IN; Chr; Chrl; CmntyWkr; HonRl; Mdrgl; NatlMeritSF; SchMus; SchPl; LetterBsktbl; LetterFtbl; Coll; Music.

BROWN, Gayle A; Ocon Sr HS; Oconomowoc, WI; 17/223 PresFrshCls; VPSophCls; VPJrCls; Chr; HonRl; NHS; SchMus; Univ Of Madison; Fine Arts.

BROWN, Geraldine L; Heritage Hills HS; Troy, IN; 22/148 Band; Chrs; CncrtBnd; HonRl; MrchBnd; NHS; PepBnd; U Of Evansville Ind; Music.

BROWN, Gregory A; Belleville HS; Ypsilanti, MI; 17/525 PresSrCls; HonRl; NHS; StuCncl; StuGov; GerCl; Bsbl; Bsktbl; CaptFtbl; Navy; Vetrinarian Med.

BROWN, Gregory T; Ithaca HS; Ithaca, MI; ALBoysSt; Band; Chr; HonRl; Mdrgl; NHS; SchMus; YthFlsp; Ftbl; ChmnTennis;.

BROWN, Jacqueline T; Anchor Bay HS; New Baltimore, MI; ChrhWkr; HonRl; NHS; John Wesley College; Elementary Teacher.

BROWN, James A; Forreston HS; Forreston, IL; 28/78 ChrhWkr; CmntyWkr; LbryAde; LetterBsbl; LetterBsktbl; LetterFtbl; LetterTrk;.

BROWN, James G; Benton Central HS; Fowler, IN; 29/289 ChrhWkr; HonRl; NHS; SctActv; YthFlsp; LetterFtbl; IMSpt; College; Professional.

BROWN, Janet L; Avoha Comm HS; Avoca, IA; SecJrCls; ALAGirlsSt; Chrs; HonRl; LbryAde; NHS; NatlThespSoc; SchMus; Teen; Chrldr; Coll; Art.

BROWN, Janice R; Caro HS; Caro, MI; 63/178 Chr; ChrhWkr; HonRl; NatlMeritCmnd; OffAde; SctActv; TchrAde; YthFlsp; FHA; PpCl; Col; Secretarial Science.

BROWN, Janis L; Wauconda HS; Wauconda, IL; 5/234 Band; HonRl; LbryAde; NHS; NatlThespSoc; SchPl; YthFlsp; FrCl; Western Michigan Univ; Physicians Asst.

BROWN, Jan M; North Putnam HS; Greencastle, IN; 5/130 HonRl; LbryAde; NHS; OffAde; 4-H; LatCl; MthCl; LetterBsktbl; GAA; 4-HAwd; Univ; Medicine.

BROWN, Jeannie R; Windsor HS; Windsor, MO; Chrs; ChrhWkr; HonRl; FHA; FTA; LatCl;.

BROWN, Jeannine A; Dilworth Public HS; Dilworth, MN; 4/45 Band; CmntyWkr; CncrtBnd; HonRl; NHS; SchMus; PresSophCls; LetterBsktbl; LetterTrk; LetterChrldr; Coll.

BROWN, Jeff A; Scranton HS; Gascoyne, ND; VPFrshCls; PresSophCls; Chrs; CncrtBnd; HonRl; PepBnd; StuCncl; 4-H; LetterBsktbl; LetterFtbl; LetterTrk; Coll; Phy Ed.

BROWN, Jeffrey; Ames Sr HS; Ames, IA; 20/394 ALBoysSt; Band; HonRl; ModUN; NatlFornLg; NatlMeritFnl; NatlMeritSchl; StuGov; Tennis; IMSpt; St Olaf Coll; Math.

BROWN, Jeffrey A; Dundee HS; Dundee, MI; Band; CncrtBnd; HonRl; MrchBnd; PepBnd; SchPl; Trade School.

BROWN, Jeffrey D; Brazil HS; Brazil, IN; Chr; HonRl; NatlThespSoc; SchMus; StuCncl; KeyCl; PpCl; LetterBsbl; LetterFtbl; LetterTrk; Clge; Pro.

BROWN, Jeffrey W; Evanston Twp HS; Evanston, IL; HonRl; NatlMeritCmnd; StuCncl; StuGov; GerCl; LetterFtbl; CaptTrk; EldAwd; Harvard Univ; Medicine.

BROWN, Jerald J; Bullock Creek HS; Midland, MI; ChrhWkr; JA; SchPl; SctActv; JAAwd;.

BROWN, Jerry A; Dickinson Area Vocational HS; Dickinson, ND; Band; CAP; CncrtBnd; HonRl; MrchBnd; NHS; PepBnd; SctActv; RptrYrbk; SciCl; Purdue U; Aerospace Engineering.

BROWN, Jerry L; North White HS; Monticello, IN; Band; HonRl; NHS; NatlThespSoc; SchMus; 4-H; Bsbl; CaptBsktbl; LetterGlf; 4-HAwd; Huntington College; Accounting.

BROWN, Jerry L; Southeastern HS; Augusta, IL; 9/35 VPFrshCls; Band; Chr; CncrtBnd; HonRl; MrchBnd; SchMus; SchPl; Yrbk; FFA; FTA; Bsbl; Trk; Trade School; Vocation.

BROWN, Jill M; Breckenridge HS; St Louis, MI; HonRl; YthFlsp; SpnCl; IMSpt; PPFtbl; Coll; Social Work.

BROWN, Joanne M; Milton Sr HS; Milton, WI; 10/186 AFS; HonRl; StuCncl; RptrYrbk; Sec4-H; VPFHA; FrCl; PpCl; 4-HAwd; College; Home Economics.

BROWN, Joanne M; Traverse City HS; Traverse City, MI; 19/700 NatlFornLg; NHS; NatlMeritSF; RedCrAde; StuCncl; StuGov; SpnCl; PpCl; SciCl; Chrldr; U Of Mich; Psychology.

BROWN, Jody L; La Salle Peru Twp HS; Peru, IL; HonRl; OffAde; Yrbk; RptrSchPpr; Illinois Valley Comm College.

BROWN, Joe D; Griggsville HS; Girggisville, IL; 5/25 PresFrshCls; Chrs; HonRl; NHS; StuCncl; YthFlsp; SpnCl; LetterBsbl; LetterBsktbl; LetterTrk; Univ Of Il; Engineering.

BROWN, John D; Logansport HS; Logansport, IN; 40/380 HonRl; OffAde; SecKeyCl; VPGerCl; MthCl; SciCl; LetterTennis; LetterTrk; Wabash College; Medicine.

BROWN, John K; Elk Point HS; Elk Point, SD; 12/51 HonRl; 4-H; Col; Math.

BROWN, Joy A; Aledo HS; Aledo, IL; 2/101 AFS; Band; ChrhWkr; CncrtBnd; HonRl; SchMus; VPYthFlsp; Yrbk; SecFNA; GAA; DanFAwd; 4-HAwd; Sterling College; Medicine.

BROWN, Joyce A; Brazil Sr HS; Brazil, IN; 9/155 HonRl; NHS; FBLA;.

BROWN, Julia; Richland HS; Gray Ridge, MO; ChrhWkr; HonRl; OffAde; SchPl; SchPpr; FHA; Semo Cape; Business.

BROWN, Julia C; A A Stagg HS; Palos Hills, IL; HonRl; JrNHS; LbryAde; NHS; SchMus; MthCl; PpCl; College; Computers.

BROWN, Julie J; Benkelman HS; Parks, NE; 2/45 ALAGirlsSt; Chrs; CncrtBnd; HonRl; HospAde; NHS; Yrbk; 4-H; Scottsbluff School Of Nursing; Nurse.

BROWN, Julie J; Bentielman HS; Parks, NE; 2/45 ALAGirlsSt; Band; Chrs; CmntyWkr; CncrtBnd; HonRl; HospAde; MrchBnd; NHS; PepBnd; Yrbk; SptEdSchPpr; Scottsbluff School Of Nursing; Nurse.

BROWN, Karen; Jennings HS; St Louis, MO; Chr; Chrs; ChrhWkr; CmntyWkr; SchPpr; Sw Baptist Coll; Religious Studies.

BROWN, Karla; Jacksonville; Jacksonville, IL; 61/363 Band; Chr; ChrhWkr; HospAde; MrchBnd; TreasYthFlsp; SchPpr; VP4-H; DanFAwd; 4-HAwd; College; Business.

BROWN, Kathleen A; Huntington North HS; Huntington, IN; SecJrCls; Chr; ChrhWkr; HonRl; LitMag; OffAde; PolWkr; SchMus; RptrSchPpr; PpCl; Coll; Pre Law.

BROWN, Kathleen J; Clay HS; South Bend, IN; 1/385 Band; CncrtBnd; HonRl; MrchBnd; NHS; NatlMeritSF; StuCncl; SchPpr; FrCl; PPFtbl;.

BROWN, Kathryn E; Brazil Senior HS; Brazil, IN; 20/165 DrlTm; HonRl; HospAde; NHS; OffAde; YthFlsp; Yrbk; FHA; SpnCl; Ind St Univ; Registered Nurse.

BROWN, Kathy; Malden HS; Malden, MO; Chr; ChrhWkr; HonRl; OffAde; FHA; FrCl; College.

BROWN, Kathy; Northeast Nodaway Rv HS; Ravenwood, MO; Chr; HonRl; SchMus; SchPl; StuCncl; YthFlsp; RptrYrbk; University.

BROWN, Kathy J; Brownstown HS; Brownstown, IL; HonRl; LbryAde; SchPl; TchrAde; RptrYrbk; TreasFHA; GAA;.

BROWN, Keith C; Limestone HS; Bartonville, IL; 103/396 Chr; Chrl; HonRl; Mdrgl; NatlThespSoc; SchMus; SchPl; SpnCl; Univ; Pre Med.

BROWN, Kelly R; Pawnee Public HS; Pawnee City, NE; 4/36 Band; ChrhWkr; HonRl; MrchBnd; OffAde; SchMus; SchPl; StuGov; Twrl; 4-H; FHA; Bsbl; Bsktbl; Univ Of Nebraska; Criminal Justice.

BROWN, Kenneth E; Soldan HS; St Louis, MO; Aud/Vis; HonRl; JA; LetterPpCl; LetterBsktbl; LetterFtbl; CchngActv; IMSpt; College; Business Admin.

BROWN, Kenneth L; Diagonal Community HS; Diagonal, IA; ALBoysSt; LetterBand; HonRl; PolWkr; SchMus; SchPl; StuCncl; RptrSchPpr; 4-H; Bsbl; Jr College; Vocation.

BROWN, Kevin A; Rochester HS; Rochester, IN; 46/150 ALBoysSt; StuCncl; YthFlsp; GerCl; LetterBsbl; LetterBsktbl; College.

BROWN, Kevin M; Wm Henry Harrison HS; W Lafayette, IN; 34/251 Band; ChrhWkr; CncrtBnd; MrchBnd; NHS; PepBnd; SchPl; SctActv; YthFlsp; 4-H; Purdue Univ; Engineering.

BROWN, Kevin T; St Patrick HS; Chicago, IL; HonRl; JA; LbryAde; NatlMeritCmnd; StuCncl; College; Science.

BROWN, Kim A; Penn HS; Osceola, IN; Band; CncrtBnd; MrchBnd; PepBnd; SchMus; YthFlsp; PresKeyCl; FrCl; LetterTrk; Jordan College Of Music; Trombone.

BROWN, Kimberly L; Memorial HS; Joplin, MO; ChrhWkr; CncrtBnd; Chrldr; GAA; College; Special Ed.

BROWN, Kim D; Ishpeming HS; Ishpeming, MI; ChrhWkr; HonRl; LbryAde; SchPl; Yrbk; FTA; FrCl; Job.

BROWN, Kim E; Saranna HS; Savanna, IL; 24/63 HonRl; SchPl; SciCl; Nursing Sch; Nurse.

BROWN, Larry; Newton Community HS; Newton, IL; HonRl; RptrSchPpr; SchPpr; LatCl; Olney Central College.

BROWN, Laura J; Dekalb Sr HS; Dekalb, IL; 6/390 CncrtBnd; JrNHS; LitMag; SecNatlFornLg; NatlMeritCmnd; NatlThespSoc; SchPl; SecStuCncl; TchrAde; FrCl; College.

BROWN, Laurie A; Lewistown HS; Lewistown, IL; Band; Chrs; SchPl; SctActv; RptrYrbk; FHA; PpCl; Trk; College.

BROWN, Lawrence N; Webster Groves Senior HS; Webster Groves, MO; 2/465 Band; ChrhWkr; CncrtBnd; HonRl; MrchBnd; PolWkr; StuCncl; YthFlsp; SpnCl; LetterSwmmng; U Of Chicago.

BROWN, Leland D; Oldhem HS; Oldham, SD; ALBoysSt; PresStuCncl; StuGov; RptrYrbk; EdSchPpr; PpCl; Bsbl; LetterBsktbl; LetterFtbl; LetterTrk; College; Professional.

BROWN, Leslie C; Pierce City HS; Pierce City, MO; HonRl; NHS; ROTC; PpCl; SciCl; LetterBsktbl; LetterTrk; GAA; PPFtbl; University; Veterinary Medicine.

BROWN, Leslie H; Farmer City HS; Farmer City, IL; 3/74 AFS; CncrtBnd; HonRl; MrchBnd; NHS; SchMus; SctActv; EdYrBk; 4-H; LetterBsktbl; GAA; DanFAwd; 4-HAwd; College; Music.

BROWN, Linda A; Churubusco HS; Churubusco, IN; 12/105 ChrhWkr; HonRl; NHS; Quill&Scroll; TchrAde; EdSchPpr; TreasFTA; LatCl; AmLegAwd; Indiana Univ; Journalism.

BROWN, Linda A; Lourdes HS; Chicago, IL; CmntyWkr; HonRl; OffAde; SchPl; SctActv; RptrSchPpr; SchPpr; College; Vocation.

BROWN, Linda J; Benkelman HS; Parks, NE; 1/34 VPFrshCls; LetterBand; LetterChrs; DrlTm; LetterMrchBnd; NHS; 4-H; PpCl; LetterTrk; Chrldr; Univ Of Nebraska; Teaching.

BROWN, Lonae L; St Marys HS; Bentley, ND; Chr; Chrl; Chrs; HonRl; 4-H; PpCl; Trk; CaptChrldr; Wapheton Trade Sch; Occupational Therapist.

BROWN, Lori A; St Mary Academy; Rockwood, MI; ChrhWkr; CmntyWkr; LbryAde; NHS; StuCncl; PpCl; CaptChrldr; College; Art Or Science.

BROWN, Lynn D; J C Harmon HS; Kansas City, KS; Band; HonRl; LbryAde; NHS; SctActv; TchrAde; YthFlsp; Swmmng; Tennis; GAA; Johnson Cty Comm College; Dental Hygiene.

BROWN, Margarita C; Bayard HS; Mcgrew, NE; 6/43 HonRl; LbryAde; NHS; SchPl; Yrbk; SchPpr; KeyCl; EldAwd; PresAwd; College; Accounting.

BROWN, Marilyn R; Central Community HS; Carlyle, IL; SecSophCls; SecJrCls; SecTrsSrCls; HonRl; SchPl; StuCncl; FHA; SpnCl; MthCl;.

BROWN, Marilyn S; Neponset HS; Neponset, IL; HstFrshCls; TrsSophCls; Band; Chrs; SchPl; YthFlsp; Yrbk; FHA; PpCl; Chrldr;.

BROWN, Mark; Edgemont HS; Edgemont, SD; 4/16 TrsFrshCls; Chrs; ChrhWkr; HonRl; SchPl; StuCncl; RptrYrbk; MthCl; Coll; Professional.

BROWN, Mark E; Sullivan HS; Sullivan, MO; 4/159 Band; Chr; CncrtBnd; HonRl; NHS; PepBnd; StuCncl; FTA; LetterBsktbl; RotaryAwd; College; Professional.

BROWN, Mark W; Garber HS; Essexville, MI; Chr; HonRl; SchMus; SchPl; TchrAde; Bsbl; Bsktbl; Ftbl; Trk; CchngActv; College; Coaching.

BROWN, Mary A; Murphysboro HS; Murphysboro, IL; 15/180 Chrs; HonRl; SchMus; StuCncl; RptrSchPpr; 4-H; PpCl; CaptChrldr; 4-HAwd; Univ; Psychology Or Physical Ed.

BROWN, Mary A; Bishop Dwenger HS; Fort Wayne, IN; Band; Chrs; CncrtBnd; HonRl; MrchBnd; NHS; SchMus; SchPl; Twrl; RptrYrbk; Clge; Elem Ed.

BROWN, Mary C; Bishop Noll Institute; East Chicago, IN; 112/360 CmntyWkr; DrlTm; HonRl; HospAde; JA; NHS; NatlMeritSchl; UNYO; FBLA; FDA; College; Medical.

BROWN, Mary J; Grand Blanc HS; Grand Blanc, MI; 15/635 HospAde; NHS; YthFlsp; Grand Rapids Baptist College; Teacher.

BROWN, Mary L; St Thomas Apostle HS; Chicago, IL; 8/43 AFS; Chr; CmntyWkr; HonRl; HospAde; SchAde; StuCncl; GAA; College; Registered Nurse.

BROWN, Melinda A; Alma Public HS; Alma, NE; 3/27 SecTrsSrCls; Band; Chrs; HonRl; Mdrgl; NHS; TchrAde; YthFlsp; Yrbk; PpCl; U Of Nebraska; Special Education.

BROWN, Michael; New Ulm Senior HS; New Ulm, MN; Chr; Chrs; ChrhWkr; CmntyWkr; HonRl; SchAde; SctActv; StuGov; IMSpt; College; Professional.

BROWN, Michael A; Tilden HS; Chicago, IL; 85/336 HonRl; JA; NatlMeritSchl; SchAde; StuCncl; TchrAde; Bsktbl; LetterFtbl; IMSpt; JAAwd; College; Professional.

BROWN, Michelle A; Anna Jonesboro HS; Jonesboro, IL; 16/137 ALAGirlsSt; PresBand; ChrhWkr; CncrtBnd; HonRl; ModUN; NHS; SecStuCncl; FNA; PresLatCl; Se Mo St U; Rn.

BROWN, Mike A; Marion HS; Marion, IL; 1/277 Band; ChrhWkr; CncrtBnd; HonRl; MrchBnd; NatlMeritSF; SctActv; CivCl; MthCl; SciCl;.

BROWN, Monica S; North Miami HS; Macy, IN; 7/117 Chr; HonRl; Mdrgl; NHS; OffAde; SptEdSchPpr; SpnCl; PpCl; CaptBsktbl; LetterTrk; Coll; Coach, Journalism.

BROWN, Myrna L; Ancille Domini HS; Plymouth, IN; 6/15 HstSophCls; HstJrCls; Chrl; DrlTm; HonRl; SchMus; SchPl; StuCncl; StuGov; Parkview Schl; Nursing.

BROWN, Myron D; Enterprise Acad; Eureka, KS; PresFrshCls; VPSophCls; Chr; StuCncl; SchPpr; IMSpt; BttyCrckrAwd; College; Medicine.

BROWN, Nancy J; Holden HS; Centerview, MO; 2/90 SecSrCls; Band; CncrtBnd; HonRl; MrchBnd; TreasNHS; TchrAde; SecSciCl; Secretarial Work.

BROWN, Nate; St Anne HS; Momence, IL; HonRl; Bsktbl; Trk; College.

BROWN, Nola; St Mary HS; Highland Park, MI; TrsJrCls; ChrhWkr; HonRl; NHS; SchAde; Yrbk; Andrews Univ; Medicine.

BROWN, Norman; West Catholic HS; Comstock Park, MI; Band; CncrtBnd; HonRl; JA; MrchBnd; SchPl; SpnCl; MthCl; Socr;.

BROWN, Oliver E; Central HS; Minneapolis, MN; Univ Of Mn; Forensic Pathologist.

BROWN, Paige D; Dumont Community HS; Dumont, IA; PresSophCls; Chrs; ChrhWkr; HonRl; NHS; YthFlsp; Yrbk;.

BROWN, Pamela; Franklin Community HS; Franklin, IN; PpCl; GAA; PPFtbl; Trade; Business Field.

BROWN, Pamela; Clearwater HS; Piedmont, MO; 6/100 ChrhWkr; HonRl; LbryAde; OffAde; SciCl; Busniess School; Vocation.

BROWN, Pamela A; Bellmont HS; Decatur, IN; 10/251 Band; HonRl; NHS; SchPl; YthFlsp; FHA; FTA; PpCl; SciCl; IMSpt; Ball State U; Mathematics.

BROWN, Patricia M; Mt Assisi Acad; Chicago, IL; SecSophCls; Chrs; HonRl; NHS; SchPl; StuCncl; SpnCl; Glf; GAA; Loyola Univ; Pre Law.

BROWN, Patrick D; Anna Jonesboro Comm HS; Anna, IL; 16/144 Band; HonRl; JA; NHS; 4-H; FSA; KeyCl; LatCl; SciCl; LetterBsktbl; College; Professional.

BROWN, Paul E; Clarkston HS; Clarkston, MI; 5/440 ChrhWkr; HonRl; JrNHS; NHS; SptEdYrbk; CaptTrk; Albion College; Doctor.

BROWN, Peggy; Delwood Community HS; Delmar, IA; PresSrCls; Chrs; HonRl; Mdrgl; NHS; SchPl; RptrYrbk; EdSchPpr; FrCl; Bsktbl; American Inst Of Bus Sch; Secretary.

BROWN, Peggy L; Delwood HS; Delmar, IA; PresSrCls; Chrs; HonRl; LbryAde; SchMus; SchPl; RptrYrbk; EdSchPpr; FTA; Bsktbl; Amer Inst Busi; Sec.

BROWN, Penny L; Gallatin HS; Gallatin, MO; 29/52 Band; CncrtBnd; LbryAde; MrchBnd; PepBnd; FHA;.

BROWN, Peter A; Gilman HS; Danforth, IL; 1/50 PresFrshCls; ALBoysSt; Band; Chr; Chrl; Chrs; CncrtBnd; HonRl; MrchBnd; NHS; PepBnd; SchPl; EdYrBk; LetterTrk; University Of Illinois; Engineering.

BROWN, Phillip L; Nebraska Cty Sr HS; Nebraska City, NE; Band; ChrhWkr; CmntyWkr; CncrtBnd; HonRl; MrchBnd; NHS; PepBnd; Quill&Scroll; SchMus; LetterBsktbl; LetterFtbl; LetterTrk; University Of Nebraska; Dentistry.

BROWN, Phyllis E; Bellevue HS; Bellevue, NE; 37/550 HonRl; NHS; StuCncl; FTA; LetterSwmmng; GAA; IMSpt; PPFtbl; U Of S Cal; Lawyer.

BROWN, Rachel D; Clay Center Public HS; Clay Center, NE; 1/29 Band; Chr; Chrs; HonRl; NHS; Teen; 4-H; LetterTrk; DARAwd; PresAwd; College; Police.

BROWN, Randall D; South Callaway Rii HS; Fulton, MO; 11/28 ChrhWkr; HonRl; SchPl; StuCncl; Yrbk; FBLA; Bsbl; Bsktbl; Trk; Westminster; Accounting.

BROWN, Randy A; Oshkosh West HS; Oshkosh, WI; Ftbl; College; Carpenter.

BROWN, Rebecca; Kewanee HS; Kewanee, IL; HonRl; SchPl; GerCl; PpCl; Chrldr; Trade Sch; Lpn.

BROWN, Rebecca A; John Glenn HS; Westland, MI; 45/678 Band; HonRl; JrNHS; NHS; GerCl; Tennis; Western Michigan Univ; Law.

BROWN, Rebecca L; Gillett HS; Gillett, WI; 9/76 TrsFrshCls; PresJrCls; PresSrCls; ALAGirlsSt; CncrtBnd; MrchBnd; NatlFornLg; VPFHA; Chrldr; DARAwd; Lakeland Medical & Dental Acad; Med Assist.

BROWN, Regina; Calumet HS; Chicago, IL; 3/370 PresJrCls; Chrs; ChrhWkr; HonRl; NatlMeritCmnd; SpnCl; SciCl; Northwestern Univ; Law.

BROWN, Renee L; Paxton Consolidated HS; Paxton, NE; ChrhWkr; HonRl; NHS; SchMus; YthFlsp; PpCl; LetterBsktbl; LetterTrk; Chrldr; GAA; College; Professional.

BROWN, Richard; Madison Sr HS; Madison, IL; 26/117 VPFrshCls; TrsSophCls; VPJrCls; ALBoysSt; ChrhWkr; HonRl; JA; PolWkr; StuCncl; FrCl; Columbia College Chicago; Communications.

BROWN, Richard D; Lutheran West HS; Southfield, MI; ChrhWkr; HonRl; NHS; NatlMeritCmnd; TreasStuCncl; GerCl; Bsbl; Bsktbl; LetterFtbl; Trk; CaptWrstlng; University Of Michigan; Architect.

BROWN, Richard R; Harlan Comm HS; Harlan, IA; VPFrshCls; HonRl; JA; StuCncl; TreasFFA; Bsktbl; Ftbl; Tennis; CchngActv; JAAwd; College; Business.

BROWN, Robert E; Dekalb HS; Dekalb, IL; 21/355 Band; CncrtBnd; HonRl; MrchBnd; Orch; PepBnd; PresSpnCl; Univ; Bio/photography.

BROWN, Robin J; Barnum HS; Barnum, MN; HonRl; JrNHS; NHS; TchrAde; Yrbk; EdSchPpr; VPFTA; PpCl; CaptBsktbl; CchngActv; Brainerd Jr Clge; Special & Phy Ed.

BROWN, Rodney D; St Francis De Saces HS; Chicago, IL; 38/296 HonRl; JrNHS; NHS; StuCncl; Bsktbl; Univ Of Il; Law.

BROWN, Roger K; South Page HS; Clarinda, IA; 2/38 VPFrshCls; PresSophCls; Band; CncrtBnd; HonRl; MrchBnd; NHS; PepBnd; SchPl; LetterBsktbl; Engineering.

BROWN, Ronice J; Batavia Sr HS; Batavia, IL; 5/221 CncrtBnd; HonRl; MrchBnd; OffAde; SchPl; TchrAde; 4-H; FrCl; MthCl; Iowa State Univ; Veterinarian.

BROWN, Rose D; John Marshall Haran HS; Chicago, IL; 9/707 HonRl; NHS; StuCncl; MthCl; PpCl; George Washington Univ; Cpa.

BROWN, Ruth; Greenway HS; Grand Rapids, MN; Band; Chr; ChrhWkr; HonRl; NHS; OffAde; TchrAde; Chrldr; GAA; PPFtbl; College; Nursing.

BROWN, Sally; Ludington HS; Ludington, MI; 7/217 ALAGirlsSt; NHS; SchMus; StuCncl; 4-H; LatCl; RusCl; SpnCl; 4-HAwd; Mi St Univ.

BROWN, Sally R; O Fallon Township HS; O Fallon, IL; VPJrCls; Chrs; HonRl; JrNHS; Mdrgl; NHS; NatlThespSoc; SchMus; SchPl; Carnegie Mellon; Theatre Arts.

BROWN, Sarah J; Charleston HS; Charleston, MO; 1/167 ALAGirlsSt; Chrs; HstFrshCls; HonRl; Mdrgl; NHS; NatlMeritCmnd; SchMus; PresStuCncl; Twrl; Vanderbilt U; Medicine.

BROWN, Scott D; Oconomowoc HS; Oconomowoc, WI; 11/450 ALBoysSt; Chr; Chrl; Chrs; ChrhWkr; SecNHS; SchPl; StuCncl; LetterWrstlng; U Of Wis Eau Claire; Journalism.

BROWN, Scott M; Hammond Baptist HS; Alsip, IL; 66/88 HstFrshCls; Band; Chrl; ChrhWkr; CncrtBnd; MrchBnd; Orch; PepBnd; SchMus; SchPl; PpCl; Bsbl; Bsktbl; Ftbl; Tenn Temple; Ministry.

BROWN, Sharon; Lasalle HS; Cedar Rapids, IA; Chr; Undecided; Accountant Teacher.

BROWN, Shelby R; Bernie HS; Bernie, MO; HonRl; SchPl; Jr College.

BROWN, Sherry L; Diagonal Community HS; Diagonal, IA; LetterBand; CncrtBnd; HonRl; StuCncl; 4-H; Bsktbl; Trk; LetterChrldr; DanFAwd; 4-HAwd; Jr College; Vocaton Sec Clerical.

BROWN, Stephen; Memorial HS; Beloit, WI; 56 Aud/Vis; CncrtBnd; PepBnd; ROTC; RptrSchPpr; Tennis; VFWAwd; Marquette Univ; Bs Major In Physics.

BROWN, Stephen A; Winona R 3 HS; Winona, MO; Band; CncrtBnd; HonRl; JrNHS; SchPl; Sec4-H; LetterBsbl; LetterBsktbl; Us Coast Guard; Math.

BROWN, Stephen J; Appleton West HS; Appleton, WI; Aud/Vis; LbryAde; PolWkr; SchPl; SctActv; U Of Wisc; Eng.

BROWN, Steve A; Orrick Public HS; Camden, MO; 2/47 VPJrCls; PresSrCls; PresNHS; StuCncl; TchrAde; PresFFA; Bsktbl; CaptFtbl; CaptTrk; Univ Of Missouri; Agriculture Ed.

BROWN, Steve K; Abingdon HS; Abingdon, IL; HonRl; NHS; 4-H; PresFFA; LatCl; Bsktbl; LetterFtbl; LetterTrk; IMSpt; Western Illinois University; Agriculture.

BROWN, Steven J; Roosevelt HS; Minneapolis, MN; ChrhWkr; YthFlsp; SciCl; Ftbl; Socr; Swmmng; LetterTrk; United Theol Seminary; Psychology.

BROWN, Steven P; Carl Brablec HS; Roseville, MI; 9/418 HonRl; NHS; SchMus; SctActv; YthFlsp; SciCl; Trk; Albion Coll; Elec Engr.

BROWN, Steven W; Sioux Valley HS; Volga, SD; 11/66 HonRl; IMSpt; University; Architect.

BROWN, Tamara A; Highland HS; Anderson, IN; 24/251 HonRl; TchrAde; 4-H; FrCl; 4-HAwd; Purdue University; Engineering.

BROWN, Teresa D; Blue Mound HS; Macon, IL; 2/50 PresSophCls; PresChrs; ChrhWkr; HonRl; TreasNHS; SecStuCncl; PresYthFlsp; Pres4-H; CaptChrldr; CitAwd; College; Medicine.

BROWN, Terry L; Boyne City HS; Boyne City, MI; Band; HonRl; SchMus; TchrAde; PpCl; Chrldr; Univ Of Mich; Med Tech.

BROWN, Terry L; Castle HS; Chandler, IN; HonRl; NatlThespSoc; PolWkr; SchMus; StuCncl; FTA; Indiana University; Biology.

BROWN, Tessie J; Normandy HS; St Louis, MO; ChrhWkr; HonRl; JA; NHS; PpCl; Univ; Psychology.

BROWN, Thomas D; Forest Hills Central HS; Grand Rapids, MI; 10/180 Band; HonRl; LbryAde; MrchBnd; ModUN; NHS; NatlMeritCmnd; PepBnd; TreasYthFlsp; LatCl; Trk; Michigan St Univ; Veterinarian.

BROWN, Thomas G; Fenwick HS; Oak Park, IL; SpnCl; Ftbl; Univ Of Arizona; Pharmacy.

BROWN, Thomas G; Crossville Community HS; Crossville, IL; VPJrCls; StuCncl; MthCl; Trade School; Professional.

BROWN, Thomas M; Marist HS; Oak Lawn, IL; 36/390 CtyCnl; CmntyWkr; HonRl; NHS; NatlMeritFnl; PolWkr; StuCncl; StuGov; Bsktbl; Ftbl;.

BROWN, Thomas R; Marion Sr HS; Marion, IL; ChrhWkr; CmntyWkr; HonRl; SctActv; SciCl; LetterWrstlng; University.

BROWN, Todd D; Bishop Dwenger HS; Ft Wayne, IN; 110/245 JA; JAAwd; Col; Professional.

BROWN, Todd F; Bremen HS; Markham, IL; 2/440 Chr; ChrhWkr; PresNHS; NatlThespSoc; SchMus; SchPl; StuCncl; Tennis; Lincoln Christian College.

BROWN, Tony K; Melrose Mindoro HS; Melrose, WI; 12/84 PresFrshCls; HonRl; StuCncl; RptrSchPpr; FFA; CaptBsbl; LetterBsktbl; CaptFtbl; CaptTrk; Technical School; Air Conditioning Tech.

BROWN, Tresa M; Bluffs HS; Winchester, IL; 3/34 TrsSrCls; ALAGirlsSt; CmntyWkr; HonRl; NHS; OffAde; StuCncl; Yrbk; PresFHA; SpnCl; DanFAwd; DARAwd; SARAwd; College; Nurse.

BROWN, Valerie J; Gordon HS; Porcupine, SD; 3/67 HonRl; LbryAde; SecStuCncl; TchrAde; FBLA; PresFTA; DARAwd; 4-HAwd; College; Elementary Education.

BROWNE, Valerie K; Lawton HS; Lawton, MI; HstSophCls; DrlTm; SpnCl; PpCl; Bsbl; Bsktbl; Chrldr;.

BROWN, Vanessa; Thornton Township HS; Harvey, IL; ChrhWkr; HonRl; TchrAde; PpCl; IMSpt; CitAwd; College.

BROWN, Vern A; Jonesville HS; Jonesville, MI; 1/80 HonRl; StuCncl; 4-H; FFA; Michigan State Univ; Farming.

BROWN, Virginia J; Douglas Mac Arthur HS; Saginaw, MI; 49/278 SecFrshCls; HonRl; NHS; OffAde; PolWkr; YthFlsp; EdYrBk; PpCl; Weber State College; Social Worker.

BROWN, Wanda S; Avoha Comm HS; Avoca, IA; 7/45 PresJrCls; Chrs; HonRl; Mdrgl; NHS; StuGov; Yrbk; LetterBsktbl; LetterTrk; JETSAwd; Iowa State U.

BROWN, Ward W; Decatur Comm HS; Seldon, KS; PresFrshCls; PresSophCls; PresJrCls; PresSrCls; ALBoysSt; NHS; Pres4-H; Bsbl; LetterFtbl; LetterTrk; College; Professional.

BROWN, Wendy R; Wayland Academy; Beaver Dam, WI; Chr; NatlMeritSF; Univ Of Wisconsin; Medicine.

BROWNE, Alicia M; Elgin Acad; Elgin, IL; 4/18 VPJrCls; HonRl; SchPl; StuCncl; StuGov; TchrAde; SpnCl; PpCl; Chrldr; RotaryAwd; U Of Wisc; Certified Public Accountant.

BROWNE, Katherine S; Naperville Central HS; Naperville, IL; 79/820 ChrhWkr; CmntyWkr; HonRl; HospAde; LbryAde; NHS; TchrAde; YthFlsp; PpCl; U Of Il; Psychologist.

BROWNE, Margaret; Holy Cross HS; Marine City, MI; 5/35 SecSophCls; SecJrCls; Chr; HonRl; JrNHS; NHS; SchPl; EdYrBk; 4-H; GAA; St Clair Co Comm Col; Executive Secretary.

BROWNE, Marilyn B; Regina Dominican HS; Skokie, IL; 11/206 HonRl; HospAde; NatlMeritSF; LatCl; Marquette Univ; Nursing.

BROWNE, Sue C; Brookfield East HS; Brookfield, WI; CmntyWkr; HonRl; SchAde; SptEdYrbk; Yrbk; LetterTrk; Uw Milwaukee; Phy Ed.

BROWNELL, Steven D; John Adams HS; South Bend, IN; 120/500 VPSrCls; HonRl; OffAde; LetterFtbl; LetterWrstlng; KiwanAwd; In Univ; Major Police Adm.

BROWNELL, Thomas P; Ft Zumwalt HS; Wentzville, MO; Band; CncrtBnd; HonRl; MrchBnd; NHS; University Of Missouri; Computer Science.

BROWNELL, Tim; Lourder HS; Rochester, MN; SctActv; Ftbl; Trk; EldAwd; Coll; Pro.

BROWNFIELD, David L; Griffin HS; Springfield, IL; Band; CncrtBnd; HonRl; JA; MrchBnd; SctActv; TchrAde; Univ Of Illinois; Engineering.

BROWNFIELD, Kenneth J; South Vigo HS; Terre Haute, IN; HonRl; TchrAde; RptrSchPpr; Indiana State Univ; Science.

BROWNING, Jayne E; Goshen HS; Goshen, IN; 51/254 HonRl; LatCl; Indiana U; Medical Technlogy.

BROWNING, Lavonne; Von Steuben Hs; Chicago, IL; 24/231 HonRl; NatlFornLg; NHS; Orch; GAA; U Of Illinois; Psychology.

BROWNING, Lesa A; Meredosia Chambersburg HS; Chambersburg, IL; 2/40 SecJrCls; Band; Chrs; ChrhWkr; HonRl; NHS; StuCncl; SciCl; College; Nurse.

BROWNING, Mary E; Ridgway HS; New Haven, IL; 3/50 ChrhWkr; DrmMjrt; HonRl; MrchBnd; PolWkr; StuCncl; TchrAde; EdYrBk; RptrSchPpr; SpnCl; Bauder Fashion Coll; Fashin Merchandising.

BROWNING, Michael R; Madison West HS; Madison, WI; 183/583 SctActv; Ftbl; IMSpt; Uw; Marketing.

BROWNING, Rita K; Southern HS; Media, IL; Chrs; HonRl; Yrbk; FHA; GAA; Southeastern Comm Clge; Rn.

BROWNING, Ron W; Butler HS; Butler, MO; 5/80 AFS; HonRl; PresNHS; SchPl; EdYrBk; FrCl; Sw Mo Univ; Business Mgmt.

BROWNING, Sandy; Knox County Hs; Knox City, MO; Band; ChrhWkr; MrchBnd; PepBnd; 4-H; FDA; LetterTrk; 4-HAwd;.

BROWNLEE, David L; Farragut Community HS; Farragut, IA; 13/35 HonRl; 4-H; FFA; Bsbl; Bsktbl; Ftbl; Trk; 4-HAwd;.

BROWNLEE, Diane E; Shawnee Mission East HS; Prairie Village, KS; ChrhWkr; HonRl; HospAde; NatlFornLg; NatlMeritSF; SctActv; PpCl; IMSpt; Texas Christian Univ.

BROWNLEE, Edward G; Austin HS; St Clair Shores, MI; 8/135 Chr; HonRl; NHS; Sacrstn; SchMus; Univ Of Michigan; Mathematics.

BROWNLEE, Janice J; Lincoln HS; Kansas City, MO; Chr; DrlTm; JA; NatlMeritCmnd; RptrSchPpr; 4-H; Bsbl; Bsktbl; 4-HAwd; CitAwd; Coll; Professional.

BROWNLEE, Kathy L; Rockwell City Comm HS; Rockwell City, IA; 10/64 Band; Chrs; ChrhWkr; CncrtBnd; HonRl; MrchBnd; Orch; PepBnd; SchMus; SchPl; RptrSchPpr; FrCl; LetterBsbl; LetterBsktbl; Iowa State University; Political Science.

BROWNLEE, Marcia A; Sabetha Sr HS; Sabetha, KS; ALAGirlsSt; Band; SecNHS; 4-H; FFA; FHA; CaptBsktbl; Chrldr; 4-HAwd; Kansas State University; Dentistry.

BROWNLEE, Mary L; Williamston HS; Williamston, MI; 8/148 SecAFS; Band; Chr; ChrhWkr; MrchBnd; SchPl; YthFlsp; Spring Arbor Clge; French Translator.

BROWNSBERGER, Edith; Ballard R Ii HS; Montrose, MO; 1/14 SecFrshCls; VPJrCls; Chrs; ChrhWkr; HonRl; SchPl; Yrbk; EdSchPpr; BttyCrckrAwd; CitAwd; Central Mo State Univ; Science.

BROXTERMAN, Dona M; Marian HS; Chicago Hts, IL; 23/365 HonRl; NHS; Sdlty; TchrAde; Yrbk; Prairie St College; Secretary.

BROXTERMAN, Sandra; B&b HS; Baileyville, KS; 4/36 VPJrCls; Chrs; ChrhWkr; HonRl; SchPl; FHA; EngCl; PpCl; Trk; College; Computer Programmer.

BROYHILL, Clifford L; So Soo Sr HS; Dakota City, NE; 30/200 HonRl; JA; SpnCl; Bsktbl; Ftbl; Trk; Business Schl; Business Admin.

BROYLES, Barbara L; Rossville HS; Delia, KS; 2/45 HonRl; MrchBnd; SchMus; VPStuCncl; TchrAde; CaptBsktbl; LetterTrk; IMSpt; BttyCrckrAwd; 4-HAwd; Washburn Univ.

BROYLES, Deborah A; Streator HS; Streator, IL; 14/390 NHS; College; Cpa.

BROYLES, Gary L; Westfield Washington HS; Westfield, IN; 18/89 TrsFrshCls; Aud/Vis; HonRl; NatlThespSoc; StuCncl; YthFlsp; Bsktbl; Ftbl; Trk; Wrstlng; Univ; Pro.

BROZ, John A; Immaculate Conception HS; Hillside, IL; 33/140 NatlMeritCmnd; SctActv; LatCl; Bsktbl; LetterFtbl; LetterTrk; Univ Of Illinois; Engineering.

BROZEK, Jeffrey E; La Crosse HS; La Crosse, KS; 1/35 TrsFrshCls; HstSophCls; PresJrCls; Chrs; HonRl; NatlFornLg; NHS; NatlMeritCmnd; SchPl; PresStuCncl; PpCl; LetterBsktbl; LetterGlf; Trk; Univ Of Kansas; Medicine.

BROZKA, Robert; Griffin HS; Rochester, IL; HonRl; NHS; SctActv; PpCl; Ftbl; Springfield Coll; Biology.

BRTKO, Carolyn A; Bishop Noll Institute HS; Whiting, IN; 19/360 ChrhWkr; HonRl; TchrAde; SpnCl;.

BRUCE, Camilla L; West Side HS; Gary, IN; 56/700 ChrhWkr; HonRl; ROTC; YthFlsp; Indiana U; Rn.

BRUCE, Coy W; Fairfield Comm HS; Fairfield, IL; Chr; Chrs; LbryAde; Florida Inst Of Tech; Marine Biology.

BRUCE, Deborah E; Sherwood Public HS; Sherwood, ND; VPJrCls; PresSrCls; ALAGirlsSt; DrlTm; HonRl; MrchBnd; SchPl; StuCncl; SchPpr; Bsktbl; Coll; Secretarial.

BRUCE, Jeanne A; Putnam Co HS; Lucerne, MO; SecFrshCls; HonRl; SchPl; StuCncl; RptrYrbk; 4-H; PpCl; LetterBsktbl; LetterTrk; IMSpt; AmLegAwd; Univ Of Missouri; Journalism.

BRUCE, Jeff; Belton HS; Richard Gebaur Afb, MO; 1/282 HonRl; NHS; ROTC; StuCncl; TchrAde; FrCl; Socr; OptClAwd; Central Missouri State U; Political Science.

BRUCE, Kristine L; Le Roy HS; Le Roy, IL; Chrs; DrlTm; HonRl; LitMag; Mdrgl; SchMus; SchPl; YthFlsp; 4-H; PpCl; LetterTrk; GAA; IMSpt; College.

BRUCE, Lesley E; Glenbrook South HS; Glenview, IL; 111/600 ChrhWkr; HonRl; TchrAde; CaptBsbl; LetterSwmmng; Univ Of Illinois; Architect.

BRUCE, Linda J; Smithville HS; Smithville, MO; 10/75 Band; HonRl; JrNHS; NHS; SchPl; PpCl; Bsbl; LetterBsktbl; LetterTrk; BttyCrckrAwd; Central Missouri State Univ.

BRUCE, Patty; Norris City Omaha HS; Norris City, IL; Chrs; HonRl; SchPl; RptrYrbk; PpCl; GAA; IMSpt; Southern Ill Univ; Mathematics Teacher.

BRUCE, Terri L; Senath Hornersville HS; Senath, MO; SecJrCls; Chr; Chrs; ChrhWkr; LbryAde; TchrAde; FTA; PpCl; Swmmng; College.

BRUCE, T Jeffery; Andrean HS; Merrillville, IN; 12/306 HonRl; NHS; MthCl; LetterWrstlng; Notre Dame Univ; Computer Science.

BRUCH, Julie J; Smithville HS; Kansas City, MO; 7/75 Chr; Chrs; ChrhWkr; HonRl; NatlMeritCmnd; SchMus; SchPl; Yrbk; RptrSchPpr; Clge; Math.

BRUCH, Kathy J; Whitewater HS; Whitewater, WI; AFS; Band; HonRl; NHS; NatlThespSoc; SchMus; SchPl; LetterTrk; GAA; IMSpt; Marquette Univ; Dental Hygeine.

BRUCK, Susan; Rock Island Hs; Rock Ilsland, IL; Band; CmntyWkr; NHS; Orch; PepBnd; SchPl; SctActv; KeyCl; MthCl;.

BRUCKER, Gary G; Seneca Twp HS; Seneca, IL; HonRl; SptEdYrbk; GerCl; PpCl; Bsbl; CaptBsktbl; Ftbl; LetterGlf; LetterTrk; Illinois State Univ; Accounting.

BRUCKNER, Corinna M; Mather HS; Chicago, IL; 40/422 Chrs; ChrhWkr; HonRl; NHS; TchrAde; Yrbk; Augustana College; English.

BRUCKNER, Diane D; Sevastopol HS; Sturgeon Bay, WI; Chrs; LbryAde; TchrAde; FHA; Clerical Field.

BRUCKNER, John J; St Johns Mil Academy; Thiensville, WI; 3/48 DrlTm; HonRl; NHS; ROTC; RptrSchPpr; SpnCl; Bsbl; Bsktbl; CaptFtbl; Marquette Univ; Medicine.

BRUCKS, Jayne M; Glasgow Rii HS; Glasgow, MO; TrsJrCls; HonRl; SctActv; FHA; Bsbl; Bsktbl; Swmmng; Tennis; Trk; PresAwd; Univ; Nursing.

BRUCKS, Richard M; Weber HS; Chicago, IL; 26/192 DrmBgl; LetterTennis; Unif Of I Circle; Medicine.

BRUDE, Jan; Wellcome Memorial HS; Good Thunder, MN; 13/45 SecFrshCls; SecSrCls; Band; Chr; Chrs; ChrhWkr; CmntyWkr; CncrtBnd; HonRl; LbryAde; Trade Sch; Vocation.

BRUDER, Linda; Crofton Public HS; Crofton, NE; 4/65 HonRl; NHS; OffAde; SchMus; SchPl; SctActv; StuCncl; RptrYrbk; EdYrBk; RptrSchPpr; Bus Sch; Accounting.

BRUDNICKI, Gregory J; Marist HS; Chicago Ridge, IL; HonRl; U S Air Force; Electronics.

BRUDOS, Julie; Tomah Sr HS; Tomah, WI; 6/283 Chr; HonRl; NHS; SchMus; Univ; Special Education.

BRUE, Daniel; Mt Horeb HS; Hollandale, WI; College; Farming.

BRUECK, Christine M; Notre Dame HS; Burlington, IA; 20/80 DrlTm; HonRl; HospAde; RptrYrbk; RptrSchPpr; PpCl; LetterTennis; IMSpt; College; Professional.

BRUEGGEMAN, George V; St Louis University HS; St Louis, MO; 19/190 HonRl; U Of Missouri; Bus Admin.

BRUEGGEMAN, Rose; Athens HS; Hamburg, WI; VPSophCls; Band; CncrtBnd; HonRl; LbryAde; NHS; PepBnd; FBLA; FHA; PpCl; College; Business Course.

BRUEGGEMANN, Barbara A; Union HS; Beaufort, MO; 2/174 PresJrCls; ALAGirlsSt; Band; CncrtBnd; HonRl; MrchBnd; PepBnd; College; Medicine.

BRUEGGEMANN, Brenda J; Greeley County HS; Tribune, KS; TrsSrCls; Band; CncrtBnd; HonRl; MrchBnd; NatlThespSoc; PepBnd; SchPl; StuCncl; Yrbk; University; Psychology.

BRUEGGEMANN, Susan; Burke HS; Omaha, NE; ChrhWkr; HonRl; NHS; StuGov; FHA; LatCl; PpCl; IMSpt; U Of Nebr At Omaho; Business Clothing.

BRUEGGEN, Carol; Cashton HS; Cashton, WI; 10/66 Band; Chrs; CncrtBnd; HonRl; Mdrgl; MrchBnd; NHS; RptrYrbk; RptrSchPpr; FHA; Viterbo College; Registered Nurse.

BRUEGGER, Lori K; Nauvoo Colusa HS; Nauvoo, IL; HonRl; SchPl; TreasStuCncl; SptEdYrbk; FBLA; FHA; PpCl; Glf; CaptChrldr; GAA;.

BRUEHLMAN, Jodine K; Black Hawk HS; South Wayne, WI; HonRl; LbryAde; NatlFornLg; SchPl; RptrYrbk; FHA; VPFrCl; PpCl; Trk; University; French Interperter.

BRUEHLMAN, Laurel J; Argyle HS; Argyle, WI; Band; Chr; ChrhWkr; CncrtBnd; HonRl; Mdrgl; MrchBnd; PepBnd; SchMus; EdYrBk; EdSchPpr; LetterTrk; IMSpt; 4-HAwd; College; Insurance Secretary.

BRUEHLMAN, Loren J; Arayle HS; Argyle, WI; ModUN; Ftbl; Coll; Aeronautical Engineering.

BRUELAND, Barry L; Walker HS; Ah Gwah Ching, MN; Band; Chr; Chrs; ChrhWkr; CncrtBnd; HonRl; Mdrgl; NatlFornLg; SchPl; College; Professional.

BRUER, Patrick J; Regis HS; Eau Claire, WI; PresFrshCls; Band; HonRl; MrchBnd; Orch; StuCncl; FrCl; Tennis; IMSpt; OptClAwd;.

BRUESS, Connie A; Turkey Valley HS; Jackson Jct, IA; HonRl; NHS; SptEdYrbk; Bsbl; Bsktbl; AmLegAwd;.

BRUGGEMAN, Clair J; O Gorman HS; Sioux Falls, SD; PresJrCls; PresSrCls; ALBoysSt; ChrhWkr; HonRl; NatlFornLg; NHS; PolWkr; SchMus; St Johns Univ; Humanities.

BRUGGEMAN, Clair J; Ogorman HS; Sioux Falls, SD; PresJrCls; PresSrCls; ALBoysSt; ChrhWkr; NatlFornLg; NHS; SchMus; CivCl; IMSpt; Univ Of South Dakota; Law.

BRUGGEMAN, Dave J; Leo HS; Guttenberg, IA; Chrs; CmntyWkr; HonRl; SchMus; SchPl; LetterBsbl; Trk; IMSpt; CitAwd; Professional.

BRUGGER, Lorna K; Cotter HS; Winona, MN; DrlTm; HonRl; PresAwd; Winona Voc Sch; Med Sec.

BRUGGER, Zoanne E; Bullock Creek HS; Midland, MI; 19/170 Chr; ChrhWkr; HonRl; NHS; TchrAde; 4-H; GerCl; 4-HAwd; Business Schooling; Secretary.

BRUGMAN, Karla K; South Clay Community HS; Webb, IA; 3/29 VPSrCls; Chr; HonRl; SchPl; EdYrBk; LetterBsktbl; Trk; BttyCrckrAwd; 4-HAwd; U Of Northern Ia.

BRUHN, Charles A; River Valley HS; Spring Green, WI; LetterBsbl; LetterBsktbl; IMSpt; College; Carpenter.

BRUHN, Patricia; St Louise De Marillac Hs; Glenview, IL; 18/254 Chrs; LitMag; Orch; SchMus; SchPl; StuCncl; StuGov; Columbia College; Communication.

BRUICK, David; New Haven HS; New Haven, IN; Band; CncrtBnd; MrchBnd; RptrYrbk; RptrSchPpr; SptEdSchPpr; SciCl; Trk; In Inst Of Tech; Engr.

BRUKER, Sarah J; Edwardsville Sr HS; Edwardsville, IL; Chr; Chrs; HonRl; Trk; Illinois State University.

BRUKETTA, Stephen P; Farmington East HS; Farmington, IL; Aud/Vis; LbryAde; SchPl; TchrAde; University; Osteopathacy.

BRULE, Mary P; Lafayette HS; Red Lake Falls, MN; 11/69 CncrtBnd; HonRl; PepBnd; Yrbk; 4-H; FHA; LetterBsktbl; LetterTrk; 4-HAwd; CitAwd; College; Vet Med.

BRULEY, Darcy L; St Peter HS; St Peter, MN; 18/186 Chr; PresLbryAde; NatlThespSoc; Quill&Scroll; SchPl; StuGov; RptrSchPpr; FHA; PpCl; GAA; St Cloud St; Mass Communications.

BRULLO, Raymond W; Saint Patrick HS; Chicago, IL; 5/425 HonRl; PresFDA; SpnCl; BauchLmbAwd; Loyola University; Medicine.

BRUMBAUGH, Curtis A; Pittsburg HS; Pittsburg, KS; HonRl; Bsktbl; Tennis; IMSpt; Kansas State College; Mechanical Engineer.

BRUMBAUGH, Peggy J; L C Mohr HS; South Haven, MI; Chrs; CmntyWkr; HonRl; Orch; SchMus; SchPl; College; Art.

BRUMLEY, David W; East Prairie HS; East Prairie, MO; 2/100 ALBoysSt; Band; Chr; NHS; Orch; SchPl; StuCncl; EdYrBk; LetterFtbl; Missouri University; Music.

BRUMLEY, Patricia F; Union HS; Losantville, IN; Chr; HonRl; NHS; TchrAde; FHA; SpnCl; College.

BRUMLEY, Rhonda L; Carson Macedonia HS; Carson, IA; 10/42 ALAGirlsSt; SecBand; Chr; HonRl; HospAde; NHS; StuGov; YthFlsp; Yrbk; 4-H; Bsktbl; 4-HAwd; Ankeny Comm College; Lab Technology.

BRUMM, Margaret M; Marquette HS; Marquette, MI; Band; CncrtBnd; DrmBgl; MrchBnd; NatlMeritSF; Orch; PepBnd; SchPl; SciCl; Univ; Chem Engr.

BRUMMEL, Howard A; Watertown HS; Watertown, WI; SecJrCls; Chrs; ChrhWkr; HonRl; SchMus; StuCncl; 4-H; LetterWrstlng; Univ Wi; Teaching Pro.

BRUMMEL, Michael; Aurora Central Catholic HS; Aurora, IL; 5/195 HonRl; Wrstlng; IMSpt;.

BRUMMEL, Michael P; Aurora Central Catholic HS; Aurora, IL; 5/164 College; Business.

BRUMMER, Cynthia A; Lafayette HS; Red Lake Falls, MN; 8/69 PresChrhWkr; HonRl; PolWkr; Sacrstn; VPStuCncl; RptrYrbk; RptrSchPpr; PresSpnCl; PresSciCl; IMSpt; St Benedict Col; Sociology.

BRUMMET, Barbara C; Nokomis HS; Nokomis, IL; ChrhWkr; HonRl; 4-H;.

BRUMMETT, Kathy A; Diamond R 4 HS; Diamond, MO; 7/52 Chr; HonRl; NHS; OffAde; FHA; Crowder College; Teacher.

BRUMMETT, Mark L; Frontier HS; Brookston, IN; VPFrshCls; HstJrCls; HonRl; NHS; SchAde; PresStuCncl; StuGov; TchrAde; SptEdYrbk; PpCl; SciCl; CaptFtbl; IMSpt; PresAwd; College; Professional.

BRUNDAGE, Christine D; United Community HS; Luther, IA; 7/38 Band; Chr; Chrs; SchMus; SchPl; TchrAde; 4-H; PpCl; SciCl; CaptBsbl; Iowa State Univ; Professional.

BRUNDIN, Karla A; Central HS; Glenwood, MN; Chr; HonRl; HospAde; SctActv; StuCncl; FHA; FNA; GerCl; College; Dental Hygienist.

BRUNE, Kathleen; Warren County R Iii HS; Warrenton, MO; 9/102 ChrhWkr; HonRl; MrchBnd; FHA; PpCl; Nw Mo St Univ; Elem Education.

BRUNE, Kellie A; Richmond Senior HS; Richmond, IN; SecTrsFrshCls; TrsSrCls; SecBand; CncrtBnd; DrmMjrt; MrchBnd; NHS; Pres4-H; Chrldr; CchngActv; Purdue; Zoologist.

BRUNEEL, Tammy A; Holy Cross HS; Richmond, MI; Chrl; ChrhWkr; LbryAde; 4-H; PpCl; Bsktbl; Trk; GAA; 4-HAwd; College.

BRUNELL, Gary A; Homewood Flossmoor HS; Glenwood, IL; 13/1040 Band; CncrtBnd; HonRl; PepBnd; FDA; FrCl; Univ Of Illinois; Biology.

BRUNER, Douglas; Drake Public HS; Drake, ND; Band; Chr; CncrtBnd; HonRl; MrchBnd; StuCncl; EdYrBk; RptrSchPpr; FFA; Trk; University Of Montana; Psychology.

BRUNER, Gail A; Marion HS; Florence, KS; VPFrshCls; ALAGirlsSt; Chrs; HonRl; LbryAde; FHA; SpnCl; PpCl; Bsktbl; Trk; Univ; Medical Prof.

BRUNER, Gary C; Uniontown HS; Uniontown, KS; PresFrshCls; PresSophCls; Band; ChrhWkr; CmntyWkr; StuCncl; StuGov; 4-H; FFA; Bsbl; LetterBsktbl; LetterFtbl; Glf; Swmmng; Kansas State Univ; Agriculture.

BRUNER, Janet M; Ladysmith HS; Ladysmith, WI; 6/124 HonRl; NHS; SchPl; StuCncl; Twrl; RptrYrbk; FHA; SecSpnCl; Chrldr; GAA; 4-HAwd; Western Wi Tech Inst; Medical Lab Tech.

BRUNER, John D; Mishawaka HS; Mishawaka, IN; 2/422 Band; Chr; HonRl; NHS; NatlMeritSF; SchMus; SchPl; SctActv; GerCl; SciCl; College; Electrical Eng Or Computer Science.

BRUNER, Judy; Dillsboro Public HS; Dillsboro, IN; 1/42 ALAGirlsSt; SchPpr; Trk; Chrldr; GAA; College;certified Public Accountant.

BRUNETT, Jeffrey L; Paul Harding HS; Fort Wayne, IN; 1/275 HonRl; JrNHS; StuCncl; Bsbl; Bsktbl; ChmbCommrsAwd; Wheaton College; Medicine.

BRUNETTE, Lisa A; West Bend West HS; West Bend, WI; 1/303 ALAGirlsSt; ChrhWkr; NatlFornLg; PresNHS; NatlMeritFnl; SchPl; TchrAde; RptrSchPpr; MthCl; VoiceDemAwd; College; Law.

BRUNGARDT, David J; Ellis HS; Ellis, KS; ChrhWkr; HonRl; PpCl; LetterFtbl; LetterTrk; LetterWrstlng;.

BRUNGARDT, Karla J; Forest Lake HS; Forest Lake, MN; 4/460 CncrtBnd; HonRl; MrchBnd; NatlFornLg; PepBnd; SchMus; Yrbk; LetterBsktbl; Tennis; LetterTrk; PresAwd; St Benedicts; Medicine.

BRUNGARDT, Mark W; Washington HS; Washington, KS; LetterTrk; Employment.

BRUNGARDT, Randall R; Auburn HS; Auburn, NE; 9/86 ALBoysSt; Band; CtyCnl; CmntyWkr; CncrtBnd; HonRl; NHS; Yrbk; SpnCl; MthCl; U Of Ne; Dentistry.

BRUNI, Susan C; Port Huron Northern HS; Port Huron, MI; 1/432 Chr; ChrhWkr; HonRl; NatlMeritCmnd; TreasStuCncl; PresFrCl; Valparaiso Univ; Business Admin.

BRUNIK, Paul H; Paynesville HS; Paynesville, MN; 9/117 ALBoysSt; Band; Chr; CncrtBnd; HonRl; MrchBnd; SchMus; SchPl; SctActv; YthFlsp; LetterBsbl; LetterBsktbl; Ftbl; EldAwd; College; Medicine.

BRUNING, Dean J; St Bernards HS; Breda, IA; PresJrCls; Chrs; HonRl; RedCrAde; SchPl; PresStuCncl; Bsktbl; College.

BRUNING, Dee A; Le Roy HS; Le Roy, IL; HonRl; NHS; StuCncl; 4-H; FHA; PpCl; PresGAA; PPFtbl; Il St U; Elemetray Ed.

BRUNING, Donna F; Ellsworth HS; Ellsworth, KS; Chrs; HonRl; RptrYrbk; Us Navy; Nursing.

BRUNING, Kenneth D; Winnebago HS; Winnebago, IL; 12/108 ChrhWkr; HonRl; JA; NHS; YthFlsp; 4-H; FTA; GerCl; PpCl; 4-HAwd; Western Ill U; Banking.

BRUNINK, Debra K; Holland Christian HS; Zeeland, MI; SecFrshCls; Chr; HonRl; JrNHS; FshEdSchPpr; Bsbl; Swmmng; PressSrCls; Trk; IMSpt; Central Mich U; Speech Pathologist.

BRUNK, Christine E; Brownstown HS; Brownstown, IL; 1/32 SecFrshCls; VPJrCls; SecBand; Chr; Chrs; DrlTm; HonRl; PepBnd; SchPl; StuCncl; TchrAde; FHA; SecFrCl; GAA; Univ; Professional.

BRUNK, Lars E; Badger HS; Lake Geneva, WI; 40/260 HonRl; OffAde; SchPl; StuCncl; StuGov; YthFlsp; Ftbl; Swmmng; Tennis; KiwanAwd; College; Professional.

BRUNKE, Susanne M; Cabrini HS; Allen Park, MI; 87/157 Chr; Chrs; HospAde; OffAde; SctActv; RptrYrbk; RptrSchPpr; FNA; GAA; College; Nursing.

BRUNKEN, Jeffrey E; Rochester HS; Rochester, IL; Band; CncrtBnd; HonRl; MrchBnd; PepBnd; SchMus; Univ; Wildlife Management.

BRUNKEN, Karen J; Clarks Public HS; Clarks, NE; 4/25 Band; Chrs; HonRl; LbryAde; PepBnd; SchPl; TchrAde; Doane College; Teacher.

BRUNKEN, Rodney D; Oak Park Academy; Burlington, IA; PresFrshCls; Chr; Chrl; College; Minister.

BRUNKER, Tim R; Reavis HS; Burbank, IL; 22/780 CAP; CmntyWkr; DrlTm; HonRl; JA; JrNHS; NHS; PolWkr; ROTC; SctActv; StuGov; YthLg; RusCl; MthCl; Air Force Academy; Engineering.

BRUNKO, Anne Marie S; Independence HS; Brandon, IA; 2/150 Band; ChrhWkr; CncrtBnd; HonRl; MrchBnd; NHS; NatlMeritCmnd; Pres4-H; Bsbl; Bsktbl; LetterTrk; GAA; 4-HAwd; Iowa St Univ; Science.

BRUNKOW, Susan R; Bay View HS; Milwaukee, WI; Band; Chr; ChrhWkr; CncrtBnd; HonRl; TreasJA; TreasLbryAde; MrchBnd; NatlMeritSF; Orch; University; Bio Medical Engineering.

BRUNMEIER, Kila M; Sully Buttes HS; Onida, SD; ALAGirlsSt; Chrs; HonRl; PpCl; Trade School; Secretary.

BRUNMEIER, Pamela M; Hazen Public HS; Hazen, ND; Chr; ChrhWkr; HonRl; Minot Bus Coll; Secretarial.

BRUNNER, Allan D; Riceville Comm HS; Le Ray, MN; HonRl; NHS; SchPl; Yrbk; SptEdYrbk; SchPpr; Univ; Physician.

BRUNNER, Karen S; Mason Co Eastern HS; Custer, MI; 3/45 SecJrCls; SecSrCls; HonRl; NHS; SchPl; TchrAde; SecFHA; FTA; EldAwd; Ferris State College; Business.

BRUNNER, Maureen K; Providence HS; Mokena, IL; 1/121 PresFrshCls; Chrs; HonRl; NHS; Yrbk; EdSchPpr; PresFrCl; SciCl; GAA; DARAwd; Lewis Univ; Nursing.

BRUNNER, Michael; Allen Park HS; Allen Park, MI; 5/515 HonRl; JrNHS; NHS; StuCncl; TchrAde; AmLegAwd; KiwanAwd; Michigan State Univ; Veterinarymedicine.

BRUNNER, Pamela; Riverside Brookfield Hs; N Riverside, IL; 7/489 HonRl; HospAde; NHS; LetterSwmmng; GAA; Loyola U; Pre Med And French.

BRUNNER, Richard; Manhattan HS; Manhattan, KS; 40/450 Chr; Chrs; HonRl; NatlFornLg; NatlThespSoc; Orch; SchMus; SchPl; OptClAwd; Univ Kansas State; Curriculum Of Major Stud.

BRUNNER, Richard J; Napoleon HS; Bismarck, ND; FFA; Ftbl; Wrstlng; Construction Work.

BRUNNER, Roni Marie; Cook HS; Angora, MN; 2/58 LetterBand; LetterChrs; HonRl; NHS; SchPl; SpnCl; LetterTrk; LetterChrldr; GAA; DARAwd; VoiceDemAwd; St Benedicts College; Lawyer.

BRUNNERT, Gerald G; Central Catholic HS; West Point, NE; Chr; Chrs; SchMus; SchPl; 4-H; SciCl; Bsbl; 4-HAwd; CitAwd; Trade Sch; Dairy Farmer.

BRUNNGRABER, Eric H; Proviso West HS; Westchester, IL; NatlFornLg; PolWkr; College.

BRUNS, Debra L; Greenway HS; Grand Rapids, MN; SecFrshCls; SecSrCls; NHS; NatlMeritCmnd; SchPl; EdSchPpr; FHA; CaptBsktbl; Chrldr; GAA; PPFtbl;.

BRUNS, Henry R; Liberal HS; Liberal, KS; Band; Chrs; ChrhWkr; CncrtBnd; PepBnd; Kansas State University.

BRUNS, Kevin J; Janesville HS; Janesville, IA; HonRl; TchrAde; Yrbk; Trade School; Commercial Art.

BRUNS, Steven R; Cal Comm HS; Alexander, IA; Band; Chrs; VPNHS; SchMus; SchPl; PresStuCncl; PresYthFlsp; Yrbk; LetterBsbl; LetterBsktbl; College; Commercial Art.

BRUNS, Teresa J; St Marys HS; Kansas City, MO; 2/74 VPJrCls; TrsSrCls; HonRl; ModUN; NHS; SchMus; SchPl; StuCncl; FrCl; IMSpt; Creighton Univ; Psychology.

BRUNS, Wayne A; Titonka Consolidated HS; Titonka, IA; Band; Chrs; HonRl; PresNHS; SchMus; 4-H; Bsktbl; LetterTrk; 4-HAwd; CitAwd; Iowa St Univ; Engineering.

BRUNSCHER, Patsy A; Tina Avalon HS; Bogard, MO; PresJrCls; Chrs; HonRl; NHS; StuCncl; RptrYrbk; RptrSchPpr; EdSchPpr; FHA; LetterBsktbl; College; English Teacher.

BRUNSINK, Holly R; Southfield Christian HS; Detroit, MI; 1/50 TrsSrCls; Chrs; ChrhWkr; CmntyWkr; HonRl; NHS; NatlMeritSF; SctActv; TreasStuGov; YthFlsp; SpnCl; MthCl; Univ Of Michigan; Language.

BRUNSMAN, Wayne; Dyersville Beckman HS; Dyersville, IA; 1/140 Chrs; NHS; NatlMeritCmnd; SchMus; SchPl; GerCl; IMSpt; Ia State Col; Engineering.

BRUNSMANN, Carla; Beckman HS; New Vienna, IA; Chrs; NHS; SchMus; StuCncl; GAA; Univ North Ia; Interior Design.

BRUNSVOLD, David A; Northwood Kensett HS; Kensett, IA; TrsSophCls; TrsJrCls; ALBoysSt; Chr; Chrl; LetterTrk; Coll; Journalism.

BRUNTON, Judith L; Bellmont HS; Decatur, IN; 8/249 HonRl; NHS; SecSpnCl; PresPpCl; SciCl; Univ; Fashion Retailing.

BRUSATTI, Kathleen M; Bishop Dubourg HS; St Louis, MO; 24/419 HonRl; HospAde; OffAde; Socr; IMSpt; PPFtbl; College; Medical Therapist.

BRUSCHER, David R; Sac Community HS; Sac City, IA; LetterTrk; Trade Schl; Elec Tech.

BRUSCHNIG, Terri J; Oconomowoc HS; Oconomowoc, WI; 9/468 Band; CncrtBnd; HonRl; JrNHS; MrchBnd; NHS; PepBnd; Univ; Spec Education.

BRUSE, Jo E; Aberdeen Central HS; Aberdeen, SD; ChrhWkr; HonRl; StuCncl; StuGov; PpCl; Chrldr; PPFtbl; College; Professional.

BRUSKY, Ron H; Whithall HS; Greenfield, WI; Band; CncrtBnd; HonRl; MrchBnd; ModUN; NHS; PepBnd; MthCl; SciCl; College; Engineering.

BRUSSLAN, James D; Highland Park HS; Highland Park, IL; PresSophCls; NHS; SchMus; StuCncl; StuGov; TchrAde; College.

BRUSSOLO, Robert F; Huron HS; Ann Arbor, MI; CmntyWkr; CncrtBnd; HonRl; MrchBnd; NatlMeritCmnd; PolWkr; SctActv; FrCl; IMSpt; U Of Mi; Engineering.

BRUSUEN, Myron K; Mahnomen HS; Mahnomen, MN; Band; Chr; HonRl; PepBnd; SchMus; Bsbl; CaptBsktbl; CaptFtbl; Trk; 4-HAwd; PresAwd; College; Professional.

BRUTCHER, Brian E; Princeton HS; Princeton, IL; 10/200 PresFrshCls; Chrs; HonRl; NHS; StuGov; GerCl; CaptFtbl; Trk; Wrstlng; CchngActv; Coll; Sci.

BRUXVOORT, Byron; Pella Christian HS; Oskaloosa, IA; Band; ChrhWkr; HonRl; MrchBnd; PepBnd; 4-H; IMSpt; 4-HAwd; Bus Sch; Vocation.

BRYAN, Candy K; Morton Sr HS; Hammond, IN; 12/478 HonRl; JrNHS; TreasNHS; 4-H; FHA; FTA; SpnCl; GAA; PPFtbl; University; Engineering.

BRYAN, Daniel S; Frederic Senior HS; Frederic, WI; 4/68 HonRl; JrNHS; NatlFornLg; NHS; NatlMeritSchl; NatlSciFnd; SchPl; StuCncl; 4-H; FBLA; Collge; Neuclear Physiology.

BRYAN, Jana; Joliet East HS; Elwood, IL; 126/381 Chr; HonRl; HospAde; College; Nursing.

BRYAN, Nora E; Turpin HS; Liberal, KS; Chr; HonRl; SchPl; Yrbk; FHA; FrCl; PpCl; LetterBsktbl; Swmmng; Trk; Clge; Vet.

BRYAN, Stuart W; Manistee HS; Manistee, MI; VPJrCls; ALBoysSt; Band; CncrtBnd; HonRl; MrchBnd; NatlFornLg; NHS; NatlMeritSchl; YthFlsp; Kalamazoo College; Pre Med.

BRYANS, Sarah A; Carpio Public HS; Carpio, ND; 2/24 CncrtBnd; HonRl; LbryAde; SchPl; RptrSchPpr; IMSpt; AmLegAwd; 4-HAwd; MasAwd; CitAwd; Coll.

BRYANT, Barbara L; Pepin HS; Pepin, WI; VPJrCls; Chrs; HonRl; RptrSchPpr; Business School; Vocational.

BRYANT, Belinda A; Josephinum HS; Chicago, IL; 12/104 PresFrshCls; HonRl; LbryAde; NHS; NatlMeritSchl; StuCncl; College; Professional.

BRYANT, Ben R; Richmond HS; Richmond, IN; CmntyWkr; HonRl; Swmmng; LetterWrstlng; IMSpt; College; Physician.

BRYANT, Cindy; Bishop Miege HS; Fairway, KS; 14/250 Chrl; ChrhWkr; HonRl; HospAde; ModUN; NHS; PolWkr; SchMus; Benedictine Coll; Physician.

BRYANT, Donald E; Central HS; Omaha, NE; 125/578 VPFrshCls; TrsJrCls; VPSrCls; Chrs; CmntyWkr; HonRl; JA; LbryAde; ModUN; NatlMeritCmnd; LetterFtbl; LetterTrk; Chrldr; CchngActv; University; Computer Technology.

BRYANT, Helen M; Franklin HS; Murrayville, IL; 7/40 HonRl; NHS; StuGov; EdYrBk; 4-H; FFA; FHA; SpnCl; PpCl; 4-HAwd; Western Ill Univ; Law Enforcement.

BRYANT, James; New Haven HS; New Haven, IN; 3/240 HonRl; NHS; SctActv; FSA; SciCl; Trk; AmLegAwd; Purdue Univ; Mech Engrg.

BRYANT, Jeffrey M; Amos Alonzo Stagg HS; Hickory Hills, IL; Band; CncrtBnd; HonRl; LitMag; MrchBnd; NHS; NatlMeritCmnd; PepBnd; StuCncl; RptrYrbk; SptEdYrbk; CaptBsbl; CaptBsktbl; College.

BRYANT, Jerri; Centerville HS; Centerville, IA; Chrs; HonRl; RptrYrbk; RptrSchPpr; EdSchPpr; SpnCl; PpCl; MasAwd; Jr Coll; Comm Art.

BRYANT, Jody A; Medicine Valley HS; Curtis, NE; Band; Chrs; DrmMjrt; HonRl; NHS; StuCncl; FNA; PpCl; LetterTrk; CchngActv; GAA; 4-HAwd; MasAwd; Nursing Schl; Professional.

BRYANT, Kenneth J; Westside HS; Hoffman Estates, IL; HonRl; Trk; CchngActv; IMSpt; CitAwd; College Ottawa Ks; Business.

BRYANT, Kevan L; Morgan Park HS; Chicago, IL; 132/493 PresSrCls; HonRl; NHS; NatlMeritFnl; College; Medicine.

BRYANT, Mark; Malden HS; Malden, MO; Band; Chr; ChrhWkr; CncrtBnd; DrmMjrt; MrchBnd; Trhee Rivers Junior Col; Music.

BRYANT, Mary; Floyd Central HS; New Albany, IN; 3/275 ALAGirlsSt; Chr; HonRl; JrNHS; NHS; Orch; StuGov; RptrSchPpr; BttyCrckrAwd; RotaryAwd; Univ Of Cincinnati; Music.

BRYANT, Nancy C; Warren Central HS; Indianapolis, IN; HonRl; NatlMeritCmnd; StuGov; TchrAde; SciCl; Swmmng; Trk; GovHonPrgAwd; Iupui; Sociology.

BRYANT, Randy; Westville HS; Westville, IL; Band; CmntyWkr; HonRl; SchPl; Yrbk; SpnCl; SciCl; Trk; College; Vocation.

BRYANT, Ronald D; Sullivan HS; Sullivan, MO; 26/161 HonRl; NHS; Bsktbl; Ftbl;.

BRYANT, Russell; Morning Son Hs; Morning Sun, IA; PresJrCls; Band; HonRl; SchPl; SctActv; YthFlsp; Bsbl; Bsktbl; Ftbl; Trk; College ; Professional.

BRYANT, Vania L; Southeast HS; Kansas City, MO; DrlTm; HonRl; SchAde; 4-H; FrCl; PpCl; Chrldr; CitAwd; College; Law Or Social Work.

BRYANT, Vicki T; University HS; Cape Girardeau, MO; /38 NHS; StuCncl; RptrSchPpr; MthCl; PpCl; U Semo State; Professional.

BRYANT, Zeanta; Lindblom Tech HS; Chicago, IL; 33/722 Chr; HonRl; NHS; SchAde; TchrAde; RptrSchPpr; LatCl; University; Law.

BRYCE, Patricia C; Our Lady Star Of The Sea HS; Grosse Pte Woods, MI; 6/58 SecFrshCls; SecSrCls; ChrhWkr; CtyCnl; HonRl; NHS; Bsktbl; Socr; CaptSwmmng; IMSpt; U Of Mi; Dental Hygienist.

BRYCE, Patricia C; Our Lady Star Of The Sea; Grosse Pointe Wood, MI; 6/65 SecFrshCls; SecSrCls; HonRl; NHS; StuCncl; RptrSchPpr; Bsktbl; ChmnSwmmng; IMSpt; U Of Mich; Biological Science.

BRYCELAND, Janis M; Regina Dominican HS; Chicago, IL; 28/207 Chrs; PresFrCl; Univ Of Ill; Med Tech.

BRYCESON, Deborah D; West Harrison HS; Mondamin, IA; Band; Chrs; CncrtBnd; HonRl; LbryAde; MrchBnd; SchMus; SchPl; StuCncl; YthFlsp; LetterBsktbl; College.

BRYCK, Sue K; Plain Well HS; Plainwell, MI; 24/235 HonRl; NHS; PepBnd; Yrbk; FrCl; LetterBsbl; LetterBsktbl; LetterTennis; PPFtbl; Mi State U; Phys Ed Or Architecture.

BRYDA, Charles A; Maine Township HS; Niles, IL; 7/900 HonRl; JrNHS; NHS; NatlThespSoc; SchMus; SchPl; StuCncl; StuGov; PresMthCl; LetterFtbl; U Of Il; Electrical Engineering.

BRYNILDSON, Sanee M; Greenfield HS; Greenfield, WI; 6/395 Band; ChrhWkr; CncrtBnd; HonRl; HospAde; MrchBnd; NHS; PepBnd; YthFlsp; RptrYrbk; Coll; Medical Tech.

BRYSK, Judith G; Huron HS; Ann Arbor, MI; 6/576 HonRl; NatlMeritCmnd; TchrAde; SchPpr; RusCl; SpnCl; Univ; Medicine.

BRYSK, Judy G; Huron HS; Ann Arbor, MI; 6/576 HonRl; ChmnLitMag; NatlMeritCmnd; StuGov; TchrAde; RusCl; SpnCl; Univ; Medicine.

BRYSON, Debra K; Thomas Jefferson HS; Council Bluffs, IA; HonRl; NHS; StuCncl; SptEdYrbk; RptrSchPpr; LetterBsktbl; LetterGlf; LetterTennis; CchngActv; PPFtbl; DARAwd; PresAwd; University; Mathematics.

BRYSON, Stephen T; Lane Technical HS; Chicago, IL; 313/1200 Chr; Chrs; HonRl; Mdrgl; OffAde; Yrbk; RusCl; MthCl; PresSciCl; Northwestern Univ; Astronomer.

BRYSON, Vickie R; New Franklin HS; New Franklin, MO; Band; Chr; ChrhWkr; HonRl; SchPl; TreasFHA; SpnCl; PpCl; Bsbl; Bsktbl; Chrldr; GAA; College; Professional.

BRZEZINSKI, Alexandra A; Holy Family Academy; Schaumburg, IL; 1/104 SecJrCls; PresAud/Vis; Chr; Chrs; HonRl; JrNHS; LbryAde; NHS; OffAde; SchAde; SchMus; SecStuCncl; StuGov; TchrAde; University; Pharmacy.

BRZEZINSKI, Mathew J; Plymouth Canton HS; Plymouth Twp, MI; CmntyWkr; NatlMeritSF; PolWkr; StuGov; RptrSchPpr; Schoolcraft Coll; Jounralism.

BRZEZINSKI, Monica A; St Joseph HS; Chicago, IL; 1/124 HonRl; VPNHS; NatlMeritSF; Quill&Scroll; RptrSchPpr; SchPpr; FrCl; VPMthCl; Loyola U; Communication Arts.

BRZEZNIAK, Thaddeus N; St Rita HS; Chicago, IL; 51/454 HonRl; SctActv; LetterSocr; IMSpt; University; Law Enforcement Officer.

BRZOZOWSKI, Barbara; Maine South Hs; Morridge, IL; HonRl; LitMag; NHS; PolWkr; Quill&Scroll; SchMus; SchPpr; FrCl; GAA; Rosary College; International Finance.

BRZOZOWSKI, Cindy A; St Louise De Marillac HS; Glenview, IL; 10/256 Chrs; ChrhWkr; HospAde; NHS; SchPl; SctActv; RptrYrbk; EdYrBk; Illinois Wesleyan Univ; Nursing.

BRZOZOWSKI, Lori J; St Louise De Marillac HS; Glenview, IL; 42/249 Chrs; Teen; Yrbk; SpnCl; Pharmacy School.

BSSTONE, Peter F; Latin Sch Of Chicago; Chicago, IL; PresSrCls; ChrhWkr; CmntyWkr; ChmnHospAde; PolWkr; PresStuCncl; PresStuGov; Ftbl; CchngActv; CitAwd; Harvard Univ; Medicine.

BUBACH, Renee; Sheyenne Public Hs; Sheyenne, ND; Band; CncrtBnd; HonRl; SchPl; StuCncl; RptrSchPpr; 4-H; FHA; LetterBsktbl; LetterTrk; College; Professional.

BUBACH, Renel E; Sheyenne Public HS; Sheyenne, ND; CmntyWkr; CncrtBnd; HonRl; SchPl; RptrSchPpr; 4-H; FHA; PpCl; LetterBsktbl; LetterTrk; College; Professional.

BUBAK, Mark W; Sisseton HS; Sisseton, SD; PresFrshCls; PresSrCls; Band; HonRl; NatlThespSoc; SchPl; StuCncl; KeyCl; Ftbl; Trk; IMSpt; Univ Of South Dakota; Professional.

BUBB, Paul A; V I T HS; Ipava, IL; 7/58 NHS; SchPl; StuCncl; TchrAde; Yrbk; Bsbl; CaptBsktbl; CaptFtbl; LetterTrk; SARAwd; Us Air Force Acad; Pilot Training.

BUBENYAK, Michael T; Camanche HS; Camanche, IA; 25/116 PresSrCls; HonRl; NHS; ROTC; StuGov; Ftbl; Trk; IMSpt; GovHonPrgAwd; JAAwd; PresAwd; Univ; Pre Law.

BUBOLZ, Catherine G; Rio HS; Rio, WI; Band; HonRl; LbryAde; NHS; PepBnd; 4-H; 4-HAwd; VFWAwd; CitAwd; College; Home Ec.

BUCARO, Mary A; Maine Township HS; Park Ridge, IL; ChrhWkr; HonRl; NatlThespSoc; PolWkr; SchMus; SchPl; SpnCl; PpCl; Northern Illinois Univ; Art.

BUCCELLATO, Robert J; Cabrini HS; Allen Park, MI; 22/139 NHS; Quill&Scroll; EdYrBk; EdSchPpr; IMSpt; Lawrence Inst Of Tech; Mech Engineer.

BUCCI, Cathey; Theodore Roosevelt HS; Wyandotte, MI; Chr; ChrhWkr; HonRl; NHS; NatlMeritSF; YthFlsp; RptrYrbk; RptrSchPpr; SchPpr; EngCl; Olivet College; Minister.

BUCCI, Patricia A; Morton West HS; Berwyn, IL; 3/700 HonRl; JrNHS; NatlFornLg; NatlThespSoc; SchMus; Illinois St Univ; Agriculture.

BUCEK, Kimberly A; Lourdes HS; Chicago, IL; CmntyWkr; HonRl; HospAde; SchPl; TchrAde; EdYrBk; Ill State Univ; Speech Pathologist.

BUCH, Gordon R; Clarinda Comm HS; Clarinda, IA; ChrhWkr; HonRl; YthFlsp; 4-H; FFA; LetterBsbl; LetterBsktbl; LetterFtbl; IMSpt; 4-HAwd; College; Agri Bus.

BUCHANAN, Dennis D; Osmond Comm HS; Osmond, NE; SecFrshCls; Chr; PepBnd; SchPl; YthFlsp; EdYrBk; GerCl; Bsktbl; Ftbl; Wrstlng; IMSpt; Trade School; Professional.

BUCHANAN, Diana; Les Cheneaux HS; Hessel, MI; Chr; CncrtBnd; HonRl; PolWkr; TchrAde; Teen; YthFlsp; FHA; MthCl; BttyCrckrAwd; Marriage.

BUCHANAN, Diane G; Hamilton HS; Hamilton, IN; 3/60 SecJrCls; ALAGirlsSt; HonRl; NHS; SchMus; VPStuCncl; TchrAde; RptrYrbk; EdYrBk; SchPpr; Ball State U; Elem Ed.

BUCHANAN, Gary R; Kingman HS; Kingman, KS; 30/124 TrsJrCls; PresSrCls; Chr; HonRl; SctActv; LetterBsktbl; Ftbl; Trk; CchngActv; Univ.

BUCHANAN, James S; Jennings Co HS; North Vernon, IN; Aud/Vis; IntrClCncl; OffAde; SctActv; VPSpnCl; PpCl; SciCl; Bsbl; LetterFtbl; LetterTrk; Annapolis Naval Academy; Navy Pilot.

BUCHANAN, Jennifer S; Notre Dame De Sion HS; Overland Park, KS; 2/42 SecJrCls; Chr; ChrhWkr; HonRl; HospAde; NHS; SchMus; College; Physician.

BUCHANAN, Kelly P; Craig HS; Janesville, WI; 84/474 CmntyWkr; HonRl; StuCncl; LetterFtbl; LetterWrstlng; CitAwd; Chico State College; Forestry.

BUCHANAN, Lois E; North Posey HS; Wadesville, IN; 7/163 HonRl; HospAde; NHS; OffAde; 4-H; VPFHA; IMSpt; PPFtbl; 4-HAwd; Brescia College; Special Education.

BUCHANAN, Patti L; Leland HS; Leland, IL; 1/32 ALAGirlsSt; Chrs; ChrhWkr; CncrtBnd; HonRl; LbryAde; NHS; OffAde; PepBnd; PolWkr; SchAde; SchPl; LetterGlf; GAA; South Ill Univ; Journalism.

BUCHANAN, Richard E; Jacksonville HS; Jacksonville, IL; 43/363 Band; ChrhWkr; PresCncrtBnd; HonRl; MrchBnd; NHS; SctActv; KeyCl; Glf; GodCntryAwd; Univ Of Illinois; Medicine.

BUCHANAN, Sharon L; South Decatur HS; Greensburg, IN; ChrhWkr; HospAde; FHA; SpnCl; Trade School.

BUCHANAN, Stanley R; Marquette Manor Christian HS; Chicago, IL; PresJrCls; HonRl; Devry Tech Inst; Elec Engineer.

BUCHANAN, Tony D; Fair Grove HS; Elkland, MO; Aud/Vis; Chrl; Chrs; HonRl; SchPl; StuCncl; EdSchPpr; MthCl; IMSpt; CitAwd; College.

BUCHANAN, Wayne; Lindblom Tech HS; Chicago, IL; HonRl; JA; NatlMeritSF; SchAde; StuCncl; StuGov; TchrAde; RptrYrbk; FrCl; IMSpt; Univ Miami; Music.

BUCHBERGER, Laurie L; North HS; Eau Claire, WI; Band; ChrhWkr; HonRl; NHS; Orch; TchrAde; VPGerCl; Univ Of Wis; Accounting.

BUCHBERGER, Scott L; North HS; Eau Claire, WI; ChrhWkr; HonRl; University; Art Major.

BUCHDA, Timothy C; Melrose Mindoro HS; Melrose, WI; Band; CncrtBnd; MrchBnd; NatlMeritCmnd; Orch; YthFlsp; LetterFtbl; CaptTrk; LetterWrstlng; RotaryAwd; Univ; Physics.

BUCHE, Michael; Girard Hs; Mulberry, KS; VPFrshCls; CmntyWkr; Sacrstn; SctActv; CivCl; Bsbl; Bsktbl; Ftbl; Glf;.

BUCHEN, Jeri; United Township HS; East Moline, IL; Chr; HonRl; FrCl; Bsktbl; Trk; GAA; IMSpt; College; Unsure.

BUCHER, David K; Valley HS; Des Moines, IA; 3/440 AFS; Band; HonRl; JrNHS; NHS; NatlMeritSF; SctActv; StuGov; RptrSchPpr; EldAwd; Univ Of Ia; Medicine.

BUCHER, Margaret E; Bishop Mcnamara HS; Bourbonnais, IL; HonRl; NHS; GAA; St Xavier; English Or Political Science.

BUCHHEIM, Connie J; Wolsey Public HS; Wolsey, SD; TrsFrshCls; TrsSophCls; Chrs; HonRl; StuCncl; TchrAde; Yrbk; RptrSchPpr; LetterTrk; Chrldr; School Of Mines; Engineer.

BUCHHEIT, Deborah; 2727 Campbell Street HS; Valparaiso, IN; 8/429 ChrhWkr; CmntyWkr; HonRl; NHS; StuCncl; TchrAde; RptrSchPpr; PpCl; Valparaiso Univ; Pedodontist.

BUCHHOLTZ, Mark; Tolley Public HS; Kenmare, ND; PresFrshCls; PresSophCls; VPJrCls; ALBoysSt; HonRl; SchPl; RptrYrbk; PpCl; PresAwd; University;.

BUCHHOLZ, C Jeanne; Hartford HS; Hartford, MI; 3/83 ALAGirlsSt; Band; ChrhWkr; HospAde; NHS; SecStuCncl; TchrAde; 4-H; BttyCrckrAwd; DARAwd; College; Elem Ed.

BUCHHOLZ, Joyce A; Bonduel HS; Bonduel, WI; 10/122 Band; HonRl; PepBnd; Yrbk; 4-H; FTA; MthCl; SciCl; 4-HAwd; College; Business Admin.

BUCHHOLZ, Kathie L; Albert City Truesdale HS; Albert City, IA; 9/50 Chr; Chrs; ChrhWkr; HonRl; OffAde; SchMus; SchPl; StuCncl; RptrYrbk; FHA; SpnCl; Univ Of S Dakota; Med Technology.

BUCHHOLZ, Kathryn A; Lutheran HS; Kenosha, WI; 7/83 Band; HonRl; NHS; PepBnd; PpCl; Condordia College; Respiratory Therapist.

BUCHHOLZ, Mary A; Green Lake HS; Green Lake, WI; 6/36 ALAGirlsSt; Chr; Chrs; NHS; NatlThespSoc; SchPl; 4-H; GerCl; LetterBsktbl; 4-HAwd; Medicine.

BUCHHOLZ, Sandra J; West HS; Green Bay, WI; 32/390 HonRl; HospAde; OffAde; SchAde; FNA; GAA; Tech Schl; Electroencephalograph Technician.

BUCHHOLZ, Tammie L; Brazil HS; Brazil, IN; 23/167 HonRl; HospAde; NHS; OffAde; SctActv; 4-H; FHA; SpnCl; PpCl; Chrldr; Coll; X Ray Tech.

BUCHHOLZ, Theresa L; Osseo Fairchild HS; Osseo, WI; Aud/Vis; Band; HonRl; NHS; GerCl; GAA; College; Language.

BUCHKO, Paul O; Ironwood Catholic HS; Ironwood, MI; Chrs; ChrhWkr; CmntyWkr; NHS; SchMus; PresStuCncl; Bsktbl; AmLegAwd; DanFAwd; CitAwd; College.

BUCHL, Elizabeth A; Rock Lake Public HS; Rock Lake, ND; 1/21 SecTrsSophCls; HstJrCls; Band; Chrs; HonRl; StuCncl; EdSchPpr; Bsktbl; Chrldr; College; Political Science.

BUCHL, Mary C; Rock Lake HS; Rock Lake, ND; SecTrsSrCls; ALAGirlsSt; PresBand; PresChrs; HonRl; PepBnd; SchPl; EdYrBk; PresFHA; PpCl; Trk; 4-HAwd; Mary College; Music.

BUCHLER, Gary M; Marist HS; Chicago, IL; 43/374 CmntyWkr; HonRl; PolWkr; CaptBsbl; Bsktbl; LetterFtbl; Trk; University; Elec Engineering.

BUCHLER, Karen L; Lake Central HS; Dyer, IN; TrsJrCls; TrsSrCls; HonRl; Quill&Scroll; StuCncl; StuGov; SchPpr; PpCl; Chrldr; Business Schl; Secretary.

BUCHNER, Diann M; Bloomer HS; Bloomer, WI; Band; ChrhWkr; HonRl; NHS; StuCncl; Chrldr; College; Nursing.

BUCHNER, Michael P; Luke M Powers HS; Flint, MI; 41/306 HonRl; JA; NHS; SchMus; SchPl; C S Mott; Pharmacy.

BUCHOLZ, Romaine; Bonduel Community HS; Bonduel, WI; 11/122 CmntyWkr; HonRl; SchPl; Yrbk; RptrSchPpr; FHA; PpCl; GAA; Technical Coll; Commercial Artist.

BUCHSBAUM, Andrew P; Oak Park River Forest HS; Oak Park, IL; 5/1100 Band; LitMag; NHS; NatlMeritFnl; NatlMeritSchl; NatlMeritSF; StuCncl; CaptBsktbl; AmLegAwd; BauchLmbAwd; Harvard Clge.

BUCHWALD, Randall H; Brookfield E HS; Brookfield, WI; 4/509 AFS; HonRl; NHS; NatlMeritCmnd; Yrbk; KeyCl; MthCl; Marquette Univ; Electrical Engineering.

BUCK, Carol M; Stillwater HS; Stillwater, MN; 9/617 Chr; HonRl; NHS; NatlMeritSF; StuGov; Concordia College.

BUCK, Christopher; Ashwaubenon HS; Green Bay, WI; HonRl; JA; NHS; 4-H; KeyCl; SpnCl; SciCl; Trk; 4-HAwd; JAAwd; Marguette Dental School; Dentist.

BUCK, Debbie L; Seneca HS; Seneca, IL; 6/60 SecFrshCls; SecTrsJrCls; PresBand; CncrtBnd; NHS; StuCncl; Yrbk; VPGerCl; Chrldr; SecGAA; Illinois St Univ; Med Technician.

BUCK, Diana; Saline HS; Saline, MI; 2/204 Aud/Vis; Chrs; ChrhWkr; HonRl; LbryAde; NHS; E Mi Univ; Counselor.

BUCK, Donald D; Ashley HS; Ashley, ND; TrsSophCls; TrsJrCls; PresSrCls; Chr; HonRl; Mdrgl; SchPl; TreasYthFlsp; 4-H; LetterTrk;.

BUCK, Jean M; West Marshall HS; State Center, IA; 1/90 VPJrCls; VPSrCls; TreasBand; ChrhWkr; HonRl; TreasNHS; NatlMeritCmnd; SecStuCncl; SecCaptChrldr; Ia Univ.

BUCK, Judy A; Patoka HS; Patoka, IL; 4/27 Band; Chrs; DrmMjrt; HonRl; SchPl; RptrSchPpr; FHA; College.

BUCK, Kenneth A; Forman HS; Manito, IL; 6/45 PresFrshCls; PresBand; NHS; SctActv; PresStuCncl; PresYthFlsp; EdYrBk; PresSpnCl; LetterBsbl; LetterGlf; AmLegAwd; GodCntryAwd; Knox College; Law.

BUCK, Marguerite A; Little Flower HS; Evergreen Park, IL; 9/439 HonRl; NHS; NatlMeritCmnd; YthFlsp; LatCl; PpCl; Marquette Univ; Physical Therapist.

BUCK, Mary L; Streeter HS; Bismarck, ND; 7/22 PresSrCls; Chr; CncrtBnd; HonRl; HospAde; StuCncl; Yrbk; SchPpr; LetterBsktbl; AmLegAwd; Jamestown Col; Teacher.

BUCK, Patricia D; Academy Of Mount St Scholasti; Atchison, KS; HonRl; Benedictine College; Criminal Justice.

BUCK, Randall A; North HS; Fargo, ND; Band; Chr; Chrl; CncrtBnd; HonRl; NatlFornLg; NHS; NatlMeritCmnd; GerCl; No Dakota State Univ; Electronics Eng.

BUCK, Sheila; Greencastle HS; Greencastle, IN; SecSrCls; HonRl; NHS; OffAde; RptrSchPpr; SchPpr; FTA; PpCl; Chrldr; BttyCrckrAwd; W Ky Univ; English.

BUCKBEE, Craig L; Sargent HS; Sargent, NE; SecJrCls; Chrs; HonRl; SchPl; SctActv; 4-H; FBLA; Bsktbl; Ftbl; Trk;.

BUCKEL, Robert J; Lakeville HS; Millington, MI; 17/190 SchPl; StuCncl; StuGov; RptrSchPpr; SchPpr; 4-H; LetterBsbl; LetterBsktbl; LetterFtbl; CchngActv; Central Mi Univ; Journalism.

BUCKELS, James C; Bremen HS; Midlothian, IL; 110/400 Aud/Vis; LitMag; NatlThespSoc; SchPl; StuGov; RptrYrbk; RptrSchPpr; FrCl; LetterBsbl; LetterBsktbl; Clge St Frances Joliet; Scientific Research.

BUCKENMEYER, Joel D; Algonac HS; Algonac, MI; HonRl; JrNHS; NatlMeritCmnd; PolWkr; TchrAde; RptrYrbk; SpnCl; Mi Univ.

BUCKHOLZ, Bertha; Engadine Consolidated HS; Engadine, MI; Band; HonRl; SchAde; StuCncl; TchrAde; Chrldr; IMSpt; College; Professional.

BUCKI, William E; Bishop Noll Institute HS; Harvey, IL; 1/360 Aud/Vis; ChrhWkr; HonRl; NHS; University; Medicine.

BUCKINGHAM, Marja J; Joliet Central HS; Joliet, IL; 18/491 SecJrCls; Band; NHS; StuCncl; RptrYrbk; Trk; College; Law.

BUCKLES, William; Van Buren Comm HS; Keosauqua, IA; 15/90 TrsSrCls; HonRl; JCC; NHS; PolWkr; SchPl; StuGov; Bsktbl; Glf; TIMEAwd; College; Banking.

BUCKLEY, Cindy L; Southeast HS; Springfield, IL; HospAde; SchPl; FrCl; PpCl; IMSpt; Trade Sch; Nursing.

BUCKLEY, Edward R; Centennial HS; Champaign, IL; 90/365 ALBoysSt; Band; ChrhWkr; CmntyWkr; CncrtBnd; LbryAde; MrchBnd; StuGov; SptEdYrbk; LetterFtbl; LetterTrk; CchngActv; AmLegAwd; Oral Roberts Univ; Business Admin.

BUCKLEY, Janis M; Portland HS; Portland, MI; SecFrshCls; Band; CncrtBnd; HonRl; MrchBnd; PepBnd; TchrAde; FTA; SpnCl; Chrldr; College; Elementary Teacher.

BUCKLEY, Jean M; Immaculate Heart Of Mary HS; Westchester, IL; 17/272 TrsFrshCls; VPSrCls; NatlMeritCmnd; StuGov; RptrSchPpr; SpnCl; MthCl; CchngActv; Univ; Communications.

BUCKLEY, John J; Allegan HS; Allegan, MI; ChrhWkr; HonRl; SchPl; LatCl; Ftbl; University.

BUCKLEY, Pam K; Eldora Community HS; Eldora, IA; 15/63 PresSrCls; ALAGirlsSt; CmntyWkr; HonRl; NHS; PepBnd; StuCncl; RptrYrbk; LetterBsktbl; CitAwd; Trade School; Secretary.

BUCKLEY, Patrick J; Notre Dame HS; Morton Grove, IL; 26/264 Chrs; CmntyWkr; HonRl; PolWkr; SchMus; StuGov; TchrAde; Trk; Notre Dame Univ; Eng.

BUCKLEY, Peggy L; North Side HS; Fort Wayne, IN; SecSrCls; CmntyWkr; HospAde; JrNHS; NHS; NatlMeritSF; PpCl; Trk; JAAwd; CitAwd; College; Art.

BUCKLEY, Randall E; Burr Oak HS; Burr Oak, KS; Chr; SchPl; StuCncl; YthFlsp; Yrbk; SchPpr; LetterBsktbl; LetterFtbl; Vo Tech School; Rancher.

BUCKLEY, Scott D; Central HS; Grand Forks, ND; VPFrshCls; PresJrCls; ALBoysSt; ChrhWkr; HonRl; SctActv; StuCncl; SptEdSchPpr; Bsktbl; Ftbl; College; Professional.

BUCKLEY, Terrance M; Reddick HS; Buckingham, IL; HonRl; SchPl; TreasStuCncl; Yrbk; FFA; AmLegAwd; Joliet Jr College; Art.

BUCKLEY, Thomas; Hartford HS; Hartford, MI; SchPpr; College.

BUCKNELL, Craig D; Riceville Community HS; Chester, IA; PresFrshCls; HonRl; SchPl; YthFlsp; Bsktbl; Ftbl; Trk; AmLegAwd; Austin Comm Coll; History.

BUCKNER, Lynn; Sycamore Hs; Sycamore, IL; ChrhWkr; HonRl; SchMus; SchPl; YthFlsp; GAA; College; Psychology.

BUCKNER, Sharon K; South Iron R 1 HS; Annapolis, MO; TrsSophCls; HonRl; SchMus; StuCncl; TchrAde; FHA; PpCl; Chrldr;.

BUCKNER, Sherry; Belleville HS; Ypsilanti, MI; 27/525 Chr; HonRl; SchMus; FrCl; PpCl; GAA; Eastern Michigan Univ; Businessadministrati.

BUCKNER, Simon B; Southwest HS; Kansas City, MO; AFS; Band; HonRl; NatlFornLg; NatlMeritSF; SchMus; SctActv; StuCncl; StuGov; FrCl; Williams College; Law.

BUCKNER, Teresa G; Rossville Alvin HS; Henning, IL; Chr; Chrs; HonRl; LbryAde; LitMag; SchPpr; 4-H; GAA; IMSpt; JAAwd; Danville Jr Col ;child Care.

BUCKNER, Vanderbilt; Cass Technical HS; Detroit, MI; HonRl; NHS; GerCl; Univ Of Michigan; Architecture.

BUCKNER, William B; Mexico HS; Mexico, MO; PresFrshCls; ALBoysSt; Chr; CmntyWkr; SchMus; SctActv; StuCncl; KeyCl; LetterGlf; LetterTrk; Univ Of Mo; Conservation Or Agriculture.

BUCKO, Robert J; Culver Military Academy; Merrillville, IN; 100/183 Chr; Chrl; Chrs; CmntyWkr; DrlTm; HonRl; PolWkr; ROTC; StuCncl; StuGov; SpnCl; Bsktbl; CaptFtbl; IMSpt; Texas Christian Univ; Law.

BUCKOSKI, Katherine L; Port Huron Northern HS; Port Huron, MI; Band; CncrtBnd; MrchBnd; PepBnd; StuCncl; College; Broadcasting.

BUCKSHAW, Mary A; Chadsey HS; Detroit, MI; HonRl; LbryAde; StuCncl; AmLegAwd; College; Business Administration.

BUCREK, Mary J; Lumen Christi HS; Jackson, MI; 9/222 ChrhWkr; HonRl; NHS; SchPpr; PpCl; IMSpt; U Of Mi; Pharmacy.

BUCY, Sheryl E; Owen Valley HS; Spencer, IN; 11/190 ALAGirlsSt; Band; HonRl; NHS; PepBnd; TchrAde; YthFlsp; LatCl; PpCl; DARAwd; In U Bloomington; Premed Chemistry.

BUCZKOWSI, James A; Southfield Lathrup HS; Lathrup Village, MI; 28/683 U Of Mi; Electrical Engin.

BUDD, Beth E; Benson HS; Omaha, NE; Aud/Vis; CmntyWkr; LbryAde; Military.

BUDD, Don R; Webberville HS; Webberville, MI; TrsSrCls; HonRl; StuCncl; FrCl; LetterTrk; Central Mi Univ; Tchr.

BUDD, Joan; Emporia HS; Emporia, KS; ModUN; NatlMeritFnl; NatlMeritSF; TchrAde; Kansas Univ.

BUDD, Susan E; Winamac Comm HS; Winamac, IN; Band; ChrhWkr; HonRl; MrchBnd; NHS; 4-H; LatCl; College.

BUDD, Zoe Ann; Thornton Twp HS; Riverdale, IL; 2/674 VPCncrtBnd; HonRl; MrchBnd; NHS; Orch; SptEdYrbk; LetterSwmmng; Illinois State University.

BUDDE, Deborah; Ladywood HS; Detroit, MI; Chrs; HonRl; NatlFornLg; NHS; SchMus; StuCncl; Bsbl; Trk; Univ Of Mi; Nursing.

BUDDE, Melody L; Minonk Dana Rutland HS; Flanagan, IL; AFS; Chrs; ChrhWkr; HonRl; TchrAde; RptrYrbk; PpCl; GAA; Univ; Veterinarian.

BUDDEN, Nanette A; New Haven HS; New Haven, MI; 10/100 HonRl; JA; LbryAde; OffAde; TchrAde; Art School; Photography.

BUDDENBERG, Roger R; Gothenburg HS; Gothenburg, NE; 4/84 ALBoysSt; ChrhWkr; HonRl; Mdrgl; SchMus; PresStuCncl; YthFlsp; RptrSchPpr; 4-H; 4-HAwd; U Of Neb; Journalism.

BUDDING, Wayne F; Wilton Community HS; Wilton, IA; 2/70 ALBoysSt; Band; Chrs; HonRl; NHS; NatlMeritCmnd; PresStuCncl; CaptFtbl; Trk; PPFtbl; Iowa St Univ; Veterinarian.

BUDDY, Ellen M; Dodge City Sr HS; Dodge, KS; PresJrCls; ALAGirlsSt; ChrhWkr; HonRl; NHS; PolWkr; SchPl; StuCncl; RptrSchPpr; FrCl; LetterTennis; Trk; IMSpt; University; Professional.

BUDEK, Christine A; Goodman HS; Goodman, WI; 1/21 SecSrCls; Band; ChrhWkr; CmntyWkr; DrlTm; HonRl; NHS; Yrbk; Chrldr; DARAwd; Nursing.

BUDEK, Debra; St Mary Acad; New Boston, MI; CmntyWkr; Trk; Concordia; Social Work.

BUDISIC, Chris; Goshen HS; Goshen, IN; Band; Chr; ChrhWkr; CmntyWkr; HonRl; NatlFornLg; NatlThespSoc; RedCrAde; SchPl; StuCncl; College; Social Worker.

BUDKE, Michelle L; Sacred Heart HS; Salina, KS; CmntyWkr; CncrtBnd; HonRl; MrchBnd; StuCncl; TchrAde; FBLA; CaptBsktbl; IMSpt; PresAwd; College; Doctor.

BUDLONG, Audrey M; De Tour Area HS; De Tour Village, MI; 2/47 HonRl; NHS; Lake Superior St College; Psychology.

BUDNILKI, Timothy R; Collinsville HS; Collinsville, IL; 120/670 Aud/Vis; ChrhWkr; HonRl; LbryAde; NHS; YthFlsp; KeyCl; Bsbl; SecJrCls; CchngActv; Coll; State Police.

BUDREAU, Jeannie M; Benton Central HS; Earl Park, IN; 8/260 SecSrCls; HonRl; JrNHS; NHS; NatlMeritCmnd; Quill&Scroll; StuCncl; RptrSchPpr; IMSpt; PPFtbl; Univ; Interior Designer.

BUDWEIL, Barbara M; Dominican HS; Hamtramck, MI; Chrl; CmntyWkr; HospAde; College; Disc Jockey.

BUDZYN, Martha H; Burlington HS; Burlington, IA; CncrtBnd; DrlTm; HonRl; JrNHS; NHS; StuCncl; Yrbk; PpCl; College; Fashion Merchandising.

BUDZYNSKI, Carol L; Crestwood HS; Dearborn Hgts, MI; HonRl; Coll; Psychology.

BUECH, Rosemarie S; Winneconne HS; Winneconne, WI; ChrhWkr; HonRl; NHS; SchPl; SchPpr; 4-H; University; Professional.

BUECHEL, Kim M; Elkhart Lake Glenbeulah HS; Elkhart Lake, WI; 2/65 Band; CncrtBnd; HonRl; MrchBnd; NatlFornLg; PepBnd; SchPl; RptrYrbk; RptrSchPpr; U Of Wi; Lawyer.

BUECHLER, Carolyn S; Forest Park HS; Ferdinand, IN; Chrs; HonRl; PpCl; GAA; Indiana State U; Nursing.

BUECHLER, Jerae L; Bowdle Public HS; Bowdle, SD; 8/25 ALBoysSt; Band; HonRl; SchPl; StuCncl; YthFlsp; Bsktbl; Ftbl; Trk; Trade School; Radio Repair.

BUECHLER, Stephen R; Dubois HS; Jasper, IN; SecFrshCls; HonRl; SctActv; PpCl; Trade.

BUECHLER, William F; Colver Military Academy; Elwood, IN; Band; CncrtBnd; DrmBgl; MrchBnd; NatlMeritCmnd; PepBnd; ROTC; GerCl; SciCl; Vanderbilt Univ; Medicine.

BUECHNER, Louise B; Butternut Public HS; Butternut, WI; ALAGirlsSt; Chrs; HonRl; NHS; OffAde; PepBnd; 4-H; SpnCl; PpCl; Technical Sch; Vocation.

BUECHNER, Randall; Northrop HS; Fort Wayne, IN; 15/643 Aud/Vis; HonRl; LitMag; NatlFornLg; Univ.

BUECHTER, Mark J; Lafayette Co C 1 HS; Higginsville, MO; 3/99 ALBoysSt; Chr; HonRl; PresNHS; PepBnd; StuCncl; PresSciCl; LetterFtbl; LetterTrk; AmLegAwd; Us Air Force Acad; Aeronautical Eng.

BUEHLER, Bonnie M; Wesclin Sr HS; Trenton, IL; 4/100 HonRl; NHS; SchPpr; FBLA; GerCl;.

BUEHLER, Bruce S; Ofallon Township HS; Belleville, IL; HonRl; SctActv; Bsbl; IMSpt; S Illinois Of Dental Medicine; Dentristry.

BUEHLER, Jennifer A; Carrollton HS; Carrollton, MO; VPFrshCls; Band; Chrs; CncrtBnd; HonRl; MrchBnd; NatlThespSoc; SchPl; TchrAde; Twrl; GerCl; Univ Of Missouri; Speech Pathology.

BUEHNE, Cynthia A; Mater Dei HS; Highland, IL; Chrs; HonRl; LbryAde; SchMus; RptrSchPpr; SchPpr; 4-H; LatCl; 4-HAwd; College.

BUEHNER, Marvin E; Tripp Independent HS; Tripp, SD; VPSrCls; Band; Chrs; CncrtBnd; HonRl; MrchBnd; NatlFornLg; NHS; NatlMeritCmnd; PepBnd; SctActv; StuCncl; StuGov; Bsktbl; LetterFtbl; Univ Of South Dakota.

BUEHNER, Sharon M; Emery HS; Emery, SD; 1/525 Band; CncrtBnd; HonRl; MrchBnd; PepBnd; SchPl; FHA; PpCl; LetterTrk; University; Physical Theropy,child Dev,muci.

BUEHRER, Judith A; Litchfield HS; Litchfield, IL; 2/138 VPJrCls; Chrs; PresChrhWkr; CncrtBnd; MrchBnd; PresNHS; StuCncl; FrCl; Chrldr; GAA; Millikin Univ; Music.

BUEHRER, Linda R; Morton HS; Morton, IL; 89/286 Chrs; HonRl; LatCl; College; Secretary.

BUELER, Charles M; Hannibal HS; Hannibal, MO; 22/240 HonRl; NHS; Yrbk; LetterFtbl; IMSpt; Culver Stockton Coll; Biology Major.

BUELIGEN, Daniel D; New Salem HS; New Salem, ND; ALBoysSt; Chrs; ChrhWkr; HonRl; SchMus; FFA; LetterBsktbl; LetterFtbl; Trade School; Vocation.

BUELL, Cynthia M; Bishop Noll HS; Calumet City, IL; Chr; SctActv; Yrbk; PpCl; LetterTrk; College; Professional.

BUELL, Peggy; Stephen Hempstead HS; Dubuque, IA; 35/455 Aud/Vis; HonRl; JrNHS; NHS; Quill&Scroll; SchPl; StuGov; RptrYrbk; EdYrBk; Yrbk; LetterTennis; College; Lawyer.

BUELLESBACH, John C; Marquette University; Elm Grove, WI; Band; ChrhWkr; CmntyWkr; CncrtBnd; HonRl; MrchBnd; NatlFornLg; Orch; PepBnd; SchMus; Purdue University; Engineering.

BUELTEL, Alan C; Creighton Prep HS; Omaha, NE; 37/249 CmntyWkr; HonRl; SchPl; SctActv; Swmmng; IMSpt; Creighton Univ; Medicine.

BUENDORF, Randy; Wells Easton HS; Wells, MN; 32/118 ALBoysSt; Band; Chrs; ChrhWkr; CncrtBnd; HonRl; MrchBnd; Orch; PepBnd; SchMus; Vocational School; Farming.

BUENING, Gerry E; Kirksville Sr HS; Kirksville, MO; Band; ChrhWkr; CncrtBnd; HonRl; College; Science.

BUENING, Joyce; Teutopolis Hs; Effingham, IL; 5/113 TrsFrshCls; TrsJrCls; PresSrCls; HonRl; SchPl; FHA; PpCl; CaptChrldr;.

BUENING, Sandra E; Prairie Sr HS; Prairie Du Chien, WI; HonRl; NHS; 4-H; LatCl; LetterBsktbl; LetterGAA; IMSpt; Viterbo College; Medical Dietetics.

BUENZLI, Nancy R; Central HS; Elkhart, IN; Band; Chr; ChrhWkr; HonRl; NatlThespSoc; Orch; SchMus; SchPl; StuCncl; RptrYrbk; Indiana Univ; Ecology.

BUERGER, Scott; Cudahy Sr HS; Cudahy, WI; HstFrshCls; HonRl; NHS; TchrAde; Univ Of Wi;pre Med.

BUERGES, Jeanne; Duchesne HS; St Charles, MO; 7/185 Chrs; HonRl; NHS; RedCrAde; RptrYrbk; FrCl; PpCl; CitAwd; Nursing School; Rn.

BUERKETT, William T; Griffin HS; Springfield, IL; 93/169 HonRl; PpCl; Ftbl; Trk; College.

BUESCHER, Cynthia L; Adlai E Stevenson HS; Deerfield, IL; 2/231 PresAFS; ChrhWkr; NHS; SchMus; StuCncl; EdYrBk; GerCl; LetterTrk; CaptChrldr; University; Food Science.

BUESCHER, Nancy; Lawrence Public HS; Lawrence, NE; 10/30 Band; Chrs; HonRl; JCC; NHS; PepBnd; RedCrAde; RptrYrbk; Chrldr; National College Of Bus; Airlines.

BUESING, Joni A; Lees Summit HS; Lees Summit, MO; 50/380 CmntyWkr; CncrtBnd; NHS; SctActv; YthFlsp; EdYrBk; SchPpr; PresSpnCl; Trk; GodCntryAwd; OptClAwd; CitAwd; Univ Of Missouri; Nursing.

BUESING, Keith M; Tracy HS; Garvin, MN; 27/124 Band; ChrhWkr; CmntyWkr; Bsbl; Bsktbl; Ftbl; Trk; LetterWrstlng; CchngActv; IMSpt; Clge; Industrial Arts.

BUESKING, Andrew; Stewardson Strasburg HS; Strasburg, IL; PresFrshCls; ChrhWkr; HonRl; LbryAde; NHS; Bsktbl; Univ Or Military Acad; Professional.

BUESKING, Kathryn J; Fox Senior HS; Arnold, MO; ChrhWkr; HonRl; OffAde; SchAde; FHA; FrCl; PpCl; Chrldr; GAA; College; Registered Nurse.

BUESKING, Perrie S; Stewardson Strasburg HS; Strasburg, IL; 1/48 VPJrCls; Aud/Vis; ChrhWkr; CmntyWkr; HonRl; NHS; SchPl; Yrbk; FHA; University; Medical Technology.

BUESSER, Lori J; Rice Lake HS; Rice Lake, WI; HonRl; NHS; RptrYrbk; Yrbk; Coll; Pro.

BUETTNER, Randall H; Columbia HS; Columbia, IL; 2/110 ChrhWkr; HonRl; NHS; VPStuCncl; YthFlsp; SptEdYrbk; FBLA; FTA; PresFrCl; MthCl; LetterTennis; Southeast Missouri Univ; Business Admin.

BUFFETT, Judith K; Kewanee Sr HS; Kewanee, IL; AFS; Band; CncrtBnd; MrchBnd; TchrAde; Chrldr; Blackhawk East.

BUFFINGTON, Beth J; Marietta Public HS; Marietta, MN; HonRl; SchPl; StuCncl; YthFlsp; Yrbk; 4-H; PresFHA; LetterBsktbl; Chrldr; 4-HAwd; State College; Home Ec.

BUFFINGTON, David B; Glenwood Comm HS; Glenwood, IA; HonRl; NatlMeritFnl; NatlMeritSchl; NatlSciFnd; SchMus; SchPl; EdYrBk; LetterTrk; BauchLmbAwd; PresAwd; Washington University; Biology.

BUFFINGTON, Jean M; Titonka Consolidated HS; Titonka, IA; VPSrCls; Chrl; ChrhWkr; HonRl; HospAde; PresYthFlsp; EdSchPpr; PresFHA; CaptBsktbl; LetterTrk; PPFtbl; Iowa Lakes Community College; Nursing.

BUFFO, Janine; Knoxville Sr Hs; Knoxville, IA; CmntyWkr; HonRl; NatlThespSoc; RedCrAde; SchPl; SecStuCncl; Yrbk; RptrSchPpr; LetterTennis; DanFAwd; University; Professional.

BUGAN, Rhonda T; Evergreen Park Comm HS; Evergreen Park, IL; 7/439 HonRl; NHS; TchrAde; PresFTA; RusCl; PpCl; College; Special Education.

BUGARIN, John R; Tomahawk HS; Tomahawk, WI; 2/160 PresFrshCls; ALBoysSt; CncrtBnd; HonRl; MrchBnd; NatlFornLg; SchMus; SchPl; RptrYrbk; RptrSchPpr; MthCl; Glf; College; Mathematics.

BUGBEE, Ernest E; Phillipsburg HS; Republican City, NE; 18/87 PresJrCls; ChrhWkr; HonRl; NHS; PresStuCncl; TchrAde; CaptFtbl; CchngActv; PPFtbl; Fort Hays College; Business Admin.

BUGENSKI, Patricia G; Romeo HS; Romeo, MI; 14/321 HonRl; HospAde; NHS; PolWkr; SchPl; RptrYrbk; FHA; SpnCl; IMSpt; University; Nursing.

BUGOS, Joseph T; Marist HS; Oaklawn, IL; 2/393 ChrhWkr; HonRl; JrNHS; NHS; SchMus; SchPl; SchPpr; Glf; IMSpt; Northwstern; Law.

BUHLER, Ron K; Bristol HS; Milbank, SD; HonRl; Bsktbl; Ftbl; Trade Sch; Meat Cutting.

BUHNERKEMPE, James W; Teutopolis HS; Effingham, IL; HonRl; NatlMeritCmnd; Eastern Ill Univ; Business Management.

BUHR, Elaine L; Parkersburg Comm HS; Parkersburg, IA; SecFrshCls; SecSophCls; Band; Chr; ChrhWkr; HonRl; NHS; SchMus; StuCncl; VPSpnCl; Bethany Luth Clge; Vocation.

BUHR, Joy; Ponca Public HS; Ponca, NE; SecFrshCls; Chr; Chrs; HonRl; NHS; SchPl; StuGov; RptrYrbk; SchPpr; PpCl; Nettleton Bus School.

BUHR, Mary; Marion HS; Marion, WI; 4/84 Band; ChrhWkr; HonRl; NHS; StuCncl; TchrAde; 4-H; SpnCl; Bsktbl; Trk; Univ Of Wis; Pre Veterinary Medicine.

BUHRMASTER, Betty J; Paxton HS; Paxton, IL; TrsSrCls; ChrhWkr; HonRl; NatlThespSoc; SchPl; YthFlsp; RptrSchPpr; Trk; PresGAA; IMSpt; Wiu; Elementary Education.

BUHROW, Paul; Edgerton HS; Edgerton, WI; SecFrshCls; PresSophCls; ModUN; StuCncl; FFA; Chrldr; CchngActv; Az State Univ; Psychologist.

BUIE, Janet L; Wamego HS; Wamego, KS; Band; Chrs; CncrtBnd; HonRl; MrchBnd; NHS; OffAde; PepBnd; StuCncl; SpnCl; University.

BUIKEMA, Nancy K; Fulton HS; Fulton, IL; 3/150 Chr; Chrs; ChrhWkr; HonRl; LbryAde; NHS; FTA; Univ; Library Science.

BUIKEMA, Robert H; Chicago Christian HS; Oaklawn, IL; 10/180 Chr; Chrl; HonRl; Mdrgl; RptrYrbk; SptEdSchPpr; GerCl; Bsktbl; Glf; Calvin College; Lawyer.

BUILTA, Cheryl R; Tri Valley HS; Ellsworth, IL; 12/45 SecFrshCls; Band; Chrs; HonRl; PepBnd; SchMus; SchPl; FHA; PpCl; Chrldr;.

BUJA, Maureen; Sycamore Sr HS; Genoa, IL; Band; CncrtBnd; HonRl; MrchBnd; NatlThespSoc; PepBnd; FrCl; University; History Of Music.

BUJA, Timothy K; Sycamore HS; Genoa, IL; 5/201 ALBoysSt; Band; Chr; Chrl; Chrs; CncrtBnd; HonRl; LbryAde; Mdrgl; MrchBnd; PresNHS; Univ Of Ill; Pharmacy.

BUJAK, Andrew J; Deckerville HS; Pt Sanilac, MI; HonRl; JA; NHS; SchPl; TchrAde; Bsbl; CaptBsktbl; CaptFtbl; Trk; CchngActv; Suomi Coll; Data Processing.

BUJEL, Elizabeth; St Marys Of Redford HS; Detroit, MI; Band; ChrhWkr; HospAde; OffAde; SchAde; SchPl; StuCncl; PpCl; Swmmng; College; Nurse.

BUKER, Myron L; Trico HS; Ava, IL; LetterBand; LetterChrs; LetterChrhWkr; LetterCncrtBnd; LetterHonRl; LetterMrchBnd; LetterPepBnd; LetterSchMus; LetterSctActv; Pres4-H; Southern Ill Univ; Musician.

BUKOVAC, Janice L; Okemos HS; East Lansing, MI; 7/280 Band; CncrtBnd; HonRl; MrchBnd; NHS; Orch; PepBnd; SchAde; SchMus; EngCl; GerCl; Univ Of Michigan; Architecture.

BUKOVICH, Barbara M; Houghton HS; Houghton, MI; 3/111 HonRl; OffAde; Yrbk; PpCl; PPFtbl; Coll; Bus.

BUKOWSKI, John M; Humboldt HS; St Paul, MN; 16/223 HonRl; NHS; LetterBsbl; LetterFtbl; U Of Minn; Accounting.

BULEMORE, Kathryn E; Corunna HS; Corunna, MI; 9/200 ChrhWkr; HonRl; NHS; SchAde; StuCncl; TchrAde; YthFlsp; 4-H; PpCl; CaptChrldr; Central Michigan Univ; Business Secretary.

BULGARELLI, Valerie A; Lakeview HS; St Clair Shores, MI; TrsFrshCls; Chr; HonRl; HospAde; NHS; NatlMeritCmnd; NatlThespSoc; SchMus; SchPl; RptrYrbk; FNA; Mich St Univ; Nursing.

BULIN, Bonnie; Weston Union HS; Lavalle, WI; Band; CncrtBnd; HonRl; MrchBnd; NHS; PepBnd; RptrYrbk; RptrSchPpr; PpCl; IMSpt; Vocational School; General Secretarial.

BULIN, Jeanette L; Meridian HS; Alexandria, NE; ALAGirlsSt; Chrs; CmntyWkr; HonRl; OffAde; Twrl; YthFlsp; SchPpr; 4-H; PpCl; Business School.

BULKEMA, June E; Grand Rapids Christian HS; Grand Rapids, MI; ChrhWkr; CmntyWkr; HospAde; Orch; 4-H; Calvin College; Sociology.

BULKO, Joseph J; Vassar HS; Vassar, MI; 1/141 HonRl; NatlFornLg; NHS; NatlSciFnd; Trk; Central Michigan Univ; Secondary Ed.

BULL, Alan L; Forreston HS; Forreston, IL; 17/65 ALBoysSt; HonRl; SchPl; StuCncl; SptEdSchPpr; Bsbl; Bsktbl; Ftbl; Bradley Univ; Computer Science.

BULL, Charles E; Northville HS; Northville, MI; Aud/Vis; NHS; Univ; Engi.

BULL, Donald; Luther L Wright HS; Ironwood, MI; Chr; HonRl; SchMus; YthFlsp; SptEdSchPpr; Ftbl; Trk; IMSpt; Coll; Medicine.

BULL, Linda; Clark HS; Clark, SD; 4/50 TrsFrshCls; ALAGirlsSt; Band; HonRl; NHS; Quill&Scroll; SchMus; Yrbk; Chrldr; South Dakota State U; Secretarial.

BULL, Theresa A; Yutan Public HS; Yutan, NE; 2/25 SecFrshCls; SecSophCls; ALAGirlsSt; CncrtBnd; HonRl; SchPl; EdSchPpr; LetterTrk; Chrldr; 4-HAwd; Univ.

BULLA, Susan L; Lake Orion HS; Lake Orion, MI; 7/334 CmntyWkr; HonRl; HospAde; NHS; TchrAde; LetterTrk; Univ Of Mi; Physical Therapy.

BULLEN, Susan S; Glenwood HS; Springfield, IL; 21/143 AFS; ALAGirlsSt; Chr; ChrhWkr; HonRl; NatlThespSoc; SchMus; TchrAde; FTA; Carthage College.

BULLER, Galen; Burrton HS; Burrton, KS; ALBoysSt; Band; CncrtBnd; HonRl; NHS; SchPl; StuCncl; 4-H; Ftbl; Bether College.

BULLER, Libby J; Stromsburg HS; Stromsburg, NE; ALAGirlsSt; Band; Chr; Chrl; Chrs; ChrhWkr; CncrtBnd; HonRl; MrchBnd; NHS; College.

BULLER, Robert G; Henderson Comm HS; York, NE; PresSophCls; HonRl; LetterFtbl; LetterTrk; IMSpt;.

BULLINGER, Bonnie L; Central HS; Grand Forks, ND; HospAde; JrNHS; NHS; NatlMeritSchl; UNYO; YthFlsp; 4-H; PpCl; LetterBsktbl; LetterChrldr; 4-HAwd; GovHonPrgAwd; PresAwd; University Of North Dakota; Stewardess.

BULLIS, Paul A; Mariner HS; White Bear Lk, MN; Band; CncrtBnd; NatlFornLg; NHS; NatlMeritFnl; NatlMeritCmnd; PolWkr; StuGov; Yrbk; GerCl; U Of Arizona; Pre Law.

BULLOCH, Jack A; Lincoln HS; Wisconsin Rapids, WI; ChrhWkr; HonRl; GerCl; IMSpt; U Of Wis Whitewater; Accounting.

BULLOCK, Andrew R; Southmont HS; New Market, IN; 32/186 PresFrshCls; CmntyWkr; HonRl; NHS; YthFlsp; SptEdSchPpr; Bsktbl; LetterFtbl; LetterTrk; PresAwd; Trade; Vocation.

BULLOCK, Bernadette; Immaculate Conception HS; Elmhurst, IL; TrsFrshCls; CmntyWkr; DrlTm; HonRl; JA; StuCncl; TchrAde; RptrYrbk; FrCl;.

BULLOCK, Charles; William Chrisman HS; Independence, MO; AFS; HonRl; JrNHS; VPNatlFornLg; NHS; PresNatlThespSoc; SchPl; StuCncl; OptClAwd; Baker Univ; Communications.

BULLOCK, Madonna S; Barr Reeve HS; Montgomery, IN; VPJrCls; PresSrCls; PresBand; CncrtBnd; HonRl; MrchBnd; SpnCl; PpCl; Bsktbl; Chrldr; College; Major Study.

BULLOCK, Marion E; Smithville R Ii HS; Smithville, MO; 2/73 Band; HonRl; JrNHS; NHS; RedCrAde; StuCncl; TchrAde; FBLA; FHA; William Jewel Col; Nursing.

BULLOCK, Nancy F; Forman HS; Manito, IL; 5/48 Band; Chrs; CncrtBnd; HonRl; JrNHS; NHS; PepBnd; SchMus; StuCncl; FHA; SpnCl; Icc; Chiropractor.

BULLOCK, Robert K; Wichita West HS; Wichita, KS; 50/621 ALBoysSt; Band; ChrhWkr; HonRl; MrchBnd; PepBnd; Ks St Univ; Engineering.

BULLOCKS, Tina M; North Chicago Community HS; North Chicago, IL; ChrhWkr; HonRl; HospAde; JA; NHS; StuGov; EdYrBk; FNA; FTA; JAAwd; College; Nurse.

BULLUCK, Veda R; Providence St Mel HS; Chicago, IL; 2/50 VPSrCls; TrsSrCls; Chrs; CmntyWkr; HonRl; NHS; OffAde; StuCncl; TchrAde; FTA; SpnCl; Wells College; Law.

BULMAN, Debra A; Caledonia HS; Caledonia, MN; Chr; Chrs; ChrhWkr; CmntyWkr; HonRl; SchPl; YthFlsp; FHA; SpnCl; PpCl; Trade School.

BULMER, Shari L; D C Everest Sr HS; Schofield, WI; 7/338 ChrhWkr; CncrtBnd; HonRl; MrchBnd; NatlFornLg; NHS; NatlThespSoc; SchPl; StuCncl; RptrSchPpr; Univ; Medicine.

BULOW, David; Manistee HS; Manistee, MI; VPSrCls; Band; CmntyWkr; CncrtBnd; HonRl; MrchBnd; Teen; Col.

BULS, Gary D; Riceville Comm HS; Riceville, IA; 11/84 Chr; Chrs; HonRl; NHS; YthFlsp; LetterBsktbl; Trk; Coll; Computer Science.

BULSON, Paul C; Forest Hills Northern HS; Grand Rapids, MI; 15/162 Chr; CmntyWkr; HonRl; ModUN; SctActv; StuGov; FDA; SpnCl; MthCl; Bsbl; Bsktbl; LetterFtbl; IMSpt; University; Professional.

BULTMAN, Lydia; Kalamazoo Christian HS; Decatur, MI; 38/136 Chr; ChrhWkr; HonRl; SchMus; SchPl; Yrbk; SchPpr; College; Nursing.

BULTMAN, Steven J; Kewaunee HS; Kewaunee, WI; 47/137 HonRl; SciCl; CaptBsktbl; LetterFtbl; CaptTrk; Uw Whitewater; Accountant.

BULTSMA, Cheryl; Platte HS; Platte, SD; Chrs; HonRl; HospAde; JA; RptrYrbk; Yrbk; 4-H; FNA; PpCl; 4-HAwd; Coll; Nurse.

BUMAN, James L; Harlan Comm HS; Portsmouth, IA; ChrhWkr; CmntyWkr; HonRl; NHS; StuCncl; StuGov; SchPpr; FFA; Ftbl; IMSpt;.

BUMANN, Brian L; Maple Valley HS; Castana, IA; CmntyWkr; StuCncl; YthFlsp; 4-H; TreasFFA; Swmmng; CaptWrstlng;.

BUMGARDNER, Leigh A; Rosedale HS; Rosedale, IN; Chr; ChrhWkr; ModUN; OffAde; SchMus; TchrAde; 4-H; PpCl; GAA; IMSpt; 4-HAwd; Trade; Medicial Field.

BUMGARNER, Jonathan S; Putnam County HS; Hennepin, IL; Chrs; SchPl; RptrYrbk; Yrbk; RptrSchPpr; 4-H; FFA; FrCl; RusCl; 4-HAwd; Southern Il U; Business Marketing.

BUMGARNER, Laura L; J C Senior HS; Jefferson City, MO; AFS; Chr; Chrs; ChrhWkr; OffAde; RedCrAde; SchPl; SctActv; YthFlsp; LatCl; PpCl; SciCl; Sw Missouri State Univ; Physical Education.

BUMGARNER, Randy L; Triopia HS; Concord, IL; ALBoysSt; Band; Chrs; CncrtBnd; HonRl; SchPl; 4-H; Bsktbl; LetterFtbl; LetterTrk; 4-HAwd; College; Engineering.

BUMPUS, John M; Edwards Cty HS; Albion, IL; 10/125 HonRl; Old Dominion Univ; Optometry.

BUMRUNGCHIT, Naowarat Y; Louisiana HS; Louisiana, MO; AFS; HonRl; StuCncl; FrCl; SpnCl; Chulalungkorn Univ; Sociology.

BUNCE, Polly; St Johns HS; St Johns, MI; 9/325 Band; ChrhWkr; HonRl; MrchBnd; NHS; YthFlsp; RptrYrbk; 4-H; CaptBsktbl; IMSpt; Ferris St Clg; Exec Sec.

BUNCH, Beverly; Macomb Senior HS; Macomb, IL; 1/242 HonRl; VPNHS; PresOrch; SctActv; RptrYrbk; 4-H; PresSpnCl; SciCl; Bsktbl; Trk;.

BUNCH, Cheryl K; Adair County Rii HS; Hurdland, MO; Chrs; HonRl; SchPl; LetterBsbl; LetterBsktbl; LetterTrk; Chrldr; CchngActv; University; Physical Educ.

BUNCH, Debra L; Dixon HS; Dixon, IL; 7/330 Chrs; SecCncrtBnd; MrchBnd; VPNHS; NatlMeritCmnd; StuCncl; Yrbk; PresFDA; AmLegAwd; Univ; Medical.

BUNCH, Jan; Randolph Southern HS; Lynn, IN; VPFrshCls; PresSophCls; ChrhWkr; HonRl; NHS; PepBnd; CitAwd; Taylor Univ; Music Major.

BUNCH, Jan W; Randolph Southern HS; Lynn, IN; 7/65 VPFrshCls; PresSophCls; Band; HonRl; NHS; StuCncl; YthFlsp; Yrbk; Tennis; LetterTrk; Taylor U.

BUNCH, Ray C; Northwestern HS; Blandinsville, IL; 18/53 ChrhWkr; CmntyWkr; PolWkr; SchPl; YthFlsp; SptEdSchPpr; VP4-H; FFA; MthCl; SciCl; LetterBsbl; LetterBsktbl; LetterFtbl; Western Illinois Univ; Agri Economics.

BUNDY, Debra K; Taylorville HS; Taylorville, IL; 23/271 Band; Chr; ChrhWkr; CncrtBnd; HonRl; HospAde; MrchBnd; OffAde; PepBnd; YthFlsp; FTA; SpnCl; PpCl; Univ Of Ill; Elem Educ Teacher.

BUNDY, Jay S; Marquette HS; Elm Grove, WI; 2/256 VPFrshCls; SecJrCls; VPSrCls; DrlTm; NHS; NatlMeritCmnd; Quill&Scroll; RptrYrbk; KeyCl; University; Music.

BUNDY, Mary R; Gull Lake HS; Battle Creek, MI; 31/150 Band; CncrtBnd; HonRl; HospAde; JrNHS; MrchBnd; Chrldr; GAA; PPFtbl; 4-HAwd; Coll; Bus Mang.

BUNDY, Randall R; Tekamah Herman HS; Tekamah, NE; Band; Chrs; CncrtBnd; HonRl; Mdrgl; MrchBnd; NHS; PepBnd; SchMus; Univ Of Nebraska; Elect Engineering.

BUNE, Michael R; Potosi HS; Cadet, MO; 43/246 HonRl; Ftbl; College; Engineer.

BUNESCU, Christine; Rolling Meadows Hs; Arlington Heights, IL; 1 ChrhWkr; HonRl; NHS; NatlMeritCmnd; Trk; College;engineering.

BUNGART, Pete W; Deckerville HS; Deckerville, MI; PresStuCncl; Alma College; Business Admin.

BUNGE, Barbara A; Central HS; Davenport, IA; 1/612 Chr; ChrhWkr; HonRl; NatlMeritSF; SchPpr; College; Education.

BUNGE, Kathy G; Du Quoin HS; Du Quoin, IL; 32/143 Chrs; DrlTm; HonRl; SchMus; FHA;.

BUNGE, Loretta K; Brown County HS; Nashville, IN; 12/169 Band; ChrhWkr; HonRl; NHS; SctActv; YthFlsp; LatCl; SpnCl; Trk; CchngActv; Franklin College; Physical Therapist.

BUNGE, Martin; Osage Comm HS; Osage, IA; 10/120 HonRl; ModUN; Ftbl; Trk; Iowa State Univ; Electrical Engineer.

BUNGERT, Terri L; Academy Of The Holy Angels; Bloomington, MN; 7/106 Band; Chrs; CncrtBnd; HonRl; MrchBnd; NHS; NatlMeritSchl; StuCncl; RptrYrbk; CaptChrldr; College Of St Teresa; Nursing.

BUNGUM, Sharon P; Mentor HS; Mentor, MN; SecSophCls; TrsSophCls; Band; Chr; Chrs; ChrhWkr; HonRl; LbryAde; Mdrgl; MrchBnd; Concordia Clg; Ecology.

BUNK, Diane K; Hazen Public HS; Hazen, ND; SecFrshCls; Chrs; CncrtBnd; HonRl; MrchBnd; PepBnd; StuCncl; RptrSchPpr; FHA;.

BUNKER, Brenda K; Sault Area HS; Sault Ste Marie, MI; Band; CncrtBnd; HonRl; LitMag; MrchBnd; Orch; PepBnd; Swmmng; Business School; Secretarial Field.

BUNKER, Cheryl D; Century HS; Karnak, IL; 5/58 TrsFrshCls; TrsSophCls; HonRl; MrchBnd; StuCncl; RptrYrbk; RptrSchPpr; FHA; PpCl; Chrldr; S I U.

BUNKER, Karen K; Swartz Creek HS; Swartz Creek, MI; HonRl; SchAde; Central Mi; Education.

BUNKER, Louis C; Monroe HS; Monroe, WI; 35/200 HonRl; YthFlsp; KeyCl; Ftbl; Trk; Wrstlng; IMSpt; College; Professional.

BUNNELL, Bernie S; Oxford Community HS; Oxford, NE; 2/36 HonRl; Mdrgl; OffAde; SchMus; SchPl; RptrYrbk; 4-H; PpCl; LetterTrk; Chrldr; College; Physical Education.

BUNNO, Linda; Gladstone Area HS; Gladstone, MI; 8/171 PresSrCls; HonRl; JA; MrchBnd; NHS; FDA; FSA; FTA; PresAwd; CitAwd; College; Veterinary Medicine.

BUNSE, Larry M; Savannah R Iii HS; Cosby, MO; Band; Chr; ChrhWkr; CncrtBnd; DrmMjrt; HonRl; NHS; SchMus; StuCncl; FFA; College; Agri.

BUNTEN, Susan L; St Alberts HS; Council Bluffs, IA; Chr; HonRl; SchMus; PpCl; Ia Western Comm Coll; Nursing.

BUNTING, Carolyn L; New Trier East HS; Wilmette, IL; 117/847 Chrs; HonRl; LbryAde; SctActv; RptrSchPpr; VPGAA; College; Veterinary Medicine.

BUNTING, Darrell K; Anamosa Community HS; Springville, IA; ALBoysSt; Band; ChrhWkr; CncrtBnd; HonRl; MrchBnd; PepBnd; SctActv; SciCl; Rotc; Engi.

BUNTING, Della M; South Callaway Rii HS; Tebbetts, MO; HonRl; NHS; StuCncl; EdYrBk; EdSchPpr; 4-H; Trk; GAA; DARAwd; SARAwd; College; Pharmacist.

BUNTING, James H; Mehlville Sr HS; St Louis, MO; 7/500 NHS; NatlMeritSF; SchMus; St Louis Univ; Physician.

BUNTON, Irving; Lindblom Tech HS; Chicago, IL; 59/610 Chr; Chrs; NatlMeritCmnd; FrCl; Univ; Engineering.

BUNYER, Bruce; Galena HS; Galena, IL; 29/110 HonRl; Bsbl; Bsktbl; Ftbl; Trk; IMSpt; College; Prof.

BUNZEL, Brian L; Greendale HS; Milwaukee, WI; HonRl; SchMus; SchPl; SciCl; Swmmng; Univ; Vocation.

BUOSCIO, Joseph R; St Francis De Sales HS; Chicago, IL; 27/292 VPSrCls; HonRl; NHS; OffAde; StuCncl; StuGov; College.

BUOY, Kimberly A; Concordia HS; Jamestown, KS; Band; Chr; CmntyWkr; CncrtBnd; HonRl; MrchBnd; PepBnd; FrCl; LetterBsktbl;.

BURACK, Gail E; Waynesville HS; Ft Leonard Wood, MO; 1/253 TrsJrCls; SecAFS; HonRl; PresNHS; NatlMeritCmnd; SpnCl; VPMthCl; CaptTennis; Northwestern Univ; Computer Science.

BURAGES, John M; St Charles HS; Saginaw, MI; CmntyWkr; HonRl; SctActv; LetterBsbl; LetterBsktbl; LetterFtbl; University; Professional.

BURAGES, William M; St Charles HS; Saginaw, MI; CmntyWkr; HonRl; SctActv; LetterBsbl; LetterBsktbl; LetterFtbl; College; Professional.

BURAGLIO, Renee A; Lincoln HS; Park Falls, WI; CmntyWkr; HonRl; FHA; College; Art.

BURAU, Greg D; Roosevelt HS; Fergus Falls, MN; Pres4-H; SecFFA; 4-HAwd; Tech School; Dairy Farmer.

BURAU, Shannon R; Columbus HS; Larson, ND; VPJrCls; Band; Chr; HonRl; PresStuCncl; RptrYrbk; Bsktbl; CaptFtbl; Trk; State Schl Of Science; Diesel Mechanic.

BURBACH, Dennis D; Wynot HS; Wynot, NE; PresFrshCls; PresSophCls; PresJrCls; ChrhWkr; HonRl; Bsbl; Bsktbl; Ftbl; Trk; VoiceDemAwd; U Of Ne; Business.

BURBACH, Jeffrey J; Wahlert HS; Dubuque, IA; 77/401 HonRl; SctActv; TchrAde; LetterFtbl; College; Lawyer.

BURBANK, Deyon D; Proctor Hug HS; Lemmon Valley, NE; DrlTm; HonRl; 4-H; FrCl; PpCl; 4-HAwd; Univ; Lab Tech.

BURBEE, Steven C; Lees Summit Senior HS; Lees Summit, MO; 12/370 ALBoysSt; Chr; CncrtBnd; HonRl; NHS; NatlMeritCmnd; RedCrAde; LetterFtbl; LetterTennis; College; Methodist Minister.

BURBRIDGE, Marshall L; Clopton HS; Eolia, MO; 28/60 LetterBsbl; LetterLetterTrk; Clg Of Jefferson County; Electronics.

BURBRIDGE, Thomas E; Jennings HS; Jennings, MO; 1/252 Chr; NHS; NatlSciFnd; NatlThespSoc; SchPl; U Of Mo; Electrical Engineering.

BURCH, Anna; Moose Lake HS; Barnum, MN; Chr; HonRl; HospAde; NHS; 4-H; College; Nursing.

BURCH, Mark W; Estherville HS; Estherville, IA; Band; Chr; Chrl; Chrs; CncrtBnd; HonRl; Mdrgl; PepBnd; College.

BURCH, Paul J; Barr Reeve HS; Loogootee, IN; HonRl; LatCl;.

BURCH, Phyllis M; Frank L Peterson HS; Detroit, MI; SecSrCls; Chr; HonRl; SchAde; StuCncl; Mercy College Of Detroit; Med Rec Science.

BURCHAM, Robert K; Bismarck HS; Bismarck, ND; Band; CncrtBnd; HonRl; MrchBnd; NHS; Orch; PepBnd; College; Engineer.

BURCHAM, Sharon; Crane HS; Crane, MO; 2/26 HonRl; NHS; StuCncl; EdYrBk; RptrSchPpr; GAA; IMSpt; Trade School; Professional.

BURCHAM, Virginia M; Plato HS; Plato, MO; SecSrCls; ChrhWkr; HonRl; LbryAde; SchPl; Yrbk; FBLA; FHA; BttyCrckrAwd;.

BURCHETT, Mary E; Our Lady Star Of The Sea; Grosse Pt Woods, MI; 3/65 TrsSrCls; HonRl; NHS; NatlThespSoc; SchMus; RptrYrbk; RptrSchPpr; FrCl; LetterSwmmng; GAA; University.

BURCHETT, Mary E; Our Lady Star Of The Sea HS; Grosse Pte Woods, MI; 3/58 TrsSrCls; CmntyWkr; NatlFornLg; NHS; NatlThespSoc; SchMus; RptrYrbk; FrCl; LetterSwmmng; DARAwd; Notre Dame.

BURCHETT, Patricia L; No Vermillion HS; Cayuga, IN; SecFrshCls; SecSophCls; SecJrCls; SecSrCls; ALAGirlsSt; Band; CncrtBnd; HonRl; NHS; OffAde; 4-H; SpnCl; PpCl; Chrldr; Indiana St Univ; Physical Educ Teacher.

BURCHFIEL, Cherie D; Maize HS; Wichita, KS; Chr; Chrl; Chrs; ChrhWkr; HonRl; Mdrgl; MrchBnd; SchPl; RptrYrbk; Friends Univ; Social Science.

BURCHFIELD, Elizabeth M; Tekonsha HS; Tekonsha, MI; 9/40 ChrhWkr; LbryAde; RptrYrbk; Yrbk; RptrSchPpr; EdSchPpr; College; Social Work.

BURCK, William C; Morgan Park HS; Chicago, IL; 12/550 Chr; Chrs; HonRl; NHS; SchPpr; KeyCl; FrCl; Ftbl; Univ Of Illinois; Engineering.

BURCKHARD, Rita M; Newport Public HS; Towner, ND; PresJrCls; ALAGirlsSt; SchPl; Yrbk; 4-H; PpCl; Bsktbl; GAA; Univ Of Nd; Psychology.

BURCKLE, Joseph W; Goodrich HS; Fond Du Lac, WI; ChrhWkr; LitMag; Orch; SchPl; RptrSchPpr; GerCl; Technical School; Agricultural Sales.

BURD, John C; Willow Springs HS; Willow Springs, MO; HonRl; SctActv; FFA; SciCl; U Of Mo; Veterinary Medicine.

BURD, L C; Washington HS; Washington, IL; 102/445 Chr; Chrl; Chrs; ChrhWkr; CmntyWkr; Mdrgl; YthFlsp; RptrSchPpr; LetterBsbl; IMSpt; College; Phy Ed.

BURD, Lois; Conway HS; Phillipsburg, MO; Orch; SctActv; YthFlsp; SchPpr; 4-H; FTA; EngCl; SpnCl; CchngActv; Univ; Professional.

BURDEN, Thomas A; Carl Sandburg HS; Palos Heights, IL; 104/700 SctActv; TchrAde; SchPpr; GerCl; Univ Of Il; Engineering.

BURDESS, Terri S; Blair HS; Ft Calhoun, NE; Chr; DrlTm; HonRl; HospAde; MrchBnd; FTA; Business Ed; Accounting.

BURDETTE, Jay J; Catholic Central HS; Monroe, MI; TrsJrCls; TrsSrCls; CmntyWkr; HonRl; NHS; StuCncl; StuGov; IMSpt; DARAwd; CitAwd; U Of Mich; Pediatrician.

BURDETTE, Tracy D; Bishop Ward HS; Kansas City, KS; ALAGirlsSt; ChrhWkr; CmntyWkr; DrlTm; HonRl; ModUN; NHS; SchAde; SctActv; StuGov; TchrAde; YthFnd; PpCl; College; Professional.

BURDICK, Anthony M; Pontiac Central HS; Pontiac, MI; Chr; HonRl; LitMag; NatlMeritSF; SchMus; SchPl; StuCncl; RptrSchPpr; FrCl; LetterTennis; Clge; Philosophy & Literature.

BURDICK, Carol A; Unity HS; Sadorus, IL; Band; CncrtBnd; HonRl; MrchBnd; NHS; PepBnd; 4-H; FrCl; PpCl; 4-HAwd; Southern Illinois U; Reatailor.

BURDICK, James; Huron Senior HS; Huron, SD; 4-H; FFA; 4-HAwd; Vocaional School; Farm.

BURDICK, Larry F; Jackson Heights HS; Whiring, KS; PresFrshCls; VPJrCls; ChrhWkr; HonRl; StuCncl; TchrAde; PpCl; Ftbl; Trk;.

BURDS, Jeffrey P; Catholic Central HS; Detroit, MI; SecFrshCls; HonRl; JrNHS; NatlFornLg; NHS; PolWkr; StuGov; FrCl; Swmmng; Harvard University; Law.

BURDZILAUSKAS, Joan M; Illiopolis HS; Illiopolis, IL; 1/40 SecSrCls; Band; Chrs; HonRl; PresNHS; NatlThespSoc; OffAde; SchPl; EdYrBk; FHA; FTA; SecGAA; Illinois State Univ; Business Admin.

BURESH, Diane K; Prairie Sr HS; Cedar Rapids, IA; Chr; ChrhWkr; CmntyWkr; CaptDrlTm; HonRl; JrNHS; NatlFornLg; OffAde; PresYthFlsp; Pres4-H; Bsktbl; 4-HAwd; Coe College; Pharmacist.

BURESH, Douglas J; Central Public HS; Valparaiso, NE; 30/62 Chr; Chrs; ChrhWkr; HonRl; SchMus; SchPl; StuCncl; TchrAde; 4-H; FBLA; FFA; Bsbl; Bsktbl; LetterFtbl;.

BURFEIND, Barbara A; Lewiston HS; Winona, MN; Band; CncrtBnd; NHS; RptrYrbk; Yrbk; RptrSchPpr; 4-H; Trk; GAA; 4-HAwd; U Of Wis; Photo.

BURFORD, Bobbi J; Norwich HS; Milton, KS; TrsFrshCls; VPSophCls; TrsJrCls; Band; Chr; Chrs; CmntyWkr; CncrtBnd; HonRl; HospAde; MrchBnd; Tennis; Trk; Chrldr; College.

BURG, Beth A; Lawton Bronson HS; Lawton, IA; Band; Chrs; CncrtBnd; MrchBnd; PresNatlThespSoc; StuCncl; YthFlsp; PpCl; LetterTrk; Chrldr; Coll; Professnl.

BURG, Connie R; Wisconsin Academy; Hinsdale, IL; HonRl; LbryAde; StuCncl; Andrews University; Vet.

BURG, Edward G; Palatine HS; Palatine, IL; 3/440 VPBand; TreasNHS; NatlMeritCmnd; Quill&Scroll; EdSchPpr; NCTE; Univ Of Calif; Writer.

BURG, Helen J; Caledonia HS; Caledonia, MN; HonRl; SchPl; StuCncl; Yrbk; FHA; SpnCl; LetterBsktbl; LetterTrk; GAA; IMSpt; College; Biology Major.

BURGAN, John G; St Catherines HS; Racine, WI; 11/250 HonRl; NHS; SchMus; StuCncl; StuGov; RusCl; College; Engineering.

BURGAR, Laurie A; Springfield Southeast HS; Springfield, IL; 26/500 NHS; Trk; College; English.

BURGARD, Jean; Central HS; Aberdeen, SD; Chrs; ChrhWkr; CmntyWkr; HonRl; HospAde; SchAde; SchMus; SchPl; IMSpt; Northern St Coll; Special Education.

BURGARD, Theresa; Ypsilanti HS; Ypsilanti, MI; 8/520 ChrhWkr; HonRl; LitMag; NHS; StuCncl; SpnCl; Bsktbl; College; Unknown.

BURGARDT, Mary E; Sacred Heart HS; Salina, KS; VPFrshCls; LetterBand; ChrhWkr; CmntyWkr; CncrtBnd; HonRl; MrchBnd; Orch; LetterBsktbl; PresAwd; College; Special Education.

BURGARDT, Michael A; Wheatland HS; Park, KS; ALBoysSt; SchMus; SchPl; StuGov; RptrYrbk; SptEdYrbk; Yrbk; RptrSchPpr; SptEdSchPpr; SchPpr; Bsbl; LetterBsktbl; LetterFtbl;.

BURGAUER, James O; Libertyville HS; Libertyville, IL; HonRl; NHS; NatlMeritCmnd; SctActv; StuCncl; SciCl; Univ Of Il; Economist.

BURGE, Alan J; Stewart Public HS; Brownton, MN; ChrhWkr; HonRl; StuCncl; StuGov; RptrSchPpr; SptEdSchPpr; SchPpr; LetterBsbl; LetterFtbl; IMSpt; Coll; Professional.

BURGE, Billie J; Girard HS; Girard, KS; 3/89 ALAGirlsSt; Band; CncrtBnd; DrlTm; HonRl; MrchBnd; VPNHS; PepBnd; SchPl; StuCncl; Teen; SchPpr; Bsktbl; PPFtbl; Kansas State Univ; Fashion Retailing.

BURGE, Melia L; Howell HS; Howell, MI; 19/362 Band; ChrhWkr; CmntyWkr; CncrtBnd; HonRl; MrchBnd; NHS; PepBnd; SctActv; 4-H; GerCl; Kalamazoo College; Medicine.

BURGE, Rodney; Superior HS; Webber, KS; HonRl; 4-H; Bsktbl; Wrstlng; MasAwd; College; Lab Technician.

BURGENER, Mary J; West Richland HS; Noble, IL; 4/36 Band; Chrs; ChrhWkr; HonRl; SchPl; PresYthFlsp; Yrbk; FrCl; PpCl; 4-HAwd; C C E Il Univ; Med Tech.

BURGER, Christine M; Larkin HS; Elgin, IL; 9/625 Chrs; DrlTm; HonRl; FrCl; Univ; Liberal Arts.

BURGER, David H; Kapaun Mt Carmel HS; Wichita, KS; HonRl; PolWkr; SctActv; FrCl; IMSpt; CitAwd; College.

BURGER, Edith A; Newman HS; Wausau, WI; 5/130 HonRl; LbryAde; NHS; StuGov; RptrSchPpr; SpnCl; MthCl; Univ Of Wisconsin; Medicine.

BURGER, Elizabeth M; Burris Laboratory HS; Muncie, IN; 3/49 ChrhWkr; LitMag; NatlMeritCmnd; NatlMeritSF; PolWkr; Yrbk; EdSchPpr; 4-H; LatCl; Univ Of Notre Dame; Law.

BURGER, Karla J; Clay Center Community HS; Clay Center, KS; Band; Chr; CncrtBnd; HonRl; MrchBnd; SchPl; Yrbk; PpCl; Manhattan Area Vo Tech.

BURGER, Robert M; Summerfield HS; Summerfield, KS; 4/21 Chrs; HonRl; Bsktbl; LetterFtbl; College; Teaching.

BURGESON, Keith J; Park River HS; Park River, ND; Chr; Chrs; ChrhWkr; HonRl; SchPl; StuCncl; YthFlsp; College; Missionary.

BURGESS, Ann M; Pekin Community HS; Pekin, IL; 69/759 HonRl; SchPl;.

BURGESS, Barbara A; Vestaburg Comm HS; Blanchard, MI; 27/63 Band; Chr; ChrhWkr; CmntyWkr; HonRl; TchrAde; YthLg; RptrYrbk; 4-H; Chrldr; CchngActv; John Wesley College; Social Work.

BURGESS, Bonnie L; North Putman HS; Fillmore, IN; 12/130 Band; HonRl; NHS; OffAde; PepBnd; TchrAde; RptrYrbk; RptrSchPpr; LatCl; MthCl; College; English Teacher.

BURGESS, Bruce J; Assumption HS; Wisconsin Rapids, WI; TrsJrCls; HonRl; StuCncl; StuGov; SptEdSchPpr; SpnCl; MthCl; Bsktbl; LetterFtbl; IMSpt; Univ Of Minnesota; History.

BURGESS, Connie C; O Fallen Twp HS; Caseyville, IL; ChrhWkr; HonRl; NHS; StuCncl; YthFlsp; College; Medicine.

BURGESS, David B; Stevens HS; Rapid City, SD; 182/413 Band; CncrtBnd; MrchBnd; College; Engineering.

BURGESS, Karen; Oakville Senior HS; St Louis, MO; 1/365 CmntyWkr; HonRl; NHS; PolWkr; TchrAde; FHA; MthCl; PpCl; IMSpt; PresAwd; Univ Of Md; Ceramic Engineer.

BURGESS, Karen K; Darlington HS; Shullsburg, WI; TrsSrCls; ALAGirlsSt; CmntyWkr; HonRl; FHA; SpnCl; PpCl; CaptChrldr; GAA; 4-HAwd; Accountant.

BURGESS, Karla A; Wesclin HS; New Baden, IL; Chrs; DrlTm; DrmBgl; LbryAde; NatlFornLg; NatlThespSoc; RedCrAde; Twrl; FNA; LatCl; College; Professional.

BURGESS, Kenneth G; Portland HS; Mulliken, MI; 23/126 HonRl; Military Training; Electronics.

BURGESS, Leenette M; Newberry HS; Newberry, MI; 1/120 SecSophCls; Band; ChrhWkr; CncrtBnd; HonRl; JrNHS; NHS; RptrSchPpr; Bsktbl; Chrldr; Coll; Med Tech.

BURGESS, Paula L; Croswell Lexington HS; Croswell, MI; TrsJrCls; TrsSrCls; CncrtBnd; HonRl; MrchBnd; OffAde; StuCncl; StuGov; TchrAde; College; Social Service.

BURGESS, Ronald L; Batavia Sr HS; Aurora, IL; 4/219 PresJrCls; Band; ChrhWkr; CncrtBnd; HonRl; JrNHS; LitMag; MrchBnd; NHS; PepBnd; Univ Of Illinois; Architecture.

BURGESS, Timothy L; Bloomer HS; Bloomer, WI; 60/127 AFS; Chr; Chrs; SctActv; FFA; PpCl; LetterBsbl; LetterFtbl; LetterWrstlng; IMSpt; Air Force.

BURGET, Cindy L; Southeast Polk HS; Altoona, IA; 16/216 Chr; NHS; SctActv; 4-H; IMSpt; Clge; Prof.

BURGHOFFER, Becky L; Central HS; Donnellson, IA; HonRl; HospAde; SchPl; SctActv; YthFlsp; RptrSchPpr; FBLA; PpCl; LetterBsktbl; Technical School; Medical Assistant.

BURGOON, Deborah A; Wayne Memorial HS; Wayne, MI; 4/638 HonRl; JrNHS; NHS; FrCl; GAA; Univ; Elementary Teacher.

BURHANS, Laura S; Wheaton Warrenville HS; Warrenville, IL; 13/225 SecSrCls; HonRl; NHS; SchMus; SchPl; StuCncl; StuGov; TchrAde; VPSpnCl; PpCl; Trk; CaptChrldr; BauchLmbAwd; College; Nursing.

BURHANS, Maxine L; Northwestern HS; Brule, WI; Chr; LbryAde; OffAde; 4-H; FHA; FNA; Trk; GAA; Trade Sch; Voc.

BURHANS, William J; Anamosa Comm HS; Anamosa, IA; 19/140 PresFrshCls; HonRl; ModUN; StuCncl; PpCl; LetterBsbl; CaptBsktbl; CaptFtbl; LetterTrk; CchngActv; Univ Of Arizona; Business Admin.

BURHOP, Debbie L; Grafton HS; Grafton, WI; Band; HonRl; MrchBnd; TreasStuCncl; 4-H; Bsbl; Trk; CaptChrldr; DARAwd; Professional.

BURICH, Richard J; Premontre HS; Green Bay, WI; Band; CncrtBnd; HonRl; PepBnd; SchMus;.

BURINGTON, Colleen R; E Waterloo HS; Waterloo, IA; 13/300 ChrhWkr; NHS; SchPl; 4-H; CaptBsktbl; CaptSwmmng; CaptTrk; 4-HAwd; PresAwd;.

BURK, Janene R; Ida Grove HS; Ida Grove, IA; ALAGirlsSt; Chrs; ChrhWkr; HonRl; NHS; YthFlsp; 4-H; Bsktbl; Trk; Business School.

BURK, Jo Ann; Manual HS; Peoria, IL; 13/329 SecChr; ChrhWkr; CmntyWkr; LbryAde; NHS; TchrAde; PresYthFlsp; FTA; Tennis; CchngActv; Texas Lutheran College; Elem Education.

BURK, Joyce A; Perry Meridian HS; Indianapolis, IN; Aud/Vis; HonRl; JA; LbryAde; OffAde; SchAde; StuCncl; FBLA; MthCl; PpCl; IMSpt; 4-HAwd; College; Pharmacy.

BURK, Nancy D; Twin Rivers HS; Qulin, MO; 4/101 ChrhWkr; HonRl; SchPl; TreasFHA; Three River Comm Coll; Bus Admin.

BURK, Thomas K; Boone Valley HS; Renwick, IA; TrsSophCls; VPJrCls; CncrtBnd; HonRl; SchPl; StuCncl; StuCncl; SptEdYrbk; SciCl; Bsktbl; Trk; D M Area Comm Clg; Masonry.

BURKART, John D; Premontre HS; Green Bay, WI; 1/123 Band; CncrtBnd; HonRl; ROTC; SchMus; SctActv; StuCncl; KeyCl; SpnCl; PpCl; Marquette; Dentistry.

BURKART, Michael D; Sycamore HS; Sycamore, IL; 16/201 VPJrCls; PresSrCls; AFS; ALBoysSt; CAP; HonRl; NHS; SctActv; StuCncl; SptEdYrbk; Yrbk; SchPpr; Bsbl; Bsktbl; Univ Of Illinois; Business Admin.

BURKART, Susan L; Larkin HS; Elgin, IL; 57/573 Chrl; Chrs; HonRl; SchMus; SchPl; TchrAde; RptrYrbk; SecRptrSchPpr; EngCl; PpCl; Illinois State Univ; Biology.

BURKE, Bonnie L; Mason County Central HS; Branch, MI; 11/150 Chr; CmntyWkr; HonRl; NatlMeritCmnd; TchrAde; RptrYrbk; 4-H; 4-HAwd; West Shore Comm Clge; Gen Ed.

BURKE, Brian; Pius Xi HS; Wauwatosa, WI; IMSpt; Univ; Business Administration.

BURKE, Daniel J; Benedictine HS; Detroit, MI; 28/135 ChrhWkr; HonRl; LbryAde; NatlMeritSF; University Of Michigan; Mechanical Engineer.

BURKE, Darrell E; Midway Denton HS; Huron, KS; PresFrshCls; Band; Chrs; CncrtBnd; HonRl; NHS; PepBnd; SchPl; LetterBsktbl; LetterTrk; Coll; Med Tech.

BURKE, Debra J; St John HS; Independence, IA; 7/27 SecSophCls; Chr; HonRl; NHS; StuCncl; StuGov; RptrYrbk; LetterBsktbl; Trk; LetterChrldr; GAA; College; Med Records Librarian.

BURKE, Denise J; Center Sr HS; Kansas City, MO; 25/431 Band; ChrhWkr; CncrtBnd; HonRl; MrchBnd; PepBnd; Yrbk; SpnCl; Coll; Special Ed.

BURKE, Diane M; Mendota Twp HS; Mendota, IL; Chr; Chrl; PresChrs; HonRl; OffAde; SchAde; PresSpnCl; College; Liberal Arts.

BURKE, Donna M; Ernest W Seaholm HS; Birmingham, MI; TrsSophCls; NatlMeritCmnd; StuGov; FrCl; U Of Mi; Medicine.

BURKE, Ed J; St Agnes HS; Alliance, NE; 11/21 Chr; HonRl; SchMus; 4-H; CaptBsktbl; Ftbl; Trk; 4-HAwd;.

BURKE, Edward J; St Ignatius HS; Chicago, IL; CmntyWkr; HonRl; RptrYrbk; Yrbk; LetterTennis; IMSpt; Notre Dame Univ; Business.

BURKE, Hal D; South Knox HS; Monroe City, IN; 6/99 ALBoysSt; NHS; RptrSchPpr; MthCl; Bsktbl; Glf; CchngActv; Purdue Univ; Aeronautics.

BURKE, James J; Greendale HS; Greendale, WI; 110/375 ModUN; TchrAde; GerCl; Bsktbl; Ftbl; Univ; Professional.

BURKE, Jill R; Beaverton HS; Beaverton, MI; 8/140 Band; Chr; HonRl; NHS; SchMus; TchrAde; YthFlsp; College; Secondary Education.

BURKE, John A; Brother Rice HS; Chicago, IL; 77/416 HonRl; Loyola Univ; Dentistry.

BURKE, John R; Lake Central HS; Dyer, IN; 24/461 NHS; Purdue Univ; Elect Engr.

BURKE, Kathleen E; Cahokia Senior HS; Cahokia, IL; 8/533 DrlTm; HonRl; NHS; College; Professional.

BURKE, Kathy M; Ashton HS; Ashton, IL; SecSrCls; Band; Chrs; StuCncl; RptrSchPpr; Chrldr; College; Management.

BURKE, Lauren B; Zeeland HS; West Olive, MI; ChrhWkr; HonRl; NHS; SchPl; TchrAde; SchPpr; Retail Sales.

BURKE, Luke; Stevenson HS; Livonia, MI; ChrhWkr; HonRl; SctActv; Mi Univ; Astrophysics.

BURKE, Margaret M; Academy Of Our Lady; Chicago, IL; 7/160 JA; NatlSciFnd; SchMus; SchPl; Sdlty; EdYrBk; SchPpr; 4-H; PpCl; BttyCrckrAwd; Northwestern University; Chemistry.

BURKE, Martin W; Cedar Catholic HS; Coleridge, NE; Band; Chrs; CncrtBnd; HonRl; MrchBnd; NHS; PepBnd; SchMus; 4-H; Ftbl; Trk; College.

BURKE, Maureen E; Our Lady Star/sea HS; Grosse Pt Shrs, MI; PresFrshCls; Aud/Vis; ChrhWkr; CmntyWkr; SchPl; Sdlty; TchrAde; RptrSchPpr; SptEdSchPpr; FrCl; Bsbl; Swmmng; Tennis; Villanova Univ; History.

BURKE, Michael A; North Side HS; Fort Wayne, IN; Band; CncrtBnd; HonRl; MrchBnd; NHS; Orch; PepBnd; SchMus; SchPl; SecKeyCl; LetterTennis; IMSpt; Ball State University; Business Admin.

BURKE, Patricia A; St Marys HS; Kansas City, MO; 11/75 NHS; OffAde; PolWkr; SchMus; SchPl; Yrbk; PpCl; Central Mo State; Special Educ.

BURKE, Patrick; Shelbyville Hs; Shelbyville, IL; HonRl; RptrSchPpr; 4-H; Bsktbl; Ftbl; Lakeland Jr College;architectural Of Draft.

BURKE, Richard W; Divernon HS; Divernon, IL; PresSrCls; NHS; NatlMeritFnl; NatlMeritCmnd; NatlMeritSchl; CivCl; AmLegAwd; DARAwd; MasAwd; CitAwd; Architect.

BURKE, Ross D; California HS; California, MO; 34/99 PresFrshCls; HonRl; StuCncl; LetterBsktbl; LetterFtbl; College; Political Science.

BURKE, Sharon E; Dekalb HS; De Kalb, IL; 24/370 HonRl; NHS; StuCncl; PpCl; IMSpt; PPFtbl; College.

BURKE, Timothy J; Northrop HS; Fort Wayne, IN; VPSophCls; HonRl; StuCncl; StuGov; Tennis; CchngActv; IMSpt; PPFtbl; U Of Virginia.

BURKE, Victoria S; Macomb HS; Macomb, IL; 76/247 IMSpt; College.

BURKERT, David; Hammond Baptist Hs; Crete, IL; SecTrsJrCls; ChrhWkr; HonRl; EdYrBk; LetterFtbl; LetterSocr; LetterLetterCchngActv; Bob Jones U; Lawyer Or Coach.

BURKERT, James; Tipton HS; Elwood, IN; 6/173 HonRl; NHS; KiwanAwd; Purdee Univ; Agronomy.

BURKETT, Connie L; Marshall HS; Marshall, IL; 40/115 FTA; SpnCl; Trk; Schooling; Voc.

BURKETT, Eldon L; Breckenridge Jr/sr HS; Breckenridge, MI; SecSophCls; Band; ChrhWkr; HonRl; LbryAde; MrchBnd; PepBnd; RedCrAde; SchPl; 4-H; Univ.

BURKETT, Michael; La Porte City HS; Laporte City, IA; 20/70 SchPl; FFA; LetterWrstlng; Ellsworth Comm Iowa State;agriculture Busin.

BURKETT, Michael L; La Porte City HS; La Porte City, IA; 17/90 CmntyWkr; HonRl; SchPl; 4-H; FFA; Bsbl; CaptWrstlng; 4-HAwd; Ellsworth Comm Coll; Agriculture.

BURKETT, Vickie L; Northwest HS; Dittmer, MO; ChrhWkr; HonRl; LbryAde; TchrAde; FTA; PpCl;.

BURKEY, Paul S; Zion Benton Township HS; Zion, IL; 1/431 Band; CncrtBnd; HonRl; MrchBnd; Loyola Univ; Orthodontics.

BURKEY, Susanne M; Elm Creek Public HS; Elm Creek, NE; 3/29 Chr; Chrs; HonRl; JrNHS; PresNHS; SchPl; EdYrBk; 4-H; PpCl; LetterTrk; Grand Island Sch Of Bus; Exec Sec.

BURKHALTER, Laureen; Black Hawk HS; South Wayne, WI; SecFrshCls; SecJrCls; Band; Chr; DrmMjrt; HonRl; Mdrgl; NHS; Chrldr; La Crosse Univ; Phy Ed Teacher.

BURKHARD, Doreen M; St Benedict HS; Chicago, IL; 46/183 SecFrshCls; SecSophCls; VPSrCls; Chrs; HonRl; LbryAde; SchMus; SchPl; StuCncl; MthCl; PpCl; Northeastern Il Univ; English Teacher.

BURKHARDT, Anita J; East HS; Kansas City, MO; 4/250 Band; Chr; HonRl; HospAde; JrNHS; NHS; SchMus; RptrYrbk; Yrbk; College; Nursing.

BURKHARDT, Debra L; Northridge HS; Middlebury, IN; Chr; DrlTm; HonRl; HospAde; Yrbk; 4-H; College; Social Work.

BURKHARDT, Michael A; Howards Grove HS; Howards Grove, WI; 1/74 ChrhWkr; CncrtBnd; NHS; TchrAde; YthFlsp; RptrSchPpr; EdSchPpr; Trk; IMSpt; RotaryAwd; Lawrence University; Music Education.

BURKHART, Kim A; Leaf River HS; Egan, IL; SchPl; 4-H; FFA; Bsktbl; Ftbl; 4-HAwd; Trade School; Farming.

BURKHART, Sheri C; Grand Haven HS; Grand Haven, MI; ChrhWkr; HonRl; HospAde; PolWkr; Bsktbl; Trk; Coll; Elem Educ.

BURKHART, Timothy J; Washington HS; Sioux Falls, SD; ALBoysSt; HonRl; NHS; StuCncl; LetterTrk; Sdsu; Forestry.

BURKHART, Vickie; Olympia HS; Stanford, IL; Chrs; HonRl; 4-H; Trk; Beauty College; Beautician.

BURKHEAD, Lisa; Adams Central HS; Monroe, IN; 9/123 TrsJrCls; Chr; HonRl; LbryAde; NHS; StuCncl; YthFlsp; 4-H; FrCl; IMSpt; Indiana Univ; Journalism.

BURKHOLDER, Anne C; West HS; Madison, WI; NatlMeritSF; Quill&Scroll; StuCncl; RptrYrbk; Univ Of Wi; Biological Research.

BURKHOLDER, Scott G; Smith Cotton HS; Sedalia, MO; Band; HonRl; MrchBnd; SchMus; StuGov; YthLg; MthCl; Bsktbl; Glf; Socr; Univ; Prof.

BURKHOLZ, Robert C; Lake Michigan Catholic HS; Benton Harbor, MI; 14/96 ChrhWkr; HonRl; JA; ModUN; NHS; PolWkr; RptrYrbk; JAAwd; KiwanAwd; RotaryAwd; Univ Mi; Law Field.

BURKI, Marlan M; Gordon HS; Gordon, NE; Chr; NatlThespSoc; StuCncl; TchrAde; YthFlsp; GerCl; Ftbl; Wrstlng; Univ; Physical Therapy.

BURKI, Sharon K; Parkview HS; Footville, WI; 7/163 Band; CncrtBnd; HonRl; MrchBnd; NHS; PepBnd; StuCncl; Twrl; EdYrBk; GAA; College; Professional.

BURKLAND, Mark E; Rochelle Twp HS; Rochelle, IL; 11/230 CncrtBnd; Mdrgl; MrchBnd; NatlFornLg; NatlThespSoc; Orch; SchPl; StuCncl; KeyCl; LatCl; Trk; Univ Of Illinois; Law.

BURKS, Linda D; Southwestern HS; Brighton, IL; Chrs; HonRl; Army Military Police.

BURKS, Michael G; Forman HS; Manito, IL; 12/60 PresChrs; HonRl; SchMus; SchPl; StuCncl; PresYthFlsp; RptrYrbk; RptrSchPpr; LetterBsbl; LetterBsktbl; LetterTrk; Il State; Art.

BURLESON, Donald E; Riceville Community HS; Riceville, IA; 4/63 HonRl; NatlMeritCmnd; SchPl; RptrSchPpr; LetterGlf; Wrstlng; University; Accounting.

BURLESON, Randall R; Verona R 7 HS; Verona, MO; PresSophCls; HonRl; NHS; SchPl; StuCncl; StuGov; LetterBsbl; LetterBsktbl; College; Vocation.

BURLET, Chad R; Mound Westonka; Mound, MN; PresChrhWkr; HonRl; NHS; Quill&Scroll; SchAde; SctActv; EdSchPpr; SptEdSchPpr; MthCl; Ftbl; University; Professional.

BURLEY, David M; Cedar Lake Acad; Frankfort, MI; 24/78 ChrhWkr; HonRl; OffAde; StuCncl; StuGov; Bsbl; Bsktbl; Socr; IMSpt; Andrews U; Political Sci.

BURLEY, Kevin; John Glenn HS; Bay City, MI; 35/335 SchPl; Bsktbl; Michigan Tech Univ; Metallurgical Engineer.

BURLING, Richard; Oregon HS; Oregon, WI; TrsFrshCls; CncrtBnd; HonRl; MrchBnd; RptrYrbk; MthCl; College; Biological Sciences.

BURLINGAME, Beth M; North HS; Eau Claire, WI; Chr; HonRl; HospAde; NHS; NatlThespSoc; Orch; SchMus; SchPl; College; Home Economics.

BURMAN, Janel N; Badger HS; Lake Geneva, WI; 15/244 AFS; Chr; HonRl; Mdrgl; NatlFornLg; NHS; NatlThespSoc; SchMus; SchPl; Judson Baptist College; Writer.

BURMAN, Kathleen; New Monroe Comm HS; Monroe, IA; Band; CncrtBnd; HonRl; MrchBnd; TchrAde; RptrYrbk; SchPpr; Bsbl; Bsktbl; Univ Of N Ia; Teaching Math Accand Coaching.

BURMAYER, Doreen; Walker HS; Walker, MN; TrsFrshCls; TrsSophCls; Band; Chr; Chrs; ChrhWkr; CmntyWkr; CncrtBnd; IMSpt; Bus School; Vocation.

BURMEISTER, Debra L; Port Washington HS; Port Washington, WI; Band; CncrtBnd; HonRl; MrchBnd; NHS; SctActv; RptrYrbk; EdYrBk; SchPpr; MthCl; College; Professional.

BURMEISTER, James H; Perry Community HS; Perry, IA; ChrhWkr; HonRl; StuCncl; SpnCl; PpCl; Bsktbl; LetterGlf; College; Major Study.

BURMEISTER, Paul I; Shelby Public HS; New Era, MI; 7/120 PresJrCls; Chr; HonRl; Mdrgl; NHS; SchPl; SctActv; StuCncl; TchrAde; YthFlsp; College; Professional.

BURMEISTER, Wendy Sue; Saint Marys HS; Storm Lake, IA; 11/45 Band; Chrs; CncrtBnd; MrchBnd; PepBnd; SchMus; Univ Of S D; Library Sci.

BURMESTER, Donald A; Beaver Dam HS; Beaver Dam, WI; 100/301 Chr; NHS; StuCncl; StuGov; YthFlsp; Yrbk; Ftbl; PresAwd; VoiceDemAwd; College; Professional Photographer.

BURMOOD, Nancy L; Shelton HS; Shelton, NE; 2/32 SecTrsSrCls; ALAGirlsSt; Band; CncrtBnd; DrlTm; HonRl; MrchBnd; PepBnd; SchPl; RptrYrbk; FHA; FrCl; Kearney St College; Computer Science.

BURNELL, Frances; Triton Central HS; Shelbyville, IN; 41/150 ChrhWkr; HonRl; LbryAde; StuCncl; TchrAde; PpCl; Bsktbl; Chrldr; GAA;.

BURNER, Debra; Owosso HS; Owosso, MI; 35/438 Chr; ChrhWkr; HospAde; Mdrgl; NHS; StuCncl; YthFlsp; LatCl; DARAwd; RotaryAwd; Mich State; Business Maj.

BURNETT, Ann C; Shrine HS; Royal Oak, MI; 50/170 CmntyWkr; HonRl; HospAde; SchMus; SctActv; StuCncl; StuGov; Yrbk; SchPpr; PpCl; U Of Mi; Business Law.

BURNETT, Diane R; Webber Twp HS; Obdyke, IL; HonRl; FHA; PpCl; Chrldr; College.

BURNETT, Douglas; Urbana Hs; Urbana, IL; 1/428 SchPpr; U Of Illinois; Commercial Art.

BURNETT, Jackie S; Woodruff HS; Peoria, IL; ChrhWkr; HonRl; College; Physical Therapy.

BURNETT, Kenneth; Jefferson Senior HS; Jefferson, WI; HstFrshCls; HstSophCls; HstJrCls; HstSrCls; CmntyWkr; HonRl; SchPl; TchrAde; SchPpr; Univ; Forestry Conservation.

BURNETT, Nancy L; Casey HS; Casey, IL; 11/94 Band; HonRl; NHS; SecStuCncl; Sec4-H; SpnCl; SecPpCl; Chrldr; IMSpt; 4-HAwd; Col; Vocation.

BURNETT, Rebecca; Macon Senior HS; Macon, MO; 3/117 CncrtBnd; HonRl; MrchBnd; PepBnd; SctActv; StuCncl; Twrl; SpnCl; PpCl; Chrldr; Univ Of Mo; Phys Educ.

BURNETT, Tamra L; Council Grove HS; Ahavista, KS; Chrs; ChrhWkr; DrlTm; OffAde; YthFlsp; RptrYrbk; SchPpr; PpCl; Bsbl; Ks State U; Rn.

BURNEY, Glenda D; C 4 HS; Viburnum, MO; 17/59 CncrtBnd; HonRl; LbryAde; MrchBnd; NHS; NatlThespSoc; PepBnd; PresFHA; FTA; VPPpCl; College; Liberal Arts.

BURNHAM, Charleen M; Avondale Senior HS; Rochester, MI; ChrhWkr; HonRl; OffAde; RedCrAde; SchAde; SctActv; TchrAde; College; X Ray Tech.

BURNHAM, Donna J; Fredericktown HS; Fredericktown, MO; 22/125 PresSophCls; HonRl; NHS; NatlThespSoc; PolWkr; TreasStuCncl; RptrYrbk; RptrSchPpr; SpnCl; CaptChrldr; Se Mo St Univ; Bus Ad & Public Rela.

BURNHAM, Shari L; Walnut Grove Public HS; Walnut Grove, MN; Chrs; LbryAde; 4-H; FFA; SpnCl; Trk; 4-HAwd; Univ Of Minnesota; Veterinary Medicine.

BURNHAM, Teya; Mahomet Seymour HS; Mahomet, IL; Chr; Chrs; Mdrgl; NatlMeritSF; NatlThespSoc; SchPl; RptrYrbk; RptrSchPpr; FrCl; VPSciCl; Trk; College; Doctor.

BURNISON, Charles S; Reese Public HS; Reese, MI; 22/127 TrsJrCls; HonRl; NatlMeritFnl; StuGov; SptEdSchPpr; Bsbl; Bsktbl; Ftbl; Glf;.

BURNS, Betty L; Laurel PublicHS; Laurel, NE; 10/61 ALAGirlsSt; Band; Chrs; HonRl; PepBnd; StuCncl; RptrYrbk; FHA; PpCl; IMSpt;.

BURNS, Cindi L; Macon HS; Macon, IL; 11/56 HonRl; TchrAde; Yrbk; EdSchPpr; FBLA; SpnCl; PpCl; Chrldr; ChmbCommrsAwd; William R Harper Jr Clg; Legal Technology.

BURNS, Colleen A; Wrightstown HS; Brillion, WI; Chrs; HospAde; NatlFornLg; SchPl; 4-H; SpnCl; GAA; IMSpt; AmLegAwd; 4-HAwd; Nursing Schl; Rn.

BURNS, Cynthia R; St Marys HS; Storm Lake, IA; 1/45 SecSophCls; Band; Chrs; ChrhWkr; CncrtBnd; DrlTm; HonRl; MrchBnd; NatlMeritSF; PepBnd; SctActv; RptrSchPpr; Briar Cliff College; Medical Tech.

BURNS, David W; Vienna HS; Vienna, IL; 12/120 ChrhWkr; CmntyWkr; HonRl; Mdrgl; SchAde; SchPl; SpnCl; PpCl; Trk; IMSpt; Shawnee Jr Siu; Bus Mgmnt.

BURNS, Deanna L; Gibson Southern HS; Ft Branch, IN; MrchBnd; SecNatlThespSoc; SchMus; EdYrBk; RptrSchPpr; FHA; LatCl; PpCl; OptClAwd; Univ; Radio Tv Broadcasting.

BURNS, Eric H; West La Fayette HS; West Lafayette, IN; 20/215 PresSrCls; ALBoysSt; HonRl; NHS; NatlMeritCmnd; StuCncl; RptrSchPpr; LetterFtbl; Wrstlng; RotaryAwd; Wabash Clge; Pre Med.

BURNS, James L; Hartford Union HS; Hartford, WI; VPJrCls; ALBoysSt; HonRl; JA; JrNHS; NHS; SctActv; StuCncl; Glf; Swmmng; Univ; Lawyer.

BURNS, James W; Richland Center HS; Richland Center, WI; Chr; ChrhWkr; HonRl; LitMag; NHS; PresYthFlsp; FBLA; Trk;.

BURNS, Jeanne M; Everly Comm HS; Hartley, IA; 7/34 SecSrCls; TreasBand; Chr; Chrs; HonRl; Mdrgl; MrchBnd; NHS; PepBnd; SchMus; Morningside Clg; Music Education.

BURNS, Jo Anne; Raymond Lincolnwood HS; Waggoner, IL; HonRl; LbryAde; TchrAde; YthFlsp; FHA; FTA; SciCl; Coll; Pro.

BURNS, John P; North HS; Eau Claire, WI; 15/375 ChrhWkr; CncrtBnd; HonRl; MrchBnd; NHS; SctActv; Ftbl; LetterTennis; AmLegAwd; RotaryAwd; Apostolic Bible Institute; Ministry.

BURNS, Julie L; East Dubuque HS; East Dubuque, IL; Band; Chr; Chrs; CncrtBnd; HonRl; MrchBnd;.

BURNS, Karen G; Lake Forest HS; Lake Forest, IL; Chr; HonRl; HospAde; LbryAde; NHS; NatlMeritFnl; SchMus; Yrbk; Tennis; U Of Notre Dame; Biology Major.

BURNS, Karen J; Millington HS; Millington, MI; HonRl; NHS; Nursing School; Nurse.

BURNS, Karen S; Alpena Senior HS; Alpena, MI; 43/750 ChrhWkr; HonRl; NatlMeritSF; OffAde; SchAde; YthFlsp; 4-H; GerCl; SpnCl; 4-HAwd; Business School; Secretarial.

BURNS, Kathleen P; Waterville Elysian HS; Waterville, MN; 10/75 Band; Chrs; CncrtBnd; HonRl; PepBnd; SchMus; SchPl; Twrl; FHA; College; Elementary Educ.

BURNS, Martin A; Joliet Catholic HS; Joliet, IL; 32/176 SecSrCls; Chrl; ChrhWkr; HonRl; StuCncl; Yrbk; FrCl; GerCl; St Marys College; Ecology.

BURNS, Michele K; Moline Sr HS; Moline, IL; 26/845 HonRl; JrNHS; NHS; Orch; PolWkr; TchrAde; EdYrBk; FrCl; LetterTennis; GAA; Western Illinois Univ; Elem Education.

BURNS, Moira A; Dominican HS; Detroit, MI; Band; Chr; LbryAde; NHS; Orch; PolWkr; SchMus; SchPl; Yrbk; Univ; Medical Tech.

BURNS, Nancy; Steamboat Rock Comm HS; Steamboat Rock, IA; PresSophCls; Band; Chrs; HonRl; SchPl; StuCncl; EdSchPpr; Bsktbl; LetterCollege Or Univ; Math Teacher.

BURNS, Nancy R; Nauvoo Colusa HS; Nauvoo, IL; Band; ChrhWkr; CncrtBnd; HonRl; LbryAde; MrchBnd; PepBnd; SchPl; SctActv; YthFlsp; PresFBLA; College; Accounting.

BURNS, Pamela; Moline HS; Rock Island, IL; CmntyWkr; HonRl; NatlMeritFnl; OffAde; PolWkr; RptrYrbk; SciCl; Western Ill Univ; Professional.

BURNS, Rita G; Chaffee HS; Chaffee, MO; 24/60 Chr; ChrhWkr; DrlTm; HonRl; MrchBnd; NHS; SchAde; FHA; PpCl; SciCl; Trade School; Interior Decorating.

BURNS, Robert A; North HS; Eau Claire, WI; HonRl; NatlMeritCmnd; Orch; SchMus; GerCl; College; Medicine.

BURNS, Sandra A; Bradley Bourbonnais Comm HS; Bourbonnais, IL; 5/360 HonRl; NHS; OffAde; StuCncl; Teen; SpnCl; Air Force.

BURNS, Scott A; Downers Grove S HS; Downers Grove, IL; 31/830 HonRl; NHS; FSA; Univ Of Ill; Engineering.

BURNS, Sherry L; Sparta HS; Coulterville, IL; Chr; HonRl; PolWkr; SchMus; SchPl; TchrAde; YthFlsp; Yrbk; 4-H; FBLA; FTA; FrCl; PpCl; Se Missouri State; History Teacher.

BURNS, Steven A; East Dubuque HS; East Dubuque, IL; 6/50 SecSophCls; Band; Chr; Chrs; CncrtBnd; HonRl; MrchBnd; PepBnd; Yrbk; College; Accounting.

BURNS, Stuart; Stoutland HS; Lebanon, MO; SecTrsSophCls; VPJrCls; TrsSrCls; HonRl; RptrYrbk; Yrbk; Bsktbl; Missouri Univ; Agriculture.

BURNS, Timothy E; Richland R 1 HS; Essex, MO; ChrhWkr; HonRl; TreasFFA; Tradef; Vocation.

BURNS, Victor T; Hammond HS; Hammond, IN; Chr; ChrhWkr; CmntyWkr; Mdrgl; OffAde; SchMus; StuCncl; StuGov; RptrYrbk; SchPpr; Indiana U At Gary; Radiologic Technology.

BURNSIDE, Philip E; Udall HS; Douglass, KS; 3/30 SecTrsJrCls; ALBoysSt; PresBand; ChrhWkr; HonRl; MrchBnd; PepBnd; SchMus; StuCncl; Bsktbl; College; Teaching Music.

BURNSIDE, Robert R; Spoon River Valley HS; Fairview, IL; 1/82 Band; Chr; Chrs; ChrhWkr; HonRl; LbryAde; PepBnd; SchMus; FFA; SecLatCl; Univ Of Illinois; Engineering.

BURNSIDE, William; Hammond Baptist Hs; Munster, IN; 13/88 ChrhWkr; HonRl; NHS; EdYrBk; EdSchPpr; GerCl; U; Professional.

BURR, Cynthia L; Our Lady Of Providence HS; New Albany, IN; 3/138 SecSrCls; Chr; DrlTm; HonRl; SchMus; SchPl; StuCncl; PpCl; Tennis; IMSpt; Univ.

BURR, Diane E; Faulkton HS; Faulkton, SD; 4/49 SecFrshCls; Band; Chrs; CtyCnl; HonRl; PolWkr; RptrSchPpr; SpnCl; Bsktbl; Glf; Tennis; University Of South Dakota; Science.

BURR, William D; Sullivan HS; Carlisle, IN; 9/154 ChrhWkr; HonRl; NHS; StuCncl; SecFFA; Purdue; Agru.

BURRAGE, Margery J; So Milwaukee Sr HS; So Milwaukee, WI; 38/435 ChrhWkr; HonRl; LbryAde; College; Professional.

BURRELL, Donna Y; Liberty Sr HS; Liberty, MO; 57/288 AFS; JA; LitMag; SctActv; Trk; GAA; AmLegAwd; Nw Missouri St; Commercial Art.

BURRELL, Lyle; Washington HS; Sioux Falls, SD; TchrAde; SpnCl; Ftbl; Trk; IMSpt; College; Physical Education.

BURRELL, Nancy J; Lake Central HS; Crown Point, IN; 99/431 SecSrCls; Quill&Scroll; StuGov; Teen; EdSchPpr; Sec4-H; SecPpCl; CaptPPFtbl; Purdue Univ Lafayette; Zoology.

BURRELL, Paula J; Madison HS; Madison, SD; Band; ChrhWkr; CncrtBnd; HonRl; MrchBnd; NHS; 4-H; FBLA; PpCl; Dakota State Clge; Data Processing.

BURRER, Douglas A; Harrold HS; Harrold, SD; ALBoysSt; Band; HonRl; SchPl; StuCncl; RptrYrbk; SptEdSchPpr; SciCl; Bsktbl; Ftbl; Swmmng; IMSpt; Army; Veterinarian.

BURRIDGE, Jean A; Libertyville HS; Libertyville, IL; HonRl; NHS; University; Zoology.

BURRIGHT, Beth J; Kingsley Pierson HS; Pierson, IA; Band; Chr; Chrs; ChrhWkr; CncrtBnd; MrchBnd; PepBnd; SchMus; TchrAde; YthFlsp; College; Elementary Education.

BURRINGTON, James H; Monroe HS; Monroe, MI; College; Business.

BURRIS, Andrew S; Platteville HS; Platteville, WI; Aud/Vis; ModUN; NatlFornLg; NatlMeritCmnd; SchMus; SchPl; SchPpr; FSA; SciCl; Swmmng; College; Biologist.

BURRIS, Brenda; Monroe City R 1 HS; Monroe City, MO; 7/92 Band; Chr; Chrs; ChrhWkr; CncrtBnd; HonRl; MrchBnd; NHS; PepBnd; FHA; Ne Mo St Univ; Math.

BURRIS, Cheri J; Centerville HS; Centerville, IN; 7/128 SecJrCls; SecSrCls; ALAGirlsSt; Band; Chr; Chrs; ChrhWkr; CncrtBnd; HonRl; HospAde; JrNHS; MrchBnd; NHS; PepBnd; College; Lab Technician.

BURRIS, Joe; Laurel HS; Laurel, IN; HonRl; NHS;.

BURRIS, Scott C; Evanston Twnshp HS; Evanston, IL; Chr; Chrl; HonRl; Mdrgl; NatlMeritFnl; NatlMeritSF; University; Novelist.

BURRITT, Sheryl S; Morton HS; Morton, IL; 1/292 HonRl; HospAde; NHS; NatlMeritCmnd; Bradley Univ; Accounting.

BURROUGHS, Bob; Menasha HS; Menasha, WI; Ftbl; IMSpt; Marine Corps.

BURROUGHS, Dianne; Beaumont HS; Saint Louis, MO; 41/697 ChrhWkr; CmntyWkr; HonRl; JA; JrNHS; NHS; OffAde; SchAde; SchMus; SchPl; Coll; Psychologist.

BURROUGHS, Rebecca; Goreville HS; Goreville, IL; SecFrshCls; ChrhWkr; HonRl; LbryAde; TchrAde; YthFlsp; FHA; FrCl;.

BURROW, James L; Fort Atkinson Sr HS; Fort Atkinson, WI; 40/233 Band; CncrtBnd; HonRl; MrchBnd; PepBnd; Bsktbl; Trk; Univ Of Wisconsin; Medicine.

BURROW, Melanie E; West Platte Rii HS; Weston, MO; AFS; HonRl; ModUN; NHS; 4-H; PpCl; Chrldr; DanFAwd; 4-HAwd; LionAwd; College; Medical Technology.

BURROW, Patricia A; Malden HS; Malden, MO; ChrhWkr; HonRl; LbryAde; OffAde; StuGov; TchrAde; YthLg; FHA; FrCl; PpCl; College; Dietician.

BURROW, Robert B; Wichita North HS; Wichita, KS; EdSchPpr; LatCl; SpnCl; PpCl; CaptFtbl; CaptTrk; IMSpt; Texas A&m Univ; Veterinarian.

BURROWS, Gerald G; Harbor Springs HS; Harbor Springs, MI; OffAde; SchAde; TchrAde; YthFlsp; Trk; College.

BURROWS, Victoria A; Shepherd HS; Shepherd, MI; 2/129 Band; ChrhWkr; CncrtBnd; HonRl; MrchBnd; NHS; StuCncl; LatCl; Central Mi Univ.

BURRUS, Roger L; Zionsville Community HS; Zionsville, IN; 14/122 ChrhWkr; HonRl; NHS; SptEdYrbk; 4-H; LetterFtbl; IMSpt; 4-HAwd; Valparaiso U; Law.

BURRUS, Tami R; Brookport HS; Brookport, IL; SecFrshCls; TrsJrCls; HonRl; NHS; SchPl; Yrbk; 4-H; FHA; PpCl; Chrldr; College; Art.

BURSICK, James; Hale HS; Hale, MI; 8/60 PresFrshCls; CncrtBnd; HonRl; MrchBnd; SchAde; RptrSchPpr; SchPpr; Bsbl; Bsktbl; Ftbl; College; Vocational.

BURSICK, Linda A; Daniel J Gross HS; Omaha, NE; HonRl; NHS; StuCncl; TchrAde; FBLA; FNA; PpCl; GAA; PresAwd; CitAwd; Metro Tech; Denta Asst Or Pe Teacher.

BURSON, Bobbi J; Casey Jr Sr HS; Casey, IL; 13/94 Band; CncrtBnd; HonRl; MrchBnd; StuCncl; FHA; FTA; PpCl; GAA; Jr College; Vocation.

BURSOTT, Douglas E; West Richland HS; Noble, IL; CtyCnl; CAP; JA; PolWkr; RedCrAde; ROTC; StuGov; LetterBsbl; LetterBsktbl; LetterTrk; College; Professional.

BURT, Diane M; Calumet HS; Gary, IN; HonRl; JrNHS; RptrYrbk; GAA; Clge.

BURT, Karen D; Bennington HS; Salina, KS; Chrs; HonRl; SchMus; SchPl; PpCl; LetterBsktbl; LetterTrk; Chrldr; GAA; Col; Vocation.

BURT, Mark E; Argo Community HS; Bridgeview, IL; 7/502 HonRl; ModUN; NHS; Bsbl; Bsktbl; Univ Of Illinois.

BURT, Randy R; Hartley Comm HS; Hartley, IA; Band; Chr; Chrs; CncrtBnd; HonRl; MrchBnd; Orch; PepBnd; YthFlsp; Ftbl; Morningside Clg; Music Teacher.

BURT, Tamara L; Belding HS; Belding, MI; 1/165 ChrhWkr; CncrtBnd; HonRl; MrchBnd; NHS; TchrAde; 4-H; MthCl; Chrldr; PPFtbl; Mi St;teach Art.

BURT, Tina M; Eastern HS; Lansing, MI; Band; HonRl; Central Mich Univ; Music.

BURT, Virginia; Lexington HS; Lexington, IL; AFS; Band; CncrtBnd; HonRl; MrchBnd; PepBnd; TchrAde; Yrbk; PpCl; GAA; College; Social Worker.

BURTCH, Janie M; Medicine Valley HS; Curtis, NE; TrsSophCls; VPSrCls; Band; Chr; Chrs; ChrhWkr; CncrtBnd; HonRl; MrchBnd; NHS; PepBnd; YthFlsp; EdYrBk; Kearney St College; Elem Education.

BURTCH, Kimberly R; Breckenridge Jr Sr HS; Wheeler, MI; HonRl; MrchBnd; NHS; StuCncl; YthFlsp; RptrSchPpr; SpnCl; PpCl; Trk; Chrldr; Lansing Business U; Data Process.

BURTHER, Donald D; Southwestern HS; Hanover, IN; Band; HonRl; SchPl; StuCncl; YthFlsp; SptEdSchPpr; FFA; LetterBsbl; LetterBsktbl; LetterTrk; Trade Sch; Professional.

BURTHOLD, Marcia C; Tolra Public HS; Pekin, ND; 3/24 SecFrshCls; TrsSrCls; ALAGirlsSt; Band; ChrhWkr; HonRl; PresNHS; SchPl; EdSchPpr; Nd Univ; Nursing.

BURTLE, Nancy H; Auburn HS; Auburn, IL; HstJrCls; Band; Chrs; JA; NHS; SchMus; Yrbk; Pres4-H; PpCl; GAA; 4-HAwd; JAAwd; College; Accounting.

BURTNER, Orval R; Noblesville HS; Noblesville, IN; CtyCnl; JA; ROTC; EngCl; MthCl; LetterTrk; IMSpt; Trade Sch; General Contracter.

BURTNESS, Jill A; Parkview HS; Orfordville, WI; 55/150 HonRl; StuCncl; PpCl; Chrldr; GAA; U Of Wi; Curriculum Of Major Studies.

BURTON, Bruce J; Catholic Central HS; Detroit, MI; HonRl; LetterBsktbl; LetterFtbl; IMSpt; Univ; Pre Law Or Bus Admin.

BURTON, Courtney A; St Marys Acad; Gary, IN; ChrhWkr; CncrtBnd; HonRl; JrNHS; LbryAde; MrchBnd; NHS; PepBnd; SchMus; LatCl; Clg; Law.

BURTON, Debbie L; Woodland R 4 HS; Marble Hill, MO; 3/83 ChrhWkr; CmntyWkr; HonRl; PresNHS; PepBnd; StuCncl; VPYthFlsp; FHA; FrCl; PresPpCl; University; Doctor.

BURTON, Diane C; North Greene HS; Hillview, IL; 7/107 SecSophCls; Band; HonRl; MrchBnd; NHS; FFA;.

BURTON, Jennifer; Avon HS; Danville, IN; 153/171 HonRl; HospAde; NHS; OffAde; TchrAde; YthFlsp; FrCl; PpCl; Bsktbl; GAA; Ind Cent Bus College; Executive Secretary.

BURTON, Jocelyn P; Academy Of Our Lady; Chicago, IL; 11/199 Chr; HonRl; LbryAde; NHS; SchPl; PpCl; Elmhurst College; Psychologist.

BURTON, Karla J; Southwestern HS; West Point, IN; 9/104 SecSophCls; HonRl; NHS; Yrbk; 4-H; FHA; PpCl; GAA; IMSpt;.

BURTON, Marilyn K; Auburn HS; Auburn, IL; 3/59 SecJrCls; Band; Chrs; HonRl; PresNHS; StuCncl; EdYrBk; Pres4-H; Chrldr; VFWAwd; St Louis College Of Pharm; Pharmacy.

BURTON, Martha M; Brookfield E HS; Brookfield, WI; 12/523 HonRl; NHS; NatlMeritSF; Univ; Mathematics.

BURTON, Penny A; Unity HS; Tolono, IL; VPFrshCls; PresSrCls; LbryAde; NHS; OffAde; StuCncl; TchrAde; RptrYrbk; FHA; Business School; Secretary.

BURTON, Rowly D; Irwin Kirkman Comm HS; Irwin, IA; VPSophCls; Band; Chr; ChrhWkr; HonRl; GerCl; LetterFtbl; Trk; IMSpt; 4-HAwd; College; Veterinarian.

BURTON, Sally J; Rolla HS; Rolla, MO; 10/307 ALAGirlsSt; HonRl; FDA; FrCl; LatCl; College.

BURTON, Tammy; Central Noble HS; Albion, IN; Band; HonRl; MrchBnd; OffAde; SchPl; SctActv; Twrl; PpCl; Tennis; GAA;.

BURWELL, Dale; Bridgman HS; Bridgman, MI; PresSrCls; Band; CncrtBnd; HonRl; MrchBnd; NHS; TchrAde; Bsktbl; Ftbl; Andrewsn Univ; Vocation.

BURWELL, Sharyle; Marion Adams HS; Sheridan, IN; 4/99 Band; Chr; HonRl; Mdrgl; PepBnd; TchrAde; 4-H; FTA; Iupui.

BURY, Ann L; Bristol HS; Webster, SD; Chrs; HonRl; HospAde; RptrSchPpr; FNA; VoiceDemAwd; College; Registered Nurse.

BURY, Peter J; Glenbrook South HS; Glenview, IL; 22/580 HonRl; JrNHS; NHS; NatlMeritSchl; LetterBsbl; CaptBsktbl; LetterSocr; Bucknell Univ; Accounting.

BURY, Robert J; Bogan HS; Chicago, IL; 5/704 AFS; NHS; NatlMeritFnl; PolWkr; PresStuCncl; CaptGlf; JETSAwd; Univ Of Illinois; Engineering.

BUSAM, Philip W; Lakeview HS; St Clair Shores, MI; HonRl; NatlMeritSF; LetterFtbl; IMSpt; College.

BUSAROW, Philip L; Collinsville HS; Collinsville, IL; 49/645 Band; CncrtBnd; HonRl; MrchBnd; Coast Guard Academy; Electrical Engineer.

BUSBY, Jeri; Ulen Hitterdal HS; Hitterdal, MN; 1/43 PresFrshCls; Chr; HonRl; NHS; SchMus; SchPl; StuCncl; EdYrBk; RptrSchPpr; FHA; Mooread St Coll; Accounting.

BUSCH, Carolyn E; Gull Lake HS; Richland, MI; CncrtBnd; DrlTm; HonRl; NHS; StuGov; TchrAde; FrCl; PpCl; LetterTrk; PPFtbl; College; French Or English.

BUSCH, Darcy L; Forest View HS; Mt Prospect, IL; Chr; DrlTm; HonRl; Mdrgl; NHS; Quill&Scroll; SchMus; De Paul Univ; Nursing.

BUSCH, Darrell; Delwood Comm HS; Lost Nation, IA; 7/29 Band; CncrtBnd; HonRl; MrchBnd; YthFlsp; Trk; Iowa St Univ; Engin.

BUSCH, David A; Westview HS; Kankakee, IL; 11/223 Band; ChrhWkr; CncrtBnd; NHS; Orch; PepBnd; SchMus; Ftbl; Swmmng; College; Law Enforcement.

BUSCH, Debby L; Forest View HS; Mt Prospect, IL; 20/636 Band; Chr; CmntyWkr; DrlTm; HonRl; Mdrgl; NHS; Quill&Scroll; SchMus; RptrYrbk; De Paul Univ; Nursing.

BUSCH, Michael D; Marist HS; Alsip, IL; 18/364 NatlMeritCmnd; SctActv; SciCl; Trk; Purdue University.

BUSCH, Michael S; Lebanon HS; Lebanon, IL; Band; HonRl; StuCncl; RptrYrbk; RptrSchPpr; Glf; Swmmng;.

BUSCH, Nancy E; Underwood Public HS; Underwood, ND; ALAGirlsSt; CmntyWkr; HonRl; NHS; StuCncl; SciCl; LetterBsktbl; CaptTrk; Chrldr; PPFtbl; College; Botanist.

BUSCH, Paul G; Ryan HS; Minot, ND; 3/90 VPSophCls; CmntyWkr; JrNHS; NHS; StuCncl; TreasKeyCl; GerCl; LetterBsktbl; LetterFtbl; LetterTrk; Mary Coll; Banker.

BUSCH, Scott; Maine East HS; Park Ridge, IL; HonRl; NHS; GerCl; IMSpt; Marquette Univ; Cpa.

BUSCH, Stephen M; Lebanon HS; Lebanon, IL; 14/100 CncrtBnd; ModUN; NHS; NatlMeritSchl; RptrYrbk; RptrSchPpr; MthCl; SciCl; Swmmng; Trk; Kevirg Tech; Elect.

BUSCH, William T; East Gary Edison HS; Garg, IN; Band; Chr; CncrtBnd; Mdrgl; PepBnd; SchMus; FrCl; LetterBsbl; LetterBsktbl; LetterFtbl; Lincoln Tech Inst; Disel Truck Tech.

BUSCHE, Karen J; Topeka West HS; Topeka, KS; HonRl; NatlMeritSF; Orch; SctActv; SpnCl; PpCl; Bsktbl; Univ; Math.

BUSCHE, Roger O; Woodlan HS; Spencerville, IN; 19/144 Chr; Chrs; ChrhWkr; HonRl; LbryAde; NHS; NatlThespSoc; SchMus; FFA; Mech Trade School; Mechanic.

BUSCHER, Mary L; Mankato West HS; Mankato, MN; 10/300 SecFrshCls; VPSophCls; VPSrCls; Chrs; DrlTm; HonRl; SchMus; StuCncl; SciCl; Chrldr; CchngActv; Hamline Univ; Health.

BUSCHING, Carol S; Plainfield HS; Joliet, IL; 37/297 DrlTm; HonRl; Quill&Scroll; Yrbk; MthCl; Univ Of Illinois; Medicine.

BUSCHJOST, Carol; Blair Oaks HS; St Thomas, MO; TrsFrshCls; SecSophCls; HonRl; 4-H; FBLA; FHA; MthCl; PpCl; 4-HAwd; College.

BUSCHMANN, Paul; Ofallon Township HS; Ofallon, IL; Band; CncrtBnd; PepBnd; LetterBsbl; LetterFtbl; College; Baseball.

BUSCHOR, Michelle R; Darlington HS; Darlington, WI; HonRl; SchPl; StuCncl; Yrbk; 4-H; FHA; SpnCl; PpCl; 4-HAwd; Univ; Art.

BUSE, Galyn; Lennox HS; Lennox, SD; Band; Chr; Chrs; ChrhWkr; HonRl; MrchBnd; Bsktbl; Ftbl; Trk; Farmer.

BUSE, Marlin R; Brandon HS; Brandon, MN; VPJrCls; VPSrCls; ALBoysSt; PresBand; HonRl; SchPl; StuCncl; PresFFA; LetterBsktbl; LetterFtbl; College; Vocation.

BUSEMAN, Brenda; Marion HS; Marion, SD; 5/44 Chrs; ChrhWkr; HonRl; MrchBnd; PepBnd; YthFlsp; Yrbk; SchPpr; PpCl; SciCl; Sd St Iniv; Rn.

BUSENBARK, Nancy A; Sesser F Comm Unit HS; Sesser, IL; 1/43 Band; HospAde; Yrbk; RptrSchPpr; SecPpCl; SciCl; GAA; TIMEAwd; Univ Of Illinois; Veterinarian.

BUSER, Diana L; Arlington HS; Indianapolis, IN; 16/465 CncrtBnd; MrchBnd; NatlFornLg; NHS; PresNatlThespSoc; SchMus; SchPl; StuCncl; TchrAde; FrCl; University; Elementary Teacher.

BUSER, Teresa; Palestine HS; Palestine, IL; 2/48 Chr; HonRl; SchMus; YthFlsp; RptrYrbk; 4-H; EngCl; DanFAwd; 4-HAwd; JAAwd; Vincennes U; Profession In Health.

BUSH, Alan D; Ellsworth Public HS; Magnolia, MN; SecFrshCls; TrsFrshCls; PresSophCls; HonRl; StuCncl; 4-H; Bsktbl; Ftbl; Trk; IMSpt; College.

BUSH, Barbara L; Wauneta Public HS; Hamlet, NE; 9/36 PresSophCls; ChrhWkr; HonRl; StuCncl; YthFlsp; RptrYrbk; 4-H; PpCl; LetterTrk; 4-HAwd; Univ Of Nebraska; Horticulture.

BUSH, Charles E; Oscoda Area HS; Oscoda, MI; ChrhWkr; HonRl; TchrAde; FrCl; Michigan Tech Univ; Master Architect.

BUSH, Gary R; Elwood Comm HS; Elwood, IN; 73/200 HonRl; PolWkr; StuCncl; Ftbl; Trk; IMSpt; JCAwd; College; Law Enforcement.

BUSH, Jane L; Carroll HS; Bringhurst, IN; 11/131 TrsJrCls; HonRl; NHS; TreasSpnCl;.

BUSH, Jeffery G; Davis County Comm HS; Keota, IA; 10/140 HonRl; SecNHS; TchrAde; YthFlsp; 4-H; Ftbl; 4-HAwd; PresAwd; Ne Missouri St University; Osteopath.

BUSH, John; Franklin Central HS; Indianapolis, IN; Band; CmntyWkr; HospAde; JA; MrchBnd; SctActv; RptrSchPpr; 4-H; Tennis; 4-HAwd; Army; Electricity & Communications.

BUSH, John E; Southwestern HS; Flint, MI; Aud/Vis; Chrs; ChrhWkr; CmntyWkr; HonRl; NHS; TchrAde; YthFlsp; GerCl; U Of Mich; Medicine.

BUSH, John M; Portage Northern HS; Portage, MI; HonRl; NatlMeritCmnd; NatlMeritSchl; CaptBsbl; Michigan State Univ; Doctor.

BUSH, Karen L; Effingham HS; Effingham, IL; 21/225 Band; HonRl; JA; StuCncl; YthFlsp; MthCl; Bsktbl; Swmmng; Tennis; Trk; GAA; Eastern Ill Univ; Accountant.

BUSH, Karen M; St Augustine HS; Chicago, IL; HonRl; HospAde; OffAde; SctActv; TchrAde; PpCl; College; Accountant.

BUSH, Kathryn; Roncalli; Manitowoc, WI; 4;140 AFS; Band; HonRl; NHS; MthCl; Trk; Uw Madison;health.

BUSH, Linda A; Northwest HS; St Louis, MO; ChrhWkr; HonRl; JA; StuCncl; PpCl; JAAwd; College; Data Processing.

BUSH, Lisa; Whiteford HS; Ottawa Lake, MI; 19/80 Band; HonRl; LbryAde; NHS; SchMus; StuCncl; RptrYrbk; 4-H; SpnCl; College, Law.

BUSH, Lisa D; Bonner Spgs HS; Edwardsville, KS; 18/197 CncrtBnd; HonRl; MrchBnd; PepBnd; TchrAde; TreasYthFlsp; LatCl; PpCl; College; Math.

BUSH, Loretta L; Hononegah HS; Roscoe, IL; 6/188 Band; ChrhWkr; CncrtBnd; HonRl; JA; MrchBnd; SchMus; SchPl; 4-H; SpnCl; 4-HAwd; Ball State Univ; Nurse.

BUSH, Martin P; Prospect HS; Mt Prospect, IL; 109/610 Band; CncrtBnd; HonRl; MrchBnd; SchMus; Coll; Pe.

BUSH, Naomi R; Lancaster HS; Lancaster, WI; Band; Chr; HonRl; HospAde; NHS; Orch; SchMus; Yrbk; FHA; SpnCl; College; Nurse.

BUSH, Peggy L; Taylor HS; Taylor, WI; Chrs; HonRl; LbryAde; NatlFornLg; NatlMeritSchl; StuCncl; EdSchPpr; SchPpr; FHA; GerCl; SecGAA; College; Business.

BUSH, Sally E; Marian HS; Birmingham, MI; HonRl; HospAde; ModUN; Quill&Scroll; SchPl; Yrbk; College; Medical.

BUSH, Samuel D; Franklin Comm HS; Franklin, IN; 18/254 ChrhWkr; CmntyWkr; HonRl; JrNHS; ModUN; NHS; Pres4-H; LatCl; SciCl; CaptTennis; 4-HAwd; Indiana Central College; Banking.

BUSH, Stephanie L; Jefferson W HS; Meriden, KS; PresJrCls; HonRl; StuCncl; FFA; LetterTrk; Chrldr; AmLegAwd; 4-HAwd; Kansas St Univ; Veterinarian.

BUSH, Terrie; Lewis St HS; Lilbourn, MO; 11/80 HonRl; TchrAde; Yrbk; PpCl;.

BUSH, Wayne M; Grant Comm HS; Ingleside, IL; 8/200 CAP; HonRl; NHS; StuGov; Teen; PpCl; LetterTrk; IMSpt; ALAGirlsSt; Law.

BUSHBY, Daniel J; West Sioux HS; Ireton, IA; Band; ChrhWkr; CncrtBnd; HonRl; MrchBnd; PepBnd; YthFlsp; FFA; Trade School; Vocaton.

BUSHEE, Dixie K; Fennville HS; Fennville, MI; 20/84 HonRl; StuCncl; TchrAde; Western Michigan Univ; Medical Technology.

BUSHEY, Jon; Bismarck HS; Bismarck, ND; SchPl; SctActv; Yrbk; SchPpr; Trk; GodCntryAwd; MasAwd; Univ; Electrcl Eng.

BUSHEY, Kerry; Alcona HS; Spruce, MI; CtyCnl; CncrtBnd; HonRl; NHS; RedCrAde; StuCncl; StuGov; RptrSchPpr; Chrldr; 4-HAwd; Ferris State College; Med Assistant.

BUSHINSKI, Mark J; Vandercook Lake HS; Jackson, MI; 18/115 HonRl; SctActv; StuCncl; TchrAde; Bsbl; Bsktbl; Ftbl; University; Mathematics.

BUSHKO, Jon N; Rhinelander HS; Rhinelander, WI; 59/331 HonRl; NatlFornLg; NatlSciFnd; NatlThespSoc; SchPl; SchPpr; FSA; GerCl; MthCl; Univ Of Wisconsin; Elec Engineer.

BUSHMAKER, Stacey A; Lincoln HS; Rudolph, WI; HonRl; Trade School.

BUSHNELL, Paul T; University HS; Normal, IL; 29/125 Band; Chrs; NatlMeritFnl; PolWkr; LetterTrk; Oberlin College; Social Science.

BUSHNO, Rose M; Annawan HS; Prophetstown, IL; Band; Chr; Chrs; CncrtBnd; HonRl; JrNHS; LbryAde; MrchBnd; NatlMeritCmnd; SchPl; TchrAde; 4-H; FHA; GAA; Illinois State University; Psychology.

BUSHOLD, Thomas R; Chaminade College Prep HS; Des Peres, MO; 43/113 Band; CncrtBnd; HonRl; PepBnd; StuCncl; StuGov; LetterBsbl; LetterFtbl; IMSpt; College.

BUSHONG, Pamela K; Handy HS; Bay City, MI; 3/365 Band; ChrhWkr; CncrtBnd; MrchBnd; NHS; NatlMeritSchl; NatlMeritSF; PepBnd; LetterTennis; University Of Michigan; Physical Therapy.

BUSHRE, Ricky; Chippewa Hills HS; Weidman, MI; Band; CncrtBnd; HonRl; MrchBnd; Orch; SpnCl; Bsbl; Bsktbl; IMSpt; College; Professional.

BUSHUR, Karla R; St Anthony HS; Effingham, IL; 1/79 Band; Chrs; CncrtBnd; HonRl; NHS; SchMus; RptrSchPpr; FTA; PpCl; Chrldr; Eastern Il Univ.

BUSJAHN, Sandra R; Orangeville HS; Orangeville, IL; TrsSophCls; Chrs; HonRl; NHS; College; Accounting.

BUSKEVICIUS, Steven V; W J Bryan HS; Omaha, NE; 39/418 DrlTm; HonRl; College; Architecture.

BUSKIRK, William D; Bayard HS; Bayard, NE; CmntyWkr; Ftbl;.

BUSKO, Marianne; Breckenridge HS; Breckenridge, MN; HonRl; FBLA; Trade School.

BUSMAN, Sandra K; Coopersville Senior HS; Coopersville, MI; Chr; HonRl; VPNHS; SchMus; SchPl; GerCl; PpCl; PPFtbl; Hope College; Psychology.

BUSS, Charles H; Bonduel HS; Bonduel, WI; VPFrshCls; PresStuCncl; Yrbk; FTA; TreasSciCl; Bsktbl; LetterFtbl; LetterTrk; Clg; Automotive.

BUSS, Dale D; Webb HS; Reedsburg, WI; ChrhWkr; HonRl; NatlThespSoc; SchPl; StuCncl; SchPpr; KeyCl; LatCl; Tennis; Univ Wi Madison; Journalism.

BUSS, James G; Luther North HS; Chicago, IL; 6/250 HonRl; NHS; SctActv; SchPpr; LetterFtbl; LetterTrk; College; Medical Science.

BUSS, John; Perkins County HS; Brule, NE; 1/40 PresSophCls; Chr; HonRl; NHS; SchMus; EdYrBk; 4-H; Glf; BauchLmbAwd; EldAwd; Univ Of Ne; Math.

BUSS, Mary K; Wittenberg Birnamwood HS; Eland, WI; 1/153 HonRl; NHS; SchMus; RptrYrbk; EdYrBk; FHA; SpnCl; LetterTennis; LetterTrk; GAA; Uw Eau Claire; Nursing.

BUSS, Randall; United Township HS; East Moline, IL; Chr; ChrhWkr; HonRl; YthFlsp; Univ Of Illinois; Professional.

BUSS, Sharon K; Plainview HS; Plainview, NE; SecTrsSophCls; SecTrsSrCls; Chrs; ChrhWkr; CmntyWkr; LbryAde; PpCl; Trk; Chrldr; Lincoln Sch Of Commerce; Business.

BUSSA, Donna L; Glenbard East HS; Lombard, IL; 33/647 VPJrCls; HonRl; NHS; StuCncl; PpCl; Chrldr; Trade School; Business.

BUSSAN, Kathy A; Pardeeville HS; Pardeville, WI; ChrhWkr; HonRl; LbryAde; SchPl; TchrAde; LetterTrk; GAA; IMSpt; Beauty School; Cosmetician.

BUSSAN, Martha A; Galena HS; Galena, IL; 8/105 VPSophCls; VPSrCls; AFS; Band; CncrtBnd; HonRl; HospAde; MrchBnd; NatlMeritCmnd; PepBnd; Yrbk; 4-H; SpnCl; Glf; College; Physician.

BUSSCHER, James C; Holland Christian HS; Holland, MI; Chr; LetterSocr; LetterTrk; IMSpt; College; Physical Ed.

BUSSCHER, Timothy D; Zeeland HS; Zeeland, MI; TchrAde; Bsktbl; Ftbl; Trk; IMSpt;.

BUSSE, Steve S; Hyde Co Ind HS; Highmore, SD; 12/60 ALBoysSt; ChrhWkr; HonRl; SchPl; FBLA; SciCl; LetterBsktbl; Ftbl; Trk; S D S U; Pharmacy.

BUSSELL, Paul H; Grand Meadow HS; Grand Meadow, MN; ALBoysSt; Band; ChrhWkr; HonRl; NHS; SchPl; PresStuCncl; CaptBsktbl; LetterTrk; PresAwd; University; Professional.

BUSSEN, Patrick J; St Thomas Academy; Minneapolis, MN; Chrs; CmntyWkr; ROTC; Sacrstn; SctActv; RptrYrbk; LetterFtbl; LetterTrk; IMSpt; St Johns Univ; Business.

BUSSEN, Thomas J; Wallace County HS; Wallace, KS; NHS; SchPl; TchrAde; SchPpr; College; General Science.

BUSSERT, Luther W; Kewanna HS; Kewanna, IN; 5/32 TrsFrshCls; TrsSophCls; TrsJrCls; TrsSrCls; HonRl; LbryAde; SchPl; StuCncl; TchrAde; EdYrBk; 4-H; FrCl; PpCl; SciCl; Purdue Univ; Archaeology.

BUSSERT, Victoria M; Munster HS; Munster, IN; 81/430 Chr; Chrs; HonRl; NHS; NatlThespSoc; Orch; SchMus; SchPl; TchrAde; 4-H; College; Communications.

BUSSEY, Robin S; Forest Lake HS; Wyoming, MN; 7/500 HonRl; JrNHS; SchPl; RptrSchPpr; FHA; FrCl; PpCl; GAA; Bus School; Med Secretary.

BUSSICK, Kimberly A; Snider HS; Fort Wayne, IN; ChrhWkr; HonRl; HospAde; IntrClCncl; LitMag; SptEdYrbk; LatCl; PpCl; LetterTrk; PPFtbl; Indiana Univ; Liberal Arts.

BUSSING, Stephen A; Brazil HS; Brazil, IN; HonRl; LetterBsktbl; LetterFtbl; College; Lawyer.

BUSSING, Tom; Reitz Memorial HS; Evansville, IN; HonRl; SchPl; IMSpt; Purdue Univ; Architecture.

BUSSMAN, Denise M; Warren HS; Warren, IL; 8/58 ALAGirlsSt; Band; Chrs; Mdrgl; NHS; StuCncl; RptrSchPpr; FTA; Chrldr; GAA; N Ill Univ; Med Tech.

BUSSMANN, Jayne; Lutheran HS; Norwood, MN; 16/62 Chrs; ChrhWkr; CmntyWkr; HonRl; PolWkr; FTA; SciCl; GAA; PPFtbl; St Marys Junior College; Physical Therapy.

BUSSONE, John L; Green Valley Comm HS; Green Valley, IL; PresSophCls; Chrs; HonRl; 4-H; LetterBsbl; LetterBsktbl; LetterGlf; Minn St Univ; Forestry.

BUSSONE, Stephen J; Gwinn HS; Gwinn, MI; HonRl; SchPl; StuCncl; StuGov; RptrYrbk; Yrbk; College; Administrator.

BUSTA, Debbie A; Turkey Valley HS; Lawler, IA; Chr; ChrhWkr; HonRl; StuCncl; StuGov; TchrAde; RptrYrbk; FTA; CaptChrldr; CchngActv; Univ Of Northern Ia; Special Educ Teacher.

BUSTA, Marilyn K; Turkey Valley Comm HS; Fort Atkinson, IA; Chrs; HonRl; Sdlty; 4-H; SpnCl; Bsktbl; Trk; IMSpt; Jr College; Rn.

BUSTAMANTE, Carol S; St Barbara HS; Chicago, IL; 8/88 CmntyWkr; HonRl; LitMag; SptEdYrbk; SchPpr; College; Professional.

BUSTAMANTE, Monica D; Turner HS; Kansas, KS; ChrhWkr; CmntyWkr; DrlTm; HonRl; PolWkr; SchAde; SchPl; 4-H; FBLA; PpCl;.

BUSTEED, Terry W; Madison HS; Madison, NE; VPSophCls; PresJrCls; Chr; Chrs; ChrhWkr; SchPl; StuGov; Bsktbl; CaptFtbl; LetterTrk; Working.

BUSTRAK, Julie A; South Shore HS; Corhucopia, WI; Band; Chrs; CncrtBnd; DrlTm; Orch; PepBnd; SchMus; RptrYrbk; RptrSchPpr; CchngActv; University Of Wisconsin; Psychology.

BUSWELL, Roxanne S; Holcombe Public HS; Holcombe, WI; Band; Chrs; HonRl; TchrAde; YthFlsp; Yrbk; 4-H; FHA; IMSpt; CitAwd; Tech Institute; Data Processing.

BUTCHER, Barbara L; St Alphonsus HS; Dearborn, MI; SecJrCls; Chr; Chrs; HonRl; JrNHS; Mdrgl; NHS; SchMus; SchPl; StuCncl; Swmmng; Chrldr; GAA; Univ Of Mich; Pre Medicine.

BUTCHER, Craig E; Monona Grove HS; Cottage Grove, WI; PresFrshCls; VPSrCls; ALBoysSt; HonRl; NHS; StuCncl; YthFlsp; LetterBsbl; CaptWrstlng; IMSpt; AmLegAwd; Madison Area Tech College; Electronics.

BUTCHER, Lisa M; Virden Comm HS; Virden, IL; Aud/Vis; Band; Chrs; CncrtBnd; MrchBnd; SchMus; SchPl; RptrYrbk; Yrbk; FHA; University.

BUTCHER, Nancy J; Lincoln Way HS; New Lenox, IL; 19/566 HonRl; NHS; SchPl; TchrAde; Chicago Natl College; Medicine.

BUTCHER, Renea S; Holstein HS; Holstein, IA; 8/37 Band; Chr; HonRl; HospAde; RptrSchPpr; 4-H; PpCl; LetterBsktbl; 4-HAwd; GodCntryAwd; Iowa State Univ; Home Economics.

BUTEAU, Diane L; John Hersey HS; Mount Prospect, IL; 1/739 Chrs; DrlTm; PresMdrgl; NHS; NatlMeritCmnd; OffAde; SchMus; SchPl; Univ; Theatre.

BUTER, Gregory W; W Michigan Christian HS; Muskegon, MI; MthCl; LetterBsbl; LetterBsktbl; LetterSocr; LetterTrk; Ferris St College; Med Technology.

BUTERBAUGH, Richard D; Winfield Senior HS; Winfield, KS; Chr; Chrl; CncrtBnd; HonRl; MrchBnd; NatlFornLg; StuCncl; TchrAde; Bsktbl; College; Teaching.

BUTEYN, Michelle M; Sheboygan North HS; Sheboygan, WI; 29/538 Chr; Chrl; Chrs; HonRl; NHS; StuCncl; StuGov; Chrldr; IMSpt; College; Elem Teaching.

BUTHE, Dorothy A; O Gorman HS; Sioux Falls, SD; VPFrshCls; CmntyWkr; OffAde; SchAde; SchMus; StuCncl; TchrAde; Bsktbl; CaptTrk; IMSpt; Coll; Teaching.

BUTKIEWICZ, Doyle E; Moose Lake HS; Kettle River, MN; 2/75 NHS; StuCncl; StuGov; Yrbk; LetterFtbl; LetterTrk; Concordia Clg.

BUTKIEWICZ, Gloria; Taft Hs; Chicago, IL; 126/790 Band; HonRl; OffAde; EdSchPpr; VPKeyCl; GAA; College; Business Administration.

BUTLER, Ann E; Carmel High School For Girls; Libertyville, IL; 4/185 Chrs; HonRl; NatlMeritSF; LatCl; College; Pre Med.

BUTLER, Becky S; Northeastern HS; Richmond, IN; 20/120 SecJrCls; TchrAde; EdSchPpr; SpnCl; Chrldr; GAA; PresAwd; Ball State Univ; Phy Ed.

BUTLER, Betsy A; Crothersville HS; Crothersville, IN; 6/54 Band; Chr; CncrtBnd; DrlTm; HonRl; NHS; SchMus; YthFlsp; PpCl; College.

BUTLER, Brenda M; Illini Bluffs HS; Hanna City, IL; 1/79 VPSophCls; PresJrCls; NHS; SchMus; SchPl; StuCncl; StuGov; 4-H; Chrldr; Univ Of Illinois; Psychology.

BUTLER, Carolyn L; Central Catholic HS; Grand Island, NE; SecTrsFrshCls; Chrs; HonRl; NHS; SchMus; StuCncl; EdYrBk; PpCl; CaptChrldr; PPFtbl; University; Professional.

BUTLER, Daniel A; Lapeer Sr HS; Lapeer, MI; Chr; ChrhWkr; HospAde; PolWkr; SchPl; Coll; Criminal Law.

BUTLER, Deborah L; Forrest Strawn Wing HS; Forrest, IL; Band; Chrs; CncrtBnd; HonRl; SchPl; Yrbk; FHA; FNA; ChmnSpnCl; ChmnGAA; Northern Il U; Physical Therapy.

BUTLER, Diane J; Algonac HS; Algonac, MI; Band; CncrtBnd; HonRl; MrchBnd; PepBnd; SctActv; 4-H; KeyCl; LatCl; 4-HAwd; University; Veterinary Science.

BUTLER, Di Anne E; Lawrence Central HS; Indianapolis, IN; ChrhWkr; DrlTm; HonRl; MrchBnd; OffAde; SctActv; TchrAde; YthFlsp; College; Elementary Ed.

BUTLER, Drynda K; Milan C 2 HS; Milan, MO; TrsSrCls; ChrhWkr; HonRl; HospAde; OffAde; SchPl; StuCncl; Yrbk; FBLA; SecFHA; VPSpnCl; JCAwd; College; Professional.

BUTLER, Gary D; St Joseph Ogden HS; St Joseph, IL; 18/103 HonRl; RptrSchPpr; SpnCl; PpCl; LetterBsbl; LetterWrstlng; Univ Of Ill; Teacher.

BUTLER, Gina A; Chicago Vocational HS; Chicago, IL; 32/677 HonRl; IntrClCncl; JrNHS; NHS; OffAde; SchAde; StuCncl; StuGov; Bsktbl; Tennis; U Of Il; Obstetrician Gyneocologist.

BUTLER, Grace W; Appleton East HS; Appleton, WI; 15/550 CmntyWkr; NatlFornLg; NHS; SchPl; StuGov; Yrbk; EdSchPpr; Tennis; Trk; CchngActv; Bowdoin College; Psychairty.

BUTLER, James K; Columbus North HS; Columbus, IN; 9/460 Chr; Chrl; Chrs; ChrhWkr; HonRl; ModUN; NatlFornLg; NatlThespSoc; SchMus; TchrAde; Indiana U; Music Education.

BUTLER, Jeffery; Unionville HS; Unionville, MO; 4/86 PresSophCls; ChrhWkr; HonRl; 4-H; Central Christian Col; Elementary Councilng.

BUTLER, Jeffrey; Arcola HS; Arcola, IL; 2/65 ALBoysSt; ChrhWkr; HonRl; Ftbl; Trk; AmLegAwd; SARAwd; Parkland Jr College; Math And Education.

BUTLER, Jerry L; Eastern Heights HS; Agra, KS; Chrs; HonRl; SctActv; Bsktbl; Ftbl; Trk; Trade School; Vocation.

BUTLER, Joan E; Washington Catholic HS; Washington, IN; TrsJrCls; Chrl; HonRl; HospAde; SchPl; PpCl; Chrldr; GAA; College; Medical Career.

BUTLER, Joan K; Morton Township HS; Pekin, IL; PresSrCls; Chr; Chrs; HonRl; NatlFornLg; NatlThespSoc; StuCncl; StuGov; PresPpCl; GAA; Trade; Cosmotologist.

BUTLER, John K; St Viator HS; Palatine, IL; 5/275 HonRl; JrNHS; NHS; StuGov; LetterWrstlng; Marquette Univ; Engineering.

BUTLER, Karen S; Carmel Sr Girls HS; Deerfield, IL; 14/185 Chr; Chrs; HonRl; NHS; NatlMeritCmnd; University; Biology.

BUTLER, Kathleen A; Carmel HS; Deerfield, IL; Chr; Chrs; HonRl; NHS; Marquette Univ; Nurse.

BUTLER, Kevin J; Memorial HS; Joplin, MO; Chr; ChrhWkr; HonRl; LitMag; NatlFornLg; NatlThespSoc; Quill&Scroll; SchMus; RptrYrbk; RptrSchPpr; Mssc.

BUTLER, Lori J; Larimore HS; Northwood, ND; ALAGirlsSt; HonRl; Univ; Occupational Therapist.

BUTLER, Lucinda M; Marysville HS; Marysville, KS; VPSophCls; HonRl; PolWkr; SchPl; FHA; VPPpCl; IMSpt; Social Worker.

BUTLER, Mary; Franklin Central HS; Indianapolis, IN; 17/240 HonRl; ModUN; NHS; SctActv; 4-H; SpnCl; PresAwd; College.

BUTLER, Nancy I; Sullivan HS; Sullivan, IN; 7/139 ChrhWkr; HonRl; NHS; StuGov; YthFlsp; 4-H; FHA; MthCl; Chrldr; PresAwd; Purdue University; Pharmacy.

BUTLER, Nicholas K; Mt Morris HS; Mt Morris, IL; Aud/Vis; HonRl; SchPl; StuCncl; RptrYrbk; RptrSchPpr; GerCl; PpCl; LetterTennis; Southern Ill Univ; Psychology.

BUTLER, Randy; Homer Comm Hs; Homer, MI; HonRl; NatlFornLg; ROTC; SchPl; StuCncl; StuGov; TchrAde; FFA; CaptBsktbl; LetterTrk; College; Electrical Engineering.

BUTLER, Rebecca J; Central HS; Burden, KS; ALAGirlsSt; Chr; Chrs; ChrhWkr; CncrtBnd; HonRl; MrchBnd; NHS; PepBnd; SchPl; YthFlsp; 4-H; Southwestern College; Medicine.

BUTLER, Rebecca J; U S D #462; Burden, KS; Chrs; ChrhWkr; CncrtBnd; HonRl; HospAde; MrchBnd; PepBnd; YthFlsp; 4-H; College; Medicine.

BUTLER, Reginald F; De Andreis HS; St Louis, MO; 17/80 VPFrshCls; VPJrCls; Band; Chrs; HonRl; LitMag; SchMus; RptrYrbk; RptrSchPpr; PpCl; Washington Univ; Music And Theater Arts.

BUTLER, Richard; Union City Senior HS; Sherwood, MI; 27/100 CmntyWkr; HonRl; SctActv; SpnCl; Bsbl; Ftbl; College; Professional.

BUTLER, Stan M; Lamar HS; Lamar, MO; 9/104 AFS; Chr; HonRl; NatlFornLg; CaptFtbl; Trk; DARAwd; Collge.

BUTLER, Susan R; Paris HS; Paris, IL; Band; CncrtBnd; HonRl; MrchBnd; NHS; PepBnd; 4-H; SpnCl; SciCl; E Illinois Univ; Optometry.

BUTLER, Timothy; St Alphonsus HS; Dearborn, MI; 1/145 TrsFrshCls; LatCl; LetterBsktbl; CaptTrk; University.

BUTLER, Victor; Romulus Senior HS; Romulus, MI; HonRl; OffAde; StuGov; TchrAde; Ftbl; CchngActv; Central Mi Univ; Lay.

BUTMAN, William D; Libertyville HS; Libertyville, IL; Band; CncrtBnd; HonRl; MrchBnd; Carthage College; Business Admin.

BUTNER, Brenda; Bonner Springs HS; Bonner Springs, KS; SecFrshCls; TrsSophCls; SecSrCls; ALAGirlsSt; Chr; HonRl; SchPl; TchrAde; SpnCl; PpCl; College; Professional.

BUTNER, Jolitta O; Slater HS; Slater, MO; Chrs; HonRl; VPStuCncl; SchPpr; FHA; FTA; FrCl; PpCl; Chrldr; GAA; IMSpt; College; Business Management.

BUTT, Lisa A; Lewistown Community HS; Lewistown, IL; Chrs; CmntyWkr; HonRl; IntrClCncl; TreasStuCncl; Teen; YthLg; Yrbk; VPSpnCl; PpCl; LetterGlf; Chrldr; GAA; College; Biology.

BUTT, M S; South Page HS; Clarinda, IA; Band; CncrtBnd; MrchBnd; 4-H; FHA; CaptBsktbl; CaptTrk; 4-HAwd; PresAwd; Nw Mo State U; Pe & Business.

BUTTCHEN, Terry G; Evansville HS; Brooklyn, WI; ChrhWkr; CmntyWkr; HonRl; TchrAde; RptrSchPpr; FFA; University; Professional.

BUTTELL, Laurine; Caledonia HS; Caledonia, MN; SecSophCls; PresJrCls; Aud/Vis; HonRl; SchPl; StuCncl; SptEdYrbk; College Or Trade School.

BUTTERBRODT, Michael J; Beaver Dam HS; Beaver Dam, WI; PresSrCls; StuCncl; PpCl; LetterBsktbl; LetterFtbl; IMSpt;.

BUTTERFIELD, Diane M; Washington HS; Cedar Rapids, IA; 9/460 SecSrCls; Band; Chr; Chrl; HonRl; NHS; NatlMeritSF; StuCncl; StuGov; FrCl; College; Professional.

BUTTLER, Pamela S; Guthrie Center HS; Guthrie Center, IA; 24/66 Band; CncrtBnd; HonRl; MrchBnd; PepBnd; SctActv; YthFlsp; Bsktbl; LetterTrk; College; English Or Science.

BUTTLER, Patricia A; Guthrie Center HS; Guthrie Center, IA; 13/55 Band; Chr; HonRl; MrchBnd; PresNHS; SctActv; YthFlsp; RptrSchPpr; LetterBsktbl; BttyCrckrAwd; Marshalltown Comm Clg; Nursing.

BUTTON, Roger D; Dodge City Sr HS; Dodge City, KS; 30/276 Band; ChrhWkr; CmntyWkr; CncrtBnd; HonRl; MrchBnd; PepBnd; SchPl; StuCncl; Univ; Doctor.

BUTTRY, Diane J; East Alton Wood River HS; Wood River, IL; 23/287 Band; ChrhWkr; DrlTm; HonRl; JrNHS; MrchBnd; StuCncl; YthFlsp; FHA; SpnCl; College; Pro.

BUTTS, Judy K; Mt Zion HS; Mt Zion, IL; ChrhWkr; HonRl; NHS; TchrAde; 4-H; PpCl; E I U; English.

BUTTS, Michael D; Rogers HS; Michigan City, IN; 58/483 Chr; ChrhWkr; CmntyWkr; HonRl; NHS; VPSctActv; PresYthFlsp; RptrYrbk; AmLegAwd; EldAwd; Heidelberg College; Musician.

BUTTS, Rita H; Laboure HS; St Louis, MO; 1/61 HonRl; HospAde; NHS; PresStuCncl; StuGov; TchrAde; St Louis Col Of Pharmacy; Professional.

BUTTS, Rita S; Humboldt HS; Humboldt, KS; ALAGirlsSt; HonRl; NHS; SchPl; StuCncl; Sec4-H; VPPpCl; Bsktbl; 4-HAwd; College.

BUTULA, Betty J; John Marshall HS; Milwaukee, WI; 71/711 ChrhWkr; DrlTm; HonRl; LbryAde; NHS; SctActv; Trk; Coll; Statistician.

BUTZ, Marjorie; Maine Township Hs; Park Ridge, IL; HonRl; VPJA; NHS; PolWkr; Illinois State U; Accountant.

BUTZER, Mary F; O Gorman HS; Sioux Falls, SD; Band; CncrtBnd; HonRl; MrchBnd; PepBnd; SchPl; StuGov; TchrAde; EngCl; FrCl; Bsktbl; Swmmng; Tennis; Arizona State Univ; Interpretor.

BUXA, Stanley J; Anamoose Public HS; Anamoose, ND; 5/19 CncrtBnd; HonRl; NatlThespSoc; PepBnd; StuCncl; CaptBsktbl; LetterFtbl; LetterTrk; Bismarck Jr College; Education.

BUXTON, David K; Belleville Twp HS; Fairview Hgts, IL; CncrtBnd; MrchBnd; SctActv; YthFlsp; LatCl; Trk; Wrstlng; Sch Of Ozards; Crime.

BUXTON, Phil L; Glendale HS; Springfield, MO; Band; CncrtBnd; HonRl; MrchBnd; MthCl; Bsktbl; JETSAwd; School Of Architecture; Architecture.

BUYARSKI, Daniel G; Menominee HS; Menominee, MI; 4-H; Univ Of Wisconsin; Physical Educ.

BUYARSKI, Susan M; Menominee HS; Menominee, MI; 4/280 Band; ChrhWkr; HonRl; MrchBnd; NHS; NatlMeritSF; Orch; SchPl; College; Medical Technology.

BUYER, John J; North White HS; Monticello, IN; 31/99 PresFrshCls; Band; Chrs; CncrtBnd; HonRl; Mdrgl; MrchBnd; NatlThespSoc; Orch; PepBnd; Bsktbl; LetterFtbl; LetterTrk; IMSpt; Citadel College; Dentist.

BUYSSE, Beverly A; Tracy HS; Tracy, MN; Chr; Chrs; ChrhWkr; HonRl; JCC; LbryAde; SchMus; SchPl; StuCncl; FHA; Vocational Schl; Bus.

BUYSSE, Julie A; Minneota HS; Minneota, MN; ALAGirlsSt; Band; Chrs; CncrtBnd; HonRl; MrchBnd; NHS; SchPl; 4-H; Trade School; Vocation.

BUZALSKY, Pamela J; St Gertrudes HS; Amidon, ND; 5/26 Chr; ChrhWkr; LetterBsktbl; LetterTrk; LetterChrldr; CchngActv; IMSpt; 4-HAwd; JAAwd; CitAwd; Carroll Clg; English.

BUZZELL, Eric J; Frankfort HS; Frankfort, MI; VPJrCls; ALBoysSt; HonRl; NHS; LetterGlf; LetterTennis; Piedmont Col; Biology.

BUZZELL, Mark A; Manistee HS; Manistee, MI; 9/171 ALBoysSt; ChrhWkr; HonRl; MrchBnd; NHS; PepBnd; YthFlsp; AmLegAwd; RotaryAwd; VoiceDemAwd; Mi Tech U; Engineering.

BYALL, Mark A; Bladeford HS; Hartford City, IN; ALBoysSt; Aud/Vis; HonRl; PpCl; Bsbl; Chrldr; IMSpt; College; Physical Education.

BYARS, Mary S; Rockford West HS; Rockford, IL; 42/339 ChrhWkr; HonRl; LbryAde; Orch; SchAde; SpnCl; Evangel Coll.

BYBEE, Anne E; Stillman Valley HS; Oregon, IL; 2/100 Band; HonRl; NHS; RptrYrbk; 4-H; FHA; FTA; GAA; DanFAwd; Univ Of Wisconsin; Teaching.

BYBEE, Carolyn L; Humboldt HS; Humboldt, IA; Band; Chr; Chrl; CncrtBnd; HonRl; MrchBnd; NHS; PepBnd; SchMus; StuGov; Iowa State Univ; Instrumental Music.

BYBEE, Jonathan K; Cannelton HS; Cannelton, IN; Aud/Vis; ChrhWkr; HonRl; StuCncl; Trk; CitAwd; College;.

BYBEE, Rodger D; Medicine Valley HS; Curtis, NE; PresFrshCls; HstSophCls; Band; ChrhWkr; CmntyWkr; SctActv; StuCncl; LetterBsktbl; LetterFtbl; CitAwd; Clge; Pro.

BYBEE, William D; United Township HS; East Moline, IL; 80/625 HonRl; LetterFtbl; LetterTrk; Wrstlng; Augustana Clge; Dentistry.

BYE, Gail; Cudahy Sr HS; Cudahy, WI; 12/344 Band; ChrhWkr; CmntyWkr; NHS; StuCncl; SpnCl; CchngActv; Caroll Univ; Medical Technologist.

BYE, Mary A; Marengo HS; Marengo, IN; Chr; ChrhWkr; HonRl;.

BYER, Christie L; Northrop HS; Ft Wayne, IN; 185/643 HonRl; Orch; LetterBsktbl; LetterTennis; PresAwd; Col; Architect.

BYER, Richard; Knox HS; Knox, IN; SchPpr; Ftbl; Wrstlng; Vincennes Univ; Law Enforce.

BYERLY, Juanita M; North Harrison HS; Palmyra, IN; Band; ChrhWkr; CmntyWkr; CncrtBnd; CaptDrlTm; MrchBnd; OffAde; SchPl; YthFlsp; 4-H; Indiana University Southeast; Nurse.

BYERLY, Kevin D; Marengo HS; Marengo, IN; PresFrshCls; PresSophCls; PresJrCls; LetterTrk; College; Electronic Engineer.

BYERS, Brian; Walnut Grove HS; Revere, MN; VPSrCls; ChrhWkr; CmntyWkr; HonRl; StuGov; SptEdSchPpr; Wrstlng; College.

BYERS, Carl; Montezuma Community HS; Montezuma, IA; 3/56 SecSrCls; Chrs; CncrtBnd; HonRl; NHS; NatlMeritCmnd; StuCncl; YthFlsp; Us Air Force Academy.

BYERS, David; Montezuma Community HS; Montezuma, IA; CncrtBnd; HonRl; NHS; Orch; SchMus; SctActv; YthFlsp; RptrSchPpr; Bsbl; Ftbl; Univ; Commercial Art.

BYERS, Larry B; Rosemount Senior HS; Apple Valley, MN; RptrSchPpr; GerCl; College; Mathematics.

BYERS, Randall; Southwestern Hs; Lafayette, IN; 13/115 PresFrshCls; PresSophCls; PresJrCls; Band; Chr; NHS; SecFrshCls; Pres4-H; 4-HAwd; Purdue U; Communications.

BYERS, Shari L; Southridge HS; Huntingburg, IN; Band; ChrhWkr; CncrtBnd; HonRl; HospAde; MrchBnd; PepBnd; SchMus; FrCl; PpCl; College; Speech.

BYERS, Tracy A; Marion HS; Marion, WI; ALAGirlsSt; Chrs; CncrtBnd; DrmMjrt; HonRl; NatlFornLg; NHS; SchPl; RptrYrbk; FTA; Bsktbl; University; Education.

BYERS, Wendy A; Amos Alonzo Stagg HS; Worth, IL; 2/468 CncrtBnd; HonRl; NHS; NatlMeritCmnd; TchrAde; FrCl; Bsbl; Bsktbl; Glf; PresSwmmng; GAA; Stephens College; Fashion Design.

BYLAND, Eugene V; Concordia Acad; St Paul, MN; 8/49 HonRl; LbryAde; LetterTennis; LetterTrk; LetterWrstlng; Univ Of Minn; Computer Prog.

BYLANDER, Thomas C; Beresford HS; Beresford, SD; 2/67 VPJrCls; ChrhWkr; HonRl; NatlFornLg; NatlMeritFnl; StuCncl; 4-H; LetterTrk; 4-HAwd; Univ; Math.

BYLIN, Julie R; Adams Public HS; Adams, ND; PresJrCls; HonRl; StuCncl; Twrl; 4-H; Bsktbl; Trk; Chrldr; AmLegAwd; 4-HAwd; Univ.

BYRD, Benjamin H; Walter P Chrysler HS; New Castle, IN; Band; ChrhWkr; CncrtBnd; MrchBnd; PepBnd; YthFlsp; Olivet Nazarene College; Radio Broadcasting.

BYRD, Debra L; Laurel HS; Rushville, IN; Chrs; ChrhWkr; DrlTm; HonRl; LbryAde; NHS; OffAde; SchAde; TchrAde; RptrYrbk; RptrSchPpr; Trade School; Professional.

BYRD, Denise R; Hamilton Southeastern HS; Noblesville, IN; Chr; Chrs; HonRl; JA; NHS; OffAde; SchAde; SctActv; YthFlsp; RptrSchPpr; GerCl; Ball State University.

BYRD, John D; Wyoming Park HS; Wyoming, MI; 35/256 ChrhWkr; HonRl; NHS; SchPl; PresYthFlsp; Ftbl; IMSpt; Grand Rapids Jr College; Engineering.

BYRD, Julius G; Osborn HS; Detroit, MI; CmntyWkr; HonRl; NHS; NatlMeritFnl; PolWkr; StuCncl; LatCl; Bsbl; College; Medicine.

BYRD, Kendall W; Lyons Twp HS; Western Sprgs, IL; ALBoysSt; Band; ChrhWkr; CncrtBnd; HonRl; MrchBnd; NHS; Orch; SchMus; SctActv; Purdue Univ; Engineering.

BYRD, Mary A; Iowa Falls HS; Iowa, IA; Band; Chr; HonRl; NatlMeritSF; NatlThespSoc; PepBnd; FTA; LetterChrldr; College; Special Ed.

BYRD, Mary E; Trico HS; Percy, IL; Chrs; ChrhWkr; CmntyWkr; HonRl; FHA; PresFrCl; Univ; Professional.

BYRD, Ruth E; East HS; Kansas City, MO; HonRl;.

BYRD, Sharon D; Chicago Vocational HS; Chicago, IL; 66/1200 Chr; ChrhWkr; CmntyWkr; HonRl; TchrAde; GAA; Northwestern Univ; Interpreter.

BYRER, Ann L; Triton HS; Bourbon, IN; 7/100 ALAGirlsSt; Chr; HonRl; NHS; SchMus; SchPl; StuCncl; TchrAde; YthFlsp; 4-H; FTA; Glf; CaptChrldr; AmLegAwd; College; Professional.

BYRNE, Allen D; Lasalle Peru Twp HS; Oglesby, IL; 51/516 HonRl; Glf; Univ Of Il; Electrical Engineer.

BYRNE, Dale J; George S Parker HS; Janesville, WI; 49/387 Band; CncrtBnd; DrmBgl; HonRl; MrchBnd; NHS; PepBnd; Quill&Scroll; SctActv; RptrSchPpr; College; Teacher.

BYRNE, Joanne M; Bishop Borgess HS; Detroit, MI; HonRl; JrNHS; NHS; SchPl; TchrAde; Yrbk; Tennis; Univ; Artist.

BYRNE, Raymond J; Gordon Tech HS; Chicago, IL; 6/618 HonRl; NHS; RptrSchPpr; LetterBsbl; Northwestern Univ; Medicine.

BYRNE, Richard P; Aurora Central Catholic HS; Aurora, IL; 2/135 HonRl; NHS; SciCl; Univ Of Ill; Civil Engineer.

BYRNES, Colleen D; Lourdes HS; Chicago, IL; HonRl; JA; Quill&Scroll; SchMus; SchPl; EdSchPpr; Lawrence Univ; Jour.

BYRNES, Robert J; Waukon HS; Waukon, IA; HonRl; RptrSchPpr; 4-H; 4-HAwd; U Of Wi; Animal Science.

BYRNES, Sylvia K; Fort Scott HS; Fort Scott, KS; ChrhWkr; CmntyWkr; HonRl; HospAde; NatlFornLg; NatlMeritSF; SchPl; Sdlty; TchrAde; 4-H; IMSpt; Univ Of Ks; Law.

BYRUM, Carol A; Dieterich HS; Dieterich, IL; Chrs; HonRl; SpnCl; College.

BYRUM, George; South Central HS; Laconia, IN; 14/62 PresJrCls; VPSrCls; Band; SctActv; StuCncl; YthFlsp; 4-H; FrCl; CchngActv; Indiana Univ S E;.

BYTNAR, Rita M; Tamaroa HS; Tamaroa, IL; SecSophCls; VPJrCls; Chrl; Chrs; HonRl; SchMus; SchPl; StuCncl; PresFHA; CaptChrldr; College; Education.

BYWATER, Carmen D; Tarkio HS; Tarkio, MO; 10/63 Band; HospAde; SecNHS; Twrl; RptrYrbk; FHA; SecLetterBsktbl; CaptTrk; CaptChrldr; Northwest Mo Univ; Elementary Education.

BZDOK, Deborah; St Ladislaus Hs; Hamtramck, MI; 3 HonRl; NHS; RedCrAde; SchMus; SchPl; SctActv; EdYrBk; FNA; FTA; Trk; U Detroit ; Drama.

C

CABAJ, Christopher R; J H Bowen HS; Chicago, IL; 2/571 CncrtBnd; HonRl; NHS; StuCncl; FSA; FrCl; MthCl; SciCl; Swmmng; JETSAwd; Univ Of Il; Engineering.

CABAN, Mary T; Edwardsville HS; Edwardsville, IL; 1/461 Band; Chr; Chrs; CncrtBnd; HonRl; NHS; NatlMeritCmnd; GerCl; U Of Il; Eng.

CABARGA, Vivian M; Derham Hall HS; St Paul, MN; 14/139 Chrs; LitMag; LbryAde; TchrAde; Yrbk; SchPpr; CitAwd; St Marys Clge; Engineering.

CABLE, Dan E; Jennings Co HS; North Vernon, IN; 10/342 CmntyWkr; HonRl; NHS; SpnCl; Purdue Univ; Eng Field In Air Force.

CABLE, James D; Fairfield Comm HS; Fairfield, IL; 5/165 ALBoysSt; PresBand; Chrs; ChrhWkr; CncrtBnd; HonRl; MrchBnd; VPNHS; SctActv; SchPl; PresStuCncl; EldAwd; Southern Illinois Univ; Medicine.

CABLE, John H; New Trier West HS; Wilmette, IL; NatlFornLg; PolWkr; University; Political Science.

CABRERA, Michael A; Downers Grove North HS; Downers Grove, IL; AFS; ChrhWkr; HonRl; JA; NatlMeritCmnd; TchrAde; Tennis; Univ Of Illinois; Elementary Education.

CACIC, Donna J; Montello HS; Montello, WI; 4/67 Band; CncrtBnd; HonRl; MrchBnd; NHS; PepBnd; SchPl; FrCl; PpCl; GAA; U Of Wi Madison; Law.

CACIOPPO, Margie A; St Pius X HS; Kansas City, MO; 21/129 TrsSophCls; HonRl; StuCncl; PpCl; Coll Or Trade.

CACKLER, Steven D; Moline Sr HS; Coal Valley, IL; ChrhWkr; HonRl; NHS; NatlMeritCmnd; SpnCl; Univ Of Wisc; Biology.

CADALBERT, Mary C; Derham Hall HS; St Paul, MN; HospAde; LbryAde; NHS; SchMus; SchPl; StuCncl; RptrYrbk; SpnCl; Univ Of Mn; Medicine.

CADANAU, Rodney D; Willow Springs HS; Willow Springs, MO; 3/100 VPSophCls; ALBoysSt; HonRl; SctActv; SciCl; LetterTrk; LetterWrstlng;.

CADE, Sarah; Fountain Central HS; Veedersburg, IN; 14/127 ALAGirlsSt; Band; Chr; DrlTm; HonRl; LbryAde; Mdrgl; SchMus; SchPl; YthFlsp; 4-H; FHA; PpCl; 4-HAwd; Purdue U; Sociology.

CADENA, Julia; Buena Vista HS; Saginaw, MI; 13/200 PresSophCls; HonRl; PresNHS; SchPl; StuGov; SpnCl; PpCl; IMSpt; PPFtbl; College; Lawyer.

CADIEUX, Laurie J; Shelbyville HS; Shelbyville, IN; 1/265 Band; HonRl; NHS; NatlMeritSF; Yrbk; SpnCl; SciCl; Swmmng; GAA; DARAwd; Purdue Univ; Engr.

CADLE, Mona; Chippewa Valley HS; Mt Clemens, MI; HonRl; JA; OffAde; SchAde; TchrAde; SpnCl; JAAwd; College; Professional.

CADMAN, Craig A; Humboldt HS; Humboldt, IA; Band; Chr; CncrtBnd; HonRl; MrchBnd; SchMus; SctActv; LetterBsktbl; LetterFtbl; LetterTrk; Business Management.

CADWALLADER, Diana L; Stuart Public HS; Stuart, NE; Band; MrchBnd; PepBnd; SchPl; Yrbk; RptrSchPpr; 4-H; PpCl; Bsktbl;.

CADWALLADER, Mark W; Ypsilanti HS; Ypsilanti, MI; HonRl; NHS; SctActv; EdSchPpr; College; Agricultural Tech.

CADWELL, Gina A; Raytown HS; Raytown, MO; 20/605 Chr; HonRl; JA; SchPpr; GerCl; SpnCl; SciCl; IMSpt; Umkc College; Pharmacy.

CADWELL, Tamie; West Pike HS; Kinderhook, IL; PresJrCls; Band; HonRl; NHS; SchPl; FHA; Bsktbl; Trk; Chrldr; PresAwd; Coll; Physical Therapy.

CADWELL, Theresa; Sacred Heart Academy; Springfield, IL; PresSophCls; HonRl; StuCncl; Springfield College; Medicine.

CADY, Carol J; Summerfield HS; Petersburg, MI; Band; ChrhWkr; CncrtBnd; HonRl; MrchBnd; OffAde; SchAde; SchPl; TchrAde; RptrYrbk; Monroe Comm Clge; Prof.

CADY, Kati A; Brookfield Central HS; Brookfield, WI; LetterBsktbl; College; Professional.

CADY, Mark; Elmwood HS; Elmwood, IL; 13/56 PresFrshCls; VPSophCls; TrsJrCls; HonRl; SptEdYrbk; PpCl; SciCl; Bsbl; Bsktbl; College; Law.

CAES, Suzanne M; Durant HS; Stockton, IA; Band; HonRl; MrchBnd; NHS; PepBnd; SchPl; RptrSchPpr; 4-H; FHA; Trk; C; Pediatrics.

CAFARELLI, Nicholas E; Charles Stewart Mott HS; Warren, MI; LetterTrk; Clge; Prof.

CAFFREY, Dick R; Wichita HS East; Wichita, KS; 35/657 HonRl; HospAde; NatlFornLg; NatlMeritSF; SctActv; TchrAde; RptrYrbk; SciCl; Trk; IMSpt; College; Medicine.

CAFFREY, Linda K; Frankfort HS; Vermillion, KS; 3/41 VPSrCls; Chrs; PresPpCl; Chrldr; GAA;.

CAGLE, Michael S; Brown County HS; Nashville, IN; LitMag; NatlMeritFnl; NatlMeritSF; NatlThespSoc; SchPl; StuCncl; TchrAde; RptrYrbk; Yrbk; SchPpr; College; Design Science.

CAGLE, Philip V; Plainfield HS; Plainfield, IN; 5/310 ALBoysSt; Band; CncrtBnd; HonRl; JrNHS; MrchBnd; NHS; StuCncl; GerCl; DARAwd; Univ; Engineer.

CAGNEY, Colleen M; Portage Central HS; Scotts, MI; ChrhWkr; CmntyWkr; NatlFornLg; NHS; SchAde; StuCncl; TchrAde; Pres4-H; PresPpCl; DanFAwd; 4-HAwd; KiwanAwd; Nazareth College; Social Work.

CAHA, Phyllis J; Wahoo Public HS; Wahoo, NE; PresSophCls; ChrhWkr; HonRl; SchPl; StuGov; YthFlsp; 4-H; SpnCl; Trk; Coll; Major Study.

CAHALAN, James L; Moline Sr HS; Moline, IL; 43/850 Band; CncrtBnd; HonRl; JrNHS; MrchBnd; NHS; SchPpr; LetterFtbl; LetterTrk; LetterWrstlng; Columbia Univ; Law.

CAHILL, Barbara E; Mother Mcauley HS; Chicago, IL; 35/477 ChrhWkr; CmntyWkr; HonRl; JrNHS; NHS; PolWkr; FshEdYrbk; St Xaviers College; Education.

CAHILL, Bill P; Preston HS; Preston, IA; Aud/Vis; ChrhWkr; HonRl; LbryAde; SctActv; StuCncl; RptrSchPpr; Iowa State Univ; Architect.

CAHILL, Debbie S; Civic Memorial HS; Bethalto, IL; HonRl; NHS; NatlThespSoc; SchPl; EdSchPpr; FNA; VPFrCl; PpCl; LetterTennis; GAA; Ozark Bible College; Medicine.

CAHILL, Grace E; Trinity HS; Chicago, IL; 11/214 ChrhWkr; CmntyWkr; HonRl; NHS; StuGov; RptrSchPpr; University; Professional.

CAHILL, Joseph A; Preston Comm HS; Preston, IA; 3/30 SecFrshCls; VPJrCls; ALBoysSt; HonRl; PresNHS; Bsbl; Bsktbl; Ftbl; CaptTrk; CitAwd; Univ;.

CAHILL, Karen A; Academy Of Our Lady; Chicago, IL; 4/160 HonRl; Mdrgl; NHS; SchMus; SchPl; VPSdlty; Yrbk; FNA; SpnCl; PpCl; Chrldr; GAA; Univ Of Illinois; Physical Therapy.

CAHILL, Mary J; St Edward HS; St Edward, NE; SecFrshCls; TrsJrCls; VPBand; Chrs; HonRl; Mdrgl; StuCncl; Yrbk; VPPpCl; CitAwd; U Of Ne; Engineering.

CAHILL, Michael E; St Bede Acad; Ransom, IL; CmntyWkr; HonRl; SchMus; SchPl; StuGov; SptEdYrbk; LetterBsbl; LetterFtbl; LetterTrk; IMSpt; Coll; Civil Engi.

CAHN, Naomi R; Clayton HS; St Louis, MO; 11/200 SecSrCls; Band; CmntyWkr; LitMag; ModUN; NHS; NatlMeritFnl; TchrAde; RptrYrbk; EdSchPpr; Princeton University.

CAHOON, Timothy G; Saranac HS; Clarksville, MI; 2/82 TrsJrCls; PresSrCls; ALBoysSt; Band; HonRl; MrchBnd; NHS; SctActv; TchrAde; 4-H; Eastern Michigan Univ; Computer Science.

CAHOY, Thomas J; Hudson Sr HS; Hudson, WI; VPSophCls; Bsktbl; LetterFtbl; Trk;.

CAIN, Candice L; Lenox HS; Lenox, IA; SecFrshCls; SecJrCls; Band; HonRl; NHS; Yrbk; CaptBsktbl; LetterGlf; BttyCrckrAwd; CitAwd; Business School;.

CAIN, Colleen M; Parkway North HS; Creve Coeur, MO; 35/459 NHS; SchAde; College; Bus Ed.

CAIN, Donna J; Peoria HS; Peoria, IL; 20/450 Chr; Chrs; ChrhWkr; CmntyWkr; HonRl; NHS; Illinois Wesleyan Univ; Music.

CAIN, Jean L; Hayward HS; Hayward, WI; 2/150 HonRl; NHS; Twrl; SchPpr; VPFHA; Dst #1 Tech Inst Eau Claire; Sec Sci.

CAIN, Joy L; Buffalo Grove HS; Buffalo Grove, IL; ChrhWkr; CmntyWkr; HonRl; HospAde; NHS; Northwestern Univ; Medicine.

CAIN, Lyle J; U S D #440 HS; Halstead, KS; 4/69 ALBoysSt; Band; Chr; Chrl; Chrs; ChrhWkr; CmntyWkr; CncrtBnd; HonRl; MrchBnd; Glf; Kansas St Univ; Music.

CAIN, Margaret M; Edgewood HS; Madison, WI; 15/138 ALAGirlsSt; Chrs; HonRl; NHS; SchMus; StuCncl; SptEdYrbk; PpCl; LetterBsktbl; GAA; College; Medicine.

CAIN, Michelle M; Marquette HS; Alton, IL; CmntyWkr; HonRl; JA; NatlMeritFnl; NatlMeritSchl; NatlThespSoc; StuGov; RptrSchPpr; Swmmng; IMSpt; Univ; Anesthesiologist.

CAIN, Patricia L; Marysville HS; Beattie, KS; HonRl; StuCncl; FHA; PpCl; Bsbl; University; Vocation.

CAIN, Tim J; Prairie Heights HS; Orland, IN; PresJrCls; Aud/Vis; HonRl; StuCncl; FrCl; GerCl; Ftbl; CaptGlf; IMSpt; College; Law.

CAIN, Timothy T; Hastings HS; Hastings, MN; 16/321 HonRl; NHS; StuCncl; TchrAde; Bsbl; Bsktbl; LetterGlf; St Cloud State Clg; Business.

CAINE, Candace A; Hickman HS; Columbia, MO; TrsFrshCls; Chr; ChrhWkr; HonRl; Mdrgl; NHS; SchMus; TchrAde; GAA; College; Doctor.

CAINE, Junie A; Harry E Wood HS; Indianapolis, IN; 29/233 Chr; Chrl; Chrs; HonRl; SchAde; SchMus; TchrAde; Law.

CAINE, Kerry L; Heritage Christian HS; Indianapolis, IN; Band; Chr; HonRl; Orch; SctActv; SchPpr; LetterBsbl; LetterBsktbl; LetterSocr; LetterTrk; Tennessee Temple School; Business Admin.

CAIRNS, Mary; Ottawa Twp Hs; Ottawa, IL; HonRl; NHS; 4-H; Illinois State U;psychologist.

CAIRNS, Melvin; Santa Fe Trail HS; Carbondale, KS; 2/95 HonRl; MrchBnd; NHS; PepBnd; StuCncl; RptrYrbk; Glf; IMSpt; Kansas St Univ; Chem Eng.

CALABRESE, Michael A; Taft HS; Chicago, IL; 3/820 PresSrCls; HonRl; IntrClCncl; NHS; NatlMeritCmnd; NatlSciFnd; SctActv; StuCncl; EdSchPpr; LetterBsbl; Univ;proffesional.

CALABRESE, Peter J; Notre Dame HS; Morton Grove, IL; 9/276 ChrhWkr; HonRl; JA; JrNHS; SchAde; SchPl; YthFlsp; CaptBsktbl; Notre Dame College; Professional.

CALABRESE, Rose M; D D Eisenhower HS; Calumet Park, IL; Chrs; HonRl; JrNHS; LitMag; NatlThespSoc; OffAde; SchPl; Northwestern Univ; Communications.

CALAHAN, Vicki L; Bruning Public HS; Carleton, NE; 4/17 Chr; ChrhWkr; CmntyWkr; HonRl; SchPl; SctActv; StuGov; YthFlsp; PpCl; PPFtbl; College.

CALAMARI, Arthur A; T Roosevelt HS; Chicago, IL; 23/297 HonRl; NHS; Bsbl; CaptFtbl; College; Business Admin.

CALBERT, Robert H; Greenwood HS; Springfield, MO; SecTrsFrshCls; Chrs; HonRl; LatCl; SpnCl; Ftbl; Glf; Smsu.

CALCATERRA, Pamela; St Marys Acad; Mount Prospect, IL; HonRl; OffAde; SchPl; StuCncl; FBLA; Bsbl; Tennis; CchngActv; GAA; Jr Coll; Business.

CALDER, James S; Neil Armstrong HS; Minneapolis, MN; 57/600 Band; ChrhWkr; CmntyWkr; HonRl; PolWkr; LetterBsktbl; LetterFtbl; LetterTrk; CchngActv; Creighton Univ; Medicine.

CALDWELL, Becky K; Osborne HS; Portis, KS; ALAGirlsSt; Chrs; ChrhWkr; CncrtBnd; HonRl; MrchBnd; PepBnd; CivCl; FHA; PpCl; Bsktbl; Trk; Chrldr; College; Professional.

CALDWELL, Chris A; Winola HS; Viola, IL; 8/65 HonRl; NHS; Twrl; Yrbk; TreasFHA; SecFNA; SpnCl; PpCl; Chrldr; IMSpt; 4-HAwd; Black Hawk Clge; Med Secretary.

CALDWELL, Christopher G; Shawnee Mission South HS; Overland Park, KS; AFS; HonRl; NHS; NatlMeritFnl; NatlMeritSchl; SchPl; SctActv; SchPpr; U Of Kansas; Internatl Law.

CALDWELL, Cynthia J; Dunkirk HS; Dunkirk, IN; HonRl; FrCl; LatCl; PpCl; SciCl; Bsktbl; GAA;.

CALDWELL, Dalonda; Clinton Prairie Hs; Frankfot, IN; 15/100 SecTrsFrshCls; HonRl; NHS; EdYrBk; SpnCl; PpCl; SciCl; Hanover College; Political Cienec.

CALDWELL, David L; Wellington HS; Wellington, IL; TrsSophCls; ALBoysSt; Chrs; HonRl; PpCl; LetterBsbl; LetterBsktbl; LetterTrk; College; Teacher Coach.

CALDWELL, Kenneth R; Lake Forest HS; Lake Bluff, IL; 26/435 Band; CncrtBnd; HonRl; LitMag; MrchBnd; NHS; OffAde; YthFlsp; SptEdSchPpr; CaptTrk; College; Geology.

CALDWELL, Marilyn; Oakville Senior HS; St Louis, MO; 15/336 HonRl; NHS; OffAde; FTA; Coll; Art Ther.

CALDWELL, Mark L; Sparta HS; Sparta, WI; 15/197 HonRl; NHS; GovHonPrgAwd; CitAwd; Work; Vocation.

CALDWELL, Michael L; Waynesville HS; Waynesville, MO; 96/257 SecTrsFrshCls; HstSophCls; TrsJrCls; HstSrCls; Band; HonRl; NHS; StuCncl; SptEdSchPpr; Bsktbl; Coll; Vet.

CALDWELL, Patricia; Festus Sr HS; Festus, MO; 4/157 Band; Chrs; ChrhWkr; ALAGirlsSt; HonRl; MrchBnd; NHS; Chrldr; Nursing Chool.

CALDWELL, Robin L; Woodland R 4 HS; Lutesville, MO; 1/75 Band; CncrtBnd; DrmMjrt; HonRl; PepBnd; Twrl; FHA; PpCl; Southeast Missouri St Univ; Physical Therap.

CALDWELL, Sandra L; Gallatin R 5 HS; Gallatin, MO; 5/54 PresJrCls; ALAGirlsSt; VPBand; HonRl; NHS; SchPl; StuCncl; EdYrBk; PresFHA; DARAwd; College; Home Economics.

CALDWELL, Twyla D; Egyptian HS; Thebes, IL; 12/67 HonRl; VPStuCncl; Yrbk; SchPpr; FHA; SciCl; Shawnee Junior College; Law.

CALDWELL, Wendie; Howell Sr HS; Howell, MI; 39/372 Chr; HonRl; JA; SchAde; FrCl; GerCl; Lake Superior State College; Computer Engin.

CALDWELL, William C; Cherryvale HS; Cherryvale, KS; 4/52 HonRl; NHS; SchAde; TchrAde; PresFFA; IMSpt; College; Agriculture.

CALGARO, Catherine L; Holdingford HS; Avon, MN; SecTrsFrshCls; PresSrCls; Band; CncrtBnd; HonRl; MrchBnd; Yrbk; 4-H; GAA; 4-HAwd; College.

CALHOON, Karen M; Winner Sr HS; Winner, SD; Chr; Chrs; DrlTm; Mdrgl; YthFlsp; RptrYrbk; Yrbk; RptrSchPpr; Nettleton College; Fashion Mdse.

CALHOUN, Carol; Waukegan East HS; Waukegan, IL; 20/502 HonRl; JrNHS; NHS; GerCl; College; Medical Doctor.

CALHOUN, George D; East HS; Sioux City, IA; Aud/Vis; HonRl; LbryAde; NatlMeritSF; YthFlsp; GovHonPrgAwd; Univ; Engineer.

CALHOUN, James M; Bowen HS; Chicago, IL; 35/571 PresSrCls; Aud/Vis; Chr; ChrhWkr; HonRl; StuCncl; FrCl; LetterFtbl; Univ; Vocation.

CALHOUN, Levon P; Lindblom Tech HS; Chicago, IL; 131/657 LitMag; NatlMeritCmnd; Quill&Scroll; StuCncl; YthFlsp; EdSchPpr; PepBnd; FrCl; PresJETSAwd; Unofroch ;lawyer.

CALHOUN, Timothy A; New Haven HS; New Haven, MI; CmntyWkr; HonRl; LbryAde; NHS; TreasStuCncl; TchrAde; FrCl; GerCl; CitAwd; Central Mi; Psychology.

CALHOUN, William V; Andale HS; Goddard, KS; Mdrgl; SchMus; SchPl; SpnCl; Wichita State Univ.

CALICH, Victoria A; Bremen HS; Posen, IL; 62/484 Chrs; NHS; SchPl; SctActv; PresStuCncl; RptrSchPpr; 4-H; PpCl; GAA; College; Journalism.

CALIGURI, Janet D; East Detroit HS; East Detroit, MI; HonRl; NHS; OffAde; RedCrAde; SchAde; TchrAde; SptEdSchPpr; Bsbl; LetterBsktbl; Trk; University ; Vocational.

CALISE, Christopher P; Kirksville R Iii Sr HS; Kirksville, MO; VPSophCls; CmntyWkr; StuCncl; StuGov; Bsbl; Bsktbl; College; Medicine.

CALKINS, Bernice L; Haslett HS; Haslett, MI; 9/144 Chr; Chrl; ChrhWkr; SchAde; SchMus; TchrAde; Teen; FHA; College; Rn.

CALKINS, James B; Brookfield East HS; Elm Grove, WI; AFS; ChrhWkr; HonRl; YthFlsp; Univ Of Minnesota; Veterinary Medicine.

CALKINS, Keith; Cedar Lake Acad; Tustin, MI; 7/72 HonRl; NatlMeritCmnd; MthCl; IMSpt; Andrews Univ; Mathematician.

CALKINS, Marchia L; Florence HS; Iron Mountain, MI; 7/70 Chrs; CmntyWkr; HonRl; NatlFornLg; NHS; Quill&Scroll; SchPl; StuCncl; Twrl; EdYrBk; GAA; Marinette Tech School; Clerk Typist.

CALL, William W; United Township HS; East Moline, IL; 23/800 Chr; ChmnChrhWkr; HonRl; VPJA; JrNHS; Mdrgl; NHS; FrCl; Trk; JAAwd; Jr Clge; Music Pro.

CALLAGHAN, Barb E; Frederick HS; Frederick, SD; Band; Chrs; CncrtBnd; HonRl; MrchBnd; PepBnd; SchPl; PpCl; Sd Univ; Journalism.

CALLAGHAN, Dennis F; Riverside Brookfield HS; Riverside, IL; HonRl; LetterFtbl; LetterTrk; Loyola University; Medicine.

CALLAHAN, Bill; Anderson HS; Anderson, IN; 7/600 Aud/Vis; ChrhWkr; HonRl; NatlMeritSF; YthFlsp; DARAwd; CitAwd; Purdue; Teacher.

CALLAHAN, Cynthia; Brady Public HS; Farnam, NE; SecFrshCls; SecSophCls; VPJrCls; HonRl; SchPl; RptrYrbk; PpCl; GAA; PPFtbl; 4-HAwd; National School Of Business; Secretary.

CALLAHAN, Dan F; Rochester HS; Rochester, IN; Aud/Vis; Chr; HonRl; FrCl; PpCl; Bsktbl; LetterFtbl; CchngActv; IMSpt; College; Science.

CALLAHAN, Glenn A; Tomahawk HS; Tomahawk, WI; PresJrCls; HonRl; NatlThespSoc; SchPl; StuCncl; StuGov; 4-H; LetterFtbl; 4-HAwd; JETSAwd; Col; Engineering.

CALLAHAN, Joyce E; Troy HS; Troy, KS; ChrhWkr; HonRl; NHS; SchPl; TchrAde; YthFlsp; SchPpr; Treas4-H; VPPpCl; 4-HAwd; Nursing School; Nurse.

CALLAHAN, Mary E; Naperville Central HS; Naperville, IL; ChrhWkr; DrlTm; HonRl; OffAde; StuGov; TchrAde; SpnCl; CaptChrldr; PresAwd; St Marys College; Nursing.

CALLAHAN, Susan R; Richwoods HS; Peoria, IL; HospAde; SctActv; IMSpt; College; Policewoman.

CALLAHAN, Thomas W; Brother Rice HS; Chicago, IL; 60/416 CmntyWkr; HonRl; LitMag; NHS; PolWkr; SchAde; Univ Of Illinois; Psychology.

CALLAN, Donna M; Benton Community HS; Watkins, IA; Band; ChrhWkr; CncrtBnd; MrchBnd; PepBnd; FHA; GAA; PPFtbl; College; Nursing.

CALLAN, Paul J; Marquette University HS; Milwaukee, WI; 10/250 HonRl; NatlFornLg; FrCl; MthCl; University Of Notre Dame; Business.

CALLAWAY, Deborah A; West Platte HS; Rushville, MO; AFS; ChrhWkr; CmntyWkr; HonRl; NHS; NatlMeritSchl; TchrAde; YthFlsp; Trade School; Professional.

CALLAWAY, Lorie L; Waverly HS; Lincoln, NE; Chr; HonRl; SchPl; StuCncl; StuGov; RptrYrbk; PpCl; SciCl; LetterTrk; CaptChrldr; U Of Ne Lincoln; Psych.

CALLAWAY, Tonja; Palestine HS; Palestine, IL; 3/40 VPJrCls; Band; Chrs; CncrtBnd; DrmMjrt; HonRl; SchMus; 4-H; FHA; GAA; Coll; Vocation.

CALLEJA, Michael A; Somerset Public HS; Somerset, WI; ChrhWkr; CmntyWkr; HonRl; JA; SctActv; EngCl; GerCl; PpCl; Bsbl; Bsktbl; Ftbl; IMSpt; College; Professional.

CALLEN, Edward J; St Laurence HS; Chicago, IL; Band; CncrtBnd; HonRl; MrchBnd; PepBnd; SchMus; StuCncl; StuGov; Ftbl; Loyola Univ; Radiologist.

CALLEN, Tammie J; Grundy Co R V HS; Galt, MO; SecSophCls; ALAGirlsSt; Band; ChrhWkr; NHS; Twrl; FHA; College.

CALLICOTT, Michael J; Hannibal Sr HS; Hannibal, MO; ALBoysSt; Band; CncrtBnd; HonRl; MrchBnd; NHS; SchPl; EdSchPpr; College; Journalism.

CALLIES, David W; Lutheran East HS; Roseville, MI; HonRl; NHS; Bsktbl; LetterTrk; IMSpt; Macomb County Comm Coll; Bus Admin.

CALLIES, Debra J; Leigh Community HS; Leigh, NE; SecJrCls; Band; CncrtBnd; HonRl; MrchBnd; PepBnd; SchPl; 4-H; FHA; PpCl; Wayne State College; Accountant.

CALLIHAN, Lloyd; Lowell Senior HS; Lowell, MI; 9/197 HonRl; NHS; LionAwd; Univ; Computer Programmer.

CALLINAN, Mary K; Derham Hall HS; St Paul, MN; 59/128 Chr; Chrs; HospAde; SchPl; StuCncl; StuGov; SpnCl; IMSpt; St Marys Jr Clg; Medical Tech.

CALLIS, Kevin D; Shawnee HS; Grand Tower, IL; 12/62 HonRl; FFA; Shawnee Jr Col; Science.

CALLIS, Sherry A; Madison Consolidated HS; Madison, IN; Chr; ChrhWkr; HonRl; NHS; TchrAde; YthFlsp; Trade Sch; Voc.

CALLIS, Timothy A; Madison Consolidated HS; Madison, IN; PresSophCls; VPJrCls; StuCncl; SpnCl; LetterBsbl; IMSpt; Collge; Professional.

CALLISON, Kathleen S; Franklin Center HS; Franklin Grove, IL; 6/48 SecFrshCls; SecSophCls; PresJrCls; SecSrCls; Band; Chrs; CncrtBnd; HonRl; HospAde; MrchBnd; NHS; PepBnd; SchPl; 4-H; PpCl; Nursing School; Registered Nurse.

CALLISTER, Brian J; Osseo Fairchild HS; Osseo, WI; VPSophCls; Band; CncrtBnd; HonRl; MrchBnd; PepBnd; Yrbk; LetterBsbl; LetterFtbl; LetterGlf; College; Architecture.

CALLON, Catherine A; Whiteland Comm HS; Whiteland, IN; 6/204 ChrhWkr; CncrtBnd; MrchBnd; NHS; StuCncl; Sec4-H; FTA; SecSpnCl; CaptBsktbl; LetterTrk; Franklin College; Phys Educ.

CALLOWAY, B; Sts Peter And Paul HS; Saginaw, MI; RptrYrbk; LetterFtbl; LetterTrk; IMSpt; Art College; Advertising.

CALTEUX, Kenneth J; Thomas More HS; St Francis, WI; ChrhWkr; HonRl; StuCncl; LetterFtbl; School; Science Field.

CALVERT, Bruce D; Marissa Unit Dist #40 HS; Marissa, IL; 22/74 VPJrCls; Band; HonRl; MrchBnd; SchMus; SctActv; LetterBsbl; LetterBsktbl; College; Vocational.

CALVERT, Gregory S; Du Quoin HS; Du Quoin, IL; 9/143 Band; CncrtBnd; HonRl; MrchBnd; PepBnd; SpnCl; LetterBsktbl; LetterFtbl; LetterTrk; CchngActv; Univ; Journalism.

CALVERT, Karen E; Edinburg Community HS; Edinburg, IN; 5/64 TrsJrCls; SecSrCls; ALAGirlsSt; HonRl; HospAde; NHS; YthFlsp; FHA; FrCl; AmLegAwd; Ind Central; Health Careet.

CALVERT, Ronda A; Savannah HS; Savannah, MO; CmntyWkr; HonRl; JrNHS; LbryAde; NHS; FrCl; SpnCl; PpCl; GAA; Univ; Pro.

CALVIN, Candace; Pacific HS; Pacific, MO; Band; ChrhWkr; CncrtBnd; HonRl; MrchBnd; PepBnd; PolWkr; FrCl; LatCl; SpnCl; Webster Groves; Lawyer.

CALVIN, Cindy J; Hillsdale HS; Hillsdale, MI; 13/180 Chr; ChrhWkr; HonRl; NHS; TchrAde; Yrbk; CivCl; PresFBLA; SpnCl; Southern Bible Coll; Bus.

CALYO, Lisa D; Momence Community HS; Momence, IL; 6/130 SecJrCls; HonRl; NHS; NatlMeritCmnd; SchPl; PresStuCncl; RptrYrbk; Yrbk; RptrSchPpr; SchPpr; Southern Ill Univ; Art Major.

CALZAVARA, Carolyn M; Amos Alonzo Stagg HS; Palos Hills, IL; ChrhWkr; HonRl; StuCncl; YthLg; FNA; St Ambrose College; Liberal Arts.

CAMATTI, Cathy L; La Salle Peru Twp HS; Oglesby, IL; 28/485 HonRl; Chrs; SctActv; FrCl; PpCl; College; Mathematics.

CAMBRON, Joan M; Bergan HS; Peoria, IL; 12/200 ALAGirlsSt; CmntyWkr; HonRl; SchAde; RptrYrbk; SpnCl; Illinois State Univ; Medical Technology.

CAMBRON, Thomas G; Mercy HS; St Louis, MO; HonRl; NHS; IMSpt; CitAwd; Univ Of Mo; Business Admin.

CAMBURN, Kathleen A; Granite City South HS; Granite City, IL; College.

CAMERA, Philip R; Mendel Catholic Prep HS; Dolton, IL; 3/200 Aud/Vis; ChrhWkr; CmntyWkr; HonRl; IntrClCncl; RedCrAde; SchAde; SctActv; StuCncl; StuGov; College; Chemical Engineering.

CAMERINO, Nestor H; North Chicago Comm HS; Great Lakes, IL; 6/300 HonRl; NHS; NatlMeritCmnd; Yrbk; SchPpr; LetterTennis; Us Naval Academy; Nuclear Physics.

CAMERON, Anne M; Dowling HS; Des Moines, IA; 1/385 Chrs; HonRl; JA; NatlMeritSF; StuCncl; FrCl; College; Law.

CAMERON, Barbara; Fisher Public HS; Fisher, MN; Band; ChrhWkr; HonRl; JA; SchPl; Yrbk; PpCl; Bsktbl; JAAwd; Trade; Vocation.

CAMERON, Carol J; Bishop Foley HS; Madison Hts, MI; 16/150 HonRl; JrNHS; NHS; Ctr For Creative Studies; Fine Arts.

CAMERON, Charles D; Paw Paw HS; Paw Paw, MI; 26/169 HonRl; NHS; Trade School; Design.

CAMERON, Donald L; Seaholm HS; Birmingham, MI; PresFrshCls; PresSrCls; HonRl; NHS; ModUN; NHS; SchMus; SctActv; StuCncl; LetterFtbl; OptClAwd; Univ Of Mi; Naval Architecure & Marine Eng.

CAMERON, Douglas C; Proviso West HS; Westchester, IL; 30/1100 ChrhWkr; HonRl; NHS; EdSchPpr; Ftbl; LetterSocr; LetterTrk; University; Engineer.

CAMERON, Jo Ellen K; Adair Co Rii HS; Brasher, MO; SecFrshCls; SecJrCls; Chrs; HonRl; SchPl; CaptBsktbl; LetterTrk; IMSpt; Bus Sch; Secretarial Work.

CAMERON, Kathy L; Chambers Public HS; Chambers, NE; 6/24 Band; Chr; Chrs; ChrhWkr; CncrtBnd; HonRl; LbryAde; MrchBnd; NHS; PepBnd; SctActv; BttyCrckrAwd; Mount Marty College; Nurse.

CAMERON, Kenneth; Frontenac Hs; Pittsburg, KS; ALBoysSt; HonRl; NHS; SchPl; StuCncl; SpnCl; College;professional.

CAMERON, Leigh A; Lyman HS; Presho, SD; Band; Chr; CncrtBnd; DrlTm; HonRl; NHS; PepBnd; RedCrAde; YthFlsp; Yrbk; College; Professional.

CAMERON, Robert B; Magic City Campus HS; Minot, ND; ALBoysSt; Band; CncrtBnd; HonRl; JrNHS; NatlMeritSchl; PepBnd; GerCl; Bsktbl; LetterTrk; College; Medicine.

CAMERON, Robert W; Greenville HS; Greenville, MI; ALBoysSt; HonRl; SctActv; StuCncl; YthFlsp; LetterBsbl; LetterBsktbl; LetterFtbl; IMSpt; Grand Valley St Coll; Accounting.

CAMFERDAM, Janet L; Moline Sr HS; Moline, IL; 27/822 Chr; HonRl; LitMag; NHS; OffAde; PolWkr; StuCncl; StuGov; SchPpr; LatCl; SciCl; LetterSwmmng; GAA; College; Medicine.

CAMP, Dane R; Walther Lutheran HS; Elmhurst, IL; Chrs; HonRl; RptrSchPpr; College.

CAMP, David J; Normandy Sr HS; Pine Lawn, MO; 11/514 HonRl; HospAde; NHS; StuCncl; FrCl; Wa Univ St Louis; College Professor.

CAMP, Debra; Waltonville HS; Bonnie, IL; ChrhWkr; HonRl; LbryAde; SchPl; GerCl; PpCl; Chrldr; GodCntryAwd; Rend Lake College; Biology Major.

CAMP, Melvin D; Bedford North Lawrence HS; Bedford, IN; 103/397 PresJrCls; ALBoysSt; NHS; SctActv; StuCncl; LetterBsbl; LetterBsktbl; In St Univ; Pre Law.

CAMP, Norman J; Hammond Technical Voc HS; Hammond, IN; ChrhWkr; HonRl; SchMus; SchPl; StuCncl; SchPpr; GerCl; LetterFtbl; LetterSocr; LetterWrstlng; Navy.

CAMP, Tracy L; Immaculata HS; Leavenworth, KS; SecFrshCls; Band; CncrtBnd; HonRl; PepBnd; SctActv; RptrYrbk; 4-H; College; Journalism.

CAMP, Wanda K; Thornton Fractional No HS; Burnham, IL; Chr; ChrhWkr; CmntyWkr; HonRl; NHS; PolWkr; Quill&Scroll; TchrAde; RptrSchPpr; SchPpr; SpnCl; College; Social Work.

CAMPAU, Dale; Greenfield Central HS; Greenfield, IN; 10/360 HonRl; MrchBnd; NHS; NatlMeritCmnd; TchrAde; Bsktbl; Trk; JETSAwd; Rose Hulman Institute Of Tech; Chemistry.

CAMPBELL, Alan V; Oskaloosa Sr HS; Oskaloosa, IA; 40/197 HonRl; PolWkr; SchPl; StuCncl; KeyCl; Wm Penn College; Politics.

CAMPBELL, Amy J; Lawrenceville HS; Lawrenceville, IL; 8/180 SecBand; Chr; ChrhWkr; HonRl; NHS; TchrAde; SpnCl; PpCl; SciCl; GAA; Eastern; Elementary Education.

CAMPBELL, Amy M; Holy Angels HS; Edina, MN; ChrhWkr; CmntyWkr; StuCncl; College; Counseling.

CAMPBELL, Anita; West Nodaway Hs; Elmo, MO; 2/43 Band; Chrs; HonRl; NHS; SchPl; StuCncl; 4-H; VPPpCl; Bsktbl; Chrldr; University; Medical Technology.

CAMPBELL, Bride E; Brainerd HS; Brainerd, MN; Chr; HonRl; StuCncl; StuGov; RptrYrbk; SptEdYrbk; Swmmng; Chrldr; IMSpt; PPFtbl; Bus Sch; Vocation Or Professnl.

CAMPBELL, Christie K; Garden County HS; Oshkosh, NE; 4/30 HonRl; HospAde; SchPl; SctActv; RptrYrbk; RptrSchPpr; SpnCl; PpCl; Trk; Chrldr; AmLegAwd; University Of Nebraska; Nursing.

CAMPBELL, Christine; Falls City HS; Falls City, NE; Band; Chr; Chrs; CncrtBnd; DrlTm; DrmMjrt; MrchBnd; NHS; PepBnd; SchMus; College Of Bus Sch; Music Or Secretary.

CAMPBELL, Christopher W; Lansing HS; Leavenworth, KS; 40/98 Band; CmntyWkr; CncrtBnd; HonRl; MrchBnd; PepBnd; StuCncl; 4-H; SciCl; 4-HAwd; College Or Univ; Animal Husbandry.

CAMPBELL, Claire A; Bishop Dwenger HS; Fort Wayne, IN; HonRl; PolWkr; RptrYrbk; FrCl; PpCl; GAA; University; Education.

CAMPBELL, Cynthia S; Lincoln Community HS; Lincoln, IL; 19/273 Chr; Chrs; HonRl; HospAde; SchMus; PresFNA; PpCl; SciCl; College; Chemistry.

CAMPBELL, Dana J; Sarcoxie HS; La Russell, MO; 6/63 ChrhWkr; Mdrgl; SecNHS; StuCncl; FFA; FHA; FTA; MthCl; CaptBsktbl; Chrldr; Southwest Baptist College; Elementary Ed.

CAMPBELL, David W; Grand Blanc HS; Grand Glanc, MI; 151/666 CncrtBnd; MrchBnd; Orch; PepBnd; SchMus; SctActv; EldAwd; RotaryAwd; Central Michigan Univ; Optometry.

CAMPBELL, Deborah J; Litchville HS; Sanborn, ND; Band; Chrs; CncrtBnd; HonRl; MrchBnd; PepBnd; SchMus; FHA; PpCl; College; Medicine.

CAMPBELL, Debra A; La Grove Comm HS; Farina, IL; PresSophCls; Band; Chrs; HonRl; SchPl; FrCl; SciCl; LetterTrk; ChmnChrldr; IMSpt; University; Accountant.

CAMPBELL, Debra S; Humansville HS; Humansville, MO; 2/35 SecTrsSrCls; Chr; ChrhWkr; HonRl; SchPl; TchrAde; SchPpr; Cmsu; Elementary Ed.

CAMPBELL, Don E; Allegan HS; Allegan, MI; PresSophCls; ALBoysSt; PresNHS; NatlMeritSF; Bsktbl; CchngActv; RotaryAwd; Univ Of Mi; Medical.

CAMPBELL, Faith M; Midway HS; Inkster, ND; 6/40 SecALAGirlsSt; HonRl; SchMus; SchPl; RptrYrbk; FHA; PpCl; U Of Nd; Social Worker.

CAMPBELL, Frank; Highland HS; Anderson, IN; 145/271 Band; Chr; ChrhWkr; CncrtBnd; MrchBnd; SctActv; Ftbl; Swmmng; Trk; Wrstlng; Indiana University; Psychologist.

CAMPBELL, Gerald D; North Crawford HS; Gays Mills, WI; ALBoysSt; Band; HonRl; StuGov; YthFlsp; MthCl; Bsbl; Bsktbl; Ftbl;.

CAMPBELL, Gerald G; Burrton HS; Burrton, KS; PresSrCls; Band; CncrtBnd; HonRl; MrchBnd; PepBnd; RptrYrbk; RptrSchPpr; 4-H; Kansas State Univ; Veterinary Medicine.

CAMPBELL, Gordon L; Streator Township HS; Streator, IL; MrchBnd; NHS; NatlThespSoc; PepBnd; SchMus; SchPl; StuCncl; YthFlsp; GerCl; LetterWrstlng; Us Air Force Acad; Air Force Career.

CAMPBELL, Gregory D; Hillsdale HS; Hillsdale, MI; 15/120 Chr; Chrl; HonRl; NHS; SchMus; SchPpr; LetterFtbl; LetterTrk; IMSpt; Coll; Music Ed.

CAMPBELL, Gregory L; East Central HS; Sunman, IN; VPFrshCls; TreasAud/Vis; Band; ChrhWkr; CncrtBnd; MrchBnd; PepBnd; LetterBsbl; LetterGlf; College; Business.

CAMPBELL, Gregory P; Dixon R 1 HS; Dixon, MO; HstJrCls; Aud/Vis; Band; Chrs; CmntyWkr; CncrtBnd; DrmMjrt; HonRl; JA; MrchBnd; PepBnd; SchAde; Glf; College; Broadcaster.

CAMPBELL, James A; Stevens Point Area Senior HS; Stevens Point, WI; 101/568 Chr; NHS; NatlMeritCmnd; LetterBsktbl; LetterFtbl; LetterTrk; IMSpt; U W Eau Claire; Law.

CAMPBELL, James K; Bennington HS; Salina, KS; VPJrCls; VPSrCls; Band; Chrs; HonRl; MrchBnd; SchPl; TchrAde; RptrYrbk; SchPpr; Bsktbl; AmLegAwd; Oklahoma Baptist Univ; Music.

CAMPBELL, Jane A; Jasper R 5 HS; Jasper, MO; Band; Chr; ChrhWkr; CmntyWkr; HospAde; FHA; FTA; PpCl; Chrldr; IMSpt; Trade Sch; Voc.

CAMPBELL, Jane L; Ladysmith Hawkins HS; Hawkins, WI; HonRl; LbryAde; NHS; College.

CAMPBELL, Jane M; Brentwood HS; Richmond Hts, MO; ChrhWkr; DrlTm; HospAde; NatlThespSoc; SchAde; TchrAde; YthFlsp; RptrSchPpr; SpnCl; GAA; Coll; Prof.

CAMPBELL, Jeanette I; Valley R6 HS; Belleview, MO; 3/48 SecTrsFrshCls; Chrs; HonRl; JrNHS; LbryAde; NHS; PepBnd; SchPl; VPStuCncl; TchrAde; EdYrBk; SecFHA; Chrldr; Col; Conservationist.

CAMPBELL, Jeffery L; Carson City Crystal Area HS; Crystal, MI; 18/114 Band; HonRl; NHS; OffAde; SchAde; SctActv; YthFlsp; Ferris St Clg; Elec Engr.

CAMPBELL, Jeffrey; E Gary Edison Sr Hs; East Gary, IN; Band; HonRl; JrNHS; NHS; LetterBsbl;.

CAMPBELL, Jodie B; Lyons Township HS; Western Springs, IL; 160/1214 HonRl; IntrClCncl; NHS; StuGov; TchrAde; YthFlsp; Univ Of Ill; Home Economics.

CAMPBELL, Judith; Westville HS; Danville, IL; ChrhWkr; DrlTm; HonRl; NHS; OffAde; PpCl; SciCl; Chrldr; IMSpt; Coll; Teacher.

CAMPBELL, Judy; Northrop HS; Fort Wayne, IN; Aud/Vis; ChrhWkr; HonRl; LbryAde; TchrAde; 4-H; 4-HAwd; CitAwd;.

CAMPBELL, Julie R; Noblesville HS; Noblesville, IN; 21/250 HonRl; NHS; FTA; SpnCl; CaptBsktbl; Trk; GAA; IMSpt; Purdue Univ; Phys Therapist.

CAMPBELL, Karen; Manchester Hs; Manchester, MI; ALAGirlsSt; HonRl; SchMus; SchPl; YthFlsp; FrCl; College;drama.

CAMPBELL, Karen V; Chicago Vocational HS; Chicago, IL; HonRl; College.

CAMPBELL, Kay A; Fairfield HS; Arlington, KS; 4/64 Bsktbl; Chr; CncrtBnd; HonRl; SchPl; StuCncl; TchrAde; YthFlsp; RptrYrbk; Tennis; U Of Kan; Medicine.

CAMPBELL, Keith M; Kalkaska HS; Kalkasko, MI; TrsSophCls; Band; CncrtBnd; MrchBnd; SchPl; Bsbl; Bsktbl; Ftbl; Trk; PresAwd; Coast Guard Acad; Doctor.

CAMPBELL, Keith R; Ashland HS; Ashland, IL; 5/37 PresJrCls; Chrs; CncrtBnd; HonRl; NHS; SchMus; PresStuCncl; RptrYrbk; SptEdSchPpr; TreasFFA; College.

CAMPBELL, Kimberly D; Central HS; Red Wing, MN; Chr; ChrhWkr; HonRl; TchrAde; YthFlsp; FBLA; FHA; FTA; Quachita Baptist Univ; Elementary Ed.

CAMPBELL, Kimberly K; Blair HS; Blair, NE; DrlTm; HonRl; HospAde; TreasNatlThespSoc; SchMus; SchPl; FBLA; Bus Sch; Med Sec.

CAMPBELL, Laura; Batavia HS; Batavia, IL; Chr; LitMag; SchPl; StuGov; LatCl; Northern Ill Univ; Fine Arts.

CAMPBELL, Laura J; Alcona HS; Lincoln Mi, MI; 7/121 NHS; TchrAde; LetterBsbl; LetterTrk; GAA; PPFtbl; E Mich U; Occup Therapy.

CAMPBELL, Leslie C; Chenoa HS; Chenoa, IL; 11/57 VPJrCls; AFS; Band; Chrs; CncrtBnd; HonRl; MrchBnd; StuCncl; FTA; Univ Of Illinois.

CAMPBELL, Lisa K; Corunna HS; Corunna, MI; Band; HonRl; NHS; TchrAde; Yrbk; Bsbl; Bsktbl; Ftbl; GAA; PpCl;.

CAMPBELL, Marcia D; Coleman HS; Coleman, MI; 2/84 Band; ChrhWkr; CncrtBnd; HonRl; MrchBnd; NHS; PepBnd; TchrAde; CaptBsktbl; DARAwd; Evangel College.

CAMPBELL, Marilyn K; Nashua Comm HS; Nashua, IA; 1/71 Band; HonRl; NHS; NatlThespSoc; SchPl; RptrYrbk; RptrSchPpr; FHA; FrCl; LetterGlf; Luther College; Home Economics.

CAMPBELL, Mark K; Aurora HS; Aurora, NE; Chr; Chrl; Chrs; HonRl; NHS; SchMus; Neb Esleyan U; Teacher.

CAMPBELL, Mart; Van Buren Community HS; Keosauqua, IA; 10/90 VPSrCls; HonRl; NHS; SchPpr; SecTrsSophCls; Bsbl; Bsktbl; IMSpt; AmLegAwd; Central College; Business.

CAMPBELL, Mary B; Oak Grove Lutheran HS; Stanton, ND; 1/50 Chr; ChrhWkr; HonRl; JrNHS; Mdrgl; NHS; OffAde; Orch; SchMus; BauchLmbAwd; Concordia Clg; Optometry.

CAMPBELL, Mary C; Mother Mc Auley HS; Chicago, IL; 41/474 Chrs; HonRl; NHS; Yrbk; St Marys College; Business.

CAMPBELL, Mary M; Bay City All Saints HS; Essexville, MI; VPFrshCls; ChrhWkr; HonRl; NHS; StuGov; RptrYrbk; 4-H; SpnCl; Chrldr; College; Medicine.

CAMPBELL, Michael D; Irving Crown HS; Carpentersville, IL; 42/355 HonRl; NHS; StuCncl; RptrYrbk; SptEdYrbk; CaptBsbl; LetterBsktbl; LetterFtbl; Michigan State Univ; Law Enforcement.

CAMPBELL, Milton R; Wisconsin Academy; Janesville, WI; Chr; HonRl; TchrAde; Bsbl; College; Major Study.

CAMPBELL, Myrna; Roosevelt HS; Minneapolis, MN; Band; ChrhWkr; CncrtBnd; HospAde; MrchBnd; OffAde; PepBnd; TchrAde; IMSpt; U Of Minn; Physician.

CAMPBELL, Nancy A; Mercy HS; Overland, MO; 2/200 HonRl; NHS; SchMus; SchPl; Sdlty; TchrAde; RptrYrbk; PpCl; LetterBsktbl; IMSpt; Univ.

CAMPBELL, Pamela A; Athens Community HS; Springfield, IL; 1/54 Band; ChrhWkr; CncrtBnd; HonRl; JrNHS; MrchBnd; RptrYrbk; RptrSchPpr; Bsktbl; GAA;.

CAMPBELL, Patrice; Mackenzie HS; Detroit, MI; HonRl; JrNHS; TchrAde; FTA; CitAwd; Wayne St Univ; Registered Nurse.

CAMPBELL, Paula K; Jennings HS; Clayton, KS; Chrs; HonRl; SchPl; TchrAde; 4-H; PpCl; LetterBsktbl; 4-HAwd; College; Business.

CAMPBELL, Peggy C; Valley Park HS; Valley Park, MO; SecFrshCls; HonRl; TreasNatlThespSoc; SchPl; FHA; PpCl; Beauty College; Professional.

CAMPBELL, Penny; Wellington HS; Milford, IL; TrsSophCls; NHS; StuCncl; SchPpr; 4-H; FHA; PpCl; College; Secretary.

CAMPBELL, Priscilla L; Calhoun HS; Kampsville, IL; SecFrshCls; VPSophCls; HonRl; NHS; StuCncl; Yrbk; LetterChrldr; 4-HAwd;.

CAMPBELL, Ralph W; Lake Crystal HS; Lake Crystal, MN; VPFrshCls; PresSophCls; PresJrCls; PresSrCls; Band; CncrtBnd; MrchBnd; Bsktbl; Ftbl; Trade School; Vocation.

CAMPBELL, Rebecca; Clear Creek HS; Oxford, IA; 3/65 NHS; NatlThespSoc; SchMus; SchPl; FrCl; BttyCrckrAwd; Univ Iowa; Special Education.

CAMPBELL, Robert C; Carmel HS; Carmel, IN; 38/550 Chrl; ChrhWkr; HonRl; NHS; NatlMeritSF; NatlThespSoc; SchMus; SchPl; StuGov; YthFlsp; IMSpt; Univ.

CAMPBELL, Robin E; Cass Tech HS; Detroit, MI; Band; Chr; CmntyWkr; CncrtBnd; HonRl; NatlMeritCmnd; Orch; ROTC; SchPl; TchrAde; Mit; Urban Planing.

CAMPBELL, Rose; Borden HS; Pekin, IN; 7/64 Band; DrmMjrt; HonRl; NHS; SchPl; StuCncl; EdYrBk; FHA; DanFAwd; PresAwd; In Univ Se; Interior Deco.

CAMPBELL, Scott O; Palestine HS; Robinson, IL; 7/47 VPFrshCls; VPSophCls; Band; HonRl; MrchBnd; SchMus; TchrAde; YthFlsp; Yrbk; 4-H; LatCl; CaptBsktbl; LetterTrk; CchngActv; Univ Of Illinois; Elec Engineer.

CAMPBELL, Scott W; Lawrence HS; Lawrence, KS; ALBoysSt; CmntyWkr; HonRl; NatlMeritCmnd; PolWkr; StuGov; TchrAde; SciCl; Ks Univ; Aquatic Biology.

CAMPBELL, Sheryl L; Marion HS; Marion, IA; 6/165 Chr; Chrs; ChrhWkr; HonRl; NHS; Quill&Scroll; TchrAde; SecYthFlsp; RptrYrbk; BttyCrckrAwd; Iowa State U; Home Ec.

CAMPBELL, Steven P; Roxana HS; East Alton, IL; 7/275 ChrhWkr; HonRl; VPNHS; NatlMeritCmnd; SchMus; GerCl; VPMthCl; Trk; South Ill U At Edwsvlle; Dentistry.

CAMPBELL, Stuart T; Barr Reeve HS; Montgomery, IN; PresSophCls; ALBoysSt; ChrhWkr; HonRl; SctActv; SpnCl; PpCl; LetterBsbl; IMSpt; AmLegAwd; Indiana State Univ; Accounting & Bus.

CAMPBELL, Susan; Cass Technical HS; Detrit, MI; AFS; Chr; HonRl; NHS; NatlMeritCmnd; OffAde; Orch; PolWkr; TchrAde; SpnCl; Univ; Environmental & Sociological.

CAMPBELL, Susan E; Houston HS; Bucyrys, MO; Band; ChrhWkr; CncrtBnd; HonRl; HospAde; MrchBnd; NHS; FBLA; College; Nurse.

CAMPBELL, Susan M; Clio HS; Clio, MI; ChrhWkr; HonRl; LbryAde; NHS; SpnCl; LetterBsbl; LetterBsktbl; GAA; PPFtbl; MasAwd; U Of Mi; Physician.

CAMPBELL, Susie; Lincoln HS; Beverly, KS; 1/60 TrsFrshCls; ALAGirlsSt; Band; Chrs; DrmMjrt; HonRl; NatlFornLg; PepBnd; TchrAde; College; Music.

CAMPBELL, Thomas D; Newburg Rii HS; Newburg, MO; 5/48 ChrhWkr; HonRl; NHS; PresStuCncl; Bsbl; Trk; MasAwd; CitAwd; Air Force; History.

CAMPBELL, Timothy E; St Thomas Academy; Minneapolis, MN; Band; LitMag; NatlFornLg; NatlMeritFnl; PolWkr; ROTC; SchMus; SchPl; Yrbk; College; Journalism.

CAMPBELL, Trudy D; Greenfield HS; Greenfield, MO; 1/36 PresSophCls; HonRl; StuCncl; 4-H; FHA; FTA; MthCl; College; Teaching.

CAMPBELL, William; Princeton R 5 HS; Cainsville, MO; 11/51 HonRl; NHS; StuCncl; RptrYrbk; SpnCl; Nemsu; Medical Technology.

CAMPION, Stephen R; Lincoln HS; Lake City, MN; 14/130 Chrs; CncrtBnd; HonRl; MrchBnd; NHS; PepBnd; SchMus; SchPl; LetterBsbl; LetterBsktbl; College.

CAMPISE, Karen A; Bishop Du Bourg HS; St Louis, MO; 29/478 HonRl; NHS; Orch; Trade Sch; Med Lab Tech.

CAMPISI, Alda; Thornwood Hs; Calumet City, IL; 43/852 HonRl; NatlFornLg; NHS; OffAde; StuCncl; PpCl;.

CAMPISI, Alda C; Thornwood HS; Calumet City, IL; HonRl; NatlFornLg; NHS; StuCncl; Thornton Com College; Accounting.

CAMPO, Michael J; St Agatha HS; Detroit, MI; VPSophCls; HonRl; StuCncl; LetterBsktbl; AmLegAwd; College; Professional.

CAMPO, Terry; Spfld Southeast Hs; Springfield, IL; OffAde; PolWkr; YthLg; Millikin University; Attorney.

CAMPOS, Monica; Pacelli HS; Austin, MN; Chr; Chrl; Chrs; HonRl; NatlCathMusEdAsoc; SchMus; SchPl; SpnCl; PpCl;.

CAMREN, Carla J; De Forest Area HS; De Forest, WI; VPFrshCls; ALAGirlsSt; Band; DrmMjrt; HonRl; PepBnd; Twrl; Swmmng; Chrldr;.

CANADA, Curtis V; Geneva Comm HS; Geneva, IL; 2/240 Aud/Vis; Band; HonRl; NHS; NatlMeritCmnd; TreasKeyCl; MthCl; Valparaiso Univ; Physics.

CANARD, Dwight; Oklee Hs; Trail, MN; 4/37 Chrs; HonRl; SchPl; StuCncl; Yrbk; Vocational School; Salesman.

CANARD, Dwight W; Oklee Public HS; Trail, MN; 4/36 Chrs; HonRl; SchPl; StuCncl; Yrbk; Voc School; Marketing.

CANARD, Marcia L; Bedford HS; Temperance, MI; 90/450 ChrhWkr; SchPl; StuCncl; YthFlsp; PpCl; College; Professional.

CANARY, Mary R; Washington Catholic HS; Washington, IN; 13/40 Chrs; HonRl; TchrAde; Icbt; Electronic Acc.

CANCHOLA, Carolina; Robert A Waller HS; Chicago, IL; 24/214 Band; SchMus; SchPl; RptrSchPpr; SchPpr; PpCl; LetterTennis; LetterTrk; CaptChrldr; GAA; CitAwd; College; English.

CANCIAMILLE, Andria M; Boylan Central Catholic HS; Rockford, IL; NatlMeritCmnd; Illinois State Univ; Business.

CANDELA, Kevin A; East Alton Wood River HS; Wood River, IL; 10/350 HonRl; JrNHS; LitMag; NHS; NatlMeritSF; RptrSchPpr; SchPpr; Univ; Aerospace Eng.

CANDELA, Kevin A; E Alton Wood River HS; Wood River, IL; HonRl; JrNHS; NHS; NatlMeritFnl; NatlMeritSF; RptrSchPpr; SchPpr; LatCl; Parks College; Aerospace Eng.

CANDIDO, Mary C; Bishop Dubourg HS; St Louis, MO; ChrhWkr; CmntyWkr; HonRl; StuCncl; LetterBsktbl; IMSpt; Washington Univ; Interior Design.

CANDLER, William J; South Knox HS; Vincennes, IN; 8/130 ChrhWkr; HonRl; NHS; Quill&Scroll; SchMus; YthFlsp; Yrbk; SchPpr; 4-H; SecFFA; MthCl; Wrstlng; CaptIMSpt; 4-HAwd; Harvard University; Lawyer.

CANDOS, Alan A; St Laurence HS; Chicago, IL; HonRl; StuGov; College; Professional.

CANE, Diane M; Drummond HS; Drummond, WI; Band; HonRl; MrchBnd; NHS; PepBnd; StuGov; GerCl; LetterBsktbl; LetterTrk; College.

CANFIELD, Jerry; Walker HS; Walker, MN; PresFrshCls; VPJrCls; Band; Chr; CncrtBnd; HonRl; ROTC; SctActv; College; Professional.

CANGELOSI, William M; New Trier East HS; Wilmette, IL; 160/837 Chr; HonRl; College; Veterinarian.

CANIFF, Chawn E; Wood Memorial HS; Oakland City, IN; 3/118 ALBoysSt; Aud/Vis; ChrhWkr; CmntyWkr; HonRl; IntrClCncl; SchAde; SctActv; TchrAde; YthFlsp; EdYrBk; SptEdSchPpr; MthCl; Bsktbl; Purdue Univ; Mechanical Eng.

CANKOVIC, Ann M; Morton West HS; Stickney, IL; HonRl; HospAde; JA; LitMag; OffAde; Morton Nursing School; Nurse.

CANNADY, Joene; Hutsonville HS; West York, IL; ChrhWkr; HonRl; StuCncl; Yrbk; SchPpr; 4-H; FHA; DanFAwd; 4-HAwd; JAAwd; Beautician.

CANNING, Helen; Lindbergh Sr HS; Mtkd, MN; PresSophCls; AFS; ChrhWkr; LitMag; OffAde; SpnCl; GAA; IMSpt; RotaryAwd; Medicine.

CANNINGHAM, Margaret; Atwater Public HS; Atwater, MN; Band; CncrtBnd; HonRl; MrchBnd; NHS; PepBnd; EdYrBk; Coll; Voc.

CANNON, Carlis M; Delta C N HS; Steele, MO; Chrs; ChrhWkr; MrchBnd; SchMus; StuCncl; FHA; PpCl;.

CANNON, Cathy A; Glendale HS; Springfield, MO; AFS; ChrhWkr; DrmBgl; HonRl; OffAde; YthFlsp; FTA; Univ; Teach.

CANNON, Faith A; Glenbrook South HS; Glenview, IL; 28/579 HonRl; JrNHS; LbryAde; NHS; OffAde; Quill&Scroll; TchrAde; SchPpr; SpnCl; Univ Of Ne Ill; Business Adm.

CANNON, Gail E; Mother Guerin HS; Chicago, IL; 23/409 HonRl; Northeastern University.

CANNON, Kay M; Mason City HS; Mason City, IA; Chr; HonRl; N Iowa Area Comm College; Merchandising.

CANNON, Kevin P; Creighton Prep HS; Omaha, NE; 6/218 ChrhWkr; HonRl; JrNHS; NHS; NatlMeritSF; Sdlty; MthCl; CaptBsktbl; IMSpt; University; Doctor.

CANNON, Mary E; Brooklyn Guernsey Malcom HS; Brooklyn, IA; TrsSophCls; ALAGirlsSt; HonRl; NHS; SctActv; StuCncl; EdYrBk; PpCl; Bsktbl; CitAwd; Iowa State U; Art.

CANNON, Philip J; Southfield Sr HS; Southfield, MI; NHS; LetterSwmmng; Central Michigan Univ; Liberal Arts.

CANNON, Terrence K; Glenbard East HS; Lombard, IL; Band; CAP; CncrtBnd; HonRl; NatlMeritCmnd; SchPl; FrCl; Swmmng; University; Profession.

CANNON, Valerie L; Andrean HS; Gary, IN; 100/300 Band; CncrtBnd; HonRl; JrNHS; MrchBnd; PepBnd; SchMus; LatCl; GAA; PPFtbl; St Mary Coll; Nuclear Medicine.

CANNON, Wendy K; Villa Grove HS; Camargo, IL; 1/75 Chrs; ChrhWkr; HonRl; MrchBnd; NHS; SchMus; Pres4-H; TreasFHA; GAA; 4-HAwd; Eastern Ill Univ; Family Services.

CANNOY, Jess A; Windsor HS; Gays, IL; ALBoysSt; HonRl; PresNHS; TreasFFA; VPSciCl; LetterTrk; Lakeland Jr Coll; Engineering.

CANNOY, Rhonda J; Windsor HS; Gays, IL; .

CANONACO, Adeline A; Notre Dame HS; Norridge, IL; 20/260 HonRl; NHS; StuCncl; StuGov; TchrAde; MthCl; PpCl; IMSpt; University.

CANTERBURY, Cynthia A; Athens HS; Cantrall, IL; Band; Chr; Chrs; ChrhWkr; HonRl; NHS; 4-H; FTA; GAA; 4-HAwd; Lincoln Clge; Musician.

CANTIN, Daniel M; Southwestern HS; Flint, MI; 36/570 Chr; Chrl; ChrhWkr;.

CANTRELL, Donald A; Carmi Comm HS; Carmi, IL; 1/139 ChrhWkr; CAP; DrlTm; HonRl; PresNHS; RedCrAde; TchrAde; FSA; PresMthCl; SciCl; Bsktbl; Univ Of Ill; Nuclear Engineer.

CANTRELL, Joyce; Plano HS; Plano, IL; HonRl; RptrSchPpr; SpnCl; College; Home Ec.

CANTRELL, Karen A; Holt HS; Dimondale, MI; 10/254 HonRl; TreasJA; NHS; TchrAde; KeyCl; SpnCl; PpCl; Trk; Northwood Inst; Bus Mgmt.

CANTRELL, Rita D; Flora HS; Xenia, IL; 3/138 Chrs; ChrhWkr; HonRl; SecNHS; Quill&Scroll; EdSchPpr; FBLA; FHA; FTA; SpnCl; GAA; DARAwd; Oakland City College; English Teacher.

CANTWELL, Kim R; Frederick Public HS; Barnard, SD; 4/30 VPSophCls; Chrs; HonRl; SchPl; StuCncl; StuGov; RptrYrbk; PpCl; Chrldr; BttyCrckrAwd; Sd State Univ; Nursing.

CANTWELL, Paul F; St Joseph HS; Kenosha, WI; 7/170 PresJrCls; ALBoysSt; Chrs; HonRl; NHS; SchMus; SchPl; StuCncl; StuGov; Bsktbl; Glf; LetterTrk; IMSpt; College.

CANTY, Elizabeth A; Thornwood HS; So Holland, IL; 3/852 CncrtBnd; HonRl; JrNHS; MrchBnd; NHS; TchrAde; SecGerCl; MthCl; DARAwd; Univ Of Ill; Chemical Engineer.

CANUTE, Christie P; United Community HS; Ames, IA; VPJrCls; VPSrCls; Chr; Chrl; SchMus; SchPl; StuCncl; StuGov; PpCl; CaptBsbl; LetterBsktbl; LetterTrk; Chrldr; Area College; Commercial & Advertising Arts.

CANUTE, Mark A; East Richland HS; Olney, IL; PresJA; LbryAde; StuCncl; SpnCl; SciCl; LetterGlf; Tennis; JAAwd; College; Accounting.

CAOUETTE, Susan M; Patrick Henry HS; Minneapolis, MN; Band; CncrtBnd; HonRl; MrchBnd; NHS; PepBnd; SctActv; StuGov; TchrAde; Teen; College; Home Ec.

CAP, Mary Ellen; Elizabeth Seton HS; Chicago, IL; 31/239 SecJrCls; HonRl; SecNHS; StuCncl; EdYrBk; RptrSchPpr; LatCl; MthCl; SciCl; St Marys; Medical Technology.

CAP, Thaddeus J; Bishop Noll Institute HS; Chicago, IL; 43/367 ChrhWkr; CmntyWkr; De Paul Univ; Lawyer.

CAPEHART, John S; Miller HS; La Russel, MO; HonRl; LbryAde; NHS; SecStuCncl; SchPpr; FTA; MthCl; VFWAwd; College.

CAPEHART, Susan L; Central HS; St Joseph, MO; 111/524 CncrtBnd; DrlTm; HonRl; MrchBnd; Orch; SchMus; FrCl; GAA; IMSpt; PPFtbl; Clge; Pro Musician.

CAPEK, Deborah E; Maine Twp HS; Niles, IL; 8/431 PresCncrtBnd; HonRl; MrchBnd; Orch; PepBnd; SchMus; TreasYthFnd; PpCl; Univ Of Ill; Chemist.

CAPEK, Debra L; Milligan HS; Milligan, NE; 2/10 PresJrCls; Band; Chrs; DrmMjrt; SchPl; RptrYrbk; 4-H; PpCl; LetterTrk; Chrldr; U Of Ne; Fashion Design.

CAPEK, Paul; Forest View HS; Des Plaines, IL; 30/650 HonRl; NHS; SctActv; GerCl; College; Medicine.

CAPEL, Kim D; Anna Jonesboro C HS; Anna, IL; 7/136 ALBoysSt; ChrhWkr; HonRl; ModUN; NHS; NatlMeritSchl; StuCncl; Yrbk; SptEdSchPpr; FTA; KeyCl; LatCl; LetterBsbl; Purdue Univ; Pharmacy.

CAPELLI, John A; St Josephs HS; Kenosha, WI; 31/158 Band; ChrhWkr; CncrtBnd; HonRl; HospAde; JrNHS; MrchBnd; PepBnd; KeyCl; Trk; CaptWrstlng; CchngActv; IMSpt; Marquette Univ; Medicine.

CAPERTON, Patricia A; Thornton Twn HS; Dolton, IL; CncrtBnd; HonRl; JrNHS; MrchBnd; NHS; College.

CAPERTON, Valentina M; Emil Hirsch HS; Chicago, IL; 2/294 HonRl; JrNHS; NHS; Univ; Busi Admin.

CAPITANI, Norman E; Mendota Twp HS; Mendota, IL; 3/201 Band; CncrtBnd; DrlTm; HonRl; MrchBnd; NHS; PepBnd; YthFlsp; SpnCl; Jr College; Accounting.

CAPITANI, Randy L; Putnam County HS; Granville, IL; ALBoysSt; Band; Chrs; CncrtBnd; DrmBgl; HonRl; MrchBnd; NHS; Orch; PepBnd; LetterBsktbl; LetterTrk; College; Professional.

CAPLAN, Mark A; Stephen T Mather HS; Chicago, IL; 43/442 Band; CncrtBnd; HonRl; MrchBnd; NHS; NatlMeritCmnd; Univ Of Ill; Medicine.

CAPLE, Cheryl K; Labette County HS; Altamont, KS; 8/150 HonRl; NHS; TchrAde; RptrSchPpr; FBLA; SpnCl; PpCl; SciCl; Labette Co Jr Clg; Teach Handicapped.

CAPLE, Jeffrey S; Lakeshore HS; Stevensville, MI; HonRl; RptrSchPpr; Bsbl; Western Michigan Univ;.

CAPLING, Patti; Trinity HS; Chicago, IL; 28/204 ChrhWkr; HonRl; NHS; SchMus; Univ; Engineering.

CAPODICE, Christina M; Central Catholic HS; Bloomington, IL; 7/87 Chrs; HonRl; OffAde; FrCl; PpCl; College; Business Admin.

CAPONI, Robert E; Proviso West HS; Hillside, IL; 103/1184 HonRl; NHS; LetterBsbl; LetterBsktbl; Ftbl; Ill Inst Of Tech; Engineering.

CAPOUCH, Kevin E; Central HS; Grafton, ND; PresFrshCls; ALBoysSt; Chrs; HonRl; NHS; SchPl; StuCncl; MthCl; SciCl; Bsbl; CaptFtbl; College; Professional.

CAPOZZOLI, Terry M; Prospect HS; Mt Prospect, IL; 33/610 Moser College; Legal Secretary.

CAPPELLO, Ronald A; Daniel J Gross HS; Omaha, NE; HonRl; Bsbl; College; Dentist.

CAPPER, Kristie S; Central Community HS; Dewitt, IA; 25#29#30 Chrs; ChrhWkr; CncrtBnd; HonRl; SchMus; Trk; PPFtbl; Univ; Theater.

CAPPETTA, Thomas J; St Ignatius College Prep; Chicago, IL; 35/200 HonRl; SchAde; TchrAde; IMSpt; De Paul Univ; Pharmacist.

CAPPOZZO, Glynis L; Rich Central HS; Park Forest, IL; 7/413 AFS; Chr; Chrl; HonRl; NHS; SctActv; FrCl; LetterTennis; Clge; Medicine.

CAPPS, Russell A; Pekin Comm HS; Packwood, IA; 8/46 ChrhWkr; HonRl; 4-H; FFA; Bsktbl; Trk;.

CAPRA, Gina C; Waukegan East HS; Waukegan, IL; Chrs; HonRl; NatlSciFnd; NatlThespSoc; Orch; SchMus; SchPl; TchrAde; University; Professional.

CAPRA, Mark; St Pius X HS; Kansas City, MO; Chr; Chrs; CmntyWkr; StuCncl; CchngActv; Univ Of Missouri; Business.

CAPRIO, Thomas G; Taft HS; Chicago, IL; ChrhWkr; CmntyWkr; DrlTm; HonRl; PolWkr; ROTC; SctActv; College; Professional.

CAPRON, Brenda L; Dunlap HS; Edwards, IL; DrlTm; HospAde; SchPl; 4-H; SpnCl; PpCl; LetterBsktbl; Chrldr; GAA; IMSpt; College.

CAPUTO, Valorie K; Mother Of Sorrows HS; Blue Island, IL; 3/115 HonRl; NHS; TchrAde; Yrbk; PpCl; College; History.

CARAGHER, Keith E; Christian Brothrs Col HS; Manchester, MO; TrsSophCls; JA; ROTC; LetterBsbl; LetterTreasJAAwd; Clge; Pro.

CARAKER, John C; Benton Consolidated HS; Benton, IL; 50/168 SecSrCls; HonRl; Quill&Scroll; SctActv; RptrSchPpr; KeyCl; PpCl; SciCl; LetterFtbl; GodCntryAwd; Bradley University; Electrical Engineer.

CARAWAY, Sherri L; Gallatin Rv HS; Gallatin, MO; 8/47 SecFrshCls; VPJrCls; HonRl; LbryAde; NHS; OffAde; Yrbk; FHA;.

CARBARY, Diane T; Sacred Heart HS; Dearborn, MI; Chrl; HonRl; SchPl; StuGov; Yrbk; Michigan State Univ; Animal Tech.

CARBAUGH, Malcolm L; Holdrege Sr HS; Holdrege, NE; HonRl; Ftbl; College.

CARBERRY, Susan; Benton Community HS; Benton Community, IA; 3/108 HonRl; StuCncl; RptrSchPpr; SpnCl; IMSpt; PPFtbl; 4-HAwd; Iowa State University; Unfeclared Math Or S.

CARBONARA, Lynn M; Salem Central HS; Antioch, IL; 45/200 HonRl; NHS; RedCrAde; SchAde; SchPl; TchrAde; Yrbk; FrCl; PpCl; GAA; Univ Wisc Milwaukee; Microbiology.

CARBONARA, Richard M; Loyola Academy; Chicago, IL; HonRl; JrNHS; LitMag; NHS; SchMus; RptrSchPpr; Trk; Loyola Univ Of Chicago; Dentist.

CARBONE, Angela M; Thornton Frac HS; Lansing, IL; Aud/Vis; HonRl; LbryAde; FrCl; Eastern Illinois Univ; Accounting.

CARD, Mary A; Adelphian Acad; Midland, MI; HstSophCls; Chr; HonRl; SchAde; StuCncl; StuGov; TchrAde; SchPpr; PpCl; Tennis; Andrews Univ.

CARD, Steven J; Arthur Hill HS; Saginaw, MI; HonRl; JCC; NHS; FDA; University Of Michigan; Dentist.

CARDA, Betty J; Armour HS; Armour, SD; 3/31 Chr; Chrs; ChrhWkr; HonRl; NHS; SchMus; SchPl; FHA; PpCl; Trk; Mount Mary College; Nursing.

CARDELLA, Mark A; Midland HS; Midland, MI; 60/433 HonRl; NHS; StuCncl; StuGov; GerCl; Univ Of Mi; Eng.

CARDER, Brenda L; Columbus Unified HS; Columbus, KS; DrmBgl; HonRl; OffAde; College; Special Ed.

CARDIFF, Patrick J; Badger HS; Lake Geneva, WI; 13/240 ALBoysSt; ChrhWkr; HonRl; NHS; SchPl; Bsktbl; LetterFtbl; LetterTrk; University Of Wisconsin; Veterinarian.

CARDINAL, Kent L; Jennings County HS; North Vernon, IN; 50/381 ChrhWkr; PepBnd; YthFlsp; Ftbl; Trk; Wrstlng; Ball State; Police Work.

CARDONA, Teresa M; East Leyden HS; Franklin Park, IL; 31/586 CmntyWkr; HonRl; LbryAde; NHS; Orch; SctActv; Twrl; College.

CARDONI, Debra K; Mt Pulaski HS; Mt Pulaski, IL; 1/105 ALAGirlsSt; Chrs; HonRl; LbryAde; NHS; SchMus; SpnCl; Tennis; GAA; IMSpt; College; Medical Technology.

CARDWELL, Cynthia A; St Augustine HS; Chicago, IL; 6/85 Chrs; ChrhWkr; HonRl; LbryAde; NHS; SchPl; SctActv; TreasStuCncl; Yrbk; RptrSchPpr; College; Professional.

CARDWELL, Mary L; Woodlands Acad/sacred Heart; Winnetka, IL; 7/75 ChrhWkr; CmntyWkr; HospAde; LitMag; PolWkr; SchPl; Sdlty; RptrYrbk; CivCl; Williams College; Business.

CARENDER, Nancy; Southside HS; Muncie, IN; 6/369 Band; HonRl; LbryAde; NHS; OffAde; Orch; FHA; OptClAwd; Ball State Univ; Home Economics.

CAREW, Kelly J; West HS; Green Bay, WI; 4/407 HonRl; NHS; SctActv; StuCncl; SchPpr; MthCl; LetterWrstlng; IMSpt; College; Electrical Engineering.

CAREW, Mary L; Little Wolf HS; New London, WI; 3/79 SecSophCls; Band; HonRl; MrchBnd; NatlFornLg; NHS; SchPl; RptrYrbk; Chrldr; GAA; University; Elementary Education.

CAREY, Catherine E; Glenbrook North HS; Northbarook, IL; 8/655 HonRl; NHS; NatlMeritSF; GAA; Vanderbilt Univ; Teacher.

CAREY, Catherine E; Glenbrook North HS; Northbrook, IL; 6/607 NHS; NatlMeritFnl; NatlMeritSF; College; Special Education.

CAREY, Catherine; Mother Of Sorrows HS; Chicago, IL; 17/143 VPSrCls; Chrs; HonRl; HospAde; JrNHS; StuCncl; RptrSchPpr; FBLA; GAA; AmLegAwd; Business School; Professional.

CAREY, Dayna J; Boyceville HS; Boyceville, WI; VPSrCls; Band; ChrhWkr; CncrtBnd; HonRl; MrchBnd; NHS; SpnCl; SciCl; College; Nursing.

CAREY, Joseph K; New Trier West HS; Northfield, IL; 90/698 ChrhWkr; HonRl; RptrYrbk; RptrSchPpr; LetterBsktbl; LetterGlf; CchngActv; Univ Of Notre Dame; Journalism.

CAREY, Michelle M; Mt Pleasant HS; Mt Pleasant, MI; 41/348 Band; CncrtBnd; HonRl; LbryAde; MrchBnd; NHS; NatlMeritCmnd; RptrSchPpr; 4-H; 4-HAwd; Mi State Clg; Computer Science.

CAREY, Patricia A; Mt Carmel HS; Mt Carmel, IL; 5/183 NHS; GAA; KiwanAwd; PresAwd;.

CAREY, Rebecca S; West Liberty HS; West Liberty, IA; 3/92 Chrs; CncrtBnd; HonRl; NHS; FHA; Iowa State Univ; Music.

CAREY, Ronald W; Fredericksburg Comm HS; Fredericksburg, IA; 2/38 VPSophCls; ChrhWkr; HonRl; PolWkr; StuCncl; Bsbl; Bsktbl; Ftbl; Bethel College; Political Science.

CAREY, Roy O; Carl Sandburg HS; Palos Park, IL; 50/700 HonRl; MthCl; LetterTrk; IMSpt; College; Math.

CAREY, Sharon L; O Gorman HS; Sioux Falls, SD; DrlTm; NHS; Univ Of Nebraska; Speech Pathology.

CARINGER, Douglas O; Litchfield Sr HS; Litchfield, IL; 10/150 HonRl; JrNHS; NHS; Quill&Scroll; SchMus; SchPl; KeyCl; FrCl; SpnCl; MthCl; Bsbl; Bsktbl; Univ Of Illinois; Chemical Engineer.

CARIVEAU, Thomas; Central HS; Grand Forks, ND; 5/300 HonRl; NHS; StuCncl; SciCl; Bsktbl; Ftbl; Tennis; Trk; EldAwd; Nd Univ; Medicine.

CARL, Beth; William G Mather HS; Munising, MI; SecFrshCls; SecSophCls; Band; CncrtBnd; NatlMeritSF; PepBnd; StuCncl; RptrYrbk; SchPpr; PpCl; College; Biological Science Major.

CARL, Diane; Gull Lake HS; Kalamazoo, MI; ALAGirlsSt; HonRl; PolWkr; YthFlsp; Yrbk; 4-H; SciCl; Bsktbl; GAA; PPFtbl; Univ; Vet.

CARL, Jean; Waconda East HS; Cawder City, KS; 1/25 Band; Chrs; HonRl; MrchBnd; PepBnd; PpCl; Chrldr; CitAwd; Ncka Vocational School; Business.

CARL, Randy R; St Johns Military Academy; Manawa, WI; 11/37 SecJrCls; SecSrCls; Quill&Scroll; ROTC; SptEdSchPpr; SpnCl; Bsktbl; Socr; College; Business Admin.

CARLAW, Clinton L; Shell Lake HS; Shell Lake, WI; 19/55 TrsSrCls; Aud/Vis; HonRl; NatlFornLg; SctActv; StuGov; TchrAde; YthFlsp; FHA; Bsbl; LetterFtbl; Swmmng; Trk; Wrstlng; College; Conservation.

CARLBLOM, Carol R; Lisbon HS; Milnor, ND; 16/75 VPJrCls; HonRl; HospAde; TchrAde; 4-H; FHA; PpCl; St Lukes Hosp Sch; Nursing.

CARLE, Michelle M; St Marys Academy; Monroe, MI; Chrl; NHS; SchMus; RptrYrbk; LatCl; St Vincents Hospital; Radiological Tech.

CARLE, Wendy C; Donald E Gavit HS; Hammond, IN; Chr; NatlFornLg; NHS; Quill&Scroll; StuCncl; Yrbk; RptrSchPpr; FrCl; LetterBsktbl; LetterTrk; College; Biochemical Research.

CARLETTA, Daniel A; Hill Murray HS; St Paul, MN; HonRl; NHS; RptrSchPpr; College Of St Thomas; Engineer.

CARLILE, Randy S; Cheney HS; Chengy, KS; 28/40 Chr; SchPl; TchrAde; YthFlsp; Yrbk; SchPpr; FFA; SpnCl; Bsktbl; Trk; Univ Of Wichita State; Graphic Design.

CARLIN, Joan M; Mitchell Sr HS; Mitchell, SD; Chr; CmntyWkr; HonRl; SchPl; SctActv; College; Cpa.

CARLIN, Kenneth E; Whitko HS; Warsaw, IN; 27/153 LetterFtbl; LetterTrk; LetterWrstlng; Iu Purue Extension; Farming.

CARLIN, Mary M; Spalding Acad; Spalding, NE; Chr; Chrs; SchAde; SchPl; StuGov; Yrbk; 4-H; SpnCl; MthCl; LetterTrk; St Marys Coll; Med Lab Tech.

CARLIN, Robin H; Mc Donald County HS; Anderson, MO; HstFrshCls; DrlTm; HonRl; PepBnd; RptrSchPpr; SchPpr; 4-H; FHA; FTA; Chrldr; Col; Social Worker.

CARLIN, Sharon R; Corunna HS; Corunna, MI; 1/250 ALAGirlsSt; Band; ChrhWkr; CmntyWkr; HonRl; MrchBnd; NHS; 4-H; 4-HAwd; PresAwd; College.

CARLIN, William L; Spalding Academy; Spalding, NE; PresSophCls; ALBoysSt; Chr; Chrs; ChrhWkr; CmntyWkr; HonRl; LbryAde; NHS; CaptBsbl; CaptBsktbl; CaptFtbl; CaptTrk; Univ Of Nebraska; Medicine.

CARLISLE, Kimberly A; Douglas Mac Arthur HS; Saginaw, MI; 8/270 HonRl; JrNHS; NHS; FrCl; TreasLatCl; Delta College; Medicine.

CARLOCK, Shirley A; Chandlerville HS; Chandlerville, IL; TrsSophCls; Band; Chrs; CncrtBnd; HonRl; MrchBnd; NHS; FHA; PpCl; CaptChrldr; College; Social Work.

CARLOCK, Steve; Nokomis HS; Fillmore, IL; Chrs; ChrhWkr; HonRl; SchMus; Eastern Illinois Univ; Business Management.

CARLOCK, Susan E; Gardner South Wilmington HS; Braceville, IL; ChrhWkr; HonRl; HospAde; LbryAde; NatlMeritCmnd; SchAde; YthFlsp; RptrYrbk; RptrSchPpr; 4-H; SpnCl; Chrldr; GAA; Univ Of Ill; Doctor.

CARLON, Roger L; Prairie Comm HS; Gowrie, IA; 6/78 ALBoysSt; Chrs; ChrhWkr; CncrtBnd; HonRl; NHS; FFA; LetterBsktbl; Iowa State Univ; Ag Business.

CARLS, Kathleen A; Triopia HS; Arenzville, IL; 11/51 Band; Chr; HonRl; SchMus; SchPl; YthFlsp; Yrbk; 4-H; PpCl; Trk; Univ Of Il.

CARLS, Philip W; Sheffield Chapin HS; Sheffield, IA; 1/46 TrsSrCls; Band; Chrs; LitMag; NatlMeritSchl; Orch; SchPl; PresSciCl; CaptBsktbl; LetterTrk; Wartburg College;.

CARLS, Steve A; Triopia Jr Sr HS; Arenzville, IL; 6/50 ChrhWkr; HonRl; SchPl; StuCncl; VP4-H; LetterBsktbl; LetterFtbl; AmLegAwd; DanFAwd; 4-HAwd; U Of Il; Agriculture.

CARLSEN, Mary; Stillwater HS; Stillwater, MN; 16/606 Band; Chr; ChrhWkr; CmntyWkr; CncrtBnd; HonRl; NHS; NatlMeritCmnd; SchMus; StuCncl; College; Social Work.

CARLSON, Alan R; Forest Lake Sr HS; Forest Lake, MN; 1/416 ChrhWkr; HonRl; Pres4-H; FFA; Bsbl; 4-HAwd; Univ Of Minnesota; Sociology.

CARLSON, Barbara; Riverdale HS; Port Byron, IL; 10/107 Band; CncrtBnd; DrmMjrt; HonRl; MrchBnd; PepBnd; SchMus; ChmbCommrsAwd; Augustana College; Music Ed.

CARLSON, Barbara; Wm G Mather HS; Munising, MI; Band; Chr; CmntyWkr; CncrtBnd; HonRl; MrchBnd; 4-H; FHA; Bsktbl; GAA; College; Art.

CARLSON, Barbara L; Moline Sr HS; Moline, IL; 16/845 Band; ChrhWkr; HonRl; MrchBnd; NHS; Orch; PepBnd; RptrYrbk; Blackhawk College.

CARLSON, Barry L; Madison HS; Madison, MN; Band; Chr; HonRl; NHS; SchPl; StuCncl; YthFlsp; Bsktbl; CaptTennis; AmLegAwd; St Olaf College; Social Science.

CARLSON, Bill E; Willman Sr HS; Willman, MN; SecFrshCls; ChrhWkr; SctActv; StuCncl; TchrAde; RptrSchPpr; KeyCl; Bsbl; Bsktbl; Ftbl; Trk; CchngActv; College.

CARLSON, Bonnie E; Batavia Sr HS; Batavia, IL; VPSophCls; VPJrCls; VPSrCls; HonRl; NHS; TchrAde; 4-H; Bsktbl; Trk; GAA; IMSpt; Purdue University.

CARLSON, Carol J; Spencer HS; Spencer, WI; Chrs; HonRl; NatlFornLg; 4-H; PpCl; Home Study Course; Art Studies.

CARLSON, Carolyn J; Palatine HS; Palatine, IL; 4/450 Band; SecChr; Chrl; Chrs; ChrhWkr; HonRl; HospAde; Mdrgl; PresNHS; NatlThespSoc; SchMus; University Of Illinois; Chemical Engineer.

CARLSON, Cheryl; Wisconsin Acad; Green Bay, WI; ChrhWkr; CmntyWkr; NHS; PolWkr; FFA; FHA; FSA; PresAwd; CitAwd; VoiceDemAwd; College; Journalism.

CARLSON, Christina L; J D Darnall Sr HS; Geneseo, IL; HonRl; NatlFornLg; NHS; NatlThespSoc; SchMus; Illinois State Univ; Theatre.

CARLSON, Christopher D; Heritage Christian HS; Carmel, IN; VPFrshCls; Band; ChrhWkr; CncrtBnd; HonRl; YthFlsp; LetterBsktbl; LetterSocr; LetterTrk; Indiana University; Medicine.

CARLSON, Cindy D; Central Webster HS; Gowrie, IA; 5/43 Band; Chrs; HonRl; SchMus; SchPl; StuCncl; RptrYrbk; RptrSchPpr; 4-H; Chrldr; Iowa State Univ.

CARLSON, Cindy M; Deer River HS; Spring Lake, MN; 4/83 HonRl; NHS; OffAde; RptrYrbk; RptrSchPpr; 4-H; FHA; Bemidji St College; Lab Technician.

CARLSON, Collette M; Bowdie HS; Bowdie, SD; Band; ChrhWkr; HonRl; SchPl; StuCncl; RptrSchPpr; Bsbl; LetterBsktbl; LetterTrk; GAA; IMSpt; 4-HAwd; CitAwd; Sd State Univ; Nursing.

CARLSON, Connie E; Pecatonica Area HS; Hollandale, WI; ChrhWkr; HonRl; SchAde; TchrAde; YthFlsp; RptrYrbk; College; Nurse.

CARLSON, Crystal K; Higbee HS; Higbee, MO; 1/24 Chrs; ChrhWkr; HonRl; NatlMeritCmnd; SchPl; Yrbk; FHA; Bsktbl; BttyCrckrAwd; DARAwd; 4-HAwd; Ne Missouri St Univ; Foreign Service.

CARLSON, Daniel; Ishpeming HS; Ishpeming, MI; 50/199 HonRl; Glf; Michigan Tech Univ; Mechanical Engineer.

CARLSON, Darla G; Harvard Comm HS; Harvard, IL; TreasAFS; Chr; Chrs; ChrhWkr; Mdrgl; SchMus; YthFlsp; 4-H; FrCl; CaptChrldr; Coll At Greenville; Spec Ed.

CARLSON, David; Tinley Park Hs; Tinley Park, IL; CmntyWkr; HonRl; NHS; SchPpr; LatCl; MthCl; LetterTennis; Loyola U; Medicine.

CARLSON, David B; Minot HS; Minot, ND; HonRl; LitMag; ModUN; NatlFornLg; NatlMeritSF; PolWkr; StuGov; RptrSchPpr; GerCl; SciCl; IMSpt; AmLegAwd; Univ; Doctor.

CARLSON, David W; Shawnee Mission West HS; Overland Park, KS; 138/640 AFS; HonRl; HospAde; NHS; ROTC; SctActv; LetterSwmmng; Trk; GodCntryAwd; Military Academy; Chemical Engineer.

CARLSON, Debbie M; Faulkton HS; Seneca, SD; HonRl; LbryAde; FHA; PpCl; Nursing School; Lpn.

CARLSON, Deborah K; Central Comm HS; Argyle, IA; Band; Chr; Chrs; ChrhWkr; CncrtBnd; HonRl; MrchBnd; PepBnd; SchPl; SpnCl; College; Nursing.

CARLSON, Debra J; Prairie Comm HS; Fort Dodge, IA; Band; ChrhWkr; CncrtBnd; HonRl; MrchBnd; Yrbk; 4-H; FHA; Chrldr; 4-HAwd; Ia Central Cm Col; Home Ec.

CARLSON, Debra K; Moose Lake HS; Mooselake, MN; SecSophCls; ALAGirlsSt; Band; Chr; CncrtBnd; HonRl; HospAde; NHS; PepBnd; SchMus; Bemidji State Univ; Music.

CARLSON, Debra L; Hiawatha HS; Kirkland, IL; Band; Chrs; ChrhWkr; HonRl; Mdrgl; MrchBnd; NHS; NatlThespSoc; PepBnd; SchMus; SchPl; StuCncl; TchrAde; RptrSchPpr; Simmons College; Communications.

CARLSON, Diane; Clayton HS; Clayton, WI; VPSophCls; SchPl; 4-H; PpCl; GAA; IMSpt; 4-HAwd; Us Wac.

CARLSON, Dianne M; Mitchell Sr HS; Mitchell, SD; 15/288 Band; DrlTm; HonRl; HospAde; JrNHS; NHS; FrCl; PpCl; Univ Of So Dakota.

CARLSON, Donald L; Guilford HS; Rockford, IL; 78/656 Band; ChrhWkr; HonRl; Bsktbl; Wheaton College.

CARLSON, Donna L; Sherrard HS; Sherrard, IL; 5/95 Band; HonRl; NHS; SchMus; PresSctActv; Yrbk; FHA; PresFTA; CaptChrldr; BttyCrckrAwd; Ill State Univ; Special Education.

CARLSON, Eileen C; Jefferson HS; Rockford, IL; Chr; HonRl; NHS; College; Education.

CARLSON, Elaine M; Decatur Jr/sr HS; Dowagiac, MI; 8/74 ChrhWkr; HonRl; NHS; SchPl; TchrAde; RptrYrbk; RptrSchPpr; FrCl; PresPpCl; Southwestern Mi Coll; Psychology.

CARLSON, Eric A; Parker Sr HS; Janesville, WI; 207/517 Ftbl; IMSpt; Trade; Vocation.

CARLSON, Gail D; Hancock Central HS; Hancock, MI; 26/90 ALAGirlsSt; HonRl; SchPl; CaptStuCncl; VPTeen; 4-H; FTA; PpCl; Chrldr; 4-HAwd; Gogebic Com Col; Cosmetology.

CARLSON, Gerald J; Waynesville HS; Ft Leonardwood, MO; HonRl; SctActv; Swmmng; Wrstlng; College;.

CARLSON, Grant E; Laurens Comm HS; Laurens, IA; 10/57 PresJrCls; Band; Chr; Chrs; ChrhWkr; CmntyWkr; CncrtBnd; HonRl; NHS; PepBnd; CaptFtbl; Swmmng; Trk; LetterWrstlng; William Penn College.

CARLSON, Greg A; North Bend Central HS; North Bend, NE; 21/68 Chr; Chrs; HonRl; SchMus; SchPl; Yrbk; SchPpr; FTA; LetterBsktbl; LetterFtbl; Electronics School.

CARLSON, Helen; Potter HS; Potter, NE; TrsFrshCls; ALAGirlsSt; Chrs; HonRl; NHS; SchPl; RptrYrbk; RptrSchPpr; SchPpr; Chrldr; Western Ne Tech College; Secretary.

CARLSON, James C; Homewood Flossmoor HS; Homewood, IL; 72/910 Chrs; HonRl; JA; NatlMeritCmnd; YthFlsp; Rose Hulman Inst Of Tech; Chemical Engineer.

CARLSON, Jay W; Lincoln HS; Lake City, MN; Chrs; HonRl; NHS; SchMus; SctActv; StuCncl; StuGov; RptrSchPpr; LetterFtbl; LetterWrstlng; Navel Acd; Professional.

CARLSON, Jeanie M; Rock County HS; Bassett, NE; Band; HonRl; PepBnd; SchMus; StuCncl; YthFlsp; FHA; Swmmng; Trk; Chrldr; Univ Of Neb; Medical.

CARLSON, Jill A; Cassville HS; Shell Knob, MO; Chr; Chrs; OffAde; SchPl; StuCncl; StuGov; TchrAde; MthCl; PpCl; GAA; College; Professional.

CARLSON, Joy; Cornell HS; Cornell, WI; Band; Chrs; HonRl; Mdrgl; SchPl; EdYrBk; Chrldr; AmLegAwd; Univ; Physical Ed Teacher.

CARLSON, Judy A; North Bend Central HS; North Bend, NE; ChrhWkr; CmntyWkr; SchPl; SctActv; RptrSchPpr; FBLA; FFA; PpCl; Bsktbl; Trk; College.

CARLSON, Karlene A; Grand Haven Sr HS; West Olive, MI; HonRl; NHS; RptrYrbk; RptrSchPpr; 4-H; Trk; 4-HAwd; College; Teacher.

CARLSON, Karlene L; Bancroft Public HS; Bancroft, NE; 9/32 Band; Chr; Chrl; Chrs; CncrtBnd; HonRl; MrchBnd; NHS; PepBnd; PpCl; Northeast Ne Tech Coll; Secretary.

CARLSON, Kathryn L; Greenway HS; Coleraine, MN; Band; HonRl; HospAde; MrchBnd; SchPl; TchrAde; EdYrBk; FrCl; PpCl; Bsktbl; Trk; College.

CARLSON, Kenneth F; Roosevelt HS; Minneapolis, MN; 19/638 TrsSrCls; AFS; HonRl; LitMag; SchPl; TchrAde; EdYrBk; Trk; PresAwd; Ma Inst Of Tech; Physics.

CARLSON, Kent; Twin Valley HS; Twin Valley, MN; 7/32 Aud/Vis; HonRl; NHS; SchPl; StuCncl; SptEdYrbk; Moorhead St College, Engrn.

CARLSON, Kevin W; Taylors Falls HS; Shafer, MN; Band; Chr; HonRl; MrchBnd; PepBnd; SchPl; SciCl; LetterBsbl; LetterBsktbl; LetterFtbl; College; Vocation.

CARLSON, Lance H; Elk Grove HS; Elk Grove Vlg, IL; CncrtBnd; HonRl; HospAde; MrchBnd; NHS; PepBnd; SctActv; Glf;.

CARLSON, Larry E; L & M Community HS; Fruitland, IA; 9/51 HonRl; IMSpt; Muscatine Clg.

CARLSON, Laurel A; Lyons Township HS; La Grange, IL; Chr; ChrhWkr; HonRl; NHS; NatlMeritCmnd; OffAde; SchPl; YthFlsp; College; Spanish Interpreter.

CARLSON, Lewis A; St Edward Public HS; St Edward, NE; 4/29 SecSophCls; PresSrCls; HonRl; SchPl; StuCncl; FFA; Bsbl; Ftbl; Trk; Clge; Vocation.

CARLSON, Linda G; Stewart Public HS; Stewart, MN; 8/37 ALAGirlsSt; Band; ChrhWkr; HonRl; SchPl; SchPpr; FHA; CaptBsktbl; Chrldr; GAA; Univ Of Minn; Veterinarian.

CARLSON, Lori A; Central Community HS; Camanche, IA; AFS; HonRl; HospAde; 4-H; FrCl; SpnCl; PpCl; SciCl; Bsbl; Trk; Clinton Community Clg; Nursing Rn.

CARLSON, Lyle F; Benson HS; Omaha, NE; 13/485 Band; TreasChrhWkr; TreasCncrtBnd; HonRl; MrchBnd; NHS; PepBnd; SpnCl; Iowa St Univ; Engineer.

CARLSON, Lynee J; Grayslake Comm HS; Grayslake, IL; 25/243 CncrtBnd; HonRl; MrchBnd; NHS; NatlMeritCmnd; PepBnd; RptrYrbk; PpCl; Chrldr; Carthage College; Physical Education.

CARLSON, Lynette J; South Clay HS; Dickens, IA; 8/29 SecFrshCls; SecJrCls; Chr; HonRl; SchPl; StuCncl; RptrYrbk; 4-H; PpCl; CaptChrldr; Univ Of South Dakota; Professional.

CARLSON, Lynnette M; Madrid Community HS; Madrid, IA; VPJrCls; VPSrCls; Chrs; ChrhWkr; NatlCathMusEdAsoc; NHS; LetterChrldr; Dana College; Chemistry.

CARLSON, Lynnette R; New Berlin HS; New Berlin, IL; 1/63 ALAGirlsSt; Chr; ChrhWkr; CncrtBnd; HonRl; NHS; NatlMeritCmnd; SchMus; PresStuCncl; YthFlsp; GAA; Ill Wesleyan Univ; Minister.

CARLSON, Marie P; Mt Assisi Academy; Chicago, IL; 4/198 HonRl; HospAde; LitMag; St Mary Of Nazareth; Nursing.

CARLSON, Marie P; Mount Assisi Academy; Chicago, IL; 2/199 HonRl; LitMag; 4-H; St Mary Of Nazareth Univ; Nursing.

CARLSON, Matthew C; Homewood Flossmoor HS; Homewood, IL; Aud/Vis; HonRl; LbryAde; NatlFornLg; Quill&Scroll; SchPpr; IMSpt; Marquette Univ; Communications.

CARLSON, Pamela J; South Hamilton HS; Stanhope, IA; Band; Chr; Chrs; ChrhWkr; CncrtBnd; HonRl; Mdrgl; MrchBnd; NHS; PepBnd; LetterBsktbl; CaptTrk; Waldorf College; Elementary Educ.

CARLSON, Pamela S; Wyanet HS; Wyanet, IL; 3/29 Band; ChrhWkr; CncrtBnd; HonRl; LbryAde; NHS; NatlFornLg; SpnCl; Chrldr; AmLegAwd; Bible Coll.

CARLSON, Patricia A; Spencer HS; Marshfield, WI; 2/59 ALAGirlsSt; Band; Chrs; HonRl; Mdrgl; LetterTrk; CaptChrldr; EldAwd; LionAwd; PresAwd; Uw Lacrosse; Phy Ed.

CARLSON, Patrick R; Beloit Memorial HS; Beloit, WI; HonRl; NHS; SchPl; Univ Or Wis River Falls; Physics Major.

CARLSON, Paula D; Kirksville Sr HS; Kirksville, MO; Chrs; ChrhWkr; HonRl; LbryAde; TchrAde; RptrYrbk; FHA; FrCl; PpCl; College.

CARLSON, Randall K; Salina HS; Salina, KS; 68/313 Aud/Vis; ChrhWkr; HonRl; LbryAde; Bethany College; Chemistry.

CARLSON, Randy E; Belle Plaine HS; Belle Plaine, MN; 12/96 PresSophCls; ChrhWkr; CmntyWkr; HonRl; StuCncl; TchrAde; LetterBsbl; LetterBsktbl; LetterFtbl; CchngActv; College; Math.

CARLSON, Randy S; L L Wright HS; Ironwood, MI; 32/201 HonRl; NHS; NatlThespSoc; Michigan Tech Univ; Civil Engineer.

CARLSON, Rebecca S; Cardinal Stritch HS; Keokuk, IA; 11/33 LbryAde; SchAde; SctActv; TchrAde; LetterBsbl;.

CARLSON, Richard A; Caledonia HS; Caledonia, MN; HonRl; Ftbl; Trk; College; Professnl.

CARLSON, Richard R; John Marshall HS; Indianapolis, IN; 9/444 Band; VPNHS; NatlMeritCmnd; StuCncl; GerCl; BauchLmbAwd; Butler Univ; Mathematics.

CARLSON, Rick G; Chisago Lakes HS; Lindstrom, MN; Band; Chr; CncrtBnd; HonRl; MrchBnd; Orch; PepBnd; SchMus; LetterGlf; CchngActv; College; Business Administration.

CARLSON, Rick J; Pecatonica Area HS; Hollandale, WI; Band; ChrhWkr; OffAde; SchPl; YthFlsp; EdYrBk; FFA; LetterBsktbl; Trk; Sw Voc Tech School; Agriculture.

CARLSON, Rick J; Pecatonica HS; Hollandale, WI; Band; PepBnd; YthFlsp; Yrbk; FFA; LetterBsktbl; Trk; College; Vocation.

CARLSON, Rojean M; St Augustine HS; Chicago, IL; PresFrshCls; HonRl; JrNHS; SchPl; SctActv; Maccormac Jc; Paralegal Assistant.

CARLSON, Sandra K; Garrison HS; Ryder, ND; TrsJrCls; Band; ChrhWkr; CncrtBnd; HonRl; MrchBnd; PepBnd; SchMus; RptrSchPpr; SchPpr; GAA; DanFAwd; College; Business Mgmt.

CARLSON, Shane A; Republic Michigan HS; Republic, MI; HonRl; NatlMeritSchl; SctActv; StuCncl; Teen; YthFlsp; EngCl; Bsbl; LetterBsktbl; LetterTrk; Msu; Law.

CARLSRON, Sharon; Highland Hs; Highland, IN; 4/573 Chr; ChrhWkr; CncrtBnd; MrchBnd; SchMus; YthFlsp; Pres4-H; GerCl; 4-HAwd; College; Mathematics Teacher.

CARLSON, Steven M; Abingdon HS; Abingdon, IL; 3/100 Band; ChrhWkr; HonRl; NHS; PepBnd; LatCl; LetterFtbl; LetterGlf; Chrldr; CaptIMSpt; Knox College; Lawyer.

CARLSON, Susie L; North Platte HS; North Platte, NE; ChrhWkr; HonRl; RedCrAde; TchrAde; YthFlsp; PpCl; GAA; PPFtbl; Jr Coll; Medical Field.

CARLSON, Thomas; Constantine HS; Constantine, MI; StuCncl; Univ Of Mi;.

CARLSON, Tim P; Forest Lake H S; Forest Lake, MN; Band; CncrtBnd; HonRl; MrchBnd; PepBnd; Col; Cpa.

CARLSON, Wade A; Rock HS; Rock, MI; 1/30 PresSophCls; TrsJrCls; ALBoysSt; Band; ChrhWkr; PepBnd; SchPl; EdYrBk; RptrSchPpr; College; Business.

CARLSON, Wanda L; Forest Park HS; Crystal Falls, MI; Chrs; HonRl; Lake Superior State College; Secretary.

CARLSRUD, Victoria B; Rothsay HS; Rothsay, MN; SecSrCls; HonRl; SchMus; StuCncl; PpCl; LetterBsktbl; GAA; Fergus Falls Comm Clge; Nursing.

CARLSTROM, Jane E; Grantsburg Integrated HS; Grantsburg, WI; 2/69 SecSophCls; ALAGirlsSt; Band; CncrtBnd; HonRl; MrchBnd; PepBnd; RptrYrbk; FHA; LetterTrk; Chrldr; GAA; DARAwd; College; Fashion Merch.

CARLTON, Douglas W; Taylorville HS; Taylorville, IL; Band; HonRl; YthFlsp; KeyCl; Bsktbl; LetterFtbl; LetterTrk; Univ Of Illinois.

CARLTON, Julie M; Astoria HS; Astoria, IL; LetterBand; Chrs; HospAde; SchAde; YthFlsp; SpnCl; PpCl; SciCl; LetterTrk; GAA; Col; Professional.

CARLTON, Linda; Junction City Sr HS; Ft Riley, KS; 60/305 Band; ChrhWkr; DrlTm; HonRl; StuCncl; RptrYrbk; GerCl; GAA; IMSpt; Kansas State Univ; Forestry.

CARLTON, Ronald R; Chesaning Union HS; Oakley, MI; Chr; HonRl; TchrAde; EdSchPpr; FrCl; Mich State U; Medicine.

CARLUE, Andrea L; Southport HS; Indianapolis, IN; 8/500 ChrhWkr; HonRl; NHS; OffAde; StuCncl; StuGov; FrCl; Hanover College; Law.

CARLYLE, Joyce; Mona Shores HS; Muskegon, MI; Band; HonRl; MrchBnd; SchPl; SctActv; PpCl; SciCl; Swmmng; Tennis; GAA; College; Physical Educ.

CARMAN, Cindy K; North Platte HS; North Platte, NE; 1/393 ALAGirlsSt; DrlTm; HonRl; NatlMeritSF; Quill&Scroll; SchPl; TreasStuCncl; TreasYthFlsp; EdSchPpr; PpCl; LetterTrk; VPGAA; IMSpt; College; Journalism.

CARMAN, Cynthia L; Pleasanton HS; Amherst, NE; Band; Chr; ChrhWkr; CncrtBnd; HonRl; MrchBnd; SchPl; YthFlsp; SchPpr; LetterBsktbl; College; Nursing.

CARMAN, Dennis E; Crestwood HS; Lime Springs, IA; ChrhWkr; HstFrshCls; HonRl; 4-H; FFA; Ftbl; Wrstlng; IMSpt; Waldort Coll; Agra Business.

CARMAN, Elizabeth A; Lake Forest HS; Lake Forest, IL; 81/435 HonRl; NHS; TchrAde; RptrSchPpr; CchngActv; PresGAA; Illinois State University; Accounting.

CARMAN, Micky R; Rosiclare HS; Rosiclare, IL; 7/31 Chr; ChrhWkr; CmntyWkr; SchPl; RptrYrbk; SchPpr; SpnCl; Millikin U; Business.

CARMAN, Peggy A; Rock Island HS; Rock Island, IL; CmntyWkr; LitMag; FHA; BttyCrckrAwd; Scott Co ;lab Tech.

CARMAN, Philip A; Mason City HS; Mason City, IA; 1/458 HonRl; Quill&Scroll; SctActv; Yrbk; Ia State Univ; Engineering.

CARMELL, Kerry E; Pennfield HS; Battle Creek, MI; 9/186 SpnCl; MthCl; SciCl; Kellogg Comm College; Medical.

CARMICHAEL, Beverly A; Harper HS; Chicago, IL; 35/251 Chrs; ChrhWkr; YthFlsp; MthCl; PpCl; SciCl; Bsktbl; CchngActv; GAA; Univ Of Il; Engineering.

CARMICHAEL, Carol; Rochelle Township HS; Rochelle, IL; 5/210 TrsJrCls; Chr; Chrs; HonRl; MrchBnd; Orch; StuCncl; Univ Of Il; Med Tech.

CARMICHAEL, Carol L; Rochelle Twp HS; Rochelle, IL; 5/225 TrsJrCls; Chr; HonRl; PresOrch; StuCncl; Treas4-H; SecSpnCl; LetterBsktbl; LetterTennis; GAA; 4-HAwd; Univ Of Il; Medical Technology.

CARMICHAEL, John L; Wichita Heights HS; Wichita, KS; ALBoysSt; HonRl; ModUN; NatlFornLg; NatlMeritSF; SctActv; RptrSchPpr; CivCl; MasAwd; OptClAwd; Coll Ksu; Architecture.

CARMICHAEL, Kevin L; Harrisonville HS; Harrisonville, MO; HonRl; SciCl; Bsbl; Bsktbl; LetterFtbl; LetterTrk; CaptWrstlng; IMSpt;.

CARMICHAEL, Susan K; North Nodaway R Vi HS; Pickering, MO; TrsFrshCls; TrsSophCls; HonRl; StuCncl; TchrAde; 4-H; FHA; PpCl; LetterBsktbl; LetterTrk; Clge; Prof.

CARMIEN, Catherine E; Huntington North HS; Huntington, IN; Chr; ChrhWkr; CncrtBnd; MrchBnd; PepBnd; SchMus; GerCl; GAA; Purdue Univ; Chemical Engineer.

CARMIEN, Tammy L; St Joseph Ogden HS; St Joe, IL; 20/107 HonRl; MrchBnd; NHS; 4-H; GerCl; PpCl; Trk; Chrldr; 4-HAwd; LionAwd; College; Business.

CARMODY, Karen A; Owosso HS; Owosso, MI; 18/452 Bsktbl; GAA; IMSpt; Dental Hygienist.

CARMODY, Kelly L; Armour HS; Armour, SD; 2/31 Band; Chrs; HonRl; NHS; RedCrAde; SecStuCncl; FHA; PpCl; Trk; BttyCrckrAwd; South Dakota State Univ; Sociology.

CARMODY, Mollie; Central Catholic HS; Bloomingtn, IL; CmntyWkr; HonRl; NHS; StuCncl; SchPpr; FrCl; PpCl; College.

CARMODY, Teresa L; Calhoun HS; Hardin, IL; HonRl; NHS; StuCncl; CivCl; 4-H; GAA; AmLegAwd; DanFAwd; 4-HAwd; Blackburn College; Anthropologist.

CARNAHAN, David M; Hartland HS; Hartland, MI; ChrhWkr; SctActv; LetterFtbl; LetterTennis;.

CARNAHAN, Kathleen M; Sioux County HS; Harrison, NE; TrsSrCls; Chrs; HonRl; NatlFornLg; NHS; StuCncl; RptrYrbk; FHA; SciCl; Chrldr; College.

CARNEGIE, Josephine M; Edison Sr HS; East Gary, IN; Chr; HonRl; FTA; PresSpnCl; PpCl; College; Medicine.

CARNELL, Susan A; Gull Lake HS; Augusta, MI; ChrhWkr; CncrtBnd; HonRl; MrchBnd; NHS; PepBnd; Bsktbl; PPFtbl; Western Mi U; Accounting.

CARNER, Kathryn A; Union HS; Kirkwood, IL; 4/72 Band; Chr; ChrhWkr; CncrtBnd; HonRl; Mdrgl; NHS; StuCncl; 4-H; FTA; Ill Wesleyan U; Elem Educ.

CARNES, Jeffrey S; Cass Technical HS; Detroit, MI; 5/220 HonRl; NatlMeritSF; RptrSchPpr; EdSchPpr; SchPpr; CaptGlf; Wayne State Univ; Lawyer.

CARNES, Kevin D; Field Kindley Memorial HS; Coffeyville, KS; 1/249 ALBoysSt; HonRl; NHS; NatlMeritSF; SctActv; StuCncl; AmLegAwd; Baker Univ; Scientist.

CARNEY, Donna J; Rockford HS; Marble Rock, IA; 1/71 Band; Chr; CncrtBnd; HonRl; MrchBnd; NHS; SchMus; SchPl; Yrbk; DanFAwd; Univ; Interior Design.

CARNEY, Iva L; Craig Riii HS; Bigelow, MO; CaptBsktbl; College; Conservation Work.

CARNEY, Lucinda A; Lakeland HS; Lagrange, IN; SecJrCls; Band; HonRl; StuCncl; Teen; 4-H; PpCl; Tennis; CaptChrldr; PresAwd; Ball St Univ.

CARNEY, Mark D; Logansport HS; Logansport, IN; 5/324 HonRl; JrNHS; PolWkr; SchPl; YthFlsp; KeyCl; GerCl; Swmmng; EldAwd; Indiana Univ; Professional.

CARNEY, Robert M; Immaculate Conception HS; Elmhurst, IL; 9/174 VPJrCls; PresSrCls; HonRl; VPNHS; StuCncl; SpnCl; SciCl; Bsbl; Bsktbl; Ftbl; CchngActv; IMSpt; University; Law.

CAROH, Tom; Bloomer HS; Bloomer, WI; HonRl; SchPpr; FFA; PpCl; Bsktbl; IMSpt; 4-HAwd; College; Professional.

CAROL, Albert F; St Agatha HS; Detroit, MI; Chr; Chrl; Chrs; HonRl; SctActv; College; Biology.

CAROLAN, Mary D; St Scholastica HS; Park Ridge, IL; CmntyWkr; HonRl; NHS; NatlMeritCmnd; PolWkr; TchrAde; Lawrence Univ; Anthropology.

CAROLLO, Cathy A; Kingsford HS; Kingsford, MI; 4/168 VPSophCls; HonRl; NHS; StuCncl; EdYrBk; TreasPpCl; IMSpt; Mi Tech Univ; Biological Science.

CAROW, Elizabeth A; Portage Northern HS; Kalamazoo, MI; TrsFrshCls; Chr; LitMag; LbryAde; RedCrAde; TchrAde; LetterTennis; Univ Of Ky; Nursing.

CARPENTER, Charles E; Monroe HS; Monroe, WI; 13/220 ChrhWkr; CncrtBnd; HonRl; PepBnd; LetterFtbl; LetterWrstlng; U Of Wi Madison; Veterinarian.

CARPENTER, Charles R; Ann Arbor Huron HS; Ann Arbor, MI; 109/570 PresFrshCls; HonRl; PolWkr; StuCncl; StuGov; TchrAde; Yrbk; FrCl; CaptFtbl; Wrstlng; Coll; Urban Planning.

CARPENTER, David D; Dwight HS; Dwight, IL; 58/111 Aud/Vis; Chrs; ChrhWkr; CmntyWkr; LbryAde; PolWkr; SchMus; SchPl; RptrSchPpr; FFA; Ftbl; Tennis; Ill State Univ; Agriculture Business.

CARPENTER, Debbie L; John Glenn HS; Bay City, MI; 15/320 HonRl; JrNHS; NHS; OffAde; SchMus; TchrAde; Yrbk; PpCl; Chrldr; Saginaw Valley St College; Business Admin.

CARPENTER, Denise M; Fingal Public HS; Fingal, ND; 8/21 VPJrCls; Chr; CncrtBnd; HonRl; PepBnd; SchPl; Yrbk; RptrSchPpr; Chrldr; Nd Sss Wahpeton; Secretary.

CARPENTER, Donald L; Hinsdale Twp Central HS; Hinsdale, IL; 70/583 ChrhWkr; CncrtBnd; HonRl; NHS; PolWkr; SchAde; LatCl; Tufts University.

CARPENTER, Douglas J; Hinsdale Central HS; Hinsdale, IL; 204/583 VPFrshCls; ChrhWkr;

HonRl; OffAde; StuGov; RptrYrbk; Denison Univ; Medicine.

CARPENTER, Jody J; Forest Lake HS; Forest Lake, MN; 13/353 Band; ChrhWkr; CncrtBnd; HonRl; MrchBnd; NHS; PepBnd; Bible Coll; Religious Work.

CARPENTER, Kevin N; Mc Cluer North HS; Florissant, MO; ChrhWkr; HonRl; NHS; TchrAde; GerCl; Lake Forest Sch; Physics.

CARPENTER, Lawrence; Monroe Sr HS; Monroe, WI; 20/220 ChrhWkr; CncrtBnd; HonRl; PepBnd; GerCl; Bsbl; Bsktbl; Ftbl; PresAwd; U Of Wis Madison; Medicine.

CARPENTER, Lisa M; Orangeville HS; Orangeville, IL; 10/58 SecBand; NHS; StuCncl; Yrbk; FBLA; FrCl; GAA; 4-HAwd;.

CARPENTER, Nyla J; Tri HS; Straughn, IN; 3/93 ChrhWkr; HonRl; LbryAde; NHS; University; Nursing.

CARPENTER, Pamela; Maysville HS; Maysville, MO; Chrs; CmntyWkr; CncrtBnd; HonRl; HospAde; NHS; SchPl; SctActv; StuGov; Chrldr; PresAwd; College; Major Communications.

CARPENTER, Patti L; Oak Park River Forest HS; Oak Park, IL; PresSrCls; HonRl; Bsktbl; College; Professional.

CARPENTER, Ricky L; South Putnam HS; Greencastle, IN; 2/100 ALBoysSt; Band; CncrtBnd; HonRl; MrchBnd; VPNHS; PresNatlThespSoc; SchPl; EdYrBk; SpnCl; Indiana State Univ; Teaching.

CARPENTER, Robert; Brillion Public HS; Brillion, WI; VPFrshCls; PresJrCls; ALBoysSt; NHS; StuCncl; GerCl; PpCl; Marquette Univ; Mechanical.

CARPENTER, Sandra; Switzerland County HS; Veucay, IN; 28/120 Chr; Chrs; CmntyWkr; DrlTm; LbryAde; SchAde; TchrAde; 4-H; FHA; SpnCl; Clothing.

CARPENTER, Stephanie M; Immaculate Heart Of Mary HS; Cicero, IL; 38/244 HospAde; SchMus; SpnCl; Trk; GAA; Loyola Univ.

CARPENTER, Susan A; Harbor Springs HS; Harbor Springs, MI; PresSophCls; ALAGirlsSt; Band; CncrtBnd; HonRl; MrchBnd; PepBnd; TchrAde; Yrbk; 4-H; College; Professional.

CARPENTER, Su Zan; Robbinsdale Sr HS; Minneapolis, MN; 1/761 Band; CncrtBnd; HonRl; MrchBnd; NHS; NatlMeritSF; NatlSciFnd; PepBnd; PolWkr; SchMus; SctActv; StuGov; RptrYrbk; Yrbk; College; Science.

CARPENTER, Thomas W; Saginaw HS; Saginaw, MI; 2/500 Chr; Chrs; HonRl; NHS; PepBnd; SctActv; CaptFtbl; CaptSwmmng; CaptTennis; OptClAwd; College; Engineering.

CARPENTER, Victoria J; Marillac HS; Arlington Hts, IL; 37/265 CmntyWkr; Orch; College; Journalism.

CARPENTER, Wilma R; 326 Eagle HS; Burr Oak, MI; 2/40 HonRl; LbryAde;.

CARPER, Diane G; Mahomet Seymour HS; Seymour, IL; 24/134 CmntyWkr; HonRl; NHS; SctActv; RptrYrbk; Pres4-H; FFA; LetterTrk; 4-HAwd; Univ Of Il; Veterinarian.

CARPER, Douglas L; East HS; Waterloo, IA; PresFrshCls; PresSrCls; Band; CncrtBnd; JrNHS; NHS; SchMus; StuCncl; LetterBsbl; LetterBsktbl; LetterFtbl; LetterGlf; College.

CARPER, Susan K; Highland HS; La Belle, MO; Chr; HonRl; JrNHS; NHS; VPFHA; FSA; PpCl; Bsktbl; Trk; Chrldr; College; Fashion.

CARPEROS, Diane B; Proviso West HS; Hillside, IL; ChrhWkr; HonRl; NHS; SpnCl; GAA; College.

CARR, Audrey L; Maywood HS; Maywood, NE; 1/26 Chr; Chrs; CmntyWkr; HonRl; LbryAde; NHS; SchMus; SchPl; StuCncl; PpCl; Chrldr; CchngActv; IMSpt; Colorado Univ; Graphic Arts.

CARR, Cynthia; Union R Ii HS; Union, MO; Band; CncrtBnd; HonRl; HospAde; JA; NHS; StuCncl; Twrl; 4-H; SpnCl; PpCl; CchngActv; PPFtbl; E Central Jr Coll; Ele Ed.

CARR, Cynthia S; Mid County HS; Varna, IL; 2/60 SecSophCls; TrsJrCls; SecSrCls; DrlTm; HonRl; FrCl; PpCl; Bsktbl; Trk; Chrldr; GAA; Bradley Univ; Medical Tech.

CARR, David V; Connersville HS; Connersville, IN; /400 StuCncl; 4-H; Bsbl; Bsktbl; Ftbl; IMSpt; CAP; College; Pro Ball Or Professional.

CARR, Diana M; Medicine Valley HS; Wellfleet, NE; Band; ChrhWkr; HonRl; NHS; SchMus; StuCncl; RptrYrbk; LetterTrk; CaptChrldr; 4-HAwd; PresAwd; Univ Of Nebraska.

CARR, Don; Sutherland HS; Sutherland, NE; 8/26 SecFrshCls; VPSophCls; VPSrCls; HonRl; OffAde; TchrAde; LetterBsktbl; Ftbl; IMSpt; AmLegAwd; Jr Col; Agriculture.

CARR, Karen J; Hinsdale South HS; Clarendon Hills, IL; 2/381 Band; ChrhWkr; CmntyWkr; HonRl; HospAde; TreasNHS; NatlMeritCmnd; GAA; College; Business.

CARR, Laurie L; Van Meter Community HS; Adel, IA; Chrs; HonRl; SchMus; SchPl; PpCl; Trk; Chrldr; University; Math Or Computer Science.

CARR, Leisa L; Fenton HS; Fenton, MI; Chr; HonRl; NHS; RptrSchPpr; Trk; Chrldr; Clge.

CARR, Linda; Lincoln Senior HS; Warren, MI; HonRl; JrNHS; NatlFornLg; NHS; OffAde; SchMus; SchPl; Trk; CchngActv; College; Teacher Or Photojournalist.

CARR, Lori K; Durand Area HS; Durand, MI; 23/189 Band; CncrtBnd; HonRl; HospAde; MrchBnd; NatlMeritCmnd; OffAde; YthFlsp; FNA; Mott Comm College; Business.

CARR, Marsha L; Sullivan HS; Sullivan, MO; 41/150 ALAGirlsSt; Band; HonRl; NHS; SchPl; StuCncl; TchrAde; EdYrBk; EdSchPpr; PresFTA; PPFtbl; Southwest Missouri State University.

CARR, Mary L; Collinsville HS; Collinsville, IL; Aud/Vis; CaptDrlTm; HonRl; NHS; SchPl; FrCl; PpCl; Trk; Socr; College.

CARR, Robert G; Carl Sandburg HS; Palos Park, IL; 38/700 GerCl; College; Engineering.

CARR, Robert S; Northview HS; Grand Rapids, MI; 3/231 CncrtBnd; HonRl; LitMag; MrchBnd; ModUN; NHS; NatlMeritFnl; PepBnd; PolWkr; RotaryAwd; Yale Univ; Physics.

CARR, Robert S; Emerson HS; Gary, IN; 8/223 Band; CncrtBnd; HonRl; MrchBnd; NHS; Orch; PepBnd; SchPl; LetterBsbl; Tennis; Army; Vet.

CARR, Robin H; Adelphian Academy; Holly, MI; Chrs; ChrhWkr; HonRl; RptrYrbk; FshEdYrbk; Yrbk; RptrSchPpr; SchPpr; EngCl; Chrldr; Univ Of Mich Flint; Teaching.

CARR, Ronald J; Garden City West HS; Garden City, MI; 30/415 HonRl; StuGov; RptrYrbk; SchPpr; Bsktbl; IMSpt; College Albion Mi; Phys Ed Teacher.

CARR, Susan A; Medicine Valley HS; Wellfleet, NE; 1/32 SecSophCls; TrsJrCls; TrsJrCls; Band; Chr; Chrs; HonRl; MrchBnd; NHS; PepBnd; College; Professional.

CARRAHER, Donald F; Westview HS; Kankakee, IL; 11/250 HonRl; Kankakee Comm College; Psychology.

CARRARA, Mark E; Naperville Central HS; Naperville, IL; CmntyWkr; HonRl; JrNHS; NHS; NatlMeritFnl; 4-H; FFA; AmLegAwd; 4-HAwd; North Central College; Nuclear Physics.

CARREL, Ann M; Wamego HS; Wamego, KS; 10/96 ChrhWkr; HonRl; NHS; SchPl; StuCncl; RptrYrbk; RptrSchPpr; SpnCl; PpCl; College; English.

CARREL, Cheri L; Maysville HS; Clarksdale, MO; HonRl; PresNHS; StuCncl; RptrYrbk; EdSchPpr; FFA; FHA; SpnCl; PpCl;.

CARREL, James A; Rogers HS; Wyoming, MI; 16/268 Band; HonRl; NHS; Orch; PepBnd; LetterBsbl; LetterBsktbl; LetterFtbl; IMSpt; Western Michigan Univ; Engineering.

CARRELL, Mary H; Oregon HS; Madison, WI; HonRl; StuCncl; CaptTrk; PPFtbl; Uw; Vet Asst.

CARRICK, Cathy J; Vestaburg HS; Vestaburg, MI; 5/65 ChrhWkr; HonRl; NHS; RptrYrbk; SpnCl; DARAwd; CitAwd; Graceland Clg; Social Work.

CARRICK, Christie L; Gurdon S Hubbard HS; Chicago, IL; 31/620 HonRl; NHS; StuCncl; RptrYrbk; Bsktbl; Socr; Trk; GAA; IMSpt; PPFtbl; College; Special Ed Teacher.

CARRICO, Michelle; Bedford North Lawrence HS; Bedford, IN; 31/483 HonRl; NHS; OffAde; TchrAde; AmLegAwd; KiwanAwd; Trade Or Bus School; Vocation.

CARRIE, Susan E; Franklin HS; Westland, MI; CncrtBnd; HonRl;.

CARRIER, Daniel S; Cardinal Ritter HS; Indianapolis, IN; 26/151 Band; Chrs; CncrtBnd; HonRl; MrchBnd; NHS; PepBnd; SchMus; StuGov; SpnCl; Marian Clge; Accounting.

CARRIER, Nancy J; Addison Trail HS; Addison, IL; 106/604 Chr; ChrhWkr; HonRl; SctActv; PpCl; Trk; GAA; Vocational School; Nursing.

CARRIER, Rebecca L; Guttenberg Community HS; Guttenberg, IA; 1/64 SecJrCls; Chr; Chrs; HonRl; Mdrgl; NHS; PpCl; U Of N Ia; Professional.

CARRIER, Sharon K; Buena Vista HS; Saginaw, MI; 5/259 HonRl; Secretary.

CARRIERE, Denise L; Bishop Hogan HS; Kansas City, MO; CmntyWkr; HonRl; PpCl; Chrldr; College; Nursing.

CARRIGAN, Dana K; Bergan HS; Peoria, IL; 64/210 HonRl; RptrSchPpr; SchPpr; GerCl; Ftbl; Illinois State; Science.

CARRINGTON, Ronald E; Shiloh HS; Redmon, IL; 5/41 HstJrCls; ChrhWkr; CmntyWkr; HonRl; Bsktbl; Rose Hulman Inst Of Tech; Chemical Engineer.

CARROL, Lisa H; Hockaday HS; Bloomington, IN; SecFrshCls; PresJrCls; PresSrCls; Band; HonRl; Orch; StuCncl; StuGov; TchrAde; SpnCl; MthCl; LetterBsbl; LetterBsktbl; College; Business.

CARROLL, Cynthia D; Morgan Park HS; Chicago, IL; 45/600 Chr; CmntyWkr; HonRl; NHS; NatlMeritCmnd; Quill&Scroll; StuCncl; RptrYrbk; RptrSchPpr; FrCl; GAA; Yale Univ; Pre Med.

CARROLL, Darlene M; Marion Co R2 HS; Philadelphia, MO; 1/11 Chrs; ChrhWkr; HonRl; SchPl; StuCncl; EdYrBk; SchPpr; FHA; FrCl; AmLegAwd; Baptist Bible College; Vocal Music.

CARROLL, David G; Lyons Twp HS; La Grange Park, IL; 198/1250 HonRl; NHS; Sacrstn; Bsbl; Bsktbl; Ftbl; Dartmouth Univ; Math.

CARROLL, David W; Warsaw HS; Warsaw, MO; ALBoysSt; NHS; SchMus; RptrYrbk; RptrSchPpr; Community College; Photo Journalism.

CARROLL, Deborah; Port Huron HS; Port Huron, MI; HonRl; SchPpr; College.

CARROLL, Eileen J; Oak Lawn HS; Oak Lawn, IL; 19/667 VPChr; Chrs; HonRl; JrNHS; Mdrgl; NHS; SchMus; StuGov; TchrAde; PresSciCl; College; Art.

CARROLL, George L; Crown Point HS; Crown Point, IN; 33/458 HonRl; NHS; LetterGlf; Univ Of Notre Dame; Chem Engineer.

CARROLL, Gregory L; St Charles HS; St Charles, MO; Band; CncrtBnd; HonRl; MrchBnd; NHS; Orch; PepBnd; MthCl; College.

CARROLL, James A; Fenton HS; Wood Dale, IL; 33/356 HonRl; NatlMeritCmnd; Univ Of Ill; Political Science.

CARROLL, James G; St Marys HS; St Louis, MO; SchPl; SctActv; Socr; Trk; Meramec Jr College; Law Enforcement.

CARROLL, Jane L; Central Catholic HS; Bloomington, IL; 22/84 HonRl; PpCl; Il Univ.

CARROLL, Joan D; Pekin Com HS; Pekin, IL; 308/744 Chr; SchMus; SchPl; College; Physical Therapist.

CARROLL, John C; St Thomas Prep; Rolla, MO; 3/11 PresSophCls; HonRl; NatlMeritCmnd; EdSchPpr; LatCl; LetterSocr; Univ; Radio Television.

CARROLL, Judith M; Granite City No HS; Granite City, IL; Chrs; HospAde; LbryAde; NHS; OffAde; TchrAde; 4-H; SpnCl; PpCl; Univ Of Illinois; Veterinarian.

CARROLL, Laura S; Duchesne HS; St Charles, MO; Chrs; ChrhWkr; HonRl; SchMus; Yrbk; TreasFrCl; PpCl; CchngActv; GAA; PPFtbl; College; Cpa.

CAROLL, Laurie; Waverly HS; Lansing, MI; 2/400 AFS; MrchBnd; PepBnd; SchMus; SchPl; TchrAde; PpCl; Univ Of Mich; Nursing.

CARROLL, Ledonna S; Stanberry R Ii HS; Stanberry, MO; 6/40 SecFrshCls; SecSophCls; SecJrCls; HonRl; YthFlsp; FHA; PpCl; CaptBsktbl; LetterTrk; IMSpt; Univ; Bs In Art.

CARROLL, Lori A; Jefferson City Sr HS; Jefferson City, MO; ChrhWkr; CncrtBnd; MrchBnd; NHS; PepBnd; SchMus; SctActv; StuCncl; LatCl; PpCl; College; Education.

CARROLL, Mary E; Crown Point HS; Crown Point, IN; 1/492 Band; CncrtBnd; HonRl; MrchBnd; NHS; NatlMeritSF; SchPl; RptrYrbk; FrCl; LetterTennis; KiwanAwd; Coll; Psych.

CARROLL, Mary J; Lancaster Sr HS; Lancaster, WI; 9/159 VPChrs; HonRl; HospAde; NHS; Sacrstn; YthFlsp; RptrYrbk; EdSchPpr; SpnCl; IMSpt; Col; Social Work.

CARROLL, Michelle A; Kokomo HS; Kokomo, IN; 20/356 ChrhWkr; HonRl; NHS; Purdue Univ; Interior Design.

CARROLL, Nancy A; St Marys HS; Sleepy Eye, MN; Band; Chrs; CncrtBnd; MrchBnd; OffAde; Quill&Scroll; TchrAde; EdSchPpr; Swmmng; GAA; Business School; Vocation.

CARROLL, Ned J; Spencer HS; Spencer, IA; Band; HonRl; NHS; NatlThespSoc; Quill&Scroll; SchMus; SchPl; StuCncl; Yrbk; Ftbl; Cornell Coll; Law.

CARROLL, Shawn W; Greenfield HS; Greenfield, WI; 13/397 Band; ChrhWkr; HonRl; NHS; StuGov; RptrYrbk; RptrSchPpr; SchPpr; PpCl; Bsktbl; Ftbl; St Olaf College; Law.

CARROLL, Sheila; St Joseph HS; Kenosha, WI; 15/150 Chr; Chrs; ChrhWkr; HonRl; HospAde; JrNHS; NHS; StuCncl; KiwanAwd; NCTE; Marquette Univ; Nursing.

CARROLL, Shelly K; Dickinson HS; Dickinson, ND; Band; Chr; CncrtBnd; HonRl; MrchBnd; OffAde; PepBnd; GerCl; PpCl; Chrldr; College; Professional.

CARROLL, Vickie A; Webb HS; Platteville, WI; Band; CncrtBnd; HonRl; MrchBnd; Orch; PepBnd; Univ; Nursing.

CARRUTHERS, David A; St Bede HS; Ladd, IL; 5/92 Chr; ChrhWkr; HonRl; Quill&Scroll; SchMus; StuGov; SpnCl; LetterFtbl; AmLegAwd; PresAwd; Univ; Psychiatrist Psychologist.

CARRUTHERS, David A; St Bede Academy; Ladd, IL; 7/90 Chrs; HonRl; LitMag; StuGov; SpnCl; LetterBsktbl; LetterFtbl; IMSpt; AmLegAwd; PresAwd; CitAwd; University; Psychiatry.

CARRUTHERS, Janetta L; Vandalia Comm HS; Vandalia, IL; Chrs; TreasNHS; SchPl; PresFHA; VPSciCl; Blackburn Univ; Medicine.

CARRY, Carl D; Pekin Comm HS; Pekin, IL; 56/800 Chr; ChrhWkr; HonRl; NHS; SchMus; Illinois Central College; Data Processing.

CARSELLO, Susan J; Notre Dame HS For Girls; Chicago, IL; 31/302 HonRl; NHS; StuGov; SpnCl; Univ Of Illinois.

CARSON, Carol J; Ofallon Township HS; O Fallon, IL; SchPpr; College.

CARSON, Cecilia A; St Mary Acad; Indianapolis, IN; 4/45 VPSophCls; HstJrCls; PresSrCls; Chrs; HonRl; NHS; StuCncl; 4-H; FrCl; John Herron Art Schl; Commercial Artist.

CARSON, Debbie L; Victoria HS; Victoria, KS; Chr; DrlTm; HonRl; HospAde; NatlMeritCmnd; SchPl; FHA; SpnCl; PpCl; Swmmng; College; Lab Tech.

CARSON, Gay L; Osceola HS; Osceola, MO; ChrhWkr; HonRl; HospAde; LbryAde; NHS; 4-H; FHA; FNA; SpnCl; College; Medical Technology.

CARSON, Greg L; Orion HS; Coal Valley, IL; 6/130 HonRl; NHS; SchPl; SchPpr; SpnCl; Trk; Wrstlng; College; Engineer.

CARSON, James M; Wabash HS; Wabash, IN; Band; Chr; CncrtBnd; MrchBnd; NatlFornLg; NHS; NatlMeritSF; SchMus; SchPl; StuCncl; Indiana St Univ; Teach.

CARSON, Janice S; Alexis HS; Gerlaw, IL; Chr; ChrhWkr; CmntyWkr; CncrtBnd; MrchBnd; PepBnd; RptrSchPpr; SecFHA; GAA; College; Vocation.

CARSON, Kathleen L; Tiskilwa HS; Tiskilwa, IL; 3/42 PresSophCls; PresJrCls; HospAde; NHS; VPStuCncl; EdSchPpr; Bsktbl; Trk; PresGAA; DARAwd; Northern Ill Univ; Mathematics.

CARSON, Keith; Boyne Falls Public HS; Boyne Falls, MI; HonRl; SchMus; SchPl; 4-H; SciCl; Bsbl; Bsktbl; AmLegAwd; 4-HAwd; College; Professional.

CARSON, Luann; Savannah HS; Savannah, MO; Band; Chr; CncrtBnd; Mdrgl; MrchBnd; NHS; PepBnd; SchMus; PpCl; College.

CARSON, Mark D; T L Handy HS; Bay City, MI; 5/400 HonRl; NHS; NatlMeritCmnd; GerCl; MthCl; LetterBsktbl; LetterFtbl; Tennis; Trk; Usaf Acad; Engineer.

CARSON, Martha A; Decatur HS; Decatur, MI; Band; CncrtBnd; MrchBnd; NHS; PepBnd; SchPl; StuGov; YthFlsp; PpCl; LetterChrldr; Hope Clge; Pro Math.

CARSON, Raymond; Hesperia Community HS; Hesperia, MI; 26/85 HonRl; Michigan State Univ; Law.

CARSON, Robin L; Parkview HS; Springfield, MO; Chr; ChrhWkr; CmntyWkr; HonRl; Mdrgl; SchMus; YthFlsp; FBLA; IMSpt; College; Secretary.

CARSON, Stephanie A; Laboure HS; St Louis, MO; Chrs; CmntyWkr; HospAde; JA; ROTC; SchMus; StuGov; SchPpr; FNA;.

CARSON, William S; Big Rapids HS; Big Rapids, MI; Band; Chr; DrmMjrt; HonRl; NHS; NatlMeritFnl; NatlMeritSchl; SchMus; SchPl; LatCl; Trk; Macalester College; Music.

CARSTENS, Dorene K; Alta Community HS; Alta, IA; 1/65 Band; Chrs; ChrhWkr; CncrtBnd; HonRl; MrchBnd; TreasNHS; PepBnd; SchMus; SecGerCl; Isu ;med Or Music.

CARSTENS, Jean M; Pierce Public HS; Pierce, NE; Chr; HonRl; PpCl; Bsbl; LetterTrk; Chrldr; IMSpt; PresAwd; VoiceDemAwd; Ne Methodist Sch Of Nursing; Nursing.

CARSTENS, Karen K; Perham HS; Frazee, MN; Band; CncrtBnd; HonRl; HospAde; LbryAde; MrchBnd; PepBnd; EdSchPpr; LatCl; PPFtbl; Rochester Comm Coll; Registered Nurse.

CARSTENSEN, Diane; Wilson Campus HS; Mankato, MN; Chr; TchrAde; PpCl; GAA; College; Nursing.

CARSWELL, Roger; Quenemo HS; Quenemo, KS; 1/13 TrsFrshCls; VPSophCls; PresSrCls; Chrs; SchPl; StuCncl; EdSchPpr; AmLegAwd; Mcpherson College; Secondary Education.

CART, Shelley; Fairfield HS; Millersburg, IN; ALAGirlsSt; Band; Chr; Mdrgl; MrchBnd; Yrbk; 4-H; PpCl; Ferris State College; Business Major.

CARTER, Annette; Kettering HS; Detroit, MI; Chrs; ChrhWkr; CmntyWkr; HonRl; JA; LbryAde; OffAde; PolWkr; SchAde; SchMus; SchPl; Bsktbl; Swmmng; Detroit Institute Of Tech; X Ray Technician.

CARTER, Beverlee; Plainfield HS; Joliet, IL; HonRl; HospAde; NHS; OffAde; RptrYrbk; GAA; IMSpt; PPFtbl; Univ; Major Study.

CARTER, Brent L; Chappell HS; Chappell, NE; 4/28 TrsSophCls; ChrhWkr; HonRl; NHS; YthFlsp; Treas4-H; SecFFA; LetterBsktbl; LetterTrk; CitAwd; Univ Ne; Economics.

CARTER, Charles M; Campus HS; Haysville, KS; 22/215 ChrhWkr; HonRl; NatlMeritSF; Wichita State Univ; Engineering.

CARTER, Cheryl A; Springfield HS; Springfield, IL; Chr; PolWkr; StuCncl; TchrAde; LatCl; Bradley Univ; Biology.

CARTER, Christine A; Rushville Consolidated HS; Milroy, IN; 28/263 ALAGirlsSt; ChrhWkr; HonRl; NHS; TreasTeen; PresYthFlsp; VPFDA; SpnCl; MthCl; PpCl; 4-HAwd; Butler U; Pharmacy.

CARTER, Christy; Mexico Senior HS; Mexico, MO; Chr; ChrhWkr; NHS; StuCncl; SpnCl; PpCl; Central Methodist Coll; Business.

CARTER, Cora M; Kokomo HS; Kokomo, IN; 10/331 ALAGirlsSt; HonRl; JrNHS; NHS; OffAde; StuCncl; Chrldr; Indiana Univ; Professional.

CARTER, David E; William Chrisman HS; Independence, MO; ChrhWkr; HonRl; JrNHS; PresNHS; SctActv; PresYthFlsp; KeyCl; FrCl; LetterTrk; GodCntryAwd; Univ Of Missouri; Military Commercial Pilot.

CARTER, David S; Zionsville Comm HS; Zionsville, IN; ALBoysSt; Band; CncrtBnd; DrlTm; HonRl; MrchBnd; PepBnd; FrCl; In Sch Of Bus; Business.

CARTER, Deborah S; North Clay Comm HS; Louisville, IL; HonRl; SchPl; RptrSchPpr; Treas4-H; SpnCl; PpCl; Bsktbl; Trk; GAA; 4-HAwd; Air Force; Secretarial.

CARTER, Dennis J; Hale Area HS; South Branch, MI; Band; ChrhWkr; CncrtBnd; HonRl; LbryAde; MrchBnd; SchPl; SctActv; SptEdSchPpr; Clg; History Teacher.

CARTER, Dennis R; Carrollton HS; Carrollton, IL; VPSrCls; HonRl; StuCncl; FBLA; FSA; FTA; PpCl; LetterFtbl; Western Illinois Univ; Business Admin.

CARTER, Dorval R; The Faulkner HS; Chicago, IL; 3/10 VPJrCls; Chr; HonRl; TreasNatlThespSoc; SchPl; StuCncl; PresStuGov; RptrYrbk; SptEdSchPpr; CaptBsktbl; Coll; Pre Med.

CARTER, Elizabeth L; Carmel HS; Carmel, IN; 16/523 Band; ChrhWkr; HonRl; MrchBnd; NHS; NatlMeritSF; StuGov; PresYthFlsp; FrCl; PPFtbl; Earlham College; Government.

CARTER, Elizabeth L; Roxana Sr HS; East Alton, IL; Chrs; ChrhWkr; HonRl; HospAde; LbryAde; SctActv; FHA; SecFNA; PpCl; LetterTrk; St Lukes Hosp; Nursing.

CARTER, H R; North Greene HS; Roadhouse, IL; HonRl; NHS; SchPl; FTA; IMSpt; Univ; Professnl.

CARTER, H Randall; North Greene HS; Roodhouse, IL; HonRl; NHS; FTA; College; Professional.

CARTER, Janice D; Chicago Vocational HS; Chicago, IL; 52/776 HonRl; SchAde; SchPl; StuCncl; Stu-

Gov; TchrAde; Chrldr; GAA; IMSpt; De Paul U; Political Science.

CARTER, Janice M; Franklin HS; Livonia, MI; CmntyWkr; HonRl; SchAde; TchrAde; VPSpnCl; Wayne State Univ; Psychology.

CARTER, Jeff A; Neosho HS; Neosho, MO; ALBoysSt; Band; ChrhWkr; HonRl; MrchBnd; NatlFornLg; PolWkr; YthFlsp; 4-H; MthCl; Bsktbl; DanFAwd; College; Political Science.

CARTER, Joye M; Shortridge HS; Indianapolis, IN; 8/390 SecSrCls; Chr; ChrhWkr; CmntyWkr; HonRl; ModUN; NHS; NatlThespSoc; PolWkr; SchPl; StuCncl; StuGov; RptrYrbk; Univ Of Wittenberg; Lawyer.

CARTER, Judyth A; Stes Peter & Paul Area HS; Saginaw, MI; 2/105 ChrhWkr; CmntyWkr; HonRl; NHS; OffAde; SchPl; CivCl; Univ Of Michigan; Occupational Therapy.

CARTER, Julie E; Mediapolis HS; Morning Sun, IA; 5/80 Band; Chrs; CncrtBnd; HonRl; MrchBnd; PepBnd; YthFlsp; RptrYrbk; EdSchPpr; SchPpr; Clg; Mathematics.

CARTER, Julie E; Altoona Midway Sr HS; Altoona, KS; 1/36 ChrhWkr; HonRl; LbryAde; SchPl; Yrbk; Bsktbl; College; Accounting.

CARTER, Karen; Turner HS; Kansas City, KS; DrlTm; HonRl; SecJrNHS; NatlCathMusEdAsoc; SecStuCncl; Yrbk; SecFrCl; PpCl; Bsbl; GAA; College; Commercial Art.

CARTER, Karen A; Staunton HS; Brazil, IN; 12/65 VPFrshCls; TrsSophCls; SecJrCls; Chr; Chrs; HonRl; SchMus; RptrYrbk; RptrSchPpr; FHA; Nursing.

CARTER, Kerry D; Mazon Verona Kinsman HS; Mazon, IL; 7/42 ALBoysSt; HonRl; SchPl; SctActv; PresStuCncl; StuGov; TreasFTA; PpCl; LetterBsktbl; Glf; LetterWrstlng; College; Engineering.

CARTER, Kimberly A; Homer HS; Homer, IL; Band; Chrs; ChrhWkr; HonRl; NHS; SchPl; StuCncl; FHA; Trk; Chrldr; GAA; College; Psychology.

CARTER, Kim L; Charlevoix HS; Charlevoix, MI; 8/148 CncrtBnd; MrchBnd; PepBnd; SchMus; PresStuCncl; SecYthFlsp; Yrbk; PresSpnCl; Spring Arbor College; Philosophy.

CARTER, Kristine; Langdon HS; Langdon, ND; 1/107 HonRl; LbryAde; NHS; YthFlsp; Yrbk; FrCl; GerCl; SpnCl; PpCl; Univ Of Nd; Foreign Languages.

CARTER, Linda; Omaha Central HS; Omaha, NE; 7/446 Band; ChrhWkr; CncrtBnd; HonRl; MrchBnd; PepBnd; TchrAde; FFA; Univ Of Ne.

CARTER, Marcia E; Eastbrook HS; Van Buren, IN; ChrhWkr; YthFlsp; Sec4-H; FBLA; SecFHA; GerCl; PpCl; 4-HAwd; College; Business.

CARTER, Mary K; Streator Township HS; Streator, IL; HonRl; NatlThespSoc; SchPl; SpnCl; PpCl; Illinois Vly Jr College; Med Lab Technician.

CARTER, Mary L; Yale HS; Yale, MI; Chr; Chrl; Chrs; HonRl; StuCncl; FHA; College; Music.

CARTER, Michael L; Hillman Community HS; Hillman, MI; TrsFrshCls; TrsSophCls; HonRl;.

CARTER, Michael L; Oak Park Sr HS; Kansas City, MO; ChrhWkr; HonRl; Orch; SchMus; College; Professional.

CARTER, Millicent F; Cahokia Sr HS; Centerville, IL; 37/534 Chrs; ChrhWkr; HonRl; JA; NHS; MthCl; PpCl; Trk; College; Public Accountant.

CARTER, Nancy L; Huntington North HS; Huntington, IN; ChrhWkr; OffAde; PolWkr; StuGov; TchrAde; RptrSchPpr; SptEdSchPpr; GerCl; LetterBsktbl; LetterGlf; LetterTennis; CchngActv; GAA; Indiana University; Physical Education.

CARTER, Pamela R; Norborne Public HS; Norborne, MO; PresFrshCls; SecJrCls; Band; Chrs; HonRl; NHS; SchPl; StuCncl; FHA; FrCl; College.

CARTER, Patricia A; Dixon R 1 HS; Dixon, MO; Chr; HonRl; MrchBnd; NHS; TchrAde; Yrbk; FBLA; TreasFHA; FTA; AmLegAwd; Univ Of Missouri; Home Economics.

CARTER, Patricia A; Leroy HS; Leroy, IL; 17/68 Chrs; HospAde; Mdrgl; TreasFHA; Bsktbl; GAA; IMSpt; College; Nursing.

CARTER, Patricia G; Mitchell HS; Mitchell, IN; 16/119 ALAGirlsSt; Band; ChrhWkr; DrlTm; HonRl; NHS; NatlThespSoc; SchPl; Vincennes University; Nursing.

CARTER, Randy P; St Clair HS; St Clair, MO; PresFrshCls; PresSophCls; PresJrCls; PresSrCls; ChrhWkr; YthFlsp; Yrbk; CaptBsbl; Bsktbl; ChmnFtbl; Coll.

CARTER, Robert K; East HS; Rockford, IL; 25/650 CncrtBnd; HonRl; JrNHS; MrchBnd; NHS; StuCncl; Rock Valley College; Accountant.

CARTER, Ronald; East Central HS; Miles, IA; 2/59 Band; Chrs; CncrtBnd; HonRl; NHS; PepBnd; SchPpr; Trk; IMSpt; GovHonPrgAwd; Iowa State Univ; Electrcl Engrg.

CARTER, Sandra L; Western Dubuque HS; Peosta, IA; 23/243 CmntyWkr; HonRl; VPModUN; UNYO; SpnCl; Glf; Trk; IMSpt; Wartburg College; Orthodontist.

CARTER, Stephen A; St Ignatius HS; Chicago, IL; SecSophCls; HonRl; JA; StuCncl; YthFlsp; 4-H; SpnCl; Swmmng; CaptTrk; IMSpt; Col; Medicine.

CARTER, Steven R; Dallas Community HS; Dallas Center, IA; Band; Chr; Chrs; ChrhWkr; CncrtBnd; Mdrgl; MrchBnd; PepBnd; SchMus; SchPl; College.

CARTER, Susan L; Trico HS; Ava, IL; Chr; SchMus; StuCncl; Yrbk; 4-H; KeyCl; SecPpCl; DanFAwd; 4-HAwd; CitAwd;.

CARTER, Suzette; Bradley Bourbonnais HS; Bradley, IL; SchPl; RptrYrbk; EdYrBk; Yrbk; PpCl; AmLegAwd; Comm Coll; Nursing.

CARTER, Terry E; Jersey Comm HS; Jerseyville, IL; 25/277 HonRl; NHS; SchPpr; FrCl; MthCl; LetterTrk; LetterWrstlng; IMSpt; Lewis & Clark Comm College; Business Mgmt.

CARTER, Timothy; Marion HS; Marion, IA; 39/168 Band; CncrtBnd; HonRl; MrchBnd; NHS; PepBnd; TchrAde; Nw Mo St Univ; English.

CARTER, Tina D; Rolla Senior HS; Rolla, MO; 5/307 Band; ChrhWkr; CncrtBnd; HonRl; MrchBnd; PepBnd; SchMus; StuCncl; StuGov; YthFlsp; FrCl; Drury College; Music.

CARTER, Victoria L; Lockport Cntrl HS; Lockport, IL; ChrhWkr; LbryAde; OffAde; SchAde; SchMus; SchPl; StuCncl; Teen; 4-H; Bsbl; College; Nursing.

CARTER, Virgil R; Storden Jeffers HS; Jeffers, MN; VPFrshCls; HonRl; LbryAde; YthFlsp; SciCl; LetterBsbl; LetterBsktbl; LetterFtbl; Trk; IMSpt; Voc Tech; Vocation.

CARTER, William; Whitewater Senior HS; Whitewater, WI; 4/192 ALBoysSt; Band; Chr; HonRl; NHS; Bsktbl; Wrstlng; GovHonPrgAwd; Us Air Force Acad; Test Engineer.

CARTHRAE, Kathryn F; South Barber HS; Lake City, KS; Band; HonRl; OffAde; 4-H; 4-HAwd;.

CARTMELL, Jo E; Mooresville HS; Martinsville, IN; 1/269 ALAGirlsSt; ModUN; NHS; NatlMeritCmnd; VPFHA; VPFrCl; PresSciCl; AmLegAwd; BttyCrckrAwd; DARAwd; In Univ; Nursng.

CARTMILL, Candy J; Wheatland HS; Gove, KS; SecSophCls; Chrs; HonRl; Pres4-H; 4-HAwd; College; English.

CARTMILL, John T; Elk Mound HS; Elk Mound, WI; ChrhWkr; HonRl; SchPl; 4-H; PpCl; Bsktbl; Trade Sch.

CARTWRIGHT, Jan M; Lew Wallace HS; Gary, IN; Chr; HonRl; LitMag; NHS; SchMus; SchPl; TchrAde; Drama School; Actress.

CARTWRIGHT, Linda L; Northfield HS; Andrews, IN; 62/110 Chrs; ChrhWkr; PolWkr; SchPl; TchrAde; YthFlsp; RptrYrbk; RptrSchPpr; 4-H; SpnCl; PpCl; GAA; Huntington College; Journalism.

CARTWRIGHT, Randy K; New Monroe Community HS; Monroe, IA; HonRl; SchPl; VP4-H; TreasFFA; SciCl; Bsktbl; LetterFtbl; LetterTrk; 4-HAwd;.

CARTWRIGHT, Steve W; Hays HS; Hays, KS; HonRl; College; Professional.

CARTWRIGHT, Valerie L; New Monroe Community HS; Monroe, IA; SecSophCls; HonRl; MrchBnd; SchPl; StuCncl; RptrSchPpr; SchPpr; LetterBsktbl; LetterTrk; Chrldr; Bus Sch; Secretary.

CARUSO, Frank J; Wm A Wirt HS; Gary, IN; Aud/Vis; Band; CncrtBnd; MrchBnd; OffAde; Orch; PepBnd; Bsktbl; Musician.

CARUSO, Margaret; Montini HS; Lombard, IL; 21/152 HonRl; OffAde; SchAde; EngCl; SpnCl; Rosary Col River Forest Il; Language.

CARUSO, Michael J; Proviso West HS; Hillside, IL; Band; DrmBgl; PolWkr; SctActv; Univ.

CARUTHERS, Donald R; Wellsville HS; Wellsville, KS; ALBoysSt; HonRl; ModUN; NHS; SctActv; StuCncl; LetterFtbl; LetterTrk; AmLegAwd; GodCntryAwd; College; Drafting.

CARUTHERS, John S; R Nelson Snider HS; Ft Wayne, IN; HonRl; LatCl; Tennis; University; Professional.

CARVELLI, Dawn M; Thornton Township HS; Harvey, IL; 43/701 Chr; HonRl; HospAde; JrNHS; NHS; NatlMeritFnl; NatlMeritCmnd; NatlMeritSchl; NatlMeritSF; College; Professional.

CARVER, Jane M; Humboldt HS; Humboldt, IA; 21/140 Chr; Chrs; ChrhWkr; HonRl; HospAde; SchMus; SchPpr; Mount Mercy Clge; Medical Technologist.

CARVER, Jeffrey; Cornell HS; Cornell, WI; 10/57 Aud/Vis; ChrhWkr; CmntyWkr; OffAde; SchAde; SchPl; YthFlsp; Yrbk; SchPpr; Trade Sch; Photography.

CARVER, Mary L; Rockwell City Comm HS; Rockwell City, IA; 3/64 Band; ChrhWkr; CncrtBnd; HonRl; MrchBnd; NatlMeritSF; PepBnd; RedCrAde; SchMus; SchPl; Univ Of Iowa; Psychology.

CARVER, Penny K; Oak Park HS; Kansas City, MO; 27/603 SecChr; SecChrl; ChrhWkr; HonRl; Mdrgl; SecNatlThespSoc; SchMus; SchPl; TchrAde; VPYthFlsp; IMSpt; Nw Missouri St University.

CARVER, Philip H; Cedar Falls HS; Cedar Falls, IA; Chr; Chrs; HonRl; Mdrgl; Orch; SchMus; SchPl; KiwanAwd; Cornell College; Music.

CARVER, Tara L; Valentine HS; Crookston, NE; Chrs; DrlTm; HonRl; NHS; StuCncl; TreasFFA; SecSpnCl; PresPpCl; SciCl; IMSpt; University Of Nebraska; Animal Science.

CARVIOU, Howard H; Marinette Sr HS; Marinette, WI; 77/260 Band; CncrtBnd; DrmMjrt; MrchBnd; PepBnd; Univ Of Wisconsin; Geology.

CARY, Debbra; Chandlerville HS; Virginia, IL; SecSophCls; Chrs; HonRl; LbryAde; NHS; StuCncl; FHA; Business School; Curriculum Of Study.

CARY, Paul W; Oxford HS; Leonard, MI; VPAud/Vis; RptrSchPpr; SptEdSchPpr; LetterTrk; LetterWrstlng; Army; Carpenter.

CARY, Peggy S; Rivet HS; Vincennes, IN; 2/47 HonRl; ModUN; EdYrBk; TreasFHA; PpCl; Trk; In Univ; Law.

CASADY, Danny J; Chillicothe HS; Chillicothe, MO; 33/185 ChrhWkr; HonRl; RedCrAde; SchPl; 4-H; VPFFA; LatCl; SciCl; IMSpt; Univ Of Missouri; Veterinarian.

CASALENDA, Martin S; Humboldt HS; St Paul, MN; 6/220 HonRl; TchrAde; SchPpr; IMSpt; College; Math.

CASALETTO, Paul; Maine South HS; Park Ridge, IL; HonRl; JrNHS; NHS; Univ Of Ill; Medicine.

CASANOVA, Dan K; Central HS; Aberdeen, SD; CmntyWkr; HonRl; Bsbl; Bsktbl; Ftbl; Business School; Accounting.

CASAREZ, Jorge A; Gabriel Richard HS; Detroit, MI; VPSophCls; HonRl; JA; NHS; SchPl; StuCncl; StuGov; SpnCl; Michigan State U; Psychiatry.

CASAS, Alfred; Almond Pub HS; Bancroft, WI; PresSophCls; ALBoysSt; CmntyWkr; PpCl; LetterBsbl; LetterBsktbl; LetterFtbl; Trk; Photography.

CASBON, Karen L; Boone Grove HS; Hebron, IN; 10/64 SecBand; ChrhWkr; HonRl; NHS; SchPl; VPYthFlsp; Yrbk; Pres4-H; VPPpCl; PresGAA; Winona State; Guidance Counslng.

CASCIO, Karen J; Forest View HS; Arlington Heights, IL; 63/597 ChrhWkr; HonRl; HospAde; NHS; Quill&Scroll; TchrAde; RptrYrbk; Wm Rainey Harper Comm College; Business Adm.

CASCIO, Shirley A; Jefferson HS; Rockford, IL; 4/335 TrsFrshCls; TrsSophCls; TrsJrCls; TrsSrCls; HonRl; JrNHS; NHS; SchMus; Trk; GovHonPrgAwd; U Of Il; Medical.

CASE, Blane J; Marcus HS; Marcus, IA; 6/73 HonRl; StuCncl; SpnCl; LetterFtbl; Trk; Wrstlng; University; Professional.

CASE, Brenda L; Shelbyville HS; Shelbyville, IN; HonRl; Civil Service; Post Office Clerk.

CASE, Colin J; Plattsmouth HS; Plattsmouth, NE; 6/163 Band; ChrhWkr; CncrtBnd; HonRl; MrchBnd; NHS; Orch; PolWkr; SctActv; MthCl; Bsktbl; Ftbl; Univ.

CASE, Deborah L; Marshall HS; Marshall, MO; LbryAde; OffAde; TchrAde; PresYthFlsp; RptrSchPpr; FHA; LetterBsktbl; LetterTennis; CaptTrk; Central Mo St Univ; College Coach.

CASE, James R; Capital City Christian HS; Okemos, MI; 1/16 VPFrshCls; PresSophCls; ChrhWkr; HonRl; JrNHS; NHS; StuCncl; RptrYrbk; Bsbl; Ftbl; Christian Work.

CASE, Janice L; Durand Area HS; Durand, MI; Band; Chr; ChrhWkr; HonRl; MrchBnd; SctActv; TchrAde; 4-H; FrCl; Univ Of Mi; Physical Therapy.

CASE, Kathleen M; Plattsmouth HS; Plattsmouth, NE; 1/169 Band; ChrhWkr; CncrtBnd; DrmMjrt; HonRl; MrchBnd; NHS; StuCncl; Twrl; 4-H; VPGAA; PPFtbl; DARAwd; University; Medical Field.

CASE, Louise A; Lancaster Sr HS; Lancaster, WI; VPFrshCls; AFS; Band; Chrs; CncrtBnd; DrlTm; HonRl; MrchBnd; PepBnd; StuCncl; GAA; IMSpt; 4-HAwd; Col; Engineering.

CASE, Robert G; Wapahani HS; Parker City, IN; 1/8/80 ALBoysSt; HonRl; JrNHS; LbryAde; NHS; Quill&Scroll; EdYrBk; SpnCl; LetterBsktbl; LetterTrk; College; Professional Air Lines.

CASE, Sharon L; Rich Central HS; Olympia Fields, IL; 22/400 Chr; DrlTm; HonRl; Mdrgl; NHS; SchMus; SpnCl; Iowa State Univ; Dietetics.

CASE, Steven P; Plattsmouth HS; Plattsmouth, NE; 1/133 Band; ChrhWkr; CmntyWkr; HonRl; MrchBnd; NHS; PepBnd; SctActv; MthCl; Bsbl; Bsktbl; Ftbl; DARAwd; University; Law.

CASEBEER, Francesca; Elizabeth Seton HS; Riverdale, IL; 15/239 HonRl; SpnCl; MthCl; SciCl; College; Art.

CASELMAN, Teresa J; Tri County R 7 HS; Jamesport, MO; HstFrshCls; SecJrCls; Band; Chr; Chrs; Chrs; ChrhWkr; CncrtBnd; DrmBgl; HonRl; Platte Guard Business College; Accountant.

CASELTON, Darrel J; Calhoun HS; Hardin, IL; TrsFrshCls; TrsSophCls; VPJrCls; Band; CmntyWkr; CncrtBnd; HonRl; PepBnd; RptrYrbk; SptEdYrbk; Trade School; Carpenter.

CASEY, Ann E; St Joseph HS; Kenosha, WI; 2/165 HonRl; JA; LbryAde; NHS; SctActv; StuCncl; RptrYrbk; Yrbk; LetterTennis; Univ; Accounting.

CASEY, Anne T; Mother Mc Auley HS; Chicago, IL; 44/474 Chrs; ChrhWkr; HonRl; NHS; StuCncl; Teen; 4-H; FTA; SpnCl; Bsktbl; Clarke Clge; Soc Wrkr.

CASEY, Bruce; Mitchell Sr HS; Mitchell, SD; 10/295 HonRl; JrNHS; NHS; StuCncl; KeyCl; College; Biology.

CASEY, Colleen A; Holy Angels HS; Richfield, MN; 4/110 HonRl; HospAde; JrNHS; NHS; SchMus; PPFtbl; Univ Of Mn; Med Tech.

CASEY, Jay H; Schulte HS; Terre Haute, IN; LetterBsktbl; LetterTennis; College.

CASEY, Kathleen M; Whiting HS; Whiting, IN; 10/106 HonRl; LbryAde; SchMus; SpnCl; KiwanAwd; Bus School; Professional.

CASEY, Marie A; Rosati Kain HS; St Louis, MO; PresSophCls; Chrs; ChrhWkr; CmntyWkr; NHS; Orch; PresStuCncl; RptrSchPpr; Swmmng; VoiceDemAwd; S Ill U; Law.

CASEY, Mary; St John HS; Independence, IA; 3/27 VPSophCls; PresJrCls; Chr; HonRl; NHS; StuCncl; RptrYrbk; Bsktbl; Trk; 4-HAwd; Clarke College; Social Worker.

CASEY, Michele M; North HS; Omaha, NE; Chr; Chrl; Chrs; CmntyWkr; HonRl; HospAde; SchMus; SchPl; SctActv; SchPpr; FNA; PpCl; Bsktbl; College; Professional.

CASEY, Monica D; Harlan HS; Chicago, IL; CmntyWkr; HonRl; NHS; 4-H; PpCl; 4-HAwd; Illinois State; Accountin.

CASEY, Patricia A; Hillsboro HS; Hillsboro, IL; 8/180 Band; Chr; CncrtBnd; HonRl; MrchBnd; NatlMeritCmnd; VPQuill&Scroll; SchMus; SchPl; SctActv; RptrSchPpr; PresFrCl; College; Journalist.

CASEY, Patty K; Emerson Hubbard HS; Winnebago, NE; 6/56 VPSophCls; ALAGirlsSt; HonRl; LbryAde; NHS; TchrAde; College; Teaching.

CASEY, Roberta L; Mundelein HS; Mundelein, IL; 12/340 Chr; Chrs; HonRl; JrNHS; LitMag; NHS; SchAde; SchPl; TchrAde; College; Business Admin.

CASEY, Robin M; Robert Lindblom Tech HS; Chicago, IL; HonRl; LbryAde; NHS; Quill&Scroll; StuCncl; RptrSchPpr; MthCl; Bsktbl; Tennis; Univ Of Michigan; Cpa.

CASEY, Sibyl L; Whiteland Comm HS; New Whiteland, IN; 35/210 Chr; ChrhWkr; HonRl; HospAde; YthFlsp; FHA; LetterTennis; GAA; Cumberland College; Medical Tech.

CASEY, Stephen; Lakeville HS; Burnsville, MN; HonRl; RptrSchPpr; 4-H; Vocational School; Telephone Communications.

CASEY, Thomas C; Marquette Jr HS; Brookfield, WI; 66/250 HonRl; SchAde; SctActv; LatCl; CaptFtbl; LetterTrk; College; Science.

CASH, Brenda S; Mckinley HS; St Louis, MO; 8/171 VPJrCls; SecSrCls; HonRl; SecYrbk; Chrldr; DARAwd; KiwanAwd; Se Missouri State Univ; Business.

CASH, Donna; St Pius X HS; Kansas City, MO; 50/140 Band; Chrs; HospAde; PepBnd; SchMus; PpCl; CaptBsktbl; GAA; Forestry.

CASH, John F; Dekalb HS; Dekalb, IL; Aud/Vis; HonRl; LitMag; StuCncl; TchrAde; RptrYrbk; RptrSchPpr; FrCl; SpnCl; LetterSwmmng; U Of Mo; Business.

CASHEL, Therese A; Springfield Catholic HS; Springfield, MO; SecFrshCls; VPSrCls; Chr; HonRl; StuCncl; StuGov; LetterBsbl; Bsktbl; GAA; IMSpt; Sw Mo State Univ.

CASHEN, Michael E; Pawnee HS; Pawnee, IL; 1/55 PresJrCls; Band; CncrtBnd; HonRl; JrNHS; LbryAde; MrchBnd; NHS; FrCl; SARAwd; Coll; Writing Or Teaching.

CASKEY, Sue A; Lasalle Peru Twp HS; Lasalle, IL; 48/516 HonRl; NHS; StuCncl; PresLatCl; LetterTennis; LetterTrk; Illinois State University; Physical Educ.

CASPALL, Laura J; Macomb Sr HS; Macomb, IL; 30/235 Chr; ChrhWkr; HonRl; NHS; SchMus; RptrYrbk; FrCl; Western Ill University.

CASPER, Angela M; Harrison HS; Harrison, MI; 3/141 HonRl; PolWkr; TchrAde; FrCl; Central Mi.

CASPER, Deborah S; Anna Jonesboro Comm HS; Anna, IL; 17/139 TrsSophCls; TrsJrCls; Band; CncrtBnd; DrlTm; LbryAde; MrchBnd; PepBnd; RptrYrbk; Yrbk; EdSchPpr; FHA; FTA; SpnCl; Univ; Professional.

CASPER, Janice M; Greenfield HS; Greenfield, WI; Band; Chrs; HonRl; ModUN; NHS; RptrYrbk; RptrSchPpr; Univ Of Wisconsin; Music.

CASPER, Judy S; Vienna Community HS; Cypress, IL; 8/106 Chrs; OffAde; SchAde; SchPl; StuCncl; TchrAde; 4-H; FHA; PpCl; Trk; Shawnee Jr Clge; Rn.

CASPER, Rex A; Madison HS; Madison Hts, MI; 40/240 ChrhWkr; HonRl; NHS; SciCl; Swmmng; Lawrence Inst Of Tech; Electrical Engr.

CASPERS, Mary; Bird Island Public HS; Bird Island, MN; Band; Chr; CncrtBnd; HonRl; NatlMeritCmnd; SchMus; SchPl; Coll; Med.

CASPERS, Sandra D; Smith Center HS; Gaylord, KS; ALAGirlsSt; Band; Chr; Chrs; ChrhWkr; CncrtBnd; DrlTm; RptrSchPpr; PpCl; IMSpt; Beauty Academy; Cosmotology.

CASPERS, Steven L; Smith Center HS; Gaylord, KS; 11/61 CncrtBnd; HonRl; MrchBnd; PepBnd; SchMus; SctActv; Yrbk; SchPpr; Ftbl; CaptWrstlng; Kansas St Univ; Gen Engineering.

CASPERSON, Christine M; Greeburg Comm HS; Freeburg, IL; Band; HonRl; ModUN; NHS; NatlThespSoc; SchPl; SecStuCncl; RptrYrbk; PpCl; Chrldr;.

CASS, Jack R; St Marys HS; Gaylord, MI; 1/256 PresFrshCls; PresSophCls; PresJrCls; PresSrCls; JA; ROTC; FDA; LetterBsbl; LetterBsktbl; LetterFtbl; Univ Of Mi; Doctor.

CASS, Janice P; Kirksville Sr HS; Kirksville, MO; HonRl; HospAde; TchrAde; RptrSchPpr; SchPpr; FHA; FrCl; Trk; College; Veterinarian.

CASS, Kimberley; United Township HS; E Moline, IL; 16/843 Chr; HonRl; HospAde; JrNHS; NHS; StuCncl; GerCl; Tennis; Lutheran Sch Of Nursing; Nurse.

CASS, Laura; United Township HS; Siluis, IL; 9/800 Chr; Chrl; ChrhWkr; HonRl; NHS; OffAde; SchMus; SchPl; GAA; College.

CASS, Marla J; Sullivan HS; Chicago, IL; PresSophCls; HonRl; NHS; OffAde; SchAde; StuCncl; RptrYrbk; RptrSchPpr; EdSchPpr; University; Attorney.

CASSAVAUGH, Glenda L; North Nodaway R 6 HS; Hopkins, MO; SecSophCls; DrlTm; HonRl; LbryAde; SecStuCncl; VPFHA; PpCl; SecSciCl; Bsktbl; Trk; Nwmsu; Acct.

CASSELL, Patrick E; Anita HS; Anita, IA; 16/61 PresFrshCls; VPSophCls; PresJrCls; ChrhWkr; CmntyWkr; HonRl; NatlFornLg; PolWkr; StuCncl; StuGov; Bsbl; Bsktbl; Ftbl; Trk; Jamestown College; Business Mgmt.

CASSERLY, Kimberly; Mulberry Grove Unit 1 HS; Mulberry Grove, IL; 15/39 DrmMjrt; HonRl; HospAde; NHS; Yrbk; RptrSchPpr; FFA; GAA; Nursing School; Registered Nurse.

CASSIDAY, William C; Alton Sr HS; Alton, IL; Band; HonRl; MrchBnd; TchrAde; Southern Ill Univ; Physics.

CASSIDY, James; Jasper HS; Jasper, IN; ChrhWkr; HonRl; SctActv; Bsktbl; Ftbl; Trk; IMSpt; Indiana State Univ; Stock Broker.

CASSIDY, Jill L; Aurora Sr HS; Aurora, IN; 4/135 ALAGirlsSt; Band; Chr; ChrhWkr; CncrtBnd; HonRl; SecNHS; PpCl; GAA; IMSpt; College; Health Sciences.

CASSIDY, Mary L; Jeffersonville HS; Jeffersonville, IN; 44/650 Band; ChrhWkr; DrmMjrt; HonRl; JrNHS; SctActv; Pres4-H; LatCl; 4-HAwd; University; Science Music.

CASSIDY, Pamela K; Nokomis HS; Ohlman, IL; VPSrCls; Chrs; ChrhWkr; CmntyWkr; HonRl; SchMus; Yrbk; 4-H; GAA; St Johns School Of Nursing; Nursing.

CASSIDY, Steven J; St Patrick HS; Norridge, IL; 14/376 HonRl; StuGov; SciCl; Science Field.

CASSIDY, Thomas M; Monroe HS; Monroe, MI; 85/540 ChrhWkr; JA; RedCrAde; StuGov; SciCl; LetterFtbl; Trk; Wrstlng; IMSpt; Monroe Cty Comm College; Engineering.

CASSINO, Mark C; Adrian HS; Adrian, MI; 11/400 RptrSchPpr; FrCl; U Of Michigan; Writer.

CASSIOPPI, Gerald A; Guilford HS; Rockford, IL; 67/658 HonRl; NatlMeritCmnd; LetterBsbl; LetterSwmmng; Univ Of Illinois; Accounting.

CASSMEYER, Karen; Duchesne HS; Bridgeton, MO; 26/200 ALAGirlsSt; HonRl; NHS; SchMus; SctActv; FrCl; PpCl; Bsktbl; Trk; GAA; College; Accountant.

CASSON, Karen J; Pontiac Twp HS; Pontiac, IL; 3/202 TrsFrshCls; TrsSophCls; SecJrCls; CmntyWkr; HonRl; NHS; EdYrBk; VPFrCl; MthCl; PpCl; Illinois Wesleyan University.

CASSUTT, Deborah A; Ramona HS; Ramona, SD; 2/18 VPSophCls; SecJrCls; Chrs; HonRl; SchPl; SecStuCncl; Yrbk; SecFHA; Chrldr; College.

CASTANEDA, Cynthia A; Escanaba Area Public HS; Escanaba, MI; NatlFornLg; Quill&Scroll; StuGov; RptrYrbk; RptrSchPpr; EdSchPpr; SchPpr; SpnCl; CaptSocr; GAA; Central Michigan Univ; Journalism.

CASTANEDA, Lucia; St Catherines HS; Racine, WI; 86/250 VPFrshCls; VPSophCls; HonRl; PolWkr; Bsbl; Bsktbl; Chrldr; IMSpt; PPFtbl; PresAwd;.

CASTANEDA, Maria; St Stanislaus Kostka HS; Chicago, IL; 25/64 PresFrshCls; TrsSophCls; TrsJrCls; TrsSrCls; ChrhWkr; StuCncl; RptrSchPpr; FTA; SpnCl; Rosary Coll;spec Educ.

CASTEEL, Marcia L; Pittsfield HS; Pittsfield, IL; 3/126 SecJrCls; Chrs; ChrhWkr; HonRl; Mdrgl; NHS; NatlThespSoc; SchMus; SchPl; SctActv; Swmmng; LetterTennis; Trk; Univ Of Ill; Physical Education.

CASTEGNARO, Anthony M; Seymour HS; Plainville, IL; 14/65 Band; CncrtBnd; HonRl; MrchBnd; PepBnd; SchMus; StuCncl; LetterBsbl; LetterTrk; College.

CASTELLANO, Marcella; Marion Sr HS; Marion, IL; CaptDrlTm; MrchBnd; PpCl; S Il Univ; Elem Teacher.

CASTELLARIN, Peter F; Mount Carmel HS; Burnham, IL; 29/197 VPSrCls; Band; HonRl; NHS; NatlMeritCmnd; SctActv; StuCncl; De Paul Univ; Law.

CASTELLI, Bartolomeo J; Chaminade College Prep; Crestwood, MO; 28/110 Band; CmntyWkr; HonRl; JA; SchPl; StuGov; RptrSchPpr; Bsbl; Bsktbl; Ftbl; Chrldr; CchngActv; St Marys Univ; Medicine.

CASTELNUOVO, Richard M; Evanston Twp HS; Evanston, IL; 50/1040 HonRl; Ftbl; College; Law.

CASTIC, Susan J; Egyptian HS; Olive Branch, IL; 6/70 HonRl; LbryAde; Orch; SchMus; TchrAde; GAA; College; Wildlife Technology.

CASTILLO, Robert; Willowbrook Hs; Villa Park, IL; 80 PresFrshCls; HonRl; ModUN; NHS; SctActv; StuCncl; YthFlsp; LetterBsbl; LetterBsktbl; LetterFtbl; U Of Illinois;ba Finance Vuris Doctor.

CASTLE, Linda K; Chase County HS; Imperial, NE; 8/60 ALAGirlsSt; Band; CncrtBnd; DrmMjrt; HospAde; MrchBnd; NHS; PepBnd; TchrAde; 4-H; FHA; Trk; Chrldr; Kearney St College; Physicians Asst.

CASTLE, Nancy; Mona Shores HS; Norton Shores, MI; 15/500 Band; CncrtBnd; HonRl; LbryAde; NatlFornLg; NatlMeritSchl; PolWkr; SctActv; FrCl; PpCl; Mi State; Radio Announcer.

CASTLEBERRY, Roxlynn; Kimball County HS; Kimball, NE; 4/88 Band; Chrs; CncrtBnd; HonRl; HospAde; Mdrgl; MrchBnd; NHS; SchMus; SchPl; EdYrBk; 4-H; PpCl; Trk; Larmie County Comm Col; Law Enforcement.

CASTLEMAN, Lori; Ofallon Twsp HS; Ofallon, IL; 9/270 Chrs; DrlTm; HonRl; NHS; StuCncl; RptrYrbk; EdYrBk; SchPpr; Trk; Southern Ill Univ At Carbondale; Journalism.

CASTLEMAN, Lori A; O Fallon Township HS; O Fallon, IL; 9/301 CmntyWkr; HonRl; NHS; SchMus; StuCncl; YthFlsp; RptrYrbk; EdYrBk; Trk; Siu; Journalism.

CASTOR, Loretta; Huron HS; Ann Arbor, MI; 30/600 HonRl; LbryAde; Orch; SchMus; SctActv; FrCl; Bsktbl; Univ Of Michigan; Music.

CASTRO, Rito; Kewaunee HS; Kewaunee, WI; 12/139 PresSophCls; Aud/Vis; HonRl; SchAde; TchrAde; SchPpr; PresSciCl; Ftbl; Wrstlng; University; Ecology.

CASTROGIOVANNI, Gary J; Marmion Military Academy; Chicago, IL; 7/69 PresSophCls; Band; CncrtBnd; HonRl; MrchBnd; NHS; NatlMeritCmnd; ROTC; StuCncl; PpCl; Ftbl; Loyola Univ; Business Adm.

CASTROGIOVANNI, Ronald R; Marmion Military Academy; Chicago, IL; 4/89 PresSrCls; Band; CncrtBnd; HonRl; JrNHS; MrchBnd; NatlMeritCmnd; PepBnd; ROTC; SchMus; StuCncl; StuGov; Bsbl; Ftbl; College; Dentistry.

CASURELLA, James E; Rolling Meadows HS; Arlington Hts, IL; PresSrCls; HonRl; NHS; NatlMeritSF; SchMus; StuGov; LetterFtbl; CchngActv; Harvard College; Law.

CASWELL, Steven; Walled Lake Central HS; Union Lake, MI; 35/365 HonRl; ModUN; NHS; StuGov; Coll; Poli Sci.

CATALFIO, Maria R; Lakeview HS; St Clair Shrs, MI; 11/658 PresFrshCls; HonRl; LitMag; LbryAde; NatlFornLg; NHS; PolWkr; StuCncl; StuGov; SchPpr; Univ Of Michigan; Journalism.

CATCHINGS, Kathy J; Cahokia Sr HS; Centreville, IL; Band; CncrtBnd; DrlTm; DrmMjrt; HonRl; MrchBnd; NatlMeritCmnd; OffAde; Orch; Quill&Scroll; SchPl; RptrSchPpr; IMSpt; Washington Univ; Journalism.

CATE, Mike B; Clio Area HS; Clio, MI; 22/366 PresSrCls; HonRl; LitMag; StuCncl; StuGov; Ftbl; Trk; IMSpt; Mi St; Clinical Psychologist.

CATENACCI, Donald L; Pardeeville HS; Wyocena, WI; College.

CATENZARO, Mary L; Marian Central HS; Crystal Lake, IL; 8/116 Chrl; ChrhWkr; HonRl; NHS; TchrAde; Yrbk; EdSchPpr; Mc Henry Co College; Psychology.

CATER, John M; Washburn Rural HS; Topeka, KS; 6/180 Band; ChrhWkr; CncrtBnd; HonRl; NatlMeritFnl; NatlMeritSF; PepBnd; SchMus; SchPl; MthCl; College; Engineer.

CATES, Joe M; Griffin HS; Springfield, IL; HonRl; JA; Univ Of Illinois; Law.

CATES, Larry D; Anna Jonesboro HS; Jonesboro, IL; 33/137 CmntyWkr; HonRl; NHS; Bsbl; Bsktbl; Ftbl; Trk; CchngActv; IMSpt; S Il Univ; Civil Engineering.

CATES, Sandra D; East Prairie HS; East Prairie, MO; 3/84 Band; ChrhWkr; CncrtBnd; HonRl; MrchBnd; PresNHS; PepBnd; RptrSchPpr; SpnCl; SciCl; Southeast Missouri State Univ; Cpa.

CATES, Terris; Mt Vernon HS; Mt Vernon, MO; 1/94 PresJrCls; Band; CncrtBnd; HonRl; MrchBnd; ModUN; MthCl; Trk; DanFAwd; Univ Of Mo; Physics.

CATHCART, Patty A; R 1 North Callaway HS; Auxvasse, MO; 2/71 TrsFrshCls; ChrhWkr; HonRl; LbryAde; StuCncl; 4-H; PpCl; University; Accountant.

CATHEY, Cameron H; Fairfield HS; Fairfield, IA; 1/200 Band; CncrtBnd; HonRl; MrchBnd; NHS; PepBnd; Quill&Scroll; EdYrBk; RptrSchPpr; SciCl; Iowa St Univ; Engineering.

CATHEY, Donald G; Topeka West HS; Topeka, KS; 54/419 LitMag; GerCl; LetterTrk; Univ; Prof Bus.

CATHEY, Spencer O; Monticello HS; Monticello, IL; 17/190 CncrtBnd; NHS; StuCncl; Yrbk; LatCl; Univ Of Ill; Math.

CATHOLOS, Jo Ellen; Northwest HS; Grand Island, NE; Chr; CmntyWkr; CncrtBnd; HonRl; MrchBnd; StuCncl; FHA; Trk; CaptChrldr; School Of Music; Pianist.

CATLIN, Rick J; Gibbon HS; Gibbon, NE; 6/60 VPFrshCls; HonRl; SctActv; TchrAde; LetterFtbl; LetterTrk; CaptWrstlng; CchngActv; University; Professional.

CATO, Charlotte A; Zalma HS; Zalma, MO; TrsSophCls; TrsJrCls; Chr; ChrhWkr; HonRl; FHA; College.

CATOE, Dianne M; Ashby Public HS; Ashby, MN; Band; Chr; DrmMjrt; HonRl; HospAde; NHS; TchrAde; Yrbk; FHA; PpCl; LetterBsktbl; Trk; Chrldr; GAA; College; Secretary.

CATON, Mary S; Regis HS; Eau Claire, WI; 15/138 HonRl; MrchBnd; NatlFornLg; RptrSchPpr; SpnCl; PpCl; U Of Wis; Commercial Art.

CATRON, Joseph K; Frankfort Sr HS; Frankfort, IN; 35/250 ALBoysSt; NHS; StuCncl; TchrAde; KeyCl; LetterTrk; Wabash College; Law.

CATRON, Tim D; Clinton Central HS; Russiaville, IN; 15/105 Chr; Chrs; HonRl; YthFlsp; FFA; PpCl; LetterTrk; Wrstlng;.

CATT, Diane M; Independence Comm HS; Independence, IA; 16/146 CncrtBnd; HonRl; MrchBnd; NHS; SchMus; SchPl; 4-H; LetterTrk; IMSpt; 4-HAwd; Winona St In Mn; Bio.

CATT, Lawrence R; Brazil HS; Brazil, IN; Chr; Chrs; HonRl; NatlThespSoc; RedCrAde; SctActv; SpnCl; PpCl; SciCl; Glf; University; Professional.

CATTANACH, Curt D; Neillsville HS; Neillsville, WI; HonRl; SchPl; StuCncl; StuGov; Yrbk; SpnCl; PpCl; LetterFtbl; Swmmng; IMSpt; Coll; Pharmacy.

CATTLEDGE, Antionette; Southeast HS; Springfield, IL; 9/503 Band; Chr; HonRl; JrNHS; VPNHS; NatlMeritCmnd; StuCncl; VPMthCl; Chrldr; PresAwd; Univ Of Il; Accounting.

CAUDILL, Anthony R; Springville Comm HS; Springville, IA; ALBoysSt; ChrhWkr; PolWkr; StuCncl; StuGov; TchrAde; YthFlsp; FSA; FrCl; University Of Iowa; Engineer.

CAUDILL, David A; Whitko HS; Pierceton, IN; ALBoysSt; ChrhWkr; HonRl; NatlThespSoc; SchPl; GerCl; SciCl; LetterFtbl; LetterGlf; Fl Inst; Ocean.

CAUDILL, Rhonda J; Oscoda Area HS; Elkhart, IN; Band; Chr; ChrhWkr; CncrtBnd; HonRl; MrchBnd; Freed Hardeman College; Social Work.

CAUDILL, Viki L; Milan Jr Sr HS; Milan, IN; HonRl; LbryAde; SchAde; SchPl; TchrAde; EdSchPpr; FTA; VPSpnCl; PpCl; IMSpt; Indiana State Univ; Archaeologist.

CAUDLE, Clinton D; South Pemiscot HS; Steele, MO; Band; CmntyWkr; CncrtBnd; HonRl; JrNHS; MrchBnd; PepBnd; RedCrAde; SctActv; FFA; KeyCl; EngCl; SpnCl; University; Agriculture.

CAUDLE, Richard L; Parkwood HS; Joplin, MO; Chr; ChrhWkr; HonRl; YthFlsp; Ftbl; Oral Roberts U; Engr.

CAULEY, Kathryn L; Lesterville HS; Black, MO; Chr; Chrs; HonRl; LbryAde; SchPl; PpCl; GAA; Trade Sch; Vocational.

CAULFIELD, Shirley A; Willow Lake HS; Willow Lake, SD; Chr; Chrs; HonRl; LbryAde; PresFrshCls; SchPl; RptrYrbk; Trk; Chrldr; AmLegAwd; Nettleton Col; Pro Acct.

CAUSEY, Steven L; Cass Technical HS; Detroit, MI; StuCncl; Univ Of Michigan; Medicine.

CAUVEL, Teri L; Oak Park Sr HS; Gladstone, MO; AFS; Chr; ChrhWkr; HonRl; LbryAde; SchMus; SctActv; FrCl; Business School; Secretary.

CAVA, Roberta A; Nazareth Academy; Cicero, IL; VPJrCls; SchAde; StuGov; PpCl; GAA; IMSpt; College; Law Enforcement.

CAVALIGOS, George K; Curie HS; Chicago, IL; HonRl; LetterWrstlng; De Paul Univ; Biochemistry.

CAVALLARO, Diane B; Resurrection HS; Chicago, IL; 116/252 PresSophCls; HonRl; HospAde; GerCl; GAA;.

CAVALLO, Laura L; Highland Park HS; Highland Park, IL; Chrs; NHS; SchMus; SchPl; Georgetown Univ; International Affairs.

CAVANAGH, Nancy J; Mother Mc Auley HS; Chicago, IL; 47/475 Chrs; HonRl; NHS; SchMus; Northern Illinois University.

CAVANAUGH, James M; Monticello HS; Monticello, IL; ChrhWkr; HonRl; RptrSchPpr; Tennis; Southern Illinois; Journalism.

CAVANAUGH, Kathleen M; Ottawa HS; Ottawa, IL; 23/420 Band; CncrtBnd; HonRl; HospAde; MrchBnd; NHS; PepBnd; YthFlsp; College; Pharmacy.

CAVANAUGH, Kerry L; Assumption HS; Wis Rapids, WI; 1/110 HonRl; NatlFornLg; NHS; SchPl; StuCncl; TchrAde; RptrSchPpr; SpnCl; MthCl; Chrldr; Univ; Law.

CAVANAUGH, Kevin M; S County Tech HS; Affton, MO; 1/20 Aud/Vis; Chrs; HonRl; SchAde; SchMus; SchPl; SctActv; TchrAde; College; Business.

CAVANESS, Terry L; Shawnee HS; Mcclure, IL; SecTrsSophCls; HonRl; TchrAde; FBLA; FHA; FTA; PpCl; GAA; Brigham Young U; Teach Deaf.

CAVE, Betty L; Marcus Comm HS; Marcus, IA; 8/71 Band; ChrhWkr; CncrtBnd; NHS; YthFlsp; Bsktbl; Trk; CaptChrldr; CaptIMSpt; PPFtbl; Business Sch; Vocation.

CAVE, Cynthia A; Northridge HS; Bristol, IN; TrsJrCls; Chr; HonRl; NHS; SctActv; RptrSchPpr; FHA; SpnCl; PpCl; CaptChrldr; Coll; Nursing.

CAVEDONI, Jean; Dominican HS; East Detroit, MI; HonRl; NHS; LetterBsbl; LetterBsktbl; Ftbl; CchngActv; GAA; Univ Of Michigan; Marine Biology.

CAVEN, James; Catholic Memorial HS; Waukesha, WI; RptrYrbk; EdYrBk; IMSpt; Univ Of Wi Madison; Social Sci.

CAVEN, Louise M; Wellcome Memorial HS; Amboy, MN; 6/45 PresSophCls; ALAGirlsSt; Band; Chrs; CncrtBnd; HonRl; SchMus; StuCncl; EdYrBk; Trk; College.

CAVENAUGH, Timothy R; Loyola Academy; Deerfield, IL; 12/442 HonRl; LbryAde; NHS; NatlMeritCmnd; SchMus; RptrYrbk; GerCl; LetterBsbl; LetterSwmmng; Univ Of Ill; Architect.

CAVENEE, Charles J; Manhattan HS; Manhattan, KS; Univ; Engineering.

CAVENY, Catherine L; Marian Central HS; Algonquin, IL; 8/114 Chr; ChrhWkr; CmntyWkr; HonRl; NHS; SchAde; TchrAde; Yrbk; Blackburn College; Lawyer.

CAVES, Jim G; Wildrose Public HS; Wild Rose, WI; ALBoysSt; Band; ChrhWkr; CncrtBnd; HonRl; MrchBnd; PepBnd; SchMus; SchPl; SctActv; Bsbl; Bsktbl; Trade School; Vocation.

CAVEYE, Julie A; Bryan Sr HS; Omaha, NE; ChrhWkr; HonRl; NHS; SpnCl; Trk; CchngActv; University; Dental Hygiene.

CAVIN, Patricia A; St Mark HS; St Louis, MO; TrsSophCls; SecJrCls; HonRl; LbryAde; SchMus; SctActv; EdSchPpr; College; Human Relation.

CAVITT, Christina M; Richfield HS; Richfield, MN; DrlTm; DrmBgl; StuGov; RptrYrbk; LetterBsktbl; Trk; IMSpt; Coll; Mass Communications.

CAWLEY, Mary; Arthur Hill HS; Saginaw, MI; JrNHS; FrCl; Bsktbl; Tennis; Alma College; Medicine.

CAYLOR, Duane K; Linn Mar HS; Marion, IA; VPSophCls; ALBoysSt; ChrhWkr; HonRl; NHS; NatlMeritSF; NatlThespSoc; SchMus; Bsktbl; Trk; Iowa State;medicine.

CAZARES, Mary; Jones Commercial HS; Chicago, IL; 66/437 Chrs; HonRl; StuCncl; FBLA; Bsbl; Bsktbl; Swmmng; Trk; Chrldr; GAA; College; Professional.

CAZZELL, Cindy L; Ex Springs West HS; Excelsior Springs, MO; 27/240 HonRl; JrNHS; NHS; TchrAde; FTA; SciCl; LetterTennis; Chrldr; AmLegAwd; College; Teacher.

CEARLOCK, Cathy; Arthur HS; Arthur, IL; 12/48 ALAGirlsSt; Band; Chrs; ChrhWkr; HonRl; MrchBnd; SctActv; SptEdYrbk; FHA; College;vocation.

CEBAR, Paul R; Pius Xi HS; Milwaukee, WI; 3/375 PresSophCls; PresJrCls; Chrs; HonRl; NHS; NatlMeritSF; SchMus; SchPl; StuCncl; StuGov; Yrbk; RptrSchPpr; College; Communication.

CEBELAK, Carol M; Pennfield HS; Battle Creek, MI; SecSophCls; HonRl; NHS; SchPl; StuGov; TchrAde; FBLA; PpCl; GAA; DanFAwd; Western Michigan Univ; Bus Adm.

CEBULA, Casey M; Rhinelander HS; Rhinelander, WI; StuCncl; CaptBsktbl; Tennis; Trk; College.

CECERE, Mary R; Resurrection HS; Norridge, IL; 25/285 SecFrshCls; PresSophCls; PresJrCls; Chr; HonRl; JrNHS; NHS; SchMus; SpnCl; Rosary Coll; Business.

CECH, Gail A; Saginaw HS; Saginaw, MI; HonRl; JA; JrNHS; Trade Sch; Office Work.

CECH, Hildegard; Sts Peter And Paul HS; Saginaw, MI; Chrs; DrlTm; JA; Mdrgl; NHS; GerCl; Univ; Professional.

CECH, Richard; St Patrick HS; Chicago, IL; HonRl; JrNHS; MthCl; Trk; Univ; General Business Accountancy.

CECICH, Diane R; Lourdes HS; Chicago, IL; 97/293 PresFrshCls; PresSrCls; HonRl; StuCncl; StuGov; LatCl; IMSpt; Evangelical Sch; Rn.

CECIL, Carl P; Greenwood Community HS; Greenwood, IN; 7/238 ALBoysSt; ChrhWkr; CmntyWkr; NHS; PolWkr; PresSctActv; StuCncl; YthLg; SecKeyCl; Ftbl; LetterTrk; LetterWrstlng; Us Military Academy; Law.

CEDARHOLM, Sara L; Marquette HS; Marquette, KS; 5/24 SecSophCls; Band; Chr; Chrl; Chrs; ChrhWkr; CmntyWkr; CncrtBnd; DrlTm; DrmMjrt; HonRl; Trk; Chrldr; Seattle Pacific College; Humanities.

CEDERBERG, Kyle D; Luray HS; Luray, KS; PresSophCls; ChrhWkr; CmntyWkr; HonRl; StuCncl; TchrAde; LetterBsktbl; CaptFtbl; LetterTrk; 4-HAwd; Ft Hays Kansas St College; Biology.

CEDERSTROM, Steven R; Velva Public HS; Velva, ND; 6/48 PresSrCls; Band; HonRl; NHS; PepBnd; SctActv; StuCncl; TchrAde; Bsbl; Bsktbl; College; Pharmacy.

CEDZO, Cathy M; Rib Lake HS; Rib Lake, WI; Chrs; HonRl; LbryAde; RptrYrbk; RptrSchPpr; Bsktbl; Stewardess.

CEGIELSKI, Terry P; Marian HS; South Bend, IN; RotaryAwd; Purdue Univ; Forestry.

CEHULA, Linda; Grosse Pte Pk HS; Grosse Pte Pk, MI; 147/630 Band; ChrhWkr; CmntyWkr; CncrtBnd; HonRl; PepBnd; SchPl; Michigan Univ; Professional.

CEJDA, Cindy L; Wamego HS; Wamego, KS; SecTrsJrCls; Band; DrlTm; HonRl; OffAde; SchPl; Twrl; PresFBLA; PpCl; Chrldr; College Or University.

CEJKA, Darrell G; Dorchester HS; Dorchester, NE; 3/26 VPSrCls; Chr; ChrhWkr; HonRl; SchPl; EdSchPpr; LetterBsbl; LetterBsktbl; LetterFtbl; LetterTrk; Doane Coll; Journalism.

CEKANDER, Linda; Mahomet Seymour HS; Champaign, IL; ALAGirlsSt; Band; ChrhWkr; HonRl; SchMus; StuCncl; Yrbk; SpnCl; Trk; AmLegAwd; College Of Nursing; Rn.

CELESCHI, Rebecca M; Glenbard West HS; Glen Ellyn, IL; 36/545 HonRl; NHS; NatlMeritCmnd; NatlThespSoc; SchMus; SchPl; College Of Dupage; Medicine.

CELING, Lynn A; Mundelein HS; Mundelein, IL; 12/336 CncrtBnd; HonRl; LitMag; MrchBnd; Quill&Scroll; StuGov; GerCl; LatCl; Il State Univ;.

CELINSKY, Cindy A; South Shore HS; Herbster, WI; Band; Chr; Chrl; Chrs; ChrhWkr; CncrtBnd; HonRl; SchPl; RptrSchPpr; Chrldr;.

CELIS, Jorge; Oak Park & River Forest HS; River Forest, IL; 187/1012 HonRl; Ftbl; Loyola University; Biology.

CELLA, Michael J; Naperville Central HS; Naperville, IL; 1/800 HonRl; NHS; StuGov; LatCl; MthCl; LetterBsbl; LetterBsktbl; AmLegAwd; Univ Of Illinois; Mathematics.

CEMENO, William T; Joliet Catholic HS; Joliet, IL; 7/170 HonRl; NHS; FSA; RusCl; SciCl; LetterTrk; Southern Illinois Univ; Zoology.

CENEK, Kurt J; Cedarburg HS; Cedarburg, WI; HonRl; NatlMeritSF; Ftbl; Wrstlng; Univ Of Wi; Mathematics.

CENEY, Pamela J; Hillsboro HS; Hillsboro, IL; Band; Chrs; HonRl; NatlMeritSF; SchAde; SctActv; TchrAde; EdSchPpr; PresGerCl; AmLegAwd; College ; Foresty.

CENTELLA, Celeste V; St Edward HS; Carpentersville, IL; 16/128 Band; ChrhWkr; CmntyWkr; CncrtBnd; HonRl; MrchBnd; NatlMeritCmnd; StuCncl; MthCl; Barat College; Education.

CEPA, Jerome M; Saint Rita HS; Chicago, IL; Band; CncrtBnd; MrchBnd; NHS; Univ; Professional.

CEPLECHA, Kari Sue A; Bethlehem Academy; Northfield, MN; 9/95 Chrs; HonRl; SchMus; SchPl;

StuCncl; TchrAde; RptrSchPpr; SpnCl; Trk; College; Teaching.

CEPRESS, Randal G; Assumption HS; Vesper, WI; 8/121 HonRl; 4-H; KeyCl; CaptFtbl; CaptWrstlng; PresAwd; Uw Lacrosse;computers.

CEREK, Gail M; Resurrection HS; Chicago, IL; 18/261 HonRl; HospAde; Quill&Scroll; SchPl; RptrYrbk; RptrSchPpr; SchPpr; Northern Ill Univ; Dietetics.

CERMAK, Blythe S; Nerinx Hall HS; St Louis, MO; Chrl; CmntyWkr; HonRl; NatlThespSoc; OffAde; SchPl; RptrYrbk; RptrSchPpr; PpCl; LetterSwmmng; Univ; Archeology.

CERNIVIVO, Diane; Lourdes HS; Chicago, IL; 7/250 HonRl; NHS; SchMus; SchPl; SpnCl; Mac Cormac Jr College; Court Reporter.

CERNY, Bridget J; Edwardsville HS; Edwardsville, IL; Trk; GAA; Southern Il Univ; Accounting.

CERNY, Danette K; Scotus Central Catholic HS; Columbus, NE; 11/60 TrsFrshCls; TrsSophCls; Chr; Chrs; HonRl; HospAde; NHS; TchrAde; EdSchPpr; SecPpCl; Trk; IMSpt; College; Professional.

CERNY, Diane L; J A Craig HS; Janesville, WI; Band; HonRl; JrNHS; NHS; OffAde; StuCncl; TchrAde; RptrSchPpr; Chrldr; GAA; University Of Wisconsin; Occupational Thera.

CERNY, Stephen R; Cobden Unit HS; Cobden, IL; 1/55 PresFrshCls; VPSophCls; PresJrCls; Band; Chrs; ChrhWkr; HonRl; MrchBnd; NHS; PepBnd; Millikin University; Biology.

CERVANTES, Susan M; Calumet HS; Gary, IN; 3/330 HonRl; JrNHS; SchPl; SpnCl; College; Medical Tech.

CERVENKA, Dean A; West Central HS; Francesville, IN; SecFrshCls; HonRl; VPNHS; StuCncl; PresYthFlsp; 4-H; LetterBsktbl; Trk; 4-HAwd; College.

CERVENY, Diana; Fennville HS; Pullan, MI; 2 84 HonRl; LbryAde; Davenport Coll; Secretarial.

CESAREK, Bruce; Sterling HS; Sterling, IL; 4/390 ALBoysSt; HonRl; NatlFornLg; NHS; Quill&Scroll; Yrbk; SchPpr; GerCl; Illinois State U; Mathematics.

CESARIO, John R; Marmion Academy; Elburn, IL; 8/87 ChrhWkr; HonRl; Sacrstn; SctActv; RptrYrbk; RptrSchPpr; SchPpr; LetterFtbl; Trk; AmLegAwd; Loyola University; Lawyer.

CESARONE, Diane; Trinity HS; Chicago, IL; 20/204 Chrs; HonRl; NHS; University; Communication.

CESNE, Ann; Union HS; Caledonia, WI; 1/225 ALAGirlsSt; HonRl; NatlFornLg; NHS; StuCncl; GAA; BauchLmbAwd; 4-HAwd; Univ Of Wi Oshkosh; Pre Law.

CESSNA, Michael M; Unit 226 HS; Mineral, IL; 25/52 PresStuCncl; Pres4-H; FFA; FTA; Bsbl; CaptBsktbl; CaptFtbl; 4-HAwd; Illinois State Univ; Teaching,coaching.

CESTKOWSKI, Theresa A; Watersmeet HS; Watersmeet, MI; 3/14 PresJrCls; HonRl; OffAde; PepBnd; StuCncl; RptrYrbk; RptrSchPpr; 4-H; Bsktbl; No Michigan Univ; Nurse.

CEVIGNEY, Connie D; Republic Michigamme HS; Michigamme, MI; PresSrCls; Band; HonRl; OffAde; StuGov; EdSchPpr; SecFrCl; Coll; Business.

CEZAR, William; Council Grove HS; Dwight, KS; ALBoysSt; Chrs; HonRl; SchMus; SchPl; RptrYrbk; Glf; AmLegAwd; Col; Prof.

CHACHICH, Alan C; Waterford Kettering HS; Drayton Plains, MI; 5/423 Aud/Vis; HonRl; JA; NHS; NatlMeritSchl; OffAde; LetterTennis; LetterTrk; JAAwd; Oakland Univ; Physicist.

CHACZYK, Edward A; Holy Redeemer HS; Detroit, MI; 10/190 HonRl; RptrYrbk; Col; Artist.

CHADIMA, Michael J; Washington Sr HS; Cedar Rapids, IA; 50/470 TrsSrCls; CtyCnl; SchPl; Treas-StuCncl; TchrAde; GodCntryAwd; Univ; Vocational.

CHADWICK, Nina; Mississinewa HS; Gas City, IN; 42/222 Chr; ChrhWkr; HonRl; CitAwd; Nursing School; Professional Nurse.

CHADWICK, Robert L; Galesburg Sr HS; Galesburg, IL; Band; ChrhWkr; CncrtBnd; HonRl; MrchBnd; Orch; PepBnd; SchMus; YthFlsp; No Illinois Univ; Music.

CHADY, Linda C; Benton HS; Benton, IL; 25/168 Band; ChrhWkr; HonRl; Quill&Scroll; SchPpr; FTA; SpnCl; MthCl; GAA; DARAwd; Coll; Math.

CHAFFEE, Mark S; Pinconning Area HS; Pinconning, MI; PresFrshCls; ALBoysSt; CmntyWkr; HonRl; NHS; SctActv; StuCncl; Bsbl; Bsktbl; Ftbl; Tennis; Ferris State College; Pharmacy.

CHAFFEE, Sarah; Taylor HS; Kokomo, IN; 10/160 HonRl; LbryAde; NHS; NatlThespSoc; OffAde; SchAde; SchMus; Yrbk; PpCl; PPFtbl; Ball St Univ; Bus.

CHAFFIN, Mark S; Central HS; Evansville, IN; 15/698 HonRl; JrNHS; NHS; RedCrAde; StuGov; TchrAde; IMSpt; College; Cpa.

CHAFIN, Robert; Richland Senior HS; Gray Ridge, MO; HonRl; NHS; PolWkr; StuCncl; StuGov; YthFlsp; EngCl; Bsktbl; GodCntryAwd; CitAwd; School Of Heavy Equip; Operate Heavy Equip.

CHAKOS, Kathi; Calumet HS; Gary, IN; 6/250 TrsSrCls; HonRl; NHS; StuCncl; YthFnd; PpCl; SciCl; Chrldr; LetterGAA; PPFtbl; DARAwd; Indiana Univ; Nursing.

CHALENDER, Robert A; Manhattan Sr HS; Manhattan, KS; ALBoysSt; Band; Chrl; HonRl; SchMus; SchPl; StuCncl; IMSpt; University; Fine Arts.

CHALFANT, David; De Kalb HS; Auburn, IN; 37/300 ALBoysSt; Aud/Vis; ChrhWkr; SchAde; StuCncl; YthFlsp; Bsbl; Bsktbl; IMSpt; Hillsdale Coll; Chiropractic.

CHALFANT, Larry; Monroe Central HS; Parker City, IN; 9/73 Aud/Vis; HonRl; NHS; RptrSchPpr;.

CHALKER, Mary Beth; Gull Lake HS; Galesburg, MI; 1/216 ChrhWkr; HonRl; NHS; Calvin Col; Christian Service.

CHALKEY, Denise E; Streator Twp HS; Streator, IL; 11/283 NHS; StuCncl; TchrAde; EdYrBk; FHA; PresFTA; SpnCl; DARAwd; 4-HAwd; I S U; Elem Ed.

CHALL, Mark E; Frankenmuth HS; Frankenmuth, MI; Aud/Vis; HonRl; NHS; NatlMeritCmnd; SchPl; Trk; Wayne State Univ; Med.

CHALMERS, Beth Anne; Airport Community HS; Carleton, MI; 13/273 Band; Chrs; HonRl; PepBnd; TchrAde; YthFlsp; RptrSchPpr; SpnCl; Trk; PresAwd; College; Nursing Or Social Wk.

CHALONER, Carole A; New Trier East HS; Wilmette, IL; TrsFrshCls; SecSophCls; SecSrCls; Chr; Chrs; ChrhWkr; CmntyWkr; HonRl; HospAde; OffAde; SchAde; SchMus; GAA; OptClAwd; Butler Univ; Physical Therapy.

CHALOUPKA, Patricia J; Stevens HS; Rapid City, SD; 23/431 HonRl; LetterNatlFornLg; StuCncl; LetterTrk; DARAwd; Schl Of Mines & Tech; Medicine.

CHALOUPKA, Richard A; Milbank HS; Twin Brooks, SD; TrsSrCls; HonRl; Col; Pro.

CHALTRY, Richard A; W G Mather HS; Munising, MI; Band; CncrtBnd; HonRl; MrchBnd; PepBnd; SctActv; Univ; Professional.

CHAMBERLAIN, Dawn D; Grant HS; Grant, MI; TrsFrshCls; HonRl; StuCncl; Yrbk; 4-H; FNA; FSA; FTA; SciCl; CitAwd; Ferris State Coll; Lab Tech.

CHAMBERLAIN, Debra K; Whitewater HS; Whitewater, WI; 12/190 ChrhWkr; HonRl; NHS; Quill&Scroll; RptrSchPpr; SchPpr; 4-H; FrCl; Trk; GAA; Uw Whitewater; Math.

CHAMBERLAIN, Ellen A; Glenbrook North HS; Northbrook, IL; 92/565 HonRl; OffAde; PolWkr; TchrAde; YthFlsp; LetterSwmmng; GAA; In Univ; Foreign Lang.

CHAMBERLAIN, Jerome; Greenway HS; Taconite, MN; 1/158 Chr; NHS; PepBnd; SchPl; RptrYrbk; GerCl; MthCl; SciCl; Swmmng; AmLegAwd; Coll; Engrg.

CHAMBERLAIN, Paul; Thornton Township Hs; Harvey, IL; 106/742 OffAde; StuGov; MthCl; LetterTrk; College; Electronic Engineering.

CHAMBERLAIN, Raella M; Webberville HS; Williamston, MI; 4/60 TrsFrshCls; VPJrCls; HonRl; NHS; Yrbk; 4-H; Michigan St Univ; Teaching.

CHAMBERLAIN, William D; Arthur Hill HS; Saginaw, MI; ChrhWkr; HonRl; IntrClCncl; SctActv; College; Acct.

CHAMBERLAND, Michael A; O Fallon Township HS; O Fallon, IL; TchrAde; Yrbk; SchPpr; FrCl; LetterBsbl; LetterFtbl; IMSpt; Belleville Area College; General Education.

CHAMBERLIN, Patricia S; Olin Consolidated HS; Olin, IA; 6/24 SecSophCls; ChrhWkr; MrchBnd; SchPl; StuCncl; RptrSchPpr; PpCl; Bsbl; CchngActv; Bus Sch.

CHAMBERLIN, Rick; Olin Consolidated HS; Olin, IA; 4/31 PresSophCls; Chr; Chrs; HonRl; Mdrgl; NatlThespSoc; SchMus; SchPl; YthFlsp; LetterBsbl; CaptBsktbl; CaptFtbl; LetterTrk; College; Science.

CHAMBERS, Ann R; York HS; York, NE; 20/125 Chr; Chrs; ChrhWkr; HonRl; Mdrgl; NHS; SchMus; SchPl; PpCl; LetterTrk; Doane Col Crete; Special Ed Teacher.

CHAMBERS, Carol A; North Huron HS; Filion, MI; Band; Chr; ChrhWkr; CncrtBnd; HonRl; MrchBnd; OffAde; PepBnd; TchrAde; YthFlsp; 4-H; FBLA; Business College.

CHAMBERS, Cinda A; Greenview HS; Greenview, IL; 3/45 ChrhWkr; HonRl; TchrAde; SchPpr; IMSpt; Evangel College; Nursing.

CHAMBERS, Clark A; Bemidji HS; Bemidji, MN; ChrhWkr; HonRl; JrNHS; NHS; SchMus; SchPl; Bsbl; Bsktbl; LetterFtbl; IMSpt; College; Dentist.

CHAMBERS, Craig M; Mayo HS; Rochester, MN; 11/430 ChrhWkr; SecNHS; NatlMeritCmnd; SctActv; PresSciCl; Univ Of Minnesota; Biochemistry.

CHAMBERS, David; Dundee Community Hs; Carpentersville, IL; 70/366 AFS; Band; ChrhWkr; CncrtBnd; HonRl; NHS; SchPl; StuCncl; LatCl; SciCl; College; Marine Biologist.

CHAMBERS, Deborah L; Parker HS; Chicago, IL; 4/245 PresSrCls; Band; Chr; ChrhWkr; CncrtBnd; HonRl; JA; NHS; OffAde; SctActv; Twrl; SchPpr; Bsktbl; Univ Of Il; Accountant.

CHAMBERS, Elden G; Turner HS; Kansas City, KS; PresFrshCls; PresSrCls; CmntyWkr; HonRl; NHS; SctActv; StuCncl; YthFlsp; PpCl; Ftbl; Glf; Trk; CaptWrstlng;.

CHAMBERS, Jonae; Tri Center HS; Neola, IA; 3/72 Band; ChrhWkr; CmntyWkr; HonRl; MrchBnd; NHS; YthFlsp; RptrYrbk; RptrSchPpr; 4-H; School Of Nursing; Registered Nurse.

CHAMBERS, Kenneth T; Grover Cleveland HS; St Louis, MO; 175/675 LetterBsbl; LetterBsktbl; Ftbl; Socr; Pro.

CHAMBERS, Kevin M; North Miami HS; Maccy, IN; ModUN; YthFnd; SptEdSchPpr; FFA; SpnCl; LetterWrstlng; College.

CHAMBERS, Leola; Two Harbors HS; Duluth, MN; 14 NHS; College; Prof.

CHAMBERS, Michelle; Senior HS; Traverse City, MI; StuCncl; PpCl; Mi State Univ; Journalism.

CHAMBERS, Peggy S; Maires R I HS; Vienna, MO; VPFrshCls; PresSophCls; ALAGirlsSt; MrchBnd; SchPl; FHA; FTA; Bsktbl; Trk; Chrldr; Univ; Professional.

CHAMBERS, Robert S; Lesterville R 4 HS; Lesterville, MO; VPFrshCls; VPSophCls; Band; HonRl; PepBnd; College; Professional.

CHAMBERS, Steven L; Hammond Baptist HS; Lansing, IL; Band; ChrhWkr; CncrtBnd; HonRl; YthFlsp; RptrSchPpr; LetterBsbl; LetterBsktbl; CaptFtbl; Hyles Anderson College.

CHAMBERS, Theresa; Cahokia HS; Centerville, IL; Chrs; ChrhWkr; HonRl; LbryAde; 4-H; FDA; Southern Illinois Univ; Medicine.

CHAMBLEE, Marquita T; St Josephs HS; South Bend, IN; 47/232 ChrhWkr; HonRl; NHS; NatlMeritCmnd; SchPpr; FDA; SpnCl; College; Veterinary Medicine.

CHAMBLIN, Ivy K; Gideon HS; Gideon, MO; 5/40 Band; Chrs; CncrtBnd; HonRl; MrchBnd; PepBnd; VPJrCls; Bsbl; LetterBsktbl; IMSpt; U Of Ms; Pharmacy.

CHAMBLIN, Kathie J; Gideon HS; Gideon, MO; Chrs; HonRl; JrNHS; NHS; FrCl; PpCl; LetterBsbl; Chrldr; Business Major.

CHAMBLISS, Patricia; Cairo HS; Cairo, IL; 2/67 VPSophCls; ChrhWkr; HonRl; MrchBnd; NHS; SchPl; StuCncl; RptrYrbk; FrCl; GAA; College; Biology.

CHAMNESS, Leon L; Fairfield Comm HS; Fairfield, IL; 22/180 ALBoysSt; Band; CncrtBnd; HonRl; MrchBnd; NHS; FTA; SpnCl; Southern Illinois Univ; Architecture.

CHAMNESS, Marsha L; Herrin HS; Herrin, IL; 7/209 Chrs; DrlTm; HonRl; NHS; OffAde; TchrAde; RptrYrbk; Yrbk; RptrSchPpr; SchPpr; Eastern Ill Univ; Medical Tech.

CHAMNESS, Melinda S; Trico HS; Ava, IL; Chr; Chrs; HonRl; SchMus; StuCncl; RptrYrbk; Pres4-H; PresFHA; VPPpCl; Chrldr; DanFAwd; 4-HAwd; John A Logan Jr Col; Legal Stenographer.

CHAMNESS, Ricky L; Anna Jonesboro Comm HS; Jonesboro, IL; Chrl; CmntyWkr; CncrtBnd; MrchBnd; PolWkr; 4-H; FFA; Bsktbl; Trk; 4-HAwd; University; Business Admin.

CHAMP, Timothy E; Woodlawn Community HS; Woodlawn, IL; ChrhWkr; HonRl; NHS; YthFlsp; FFA; Bsbl; Bsktbl; Business School.

CHAMPAGNE, Mitchell P; Duchesne HS; St Charles, MO; CmntyWkr; HonRl; SpnCl; Col; Major Study.

CHAMPAGNE, Paul; Central Catholic HS; Normal, IL; ALBoysSt; HonRl; StuCncl; PpCl; Univ; Eng.

CHAMPINE, Laurie A; Beaver Dam Sr HS; Beaver Dam, WI; 32/349 AFS; SpnCl; University.

CHAMPION, Anita; Lee HS; Wyoming, MI; Band; CncrtBnd; HonRl; MrchBnd; PepBnd; SpnCl; Bsbl; Swmmng; Cllege;professional.

CHAMPION, Leesa M; Carmel HS; Carmel, IN; ChrhWkr; CncrtBnd; HonRl; MrchBnd; OffAde; PolWkr; SchMus; SchPl; GAA; PPFtbl; Univf Forester.

CHAMPION, Susan M; Msd Of Fremont HS; Fremont, IN; PresSrCls; ALAGirlsSt; Chr; HonRl; NHS; SchMus; SchPl; RptrSchPpr; 4-H; FHA; LatCl; MthCl; College; Medical Technology.

CHAMPLIN, Michael E; High School; Cedar Vale, KS; 4/19 ALBoysSt; Band; Chrs; CncrtBnd; HonRl; MrchBnd; NHS; SchPl; StuCncl; Bsktbl; Ftbl; Trk; AmLegAwd; University; History.

CHAMPNEY, Joan M; Concord HS; Horton, MI; 2/72 TrsSrCls; Band; ChrhWkr; CmntyWkr; PresLbryAde; NHS; OffAde; PresYthFlsp; Coll; Medical Assistant.

CHAMULAK, Glenn A; George G Schafer HS; Allen Park, MI; 1/290 Band; HonRl; JA; MrchBnd; NHS; NatlMeritSF; NatlSciFnd; StuCncl; PresSophCls; MthCl; U Of M; Medical Field.

CHANCE, Jerry L; Stuart Menlo HS; Menlo, IA; HonRl; Trade School; Auto Mechanic.

CHANCE, Lou Ann; Warsaw HS; Warsaw, MO; 9/61 HonRl; JrNHS; NHS; SctActv; StuCncl; YthFlsp; GAA; BttyCrckrAwd; College; Accounting.

CHANCELLOR, Patricia; Harrisonville Senior Hs; Harrisonville, MO; 8/153 ChrhWkr; HonRl; NatlFornLg; Quill&Scroll; SchPl; StuCncl; SchPpr; FTA; Chrldr; IMSpt; College; Accounting Major.

CHAND, Krishna K; Cass Technical HS; Detroit, MI; AFS; HonRl; NatlSciFnd; TchrAde; MthCl; SciCl; Univ; Medicine.

CHANDLER, Charles H; Metropolis Comm HS; Metropolis, IL; 1/151 Band; Chrs; ChrhWkr; CmntyWkr; HonRl; NHS; NatlThespSoc; SchPl; SctActv; StuCncl; Bsbl; Bsktbl; LetterFtbl; VFWAwd; Samford Univ; Medicine.

CHANDLER, Karen S; Garnett HS; Richmond, KS; 2/130 ChrhWkr; CmntyWkr; HonRl; NHS; NatlMeritCmnd; TchrAde; Sec4-H; FHA; PpCl; 4-HAwd; Kansas State University; Engineering.

CHANDLER, Rayann; Bay View HS; Milwaukee, WI; HonRl; JA; LbryAde; NatlMeritSF; SctActv; StuGov; TchrAde; RptrYrbk; RptrSchPpr; SpnCl; Carroll Univ; Education.

CHANDLER, Sherry L; Metropolis Comm HS; Metropolis, IL; Chr; ChrhWkr; SctActv; ChmnStuCncl; RptrYrbk; GerCl; PpCl; SciCl; LetterChrldr; GAA; Samford Univ; Nursing.

CHANDLEY, Debra E; Central HS; Evansville, IN; Chr; HonRl; NHS; StuCncl; CivCl; PPFtbl; CitAwd; U Of Evansville; Nursing.

CHANEY, Andrew J; St Mary Of P H HS; Chicago, IL; VPSrCls; SchMus; SchPl; StuCncl; StuGov; Yrbk; SchPpr; CaptBsktbl; LetterTrk; IMSpt; Univ Of No Il; Bus Admini.

CHANEY, Barbara S; Rochester Comm HS; Rochester, IN; 6/170 NHS; SctActv; Yrbk; Col; Ecology.

CHANEY, Gregory A; Cathedral HS; Indianapolis, IN; 20/126 ChrhWkr; HonRl; ModUN; NHS; PolWkr; LetterGlf; IMSpt; Univ; Engr.

CHANEY, Louie; Centerville Sr HS; Centerville, IN; Band; HonRl; JA; NHS; StuGov; YthFlsp; FFA; MthCl; Bsbl; Bsktbl; Ftbl; CchngActv; Univ; Business.

CHANG, Cynthia L; Okemos HS; Okemos, MI; 5/240 Chr; Chrs; CncrtBnd; Mdrgl; MrchBnd; SecNHS; SchMus; SecFrCl; Univ Of Michigan; Medical Tech.

CHANG, Paul J; Shawnee Mission East HS; Mission Hills, KS; 1/605 HonRl; NHS; NatlMeritSF; SctActv; StuCncl; StuGov; TchrAde; YthFlsp; EdSchPpr; PpCl; SciCl; IMSpt; University; Medicine.

CHANG, Stillma; Schaumburg HS; Hanover Park, IL; 5/537 HonRl; StuCncl; StuGov; FDA; Northwestern Univ; Medicine.

CHANNELL, Brenda K; South Pemiscot HS; Steele, MO; Chr; Chrs; HonRl;.

CHANTINY, Carol I; Central HS; Standish, MI; 10/155 HonRl; SchPl; TchrAde; 4-H; FrCl; Michigan Univ; Psychologist.

CHAO, Joan; York Comm HS; Elmhurst, IL; HonRl; NHS; Quill&Scroll; EdYrBk; PresFrCl; Northwestern Univ; Medicine.

CHAPA, Deborah J; Lake Zurich Sr HS; Lake Zurich, IL; 38/157 TrsJrCls; TrsSrCls; AFS; ChrhWkr; CncrtBnd; NHS; NatlThespSoc; SchMus; Chrldr; GAA; DanFAwd; Augustana College; Mathematics.

CHAPIN, Norman A; Millington HS; Millington, MI; 28/180 Band; ChrhWkr; HonRl; TchrAde; YthFlsp; SecSophCls; SptEdSchPpr; LetterFtbl; CaptTrk; LetterWrstlng; Coll; Prof.

CHAPINSKI, Mary P; Newman Central Catholic HS; Rock Falls, IL; VPFrshCls; Chrs; SchMus; SchPl; StuCncl; RptrYrbk; RptrSchPpr; CaptChrldr; GAA; College; Social Worker.

CHAPLA, Robin L; West Iron County HS; Gaastra, MI; 68/172 HonRl; SchPpr; Central Mich Univ; Psychology.

CHAPLIN, Brian S; Carmel HS; Indianapolis, IN; 11/500 ChrhWkr; CncrtBnd; HonRl; NatlMeritSF; SchPl; YthFlsp; Yrbk; Tennis; JETSAwd; VoiceDemAwd; Univ; Social Sci.

CHAPLIN, Monty; Fox Valley Hs; Milton, IA; TrsSrCls; CmntyWkr; CncrtBnd; MrchBnd; PepBnd; StuCncl; RptrYrbk; 4-H; LetterBsktbl; LetterTrk; College; Agriculture.

CHAPLOW, Beata; Dominican HS; Grosse Point Park, MI; Chrl; PepBnd; SecStuCncl; TchrAde; Ftbl; University; Professional.

CHAPMAN, Brian S; Edwardsville HS; Edwardsville, IL; Swmmng;.

CHAPMAN, Brian W; New Haven HS; New Haven, IN; 54/229 Band; MrchBnd; PepBnd; YthFlsp; Purdue Univ At Fort Wayne; Mechanical Eng.

CHAPMAN, Chris M; Farmington HS; Farmington, MI; RptrSchPpr; EdSchPpr; U Of Mi; Liberal Arts.

CHAPMAN, Donna L; Herndon HS; Herndon, KS; 1/8 SecTrsSophCls; SecTrsSrCls; Band; Chrs; SchPl; RptrYrbk; PpCl; LetterBsktbl; Trk; Chrldr; BttyCrckrAwd; Kansas Univ; Biology.

CHAPMAN, Jacquilan L; Concordia Academy; St Paul, MN; 14/40 SecFrshCls; TrsSophCls; VPJrCls; ChrhWkr; Nursing School; Nurse.

CHAPMAN, James M; Chippewa Hills HS; Remus, MI; 27/141 Band; CncrtBnd; HonRl; LbryAde; MrchBnd; NHS; NatlThespSoc; PepBnd; SchPl; Ferris St Coll; Law Enfor.

CHAPMAN, Jeffery; Monroe HS; Monroe, MI; Chrs; ChrhWkr; CncrtBnd; HonRl; MrchBnd; NatlMeritCmnd; NatlMeritSF; RedCrAde; SchMus; FDA; V Ofm Mich State; Medicine.

CHAPMAN, Jill M; Dearborn HS; Dearborn, MI; ChrhWkr; CmntyWkr; HonRl; NatlFornLg; NatlThespSoc; OffAde; SchPl; Teen; RptrSchPpr; GerCl; College; Lawyer In Economics.

CHAPMAN, John C; Greenfield Central HS; Greenfield, IN; 5/265 ALBoysSt; HonRl; NHS; StuCncl; Pres4-H; PresFFA; MthCl; College; Architecture.

CHAPMAN, John S; Comstock Park HS; Comstock Park, MI; 2/150 ChrhWkr; HonRl; NHS; SchPl; StuCncl; TchrAde; Trk; Davenport Coll; Acct.

CHAPMAN, Joyce; Dryden Comm HS; Dryden, MI; ChrhWkr; HonRl; NHS; NatlMeritSchl; NatlMeritSF; EdYrBk; FHA; BttyCrckrAwd; DARAwd; College; Therapy.

CHAPMAN, Kathryn M; Elmhurst HS; Fort Wayne, IN; HonRl; TreasJA; LbryAde; YthFlsp; Indiana U; Library Sci.

CHAPMAN, Kirby J; Fairmount Public HS; Fairmount, ND; ALBoysSt; Band; ChrhWkr; CncrtBnd; HonRl; MrchBnd; PepBnd; SchPl; YthFlsp; RptrYrbk; LetterFtbl; AmLegAwd; RotaryAwd; Trade School; Diesel Mechanics.

CHAPMAN, Lisa J; Hutsonville HS; West Union, IL; 3/38 TrsFrshCls; Band; VPNHS; EdYrBk; RptrSchPpr; Pres4-H; VPFHA; AmLegAwd; DARAwd; 4-HAwd; Eastern Il Univ; Home Ec.

CHAPMAN, Marilyn K; Mt Carmel HS; Mt Carmel, IL; 12/185 PresSrCls; Chrs; HospAde; PresNHS; OffAde; SchPl; TreasStuCncl; VPGAA; DARAwd; Eastern Ill Univ; Cpa.

CHAPMAN, Mark R; Allen Cons HS; Allen, NE; Chr; ChrhWkr; HonRl; SchPl; RptrSchPpr; 4-H; FFA; Bsktbl; 4-HAwd; Univ Of Ne; Agriculture Ed.

CHAPMAN, Michael D; Rosedale HS; Carbon, IN; 1/60 PresChrhWkr; CmntyWkr; HonRl; ModUN; YthFlsp; Pres4-H; LatCl; MthCl; SciCl; Bsktbl; 4-HAwd; Rose Hulman Inst; Engineer.

CHAPMAN, Monica A; Elisabeth Ann Johnson HS; Mt Morris, MI; 22/270 VPSophCls; PresJrCls; PresSrCls; JrNHS; NHS; StuCncl; StuGov; SpnCl; CaptBsktbl; IMSpt; Univ; Medicine Or Teaching.

CHAPMAN, Olif B; St Johns Military HS; Liberty, MO; DrlTm; HonRl; JCC; MrchBnd; ROTC; RptrYrbk; RptrSchPpr; LetterFtbl; LetterTennis; LetterWrstlng; Norwich Univ; Psychology.

CHAPMAN, Ronald J; North Bend Central HS; North Bend, NE; Aud/Vis; Band; Chrs; CmntyWkr; CncrtBnd; MrchBnd; PepBnd; SchMus; SctActv;.

CHAPMAN, Scott J; Ss Peter & Paul Area HS; Saginaw, MI; Chrs; CmntyWkr; HonRl; SchAde; Tennis; College; Professional.

CHAPMAN, Sherry L; Clinton HS; Clinton, IL; Chrs; CncrtBnd; HonRl; MrchBnd; NHS; PepBnd; SchAde; FrCl; PpCl; GAA;.

CHAPPEL, David L; Whitko HS; South Whitley, IN; SecSophCls; Quill&Scroll; RptrSchPpr; SchPpr; LetterFtbl; IMSpt; College; Journalism.

CHAPPELL, Bobby; Southwest HS; Washburn, MO; 2/42 VPSophCls; HonRl; SchPl; StuCncl; Yrbk; FHA; Bsbl; Bsktbl; Drury; Prof.

CHAPUT, John F; Loyola Academy; Wilmette, IL; 67/442 CmntyWkr; Loyola Univ; Business.

CHARBONEAU, Mary; St Pius X HS; De Soto, MO; 9/100 SecSrCls; Chrs; HonRl; NHS; SchMus; Bsktbl; Jr Coll; Nursing.

CHARBONEAU, Richard G; Rosemount HS; Rosemount, MN; 39/355 HonRl; CaptTennis; U Of Wi At Green Bay; Science.

CHARD, Kevin; Rockridge HS; Illinois City, IL; ALBoysSt; HonRl; YthFlsp; SpnCl; Bsbl; Trk; AmLegAwd; PresAwd; College; Business Administration.

CHARETTE, John G; Haslett HS; E Lansing, MI; StuCncl; Bsbl; Bsktbl; Ftbl; CchngActv; IMSpt; Univ; Agriculture.

CHARGING, Anita F; White Shield HS; Roseglen, ND; 5/13 TrsSophCls; VPJrCls; Chrs; ChrhWkr; HonRl; SchPl; PresStuCncl; StuGov; RptrSchPpr; FHA; LetterBsktbl; Trk; Chrldr; North Dakota St University.

CHARGING, Clarice M; White Shield HS; Roseglen, ND; SecFrshCls; VPSophCls; Chr; Chrs; HonRl; StuCncl; EdYrBk; FHA; PpCl; Bsbl; College; Special Education.

CHARIPAR, Lisa M; La Salle HS; Cedar Rapids, IA; HonRl; PpCl; Bsktbl; GAA; IMSpt; Coll.

CHARKEWYCZ, Christine M; Trinity HS; Elmwood Park, IL; 3/204 Chr; Chrs; HonRl; NHS; SchMus; StuCncl; University Of Illinois; Law.

CHARLES, Albert L; Goreville HS; Creal Springs, IL; HonRl; SctActv; Univ Of Missouri; Engineer.

CHARLES, Cecilia A; Labette County HS; Altamont, KS; HonRl; PresStuCncl; EdYrBk; PresFHA; DanFAwd; PresAwd; Labette Comm Jr College; Dietician.

CHARLES, Kathy; Sabetha HS; Siawatha, KS; ChrhWkr; HonRl; StuCncl; SpnCl; PpCl; DARAwd; Missouri Western St Coll; Rn.

CHARLES, Lonnie W; Zionsville Comm HS; Zionsville, IN; Band; CncrtBnd; DrlTm; HonRl; JrNHS; MrchBnd; NHS; PepBnd; SctActv; Yrbk; LetterFtbl; Trk; IMSpt; MasAwd; Purdue College; Electrical Engineer.

CHARLES, Randal D; Marenisco HS; Marenisco, MI; 3/19 VPChrs; HonRl; SchPl; PresStuCncl; Yrbk; SptEdSchPpr; 4-H; PresFTA; LetterBsktbl; Trk; IMSpt; College.

CHARLES, Stephanie; St Thomas Apostle HS; Chicago, IL; 3/45 SecFrshCls; TrsJrCls; HonRl; TreasGAA; College; Teachers Ed.

CHARLES, Susan J; Stockton HS; Mt Carroll, IL; 7/84 Band; CncrtBnd; HonRl; LbryAde; MrchBnd; TchrAde; Yrbk; RptrSchPpr; FBLA; Mac Murray College; Special Ed.

CHARLES, Susan M; Unity HS; Chicago, IL; ChrhWkr; College; Liberal Arts.

CHARLES, Tia B; Kirksville Senior HS; Kirksville, MO; Chrs; ChrhWkr; HonRl; SchMus; TchrAde; College; Elementary Education.

CHARLESWORTH, Kay; Airport HS; South Rockwood, MI; 4/225 ChrhWkr; HonRl; NHS; TchrAde; YthFlsp; RptrSchPpr; 4-H; FHA; LionAwd; VoiceDemAwd;.

CHARLEY, Alan J; Jayhawk Linn HS; Mound City, KS; CncrtBnd; HonRl; MrchBnd; SchPl; 4-H; MthCl; SciCl; 4-HAwd; Ft Hays St; Elct.

CHARLSTON, Rondi E; Metro HS; Chicago, IL; ChrhWkr; CmntyWkr; HonRl; SchMus; College; Theatre.

CHARLTON, Jeffrey; Cardinal Ritter HS; Indianapolis, IN; 5/151 Band; Chrs; CncrtBnd; HonRl; MrchBnd; NHS; PepBnd; SchMus; RptrYrbk; IMSpt; In Univ; Business.

CHARLTON, Katherine L; Primghar Community HS; Primghar, IA; VPFrshCls; CncrtBnd; HonRl; NHS; SptEdSchPpr; CivCl; LetterBsktbl; LetterTrk; AmLegAwd; College; Political Science.

CHARNEKAR, Anita M; Gavit Jr Sr HS; Hammond, IN; 43/360 Chr; HonRl; NHS; NatlThespSoc; SchMus; StuCncl; PpCl; GAA; IMSpt; PPFtbl; U Of Evansville; Communications.

CHARNESKEY, Walter J; Bloomington HS; Bloomington, IL; 46/391 HonRl; SptEdSchPpr; Bsbl; Illinois Wesleyan Univ; Journalism.

CHARNEY, David L; Boystown HS; Boystown, NE; HonRl; NHS; Bsbl; College.

CHARRON, John P; Columbus HS; Marshfield, WI; Chrs; HonRl; RptrSchPpr; FrCl; IMSpt; Coll; Cpa.

CHARRON, Sandra J; Fitzgerald HS; Warren, MI; 11/430 HonRl; JA; NHS; NatlMeritCmnd; TchrAde; FrCl; PpCl; GAA; U Of Mi; Computer Science.

CHARTIER, Colette A; Eisenhower HS; New Berlin, WI; 54/232 HonRl; OffAde; Stenographer.

CHARTRAND, Gregg R; Chisago Lakes HS; Lindstrom, MN; ALBoysSt; CmntyWkr; HonRl; SchPl; SctActv; StuCncl; StuGov; LetterBsktbl; CaptTrk; College; Professional.

CHASANOV, Elliot L; Homewood Flossmoor HS; Homewood, IL; 89/980 Band; CncrtBnd; HonRl; MrchBnd; NatlMeritCmnd; Orch; PepBnd; SchMus; Yrbk; Univ Of Miami; Music.

CHASCO, Debra; Washington Community HS; Washington, IL; 36/355 HonRl; NHS; StuCncl; RptrSchPpr; SpnCl; Illinois Central Col; Registered Nurse.

CHASE, Cynthia; Western HS; Bay City, MI; Chr; HonRl; SchMus; College; Biology.

CHASE, Cynthia M; Waukesha North HS; Pewaukee, WI; 1/326 AFS; ChrhWkr; HonRl; NHS; NatlMeritCmnd; FrCl; SpnCl; Swmmng; University; Major In Physics.

CHASE, Diane; Welcome HS; Welcome, MN; 5/19 VPJrCls; SecSrCls; ALAGirlsSt; Chrs; MrchBnd; NHS; StuGov; Twrl; Chrldr; AmLegAwd; Winona State.

CHASE, Jacqueline M; Tecumseh HS; Tecumseh, MI; 12/240 Band; ChrhWkr; CncrtBnd; MrchBnd; NHS; YthFlsp; SpnCl; Cleary College; Secretary.

CHASE, Philip; Glenbard West HS; Wheaton, IL; 37/508 ChrhWkr; HonRl; NHS; IMSpt; DARAwd; College; Science Major.

CHASE, Susan M; Mason Co Central HS; Scottville, MI; 24/133 Chr; ChrhWkr; SchMus; SctActv; SpnCl; Grand Rapids Baptist Clg; Teach.

CHASE, Thomas R; Sisseton HS; Sisseton, SD; ALBoysSt; Band; ChrhWkr; CmntyWkr; CncrtBnd; HonRl; MrchBnd; NatlFornLg; NatlThespSoc; PolWkr; Sacrstn; Ftbl; Wrstlng; S Dakota State Univ; Wildlife.

CHASKA, Lorraine C; Beach HS; Beach, ND; 3/39 TrsSophCls; Band; Chr; Chrs; ChrhWkr; CmntyWkr; CncrtBnd; DrlTm; HonRl; MrchBnd; PepBnd; LetterTrk; Chrldr; PPFtbl; N Dakota State Univ; Psychology.

CHASTAIN, Rhonda J; West Washington HS; Campbellsburg, IN; 1/93 SecFrshCls; VPSophCls; SecJrCls; SecTrsSrCls; Band; NHS; SpnCl; LetterBsktbl; LetterTrk; DARAwd; University; Professional.

CHATELAIN, Jeanne M; Shawnee Mission W HS; Prairie Vlg, KS; 9/700 ChrhWkr; CncrtBnd; DrmMjrt; NHS; Orch; PolWkr; SchMus; YthFlsp; LetterBsbl; Bsktbl; LetterSocr; Chrldr; CchngActv; Univ Of Kansas; Business Admin.

CHATHAM, Pamela J; Brazil Senior HS; Brazil, IN; HonRl; NHS; OffAde; SchMus; SchPl; Yrbk; SchPpr; FHA; College.

CHATMAN, Jerry; Chicago Vocational; Chicago, IL; 13/1177 HonRl; Il Inst Of Tech; Electronic Engineer.

CHATMAN, Willie H; Chicago Vocational HS; Chicago, IL; HonRl; NHS; OffAde; SchAde; StuCncl; StuGov; TchrAde; RptrSchPpr; SchPpr; University Of Illinois; Mathematics.

CHATT, Susan; Morton West Hs; Berwyn, IL; HospAde; NHS; NatlMeritCmnd; TchrAde; YthFlsp; U; Pharmacy.

CHATTERS, Rachel C; West Side HS; Gary, IN; HonRl; NHS; Chrldr;.

CHATTIN, Beverly J; South Knox HS; Vincennes, IN; 1/96 PresSophCls; ALAGirlsSt; ChrhWkr; HonRl; NHS; Quill&Scroll; StuCncl; Yrbk; EdSchPpr; VP4-H; PpCl; Indiana Univ; Dental Hygiene.

CHATTIN, Linda M; Jefferson HS; Osakis, MN; 21/340 LitMag; Yrbk; U Of Minnesota; English.

CHAUSSE, Diane M; Nokomis HS; Nokomis, IL; 8/92 Chrs; HonRl; OffAde; FHA; GAA; Nursing School; Nursing.

CHAUVIN, Kerry A; Merrill HS; Merrill, WI; ChrhWkr; HonRl; HospAde; SchMus; SchPl; StuCncl; Yrbk; RptrSchPpr; PresPpCl; GAA; North Central Tech; Rn.

CHAVERS, Miriam; Richmond HS; Richmond, IN; 9/634 HonRl; HospAde; JrNHS; NHS; Teen; YthFlsp; YthLg; RptrYrbk; EdSchPpr; PpCl; U Of Arizona; Journalism Or Sociology.

CHAVEZ, Carlos M; Immaculata HS; Leavenworth, KS; 1/56 ALBoysSt; Chr; HonRl; ModUN; NatlFornLg; SchMus; SctActv; KeyCl; PresSpnCl; Ftbl; University; Medicine.

CHAVEZ, Pedro; Capac HS; Capac, MI; HonRl; SciCl; LetterFtbl; Trk; College; Professional.

CHAYER, Rebecca A; Chatsworth HS; Chatsworth, IL; 4/27 TrsFrshCls; TrsSrCls; ALAGirlsSt; Band; Chrs; HonRl; NHS; SchPl; StuCncl; RptrYrbk;.

CHEATHAM, Lisa R; Pike HS; Indianapolis, IN; 23/243 Chr; ChrhWkr; HonRl; NHS; NatlMeritCmnd; PresQuill&Scroll; PresYthFlsp; SchPpr; PpCl; CaptBsktbl; CaptTrk; Chrldr; IMSpt; Indiana State Univ; Journalism.

CHEATHAM, Richard G; South Iron HS; Vulcan, MO; 5/35 Chrs; HonRl; LbryAde; SctActv; PpCl; PresSciCl; Se Mo U; Dental.

CHEATUM, Brenda G; Buhler HS; Hutchinson, KS; Band; CncrtBnd; HonRl; MrchBnd; PepBnd; SctActv; YthFlsp; PpCl; LetterTennis; PPFtbl; Jr Clge;.

CHEEK, Cathy E; Sheldon HS; Sheldon, IL; 2/31 Band; ROTC; HonRl; Quill&Scroll; RptrSchPpr; 4-H; PpCl; Bsktbl; GAA; 4-HAwd; Univ; Secretary.

CHEEK, Kathleen D; Eminence HS; Quincy, IN; 2/32 CmntyWkr; HonRl; NHS; OffAde; EdYrBk; 4-H; CaptBsktbl; GAA; IMSpt; 4-HAwd;.

CHEEK, William D; Cranbrook HS; Troy, MI; 3/110 HonRl; NHS; NatlMeritFnl; NatlMeritCmnd; FrCl; Bsbl; Ftbl; Harvard; Oceanography.

CHEESMAN, Douglas; Northside HS; Muncie, IN; 59/316 HonRl; NHS; SctActv; LatCl; Bsktbl; Ftbl; Trk; IMSpt; Purdue Univ; Engineer.

CHEHEY, Gregory M; School Dist #46 HS; Maywood, NE; 6/22 PresJrCls; Band; Chr; Chrs; CncrtBnd; HonRl; MrchBnd; NHS; SchPl; StuCncl; University Of Nebraska; Vicil Engineering.

CHEJLAVA, Edward J; Riverside Brookfield HS; North Riverside, IL; 18/498 HonRl; JA; NHS; NatlMeritCmnd; NatlSciFnd; BauchLmbAwd; Harvey Mudd College; Chemistry.

CHEJLAVA, Pamela A; Proviso West HS; Westchester, IL; 81/964 ChrhWkr; HonRl; NHS; SchAde; YthFlsp; Swmmng; GovHonPrgAwd; U Of Il; Med Laboratory.

CHELGREN, Donnette F; Wahpeton HS; Wahpeton, ND; SecFrshCls; Band; Chrs; CncrtBnd; HonRl; HospAde; MrchBnd; PepBnd; RedCrAde; PpCl; College; Nursing.

CHELSVIG, Deborah K; South Hamilton HS; Jewell, IA; 16/91 Band; Chrs; ChrhWkr; HonRl; MrchBnd; NHS; SchMus; MthCl; Glf; IMSpt; Waldorf Coll; Bus Admin.

CHEN, Co Co; Lakeview HS; St Clair Shores, MI; 4/650 CmntyWkr; HonRl; Orch; SctActv; StuCncl; Univ Of Michigan; Medicine.

CHENEVERT, Mary J; St Joseph Acad; Detroit, MI; HonRl; StuCncl; RptrYrbk; EdYrBk; GAA; Mich Tech U; Doctor.

CHENEVERT, Renee M; Granite City Sr HS; Granite City, IL; 100/630 CmntyWkr; HospAde; RedCrAde; SchAde; SchPl; SctActv; RptrSchPpr; SptEdSchPpr; SchPpr; GerCl; Southern Ill Univ; Pre Medical.

CHENEY, Janet L; Palmyra HS; Bennet, NE; 9/37 ALAGirlsSt; Band; Chrs; CncrtBnd; MrchBnd; StuCncl; PpCl; College; English.

CHENEY, Pamela J; Central Catholic HS; Bloomington, IL; 1/84 SecJrCls; SecSrCls; PresNHS; StuCncl; TchrAde; Yrbk; FrCl; LetterTennis; BttyCrckrAwd; DARAwd; Univ Of Illinois; Biology.

CHENEY, Pamela R; Sylvan Unified #299 HS; Sylvan Grove, KS; 5/22 SecJrCls; ChrhWkr; CmntyWkr; HonRl; NHS; EdYrBk; 4-H; LetterBsktbl; LetterTrk; Chrldr; 4-HAwd; CitAwd; Cloud Cty Comm College; Elem Teacher.

CHENEY, Stephanie L; Dekalb Sr HS; Dekalb, IL; HonRl; HospAde; LbryAde; NHS; StuCncl; PpCl; Univ Of Illinois.

CHENG, Katherine H; Midland HS; Midland, MI; Band; CncrtBnd; HonRl; MrchBnd; NHS; NatlMeritFnl; Orch; TchrAde; RptrYrbk; FrCl; Mich St Univ; Math Tchr.

CHENG, Mini K; Lindblom Tech HS; Chicago, IL; TchrAde;.

CHENG, Vernon S; New Trier East HS; Winnetka, IL; HonRl; Orch; SchAde; StuCncl; MthCl; Univ Of Illinois; Engineering.

CHENOWETH, Kimberley J; East Alton Wood Rvr Comm HS; Wood River, IL; ChrhWkr; JrNHS; NatlFornLg; NHS; NatlThespSoc; PolWkr; SchPl; TchrAde; CchngActv; University; Professional.

CHEOLAS, Gregory W; Brown City HS; Melvin, MI; HonRl; NHS; TchrAde; FFA; Glf; Mi State Univ; Biology.

CHERESKIN, James A; Florence HS; Iron Mt, MI; Band; CncrtBnd; HonRl; MrchBnd; PolWkr; RptrSchPpr; Bsktbl; LetterFtbl; LetterTrk; LetterWrstlng; College; Lawyer.

CHERESKIN, Samuel; Lincoln Way HS; New Lenox, IL; 36/566 Chr; HonRl; NHS; LetterFtbl; Dartmouth Clg; Architecture.

CHERF, Susan M; Central HS; Lacrosse, WI; 15/527 HonRl; NHS; OffAde; Quill&Scroll; SchPl; StuCncl; StuGov; Yrbk; RptrSchPpr; SpnCl; Uwl; Business Admin.

CHERKINIAN, Nancy A; William Horlick HS; Racine, WI; Band; CncrtBnd; HonRl; HospAde; Orch; PepBnd; SchMus; RptrSchPpr; Chrldr; U Of Wi; Bba.

CHERN, Lydia A; Appleton HS; Appleton, WI; 1/523 Chr; Chrl; Chrs; ChrhWkr; Mdrgl; NatlMeritSF; SchMus; Lawrence Univ; Music.

CHERNEY, Michael G; Marquette Univ HS; Milwaukee, WI; 5/270 NatlFornLg; SctActv; StuGov; PresSciCl; LetterGlf; Marquette Univ; Mathematics.

CHERNICH, Barbara J; Park Hill HS; Kansas City, MO; 21/410 ChrhWkr; HonRl; NatlFornLg; NHS; SchMus; FHA; FrCl; PpCl; LetterSwmmng; Nd State Univ; Pharmacy.

CHERRY, Debra; Marion Adams HS; Sheridan, IN; 3/99 ALAGirlsSt; Chr; HospAde; JrNHS; FHA; LatCl; Vincennes Univ; Nursing.

CHERRY, Gilda D; Chicago Vocational HS; Chicago, IL; 6/1176 Chr; ChrhWkr; HonRl; OffAde; YthFlsp; RptrYrbk; FHA; GAA; Univ Of Wisc; Clinical Psychology.

CHERRY, Kathy J; Girard HS; Girard, IL; VPSophCls; SecJrCls; Chrs; HonRl; JrNHS; VPNHS; OffAde; SchPl; Yrbk; LetterTrk; College; Business Admin.

CHERRY, Pamela G; Highland HS; Highland, IN; 147/543 HospAde; OffAde; SctActv; StuCncl; RptrYrbk; FHA; PpCl; Chrldr; GAA; GodCntryAwd; Colleg; Nursing.

CHERRY, Rosalee; Trico HS; Cutler, IL; 6/78 HonRl; LbryAde; OffAde; SchAde; TreasStuCncl; YthFlsp; Yrbk; RptrSchPpr; Pres4-H; PresFHA; GAA; AmLegAwd; 4-HAwd; JAAwd; Jr College; Cosmetology.

CHERRY, Zoe E; Loup City HS; Loup City, NE; 4/64 SecSophCls; SecJrCls; SecSrCls; ALAGirlsSt; Band; Chrs; DrmMjrt; PresNHS; NatlMeritCmnd; NatlSciFnd; Univ Of Nebraska; Medicine.

CHESHURE, Darlene; Waterford Township HS; Pontiac, MI; VPJrCls; HonRl; NHS; StuGov; TchrAde; RptrYrbk; Yrbk; PpCl; Western Michigan U; Liberal Arts.

CHESNEY, Debra A; Elk Grove HS; Elk Grove Village, IL; 23/505 HonRl; NatlMeritCmnd; OffAde; PolWkr; SchAde; GerCl; W Rainey Harper Clg; Business.

CHESNIK, Carrie A; Redfield HS; Redfield, SD; AFS; Band; Chrs; CncrtBnd; HonRl; MrchBnd; PepBnd; SchMus; SchPl; TchrAde; 4-H; South Dakota State Univ; Professional.

CHESTER, Brenda; Vienna Township Hs; Ozark, IL; SecTrsSrCls; HonRl; TchrAde; FTA; MthCl; Southeastern Ill Junior College; Business L.

CHESTER, Janet M; Madison Public HS; Madison, MN; ChrhWkr; CmntyWkr; HonRl; HospAde; MrchBnd; SctActv; IMSpt; PPFtbl; College; Professional.

CHESTER, Mary E; New Haven HS; New Haven, IN; 5/250 HonRl; NatlFornLg; 4-H; GerCl; PpCl; GAA; College; Physical Ed Teacher.

CHESTER, Ralph L; Lampion HS; Chicago, IL; 1/100 PresJrCls; PresSrCls; CmntyWkr; ModUN; NatlMeritCmnd; OffAde; PolWkr; SchPl; StuGov; UNYO; Ftbl; Socr; Tennis; College; Medicine.

CHESTER, Ralph L; Campion HS; Chicigao, IL; 1/100 PresJrCls; PresSrCls; CmntyWkr; ModUN; NHS; NatlMeritCmnd; SchPl; StuCncl; StuGov; TchrAde; Col ;med.

CHESTNUT, Karen F; West Vigo HS; W Terre Haute, IN; 1/192 VPSrCls; Band; CaptDrlTm; NatlFornLg; NHS; VPStuCncl; 4-H; PresFBLA; FTA; DARAwd; De Pauw Univ; Public Relations.

CHESTNUT, Marcia L; Dubois HS; Celestine, IN; Band; Chr; Chrs; ChrhWkr; CncrtBnd; HonRl; MrchBnd; PepBnd; SchPl; TchrAde; Trk; GAA; Indiana St Univ; Teacher.

CHETKOVICH, John M; Gladwin HS; Gladwin, MI; Bsktbl; College; Professional.

CHEUNG, Eva; Ladywood St Agnes HS; Indianapolis, IN; CmntyWkr; HospAde; RedCrAde; SchMus; StuCncl; TchrAde; YthFlsp; SchPpr; SpnCl; Indiana Univ; Social Work.

CHEUNG, Frances S; Niles Twp West HS; Morton Grove, IL; 28/660 Chr; ChrhWkr; HonRl; IntrClCncl; LitMag; NatlFornLg; NHS; YthFlsp; SciCl; Northwestern Univ; Mathematics.

CHEVALIA, Timothy C; Marseilles HS; Marseilles, IL; VPSophCls; ALBoysSt; Band; DrmBgl; HonRl; MrchBnd; NHS; PepBnd; SchMus; LetterWrstlng; No Illinois Univ; Computer Science.

CHEVALIER, Ann E; Catholic Central HS; Marinette, WI; SecSrCls; HonRl; StuCncl; LetterBsktbl; PPFtbl; Cardinal Stritch; Spec Ed.

CHEVREMONT, Jacque M; Milwaukee Trade & Tech HS; Milwaukee, WI; PresSrCls; HonRl; StuCncl; LetterFtbl; LetterTrk; College; Vocational.

CHEW, Jean; East Jordan HS; East Jordan, MI; HonRl; EdSchPpr; Bsktbl;.

CHEW, John; East Jordan HS; East Jordan, MI; HonRl; StuCncl;.

CHEYNE, Karen D; Athens HS; Athens, MI; 52/62 CmntyWkr; HonRl; HospAde; NHS; PepBnd; SchPl; StuCncl; YthFlsp; LetterTrk; GAA; Kell Com College; Nursing.

CHIAPPETTA, James L; Niles West HS; Niles, IL; 169/666 HonRl; NHS; LetterBsktbl; Loyola Univ; Lawyer.

CHIBE, Russell J; Luther South HS; Chicago, IL; VPJrCls; Chr; ChrhWkr; HonRl; NHS; StuCncl; Bsbl; LetterFtbl; AmLegAwd; Concordia River Forest; Professional.

CHICANTEK, Thomas P; Greenfield HS; Greenfield, WI; 42/367 NHS; Yrbk; SchPpr; CaptWrstlng; Marquette U; Pre Med.

CHICHESTER, John C; Marshall HS; Marshall, MI; JA; NatlFornLg; StuGov; JAAwd; Central Mi Univ; History Law.

CHICOINE, Mary T; Elk Point HS; Elk Point, SD; PresJrCls; Band; HonRl; SchPl; SecStuCncl; TchrAde; EdSchPpr; VPPpCl; Trk; Chrldr; Sd State Col; Nursing.

CHICOUSKY, Janet L; Roseville HS; Roseville, MI; PresSrCls; Band; Chrs; HonRl; NatlFornLg; NHS; NatlMeritSchl; StuCncl; Bsbl; VoiceDemAwd; College; Nursing Registered.

CHICRAS, Desiree A; Superior HS; Superior, WI; HonRl; HospAde; NHS; StuCncl; PpCl; LetterTrk; CaptChrldr; GAA; Col; Pro.

CHICVARA, Michele M; Mt Assisi Academy; Chicago, IL; 10/144 Chrs; Trade; Secretary.

CHIDESTER, Christine L; Mormon Trail HS; Weldon, IA; Band; HonRl; Yrbk; 4-H; FHA; VPPpCl; LetterBsktbl; LetterTrk; DanFAwd; 4-HAwd; College.

CHIGLO, Katherine; Lanesboro Hs; Whalon, MN; Band; Chrs; HonRl; TreasStuCncl; Pres4-H; PresFFA; CaptBsktbl; CaptTrk; GAA; 4-HAwd;.

CHIHAK, Joan M; Benton Community HS; Atkins, IA; HonRl; PolWkr; 4-H; SpnCl; MthCl; IMSpt; University.

CHIHOS, Marie; Browerville HS; Browerville, MN; 9/64 Band; Chr; CncrtBnd; HonRl; MrchBnd; SchAde; SchPl; Yrbk; FHA; BttyCrckrAwd; Brainerd Vo Tech; Dental Assist.

CHILCOAT, Lorri; Perry Lecompton HS; Perry, KS; Band; Chrs; HonRl; MrchBnd; SchMus; TchrAde; YthFlsp; FHA;.

CHILCUTT, Cathy; Maconaquah HS; Perv, IN; Band; CncrtBnd; DrlTm; HonRl; MrchBnd; NHS; TchrAde; 4-H; 4-HAwd;.

CHILDERS, Jona; Westville Township HS; Danville, IL; 10/112 ALAGirlsSt; Band; ChrhWkr; NHS; SchMus; SchPl; StuCncl; AmLegAwd; Danville Jr College; Child Ed.

CHILDERS, Kevin J; Marion Senior HS; Marion, IL; 7/300 Band; ChrhWkr; CncrtBnd; HonRl; MrchBnd; NHS; PepBnd; CivCl; MthCl; PpCl; Bsktbl; Southern Ill Univ; Professional.

CHILDERS, Marcia; Central HS; Farmington, MO; 12/175 ChrhWkr; HonRl; MrchBnd; NHS; OffAde; PepBnd; SchMus; StuCncl; TchrAde; Sch Of The Ozarks; Concert Flutist.

CHILDRESS, Cynthia A; Tremont HS; Tremont, IL; Chrs; ChrhWkr; DrlTm; SchAde; FHA; Bsbl; LetterBsktbl; GAA; IMSpt; PresAwd;.

CHILDRESS, Deanna D; Oakland HS; Oakland, IL; 7/44 Band; Chrs; CncrtBnd; HonRl; MrchBnd; PepBnd; SchMus; YthFlsp; Yrbk; 4-H; FHA; PpCl; GAA; Lake Land Col; Business.

CHILDRESS, Mary J; Brown County HS; Morgantown, IN; 23/206 Band; VPDrlTm; HonRl; MrchBnd; TchrAde; FHA; Bsbl; Trk; GAA; IMSpt; In U; Social Work.

CHILDS, Denise L; Elmore Public HS; Blue Earth, MN; SecSophCls; TrsJrCls; Band; Chr; Chrl; Chrs; ChrhWkr; CncrtBnd; HonRl; Mdrgl; MrchBnd; OffAde; Chrldr; College; Elem Ed.

CHILDS, Victoria L; Evergreen Pk Comm HS; Evergreen Park, IL; 44/450 Chrs; LitMag; NHS; TchrAde; FTA; PresMthCl; IMSpt; Saint Xavier College; Elementary Education.

CHILES, Jennifer P; Smithville Rii HS; Smithville, MO; 3/85 HonRl; HospAde; JrNHS; NHS; OffAde; StuCncl; StuGov; TchrAde; PresFHA; EngCl; AmLegAwd; CitAwd; College; Vocation.

CHILSEN, Elizabeth R; Newman HS; Wausau, WI; 23/135 Band; CmntyWkr; DrlTm; HonRl; SchMus; SctActv; StuGov; Yrbk; SpnCl; PpCl; Coll; Professional Photographer.

CHILSON, Jana; Clio HS; Clio, MI; HonRl; JrNHS; NHS; RedCrAde; SctActv; TchrAde; YthFlsp; Swmmng; Univ; Elementary Ed.

CHIN, Darcy; Benson HS; Omaha, NE; AFS; HonRl; NHS; FrCl; GAA; PPFtbl; DARAwd; Univ Neb; Biological Sci.

CHIN, Sue G; Lindblom Tech HS; Chicago, IL; 5/686 HonRl; NHS; TchrAde; MthCl; Tennis; University; Business.

CHIN, Susan H; Sullivan HS; Chicago, IL; 15/276 SecJrCls; Chr; HonRl; JrNHS; LbryAde; NHS; OffAde; KeyCl; PpCl; College.

CHINBERG, Sheri K; Mc Pherson HS; Mcpherson, KS; Chr; HonRl; College; Elementary Education.

CHING, Kenneth D; Nw Military & Naval Academy; Wheeling, IL; CAP; DrlTm; HonRl; JA; MrchBnd; ROTC; StuCncl; RptrYrbk; KeyCl; Tennis; Florida Tech Univ; Law.

CHINICK, Donald A; Lake Mi Cath HS; Benton Harbor, MI; VPJrCls; Chrl; ModUN; StuGov; TchrAde; MthCl; SciCl; LetterBsbl; LetterFtbl; KiwanAwd; Kalamazoo Coll; Medicine.

CHINN, Elizabeth; Edina East HS; Edina, MN; 67/449 Chr; ChrhWkr; HonRl; HospAde; FrCl; Swmmng; College; Liberal Arts.

CHINN, Victoria; Columbus East HS; Columbus, IN; 17/365 Band; CncrtBnd; HonRl; MrchBnd; NatlMeritCmnd; Orch; PepBnd; 4-H; 4-HAwd; Indiana Univ; Mathematics.

CHINSKI, Paul J; Schlarman HS; Loda, IL; 1/70 CmntyWkr; HonRl; NHS; SctActv; StuCncl; RptrYrbk; NatlSciFnd; FrCl; SpnCl; SciCl; U Of Il; Pre Md.

CHIPLIS, Mary E; St Mary Acad; Indianapolis, IN; Chrs; HonRl; SecRedCrAde; EdYrBk; FrCl; PpCl; College; Natural Science.

CHISHOLM, Cynthia L; Kapaun Mt Carmel HS; Wichita, KS; 14/127 CmntyWkr; HonRl; HospAde; University; Genetics Counselor.

CHISM, Denise D; West Platte HS; Rushville, MO; 7/75 AFS; Chr; Chrs; DrmBgl; HonRl; NHS; SchAde; SchPl; TchrAde; FBLA; FrCl; PpCl; SciCl; Maryville Col; Teacher.

CHISM, Shelly K; Senath Hornersville HS; Hornersville, MO; Chr; Chrs; HonRl; LbryAde; TchrAde; YthFlsp; FHA; FTA; PpCl; Registered Nurse.

CHITTENDEN, Sue A; Fremont HS; Fremont, MI; 13/190 Band; CncrtBnd; HonRl; MrchBnd; Orch; PepBnd; Swmmng; University.

CHITTY, Harriet A; Frontier HS; Chalmers, IN; 2/72 VPBand; ChrhWkr; HonRl; NHS; SchPl; VPYthFlsp; EdYrBk; Pres4-H; PresPpCl; GAA; College; Physical Ed Or Therapy.

CHITTY, Regina A; Butler HS; Butler, MO; TreasAFS; PresBand; CncrtBnd; DrlTm; HonRl; MrchBnd; NHS; PepBnd; FrCl; PpCl; IMSpt; PPFtbl; Southwest Mo St Univ; Pharmacist.

CHITWOOD, Kathleen A; Limestone HS; Bartonville, IL; 7/400 HonRl; OffAde; TreasStuCncl; TchrAde; SecPpCl; Chrldr; Illinois Central College; Dental Hygienist.

CHITWOOD, Michelle; Evansville HS; Evansville, WI; 3/119 ALAGirlsSt; Band; Chr; DrlTm; HonRl; MrchBnd; NHS; NatlThespSoc; SchMus; SchPl; RptrSchPpr; Madison Tech Col; Accounting.

CHIVETTA, Anthony J; Chaminade HS; St Louis, MO; Yrbk; SchPpr; Swmmng; IMSpt; Univ; Architecture.

CHIVINGTON, Carol R; Gavit HS; Hammond, IN; 18/300 HonRl; JrNHS; NatlFornLg; NHS; NatlMeritSF; TchrAde; College; Nursing.

CHLAPIK, John J; J Sterling Morton East HS; Cicero, IL; 2/771 Band; HonRl; IntrClCncl; PresJrNHS; PresNHS; Orch; SchMus; Tennis; Trk; SARAwd; University; Chemical Engineering.

CHLEBOROD, William; Bergan HS; Fremont, NE; 2/49 PresSophCls; ALBoysSt; HonRl; IntrClCncl; NatlFornLg; NHS; NatlThespSoc; FDA; OptClAwd; Doane Coll; Pre Med.

CHLOPEK, Daniel L; St Francis HS; Tarnov, NE; HonRl; LbryAde; Sacrstn; Bsktbl; Ftbl; Univ; Professional.

CHLOUPEK, Joe; Dilworth Public HS; Dilworth, MN; HonRl; NHS; College; Journalist.

CHLYSTEK, Edward E; Homer HS; Homer, MI; 16/86 VPSophCls; PresJrCls; PresSrCls; Band; CncrtBnd; DrmMjrt; MrchBnd; NHS; PepBnd; SchMus; SchPl; LetterBsktbl; Western Univ; Foreign Relations.

CHMIEL, Anthony M; St Laurence HS; Chicago, IL; 7/379 HonRl; NatlFornLg; NatlSciFnd; PolWkr; FSA; SciCl; Bsktbl; Ftbl; IMSpt; Mass Inst Tech; Nuclear Engineering.

CHMIEL, Edward; Gordon Tech HS; Chicago, IL; 155/591 IMSpt; Coll.

CHMIELEWSKI, Chester S; N Decatur HS; Greensburg, IN; Band; CncrtBnd; HonRl; MrchBnd; NatlMeritCmnd; Orch; RptrYrbk; LatCl; MthCl; Indiana Univ; Doctor.

CHMIELEWSKI, Joyce M; Catholic Central HS; Manistee, MI; 5/69 Band; CmntyWkr; CncrtBnd; HonRl; MrchBnd; NHS; OffAde; Quill&Scroll; SchPl; IMSpt; Davenport; Accounting.

CHMIELEWSKI, Karen S; Jackson HS; Jackson, MI; Chr; ChrhWkr; HonRl; Mdrgl; NHS; SchMus; YthFlsp; PpCl; CaptChrldr; PPFtbl; College; Music.

CHMIELIK, Joseph S; St Patrick HS; Chicago, IL; 34/377 PresFrshCls; PresSophCls; HstJrCls; PresChrs; HonRl; JrNHS; SecNHS; StuCncl; StuGov; LetterWrstlng; Loyola Univ; Cpa.

CHMIELOWIEC, David M; St Josephs HS; South Bend, IN; 61/250 HonRl; IMSpt; Notre Dame; Accounting.

CHOAT, Cheryl L; O Fallon Township HS; O Fallon, IL; Chr; Chrs; HonRl; Mdrgl; SchMus; RptrSchPpr; SchPpr; FrCl;.

CHOAT, Ralph F; Lockport Central HS; Lockport, IL; ChrhWkr; HonRl; SctActv; GerCl; MthCl; SciCl; IMSpt; College; Archaeologist.

CHOATE, Jeffrey; Anna Jonesboro Chs; Jonesboro, IL; 40/137 VPFrshCls; TrsSophCls; VPJrCls; HonRl; KeyCl; Bsbl; Bsktbl; Ftbl; Trk; AmLegAwd; Eastern Illinois U; Business Administration.

CHOATE, Lisa E; Anna Jonesboro HS; Anna, IL; 13/137 CmntyWkr; HonRl; Yrbk; PresFTA; LatCl; Eastern Illinois Univ; Special Education.

CHOATE, Nancy L; Vienna Township HS; Grantsburg, IL; HonRl; StuCncl; FHA; FNA; SpnCl; PpCl; CaptBsktbl; CaptChrldr; GAA; College; Professional.

CHOBANIAN, Patricia R; West Allis Central HS; West Allis, WI; 1/461 Band; CncrtBnd; DrlTm; HonRl; MrchBnd; NHS; Orch; PepBnd; Carroll College; Medical Tech.

CHOCA, Maria; Academy Of Our Lady; Chicago, IL; 1/160 PresSophCls; HonRl; PresNHS; SpnCl; PpCl; Bsktbl; CchngActv; SecGAA; DARAwd; JCAwd; Univ Of Notre Dame; History.

CHOCA, Maria; Academy Of Our Lady HS; Chicago, IL; 1/180 PresSophCls; HonRl; NHS; StuGov; SpnCl; PpCl; Bsktbl; CaptFtbl; GAA; IMSpt; PPFtbl; JCAwd; Notre Dame; Archaeology.

CHOCHOLOUSEK, Julie A; Gregory HS; Dixon, SD; 5/58 ALAGirlsSt; HonRl; NHS; NatlThespSoc; SchPl; VPFHA; CaptBsktbl; Glf; Trk; Chrldr; GAA; Mitchell Vo Tech College; Med Lab Asst.

CHOCK, Mark T; New Trier HS; Glenview, IL; CncrtBnd; HonRl; LbryAde; StuGov; LetterTrk;.

CHOCK, Theresa M; Taylors Falls Public HS; Shafer, MN; 3/27 SecSrCls; Band; Chrs; ChrhWkr; HonRl; NatlFornLg; OffAde; SchPl; SchPpr; LetterTrk; Pillsbury Baptist Bible Col; Acct.

CHOHREK, Joan P; Bremen HS; Posen, IL; 1/427 ChrhWkr; HonRl; NHS; TchrAde; Twrl; MthCl; Chrldr; GAA; AmLegAwd; Coll; Attroney.

CHOI, Chi; Lane Tech; Chicago, IL; 82 PresFrshCls; SecSophCls; TrsSrCls; HonRl; StuCncl; StuGov; RptrSchPpr; EngCl; GerCl; Trk; U Ill Urbana ; Doctorate Medical Engineerin.

CHOICE, Mary A; Chicago Voc HS; Chicago, IL; 88/778 ChrhWkr; CmntyWkr; HonRl; SchMus; StuCncl; Bsktbl; GAA; U Of Ill;.

CHOITZ, Jon E; Buhler HS; Hutchinson, KS; 1/134 PresJrCls; ChrhWkr; HonRl; NHS; StuCncl; SchPpr; GerCl; College; Business Major.

CHOJNICKI, John A; West Sr HS; Rockford, IL; 14/335 HonRl; JrNHS; NHS; LetterFtbl; Southern Ill University.

CHOLEWA, Bertram J; Marist HS; Chicago, IL; 10/393 CncrtBnd; HonRl; MrchBnd; NHS; PpCl; SciCl; IMSpt; Univ; Masters Engineering.

CHOLLY, Thomas A; Brother Rice HS; Chicago, IL; Aud/Vis; CmntyWkr; SpnCl; MthCl; Bsbl; Swmmng;.

CHONIS, Cynthia; Mercy HS; Omaha, NE; JA; SchMus; SchPl; Sdlty; StuCncl; SpnCl; PpCl; Bsbl; Trk; GAA; Univ Of Nebr; Professional In Fashion.

CHOPONIS, Richard J; Pine River HS; Luther, MI; PresSophCls; Band; ChrhWkr; CncrtBnd; HonRl; MrchBnd; NHS; SchPl; SctActv; StuGov; College; Vocation.

CHOPP, Brian S; Frank Cody HS; Detroit, MI; 2/238 PresSrCls; AFS; HonRl; NHS; SpnCl; MthCl; SciCl; University Of Michigan; Mathematics.

CHOPP, Joseph G; St Laurence HS; Chicago, IL; 70/364 CmntyWkr; HonRl; NatlMeritSF; OffAde; LetterTennis; U Of Ill; Architecture.

CHORLEY, Cathy J; West Chicago Comm HS; Winfield, IL; ChrhWkr; DrmMjrt; MrchBnd; SchMus; StuCncl; Twrl; SpnCl; PpCl; Chrldr; GAA; College; Teach Spec Educ.

CHOSKEY, Larry B; Bishop Borgess HS; Detroit, MI; ChrhWkr; HonRl; RptrSchPpr; College; Chemistry.

CHOU, Raymond H; Niles North HS; Skokie, IL; 16/650 HonRl; SchPl; Univ Of Ill; Architecture.

CHOUTKA, Carol A; Riverside Brookfield HS; Riverside, IL; 75/483 ChrhWkr; HonRl; LbryAde; NHS; PolWkr; SchPl; TchrAde; Swmmng; Univ Of Illinois; Liberal Arts.

CHOVANEC, Susan; St Francis De Sales HS; Chicago, IL; SecJrCls; SecSrCls; Chrs; HonRl; StuCncl; StuGov; GAA; Western Univ; Med Tech.

CHOW, Christopher V; University HS; Champaign, IL; 1/50 Orch; GerCl; Bsktbl; Trk; IMSpt; U Of Il; Civil Engineering.

CHRENCIK, Elaine; Lyons Township HS; La Grange Park, IL; HonRl; NHS; OffAde; TchrAde; Northern Illinois Univ; Nursing.

CHRISLAW, Charles W; Clinton HS; Clinton, WI; 8/96 VPSrCls; ChrhWkr; HonRl; StuCncl; Pres4-H; PresFFA; Bsktbl; 4-HAwd; KiwanAwd; University Of Wis Madison; Vocational.

CHRISMAN, Cindy G; Onaga HS; Onaga, KS; 4/45 ChrhWkr; HonRl; NHS; StuCncl; YthFlsp; Newman Hosp Schl; Nursing.

CHRISMAN, Kim M; Florence HS; Iron Mountain, MI; 5/68 Chr; HonRl; NHS; Quill&Scroll; SchPl; StuCncl; RptrSchPpr; FHA; Chrldr; GAA; College; X Ray Technician.

CHRISMAN, Patricia; Boone County Rvi HS; Centralia, MO; CmntyWkr; HonRl; SchPl; RptrYrbk; EdSchPpr; FHA; SpnCl; SciCl; GAA; IMSpt; Sw Mo State; Psychology.

CHRISMAN, Stephen L; Streator HS; Streator, IL; PresJrCls; CncrtBnd; SchPl; FrCl; LetterTrk; AmLegAwd; College; Horticulture.

CHRIST, Audrey M; Wheaton North HS; Wheaton, IL; 1/308 Chr; Chrs; ChrhWkr; HonRl; VPNHS; StuCncl; TchrAde; VPYthFlsp; RptrSchPpr; SpnCl; Bsktbl; CaptChrldr; GAA; Wellesley College; Mathematics.

CHRIST, Cathy R; Roosevelt HS; Minneapolis, MN; 19/575 AFS; ChrhWkr; HonRl; HospAde; LitMag; NHS; RptrYrbk; Yrbk; Trk; CaptChrldr; University; Architect.

CHRIST, Dallas M; Tri County HS; Plymouth, NE; Chr; Chrs; HonRl; JCC; SchAde; StuCncl; TchrAde; 4-H; SciCl; Bsktbl; Univ Of Ne; Business Administration.

CHRIST, Julie A; Lowpoint HS; Washburn, IL; 15/66 Band; HonRl; PresYthFlsp; SchPpr; 4-H; SecFFA; GAA; IMSpt; DanFAwd; 4-HAwd; University; Vet Med Or Dairy Animal Science.

CHRISTEL, Mary T; Maria HS; Chicago, IL; ChrhWkr; HonRl; LitMag; NHS; PresNatlThespSoc; PolWkr; SchMus; SchPl; RptrSchPpr; SpnCl; Northwestern Univ; Theatre.

CHRISTELL, Lori J; Westside HS; Omaha, NE; CmntyWkr; LbryAde; TchrAde; PpCl; Swmmng; Chrldr; GAA; PPFtbl; CitAwd; College; Travel Consultant.

CHRISTEN, Neil L; Jersey Comm HS; Jerseyville, IL; 10/277 Band; ChrhWkr; CmntyWkr; CncrtBnd; HonRl; LitMag; MrchBnd; NHS; PepBnd; 4-H; SpnCl; MthCl; PpCl; College; Professional.

CHRISTEN, Rosemary; Anselmo Merna HS; Anselmo, NE; Chrs; CncrtBnd; HonRl; Sdlty; TchrAde; FBLA; Bsbl; LetterTrk; 4-HAwd; PresAwd; College; Professional.

CHRISTEN, Timothy L; Belmont HS; Belmont, WI; ALBoysSt; CmntyWkr; HonRl; PpCl; Ftbl; Tennis; Wrstlng; AmLegAwd; PresAwd; Coll; Business.

CHRISTENSEN, Alan B; Napoleon HS; Kintyre, ND; NHS; FFA; Bsktbl; Univ; Prof.

CHRISTENSEN, Ann L; West Iron County HS; Iron River, MI; 3/176 HonRl; LbryAde; NHS; 4-H; LatCl; GAA; BauchLmbAwd; 4-HAwd; Mi State U; Dvm.

CHRISTENSEN, Betty J; Guthrie Center HS; Guthrie Center, IA; VPSophCls; Band; CncrtBnd; HonRl; LbryAde; MrchBnd; NatlSciFnd; PepBnd; Glf; Coll; Biology.

CHRISTENSEN, Carla A; Loup County HS; Taylor, NE; 2/15 PresSrCls; Band; HonRl; TreasNHS; StuCncl; Sec4-H; PresPpCl; LetterTrk; Mid Plains Comm College; Secretary.

CHRISTENSEN, Charles R; Dekalb Sr HS; De Kalb, IL; Aud/Vis; HonRl; SctActv; Trk; Augustana; Elem Ed.

CHRISTENSEN, Craig E; Loganview HS; Fremont, NE; Band; Chr; Chrl; Chrs; ChrhWkr; CncrtBnd; LbryAde; Mdrgl; MrchBnd; PepBnd; TchrAde; SciCl; Ftbl; LetterWrstlng; Bethony Clge; Contractor.

CHRISTENSEN, Craig H; Enderlin HS; Nome, ND; 2/44 ALBoysSt; Aud/Vis; HonRl; NatlMeritSchl; Yrbk; FFA; Bsktbl; 4-HAwd; VoiceDemAwd; Univ; Engineering.

CHRISTENSEN, Cynthia R; Gardner So Wilmington HS; Gardner, IL; 3/60 Band; Chrs; HonRl; LbryAde; SchPl; RptrYrbk; RptrSchPpr; SchPpr; SecMthCl; Chrldr; Jr College; Music Teacher.

CHRISTENSEN, Dean C; New Town HS; New Town, ND; Chrs; ChrhWkr; HonRl; SctActv; GerCl; SciCl; Trk; Wrstlng; IMSpt; DanFAwd; Univ Of N Dak; Engineering.

CHRISTENSEN, Denise A; Browns Valley HS; Browns Valley, MN; SecJrCls; CncrtBnd; DrmMjrt; OffAde; PpCl; Bsktbl; Trk; Chrldr; IMSpt; College.

CHRISTENSEN, Diane K; Clay Central HS; Royal, IA; Band; Chr; Chrs; ChrhWkr; CmntyWkr; CncrtBnd; HonRl; MrchBnd; PepBnd; College.

CHRISTENSEN, Diane L; Wakonda Public HS; Volin, SD; HstFrshCls; TrsJrCls; VPSrCls; Band; Chrs; CncrtBnd; DrlTm; HonRl; Bsktbl; 4-HAwd; Stenotype Inst; Court Room Reporter.

CHRISTENSEN, Donna L; Nishna Valley HS; Hastings, IA; 2/32 Band; SecChrs; HonRl; TreasNHS; SchMus; SecYthFlsp; EdYrBk; Pres4-H; LetterBsktbl; TreasChrldr; Ia St Univ; Home Ec.

CHRISTENSEN, Gary L; Elk Horn Kimballton Comm HS; Eok Horn, IA; Band; Chrs; CncrtBnd; Mdrgl; MrchBnd; PepBnd; SchPl; Wrstlng; St Univ.

CHRISTENSEN, James; Clay Central HS; Royal, IA; 2/43 ALBoysSt; Chr; HonRl; SchPl; Iowa State At Ames; Farming.

CHRISTENSEN, James R; Clay Central HS; Royal, IA; 2/42 SecTrsFrshCls; Band; Chrs; HonRl; PresYthFlsp; Pres4-H; SecFFA; LetterBsbl; LetterBsktbl; LetterFtbl; Univ; Agriculture.

CHRISTENSEN, Janene K; Underwood Comm HS; Honey Creek, IA; 10/60 Chr; ChrhWkr; CncrtBnd; HonRl; MrchBnd; NHS; PepBnd; SchMus; YthFlsp; 4-HAwd; Western Comm Col; Special Ed.

CHRISTENSEN, Janice M; Verona Public HS; Verona, ND; ALAGirlsSt; Band; Chr; ChrhWkr; SchPl; 4-H; PpCl; IMSpt; State School Of Science; Data Processing.

CHRISTENSEN, Jean A; North Platte Sr HS; North Platte, NE; OffAde; 4-H; FFA; PpCl; PPFtbl; 4-HAwd; JAAwd; Cosmetology; Cosmetologist.

CHRISTENSEN, Jill A; Joliet West HS; Joliet, IL; 23/498 Band; CmntyWkr; CncrtBnd; HonRl; JrNHS; MrchBnd; NHS; FrCl; Univ Of Iowa; Pharmacy.

CHRISTENSEN, Kathleen M; Cleveland Public HS; Madison Lake, MN; 1/41 Chr; HonRl; LbryAde; NHS; NatlThespSoc; SchPl; RptrYrbk; PpCl; GAA; College; Psychology.

CHRISTENSEN, Kathy; North Bend Central HS; Ames, NE; HonRl; FHA; PpCl; PPFtbl; Bus Sch; Professional.

CHRISTENSEN, Kathy L; Alma HS; Alma, NE; 3/30 SecFrshCls; TrsFrshCls; Band; ChrhWkr; HonRl; YthFlsp; Yrbk; 4-H; PpCl; 4-HAwd; GovHonPrgAwd; University Of Nebraska.

CHRISTENSEN, Ken; Centura HS; Dannebrog, NE; Band; ChrhWkr; SchPl; SctActv; StuCncl; TchrAde; Bsktbl; Ftbl; AmLegAwd; Farming.

CHRISTENSEN, Kenneth R; Wisconsin Dells HS; Wis Dells, WI; Band; CncrtBnd; YthFlsp; RptrSchPpr; KeyCl; Bsktbl; Ftbl; Trk; Uw La Crosse; Architect.

CHRISTENSEN, Kim E; Minden HS; Minden, NE; Chr; Chrs; OffAde; TchrAde; YthLg; RptrSchPpr; LetterBsktbl; College; Criminal Justice.

CHRISTENSEN, Madonna J; St Louise De Marillac HS; Northbrook, IL; 1/250 HstSrCls; Chrs; ChrhWkr; LitMag; NHS; NatlMeritCmnd; StuCncl; SchPpr; College; Law.

CHRISTENSEN, Mark L; Jackson HS; Jackson, MN; Band; Chr; HonRl; SctActv; 4-H; FFA; LetterWrstlng;.

CHRISTENSEN, Marsha M; R 1 North Callaway HS; Auxvasse, MO; Chrs; HonRl; NatlThespSoc; SchMus; StuCncl; FHA; PresFTA; LetterTrk; Treas4-HAwd; William Woods College; Math.

CHRISTENSEN, Mary B; Bridgewater Fontanelle HS; Fontanelle, IA; 3/43 ALAGirlsSt; Band; ChrhWkr; HonRl; SecNHS; SchPl; RptrYrbk; Chrldr; AmLegAwd; BttyCrckrAwd; Southwestern Comm College; English.

CHRISTENSEN, Mary D; Madison East HS; Madison, WI; 18/563 Chrl; HonRl; HospAde; LbryAde; NHS; FrCl; RotaryAwd; Milaukee Co General Hosp Sch; Nurse.

CHRISTENSEN, Max C; Anita HS; Anita, IA; 8/43 ALBoysSt; HonRl; FTA; SciCl; Trade Schoo6; Professional.

CHRISTENSEN, Merri; Hamlin HS; Bryant, SD; TrsJrCls; Band; Chrs; HonRl; Yrbk; SchPpr; 4-H; GerCl; PpCl; 4-HAwd; Sd State Univ.

CHRISTENSEN, Neal D; Elk Horn HS; Exira, IA; 6/37 HonRl; NHS; SchPl; FFA; Ftbl; LetterWrstlng; IMSpt; Iowa Stat Univ; Accountant.

CHRISTENSEN, Pamela G; Eastwood HS; Correctionville, IA; 1/44 ALAGirlsSt; Band; CaptDrlTm; NHS; NatlMeritSF; SchPl; StuCncl; EdYrBk; LetterGlf; LetterTrk; CaptChrldr; Iowa St Univ; Engineering.

CHRISTENSEN, Rebecca; Harmony HS; Hillsboro, IA; 14/40 TrsJrCls; AFS; Band; Chr; CncrtBnd; HonRl; MrchBnd; SchPl; Ne Missouri St Univ; Sp Education.

CHRISTENSEN, Rhoda E; Wilmot Public HS; Wilmot, SD; 1/37 ALAGirlsSt; Band; HonRl; NHS; NatlMeritSF; SchPl; EdYrBk; RptrSchPpr; FHA; DARAwd; Univ; Art.

CHRISTENSEN, Robert; Grant Deuel HS; Revillo, SD; Band; Chr; Chrs; ChrhWkr; NatlMeritSchl; NatlThespSoc; SchPl; SciCl; Trk; College; Professional.

CHRISTENSEN, Sharon K; Fremont HS; Fremont, NE; TrsSophCls; StuCncl; PpCl;.

CHRISTENSEN, Stanley C; Stromsburg HS; Stromsburg, NE; 10/41 Band; CncrtBnd; HonRl; MrchBnd; NHS; PepBnd; SchAde; SctActv; College.

CHRISTENSEN, Steve A; Underwood Community HS; Underwood, IA; 5/60 Band; Chr; ChrhWkr; HonRl; Mdrgl; NHS; SchMus; YthFlsp; LetterBsktbl; BttyCrckrAwd; Ia State Univ; Vet Med.

CHRISTENSEN, Steven A; Windom Area HS; Windom, MN; 58/148 Chr; HonRl; SchPl; SctActv; 4-H; Bsbl; Bsktbl; 4-HAwd; JAAwd; Southwest State Clge Marshall; Hotel Manage.

CHRISTENSEN, Thomas M; Mounds View HS; New Brighton, MN; ALBoysSt; JrNHS; ModUN; NatlFornLg; NHS; NatlMeritSF; Orch; Univ Of Mn; Physical Sciences.

CHRISTENSEN, Todd E; Manilla Co HS; Monilla, IA; 5/44 TrsJrCls; Band; HonRl; MrchBnd; NHS; NatlMeritCmnd; SchMus; StuCncl; YthFlsp; SciCl; Univ; Zoology.

CHRISTENSEN, Troy E; Sr HS; Fremont, NE; HonRl; LetterFtbl; LetterTrk; Wrstlng; IMSpt; MasAwd; Univ Of Nebraska; Draftsman.

CHRISTENSEN, Vonda J; Oswego HS; Oswego, IL; Chrs; ChrhWkr; HonRl; SchMus; SchPl; YthFlsp; PpCl; Tennis; College; Nursing.

CHRISTENSON, Caryn J; Mahnomen HS; Mahnomen, MN; 2/85 ALAGirlsSt; Band; Chrs; HonRl; EdSchPpr; 4-H; CaptBsktbl; Tennis; CchngActv; GAA; College; Professional.

CHRISTENSON, Charles; Mankato East HS; Mankato, MN; Band; ChrhWkr; CmntyWkr; CncrtBnd; HonRl; PepBnd; SchPl; SctActv; Concordia Coll; Religion.

CHRISTENSON, Diane L; Wausau East HS; Wausau, WI; 5/300 Band; ChrhWkr; HonRl; NHS; Quill&Scroll; StuCncl; RptrYrbk; Yrbk; GerCl; GAA; Clge; Christian Social Worker.

CHRISTENSON, Donnabelle; St Marys HS; Storm Lake, IA; 4/43 Chr; HonRl; SchMus; TchrAde; PpCl; IMSpt; College Of St Benedicts; Mathematics.

CHRISTENSON, Jane; Newburg Public HS; Macbass, ND; SecTrsFrshCls; SecTrsSophCls; PresJrCls; Band; Chr; Chrs; ChrhWkr; HonRl; PepBnd; Chrldr; College.

CHRISTENSON, Jennifer L; Bentley HS; Livonia, MI; 25/700 Chr; ChrhWkr; HonRl; Orch; Spring Arbor College; Elem Teacher.

CHRISTENSON, John L; Clark HS; Clark, SD; 18/54 ALBoysSt; Chr; ChrhWkr; HonRl; SctActv; StuCncl; KeyCl; Bsbl; Bsktbl; Ftbl; Univ Of Wisconsin; Business.

CHRISTENSON, Judith J; Oak Park Academy; Dodge Center, MN; Band; Chr; ChrhWkr; CncrtBnd; HonRl; TchrAde; Union College; Physical Therapy.

CHRISTENSON, Karen; Chosen Valley HS; Chatfield, MN; AFS; Chr; ChrhWkr; HonRl; NHS; OffAde; SchMus; Yrbk; Chrldr; Coll.

CHRISTENSON, Lorna M; Plano HS; Plano, IL; 7/112 Band; CncrtBnd; HonRl; MrchBnd; NHS; Twrl; Yrbk; LetterChrldr; Waubonsee Comm College; Business.

CHRISTENSON, Marcy; Drayton Public HS; Bowesmont, ND; 1/35 ALAGirlsSt; Band; Chrs; CncrtBnd; HonRl; MrchBnd; PepBnd; StuCncl; FHA; PpCl; N Dak St Univ; Teach English Or Spanish.

CHRISTENSON, Mark A; Chippewa Falls HS; Chippewa Falls, WI; ChrhWkr; HonRl; NHS; 4-H; FFA; Wrstlng; Univ Of Wisconsin; Animal Science.

CHRISTENSON, Nancy; Marathon Cons HS; Marathon, IA; Chrs; CncrtBnd; HonRl; MrchBnd; UNYO; 4-H; SpnCl; Trk; Vocational School; Medical Health Field.

CHRISTENSON, Paul D; Velva Public HS; Velva, ND; 2/47 Band; HonRl; NHS; Yrbk; Missionary.

CHRISTENSON, Saundra R; De Soto HS; Dittmer, MO; Chrs; ChrhWkr; HonRl; TchrAde; FBLA; College; Professional.

CHRISTIAENS, Carine M; St Willibrord HS; Chicago, IL; 1/72 TrsSrCls; HonRl; NHS; SchMus; SchPl; VPStuCncl; RptrYrbk; MthCl; SecSciCl; JCAwd; Univ Of Illinois; Chemistry.

CHRISTIAN, Joseph; Grantsburg HS; Grantsburg, WI; Band; ChrhWkr; CncrtBnd; PepBnd; YthFlsp; PpCl; Bsbl; Bsktbl; Ftbl; Glf; Coll.

CHRISTIAN, Mary Jo; Catherdral HS; New Ulm, MN; 20/95 Chrs; ChrhWkr; HonRl; HospAde; LbryAde; NHS; SchMus; Sdlty; EdYrBk; DARAwd; St Cloud St Coll; Comm Art.

CHRISTIAN, Patty J; Draper HS; Draper, SD; 2/9 PresFrshCls; TrsJrCls; ALAGirlsSt; Band; Chrs; CncrtBnd; DrlTm; HonRl; JA; MrchBnd; PepBnd; YthFlsp; 4-H; Bsktbl; College; Nurse.

CHRISTIAN, Renny L; Junction City Sr HS; Junction City, KS; 70/310 Chr; ChrhWkr; HonRl; HospAde; PolWkr; SchMus; SctActv; StuGov; FrCl; Chrldr; Kansas University; Social Welfare.

CHRISTIANA, Dan P; Bishop Noll Institute; Hammond, IN; 1/342 HonRl; NHS; MthCl; Bsbl; IMSpt; BauchLmbAwd; Purdue Univ; Engineering.

CHRISTIAN GAINES, Betty R; Richland HS; Dexter, MO; HonRl; RptrSchPpr; FHA; PresAwd; Bus Sch; Sec Or Bus.

CHRISTIANS, Bruce C; Kanawha Comm HS; Kanawha, IA; 8/22 TrsSophCls; VPSrCls; Band; Chrs; HonRl; Mdrgl; MrchBnd; Yrbk; Pres4-H; PresFFA; LetterTrk; 4-HAwd; College; Agriculture.

CHRISTIANS, Dawn; Mpls Lutheran HS; Bloomington, MN; 3/40 ALAGirlsSt; Band; Chr; CncrtBnd; HonRl; NatlMeritCmnd; RptrYrbk; RptrSchPpr; Bsktbl; Coll; Doctor.

CHRISTIANS, Dawn M; Minneapolis Lutheran HS; Minneapolis, MN; Band; Chr; HonRl; RptrYrbk; RptrSchPpr; Bsktbl; Trk; LetterChrldr; College; Doctor.

CHRISTIANS, Julia A; Ellsworth Public HS; Ellsworth, MN; 1/31 ChrhWkr; HonRl; MrchBnd; SchPl; VPStuCncl; StuGov; TchrAde; Pres4-H; Chrldr; 4-HAwd; Col; Vocational.

CHRISTIANSEN, Conrad P; Maplewood Academy; Hager City, WI; 11/75 TrsFrshCls; Aud/Vis; ChrhWkr; CncrtBnd; HonRl; JA; MrchBnd; PepBnd; 4-H; College; Professional.

CHRISTIANSEN, Debbie; Reedsville HS; Whitelaw, WI; 28/101 TchrAde; FHA; FTA; Army; Professional Operating Room Ass.

CHRISTIANSEN, Gary D; Huron HS; Huron, SD; HonRl; JCC; JrNHS; NHS; GovHonPrgAwd; JAAwd; SARAwd; MasAwd; PresAwd; VoiceDemAwd; Service Navy; Vocation.

CHRISTIANSEN, Jack R; Rock Island Sr HS; Rock Island, IL; ChrhWkr; NHS; PolWkr; StuCncl; StuGov; YthLg; Western Illinois Univ; Psychiatry.

CHRISTIANSEN, Jill C; Mc Henry Public HS; Mchenry, ND; 2/13 PresFrshCls; PresJrCls; Band; HonRl; MrchBnd; RptrYrbk; RptrSchPpr; Bsktbl; Trk; Chrldr; Collge; Teacher Or Accountant.

CHRISTIANSEN, Kendall S; Morton HS; Morton, IL; 13/295 PresSrCls; Band; CmntyWkr; HonRl; NHS; StuCncl; YthFlsp; YthLg; SchPpr; Trk; Univ ; Admin.

CHRISTIANSEN, Marcia G; Niles West HS; Morton Grove, IL; 25/666 HonRl; NHS; SchPl; Univ Of Wisconsin; Laboratory Science.

CHRISTIANSEN, Richard G; Harlan Comm HS; Harlan, IA; TrsSophCls; HonRl; StuCncl; YthFlsp; LetterBsbl; LetterFtbl; LetterTrk; IMSpt; JAAwd; College; Business Admin.

CHRISTIANSON, Brenda L; Canby HS; Canby, MN; Chr; Chrs; HonRl; Mdrgl; SchPl; Yrbk; Trade; Work With Animals.

CHRISTIANSON, Denise K; Glenburn Public HS; Glenburn, ND; Chrs; CncrtBnd; HonRl; PepBnd; SchPl; PpCl; CaptBsktbl; LetterTrk; LetterChrldr; GAA; Coll.

CHRISTIANSON, Enid A; Enderlin Public HS; Enderlin, ND; 4/44 ALAGirlsSt; Chr; ChrhWkr; CncrtBnd; HonRl; NatlMeritSF; SchMus; EdYrBk; Univ Of Nd; Nursing & Med Tech.

CHRISTIANSON, Janey L; Oakes HS; Oakes, ND; 3/63 ALAGirlsSt; Band; Chrs; HonRl; NHS; SchPl; TreasStuCncl; FHA; Bsktbl; Chrldr; College; Rn Nursing.

CHRISTIANSON, Julie M; Memorial HS; Eau Claire, WI; CmntyWkr; HospAde; LetterSwmmng; College; Nursing.

CHRISTIANSON, Kathryn; Zion Benton Township Hs; Zion, IL; 1/405 Chr; ChrhWkr; HonRl; NHS; Orch; U Of Illinois; Math.

CHRISTIANSON, Leon R; Lake Mills Community HS; Lake Mills, IA; PresFrshCls; TrsSophCls; SecJrCls; CmntyWkr; SchPl; StuCncl; YthFlsp; Yrbk; 4-H; FFA; PpCl; Bsktbl; Iowa State Univ; Ag Business.

CHRISTIANSON, Robert D; Waukon HS; Waukon, IA; PresChrhWkr; HonRl; SchPl; SchPpr; SpnCl; Wrstlng; Farming.

CHRISTIANSON, Sandi J; Butterfield Public HS; Butterfield, MN; 2/28 VPJrCls; TrsSrCls; Band; Chr; CncrtBnd; HonRl; MrchBnd; SchPl; StuCncl; RptrYrbk; Mankato State College.

CHRISTIANSON, Steven L; Hendricks HS; Astoria, SD; PresSrCls; ALBoysSt; Chrs; HonRl; StuCncl; 4-H; FFA; LetterFtbl; LetterTrk; AmLegAwd; South Dakota State Univ; Ag Teacher.

CHRISTIANSON, Susan K; Hendricks HS; Astoria, SD; Chrs; HonRl; MrchBnd; 4-H; GerCl; PpCl; LetterBsktbl; LetterTrk; Chrldr; 4-HAwd; College; Vocational.

CHRISTIE, Donald; Carman HS; Flint, MI; Band; CncrtBnd; MrchBnd; SctActv;.

CHRISTIE, Jeanne M; Bemidji HS; Bemidji, MN; 7/363 Band; CncrtBnd; HonRl; JrNHS; MrchBnd; NHS; NatlMeritCmnd; OffAde; Orch; PepBnd; LetterBsktbl; Swmmng; LetterTrk; IMSpt; College; Mass Media.

CHRISTIE, Karen S; Central HS; St Joseph, MO; 33/535 Chr; Chrs; HonRl; SchMus; SchPl; StuGov; MthCl; SciCl; College; Professional.

CHRISTIFANO, Anna M; St Pius X HS; Kansas City, MO; 20/125 TrsSrCls; Chrs; DrlTm; HonRl; StuCncl; SpnCl; Stenographer.

CHRISTLIEB, Arthur D; Plymouth HS; Plymouth, IN; FBLA; LatCl; College; Law.

CHRISTMAN, Gregory M; Clintonville Sr HS; Clintonville, WI; Band; ChrhWkr; CmntyWkr; CncrtBnd; NHS; PepBnd; SchPl; LetterTennis; RotaryAwd; Univ Of Wisconsin; Biology.

CHRISTMAN, Rodney J; Hazen HS; Hazen, ND; 30/40 Band; Chr; ChrhWkr; CncrtBnd; MrchBnd; PepBnd; FFA; Ftbl; Wahpeton State Sch Of Sci; Auctioneener.

CHRISTMAS, Gail Y; Whse HS; Waukegan, IL; Chr; ChrhWkr; DrlTm; HonRl; HospAde; JA; JCC; StuCncl; Twrl; RptrSchPpr; College; Journalism.

CHRISTMON, Sarita R; Tri City HS; Buffalo, IL; 15/52 ChrhWkr; HonRl; SchMus; SchPl; SctActv; SchPpr; FTA; CaptTrk; GAA; IMSpt; 4-HAwd; College.

CHRISTNER, Kimberly A; St Benedict HS; Chicago, IL; 6/190 Chrs; HonRl; LbryAde; VPNHS; NatlMeritCmnd; Orch; SchMus; SchPl; SchPpr; SpnCl; CchngActv;.

CHRISTOFFEL, Cindy J; Prairie Hts HS; Angola, IN; 13/103 Band; CncrtBnd; HonRl; MrchBnd; PepBnd; Ravenscroft Beauty College; Cosmetology.

CHRISTOFFEL, Lester A; Andrews Academy; Berrien Springs, MI; Chr; ChrhWkr; JrNHS; NHS; EdYrBk; FrCl; Bsktbl; Ftbl; DanFAwd; CitAwd; Andrews U; Business Ad.

CHRISTOFFERSEN, Kim Y; Fremont HS; Fremont, MI; 3/200 Band; CncrtBnd; HonRl; HospAde; MrchBnd; NatlMeritSF; OffAde; PepBnd; StuCncl; TchrAde; 4-H; FTA; College; Elem Education.

CHRISTOFFERSON, Randy L; Grosse Pointe South HS; Grosse Pointe, MI; 25/650 ALBoysSt; Band; ChrhWkr; HonRl; MrchBnd; PresNHS; NatlMeritSF; Orch; NCTE; LetterTrk; Michigan St Univ; Bio Med Engin.

CHRISTOPH, Terri; Woodlands Academy; Lake Forest, IL; 6/76 Chrs; CmntyWkr; HonRl; HospAde; NHS; StuCncl; StuGov; TchrAde; FshEdYrbk; IMSpt; Southern Methodist U.

CHRISTOPH, Terri; Woodland Academy; Lake Forest, IL; 5/75 Chrl; ChrhWkr; CmntyWkr; HonRl; HospAde; NHS; StuGov; TchrAde; FshEdYrbk; Southern Methodist Univ; Business.

CHRISTOPHER, Betty; Northwood HS; Emerado, ND; Band; Chrs; ChrhWkr; CncrtBnd; HonRl; PepBnd; SchPl; 4-H; FHA; 4-HAwd; N Daleota St Univ; Interior Design.

CHRISTOPHER, David D; Southwestern HS; Shipman, IL; VPJrCls; VPSrCls; Band; HonRl; Sacrstn; StuCncl; FFA; Bsktbl; DanFAwd; 4-HAwd; Farming.

CHRISTOPHER, Kerry; North Miami HS; Peru, IN; 11/120 ALBoysSt; Aud/Vis; HonRl; NHS; GerCl; SciCl; Glf; Wrstlng;.

CHRISTOPHER, Susan; North Winneshiek HS; Decorah, IA; 7/34 Chrs; HonRl; NHS; SchPl; StuCncl; EdSchPpr; FHA; PpCl; LetterChrldr; PresAwd; Trade School.

CHRISTOPHERSON, Becky L; Wolsey Public HS; Wolsey, SD; Chrs; CncrtBnd; HonRl; MrchBnd; PepBnd; TchrAde; RptrSchPpr; Bsbl; Bsktbl; LetterTrk; Business School.

CHRISTOPHERSON, Dale H; Ashby Public HS; Dalton, MN; ALBoysSt; Band; Chr; ChrhWkr; CncrtBnd; HonRl; NHS; FFA; LetterBsbl; LetterFtbl; College; Professional.

CHRISTOPHERSON, Donna J; Ballard Comm HS; Cambridge, IA; 13/82 Chr; Chrs; ChrhWkr; HonRl; NHS; NatlThespSoc; SchMus; SchPl; FshEdYrbk; 4-H; Area Xi Comm Col; Secretarial.

CHRISTY, Julie A; Nevada HS; Nevada, IA; 20/123 SecSophCls; SecJrCls; SecSrCls; Band; CncrtBnd; HonRl; NHS; StuCncl; RptrSchPpr; 4-H; PpCl; LetterBsktbl; LetterTrk; CchngActv; Ia State Univ; Teaching.

CHRISTY, Linda; St Joseph HS; St Joseph, MI; Chr; HospAde; Quill&Scroll; SchAde; SchMus; RptrYrbk; SpnCl; GAA; Western Mich Univ; Secondary Education.

CHROMIZKY, Karen V; Lourdes HS; Chicago, IL; 1/276 HonRl; NHS; FrCl; SciCl; Tennis; IMSpt; Illinois Inst Tech; Bio Med Engineer.

CHRON, Edward G; Lane Tech HS; Chicago, IL; 126/1183 HonRl; RptrYrbk; RptrSchPpr; Ftbl; Trk; Illinois Wesleyan University.

CHRUN, Karen M; Laboure HS; St Louis, MO; 5/79 SecSophCls; JrNHS; RptrYrbk; EdYrBk; FshEdYrbk; SptEdYrbk; Yrbk; Bsbl; Socr; Chrldr; Hickey Bus Sch; Secretary.

CHRUSZCH, Cheryl A; Belfield Public HS; Belfield, ND; Chrs; HonRl; NHS; StuCncl; FHA; PpCl; Bsktbl; Trk; Chrldr; VoiceDemAwd; Clge; Prof.

CHRZAN, David; Elmhurst HS; Ft Wayne, IN; SptEdYrbk; Bsktbl; Ftbl; College.

CHRZANOWSKI, Gregory J; St Clement HS; Warren, MI; 45/98 HonRl; RptrYrbk; SptEdYrbk; LetterBsbl; CaptBsktbl; CaptFtbl; IMSpt; Eastern Michigan Univ; Physical Ed.

CHUBB, Jo Ann; Notre Dame HS; W Burlington, IA; ChrhWkr; HonRl; PolWkr; SctActv; StuCncl; YthFlsp; 4-H; SciCl; College; Medicine.

CHUHRAN, Barbara A; St Agatha HS; Detriot, MI; HonRl; PpCl; Univ Of Mi ; Scie.

CHUKEL, Thomas P; Elmwood HS; Elmwood, WI; Chr; Chrs; HonRl; NatlFornLg; SchMus; SchPl; RptrYrbk; FHA; LetterFtbl; LetterWrstlng; Coll; Curr Study.

CHUKMAN, Gloria M; Nazareth Academy; La Grange, IL; Chrs; HonRl; JrNHS; NHS; NatlMeritCmnd; SchMus; SchPpr; FrCl; Purdue University; Engineering.

CHULSKI, Linda M; West Catholic HS; Grand Rapids, MI; Chrs; HonRl; JA; NHS; NatlMeritCmnd; FHA; Tennis; IMSpt; Davenport Coll; Accounting.

CHULSKI, Victoria J; Big Rapids HS; Big Rapids, MI; VPSophCls; Band; CncrtBnd; HonRl; NatlFornLg; NHS; NatlMeritSF; FrCl; LatCl; MthCl; Central Mi; Sec Educ.

CHUMBLEY, Berlin R; Rantoul HS; Ludlow, IL; ChrhWkr; HonRl; PolWkr; SchMus; SchPl; StuCncl; IMSpt; Florida College; Lawyer.

CHUNG, Dorothy A; Maine South HS; Park Ridge, IL; HonRl; LbryAde; NHS; NatlMeritSF; NatlThespSoc; Orch; SchMus; FrCl; PpCl;.

CHUPINSKY, Kenneth J; Bishop Foley HS; Madison Hgts, MI; 2/177 HonRl; NHS; NatlMeritCmnd; SchPl; StuCncl; RptrYrbk; Univ; Bs Med School.

CHUPP, Alice E; Kirkwood HS; Kirkwood, MO; 3/662 NatlMeritSF; PolWkr; YthFlsp; SchPpr; GerCl; NCTE; Coll; Engr.

CHURA, Michael F; St Louis University HS; Scott Afb, IL; RptrSchPpr; LetterFtbl; Trk; Wrstlng; College; Professional.

CHURCH, Brian D; Catlin HS; Catlin, IL; 14/93 ALBoysSt; HstFrshCls; HonRl; Bsbl; Bsktbl; Ftbl; VPSrCls; IMSpt; AmLegAwd; CitAwd; U Of Il; Special Education.

CHURCH, Cindy M; Coon Rapids HS; Coon Rapids, MN; ChrhWkr; HonRl;.

CHURCH, Colleen A; Ithaca HS; Ithaca, MI; 28/144 Band; HonRl; MrchBnd; TchrAde; 4-H; VPFTA; SpnCl; LetterBsktbl; College.

CHURCH, Connie L; Tomah HS; Tomah, WI; 16/283 TrsJrCls; ChrhWkr; HonRl; NHS; StuCncl; RptrSchPpr; Bsktbl; Trk; Chrldr; GAA; Bible Clge; Pro Teacher.

CHURCH, Kerri L; Pittsburg HS; Pittsburg, KS; Chrs; HospAde; StuCncl; FHA; FrCl; PpCl; Glf; Trk; Chrldr; PresAwd; College; Medicine.

CHURCH, Kristin A; Gaylord HS; Gaylord, MI; Band; Chr; HonRl; SchPl; StuCncl; Tennis; Michigan Tech Univ; Acct.

CHURCH, Marsha K; Lutheran West HS; Detroit, MI; ChrhWkr; HonRl; OffAde; StuCncl; RptrSchPpr; SchPpr; LatCl; PpCl; Trk; Chrldr; Univ Of Michigan; Journalism.

CHURCH, Russell; Riceville Comm HS; Riceville, IA; Chrs; ChrhWkr; YthFlsp; 4-H; Trade School; Vocatonal.

CHURCHILL, Jane; Newton Sr HS; Newton, IA; Band; Chrs; CncrtBnd; DrmMjrt; HonRl; MrchBnd; PepBnd; YthFlsp; 4-H; LatCl; LetterBsktbl; 4-HAwd; Des Moines Area Comm College; Medical Tech.

CHURCHILL, Laura L; Dow City HS; Dow City, IA; 1/30 TrsSrCls; ALAGirlsSt; Band; Chr; Chrs; CncrtBnd; HonRl; LitMag; LbryAde; MrchBnd; Trk; Iowa Central College; Nurse.

CHURCHILL, Leslie; Chillicothe HS; Chillicothe, MO; 17/185 ALAGirlsSt; HonRl; RedCrAde; StuCncl; EdYrBk; FHA; FTA; PpCl; GAA; Univ Of Mo; Interior Design.

CHURCHILL, Rosalie; U I T Hs; Ipava, IL; 3/56 DrlTm; HonRl; NHS; SchPl; 4-H; FFA; FHA; AmLegAwd; 4-HAwd; JAAwd; Midstate College; Accounting.

CHWALINSKI, Daniel F; Wheeling HS; Wheeling, IL; 40/462 HonRl; NHS; NatlMeritCmnd; GerCl; MthCl; SciCl; LetterBsbl; LetterFtbl; LetterGlf; LetterTennis; IMSpt; Northern Illinois Univ; Business.

CHWALISZ, Christine; Woodstock HS; Woodstock, IL; ChrhWkr; HonRl; PresNatlMeritCmnd; TchrAde; SptEdSchPpr; 4-H; Bsktbl; BttyCrckrAwd; 4-HAwd; U Of Whitewater;newspaper Journalism.

CHYE, Dorothy A; Mason County Eastern HS; Custer, MI; 9/43 Band; Chr; HonRl; MrchBnd; SchPl; LetterBsbl; LetterSocr; LetterTrk; LetterChrldr; GAA; Mi State U.

CIARA, Damaris; Maria HS; Chicago, IL; 5/301 PresFrshCls; PresSrCls; ChrhWkr; HonRl; NHS; VPStuCncl; RptrSchPpr; SpnCl; Bsktbl; Chrldr; Loyola Univ; Nursing.

CICHY, Neil T; Manistee Catholic Central HS; Manistee, MI; 1/76 HonRl; NHS; SchPpr; Bsktbl; ChmnGlf; IMSpt; College.

CICIULLA, Peggy A; Marian HS; Omaha, NE; ChrhWkr; HospAde; Creighton Univ; Biologist.

CIECKO, Georgine; Resurrection Hs; Chicago, IL; 5/261 HonRl; HospAde; NHS; FNA; MthCl; Bsktbl; GAA; College; Nursing.

CIEGLER, Laura B; Richwoods HS; Peoria, IL; 61/424 Chr; Chrs; HonRl; Mdrgl; SchMus; SctActv; YthFlsp; Univ Of Illinois; Social Worker.

CIEMNIAK, Claudia; St Clare Academy; Yale, MI; Chrs; HonRl; HospAde; StuCncl; RptrSchPpr; SchPpr; 4-H; Bsbl; Trk; Univ; Pt.

CIERLIK, Gregory; St Benedict HS; Chicago, IL; 23/200 Band; Chrs; HonRl; SchMus; SchPl; StuCncl; GerCl; IMSpt; Depaul University; Flight Engineering.

CIERS, Bill; Whiting HS; Whiting, IN; GerCl; Trk;.

CIERS, Jeanelle R; Whiting HS; Whiting, IN; 11/104 Chr; Chrs; HonRl; JA; JrNHS; NHS; OffAde; StuCncl; TchrAde; SptEdYrbk; Yrbk; Swmmng; LetterTrk; Purdue; Chemistry.

CIESLAK, Joseph G; Brother Rice HS; Chicago, IL; 35/416 Band; CncrtBnd; HonRl; MrchBnd; NHS;

NatlMeritCmnd; PepBnd; SchMus; Univ Of Illinois; Civil Engineering.

CIESLAK, Mark E; Lane Tech HS; Chicago, IL; 24/1042 ChrhWkr; CmntyWkr; NHS; SchAde; StuCncl; StuGov; TchrAde; KeyCl; Bsktbl; Northwestern Univ; Medicine.

CIESLEWICZ, Stanley J; Craig HS; Janesville, WI; 23/472 HonRl; CaptNatlFornLg; NHS; VPStuCncl; SchPpr; EldAwd; Ripon Clge; Law.

CIESLINSKI, Brian; Bay City All Saints; Bay City, MI; HstSophCls; HstJrCls; Chrs; HonRl; NatlMeritCmnd; OffAde; StuCncl; StuGov; YthFnd; Coll; Vet.

CIESLINSKI, Steven D; Hazel Park HS; Hazel Park, MI; 92/410 Aud/Vis; Wayne St University.

CIGAN, Linda; Lake Holcombe Public HS; Gilman, WI; 8/39 SecJrCls; Band; Chrs; StuCncl; RptrYrbk; EdYrBk; RptrSchPpr; FHA; AmLegAwd; BttyCrckrAwd; Uw Eau Claire; Pysical Therapist.

CIHA, James A; Kewaskum HS; Allenton, WI; HonRl; NHS; SchPl; RptrYrbk; RptrSchPpr; SptEdSchPpr; Ftbl; Glf; IMSpt; College; Landscape Architect.

CIHASKY, Christina E; Rib Lake HS; Rib Lake, WI; Band; Chr; CncrtBnd; DrmMjrt; MrchBnd; NatlFornLg; SecFrshCls; RptrSchPpr; PpCl; Chrldr;.

CIMINO, Joanna M; Burris HS; Muncie, IN; 2/50 Band; Chr; Mdrgl; Orch; PepBnd; RptrSchPpr; Ball State Univ; Music.

CIMINO, John J; Creighton Prep HS; Omaha, NE; 29/229 HonRl; JrNHS; Sdlty; RptrYrbk; Ftbl; LetterTrk; CaptWrstlng; Univ Of Notre Dame; Medicine.

CINCOTTA, Toni M; South Adams HS; Geneva, IN; Chr; SctActv; TchrAde; LatCl; PpCl; Ftbl; Wrstlng; Chrldr; Ball St Univ; Nursing.

CINNAMON, William M; Brimfield HS; Brimfield, IL; ChrhWkr; Pres4-H; VPFFA; LetterBsbl; LetterBsktbl; College; Architecture.

CINQUEPALMI, Bruno P; Wayne Mem HS; Westland, MI; Band; CncrtBnd; HonRl; MrchBnd; NHS; Univ Of Michigan; Engineering.

CIOCAN, Jane; Dearborn HS; Dearborn, MI; ChrhWkr; CmntyWkr; HonRl; LatCl; PpCl; CitAwd; College; Professional.

CIOCHETTO, Donna M; West Iron County HS; Stambaugh, MI; Chrs; HonRl; NHS; Twrl; RptrYrbk; FrCl; Central Michigan Univ; Psychology.

CIOLKOSZ, Eugene F; Thorp HS; Stanley, WI; 20/90 HonRl; Yrbk; LetterBsktbl; LetterTrk; College.

CIPRIANO, Susan; Glenbard East Hs; Lombard, IL; 28 DrlTm; HonRl; NHS; FrCl; U Of Illinois;interior Designer.

CIRA, Roseanne M; A A Stagg HS; Hickory Hills, IL; 25/468 CncrtBnd; HonRl; MrchBnd; NHS; PepBnd; SchAde; De Paul Univ; Accounting.

CIRESI, Michael; Pike HS; Indianapolis, IN; 32/231 HonRl; NHS; MthCl; Bsktbl; Trk; IMSpt; Purdue Univ; Industrial Management.

CIRKS, Julie; Nevis HS; Nevis, MN; 3/28 Chr; HonRl; PolWkr; SchPl; StuCncl; StuGov; SchPpr; Chrldr; St Marys Jr Coll Mpls; Physical Therapy Ass.

CISAR, Cindy R; College Community 'S; Cedar Rapids, IA; Band; Chrs; HonRl; JrNHS; OffAde; TreasStuCncl; YthFlsp; 4-H; Bsktbl; LetterTrk; Iowa College; Chemistry.

CISCO, Leslie S; Clinton Community HS; Clinton, IL; 30/154 Band; CncrtBnd; MrchBnd; SchMus; SctActv; Yrbk; IMSpt; JETSAwd; University.

CISEK, Joseph; Proviso West Hs; Berkeley, IL; 90/940 HonRl; NHS; Bsktbl; LetterTennis; Triton College; Social Studies.

CISEWSKI, Thomas J; Rosholt HS; Rosholt, WI; TreasStuCncl; MthCl; CaptFtbl; LetterTrk; LetterWrstlng; Trade Sch; Barber Haristyling.

CISKE, Julia C; Appleton West HS; Appleton, WI; PresAFS; Band; ChrhWkr; CmntyWkr; CncrtBnd; HonRl; MrchBnd; PepBnd; SpnCl; PpCl; Lacrosse Univ; Physical Therapist.

CISLER, Donald K; Caledonia HS; Caledonia, MI; Band; CncrtBnd; HonRl; MrchBnd; PepBnd; 4-H; FrCl; Ftbl; 4-HAwd; Jr College & College.

CISNEROS, John L; Harrison HS; Chicago, IL; 91/388 Band; ChrhWkr; CmntyWkr; CncrtBnd; DrlTm; HonRl; MrchBnd; Orch; PepBnd; ROTC; Chicago St Univ; Music Director.

CISOWSKI, Doreen A; Andrean HS; Gary, IN; 2/306 ChrhWkr; HonRl; NHS; NatlMeritCmnd; SchMus; SchPl; StuCncl; Yrbk; FrCl; MthCl; U Of Evansville; Social Work.

CISSELL, Robert G; Mercy HS; St Awn, MO; 18/187 HonRl; JrNHS; NHS; SchPl; U Of Missouri; Political Science.

CISTON, Melanie A; St Joseph HS; Chicago, IL; 15/121 Chr; HonRl; LbryAde; SchAde; TchrAde; RptrYrbk; Yrbk; FrCl; SciCl; IMSpt; Loyola Univ Sch Of Dentistry; Professional.

CIZEK, Donna J; Bloom Twp HS; Steger, IL; 48/900 Band; Chr; Chrs; CmntyWkr; CncrtBnd; HonRl; HospAde; JrNHS; LbryAde; MrchBnd; NHS; OffAde; Orch; PepBnd; SchAde; College; Librarian.

CLAASSEN, Daniel L; Rose Hill HS; Rose Hill, KS; Chr; Chrl; ChrhWkr; HonRl; OffAde; SchPl; TchrAde; RptrSchPpr; EdSchPpr; College; Professional.

CLAASSEN, David A; Chase County HS; Imperial, NE; 16/58 Band; Chr; SchMus; SchPl; YthFlsp; 4-H; VPFFA; Bsktbl; LetterFtbl; LetterTrk; LetterWrstlng; IMSpt; Mc Pherson College; Music.

CLAES, Jocelyn; Finney HS; Detroit, MI; Chrs; HonRl; JA; TchrAde; EdYrBk; FshEdYrbk; RptrSchPpr; GerCl; Univ Of Mich;psychologist.

CLAEYS, Chris M; United Township HS; East Moline, IL; AFS; Chr; Chrl; HonRl; NatlThespSoc; PolWkr; SchMus; SchPl; Illinois State University.

CLAEYS, Denise; Central Comm HS; Welton, IA; 7/166 HonRl; NHS; EdYrBk; RptrYrbk; Yrbk; 4-H; SciCl; Trk; 4-HAwd; Ia Wesleyan Coll; Art.

CLAEYS, Eric C; Buffalo Grove HS; Arlington Hts, IL; 20/280 Aud/Vis; HonRl; NHS; SctActv; SchPpr; KeyCl; Trk; Southern Illinois Univ; Photography.

CLAFLIN, Cheryl A; Southern Door HS; Sturgeon Bay, WI; Chrs; HonRl; JrNHS; NHS; TchrAde; RptrYrbk; EdYrBk; RptrSchPpr; SpnCl; Technical Sch; Interior Decorating.

CLAIBORNE, Ronald B; Baxter HS; Baxter Springs, KS; HonRl; LbryAde; VPKeyCl; SpnCl; College; Conservationist.

CLAIR, Michael; Marquette HS; Ottawa, IL; 14/96 HonRl; NHS; FFA; KeyCl; Ftbl; Trk; IMSpt; College; Agriculture.

CLAMPITT, Mark; Orchard Farm HS; St Charles, MO; HonRl; JrNHS; KeyCl; Ftbl; Trk; College; Professional.

CLANCY, Jeffrey; Sisseton HS; Sisseton, SD; HonRl; SchPl; RptrSchPpr; Ftbl; Northwestern State Coll; Business.

CLANCY, Maribeth; St Paul HS; Highland, IL; 7/53 SecTrsFrshCls; VPSophCls; VPJrCls; VPSrCls; Chrs; HonRl; LbryAde; SchPl; StuCncl; RptrYrbk; PpCl; Southern Ill Univ; Accounting.

CLANCY, Sara J; Lawrence Central HS; Indianapolis, IN; ALAGirlsSt; HonRl; NHS; OffAde; Quill&Scroll; StuCncl; StuGov; EdYrBk; PPFtbl; AmLegAwd;.

CLANIN, James; Toluca HS; Toluca, IL; 1/24 Band; CncrtBnd; HonRl; MrchBnd; NHS; Orch; PepBnd; StuCncl; Univversity; Law.

CLANIN, James M; Toluca HS; Toluca, IL; Band; CncrtBnd; HonRl; NHS; PepBnd; StuCncl; FrCl; PpCl; SciCl; LetterBsbl; LetterBsktbl; LetterTrk;.

CLANTON, Janie J; Cary Grove HS; Cary, IL; 13/280 Band; Chrs; CmntyWkr; CncrtBnd; HonRl; MrchBnd; NHS; PepBnd; TchrAde; RptrSchPpr; Illinois State Univ; Special Education.

CLAPHAM, Daniel J; Grafton HS; Grafton, WI; 2/210 Band; CncrtBnd; DrmBgl; HonRl; MrchBnd; NHS; PepBnd; TchrAde; MthCl; Mil School Of Engineering; Elec Eng Tech.

CLAPP, Christi; Mccook Sr HS; Mccook, NE; 16/162 AFS; HonRl; NHS; FBLA; MthCl; PpCl; Trk; Chrldr; IMSpt; College; Secretarial Science.

CLAPP, John R; Mc Cook HS; Mc Cook, NE; Bsbl; LetterBsktbl; LetterTennis; College; Professional.

CLAPP, Kathleen D; Hendricks Public HS; Hendricks, MN; 1/50 Band; Chr; ChrhWkr; CmntyWkr; CncrtBnd; HonRl; LbryAde; MrchBnd; PepBnd; PpCl; Nursing School; Registered Nurse.

CLAPP, Rodney R; Forgan HS; Liberal, KS; PresFrshCls; SecTrsSophCls; HstJrCls; PresSrCls; ALBoysSt; Band; Chr; ChrhWkr; CncrtBnd; HonRl; SchPl; StuCncl; EdSchPpr; Ftbl; Oklahoma St Univ; Journalism.

CLAPPER, Jo A; Ainsworth HS; Ainsworth, NE; 5/67 ALAGirlsSt; Band; NHS; NatlThespSoc; StuCncl; Univ Of Nebraska; Veterinarian.

CLARADY, Clara L; Evart HS; Evart, MI; 8/90 HonRl; LbryAde; College; Pharmacy.

CLARAHAN, Daniel A; Bloomington HS; Bloomington, IL; ChrhWkr; CmntyWkr; HonRl; NHS; YthFlsp; SchPpr; GerCl; MthCl; PpCl; SciCl; Univ Of Illinois; Chemical Engineer.

CLARAHAN, Richard; Regina HS; Iowa City, IA; 18/60 TrsFrshCls; HonRl; NHS; SchMus; SchPl; SptEdYrbk; SptEdSchPpr; LetterFtbl; LetterWrstlng; Air Force; Pro.

CLARE, Kathryn J; Ida HS; Temperance, MI; HonRl; NHS; SchPl; RptrYrbk; RptrSchPpr; Monroe Comm Clg; Data Processing.

CLARE, Kelly L; Oak Forest HS; Oak Forest, IL; CmntyWkr; HonRl; LitMag; NHS; OffAde; RptrSchPpr; SpnCl; Loyola Univ; Psychology.

CLARK, Alice M; Barrington HS; Barrington, IL; 94/642 TrsSrCls; Band; CncrtBnd; HonRl; MrchBnd; NHS; Orch; PepBnd; StuCncl; StuGov; YthFlsp; Yrbk; IMSpt; Afs; Sociology.

CLARK, Audrey D; Fountain Central HS; Lingman, IN; 7/126 Band; ChrhWkr; DrlTm; HonRl; NHS; SchMus; SchPl; Yrbk; PresFHA; BttyCrckrAwd;.

CLARK, Aurelia J; Lindblom Tech HS; Chicago, IL; 17/722 HonRl; OffAde; Quill&Scroll; SchAde; TchrAde; RptrSchPpr; SchPpr; Northwestern Univ; Law.

CLARK, Bret; J C Harmon HS; Kansas City, KS; HonRl; NHS; Quill&Scroll; Yrbk; SchPpr; SciCl; College; Professional.

CLARK, Bruce; Western HS; Kokomo, IN; HonRl; YthFlsp; RptrSchPpr; Glf;.

CLARK, Carla A; Concordia HS; Ft Wayne, IN; ChrhWkr; HonRl; HospAde; FrCl; PpCl; College; Nurse.

CLARK, Carol A; Dow City Arion Comm HS; Dow City, IA; 3/40 Chrs; DrlTm; HonRl; YthFlsp; RptrSchPpr; FTA; PpCl; PPFtbl;.

CLARK, Carol F; Montgomery County R2 HS; Montgomery City, MO; Chr; CmntyWkr; HonRl; NHS; NatlMeritSF; DARAwd; 4-HAwd; Nursing Sch; Nursing.

CLARK, Catherine C; St Josephs Academy; St Louis, MO; PresSrCls; HonRl; LitMag; NHS; FrCl; LetterFtbl; GAA; IMSpt; College; Lawyer.

CLARK, Chipper W B; North Linn HS; Central City, IA; 5/67 VPFrshCls; VPSophCls; Chrs; HonRl; JrNHS; SchMus; SchPl; StuCncl; FFA; Bsbl; Ftbl; College; Vocation.

CLARK, Christine M; Oregon Davis HS; Walkerton, IN; Chr; Chrl; HonRl; SchMus; SchPl; StuCncl; 4-H; Chrldr; GAA; 4-HAwd; Coll.

CLARK, Cindy J; Centralia HS; Centralia, IL; CmntyWkr; DrlTm; JrNHS; NHS; OffAde; RedCrAde; PresSciCl; Swmmng; Trk; PPFtbl; College; Physical Education.

CLARK, Cindy K; R Nelson Snider HS; Ft Wayne, IN; 70/510 Chr; HonRl; PolWkr; SchMus; SchPl; StuCncl; TchrAde; Chrldr; Indiana Univ; Lawyer.

CLARK, Connie S; Pawnee City Public HS; Pawnee City, NE; TrsFrshCls; SecTrsSophCls; Chrs; HonRl;.

CLARK, Cynthia S; Kewaunee HS; Kewaunee, WI; 8/138 AFS; HonRl; NHS; SecStuCncl; EdYrBk; FHA; DARAwd; PresAwd; Uw Stevens Point;english Journalism.

CLARK, Dale; Green Bay Southwest HS; Green Bay, WI; HonRl; Univ; Business.

CLARK, Dale D; North White HS; Monon, IN; Band; Chrs; ChrhWkr; HonRl; NHS; NatlThespSoc; PepBnd; PolWkr; SchMus; Florida Inst Of Tech; Pilot.

CLARK, Dan T; New England Public HS; New England, ND; PresFrshCls; ALBoysSt; HonRl; NHS; SchPl; FFA; LetterBsktbl; LetterFtbl; LetterGlf; LetterTrk; Coll.

CLARK, David L; Rushville Con HS; Rushville, IN; 50/267 ALBoysSt; CncrtBnd; MrchBnd; NatlFornLg; NHS; PepBnd; PolWkr; SctActv; RptrYrbk; LetterTrk; Indiana Univ; Medicine.

CLARK, David M; Bentley Sr HS; Burton, MI; ALBoysSt; Chr; HonRl; Mdrgl; NHS; SchMus; YthFlsp; Univ Of Michigan; Dentistry.

CLARK, Debbie; Virden HS; Virden, IL; Band; ChrhWkr; CncrtBnd; HonRl; HospAde; MrchBnd; TchrAde; Twrl; FHA; SciCl; Tennessee Temple Schools; Work With Handica.

CLARK, Debora; Walhalla Public HS; Walhalla, ND; 5/58 ALAGirlsSt; ChrhWkr; HonRl; LbryAde; SchAde; YthFnd; FBLA; BttyCrckrAwd; 4-HAwd; Univ; Nursing.

CLARK, Debra S; Gull Lake HS; Richland, MI; 2/239 HonRl; JA; NatlMeritSF; PolWkr; SchPl; 4-H; FrCl; SpnCl; SciCl; IMSpt; Mich St Univ; Biological Science.

CLARK, Denise A; Mankato East HS; Mankato, MN; CncrtBnd; HonRl; Clge; Pro.

CLARK, Diana; Lindblom Tech HS; Chicago, IL; 67/722 Chr; ChrhWkr; HonRl; TchrAde; YthFlsp; SpnCl; Trk; GAA; College; Secondary Education Mathematics.

CLARK, Donald E; Douglass Macarthur HS; Decatur, IL; 14/410 Band; HonRl; NHS; EdYrBk; Yrbk; RptrSchPpr; Univ Of Ill; French.

CLARK, Edgar D; Peoria HS; Peoria, IL; Band; Orch; Socr; Univ Of Illinois; Agriculture.

CLARK, Floyd D; Elverado HS; Murphysboro, IL; HonRl; SchPl; YthFlsp; 4-H; FBLA; FFA; PresFrCl; Ftbl; College; Mining Engineering.

CLARK, Gaynell G; Chicago Voc HS; Chicago, IL; 18/789 Chr; Chrs; HonRl; NHS; Col; Vocation.

CLARK, Gwen S; Raymond Central HS; Ceresco, NE; HonRl; SchPl; StuCncl; StuGov; TchrAde; 4-H; FHA; PpCl; LetterBsktbl; LetterTrk; Chrldr; GAA; 4-HAwd; University; Psychology.

CLARK, Jacki D; Keya Paha Co HS; Springview, NE; 4/26 Chrs; DrmMjrt; MrchBnd; SchPl; StuCncl; Yrbk; FHA; PpCl; Bsbl; Bsktbl; Trk; College.

CLARK, James B; Knox County HS; Edina, MO; PresJrCls; Chr; Chrs; ChrhWkr; HonRl; SchMus; StuCncl; StuGov; FFA; Bsktbl; College; Professional Or Voc.

CLARK, Jane M; Delwein Comm HS; Delwein, IA; HonRl; JrNHS; LitMag; LbryAde; PpCl;.

CLARK, Janette L; Norton Community HS; Norton, KS; Chrs; SchMus; StuCncl; RptrYrbk; Yrbk; FHA; PpCl; Glf; Collegef Animal Technician.

CLARK, Jaynan R; Lyle Public HS; Austin, MN; 2/32 Band; Chr; HonRl; JrNHS; MrchBnd; SchMus; EdYrBk; FHA; LetterTrk; PresAwd; College; Professional.

CLARK, Jeff J; Murray HS; St Paul, MN; Band; CmntyWkr; CncrtBnd; HonRl; PepBnd; RedCrAde; SctActv; College Of St Thomas; Lawyer.

CLARK, Joseph M; Sault Area Public HS; Sault Ste Marie, MI; Chr; ChrhWkr; LitMag; PolWkr; Bsbl; LetterFtbl; LetterGlf; Swmmng; IMSpt; RotaryAwd; Law School; Lawyer Politics.

CLARK, Joyce E; Rich Hill HS; Rich Hill, MO; VPJrCls; ChrhWkr; HonRl; StuCncl; Yrbk; RptrSchPpr; FBLA; FHA; Chrldr; CitAwd; College; Professional.

CLARK, Julie; Century HS; Karnak, IL; 1/54 PresFrshCls; VPSophCls; HonRl; TchrAde; Twrl; Yrbk; RptrSchPpr; FHA; PpCl; IMSpt; Draughons Bus Col; Accounting.

CLARK, Julie A; Minot HS; Minot, ND; HonRl; NHS; SciCl; IMSpt; Univ Of Co Boulder; Art, Meteorologest.

CLARK, Karen; Urbana Hs; Urbana, IL; 1 College Of Liberial Arts ; Religious Studie.

CLARK, Karen L; Wethersfield HS; Kewanee, IL; VPBand; ChrhWkr; CncrtBnd; HonRl; LbryAde; MrchBnd; PepBnd; SchPl; StuCncl; VPYthFlsp; Blackhawk East Campus; Home Ec.

CLARK, Karen L; John F Kennedy HS; Chicago, IL; 32/610 TreasChrs; HonRl; JrNHS; NHS; SchMus; SchPl; Yrbk; Univ Of Illinois; Psychology.

CLARK, Karen L; Thornton Fractional So HS; Lansing, IL; 11/650 Chr; ChrhWkr; CmntyWkr; HonRl; HospAde; NHS; NatlMeritFnl; NatlMeritCmnd; OffAde; SchAde; SctActv; SpnCl; PpCl; School Radiologic Tech; X Ray Technician.

CLARK, Kimberly; Mauston Area HS; Mauston, WI; Band; CncrtBnd; HonRl; MrchBnd; 4-H; PpCl; Chrldr; PPFtbl; 4-HAwd; Coll; Professional.

CLARK, Kimberly C; Paw Paw HS; Paw Paw, MI; VPSrCls; CaptDrlTm; HonRl; StuCncl; Pres4-H; Bsbl; Tennis; CaptChrldr; CchngActv; 4-HAwd;.

CLARK, Kim N; Larkin HS; Elgin, IL; HonRl; University Of Illinois.

CLARK, Leesa A; St Pius X HS; Kansas City, MO; HonRl; SchPpr; Mo Univ At Columbia; Public Relations.

CLARK, Leslie R; Alton Senior HS; Alton, IL; 210/1200 Aud/Vis; Chr; Chrs; ChrhWkr; HonRl; LbryAde; TchrAde; PresGerCl; SciCl; Southern Ill Univ.

CLARK, Louise H; Johannesbg Lewiston Area HS; Johannesburg, MI; 1/56 PresSophCls; CncrtBnd; HonRl; PepBnd; SchPl; StuCncl; TchrAde; RptrSchPpr; SciCl; U Of Mi; Medicine.

CLARK, Marian K; Beal City HS; Mt Pleasant, MI; 3/54 HonRl; LbryAde; NHS; SchPl; 4-H; Bsktbl; Trk; GAA; 4-HAwd; Ferris State Col; Acctg.

CLARK, Mariann E; Quincy Senior HS; Quincy, IL; StuGov; Univ Of Illinois; Engineering.

CLARK, Mary; Wes Del HS; Muncie, IN; 3/110 ChrhWkr; HonRl; NHS; BttyCrckrAwd; Ball State Univ; Music Major.

CLARK, Mary E; Sparta HS; Sparta, WI; VPSophCls; Chrs; ChrhWkr; HonRl; NatlFornLg; SchMus; SchPl; PpCl; CaptChrldr; College; Commercial Art.

CLARK, Melanie; Ottawa Hs; Grand Ridge, IL; HonRl; NHS; GerCl; Collge Ivcc;accounting.

CLARK, Melanie A; Brighton HS; Brighton, MI; HonRl; NHS; StuCncl; StuGov; GAA; PPFtbl; Univ.

CLARK, Michael; Clinton Sr HS; Clinton, WI; 13/96 AFS; Band; HonRl; MrchBnd; SchMus; GerCl; Bsbl; Bsktbl; KiwanAwd; College; Lawyer.

CLARK, Michael A; Chandler Lake Wilson HS; Chandler, MN; Band; HonRl; OffAde; Col; Professional.

CLARK, Michael L; Gibson Southern HS; Fort Branch, IN; HonRl; TchrAde; SchPpr; Lockyear Bus Coll; Accountant.

CLARK, Nancy J; St Teresa HS; Decatur, IL; 18/118 ALAGirlsSt; HonRl; JrNHS; NHS; NatlMeritCmnd; OffAde; Sacrstn; Yrbk; Eastern Ill Univ; Accounting.

CLARK, Niles; Westfield; Westfield, IN; 40/128 Band; Chr; ChrhWkr; CncrtBnd; HonRl; MrchBnd; SchMus; 4-H; FFA; Army College; Professional.

CLARK, Pam A; Lovington HS; Lovington, IL; 12/38 ChrhWkr; CmntyWkr; HonRl; HospAde; SchPl; FNA; Bsktbl; GAA; IMSpt; KiwanAwd; Wiu; Rn.

CLARK, Pamela J; New England Public HS; New England, ND; 2/49 Band; Chr; HonRl; NHS; SchPl; StuCncl; PpCl; CaptBsktbl; LetterTrk; Chrldr; State Sch Of Science; Occupational Therapis.

CLARK, Pamela K; West Harrison HS; Pisgah, IA; Band; Chr; Chrs; ChrhWkr; CncrtBnd; HonRl; MrchBnd; NHS; SchMus; SchPl; StuGov; Twrl; YthFlsp; 4-H; LetterBsktbl; Iowa Western Com College; Dental Asst.

CLARK, Patricia K; Lees Summit HS; Lees Summit, MO; Chr; ChrhWkr; HonRl; Mdrgl; Central Missouri State College; Typing.

CLARK, Patty B; Peoria Heights HS; Peoria Heights, IL; 12/93 CncrtBnd; HonRl; MrchBnd; NHS; Quill&Scroll; SchMus; SptEdYrbk; EdSchPpr; CaptTrk; CaptChrldr; Physical Educ.

CLARK, Paul; Clinton HS; Clinton, MO; 24/143 AFS; Chr; Chrl; Chrs; ChrhWkr; Mdrgl; SctActv; 4-H; Trk; Wrstlng; Ks St Univ; Physcial Therapy.

CLARK, Peter A; Stevens HS; Rapid City, SD; Liberal Arts College; Writer.

CLARK, Randall N; Mona Shores HS; Muskegon, MI; Band; ChrhWkr; CncrtBnd; HonRl; NHS; NatlMeritSF; PepBnd; StuCncl; LetterFtbl; LetterTrk; Hope Clge Holland Mi; Pre Med.

CLARK, Richard D; Mills Prairie HS; Mill Shoals, IL; VPJrCls; HonRl; 4-H; FFA; EngCl; Bsbl; Bsktbl; Trk; AmLegAwd; College.

CLARK, Richard E; Enterprise Academy; Topeka, KS; 1/39 TrsSophCls; PresChr; HonRl; StuCncl; IMSpt; College.

CLARK, Rickie J; Princeton R 5 HS; Princeton, MO; 17/52 VPFrshCls; VPSophCls; VPJrCls; VPSrCls; Chr; HonRl; StuGov; Bsktbl; Ftbl; Trk; Highland Jr Coll.

CLARK, Rita M; Elgin Public HS; Elgin, NE; Chrs; HonRl; SchPl; FHA; Trk; Trade Or Bus School.

CLARK, Sharon; Jackson County Western HS; Jackson, MI; 1/150 Band; ChrhWkr; CncrtBnd; HonRl; MrchBnd; NHS; TchrAde; RptrYrbk; SchPpr; Spring Abor College; Teacher Education.

CLARK, Steve A; Alton Sr HS; Godfrey, IL; 78/804 HonRl; NHS; PolWkr; TreasStuCncl; PresStuGov; SchPpr; GerCl; Bsktbl; LetterTrk; AmLegAwd; Purdue Univ; Chemical Engineering.

CLARK, Steven A; Marist HS; Chicago Ridge, IL; HonRl; NatlMeritSF; Coll; Pre Med.

CLARK, Steven J; Houghton HS; Houghton, MI; 1 117 HonRl; NatlMeritSF; PolWkr; RptrYrbk; SpnCl; LetterTrk; Kalamazoo Clg; Math.

CLARK, Sue A; Adrian HS; Adrian, MI; 7/411 ALAGirlsSt; Chr; ChrhWkr; NHS; NatlThespSoc; SchMus; SchPl; SecYthFlsp; Yrbk; IMSpt; Malone Coll; Eng.

CLARK, Susan K; United Township HS; East Moline, IL; 25/687 Chr; HonRl; HospAde; JA; LbryAde; NHS; S Illinois Univ; Theater.

CLARK, Susanna M; Brimfield Comm Unit HS #309; Brimfield, IL; 4/50 Chr; Chrs; ChrhWkr; HonRl; NHS; SctActv; FHA; SpnCl; PpCl; Univ.

CLARK, Susan P; Nazareth Academy; Chicago, IL; 37/154 LbryAde; OffAde; Rosary College; Business Admin.

CLARK, Teri K; Sutherland Public HS; Sutherland, NE; Chr; Chrl; Chrs; ChrhWkr; CmntyWkr; DrlTm; HonRl; Mdrgl; SchAde; SchPl; Trade; Vocation.

CLARK, Teri L; Centerville Sr HS; Richmond, IN; Band; DrlTm; HonRl; LbryAde; OffAde; TchrAde; GAA;.

CLARK, Terry N; Northwestern R I HS; Rothville, MO; PresSophCls; TrsJrCls; NHS; TreasFFA; SciCl; Bsbl; LetterBsktbl; North East Mo State Univ; Vocational Agricu.

CLARK, Thomas; Bishop Miege HS; Arairie Village, KS; Aud/Vis; HonRl; NHS; PolWkr; TchrAde; College; Professional.

CLARK, Tom G; Big Springs HS; Big Springs, NE; PresSophCls; Band; HonRl; PepBnd; SctActv; TchrAde; 4-H; College.

CLARK, Virginia L; Durand HS; Durand, IL; 5/62 AFS; HonRl; SchMus; SchPl; EdYrBk; SpnCl; Rockford College; English.

CLARK, Vivian L; Lake City Community HS; Lake City, IA; 2/61 Band; Chr; CncrtBnd; HonRl; HospAde; LbryAde; MrchBnd; PepBnd; FSA; PpCl; Coll; Nursing.

CLARK, Vonda L; Mulvane HS; Wichita, KS; Chrs; CmntyWkr; HonRl; NHS; SchPl; RptrYrbk; FHA; PpCl; Clge; Prof.

CLARK, Wayne; Black River Falls HS; Black River Falls, WI; 50/149 Band; Chr; ChrhWkr; HonRl; Mdrgl; SchMus; StuCncl; 4-H; College; Pre Law.

CLARK, William R; Hinsdale Twp HS; Hinsdale, IL; ChrhWkr; HonRl; LitMag; NatlMeritCmnd; RptrSchPpr; LetterBsktbl; College; Communications.

CLARKE, Anthony W; Beecher HS; Flint, MI; 45/350 PresFrshCls; PresSophCls; PresJrCls; HonRl; HospAde; SchMus; SchPl; StuCncl; StuGov; FDA; College.

CLARKE, Charles P; Gwinn HS; K I Sawyer Afb, MI; 8/160 CncrtBnd; MrchBnd; NHS; SpnCl; SciCl; IMSpt; Mich Tech U; Applied Physics.

CLARKE, Jennifer L; Climax Scotts HS; Scotts, MI; 6/53 Band; ChrhWkr; HonRl; NatlFornLg; OffAde; SchPl; RptrYrbk; 4-H; MthCl; Chrldr; Kalamazoo Coll; Foreign Lang.

CLARKE, Kathy; Cass City HS; Cass City, MI; 10/160 ChrhWkr; HonRl; JrNHS; NHS; 4-H; FHA; KeyCl; FrCl;.

CLARKE, Michael G; St Rita HS; Chicago, IL; 35/437 HonRl; RptrSchPpr; Bsktbl; College; Accounting.

CLARKE, Nancy R; Valley R 6 HS; Bismarck, MO; 1/50 PresSophCls; SecJrCls; SecSrCls; Band; HonRl; StuCncl; SptEdSchPpr; Trk; IMSpt; DARAwd; Mineral Area College; Business.

CLARKE, Patrick R; Homer HS; Homer, IL; 2/36 PresJrCls; ALBoysSt; PresBand; ChrhWkr; CncrtBnd; NHS; NatlMeritCmnd; SchMus; PresStuCncl; EdYrBk; FSA; Ftbl; LetterGlf; University Of Illinois; Veterinarian.

CLARKE, P Ryan; Homer HS; Homer, IL; 2/37 PresJrCls; ALBoysSt; PresBand; HonRl; NatlMeritCmnd; PresStuCncl; EdYrBk; Ftbl; Glf; AmLegAwd; Univ Of Illinois; Veterinarian.

CLARKE, Randy C; Auburn HS; Auburn, NE; ChrhWkr; HonRl; LbryAde; SciCl; College; Data Processing.

CLARKE, Robert; Jetmore HS; Jetmore, KS; 1/44 PresSophCls; Chr; Chrs; HonRl; SctActv; StuGov; Trk; GodCntryAwd; Univ Of Kansas; Major In Science.

CLARKE, Stewart M; Roger C Sullivan HS; Chicago, IL; ChrhWkr; HonRl; JA; NatlMeritFnl; OffAde; StuCncl; StuGov; TchrAde; KeyCl; GerCl; Univ Of Ill; Accounting.

CLARKSEGN, Wayne R; Cavalier Public HS; Cabalier, ND; /84 Band; HonRl; PepBnd; SciCl; Ftbl; Glf; Wahpeton School Of Science; Accouting.

CLARY, Aaron R; St Johns Military HS; Herington, KS; Band; Chr; ChrhWkr; SchAde; SchMus; SpnCl; SciCl; Ftbl; Trk; Wrstlng; IMSpt; KiwanAwd; College; Law.

CLARY, Deborah J; Saline HS; Saline, MI; 12/199 TrsSrCls; Band; HonRl; HospAde; MrchBnd; OffAde; SchMus; YthFlsp; PpCl; Eastern Mich; Medicine.

CLARY, Ellen; Peru HS; Peru, IN; 67/231 Band; CncrtBnd; HonRl; NatlFornLg; OffAde; FTA; SpnCl; PpCl; LetterChrldr; LetterGAA;.

CLARY, Linda K; Macomb HS; Macomb, IL; Chr; Chrs; ChrhWkr; CncrtBnd; HonRl; LbryAde; MrchBnd; NHS; PepBnd; YthFlsp; Yrbk; Western Illinois Univ; Music.

CLARY, Randall A; Peoria HS; Peoria, IL; 1/481 ChrhWkr; HonRl; JrNHS; LatCl; LetterFtbl; Trk; Wrstlng; SARAwd; College; Medicine.

CLARY, Ricky L; Troy HS; Troy, KS; 10/30 Chrs; HonRl; SchPl; TchrAde; SchPpr; Pres4-H; Ftbl; Trk; 4-HAwd; Highland Jr College; Engineer.

CLASEN, Edward A; Winneconne Community HS; Winneconne, WI; 22/144 HonRl; NHS; SchPl; PresStuCncl; TchrAde; Bsktbl; Trk; College.

CLASEN, Jaclynn R; Rich Central HS; Olympia Fields, IL; 18/400 CmntyWkr; HonRl; NHS; RptrSchPpr; Univ Of Illinois; Medicine.

CLASEN, Jim; Douglass HS; Douglass, KS; 5/45 HonRl; OffAde; SchAde; TchrAde; Bsbl; Bsktbl; Trk; DanFAwd; CitAwd; Friends Univ; Teacher Col Coaching.

CLASING, Kevin; Graettinger Community Hs; Ruthven, IA; HonRl; NHS; SchMus; SchPl; StuCncl; 4-H; FFA; Ftbl; Chrldr;.

CLASS, Cynthia J; St Louise De Marillac HS; Northbrook, IL; 52/252 Chrl; Chrs; HospAde; NHS; SchMus; Sdlty; StuCncl; SpnCl; St Marys College; Social Worker.

CLASSEN, Bruce D; Adams Central HS; Glenvil, NE; 12/54 ALBoysSt; Band; Chr; HonRl; NHS; SchMus; SchPl; EdYrBk; Yrbk; 4-H; Wrstlng; AmLegAwd; Wayne State College; Business Admin.

CLASSEN, Mary; Adams Central HS; Ayr, NE; 14/54 SecTrsSrCls; Band; Chr; HonRl; MrchBnd; PepBnd; StuGov; Yrbk; EdSchPpr; ChmbCommrsAwd; Ne Univ; Business Admin.

CLASSEN, Suzanne; Lourdes HS; Rochester, MN; Chr; Chrl; Chrs; ChrhWkr; TchrAde; SpnCl; St Teresas College; Spanish Interpreter.

CLATTS, Michael C; St Alberts Jr Seminary; Scottarb, IL; ChrhWkr; CmntyWkr; HonRl; LbryAde; OffAde; Sacrstn; SchAde; SchPl; SctActv; StuCncl; TchrAde; CivCl; FrCl; Bsktbl; Orange County Comm College; Priest.

CLAUDE, Sharon L; Public Senior HS; Sauke Centre, MN; Band; Chr; HonRl; 4-H; 4-HAwd; U Of Mn; Mathematics.

CLAUNCH, Larry O; Osceola Public HS; Osceola, MO; 19/57 HonRl; NHS; PolWkr; SchPl; FBLA; FFA; LetterPpCl; Bsktbl; Ftbl; CchngActv; College; Business.

CLAUS, Diana J; East Pike HS; Milton, IL; 3/25 TrsSophCls; PresJrCls; HonRl; NHS; SchPl; EdYrBk; 4-H; FHA; Trk; Chrldr;.

CLAUSE, Joy L; E Greene Comm HS; Grand Jct, IA; ChrhWkr; CmntyWkr; ModUN; NHS; PolWkr; TchrAde; EdSchPpr; Bsktbl; Trk; 4-HAwd; JAAwd; Iowa St Univ; Law.

CLAUSEN, Amy M; Edina East HS; Edina, MN; CncrtBnd; MrchBnd; LatCl; Chrldr; IMSpt; College; Professional.

CLAUSEN, Jeanne; Northwestern HS; Ashton, SD; 14/35 Band; Chrs; HonRl; HospAde; NatlThespSoc; SchPl; Yrbk; 4-H; DARAwd; LionAwd; Presentation College; Registered Nurse.

CLAUSEN, Kirk A; Winnebago HS; Rockford, IL; 9/125 Chr; Chrl; Chrs; HonRl; Mdrgl; SchMus; SchPl; TchrAde; PresYthFlsp; 4-H; 4-HAwd; University; Math.

CLAUSEN, Kristen A; Seward Sr HS; Seward, NE; TrsJrCls; HonRl; SchPl; StuCncl; StuGov; Teen; College; Teaching.

CLAUSEN, Mary P; Henry Ind #27 HS; Henry, SD; TrsJrCls; Chr; PresFrshCls; SchPl; StuCncl; RptrSchPpr; PpCl; Bsktbl; Trk; GAA; Business School; Business.

CLAUSEN, Paula; Luck Public HS; Luck, WI; 3/49 VPJrCls; Band; CncrtBnd; HonRl; MrchBnd; PepBnd; TchrAde; FHA; PpCl; Vocational School; Secretary.

CLAUSEN, Robert E; Sycamore HS; Genoa, IL; ChrhWkr; HonRl; 4-H; FFA; Wrstlng; ChmbCommrsAwd; College; Agriculture.

CLAUSEN, Rodney P; Charter Oak Ute Comm HS; Charter Oak, IA; 10/45 Band; ChrhWkr; CncrtBnd; HonRl; MrchBnd; NHS; SchPl; StuCncl; Bsktbl; LetterFtbl; LetterTrk; Iowa State University; Conservation.

CLAUSON, Steven R; Lakota HS; Lakota, ND; ALBoysSt; HonRl; SchPl; SctActv; FFA; CaptBsbl; LetterFtbl; LetterTrk; LetterWrstlng; University.

CLAUSS, Linda S; Triton HS; Bourbon, IN; Band; ChrhWkr; CncrtBnd; HonRl; NHS; PepBnd; SchMus; FHA; FTA; PpCl; Bus Sch; Accountant.

CLAUSS, Lynn M; Tri County HS; Walcott, IN; 5/86 Band; NHS; OffAde; Orch; PepBnd; EdYrBk; 4-H; FrCl; PpCl; GAA; In Voc & Tech Clge; Clinical Lab Assistant.

CLAUSSEN, Cheryl K; Porta HS; Petersburg, IL; SecBand; Chr; CncrtBnd; VPJA; MrchBnd; Orch; PepBnd; RptrSchPpr; GAA; IMSpt; College; Data Processing.

CLAUSSEN, David P; Schleswig Comm HS; Ricketts, IA; Band; Chr; CmntyWkr; HonRl; Orch; SchMus; StuCncl; RptrSchPpr; EdSchPpr; FTA; Ftbl; Glf; Drake Univ; Law.

CLAUSSEN, Dennis W; Porta HS; Petersburg, IL; 23/97 LbryAde; Mdrgl; NHS; SchMus; TchrAde; RptrSchPpr; KeyCl;.

CLAUSSEN, Kimberly S; Fremont Senior HS; Fremont, NE; Chrs; 4-H; GerCl; 4-HAwd; Univ Of Nebr; Lab Tech.

CLAVEL, Nanette; Grosse Pointe South HS; Grosse Pointe Cy, MI; 35/614 CmntyWkr; HonRl; NHS; SchAde; TchrAde; Yrbk; FTA; PPFtbl; Univ Of Michigan.

CLAVON, Kimberly A; Immaculata HS; Detroit, MI; ChrhWkr; HonRl; LbryAde; NatlMeritSchl; NatlSciFnd; StuGov; YthLg; FDA; SciCl; Trk; JCAwd; Univ Of Michigan; Medicine.

CLAWSON, Carol A; John Marshall HS; Indianapolis, IN; 17/538 HonRl; NHS; LetterChrldr; College; Professional.

CLAWSON, Debra K; Industry HS; Industry, IL; 1/35 SecFrshCls; TrsJrCls; Band; Chrs; CncrtBnd; HonRl; MrchBnd; NatlMeritSF; StuCncl; EdYrBk; RptrSchPpr; Pres4-H; GAA; 4-HAwd; Western Ill Univ; Math.

CLAWSON, Lary D; Annapolis HS; Dearborn Heights, MI; 21/435 ChrhWkr; HonRl; NHS; SchAde; SchPl; Univ Of Michigan; History.

CLAWSON, Rae L; Edgerton HS; Edgerton, WI; AFS; DrlTm; NHS; SchPl; SctActv; Tennis; College; Business Education.

CLAXTON, Delbert L; Finney HS; Detroit, MI; Band; CncrtBnd; HonRl; JrNHS; MrchBnd; LetterBsbl; LetterFtbl; Swmmng; Trk; Wrstlng; IMSpt; AmLegAwd; Michigan St Univ; Medicine.

CLAY, Betty J; Green City R I HS; Green Castle, MO; 5/30 VPFrshCls; ALAGirlsSt; Band; DrmMjrt; HonRl; NHS; StuCncl; Bsbl; Bsktbl; CaptTrk; Northeast Missouri; Secretarial.

CLAY, Charles; North Division HS; Milwaukee, WI; Band; CmntyWkr; CncrtBnd; HonRl; MrchBnd; PepBnd; SchAde; YthFnd; Bsktbl; Ftbl; Coll;.

CLAY, Cynthia A; Taft HS; Chicago, IL; VPSrCls; Chrs; HonRl; VPJA; JrNHS; NHS; TchrAde; KeyCl; SpnCl; PpCl; Trk; GAA; Business School; Legal Secretary.

CLAY, Gilbert; Cregier Voc; Chicago, IL; 20/106 PresSrCls; CmntyWkr; HonRl; SchAde; StuCncl; Bsbl; Wrstlng; Tennessee State U; Architectural Drafting.

CLAY, Jimmy R; Richland HS; Essex, MO; Band; ChrhWkr; HonRl; FFA; LetterBsbl; LetterBsktbl; College; Professional.

CLAY, Larry D; Le Roy HS; Le Roy, KS; ALBoysSt; Chrs; HonRl; SchPl; Yrbk; Bsktbl; Ftbl; IMSpt; Butler Co Com Coll; Electronics.

CLAY, Marilyn L; Plainfield HS; Plainfield, IL; 28/273 HonRl; JrNHS; NHS; FNA; SpnCl; GAA; IMSpt; College.

CLAY, Sophia; St Thomas Apostle; Chicago, IL; CmntyWkr; NatlMeritFnl; NatlMeritCmnd; OffAde; SchAde; TchrAde; YthFnd; Univ; Computer Programming.

CLAY, Susan A; Hannibal HS; Hannibal, MO; SecBand; CncrtBnd; MrchBnd; SctActv; PpCl; GAA; Univ; Architecture.

CLAY, Wanda C; Rosati Kain HS; St Louis, MO; 38/116 PresFrshCls; Chrs; NHS; NatlThespSoc; SchPl; MthCl; GAA; Univ Of Detroit; Professional.

CLAY, William E; King City R1 HS; King City, MO; Band; Chr; CncrtBnd; DrmMjrt; HonRl; NHS; SchPl; StuCncl; StuGov; SptEdYrbk; University; Social Anthropology.

CLAYBAUGH, Janet L; Hillsdale HS; Hillsdale, MI; 6/180 Band; Chr; NHS; PepBnd; TchrAde; 4-H; FTA; FrCl; EldAwd; College; Teacher.

CLAYCAMP, Lonny P; Trego Community HS; Wakeeneg, KS; Chrs; ChrhWkr; CmntyWkr; SctActv; TchrAde; YthFlsp; CivCl; FFA; KeyCl; IMSpt; Fort Hays St Col; Business.

CLAYCOMB, Richard; Wyoming Park HS; Wyoming, MI; HonRl; SpnCl; Grand Valley State Col; Special Ed Teacher.

CLAYPOOL, Brenda J; Bismarck Henning HS; Bismarck, IL; Chrs; ChrhWkr; HonRl; OffAde; SchMus; PresEdYrBk; PresPpCl; ChmnGAA; PPFtbl; 4-HAwd; Beauty School.

CLAYPOOL, Forrest E; St Elmo HS; St Elmo, IL; PresFrshCls; Band; PresChrs; CncrtBnd; HonRl; PresJrNHS; NHS; SchMus; RptrSchPpr; EdSchPpr; LetterBsbl; LetterTrk; CchngActv; Southern Il Univ; Journalism.

CLAYPOOLE, Byron P; Maine South HS; Park Ridge, IL; 80/800 Band; CncrtBnd; HonRl; MrchBnd; Univ Of Illinois; Architect.

CLAYTON, Cheryl L; Glenwood HS; Pawnee, IL; 12/143 AFS; ChrhWkr; CmntyWkr; HospAde; NHS; NatlMeritSchl; PepBnd; SctActv; StuGov; YthFlsp; Illinois Wesleyan Univ; Political Science.

CLAYTON, Debby J; Belmont HS; Belmont, WI; 5/46 VPFrshCls; VPSophCls; PresJrCls; Band; Chr; Chrs; HonRl; LbryAde; SchMus; SchPl; StuCncl; RptrYrbk; RptrSchPpr; 4-H; FHA; College; Elementary Teacher.

CLAYTON, Gary L; Stuart Menlo HS; Menlo, IA; VPJrCls; HonRl; FFA; Trade School; Farming.

CLAYTON, Keith; Oak Park River Forest Hs; Oak Park, IL; HonRl; PresNatlFornLg; NatlMeritCmnd; Northwestern U; Journalism.

CLAYTON, Kevin D; Newton Community HS; Newton, IA; 11/330 HonRl; NHS; KeyCl; Swmmng; Ia St U; Archi.

CLAYTON, Kim A; Franklin HS; Franklin, IL; SecSophCls; Band; Chrs; LitMag; NHS; SchPl; Yrbk; 4-H; Chrldr; 4-HAwd; Business School; Vocation.

CLAYTON, Marilyn D; Neosho HS; Joplin, MO; SecTrsSrCls; Chr; HonRl; LbryAde; StuGov; FBLA; EngCl; Mssc Joplin.

CLAYTON, Randy W; Bond County Comm Unit #2 HS; Pocahontas, IL; VPJrCls; PresSrCls; Band; Chrs; CncrtBnd; MrchBnd; PepBnd; SchMus; FrCl; PpCl; LetterBsbl; Bsktbl; Kaskaskia Jr College; Computer Science.

CLAYTON, Scott E; Pinckney HS; Hamburg, MI; HonRl; NHS; Bsbl; University; Professional.

CLAYTON, Wendi J; Unity HS; Chicago, IL; 6/182 Chrs; SchMus; TchrAde; EdYrBk; 4-H; Northwestern Univ; Physicist.

CLAYWELL, Deborah C; Ben Davis HS; Indianapolis, IN; ChrhWkr; HonRl; NatlMeritCmnd; OffAde; FBLA; Job; Bookkeeper Or Secretary.

CLAYWELL, Howard J; Union HS; Losantville, IN; PresFrshCls; HonRl; LbryAde; 4-H; FFA; LetterBsktbl; Trade Schl; Mechanic.

CLEAVELIN, Leonard R; Bishop Du Borg HS; St Louis, MO; 45/470 HonRl; LbryAde; SchMus; SchPl; RptrYrbk; Yrbk; RptrSchPpr; LatCl; CchngActv; U Of Washington; Philosophy.

CLEAVER, Charles R; Centerville HS; Centerville, IN; HonRl; JA; JrNHS; NHS; StuCncl; SpnCl; SciCl; LetterBsbl; LetterFtbl; JAAwd; KiwanAwd; CitAwd; College; Accounting.

CLEAVER, Cynthia A; West Chicago Community HS; Winfield, IL; 27/321 AFS; HonRl; NHS; StuCncl; YthFlsp; Yrbk; Bsktbl; Tennis; CchngActv; DARAwd; University Of Il; Accounting.

CLEAVER, John; Mark Twain HS; Perry, MO; 21/69 Band; CncrtBnd; HonRl; MrchBnd; PepBnd; SctActv; Yrbk; FTA; SecJrCls; Trk; Mo Univ; Law.

CLEAVER, Max B; Yorktown HS; Muncie, IN; TrsJrCls; RedCrAde; TchrAde; FBLA; SpnCl; SciCl; LetterBsbl; Bsktbl; Ftbl; LetterSwmmng; Trk; PresAwd; Ball State Univ; Civil Engineering.

CLEAVER, Phillip J; Homestead HS; Ft Wayne, IN; Band; HonRl; MrchBnd; StuCncl; Ftbl; Swmmng; IMSpt; Indiana Univ; Bus Law.

CLEAVINGER, Jean A; Tonganoxie HS; Leavenworth, KS; 6/95 DrlTm; HonRl; NHS; PresNatlThespSoc; SchPl; YthFlsp; VP4-H; SecFBLA; FHA; 4-HAwd; Ks City Ks Comm College; Nursing.

CLEETER, Joyce A; Dillsboro HS; Dillsboro, IN; SecBand; ChrhWkr; CncrtBnd; HonRl; MrchBnd; SchPl; Yrbk; RptrSchPpr; SchPpr; GAA; College; Nursing.

CLEGG, Jill L; Churchill HS; Westland, MI; ChrhWkr; HonRl; StuCncl; TchrAde; Coll; Cpa.

CLELAND, Joan C; Deckerville HS; Deckerville, MI; 2/79 SecJrCls; ALAGirlsSt; ChrhWkr; HonRl; NHS; OffAde; StuCncl; TchrAde; Central Mi Univ; Elem Educ.

CLELAND, Linda A; Baldwin HS; Baldwin, KS; HonRl; NatlFornLg; SchMus; StuCncl; 4-H; FHA; DanFAwd; 4-HAwd; College; Oral Communication.

CLEM, Deborah L; Abl HS; Broadlands, IL; 4/23 Band; Chr; Chrs; ChrhWkr; CmntyWkr; HonRl; NHS; PepBnd; SchPl; StuCncl; Eastern Il U; Special Ed.

CLEMEN, Mary S; Leo HS; Holy Cross, IA; Chrs; HonRl; LbryAde; OffAde; SchAde; SchMus; TchrAde; PresPpCl; IMSpt; Trade HS.

CLEMENIC, Bonnie; Walther Lutheran Hs; Willow Springs, IL; 6/91 Chrs; HonRl; RptrSchPpr; Swmmng; College; Pharmacy.

CLEMENIC, Bonnie; Walther Lutheran HS; Willow Springs, IL; 6/91 Chrs; HonRl; JrNHS; RptrSchPpr; Swmmng; Univ Of Il; Pharmacy.

CLEMENS, Cathleen M; Mother Of Sorrows HS; Chicago, IL; 15/143 TrsJrCls; CmntyWkr; HonRl; NHS; StuCncl; TchrAde; GAA; IMSpt; VoiceDemAwd; College; Diatician.

CLEMENS, Elaine; Odessa HS; Odessa, MO; VPJrCls; NatlThespSoc; YthFlsp; RptrYrbk; Yrbk; RptrSchPpr; EdSchPpr; FTA; Ftbl; Tennis; Modeling School; Modeling.

CLEMENS, Gale R; Excelsior Springs HS; Excelsior Springs, MO; 52/240 Chr; DrlTm; HonRl; JrNHS; NHS; SchMus; StuCncl; TchrAde; FTA; IMSpt; Univ Of Mo; Music.

CLEMENS, Mary; Providence Hs; New Lenox, IL; SecJrCls; Chrs; HonRl; NHS; RptrYrbk; RptrSchPpr; PresSpnCl; MthCl; GAA; BttyCrckrAwd; College; Psychology.

CLEMENS, Patricia H; New Trier West HS; Northfield, IL; 64/694 AFS; Aud/Vis; Chrs; CmntyWkr; HonRl; NatlMeritCmnd; NatlMeritSF; SchMus; SchPl; College; Theatre.

CLEMENS, Polly R; Luther L Wright HS; Ironwood, MI; Band; CncrtBnd; HonRl; HospAde; NHS; SchMus; SchPl; VPStuCncl; Yrbk; RptrSchPpr; PpCl; Univ Of River Falls; Business Admin.

CLEMENS, Teri; Marshfield HS; Marshfield, MO; 4/135 ChrhWkr; HonRl; JrNHS; NHS; SchPl; RptrYrbk; RptrSchPpr; FHA; FNA; Univ; Vocation.

CLEMENT, David R; Miller Co Riii HS; Tuscumbia, MO; ALBoysSt; Chr; HonRl; LbryAde; OffAde; SchPl; SctActv; VPStuCncl; RptrYrbk; SptEdYrbk; FFA; LetterBsbl; LetterBsktbl; College; Wildlife Biology.

CLEMENT, Jane L; Redfield Public HS; Zell, SD; SecTrsFrshCls; Band; Chrs; HonRl; HospAde; RptrSchPpr; SchPpr; FNA; FTA; PpCl; LetterBsktbl; Univ Of So Dakota; Nursing.

CLEMENT, Mary C; Jacksonville HS; Jacksonville, IL; CncrtBnd; HonRl; MrchBnd; NHS; NatlMeritCmnd; 4-H; PresFrCl; SpnCl; BttyCrckrAwd; DanFAwd; Univ Of Il; Foreign Language.

CLEMENT, Nora E; Cassopolis HS; Cassopolis, MI; Band; ChrhWkr; CncrtBnd; HonRl; MrchBnd; NHS; PepBnd; 4-H; Michigan St University.

CLEMENT, Ruth M; Mc Bain Rural Agric HS; Mc Bain, MI; Chr; Chrs; Mdrgl; NHS; EdSchPpr; Interlochen Arts Academy; Musician.

CLEMENT, Sheila D; Sault Area HS; Sault Ste Marie, MI; Chr; CmntyWkr; HonRl; TchrAde; Bsbl; College; Professional.

CLEMENTS, Denise A; Howell Senior HS; Howell, MI; 81/372 Chr; HonRl; JA; NHS; SchMus; 4-H; LatCl; 4-HAwd; N Mich Univ; Nursing.

CLEMENTS, Diana J; Mt Vernon HS; Fortville, IN; 7/140 ALAGirlsSt; Band; ChrhWkr; DrlTm; HonRl; NHS; SchMus; PpCl; Trk; Ball State Univ; Social Worker.

CLEMENTS, Doreen E; Trico HS; Percy, IL; ChrhWkr; HonRl; RptrSchPpr; PpCl; SciCl; College; Social Work.

CLEMENTS, Gerald A; Shelbyville Sr HS; Shelbyville, IN; Band; CncrtBnd; HonRl; LitMag; MrchBnd; PepBnd; SchPpr; 4-H; FrCl; PpCl; Purdue Univ; Business Administration.

CLEMENTS, Janell; Fairfield HS; Fairfield, IA; ChrhWkr; HonRl; YthFlsp; SptEdYrbk; SptEdYrbk; RptrSchPpr; Bsktbl; College; Journalism.

CLEMENTS, Karen L; St Clair HS; St Clair, MI; 36/191 VPJrCls; HonRl; SchPl; TchrAde; Yrbk; RptrSchPpr; FrCl; JCAwd; Central Mi Univ; Foreign Languages.

CLEMENTS, Maria A; Western Dubuque HS; Epworth, IA; 9/248 PresSrCls; Band; Chrs; HonRl; NHS; SchMus; SchPl; StuCncl; 4-H; LetterBsktbl; VoiceDemAwd; College; Medicine.

CLEMMENS, Mary; Galena HS; Galena, KS; HonRl; HospAde; JrNHS; NHS; YthFlsp; FNA; GovHonPrgAwd; JAAwd; CitAwd; VoiceDemAwd; Franklin Technical; Lpn.

CLEMON, Lonnie L; South Sioux City HS; So Sioux City, NE; HonRl; NHS; Trk; College; Accounting.

CLEMONS, Bradley W; North Miami HS; Macy, IN; Aud/Vis; Chr; LbryAde; TchrAde; FFA; Lincoln Tech Inst; Diesel Truck Mechanic.

CLEMONS, Kirby R; Arthur HS; Arthur, IL; Band; HonRl; SchPl; SctActv; LetterFtbl; LetterTrk; College; Industrial Arts.

CLEMONS, Paul; Waseca HS; Waseca, MN; 65/216 ChrhWkr; HonRl; Sacrstn; StuGov; Bsktbl; Ftbl; Glf; Mankato State College; Accounting.

CLENDENIN, Betsy; Shellsburg Comm HS; Shellsburg, IA; 1/23 SecSophCls; ALAGirlsSt; Chrs; ChrhWkr; HonRl; NHS; SchMus; SchPl; YthFlsp; Yrbk; College.

CLENDENIN, Cathy A; Trico HS; Ava, IL; Chrs; ChrhWkr; HonRl; NHS; SchPl; EdSchPpr; 4-H; FHA; PpCl; 4-HAwd; Coll.

CLENNAN, Eileen K; Harrison HS; Harrison, MI; Chr; HonRl; SctActv; TchrAde; Yrbk; Delta College; Nursing.

CLEPPE, Ruth M; Hlv Comm HS; Victor, IA; VPJrCls; SecTrsSrCls; HonRl; OffAde; StuCncl; Yrbk; FTA; LetterBsktbl; CaptTrk;.

CLEVELAND, Douglas B; Brookfield HS; Brookfield, MO; 3/105 Chrs; HonRl; NHS; SctActv; StuCncl; LetterBsktbl; CaptFtbl; LetterTrk; IMSpt; Mos Univ; Med.

CLEVELAND, Jean D; Central HS; Detroit, MI; 13/102 ChrhWkr; JA; NatlMeritCmnd; OffAde; SchAde; StuCncl; RptrYrbk; RptrSchPpr; PresFrCl; LetterTennis; Oakland U; Law.

CLEVELAND, Mary K; Morton HS; Morton, IL; ChrhWkr; HospAde; YthFlsp; 4-H; LatCl; LetterBsbl; LetterBsktbl; GAA; PPFtbl; 4-HAwd; Col; Psychology.

CLEVELAND, Rick J; North Knox HS; Sandborn, IN; 10/150 HonRl; NHS; MthCl; Bsbl; Purdue Univ; Science.

CLEVELAND, Shannon; Independence HS; Independence, IA; 3/160 AFS; Band; Chr; HonRl; NHS; StuCncl; Bsktbl; PPFtbl; Iowa State U; Chemical Engineering.

CLEVENGER, Alisa B; Randolph Southern HS; Winchester, IN; 5/51 HonRl; StuCncl; YthFlsp; Yrbk; 4-H; PpCl;.

CLEVENGER, Katherine; Muncie Southside HS; Muncie, IN; 93/427 Band; DrmMjrt; LbryAde; MrchBnd; OffAde; StuCncl; Bsktbl; Glf; GAA; Ball State Univ; Airline Stewardess.

CLEVENGER, Kelli L; Milan HS; Milan, MO; 9/49 SecSrCls; ALAGirlsSt; HonRl; NHS; SecStuCncl; Yrbk; RptrSchPpr; SecFBLA; Chrldr; Univ; Spec Educ.

CLEVENGER, Robin L; John Marshall HS; Indianapolis, IN; Chr; Chrs; HonRl; Mdrgl; NatlThespSoc; SchAde; SctActv; StuCncl; FrCl; College; Nursing.

CLEVENGER TARR, Pamela M; Stet R Xv HS; Carrollton, MO; TrsFrshCls; Band; Chrs; ChrhWkr; StuCncl; RptrYrbk; RptrSchPpr; FHA; Bsbl; Bsktbl; Business School; Secretarial.

CLEVER, Henry; Duchesne HS; St Charles, MO; 33/180 PresSrCls; Aud/Vis; HonRl; NHS; PolWkr; SchMus; StuCncl; SchPpr; Ftbl; Socr; Mo Univ; Journal.

CLICK, Mary S; Arcadia Valley HS; Arcadia, MO; 7/87 HonRl; TchrAde; SecFBLA; FTA; FrCl; PpCl; SecJrCls; Mineral Area College; Secretarial.

CLIFFORD, Cindy; North Knox Hs; Freelandville, IN; 6/140 DrlTm; HonRl; SecNHS; SecYthFlsp; Pres4-H; Bsbl; CaptChrldr; AmLegAwd; 4-HAwd; PresAwd; Iupui; Nurse.

CLIFFORD, Cynthia A; North Knox HS; Edwardsport, IN; ALAGirlsSt; Aud/Vis; ChrhWkr; DrlTm; HonRl; HospAde; JrNHS; SecNHS; StuCncl; TchrAde; SecYthFlsp; Pres4-H; Bsbl; Chrldr; College; Nursing.

CLIFFORD, Deborah K; Richmond Senior HS; Richmond, IN; 46/647 JA; NHS; PpCl; JAAwd; Earlham College; Missionary.

CLIFFORD, John; Lawrence HS; Lawrence, KS; HonRl; SchMus; SchPl; Univ; Biological Sciences.

CLIFFORD, Nancy R; St Mary Central HS; Neenah, WI; JA; NatlFornLg; RedCrAde; RptrYrbk; SpnCl; LetterGAA; JAAwd; Marquette Univ; Nurse.

CLIFFORD, Sherri L; Hayes Co HS; Hayes Center, NE; Band; Chr; Chrs; ChrhWkr; CncrtBnd; HonRl; MrchBnd; PepBnd; 4-H; PpCl; Chrldr; GAA; College; Nursing.

CLIFFTON, Thomas F; North HS; Omaha, NE; Band; CncrtBnd; HonRl; MrchBnd; Orch; PepBnd; SchMus; TchrAde; GerCl; Univ; Pro.

CLIFT, Bradley E; Davenport West HS; Davenport, IA; 224/900 HonRl; Yrbk; SchPpr; LetterTrk; College; Photography.

CLIFT, Debra D; Indiana St U Laboratory HS; Terre Haute, IN; 15/50 JrNHS; ModUN; SecNHS; SecStuCncl; TchrAde; Teen; RptrYrbk; EdSchPpr; Bsktbl; Chrldr; GAA; College; Banking.

CLIFT, Sandra; Fountain Central HS; Veedersburg, IN; 28/131 Band; ChrhWkr; HonRl; MrchBnd; OffAde; TchrAde; YthFlsp; 4-H; FHA; GAA;.

CLIFTON, Janice; Decatur Central HS; Indianapolis, IN; Band; ChrhWkr; CmntyWkr; CncrtBnd; HonRl; OffAde; SctActv; YthFlsp; 4-HAwd; Iupui; Occupational Therapy.

CLIFTON, Jay D; Plainfield HS; Plainfield, IL; 21/300 HonRl; SptEdYrbk; GerCl; MthCl; Bsbl; Socr; Tennis; University Of Illinois; Medicine.

CLIMO, Ted J; Pittsford Area HS; Hudson, MI; ALBoysSt; HonRl; SctActv; LatCl; SpnCl; PpCl; AmLegAwd; College; Engineering.

CLIMPSON, Susan R; Gibson City HS; Gibson City, IL; 4/89 Band; Chr; Chrs; ChrhWkr; HonRl; Mdrgl; MrchBnd; Quill&Scroll; SchMus; SchPl; SctActv; Swmmng; Tennis; Oral Roberts Univ; Social Work.

CLINANSMITH, Cindy M; Bronson HS; Burr Oak, MI; 1/139 Band; ChrhWkr; CncrtBnd; HonRl; MrchBnd; NHS; PepBnd; SchPl; 4-H; FNA; Mi St Univ; Nursing.

CLINARD, Charles R; Thomas Carr Howe HS; Indianapolis, IN; 23/447 HonRl; JA; NHS; NatlMeritSF; SciCl; Rose Hulman Inst Of Tech; Chemical Eng.

CLINE, Carolyn; South East HS; Wichita, KS; 38/650 Band; ChrhWkr; CncrtBnd; HonRl; HospAde; MrchBnd; NHS; Orch; PepBnd; SchMus; Wichita State Univ; Music Major.

CLINE, Debra R; Edison HS; East Gary, IN; HonRl; RptrSchPpr; GAA; IMSpt; College; Bookkeeper.

CLINE, Emilee F; Mexico HS; Mexico, MO; SecFrshCls; Chr; HospAde; NatlFornLg; StuCncl; LatCl; PpCl; Chrldr; Univ Of Mo; Fashion Design.

CLINE, Jane T; Ladywood St Agnes HS; Inidanapolis, IN; 5/116 CmntyWkr; HonRl; PolWkr; SchMus; SctActv; StuCncl; StuGov; Yrbk; SpnCl; LetterTennis; U Of Vermont; Environmentalist.

CLINE, Kimberly J; Mexico Senior HS; Mexico, MO; 15/256 NHS; 4-H; SpnCl; LetterTrk; SecGAA; Central Missouri State Univ; Chemistry.

CLINE, Linda R; Franklin HS; Franklin, NE; Band; Chrs; MrchBnd; PepBnd; StuCncl; TchrAde; 4-H; PpCl;.

CLINE, Michael A; Clinton Central HS; Sheridan, IN; 60/106 Band; CncrtBnd; MrchBnd; PepBnd; SchMus; TchrAde; 4-H; FFA; PpCl; LetterFtbl; CaptWrstlng; Purdue Univ; Horticulture.

CLINE, Rick L; Kingsville HS; Kingsville, MO; Chr; Chrs; ChrhWkr; HonRl; Mdrgl; SchPl; RptrYrbk; Yrbk; SptEdSchPpr; Bsbl; Cmsu; Law.

CLINE, Roberta B; Trenton HS; Inkster, MI; 45/571 HonRl; NHS; NatlMeritCmnd; NatlMeritSF; ROTC; Michigan State University; Mathematics.

CLINGENPEEL, Brenda S; Tippecanoe Valley HS; Warsaw, IN; HospAde; Bsktbl; College; Major Psychology.

CLINGMAN, Jonathan R; Galena HS; Galena, IL; 22/119 AFS; CncrtBnd; HonRl; Orch; SchMus; TchrAde; SchPpr; LetterFtbl; LetterTennis; LetterWrstlng; U Of Ia; Pharmacy.

CLINKENBEARD, Beth A; Herbert Henry Dow HS; Midland, MI; HonRl; NHS; Swmmng; College.

CLINNIN, David D; Wells Easton HS; Easton, MN; 74/108 ALBoysSt; Band; ChrhWkr; CncrtBnd; HonRl; MrchBnd; Orch; PepBnd; SchMus; YthFlsp; IMSpt; College; Professional.

CLINTON, Patricia S; Keith Country Day HS; Rockford, IL; 2/14 HonRl; SchPl; StuGov; TchrAde; PpCl; LetterTrk; GAA; College.

CLINTON, Ruth A; Lancaster Public HS; Lancaster, MN; Chrs; HonRl; StuCncl; TchrAde; RptrSchPpr; PpCl; Voc Tech; Med Sec.

CLISCH, Lisa A; Baraga HS; Baraga, MI; SecFrshCls; CncrtBnd; HonRl; MrchBnd; NHS; OffAde; PepBnd; StuCncl; FHA; Trk; Mich Tech Univ; Medical Technology.

CLOBES, Julie A; Lyle Public HS; Austin, MN; 3/30 Band; Chr; CncrtBnd; HonRl; JrNHS; NHS; RptrYrbk; FHA; Trk; GAA; Comm College ;lab Tech.

CLODJEAUX, Timothy; Central Catholic HS; Lafayette, IN; 1/135 Ftbl; LetterGlf; IMSpt; Coll; Accounting, Sports Broadcasting.

CLOGHESSY, Michael P; Bishop Noll Inst HS; Dyer, IN; 53/360 ChrhWkr; HonRl; College; Architecture.

CLORE, Deborah; Hanover Horton HS; Jackson, MI; Band; Chrs; CncrtBnd; HonRl; MrchBnd; PepBnd; SchMus; SchPl; College;professional.

CLOSE, Dana; Green Ridge R 8 HS; Green Ridge, MO; SecSrCls; Band; Chrs; CncrtBnd; DrmMjrt; HonRl; MrchBnd; PepBnd; SchMus; College.

CLOSE, James M; Edwardsville HS; Edwardsville, IL; 1/463 HonRl; JrNHS; NHS; Bsktbl; IMSpt; Univ; Medicine Sci.

CLOSE, Jonathan C; Fremont HS; Fremont, IN; 3/66 TrsSrCls; HonRl; NHS; NatlMeritCmnd; SchMus; StuCncl; YthFlsp; FrCl; PpCl; LetterTrk; Univ; Actuarial Sci.

CLOSE, Lori J; Birch Run HS; Birch Run, MI; SecJrCls; HonRl; SchPl; Delta College.

CLOSE, Stephen G; Glencoe HS; Glencoe, MN; Band; Chr; CncrtBnd; HonRl; MrchBnd; Taylor University.

CLOSE, Timothy P; Carl Sandburg HS; Orland Park, IL; 60/700 HonRl; MthCl; LetterTrk; University Of Illinois; Math.

CLOSSER, Jerry L; Alexandria Monroe HS; Alexandria, IN; 9/223 VPSophCls; Chr; HonRl; NHS; StuCncl; YthFlsp; CaptBsbl; CaptBsktbl; CaptFtbl; Trk; Butler U; Acctng.

CLOTFELTER, Kathryn; Arlington Hs; Arlington Hts, IL; 23 SecSophCls; Band; HonRl; MrchBnd; SecNHS; StuCncl; SptEdSchPpr; LetterSwmmng; GAA; College;journalism.

CLOUD, Duane; Hill Murray HS; St Paul, MN; HonRl; NHS; College;math And Science.

CLOUGH, Dwight A; Monona Grove HS; Monona, WI; ChrhWkr; HonRl; NatlFornLg; NHS; NatlMeritCmnd; StuCncl; StuGov; AmLegAwd; OptClAwd; Moody Bible Institute; Pastor.

CLOUGH, Patrick D; Logan View HS; Hooper, NE; 17/53 TrsFrshCls; Chr; Chrs; HonRl; SchPl; StuCncl; RptrYrbk; LetterBsktbl; LetterFtbl; LetterGlf; Northeast Ne Tech Coll; Architectural Draw.

CLOUSE, James; Taylor HS; Kokomo, IN; 7/175 ChrhWkr; HonRl; NHS; SchAde; TchrAde; YthFlsp; Bsbl; Bsktbl; Ftbl; IMSpt; Indiana Stae Univ; Basebal.

CLOUSE, Linda D; West Central Jr Sr HS; Francesville, IN; 3/83 Chr; HonRl; NHS; SchMus; Yrbk; Sec4-H; FHA; FTA; College.

CLOUSE, Stanley A; Brady Public HS; Brady, NE; 4/16 PresSrCls; Band; Chrs; HonRl; NHS; SchMus; EdYrBk; EdSchPpr; Bsktbl; Trk; CchngActv; IMSpt; Mid Plains Voc Tech; Carpenter.

CLOUSE, Susan M; West Central HS; Francesville, IN; 2/90 SecFrshCls; TrsJrCls; Band; ChrhWkr; HonRl; NHS; PresFHA; GAA; DARAwd; CitAwd; X Ray Tech; Radiologic Tech.

CLOUTIER, Diane M; Escanaba Area HS; Escanaba, MI; 11/400 HonRl; HospAde; JrNHS; LbryAde; NHS; NatlMeritFnl; NatlMeritSchl; NatlMeritSF; CivCl; Trk; College; Accountant.

CLOUTIER, Suzanne M; Argo Comm HS; Bridgeview, IL; 3/509 HonRl; LitMag; ModUN; VPNHS; NatlThespSoc; OffAde; SchPl; SctActv; SciCl; BauchLmbAwd; Bradley Univ; Pharmacy.

CLOYD, Chuck H; Platteview Jr Sr HS; Springfield, NE; VPSophCls; Band; CncrtBnd; HonRl; MrchBnd; LetterBsbl; LetterBsktbl; LetterFtbl; LetterTrk; CchngActv; College; Communications.

CLUBB, Duane L; Van Buren Comm HS; Keosauqua, IA; Band; Chrs; CmntyWkr; CncrtBnd; MrchBnd; PepBnd; PolWkr; SchMus; SchPl; 4-H; 4-HAwd; College; Farming.

CLUBB, Mary K; Academy Of The Holy Angels; Burnsville, MN; 18/108 Chr; ChrhWkr; JrNHS; SchMus; RptrYrbk; EdYrBk; Yrbk; Bsktbl; CaptFtbl; PPFtbl; Col Of St Catherines; Journalism Bus.

CLUCK, Cathy E; Gideon HS; Gideon, MO; 2/39 SecFrshCls; Band; CncrtBnd; HonRl; MrchBnd; NHS; PepBnd; StuCncl; Yrbk; FrCl; Mo Univ; Modern Language.

CLUEVER, Linda J; Eagle Bend Public HS; Eagle Bend, MN; Band; Chr; CncrtBnd; HonRl; Twrl; EdYrBk; Wadena Area Voc Tech Inst; Accounting.

CLUTS, Patricia E; Tremont Unit Dist 702 HS; Tremont, IL; AFS; Band; Chrs; ChrhWkr; HonRl; HospAde; NatlThespSoc; SchMus; FNA; GerCl; Col; Professional Nursing.

CLUTTS, Carey M; Pontiac Township HS; Pontiac, IL; CncrtBnd; NatlMeritSF; Quill&Scroll; SchMus; StuCncl; SptEdSchPpr; Ill Wesleyan Univ; Biology.

CLUVER, Andrew H; Cissna Park HS; Cissna Park, IL; 8/45 PresSophCls; ALBoysSt; HonRl; NHS; SctActv; PresStuCncl; Bsktbl; Trk; Univ Of Illinois; Computer Science.

CLUVER, Ann C; Cissne Park HS; Cissna Park, IL; 3/44 ALAGirlsSt; Band; Chrs; HonRl; NHS; SchMus; SctActv; TchrAde; FHA; GAA; St Olaf College; Teacher.

CLYNE, Jennifer M; Waukegan East HS; Waukegan, IL; Band; ChrhWkr; CncrtBnd; HonRl; HospAde; JrNHS; MrchBnd; NHS; PepBnd; SchMus; Purdue University; Pharmacist.

CNOCKAERT, Thomas G; Austin Catholic Prep; Grosse Pt Woods, MI; 51/115 HonRl; SchMus; SchPl; GerCl; LetterFtbl; CchngActv; College; Biology.

COAD, Marie K; Mahomet Seymour HS; Mahomet, IL; HonRl; NHS; NatlThespSoc; Quill&Scroll; EdYrBk; RptrSchPpr; SpnCl; University Of Illinois; Medicine.

COADY, Todd M; Paxton HS; Paxton, IL; NHS; NatlThespSoc; SchPl; TchrAde; SciCl; LetterTennis; University; Medicine.

COAKLEY, Brian J; Dixon HS; Dixon, IL; HonRl; JA; College; Oceanographer.

COALWELL, Rick L; Dilworth HS; Dilworth, MN; 1/65 Band; CncrtBnd; HonRl; MrchBnd; NHS; PepBnd; SctActv; LetterBsktbl; LetterFtbl; LetterTrk; Military Academy;.

COATE, Barbara; Essex HS; Essex, IA; 20/35 PresSophCls; HonRl; OffAde; Yrbk; RptrSchPpr; 4-H; PpCl; Bsktbl; PPFtbl; 4-HAwd; Bus School; Vocation.

COATES, Richard; Lapeer Senior HS; Lapeer, MI; 31/426 HonRl; SctActv; Central Michigan Univ; Accounting.

COATES, Robert D; Switzerland Co HS; Vevay, IN; Band; Chr; ChrhWkr; CncrtBnd; MrchBnd; PepBnd; SchPl; Bsbl; Bsktbl; Trk; College; Professional.

COATES, Robert R; Marseilles HS; Marseilles, IL; 9/65 VPJrCls; Chrs; HonRl; Illinois Wesleyan Univ; Political Science.

COATNEY, Billy E; Monett HS; Monett, MO; ChrhWkr; HonRl; PresYthFlsp; FTA; KeyCl; SpnCl; Bsbl; LetterBsktbl; Ftbl; Trk; IMSpt; College.

COATS, Barbara S; Hutchinson HS; Hutchinson, KS; AFS; HonRl; NatlMeritCmnd; Orch; SchMus; StuCncl; RptrSchPpr; SciCl; GAA; PPFtbl; U Of Ks; Pre Med.

COATS, Debra L; C S Mott HS; Warren, MI; HonRl; NHS; NatlMeritSF; PolWkr; StuGov; YthFlsp; SpnCl; Bsktbl; GAA; IMSpt; Coll; Education.

COAUETTE, Timmy; Crookston Central HS; Crookston, MN; VPSrCls; StuCncl; SchPpr; CchngActv; College; Farm.

COBAN, Mary E; Mother Theodore Guerin HS; Norridge, IL; 17/409 ChrhWkr; HonRl; NHS; StuCncl; RptrSchPpr; SptEdSchPpr; GAA; Northeastern Ill Univ; Teacher.

COBB, Edward B; East Waterloo HS; Evansdale, IA; HonRl; StuCncl; StuGov; LetterBsbl; Ftbl; Wrstlng; College; Industrial Lab Tech.

COBB, Joyce; Mason HS; Erie, MI; 8/121 HonRl; NHS; OffAde; PepBnd; RedCrAde; TchrAde; RptrSchPpr; SchPpr; PpCl; PresAwd; Univ; Special Education.

COBB, Larry K; Ritenour HS; St Louis County, MO; ChrhWkr; HonRl; JrNHS; NHS; YthFlsp; Trk; CchngActv; College; Computer Science.

COBB, Mary E; Montgomery County R Ii HS; New Florence, MO; ALAGirlsSt; Chr; HonRl; SchPl; TchrAde; 4-H; FHA; PpCl; Chrldr; 4-HAwd; Cmsu Warrensburg; Home Ec.

COBB, Peggy; Maysville R 1 HS; Maysville, MO; 2/65 ALAGirlsSt; ChrhWkr; CncrtBnd; HonRl; MrchBnd; NHS; SchPl; TchrAde; FHA; SciCl; Univ Miss; Business Adm.

COBB, Richard E; Valley Falls HS; Valley Falls, KS; 6/55 ALBoysSt; HonRl; SchPl; RptrSchPpr; EdSchPpr; LetterBsbl; LetterBsktbl; LetterFtbl; LetterTrk; AmLegAwd; Kansas University; Chemistry Or Biology.

COBB, Richard K; Meadville HS; Wheeling, MO; HonRl; NHS; SchPl; 4-H; PpCl; LetterBsbl; Bsktbl; LetterTrk; Coll; Physical Educ.

COBB, Richelle; Millington HS; Millington, MI; 5/173 SecSophCls; PresSrCls; HonRl; NHS; SchPl; FHA; Trk; Delta College; Fashion Merchandising.

COBB, Vicky S; Harrison HS; Harrison, MI; Band; HonRl; MrchBnd; LetterBsktbl; GAA; IMSpt; PPFtbl; PresAwd;.

COBERLEY, Lisa; Onsted HS; Brooklyn, MI; 1/114 PresJrCls; LitMag; NHS; RptrYrbk; FHA; Bsbl; Bsktbl; Trk; DanFAwd; 4-HAwd; College.

COBIE, Rick A; Ackley Geneva HS; Ackley, IA; 25/54 Band; CncrtBnd; HonRl; MrchBnd; SchMus; SchPl; Bsbl; Bsktbl; Ftbl; Glf; Coll;.

COBLE, Lori D; Lyman HS; Vivian, SD; PresSophCls; Band; HonRl; NHS; RedCrAde; StuCncl; 4-H; CaptBsktbl; Chrldr; GAA; Univ, Col; Bs In Pe & Psch.

COBURN, Scott K; North Platte HS; North Platte, NE; ChrhWkr; CncrtBnd; HonRl; MrchBnd; StuCncl; YthFlsp; KeyCl; LetterBsktbl; LetterFtbl; AFS; Univ Of Neb.

COBURN, Sheryl A; Lincoln Consolidated HS; Willis, MI; 18/168 ChrhWkr; HonRl; NatlFornLg; NHS; NatlThespSoc; OffAde; SchMus; TchrAde; YthFlsp; 4-H; FrCl; Mich Tech; Med Tech.

COBURN, Susan A; West Holt HS; O Neill, NE; 5/84 Band; CncrtBnd; HonRl; MrchBnd; PepBnd; RptrYrbk; RptrSchPpr; 4-H; FHA; PpCl; CaptChrldr; 4-HAwd; Univ Of Nebraska; Music.

COBY, Geneva; Culver Community HS; Leiters Ford, IN; CncrtBnd; HonRl; HospAde; MrchBnd; Orch; SctActv; FDA; Chrldr; AmLegAwd; N Manchester; Physician.

COCHLEY, Judith E; Wabash HS; Wabash, IN; 1/209 PresSophCls; SchMus; StuCncl; StuGov; YthFlsp; GerCl; PpCl; Chrldr; EldAwd; OptClAwd; Purdue Univ; Math Computer Science.

COCHRAN, Cindy; Sullivan HS; Sullivan, IL; 1/108 PresJrCls; Band; CncrtBnd; HonRl; MrchBnd; NHS; StuCncl; FTA; FrCl; SciCl; U Of Il; Undecided.

COCHRAN, Diana; Decatur Community HS; Oberlin, KS; 8/85 Band; Chr; CncrtBnd; HonRl; NHS; PepBnd; SchMus; SchPl; YthFlsp; PresAwd; Emporia Kansas St College; Medical Tech.

COCHRAN, Doug R; Edison HS; E Gary, IN; ALBoysSt; Band; CncrtBnd; HonRl; MrchBnd;

PepBnd; StuCncl; StuGov; Trk; In U; Medical Profession.

COCHRAN, Glenda K; Niantic HS; Harristown, IL; HonRl; SctActv; PpCl; Bsbl; Trk; GAA;.

COCHRAN, Janis L; Allegan HS; Allegan, MI; 19/210 HonRl; JrNHS; NHS; OffAde; YthFlsp; 4-H; LatCl; PpCl; Trk; PPFtbl; Calvin Coll; Math.

COCHRAN, John M; Griswold Comm HS; Griswold, IA; SecTrsFrshCls; ALBoysSt; Chrs; ChrhWkr; CmntyWkr; CncrtBnd; HonRl; SchMus; SchPl; LetterBsktbl; LetterFtbl; CaptTrk; DanFAwd;.

COCHRAN, Karen S; Grand Blanc HS; Grand Blanc, MI; 1/637 ALAGirlsSt; NHS; NatlMeritCmnd; PresSciCl; Univ Of Michigan; Science.

COCHRAN, Marc A; Anita HS; Anita, IA; SecJrCls; SctActv; YthFlsp; PpCl; Bsbl; Ftbl; Glf; Trk; Wrstlng; College.

COCHRAN, Ronald; Charleston Hs; Cahrleston, IL; 56/259 ChrhWkr; HonRl; StuCncl; YthFlsp; JCAwd;.

COCHRAN, Sandra J; Nevada HS; Nevada, IA; 31/117 Chr; ChrhWkr; HonRl; HospAde; 4-H; FHA;.

COCHRAN, Timothy; Allegan HS; Allegan, MI; 13/204 ChrhWkr; CmntyWkr; HonRl; PolWkr; StuGov; VPSophCls; LetterTrk; IMSpt; 4-HAwd; Univ; Vet.

COCHRAN, Virginia A; Fairfield Community HS; Fairfield, IL; Band; CncrtBnd; HonRl; MrchBnd; RptrYrbk; FTA; SecSpnCl; PpCl; GAA; College.

COCHRANE, Hamilton E; St Thomas Acad; W St Paul, MN; VPFrshCls; VPSophCls; TrsJrCls; DrlTm; HonRl; NatlMeritCmnd; PresStuCncl; Bsbl; Bsktbl; Ftbl; College; Law.

COCHRANE, Mary Ann; Huron HS; Ann Arbor, MI; 6/530 Orch; SchMus; Yrbk; GerCl; GAA; Duke U; Management Sciences.

COCKERILL, Julie A; Rock Island HS; Rock Island, IL; 35/700 SecFrshCls; Chrs; CncrtBnd; HonRl; MrchBnd; NHS; PepBnd; StuCncl; StuGov; FshEdSchPpr; FrCl; LetterTennis; GAA; Bradley Univ; Math.

COCKERILL, Thomas J; Putnam County HS; Mc Nabb, IL; Band; CncrtBnd; HonRl; MrchBnd; NHS; FrCl; Univ.

COCKRAM, Michael R; University HS; Centerview, MO; VPSrCls; Chr; HonRl; SchPl; StuCncl; 4-H; FFA; Bsktbl; University; Liberal Arts.

COCKRELL, Janet M; Wheaton North HS; Wheaton, IL; Chr; HonRl; Swmmng; Southern Illinois Univ; Accounting.

COCKRELL, Nancy P; Redford Union HS; Detroit, MI; CmntyWkr; HonRl; JA; NHS; FrCl; SpnCl; GAA; Univ Mi Dearborn.

COCKRUM, Larry R; Waltonville HS; Waltonville, IL; TrsSophCls; ChrhWkr; HonRl; 4-H; FFA; PpCl; LetterBsbl; LetterBsktbl; LetterTrk; IMSpt; College; Professional.

COCOS, James P; Oakville HS; St Louis, MO; 67/340 HonRl; NHS; PolWkr; StuCncl; GerCl; Ftbl; OptClAwd; Univ Of Mo Rollo.

COCQUYT, Donald A; Niagara Public HS; Niagara, WI; 10/66 ChrhWkr; HonRl; NHS; RptrSchPpr; EdSchPpr; PpCl; Bsktbl; Ftbl; Trk; Univ Of Wisconsin; Business Admin.

CODEMO, Julie; Ofallon Township HS; Caseyville, IL; Chrs; HonRl; NHS; SchPl; Univ Of Il; Creative Writing.

CODIANO, Karen; Brookville HS; Brookville, IN; 14/189 ALAGirlsSt; HonRl; NHS; RedCrAde; TchrAde; EdYrBk; FTA; GAA; Miami Univ.

CODY, Cathy J; Moberly HS; Moberly, MO; 17/215 AFS; Band; Chr; Chrl; Chrs; CncrtBnd; Trk; Chrldr; PPFtbl; AmLegAwd; Northeast Mo State U; Vocal Music.

CODY, Joan M; Mandan HS; Mandan, ND; Chr; Mdrgl; StuCncl; RptrYrbk; RptrSchPpr; LetterTennis; Bismarck Jr Col; Sociology Psychology.

CODY, Mac A; El Dorado HS; El Dorado, KS; 37/187 HonRl; NatlFornLg; Kansas State Univ; Electrical Engineer.

CODY, William; Riceville HS; Riceville, IA; Band; CncrtBnd; HonRl; MrchBnd; PepBnd; StuCncl; FrCl; Glf; CchngActv; Upper Iowa U; Professional.

COE, Bonnie J; St Stephens HS; Saginaw, MI; 15/104 TrsSophCls; TrsSrCls; CmntyWkr; HonRl; NHS; Yrbk; CaptBsbl; LetterBsktbl; Swmmng; Chrldr; College; Professional.

COE, Jim; William Chrisman HS; Independence, MO; StuCncl; TchrAde; YthFlsp; IMSpt; College.

COE, Kathleen S; Wahlert HS; Dubuque, IA; 35/400 HstFrshCls; HstSophCls; HstJrCls; HonRl; PolWkr; StuCncl; StuGov; SpnCl; PpCl; LetterSwmmng; College; Dietetics.

COE, Pam J; Chadwick HS; Chadwick, MO; 3/9 SecTrsFrshCls; SecTrsSophCls; SecTrsJrCls; SecTrsSrCls; Chrs; HonRl; LbryAde; SchPl; TchrAde; Bsktbl; Bus Sch; Curr Of Maj Study.

COE, Robert W; Newton HS; Newton, KS; Chrs; CncrtBnd; HonRl; PolWkr; SctActv; StuCncl; RptrYrbk; RptrSchPpr; CaptBsktbl; LetterGlf; SARAwd; Kansas St Univ; Law.

COEN, Marcia; Craig HS; Janesville, WI; 67/500 HonRl; NHS; RptrSchPpr; 4-H; FBLA; LatCl; Wi Univ; Nursing.

COENEN, Douglas W; Xavier HS; Appleton, WI; 15/110 VPSrCls; ALBoysSt; Chrs; NHS; SchPl; StuCncl; SptEdYrbk; EdSchPpr; SptEdSchPpr; KeyCl; Univ Of Wis; Engineering.

COENEN, Judith M; Menasha HS; Menasha, WI; CmntyWkr; DrlTm; OffAde; SchPl; StuGov; TchrAde; SpnCl; PpCl; Bsktbl; Swmmng; Trk; University Of Wisconsin; Home Economics.

COENEN, Richard A; New London HS; Dale, WI; ChrhWkr; CtyCnl; CmntyWkr; HonRl; LbryAde; NHS; CivCl; FFA; IMSpt; PresAwd; College; Agricultural Engineer.

COERS, Wendy S; Amboy HS; Dixon, IL; 10/117 Chr; ChrhWkr; CncrtBnd; HonRl; MrchBnd; NHS; PresYthFlsp; RptrYrbk; FBLA; FrCl; Jr College; Business.

COFER, Donna S; Wheeling HS; Buffalo Grove, IL; 29/459 Band; CncrtBnd; HonRl; MrchBnd; NHS; College; Medicine.

COFFEY, Colleen A; Crete Public HS; Crete, NE; 5/115 HonRl; FBLA; PpCl; SciCl; Trk; College; Doctor.

COFFEY, Elva M; Lincoln Way HS; Mokena, IL; 48/566 HonRl; OffAde; SctActv; RptrSchPpr; PresSpnCl; Loyola Univ; Pre Law.

COFFEY, Fredrick L; Spaulding HS; Chicago, IL; PresFrshCls; PresSophCls; PresJrCls; PresSrCls; ChrhWkr; HonRl; NatlMeritSchl; FDA; FFA; FSA;.

COFFEY, Kevin W; Queen Of Apostles HS; Madison, WI; ChrhWkr; Bsktbl; Ftbl; Trk; College; Architact.

COFFEY, Sandra S; Kansas HS; Kansas, IL; 8/26 HonRl; NHS; NatlMeritCmnd; Yrbk; 4-H; Southern Illinois Univ; Medicine.

COFFIELD, Theodore C; Swartz Creek HS; Durand, MI; 7/365 HonRl; NHS; NatlMeritCmnd; SctActv; MthCl; General Motors Insti; Engineer.

COFFIN, Harley S; South Putnam HS; Fillmore, IN; Aud/Vis; VPNatlThespSoc; OffAde; SchPl; PresStuCncl; YthFlsp; PpCl; SciCl; LetterBsktbl; Ftbl; LetterTrk; Indiana Mortuary College; Law Enforcement.

COFFIN, Michael J; Lincoln HS; Manitowoc, WI; Band; CncrtBnd; HonRl; JA; MrchBnd; Orch; PepBnd; SchMus; Ftbl; College; Law.

COFFIN, Philip J; Hinsdale Central HS; Hinsdale, IL; HonRl; NHS; SchAde; RptrSchPpr; KeyCl; Bsktbl; Dartmouth College; Psychology.

COFFIN, Rebecca; Ar We Va HS; Westside, IA; 4/42 VPFrshCls; Band; Chr; Chrs; ChrhWkr; CncrtBnd; HonRl; Mdrgl; MrchBnd; Yrbk; U Of Iowa; Journalism Major.

COFFMAN, Craig K; Boone HS; Boone, IA; ChrhWkr; Wrstlng; Coll; Math.

COFFMAN, Jeff L; High School; New Virginia, IA; ALBoysSt; Chrs; HonRl; SchMus; SchPl; 4-H; PpCl; SciCl; Wrstlng; 4-HAwd; College; Electronics.

COFFMAN, Lisa E; Northern Heights HS; Allen, KS; TrsSophCls; Band; Chrs; HonRl; NHS; YthFlsp; Bsbl; LetterBsktbl; PPFtbl; University.

COFFMAN, Nancy K; Edison Sr HS; East Gary, IN; SecSophCls; SecJrCls; ALAGirlsSt; HonRl; NHS; VPStuCncl; FrCl; SciCl; GAA; IMSpt; PPFtbl; University; X Ray Technician.

COFFMAN, Pamela S; English Valleys HS; South English, IA; 1/65 VPBand; VPCncrtBnd; HonRl; VPMrchBnd; NHS; TchrAde; YthFlsp; VPFTA; Bsktbl; Trk; LetterChrldr; Ia State Univ; Home Economics.

COFFMAN, Rebecca L; Riverton HS; Galena, KS; 1/50 Band; Chr; ChrhWkr; CncrtBnd; HonRl; MrchBnd; NHS; Orch; PepBnd; SchPl; FHA; FrCl; MthCl; Kansas St College; Accounting.

COFFMAN, Terri L; William Borden HS; Borden, IN; 1/64 ALAGirlsSt; Band; CncrtBnd; HonRl; MrchBnd; NHS; StuCncl; Yrbk; FHA; OptClAwd; Ius College; Political Sci.

COFOID, Lisa J; Tonica HS; Tonica, IL; Band; Chr; Chrs; HonRl; YthFlsp; 4-H; SpnCl; Nursing Sch; Nursing.

COFOID, Maureen A; Tonica Comm HS; Tonica, IL; 2/50 Chrs; HonRl; LbryAde; NHS; SchMus; SchPl; RptrSchPpr; SchPpr; FHA; SpnCl; PpCl; SciCl; Illinois Valley Comm Col; Sec Science.

COFRIN, Tom M; Southern Door HS; Sturgeon Bay, WI; VPFrshCls; Band; CncrtBnd; MrchBnd; Orch; PepBnd; SchMus; SchPl; PpCl; SciCl; College; Medicine.

COGDAL, Pamela A; La Salle Peru HS; Utica, IL; HonRl; PolWkr; SchPpr; FrCl; Illinois Valley Comm College; Journalism.

COGGINS, Jerome L; Olympio HS; Minier, IL; ALBoysSt; HonRl; NHS; SpnCl; MthCl; SciCl; Trk; University; Engineering.

COGGINS, Lynn E; Raymond Central HS; Raymond, NE; Chr; Chrs; ChrhWkr; HonRl; NHS; SchMus; SchPl; StuCncl; StuGov; 4-HAwd; Oral Roberts Univ; Creative Arts.

COGSWELL, James W; Galena HS; Galena, IL; 1/120 Band; HonRl; ModUN; PolWkr; Yrbk; Tennis; University; Research Of High Energy.

COHAN, Cheryl P; Niles East HS; Skokie, IL; 29/573 CmntyWkr; HonRl; Univ; Speech Therapist.

COHAN, Mary K; Our Lady Star Of The Sea HS; Grosse Pte, MI; SecJrCls; HonRl; LbryAde; NHS; SchMus; SchPl; TchrAde; Tennis; GAA; IMSpt; College; Prof.

COHEN, Edward A; Jefferson City Sr HS; Jefferson City, MO; PresSrCls; NatlFornLg; NHS; PolWkr; Quill&Scroll; SchPpr; VPLatCl; Ftbl; LetterTennis; AmLegAwd; Tulane U; Poli Sci.

COHEN, Elena N; New Trier East HS; Wilmette, IL; 5/347 AFS; CmntyWkr; HonRl; LitMag; PolWkr; Yrbk; LetterTennis; College; Political Science.

COHEN, Elizabeth R; Saline HS; Saline, MI; SecCncrtBnd; HonRl; HospAde; MrchBnd; NHS; SchMus; SchPl; 4-H; FrCl; GAA; College; Teacher, Drama.

COHEN, Gail E; Maine East HS; Morton Grove, IL; HonRl; OffAde; Quill&Scroll; SchAde; RptrYrbk; SptEdYrbk; FBLA; Bsktbl; Univ Of Tulsa; Special Education.

COHEN, Gordon; Horton Watkins HS; St Louis, MO; 56/502 ChrhWkr; CmntyWkr; HonRl; ModUN; NatlFornLg; StuCncl; StuGov; SpnCl; Vanderbilt Univ; Law.

COHEN, Judith L; Niles North HS; Skokie, IL; 1/600 TrsSrCls; HonRl; NHS; PolWkr; TchrAde; Univ Of Michigan.

COHEN, Judith S; Deerfield HS; Deerfield, IL; 17/561 RptrYrbk; Univ Of Illinois; Chemistry.

COHEN, Julie E; New Trier West HS; Wilmette, IL; Chr; ChrhWkr; LbryAde; NatlMeritCmnd; University Of Michigan.

COHEN, Karen A; Evanston Township HS; Skokie, IL; HonRl; U Of Illinois; Medicine.

COHEN, Penelope S; Petoskey HS; Petoskey, MI; 14/287 ChrhWkr; NatlFornLg; NHS; NatlMeritCmnd; SchMus; SchPl; StuCncl; EldAwd; U Of Mi; Architect.

COHEN, Randi S; New Trier West HS; Wilmette, IL; HonRl; PpCl; Bsbl; Bsktbl; Tennis; Trk; College; Art.

COHEN, Sheryl B; Highland Park HS; Highland Park, IL; 50/643 Chrs; CmntyWkr; PolWkr; SchPl; PpCl; Clge.

COHN, Allan L; Maine Twp HS East; Niles, IL; 5/900 HonRl; NHS; GerCl; MthCl; Bsbl; Trk; CchngActv; College; Medicine.

COHN, Howard F; Cass Tech; Detroit, MI; 3/200 HonRl; NHS; PolWkr; Quill&Scroll; TchrAde; RptrSchPpr; Univ Of Mi; Pro Journalism.

COHROY, Gregory L; Dist 101 R HS; Oconto, NE; VPSrCls; Band; CmntyWkr; CncrtBnd; HonRl; MrchBnd; PepBnd; SchMus; SchPl; StuCncl; StuGov; Yrbk; 4-H; Bsktbl; Ftbl; College; Professional.

COHRS, Janice L; Bennington HS; Bennington, NE; 1/34 SecSophCls; Chrs; HonRl; SchPl; StuCncl; TchrAde; RptrYrbk; 4-H; PpCl; AmLegAwd; PresAwd; Hastings College; Mathematics.

COHRS, Nancy J; Vicksburg Community HS; Vicksburg, MI; Band; NHS; PepBnd; StuCncl; CaptBsktbl; Tennis; Mi State U; Engr Arts.

COIL, Jon C; Petersburg Porta HS; Petersburg, IL; 32/131 JA; SchPl; KeyCl; FrCl; Bsktbl; LetterGlf; University.

COIL, Kathy D; Mexico HS; Mexico, MO; ALAGirlsSt; Band; CncrtBnd; HospAde; MrchBnd; Yrbk; LatCl; PpCl; LetterTrk; School Of Nursing; Anesthesiest Or O R Tech.

COIL, Vicky S; R 1 North Callaway HS; Auxvasse, MO; 5/76 TrsJrCls; ALAGirlsSt; HonRl; NHS; SchPl; StuCncl; 4-H; FHA; FTA; FrCl; 4-HAwd; College; Secretary.

COIN, David L; Kirksville Sr HS; Kirksville, MO; CtyCnl; FBLA; FDA; FFA; FHA; FNA; FSA; FTA; DARAwd; Trade School; Architect.

COKER, Brenda K; North Knox HS; Bicknell, IN; DrlTm; HonRl; NHS; OffAde; SchAde; FHA; PpCl; ChmnBsktbl; GAA; PresAwd; Business College.

COLASANTI, Bruce T; Brother Rice HS; Royal Oak, MI; 25/215 Chrl; HonRl; NatlMeritSchl; SctActv; IMSpt; Mi State Univ; Business Major.

COLASINSKI, William D; Allen Park HS; Allen Park, MI; CmntyWkr; HonRl; JrNHS; RptrYrbk; FrCl; Bsbl; Ftbl; CaptSocr; Swmmng; Wrstlng; Rets Electronics; Nuclear Medicine.

COLBERG, Linda M; George Rogers Clark HS; Whiting, IN; TrsFrshCls; Chr; StuCncl; SecYthFlsp; SchPpr; Chrldr; College Or Univ; Elementary Education.

COLBERT, Charles W; Tri County HS; Delta, IA; ALBoysSt; Band; Chrs; ChrhWkr; PepBnd; SchMus; VPFFA; Bsktbl; LetterTrk; LetterWrstlng; Trade Sch; Farming.

COLBERT, Patricia; Zalma HS; Kinder, MO; SecJrCls; HonRl; NHS; SchPpr; FHA;.

COLBERT, Raymond O; Jacksonville HS; Jacksonville, IL; 36/362 TrsJrCls; Chrs; HonRl; NHS; NatlMeritCmnd; SchPl; SctActv; Bsbl; Bsktbl; LetterFtbl; College; Engineering.

COLBURN, Chris; Manchester HS; North Manchester, IN; Band; CncrtBnd; HonRl; MrchBnd; NatlFornLg; KeyCl; Bsktbl; Ftbl; Trk; Wrstlng; Purdue Univ; Pharmacy.

COLBURN, Cynthia A; Cloquet Sr HS; Cloquet, MN; 13/250 VPJrCls; Chr; Chrs; NHS; VPStuCncl; RptrSchPpr; PpCl; PPFtbl; U Of Mn.

COLBURN, Jerome S; Carl Sandburg HS; Palos Pk, IL; 32/700 Chr; Chrs; HonRl; LitMag; NatlMeritSF; StuCncl; RptrSchPpr; SchPpr; Univ Of Illinois.

COLBURN, Patrick J; Creighton Prep HS; Omaha, NE; HonRl; NHS; Bsktbl; Socr; LetterTrk; Chrldr; IMSpt; University Of Nebraska; Dentistry.

COLBY, Ronald F; St Charles Borremeo Sem; Woodridge, IL; Chrl; ChrhWkr; HonRl; TchrAde; LatCl; College; Education.

COLBY, Susan K; Caledonia HS; Al Lo, MI; Band; HonRl; NHS; PepBnd; SchPl; TchrAde; RptrYrbk; 4-H; ALBoysSt; 4-HAwd; Ferris St Clge; Med Tech.

COLDWELL, E Jay; D C Everest HS; Rothschild, WI; 2/350 AFS; ALBoysSt; Band; Chr; CncrtBnd; DrmBgl; HonRl; MrchBnd; NHS; NatlMeritFnl; NatlThespSoc; Orch; PepBnd; IMSpt; Univ Of Wisc; Physics.

COLE, Alice M; Alliance HS; Alliance, NE; 1/150 Aud/Vis; DrlTm; HonRl; JrNHS; TchrAde; RptrYrbk; College.

COLE, Angela F; John Marshall Harlan HS; Chicago, IL; 6/920 ChrhWkr; CmntyWkr; HonRl; NHS; SchAde; TchrAde; MthCl; AmLegAwd; CitAwd; Fisk U;interpreter.

COLE, Cinda J; Mattoon Sr HS; Mattoon, IL; 15/450 HonRl; LbryAde; NHS; Parkland Jr College; Nurse.

COLE, Cynthia F; Prospect HS; Arlington Hts, IL; 12/615 ChrhWkr; CmntyWkr; DrlTm; HonRl; NHS; SchPl; Univ Of Illinois; Business.

COLE, Darlene F; Kelly HS; Sikeston, MO; Band; HonRl; PepBnd; FHA; Univ; Prof.

COLE, Deborah; Houston HS; Houston, MO; Band; CncrtBnd; HonRl; MrchBnd; PepBnd; 4-H; Bsktbl; Trade Sch; Voc.

COLE, Debra K; Jefferson HS; Jefferson, SD; TrsSophCls; SecJrCls; VPSrCls; Chrs; HonRl; SctActv; YthFlsp; PpCl; LetterChrldr; IMSpt; Trade Schl; Secretary.

COLE, Franklin T; Aurora Hoyt Lakes HS; Hoyt Lakes, MN; SecSrCls; NHS; NatlThespSoc; SchPl; Yrbk; MthCl; LetterBsktbl; Trk; Univ Of Mn; Medicine.

COLE, Glenn P; Bloom Township HS; E Chicago Hts, IL; 46/945 ALBoysSt; HonRl; NHS; NatlMeritFnl; NatlMeritSchl; Bsbl; LetterFtbl; Stanford University; Business.

COLE, Jackie W; Paxton HS; Paxton, IL; 4/137 HonRl; TreasNHS; SciCl; IMSpt; College; Professional.

COLE, Jeffrey; Lyman HS; Kennebec, SD; ALBoysSt; Band; Chrs; CncrtBnd; HonRl; MrchBnd; PepBnd; YthFlsp; Ftbl;.

COLE, Jeffrey; Michigan Center HS; Michigan Center, MI; 1/159 HonRl; NHS; TchrAde; RptrYrbk; EdYrBk; RptrSchPpr; SciCl; Comm College.

COLE, Jill A; Liggett University; Detroit, MI; AFS; Chr; CmntyWkr; HonRl; SchMus; SchPl; Yrbk; IMSpt; PPFtbl; Univ Of Mich; Pharmacy.

COLE, John E; Highland HS; Highland, IL; 11/190 CncrtBnd; HonRl; NHS; NatlMeritCmnd; StuCncl; RptrSchPpr; Trk; OptClAwd; VFWAwd; VoiceDeMAwd; Wash Univ; Bus Admin.

COLE, Joyce L; Diamond HS; Neosho, MO; 22/54 ChrhWkr; HonRl; NatlFornLg; OffAde; SchAde; SchPl; TchrAde; PresYthFlsp; FHA; College; Vocational.

COLE, Judy M; Medicine Valley HS; Curtis, NE; 2/34 SecJrCls; Band; Chrs; HonRl; NHS; SchMus; FHA; PpCl; Chrldr; PresAwd; Cosmotology Sch; Professional.

COLE, Karen; The Immaculata Hs; Chicago, IL; 1/201 HonRl; NHS; TchrAde; RptrYrbk; RptrSchPpr; SpnCl; PpCl; U; Biology.

COLE, Kenneth; Lincoln HS; Beverly, KS; PresFrshCls; CmntyWkr; HonRl; PolWkr; EdSchPpr; GerCl; Bsbl; Ftbl; Trk; PresAwd; University; Professional.

COLE, Kim L; Wellington Napoleon R 9 HS; Wellington, MO; 14/38 SecFrshCls; TrsSophCls; HonRl; SchPpr; FHA; PpCl; Chrldr; PPFtbl; Cmsu.

COLE, Lani; O Neill HS; Oneill, NE; Chr; HonRl; NHS; SchMus; StuCncl; YthFlsp; Yrbk; 4-H; PpCl; 4-HAwd; Coll.

COLE, Lisa N; Greenfield HS; Greenfield, IL; 2/58 HstJrCls; SecSrCls; ALAGirlsSt; Band; ChrhWkr; HonRl; SecNHS; SecStuCncl; PresFHA; Trk; Chrldr; GAA; IMSpt; College; Home Economics.

COLE, Marlys M; Ringsted Comm HS; Ringsted, IA; 5/21 Band; CncrtBnd; LbryAde; MrchBnd; PepBnd; SchPpr; Sec4-H; FTA; 4-HAwd; Iowa Lakes Comm Col; Vocation Clerical.

COLE, Mary A; Anselmo Merna HS; Merna, NE; 2/25 PresFrshCls; PresSophCls; Band; Chr; Chrs; CmntyWkr; CncrtBnd; HonRl; MrchBnd; NHS; NatlSciFnd; Trk; Chrldr; GAA; College; Biology.

COLE, Mary E; St Joseph Academy; Northville, MI; 2/23 Chrl; HonRl; NHS; NatlMeritSF; SchPl; SecStuCncl; Bsktbl; GAA; PPFtbl; College; Psychology.

COLE, Mary M; Farmington HS; Farmington Hills, MI; Chr; ChrhWkr; HonRl; College; Professional Art Ed.

COLE, Meg; Wtn HS; Watertown, SD; 120/300 AFS; ALBoysSt; Chrs; ChrhWkr; CmntyWkr; SctActv; TchrAde; UNYO; GAA; PPFtbl; College; Professional.

COLE, Patrick; Central Noble HS; Albion, IN; PresFrshCls; PresSophCls; PepBnd; EdYrBk; Coll; Acc.

COLE, Paula D; Warren HS; Warren, IL; SecFrshCls; Band; Chrs; HonRl; SchMus; SchPl; 4-H; FHA; GAA; College; Elem Teacher.

COLE, Randy; West Delaware HS; Manchester, IA; CAP; HonRl; NHS; NatlMeritFnl; NatlMeritCmnd; NatlMeritSchl; NatlSciFnd; FBLA; ChmbCommrsAwd; GovHonPrgAwd; Hawkeye School Of Tech; Police Science.

COLE, Ray; Central HS; Waterloo, IA; SchPl; PpCl; Ftbl; Trk; Wrstlng; College.

COLE, Renae M; Breckenridge Jr Sr HS; Breckenridge, MI; 5/94 Band; Chr; CncrtBnd; HonRl; Mdrgl; MrchBnd; NHS; PepBnd; SchMus; Central Michigan Univ; Music.

COLE, Rex A; Medicine Valley Jr Sr HS; Curtis, NE; Chr; CncrtBnd; MrchBnd; PepBnd; 4-H; FFA; Bsktbl; Trade School; Automotive Mechanic.

COLE, Rhonda A; Southwest HS; St Louis, MO; 12/

597 ChrhWkr; HonRl; ModUN; MthCl; Harvard Univ; Physician.

COLE, Rhonda D; Assumption HS; Assumption, IL; HonRl; NHS; RptrSchPpr; FHA; Bsbl; Trk; CaptChrldr; IMSpt; PresAwd; College; Teacher.

COLE, Richard; Addison HS; Addison, MI; HonRl; LbryAde; NatlMeritCmnd; GerCl; IMSpt; KiwanAwd; Msu Univ; Physics.

COLE, Robin M; Cardinal Ritter HS; Indianapolis, IN; 9/165 HonRl; JA; College; Medical Technology.

COLE, Sandra; East High School; Rockford, IL; 5/665 ChrhWkr; HonRl; JA; NHS; 4-H; GAA; BttyCrckrAwd; 4-HAwd; JAAwd; Northern Illinois U; Accounting.

COLE, Terry; East HS; Waterloo, IA; Band; HonRl; SctActv; Bsktbl; Ftbl; Trade Sch; Prof Photography.

COLE, Terry R; Memorial HS; Joplin, MO; DrlTm; HonRl; LbryAde; ROTC; AmLegAwd; VFWAwd; Coll.

COLE, Willie M; Harvard St George HS; Chicago, IL; 2/20 Chrs; CmntyWkr; HonRl; JA; NHS; NatlMeritSF; OffAde; StuCncl; RptrYrbk; Bsktbl; JCAwd; College; Journalism.

COLEBANK, Kimberly A; Litchville Public HS; Litchville, ND; PresFrshCls; ChrhWkr; CmntyWkr; HonRl; NHS; PpCl; Chrldr; Wahpeton St Sch; Occ Therp Asst.

COLEGROVE, Terry; Morton HS; Morton, IL; 20/297 Band; CncrtBnd; HonRl; MrchBnd; NatlMeritCmnd; Orch; PepBnd; SpnCl; Il Central Col; Architecture.

COLEHOUR, Jeanne S; Fourth Baptist Christian HS; Minneapolis, MN; Chr; Chrs; HonRl; HospAde; Mdrgl; SctActv; RptrYrbk; RptrSchPpr; Trk; Chrldr; College; Major In Art Or English.

COLEMAN, Barbara K; Bloom Twp HS; Crete, IL; JrNHS; LitMag; Quill&Scroll; College; Writer.

COLEMAN, Charles L 9; Lindblom Technical HS; Chicago, IL; 26/650 HonRl; NatlMeritCmnd; SchAde; StuCncl; TchrAde; LatCl; MthCl; Trk; University; Physics.

COLEMAN, David W; St Edmond HS; Fort Dodge, IA; VPBand; CncrtBnd; HonRl; PepBnd; SchPl; StuCncl; LetterBsbl; Bsktbl; Trk; IMSpt; College; Retail Marketing.

COLEMAN, Edward E; Chicago Vocational HS; Chicago, IL; ChrhWkr; HonRl; StuCncl; MthCl; Univ; Professional.

COLEMAN, Gary D; Valentine HS; Valentine, NE; ALBoysSt; ALAGirlsSt; HonRl; TchrAde; RptrSchPpr; Bsbl; LetterBsktbl; IMSpt; AmLegAwd; CitAwd; College; English.

COLEMAN, Gary N; Paxton HS; Paxton, IL; VPSrCls; HonRl; NHS; SchPl; StuCncl; RptrSchPpr; SciCl; Bsbl; College; Civil Engineering.

COLEMAN, Glenn E; Pleasant Hill HS; Peculiar, MO; 44/104 StuGov; 4-H; FFA; Ftbl; LetterTrk; CaptWrstlng; Longview Comm College; Mech Husbandry.

COLEMAN, Janet A; Paxton HS; Paxton, IL; ChrhWkr; HonRl; JrNHS; NHS; RptrYrbk; Yrbk; College.

COLEMAN, Keith R; Austin HS; Chicago, IL; Band; Trk; Coll; Pharmacy.

COLEMAN, Kim; Valentine HS; Valentine, NE; TrsSophCls; Chr; Chrs; HospAde; SctActv; StuCncl; TchrAde; YthFlsp; FHA; Chrldr; Patricia Stevens Coll; Airlines.

COLEMAN, Kimberly A; Our Lady Of The Lakes HS; Clarkston, MI; 9/53 CmntyWkr; HonRl; TchrAde; Yrbk; FrCl; Bsbl; Chrldr; IMSpt; Central Michigan University.

COLEMAN, Lindell A; Potosi HS; Richwoods, MO; 10/186 Chr; ChrhWkr; HonRl; PresNHS; SchAde; LetterBsbl; LetterFtbl; LetterTrk; IMSpt; DanFAwd; Southeast Mo State U; Teaching.

COLEMAN, Mike; Elgin HS; Elgin, IL; 11/827 Aud/Vis; HonRl; NatlMeritCmnd; Orch; SchMus; SctActv; SchPpr; Mit; Engineering.

COLEMAN, Pamela K; Trico HS; Percy, IL; SecSophCls; Band; Chr; Chrs; ChrhWkr; CtyCnl; CmntyWkr; Chrldr; GAA; PresAwd; Baptist Nursing College; Nursing.

COLEMAN, Patricia M; Fridley HS; Fridley, MN; HonRl; NHS; RptrSchPpr; SpnCl; Trk; Univ; Doctor.

COLEMAN, Robert J; St Joseph HS; Glendale Heights, IL; 46/206 VPFrshCls; VPSophCls; VPJrCls; HonRl; StuCncl; StuGov; Bsbl; Bsktbl; Ftbl; IMSpt; Lewis Univ; Accting.

COLEMAN, Ron C; Shelby HS; Shelby, MI; Band; ChrhWkr; CncrtBnd; HonRl; MrchBnd; PepBnd; SctActv; PpCl; Trk; Michigan State Univ; Professional.

COLEMAN, Vernita J; Chicago Vocational HS; Chicago, IL; 37/900 ChrhWkr; CmntyWkr; HonRl; JA; OffAde; SchAde; StuCncl; TchrAde; Col; Professional.

COLEMAN, William; Northrop HS; Ft Wayne, IN; RptrSchPpr; Glf; In Univ; Accounting.

COLESON, Kathy A; West Delaware HS; Manchester, IA; 1/217 Band; Chr; CncrtBnd; HonRl; MrchBnd; NHS; PepBnd; Quill&Scroll; EdSchPpr; Univ; Med Or Ecology.

COLESTOCK, Helen A; Normandy HS; Northwoods, MO; 5/600 PresBand; ChrhWkr; CncrtBnd; MrchBnd; PresNHS; NatlMeritSF; Orch; PepBnd; SchMus; RptrSchPpr; Col; Music.

COLETTA, Michael A; Northwestern HS; Lake Nebagamon, WI; CmntyWkr; HonRl; SciCl; LetterFtbl; College; Law.

COLETTI, Mary E; Grand Blanc HS; Grand Blanc, MI; 57/637 Chr; Chrs; HonRl; NHS; NatlMeritSchl; NatlMeritSF; Ferris St College; Pharmacy.

COLEY, Jeri; Wysses HS; Ulysses, KS; PresSophCls; HonRl; NHS; TchrAde; FHA; GerCl; PpCl; Trk; Chrldr; PPFtbl; Rotc Univ; Air Force.

COLGAN, Lucinda R; Holdrege HS; Holdrege, NE; Band; Chr; Chrs; ChrhWkr; CmntyWkr; CncrtBnd; MrchBnd; PepBnd; SchPl; YthFlsp; RptrSchPpr; Pres4-H; FBLA; PpCl; Chrldr; College; Professional.

COLGLAZIER, John T; Salem HS; Salem, IN; 19/168 HonRl; StuCncl; TchrAde; Yrbk; LatCl; Bsktbl; LetterGlf; Indiana Univ Se; Business Major.

COLGLAZIER, Patrick D; Lewistown Comm HS; Lewistown, IL; 38/104 ChrhWkr; CmntyWkr; HonRl; SchPl; StuCncl; SptEdYrbk; FFA; PpCl; LetterFtbl; LetterGlf; LetterTrk; LetterWrstlng; College; Agriculture.

COLGROVE, Charlotte J; Lemmon HS; Lemmon, SD; 3/69 PresJrCls; ALAGirlsSt; ChrhWkr; HonRl; HospAde; JrNHS; NHS; SchPl; GerCl; Bsktbl; S Dakota St Univ; Nursing.

COLGROVE, Kip D; West Pike HS; Kinderhook, IL; 3/35 PresSrCls; HonRl; NHS; SchPl; VPStuCncl; EdYrBk; SchPpr; EngCl; SpnCl; PpCl; Bsbl; So Ill Univ; Broadcasting.

COLHT, Judy A; St Barbara HS; Chicago, IL; 26/88 SecSrCls; HonRl; HospAde; SchPl; College; Child Development.

COLLARD, Linda M; Douglas Mac Arthur HS; Saginaw, MI; HonRl; NHS; PolWkr; TchrAde; PpCl; LetterTennis; Central Michigan Univ; Law.

COLLARD, Mary P; Marinette Cath Central HS; Menominee, MI; HonRl; LbryAde; SchPl; PpCl; N Mi Univ; Social Worker.

COLLARENO, Philip A; Bentley HS; Livonia, MI; CmntyWkr; HonRl; NatlMeritSF; SchPl; StuCncl; StuGov; Teen; SptEdSchPpr; Ftbl; JCAwd; U Of Mi; Engineering.

COLLATZ, Pamela D; Roosevelt HS; River Forest, IL; 9/293 Band; CncrtBnd; HonRl; NHS; Orch; SchAde; SctActv; YthFlsp; Swmmng; IMSpt; U Of Illinois; Accounting.

COLLE, Joni D; Waltonville Comm HS; Nason, IL; 7/40 ChrhWkr; HonRl; SchPl; VPFHA; PresGerCl; PpCl; SecGAA; Rend Lake Jr College.

COLLETTA, Louis; Lakeview HS; St Clair Shores, MI; 21/670 HonRl; University; Professional.

COLLETTE, Mark A; Eastridge HS; Kankakee, IL; 385/425 Chr; HonRl; LbryAde; NatlThespSoc; PolWkr; SchMus; SchPl; 4-H; FFA; LetterFtbl; Wrstlng; Us Marine Corp; Avionics.

COLLICK, Betty; Negaunee HS; Palmer, MI; 36/149 SecJrCls; Chrs; HonRl; Mdrgl; SctActv; StuGov; SpnCl; Bsbl; Bsktbl; Trk; Northern Mich Univ;med Sec.

COLLIER, Jerome A; Effingham HS; Effingham, IL; ALBoysSt; CtyCnl; RptrYrbk; 4-H; KeyCl; Bsktbl; LetterFtbl; LetterTrk; IMSpt; AmLegAwd; 4-HAwd; College; Law Enforcement.

COLLIER, Laura L; Campbellsport HS; Campbellsport, WI; 6/147 HonRl; NatlFornLg; NHS; Sdlty; FHA; SpnCl; GAA; IMSpt; Uw Stevens Point; Business Administration.

COLLIER, Lynda; Dekalb Senior HS; Dekalb, IL; 30/370 SecTrsSrCls; DrlTm; HonRl; LbryAde; NHS; StuCncl; Teen; PpCl; IMSpt; Univ Of Il; Engineering.

COLLIER, Lynda A; De Kalb Sr HS; De Kalb, IL; 29/370 SecTrsSrCls; DrlTm; HonRl; LbryAde; NHS; StuCncl; Univ Of Ill; Engineer.

COLLIER, Robert J; Luther South HS; Chicago, IL; Aud/Vis; Band; ChrhWkr; CmntyWkr; HonRl; SchAde; Ftbl; Wrstlng; Arizona State University; Engineering.

COLLIN, Sylvia; Holdrege Sr HS; Funk, NE; Band; Chrs; ChrhWkr; CncrtBnd; HonRl; MrchBnd; PepBnd; SchMus; Univ Of Nebraska; Physical Terapy.

COLLINGS, Richard H; Buckley Loda HS; Loda, IL; ALBoysSt; HonRl; JCC; NHS; NatlMeritSchl; SchPl; StuGov; FBLA; PresSpnCl; AmLegAwd; U Of Co; Accounting.

COLLINS, Becky A; Logan HS; La Crosse, WI; Chr; ChrhWkr; HonRl; NatlFornLg; AmLegAwd;.

COLLINS, Bobbie; Kirksville Sr HS; Kirksville, MO; HonRl; RedCrAde; SctActv;.

COLLINS, Brad L; Bourbon HS; Bourbon, MO; ALBoysSt; HonRl; NHS; NatlMeritCmnd; East Central Jr College; Lawyer.

COLLINS, Catherine M; Williamsburg HS; Williamsburg, KS; 3/28 SecFrshCls; SecJrCls; TrsSrCls; Chr; ChrhWkr; HonRl; NHS; LetterTrk; DARAwd; CitAwd; Emporia Ks St Coll; Nursing.

COLLINS, Christopher; Corunna HS; Corunna, MI; 15/220 HonRl; Ftbl; Univ; Engineering.

COLLINS, Cindy R; Burrton HS; Burrton, KS; HonRl; PolWkr; SchPl; StuCncl; TchrAde; Teen; RptrYrbk; Trk; Chrldr; PPFtbl; College; Radiology.

COLLINS, Crystal L; White Lake Ind HS; White Lake, SD; Chr; ChrhWkr; CmntyWkr; HonRl; LbryAde; YthFlsp; PpCl; 4-HAwd; College.

COLLINS, Cynthia K; Harry A Burke HS; Omaha, NE; Chrs; JA; OffAde; SchAde; SchMus; SchPl; TchrAde; IMSpt; PresJAAwd; Uno; Law Accounting Majors.

COLLINS, Edward R; St Patrick HS; Chicago, IL; 32/358 CmntyWkr; HonRl; SctActv; StuCncl; StuGov; SchPpr; College.

COLLINS, Eileen T; Acad Of Our Lady; Chicago, IL; 9/168 HonRl; NHS; SchPl; Sdlty; TchrAde; Yrbk; SchPpr; PpCl; Univ; Prof.

COLLINS, Fred R; Fort Dodge Sr HS; Fort Dodge, IA; ALBoysSt; HonRl; LitMag; ModUN; NHS; Orch; SchPl; SctActv; EdSchPpr; MasAwd; College; Law.

COLLINS, Gary L; L & M Comm HS; Letts, IA; PresJrCls; VPSrCls; ChrhWkr; HonRl; VPNHS; SctActv; PresStuCncl; PresYthFlsp; RptrYrbk; RptrSchPpr; Bsbl; Muscatine Jc; Engineer.

COLLINS, Gerald R; Dwight D Eisenhower HS; Decatur, IL; 53/331 FBLA; FrCl; College; Business.

COLLINS, Gregory A; Dekalb HS; Auburn, IN; 19/279 VPBand; MrchBnd; NHS; PepBnd; SchMus; PresStuCncl; FrCl; Tennis; DanFAwd; KiwanAwd; Indiana Univ; Business Administration.

COLLINS, Howard S; Hillsdale HS; Hillsdale, MI; Chr; Chrl; Chrs; Univ; Music.

COLLINS, James D; Hutchinson HS; Hutchinson, KS; Band; CncrtBnd; HonRl; MrchBnd; NatlMeritCmnd; Orch; PepBnd; GerCl; Univ; Physical Science.

COLLINS, Janet K; Overton Public HS; Overton, NE; 2/21 PresJrCls; PresBand; Chrs; ChrhWkr; CncrtBnd; HonRl; MrchBnd; SchPl; StuCncl; YthFlsp; Chrldr; Business School.

COLLINS, Jeanne M; St Francis HS; Wheaton, IL; 8/130 ChrhWkr; HonRl; NHS; SchPl; StuCncl; SpnCl; PpCl; Illinois State Univ; Art.

COLLINS, Jeffery C; Springfield Southeast HS; Springfield, IL; 1/504 JrNHS; NHS; NatlMeritCmnd; StuCncl; StuGov; MthCl; SciCl; LetterSwmmng; LetterTrk; University Of Illinois; Physics.

COLLINS, Jody R; Lewellen Rural HS; Lewellen, NE; 4/14 Chrs; HonRl; JA; SchPl; Twrl; YthFlsp; EdSchPpr; 4-H; FHA; PpCl; LetterBsktbl; Tennis; LetterTrk; Kearney St College; Physical Educ.

COLLINS, John W; Madison Consolidated HS; Madison, IN; 30/300 NatlMeritCmnd; YthFlsp; LatCl; LetterTrk; LetterWrstlng; Rose Hulman Inst; Mech Engineering.

COLLINS, Joseph A; Marist HS; Chicago, IL; 102/393 Aud/Vis; ChrhWkr; CmntyWkr; HonRl; SchMus; SchPl; YthLg; RptrSchPpr; PpCl; College; Journalism.

COLLINS, Julie L; St Francis Academy; Joliet, IL; PresSrCls; HonRl; LitMag; SchMus; StuCncl; RptrYrbk; GerCl; Joliet Jr College; Art.

COLLINS, Keith M; Harry S Truman HS; Taylor, MI; Band; ChrhWkr; CmntyWkr; HonRl; LitMag; PolWkr; StuCncl; SchPpr; LatCl; Wayne St Univ; Medicine.

COLLINS, Leonard; Manistee HS; Manistee, MI; ChrhWkr; HonRl; NHS; Coll; Soc Sci.

COLLINS, Mark A; Kalamazoo Central HS; Kalamazoo, MI; 8/549 SptEdSchPpr; LetterBsktbl; IMSpt; Univ Mi; Prof/science.

COLLINS, Marsha L; Riii Central HS; Flat River, MO; Band; Chrs; CncrtBnd; HonRl; MrchBnd; NHS; SchPl; FTA; PpCl; LetterTrk; Mineral Area Jr College.

COLLINS, Marva K; Liberty HS; Liberty, MO; 9/279 AFS; Chrs; ChrhWkr; HonRl; NHS; SchMus; FTA; TreasPpCl; DARAwd; RotaryAwd; William Jewell Col; Elementary Ed.

COLLINS, Mary E; Big Bay De Noc HS; Cooks, MI; PresSophCls; ChrhWkr; HonRl; SchPl; StuCncl; TchrAde; 4-H; 4-HAwd; U ;physchology.

COLLINS, Matthew R; Flat Rock HS; Flat Rock, MI; 4/131 CmntyWkr; CncrtBnd; NHS; NatlMeritCmnd; Orch; PolWkr; SctActv; MthCl; SciCl; LetterTennis; Univ Of Mich; Bus Admin.

COLLINS, Micki J; Beaumont HS; St Louis, MO; 31/539 HonRl; JA; JrNHS; TchrAde; YthFlsp; FBLA; PpCl; Florissant Vlly Comm Clge; Legal Secretary.

COLLINS, Nina F; Traverse City Sr HS; Traverse City, MI; 7/650 SecChr; HonRl; Mdrgl; NHS; PolWkr; SchMus; StuCncl; CivCl; Chrldr; KiwanAwd; Central Mich U; Psych.

COLLINS, Noreen M; Immaculate Heart Of Mary HS; Broadview, IL; VPSophCls; PresJrCls; Aud/Vis; NHS; StuCncl; SchPpr; CaptBsktbl; Trk; GAA; IMSpt; Triton Jr College; Law Enforcement.

COLLINS, Patricia A; Good Counsel HS; Chicago, IL; 1/247 HonRl; PresNHS; NatlMeritFnl; Quill&Scroll; StuCncl; EdYrBk; RptrSchPpr; SpnCl; St Marys College; Social Work.

COLLINS, Peter; Regina HS; Coralville, IA; HonRl; NHS; SchMus; SchPl; SctActv; RptrYrbk; Yrbk; RptrSchPpr; SchPpr; JAAwd; College.

COLLINS, Reuben T; Mason City HS; Mason City, IA; NHS; NatlMeritCmnd; Quill&Scroll; Yrbk; BauchLmbAwd; CitAwd; University; Science.

COLLINS, Robert W; Rockford East HS; Rockford, IL; 87/660 HonRl; NHS; LetterFtbl; LetterWrstlng; Iowa St University.

COLLINS, Robin S; Cass Tech HS; Detroit, MI; 19/181 HonRl; JrNHS; TreasNHS; TchrAde; Teen; LetterTrk; CchngActv; Michigan St Univ; Medicine.

COLLINS, Scott J; Midland Community HS; Onslow, IA; Aud/Vis; Chrs; SchMus; SchPl; 4-H; SciCl; Bsbl; Bsktbl; Ftbl; LetterTrk; College.

COLLINS, Sheila A; North HS; Sheboygan, WI; JAAwd; College.

COLLINS, Teresa K; Gallatin Rv HS; Gallatin, MO; 11/47 Band; CncrtBnd; HonRl; MrchBnd; NHS; OffAde; Yrbk; SchPpr; FHA; PpCl; Trk; College; Journalist.

COLLINS, Thomas; Black Hawk HS; Gratiot, WI; HstFrshCls; CmntyWkr; HonRl; OffAde; RptrSchPpr; Bsbl; Bsktbl; Ftbl; IMSpt; College; Phy Ed Education.

COLLINS, Timothy C; Mexico HS; Mexico, MO; ALBoysSt; Chr; LbryAde; NatlMeritCmnd; PolWkr; SctActv; StuCncl; YthFlsp; KeyCl; LetterTrk; College; Conservation Worker.

COLLINS, Vanessa; Grafton HS; Grafton, WI; Band; CncrtBnd; HonRl; MrchBnd; NatlThespSoc; PepBnd; SchMus; SchPl; RptrSchPpr; U W Oshkosh; Music Education.

COLLINS III, William; Cheboygan HS; Cheboygan, MI; Band; Chr; CncrtBnd; HonRl; PepBnd; StuGov; 4-H; FFA; Northern Mich Univ; Professional.

COLLINSWORTH, Mary J; Chase Co HS; Cottonwood Falls, KS; Chrl; Chrs; HonRl; LbryAde; OffAde; SchMus; Twrl; YthFlsp; SpnCl; PpCl; Trk; Ks State U.

COLLISON, Jana L; W Platte R 11 HS; Weston, MO; 4/75 TrsSophCls; VPJrCls; SecAFS; HonRl; NHS; StuCncl; PresFHA; PpCl; LetterGlf; Chrldr; College; Business.

COLLISTER, Lori A; Colfax HS; Colfax, IA; 8/61 ALAGirlsSt; Band; Chr; Chrs; CncrtBnd; HonRl; MrchBnd; PepBnd; SchMus; SchPl; College; Speech Therapy.

COLLMAN, Janice L; Forreston HS; Freeport, IL; 3/68 VPSophCls; TrsSrCls; ALAGirlsSt; HonRl; PresYthFlsp; Yrbk; EdSchPpr; Pres4-H; Trk; PresGAA; 4-HAwd; Bradley Univ; Business Management.

COLLMANN, Ann M; Oxford HS; Winfield, KS; 12/39 Chrs; HonRl; TchrAde; Yrbk; RptrSchPpr; SchPpr; FHA; Cowley County Comm Jr Clge; Police Science.

COLMAN, Steven A; Cumberland HS; Cumberland, WI; 8/108 PresFrshCls; PresSophCls; HonRl; SchPl; RptrYrbk; RptrSchPpr; Bsktbl; Ftbl; AmLegAwd; GovHonPrgAwd; Macalester Clg; Business & Economics.

COLOGNA, Rosemary L; Norway HS; Norway, MI; ChrhWkr; CmntyWkr; HonRl; Sacrstn; SchPl; Yrbk; RptrSchPpr; 4-H; FHA; Trk; Bay De Noc C Col ;social Worker.

COLOSIA, Mark; Marist HS; Willow Springs, IL; 21/364 HonRl; LitMag; TchrAde; LatCl; SciCl; 4-HAwd; Bradley Univ; Electrical Engineer.

COLOSIA, Mark; Marist HS; Willow Springs, IL; 23/370 HonRl; LitMag; TchrAde; LatCl; SciCl; College; Electicial Engineering.

COLOVAS, Stephen W; Riverside HS; Dearborn Heights, MI; 16#26#30 SchMus; StuGov; SchPpr; Bsktbl; Ftbl; Trk; CchngActv; Wayne St Univ; Law.

COLSCH, Bonnie K; Waukon Sr HS; Waukon, IA; 10/150 Chr; ChrhWkr; HonRl; NHS; 4-H; SpnCl; PpCl; Bsktbl; 4-HAwd; Clarke Coll; Medical Technology.

COLSTAD, Mary; Beaver Dam Sr HS; Beaver Dam, WI; 39/318 HonRl; Mdrgl; MrchBnd; PepBnd; SchMus; StuCncl; Yrbk; SpnCl; PpCl; IMSpt; College; Elem Ed.

COLTMAN, Ross M; Calumet HS; Lavrium, MI; Band; ChrhWkr; CncrtBnd; MrchBnd; PepBnd; LetterFtbl; LetterTrk; College.

COLTON, Teri L; Gretna HS; Gretna, NE; Band; Chr; Chrs; CncrtBnd; HonRl; MrchBnd; NHS; Orch; PepBnd; SchMus; SchPl; TchrAde; LetterSwmmng; Chrldr; College; Music.

COLTON, Timothy D; Durand Area HS; Durand, MI; HonRl; Quill&Scroll; SchPl; RptrYrbk; RptrSchPpr; EdSchPpr; SptEdSchPpr; SchPpr; Mich State Univ; Hotel Management.

COLVARD, Cyril S; Mt Vernon HS; Fortville, IN; 5/143 ALBoysSt; Aud/Vis; Band; CncrtBnd; HonRl; NHS; SchMus; SchPl; Yrbk; 4-H; LetterGlf; 4-HAwd; GovHonPrgAwd; Univ; Medicine.

COLVIN, Daniel E; East Peoria Comm HS; East Peoria, IL; PresFrshCls; Band; CncrtBnd; HonRl; SchAde; StuCncl; LetterFtbl; LetterTrk; GovHonPrgAwd; Univ Of Illinois; Engineering.

COLVIN, Frederick A; Illiana Christian HS; Lansing, IL; Band; CncrtBnd; MrchBnd; PepBnd; GerCl; Bsbl; Socr; Dordt Christian College; Cpa.

COLVIN, Heidi J; Hammond Tech Voc HS; Hammond, IN; 35/300 HonRl; LbryAde; NHS; OffAde; TchrAde; ChmnFHA; VPEngCl; Armed Services; Accountant.

COLVIN, Janis J; Haven HS; Hutchinson, KS; Band; CncrtBnd; HonRl; MrchBnd; TchrAde;.

COLVIN, Julie; Washington Catholic HS; Montgomery, IN; Chrs; HonRl; NHS; TchrAde; 4-H; PpCl;.

COLVIN, Kevin W; Divernon HS; Divernon, IL; 4/28 HonRl; SchPl; StuGov; LetterFtbl; LetterTrk; LetterWrstlng; College; Engineer Mechanic.

COLVIN, Paula; Bloomfield Community HS; Bloomfield, NE; 15/66 Yrbk; FHA; PpCl; Business School; Accountant.

COLWELL, Diane L; Franklin HS; Meredosia, IL; ALAGirlsSt; Chrs; HonRl; HospAde; PresNHS; OffAde; StuCncl; YthFlsp; FHA; PresSpnCl; LetterChrldr; GAA; College; Professional.

COLWELL, Julia B; New Trier East HS; Wilmette, IL; 27/847 Band; HonRl; NatlMeritSF; SctActv; ChmnBsbl; LetterBsktbl; PresGAA; NCTE; Univ Of Mi; Medicine.

COLWELL, Mary Lou; Alliance HS; Alliance, NE; 5/155 AFS; ALAGirlsSt; Chr; ChrhWkr; CmntyWkr; HonRl; JrNHS; NHS; NatlThespSoc; Quill&Scroll; Creighton Univ; Bs In Nursing.

COLWELL, Maureen R; Hill Murray HS; St Paul, MN; VPSrCls; Chr; Chrs; HonRl; Trk; College; Counselor.

COLWELL, Patrick D; Cedar Falls HS; Cedar Falls, IA; 9/381 HonRl; NatlMeritCmnd; KiwanAwd; Univ; Engr.

COLWELL, Starlyn L; Genesee HS; Mt Morris, MI; SecFrshCls; Chr; Chrs; HonRl; LbryAde; Mdrgl; NHS; SchPl; StuCncl; Chrldr; College; Social Work.

COLWELL, Willa M; Austin HS; Austin, IN; 12/68 TrsSrCls; Chrs; HonRl; PresHospAde; NHS; SchPl; SctActv; TchrAde; FTA; PpCl; Trade Sch; Therapis.

COLZA, Carol A; Andrean HS; Gary, IN; 20/301 Chr; HonRl; StuCncl; FrCl; PpCl; GAA; Franklin College; Pre Law.

COMANSE, Richard A; Roosevelt HS; East Chicago, IN; 26/200 CncrtBnd; HonRl; MrchBnd; Orch; SchPl; StuGov; RptrYrbk; MthCl; Tennis; Wrstlng; Army.

COMASTRO, Kim M; Fenton HS; Itasca, IL; PresSophCls; PresSrCls; Band; Chr; HonRl; StuCncl; Yrbk; College; Teacher.

COMBES, Marilyn S; Waverly HS; Waverly, KS; 4/24 VPFrshCls; Chrs; CncrtBnd; HonRl; SchPl; YthFlsp; EdYrBk; 4-H; Chrldr; 4-HAwd; Washburn U; Business.

COMBS, Cherylyn A; Rantoul Township HS; Rantoul, IL; HonRl; JrNHS; SpnCl; AmLegAwd; College; Language.

COMBS, Connie L; Laurel HS; Laurel, IN; VPSophCls; ChrhWkr; HonRl; NHS; OffAde; Business School; Vocation.

COMBS, David; Wabash HS; Wabash, IN; ALBoysSt; HonRl; RedCrAde; StuCncl; StuGov; IMSpt; Univ; Science.

COMBS, Donna G; Newton Community HS; Newton, IL; 20/187 HonRl; LbryAde; NHS; FNA; College; Professional.

COMBS, Donna M; Dillsboro Public HS; Dillsboro, IN; 2/31 HstSrCls; Chrs; CncrtBnd; HonRl; NatlMeritSchl; Yrbk; EdSchPpr; GAA; DARAwd; CitAwd; E Ky U; Business.

COMBS, Kathy A; Northrop HS; Ft Wayne, IN; Chr; CmntyWkr; LbryAde; PolWkr; Quill&Scroll; RedCrAde; SctActv; TchrAde; SchPpr; PpCl; Travel Agency.

COMBS, Lavonda R; Charlestown HS; Charlestown, IN; 10/146 CncrtBnd; CaptDrlTm; MrchBnd; NHS; StuCncl; FshEdSchPpr; FHA; LatCl; PresSciCl; GAA; Indiana Univ; Archaeology.

COMBS, Linda S; Valley Center HS; Wichita, KS; 18/119 Chr; ChrhWkr; HonRl; NHS; NatlMeritSchl; OffAde; SchAde; StuCncl; YthFlsp; RptrSchPpr; Evangel College; Music.

COMBS, Roxanne; West Ottawa HS; Holland, MI; 11/270 HonRl; NHS; Orch; SchMus; SchPl; GerCl; Western Mi Univ; Music Therapy.

COMBS, Sherry; Sunnydale Academy; Kansas City, MO; 2/42 Chr; Chrl; ChrhWkr; HonRl; LbryAde; NHS; SchPl; TchrAde; Yrbk; IMSpt; College; Teacher.

COMBS, Susan J; Couch HS; Couch, MO; 5/28 PresFrshCls; VPSophCls; TrsJrCls; Band; Chr; HonRl; OffAde; PresStuCncl; VPFHA; Colege; Business.

COMBS, Terri L; Joplin Memorial HS; Webb City, MO; Band; Chr; HonRl; JCC; Mdrgl; NHS; Trk; GAA; IMSpt; Sw Missouri St Univ; Law.

COMER, Carolyn R; Unity HS; Chicago, IL; Chr; Chrs; ChrhWkr; NatlCathMusEdAsoc; SchMus; SchPl; StuCncl; Univ Of Illinois; Secretary.

COMER, Cindy G; Seeger Memorial HS; Attica, IN; 15/125 Band; NHS; Twrl; RptrSchPpr;.

COMERFORD, Nancy A; Brookfield Central HS; Elm Grove, WI; OffAde; StuCncl; EdSchPpr; LetterTrk; GAA; IMSpt; College; Journalist.

COMERFORD, Robert; North Miami Hs; Denver, IN; 93/122 4-H; FFA; Glf; 4-HAwd; Navy;navy.

COMFORD, Mary H; St Teresas Academy; Kansas City, MO; Chr; Chrs; SchAde; Bsktbl; Ftbl; Trk; CchngActv; GAA; IMSpt; PPFtbl; U M K C Col; Phy Ed.

COMFORD, Peggy J; Wildrose Public HS; Wildrose, ND; PresSrCls; Band; Chr; Chrs; ChrhWkr; CncrtBnd; LetterBsktbl; LetterTrk; Chrldr; GAA; Und Grand Forks.

COMFORT, Keith C; Mt Pleasant HS; Mt Pleasant, IA; 24/170 ChrhWkr; HonRl; NHS; SctActv; SpnCl; SciCl; Bsktbl; Trk; IMSpt; Ottawa U; Statistician.

COMMENT, Roland D; Edwardsburg HS; Edwardsburg, MI; Yrbk; Ivy Tech; Electronics Master.

COMMERFORD, Mary; St Pius X HS; Crystal City, MO; 6/124 Band; Chrs; CncrtBnd; HonRl; MrchBnd; NHS; PepBnd; StuCncl; CivCl; HstSophCls; Coll; Voc Rehab.

COMMONS, Daniel L; Salina HS; Salina, KS; HonRl; LbryAde; Wichita State Univ; Chemistry.

COMPORA, Judith A; Monroe HS; Monroe, MI; 80/524 Chrs; HonRl; NatlMeritCmnd; OffAde; TchrAde; Com College; Elementary Teaching.

COMPTON, Brenda G; Nevada HS; Nevada, MO; Chr; Chrs; ChrhWkr; CmntyWkr; OffAde; SctActv; 4-H; FHA; MthCl; Bsbl; Col; Bus.

COMPTON, Laura L; Lindbergh Sr HS; St Louis, MO; HonRl; NHS; NatlMeritSF; NatlThespSoc; SchPl; RptrYrbk; Yrbk; EngCl; SpnCl; College; Law.

COMPTON, Michael L; Peoria HS; Peoria, IL; 14/450 HonRl; JrNHS; NHS; SchPl; Univ Of Illinois; Dentistry.

COMPTON, Sally L; Tiskilwa HS; Tiskilwa, IL; PresSophCls; TrsJrCls; Chrs; CmntyWkr; StuCncl; YthFlsp; FHA; Trk; Chrldr; GAA; Il St U; Teacher.

COMSTOCK, Diane D; St Louis HS; St Louis, MI; 5/114 HonRl; NHS; OffAde; SchMus; SchPl; StuCncl; YthFlsp; SpnCl; PpCl; Western Mich Univ; Mathematics.

COMSTOCK, Jerry P; Kuemper HS; Vail, IA; ALBoysSt; ChrhWkr; SctActv; Sdlty; 4-H; Ftbl; Univ; Professional.

COMSTOCK, Joni B; Lincoln Comm HS; Lincoln, IL; 25/272 VPFrshCls; PresBand; ChrhWkr; CncrtBnd; HonRl; JrNHS; MrchBnd; NHS; NatlMeritCmnd; NatlMeritSchl; CaptBsktbl; Tennis; Trk; GAA; E Illinois Univ; Physical Educ.

COMSTOCK, Kathy M; Blair HS; Blair, NE; Chr; TchrAde; FNA; PpCl; LetterTrk; Chrldr; GAA; IMSpt; PresAwd; College; Nursing.

COMSTOCK, Timothy J; Unionville HS; Unionville, MO; Band; ChrhWkr; CncrtBnd; HonRl; MrchBnd; Orch; PepBnd; 4-H; SpnCl; LetterBsktbl; CaptFtbl; Glf; LetterTrk; Drury College; Business Admin.

COMSTOCK, Wanita J; Belton HS; Belton, MO; CmntyWkr; HonRl; TchrAde; FHA; PpCl; GAA; Culver Stockton College; Physical Educ.

COMSTOCK, Wendy; Cary Grove Community HS; Cary, IL; 29/300 Chr; Chrs; HonRl; JrNHS; LitMag; NHS; SchMus; RptrSchPpr; Chrldr; Miami Univ; Law School.

CONARD, Lois A; Fairfield HS; Arlington, KS; Chr; HonRl; SchPl; SecYthLg; RptrYrbk; 4-H; FDA; Bsbl; Bsktbl; LetterTennis; Hutchinson Juco; Nursing.

CONAWAY, Louise A; Highland Sr HS; Highland, IN; 14/543 ChrhWkr; HonRl; SctActv; YthFlsp; VP4-H; VPGerCl; GAA; PPFtbl; 4-HAwd; Ball State Or Valparaiso.

CONBOY, Maire E; Leavenworth HS; Ft Leavenworth, KS; HonRl; JrNHS; NatlFornLg; NatlMeritSF; SctActv; Northwestern Univ; Physician.

CONBOY, Terry; Northwest HS; High Ridge, MO; HonRl; HospAde; NHS; SctActv; PpCl; Coll; Medical Profession.

CONDIT, Jeffrey J; Mt Morris HS; Mt Morris, IL; 9/90 HonRl; StuCncl; SpnCl; Bsktbl; LetterFtbl; LetterGlf; College; Math.

CONDON, Beverly A; Mascoutah HS; Mascoutah, IL; 39/220 Band; HonRl; NHS; StuCncl; LetterTrk; GAA; College; Physical Education.

CONDON, Edward F; Loyola Academy; Northbrook, IL; 43/442 HonRl; JrNHS; NHS; NatlMeritCmnd; SchPl; TchrAde; RptrSchPpr; CaptBsktbl; Univ Of Notre Dame; Sociology.

CONDON, Mark W; Catholic Memorial HS; Waukesha, WI; 12/197 HstSophCls; ALBoysSt; HonRl; JrNHS; NHS; StuCncl; SptEdYrbk; RptrYrbk; CaptFtbl; St Norbert Coll; Sci Res.

CONDON, Mary E; Adlai E Stevenson HS; Buffalo Grove, IL; 16/231 PresSophCls; HonRl; LbryAde; NHS; SchPl; StuCncl; Yrbk; Loyola Univ; Pre Medicine.

CONDON, Peter J; Saint Laurence HS; Chicago, IL; 253/380 ChrhWkr; HonRl; SpnCl; Trk; University; Marine Biology.

CONDOTTI, Carol; Lyons Township Hs; La Grange Park, IL; SecSrCls; HonRl; HospAde; JrNHS; NHS; OffAde; Quill&Scroll; SchPl; StuGov; EdYrBk; Illinois U;child Devolopment.

CONDRAY, Robin; Clifton HS; Clifton, KS; Band; ChrhWkr; CncrtBnd; JA; LbryAde; YthFlsp; RptrYrbk; 4-H; FHA; Univ; Registered Nurse.

CONE, Elizabeth; Elkhart Central HS; Elkhart, IN; Chr; ChrhWkr; HonRl; HospAde; LbryAde; Orch; SchMus; FTA; FrCl; IMSpt; Coll; Biol.

CONE, Jacqueline S; Hermitage Public HS; Hermitage, MO; SecTrsJrCls; PresSrCls; HonRl; StuCncl; RptrYrbk; Yrbk; FHA; PpCl; Chrldr; BttyCrckrAwd; Business School.

CONE, Marla; Waukegan East Hs; Waukegan, IL; AFS; CmntyWkr; HonRl; NHS; EdSchPpr; U Of Wisc; Journalist.

CONETZKEY, Demer J; Lane Technical HS; Chicago, IL; 135/1209 CmntyWkr; SctActv; College; Engineering.

CONGER, Kirk J; North Platte HS; North Platt, NE; VPJrCls; HonRl; NatlMeritSF; PepBnd; SctActv; StuCncl; VPYthFlsp; KeyCl; Wrstlng; GodCntryAwd; College; Engineer.

CONGER, Marla; Gaylord HS; Gaylord, MI; 6/205 Band; CncrtBnd; HonRl; JrNHS; NatlFornLg; NHS; SchAde; StuCncl; FrCl; College; General Practitioner.

CONGER, Micki; Gaylord HS; Gaylord, MI; VPFrshCls; VPJrCls; Band; HonRl; HospAde; NHS; StuCncl; TchrAde; YthFlsp; Chrldr; N Central Mich Coll; Nursing.

CONGIOUS, Tammy L; Lindblom Tech HS; Chicago, IL; Chr; Chrs; ChrhWkr; LbryAde; University; Law.

CONKLE, Kathy M; Walkerville HS; Walkerville, MI; 5/27 TrsFrshCls; TrsSophCls; TrsJrCls; TrsSrCls; CmntyWkr; HonRl; PepBnd; LetterChrldr; IMSpt; EldAwd; Bus College; Pro Exec Sec.

CONKLIN, Colette R; Stratford Comm HS; Stratford, IA; 2/33 PresSophCls; Chrs; ChrhWkr; HonRl; StuCncl; RptrYrbk; EdSchPpr; FTA; CaptChrldr; 4-HAwd; U Of Northern Iowa; Music.

CONKLIN, Elizabeth A; Williamston HS; Williamston, MI; 8/160 SecJrCls; HonRl; StuGov; Trk; Chrldr; EldAwd; Michigan State Univ; Math & English Educ.

CONKLIN, Kimberly K; Durand Area HS; Durand, MI; 16/202 SecTrsJrCls; SecTrsSrCls; Chr; ChrhWkr; CmntyWkr; HonRl; Mdrgl; NHS; OffAde; StuCncl; Ferris State; Law.

CONKLIN, Stephanie; Earlham Comm HS; Earlham, IA; Chrs; DrlTm; HonRl; SchMus; TchrAde; RptrSchPpr; FrCl; College; Elementary Teaching.

CONLEY, Cary; Notre Dame Hs; Parkridge, IL; 11 CmntyWkr; HonRl; NatlMeritSchl; Bsbl; Bsktbl;.

CONLEY, Cindy S; Rock Falls Township HS; Rock Falls, IL; 25/259 HonRl; JrNHS; NHS; NatlMeritCmnd; OffAde; PolWkr; SpnCl; PpCl; Tennis; IMSpt; College; Pharmacy.

CONLEY, Donal T; Waterford Union HS; Waterford, WI; AFS; HonRl; NHS; NatlMeritCmnd; Yrbk; SchPpr; FrCl; Univ Of Wisconsin.

CONLEY, Pamela M; Laurel HS; Laurel, IN; SecTrsJrCls; Chrs; HonRl; NHS; StuCncl; Yrbk; Bus Sch.

CONLEY, Patricia M; St Elizabeth Academy; St Louis, MO; 9/115 PresJrCls; HonRl; NHS; PresGerCl; LetterBsktbl; LetterTrk; GAA; Quincy College; Mathematics.

CONLEY, Robert R; Mt Vernon HS; Greenfield, IN; HonRl; SchPl; Bsktbl; Trk; Purdue Univ; Engineering.

CONLEY, Susan J; Stockbridge HS; Munith, MI; 6/123 Band; NHS; College; Data Processing.

CONLIN, James D; Olympia HS; Mc Lean, IL; 21/230 PresAFS; HonRl; NHS; SchMus; SchPl; StuCncl; TreasGerCl; MthCl; PpCl; SciCl; LetterFtbl; Glf; Univ Of Illinois; Agriculture.

CONLIN, Margaret M; Derham Hall HS; St Paul, MN; Chrs; NHS; SchMus; RptrSchPpr; FrCl; SpnCl; College; Bus Admin.

CONLIN, Richard; Garber HS; Essexville, MI; TrsFrshCls; Chr; HonRl; SchMus; SchPl; StuCncl; TchrAde; Ftbl; Swmmng; Trk; Mi State Univ; Md Surgeon.

CONLIN, Robert G; Arthur HS; Arthur, IL; 5/52 TrsJrCls; CncrtBnd; HonRl; MrchBnd; RedCrAde; RptrSchPpr; TreasFFA; MthCl; LetterBsktbl; LetterFtbl; College; Doctor.

CONLIN, Suzanne M; St Thomas HS; Ann Arbor, MI; 8/79 HonRl; NHS; NatlMeritCmnd; NatlMeritSF; StuCncl; SpnCl; PpCl; CaptBsktbl; CaptGlf; GAA; U Of Fl; Law Political Science.

CONLON, Elizabeth J; Andrean HS; Crown Point, IN; 31/301 HonRl; NHS; PolWkr; Quill&Scroll; SctActv; StuCncl; StuGov; RptrYrbk; LatCl; PpCl; St Josephs Col; Medical Tech.

CONN, Dan R; Pleasantville Comm HS; Pleasantville, IA; ALBoysSt; Chr; Chrs; ChrhWkr; HonRl; Mdrgl; SchPl; SctActv; YthFlsp; Bsbl; College; The Ministry.

CONN, Julie; Corunna HS; Owosso, MI; 27/201 TrsFrshCls; TrsSophCls; TrsJrCls; TrsSrCls; HonRl; TchrAde; YthFlsp; 4-H; Chrldr; GAA; Ferris State College; Respiratory Therapy.

CONN, Warren A; St Johns Mil Academy; Chicago, IL; 1/38 ALBoysSt; HonRl; NHS; ROTC; StuGov; RptrSchPpr; RusCl; Swmmng; Univ; Professional.

CONNAUGHTON, Steven R; Washington HS; Washington, IN; Band; ChrhWkr; JA; PresKeyCl; I T T Tech Inst; Electronics.

CONNELL, Craig; Spencer HS; Spencer, IA; 19/163 Chr; HonRl; JrNHS; NHS; SchMus; SchPl; SctActv; FTA; IMSpt; College; Engineering.

CONNELL, Gail E; Genesse Street HS; Frakenmuth, MI; 11/195 Band; PresChrhWkr; HonRl; MrchBnd; NHS; SchPl; StuCncl; RptrYrbk; Chrldr; SecGAA; Ferris Univ; Pharmicist.

CONNELL, Linda K; Frederick HS; Frederick, SD; ChrhWkr; DrlTm; HonRl; 4-H; PpCl; Trade School; Upholsterer.

CONNELL, Lisa D; Eldon HS; Eldon, MO; HonRl; NHS; StuCncl; RptrYrbk; Yrbk; RptrSchPpr; PpCl; College.

CONNELL, Mark A; Memorial HS; Eau Claire, WI; HonRl; SctActv; Ftbl; IMSpt; Univ; Prof.

CONNELLY, Brian C; Davison HS; Burton, MI; 4/461 Chr; Chrl; ChrhWkr; HonRl; Mdrgl; NHS; NatlMeritSF; SchMus; SchPl; TchrAde; State Col; Prof Music History.

CONNELLY, Charlotte L; Casey HS; Casey, IL; Chr; HonRl; NatlThespSoc; OffAde; SchMus; SchPl; SctActv; StuCncl; FTA; PpCl; SciCl; GAA;.

CONNELLY, Christina S; Marshall HS; Marshall, MI; 63/275 Band; HonRl; SpnCl; PpCl; LetterBsktbl; Swmmng; GAA; IMSpt; PPFtbl; College; Occupational Therapy.

CONNELLY, Christine A; Salem Central HS; Salem, WI; TrsSophCls; HonRl; SchPl; TchrAde; RptrYrbk; RptrSchPpr; PpCl; Trk; Chrldr; GAA; Uw Whitewater; Spec Educ.

CONNELLY, Karen; R Nelson Snider HS; Fort Wayne, IN; 51/515 Chr; HonRl; JA; RptrYrbk; FrCl; JAAwd; Depauw Univ.

CONNELLY, Kathleen A; Visitation HS; St Paul, MN; 1/45 Chrs; HospAde; LbryAde; SchMus; SchPl; TchrAde; RptrYrbk; Yrbk; SpnCl; College; Horticulture.

CONNELLY, Kimberly J; Glenwood HS; Chatham, IL; 8/140 Band; HonRl; HospAde; NHS; SchMus; SchPl; TchrAde; FNA; Univ Of Ill; Engineering.

CONNELLY, Louis; Bridgeport HS; Saginaw, MI; 4/330 ChrhWkr; HonRl; NHS; Tennis; CchngActv; IMSpt; General Motors Institute; Industrial Adm.

CONNELLY, Mary A; Brady Public HS; Brady, NE; TrsJrCls; TrsSrCls; ALAGirlsSt; ChrhWkr; HonRl; SchPl; RptrYrbk; 4-H; PpCl; Chrldr; Business School; Secretary.

CONNELLY, Michael C; Assumption HS; Moweaqua, IL; 1/35 TrsSophCls; SecSrCls; HonRl; NHS; RptrYrbk; CivCl; 4-H; FFA; 4-HAwd; Univ Of Illinois; Agriculture.

CONNELLY, Michael D; Roger C Sullivan HS; Chicago, IL; HonRl; LitMag; PolWkr; StuCncl; RptrSchPpr; EdSchPpr; SchPpr; College; Journalism.

CONNELLY, Michael K; Cedar Falls HS; Cedar Falls, IA; 4/374 HonRl; ModUN; NatlFornLg; NatlMeritCmnd; PolWkr; TchrAde; GerCl; U Of Ia; Government.

CONNELLY, Patricia A; Laboure HS; St Louis, MO; SecJrCls; TrsSrCls; CmntyWkr; HonRl; StuCncl; StuGov; CivCl; Socr; Tennis; IMSpt; College; Elementary Education.

CONNELLY, Richard J; Carl Sandburg HS; Orland Park, IL; NatlMeritCmnd; StuCncl; RptrSchPpr; FrCl; MthCl; Univ; Engineering.

CONNER, David P; Benton HS; Benton, IL; 3/175 Aud/Vis; HonRl; NHS; FDA; LatCl; MthCl; PpCl; CaptTrk; IMSpt; LionAwd; Southern Illinois Univ; Medicine.

CONNER, Elizabeth L; Heritage Christian HS; Indianapolis, IN; 6/24 SecFrshCls; SecTrsSophCls; Chr; ChrhWkr; HonRl; SchMus; TchrAde; YthFlsp; CaptChrldr; GAA; Butler Univ; Nursing.

CONNER, Karen E; Richland HS; Parma, MO; ChrhWkr; StuCncl; Yrbk; RptrSchPpr; FHA; Chrldr; CchngActv; College.

CONNER, Kimberly S; Scottsbluff HS; Scottsbluff, NE; Band; Chr; HonRl; SchMus; PpCl; LetterTrk; Chrldr; College; Sociology.

CONNER, Marcia A; Arnold HS; Arnold, NE; ChrhWkr; HonRl; TchrAde; 4-H; FHA; PpCl; LetterBsktbl; Glf; Swmmng; Trk; Wrstlng; Chrldr; 4-HAwd; College; Reading Specialist.

CONNER, Mark V; Parker HS; Chicago, IL; 2/240 ChrhWkr; HonRl; NHS; TchrAde; College; Professional.

CONNER, Mary Ann; Riverdale HS; Avoca, WI; HonRl; SpnCl; PpCl; SciCl; School Of Nursing; Nursng.

CONNER, Mary E; Columbus HS; Marshfield, WI; 6/117 HonRl; NHS; SchPl; StuCncl; RptrSchPpr; FrCl; PpCl; GAA; College; Law.

CONNER, Meredith A; Red Bud HS; Prairie Du Rocher, IL; HonRl; 4-H; FBLA; FTA; SpnCl; Fontbonne College; Business.

CONNERS, Annette J; Jefferson West HS; Grantville, KS; 2/55 VPFrshCls; HonRl; SecSctActv; StuCncl; TchrAde; RptrYrbk; Sec4-H; PresFHA; PpCl; 4-HAwd; Ks St Univ; Social Studies.

CONNERY, Jean; Mt Horeb HS; Blue Mounds, WI; 14 Band; CncrtBnd; MrchBnd; NHS; PepBnd; SctActv; EdYrBk; Yrbk; FHA; IMSpt; Univ; Major Science.

CONNERY, Philip J; Homewood Flossmoor HS; Flossmoor, IL; 149/940 Univ Of Illinois.

CONNESS, Diane M; Marquette HS; Ottawa, IL; 3/96 ChrhWkr; CmntyWkr; HonRl; NatlThespSoc; SchMus; SchPpr; 4-H; PpCl; Chrldr; GAA; IMSpt; Illinois St Univ; Speech Pathology.

CONNOLLY, Brian J; New Trier West HS; Northfield, IL; HonRl; CaptSwmmng; Bowdoin College.

CONNOLLY, Daniel G; Mason Sr HS; Erie, MI; VPFrshCls; PresSophCls; VPJrCls; JrNHS; PresStuCncl; TchrAde; FTA; GerCl; CaptSwmmng; CaptTrk; University Of Arizona; Biology.

CONNOLLY, James; Oconomowoc HS; Oconomowoc, WI; PresSophCls; HonRl; StuCncl; Bsktbl; Uw Eau Claire; Law.

CONNOLLY, Kevin G; St Viator HS; Palatine, IL; 23/257 HonRl; TchrAde; Yrbk; RptrSchPpr; University; Journalism.

CONNOLLY, Mary P; St Francis HS; Traverse City, MI; 2/81 TrsSrCls; HonRl; JrNHS; NHS; OffAde; StuCncl; PpCl; Chrldr; KiwanAwd; Northwestern Mi Col; Liberal Arts.

CONNOLLY, Maureen A; Mehlville HS; St Louis, MO; 35/556 CmntyWkr; HonRl; PolWkr; Univ; Teacher.

CONNOLLY, Rosemary R; Western Dubuque HS; Holy Cross, IA; 25/243 ChrhWkr; CmntyWkr; HonRl; ModUN; SchMus; Sdlty; RptrYrbk; 4-H; FTA; IMSpt; Franciscan Sch Of Nursing; Nurse.

CONNOLLY, Sheila M; Bishop Luers HS; Fort Wayne, IN; ChrhWkr; CmntyWkr; HonRl; HospAde; PolWkr; SctActv; FrCl; PpCl; LetterBsbl; CaptBsktbl; Xavier Univ; Social Worker.

CONNOLLY, Theresa; Mount Assisi Academy; Chicago, IL; 7/129 SecSophCls; ChrhWkr; HonRl; JrNHS; SchAde; SctActv; StuCncl; StuGov; College; Law.

CONNOR, Carolyn; Chatard HS; Indianapolis, IN; 14/192 VPJrCls; HonRl; NHS; Quill&Scroll; SchMus; SecStuCncl; RptrYrbk; CchngActv; IMSpt; Purdue University; Mathematics.

CONNOR, David M; Illinois Valley Central HS; Chillicothe, IL; 16/230 ChrhWkr; HonRl; SctActv; Univ Of Illinois; Mechanical Engineer.

CONNOR, Elizabeth M; Good Counsel HS; Chicago, IL; Chrs; HonRl; JA; NHS; SchMus; SchPpr; GerCl; College; Fine Arts.

CONNOR, Gerald A; Hillsboro HS; Hillsboro, IL; HonRl; JrNHS; NatlMeritFnl; NatlMeritCmnd; 4-H; GerCl; SciCl; Wrstlng; U Of Il; Busi Admin.

CONNOR, Julie A; Jennings Sr HS; St Louis, MO; Chr; HonRl; HospAde; NHS; PresNatlThespSoc;

SchMus; SchPl; SctActv; SecFHA; GAA; Cntrl Missouri St Univ; Occup Therapy.

CONNOR, Mary K; St Francis Academy; Joliet, IL; 32/178 HonRl; HospAde; LitMag; StuCncl; RptrYrbk; EdYrBk; Yrbk; College; Accountant.

CONNOR, Scott A; Lanse HS; L Anse, MI; 16/88 HonRl; Glf; Mich Tech U; Dentist.

CONNORS, Carla J; Vermillion HS; Vermillion, SD; 1/125 SecBand; PresChrs; HonRl; NHS; NatlMeritSF; SecStuCncl; EdYrBk; SecMthCl; LetterTennis; CaptChrldr; DARAwd; VoiceDemAwd; Univ; Music.

CONNORS, Margaret M; Snider HS; Fort Wayne, IN; 4/515 HonRl; HospAde; Quill&Scroll; Yrbk; CivCl; SecSpnCl; ChmbCommrsAwd; Purdue Univ; Mathematics.

CONOPEOTIS, Theodora M; North Chicago HS; No Chicago, IL; 7/250 Band; ChrhWkr; HonRl; NHS; SchPl; EdYrBk; Chrldr; College; Professional.

CONOVER, Amy; Anderson Senior HS; Anderson, IN; CmntyWkr; HonRl; PolWkr; StuGov; TchrAde; FrCl; Ball State Univ; Social Work.

CONOVER, Blake R; Holstein Comm HS; Holstein, IA; 8/36 SecFrshCls; Chr; Chrs; ChrhWkr; HonRl; Mdrgl; SchPl; 4-H; LetterFtbl; LetterWrstlng; 4-HAwd; Isu; Animal Science.

CONRAADS, Yvonne E; Milbank HS; Twin Brooks, SD; TrsSophCls; TrsJrCls; Band; Chrs; DrmMjrt; HonRl; Mdrgl; SchMus; SchPl; YthFlsp; College; Music.

CONRAD, Annette L; South Barber HS; Kiowa, KS; 4/38 SecTrsFrshCls; Band; CncrtBnd; PepBnd; RptrYrbk; RptrSchPpr; VPFHA; PresFNA; TreasPpCl; PPFtbl; College.

CONRAD, Bob; Hoisington Rural HS; Hoisington, KS; Chr; HonRl; FFA; SciCl; Bsbl; Bsktbl; Ftbl; Trk; IMSpt; Benton County Jr College; Stockman.

CONRAD, Brenda J; Marquette HS; Hillsboro, IA; 9/49 PresJrCls; Chr; HonRl; NHS; StuCncl; 4-H; PpCl; Trk; Chrldr; 4-HAwd; Iowa U Iowa City; Pharmacy.

CONRAD, Debbie J; Bloomer Senior HS; Cornell, WI; SchAde; TchrAde; Vocational School; Health Occupation.

CONRAD, Jack G; St Joseph HS; Kenosha, WI; 5/140 ChrhWkr; CmntyWkr; HonRl; NHS; SctActv; StuCncl; StuGov; Ftbl; IMSpt; Marquette Univ; Electrical Engineering.

CONRAD, Jacob B; Marquette HS; Wauwatosa, WI; LitMag; ModUN; NHS; NatlMeritSF; PolWkr; College.

CONRAD, Kathy; Sidney St Pats HS; Sidney, NE; SecSophCls; SecJrCls; Chrs; CmntyWkr; HonRl; HospAde; NHS; SchPl; Chrldr;.

CONRAD, Mark; Manual HS; Peoria, IL; 4/367 Band; HonRl; NHS; NatlMeritCmnd; PolWkr; SchPl; SchPpr; LetterTrk; AmLegAwd; RotaryAwd; Mac Murray; Law.

CONRAD, Michael G; Memorial Sr HS; Joplin, MO; LetterDrlTm; HonRl; JrNHS; LitMag; ROTC; MthCl; College; Illustrator.

CONRAD, Randolph F; Tri County Comm HS; Rose Hill, IA; VPFrshCls; PresSophCls; PresJrCls; Band; Chrs; HonRl; MrchBnd; SchMus; Ftbl; Trk;.

CONRAD, Robin R; St Johns HS; St Johns, MI; 26/325 Chr; Chrs; ChrhWkr; HonRl; JA; NatlMeritCmnd; SchMus; College; Medical Technology.

CONRAD, Thomas M; Osawatomie HS; Osawatomie, KS; FrCl; LetterBsktbl; LetterFtbl; LetterTrk; College.

CONRAD, Walter R; Glenwood Community HS; Glenwood, IA; LbryAde; SchPl; YthFlsp; OptClAwd; University; Broadcasting.

CONRAD, Winona; Hoisington HS; Hoisington, KS; Band; CncrtBnd; HonRl; MrchBnd; PepBnd; SchPl; TchrAde; PpCl; MasAwd; College; Registered Nurse.

CONRADY, Janet S; Northwestern HS; Hettick, IL; 5/53 CmntyWkr; HonRl; PresLbryAde; NatlMeritCmnd; SchPl; Yrbk; Pres4-H; SecFTA; DARAwd; 4-HAwd; Valparaiso Univ; Education.

CONROY, Donna M; Wheaton HS; Dumont, MN; 11/87 CncrtBnd; HonRl; HospAde; MrchBnd; PepBnd; FHA; SpnCl; LetterBsktbl; Chrldr; GAA; U Of Mn; Home & Family Services.

CONROY, Kelley L; Port Huron HS; Port Huron, MI; Band; CncrtBnd; HonRl; MrchBnd; PepBnd; TchrAde; College; Psychologist.

CONROY, Michael L; St Ann HS; Oconto, NE; VPSrCls; HonRl; RptrYrbk; 4-H; Ftbl; Trk; 4-HAwd; College.

CONROY, William F; Brother Rice HS; Oak Lawn, IL; ChrhWkr; HonRl; SctActv; LetterSwmmng; IMSpt; Us Air Force Academy; Officer.

CONSIDINE, Timothy P; Joliet Catholic HS; Romeoville, IL; 35/175 CmntyWkr; HonRl; NHS; Illinois State Univ; Law.

CONSIGLIO, Angelo; De La Salle Inst; Chicago, IL; 1/255 SecJrCls; SecSrCls; HonRl; NHS; StuCncl; StuGov; RptrSchPpr; SptEdSchPpr; Bsbl; Ill Benedictine Coll; Physician.

CONSIGLIO, Angelo R; De La Salle HS; Chicago, IL; 1/250 HstFrshCls; VPSophCls; SecJrCls; SecSrCls; HonRl; NHS; StuCncl; SptEdSchPpr; LetterBsbl; Ill Benedictine Col; Physician.

CONSOLINO, Julia F; Wateruliet HS; Wateruliet, MI; HonRl; HospAde; NHS; 4-H; SpnCl; Michigan State Univ; Veterinarian.

CONSOLO, Linda S; Marillac HS; Chicago, IL; TrsSophCls; SecSrCls; NHS; NatlMeritSF; OffAde; PolWkr; SchPl; StuCncl; StuGov; TchrAde; College; Law Phychology.

CONSTANCE, Chris; South HS; Sheboygan, WI; 16/496 ALBoysSt; CmntyWkr; NHS; PresOrch; TreasSctActv; SecStuGov; LionAwd; Marquette U; Physician.

CONSTANS, Patricia; Southwest HS; Green Bay, WI; 92;420 CncrtBnd; HonRl; MrchBnd; PepBnd; SchMus; FBLA; LatCl; PpCl; Glf; GAA; Uw Madison;physical Therapy.

CONSTANT, Steven M; Godwin Heights HS; Wyoming, MI; 2/186 HonRl; NHS; LatCl; PpCl; LetterBsbl; Grand Rapids Junior College; Medicine.

CONSTANTINE, Sandra; University HS; Milwaukee, WI; CmntyWkr; HonRl; HospAde; NatlMeritFnl; StuGov; RptrYrbk; SchPpr; Harvard.

CONSTANTZ, Elizabeth G; Northwest HS; House Springs, MO; 26/389 SecFrshCls; SecJrCls; PresSrCls; DrlTm; NHS; StuCncl; RptrSchPpr; PpCl; IMSpt; College; Professional.

CONTENTO, Elise M; Evergreen Park HS; Evergreen Park, IL; 1/450 HonRl; JrNHS; NHS; OffAde; MthCl; PpCl; Trk; Chrldr; GAA; University Of Illinois; Dance.

CONTRERAS, Magda D; Rosarian Academy; Addison, IL; ChrhWkr; HonRl; LbryAde; NatlCathMusEdAsoc; NatlFornLg; SchMus; SchPl; StuCncl; FDA; Univ Of Illinois; Medicine.

CONTRO, Antonia J; Galesburg HS; Galesburg, IL; SecJrCls; HonRl; NHS; StuCncl; SchPpr; FrCl; University.

CONVEISE, Diane E; Larned HS; Garfield, KS; SecTrsFrshCls; Band; Chrs; CncrtBnd; HonRl; Orch; PepBnd; RptrSchPpr; Trk; Chrldr; Ks Univ; Music Teacher Or Dancer.

CONVERSE, Luretta L; Council Grove HS; Council Grove, KS; FBLA; TreasFHA; Nurses Training School; Nurse.

CONVERSE, Peter E; Ann Arbor Pioneer HS; Ann Arbor, MI; NatlMeritSF; PolWkr; Univ Of Wisc; Economics.

CONVIS, Margaret J; Fairbury Cropsey HS; Fairbury, IL; 47/98 TreasBand; CncrtBnd; HonRl; MrchBnd; PepBnd; SchPl; RptrYrbk; SecSophCls; MthCl; Trk; Illinois Central College; Radiologic Tech.

CONWAY, Cathy R; Leeds Public HS; Leeds, ND; TrsSophCls; Band; Chr; HonRl; MrchBnd; 4-H; FHA; LetterBsktbl; LetterTrk; LetterChrldr; College; Music.

CONWAY, Christopher J; Cretin HS; St Paul, MN; VPSophCls; PresJrCls; HonRl; ROTC; StuCncl; StuGov; RptrSchPpr; Trk; Wrstlng; IMSpt; Coll Forestry; Environmental Sciences.

CONWAY, David B; Center Sr HS; Kansas City, MO; 2/421 CncrtBnd; HonRl; MrchBnd; NHS; Orch; SchMus; SctActv; KeyCl; GerCl; Univ; Physical Science.

CONWAY, Debra J; Mallard Community HS; Mallard, IA; 5/33 Chrs; DrlTm; HonRl; NatlMeritCmnd; SchPl; Twrl; RptrYrbk; Bsktbl; LetterTrk; IMSpt; College; Accounting.

CONWAY, Diane; Albia Comm HS; Albia, IA; 20/164 HonRl; FHA; GAA;.

CONWAY, Jill M; Elizabeth Seton HS; Tinley Park, IL; HonRl; NHS; NatlMeritCmnd; SchMus; SchPl; SecStuCncl; RptrYrbk; RptrSchPpr; FrCl; Univ Of Notre Dame; Accounting.

CONWAY, Johnita F; Bunker HS; Bunker, MO; 2/20 SecJrCls; HonRl; LbryAde; OffAde; SchPl; StuCncl; FHA; PpCl; CaptChrldr;.

CONWAY, Kimberly K; Leeds HS; Leeds, ND; Band; Chr; ChrhWkr; CncrtBnd; HonRl; SchPl; RptrYrbk; 4-H; Bsktbl; Trk; Chrldr; College; Phy Ed.

CONWAY, Mary A; Hoxie HS; Hoxie, KS; 1/70 Chrs; DrlTm; HonRl; OffAde; SchPl; 4-H; FHA; FrCl; Kansas St Univ; Journalism.

CONWAY, Mary T; Parker Senior HS; Janesville, WI; 19/423 HonRl; NHS; NatlMeritCmnd; VPQuill&Scroll; RptrYrbk; SchPpr; PresFrCl; EdAwd; LionAwd; College; Journalism.

CONWAY, Patrick W; Leo HS; Chicago, IL; 39/200 HonRl; NHS; Quill&Scroll; StuCncl; RptrYrbk; Yrbk; RptrSchPpr; SchPpr; Univ Of Illinois; Journalism.

CONWAY, Richard A; North West HS; House Springs, MO; Chr; Chrs; ChrhWkr; CmntyWkr; HonRl; NHS; SchMus; YthFlsp; RptrSchPpr; PpCl; LetterBsktbl; College; Architecture.

CONWAY, Ronald; Pecatonica HS; Hollandale, WI; HonRl; NatlFornLg; College; Architectural.

CONWAY, Rosalie; Kee HS; Harpers Ferry, IA; 12/53 ChrhWkr; HonRl; NHS; SchPl; StuCncl; Yrbk; 4-H; PpCl; 4-HAwd; Work.

CONWAY, Sharon A; Mother Of Sorrows HS; Chicago, IL; VPSrCls; HonRl; NHS; SchPl; StuGov;.

CONWAY, Shawn C; Aledo HS; Reynolds, IL; 3/110 PresSophCls; AFS; ChrhWkr; CmntyWkr; HonRl; IntrClCncl; NHS; NatlMeritCmnd; StuCncl; StuGov; EdSchPpr; LetterFtbl; LetterTrk; Junior College; Professional.

CONWAY, Tamara M; Monroe HS; Monroe, WI; HonRl; StuGov; Yrbk; Tech College; Marketing.

COOGAN, Sheila; Spalding Acad; Peoria, IL; 8/92 HonRl; NHS; NatlMeritCmnd; SchPl; EdYrBk;.

COOK, Alan D; Madison HS; Madison Heights, MI; 14/240 CncrtBnd; HonRl; NHS; NatlThespSoc; PolWkr; SchPl; RptrYrbk; RptrSchPpr; TreasSpnCl; DanFAwd; Wayne State Univ; Theatre.

COOK, Brenda J; Stonington HS; Stonington, IL; 8/33 HstJrCls; PresBand; Chrs; ChrhWkr; CncrtBnd; HonRl; HospAde; Mdrgl; MrchBnd; OffAde; Eastern Ill Univ; Music Education.

COOK, Brian R; Dupo HS; Dupo, IL; TrsFrshCls; Aud/Vis; HonRl; PepBnd; StuCncl; YthFlsp; SciCl; Bsbl; Bsktbl; Ftbl; College; Professional.

COOK, Bruce D; Highland HS; Anderson, IN; 3/251 PresFrshCls; TrsSophCls; CtyCnl; HonRl; NHS; StuCncl; RptrYrbk; Bsktbl; Glf; College; Professional.

COOK, Carie E; Tomahawk HS; Tomahawk, WI; Band; CncrtBnd; MrchBnd; PepBnd; SctActv; Twrl; PpCl; Trk; Chrldr; GAA; College; Professional.

COOK, Cheryl L; Joliet West HS; Joliet, IL; Chr; HonRl; Mdrgl; StuCncl; FrCl; Chrldr; Jr High Music Teacher.

COOK, Christopher C; Quincy HS; Quincy, IL; 124/655 Chr; CncrtBnd; DrmMjrt; MrchBnd; Orch; FrCl; Univ Of Missouri.

COOK, Clifford L; Bergland Comm HS; Merriweather, MI; HonRl; NatlSciFnd; StuGov; LetterBsbl; LetterBsktbl; LetterTrk; Northland College; Computer Programing.

COOK, Colette M; Lincoln Community HS; Mechanicsville, IA; ChrhWkr; HonRl; JrNHS; StuCncl; Yrbk; SchPpr; LetterBsbl; Bsktbl; LetterTrk; CchngActv; Univ; Voc.

COOK, Crandle; Centerville HS; Centerville, IN; HonRl; YthFlsp; Bsbl; Bsktbl; Ftbl; College; Professional.

COOK, David; Carrollton HS; Wakenda, MO; 12/104 HonRl; NHS; TchrAde; Bsbl; Central Mo St Univ; Law Enforcement.

COOK, David B; East HS; Des Moines, IA; 2/500 ALBoysSt; CncrtBnd; HonRl; NatlFornLg; SciCl; LetterTennis; Air Force Academy; Aeronautics.

COOK, David L; Brimfield HS; Brimfield, IL; 2/52 Aud/Vis; HonRl; NHS; SchPl; SctActv; Trk; Univ; Engineer.

COOK, Debra; Gothenburg Public HS; Gothenburg, NE; 2/84 ChrhWkr; CncrtBnd; HonRl; NHS; PepBnd; TchrAde; 4-H; PpCl; AmLegAwd; Kearney State; Elem Education.

COOK, Debra R; Beal City HS; Mt Pleasant, MI; 2/52 SecSrCls; Band; ChrhWkr; HonRl; NHS; SchPl; SpnCl; Bsktbl; Tennis; Trk; Alma College; Teacher.

COOK, Dennis L; Flora HS; Rinard, IL; 6/138 ChrhWkr; HonRl; VPNHS; YthFlsp; VPFFA; FHA; VPSciCl; College; Farming.

COOK, Donald D; Du Quoin HS; Du Quoin, IL; SchPl; StuCncl; RptrYrbk; RptrSchPpr; PpCl; Southern Illinois Univ; Journalism.

COOK, Eugene D; East Side HS; Butler, IN; ChrhWkr; CmntyWkr; HonRl; YthFlsp; FrCl; Bsktbl; LetterFtbl; LetterTrk; Wrstlng; College; Teacher.

COOK, Gene D; Arcadia Valley HS; Arcadia, MO; Band; CncrtBnd; HonRl; MrchBnd; NHS; PolWkr; VPFBLA; FTA; PpCl; Bsbl; Missouri Univ; Business Admin.

COOK, Gloria S; Chesaning Union HS; Burt, MI; 4/248 SecJrCls; Chr; ChrhWkr; HonRl; JrNHS; NHS; GAA; IMSpt; Western Mich Univ; Psychology.

COOK, Jack; Ovid Elsie HS; Ovid, MI; 1/165 Aud/Vis; HonRl; NHS; Glf; AmLegAwd; VoiceDemAwd; Ferris State College; Chemistry.

COOK, James P; Carrington HS; Carrington, ND; VPJrCls; Band; Chr; CncrtBnd; HonRl; MrchBnd; PepBnd; StuCncl; PresFFA; CaptFtbl; LetterTrk; LetterWrstlng; College.

COOK, James W; Sullivan HS; Sullivan, IL; Chr; Chrs; HonRl; Bsktbl;.

COOK, Jeffrey A; Corning HS; Corning, IA; 8/86 ALBoysSt; Chrs; CmntyWkr; HonRl; NHS; NatlThespSoc; SchMus; SchPl; LetterFtbl; Glf; Simpson College; Business.

COOK, Jeffrey A; Sidney HS; Sidney, NE; HonRl; JrNHS; NHS; PolWkr; SctActv; LetterGlf; Univ; Optometrist.

COOK, Joellen; Mercy HS; Omaha, NE; CAP; OffAde; Sdlty; TchrAde; SchPpr; MthCl; Bsbl; Univ Of Ne At Omaha; Math Teacher.

COOK, Karen Z; Glendale HS; Springfield, MO; AFS; HospAde; FHA; FrCl; OptClAwd; Nursing.

COOK, Kathryn S; Dixon HS; Dixon, IL; 1/350 CncrtBnd; NHS; NatlThespSoc; StuCncl; SchPpr; LetterBsktbl; LetterTrk; PresGAA; Univ.

COOK, Kay A; Brown City Comm HS; Melvin, MI; Chr; ChrhWkr; HonRl; LbryAde; YthFlsp; 4-H; College; Library Work.

COOK, Kevin B; Warren Central HS; Indianapolis, IN; 10/800 HonRl; PresNatlFornLg; NHS; NatlMeritSF; NatlThespSoc; PolWkr; StuGov; LetterBsbl; LetterGlf; LetterTennis; Univ; Theater.

COOK, Kevin G; High School; Pewamo, MI; HonRl; SchMus; SchPl; StuGov; RptrYrbk; RptrSchPpr; Bsktbl; Ftbl; Lansing Comm College; Social Work.

COOK, Kurt I; Granton HS; Granton, WI; SecFrshCls; Band; CncrtBnd; HonRl; MrchBnd; PepBnd; University; Agriculture.

COOK, Laurel D; Adams Central HS; Juniata, NE; 1/54 Band; HonRl; JrNHS; NHS; PepBnd; SchMus; SchPl; Yrbk; SchPpr; Trk; Univ Of Ne; Art Major.

COOK, Laurie; Frankfort HS; Frankfort, MI; 67 TrsSophCls; ChrhWkr; CmntyWkr; HonRl; OffAde; SchAde; StuCncl; YthFlsp; CaptBsktbl; CaptTrk; Centralmichiganuniversity;phyedteaching.

COOK, Linda D; New Providence Comm HS; New Providence, IA; 1/7 PresSophCls; ChrhWkr; HonRl; SchPl; StuCncl; YthFlsp; EdYrBk; 4-H; Bsktbl; Chrldr; BttyCrckrAwd; Iowa State Univ; Elem Education.

COOK, Madonna L; Gibault Cath HS; Red Bud, IL; Chrs; HonRl; OffAde; SchPl; TchrAde;.

COOK, Maria V; St Patricks HS; Portland, MI; PresJrCls; HonRl; LbryAde; NHS; TchrAde; EdYrBk; PPFtbl; PresAwd; CitAwd; Correspondence School; Arts.

COOK, Marie E; Derham Hall HS; St Paul, MN; CmntyWkr; HospAde; NHS; StuCncl; SchPpr; FrCl; St Catherines Clg; Nursing.

COOK, Marilyn M; Springville Comm HS; Springville, IA; 2/60 VPSophCls; Chr; HonRl; NHS; SchPl; YthFlsp; Bsktbl; LetterTrk; Chrldr; CitAwd; Elem Ed.

COOK, Marion H; Martinsville HS; Martinsville, IL; Chrs; CncrtBnd; HonRl; MrchBnd; SchMus; RptrYrbk; 4-H; FBLA; SciCl; College; Pharmacist.

COOK, Mary A; De Witt HS; De Witt, MI; 22/128 TrsSophCls; HonRl; NatlThespSoc; SchMus; SchPl; FrCl; PpCl; Chrldr; PPFtbl; Lansing Comm Coll; Social Work.

COOK, Michael J; College HS; Cape Girardeau, MO; 6/36 PresSophCls; NHS; StuCncl; MthCl; PpCl; LetterBsktbl; Univ; Professional.

COOK, Paul W; Viroqua HS; Viroqua, WI; 17/121 Band; CncrtBnd; HonRl; MrchBnd; PepBnd; Univf Dentistry.

COOK, Phyllis I; Adrian HS; Adrian, MI; 39/370 Band; ChrhWkr; CncrtBnd; MrchBnd; NHS; SchMus; YthFlsp; Malone College; Education.

COOK, Raymond A; A E Stevenson HS; Long Grove, IL; 14/235 Band; CncrtBnd; HonRl; MrchBnd; NHS; Orch; PepBnd; RedCrAde; SchMus; SchPl; StuCncl; Univ Of Illinois; Biochemistry.

COOK, Rhonda; Meadow Heights HS; Lutesville, MO; 4/51 CmntyWkr; HonRl; FHA; PpCl; SciCl; Chrldr; Semo College; Business Education.

COOK, Ricky L; Meadow Heights HS; Lutesville, MO; ChrhWkr; HonRl; Business School; Business.

COOK, Robert F; Roseville Unit HS; Roseville, IL; Band; HonRl; MrchBnd; PepBnd; Sdlty; YthFlsp; SpnCl; Ftbl; LetterTrk; Wrstlng; Jr College; Business Adm.

COOK, Roger A; Lincoln Way HS; Manhattan, IL; 120/560 HonRl; OffAde; SchAde; StuGov; TchrAde; MthCl; LetterTrk; U Of W Ill; Acctng.

COOK, Steve; Roosevelt HS; Gary, IN; HonRl; NHS; OffAde; TchrAde; IMSpt; In St Univ; Mathematics.

COOK, Susan V; Hillsdale HS; Hillsdale, MI; HonRl; NHS; Orch; SchPl; TchrAde; RptrSchPpr; SchPpr; 4-H; 4-HAwd; Olivet College; Music Teacher.

COOK, Terri; Grosse Ile HS; Grosse Ile, MI; CmntyWkr; HospAde; JA; RedCrAde; StuGov; TchrAde; YthLg; CivCl; SpnCl; College; Lawyer.

COOK, Terri S; Glenwood HS; Springfield, IL; SecChr; ChrhWkr; HonRl; JrNHS; SecNHS; NatlThespSoc; SchMus; SchPl; StuCncl; TchrAde;.

COOK, Thomas; Ionia HS; Ionia, MI; 30/229 HonRl; Lake Superior State; Political Science.

COOK, Timothy; Cherry Hill HS; Portage, MI; 8/325 ALBoysSt; HonRl; NHS; NatlMeritCmnd; NatlMeritSF; PolWkr; FrCl; IMSpt; University; Pre Law.

COOK, Tommy J; Holbomc HS; Holcomb, MO; TrsFrshCls; CmntyWkr; HonRl; SchPl; StuGov; TchrAde; PpCl; Bsbl; Bsktbl; Farming.

COOK, William L; Gladstone Area HS; Gladstone, MI; HonRl; NHS; RptrSchPpr; College; Commercial Art.

COOK, William R; Northwest HS; Cedar Hills, MO; Chr; HonRl; LitMag; NHS; SciCl; CaptFtbl; College; Doctoral Work In Math.

COOKE, Dalee; Westville HS; Westville, IL; HonRl; OffAde; SctActv; Twrl; Yrbk; SchPpr; PpCl; GAA; Danville Jr College;.

COOKE, Virginia T; Queen Of Peace HS; Chicago, IL; Chrs; CmntyWkr; IntrClCncl; NHS; SchAde; SchPl; StuCncl; StuGov; TchrAde; Bsbl; Bsktbl; GAA; IMSpt; Northeastern University.

COOKE, William D; Haven 'S; Haven, KS; ALBoysSt; Chr; ChrhWkr; HonRl; SchMus; StuCncl; TchrAde; PresFrCl; LetterFtbl; LetterWrstlng; College Wyo; Wildlife Management.

COOKSEY, Darrell W; Savannah Senior HS; St Joseph, MO; Chr; Mdrgl; SchMus; SctActv; StuCncl; Bsktbl; LetterFtbl; LetterTrk; Wrstlng; GodCntryAwd; College; Electioncal Eng.

COOKSEY, John D; Wheatland HS; Park, KS; ChrhWkr; SchPl; Bsktbl; LetterTrk; Trade Sch; Vocation.

COOKSEY, Tambi L; L & M HS; Lyons, IN; 1/35 TrsSrCls; ChrhWkr; TreasDrlTm; HonRl; RptrYrbk; FHA; PpCl; Bsbl; Bsktbl; GAA; Vocational Schl; Med Assistant.

COOLEY, Christine Z; Morrill HS; Morrill, NE; NHS; SecNatlThespSoc; SchPl; StuGov; Twrl; PresPpCl; SecGAA; PPFtbl; College; Mathematics.

COOLEY, Debra E; Hillsboro HS; Hillsboro, IL; 4/179 CmntyWkr; HonRl; NatlMeritCmnd; RptrYrbk; RptrSchPpr; SpnCl; Univ Of Il; Civil Engineering.

COOLEY, Holland S; Litchfield HS; Litchfield, MI; 3/55 TrsSophCls; HonRl; SchPl; StuCncl; StuGov; TchrAde; LatCl; Ftbl; Trk; CchngActv; Adrian College; Physics.

COOLEY, Keith; Southeast Of Saline HS; Gypsum, KS; 6/51 VPFrshCls; Univ;forestry.

COOLEY, Laura R; Glenwood HS; Lowry, MN;

TchrAde; FTA; GerCl; LetterBsktbl; LetterTrk; CchngActv; GAA; Cllege; Peace Corps.

COOLEY, Michael G; Corning Comm HS; Mt Etna, IA; ChrhWkr; CncrtBnd; HonRl; SancSoc; Pres4-H; Bsbl; Bsktbl; Ftbl; 4-HAwd; Univ; Agric.

COOLEY, Sandra J; Centralia HS; Centralia, IL; 7/360 Band; CncrtBnd; DrmMjrt; HonRl; JrNHS; MrchBnd; NHS; PepBnd; SchMus; VPFrCl;.

COOLEY, Sheryl A; Mahomet Seymour HS; Seymour, IL; Band; ChrhWkr; CncrtBnd; HonRl; MrchBnd; SchMus; FTA; SpnCl; GAA; PPFtbl; Univ; Elementary Teacher.

COOLICH, Cindy L; Northern HS; Flint, MI; PolWkr; SpnCl; Univ Of Mi Flint; Biology Or Ecology.

COOLIDGE, Kevin L; Rantoul Township HS; Rantoul, IL; Aud/Vis; ChrhWkr; HonRl; NHS; StuCncl; TchrAde; RptrYrbk; LatCl; CitAwd; University Of Illinois; Physics.

COOLIDGE, Sarah R; West HS; Iowa City, IA; 7/286 HonRl; JrNHS; LitMag; NatlFornLg; FrCl; U Of Iowa; Zoology.

COOMBS, Carol M; Bolingbrook HS; Bolingbrook, IL; 11/219 HonRl; NHS; OffAde; SecStuGov; RptrYrbk; Univ; Business Adm.

COOMES, Stephen; Avon HS; Plainfield, IN; 1/159 ALBoysSt; ChrhWkr; HonRl; FrCl; SciCl; Wabash College; Dentistry.

COOMES, Thomas R; Avon HS; Plainfield, IN; PresSrCls; ALBoysSt; Aud/Vis; HonRl; VPNHS; StuCncl; Yrbk; FrCl; LetterGlf; Univ; Lawyer.

COON, Cynthia A; Jackson Co Western HS; Jackson, MI; SecSophCls; PresJrCls; CncrtBnd; HonRl; OffAde; SchMus; StuCncl; YthFlsp; SpnCl; GAA; College.

COON, Duane E; East Greene HS; Grand Jct, IA; 4/43 Band; Chr; CncrtBnd; HonRl; NHS; StuCncl; Yrbk; SchPpr; 4-H; VPFFA; Iowa State Univ; Engineering.

COON, Gary J; Charleston HS; Charleston, MO; VPFrshCls; Band; Chrs; HonRl; Mdrgl; NHS; SchMus; SchPl; SctActv; EdSchPpr; Univ Of Tennessee; Communications.

COON, Lisa A; North HS; Wichita, KS; ChrhWkr; HonRl; HospAde; OffAde; RptrSchPpr; LatCl; SpnCl; PpCl; University; Nursing.

COON, Robin J; Hillsdale HS; Hillsdale, MI; ALAGirlsSt; Chr; Chrl; Chrs; ChrhWkr; CmntyWkr; HonRl; HospAde; JrNHS; College; Professional.

COON, Tammy K; Alba Public HS; Alba, MI; VPSophCls; TrsJrCls; Chrs; HonRl; LbryAde; SctActv; TchrAde; YthFlsp; 4-H; Bsktbl; College; Teacher.

COONCE, Trent A; South Knox HS; Monroe City, IN; 18/130 Band; ChrhWkr; CncrtBnd; HonRl; MrchBnd; PepBnd; 4-H;.

COONEY, Dale S; Wheeling HS; Prospect Hts, IL; 69/459 HonRl; NHS; SciCl; LetterGlf; IMSpt; College; Lawyer.

COONEY, Gregory C; Montgomery HS; Montgomery, MN; HonRl; NHS; StuCncl; Bsbl; Trk; Northwest Tech Inst Inc; Drafting & Enginee.

COONEY, James P; New Trier HS; Wilmette, IL; 110/887 NatlFornLg; NatlMeritCmnd; PolWkr; StuCncl; StuGov; College; Teaching.

COONEY, John A; La Salle HS; Cedar Rapids, IA; 4/156 HonRl; ModUN; NHS; StuGov; LetterFtbl; LetterTrk; Notre Dame; Law.

COONEY, Maureen C; Marian HS; Omaha, NE; 21/170 PresFrshCls; ALAGirlsSt; Chr; SecNatlFornLg; NHS; NatlThespSoc; SecStuCncl; VPAmLegAwd; VoiceDemAwd; College; Government.

COONEY, Michael J; Homestead HS; Mequon, WI; HonRl; NatlFornLg; Ftbl; Trk; U Of Wisc; Pre Law.

COONEY, William B; St Agatha HS; Detroit, MI; PresJrCls; Band; Chr; SchPl; RptrYrbk; Yrbk; SpnCl; Trade School; Disc Jockey.

COONLEY, Colleen A; Belvidere HS; Belvidere, IL; 30/348 Chrs; FrCl; PpCl; College; Legal Secretary.

COONROD, Chet L; Carrollton HS; Carrollton, IL; 4/90 VPFrshCls; Band; Chrs; CncrtBnd; HonRl; MrchBnd; NHS; NatlMeritCmnd; PepBnd; SchPl; Ill College; Journalism.

COONROD, Doris L; Greenfield HS; Greenfield, IL; 23/58 Chrs; HonRl; SchMus; Yrbk; PpCl; Chrldr; GAA; Beauty School; Beautician.

COONS, Robin J; Collinsville Sr HS; Collinsville, IL; HonRl; NHS; Southern Illinois Univ; Psychologist.

COOPER, Andrea M; Murray Wright HS; Detroit, MI; HonRl; Univ Of Michigan State; Engineering.

COOPER, Arnold R; Alb HS; Alerton, IL; HonRl; Bsktbl; Trk;.

COOPER, Brian K; Buchanan HS; Buchanan, MI; ALBoysSt; CmntyWkr; JA; OffAde; SchAde; SctActv; TchrAde; AmLegAwd; JAAwd; Coll; Lawyer.

COOPER, Calvin C; Lyons Twp HS; Lagrange, IL; Aud/Vis; HonRl; NatlMeritCmnd; NatlThespSoc; OffAde; Quill&Scroll; SchMus; SchPl; RptrSchPpr; College; Lawyer.

COOPER, Carol M; Lyons Twp HS; Western Springs, IL; Chr; HonRl; LitMag; NHS; SchMus; RptrSchPpr; 4-H; Tennis; GAA; 4-HAwd; U Of Wi; Med.

COOPER, Christine; Winchester HS; Winchester, IL; 14/77 ChrhWkr; CmntyWkr; HonRl; LbryAde; SchPl; Yrbk; FHA; FrCl; AmLegAwd; DARAwd; School Of Nursing; Registered Nurse.

COOPER, Claudia A; Randolph Southern HS; Lynn, IN; 8/60 HonRl; TchrAde; 4-H; College; Teacher.

COOPER, Connie L; Bladen Public HS; Bladen, NE; 5/11 Band; Chr; Chrl; Chrs; CncrtBnd; HonRl; JA; Mdrgl; MrchBnd; PepBnd; LetterTrk; Chrldr; GAA; IMSpt; Kearney St College; Music.

COOPER, Curtis L; Dayton Community HS; Dayton, IA; SecFrshCls; TrsSophCls; SchPl; StuCncl; IMSpt; AmLegAwd; Trade School; Vocation.

COOPER, Cynthia A; Lewistown HS; Lewistown, IL; 2/87 HonRl; NHS; SchPl; Yrbk; FTA; SpnCl; PpCl; AmLegAwd; Western Ill Univ; Speech Pathology.

COOPER, Daniel R; Tippecanoe Valley HS; Mentone, IN; 8/145 Aud/Vis; HonRl; NHS; SchPl; StuCncl; FTA; MthCl; PpCl; SciCl; LetterGlf; College; Law.

COOPER, David; Divernon HS; Divernon, IL; 10/28 VPFrshCls; VPSophCls; PresJrCls; HonRl; StuGov; SciCl; Bsktbl; College; Prof.

COOPER, David; Milwaukee Lutheran HS; Hartford, WI; NHS; YthFlsp; 4-H; Ftbl; Tennis; IMSpt; 4-HAwd; Coll; Sci.

COOPER, David R; Doniphan HS; Doniphan, MO; VPFrshCls; PresSophCls; Band; ChrhWkr; CncrtBnd; MrchBnd; PepBnd; StuCncl; College; Medicine.

COOPER, Debra L; East Kentwood HS; Kentwood, MI; Band; HonRl; College; Social Science.

COOPER, Erin M; Okawville HS; Okawville, IL; SecJrCls; Band; CncrtBnd; HonRl; StuCncl; YthFlsp; 4-H; PpCl; DanFAwd; Decconess Hosp; Nursing.

COOPER, Gary; Chetopa HS; Chetopa, KS; PresFrshCls; Band; Chrs; ChrhWkr; HonRl; MrchBnd; StuCncl; Bsktbl; Ftbl; Trk; Mo S State Coll; Archi Drafting.

COOPER, Glenna S; Sargent Public HS; Sargent, NE; PresFrshCls; Band; Chr; Chrs; HonRl; NHS; PepBnd; StuCncl; PpCl; Chrldr; College.

COOPER, Hope; Beaumont HS; St Louis, MO; PresFrshCls; SecTrsJrCls; Band; ChrhWkr; JA; TchrAde; PpCl; JAAwd; MasAwd; CitAwd; Col; Law.

COOPER, Janet L; Chase County HS; Emporia, KS; 9/57 Chrs; ChrhWkr; CmntyWkr; HonRl; LbryAde; ModUN; OffAde; SchAde; Bsktbl; 4-HAwd; Emporia Kansas State; Physical Ed.

COOPER, Jeffery L; Staunton HS; Brazil, IN; HonRl; SctActv; StuCncl; KeyCl; Bsbl; Bsktbl; College.

COOPER, Jeffrey D; Nicholas Senn HS; Evanston, IL; 70/380 EdSchPpr; SptEdSchPpr; LetterBsktbl; LetterFtbl; CaptGlf; Wrstlng; Loyola University; Journalism.

COOPER, Jeffrey M; Richmond Sr HS; Richmond, IN; 42/800 ChrhWkr; HonRl; NHS; YthLg; SchPpr; Bsktbl; Purdue Or Rose Hulman Tech; Science Math En.

COOPER, Joy E; New Lothrop HS; New Lothrop, MI; 1/81 SecJrCls; NHS; OffAde; PepBnd; SchPl; RptrYrbk; FHA; SecSpnCl; Trk; BttyCrckrAwd; Alma College; Business Admin.

COOPER, Judith K; Escanaba Senior HS; Escanaba, MI; 35/383 Band; Chr; ChrhWkr; CncrtBnd; HonRl; MrchBnd; PepBnd; SchMus; SchPl; Yrbk; Western Mich; Psychology.

COOPER, Karl E; Wheaton HS; Wheaton, MO; 1/34 ALBoysSt; HonRl; NHS; SchPl; StuCncl; FFA; CitAwd; U Of Mo; Analytical Chemist.

COOPER, Karyl J; Jefferson City HS; Jefferson City, MO; Aud/Vis; Chr; ChrhWkr; SpnCl; PpCl; Chrldr; PPFtbl; College; Nursing.

COOPER, Lisa J; East Troy HS; East Troy, WI; 8/126 Chr; Chrs; ChrhWkr; HonRl; Mdrgl; NHS; SchPl; SctActv; SpnCl; IMSpt; PPFtbl; Univ Of Wisconsin; Political Science.

COOPER, Lynnae L; Wilmot Union HS; Twin Lakes, WI; DrlTm; HonRl; MrchBnd; NHS; Quill&Scroll; EdYrBk; Yrbk; PpCl; CaptChrldr; GAA; College; Math.

COOPER, Martha M; Liberal R 2 HS; Liberal, MO; Band; Chrs; ChrhWkr; LbryAde; MrchBnd; SchPl; Twrl; FHA; PpCl; College; Vocation.

COOPER, Mary A; Lincoln HS; Vincennes, IN; 1/324 ALAGirlsSt; Band; CncrtBnd; HonRl; MrchBnd; StuCncl; EdSchPpr; FrCl; Tennis; KiwanAwd; Indiana University; Medicine.

COOPER, Michael R; Anderson HS; Anderson, IN; ALBoysSt; CmntyWkr; HonRl; PolWkr; Quill&Scroll; VPStuCncl; YthFlsp; SptEdYrbk; LetterFtbl; LetterWrstlng; Coll; Law & Politics.

COOPER, Mike A; Centennial HS; Beaver Crossing, NE; PresSophCls; VPJrCls; ALBoysSt; Chrs; NHS; SchPl; StuCncl; SciCl; LetterFtbl; LetterTrk; College; Professional.

COOPER, Pamela S; Duchesne HS; St Charles, MO; 10/200 HonRl; SchMus; SchPl; LatCl; Col; Research Asst Biology.

COOPER, Peggy J; Beardstown Senior HS; Beardstown, IL; 21/134 ALAGirlsSt; HonRl; OffAde; RedCrAde; StuCncl; StuGov; Yrbk; 4-H; SpnCl; Chrldr; IMSpt; 4-HAwd; College; Professional.

COOPER, Penny L; Cadillac HS; Cadillac, MI; 11/285 ChrhWkr; HonRl; NatlFornLg; NHS; TreasStuCncl; StuGov; YthFlsp; BttyCrckrAwd; Michigan State Univ; Child Development.

COOPER, Phillip L; Ben Davis HS; Indianapolis, IN; VPBand; CncrtBnd; HonRl; MrchBnd; ModUN; YthFlsp; 4-H; 4-HAwd; University; Band Director.

COOPER, Randall M; Kalamazoo Central HS; Kalamazoo, MI; 12/512 Aud/Vis; ChrhWkr; HonRl; TchrAde; RptrSchPpr; Tennis; Valparaiso Univ; Entomology.

COOPER, Randy D; Mc Donald Cty HS; Rocky Comfort, MO; HonRl; LbryAde; StuCncl; TchrAde; FFA; FTA; SpnCl; Bsbl; Bsktbl; Ftbl; College; Doctor.

COOPER, Reba V; Glasgow HS; Glasgow, MO; PresSrCls; CmntyWkr; HonRl; NHS; EdYrBk; FDA; FSA; BttyCrckrAwd; University; Professional.

COOPER, Rita F; Heritage Hills HS; Dale, IN; 10/148 ALAGirlsSt; CncrtBnd; HonRl; MrchBnd; NHS; PepBnd; RptrYrbk; VPFrCl; PpCl;.

COOPER, Robert G; Lapeer Sr HS; Lapeer, MI; 3/450 LetterTennis; IMSpt; Central Mich Univ; Business Education.

COOPER, Robert J; Loyola Academy; Wilmette, IL; HonRl; LbryAde; NHS; LetterBsbl; LetterBsktbl; LetterFtbl; Univ Of Notre Dame.

COOPER, Robert S; Covington HS; Covington, IN; 17/120 VPFrshCls; VPSophCls; Band; CncrtBnd; HonRl; SchMus; StuCncl; SciCl; LetterBsbl; LetterBsktbl; Coll; Business.

COOPER, Russell L; Central Heights HS; Richmond, KS; VPFrshCls; HonRl; SchPl; StuCncl; StuGov; TchrAde; 4-H; Ftbl; IMSpt; 4-HAwd; Clge; Agribusiness.

COOPER, Scott E; Octavia HS; Colfax, IL; 12/50 ChrhWkr; CmntyWkr; HonRl; SchMus; SchPl; YthFlsp; RptrSchPpr; Ftbl; LetterTrk; LetterWrstlng; Fla Inst Of Tec; Oceanography.

COOPER, Teresa B; Galena HS; Galena, MO; 6/36 VPFrshCls; SecTrsSophCls; HstJrCls; Band; Chrs; CncrtBnd; HonRl; FHA; Chrldr; Trade School; Dental Assistant.

COOPER, Timothy R; Northrop HS; Fort Wayne, IN; 74/568 Aud/Vis; ChrhWkr; HonRl; MrchBnd; NatlMeritSF; Orch; PepBnd; TchrAde; Teen; YthFlsp; Purdue; Physicist Research.

COOPER, Wanda I; Chase County HS; Emporia, KS; Band; Chrs; CncrtBnd; HonRl; IntrClCncl; MrchBnd; PepBnd; 4-H; Bsktbl; 4-HAwd; Farming.

COOPERRIDER, Daniel J; Waterford Mott HS; Pontiac, MI; 14/444 ChrhWkr; CmntyWkr; HonRl; StuCncl; LetterBsbl; LetterBsktbl; LetterFtbl; LetterTrk; Univ Of Mi;.

COOPWOOD, Janet A; Calumet HS; Gary, IN; 10/330 Band; Chr; CncrtBnd; HonRl; HospAde; JrNHS; MrchBnd; NHS; PepBnd; SctActv; YthFlsp; JAAwd; Evansville; Architect.

COOSE, Cathy; Van Far Ri HS; Vandalia, MO; 12/102 HonRl; MrchBnd; NHS; OffAde; Quill&Scroll; StuCncl; Twrl; Yrbk; PpCl; GAA; Coll; Prof.

COOTS, Dennas R; La Porte City HS; Mt Auburn, IA; VPJrCls; ALBoysSt; StuCncl; YthFlsp; LetterBsbl; LetterBsktbl; LetterFtbl; LetterTennis; PresAwd;.

COPE, Barbara; Roxana Hs; Wood River, IL; 25 Chr; HonRl; HospAde; TchrAde; PpCl;.

COPE, Debra R; Yates Center HS; Yates Center, KS; Chr; HonRl; OffAde; TchrAde; 4-H; FHA; PpCl; Trk; Trade School; Airline Hostess.

COPE, Desarae J; Onaway HS; Onaway, MI; SecSrCls; Band; CncrtBnd; DrmMjrt; LbryAde; MrchBnd; Twrl; TreasYthFlsp; RptrYrbk; Chrldr; Coll; Art.

COPE, Pamela A; St Clement HS; Warren, MI; 15/127 HonRl; SctActv; PpCl; CaptChrldr; IMSpt; Macomb College; Accounting.

COPEK, Stephanie J; Fort Zumwalt HS; St Peters, MO; TrsJrCls; SecSrCls; Chrl; HonRl; OffAde; StuCncl; FNA; MthCl; PpCl; Chrldr; College; Nursing.

COPELAND, Debra; North Central HS; Shelburn, IN; 19/120 Band; Chr; Chrs; CncrtBnd; HonRl; LbryAde; MrchBnd; OffAde; PepBnd; GAA; In State Univ; Nursing.

COPELAND, Diana L; Althoff Catholic HS; Fairview Heights, IL; 89/317 HonRl; LbryAde; NHS; FTA; PpCl; College; Accounting.

COPELAND, Gary L; Glasgow HS; Glasgow, MO; HonRl; NHS; 4-H; FFA; DARAwd; 4-HAwd; CitAwd; U Of Mo; Agricultrure.

COPELAND, Nancy R; Logan Rogersville HS; Rogersville, MO; VPFrshCls; Chrs; ChrhWkr; HonRl; OffAde; SchPl; YthFlsp; SptEdSchPpr; VPFHA; LetterBsbl; Business School; Medical Secretary.

COPELAND, Pat G; Edwards County HS; Albion, IL; 7/102 VPFrshCls; HonRl; VPFrCl; LetterBsbl; LetterBsktbl; Coll;accountant.

COPELAND, Peter M; New Trier East HS; Winnetka, IL; 204/850 AFS; CmntyWkr; HonRl; LatCl; SpnCl; Lawrence Univ; Government.

COPELAND, Randal R; North Central HS; Wilson, MI; Aud/Vis; HonRl; HospAde; SctActv; 4-H; Bsktbl; Ftbl; Trk; IMSpt; U Of Mi; Physical Therapy.

COPELAND, Robert; Elk Grove Hs; Elk Grove, IL; 23/505 CncrtBnd; HonRl; MrchBnd; PolWkr; SchMus; StuGov; GerCl; Ftbl; GovHonPrgAwd; JCAwd; College; Business.

COPELAND, Robert C; United Twp HS; Silvis, IL; 61/517 HonRl; Mc Murrey College; Chemistry.

COPELAND, Robin L; Niles Township No HS; Skokie, IL; 77/640 HonRl; HospAde; OffAde; FNA; SpnCl; VPMthCl; Univ Of Illinois; Mathematics.

COPELAND, Sandra L; Charlotte HS; Charlotte, MI; 52/262 ChrhWkr; HonRl; SchMus; SchPl; SctActv; RptrYrbk; 4-H; RotaryAwd; Brigham Young U; Art.

COPELAND, Timothy S; Mahtomedi Sr HS; White Bear, MN; Aud/Vis; HonRl; SchPl; StuCncl; PresSophCls; RptrSchPpr; GerCl; Glf; Col;.

COPELAND, Vicki S; Union HS; Union, MO; 14/174 Chr; CncrtBnd; DrmMjrt; HonRl; JA; MrchBnd; NHS; SchMus; SpnCl; University; Lawyer.

COPLAN, Marcia; Colchester HS; Colchester, IL; Band; CncrtBnd; HonRl; LitMag; LbryAde; StuCncl; RptrYrbk; MthCl; PpCl; Business.

COPLAN, Margaret M; Watertown HS; Hazel, SD; 91/297 HonRl; 4-H; Col; Med Lab Tech.

COPLEA, Cynthia L; Fairfield Comm HS; Fairfield, IL; ChrhWkr; HonRl; FHA; LatCl; SciCl;.

COPLEY, Craig W; Little Falls Community HS; Randall, MN; ChrhWkr; HonRl; TchrAde; MthCl; SciCl; College; Professional.

COPLEY, Ruth E; Clarence M Kimball HS; Royal Oak, MI; Band; Chr; ChrhWkr; LetterMrchBnd; Orch; PepBnd; SchMus; RptrYrbk; PresFTA; GAA; PPFtbl; GodCntryAwd; Western Michigan Univ; Music.

COPLEY, Shirley A; Gwinn HS; Gwinn, MI; 9/167 Band; CncrtBnd; HonRl; MrchBnd; NHS; SchPl; StuCncl; StuGov; Yrbk; RptrSchPpr; Trk; PPFtbl; EldAwd; Northern Michigan Univ; Banker.

COPLEY, Tamberly M; Cooter HS; Cooter, MO; Chr; ChrhWkr; CncrtBnd; HonRl; MrchBnd; PepBnd; Twrl; FHA; PpCl; Chrldr; Univ; Pharmacy.

COPLIEN, Brenda L; Monroe HS; Monroe, WI; CmntyWkr; HospAde; NatlFornLg; OffAde; SchAde; TchrAde; YthFlsp; PpCl; College; Elem Teacher.

COPLIN, Michelle E; Academy Of Our Lady; Chicago, IL; HonRl; NHS; NatlMeritCmnd; SchPl; StuGov; SchPpr; Chrldr; GAA; College; Medical Tech.

COPP, Karen A; Nazareth Academy; Lyons, IL; 4/180 SecSophCls; Chrs; DrlTm; HonRl; JrNHS; NHS; OffAde; SchMus; SctActv; StuCncl; StuGov; TchrAde; SchPpr; College; Nursing.

COPPENS, Cheryl; Charlevoix HS; Charlevoix, MI; 5/147 Band; CncrtBnd; HonRl; MrchBnd; PepBnd; StuCncl; LatCl; PpCl; Bsktbl; GAA; Central Mi Univ; Bus Adm.

COPPESS, Frank R; Adams Central HS; Monroe, IN; Band; CncrtBnd; HonRl; MrchBnd; PepBnd; SchPl; LetterGlf; Indiana University; Business Management.

COPPESS, William; Lincoln Community HS; Stanwood, IA; TrsFrshCls; ALBoysSt; Band; CncrtBnd; HonRl; MrchBnd; PepBnd; SctActv; FFA; Ftbl; Coll.

COPPINGER, Thomas R; St Edmond HS; Barnum, IA; Chrs; ChrhWkr; HonRl; NHS; StuCncl; Yrbk; LetterBsbl; LetterBsktbl; LetterTrk; St Johns Univ; Physics.

COPPLE, Brad D; Sycamore HS; Sycamore, IL; 20/200 ChrhWkr; CmntyWkr; HonRl; NHS; OffAde; StuCncl; RptrSchPpr; FFA; LetterBsbl; LetterBsktbl; College.

COPPLE, Jamie L; Lawrenceburg HS; Lawrence Burg, IN; TrsFrshCls; TrsSophCls; TrsJrCls; HonRl; TchrAde; FHA; Bsbl; Chrldr; GAA; Indiana Univ; Air Line Stewardess.

COPPLE, Vivian A; Charlestown HS; Charlestown, IN; 2/145 ALAGirlsSt; Chrs; HonRl; NHS; SchPl; 4-H; FrCl; 4-HAwd; Sullivan Bus Coll; Computer Programmer.

CORBA, Michelle L; Millington HS; Birch Run, MI; 10/150 SecSrCls; Band; CncrtBnd; HonRl; HospAde; MrchBnd; NHS; 4-H; FrCl; General Motors Inst; Engineering.

CORBETT, Catherine M; Ursuline Academy; Springfield, IL; 6/85 Band; Chrs; LbryAde; NHS; Quill&Scroll; StuCncl; TchrAde; EdYrBk; 4-H; GAA; College; Elementary Education.

CORBIN, Debra J; Northeast HS; Kansas City, MO; AFS; HonRl; NatlThespSoc; SchPl; StuGov; VPTeen; RptrYrbk; SptEdYrbk; VPPpCl; PPFtbl; Northeast Mo St Univ; Business Admin.

CORBIN, Laura; Charlevoix HS; Charlevoix, MI; ChrhWkr; HonRl; SctActv; RptrSchPpr; 4-H; LetterBsktbl; Swmmng; Univ Mi; Veterinary Science.

CORBIN, Rhonda J; Webster Public HS; Webster, SD; SecSophCls; ChrhWkr; CncrtBnd; HonRl; PepBnd; SchPl; EdYrBk; FHA; GerCl; Chrldr; College; Fashion Merch.

CORBIN, Stephen E; Nauroo Colusa HS; Niota, IL; VPJrCls; Chr; Chrs; HonRl; SchPl; SctActv; RptrSchPpr; Trk; LetterWrstlng; Coll; Law.

CORBITT, Betty A; Chicago Vocational HS; Chicago, IL; Band; CncrtBnd; DrmMjrt; HonRl; JrNHS; MrchBnd; NHS; Orch; Twrl; CaptBsbl; GAA; JAAwd; JETSAwd; Illinois Inst Of Tech; Electrical Eng.

CORBY, John T; Union HS; Grand Rapids, MI; SpnCl; LetterTrk; Univ Of Michigan; Law.

CORCORAN, Brian J; Whitefish Bay HS; Milwaukee, WI; 39/420 HonRl; NatlMeritCmnd; SpnCl; Bsbl; Bsktbl; Ftbl; IMSpt; College; Business Mngmnt.

CORCORAN, Kathy M; Duchesne Acad; Omaha, NE; 4/45 Chrs; HonRl; Sdlty; TchrAde; RptrSchPpr; IMSpt; Ariz State U; Social Psychology.

CORD, Barbara; Shelbyville Senior HS; Shelbyville, IN; Chrs; OffAde; RptrSchPpr; SciCl; Swmmng; GAA; Univ; Teaching.

CORD, David J; Shelby Sr HS; Shelbyville, IN; 19/257 HonRl; NHS; SctActv; FrCl; SciCl; LetterWrstlng; Indiana Univ; Law.

CORD, Mary T; Schaumburg HS; Hanover Park, IL; ChrhWkr; College.

CORDER, Debra; Decatur Community HS; Seldon, KS; Chr; ChrhWkr; HonRl; SchMus; SpnCl; Fort Hays St Coll.

CORDER, Rhoda J; Marion HS; Marion, IL; 18/273 ChrhWkr; HonRl; HospAde; NHS; OffAde; PolWkr; SecStuCncl; PresFBLA; Chrldr; GovHonPrgAwd; So Ill Univ; Business Administration.

CORDES, Cynthia A; Wanamingo Public HS; Kenyon, MN; Band; Chrs; ChrhWkr; HonRl; NHS; NatlThespSoc; SchPl; StuGov; RptrYrbk; 4-H; Mankato State; Nursing.

CORDES, Joan; Hillman Community HS; Hillman, MI; 1/61 VPSophCls; TrsSrCls; ChrhWkr; HonRl; SchPl; StuCncl; SptEdYrbk; GAA; Univ; Professional.

CORDES, Lynn D; Lawrenceville HS; Lawrenceville, IL; 18/186 ChrhWkr; HonRl; HospAde; NHS; YthFlsp; SpnCl; Vincennes Univ; Business.

CORDES, Marlene M; Monroe HS; Browntown, WI; 2/253 Chr; Chrs; HonRl; SchPpr; FFA; PpCl; Trk; PPFtbl; Univ; Agriculture.

CORDES, Morris E; Meade HS; Meade, KS; 16/52 ALBoysSt; Chrs; ChrhWkr; HonRl; TchrAde; PresYThFlsp; VP4-H; VPKeyCl; CaptBsktbl; CaptFtbl; Tennis; Trk; College; Business.

CORDES, Scott D; Eisenhower HS; Decatur, IL; 11/309 HonRl; PresNHS; NatlMeritCmnd; SctActv; PresStuCncl; EdSchPpr; GerCl; LetterTrk; SARAwd; Northwestern Univ; Medicine.

CORDIA, Donna L; John A Evans HS; Richwoods, MO; ChrhWkr; CmntyWkr; HonRl; HospAde; StuCncl; YthLg; 4-H; FBLA; College; Secretary.

CORDIO, Carol J; La Follete Sr HS; Madison, WI; 52/560 Chrs; CncrtBnd; HonRl; HospAde; MrchBnd; SctActv; StuCncl; RptrYrbk; LetterTennis; Madison Area Tech College; Fashion Merchand.

CORDLE, Julie; Nashua HS; Nashua, IA; 3/80 ALAGirlsSt; Band; Chrs; HonRl; NHS; SchPl; RptrYrbk; RptrSchPpr; FTA; SciCl; Bsktbl; GAA; Univ Of Iowa; X Ray Tech.

CORDRY, Jeff T; West Depere HS; Depere, WI; HonRl; College; Bus Admin.

CORE, Donna J; Union HS; Union, MO; Chr; Chrs; ChrhWkr; HonRl; SchMus; SchPl; University; Music.

CORE, Mary A; Sacred Heart HS; Dearborn, MI; ChrhWkr; LbryAde; NatlFornLg; NHS; NatlMeritFnl; Sacrstn; SctActv; StuGov; RptrSchPpr; FrCl; Eastern Mi Univ; Speech Ther.

CORE, Phillip L; Pleasantville; Pleasantville, IA; 8/55 HonRl; NHS; StuCncl; TchrAde; 4-H; PresFFA; CaptBsktbl; CaptFtbl; CaptTrk; 4-HAwd; Isu; Vet Med.

COREN, Linda R; Highland Park HS; Highland Pk, IL; 45/750 CmntyWkr; NHS; SchMus; SchPl; TchrAde; FHA; Emory University; Lawyer.

COREY, Lynn J; Neillsville HS; Neillsville, WI; Band; Chr; CncrtBnd; DrmMjrt; HonRl; NHS; PepBnd; SchPl; PpCl; Chrldr; Univ Of Wi Eau Claire.

COREY, Mary L; Benton HS; Whittington, IL; 46/185 Band; ChrhWkr; CmntyWkr; HonRl; NHS; SchMus; StuCncl; YthFlsp; FBLA; IMSpt;.

CORGAN, Carol L; Virden HS; Virden, IL; Chrs; HonRl; NHS; NatlMeritCmnd; SchMus; SchPl; StuCncl; FTA; College; Law.

CORL, Mary A; Waterford Mott HS; Pontiac, MI; 28/400 Chr; ChrhWkr; HonRl; HospAde; Mi State U; Computer Science.

CORLEY, Cathy J; William Chrisman HS; Independence, MO; 1/437 ChrhWkr; CncrtBnd; MrchBnd; NatlFornLg; NHS; NatlMeritCmnd; Orch; TchrAde; Twrl; FrCl; Missouri Valley College; Mathematics.

CORLISS, Bill J; Gordon Tech HS; Chicago, IL; SctActv; Teen; College; Vocation.

CORMAN, Marilyn D; Ruskin HS; Ruskin, NE; 1/9 TrsSophCls; Band; Chrs; ChrhWkr; DrlTm; HonRl; PepBnd; PpCl; LetterTrk; College; Interior Design.

CORMAN, Robert S; Willow Springs HS; Pomona, MO; 5/95 PresFrshCls; ALBoysSt; HonRl; StuCncl; 4-H; FFA; CaptBsktbl; Ftbl; Trk; University Of Columbis; Animal Husbandry.

CORMICAN, Duane A; Boyceville HS; Glenwood City, WI; HonRl; FFA; LetterWrstlng; College.

CORMIER, Alicia H; Arthur Hill HS; Saginaw, MI; Chr; Chrs; Mdrgl; NatlThespSoc; OffAde; RedCrAde; SchMus; RptrYrbk; SpnCl; Swmmng; Col; Professional.

CORN, Melinda K; Warsaw Community HS; Warsaw, IN; Band; CncrtBnd; JA; MrchBnd; SchPl; Yrbk; PpCl; JAAwd; PresAwd; Business School; Vocation.

CORNEJO, Nicholas; Saint Francis De Sales HS; Chicago, IL; College; Medicine.

CORNELIUS, Kittie C; Whitko HS; Columbia City, IN; HonRl; NatlFornLg; NHS; NatlThespSoc; Quill&Scroll; SchPl; Yrbk; EdSchPpr; Trade Sch; Cosmetology.

CORNELIUS, Susan C; Wheatland HS; Madrid, NE; VPFrshCls; SecTrsJrCls; ALAGirlsSt; Band; Chrs; ChrhWkr; CmntyWkr; Chrldr; IMSpt; 4-HAwd; Univ Of Ne; Professional.

CORNELL, Cynthia L; Vandercook Lake HS; Jackson, MI; 2/90 VPSophCls; TrsSrCls; Band; ChrhWkr; CmntyWkr; DrlTm; HonRl; NHS; SchPl; TchrAde; SchPpr; Eastern Michigan Univ; Teaching.

CORNELL, Karen A; Mona Shores HS; Muskegon, MI; HonRl; HospAde; JrNHS; NHS; FrCl; GAA; Muskegon Comm Clg.

CORNELL, Kathleen A; Mona Shores HS; Muskegon, MI; HonRl; HospAde; NHS; FrCl; GAA; Muskegon Community College.

CORNELL, Kevin A; Parkwood HS; Joplin, MO; HonRl; ROTC; IMSpt; Univ Of Oklahoma; Architecture.

CORNELL, Michael C; Memorial HS; Joplin, MO; 8/221 Band; CncrtBnd; HonRl; LbryAde; MrchBnd; NHS; PepBnd; SctActv; Missouri So State College.

CORNELL, Michael R; Thurston HS; Detroit, MI; 60/600 College; Accountant.

CORNELL, Patty L; S Sioux HS; S Sioux City, NE; DrlTm; HonRl; JrNHS; LbryAde; OffAde; SchAde; TchrAde; EdYrBk; SpnCl; PpCl; College; Professional.

CORNELL, Pete M; Kimball HS; Royal Oak, MI; Band; CncrtBnd; MrchBnd; Orch; TchrAde; Tennis; CchngActv; Mi State; Law Enforcement.

CORNET, James L; Chatard HS; Indianapolis, IN; SciCl; In Purdue Univ; Engineering.

CORNETT, Galen L; El Paso HS; El Paso, IL; 6/87 TrsFrshCls; VPSophCls; HonRl; NHS; NatlMeritCmnd; StuCncl; MthCl; LetterBsbl; LetterBsktbl; CaptFtbl; Univ; Professional Dentist.

CORNETT, Julie A; Winfield HS; Winfield, KS; Band; Chr; ChrhWkr; CncrtBnd; HonRl; MrchBnd; PepBnd; SchMus; SctActv; YthFlsp; Ks State U; Vet Medicine.

CORNETT, Phillip A; Elkhorn Valley HS; Oakdale, NE; CmntyWkr; HonRl; HospAde; JrNHS; StuGov; YthFlsp; Bsktbl; LetterFtbl; CchngActv; IMSpt;.

CORNETT, Russell; William Chrisman HS; Independence, MO; JrNHS; Ftbl; Trk; Coll; Electronics Engineer.

CORNILSEN, Diane M; Calamus Com HS; Grand Mound, IA; TrsFrshCls; TrsJrCls; SecSrCls; HonRl; SchMus; SchPl; TchrAde; 4-H; GerCl; LetterBsktbl; Moline Lutheran School For Nurses; Rn Nurse.

CORNING, Paul E; Glenbard East HS; Lombard, IL; 1/615 HonRl; VPJrNHS; VPNHS; NatlMeritCmnd; GerCl; MthCl; LetterTennis; Augustana College; Medicine.

CORNING, Vicki L; Paxton HS; Paxton, IL; 10/137 HonRl; HospAde; PresNHS; NatlMeritCmnd; SchAde; TchrAde; EngCl; LatCl; SciCl; GAA; C; Teaching.

CORNISH, K C; Sigourney Comm HS; Sigourney, IA; 1/78 ALBoysSt; Chrs; NHS; NatlThespSoc; PresStuCncl; CaptFtbl; LetterSwmmng; LetterTrk; Univ Of Northern Ia; Marine Bio.

CORNO, Edward C; Kirkwood HS; Kirkwood, MO; 121/636 CmntyWkr; HonRl; EdYrBk; PpCl; CaptFtbl; LetterTrk; College; Art.

CORNO, Marie E; Incarnate Word Academy; Ferguson, MO; PresJrCls; Chr; HonRl; JA; PolWkr; StuCncl; RptrSchPpr; University Of Missouri; Journalism.

CORNOG, Roy J; Spokane R 7 HS; Spokane, MO; Band; Chr; ChrhWkr; HonRl; JA; NatlMeritCmnd; SchPl; RptrYrbk; SptEdYrbk; Yrbk; Draughtons Bus Col; Ibm.

CORNWALL, Gail A; Hudson Senior HS; Hudson, WI; SecFrshCls; Chrs; HonRl; SchPpr; GerCl; PresAwd; VoiceDemAwd; College; Science.

CORNWALL, Jeffrey R; Ripon HS; Green Lake, WI; 9/179 Chr; ChrhWkr; HonRl; Mdrgl; NHS; NatlThespSoc; PolWkr; SchMus; StuGov; Glf; St Olaf; Radio Tv Broadcasting.

CORNWALL, Juanita R; Thornton Township HS; South Holland, IL; 1/761 ChrhWkr; HonRl; NHS; NatlMeritSF; YthFlsp; MthCl; AmLegAwd; Univ Of Illinois; Engineering.

CORNWALL, Susan C; Benet Academy; Downers Grove, IL; HonRl; HospAde; RedCrAde; SchPl; StuGov; RptrSchPpr; FrCl; Creighton Univ; Pre Medicine.

CORNWELL, Darrell D; Hilbert HS; Hilbert, WI; 21/67 Chr; CncrtBnd; HonRl; Mdrgl; MrchBnd; KeyCl; SciCl; Bsktbl; Ftbl; LetterTrk; Coll; Inhalation Ther.

CORNWELL, Mary M; Clio Area HS; Clio, MI; 48/366 Band; ChrhWkr; CncrtBnd; MrchBnd; PepBnd; LatCl; PresGAA; Northern Michigan Univ; Medicine.

CORNWELL, Sheryl; Clio HS; Clio, MI; LatCl; Trk; GAA; College.

CORNYN, David G; Marist HS; Midlothian, IL; 18/393 HonRl; PepBnd; PpCl; Bsktbl; IMSpt; University; Engineering.

CORNYN, James T; St Lawrence HS; Chicago, IL; HonRl; StuCncl; StuGov; RptrSchPpr; SciCl; LetterSocr; Trk; Univ Of Illinois; Computer Sciences.

CORONA, George S; Austin Catholic Prep; Detroit, MI; 6/135 HonRl; NHS; Univ Of Michigan; Law.

CORONADO, Theresa; Hazel Park HS; Hazel Park, MI; 20/410 HonRl; NHS; OffAde; StuCncl; StuGov; Tennis; GAA; VFWAwd; College; Marketing.

CORP, Ann E; Joliet West HS; Joliet, IL; 123/495 Chr; HonRl; SchMus; College; Medicine.

CORPSTEIN, Barbara A; Tipton HS; Tipton, KS; VPFrshCls; VPJrCls; Chrs; ChrhWkr; CmntyWkr; HonRl; StuCncl; Yrbk; 4-H; LetterTrk; Clg; Nursing.

CORPSTEIN, Joanne; Mss Academy; Atchison, KS; Chrs; HonRl; SchMus; Sdlty; PpCl; GAA; Coll; Nursing.

CORPUZ, Maryann; Kenwood Hs; Chicago, IL; 17 Band; HonRl; HospAde; NHS; TchrAde; GAA; College ; Engineering.

CORRAL, Karen; Howell HS; Howell, MI; 17/372 CmntyWkr; NHS; Coll; Professional.

CORRAL, Lisa A; Humboldt HS; St Paul, MN; ChrhWkr; CmntyWkr; HonRl; TchrAde; SchPpr; FrCl; Univ Of Mn; Journalism.

CORRAO, Pamela A; St John Cathedral; Milwaukee, WI; 4/110 Band; CncrtBnd; MrchBnd; SecOrch; PepBnd; SchMus; SchPl; Yrbk; IMSpt; U Of Wi; Math.

CORREA, Jerome A; Marist HS; Alsip, IL; 33/364 HonRl; NHS; SpnCl; SciCl; LetterTrk; IMSpt; Loyola Univ; Pre Med, Bio.

CORREA, Sergio; Harris HS; Chicago, IL; DrlTm; ROTC; SchAde; Chicago Circle Campus; Social Work.

CORRELL, Bruce E; Mc Pherson County HS; Tryon, NE; 1/12 PresFrshCls; VPSophCls; ALBoysSt; Chrs; HonRl; SchPl; LetterBsktbl; LetterFtbl; LetterTrk; IMSpt; College; Math.

CORRELL, Christona L; Satanta HS; Satanta, KS; SecFrshCls; PresJrCls; Band; Chr; CncrtBnd; HonRl; JrNHS; MrchBnd; PepBnd; SchPl; Univ; Professional.

CORRELL, James N; Collinsville HS; Collinsville, IL; 10/645 HonRl; NHS; LetterFtbl; LetterWrstlng; Univ Of Illinois; Engineering.

CORRELL, Janet L; Caruthersville HS; Caruthersville, MO; ALAGirlsSt; CncrtBnd; LbryAde; MrchBnd; NHS; SchPl; SctActv; FrCl; Se Missouri State Univ; Music Major.

CORRELL, Leann K; Oak Park HS; Kansas City, MO; Chr; HonRl; OffAde; SchMus; SctActv; VPSpnCl; PpCl; IMSpt; College; Psychology.

CORRELL, Terry L; Stapleton HS; Tyron, NE; VPFrshCls; PresSophCls; Chr; Chrs; HonRl; StuCncl; 4-H; LetterBsktbl; LetterFtbl; LetterTrk; Coll.

CORRELL, Terry L; Stapleton HS; Tryon, NE; PresSrCls; ALBoysSt; NHS; SchPl; StuCncl; 4-H; LetterBsktbl; LetterFtbl; LetterTrk; 4-HAwd; College.

CORRICK, Beth A; Mccook Sr HS; Mccook, NE; AFS; Chr; HonRl; StuGov; YthFlsp; RptrYrbk; PpCl; Chrldr; IMSpt; University Of Nebraska; Airline Hostess.

CORRIGAN, Kathleen; Mayo HS; Rochester, MN; 21/456 DrlTm; NHS; NatlMeritCmnd; StuCncl; PpCl; SciCl; College; Chemical Engineer.

CORRIGAN, Margaret S; Wahlert HS; Dubuque, IA; IMSpt; Ia State; Forestry.

CORRIGAN, Timothy; Unity HS; Loraine, IL; TrsSophCls; ChrhWkr; CmntyWkr; HonRl; YthFlsp; 4-H; FFA; MthCl; SciCl; Ftbl; Wrstlng; College.

CORRIN, Jane L; Tri Center HS; Neola, IA; 2/71 PresJrCls; PresSrCls; Band; HonRl; MrchBnd; PresNHS; Twrl; RptrSchPpr; PpCl; LetterBsktbl; Bishop Clarkson Hospital; Nurse.

CORRINGTON, Bonnie M; Mitchell Sr HS; Mitchell, SD; 5/289 ALAGirlsSt; Chr; ChrhWkr; HonRl; JrNHS; NatlFornLg; NHS; SchMus; SchPl; ElDAwd; Dakota Wesleyan Univ; Med Lab Tech.

CORRIVEAU, Jeanine L; West HS; Green Bay, WI; 6/390 Chrs; ChrhWkr; CmntyWkr; HospAde; PolWkr; SchPl; RptrYrbk; PresFNA; TreasFrCl; Uw Eau Claire; Rn.

CORRY, William K; Port Huron HS; Port Huron, MI; StuCncl; StuGov; Bsbl; St Clair County Clge; Dentist.

CORSER, Diana M; Aquinas HS; La Crosse, WI; 8/215 CmntyWkr; HospAde; NatlFornLg; NHS; Quill&Scroll; StuGov; RptrYrbk; EdSchPpr; CivCl; FrCl; Eau Claire U; Journalism.

CORSER, Joseph A; Winona HS; Hastings, MN; LitMag; NHS; SctActv; StuCncl; YthLg; SecSciCl; Ftbl; Glf; Tennis; Wash Univ.

CORSO, Roger L; Frank Cody HS; Detroit, MI; 5/250 HonRl; SpnCl; MthCl; SciCl; College.

CORSON, Linda; Sparta HS; Sparta, IL; 24/170 Band; Chr; Orch; ChrhWkr; HonRl; YthFlsp; 4-H; FBLA; GAA; Belleville Area Col; Legal Court Secretary.

CORTESE, Frank J; Holy Cross HS; Norridge, IL; 9/308 HonRl; NHS; Northwestern University; Professional.

CORTEZ, Maria R; Holy Name Cathedral HS; Chicago, IL; Chrs; CmntyWkr; HonRl; SchPl; TchrAde; SpnCl; Swmmng; Univ; Lawyer.

CORTEZ, Marybeth; Marian HS; Lathrup Village, MI; VPFrshCls; HstSrCls; HonRl; ModUN; NHS; StuGov; U Of Mich; Professional.

CORVALLIS, Rose Mary; Collinsville HS; Collinsville, IL; 18/654 SecDrlTm; Pres4-H; SecSpnCl; SciCl; 4-HAwd; College; Spanish.

CORVINO, Robert F; Fenwick HS; Westchester, IL; 41/286 CmntyWkr; HonRl; PolWkr; StuCncl; SptEdSchPpr; MthCl; Bsbl; LetterFtbl; Glf; Univ Of Ill; Business.

CORY, Dennis W; Carrollton HS; Kane, IL; 7/78 ChrhWkr; CmntyWkr; HonRl; YthFlsp; PpCl; LetterBsktbl; LetterFtbl; LetterTrk; 4-HAwd; College; Vocation.

CORY, Kathleen A; Carroll HS; Flora, IN; 9/132 Chr; HonRl; NHS; YthFlsp; 4-H; KeyCl; FrCl; PpCl; BttyCrckrAwd; 4-HAwd; Purdue University; Home Economics.

CORYELL, Catherine L; St Anns HS; Lexington, NE; SecSophCls; PresJrCls; Chrs; HonRl; NHS; SchMus; SchPl; SctActv; CivCl; 4-H;.

CORYELL, Jerome E; Martin HS; Shelbyville, MI; Band; ChrhWkr; CncrtBnd; HonRl; MrchBnd; PepBnd; SchMus; SctActv; LetterBsbl; LetterFtbl; Us Naval Acad; Aviator.

CORZILIUS, Constance; Granite City HS S; Granite City, IL; Chr; HonRl; LitMag; NHS; PresQuill&Scroll; SchPl; StuCncl; YthFlsp; EdSchPpr; PresAwd; University; Journalism Major.

CORZINE, Steven A; Roxana Sr HS; East Alton, IL; 26/300 ALBoysSt; HonRl; NHS; SctActv; GerCl; Ftbl; Eastern Illinois Univ; Medicine.

CORZINE, Suzanne; Dongola HS; Dongola, IL; 1/23 Band; HonRl; StuCncl; 4-H; SecFHA; GAA; AmLegAwd; DanFAwd; 4-HAwd; JAAwd; Se Missouri State Univ; Business.

CORZINE, Tamma W; Century HS; Karnak, IL; 1/60 TrsFrshCls; ChrhWkr; HonRl; SchPl; VPStuCncl; EdYrBk; SecFHA; PresPpCl; BttyCrckrAwd; St Louis Univ; Physical Therapy.

CORZINE, Vicki K; Dongola HS; Dongola, IL; 3/23 PresJrCls; VPBand; CncrtBnd; HonRl; MrchBnd; PepBnd; Yrbk; PpCl; Chrldr; GAA; Barnes School; Nursing.

COSATINO, Marian J; Kelvyn Park HS; Chicago, IL; 3/299 CmntyWkr; HonRl; SchMus; SctActv; StuCncl; TchrAde; De Paul Univ; Accounting.

COSBY, Lillie K; Paseo HS; Kansas City, MO; VPJrCls; Chrs; HonRl; SctActv; StuCncl; YthFlsp; RptrYrbk; RptrSchPpr; FHA; SciCl; College; Professional.

COSBY, Linda R; North Branch Sr HS; North Branch, MI; 2/150 TrsSophCls; Band; ChrhWkr; CncrtBnd; HonRl; MrchBnd; NHS; PepBnd; FrCl; DARAwd; Bible College; Elementary Education.

COSCARELLI, Carolyn; Hillsdale HS; Hillsdale, MI; HonRl; HospAde; SchPl; 4-H; FDA; FNA; FrCl; University; Nurse.

COSCARELLY, Christine M; Coldwater HS; Coldwater, MI; ALAGirlsSt; Chr; HonRl; NHS; SchMus; SchPpr; SpnCl; PpCl; IMSpt; PPFtbl; College; Professional.

COSENTINO, Agostina; Ridgewood Hs; Norridge, IL; 27/369 CmntyWkr; HonRl; NHS; SchMus; SchPl; TchrAde; YthFlsp; Yrbk; PpCl; GAA; Northeastern Illinois; Teaching.

COSENTINO, Patricia L; Elizabeth Seton HS; Chicago, IL; 43/252 HonRl; NHS; RptrYrbk; RptrSchPpr; LatCl; Univ Of Il; Accountant.

COSGRAY, Mark D; Twin Lakes HS; Idaville, IN; 43/206 ChrhWkr; CmntyWkr; HonRl; NHS; YthFlsp; 4-H; FFA; MthCl; Purdue Univ; Veterinarian.

COSGRIFF, Susan M; Elk Grove HS; Elk Grove Vlg, IL; 48/500 Chrs; HonRl; SctActv; University Of Wisconsin; Physical Therapy.

COSGROVE, Sarah A; St Bede Academy; Spring Valley, IL; 15/120 Chrs; HonRl; SchMus; FrCl; GAA; Notre Dame Univ; Medicine.

COSGROVE, Thomas C; Hempstead HS; Dubuque, IA; ChrhWkr; SctActv; StuGov; TchrAde; Bsktbl; Ftbl; LetterTrk; IMSpt; DARAwd; College; Doctor.

COSLET, Julia M; Oakland HS; Tuscola, IL; 2/44 HonRl; Lakeland College; Business.

COSSAIRT, Vickie A; Dixon HS; Dixon, IL; 15/333 PresJA; SchMus; SchPl; SchPpr; SecJAAwd; Sauk Valley College; Mathematics.

COSTA, George S; Lane Technical HS; Chicago, IL; 33/1210 SecSrCls; HonRl; JA; NHS; OffAde; SchMus; StuCncl; StuGov; TchrAde; Yrbk; KeyCl; PresFrCl; PpCl; JAAwd; Northwestern Univ; Law.

COSTA, Timothy J; Morton Sr HS; Hammond, IN; PresJrCls; CmntyWkr; StuCncl; StuGov; TchrAde; LetterFtbl; LetterSocr; LetterSwmmng; College; Professional.

COSTANDINE, Cindy L; Monroe Jr Sr HS; St Paul, MN; 40/160 Chrs; HonRl; JA; NatlFornLg; SchMus; SchPl; SctActv; TchrAde; 4-H; FHA; Inver Hills Community; Probation Officer.

COSTANTINO, Antoinette F; Thornwood HS; South Holland, IL; 1/852 PresAFS; ChrhWkr; CmntyWkr; HonRl; NHS; OffAde; StuCncl; RptrYrbk; SpnCl; MthCl; College; Computer Science.

COSTANTINO, Peter D; Macomb HS; Macomb, IL; PresSophCls; HonRl; NHS; PolWkr; StuCncl; StuGov; RptrYrbk; Yrbk; SpnCl; Tennis; IMSpt; Notre Dame; Medicine.

COSTELLO, Anthony L; Mendota HS; Mendota, IL; Agriculture.

COSTELLO, Barbara A; Catholic Central HS; Grand Rapids, MI; Chrs; HonRl; JrNHS; Mdrgl; NHS; SchMus; IMSpt; St Leo College; Business Education.

COSTELLO, Dennis; Fremont Bergan HS; Fremont, NE; 5/48 VPSrCls; ALBoysSt; HonRl; StuCncl; RptrYrbk; SptEdYrbk; Bsktbl; Ftbl; Trk; Creighton Univ; Accountant.

COSTELLO, Elizabeth M; O Fallon Township HS; O Fallon, IL; Band; CncrtBnd; MrchBnd; LatCl; College; Professional.

COSTELLO, Gene A; New Hampton Comm HS; Elma, IA; Chr; HonRl; JA; StuCncl; StuGov; YthFlsp; 4-H; Wrstlng; 4-HAwd; JAAwd; College; Conservationist.

COSTELLO, Julie L; Nazareth Academy; Hinsdale, IL; Chrs; NatlMeritCmnd; SchPl; TchrAde; SecSophCls; FrCl; MthCl; Xavier Univ; Doctor.

COSTELLO, Linda L; Nishna Valley HS; Imogene, IA; 1/31 Band; Chrs; HonRl; NHS; NatlMeritCmnd; SchMus; Pres4-H; LetterBsktbl; LetterTrk; GovHonPrgAwd; Oral Roberts U; Med.

COSTELLO, Melissa K; Immaculata HS; Chicago, IL; 14/201 HonRl; PresNHS; PepBnd; RedCrAde; StuCncl; StuGov; Bsktbl; Chrldr; Univ Of Notre Dame; Advertising.

COSTELLO, Patrick A; Gibault HS; Waterloo, IL; Band; CmntyWkr; CncrtBnd; MrchBnd; PepBnd; SctActv; PpCl; Socr; CchngActv; IMSpt; Il Col; Chemical Engineer.

COSTELLO, Robert J; Boylan Central Catholic HS; Rockford, IL; HonRl; StuGov; LetterFtbl; LetterWrstlng; IMSpt; University; Professional.

COSTELLO, Thomas M; Austin Catholic Prep; Grosse Pt Woods, MI; VPSrCls; StuGov; LetterBsbl; College; Business Administration.

COSTEPHENS, Donna K; Malden HS; Malden, MO; ChrhWkr; HonRl; College.

COSTER, Diane L; Rock Island Sr HS; Rock Island, IL; Chr; CmntyWkr; HonRl; LitMag; SchMus; StuCncl; StuGov; TchrAde; Teen; LetterTrk; Univ Of Iowa; Commercial Artist.

COTA, Michael J; Ogorman HS; Sioux Falls, SD; ChrhWkr; NHS; TchrAde; Bsktbl; LetterFtbl; LetterTrk; Univ; Teaching.

COTE, Darlene D; Riverview HS; Riverview, MI; 12/241 HonRl; NHS; TchrAde; RptrSchPpr; Bsbl; LetterBsktbl; GAA; PPFtbl; Wayne St Univ; Pharmacy.

COTEY, Annette M; W G Mather HS; Munising, MI; TrsFrshCls; Band; CmntyWkr; HonRl; MrchBnd; PepBnd; SchPl; TchrAde; SchPpr; PpCl; SciCl; Coll; Social Work.

COTHERMAN, Scott; Burris HS; Muncie, IN; 17/72 PresJrCls; Band; PepBnd; PolWkr; SchPl; RptrYrbk; SptEdSchPpr; FrCl; Bsktbl; Univ; Business Administration.

COTHRAN, David; Effingham HS; Effingham, IL; FFA; Fulton Coll; Military.

COTTER, Susan A; Queen Of Peace HS; Chicago, IL; 30/415 HonRl; NHS; StuCncl; YthLg; FrCl; Ftbl;.

COTTER, Teresa C; Randolph Southern HS; Lynn, IN; Band; ChrhWkr; CncrtBnd; HonRl; MrchBnd; RptrYrbk; 4-H; PpCl; 4-HAwd; Coll; Major Study.

COTTER, Terry T; Walled Lake Western HS; Orchard Lk, MI; HonRl; RedCrAde; YthFlsp; SpnCl; U Of Detroit; Dentistry.

COTTERELL, Donita J; Red Hill HS; Sumner, IL; 2/125 ALAGirlsSt; SecBand; Chrs; ChrhWkr; CncrtBnd; HonRl; IntrClCncl; MrchBnd; NHS; PepBnd; Chrldr; VPGAA; DanFAwd; 4-HAwd; University; Music.

COTTINGHAM, Lora A; Forman HS; Manito, IL; ChrhWkr; CmntyWkr; HospAde; NHS; SchPl; SecSctActv; SecYthFlsp; RptrYrbk; RptrSchPpr; FHA; IMSpt; College; Business.

COTTON, Brian F; Harper Creek HS; E Leroy, MI; ALBoysSt; Band; SctActv; Bsbl; Bsktbl; Ftbl; College.

COTTON, Lucretia L; Arlington HS; Indianapolis, IN; Band; ChrhWkr; CmntyWkr; CncrtBnd; DrlTm; HonRl; JA; MrchBnd; NatlMeritCmnd; SctActv; Indiana University; Accountant.

COTTON, Mary; Woodbine Community HS; Woodbine, IA; 13/58 VPSophCls; DrlTm; HonRl; NHS; YthFlsp; RptrYrbk; IMSpt; AmLegAwd; College; Physical Education.

COTTON, Michelle P; Soldan HS; St Louis, MO; Band; Chr; ChrhWkr; CmntyWkr; HonRl; NHS; SctActv; StuCncl; TchrAde; YthFlsp; Univ; Professional.

COTTRELL, Ronda L; Marysville HS; Marysville, KS; 2/105 SecBand; CncrtBnd; HonRl; MrchBnd; PepBnd; VPYthFlsp; PpCl; DARAwd; KiwanAwd; Ft Hays Kansas St College; Business.

COUBARD, Ann M; Eisenhower HS; Utica, MI; HonRl; FrCl; GerCl; PpCl; Arline Sch; Travel.

COUCH, Carol; Downers Grove South HS; Downers Grove, IL; 4/850 HonRl; NHS; NatlThespSoc; SchPl; College.

COUCH, Heather E; Culver Academy; Indianola, IA; 6/169 Band; Chr; Chrl; Chrs; CmntyWkr; CncrtBnd; HonRl; Mdrgl; TchrAde; LetterBsbl; IMSpt; CitAwd; Vanderbilt Univ; Russian.

COUCH, Janice G; Meadville R 4 HS; Linneus, MO; HstFrshCls; VPJrCls; HonRl; NHS; Twrl; Yrbk; SchPpr; FHA; LetterBsbl; CaptChrldr; Nw Missouri St University.

COUCH, Kelly K; Mark Twain HS; Perry, MO; VPFrshCls; CmntyWkr; HonRl; RedCrAde; FNA; PpCl; LetterBsktbl; CchngActv; IMSpt; PPFtbl; University; Art.

COUDEN, Julia K; Hamilton Heights HS; Arcadia, IN; Chrs; HonRl; Quill&Scroll; SchPl; Yrbk; SchPpr; FTA; PpCl; SciCl; Patricia Stevens; Fashion Mrch.

COUDRON, Tanya K; Adrion HS; Adrion, MI; HonRl; JrNHS; NHS; SpnCl; Bsktbl; Trk; GAA; University; Journalism.

COUFAL, Marlene K; Howells Public HS; Howells, NE; 1/43 HstJrCls; Chrs; HonRl; LbryAde; OffAde; SchPl; TchrAde; SchPpr; SecFHA; PpCl; Bus Col; Secretary.

COUGHENOUR, Betty; Colo HS; Colo, IA; 2/27 Band; Chrs; HonRl; NHS; SchMus; 4-H; FTA; SpnCl; Bsktbl; Trk; Iowa Stae Univ; Pre Vet Study.

COUGHLIN, Beth I; Oak Grove Lutheran HS; Fargo, ND; 5/50 Band; Chr; Chrl; Chrs; CncrtBnd; HonRl; JrNHS; MrchBnd; NHS; PepBnd; StuCncl; YthFlsp; Yrbk; LetterBsktbl; Pacific Lutheran Univ; Physical Education.

COUGHLIN, Bonnie M; Oak Grove Lutheran HS; Fargo, ND; 4/50 Band; Chr; Chrl; Chrs; CncrtBnd; HonRl; MrchBnd; NHS; PepBnd; YthFlsp; PpCl; SciCl; LetterBsktbl; LetterTrk; Pacific Lutheran Univ.

COUGHLIN, Brian C; Brother Rice HS; Oak Lawn, IL; 95/440 HonRl; StuCncl; RptrSchPpr; KeyCl; Bsktbl; LetterFtbl; CaptTrk; Univ Of Illinois.

COUGHLIN, Julie M; Albia Comm HS; Melrose, IA; Band; Chrs; CncrtBnd; HonRl; HospAde; MrchBnd; PepBnd; FHA; FNA; LetterGlf; Indian Hills Comm Col; Rn.

COUGHLIN, Mary L; Wethersfield HS; Kewanee, IL; SecJrCls; HonRl; NHS; SchMus; SchPl; RptrSchPpr; FrCl; Chrldr; AmLegAwd; N Ill Univ; Nursing.

COUGHLIN, Michael L; Kenmare HS; Kenmare, ND; 1/52 Chrl; Chrs; ChrhWkr; HonRl; StuCncl; YthFlsp; SptEdYrbk; Yrbk; Bsbl; LetterBsktbl; LetterFtbl; Glf; CchngActv; Nw Bible College; Accounting.

COUGHLIN, Richard; Lawrence Central HS; Indpls, IN; 150/700 SchPl; TchrAde; Univ; Psychology.

COUGILL, Debra D; Aurelia Community HS; Aurelia, IA; PresFrshCls; Band; CncrtBnd; DrlTm; HonRl; SecLbryAde; MrchBnd; PepBnd; SchPl; RptrSchPpr; CaptChrldr; PresGAA; AmLegAwd; CitAwd;.

COUGILL, Mary C; Central HS; Evansville, IN; HonRl; JrNHS; NHS; StuCncl; StuGov; YthFlsp; SptEdSchPpr; SecCivCl; GerCl; Tennis; PPFtbl; Ball State University; Medical Technology.

COUILLARD, Daniel; Holy Angels HS; Richfield, MN; College; History.

COULIS, Louie; Bishop Noll Institute; East Chicago, IN; ALBoysSt; HonRl; NHS; RptrYrbk; SptEdYrbk; MthCl; LetterBsktbl; IMSpt; AmLegAwd; CitAwd; University; Professional.

COULMAN, Roseanne M; Flint Northern HS; Clio, MI; 1/619 HospAde; NHS; TreasFrCl; PpCl; LetterChrldr; Univ Of Mich Flint; Medical Profession.

COULSON, Bruce E; Blackford HS; Hartford City, IN; HonRl; NatlFornLg; NatlThespSoc; SchPl; LatCl; Clge; Computers/law.

COULSON, Catherine A; Springfield Catholic HS; Springfield, MO; 1/64 TrsJrCls; PresSrCls; HonRl; NatlMeritSF; SchPl; SpnCl; LetterBsbl; Bsktbl; GAA; EldAwd; Southwest Mo State Clge; Data Processing.

COULSON, Joseph P; East Detroit HS; East Detroit, MI; Chr; HonRl; NHS; Teen; Wayne State Univ; Pre Med Studies.

COULTER, Cynthia A; Marian HS; Hays, KS; ChrhWkr; HonRl; HospAde; SctActv; TchrAde; PpCl; IMSpt; College; Beauty Consultant.

COULTER, J Kevin; Eureka HS; Goodfield, IL; 45/100 4-H; FFA; LetterTrk; CaptWrstlng; 4-HAwd; College; Agriculture.

COULTER, Robert L; Westmer HS; New Boston, IL; PresSophCls; VPJrCls; PresSrCls; HonRl; StuCncl; SpnCl; SciCl; PresJrCls; CaptBsktbl; LetterFtbl; Trade Sch; Vocational.

COULTER, Timothy G; Glenbrook North HS; Northbrook, IL; 14/654 ChrhWkr; CmntyWkr; HonRl; NHS; NatlMeritCmnd; SctActv; StuCncl; YthFlsp; LatCl; LetterSwmmng; Trk; Brown Univ; Business Admin.

COULTER, Viola; Belcourt HS; Belcourt, ND; ALAGirlsSt; HonRl; StuCncl; RptrYrbk; RptrSchPpr; PpCl; Chrldr; Univ; Professional.

COUMANS, Darlene T; Lanse Creuse HS; New Baltimore, MI; HonRl; JrNHS; LitMag; NHS; NatlMeritSchl; PpCl; Chrldr; VoiceDemAwd; Central Mi; Rn.

COUMBES, Kendra; Jacksonville HS; Murrayville, IL; 152/352 ChrhWkr; CmntyWkr; StuGov; FrCl; Lincoln Land Comm Coll; Acc.

COUNSELL, Patricia M; Catholic Memorial HS; Oconomowoc, WI; ChrhWkr; CmntyWkr; HospAde; JrNHS; SctActv; RptrYrbk; PpCl; College; Journalism.

COUNTERMAN, Karen S; Martin Public HS; Otsego, MI; VPSophCls; PresJrCls; Chr; CncrtBnd; HonRl; MrchBnd; StuCncl; LetterBsktbl; LetterChrldr; Univ; Professional.

COUNTERMAN, Rex A; Heritage HS; Hoagland, IN; ChrhWkr; YthFlsp; KeyCl; LetterBsbl; LetterBsktbl; LetterFtbl; College; Professional.

COUNTRYMAN, Lyn L; 215 North 11th HS; Adel, IA; HonRl; NHS; NatlThespSoc; SchMus; SchPl; StuCncl; Bsktbl; Gif; Trk; IMSpt; Clge; Nurse.

COUNTS, Mary L; St Pius X HS; Festus, MO; 17/120 ALAGirlsSt; Band; CncrtBnd; HonRl; MrchBnd; NHS; PepBnd; PpCl; SecSciCl; LetterTrk; College; Med Technologist.

COUPANGER, Sheila; Elmore Public HS; Elmore, MN; 8/26 Band; Chr; ChrhWkr; CncrtBnd; HonRl; RptrYrbk; GerCl; Chrldr; GAA; IMSpt; College; Secreterial.

COUPE, Denise; Falls City HS; Falls City, NE; 14/91 SecJrCls; Band; Chr; Chrs; NHS; StuCncl; Yrbk; 4-H; Bsktbl; Trk; Pru State College; Teacher In Phy Ed.

COURIER, Terry L; Franklin HS; Franklin, IL; ChrhWkr; FFA; Farming.

COURSE, Jeannine V; Lakeview HS; St Clair Shores, MI; Band; CncrtBnd; HonRl; MrchBnd; Orch; PepBnd; College; Musician.

COURSE, Timothy D; Bay City Western HS; Auburn, MI; Aud/Vis; SchMus; SchPl; RptrSchPpr; FrCl; Mich St Univ; Tele/radio Brodct.

COURSER, Larry L; Pope County Com HS; Brownfield, IL; TchrAde; FFA; PpCl; College.

COURT, Jennifer L; Northwest HS; High Ridge, MO; HonRl; NHS; TchrAde; FTA; Correspondence Course; Interior Decorator.

COURT, Mary C; Regis HS; Eau Claire, WI; ChrhWkr; CmntyWkr; DrlTm; HonRl; HospAde; RptrSchPpr; FBLA; LatCl; PpCl; GAA; U Of W; Business Fashions.

COURTER, Annette; Comstock HS; Kalamazoo, MI; VPJrCls; PresSrCls; Band; HonRl; MrchBnd; NHS; PepBnd; SchPl; Tennis; Trk; University; Anthropology Ph D.

COURTER, Mark D; Pomeroy Comm HS; Jolley, IA; 3/32 Chrs; HonRl; NHS; SchPl; YthFlsp; SptEdSchPpr; FFA; Bsktbl; Ftbl; Trk; U Of N Ia; Accounting.

COURTNEY, John L; Mt Vernon Township HS; Mt Vernon, IL; ALBoysSt; CncrtBnd; DrmMjrt; HonRl; MrchBnd; NHS; Orch; PepBnd; SchMus; Round Lake College; Optometry.

COURTNEY, Karen M; Notre Dame HS; Milwaukee, WI; VPSophCls; VPJrCls; Chr; ChrhWkr; HonRl; NHS; NatlMeritSchl; SchPl; PpCl; SciCl; Marquette Univ; Undecided.

COURTNEY, Kenneth R; St Pius X HS; Kansas City, MO; 29/136 Chrs; ChrhWkr; HonRl; JrNHS; NHS; SchMus; SchPl; StuCncl; Univ Of Missouri; Communications.

COURTNEY, Mary E; Proviso West HS; Melrose Park, IL; 2/1086 HonRl; LbryAde; NHS; NatlMeritSchl; Clge; Math.

COURTNEY, Ronald S; Chippewa Valley HS; Mt Clemens, MI; HonRl; NHS; NatlMeritSF; Creighton Univ; Doctor.

COURTRIGHT, Jeffrey L; Prairie Heights HS; Hudson, IN; 4/102 Band; Chrs; CncrtBnd; MrchBnd; NHS; PepBnd; SchMus; SchPl; Ftbl; 4-HAwd; Manchester Clge; Speech Communications.

COURTRIGHT, Mary A; O L Mount Carmel HS; Wyandotte, MI; 1/58 Chr; Chrl; NHS; NatlMeritSF; Sdlty; StuCncl; StuGov; EdYrBk; EdSchPpr; PpCl; Msu.

COURTRIGHT, Michael J; Illini Bluffs HS; Mapleton, IL; 2/100 ALBoysSt; HonRl; NHS; SchMus; SchPl; StuCncl; VPStuGov; FrCl; OptClAwd; University; Engineer.

COUSE, Debra A; Assumption HS; Wisconsin Rapids, WI; 12/120 VPFrshCls; HonRl; Sacrstn; StuCncl; PpCl; CaptBsktbl; Swmmng; Chrldr; College; Secretary.

COUSIN, Peter E; Marshall U HS; Minneapolis, MN; PresJrCls; Aud/Vis; StuGov; TchrAde;.

COUSSENS, Linda; United Township HS; East Moline, IL; 1/687 HonRl; TchrAde; GerCl; ChmbCommrsAwd; College; Banking And Finance.

COUTRE, Nanette L; Carmel For Girls HS; Mundelein, IL; 12/173 TrsJrCls; Chrs; HonRl; NHS; OffAde; SchMus; StuCncl; TchrAde; JCAwd; College; Elem Educ.

COUTTS, Julia E; Cass Tech HS; Detroit, MI; HospAde; JA; Mi State Univ; Veterinarian.

COUTURE, James M; Ames Sr HS; Ames, IA; HonRl; NatlThespSoc; SchMus; SchPl; IMSpt; Iowa U; Actor.

COUWENHOVEN, Laurel; Illiana Christian Hs; Lansing, IL; 1/189 SecSrCls; TrsSrCls; Chr; ChrhWkr; HospAde; NHS; NatlMeritCmnd; Calvin College; Bs In Nursing.

COVEN, Sandra S; Kewanee HS; Kewanee, IL; Band; CncrtBnd; HonRl; MrchBnd; RptrYrbk; RptrSchPpr; SchPpr; 4-H; FHA; College; Secretary.

COVENEY, Anne M; Columbus North HS; Columbus, IN; 2/468 Chr; HonRl; ModUN; NatlFornLg; NatlThespSoc; Quill&Scroll; SchMus; SchPpr; NCTE; OptClAwd; St Mary Of The Woods Coll; French.

COVER, Christianne; Northfield Sr HS; Northfield, MN; 35/256 Aud/Vis; ChrhWkr; CncrtBnd; HonRl; MrchBnd; NHS; SchAde; YthFlsp; Calvin College; Medical Tech.

COVERT, Karen E; Rochester Adams HS; Rochester, MI; CncrtBnd; JA; NHS; NatlMeritCmnd; PepBnd; SchPl; StuGov; RptrYrbk; VPGerCl; Michigan State U; Eng.

COVERT, Karen J; Inland Lakes HS; Alanson, MI; 4/40 SecFrshCls; SecSophCls; VPJrCls; HonRl; StuCncl; 4-H; Chrldr; College; Art.

COVILLE, Mark P; O Fallon Township HS; O Fallon, IL; 16/297 ChrhWkr; CmntyWkr; HonRl; ModUN; NHS; SctActv; YthFlsp; FrCl; Bsbl; Ftbl; Univ Of Connecticut; Statistician.

COVILLI, Thomas M; Duchesne HS; St Charles, MO; 21/182 HonRl; VPStuCncl; LetterFtbl; LetterSocr; LetterTrk; College.

COVINGTON, Andre E; Fenger HS; Chicago, IL; 16/593 PresFrshCls; VPFrshCls; SecFrshCls; TrsFrshCls; Band; Chr; ChrhWkr; HonRl; IntrClCncl; NHS; Quill&Scroll; StuCncl; College; Liberal Arts.

COWAN, Dawn M; Climax Scotts HS; Climax, MI; 33/53 Band; ChrhWkr; CncrtBnd; HonRl; NatlFornLg; TchrAde; RptrYrbk; Yrbk; FHA; PPFtbl; Col; Secretarial Sceince.

COWAN, Dewey; Unionville HS; Unionville, MO; VPSrCls; HonRl; NHS; FFA; College; Lawyer.

COWAN, Robert M; Rock Island HS; Rock Island, IL; 96/700 HonRl; NHS; RedCrAde; SchAde; SctActv; StuCncl; StuGov; KeyCl; SpnCl; CaptSwmmng; Univ; Bus.

COWART, Ruth M; Arlington HS; Indianapolis, IN; Chr; ChrhWkr; CmntyWkr; HonRl; JrNHS; Mdrgl; NHS; Orch; TchrAde;.

COWART, Virginia; Oak Lawn Community HS; Oak Lawn, IL; 38/711 HonRl; LbryAde; NHS; SchAde; SchPl; StuGov; RptrSchPpr; GAA; IMSpt; Coll; Med Lab Tech.

COWDEN, Valerie S; Viroqua HS; Viroqua, WI; SecSophCls; SecSrCls; Band; Chrs; ChrhWkr; CncrtBnd; HonRl; MrchBnd; NatlFornLg; PepBnd; StuCncl; RptrSchPpr; FHA; FrCl; Minnesota Bible College; Social Work.

COWELL, George A; Wm G Mather HS; Munising, MI; ALBoysSt; Band; CncrtBnd; PepBnd; HstJrCls; Trk; Michigan Tech Univ.

COWELL, Margie E; Lewistown HS; Lewistown, IL; Chrs; HonRl; College; Professional.

COWGILL, Gerald M; Macarthur HS; Decatur, IL; Band; CncrtBnd; Bsbl; LetterFtbl; LetterWrstlng; College.

COWHERD, Terrence E; Northwestern Military Academy; Chicago, IL; HonRl; NatlMeritCmnd; CaptBsbl; LetterBsktbl; LetterFtbl; Trk; CchngActv; JAAwd; College; Professional.

COWIE, Denise M; Reed Custer HS; Braidwood, IL; VPSrCls; HonRl; NHS; OffAde; PresStuCncl; Yrbk; RptrSchPpr; SchPpr; VPSpnCl; Chrldr; Business Schl; Legal Secretary.

COWIE, Islay J; Springfield HS; Springfield, IL; 12/585 Band; CncrtBnd; MrchBnd; NHS; Orch; SchMus; Bradley Univ; Chemistry.

COWIE, Jean M; Rothsay HS; Rothsay, MN; Band; Chrs; CncrtBnd; HonRl; Mdrgl; PepBnd; SchMus; SchPl; RptrSchPpr; GerCl; College.

COWIN, Deborah J; R 2 Reynolds HS; Ellington, MO; Band; Chr; ChrhWkr; HonRl; MrchBnd; SchPl; Twrl; FHA; PpCl; Chrldr;.

COWLES, Denise A; Belding HS; Belding, MI; PresSrCls; SchPpr; CmntyWkr; HonRl; StuCncl; StuGov; YthFlsp; CaptChrldr; IMSpt; PPFtbl; College; Vocation.

COWLES, Geralyn; Albia HS; Albia, IA; 4/150 Band; ChrhWkr; CncrtBnd; HonRl; MrchBnd; NHS; SchPl; RptrYrbk; SpnCl; PpCl; Maryerest Coll; Math Major.

COWLES, James; Albia HS; Albia, IA; 2/150 Band; Chrs; CncrtBnd; HonRl; MrchBnd; PepBnd; FFA; Univ; Professional.

COWLES, John E; Southeast HS; Wichita, KS; PresFrshCls; NatlFornLg; SchPl; Bsktbl; Tennis; Tx Critian U; Law.

COWLEY, Beverly; Ovid Elsie HS; Elsie, MI; 10/165 Band; Chr; ChrhWkr; CmntyWkr; CncrtBnd; HonRl; Mdrgl; Orch; SchPl; FNA; Nursing School; Registered Nurse.

COWLEY, Marquetta; Onaga HS; Onaga, KS; Chrs; HonRl; RptrSchPpr; 4-H; Bus School;comp Tech.

COWLEY, Nina S; Rolla HS; Rolla, MO; 28/307 HonRl; JrNHS; OffAde; TchrAde; PpCl; LetterBsktbl; Trk; GAA; Vocational School; Secretary.

COX, Brian W; Pittsfield HS; Pittsfield, IL; CmntyWkr; HonRl; NatlThespSoc; PolWkr; SchPl; Yrbk; PpCl; Bsktbl; Ftbl; IMSpt; College; Conservationist.

COX, Byron E; Ogilvie HS; Ogilvie, MN; ChrhWkr; YthFlsp; Ftbl; CaptTrk; LetterWrstlng; IMSpt; Christian Clg; Ministry.

COX, Catherine J; Tipton HS; Tipton, IN; 29/177 SecSrCls; HonRl; Twrl; Yrbk; PpCl; LetterTennis; Trk; Purdue Univ; Bus.

COX, Cathy D; Randolph Southern HS; Lynn, IN; 9/64 Chrs; HonRl; NHS; OffAde; SchMus; Business Schl; Secretary.

COX, Cheryl J; Waukesha South HS; Waukesha, WI; SecSrCls; AFS; HonRl; NHS; StuGov; RptrYrbk; RptrSchPpr; FrCl; TrsSophCls; U Of Wi; Inter Relations.

COX, Christine; Beloit Memorial HS; Beloit, WI; 1/465 SecTrsJrCls; AFS; ALAGirlsSt; Band; ChrhWkr; CncrtBnd; DrmMjrt; HonRl; MrchBnd; Swmmng; Univ; Oceanography.

COX, Cindy A; Cuba HS; Cuba, IL; 3/65 Band; Chrs; ChrhWkr; HonRl; NHS; PepBnd; YthFlsp; 4-H; FrCl; Chrldr; College.

COX, Colleen M; Prophetstown HS; Prophetstown, IL; 12/100 AFS; Aud/Vis; Chr; Chrs; HonRl; JrNHS; NHS; OffAde; TchrAde; 4-H; FTA; Bsktbl; Univ Of Illinois; Business.

COX, Cynthia L; Rosehill HS; Rose Hill, KS; 2/60 VPFrshCls; PresSophCls; HonRl; NatlFornLg; SchPl; StuCncl; RptrSchPpr; EdSchPpr; FHA; Junior College; English Teacher.

COX, David E; Metawora HS; East Peoria, IL; SctActv; StuCncl; RptrSchPpr; Univ Of Ill; Law.

COX, Deirdre; Tipton HS; Tipton, IA; ALAGirlsSt; Chr; Chrs; HonRl; NHS; OffAde; SchPl; StuCncl; RptrYrbk; SchPpr; FrCl; College; Communications.

COX, Diane; Dekalb Senior Hs; Dekalb, IL; HonRl; NHS; TchrAde; Teen; 4-H; FrCl; PpCl; 4-HAwd; University; Business.

COX, Elaine G; Rosiclare HS; Rosiclare, IL; 1/32 SecFrshCls; PresSrCls; Band; Chrs; ChrhWkr; CmntyWkr; CncrtBnd; HonRl; MrchBnd; NHS; PolWkr; Bsktbl; BttyCrckrAwd; Murray State Univ; Special Education.

COX, Emily M; Pecatonica HS; Winnebago, IL; 6/60 PresFrshCls; PresBand; PresChrs; CncrtBnd; HonRl; JrNHS; Mdrgl; MrchBnd; NHS; PepBnd; Bsktbl; Chrldr; GAA; 4-HAwd; College; Vocation.

COX, Frances L; Normal Comm HS; Normal, IL; 1/480 VPChr; ChrhWkr; SecCncrtBnd; SecMdrgl; TreasNHS; SecNatlThespSoc; Orch; SchMus; SchPl; GAA; William Jewell College; History.

COX, Heidi L; East HS; Des Moines, IA; AFS; Aud/Vis; HonRl; JA; ModUN; PolWkr; RedCrAde; StuGov; Teen; UNYO; FrCl; PpCl; IMSpt; Iowa State Univ; Engineering.

COX, Jennifer L; Wawasee HS; Syracuse, IN; SecTrsJrCls; Chr; HonRl; JrNHS; NHS; StuCncl; PpCl; Chrldr; College; Medicine.

COX, Joann M; Wellcome Memorial HS; Garden City, MN; 7/45 Band; Chrs; ChrhWkr; CncrtBnd; HonRl; HospAde; PepBnd; SecYrbk; SchPpr; FHA;.

COX, Julie K; Eisenhower HS; Decatur, IL; 1/301 NHS; Millikin Univ; Chemistry.

COX, Kathleen A; Fort Atkinson Sr HS; Fort Atkinson, WI; 41#54#60 SchMus; Yrbk; PpCl; Uw Oshkosh; Nursing.

COX, Kathleen M; Bishop Borgess HS; Detroit, MI; ChrhWkr; CmntyWkr; HonRl; HospAde; NHS; Quill&Scroll; RptrYrbk; FrCl; College; Nursing.

COX, Lawrence M; Cass Tech HS; Detroit, MI; 52/1003 HonRl; TreasNHS; IMSpt; Univ Of Michigan; Mathematics.

COX, Lois K; Nevada HS; Nevada, MO; SchPl; RptrSchPpr; SchPpr; LatCl; PpCl; University; Business.

COX, Mark A; Frankton Sr HS; Frankton, IN; 21/168 TreasBand; CncrtBnd; HonRl; TreasMrchBnd; NHS; VPYthFlsp; FTA; CaptBsbl; Ftbl; Glf; Purdue Univ; Math Teacher.

COX, Marla F; Jayhawk Linn HS; Prescott, KS; VPJrCls; ChrhWkr; DrlTm; HonRl; TchrAde; RptrYrbk; EdYrBk; RptrSchPpr; SchPpr; FHA; PresSpnCl; PpCl; Trade School; Professional.

COX, Michael D; South Decatur HS; Greensburg, IN; 14/92 PresJrCls; Chrs; HonRl; NHS; StuCncl; FFA; KeyCl; PpCl; Bsbl; LetterBsktbl; LetterTrk; Purdue Univ; Liberal Arts.

COX, Michael W; Hutsonville HS; Hutsonville, IL; Band; Chr; ChrhWkr; CncrtBnd; HonRl; Mdrgl; MrchBnd; PepBnd; SchPl; MthCl; Coll; Prof.

COX, Nancy A; Sullivan HS; Sullivan, IN; 7/152 Chr; Chrs; DrlTm; HonRl; JrNHS; NHS; SchMus; 4-H; SpnCl; Chrldr; Indiana St Univ; Nursing.

COX, Nancy K; Coldwater HS; Coldwater, KS; 27#29#30 HonRl; NHS; SchMus; SchPl; StuCncl; VPSophCls; RptrSchPpr; College.

COX, Paul; Fayette HS; Fayette, MO; Chrs; HonRl; NHS; StuCncl; College; Forestry.

COX, Rebecca M; Lake Central HS; St John, IN; Aud/Vis; Chr; Chrs; HonRl; Mdrgl; NatlThespSoc; SchMus; SchPl; TchrAde; YthFlsp; College; Theater.

COX, Rick M; Lindbergh HS; St Louis, MO; 1 1000 HonRl; NHS; NatlMeritSF; SchAde; RusCl; Trk; Wa Univ; Elec Engin.

COX, Rick M; Brownstown HS; Brownstown, IL; 2/35 PresFrshCls; ChrhWkr; CmntyWkr; HonRl; HospAde; LbryAde; SchPl; StuCncl; Yrbk; Univ Of Il; Physician.

COX, Roberta M; Central Heights HS; Princeton, KS; DrlTm; NHS; SchPl; StuCncl; Pres4-H; FFA; FHA; PpCl; LetterBsktbl; Trk; 4-HAwd; PresAwd;.

COX, Robert J; Pennville HS; Dunkirk, IN; 10/43 Aud/Vis; Chr; HonRl; NHS; StuCncl; TchrAde; 4-H; FFA; Bsktbl; Trk;.

COX, Robert L; Truman HS; Independence, MO; Chr; ChrhWkr; CmntyWkr; HonRl; JrNHS; Mdrgl; NHS; NatlThespSoc; PolWkr; SchMus; SctActv; StuCncl; Trk; College; Music.

COX, Sandra L; Flora HS; Flora, IL; 2/138 HonRl; NHS; TchrAde; RptrSchPpr; SchPpr; FBLA; PresFHA; FTA; SpnCl; MthCl; SciCl; College; Teaching.

COX, Sara J; Beardstown Jr Sr HS; Beardstown, IL; 1/128 ALAGirlsSt; Chrs; ChrhWkr; HonRl; NHS; 4-H; College; Forestry.

COX, Stephen; United Township HS; Hampton, IL; HonRl; TchrAde; SchPpr; LetterFtbl; LetterTennis; Univ; Chemistry.

COX, Tamra L; Tri Center Community HS; Persia, IA; Chr; Chrs; CncrtBnd; HonRl; MrchBnd; NHS; SchMus; PpCl; Bsktbl; LetterTrk; Jennie Edmundson Nursing School; Nursing.

COX, Theresa L; Hillsboro HS; Hillsboro, IL; 13/183 HonRl; OffAde; StuCncl; RptrSchPpr; SchPpr; SpnCl; PpCl; S I U ; Law.

COX, Toni M; Mattoon HS; Mattoon, IL; Band; CncrtBnd; HospAde; MrchBnd; OffAde; Orch; SchAde; 4-H; 4-HAwd; College.

COX, Wendy A; High School; De Soto, KS; 49/107 Chr; Chrs; RptrYrbk; RptrSchPpr; 4-H; FBLA; FHA; PpCl;.

COX, William H; Wabeno HS; Wabeno, WI; 4/33 ALBoysSt; ChrhWkr; CmntyWkr; HonRl; SchPl; StuCncl; TchrAde; PpCl; LetterBsktbl; CaptFtbl; 4-HAwd; U W Stevens Point; Computer.

COYLE, Brian G; Murdock HS; Murdock, MN; Chr; SchPl; YthFlsp; 4-H; LetterBsbl; LetterBsktbl; LetterFtbl; LetterTrk; 4-HAwd; College.

COYLE, Lisa A; Jacksonville HS; Jacksonville, IL; 19/363 SecJrCls; Chr; HonRl; NHS; SchMus; StuGov; UNYO; SptEdYrbk; FTA; Illinois St Univ; Special Education.

COYLE, Mary; Catholic Memorial HS; Waukesha, WI; 4/140 TrsJrCls; ChrhWkr; HonRl; JrNHS; NHS; SctActv; StuCncl; EdSchPpr; PpCl; Marquette Univ; Nursing.

COYLE, Peter J; Lincoln HS; Lake City, MN; 14/147 PresFrshCls; PresSophCls; Chr; Chrl; HonRl; NHS; PolWkr; SchMus; LetterBsbl; CaptFtbl; College; Law.

COYLE, Richard; Maquoketa Valley HS; Hopkinton, IA; 15/108 VPJrCls; Band; HonRl; NatlThespSoc; Quill&Scroll; SchMus; SchPl; StuCncl; RptrSchPpr; EdSchPpr; Coll;md.

COYNE, Catherine M; Nazareth HS; Western Springs, IL; SecSophCls; Chrs; ChrhWkr; SchMus; SchPl; SctActv; Teen; YthFlsp; SpnCl; Chrldr; Univ; Marketing.

COYNE, David J; Gordon Tech HS; Chicago, IL; 21/647 CAP; HonRl; NHS; SchPl; StuCncl; RptrSchPpr; FrCl; MthCl; Univ Of Ill; Pilot.

COYNE, Denise A; Bluffton HS; Bluffton, IN; TrsFrshCls; Chrs; HonRl; SchPl; TreasStuCncl; LatCl; LetterBsktbl; Chrldr; GAA; Depauw Univ; Dentist.

COYNE, Raymond M; Hinsdale So HS; Westmont, IL; 90/448 AFS; StuCncl; RptrSchPpr; SchPpr; Univ Of Illinois; Social Studies.

COYNE, Terrance S; Maine South HS; Park Ridge, IL; HonRl; NatlMeritCmnd; Coll; Chem Eng.

COZAD, David C; Bay City Central HS; Bay City, MI; HonRl; NHS; LetterGlf; Tennis; Alma College; Medicine.

COZIAHR, Mary K; Thomas Jefferson HS; Council Bluffs, IA; 4/454 Band; NHS; Orch; SctActv; TreasStuCncl; EdYrBk; PresSciCl; LetterBsktbl; LetterTrk; SecGAA; Univ Of Northern Ia; Medicine.

COZIAR, Faith L; Ofallon Twnsp HS; Caseyville, IL; SecChrs; Mdrgl; VPSpnCl; College; Teaching.

COZZA, John F; Lyons Township HS; Western Springs, IL; VPSrCls; HonRl; NHS; JrNHS; Teen; Socr; Univ Of Illinois; Law.

COZZAGLIO, Bonnie L; Fordson HS; Dearborn, MI; Chrl; Chrs; CmntyWkr; HonRl; HospAde; JrNHS; LitMag; NHS; StuGov; SpnCl; College.

CRABB, Kathleen A; Sac Comm HS; Sac City, IA; AFS; HonRl; LbryAde; Quill&Scroll; RptrSchPpr; FBLA; FHA; PpCl; Bsktbl; Trk; College.

CRABBS, Cheryl J; Guthrie Center HS; Guthrie Center, IA; Chrl; HonRl; NHS;.

CRABTREE, David M; Hartford HS; Hartford, MI; Band; TchrAde; Michigan St Univ; Math.

CRABTREE, Elayne L; Hancock Public HS; Hancock, MN; Band; Chr; Chrs; ChrhWkr; HospAde; NatlThespSoc; PepBnd; SchAde; SchPl; RptrSchPpr; U Of Mn.

CRABTREE, Jean L; Wauwatosa East HS; Wauwatosa, WI; CncrtBnd; HonRl; MrchBnd; NHS; MthCl; Col;.

CRABTREE, Pamela K; Central HS; St Jospeh, MO; 49/507 Chrs; HonRl; HospAde; LbryAde; SctActv; LatCl; Univ; Professional.

CRABTREE, Ronald C; Waterloo Public HS; Columbia, IL; 1/147 ALBoysSt; Band; Chrs; ChrhWkr; CncrtBnd; HonRl; JrNHS; MrchBnd; NHS; PepBnd; SchMus; AmLegAwd; West Point; Electronics Engineer.

CRABTREE, Susan R; Moravia HS; Blakesburg, IA; SecFrshCls; Band; Chr; Chrs; CncrtBnd; HonRl; MrchBnd; PepBnd; SchMus; RptrYrbk; EdYrBk; RptrSchPpr; FHA; SpnCl; CaptChrldr; Central College; Music.

CRACCHIOLA, Vickie; Berkeley Sr Hs; Berkeley, MO; SecJA; NHS; StuCncl; College; Doctor.

CRACKEL, Michael D; Serena HS; Earlville, IL; PresSrCls; ChrhWkr; CmntyWkr; SchPl; StuCncl; SptEdYrbk; FTA; LetterBsbl; LetterBsktbl; LetterFtbl; LetterGlf; IMSpt; College; Accounting.

CRACKEL, Philip R; Miller HS; Miller, SD; 8/100 ALBoysSt; Band; ChrhWkr; HonRl; NatlFornLg; NHS; NatlMeritSF; SchPl; SchPpr; College; Engineering.

CRACRAFT, Cindy J; Macomb Sr HS; Macomb, IL; 1/250 Chr; ChrhWkr; HonRl; NHS; SctActv; PresYthFlsp; EdSchPpr; FrCl; PresSpnCl; Univ Of Ill; Foreign Correspondent.

CRADDOCK, Richard D; Brookings HS; Brookings, SD; ALBoysSt; StuCncl; 4-H; CaptFtbl; CaptWrstlng; 4-HAwd; KiwanAwd; LionAwd; Univ; Biology.

CRADER, Bernard V; Woodland R Iv HS; Glen Allen, MO; HonRl; MrchBnd; NatlMeritCmnd; ROTC; StuCncl; RptrSchPpr; LatCl; SpnCl; MasAwd; Coll; Law.

CRADER, Patsy R; Woodland HS; Lutesville, MO; CmntyWkr; HonRl; NHS; NatlMeritSchl; RedCrAde; StuCncl; StuGov; FBLA; FSA; LetterChrldr; Col; Professional.

CRAFT, Cary L; Argyle HS; Gratiot, WI; Chrs; HonRl; 4-H; FFA; Univ Of Wisconsin; Animal Science.

CRAFT, David L; Auburn HS; Rockford, IL; 1/300 Illinois College.

CRAFT, Le Ann; Argyle HS; Gratiot, WI; 4/44 ALAGirlsSt; Chr; HonRl; TreasLbryAde; CaptTwrl; Pres4-H; FFA; TreasFHA; 4-HAwd; Univ Of Wisconsin; Agriculture.

CRAFTON, Curtis R; Clay City HS; Terre Haute, IN; VPJrCls; HonRl; StuCncl; 4-H; FFA; LetterWrstlng; Purdue Univ.

CRAGLE, David R; Hudson Community HS; Hudson, IA; 5/61 Band; Chr; HonRl; NHS; SchMus; SchPpr; LetterBsbl; Bsktbl; LetterFtbl; LetterTrk; College; Math Or Physics.

CRAGO, Carrie D; Belleville Twp East HS; Fairview Hts, IL; 35/674 Chr; Chrl; Chrs; ChrhWkr; CmntyWkr; HonRl; JrNHS; NHS; Orch; SchMus; Ball State Univ; Music.

CRAHAN, Kevin F; High School; Dubuque, IA; ChrhWkr; CmntyWkr; OffAde; PolWkr; SctActv; StuCncl; StuGov; SchPpr; PpCl; Ftbl; Wrstlng; CchngActv; St Thomas College; Law.

CRAIG, Beth A; Trenton HS; Trenton, MO; AFS; HonRl; NHS; SctActv; StuCncl; FHA; SpnCl; PpCl; SciCl; Chrldr; College.

CRAIG, Brenda C; Kirksville Sr HS; Kirksville, MO; Chr; ChrhWkr; HonRl; OffAde; PresYthFlsp; Yrbk; SchPpr; 4-H; FHA; FTA; Ne Missouri St Univ; English.

CRAIG, Carol D; Normal Comm HS; Normal, IL; AFS; ALAGirlsSt; LbryAde; NHS; Quill&Scroll; TchrAde; EdYrBk; PresFrCl; Illinois Wesleyan Univ; Law.

CRAIG, Catheryn E; Central HS; Flint, MI; 42/470 SecSophCls; HonRl; HospAde; MrchBnd; NHS; Orch; SchPl; StuGov; TchrAde; Spring Arbor College; Medicine.

CRAIG, Dennis L; Waukegan HS; Waukegan, IL; 1/856 Chr; CncrtBnd; HonRl; JrNHS; LbryAde; MrchBnd; PresNatlFornLg; PresNHS; NatlMeritCmnd; PepBnd; Univ Of Ill; Architectural Studies.

CRAIG, James P; West HS; Davenport, IA; VPJrCls; ALBoysSt; Chr; HonRl; StuCncl; StuGov; LatCl; Ftbl; Trk; AmLegAwd; Coll; Law.

CRAIG, Johnetta M; Mary Inst HS; St Louis, MO; AFS; Aud/Vis; Band; Chr; ChrhWkr; CmntyWkr; HonRl; HospAde; JA; LbryAde; Chrldr; GAA; IMSpt; Univ; Pediatrician.

CRAIG, Joy L; Regina Dominican HS; Highland Park, IL; 18/207 Chrs; HonRl; LitMag; Mdrgl; SchMus; SchPl; Sdlty; StuCncl; College; Therapist.

CRAIG, Katrina E; Brazil Sr HS; Brazil, IN; Chr; HonRl; NHS; SchMus; Yrbk; 4-H; FrCl; PpCl; GAA; University; Professional.

CRAIG, Kevin A; Maine Twp South HS; Park Ridge, IL; 200/800 HonRl; SctActv; Univ Of Ill Urbana; Agriculture.

CRAIG, Kevin L; Maywood HS; Maywood, NE; Chrs; ChrhWkr; CncrtBnd; HonRl; NHS; SchPl; Yrbk; Bsktbl; Ftbl; Trk; College; Business Management.

CRAIG, Lawrence A; Finney HS; Detroit, MI; 10/100 Band; ChrhWkr; CncrtBnd; HonRl; IntrClCncl; OffAde; TchrAde; YthFlsp; MthCl; SciCl; Wayne St Univ; Engineering.

CRAIG, Mark K; Fairbury HS; Fairbury, NE; 12/138 ChrhWkr; HonRl; FBLA; FFA; Ftbl; Trk; IMSpt; Trade; Computer Programming.

CRAIG, Marvin E; Delavan HS; Delavan, IL; LbryAde; StuCncl; SchPpr; FFA; SciCl; Bsktbl; LetterTrk; IMSpt; Working.

CRAIG, Michael B; Libertyville HS; Libertyville, IL; 67/458 Chr; HonRl; NHS; SchMus; SchPl; Northwestern Univ; Broadcasting.

CRAIG, Robin D; Elgin HS; Streamwood, IL; Band; HonRl; NatlFornLg; NatlMeritCmnd; Orch; PepBnd; PolWkr; SchPl; TchrAde; Univ; Law.

CRAIG, Sharon L; Baldwin HS; Baldwin City, KS; 1/70 TrsJrCls; Band; HonRl; HospAde; NHS; PepBnd; StuCncl; FHA; SpnCl; College; Home Economics.

CRAIG, Teresa L; St Joseph Ogden HS; St Joseph, IL; 13/107 VPSophCls; Band; Chrs; HonRl; NHS; SchMus; Yrbk; SchPpr; FrCl; Chrldr; Western Ky U; History Teacher.

CRAIG, Terrence E; Northern HS; Detroit, MI; PresSrCls; VPSrCls; HonRl; JrNHS; NHS; NatlMeritCmnd; NatlMeritSchl; GovHonPrgAwd; KiwanAwd; Johnson C Smith U.

CRAIGHEAD, Lois J; R I North Callaway HS; Fulton, MO; 3/76 TrsSophCls; TrsJrCls; SecBand; NHS; TreasStuCncl; Yrbk; Sec4-H; PresFTA; FrCl; PresPpCl; College.

CRAIGHEAD, Lois J; Ri North Callaway HS; Fulton, MO; 3/77 TrsSophCls; TrsJrCls; SecBand; HonRl; NHS; TreasStuCncl; RptrYrbk; PresFTA; PresPpCl; CitAwd; College.

CRAIGMILE, Deborah A; Lake Forest HS; Lake Forest, IL; 37/435 ChrhWkr; HonRl; NHS; NatlMeritCmnd; Orch; Trk; Drake Univ; Interior Design.

CRAIGMILE, James L; Dilworth Public HS; Dilworth, MN; PresFrshCls; PresJrCls; ALBoysSt; NHS; StuCncl; Bsktbl; Ftbl; Glf; Trk; U Of Nd ;law.

CRAIL, Erick E; Belfield HS; Belfield, ND; 1/58 ALBoysSt; TreasCncrtBnd; HonRl; ModUN; PresNHS; NatlMeritCmnd; PresStuCncl; StuGov; SchPpr; LetterBsktbl; U Of Nd; Corporate Law.

CRAIN, Jeanne M; Riverside Brookfield HS; Brookfield, IL; 14/485 Band; CncrtBnd; DrmMjrt; HonRl; HospAde; LbryAde; MrchBnd; NHS; SchMus; Northern Il; Ele Ed.

CRAIN, Jeffery F; Franklin Public HS; Morton, MN; Band; Chr; ChrhWkr; CncrtBnd; MrchBnd; PepBnd; SchPl; StuGov; RptrSchPpr; FFA; Willmar Cc.

CRAIN, Karla F; Jackson HS; Jackson, MO; Band; HonRl; MrchBnd; PepBnd; Yrbk; FrCl; PpCl; Univ; Registered Nurse.

CRAIN, Linda F; Thomas Jefferson HS; Rockford, IL; 28/355 HonRl; TchrAde; Medical Secretary.

CRAIN, Michael M; Alexander Hamilton HS; Milwaukee, WI; 56/786 Chr; ChrhWkr; Orch; SctActv; Marquette Univ; Physics.

CRAIN, Rhonda K; Laurel HS; Laurel, IN; HonRl; RptrYrbk; RptrSchPpr; Vocational Training.

CRAINE, Mary Caren; Carme For Girls HS; Barrington, IL; 28/195 SecJrCls; HonRl; StuCncl; StuGov; Coll; Pro.

CRAINE, Patrick J; Gordon Tech HS; Chicago, IL; ChrhWkr; CmntyWkr; OffAde; PepBnd; PolWkr; SctActv; Teen; LetterBsbl; IMSpt; University Of Arizona.

CRAINE, Sharri; Lincoln Park HS; Lincoln Park, MI; Band; LbryAde; StuCncl; SchPpr; Swmmng; Chrldr; College; Pychologist.

CRALL, Catherine M; Albia Community HS; Albia, IA; TrsFrshCls; HonRl; MrchBnd; RedCrAde; Twrl; Yrbk; 4-H; College; Liberal Arts.

CRAMBLET, Richard; Holton HS; Holton, MI; 4/63 PresFrshCls; PresSophCls; VPSrCls; Band; ChrhWkr; MrchBnd; PepBnd; SchPl; Yrbk; Alma College.

CRAME, Richard; Rockford Sr HS; Rockford, MI; HonRl; NHS; CivCl; SciCl; Bsktbl; RotaryAwd; Western Mich Univ; Broascastig.

CRAMER, Kathleen S; Casey Jr/sr HS; Yale, IL; 21/98 SecJrCls; Band; ChrhWkr; CncrtBnd; HonRl; MrchBnd; PepBnd; StuCncl; Yrbk; FHA; Univf Health Career Nursing.

CRAMER, Laura A; Manistee HS; Manistee, MI; ALAGirlsSt; Band; CncrtBnd; HonRl; JrNHS; MrchBnd; SchPpr; VoiceDemAwd; Olivet Col; Music.

CRAMER, Mary C; Bristol HS; Bristol, SD; TrsJrCls; Band; Chrs; HonRl; HospAde; PepBnd; RptrYrbk; RptrSchPpr; FHA; FNA; Univ.

CRAMER, Pamela S; Greenview HS; Greenview, IL; 3/25 PresSophCls; PresSrCls; Band; Chrs; NHS; PresStuCncl; YthFlsp; Yrbk; RptrSchPpr; Glf; GAA; IMSpt; College; Public Relations.

CRAMER, Paul E; Centura HS; Dannebrog, NE; 21/70 Band; Chr; Chrs; CncrtBnd; MrchBnd; PepBnd; FBLA; Wrstlng; Grace Bible Inst;electronics Technician.

CRAMER, Radley B; Southeastern HS; Bowen, IL; 3/50 PresSophCls; PresJrCls; HonRl; NHS; StuCncl; Coburn Fashion School; Fashion Buying.

CRANDAL, Verla E; Clark County Ri HS; Alexandria, MO; Band; Chrs; CncrtBnd; DrmMjrt; HonRl; MrchBnd; PepBnd; SchPl; Yrbk; FHA; Northeast Mo State U Kirksville.

CRANDALL, Julie; Winnebago HS; Rockford, IL; 22/105 Band; ChrhWkr; CncrtBnd; HonRl; LbryAde; MrchBnd; OffAde; FTA; Trk; Univ Of Illinois; Economics.

CRANDALL, Kerry L; East Union HS; Afton, IA; PresSophCls; Band; ChrhWkr; CncrtBnd; DrmMjrt; HonRl; MrchBnd; RptrSchPpr; Bsktbl; LetterGlf; College; Professional.

CRANDALL, Lori L; Msd Of Fremont HS; Fremont, IN; 10/63 PresSrCls; PresChr; ChrhWkr; NHS; PolWkr; SchPl; EdYrBk; PresKeyCl; Wrstlng; DARAwd; University.

CRANDALL, Paul; Drake HS; Drake, ND; ChrhWkr; HonRl; SchPl; StuCncl; YthFlsp; Bsbl; Bsktbl; Ftbl; Trk; Coll; Coaching.

CRANDELL, James F; Libertyville HS; Libertyville, IL; 26/416 Band; CncrtBnd; HonRl; MrchBnd; NHS; Orch; PepBnd; SchPl; Bsktbl; College.

CRANDELL, Karen; Central HS; St Joseph, MO; 87/505 HonRl; TchrAde; LatCl; SpnCl; MthCl; SciCl; U Mo Columbia; Mathematics.

CRANE, Christopher M; New Trier East HS; Winnetka, IL; Band; CncrtBnd; HonRl; LitMag; Orch; StuGov; College; Professional.

CRANE, Dwight; Savannah HS; Savannah, MO; TrsFrshCls; TrsSophCls; HonRl; NHS; SpnCl; PpCl; CchngActv; Univ Of M U At Columbia; Engineering.

CRANE, Jeffrey B; Hallsville HS; Hallsville, MO; VPFrshCls; Chrs; ChrhWkr; CmntyWkr; HonRl; RptrSchPpr; SptEdSchPpr; SciCl; CaptBsbl; CaptBsktbl; Jr College; Pro Ball.

CRANE, Jolene; Northwood Kensett HS; Northwood, IA; 2/50 Band; Chr; ChrhWkr; CncrtBnd; HonRl; NHS; SchPl; Bsktbl; Trk; GAA; Univ Of Northern Ia; Doctor.

CRANE, Linda K; Savannah HS; Savannah, MO; TrsFrshCls; VPSophCls; Band; Chr; CncrtBnd; HonRl; MrchBnd; NHS; SchMus; PpCl; CaptChrldr; IMSpt; Univ Of Mo; Occupational Therapy.

CRANE, Raymond E; Princeton R 5 HS; Princeton, MO; 14/52 HonRl; NHS;.

CRANE, William M; Salem Community HS; Salem, IL; 14/213 HonRl; JrNHS; NHS; SchPl; SpnCl; PpCl; Bsktbl; CaptFtbl; CaptTrk; Univ Of Il; Pilot.

CRAPP, Debra; Potosi HS; Potosi, WI; 7/70 DrmMjrt; HonRl; JrNHS; MrchBnd; NHS; SchPl; StuCncl; Twrl; RptrSchPpr; FHA; College; Psychology.

CRAPSON, Jeffrey; Tarkio HS; Tarkio, MO; 1/62 Band; ChrhWkr; CncrtBnd; HonRl; MrchBnd; PepBnd; StuCncl; YthFlsp; IMSpt; Coll; Math.

CRARY, Frances I; Onalaska HS; Onalaska, WI; ChrhWkr; HonRl; NHS; RptrYrbk; PpCl; CaptChrldr; GAA; IMSpt; Univ; Med Lab Tech.

CRASE, Michael W; Belmont HS; Mineral Point, WI; Band; HonRl; ModUN; PepBnd; SchMus; SchPl; StuCncl; 4-H; Bsbl; Trk; College; Communications.

CRATES, April A; Cassville HS; Shell Knob, MO; 16/103 HonRl; NHS; SchMus; PresSophCls; SctActv; TchrAde; Art Sch; Commercial Art.

CRAUN, Kathleen; Maple Valley HS; Vermontville, MI; HonRl; 4-H; SpnCl; Bsktbl; GAA; PPFtbl; 4-HAwd; Msu; Nursing.

CRAVATTA, Christine A; Savanna Community HS; Savanna, IL; PresSophCls; PresJrCls; Band; Chrs; HonRl; NHS; SchPl; SecStuCncl; EdYrBk; University.

CRAVEN, Carla R; Mcpherson Senior HS; Mcpherson, KS; 10/232 HonRl; LbryAde; NHS; StuCncl; FHA; PresSpnCl; College Graduate; Sociology.

CRAVEN, Chris D; Catholic Boys HS; Quincy, IL; 7/75 HonRl; StuCncl; FBLA; College; Professional.

CRAVEN, Paula J; Union HS; Caledonia, WI; 3/204 SecJrCls; SecSrCls; SecAFS; Trk; Chrldr; GAA;

PPFtbl; 4-HAwd; GovHonPrgAwd; CitAwd; Clge; Physical Therapy.

CRAVEN, Rex P; Randolph HS; Randolph, NE; HonRl; PresNHS; NatlThespSoc; SchMus; SchPl; StuCncl;.

CRAVEN, Valerie A; Crystal Lake HS; Crystal Lake, IL; 23/477 HonRl; NHS; SchPpr; Tennis; Madison College; Physical Therapy.

CRAVENS, Roy E; Fairfield Comm HS; Fairfield, IL; HonRl; LatCl; MthCl; Univ Of Illinois; Mathematics.

CRAVENS, Roy E; Fairfield Community HS; Fairfield, IL; HonRl; LatCl; MthCl; Univ Of Illinois; Mathematics.

CRAVENS, Roy E; Fairfield Comm HS; Fairfield, IL; HonRl; LatCl; MthCl; Univ Of Ill; Math.

CRAW, Jacki R; Benkelman HS; Max, NE; 7/34 Band; Chrs; CncrtBnd; HonRl; PepBnd; PpCl; Swmmng; LetterTrk; Chrldr; Univ Of Nebraska; Accounting.

CRAW, Lori C; Stratton Public HS; Stratton, NE; 1/19 SecJrCls; Band; CncrtBnd; HonRl; MrchBnd; NHS; TchrAde; RptrYrbk; PpCl; Trk; College; Business.

CRAWFORD, Berit A; Guilford HS; Rockford, IL; 38/656 HonRl; Quill&Scroll; Illinois State Univ; Biology.

CRAWFORD, Bonnie; Sterling Heights HS; Sterling Heights, MI; 20/500 NHS; NatlThespSoc; SchAde; SchPl; TchrAde; SciCl; Bsbl; GAA; Mi Tech; Assoc Degree In Nrsng.

CRAWFORD, Carol A; Woodruff HS; Peoria, IL; CmntyWkr; HonRl; OffAde; Yrbk; Social Work.

CRAWFORD, Cheryl A; Antigo HS; Antigo, WI; 3/368 Band; ChrhWkr; CncrtBnd; PepBnd; CivCl; LatCl; MthCl; Trk; LetterChrldr; University Of Wisconsin; Nuclear Eng.

CRAWFORD, Cheryl A; Appleton West HS; Appleton, WI; HospAde; SecYthFlsp; GerCl; Uw Platteville; Criminal Justice.

CRAWFORD, Dan L; Winona HS; Winona, MN; HonRl; JrNHS; NHS; SpnCl; Bsbl; Bsktbl; Ftbl; Tennis; IMSpt; RotaryAwd; Winona St U; Geology Oceanography.

CRAWFORD, Delia L; Lindblom Tech HS; Chicago, IL; 227/900 Chr; PresChrhWkr; OffAde; SchAde; StuCncl; StuGov; TchrAde; SpnCl; PpCl; Bsktbl; GAA; Michigan Tech; Physical Therapist.

CRAWFORD, James A; Pierce City HS; Pierce City, MO; 12/60 ChrhWkr; CncrtBnd; HonRl; MrchBnd; ModUN; NHS; SchAde; TchrAde; MthCl; LetterFtbl; Work.

CRAWFORD, James P; Vianney HS; Kirkwood, MO; 4/170 Chrs; HonRl; NHS; SchMus; SpnCl; LetterFtbl; LetterTrk; IMSpt; RotaryAwd; University Of Dayton; History.

CRAWFORD, Jayne M; Columbus North Senior HS; Columbus, IN; 34/513 Chr; ChrhWkr; CmntyWkr; HonRl; JA; YthFlsp; SpnCl; PpCl; Vincennes University; Dental Hygienest.

CRAWFORD, Jeffrey G; Forest Lake HS; Forest Lk, MN; CncrtBnd; HonRl; MrchBnd; PepBnd; SpnCl; Bsktbl; Trk; Univ Of Mn ; Law.

CRAWFORD, John R; Savannah Riii HS; Savannah, MO; PresSophCls; PresJrCls; ALBoysSt; CmntyWkr; NHS; SctActv; SchPpr; Bsktbl; Ftbl; Tennis; Wrstlng; AmLegAwd; Univ Of Missouri.

CRAWFORD, Katherine A; Notre Dame HS; Chicago, IL; HstFrshCls; SecTrsSophCls; SecTrsJrCls; CmntyWkr; RedCrAde; TchrAde; Yrbk; SpnCl; Bsktbl; IMSpt; Col; Special E.

CRAWFORD, Kendra L; Wolverine Comm HS; Wolverine, MI; 4/18 TrsSrCls; HonRl; NHS; Yrbk; Business Schl; Accounting.

CRAWFORD, Leo J; Heelan HS; Sioux City, IA; 9/250 Band; HonRl; Bsktbl; CaptFtbl; Trk; IMSpt; Univ Of South Dakota; Business Adm.

CRAWFORD, Mary A; TriHS; Lewisville, IN; Chr; PpCl; SciCl; PresGAA; Vocational School; Health.

CRAWFORD, Matthew T; St Louis Univ HS; Richmond Heights, MO; Chr; LetterTrk; Univ.

CRAWFORD, Michael E; Triopia HS; Jacksonville, IL; Chrs; ChrhWkr; HonRl; StuCncl; YthFlsp; Bsktbl; Ftbl; Trk; AmLegAwd; JAAwd; Univ; Vocation.

CRAWFORD, Randal L; California HS; California, MO; PresSrCls; Chr; Chrs; HonRl; NHS; StuCncl; YthFlsp; MthCl; ChmnBsktbl; Ftbl; Univ Of Mo; Civil Engineering.

CRAWLEY, Joanne L; St Frances Cabrini HS; Allen Park, MI; 1/167 ChrhWkr; CmntyWkr; HonRl; NHS; StuGov; RptrSchPpr; LetterTrk; GAA; JCAwd; PresAwd; College Or University; Probably Sciences.

CRAWLEY, Therese N; Riverside Brookfield HS; La Grange Park, IL; CaptDrlTm; HonRl; LbryAde; OffAde; GAA; Northern Illinois Univ; Nursing.

CRAY, Nicholas K; St Laurence HS; Oak Lawn, IL; 16/385 HonRl; NHS; SciCl; Northwestern Univ; Engineering.

CRAY, Patricia J; West Platte R Ii HS; Weston, MO; AFS; Chr; DrlTm; DrmMjrt; HonRl; ModUN; NHS; SchPl; SecStuCncl; PresFBLA; CaptBsktbl; LetterTrk; Chrldr; College; Theatrical Arts.

CRAY, Terrence B; Clinton Comm HS; Clinton, IL; 8/156 SecSophCls; HonRl; NHS; PresStuCncl; Bsbl; Bsktbl; Ftbl; Trk; SARAwd; Univ Of Ill; Teacher.

CRAYCRAFT, Robert H; Culver HS; Culver, IN; 13/95 VPSrCls; ALBoysSt; VPChr; ChrhWkr; CmntyWkr; IntrClCncl; VPNHS; SchMus; StuCncl; Bsktbl; Business College; Cpa.

CRAYTON, Rebecca S; Washington Comm HS; Washington, IL; 2/325 PresAFS; Band; Chr; Chrs; ChrhWkr; HonRl; NHS; NatlMeritFnl; SchMus; StuCncl; FrCl; BttyCrckrAwd; Eastern Ill Univ; Elem Ed.

CREAGER, Richard G; Ja Craig HS; Janesville, WI; AFS; ChrhWkr; CmntyWkr; HonRl; NHS; NatlMeritSF; UNYO; FrCl; MthCl; LetterSwmmng;.

CREASER, Cynthia L; Elk Mound HS; Elk Moundl, WI; 16/41 LetterBand; CncrtBnd; HonRl; MrchBnd; PepBnd; SchPl; TchrAde; RptrYrbk; GAA; IMSpt; Eau Cliare Tech; Accounting.

CREASER, John W; Durand Unified HS; Menomonie, WI; 4-H; PresFFA; Trade; Mechanic.

CREASEY, Jennifer; Clinton Community HS; Clinton, IL; 11/180 Chrs; HonRl; StuCncl; FrCl; Bsktbl; GAA; IMSpt; Lincolnland Vocational; Cosmetologist.

CREASMAN, Craig N; Lincoln Park HS; Lincoln Pk, MI; PresJrCls; PresSrCls; Aud/Vis; HonRl; NHS; NatlSciFnd; StuCncl; FDA; CaptTrk; Wayne St Univ; Doctor.

CREECH, Kae; Cardinal Comm HS; Eldon, IA; PresSophCls; PresSrCls; Band; CncrtBnd; HonRl; PepBnd; 4-H; MasAwd; CitAwd; U Of Ia; Nursing.

CREECH, Kimberly; Hannibal Senior HS; Hannibal, MO; Chrs; StuGov; FrCl; PpCl; Chrldr; IMSpt; PPFtbl; Ne Mo St Univ; Medical Secretary.

CREED, Rick L; Walnut Grove HS; Walnut Grove, MO; 2/27 PresFrshCls; ALBoysSt; Band; HonRl; MrchBnd; StuCncl; LetterBsbl; CaptBsktbl; CitAwd; College; Professional.

CREEK, Reta J; Gillespie HS; Gillespie, IL; 3/133 Band; ChrhWkr; HonRl; HospAde; JrNHS; TchrAde; YthFlsp; Illinois Weselyn Univ; Nursing.

CREGER, Bill E; Maxwell Comm HS; Maxwell, IA; 3/24 Band; Chrs; HonRl; NHS; SchPl; LetterBsbl; LetterBsktbl; LetterFtbl; LetterTrk; College; Pro Athlete.

CREGER, Deborah L; Wauneta Public HS; Wayneta, NE; 5/34 HstSophCls; Band; HonRl; NHS; StuCncl; TchrAde; VPPpCl; LetterTrk; GAA; PresAwd; Univ.

CREGER, Timothy L; Wauneta Pub HS; Wauneta, NE; 12/34 TrsJrCls; CncrtBnd; HonRl; MrchBnd; PepBnd; SctActv; StuCncl; RptrYrbk; RptrSchPpr; University; Vocational.

CREHAN, Cynthia L; Wheeling HS; Wheeling, IL; AFS; DrlTm; HonRl; JrNHS; NHS; SciCl;.

CREIGHTON, Rhonda L; Laville Jr Sr HS; Lakeville, IN; SecFrshCls; ALAGirlsSt; PresNatlFornLg; SecSctActv; StuCncl; Yrbk; RptrSchPpr; 4-H; PresGerCl; PpCl; College; Professional.

CREMEAN, Michele L; Garden City E HS; Garden City, MI; CncrtBnd; HonRl; JrNHS; OffAde; Quill&Scroll; SchMus; SchPl; StuCncl; SchPpr; College; Nursing.

CREMEENS, Penny R; Carbondale Community HS; Carbondale, IL; Chr; ChrhWkr; HonRl; NatlMeritCmnd; NatlThespSoc; YthLg; Yrbk; Southern Illinois Univ; Art.

CREMER, D Mark; Clinton HS; Camanche, IA; 5/506 Chrs; HonRl; NHS; NatlMeritSF; NatlThespSoc; SchMus; SchPl; StuCncl; Bsktbl; Glf; Tennis; Univ; Business Management.

CRENSHAW, Randy; Kirksville Senior HS; Kirksville, MO; Band; CncrtBnd; HonRl; MrchBnd; Bsbl; Glf; CchngActv; Coll; Pro.

CRENSHAW, Susan; Rock Falls Hs; Rock Falls, IL; Chrs; ChrhWkr; HonRl; JrNHS; NHS; 4-H; FrCl; Chrldr; GAA; 4-HAwd; Western Ill U; Veterinarian.

CRESPI, Charles L; Benet Acad; Downers Grove, IL; 17/230 Aud/Vis; ChrhWkr; HonRl; NHS; NatlMeritCmnd; 4-H; 4-HAwd; Coll; Architecture.

CRESPI, C J; Bishop Du Bourg HS; St Louis, MO; ChrhWkr; CmntyWkr; HonRl; PolWkr; FTA; PpCl; GAA; IMSpt; PPFtbl; CitAwd; College; Pre Law.

CRESS, Andrew R; Okemos HS; Okemos, MI; HonRl; NHS; StuGov; GerCl; MthCl; Trk; Univ Of Mich; Pre Law.

CRESS, Cynthia G; Abl HS; Allerton, IL; Chr; HonRl; FHA; Trk; Chrldr; College.

CRESS, John; Wayland Acad; Beaver Dam, MI; 16/74 HonRl; PpCl; LetterBsktbl; LetterGlf;.

CRESS, Karen L; Luther South HS; Oak Lawn, IL; 25/215 SecFrshCls; CncrtBnd; HonRl; HospAde; MrchBnd; NHS; OffAde; TreasStuCncl; TchrAde; RptrSchPpr; GAA; College; Accounting.

CRESSLER, Gwendolyn F; Jennings HS; Jennings, KS; SecTrsFrshCls; SecSophCls; Band; Chr; ChrhWkr; CncrtBnd; MrchBnd; PepBnd; SchPl; Yrbk;.

CRESSWELL, Lisa A; Manchester HS; Manchester, MI; 8/102 ALAGirlsSt; CmntyWkr; SchPl; SctActv; EdYrBk; SchPpr; SecPpCl; CaptBsktbl; Trk; CchngActv; Univ; Science.

CREW, Connie J; Lasalle Peru HS; La Salle, IL; Chrs; HonRl; SpnCl; Illinois Vllaey Comm Clg; Music.

CREWS, Cindy; Granite City HS; Granite City, IL; 41/630 Chr; Chrs; ChrhWkr; HonRl; NHS; Quill&Scroll; RptrYrbk; EdYrBk; PpCl; GAA; Siu Edwardsville;nursing.

CREWS, Jennifer R; Glendale HS; Springfield, MO; HonRl; NatlFornLg; Quill&Scroll; EdSchPpr; College; Journalism.

CREWS, Mitch; English HS; English, IN; 5/34 PresFrshCls; PresSophCls; VPJrCls; ALBoysSt; NHS; Trk; College.

CREWS, Steven E; Fairbury Cropsey HS; Fairbury, IL; HonRl; LetterBsbl; Bsktbl; CaptFtbl; Trk; Wrstlng; Parkland Jr Clge; Construct & Draft.

CREYTS, David M; Everett HS; Lansing, MI; 19/491 ChrhWkr; HonRl; JrNHS; NHS; Michigan State Univ; Math.

CRIDER, Janice; Eagle Bend Public HS; Eagle Bend, MN; 1/33 ChrhWkr; CncrtBnd; HonRl; RptrYrbk; FFA; AmLegAwd; CitAwd; College; Court Reporter.

CRIDER, Steve M; Berkeley Sr HS; Berkeley, MO; 2/352 Band; CncrtBnd; HonRl; PresNHS; PepBnd; SchMus; Bsbl; Bsktbl; LetterFtbl; CaptTrk; College.

CRIFASE, Steve A; Maine East HS; Park Ridge, IL; HonRl; NHS; StuCncl; CaptSocr; Tennis; Wrstlng; Drake Univ; Law.

CRIM, Daniel; Stratford Comm HS; Stratford, IA; 1/32 PresSrCls; HonRl; NatlMeritFnl; PepBnd; YthFlsp; RptrYrbk; SptEdYrbk; GerCl; Iowa State Univ; Computer Science.

CRIM, Daniel E; Stratford Comm HS; Stratford, IA; 1/32 PresSrCls; ALBoysSt; Chrs; ChrhWkr; CmntyWkr; NatlMeritSF; PresStuCncl; ChmnBsbl; ChmnBsktbl; LetterTrk; Ia St U; Computer Science.

CRIM, Paul D; Seymour HS; Plainville, IL; 17/65 ChrhWkr; HonRl; OffAde; 4-H; FFA; PpCl; IMSpt; Carpenter.

CRIM, Robert A; Greenhills HS; Saline, MI; 1/20 NatlMeritFnl; NatlMeritSchl; StuCncl; Yrbk; CaptBsktbl; CaptSocr; OptClAwd; Harvard College.

CRIMMINS, Gilbert L; Pioneer HS; Lucerne, IN; 22/120 ChrhWkr; HonRl; Treas4-H; KeyCl; SpnCl; Bsktbl; Trk; IMSpt; 4-HAwd; Purdue College; Education Coaching.

CRINER, Terri; Boone Jr Sr HS; Boone, IA; Band; CncrtBnd; DrmMjrt; HonRl; MrchBnd; PepBnd; StuCncl; FNA; LatCl; College; Professional.

CRIPE, Debra J; Goshen HS; Goshen, IN; Band; CncrtBnd; HonRl; HospAde; MrchBnd; NatlFornLg; TchrAde; YthFlsp; GerCl; Bsktbl; Coll; Rn.

CRIPE, Lori L; Central City Community HS; Central City, IA; ChrhWkr; HospAde; LbryAde; NatlFornLg; PepBnd; RedCrAde; TchrAde; FrCl; GAA; College; Nursing Ba.

CRIPE, Robert M; Sterling HS; Sterling, IL; TreasAFS; Band; CncrtBnd; HonRl; TreasJA; MrchBnd; NHS; PepBnd; SchPl; FrCl; AmLegAwd; GovHonPrgAwd; Loyola Univ; Doctor.

CRIPE, Tammie S; Vandalia Comm HS; Vandalia, IL; Chr; Chrs; ChrhWkr; LbryAde; NHS; SecFrCl; SecSpnCl; Greenville College; English Teacher.

CRIPPEN, Cindy L; Huron Sr HS; Huron, SD; Band; CncrtBnd; MrchBnd; OffAde; Orch; PpCl; Dakota Wesleyan Univ; Nurse.

CRIPPEN, Karen L; Elmhurst HS; Fort Wayne, IN; Chr; HonRl; JA; LbryAde; RptrSchPpr; JAAwd; University; Biochemistry.

CRIPPEN, Patty; West Holt HS; Atkinson, NE; Chrs; HonRl; HospAde; SctActv; Yrbk; FFA; FHA; FrCl; PpCl; Trade School; Nurse.

CRIPPEN, Terri E; Faith Baptist Academy; Kalamazoo, MI; 1/9 Band; Chr; Chrl; ChrhWkr; HonRl; SchAde; TchrAde; RptrSchPpr; Tennessee Temple College; Secretary.

CRIQUELION, Susan K; Auburn HS; Auburn, IL; 2/58 HonRl; NHS; Yrbk; SchPpr; 4-H; Trk; Chrldr; GAA; IMSpt; BttyCrckrAwd; College; Pharmacy.

CRISCUOLO, Joseph; Fordson HS; Dearborn, MI; Aud/Vis; HonRl; StuCncl; LetterBsbl; LetterFtbl; CchngActv; Northwood Inst; Accounting.

CRISCUOLO, Mark A; Marmion Military Acad; Elgin, IL; 29/97 ChrhWkr; HstFrshCls; HonRl; OffAde; ROTC; StuGov; SchPpr; LatCl; Swmmng; Ill Benedictine Coll; Medical.

CRISMAN, Gregory; White Bear Sr HS; White Bear Lake, MN; Band; SctActv; Ftbl; Trk; IMSpt; College; Veternary Medicine.

CRISP, David; Waldron HS; Shelbyville, IN; 7/68 Band; Chr; ChrhWkr; HonRl; YthFlsp; KeyCl; LatCl; IMSpt; Indiana Central; Medical Technology.

CRISPIN, William K; Chrisman HS; Chrisman, IL; 10/47 PresJrCls; ALBoysSt; Aud/Vis; Band; NHS; PresStuCncl; YthFlsp; LetterBsbl; CaptBsktbl; GovHonPrgAwd; Univ Of Illinois; Law.

CRIST, Deborah J; Harry A Burke HS; Omaha, NE; Chr; Chrs; HonRl; HospAde; NHS; OffAde; SchMus; FNA; FrCl; Trk; Univ Neb Medical Center; Nursing.

CRIST, Elaine M; Milford HS; Milford, IL; 6/70 Band; Chrs; CncrtBnd; Mdrgl; MrchBnd; NHS; StuCncl; YthFlsp; LatCl; Bsktbl; GAA; Illinois State University.

CRIST, Marlys L; Chariton Comm HS; Chariton, IA; Chr; HonRl; NHS; NatlMeritSF; NatlThespSoc; SchMus; CivCl; 4-H; Bsktbl; Drake Univ; Accounting.

CRISTAN, Carol A; Pius Xi HS; Milwaukee, WI; CmntyWkr; LbryAde; SchAde; TchrAde; Yrbk; SchPpr; FBLA; FTA; SpnCl; GAA; Mt Mary Clg; Fashion Mrch.

CRISTE, Joseph A; Monroe HS; Monroe, MI; Band; CncrtBnd; JA; MrchBnd; NatlMeritSF; Mi Univ; Law.

CRISTO, Patricia A; Ft Calhoun HS; Omaha, NE; 1/35 Chrs; CncrtBnd; HonRl; Mdrgl; MrchBnd; NHS; PepBnd; 4-H; BttyCrckrAwd; DanFAwd; Berklee Clg Of Music; Composition.

CRISTO, Patricia A; Fort Calhoun HS; Omaha, NE; SecBand; Chr; CncrtBnd; HonRl; MrchBnd; TreasNHS; PepBnd; 4-H; Trk; 4-HAwd; College; Music Composition.

CRISWELL, Theresa L; Heritage Christian HS; Indianapolis, IN; 11/54 Chr; ChrhWkr; HonRl; SchMus; College; Art.

CRITCHFIELD, Galen; Burrton HS; Moundridge, KS; Band; CncrtBnd; HonRl; PepBnd; LetterFtbl; LetterTrk; College.

CRITTEN, Deborah J; Gallatin HS; Gallatin, MO; 7/47 PresBand; Chr; Chrs; ChrhWkr; CmntyWkr; DrmMjrt; HonRl; NHS; YthFlsp; FHA; LetterBsktbl; Chrldr; 4-HAwd; GodCntryAwd; Mo Methodist; Nursing.

CRITTENDEN, John H; Community HS; West Chicago, IL; 46/321 PresJrCls; HonRl; NHS; StuCncl; Ftbl; Univ Of Illinois; Architecture.

CRNEKOVIC, Barbara P; Nazareth Academy; Chicago, IL; 1/154 HonRl; NHS; NatlMeritFnl; NatlMeritSchl; NatlMeritSF; SchMus; Yrbk; Duke University; Oceanography.

CROCI, Carl L; St Thomas Aquinas HS; Hazelwood, MO; 30/360 ALBoysSt; JA; SchMus; SchPl; EdYrBk; PresLatCl; AmLegAwd; Se Missouri St Univ; Agriculture.

CROCKER, Georgean M; Onsted Public HS; Onsted, MI; SecJrCls; SecSrCls; Band; CmntyWkr; CncrtBnd; MrchBnd; OffAde; PepBnd; SchPl; StuGov; College; Professional.

CROCKETT, Catharine J; Terre Haute North Vigo HS; Terre Haute, IN; 1/600 ChrhWkr; CmntyWkr; HonRl; ModUN; NHS; NatlMeritFnl; PolWkr; RedCrAde; SctActv; StuCncl; RptrSchPpr; CivCl; VPFrCl; CaptSwmmng; De Paul Univ; Medicine.

CROCKETT, Cathy M; West Vigo HS; West Terre Haute, IN; Band; ChrhWkr; CncrtBnd; HonRl; MrchBnd; NHS; PepBnd; FBLA; FTA; Univ; Busines.

CROCKETT, Lesli; Davenport Comm HS; Davenport, NE; 1/23 PresJrCls; Band; ChrhWkr; HonRl; Bsktbl; Glf; Tennis; Trk; Chrldr; 4-HAwd; U Of Nebr; Mathematics.

CROCKETT, Robert D; West Platte R Ii HS; Rushville, MO; VPSophCls; VPJrCls; AFS; ALBoysSt; Chr; HonRl; ModUN; RptrYrbk; Yrbk; Bsbl; Bsktbl; CaptFtbl; CaptGlf; Trk; College; Accounting.

CROCKRELL, Denise M; Harper HS; Chicago, IL; 12/512 Band; CmntyWkr; CncrtBnd; HonRl; MrchBnd; NHS; OffAde; SchMus; StuCncl; TchrAde; University; Law.

CRODY, Rebecca R; Central HS; Jasonville, IN; 11/47 Band; CncrtBnd; HonRl; MrchBnd; NHS; OffAde; TchrAde; Business School.

CROEGAERT, Richard; Annawan Hs; Mineral, IL; 11/85 PresSophCls; ChrhWkr; HonRl; StuCncl; FFA; LetterBsktbl; Ftbl; LetterTrk; AmLegAwd; DanFAwd; College;agriculture.

CROEGAERT, Richard R; Annawan HS; Mineral, IL; 11/80 ChrhWkr; HonRl; StuCncl; 4-H; FFA; LetterBsktbl; LetterFtbl; LetterTrk; AmLegAwd; DanFAwd; 4-HAwd; University.

CROFOOT, Daniel W; Sparta HS; Sparta, MI; 19/209 Band; CncrtBnd; HonRl; MrchBnd; NHS; SchPl; TchrAde; FTA; Calvin Coll; English.

CROFOOT, Rhonda J; St Charles HS; Brant, MI; CncrtBnd; HospAde; NHS; StuCncl; 4-H; LetterBsktbl; GAA; IMSpt; Coll; Botany.

CROFT, Candace A; Lancaster HS; Lancaster, WI; Band; Chr; HonRl; MrchBnd; NatlFornLg; SchMus; RptrYrbk; SpnCl; PpCl; Chrldr; Uw;dr.

CROFT, Cathy D; Fennimore HS; Fennimore, WI; Band; Chrs; ChrhWkr; CncrtBnd; HonRl; MrchBnd; PepBnd; FHA; GAA; U W Platteville; Teacher.

CROM, Steven; Beloit Memorial HS; Beloit, WI; 1/638 ALBoysSt; Band; HonRl; NHS; StuGov; FrCl; Bsktbl; Beloit Coll; Foreign Service.

CROMBIE, Janet A; Joliet Central HS; Joliet, IL; 5/491 HonRl; NHS; YthFlsp; FrCl; Tennis; Univ Of Illinois; Business.

CROMER, Toni M; Madison HS; Madison, IL; HonRl; JA; Yrbk; S Ill Univ; Business.

CROMLEY, Carolyn L; Carrollton HS; Carrollton, MO; 1/100 VPJrCls; Band; HonRl; NHS; NatlMeritCmnd; NatlThespSoc; TchrAde; GerCl; SecPpCl; IMSpt; College; Medicine.

CROMWELL, Kimberly A; Genoa Public HS; Genoa, NE; PresFrshCls; VPJrCls; Band; ChrhWkr; JrNHS; SchPl; EdYrBk; FFA; 4-HAwd; LionAwd; College.

CROMWELL, Teri K; Deer River HS; Deer River, MN; 18/85 Band; CncrtBnd; HonRl; PepBnd; SchPpr; PpCl; CaptTrk; GAA; IMSpt; VFWAwd; Col; Pro Law.

CRONCE, Anita; West Milwaukee HS; West Allis, WI; 7/182 Chrs; ChrhWkr; HonRl; JA; NHS; SchMus; RptrSchPpr; Bsktbl; Trk; IMSpt; Univ; Occupational Therapy.

CRONENWETT, Amy; Airport HS; Carleton, MI; 1/220 ALAGirlsSt; Chrs; HonRl; NHS; StuCncl; Yrbk; 4-H; Chrldr; 4-HAwd; College; Landscape Architect.

CRONIN, Daniel J; Thorton Frac South HS; Lansing, IL; 14/560 ChrhWkr; HonRl; NHS; RptrYrbk; RptrSchPpr; SptEdSchPpr; LetterBsbl; LetterFtbl; LetterGlf; Univ Of Illinois; Lawyer.

CRONIN, David J; Thompson Public HS; Thompson, ND; ALBoysSt; Band; Chrs; HonRl; SchPl; 4-H; Bsktbl; College.

CRONIN, Joseph E; St Francis HS; W Chicago, IL; 13/120 HonRl; NHS; SchPl; 4-H; Bsbl; LetterBsktbl; LetterTrk; Notre Dame Univ; Liberal Arts.

CRONIN, Kevin P; St Ignatius C P HS; Chicago, IL; 40/155 CmntyWkr; HonRl; NatlMeritCmnd; RedCrAde; IMSpt; Northwestern Univ; Medicine.

CRONIN, Margaret M; St Augustine HS; Chicago, IL; 8/85 VPSophCls; VPJrCls; Chrs; ChrhWkr; HonRl; NHS; SchPl; RptrYrbk; RptrSchPpr; VFWAwd;.

CRONIN, Margie A; Roncalli HS; Omaha, NE; PpCl; Trk; Chrldr; IMSpt; Coll; Bus Ed.

CRONIN, Marian D; Mother Mcauley HS; Oak Lawn, IL; 62/474 HonRl; NHS; SchMus; Eastern Illinois Univ; Medical Tech.

CRONK, Julie E; Oneill Public HS; Page, NE; 5/66 Band; HonRl; NHS; SchMus; RptrYrbk; EdSchPpr; PpCl; Bsktbl; Trk; VoiceDemAwd; Univ Of Nebr.

CRONKRIGHT, Sally A; Vale HS; Goodells, MI; 31/139 Band; CmntyWkr; CncrtBnd; HonRl; MrchBnd; OffAde; SchPl; FHA; LetterBsbl; PPFtbl; St Clair County Comm College; Art.

CRONN, Susan; Trego Community HS; Wakeeney, KS; Band; CncrtBnd; DrlTm; HonRl; MrchBnd; PepBnd; 4-H; FHA; PpCl; SciCl; Coll; Physical Therapy.

CRONOVER, Terry L; Hastings HS; Hastings, MI; SecTrsSrCls; HonRl; TchrAde; FrCl; CaptBsktbl; GAA; Kellogg Comm College; Sociology.

CROOK, Barbara A; Archie HS; Archie, MO; Band; Chr; Chrs; ChrhWkr; CncrtBnd; DrlTm; HonRl; MrchBnd; SchPl; 4-H; FHA; PpCl; Bsbl; Business Schl; Vocation.

CROOK, Delorse; Naylor HS; Naylor, MO; Chrs; ChrhWkr; HonRl; SchMus; SchPl; StuCncl; FHA; FTA; SciCl; Bsktbl; Three Rivers Jr Coll; Teach Special Ed.

CROOK, Patrick V; Crown Point HS; Crown Pt, IN; HonRl; NatlMeritSF; PolWkr; Quill&Scroll; RptrSchPpr; University; Journalism.

CROOK, Rodney E; Rising City Public HS; Rising City, NE; Band; Chr; Chrs; ChrhWkr; CmntyWkr; SchPl; StuCncl; StuGov; TchrAde; YthFlsp; RptrYrbk; Yrbk; 4-H; Bsbl; CaptBsktbl; Platte College; Agriculture.

CROOKS, Corinne F; Rockwell Sweldale HS; Rockwell, IA; Chrs; ChrhWkr; HonRl; HospAde; SchMus; TchrAde; PresYthFlsp; FNA; FTA; PpCl; College; Physciologist.

CROOKS, Roy G; Pembroke Country Day HS; Kansas City, MO; 20/49 HonRl; LitMag; NatlMeritSF; SchPpr; LetterTrk; College; Banking.

CROOKSHANKS, Cheri; Meadville HS; Browning, MO; 6/38 VPSrCls; Band; HonRl; NHS; StuCncl; RptrYrbk; RptrSchPpr; PpCl; Central Missouri State Univ; Accountant.

CROPPER, Connie S; Orchard Farm HS; St Charles, MO; Harding Col; Art.

CROSBY, Dale; Jefferson HS; Cedar Rapids, IA; Band; SctActv; Ftbl; Glf; Trk; Wrstlng; IMSpt; CitAwd; Univ; Engineering.

CROSBY, Dinella L; Ann Arbor Huron HS; Ann Arbor, MI; ChrhWkr; HonRl; StuGov; Yrbk; SpnCl; PpCl; Trk; LetterChrldr; CchngActv; Mt Holyoke Coll; Psy Or Pol Sci.

CROSBY, Kent D; Twin Lakes HS; Monticello, IN; 6/225 Chrs; ChrhWkr; HonRl; TreasNatlFornLg; SchPl; YthFlsp; 4-H; FFA; SciCl; OptClAwd; Purdue 1; Ag Research.

CROSBY, Jr,Robert; Eagle Grove Community; Woolstock, IA; 4/126 HonRl; NHS; NatlThespSoc; SchMus; SchPl; Iowa State U; Chemical Eng.

CROSE, David L; Alexis HS; Alexis, IL; VPFrshCls; PresJrCls; HonRl; StuCncl; SpnCl; Bsktbl; Ftbl; Trk; IMSpt; Coll; Vocational.

CROSS, Colette P; Jefferson City HS; Jefferson City, MO; 6/475 CncrtBnd; HonRl; HospAde; JrNHS; MrchBnd; VPNHS; PresYthFlsp; SpnCl; TreasPpCl; AmLegAwd; William Jewell Clg; Sociology.

CROSS, Colette P; Jefferson City Sr HS; Jefferson City, MO; 7/480 Chr; CmntyWkr; CncrtBnd; HonRl; JrNHS; MrchBnd; NHS; SctActv; SpnCl; PpCl; William Jewell College; Sociology.

CROSS, Cynthia L; Union City HS; Sherwood, MI; 6/80 Band; CncrtBnd; HonRl; MrchBnd; SchPl; StuCncl; TchrAde; RptrYrbk; FTA; PPFtbl; Col; Blackburn Col; Child Psychology.

CROSS, Denise G; Union City HS; Sherwood, MI; Band; CncrtBnd; HonRl; ModUN; PepBnd; SchPl; StuCncl; TchrAde; FTA; PPFtbl; College.

CROSS, Eddie W; Kennett Sr HS; Kennett, MO; 39/154 CmntyWkr; Bsbl; Bsktbl; Ftbl; Trk; DanFAwd;.

CROSS, Ellen M; Fairfield HS; New Pairs, IN; 3/108 Chr; Chrl; ChrhWkr; HonRl; SchMus; 4-H; PpCl; BttyCrckrAwd; 4-HAwd; Fort Wayne Bible Clge.

CROSS, Francine M; Armada HS; Allenton, MI; 16/150 CncrtBnd; HonRl; MrchBnd; Orch; PpCl; CaptBsktbl; Tennis; Trk; GAA; IMSpt; College; Professional.

CROSS, Gaila M; Stockton HS; Stockton, MO; 1/66 PresSrCls; Band; Chrs; ChrhWkr; PresNHS; StuCncl; EdSchPpr; Pres4-H; PresFBLA; PresFHA; Univ Of Mo Columbia; Business.

CROSS, Gregory J; Fridley HS; Fridley, MN; ChrhWkr; HonRl; PolWkr; Bsktbl; IMSpt; College.

CROSS, Jacque; West Ohawa HS; Holland, MI; 19/270 Chr; ChrhWkr; HonRl; NHS; SchMus; SchPl; YthFlsp; 4-H; 4-HAwd; Northern Michigan U; Nursing.

CROSS, Jimmy K; West Side HS; Gary, IN; Orch; Bsktbl; Ftbl; Trk; Purdue U;elec Eng.

CROSS, Joel L; Hartsburg Emden HS; Emden, IL; 3/20 ChrhWkr; CmntyWkr; HonRl; JrNHS; NHS; NatlMeritSchl; StuCncl; SchPpr; LetterBsbl; LetterBsktbl; Trk; AmLegAwd; GodCntryAwd; College; Conservation.

CROSS, Margaret C; Hayti HS; Hayti, MO; PresFrshCls; TrsJrCls; Chr; ChrhWkr; HonRl; NHS; NatlThespSoc; SchMus; SchPl; StuCncl; YthFlsp; Memphis State Univ.

CROSS, Martha C; Murphysboro Township HS; Murphrsboro, IL; 28/210 Band; PresChrs; DrlTm; HonRl; MrchBnd; SchMus; StuCncl; SciCl; MasAwd; Siu Carbondale; Adminsitarion Of Justice.

CROSS, Mary; Lake Michigan Catholic HS; St Joseph, MI; HonRl; SchPl; Bsbl; Bsktbl; GAA; IMSpt; College; Major Study.

CROSS, Steven R; Baxter Community HS; Baxter, IA; PresFrshCls; PresSophCls; PresJrCls; ALBoysSt; Band; Chr; Chrs; CncrtBnd; HonRl; MrchBnd; NatlThespSoc; Broadcasting.

CROSS, Tom H; Yorkville HS; Yorkville, IL; Band; CncrtBnd; MrchBnd; PepBnd; SchPl; YthFlsp; 4-H; LetterBsbl; Bsktbl; LetterTrk; Univ; Professional.

CROSSER, Ann; Brookings HS; Volga, SD; Band; CncrtBnd; MrchBnd; NHS; PepBnd; 4-H; FHA; LionAwd; Col; Med Tech.

CROSSER, Brian; North Platte HS; North Platte, NE; ALBoysSt; ChrhWkr; HonRl; Wrstlng; Graceland College; Oceanography.

CROSSER, Diane R; L D F Comm HS; Marshalltown, IA; 3/46 VPFrshCls; PresSophCls; Band; Chr; Chrs; CncrtBnd; HonRl; MrchBnd; NHS; PepBnd; LetterChrldr; VoiceDemAwd; College; Professional.

CROSSER, Diane R; Ldf Community HS; Marshalltown, IA; 4/44 Chr; Chrs; CncrtBnd; HonRl; NHS; SchMus; SchPl; PpCl; LetterChrldr; Ia State U; Professnl.

CROSSEY, Mary Kay; Saline HS; Saline, MI; ALAGirlsSt; Band; HonRl; NHS; FHA; Bsktbl; Trk; College.

CROSSLAND, Diana L; East Peoria Community HS; East Peoria, IL; 25/440 ChrhWkr; CmntyWkr; HonRl; VPYthFlsp; FHA; GAA; Illinois Central College.

CROSSLAND, Karen E; Shortridge HS; Indianapolis, IN; HstJrCls; HonRl; HospAde; OffAde; Quill&Scroll; Yrbk; SpnCl; Socr; Chrldr; IMSpt; College; Medicine.

CROSSMAN, Margaret A; Morton West HS; Berwyn, IL; 22/750 HonRl; TreasNHS; TchrAde; College; Special Education.

CROSSWHITE, Patricia; Moberly Senior HS; Moberly, MO; 41/221 ChrhWkr; HonRl; Mdrgl; NHS; SchMus; SchPl; YthFlsp; PpCl; College; Speech.

CROSTHWAIT, Camela; Crown Point HS; Crown Point, IN; 95/500 Chr; HonRl; MrchBnd; SchMus; StuCncl; EdSchPpr; SpnCl; Trk; GAA; IMSpt; PPFtbl; Indiana Univ; Medicine.

CROTTEAU, Gayanne M; Lincoln HS; Esko, MN; HonRl; JA; LbryAde; TchrAde; FHA; EldAwd; College; Occupational Therapy.

CROTTY, Mary Jo; Queen Of Peace HS; Chicago, IL; 6/430 ChrhWkr; CmntyWkr; HonRl; NHS; PolWkr; SctActv; PresLatCl; Loyola University; Medicine.

CROTTY, Robert A; Highland Park HS; Highland Park, IL; 60/561 HonRl; Univ Of Ill; Chemistry.

CROTWELL, Vicki E; Edison HS; Morrisville, MO; HonRl; TchrAde; GAA; Southwest Mo State Univ; Teacher.

CROUCH, Kelly J; Sevastopol HS; Sturgeon Bay, WI; Aud/Vis; SchMus; SchPpr; Bsktbl; Trk; IMSpt; Coll; Business.

CROUCH, Merry J; Bettendorf HS; Bettendorf, IA; HonRl; SchPl; TchrAde; SpnCl; PpCl; College.

CROUCH, Michael S; Diamond HS; Joplin, MO; 2/63 TrsJrCls; ChrhWkr; HonRl; VPNHS; SchPl; TchrAde; RptrYrbk; RptrSchPpr; FFA; MthCl; Missouri So St College; Medicine.

CROUCH, Samuel D; Monett Sr HS; Verona, MO; Band; CncrtBnd; MrchBnd; PepBnd; 4-H; DanFAwd;.

CROUDY, Doug P; Estherville HS; Estherville, IA; 14/189 AFS; Chr; Chrs; ChrhWkr; HonRl; StuCncl; LetterBsbl; Bsktbl; LetterFtbl; Glf; Trk; LetterWrstlng; College; Engineering.

CROUSE, Carol; Orangeville Comm Hs; Winslow, IL; 4/55 SecSrCls; SecNHS; SchMus; StuCncl; EdYrBk; Pres4-H; PresFHA; PresFrCl; BttyCrckrAwd; DARAwd; Iowa State U Of S & T; Home Economics.

CROUSE, Carol E; Appleton East HS; Appleton, WI; 33/498 VPAFS; SecBand; ChrhWkr; CncrtBnd; HonRl; MrchBnd; Orch; PepBnd; RptrYrbk; FrCl; Colorado State U; Business.

CROUSE, Cheryl; Staunton HS; Brazil, IN; 8/59 Band; ChrhWkr; HonRl; LbryAde; NHS; OffAde; TchrAde; 4-H; PpCl; 4-HAwd; Trade School; Vocation Secretarial.

CROUSE, Gordon J; Lincoln HS; Wisconsin Rapids, WI; HonRl; NatlFornLg; NatlMeritSF; Orch; SctActv; GerCl; PresSciCl; RotaryAwd; VoiceDemAwd; Univ Of Wis; Lawyer.

CROUSE, Janet L; Princeton R 5 HS; Cainsville, MO; 9/52 ChrhWkr; CmntyWkr; HonRl; NHS; SchPl; RptrYrbk; RptrSchPpr; FHA; EngCl; SpnCl; Trenton Jr College; Elementary Education.

CROUSE, Janice K; Princeton HS; Cainsville, MO; 5/52 ChrhWkr; CmntyWkr; HonRl; NHS; SchPl; RptrYrbk; RptrSchPpr; FHA; EngCl; TreasSpnCl; Trenton Jr College; Elementary Educ.

CROW, Christine A; Dexter HS; Dexter, KS; SecFrshCls; TrsSophCls; VPSrCls; Band; Chrs; HonRl; NHS; OffAde; RptrYrbk; RptrSchPpr; Bsktbl; Trk; College; Teacher.

CROW, Connie L; North Platte HS; North Platte, NE; Band; HonRl; HospAde; JA; RedCrAde; TchrAde; 4-H; 4-HAwd; College; Marine Biology.

CROW, Danny; Culver Com HS; Culver, IN; ChrhWkr; HonRl; 4-H; 4-HAwd; College; Teaching.

CROW, Pamala; Elverado HS; Elkville, IL; Chrs; HonRl; LbryAde; SchPl; SchPpr; 4-H; FHA; PpCl; Bsktbl; GAA; John A Logan; Nursing.

CROW, Randy; Mediapolis HS; Mediapolis, IA; HonRl; LetterTrk; IMSpt; Vocation.

CROW, Sharla J; East HS; Kansas City, MO; Chr; HonRl; JrNHS; OffAde; StuCncl; RptrSchPpr; PpCl; CaptBsktbl; GAA; IMSpt; College; Receptionist.

CROWDER, Brian; New Palestine HS; New Palestine, IN; HonRl; Yrbk; SciCl; Us Coast Guard Acad; Marine Sci.

CROWDER, Justin H; New Palestine HS; New Palestine, IN; 3/132 ALBoysSt; ChrhWkr; HonRl; NHS; NatlSciFnd; SchAde; TchrAde; Yrbk; FFA; College; Teach School.

CROWDER, Leona J; West HS; Aurora, IL; 226/590 TreasJA; RptrYrbk; RptrSchPpr; 4-H; FBLA; BttyCrckrAwd; 4-HAwd; JAAwd; Business School; Transportation.

CROWDER, Wayne T; Whitko HS; South Whitley, IN; Band; CncrtBnd; HonRl; MrchBnd; PepBnd; GerCl; SciCl; College; Pharmacy.

CROWE, Alison A; Lanphier HS; Springfield, IL; Chr; HospAde; OffAde; SchAde; SchPl; SctActv; PpCl; College; Theatre.

CROWE, Deborah J; Morton West HS; Berwyn, IL; 38/750 Chr; Chrs; ChrhWkr; HonRl; NHS; SctActv; YthFlsp; College; Accounting.

CROWE, Greg A; Plainfield Jr Sr HS; Plainfield, IN; 7/250 HonRl; NHS; CaptBsktbl; LetterFtbl; LetterTrk; Rose Hulman Inst Of Tech; Engineering.

CROWE, James M; Cahokia HS; Cahokia, IL; 13/500 HonRl; JrNHS; NHS; LetterFtbl; LetterWrstlng; Jr Col; Vocation.

CROWE, Mike F; Eastern HS; Bloomfield, IN; 9/70 ALBoysSt; Quill&Scroll; StuCncl; TchrAde; RptrYrbk; EdSchPpr; College.

CROWE, Stacy L; John Marshall HS; Indianapolis, IN; CmntyWkr; StuCncl; TchrAde; Bsktbl; Trk; Chrldr; CchngActv; GAA; IMSpt; JAAwd; College; Business.

CROWE, Thomas J; Maine Twp South HS; Park Ridge, IL; HonRl; NHS; NatlMeritCmnd; NatlSciFnd; Bsbl; Clge; Chemical Engineer.

CROWELL, Bret; Connersville HS; Connersville, IN; HonRl; JA; StuGov; SpnCl; Ftbl; Trk; IMSpt; JAAwd; Purdue; Forestry.

CROWELL, Debra M; Patoka HS; Vernon, IL; 3/26 Chr; SchPl; StuCncl; EdYrBk; FHA; KeyCl; PpCl; Kaskaskia College; Dental Asst.

CROWELL, Gregg J; Maine West HS; Des Plaines, IL; HonRl; JrNHS; NHS; College; Engineering.

CROWELL, Mary; Chetapa HS; Chetopa, KS; Band; Chrs; CncrtBnd; HonRl; MrchBnd; SchPl; FHA; PpCl; PPFtbl; Kansas State College; Nursing.

CROWL, Karen M; Mayville HS; Mayville, MI; Band; ChrhWkr; CncrtBnd; HonRl; LbryAde; MrchBnd; PepBnd; StuCncl; TchrAde; VPFHA; PpCl; College; Professional.

CROWL, Randy D; Hamilton HS; Pleasant Lake, IN; 5/58 HonRl; StuCncl; StuGov; SecFFA; College; Biology.

CROWLEY, Catherine A; Birch Run HS; Birch Run, MI; 9/157 HonRl; LbryAde; NHS; TchrAde; RptrSchPpr; SpnCl; Flint University Michigan; Pre Law.

CROWLEY, Christopher R; Marian Central HS; Algonquin, IL; 34/162 Sacrstn; SctActv; SciCl; Military Academy; Engineering.

CROWLEY, David S; Shenandoah Community HS; Shenandoah, IA; ALBoysSt; ChrhWkr; CmntyWkr; HonRl; Bsbl; Bsktbl; Glf; AmLegAwd; Col;.

CROWLEY, Jane; Elk Grove HS; Elk Grove Vlg, IL; DrlTm; HonRl; NHS; Quill&Scroll; StuCncl; StuGov; RptrYrbk; Yrbk; Bradley University.

CROWLEY, John S; Rolla Sr HS; Rolla, MO; 9/317 ChrhWkr; HonRl; HospAde; YthFlsp; PresFDA; LatCl; LetterTennis; College; Medicine.

CROWNOVER, Earl L; Park Hill HS; Kansas City, MO; HonRl; IMSpt; College; Teaching Art.

CROWSER, Tami L; W J Brown HS; Sturgis, SD; PresFrshCls; SecSophCls; VPJrCls; ALAGirlsSt; ChrhWkr; VPStuCncl; TchrAde; Chrldr;.

CROY, Paula M; Clay City Unit Dist #10 HS; Clay City, IL; SecTrsJrCls; HonRl; Yrbk; SchPpr; PresSpnCl; PpCl; Trk; Chrldr; College.

CROZIER, Terry L; Hoopeston East Lynn HS; Hoopeston, IL; 15/137 Univ Of Notre Dame; Lawyer.

CRUELL, Linda; Parker HS; Chicago, IL; 1/240 Chr; Chrs; ChrhWkr; HonRl; Mdrgl; NHS; SchMus; StuCncl; TchrAde; FBLA; Roosevelt Univ; Opera Singer.

CRULL, Brenda D; Wabash HS; Wabash, IN; Chr; HonRl; NatlMeritCmnd; SctActv; 4-H; FBLA; SpnCl; PpCl; 4-HAwd; Secretarial Position.

CRULL, Gregory J; North Boone HS; Capron, IL; SecJrCls; HonRl; SchMus; FFA; Bsktbl; Ftbl; College; Farming.

CRULL, Robert J; South Callaway R Ii HS; Portland, MO; 2/28 HonRl; NHS; SchPl; StuCncl; Yrbk; FSA; Univer Of Mo/rolla; Aerospace Engineering.

CRUM, Anita A; St Elmo HS; St Elmo, IL; 3/53 VPJrCls; HonRl; JrNHS; NHS; StuCncl; PpCl; GAA; E Il U; Teaching.

CRUM, David W; Milan HS; Milan, IN; 5/63 ALBoysSt; Band; Chrs; CncrtBnd; HonRl; MrchBnd; NHS; SchPl; YthFlsp; LatCl; University; Professional.

CRUM, James A; Virginia HS; Virginia, IL; ChrhWkr; HonRl; SptEdYrbk; Pres4-H; PresFFA; 4-HAwd; Lincoln Land Jr College; Agriculture.

CRUM, Melanie D; Flat River Central R3 HS; Flat River, MO; 31/156 ChrhWkr; HonRl; NHS; OffAde; StuCncl; StuGov; VPFBLA; FTA; SecSpnCl; SecPpCl; College; Nursing.

CRUME, Cynthia; Hillsdale HS; Hillsdale, MI; 39/200 Chr; HonRl; HospAde; NHS; SchMus; N Cent Michigan; Inhalation Therapist.

CRUME, Howard; California R1 HS; California, MO; Aud/Vis; Band; Chr; Chrs; CncrtBnd; MrchBnd; Orch; PepBnd; SpnCl; Ftbl;.

CRUME, Sarah J; Tipton HS; Tipton, IN; 12/193 NHS; 4-H; SciCl; College; Biological Sciences.

CRUMMEL, Anna L; Mason Consolidated HS; Erie, MI; 7/118 Chr; Chrs; HonRl; JrNHS; NHS; GerCl; College.

CRUMMEL, Betty J; Mason Consolidated HS; Erie, MI; TrsJrCls; Chrs; HonRl; JrNHS; NatlFornLg; StuCncl; Hospital Training; X Ray Tech.

CRUMP, Abigail; New Trier East Hs; Winnetka, IL; ChrhWkr; HonRl; NatlMeritCmnd; StuCncl; StuGov; Yrbk; PpCl; LetterTennis; Trk; Chrldr; U Of Illinois; Professional.

CRUMP, Carole J; Elkhart Central HS; Elkhart, IN; 39/475 TrsFrshCls; ChrhWkr; MrchBnd; NHS; NatlThespSoc; PolWkr; PresStuCncl; YthFlsp; SpnCl; GAA; College; Medicine.

CRUMP, Deborah L; Blue Mound HS; Boody, IL; 12/38 Band; HonRl; OffAde; PepBnd; SchPl; TchrAde; RptrYrbk; EdSchPpr; FTA; SecGAA; Illinois State University; Education.

CRUMP, Ward J; Sullivan HS; Sullivan, MO; VPSrCls; CmntyWkr; HonRl; StuCncl; FFA; OptClAwd; RotaryAwd; Univ Of Mo; Agriculture.

CRUMPECKER, Gail A; Thomas W Kelly HS; Benton, MO; VPJrCls; Band; CncrtBnd; HonRl; MrchBnd; PepBnd; FHA; PpCl; Chrldr; College.

CRUMRIN, Lou E; Marshall HS; Marshall, IL; 28/115 Band; Chrs; ChrhWkr; CmntyWkr; CncrtBnd; MrchBnd; PepBnd; 4-H; FBLA; FSA; University; Professional.

CRUSE, Robyn E; Springfield Catholic HS; Springfield, MO; PresFrshCls; HstJrCls; HonRl; StuCncl; SchPpr; SpnCl; LetterBsbl; LetterBsktbl; Chrldr; GAA; Coll.

CRUSIUS, Martha; Southwest HS; St Louis, MO; 4/500 Chr; ChrhWkr; HonRl; Quill&Scroll; SchMus; SctActv; RptrYrbk; GAA;.

CRUSOR, Anthony Q; Metro HS; Chicago, IL; Prescott; Politics.

CRUTCHER, Donna M; Jennings Sr HS; Jennings, MO; Chr; HonRl; NHS; NatlThespSoc; SchPl; TchrAde; EdYrBk; FHA; FTA; EngCl; LetterSwmmng; GAA; IMSpt; University; Mathematics.

CRYDER, Lois E; Wesclin Sr HS; Trenton, IL; 42/100 Band; ChrhWkr; MrchBnd; NatlThespSoc; SchMus; Yrbk; SchPpr; FrCl; PpCl; Trk; GAA; E Illinois Univ; Physical Educ.

CRYE, Lisa J; Auburn HS; Auburn, IL; 11/59 Chr; Chrs; HonRl; LbryAde; SchMus; SchPl; YthFlsp; Yrbk; EdSchPpr; FFA; PpCl; Trk; GAA; Ill State Univ; Law.

CRYSTAL, Laurel A; Lees Summit HS; Lees Summit, MO; Chr; CmntyWkr; HonRl; NHS; NatlMeritCmnd; NatlThespSoc; PolWkr; SchMus; PpCl; PPFtbl; Central Mo State Univ; Law.

CRYSTAL, Thomas W; Bentley Senior HS; Burton, MI; HonRl; JA; NHS; Bsbl; Bsktbl; Glf; Baker Jr College Of Business; Data Process.

CSERI, Jeanne B; Oak Creek HS; Oak Creek, WI; 10/361 AFS; ChrhWkr; CmntyWkr; HonRl; SchPl; SctActv; TchrAde; RptrYrbk; RptrSchPpr; FTA; Uw Milwaukee; Chemical Engineering.

CSICSKO, David L; Morton Sr HS; Hammond, IN; CmntyWkr; RedCrAde; SchMus; SchPl; StuCncl; StuGov; TchrAde; LetterSwmmng; Cleveland Inst Of Art; Illustration.

CSIKOS, Mindy C; Lake Central HS; Dyer, IN; Chr; Chrs; ChrhWkr; CmntyWkr; HonRl; SchMus; SchPl; Teen; 4-H; GerCl; PpCl; College; Marine Biologist.

CSONT, Donald W; Lincoln Park HS; Lincoln Park, MI; 130/560 Chr; ModUN; SchMus; PresStuCncl; RptrSchPpr; Tennis; Ferris St College; Journalism.

CUBERT, David L; Taylor HS; Kokomo, IN; 31/181 Band; HonRl; MrchBnd; PepBnd; TchrAde; PpCl; Bsktbl; Ftbl; Trk; CchngActv; Clge; Nerology.

CUCCHIARA, Anna C; St Pius X HS; Kansas City, MO; 35/129 Chr; Chrs; ChrhWkr; HonRl; ModUN; RedCrAde; StuCncl; FDA; FHA; Chrldr; BttyCrckrAwd; Clge; Pro Dental Assistant.

CUCKIE, Nancy; Northwest Webster HS; Clare, IA; 2/20 VPSophCls; Chrs; HonRl; SchPl; StuCncl; RptrYrbk; Bsbl; Bsktbl; Trk; J College; Secretary.

CUDAHY, George C; Deerfield Academy; Omaha, NE; PresSrCls; NatlMeritSF; StuGov; EdYrBk; Socr; LetterTennis; IMSpt; Princeton; Architecture.

CUENE, Barbara; St Joseph Academy; Depere, WI; Chrs; CmntyWkr; HospAde; TchrAde; Yrbk; Col Of St Teresa; Nurse.

CUENGROS, Mary E; Glenbard West HS; Glen Ellyn, IL; Chr; Chrl; Chrs; HonRl; OffAde; Teen; YthFlsp; SpnCl; College; Medicine.

CUEVA, Ivonne C; Immaculata HS; Chicago, IL; 3/205 CmntyWkr; HonRl; LitMag; NHS; Quill&Scroll; StuCncl; StuGov; EdSchPpr; FrCl; PpCl; Bsktbl; Tennis; Northwestern University; Journalism.

CULBERTSON, Denice; Fredericksburg Community HS; Fredricksburg, IA; 7/33 Band; ChrhWkr; CncrtBnd; HonRl; MrchBnd; SchPl; RptrSchPpr; Bsktbl; Trk; Wartburg Col; Elementary Ed.

CULBERTSON, Kim M; Plainview HS; Plainview, NE; Band; Chrs; CncrtBnd; HonRl; MrchBnd; PepBnd; SchMus; SchPl; TchrAde; FHA; College; Major Study.

CULHANE, John; Rushford HS; Rushford, MN; Chrs; LbryAde; TchrAde; RptrSchPpr; FTA; Bemedji State Coll; Physical Ed Teacher.

CULICH, Jean M; George Washington HS; Chicago, IL; 32/481 SecTrsSrCls; Chr; ChrhWkr; CmntyWkr; HonRl; NHS; StuCncl; TchrAde; MthCl; Illinois St Univ; Social Worker.

CULKIN, Mary D; Chatsworth HS; Chatsworth, IL; 3/27 SecSophCls; SecTrsJrCls; Band; HonRl; NHS; SchMus; SchPl; TreasStuCncl; SecFHA; Chrldr; Jr College; Nurse.

CULLAN, Stephen L; Hemingford HS; Hemingford, NE; 2/55 HonRl; SciCl; Ftbl; Us Merchant Marine Acad; Marine Eng.

CULLEN, Joanne; Menomonee Falls HS; Menomonee Falls, WI; ChrhWkr; CncrtBnd; DrlTm; DrmMjrt; HonRl; Twrl; GAA; College; Medicine.

CULLEN, Kathleen E; Gage Park HS; Chicago, IL; 5/600 PresJrCls; SecSrCls; Chrs; ChrhWkr; HonRl; NHS; OffAde; Twrl; LetterTennis; LionAwd; Clge; Medicine.

CULLEN, Steve; Greenfield HS; Greenfield, IA; StuCncl; Ftbl; College; Accounting.

CULLERS, Kathy A; Kewanee HS; Kewanee, IL; 28/213 Chr; HonRl; OffAde; StuCncl; TchrAde; FTA; SpnCl; Black Hawk Jr Clg; Spanish.

CULLEY, Melody L; Decatur Central HS; Indianapolis, IN; 15/325 HonRl; JA; NHS; PolWkr; Quill&Scroll; SctActv; 4-H; Swmmng; GAA; IMSpt; Butler U; Pharmacy.

CULLIGAN, Patrick E; Benet Academy; Naperville, IL; HonRl; StuCncl; StuGov; RptrYrbk; SptEdYrbk; RptrSchPpr; GerCl; Bsktbl; Swmmng; Purdue Univ; Professional.

CULLIGAN, Sheila A; Derham Hall HS; St Paul, MN; NHS; StuCncl; IMSpt; PPFtbl; Univ; Professional.

CULLINAN, Carol; Duchesne HS; St Charles, MO; 39/190 Chrs; CmntyWkr; HonRl; SchMus; SchPl; SpnCl; PpCl; Chrldr; IMSpt; PPFtbl; Coll.

CULLOM, Linda S; Mt Olive HS; Mt Olive, IL; 3/56 SecSophCls; Band; Chrs; ChrhWkr; CncrtBnd; HonRl; MrchBnd; PepBnd; StuCncl; YthFlsp; LetterTrk; SecGAA; Univ Of Illinois; Physical Ed.

CULLOM, Linda S; Mt Olive Comm HS; Mt Olive, IL; 3/56 SecSophCls; Band; Chrs; ChrhWkr; CncrtBnd; HonRl; MrchBnd; PepBnd; StuCncl; YthFlsp; RptrYrbk; FHA; SpnCl; LetterTrk; GAA; College; Physical Ed.

CULP, Kathy L; R Iv HS; St Joseph, MO; 12/43 HonRl; OffAde; TchrAde; EdYrBk; Missouri W St College; Special Ed.

CULVER, Becky; Osceola HS; Osceola, WI; Chr; ChrhWkr; FrCl; GAA; Coll;.

CULVER, Cassie; Mona Shores HS; Muskegon, MI; Band; HonRl; HospAde; MrchBnd; NHS; SciCl; Trk; Michigan State.

CULVER, David L; Orleans HS; Orleans, NE; 3/17 SecSrCls; Band; Chr; ChrhWkr; VPCncrtBnd; HonRl; SchMus; VPYthFlsp; FrCl; BttyCrckrAwd; Central Tech Comm College; Radio & Tv Elect.

CULVER, Debra; R I North Callaway Hs; Auxvasse, MO; Band; Chrs; CncrtBnd; HonRl; NHS; SchMus; SchPl; StuCncl; FHA; SpnCl;.

CULVER, Jean A; Lake Central HS; Griffith, IN; 73/443 HonRl; OffAde; SchAde; TchrAde; Teen; Bus College.

CULVER, Laurel A; Mt Pleasant HS; Mt Pleasant, MI; 32/325 Band; CncrtBnd; HonRl; NHS; PepBnd; SchMus; 4-H; GerCl; Bsktbl; IMSpt; Mi State Univ; Veterinarian.

CULVER, Robert D; Cimarron HS; Cimarron, KS; 2/36 PresFrshCls; ALBoysSt; Band; Chrs; HonRl; NHS; Bsktbl; Ftbl; Tennis; Trk; College; Business.

CULVER, Robert E; Crawford County HS; Bourbon, MO; ChrhWkr; HonRl; YthFlsp; SpnCl; Univ Of Missouri Rolla; Electrical Eng.

CULY, Jeffrey; Hagerstown Jr Sr HS; Hagerstown, IN; JA; NHS; SctActv; SciCl; Swmmng; JAAwd; Univ; Engineering.

CUMBERLAND, Michael; Lane Technical Hs; Chicago, IL; 88 CncrtBnd; DrmBgl; MrchBnd; NHS; NatlMeritCmnd; ROTC; TchrAde; SciCl; Trk; AmLegAwd; College;medical Doctor.

CUMBO, Linda; Addison Trail HS; Villa Park, IL; SecJrCls; SecSrCls; Chr; DrlTm; StuCncl; Chrldr; GAA; IMSpt; College; Airlines.

CUMBY, Brenda E; Carrollton HS; Carrollton, IL; 5/77 SecFrshCls; SecSophCls; SecJrCls; ChrhWkr; HonRl; NatlThespSoc; SchPl; StuCncl; Pres4-H; FBLA; SecFHA; Chrldr; GAA; PPFtbl; Western Ill Univ; Foreign Relations.

CUMMER, Jeffrey A; Normal Comm HS; Normal, IL; 18/450 HonRl; NHS; StuCncl; LetterTennis; College; Actuarial Science.

CUMMING, Carol; St Edward HS; Genoa, NE; 2/30 SecSrCls; Chr; Chrs; ChrhWkr; HonRl; Mdrgl; NatlThespSoc; 4-H; PpCl; 4-HAwd; Tech College;.

CUMMINGS, Abigail C; Williamsville HS; Williamsville, IL; 5/43 NHS; OffAde; SchPl; PresStuCncl; RptrYrbk;.

CUMMINGS, Barbara A; Springville Comm HS; Springville, IA; 1/57 Chr; HonRl; NHS; TchrAde; FSA; College; Sociology.

CUMMINGS, Brenda K; Mt St Scholastica Academy; Potter, KS; TrsSophCls; Chrs; HonRl; PolWkr; SchMus; 4-H; FTA; PpCl; SciCl; LetterBsktbl; College; Law.

CUMMINGS, Christina; Harbor Springs HS; Harbor Springs, MI; 1/75 Band; CmntyWkr; CncrtBnd; HonRl; MrchBnd; PepBnd; StuCncl; Trk; Albion College; Health Field.

CUMMINGS, Eileen M; Mount Assisi Academy; Chicago Ridge, IL; 20/144 Band; HonRl; JrNHS; LbryAde; MrchBnd; OffAde; SchPl; SctActv; Bsbl; Chrldr; Hosp School; Nurse.

CUMMINGS, Kevin R; Seymour HS; Plainville, IL; 14/66 CncrtBnd; MrchBnd; FrCl; Bsktbl; Ibew Local; Electrician.

CUMMINGS, Minda; Barr Reeve Hs; Cannelburg, IN; 12/64 Band; Chr; CncrtBnd; DrmMjrt; HonRl; VPLbryAde; Yrbk; SecSecSpnCl; CaptChrldr; Lockyear Business College; Secretarial.

CUMMINGS, Sharon E; Burke HS; Omaha, NE; 23/536 ChrhWkr; CmntyWkr; TchrAde; YthFlsp; PpCl; University Of Ne. At Omaha; Elementary Teac.

CUMMINS, Deshae; Puxico HS; Puxico, MO; HonRl; PpCl; IMSpt; College.

CUMMINS, Douglas W; Assumption HS; Tower Hill, IL; 2/52 HonRl; Bradley Univ; Engineering.

CUMMINS, Jennifer; Carrier Mills HS; Carrier Mills, IL; Band; Chrs; CncrtBnd; MrchBnd; PepBnd; SchPl; RptrSchPpr; PpCl; LetterChrldr; IMSpt; Southern Il Univ; Interpeter.

CUMMINS, Kathy I; Carthage Sr HS; Carthage, MO; 3/243 ChrhWkr; HonRl; NHS; TchrAde; PresFBLA; FHA; PresFTA; Business School; Accounting.

CUMMINS, Mary C; Whitefish Bay HS; Milwaukee, WI; AFS; Band; CncrtBnd; HonRl; MrchBnd; NHS; PepBnd; SchPl; RptrSchPpr; GerCl; University; Medicine.

CUMMINS, Nancy; Risco Hs; Risco, MO; 4/28 SecSrCls; ChrhWkr; HonRl; EdYrBk; 4-H; FHA; Chrldr; DanFAwd; DARAwd; 4-HAwd;.

CUMMINS, Wesely W; Oak Forest HS; Midlothian, IL; Univ Of Illinois; Engineering.

CUMPIAN, Medora D; Chicago Public HS; Chicago, IL; Chr; HonRl; LbryAde; SchAde; StuCncl; StuGov; TchrAde; UNYO; SpnCl; College; Literature.

CUMPSTON, Carla L; Arapahoe Pulbic HS; Arapahoe, NE; 2/35 Band; Chr; ChrhWkr; CncrtBnd; HonRl; PepBnd; SchPl; StuCncl; YthFlsp; PpCl; U Of Neb; Medical Tecnology.

CUMPTON, Christopher E; Mclouth HS; Oskaloosa, KS; 4/48 PresSrCls; HonRl; ModUN; NHS; StuCncl; StuGov; RptrYrbk; Yrbk; LetterFtbl; LetterTrk; College; Professional.

CUNARD, Peggy; Missouri Valley Public HS; Missouri Valley, IA; 16/106 Chr; ChrhWkr; CmntyWkr; HonRl; StuCncl; TchrAde; FTA; PpCl; Bsbl; Bsktbl; Mid Am Nazarene College; Elem Ed Missionary.

CUNDALL, Brad L; Louisville HS; Cedar Creek, NE; VPSophCls; VPJrCls; Chr; Chrl; Chrs; HonRl; Yrbk; FrCl; LetterBsktbl; LetterFtbl; Univ; Professional.

CUNDIFF, Charles A; Maconaquah HS; Grissom Air Base, IN; Chrl; ChrhWkr; Mdrgl; NatlThespSoc; SchMus; SchPl; TchrAde; SchPpr; Bsbl; College; Commercial Art.

CUNDIFF, Nancy J; Huntington North HS; Huntington, IN; Chr; LbryAde; SchMus; SchPl; Coll; Teaching.

CUNDIFF, Phyllis A; Collinsville HS; Collinsville, IL; Band; HonRl; NHS; Quill&Scroll; SchPl; RptrSchPpr; PresSpnCl; SciCl; PPFtbl; 4-HAwd;.

CUNDIFF, Rita M; Lathrop HS; Lathrop, MO; SecSrCls; PresBand; HonRl; MrchBnd; OffAde; TchrAde; YthFlsp; TreasFHA; VPPpCl; Chrldr; IMSpt; PPFtbl; Mo Western Col; Business Economics.

CUNNICK, Joan E; Mc Pherson HS; Mc Pherson, KS; 6/222 HonRl; NHS; NatlMeritCmnd; Yrbk; SpnCl; SciCl; BttyCrckrAwd; Mc Pherson College; Major Biology.

CUNNIFF, Margaret B; St Scholastica HS; Chicago, IL; Chrs; CmntyWkr; HospAde; RedCrAde; StuCncl; StuGov; Teen; RptrSchPpr; EdSchPpr; CitAwd; Loyola Univ; Lawyer.

CUNNING, Scott A; Terre Haute North Vigo HS; Terre Haute, IN; 152/611 Aud/Vis; CncrtBnd; HonRl; MrchBnd; NHS; SchMus; SpnCl; Bsbl; Swmmng; IMSpt; Univ; Medical Field.

CUNNINGHAM, Anne M; Emmons HS; Twin Lakes, MN; 5/27 SecSrCls; Band; Chrs; CncrtBnd; HonRl; MrchBnd; PepBnd; SchPl; StuCncl; RptrSchPpr; FHA; Trk; Chrldr; College.

CUNNINGHAM, Becky S; Trego Community HS; Wakeeney, KS; Chrs; HospAde; LbryAde; SchPl; Teen; FHA; PpCl; SciCl; LetterTrk; LetterChrldr; Collene; Nursing.

CUNNINGHAM, Beverly G; Montgomery County R Ii HS; New Florence, MO; Chr; ChrhWkr; HonRl; StuCncl; YthFlsp; 4-H; FHA; PpCl; Chrldr; Patricia Stevens Career College; Fashion Ca.

CUNNINGHAM, Brian R; Delavan Comm HS; Delavan, IL; HonRl; SchPl; VPJrCls; Trk; CaptWrstlng; IMSpt;.

CUNNINGHAM, Carol; Mount Assisi Acad; Chicago, IL; 23/189 NHS; SchPl; SpnCl; GAA; College; Doctor Bio Chemistry.

CUNNINGHAM, Carol A; Mt Assisi Acad; Chicago, IL; 27/194 HonRl; SchPl; SpnCl; Univ;bio Chem Pre Med.

CUNNINGHAM, Carol A; Hudson HS; Hudson, WI; HonRl; PresGerCl; LetterTrk; College.

CUNNINGHAM, Carol L; Lakewood HS; Lake Odessa, MI; 5/203 ChrhWkr; HonRl; NHS; SchPl; TchrAde; YthFlsp; SpnCl; DARAwd; Coll; Social Worker.

CUNNINGHAM, Clifford; Westfield Washington HS; Westfield, IN; HonRl; ModUN; Wrstlng; Iupui; Dentistry.

CUNNINGHAM, Connie J; Smithton Rr 1 HS; Smithton, MO; VPJrCls; Chr; Chrs; HonRl; NHS; SchMus; SchPl; Yrbk; FHA; College; Medicine.

CUNNINGHAM, Darcy S; Rolla HS; Rolla, MO; 58/307 HonRl; SchMus; SchPl;.

CUNNINGHAM, Dick P; North Muskegon HS; North Muskegon, MI; HonRl; SchAde; TchrAde; CaptFtbl; IMSpt; DanFAwd; Muskegon Comm College; Teacher.

CUNNINGHAM, Edward; Kent City HS; Casnovia, MI; 37/90 Chrs; HonRl; NHS; StuGov; FFA; SciCl; College; Heavy Equip Ser.

CUNNINGHAM, Elizabeth C; Grosse Pte South HS; Grosse Pointe, MI; ChrhWkr; CmntyWkr; HonRl; MrchBnd; NHS; Orch; SchPl; GerCl; Western Michigan U; Occupational Therapy.

CUNNINGHAM, Gail M; Center Line HS; Warren, MI; 4/430 Band; ChrhWkr; HonRl; JrNHS; MrchBnd; NHS; StuCncl; Bsbl; Bsktbl; OptClAwd; Wayne St Univ; Bs Degree, Crime Lab.

CUNNINGHAM, Jaclyn K; Bridgeport HS; Bridgeport, IL; Band; Chrs; HonRl; NHS; SchMus; StuCncl; Yrbk; Chrldr; SecGAA; DARAwd; Eastern Illinois Univ; Zoology.

CUNNINGHAM, Jill A; Bismarck Henning HS; Bismarck, IL; 1/74 SecFrshCls; PresJrCls; HonRl; SchPl; StuCncl; RptrYrbk; SchPpr; FTA; SpnCl; PpCl; Coll; Eng Teacher.

CUNNINGHAM, Karla G; So Boone Co R 1 HS; Hartsburg, MO; ALAGirlsSt; Band; Chr; ChrhWkr; HonRl; SchPl; YthFlsp; YthLg; 4-H; Univ; Nurse.

CUNNINGHAM, Kathleen M; Mother Guerin HS; River Grove, IL; 53/409 HospAde; MthCl; Bsktbl; College.

CUNNINGHAM, Leanna J; Greenfield HS; Greenfield, IL; ChrhWkr; CncrtBnd; HonRl; RedCrAde; Yrbk; FHA; FrCl; GAA; IMSpt; AmLegAwd; Nursing Sch; Medicine.

CUNNINGHAM, Leslie D; Grosse Pointe South HS; Grosse Pointe, MI; ChrhWkr; HonRl; Orch; SchMus; GerCl; College; Humanities.

CUNNINGHAM, Lisa K; Roseville HS; Roseville, IL; VPFrshCls; Chrs; CmntyWkr; HonRl; SchMus; SctActv; SchPpr; 4-H; SpnCl; PpCl; GAA; AmLegAwd; Univ Of Illinois; Youth Extension Advisor.

CUNNINGHAM, Lynn M; Marian HS; Troy, MI; ModUN; NHS; RptrYrbk; College.

CUNNINGHAM, Margaret M; Mercy HS; Omaha, NE; 5/66 SchMus; SpnCl; GAA; Univ; Medicine.

CUNNINGHAM, Marion O; Lindblom Tech HS; Chicago, IL; 6/740 Chr; Chrs; ChrhWkr; HonRl; NatlThespSoc; SchPl; TchrAde; College; Medicine.

CUNNINGHAM, Mary K; Rosati Kain HS; St Louis, MO; Chrs; HonRl; Mdrgl; SchMus; StuCncl; College; Accountant.

CUNNINGHAM, Norma; Central R Iii HS; Flat River, MO; 18/137 Band; Chr; DrmMjrt; HonRl; JrNHS; MrchBnd; NHS; Twrl; PpCl; Trk; College; Math Or English.

CUNNINGHAM, Peggy; Central Heights HS; Princeton, KS; 6/40 Band; Chrs; HonRl; TrsFrshCls; NHS; PepBnd; SchPl; PpCl; Bsktbl; Trk; Jr Coll; Teach.

CUNNINGHAM, Peggy A; East HS; Kansas City, MO; 16/200 HonRl; Central Missouri State U; Distributive Educ.

CUNNINGHAM, Sharon L; Klemme Comm HS; Goodell, IA; HstFrshCls; PresSophCls; Chr; Chrs; ChrhWkr; HonRl; YthFlsp; SciCl; College; Vocational.

CUNNINGHAM, Sheila M; Maria HS; Chicago, IL; PresJrCls; Chrs; CmntyWkr; HonRl; NatlMeritSF; StuCncl; SpnCl; Bsktbl; Chrldr; College; Police.

CUNNINGS, Stephen W; Memphis HS; Memphis, MI; 1/76 HonRl; NatlMeritSF; StuGov; RptrYrbk; EdYrBk; BauchLmbAwd; Univ; Special Education.

CUNY, Cari L; East Catholic HS; Detroit, MI; 1/90 TrsSophCls; CncrtBnd; HonRl; NHS; SctActv; StuCncl; StuGov; FrCl; Chrldr; Trade School; Art.

CUPANI, Teresa M; Resurrection HS; Chicago, IL; 18/273 HonRl; PresNHS; NatlMeritCmnd; StuCncl; FNA; SpnCl; MthCl; SciCl; GAA; Univ Of Illinois; Pharmacy.

CUPERUS, Steven B; Graceville HS; Dumont, MN; 2/50 ChrhWkr; HonRl; NHS; FFA; SciCl; Ftbl; Nd State School; Electronics.

CUPIDO, Cathy A; James Madison HS; Milwaukee, WI; 13/850 NHS; SpnCl; PpCl; LetterTennis; GAA; BauchLmbAwd; BttyCrckrAwd; GovHonPrgAwd; University Of Wisconsin; Chemistry.

CUPP, Gary; South Newton Hs; Brook, IN; 17/97 HonRl; EdYrBk; 4-H; FBLA; FFA; FTA; LatCl; LetterBsbl; LetterBsktbl; LetterFtbl; Purdue;professional.

CUPPLES, William T; Hoxie HS; Hoxie, KS; HonRl; StuCncl; StuGov; FshEdYrbk; SptEdSchPpr; SchPpr; CaptBsktbl; CaptFtbl; LetterGlf; Swmmng; Colby Comm College; Physical Educ.

CUPRISIN, Timothy E; Lakeshore HS; Stevensville, MI; HonRl; Quill&Scroll; TchrAde; EdSchPpr; Clg; Journalism.

CURATOLO, Thomas A; Thornton Twp HS; Dolton, IL; CmntyWkr; HonRl; Ill State Univ; Computer Science.

CURBOW, David W; Clever HS; Billings, MO; 10/23 TrsFrshCls; VPSophCls; Band; Chrs; CncrtBnd; HonRl; PepBnd; SchPl; FFA; MthCl; Smsu; Architecture.

CURBY, Debora A; Donovan HS; Beaverville, IL; VPFrshCls; Band; NHS; Quill&Scroll; SchMus; SchPl; RptrYrbk; EdSchPpr; Chrldr; DARAwd; U Of Il; Special Ed.

CURDA, Carol E; Lyons Twp HS; La Grange, IL; 8/1245 HospAde; JrNHS; NHS; TreasFHA; RusCl; Tennis; AmLegAwd; BttyCrckrAwd; Univ Of Ky; Nutritional Therapy.

CUREMAN, Mavon; Prophetstown HS; Prophetstown, IL; 5/98 Band; CmntyWkr; CncrtBnd; HonRl; MrchBnd; NHS; PepBnd; SctActv; PpCl; College; Bachelors Degree In Nursing.

CUREY, Victoria; Litchfield HS; Litchfield, MI; SecFrshCls; SecJrCls; Chr; HonRl; RptrSchPpr; Chrldr; GAA; Lake Superior State; Conservation.

CUREY, Victoria; Litchfield HS; Litchfield, MI; VPFrshCls; SecJrCls; Band; HonRl; SchPl; CaptFFA; LetterBsktbl; LetterTrk; Chrldr; GAA; Lake Superior State College;conservation.

CURFMAN, Darcey A; Perry HS; Griggsville, IL; 4/17 SecSophCls; TrsJrCls; Chrs; HonRl; StuCncl; Yrbk; CivCl; FHA; Bsktbl; DanFAwd; Coll; Professional.

CURLEY, Carol A; Msgr Hackett HS; Kalamazoo, MI; 5/143 Band; CmntyWkr; CncrtBnd; HonRl; IntrClCncl; MrchBnd; NHS; Orch; SchMus; StuCncl; IMSpt; Ferris State College; Office Admin.

CURLEY, Shawn P; U Of D HS; Detroit, MI; 1/204 CmntyWkr; HonRl; NHS; NatlMeritFnl; StuGov; Yrbk; SciCl; LetterFtbl; CaptTrk; IMSpt; Dartmouth Clg; Math.

CURNOW, Candace M; Harbor Springs HS; Harbor Springs, MI; 5/75 Chrs; CncrtBnd; HonRl; HospAde; LbryAde; PepBnd; SchPl; SpnCl; PpCl; IMSpt; College.

CURPHY, Cary E; Topeka West HS; Topeka, KS; 13/500 Band; HonRl; NatlMeritSF; LatCl; SciCl; Trk; Kansas Univ; Computer Science.

CURRAN, Colleen M; Escanaba Area HS; Escanaba, MI; 5/382 Chrs; ChrhWkr; CmntyWkr; NHS; SchAde; SchMus; College; Interior Designer.

CURRAN, Lawrence S; Greeley Public HS; Greeley, NE; SecFrshCls; ChrhWkr; HonRl; SchPl; SctActv; SptEdYrbk; SptEdSchPpr; Bsbl; Bsktbl; Ftbl; Physical Education.

CURRAN, Lisa F; Edgewood HS; Madison, WI; Chrs; HonRl; OffAde; SchMus; Trade Schl; Business.

CURRAN, Mary E; St Agatha HS; Redford Twp, MI; HonRl; NHS; PolWkr; TreasStuCncl; LetterBsbl; LetterBsktbl; LetterChrldr; CchngActv; Mich St U; Rn.

CURRAN, Mary Elle; St Agatha HS; Redford Twp, MI; HonRl; NHS; TreasStuCncl; CaptBsbl; LetterChrldr; CchngActv; Mi St Univ; Registerd Nurse.

CURRAN, Steven M; O Fallon Twp HS; O Fallon, IL; 19/301 HonRl; NHS; StuCncl; SptEdYrbk; EdSchPpr; SptEdSchPpr; Bsbl; Bsktbl; Ftbl; Univ Of Missouri; Geology.

CURRENT, Thomas R; Maquoketa Comm HS; Maquoketa, IA; 3/155 Band; PresChrs; HonRl; ModUN; NHS; SctActv; Ftbl; Wrstlng; GovHonPrgAwd; RotaryAwd; University Of Iowa; Lawyer.

CURRIE, Daniel; Bishop Dwenger HS; Fort Wayne, IN; CmntyWkr; HonRl; PolWkr; FrCl; College; Professional.

CURRIE, Edward; St Martin De Porres HS; Detroit, MI; HonRl; JA; JrNHS; NHS; ROTC; StuGov; LetterBsktbl; IMSpt; University; Aerospace.

CURRIE, James A; High School; Powhattan, KS; PresFrshCls; PresSophCls; SecTrsSrCls; HonRl; Bsktbl; Ftbl; Trk; Washburn Univ.

CURRIE, Patricia M; Maine East HS; Park Ridge, IL; ChrhWkr; HonRl; JrNHS; NHS; NatlMeritCmnd; SctActv; StuGov; SecMthCl; Swmmng; Univ Of Ill; Finance.

CURRIE, Rebecca L; Springfield HS; Springfield, IL; Chr; ChrhWkr; CmntyWkr; PolWkr; SchMus; SctActv; College; Nursing.

CURRIER, Bobbi K; Burr Oak HS; Burr Oak, MI; 9/34 Band; DrmMjrt; HonRl; SecNHS; SchMus; SchPl; TchrAde; EdYrBk; CaptChrldr; PPFtbl; Glen Oaks Comm College; Drama.

CURRIN, Archie L; Luther South HS; Chicago, IL; 60/204 TrsSophCls; VPJrCls; PresSrCls; SptEdSchPpr; LetterBsbl; CaptFtbl; Wrstlng; College; Law.

CURRIN, Sharon L; Streator Twp HS; Streator, IL; 82/385 CmntyWkr; HonRl; StuGov; TchrAde; Yrbk; Illinois State Univ; Corrections.

CURRO, Julie G; Ashwaubenon HS; Green Bay, WI; PresFrshCls; SecSophCls; SecJrCls; NHS; SchPl; SecFBLA; PpCl; Chrldr; College.

CURRY, Beverly K; Jayhawk Linn HS; Kincaid, KS; Band; CncrtBnd; HonRl; Mdrgl; Ottawa U; Art.

CURRY, Denis R; Morton HS; Pekin, IL; Chrs; CmntyWkr; HonRl; SchMus; 4-H; Illinois Central College; Mortuary Science.

CURRY, Dwight H; Nebraska Christian HS; Ponca, NE; VPSrCls; Chr; Chrl; Chrs; ChrhWkr; SchPl; 4-H; Bsktbl; Ftbl; Trk; Lynchburg Baptist College.

CURRY, Julie; Elk Point HS; Elk Point, SD; 3/39 ALAGirlsSt; Band; CncrtBnd; HonRl; MrchBnd;

Orch; PepBnd; RptrYrbk; EdYrBk; CitAwd; Sd St Univ; Home Ec.

CURRY, Kenneth B; Morton HS; Pekin, IL; 22/292 ChrhWkr; HonRl; 4-H; FFA; SciCl; Glf; Drake Univ; Pharmacy.

CURRY, Lucia A; Bucklin Rii HS; Bucklin, MO; SecFrshCls; TrsSophCls; TrsJrCls; TrsSrCls; ALAGirlsSt; Chr; Chrs; ChrhWkr; HonRl; HospAde; NHS; Bsktbl; DanFAwd; Univ Of Missouri; Nursing.

CURRY, Lynn M; Excelsior Springs HS; Excelsior Springs, MO; HonRl; NHS; OffAde; FBLA; PpCl; SciCl; CaptBsktbl; Tennis; Chrldr; GAA; University.

CURRY, Mark A; Wichita North HS; Wichita, KS; Aud/Vis; Band; ChrhWkr; CncrtBnd; MrchBnd; Orch; PepBnd; SchMus; SctActv; YthFlsp; SptEdYrbk; College; Business Adm.

CURRY, Pamala G; Ponca Public HS; Ponca, NE; Band; Chrs; CncrtBnd; HonRl; Mdrgl; MrchBnd; NHS; PepBnd; SchPl; YthFlsp; 4-H;.

CURRY, Phyllis L; St James HS; St James, MN; 82/148 VPJrCls; Chr; DrmMjrt; HonRl; StuCncl; YthFlsp; RptrYrbk; Swmmng; Trk; Chrldr; College; Busness Field.

CURRY, Robert G; Ponca HS; Ponca, NE; PresFrshCls; Chr; SchPl; StuCncl; RptrYrbk; 4-H; CaptBsktbl; Ftbl; Trk; CitAwd; U Of Sd; Education.

CURRY, Tamara S; Octavia HS; Colfax, IL; Band; HonRl; SchPl; StuCncl; YthFlsp; RptrSchPpr; MthCl; SciCl; Trk; GAA; PPFtbl; Trade School; Vocation.

CURRY, Thomas M; Owen Valley HS; Spencer, IN; 8/190 HonRl; NHS; TchrAde; 4-H; DanFAwd; Purdue; Forestry.

CURRY, Tyray; Concordia HS; Ft Wayne, IN; Chr; NatlMeritCmnd; ROTC; TchrAde; Bsktbl; LetterFtbl; Clge; Law.

CURTIN, Brigid A; Good Counsel Acad; St Paul, MN; 5/64 NatlMeritSF; SchPl; StuCncl; EdSchPpr; GerCl; GAA; Coll; Theology.

CURTIN, John F; Stonington HS; Blue Mound, IL; 2/48 PresFrshCls; ChrhWkr; HonRl; Pres4-H; VPFFA; Bsbl; LetterBsktbl; 4-HAwd; Univ Of Illinois; Farmer.

CURTIN, John M; Algoma HS; Algoma, WI; VPSrCls; Chrs; HonRl; Mdrgl; NatlFornLg; SchMus; SchPl; TchrAde; RptrYrbk; SchPpr; Univ; Advertising Journalism.

CURTIN, Mark T; Logansport HS; Logansport, IN; NatlMeritCmnd; NatlMeritSF; PolWkr; SchMus; SchPl; SctActv; FrCl; MthCl; SciCl; Trk; Indiana Univ; Medicine.

CURTIN, Patrick P; So Milw HS; So Milw, WI; 76/446 CAP; HonRl; SciCl; Ftbl; LetterSwmmng; IMSpt; Pudue Univ; Civil Engineer.

CURTINDOLPH, Calvin A; Fenger HS; Dixmoor, IL; ChrhWkr; NatlMeritCmnd; OffAde; StuCncl; TchrAde; RptrSchPpr; FTA; MthCl; Coll; Mathematics Teacher.

CURTIS, Cheryl L; Burt Community HS; Burt, IA; HonRl; LbryAde; TchrAde; FTA; College; Social Services.

CURTIS, Clifford; Chariton Community HS; Chariton, IA; VPJrCls; ALBoysSt; ChrhWkr; StuCncl; StuGov; YthFlsp; Bsktbl; Ftbl; Glf; CchngActv; College; Professional.

CURTIS, Connie J; Fremont Mills HS; Tabor, IA; SecBand; CmntyWkr; CncrtBnd; DrmMjrt; HonRl; NatlThespSoc; SchPl; PresStuCncl; YthFlsp; Yrbk; CaptBsktbl; LetterTrk; CchngActv; Iowa W Comm College; Secretary.

CURTIS, Danny R; Central Comm HS; De Witt, IA; 24/166 Chrs; HonRl; NHS; OffAde; SchAde; 4-H; FFA; LetterFtbl; Trk; Wrstlng; Iowa State Univ; Veterinarian.

CURTIS, Diana K; St Pius X HS; Kansas City, MO; 18/132 Chrs; HonRl; OffAde; SchMus; TchrAde; RptrSchPpr; PpCl; Coll; Med Lab Tech.

CURTIS, James; E Alton Wood River HS; Wood River, IL; 5/290 HonRl; LitMag; NatlFornLg; NHS; NatlThespSoc; SchMus; SchPl; AmLegAwd; KiwanAwd; Univ; Professional Speech.

CURTIS, James B; East Alton Wood River HS; Wood River, IL; 4/331 ChrhWkr; HonRl; LitMag; NatlFornLg; NHS; NatlThespSoc; SchMus; SchPl; StuCncl; RptrSchPpr; LatCl; Univ; Law.

CURTIS, Joan M; Arthur Hill HS; Sagninaw, MI; Band; Chr; HonRl; College; Professional.

CURTIS, John; West Grant HS; Prairie Du Chien, WI; SecJrCls; Band; CncrtBnd; HonRl; MrchBnd; PepBnd; SchMus; Vocational Sch.

CURTIS, Kim A; South Newton Jr Sr HS; Kentland, IN; 8/100 Band; Chr; Chrs; CncrtBnd; HonRl; MrchBnd; NHS; Orch; PepBnd; Quill&Scroll; GAA; Indiana Univ; Optometry.

CURTIS, Lisa M; La Crosse HS; La Crosse, KS; Band; Chr; HonRl; PepBnd; SchPl; StuCncl; TchrAde; FHA; SpnCl; Fort Hays State College; Airline Stewardess.

CURTIS, Michael D; Franklin HS; Franklin, IL; Band; HonRl; College; Professional.

CURTIS, Nancy A; Brown County HS; Nashville, IN; 15/166 Chrs; ChrhWkr; HospAde; NHS; NatlThespSoc; SchMus; SctActv; StuCncl; TchrAde; 4-H; College; Physical Therapist.

CURTIS, Patrice J; Cus HS; Chicago, IL; 99/1200 TrsFrshCls; Chr; ChrhWkr; HonRl; HospAde; MrchBnd; OffAde; SchAde; StuCncl; GAA; Northern Univ; Pharmacist.

CURTIS, Paul E; West Sr HS; North Aurora, IL; Chr; Chrs; ChrhWkr; NHS; SctActv; College; Professional.

CURTIS, Sharon; St Pius X HS; Kansas City, MO; 7/130 Chrs; HonRl; SchMus; PpCl; Bus School; Secretarial.

CURTIS, Shayne P; Hill City HS; Hill City, MN; VPJrCls; HonRl; StuGov; Ftbl; CchngActv; Aerospace Engr.

CURTIS, Sherry L; Macomb HS; Macomb, IL; 16/235 Band; Chr; CncrtBnd; HonRl; MrchBnd; NHS; SchPpr; FHA; SpnCl; Western Ill Univ; Bi Lingual Education.

CURTISS, Jay L; Sidney HS; Sidney, NE; Chrs; CncrtBnd; HonRl; JrNHS; Mdrgl; NHS; SchMus; MthCl; LetterBsktbl; LetterFtbl; Glf; University Of Nebraska; Agriculture.

CURTISS, Michael S; Springfield HS; Springfield, IL; 83/585 PolWkr; ROTC; SctActv; RptrYrbk; KeyCl; Bsbl; Ftbl; Vanderbilt Univ; Medicine.

CURTNER, Rosa L; Crab Orchard HS; Stonefort, IL; SecTrsJrCls; ChrhWkr; HonRl; YthFlsp; RptrYrbk; RptrSchPpr; FHA; PpCl; John R Logan Coll; Business.

CURTRIGHT, Patsy; Senath Hornersville HS; Senath, MO; Chrs; ChrhWkr; HonRl; TchrAde; Secretarial.

CURTSINGER, Tracee; Rochester HS; Rochester, IL; Chr; HonRl; RptrSchPpr; FHA; GerCl; Trk; Chrldr; GAA; Trade Or Bus; Vocation.

CURY, Steve; Benton HS; Benton, IL; NHS; FDA; SpnCl; Bsktbl; IMSpt; Southern Il Univ; Med.

CUSACK, Maureen T; Academy Of Our Lady; Chicago, IL; 7/189 HonRl; NHS; SchPl; Yrbk; FrCl; PpCl; CchngActv; GAA; PPFtbl; LionAwd; U Of Chicago; Special Ed Teach.

CUSHING, Melisa A; Lawrence Central HS; Indianapolis, IN; 89/704 DrlTm; HonRl; TreasJA; SchAde; TchrAde; Yrbk; Butler Univ; Pre Law.

CUSHING, Thomas C; Craig Sr HS; Janesville, WI; HonRl; Quill&Scroll; StuCncl; RptrSchPpr; SptEdSchPpr; LetterFtbl; Glf; U Of Wi Madison; Optometry.

CUSHINGBERRY, Matthew P; East HS; Des Moines, IA; Band; CncrtBnd; MrchBnd; PepBnd; StuCncl; Trade School; Computer Science.

CUSHMAN, David; Fort Atkinson Senior HS; Fort Atkinson, WI; 16/262 Band; ChrhWkr; CAP; CncrtBnd; HonRl; MrchBnd; NHS; PepBnd; SctActv; KeyCl; College; Electrical Engineer.

CUSHMAN, Donna J; Fountain Central HS; Attica, IN; 15/127 ALAGirlsSt; SecBand; Chr; ChrhWkr; CmntyWkr; HonRl; Mdrgl; NHS; SchAde; PresYthFlsp; SecFHA; PpCl; Indiana Univ; Special Ed.

CUSHMAN, Neal D; Fraser HS; Fraser, MI; 12/500 Band; ChrhWkr; CncrtBnd; HonRl; MrchBnd; NHS; IMSpt; Bob Jones Univ; Professional.

CUSIMANO, Scott A; Marmion Military Acad; Oak Park, IL; 5/89 PresFrshCls; PresSophCls; PresJrCls; Band; HonRl; NHS; ROTC; StuCncl; SpnCl; LetterBsbl; Univ; Military Or Lawyer.

CUSSEN, Diane T; Maria HS; Oak Lawn, IL; 17/335 SecSophCls; Chrl; HonRl; HospAde; SchMus; SctActv; GerCl; Swmmng; GAA; IMSpt; College; Home Ec Art.

CUSSICK, Gwendolyn M; Forest View HS; Mt Prospect, IL; PresFrshCls; Chr; ChrhWkr; SchMus; SctActv; TchrAde; SchPpr; Northern Illinois Univ; Fashion Merch.

CUSSON, Jody M; George Washington HS; Indianapolis, IN; 13/359 PresJrCls; PresSrCls; VPChr; ModUN; VPNatlFornLg; NHS; StuCncl; DARAwd; Indiana Univ; Social Service.

CUSTARD, Richard W; New Bloomfield R Iii HS; New Bloomfield, MO; Chrs; HonRl; StuCncl; SptEdSchPpr; PpCl; SciCl; LetterBsbl; CaptBsktbl; College.

CUSTER, Judith K; Lyons Township HS; Western Springs, IL; 20/1300 AFS; Chrs; ChrhWkr; HonRl; JrNHS; NHS; SchAde; SchMus; SctActv; TchrAde; YthFlsp; PpCl; Chrldr; College; Medicine.

CUSTER, Marie; Waukesha North HS; Waukesha, WI; 40/326 Chr; Chrs; NHS; SctActv; RptrSchPpr; PpCl; Trk; GAA; PPFtbl; PresAwd; U Of Wis Waukesha; Acct.

CUSTER, Robert A; Summerfield HS; Petersburg, MI; 3/75 ALBoysSt; HonRl; NHS; SchAde; SchPl; Trk; Monroe Comm Col; Drafting.

CUSTIS, David; Scotland HS; Scotand, SD; HonRl; OffAde; SchMus; SchPl; IMSpt; Mount Marty Coll; Nursing.

CUTBERTH, Jeffrey L; Central HS; St Joseph, MO; 21/540 PresSrCls; HonRl; JrNHS; NHS; SchMus; StuCncl; StuGov; PresSciCl; LetterTennis; Ks Univ; Arcitct Engin.

CUTKA, Mary S; George Rogers Clark HS; Whiting, IN; 4/260 ALAGirlsSt; PresChrhWkr; HospAde; NHS; PresNatlThespSoc; Quill&Scroll; SchPl; RptrYrbk; FNA; SpnCl; College; Nursing.

CUTLER, Pamela E; Christopher HS; Christopher, IL; Band; CncrtBnd; HonRl; NHS; Twrl; Yrbk; FHA; Business School; Stenographer.

CUTLER, Sandra L; Groton HS; Claremont, SD; 4/60 Chrs; CncrtBnd; HonRl; NatlSciFnd; NHS; SchPl; RptrSchPpr; Trk; BttyCrckrAwd; 4-HAwd; Concordia Col; Music Ed.

CUTLER, Sharon L; Auburndale HS; Arpin, WI; 40/100 Band; CncrtBnd; HonRl; MrchBnd; PepBnd; SctActv; RptrSchPpr; FFA; FHA; Bsktbl; Trk; EldAwd; Univ Of La Crosse; Physical Education.

CUTRIGHT, David E; Charleston HS; Ashmore, IL; 36/251 HonRl; SpnCl; Ftbl; University Of Illinois; Electrical Engineer.

CUTRIGHT, Jennifer J; Casey HS; Casey, IL; Chr; Chrs; ChrhWkr; CmntyWkr; HonRl; SchMus; Yrbk; SchPpr; FHA; PpCl; Missouri Schl For Doctors; Medical Tech.

CUTSHAW, Linda L; Louisburg HS; Louisburg, KS; 7/63 HstSrCls; ALAGirlsSt; DrlTm; HonRl; FNA; FSA; SpnCl; MthCl; PpCl; Swmmng;.

CUTTER, Peggy J; Dillsboro Public HS; Dillsboro, IN; 4/30 SecJrCls; SecSrCls; Band; Chrs; ChrhWkr; HonRl; Yrbk; 4-H; SecGAA; DanFAwd; Marian Coll; Medical Technology.

CUTTING, Betsy; St Pius X HS; Kansas City, MO; 28/131 Chrs; HonRl; SchMus; SchPl; 4-H; 4-HAwd; College; Foreign Lang.

CUTTING, Loretta C; Alvernia HS; Chicago, IL; 10/280 PresFrshCls; HospAde; NHS; StuCncl; StuGov; FrCl; No Illinois Univ; Physical Therapist.

CUTTS, Beth M; Stillman Valley HS; Stillman Valley, IL; 6/100 SecBand; DrlTm; HonRl; LbryAde; NHS; YthFlsp; 4-H; FHA; FTA; PPFtbl; Carthage Col ;pre School Ed.

CUVA, Susan K; North HS; Omaha, NE; HonRl; JA; LbryAde; OffAde; TchrAde; SpnCl; MthCl; IMSpt; PPFtbl; Uno; Social Work.

CUVELIER, Ronald L; Harrison HS; Harrison, MI; 8/120 NHS; LetterBsbl; LetterBsktbl; ChmnFtbl; LetterWrstlng; Clge.

CVACH, Barbara A; Kadoka HS; Kadoka, SD; ALAGirlsSt; Band; DrlTm; HonRl; LbryAde; PolWkr; RptrSchPpr; 4-H; FHA; LetterTrk;.

CWACH, Nancy L; Yankton Sr HS; Yankton, SD; HonRl; RptrYrbk; Pres4-H; FTA; MthCl; SciCl; Trk; 4-HAwd; PresAwd; College; Professional.

CWIAKALA, Debra A; Grand Blanc HS; Grand Blanc, MI; 52/618 CmntyWkr; HonRl; NHS; 4-H; PpCl; PPFtbl; Univ Of Michigan; Medical Technology.

CWIK, Linda; Taft HS; Chicago, IL; 30/850 HonRl; JrNHS; Orch; GAA; College; Private Teacher Of Music.

CWIK, Michael C; Catholic Central HS; Detroit, MI; Chrl; HonRl; IMSpt; Univ Of Detroit; Business.

CYCENAS, Mary N; Siren HS; Siren, WI; TrsFrshCls; PresJrCls; TrsSrCls; Band; ChrhWkr; HonRl; PepBnd; 4-H; FHA; PpCl; Marriage.

CYCON, Cynthia A; Taft HS; Chicago, IL; 11/857 Band; Chr; Chrs; ChrhWkr; HonRl; JA; LbryAde; NHS; GAA; AmLegAwd; College; Physical Science.

CYGAN, John L; St Paul HS; Highland, IL; 1/53 Chrs; HonRl; ModUN; SchMus; SpnCl; LetterBsbl; CaptLetterSocr; PresAwd; Univ Of Chicago.

CYPHERS, Robert L; Litchfield HS; Litchfield, IL; ChrhWkr; CmntyWkr; PolWkr; StuGov; YthFlsp; EdYrBk; EdSchPpr; SptEdSchPpr; Glf; IMSpt; College; Journalism.

CYR, Anita; Hastings Sr HS; Hastings, MN; 2/428 HonRl; JrNHS; NHS; NatlThespSoc; SchPl; TchrAde; Twrl; FrCl; Inver Hills Jr Col.

CYR, Ann M; Oconto Falls HS; Oconto Falls, WI; 26/157 Chrs; HonRl; NatlFornLg; VPFHA; Uw Stevens Point; Home Economics.

CYR, Vicki R; Clyde Rural HS; Clyde, KS; Chrs; ChrhWkr; HonRl; LbryAde; SpnCl; Beloit Vo Tech; Lpn.

CYRUS, Mary K; Macks Creek HS; Macks Creek, MO; SecFrshCls; PresSophCls; PresJrCls; Chr; ChrhWkr; HonRl; PresStuCncl; EdYrBk; RptrSchPpr; FHA; MthCl; SciCl; Bsktbl; College; Home Economics.

CZAJKA, Peni S; Frank Cody HS; Detroit, MI; Band; CncrtBnd; HonRl; MrchBnd; Business School; Vocation.

CZAPLA, Edward; Bishop Noll Institute; East Chicago, IN; 123/365 HonRl; MthCl; IMSpt; Univ; Industrial Engineer.

CZAPLEWSKI, Kellen K; Loup City Public HS; Loup City, NE; 11/63 Chrs; ChrhWkr; HonRl; StuCncl; Yrbk; Bsbl; LetterBsktbl; LetterFtbl; LetterGlf; LetterTrk; Kearney St College; Biology.

CZARNECKI, Douglas L; Comstock Park HS; Comstock Park, MI; NatlFornLg; SchPl; StuCncl; Yrbk; RptrSchPpr; Bsktbl; LetterFtbl; AmLegAwd; Clge; Psychology.

CZARNECKI, Thomas N; St Joseph HS; Kenosha, WI; 20/150 Chr; HonRl; NatlFornLg; NHS; SctActv; PpCl; LetterBsktbl; Ftbl; Glf; IMSpt; Col; Professional.

CZECH, Julie A; Collinsville HS; Collinsville, IL; HonRl; NHS; TchrAde; TreasPpCl; LetterTrk; LetterGAA; College; Pe.

CZECH, Melanie S; Thornridge HS; Harvey, IL; HonRl; HospAde; NHS; Purdue University; Nursing.

CZECHOWSKI, Christopher; Milwaukee Tech HS; Milwaukee, WI; 72/584 HonRl; NHS; Bsktbl; Uw Milwaukee; Physician.

CZERANKO, Michael J; Creighton Preparatory HS; Omaha, NE; 33/249 Chrs; HonRl; NatlFornLg; SchAde; SchMus; SchPl; Sdlty; TchrAde; Yrbk; Univ Of Nebraska; Drama.

CZERKIES, Lawrence; Boyne Falls Public HS; Boyne Falls, MI; 1/18 VPJrCls; ChrhWkr; CncrtBnd; HonRl; MrchBnd; PepBnd; TchrAde; Bsbl; Bsktbl; N Central Mi College; Research.

CZERNYCZUK, Nicholas W; Notre Dame HS; Milwaukee, WI; PresSophCls; HonRl; NatlMeritSchl; SchMus; StuCncl; College; Professional.

CZERWINSKI, Janet; Fairfield HS; Fairfield, IA; ChrhWkr; CmntyWkr; HonRl; NHS; FrCl; PpCl; Bsktbl; CchngActv; College; Professional.

CZERWINSKI, Thomas; Round Lake Sr HS; Round Lake, IL; 37/217 HonRl; LitMag; RptrSchPpr; IMSpt; Northern Illinois Univ; Journalism.

CZERWONKA, Frederick W; Newton HS; Newton, IL; VPJrCls; ChrhWkr; Glf; Tennis; College; Professional.

CZIOK, Pamela A; Onamia HS; Onamia, MN; TrsSrCls; Band; CncrtBnd; HonRl; MrchBnd; PepBnd; TchrAde; PpCl; Trk; CaptChrldr; College; Phy Educ.

CZISNY, Carole; Port HS; Port Washington, WI; HonRl; StuCncl; RptrYrbk; KiwanAwd; Milw Area Tech Coll; Accounting.

CZMIEL, Timothy P; Mendel Catholic Prep HS; Chicago, IL; 13/169 HonRl; MthCl; Villanova Univ; Priest.

CZMIEL, Timothy P; Mendel Catholic Prep; Chicago, IL; HonRl; PolWkr; MthCl; PpCl; Univ; Theologian.

CZUBA, Daniel M; St Paul & Kennedy HS; Chicago, IL; 206/610 Chrs; SctActv; StuCncl; Ftbl; CaptTrk; Siu.

CZUBA, John C; Lake Michigan Catholic HS; Sodus, MI; Band; HonRl; PepBnd; RptrSchPpr; University; Accounting.

CZUBA, Stanley J; J F Kennedy HS; Chicago, IL; 57/544 HonRl; OffAde; University Of Illinois; Mechanical Engineer.

CZUPRYN, Kurt; East Noble; Kendallville, IN; 14/279 Band; ChrhWkr; HonRl; NHS; YthFlsp; SptEdSchPpr; Wrstlng; IMSpt; GovHonPrgAwd; Ind Univ; Phys Ed.

CZUPRYNSKI, James S; St Rita HS; Chicago, IL; 4/424 Chrs; HonRl; NHS; NatlMeritCmnd; SchPl; Bradley Univ; Journalism.

CZYZEWSKI, John E; Lake Park HS; Bloomingdale, IL; HonRl; SctActv; University; Medicine.

D

D AMATO, Riki C; Waukesha South HS; Waukesha, WI; AFS; SchMus; SchPl; TchrAde; RptrSchPpr; EdSchPpr; U Of Wi Whitewater; Journalism.

D ANDREA, Kathleen E; W L Western HS; Walled Lake, MI; 1/400 HonRl; TreasNHS; StuCncl; StuGov; PpCl; LetterBsktbl; GAA; IMSpt; Mercy Col; Medical Technology.

D AQUILA, Margaret M; Hibbing HS; Hibbing, MN; HonRl; PolWkr; SchMus; SchPl; CaptSwmmng; GAA; IMSpt; St Marys College Of Notre Dame; Medicine.

D ARCY, Diane; Gladstone Area HS; Gladstone, MI; CncrtBnd; HonRl; MrchBnd; SctActv; TchrAde; CaptBsktbl; CaptTrk; GAA; IMSpt; PPFtbl; Univ Central Mi; Physical Ed.

D ARCY, Jean M; Munster HS; Munster, IN; ChrhWkr; HonRl; JA; JrNHS; NatlFornLg; 4-H; FBLA; JCAwd; JAAwd; KiwanAwd; College; Professional.

D ARPINI, Harold A; Jefferson HS; Monroe, MI; 17/150 Band; ChrhWkr; CncrtBnd; HonRl; MrchBnd; NatlThespSoc; PepBnd; SchPl; SctActv; RptrSchPpr; FrCl; Alma College; Actor.

D AUBEN, Michael J; Thornridge HS; Dolton, IL; Aud/Vis; HonRl; Quill&Scroll; RptrYrbk; Univ Of Illinois; Architect.

D OYLY, Michael R; Interlochen Arts Academy; Grand Haven, MI; Band; Chr; Chrl; Chrs; CncrtBnd; HonRl; NHS; Orch; SchMus; StuCncl; Hope Coll; Music.

D SOUZA, Anita M; Kirksville Sr HS; Kirksville, MO; Chrs; ChrhWkr; CmntyWkr; HonRl; JA; Orch; SchMus; 4-H; SciCl; College; Business Admin.

D URSO, Mary L; Urbana Sr HS; Urbana, IL; 48/483 AFS; ChrhWkr; HonRl; TchrAde; 4-H; FTA; PresFrCl; Chrldr; Univ Of Illinois; Social Studies.

D VALENTINE, Christie; East Lansing HS; East Lansing, MI; 28/357 Chrl; Chrs; LitMag; NHS; OffAde; SctActv; TchrAde; FTA; Mi Tech Univ; Med Tech.

DABBS, Regina M; Union HS; Sturtevant, WI; 5/198 Band; Chr; ChrhWkr; CncrtBnd; HonRl; MrchBnd; NHS; NatlMeritSF; PepBnd; 4-H; St Lukes Hosp School; Nursing.

DABERKOW, Laurie; Bancroft Public HS; Bancroft, NE; HstSophCls; PresJrCls; ALAGirlsSt; Chrs; HonRl; NHS; 4-H; SciCl; Chrldr; Coll Trade.

DABLER, Robert E; Maysville HS; Amity, MO; Chrs; ChrhWkr; CmntyWkr; HonRl; JrNHS; SchPl; StuCncl; YthFlsp; 4-H; FFA; Univ; Professnl.

DABNEY, Kirk A; Davis Co Comm HS; Bloomfield, IA; VPSophCls; ALBoysSt; ChrhWkr; HonRl; PolWkr; SctActv; StuCncl; HstFrshCls; Bsktbl; Glf; Coll; Prof.

DABROWSKI, Edward J; Morton West HS; Stickney, IL; Aud/Vis; HonRl; Quill&Scroll; TchrAde; Illinois Inst Of Tech; Electronics.

DACHNIWSKYJ, Maria T; Immaculata HS; Chicago, IL; 11/220 Chr; HonRl; SctActv; TchrAde; Univ Of Illinois.

DADAH, Ann Marie; St Mary Of Redford HS; Detroit, MI; 22/163 Chrl; HonRl; LitMag; NHS; NatlMeritSF; StuGov; SchPpr; Univ Of Detroit; Lawyer.

DA DAN, Jami S; Lake Michigan Catholic HS; St Joseph, MI; 5/86 Chrl; HonRl; NHS; NatlThespSoc; SchMus; StuGov; Yrbk; PpCl; Swmmng; CaptChrldr; Clge; Med Tech.

DADO, Claudia M; Maria HS; Chicago, IL; 38/301 HonRl; NHS; TchrAde; St Xavier College; Biology.

DADY, Therese A; Mobridge HS; Mobridge, SD; Band; Chrs; CncrtBnd; DrlTm; HonRl; NatlThespSoc; SchMus; StuGov; CaptBsktbl; CchngActv; Univ; Nursing.

DAEHLER, Joann L; Chadwick HS; Chadwick, IL; 2/26 VPSrCls; Chrs; HonRl; SchMus; SchPl; SctActv; StuCncl; Yrbk; FHA; Chrldr; University.

DAEHLER, Kathleen; Chadwick HS; Chadwick, IL; /33 ALAGirlsSt; Band; Chrs; HonRl; PepBnd; SchPl; Yrbk; FHA; Glf; Chrldr; Coll;.

DAEHLER, Ruth M; Chadwick HS; Chadwick, IL; Chr; Chrs; CncrtBnd; HonRl; LbryAde; SchMus; SchPl; Yrbk; FHA; Trk; College; Curriculum Of Major Study.

DAENTL, William; Dodgeville Hs; Dodgeville, WI; 20/120 HonRl; StuCncl; 4-H; FFA; PpCl; U Wisconsin; Dairy.

DAFFER, Kevin L; Beaver Valley HS; Danbury, NE; 2/16 VPSrCls; HonRl; ROTC; StuGov; YthFlsp; RptrYrbk; CaptBsktbl; LetterFtbl; LetterTrk; AmLegAwd; University; Professional.

DAGE, Sharon K; Montabella HS; Edmore, MI; 12/97 VPJrCls; VPSrCls; Band; CncrtBnd; HonRl; MrchBnd; SecNHS; OffAde; PepBnd; SchMus; PPFtbl; AmLegAwd; University Of Michigan; Physical Therapy.

DAGEL, Karen M; Moose Lake HS; Willow River, MN; Band; CmntyWkr; CncrtBnd; HonRl; LbryAde; MrchBnd; NHS; OffAde; Trk; Vocational Tech; Secretary.

DAGER, Debra A; Fenton Senior HS; Fenton, MI; TrsJrCls; ALAGirlsSt; Chrs; HonRl; NHS; LetterChrldr; PPFtbl; College; Art.

DAGES, Kevin F; St Laurence HS; Chicago, IL; 8/385 HonRl; NHS; NatlMeritSF; TreasStuCncl; StuGov; Bsktbl; IMSpt; College; Business Adm.

DAGGETT, Kathi A; Melvin Community HS; Sanborn, IA; 2/15 PresJrCls; Band; Chr; CncrtBnd; HonRl; MrchBnd; PresNHS; SecStuCncl; PresYthFlsp; LetterBsktbl; U Of Ia; Accountant Cpa.

DAGGETT, Sondra; Clarion Community HS; Clarion, IA; 3/94 HstSrCls; Band; Orch; PepBnd; SchMus; StuCncl; StuGov; YthFlsp; SchPpr; Univ; Mass Communications Public Relations.

DAGHER, Jehad; Loy Norrix HS; Kalamazoo, MI; Michigan State Univ; Engineering.

DAHER, Elizabeth A; Marquette HS; Michigan City, IN; Chrl; ChrhWkr; HonRl; JrNHS; NHS; Quill&Scroll; SchMus; SptEdYrbk; LetterGlf; CaptChrldr; Coll; Pysch.

DAHL, Carla; Adams Public HS; Adams, ND; TrsFrshCls; Band; Chr; HonRl; YthFlsp; RptrYrbk; EdYrBk; RptrSchPpr; 4-H; PpCl; Univ; Prof.

DAHL, Cherie B; Gary HS; Gary, MN; 3/15 Band; HonRl; MrchBnd; PepBnd; StuCncl; RptrSchPpr; PresCivCl; PresFHA; PpCl; Chrldr; Moorehead St; Social Work.

DAHL, Cynthia A; Harding HS; St Paul, MN; 2/724 TrsSophCls; PresSrCls; HonRl; TreasJA; VPNHS; StuCncl; TreasPpCl; PresGAA; JAAwd; RotaryAwd; U Of Mn; Pharmacy.

DAHL, Debra A; Lyle Public HS; Lyle, MN; 1/27 Band; Chrs; HonRl; NHS; StuCncl; RptrSchPpr; TreasFHA; Chrldr; IMSpt; AmLegAwd; Fairview Schl; Radiology.

DAHL, Elfriede; Immaculata HS; Chicago, IL; 2/201 Chrs; HonRl; NHS; NatlMeritCmnd; StuCncl; RptrYrbk; GerCl; PpCl; GAA; Carroll College; Pediatrician.

DAHL, Kenn T; Central Cass HS; Casselton, ND; 5/60 PresSrCls; ALBoysSt; ChrhWkr; CmntyWkr; SchPl; SctActv; StuGov; LetterFtbl; LetterTrk; University; Engineering.

DAHL, Mark J; Rushford HS; Rushford, MN; HonRl; Bsktbl; Ftbl; Trk; Trade Sch; Aviation.

DAHL, Robert A; West HS; Minneapolis, MN; Band; CncrtBnd; HonRl; MrchBnd; NHS; PepBnd; Navy; Nuclear Power.

DAHLAGER, Nancy J; Sacred Heart Public HS; Sacred Heart, MN; SecSophCls; SecSrCls; Band; Chr; ChrhWkr; HonRl; NHS; YthFlsp; Yrbk; FHA; Jr College; Interior Decorating.

DAHLBERG, David F; C A Lindbergh HS; Minnetonka, MN; 12/390 ALBoysSt; Band; ChrhWkr; CncrtBnd; MrchBnd; Orch; PepBnd; College; Medicine.

DAHLBERG, Karen A; Dekalb Senior HS; Dekalb, IL; HospAde; SchMus; StuGov; FrCl; PpCl; University Of Iowa; Physians Asst.

DAHLE, Jodi L; Harlem HS; Rockford, IL; 5/559 Band; HonRl; NatlMeritSF; Quill&Scroll; Twrl; College; History.

DAHLE, Linda; Carpio HS; Carpio, ND; Chrs; SchPl; YthFlsp; SchPpr; PpCl; Chrldr; IMSpt; Coll; Legal Secretary.

DAHLE, Nancy L; Milbank HS; Milbank, SD; ALAGirlsSt; Chr; Chrl; Chrs; ChrhWkr; HonRl; Mdrgl; NatlFornLg; NHS; SchAde; KiwanAwd; CitAwd; College; Music.

DAHLE, Pamela J; Carpio HS; Carpio, ND; SecFrshCls; PresJrCls; Band; Chrs; DrmMjrt; HonRl; StuCncl; YthFlsp; Bsktbl; College; Special Education.

DAHLEN, Carolyn S; Goodridge HS; Goodridge, MN; 3/35 VPJrCls; SecSrCls; HonRl; NHS; SchPl; EdSchPpr; SecFTA; CaptBsktbl; Chrldr; PresGAA; Voc Sch; Business.

DAHLEN, Diane K; Winona Senior HS; Winona, MN; 25/431 Band; ChrhWkr; CncrtBnd; HonRl; MrchBnd; NHS; NatlMeritSchl; PepBnd; YthFlsp; College; Math Major.

DAHLEN, Karen J; Westby HS; Coon Valley, WI; 8/115 ChrhWkr; CncrtBnd; MrchBnd; NatlFornLg; NHS; PepBnd; Yrbk; FHA; AmLegAwd; LionAwd; Wwti; Registered Nurse.

DAHLGREN, Denise D; Tipton Community HS; Tipton, IA; ChrhWkr; HonRl; HospAde; OffAde; StuCncl; Swmmng; Trk; Chrldr; College; Professional Teacher.

DAHLGREN, Sandra L; Clarion Community HS; Clarion, IA; 9/82 Chrs; CncrtBnd; HonRl; MrchBnd; PepBnd; Pres4-H; TreasFTA; LetterBsktbl; Chrldr; 4-HAwd; Collge; Science Pe.

DAHLIN, Jeffrey W; Mounds View HS; New Brighton, MN; NHS; Socr; IMSpt; U Of Mn; Dr.

DAHLIN, Susan M; Green Bay Southwest HS; Green Bay, WI; Chrl; Chrs; HonRl; Orch; SchMus; SctActv; RptrYrbk; Yrbk; PpCl; Trk; U Of Oshkosh; Nursing.

DAHLKE, Madonna M; Neenah HS; Neenah, WI; 54/571 Band; Chr; HonRl; LbryAde; MrchBnd; Orch; PepBnd; SchMus; RptrSchPpr; Univ Of Wisc; Nursing.

DAHLKE, Mark; Wonewa Center HS; Wonewoc, WI; PresSophCls; PresJrCls; Band; CncrtBnd; LbryAde; MrchBnd; Bsbl; Bsktbl; Ftbl; IMSpt; Univ; Conservation.

DAHLKE, Susan G; Raymond HS; Raymond, MN; 1/29 PresCncrtBnd; HonRl; MrchBnd; NHS; NatlMeritSF; PepBnd; EdYrBk;.

DAHLMAN, Peter B; Chesaning Union HS; Chesaning, MI; Chr; Chrs; HonRl; SchMus; SctActv; StuCncl; YthFlsp; Yrbk; LetterTrk; LetterWrstlng; Mich St Univ; Fisheries & Wildlife.

DAHLSON, Kimberly A; Technical HS; St Cloud, MN; 20/411 Band; CncrtBnd; JrNHS; MrchBnd; NHS; PepBnd; StuCncl; GAA; ChmbCommrsAwd; University; Professional.

DAHLSTROM, Eric L; Ridgewood HS; Norridge, IL; Band; CncrtBnd; DrmBgl; HonRl; MrchBnd; PepBnd; PolWkr; SchMus; SctActv; Yrbk; Bsktbl; LetterTennis; University; Vocational.

DAHLSTROM, Timothy G; Lincoln HS; Thief River Falls, MN; 72/254 Chr; Chrs; ChrhWkr; HonRl; LbryAde; SchMus; SciCl; Swmmng; Dunwoody Indus Inst; Elec.

DAHMER, Mary Ann; Crab Orchard HS; Marion, IL; Chrs; ChrhWkr; CmntyWkr; HonRl; SchPl; StuCncl; RptrYrbk; RptrSchPpr; 4-H; FHA; CaptChrldr; DanFAwd; 4-HAwd; College; Physical Ed.

DAHMKE, Mark C; David City Public HS; David City, NE; Chr; HonRl; LbryAde; NatlThespSoc; Quill&Scroll; SchMus; Yrbk; Univ Of Nebraska; Engineering.

DAHMS, Cheryll A; West Concord HS; West Concord, MN; 14/44 VPSophCls; Band; HonRl; LbryAde; NHS; SchMus; SchPl; SecStuCncl; RptrYrbk; PresFTA; PpCl; CaptBsktbl; Chrldr; Rochester Voc Schl; Dental Asst.

DAHN, Linda M; South Broward HS; Columbus, IN; ChrhWkr; CmntyWkr; Army; Nursing.

DAIBER, Thomas A; St Paul HS; Highland, IL; 3/56 HonRl; LetterSocr; U Of Si; Mathematics.

DAIDONE, Robert E; Hamilton HS; Hamilton, IL; 1/70 TrsJrCls; TrsSrCls; Chrs; HonRl; JrNHS; SchPl; SctActv; StuCncl; EdSchPpr; KeyCl; SpnCl; Bsktbl; LetterGlf; Harvard; Law.

DAIGH, Toni L; Parsons Sr HS; Parsons, KS; 4/165 Band; Chr; DrmMjrt; HonRl; NHS; OffAde; SchMus; Twrl; PpCl; PPFtbl; Labette Community Jr College; English.

DAILEY, Carol A; Oskaloosa HS; Oskaloosa, KS; Band; Chr; ChrhWkr; CncrtBnd; HonRl; MrchBnd; PepBnd; SchPl; YthFlsp; PpCl; College; Vet.

DAILEY, Cathy; Acad Of Our Lady Spalding Ins; Washington, IL; 7/89 Chr; Chrl; ChrhWkr; CmntyWkr; HonRl; NHS; SchPl; RptrYrbk; RptrSchPpr; FNA; U; Pharmacy.

DAILEY, Cathy A; Academy Of Our Lady; Washington, IL; 7/89 Chr; PresChrl; Chrs; ChrhWkr; HonRl; NHS; SchMus; SchPl; RptrYrbk; Yrbk; RptrSchPpr; 4-H; FNA; GAA; Butler Univ; Pharmacy.

DAILEY, Clifford L; Stapleton Public HS; Gandy, NE; VPJrCls; TrsSrCls; Chr; Chrs; HonRl; SchPl; EdYrBk; Yrbk; LetterFtbl; LetterTennis;.

DAILEY, Edward G; Jonesville HS; Jonesville, MI; 2/87 VPJrCls; PresSrCls; Band; PresStuGov; UNYO; YthFlsp; FTA; Adrian College; Scientist.

DAILEY, Janice; Alleman Hs; Rock Island, IL; 3/200 ChrhWkr; CmntyWkr; NHS; StuCncl; TchrAde; Illinois State U; Teacher In Special Ed.

DAILEY, John A; Glenbard East HS; Lombard, IL; 35/653 ChrhWkr; HonRl; NHS; TchrAde; 4-H; LetterTrk; Cedarville College.

DAILEY, Lemoyne E; Stampleton Public HS; Gandy, NE; 6/30 TrsSophCls; TrsSrCls; Chrs; NHS; SchPl; Bsktbl; Ftbl;.

DAILEY, Lemoyne E; Stapleton HS; Gandy, NE; TrsSophCls; Chr; Chrs; HonRl;.

DAILL, Kristen M; Downers Grove South HS; Downers Grove, IL; HonRl; NHS; SpnCl; Univ Of Illinois; Medicine.

DAILY, Dan M; Goodland HS; Kanorado, KS; HonRl;.

DAILY, Dawn M; Wagner HS; Wagner, SD; /74 Band; ChrhWkr; CncrtBnd; HonRl; OffAde; StuCncl; SchPpr; FNA; PpCl; LetterBsktbl; U Of Sd Vermillion; Help The Handicapped.

DAILY, Susan E; Columbus East HS; Columbus, IN; 2/336 SecSophCls; SecJrCls; SecSrCls; AFS; NatlMeritSchl; StuGov; 4-H; BttyCrckrAwd; DARAwd; OptClAwd; Hanover Clg; Psychology.

DAINIUS, Paul W; Schaumburg HS; Schaumburg, IL; 45/539 HonRl; StuCncl; TchrAde; Univ Of Illinois; Chemical Engineer.

DAINS, Darcee M; Marion Public HS; Marion, SD; 2/42 Band; Chrs; HonRl; MrchBnd; NatlMeritCmnd; SchPl; Yrbk; FHA; Trk; AmLegAwd; Sd U; Med Tech.

DALBEC, Annette M; Northwestern HS; Maple, WI; Chr; HonRl; Twrl; 4-H; FBLA; FrCl; LetterTrk; IMSpt; PresAwd; Hi Univ; Law Field.

DALBEY, Timothy W; Tarkio HS; Tarkio, MO; Band; ChrhWkr; CncrtBnd; HonRl; MrchBnd; SchMus; SchPl; YthFlsp; LetterBsktbl; Glf; Tarkio College; Commercial Pilot.

DALBOM, William E; East Newton HS; Stella, MO; TrsFrshCls; HonRl; NHS; SctActv; PresStuCncl; YthFlsp; FFA; Bsktbl; Ftbl; Trk; Missouri Valley College; Science.

DALCHOW, Diane M; Robbinsdale HS; Robbinsdale, MN; 13/714 Chr; ChrhWkr; HonRl; HospAde; NHS; SchPl; GerCl; PpCl; Univ Of Mn; Science & Math.

DALCHOW, Karen; Wapello Community HS; Wapello, IA; Band; Chr; HonRl; SchPl; YthFlsp; SpnCl; Bsktbl; Trk; IMSpt; 4-HAwd; College; Science.

DALDIN, Victoria; Seaholm HS; Birmingham, MI; Mi St U; Animal Tech.

DALE, Bruce A; Alexander Hamilton HS; Milwaukee, WI; 25/786 ALBoysSt; Aud/Vis; Band; Chr; Chrs; HonRl; MrchBnd; LetterTennis; LionAwd; Coll; Engineering.

DALE, Dorothy A; Mundelein HS; Mundelein, IL; HonRl; LitMag; GAA; U Of Il; History Journalism.

DALE, Jeffrey M; Clare HS; Clare, MI; 32/150 HonRl; NHS; SctActv; SciCl; LetterFtbl; Michigan Tech; Bus Admin.

DALE, Julia A; Sacred Heart HS; Sedalia, MO; Chr; Chrs; HonRl; NatlCathMusEdAsoc; NatlMeritSchl; OffAde; SchMus; SchPl; TchrAde; LatCl; College; Spec Education.

DALE, Kathy A; Wyaconda C 1 HS; Wyaconda, MO; 2/18 PresSrCls; Chrs; ChrhWkr; CmntyWkr; HospAde; RedCrAde; SchPl; EdYrBk; 4-H; Chrldr; College; Physical Therapy.

DALE, Rosalind R; Ruskin HS; Kansas City, MO; Band; ChrhWkr; DrlTm; HonRl; HospAde; Twrl; RptrYrbk; FHA; PpCl; Swmmng; Chrldr; Fisk Univ; Health Care Admin.

DALE, Scott J; Montpelier HS; Montpelier, ND; TrsFrshCls; TrsSophCls; ALBoysSt; Band; Chr; TrsSrCls; CncrtBnd; HonRl; LetterBsktbl; LetterTrk; Un Of N Dakota; Farming.

DALEY, Neal A; Charles City Comm HS; Charles City, IA; ALBoysSt; Chrl; HonRl; NHS; PresOrch; SctActv; StuCncl; FDA; MthCl; CaptFtbl; Univ Of Ia; Pharmacy.

DALEY, Robert J; Quigley South HS; Chicago, IL; 30/200 VPFrshCls; HonRl; StuCncl; SpnCl; Glf; CaptSocr; St Marys College; Physician.

DALKE, Douglas; Beatrice Senior HS; Beatrice, NE; Band; HonRl; ModUN; KeyCl; IMSpt; Ne Wesleyan Univ; Medical Research.

DALL, Rebecca; Goodrich HS; Fond Du Lac, WI; Band; ChrhWkr; CncrtBnd; DrlTm; JrNHS; Trk; Chrldr; GAA; IMSpt; Univ Of Madison; Pharmacy.

DALLAS, Elena M; Ofallon Township HS; Ofallon, IL; 47/296 Band; Chrs; CncrtBnd; HonRl; HospAde; JrNHS; Mdrgl; MrchBnd; NHS; Murray St Univ; Music Therapy.

DALLAS, Lyndall W; Tuscola HS; Tuscola, IL; 4/128 Aud/Vis; HonRl; FFA; Univ Of Illinois; Agronomy.

DALLE AVE, Margaret A; Lincoln HS; Vincennes, IN; 36/328 LbryAde; 4-H; FBLA; Bsktbl; Trk; GAA; IMSpt; Indiana Univ; Accounting.

DALLIN, Rodney G; Cooper Sr HS; Minneapolis, MN; Chr; ChrhWkr; HonRl; St Paul Bible Clg; Theology.

DALLINGER, Barbara L; Morton HS; Morton, IL; Band; ChrhWkr; CmntyWkr; CncrtBnd; HonRl; MrchBnd; PepBnd; PpCl; GAA; College; Music Education.

DALLMAN, Barbara; Wauwatosa East HS; Wauwatosa, WI; RptrYrbk; Stout St Wi; Home Econ.

DALLMAN, David F; Markesan HS; Markesan, WI; 15/113 ALBoysSt; Chrs; ChrhWkr; NHS; 4-H; Bsktbl; 4-HAwd; Collge; Engineering.

DALLMAN, Sheryl L; Franklin Public HS; Franklin, NE; ALAGirlsSt; Chrs; ChrhWkr; HonRl; LbryAde; SchPl; Sec4-H; PresFHA; TreasPpCl; 4-HAwd; Beauty School; Beautician.

DALLMIER, Judith; Newton HS; Newton, IL; 3#13#32# ChrhWkr; HonRl; MrchBnd; NHS; SecTrsFrshCls; 4-H; FNA; Univ Of Illimois; Physical Therapy.

DALLMIER, Rebecca S; Newton Community HS; Willow Hil, IL; Chr; HonRl; NHS; RptrYrbk; RptrSchPpr; Sec4-H; GAA; IMSpt; 4-HAwd; Jr College; Pe Teacher.

DALMAN, Gregory L; Homestead HS; Ft Wayne, IN; HonRl; StuCncl; YthFlsp; SecSophCls; SptEdSchPpr; LetterFtbl; LetterTrk; Col; Mission Piolet.

DAL PIAN, Margaret P; Verdigre HS; Verdigre, NE; Chrs; ChrhWkr; HonRl; HospAde; SchPl; YthFlsp; RptrYrbk; RptrSchPpr; PpCl; LetterTrk; PresAwd;.

DALRYMPLE, Linda K; Shawnee Mission South HS; Overland Park, KS; HonRl; HospAde; JrNHS; LbryAde; NHS; OffAde; StuCncl; TchrAde; PpCl; College; Physical Therapy.

DALSING, Joseph G; Wahlert HS; Hazel Green, WI; 6/450 NHS; StuCncl; StuGov; TchrAde; MthCl; IMSpt; Marquette Univ; Medicine.

DALTON, Dan; Bishop Ward HS; Kansas City, KS; 13/219 HonRl; NHS; FrCl; Rockhurst College; Communications.

DALTON, Daniel P; Lyons Township HS; Western Springs, IL; 163/1226 Band; CncrtBnd; HonRl; MrchBnd; Orch; PepBnd; SchMus; SchPl; LetterFtbl; Tulane Univ; Medicine.

DALTON, Danniel C; Monroe HS; Monroe, WI; Aud/Vis; VPLbryAde; OffAde; SchAde; SptEdSchPpr; SchPpr; Police Or Carpenter.

DALTON, Dawn M; Immaculata HS; Chicago, IL; 10/200 ChrhWkr; HonRl; NHS; SctActv; SecStuCncl; StuGov; YthFlsp; RptrYrbk; FrCl; PpCl; Bsktbl; Chrldr; GAA; Univ Of Illinois; Medicine.

DALTON, Dennis P; Monroe Sr HS; Monroe, WI; Aud/Vis; LbryAde; SchAde; Yrbk; Trade Sch; Photographer.

DALTON, Lisa I; Joliet Twnshp East HS; Joliet, IL; 4/450 Chr; HonRl; PresNHS; NatlMeritSF; SchMus; YthFlsp; FrCl; GAA; N Il Univ; Engr.

DALTON, Mary C; Helias HS; Jefferson City, MO; TreasBand; CncrtBnd; PresDrmBgl; HonRl; MrchBnd; NHS; PepBnd; SchMus; SchPl; SchPpr; Clge; Bus & Public Admin.

DALTON, Rhonda J; Southwest HS; Seligman, MO; HstSophCls; HstJrCls; HonRl; NHS; SchPl; StuCncl; RptrSchPpr; VPSpnCl; PpCl; Chrldr; Coll; Actress.

DALTON, Susan L; Glenbrook North HS; Northbrook, IL; 137/604 SecFrshCls; HonRl; StuCncl; StuGov; Yrbk; Tennis; Chrldr; Univ; Business Admin.

DALTON, Teresa A; North Clay Comm HS; Farina, IL; 13/63 HonRl; JA; LbryAde; SpnCl; PpCl; Univ Of Illinois; Teacher.

DALTON, Theresa A; St Louise De Mavillac HS; Des Plaines, IL; 20/254 NHS; NatlMeritSF; SchMus; IMSpt; College; Psychology.

DALUGA, Daniel J; Pontiac Twp HS; Pontiac, IL; 1/206 CmntyWkr; HonRl; NHS; EdYrBk; SptEdYrbk; KeyCl; FrCl; MthCl; SciCl; LetterBsktbl; LetterFtbl; LetterTrk; Augustana College; Optometry.

DALY, Ann; Desham Hall HS; St Paul, MN; SecTrsFrshCls; CmntyWkr; DrlTm; SchPl; StuCncl; SptEdSchPpr; FrCl; Chrldr; IMSpt; OptClAwd; Univ Of Mn; Criminal Lawyer.

DALY, Charles E; Thedford HS; Stapleton, NE; 1/19 TrsSrCls; Chrs; HonRl; SchPl; Yrbk; 4-H; LetterBsktbl; LetterFtbl; LetterTrk; DARAwd; Business School; Ranch.

DALY, Edward M; St Joseph HS; Hillside, IL; 10/184 HonRl; NHS; PpCl; Bsbl; Ftbl; College; Business Admin.

DALY, Kathleen S; Cherry Hill HS; Inkster, MI; HonRl; NatlMeritSF; LetterTennis; American Junior College; Art.

DALY, Lynn K; Assumption HS; Wis Rapids, WI; 11/117 SecTrsFrshCls; VPSophCls; PresJrCls; ALAGirlsSt; Chrs; HonRl; NatlFornLg; NHS; NatlThespSoc; StuCncl; CaptGAA; AmLegAwd; Univ Of Wi; Journalism.

DALY, Nancy M; Notre Dame HS; Quincy, IL; 5/109 VPSophCls; TrsSrCls; Band; Chr; Chrs; CncrtBnd; MrchBnd; NHS; SchMus; StuCncl; Bradley University; Music Educ.

DALY, Patrice M; Pontiac Central HS; Pontiac, MI; HonRl; NHS; Bsbl; PPFtbl; Univ Central Mi.

DALY, Patrick T; Waterford Twp HS; Pontiac, MI; HonRl; PolWkr; CaptTennis; Wayne State U; Law.

DALY, Sheryl L; Sutherland HS; Sutherland, NE; Band; HonRl; 4-H; FHA; LetterTrk; Chrldr; GAA; DARAwd; 4-HAwd; PresAwd; College; Professional.

DALY, Thomas J; Loyola Academy; Lake Forest, IL; 30/442 Band; HonRl; MrchBnd; NatlMeritCmnd; RusCl; University; Chemical Engineer.

DALZEN, Becky; Fridley Sr HS; Fridley, MN; Minn School Of Business; Legal Secretary.

DAME, David G; Papillion HS; Papillion, NE; 8/317 ChrhWkr; CncrtBnd; HonRl; MrchBnd; NHS; PepBnd; GerCl; LetterBsbl; LetterBsktbl; LetterFtbl; University; Medicine.

DAMERON, John A; Chilhowee HS; Chilhowee, MO; 2/18 HstSophCls; HonRl; EdYrBk; Yrbk; RptrSchPpr; 4-H; OptClAwd; Central Missouri State University; Vet.

DAMERON, Julie M; Virden HS; Virden, IL; Band; CncrtBnd; HonRl; HospAde; LbryAde; MrchBnd; NHS; PepBnd; SchMus; SchPl; FHA; Community College; Vocation.

DAMERY, Shelly M; Blue Mound HS; Blue Mound, IL; AFS; ChrhWkr; HonRl; PresNHS; SchPl; SctActv; StuCncl; YthFlsp; VP4-H; GAA; Univ; Zoology.

DAMHOF, Virgil D; Willmar HS; Blomkest, MN; Aud/Vis; StuCncl; RptrYrbk; VP4-H; FFA; LetterBsktbl; LetterTrk; 4-HAwd; U Of Mn; Ag.

DAMISCH, David M; Dundee Senior HS; Hampshire, IL; 38/396 DrmBgl; ChrhWkr; CncrtBnd; HonRl; MrchBnd; PepBnd; YthFlsp; 4-H; University; Professional.

DAMJANOVICH, Alexander; Campion HS; Berwyn, IL; 1/70 LbryAde; ModUN; Bsktbl; Loyola U; Medicine.

DAMMAN, David L; West Allis Central HS; West Allis, WI; Band; CncrtBnd; HonRl; MrchBnd; LetterFtbl; CaptTrk; IMSpt; JCAwd; Platville; Police Work.

DAMMANN, Carol; Lincoln HS; Lake City, MN; 25/145 ALAGirlsSt; Band; Chr; ChrhWkr; HonRl; MrchBnd; NHS; 4-H; FHA; GAA; Winona State College; Nursing.

DAMMANN, Marla J; Lester Prairie Public HS; Glencoe, MN; Band; Chr; CncrtBnd; HonRl; NHS; YthFlsp; Bsktbl; CaptTrk; LetterChrldr; VPGAA; Medical Inst Of Mn; Vocation.

DAMPER, Herbert K; Kinloch Sr HS; Kinloch, MO; 5/65 Chr; HonRl; SchPl; StuCncl; Bsbl; Bsktbl; Trk; Southern Illinois Univ; Business Admin.

DAMS, Phyllis; Yale HS; Avoca, MI; 23/137 Band; DrmMjrt; St Clair Co Comm Coll; Law Enforcement.

DAMS, Sheree G; Kingsford HS; Kingsford, MI; 7/164 Band; ChrhWkr; CncrtBnd; HonRl; HospAde; MrchBnd; NHS; StuCncl; PpCl; CaptChrldr; Northern Mi Univ; Radiologic Tech.

DANA, Jay A; Waverly Shell Rock HS; Waverly, IA; Bsktbl; Ftbl; Trk;.

DANAHER, Patty E; Le Blond HS; St Joseph, MO; 11/116 HonRl; Yrbk; LionAwd; College; Vocational.

DANCE, Debra S; Highland HS; Lewistown, MO; Chr; Chrs; ChrhWkr; CmntyWkr; HonRl; JrNHS; Mdrgl; NHS; SchMus; FSA; Hannibal Lagrange Col; Music.

DANCE, Roger; Wayne Memorial HS; Wayne, MI; 28/638 ChrhWkr; HonRl; JrNHS; MrchBnd; NHS; Orch; IMSpt; E Mi Univ; Industrial Echnology.

DANCY, James N; Slater HS; Slater, MO; Aud/Vis; HonRl; YthLg; Yrbk; SchPpr; PpCl; LetterBsbl; LetterBsktbl; LetterFtbl; LetterTrk; College.

DANCZAK, Karen E; Mother Of Sorrows HS; Alsip, IL; 6/143 Chrs; HonRl; LitMag; LbryAde; NHS; SchPl; TchrAde; VPMthCl; Trk; VoiceDemAwd; College; Law.

DANCZYK, Gary M; Hayward Comm HS; Hayward, WI; 1/150 SchAde; SchPl; Bsbl; Bsktbl; Ftbl; CchngActv;.

DANEHEY, Nancy L; Blue Hill Community HS; Blue Hill, NE; 3/39 SecTrsSrCls; Band; Chrs; CncrtBnd; HonRl; MrchBnd; PepBnd; RptrYrbk; RptrSchPpr; SecPpCl; Univ Of Nebraska; Business Management.

DANEKAS, Janet; Clark HS; Raymond, SD; 9/60 PresSophCls; ALAGirlsSt; Chrs; CncrtBnd; SchMus; Yrbk; Sd State Univ; Music.

DANELSKI, Franklin E; Albany Senior HS; Albany, MN; Band; Chr; Chrs; CncrtBnd; HonRl; MrchBnd; PepBnd; SchPl; Ftbl; Trk; Trade Sch; Professional.

DANGERFIELD, Diane L; Mt Horeb HS; Mount Horeb, WI; 1/137 ALAGirlsSt; Chr; VPNHS; PpCl; LetterBsktbl; Trk; IMSpt; University; Conservation.

DANGREMOND, Debra J; Oak Lawn Comm HS; Oak Lawn, IL; 2/700 Band; PresCncrtBnd; HonRl; MrchBnd; NHS; NatlMeritCmnd; Orch; PepBnd; SchMus; MthCl; College; Music.

DANHOF, Brenda G; Montague HS; Rothbury, MI; Chr; HonRl; PresNHS; VPStuCncl; GerCl; PpCl; Chrldr; GAA; IMSpt; PPFtbl; Central Michigan Univ; Social Work.

DANIEL, Barbara A; Columbus HS; Marshfield, WI; SecTrsJrCls; Chrs; ChrhWkr; StuCncl; SecGerCl; PresPpCl; Bsktbl; LetterTrk; SecGAA; Marshfield Wood County Campus; Elem Ed.

DANIEL, Dana A; Mundelein HS; Mundelein, IL; Chr; LitMag; OffAde; SchAde; Sdlty; Bradley Univ; Nursing.

DANIEL, Denise M; Cass Tech HS; Detroit, MI; Chr; NHS; OffAde; ROTC; StuCncl; TchrAde; FTA; SpnCl;.

DANIEL, James R; Elmwood Park HS; Elmwood Park, IL; 24/327 HonRl; IntrClCncl; RptrSchPpr; KeyCl; CaptTrk; Univ Of Ill; Accounting.

DANIEL, Jennie S; East Peoria Comm HS; Creve Coeur, IL; 87/435 HonRl; SchAde; SchPl; TchrAde; FTA; GerCl; Ill Central College; Elem Education.

DANIEL, Rebecca; Thomas W Kelly HS; Benton, MO; 11/54 Band; CncrtBnd; HonRl; MrchBnd; PepBnd; Twrl; EdYrBk; SchPpr; FHA; SpnCl; Chrldr; Univ; Biological Sciences.

DANIEL, Ronald E; Mitchell HS; Mitchell, IN; Band; CncrtBnd; HonRl; MrchBnd; NatlMeritSchl; NatlThespSoc; PepBnd; SchMus; Us Naval Acad; Professional.

DANIEL, Thomas M; St Louis V HS; St Louis, MO; StuCncl; StuGov; Yrbk; SchPpr; IMSpt; OptClAwd; College.

DANIELS, Ceandra L; Lindblom Tech HS; Chicago, IL; 26/722 HonRl; LitMag; TchrAde; RptrSchPpr; SciCl; Trk; Univ; Pharmacy.

DANIELS, Curtis D; Seneca HS; Seneca, MO; ChrhWkr; CmntyWkr; SchPl; SpnCl; MthCl; PpCl; LetterBsbl; LetterBsktbl; Tennis; Trk; JAAwd; College; Art.

DANIELS, Curtis L; East Central HS; Miles, IA; PresFrshCls; PresJrCls; ALBoysSt; HonRl; NHS; SchMus; StuCncl; YthFlsp; LetterBsbl; LetterBsktbl; Undecided.

DANIELS, Deborah D; Manistee Catholic Central HS; Manistee, MI; Band; CncrtBnd; DrmMjrt; MrchBnd; PepBnd; SchMus; College; Professional.

DANIELS, Gregory; Bellmont HS; Decatur, IN; 40/251 HonRl; Mechanical Engineering.

DANIELS, James A; Northwestern HS; Mendon, MO; VPSrCls; ALBoysSt; Band; HonRl; SchPl; StuCncl; YthFlsp; Bsbl; Trk; AmLegAwd; U Of Mo; Farmer.

DANIELS, James M; Griffin HS; Springfield, IL; HonRl; PresKeyCl; Socr; LetterTrk; University; Biology.

DANIELS, Jean A; Carrier Mills HS; Carrier Mills, IL; Chrs; HonRl; LbryAde; PresNHS; SchPl; TchrAde; Yrbk; PresFHA; SpnCl; Coll; Deaf Teachr.

DANIELS, Joan D; Merrill HS; Merrill, MI; 5/112 Band; Chr; HonRl; NHS; Nursing School; Nurse.

DANIELS, Kathleen; Kapaun Mt Carmel HS; Wichita, KS; 8/135 SecSophCls; VPJrCls; PresSrCls; CmntyWkr; HonRl; NHS; SchMus; SchPl; StuCncl; Ku; Pro.

DANIELS, Koleen K; Northwest HS; Jackson, MI; Band; CncrtBnd; HonRl; HospAde; MrchBnd; NHS; NatlMeritSchl; PepBnd; 4-H; PresFrCl; Lansing Comm Clg; Nursing.

DANIELS, Robert M; Mona Shores HS; Muskegon, MI; ChrhWkr; HonRl; NHS; NatlMeritFnl; SchPl; TchrAde; LetterFtbl; Glf; Trk; IMSpt; Univ Of Mi; Law.

DANIELS, Scott A; Fayette Comm HS; Fayette, IA; HonRl; TreasNHS; StuCncl; YthFlsp; EdSchPpr; LetterBsbl; LetterBsktbl; LetterFtbl; LetterGlf; LetterTrk; Univ Of Iowa; Business Admin.

DANIELS, Scott M; Bluffton HS; Bluffton, IN; Band; CncrtBnd; HonRl; MrchBnd; PepBnd; Quill&Scroll; SchPl; SctActv; RptrYrbk; SptEdYrbk; College; Medicine.

DANIELS, Sharon G; South Pemiscot HS; Steele, MO; 18/67 SecTrsSrCls; Chr; ChrhWkr; CncrtBnd; HonRl; JrNHS; NHS; SchPl; SchPpr; College; Home Economics.

DANIELS, Thomas G; Pacelli HS; Stevens Point, WI; Band; CtyCnl; CmntyWkr; ModUN; PolWkr; PresStuCncl; YthLg; SchPpr; Tennis; IMSpt; GodCntryAwd; University; Law.

DANIELS, William; Fayette HS; Fayette, MO; 4/67 SecSophCls; PresJrCls; ALBoysSt; NHS; AmLegAwd; OptClAwd; CitAwd; University Of Mo; Pre Med.

DANIELSON, Chris; Pioneer HS; Ann Arbor, MI; 37/675 Band; Chr; ChrhWkr; HonRl; MrchBnd; Orch; Socr; Kalamozoo College; Biology Major.

DANIELSON, Janice M; Woodstock HS; Woodstock, IL; CncrtBnd; HonRl; PresMdrgl; MrchBnd; VPNHS; NatlThespSoc; SchMus; SchPl; GAA; Ill State Univ; Music.

DANIELSON, Kari B; Willmar Senior HS; Kandiyohi, MN; ChrhWkr; OffAde; SchPl; RptrSchPpr; Pres4-H; FrCl; 4-HAwd; PresAwd; College; Journalism.

DANIELSON, Kathy; Deer River HS; Deer River, MN; HonRl; LbryAde; EdSchPpr; 4-H;.

DANIELSON, Pam; Grand Island Senior HS; Grand Island, NE; CncrtBnd; DrlTm; HonRl; MrchBnd; FrCl; PpCl; Univ Of Ne;.

DANIELSON, Penny G; Grantsburg HS; Grantsburg, WI; Band; Chr; ChrhWkr; SchMus; SchPl; 4-H; LetterBsktbl; LetterTrk; Chrldr; GAA; DARAwd; PresAwd; Northwestern College; Physical Ed.

DANIELSON, Sheryl; Brookfield East HS; Brookfield, WI; Band; HonRl; MrchBnd; PepBnd; Coll; Special Educ.

DANIELSON, Susan G; Albert Lea Sr HS; Albert Lea, MN; 31/526 TrsJrCls; Chrs; CncrtBnd; HonRl; NatlMeritCmnd; Orch; StuCncl; FrCl; LetterTennis; College; Fine Arts.

DANIELSON, Theodore L; Geneva Comm HS; Geneva, IL; Chr; HonRl; NHS; NatlMeritCmnd; Univ Of Illinois; Law.

DANIELSON, Theresa D; J A Craig HS; Janesville, WI; AFS; ChrhWkr; LbryAde; 4-H; College; Professional.

DANILLS, Victoria L; Goodland HS; Goodland, KS; 30/131 PresAFS; Band; HonRl; Quill&Scroll; SchPl; Twrl; Yrbk; GerCl; Coll; Psychology.

DANISZEWSKI, Allen; Bishop Noll Institute; Calumet City, IL; MthCl; Northwestern Univ; Mathematics.

DANKE, Kitty M; Cadillac HS; Cadillac, MI; VPJrCls; Band; ChrhWkr; CncrtBnd; HonRl; MrchBnd; NHS; StuCncl; StuGov; IMSpt; Mi St Univ; Pediatrician.

DANKER, Roshell L; Oakland Comm HS; Minden, IA; 4/39 Band; Chr; Chrs; CncrtBnd; HonRl; MrchBnd; PepBnd; YthFlsp; RptrYrbk; RptrSchPpr; Bsktbl; College; Professional.

DANKS, Paula; Blue Earth HS; Blue Earth, MN; 8/103 HonRl; PolWkr; Tennis; GAA; IMSpt; MasAwd; Uinona St College; Math And Business.

DANNEHOLD, Sandra A; Gibault Catholic HS; Waterloo, IL; 1/101 NHS; NatlMeritSF; StuCncl; RptrYrbk; St Louis Univ; Law.

DANNELLY, Diane; Genoa Public HS; Genoa, NE; 1/50 Band; NHS; YthFlsp; Chrldr; GAA; IMSpt; PPFtbl; 4-HAwd; College; High School Teacher.

DANNEN, Tammy D; Estherville HS; Estherville, IA; HonRl; HospAde; VP4-H; VPFHA; Bsktbl; IMSpt; Univ Of Iowa; Medicine.

DANNENBRING, Daniel O; Tri County Emery HS; Freeman, SD; PresFrshCls; ChrhWkr; HonRl; FFA; Ftbl; Trk; University; Vocation.

DANNENBRING, Terrance J; Burlington Community HS; Burlington, IA; Chr; ChrhWkr; HonRl; SchAde; StuCncl; Bsktbl; IMSpt; College; Professional.

DANNER, Bryan L; L P Goodrich HS; Fond Du Lac, WI; HonRl; TchrAde; Yrbk; SchPpr; GerCl; MthCl; JAAwd; College.

DANNER, Elaine; Elkhart Memorial HS; Elkhart, IN; DrlTm; HonRl; NatlFornLg; NHS; NatlMeritCmnd; SchPl; TreasStuGov; College; Broadcasting.

DANNER, James E; Savannah HS; Savannah, MO; HonRl; LbryAde; NHS; StuGov; LatCl; SpnCl; AmLegAwd; Coll; Special Ed.

DANNER, Jeffrey R; Terre Haute South Vigo HS; Terre Haute, IN; Band; CncrtBnd; HonRl; MrchBnd; Orch; PepBnd; SciCl; Ftbl; Wrstlng; College; Science.

DANNER, Susan E; South Newton Jr Sr HS; Kentland, IN; 5/100 Band; ChrhWkr; HonRl; MrchBnd; NHS; RedCrAde; SchMus; StuCncl; Twrl; Yrbk; 4-H; LetterBsbl; Chrldr; PPFtbl; Univ; Industrial Management.

DANON, Nitza; Oak Park River Forest HS; Oak Park, IL; 119/1040 HonRl; JA; SchMus; Research Medicine & Biochemistry.

DANSBY, Helayne C; Lindblom HS; Chicago, IL; 3/652 CmntyWkr; PresHonRl; HospAde; NHS; NatlMeritCmnd; OffAde; SctActv; TchrAde; YthFlsp; FSA; VPMthCl; SciCl; GAA; Ill Inst Of Tech; Biomedical Engineering.

DANSDILL, Richard J; Burlington Comm HS; Burlington, IA; 94/527 PresFrshCls; Chr; HonRl; Mdrgl; NHS; StuCncl; Bsktbl; Ftbl; College; Business.

DANZ, Ann; Gabriel Richard HS; Wyandotte, MI; 7/155 ChrhWkr; HonRl; FrCl; Bsktbl; Tennis; Trk; Univ Of Mich; Physical Therapy.

DANZ, William D; Wisconsin Heights HS; Black Earth, WI; Band; CncrtBnd; MrchBnd; PresNHS; NatlMeritSF; PepBnd; Univ Of Wi; Accounting.

DAPPER, Joan M; Resurrection HS; Chicago, IL; 9/267 Chr; HonRl; HospAde; LitMag; LbryAde; Mdrgl; NHS; SchMus; TchrAde; FNA; Loyola Univ; Nursing.

DA PRA, David P; A D Johnston HS; Bessemer, MI; 6/104 TrsFrshCls; HonRl; PpCl; SciCl; CaptBsbl; CaptFtbl; Trk; IMSpt; Gogebic Comm College; Teacher.

DA PRA, Deborah A; A D Johnston HS; Bessemer, MI; 16/104 Band; HonRl; PepBnd; SchPpr; PpCl; Gogebic Community College; Social Worker.

DARABAN, Joan; Roanoke Benson HS; Roanoke, IL; 1/100 TrsSrCls; Band; CncrtBnd; HonRl; HospAde; MrchBnd; NHS; Bsbl; Bsktbl; Trk; GAA; Univ Of Illinois.

DARBIN, Steve P; Mishawaka HS; Michawaka, IN; ChrhWkr; CmntyWkr; HonRl; NatlMeritFnl; NatlMeritSF; OffAde; SctActv; YthFlsp; RptrSchPpr; LatCl; Rose Hulman Inst; Electrical Engineer.

DARBO, Doug D; Aurora Hoyt Lakes HS; Hoyt Lakes, MN; AFS; ChrhWkr; HonRl; NHS; StuCncl; YthFlsp; LetterBsktbl; LetterFtbl; LetterGlf; College.

DARBY, Bradley A; Chicago Voc HS; Chicago, IL; Chr; ChrhWkr; HonRl; YthFlsp; Business; Computer Programmer.

DARCY, Anita; Notre Dame Hs; Chicago, IL; HonRl; JA; NatlFornLg; NHS; SchMus; SctActv; TchrAde; RptrSchPpr; FrCl; Loyola U; Politcal Science And Law.

DARDA, David M; Hillsboro HS; Hillsboro, IL; 1/185 HonRl; NatlMeritCmnd; GerCl; PresSciCl; Tennis; IMSpt; AmLegAwd; RotaryAwd; Univ Of Illinois; Dentistry.

DARDEN, Cheryl D; Madison HS; Madison, IL; 16/119 HonRl; NHS; OffAde; Univ; Anesthetist.

DARDUGNO, Thomas; Oak Park & River Forest Hs; Oak Park, IL; 250/1100 HonRl; CaptTrk; University;medicine.

DARFLER, Jill L; Chicago Christian HS; Blue Island, IL; Chrl; ChrhWkr; HonRl; HospAde; LbryAde; Mdrgl; StuCncl; Yrbk; GerCl; Tennis; College; Biology.

DARGA, Lorelei L; St Agatha HS; Det, MI; 10/100 CncrtBnd; HonRl; NHS; Orch; SctActv; StuCncl; TchrAde; YthFlsp; RptrYrbk; SecLatCl; U Of M; Counselor.

DARGAN, Crystal L; Rantoul Township HS; Paxton, IL; ChrhWkr; HonRl; StuCncl; VPFHA; Univ Of Ill; Elementary Teacher.

DA RIF, James F; Ottawa Twp HS; Ottawa, IL; Chr; DrlTm; NHS; NatlThespSoc; ROTC; SchPl; SctActv; LetterFtbl; AmLegAwd; Purdue Univ; Chemical Engineer.

DARIGO, Nancy; University City HS; University City, MO; 25/550 HonRl; Orch; PolWkr; GAA; IMSpt; Southern Ill College; Major Study.

DARK, William A; Decatur Community HS; Oberlin, KS; TrsFrshCls; SecSophCls; SecJrCls; ALBoysSt; HonRl; NHS; SchPl; TreasSpnCl; Wrstlng; Univ Of Kansas; Accounting.

DARLING, Carla D; Raymore Peculiar HS; Peculiar, MO; 12/86 Band; Chrs; ChrhWkr; HonRl; NHS; PepBnd; 4-H; FrCl; Chrldr; GAA; Central Mo State U; Bus Data Procesing.

DARLING, Doug A; Kee HS; New Albin, IA; LetterBsbl; IMSpt; College; Professional.

DARLING, Jane J; Burwell Jr Sr HS; Burwell, NE; 3/36 Aud/Vis; Chrs; HonRl; LbryAde; Mdrgl; SchMus; SchPl; PresStuCncl; PresSpnCl; Northeastern Jr College; Accounting.

DARLING, Nina M; Emerson HS; Gary, IN; Chr; HonRl; NHS; OffAde; PpCl; GAA; College; Doctor.

DARLING, Sayre K; Lincoln Northeast HS; Lincoln, NE; 71/555 HonRl; SchPl; StuCncl; EdYrBk; RptrSchPpr; FFA; PpCl; GAA; College; Journalism.

DARLINGTON, Lloyd R; Normandy HS; St Louis, MO; 52/542 Band; Chr; CmntyWkr; CncrtBnd; HonRl; JA; MrchBnd; NHS; PresSctActv; PresYthFlsp; GerCl; LetterTrk; West Point Military Academy; Officer.

DARNELL, Frances V; Hanover Central HS; Cedar Lake, IN; 2/140 HonRl; JrNHS; NHS; SecStuCncl;.

DARNELL, Jeffrey L; Lynch Public HS; Lynch, NE; VPSophCls; HonRl; NHS; SchPl; StuCncl; RptrSchPpr; Bsktbl; Ftbl; University Of Nebraska.

DARNELL, Robyn E; Cahokia Senior S; Cahokia, IL; 110/550 PresSophCls; Chr; HonRl; PolWkr; TreasStuGov; TchrAde; Yrbk; SchPpr; LetterBsktbl; LetterTrk; Eastern Il Univ; Special Ed Teacher.

DARNELL, Teresa J; Liberal HS; Liberal, KS; 12/256 Band; HonRl; LbryAde; NHS; LetterBsktbl; College; Curriculm.

DAROSZEWSKI, Albert F; A G Lane Tech HS; Chicago, IL; 68/1213 HonRl; JrNHS; NHS; SchAde; TchrAde; Yrbk; SchPpr; GerCl; University Of Illinois; Urban Planning.

DARRAH, John; Union HS; Monmouth, IL; 1/70 Chrs; ChrhWkr; HonRl; NHS; SchMus; SchPl; StuCncl; RptrSchPpr; College; Business.

DARRELL, David J; Lyons Township HS; Western Springs, IL; ALBoysSt; Band; HonRl; Butler Univ; Law.

DARRING, Paul L; Lindblom Tech; Chicago, IL; 205/637 Aud/Vis; Chrl; NatlMeritFnl; NatlMeritSchl; NatlMeritSF; OffAde; LetterBsktbl; LetterFtbl; Trk; IMSpt; Us Naval Academy; Engineering.

DARRINGTON, Jolene; Underwood Comm HS; Underwood, IA; CncrtBnd; HonRl; PepBnd; SchMus; SchPl; YthFlsp; RptrYrbk; 4-H; FHA; IMSpt; Coll; Elem Education.

DARROW, Michael R; Washington Comm HS; Washington, IL; 14/325 Bradley Univ; Mechanical Engineer.

DART, Michael L; Oblong HS; Oblong, IL; HonRl; RptrYrbk; LetterBsktbl; LetterFtbl; IMSpt; Lincoln Trail College; Farmer.

DASCH, Steve D; West Richard S; Noble, IL; HonRl; 4-H; Vocational.

DASCHNER, Karen J; Watseka Community HS; Watseka, IL; TreasAFS; Band; HonRl; NHS; Quill&Scroll; StuCncl; TchrAde; Yrbk; FTA; SpnCl; College; Social Worker.

DASEN, Catherine E; Sanborn Community HS; Sanborn, IA; Band; Chrs; CncrtBnd; HonRl; HospAde; MrchBnd; SchPl; TchrAde; Bsktbl; LetterTrk; Nursing; Reg Nurse.

DASEN, Joanne M; Corunna HS; Corunna, MI; SecJrCls; SecSrCls; HospAde; NHS; RedCrAde; TchrAde; Ferris State College; Medical Assistant.

DASHER, Richard A; Leo HS; Calumet Pk, IL; 25/197 HonRl; SctActv; Eastern Illinois Univ; Accounting.

DASKOLIAS, Anna M; Maine Township South HS; Park Ridge, IL; 136/849 ChrhWkr; HonRl; PolWkr; Quill&Scroll; RptrSchPpr; Univ Of Illinois; Architecture.

DASSINGER, Laverne D; Dickinson HS; Gladstone, ND; 7/186 Chr; CmntyWkr; HonRl; HospAde; JrNHS; ModUN; NatlFornLg; NHS; StuCncl; 4-H; EldAwd; Mary College; Nursing.

DASSINGER, Loraine; Dickinson HS; Gladstone, ND; 20/209 HonRl; JrNHS; NHS; NatlSciFnd; 4-H; FFA; SpnCl; EldAwd; University; Animal Science.

DAUB, Bruce K; Winnebago HS; Pecatonica, IL; HonRl; 4-H; SpnCl; PpCl; Bsktbl; Ftbl; Trk; College; Professional.

DAUBER, Sharon G; Backus Public HS; Pine River, MN; 2/20 VPJrCls; SecTrsSrCls; Band; HonRl; SchPl; EdYrBk; CaptBsktbl; Vernnard Col.

DAUBY, Randall W; Enfield HS; Springerton, IL; 1/30 Chrs; Yrbk; SpnCl; Univ Of Il; Engineering.

DAUER, Cindy J; Waldron Area HS; Camden, MI; 6/42 ChrhWkr; HonRl; NHS; SchPl; StuCncl; Yrbk; FHA; College; Home Economics.

DAUER, Cynthia J; Waldron HS; Camaen, MI; 6/42 ChrhWkr; HonRl; NHS; SchPl; StuCncl; Yrbk; FHA; Chrldr; College.

DAUER, Elaine K; Wahpeton Sr HS; Wahpeton, ND; HonRl; 4-H; 4-HAwd; Nd S S S; Accounting.

DAUFELDT, Cynthia A; West Liberty Community HS; West Liberty, IA; Band; ChrhWkr; CncrtBnd; MrchBnd; StuCncl; RptrSchPpr; 4-H; FFA; FHA; Bsktbl; Business School; Vocation.

DAUGHERTY, Arlene K; Terre Haute North Vigo HS; Terre Haute, IN; Aud/Vis; Band; ChrhWkr; CncrtBnd; HonRl; HospAde; JA; MrchBnd; OffAde; PepBnd; Indiana Voca Tech Clg; Xray Technician.

DAUGHERTY, Candice D; Pana Senior HS; Pana, IL; CmntyWkr; HonRl; OffAde; Yrbk; FTA; GAA; Millikin Univ; Nursing.

DAUGHERTY, Carolyn; St Louia Sr HS; E St Louis, IL; 74/896 HonRl; OffAde; PpCl; SciCl; Univ; Medical Tech.

DAUGHERTY, Caroyln M; Bellevue Comm HS; Bellevue, IA; TrsFrshCls; Band; Chrs; CncrtBnd; DrmMjrt; HonRl; MrchBnd; NHS; PepBnd; SchPl; 4-H; FHA; PpCl; Bsktbl; College; Home Economics.

DAUGHERTY, James; Concordia Sr HS; Concordia, KS; HonRl; College; Electronics.

DAUGHERTY, Kimberly; Southeast Warren HS; Lacona, IA; 10/54 ChrhWkr; HonRl; YthFlsp; RptrYrbk; SchPpr; SpnCl; Chrldr; Pres4Awd;.

DAUGHERTY, Leonard J; Rio HS; Rio, WI; 16/53 HonRl; Glf; College; Engineer.

DAUGHERTY, Matthew S; Depue HS; Depue, IL; Cornell University; Hotel Management.

DAUGHERTY, Randy L; Puxico HS; Puxico, MO; ChrhWkr; HstFrshCls; HonRl; IntrClCncl; SchPl; StuCncl; Bsbl; Bsktbl; Ftbl; Trk; Coll; Computer Tech.

DAUGHERTY, Sandra; Edinburg HS; Edinburg, IL; 4/ Chr; Chrs; HonRl; LbryAde; OffAde; SchAde; SchPl; Trk; Chrldr; GAA; Eureka Coll; Phy Ed.

DAUGHERTY, Sharon A; St Teresas Academy; Kansas City, MO; Chrs; ChrhWkr; Mdrgl; NatlMeritCmnd; RedCrAde; SchPl; StuCncl; StuGov; TchrAde; RptrSchPpr; Umkc; Theatre Arts.

DAUGHERTY, Tammy J; St Teresa HS; Decatur, IL; SecTrsSophCls; CmntyWkr; HonRl; NatlThespSoc; SchPl; StuCncl; PpCl; Chrldr; College.

DAUGHERTY, Timothy P; Bellevue Comm HS; Bellevue, IA; 1/44 PresFrshCls; ALBoysSt; HonRl; PresNHS; PresStuCncl; PpCl; LetterBsbl; LetterBsktbl; LetterFtbl; Trk; State Univ Of Iowa; Accounting.

DAUGHHETEE, Gregory D; Courtland HS; Courtland, KS; SecJrCls; Chr; Chrs; HonRl; SchPl; SctActv; LetterBsktbl; Ftbl; Trk; KiwanAwd; College; Accounting.

DAUGIRDA, Colette S; Mt Assisi HS; Evergreen Park, IL; 7/189 HonRl; HospAde; NHS; RedCrAde; StuCncl; Little Co Of Mary Schl; Nursing.

DAUGS, Douglas W; Buchanan HS; Buchanan, ND; 7/10 PresFrshCls; VPSophCls; Chrs; HonRl; SchPl; StuCncl; StuGov; SchPpr; CaptBsktbl; BttyCrckrAwd; DanFAwd; Univ Of North Dakota.

DAUL, Darlene M; Preble HS; Green Bay, WI; HonRl; JrNHS; NHS; OffAde; SchAde; StuCncl; TchrAde; RptrSchPpr; SchPpr; Clge; Biology.

DAULT, Michelle L; Musk Catholic Central HS; Muskegon, MI; 12/215 PresJrCls; Chrl; HonRl; JA; NHS; SchPl; StuCncl; FrCl; PpCl; Musk Jr College; Nursing.

DAUM, Laura L; Castle HS; Newburgh, IN; 27/311 Chr; HonRl; NHS; NatlThespSoc; SchMus; YthFlsp; CivCl; FTA; LatCl; PpCl; College; Computer Science.

DAUN, Judy; New Holstein HS; St Cloud, WI; 60/198 AFS; ChrhWkr; HonRl; LitMag; LbryAde; NatlFornLg; TchrAde; SchPpr; SpnCl; GAA; Univ Of Wi Eau Claire; Special Educ.

DAUNER, Mike L; Hawley HS; Hawley, MN; 10/54 CmntyWkr; HonRl; SchMus; SchPl; SchPpr; 4-H; FFA; Bsktbl; Ftbl; Tech School.

DAUNIS, Diane M; Regina HS; Detroit, MI; CmntyWkr; HonRl; NatlThespSoc; SchPl; PPFtbl; U Michigan State; Communications Brdcstng.

DAUPHIN, Rebecca J; Mt Carroll HS; Savanna, IL; 4/69 PresJrCls; PresSrCls; HonRl; NHS; 4-H; Western Illinois Univ; Mathematics.

DAUPHIN, Susan M; Mt Carroll HS; Savanna, IL; 25/70 Band; Chr; HonRl; HospAde; RptrSchPpr; 4-H; KeyCl; PpCl; Trk; DanFAwd; College; Nursing.

DAUTENHAHN, David P; Marshall HS; Marshall, MO; HonRl; RedCrAde; SchPl; StuCncl; VPStuGov; SecYthFlsp; LetterGlf; LetterSwmmng; IMSpt; Missouri Valley College; Mathematics.

DAVENPORT, Alan M; Sandy Creek HS; Fairfield, NE; 8/47 VPFrshCls; VPSophCls; TrsJrCls; NHS; LetterBsbl; LetterBsktbl; LetterFtbl; CaptGlf; Trk; PresAwd; College; Pro Athletics.

DAVENPORT, Janet R; Galva Community HS; Galva, IA; 11/22 Band; CncrtBnd; HonRl; LbryAde; MrchBnd; SchPl; PpCl; Trade Sch; Child Care.

DAVENPORT, Jim V; Central Noble HS; Albion, IN; Band; SctActv; PresSciCl; Us Air Force; Law Enforcement.

DAVENPORT, Judy A; New Leipzig HS; New Leipzig, ND; 4/15 ALAGirlsSt; Chr; Chrs; DrmMjrt; OffAde; RedCrAde; SchPl; StuCncl; RptrYrbk; RptrSchPpr; Jamestown College; Nursing.

DAVENPORT, Nancy E; Northwest HS; House Springs, MO; VPJrCls; ChrhWkr; HonRl; NHS; PresStuCncl; TchrAde; YthFlsp; PpCl; Chrldr; PresAwd; Univ Of Missouri; Home Economics.

DAVENPORT, Terri L; Terre Haute North Vigo HS; Terre Haute, IN; 1/642 Band; HonRl; MrchBnd; NatlMeritCmnd; SctActv; StuGov; 4-H; MthCl; SciCl; GAA; In State Univ; Art.

DAVES, Susan; Greenville HS; Silva, MO; Chrs; HonRl; MrchBnd; PolWkr; 4-H; FHA; Trk; Chrldr; IMSpt; 4-HAwd; College; Lab Tech.

DAVEY, Russell L; Rocwell City Com HS; Rockwell City, IA; Band; CncrtBnd; HonRl; MrchBnd; PepBnd; SchMus; JCAwd; American Inst Of Bus; Bus Admin.

DAVEY, Ruth; Gp North HS; Grosse Pointe, MI; Chr; ChrhWkr; CmntyWkr; Orch; SchMus; SctActv; YthFlsp; FrCl; Univ; Professional.

DAVEY, Ruth E; Ludington HS; Ludington, MI; 55/234 Band; SecChr; Chrs; ChrhWkr; CncrtBnd; HonRl; MrchBnd; PepBnd; SchMus; Coll; Music.

DAVID, Dixon; Englewood HS; Chicago, IL; 6/347 CncrtBnd; HonRl; PresJrNHS; NatlMeritSF; SptEdSchPpr; VPFTA; Trk; AmLegAwd; CitAwd; College; Doctor.

DAVID, Elmer A; Union County HS; Liberty, IN; HonRl; NHS; YthFlsp; FrCl; LetterTrk; LetterWrstlng; Purdue Univ; Engineering.

DAVID, Kathy E; Watertown HS; Henry, SD; ChrhWkr; HonRl; SchAde; TchrAde; Yrbk; 4-H; FTA; GerCl; CchngActv; Pres4-HAwd; Clge; Elem Teacher.

DAVID, Kimberly J; Alma HS; Alma, NE; 1/27 ChrhWkr; DrmMjrt; Mdrgl; NHS; SchPl; StuCncl; 4-H; Chrldr; BttyCrckrAwd; Univ Of Nebraska; Fashion Merchandising.

DAVID, Larry F; Marine City HS; Fair Haven, MI; 9/165 HonRl; NHS; OffAde; LetterFtbl; Wrstlng; Michigan St Univ; Criminology.

DAVID, Lynn A; Univ Of Chicago Lab HS; Chicago, IL; TrsSophCls; VPSrCls; StuGov; Yrbk; SchPpr; PpCl; LetterBsktbl; College; Special Educ.

DAVID, Mary J; Medford Public HS; Faribault, MN; 12/42 HonRl; Mdrgl; SchMus; SchPl; StuCncl; Twrl; RptrSchPpr; FTA; Chrldr; IMSpt; College; Rn.

DAVID, Robert L; Trico HS; Campbell Hill, IL; HonRl; 4-H; FFA; SciCl; DanFAwd; Us Air Force Academy; Md.

DAVIDO, Cindy L; Pembine HS; Pembine, WI; 6/21 TrsSophCls; TrsSrCls; Band; Chrs; CncrtBnd; HonRl; MrchBnd; NatlThespSoc; PepBnd; SchMus; Boradcasting.

DAVIDSAVER, Mary A; Duchesne Academy; Omaha, NE; 3/46 Chrs; ChrhWkr; HonRl; HospAde; NHS; SchMus; Sdlty; FrCl; Loyola Univ; Accounting.

DAVIDSMEYER, Bruce A; Virginia HS; Virginia, IL; TrsFrshCls; HonRl; NHS; Bsbl; Ftbl; AmLegAwd; College ;professional.

DAVIDSON, Brett M; Haworth HS; Kokomo, IN; OffAde; TchrAde; Bsktbl; Ftbl; Trk; CchngActv; IMSpt; College; Law.

DAVIDSON, Cheryl L; North Platte R I HS; Edgerton, MO; StuCncl; 4-H; FHA; PpCl; Chrldr; DanFAwd; 4-HAwd; U Of Mo; Teacher Of Blind.

DAVIDSON, Craig G; Roseau HS; Roseau, MN; 1/125 VPJrCls; HonRl; NatlMeritFnl; NatlMeritCmnd; NatlMeritSF; StuCncl; LetterBsbl; LetterFtbl; Univ; Engineering.

DAVIDSON, Debra K; Zionsville Comm HS; Zionsville, IN; ChrhWkr; HonRl; LbryAde; YthFlsp; FrCl; PpCl; Univ; Medicine.

DAVIDSON, Delight M; Boone Jr HS; Boone, IA; ChrhWkr; SctActv; RptrSchPpr; Bsktbl; IMSpt; Housewife.

DAVIDSON, Elizabeth E; Lewis Central HS; Council Bluffs, IA; HonRl; HospAde; JA; LbryAde; NHS; SctActv; TchrAde; FNA; Tennis; College; Pediatric Nurse.

DAVIDSON, Holly A; Loretto HS; Kansas City, MO; Chrl; Chrs; DrlTm; HonRl; SchMus; SchPl; SctActv; StuGov; TchrAde; Stephens College; Fashion Mdse.

DAVIDSON, Janell S; L And M HS; Bloomfield, IN; 2/38 PresSrCls; ALAGirlsSt; ChrhWkr; HonRl; NHS; Bsbl; Bsktbl; GAA; DARAwd; Indiana State University.

DAVIDSON, Joan E; Homewood Flossmoor HS; Homewood, IL; NHS; Orch; SchMus; College; Music.

DAVIDSON, Kevin L; Wilmington HS; Wilmington, IL; 7/129 Band; Chrl; ChrhWkr; CncrtBnd; HonRl; Mdrgl; NHS; SchMus; SchPl; RptrSchPpr; SchPpr; MthCl; Harding College; Chemical Engineer.

DAVIDSON, Kevin W; Riverview Gardens HS; St Louis, MO; Band; HonRl; VPNHS; NatlMeritCmnd; NatlThespSoc; SchMus; SchPl; BauchLmbAwd; DanFAwd; Saint Louis Univ; Dramatic Arts.

DAVIDSON, Lorilee M; Webster HS; Webster, SD; SecTrsSrCls; Chr; Chrs; DrlTm; HonRl; HospAde; Mdrgl; OffAde; SchPl; 4-H; FHA; FNA; BttyCrckrAwd; Jr College; Occupational Therapy.

DAVIDSON, Maurice A; Greenwood Comm HS; Greenwood, IN; Chr; ChrhWkr; HonRl; SchMus; SchPl; PpCl; Ftbl; Trk; William Penn College; Business Education.

DAVIDSON, Robert F; Elmwood Park Comm HS; Elmwood Park, IL; 16/307 SchMus; SchPl; TchrAde; KeyCl;.

DAVIDSON, Robin; Hillcrest Hs; Markham, IL; 67 ChrhWkr; OffAde; SchAde; PpCl; LetterTennis; Lewis U;nursing Rnbs.

DAVIDSON, Tamara S; Walled Lake Central HS; Orchard Lake, MI; 49/375 Band; ChrhWkr; CncrtBnd; HonRl; MrchBnd; NHS; Orch; PepBnd; SchMus; Albion Clg; Chemist.

DAVIE, Barbara J; S Mumford HS; Detroit, MI; 27/750 Chr; HonRl; NHS; OffAde; RptrYrbk; RptrSchPpr; Clark Clg; Medicine.

DAVIE, Denese K; Airport HS; Belleville, MI; Chr; Chrs; ChrhWkr; CmntyWkr; HonRl; FBLA; PpCl; Business College; Business Administration.

DAVIE, Janet A; Homer HS; Homer, MI; 10/86 HonRl; TchrAde; FHA; Lansing Business Univ; Court Conference Rep.

DAVIED, Daniel J; Girard HS; Girard, KS; 6/88 ChrhWkr; HonRl; NHS; FrCl; MthCl; College; Professional.

DAVIES, Brian S; Aberdeen Central HS; Aberdeen, SD; HonRl; StuCncl; Bsbl; LetterFtbl; Trk; CitAwd; College; Biological Science.

DAVIES, Cheryl A; Lancaster Sr HS; Lancaster, WI; 29/159 AFS; Band; Chrs; HonRl; NHS; StuCncl; Twrl; RptrYrbk; RptrSchPpr; 4-H; GAA; IMSpt; 4-HAwd; College; Education.

DAVIES, Cindy S; Mar Mac HS; Mcgregor, IA; 2/36 VPSrCls; Band; Chrs; HonRl; NHS; SchMus; YthFlsp; 4-H; Bsbl; Bsktbl; Tennis; Trk; University Of Iowa; Medicine.

DAVIES, Diane; Moberly HS; Moberly, MO; Chrs; ChrhWkr; DrlTm; HonRl; NHS; SchMus; FBLA; Chrldr; PPFtbl;.

DAVIES, James R; Canton Sr HS; Canton, IL; Band; CncrtBnd; HonRl; MrchBnd; NHS; NatlMeritSF; PepBnd; SctActv; Buddley Univ; Math.

DAVIES, John M; Lancaster HS; Lancaster, WI; 6/154 HonRl; NHS; NatlMeritCmnd; SctActv; YthFlsp; LetterBsbl; Bsktbl; LetterFtbl; Trk; Pro.

DAVIES, Kristeen; Lancaster Sr Hs; Lancaster, WI; ALAGirlsSt; Band; Chrs; HonRl; Mdrgl; NatlFornLg; NHS; Orch; SchMus; StuCncl; Uw Madison;xray Technologist.

DAVIES, Nancy J; Arlington HS; Arlington Hts, IL; 44/581 Chrs; HonRl; OffAde; FrCl; Harper College; Occup Therapy.

DAVIES, Pamela; Kenwood HS; Chicago, IL; HonRl; OffAde; StuCncl; Western Michigan Univ; African Studies Prof.

DAVIES, Susan L; Evanston Township HS; Evanston, IL; Chr; ChrhWkr; HonRl; SecYthFlsp; GerCl; GAA; DARAwd; Western Illinois Univ; History.

DAVILA, Rojelio; Beecher HS; Mt Morris, MI; HonRl; NHS; PolWkr; SctActv; PpCl; Swmmng; Trk; U Of Mich Flint; Lawyer.

DAVINROY, Benjamin; Assumption Hs; Fairview Heights, IL; ALBoysSt; CmntyWkr; HonRl; LetterBsbl; AmLegAwd; College; Professional.

DAVIS, Amy J; Delta HS; Braggadocio, MO; 2/21 PresJrCls; Band; HonRl; VPNHS; StuCncl; Yrbk; FHA; SecFTA; PpCl; Chrldr; Univ Of Missouri; Guidance Counselling.

DAVIS, Andrea; Proctor HS; Duluth, MN; ChrhWkr; CmntyWkr; HonRl; PolWkr; 4-H; FHA; PpCl; SciCl; 4-HAwd; College; Social Work.

DAVIS, Annette S; John Marshall Harlan HS; Chicago, IL; LetterBand; CncrtBnd; HonRl; JA; MrchBnd; PepBnd; SchMus; SctActv; StuCncl; RptrSchPpr; FshEdSchPpr; JAAwd; Bradley Univ; Pre Law.

DAVIS, Ann M; Tekamah Herman HS; Tekamah, NE; SecChrs; NHS; NatlThespSoc; PepBnd; StuCncl; YthFlsp; RptrYrbk; 4-H; FHA; PpCl; Univ Of Ne At Lincoln; Instrumental Music.

DAVIS, Ann M; Bay City Western HS; Bay City, MI; VPFrshCls; VPSophCls; ChrhWkr; HonRl; NHS; RptrYrbk; Bsbl; Bsktbl; Chrldr; JCAwd; Jr Coll; Physical Ther.

DAVIS, Arletta G; Galena HS; Highlandville, MO; Band; Chrs; HonRl; HospAde; RedCrAde; PpCl; LetterBsbl; LetterBsktbl; Chrldr; PresAwd;.

DAVIS, Barbara A; Odell Comm HS; Odell, IL; Chrs; HonRl; SchPl; SecStuCncl; TchrAde; Pres4-H; FHA; GAA; 4-HAwd; College.

DAVIS, Barbara L; David City HS; David City, NE; Band; CmntyWkr; CncrtBnd; HonRl; MrchBnd; NatlThespSoc; PepBnd; SchMus; SchPl; RptrSchPpr; PpCl; Glf; Tennis; LetterTrk; Univ Of Nebraska; Music.

DAVIS, Belinda K; Dongola Unit HS; Dongola, IL; 3/27 SecFrshCls; Band; Chrs; CncrtBnd; HonRl; MrchBnd; PepBnd; SchMus; StuCncl; Twrl; Treas4-H; CaptChrldr; VPGAA; Shawnee Jr Col; Exec Secretary.

DAVIS, Benjamin F; West Side HS; Gary, IN; Band; Chr; HonRl; NatlMeritCmnd; SctActv; TchrAde; LatCl; PresSciCl; CaptSwmmng; College; Professional.

DAVIS, Benjamin L; Roosevelt HS; St Louis, MO; 16/400 Band; HonRl; NHS; SctActv; StuCncl; RptrYrbk; Washington Univ; Architecture.

DAVIS, Benjamin L; Park Tudor HS; Indianapolis, IN; ChrhWkr; CmntyWkr; SchPl; KeyCl; FrCl; Bsbl; CaptFtbl; Glf; LetterTrk; Wrstlng; University; Medicine.

DAVIS, Beverly; Bunker R3 HS; Bunker, MO; 2/27 TrsFrshCls; Band; Chrs; HonRl; MrchBnd; PepBnd; EdYrBk; SchPpr; BttyCrckrAwd; College; Home Economics.

DAVIS, Blake E; Casey HS; Casey, IL; NHS; LetterFtbl; LetterTrk; Univ; Industrial Engr.

DAVIS, Bob D; Mt Pleasant Comm HS; Mt Pleasant, IA; 35/163 HonRl; Bsktbl; LetterFtbl; Trk; U Of Iowa; Pharmacey.

DAVIS, Brenda A; Muskego HS; Muskego, WI; 13/350 Chr; ChrhWkr; HonRl; NHS; SchPl; RptrYrbk; 4-H; SecFrCl; PpCl; 4-HAwd; Uw Milwaukee; Architecture.

DAVIS, Brenda A; Hope HS; Hope, KS; Band; Chrs; HonRl; NatlFornLg; YthFlsp; Sec4-H; SecFHA; CaptBsktbl; LetterTrk; Chrldr;.

DAVIS, Brian J; Lake Shore HS; St Clair Shores, MI; HonRl; NHS; Oakland University; Math.

DAVIS, Bryan C; East Prairie HS; East Prairie, MO; VPFrshCls; HstJrCls; Chr; ChrhWkr; CmntyWkr; CncrtBnd; HonRl; JrNHS; MrchBnd; NHS; SchMus; SchPl; SctActv; Bsbl; LetterFtbl; University; Agronomy.

DAVIS, Carla L; Marshfield HS; Marshfield, MO; SecSophCls; AFS; Band; CncrtBnd; MrchBnd; SchPl; StuCncl; FTA; PpCl; College; Elementary Ed.

DAVIS, Carol; Garrigan HS; Algana, IA; Chrs; CmntyWkr; HonRl; LbryAde; SchAde; SchMus; YthFlsp; CivCl; IMSpt; Business School; Secretarial.

DAVIS, Carol A; Waukegan HS; Waukegan, IL; AFS; College; Wildlife Management.

DAVIS, Carol S; Harrisonville Sr HS; Harrisonville, MO; 4/161 TrsJrCls; Band; Chrs; HonRl; MrchBnd; Quill&Scroll; SchMus; Yrbk; RptrSchPpr; Kansas City Business; Court Reporter.

DAVIS, Caryn; Muskego HS; Muskego, WI; 8/325 Chr; HonRl; Mdrgl; NHS; NatlMeritSF; NatlThespSoc; StuCncl; Swmmng; Ripon College; Law.

DAVIS, Cassandra R; East Catholic HS; Highland Park, MI; 6/90 HonRl; PresJA; VPLbryAde; NHS; NatlMeritSF; NatlSciFnd; Yrbk; ChmnFrCl; SciCl; JAAwd; Engingeering.

DAVIS, Cecile A; Neutown Harris HS; Lucerne, MO; 6/24 TrsJrCls; HstSrCls; Band; ChrhWkr; CmntyWkr; CncrtBnd; HonRl; LbryAde; MrchBnd; PepBnd; Bsbl; Bsktbl; Trk; William Penn Col; Physical Educ.

DAVIS, Cheryl R; Greenville Senior HS; Greenville, MI; Band; HonRl; MrchBnd; NatlFornLg; SchPl; StuCncl; Twrl; FrCl; PpCl; Glf; Trk; Michigan State University.

DAVIS, Christy A; Illmo Scott City HS; Scott City, MO; 10/100 PresJrCls; Band; Chrs; ChrhWkr; HonRl; NHS; SchPl; StuCncl; YthFlsp; Chrldr; University; Professional.

DAVIS, Cindy; Ripon Senior HS; Ripon, WI; College; Curriculum Of Major Study.

DAVIS, Clayton G; Glenwood Comm HS; Glenwood, IA; 2/110 PresBand; ChrhWkr; HonRl; PresNHS; FrCl; CaptGlf; AmLegAwd; BauchLmbAwd; DARAwd; RotaryAwd; Iowa State U; Computer Scinece.

DAVIS, Coralie; Pine River HS; Leroy, MI; Band; HonRl; NHS; StuCncl; YthFlsp; Yrbk; RptrSchPpr; SpnCl; LetterBsktbl; Trk; Ferris State Coll.

DAVIS, Cynthia; Mullinville HS; Mullinville, KS; TrsSophCls; PresJrCls; Chrs; ChrhWkr; CncrtBnd; MrchBnd; PepBnd; PpCl; Bsktbl; Trk; Hutchinson Juco Ks State; Home Economics.

DAVIS, Daniel; Central Lyon HS; Rock Rapids, IA; Chr; NatlThespSoc; SchMus; SchPl; RptrYrbk; RptrSchPpr; Coll; Advertiz.

DAVIS, Daniel B; Lexington HS; Lexington, IL; VPJrCls; VPSrCls; Band; CmntyWkr; LbryAde; PepBnd; YthFlsp; 4-H; FFA; PpCl; LetterBsbl; CaptBsktbl; CaptFtbl; College; Law Enforcement.

DAVIS, Darlene S; Walter P Chrysler Mem HS; New Castle, IN; Chr; Chrl; HonRl; SctActv; StuCncl; YthFlsp; Pres4-H; PresFHA; BttyCrckrAwd; Pres4-HAwd;.

DAVIS, Daryl N; De La Salle HS; Chicago, IL; 9/258 HonRl; NatlFornLg; SecNHS; NatlMeritCmnd; SchMus; SchPpr; IMSpt; VoiceDemAwd; College; Prelaw.

DAVIS, Deborah D; Chicago Vocational HS; Chicago, IL; College; Secretary.

DAVIS, Deborah M; Blair Comm HS; Blair, NE; VPFrshCls; FHA; LetterTrk; LetterTrk; PresAwd;.

DAVIS, Deborah S; Pana Sr HS; Pana, IL; 6/160 ChrhWkr; HonRl; LbryAde; NHS; YthFlsp; RptrSchPpr; Olivet Nazarene College; Psychology.

DAVIS, Debora R; Garber HS; Essexville, MI; ChrhWkr; HonRl; TchrAde; Nursing.

DAVIS, Debra; Creston HS; Creston, IA; 7/154 HonRl; FNA; GAA; Amer Inst Of Bus; Secretarial.

DAVIS, Debra D; Maple Valley HS; Castana, IA; ChrhWkr; CncrtBnd; HonRl; HospAde; MrchBnd; ModUN; 4-H; FNA; 4-HAwd; Ne Methodist; Nurse.

DAVIS, Diana L; Comstock HS; Kalamazoo, MI; PresAFS; HonRl; NatlFornLg; NHS; SchPl; TchrAde; SecGerCl; Univ Of Michigan; Doctor.

DAVIS, Diane E; Tuscola HS; Tuscola, IL; 3/128 Band; Chr; Chrs; CncrtBnd; HonRl; MrchBnd; RptrSchPpr; FTA; LatCl; PpCl; SciCl; Trk; University Of Illinois; Liberal Arts.

DAVIS, Dianne C; Bedford North Lawrence HS; Bedford, IN; 20/360 VPSrCls; ALAGirlsSt; VPChr; HonRl; NHS; StuCncl; SpnCl; SecMthCl; Chrldr; GAA; Univ; Medical Field.

DAVIS, Donna; Huteonville HS; West York, IL; HonRl; MthCl; Coll.

DAVIS, Donovan; Wisconsin Acad; Rockford, IL; ChrhWkr; College.

DAVIS, Elaine; Tuscola Hs; Tuscola, IL; 3/128 Band; HonRl; RptrSchPpr; FTA; LatCl;.

DAVIS, Elizabeth A; East Prairie HS; E Prairie, MO; SecTrsFrshCls; SecSophCls; TrsSrCls; Band; Chr; Tennis; Trk; Chrldr; IMSpt; PPFtbl; Univ Co Boulder; Architect.

DAVIS, Elizabeth M; Mother Of Sorrows HS; Calumet Park, IL; 3/125 ChrhWkr; HonRl; PresNHS; SchAde; StuCncl; TchrAde; GAA; Millikin Univ; Physical Therapy.

DAVIS, Eva L; Thornton Township HS; Harvey, IL; 13/727 Band; CncrtBnd; HonRl; MrchBnd; NHS; Purdue Univ; Engineer.

DAVIS, Fawn L; Esbon HS; Esbon, KS; 1/14 Band; Chr; HonRl; SchPl; StuCncl; Yrbk; 4-H; PpCl; LetterBsktbl; LetterTrk; Ks St U; Fine Arts.

DAVIS, Gail N; Madonna HS; Chicago, IL; 73/293 VPFrshCls; VPSophCls; SecJrCls; SecSrCls; Chr; ChrhWkr; CmntyWkr; HonRl; HospAde; NatlMeritCmnd; StuCncl; Loyola Univ; Nurse.

DAVIS, Gayle L; Jetmore HS; Jetmore, KS; Band; CncrtBnd; HonRl; MrchBnd; PepBnd; StuCncl; 4-H; PpCl; 4-HAwd; Kansas State Univ; Veterinary Med.

DAVIS, Gregory A; North Liberty HS; North Liberty, IN; 1/91 SecSophCls; ALBoysSt; HonRl; NHS; NatlMeritFnl; NatlMeritSchl; PresStuCncl; Yrbk; FrCl; Mi State U; Astrophysics.

DAVIS, Ivan S; Clare HS; Clare, MI; 50/155 HonRl; CaptBsbl; CaptBsktbl; CaptGlf; CchngActv; KiwanAwd; Albion College; Physics.

DAVIS, Jacqueline A; Climax Scotts HS; Climax, MI; 4/53 VPFrshCls; SecSophCls; SecSrCls; Band; HonRl; NatlFornLg; StuCncl; RptrYrbk; MthCl; Trk; 4-HAwd; Aquinas College; Social Work.

DAVIS, James E; St Joseph HS; St Joseph, MI; Chr; CncrtBnd; HospAde; JA; MrchBnd; NHS; Orch; PepBnd; SchAde; SchMus; MthCl; SciCl;.

DAVIS, Janet K; Richland HS; Richland, MO; 5/65 Band; SecChrhWkr; DrmMjrt; HonRl; RptrYrbk; RptrSchPpr; FHA; LetterBsktbl; LetterTrk; Chrldr; Midamerican Bus Coll; Pro Sec.

DAVIS, Janet K; Lincoln Co R Ii; Elsberry, MO; 2/62 Band; Chr; CncrtBnd; HonRl; NHS; 4-H; SciCl; Chrldr; GAA; 4-HAwd; Univ; Prof.

DAVIS, Jeff E; Cloverdale HS; Cloverdale, IN; 4/70 ALBoysSt; Band; CncrtBnd; HonRl; MrchBnd; NatlThespSoc; PepBnd; SchMus; SchPl; RptrYrbk; College Or University; Professional.

DAVIS, Jeffery B; Casey HS; Casey, IL; HonRl; Ftbl; E Illinois Univ; Medicine.

DAVIS, Jeffery D; Cambridge HS; Cambridge, NE; SchPl; SctActv; Bsbl; Bsktbl; LetterFtbl; LetterTrk; Wrstlng; College.

DAVIS, Jeffrey R; Lincoln HS; Vincennes, IN; 34/350 Band; ChrhWkr; HonRl; NatlFornLg; StuCncl; PresYthFlsp; MthCl; SciCl; Tennis; College; Engineering Chemistry.

DAVIS, Jennifer A; Adrian HS; Adrian, MI; NatlFornLg; SchPl; SctActv; StuCncl; PpCl; SciCl; Tennis; Trk; IMSpt; College; Professnl.

DAVIS, Jerome J; Dc Everest HS; Schofield, WI; 10/337 Aud/Vis; HonRl; NHS; NatlMeritSF; SctActv; MthCl; Bsktbl; Ftbl; IMSpt; MasAwd; Univ Of Wi; Professional, Engineering.

DAVIS, Jim V; Hammond Baptist HS; Crown Point, IN; 11/88 HonRl; NHS; Quill&Scroll; Yrbk; RptrSchPpr; LetterWrstlng; Trade School; Vocation.

DAVIS, Joan E; Zion Benton Township HS; Zion, IL; 20/405 HonRl; JrNHS; LitMag; NHS; VPGerCl; Florida College; Laboratory Technician.

DAVIS, Joan R; Crab Orchard HS; Marion, IL; 6/27 PresJrCls; Chrs; HonRl; SchPl; RptrYrbk; FHA; John A Logan Jr Clg.

DAVIS, John; Maine Twp Hs South; Park Ridge, IL; 76/850 HonRl; JrNHS; NHS; NatlMeritCmnd; Orch; SchMus; College; Biology Research.

DAVIS, Joyce A; Kalamazoo Loy Norrix HS; Kalamazoo, MI; ChrhWkr; CaptBsktbl; CaptTrk; Mississippi Univ; Math.

DAVIS, Juanita; Platte Valley Academy; North Platte, NE; TrsSophCls; Band; Chr; ChrhWkr; HonRl; NHS; SchMus; SchPl; StuGov; TchrAde; Union College; Physical Therapy.

DAVIS, Julia A; Richland HS; Richland, MO; Band; Chrs; SecChrhWkr; CncrtBnd; DrmBgl; HonRl; FHA; Bsbl; Bsktbl; Chrldr;.

DAVIS, Julie A; Lew Wallace HS; Gary, IN; 27/513 HonRl; NHS; SciCl; IMSpt; Indiana Univ; Communications.

DAVIS, Julie M; Monett HS; Monett, MO; 25/120 Band; CncrtBnd; MrchBnd; ModUN; NatlFornLg; PepBnd; PolWkr; SchPl; StuCncl; FBLA; College; Dramatic Arts.

DAVIS, Katherine L; Orion HS; Orion, IL; 10/125 Band; ChrhWkr; DrlTm; HonRl; NHS; SchAde; TchrAde; SpnCl; Chrldr; GAA; Univ; Business.

DAVIS, Katherine R; Lincoln County R Ii HS; Elsberry, MO; 3/60 Band; CncrtBnd; HonRl; MrchBnd; NHS; PepBnd; TchrAde; YthFlsp; SciCl; GAA; Univ; Math.

DAVIS, Kathryn J; Unity HS; Chicago, IL; SecSrCls; Chrs; DrmMjrt; SchMus; SchPl; StuCncl; FrCl; College.

DAVIS, Kaye; Sullivan HS; Sullivan, MO; 23/150 Band; HonRl; LbryAde; NHS; SchMus; TchrAde; Yrbk; RptrSchPpr; SecFTA; PresPpCl; School Of The Ozarks.

DAVIS, Keith R; Coloma HS; Coloma, MI; Band; CncrtBnd; HonRl; MrchBnd; NHS; PepBnd; YthFlsp; Yrbk; LatCl; Ftbl; Trk; Albion College; Medicine.

DAVIS, Kenneth; Harris Lake Park HS; Lake Park, IA; ALBoysSt; Band; Chrs; CncrtBnd; HonRl; MrchBnd; PepBnd; SctActv; Wrstlng; Trade; Mechanic.

DAVIS, Kenneth E; Hillsboro HS; Hillsboro, IL; 6/180 ALBoysSt; HonRl; NatlMeritCmnd; RptrSchPpr; GerCl; Eastern Illinois Univ; Engineering.

DAVIS, Kenneth F; Guttenberg Comm HS; Guttenberg, IA; 7/68 ALBoysSt; Chr; NHS; SchPl; RptrYrbk; PpCl; LetterBsbl; LetterBsktbl; LetterFtbl; Trk; College; Professional.

DAVIS, Kevin L; Garden City West Sr HS; Garden City, MI; HonRl; NHS; NatlMeritSchl; SchPpr; FDA; GerCl; IMSpt; AmLegAwd; GovHonPrgAwd; PresAwd; Eastern Mich; Med Tech.

DAVIS, Kevin M; Heelan HS; Sioux City, IA; 44/244 Band; CncrtBnd; HonRl; College.

DAVIS, Kim; Cannon Falls HS; Cannon Falls, MN; HonRl; SchMus; TchrAde; FTA; SpnCl; PpCl; Chrldr; GAA; PPFtbl; Dakota County Vo Tech; Travel Agent.

DAVIS, Kimberly L; William Fremd HS; Palatine, IL; CncrtBnd; HonRl; MrchBnd; PolWkr; SchPl; StuCncl; 4-H; Iowa State Univ; Nutrition Research.

DAVIS, Kimberly R; Harian HS; Chicago, IL; 74/510 Chrs; HonRl; StuCncl; StuGov; RptrYrbk; FshEdSchPpr; 4-H; SpnCl; PpCl; 4-HAwd; Elmhurst College; Librarian.

DAVIS, Kimberly S; Nebraska City Sr HS; Nebraska City, NE; 17/123 VPSrCls; HonRl; NHS; FHA; SecPpCl; LetterBsktbl; CchngActv; Univ Of Nebraska; Physical Ed.

DAVIS, Kip D; Oblong HS; Oblong, IL; Band; HonRl; SchPl; SctActv; FFA; EngCl; Bsbl; Bsktbl; Tennis; Lincoln Trail College; Business.

DAVIS, Kristi L; Atlantic HS; Atlantic, IA; Teen; 4-H; Bsbl; Trk; Iowa Methodist School; Nursing.

DAVIS, Lee A; Southeast Sr HS; Kansas City, MO; Band; Chrs; DrlTm; DrmBgl; HonRl; MrchBnd; ROTC; SchMus; StuGov; CitAwd; College; Professional.

DAVIS, Lewis; Bullock Creek HS; Midland, MI; HonRl; NatlFornLg; YthFlsp; PpCl; SciCl; Bsktbl; Colege;.

DAVIS, Linda C; Woodruff HS; Peoria, IL; 18/225 Band; CncrtBnd; HonRl; MrchBnd; Orch; PepBnd; FrCl; Business School; Computer Programming.

DAVIS, Linda J; Parker HS; Chicago, IL; ChrhWkr; CtyCnl; CmntyWkr; HonRl; JA; SchPpr; Trk; University.

DAVIS, Linda L; Republic HS; Republic, MO; 30/114 ChrhWkr; HonRl; 4-H; FHA; PpCl; SciCl; Business School.

DAVIS, Lori D; Hot Springs HS; Hot Springs, SD; 7/79 ALAGirlsSt; ChrhWkr; CmntyWkr; HonRl; NHS; SchAde; StuCncl; TchrAde; LetterBsktbl; LetterTrk; College; Math Teacher.

DAVIS, Marcia A; Deerfield HS; Deerfield, IL; ChrhWkr; HonRl; NHS; Yrbk; University.

DAVIS, Marcia L; Farnam Public HS; Farnam, NE; PresJrCls; Band; ChrhWkr; CncrtBnd; HonRl; MrchBnd; SchPl; StuCncl; RptrYrbk; Chrldr; Kearney State; Business.

DAVIS, Mark A; Verona HS; Verona, WI; 6/125 VPSophCls; TreasAud/Vis; HonRl; NHS; TchrAde; Pres4-H; OptClAwd; Uw Madison; Electrical Eng.

DAVIS, Mark E; Fairfield Community HS; Fairfield, IL; 24/165 SecTrsSophCls; ChrhWkr; HonRl; NHS; StuGov; MthCl; SciCl; LetterBsbl; LetterBsktbl; LetterTrk; BauchLmbAwd; Eastern Ill Univ; Neurologist.

DAVIS, Mark H; Lowell Sr HS; Hebron, IN; 11/267 TrsSophCls; VPJrCls; AFS; HonRl; NHS; StuCncl; RptrYrbk; FrCl; Swmmng; Indiana U; Bus Admin.

DAVIS, Martha; Purdy R Ii HS; Purdy, MO; TrsJrCls; Chrs; HonRl; JA; LbryAde; OffAde; SchPl; Bsktbl; Chrldr; Business School; Professional.

DAVIS, Martha A; Butler HS; Butler, MO; SecFrshCls; SecJrCls; PresSrCls; AFS; HonRl; NHS; SchPl; StuCncl; FHA; Burge School; Nursing.

DAVIS, Martha E; Parkview HS; Springfield, MO; 16/380 ALAGirlsSt; HonRl; NatlFornLg; NatlMeritCmnd; PolWkr; StuCncl; PresStuGov; LatCl; PpCl; IMSpt; Newcomb College; Biological Research.

DAVIS, Martha F; North HS; Wichita, KS; 1/549 Chr; ChrhWkr; HonRl; LitMag; Mdrgl; ModUN; VPNHS; NatlMeritSF; Orch; PolWkr; SchMus; PresStuCncl; IMSpt; College; Chemistry.

DAVIS, Martha G; Waterford Mott HS; Pontiac, MI; 44/385 College; Interior Decorator.

DAVIS, Marvin R; Limestone Comm HS; Bartonville, IL; 11/390 HonRl; SecNHS; NatlMeritCmnd; KeyCl; SpnCl; PpCl; SciCl; LetterBsbl; LetterFtbl; DARAwd; Univ Of Montana; Forestry.

DAVIS, Mary A; Central Montcalm HS; Stanton, MI; 1/121 TrsSrCls; HonRl; OffAde; TchrAde; SpnCl; IMSpt; PPFtbl; BttyCrckrAwd; Montcalm Comm College; Accountant.

DAVIS, Mary L; Mancelona HS; Mancelona, MI; Band; CncrtBnd; HonRl; MrchBnd; NHS; PepBnd; TchrAde; College; Industrial Arts.

DAVIS, Mary M; Winamac Comm HS; Winamac, IN; ChrhWkr; HonRl; SchPl; College; Professional.

DAVIS, Mary R; Wilmington HS; Wilmington, IL; 16/133 Band; ChrhWkr; CncrtBnd; HonRl; JrNHS; MrchBnd; NHS; PepBnd; RptrYrbk; TreasFHA; FTA; GAA; North Central College; Elem Educ.

DAVIS, Michael D; Crown Point HS; Crown Point, IN; HonRl; NHS; YthFlsp; IMSpt; MasAwd; Us Naval Acad.

DAVIS, Michael L; Desoto Senior HS; De Soto, KS; 8/95 HonRl; NHS; SptEdYrbk; FBLA; SciCl; Ftbl; Tennis; CchngActv; Kansas State Univ; Electrical Eng.

DAVIS, Michele D; Woodruff HS; Peoria, IL; 41/232 Chr; ChrhWkr; CmntyWkr; DrlTm; HonRl; NHS; TchrAde; YthFlsp; SpnCl; KiwanAwd; Isu; Accounting.

DAVIS, Milan S; Meade HS; Meade, KS; ChrhWkr; SchMus; SchPl; SciCl; Swmmng; Tennis; Wrstlng; Univ; X Ray Tech.

DAVIS, Miles; Interlochen Arts Acad; Monroe, MI; Band; HonRl; MrchBnd; NHS; PepBnd; SchMus; StuCncl; SptEdSchPpr; Bsbl; Socr; U Of Mi; Music Performance.

DAVIS, Pamela L; Park Hill Sr HS; Kansas City, MO; 93/405 HonRl; NatlMeritCmnd; Tennis; Baker Univ; Biology.

DAVIS, Pamela S; De Soto Senior HS; Shawnee, KS; Chrl; Chrs; CncrtBnd; HonRl; JrNHS; MrchBnd; NHS; PepBnd; RptrYrbk; College.

DAVIS, Patricia I; Mahtomedi HS; Mahtomedi, MN; Band; Chr; ChrhWkr; CncrtBnd; HonRl; MrchBnd; PepBnd; TchrAde; 4-H; Bemidji State Coll; Music Major Or Law Pro.

DAVIS, Patrick O; Pine River HS; St Cloud, MN; ALBoysSt; HonRl; NHS; Yrbk; Trk; St Cloud State College; Medicine.

DAVIS, Peggy S; Beardstown HS; Beardstown, IL; Band; Chrs; ChrhWkr; CmntyWkr; OffAde; SchMus; 4-H; FTA; PpCl; SciCl; College; Teacher Lab Ass.

DAVIS, Ray M; St Charles HS; St Charles, MO; /598 HonRl; SctActv; RptrSchPpr; College; Professional.

DAVIS, Regina; Norton Community HS; Norton, KS; TrsSophCls; ALAGirlsSt; ChrhWkr; HonRl; MrchBnd; Quill&Scroll; SchMus; TchrAde; Yrbk; PpCl; College.

DAVIS, Rhonda C; Delta C 7 HS; Deering, MO; 1/20 VPSophCls; PresBand; DrmMjrt; PepBnd; VPStuCncl; Yrbk; VPFHA; FTA; PpCl; CaptChrldr; College.

DAVIS, Rickey E; Parkside HS; Jackson, MI; SecFrshCls; StuCncl; StuGov; CaptBsbl; IMSpt; Spring Arbor College; Accounting.

DAVIS, Sandra K; Emmerich Manual HS; Inidanapolis, IN; HonRl; SchMus; SchPl; Twrl; FrCl;.

DAVIS, Sandra K; Roxana Sr HS; Wood River, IL; 21/290 HonRl; HospAde; Yrbk; PpCl; Tennis; LetterTrk; Lewis & Clark College; Commercial Art.

DAVIS, Sherry L; Aurora Sr HS; Lawrenceburg, IN; HstSophCls; HstJrCls; HstSrCls; HonRl; OffAde; RedCrAde; SctActv; SchPpr; Air Force; Medical.

DAVIS, Stephen P; Beaver Dam Sr HS; Beaver Dam, WI; 13/320 VPSrCls; Band; Chrs; ChrhWkr; DrmMjrt; SchMus; CaptTennis; IMSpt; College; Psychology.

DAVIS, Steven J; Aurora Central Catholic HS; Aurora, IL; Yrbk; 4-H; LetterTrk; College Or University; Lawyer.

DAVIS, Suzanne; Bergan HS; Peoria, IL; 1/206 Chrs; DrlTm; HonRl; Yrbk; SpnCl; PpCl; Univ Of Illinois; Medical Tech.

DAVIS, Suzanne E; Bergan HS; Peoria, IL; 12/208 Chrs; CmntyWkr; DrlTm; HonRl; SpnCl; Univ Of Illinois; Medicine.

DAVIS, Terrance W; Jackson HS; Jackson, MI; 17/373 CncrtBnd; HonRl; MrchBnd; NHS; NatlMeritCmnd; NatlMeritSF; PepBnd; SctActv; GerCl; RusCl; College; Dental Health.

DAVIS, Terry L; Wentzville R Iv HS; Ofallon, MO; Band; CncrtBnd; DrlTm; HonRl; MrchBnd; SchPl; PpCl; Trk; GAA; IMSpt; Business Sch; Secretary.

DAVIS, Terry M; Cleveland HS; Cleveland, MN; 5/41 HonRl; NHS; NatlThespSoc; SchPl; Yrbk; RptrSchPpr; Mankato St Coll; History.

DAVIS, Theodore; Westmer HS; Joy, IL; ChrhWkr; HonRl; TchrAde; FTA; SciCl; Trk; IMSpt; Univ Wisc; Forester.

DAVIS, Theodore E; Westmer HS; Joy, IL; ChrhWkr; HonRl; TchrAde; FTA; SciCl; Univ Of Wisconsin; Forest Conserv.

DAVIS, Thomas C; East HS; Sioux City, IA; 8/360 HonRl; NatlMeritSF; PolWkr; SchMus; StuCncl; SchPpr; Bsktbl; Ftbl; Trk; IMSpt; Yale Univ; Phil/ecol.

DAVIS, Timothy J; East Brook HS; Upland, IN; HonRl; NatlThespSoc; SchMus; SchPl; GerCl; Bsbl; Bsktbl; Ftbl; Univ; Pro.

DAVIS, Toni R; Berkeley Sr HS; Florissant, MO; 22/279 HonRl; JA; NHS; StuCncl; Univ Of Mo; Science.

DAVIS, Tony M; St Francis HS; Cedar, MN; 1/210 Chrs; HonRl; 4-H; Bsbl; Bsktbl; Univ; Elec Eng.

DAVIS, Vicky L; Adel Community HS; Adel, IA; DrlTm; HonRl; Yrbk; SchPpr; Chrldr;.

DAVIS, Virginia M; Marinette HS; Marinette, WI; 70/283 Chr; Chrs; HonRl; RptrSchPpr; LatCl; PpCl; Trk; CchngActv; GAA; IMSpt; Uw At Marinette; Professional Cpa.

DAVIS, Wendy L; Oscoda Area HS; Oscoda, MI; 1/240 ALAGirlsSt; Chr; ChrhWkr; CncrtBnd; HonRl; LitMag; NHS; TreasSciCl; Univ Of Michigan; Art.

DAVIS, Zoe E; Lincoln HS; Cambridge City, IN; 10/120 CncrtBnd; HonRl; MrchBnd; NHS; PepBnd; SchMus; Bsktbl; LetterTennis; CchngActv; GAA; University; Professional.

DAVISON, Carol L; Sedgwick HS; Sedgwick, KS; 2/39 SecSophCls; SecJrCls; HonRl; Mdrgl; PepBnd; SchMus; SchPl; SchPpr; PpCl; LetterBsktbl; LetterTrk; Chrldr; CchngActv; College; Liberal Arts.

DAVISON, Kathleen J; Proviso West HS; Hillside, IL; Chr; Chrs; ChrhWkr; HospAde; Mdrgl; StuCncl; PpCl; Iowa State Univ; Int Design.

DAVISON, Michael A; Whitewater HS; Whitewater, WI; 7/180 ALBoysSt; Chr; CncrtBnd; DrmMjrt; Mdrgl; NHS; SchMus; StuGov; LetterBsbl; Bsktbl; LetterFtbl; CaptWrstlng; AmLegAwd; Eastman School; Music.

DAVISON, Nancy L; Highland HS; Highland, IN; 125/538 Chr; CncrtBnd; Mdrgl; MrchBnd; NatlThespSoc; SchMus; SchPl; SctActv; FHA; College; Special Education.

DAVISSON, Kathy; Oxford HS; Oxford, MI; 1/190 HonRl; ModUN; SchMus; StuCncl; RptrYrbk; 4-H; DARAwd; 4-HAwd; Mi State Univ; Poli Sci Pre Law.

DAVISSON, Sandra L; Jackson HS; Jackson, MI; 10/373 Chr; HonRl; NHS; RptrSchPpr; GerCl; Jackson Comm Coll; Engineering.

DAVITT, Timothy P; Alexander Ramsey HS; Roseville, MN; JrNHS; NHS; StuCncl; LetterSocr; IMSpt; Univ Mn.

DAVLIN, Timothy P; Creighton Prep HS; Omaha, NE; 56/249 HonRl; Sdlty; PpCl; LetterBsktbl; IMSpt; Univ; Law.

DAVY, Melvin A; Caledonia HS; Hokah, MN; Chr; Chrs; ChrhWkr; HonRl; Mdrgl; FFA; Wrstlng; Ag.

DAWES, Lisa A; Hume R 8 HS; Foster, MO; TrsSophCls; Band; Chr; Chrs; CncrtBnd; HonRl; LbryAde; MrchBnd; Orch; Orch; University; Veterinary.

DAWES, Suzanne G; Carman HS; Flint, MI; Chr; CmntyWkr; HonRl; RedCrAde; SctActv; StuCncl; StuGov; TchrAde; YthFlsp; Central Michigan Univ; Social Work.

DAWKINS, Amelia J; St Michael C HS; Chicago, IL; 15/37 VPFrshCls; SecSophCls; SecTrsJrCls; PresSrCls; Chr; ChrhWkr; HonRl; StuCncl; TchrAde; So Illinois Univ; Professional.

DAWLEY, Denise L; Southeast Polk HS; Runnells, IA; LetterChrs; ChrhWkr; StuGov; YthFlsp; 4-H; FFA; PpCl; LetterSwmmng; LetterChrldr; PPFtbl; 4-HAwd; College; Animal Science.

DAWLEY, Judith G; Lake Of The Woods HS; Baudette, MN; Band; Chrs; HonRl; NHS; TchrAde; Hospital Employment; College For Prac Nurse.

DAWSON, Cheryl A; St Charles HS; St Charles, MO; ChrhWkr; CmntyWkr; HonRl; RedCrAde; SctActv; SpnCl; PpCl; Ne Mo St Univ.

DAWSON, Elizabeth; Cardinal Ritter HS; Indianapolis, IN; 37/154 CmntyWkr; HonRl; HospAde; JA; NHS; SchMus; SchPl; SctActv; EdYrBk; SpnCl; Indiana University; Social Work.

DAWSON, Jean M; Bellaire Public HS; Bellaire, MI; VPSrCls; HonRl; NHS; TchrAde; EdYrBk; Northwestern Beauty Academy; Cosmetologist.

DAWSON, Jody A; Concord HS; Hanover, MI; 6/71 SecSophCls; PresJrCls; HonRl; NHS; OffAde; StuCncl; StuGov; RptrSchPpr; 4-H; 4-HAwd; Marriage; Work.

DAWSON, Kandace E R; Pardeeville HS; Cambria, WI; Chr; HonRl; NatlFornLg; YthFlsp; 4-H; PpCl; Trk; Chrldr; GAA; College; Nursing.

DAWSON, Kathryn; Rolla HS; Rolla, MO; 8/300 VPFrshCls; ChrhWkr; HonRl; PresAwd; Hawaii College;free Lance Writer.

DAWSON, Kelly O; Roosevelt HS; Almont, ND; ALBoysSt; HonRl; 4-H; FFA; Bsktbl; Bismarck Jr College; Farming.

DAWSON, Marcia L; Rantoul Twp HS; Rantoul, IL; ChrhWkr; CncrtBnd; MrchBnd; Orch; SchMus; 4-H; SpnCl; DanFAwd; Univ Of Illinois; Music.

DAWSON, Michael A; Catholic Memorial HS; Waukesha, WI; HonRl; JrNHS; StuCncl; Yrbk; SchPpr; Bsbl; Ftbl; Glf; U Of Wi; Biology.

DAWSON, Michael L; C B C HS; St Louis, MO; DrlTm; MrchBnd; NatlMeritSF; StuGov; Trk; Wrstlng; IMSpt; Drake U; Attorney.

DAWSON, Thomas C; St Louis Pk Sr HS; St Louis Park, MN; ChrhWkr; PolWkr; SchPl; CchngActv; College; Law.

DAY, Cynthia J; Lincoln HS; Lincoln, KS; ALAGirlsSt; Chr; CmntyWkr; CaptDrlTm; PolWkr; TchrAde; Yrbk; Pres4-H; FHA; GerCl; PpCl; Trk; 4-HAwd; Kansas State Univ; Political Science.

DAY, Dan; Grosse Pointe South HS; Grosse Pointe Park, MI; Chr; Chrs; NatlThespSoc; SchMus; SchPl; RptrSchPpr; Ftbl; Trk; Wayne State U.

DAY, Dennis A; Keokuk Sr HS; Keokuk, IA; Bsbl; Ftbl; Trk; Trade School; Professional.

DAY, Diane E; Brown HS; Sturgis, SD; 5/217 ALAGirlsSt; Band; Chrs; ChrhWkr; CncrtBnd; HonRl; HospAde; MrchBnd; NatlFornLg; NHS; NatlMeritSF; NatlThespSoc; PepBnd; PolWkr; College.

DAY, Doran; Loup City HS; Loup City, NE; Band; Chrs; CncrtBnd; HonRl; MrchBnd; PepBnd; SchAde; StuCncl; TchrAde; Chrldr; College; English Teacher.

DAY, Jennifer; Washington Community Hs; Washington, IL; 41/345 AFS; DrlTm; HonRl; MrchBnd; SchPl; StuCncl; RptrSchPpr; FrCl; Trk; Iowa State; Speech.

DAY, John C; Rantoul Township HS; Rantoul, IL; Band; CncrtBnd; MrchBnd; PepBnd; Mathematics.

DAY, Joy E; Onalaska HS; Onalaska, WI; 14/1506 Band; Chr; ChrhWkr; CncrtBnd; HonRl; Mdrgl; MrchBnd; NHS; PepBnd; YthFlsp; Chrldr; Coll; Music Teacher.

DAY, Julia L; Marshall HS; Marshall, MI; Band; HonRl; HospAde; OffAde; TchrAde; SpnCl; Western Michigan Univ; Teaching.

DAY, Julie A; Prairie Du Chien Sr HS; Prairie Du Chien, WI; 6/133 PresSophCls; PresJrCls; Chrs; NHS; StuCncl; EdSchPpr; SpnCl; GAA; KiwanAwd; OptClAwd; University; Broadcasting.

DAY, Kathy L; Kewanee HS; Kewanee, IL; 45/235 HonRl; OffAde; FHA; GAA; College.

DAY, Kevin A; Bedford North Lawrence HS; Bedford, IN; 40/431 PresFrshCls; PresSophCls; HonRl; NHS; StuCncl; KeyCl; SpnCl; SciCl; LetterBsbl; LetterBsktbl; G M I; Engineer.

DAY, Luann; Clay City HS; Clay City, IN; 1/60 Band; CncrtBnd; HonRl; HospAde; JrNHS; MrchBnd; NHS; FrCl; MthCl; PpCl; College; Surgical Nurse.

DAY, Melissa D; Clay City HS; Clay City, IN; Band; ChrhWkr; CncrtBnd; HonRl; LbryAde; MrchBnd; PepBnd; Yrbk; SchPpr; FBLA;.

DAY, Michael J; Mercy HS; St Louis, MO; 7/200 HonRl; NHS; Bsktbl; IMSpt; VoiceDemAwd; Univ; Professional.

DAY, Stephen G; Waldron Area HS; Waldron, MI; 12/53 ChrhWkr; HonRl; NHS; NatlMeritCmnd; YthFlsp; FFA; PpCl; Bsktbl; CitAwd; Tri State College; Electrical Eng.

DAY, Victoria L; Winamac Comm HS; Winamac, IN; Band; CncrtBnd; MrchBnd; PepBnd; PolWkr; SchMus; SchPl; 4-H; Glf; VoiceDemAwd; Indiana St Univ; Journalism.

DAY, Wanda B; Beaumont HS; St Louis, MO; 63/803 TrsJrCls; TrsSrCls; ChrhWkr; CmntyWkr; DrlTm; HonRl; College; Doctor.

DAY, Wayne V; Orrick HS; Orrick, MO; Band; Chr; CncrtBnd; HonRl; MrchBnd; NHS; PepBnd; RptrSchPpr; FFA; College; Music.

DAYFON, William R; B G M Comm HS; Malcom, IA; 39/76 AFS; ALBoysSt; Chrs; HonRl; SchMus; SchPl; SptEdYrbk; PpCl; Ftbl; LetterGlf;.

DAYHOFF, Scott A; Calumet HS; Gary, IN; 45/315 Band; HonRl; PresJrNHS; MrchBnd; NHS; StuCncl; LetterBsbl; Bsktbl; LetterFtbl; AmLegAwd; St Joe; Police Officer.

DAYRINGER, Sara L; Carthage HS; Webb City, MO; AFS; HonRl; HospAde; NHS; TchrAde; RptrYrbk; RptrSchPpr; FHA; FTA; FrCl; Clge.

DAYTON, Anne K; Manhattan HS; Manhattan, KS; AFS; ModUN; NatlFornLg; PolWkr; YthFnd; 4-H; FrCl; PpCl; Univ Of Ks; Law.

DAYVAULT, Mark S; Wichita Southeast HS; Wichita, KS; HonRl; LitMag; SctActv; MthCl; SciCl; Ftbl; Trk; Wrstlng; CchngActv; IMSpt; Kansas State Univ; Architecture.

DE ADAM, Suann M; St Benedict HS; Chicago, IL; Chrs; HonRl; LbryAde; SchPl; PpCl; GAA; Coll; Major Study.

DEAL, Deborah R; Manual HS; Peoria, IL; 19/339 Chrs; SecFrshCls; HonRl; NHS; OffAde; YthFlsp; PpCl; Coll; Nusing.

DEAL, James E; Brazil HS; Knightsville, IN; 1/200 Univ; Modern Languages.

DEAL, Mark D; Malden HS; Malden, MO; Band; ChrhWkr; CncrtBnd; HonRl; Bsktbl; Ftbl; Trk; College; Accounting.

DEAN, Andrew K; Centerville HS; Centerville, IN; TrsSrCls; HonRl; JrNHS; NHS; SpnCl; SciCl; Bsbl; Bsktbl; Ftbl; Glf; In Univ; Education.

DEAN, Connie; Southeast Sr HS; Kansas City, MO; Band; Chr; ChrhWkr; CncrtBnd; HonRl; MrchBnd; PepBnd; SctActv; SpnCl; CitAwd; Mu Miss Univ; Doctor.

DEAN, Debbie M; Rockridge HS; Taylor Ridge, IL; SecJrCls; Band; ChrhWkr; CncrtBnd; HonRl; MrchBnd; NHS; PepBnd; StuCncl; RptrYrbk; College.

DEAN, Diane; Collinsville HS; Collinsville, IL; HonRl; NHS; OffAde; TchrAde; GAA;.

DEAN, Dorothy L; Libertyville HS; Libertyville, IL; 42/458 PresFBLA; SpnCl; PpCl; Illinois State Univ; History.

DEAN, Glenda J; Central HS; Grenola, KS; 6/34 Band; Chrs; CncrtBnd; HonRl; MrchBnd; PepBnd; SchPl; SchPpr; FFA; PpCl; College; Nurse.

DEAN, Glenda J; Central Of Burden HS; Grenola, KS; 7/34 Band; Chr; Chrs; CncrtBnd; DrmMjrt; HonRl; LbryAde; MrchBnd; PepBnd; PolWkr; SchPl; SchPpr; FFA; FHA; University; Nurse.

DEAN, Jonathan R; Crawfordsville HS; Crawfordsville, IN; 10/230 Chr; JrNHS; NatlFornLg; NHS; NatlMeritSF; PolWkr; SchMus; SchPl; StuCncl; RptrSchPpr; Carleton College; Secondary Education.

DEAN, Joyce C; Gibbon HS; Gibbon, NE; Chrs; HonRl; FBLA; Hastings State; Music.

DEAN, Judith A; Cabrini HS; Allen Park, MI; 1/167 ChrhWkr; HonRl; NHS; StuCncl; Teen; RptrSchPpr; LatCl; CchngActv; Col; Science Field.

DEAN, Julia L; Lawton HS; Schoolcraft, MI; Band; HonRl; NHS; StuCncl; TchrAde; RptrYrbk; RptrSchPpr; VP4-H; MthCl; 4-HAwd; College; Education.

DEAN, Lita M; Lindblom HS; Chicago, IL; 28/722 HonRl; MthCl; Roosevelt Univ; Business Admin.

DEAN, Marianne; Marillac HS; Glenview, IL; HonRl; NatlMeritCmnd; GerCl; Coll; Nurse.

DEAN, Monica R; Mt Pleasant Comm HS; Mt Pleasant, IA; 8/170 Band; CmntyWkr; CncrtBnd; HonRl; MrchBnd; NHS; PepBnd; StuCncl; Chrldr; University; Medicine.

DEAN, Patricia A; Kenowa Hills HS; Marne, MI; ChrhWkr; HonRl; College; Secretary.

DEAN, Paul; Central HS; Lacrosse, WI; Band; ChrhWkr; CncrtBnd; HonRl; JrNHS; MrchBnd; PepBnd; Quill&Scroll; SchMus; TchrAde; Univ Wisconsin Lacrosse; Commercial Artist.

DEAN, Robin E; Thornapple Kellogg HS; Middleville, MI; 3/129 Band; Chrs; HonRl; NHS; NatlMeritCmnd; SchMus; SchPl; StuCncl; Wrstlng; Chrldr; Mich State U; Linguist.

DEAN, Vanessa R; Pine River Area HS; Leroy, MI; Band; Chr; ChrhWkr; CncrtBnd; HonRl; MrchBnd; OffAde; PepBnd; SchPl; Teen; Marion Clge; Nursing.

DEAN, William J; Pekin HS; Pekin, IL; 95/759 Band; CncrtBnd; 4-H; Univ Of Illinois; Elec Engineering.

DE ANGELIS, Michael L; Glenbard East HS; Lombard, IL; 32/656 HonRl; NHS; Univ Of Illinois; Interpreter.

DEANY, Michelle M; Lexington HS; Lexington, IL; 7/61 SecJrCls; AFS; HonRl; TchrAde; RptrYrbk; FHA; FTA; PpCl; Ill State Univ.

DEARBORN, John D; Davis Co Comm HS; Bloomfield, IA; 11/134 Aud/Vis; Band; CncrtBnd; MrchBnd; NHS; NatlThespSoc; RptrYrbk; Treas4-H; TreasFFA; LetterTrk; Iowa St Univ; Engineer.

DEARDEUFF, Stephen; Riverview Gardens Senior HS; Ferguson, MO; Aud/Vis; HonRl; NHS; NatlMeritCmnd; NatlThespSoc; SchMus; SchPl; Yrbk; SchPpr; Univer Of Mo; Computer Ele.

DEARING, John J; E Alton Wood River HS; Wood River, IL; HonRl; JA; GerCl; Tennis; College; Professional.

DEARMONT, David D; Burwell Jr Sr HS; Burwell, NE; ALBoysSt; HonRl; NHS; FFA; LetterBsktbl; LetterFtbl; College; Vocational.

DEARNBARGER, Dennis L; Arthur HS; Sullivan, IL; HstJrCls; LetterBand; HonRl; PepBnd; College; Law.

DEARTH, Susan; Mattawan HS; Mattawan, MI; 19/105 Band; CncrtBnd; MrchBnd; NHS; NatlMeritCmnd; NatlMeritSchl; StuCncl; StuGov; TchrAde;.

DEASON, Kimberle J; Chisago Lakes Sr HS; Chisago City, MN; ALAGirlsSt; Band; HonRl; MrchBnd; SchPl; StuCncl; RptrYrbk; Chrldr; College; Elementary Education.

DEASON, Robert; Mexico Senior HS; Mexico, MO; 16/248 ALBoysSt; Band; HonRl; MrchBnd; NatlFornLg; Orch; SchMus; SchPl; StuCncl; SchPpr; Ne Mo Univ; Mass Communication.

DEASY, James A; Bishop Noll Institute HS; Hammond, IN; 17/342 HonRl; NHS; SctActv; MthCl; Swmmng; IMSpt; Indiana Univ; Optometry.

DEATON, Charles L; Vienna Twp HS; Vienna, IL; ChrhWkr; CtyCnl; VPStuCncl; StuGov; TchrAde; VPFFA; FTA; PpCl; LetterBsbl; College; Agronomy.

DEATON, Dundri L; Bedford North Lawrence HS; Bedford, IN; 77/428 ChrhWkr; HonRl; NatlFornLg; PolWkr; YthFlsp; GerCl; Glf; CchngActv; GAA; IMSpt; Coll; Med.

DEATRICK, Shelley M; Andrews HS; Harbor Beach, MI; 2/50 Chrs; HonRl; NHS; StuCncl; RptrYrbk; EdYrBk; SchPpr; Nursing Sch; Rn.

DEATSCH, Theresa; Clear Creek Comm HS; Oxford, IA; Chr; ChrhWkr; HonRl; MrchBnd; NatlThespSoc; SchMus; SchPl; Bsktbl; Trk; College.

DEAVER, Terry V; Wheatland HS; Wheatland, NE; SecSrCls; TrsSrCls; Chrs; SchPl; TchrAde; RptrYrbk; Trk; College; Professional.

DE BACKER, Lois R; Wylie E Groves HS; Birmingham, MI; 19/681 Chr; ChrhWkr; CmntyWkr; JrNHS; LbryAde; NHS; NatlMeritSF; PolWkr; TreasYthFlsp; FrCl; Univ Of Michigan; Business.

DE BACKER, Marianne; Regina HS; Detroit, MI; HonRl; LbryAde; NHS; VPFHA; U Of Detroit; Business.

DEBANO, Dee A; South Barber HS; Hazelton, KS; 3/45 ALAGirlsSt; Band; Chr; HonRl; SchPl; Teen; PpCl; LetterBsktbl; LetterTrk; Chrldr; Kansas Univ; Optometrist.

DE BAUN, Donna M; South Iron HS; Annapolis, MO; 4/35 Chrs; ChrhWkr; FHA; PpCl; CaptChrldr;.

DEBBAN, Harold P; Kearney HS; Kearney, NE; 6/289 ChrhWkr; HonRl; ModUN; NatlMeritSF; SciCl; LetterTrk; College; Engineering.

DEBBS, Keryl; Platte HS; Platte, SD; 9/47 Band; Chrs; CncrtBnd; DrlTm; Mdrgl; NatlFornLg; SchPl; RptrYrbk; EdSchPpr; GerCl; Univ Of S Dak; Art Major.

DE BEL, Marcia A; Marian HS; Mishawaka, IN; 11/117 HonRl; LbryAde; SecNHS; StuCncl; EdYrBk; IMSpt; College; Business.

DE BENEDETTO, Mike A; St Pius V HS; Kansas City, MO; 10/129 HonRl; RptrSchPpr; PpCl; Ftbl; LetterGlf; Trk; LetterWrstlng; College; Professnl.

DEBERGE, Mary A; St Joseph HS; Kenosha, WI; Chr; HonRl; SchPl; Swmmng; Trk; GAA; IMSpt; Coll; Psychology.

DEBERTIN, Mollie A; Magic City Campus HS; Minot, ND; HonRl; JrNHS; SpnCl; College; Veterinarian.

DEBLASIO, Dominic F; St Rita HS; Chicago, IL; HonRl; SciCl; IMSpt; JAAwd; CitAwd; College; Professional.

DE BOE, Lavonne; Cedar Springs HS; Rockford, MI; HonRl; GAA; IMSpt; PPFtbl; College; Nursing Or Lab Tech.

DE BOER, Denise L; Ogilvie HS; Ogilvie, MN; Band; CncrtBnd; HonRl; NHS; SchMus; StuCncl; RptrYrbk; Yrbk; EngCl; LetterChrldr; St Cloud Beauty College; Cosmetologist.

DE BOER, Donald W; Unity Christian HS; Orange City, IA; ALBoysSt; Band; CncrtBnd; NHS; Orch; PepBnd; RptrYrbk; RptrSchPpr; College; Professional.

DEBOER, Karen; Kennedy HS; Cedar Rapids, IA; 58/446 Chr; ChrhWkr; CmntyWkr; HonRl; StuGov; YthFlsp; PpCl; Chrldr; Northwestern College; Education.

DE BOER, Mary Ann; John Glenn HS; Westland, MI; 29/700 CtyCnl; HonRl; LbryAde; NHS; SchMus; SchPl; RptrYrbk; RptrSchPpr; JCAwd; LionAwd; U Of Mi At Ann Arbor; Pks And Rec Res Mang.

DE BOER, Ruth A; St Johns HS; St Johns, MI; Band; CncrtBnd; HonRl; MrchBnd; 4-H; 4-HAwd; PresAwd; Lansing Comm Clg; Animal Tech.

DEBONDT, Dennis J; Mexico HS; Mexico, MO; ALBoysSt; Chr; Chrs; JA; SchPl; Bsktbl; Ftbl; Tennis; JAAwd; Univ Or College; Proessional.

DE BORD, Debra A; Galena HS; Galena, IL; 2/107 AFS; Chrs; ChrhWkr; HonRl; HospAde; SchMus; RptrSchPpr; SchPpr; PresFrCl; EldAwd; Illinois State University; Journalism.

DE BORD, Debra A; Greenway HS; Pengilly, MN; Band; Chrl; ChrhWkr; CncrtBnd; MrchBnd; OffAde; TchrAde; Trk; Northern Central Bible Coll.

DE BROUX, James M; Hastings HS; Hastings, MI; Band; HonRl; MrchBnd; NatlThespSoc; SchPl; Bsktbl; Adrian Coll; Dentistry.

DE BRUIN, Darlene S; Lee HS; Wyoming, MI; 1/93 Chr; HonRl; NHS; SchMus; SecStuCncl; SpnCl; PpCl; CaptChrldr; TreasGAA; IMSpt; PPFtbl; AmLegAwd; Grand Rapids Jr College; Medicine.

DE BRULER, Philip W; George Washington HS; Indianapolis, IN; 13/439 VPJrCls; ALBoysSt; HonRl; SecNatlFornLg; NHS; PresNatlThespSoc; SchMus; SchPl; StuCncl; SecGerCl; SciCl; LetterBsbl; OptClAwd; Indiana Univ; Pathology.

DEBS, Michael E; Lake Shore HS; St Clair Shores, MI; PresSrCls; CAP; HonRl; NatlMeritSchl; Bsbl; LetterFtbl; Chrldr; BttyCrckrAwd; CitAwd; Macomb Col; Pimp.

DEBUS, Janet S; Homewood Flossmoor HS; Chicago Heights, IL; Lutheran Gen Deac Hosp; Nursing.

DEBUSK, Lana C; Sullivan HS; Sullivan, IN; 1/150 CncrtBnd; HonRl; VPJrNHS; MrchBnd; NHS; PepBnd; SchMus; SchPl; 4-H; FHA; LatCl; MthCl; PpCl; Purdue Univ; Home Economics.

DE CAPP, Theresa M; United Twp HS; Silvis, IL; 9/700 Chr; ChrhWkr; HonRl; NHS; SchPl; Augustana College; Math.

DECH, Bert L; North Greene HS; Roodhouse, IL; PresSophCls; PresJrCls; Band; Chrs; StuCncl; EdYrBk; SciCl; CaptFtbl; AmLegAwd; SARAwd; Nw Univ; Med Research.

DECIO, Jay A; Woodlands Acad; Elkhart, IN; ChrhWkr; CmntyWkr; SchPl; StuGov; PpCl; Bsktbl; CchngActv; GAA; CaptIMSpt; Univ.

DECK, Randall E; Lyons Twp HS; Lagrange Pk, IL; CmntyWkr; HonRl; PolWkr; Michigan St Univ; Medicine.

DECKARD, Belinda L; Mitchell HS; Bedford, IN; 25/139 Chrs; ChrhWkr; HonRl; NatlThespSoc; OffAde; SchMus; SchPl; TchrAde; 4-H; University; Teaching.

DECKER, Carol L; E Noble HS; Avilla, IN; 4/274 HonRl; NHS; TchrAde; SpnCl; Tri State College; Chemical Engineer.

DECKER, Cyndee G; Oak Park Acad; Sioux City, IA; Chr; ChrhWkr; CmntyWkr; HonRl; HospAde; SchMus; TchrAde; YthFlsp; RptrYrbk; RptrSchPpr; College; Nursng.

DECKER, David; Marseilles Hs; Marseilles, IL; ALBoysSt; Chrs; CmntyWkr; HonRl; NHS; StuCncl; YthFlsp; LetterBsktbl; LetterFtbl; LetterGlf; Illinois Wesleyan ; Medicine.

DECKER, Debbie A; Franklin HS; Franklin, NE; 3/54 TrsJrCls; Chr; HonRl; LbryAde; SchMus; 4-H; PpCl; Business.

DECKER, Dennis A; Field Kindley HS; Coffeyville, KS; 66/244 Band; College; Computer Science.

DECKER, Diane L; Liberty Comm Unit 2 HS; Clayton, IL; 12/62 SecSophCls; Band; Chrs; HonRl; Yrbk; FHA; PpCl; Chrldr; Trade School.

DECKER, Gerald V; Aquin HS; Bernard, IA; TrsFrshCls; SecTrsSophCls; PresSrCls; ChrhWkr; HonRl; NHS; SchPl; RptrYrbk; Bsktbl; Trk; College; Professional.

DECKER, Jamie L; Edinburg HS; Edinburg, IN; 15/80 PresSophCls; Chr; HonRl; LitMag; NHS; OffAde; StuCncl; RptrYrbk; Yrbk; RptrSchPpr; FrCl; Ball State Univ; Elementary School Teacher.

DECKER, Jolene K; Watertown Sr HS; Watertown, SD; 18/326 Chr; Chrs; HonRl; NatlFornLg; NatlThespSoc; RptrSchPpr; SchPpr; College; Professional.

DECKER, Karen; Adair County HS; Kirksville, MO; ChrhWkr; HonRl; SchPl; Bsbl; GAA; University; Professional.

DECKER, Mary G; Southwest HS; St Louis, MO; 28/525 Chr; Chrs; HonRl; Mdrgl; OffAde; SchMus; YthFlsp; Umsl; Accounting.

DECKER, Nancy; Aquin HS; Cascade, IA; 10/67 Chrs; HonRl; SchPl; College; Area Of Art.

DECKER, Patricia; Fennville HS; Fennville, MI; VPSophCls; VPJrCls; StuCncl; StuGov; FHA; BttyCrckrAwd; Kalamazoo Valley Coll; Rn.

DECKER, Sandra L; Lake Orion HS; Lake Orion, MI; 13/350 HonRl; NHS; NatlMeritSF; StuGov; CivCl; Michigan State University; Retailing.

DECKER, Shelley K; Osage Community HS; Osage, IA; SecSophCls; TrsSrCls; ALAGirlsSt; Chrs; DrmBgl; Mdrgl; NHS; SchPl; EdYrBk; PpCl; Univ Of Northern Ia.

DECKER, Steven A; Lakewood HS; Lake Odessa, MI; Chrs; HonRl; Bsbl; Glf; IMSpt; College; Businessman.

DECKER, Tamara K; Springfield Southeast HS; Springfield, IL; RptrYrbk; RptrSchPpr; FBLA; PpCl; 4-HAwd; College; Proffessional.

DECKERT, Desiree K; Wing Public HS; Arena, ND; SecTrsFrshCls; PresJrCls; Band; Chrs; ChrhWkr; HonRl; PepBnd; SchMus; StuCncl; RptrSchPpr; 4-H; PpCl; LetterBsktbl; Trk; College; Nursing.

DECKERT, Randal J; Wing Public HS; Wing, ND; 6/13 PresSophCls; SecJrCls; TrsJrCls; ALBoysSt; Band; Chr; HonRl; StuCncl; SptEdSchPpr; SchPpr; College; Teach & Coach Athletics.

DECKERT, Richard W; Otis Bison Sr HS; Bison, KS; SecJrCls; ALBoysSt; PresBand; Chrs; CncrtBnd; HonRl; ModUN; NHS; PresStuCncl; Ft Hays Kansas State Clg; Agriculture.

DE CLUE, John A; Jefferson City Sr HS; Jefferson City, MO; 52/484 ALBoysSt; CmntyWkr; NHS; NatlMeritCmnd; NatlThespSoc; Quill&Scroll; PresStuCncl; Yrbk; EdSchPpr; Arizona State University; Medicine.

DE COCK, Janice M; Minneota Public HS; Minneota, MN; Band; Chrs; CncrtBnd; HonRl; MrchBnd; StuCncl; RptrYrbk; 4-H; PpCl; ChmnChrldr; College.

DE COOK, Barbara J; Guttenberg Community HS; Guttenberg, IA; 1/74 Band; Chr; Chrs; ChrhWkr; CncrtBnd; HonRl; MrchBnd; SchMus; RptrYrbk; FHA; MthCl; Bsktbl; LetterTrk; Univ Of Iowa; Medical Technology.

DE COOK, Barbara J; Guttenberg HS; Guttenberg, IA; 1/72 Band; Chrs; ChrhWkr; NHS; RptrYrbk; FHA; MthCl; SciCl; Bsktbl; GAA; U Of Iowa; Medical Technology.

DE COOK, Cheryl L; Gull Lake HS; Richland, MI; ALAGirlsSt; Chr; HonRl; HospAde; JA; NHS; PolWkr; SchPl; StuCncl; YthFlsp; SpnCl; Chrldr; IMSpt; Western Michigan Univ; Accountant.

DE CORA, Deborah S; Bridgeport HS; Bridgeport, NE; 3/62 PresFrshCls; Band; NHS; SchPl; StuCncl; YthFlsp; RptrYrbk; PpCl; Glf; Trk; GAA; IMSpt; Hastings College.

DE CORA, Kirk L; New Lisbon HS; New Lisbon, WI; 2/63 Band; CncrtBnd; HonRl; NHS; PepBnd; LetterTrk; Univ Of Madison; Medicine.

DE CORI, Nancy; Beloit Memorial HS; Beloit, WI; ALAGirlsSt; HonRl; NHS; StuCncl; SchPpr; Tennis; Chrldr; GAA; AmLegAwd; PresAwd; Madison Tech; Prof.

DE CORTE, Mark L; Bay City Central HS; Bay City, MI; HonRl; PolWkr; U Of Mi; Lawyer.

DE COURCY, James F; Granite City HS South; Granite City, IL; Band; CncrtBnd; MrchBnd; St Louis College; Pharmacist.

DEDERICH, Curt; Monona Grove HS; Monona, WI; StuCncl; StuGov; College; Communications.

DEDERT, Mark; Quincy Senior Hs; Quincy, IL; 63/816 Band; CncrtBnd; HonRl; MrchBnd; Orch; PepBnd; SchMus; 4-H; Ftbl; Trk; U Of Illinois; Music.

DEDIC, June A; Marquette Manor Christian HS; Westmont, IL; SecTrsJrCls; VPSrCls; Chr; ChrhWkr; HonRl; SchMus; StuCncl; SecSchPpr; IMSpt; AmLegAwd; College; Elem Education.

DEDINAS, Vida R; Maria HS; Chicago, IL; PresJA; TreasNHS; Orch; GerCl; Univ Of Illinois; Finance.

DEDMAN, Stanley A; Plattsburg HS; Plattsburg, MO; 19/52 Band; CncrtBnd; HonRl; PepBnd; RptrSchPpr; SptEdSchPpr; SchPpr; ChmnBsktbl; LetterFtbl; LetterTrk; Mo W State Clg; Coach.

DEDON, Peter C; Eisenhower HS; Hopkins, MN; 4/429 ALBoysSt; Band; CmntyWkr; CncrtBnd; HonRl; MrchBnd; PepBnd; Bsktbl; Medical Sch; Medicine.

DEE, Barbara; Grinnell Comm Sr HS; Malcom, IA; SecBand; CncrtBnd; HonRl; PresNHS; PepBnd; Quill&Scroll; EdYrBk; SpnCl; IMSpt; BauchLmbAwd; Northern Ia Univ; Math Science.

DEE, David; Cary Grove HS; Cary, IL; 19/250 ALBoysSt; NatlMeritCmnd; Depauw Univ; Medicine.

DEE, Mary A; Lourdes HS; Rochester, MN; Band; CncrtBnd; HonRl; MrchBnd; PepBnd; SchPl; TchrAde; Yrbk; 4-H; 4-HAwd; College; Physical Therapy.

DEEDS, William C; North Miami HS; Macy, IN; 45/122 Chr; HonRl; 4-H; FFA; SpnCl; SciCl; Bsktbl; LetterFtbl; Glf; CaptWrstlng; Trade Schl; Construction Work.

DEEG, Janet S; Mason Sr HS; Mason, MI; 16/233 CncrtBnd; HonRl; JrNHS; MrchBnd; NHS; NatlMeritCmnd; RptrYrbk; 4-H; FHA; PpCl; Lansing Comm College; Accounting.

DEEKE, Von C; Mascoutah HS; Mascoutah, IL; 6/250 Aud/Vis; Band; CncrtBnd; HonRl; ModUN; NHS; NatlMeritCmnd; PolWkr; PresSctActv; SecStuCncl; IMSpt; Univ Of Illinois; Elec Engineering.

DEEKER, Jim M; Schulte HS; Terre Haute, IN; HonRl; JA; KeyCl; MthCl; Bsktbl; Ftbl; LetterGlf; IMSpt; Clg; Bus Mangemt.

DEEM, Patricia A; Marquette HS; Alton, IL; 25/116 SecSophCls; SecJrCls; SecTrsSrCls; AFS; HonRl; NHS; StuCncl; LatCl; Bsktbl; Southern Ill Univ; Music.

DEEM, Wendy A; Sterling HS; Sterling, IL; Chr; Chrs; HonRl; HospAde; JA; GerCl; Sauk Valley Col; Med Lab Tech.

DEEMAN, Karen J; Queen Of Peace HS; Chicago, IL; 27/435 HonRl; JrNHS; NatlMeritCmnd; FrCl; Chrldr; PPFtbl; No Illinois Univ; Accounting.

DEEMER, Suzette L; Platte Valley Academy; Papillion, NE; ChrhWkr; HonRl; NHS; TchrAde; SchPpr; IMSpt; Coll; Elem Ed.

DEER, Kimberley A; John Marshall HS; Indianapolis, IN; RptrYrbk; Yrbk; FrCl; PpCl; Teacher Of Small Children.

DEERING, Cheryl L; Mt Zion HS; Mt Zion, IL; 1/198 SecSophCls; SecJrCls; SecSrCls; HonRl; NHS; NatlMeritSF; SecStuCncl; EdYrBk; 4-H; GodCntryAwd; Univ; Social Work.

DEERING, Kathy; Mother Of Sorrows HS; Chicago, IL; TrsSrCls; HonRl; StuCncl; TchrAde; PpCl; Bsktbl; GAA; Maccormac Jr Col; Court Reporter.

DEES, Kay; Maroa Forsyth HS; Decatur, IL; 4/69 Band; Chrs; HospAde; NHS; SchPl; YthFlsp; Yrbk; RptrSchPpr; VPFHA;.

DEES, Mary E; Mattoon HS; Mattoon, IL; AFS; Chr; HonRl; HospAde; Mdrgl; NatlMeritCmnd; SctActv; YthFlsp; SpnCl; GodCntryAwd; Wesleyian Univ; Spanish & Religion.

DEES, Sherry A; Plainfield HS; Plainfield, IN; HonRl; StuCncl; FHA; PpCl; Swmmng; Trk; Chrldr; GAA; 4-HAwd; CitAwd; College; Major Study.

DEES, Susan E; Springfield HS; Springfield, IL; 34/539 AFS; NHS; SchMus; PresYthFlsp; FrCl; MthCl; Iowa State Univ; Zoology.

DEETER, Teresa A; Oblong HS; Oblong, IL; Band; HonRl; StuCncl; RptrYrbk; RptrSchPpr; FTA; LatCl; PpCl; SciCl; St Louis College; Pharmacy.

DEETS, Kevin L; Polo Community HS; Polo, IL; 1/99 ALBoysSt; Band; CncrtBnd; HonRl; NHS; PepBnd; VPStuCncl; YthFlsp; FrCl; College Or Univ; Biologist.

DEFFENBAUGH, Paula J; Pius X HS; Lincoln, NE; ChrhWkr; CmntyWkr; HonRl; RptrYrbk; RptrSchPpr; 4-H; FrCl; PresAwd; College; Medicine.

DE FOE, Michael J; Pembina Public HS; Pembina, ND; 2/22 PresSrCls; ALBoysSt; PresBand; ChrhWkr; HonRl; VPStuCncl; YthFlsp; Pres4-H; CaptFtbl; LetterTrk; CchngActv; AmLegAwd; College; Music.

DE FOREST, Deborah M; Battle Creek Academy; Battle Creek, MI; TrsJrCls; Chr; Chrs; StuCncl; Andrews Univ; Special Educ.

DE FOREST, Kathleen D; Galien HS; Galien, MI; CncrtBnd; HonRl; SchPl; StuCncl; TchrAde; Twrl; Yrbk; 4-H; Bsbl; Chrldr; Collge; Art.

DE FOSSEZ, Mark E; Glenbrook North HS; Northbrook, IL; CmntyWkr; HonRl; NatlFornLg; NHS; PolWkr; StuCncl; EdSchPpr; KeyCl; LatCl; Trk; Northwestern University.

DE FOUW, Julie A; Creston HS; Grand Rapids, MI; 1/454 Chr; ChrhWkr; JrNHS; NHS; SchMus; SchPl; SpnCl; PpCl; AmLegAwd; KiwanAwd; Univ Of Mi; Bsn.

DE FRANCO, Nancy J; Henry Sibley HS; W St Paul, MN; ChrhWkr; HonRl; NatlFornLg; NatlMeritSF; SchMus; SpnCl; Univ;journalism.

DE FRANK, Deborah J; Crete Monee HS; Crete, IL; 21/326 Chr; HonRl; VPNHS; Robert Morris Sch; Dental Asst.

DE GAFTANO, Stephen; Warsaw Community HS; Warsaw, IN; 31/370 ALBoysSt; HonRl; JrNHS; StuCncl; YthFlsp; SptEdYrbk; PpCl; Swmmng; College; Pro Football.

DEGAN, Nancy; Andrean HS; Merrillville, IN; 14/250 HonRl; NHS; SchMus; SchPl; FrCl; GAA; College;.

DE GAYNER, Tarianne; Fenton HS; Linden, MI; 79/307 SecSrCls; NHS; OffAde; TchrAde; EdYrBk; SptEdYrbk; FTA; PPFtbl; DARAwd; N Michigan Univ; Teacher.

DE GEAL, Rebecca C; Greenfield HS; Rockbridge, IL; 5/55 Chr; ChrhWkr; HonRl; OffAde; TreasStuCncl; Yrbk; SchPpr; FHA; Passavant School; Nursin.

DEGEBERG, Kim R; Edina East HS; Edina, MN; Chr; HonRl; HospAde; Quill&Scroll; SptEdYrbk; Gustavus Adolphus College; Biology.

DEGENHARDT, Cathryn; Du Quoin HS; Duquoin, IL; TrsSophCls; Chrs; DrlTm; HonRl; LatCl; Junior College; Biology.

DEGER, Druann; Niles West HS; Niles, IL; 10/655 HonRl; NatlMeritCmnd; College; Home Ec.

DEGIDIO, Loreen; Luther South HS; Oak Lawn, IL; 7/241 SecJrCls; Chr; ChrhWkr; CmntyWkr; HonRl; NHS; 4-H; Bsktbl; GAA; IMSpt; Business College.

DEGLER, Aleen M; Chaska HS; Excelsior, MN; 21/216 ALAGirlsSt; Chr; ChrhWkr; HonRl; NHS; PolWkr; SchPl; FFA; Bsktbl; HstSrCls; Concordia St; Teach Elem Educ.

DEGNER, David K; Wonewoc Center HS; Wonewoc, WI; 4/36 ALBoysSt; ChrhWkr; CncrtBnd; HonRl; MrchBnd; PepBnd; SchPl; LetterBsbl; LetterBsktbl; LetterFtbl; College; Major Study.

DEGNITZ, Thomas R; Kewaskum Community HS; Kewaskum, WI; 2/172 AFS; ChrhWkr; HonRl; NHS; VPYthFlsp; 4-H; GerCl; LetterWrstlng; 4-HAwd; KiwanAwd; Lakeland College; Theology.

DE GOEY, Gary W; North Mohaska HS; New Sharon, IA; 32/62 SchPl; YthFlsp; SchPpr; FFA; LetterBsbl; LetterBsktbl; LetterTrk;.

DE GOLIER, Robert; Turtle Lake HS; Turtle Lake, WI; 29#33#37 HonRl; MrchBnd; PepBnd; YthFlsp; Bsbl; College.

DEGONIA, Pamela A; Arcadia Valley HS; Arcadia, MO; VPJrCls; SecSrCls; Band; HonRl; TreasNHS; SecStuCncl; EdYrBk; PpCl; LetterGlf; DARAwd; Univ Of Missouri.

DE GOOD, Donna S; Corunna HS; Corunna, MI; 22/240 Band; CncrtBnd; HonRl; JA; LbryAde; MrchBnd; Orch; PepBnd; SctActv; TreasTeen; YthFlsp; 4-H; 4-HAwd; University; Elementary Education.

DE GOOD, Nancy J; Peoria HS; Peoria, IL; 66/481 SecSophCls; ChrhWkr; OffAde; Quill&Scroll; SctActv; SecStuCncl; YthFlsp; EdSchPpr; SpnCl; PpCl; Iowa St Univ; Home Economics.

DE GRACE, Margaret M; Divine Savior Holy Angels HS; Wauwatosa, WI; 20/100 SecSrCls; CmntyWkr; HonRl; LitMag; NHS; TchrAde; RptrYrbk; Yrbk; Marquette Univ; English.

DEGRAEVE, Bill J; Raytown HS; Kansas City, MO; 68/650 SctActv; College; Engineering.

DE GRAEVE, Victoria J; Lakeview HS; St Clair Shores, MI; 6/670 HonRl; NHS; StuCncl; SchPpr; LetterSwmmng; CitAwd; Wayne St Univ; Engr.

DE GRAFF, Debora L; Southeast Polk HS; Runnells, IA; ChrhWkr; HonRl; NHS; Bsktbl; PPFtbl; Bible College.

DEGRASSE, Kathy L; Bishop Dwenger HS; Ft Wayne, IN; Chr; Chrs; HonRl; SchAde; SctActv; SchPpr; FrCl; Bsktbl; LetterTennis; GAA; Trade School; Business.

DE GRAVE, Kim M; Southern Door HS; Brussels, WI; SecJrCls; SecSrCls; Chrs; HonRl; NHS; StuCncl; RptrYrbk; PpCl; Nwti; Ward Clerk.

DE GRAVES, Patsy L; Harper Creek HS; Battle Creek, MI; SecJrCls; ALAGirlsSt; HonRl; JrNHS; SecNHS; StuCncl; Pres4-H; SpnCl; Trk; PPFtbl; 4-HAwd; PresAwd; Michigan State Univ; Home Economics.

DE GRAW, Nancy J; Neosho HS; Neosho, MO; 23/250 HonRl; HospAde; TchrAde; PpCl; Crowder Coll.

DE GROOT, Roger A; Morrison Community HS; Morrison, IL; Band; CncrtBnd; HonRl; MrchBnd; TchrAde; Bsbl; LetterGlf; LetterWrstlng; College; Political Science.

DE GROTE, Darla D; Edgerton Public HS; Edgerton, MN; Band; Chr; HonRl; ModUN; NHS; SctActv; FHA; PpCl; LetterTrk; GAA; Trade Scool; Computer Programer.

DE GUIRE, Ronald M; St Ladislaus HS; Hamtramck, MI; 10/112 TrsJrCls; TrsSrCls; HonRl; StuCncl; Yrbk; FBLA; FrCl; MthCl; OptClAwd; CitAwd; U Of Mi; Accounting.

DEHAAB, Debbie; Kalamazoo Christian HS; Portage, MI; 6/150 CmntyWkr; HonRl; Bsktbl; Tennis; Coll.

DE HAAN, Anita M; Jenison HS; Grandville, MI; FNA; FrCl; CaptGlf; PPFtbl; Grand Valley St Coll; Nursing.

DE HAAN, Dan R; Grand Rapids Christian HS; Grand Rapids, MI; Band; ChrhWkr; CncrtBnd; MrchBnd; PepBnd; Trk; IMSpt; Clge; Bus Accounting.

DE HAAN, Ralph J; Pella Christian HS; Pella, IA; 1/93 VPFrshCls; PresSophCls; CncrtBnd; HonRl; MrchBnd; PepBnd; StuCncl; CaptBsbl; CaptBsktbl; LetterTrk; Calvin College; Business.

DEHART, Thomas D; Cvandon HS; Cvandon, WI; VPSophCls; ALBoysSt; HonRl; PpCl; LetterBsbl; College; Professional.

DE HART, Timothy D; Van Buren Community HS; Keosauqua, IA; Chr; ChrhWkr; HonRl; SchPl; YthFlsp; Yrbk; Ftbl; LetterGlf; LetterTrk; LetterWrstlng; College; Agriculture Engineer.

DE HATE, Denise M; Pinconning HS; Pinconning, MI; 6/253 HonRl; NHS; TchrAde; RptrYrbk; PresFTA; PpCl; PPFtbl; Michigan State; Data Process.

DE HEER, Richard L; New Monroe Comm HS; Monroe, IA; JA; Yrbk; 4-H; FFA; SciCl; LetterBsbl; LetterBsktbl; LetterTrk; DanFAwd; 4-HAwd; JAAwd; College; Agriculture.

DEHN, Susan B; Center Grove HS; Greenwood, IN; 8/224 HonRl; NHS; FrCl; PpCl; LetterBsktbl; LetterTennis; GAA; PPFtbl; Purdue; Civil Engineering.

DEHNE, Helen A; Lakeland Union HS; Woodruff, WI; 44/165 Band; CncrtBnd; HonRl; MrchBnd; PepBnd; TchrAde; Twrl; FBLA; SpnCl; PpCl; Business Schl; Secretary.

DEHNER, Michelle A; Aquinas HS; David City, NE; ALAGirlsSt; Chr; Chrs; NHS; Quill&Scroll; SpnCl; MthCl; PpCl; SciCl; Chrldr; U Of Neb; Biology.

DEHNICKE, Candy; Rearis HS; Burbank, IL; PepBnd; FrCl; IMSpt; PPFtbl; College; Social Worker.

DEHNING, Mark R; Dist 80 HS; Big Springs, NE; TrsFrshCls; Band; CncrtBnd; MrchBnd; PepBnd; SctActv; 4-H; Bsktbl; Ftbl; Trk; Trade School; Rancher.

DE HOEDT, Dale L; No Mahaska HS; Searsboro, IA; 5/62 HonRl; NHS; SpnCl; Ftbl; Wrstlng; Univ Of Iowa; Medicine.

DE HOFF, Jackie R; Pennville HS; Portland, IN; 3/38 Band; ChrhWkr; CncrtBnd; HonRl; JA; MrchBnd; NHS; OffAde; Bsktbl; Trk; Chrldr; GAA; AmLegAwd; International Jr Col; Prof.

DEHRING, Terrence R; Alpena Sr HS; Alpena, MI; HonRl; College; Fisheries.

DEIBERT, Myren A; Ipswich HS; Ipswich, SD; ALBoysSt; Chrs; HonRl; NHS; PolWkr; SchMus; StuCncl; StuGov; Yrbk; Northern State College; Commercial Art.

DEICHERT, Rory L; S Sioux City Comm HS; S Sioux City, NE; Aud/Vis; CncrtBnd; HonRl; JA; JrNHS; MrchBnd; PepBnd; SchMus; SchPl; JAAwd; Univ; Engr.

DEICHERT, William; St Gertrude HS; Raleigh, ND; TrsSophCls; Chr; Chrs; HonRl; SchMus; SchPl; StuCncl; Bsktbl;.

DEIGHTON, David L; Macksville HS; Macksville, KS; ChrhWkr; PresStuCncl; StuGov; LetterBsktbl; College; Math.

DEIGNAN, Michael J; So Sioux City HS; So Sioux City, NE; VPSophCls; VPJrCls; ALBoysSt; HonRl; Bsktbl; Ftbl; Trk; IMSpt; PresAwd; College; Professional.

DEINES, Brian L; Trego Community HS; Wakeeney, KS; ALBoysSt; Band; Chrs; ChrhWkr; CncrtBnd; HonRl; MrchBnd; PepBnd; SchPl; SctActv; StuCncl; Trade School; Vocation.

DEINES, Carol A; Bayard HS; Bayard, NE; 20/43 Band; Chrs; HonRl; OffAde; Yrbk; SchPpr; FHA; SpnCl; LetterTrk; Chrldr; Col; Nursing.

DEINES, Dana C; Cedar Falls HS; Cedar Falls, IA; ALBoysSt; Chr; ChrhWkr; HonRl; PolWkr; SctActv; StuCncl; LetterBsbl; Bsktbl; Ftbl; Trk; Wrstlng; University; Doctor.

DEINES, Denith K; Beemer HS; Beemer, NE; 6/22 TrsJrCls; SecSrCls; ALAGirlsSt; Chrs; ChrhWkr; HonRl; Mdrgl; NHS; SchPl; RptrYrbk; PpCl; Concordia Teachers College; Teaching.

DEINES, Ranita S; Trego Comm HS; Ogallah, KS; 5/78 HonRl; NHS; SchPl; TchrAde; Teen; FHA; PpCl; SciCl; CaptBsktbl; Trk; IMSpt; PPFtbl; DanFAwd;.

DEITCHMAN, Robert P; Chatard HS; Indianapolis, IN; 24/192 ChrhWkr; HonRl; NatlFornLg; NHS; Quill&Scroll; SchPl; StuCncl; EdSchPpr; LetterTrk; OptClAwd; Indiana University; Business.

DEITER, Linda G; Faulkton HS; Faulkton, SD; 2/50 ALAGirlsSt; Band; Chrs; HonRl; PepBnd; StuCncl; EdYrBk; LetterBsktbl; LetterTrk; Chrldr; College.

DEITERING, Evelyn; Boylan Central Catholic Hs; Rockford, IL; CmntyWkr; HonRl; LbryAde; SctActv; TchrAde; FrCl; College; Medicine.

DEITERS, Theresa; Mater Dei HS; Breese, IL; 10/197 Chrs; HonRl; Sacrstn; SchMus; TchrAde; FBLA; LatCl; Business School; Accounting.

DEITZ, Larry J; Crofton Public HS; Crofton, NE; SchAde; SchMus; SchPl; TchrAde; FFA; Bsktbl; LetterFtbl; LetterTrk; Carpenter.

DEJARDIN, Debbie; Southern Door HS; Brussels, WI; Chrs; OffAde; SchAde; TchrAde; FBLA; PpCl; Bsktbl; IMSpt; College; Special Education Teacher.

DE JONG, Brenda K; Platte Public HS; Platte, SD; ALAGirlsSt; Band; Chrs; TreasChrhWkr; CmntyWkr; HonRl; YthFlsp; Sec4-H; PpCl; 4-HAwd; College; Veterinary.

DE JONG, Cyndi; Pella Christian HS; Pella, IA; Chr; CmntyWkr; LbryAde; SchPl; YthFlsp; Yrbk; PpCl; IMSpt; College Or U; Handicapped.

DE JONG, Penny L; Coopersville HS; Grand Rapids, MI; VPSrCls; Band; CncrtBnd; HonRl; MrchBnd; StuCncl; CmntyWkr; TchrAde; FTA; LetterBsktbl; CaptTrk; Grand Valley State Clge; Teach & Coach.

DE JONGE, Penny A; Zeeland HS; Zeeland, MI; ChrhWkr; HonRl; JA; NHS; YthFlsp; 4-H; Ftbl; Tennis; GAA; IMSpt;.

DEKAM, Bonnie; Northern Mich Christian HS; Falmouth, MI; SecSrCls; Chr; HonRl; LbryAde; SchPl; PpCl; IMSpt; 4-HAwd; College; Medical Secretary.

DE KAM, Elizabeth J; Bloomingdale HS; Gobles, MI; 6/91 SecSrCls; HonRl; SchPl; StuGov; RptrYrbk; RptrSchPpr; CivCl;.

DE KAY, Duane; Stanton Community HS; Villisca, IA; 6/35 PresSophCls; SecSrCls; Band; Chr; HonRl; NHS; PepBnd; SchPl; FFA; Bsktbl; Southwestern Community Trade; Carpenter.

DE KEZEL, Susan M; J D Darnell HS; Colona, IL; 19/207 HonRl; NHS; TchrAde; EdYrBk; GAA; College; Professional.

DEKKER, Gail; Sheboygan North HS; Sheboygan, WI; Chr; Chrs; CmntyWkr; HonRl; NatlFornLg; NatlMeritCmnd; RptrYrbk; RptrSchPpr; SpnCl; Northwetern Univ; Medicine.

DE LAET, Dwight D; Lewellen Rural HS; Lewellen, NE; Band; Chr; Chrs; ChrhWkr; CncrtBnd; HonRl; MrchBnd; NHS; PepBnd; YthFlsp; LetterBsktbl; LetterFtbl; LetterTrk; Kearney State College; Minister.

DE LA FONTE, Linda M; St Scholastica HS; Chicago, IL; CmntyWkr; JA; SchMus; SchPpr; GAA; Rosary College; Psychology.

DE LAMA, George; Gordon Tech HS; Chicago, IL; 23/618 NHS; LetterBsbl; LetterBsktbl; Northwestern Univ; Journalism.

DELAMATER, Susan C; Montabella HS; Six Lakes, MI; Band; ChrhWkr; HonRl; MrchBnd; NHS; Yrbk; SpnCl; PpCl; PPFtbl; PresAwd; Msu.

DE LANCEY, Patricia R; Fullerton HS; Fullerton, NE; 14/59 HonRl; LbryAde; TchrAde; Yrbk; FHA; Bsktbl; SecGAA; Univ Of Nebraska; Criminal Justice.

DELANEY, Barbara; Osborne HS; Alton, KS; Chr; Chrs; HonRl; NHS; SchPl; EdYrBk; PpCl; PPFtbl; Colby Comm J C.

DELANEY, Brian K; Mount Carmel HS; Chicago, IL; 39/200 HonRl; LbryAde; NHS; SciCl; Bsbl; Bsktbl; Univ Of Illinois; Liberal Arts.

DELANEY, Dennis P; Wilmington HS; Wilmington, IL; 1/130 VPNHS; SchPl; YthFlsp; RptrSchPpr; EdSchPpr; SpnCl; MthCl; LetterBsbl; LetterBsktbl; LetterFtbl; Augustana College; Chemical Engineering.

DELANEY, Dianne C; Aquinas HS; Ft Madison, IA; 2/46 VPSophCls; CmntyWkr; HonRl; MrchBnd; PresNHS; StuCncl; RptrYrbk; PpCl; ChmnChrldr; Tennis; College; Teaching.

DELANEY, Kathy A; Duchesne HS; St Charles, MO; LetterBand; Chr; Chrs; CncrtBnd; HonRl; MrchBnd; PepBnd; SchMus; SchPl; FrCl; College; Curriculum Of Major Study.

DELANEY, Margaret E; Knox County HS; Baring, MO; ChrhWkr; HonRl; NatlMeritSF; RptrSchPpr; EdSchPpr; FHA; FNA; SciCl; Univ Of Missouri; Nurse.

DELANEY, Nancy I; Regina Dominican HS; Glenview, IL; HonRl; NatlMeritCmnd; University; Business.

DELANEY, Terrence; Glenbrook North Hs; Northbrook, IL; 39/600 LetterBsktbl; Miami U; Business.

DE LANG, Jade W; Burl Comm HS; Burlington, IA; Chr; HonRl; NHS; StuCncl; PresPpCl; LetterSwmmng; Tennis; CchngActv; IMSpt; Iowa State U; Teaching.

DE LANY, Mark P; Jefferson HS; Cedar Rapids, IA; TchrAde; LetterFtbl;.

DELAPLANE, Mary Beth; Mother Mcauley Lib Arts HS; Chicago, IL; 3/474 HonRl; NHS; NatlMeritCmnd; Quill&Scroll; RedCrAde; TchrAde; SchPpr; SecFTA; FrCl; SecMthCl; Univ; Professional.

DE LA ROSA, Raul; E Dubuque HS; E Dubuque, IL; TrsJrCls; Band; HonRl; JA; SctActv; StuCncl; Yrbk; 4-H; Bsktbl; Ftbl; Trk; DanFAwd; 4-HAwd; College; Professional.

DELAY, Deborah J; Mckinley HS; St Louis, MO; Chr; Chrs; ChrhWkr; CmntyWkr; HonRl; SecJA; OffAde; SchMus; StuCncl; Twrl; College; Major Study.

DELAY, Joseph D; Lewis HS; Lewis, KS; 3/24 VPFrshCls; VPSrCls; HonRl; SchPl; StuGov; TchrAde; YthLg; EdSchPpr; CaptBsktbl; LetterFtbl; LetterTrk; PresAwd; Dodge City Comm College; Engineering.

DELCOUR, Jan A; Marshall Sr HS; Ghent, MN; 1/220 Chr; ChrhWkr; HonRl; StuCncl; TchrAde; SchPpr; FFA; FrCl; LatCl; Trk; State University; Philosophy.

DELEEUW, Thomas P; Cosmos HS; Cosmos, MN; 9/35 ALBoysSt; Chr; NHS; SchMus; SchPl; SptEdYrbk; LetterBsbl; LetterBsktbl; LetterFtbl; Trk; Sw Mn Clg; Electronics.

DE LEON, Allison L; Sullivan HS; Sullivan, MO; HonRl; SchMus; SchPl; StuCncl; FFA; GAA; IMSpt; University; Photography.

DELEON, Lorenzo; Lane Tech HS; Chicago, IL; 280/1213 HonRl; OffAde; SchAde; StuCncl; StuGov; TchrAde; RptrSchPpr; Illinois Inst Of Tech; Computer Science.

DELGADO, Victor R; Harper HS; Chicago, IL; 2/274 VPSrCls; Band; CncrtBnd; HonRl; MrchBnd; NHS; OffAde; TchrAde; RptrYrbk; RptrSchPpr; SpnCl; MthCl; College; Professional.

DELGER, Paul T; Kanawha Comm HS; Kanawha, IA; VPJrCls; HonRl; YthFlsp; SptEdYrbk; SptEdSchPpr; Bsbl; Ftbl; Col; Journalism.

DELHEIMER, Scott G; Cornell HS; Cornell, IL; PresFrshCls; Chrs; HonRl; NatlMeritCmnd; SchPl; SptEdYrbk; 4-H; SpnCl; LetterBsbl; LetterBsktbl; Coll; Commerce & Bus Admin.

DELHEY, James P; Saline HS; Saline, MI; ALBoysSt; Band; Chr; Chrl; Chrs; CncrtBnd; HonRl; MrchBnd; Sacrstn; IMSpt; Univ; Archit/law.

DE LISLE, Renee B; Hill Murray HS; St Paul, MN; PresSophCls; VPJrCls; SecTrsSrCls; HonRl; RedCrAde; StuCncl; StuGov; SpnCl; St Catherines College; Nursing.

DELK, David L; Fulton Comm HS; Albany, IL; ALBoysSt; Band; Chr; CncrtBnd; HonRl; MrchBnd; NatlThespSoc; PepBnd; Bsktbl; LetterFtbl; Glf; LetterWrstlng; IMSpt; Luther College; Computer Science.

DELK, Richard A; Fulton HS; Albany, IL; Band; CncrtBnd; HonRl; JA; MrchBnd; PepBnd; Ftbl; Wrstlng; JAAwd; Col; Accountant.

DELL, Daryl W; Union HS; Union, MO; HonRl; Bsbl; Bsktbl; Ftbl; Trk; Wrstlng; GodCntryAwd; University; Professional.

DELL, Michael J; Churubusco HS; Churubusco, IN; SctActv; SpnCl; Bsbl; LetterBsktbl; LetterFtbl; IMSpt;.

DELL, Valerie J; Watervliet HS; Watervliet, MI; HonRl; NHS; PolWkr; StuCncl; StuGov; SpnCl; University; History.

DELL ACCIO, Dennis J; Mt Pleasant HS; Mt Pleasant, MI; 97/352 Band; CncrtBnd; HonRl; MrchBnd; PepBnd; Wrstlng; IMSpt; U Of Hartford; Biology.

DELLER, Steven P; Trenton HS; Trenton, MI; CmntyWkr; HonRl; NHS; StuCncl; StuGov; LetterBsktbl; LetterTrk; KiwanAwd; PresAwd; CitAwd; Cll; Social Worker.

DELLINGER, Jeffrey; North Side HS; Fort Wayne, IN; 1/438 HonRl; NatlMeritCmnd; SciCl; IMSpt; BauchLmbAwd; DanFAwd; In Univ; Mathematics Major.

DELLINGER, Joanmarie I; St Joseph HS; Kenosha, WI; Chr; Chrs; Mdrgl; SchMus; SchPl; College Conservatory Of Music; Vocalist.

DELLORO, Michael; Horace Mann HS; Gilbert, MN; 2/65 Band; Chr; ChrhWkr; PepBnd; SchPl; StuCncl; RptrSchPpr; Bsbl; Mn Univ; Engr.'

DELLORTO, Joseph A; Thornwood HS; S Holland, IL; 1/850 HonRl; PresNHS; MthCl; LetterFtbl; LetterTrk; Massachusetts Inst Of Tech; Chem Engr.

DE LONG, Patty A; Randolph Public HS; Randolph, NE; PresJrCls; PresBand; Chrs; HonRl; MrchBnd; YthFlsp; PpCl; LetterTrk; Chrldr; PresAwd; St Lukes Medical Ctr; Nursing.

DE LONGCHAMP, Mark A; Walled Lake Central HS; Orchard Lake, MI; 29#37#50 SchPpr; Bsbl; Bsktbl; LetterFtbl; Clge; Computers.

DE LORENZO, Carol L; Mother Of Sorrows HS; Chicago, IL; 1/162 TrsFrshCls; Band; ChrhWkr; CmntyWkr; DrmMjrt; HonRl; JrNHS; PolWkr; StuCncl; VPFrCl; CaptChrldr; AmLegAwd; VoiceDemAwd; College; Special Ed.

DE LORENZO, Silvana M; Wauconda HS; Island Lake, IL; 14/265 Band; CncrtBnd; HonRl; JrNHS; MrchBnd; NHS; PepBnd; Chrldr; Univ; Nursing.

DELOSKE, Joann; Louisville HS; Lousiville, NE; 4/41 SecFrshCls; ChrhWkr; HonRl; Yrbk; 4-H; FHA; FrCl; PpCl; 4-HAwd; Col.

DELPERDANG, Paul; St Marys HS; Remsen, IA; 1/60 Band; Chrs; CncrtBnd; HonRl; NHS; SchMus; SchPl; TchrAde; Bsktbl; Glf; Iowa State Or Vermillion Co; Data Process.

DELPH, Bryan C; Taylor HS; Kokomo, IN; AL-

BoysSt; HonRl; NHS; TchrAde; Bsktbl; LetterFtbl; LetterGlf; LetterTrk; Sch Of Mining; Geology.

DEL PONTE, Patrick J; Campbellsport HS; Campbellsport, WI; 5/147 PresSrCls; HonRl; PresNHS; StuCncl; Pres4-H; CaptTrk; CaptWrstlng; EldAwd; 4-HAwd; KiwanAwd; Milwaukee Sch Of Eng; Architectual Eng.

DELSART, Nancy J; Serastopos HS; Sturgeon Bay, WI; HonRl; LatCl; SecSophCls; GAA; IMSpt;.

DEL TORO, Eva M; Morton Senior HS; Hammond, IN; 12/499 ChrhWkr; HonRl; NHS; Quill&Scroll; SctActv; TchrAde; SptEdYrbk; Bsktbl; Trk; University; Professional.

DE LUCA, Jolene M; Big Rapids HS; Stanwood, MI; HonRl; NHS; RptrSchPpr; FrCl; LatCl; GAA; IMSpt; Mi State Univ; Veterinary Medicine.

DE LUCIO, Joan; Richmond Sr HS; Richmond, IN; 16/693 Chr; HonRl; NatlFornLg; NHS; RedCrAde; SchAde; SctActv; StuGov; Yrbk; DARAwd; OptClAwd; In Univ; Socialogy.

DELVEAUX, Howard A; Oconto Falls HS; Oconto Falls, WI; HonRl; FBLA; College; Anethetist.

DELVECCHIO, Francis X; St Thomas Aquinas HS; Hazelwood, MO; 25/329 PresFrshCls; HonRl; Yrbk; LetterFtbl; LetterTrk; College; Professional.

DELVO, Sandy K; Canton HS; Canton, SD; Band; Chrs; NHS; SchMus; SchPl; SptEdYrbk; RptrSchPpr; FHA; LetterTrk; LetterChrldr; South Dakota St Univ; Pharmacy.

DELWICHE, Julie; Algoma HS; Algoma, WI; Band; ChrhWkr; DrlTm; HonRl; MrchBnd; PepBnd; RptrYrbk; SchPpr; EngCl; Glf; Technical School; Secretary.

DELZEIT, Doris; Usd 406; Wathena, KS; 3/46 PresJrCls; ALAGirlsSt; HonRl; SchPl; StuCncl; VPSophCls; 4-H; PpCl; Chrldr; College; Secretary Med Tech.

DE MARANVILLE, Diane E; Basehor HS; Basehor, KS; HonRl; TchrAde; RptrSchPpr; Chrldr; Trade Sch; Homemaker.

DEMAREE, Nancy; Malden HS; Malden, MO; 3/107 HonRl; SctActv; TchrAde; YthFlsp; 4-H; PpCl; GodCntryAwd; PresAwd; Stephens College; Veterinary Science.

DEMAREE, Rhonda L; Nevada HS; Nevada, MO; 39/199 College.

DEMAREE, Thomas M; Garden City East HS; Garden City, MI; HonRl; Ftbl; Wrstlng; Univ; Bus.

DEMARETTI, Joseph D; Frankfort Comm HS; West Frankfort, IL; 4/164 VPFrshCls; PresSrCls; HonRl; JrNHS; NHS; StuCncl; SptEdYrbk; KeyCl; SpnCl; Bsktbl; Ftbl; Trk; So Illinois Univ; Broadcasting.

DE MARR, Rick W; Coldwater HS; Coldwater, MI; 25/277 PresFrshCls; ChrhWkr; HonRl; NHS; SpnCl; LetterBsbl; CaptBsktbl; CchngActv; IMSpt; AmLegAwd; Kalamazoo College; Doctor.

DE MARTINO, Nancy A; John F Kennedy HS; Chicago, IL; 25/610 HonRl; JrNHS; NHS; OffAde; SchPl; TchrAde; SpnCl; PpCl; Univ Of Ill; Veterinarian.

DE MASO, Gregg T; Springfield HS; Springfield, MI; ChrhWkr; NatlMeritSF; StuCncl; YthFlsp; SpnCl; Bsbl; Bsktbl; Ftbl; Brigham Young Univ; Electronic Technology.

DEMASTER, Adrienne; Lakeville HS; Lakeville, MN; 6/187 HonRl; NHS; NatlMeritFnl; NatlThespSoc; SchPl; Univ Of Mn; Veterinarian.

DEMAVRO, Jeannette M; Steinmetz HS; Chicago, IL; CmntyWkr; CtyCnl; IntrClCncl; StuCncl; TchrAde; Univ; Major Study.

DEMBIEC, Stephen J; Custer HS; Milwaukee, WI; ALBoysSt; HonRl; NHS; LetterBsktbl; College; Electronic Engineer.

DEMENT, Greg A; St Louis U HS; St Louis, MO; 6/200 HonRl; LitMag; NatlMeritCmnd; SchPpr; IMSpt; Universtity; Professional Badminton Teacher.

DE MENT, Rhonda L; Clinton HS; Kenney, IL; 11/160 HonRl; HospAde; NHS; StuCncl; 4-H; FFA; FNA; DanFAwd; Univ Of Illinois; Home Economics.

DE MENT, Rhonda L; Clinton Community HS; Kenney, IL; 11/160 ChrhWkr; HonRl; HospAde; NHS; StuCncl; VP4-H; VPFFA; VPFNA; DanFAwd; 4-HAwd; Univ Of Illinois; Home Economics.

DEMENT, Robert A; Malden HS; Malden, MO; PresFrshCls; PresJrCls; HonRl; LetterBsktbl; CaptFtbl; LetterTrk; College; X Ray Tech.

DEMERATH, Joan M; Little Chute HS; Little Chute, WI; ChrhWkr; HonRl; RptrYrbk; FBLA; Univ; Therapy Rehabilitation.

DE MERITT, Robin; Avondale Sr HS; Troy, MI; Chrs; ChrhWkr; CmntyWkr; HospAde; RedCrAde; SchMus; TchrAde; FDA; FNA; PpCl; College Oakland Comm; Nursing.

DE MEYER, Gail M; Waterford Union HS; Mukwonago, WI; 3/204 HonRl; LbryAde; NHS; Treas4-H; PpCl; Trk; Alverno College Milwaukee; Registered Nurse.

DEMICH, Raymond T; Morgan Park HS; Chicago, IL; 12/550 Chr; Chrs; ChrhWkr; VPHonRl; NHS; TchrAde; KeyCl; GerCl; MthCl; Ftbl; Univ Of Illinois; Architecture.

DEMICK, Marguerite M; Pinckneyville Comm HS; Sparta, IL; 1/120 HonRl; NHS; 4-H; FHA; FrCl; PpCl; DARAwd; 4-HAwd; U Of Illinois; Mathematics.

DEMKOVICH, Jane; Whiting HS; Whiting, IN; LbryAde; NHS; StuCncl; GerCl; College; X Ray Technician.

DEMMER, David A; Foley HS; Foley, MN; 11/128 ALBoysSt; Chrs; ChrhWkr; HonRl; NHS; PresStuCncl; LetterBsktbl; LetterFtbl; LetterGlf; N Central Bible College; Religious Ed.

DEMMIN, Steve A; Sevastopol HS; Sturgeon Bay, WI; Bsbl; Ftbl; Wrstlng; St Norbert College; Accounting.

DEMMING, Carol K; New London HS; New London, WI; VPFrshCls; Band; Chrs; ChrhWkr; CmntyWkr; HonRl; NatlFornLg; SctActv; RptrYrbk; PpCl; U Of Wi La Crosse; Medical Tech.

DEMMON, Janett A; Nevis HS; Nevis, MN; Chr; Chrs; ChrhWkr; CmntyWkr; HonRl; LbryAde; PolWkr; StuCncl; TchrAde; GAA;.

DEMOREST, Mark S; Centennial HS; Champaign, IL; 1/355 Chr; JrNHS; LitMag; NHS; NatlMeritFnl; PresNatlThespSoc; SchMus; SchPl; Yrbk; SecGerCl; IMSpt; College; Law.

DEMOSKE, Tasha M; L P Goodrich HS; Fond Du Lac, WI; TrsSophCls; Chr; Chrs; ChrhWkr; NHS; SchMus; StuCncl; FrCl; Oshkosh; Music.

DE MOSS, Annetta L; Hamilton Heights HS; Arcadia, IN; 1/108 PresFrshCls; HonRl; NHS; NatlMeritFnl; NatlMeritSF; SchPl; PresStuGov; SptEdSchPpr; VPSpnCl; GAA; College; Forestry.

DE MOTT, Tina M; Granite City North HS; Granite City, IL; 16/375 LitMag; NHS; OffAde; Quill&Scroll; RptrYrbk; Yrbk; PpCl; College; Mathematics.

DEMOULIN, Michele; Mulberry Grove HS; Mulberry, IL; ChrhWkr; CmntyWkr; HonRl; NHS; SchPl; Yrbk; EdSchPpr; FHA; FNA; SciCl; GAA; Coll; Medical Technologist.

DEMPSAY, Ellen; Pierce Public HS; Norfolk, NE; VPFrshCls; TrsSophCls; Chr; HonRl; SchAde; SchPl; StuCncl; RptrYrbk; GerCl; DanFAwd; Univ Of Nebr Lincoln; Human Services.

DEMPSEY, Kathleen P; Peoria HS; Peoria, IL; 13/450 Chr; CmntyWkr; HonRl; JrNHS; NHS; NatlMeritCmnd; Quill&Scroll; SctActv; StuGov; Augustana College; Public Admin.

DEMPSKI, Donald A; Mexico HS; Mexico, MO; VPFrshCls; ALBoysSt; Chr; StuCncl; SpnCl; CaptBsbl; LetterBsktbl; PPFtbl; College; Business Admin.

DEMPSTER, Cynthia A; Baraga HS; Sheboygan, WI; PresFrshCls; HonRl; LbryAde; NHS; OffAde; TchrAde; FHA; LetterTrk; GAA; College; Major Study.

DE MURI, Bernadette A; Lena HS; Lena, WI; 1/73 SecTrsSrCls; ALAGirlsSt; Band; RptrSchPpr; Pres4-H; FHA; PpCl; LetterBsktbl; LetterTrk; CaptChrldr; Marquette Univ; Pre Med Biology Major.

DEMUS, Catherine V; Harvard Community HS; Harvard, IL; 27/165 Chr; Chrs; ChrhWkr; HonRl; Mdrgl; PresNatlThespSoc; SchMus; SchPl; College; Applied Voice.

DENARDO, Celeste M; Lakeview HS; St Clair Shores, MI; HonRl; JrNHS; NHS; SchMus; TchrAde; College; Biology.

DENAULT, Orville J; Herscher HS; Kankakee, IL; 1/155 CmntyWkr; HonRl; NHS; TchrAde; PpCl; CaptBsbl; LetterBsktbl; CchngActv; AmLegAwd; GovHonPrgAwd; Ill State Univ; Political Science.

DENBY, Dennis D; Roxana Sr HS; East Alton, IL; 8/275 CmntyWkr; HonRl; NHS; NatlMeritCmnd; PresMthCl; LetterBsktbl; CchngActv; College; Engineering.

DENBY, Stephanie; Carlinville Comm HS; Carlinville, IL; 34/170 CmntyWkr; HonRl; HospAde; OffAde; SchPl; SctActv; SpnCl; GAA; University; Professional.

DENERY, Christopher A; Memorial HS; Joplin, MO; 8/225 DrlTm; HonRl; NHS; ROTC; SchAde; SchPl; SctActv; TchrAde; RptrSchPpr; DARAwd; Westmister College; Biology.

DE NEUI, Dixie A; Rockwell City Comm HS; Rockwell City, IA; 1/72 Band; Chrs; TreasChrhWkr; HonRl; NHS; StuCncl; Yrbk; FrCl; LetterBsktbl; LetterTrk; IMSpt; College.

DENEWETH, Richard A; Austin Catholic Prep; Grosse Pt Woods, MI; 10/115 HonRl; NHS; Bsbl; CaptBsktbl; Chrldr; Univ Of Michigan; Business.

DENGER, Carol; Dows Cmmunity HS; Dows, IA; Chr; ChrhWkr; HonRl; LbryAde; SchPl; Yrbk; FHA; GerCl; Niacc; Vocal Music.

DENGLER, Amalia M; Adelphian Acad; Freeland, MI; Chr; ChrhWkr; CmntyWkr; CncrtBnd; HonRl; MrchBnd; NHS; OffAde; RptrSchPpr; SchPpr; Coll.

DENGLER, Peggy L; Durant HS; Durant, IA; 9/70 Band; Chrs; HonRl; NHS; StuCncl; YthFlsp; 4-H; Bsbl; Bsktbl; Trk; IMSpt; 4-HAwd; University; Psychology.

DEN HARTOG, Sherri L; Sheldon Community HS; Sheldon, IA; Chr; SecChrhWkr; SchMus; YthFlsp; PpCl; LetterBsktbl; LetterTrk; IMSpt; College; Business.

DENHOLM, Charlotte M; Independent School Dist #102; Fairfax, SD; 1/10 Band; Chr; Chrs; CncrtBnd; HonRl; HospAde; LbryAde; SchPl; StuCncl; RptrSchPpr; LetterTrk; College; Professional.

DENHOLM, Glenna M; Fairfax Public HS; Fairfax, SD; 2/8 Chrl; Chrs; HonRl; LbryAde; SchPl; StuCncl; RptrYrbk; RptrSchPpr; PpCl;.

DE NIER, Scott L; North Boone HS; Capron, IL; ALBoysSt; Band; Chrs; CmntyWkr; CncrtBnd; Mdrgl; SchMus; SchPl; StuGov; RptrYrbk; GerCl; PpCl; University; Education.

DENIGAN, James B; Christian Bros College HS; St Louis, MO; 9/166 HonRl; NHS; ROTC; SctActv; RptrSchPpr; BauchLmbAwd; U Of Mo St Louis; Veterinarian.

DENIS, Paul T; Austinc Atholic Prep School; Grosse Pte Woods, MI; 15/150 Chr; HonRl; NHS; Quill&Scroll; SchMus; SchPl; StuCncl; RptrYrbk; EdSchPpr; College; Law Or Psychology.

DENISE, Julie M; Boyne Falls HS; Boyne Falls, MI; SecFrshCls; SecSophCls; HonRl; Chrldr; College; Professional.

DENISON, Deanna; Climax Public HS; Shelly, MN; 11/28 U Of M Crookston; Radio Announcing.

DENK, Michael S; Phillips HS; Phillips, WI; Aud/Vis; ChrhWkr; HonRl; NatlFornLg; SchPpr; FFA; LetterBsktbl; Ftbl; LetterTrk; IMSpt; LionAwd; Vocational School; Law Enforcement.

DENKER, Lisa A; Wauneta HS; Waneta, NE; HstFrshCls; HstJrCls; ChrhWkr; HonRl; NHS; StuCncl; YthFlsp; PpCl; Bsktbl; LetterTrk; Kearney State Coll; Bus.

DENKER, Patricia L; Craig HS; Janesville, WI; Chr; ChrhWkr; HonRl; LbryAde; SchPl; SctActv; RptrYrbk; Yrbk; SpnCl; Tech Schl; Fashion Merchandising.

DENKINGER, Janet; Humphrey HS; Humphrey, NE; 1;22 SecJrCls; Chrs; HonRl; StuCncl; EdYrBk; PpCl; AmLegAwd; BttyCrckrAwd; EldAwd; 4-HAwd; Washington University;doctor.

DENKLER, Janet M; Downers Grove North HS; Downers Grove, IL; 70/560 LbryAde; SctActv; Northern Illinois Univ; Nutrition.

DENMAN, Bette J; Linton Stockton HS; Linton, IN; 2/92 TrsFrshCls; TrsSophCls; TrsJrCls; Band; Chr; NHS; StuCncl; Yrbk; FHA; AmLegAwd; Clge.

DENMAN, Richard B; Berkley HS; Huntington Woods, MI; 1/600 NHS; NatlMeritSF; RptrYrbk; Yrbk; LetterTrk; LetterWrstlng; College; Engineering.

DENN, Gordon J; Hastings HS; Hastings, MN; ChrhWkr; CtyCnl; HonRl; NHS; 4-H; Bsktbl; Swmmng; Tennis; CchngActv; 4-HAwd; University; Architectural.

DENN, Steven; Wellcome Memorial HS; Garden City, MN; SecFrshCls; Chrs; ChrhWkr; HonRl; SchMus; 4-H; FFA; 4-HAwd; PresAwd; Vocational; Management.

DENNEHY, Thomas; Austin Catholic Prep; Grosse Pointe Park, MI; 10/126 HonRl; NatlFornLg; NHS; Orch; SchMus; SchPl; RptrYrbk; IMSpt; Univ; Computer Engineering.

DENNEN, Eric P; Rich East HS; Park Forest, IL; 21/400 AFS; HonRl; NatlFornLg; NatlMeritFnl; PolWkr; Quill&Scroll; StuGov; EdSchPpr; LatCl; College; Government.

DENNERT, Randy L; Frederick HS; Westport, SD; Band; Chrs; CncrtBnd; HonRl; MrchBnd; PepBnd; SchPl; StuCncl; YthFlsp; 4-H; Sd Univ; Agric.

DENNEWITZ, Charles P; Chatsworth HS; Chatsworth, IL; 2/27 PresSophCls; VPSrCls; HonRl; NHS; NatlMeritCmnd; StuCncl; Univ Of Illinois.

DENNEY, Douglas E; Maple Valley Comm HS; Castana, IA; Band; ChrhWkr; CncrtBnd; MrchBnd; 4-H; LetterFtbl; LetterTrk; Trade Schl; Vocation.

DENNEY, Michael R; North Mabaska HS; Rose Hill, IA; TrsJrCls; Band; CncrtBnd; HonRl; MrchBnd; NHS; PepBnd; StuCncl; RptrSchPpr; Treas4-H; SpnCl; SciCl; Bsktbl; LetterTrk; Univ Of Iowa; Medicine.

DENNING, Dixie L; Elm Creek Public HS; Elm Creek, NE; 2/30 Chr; Chrs; HonRl; LbryAde; Mdrgl; NHS; OffAde; RedCrAde; SchAde; SchPl; StuCncl; Yrbk; SchPpr; College; Professional.

DENNING, Raymond B; Staples HS; Stapls, MN; 1/149 ALBoysSt; Band; Chr; CncrtBnd; MrchBnd; NHS; NatlThespSoc; SchMus; StuCncl; IMSpt; St Olaf Clg; Law.

DENNINGTON, Bill L; Collinsville Sr HS; Collinsville, IL; 58/654 Belleville Area College; Liberal Arts.

DENNIS, Bryan M; Ste Fenevieve HS; Excello, MO; 8/183 Band; CncrtBnd; HonRl; MrchBnd; MthCl; SciCl; Ftbl; Trk; College; Professional.

DENNIS, Cynthia E; Cooter HS; Cooter, MO; SecTrsFrshCls; VPSophCls; SecJrCls; ChrhWkr; HonRl; HospAde; JrNHS; OffAde; SchPl; SctActv; StuCncl; YthFlsp; RptrYrbk; FHA; Swmmng; Se Missouri State Univ.

DENNIS, Dean; Turtle Lake Mercer HS; Turtle Lake, ND; Band; Chrs; HonRl; SchPl; Yrbk; SciCl; Univ Of Nd; Pharmacy.

DENNIS, Debra A; Brookfield R Iii HS; Brookfield, MO; 5/130 Band; Chrs; CncrtBnd; HonRl; MrchBnd; NHS; PepBnd; SchMus; VPSctActv; FHA; College; Accounting.

DENNIS, Donn M; Hancock Central HS; Hancock, MI; 30/92 ChrhWkr; HonRl; YthFlsp; Bsktbl; LetterFtbl; AmLegAwd; Mi Tech U; Chem Eng.

DENNIS, Douglas E; Edwardsville Senior HS; Edwardsville, IL; 115/439 Chr; Chrs; ChrhWkr; CtyCnl; HonRl; SctActv; YthFlsp; LetterFtbl; KiwanAwd; St Louis College; Pharmacy.

DENNIS, Ellen V; Caro HS; Caro, MI; 16/180 HonRl; LbryAde; ModUN; NHS; TchrAde; EdYrBk; EdSchPpr; Trk; PresAwd; CitAwd; Central Mi U; Speech Ed.

DENNIS, Janet D; Avondale Sr HS; Troy, MI; Band; CncrtBnd; MrchBnd; OffAde; SctActv;.

DENNIS, Jay D; Joliet West HS; Joliet, IL; 94/495 Band; CncrtBnd; HonRl; MrchBnd; Southern Ill Univ; Pre Medicine.

DENNIS, Lee N; Glenbrook South HS; Glenview, IL; 5/600 Chrs; ChrhWkr; CmntyWkr; HonRl; NHS; SchPl; StuCncl; StuGov; YthFlsp; RptrSchPpr; Bsktbl; Socr; Tennis; College; Doctor.

DENNIS, Robert F; Grant Park HS; Grant Park, IL; 4/54 ALBoysSt; Band; PresNHS; NatlMeritSchl; SptEdSchPpr; SpnCl; PresMthCl; LetterBsbl; LetterBsktbl; LetterGlf; LetterTrk; Northern Illinois Univ; Law.

DENNIS, Scott A; Ann Arbor Huron HS; Ann Arbor, MI; Band; CncrtBnd; HonRl; Orch; IMSpt; Us Navy; Nuclear Propulsion.

DENNISON, Aralyn D; Southwestern HS; Flint, MI; 2/570 Chr; Chrl; HonRl; NHS; TchrAde; U Of Mich Flint; Deaf Ed Counselor.

DENNISON, David C; Richland HS; Richland, MO; Aud/Vis; Chr; ChrhWkr; CmntyWkr; SctActv; YthFlsp; SchPpr; FFA; Univ Of Missouri; Veterinarian.

DENNISON, Sheldon L; South Central HS; Laconia, IN; Band; Chrs; 4-H; LetterBsbl; LetterBsktbl; LetterTrk; 4-HAwd; College; Liberal Arts.

DENNISTON, Randal L; Nebraska City HS; Nebraska City, NE; HonRl; Bsktbl; Swmmng; College; Business Admin.

DENNY, Deborah S; Roosevelt HS; St Louis, MO; 8/430 PresSophCls; Chr; PresChrhWkr; HonRl; HospAde; LbryAde; NHS; VPStuCncl; RptrYrbk; U Of Mo St Louis; Bio.

DENNY, Jeffrey S; Haworth HS; Kokomo, IN; 217/456 Bsbl; Bsktbl; Ftbl; CchngActv; Coll; Prof Baseball.

DENNY, Leslie J; Lamar R 1 HS; Lamar, MO; 36/86 Aud/Vis; Chr; ChrhWkr; CmntyWkr; HonRl; RedCrAde; RptrYrbk; Yrbk; RptrSchPpr; SchPpr; Missouri So St College; Special Educ.

DENOMY, Mary Ellen G; Dominican HS; Detroit, MI; Chrl; CncrtBnd; Mdrgl; ModUN; NHS; Orch; Sacrstn; SchMus; StuCncl; StuGov; Wayne State Univ; Accounting.

DE NOON, Leslie J; Riverside HS; Dearborn Heights, MI; HstJrCls; ChrhWkr; CmntyWkr; HonRl; JrNHS; NHS; RedCrAde; VPStuCncl; GAA; IMSpt; Univ; Health.

DE NOOYER, Rebecca L; Gull Lake HS; Richland, MI; 26/225 VPBand; Chrl; ChrhWkr; CncrtBnd; HonRl; HospAde; MrchBnd; NHS; PepBnd; PolWkr; SchAde; College; Nurse.

DEN OTTER, Larry A; Dexter HS; Whitmore Lake, MI; Band; HonRl; JrNHS; MrchBnd; NHS; Orch; PepBnd; LetterBsbl; LetterBsktbl; LetterFtbl; Eastern Mich Univ.

DENSLOW, Craig; Midland HS; Midland, MI; Band; CncrtBnd; HonRl; MrchBnd; Orch; PepBnd; Delta College.

DENSMORE, Robert G; West Richland HS; Noble, IL; HonRl; TreasJA; Jr College; Computer Programmer.

DENSON, Bette J; Southeastern HS; Detroit, MI; 2/200 VPSrCls; ChrhWkr; HonRl; NHS; StuCncl; YthFlsp; PpCl; Swmmng; Tennis; AmLegAwd; U Of Michigan; Accounting.

DENSON, Dorothy A; Spalding Academy; Spalding, NE; 10/18 Chrl; Chrs; SchPl; Yrbk; RptrSchPpr; SptEdSchPpr; SchPpr; Business College; Professional.

DENSON, Gail; Paseo HS; Kansas City, MO; 2/350 VPSrCls; AFS; ChrhWkr; CmntyWkr; HonRl; NHS; NatlMeritCmnd; StuGov; CaptTrk; DARAwd; College; Medicine.

DENSTEDT, Debra K; Pinconning Area HS; Linwood, MI; 8/253 Band; HonRl; NHS; SchPl; TchrAde; Yrbk; 4-H; FTA; GerCl; Col; Business.

DENT, Cheryl; Andrean HS; Gary, IN; 32/256 HonRl; SctActv; FrCl; U; Teacher.

DENT, Leon C; Cass Technical HS; Detroit, MI; HonRl; NatlMeritSF; Univ Of Michigan; Physics.

DENT, Lillie K; East Catholic HS; Detroit, MI; TrsFrshCls; SecSophCls; CmntyWkr; HonRl; NHS; StuCncl; Yrbk; SchPpr; 4-H; PpCl; Univ Of Michigan.

DENTEL, Sheri L; Harbor Springs HS; Harbor Springs, MI; Band; CncrtBnd; HonRl; MrchBnd; OffAde; SchPl; TchrAde; Yrbk; FHA; SpnCl; College; Legal Secretary.

DENTON, Bradley C; Circle HS; Towanda, KS; Band; CncrtBnd; HonRl; MrchBnd; PepBnd; SchPl; StuCncl; LetterTrk; U Of Ks; Astronomy.

DENTON, Brenda K; Frontier HS; Monticello, IN; 10/71 ChrhWkr; HonRl; HospAde; SecNHS; SchPl; PresYthFlsp; Sec4-H; SpnCl; PpCl; Chrldr; GAA; 4-HAwd; Ball State Univ; Health Field.

DENTON, Carole S; Cardinal Ritter HS; Indianapolis, IN; 4/165 HonRl; NatlMeritSF; SpnCl; Univ; Science.

DENTON, Cynthia A; Ramsey HS; Ramsey, IL; ChrhWkr; HonRl; RedCrAde; SchPl; StuCncl; RptrSchPpr; 4-H; FrCl; LetterGlf; Swmmng; GAA; 4-HAwd; E Illinois Univ; Radio.

DENTON, Gregg L; Porta HS; Petersburg, IL; 35/95 Aud/Vis; Chrs; Mdrgl; NatlThespSoc; YthFlsp; Yrbk; RptrSchPpr; Ftbl; Trk; Wrstlng; Western Ill Univ; Vetrenerian.

DENTON, James; Kerkhoven Hs; Kerkhoven, MN; Band; MrchBnd; PepBnd; 4-H; 4-HAwd; College ; Electronics.

DENTON, Roger C; Glenwood HS; Springfield, IL; 7/143 AFS; HonRl; NHS; SchMus; SchPl; TchrAde; SptEdYrbk; SptEdSchPpr; Ftbl; Glf; College; Professional.

DENTON, Ronda G; Chillicothe HS; Chillicothe, MO; HospAde; JA; SchPl; TchrAde; 4-H; LatCl; PpCl; Missouri Western College; Nursing.

DENU, Alice J; Du Bois HS; Du Bois, IN; 10/76 VPFrshCls; SecSrCls; ALAGirlsSt; Band; HonRl; NHS; PolWkr; UNYO; SchPpr; Chrldr; Univ; Nursing.

DE NUCCI, Joseph F; Beloit Catholic HS; Beloit, WI; PresSrCls; HonRl; NHS; SchMus; StuCncl; Yrbk; Ftbl; LetterTennis; IMSpt; DARAwd; Marquette U; Dentist.

DE NURE, Scott A; Black Hawk HS; South Wayne, WI; TrsFrshCls; ChrhWkr; HonRl; Yrbk; RptrSchPpr; FrCl; LetterBsbl; Bsktbl; Ftbl; IMSpt; Business Sch; Vocation.

DENUYL, Jodea; South Haven HS; South Haven, MI; 1/216 HonRl; NHS; NatlMeritCmnd; Orch; StuGov; TchrAde; SciCl; Hope Coll; Med.

DEN UYL, Jo Dea A; South Haven HS; South Haven, MI; 1/216 HonRl; NHS; NatlMeritCmnd; Orch; SchAde; StuGov; TchrAde; FrCl; PpCl; SciCl; Swmmng; Trk; Hope College; Medicine.

DENYS, Scott O; Reavis HS; Burbank, IL; 156/676 ChrhWkr; HonRl; StuGov; TchrAde; YthFlsp; YthLg; Bsktbl;.

DENZER, Gary S; Normal Community HS; Bloomington, IL; 19/437 VPSrCls; ALBoysSt; HonRl; PresNHS; SchPl; StuCncl; 4-H; SecFFA; KeyCl; Bsktbl; LetterFtbl; DanFAwd; 4-HAwd; Univ Of Illinois; Agriculture.

DENZER, Scott; Lesueur HS; Lesueur, MN; Band; CncrtBnd; HonRl; JA; MrchBnd; NHS; PepBnd; SchAde; TchrAde; RptrSchPpr;.

DEOGRACIAS, Cecilia M; Our Lady Of Grace Acad; Edinburg, IN; Chrs; HonRl; ModUN; SchMus; RptrYrbk; Bsktbl; IMSpt; Coll; Nurse.

DE ORNELLAS, Janet A; North Greene HS; Roodhouse, IL; 4/120 Chrs; HonRl; LbryAde; NHS; SchPpr; Pres4-H; VPSciCl; GAA; 4-HAwd; KiwanAwd; College; Biology.

DEPA, Cynthia A; Reavis HS; Burbank, IL; 81/691 HstFrshCls; HstSophCls; HstJrCls; HstSrCls; HonRl; JrNHS; StuCncl; Yrbk; FrCl; VPMthCl; Augustana College; Engineering.

DE PAEPE, Richard C; Riley Senior HS; South Bend, IN; Bsktbl; LetterFtbl; LetterTrk; LetterWrstlng; Air Force Acad; Pilot.

DE PALMA, Gino; Crestwood HS; Drbn Hghts, MI; 10/450 HonRl; TchrAde; SciCl; Bsktbl; JETSAwd; Lawrence Tech; Elec Engr.

DE PETRO, Karen; Ladywood HS; Garden City, MI; HonRl; Orch; Quill&Scroll; SchMus; StuCncl; RptrYrbk; SpnCl; Mich Univ; Veterinary Med.

DEPIES, Cindy L; Random Lake HS; Belgium, WI; TrsFrshCls; Band; Chr; HonRl; SchMus; StuCncl; RptrYrbk; 4-H; Chrldr; 4-HAwd; Computor Field.

DE PINTO, Mary Kaye; Forest View HS; Des Plaines, IL; 9/650 ChrhWkr; DrlTm; HonRl; HospAde; NatlFornLg; NHS; TchrAde; YthFlsp; KeyCl; Wheaton College; Biology.

DEPLANTY, Richard E; Rockville HS; Rockville, IN; 28/95 VPSrCls; Band; MrchBnd; FFA; SpnCl; Bsktbl; LetterTrk; IMSpt; College.

DEPOISTER, Daonna; Mt Vernon Twp HS; Mount Vernon, IL; /387 ChrhWkr; HonRl; NatlThespSoc; Quill&Scroll; SchPl; TchrAde; RptrSchPpr; Murray State Univ;.

DE POOTER, Teresa; Rockridge HS; Andalusia, IL; HonRl; FNA; FTA; LatCl; Bsktbl; College; Nursing.

DE PORTER, Kathleen A; Sherrard HS; Milan, IL; 4/98 PresJrCls; SecSrCls; CaptDrlTm; HonRl; NHS; StuGov; Pres4-H; PresPpCl; Chrldr; DARAwd; Northern Illinois Univ; Biology.

DEPOY, James L; Danville Community HS; Danville, IN; Chr; PresLbryAde; NHS; LatCl;.

DEPPE, Cleta M; Bellevue Community HS; Bellevue, IA; Chr; Chrs; SchMus; SchPl; FHA; PpCl;.

DEPPE, Jean F; Sparta HS; Sparta, IL; Chr; Chrs; ChrhWkr; CmntyWkr; HonRl; RedCrAde; SctActv; StuGov; YthFlsp; BttyCrckrAwd; College; Vocation.

DEPPE, Michael W; Creighton Prep; Omaha, NE; CmntyWkr; Sdlty; SchPpr; Bsktbl; Ftbl; Trk; IMSpt; Univ Of Ne; Forestry.

DEPPE, Richard R; Pecatonica HS; Pecatonica, IL; 7/78 Chr; HonRl; JrNHS; NHS; Quill&Scroll; RptrSchPpr; 4-H; Bsktbl; College; Dentist.

DEPPERMANN, Ronald; Farmington East Hs; Trivoli, IL; 4-H; FFA; LetterBsbl; LetterBsktbl; University Of Illinois; Ag Economics.

DEPPERSCHMIDT, Mark W; U.s.d. #295 HS; Dresden, KS; CmntyWkr; HonRl; LbryAde; RptrYrbk; GerCl; PpCl; College; Veterinarian.

DEPPERT, David D; Pekin Community HS; Pekin, IL; 9/800 HonRl; NHS; 4-H; FFA; Ill Central College; Agriculture.

DEPPISH, Julie H; St Xaviers HS; Junction City, KS; VPJrCls; HonRl; SctActv; Yrbk; FrCl; LetterBsktbl; LetterTrk; Ks Univ; Radio Television.

DE PREE, Sara; Zeeland HS; Zeeland, MI; 5/185 SecFrshCls; Band; ChrhWkr; CncrtBnd; HonRl; NHS; YthFlsp; LatCl; PpCl; PresGAA; Hope College; Liberal Arts.

DE PRESTE, Nancy A; Glendale HS; Springfield, MO; SecFrshCls; SecSrCls; ChrhWkr; HonRl; HospAde; OffAde; SchPl; SctActv; SpnCl; PpCl; Nursing School.

DEPREY, Kristi; Waukesha South Campus HS; Waukesha, WI; Band; ChrhWkr; MrchBnd; NHS; TchrAde; Trk; GAA; College; Elementry Education.

DERADO, Jr,John; Edison Sr HS; East Gary, IN; ALBoysSt; Chr; JrNHS; Mdrgl; NHS; SchMus; Bsktbl; Ftbl; Glf; College.

DERBAS, Peggysue M; St Joseph HS; Chicago, IL; 2/117 PresSophCls; PresJrCls; HonRl; NHS; StuCncl; EngCl; MthCl; PpCl; Tennis; Loyola Univ; Teaching.

DERBY, Bonnie K; Montpelier HS; Ypsilanti, ND; SecSophCls; Chr; Chrs; HonRl; LbryAde; SchMus; SchPl; RptrSchPpr; LetterBsktbl; LetterTrk; Devils Lake Jr Col; Fashionmerchandizer.

DERBY, Debra S; Newman Public HS; Newman, IL; StuCncl; Pres4-H; FHA; PpCl; LetterBsktbl; CaptChrldr; SecGAA; IMSpt; PresAwd; College; Social Work.

DERBY, Denise D; Monroe HS; Monroe, MI; ALAGirlsSt; Chr; ChrhWkr; CmntyWkr; HonRl; LitMag; NHS; NatlMeritSF; NatlThespSoc; PolWkr; SchPl; StuGov; PresYthFlsp; Yrbk; College; Chemistry Teacher.

DERCKS, Joann; Appleton West HS; Appleton, WI; Chrl; ChrhWkr; CmntyWkr; LbryAde; SctActv; TchrAde; Pres4-H; LatCl; AmLegAwd; Technical Sch; Health Careet.

DERDALL, Jean S; Lyons Township HS; Western Springs, IL; Chrs; ChrhWkr; HonRl; NHS; RptrYrbk; U Of Ia; Math Major.

DEREN, Jeffrey D; John Adams HS; Southbend, IN; 40/440 HonRl; StuCncl; StuGov; YthFlsp; CaptSwmmng; CchngActv; DARAwd; KiwanAwd; Us Merchant Marine Acad.

DERENGOWSKI, Susan M; Lincoln Park HS; Lincoln Park, MI; 18/576 AFS; CmntyWkr; HonRl; HospAde; JA; ModUN; RedCrAde; StuCncl; YthFnd; RptrSchPpr; Henry Ford Comm Clge; Law.

DERHEIMER, Dan; Bishop Luers HS; Fort Wayne, IN; 63/224 Yrbk; SchPpr; KeyCl; Ftbl;.

DERING, Marcia A; Morgan Park Academy; Chicago, IL; Chr; Chrs; ChrhWkr; CmntyWkr; HonRl; LitMag; ModUN; NHS; SchPl; YthFlsp; FrCl; Univ; Medicine.

DERKS, Cynthia D; Stanberry R Ii HS; Stanberry, MO; 2/40 Band; Chr; Chrs; ChrhWkr; CmntyWkr; CncrtBnd; LetterGlf; CaptChrldr; IMSpt; 4-HAwd; Univ; Math/science/music.

DERKS, Susan K; Lourdes HS; Lincoln, NE; SecJrCls; Band; HonRl; NHS; Yrbk; SpnCl; MthCl; PpCl; Bsktbl; Trk; Univ Ne.

DERKSEN, Virginia A; Marquette HSLJLUMULOVELL; West Point, IA; 7/51 Band; CncrtBnd; NatlMeritCmnd; NHS; PepBnd; SchPpr; LetterTrk; Southeastern Comm College; Business Admin.

DERMAN, Betty M; Arlington HS; Nickerson, NE; SecJrCls; SecBand; ChrhWkr; CncrtBnd; HonRl; MrchBnd; NHS; PepBnd; StuCncl; 4-H; FBLA; PpCl; LetterTrk; CaptChrldr; College; Secretarial.

DERNULE, Monica M; Bishop Noll Institute; Highland, IN; 90/360 Chrl;.

DE ROCHE, Michael T; Proctor HS; Proctor, MN; 3/250 PresSophCls; Chr; ChrhWkr; HonRl; NHS; SchPl;.

DEROCHER, Dan N; Bark River HS; Bark River, MI; TrsFrshCls; VPSophCls; TrsJrCls; Band; CncrtBnd; HonRl; MrchBnd; PepBnd; SchPl; College; Engineering.

DEROCHER, David L; Menominee HS; Menominee, MI; 96/275 ChrhWkr; CmntyWkr; HonRl; TchrAde; SptEdYrbk; Bsktbl; LetterFtbl; Ferris State College; Data Processing.

DEROCHER, Ronald P; Port Huron Northern HS; Port Huron, MI; 203/437 Aud/Vis; LbryAde; SctActv; StuCncl; RptrYrbk; Clge; Law.

DE ROO, Terry; Zeeland HS; Zeeland, MI; Davenport Business Col; Business.

DE ROSA, Christine A; Thornton Twp HS; Dolton, IL; 8/727 Chr; HonRl; JrNHS; NHS; NatlMeritCmnd; TreasStuGov; PpCl; CchngActv; Univ Of Chicago; Lawyer.

DE ROSE, Christopher M; East Lansing HS; East Lansing, MI; ChrhWkr; CmntyWkr; NHS; PolWkr; StuCncl; StuGov; YthFlsp; YthFnd; YthLg; SchPpr; Kalamazoo Coll; Attorney.

DE ROSE, David J; Loyola Academy; Northbrook, IL; 5/461 ChrhWkr; CmntyWkr; HonRl; NatlFornLg; NHS; TchrAde; RptrYrbk; SchPpr; TreasGerCl; SciCl; University; Law.

DE ROSE, Robert C; Waukegan East HS; Waukegan, IL; 41/502 HonRl; TchrAde; KeyCl; LatCl; LetterBsktbl; LetterFtbl; LetterWrstlng; CchngActv; IMSpt; College; Law.

DEROSIER, Daniel P; La Fayette HS; Red Lake Falls, MN; 4/69 PresSrCls; ALBoysSt; Band; Chr; HonRl; SchMus; RptrSchPpr; LetterFtbl; LetterTrk; U Of Minn; Industrial Eng.

DE ROSIER, Joseph M; Saints Peter & Paul HS; Saginaw, MI; 21/121 ALBoysSt; Chr; CtyCnl; HonRl; JrNHS; NHS; SchPl; Ftbl; Tennis; IMSpt; Mich Tech; Gen Engr.

DEROSIER, Mary R; Lafayette HS; Red Lake Falls, MN; Chrs; CncrtBnd; HonRl; HospAde; MrchBnd; PepBnd; SchMus; SctActv; RptrYrbk; College; Social Work.

DEROUSSEAU, Michael; Clyde HS; Clyde, KS; VPFrshCls; VPSophCls; VPJrCls; VPSrCls; ALBoysSt; ChrhWkr; HonRl; EdSchPpr; Ftbl; Wrstlng; Highland Jr Coll; Agronomy.

DERR, Cynthia A; O Gorman HS; Sioux Falls, SD; Chr; ChrhWkr; HospAde; JA; TreasNHS; SctActv; PresStuCncl; TchrAde; RptrSchPpr; JAAwd; Augustana College; Childhood Development.

DERR, Debra K; St Charles HS; St Charles, MO; ChrhWkr; CmntyWkr; HonRl; IMSpt; Coll; Nurse.

DERR, Stanley D; Huntley HS; Lyman, NE; Chr; Chrs; SchPl; SctActv; YthFlsp; 4-H; LetterBsbl; LetterBsktbl; LetterTrk; 4-HAwd; Coll;.

DERRER, Linda M; Lanark HS; Lanark, IL; 1/56 Chrs; HonRl; LbryAde; NHS; Yrbk; Pres4-H; PresFHA; 4-HAwd; Jr College; Secretarial.

DERRICK, Oma J; Clarke Comm HS; Weldon, IA; 28/108 Chrs; ChrhWkr; HonRl; LbryAde; RptrYrbk; RptrSchPpr; College; Writer.

DERRICK, Sue E; Mackinaw City HS; Mackinaw City, MI; 4/21 TrsFrshCls; SecSophCls; SecJrCls; SecSrCls; HonRl; NatlMeritSF; LetterBsktbl; LetterTrk; LetterChrldr; IMSpt; Ferris State Clg; Cpa Data Processing.

DERRY, Catherine K; Greenview HS; Greenview, IL; 2/24 ChrhWkr; CmntyWkr; HonRl; RptrYrbk; FSA; FTA; SpnCl; GAA; IMSpt; Lincolnland Comm College; Mathematics.

DERRY, Jolene J; Wahpeton Sr HS; Wahpeton, ND; ALAGirlsSt; HonRl; JrNHS; StuCncl; EdYrBk; EdSchPpr; FBLA; KeyCl; PpCl; Chrldr; College; Prof Chiropractice.

DERRY, Kristie L; Frederick HS; Frederick, SD; Chr; Chrs; HonRl; OffAde; SchAde; SchPl; TchrAde; Yrbk; Trk; GAA; Col; Commercial Artist.

DERRY, Theresa; East Greene HS; Rippey, IA; 7/42 Chr; ChrhWkr; CmntyWkr; HonRl; NHS; SchMus; SchPl; RptrYrbk; 4-H; Iowa Methodist School Of Nursing; Nursing.

DERRYBERRY, Roger A; Salem HS; Salem, MO; ALBoysSt; HonRl; StuCncl; TchrAde; College; Dentist.

DERSE, Robert F; Lake Mills Public HS; Lake Mills, WI; 7/118 Band; Chr; Chrs; CncrtBnd; HonRl; Mdrgl; MrchBnd; NatlMeritSF; PepBnd; StuCncl; Ftbl; Trk; Univ Of Wisc; Business.

DE RUE, Brian A; Saint Joseph HS; South Bend, IN; 89/235 Chrs; HonRl; OffAde; PolWkr; SchAde; SchMus; SchPl; RptrYrbk; PpCl; Chrldr; Univ Of Notre Dame; Architecture.

DE RUITER, Randall A; Lincolnway HS; Frankfort, IL; 12/498 HonRl; NHS; MthCl; Univ Of Ill; Engineering.

DERUNTZ, Anne; Granite City Shs South; Granite City, IL; 1/630 LitMag; LbryAde; VPNHS; NatlMeritFnl; Quill&Scroll; RptrSchPpr; Pres4-H; PpCl; SecSciCl; AmLegAwd;.

DE RUNTZ, Anne E; Granite City Sr South HS; Granite City, IL; 1/529 LitMag; LbryAde; VPNHS; NatlMeritFnl; Quill&Scroll; RptrSchPpr; Pres4-H; ChmnPpCl; SecSciCl; AmLegAwd; William Woods College.

DERUSHA, Carol A; Menomonee Falls East HS; Menomonee Falls, WI; 35/335 CmntyWkr; HonRl; HospAde; NHS; Quill&Scroll; RptrSchPpr; EdSchPpr; SchPpr; FrCl; PpCl; Waukesha Mem Hos; Rad Tech.

DERWIN, Andrew P; Marist HS; Chicago, IL; IMSpt; Loyola Univ; Biology.

DERY, Mark W; Lake Orion HS; Lake Orion, MI; 3/335 HonRl; NHS; IMSpt; Oakland Univ; Bus Mang.

DERY, Nancy M; Ladywood HS; Livonia, MI; ChrhWkr; JA; NHS; NatlMeritCmnd; SchMus; SchPl; SciCl; LetterTrk; AmLegAwd; JAAwd; Wayne State U; Physics.

DE RYDER, Kathy A; Gull Lake HS; Hickory Corners, MI; 4/239 CmntyWkr; HonRl; NatlFornLg; NHS; NatlMeritSF; PolWkr; 4-H; GAA; IMSpt; PPFtbl; Univ; Special Ed.

DERYLO, Valerie C; West Catholic HS; Grand Rapids, MI; 13/320 HonRl; JA; NHS; NatlMeritSchl; StuCncl; FrCl; PPFtbl; Butterworth Hgs Sch Of Nursing; Nursing.

DERYNCK, Kathleen J; Tyler Public HS; Tyler, MN; 13/35 SecSrCls; Chr; SchPl; StuCncl; UNYO; PpCl; Trk; GAA; PresAwd; CitAwd; St Cloud St Col; Teacher.

DE SANTIS, John F; Homestead HS; Ft Wayne, IN; 30/240 HonRl; NHS; TchrAde; LetterFtbl; LetterTrk; Brown Univ; Economics.

DESART, Melvin; Hillsboro HS; Coffeen, IL; 5/200 Band; CncrtBnd; HonRl; LbryAde; MrchBnd; PepBnd; SpnCl; U Of Il; Astorphusics.

DESCH, John A; Houston HS; Houston, MO; Aud/Vis; HonRl; SctActv; 4-H; SciCl; Bsbl; LetterBsktbl; LetterTrk; College; X Ray Tech.

DESCH, Linda; Rhinelander HS; Rhinelander, WI; Chrs; DrmBgl; HonRl; NHS; RptrSchPpr; SchPpr; Nicolet Tech; Dietician.

DESCHNER, Bradley D; Natoma HS; Natoma, KS; SecSophCls; TrsJrCls; Band; CncrtBnd; HonRl; MrchBnd; PepBnd; FFA; LetterFtbl; Vo Tech.

DE SELM, Stephen P; Bishop Mc Namara HS; Kankakee, IL; 43/162 ChrhWkr; HonRl; NHS; LetterBsbl; LetterFtbl; LetterTrk; IMSpt; Il State Univ; Accounting.

DE SHANO, Cathy G; Bullock Creek HS; Freeland, MI; HonRl; NHS; TchrAde; Yrbk; 4-H; PpCl; GAA; 4-HAwd; College; Medical Study.

DE SHASIER, Marcia L; Paxton HS; Paxton, IL; 13/137 HonRl; NHS; NatlThespSoc; TchrAde; LetterTennis; GAA; Il State Univ; Elementary Teacher.

DESHAZER, Keith; Hyde Co Independant HS; Highmore, SD; /54 HonRl; FBLA; CaptBsktbl; CaptFtbl; Coll;acc.

DESHAZO, Henry N; Springfield Catholic HS; Springfield, MO; PresSophCls; ALBoysSt; HonRl; StuCncl; EdYrBk; PresLatCl; LetterBsbl; LetterTrk; VoiceDemAwd; College; Meteorology.

DE SIMONE, Gerald F; Arlington HS; Arlington Heights, IL; 95/585 HonRl; SctActv; StuCncl; LetterBsbl; LetterBsktbl; Ftbl; College; Business.

DESING, Dana M; North HS; Sioux City, IA; 9/324 MrchBnd; Twrl; SchPpr; PpCl; Tennis; IMSpt; U Of Ia; Biomedical Engr.

DESING, Joan; Messmer HS; Milwaukee, WI; 1/208 Chrs; HonRl; Mdrgl; NHS; NatlMeritCmnd; SchPl; Yrbk; SchPpr; FTA; SpnCl; U Of Marquette; Journalism.

DESLAURIERS, Theresa R; Canby HS; Canby, MN; Chr; CmntyWkr; CncrtBnd; HonRl; HospAde; LbryAde; PresSecFHA; PpCl; 4-HAwd; Coll; Nurse.

DESLOOVER, Irene; St Mary Acad; Monroe, MI; 8/142 HonRl; LbryAde; NHS; SchMus; SchPl; RptrSchPpr; SchPpr; Marygrove College; Accounting.

DE SLOOVER, Irene F; St Mary Academy; Monroe, MI; 8/142 HonRl; NHS; SchMus; SchPl; Teen; RptrSchPpr; Marygrove College; Accounting.

DE SMITH, Jerry G; Annawan HS; Annawan, IL; 5/50 PresFrshCls; HonRl; NHS; SchPl; StuCncl; 4-H; PresFFA; LetterFtbl; College; Vocation.

DESMOND, Susan M; Our Lady Of The Lakes HS; Clarkston, MI; 4/53 SecFrshCls; SecSophCls; ChrhWkr; HonRl; PresNHS; VPStuCncl; EdYrBk; FrCl; Central Michigan Univ; Teaching.

DESOTO, Abigail E; Faulkner HS; Chicago, IL; PresFrshCls; PresSophCls; PresJrCls; Chrs; HonRl; NHS; YthFlsp; EdYrBk; Swmmng; DARAwd; U Of Chicago;.

DESPOT, Sandra J; Hubbard HS; Chicago, IL; PresJrCls; DrmMjrt; LbryAde; StuCncl; StuGov; TchrAde; Twrl; Yrbk; Bsbl; Trk;.

DES ROCHER, Terry L; Trico HS; Percy, IL; Chr; Chrs; HonRl; SchMus; YthFlsp; FrCl; PpCl; SciCl; Bsbl; Univ; Engineer.

DESROSIERS, Kevin M; St John Vianney HS; St Louis, MO; 21/186 HonRl; JA; IMSpt; PresJAAwd; Southern Il Univ; Radio Broadcasting.

DESSALET, Sharon L; Wilson Campus HS; Mankato, MN; Chr; Chrl; Chrs; HospAde; SchMus; SctActv; TchrAde; Yrbk; CaptBsktbl; Col; Business Management.

DESTREE, Steven G; Southern Door HS; Sturgeon Bay, WI; 13/130 HonRl; NHS; SchPl; StuCncl; CaptFtbl; Trk; CaptWrstlng; IMSpt; Lakeland College; Business Administration.

DESTREE, Theresa; Southern Doos HS; Sturgeon Bay, WI; Band; CncrtBnd; HonRl; MrchBnd; PepBnd; Bsktbl; GAA;.

DESWIK, Nancy C; Maine Township South HS; Park Ridge, IL; HonRl; JrNHS; NatlMeritFnl; NatlMeritSchl; PolWkr; Quill&Scroll; StuCncl; SchPpr; IMSpt; Michigan State Univ; Food Science.

DETAMORE, Susan L; Plymouth HS; Plymouth, IN; 12/215 Band; CncrtBnd; HonRl; MrchBnd; NHS; SchMus; SctActv; MthCl; PpCl; BauchLmbAwd; Butler U; Pharmacy.

DETERDING, Karen D; Normal Comm HS; Normal, IL; 19/443 ChrhWkr; CncrtBnd; HonRl; MrchBnd; NHS; Orch; SchMus; SchPl; Univ Of Illinois; Chemical Engineer.

DETERMAN, Bonnie L; St Johns Prep; St Cloud, MN; 1/33 HonRl; NHS; St Benedicts College; Medical Technology.

DETERMAN, Robert; Daniel J Gross HS; Belleville, NE; HonRl; NatlMeritFnl; StuCncl; SpnCl; Bsktbl; Trk; IMSpt;.

DETERS, Joan A; Flanagan HS; Flanagan, IL; Band; Chr; Chrl; Chrs; CncrtBnd; HonRl; Mdrgl; MrchBnd; GAA; IMSpt; College Or Univ; Writing Music Drama Englis.

DETERS, Patricia G; Flanagan HS; Flanagan, IL; Band; Chrs; CncrtBnd; HonRl; MrchBnd; PepBnd; SchMus; 4-H; GerCl; PpCl; Socr; Chrldr; IMSpt; University; Education.

DETHERAGE, Shirley J; Macksville HS; Radium, KS; TrsSophCls; TrsJrCls; Chrs; HospAde; FHA; PpCl; Bsktbl; College.

DETHEROW, Donald E; Seymour HS; Seymour, MO; ChrhWkr; HonRl; Bsbl; Bsktbl; Trk; Mu; Sports.

DETHLEFS, Cynthia R; Loup City HS; Rockville, NE; CncrtBnd; HonRl; Mdrgl; MrchBnd; NHS; SchMus; EdYrBk; FHA; Trk; 4-HAwd; Coll; Dental Assit.

DETMERS, Peggy A; Canton HS; Canton, SD; Chr; DrlTm; DrmMjrt; HonRl; NHS; SchPl; StuCncl; LetterTrk; Chrldr; IMSpt; College; Conservation.

DETRY, Carol A; Green Bay East HS; Green Bay, WI; 50415 ChrhWkr; HonRl; NHS; NatlMeritSF; SchPl; SctActv; RptrSchPpr; SchPpr; VPFrCl; OptClAwd; Coll; Med Tech.

DETTER, Kimberly K; Winfield HS; Winfield, KS; VPFrshCls; Band; ChrhWkr; CncrtBnd; HonRl; HospAde; MrchBnd; PepBnd; TchrAde; Tennis; Col; Business.

DETTLINGER, Butch A; New Palestine HS; New Palestine, IN; HonRl; SpnCl; Bsbl; LetterBsktbl; LetterFtbl; LetterTrk; College ; Professional.

DETTLOFF, Michael J; Brown City HS; Brown City, MI; Band; CncrtBnd; HonRl; MrchBnd; PepBnd; SchMus; SchPl; StuCncl; RptrYrbk; RptrSchPpr;.

DETTMER, Angela K; Garber HS; Essexville, MI; 19/180 HonRl; 4-H; Bsktbl; Trk; College; Exec Legal Secretary.

DETTMER, David A; Plymouth HS; Plymouth, IN; PresJrCls; Chr; HonRl; NHS; StuCncl; SecFFA; LatCl; MthCl; PpCl; Ftbl; LetterTrk; Purdue University; Vet.

DETTMER, Jeanne; Cass Technical HS; Detroit, MI; LetterSwmmng; Msu; Vet Med.

DETWEILER, Mark; Chillicothe HS; Chillicothe, MO; AFS; ChrhWkr; NHS; SchMus; SctActv; StuGov; FrCl; SciCl; Glf; GodCntryAwd; Macalester College; Philospy Major.

DETWEILER, Mark P; Richwoods HS; Peoria, IL; 5/450 AFS; HonRl; NatlMeritSF; Univ Of Il; Oceanography.

DETWILER, Sara J; Tiskilwa HS; Tiskilwa, IL; 6/41 SecFrshCls; TrsSophCls; Chrs; ChrhWkr; HonRl; LbryAde; NHS; SchMus; EdYrBk; FHA; Bsktbl; TreasGAA; College; Social Work.

DETZLER, Elwin; Taylors Falls HS; Center City, MN; HonRl; SciCl; Bsktbl; Ftbl; Trk; Coll.

DEUBLER, Jane A; Camdenton R 3 HS; Camdenton, MO; HonRl; ModUN; NHS; SctActv; TchrAde; RptrSchPpr; SpnCl; MthCl; PpCl; Warrensburg St Univ; Medicine.

DEUEL, Douglas J; Center HS; Kansas City, MO; Chr; ChrhWkr; CmntyWkr; HonRl; StuCncl; StuGov; YthFlsp; Bsktbl; DARAwd; Wlliam Jewell College; Lawyer.

DEUEL, Janet L; Superior HS; Superior, NE; Band; CncrtBnd; HonRl; MrchBnd; NHS; PepBnd; Teen; VP4-H; LetterTrk; University Of Nebraska; Vet.

DEUEL, Nancy R; Lake Zurich HS; Kildeer, IL; Chr; HonRl; NHS; NatlMeritSF; StuGov; RptrSchPpr; Coll; Vet Med.

DEUEL, Nancy R; Lake Zurich Senior HS; Kildeer, IL; 9/200 Chr; HonRl; NHS; NatlMeritFnl; StuGov; Univ Of Illinois; Veterinarian.

DE URIES, Bradley D; Sioux Center Comm HS; Maurice, IA; 12/81 TrsJrCls; VPSrCls; Chr; Chrs; ChrhWkr; HonRl; NHS; PresFFA; CaptFtbl; CitAwd; Univ; Vet Med.

DEUTSCH, Cynthia L; R Nelson Snider HS; Fort Wayne, IN; 100/510 Band; ChrhWkr; CncrtBnd; HonRl; HospAde; MrchBnd; PepBnd; SchMus; College; Nursing.

DEUTSCH, Kim S; Hoisington HS; Hoisington, KS; Band; NHS; Chrldr; Barton County Jr College; Interior Design.

DEVALK, Marcia J; Prospect HS; Mount Prospect, IL; 81/612 Chr; ChrhWkr; HonRl; NatlMeritCmnd; SchMus; StuCncl; RusCl; PpCl; Bsbl; Bsktbl; Tennis; GAA; Northwestern Univ; Russian Economics.

DEVANE, Colleen M; St Xaviers HS; Junction City, KS; PresSrCls; ALAGirlsSt; HonRl; StuCncl; StuGov; TchrAde; RptrYrbk; SptEdYrbk; Trk; Chrldr; AmLegAwd; KiwanAwd; College; Professional.

DEVANEY, Leonard P; St Patrick HS; Chicago, IL; 90/460 Univ Of Illinois; Engineering.

DE VANEY, Richard M; E Gary Edison Hs; East Gary, IN; PresSophCls; Chr; Mdrgl; SchMus; StuCncl; FrCl; LetterBsktbl; Ftbl; LetterTrk;.

DE VAULT, Betsy A; Clear Lake HS; Clearlake, IA; 5/150 Chr; CncrtBnd; HonRl; MrchBnd; NHS; SchMus; EdYrBk; RptrSchPpr; LatCl; Tennis; Ia St U; Journalism.

DE VAULT, Cynthia M; North Andrew R6 HS; Rea, MO; HonRl; SchPl; RptrSchPpr; FHA; GAA; PPFtbl; Business College; Vocation.

DEVENA, Diana L; Buhler HS; Hutchinson, KS; 10/149 Band; ChrhWkr; CncrtBnd; HonRl; MrchBnd; NHS; PepBnd; SecSpnCl; PpCl; Tennis; Wichita State Univ; Medicine.

DE VERANEZ, Denise C; Lindblom Tech HS; Chicago, IL; 4/657 Chr; ChrhWkr; HonRl; HospAde; Mdrgl; NHS; TchrAde; Univ; Geneticist.

DEVEREAUX, Scott J; Kouts HS; Kouts, IN; Aud/Vis; Chr; HonRl; OffAde; SchPl; FFA; Bsbl; Bsktbl;.

DEVEREUX, Paul T; Chaminade College Prep; St Louis, MO; 3/110 HonRl; StuCncl; StuGov; RptrSchPpr; LetterBsbl; LetterFtbl; LetterSocr; IMSpt; University; Professional.

DE VETTER, Charlie D; Tracy HS; Tracy, MN; 66/98 CtyCnl; CmntyWkr; HonRl; JA; LetterFtbl; LetterTrk; Wrstlng; CchngActv; VFWAwd; VoiceDemAwd; St Thomas; Psychology.

DE VIENCE, Mark D; De La Salle HS; Chicago, IL; 12/268 HonRl; NHS; LetterTennis; University; Business Admin.

DEVILBISS, Warren; St Charles Hs; St Charles, IL; HonRl; PolWkr; LatCl; LetterTrk; College ; Professional Engineering.

DEVIN, Willa J; Lawrenceville HS; Birds, IL; HonRl; SchMus; FNA; FrCl; PpCl; SciCl; Bsktbl; GAA; Lincoln Trail College; Health.

DEVINATZ, Victor G; New Trier West HS; Wilmette, IL; 81/698 HonRl; LetterTrk; Coll; Mathematics.

DEVINE, Amy M; Rock Falls HS; Rock Falls, IL; 6/214 SecBand; CmntyWkr; HonRl; MrchBnd; NHS; PolWkr; VPStuCncl; VPFrCl; PresGAA; AmLegAwd; Il Univ; Physical Therypist Asst.

DEVINE, Diane; Herscher Hs; Herscher, IL; 13/175 Band; CncrtBnd; DrlTm; HonRl; MrchBnd; SecNHS; PepBnd; 4-H; AmLegAwd; AmLegAwd; College Siu; Special Education.

DEVINE, John J; Bishop Noll Inst; Highland, IN; 53/360 HonRl; NatlFornLg; NHS; StuCncl; LetterTrk; Coll; Med.

DEVINE, John R; Marist HS; Chicago, IL; LetterFtbl; Northern Ill; Public Relations.

DEVINE, Judy K; Emmerich Manual HS; Indianapolis, IN; Band; Chr; ChrhWkr; CncrtBnd; HonRl; MrchBnd; PepBnd; SchMus; YthFlsp; Bible College; Christian Education.

DEVINE, Randy A; St Louis HS; St Louis, MI; 2/120 ALBoysSt; Band; ChrhWkr; NHS; NatlMeritCmnd; SptEdYrbk; RptrSchPpr; CaptFtbl; CaptTrk; CaptWrstlng; Mi Tech Univ; Mechanical Engineer.

DEVINE, Robert J; Kewaskum HS; Adell, WI; AFS; HonRl; NatlFornLg; 4-H; MthCl; Trk; Wrstlng; College; Engineering.

DE VINEY, Linda M; Bolingbrook HS; Bolingbrook, IL; 3/219 Chrs; HonRl; Mdrgl; NHS; TchrAde; SchPpr; North Central College; Computer Analyst.

DE VITO, Karol A; Waterford Mott HS; Pontiac, MI; College; Medicine.

DE VITO, Susan E; Rolling Meadows HS; Arlington Hts, IL; 14/546 ChrhWkr; DrlTm; HonRl; HospAde; NHS; University; Professional.

DE VLAMINCK, Virginia A; New Haven HS; New Haven, MI; HonRl; LbryAde; NHS; College; Veterinarian.

DEVLIN, Christopher P; Benet Academy; Bolingbrook, IL; 10/230 Aud/Vis; ChrhWkr; CmntyWkr; HonRl; JrNHS; NHS; Ftbl; Illinois Inst Of Tech; Chemical Engineer.

DEVLIN, Joe; West Grant HS; Woodman, WI; TrsFrshCls; Band; CncrtBnd; HonRl; MrchBnd; SchPl; 4-H; FFA; LetterBsbl; LetterBsktbl; LetterFtbl; LetterTrk; Univ Of Wi La Crosse; Physical Education.

DEVNEY, Joann; Lourdes HS; Rochester, MN; Chrs; ChrhWkr; DrlTm; HonRl; NatlCathMusEdAsoc; OffAde; SchMus; TchrAde; UNYO; SpnCl; St Catherines Col; Math.

DEVO, Michael S; Kennedy St Paul HS; Chicago, IL; HonRl; IMSpt; College; Professional.

DEVORAK, Douglas J; Madison Public HS; Madison, MN; ChrhWkr; CmntyWkr; HonRl; TchrAde; Wrstlng; IMSpt; PresAwd; Trade; Computer Science.

DE VORE, Robert; Nevis HS; Park Rapids, MN; PresFrshCls; SecSophCls; Chrs; College; Prof.

DE VORE, Timothy G; Alma HS; Alma, MI; 36/266 Chr; Chrl; CncrtBnd; HonRl; MrchBnd; NatlFornLg; NatlThespSoc; SchMus; PresStuCncl; Yrbk; Adrian College; Music And Theatre.

DE VOS, Doreen K; Marshall HS; Marshall, MN; 40/220 Chr; ChrhWkr; CmntyWkr; HonRl; NatlFornLg; PolWkr; SchMus; SchPl; RptrSchPpr; 4-H; FHA; Bsktbl; ChmbCommrsAwd; Macalester College; Political Science.

DE VOS, Julie F; Minneota HS; Taunton, MN; ChrhWkr; CmntyWkr; HonRl; HospAde; LbryAde; SchPl; RptrSchPpr; IMSpt; BttyCrckrAwd; PresAwd; Trade School; Professional.

DEVRIES, Conda; Armour Hs; Armour, SD; 1/30 Chr; Chrs; ChrhWkr; HonRl; NHS; SchMus; SchPl; RptrYrbk; FHA; Trk; Dakota Wesleyan U; Medical Lab Tech.

DE VRIES, Dan L; Ogilvie HS; Dalbo, MN; 5/54 PresFrshCls; Chr; HonRl; Mdrgl; NHS; StuCncl; LetterBsbl; LetterBsktbl; LetterFtbl; Bemidji St Coll; Business.

DEVRIES, Deborah; Sheldon Community HS; Sheldon, IA; 20/146 ChrhWkr; CncrtBnd; HonRl; HospAde; MrchBnd; NHS; SctActv; YthFlsp; College; Professional.

DE VRIES, Donna F; Rapid City Central HS; Rapid City, SD; 29/552 ChrhWkr; HonRl; LitMag; Orch; PolWkr; PresYthFlsp; PresFHA; PresGerCl; SciCl; Dakota Wesleyan U; Abnormal Psychology.

DE VRIES, Janice; Chicago Christian HS; Evergreen Park, IL; 14/175 Chr; Chrl; ChrhWkr; HonRl; JrNHS; Mdrgl; NHS; SchPl; Yrbk; FrCl; GAA; College; Doctor.

DE VRIES, Phyllis L; Parkwood HS; Joplin, MO; 67/314 PresSrCls; HonRl; PresStuCncl; Teen; PpCl; CaptChrldr; Missouri St; Major Study.

DE VRIES, Ruth R; Corsica Public HS; Harrison, SD; 3/21 PresSophCls; VPJrCls; TrsSrCls; Chrs; HonRl; SchPl; StuCncl; RptrYrbk; PpCl; Trk; Sdsu; Pharmacy.

DE VRIES, Steven A; Pella Comm HS; Palla, IA; 17/125 PresJrCls; VPSrCls; ALBoysSt; Chrs; HonRl; Bsbl; CaptBsktbl; CaptFtbl; Trk; Coll; History Teacher.

DEVROY, Michael R; New Trier East HS; Wilmette, IL; 250/850 Band; HonRl; Yrbk; LatCl; SciCl; Ftbl; Swmmng; Wrstlng; IMSpt; Purdue; Aeronautical Engineering.

DEW, Deborah L; Browns Valley HS; Browns Valley, MN; 4/42 PresJrCls; ALAGirlsSt; Band; HonRl; NHS; SchPl; StuCncl; Yrbk; EdSchPpr; FHA; Moorehead St Coll; Special Education.

DE WAARD, Gary G; Stickney Public HS; Stickney, SD; 9/36 PresSophCls; ALBoysSt; HonRl; LbryAde; StuCncl; RptrYrbk; LetterBsktbl; LetterFtbl; LetterTrk; BttyCrckrAwd; Farming; Farming.

DE WAAY, Byron O; Sheldon Comm HS; Sanborn, IA; ChrhWkr; CmntyWkr; HonRl; YthFlsp; SecFFA; College; Science.

DEWALD, Kelly D; Meridian 303 HS; Hebron, NE; 5/35 SecJrCls; Chr; CncrtBnd; MrchBnd; SchAde; RptrYrbk; 4-H; EngCl; PpCl; PPFtbl; Daane Clg; Teaching.

DE WALD, Robert M; Meridian HS; Alexandria, NE; Chrs; HonRl; SchPl; SctActv; StuGov; SchPpr; LetterFtbl; LetterTrk; Wrstlng; Service.

DE WALL, Debra D; Pocahontas Comm HS; Pocahontas, IA; 13/72 Band; CncrtBnd; DrlTm; HonRl; HospAde; MrchBnd; PepBnd; StuCncl; TchrAde; RptrSchPpr; PpCl; Bsbl; Bsktbl; Iowa Methodist Schl Of Nursing; Nurse.

DE WALL, Diane E; Palmer Cons HS; Gilmore City, IA; 2/22 PresSophCls; Band; ChrhWkr; HonRl; ModUN; StuCncl; TreasYthFlsp; RptrSchPpr; FHA; IMSpt; LionAwd; Univ Of S Dakota; Music.

DE WALL, Jane A; Pocahontas Comm HS; Pocahontas, IA; 6/71 SecTrsSophCls; SecSrCls; Chr; ChrhWkr; CncrtBnd; HonRl; MrchBnd; NHS; SchMus; College; Medical Assistant.

DE WALT, Michael L; Kewanee HS; Kewanee, IL; Band; PepBnd; PolWkr; SchPl; TchrAde; SchPpr; FTA; Ftbl; Wrstlng; University; Business.

DE WALT, Ronda L; Charlotte HS; Charlotte, MI; 6/262 Band; CncrtBnd; HonRl; MrchBnd; NHS; NatlMeritSchl; PepBnd; PpCl; Michigan St Univ; Veterinarian.

DE WEERDT, Randall L; Fulton HS; Fulton, IL; 3/124 HonRl; NHS; College; Civil Engineering.

DEWEESE, Marlene; Austin HS; Deputy, IN; NHS; TchrAde; FTA; LatCl; SpnCl; Indiana Southeast U; Special Ed.

DE WEESE, Penny J; Goodhue HS; Goodhue, MN; Chr; Chrs; HonRl; TchrAde; YthFlsp; SchPpr; LetterBsktbl; Red Wing Avti; Data Processing.

DEWELL, Kevin W; Fowler HS; Fowler, KS; Band; CncrtBnd; MrchBnd; PepBnd; SchPl; StuCncl; SecFFA; Bsktbl; Ftbl; LetterTennis;.

DE WELLS, Cliff; Leo HS; Ft Wayne, IN; 36/116 JrNHS; SchPl; Yrbk; SciCl; IMSpt; OptClAwd; College; Prof Or Vocational.

DE WENT, Debra S; Hudsonville HS; Hudsonville, MI; Band; ChrhWkr; HonRl; NHS; StuCncl; EdYrBk; 4-H; Bsktbl; PPFtbl; Grand Rapids Jr Col; Accouging.

DEWEY, Charles R; Ashby HS; Ashby, MN; VPJrCls; TrsSrCls; Chr; Mdrgl; SchPl; StuCncl; EdYrBk; RptrSchPpr; FFA; Alexandria Area Tech Inst; Commerical Art.

DEWEY, Mark; East Kentwood HS; Kentwood, MI; SctActv; Tennis; IMSpt; College; Vocational.

DEWHIRST, Curt V; Newton HS; Newton, IL; Band; CncrtBnd; HonRl; MrchBnd; PepBnd; LatCl; College; Liberal Arts.

DE WITT, Charles C; Routt HS; Virginia, IL; 6/61 HonRl; JA; NatlMeritCmnd; Yrbk; MthCl; College; Professional.

DEWITT, Charles C; Routt HS; Virginai, IL; 5/65 HonRl; NHS; NatlMeritCmnd; MthCl; Trk; College; Professional.

DE WITT, Charles C; Routt HS; Virginia, IL; 5/65 HonRl; NHS; Yrbk; MthCl; Trk; College; Professional.

DE WITT, David J; North Mahaska HS; New Sharon, IA; HonRl; SctActv; 4-H; FFA; LetterBsbl; Bsktbl; LetterFtbl; LetterGlf; Trk; Wrstlng;.

DE WITT, Franklin S; Wisconsin Heights HS; Black Earth, WI; 10/120 PresJrCls; ALBoysSt; Band; NHS; StuCncl; SptEdSchPpr; LetterFtbl; Trk; Us Military Acad W Point; Electrical Eng.

DE WITT, Judith A; Carmel Girls HS; Zion, IL; 4/195 CmntyWkr; HonRl; NHS; TchrAde; PresSpnCl; MthCl; PpCl; GAA; University; Teacher.

DEWITT, Linda; Marquette Hs; Marquette, KS; 1/17 SecJrCls; Band; Chrs; CncrtBnd; HonRl; SchPl; StuCncl; EdYrBk; RptrSchPpr; PpCl; Wichita State U; Dental Hygiene.

DEWITT, Ray L; Hale HS; Hale, MO; ChrhWkr; CmntyWkr; SctActv; StuGov; Yrbk; 4-H; LetterBsbl; LetterBsktbl; LetterTrk; 4-HAwd; Us Army; Welder.

DE WITTE, Richard S; Hudson HS; Hudson, WI; 3/270 Aud/Vis; HonRl; SctActv; Tennis; St Cloud Mn; Conservation.

DEWULF, Karol K; Durant HS; Wilton, IA; ChrhWkr; CncrtBnd; HonRl; NatlCathMusEdAsoc; NatlFornLg; NHS; PepBnd; StuCncl; RptrSchPpr; Chrldr; Iowa State Univ; Home Ec Journalism.

DEXTER, Carol A; Wausau East HS; Wausau, WI; 45/300 HonRl; PolWkr; SctActv; RptrSchPpr; Trk; College; Sociology.

DEXTER, Julie K; Chambers HS; Chambers, NE; SecFrshCls; PresSophCls; SecJrCls; NHS; Bsbl; Bsktbl; Ftbl; Swmmng; Trk; Chrldr; College; Art.

DEXTER, Robin J; Clarks HS; Clarks, NE; Band; CncrtBnd; HonRl; MrchBnd; PepBnd; RptrSchPpr; PpCl; Trk; Col ;rn.

DEXTER, Ruth E; Century HS; Ullin, IL; 6/57 ChrhWkr; HonRl; RptrSchPpr; 4-H; FHA; PpCl; IMSpt; 4-HAwd; U Of Il; Psychology.

DEY, Justin A; Douglas Mac Arthur HS; Saginaw, MI; 45/300 HonRl; NHS; PolWkr; SctActv; TchrAde; Ftbl; Trk; Delta Univ; Dentist.

DEY, Sheryl A; Douglas Mac Arthur HS; Saginaw, MI; 21/283 Band; HonRl; MrchBnd; NHS; NatlMeritCmnd; Orch; PolWkr; SchPl; SchPpr; FrCl; Univ Of Michigan ; Professional.

DEYO, Daniel E; Millington HS; Millington, MI; NHS; RptrSchPpr; LetterTrk; LetterWrstlng; College.

DEYO, Mike D; Martin Hughes HS; Britt, MN; ALBoysSt; HonRl; Yrbk; LetterBsbl; LetterBsktbl; LetterFtbl; LetterTrk; CchngActv; Col;.

DE YONKER, Lorianne; Our Lady Star Of The Sea HS; Grosse Pointe Wood, MI; VPFrshCls; TrsJrCls; HonRl; HospAde; LbryAde; NHS; SchPl; Bsktbl; GAA; IMSpt; Mi U; Dental.

DE YOUNG, Cheryl D; Thornwood HS; S Holland, IL; 23/852 CncrtBnd; HonRl; MrchBnd; NHS; StuCncl; GerCl; Thornton Jr College; Accounting.

DE YOUNG, Merrilee D; Pella Christian HS; Pella, IA; Chr; HonRl; SchPl; RptrSchPpr; Bsbl; Trk; Iowa State University; Wildlife Biology.

DE YOUNG, Susan J; Watervliet HS; Watervliet, MI; SecFrshCls; Band; Chrl; CncrtBnd; MrchBnd; NHS; NatlMeritSchl; Orch; PepBnd; SchMus; Siena Heights Clg; Music.

DEZEEUW, Gail; Lake Benton Public HS; Lake Benton, MN; 5/37 Chrs; HonRl; LbryAde; MrchBnd; NHS; SchPl; RptrYrbk; RptrSchPpr; FHA; College; Medical Tech.

DE ZEEUW, Vera C; Orfordville Parkview HS; Evansville, WI; 44/150 Band; HonRl; NatlFornLg; NatlThespSoc; SchAde; 4-H; Bsktbl; CchngActv; IMSpt; 4-HAwd; Rock Valley Col; Recreation/police Science.

DEZELAN, Denise; Taylor HS; Kokomo, IN; 5/295 HonRl; JA; NHS; 4-H; SpnCl; GAA; Univ; Professional.

DE ZWAAN, Timothy J; Caledonia HS; Caledonia, MI; 1/172 VPJrCls; Band; CncrtBnd; PresFrshCls; MrchBnd; NatlMeritFnl; NatlMeritSF; Glf; Tennis; Trk; Univ;chem Physics.

DHAEMERS, Geralyn M; Sherrard HS; Sherrad, IL; 19/120 TrsJrCls; HonRl; StuGov; SptEdYrbk; 4-H; FHA; FrCl; PpCl; CaptChrldr; Coll; Accounting.

DHAENS, Laurie S; Cary Grove HS; Cary, IL; 14/291 Chr; HonRl; JrNHS; NHS; RptrYrbk; College; Education.

DIACZOK, Irene; Fitzgerald HS; Warren, MI; HonRl; LitMag; NHS; PolWkr; SchPl; SctActv; StuGov; FTA; PpCl; Wayne St Univ; Med.

DIAK, Robert J; Granite HS; Granite City, IL; 49/630 University; Pre Medicine.

DIAL, Denise L; Lincoln HS; Des Moines, IA; Us Army Res; Radio Field Oper.

DIAL, Sally M; Moweaqua HS; Moweaqua, IL; ChrhWkr; HonRl; LbryAde; RptrSchPpr; FHA; Cancer Research.

DIAMANT, Richard L; Parkay North HS; St Louis, MO; ALBoysSt; JrNHS; LitMag; ModUN; SchAde; TchrAde; RptrYrbk; MthCl; IMSpt; Univ Of Missouri; Law Business.

DIAMOND, Nancy; Gilman HS; Gilman, WI; SecFrshCls; Chrs; ChrhWkr; HonRl; MrchBnd; NHS; SchPl; StuCncl; YthFlsp; Bsktbl; College; Registered Nurse.

DIAZ, Gloria; Calumet HS; Gary, IN; 4/350 PresChr; Chrl; HonRl; JrNHS; LbryAde; NHS; Teen; SecFSA; SecSpnCl; SecSciCl; Bsktbl; GAA; IMSpt; Purdue Univ; Reg Nurse.

DIBBERN, Deanna K; Perry Community HS; Perry, IA; 14/145 HonRl; PolWkr; RptrSchPpr; FrCl; PpCl; LetterGlf; Chrldr; Iowa State Univ; Architecture.

DIBBERN, Joseph A; Yankton Senior HS; Yankton, SD; 3/233 ALBoysSt; Band; HonRl; MrchBnd; NHS; StuGov; YthFlsp; FDA; LetterFtbl; LetterTrk; LetterIMSpt; University Of South Dakota; Medicine.

DIBBLE, Bonnie; Lc Mohr HS; South Haven, MI; College; Artist.

DI BENEDETTO, Mike A; St Pius X HS; Kansas City, MO; 10/129 HonRl; RptrSchPpr; PpCl; Ftbl; LetterGlf; Trk; LetterWrstlng; College; Professional.

DIBENEDETTO, Vincent; Oak Park & River Forest HS; Oak Park, IL; 1/1100 ALBoysSt; Chr; HonRl; Mdrgl; NatlFornLg; NHS; NatlMeritSF; SchMus; StuCncl; AmLegAwd; College; English Major.

DIBLER, Brenda F; Virden Comm HS; Virden, IL; Chrs; ChrhWkr; HonRl; NHS; SchMus; TchrAde; Twrl; YthFlsp; Yrbk; FTA; PpCl; SciCl; Bsbl; Blackburn College; Math.

DIBLER, Daryl L; Manual HS; Peoria, IL; 11/326 Chr; HonRl; SchMus; SchPl; RptrSchPpr; EdSchPpr; Illinois Central College; Law.

DI CARO, Daneil P; Holy Cross HS; Chicago, IL; 10/314 VPFrshCls; PresJrCls; PresSrCls; HonRl; NHS; StuCncl; LetterBsbl; LetterFtbl;.

DICK, Cathy J; Northrop HS; Ft Wayne, IN; 6/587 HonRl; NatlFornLg; NatlSciFnd; SchMus; TchrAde; ChmbCommrsAwd; LionAwd; Purdue Univ; Pharmacy.

DICK, Debra S; Wayne HS; Ft Wayne, IN; 41/300 CncrtBnd; HonRl; MrchBnd; Orch; Bsktbl; Tennis; Chrldr; Ball State U; Phy Ed.

DICK, Donna J; E Prairie HS; East Prairie, MO; 4/98 Band; Chr; HonRl; TreasNHS; SctActv; Twrl; PresFHA; PpCl; SciCl; Trk; Univ Mo; Dentist.

DICK, Donna R; Boone County R Vi HS; Centraia, MO; SecTrsFrshCls; ChrhWkr; CmntyWkr; NHS; SchPl; StuCncl; TchrAde; CaptChrldr; PresGAA; IMSpt; Univ Of Mo; Special Education.

DICK, Dwayne; Buhler HS; Burrton, KS; ChrhWkr; TchrAde; 4-H; FFA; 4-HAwd; Vocational Tech; Auto Mech.

DICK, Gerry A; Clinton HS; Clinton, IN; VPFrshCls; VPSophCls; PresJrCls; ALBoysSt; ChrhWkr; CmntyWkr; StuGov; SptEdYrbk; SchPpr; LatCl; College; Communications.

DICK, Paul W; Maine West HS; Des Plaines, IL; 100/759 Bsktbl; Trk; College; Finance.

DICK, Sheila M; Bishop Borgess HS; Livonia, MI; CmntyWkr; HonRl; HospAde; NHS; Madonna College; Nursing.

DICK, Timothy; Northern Christian HS; Mc Bain, MI; 4-H; Bsktbl; Trk; IMSpt; 4-HAwd; Michigan State; Engineering.

DICKASON, Laura J; St Charles HS; St Charle, MO; Band; CncrtBnd; HonRl; MrchBnd; NHS; PepBnd; StuCncl; Jr College; Occupational Therapy.

DICKE, Martin P; Concordia Academy; St Paul, MN; PresFrshCls; PresSophCls; PresJrCls; Chr; Chrl;

HonRl; SchPl; StuCncl; RptrYrbk; Bsktbl; Ftbl; Trk; College; Music.

DICKEL, David E; J I Case HS; Des Moines, IA; 9/732 ChrhWkr; HonRl; FBLA; LetterBsbl; LetterFtbl; Univ Of Iowa; Computer Engineering.

DICKEN, Kent; Alexandria Monroe HS; Alexandria, IN; 6/223 ChrhWkr; HonRl; NHS; NatlMeritCmnd; SchPl; SctActv; TchrAde; YthFlsp; Yrbk; GerCl; Ball St Univ; Secondary Spec Ed.

DICKEN, Rebecca L; Gladwin HS; Gladwin, MI; 7/151 HonRl; JrNHS; NHS; RptrYrbk; SptEdYrbk; RptrSchPpr; FHA; LetterBsktbl; LetterTrk; U Of Mi.

DICKEN, Sharon; De Soto Sr HS; De Soto, KS; HonRl; StuCncl; PpCl; GAA; Nazarene College; Art Business.

DICKENS, David A; Central HS; St Joseph, MO; VPJrCls; SchMus; StuCncl; LatCl; Tennis; GodCntryAwd; MasAwd; Univ Mo Columbia; Law Field.

DICKENS, Linda S; Republic R 3 HS; Republic, MO; 20/113 Band; ChrhWkr; CncrtBnd; LitMag; JrNHS; MrchBnd; NHS; PepBnd; IMSpt; College.

DICKENS, Robert J; St John Cathedral HS; Milwaukee, WI; 10/120 ALBoysSt; Chr; HonRl; SchAde; SchMus; TchrAde; RptrSchPpr; SptEdSchPpr; SchPpr; SpnCl; University; Professional.

DICKENSON, Clifton R; Hermitage HS; Hermitage, MO; Chrs; HonRl; SchPl; StuCncl; PpCl; Bsbl; Military Service.

DICKENSON, Patricia; William Jennings Bryan HS; Omaha, NE; 149/390 Business School.

DICKERSON, Chris M; Newton Community HS; Newton, IL; 41/187 Band; CncrtBnd; HonRl; MrchBnd; NHS; PepBnd; VP4-H; FHA;.

DICKERSON, Deborah L; Adrian R 3 HS; Butler, MO; 4/56 SecSophCls; HonRl; PresNHS; SchPl; StuCncl; TchrAde; SecFHA; Bsbl; LetterBsktbl; BttyCrckrAwd; Lawyers Sec.

DICKERSON, Dee A; Indianola HS; Indianola, IA; VPSrCls; Band; Chrs; NHS; PepBnd; SchMus; VPPpCl; ChmnTrk; LetterChrldr; GAA; U Of N Iowa.

DICKERSON, Jo Beth; Clay City HS; Clay City, IN; CncrtBnd; DrlTm; HonRl; MrchBnd; NHS; TchrAde; SptEdYrbk; FHA; PpCl; University; Special Education.

DICKERSON, Linda S; Platte Valley Academy; Lincoln, NE; 1/39 VPFrshCls; PresSophCls; Chr; HonRl; NHS; SpnCl; College; Nursing.

DICKERSON, Sandra D; Grosse Pte North HS; Grosse Pte Woods, MI; 1/613 LetterBand; JrNHS; MrchBnd; NHS; NatlMeritFnl; SctActv; TchrAde; LetterBsbl; LetterBsktbl; CchngActv; Univ; Doctor.

DICKES, Suzanne M; Lawton Bronson HS; Sioux City, IA; Chr; Chrs; DrlTm; NHS; NatlThespSoc; Quill&Scroll; RptrSchPpr; SchPpr; Bsktbl; Wayne State U; Music.

DICKESON, Linda K; Galesburg Senior HS; Galesburg, IL; 25/588 Band; Chr; Chrs; CncrtBnd; HonRl; JrNHS; Mdrgl; MrchBnd; Orch; PepBnd; SchMus; 4-H; Bradley Univ; Accounting.

DICKEY, Collin M; St Anthony Village HS; Mpls, MN; 5/192 ALBoysSt; CncrtBnd; HonRl; NatlThespSoc; NHS; PepBnd; PresStuCncl; LetterFtbl; Trk; IMSpt; St Olaf Coll; Bus.

DICKEY, Danny L; Valley R6 HS; Caledonia, MO; 8/48 Band; ChrhWkr; CncrtBnd; HonRl; NHS; SchPl; RptrSchPpr; 4-H; Bsktbl; Col; Engineering.

DICKEY, Kevin L; Kenwood HS; Chicago, IL; CmntyWkr; NatlThespSoc; SchPl; StuCncl; Yrbk; University; Architecture.

DICKEY, Terri L; Rosedale HS; Montezuma, IN; 3/50 TrsSrCls; Chr; ChrhWkr; HonRl; NHS; SchPl; TchrAde; YthFlsp; 4-H; Bsktbl; Trk; GAA; College; Art.

DICKIE, Debra; Crosby Ironton HS; Merrifield, MN; 2/148 HonRl; NHS; TchrAde; FHA; FTA; IMSpt; BttyCrckrAwd; LionAwd; Concordia Coll.

DICKINSON, Gayle M; Logan Magnolia Comm HS; Logan, IA; 4/58 Band; Chr; Chrs; CncrtBnd; HonRl; MrchBnd; NHS; PepBnd; SchPl; FHA; PpCl; LetterBsbl; LetterBsktbl; College; Psychology.

DICKINSON, James R; North Platte HS; North Platte, NE; Chr; ChrhWkr; HonRl; Bsktbl; Ftbl; Trk; Clge; Electronics.

DICKINSON, John; Buffalo Grove HS; Arlington Hts, IL; ChrhWkr; HonRl; JA; SctActv; LetterFtbl; Socr; CaptTrk; JAAwd; University; Accountant.

DICKINSON, Katherine M; Milton Public HS; Milton, ND; PresFrshCls; PresJrCls; Chrs; HonRl; SchPl; SchPpr; FHA; Univ; Law.

DICKINSON, Kim; Mitchell Senior HS; Mitchell, SD; /296 HonRl; HospAde; NHS; Practical Nursing; Nursing.

DICKINSON, Marsyl D; Maplewood Academy; Mankato, MN; TrsSrCls; Chr; Chrl; HospAde; LbryAde; StuGov; EdYrBk; RptrSchPpr; Union Clg; Commercial Art.

DICKINSON, Matthew G; Carthage Comm HS; Carthage, IL; 1/88 ALBoysSt; HonRl; NHS; Bradley Univ; Electrical Engineering.

DICKISON, Brenda; Cabool HS; Cabool, MO; 7/72 Chr; CmntyWkr; HonRl; NHS; NatlThespSoc; SchPl; YthFlsp; EdSchPpr; FHA; PPFtbl; Southwest Mo State Univ; English.

DICKMAN, Jay W; Jacksonville HS; Jacksonville, IL; 69/352 HonRl; StuGov; KeyCl; LetterBsbl; LetterBsktbl; LetterSocr; Eastern Illinois University.

DICKMAN, Kathy A; Sac Community HS; Sac City, IA; 12/81 ChrhWkr; HonRl; HospAde; LbryAde; FNA; Hospital Schl; Nursing.

DICKMAN, Marla; Worthington Senior HS; Reading, MN; HospAde; YthFlsp; 4-HAwd; Sioux Valley School Of Nursing;nursing.

DICKMAN, Susan M; Grinnell HS; Grinnell, KS; 6/27 Band; Chr; Chrl; Chrs; CncrtBnd; HonRl; MrchBnd; PepBnd; SchPl; RptrYrbk; SchPpr; 4-H; PpCl; LetterBsktbl; College; Business.

DICKMAN, Thomas F; Zeeland HS; Zeeland, MI; ALBoysSt; Band; MrchBnd; PepBnd; SchPl; Ftbl; Ferris St Coll; Printer.

DICKMEYER, Debra; Arapahoe Public HS; Arapahoe, NE; VPJrCls; Chr; ChrhWkr; HonRl; SchPl; YthFlsp; PpCl; Trk; Trade School; Vocational.

DICKOFF, Jane E; Regis HS; Eau Claire, WI; Band; Chr; Chrs; CncrtBnd; HonRl; MrchBnd; Orch; PepBnd; SchMus; StuGov; FrCl; PpCl; GAA; Lawrence Univ; Music.

DICKRELL, Karen M; Elkhart Lake Glenbeulah HS; Elkhart Lake, WI; Band; Chrs; HonRl; NHS; PepBnd; SchPl; StuCncl; EdSchPpr; FHA; PpCl;.

DICKS, Ramona L; Brown Deer HS; Brown Deer, WI; ChrhWkr; CmntyWkr; HonRl; HospAde; NatlMeritCmnd; SctActv; YthFlsp; RptrYrbk; GerCl; Kent State Univ; Nursing.

DICKSON, Christopher W; Maine East HS; Niles, IL; ChrhWkr; JA; YthFlsp; RusCl; Socr; Swmmng; CchngActv; Indiana Univ; Computer Science.

DICKSON, Cindy L; Forest Lake HS; Forest Lake, MN; 18/354 HonRl; Coll; Law.

DICKSON, David P; Hinckley Big Rock HS; Big Rock, IL; 3/72 HonRl; NHS; NatlMeritCmnd; PepBnd; SchPl; SctActv; RptrSchPpr; SciCl; Bsktbl; Glf; LetterSocr; AmLegAwd; College; Medicine.

DICKSON, Debra G; Waldron HS; Waldron, MI; 2/44 Chrs; ChrhWkr; HonRl; NHS; StuCncl; Yrbk; EdSchPpr; FHA; PpCl; Bsbl; Trk; Chrldr; PresGAA; College.

DICKSON, Diane; Urbandale HS; Urbandale, IA; 32#41#44 NHS; PolWkr; YthFlsp; RptrYrbk; CchngActv; College; Child Development.

DICKSON, Kenneth R; Monticello Public HS; Monticello, WI; 5/38 ALBoysSt; Band; CmntyWkr; PepBnd; TchrAde; UNYO; YthFlsp; SpnCl; PpCl; Bsktbl; Professional.

DI CRISTOFARO, Lynn M; Nazareth Academy; Lyons, IL; 27/154 HonRl; JrNHS; LbryAde; NHS; OffAde; FrCl; GerCl; Control Data Inst; Computer Science.

DIDDENS, Karen G; Lanark HS; Lanark, IL; 7/57 TrsSrCls; Band; Chrs; CncrtBnd; HonRl; MrchBnd; PepBnd; SchPl; 4-H; TreasFHA; Chrldr; GAA; University; Speech Pathology.

DIDERICH, James M; Hononegah HS; Roscoe, IL; ALBoysSt; SchMus; SchPl; Univ Of Illinois; Engineering.

DIDIER, Cynthia M; Belle Fourche HS; Belle Fourche, SD; 9/116 Band; HonRl; JrNHS; MrchBnd; NHS; PepBnd; SchPl; Yrbk; PpCl; GAA; Stevens College; Secretarial.

DIDIER, Rhonda; Franklin HS; Franklin Grove, IL; 7/36 Chrs; HonRl; NHS; SchMus; SchPl; RptrSchPpr; 4-H; PpCl; TreasGAA; 4-HAwd; Parkland Coll; X Ray Tech.

DIEBEL, Thomas W; Glenbrook South HS; Glenview, IL; 58/625 Band; Chr; ChrhWkr; CncrtBnd; HonRl; MrchBnd; NHS;.

DIEBOLD, David; Hartford HS; Hartford, MI; Band; CncrtBnd; HonRl; LitMag; MrchBnd; PepBnd; RptrSchPpr; Trk; College; Business Management.

DIEBOLT, Lynn D; Corunna HS; Corunna, MI; 4/219 Band; CncrtBnd; HonRl; MrchBnd; NHS; Orch; 4-H; FFA; Michigan State Univ; Veterinarian.

DIECK, Joyce A; Franklin Central HS; Indianapolis, IN; 53/221 Chr; Chrs; ChrhWkr; Mdrgl; SchMus; FHA;.

DIECKER, Karen J; Freeburg Comm HS; St Libory, IL; 6/124 ChrhWkr; CmntyWkr; HonRl; LbryAde; ModUN; NHS; SchAde; College; Professional.

DIECKHOFF, Cynthia L; Diamond R 4 HS; Diamond, MO; 1/63 SecSophCls; Chr; Mdrgl; NHS; SchMus; TchrAde; YthFlsp; FHA; Chrldr; 4-HAwd; Sw Missouri State College; Art Teacher.

DIECKMAN, Douglas R; Benton Co R 1 HS; Cole Camp, MO; 9/52 ALBoysSt; HonRl; Pres4-H; FFA;.

DIEDE, Carla M; Ellendale Public HS; Ellendale, ND; PresSophCls; VPJrCls; ChrhWkr; HonRl; HospAde; FHA; PpCl; LetterBsktbl; Trk; Chrldr; IMSpt; CitAwd; College; Nursing.

DIEDERICH, Cynthia I; West De Pere HS; De Pere, WI; 15/187 HonRl; NHS; SchPpr; FTA; SciCl; LetterBsktbl; GAA; CitAwd; Engn Sch; Electrical Engineer.

DIEDERICH, Delores M; Hanover HS; Greenleaf, KS; TrsSophCls; TrsJrCls; Chrs; HonRl; SchMus; SchPl; Sdlty; FHA; SecTrsSophCls; Chrldr; Ks St Univ; Nursing.

DIEDRICH, Becky; Little Chute HS; Little Chute, WI; PresSrCls; ALAGirlsSt; HonRl; NHS; RptrSchPpr; Bsktbl; Trk; Chrldr; GAA; IMSpt; Technical School; Accounting.

DIEDRICH, Cynthia; Ritenour Sr HS; St Louis, MO; HonRl; JrNHS; NHS; StuCncl; PPFtbl; JCAwd; College.

DIEDRICH, Dianne M; Hilbert HS; Hilbert, WI; 7/66 Chr; LitMag; TchrAde; Yrbk; GAA; BttyCrckrAwd; Fox Valley Tech; Child Care.

DIEDRICH, Jeffery D; Oshkosh West HS; Oshkosh, WI; Band; ChrhWkr; CncrtBnd; PepBnd; SctActv; Bsbl; Ftbl; Trk; Wrstlng; IMSpt; College; Professnl.

DIEDRICH, Rae; Slayton Public HS; Iona, MN; 20/109 SecJrCls; Band; CncrtBnd; DrlTm; HonRl; MrchBnd; NHS; PepBnd; FHA; Bsktbl; Trade School; Sales Manage.

DIEDRICHSEN, Sharon E; Blair HS; Blair, NE; 7/139 ALAGirlsSt; Band; Chr; HonRl; StuGov; YthFlsp; SchPpr; FSA; FTA; TreasSpnCl; Nebraska Wesleyan; Medicine.

DIEFENBACH, Linda L; St Paul HS; E St Louis, IL; 9/51 HonRl; YthFlsp; RptrYrbk; Trade School; Computer Science.

DIEFENBACH, Randy; Carrollton HS; Saginaw, MI; HonRl; JA; NHS; NatlMeritSchl; SchAde; StuCncl; StuGov; TchrAde; PpCl; Bsktbl; Saginaw Valley State College; Engineer.

DIEFENDORF, Ellen C; Otterville Public HS; Otterville, MO; 3/22 SecTrsJrCls; Chrs; DrmMjrt; HonRl; SchMus; PresPpCl; Bsbl; Bsktbl; Trk; CaptChrldr; University; Professional.

DIEGNAU, Linda S; Fenton HS; Bensenville, IL; 37/360 AFS; CmntyWkr; CncrtBnd; LitMag; MrchBnd; NHS; SecStuCncl; Yrbk; Univ Of Ill; Business Adm.

DIEHL, David L; Rudyard HS; Kincheloe Afb, MI; Band; CncrtBnd; HonRl; MrchBnd; SctActv; LetterBsbl; IMSpt; Trade School; Vocational.

DIEHL, Debra J; Wheatland HS; Elsie, NE; 5/20 ALAGirlsSt; Chrs; HonRl; SchPl; Yrbk; College; Physical Therapist.

DIEHL, Holly L; Little Wolf HS; Manawa, WI; Band; Chrs; HonRl; NHS; RptrYrbk; EdSchPpr; 4-H; MthCl; GAA; IMSpt; 4-HAwd; Univ Of Wis; Accounting.

DIEHL, Janet; Sauk Prairie HS; Sauk City, WI; 15/223 ChrhWkr; DrlTm; HonRl; NHS; NatlMeritCmnd; SchAde; TchrAde; PpCl; College; Teacher.

DIEHL, Marilyn G; Kaneland HS; Maple Park, IL; 18/152 VPBand; CncrtBnd; HonRl; NHS; NatlThespSoc; SchMus; SchPl; RptrSchPpr; TreasFrCl; GAA; 4-HAwd; College.

DIEHL, Robert T; Morton HS; Hammond, IN; 14/529 HonRl; NHS; TchrAde; SciCl; Tennis; College; Opthalmology.

DIEKEMPER, Lisa K; Dupo Community HS; Dupo, IL; 2/127 VPFrshCls; VPSophCls; TrsSrCls; ALAGirlsSt; HonRl; NHS; StuCncl; Yrbk; MthCl; University; Liberal Arts.

DIEKEN, Benjamin R; Dell Rapids Public HS; Dell Rapids, SD; 9/52 ALBoysSt; HonRl; NHS; Univ; Pro.

DIEKHANS, Mark E; North Vigo HS; Terre Haute, IN; HonRl; NHS; SciCl; Indiana Univ; Doctor.

DIEKMANN, Connie S; Algona HS; Algona, IA; Band; Chr; Chrs; ChrhWkr; CncrtBnd; DrlTm; DrmMjrt; HonRl; Mdrgl; MrchBnd; University; Music Major.

DIEKROEGER, Lisa; Williamsville HS; Sherman, IL; 11/65 SecSophCls; Chr; Chrs; HonRl; Mdrgl; NHS; OffAde; SchPl; GAA; IMSpt; Radiology Tech.

DIEL, Bruce A; Newton HS; Newton, IL; PresSrCls; StuCncl; LatCl; LetterBsktbl; LetterTennis; Trk;.

DIEL, Nancy; Brazil HS; Center Point, IN; 47/180 ChrhWkr; DrlTm; HonRl; SchMus; SchPl; StuCncl; YthFlsp; FHA; FTA; Chrldr; College.

DIELMAN, Annette L; Petoskey Senior HS; Petoskey, MI; ChrhWkr; HospAde; TchrAde; YthFlsp; FFA; College; Teaching.

DIENBERG, Denise M; Oak Park & River Forest HS; Oak Park, IL; 42/1200 Chrs; HonRl; NHS; College; Social Worker.

DIERCKS, David J; Dodge Center Public HS; Dodge Center, MN; Band; Chr; Chrs; CncrtBnd; HonRl; MrchBnd; NHS; LetterBsbl; LetterBsktbl; LetterFtbl; Mankato State Coll; Accounting.

DIERCKS, Deborah L; James B Conant HS; Hoffman Ests, IL; 10/647 Band; CmntyWkr; DrmMjrt; HonRl; JrNHS; LitMag; MrchBnd; PresNHS; PepBnd; SchPl; FrCl; PPFtbl; Univ Of So California.

DIERICX, James L; Atkinson HS; Atkinson, IL; 16/41 PresFrshCls; CAP; HonRl; RptrSchPpr; SchPpr; FFA; SpnCl; LetterBsbl; Agr Bus.

DIERKER, Diane K; Forman HS; Manito, IL; HonRl; StuCncl; RptrYrbk; FHA; KeyCl; LetterTrk; Chrldr; DanFAwd; 4-HAwd; CitAwd; Midstate College; Court Reporter.

DIERKING, Ann C; Washington HS; Washington, MO; 28/279 CmntyWkr; HonRl; JA; NHS; SctActv; RptrYrbk; RptrSchPpr; EdSchPpr; FBLA; PresFHA; U Of Mo Columbia; Business Admin.

DIERKING, Heidi A; Kenyon HS; Nerstrand, MN; HonRl; NHS; FHA; FrCl; College.

DIERKING, Keith A; Nemaha Valley HS; Talmage, NE; 19/33 TrsFrshCls; PresSophCls; ALBoysSt; SchPl; StuGov; TreasYthFlsp; Bsbl; LetterBsktbl; LetterTrk; College; Vocation.

DIERS, Ray; Spencer HS; Spencer, WI; HonRl; Quill&Scroll; Yrbk; SchPpr; Tech Sch; Residental Design.

DIERS, Rich A; Gresham Public HS; Gresham, NE; HonRl; PepBnd; SchPl; StuCncl; YthFlsp; RptrSchPpr; Bsbl; LetterBsktbl; LetterFtbl; LetterTrk; Kearney State Col; Engineering.

DIERSCHOW, Duane L; Smithville HS; Smithville, MO; 2/73 Band; CncrtBnd; HonRl; JrNHS; MrchBnd; NHS; SchMus; SchPl; StuCncl; TchrAde; SciCl; LetterFtbl; LetterTrk; AmLegAwd; College; Professional.

DIERSEN, Deborah A; Sac Comm HS; Sac City, IA; Chrs; HonRl; LbryAde; NHS; NatlMeritSF; FHA; SpnCl; PpCl; IMSpt; College.

DIESCH, Kurt H; Ed Co Community HS; Greely, IA; PresFrshCls; PresSophCls; PresJrCls; Band; CncrtBnd; HonRl; PepBnd; SchMus; YthFlsp; Ftbl; University; Electrical Engineering.

DIESEN, Thomas W; H H Dow HS; Midland, MI; CncrtBnd; HonRl; MrchBnd; NHS; NatlMeritFnl; NatlMeritSchl; SctActv; TchrAde; YthFlsp; Wrstlng; Tech College; Chemical Engineering.

DIESER, Margaret; Southland HS; Adams, MN; 1/122 HonRl; NHS; TchrAde; Yrbk; SchPpr; FTA; GerCl; PpCl; 4-HAwd; College Of St Benedict.

DIETER, Debra J; Brewster Public HS; Brewster, MN; ALAGirlsSt; Chrs; ChrhWkr; HonRl; LbryAde; SchPl; Yrbk; RptrSchPpr; 4-H; FHA; Bethany Lutheran Clg.

DIETERLE, Gregory J; Marian Central HS; Mc Henry, IL; ChrhWkr; PolWkr; SctActv; YthFlsp; Bsbl; Ftbl; Wrstlng; IMSpt; AmLegAwd;.

DIETERLE, Laura A; Gage Park HS; Chicago, IL; 29/463 Chrs; HonRl; LbryAde; NatlMeritCmnd; OffAde; SctActv; StuCncl; Augustana College; Med Technology.

DIETERMAN, Leann; Northern Christian HS; Mcbain, MI; 9/41 ChrhWkr; HonRl; NHS; SchPl; 4-H; Bsktbl; IMSpt; 4-HAwd; Beauty School; Cosmetologist.

DIETL, Janice K; Nokomis HS; Nokomis, IL; Chrs; ChrhWkr; HonRl; HospAde; SchMus; SchPl; Yrbk; 4-H; FHA; GAA; St Johns School Of Nursing; Nurse.

DIETL, Rick E; East HS; Waterloo, IA; 13/320 Chr; JrNHS; SpnCl;.

DIETMEYER, Cheryl L; Warren Township HS; Gurnee, IL; Chr; ChrhWkr; DrlTm; HonRl; Mdrgl; MrchBnd; NHS; OffAde; SchMus; TchrAde; Clg; Music.

DIETRICH, Becky L; Edison Senior HS; East Gary, IN; 8/203 SecBand; Chr; ChrhWkr; CncrtBnd; HonRl; JrNHS; Mdrgl; MrchBnd; Orch; SchMus; SctActv; FrCl; GAA; College; Physical Therapy.

DIETRICH, Catherine M; Edison Senior HS; East Gary, IN; 6/147 ALAGirlsSt; Band; Chr; HonRl; JrNHS; VPNHS; SchMus; SctActv; VPFrCl; SpnCl; GAA; Business School; Secretary.

DIETRICH, Debra L; Henryville HS; Memphis, IN; TrsFrshCls; HstJrCls; ChrhWkr; 4-H; PpCl; Chrldr; 4-HAwd; Col; Nursing.

DIETRICH, Gregory L; Abilene HS; Topeka, KS; 14/129 ALBoysSt; Chrs; HonRl; SchMus; SchPl; TchrAde; SciCl; LionAwd; State Univ; Chemistry.

DIETRICH, Jane M; Seymour HS; Plainville, IL; 25/68 SecJrCls; PresSrCls; SchPpr; 4-H; PpCl; LetterChrldr; 4-HAwd; College.

DIETRICH, John E; Mt Horeb HS; Mt Horeb, WI; ALBoysSt; PresNHS; FrCl; MthCl; Bsktbl; Ftbl; IMSpt; College; Meteorology.

DIETRICH, John W; Dearborn HS; Dearborn, MI; 92/700 Aud/Vis; HonRl; NatlFornLg; NHS; SchPpr; FrCl; LetterTrk; IMSpt; University Of Michigan; Medicine.

DIETRICH, Joseph T; Mt Horeb HS; Mt Horeb, WI; AFS; ALBoysSt; NHS; FrCl; MthCl; Bsktbl; Ftbl; IMSpt; University; Chemistry.

DIETRICH, Karla J; Notre Dame HS; Quincy, IL; Band; HonRl; SecNHS; NatlMeritFnl; SchPpr; Quincy College; Veterinarian.

DIETRICH, Marilyn R; Lanesville HS; Corydon, IN; 7/44 HstSophCls; SecJrCls; Band; Chr; HonRl; NHS; StuCncl; Trk; GAA; IMSpt; Western Ky Univ; Home Ec.

DIETRICH, Ronald R; Luther South HS; Hickory Hills, IL; 4/214 CncrtBnd; HonRl; MrchBnd; NHS; StuCncl; YthLg; SchPpr; Trk; Wrstlng; IMSpt; Northwestern Univ; Lawyer.

DIETSCH, Joan; Chetek HS; Colfax, WI; 27/83 SecSophCls; Chr; HonRl; Mdrgl; NatlFornLg; SchPl; 4-H; FBLA; FHA; Univ Wis Eau Claire.

DIETSCH, Julie C; Scotland HS; Kaylor, SD; 6/45 TrsSrCls; ChrhWkr; HonRl; SchPl; YthFlsp; RptrYrbk; PpCl; Bus Sch; Airlines.

DIETZ, Kevin M; New Prague HS; New Progue, MN; 30/206 HonRl; StuCncl; 4-H; SpnCl; Mankato State U; Nurse.

DIETZ, Lynn E; Mt Pleasant HS; Mt Pleasant, IA; Band; Chrs; ChrhWkr; CncrtBnd; HonRl; MrchBnd; PepBnd; YthFlsp; IMSpt; Clge; Minister Of Gospel.

DIETZ, Nancy J; Lakeville HS; Farmington, MN; 6/190 AFS; Band; ChrhWkr; CncrtBnd; HonRl; PresNHS; VPNatlThespSoc; SchMus; SchPl; EdYrBk; Col; Journalism.

DIETZEL, Shirley; East Dubuque HS; East Dubuque, IL; SecSophCls; SecJrCls; HonRl; ModUN; NHS; SchPl; EdYrBk; FHA; College.

DIETZMAN, Beverly K; Richland Center HS; Muscoda, WI; Band; Chr; ChrhWkr; HonRl; MrchBnd; 4-H; LatCl; 4-HAwd;.

DIETZMAN, Sandra; Morton Sr HS; Hammond, IN; 4/497 ALAGirlsSt; Band; DrmMjrt; HonRl; Orch; PolWkr; SpnCl; PpCl; PPFtbl; College; Accounting.

DIEWALD, Jeffrey M; Portage Central HS; Portage, MI; 14/340 Aud/Vis; HonRl; ModUN; NatlMeritSF; SchMus; SchPl; GerCl; SciCl; CchngActv; U Of Mich; Engineering.

DIEZ, Robbie; Brookfield Central HS; Elm Grove, WI; ChrhWkr; CAP; OffAde; StuCncl; TchrAde; FHA; FTA; CchngActv; GAA; IMSpt; Coll; Ed.

DIFANI, James E; Perryville HS; Perryville, MO; HonRl; NHS; Quill&Scroll; Southeast Missouri St Univ; Physics.

DI GAUDIO, Kathleen M; Good Counsel HS; Chicago, IL; Chr; Chrs; HonRl; SchMus; SchPl; Tennis; College; Veterinarian.

DIGGINS, Kathryn L; Rapid City Central HS; Rapid City, SD; ChrhWkr; HonRl; Mdrgl; NatlMeritSF; NatlThespSoc; PolWkr; SchMus; SchPl; FrCl; PPFtbl; C; Political Science.

DIGGS, Anne; University HS; Urbana, IL; 1/50 CmntyWkr; NatlMeritCmnd; SchPl; Yale Univ; Theatre.

DI GIANFILIPPO, Anthony; Gordon Tech; Chicago, IL; 8/618 HonRl; HospAde; VPNHS; SchMus; StuCncl; EdYrBk; RptrSchPpr; LetterSocr; JCAwd; Northwestern U; Medicine.

DI GIULIO, Thomas A; Joliet Township HS; Joliet, IL; 40/580 PresSophCls; PresJrCls; HonRl; StuCncl; LetterBsktbl; LetterTennis; University.

DIGMAN, Tamara L; Monroe Sr HS; Monroe, WI; 29/255 SecFrshCls; VPSophCls; VPJrCls; HonRl; SchPl; StuGov; RptrYrbk; Pres4-H; TreasFrCl; 4-HAwd; University.

DIGNAN, Dennis J; Almond HS; Almond, WI; HonRl; NHS; TchrAde; Yrbk; LetterFtbl; Trk; College; Engineering.

DI JULIO, Mark E; Marist HS; Oaklawn, IL; 22/398 HonRl; Glf; LetterSocr; IMSpt; College; Professional.

DIKE, Cindy A; Aquinas HS; Fort Madison, IA; VPSrCls; Band; ChrhWkr; CncrtBnd; DrmMjrt; HonRl; MrchBnd; NHS; PepBnd; StuCncl; RptrYrbk; FrCl; PpCl; Chrldr;.

DIKOFF, Lonell G; Medina Public HS; Medina, ND; Chr; Chrs; HonRl; SchPl; SptEdSchPpr; SchPpr; PresFFA; PpCl; Bsktbl; Trk; Trade School.

DI LALLO, Michael; Proviso West HS; Hillside, IL; HonRl; NHS; NatlThespSoc; SchPl; Univ Of Illinois; Mathematics.

DILAY, Diane M; Southfield Lathrup HS; Lathrup Village, MI; 107/683 Band; CncrtBnd; CaptDrmMjrt; HonRl; MrchBnd; NHS; NatlThespSoc; SchMus; SchPl; Mi State Univ; Vet Med.

DILGER, Carol V; Heritage Hills HS; Ferdinand, IN; HonRl; StuCncl; SchPpr; FHA; FrCl; PpCl; Chrldr; Indiana State University; Physical Therapy.

DILGER, Diane M; Bogan HS; Chicago, IL; 10/689 AFS; HonRl; NHS; OffAde; SchAde; StuCncl; TchrAde; Yrbk; Univ Of Ill; Medical Technology.

DILL, David L; Vermillion HS; Vermillion, SD; ALBoysSt; HonRl; NatlFornLg; NHS; NatlMeritSF; MthCl; SciCl; VoiceDemAwd; Computer Science.

DILL, Joann M; Shepherd Public HS; Shepherd, MI; 4/124 HonRl; NatlFornLg; NHS; TchrAde; FTA; FrCl; SpnCl; College; Biology.

DILL, Thomas E; Valentine HS; Valentine, NE; 2/95 VPJrCls; ALBoysSt; Band; CncrtBnd; HonRl; MrchBnd; NHS; NatlMeritSF; PepBnd; SchPpr; Univ Of Nebraska; Geology.

DILL, Thomas W; Valders HS; Newton, WI; 5/113 PresFrshCls; ALBoysSt; Band; CncrtBnd; HonRl; MrchBnd; NHS; PepBnd; LetterFtbl; LetterWrstlng; U S Navy; Nuclear Power.

DILLARD, Carolyn J; Green City HS; Green Castle, MO; 6/30 SecFrshCls; VPSophCls; Chrs; HonRl; FBLA; FHA; SpnCl; PpCl; CaptBsktbl; LetterTrk; IMSpt; College.

DILLARD, Dennis J; Aero Mechanics HS; Detroit, MI; HonRl; NHS; NatlMeritCmnd; Univ; Business Admin.

DILLARD, Valerie G; Lindblom Tech HS; Chicago, IL; 152/757 Chr; Chrl; Chrs; ChrhWkr; Mdrgl; NatlMeritSF; SctActv; TchrAde; RptrSchPpr; Univ; Professional.

DILLEHAY, Tony S; Plattsmouth HS; Plattsmouth, NE; 9/133 PresSrCls; SecChrs; Mdrgl; NHS; SchMus; StuCncl; RptrYrbk; SptEdSchPpr; MthCl; LetterFtbl; Coll; Journalism.

DILLEMUTH, Nancy B; Rockwell City Comm HS; Rockwell City, IA; 8/62 VPFrshCls; Band; HonRl; MrchBnd; PresNHS; PepBnd; SchMus; FHA; FrCl; CaptChrldr; Iowa St Univ; English.

DILLER, Jayne R; Nashua Community HS; Nashua, IA; Chrs; ChrhWkr; CncrtBnd; DrmBgl; HonRl; MrchBnd; SctActv; FTA; Bsktbl; GAA; College; Pro.

DILLER, Terry R; Northrop HS; Fort Wayne, IN; 1/643 HonRl; StuCncl; StuGov; Bsbl; Bsktbl; Ftbl; College; Law.

DILLEY, Randy W; Lewellen Rural HS; Lewellen, NE; 5/15 Band; CncrtBnd; HonRl; MrchBnd; PepBnd; SctActv; 4-H; LetterBsktbl; LetterFtbl; LetterTrk; IMSpt; VoiceDemAwd; Univ Of Nebr; Engineering.

DILLEY, Rhonda S; High School; Sedan, KS; 4/38 ChrhWkr; HonRl; NHS; OffAde; SchPl; SecStuCncl; TchrAde; PresYthFlsp; EdSchPpr; PresFHA; PpCl; Coffeyville Comm Jr College; Elementary Ed.

DILLIE, Jayne; Markesan Sr HS; Markesan, WI; 27/121 Band; CmntyWkr; DrlTm; MrchBnd; TchrAde; YthFlsp; SpnCl; PpCl; Bsbl; GAA; U Of Stevens Point; Art Major.

DILLIVAN, Timothy I; Burr Oak HS; Burr Oak, MI; 2/32 TrsSrCls; Band; Chrs; CmntyWkr; CncrtBnd; HonRl; NHS; SchMus; SchPl; LetterTrk; Mich State Univ; Pre Dental.

DILLMAN, Diana L; Clinton Prairie HS; Frankfort, IN; 6/97 NHS; NatlMeritCmnd; OffAde; Yrbk; SpnCl; VPPpCl; Hanover College; History.

DILLMAN, Robert C; Campion Jesuit HS; Prairie Du Chien, WI; Band; DrmBgl; HonRl; JA; SctActv; YthFlsp; SciCl; LetterBsktbl; Tennis; IMSpt; Marquette University; Medicine.

DILLON, Cheryl A; Shawnee HS; Mcclure, IL; 2/62 Chrs; HonRl; SecStuCncl; FBLA; FTA; FrCl; PpCl;.

DILLON, Corrinne T; Mercy HS; Omaha, NE; Chr; Chrs; SecChrhWkr; NatlCathMusEdAsoc; SchMus; Sdlty; FrCl; LetterSwmmng; Trk; GAA; College; Music.

DILLON, Kathy J; Monrovia HS; Mooresville, IN; 40/100 CncrtBnd; DrlTm; MrchBnd; OffAde; TchrAde; 4-H; PpCl; CaptChrldr; LetterGAA; 4-HAwd; Business Schl; Vocation.

DILLON, Kathy L; Junction City HS; Junction City, KS; 24/305 ALAGirlsSt; DrlTm; HonRl; NHS; OffAde; SctActv; StuGov; TchrAde; LetterChrldr; PresAwd; Ks State U; Law.

DILLON, Marianne; Mother Mc Auley HS; Chicago, IL; 16/474 HonRl; NHS; NatlMeritCmnd; SpnCl; College; Medicine.

DILLON, Michael L; Humboldt HS; Humboldt, KS; HonRl; TchrAde; TreasFFA; IMSpt; Junior College; Business.

DILLON, Timothy M; Fox HS; Arnold, MO; 116/599 TrsJrCls; Band; ChrhWkr; HonRl; MrchBnd; StuGov; YthFlsp; LetterBsktbl; College; Professional.

DILLON, Victoria J; Centura HS; Dannesbrog, NE; Band; CncrtBnd; MrchBnd; FBLA; College; Professional.

DILLOW, Kathy A; Anna Jonesboro C HS; Anna, IL; 28/137 Band; HonRl; SctActv; StuCncl; Yrbk; FTA; LatCl; PpCl; Chrldr; South Ill Univ; Secretarial.

DILLS, Kathryn D; Alton HS; Alton, MO; 2/94 HonRl; LbryAde; NHS; NatlMeritSchl; NatlSciFnd; NatlThespSoc; FSA; MthCl; College.

DILORENZO, Carrie L; Rosati Kain HS; St Louis, MO; HonRl; NHS; PolWkr; SchPl; FrCl; GAA; IMSpt; Oberlin Clg; Doctor.

DILS, Michael D; Union County HS; Richmond, IN; ALBoysSt; ChrhWkr; HonRl; JA; YthFlsp; SchPpr; Indiana University.

DILSAVER, John S; Nixa HS; Nixa, MO; 2/86 Band; CncrtBnd; HonRl; LitMag; MrchBnd; NatlMeritCmnd; EdSchPpr; SciCl; College.

DILTHEY, Carol J; La Monte R Iv HS; Knob Noster, MO; 3/25 HstFrshCls; VPSophCls; VPJrCls; PresSrCls; ChrhWkr; HonRl; MrchBnd; SchPl; AmLegAwd; DARAwd; Ctl Missouri St Univ; Biology.

DILWORTH, Ivy L; John M Harlan HS; Chicago, IL; Chrs; CmntyWkr; HonRl; NHS; SchPl; StuCncl; TchrAde; YthFlsp; RptrSchPpr; GerCl; College; Psycho Analyst.

DILWORTH, Janice L; St Marys Center For Learning; Chicago, IL; College; Ballet Dancer.

DILWORTH, Mary M; Lee M Thurston HS; Detroit, MI; HonRl; PresJA; JrNHS; LitMag; NHS; NatlMeritSF; SpnCl; IMSpt; English.

DI MARTINO, Angelo; St Patrick HS; Chicago, IL; 25/427 HonRl; RptrSchPpr; EngCl; Loyola University; Business Administration.

DI MARTINO, Dana M; Monroe Sr HS; St Paul, MN; Band; HonRl; HospAde; PolWkr; StuCncl; StuGov; Twrl; RptrYrbk; SchPpr; College; Law.

DI MENNA, Cathy A; Rosemount Senior HS; Apple Valley, MN; SecJrCls; CmntyWkr; DrlTm; DrmMjrt; HonRl; SchPl; StuGov; Twrl; FrCl; LetterChrldr;.

DIMENT, Kirk; Western HS; Bay City, MI; /450 ChrhWkr; HonRl; NHS; GerCl; Bsktbl; Ftbl; Trk; Delta Coll Mich; Law.

DIMICK, Susan M; Platteville HS; Platteville, WI; 1/201 AFS; HonRl; MrchBnd; NatlFornLg; SchMus; StuCncl; RptrYrbk; RptrSchPpr; DARAwd; KiwanAwd; Wis State Univ Platteville.

DIMICK, Timothy R; Marysville HS; Marysville, MI; HonRl; Ftbl; Tennis; CchngActv; IMSpt; Detroit Engineering Inst; Air Conditioning.

DIMMITT, Kathleen J; Pittsfield HS; Pittsfield, IL; HonRl; NHS; PpCl; Bsbl;.

DIMMITT, Kim M; Monroe City R I Public HS; Monroe City, MO; HonRl; NHS; Pres4-H; SciCl; Bsktbl; LetterGlf; CchngActv; 4-HAwd; College; Medicine.

DIMOCK, Kimberly; Msbr Hackett HS; Kalamazoo, MI; Chr; HonRl; PpCl; Bsktbl; Glf; Chrldr; IMSpt; College; Professional.

DIMOND, Julia A; Ladywood St Agnes HS; Indianapolis, IN; VPJrCls; PresSrCls; JA; PolWkr; StuCncl; KeyCl; SpnCl; GAA; Univ; Enviromental Law.

DIMOND, William E; Lasalle Peru HS; Peru, IL; HonRl; Swmmng; Trk; IMSpt; College; Science.

DIMPERIO, Mary; Maine South Hs; Park Ridge, IL; ChrhWkr; HonRl; JrNHS; NHS; SchMus; SchPl; U Of Illinois;veterinary Medicine.

DINEEN, Judy A; Fargo North HS; Fargo, ND; 86/360 ChrhWkr; NatlThespSoc; SchMus; SchPl; TchrAde; PPFtbl; University; Medical Tech.

DINEHART, Richard L; Alexandria Monroe HS; Alexandria, IN; PresFrshCls; ALBoysSt; Chr; NHS; SchMus; SchPl; VPSpnCl; PresPpCl; CaptFtbl; LetterTrk; Military Policeman; Law Enforcement.

DING, Dean A; Shanley HS; Fargo, ND; Chrs; NHS; Quill&Scroll; StuCncl; RptrSchPpr; SchPpr; Ftbl; Ndsu; Bio.

DINGER, Brenda L; Wyndmere Public HS; Wyndmere, ND; ALAGirlsSt; Chr; HonRl; LbryAde; NHS; TchrAde; YthFlsp; MthCl; Bsktbl; GAA; College; Md.

DINGER, Charles J; Marist HS; Chicago, IL; HonRl; Univ Of Illinois; Economist.

DINGER, Linda M; Grand Blanc HS; Grand Blanc, MI; 3/630 ALAGirlsSt; HonRl; NHS; SecTrsSophCls; Bsktbl; CaptChrldr; PPFtbl; AmLegAwd; DARAwd; U Of Mi; Engineering.

DINGERSON, Gail N; Seymour HS; Payson, IL; 18/68 SecSophCls; Chrs;.

DINGES, Charles; Francis W Parker HS; Chicago, IL; VPFrshCls; PolWkr; SchMus; SchPl; StuGov; RptrSchPpr; SptEdSchPpr; Wesleyan Univ; Law.

DINGLE, Denise R; Walter P Chryler HS; New Castle, IN; 15/371 Chr; ChrhWkr; HonRl; NatlFornLg; NHS; NatlMeritSF; SchPl; LatCl; PpCl; SciCl; Univ; Doctor.

DINGLEDEIN, Michel J; Rock Island HS; Rock Island, IL; 90/685 HonRl; LetterSwmmng; U Of Ky; Mech Eng.

DINGMAN, Bruce K; Niantic Harristown HS; Decatur, IL; PresFrshCls; HonRl; NHS; Quill&Scroll; StuCncl; RptrYrbk; EdSchPpr; 4-H; 4-HAwd; Univ Of Ill; Agriculture.

DINGRANDO, Linda; Marion Hs; Marion, IL; 7/239 Chr; HonRl; PpCl; SciCl; GAA;.

DINKA, Jane M; Springfield Catholic HS; Springfield, MO; VPFrshCls; Chrs; HonRl; Orch; SctActv; RptrSchPpr; LatCl; SpnCl; Chrldr; IMSpt; College.

DINKEL, Brenda K; Oakley HS; Oakley, KS; 11/63 HonRl; FHA; PpCl; Hutchinson Jr Clg; Med Record Librn.

DINKEL, Elaine M; Marian HS; Mc Cracken, KS; HonRl; 4-H; PpCl; 4-HAwd; VoiceDemAwd; Fort Hays Ks State Col; Home Econ.

DINKEL, Susan K; Hill City HS; Hill City, KS; SecFrshCls; CmntyWkr; HonRl; IntrClCncl; SchAde; StuCncl; PpCl; CaptBsktbl; LetterTrk; Chrldr; PPFtbl; College; Professional.

DINKINS, Stephen W; Du Quoin HS; Du Quoin, IL; 14/143 Chrs; ChrhWkr; CncrtBnd; HonRl; MrchBnd; SchMus; SctActv; Yrbk; SchPpr; Harding Christian College; Accounting.

DINNDORF, Marita L; Cathedral HS; St Cloud, MN; 89/163 CmntyWkr; HospAde; LitMag; SchMus; RptrYrbk; SchPpr; PPFtbl; St Marys Col; Child Dvelop.

DINNES, Debbie S; Grundy Center Comm HS; Grandy Center, IA; Chr; Chrs; ChrhWkr; HonRl; SchPl; FTA; Tennis; Trk; Chrldr; GAA; U Of Northern Iowa; Art.

DINS, Dianne M; Beaver Dam Sr HS; Beaver Dam, WI; 2/314 AFS; HonRl; OffAde; TchrAde; RptrYrbk; RptrSchPpr; PpCl; IMSpt; Carroll College; Teacher.

DINS, Ronald L; Edgar HS; Edgar, WI; 14/85 TrsFrshCls; VPSophCls; Chrs; ChrhWkr; HonRl; Mdrgl; LetterBsbl; LetterBsktbl; LetterFtbl; LetterTrk; Trade.

DINSMORE, Nelson G; Meadville HS; Meadville, MO; PresFrshCls; Band; CncrtBnd; DrmMjrt; HonRl; JA; MrchBnd; 4-H; LetterBsbl; LetterBsktbl; LetterTrk; College; Agriculture.

DIOMBALA, Laura J; Nazareth Academy; Riverside, IL; 3/154 NHS; OffAde; SchMus; SchPl; SchPpr; Purdue Univ; Engineering.

DION, Marc J; Parchment HS; Parchment, MI; 1/180 Band; HonRl; PresNHS; NatlMeritSF; SchMus; PresStuCncl; PresLatCl; PresPpCl; Trk; IMSpt; Kalamazoo Col; Biochemistry.

DION, Mark S; Spalding Institute HS; Peoria, IL; HonRl; NHS; NatlMeritCmnd; LatCl; VPSciCl; Wrstlng; Creighton Univ; Medicine.

DIONISE, Tony R; Farwell HS; Farwell, MI; StuCncl; LetterBsktbl; Lawrence Inst Tech; Elec & Engr.

DIONNE, Cynthia S; St Anne Comm HS; St Anne, IL; 4/103 ChrhWkr; HonRl; NHS; StuCncl; FHA; FNA; Bsbl; Chrldr; College; Accounting.

DI PAOLO, Susan H; East Alton Wood River HS; Wood River, IL; 8/312 SecTrsSrCls; Chrs; DrlTm; HonRl; NHS; OffAde; StuCncl; Washington Univ; Medicine.

DIPIETRO, Christina; Charleston HS; Chaleston, IL; 32/242 AFS; HonRl; ModUN; NatlMeritCmnd; GAA; PPFtbl; Univ Of Ill; Food Science.

DIPP, Beverly J; Thornapple Kellogg HS; Freeport, MI; Band; ChrhWkr; CmntyWkr; HonRl; LitMag; NHS; RedCrAde; TchrAde; 4-H; FTA; Coll; Elem Teach.

DIPPEL, Kim M; Franklin Center HS; Franklin Grove, IL; 4/50 TrsSrCls; Band; Chrs; HonRl; SecNHS; SchMus; PresStuCncl; PresFrCl; Chrldr; DARAwd; Northern Illinois Univ; French.

DIPPOLD, Carol M; Lagrove HS; Farina, IL; 5/33 SecTrsSophCls; SecTrsSrCls; Band; Chr; Chrs; ChrhWkr; HonRl; YthFlsp; Yrbk; Southern Illinois Univ; Veterinarian.

DIRKER, Stephen J; Paul C Schulte HS; Terre Haute, IN; ChrhWkr; CmntyWkr; PolWkr; SchAde; Bsbl; Bsktbl; LetterFtbl; LetterTrk; Wrstlng; IMSpt; In S U; Officer Of Law.

DIRKES, Paula C; West Catholic HS; Grand Rapids, MI; 36/310 HonRl; JA; LitMag; NHS; RptrYrbk; RptrSchPpr; SpnCl; Trk; IMSpt; JAAwd; Mi St Univ; Phy Educ.

DIRKMAN, Anne M; Calumet HS; Ahmeek, MI; Chr; HonRl; LbryAde; TchrAde; RptrYrbk; FTA; LetterTrk; Univ Of Wisc; Lawyer.

DIRKS, Douglas; Stevens HS; Rapid City, SD; 43,417 SecTrsSrCls; CncrtBnd; HonRl; NatlFornLg; NatlThespSoc; SchMus; SchPl; StuCncl; SpnCl; Trk; Universtiy; Law.

DIRKS, Janice A; St Anthony HS; Effingham, IL; 4/79 PresFrshCls; ChrhWkr; HonRl; HospAde; NHS; StuCncl; RptrYrbk; Yrbk; 4-H; FTA; PpCl; Eastern Ill Univ.

DIRKS, Jerry A; Omaha North HS; Omaha, NE; ChrhWkr; CmntyWkr; CncrtBnd; HonRl; MrchBnd; NatlMeritCmnd; PepBnd; YthFlsp; GerCl; RotaryAwd; College; Medical.

DIRKS, Jolene K; Grundy Center Comm HS; Grundy Center, IA; 4/78 Chr; Chrs; HonRl; Mdrgl; NHS; StuGov; Yrbk; PpCl; Chrldr; Iowa Methodist Univ; Nursing.

DIRKS, Leland R; Julesburg HS; Chappell, NE; 1/41 PresSophCls; ALBoysSt; CncrtBnd; HonRl; MrchBnd; NHS; NatlThespSoc; StuCncl; SchPpr; PresSciCl; Univ Of Wyo; Study Languages Physics.

DIRKS, Leslie J; Chandlerville HS; Virginia, IL; 4/18 TrsJrCls; ALAGirlsSt; ChrhWkr; CncrtBnd; HonRl; MrchBnd; NHS; FHA; AmLegAwd; TIMEAwd; Palmer Chiropractic College; Chiropractor.

DIRKSCHNEIDER, Dawn M; Wilber Clatonia HS; Wilber, NE; 7/34 SecFrshCls; TrsSophCls; VPJrCls; SecSrCls; ALAGirlsSt; HonRl; TreasNHS; SchMus; PresStuCncl; LetterIMSpt; Univ; Business Education.

DIRTH, Caren J; Notre Dame HS; W Burlington, IA; 2/76 ChrhWkr; HonRl; SchPl; TchrAde; PpCl; Chrldr; Ia St U; Computer Math.

DISBROW, Susan R; United Township HS; East Moline, IL; 14/650 CmntyWkr; DrmMjrt; HonRl; JrNHS; NHS; NatlThespSoc; PolWkr; SchMus; SchPl; Teen; Twrl; YthFlsp; College; Medicine.

DISCH, Chandra; Monroe HS; Monroe, WI; SchPpr; GerCl; GAA; College; Physical Therapy.

DISCH, Deborah; New Glarus HS; Monticello, WI; 3/60 TchrAde; YthFlsp; RptrSchPpr; SchPpr; PpCl; Trk; GAA; College; Vocational.

DISCH, Elizabeth A; New Glarus HS; New Glarus, WI; Band; Chrs; PepBnd; SchPl; YthFlsp; RptrSchPpr; SchPpr; PpCl; Trk; GAA; College; Professional.

DISCHER, Kenneth C; Elmore Public HS; Elmore, MN; Chr; ChrhWkr; CncrtBnd; HonRl; NHS; NatlMeritCmnd; SchPl; LetterBsktbl; LetterFtbl; LetterGlf; Coll.

DISHER, Peggy A; Robert A Waller HS; Chicago, IL; HonRl; HospAde; LitMag; NHS; OffAde; Yrbk; RptrSchPpr; SpnCl; Tennis; De Paul U; Banking.

DISHER, Theresa; Alton Senior Hs; Alton, IL; Chrs; HonRl; HospAde; JA; LbryAde; OffAde; RptrSchPpr; Siu E; Major In Spanish.

DISHMAN, Vonda L; W Washington HS; Campbellsburg, IN; Band; ChrhWkr; CncrtBnd; MrchBnd; PepBnd;.

DISHMAN, William; Tri HS; Lewisville, IN; 9/93 ALBoysSt; ChrhWkr; CmntyWkr; HonRl; NHS; OffAde; YthFlsp; SpnCl; PresJrCls; Wrstlng;.

DISHNEAU, Lori M; Bergland HS; Bergland, MI; ALAGirlsSt; HonRl; OffAde; SchPl; StuCncl; EdYrBk; 4-H; LetterBsktbl; Trk; Chrldr; Coll; Pro.

DISINGER, James J; David H Hickman HS; Columbia, MO; Aud/Vis; HonRl; LbryAde; NHS; NatlMeritSF; GerCl; College; Biochemistry.

DISNEY, Lawrence L; Limestone Comm HS; Bartonville, IL; Chr; HonRl; Mdrgl; SchMus; College; Astronomy.

DISTELRATH, Christine M; St Marys Of Redford HS; Detroit, MI; NatlFornLg; SchPl; StuCncl; StuGov; TchrAde; Yrbk; RptrSchPpr; EdSchPpr; SchPpr; PpCl; College; Buyer.

DISTER, John M; Junction City HS; Fort Riley, KS; 20/300 SchPl; StuCncl; StuGov; YthFlsp; EngCl; FrCl; Bsbl; LetterBsktbl; LetterFtbl; LetterTrk; Coll; Law.

DISTERHOFT, Lisa M; Waupun HS; Waupun, WI; SecSophCls; Chr; Chrs; ChrhWkr; HonRl; SchAde; SchPpr; SpnCl; PpCl; Chrldr; Uw Oshkosh; Communications.

DITMAN, Stephen M; Carrollton Comm HS; Carrollton, IL; 1/85 VPSophCls; HonRl; NHS; NatlMeritSF; FSA; SpnCl; LetterBsbl; LetterBsktbl; LetterFtbl; College; Math.

DITMEYER, Elizabeth A; Normandy HS; St Louis, MO; 10/500 SecBand; ChrhWkr; HonRl; MrchBnd; NHS; NatlMeritCmnd; Orch; SchMus; StuCncl; FrCl; College; Registered Nurse.

DITTBRENNER, Diane; Chester Hubbell HS; Chester, NE; 1/24 SecTrsFrshCls; PresJrCls; Band; Chrs; ChrhWkr; HonRl; MrchBnd; SchPl; PpCl; BttyCrckrAwd; Busin; Secretarial.

DITTER, Mark J; Monroe Public HS; Monroe, NE; PresFrshCls; Chr; HonRl; OffAde; SctActv; YthFlsp; Bsbl; Ftbl; Trk; Trade School; Vocation.

DITTERT, Caroline E; Cor Jesu Academy; Saint Louis, MO; 6/109 Chr; ChrhWkr; HonRl; LitMag; NHS; RptrSchPpr; FNA; PpCl; CchngActv; IMSpt; Univ; Rn.

DITTERT, Rainer H; St Louis HS; St Louis, MO; Chr; HonRl; NHS; NatlMeritSF; LetterSwmmng;.

DITTMAN, Jeff L; Faith HS; Faith, SD; 3/36 ALBoysSt; Band; Chrs; NHS; SchPl; 4-H; CaptBsktbl; CaptFtbl; Trk; ChmbCommrsAwd; Northern St Clg; Coaching.

DITTMANN, Joseph A; Thornridge HS; Dolton, IL; 25/673 CmntyWkr; HonRl; NHS; NatlMeritCmnd; SctActv; U Of Il; Elec Engi.

DITTMAR, Laura; Galena HS; Galena, IL; 5/110 AFS; Band; ChrhWkr; CncrtBnd; HonRl; MrchBnd; RptrYrbk; Yrbk; SpnCl; College;.

DITTMER, Christine T; Southeast Warren HS; Lacona, IA; 5/52 Chrs; ChrhWkr; HonRl; SchMus; SchPl; EdYrBk; RptrSchPpr; SchPpr; Sec4-H; Wrstlng; 4-HAwd;.

DITTMER, Debra A; Southeast Warren HS; Lacona, IA; 6/52 Band; Chrs; HonRl; NHS; SchPl; RptrYrbk; SecCivCl; SecFTA; Univ Of Ia; Elem Ed.

DITTMER, Dixie L; Eastwood HS; Cushing, IA; 4/34 Chrs; HonRl; LbryAde; PresNHS; PresStuCncl; SchPpr; SecSpnCl; PpCl; AmLegAwd;.

DITTMER, Jerald K; Wheatland Comm HS; Wheatland, IA; 3/24 PresFrshCls; ALBoysSt; Band; Chrs; CncrtBnd; NHS; SchMus; LetterBsbl; LetterBsktbl; CaptTrk; Univ ;accounting.

DITTMER, Jo Cindy; Southeast Warren HS; Milo, IA; 22/52 DrlTm; DrmMjrt; HonRl; RedCrAde; SchPl; RptrYrbk; EdYrBk; RptrSchPpr; Wrstlng;.

DITTMER, Lisa C; Southridge HS; Huntingburg, IN; 50/136 TrsJrCls; SecSrCls; Band; CncrtBnd; DrlTm; HonRl; MrchBnd; NatlMeritSchl; Yrbk; PpCl; I S U Of Evansville; Dental Hygienist.

DITTMER, Rachel B; Central Cass HS; Wheatland, ND; Band; Chr; CncrtBnd; HonRl; MrchBnd; NHS; PepBnd; SchMus; SchPl; YthFlsp; Moorhead State U; Pro Musician.

DITTMER, Suzanne M; Southeast Warren HS; Lacona, IA; 11/52 Band; Chrs; ChrhWkr; CncrtBnd; MrchBnd; PepBnd; SchPl; SchPpr; Simpson College; Music.

DITTRICH, Deborah A; Gavit HS; Hammond, IN; 24/335 ChrhWkr; HonRl; NHS; SchAde; PpCl; Swmmng; Chrldr; GAA; Purdue Calumet Campus; Sociology.

DIVELBESS, Wayne E; Missouri Valley HS; Missouri Valley, IA; VPJrCls; Chrs; HonRl; NHS; SctActv; FSA; LetterBsbl; LetterFtbl; LetterTrk; LetterWrstlng; 4-HAwd; Univ; Professional.

DIVER, Rebecca; Lawrenceville HS; St Francisville, IL; 3/177 ALAGirlsSt; Chrs; ChrhWkr; CmntyWkr; HonRl; NHS; StuCncl; RptrSchPpr; 4-H; FHA; Univ Of Evansville; Nursing.

DI VINCENZO, Diane C; Lake Zurich HS; Lake Zurich, IL; PresSrCls; AFS; Band; CncrtBnd; HonRl; MrchBnd; NHS; SchMus; StuCncl; LionAwd; Coll; Social Work.

DIVINCENZO, Kenneth; St Patrick Hs; Chicago, IL; 4/482 HonRl; NatlMeritSF; Ui Urbana;electrical Engineer.

DIVINE, Joyce L; Osceola Public HS; Vista, MO; TrsSrCls; Chr; ChrhWkr; HonRl; NHS; SchPl; YthFlsp; FHA; SpnCl; PpCl; Airline Stewardess.

DIVINE, Patty L; Kingsford HS; Iron Mountain, MI; Band; ChrhWkr; CncrtBnd; HonRl; MrchBnd; NatlFornLg; NatlThespSoc; PepBnd; SchPl; YthFlsp; 4-H; FHA; College; Nursing.

DIVIS, Cynthia E; East Butler HS; Brainard, NE; 1/39 PresJrCls; ALAGirlsSt; Chr; ChrhWkr; CncrtBnd; NHS; SchPl; StuCncl; RptrYrbk; FHA; Bryan Mem Hosp Sch Of Nursing; Rn.

DIVIS, Dianne S; Watervliet HS; Watervliet, MI; Band; ChrhWkr; CncrtBnd; HonRl; MrchBnd; 4-H; SpnCl; Western Michigan Univ.

DIX, Donald E; Robinson HS; Robinson, IL; 26/185 Chr; ChrhWkr; HonRl; ModUN; 4-H; KeyCl; SciCl; LetterFtbl; Trk; AmLegAwd; DARAwd; SARAwd; Rose Hulman Inst Of Tech; Chemical Engineer.

DIX, Stewart W; Lincoln HS; Wisconsing Rapids, WI; ChrhWkr; CncrtBnd; HonRl; SctActv; GerCl; Ftbl; VPSocr; Wrstlng; CchngActv; IMSpt; Univ Eau Claire; Accounting.

DIXON, Barbara A; Englewood HS; Chicago, IL; 1/287 CncrtBnd; HonRl; SecJrNHS; MrchBnd; PresNHS; OffAde; StuCncl; StuGov; FTA; Trinity Col Conn; Art.

DIXON, Beverly J; Chicago Vocational HS; Chicago, IL; 6/776 ChrhWkr; CmntyWkr; HonRl; JrNHS; NHS; NatlMeritCmnd; OffAde; SctActv; GAA; IMSpt; Mundelein Coll; Math.

DIXON, Carol C; Bellevue HS; Bellevue, MI; 1/120 CncrtBnd; HonRl; MrchBnd; NHS; NatlMeritSF; PepBnd; SchPl; EdSchPpr; Ferris State College; Court Stenographer.

DIXON, Cathy L; Tri County R 7 HS; Jamesport, MO; 1/27 PresSophCls; Chr; Chrl; Chrs; HonRl; StuCncl; StuGov; YthFlsp; FHA; PpCl; Univ; Majors.

DIXON, Cheryl A; Tri County HS; Jamesport, MO; 5/17 Chrs; HonRl; SchMus; SchPl; StuGov; YthFlsp; Yrbk; SchPpr; Trk; VoiceDemAwd; College; Medical Tech.

DIXON, Cheryl L; East Grand Forks Senior HS; E Grand Forks, MN; 7/157 ChrhWkr; HonRl; NHS; SchPl; SctActv; StuCncl; Yrbk; GAA; Hopsital Nursing School; Nursing.

DIXON, Dana; Northwestern Lutheran Acad; Carson, ND; 5/24 Chrs; ChrhWkr; CncrtBnd; DrmBgl; HonRl; MrchBnd; SchPl; StuCncl; IMSpt; CitAwd; Northwestern College; Ministry.

DIXON, David; Englewood Hs; Chicago, IL; 6/347 CncrtBnd; HonRl; PresJrNHS; NatlMeritSF; SptEdSchPpr; VPFTA; Trk; AmLegAwd; College; Medicine.

DIXON, David A; Cowan HS; Muncie, IN; PresSrCls; ALBoysSt; Band; Chrl; DrmMjrt; HonRl; NHS; Orch; LetterBsktbl; LetterTrk; Alist Nazarene College; Accounting.

DIXON, Diane; Saginaw HS; Saginaw, MI; HonRl; RptrYrbk; FrCl; PpCl; Tennessee State University; Business Admin.

DIXON, Duane B; Alleman HS; Rock Island, IL; ChrhWkr; CmntyWkr; HonRl; NHS; SctActv; LetterTrk; Augustana College; Law.

DIXON, Galen W; Hartville HS; Hartville, MO; PresSophCls; ALBoysSt; Band; ChrhWkr; LbryAde; StuCncl; SciCl; Bsbl; Bsktbl; CchngActv; College.

DIXON, Glen A; Reavis HS; Burbank, IL; HonRl; NHS; RptrSchPpr; MthCl; SciCl; Northern Ill Univ; Professional.

DIXON, Jan D; Macomb Sr HS; Macomb, IL; NHS; StuCncl; RptrYrbk; 4-H; FHA; SpnCl;.

DIXON, Jayne E; St Pius X HS; Kansas City, MO; 5/140 Band; DrlTm; HonRl; NHS; SchMus; RptrYrbk; PpCl; GAA; Avila; Medicine.

DIXON, Joseph R; Crispus Attucks HS; Indianapolis, IN; PresSrCls; ChrhWkr; CmntyWkr; StuGov; TchrAde; Yrbk; Bsktbl; Ftbl; CchngActv; PresAwd; Vincennes Univ; Pro Ball.

DIXON, Larry L; Medora HS; Medora, IN; 1/32 PresSophCls; Band; Chr; HonRl; StuCncl; YthLg; EdYrBk; SchPpr; SpnCl; SciCl; In U; Pre Med.

DIXON, Lori; Homestead HS; Mequon, WI; 17/391 ALAGirlsSt; Band; HonRl; LbryAde; NatlFornLg; NHS; NatlThespSoc; SchMus; SchPl; Univ Of Wis; Occupational Therapy.

DIXON, Mardelle L; Dixon HS; Dixon, IL; ChrhWkr; CmntyWkr; DrlTm; HonRl; NatlThespSoc; SchMus; SchPl; LetterTrk; GAA; IMSpt; Univ; Teacher.

DIXON, Nancy J; Peoria HS; Peoria, IL; 56/496 Band; ChrhWkr; CmntyWkr; CncrtBnd; JrNHS; MrchBnd; OffAde; Orch; PepBnd; RedCrAde; FrCl; Purdue Univ; Chemical Engineer.

DIXON, Pamela K; Oakridge HS; Muskegon, MI; Chr; ChrhWkr; HonRl; Trade; Vocation.

DIXON, Paula L; Ann Arbor Huron HS; Ann Arbor, MI; TchrAde; College; Art.

DIXON, Priscilla R; Monona Grove HS; Madison, WI; 1/268 Chrs; HonRl; LitMag; NHS; NatlMeritCmnd; NatlThespSoc; SchMus; SchPl; FrCl; MthCl; U Of Wi Madison; Dentist.

DIXON, Rebecca R; Greenfield HS; Greenfield, IL; 3/77 SecJrCls; Band; Chrs; HonRl; MrchBnd; NHS; PepBnd; SchMus; RptrYrbk; Yrbk; 4-H; FHA; FrCl; Trk; Business School; Vocational.

DIXON, Robert; Assumption Hs; Venice, IL; 15/128 Band; CmntyWkr; HonRl; MrchBnd; SchPl; SctActv; StuCncl; StuGov; Ftbl; Southern Illinois; Business.

DIXON, Robert F; Warren County R Iii HS; Warrenton, MO; TrsFrshCls; HonRl; NatlFornLg; SchPl; StuCncl; StuGov; TchrAde; Bsbl; Bsktbl; Ftbl; University; Medicine.

DIXON, Robert W; Newton Sr HS; Newton, IA; PresSrCls; HonRl; NatlFornLg; StuCncl; KeyCl; CaptTennis; GodCntryAwd; OptClAwd; PresAwd; CitAwd; Iowa State Univ; Law.

DIXON, Sandra K; Advance HS; Advance, MO; VPJrCls; VPMrchBnd; StuCncl; RptrSchPpr; SchPpr; SecFHA; PpCl; Chrldr; IMSpt; Col; Pro.

DIXON, Stanley A; Colchester HS; Colchester, IL; 7/52 TrsJrCls; ChrhWkr; NHS; FFA; MthCl; Farming; Agriculture.

DIXON, Susan J; New Haven HS; New Haven, IN; CncrtBnd; HonRl; MrchBnd; PepBnd; Univ; Pro.

DIXON, Terri S; Ar We Va Comm HS; Westside, IA; 5/42 Band; Chr; CncrtBnd; HonRl; Mdrgl; MrchBnd; PepBnd; SchPl; Yrbk; Nw Missouri State Univ; Medical Tech.

DIXON, Thomas; Arthur Hill HS; Saginaw, MI; HonRl; Univ; Medicine.

DIXSON, Joycelyn Y; Arlington HS; Indianapolis, IN; SecJrCls; ALAGirlsSt; ChrhWkr; HonRl; HospAde; JA; NatlMeritSF; NatlThespSoc; OffAde; Univ; Broadcasting.

DJOKICH, Joann; T F South HS; Lansing, IL; 48/552 AFS; ChrhWkr; HonRl; FNA; PpCl; Rockford College; Doctor.

DLESK, David C; Downers Grove No HS; Downers Grove, IL; 5/580 HonRl; NHS; LetterFtbl; Glf; LetterTrk; Wrstlng; JETSAwd; NCTE; University Of Illinois; Engineering.

DLUGOSZ, Stephen A; St Josephs HS; South Bend, IN; 23/230 ALBoysSt; ChrhWkr; CmntyWkr; HonRl; JA; NHS; SctActv; Wrstlng; CchngActv; College; Agriculture.

DLUZAK, Pamela; Wabash HS; Wabash, IN; Chr; HonRl; LbryAde; NHS; SchMus; SpnCl; College; Nurse.

DOAK, Jill A; Clay City HS; Coal City, IN; 17/62 Band; Chrs; DrlTm; HonRl; NHS; StuCncl; YthFlsp; PpCl; Chrldr; GAA;.

DOAK, Richard L; Hedrick Comm HS; Hedrick, IA; 2/25 SecFrshCls; TrsFrshCls; SecSophCls; TrsSophCls; VPJrCls; PresSrCls; SecSrCls; TrsSrCls; HonRl; NHS; SchPl; StuCncl; LetterBsktbl; LetterFtbl; LetterTrk; Iowa State Univ; Medicine.

DOANE, Mary L; Kent City HS; Casnovia, MI; 4/90 Band; ChrhWkr; HonRl; NHS; OffAde; TchrAde; RptrSchPpr; EdSchPpr; 4-H; DARAwd; Baptist Bible Clge; Bus Career.

DOBBELS, William; Kewanee HS; Kewanee, IL; VPSrCls; Ftbl; Wrstlng; Univ; Forestry.

DOBBEN, Richard L; Thornwood HS; South Holland, IL; 95/857 HonRl; NHS; SctActv; KeyCl; LatCl; LetterSwmmng; AmLegAwd; Washington U St Louis; Pre Med.

DOBBINS, Gregory F; Glenbard No HS; Glendale Hts, IL; 12/371 HonRl; PolWkr; Bsktbl; Ftbl; LetterGlf; IMSpt; AmLegAwd; University Of Illinois; Engineering.

DOBBINS, John M; Centralia HS; Goff, KS; 3/37 ALBoysSt; Band; HonRl; MrchBnd; PresStuCncl; 4-H; SpnCl; SciCl; LetterTrk; 4-HAwd; Col; Physics.

DOBBS, Brenda L; Kirksville HS; Kriksville, MO; ChrhWkr; SchAde; SctActv; TchrAde; PpCl; Bsbl; LetterTrk; GAA; IMSpt; College; Vocational.

DOBBS, Deirdre; Deerfield HS; Deerfield, IL; AFS; Chrs; HonRl; NHS; NatlMeritCmnd; SchPl; Yrbk; Duke Univ; Medicine.

DOBBS, Deirdre W; Deerfield HS; Deerfield, IL; AFS; Chrs; HonRl; NHS; NatlMeritCmnd; SchPl; Yrbk; VPFrCl; University; Pre Medicine.

DOBBS, Teryl; Platte HS; Platte, SD; 4/47 Chrs; CncrtBnd; Mdrgl; MrchBnd; SchPl; StuCncl; EdYrBk; RptrSchPpr; FNA; GerCl; Univ Of South Dakota; Applied Music.

DOBELMANN, Mark J; Lincoln Co HS; Old Monroe, MO; 6/60 Chrs; ChrhWkr; CmntyWkr; HonRl; PresNHS; VPStuCncl; Yrbk; LetterBsbl; LetterBsktbl;.

DOBEREINER, Aimee M; United Township HS; East Moline, IL; VPFrshCls; VPSophCls; VPJrCls; VPSrCls; Chr; HonRl; NatlThespSoc; SctActv; StuCncl; Chrldr; College; Professional.

DOBERSTEIN, Nancy; Wauwatosa East HS; Wauwatosa, WI; SecSophCls; Chrs; HonRl; Orch; SchAde; StuCncl; TchrAde; PpCl; Chrldr; IMSpt; College; Phy Ed Teacher.

DOBESKI, Gail M; Marquette HS; Michigan City, IN; 5/60 HonRl; NatlMeritCmnd; StuCncl; StuGov; SpnCl; GovHonPrgAwd; Purdue U; Merchandiser.

DOBOSZ, Michelle A; St Andrew HS; Detroit, MI; 1/110 PresFrshCls; SecSrCls; Chr; HonRl; HospAde; NHS; StuCncl; EdYrBk; PpCl; DARAwd; U Of Mi; Medicine.

DOBRENSKI, Dona M; Community Sr HS; Detroit Lakes, MN; 7/251 AFS; Chr; CncrtBnd; HonRl; HospAde; NHS; PolWkr; PpCl; LetterChrldr; Denmark; Medicine.

DOBREY, Stephanie D; Bedford North Lawrence HS; Bedford, IN; 4-H; SpnCl; MthCl; Indiana Univ; Dental Hygiene.

DOBRINICH, Tina L; Mt Olive HS; Mt Olive, IL; Band; CncrtBnd; HonRl; MrchBnd; PepBnd; StuCncl; Yrbk; FBLA; FHA; Illinois State University; History.

DOBRINSKY, Mary H; Illiopolis HS; Springfield, IL; 3/38 PresJrCls; Chrl; Chrs; HonRl; HospAde; NHS; OffAde; SchAde; SctActv; StuCncl; Chrldr; GAA; College; Technology.

DOBRY, Brian R; Fenwick HS; Berwyn, IL; CaptFtbl;.

DOBRYMAN, Steven M; Niles East HS; Skokie, IL; HonRl; StuGov; FDA; Loyola University; Biology.

DOBRZYNSKI, Raymond M; Warren HS; Warren, MI; 8/380 VPSrCls; HonRl; NHS; NatlMeritSF; StuCncl; Bsktbl; LetterFtbl; Trk; IMSpt; Mi St Univ; Lawyer.

DOBSLAW, Kimberly; A A Stagg Hs; Worth, IL; 38/480 ChrhWkr; CncrtBnd; HonRl; HospAde; LitMag; MrchBnd; NHS; NatlSciFnd; PepBnd; RptrYrbk; Bradley U; Medical Technology.

DOBY, Kenneth R; Red Bud Public HS; Red Bud, IL; Band; HonRl; MrchBnd; NatlMeritCmnd; NatlMeritSchl; PepBnd; MthCl; Bsktbl; LetterTrk; Trade School; Electrician.

DOBY, Ronald A; Red Bud HS; Red Bud, IL; Band; CncrtBnd; HonRl; MrchBnd; PepBnd; College; Professional.

DOBYNS, Dawn M; Edison HS; East Gary, IN; 14/147 IntrClCncl; NHS; FrCl; PresSciCl; Bsktbl; Trk; SecGAA; PPFtbl; Purdue Or Iu Northwest; Physical Education.

DOCHERTY, Sherry D; Rockridge HS; Reynolds, IL; ChrhWkr; HonRl; StuCncl; YthFlsp; Yrbk; FTA; LatCl; Trk;.

DOCIMO, John A; York Community HS; Elmhurst, IL; Band; CncrtBnd; HonRl; MrchBnd; NHS; NatlMeritCmnd; Orch; PepBnd; College; Professional.

DOCKEN, Julie; Ej Cooper HS; New Hope, MN; HonRl; HospAde; GerCl; GAA; College; Teacher Interior Decorator.

DOCKENDORFF, John R; Danville Community HS; Danville, IA; 9/42 Band; Chrs; ChrhWkr; CncrtBnd; HonRl; Mdrgl; MrchBnd; PepBnd; SchMus; SchPl; College; Accounting.

DOCKERY, Kathleen A; Marillac HS; Northbrook, IL; 18/254 VPFrshCls; VPSophCls; LitMag; StuGov; Univ Of Illinois; Mathematics.

DOCKERY, Ray F; Engadine Consolidated HS; Gould City, MI; ChrhWkr; College; Biological Science.

DOCKERY, Sandra J; Southwestern HS; Detroit, MI; CmntyWkr; LbryAde; OffAde; SctActv; RptrYrbk; FTA; SpnCl; PpCl; Univ Of Detroit; Dentist.

DOCKHAM, Patricia A; Crawford HS; Crawford, NE; 1/41 ChrhWkr; HonRl; OffAde; SchPl; Yrbk; PpCl; LetterBsktbl; LetterTrk; IMSpt; BauchLmbAwd; Chadron State College; Medicine.

DOCKTER, Pat A; Ashley HS; Ashley, ND; Band; CncrtBnd; HonRl; PepBnd; RptrSchPpr; 4-H; 4-HAwd; Bismarck Jr Coll; Elementary Education.

DOCKTER, Steven; Anamoose HS; Anamoose, ND; Band; Chr; CncrtBnd; HonRl; NatlThespSoc; EdYrBk; Bsbl; CitAwd; VoiceDemAwd; Univ; Agriculture.

DOCKTERMAN, David A; Rock Island HS; Rock Island, IL; 2/650 ChrhWkr; CmntyWkr; NHS; NatlMeritSF; PresStuCncl; StuGov; SchPpr; 4-H; FrCl; IMSpt; AmLegAwd; RotaryAwd; CitAwd; Stanford Univ; Education.

DOCTER, Nella; Western Michigan Chr; Spring Lake, MI; Chr; ChrhWkr; HonRl; Yrbk; Trk; Miskegon Business College; Medical Secret.

DODD, Brenda L; Campus HS; Haysville, KS; Chr; ChrhWkr; DrlTm; JA; TchrAde; PpCl; JAAwd; College; Dental Hygenist.

DODD, Jeff N; Civic Memorial HS; Bethalto, IL; 4/225 Band; CncrtBnd; HonRl; JrNHS; MrchBnd; NHS; NatlMeritSF; Orch; StuGov; LetterBsktbl; LetterFtbl; LetterTrk; Univ; Computer Science.

DODD, Jeffrey D; Alton Marquette HS; Bethalto, IL; 6/120 HonRl; TchrAde; Yrbk; LatCl; Knox College; Chemical Eng Or Pharmicist.

DODD, Jerry W; Center Line HS; Waren, MI; 21/423 HonRl; Tennis; Wayne State Univ; Doctor.

DODD, Marla E; Stephen Decatur HS; Decatur, IL; 10/368 Chr; ChrhWkr; HonRl; HospAde; NHS; Bob Jones Univ; Missionary Doctor.

DODD, Terri A; Yates City HS; Yates City, IL; SecJrCls; Chrs; ChrhWkr; HonRl; SchPl; TchrAde; SchPpr; SpnCl; Chrldr; GAA; Coll; Rn.

DODD, William E; Glencoe HS; Glencoe, MN; Band; HonRl; SctActv; Ftbl; Tennis; College.

DODDS, James S; Algona HS; Lone Rock, IA; Aud/Vis; Band; Chr; Chrs; CncrtBnd; HonRl; MrchBnd; PolWkr; RptrSchPpr; Ftbl; Isu; Professional.

DODDS, Laurie L; Maplewood Acad; Sioux Falls, SD; 15/60 ChrhWkr; HonRl; OffAde; TchrAde; RptrSchPpr; Bsktbl; Clg; Pro.

DODDS, Tina D; Southeast Polk HS; Runnells, IA; 30/220 SecTrsSrCls; Band; ChrhWkr; CncrtBnd; CaptDrlTm; HonRl; MrchBnd; NHS; SchPl; SecStuCncl; 4-H; PpCl; Bsktbl; Swmmng; Trade School.

DODEN, Debra M; Mendota HS; Mendota, IL; 22/187 Band; ChrhWkr; CncrtBnd; DrmMjrt; HonRl; IntrClCncl; MrchBnd; StuCncl; YthFlsp; LatCl; Coll; Nurse.

DODGE, Carolee; Shawano HS; Keshena, WI; TrsFrshCls; CncrtBnd; HospAde; NatlFornLg; PolWkr; StuGov; TchrAde; 4-H; FBLA; SciCl; LetterTennis; Trk; GAA; College; Nursing.

DODGE, Dean B; Hanover Central HS; Cedar Lake, IN; Band; CncrtBnd; HonRl; StuCncl; 4-H; SpnCl; Bsktbl; Ftbl; Swmmng; LetterTrk; Iu; Tela Communications.

DODGE, Dirk A; Hanover Central HS; Cedar Lake, IN; Band; HonRl; Bsktbl; Swmmng; LetterTrk; IMSpt; Trade School; Building Contractor.

DODGE, Garen E; Wittenberg Birnamwood HS; Birnamwood, WI; 3/160 VPSrCls; Band; Chrs; HonRl; NHS; SchMus; StuCncl; LetterBsktbl; LetterGlf; CmntyWkr; Uw Green Bay; Professional Law.

DODGE, George M; J A Craig HS; Janesville, WI; HonRl; NatlFornLg; NHS; NatlMeritSF; Orch; PolWkr; GerCl; Socr; LetterTrk; BauchLmbAwd;.

DODGE, Teresa K; Callaway HS; Callaway, NE; ALAGirlsSt; Chrs; TchrAde; Sec4-H; FHA; PpCl; Bsktbl; LetterTrk; 4-HAwd; College; Professional.

DODGE, Thomass J; Alba Public HS; Elmira, MI; PresFrshCls; VPFrshCls; TrsSophCls; LbryAde; Bsbl; Trade School; Electronics.

DODSON, Erin C; North Platte Senior HS; North Platte, NE; CncrtBnd; HonRl; MrchBnd; StuCncl; 4-H; LatCl; PpCl; Trk; Chrldr; GAA; U Of Ne; Social Work.

DODSON, James H; Creighton Prep HS; Omaha, NE; 35/216 HstFrshCls; HstSophCls; HstJrCls; HonRl; Sdlty; StuCncl; StuGov; LetterSocr; IMSpt; Univ; Law.

DODSON, Lisa D; Mt Vernon Township HS; Mt Vernon, IL; Chr; ChrhWkr; HonRl; OffAde; PolWkr; TchrAde; IMSpt; 4-HAwd; Rend Lake College; Accounting.

DODSON, Sueanne E; Maywood HS; Maywood, NE; 5/22 Band; ChrhWkr; HonRl; JrNHS; SchPl; RptrSchPpr; PresPpCl; Bsktbl; Univ; Secretary.

DOE, Janice E; New Ulm Sr HS; Hanska, MN; ChrhWkr; CmntyWkr; HospAde; LbryAde; RedCrAde; SchPl; TchrAde; 4-H; FNA; New Ulm Schl Nursing.

DOEBEL, Martin P; University HS; Urbana, IL; ChrhWkr; SchMus; SchPl; SchPpr; 4-H; GerCl; Bsktbl; Trk; IMSpt; 4-HAwd; Univ; Us Navy Aviation.

DOEBELE, James F; Quigley Prep North HS; Chicago, IL; 1/61 CmntyWkr; HonRl; LitMag; NHS; StuCncl; EdSchPpr; LetterTrk;.

DOEDEN, Michael L; Forreston HS; Forreston, IL; 6/68.

DOEDEN, Ron H; Nemaha Valley HS; Cook, NE; ALBoysSt; ChrhWkr; SchPl; YthFlsp; RptrYrbk; SptEdYrbk; EngCl; GerCl; Coll; Professional.

DOEDERLEIN, Karen; Owosso HS; Owosso, MI; 1/452 NHS; Concordia Lutheran Jr Coll.

DOEGE, Ro Jeanne; Westfield HS; Neshkoro, WI; ALAGirlsSt; Chr; Chrs; HonRl; NHS; YthFlsp; SchPpr; GAA; Tech Sch.

DOEHNE, Thomas; Portland Public Hs; Portland, MI; 2/124 Band; CncrtBnd; HonRl; MrchBnd; NHS; NatlMeritFnl; PepBnd; EdSchPpr; FrCl; LetterWrstlng; College; Economics.

DOEHRMANN, Anita D; Williamsburg HS; Williamsburg, IA; 2/98 HonRl; NHS; FHA; VPGerCl; Bsktbl; Univ Of Northern Iowa; Mathematical Field.

DOELL, Carolyn K; North Side HS; Fort Wayne, IN; 74/475 Band; CncrtBnd; HonRl; MrchBnd; NHS; PpCl; Purdue University; Architecture.

DOELLING, Becky L; Nashville Community HS; Nashville, IL; 1/137 Band; Chr; Mdrgl; NHS; StuCncl; RptrSchPpr; Chrldr; AmLegAwd; University; Music.

DOELLING, Bruce H; Anderson HS; Anderson, IN; PresFrshCls; HonRl; NHS; TchrAde; SpnCl; LetterTennis; AmLegAwd; CitAwd; Univ; Prof.

DOELLING, Keith F; Okawville HS; Venedy, IL; Band; HonRl; NHS; PepBnd; PresYthFlsp; VPFFA; Kaskaskia College; Agriculture.

DOELLMAN, Maria A; Quincy Sr HS; Quincy, IL; Quincy College; Medical Tech.

DOEMER, Jean; Bishop Borgess HS; Detroit, MI; SecJrCls; SecSrCls; Chrs; HonRl; JrNHS; NHS; Bsktbl; Chrldr; GAA; College Or Univ; Dental Hygienist.

DOENNIG, Cathy J; Ozark HS; Ozark, MO; 1/92 Chrs; HonRl; NatlFornLg; TchrAde; RptrYrbk; EdYrBk; Coll; English.

DOERFFEL, Kathryn J; Sunnydale Academy; Kansas City, MO; VPSophCls; Chr; ChrhWkr; HonRl; OffAde; Orch; SchPl; TchrAde; College; Special Ed.

DOERFLEIN, Kenneth D; Brookville HS; Metamora, IN; HstFrshCls; Aud/Vis; LbryAde; SctActv; 4-H; SpnCl; IMSpt; 4-HAwd; OptClAwd; PresAwd; College; Vocation.

DOERFLER, Ronald W; Griffin HS; Springfield, IL; 1/189 Band; SecCncrtBnd; HonRl; MrchBnd; SecNHS; SecStuCncl; TchrAde; RptrSchPpr; BauchLmbAwd; Il College; Mathematics.

DOERING, Bonnie L; Plankinton Independent HS; Wessington Springs, SD; Chr; Chrs; DrlTm; HonRl; SchAde; SchPl; TchrAde; RptrSchPpr; FHA; PpCl; Trade School; Hair Stylist.

DOERING, Cliff G; Akron Fairgrove HS; Caro, MI; Band; ChrhWkr; HonRl; TchrAde; LetterBsktbl; Ftbl; LetterTrk; PresAwd; College; Professional.

DOERING, Linda R; Fremont HS; Fremont, MI; 35/189 ChrhWkr; HonRl; OffAde; YthFlsp; 4-H; PpCl; Secretary.

DOERNER, Mary E; Wheaton Central HS; Wheaton, IL; 19/217 Chr; ChrhWkr; HonRl; JrNHS; NHS; NatlMeritFnl; NatlMeritCmnd; NatlMeritSchl; NatlMeritSF; SchMus; SchPl; FrCl; Bradley Univ; Medical Tech.

DOERNER, Rebecca J; Bath HS; Bath, MI; 16/90 SecFrshCls; PresSophCls; HonRl; NHS; StuCncl; TchrAde; Yrbk; SchPpr; Chrldr; CitAwd; College; Physical Education.

DOERNHOEFER, Gary R; Lindbergh HS; Crestwood, MO; SecSrCls; Aud/Vis; HonRl; NHS; NatlMeritSF; NatlThespSoc; OffAde; SchPl; StuGov; RusCl; Univ ; Law.

DOERR, Lois L; Plainview HS; Creighton, NE; 4/57 Chrs; HonRl; LbryAde; NHS; OffAde; PpCl;.

DOERRES, Melinda L; D C Everest HS; Schofield, WI; LetterBand; MrchBnd; PepBnd; GerCl; PpCl; CaptTrk; CaptChrldr; GAA; IMSpt; Univ Southern Ms; Science.

DOERSTLER, Jo A; Hagerstown HS; Greensfork, IN; 6/124 HonRl; NHS; YthFlsp; 4-H; SecFBLA; FFA; SecFHA; PpCl; Chrldr; Secretary.

DOESING, Janet; Bishop Dubourg HS; St Louis, MO; HonRl; JrNHS; NHS; OffAde; PolWkr; SchAde; SctActv; TchrAde; RptrYrbk; PPFtbl;.

DOETSCH, Douglas A; Flushing HS; Flushing, MI; 38/464 VPChr; Chrl; NHS; NatlThespSoc; SchMus; SchPl; FrCl; IMSpt; OptClAwd; Kalamazoo Clge; International Relations.

DOGGETT, Kathleen E; Burwell Jr Sr HS; Burwell, NE; VPFrshCls; SecSophCls; VPJrCls; SecSrCls; Chr; Chrs; HonRl; Mdrgl; NHS; MthCl; PpCl; Trk; Chrldr; College; Med Lab Technician.

DOGWILER, Gregg R; Dixon HS; Dixon, IL; Bsbl; Glf; Coll.

DOHE, Robert S; Three Lakes HS; Rhinelander, WI; SecTrsSophCls; ALBoysSt; Band; Chr; Chrl; Chrs; CncrtBnd; HonRl; MrchBnd; NHS; PepBnd; StuCncl; StuGov; College; Professional.

DOHERTY, Barbara J; Senior HS; Superior, WI; Chr; HonRl; LbryAde; EdSchPpr; PpCl; SciCl; Swmmng; Chrldr; GAA; PPFtbl; College; Rn.

DOHERTY, Charlotte; Jennings HS; Clayton, KS; 9/22 HstJrCls; ChrhWkr; HonRl; JA; YthFlsp; 4-H; FFA; FHA; Bsbl; Trk; Trade School; Dental Career.

DOHERTY, Cindy A; Mt Assisi HS; Crestwood, IL; 82/197 ChrhWkr; CmntyWkr; DrmMjrt; HonRl; Teen; SpnCl; SciCl; Swmmng; Chrldr; College; Professional.

DOHERTY, John G; Ellsworth Public HS; Ellsworth, MN; 1/35 Band; Chr; CncrtBnd; HonRl; MrchBnd; NatlMeritSF; Yrbk; LetterBsktbl; LetterFtbl; LetterTrk; Coll.

DOHERTY, John J; Motley HS; Motley, MN; Chr; HonRl; LbryAde; SctActv; StuCncl; TchrAde; FFA; Bsbl; CaptBsktbl; LetterFtbl; LetterTrk; Vocational School; Farmer.

DOHERTY, Michael P; Cathedral HS; Indianapolis, IN; 6/123 HonRl; NHS; NatlMeritFnl; SchPl; StuCncl; LetterWrstlng; PPFtbl; OptClAwd; Wabash Col.

DOHERTY, Patrice E; New Prague HS; New Prague, MN; 14/194 Chr; HonRl; Mdrgl; NHS; EdYrBk; GerCl; PpCl; Chrldr; IMSpt; AmLegAwd; College; Business Admin.

DOHM, Della S; Grinnell HS; Grinnell, KS; SecFrshCls; Band; CncrtBnd; MrchBnd; PepBnd; SchPl; SchPpr; 4-H; PpCl; Chrldr; School; Physical Therapy.

DOHMEIER, Mark E; Browntown Public HS; Browntown, MN; 1/22 PresFrshCls; Band; Chrs; HonRl; NatlMeritCmnd; PresStuCncl; GerCl; LetterBsbl; LetterBsktbl; LetterFtbl; College; Biology.

DOHMEN, Brenda; Newman Grove HS; Newman Grove, NE; 3/40 Band; Chrs; CncrtBnd; HonRl; MrchBnd; NHS; PepBnd; SchPl; PpCl; Grand Island School Of Busi; Accountant C.

DOHMS, Denise M; D C Everest HS; Rothschild, WI; 8/344 ChrhWkr; SctActv; GerCl; PpCl; Chrldr; LionAwd; Tech Sch; Radiologist.

DOHNALEK, Cindy M; Prairie HS; Cedar Rapids, IA; Chr; HonRl; JrNHS; 4-H; Bsktbl; 4-HAwd; College; Professional.

DOHNALEK, Daniel A; Glenbrook South HS; Glenview, IL; 73/591 CmntyWkr; HonRl; NHS; PepBnd; StuCncl; StuGov; KeyCl; Bsktbl; CaptSocr; LetterTennis; Col; Pre Med.

DOHNER, Daniel E; South Newton HS; Kentland, IN; StuCncl; LatCl; SciCl; Bsbl; Ftbl; College.

DOHR, Kathi S; Round Lake Sr HS; Round Lake, IL; 51/204 CaptBsbl; LetterBsktbl; GAA; IMSpt; Univ; Physical Education Teacher.

DOHRMANN, James A; Reese HS; Reese, MI; VPSophCls; ALBoysSt; Band; HonRl; NHS; SchPl; StuCncl; LetterBsktbl; LetterFtbl; LetterTennis; College; Curriculum Of Major.

DOHRMANN, Janice A; Reese HS; Reese, MI; PresChrhWkr; CncrtBnd; HonRl; MrchBnd; NHS; StuCncl; GerCl; PpCl; CaptChrldr; CitAwd; Central Michigan Univ; Dietician.

DOIEL, Michael; Hastings HS; Hastings, NE; Band; CncrtBnd; MrchBnd; Orch; PepBnd; SchMus; SchPl; SctActv; Bsktbl; Wrstlng; Univ Of Ne; Arch.

DOIG, Nancy C; Pt Wash HS; Port Washington, WI; 39/240 AFS; HonRl; Yrbk; Uw Eau Claire; Bus.

DOIRON, Michael F; Redbud C U HS; Prairie Du Rocher, IL; 1/138 HonRl; NHS; MthCl; Bsbl; Eastern Illinois Univ; Accountant.

DOKE, Debra A; Memorial HS; Joplin, MO; 10/225 AFS; Chr; Chrs; ChrhWkr; HonRl; NHS; YthFlsp; GAA; Missouri Southern Coll; Special Education.

DOLAN, Amy M; St Louise De Marillac HS; Northbrook, IL; Chr; Chrl; Chrs; ChrhWkr; SchPl; SchPl; Sdlty; PpCl; IMSpt; Depauw U; Singing.

DOLAN, Catherine E; Bishop Miege HS; Shawnee Mission, KS; 8/211 SecJrCls; VPSrCls; HonRl; NatlFornLg; NHS; PolWkr; StuCncl; Trk; IMSpt; AmLegAwd; Drake U; Government.

DOLAN, Cheryl; John Hersey HS; Mount Prospect, IL; 31 Chrs; HonRl; JA; Mdrgl; NHS; OffAde; SchPpr; Iowa State U;veterinary Medicine.

DOLAN, James R; Marist HS; Chicago, IL; 22/365 HonRl; NHS; Yrbk; RptrSchPpr; LatCl; SciCl; LetterBsktbl; LetterFtbl; Loyola Univ; Biology.

DOLAN, John T; Chaminade Col Prep; St Louis, MO; 22/105 HonRl; JrNHS; NHS; OffAde; Swmmng; Trk; Univ Of Mo; Professional.

DOLAN, Lori J; St John HS; Rolla, ND; 2/20 VPFrshCls; PresJrCls; Band; Chr; Chrs; ChrhWkr; HonRl; PepBnd; SchMus; SchPl; StuCncl; 4-H; FHA; Trade School; Professional.

DOLAN, Madonna K; Rudd Rockford Marble Rock HS; Marble Rock, IA; Chr; HonRl; NHS; SchMus; SchPl; StuCncl; Yrbk; 4-H; FNA; Bsktbl; College; Nursing.

DOLAN, Michael; Paul C Schulte HS; Seelyville, IN; ChrhWkr; HonRl; KeyCl; Indiana Univ; Physics.

DOLAN, Moira T; Metro HS; Chicago, IL; ChrhWkr; CmntyWkr; HonRl; OffAde; SchAde; SctActv; StuCncl; StuGov; TchrAde; FTA; Hampshire College; Law.

DOLAN, Patrick J; St Marys HS; Burlington, WI; 3/76 HonRl; SchMus; SciCl; Milwaukee Sch Of Engineering; Elec Eng.

DOLAN, Robert P; Homewood Flossmoor HS; Flossmoor, IL; 33/940 HonRl; NHS; CaptSwmmng; U; Md.

DOLBEE, William B; Constantine HS; Bristol, IN; 3/110 CncrtBnd; HonRl; MrchBnd; NHS; NatlMeritFnl; PepBnd; PresStuGov; SciCl; Bsktbl; LetterFtbl; Mich St U; Math.

DOLCE, Pamela R; Peru HS; Peru, IN; 37/221 HonRl; LitMag; StuCncl; StuGov; TchrAde; SchPpr; FrCl; Chrldr; GAA; PPFtbl; College; Science.

DOLCE, Sharon K; Niles West HS; Niles, IL; 32/666 ChrhWkr; HonRl; HospAde; NHS; Loyola Univ; Nursing.

DOLDE, Sheila R; Schaller Comm HS; Schaller, IA; 15/32 Chr; Chrs; ChrhWkr; HonRl; LbryAde; SchMus; SctActv; YthFlsp; Yrbk; Nw Missouri State Univ; Ocal Music Edctn.

DOLE, Catherine L; Warren Township HS; Gurnee, IL; 18/310 Band; CncrtBnd; HonRl; MrchBnd; NHS; College.

DOLEZAL, Edward G; Riverside Brookfield HS; La Grange Park, IL; 27/489 Band; CncrtBnd; HonRl; MrchBnd; NHS; PepBnd; U Of Il; Doctor Of Medicine.

DOLIESLAGER, Montgomery P; Atkinson HS; Atkinson, IL; 13/39 ALBoysSt; HonRl; 4-H; FFA; CaptBsbl; CaptBsktbl; LetterFtbl; LetterTrk; 4-HAwd; College.

DOLIN, Sheena L; Ypsilanti HS; Ypsilanti, MI; PresSrCls; ChrhWkr; CmntyWkr; HonRl; MrchBnd; NHS; StuCncl; GovHonPrgAwd; PresAwd; Eastern Michigan Univ; Nursing.

DOLL, Betty; Northern Mi Christian HS; Mcbain, MI; 3/40 TrsFrshCls; HonRl; StuCncl; EdYrBk; KeyCl; PpCl; 4-HAwd; Calvin College; Special Education Teacher.

DOLL, Carla J; Sherwood Cass R 8 HS; Urich, MO; 4/66 ALAGirlsSt; HonRl; SecNHS; YthFlsp; FHA; MthCl; PpCl; Bsktbl; Trk; PresAwd; State Fair Comm Col; Legal Sec.

DOLL, Cheryl A; Chase HS; Chase, KS; 11/34 VPFrshCls; Band; Chrs; HonRl; SchPl; StuCncl; Yrbk; PpCl; Bsktbl; Trk;.

DOLL, Dennis J; Greenville HS; Greenville, IL; JA; StuCncl; StuGov; LatCl; Eastern Illinois Univ; Accounting.

DOLL, Diane S; Greenville HS; Pocahontas, IL; HonRl; JA; NHS; LatCl; PpCl; GAA; PPFtbl; Greenville College; Elem Educ.

DOLL, Janice K; North Knox HS; Bicknell, IN; 6/138 ChrhWkr; NHS; Sec4-H; FTA; SecFrCl; Business School; Professional.

DOLL, Lori; Blair HS; Blair, NE; FBLA; College; Computer Systems Analyst.

DOLL, Mary; Mercy HS; Omaha, NE; SchPl; StuCncl; LatCl; PpCl; Trk; College; Professional.

DOLL, Michael J; Bishop Du Bourg HS; St Louis, MO; VPJrCls; PresSrCls; HonRl; SctActv; StuCncl; LetterFtbl; LetterTrk; University; Medicine.

DOLL, Phyllis E; Bushnell Prairie City HS; Bushnell, IL; 13/89 Band; Chr; Chrl; ChrhWkr; CncrtBnd; HonRl; NHS; PepBnd; SchMus; SchPl; Stephens Coll.

DOLL, Sandra; Butler HS; Butler, MO; 22/98 AFS; Chr; Chrl; Chrs; HonRl; FBLA; FTA; SpnCl; PpCl; IMSpt; Univ Of Mo; Journalist.

DOLLAR, Julia A; Farmington East HS; Farmington, IL; 24/131 SecJrCls; Chr; HonRl; PepBnd; TreasStuGov; YthFlsp; Yrbk; PresSpnCl; SciCl; GAA; Spoon River Jr College; Business Admin.

DOLLARD, Rita A; Our Lady Star Of The Sea HS; Detroit, MI; HonRl; LbryAde; PolWkr; SchPl; StuCncl; Teen; RptrSchPpr; Chrldr; IMSpt; College; Theology.

DOLLEN, Jonette J; Tri Center HS; Shelby, IA; SecJrCls; Band; CncrtBnd; DrmMjrt; MrchBnd; SchMus; SchPl; PpCl; CaptBsktbl; Trk; Trade Or Bus Sch.

DOLLEN, Paula J; Valley Falls HS; Valley Falls, KS; Band; Chr; Chrs; ChrhWkr; CncrtBnd; DrlTm; DrmMjrt; HonRl; MrchBnd; PepBnd; Bsktbl;.

DOLLETSKI, Robert; Heritage Hills HS; Chrisney, IN; 39/147 Band; CncrtBnd; MrchBnd; College; Professional.

DOLLEY, Henry J; Holland HS; Holland, MI; ChrhWkr; HonRl; SctActv; SciCl; College; Science.

DOLLINGER, John J; Joliet Catholic HS; Plainfield, IL; 4/170 HonRl; LitMag; NHS; NatlMeritCmnd; YthLg; EdYrBk; SchPpr; GerCl; Joliet Jr College; Farming.

DOLLMAN, Pamela K; Marengo Community HS; Union, IL; 7/175 PresSrCls; Chr; ChrhWkr; DrlTm; HonRl; SchPl; TchrAde; FHA; GerCl; SecGAA; Univ; Accounting.

DOLLMEYER, Larry J; Prairie HS; Fairfax, IA; HonRl; JrNHS; SchAde; CaptBsktbl; College; Business.

DOLOHANTY, Patrick A; St Joseph HS; St Joseph, MI; HonRl; StuCncl; Trk; IMSpt; AmLegAwd; Michigan State Univ; Accounting.

DOLPHIN, Brian K; Creighton Prep HS; Omaha, NE; CmntyWkr; HonRl; NHS; SancSoc; Sdlty; StuGov; LatCl; LetterBsktbl; LetterFtbl; IMSpt; Coll; Engr/law.

DOLSON, Sheri; Grosse Pointe South HS; Grosse Pointe Farm, MI; Band; CncrtBnd; HonRl; MrchBnd; Orch; PepBnd; GAA; IMSpt; College; Music Education.

DOMANIK, Darlene M; Aquinas HS; Lincoln Park, MI; 80218 VPChr; HonRl; NatlFornLg; NHS; NatlMeritSchl; SchMus; SchPl; College; Law Enforcement.

DOMBEK, Timothy M; Warsaw Community HS; Winona Lake, IN; Aud/Vis; ChrhWkr; CmntyWkr; LbryAde; PolWkr; SchPl; SchPpr; Criminal Law.

DOMBKIEWICZ, Sherie L; Cornell HS; Cornell, WI; HonRl; LbryAde; Busi Sch; Voc.

DOMBROWSKI, Eileen A; Andrean HS; Gary, IN; 9/250 HonRl; NHS; Purdue; Geo Engr.

DOMBROWSKI, James T; Frank Cody HS; Detroit, MI; HonRl; Coll Of Art & Design; Artist And Writer.

DOMBROWSKI, Robert A; Weber HS; Chicago, IL; 1/210 ChrhWkr; HonRl; PresNHS; NatlMeritCmnd; SctActv; StuCncl; EdYrBk; LatCl; SciCl; IMSpt; Loyola Univ; Doctor.

DOMEIER, Catherine; Cathedral HS; Sleepy Eye, MN; HonRl; HospAde; LbryAde; NatlThespSoc; SchPl; StuCncl; RptrSchPpr; PPFtbl; St Cloud St Coll; Animal Sci.

DOMEIER, Douglas J; Public HS; Sleepy Eye, MN; PresFrshCls; PresSophCls; HstJrCls; ChrhWkr; HonRl; SchAde; StuCncl; StuGov; SecSophCls; PpCl; Vocational; Agriculture.

DOMEIER, Terry L; Geneva Public HS; Geneva, NE; ALBoysSt; Band; StuGov; YthFlsp; Bsktbl; Ftbl; Univ Of Nebraska; Accounting.

DOMENOSKI, Brian K; Washington HS; Two Rivers, WI; 31/222 Band; CncrtBnd; HonRl; JA; MrchBnd; NHS; PepBnd; StuCncl; StuGov; Univ Of Wisconsin; Business Admin.

DOMINA, Lynn M; Merrill HS; Merrill, MI; 2/112 HonRl; NHS; College; Journalism.

DOMINE, Melvin; Verona Public HS; La Moure, ND; VPSrCls; SchPl; StuCncl; PpCl; Trk; IMSpt; Und Grand Forks; Prof Elect Eng.

DOMINIAK, Dennis M; Casso Polis HS; Dowagiac, MI; RptrSchPpr; FFA; Ftbl;.

DOMINY, Julie T; Ringsted Comm HS; Ringsted, IA; PresJrCls; Band; HonRl; SecNHS; NatlMeritCmnd; RptrYrbk; EdSchPpr; LetterTrk; Chrldr; KiwanAwd; Univ Of Iowa.

DOMKOWSKI, Elaine; William Howard Taft Hs; Chicago, IL; 20/880 HonRl; JrNHS; NHS; TchrAde; GAA; Drake U; Mathematics.

DOMOGALLA, Gary D; Mahnomen HS; Bejou, MN; ALBoysSt; Aud/Vis; Chrs; ChrhWkr; SchMus; SchPl; College; Ministry.

DOMOKOS, Donna G; South Milwaukee Sr HS; South Milwaukee, WI; 75/442 AFS; Band; ChrhWkr; CncrtBnd; HonRl; MrchBnd; OffAde; Orch; TchrAde; YthFlsp; University; Dietician.

DOMORACKI, Linda; Madison HS; Madison, SD; 26/159 Band; HonRl; NHS; Yrbk; South Dakota State Univ; General Reg.

DOMZALSKI, Kevin R; Carl Sandburg HS; Tinley Park, IL; 20/700 CmntyWkr; HonRl; NHS; PolWkr; Quill&Scroll; StuCncl; StuGov; YthLg; SchPpr; FrCl; GerCl; SciCl; Socr; LetterTrk; Univ Of Ill; Architecture.

DONABEDIAN, Lawrence E; St Agatha HS; Livonia, MI; U Of Mi; Art.

DONAHOE, Kerry R; Lamphere HS; Madison Heights, MI; SctActv; TchrAde; LetterSwmmng; Univ Of Michigan; Business Admin.

DONAHOE, Vincent A; Chosen Valley HS; Chatfield, MN; Band; Chrs; CncrtBnd; DrmMjrt; HonRl; Mdrgl; MrchBnd; PepBnd; SchMus; Clg; Mech Engineering.

DONAHUE, Denise D; Portland HS; Portland, IN; HonRl; JrNHS; NHS; SchAde; Teen; 4-H; FrCl; MthCl; SciCl; CitAwd; Business School; Secretary.

DONAHUE, Diane L; Valders Public HS; Manitowoc, WI; Chrs; HonRl; RptrSchPpr; 4-H; PpCl; Tech School ;fashion Merch.

DONAHUE, James; Spalding Institute; Peoria, IL; 3.

DONAHUE, Jeffery L; Franklin HS; Livonia, MI; Chr; Chrl; ChrhWkr; HonRl; Orch; TreasYthFlsp; U Of Mich; Liberal Ats.

DONAHUE, Kevin C; St Pius X HS; Smithville, MO; 10/149 PresJrCls; PresSrCls; ALBoysSt; HonRl; NHS; NatlMeritCmnd; StuCncl; RptrSchPpr; EdSchPpr; CaptBsktbl; Ftbl; LetterTrk; CchngActv; University; Law.

DONAHUE, Laurie A; Marquette HS; Ottawa, IL; 5/96 HonRl; NHS; StuCncl; Pres4-H; PpCl; CaptTrk; PresGAA; IMSpt; 4-HAwd; Augustana College; Medicine.

DONAHUE, Patricia K; Taylors Falls HS; Taylors Falls, MN; Chr; HonRl; SchPl; StuCncl; KeyCl; SpnCl; PpCl; SciCl; LetterChrldr; LetterGAA; College; Medicine.

DONAHUE, Patrick M; Wahlert HS; Dubuque, IA; 121/441 CAP; HonRl; LetterTrk; College; Chemistry.

DONAHUE, William J; Regina HS; Iowa City, IA; 8/50 TrsJrCls; HonRl; SchMus; StuGov; RptrYrbk; RptrSchPpr; Bsbl; Bsktbl; CchngActv; IMSpt; U Of Ia; Teacher.

DONAIS, Patrick; St Charles HS; St Charles, MO; HonRl; MthCl; SciCl; Ftbl; Tennis; JAAwd; Univ Of Tulsa; Physicist.

DONAJKOWSKI, Ray W; Port Washington HS; Pt Washington, WI; HonRl; SchPpr; College; Accounting.

DONALD, Antonio T; Christain Fenger HS; Chicago, IL; 10/593 HonRl; JrNHS; NHS; NatlMeritCmnd; SchAde; StuCncl; Tennis; IMSpt; Coll; Mech Engr.

DONALD, Ramona; Sumner HS; Kansas City, KS; HonRl; JA; SchMus; SchPpr; PpCl; College; Fashion.

DONALDSON, Janice L; Bloomington HS; Bloomington, IL; 52/391 TrsFrshCls; HonRl; NHS; SchPpr; SecSpnCl; MthCl; PpCl; GAA; Il St U; Special Ed.

DONALDSON, Larry B; Ramsey Comm HS; Ramsey, IL; 10/46 HonRl; SchPl; PresStuCncl; Yrbk; FTA; PpCl; LetterBsbl; LetterBsktbl; College; Professional.

DONALDSON, Laura E; R Nelson Snider HS; Fort Wayne, IN; HonRl; HospAde; StuCncl; SecFrCl; SpnCl; PpCl; Chrldr; GAA; College; Foreign Languageteacher.

DONALDSON, Lori K; Roscommon HS; Grayling, MI; 1/100 TrsSrCls; Chr; Chrl; Chrs; ChrhWkr; CmntyWkr; HonRl; HospAde; PresNHS; OffAde; Lake Superior State Clge; Rn.

DONALDSON, L Tanya E; West Side HS; Gary, IN; Band; ChrhWkr; CncrtBnd; HonRl; JrNHS; MrchBnd; College; Pediatrician.

DONALDSON, Mark; Dixon HS; Dixon, IL; HonRl; IMSpt; Univ Of Wasington; Oceanography.

DONATELLI, Michael G; Hinsdale Central HS; Hinsdale, IL; 131/583 HonRl; Us Air Force Academy; Engineering.

DONATI, Joseph S; Holy Cross HS; River Grove, IL; 12/300 HonRl; NHS; University Of Illinois; Engineer.

DONDANVILLE, L John; Griffin HS; Springfield, IL; 1/200 Band; CncrtBnd; MrchBnd; PepBnd; SchMus; Univ Of Notre Dame; Civil Engineering.

DONDLINGER, Edward J; Grace HS; Minneapolis, MN; HonRl; U Of Mn; Engineering.

DONEY, Gerald L; Wakefield HS; Wakefield, MI; HonRl; 4-H; SpnCl; Bsbl; Bsktbl; Ftbl; VPSrCls; RotaryAwd; Mi Tec U ;engineering.

DONHAM, Richard G; Mason Sr HS; Erie, MI; HonRl; NatlFornLg; NHS; SchPl; SctActv; GerCl; LetterFtbl; VoiceDemAwd; College; Professional.

DONICA, John; Hauser HS; Hope, IN; 18/86 Band; CncrtBnd; MrchBnd; PepBnd; SctActv; PpCl;.

DONIGAN, Sandra L; East Detroit HS; East Detroit, MI; TreasBand; ChrhWkr; CncrtBnd; HonRl; MrchBnd; NHS; PepBnd; SchMus; FrCl; Clge; Pro.

DONK, Lisa; Parkway Central HS; Chesterfield, MO; 26/469 ALAGirlsSt; Chr; JrNHS; ModUN; NHS; NatlMeritCmnd; StuCncl; YthFlsp; PpCl; Miami.

DONLEY, Marty A; Bishop Noll Institute; East Chicago, IN; ALBoysSt; Chrl; SchMus; College; Professional.

DONLEY, Michael L; Chaminade HS; Ballwin, MO; 40/112 HonRl; StuCncl; Ftbl; Glf; OptClAwd; College; Medicine.

DONLEY, Pamela S; Harrisburg HS; Harrisburg, IL; ChrhWkr; HonRl; 4-H; Jr College; Business.

DONLEY, Reba; John Marshall Harlan HS; Chicago, IL; 2/921 Chr; Chrs; ChrhWkr; HonRl; JrNHS; ModUN; NHS; NatlSciFnd; OffAde; LetterTennis; LetterTrk; LetterGAA; IMSpt; College; Judge.

DONLEY, Sheree D; Lincoln HS; Beverly, KS; 1/60 Band; HonRl; SchPl; StuCncl; 4-H; 4-H; GerCl; PpCl; DanFAwd; 4-HAwd; CitAwd; Fort Hays Kansas St College ;math.,

DONLIN, Linda; Rock Island HS; Rock Island, IL; ChrhWkr; JrNHS; PolWkr; Teen; YthFlsp; SpnCl; PpCl; PPFtbl; JETSAwd; Engineering.

DONNAY, Linda M; Flushing HS; Flushing, MI; 42/464 Chr; Chrs; HonRl; NHS; NatlMeritSF; SecNatlThespSoc; SchMus; SchPl; SctActv; Clge; Acting & Elem Ed.

DONNELL, Daniel K; Lexington HS; Lexington, IL; 4/48 SecJrCls; PresSrCls; TreasNHS; SctActv; SecFFA; SciCl; Bsbl; Ftbl; Trk; College; Agriculture.

DONNELL, Pamela; Field Kindley Memorial HS; Coffeyville, KS; 7/244 Chr; DrmBgl; HonRl; Orch; TchrAde; YthFlsp; Ks State Univ; Education Elementary.

DONNELL, Robert F; Marist HS; Oak Lawn, IL; HonRl; Marquette University; Bio Medical Engineer.

DONNELLAN, Edward S; Memorial HS; Eau Claire, WI; 75/410 HonRl; RedCrAde; SchMus; SchPl; PpCl; Ftbl; Swmmng; Tennis; Trk; CchngActv; Univ; Professional.

DONNELLY, Andrew J; Freeport Senior HS; Freeport, IL; 8/494 HonRl; SpnCl; Highland Community Coll; Pharmacy.

DONNELLY, Deborah J; South Lake HS; St Clair Shores, MI; ChrhWkr; CmntyWkr; HonRl; JA; LitMag; NatlMeritSF; PolWkr; RptrYrbk; Mich Univ; Spec Educ.

DONNELLY, Edward B; Freeport Senior HS; Freeport, IL; 8/494 HonRl; SpnCl; Highland Community Coll; Pharmacy.

DONNELLY, Joseph P; Loyola Academy; Chicago, IL; 131/442 Band; CncrtBnd; DrmBgl; MrchBnd; Orch; SchMus; Northwestern Univ; Engineer.

DONNELLY, Julie K; New Trier West HS; Glenview, IL; AFS; LitMag; LbryAde; RptrYrbk; University Of Illinois; Liberal Arts.

DONNELLY, Mary K; Lyons Township HS; Western Springs, IL; Chr; HonRl; LitMag; LbryAde; NHS; NatlMeritFnl; Univ Of Wisc.

DONNELLY, Robert J; Central Community HS; Dewitt, IA; 5/158 Band; Chr; CncrtBnd; HonRl; HospAde; MrchBnd; NHS; NatlMeritSF; LetterBsbl; Bsktbl; U Of Ia; Physician.

DONNELLY, Sherry L; Paolo HS; Paola, KS; 41/140 VPSophCls; Chr; HonRl; SchMus; SchPl; GerCl; PpCl; Bsbl; Trk; Ks St U; Speech.

DONNER, Brian F; Columbus HS; Columbus, WI; 36/140 ChrhWkr; CmntyWkr; Trk; Wrstlng; Univ Of Wisconsin; Law.

DONNER, Kent; Reeder Public HS; Reeder, ND; 10/17 VPSrCls; Bsbl; Bsktbl; CchngActv;.

DONNER, Perry P; Lincoln HS; Park Falls, WI; Chr; Chrl; Mdrgl; 4-H; Bsktbl; Trk; Navy.

DONNER, Susan; Jackson County Western HS; Jackson, MI; 12/149 Chr; HonRl; HospAde; NHS; FrCl; Navy.

DONOGHUE, Brian T; Loyola Academy; Glenview, IL; 4/400 CmntyWkr; HonRl; NatlMeritSF; Univ Of Illinois; Computer Science.

DONOGHUE, Eugene J; Pontiac Catholic HS; Pontiac, MI; 5/149 HonRl; ModUN; NHS; PolWkr; StuCncl; StuGov; LetterBsktbl; LetterFtbl; U Of Detroit ;bus Manage.

DONOGHUE, Margaret M; Benet Academy; Naperville, IL; 98/230 PresSrCls; VPSrCls; SecSrCls; TrsSrCls; PolWkr; StuGov; Bsktbl; Ftbl; Chrldr; Univ; Business.

DONOGHUE, William J; Henry Ford HS; Detroit, MI; 1/500 HonRl; NHS; NatlMeritSchl; Quill&Scroll; RptrYrbk; EdSchPpr; SchPpr; PresLatCl; U Of Mich; Lawyer.

DONOHO, Glenda; Lincoln Way Comm Hs; New Lenox, IL; 28/498 SecBand; ChrhWkr; CncrtBnd; HonRl; MrchBnd; NHS; PepBnd; SchMus; Cedarville College; Mathematics.

DONOHOE, Loretta A; Adams HS; Rochester, MI; HonRl; LetterNHS; NatlMeritCmnd; FrCl; Swmmng; PPFtbl; DARAwd; Mi State; Public Relations.

DONOHUE, Cynthia J; Heelan HS; Sioux City, IA; 13/246 HonRl; LbryAde; NHS; StuCncl; TchrAde; PpCl; Glf; Chrldr; PPFtbl; College; Professional.

DONOHUE, Diane K; Stanton Community HS; Stanton, IA; VPFrshCls; Band; Chr; CncrtBnd; HonRl; MrchBnd; PepBnd; LetterBsbl; Bsktbl; LetterTrk; Coll; Professional.

DONOHUE, Nancy J; Mother Mcauley HS; Chicago, IL; 10/474 HonRl; JrNHS; NHS; OffAde; SchPl; TchrAde; EdYrBk; Drake Univ; Commercial Art.

DONOHUE, Steven T; Mendel Catholic Prep HS; Calumet Park, IL; 18/191 HonRl; Univ Of Il; Biology.

DONOHUE, Thomas C; Lake Fenton HS; Fenton, MI; 1/170 PresSophCls; Band; CmntyWkr; CncrtBnd; HonRl; PresNHS; PepBnd; VPStuCncl; EdSchPpr; U Of Hawaii; Science.

DONOVAN, Cynthia A; Maquoketa Community HS; Maquoketa, IA; 8/142 Band; Chrs; CmntyWkr; HonRl; ModUN; PolWkr; SchPl; RptrSchPpr; Treas4-H; PresSciCl; College; Major In Chemistry.

DONOVAN, David; Kee HS; New Aibin, IA; 3/51 PresJrCls; HonRl; JrNHS; NHS; Quill&Scroll; StuCncl; SptEdSchPpr; PpCl; Bsbl; Bsktbl; Wartburg College; Doctor.

DONOVAN, Donald G; Baltic HS; Baltic, SD; HonRl; NHS; FFA;.

DONOVAN, Jerald A; Heelan Catholic HS; Sioux City, IA; 1/249 ChrhWkr; HonRl; NHS; TchrAde; FrCl; AmLegAwd; VFWAwd; University; Medicine.

DONOVAN, Leslie S; Evanston Township HS; Evanston, IL; Chrs; HonRl; StuGov; TchrAde; LetterTennis; GAA; Rice University; Medicine.

DONOVAN, Margaret R; Roosevelt HS; Wyandotte, MI; HstFrshCls; Chr; HonRl; SchAde; 4-H; Bsktbl; GAA; PPFtbl; 4-HAwd; Business Sch.

DONOVAN, Mary L; Ionia HS; Ionia, MI; 1/250 TrsFrshCls; SecJrCls; MrchBnd; NHS; Orch; SchMus; LetterBsktbl; LetterTrk; U Of Mi; Medicine.

DONOVAN, Mary S; Odell Comm HS; Odell, IL; Band; Chr; CncrtBnd; PepBnd; SchPl; Pres4-H; FHA; PresSpnCl; PpCl; Bsbl; Glf; 4-HAwd; JAAwd; Illinois St Univ; Physical Therapist.

DONZE, James E; Valle HS; Ste Genevieve, MO; Band; ChrhWkr; CmntyWkr; CncrtBnd; HonRl; MrchBnd; PolWkr; 4-H; Bsktbl; Trk; Univ Of Missouri; Pro/business.

DONZE, Kevin; Valle HS; Ste Genevieve, MO; /80 HonRl; HospAde; SchMus; SchPl; EdYrBk; IMSpt; Univ Mo;phys Ther.

DOOD, Steven P; W Michigan Christian HS; Ferrysburg, MI; SecTrsFrshCls; HonRl; OffAde; StuCncl; MthCl; SciCl; LetterBsbl; IMSpt; College; Vocation.

DOOGE, Evelyn V; Stratford HS; Stratford, WI; 7/90 Band; Chrs; ChrhWkr; NHS; SchPl; Yrbk; FHA; DARAwd; EldAwd; VoiceDemAwd; U Of Wis Whitewater; Teach Special Ed.

DOOLEY, Angela A; West Excelsior Springs HS; Excelsior Springs, MO; 40/240 PresJrCls; Band; Chr; CncrtBnd; HonRl; JrNHS; NHS; OffAde; StuCncl; Bsktbl; Tennis; Business Schl; Secretary.

DOOLEY, Brian; Chaffee HS; Wheatland, ND; 3/11 VPJrCls; ALBoysSt; Band; Chr; HonRl; Wahpeton St Sch Science.

DOOLEY, Charlene; Freeman HS; Freeman, SD; ChrhWkr; HonRl; SchPl; YthFlsp; RptrSchPpr; FHA; College; Arts.

DOOLEY, James J; Martensdale St Marys HS; Prole, IA; TrsFrshCls; PresSrCls; Chr; SchPl; StuGov; PpCl; LetterBsbl; LetterTrk; CchngActv; College; Education.

DOOLEY, Janet L; Mount St Scholastica HS; Atchison, KS; VPFrshCls; PresSophCls; SecTrsSrCls; HonRl; Sdlty; StuCncl; RptrYrbk; EdSchPpr; PpCl; BttyCrckrAwd; Benedictine Coll.

DOOLEY, John B; Hamburg HS; Hamburg, IA; PresJrCls; Band; CncrtBnd; HonRl; MrchBnd; NHS; StuCncl; YthFlsp; RptrYrbk; Bsbl; Bsktbl; LetterFtbl; LetterTrk; University; Engineering.

DOOLEY, Julianne M; Central Cass HS; Casselton, ND; Chr; Chrs; ChrhWkr; CmntyWkr; HonRl; NHS; PolWkr; SchPl; TchrAde; Chrldr; Nd St Sch Of Sci; Occupational Therapy.

DOOLEY, Margaret A; Pacelli HS; Austin, MN; HonRl; SchMus; SchPl; Yrbk; 4-H; FrCl; PpCl; Tennis; IMSpt; 4-HAwd; Univ; Psychiatrist.

DOOLEY, Mary Carol A; Montini HS; Lombard, IL; 23/165 Band; CmntyWkr; HonRl; StuCncl; GerCl; LetterTennis; College Of St Teresa; Doctor.

DOOLEY, Michael P; St Thomas Acad; Minneapolis, MN; Band; RptrYrbk; Ftbl; Wrstlng; IMSpt; Univ; Social Sciences.

DOOLIN, James M; Routt HS; Jacksonville, IL; 20/60 HonRl; StuCncl; LatCl; SpnCl; MthCl; LetterBsbl; Ftbl;.

DOOLING, Melodi A; Blue Valley HS; Stilwell, KS; 2/93 Chr; Chrl; DrlTm; HonRl; NatlFornLg; NHS; OffAde; SchMus; SchPl; StuCncl; TchrAde; RptrYrbk; Chrldr; IMSpt; Kansas St Univ; Business Admin.

DOOLING, Timothy R; Alleman HS; Rock Island, IL; 1/240 Band; ChrhWkr; CncrtBnd; HonRl; JA; MrchBnd; NHS; NatlMeritCmnd; PepBnd; SctActv; EdSchPpr; FrCl; DARAwd; College; Elec Engineering.

DOOLITTLE, Jennifer C; Mexico HS; Mexico, MO; TrsJrCls; VPSrCls; Band; Chr; Mdrgl; SctActv; FrCl; LatCl; Swmmng; Chrldr; College; Curriculum Of Major Study.

DOOLITTLE, Mary A; Hillsdale HS; Hillsdale, MI; CmntyWkr; JA; NHS; SchPl; UNYO; Yrbk; FTA; KeyCl; Trk; Jackson Community College; Artist.

DOOLITTLE, Ross A; Clio HS; Clio, MI; 16/366 Band; CncrtBnd; HonRl; MrchBnd; NHS; PepBnd; SchMus; YthFlsp; LatCl; Mich St Univ; Pro Musician.

DOOLITTLE, Timothy B; Bishop Ward HS; Kansas City, KS; 1/195 PresFrshCls; Chrs; HonRl; LitMag; NHS; SchMus; TchrAde; MthCl; LetterSocr; Trk;.

DOOLY, David A; Mulberry Grove HS; Mulberry Grove, IL; 4/39 Band; Chrs; ChrhWkr; CncrtBnd; HonRl; NHS; SchPl; FTA; 4-HAwd; University; Vocational.

DOOM, David N; Washington HS; Washington, IL; Chr; Chrl; Chrs; Mdrgl; NatlFornLg; NatlThespSoc; OffAde; SchMus; SchPl; SchPpr; College; Education.

DOPKINS, Laura E; Wausau East HS; Wausau, WI; 33/300 ChrhWkr; HonRl; NHS; SctActv; MthCl; GAA; U W Eau Claire.

DOPP, Pierce H; Almond HS; Almond, WI; PresJrCls; HonRl; StuGov; YthFlsp; SchPpr; KeyCl; LetterBsbl; LetterBsktbl; LetterFtbl; Trk; College; Agriculture.

DOPPEL, Timothy J; Sterling Heights HS; Sterling Hts, MI; 51/519 PresChr; ChrhWkr; HonRl; Mdrgl; PresNHS; NatlMeritCmnd; YthFlsp; IMSpt; OptClAwd; Michigan State U; Social Work.

DOPPLER, Kathy J; Clark HS; Whiting, IN; Chr; Quill&Scroll; Sdlty; Twrl; Yrbk; SptEdSchPpr; GerCl; University; Pharmacy.

DORAN, Allen; Troy HS; Troy, MI; 3/530 CncrtBnd; HonRl; JrNHS; MrchBnd; NHS; NatlMeritCmnd; PepBnd; Tennis; Michigan State Univ; Math Physics.

DORAN, Janet L; Macksville HS; Macksville, KS; VPSophCls; Band; HonRl; PresNHS; SchPl; TchrAde; Yrbk; PpCl; LetterTrk; Chrldr; Ks St; Interior Design.

DORAN, Joanne D; Mt Assisi Acad; Chicago, IL; SecSophCls; PresJrCls; TrsSrCls; HonRl; ModUN; NHS; PresStuCncl; SpnCl; Glf; GAA; IMSpt; Western Ill U; Accounting.

DORBAND, Diane L; Waukegan East HS; Waukegan, IL; 19/861 HonRl; JrNHS; NHS; TchrAde; FBLA; GerCl; PpCl; Swmmng; Trk; GAA; College; Professional.

DORCH, Rebecca L; Lincoln Community HS; Lincoln, IL; 14/255 TrsSophCls; Chr; HonRl; LitMag; NHS; NatlMeritFnl; NatlMeritCmnd; NatlThespSoc; Tennis; LetterTrk; Univ Of Il; Bs.

DORE, Mary Ann; Kingswood Cranbrook HS; Birmingham, MI; Chr; Chrs; HonRl; HospAde; LbryAde; Mdrgl; SchMus; SchPl; TchrAde; Williams College; Medicine.

DOREI, Rhonda S; Mclaugh HS; Mclouth, KS; 1/45 TrsFrshCls; SecSophCls; PresJrCls; TrsSrCls; HonRl; VPNHS; PresFrCl; LetterBsktbl; LetterTrk; ChmnChrldr; Kansas State;physical Ed.

DOREN, Maryann P; Mt Pleasant Senior HS; Rosebush, MI; Band; ChrhWkr; CmntyWkr; HonRl; OffAde; SchPpr; 4-H; BttyCrckrAwd; 4-HAwd; Central Mi U; Computer Programming.

DORETHY, Linda K; Mason City HS; Mason City, IL; 3/46 DrmMjrt; NHS; TchrAde; Twrl; EdYrBk; FHA; FTA; PresGAA; Illinois State University; Mathematics.

DORF, Steven; Marissa HS; Coulterville, IL; 2/84 Band; CncrtBnd; HonRl; MrchBnd; NatlMeritSchl; PepBnd; BauchLmbAwd; Eastern Ill Univ; Dentist.

DORGAN, Roberta F; Regina HS; Harper Woods, MI; 12/142 Aud/Vis; HonRl; NatlFornLg; NHS; RedCrAde; TchrAde; Yrbk; FNA; U Of Detroit; Architecture.

DORIA, Cecilia G; Ladywood HS; Livonia, MI; 1/96 SecSophCls; PresJrCls; PresSrCls; Chr; HonRl; NatlFornLg; NHS; SchMus; StuCncl; FNA; Henry Ford Hospital; Nursing.

DORLAND, Rick L; Palco HS; Palco, KS; 5/29 ALBoysSt; Band; ChrhWkr; HonRl; NHS; SchPl; RptrYrbk; RptrSchPpr; SchPpr; FFA; Central Bible College; Minister.

DORMAN, Keith; Dundee Community Hs; Dundee, IL; ChrhWkr; HonRl; NatlFornLg; NatlThespSoc; SchMus; SchPl; LetterGlf; Augustana College; Law.

DORMAN, Robin; Jeffersonville HS; Clarksville, IN; 17/517 Chr; ChrhWkr; HonRl; NHS; PolWkr; TchrAde; PpCl; PPFtbl; David Lipscomb Coll; Acc.

DORMANS, John; Concordia Lutheran HS; Fort Wayne, IN; Chr; ChrhWkr; SciCl; Bsktbl; Trk; RotaryAwd; Indiana Univ; Biology Major.

DORMIN, John W; Loyola Academy; Park Ridge, IL; 69/442 HonRl; HospAde; LitMag; NHS; NatlMeritCmnd; PolWkr; SchPpr; PresRusCl; College; Law.

DORN, A W; Gering HS; Gering, NE; Band; ChrhWkr; CncrtBnd; HonRl; MrchBnd; PepBnd; LetterBsktbl; Nebraska Western Clg; Prelaw.

DORN, Brad; South HS; Sheboygan, WI; 25/495 HonRl; IMSpt; Coll; Comp Sci.

DORN, Brenda J; Belvidere HS; Rockford, IL; StuCncl; PpCl; Chrldr; GAA; PPFtbl; Rock Valley College; Nursing.

DORN, Brian E; South HS; Sheboygan, WI; 79/495 HonRl; Swmmng; IMSpt; Coll; Mining Engr.

DORN, Elizabeth; Walther Lutheran HS; Maywood, IL; Chr; HonRl; HospAde; Yrbk; SchPpr; GAA; Univ; Foreign Languages.

DORN, Mark S; Brookfield Central HS; Brookfield, WI; 3/480 Band; CncrtBnd; HonRl; LitMag; MrchBnd; NHS; NatlMeritFnl; NatlMeritSF; Yrbk; Tennis; IMSpt; University; Music.

DORNAUS, Rose E; Roncalli HS; Manitowoc, WI; 7/141 TreasAFS; ALAGirlsSt; Chrs; NHS; StuCncl; LatCl; CaptChrldr; Milw Cty Sch Of Nursing; Rn.

DORNBOS, Terry J; Mona Shores HS; Norton Shores, MI; HonRl; SecJA; NHS; College; Electronics.

DORNER, Doyle; New England HS; New England, ND; 5/23 HonRl; SchPl; TchrAde; FFA; College; Electrician.

DORNTON, Cyndi; Athens HS; E Leroy, MI; HonRl; JA; NHS; 4-H; SciCl; Jr College; Radiologist Assistant.

DOROCIAK, James V; Lane Tech HS; Chicago, IL; 106/1163 Aud/Vis; HonRl; NHS; TchrAde; MthCl; Bsbl; Loyola Univ; Medicine.

DOROSHKO, Anna; Jackson HS; Jackson, MI; Chr; HonRl; HospAde; StuGov; Tennis;.

DOROTHY, Leon J; Pleasanton HS; Pleasanton, NE; 2/28 HonRl; NatlMeritCmnd; RptrSchPpr; 4-H;.

DOROW, Deborah A; East Lansing HS; East Lansing, MI; LbryAde; Orch; LetterSwmmng; GAA; IMSpt; PPFtbl; MasAwd; PresAwd; College; Optometry.

DORR, Brenda K; Alcona Comm HS; Harrisville, MI; CmntyWkr; HonRl; OffAde; RedCrAde; TchrAde; RptrSchPpr; EdSchPpr; FHA; SpnCl; 4-HAwd; Lansing Comm Clge; Legal Asst.

DORR, David B; St Joseph HS; Stevensville, MI; Chr; ChrhWkr; NHS; PolWkr; SchAde; TchrAde; LetterFtbl; RotaryAwd; Michigan State Univ; Microbiology.

DORR, Diana L; Parkside HS; Jackson, MI; Chr; HonRl; SchMus; FrCl; PpCl; Olivet Clg; Psychology.

DORRANCE, Nancy J; Axtell HS; Axtell, KS; TrsJrCls; Chrs; HonRl; SchPl; StuCncl; TchrAde; 4-H; PpCl; LetterBsktbl; 4-HAwd; College.

DORRANCE, Peggy M; Rice Lake Sr HS; Rice Lake, WI; ALAGirlsSt; HonRl; NHS; FrCl; Bsktbl; GAA; PresAwd; College; Professional.

DORREL, Carol; Penney HS; Hamilton, MO; CmntyWkr; HonRl; SchPl; StuCncl; RptrSchPpr; FHA; PpCl; GAA; AmLegAwd; Nwmsu Coll; Eng Teacher.

DORREL, Jeffery G; Brookville Consolidated HS; Brookville, IN; Band; CncrtBnd; MrchBnd; NHS; PepBnd; SchPl; TchrAde; YthFlsp; 4-H; FTA; College; Teaching.

DORSCH, William C; Roseville HS; Roseville, MI; Band; CncrtBnd; DrmMjrt; HonRl; MrchBnd; NHS; SchMus; SchPl; StuCncl; Socr; Coll; Law.

DORSEY, Debra K; E Alton Wood River Comm HS; Wood River, IL; 28/307 SecTrsJrCls; Chr; HonRl; StuCncl; PpCl; Bsbl; Trk; Chrldr; IMSpt; PresAwd; College; Pe Or Biology Teacher Or Pro Coach.

DORSEY, Doug L; Winchester HS; Winchester, IL; 6/80 LetterBsbl; College; Professional.

DORSEY, Gene; Oakville Senior HS; St Louis, MO; 22/340 Band; CmntyWkr; HonRl; SchPl; StuCncl; StuGov; CivCl; Swmmng; AmLegAwd; CitAwd; St Louis Univ; Medicinal.

DORSEY, Lawrence; Lindblom Tech HS; Chicago, IL; 9/637 HonRl; NHS; NatlMeritCmnd; SchPl; FDA; MthCl; Northwestern U; Doctor Surgery.

DORSEY, Robert T; Brother Rice HS; Chicago, IL; 9/416 HonRl; Univ Of Illinois; Engineering.

DORSEY, Steven M; Freeport HS; Freeport, IL; 1/490 VPFrshCls; Band; CncrtBnd; HonRl; Orch; LetterBsktbl; LetterFtbl; LetterTrk; College; Engineering.

DORSHER, Margaret R; Marillac HS; Northbrook, IL; 7/240 Chrl; Chrs; LitMag; VPNHS; NatlMeritSchl; PolWkr; SchMus; PresSdlty; AmLegAwd; St Marys College; Law.

DORSHORST, Duane L; Hay Springs Public HS; Hay Springs, NE; PresFrshCls; Band; Chrs; HonRl; NHS; SctActv; StuCncl; Ftbl; Trk; VoiceDemAwd; Coll.

DORTMUND, Donald J; Weber HS; Chicago, IL; 50/192 Aud/Vis; HonRl; LbryAde; VPStuGov; SchPpr; IMSpt; Coll; Med.

DORVIL, Claude M; St Thomas Apostle HS; Chicago, IL; Chr; CmntyWkr; HonRl; HospAde; JA; University; Biology.

DORWICK, Keith M; Glenbard North HS; Glendale Hts, IL; Aud/Vis; Chr; Chrs; LitMag; VPNatlThespSoc; OffAde; SchMus; SchPl; StuCncl; TchrAde; RptrSchPpr; College; Speech Arts.

DORY, Craig D; Valley HS; West Des Moines, IA; Aud/Vis; Band; Chr; Chrs; CncrtBnd; HonRl; MrchBnd; Orch; PepBnd; SchMus; Iowa State Univ; Computer Programmer.

DOSDALL, Sharon E; Hancock Public HS; Hancock, MN; 2/27 Chr; Chrs; ChrhWkr; HonRl; LbryAde; SchPl; EdSchPpr; FHA; EngCl; Womens Army Corp.

DOSEMAGEN, Debra M; St Joseph HS; Kenosha, WI; HonRl; NHS; College; Secondary Educ.

DOSIER, Gail M; Greenview HS; Greenview, IL; CncrtBnd; HonRl; LbryAde; MrchBnd; PepBnd; SchMus; PresYthFlsp; RptrSchPpr; FSA; IMSpt; Coll; Secretarial.

DOSS, Roger L; Lane Tech; Chicago, IL; 197/1310 College; Electronic Technology.

DOTHAGE, C W; Lexington HS; Lexington, MO; ALBoysSt; Band; Chrs; CncrtBnd; HonRl; MrchBnd; NHS; Ftbl; Trk; LionAwd; Vo Tech School; Electronics.

DOTHAGER, Terry J; Mulberry HS; Mulberry Grove, IL; HonRl; MrchBnd; NHS; SchPl; 4-H; FHA; FTA; SpnCl; LetterTrk; GAA; College.

DOTSON, Ada R; Battle Creek Central HS; Battle Creek, MI; JrNHS; NHS; OffAde; TchrAde; PpCl; Bsbl; CaptBsktbl; Trk; IMSpt; PresAwd; Modeling School; Secretarial.

DOTSON, Dale L; Frankfort HS; Frankfort, KS; 6/44 StuGov; YthFlsp; LetterBsktbl; LetterFtbl; LetterTrk; AmLegAwd; Ks St Univ; Engineer.

DOTSON, Judy; Wapello Comm HS; Wapello, IA; VPJrCls; Band; ChrhWkr; HonRl; TchrAde; YthFlsp; 4-H; Glf; IMSpt; 4-HAwd; Univ; Physical Therapist.

DOTSON, Karen; Noth Miami HS; Macy, IN; SecYthFlsp; College; Social Sciences.

DOTSON, Mark A; Central HS; Flint, MI; 46/420 HonRl; MrchBnd; NHS; NatlMeritSchl; NatlMeritSF; StuCncl; StuGov; LetterBsbl; LetterBsktbl; IMSpt; Univ Of Michigan; Pharmacy.

DOTSON, Michael A; Mt Carmel HS; Chicago, IL; Band; HonRl; JrNHS; LitMag; PolWkr; Swmmng; IMSpt; College; Arts & Sciences.

DOTSON, Randy C; Terril Comm HS; Langdon, IA; 3/29 ALBoysSt; NHS; SchPl; StuCncl; FrCl; SpnCl; CaptFtbl; Trk; Wrstlng; Iowa State Univ.

DOTTA, Robert M; Richwoods HS; Peoria, IL; 33/449 HonRl; SchPl; College; Advertising.

DOTY, James; Pennfield HS; Battle Creek, MI; Band; CncrtBnd; HonRl; JA; MrchBnd; SancSoc; TchrAde; SpnCl; IMSpt; Ferris College; Pharmacology.

DOTY, Keith W; Parkwood HS; Joplin, MO; HonRl; SctActv; MthCl; GodCntryAwd; OptClAwd; Univ; Dentist.

DOTY, Lynda R; Crown Point HS; Crown Point, IN; 36/468 Chr; HonRl; Mdrgl; NHS; SchMus; Purdue U; Interior Decor.

DOTY, Sandra M; East HS; Rockford, IL; DrlTm; HonRl; HospAde; ROTC; SctActv; TchrAde; Junior College; Para Legal.

DOTZERT, Ellen M; Triopia HS; Beardstown, IL; SecJrCls; ChrhWkr; HonRl; LbryAde; SecNHS; RptrYrbk; Sec4-H; AmLegAwd; DanFAwd; 4-HAwd; Secretary.

DOUBET, David L; Waverly HS; Waverly, IL; 8/33 ChrhWkr; VPYthFlsp; TreasFFA; Milwaukee Sch Of Engineering; Mech Eng.

DOUBLEDAY, Lynne M; S Beloit HS; S Beloit, IL; 1/80 SecSophCls; Band; Chrs; HonRl; NHS; SctActv; Yrbk; Il Wesleyan Univ; French.

DOUCET, Michelle M; St George HS; St George, KS; HonRl; NatlMeritSchl; SchPl; TchrAde; SchPpr; FHA; PpCl; Bsktbl; GAA; College; Special Education.

DOUCETTE, Gordon; Lf Community HS; Cushing, MN; /327 ChrhWkr; CmntyWkr; PolWkr; TchrAde; SchPpr; FBLA; IMSpt; 4-HAwd; VoiceDemAwd; Bus Sch;pro.

DOUD, Deborah A; Comstock HS; Comstock, MI; SecFrshCls; SecSophCls; ALAGirlsSt; Chr; HonRl; IntrClCncl; NHS; PolWkr; SchMus; PresStuGov; Alma Clge; Speech & Audiology Therapy.

DOUD, Denny E; Hedrick Community HS; Hedrick, IA; 3/20 ALBoysSt; Band; HonRl; NatlMeritCmnd; StuCncl; RptrSchPpr; FTA; LetterBsktbl; LetterFtbl; LetterTrk; Clge; Curr Of Major Study.

DOUD, Vickie S; Fairfield HS; Fairfield, IA; HonRl; FBLA; FHA; SpnCl;.

DOUDNA, Dawn L; Richland Center HS; Richland Center, WI; Chr; ChrhWkr; CncrtBnd; DrmMjrt; LbryAde; MrchBnd; Twrl; YthFlsp; 4-H; College; Bible.

DOUGHERTY, Anne M; O Gorman HS; Sioux Falls, SD; ChrhWkr; CmntyWkr; DrlTm; PolWkr; SchPl; SctActv; TchrAde; FDA; FHA; SpnCl; PpCl; Bsktbl; Trk; College.

DOUGHERTY, Brian L; Ithaca HS; Ithaca, MI; 1/148 ALBoysSt; Band; CncrtBnd; HonRl; MrchBnd; NHS; StuGov; Trk; Mich St U;physicist.

DOUGHERTY, Cynthia; Ainsworth HS; Ainsworth, NE; 6/67 ALAGirlsSt; Band; Chr; HonRl; MrchBnd; NatlThespSoc; SchMus; StuGov; RptrSchPpr; Bsktbl; Uno Medical Center; Nursing.

DOUGHERTY, Henry R; New Trier East HS; Wilmette, IL; 94/847 HonRl; NatlMeritCmnd; SctActv; Univ Of Ill; Accounting.

DOUGHERTY, James E; Shelbyville HS; Shelbyville, IL; Band; CncrtBnd; HonRl; MrchBnd; SchPl; Bsktbl; Ftbl; College.

DOUGHERTY, John F; Larkin HS; Elgin, IL; 27/622 Band; CncrtBnd; HonRl; MrchBnd; Orch; Univ Of Illinois; Civil Engineering.

DOUGHERTY, Kelly A; Walnut Grove HS; Walnut Grove, MO; 2/29 PresFrshCls; PresJrCls; HonRl; SchPl; StuCncl; Bsbl; Bsktbl; Trk; CchngActv; College; Professional.

DOUGHERTY, Lorie; Lewiston Consolidated Hs; Burchard, NE; PresJrCls; ALAGirlsSt; Band; Chr; SchPl; Pres4-H; FHA; PpCl; Chrldr;.

DOUGHERTY, Patti L; Mansfield HS; Macomb, MO; 5/46 VPSrCls; HonRl; ModUN; NHS; SchPl; Yrbk; FHA; LatCl; MthCl; SciCl; Burge School Of Nursing; Registered Nurse.

DOUGHERTY, Richard W; Trenton Sr HS; Laredo, MO; 74/130 TrsJrCls; AFS; ALBoysSt; Band; ChrhWkr; CmntyWkr; CncrtBnd; HonRl; LbryAde; MrchBnd; LetterBsktbl; LetterFtbl; LetterTrk; Trade School; Vocation.

DOUGHETY, Sandra A; Northwestern HS; Sumner, MO; Band; CncrtBnd; HonRl; MrchBnd; NHS; RedCrAde; Yrbk; SchPpr; 4-H; SciCl; Kirksville; Secretary.

DOUGHTY, Denice; Lindblom Technical HS; Chicago, IL; 40/600 Chr; HonRl; MrchBnd; NHS; TchrAde; College; Accounting.

DOUGLAS, Connie J; Oak Park HS; Kansas City, MO; Chr; HonRl; HospAde; JrNHS; SchMus; StuCncl; RptrYrbk; PpCl; University Of Missouri; Medicine.

DOUGLAS, Dale S; Jimtown HS; Elkhart, IN; 12/101 Band; HonRl; MrchBnd; NHS; PepBnd; SchPl; VPStuCncl; StuGov; TchrAde; RptrSchPpr; FTA; PresFrCl; PpCl; Glf; Indiana Univ; Journalism.

DOUGLAS, David W; Joliet Catholic HS; Joliet, IL; 22/170 HonRl; SchAde; TchrAde; RptrYrbk; GerCl; Ftbl; College; Elementary Teacher.

DOUGLAS, Elvin S; Harrisonville HS; Harrisonville, MO; 15/165 HonRl; CaptBsktbl; LetterFtbl; LetterTrk; Missouri At Columbia; Law Field.

DOUGLAS, Jesse L; Potosi HS; Potosi, MO; 3/185 ChrhWkr; HonRl; JrNHS; NHS; PolWkr; 4-H; SpnCl; PpCl; Univ Of Missouri; Biology.

DOUGLAS, Judy K; Urbana Community HS; Vinton, IA; Chr; Chrs; HonRl; Mdrgl; SchPl; StuCncl; TchrAde; RptrYrbk; EdSchPpr; University; Art.

DOUGLAS, Kimberly; Oakland HS; Hindsboro, IL; RedCrAde; SchPl; FHA; PpCl; Chrldr; GAA; PPFtbl; PresAwd; Coll; Work With Deaf.

DOUGLAS, Lori L; Marshall HS; Marshall, IL; 4/115 Band; Chr; PepBnd; TreasYthFlsp; Pres4-H; FHA; SciCl; GAA; E Illinois Univ; Legal Secretary.

DOUGLAS, Margaret E; Charleston HS; Charleston, IL; 31/265 PresJrCls; HonRl; NHS; StuCncl; RptrSchPpr; Sec4-H; FrCl; GAA; Eastern Ill Univ; Public Acct.

DOUGLAS, Robert E; Glenbard North HS; Carol Stream, IL; 91/400 Band; HonRl; NatlFornLg; NatlThespSoc; PolWkr; SchMus; SchPl; YthLg; GerCl; Univ Of Illinois; Law.

DOUGLAS, Sharon E; Farmington HS; Farmington, MI; TrsJrCls; TrsSrCls; ALAGirlsSt; HonRl; NHS; StuCncl; YthFlsp; CaptChrldr; PPFtbl; Mich State U; Cpa.

DOUGLAS, Sheila M; La Plata HS; La Plata, MO; 3/33 TrsFrshCls; PresJrCls; Band; ChrhWkr; CtyCnl; CmntyWkr; CncrtBnd; HonRl; JrNHS; MrchBnd; NHS; OffAde; Trk; Chrldr; University; Liberal Arts.

DOUGLAS, Sheila R; Potosi HS; Mineral Point, MO; Chr; HonRl; SchPl; FBLA; FHA; FNA; Trk; Marriage; Job.

DOUGLAS, Stephen; Leavenworth HS; Leavenworth, KS; 24/350 ALBoysSt; HonRl; NHS; ROTC; SctActv; TchrAde; SciCl; BauchLmbAwd; GodCntryAwd; Ks State Univ; Medicine.

DOUGLAS, Susan E; North County R Iii HS; Bonne Terre, MO; Chrs; ChrhWkr; HonRl; OffAde; FBLA; FHA; Trk; Mineral Area College; Professional.

DOUGLAS, Ted S; Paxton HS; Paxton, IL; HonRl; NHS; SciCl; LetterBsbl; LetterBsktbl; CaptTennis; CaptTrk; So Illinois University; Business.

DOUGLAS, Timothy J; Wayne Comm HS; Corydon, IA; 4/77 PresFrshCls; VPSophCls; HonRl; MrchBnd; NHS; LetterBsbl; LetterBsktbl; LetterFtbl; LetterGlf; Trk; College; Chemistry.

DOUGLASS, Lynne M; Durand HS; Durand, MI; Band; Chr; HonRl; MrchBnd; NatlFornLg; NHS; SchPl; YthFlsp; LetterTrk; Mott Comm Coll; Dental Hygiene.

DOUNIS, Kiki S; Fitzgerald HS; Warren, MI; 28/435 Chr; ChrhWkr; CmntyWkr; HonRl; HospAde; NHS; OffAde; PolWkr; TchrAde; University Of Detroit; Professional.

DOUTHIT, Lynne; Newton HS; Newton, IL; 15/200 Band; Chrs; CncrtBnd; DrmMjrt; HonRl; IntrClCncl; JrNHS; MrchBnd; NHS; PepBnd; SchMus; Tennis; GAA; Vanderbilt Univ; Medicine.

DOUTHITT, Douglas A; Grandville HS; Grandville, MI; 2/340 Band; HonRl; JrNHS; MrchBnd; NHS; PepBnd; SctActv; LetterFtbl; LetterWrstlng; GodCntryAwd; Jr College; Chemical Engineering.

DOVE, David A; Eastside HS; Butler, IN; 20/137 ALBoysSt; HonRl; 4-H; FFA; Bsktbl; LetterFtbl; 4-HAwd; Purdue Univ; Agriculture.

DOVE, Loren D; Garrett HS; Auburn, IN; 3/148 SecSophCls; PresJrCls; HonRl; NHS; SchMus; SpnCl; LetterBsktbl; Purdue Univ; Business.

DOVE, Robert M; Dekalb HS; Waterloo, IN; 7/292 Aud/Vis; Band; ChrhWkr; HonRl; MrchBnd; PresNHS; PepBnd; SchMus; KiwanAwd; CitAwd; Manchester College; Medicine.

DOVE, Tina M; Green Ridge R8 HS; Windsor, MO; VPFrshCls; HstSophCls; Band; Chrs; SchPpr; 4-H; FHA; PpCl; SciCl; Chrldr; Vo Tech School; Home Economics.

DOVEKOT, Sheryl K; Grand Rapids Christian HS; Grand Rapids, MI; SecFrshCls; Chr; ChrhWkr; HonRl; JrNHS; NHS; RptrYrbk; Yrbk; Socr; CaptIMSpt; Davenport Sch Of Bus; Accounting.

DOVEL, Theresa C; Hamburg HS; Hamburg, IA; 11/36 HonRl; StuCncl; TchrAde; YthFlsp; RptrYrbk; SptEdYrbk; EdSchPpr; SptEdSchPpr; FTA; PpCl; Wellington School; Prof Dancer.

DOVIDAS, Carol A; Rivet HS; Vincennes, IN; 1/46 VPSophCls; PresJrCls; PresSrCls; HonRl; HospAde; StuCncl; Bsktbl; Tennis; GAA; IMSpt; Purdue Univ; Pharmacy.

DOW, Craig M; Lakewood HS; Mulliken, MI; 62/204 HonRl; MrchBnd; TchrAde; YthFlsp; RptrSchPpr; Pres4-H; PresFFA; KeyCl; IMSpt; 4-HAwd; Michigan St Univ; Agriculture.

DOW, Gayln S; Northeast HS; Lincln, NE; Band; ChrhWkr; HonRl; JA; MrchBnd; PepBnd; PpCl; IMSpt; JAAwd; U Of Neb; Interior Design.

DOWD, Evon L; North Boone HS; Poplar Rove, IL; ChrhWkr; CncrtBnd; HonRl; MrchBnd; Sec4-H; FFA; SecPpCl; Bsbl; GAA; IMSpt; School Of Nursng; Nurse.

DOWD, Kathy; Wakonda Public HS; Wokonda, SD; PresSrCls; Band; Chr; CncrtBnd; HonRl; PepBnd; StuCncl; RptrYrbk; FHA; Bsktbl;.

DOWD, Randall; Layrel HS; Layrel, IN; PresFrshCls; PresSophCls; PresJrCls; Band; CncrtBnd; HonRl; NHS; StuCncl; CaptBsktbl; LetterTrk; College.

DOWD, Ronald J; Central Sr HS; Albert Lea, MN; 19/526 CncrtBnd; HonRl; MrchBnd; PepBnd; SctActv; Univ Of Minn; Mech Eng.

DOWDY, Curtis L; Clinton HS; Clinton, MO; 14/147 HonRl; NatlFornLg; NatlThespSoc; Yrbk; Se Mo St Univ; Audio Visual Engineer.

DOWELL, Janie D; Tower Hill HS; Tower Hill, IL; TrsSrCls; Band; Chrs; HonRl; NHS; SchPl; SpnCl; SciCl; Trk; Nursing School; Nurse.

DOWELL, Michael A; Anderson Sr HS; Anderson, IN; 37/583 ChrhWkr; HonRl; LitMag; NHS; NatlMeritCmnd; GerCl; LetterTrk; GovHonPrgAwd; PresAwd; CitAwd; Purdue Univ; Pharmacist.

DOWIS, Kirby L; Sheridan R Ii HS; Sheridan, MO; 3/12 PresFrshCls; PresSophCls; HonRl; SchPl; StuCncl; RptrYrbk; PpCl; Bsktbl; Trk; AmLegAwd; Nw Missouri State Univ; Physical Education.

DOWLAND, Dawn M; South Spencer HS; Grandview, IN; HonRl; LbryAde; Univ; Nurse.

DOWLER, Debbie K; Centerville HS; Centerville, IN; TrsJrCls; TrsSrCls; Chrs; ChrhWkr; HonRl; MrchBnd; OffAde; PolWkr; Teen; LetterTennis; College; Vocation.

DOWLER, Deborah A; Union County HS; Liberty, IN; HonRl; LbryAde; FrCl; PpCl; LetterBsktbl; LetterTrk; Chrldr; GAA; Bus Sch; Social Worker.

DOWLING, Mary M; Northwest HS; Housesprings, MO; Chr; HonRl; RedCrAde; SchAde; SctActv; TchrAde; Swmmng; IMSpt; College; Physical Therapy.

DOWLING, Vickie; Protection HS; Protection, KS; Band; Chr; ChrhWkr; CncrtBnd; HonRl; MrchBnd; PepBnd; SchMus; YthFlsp; Tennis; College; Nursing.

DOWLING, William N; Wilson HS; Wilson, KS; VPFrshCls; ALBoysSt; CncrtBnd; HonRl; StuCncl; EdYrBk; RptrSchPpr; Bsbl; LetterBsktbl; CaptFtbl; Ks State U; Electric Eng.

DOWN, Nancy J; Pinckney HS; Pinckney, MI; CncrtBnd; HonRl; MrchBnd; NHS; PepBnd; 4-H; 4-HAwd; University; Professional.

DOWNER, Darwin H; Appleton City HS; Appleton City, MO; Band; ChrhWkr; CncrtBnd; HonRl; StuCncl; Bsbl; LetterBsktbl; LetterFtbl; LetterTrk; CitAwd; College; Agriculture.

DOWNER, Delia M; Saint Pius X HS; Kansas City, MO; CmntyWkr; HonRl; LbryAde; OffAde; SchAde; SctActv; TchrAde; KeyCl; College; Business.

DOWNEY, Anna; Indiana State University HS; West Terre Haute, IN; Chr; ModUN; TchrAde; PpCl; GAA; Indiana State Univ; Veterinary.

DOWNEY, Beverly J; Preston Comm HS; Preston, IA; Band; Chrs; ChrhWkr; StuCncl; TchrAde; YthFlsp; 4-H; FTA; Bsktbl; Trk; Chrldr; University; Home Economics.

DOWNEY, Cindy L; Gull Lake HS; Richland, MI; HonRl; TchrAde; 4-H; IMSpt; GodCntryAwd; Clge.

DOWNEY, Deborah A; Carthage Sr HS; Carthage, MO; 2/209 AFS; ChrhWkr; HonRl; ModUN; PresNHS; Yrbk; RptrSchPpr; FTA; CaptMthCl; PpCl; College; Teaching.

DOWNEY, Deborah S; Ohio HS; Ohio, IL; Band; Chr; Chrs; NHS; Quill&Scroll; SchMus; SchPl; Twrl; RptrYrbk; GAA; Western Illinois Univ.

DOWNEY, Gregory; Barrington HS; Barrington, IL; ChrhWkr; HonRl; StuGov; GerCl; Armyuniv;cpa.

DOWNEY, Sean; East Detroit HS; East Detroit, MI; NatlMeritSF; TchrAde; Wayne State Univ; Mathematics.

DOWNEY, Sue; Harrison HS; Harrison, MI; HonRl; SctActv; YthFlsp; RptrYrbk; EngCl; University Of Michigan; Conservation.

DOWNING, David A; Maple Valley HS; Nashville, MI; PresJrCls; HonRl; NHS; SchPl; RptrSchPpr; LetterBsbl; LetterFtbl; Bus Schl; Voc.

DOWNING, David A; Wbg HS; Warrensburg, MO; Band; ChrhWkr; CncrtBnd; HonRl; SchPl; SctActv; StuCncl; SciCl; Bsbl; Bsktbl; Trk;.

DOWNING, Desiree D; Irving Crown HS; Algonquin, IL; TrsJrCls; TrsSrCls; HonRl; JrNHS; NHS; StuCncl; 4-H; Coll; Economics.

DOWNING, Jeffrey G; Union HS; Hagerstown, IN; 6/57 PresJrCls; PresSrCls; ALBoysSt; ChrhWkr; HonRl; VPNHS; StuCncl; TchrAde; EdYrBk; Yrbk; In Univ; Psychology.

DOWNING, Michael; Aquin Central Catholic HS; Freeport, IL; 3/55 VPSrCls; HonRl; Mdrgl; NHS; SchMus; MthCl; PpCl; Drake Univ; Actuarial Science.

DOWNING, Michael D; Aquin Catholic HS; Freeport, IL; 3/46 VPSrCls; Chrs; HonRl; JA; Mdrgl; NHS; OffAde; SchMus; StuCncl; TchrAde; LetterBsktbl; LetterFtbl; LetterGlf; Drake University; Actuarial Science.

DOWNING, Mike E; Minneota Public HS; Taunton, MN; Band; Chrs; SchPl; EdYrBk; SchPpr; PpCl; Bsktbl; Ftbl; Wrstlng; Trade Sch; Carpentry.

DOWNING, Scott A; Park Hill Sr HS; Kansas City, MO; Band; ChrhWkr; CncrtBnd; HonRl; MrchBnd; NHS; PepBnd; PolWkr; SctActv; StuCncl; StuGov; YthFlsp; CaptFtbl; Trk; Sterling College; Teaching.

DOWNING, Sherri R; Irondale Sr HS; New Brighton, MN; Chr; JrNHS; Orch; SchMus; StuCncl; Military School; Vocational.

DOWNS, Brian; Waterford Township HS; Pontiac, MI; 36/414 HonRl; JA; NHS; SctActv; Central Mich U; Engineering.

DOWNS, Charles E; Langdon HS; Langdon, ND; 32/109 CncrtBnd; HonRl; MrchBnd; PepBnd; SchMus; SchPl; StuCncl; PpCl; Bsktbl; North Dakota State School; Electrical Tech.

DOWNS, Christine; Barrington HS; Barriongton, IL; 6/750 Chr; HonRl; JrNHS; SchMus; Yrbk; RusCl; IMSpt; NCTE; Univ; Law.

DOWNS, Glenda K; Risco HS; Risco, MO; Chr; ChrhWkr; HonRl; EdSchPpr; 4-H; SpnCl; Trk; LetterChrldr; 4-HAwd; College Semsu; Ibm Programer.

DOWNS, John E; Community HS; Detriot Lakes, MN; TrsSrCls; AFS; ChrhWkr; HonRl; NHS; NatlMeritSF; PolWkr; CaptBsktbl; LetterFtbl; LetterTennis; Concordia Col ;dr.

DOWNS, Michael D; Stevens HS; Rapid City, SD; 134/418 Band; CncrtBnd; MrchBnd; Orch; PepBnd; SchMus; StuCncl; IMSpt; College; Engineering.

DOWNS, Stephen G; Carmel HS; Carmel, IN; 140/720 ALBoysSt; ChrhWkr; HonRl; StuCncl; YthFlsp; Ftbl; LetterTrk; CaptWrstlng; CchngActv; AmLegAwd; College; Engineer.

DOWNS, Thomas; St Francis Hs; West Chicago, IL; HonRl; NHS; ROTC; LetterBsbl; LetterBsktbl; LetterTennis; Northern Illinois U;finance.

DOWNS, Timothy J; Maize HS; Witchita, KS; Band; Chrs; CncrtBnd; HonRl; MrchBnd; PepBnd; StuCncl; CaptFtbl; Friends Univ; Com Comp Tech.

DOWNTON, Galen E; Twin Lakes HS; Monticello, IN; 7/206 CmntyWkr; HonRl; JA; NatlFornLg; NHS; TchrAde; FTA; FrCl; IMSpt; JAAwd; Purdue Univ; Chemical Eng.

DOWSETT, Marjorie C; Our Lady Of The Lakes HS; Drayton Plains, MI; 16/53 HonRl; NHS; OffAde; SctActv; College.

DOYE, Laurel L; Bradford HS; Buda, IL; 15/45 Band; Chrs; ChrhWkr; HonRl; HospAde; OffAde; SchPl; StuCncl; TchrAde; SchPpr; Chrldr; Illinois Central College; Elementary Ed.

DOYEN, Kathy M; Lansing Catholic Central HS; Lansing, MI; 3/128 CmntyWkr; JA; NHS; OffAde; SchMus; TchrAde; Mi St Univ; Natural Science.

DOYEN, Randy L; Ovid Elsie HS; Elsie, MI; 93/195 LetterFtbl; Wrstlng; Ferris St Univ; Bus Manage.

DOYER, Terri A; Jamaica HS; Indianaola, IL; HonRl; Yrbk; 4-H; SpnCl; PpCl; Trk; GAA; IMSpt; 4-HAwd; Coll.

DOYL, Julie; North Linn HS; Walker, IA; Band; Chrs; HonRl; JrNHS; NHS; YthFlsp; College; Physical Therapist.

DOYLE, Ann M; Midland HS; Midland, MI; 35/411 Chr; Chrl; HonRl; NHS; FrCl; Kalamazoo College.

DOYLE, Cathy M; Oak Forest HS; Oak Forest, IL; 14/326 HonRl; JrNHS; NHS; NatlMeritCmnd; SchPl; StuCncl; SchPpr; FrCl; Fox Secretarial College; Executive Sec.

DOYLE, Cynthia S; La Ville HS; South Bend, IN; 25/160 Band; CncrtBnd; MrchBnd; NHS; NatlThespSoc; SchMus; StuCncl; SpnCl; PpCl; AmLegAwd; Univ; Spanish.

DOYLE, Daniel M; St Laurence HS; Chicago, IL; 106/375 HonRl; StuCncl; SciCl; CaptSocr; U S Naval Academy; Elec Engineering.

DOYLE, Debra S; Whiteland Comm HS; Whiteland, IN; 2/174 Band; CncrtBnd; HonRl; MrchBnd; NHS; PepBnd; SctActv; FHA; PpCl; Ball State U; Economics.

DOYLE, Denise M; Sturgis HS; Sturgis, MI; HonRl; NHS; Quill&Scroll; RptrYrbk; RptrSchPpr; PpCl; PPFtbl; RotaryAwd; Marquette Univ; Business.

DOYLE, Elizabeth M; Midland HS; Midland, MI; Chr; HonRl; NHS; IMSpt; College.

DOYLE, Emily A; Mother Mc Auley HS; Palos Park, IL; 31/484 ChrhWkr; HonRl; NHS; NatlMeritCmnd; RedCrAde; RptrSchPpr; SchPpr; SpnCl; Marquette Univ; Teacher.

DOYLE, Janet; Wahlert HS; Hazel Green, WI; Chrs; HonRl; HospAde; TchrAde; Mercy Medical Center; Radiologist.

DOYLE, John J; St Thomas Academy; Burnsville, MN; 5/108 ROTC; Bsbl; Ftbl; Univ Of Minnesota.

DOYLE, Kathleen; Durand Area HS; Lennon, MI; 4/178 VPSophCls; Band; DrlTm; HonRl; MrchBnd; NHS; StuCncl; SpnCl; DARAwd; Univ Of Mi Flint Branch; Medical Technologi.

DOYLE, Kevin A; Hanson HS; Alexandria, SD; TrsFrshCls; VPSophCls; VPJrCls; ALBoysSt; HonRl; Bsktbl; Ftbl; Trk; CchngActv; IMSpt; Col ; Pro.

DOYLE, Mary J; Holton HS; Holton, KS; Chrs; CncrtBnd; HonRl; MrchBnd; PepBnd; Yrbk; 4-H; FHA; PpCl; 4-HAwd; Dodge City Univ ;fashion.

DOYLE, Mary P; Good Counsel HS; Chicago, IL; 30/248 HonRl; NatlMeritCmnd; Yrbk; SchPpr; Lewis Univ; Sociology.

DOYLE, Maryteresa; Topeka West HS; Topeka, KS; VPSrCls; CmntyWkr; HonRl; JA; LitMag; NatlThespSoc; OffAde; PolWkr; SchPl; StuCncl; StuGov; Bsktbl; Trk; Univ Of Missouri; Journalism.

DOYLE, Michael L; Whitefish Bay HS; Milwaukee, WI; 9/340 HonRl; NatlMeritCmnd; Bsbl; Bsktbl; Trk; Notre Dame Univ; Engineering.

DOYLE, Pamela K; Whiteland Comm HS; Whiteland, IN; 13/210 ALAGirlsSt; Band; CncrtBnd; HonRl; MrchBnd; PepBnd; SchMus; SctActv; FFA; FTA; PpCl; College; Agriculture.

DOYLE, Sheree G; Casey HS; Casey, IL; 26/95 HonRl; StuCncl; TchrAde; FHA; FTA; SpnCl; PpCl; Chrldr; GAA; College; Spanish & Or Airline Stewardess.

DOYLE, Shirley J; Shepherd HS; Shepherd, MI; 5/124 SecJrCls; Chr; HonRl; LbryAde; SecNHS; NatlMeritSchl; NatlMeritSF; OffAde; PpCl; PPFtbl; Central Michigan Univ; Secretary.

DOZEMAN, Douglas A; Holland Christian HS; Holland, MI; CncrtBnd; HonRl; MrchBnd; ModUN; NatlFornLg; NHS; NatlMeritCmnd; SchPl; StuCncl; IMSpt; Calvin Clge; Pre Law.

DOZLER, Linda; Elgin Public HS; Elgin, NE; /26 SecFrshCls; Chrs; FHA; PpCl; Chrldr; Coll; Teach.

DRAACK, Barbara J; Frazee HS; Frazee, MN; Band; Chrs; CncrtBnd; HonRl; MrchBnd; TchrAde; Yrbk; RptrSchPpr; FHA; College.

DRAEGE, Barbara J; Oregon HS; Oregon, IL; 13/110 AFS; HonRl; NatlThespSoc; RptrYrbk; FTA; LatCl; SpnCl; Trk; TreasGAA; PPFtbl; Illinois State University; Teacher.

DRAEGER, David C; Little Wolf HS; Manawa, WI; PresFrshCls; Chrs; HonRl; Mdrgl; PpCl; LetterFtbl; Wrstlng; Tech Sch; Professional.

DRAEGER, David J; Harding HS; St Paul, MN; 27/725 ChrhWkr; HonRl; NHS; SctActv; YthFlsp; FrCl; LetterSocr; De Vry Inst Of Tech; Elec Tech.

DRAEGER, Holly A; Mukwonago HS; Eagle, WI; 42/207 HonRl; StuGov; 4-H; SpnCl; Trk; Univ Wis Milwaukee; Registered Nurse.

DRAEGER, Terry P; Napoleon HS; Napoleon, ND; ALBoysSt; Band; Chr; Chrs; CncrtBnd; MrchBnd; StuCncl; SciCl; Bsktbl; Glf; College; Professional.

DRAFKE, Allen D; Lockport Township HS; Lockport, IL; PresBand; HonRl; MrchBnd; NHS; PepBnd; Lewis Univ; Accounting.

DRAGGOO, Dalene R; Hillsdale HS; Osseo, MI; 38/200 NHS; SchPl; StuGov; YthFlsp; RptrYrbk; RptrSchPpr; Bsktbl; Trk; GAA; Univ; Business Administration.

DRAGICEVICH, Michael P; Hackett HS; Kalamazoo, MI; 18/143 HonRl; TchrAde; LetterWrstlng; IMSpt; Mi Tech Univ; Electrical Engineering.

DRAGO, Debby A; Ed W Clark HS; Lasvegas, NE; 26/734 HstJrCls; HonRl; HospAde; SecJrNHS; OffAde; PolWkr; VPStuCncl; PresStuGov; TchrAde; Northern Az U; Med Tech.

DRAHER, Stacie; Marlette HS; Marlette, MI; 31/136 PresSrCls; HonRl; OffAde; SchPl; StuCncl; SchPpr; PpCl; College; Fashion Designing.

DRAHNAK, Janet M; Mt Assisi Acad; Chicago, IL; 10/194 HonRl; LbryAde; NHS; RedCrAde; SctActv; FrCl; Morraine College; Law Enforcement.

DRAIN, Paula A; Grandview HS; Eau Claire, WI; ChrhWkr; CncrtBnd; HonRl; MrchBnd; NHS; RptrYrbk; FTA; SecPpCl; GAA; PPFtbl; U Of Wi; Journalism.

DRAIN, Thomas C; Yates Center HS; Yates Center, KS; Band; HonRl; MrchBnd; PepBnd; Coll; Teach Music.

DRAISMA, Marcia L; Holland Christian HS; Holland, MI; ChrhWkr; HospAde; RptrSchPpr; 4-H; FNA; College; Rn.

DRAKE, Cynthia L; Newman HS; Newman, IL; Band; Chr; ChrhWkr; HonRl; StuCncl; FHA; PpCl; Chrldr; GAA; PresAwd; College; Secretary.

DRAKE, Daniel L; Charleston HS; Charleston, IL; 29/237 ChrhWkr; HonRl; SpnCl; Bsktbl; Ftbl; IMSpt; U Of Il; Engineering.

DRAKE, Douglas G; Rockridge HS; Reynolds, IL; HonRl; LatCl; Trade School.

DRAKE, Jeffery A; Waazeka Public HS; Boscobel, WI; Band; Chr; StuCncl; Yrbk; FFA; LetterBsktbl; LetterFtbl; LetterTrk;.

DRAKE, Kristine; Southeastern HS; Augusta, IL; 5/49 Band; HonRl; NHS; SchPl; StuCncl; YthFlsp; FHA; DanFAwd; SARAwd; Millikin Univ; Medical Technology.

DRAKE, Marcia J; El Paso HS; El Paso, IL; AFS; ALAGirlsSt; ChrhWkr; CncrtBnd; HonRl; NHS; PepBnd; SchPl; SpnCl; Trk; College; Foreign Language.

DRAKE, Margaret A; Elwood Community HS; Elwood, IN; 6/196 ALAGirlsSt; HonRl; JrNHS; NHS; StuCncl; Chrldr; GAA; Manchester College; Accounting.

DRAKE, Mary J; Warsaw HS; Warsaw, MO; Chr; HonRl; JrNHS; NHS; SchMus; RptrYrbk; RptrSchPpr; 4-H; FHA; 4-HAwd; College.

DRAKE, Michael W; Fairfield Comm HS; Fairfield, IL; SecFrshCls; Aud/Vis; HonRl; LbryAde; PolWkr; SchMus; SchPl; Yrbk; SchPpr; FSA; FTA; SciCl; BttyCrckrAwd; Eastern Ill Univ; Stage Design.

DRAKE, Richard D; Anderson HS; Anderson, IN; 24/569 HonRl; JrNHS; NHS; NatlMeritCmnd; Quill&Scroll; EdSchPpr; KeyCl; CaptSwmmng; Trk; ChmbCommrsAwd; Indiana Univ; Med Or Marine Bio.

DRAKE, Robin E; Hanover Central HS; Crown Point, IN; 3/144 Chr; ChrhWkr; HonRl; JrNHS; LitMag; NHS; RptrSchPpr; SchPpr; Great Lakes Bible Col; Medicine.

DRAKE, Sharon E; Huntington Catholic HS; Huntington, IN; Chrs; HonRl; SchPl; SctActv; RptrYrbk; LetterBsktbl; Trk; Chrldr; Business School; Secretary.

DRAKE, Terry L; Lyons HS; Lyons, KS; PresStuCncl; PpCl; Bsktbl; CaptTrk; DanFAwd; Hutchinson Juco; Recreation Major.

DRAKE, Thomas R; Northrop HS; Fort Wayne, IN; 1/568 HonRl; SctActv; LetterGlf; Trk; DanFAwd; In U; Med.

DRANE, Walter K; Indian Creek HS; Trafalgar, IN; PresJrCls; PresChrhWkr; HonRl; NHS; NatlThespSoc; SchMus; SchPl; VPStuCncl; FFA; Bsbl; Wrstlng; IMSpt; College.

DRANGSHOLT, Lois K; Sherwood Public HS; Mohall, ND; TrsFrshCls; ALAGirlsSt; Band; Chrs; CncrtBnd; HonRl; MrchBnd; PepBnd; LetterBsktbl; IMSpt; Univ; Home Ec.

DRAPE, Sheryl K; Tripoli Comm HS; Waverly, IA; 3/53 Chr; Chrs; HonRl; SchMus; VPYthFlsp; RptrYrbk; LetterTrk; College.

DRAPER, Dennis D; Atchison HS; Atchison, KS; HonRl; ModUN; SctActv; YthFlsp; Bsbl; Ftbl; CchngActv; College; Law Enforcement.

DRAPER, Melissa J; Civic Memorial HS; Cottage Hills, IL; 3/225 Chr; HonRl; NHS; NatlThespSoc; StuCncl; RptrSchPpr; FrCl; Chrldr; PPFtbl; 4-HAwd; Law.

DRAPER, Steven J; Gurley Public HS; Dalton, NE; TrsFrshCls; VPSophCls; VPSrCls; Chr; Chrs; Mdrgl; SchMus; SchPl; StuCncl; StuGov; LetterBsktbl; LetterFtbl; LetterTrk; College; Biology.

DRAUS, Richelle M; Elizabeth Seton HS; South Holland, IL; HonRl; NHS; SchPl; Univ Of Ill; Doctor.

DRAVES, Cheryll K; Chester HS; Rockwood, IL; Band; ChrhWkr; HonRl; LbryAde; NHS; Yrbk; SchPpr; 4-H; FTA; PpCl;.

DRAVES, Kevin E; Aurora Central Catholic HS; Aurora, IL; 6/124 VPFrshCls; HonRl; NHS; SchPl; SctActv; StuCncl; StuGov; SciCl; BauchLmbAwd; College; Professional.

DRAVES, Melody A; Cumberland HS; Comstock, WI; 10/107 AFS; Band; ChrhWkr; CncrtBnd; HonRl; MrchBnd; PepBnd; SctActv; StuCncl; TchrAde; RptrYrbk; EdSchPpr; SpnCl; Marquette Univ; Dental Hygiene.

DRAVES, Sandra L; Dryden Community HS; Imlay City, MI; VPJrCls; HonRl; VPNHS; OffAde; StuCncl; TreasFrCl; LetterBsktbl; Tennis; IMSpt; Ferris St Coll; Med Tech.

DRAVES, Scott A; Murphysboro HS; Murphysboro, IL; 5/242 ALBoysSt; Band; ChrhWkr; HonRl; NHS; NatlMeritCmnd; SchPl; RptrYrbk; KeyCl; Siu; Lawyer.

DRAXLER, Francis D; Aubundale HS; Aubundale, WI; 24/103 VPSophCls; Band; TreasChrs; DrmMjrt; JrNHS; NHS; PepBnd; PolWkr; StuCncl; MthCl; Tech Sch.

DRAXTEN, Brian H; Fergus Falls HS; Fergus Falls, MN; PresSrCls; Band; NHS; SctActv; PresStuCncl; Bsbl; CaptBsktbl; CaptFtbl; LetterTrk; CchngActv; Univ Of Mn; Mortuary Science.

DRAY, Elizabeth A; Dist 219 H S; Elmore, MN; SecSrCls; ALAGirlsSt; Chr; ChrhWkr; CncrtBnd; DrmMjrt; HonRl; Mdrgl; NHS; Twrl; College; Music.

DRAYER, Julie A; United Twp HS; Silvis, IL; 40/697 Chr; ChrhWkr; HonRl; HospAde; YthFlsp; SchPpr; Univ Of Wisconsin; Occupational Therapy.

DRAYER, Wendy; Niles West HS; Lincolnwood, IL; Aud/Vis; Chrs; HonRl; SciCl; Univ Of Illinois; Psychology.

DRAZBA, Martin J; St Viator HS; Arlington Hts, IL; 21/245 ChrhWkr; HonRl; SchAde; LetterFtbl; LetterWrstlng; University Of Illinois; Engineering.

DRAZEWSKI, Scott D; Lake Park HS; Roselle, IL; 68/536 CmntyWkr; HonRl; SchMus; SctActv; StuGov; SciCl; College; Veterinarian.

DRAZY, Dean A; Bishop Mcnamara HS; Kankakee, IL; 30/174 NHS; StuCncl; TchrAde; FFA; SpnCl; Bsbl; Bsktbl; LetterFtbl; CaptTrk; Wrstlng; IMSpt; LionAwd; Washington Univ; Architecture.

DRDA, Brad A; Edwardsville Sr HS; Edwardsville, IL; PresFrshCls; StuCncl; Bsktbl; OptClAwd; Univeristy.

DREA, Carlene M; Messmer HS; Milwaukee, WI; TrsFrshCls; ChrhWkr; HonRl; LbryAde; SchAde; StuCncl; TchrAde; FTA; PpCl; IMSpt; College; Special Education.

DREBENSTEDT, Joni M; Marion Co Rii HS; Philadelphia, MO; SecFrshCls; CmntyWkr; HonRl; SchPl; StuCncl; Pres4-H; FHA; PpCl; Bsktbl; Trk; CaptChrldr; GAA; 4-HAwd; University; Liberal Arts.

DRECHSEL, Pamela S; Edwards Cty HS; Albion, IL; 3/98 Band; Chrs; ChrhWkr; HonRl; NHS; NatlMeritCmnd; SchMus; StuCncl; 4-H; PpCl; Olney Central College.

DRECHSEL, Pamela S; Edwards County HS; Albion, IL; 3/99 Band; Chrs; ChrhWkr; CncrtBnd; HonRl; NHS; NatlMeritCmnd; SchMus; StuCncl; FrCl; Olney Central College.

DRECHSEL, Suzanne R; Dwight HS; Dwight, IL; 14/111 AFS; Chrs; ChrhWkr; HonRl; OffAde; Yrbk; 4-H; LatCl; GAA; DanFAwd; Joliet Jr College; Nursing.

DRECKTRAH, Carla H; B R Falls HS; Black River Falls, WI; 36/137 Chr; HonRl; PolWkr; SchPl; TreasStuCncl; EdSchPpr; LatCl; LetterBsbl; LetterBsktbl; VPJrCls; SecTrsFrshCls; Ripon Coll; Lawyer.

DREES, Faye A; Meridian HS; Daykin, NE; 2/34 SecSophCls; Band; Chrs; ChrhWkr; CncrtBnd; HonRl; SecHospAde; MrchBnd; NHS; PepBnd; RptrYrbk; SecPpCl; LetterTrk; PPFtbl;.

DREESZEN, Bryce W; Ames HS; Ames, IA; 39/394 ChrhWkr; HonRl; NatlMeritCmnd; PolWkr; SctActv; StuCncl; StuGov; IMSpt; Coll; Chemical Eng.

DREFFS, David A; St Charles HS; Chesaning, MI; 15/128 HonRl; TreasNHS; TchrAde; SciCl; LetterBsktbl; LionAwd; Ferris State College; Comercial Art.

DREFS, Donald P; Escanaba Area Public HS; Escanaba, MI; 49/382 Aud/Vis; Band; CmntyWkr; CncrtBnd; HonRl; MrchBnd; NHS; PepBnd; YthFlsp; YthLg; Michigan Tech Univ; Electronics Eng.

DREFS, Robert C; York HS; Elmhurst, IL; HonRl; NatlFornLg; NHS; NatlMeritFnl; PolWkr; MthCl; Knox College; Pre Law.

DREGNE, David G; Kickapoo HS; Readstown, WI; TrsSophCls; VPJrCls; PresSrCls; HonRl; SchPl; PresStuCncl; RptrYrbk; Ftbl; Univ.

DREHER, Mark A; West Vigo HS; New Goshen, IN; ChrhWkr; HonRl; YthFlsp; FTA; Indiana State Univ; Geography.

DREHLE, Jeanette M; Norborne HS; Norborne, MO; Band; Chr; HonRl; MrchBnd; StuCncl; SchPpr; FHA; PpCl; LetterBsktbl; LetterTrk; College; Physical Education.

DREHOBL, Keith A; Lane Tech HS; Chicago, IL; SctActv; YthFlsp; Northeastern Univ Of Ill; Accounting.

DREIFKE, Richard C; Hubbard Comm HS; Hubbard, IA; 1/43 SecSophCls; VPSrCls; Chrs; HonRl; SchMus; EdYrBk; EngCl; MthCl; PpCl; SciCl; Ellsworth Comm College; Accounting.

DREIL, William K; West Rockford HS; Rockford, IL; 2/486 HonRl; JrNHS; NatlFornLg; NHS; Univ Of Illinois; Medicine.

DREILING, Anthony D; Thomas More Prep; Hays, KS; Band; Chr; Chrl; Chrs; HonRl; MrchBnd; PepBnd; SchMus; SchPl; StuCncl; Socr; LetterTrk; Chrldr; Marymount Col; Drama.

DREILING, Sandra M; Marian HS; Hays, KS; ChrhWkr; CmntyWkr; HonRl; NHS; PolWkr; StuCncl; StuGov; RptrYrbk; FNA; SpnCl; College; Nursing.

DRELL, Sydney F; New Trier West HS; Wilmette, IL; LitMag; NatlMeritSF; PolWkr; SchPl; StuGov; RptrYrbk; RptrSchPpr; College; Lawyer.

DREMANN, Alan; Ohio Community Hs; Ohio, IL; 1/24 ChrhWkr; CncrtBnd; HonRl; PresNHS; NatlMeritCmnd; TchrAde; SpnCl; SecTreasSciCl; Bsktbl; LetterFtbl; Bradley U; Engineering.

DRENKOW, Teresa; Melvin Community HS; Melvin, IA; 3/15 PresFrshCls; VPSrCls; Chr; HonRl; NHS; SchPl; RptrYrbk; 4-H; Nursing School; Nursing.

DRENNAN, Erin K; Monticello HS; Monticello, IL; 5/164 Chr; Chrs; HonRl; Mdrgl; NHS; SchMus; YthFlsp; RptrSchPpr; GAA; College; Secretary.

DRENNAN, James R; Baraga HS; Baraga, MI; 3/46 PresSophCls; PresJrCls; ALBoysSt; Band; Chrs; HonRl; NHS; NatlMeritSF; SchPl; Yrbk; College; Medical Doctor.

DRENNAN, Mark A; Mt Vernon Township HS; Ina, IL; Band; ChrhWkr; CncrtBnd; HonRl; JA; MrchBnd; PepBnd; SchMus; TchrAde; 4-H; PresFFA; DanFAwd; 4-HAwd; Jr College; Agriculture Production.

DRENTLAW, Karen D; Richland Center HS; Richland Center, WI; 4-H; Tech Sch Or Bus Sch; Pro Dog Trainer.

DRESCHER, Clair D; Alden Conger HS; Alden, MN; Band; Chrs; NHS; StuCncl; 4-H; FFA; LetterFtbl; LetterGlf; CaptWrstlng; 4-HAwd; Univ Of Mn; Agricultural.

DRESCHER, James H; Quincy Sr HS; Quincy, IL; 141/840 SctActv; YthFlsp; Univ Of Il; Anthropology.

DRESEN, Mary S; Edgewood HS; Madison, WI; Chrs; HonRl; NHS; TchrAde; PpCl; Tennis; Home Economics.

DRESSLER, Nancy J; Kingman HS; Kingman, KS; 4/114 ALAGirlsSt; Band; Chr; ChrhWkr; DrmMjrt; HonRl; CaptBsktbl; CaptTennis; Trk; EldAwd; PresAwd; Kansas Univ; Journalism.

DRETZKA, Ellen E; So Milwaukee Senior HS; S Milwaukee, WI; 1/435 Band; CncrtBnd; HonRl; LbryAde; MrchBnd; NHS; Orch; PepBnd; SpnCl; NCTE; University; Medicine.

DREVECKY, Seanne; Adams Public HS; Adams, ND; 4/25 VPJrCls; ALAGirlsSt; Band; Chrs; ChrhWkr; HonRl; EdSchPpr; 4-H; 4-HAwd; Nd St Univ; Home Economics.

DREVES, Kandee M; St Francis HS; Traverse City, MI; 21/84 Chr; CmntyWkr; HonRl; NHS; OffAde; FshEdYrbk; Yrbk; 4-H; PpCl; Bsktbl; Northwestern Michigan College; R N.

DREVS, Ann E; Roland Story HS; Roland, IA; VPFrshCls; Band; CncrtBnd; HonRl; MrchBnd; StuCncl; YthFlsp; 4-H; LetterBsktbl; LetterTrk; College; Pe Major.

DREW, Brett; Ft Atkinson Sr Hs; Ft Atkinson, WI; ChrhWkr; Technical School; Police Science.

DREW, Dawn; Snider HS; Ft Wayne, IN; 83/513 Chr; CmntyWkr; HonRl; JA; PolWkr; PpCl; Coll; Pre Med.

DREW, Keith T; Zeeland HS; Zeeland, MI; 8/168 ALBoysSt; Band; ChrhWkr; HonRl; ModUN; NatlThespSoc; YthFlsp; LetterFtbl; LetterWrstlng; AmLegAwd; Spring Arbor Coll; Major Math.

DREW, Roy M; Boone County HS; Centralia, MO; 5/90 VPSophCls; PresSrCls; Chr; Chrs; ChrhWkr; HonRl; JA; Ftbl; Glf; Wrstlng; U Of Mo At Rollz; Chemical Engineering.

DREW, Sandra K; Webber Twp HS; Bluford, IL; HonRl; StuCncl; Yrbk; RptrSchPpr; FBLA; FHA; PpCl; Kaskaskia Jr College; Rn.

DREW, Thomas A; Plainfield HS; Plainfield, IL; Band; HonRl; JrNHS; NHS; YthFlsp; MthCl; CaptBsktbl; CaptFtbl; Trk; Univ; Science.

DREWEK, Lynette A; Athens HS; Athens, WI; SecSophCls; HonRl; LbryAde; NHS; VPStuCncl; FBLA; VPFHA; SpnCl; PpCl; Business; Vocation.

DREWELOW, Rick L; Nashua Community HS; Ionia, IA; Band; Chrs; ChrhWkr; CncrtBnd; HonRl; MrchBnd; PepBnd; 4-H; FFA; Bsktbl; College; Music.

DREWES, David D; Central Lyon HS; Rock Rapids, IA; Band; ChrhWkr; CncrtBnd; HonRl; MrchBnd; PepBnd; PpCl;.

DREWES, Teresa A; East HS; Waterloo, IA; 1/425 Band; CncrtBnd; HonRl; JrNHS; MrchBnd; Orch; StuCncl; Twrl; 4-H; LetterSwmmng; College; Nurse.

DREWS, Deborah A; Central HS; Red Wing, MN; ChrhWkr; DrlTm; HonRl; JrNHS; NHS; NatlMeritCmnd; NatlThespSoc; OffAde; SchPl; SctActv; YthLg; GAA; PPFtbl; College Of St Benedict; Journalism.

DREXEL, Joan D; Mercy HS; Omaha, NE; Chr; JA; OffAde; Sdlty; TchrAde; SpnCl;.

DREXLER, Susan V; Chesaning Union HS; Chesaning, MI; ChrhWkr; HonRl; SchPl; SpnCl; Ferris State Coll; Medical Secretary.

DREY, Dennis J; St Marys HS; Early, IA; TrsJrCls; Chrs; PepBnd; SchMus; SchPl; RptrSchPpr; FshEdSchPpr; SptEdSchPpr; Bsktbl; Trk; Trade Schl; Mechanics.

DREY, Laurel M; St Marys HS; Early, IA; 5/45 Chrs; HonRl; NHS; SchPl; TchrAde; Yrbk; RptrSchPpr; 4-H; PpCl; 4-HAwd; Ia Lakes Comm Clge; Med Sec.

DREYER, Alec G; Murphysboro HS; Murphysboro, IL; 1/231 PresFrshCls; HonRl; NHS; StuCncl; EdSchPpr; KeyCl; Bsbl; Univ Of Illinois; Lawyer.

DREYER, Anita R; Crystal City HS; Festus, MO; 4/85 HonRl; LbryAde; NHS; NatlMeritCmnd; OffAde; PolWkr; U Of Mo; Pre Veterinary Medicine.

DREYER, David A; Rushville HS; Rushville, NE; 6/43 ALBoysSt; Chrs; ChrhWkr; HonRl; Mdrgl; YthFlsp; FFA; Ftbl; LetterTrk; Trade School.

DREYER, Donna J; Lyons Twp HS; La Grange Park, IL; 40/1226 CmntyWkr; JrNHS; NHS; NatlMeritCmnd; TchrAde; RptrYrbk; GAA; Texas Christian U; Chiropractor.

DREYER, Jeffrey; Cal Community Hs; Latimer, IA; Band; CncrtBnd; MrchBnd; PepBnd; SchMus; Yrbk; SecFFA; Bsktbl; LetterFtbl; CchngActv; College; Farming.

DREYER, Jennifer D; Flushing HS; Flushing, MI; 15/464 Chr; ChrhWkr; YthFlsp; 4-H; FrCl; Coll; French.

DREYER, Timothy L; Bluffton HS; Bluffton, IN; 40/150 HonRl; SchPl; SchPpr; LatCl; Bsktbl; Ftbl; Trk; University; Forestry.

DRIER, Susan; Arkansaw HS; Arkansaw, WI; 3/26 TrsSophCls; VPJrCls; TrsSrCls; Band; Chr; HonRl; LionAwd; Chrldr; GAA; IMSpt; College; Nursing.

DRIER, Susan M; Arkansaw HS; Arkansaw, WI; TrsSrCls; Band; HonRl; NHS; StuCncl; EdYrBk; RptrSchPpr; Bsktbl; Chrldr; GAA; Uiterbo College; Nursing.

DRIES, Mary T; St Marys Acad; Chillicothe, IL; 10/60 Chrs; HonRl; JA; StuCncl; 4-H; LetterBsktbl; Swmmng; Trk; DARAwd; PresAwd; Univ; Prof.

DRIESSEN, Sandra; Kiel HS; Kiel, WI; AFS; SctActv; RptrSchPpr; SptEdSchPpr; 4-H; GerCl; PpCl; Bsktbl; Trk; IMSpt; College.

DRIKER, Miriam S; Berkley HS; Huntington Woods, MI; SecSophCls; HonRl; HospAde; NHS; OffAde; PolWkr; StuCncl; SpnCl; SciCl; LetterTennis; Univ Of Mi.

DRILLING, Lloyd; Lakeview Aubain HS; Lakeview, IA; ALBoysSt; Band; ChrhWkr; HonRl; MrchBnd; NatlThespSoc; PepBnd; IMSpt; Univ Of N Ia; Jewelry Business.

DRINKA, Rosemary J; Waukegan Comm HS; Waukegan, IL; Chr; Chrs; CmntyWkr; HonRl; NHS; Univ; Special Ed.

DRINKWINE, Sharon Z; Westhope HS; Westhope, ND; Band; Chr; ChrhWkr; CmntyWkr; CncrtBnd; HonRl; HospAde; MrchBnd; PepBnd; PolWkr; SchPl; SctActv; LetterTrk; GAA; College.

DRISCOLL, Julie J; Sacred Heart Of Mary HS; Palatine, IL; 36/135 CmntyWkr; NHS; PPFtbl; Marquette Univ; Physical Therapy.

DRISCOLL, Kenneth J; Reavis HS; Burbank, IL; 65/676 CmntyWkr; HonRl; NHS; NatlMeritCmnd; LetterBsbl; CaptBsktbl; Ftbl; Trk; Loyola Univ; Dentistry.

DRISDEL, Renaldo C; Cahokia HS; Cahokia, IL; 57/540 MthCl; PpCl; LetterBsbl; LetterFtbl; University; Chemistry.

DRISKELL, Michael J; West Platte R Ii HS; Weston, MO; 3/51 PresJrCls; AFS; Chr; Chrs; HonRl; Mdrgl; ModUN; NHS; SchMus; SchPl; Bsbl; Bsktbl; Ftbl; College; Forestry.

DRIVER, Lori A; Danville HS; Danville, IL; AFS; ChrhWkr; CmntyWkr; JA; PolWkr; StuCncl; Teen; YthFlsp; SecLatCl; CaptTennis; VoiceDemAwd; Southern Illinois; Law.

DROBAC, Stanley H; Okemos HS; Okemos, MI; 8/280 ChrhWkr; NHS; NatlMeritSchl; Bsbl; LetterBsktbl; Ftbl; Glf; LetterTennis; IMSpt; University.

DROBNEY, Denise D; Pocahontas Comm HS; Pocahontas, IA; Band; CncrtBnd; DrlTm; HonRl; MrchBnd; PepBnd; SchMus; Twrl; Yrbk; PpCl; Chrldr; Univ Of Northern Iowa; Biology.

DROBNY, Gail; Morton West HS; Stickney, IL; 18/750 Chr; HonRl; JrNHS; NHS; GAA; Western Illinois U; General.

DROCHNER, Diane M; Triton HS; Tippecanoe, IN; TrsFrshCls; Chr; HonRl; NHS; OffAde; SchMus; 4-H; FTA; SpnCl; PpCl; SciCl; GAA; 4-HAwd; College; Business.

DROEGE, Betty L; Ashton HS; Ashton, IL; HonRl; SchPl; YthFlsp; SchPpr; FrCl; GAA; Kishwaukee Junior College; Lpn.

DROEGE, Cecelia M; St Francis Borgia HS; Washington, MO; 4/100 SecBand; CmntyWkr; HonRl; MrchBnd; NHS; PepBnd; SchMus; RptrSchPpr; OptClAwd; College Of St Teresa; Biology.

DROEGE, Ruth A; North Pasey Senior HS; Wadesville, IN; 9/165 PresBand; Chrs; CncrtBnd; HonRl; HospAde; MrchBnd; NHS; PepBnd; RptrYrbk; GAA; Indiana State University; Nursing.

DROESCH, Kevin T; Rosary HS; St Louis, MO; HonRl; SchPl; St Louis University; Business.

DRONE, Christopher P; Harrisburg HS; Harrisburg, IL; ChrhWkr; HonRl; NatlMeritSchl; SecFFA; TreasMthCl; CitAwd; Se Illinois College; Agriculture.

DROPPS, Nadine A; Tiovola Meadowlands HS; Hibbing, MN; Chr; DrlTm; HonRl; RptrSchPpr; SchPpr; FHA; PpCl; Trade School.

DROSSEL, Carey; Anthon Oto Comm HS; Anthon, IA; PresSrCls; SchPl; RptrYrbk; 4-H; PpCl; IMSpt; 4-HAwd; Trade Sch; Carpenter.

DROST, Cindy A; Harlem HS; Loves Park, IL; 17/550 AFS; Chr; CncrtBnd; HonRl; MrchBnd; NHS; SchAde; TreasFTA; Trk; GAA; St Anthony Hospital; Medicine.

DROSTE, Charles V; Mt Olive Comm HS; Mt Olive, IL; Band; Chrs; ChrhWkr; CncrtBnd; MrchBnd; LetterBsbl; LetterBsktbl; LetterTrk; VoiceDemAwd; E Illinois Univ; Teach.

DROSTE, Nanette M; Oelwein Community HS; Oelwein, IA; 10/181 Band; Chr; HonRl; JrNHS; NHS; SchMus; SchPl; EdYrBk; EdSchPpr; PpCl; College; English.

DROZD, Julie A; Allegan HS; Allegan, MI; 5/195 Band; DrmMjrt; HonRl; MrchBnd; PepBnd; SchAde; SchPl; Twrl; 4-H; SpnCl; College; Math Teacher.

DROZDOWSKI, Gerardyne M; St Philip Cc HS; Battle Creek, MI; SecJrCls; Chrl; HonRl; HospAde; RedCrAde; SchMus; SchPl; EdSchPpr; SpnCl; Bsktbl; Mi State Univ; Theatre Major.

DROZDZ, Thomas M; Main East HS; Niles, IL; HonRl; MthCl; LetterGlf; LetterSwmmng; Loyola Univ; Doctor.

DRTINA, Judy L; Grant Community HS; Mc Henry, IL; 1/250 PresBand; Chr; Chrs; ChrhWkr; CncrtBnd; DrmBgl; HonRl; JrNHS; Mdrgl; MrchBnd; Univ; Music Education.

DRUCKMILLER, Susan K; Durant Comm HS; Durant, IA; 6/73 Chr; HonRl; Mdrgl; NatlFornLg; NHS; SchMus; SchPl; RptrSchPpr; Trk; Music Or Art.

DRUEHL, Denise R; Bettendorf HS; Bettendorf, IA; 45/449 SecJrCls; SecSrCls; AFS; NHS; Quill&Scroll; SctActv; EdSchPpr; PresGAA; EldAwd; MasAwd; Drake University; Pharmacy.

DRUGOCH, Rose Ann; Melvindale HS; Allen Park, MI; Band; CncrtBnd; HonRl; MrchBnd; NHS; NatlMeritSF; PepBnd; IMSpt; PPFtbl; Eastern Mich U; Accountant.

DRUKER, Jonathan M; C R Washington HS; Cedar Rapids, IA; PresFrshCls; VPSrCls; ALBoysSt; Chrl; HonRl; NatlFornLg; NHS; StuGov; Trk; College; Biology.

DRUMM, Alison J; Benet Academy; Naperville, IL; PresChrs; CmntyWkr; HonRl; StuGov; RptrSchPpr; FrCl; St Marys College; Int Relations.

DRUMM, Deb S; Watertown Sr HS; Watertown, SD; 3/334 SecALAGirlsSt; HonRl; JrNHS; NatlFornLg; StuCncl; SpnCl; LetterTennis; LetterTrk; GAA; College; Accounting.

DRUMMER, Jennie M; Good Counsel Academy; N Mankato, MN; MrchBnd; NHS; PepBnd; RedCrAde; SchMus; SchPl; FNA; GerCl; Bsktbl; GAA; Vo Tec; Rn.

DRUMMOND, Keven; Waukegan East HS; Waukegan, IL; HstJrCls; CtyCnl; HonRl; JrNHS; NHS; OffAde; StuCncl; StuGov; TchrAde; LatCl; Coll; Pro.

DRUMMOND, William T; Derby Sr HS; Derby, KS; 45/334 PresSrCls; ALBoysSt; JrNHS; NatlFornLg; NHS; ROTC; StuCncl; GerCl; Ftbl; West Point Univ; Medicine.

DRURY, Shirley; L L Wright HS; Ironwood, MI; TrsSrCls; Chr; HospAde; NHS; NatlThespSoc; SchMus; SchPl; SchPpr; FrCl; PpCl; College; Pre Med.

DRURY, Tom J; Rockwell Swaledale HS; Swaledale, IA; 3/50 HonRl; RptrSchPpr; Bsktbl; Ftbl; Trk; College; Writer.

DRUTYS, Terese L; Maria HS; Chicago, IL; 51/335 ChrhWkr; HonRl; LitMag; NHS; RedCrAde; TchrAde; GerCl; TreasMthCl; SciCl; U Of Il Chicago Circle Campus; Medicine.

DRYANSKI, Lucia L; John Hersey HS; Arlington Hts, IL; 35/776 AFS; Chr; CmntyWkr; HonRl; NatlFornLg; NHS; NatlMeritSF; SchMus; TchrAde; Illinois State Univ; Special Educ.

DRYER, Pamela J; Hamilton Heights HS; Greentown, IN; 13/108 ALAGirlsSt; HonRl; JrNHS; NHS; OffAde; StuGov; SecFHA; SecSciCl; College; Business.

DRYMALSKI, Geralyn L; St Louise De Marillac HS; Northbrook, IL; Chr; ChrhWkr; CmntyWkr; LitMag; NHS; RedCrAde; SchMus; Kalamazoo College.

DRYSDALE, Andrea K; Rantoul Township HS; Rantoul, IL; 2/400 ChrhWkr; CncrtBnd; HonRl; MrchBnd; NHS; NatlMeritSF; Orch; SchMus; YthFlsp; FrCl; Millikin Univ; Sociologist.

DRYSDALE, Janice E; Blue Mound HS; Blue Mound, IL; 6/50 SecSophCls; SecJrCls; Chr; ChrhWkr; HonRl; SchPl; 4-H; FHA; FTA; PpCl; GAA; Richland Comm Coll.

DRZEWIECKI, Michael R; Mendel Cath Prep; Chicago, IL; 24/163 SecFrshCls; VPSophCls; VPJrCls; VPSrCls; HonRl; NHS; Sacrstn; LetterBsbl; LionAwd; VFWAwd; Coll; Med Tech.

DUBA, Douglas R; Wilber Clatonia Public HS; Wilber, NE; Aud/Vis; Band; CncrtBnd; HonRl; LbryAde; MrchBnd; PepBnd; SchMus; SchPl; TchrAde; U Of Neb; Animal Science.

DUBACH, Margaret M; Marseilles HS; Marseilles, IL; TrsJrCls; TrsSrCls; ALAGirlsSt; HonRl; NHS; RptrYrbk; RptrSchPpr; LetterSocr; College; Correctional Work.

DUBART, Christine A; Grandville HS; Wyoming, MI; DrlTm; HonRl; MrchBnd; NHS; NatlMeritCmnd; Butterworth Hosp; Registered Nurse.

DUBAS, Catherine A; Niles Township West HS; Niles, IL; 75/660 HonRl; JA; NHS; OffAde; SchAde; TchrAde; FrCl; GAA; Air Force; Dietetics.

DU BAY, Floyd D; L Anse Crewe HS; Mt Clemens, MI; ChrhWkr; HonRl; JrNHS; Univ Of Michigan; Law.

DUBAY, Michelle; Chesoning Union HS; Chesoning, MI; HonRl; JA; JrNHS; NHS; NatlMeritCmnd; SchAde; StuCncl; CitAwd; Ferris St College; Dental Hygienst.

DUBBELDEE, Cynthia; Tyler HS; Arco, MN; SecFrshCls; Chr; HospAde; Mdrgl; SchMus; StuGov; Trk; Chrldr; GAA; IMSpt; Trade School; Lpn Nursing.

DUBES, Cameron C; Aurelia HS; Aurelia, IA; 8/50 Band; PresChr; HonRl; NHS; Orch; SchPl; StuCncl; EdYrBk; PresFFA; LetterBsktbl; Ftbl; MasAwd; CitAwd; Iowa St Univ; Lawyer.

DUBKE, Janet E; Mankato West HS; N Mankato, MN; 8/327 HonRl; StuCncl; PpCl; College; Professional.

DUBLINSKI, Patrick; Muskego HS; Hales Corners, WI; HonRl; Bsktbl; Ftbl; Trk; IMSpt; Trade School.

DU BOIS, Colette E; Tremont HS; Tremont, IL; 3/80 SecSophCls; SecJrCls; ALAGirlsSt; Band; ChrhWkr; HonRl; MrchBnd; NHS; PepBnd; Chrldr; Bus Schl; Exec Sec.

DU BOIS, Denise; St Joseph Acad; Green Bay, WI; VPSrCls; Chrs; OffAde; SchAde; SchMus; StuCncl; StuGov; FrCl; Bsbl; CchngActv; Coll; Prof.

DUBOVICK, Carol J; Mt Iron HS; Mt Iron, MN; 1/68 Band; Chr; HonRl; HospAde; NHS; SchPl; Yrbk; EdSchPpr; PresFNA; BttyCrckrAwd; Augsburg Col; Communications.

DU BRAVEC, Jean M; Christopher Comm HS; Christopher, IL; Band; HonRl; NHS; SchPl; Twrl; RptrYrbk; 4-H; FHA; IMSpt; DanFAwd; 4-HAwd; University; Liberal Arts.

DUBS, Colette; Freeman Public HS; Freeman, SD; Band; Chrs; CncrtBnd; HonRl; PepBnd; SchMus; SchPl; PpCl; Trk;.

DUBSON, Michael G; Maroa Forsyth HS; Maroa, IL; Chrs; HonRl; LbryAde; RptrSchPpr; Coll; Journalsim.

DUBUISSON, Lisa E; South Haven HS; South Haven, MI; 26/216 Band; CncrtBnd; HonRl; MrchBnd; YthFlsp; RptrYrbk; Univ; Professnl.

DUBUQUE, Jeanne M; Clifton Central HS; Chebanse, IL; 4/136 Chrs; HonRl; JrNHS; PresNatlFornLg; NHS; NatlThespSoc; SchMus; SchPl; StuCncl; Yrbk; FrCl; PpCl; Chrldr; GAA; Illinois Wesleyan Univ; English.

DUCEY, Anne; Rosary HS; Florissant, MO; 2/360 Chrl; ChrhWkr; HonRl; NHS; SchMus; StuCncl; TchrAde; FrCl; CchngActv; GAA; College; Medical Technology.

DUCEY, Michael F; Unity HS; Tolono, IL; Chr; ChrhWkr; CmntyWkr; HonRl; NatlThespSoc; SchMus; StuCncl; Bsbl; Bsktbl; Construction Engineering.

DUCHAK, Gregory M; Reavis HS; Burbank, IL; 50/758 PresChrhWkr; HonRl; PresNHS; NatlThespSoc; StuCncl; RusCl; Ftbl; Glf; Trk; College; Medicine.

DU CHARME, David P; Seneca HS; La Crosse, WI; VPJrCls; Band; CncrtBnd; MrchBnd; SchPl; StuCncl; Yrbk; FFA; LetterFtbl; LetterTrk; LetterWrstlng; Technical School; Elec Technician.

DU CHARME, Myrna H; Seneca HS; Eastman, WI; 4/34 TrsJrCls; Band; CncrtBnd; HonRl; MrchBnd; NHS; Orch; PepBnd; SchPl; RptrSchPpr; SchPpr; TreasFHA; PpCl; Trk; Work; Secretary.

DUCHARME, Sally; Florence Hs; Iron Mountain, MI; TrsFrshCls; SecJrCls; Band; Chrs; NatlFornLg; NHS; SecStuCncl; PpCl; Chrldr; GAA; Ne Wi Tech Inst; Dental Assistant.

DUCHARME, Therese M; Glenbrook South HS; Glenview, IL; AFS; HonRl; Rockford College.

DUCHENE, Steven P; Plainfield HS; Plainfield, IL; HonRl; SchPl; TchrAde; GerCl; CaptWrstlng; St Josp School Of Nursing; Physical Therapy.

DUCHENEAUX, Rose J; Cheyenna Eagle Butte HS; Eagle Butte, SD; SecSophCls; Chrs; HonRl; NHS; StuCncl; FFA; FHA; Trk; Chrldr; Voc Sch; Dental Assist.

DUCHOW, Diane; Marshfield Sr HS; Marshfield, WI; 15/327 Band; Chrs; CncrtBnd; HonRl; MrchBnd; NHS; Orch; SchMus; TchrAde; Univ Of Wi Stevens Pt; Music.

DUCHSCHERE, Kevin A; Shanley HS; Fargo, ND; 17/130 ALBoysSt; Chrs; HonRl; LitMag; NHS; PolWkr; SchMus; Yrbk; SptEdSchPpr; Univ Of Virginia; Law.

DUCK, Pamela S; United Township HS; Silvis, IL; Band; Chr; Chrl; Chrs; CncrtBnd; MrchBnd; OffAde; PepBnd; Lutheran Hosp School; Nursing.

DUCKETT, Ruth I; Southeast Polk HS; Altoona, IA; 3/218 Band; Chr; ChrhWkr; CncrtBnd; HonRl; MrchBnd; NHS; NatlMeritSF; SchMus; SctActv; Culver Coll; Education.

DUCKHORN, Margaret M; St Benedict HS; Chicago, IL; 3/183 Chrs; HonRl; PresNHS; NatlMeritCmnd; SchPl; SptEdYrbk; PpCl; CitAwd; Lawyer.

DUCKLOW, Dan J; Spring Valley HS; Spring Valley, WI; TrsFrshCls; SptEdSchPpr; Bsbl; Bsktbl; Ftbl; Glf;.

DUCKWALL, Gary A; Whitnall 'S; Hales Corners, WI; 1/289 Band; HonRl; MrchBnd; NHS; PepBnd; SchMus; SchPl; UNYO; GerCl; Trk; College; Professional.

DUCKWORTH, Timothy A; Griffin HS; Springfield, IL; TreasChrhWkr; StuCncl; PresPpCl; Ftbl; CchngActv; IMSpt; University; Professional.

DU CLOS, Carol J; H L Richards HS; Palos Heights, IL; 36/1035 HonRl; NHS; OffAde; PolWkr; Univ Of Illinois; Law.

DUDEK, Catherine L; Ladywood HS; Westland, MI; HonRl; NHS; VPQuill&Scroll; SchMus; StuCncl; RptrSchPpr; CaptTennis; JAAwd; Michigan State Univ; Education.

DUDEK, David B; Chosen Valley HS; Chatfield, MN; 26/100 SecTrsSophCls; Band; Chr; Chrs; CncrtBnd; HonRl; Mdrgl; MrchBnd; SchMus; SchPl; Yrbk; Bsbl; Bsktbl;.

DUDEK, Terese C; Oak Forest HS; Oak Forest, IL; 17/495 Band; CncrtBnd; HonRl; MrchBnd; NHS; PepBnd; SptEdSchPpr; SpnCl; Tennis; Lewis Univ; Forestry.

DUDENBOSTEL, Sandra J; New Athens Comm HS; New Athens, IL; 1/66 SecFrshCls; HonRl; SecNHS; Quill&Scroll; SchPl; EdYrBk; Yrbk; FHA; VPFTA; GAA; DARAwd; 4-HAwd; Southern Illinois Univ; Mathematics.

DUDERSTADT, Mack H; Carrollton Senior HS; Carrollton, MO; ALBoysSt; Band; ChrhWkr; HonRl; NHS; NatlThespSoc; SctActv; SchPpr; KeyCl; LetterFtbl; Trk; College; Journalism.

DUDLEY, Bevely T; Holy Cross HS; Chicago, IL; 20/356 Band; CncrtBnd; HonRl; MrchBnd; PepBnd; SchMus; SctActv; MthCl; LetterTrk; IMSpt; Illinois Inst Of Tech; Computer Sciences.

DUDLEY, Cynthia E; Centerville HS; Centerville, IA; 1/151 ChrhWkr; CmntyWkr; CncrtBnd; HonRl; NHS; SchMus; 4-H; BttyCrckrAwd; 4-HAwd; CitAwd; Ia State Indian Hills; Fashion Design.

DUDLEY, Deanna; Shepherd HS; Shepherd, MI; 3/129 HonRl; NHS; TchrAde; YthFlsp; FHA; Central Mich Univ, English.

DUDLEY, Diana K; Cassville HS; Shell Knob, MO; TrsJrCls; OffAde; RptrYrbk; RptrSchPpr; Bsktbl; GAA; Trade School; Cosmotology.

DUDLEY, Michele R; Benton Harbor HS; Benton Harbor, MI; 92/418 ChrhWkr; HonRl; JA; PolWkr; StuCncl; TreasStuGov; RptrYrbk; SpnCl; LetterBsktbl; JAAwd; Michigan State Univ; Medicine.

DUDLEY, Pamela; Steeleville HS; Steeleville, IL; Chrs; MrchBnd; StuGov; RptrYrbk; FHA; RusCl; PpCl; GAA; IMSpt; College; Nursing.

DUDLEY, Steven L; Beech Grove HS; Beech Grove, IN; 43/233 Band; CncrtBnd; MrchBnd; PepBnd; PolWkr; SchPl; Indiana State Univ; Med Tech.

DUDLEY, William D; Union HS; Union, MO; HonRl; SchMus; SchPl; StuCncl; TchrAde; RptrSchPpr; Bsktbl; Southeast Missouri University; Education.

DUDRA, Douglas J; Pekin Comm HS; Pekin, IL; 75/750 HonRl; NatlFornLg; SchPl; TchrAde; EdYrBk; SchPpr; EldAwd; Southern Ill; Photography Fine Arts.

DUDZIAK, Zofia J; Little Wolf HS; Ogdensburg, WI; 17/80 AFS; ChrhWkr; HonRl; JrNHS; Mdrgl; NatlFornLg; RptrYrbk; Swmmng; GAA; JAAwd; Uw Whitewater; Spec Ed.

DUDZIK, Kathy A; Luther South HS; Chicago, IL; 19/204 Chr; ChrhWkr; HonRl; CivCl; Aurora College; Environmental Science.

DUEA, Joseph M; Yorkville HS; Yorkville, IL; 19/125 CncrtBnd; MrchBnd; SchPl; StuCncl; 4-H; VPFFA; LetterBsbl; Bsktbl; LetterFtbl; Jr College; Agriculture.

DUEBALL, Kathy L; Maine West HS; Des Plaines, IL; Aud/Vis; Chr; Chrl; ChrhWkr; HonRl; JrNHS; NatlThespSoc; RedCrAde; SchMus; SchPl; SctActv; YthFlsp; PpCl; CchngActv; Illinois Wesleyan Univ; Nursing.

DUEBBERT, Ingrid; Alton Senior Hs; Alton, IL; 42/858 Chr; Chrs; HonRl; NHS; NatlThespSoc; SchMus; TchrAde; LatCl; PpCl; SciCl; U Of Illinois; Pre Med.

DUEBER, Peter; Waconia HS; Waconia, MN; Band; CncrtBnd; HonRl; NHS; StuCncl; LionAwd; College Of St Thomas; Business.

DUEHN, Catherine J; Hutchinson HS; Hutchinson, MN; Chr; Chrs; HonRl; PepBnd; YthFlsp; PpCl; LetterBsktbl; LetterTrk; Chrldr; College; Professional Law.

DUENSING, Gyl A; Lakeshore HS; Stevensville, MI; 20/240 TrsSophCls; TrsJrCls; Chr; HonRl; JrNHS; Mdrgl; NHS; SchMus; SchPl; TreasStuCncl; TchrAde; EdSchPpr; College; Professional.

DUENSING, Lolita E; Merrill HS; Brant, MI; 10/106 HonRl; NHS; TchrAde; 4-H; SecFTA; 4-HAwd; Delta College; Medical Assistant.

DUENSING, Ronald D; Odell Public HS; Odell, NE; PresFrshCls; VPSophCls; PresJrCls; ALBoysSt; Chrs; HonRl; SchPl; Bsbl; LetterFtbl; LetterTrk; College.

DUER, Joy L; Vienna HS; Tunnel Hill, IL; SecFrshCls; TrsFrshCls; PresSophCls; ChrhWkr; CmntyWkr; NatlThespSoc; SchPl; TchrAde; FFA; FHA; Southeastern Il.

DUER, Patti J; Vienna HS; Tunnel Hill, IL; 7/104 ChrhWkr; CmntyWkr; NatlThespSoc; TchrAde; Yrbk; FHA; MthCl; PpCl; Trk; College; Vocation.

DUERINCK, Mark V; Montini HS; Lombard, IL; 3/155 HonRl; NHS; StuCncl; RptrSchPpr; Univ Of Notre Dame; Medicine.

DUERKSEN, Jolynn K; Marion Ind HS; Marion, SD; PresSrCls; PresBand; Chrs; ChrhWkr; CncrtBnd; HonRl; MrchBnd; SchPl; TreasStuCncl; LetterTrk; DARAwd; 4-HAwd; College; Music.

DUERR, Barbara S; Lidgerwood Public HS; Lidgerwood, ND; 7/49 Band; Chrs; ChrhWkr; CncrtBnd; HonRl; MrchBnd; PepBnd; SchMus; SchPl; StuCncl; EdSchPpr; FHA; SecGerCl;.

DUERRE, Jill Y; Sherwood Public HS; Norma, ND; SecFrshCls; Band; CncrtBnd; DrlTm; HonRl; MrchBnd; PepBnd; SchPl; EdYrBk; PpCl; Minot State College; Medical Technology.

DUERSON, Timothy S; Oconomowoc Senior HS; Oconomowoc, WI; Band; CncrtBnd; HonRl; JrNHS; MrchBnd; NHS; Orch; PepBnd; Northwestern University; Broadcasting Mgmt.

DUERST, Cheryl A; New Glarus HS; New Glarus, WI; Chrs; OffAde; TchrAde; YthFlsp; RptrSchPpr; PresFHA; FTA; PpCl; Wrstlng; GAA; Madison Area Tech College; Secretary.

DUERST, Susan R; Whitewater HS; Elkhorn, WI; 52/189 AFS; Band; Chr; CmntyWkr; CncrtBnd; MrchBnd; YthFlsp; Yrbk; 4-H; GAA;.

DUEZ, Teresa A; Westville HS; Danville, IL; Band; Chrs; CmntyWkr; CncrtBnd; HonRl; PepBnd; TchrAde; UNYO; Bsktbl; College; Social Worker.

DUFAULT, Roxanne; Mount St Benedict HS; Gentilly, MN; 8/48 TrsSophCls; ALAGirlsSt; ChrhWkr; CmntyWkr; LbryAde; Sdlty; TchrAde; TreasYthFlsp; PpCl; AmLegAwd; Coll; Spec Educ, Soc Work.

DUFF, Charlotte V; Mansfield HS; Macomb, MO; 2/45 TrsJrCls; SecSrCls; ChrhWkr; HonRl; NHS; SchPl; RptrYrbk; EdSchPpr; PpCl; BttyCrckrAwd; College; Professional.

DUFF, Dana J; Lincoln HS; Cambridge City, IN; 10/118 Chr; HonRl; NHS; OffAde; SchPl; Teen; YthFlsp; FTA; Chrldr; Ballstate Univ Muncie In; Teacher.

DUFF, Dannae M; Scranton Consolidated HS; Scranton, IA; VPJrCls; Band; Mdrgl; NHS; SchMus; SchPl; SctActv; Pres4-H; LetterBsktbl; Chrldr; Iowa State University; Speech Major.

DUFF, Derek A; East Catholic HS; Detroit, MI; 35/109 HonRl; JA; NatlMeritCmnd; SchMus; SchPl; SptEdYrbk; PpCl; SciCl; Trk; IMSpt; Northwood Inst; Hotel Management.

DUFF, Linda K; Ozark HS; Ozark, MO; 17/99 HonRl; StuCncl; Twrl; PresFHA; PresPpCl; Southwest Missouri State Univ.

DUFF, Marsha J; David H Hickman HS; Columbia, MO; 25/534 TrsJrCls; HonRl; NatlFornLg; NHS; NatlThespSoc; Missouri University.

DUFF, Patrick S; Shawnee Mission South HS; Overland Park, KS; Band; CAP; DrlTm; HonRl; NatlMeritSF; ROTC; StuCncl; StuGov; Swmmng; GodCntryAwd; Univ; Philosophy.

DUFF, Philip N; Central HS; Red Wing, MN; 1/330 HonRl; NHS; NatlMeritCmnd; Yrbk; SchPpr; CaptTennis; Harvard Univ; Mathematics.

DUFF, Ramona S; Lincolnwood HS; Irving, IL; VPJrCls; HonRl; JA; RptrSchPpr; 4-H; FHA; SciCl; 4-HAwd; JAAwd; CitAwd; Coll; Pro.

DUFF, Sharan P; Saint Alberts HS; Council Bluffs, IA; DrlTm; HonRl; NHS; OffAde; PolWkr; SchMus; SchPl; PpCl; Loras College.

DUFFELS, Marty; Romeoville HS; Romeoville, IL; 12/293 VPNHS; LetterBsktbl; Ftbl; LetterGlf; Illinois State University.

DUFFICY, Kathleen A; Academy Of Our Lady; Chicago, IL; 8/164 Chr; ChrhWkr; HonRl; NHS; PolWkr; Sacrstn; SchAde; SchPl; PpCl; College; Law.

DUFFIE, Cathie L; La Harpe HS; La Harpe, IL; 4/60 ChrhWkr; HonRl; NHS; SchMus; StuCncl; TchrAde; YthFlsp; RptrYrbk; SchPpr; College; Teaching.

DUFFIELD, Arnold; Lineville Clio HS; Lineville, IA; VPSophCls; VPJrCls; HonRl; StuCncl; SchPpr; Bsbl; Bsktbl; Trk; CchngActv; IMSpt; College.

DUFFIELD, Sue E; Malta HS; Malta, IL; 2/37 Band; CncrtBnd; HonRl; LitMag; MrchBnd; NHS; NatlMeritCmnd; PepBnd; SchPl; StuCncl; 4-H; LetterTrk; Chrldr; Bradley Univ; Mathematics.

DUFFIN, Scott R; Downers Grove So HS; Downers Grove, IL; 1/800 HonRl; JrNHS; NHS; NatlMeritSF; PresYthFlsp; FrCl; LetterBsktbl; Ftbl; KiwanAwd; College; Science.

DUFFITT, Rebecca; Lapel HS; Anderson, IN; 12/74 Band; HonRl; NHS; SchMus; SptEdYrbk; 4-H; FFA; SpnCl; GAA; Purdue U.

DUFFLE, Alan A; Pomona HS; Pomona, KS; PresFrshCls; PresSophCls; PresJrCls; PresSrCls; Band; CmntyWkr; CncrtBnd; HonRl; MrchBnd; TchrAde; Bsbl; Bsktbl; Ftbl; Trk; Kansas State University.

DUFFNER, Barbara J; Elizabeth Seton HS; Thornton, IL; 4/252 HonRl; NHS; NatlMeritFnl; RptrYrbk; RptrSchPpr; Purdue Univ; Electrical Engineering.

DUFFY, Deborah J; Humboldt HS; Humboldt, IA; Band; CncrtBnd; HonRl; MrchBnd; Orch; PepBnd; StuCncl; Yrbk; EdSchPpr; CaptBsktbl; LetterTrk; Iowa State Univ; Commercial Art.

DUFFY, Kathleen A; Ryan HS; Omaha, NE; SchMus; PpCl; Creighton Univ; Nursing.

DUFFY, Kevin J; Brother Rice HS; Chicago, IL; ChrhWkr; CmntyWkr; HonRl; OffAde; FDA; SecKeyCl; U Of Ill; Veterinary Md.

DUFFY, Lora M; Schaumburg HS; Roselle, IL; ChrhWkr; HonRl; HospAde; LitMag; PresNHS; NatlMeritCmnd; Quill&Scroll; StuCncl; SchPpr; FNA; Marquette Univ; Nursing.

DUFFY, Mary P; Queen Of Peace HS; Chicago, IL; LitMag; NatlMeritSF; PolWkr; SchPl; Yrbk;.

DUFFY, Patrick; Stanley County HS; Fort Pierre, SD; 12/55 PolWkr; SchPl; StuCncl; StuGov; SchPpr; SpnCl; PpCl; Ftbl; Navy; Lawyer.

DUFFY, Tama M; Westhope HS; Westhope, ND; SecTrsJrCls; Band; Chr; DrmMjrt; HonRl; StuCncl; 4-H; PpCl; Trk; Chrldr; U Of Nd St.

DUFFY, Terry M; St Mary HS; Burlington, WI; Chrs; Yrbk; VPPpCl; Trk; AFS; Col; Dramitic.

DUFOE, Penny A; Kearney HS; Kearney, MO; 10/80 Chrs; DrlTm; HonRl; JrNHS; NHS; SchPl; FrCl; RusCl; PpCl; Chrldr; College; Forestry.

DUFORT, Julie A; Mason HS; Leslie, MI; 28/233 JrNHS; NHS; PpCl; College; Interior Design.

DUFRANE, Jane; Craig Sr HS; Janesville, WI; 68/507 ALAGirlsSt; HonRl; StuCncl; YthFlsp; RptrYrbk; Swmmng; Tennis; Chrldr; JAAwd; CitAwd; Univ Of Wi; Secondary Ed.

DUFT, Mary M; Greenville HS; Greenville, IL; 1/183 ALAGirlsSt; SecBand; TreasChrs; NHS; SchMus; SchPl; StuCncl; PresLatCl; LetterTennis; GAA; College.

DUGAN, Brenda K; Cadillac Sr HS; Cadillac, MI; 4/300 Band; Chr; CncrtBnd; HonRl; MrchBnd; NHS; Olivet College; Music.

DUGAN, David A; Oak Park HS; Kansas City, MO; Band; CncrtBnd; HonRl; NHS; Orch; PepBnd; SctActv; FrCl; Bsbl; LetterFtbl; Trk; LetterWrstlng; IMSpt; College; Teach.

DUGAN, Rhonda J; Bishop Ryan HS; Mafb, ND; ChrhWkr; HonRl; HospAde; JrNHS; OffAde; Business School.

DUGAN, Tom M; St Marys HS; Oneill, NE; SchMus; StuCncl; LetterFtbl; IMSpt; College; Professional.

DUGANITZ, Diane K; Northeast HS; Lincoln, NE; 4/550 Chr; ChrhWkr; HonRl; PolWkr; SchMus; SchPl; StuCncl; TchrAde; PresPpCl; Chrldr; Concordia Teachers Col; Elementary Teacher.

DUGGAN, Lori S; Central Valley HS; Buxton, ND; 2/24 CncrtBnd; HonRl; StuCncl; EdYrBk; FHA; PpCl; Univ Of North Dakota; Business.

DUGGAN, Lynn M; Central Valley HS; Buxton, ND; 2/24 PresJrCls; Chrs; CncrtBnd; HonRl; TreasStuCncl; Yrbk; PresFHA; PresPpCl; Trk; LetterChrldr; University; Elem Education.

DUGGAN, Paula S; Lake Orion HS; Lake Orion, MI; 2/334 ChrhWkr; HonRl; NHS; OffAde; TchrAde; YthFlsp; Oakland University; Veterinarian.

DUGGER, Douglas A; Flora HS; Flora, IL; PresSrCls; HonRl; StuCncl; 4-H; SpnCl; LetterBsbl; Bsktbl; LetterFtbl; EldAwd; 4-HAwd; Indiana Univ; Hospital Adm.

DUGUAY, Pat T; Baraga HS; Baraga, MI; VPFrshCls; VPSophCls; VPJrCls; ChrhWkr; CmntyWkr; HonRl; SancSoc; StuCncl; StuGov; Bsktbl; College; Professional.

DUHAN, Michael R; Tecumseh HS; Tecumseh, MI; TrsFrshCls; ChrhWkr; OffAde; StuCncl; Bsktbl; Ftbl; CaptTrk; IMSpt; Mi Tech; Civil Engineering.

DUHR, Arleen R; Riverdale HS; Blue River, WI; AFS; Chrs; ChrhWkr; HonRl; Mdrgl; NHS; Yrbk; FHA; SciCl; Voational; Fashion.

DUITSMAN, Cynthia J; Forrestville Vly HS; Forreston, IL; 9/76 Chrs; DrmMjrt; HonRl; MrchBnd; NHS; StuCncl; RptrYrbk; LetterTrk; GAA; PresAwd;.

DUJAN, Michael J; Morton Sr HS; Hammond, IN; 11/529 HonRl; NHS; TchrAde; SciCl; Tennis; Coll; Ag Sci.

DUKE, Dennis; Madison HS; Madison, IN; 24/300 HonRl; NHS; GerCl; College; Math,science.

DUKE, James A; East Richland HS; Olney, IL; 10/260 ALBoysSt; Band; Chrs; ChrhWkr; CmntyWkr; CncrtBnd; IntrClCncl; LbryAde; MrchBnd; NHS; Orch; PepBnd; PolWkr; SchMus; StuCncl; University; French.

DUKE, Kimberly K; Marion HS; Marion, KS; 1/55 VPFrshCls; Chrs; CncrtBnd; HonRl; SchMus; StuCncl; SecYthFlsp; VPFHA; TreasPpCl; Collegef Political Science.

DUKES, Richard A; Crispus Attucks HS; Indianapolis, IN; HonRl; NHS; StuCncl; LetterTennis; Purdue Univ; Electrical Engineer.

DUKICH, Michael P; Coon Rapids HS; Blaine, MN; HonRl; JrNHS; LbryAde; NHS; TchrAde; SchPpr; Bsktbl; Ftbl; Tennis; IMSpt; Univ Of Minn; Mechanical Engineering.

DULANEY, Cheryl; Parkway West HS; Ballwin, MO; Chr; DrlTm; SchMus; StuGov; Twrl; PpCl; Chrldr; PPFtbl; Se Mo St Univ; Spec Ed.

DULCERSCHEIN, Craig S; Oregon Consolidated HS; Oregon, WI; Band; CncrtBnd; DrmBgl; MrchBnd; VPFrshCls; PepBnd; PresFrshCls; RptrYrbk; Yrbk; Barkee Col ;music.

DULEMBA, Gerard A; Benedictine HS; Detroit, MI; HonRl; NHS; RptrYrbk; EdYrBk; SptEdYrbk; RptrSchPpr; Univ Of Mich; Communications.

DULEY, Sarah J; Metropolis Community HS; Metropolis, IL; PresJrCls; HonRl; NHS; NatlThespSoc; SchPl; StuCncl; 4-H; SpnCl; MthCl; Chrldr; University Of Kentucky; Pharmacy.

DULGAR, Billie J; Brazil HS; Brazil, IN; 3/198 HonRl; NHS; Quill&Scroll; StuCncl; Yrbk; SpnCl; PpCl; DARAwd; EldAwd; PresAwd; U Of Mich; Cirminal Law.

DULGAR, Kenneth C; Brazil Sr HS; Brazil, IN; 5/180 ALBoysSt; Band; CncrtBnd; DrmMjrt; MrchBnd; NHS; KeyCl; LetterTrk; Gote College; Teach Music.

DULIN, Brian K; Leavenworth HS; Leavenworth, KS; ALBoysSt; Band; Chr; Chrl; Chrs; CmntyWkr; DrlTm; MrchBnd; Bsktbl; Ftbl; IMSpt; AmLegAwd; College; Accounting.

DULIN, Joseph W; Quincy Sr HS; Quincy, IL; PresFrshCls; Chr; HonRl; Mdrgl; NatlThespSoc; SchMus; SchPl; SctActv; Univ Of Indiana; Music.

DULING, Nancy J; Rich Central HS; Olympia Fields, IL; 30/400 Chr; HonRl; NHS; SchMus; FrCl; PpCl; Univ Of Illinois; Business.

DULL, Sharon; Platteville HS; Platteville, WI; Chr; HospAde; TchrAde; SciCl; Navy.

DULLARD, John P; Minooka HS; Minooka, IL; 31/108 HonRl; OffAde; SchAde; SchPl; TchrAde; Bsbl; Bsktbl; Ftbl; Wrstlng; IMSpt; Winona St Clg; Accounting.

DULLUM, Pamela I; Proviso West HS; Berkeley, IL; 32/948 HonRl; NatlMeritCmnd; SchPl; PresFTA; Univ Of Minnesota; Civil Engineer.

DUMAS, Cynthia; Norfolk Senior HS; Norfolk, NE; Band; ChrhWkr; CmntyWkr; CncrtBnd; DrlTm; HonRl; MrchBnd; YthFlsp; FrCl; PpCl; Coll; Psych.

DUMAS, Frederick J; Holly Sr HS; Holly, MI; 9/227 HonRl; LbryAde; SecNHS; LetterFtbl; LetterTrk; Michigan State Univ; Conservationist.

DUMAS, Mary; Lee M Thurston HS; Detroit, MI; CmntyWkr; HonRl; TchrAde; Univ Of Mich; Zoology.

DUMBECK, Susan M; Frazee HS; Frazee, MN; HonRl; SpnCl; PpCl;.

DUMMER, Susan K; Aberdeen Central HS; Aberdeen, SD; 26/423 AFS; Chr; Chrs; NatlFornLg; VPFrshCls; SchMus; SchPl; StuGov; GAA; NCTE; U Of Iowa; Psychology.

DUMMIT, Stuart E; Wentzville HS; Wentzville, MO; Band; ChrhWkr; CncrtBnd; HonRl; Mdrgl; MrchBnd; SchPl; FrCl; Coll; English Or Music.

DUMOND, Leeann M; Greenville HS; Greenville, MI; 25/220 Band; CncrtBnd; HonRl; MrchBnd; OffAde; FrCl; GAA; IMSpt; 4-HAwd; Alma College.

DUMPERT, Mark A; Eastbrook HS; Marion, IN; 40/169 CmntyWkr; JA; JCC; NatlMeritSchl; StuCncl; YthLg; FBLA; LatCl; TIMEAwd; Business School; Accountant.

DUMSKY, Coleen M; St Marys HS; Sugar Creek, MO; SecSrCls; HonRl; NHS; SchMus; SctActv; Sdlty; StuCncl; Yrbk; PpCl; Chrldr; College; Vocation.

DUNAISKY, Andrea S; Hermantown HS; Duluth, MN; 1/137 SecSophCls; Chr; HonRl; NatlFornLg; NHS; StuCncl; EdYrBk; PpCl; Chrldr; Gustavus Adolphs Clg; Medicine.

DUNAJCIK, Mark D; Mehlville HS; St Louis, MO; Chr; Chrs; ChrhWkr; CmntyWkr; CncrtBnd; HonRl; MrchBnd; NHS; Orch; SchMus; College; Professional Musician.

DUNAWAY, Stephen L; Farmington HS; Farmington, MO; 22/233 ALBoysSt; CncrtBnd; HonRl; MrchBnd; NHS; TchrAde; YthFlsp; PresFFA; PresSciCl; Univ; Law.

DUNBAR, Dana; Tecumseh HS; Tecumseh, MI; 19/240 Band; NHS; NatlMeritSF; SchMus; SchPl; StuCncl; YthFlsp; YthLg; KeyCl; Western Mich U; Business Administration.

DUNBAR, John J; Barrington HS; Barrington, IL; 63/654 NHS; NatlMeritCmnd; EdSchPpr; CaptTrk; Notre Dame; Journalism.

DUNBAR, Tim M; Clarke Comm HS; Osceola, IA; 17/110 ChrhWkr; PolWkr; StuCncl; Pres4-H; FFA; FTA; Bsktbl; Ftbl; Trk; 4-HAwd; College; Extension Service.

DUNBAR, Vicki M; Dekalb HS; Dekalb, IL; 17/350 HonRl; NHS; Orch; SchMus; YthFlsp; Sec4-H; FrCl; University; Physical Therapy.

DUNCAN, Cindy S; Dixon R 1 HS; Dixon, MO; Band; HonRl; OffAde; SchPl; StuCncl; FBLA; VPFHA; FTA; PpCl; College; Home Economics.

DUNCAN, Daniel M; Cranbrook HS; Lake Orion, MI; ChrhWkr; NatlMeritCmnd; PresYthFlsp; KeyCl; LetterTrk; LetterWrstlng; Kalamazoo Clge; Health Sci.

DUNCAN, Deborah A; St Paul/kennedy HS; Chicago, IL; Chrs; HonRl; HospAde; NHS; SchPpr; FrCl; GAA; IMSpt; Loyola;medicine.

DUNCAN, Denise M; Lake Central HS; St Johnd, IN; VPFrshCls; PresSophCls; HospAde; NHS; NatlThespSoc; Quill&Scroll; SchPl; StuGov; EdYrBk; FrCl; College; Journalism.

DUNCAN, Dianna S; Cassville HS; Cassville, MO; 17/103 Band; ChrhWkr; NHS; StuCncl; RptrSchPpr; PresFTA; PpCl; LetterBsktbl; LetterTrk; CaptChrldr; CaptIMSpt; College; Physical Educ.

DUNCAN, Gary E; Linn Co R4 HS; Meadville, MO; PresFrshCls; TrsSophCls; Band; Chr; CncrtBnd; HonRl; JrNHS; MrchBnd; NHS; PepBnd; Hannibal Lagrange; Music.

DUNCAN, Howard C; Gordon Technical HS; Chicago, IL; 76/584 HonRl; StuCncl; StuGov; Ftbl; IMSpt; Univ; Pro.

DUNCAN, James R; Santa Fe Trail HS; Overbrook, KS; 18/84 PresJrCls; ALBoysSt; Chrs; ChrhWkr; SchMus; SchPl; StuCncl; TchrAde; YthFlsp; RptrSchPpr; SptEdSchPpr; Bsbl; CaptBsktbl; CaptFtbl; Baker Univ; Teacher.

DUNCAN, Janice E; Superior HS; Superior, NE; Chr; ChrhWkr; CmntyWkr; HonRl; LbryAde; YthFlsp; RptrYrbk; Yrbk; 4-H;.

DUNCAN, Judy; Homewood Flossmoor Hs; Homewood, IL; 102/920 Band; ChrhWkr; HonRl; LitMag; MrchBnd; NatlThespSoc; PepBnd; SchPl; SctActv; YthFlsp; Bradley U; Speech Pathologist.

DUNCAN, Kenneth H; David H Hickman HS; Columbia, MO; HonRl; NHS; NatlMeritSF; SctActv; LetterSwmmng; LetterTrk; IMSpt; GodCntryAwd; Univ; Wildlife.

DUNCAN, Lesley M; Bradley Bourbonnais Comm HS; Bourbonnais, IL; Band; CncrtBnd; HonRl; HospAde; MrchBnd; PepBnd; 4-H; Northern Illinois Univ; Nursing.

DUNCAN, Lisa M; University HS; Normal, IL; SecChrs; HonRl; NatlThespSoc; Orch; StuCncl; YthFlsp; PresSpnCl;.

DUNCAN, Matthew J; Hickman Mills HS; Kansas City, MO; ALBoysSt; Band; ChrhWkr; CncrtBnd; HonRl; PresJrNHS; PresSciCl; Bsktbl; LetterFtbl; LetterTrk; Univ; Profesional.

DUNCAN, Maureen; Scecina Memorial HS; Indianapolis, IN; CmntyWkr; HonRl; TchrAde; SpnCl; Iupui; Health Field.

DUNCAN, Pamela J; Winchester HS; Roodhouse, IL; ChrhWkr; HonRl; HospAde; SchAde; Yrbk; 4-H; FrCl; PpCl; AmLegAwd; Gem City Clge Quincy Il; Business.

DUNCAN, Randy C; Arkansas City HS; Arkansas City, KS; 32/184 VPFrshCls; ALBoysSt; ChrhWkr; HonRl; PolWkr; Quill&Scroll; TchrAde; Yrbk; FTA; Baker University; Law.

DUNCAN, Robin D; Adel HS; Adel, IA; Chr; ChrhWkr; HonRl; Quill&Scroll; RptrYrbk; Yrbk; RptrSchPpr; FrCl; Bsktbl; Brigham Young Univ; Law.

DUNCAN, Ronald J; Anna Jonesboro Comm HS; Anna, IL; Chrs; ChrhWkr; CncrtBnd; NatlFornLg; SctActv; LatCl; SciCl; Ftbl; Glf; Southern Illinois Univ; Biology.

DUNCAN, Ruth A; Mexico HS; Mexico, MO; PresSrCls; Band; CncrtBnd; MrchBnd; SctActv; StuCncl; Yrbk; LatCl; PpCl; PPFtbl; Coll Or Univ; Social Studies.

DUNCAN, Scott P; Newton Community HS; Newton, IL; Chrs; HonRl; Mdrgl; SchMus; LetterFtbl; Glf; Trk; IMSpt; University; Chemical Engineering.

DUNCAN, Steve W; Savannah R 3 HS; Savannah, MO; Band; ChrhWkr; CncrtBnd; MrchBnd; PepBnd; TchrAde; TreasFFA; Business School; Bank Work.

DUNCAN, Susan E; Southridge HS; Huntingburg, IN; Band; Chr; Chrs; ChrhWkr; CncrtBnd; DrlTm; MrchBnd; PepBnd; SchMus; SchPl; In State U; Dental Technician.

DUNCAN, Terri L; Williamsville HS; Williamsville, IL; 1/42 ChrhWkr; CmntyWkr; HonRl; NHS; NatlMeritCmnd; PolWkr; SchPl; TchrAde; YthFlsp; RptrYrbk; Ftbl; Trk; BttyCrckrAwd; University; International Law.

DUNCAN, Timothy J; Hill City HS; Jacobson, MN; TrsFrshCls; ChrhWkr; HonRl; SchPl; StuCncl; YthFlsp; Yrbk; SchPpr; CaptCaptFtbl; Brainerd Comm College; Ar Teacher.

DUNCKLEE, June E; Larimore HS; Emerado, ND; 2/66 HonRl; StuCncl; SpnCl; Univ Of No Dakota; Medicine.

DUNCKLEE, June E; Larimore HS; Emerack, ND; HonRl; StuCncl; VPSpnCl; IMSpt; U Of North Dakota; Nursing.

DUNFORD, Bradley J; Langdon Public HS; Langdon, ND; 8/140 ALBoysSt; HonRl; GerCl; Trk; U; Navy.

DUNFORD, Kevin J; Milton Public HS; Milton, ND; 1/12 VPSrCls; StuCncl; TchrAde; EdYrBk; RptrSchPpr; EdSchPpr; 4-H; FFA; PpCl; LetterBsktbl; Ndsu Fargo; Health Serv Mgnt.

DUNGEY, Denise M; Wethersfield HS; Kewanee, IL; 10/64 ALBoysSt; Chrs; HonRl; SchMus; RptrYrbk; RptrSchPpr; FrCl; PpCl; College; Journalism.

DUNGEY, Paula S; Eisenhower HS; Saginaw, MI; 25/360 PresSrCls; HonRl; NHS; PolWkr; SctActv; StuCncl; StuGov; RptrYrbk; EdSchPpr; Central Michigan Univ; Mathematics.

DUNHAM, Brian; Highland HS; Chesterfield, IN; 51/298 SecFrshCls; PresSophCls; PresJrCls; SecTrsSrCls; Univ Of Hawaii; Doctor.

DUNHAM, Dianna L; Elk Point Public HS; Elk Point, SD; HonRl; SchPl; PpCl; GAA; Col; Computer Sci.

DUNHAM, Laurel S; Westville HS; Danville, IL; TrsJrCls; Band; HonRl; NHS; SchPl; StuCncl; SpnCl; Bsbl; Chrldr; GAA; Univ; Bs In Nursing.

DUNHAM, Thomas S; Valley City HS; Valley City, ND; 1/150 HonRl; NHS; CaptBsktbl; CaptFtbl; Univ Of North Dakota; Optometry.

DUNKEL, Georgia L; Mt Carmel HS; Mt Carmel, IL; 2/190 VPFrshCls; SecSophCls; SecSrCls; Chr; Chrs; SchPl; TchrAde; Yrbk; 4-H; PpCl; GAA; AmLegAwd; College; Liberal Arts.

DUNKEL, Micki R; Broken Bow HS; Broken Bow, NE; HonRl; SctActv; RptrYrbk; RptrSchPpr; PpCl; Chrldr; College; Professional Med.

DUNKEL, Norbert W; Ashton HS; Ashton, IL; 7/40 PresSrCls; ALBoysSt; HonRl; NHS; RptrSchPpr; Bsbl; Bsktbl; CaptFtbl; Trk; AmLegAwd; BauchLmbAwd; S Illinois Univ; Engineering.

DUNKEL, Patricia R; Aberdeen Central HS; Aberdeen, SD; Chrs; ChrhWkr; HonRl; JrNHS; Chrldr; CitAwd; Brookings Sdsu; Pro.

DUNKER, Debbie L; Sparta HS; Evansville, IL; ChrhWkr; HonRl; NHS; Yrbk; FNA; Bellville Area Clg; Data Processing.

DUNKER, Sandra M; Schuyler Central HS; Schuyler, NE; Band; Chrl; CmntyWkr; DrmMjrt; HospAde; NHS; StuCncl; YthFlsp; Trk; College; Liberal Arts.

DUNKIN, John R; St Mary HS; Kenosha, WI; SecTrsSrCls; HonRl; LbryAde; OffAde; StuCncl; StuGov; Bsktbl; Ftbl; Glf; AmLegAwd; Univ Wisc; Business.

DUNKIN, Robert D; Kimball County HS; Kimball, NE; Band; Chr; CncrtBnd; HonRl; Mdrgl; MrchBnd; PepBnd; SchMus; SctActv; TchrAde; Bsbl; Voc Tech School; Construction.

DUNKIN, Susan J; Pella Community HS; Pella, IA; AFS; Chrs; HonRl; MrchBnd; NatlThespSoc; Quill&Scroll; StuCncl; EdSchPpr; LetterBsktbl; LetterTrk; Central Col; Art Teacher.

DUNKLE, David L; Hinckley Big Rock HS; Big Rock, IL; ALBoysSt; Chrs; HonRl; NatlFornLg; SchMus; SchPl; Yrbk; LatCl; SciCl; Law.

DUNKLE, Sharon K; Hinckley Big Rock HS; Big Rock, IL; SecSophCls; ALAGirlsSt; Chrs; HonRl; HospAde; SchMus; Yrbk; Socr; GAA; Waukonsee Comm College; Elemen Sch.

DUNKMANN, Debra A; Orchard Farm HS; St Charles, MO; ChrhWkr; HonRl; JA; LbryAde; OffAde; 4-H; FBLA; PpCl; 4-HAwd; Work.

DUNLAP, Ann; Norfolk Public HS; Norfolk, NE; 2/306 Band; HonRl; LitMag; VPNHS; NatlMeritSF; Orch; SchMus; FrCl; MthCl; PpCl; U Of Ne; Professional Medicine.

DUNLAP, Charlotte E; Community HS; Marengo, IL; 2/179 HonRl; MrchBnd; NatlMeritCmnd; NatlThespSoc; OffAde; GerCl; Millikin Univ; Business Adm.

DUNLAP, Cheryl L; Hutsonville HS; Hutsonville, IL; 3/42 ChrhWkr; HonRl; LbryAde; NHS; Yrbk; FHA; SecFNA; PpCl; Coll; Bookkeeper.

DUNLAP, David; Whiteland HS; Greenwood, IN; 38/184 4-H; FFA; KeyCl; PpCl; Bsktbl; 4-HAwd; KiwanAwd; Purdue Univ; Ag Economics.

DUNLAP, Diane L; Urbandale HS; Urbandale, IA; 58/245 Chrs; ChrhWkr; HonRl; NatlMeritSF; PolWkr; SctActv; TchrAde; FTA; Univ; Teacher.

DUNLAP, Mary L; Mendota HS; Mendota, IL; CncrtBnd; MrchBnd; SchPl; Augustana College; Liberal Arts.

DUNLAP, Terry J; Maquoketa Valley HS; Hopkinton, IA; 25/111 HonRl; NHS; RedCrAde; SchPl; TchrAde; RusCl; MthCl; PpCl; SciCl; Tennis; Univ Of Iowa; Astronomy.

DUNLAVY, Katherine E; Davis County Comm HS; Bloomfield, IA; CmntyWkr; HonRl; HospAde; OffAde; PolWkr; StuCncl; StuGov; RptrYrbk; RptrSchPpr; 4-H; Trade School; Professional.

DUNLEVY, Amy J; Fairfield HS; Fairfield, IA; SecFrshCls; VPJrCls; ChrhWkr; HonRl; NHS; Orch; StuCncl; LetterBsktbl; LetterTrk; Chrldr; Coll; Phy Ed.

DUNLOP, Marguerite B; Proviso West HS; Westchester, IL; 19/1198 Chrs; CmntyWkr; HonRl; NHS; NatlMeritSF; PolWkr; StuCncl; Yrbk; GerCl; Triton College.

DUNN, Alice M; Mattoon Sr HS; Mattoon, IL; 7/411 SecBand; CncrtBnd; HonRl; MrchBnd; NHS; PepBnd; PpCl; GAA; Eastern Ill Univ; Zoology.

DUNN, Cheryl L; Civic Memorial HS; Bethalto, IL; 22/214 HonRl; HospAde; NHS; SchPl; StuCncl; RptrYrbk; FrCl; PpCl; College; Medical Lab Tech.

DUNN, Christopher L; Benet Acad; Downers Grove, IL; HonRl; NatlMeritFnl; NatlMeritSF; LetterBsbl; LetterFtbl; LetterTrk; IMSpt; Univ; Prof.

DUNN, Daniel L; Newell HS; Vale, SD; 10/50 ALBoysSt; HonRl; NHS; SchPl; TchrAde; 4-H; FFA; CaptFtbl; 4-HAwd; VoiceDemAwd; College; Farmer.

DUNN, Duane M; Rolla HS; Richfield, KS; 3/17 Band; HonRl; PresStuCncl; PresYthFlsp; SptEdYrbk; SptEdSchPpr; Pres4-H; LetterBsktbl; LetterFtbl; LetterTrk; DanFAwd; 4-HAwd; Colby Comm College; Agriculture.

DUNN, Holly J; Northern Heights HS; Emporia, KS; ALAGirlsSt; Band; Chrs; CncrtBnd; HonRl; LbryAde; MrchBnd; PepBnd; SchMus; SchPl; 4-H; FBLA; College.

DUNN, Jean E; Niles HS; Niles, MI; 71/361 ChrhWkr; HonRl; PresHospAde; SchMus; YthFlsp; Yrbk; IMSpt; Mich St U; Journalism.

DUNN, Kevin R; Northrop HS; Fort Wayne, IN; 73/568 HonRl; Quill&Scroll; TchrAde; SchPpr; Indiana Univ; Lawyer.

DUNN, Kristen K; Mission Valley HS; Eskridge, KS; ALAGirlsSt; Band; DrmMjrt; NHS; PolWkr; SctActv; 4-H; FHA; LetterTrk; LionAwd; College; Music Therapy.

DUNN, Lawrence A; Fitzgerald HS; Warren, MI; HonRl; NHS; PolWkr; SctActv; FSA; FrCl; CitAwd; University; Medical Field.

DUNN, Lloyd J; Irwin Community HS; Harlan, IA; Chrs; HonRl; NatlMeritSchl; SchPl; RptrYrbk; Yrbk; RptrSchPpr; SchPpr; University.

DUNN, Loren S; Holy Name Cathedral HS; Chicago, IL; 9/135 HonRl; Massachusetts Inst Of Tech; Computer Eng.

DUNN, Mary E; Marian HS; Omaha, NE; 23/162 SecTrsJrCls; Chrs; HonRl; JA; NHS; NatlMeritSF; Sdlty; PresStuCncl; FrCl; JAAwd; Colorado St Univ; Home Economics.

DUNN, Nancy L; Marshall HS; Mashall, MI; 16/255 Chr; ChrhWkr; HonRl; JA; OffAde; YthFlsp; RptrYrbk; 4-H; LatCl; Kcc; Microbiologist.

DUNN, Pamela K; Warren HS; Warren, MI; 2/450 Chrs; HonRl; NHS; SchMus; EdYrBk; DARAwd; Wayne State U; Journalism.

DUNN, Randy L; Crete HS; Crete, NE; 26/142 HonRl; SchMus; SchPl; StuGov; FBLA; FFA; Bsbl; LetterBsktbl; IMSpt; College; Athletic Trainer.

DUNN, Sandra J; Sioux County HS; Harrison, NE; 4/18 PresFrshCls; PresSophCls; PresJrCls; SecSrCls; HonRl; NatlFornLg; NHS; FHA; LetterTrk; Chrldr; College.

DUNN, Sara A; Lincoln HS; Vincennes, IN; 55/328 HonRl; FBLA; Indiana Univ; Mathematics.

DUNN, Steven L; Alma HS; Alma, NE; Band; Chrs; HonRl; MrchBnd; PresYthFlsp; Bsbl; Bsktbl; Ftbl; Trk; CchngActv; Univ Of Nebraska; Law.

DUNN, Susan; Raytown HS; Raytown, MO; Chr; NHS; NatlThespSoc; SchPl; Coll; Theatre.

DUNN, Terri S; Carlinville HS; Carlinville, IL; 10/161 HonRl; JrNHS; SchPl; SctActv; StuCncl; FHA; SpnCl; PpCl; Southern Illinois Univ; Banking.

DUNN, Thomas B; Deep River Millersburg HS; Millersburg, IA; 2/24 VPSophCls; PresJrCls; Band; CncrtBnd; HonRl; MrchBnd; NHS; PepBnd; SchPl; StuCncl; StuGov; LetterBsbl; LetterBsktbl; IMSpt; University Of Iowa.

DUNNAWAY, Cynthia R; Holton HS; Holton, MI; 5/55 Band; CmntyWkr; HonRl; NHS; PepBnd; StuGov; 4-H; PpCl; LetterBsktbl; GAA; PPFtbl; 4-HAwd; College; Mathematics.

DUNNE, George W; Thornton Fractional South HS; Lansing, IL; 83/552 HonRl; JrNHS; NHS; College; Chemistry.

DUNNE, Michael; Saint Viator Hs; Arlington Hts, IL; 67/254 HonRl; SchMus; SchPl; TchrAde; Yrbk; SchPpr; SpnCl;.

DUNNE, Timothy N; Brookfield East HS; Brookfield, WI; 9/520 VPSophCls; TrsJrCls; ALBoysSt; HonRl; JA; NHS; NatlMeritCmnd; TreasStuCncl; StuGov; TreasKeyCl; Stanford; Engineering.

DUNNEBACK, Thomas; Kenowa Hills HS; Grand Rapids, MI; 14/230 ALBoysSt; HonRl; SchPl; StuCncl; TchrAde; EdSchPpr; Grand Rapids Junior College; Math.

DUNNETTE, Jan; Kenowa Hills HS; Grand Rapids, MI; SecFrshCls; SecSrCls; ChrhWkr; CncrtBnd; HonRl; MrchBnd; NHS; StuCncl; Twrl; DARAwd; Davenport College; Legal Sec.

DUNNIGAN, Patty J; Johnston City HS; Johnston City, IL; VPJrCls; HonRl; HospAde; OffAde; SchMus; MthCl; PpCl; SciCl; CaptChrldr; GAA; Air Force; Art.

DUNNING, Douglas K; Blair HS; Blair, NE; 2/136 Chr; HonRl; NHS; NatlMeritCmnd; EdYrBk; Yrbk; Bsktbl; Kearney State College; Business Admin.

DUNNING, Robin J; Northridge HS; Middlebury, IN; 2/117 HonRl; OffAde; SctActv; SpnCl; Purdue Univ; Veterinary Med.

DUNNINGTON, Rebecca L; Ridgeway HS; Ridgeway, MO; 1/18 TrsFrshCls; SecSophCls; Band; HonRl; JrNHS; MrchBnd; PepBnd; SchPl; StuCncl; RptrYrbk; RptrSchPpr; Bsktbl; Trk; Chrldr; University; Business.

DUNSCOMBE, Laura A; Humboldt HS; Humboldt, IA; Band; Chr; Chrl; CncrtBnd; HonRl; MrchBnd; SchMus; SchPl; Twrl; CaptChrldr; IMSpt; PPFtbl; 4-HAwd; College; Professional.

DUNSCOMBE, Roxanne; Fairfield Community HS; Fairfield, IL; Chr; Chrs; SchMus; SchPpr; 4-H; FHA; SpnCl; SciCl; 4-HAwd; College; Fashion Designer.

DUNSEITH, Les; Atlanta C3 HS; Atlanta, MO; PresFrshCls; ALBoysSt; HonRl; StuCncl; SciCl; Bsbl; Trk; CchngActv; U; Prof.

DUNSKI, Barbara J; Thomas Kelly HS; Chicago, IL; Band; TreasChrs; SecCncrtBnd; HonRl; MrchBnd; PepBnd; SchMus; SchPl; Yrbk; GAA; College; Architecture.

DUNSMOOR, Debra Y; Markesan HS; Fairwater, WI; 10/110 Band; Chr; Chrl; Chrs; CncrtBnd; DrlTm; HonRl; JrNHS; MrchBnd; IMSpt; College; Professional.

DUNSMORE, Elizabeth A; Wayland Union HS; Wayland, MI; 3/150 CncrtBnd; HonRl; MrchBnd; NHS; NatlMeritSchl; SchPl; UNYO; YthFlsp; YthLg; EldAwd; Grand Valley St Col; Nursing.

DUNSMORE, Karen S; Ida HS; Ida, MI; CncrtBnd; HonRl; MrchBnd; NHS; PepBnd; StuGov; PpCl; Trk; IMSpt; PPFtbl; Adrian Clge; Elem Ed.

DUNSMORE, Sherman L; Ida HS; Ida, MI; NatlMeritFnl; StuGov; LetterBsbl; LetterBsktbl; LetterFtbl; Clge; Phys Ed.

DUPRE, Cynthia T; Centennial HS; Hugo, MN; AFS; ChrhWkr; HonRl; NHS; TchrAde; FHA; PpCl; GAA; Univ.

DUPUIS, Cheryl R; Carrollton HS; Saginaw, MI; 7/151 TrsFrshCls; ChrhWkr; CmntyWkr; HonRl; SecNHS; TchrAde; LetterBsbl; LetterBsktbl; Delta Col; Commercial Art.

DUQUAINE, Bill D; Highland HS; Anderson, IN; HonRl; 4-H; LatCl; LetterFtbl; LetterTrk; OptClAwd; PresAwd;.

DUQUAINE, Marie A; Kingsford HS; Kingsford, MI; Band; ChrhWkr; CAP; HonRl; HospAde; MrchBnd; PepBnd; SchPl; FNA; IMSpt;.

DUQUETTE, Claire; Bayfield HS; Bayfield, WI; SecTrsSophCls; SecJrCls; Band; Chr; ChrhWkr; SchMus; SecStuCncl; YthFlsp; EdYrBk; RptrSchPpr; College; Liberal Arts.

DURACK, Gary; Mt Vernon Hs; Fortville, IN; 7/168 Band; CncrtBnd; HonRl; MrchBnd; PepBnd; SchPpr; FFA; Bsbl; Glf; Ftbl; Academic U; Math Or Science.

DURAN, Andrew C; Montabella HS; Edmore, MI; Band; HonRl; MrchBnd; NHS; PepBnd; TreasStuCncl; RptrYrbk; SchPpr; Michigan State Univ; Engineering.

DURAN, Edward; Clear Lake HS; Clear Lake, IA; AFS; HonRl; SchAde; YthFlsp; Niacc Junior College; Pre Med.

DU RAND, Carole M; Oakes Public HS; Oakes, ND; 4/61 Band; ChrhWkr; CmntyWkr; CncrtBnd; HonRl; MrchBnd; NHS; PepBnd; LetterBsktbl; LetterTrk; GAA; AmLegAwd; CitAwd; North Dakota St Univ; Zoologist.

DURANT, Joanne M; Central HS; Detroit, MI; 10/250 Aud/Vis; Band; DrmMjrt; HonRl; MrchBnd; StuGov; Yrbk; SchPpr; PpCl; Trk; Mich State U; Criminal Justice.

DURANT, Larry W; Wellington HS; Wellington, KS; 18/158 ALBoysSt; Band; CncrtBnd; HonRl; MrchBnd; NatlFornLg; PepBnd; PolWkr; SctActv; LetterTrk; Kansas St Univ; Acct.

DURANT, Lynn A; Hamady HS; Flint, MI; 35/170 HonRl; Yrbk; SchPpr; LetterGlf; College; Banking.

DURAY, Dorothy J; Coon Rapids HS; Coon Rapids, MN; Chr; ChrhWkr; HonRl;.

DURAY, Michele; Whiting HS; Whiting, IN; StuCncl; RptrSchPpr; SchPpr; SpnCl; PpCl; LetterBsktbl; Tennis; Trk; GAA; Nursing School; Nursing.

DURBAHN, William; Stewartville HS; Stewartville, MN; 20/100 Chrs; HonRl; Mdrgl; SchMus; SchPl; YthFlsp; GerCl; Hamline Univ.

DURBIN, Charlie R; St Elmo HS; St Elmo, IL; VPSophCls; PresJrCls; PresSrCls; HonRl; NHS; StuCncl; Pres4-H; PresFFA; KeyCl; 4-HAwd; Siu.

DURBIN, Davjd S; Springfield HS; Springfield, IL; 60/575 Ftbl; Swmmng; Tennis; W Illinois Univ; Medicine.

DURBIN, Deirdre J; Lincoln Way HS; Mokena, IL; HonRl; NHS; No Illinois Univ; Nursing.

DURBIN, Edward M; North HS; Sioux City, IA; 28/316 HonRl; JA; LbryAde; OffAde; TchrAde; SchPpr; MthCl; Bell & Howell Schl; Electronic Mgmt.

DURBIN, Linda M; Abingdon Sr HS; Abingdon, IL; 30/93 HonRl; SchPl; TreasFHA; PpCl; Carl Sandberg Col; Secretary.

DURBIN, Mitzi K; Abingdon HS; Abingdon, IL; 15/103 HonRl; LbryAde; NHS; SchPl; SpnCl; PpCl; GAA; Northern Il U; Library Science.

DURBIN, Richard; Carlyle HS; Carlyle, IL; 36/138 TrsFrshCls; ChrhWkr; HonRl; Quill&Scroll; SctActv; StuCncl; RptrYrbk; RptrSchPpr; Univ Of Missouri; Basebal.

DURBIN, Terry R; Shelbyville HS; Shelbyville, IL; 11/133 ChrhWkr; HonRl; TreasNHS; VPFFA; Ftbl; Tennis; Lake Land College; Engineering.

DURBIN, Theresa; Northeast Nodaway Rv HS; Ravenwood, MO; 2/28 SecFrshCls; PresSophCls; VPJrCls; HonRl; NHS; RptrYrbk; PpCl; Bsktbl; CitAwd; College; Photography.

DURBOROW, Angie D; Fort Zumwalt HS; St Peters, MO; ChrhWkr; HonRl; NHS; SctActv; SchPpr; PpCl; Chrldr; GAA; PPFtbl; College; Professional.

DURCHHOLZ, Gary A; Mt Pulaski HS; Elkhart, IL; 6/105 VPFrshCls; TrsJrCls; HstSrCls; Band; ChrhWkr; CncrtBnd; DrlTm; DrmBgl; HonRl; JrNHS; MrchBnd; NatlCathMusEdAsoc; Bsbl; Bsktbl; College; Accountant.

DURDON, Eleanor M; Harrison HS; Harrison, MI; Aud/Vis; SecBand; SecCncrtBnd; HonRl; SecPepBnd; Yrbk; RptrSchPpr; FNA; Nursing.

DUREN, Cynthia A; Osage Comm HS; Osage, IA; Band; CmntyWkr; CncrtBnd; HonRl; MrchBnd; NHS; PepBnd; RptrYrbk; Yrbk; SchPpr; Univ Ia; Phy Therapy.

DURENE, Nancy; Holdingford Area Jr Sr HS; Holdingford, MN; ChrhWkr; CncrtBnd; HonRl; MrchBnd; NHS; PepBnd; TchrAde; SecYthFlsp; RptrYrbk; Yrbk; North Central Bible College; Missions.

DURGIN, Clinton W; Northern Heights HS; Americus, KS; 4/41 Chrs; ChrhWkr; HonRl; NHS; SchPl; LetterBsbl; Baker Coll; Physics.

DURHAM, Albert L; Peoria HS; Peoria, IL; NatlMeritSF; OffAde; LetterFtbl; LetterTrk; Wrstlng; IMSpt; GovHonPrgAwd; College; Law.

DURHAM, Debra E; John Marshall Harlan HS; Chicago, IL; 5/545 HonRl; JrNHS; TreasNHS; OffAde; SchAde; SchPl; StuCncl; TchrAde; MthCl; Chrldr; Loyola Univ; Nursing.

DURHAM, Debra G; Wagner HS; Wagner, SD; SecFrshCls; CncrtBnd; HonRl; MrchBnd; PepBnd; RptrSchPpr; SchPpr; FHA; Army.

DURHAM, Gregory A; Westview HS; Kankakee, IL; 3/270 HonRl; NHS; SchMus; Arizona State Univ; Graphic Design.

DURHAM, Kenneth; Delta C 7 HS; Hayti, MO; ;28 Chr; Chrs; ChrhWkr; CmntyWkr; HonRl; OffAde; PolWkr; SchAde; FshEdYrbk; SchPpr; Markwith School System;teachinghelping Othe.

DURHAM, Lisa M; Edina West HS; Edina, MN; 20/521 NatlFornLg; NatlThespSoc; SchMus; SchPl; TchrAde; FrCl; PpCl; Otterbein Col; Theatre Journalism.

DURHAM, Patty G; Dixon HS; Dixon, MO; 4/84 ALAGirlsSt; Chrl; Chrs; HonRl; JA; OffAde; SchAde; 4-H; Trk; College; Professional.

DURHAM, Ralph E; Round Lake Sr HS; Round Lake, IL; Band; Chr; ChrhWkr; CncrtBnd; HonRl; MrchBnd; Orch; PepBnd; SchMus; University Of Illinois; Architecture.

DURKALEWYCZ, Mary A; Paul Vi HS; Omaha, NE; Chrs; HonRl; NHS; SchPl; Sdlty; PpCl; CaptChrldr; University; Journalism.

DURKEE, David S; Fork Union Military Academy; Grand Rapids, MI; 7/96 DrlTm; HonRl; NHS; U S Air Force Academy; Electronic Engineer.

DURKIN, Ann; Regina Dominican HS; Chicago, IL; 1/204 HonRl; NatlFornLg; NatlMeritFnl; NatlMeritSchl; PolWkr; SctActv; StuCncl; EdSchPpr; Swmmng; AmLegAwd; Univ Of Il; Anthro.

DURKIN, Ann D; Regina Dominican HS; Chicago, IL; 1/204 HonRl; LitMag; NatlFornLg; NatlMeritSF; PolWkr; Quill&Scroll; StuCncl; EdSchPpr; ChmnSwmmng; Clge; Anthropology.

DURKIN, Kathryn J; Lourdes HS; Chicago, IL; 4/277 HonRl; HospAde; NHS; PolWkr; StuGov; Univ Of Illinois; Nursing.

DURKIN, Maureen E; Mother Mc Auley HS; Chicago, IL; 24/484 HonRl; NHS; SchAde; De Paul Univ; Accounting.

DURKOP, Diane L; Delwood HS; Maquoketa, IA; Band; Chr; CncrtBnd; HonRl; LbryAde; MrchBnd; NHS; RptrYrbk; RptrSchPpr; Bsktbl; Univ;.

DURLAND, Lori M; Britton HS; Britton, SD; SecFrshCls; TrsSophCls; PresSrCls; ALAGirlsSt; HonRl; NHS; SchPl; Yrbk; FHA; Chrldr; Sdsu; Textiles.

DURLEY, Jack O; Homewood Flossmoor HS; Chicago Hts, IL; 43/946 HonRl; JrNHS; NHS; GerCl; Univ Of Illinois; Medicine.

DURLING, Carol J; Waldron HS; Hudson, MI; 1/51 VPSophCls; SecJrCls; PresSrCls; HonRl; NHS; StuCncl; FHA; GAA; DARAwd; Grand Rapids Col; Pro.

DURLING, Sharon; Waldron HS; Hudson, MI; 6/52 SecSrCls; ChrhWkr; CncrtBnd; HonRl; MrchBnd; SchPl; FHA; Bsktbl; Bible School;.

DURLING, Sharon L; Waldron HS; Hudson, MI; 5/51 SecSrCls; Band; ChrhWkr; SecCncrtBnd; HonRl; VPNHS; SchPl; SecStuCncl; TchrAde; GAA;.

DURMAN, Michael D; Seneca HS; Joplin, MO; ChrhWkr; FTA; MthCl; LetterBsbl; LetterFtbl; College.

DUROCHER, Joanne E; Harry S Truman HS; Taylor, MI; 56/470 OffAde; StuGov; PpCl; Bsbl; Swmmng; Eastern Michigan Univ; Psychology.

DURST, David F; Northville HS; Northville, MI; ChrhWkr; CncrtBnd; MrchBnd; NHS; LetterTrk; Grand Rapids Baptist College.

DURST, Kendall R; St George HS; St George, KS; PresJrCls; ALBoysSt; Chrs; HonRl; StuCncl; Sacrstn; LetterBsktbl; LetterFtbl; LetterTrk; CchngActv; College; Psychologist.

DURST, Linda M; Lincoln HS; Lake City, MN; HonRl; SchPl; RptrSchPpr; SchPpr; Bsktbl; Trk; GAA; PPFtbl; JCAwd; PresAwd; Adams St Col; Med Tech.

DURYEA, Dana K; Lee M Thurston HS; Redford Twsp, MI; 108/633 Band; CncrtBnd; HonRl; MrchBnd; NHS; Orch; TchrAde; CaptBsktbl; LetterTrk; CchngActv; Michigan State Univ; Medicine.

DURZINSKY, Dennis S; Alexandria Monroe HS; Alexandria, IN; 1/199 Band; HonRl; MrchBnd; VPNHS; NatlMeritFnl; NatlMeritSchl; PepBnd; TchrAde; RptrYrbk; LatCl; BauchLmbAwd; EldAwd; KiwanAwd; Northwestern Univ; Medicine.

DUSA, Laura L; Ida HS; Temperance, MI; 25/175 SecSophCls; Band; CncrtBnd; HonRl; HospAde; MrchBnd; NHS; PepBnd; StuCncl; PpCl; Chrldr; College; Business.

DUSCHER, Joel W; Redwood Falls HS; Redwood Falls, MN; 65/123 Chrs; HonRl; NatlMeritSchl; SchMus; StuGov; SptEdSchPpr; PpCl; LetterBsbl; LetterGlf; Trk; St Johns U; Business Mgmnt.

DUSEK, Jill M; Washington HS; Chicago, IL; Chr; ChrhWkr; TreasCncrtBnd; HonRl; MrchBnd; NHS; Orch; YthFlsp; LatCl; GAA; Univ Of Illinois; Musician.

DUSSIAS, Penelope; Amundsen HS; Chicago, IL; 2/344 NHS; NatlMeritCmnd; StuCncl; TchrAde; Yrbk; VPFTA; SpnCl; College; Anthropology.

DUST, Marla; George Rogers Clark HS; Hammond, IN; ChrhWkr; HonRl; NHS; PpCl; Bsktbl; Trk; GAA; IMSpt; PresAwd; Navy.

DUST, Patrick J; St Anthony HS; Effingham, IL; VPFrshCls; Chrs; HonRl; NHS; SchPl; Eastern Ill Univ; Medicine.

DUSTER, Charles E; Lindblom Tech HS; Chicago, IL; 78/722 ChrhWkr; HonRl; NHS; StuCncl; TchrAde; RptrYrbk; FDA; MthCl; SciCl; Swmmng;.

DUSTER, Christopher C; Waterloo HS; Waterloo, NE; 2/31 VPFrshCls; VPJrCls; ALBoysSt; Chr; ChrhWkr; HonRl; SchPl; StuCncl; Ftbl; LetterTrk; U Of Nebr; Prof Architect.

DUSTMAN, Leslie; North Central HS; Indianapolis, IN; 67/1173 ChrhWkr; HonRl; NHS; NatlMeritSF; OffAde; TchrAde; College.

DUSZYNSKI, Paula R; Good Counsel HS; Chicago, IL; 10/259 HonRl; NatlFornLg; NHS; SciCl; GAA; Univ Of Il Chicago Circle; Mathematics.

DUTCHER, Karen L; Truman HS; Independence, MO; TrsFrshCls; HonRl; JrNHS; LbryAde; NHS; OffAde; StuCncl; TchrAde; PpCl; Chrldr; IMSpt; University; Computer.

DUTCHER, Phyllis; Wautoma HS; Redgranite, WI; Chr; FrCl; GAA; College; Phy Ed.

DUTKIEWICZ, Alan D; J F Kennedy HS; Chicago, IL; 99/544 Yrbk; SchPpr; Tennis; Clumbia Clg; Television Producer.

DUTKO, Robin; Madison HS; Madison, IL; CncrtBnd; HonRl; MrchBnd; NHS; PepBnd; LatCl; MthCl; Tennis; IMSpt; College; Curriculum.

DUTKOWSKI, James F; Luke M Powers HS; Flint, MI; 60/305 HonRl; NHS; Yrbk; RptrSchPpr; U Of Mi Flint; Architect.

DUTKOWSKI, Michele R; Steinmetz HS; Chicago, IL; DrlTm; ROTC; TchrAde; FBLA; Triton College; Horticulture.

DUTOIT, Kurt E; Dighton HS; Dighton, KS; PresSophCls; TrsSrCls; ALBoysSt; Band; CmntyWkr; CncrtBnd; HonRl; MrchBnd; LetterBsktbl; LetterFtbl; LetterTennis; LetterTrk; CchngActv; Barton County Jr College; Architecture.

DUTTERER, Deborah; Holton HS; Holton, MI; 6/65 ALAGirlsSt; HonRl; NHS; TchrAde; SpnCl; PpCl; Bsbl; Trk; PPFtbl; College; Teacher.

DUTTON, Cynthia D; Kalkaska HS; Fife Lake, MI; HonRl; NHS; StuCncl; GAA; PPFtbl; Col; Pro.

DUTTON, Katharine S; Astoria HS; Vermont, IL; 1/42 Band; Chrs; HonRl; LbryAde; MrchBnd; NHS; YthFlsp; SpnCl; SciCl; GAA; Il St Univ; Accountant.

DUTTON, Pamela A; Pope County HS; Golconda, IL; Chr; SchPl; 4-H; FHA; FTA; PpCl; Bsktbl; Trk; Chrldr; IMSpt; College; Vocation.

DUVAL, Edward G; River Valley HS; Lakeside, MI; Chr; HonRl; SchMus; SctActv; YthFlsp; Bsbl; LetterFtbl; LetterSwmmng; Trk; LetterWrstlng;.

DUVALL, Betty C; Marietta Public HS; Marietta, MN; 4/13 Band; ChrhWkr; CncrtBnd; HonRl; LbryAde; RptrYrbk; EdSchPpr; FHA; LetterBsktbl; BttyCrckrAwd; N Hennipin Comm Clg; Rn.

DUVEL, Wanda L; Lincoln County R 1 HS; Silex, MO; 2/34 PresBand; ChrhWkr; HonRl; PresNHS; SecStuCncl; Yrbk; Pres4-H; SecFHA; Bsbl; CaptBsktbl; Univ; Physical Ed.

DUVENDACK, Tamra J; Meredosia Chambersburg HS; Meredosia, IL; ChrhWkr; HonRl; NHS; StuCncl; SciCl; College; Pharmacy.

DUWE, Darryl; Meridian HS; Sanford, MI; 17/125 HonRl; NHS; TchrAde; Trk; Delta College; Engineering.

DUWE, Margaret A; Lucas HS; Lucas, KS; 1/13 Band; Chrs; HonRl; NHS; PolWkr; StuCncl; FFA; PpCl; LetterTrk; BttyCrckrAwd; Univ; Home Ec.

DUXBURY, Kathryn A; Wessington HS; Wessington, SD; 2/26 Band; Chrs; ChrhWkr; CncrtBnd; HonRl; MrchBnd; OffAde; Quill&Scroll; SchPl; TchrAde; Yrbk; RptrSchPpr; 4-H; LetterBsktbl; GAA; College; Agriculture.

DUXBURY, Kevin D; Canova Public HS; Canova, SD; 1/27 ALBoysSt; Band; HonRl; MrchBnd; PepBnd; SchPl; StuCncl; EdYrBk; EdSchPpr; Univ Of South Dakota; Business.

DVORACEK, Dawn J; Charlevoix HS; Charlevoix, MI; CncrtBnd; HonRl; 4-H; FrCl; 4-HAwd; College; History.

DVORAK, David A; Stoughton Senior HS; Stoughton, WI; ChrhWkr; SctActv; Bsbl; Ftbl; Trk; College; Conservation.

DVORAK, Doug F; Dysart Geneseo HS; Clutier, IA; PresSophCls; Band; ChrhWkr; CncrtBnd; HonRl; MrchBnd; NHS; SchMus; StuCncl; Vocational School; Farm.

DVORAK, Mary; West Holt HS; Atkinson, NE; ALBoysSt; ALAGirlsSt; HonRl; NHS; SchPl; StuCncl; FrCl; Business Sch; Secretarial.

DVORAK, Paula A; Ashton HS; Ashton, IL; 3/40 Band; HonRl; MrchBnd; NHS; NatlMeritSF; NatlThespSoc; PepBnd; SchPl; RptrSchPpr; Sauk Valley College; Physical Therapy.

DWELLE, Mary; Lincoln HS; Lake City, MN; 5/144 Band; Chr; CncrtBnd; HonRl; NHS; SchMus; SchPl; StuCncl; SpnCl; Chrldr; College; Pre Law.

DWENGER, Wendy L; Columbus East HS; Columbus, IN; 83/330 TrsSophCls; VPSrCls; ChrhWkr; CmntyWkr; StuCncl; StuGov; TchrAde; YthLg; PpCl; CaptTennis; Chrldr; PPFtbl; Indiana St Univ; Elem Education.

DWIGGINS, Jayne E; Bevier Public HS; Bevier, MO; TrsFrshCls; ChrhWkr; CncrtBnd; HonRl; StuCncl; YthFlsp; Yrbk; RptrSchPpr; FHA; Chrldr; Ne Mo State University; Professional.

DWIGGINS, Paul A; Macarthur Hs; Decatur, IL; 13/450 ChrhWkr; HonRl; JA; NHS; NatlMeritFnl; RedCrAde; SctActv; FrCl; BauchLmbAwd; U Of Illinois; Biology Major.

DWORAK, Dale J; Mendel Catholic Prep; Chicago, IL; 1/180 HonRl; Us Air Force Academy; Psychology.

DWORNICK, Robert F; Bishop Le Blond HS; St Joseph, MO; 2/110 HonRl; JA; NatlFornLg; NHS; Quill&Scroll; StuCncl; StuGov; YthLg; SptEdSchPpr; Bsbl; George Washington Univ; Business Career Law.

DWYER, Barbara S; Madison Cons HS; Madison, IN; CmntyWkr; HonRl; Quill&Scroll; SchMus; StuCncl; YthFlsp; Yrbk; PpCl; Swmmng; GAA; Ball State Univ.

DWYER, Katie; Bergan Hs; Peoria, IL; Chr; ChrhWkr; HonRl; FrCl; PpCl; Southern Ill U;english.

DWYER, Lee; William Fremo HS; Palatine, IL; JA; StuCncl; IMSpt; PPFtbl; JAAwd; Business School; Court Stenographer.

DWYER, Lynn A; West HS; Gfreen Bay, WI; 3/390 HonRl; HospAde; NHS; SctActv; RptrYrbk; FNA; FrCl; PpCl; Trk; Chrldr; College; Medical Educational.

DWYER, M; Humboldt HS; St Paul, MN; DrlTm; HonRl; SchPl; StuCncl; Bsktbl; College; Languages.

DWYER, Maren; Homewood Flossmoor HS; Homewood, IL; 57/932 Chr; Chrs; HonRl; NHS; NatlMeritCmnd; Orch; SchMus; RusCl; SpnCl; Music.

DWYER, Mark S; Brother Rice HS; Birmingham, MI; 1/212 ChrhWkr; HonRl; JrNHS; NHS; TchrAde; Tennis; University Of Michigan; Mathematics.

DWYER, Mary R; Mother Guerin HS; Chicago, IL; SctActv; StuGov; Western Ill Univ; Veterinarian.

DWYER, Michael K; Brother Rice HS; Birmingham, MI; 9/215 VPJrCls; VPSrCls; HonRl; NHS; StuCncl; IMSpt; U Of M; Chemistry.

DWYER, Richard; Wakonda Public HS; Wakonda, SD; 8/20 TrsJrCls; Chrs; ChrhWkr; HonRl; NHS; SchPl; StuCncl; Trk; Sd St Univ; Journalism.

DWYER, Thomas; J F Kennedy Hs; Chicago, IL; 15/610 VPCncrtBnd; HonRl; NHS; OffAde; SctActv; YthFlsp; KeyCl; Swmmng; Tennis; Trk; U; Medicine.

DYBALL, Kevin D; Maine East HS; Park Ridge, IL; HonRl; NHS; NatlMeritSchl; Notre Dame Univ; Architecture.

DYBDAHL, Naomi R; Mt Horeb HS; Mt Horeb, WI; Band; Chr; Chrs; ChrhWkr; CncrtBnd; HonRl; MrchBnd; Orch; SchMus; GerCl; Coll; Biology.

DYBDAL, Douglas R; Cambridge HS; Cambridge, IL; 12/60 TrsSophCls; HonRl; NHS; SchPl; StuCncl; SchPpr; FTA; Illinois College; Business Admin.

DYBING, Parry; Brookings HS; Brookings, SD; Band; CncrtBnd; MrchBnd; NatlFornLg; NHS; Orch; PepBnd; SchMus; SctActv;.

DYE, Carol L; Quincy Senior HS; Quincy, IL; 1/713 ChrhWkr; CncrtBnd; HonRl; MrchBnd; NHS; PepBnd; StuGov; AmLegAwd; College; Mathematics.

DYE, Craig D; Onawat Area Comm HS; Millersburg, MI; 15/104 VPJrCls; SchAde; SciCl; Ftbl; Trk; Wrstlng; Michigan St Univ; Veterinarian.

DYE, Kevin R; Maries Co Rii HS; Vichy, MO; 2/54 ChrhWkr; HonRl; JrNHS; NHS; SchPl; SctActv; PresStuCncl; Yrbk; LetterBsbl; LetterTrk; Med School; Medical Missionary.

DYE, Robin L; Douglas Macarthur HS; Saginaw, MI; CmntyWkr; DrlTm; HonRl; OffAde; SchAde; TchrAde; Mich Tech Univ; Mech Engineer.

DYE, Susan K; Davison HS; Burton, MI; SecFrshCls; JA; SecNHS; NatlMeritSchl; NatlMeritSF; SchMus; SpnCl; IMSpt; Coll; Bus & Music.

DYER, Cary; Grand Blanc HS; Flint, MI; 10/600 NHS; PpCl; PPFtbl; College.

DYER, Dennis P; Tell City HS; Tell City, IN; 2/230 ALBoysSt; Band; CncrtBnd; HonRl; MrchBnd; NHS; NatlMeritSF; SctActv; FrCl; Tennis; College; Science.

DYER, Douglas D; Hyannis HS; Hyannis, NE; 7/29 Band; Chrs; HonRl; NHS; SchMus; LetterBsktbl; LetterFtbl; Trk; 4-HAwd; PresAwd; U Of Nebraska.

DYER, James; Novinger R 1 HS; Novinger, MO; 3/30 TrsFrshCls; VPSophCls; ChrhWkr; CmntyWkr; HonRl; PpCl; Univ; Engineering.

DYER, Kathleen M; Dickinson HS; Dickinson, ND; 8/200 ALAGirlsSt; Chr; Chrl; HonRl; NHS; NatlThespSoc; SchMus; SchPl; GerCl; SciCl; College; Science.

DYER, Marilyn S; Edinburg HS; Edinburg, IN; HonRl; HospAde; RedCrAde; SctActv; FHA; Trade School; Data Processing.

DYER, Rick D; Adel Community HS; Adel, IA; TrsFrshCls; SecSophCls; PresJrCls; PolWkr; StuCncl; PresStuGov; YthFlsp; RptrYrbk; SptEdYrbk; Yrbk; RptrSchPpr; Bsbl; Ftbl; Trk; Wrstlng; College; Business Mgmt.

DYK, Dennis D; Strasburg HS; Strasburg, ND; 2/23 PresSophCls; Chrs; ChrhWkr; HonRl; SctActv; 4-H; PpCl; IMSpt; Nd Schl Sci; Mech Auto.

DYKE, Wade T; Mt Horeb HS; Mt Horeb, WI; 6/120 ALBoysSt; HonRl; NHS; PresStuCncl; RptrYrbk; MthCl; Ftbl; LetterTrk;.

DYKES, Brent; Estherville HS; Estherville, IA; 36/156 Band; Chr; CncrtBnd; HonRl; MrchBnd; NHS; PepBnd; StuCncl; DanFAwd; Buena Vista College; Teacher.

DYKES, Larry W; Avon HS; Plainfield, IN; 20/159 ModUN; NHS; NatlMeritCmnd; SchPl; LetterBsktbl; CaptFtbl; CaptTrk; Univ; Radio Tv.

DYKES, Mary A; Althoff Catholic HS; East St Louis, IL; Chrs; ChrhWkr; HonRl; LbryAde; TreasSpnCl; CchngActv; GAA; BttyCrckrAwd; Belleville Area College; Nursing.

DYKHUIZEN, Sherry L; Minnehaha Academy; Bloomington, MN; Chr; ChrhWkr; HonRl; FrCl; Calvin College; Undecided.

DYKMAN, Janis; Fremont HS; Fremont, MI; ChrhWkr; HonRl; FTA; GerCl; Central Mi Univ; Stewadess.

DYKO, Debra J; Fowlerville HS; Fowlerville, MI; Chrl; CncrtBnd; MrchBnd; PepBnd; College; Music.

DYKOWSKI, Mark D; Fordson HS; Dearborn, MI; HstSrCls; AFS; CAP; CtyCnl; CmntyWkr; HonRl; IntrClCncl; JA; NHS; Bsktbl; Univ; Doctor.

DYKSTRA, Cathye; Holland Chr HS; Holland, MI; Band; HonRl; MrchBnd; NHS; PepBnd; SchPl; RptrYrbk; GerCl; Swmmng; Bronson Sch Of Nursng; Nursing.

DYKSTRA, Charles A; Kalamazoo Christian HS; Kalamazoo, MI; 14/142 Chr; ChrhWkr; HonRl; JA; NHS; SchMus; SchPl; Yrbk; PresAwd; VoiceDemAwd; Calvin College; Medical.

DYKSTRA, Dale A; Fulton HS; Fulton, IL; 9/122 Sauk Valley College; Accounting.

DYKSTRA, David W; Cal Community HS; Sheffield, IA; PresJrCls; Band; Chrs; MrchBnd; SchMus; SchPl; Yrbk; Bsbl; Ftbl; Trk; College.

DYKSTRA, Fredrick; La Salle HS; St Ignace, MI; ModUN; NHS; NatlMeritCmnd; College; Electrical Engineer.

DYKSTRA, Marcia; Wapello Community HS; Wapello, IA; 4/66 SecJrCls; Chrs; HonRl; OffAde; SctActv; TchrAde; SecFHA; SecSciCl; Kirkwood Comm Coll; Exec Sec.

DYKSTRA, Nancy J; St Anne Community HS; St Anne, IL; 1/90 ChrhWkr; HonRl; SecNHS; SecStuCncl; PresYthFlsp; SecFTA; GAA; Wheaton College; Psychology.

DYKSTRA, Robin S; Southwestern HS; Flint, MI; 5/570 Band; Chrl; CncrtBnd; HonRl; JrNHS; MrchBnd; NHS; NatlMeritCmnd; NatlMeritSF; SchPl; U Of Mi.

DYKSTRA, Ronald L; Unity Christian HS; Jenison, MI; HonRl; LetterSocr; IMSpt; College; Architecture.

DYKSTRA, Sandra; Everly Community HS; Everly, IA; 1/34 SecJrCls; HonRl; NHS; OffAde; YthFlsp; Trk; 4-HAwd; CitAwd; Ia Central Comm Col; Business Adm.

DYKSTRA, Susan; Oostburg HS; Hingahm, WI; 6/68 SecFrshCls; ALAGirlsSt; Band; Chr; HonRl; Mdrgl; NHS; YthFlsp; Yrbk; SchPpr;.

DYLHOFF, Randy L; Gobles HS; Gobles, MI; Band; ChrhWkr; CncrtBnd; SchAde; SctActv; TchrAde; 4-H; LetterBsktbl; Ftbl; 4-HAwd; Police Cadet; Law Enforce.

DYLLA, Brenda; Webster Public Hs; Webster, SD; 21/76 SecSophCls; TrsSophCls; Chr; ChrhWkr; HonRl; HospAde; StuCncl; EdSchPpr; Chrldr; GAA; Jr College;vocational.

DYMOND, Cheryl L; Saginaw HS; Saginaw, MI; 1/443 ChrhWkr; CncrtBnd; HonRl; JrNHS; Michigan St University.

DYMOND, Susan C; Birch Run HS; Birch Run, MI; 7/154 ChrhWkr; CncrtBnd; HonRl; MrchBnd; PresNHS; PepBnd; VPYthFlsp; SciCl; LetterBsktbl; Trk; Asbury Col; Md.

DYNDA, Nancy K; Hoffman HS; Hoffman, MN; 1/29 VPJrCls; PresSrCls; ALAGirlsSt; Band; Chrs; HonRl; MrchBnd; SchPl; StuCncl; Yrbk; Univ Of Minn; Nursing.

DYNDIUK, Deborah A; Rosemount HS; Apple Valley, MN; 91/444 Chr; ChrhWkr; HonRl; SchAde; SchPl; TchrAde; YthFlsp; PpCl; Coll; Med Tech.

DYNEK, Robert J; Gordon Technical HS; Chicago, IL; 6/584 ChrhWkr; NHS; Univ; Pharmacy.

DYNES, Julie E; Dickinson HS; Dickinson, ND; PresFrshCls; Chrl; HonRl; NatlFornLg; NHS; StuCncl; GerCl; Tennis; Trk; Chrldr; Univ.

DYRA, Jeanne M; Mother Mcauley Lib Arts HS; Oak Lawn, IL; Aud/Vis; ChrhWkr; CmntyWkr; HonRl; HospAde; NatlMeritSF; PolWkr; SchMus; EdYrBk; FrCl; MthCl; SciCl; St Marys College; Business Law.

DYRDA, Jeffrey A; St Laurence HS; Chicago, IL; Band; CncrtBnd; HonRl; MrchBnd; PepBnd; SctActv; College; Liberal Arts.

DYSART, Mary; Kearney HS; Kearney, MO; 12/77 DrlTm; HonRl; JrNHS; TchrAde; 4-H; PpCl; Northwest Mo St Univ;secretarial.

DYSCHKANT, Roman P; Fenton HS; Wood Dale, IL; 51/407 CncrtBnd; HonRl; MrchBnd; NatlMeritSchl; College; Medicine.

DYSE, Cassandra L; Chicago Voc HS; Chicago, IL; 55/788 ChrhWkr; CmntyWkr; HonRl; JA; NHS; TchrAde; YthFlsp; 4-H; Bsktbl; GAA; College.

DYWAN, Mary E; Bishop Noll Inst; East Chicago, IN; 52/360 HonRl; OffAde; MthCl; PpCl; GAA; AmLegAwd; College.

DZIADEK, Linda M; New Holstein HS; Malone, WI; AFS; HonRl; Fox Valley Tech Sch; Truck Driver.

DZIAK, Irene; St Hedwig HS; Dearborn Heights, MI; Chrs; HonRl; HospAde; JA; NHS; Yrbk; FNA; FrCl; GAA; VoiceDemAwd; College; Nursing.

DZIALOWY, Paul J; High School; Chicago, IL; 7/544 CncrtBnd; HonRl; NHS; StuCncl; KeyCl; University Of Illinois.

DZIECHCIARZ, Irene D; Dwight D Eisenhower HS; Washington, MI; Chrs; ChrhWkr; HonRl; NHS; Orch; SchMus; StuCncl; TchrAde; FrCl; GerCl; Univ Of Michigan; Pharmacy.

DZIEDZIC, Linda; Rosholt HS; Rosholt, WI; HonRl; NatlFornLg; SchPl; FHA; MthCl; GAA; College; Police Officer.

DZIEGLOWICZ, Carol M; T Roosevelt HS; East Chicago, IN; 2/217 HonRl; PresNHS; SpnCl; MthCl; PpCl; SciCl; AmLegAwd; CitAwd; St Josephs Calumet College; Business Mgmt.

DZIEKAN, Wayne H; Brother Rice HS; Chicago, IL; 12/416 Chr; HonRl; NatlMeritCmnd; SchMus; SchPl; University; Music.

DZIENKOWSKI, Roxi M; Cadott Public HS; Boyd, WI; HonRl; LbryAde; NatlMeritCmnd; OffAde; SchAde; TchrAde; FHA; PpCl; Chrldr; GAA; College; Social Work.

DZIERLEGA, Mary; Josephinum HS; Chicago, IL; 7/104 HonRl; JrNHS; NHS; StuGov; Loyola Univ; Professional.

DZIESINSKI, Judy A; Alpena HS; Alpena, MI; Business School ; Business.

DZIEWECZYNSKI, Cynthia; Grace HS; Columbia Heights, MN; 8 240 NHS; SchPpr; Trk; University; Midicine.

DZIEWIOR, Janice M; Mauston Area HS; Mauston, WI; 4/135 PresFrshCls; AFS; Chr; HonRl; HospAde; NHS; NatlMeritSchl; EdYrBk; LatCl; PpCl; LetterTrk; GAA; GovHonPrgAwd; College; Nursing.

DZIEWIOR, Suzanne; Mauston Area HS; Mauston, WI; 8/140 AFS; Band; Chr; CncrtBnd; HonRl; JrNHS; NHS; EdYrBk; LatCl; Viterbo College; Nursing.

DZIEWIT, Mary C; St Alphonsus HS; Dearborn, MI; 6/115 Chrl; HonRl; JA; SchMus; SctActv; SchPpr; LatCl; IMSpt; PPFtbl; JAAwd; Wayne St; Med Tech.

DZIEWIT, Renee F; Benzie Central HS; Copennish, MI; 8/120 PresSrCls; HonRl; IntrClCncl; ModUN; NHS; NatlMeritFnl; NatlMeritCmnd; StuCncl; StuGov; LetterTrk; IMSpt; EldAwd; KiwanAwd; Northern Michigan Univ; Law.

DZIVBAN, Elizabeth A; Standish Sterling Central HS; Standish, MI; 5/160 Band; CncrtBnd; HonRl; MrchBnd; NatlSciFnd; PepBnd; TchrAde; LetterBsktbl; LetterTrk; CchngActv; Central Mi U; Teach Math & Phyed.

E

EADE, Billy D; Okawville HS; Addieville, IL; 8/67 Band; HonRl; MrchBnd; TreasNHS; EdYrBk; Pres4-H; SecFFA; PresPpCl; LetterBsbl; LetterBsktbl; Jr Coll; Agricultural Production.

EADES, Linda S; Madison Consolidated HS; Madison, IN; Band; ChrhWkr; CmntyWkr; HonRl; MrchBnd; SchMus; TchrAde; Pres4-H; GAA; IMSpt; DARAwd; 4-HAwd; College; Professional.

EADS, Becky L; Lovington HS; Lovington, IL; SecJrCls; PresTeen; Yrbk; VPFHA; PresPpCl; Bsbl; Bsktbl; Chrldr; GAA; College; Teaching.

EADS, Gregory I; Mc Donald Co HS; Anderson, MO; 20/168 Band; CncrtBnd; HonRl; MrchBnd; NHS; LetterFtbl; Crowder College; Pharmacy.

EADS, Margerie R; Shiloh HS; Hume, IL; Band; Chrs; CncrtBnd; MrchBnd; SchMus; SchPl; FHA; Chrldr; GAA; IMSpt; College; X Ray Or Lab Technician.

EADS, Mark D; Poplar Bluff HS; Poplar Bluff, MO; 49/397 Band; CncrtBnd; HonRl; MrchBnd; IMSpt; Three Rivers Jr Col; Law.

EADS, Mark E; Charleston HS; Charleston, IL; 12/257 ALBoysSt; HonRl; NHS; Ftbl; Glf; IMSpt; Univ; Medicine.

EADS, Richard P; Alleman HS; Rock Island, IL; HonRl; NatlMeritSchl; PresFrCl; IMSpt; St Ambrose College; Accounting.

EAGAN, Dianne M; Pacific HS; Villa Ridge, MO; 18/190 HonRl; TchrAde; FBLA; College; Vocation.

EAGAN, Donna S; Pacific HS; Villa Ridge, MO; ChrhWkr; HonRl; TchrAde; FBLA; PresAwd; Secretary.

EAGAN, Glenda F; Mt Vernon HS; Mt Vernon, MO; Chrs; TchrAde; FHA; FTA; PpCl; Trade School; Vocation.

EAGER, Carol H; Kimball HS; Royal Oak, MI; Band; ChrhWkr; CncrtBnd; DrlTm; HonRl; HospAde; MrchBnd; SctActv; YthFlsp; Trk; Mi St Univ; Vet.

EAGLE, Eileen; Rock Island Senior HS; Rock Island, IL; SecNHS; StuGov; SpnCl; PpCl; Chrldr; AmLegAwd; University; Uncertain.

EAGLESON, Jodi L; Concordia HS; Concordia, KS; 61/141 Chr; ChrhWkr; YthFlsp; FHA; FTA; PpCl; IMSpt; College.

EAGLESON, Ronda M; Concordia HS; Concordia, KS; 18/141 Aud/Vis; Chr; ChrhWkr; HonRl; HospAde; FTA; PpCl; SciCl; LetterTennis; Marymount College; Nursing.

EAGLESTON, Robert L; Mansfield R 4 HS; Mansfield, MO; 4/45 HonRl; FFA; MthCl; Farming.

EAKER, Robert J; St Patrick HS; Chicago, IL; 46/489 College; Engineering.

EAKIN, Douglas J; Princeton HS; Princeton, IL; 10/188 Chrs; HonRl; NatlFornLg; YthFlsp; Bsktbl; Ftbl; LetterTrk; IMSpt; College; Engineering.

EAKINS, Clayton W; Davis Co Community HS; Bloomfield, IA; HonRl; 4-H; FFA; LetterFtbl; IMSpt; Trade Sch; Carpenter.

EAKLE, Mary J; Elkhart Central HS; Elkhart, IN; SecFrshCls; Chr; HonRl; HospAde; SchMus; StuCncl; FNA; PpCl; LetterTennis; GAA; Univ Of No Colorado; Nursing.

EAKMAN, Larry A; Dunlap HS; Dunlap, IL; AFS; Band; ChrhWkr; CncrtBnd; MrchBnd; SchMus; LatCl; College; Engineering.

EALES, Christopher J; Excelsior Springs West HS; Excelsior Springs, MO; 30/220 ALBoysSt; JrNHS; NHS; SctActv; TchrAde; FTA; Bsbl; LetterFtbl; CaptWrstlng; OptClAwd; Rolla Univ Of Mo; Civil Engineer.

EALY, Maurice L; Medicine Valley HS; Moorefield, NE; Band; Chr; CncrtBnd; HonRl; Twrl; SecYthFlsp; RptrYrbk; RptrSchPpr; PresFNA; PpCl; Univ; Nurse.

EALY, Wanda R; Henry Ford HS; Detroit, MI; 95/505 HstFrshCls; CmntyWkr; HonRl; HospAde; SchAde; SctActv; Univ Of Michigan; Dietetics.

EANNARINO, Joyce M; Jesse Spalding HS; Chicago, IL; 3/47 TrsSrCls; Chrs; HonRl; JA; Northeastern Univ; Special Ed.

EARHART, Kathy A; Edwards County Sr HS; Albion, IL; 9/102 Band; HonRl; FHA; Business School.

EARL, Denise L; Albion Sr HS; Albion, MI; 20/256 DrlTm; HonRl; NHS; Twrl; RptrSchPpr; 4-H; FrCl; SciCl; Albion College; Math.

EARL, Donna K; Airport HS; Carleton, MI; 42/263 ChrhWkr; CmntyWkr; HospAde; JA; LbryAde; NHS; OffAde; PolWkr; RedCrAde; StuGov; Monroe Community Clg; Secretarial.

EARL, John; Trego Community HS; Wakeeney, KS; Band; Chr; HonRl; PepBnd; SchPl; YthFlsp; SciCl; Ftbl; LetterTennis;.

EARL, Karen K; Elkhorn Valley HS; Tilden, NE; 29/50 Chrs; OffAde; SctActv; FHA; Colorado State University; Fashion Merch.

EARL, Kathleen A; Crete HS; Crete, NE; CncrtBnd; HospAde; LbryAde; MrchBnd; SchAde; SctActv; TchrAde; SptEdYrbk; FNA; College; Nurse.

EARLE, Laura D; Thornridge HS; South Holland, IL; Chr; Chrl; ChrhWkr; HonRl; LbryAde; OffAde; TchrAde; YthFlsp; 4-H; College.

EARLE, Monica; Saint Mary Acad; Indianapolis, IN; 13/43 Chr; Chrl; Chrs; CmntyWkr; HonRl; RedCrAde; RptrSchPpr; JAAwd; College; Music Education.

EARLE, Rhonda K; Earlville HS; Earlville, IL; Band; Chrs; ChrhWkr; CncrtBnd; MrchBnd; PepBnd; FrCl; College; Nursing.

EARLEY, Maureen A; New Richmond Sr HS; New Richmond, WI; AFS; Band; ChrhWkr; CncrtBnd; HonRl; MrchBnd; PepBnd; PolWkr; SchPl; SchPpr; College; English Journalism Econ.

EARLL, Michael D; Sibley Comm HS; Bigelow, MN; PresChr; Chrs; HonRl; Mdrgl; PresNHS; SchMus; SchPl; PresStuCncl; Pres4-H; PresFFA; DanFAwd; 4-HAwd; Worthington State Jr Col; Agriculture.

EARLS, Nancy S; Rolla HS; Rolla, MO; 4/289 ALAGirlsSt; HonRl; NatlMeritCmnd; PresFrCl; PpCl; DARAwd; CitAwd; Univ Of Missouri; Business Admin.

EARLY, Jeanne M; St Stephen Area HS; Saginaw, MI; PresSophCls; PresJrCls; VPSrCls; Chr; ChrhWkr; OffAde; Sdlty; StuCncl; StuGov; Glf; College; Airline Hostess.

EARLY, Marion J; John Hersey HS; Arlington Hts, IL; 84/739 AFS; HonRl; NHS; SpnCl; Univ; Art.

EARLY, Theresa S; Knox County HS; Baring, MO; SecSophCls; HonRl; NatlMeritFnl; SchPl; RptrYrbk; SchPpr; VPSciCl; GAA; College; Mathematics.

EARNEST, Jeanett F; Stratton HS; Stratton, NE; NHS; NatlMeritSchl; NatlSciFnd; SancSoc; YthLg; FSA; AmLegAwd; ChmbCommrsAwd; GodCntryAwd; VoiceDemAwd; Trade School; Vocation.

EARNHART, Irene S; Churubusco HS; Avilla, IN; 10/105 Band; CncrtBnd; HonRl; MrchBnd; NHS; PepBnd; SchMus; Bsktbl; Trk; IMSpt; In Univ; Med Tech.

EASDON, Jerry; Buhler HS; Hutchinson, KS; Band; ChrhWkr; CncrtBnd; HonRl; MrchBnd; PepBnd; SctActv; TchrAde; Bethang Nazarene College; Chemistry.

EASH, Sheryl E; Washington HS; Washington, IA; 3/172 Chr; CncrtBnd; NHS; SchMus; GovHonPrgAwd; Univ Of No Iowa; Interior Design.

EASLEY, Jacqueline R; Roosevelt Senior HS; Des Moines, IA; TrsFrshCls; SecTrsJrCls; ChrhWkr; StuCncl; UNYO; SchPpr; SpnCl; KiwanAwd; Liberal Arts Clg; Law.

EASLEY, Kevin L; Macon County R 1 HS; Macon, MO; 1/120 PresSophCls; PresSrCls; Chr; HonRl; StuGov; SptEdYrbk; Yrbk; BauchLmbAwd; DanFAwd; Univ Of Mo Col; Major.

EASLICK, Stephanie; Unionville Elewaing Area HS; Sebewaing, MI; 6/125 ALAGirlsSt; Band; HonRl; HospAde; FHA; PpCl; Chrldr; Ferris State College; Technicalnursing.

EASON, Amy M; Scranton Consolidated HS; Scranton, IA; 2/18 Band; Chrs; DrmMjrt; NHS; NatlMeritCmnd; SchMus; SchPl; EdYrBk; BttyCrckrAwd; DARAwd; Simpson Clg.

EASON, Curtis; Mount Ayr Comm HS; Mount Ayr, IA; Band; HonRl; MrchBnd; PepBnd; SchMus; SchPl; Electronics.

EAST, Cynthia; Fredericktown HS; Fredericktown, MO; 20/130 Chrs; HonRl; SctActv; TchrAde; RptrSchPpr; PpCl; De Paul Hos School Of Nursing; Rn.

EAST, Ricky E; Oakland HS; Hindsboro, IL; 2/43 HonRl; VPNHS; PresStuCncl; Yrbk; Pres4-H; PresFFA; LetterBsktbl; 4-HAwd; Lakeland Jr Col; Agriculture.

EASTBURG, Paul D; Central HS; Glenwood, MN; 3/139 ChrhWkr; HonRl; GerCl; CaptBsktbl; Ftbl; LetterTennis; LetterWrstlng; Coll; Professional.

EASTER, Barbara J; Princeton R 5 HS; Princeton, MO; TrsJrCls; Band; HonRl; NHS; SchPl; Twrl; 4-H; FFA; FHA; Trenton Junior College; Secretary.

EASTER, David A; Tremont HS; Tremont, IL; AFS; Chrs; ChrhWkr; HonRl; EdYrBk; Ftbl; Trk; College; Mechanical Engineering.

EASTERLING, O Dale; Central HS; Duluth, MN; LetterBsktbl; LetterTrk; IMSpt; Lakewood College; Data Processing.

EASTERN, Cynthia R; Wisconsin Lutheran HS; Milwaukee, WI; Chr; DrlTm; HonRl; NHS; NatlMeritCmnd; StuCncl; RptrSchPpr; Fisk Univ; Journalism.

EASTHOUSE, Karen E; Goodridge HS; Goodridge, MN; VPBand; Chrs; HonRl; OffAde; TchrAde; Yrbk; Pres4-H; FHA; FTA; PpCl; Bsktbl; GAA; College; Elem Ed.

EASTIN, Chris J; North Clay Comm HS; Louisville, IL; HonRl; 4-H; SpnCl; SciCl; Trk; DanFAwd; 4-HAwd; College; Professional.

EASTIN, Cindy R; Eldon HS; Eldon, MO; 26/129 Band; CncrtBnd; DrlTm; DrmMjrt; HonRl; MrchBnd; PepBnd; StuCncl; Chrldr; GAA; University.

EASTMAN, Dennis; H H Dow HS; Midland, MI; NatlFornLg; 4-H; Ftbl; Trk; Wrstlng; College Cmv; Physical Edvoation.

EASTMAN, Michelle L; Giltner Public HS; Giltner, NE; 3/19 SecFrshCls; SecSophCls; SecJrCls; DrlTm; HonRl; SchPl; EdYrBk; SptEdSchPpr; LetterTrk; Chrldr; GAA; Business School.

EASTO, William D; Crown Point HS; Crown Point, IN; 10/500 HonRl; NHS; AmLegAwd; Purdue Univ; Elec Engineering.

EASTOM, Mark C; Northrop HS; Fort Wayne, IN; 168/568 Aud/Vis; VPJA; PpCl; JAAwd; University; Professional.

EASTON, Luann; Patoka HS; Patoka, IL; 1/28 HstFrshCls; VPSrCls; Chrs; ChrhWkr; HonRl; SchPl; StuCncl; TchrAde; EdYrBk; FHA; Chrldr; E Illinois Univ; Physical Educ.

EASTON, Pamela R; Hanson Ind #40 HS; Fulton, SD; Chrs; DrlTm; HonRl; Mdrgl; Quill&Scroll; SchPl; Yrbk; RptrSchPpr; 4-H; FHA; PpCl; College; X Ray Technician.

EASTWOOD, Vicki L; Vienna Township HS; Cypress, IL; 17/100 4-H; FBLA; FDA; FFA; FHA; FNA; FSA; FTA; Col ; Vocation.

EATON, Albert J; Calumet HS; Gary, IN; 42/350 HonRl; NHS; Quill&Scroll; StuCncl; Bsbl; Ftbl; College; Engineering.

EATON, Audrey L; Manistee Catholic Central HS; Manistee, MI; Chr; HonRl; OffAde; SchMus; PpCl; Interior Design; Designing.

EATON, Beth A; Edison Sr HS; East Gary, IN; PresSrCls; Chr; OffAde; SchMus; StuCncl; FTA; SpnCl; PpCl; Purdue Univ; Biology.

EATON, Beverly G; Monrovia HS; Monrovia, IN; HonRl; 4-H;.

EATON, Carolyn R; Waynesville HS; A Leonard Wood, MO; TrsFrshCls; Chr; ChrhWkr; HonRl; Orch; SchPl; SctActv; YthFlsp; GerCl; MthCl; Bsktbl; Oregon College; Veterinary Medicine.

EATON, Donald L; Campbell HS; Campbell, MO; ChrhWkr; CmntyWkr; 4-H; FFA; LetterBsktbl; DanFAwd; 4-HAwd; College; Agriculture.

EATON, Donald L; North County HS; Desloge, MO; 4/170 VPJrCls; HonRl; JrNHS; TreasNHS; OffAde; SecStuCncl; RptrSchPpr; FrCl; LetterBsktbl; LetterFtbl; LetterGlf; LetterTennis; College; Accounting.

EATON, Lillian J; Atlanta C 3 HS; Elmer, MO; ChrhWkr; HonRl; 4-H; FHA; Bsbl; Chrldr; 4-HAwd; College; Vocation.

EATON, Peggy A; North Platte Sr HS; North Platte, NE; 156/404 ALAGirlsSt; Chrs; ChrhWkr; SchPl; SctActv; YthFlsp; Treas4-H; SecPpCl; GAA; PPFtbl; Nursing School; Nurse.

EATON, Ralph A; Westview HS; La Grange, IN; Band; Chr; ChrhWkr; CncrtBnd; MrchBnd; YthFlsp; 4-H; FFA; CaptBsktbl; 4-HAwd; Anderson Col; Music.

EATON, Sabrina; Stanberry HS; King City, MO; Band; Chr; Chrs; ChrhWkr; CncrtBnd; MrchBnd; PepBnd; FHA; FTA; PpCl; Nursing School; Rn.

EBACH, Rebecca S; Arthur Hill HS; Saginaw, MI; Chr; HonRl; Business School; Professional.

EBAUGH, Kristel K; South Sioux City HS; South Sioux City, NE; 8/176 PresAFS; ALAGirlsSt; Chr; HonRl; JrNHS; SecNHS; PpCl; Chrldr; AmLegAwd; Univ Of South Dakota; Computer Science.

EBBEN, Robert J; Thorp HS; Thorp, WI; TrsSophCls; Band; HonRl; SctActv; StuCncl; SptEdYrbk; SchPpr; CaptBsbl; Bsktbl; Ftbl; Police Science.

EBBEN, William F; Thorp HS; Thorp, WI; ALBoysSt; HonRl; SctActv; StuCncl; Yrbk; 4-H; FFA; Bsbl; Bsktbl; Ftbl;.

EBBERS, Nancy L; Timothy Christian HS; Cicero, IL; 4/80 ChrhWkr; CmntyWkr; HonRl; HospAde; NHS; Yrbk; Calvin College; Biology.

EBBERSTEN, Darrell L; Mt Pulaski HS; Elkhart, IL; PresSophCls; HonRl; NHS; StuCncl; FFA; Bsktbl; Farming.

EBBESMEYER, Karen A; Mercy HS; St Louis, MO; 18/172 ALAGirlsSt; ChrhWkr; CmntyWkr; DrlTm; HonRl; HospAde; NHS; SchAde; SchMus; StuCncl; TchrAde; GerCl; PpCl; St Johns Nursing Sch; Nursing.

EBEL, David M; St Louis University HS; St Louis, MO; HonRl; JrNHS; SciCl; Trk; IMSpt; College; Meteorology.

EBEL, Linda; Grand Haven HS; West Olive, MI; 27/396 Band; CncrtBnd; HonRl; JrNHS; MrchBnd; NHS; PepBnd; SctActv; RusCl; GAA; Univ Of Mic; Orean Sciences.

EBEL, Michael J; Aquinas HS; Bellwood, NE; 8/97 TreasStuCncl; RptrSchPpr; LatCl; MthCl; SecSciCl; Bsbl; Wrstlng; University; Engineering Physics.

EBEL, Patty A; Aquinas HS; Bellwood, NE; Band; CmntyWkr; CncrtBnd; MrchBnd; PepBnd; SchMus; PresStuCncl; SecSpnCl; SciCl; Glf; Lincoln Sch Of Commerce; Secretarial.

EBELHERR, Karen A; Lincoln Comm HS; Lincoln, IL; 17/255 ChrhWkr; HonRl; HospAde; JrNHS; NHS; OffAde; StuCncl; TchrAde; FTA; FrCl; College; Accounting.

EBELING, Glenn J; Manitowoc Lutheran HS; Maribel, WI; 1/79 Bsktbl; LetterFtbl; LetterTrk; Dr Martin Luther College; Education.

EBEN, John E; Oak Creek HS; Oak Creek, WI; 15/323 HonRl; NatlFornLg; NHS; TchrAde; GerCl; SciCl; Mbti Tech Schl; Data Processing.

EBEN, Larry; George Community HS; George, IA; Chr; Chrs; HonRl; SchMus; SchPl; Coll.

EBENEZER, Cindy R; Rock Falls Twp HS; Rock Falls, IL; 3/263 SecJrCls; Band; CncrtBnd; HonRl; LitMag; MrchBnd; NHS; SchPl; VPStuCncl; Twrl; RptrYrbk; CaptChrldr; AmLegAwd; DARAwd; Augustana College; Medical Tech.

EBENHOEH, Margo A; New Lothrop HS; Chesaning, MI; 17/81 HonRl; LbryAde; NHS; TchrAde; CaptChrldr; Central Michigan Univ; Law Enforcement.

EBENHOEH, Richard L; New Lothrop HS; New Lothrop, MI; PresSophCls; VPJrCls; HonRl; NHS; Yrbk; LetterFtbl; CaptTrk; IMSpt; Univ Of Michigan; Lawyer.

EBENSPERGER, Sharon A; Plum City HS; Plum City, WI; 2/37 TrsSophCls; Band; Chr; CncrtBnd; HonRl; MrchBnd; PepBnd; RptrYrbk; Yrbk; Bsktbl; Chrldr; GAA; PPFtbl; College.

EBERHARDT, Catherine L; William J Bogan HS; Chicago, IL; Chrs; HonRl; JrNHS; NHS; OffAde; SchMus; TchrAde; GerCl; SciCl; Northwestern Univ; Pediatrician.

EBERHARDT, Douglas; North Side HS; Ft Wayne, IN; 11/491 Band; CncrtBnd; HonRl; MrchBnd; NHS; PepBnd; SctActv; KeyCl;.

EBERHARDT, Nancy J; Schlarman HS; Danville, IL; 6/74 HonRl; JA; StuCncl; StuGov; RptrYrbk; St Josephs Col; Computer Science.

EBERHARDT, Thomas G; Marist HS; Oak Lawn, IL; CmntyWkr; LbryAde; PpCl; LetterBsktbl; LetterFtbl; IMSpt; Knox College; Advertising.

EBERLE, Catherine M; Nerinx Hall HS; St Louis, MO; NHS; NatlMeritSF; StuCncl; LetterBsktbl; GAA; IMSpt; Coll.

EBERLE, Mark A; Brookfield East HS; Brookfield, WI; 2/500 Band; HonRl; JrNHS; NHS; NatlMeritCmnd; PepBnd; SchMus; SchPl; StuCncl; KeyCl; GerCl; MthCl; Bsbl; LetterTennis; Columbia College; Medicine.

EBERLING, Teresa J; Postville Community HS; Postville, IA; 12/90 Band; ChrhWkr; NHS; YthFlsp; Yrbk; 4-H; FHA; LetterTrk; 4-HAwd; GodCntryAwd; St Lukes Nursing Schl; Rn.

EBERLY, Rick J; Clarinda Comm HS; Clarinda, IA; LetterBsbl; LetterBsktbl; LetterFtbl; LetterTennis; Trk; College; Wildlife Management.

EBERS, Sharon S; Steeleville HS; Chester, IL; 12/57 Chr; Chrs; ChrhWkr; HonRl; StuCncl; FBLA; FHA; PpCl; CaptChrldr; GAA; University; Secretarial.

EBERSOLE, Donna; Windsor HS; Windsor, MO; 6/52 SecSrCls; Chrs; HonRl; Quill&Scroll; RptrSchPpr; FBLA; FHA; MthCl; PpCl; Coll; Medical Secretarial Science.

EBERT, Jody A; New Prague HS; New Prague, MN; 11/194 Chr; HonRl; NHS; SchPpr; 4-H; SpnCl; PpCl; IMSpt; U Of Minn; English.

EBERT, Mark H; Mounds View HS; New Brighton, MN; ChrhWkr; HonRl; JrNHS; NHS; SchPl; StuCncl; TchrAde; GerCl; VFWAwd; Concordia College; Ministry.

EBERT, Steven L; John Marshall HS; Indianapolis, IN; 84/600 HonRl; LitMag; OffAde; Ftbl; Trk; Univ.

EBKE, David; High School; Daykin, NE; Chrs; ChrhWkr; Milford Tech College; Electronics.

EBLIN, Douglas; Salem Comm HS; Salem, IL; FFA; PpCl; Bsbl; Ftbl; IMSpt; College; Agri.

EBSCH, Christine E; Tomorrow River HS; Amherst, WI; 2/34 VPFrshCls; PresSophCls; TrsSrCls; Band; Chr; HonRl; StuCncl; EdYrBk; Chrldr; DARAwd; Uw Gb.

EBSTEIN, David H; Highland Park HS; Highland Park, IL; Band; ChrhWkr; CmntyWkr; CncrtBnd; MrchBnd; NHS; Orch; SchPl; TchrAde; LetterTennis; College; International Relations.

EBY, Brent C; Camden Frontier HS; Camden, MI; 3/44 VPSrCls; Band; HonRl; NHS; SchAde; SchMus; SchPl; TchrAde; FFA; Bsbl; College; Vocational.

EBY, Jonathan S; Andover HS; Bloomfield Hills, MI; Aud/Vis; CmntyWkr; HonRl; YthFlsp; GerCl; LetterTrk; Coll; Med.

EBY, Joseph H; Streator Twp HS; Streator, IL; 69/378 Band; CncrtBnd; HonRl; Mdrgl; MrchBnd; NatlThespSoc; PepBnd; SchMus; SchPl; Ill State Univ; Communications.

EBY, Kathleen G; St Marys Academy; Monroe, MI; TreasChrl; HonRl; NHS; RptrYrbk; EdYrBk; LatCl; GAA; College.

EBY, Tamra K; Public HS; Oneill, NE; Band; CncrtBnd; HonRl; MrchBnd; NHS; PepBnd; PpCl; LetterBsktbl; LetterGlf; LetterTrk; Univ Of Ne; Rn Nurse.

ECCLES, Eloise A; Kalamazoo Loy Norrix HS; Kalamazoo, MI; Chr; HonRl; LetterTrk; Michigan Tech Univ; Engineer.

ECHAVARRIA, Donna; Lourdes HS; Chicago, IL; 110/299 HonRl; Teen; SpnCl; Bsbl; Trade School; Stewardess.

ECHELE, Mary; St Charles HS; St Charles, MO; 15/560 Chrs; HonRl; JrNHS; NHS; SchMus; RptrYrbk; SchPpr; FBLA; PpCl;.

ECHER, Jill; Lucas HS; Lucus, KS; VPSophCls; Band; Chr; Chrs; ChrhWkr; CncrtBnd; HonRl; Bsktbl; Trk; Chrldr; College.

ECHER, Kristy L; Luray HS; Lucas, KS; 6/19 Band; HonRl; SchMus; SchPl; StuCncl; Bsbl; CaptBsktbl; LetterTrk; DanFAwd; 4-HAwd; GodCntryAwd; Ft Hays Kansas St College; Social Work.

ECHEVARRIA, Annette; Rudyard HS; Kincheloe Afb, MI; Band; Chr; ChrhWkr; CncrtBnd; HonRl; MrchBnd; PepBnd; SchAde; TchrAde; SpnCl; Coll.

ECHOLA, Donald; Forest Park HS; Crystal Falls, MI; 41#64#.

ECHOLA, Jean; Forest Park HS; Crystal Falls, MI; 8/89 Band; CncrtBnd; HonRl; MrchBnd; PepBnd; SchPl; TchrAde; FNA; IMSpt; Ferris Stae Coll; Dental Assistant.

ECHTENKAMP, Lee E; Wakefield HS; Wakefield, NE; ChrhWkr; HonRl; NHS; Pres4-H; FBLA; LetterBsktbl; LetterFtbl; 4-HAwd; College; Computer Program.

ECHTENKAMP, Victoria; West HS; Sioux City, IA; ChrhWkr; HonRl; SchPl; RptrYrbk; FrCl; PpCl; BttyCrckrAwd; College; Dentistry.

ECK, Grace M; Oak Lawn Comm HS; Hometown, IL; 75/686 HonRl; LitMag; TchrAde; College; Medicine.

ECK, Margaret L; St Johns HS; St Louis, MO; 4/83 HonRl; JrNHS; LbryAde; SecNHS; SchMus; StuCncl; EdYrBk; IMSpt; Meremac Comm Coll; Engineering.

ECK, Steven R; Niles West HS; Niles, IL; 129/666 HonRl; Univ Of Ill; Business Admin.

ECK, Tami L; Venice HS; Venice, IL; 2/50 PresFrshCls; VPSophCls; TrsJrCls; Band; Chrs; HonRl; OffAde; SchPl; SctActv; StuCncl; StuGov; YthFlsp; RptrSchPpr; FHA; Chrldr; S Illinois Univ; Business.

ECK, William B; York Comm HS; Elmhurst, IL; ChrhWkr; HonRl; LitMag; NHS; NatlMeritSF; College; Law.

ECKARDT, Alice A; Ogilvie HS; Ogilvie, MN; TrsSophCls; Chr; ChrhWkr; CncrtBnd; HonRl; NHS; ChmnBsktbl; LetterTrk; GAA; PPFtbl; Mankato State College; Pre Law.

ECKEHRECHT, Steven; Charles City Community HS; Charles City, IA; Aud/Vis; HonRl; JrNHS; NHS; SctActv; BttyCrckrAwd; Univ Of N Iowa; Biology.

ECKEL, Christopher W; Bethany HS; Sullivan, IL; Band; Chr; Chrl; Chrs; CncrtBnd; Mdrgl; MrchBnd; Orch; PepBnd; SchMus; Music Course In Jr College.

ECKEL, Elizabeth A; Bishop Ryan HS; Minot, ND; Chrs; DrlTm; HonRl; JrNHS; NHS; Sdlty; GerCl; Chrldr; Coll; Art Tchr.

ECKEL, Michael W; Danville HS; Danville, IL; 31/613 CmntyWkr; HonRl; JA; StuCncl; StuGov; SchPpr; CivCl; Bsktbl; Ftbl; Trk; College; Professional.

ECKENRODE, Craig C; Austin Catholic Prep HS; Detroit, MI; 66/115 ChrhWkr; HospAde; SchPl; SctActv; TchrAde; GerCl; LetterFtbl; Oakland Univ; Physician Assistant.

ECKER, Lori D; Jacksonville HS; Jacksonville, IL; 10/363 SecAFS; HonRl; NHS; College; Psychology.

ECKER, Michael J; Wayland Acad; Downers Grove, IL; VPFrshCls; SecTrsSophCls; HonRl; StuCncl; StuGov; LetterBsbl; LetterSocr; Wrstlng; Political Science.

ECKERLE, Beverly A; Jasper HS; Jasper, IN; 5/286 Chrs; HonRl; NHS; SchPpr; 4-H; PpCl; Indiana University; Medical Technology.

ECKERLE, Duane J; Jasper HS; Jasper, IN; Chr; Chrs; ChrhWkr; CmntyWkr; SchMus; 4-H; Trade School.

ECKERLE, Russell A; Otterville HS; Otterville, MO; HstFrshCls; ALBoysSt; Band; Chrs; CncrtBnd; HonRl; MrchBnd; PepBnd; PpCl; LetterBsktbl; College; Data Processing.

ECKERMAN, Virginia J; Warren HS; Warren, IL; Band; SecChrs; CmntyWkr; CncrtBnd; DrlTm; HonRl; LbryAde; Mdrgl; MrchBnd; PepBnd; GAA; 4-HAwd; JAAwd; Univ Of Wisconsin; Elem Education.

ECKERT, Charles S; Hutsonville HS; Palestine, IL; PresJrCls; Band; HonRl; PolWkr; SchPl; StuCncl; Yrbk; EdSchPpr; SARAwd; Rend Lake Com Coll; Liberal Arts.

ECKERT, Cheryl; Huntington North HS; Huntington, IN; ALAGirlsSt; Band; CncrtBnd; MrchBnd; PepBnd; StuCncl; Twrl; Purdue Univ; Nutrition.

ECKERT, Donald J; Divine Word Seminary; Janesville, WI; HonRl; Sacrstn; StuCncl; RptrSchPpr; LetterBsbl; Bsktbl; LetterFtbl; IMSpt; College; Missionary Brother.

ECKERT, Gary S; Hobart HS; Hobart, IN; 80/400 HonRl; NHS; TchrAde; CaptFtbl; PPFtbl; Wrstlng; IMSpt; PPFtbl; ChmbCommrsAwd; JAAwd; In U; Major Study.

ECKERT, Karen L; New Athens Community HS; Lenzburg, IL; 7/67 Band; Chrs; HonRl; PepBnd; Quill&Scroll; SchPl; TchrAde; Yrbk; FHA; PresFTA; GAA; University; Music.

ECKERT, Marcia A; Dubois HS; Celestine, IN; 4/86 Band; Chrs; HonRl; Sdlty; 4-H; Business School; Secretary.

ECKERT, Michael A; Jasper HS; Jasper, IN; 91/320 HonRl; NHS; SpnCl; MthCl; PpCl; Ftbl; Wrstlng; JAAwd; JETSAwd; CitAwd; College; Electronics Or Engr.

ECKERT, Michael L; Racine Lutheran HS; Racine, WI; 2/69 Band; CncrtBnd; HonRl; NHS; PepBnd; IMSpt; RotaryAwd; Concordia Lutheran College; Lutheran Minist.

ECKERT, Paula D; Hoopeston East Lynn HS; Hoopeston, IL; 3/127 Band; HonRl; PresNHS; NatlThespSoc; SchMus; RptrSchPpr; PpCl; GAA; IMSpt; DanFAwd; RotaryAwd; Illinois St Univ; Accounting.

ECKERT, Sonia K; L P Goodrich HS; Fond Du Lac, WI; Chr; CncrtBnd; HonRl; MrchBnd; Yrbk; College.

ECKHARDT, John J; Loyola Academy; Chicago, IL; 100/442 Chrs; CmntyWkr; HonRl; LitMag; NatlMeritCmnd; SchPpr; University; Medicine.

ECKHOFF, Cindy M; Rock Bridge HS; Columbia, MO; 111/265 HonRl; SctActv; Twrl; PpCl; LetterBsktbl; Chrldr; Dallas Fm College; Fashion Merchandising.

ECKHOFF, Janice L; Sweet Springs HS; Sweet Springs, MO; Band; ChrhWkr; CncrtBnd; HonRl; MrchBnd; PepBnd; TchrAde; Yrbk; FHA; FTA; Univ; Secretary.

ECKHOFF, Marsha E; Cal Comm HS; Alexander, IA; Band; ChrhWkr; CncrtBnd; HonRl; MrchBnd; PepBnd; SchPl; YthFlsp; SchPpr; FHA; Bus School; Vocational.

ECKHOLM, Candice F; Wing Public HS; Wing, ND; Band; Chr; Chrs; ChrhWkr; CncrtBnd; DrmMjrt; HonRl; MrchBnd; PepBnd; SchMus; Bsktbl; Wahpeton St Sch Of Science.

ECKHOUSE, Richard; N Lincoln Hs; Chicago, IL; CmntyWkr; HonRl; LbryAde; Teen; MthCl; Ftbl; Swmmng; U Of Illinois;chemical Engineering Chemist.

ECKLES, William F; Ida HS; Monroe, MI; 5/175 ALBoysSt; ChrhWkr; HonRl; NHS; SctActv; StuCncl; StuGov; Bsktbl; Us Naval Academy; Engineer.

ECKLUN, Patti A; Holdrege Sr HS; Holdrege, NE; Chrs; CmntyWkr; HonRl; SchMus; StuGov; SecTeen; Pres4-H; SecFBLA; 4-HAwd; Univ; Math.

ECKLUND, Robert S; Falls Sr HS; International Fls, MN; CmntyWkr; HonRl; PolWkr; Teen; SptEdSchPpr; Ftbl; Trk; IMSpt; College Or Univ; Professional.

ECKMAN, Charles D; Northrop HS; Fort Wayne, IN; 17/568 CncrtBnd; HonRl; MrchBnd; PepBnd; PolWkr; TchrAde; In U; Law.

ECKMAN, Suzanne L; Huntington North HS; Warren, IN; StuCncl; RptrYrbk; SptEdYrbk; PpCl; CaptChrldr; Indiana University.

ECKMANN, Beverly; Tri Center HS; Persia, IA; Band; ChrhWkr; CncrtBnd; HonRl; JA; MrchBnd; PepBnd; RptrYrbk; RptrSchPpr; IMSpt; College; Home Ec.

ECKSTAINE, Terry J; Winner Sr HS; Winner, SD; 32/156 ChrhWkr; StuCncl; StuGov; FTA; Bsbl; CaptBsktbl; CaptFtbl; CaptTrk; University Of So Dakota; Professional.

ECKSTEIN, Jeff S; Dubois HS; Jasper, IN; ALBoysSt; Band; HonRl; PpCl; College; Transportation Management.

EDDLEMAN, Judith A; Dongola Unit HS; Dongola, IL; VPBand; Chrs; CncrtBnd; MrchBnd; PepBnd; SchMus; StuCncl; FHA; Chrldr; PpCl; Fashion Merchandising.

EDDLEMAN, Tony D; Dongola Unit HS; Dongola, IL; 2/30 Band; HonRl; StuCncl; SchPpr; 4-H; SciCl; LetterBsktbl; LetterTrk; DanFAwd; 4-HAwd; So Ill Univ; Journalism.

EDDY, Debi A; Campus HS; Wichita, KS; HonRl; College; Vocation.

EDDY, Joseph P; Helias HS; Jefferson City, MO; HonRl; NHS; NatlMeritSF; RptrYrbk; SptEdYrbk; LetterBsktbl; Ftbl; LetterTrk; College; Engineering.

EDDY, Mark; Wauwatosa West HS; Wauwatosa, WI; 1/436 AFS; Band; HonRl; NHS; NatlMeritFnl; Orch; PepBnd; Quill&Scroll; RptrSchPpr; MthCl; Northwestern Univ; Music Education.

EDDY, Randall C; Centerville HS; Centerville, IA; ChrhWkr; HonRl; YthFlsp; Letter4-H; LetterFFA; CaptFtbl; Trk; 4-HAwd; College; Science.

EDDY, Raymond H; Newark Comm HS; Newark, IL; 12/59 PresSophCls; ChrhWkr; CmntyWkr; HonRl; SchMus; SchPl; SctActv; TchrAde; YthFlsp; FTA; Bsbl; Bsktbl; Socr; College; Professional.

EDDY, Roger L; Newark HS; Newark, IL; CmntyWkr; HonRl; StuCncl; StuGov; LetterBsbl; Bsktbl; LetterSocr; LetterTrk; CchngActv; IMSpt;.

EDDY, Stanley M; Parker HS; Beloit, WI; ALBoysSt; HonRl; NHS; TchrAde; 4-H; TreasFFA; PresSciCl; Bsktbl; LetterFtbl; IMSpt; U Of Wis Whitewater; Accounting Phy Ed.

EDDY, Steven A; United Township HS; Silvis, IL; 2/517 PresSrCls; HonRl; NHS; StuCncl; Yale Univ; Medicine.

EDDY, Vivian A; Onaga HS; Onaga, KS; DrmMjrt; HonRl; MrchBnd; SchMus; SchPl; StuCncl; Yrbk; LetterBsktbl; Chrldr; PresAwd; Kansas Univ; Nursing.

EDEL, Susan S; Bad Axe HS; Bad Axe, MI; 3/150 SecJrCls; CmntyWkr; HonRl; NHS; SchMus; SctActv; TchrAde; FHA; FrCl; CaptChrldr; Central Michigan Univ; Elementary Education.

EDEMA, Ruth A; Wheaton Christian HS; Wheaton, IL; VPJrCls; Chr; HonRl; NHS; StuCncl; RptrYrbk; PpCl; GAA; Calvin Coll; Special Ed (deaf).

EDEN, Deborah D; Diller HS; Diller, NE; 3/19 TrsSrCls; Band; Chr; Chrs; CncrtBnd; HonRl; MrchBnd; Orch; PepBnd; SchMus; SchPl; SctActv; StuGov; Teen; Lincoln School; Accountant.

EDEN, Lori; Holy Family HS; Monroe, NE; 14/33 HonRl; NHS; PpCl; College; Social Work.

EDEN, Ronnie; Woden Crystal Lake HS; Britt, IA; HonRl; NHS; StuCncl; CitAwd; Trade; Agriculture.

EDER, Margaret T; Waterford Union HS; Waterford, WI; 6/210 Chr; ChrhWkr; DrlTm; HonRl; Mdrgl; NHS; SchMus; SchPl; Nursing School; Nursing.

EDER, Margaret T; Waterford HS; Waterford, WI; 7/211 AFS; Chrs; ChrhWkr; DrlTm; HonRl; NHS; SchMus; FrCl; PpCl; Columbia Hosp School; Nurse.

EDER, Thomas A; St Laurence HS; Chicago, IL; 1/381 Aud/Vis; Band; CncrtBnd; HonRl; MrchBnd; NatlFornLg; PepBnd; Quill&Scroll; EdSchPpr; SciCl; Glf; IMSpt; KiwanAwd; Univ Of Notre Dame; Accounting.

EDER, Tim A; Chelsea HS; Chelsea, MI; MrchBnd; NHS; NatlMeritSchl; StuCncl; Ftbl; Central Mich Univ.

EDGAR, Jacqueline A; Shawnee Mission East HS; Prairie Village, KS; ALAGirlsSt; Chr; Chrl; HonRl; SecNatlFornLg; NHS; NatlThespSoc; SchMus; SchPl; StuCncl; FrCl; LatCl; PpCl; IMSpt; University; Law.

EDGAR, Jeanine A; Faulkton HS; Orient, SD; ChrhWkr; HonRl; LbryAde; SchAde; SchPl; TchrAde; RptrSchPpr; 4-H; FHA; PpCl; College; Vocational.

EDGAR, Keith A; Cedar Lake Academy; Troy, MI; 2/72 PresJrCls; TrsSrCls; Chr; HonRl; NHS; Bsbl; Ftbl; IMSpt; Andrews Univ; Optometry.

EDGAR, Timothy M; Coulterville Public HS; Coulterville, IL; 1/23 ChrhWkr; HonRl; SchPl; StuCncl; EdSchPpr; SpnCl; LetterBsbl; BttyCrckrAwd; Eastern Il Univ.

EDGAR, Tonia D; Trico HS; Ava, IL; Chr; Chrs; ChrhWkr; CmntyWkr; HonRl; OffAde; SchMus; StuCncl; Bsktbl; PresAwd;.

EDGE, Cynthia; Newton Sr HS; Newton, IA; 22/300 Band; Chr; Chrl; Chrs; ChrhWkr; CncrtBnd; HonRl; Mdrgl; MrchBnd; IMSpt; 4-HAwd; Seminary; Ministry.

EDGECOMB, Cindy L; River Valley HS; Three Oaks, MI; ChrhWkr; HonRl; TchrAde; 4-H; FFA; PpCl; Trk; 4-HAwd; PresAwd; Teaching.

EDGERLY, Curtis L; Alburnett Comm HS; Central City, IA; 18/42 VPSrCls; Chr; SchMus; FTA; LetterBsktbl; LetterBsbl; LetterFtbl; LetterTrk; LetterWrstlng; Coe College; Certified Public Accountant.

EDGERTON, Richard M; Creighton Prep HS; Omaha, NE; HonRl; JA; Sdlty; Ftbl; Trk;.

EDGETT, Pamela; Lyons Township Hs; La Grange, IL; 125/1226 Chrs;.

EDGREN, Lucinda J; Oskaloosa Sr HS; Oskaloosa, IA; Aud/Vis; Chr; Chrs; HonRl; NatlFornLg; PolWkr; StuCncl; SchPpr; 4-H; University; Law.

EDIGER, Mark D; Newton HS; North Newton, KS; 3/309 VPSrCls; Chr; ChrhWkr; HonRl; PresNatlFornLg; PresSctActv; StuCncl; LetterTennis; IMSpt; AmLegAwd; Bethel Coll; Chemistry.

EDIN, Julie; New Richmond HS; New Richmond, WI; Chr; Chrs; Mdrgl; SchMus; SchPl; FrCl; Univ Of Eau Claire; Entertainer.

EDIN, Napoleon B; Culhanee Gap Military Prep; Jamestown, ND; 1/137 PresSrCls; AFS; HonRl; NatlMeritFnl; SptEdYrbk; EdSchPpr; FBLA; Bsbl; Bsktbl; Tennis; Yale; Research In Time Physics.

EDINGTON, Max; Bluffton HS; Bluffton, IN; Aud/Vis; SchPl; SctActv; StuCncl; SptEdSchPpr; SpnCl; IMSpt; Ball State U; Natural Resources.

EDINGTON, Sharon A; West Vigo HS; West Terre Haute, IN; HonRl; NHS; OffAde; TchrAde; SptEdSchPpr; FTA; GAA; Isu; Spec Ed.

EDISON, Janice M; Sterling HS; Sterling, IL; HonRl; College; Professional.

EDISON, Pamela G; Highland Park HS; Highland Park, IL; 111/638 ChrhWkr; JrNHS; NHS; NatlMeritSF; SchPl; StuGov; PresFHA; GAA; Univ; Psychologist.

EDLER, Jill; West Marshall HS; State Center, IA; 10/88 Band; Chr; Chrs; CncrtBnd; HonRl; Mdrgl; MrchBnd; NHS; PepBnd; Iowa State Univ; Elementary Ed.

EDLER, Jo Jean; Pearl City HS; Pearl City, IL; LbryAde; StuCncl; RptrSchPpr; EdSchPpr; SptEdSchPpr; FHA; PpCl; Chrldr;.

EDLER, Randy; Shannon Hs; Shannon, IL; 18/31 ALBoysSt; SecFrshCls; PresSophCls; 4-H; FFA; LetterBsbl; LetterTrk; DanFAwd; 4-HAwd; JAAwd;.

EDLING, Cindy A; Elston Sr HS; Michigan City, IN; ALAGirlsSt; HonRl; NHS; SpnCl; Chrldr; Univ Notre Dame; Engineering.

EDMINSTER, Jean E; Andrews Academy; Berrien Springs, MI; Chr; NatlMeritSchl; TchrAde; IMSpt; Marriage; Secretarial.

EDMISTON, Laura L; Abingdon HS; Abingdon, IL; Band; Chrs; HonRl; LitMag; YthLg; EdSchPpr; SecFTA; LetterBsktbl; GAA; BttyCrckrAwd; University Of Illinois; Sec English Educ.

EDMISTON, Virginia L; Lafayette HS; Ballwin, MO; 1/480 Chrs; ChrhWkr; HonRl; LbryAde; NHS; NatlMeritSF; NatlSciFnd; PresSctActv; PresYthFlsp; GAA; Univ; Chemical Engineering.

EDMOND, Patricia A; Ecorse HS; Ecorse, MI; Chr; CncrtBnd; HonRl; LbryAde; NHS; NatlMeritSF; SchPl; TchrAde; RptrSchPpr; EdSchPpr; Mich State Univ; Fashion Merchandising.

EDMONDS, Dale S; Oshkosh West HS; Oshkosh, WI; 1/435 ALAGirlsSt; Chr; HonRl; PresJrNHS; Mdrgl; NHS; NatlMeritSF; SchPl; PresStuCncl; NCTE; College; Psychology.

EDMONDS, Douglas J; Leavenworth HS; Leavenworth, KS; HonRl; NHS; NatlMeritSF; ROTC; StuCncl; SciCl; Ftbl; Trk; Wrstlng; RotaryAwd; Ks Univ; Law.

EDMONDS, John R; Niles West HS; Morton Grove, IL; 119/666 HonRl; NHS; SctActv; LetterTrk; GodCntryAwd; Univ Of Illinois; Liberal Arts.

EDMONDS, Kenneth K; Mc Louth HS; Mc Louth, KS; VPSophCls; ALBoysSt; Chr; ChrhWkr; CncrtBnd; NHS; SchPl; YthFlsp; 4-H; University; Professional.

EDMONDS, Lionel; Northrop HS; Ft Wayne, IN; LbryAde; TchrAde; LatCl; PpCl; Bsktbl; Coll; Professional.

EDMONDS, R Michael; Wauwatosa West HS; Wauwatosa, WI; 37/437 AFS; CmntyWkr; JrNHS; NatlMeritCmnd; SchPl; StuGov; University; Medicine.

EDMONDSON, James R; Perry Community HS; Perry, IA; CmntyWkr; HonRl; College.

EDMONDSON, Mary; Chanute Senior HS; Chanute, KS; ALAGirlsSt; Band; CncrtBnd; HonRl; MrchBnd; OffAde; PepBnd; SctActv; YthFlsp; PpCl;.

EDMUND, Laura J; Cambridge HS; Cambridge, IL; AFS; Chrs; ChrhWkr; HonRl; NHS; SchPl; SctActv; StuCncl; RptrYrbk; 4-H; Bsbl; LetterBsktbl; GAA; Univ Of Ill; Home Economics.

EDMUNDS, Teresa A; Northern Heights Hs; Dunlap, KS; Band; Chrs; CncrtBnd; HonRl; NHS; SchMus; SchPl; StuCncl; FBLA; PpCl; PPFtbl; College; Professional.

EDNEY, Geoffrey A; Arlington HS; Indianapolis, IN; 52/463 HonRl; PolWkr; Quill&Scroll; StuCncl; SptEdSchPpr; LetterBsktbl; Glf; IMSpt; In Un Ca; Medical Profession.

EDSON, David V; Nashua HS; Ionia, IA; 20/75 Band; ChrhWkr; CncrtBnd; HonRl; MrchBnd; NHS; StuCncl; YthFlsp; 4-H; CaptBsktbl; LetterFtbl; LetterTrk; College; Agriculture.

EDSON, Jeffrey; Webber Township HS; Mt Vernon, IL; HonRl; PpCl; Trk;.

EDSON, Rodney M; Gothenburg HS; Gothenburg, NE; Band; CmntyWkr; YthFlsp; SchPpr; Bsbl; LetterBsktbl; LetterFtbl; LetterTrk; CchngActv; IMSpt; Col; Coaching.

EDSTROM, Cynthia S; Waterford Union HS; Waterford, WI; 1/190 Chr; Chrs; CtyCnl; CncrtBnd; HonRl; MrchBnd; NHS; PepBnd; StuCncl; YthFlsp; College.

EDWALL, Alfred; No St Paul Sr HS; No St Paul, MN; HonRl; StuGov; YthLg; RptrSchPpr; Ftbl; Wrstlng; IMSpt; College; Indefinite.

EDWARDS, Ada E; Mitchell HS; Mitchell, IN; 11/120 ChrhWkr; SecCncrtBnd; MrchBnd; NHS; Quill&Scroll; SchPpr; RotaryAwd; Univ; Special Education Teacher.

EDWARDS, Anthony B; Deland Weldon HS; Weldon, IL; AFS; ALBoysSt; Band; Chrs; HonRl; SchMus; SchPl; RptrSchPpr; FrCl; Eastern Ill Univ; Sociology.

EDWARDS, Barbara D; Rantoul Township HS; Rantoul, IL; ChrhWkr; HonRl; Orch; SchMus; StuCncl; TchrAde; Illinois State; Art.

EDWARDS, Carol; Kirkwood Sr HS; Kirkwood, MO; VPFrshCls; AFS; HonRl; HospAde; Quill&Scroll; SchMus; StuCncl; Yrbk; FrCl; PpCl; U Of Mo; Home Economics.

EDWARDS, Charles H; Putnam County HS; Mc Nabb, IL; 5/86 VPSrCls; HonRl; NHS; SctActv; FrCl; MthCl; Univ Of Illinois; Biology.

EDWARDS, Cheryl A; Usd 279 Jewell HS; Jewell, KS; ALAGirlsSt; Band; Chrs; CncrtBnd; HonRl; HospAde; MrchBnd; PepBnd; SchPl; Chrldr; U Of Kansas; Rn.

EDWARDS, Cindy L; Greenview HS; Greenview, IL; 18/50 PepBnd; CmntyWkr; DrmMjrt; SchMus; 4-H; FHA; Chrldr; IMSpt; DanFAwd; 4-HAwd; Business School; Secretarial Work.

EDWARDS, Connie J; East HS; Wichita, KS; Chrs; ChrhWkr; HonRl; JCC; OffAde; StuGov; RptrYrbk; EdSchPpr; PpCl; Chrldr; Ks St U; Elem Ed.

EDWARDS, Daniel G; Lewistown Community HS; Lewistown, IL; ChrhWkr; CmntyWkr; FFA; Ftbl; Trk; AmLegAwd; College; Farmer.

EDWARDS, Danny L; Ashland Greenwood HS; Ashland, NE; 10/64 VPFrshCls; TrsSrCls; Band; CncrtBnd; HonRl; MrchBnd; LetterBsktbl; LetterFtbl; LetterGlf; LetterTrk; LetterWrstlng; Univ Of Nebraska; Physical Education.

EDWARDS, Debra J; Danville HS; Danville, IL; 61/613 Aud/Vis; HonRl; JA; StuCncl; SchPpr; Parkland College; Dental Hygiene.

EDWARDS, Debra L; Paxton HS; Loda, IL; 23/136 PresJrCls; Band; DrmMjrt; HonRl; NHS; SchPl; StuCncl; YthFlsp; GAA; Illinois State Univ; Special Education.

EDWARDS, Debra L; Tri HS; Straughn, IN; HonRl; NHS; OffAde; SpnCl; PpCl; SciCl; Chrldr; GAA; Clge; Physical Therapy.

EDWARDS, Deland J; Beaumont HS; Saint Louis, MO; Chr; ChrhWkr; DrmBgl; LatCl; Swmmng; Clg; Civil Engineer.

EDWARDS, Dennis G; Fulton HS; Fulton, IL; Chr; ChrhWkr; CncrtBnd; PresNatlThespSoc; SchMus; SchPl; TchrAde; Ftbl; Trk; Wrstlng; Univ Of Iowa; Theater Arts.

EDWARDS, Floyd W; Nickerson HS; So Hutchinson, KS; 21/120 SctActv; TchrAde; SciCl; GodCntryAwd; Ks St U; Chem Engineer.

EDWARDS, Frances R; Greenview HS; Greenview, IL; 5/24 PresJrCls; ALAGirlsSt; HonRl; HospAde; NHS; TchrAde; EdYrBk; FSA; FTA; GAA; College; Nursing.

EDWARDS, Gloria K; Walnut Grove HS; Walnut Grove, MO; 5/18 HstSrCls; ChrhWkr; HonRl; HospAde; OffAde; SchPl; Yrbk; SchPpr; FHA; PpCl; Nursing ;rn.

EDWARDS, Gregory; Grosse Pte North HS; Grosse Pte Woods, MI; Band; ChrhWkr; CncrtBnd; HonRl; MrchBnd; NHS; NatlMeritFnl; PepBnd; CivCl; Mich Technological U; Chemical Engineering.

EDWARDS, James M; Rock Island HS; Rock Island, IL; 140/690 TchrAde; LetterFtbl; Univ Of Notre Dame; Attorney.

EDWARDS, Janet M; Ottawa HS; Ottawa, IL; 9/420 HonRl; HospAde; NHS; OffAde; TchrAde; SchPpr; Univ Of Illinois; Dance.

EDWARDS, Jayne E; Chatsworth HS; Chatsworth, IL; AFS; Band; CncrtBnd; HonRl; MrchBnd; SchMus; SchPl; YthFlsp; 4-H; SpnCl; Parkland Jr College.

EDWARDS, Jeffrey A; Lincoln HS; Warren, MI; 18/347 HonRl; Clge; Astronomy.

EDWARDS, Jeffrey B; Watertown HS; Watertown, SD; ALBoysSt; Band; SecNatlFornLg; VPNatlThespSoc; Orch; PolWkr; Quill&Scroll; SchPl; EdSchPpr; Trk; Sdsu; Journalism.

EDWARDS, Jeffrey N; Hardy HS; Hardy, NE; PresSophCls; Band; Chr; PresChrhWkr; SctActv; PresYthFlsp; KeyCl; Bsbl; LetterBsktbl; LetterFtbl; LetterTrk; GodCntryAwd; College; Agriculture.

EDWARDS, Joann; Walter P Chrysler HS; New Castle, IN; CmntyWkr; JA; OffAde; PolWkr; 4-H; FHA; LatCl; PpCl; Bsbl; AmLegAwd; Univ Of Evansville; Accounting.

EDWARDS, Joel J; Streator Twp HS; Streator, IL; HonRl; StuCncl; YthFlsp; KeyCl; CaptSwmmng; KiwanAwd; Univ; Law.

EDWARDS, John C; Belleville Township HS; Belleville, IL; 1/803 NHS; NatlMeritSF; NatlThespSoc; SchMus; SchPl; SctActv; SchPpr; GerCl; MthCl; DARAwd; Major In Biology.

EDWARDS, Joni K; Meridian HS; Villa Ridge, IL; ChrhWkr; HonRl; College; Computer Science.

EDWARDS, Judith A; Benton Consolidated HS; Macedonia, IL; Chrs; ChrhWkr; CmntyWkr; HonRl; NHS; OffAde; SchPpr; 4-H; FBLA; SpnCl; Jr College; Business.

EDWARDS, Julie A; Meridian HS; Villa Ridge, IL; ChrhWkr; HonRl; College; Computer Science.

EDWARDS, Keith A; E Alton Wood River HS; Wood River, IL; ChrhWkr; CncrtBnd; HonRl; JrNHS; NHS; PepBnd; LetterBsktbl; LetterTrk; AmLegAwd; Southern Ill Univ; Biology.

EDWARDS, Kimberly J; Norfolk Sr HS; Norfolk, NE; 38/292 ChrhWkr; HonRl; SecNatlFornLg; SchPl; SctActv; RptrSchPpr; 4-H; FHA; PpCl; PPFtbl; 4-HAwd; College; Legal Secretary.

EDWARDS, Linda M; Fairbury HS; Fairbury, NE; 34/132 Chr; ChrhWkr; HonRl; FHA; GerCl; College Of Beauty Cosmotolgy; Beautician.

EDWARDS, Mark R; North Platte HS; North Platte, NE; SctActv; Bsbl; Bsktbl; Ftbl; Tennis; Wrstlng; CchngActv; College; Forestry.

EDWARDS, Marla G; Zion Benton Twp HS; Zion, IL; PresSophCls; Chrs; HonRl; OffAde; StuCncl; StuGov; RptrYrbk; GerCl; Secretary At Bank Of Zion.

EDWARDS, Mary A; Luray Public HS; Luray, KS; Chrs; HonRl; SchMus; SchPl; TchrAde; RptrYrbk; RptrSchPpr; FrCl; PpCl; College; Nursing.

EDWARDS, Nancy J; Ankeny Senior HS; Ankeny, IA; 34/300 Chr; Chrs; HonRl; Mdrgl; NHS; TchrAde; YthFlsp; FTA; SciCl; Trk; College; Music Major.

EDWARDS, Raymond M; Rich Central HS; Matteson, IL; 33/400 Band; CncrtBnd; HonRl; MrchBnd; NatlFornLg; NHS; NatlMeritCmnd; PepBnd; StuCncl; SchPpr; MthCl; Purdue Univ; Engineering.

EDWARDS, Richard A; Minot HS; Minot, ND; ALBoysSt; HonRl; JrNHS; NHS; FFA; SpnCl; Bsbl; Wrstlng; IMSpt; Coll.

EDWARDS, Robb A; Tuscaloosa HS; Nebraska City, NE; 58/558 Band; Chr; Chrs; CncrtBnd; HonRl; JrNHS; MrchBnd; NHS; NatlThespSoc; PepBnd; SchPl; SctActv; StuCncl; YthFlsp; University; Computer Science.

EDWARDS, Ronald D; Pittsburg HS; Pittsburg, KS; 18/230 ALBoysSt; LetterFtbl; LetterTrk; College; Medicine.

EDWARDS, Sally A; Lawrence HS; Lawrence, MI; VPBand; CncrtBnd; HonRl; MrchBnd; Orch; PepBnd; SchMus; TchrAde; 4-H; 4-HAwd; Western Mich Univ; Music.

EDWARDS, Scott; Benton HS; St Joseph, MO; 24/174 ALBoysSt; DrlTm; HonRl; LbryAde; OffAde; ROTC; StuCncl; StuGov; Bsktbl; Rice Univ.

EDWARDS, Susan M; Bentley HS; Livonia, MI; Band; Chr; CncrtBnd; HonRl; JA; MrchBnd; Orch; PepBnd; SchPl; RptrYrbk; Mich State Univ.

EDWARDS, Thomas C; Jefferson City Sr HS; Jefferson City, MO; 13/490 VPSrCls; Band; ChrhWkr; HonRl; JrNHS; NHS; Quill&Scroll; SctActv; PresMthCl; Bsktbl; Wrstlng; IMSpt; GodCntryAwd; Univ Of Mo; Doctor.

EDWARDS, William G; Wayne Memorial HS; Wayne, MI; PresSrCls; HonRl; IntrClCncl; JrNHS; StuGov; Bsbl; Bsktbl; LetterFtbl; LetterTrk; LetterWrstlng; Mi State Univ; Veterinary.

EDWARDS, William J; Brother Rice HS; Oak Lawn, IL; 5/735 CmntyWkr; HonRl; NHS; NatlMeritCmnd; StuCncl; LetterFtbl; LetterSocr; University.

EDWARDSON, Lora L; Sioux Rapids Community HS; Sioux Rapids, IA; 2/19 VPFrshCls; PresSrCls; Chr; Chrs; ChrhWkr; HonRl; NHS; NatlMeritCmnd; SchPl; Yrbk; LetterBsbl; LetterBsktbl; LetterTrk; BttyCrckrAwd; College; Interior Decorating.

EEFTINK, Leon L; Leopold R 3; Leopold, MO; PresFrshCls; TrsJrCls; SchPl; StuCncl; Bsbl; Bsktbl; S Mo Univ;.

EENIGENBURG, Donald M; Thornton Frac South HS; Chicago Hts, IL; 11/552 Chr; ChrhWkr; HonRl; NHS; Bsktbl; Ftbl; Moody Bible Institute; Christian Science.

EETEN, Rochelle J; Green Valley HS; Green Valley, IL; 1/22 HonRl; JrNHS; NHS; RedCrAde; EdYrBk; Chrldr; University; Accounting.

EFFERTZ, Kevin P; Velva HS; Velva, ND; HonRl; VP4-H; VPFFA; LetterBsbl; LetterBsktbl; LetterFtbl; 4-HAwd; College; Agriculture.

EFFERTZ, Michelle E; Velva Public HS; Velva, ND; 6/48 ALAGirlsSt; Band; HonRl; NHS; TchrAde; 4-H; FFA; FHA; LetterBsktbl; Trk; College.

EFFINGER, Linda; Normandy Sr HS; St Louis, MO; HonRl; NHS; Quill&Scroll; TchrAde; YthFlsp; RptrYrbk; Yrbk; GerCl; Univ Of Mo; Special Education Instruc.

EFFKEN, David J; Nemaha Valley HS; Cook, NE; 7/33 Band; Chrl; Chrs; HonRl; MrchBnd; PepBnd; TreasYthFlsp; Yrbk; GerCl; Bsktbl; U Of Ne; Pharmacy.

EFFKEN, Sarah J; Nemaha Valley HS; Cook, NE; 3/23 PresJrCls; ALAGirlsSt; PresBand; Yrbk; Pres4-H; SecTrsSophCls; LetterBsktbl; LetterTrk; Chrldr; BttyCrckrAwd; U Of Nebr Lincoln; Home Econ.

EFFLAND, Claudia L; Lincoln HS; Lincoln, KS; 10/60 VPSrCls; Band; Chrs; MrchBnd; PepBnd; SchPl; SecStuCncl; Twrl; Kansas St Univ; Audiology.

EFFLAND, David L; Southern HS; Stronghurst, IL; 1/55 ALBoysSt; ChrhWkr; HonRl; NHS; SchPl; SctActv; RptrSchPpr; FrCl; Ftbl; Trk; Univ Of Illinois; Computer Science.

EFFLAND, Kimberly K; Lincoln HS; Lincoln, KS; Band; Chr; Chrs; ChrhWkr; CncrtBnd; MrchBnd; PepBnd; SchPl; College; Business.

EFLIN, Lila; Gladbrook Comm HS; Beaman, IA; ALAGirlsSt; ChrhWkr; HonRl; SchPl; StuCncl; FTA; College; Special Education Teacher.

EFTHIM, Frank P; Southwest HS; St Louis, MO; 105/570 Aud/Vis; Band; ChrhWkr; CncrtBnd; DrmBgl; MrchBnd; OffAde; Orch; PepBnd; SchMus; College; Engineer.

EFTINK, Eva M; Leopold R 3 HS; Lutesville, MO; SecJrCls; CmntyWkr; HonRl; SchMus; SchPl; StuCncl; EdYrBk; RptrSchPpr; PpCl; Chrldr;.

EFTINK, Jeffrey J; Leopold HS; Lutesville, MO; VPSrCls; HonRl; SchPl; SctActv; StuCncl; YthLg; PpCl; Bsbl; Bsktbl; CchngActv;.

EFTINK, Mary L; Notre Dame HS; Quincy, IL; 6/110 Band; Chr; CmntyWkr; HonRl; TreasNHS; PresStuCncl; SchPpr; SecFrCl; Tennis; GAA; DARAwd; Illinois State Univ; Special Education.

EGAN, Brian D; Wayne Memorial HS; Westland, MI; HonRl; StuCncl; IMSpt; Clg; Lawyer.

EGAN, Daniel J; Appleton West HS; Appleton, WI; PresFrshCls; Band; NHS; NatlThespSoc; SchMus; StuGov; EdSchPpr; FrCl; KiwanAwd; NCTE; College.

EGAN, Deborah; O Gorman HS; Sioux Falls, SD; DrlTm; SchMus; StuGov; TchrAde; PpCl; Chrldr; GAA; IMSpt; College; Physical Education.

EGAN, James F; Grosse Pte North HS; Grosse Pte Shores, MI; HonRl; FrCl; PPFtbl; College; Dentistry.

EGAN, Jeffrey C; Willowbrook HS; Lombard, IL; Band; HonRl; LitMag; MrchBnd; NHS; PepBnd; RptrSchPpr; SciCl; LetterTennis; Univ Of Ill; Writer.

EGAN, Joseph P; Thornridge HS; Dolton, IL; 2/670 HonRl; NHS; NatlMeritCmnd; Quill&Scroll; EdYrBk; KeyCl; MthCl; Univ Of Illinois; Engineering.

EGAN, Marlene R; Cuba City HS; Cuba City, WI; 20/120 Band; Chrs; ChrhWkr; Mdrgl; NHS; StuCncl; RptrYrbk; RptrSchPpr; Chrldr; GAA; 4-HAwd; LionAwd; Columbia College; Journalism.

EGAN, Matthew J; Brother Rice HS; Chicago, IL; 100/435 HonRl; LbryAde; NatlMeritCmnd; StuCncl; StuGov; Univ Of Illinois; Law.

EGAN, Michael D; Springfield HS; Battle Creek, MI; HonRl; NatlMeritFnl; NatlMeritSF; SchMus; SchPl; Michigan St Univ; Music.

EGAN, Nancy; Riverside HS; Dearborn, MI; Band; CncrtBnd; HonRl; JA; MrchBnd; NHS; PepBnd; SchMus; StuCncl; FrCl; Univ Mi; Computer Sci.

EGAN, Sharon P; Roncalli HS; Omaha, NE; HonRl; NHS; 4-H; FBLA; SpnCl; Univ Of Omaha; Legal Sec.

EGAN, Thomas P; Weber HS; Cicero, IL; 30/209 HonRl; RptrSchPpr; SciCl; Bsbl; Loyola Univ; Lawyer.

EGAN, Timothy J; St Johns Prep; Melrose, MN; PresJrCls; Band; SchAde; StuCncl; StuGov; RptrYrbk; Bsktbl; Ftbl; CchngActv; College;.

EGBERT, Brian D; Buhler HS; Hutchinson, KS; ModUN; TchrAde; FFA; PpCl; Ftbl; Trk; Kansas Univ; Professional.

EGE, Sheila L; North Miami HS; Roann, IN; VPSophCls; VPJrCls; Band; ChrhWkr; CncrtBnd; HonRl; MrchBnd; ModUN; NHS; PepBnd; College; Social Studies.

EGEBRECHT, Ruth D; Luther HS; Chicago, IL; 17/225 Chrs; ChrhWkr; HonRl; NHS; NatlMeritSchl; SchAde; StuCncl; RptrSchPpr; GerCl; North Park College; Medicine.

EGEBRECHT, Ruth D; Luther North HS; Chicago, IL; 17/220 HonRl; LbryAde; NHS; NatlMeritFnl; NatlMeritSchl; OffAde; SchMus; StuCncl; RptrSchPpr; GerCl; North Park Col; Physician.

EGELAND, Kay L; Morris Community HS; Morris, IL; 7/240 Band; Chr; Chrs; ChrhWkr; CncrtBnd; HonRl; MrchBnd; SecNHS; Pres4-H; Bsktbl; Aurora College; Criminal Justice System.

EGELER, Susan J; Leland Public HS; Leland, MI; 1/22 ALAGirlsSt; PresBand; ChrhWkr; Mdrgl; VPNHS; NatlMeritCmnd; RedCrAde; EdYrBk; RptrSchPpr; 4-H; Olivet; Professional Accompanist.

EGER, Kyla J; Tell City HS; Tell City, IN; 29/200 ALAGirlsSt; Band; Chrs; CncrtBnd; HonRl; MrchBnd; PepBnd; StuCncl; Sec4-H; GerCl; PpCl; 4-HAwd; College; Veterinarian.

EGGE, Kimberly T; West HS; Green Bay, WI; SecBand; CncrtBnd; HonRl; HospAde; LbryAde; MrchBnd; NHS; Orch; PepBnd; VPFrCl; Coll; Medical.

EGGEMAN, Cindy L; Valley R 6 HS; Potosi, MO; Chrs; HonRl; TchrAde; YthFlsp; Yrbk; SchPpr; Trade School; Vocation.

EGGEMEYER, Cathy D; Steeleville HS; Steeleville, IL; SecSophCls; SecJrCls; Chrs; StuCncl; FBLA; FHA; SpnCl; PpCl; University; Nursing.

EGGEN, Gloria; Helias HS; Jefferson City, MO; 14/175 Chrs; DrmBgl; HospAde; SchMus; RptrYrbk; PpCl; Avila College; Bs In Nursing.

EGGER, Larry M; Alleman HS; Rock Island, IL; ChrhWkr; HonRl; LetterBsktbl; IMSpt; College; Biology.

EGGERMAN, Anita; Lockwood HS; Lockwood, MO; 3/44 SecSophCls; HonRl; SchPl; RptrYrbk; RptrSchPpr; FTA; PpCl; Chrldr; PPFtbl; Univ; Teacher Special Educ.

EGGERMAN, Wiladine M; Lockwood HS; Lockwood, MO; TrsJrCls; VPSrCls; ALAGirlsSt; SchPl; HonRl; LitMag; RptrYrbk; FTA; PpCl; IMSpt; College;.

EGGERS, Carol A; Rock Bridge Sr HS; Columbia, MO; 7/213 Chrl; Mdrgl; NatlFornLg; NHS; NatlMeritSF; SchMus; SchPl; StuGov; PpCl; Chrldr; TreasGAA; IMSpt; OptClAwd; College; Psychiatry.

EGGERS, Cindy G; Carson HS; Carson, ND; Chr; Chrs; ChrhWkr; HonRl; SchPl; RptrSchPpr; SchPpr; LetterBsktbl; Secretary.

EGGERS, Debbie J; Corsica HS; Corsica, SD; PresJrCls; Chrs; HonRl; SchMus; StuCncl; Yrbk; PpCl; Trk; Chrldr; College; Nursing.

EGGERS, Kenneth G; Farragut Comm HS; Riverton, IA; 13/41 SctActv; YthFlsp; LetterFtbl; LetterTrk; CaptWrstlng; Southeast Comm Coll; Auto Mech.

EGGERS, Mark D; Philip HS; Philip, SD; 4/40 TrsSophCls; ALBoysSt; Band; Chr; Chrs; ChrhWkr; CncrtBnd; HonRl; MrchBnd; NHS; Ftbl; Trk; AmLegAwd; University.

EGGERS, Richard D; Andrew Comm HS; Bellevue, IA; 14/46 SecFrshCls; TrsSophCls; Chrs; HonRl; SchPl; PpCl; Bsbl; Bsktbl; Trk; 4-HAwd; Coll.

EGGERS, Robert L; Walther Lutheran HS; Villa Park, IL; PresJrCls; Chr; HonRl; NHS; SchMus; TreasStuCncl; Ftbl; Trk; AmLegAwd; Univ Of Tennessee.

EGGERS, Terrie K; Custer HS; Custer, SD; VPJrCls; Band; Chr; ChrhWkr; CmntyWkr; NatlThespSoc; LetterBsktbl; LetterVFWAwd; Chrldr; GAA; College.

EGGERT, Carol E; St Agatha HS; Detroit, MI; 25/108 Chrl; HonRl; Trade School; Performing Arts.

EGGERT, James R; Russell HS; Russell, KS; ALBoysSt; Band; ChrhWkr; CncrtBnd; HonRl; LitMag; PresNatlFornLg; NatlMeritSF; GerCl; VoiceDemAwd; Coll.

EGGERT, Linda L; Algoma HS; Algoma, WI; ChrhWkr; CmntyWkr; HonRl; TchrAde; RptrSchPpr; SchPpr; GAA; IMSpt; Collge; Vocation.

EGGERTH, Richard A; Swea City Community HS; Swea City, IA; PresSophCls; ALBoysSt; Aud/Vis; ChrhWkr; HonRl; StuCncl; YthFlsp; 4-H; SpnCl; LetterTrk; Technical Sch; Elec Tech.

EGGING, Linda; St Patricks HS; Gurley, NE; NHS; Yrbk; 4-H; PpCl; Chrs; 4-HAwd; Coll; Pro.

EGLAND, Annette L; John F Kennedy HS; Bloomington, MN; HstFrshCls; Chr; CmntyWkr; HonRl; SchAde; Patricia Stevens College; Fashion Mdse.

EGLAND, Cindy A; Colo Comm HS; Nevada, IA; PresJrCls; HonRl; NHS; StuCncl; Pres4-H; SpnCl; PresPpCl; LetterBsktbl; CaptChrldr; 4-HAwd; Univ Of No Iowa; Teaching.

EGLAND, Lois J; New London Sr HS; New London, WI; ALAGirlsSt; ChrhWkr; CmntyWkr; HonRl; NHS; StuCncl; StuGov; PresPpCl; GAA; AmLegAwd; DARAwd; GovHonPrgAwd; PresAwd; Univ Of Wisconsin; Dietetics.

EGLER, Elizabeth A; Charlevoix HS; Charlevoix, MI; ChrhWkr; TchrAde; SpnCl; PpCl; Bsktbl; Swmmng; Trk; GAA; IMSpt; Trade Sch.

EGLESTON, Winifred P; White River Independence HS; Whiteriver, SD; 1/37 ALAGirlsSt; Band; HonRl; SchPl; Yrbk; 4-H; LetterTrk; Chrldr; 4-HAwd; CitAwd; Sd State Univ; Extension Home Ec.

EGLETON, James J; Toluca HS; Toluca, IL; 3/26 VPSophCls; VPJrCls; HonRl; NHS; SchPl; PpCl; LetterBsbl; LetterBsktbl; LetterTrk; College.

EGLEY, Judy D; Crestview HS; Decatur, IN; 17/75 Band; HospAde; JA; TchrAde; 4-H; SpnCl; SciCl; Trk; IMSpt; 4-HAwd; JAAwd;.

EGLINTON, Carol R; Houston HS; Houston, MN; Band; SchMus; SchPl; RptrYrbk; VP4-H; FTA; Clg; English.

EGLSEDER, Patty M; Guttenberg Comm HS; Guttenbert, IA; Chr; Chrs; HonRl; Mdrgl; SchMus; SchPl; Bsktbl; LetterTrk; U Of N Iowa.

EGNER, Katherine R; Lake Orion HS; Lake Orion, MI; 33/332 Chrs; ChrhWkr; HonRl; NHS; OffAde; SchMus; StuGov; TchrAde; Col ;elem Ed.

EHALT, Jan K; Floyd Central HS; Georgetown, IN; PresBand; Chr; CmntyWkr; HonRl; PolWkr; VPStuCncl; TchrAde; Pres4-H; PresPpCl; 4-HAwd; Indiana Univ Se; Registered Nurse.

EHALT, Roseann; Floyd Central HS; Georgetown, IN; PresJrCls; Band; Chr; HonRl; StuGov; SchPpr; SpnCl; Bsktbl; Chrldr; 4-HAwd; College; Major In Political Science.

EHARDT, Paul H; Croswell Lexington HS; Lexington, MI; 4/187 TrsFrshCls; ALBoysSt; HonRl; NHS; StuCncl; LetterBsktbl; LetterGlf; LetterTrk; W Mich U; Pre Medicine.

EHLEN, Ann M; Salem Central HS; Salem, WI; Chr; ChrhWkr; CmntyWkr; DrlTm; HonRl; NatlFornLg; NHS; SchPl; TchrAde; Yrbk; FNA; SpnCl; MthCl; Nursing School; Nurse.

EHLEN, James K; John Hersey HS; Mt Prospect, IL; Illinois State Univ; Special Education.

EHLENBACH, Paul J; Marquette Univ HS; Milwaukee, WI; 16/240 Chrs; HonRl; LitMag; NatlMeritSF; SchPl; TchrAde; RptrYrbk; SciCl; LetterTrk; Univ; Medical Doctor.

EHLENZ, Michael E; White Bear Sr HS; White Bear Lake, MN; Band; Chr; Chrl; CncrtBnd; MrchBnd; NHS; PepBnd; Coll.

EHLER, Del R; Raatool HS; Thomasboro, IL; TrsJrCls; HonRl; FFA; Bsktbl; LetterTrk; Ag.

EHLERS, Angela A; Lyman HS; Presho, SD; 1/53 ALAGirlsSt; Band; HonRl; NHS; SchPl; Yrbk; RptrSchPpr; Trk; PPFtbl; 4-HAwd; Univ Of Sd; Pharmacy.

EHLERS, D; Sevastopol HS; Sturgeon Bay, WI; 4/89 TrsJrCls; TrsSrCls; Chrl; ChrhWkr; NHS; StuGov; RptrYrbk; RptrSchPpr; IMSpt; GovHonPrgAwd; Coll.

EHLERS, Ginger R; Deshler HS; Deshler, NE; ChrhWkr; HonRl; JrNHS; NHS; OffAde; SchAde; SchMus; StuGov; TchrAde; LetterPpCl; GAA; PPFtbl; So Central Comm College; Secretary.

EHLERS, Jeffery; Nebraska City HS; Nebraska City, NE; TrsJrCls; Band; NHS; Orch; PepBnd; PresFrshCls; StuGov; GerCl; College; Professional.

EHLERS, Leigh A; Gordon HS; Gordon, NE; 14/68 HonRl; SchPl; TchrAde; EdYrBk; RptrSchPpr; FHA; Trk; IMSpt; Chadron St College; Elem Education.

EHLERS, Victoria L; Colby HS; Dorchester, WI; HonRl; HospAde; LbryAde; SecYthFlsp; FHA; FrCl; Technical School; Respiratory Therapy.

EHLERT, Jilleen A; Geo S Parker HS; Janesville, WI; 12/387 ChrhWkr; HonRl; NHS; StuCncl; TchrAde; SchPpr; GAA; U Of Wi Whitewater; Acct Business.

EHLI, Charlene I; Dodge Public HS; Dodge, ND; TrsFrshCls; Chrs; TchrAde; SchPpr; LetterBsktbl; LetterChrldr; IMSpt; College.

EHLINGER, Lois A; Andrew Community HS; La Motte, IA; PresJrCls; Chrs; HonRl; NHS; NatlThespSoc; SchMus; SchPl; StuCncl; Yrbk; GerCl; College; Nursing.

EHLY, Milton F; Sutton HS; Sutton, NE; 2/56 PresFrshCls; Chrs; HonRl; NHS; SchPl; LetterBsktbl; LetterFtbl; College; Architecture.

EHM, Mike; Wisconsin Acad; Milwaukee, WI; ChrhWkr; StuCncl; StuGov; Trk; IMSpt; Adnrews Univ; Theology.

EHMEN, Randall L; Adams HS; Pickrell, NE; 8/26 PresJrCls; Aud/Vis; Band; Chrs; CncrtBnd; DrmMjrt; LbryAde; Bsktbl; Ftbl; Trk; Univ; Pol Sci.

EHN, Linda K; Laurens Comm HS; Laurens, IA; 34/51 ChrhWkr; HonRl; SchPl; Teen; Yrbk; RptrSchPpr; PpCl; Bsktbl; Trk; Iowa Central Comm College; Clerical.

EHNERT, Beverly; Kewaskum HS; Kewaskum, WI; Aud/Vis; ChrhWkr; HonRl; RptrSchPpr; SchPpr; Bsktbl; Trk; Service; Photography.

EHNI, Mark G; Richwoods HS; Peoria, IL; 31/447 HonRl; NHS; TchrAde; CaptWrstlng; Air Force Academy; Air Force Officer.

EHR, Yvette L; Dominican HS; Milwaukee, WI; PresSophCls; ChrhWkr; HonRl; NHS; NatlMeritSF; SchPl; StuCncl; StuGov; YthFlsp; IMSpt; Univ Of Co; Astronomy.

EHRENSTROM, Peter G; Boylan Central Catholic HS; Rockford, IL; 32/400 Band; CncrtBnd; HonRl; NatlMeritSF; SchMus; SchPl; SchPpr; LatCl; SciCl; LetterTrk; Coll;.

EHRESMANN, Karl J; Northwestern HS; Maple, WI; Bsktbl; LetterFtbl; LetterTrk; CchngActv; College; Farming.

EHRHARD, Michael; St Thomas Aquinas HS; St Louis, MO; HonRl; Trk; Univ; Professional.

EHRHARDT, Danielle K; St Pauls College HS; Lohman, MO; VPSophCls; Chrs; HonRl; NHS; SchPl; SctActv; TreasSciCl; LetterBsktbl; IMSpt; College; Elem Teaching.

EHRHARDT, David A; West Richland HS; Noble, IL; Chrs; ChrhWkr; HonRl; SchMus; SchPl; RptrSchPpr; SchPpr; PpCl; Bsbl; Trk; College; Engineering.

EHRHARDT, John M; Putnam County HS; Mcnabb, IL; 4/80 PresSophCls; HonRl; NHS; NatlMeritSchl; SchMus; StuCncl; 4-H; Trk; AmLegAwd; Univ Of Il; Veterinary Science.

EHRHART, Janice M; Notre Dame HS; Quincy, IL; 3/109 VPJrCls; TrsSrCls; Chrs; NHS; StuCncl; FrCl; PpCl; Bsktbl; Tennis; GAA; University Of Illinois.

EHRHART, Mark J; Durand HS; Durand, MI; NatlMeritSchl; TchrAde; FrCl; Bsbl; Bsktbl; Ftbl; LetterTennis; College; Comm Pilot.

EHRINGER, Paul D; Borden HS; Sellersburg, IN; ChrhWkr; HonRl; LetterTrk; Coll;accounting.

EHRINGER, Stephen A; Borden HS; Sellersburg, IN; ChrhWkr; HonRl; I U S; Electronics.

EHRKE, Julienne K; Lester Prairie Public HS; Lester Prairie, MN; TrsJrCls; Chr; CncrtBnd; HonRl; MrchBnd; PepBnd; YthFlsp; Yrbk; Chrldr; GAA; Trade School; Vocation.

EHRKE, Thomas; Columbus HS; Columbus, WI; FFA;.

EHRLICH, Abraham; Cass Technical HS; Detroit, MI; PresAFS; Aud/Vis; CmntyWkr; HonRl; LbryAde; NHS; NatlMeritFnl; PolWkr; PresSpnCl; Univ Mi; Biology Research.

EHRLICH, Jeffrey P; Niles North HS; Skokie, IL; 95/650 HonRl; NatlMeritSF; NatlThespSoc; SchMus; SchPl; StuCncl; University Of Illinois; Medicine.

EHRLICH, Karen; Resurrection HS; Chicago, IL; 1/294 Band; HonRl; JrNHS; NHS; Quill&Scroll; RptrSchPpr; SchPpr; FrCl; GerCl; GAA; College; Ocean Engineering.

EHRLICH, Karen K; Wahlert HS; Dubuque, IA; 17/441 CmntyWkr; HonRl; LitMag; NHS; StuGov; TchrAde; SchPpr; SpnCl; MthCl; Clarke Clg; Computer Science.

EHRLICH, Karen M; Resurrection HS; Chicago, IL; 1/294 CncrtBnd; JrNHS; NHS; Quill&Scroll; SchMus; SchPpr; FrCl; GerCl; Bsktbl; GAA; College; Ocean Engr.

EHRLICH, Robert A; Loyola Academy; Chicago, IL; College; Physics.

EHRMAN, Jacqueline A; Roseland Public HS; Roseland, NE; Chr; Chrs; HonRl; SchMus; YthFlsp; GerCl; TreasPpCl; Col; Pro.

EHRNTHALLER, James; Toluca HS; Toluca, IL; 6/24 Chrs; HonRl; SchPl; StuCncl; 4-H; FFA; FSA; PpCl; SciCl; Bsktbl; Univ; Unknown.

EHRNTHALLER, Judith C; Toluca HS; Toluca, IL; 2/40 SecJrCls; Band; Chr; Chrs; ChrhWkr; CmntyWkr; CncrtBnd; HonRl; LbryAde; MrchBnd; GAA; St Francis Sch Of Nursing; Nursing.

EHRSAM, Anne E; Bern HS; Bern, KS; ALAGirlsSt; Mdrgl; NHS; PresStuCncl; YthFlsp; EdYrBk; RptrSchPpr; Bsktbl; Trk; Chrldr; Univ; Professional.

EICH, Kelly S; Geneva Public HS; Geneve, NE; 20/56 Chr; Chrl; Chrs; CmntyWkr; CncrtBnd; Mdrgl; PepBnd; SchMus; SchPl; EdYrBk; Univ Of Ne; Animal Science.

EICH, Linda; Green Mountain HS; Marshalltown, IA; VPSophCls; SecJrCls; Chrs; HonRl; Mdrgl; SchMus; SchPl;.

EICH, Linda K; Mendota HS; Mendota, IL; 42/205 DrlTm; HonRl; HospAde; FNA; GAA; Coll; Nurse.

EICHELBERGER, Cynthia R; Shickley Public HS; Shickley, NE; 7/29 HonRl; LbryAde; SchPl; Yrbk; College; Accounting.

EICHELBERGER, Sharon L; Muscatine HS; Muscatine, IA; 61/382 Chr; Chrs; NHS; YthFlsp; 4-H; Bsktbl; Trk; IMSpt; PPFtbl; College.

EICHELBERGER, Susan M; Muscatine HS; Muscatine, IA; 14/348 Band; Chr; NHS; StuCncl; YthFlsp; 4-H; LetterTrk; IMSpt; PPFtbl; 4-HAwd; Muscatine Community College; Social Worker.

EICHELMAN, Julie A; Prospect HS; Arlington Heights, IL; 13/610 Chr; DrlTm; HonRl; NHS; Quill&Scroll; SctActv; RptrYrbk; Yrbk; PpCl; College; Journalism.

EICHHOLZ, Deborah A; Washington HS; Washington, MO; 1/272 Band; HonRl; LitMag; NHS; NatlMeritSF; SchMus; SctActv; EngCl; GerCl; IMSpt; College; Secondary Educ.

EICHHORN, Brian H; Southeastern HS; Augusta, IL; 17/49 Chrs; ChrhWkr; CmntyWkr; LbryAde; SchMus; YthFlsp; 4-H; FTA; PpCl; IMSpt; Catepilllartractor Co; Electrician With The.

EICHHORN, Jeffrey M; Middleton HS; Middleton, WI; 23/290 HonRl; NHS; Bsbl; LetterFtbl; Wrstlng; College; Profession Dvm.

EICHLER, Edward J; St Thomas Academy; Minneapolis, MN; ChrhWkr; HonRl; ROTC; Bsktbl; St Thomas College; Engineering.

EICHLER, Kelly J; Duchesne Academy; Omaha, NE; Band; Chr; Chrs; ChrhWkr; CmntyWkr; HospAde; ModUN; RedCrAde; FrCl; PpCl; Creighton Univ; Nursing.

EICHMANN, Judith A; Random Lake HS; Random Lake, WI; Chrs; ChrhWkr; DrlTm; HonRl; Mdrgl; SchMus; YthFlsp; RptrYrbk; Yrbk; RptrSchPpr; FHA;.

EICHORN, Cheryl A; Greenway HS; Bovey, MN; SctActv; 4-H; FHA; GAA; 4-HAwd; Hibbing Coll; Dental Assit.

EICHSTEDT, Bonnie L; Ripon Sr HS; Ripon, WI; Chr; Chrs; CmntyWkr; SchMus; StuCncl; YthFlsp; LetterBsbl; LetterChrldr; GAA; College; Nursing.

EICHTEN, Jerry J; Cathedral HS; New Ulm, MN; Aud/Vis; HonRl; NHS; SchMus; RptrSchPpr; LetterBsktbl; LetterGlf; Tennis; IMSpt; College.

EICKERT, Carol A; Carl Schurz HS; Chicago, IL; 6/809 HonRl; LbryAde; NHS; OffAde; TreasYthFlsp; FrCl; DARAwd; Northeaster Il U; Biology.

EICKERT, Patricia A; Byron HS; Oregon, IL; Band; ChrhWkr; DrlTm; HonRl; MrchBnd; PepBnd; YthFlsp; Arizona St Univ; Music.

EICKHOFF, Karla J; Ava HS; Ava, MO; 11/101 FHA; SpnCl; Trk;.

EICKMAN, Cynthia L; Derry Meridian HS; Indianapolis, IN; 109/573 PresFrshCls; SecTrsSophCls; SecTrsJrCls; Chrs; HonRl; StuCncl; RptrYrbk; SpnCl; PpCl; Chrldr; Indiana University; Psychologist.

EIDE, Beth A; Oelwein Comm HS; Oelwein, IA; 5/183 Band; Chrs; ChrhWkr; HonRl; NHS; PolWkr; RptrSchPpr; LetterBsbl; Bsktbl; Glf; LetterTrk; PPFtbl; Univ Of Iowa; Lawyer.

EIDE, Sandra L; Robbinsdale Sr HS; Robbinsdale, MN; Band; ChrhWkr; CncrtBnd; HonRl; MrchBnd; Orch; PepBnd; LetterSwmmng; College; Surgical Nurse.

EIDEM, Michael; St Louis Park HS; St Louis Park, MN; ChrhWkr; HonRl; Bsbl; Ftbl; Swmmng; CchngActv; IMSpt; Coll.

EIDEM, Nancy K; Marietta Public HS; Marietta, MN; Band; Chr; HonRl; SchPl; StuCncl; Yrbk; EdSchPpr; FHA; EngCl; PpCl; Medical Institute Of Minn; Medical Assistan.

EIDEM, Richard; Fridley 14 HS; Fridley, MN; .

EIDSON, Michael K; Macks Creek R V; Macks Creek, MO; 1/16 TrsFrshCls; Band; Chr; CncrtBnd; HonRl; StuCncl; TchrAde; MthCl; SciCl; Cmsu; Math.

EIDSON, Shela J; Ash Grove HS; Springfield, MO; 5/55 Band; Chrs; ChrhWkr; HonRl; NHS; Twrl; 4-H; FHA; PpCl; PPFtbl; Burge Sch Nursing; Rn.

EIERMANN, Jean; Metamora Twp Hs; East Peoria, IL; Chrs; ChrhWkr; DrlTm; SchMus; FTA; GerCl; PpCl; GAA; Augustana College; Elementary Teaching.

EIFERT, Diana L; Chaffee HS; Chaffee, MO; 2/63 SecSophCls; SecJrCls; ALAGirlsSt; DrlTm; HonRl; MrchBnd; NHS; SchPl; EdYrBk; PpCl; College; Speech Pathology.

EIFFERT, Kenton L; Harrisonville Sr HS; Harrisonville, MO; 5/166 HonRl; NHS; StuCncl; PpCl; LetterLetterGlf; LetterTennis; IMSpt; PresAwd; College.

EIFLER, Mark A; Castle HS; Chandler, IN; 5/291 ALBoysSt; Band; CncrtBnd; PresJrNHS; CaptMrchBnd; NHS; YthFlsp; Pres4-H; PresKeyCl; DanFAwd; College; Music.

EIGSTI, Calvin; Western Community Unit HS; Buda, IL; Chrs; HonRl; StuCncl; YthFlsp; 4-H; FFA; Bsbl; Ftbl; College; Science Major.

EIKENS, John; Caledonia HS; Caledonia, MN; 3/145 HonRl; NHS; NatlMeritCmnd; SchPl; SchPpr; 4-H; SpnCl; 4-HAwd; St Johns; Medicine.

EIKMEIER, James; Dodge Public HS; Dodge, NE; SchPl; 4-H; Bsbl; Bsktbl; Ftbl; Trk; Bus Sch.

EIKMEIER, Jeanine; Dodge HS; Dodge, NE; PresSophCls; Band; Chrs; CncrtBnd; DrmMjrt; HonRl; MrchBnd; PepBnd; Chrldr; IMSpt; PPFtbl; Coll;med.

EIKMEIER, Tami M; Rocori HS; St Cloud, MN; CncrtBnd; HonRl; MrchBnd; PepBnd; SchMus; TchrAde; 4-H; Bsktbl; GAA; College; Teacher.

EILAND, Anthony G; Campion Jesuit HS; Chicago, IL; CncrtBnd; LitMag; LbryAde; ModUN; NatlMeritSF; PolWkr; StuCncl; StuGov; Trk; IMSpt; Univ; Prof.

EILDERTS, Lisa M; Parkersburg Comm HS; Parkersburg, IA; PresJrCls; Band; Chr; Chrl; Chrs; ChrhWkr; HonRl; NHS; SchMus; SpnCl; Bsktbl; Trade Schl.

EILER, Mark E; Northfield HS; Roann, IN; ChrhWkr; FFA; Ftbl; Trk; Wrstlng; IMSpt; 4-HAwd; College; Farm General Ag.

EILER, Mark V; Markesan Sr HS; Markesan, WI; VPSrCls; HonRl; ROTC; SpnCl; Ftbl; CaptTrk; KiwanAwd; LionAwd; PresAwd; Univ Of Wisconsin; Geology.

EILERING, Barbara J; Routt HS; Jacksonville, IL; 11/62 CmntyWkr; HonRl; NHS; SctActv; RptrYrbk; SchPpr; SpnCl; SciCl; AmLegAwd; EldAwd; Il Coll; Teacher Of Deaf.

EILERS, David G; Central HS; Waterloo, IA; ALBoysSt; Band; Orch; SchPl; SctActv; StuCncl; SpnCl; CaptBsbl; Bsktbl; CaptFtbl; CchngActv; AmLegAwd; Wartburg College; Biology.

EILERT, Sandra S; Mt Olive Public HS; Walshville, IL; 1/56 VPSrCls; ALAGirlsSt; Band; ChrhWkr; HonRl; NHS; Yrbk; 4-H; FHA; GAA; Univ Of Illinois; Mathematics.

EILERT, Sandra S; Mt Olive Community HS; Walshville, IL; 1/60 ALAGirlsSt; Band; ChrhWkr; NHS; Yrbk; 4-H; FHA; GAA; 4-HAwd; VoiceDemAwd; Univ Of Il; Math, Or Education.

EIMERS, Karen L; Burt Community HS; Burt, IA; PresJrCls; ALAGirlsSt; HonRl; NHS; StuCncl; Yrbk; Bsbl; Bsktbl; Trk; 4-HAwd; Bus Sch; Office Work.

EINAN, Kathleen; Rich East HS; Park Forest, IL; 81/326 ChrhWkr; CmntyWkr; HonRl; YthFlsp; SecTrsFrshCls; PpCl; Il St Univ; Med Art.

EINBECKER, Kurt W; Thornton Twp HS; Dolton, IL; 30/750 HonRl; NHS; StuCncl; College; Medicine.

EINEICHNER, Beverly K; Glidden Public HS; Glidden, WI; Band; Chr; ChrhWkr; CncrtBnd; HonRl; MrchBnd; NatlFornLg; PepBnd; TchrAde; FTA; Technical School.

EINFELDT, Dennis L; United Township HS; East Moline, IL; LetterBsbl; LetterFtbl; College.

EINFELDT, James P; Durant Comm HS; Durant, IA; VPFrshCls; PresJrCls; Chrs; SchMus; SchPl; StuCncl; Teen; 4-H; Ftbl; CaptWrstlng; CchngActv; 4-HAwd; University Of Iowa.

EINHAUS, John W; Jac Cen Del HS; Osgood, IN; 41/72 Band; ChrhWkr; HonRl; PolWkr; SchPl; StuCncl; 4-H; PpCl; LetterBsktbl; Trk; CchngActv; 4-HAwd; College; Business Admin.

EINSEL, Jayne; Greensburg HS; Greensburg, KS; ALAGirlsSt; Band; Chrs; DrmMjrt; HonRl; Mdrgl; NatlFornLg; NHS; PepBnd; SchMus; SchPl; PresStuCncl; PpCl; LetterTennis; College; Medicine.

EINSPAHR, Kevin D; Hildreth HS; Hildreth, NE; PresFrshCls; PresSrCls; Chrs; CncrtBnd; HonRl; MrchBnd; StuCncl; RptrYrbk; Bsktbl; CaptFtbl; LionAwd; Kearney State College; Physical Therapist.

EINSTADTER, Douglas; Huron HS; Ann Arbor, MI; Band; HonRl; MrchBnd; Univ Of Calif; Chemistry.

EINSWEILER, Dirk A; Galena HS; Galena, IL; VPFrshCls; PresSophCls; PresJrCls; PresSrCls; HonRl; StuCncl; StuGov; CaptFtbl; University; Engineering.

EIS, Beth A; Radcliffe Community HS; Hubbard, IA; 6/34 Band; Chr; Chrs; ChrhWkr; NHS; TchrAde; YthFlsp; Yrbk; FHA; Simpson College; Elem Education.

EIS, Victoria L; Perry Lecompton HS; Perry, KS; Aud/Vis; HonRl; LbryAde; NHS; NatlMeritSF; SchPl; PpCl; Bsktbl; LetterTrk; Washburn Col; Rn.

EISBRENNER, Timothy B; Austin HS; St Clair Shores, MI; 33/115 Business College; Accountant.

EISCHEID, Marian C; Pope John Central HS; Elgin, NE; SecSophCls; ALAGirlsSt; Chrs; ChrhWkr; NHS; SchMus; StuGov; RptrSchPpr; EdSchPpr; College; Nursing.

EISCHENS, Steven M; Moline Sr HS; Moline, IL; Band; CncrtBnd; HonRl; MrchBnd; PepBnd; TchrAde; Illinois State University; Medicine.

EISELE, Charles T; Elmore Public HS; Elmore, MN; 3/27 VPFrshCls; TrsSophCls; VPJrCls; HonRl; NHS; Quill&Scroll; StuCncl; GerCl; Ftbl; Trk; St Johns; Math Journalism.

EISELE, Hermann H; Christian Brothers Col HS; St Louis, MO; 30/160 DrlTm; HonRl; JA; NHS; ROTC; SchMus; RptrSchPpr; LetterFtbl; LetterTrk; JAAwd; St Marys University; Lawyer.

EISEN, Richard B; Unity Chr HS; Allendale, MI; TrsFrshCls; Chr; HonRl; 4-H; Calvin Col; Teacher Major Art.

EISENACH, Marybeth; Mc Cook HS; Culbertson, NE; AFS; Chrs; ChrhWkr; HonRl; NHS; Orch; SchMus; YthFlsp; MthCl; PpCl; U Ne Lincoln; Professional.

EISENBEIS, Julie M; St Pius X HS; Festus, MO; HonRl; TchrAde; Teen; PpCl; SciCl; College; Professional.

EISENBEISZ, Cynthia; Bowdle HS; Bowdle, SD; Chr; Chrs; HonRl; SchAde; SchPl; StuCncl; Yrbk; SchPpr; FTA; PpCl; Presentation Coll; Nursing.

EISENBERG, Sarah; Highland Park HS; Highland Park, IL; NatlMeritCmnd; College; Special Education.

EISENBRAUN, Ruth A; Flanagan HS; Gridley, IL; 2/60 HonRl; NHS; SchPl; TchrAde; YthFlsp; RptrYrbk; VPGerCl; TreasSciCl; LetterBsktbl; LetterTrk; GAA; Wheaton College; Liberal Arts.

EISENHUTH, Lori H; West Aurora HS; Aurora, IL; Chr; Chrs; HonRl; JA; NHS; TchrAde; YthFlsp; PpCl; College; Liberal Arts.

EISENMANN, David; Madison HS; Madison, NE; HonRl; NHS; SctActv; StuCncl; FBLA; FFA; MthCl; Swmmng; Northeast Ne Tech Colllege; Agriculture.

EISENREICH, Jami L; Downers Grove S HS; Woodridge, IL; Chrs; DrlTm; HonRl; SchMus; SchPl; SctActv; TchrAde; PpCl; Swmmng; ChmnChrldr; IMSpt; College; R N.

EISENRICH, Heidi L; Mt St Benedict HS; Redby, MN; Band; CmntyWkr; CncrtBnd; HonRl; PepBnd; SchPl; Sdlty; StuCncl; RptrYrbk; RptrSchPpr; PpCl; College; Physical Therapy.

EISENZIMMER, Lona J; Lalcota HS; Lakota, ND; ALAGirlsSt; Chr; HonRl; OffAde; RptrYrbk; RptrSchPpr; FHA; PpCl; CaptBsktbl; CaptTrk; Business Sch; Certified Public Accountant.

EISFELLER, James D; Chadwick HS; Chadwick, IL; 1/34 ChrhWkr; HonRl; SchPl; YthFlsp; SciCl; Bsbl; LetterBsktbl; IMSpt; CitAwd;.

EISMA, Janice; West Sioux HS; Ireton, IA; SecFrshCls; SecTrsJrCls; Chr; Chrs; HonRl; LitMag; SchMus; YthFlsp; IMSpt; Univ; Music Education.

EISOLD, Kim R; Morris HS; Morris, IL; 5/250 Chr; Chrs; ChrhWkr; HonRl; NHS; College; Professional.

EISSENS, Linda S; Fulton Comm HS; Fulton, IL; AFS; ChrhWkr; CmntyWkr; HonRl; HospAde; SctActv; RptrYrbk; RptrSchPpr; Bsktbl; College; Political Science.

EISSINGER, Paul M; Medina HS; Medina, ND; 8/18 ALBoysSt; Band; Chr; CncrtBnd; HonRl; PepBnd; SchPl; YthFlsp; RptrSchPpr; 4-H; FFA; PpCl; LetterBsktbl; LetterTrk; North Dakota St Univ; Agriculture.

EISSLER, Holly K; Willowbrook HS; Lombard, IL; 4/890 HonRl; JrNHS; NHS; NatlMeritSF; Univ Of Ill; Math.

EISSMAN, Mark P; Niles West HS; Lincolnwood, IL; CmntyWkr; HonRl; PolWkr; StuCncl; StuGov; GerCl; IMSpt; College; Lawyer.

EITEN, Gary; Steamboat Rock Comm HS; Steamboat Rock, IA; PresJrCls; Chrs; HonRl; NatlFornLg; NatlThespSoc; PolWkr; SchMus; SchPl; StuCncl; SchPpr; College; Professional.

EITLAND, Trina E; Central Cass HS; Casselton, ND; ALAGirlsSt; PresChrhWkr; HonRl; NHS; SchPl; RptrYrbk; Yrbk; PresFHA; LetterBsktbl; LetterFtbl; Military; Home Economics.

EITRHEIM, Elizabeth; Tri Valley HS; Renner, SD; 3/65 ALAGirlsSt; ChrhWkr; HonRl; NatlFornLg; NHS; StuCncl; RptrYrbk; RptrSchPpr; BttyCrckrAwd; VoiceDemAwd; Augustana College; Journalism.

EKART, Jay F; South Central HS; Laconia, IN; 12/57 PresJrCls; Band; HonRl; NHS; PepBnd;.

EKBERG, Christine L; St Pius X HS; Kansas City, MO; SecSrCls; DrlTm; OffAde; StuCncl; PpCl; Bsbl; Trk; Univ; Psychology.

EKBLAD, Karen A; Evergreen Park Community HS; Evergreen Park, IL; 14/442 HonRl; NHS; TchrAde; VPFTA; GerCl; PpCl; Trk; GAA; IMSpt; U Of Il; Phy Ed.

EKDAHL, Clayton C; White Pine HS; Ontonagon, MI; VPSophCls; Band; ChrhWkr; CncrtBnd; HonRl; MrchBnd; PepBnd; StuCncl; SptEdYrbk; College; Music.

EKELAND, Mark A; Prairie Comm HS; Callender, IA; PresSrCls; ALBoysSt; FFA; LetterTrk; Grace Bible Inst; Veterinary Med.

EKES, Bette L; Grant HS; Fox Lake, IL; 5/199 Band; Chr; VPChrs; HonRl; NHS; PresNatlThespSoc; PepBnd; SchMus; SchPl; Yrbk; GAA; AmLegAwd; University; Art.

EKINS, Kenneth P; St Rita HS; Chicago, IL; 11/442 CmntyWkr; HonRl; NHS; SctActv; EdYrBk; SptEdYrbk; LetterGlf; Northern Illinois Univ; Mathematics.

EKSTROM, Ann; Sacred Heart Of Mary HS; Elk Grove Village, IL; 40/135 HonRl; OffAde; TchrAde; FDA; Coll Of Saint Theresas; Biology.

EKSTROM, Debra A; South Newton HS; Brook, IN; ALAGirlsSt; Band; CncrtBnd; LbryAde; MrchBnd; PepBnd; SchMus; 4-H; PPFtbl; AmLegAwd; Indiana State; Nursing.

ELAM, Arnold L; Harrisburg HS; Harrisburg, IL; 24/186 HonRl; Se Illinois College; Teacher.

ELARDE, Karen A; Good Counsel HS; Chicago, IL; TrsJrCls; HonRl; JrNHS; LbryAde; NHS; OffAde; SchAde; FrCl; MthCl; SciCl; GAA; College; Zoology.

ELBERT, Carolee A; Metamora Twp HS; Metamora, IL; 10/171 SecTrsFrshCls; SecTrsSophCls; PresJrCls; ALAGirlsSt; NHS; SchMus; EdYrBk; FTA; FrCl; Illinois Central College; Elem Education.

ELBERT, Charles M; Pierce City HS; Pierce City, MO; ALBoysSt; HonRl; StuCncl; KeyCl; MthCl; SciCl; College; Liberal Arts.

ELBERT, Karen M; Metamora Township HS; Metamora, IL; 14/174 AFS; Aud/Vis; ChrhWkr; DrlTm; HonRl; HospAde; NHS; NatlMeritCmnd; SchMus; FTA; FrCl; Western Ill Univ; Broadcasting.

ELBS, Thomas E; Marshall University HS; Minneapolis, MN; NatlFornLg; NatlMeritCmnd; PolWkr; StuGov; Yrbk; U Of Minn; Design Engr.

ELDER, Brian L; Thomas Jefferson HS; Council Bluff, IA; 101/469 HonRl; PresModUN; NHS; SchPl; SctActv; StuCncl; Yrbk; Ftbl; LetterSwmmng; Iowa State U; Navy & Law.

ELDER, E A; Columbus HS; Columbus, WI; AFS; Chrs; ChrhWkr; CmntyWkr; HospAde; YthFlsp; Yrbk; 4-H; SpnCl; 4-HAwd; Univ; Foreign Languages.

ELDER, Gina M; Midway HS; Severance, KS; CncrtBnd; HonRl; MrchBnd; PepBnd; Bsbl; LetterBsktbl; LetterTrk; Chrldr; AmLegAwd; 4-HAwd; Coll; Pro.

ELDER, John E; Alexis HS; Alexis, IL; 4/48 TrsSophCls; ChrhWkr; HonRl; NHS; SchPl; FrCl; Bsktbl; Ftbl; Trk; DARAwd; University; Professional.

ELDER, Leslie A; Lake Park HS; Lake Park, MN; 3/41 HonRl; JrNHS; NHS; TreasStuCncl; SptEdSchPpr; LetterBsktbl; LetterChrldr; CchngActv; GAA; AmLegAwd; Moorhead State College; Physical Ed Teacher.

ELDER, Patricia G; Tipton HS; Tipton, MO; TrsFrshCls; Chrs; CncrtBnd; HonRl; MrchBnd; PepBnd; StuCncl; Twrl; PpCl; Chrldr; State Fair Jr College; Lgal Secretary.

ELDERT, Donald K; Gilman HS; Gilman, IL; TrsFrshCls; HonRl; NHS; Yrbk; FFA; LetterFtbl; Trk; IMSpt; Univ Of Illinois; Agriculture.

ELDRED, Sheri L; Homer HS; Homer, MI; Aud/Vis; CAP; NHS; NatlMeritFnl; SancSoc; SctActv; FSA; AmLegAwd; VFWAwd; CitAwd; Trade School; Professional.

ELDRED, Wayne A; Jasper R 5 HS; Oronogo, MO; ChrhWkr; YthFlsp; IMSpt; Mo College.

ELDRIDGE, Dorothy A; John Glenn HS; Bay City, MI; CncrtBnd; HonRl; NHS; PepBnd; SchPl; Twrl; RptrYrbk; PPFtbl; Mich St Univ; Science.

ELDRIDGE, Eugene J; Sturgis HS; Sturgis, MI; TrsSrCls; HonRl; TreasJA; PresNHS; NatlMeritCmnd; SchPl; LatCl; LetterBsbl; CaptIMSpt; RotaryAwd; University Of Notre Dame; Medicine.

ELDRIDGE, Judy R; Moline Public HS; Moline, IL; ChrhWkr; YthFlsp; 4-H; GerCl; Swmmng; Western Illinois Univ; Chemistry.

ELDRIDGE, Melody H; Morrice HS; Morrice, MI; 1/51 TrsSophCls; TrsJrCls; TrsSrCls; Band; HonRl; NHS; LetterBsktbl; Baker Jr College; Secretary.

ELEFSON, Steve M; Mt Pleasant HS; Mt Pleasant, IA; Chr; HonRl; NHS; StuGov; RptrYrbk; RptrSchPpr; Bsktbl; LetterGlf; College; Business.

ELENBAAS, Julie B; Allendale HS; Allendale, MI; 3/38 Band; HonRl; PepBnd; StuCncl; Yrbk; FHA; PpCl; LetterBsktbl; Trk; Muskegon Business Coll; Business.

ELENBAUM, Tammy J; Lakers HS; Sebewaing, MI; Band; CncrtBnd; HonRl; MrchBnd; NHS; SctActv; YthFlsp; 4-H; FHA; PpCl; Bsktbl; Chrldr; Michigan State Univ; Horticulture.

ELESON, Kay; Chadron HS; Whitney, NE; 7/116 TrsSrCls; ChrhWkr; HonRl; NHS; StuCncl; FBLA; College.

ELEY, Joyce A; Nesco Comm HS; Zearing, IA; PresJrCls; Band; Chr; Chrs; CncrtBnd; HonRl; NHS; PepBnd; SchMus; Chrldr; Univ; Home Ec.

ELFERING, Douglas A; Central HS; Kenosha, WI; 21/201 Band; ChrhWkr; StuCncl; Yrbk; LetterFtbl; LetterWrstlng; 4-HAwd; Gateway Tech Aviation Schl; Pilot.

ELFORD, Craig; Lafayette HS; St Joseph, MO; 10/256 ChrhWkr; HonRl; JA; StuCncl; YthFlsp; Bsbl; Bsktbl; Ftbl; Glf; Colege; Architecture.

ELFRANK, Betty J; Festus HS; Festus, MO; 31/157 Chr; Chrs; HonRl; NatlMeritCmnd; TchrAde; LetterTrk; LetterGAA; Business School; Legal Secretary.

ELFRINK, Jane E; Advance HS; Advance, MO; ChrhWkr; CncrtBnd; HonRl; SecStuCncl; SchPpr; FHA; PresPpCl; CaptChrldr; IMSpt; PresAwd; Coll; Nursing.

ELFRINK, Joan; Assumption HS; Cahokia, IL; 19/96 Chrs; ModUN; OffAde; RptrSchPpr; Univ Of Illinois; Elem Education.

ELFRINK, Roy J; Jennings Sr HS; Jennings, MO; HonRl; StuCncl; EngCl; FrCl; PpCl; Bsktbl; Swmmng; College; Professional.

ELFRINK, Shirley J; Leopold R 3 HS; Leopold, MO; SecFrshCls; PresJrCls; Chr; Chrs; CmntyWkr; HonRl; SchPl; SchPpr; PpCl; Chrldr;.

ELG, Douglas J; Fenton HS; Bensenville, IL; 10/407 HonRl; NHS; NatlMeritCmnd; LetterWrstlng; Univ Of Illinois; Engineering.

ELGASS, James A; Ann Arbor Huron HS; Ann Arbor, MI; HonRl; LbryAde; NatlMeritSF; SchPl; SctActv; StuGov; FrCl; Tennis; College; Lawyer.

ELGIN, Richard Q; Heelan Catholic HS; Sioux City, IA; 67/245 HonRl; StuCncl; Bsbl; Chrldr; IMSpt; Technical School; Radio Broadcasting.

ELGIN, Sheila L; Olympia HS; Danvers, IL; Chrs; HonRl; NHS; StuCncl; YthFlsp; 4-H; PpCl; GAA; 4-HAwd;.

ELGIN, Terri L; Center Point Cons HS; Center Point, IA; 4/45 TrsSophCls; VPJrCls; VPSrCls; ALAGirlsSt; Band; NHS; YthFlsp; 4-H; FNA; LetterBsktbl; Coll; Nursing.

ELHARD, Julie Ann; Cambridge HS; Isanti, MN; Band; ChrhWkr; CncrtBnd; MrchBnd; NHS; PepBnd; SchPl; Bsktbl; LetterTrk; College; Law.

ELIAS, Ken L; Prairie HS; Cedar Rapids, IA; Band; CncrtBnd; HonRl; MrchBnd; NHS; StuCncl; SpnCl; Bsktbl; Tennis; College.

ELIAS, Kimberly M; Camelot HS; Cairo, IL; 1/16 VPFrshCls; PresSophCls; PresJrCls; Chr; ChrhWkr; HonRl; NHS; PresStuCncl; TchrAde; RptrSchPpr; PresFBLA; LetterBsbl; Bsktbl; Chrldr; Shawnee College; Broadcasting.

ELIAS, Mark A; Munster HS; Munster, IN; Band; ChrhWkr; CmntyWkr; HonRl; SchMus; TchrAde; SciCl; LetterFtbl; Socr; LetterTrk; In U; Pre Med.

ELIAS, Sandi; Munster HS; Munster, IN; 62/450 Band; ChrhWkr; HonRl; SchMus; SchPl; StuGov; TchrAde; FNA; HstSophCls; SecFrshCls; PPFtbl;.

ELIASON, Becky J; Superior Sr HS; Superior, WI; 49/550 Band; CncrtBnd; HonRl; MrchBnd; FrCl; College; Nursing.

ELIASON, Christen M; East Troy HS; East Troy, WI; 10/117 Chr; ChrhWkr; HonRl; NHS; PolWkr; SchPl; FshEdYrbk; FBLA; PresFrCl; GodCntryAwd; College; History Political Science.

ELIKER, Margaret M; Overton Public HS; Overton, NE; 2/20 PresSophCls; PresJrCls; PresSrCls; ALAGirlsSt; Band; Chr; Chrs; ChrhWkr; CncrtBnd; DrmMjrt; HonRl; Chrldr; Kearney State University; Mathematics.

ELIOT, Christopher G; Community HS; Ann Arbor, MI; 4/138 HonRl; LbryAde; NatlMeritFnl; NatlMeritSF; RedCrAde; SchAde; RptrYrbk; OptClAwd; Mit; Elec Engr.

ELIZER, Steven H; Carbondale Comm HS; Carbondale, IL; 8/289 PresFrshCls; HonRl; VPJrNHS; ModUN; NatlFornLg; NHS; NatlMeritCmnd; StuCncl; StuGov; YthLg; LetterBsbl; DARAwd; EldAwd; Washington Univ; Lawyer.

ELKIN, Bradley C; St Louis Park HS; Minneapolis, MN; 1/749 Aud/Vis; ChrhWkr; CmntyWkr; HonRl; NatlMeritFnl; NatlMeritSF; SchPl; U Of Minn; Chemical Engineer.

ELKINS, Evelyn S; Maquoketa Comm HS; Maquoketa, IA; 2/148 Band; CncrtBnd; HonRl; LitMag; MrchBnd; ModUN; NHS; NatlMeritSF; NatlThespSoc; PepBnd; PolWkr; SchPl; StuCncl; RptrSchPpr; EdSchPpr; Univ Of Iowa; Photojournalism.

ELKINS, Maurice; Edgewood HS; Ellettsville, IN; PolWkr; SchPpr; GerCl; PpCl; Bsktbl; MasAwd;.

ELKINS, Peggy L; Campus HS; Wichita, KS; Band; Chr; HonRl; JA; NHS; SctActv; YthFlsp; EdYrBk; PpCl; JAAwd; College; Nursing.

ELLA, Roxanne M; Worthington Sr HS; Worthington, MN; Chr; Chrs; OffAde; SchMus; TchrAde; GAA; Vocational School; Business Field.

ELLANSON, Douglas K; New Ulm Sr HS; New Ulm, MN; Band; MrchBnd; PepBnd; 4-H; LetterFtbl; LetterTrk; IMSpt; Coll; Teaching.

ELLEBRACHT, Edward T; Mercy HS; St Ann, MO; JrNHS; NHS; GerCl; Coll; Engi.

ELLEDGE, Marcia A; Superior HS; Superior, NE; 8/78 SecSophCls; PresJrCls; Band; CncrtBnd; HonRl; MrchBnd; PepBnd; Chrldr; AmLegAwd; Coll; Nurse.

ELLEDGE, Scott P; Burlington Community HS; Burlington, IA; 14 501 HonRl; SchPl; EdSchPpr; Coll; Pro.

ELLEFSON, Valerie L; Lafayette HS; Red Lake Falls, MN; PresJrCls; Band; PepBnd; Bsbl; Bsktbl; Trk; CchngActv; IMSpt; 4-HAwd; CitAwd; Clg; Teaching/ministry/coaching.

ELLEGOOD, Sherry L; New Holland HS; Middletown, IL; VPJrCls; CmntyWkr; HonRl; SchPl; StuCncl; Twrl; SchPpr; SpnCl; LetterBsktbl; GAA; College; Teach.

ELLENA, John T; Virden HS; Virden, IL; HonRl; NHS; PresStuCncl; PresSciCl; So Illinois Univ; Medicine.

ELLENBY, Alan M; Niles East HS; Skokie, IL; 1/585 NHS; NatlMeritCmnd; IMSpt; University Of Illinois; Actuarial Science.

ELLENS, Debra K; Rutland Inde HS; Wentworth, SD; 3/15 PresFrshCls; VPJrCls; PresSrCls; Band; HonRl; NHS; StuCncl; EdYrBk; FHA; Dakota State College; Business.

ELLENWOOD, Terry L; Chelsea HS; Chelsea, MI; Chr; SctActv; StuCncl; LetterFtbl; LetterTrk; LetterWrstlng; Nw Michigan College; Conservation.

ELLER, Sheree; Sylvan Unified 299 HS; Sylvan Grove, KS; 3/22 SecTrsFrshCls; Chrs; HonRl; NHS; StuCncl; RptrSchPpr; Bsbl; Trk; Chrldr; Fort Hays Kansas State College.

ELLERBROCK, Beth A; St Mary Academy; Monroe, MI; 6/142 HonRl; NHS; SchMus; SchPl; StuCncl; FrCl; SpnCl; Swmmng; Eastern Mich Univ; Languages.

ELLERBROCK, Beth A; St Mary Acad; Monroe, MI; 6/139 HonRl; NHS; SchPl; StuCncl; FrCl; Swmmng; Eastern Mi Univ; International Business.

ELLERT, David J; Mater Dei HS; Evansville, IN; SctActv; 4-H; PpCl; Ftbl; Tennis; Trk; Wrstlng; IMSpt; 4-HAwd; CitAwd; Purdue Univ; Engineering.

ELLESTAD, Susan A; Valders HS; Valders, WI; Chrs; DrlTm; HonRl; Mdrgl; OffAde; FHA; VPJrCls; HstSophCls; IMSpt; PPFtbl; Marion College; Registered Nurse.

ELLET, Linda G; Shawnee HS; Grand Tower, IL; Chrs; ChrhWkr; HonRl; 4-H; FBLA; FHA; FTA; Southern Il Univ; Law Enforcement.

ELLICOTT, Donald P; Sioux County HS; Harrison, NE; 2/15 TrsFrshCls; TrsSophCls; TrsJrCls; Chr; NatlFornLg; NHS; NatlMeritSF; SchPl; 4-H; College; Computer Science.

ELLIFF, Julie M; Prairie HS; Swisher, IA; SecSophCls; HospAde; NHS; StuCncl; RptrYrbk; Trk; Chrldr; Clge; Rn.

ELLINGBOE, Brad R; Lakeville Sr HS; Lakeville, MN; 42/205 Band; Chr; ChrhWkr; CncrtBnd; HospAde; MrchBnd; StuCncl; LetterBsktbl; LetterFtbl; LetterTrk; College; Business Teach.

ELLINGER, Lisa G; Illmo Scott City HS; Scott City, MO; Band; CncrtBnd; HonRl; MrchBnd; OffAde; TchrAde; SpnCl; PpCl; Chrldr; PPFtbl;.

ELLINGER, Paul N; Saunemin Unit #6 HS; Pontiac, IL; 1/21 PresSophCls; HonRl; NHS; SchPl; StuCncl; LetterBsbl; LetterBsktbl; LetterTrk; College.

ELLINGSON, Carolee; Park River HS; Park River, ND; VPSophCls; ALAGirlsSt; Band; Chrs; ChrhWkr; HonRl; NHS; SchPl; FrCl; Chrldr; Concordia College.

ELLINGSON, Dale; New Effington Ind HS; New Effington, SD; 7/17 SecJrCls; Chr; ChrhWkr; HonRl; LbryAde; StuGov; Bsktbl; Ftbl; Trk; VoiceDemAwd; Sosu At Brookings;.

ELLINGSON, Evonne I; Ada HS; Ada, MN; Univof Minn At Crookston; Children Day Care.

ELLINGSON, Greg A; Evansville HS; Ashby, MN; Band; Chr; HonRl; SchPl; TreasStuCncl; 4-H; VPFFA; LetterBsbl; LetterFtbl; LetterTrk; CaptWrstlng; 4-HAwd; Alexandria Tech; Accountant.

ELLINGSON, Larry; Bemidji Senior HS; Bemidji, MN; ALBoysSt; ALAGirlsSt; CtyCnl; ModUN; OffAde; PolWkr; StuCncl; StuGov; UNYO; YthLg; College; Accounting.

ELLINGSON, Luann J; Brainerd Sr HS; Brainerd, MN; HospAde; 4-H; SpnCl; Jr College; Stewardess.

ELLINGSON, Mark J; Orangeville HS; Orangeville, IL; 5/59 HonRl; NHS; SptEdSchPpr; PpCl; LetterBsktbl; LetterFtbl; LetterGlf; College; Professional.

ELLINGSON, Rynae E; Richland #44 HS; Christine, ND; Band; Chrs; CncrtBnd; MrchBnd; PepBnd; SchPl; RptrYrbk; RptrSchPpr; 4-H; FHA; PpCl; Bsktbl; College; Nursing.

ELLINGSWORTH, David P; Van Horn HS; Independence, MO; HonRl; SctActv; Ftbl; Swmmng; Trk; Wrstlng; GodCntryAwd; Cmsu; Accounting.

ELLINGTON, Paula L; Union Corporation HS; Modoc, IN; 3/75 SecFrshCls; SecSophCls; HonRl; NHS; OffAde; Yrbk; SchPpr; SpnCl; College; Business.

ELLINOR, Martha J; Lanark HS; Lanark, IL; 20/56 Chrs; HonRl; SchMus; VP4-H; FHA; FNA; SpnCl; SecGAA; DanFAwd; 4-HAwd; Nursing Sch; Nurse.

ELLIOT, Julie A; Starmont HS; Strawberry Point, IA; 3/108 Band; ChrhWkr; NHS; PepBnd; SchPl; EdYrBk; RptrSchPpr; FBLA; BttyCrckrAwd; Univ; Journalism.

ELLIOTT, Barbara S; Randolph Southern HS; Lynn, IN; 3/64 Chrs; HonRl; PolWkr; SchMus; Yrbk; RptrSchPpr; IMSpt; DARAwd; Coll; Art.

ELLIOTT, Bill; Ash Grove HS; Bois Darc, MO; 6/57 Band; Chrs; CncrtBnd; HonRl; MrchBnd; ModUN; PepBnd; SchPl; TchrAde; MthCl; Univ; Professional.

ELLIOTT, Brenda K; Carmi Comm HS; Carmi, IL; 3/139 ALAGirlsSt; Chr; HonRl; NHS; Quill&Scroll; Yrbk; RptrSchPpr; 4-H; PpCl; DanFAwd; 4-HAwd; Southern Illinois Univ; Law.

ELLIOTT, Bruce L; Granite City South HS; Granite City, IL; 138/630 Aud/Vis; ChrhWkr; HospAde; PolWkr; RedCrAde; SchMus; SchPl; YthFlsp; Bsbl; Ftbl; U Of S Il; Dentistry.

ELLIOTT, Carolyn D; Barr Reeve HS; Montgomery, IN; 9/67 TrsFrshCls; SecSrCls; Band; ChrhWkr; HonRl; JrNHS; 4-H; FHA;.

ELLIOTT, Craig S; Geneva Comm HS; Geneva, IL; HonRl; SctActv; YthFlsp; KeyCl; Bsktbl; College; Construction Engineer.

ELLIOTT, Cynthia L; Oak Forest HS; Oak Forest, IL; 6/346 HonRl; JrNHS; VPNHS; NatlMeritCmnd; OffAde; VPStuCncl; StuGov; FrCl; PpCl; SciCl; LetterBsktbl; Trk; GAA; Univ Of Illinois; Doctor.

ELLIOTT, Deann; Leroy Ostrander HS; Leroy, MN; 3/40 Chrs; HonRl; NHS; SchPl; RptrSchPpr; SptEdSchPpr; IMSpt; PresAwd; Trade School; Computer Programmer.

ELLIOTT, Diana L; Warrensburg Latham HS; Warrensburg, IL; 3/77 PresAFS; Band; TreasChrs; ChrhWkr; HonRl; JrNHS; Quill&Scroll; SchMus; EdYrBk; Pres4-H; University; Math.

ELLIOTT, Donald L; Delta HS; Albany, IN; ChrhWkr; HonRl; NHS; NatlMeritSF; FrCl; MthCl; SciCl; Coll.

ELLIOTT, Donna S; Usd 237 HS; Gaylord, KS; Band; Chrs; ChrhWkr; CncrtBnd; DrlTm; DrmMjrt; HonRl; MrchBnd; PepBnd; Twrl; PpCl; Ft Hays Kansas St College; Education.

ELLIOTT, Eric G; Charleston HS; Charleston, IL; 27/237 Chrs; ChrhWkr; HonRl; NHS; IMSpt; Eastern Il U; Investment Counsellor.

ELLIOTT, Gary L; Shawnee HS; Grand Tower, IL; 3/63 TrsSophCls; Band; CncrtBnd; HonRl; NHS; PepBnd; FFA; GerCl; LetterBsbl; Bsktbl; Naval Academy; Military.

ELLIOTT, Janet; Eastern Heights HS; Kirwin, KS; /19 TrsFrshCls; PresJrCls; Band; Chr; DrlTm; HonRl; PpCl; LetterBsktbl; LetterTrk; Chrldr; Coll; Modeling And Fashion Design.

ELLIOTT, Jon C; Brother Rice HS; Birmingham, MI; 34/213 ALBoysSt; HonRl; MrchBnd; ModUN; NatlFornLg; NHS; NatlMeritCmnd; SchMus; RptrYrbk; PresSciCl; Trk; IMSpt; College; Pre Law.

ELLIOTT, Julie A; Sullivan HS; Sullivan, IL; DrlTm; FTA; Lakeland College; Accounting.

ELLIOTT, Karla M; Windsor HS; Windsor, IL; SecFrshCls; TrsFrshCls; ChrhWkr; HonRl; JrNHS; NHS; SchPl; Yrbk; EdSchPpr; 4-H; SpnCl; PpCl; Trk; GAA; Lake Land Jr College; Secretary.

ELLIOTT, Larry E; Winnetonka HS; Kansas City, MO; 17/515 HonRl; RedCrAde; SctActv; TchrAde; SchPpr; Ftbl; Univ; Engineering.

ELLIOTT, Lisa L; Taylor Center HS; Taylor, MI; ALAGirlsSt; HonRl; NHS; PpCl; Swmmng; GAA; IMSpt; Univ; Ecology.

ELLIOTT, Lois A; Waterford Township HS; Pontiac, MI; Band; CncrtBnd; HonRl; MrchBnd; NHS; PepBnd; Ferris State Clg; Optometry.

ELLIOTT, Lucinda A; Rockridge HS; Reynolds, IL; VPBand; CmntyWkr; HonRl; Twrl; PresYthFlsp; 4-H; LatCl; GAA; IMSpt; PresAwd; College; Nurse.

ELLIOTT, Margaret J; Clifford Galesburg HS; Galesburg, ND; 5/21 VPFrshCls; Chrs; HonRl; SchPl; RptrYrbk; RptrSchPpr; 4-H; FHA; CaptBsktbl; LetterTrk; Nd St School Of Science; Dental Hygiene.

ELLIOTT, Marsha; Brunswick R Ii HS; Brunswick, MO; 20/46 CmntyWkr; HonRl; LbryAde; OffAde; SchAde; SchPl; Yrbk; RptrSchPpr; 4-H; 4-HAwd; Univ Of Mo;home Econ.

ELLIOTT, Michael; Chosen Valley HS; Chatfield, MN; ChrhWkr; HonRl; NHS; SchMus; SchPl; Bsbl; Trk; PresAwd; College; Science Or Math.

ELLIOTT, Randolph L; Goddard HS; Goddard, KS; 2 140 Band; Chr; HonRl; ModUN; NatlFornLg; NHS; NatlMeritSF; FSA; Glf; College.

ELLIOTT, Rita J; Fairfield Comm HS; Golden Gate, IL; 14/165 ChrhWkr; HonRl; NHS; OffAde; Quill&Scroll; SchPpr; 4-H; Southern Il Univ; Journalism.

ELLIOTT, Susan M; Prospect HS; Mt Prospect, IL; 140/614 Chr; Chrs; ChrhWkr; CmntyWkr; NatlThespSoc; SchMus; SchPl; RptrYrbk; Millikin University.

ELLIOTT, Susanne J; Fenton Sr HS; Fenton, MI; Band; CmntyWkr; CncrtBnd; HonRl; MrchBnd; PepBnd; SchPl; College; Teacher.

ELLIOTT, Walter M; Mc Cluer HS; Ferguson, MO; Aud/Vis; HonRl; SctActv; TchrAde; SciCl; Swmmng; IMSpt; U Of Mo Columbia; Ocean Engineer.

ELLIOTT, William C; Park Tudor HS; Indianapolis, IN; StuGov; KeyCl; Ftbl; Tennis; Univ; Medicine.

ELLIS, Alice J; Princeton HS; Princeton, IL; 5/163 SecSrCls; VPAFS; PresNHS; SecNatlThespSoc; Yrbk; 4-H; PresGAA; Univ Of Illinois; Medicine.

ELLIS, Amanda M; Chicago Voc HS; Chicago, IL; 99/796 JA; OffAde; TchrAde; Bsktbl; Tennis; GAA; College; Physical Educ.

ELLIS, Bradley H; Rock Island HS; Rock Island, IL; Band; Chr; HonRl; JrNHS; Mdrgl; PolWkr; StuGov; YthFlsp; PpCl; LetterGlf; U Of Il; Law.

ELLIS, Brian K; Roseville HS; Roseville, MI; ChrhWkr; HonRl; SchAde; SchMus; SchPl; StuCncl; StuGov; TchrAde; Yrbk; CitAwd; Macomb Clg; Data Processing.

ELLIS, Christopher A; New Trier East HS; Glencoe, IL; VPFrshCls; VPSophCls; Chr; ChrhWkr; CmntyWkr; HonRl; NatlMeritCmnd; SchPl; StuGov; YthFlsp; U Of Puget Sound; Marine Bio.

ELLIS, Cynthia L; Croswell Lexington HS; Lexington, MI; College; Youth Services.

ELLIS, David; Downers Grove South Hs; Darien, IL; Aud/Vis; HonRl; SctActv; StuCncl; Swmmng; GovHonPrgAwd; Southern Il U; Zoology.

ELLIS, Fawnda K; South Pemiscot HS; Steele, MO; 1/67 Band; ChrhWkr; CmntyWkr; CncrtBnd; HonRl; JrNHS; MrchBnd; NHS; OffAde; PepBnd; VPStuCncl; CaptChrldr; Harding College; Occupational Therapist.

ELLIS, Frederick P; Assumption HS; Wisconsin Rapids, WI; ALBoysSt; Chrs; ChrhWkr; HonRl; PolWkr; SchPl; Sdlty; StuGov; Yrbk; PpCl; LetterFtbl; LetterTrk; Wrstlng; St Johns Univ; Broadcasting.

ELLIS, George; Northrop HS; Fort Wayne, IN; ModUN; FrCl; Ftbl; Trk; Coll; Acc.

ELLIS, Gregory K; Lincoln HS; Vincennes, IN; 34/328 HonRl; Indiana University; Business.

ELLIS, James E; Ness City HS; Ness City, KS; 15/52 Band; Chr; CncrtBnd; HonRl; MrchBnd; NatlThespSoc; PepBnd; SchMus; SchPl; Bsktbl; LetterFtbl; LetterGlf; CitAwd; Sterling College; Medicine.

ELLIS, Jane E; Pittsfield HS; Pittsfield, IL; Chrs; ChrhWkr; CmntyWkr; HonRl; NHS; 4-H; Central Christian College; Floriculturist.

ELLIS, Jerry R; Southwest R 5 HS; Seligman, MO; VPFrshCls; PresSophCls; ChrhWkr; HonRl; SchPl; StuCncl; EdYrBk; FHA; LetterBsbl; CaptBsktbl; LetterTrk; College; Coaching.

ELLIS, Joan; Luther South HS; Chicago, IL; 7/241 Chr; HonRl; JA; NHS; OffAde; SchAde; GAA; IMSpt; Millikin U; Pre Med.

ELLIS, John C; Lincoln Co HS; Silex, MO; 1/33 PresSophCls; Band; HonRl; SchPl; StuCncl; College; Professional.

ELLIS, Karen L; Brighton Area HS; Brighton, MI; Band; CncrtBnd; HonRl; MrchBnd; NHS; NatlMeritSF; PepBnd; Michigan State Univ; Accounting.

ELLIS, Kelly J; Holdrege Sr HS; Holdrege, NE; Chr; Chrs; SchMus; 4-H; Trk; Agricultural College; Veterinary Tech.

ELLIS, Leslie R; Central HS; Albert Lea, MN; 22/495 CmntyWkr; HonRl; College; Business Administration.

ELLIS, Lynette; St Marys HS; Saint Marys, KS; 1/68 ChrhWkr; HonRl; LbryAde; NHS; SctActv; TchrAde; EdYrBk; RptrSchPpr; FHA; PpCl; Kansas State Univ; Wildlife Biology.

ELLIS, Mareth V; Jeffersonville HS; Charlestown, IN; Bsktbl; LetterTennis; College.

ELLIS, Margaret C; Rising Sun HS; Bennington, IN; 3/65 PresFrshCls; PresSophCls; PresSrCls; HonRl; PresNHS; RedCrAde; RptrYrbk; EdSchPpr; FrCl; PresSciCl; College; Pre Medicine.

ELLIS, Mary D; Mukwonago HS; Big Bend, WI; Chrs; HonRl; Mdrgl; StuGov; Trk; GAA; PresAwd; IMSpt; Chrl; College; Professional.

ELLIS, Michael S; Mendel College Prep HS; Chicago, IL; HonRl; NHS; NatlMeritFnl; NatlMeritCmnd; RptrYrbk; SptEdSchPpr; Univ; Psychology.

ELLIS, Michael W; Harrisonville Sr HS; Harrisonville, MO; 1/154 PresSrCls; PresBand; ChrhWkr; PresCncrtBnd; HonRl; MrchBnd; TreasNatlFornLg; PepBnd; StuCncl; PresFFA; Bsktbl; Ftbl; Univ Of Mo; Agricultural Engineer.

ELLIS, Michael W; Harrisonville HS; Harrisonville, MO; 1/156 PresSrCls; PresBand; PresChrhWkr; PresCncrtBnd; HonRl; IntrClCncl; TreasNatlFornLg; PresFFA; Bsktbl; Ftbl; U Of Mo; Agricultural Engineering.

ELLIS, Michael W; Harrisonville Sr HS; Harrisonville, MO; 1/154 PresSrCls; PresBand; PresChrhWkr; PresCncrtBnd; HonRl; IntrClCncl; MrchBnd; TreasNatlFornLg; PepBnd; StuCncl; PresFFA; Bsktbl; Ftbl; Univ Of Missouri; Agriculture.

ELLIS, Renee H; Lincoln HS; Bloomington, MN; Band; ChrhWkr; HonRl; GerCl; Univ.

ELLIS, Rex E; Whiteland Community HS; New Whiteland, IN; 23/174 Chr; HonRl; NHS; FBLA; Tennis; IMSpt; Iupui ;business.

ELLIS, Robert B; Mt Morris HS; Mt Morris, IL; AFS; Chr; HonRl; NHS; SchPl; SctActv; Swmmng; Tennis; Florida Inst Of Tech; Marine Biology.

ELLIS, Tim; Sheboygan South HS; Sheboygan, WI; 73/526 HonRl; NHS; Lakeland Coll; Bus Admin.

ELLISON, Averil D; Detroit Central HS; Detroit, MI; 4/92 CmntyWkr; HonRl; NHS; TchrAde; Ftbl; CitAwd; Wayne State Univ; Elec Eng.

ELLISON, Betty A; Arthur HS; Arthur, IL; 3/52 SecTrsJrCls; HonRl; NHS; SchPl; FHA; FNA; FTA; MthCl; Bsbl; Bsktbl; Southern Illinois Univ; Mathematics.

ELLISON, Bruce; Belvidere Hs; Caledonia, IL; Chrs; ChrhWkr; YthFlsp; VP4-H; PresFFA; Kishwaukee Jr College; Agriculture.

ELLISON, Daniel J; Oakes HS; Oakes, ND; 7/75 Chr; Chrs; ChrhWkr; HonRl; NHS; SchPl; Mayville State College; Lawyer.

ELLISON, Luanne; Senn HS; Chicago, IL; HonRl; LitMag; NHS; NatlMeritCmnd; OffAde; SchAde; TchrAde; Northwestern University; Law.

ELLISTON, Cheryl L; Maple Valley HS; Nashville, MI; HonRl; SchPl; SctActv; StuGov; TchrAde; SptEdSchPpr; Bsktbl; Chrldr; GAA; 4-HAwd; Central Mi Coll; Phy Ed Teacher & Coach.

ELLMORE, Mark; Covington HS; Covington, IN; ChrhWkr; SchPl; StuCncl; College; Farmer.

ELLSWORTH, Lorna K; Memence HS; Momence, IL; HonRl; NHS; NatlMeritCmnd; PpCl; Bsbl; College; Engineer.

ELLSWORTH, Mary C; Derham Hall HS; Audubon, MN; PresFrshCls; SecSophCls; SchPl; StuCncl; StuGov; RptrYrbk; Yrbk; FHA; Trk; Chrldr; Moorhead State College; Journalism.

ELLSWORTH, Michael L; Greenville HS; Greenville, IL; 7/183 ALBoysSt; ChrhWkr; HonRl; NHS; NatlMeritCmnd; YthFlsp; Greenville College; Physics.

ELLSWORTH, Thomas J; St Viator HS; Arlington Hts, IL; 13/270 ALBoysSt; PolWkr; SchAde; SpnCl; Univ Of Illinois; Law.

ELLWANGER, Shari A; Butte Public HS; Butte, NE; Aud/Vis; Band; Chrs; ChrhWkr; HonRl; MrchBnd; PepBnd; YthFlsp; EdSchPpr; PpCl; Nettleton Clge Sioux Fls Sd; Medical Asst.

ELLWOOD, Victoria; New Trier East HS; Winnetka, IL; Chrs; ChrhWkr; CmntyWkr; HospAde; LitMag; PolWkr; FrCl; College; Psychology.

ELMER, Barbara A; Chippewa Falls HS; Chippewa Falls, WI; 60/370 AFS; HonRl; HospAde; NatlFornLg; NHS; TchrAde; Univ Of Wisconsin; Nursing.

ELMER, Connie; Benton County R 2 HS; Warsaw, MO; 2/39 SecTrsFrshCls; PresSophCls; PresJrCls; Chr; ChrhWkr; HonRl; Mdrgl; NHS; SchPl; SchPpr; Burge School Of Nursing; Nursing.

ELMORE, Barbara J; West Nodaway R I HS; Burlington Jct, MO; 5/43 Band; Chrs; CncrtBnd; HonRl; MrchBnd; NHS; SchPl; StuCncl; PpCl; LetterBsktbl; Chrldr; College; Vocation.

ELMORE, Catherine A; Heelan HS; Sioux City, IA; Chr; CmntyWkr; HospAde; OffAde; RedCrAde; SpnCl; Morningside College; Elementary Ed.

ELMORE, Diana G; Malden Comm HS; Princeton, IL; 2/13 PresFrshCls; HstSophCls; HstJrCls; TrsSrCls; Chrs; ChrhWkr; HonRl; SchPl; Yrbk; EdSchPpr; GAA; College; Professional.

ELMORE, Jill D; Frontier HS; Brookston, IN; Band; ChrhWkr; HonRl; PolWkr; PpCl; Secretary.

ELONICH, Diane M; York Comm HS; Elmhurst, IL; Chrs; ChrhWkr; HonRl; NHS; NatlMeritSF; Quill&Scroll; SchMus; RptrSchPpr; TreasFrCl; Univ; Medicine.

ELOPH, Susan K; Elmhurst HS; Ft Wayne, IN; ChrhWkr; PresJA; OffAde; JAAwd; Baptist Bible College; Christian Educ.

ELOWSKY, Earl F; Clarence Lowden HS; Lowden, IA; 2/46 VPSophCls; ALBoysSt; CncrtBnd; NHS; NatlMeritCmnd; SctActv; YthFlsp; GerCl; LetterFtbl; LetterTennis; Cornell Col; Medicine.

ELPERS, Elaine; Central HS; Evansville, IN; 1/650 ChrhWkr; HonRl; JrNHS; NHS; NatlMeritCmnd; SchMus; RptrYrbk; 4-H; 4-HAwd; CitAwd; Purdue Univ; Engineering.

ELPERS, Kevin L; Anderson HS; Anderson, IN; 8/700 NHS; StuCncl; StuGov; LetterFtbl; LetterSwmmng; OptClAwd; PresAwd; Univ; Pre Med.

ELROD, Donna L; Zion Benton Township HS; Zion, IL; .

ELROD, Jane M; Clinton HS; Clinton, MO; 9/161 ALAGirlsSt; HonRl; HospAde; TchrAde; YthFlsp; 4-H; FHA; PpCl; Tennis; Chrldr; Cntrl Mo St Univ; Physical Therapy.

ELSBERND, Nora A; Turkey Valley HS; Fort Atkinson, IA; Chr; HonRl; NHS; Sdlty; VP4-H; LetterBsktbl; IMSpt; 4-HAwd; GodCntryAwd; Voc Sch; Nursing.

ELSBERRY, Terry L; Bishop Ryan HS; Minot, ND; 24/90 ALBoysSt; CtyCnl; CmntyWkr; NHS; RedCrAde; StuCncl; StuGov; RptrYrbk; SptEdYrbk; Bsktbl; Trade School; Meat Cutter.

ELSBURY, Michael; Greenfield Central HS; Greenfield, IN; 9/365 HonRl; NHS; SchPpr; 4-H; FFA; MthCl; IMSpt; 4-HAwd; Indiana Univ; Optometry.

ELSE, Thomas A; Proviso West HS; Westchester, IL; 200/1206 HonRl;.

ELSEN, Laurie A; Holy Angels Acad; Richfield, MN; 24/119 CmntyWkr; HonRl; Col Of St Benedict; Psychology Counselor.

ELSEN, Michael J; Quigley South HS; Oak Lawn, IL; 6/179 Chrs; HonRl; NHS; NatlMeritCmnd; StuGov; RptrYrbk; CaptSwmmng; University; Professional.

ELSEN, Renee; Benilde St Margarets HS; Loretto, MN; NHS; StuGov;.

ELSEN, Susan L; Edina East HS; Edina, MN; 13/489 VPChr; HonRl; LbryAde; Mdrgl; NatlThespSoc; Gustavus Adolphus Col; Music & Theatre.

ELSHOFF, Martha K; Southridge HS; Huntingburg, IN; 39/135 Chr; ChrhWkr; CmntyWkr; HonRl; SchMus; PresYthFlsp; Pres4-H; Chrldr; PPFtbl; Columbia St Comm College; Veterinarian.

ELSKAMP, Juanita A; Potosi HS; Potosi, WI; 2/70 Aud/Vis; HonRl; MrchBnd; NHS; SchPl; RptrSchPpr; FBLA; FHA; PpCl; IMSpt; College; Engineering.

ELSNER, Kenneth S; Ewen Trout Creek HS; Ewen, MI; 21/70 HonRl; NHS; SctActv; Bsktbl; Ftbl; Trk; Army; Elect Engr.

ELSNER, Steve J; Jennings Co HS; North Vernon, IN; 2/381 PresSrCls; HonRl; NHS; NatlMeritFnl; NatlMeritSchl; StuCncl; Bsbl; College; Engineer.

ELSON, Michael; Maconaquah HS; Gafb Peru, IN; ALBoysSt; ChrhWkr; IMSpt; College; Police Science Law.

ELSTER, John M; Riverside HS; Dearborn Hts, MI; NatlMeritCmnd; Univ Of Michigan; Journalism.

ELSTERMEYER, Elizabeth R; Lutheran North HS; St Louis, MO; CncrtBnd; HonRl; SchMus; Bsktbl; Tennis; GAA; IMSpt; College; Veterianrian.

ELSTOEN, Glenn; Berthold Public HS; Berthold, ND; SecTrsFrshCls; PresJrCls; ALBoysSt; HonRl; StuCncl; 4-H; DanFAwd; Ndsu; Ag Eng.

ELSTON, Carl G; Flanagan HS; Flanagan, IL; 1/37 Band; HonRl; TreasNHS; Bsktbl; LetterTrk;.

ELSTON, John B; Deerfield HS; Deerfield, IL; 55/560 ChrhWkr; HonRl; NHS; NatlMeritFnl; SctActv; StuCncl; LatCl; Duke Univ; Mathematics.

ELSTON, Kathleen A; Brown City HS; Brown City, MI; Chr; Chrs; HonRl; OffAde; TchrAde; 4-H; TreasFFA; Chrldr; Business School; Secretary.

ELSTUN, Jean; Blair HS; Blair, NE; Band; ChrhWkr; HonRl; FBLA; Chrldr; Coll; Professional.

ELTZ, Kimberly C; Sherwood HS; Sherwood, ND; VPFrshCls; DrlTm; HonRl; SchPl; StuCncl; Yrbk; PpCl; LetterTrk; Minot St University.

ELVER, Steven; Mt Horeb HS; Mt Horeb, WI; ALBoysSt; Band; CncrtBnd; HonRl; MrchBnd; NHS; PepBnd; SchMus; SctActv; Ftbl; Glf; M A T C; Architech.

ELVERUD, Dale E; Leeds HS; Leeds, ND; PresFrshCls; Band; HonRl; PepBnd; StuCncl; 4-H; FFA; CaptFtbl; Dickinson State Col; Business Admin.

ELWOOD, Steven E; Riceville Comm HS; Mc Intire, IA; 4/65 TrsJrCls; TrsSrCls; ChrhWkr; HonRl; NHS; SchPl; StuGov; YthFlsp; EdSchPpr; LetterFtbl; Trk; College; Professional.

ELY, Cynthia A; Normandy HS; St Louis, MO; Chr; Chrs; DrlTm; NHS; NatlThespSoc; Quill&Scroll; SchMus; SchPl; StuCncl; SptEdYrbk; University; Music.

ELY, Susan; Wilsonville HS; Hartville, NE; Chr; HonRl; LbryAde; SchPl; TchrAde; School Of The Ozarks; Home Ec Teacher.

ELY, Tanya E; Thorton Fractional North HS; Calumet City, IL; ChrhWkr; CncrtBnd; HonRl; JrNHS; MrchBnd; NHS; NatlMeritCmnd; Orch; SchMus; Univ Of Illinois; Biology.

ELZEA, Donna M; Erskine Public HS; Erskine, MN; 2/30 Band; Chr; CncrtBnd; NHS; TchrAde; RptrYrbk; RptrSchPpr; EdSchPpr; SchPpr; GAA; Business School; Secretary.

ELZY, Lisa D; Beecher HS; Flint, MI; 22/285 Chr; ChrhWkr; HonRl; HospAde; JA; NHS; RptrYrbk; FTA; SpnCl; SecPpCl; U Of Mich Ann Arbor; Doctor.

ELZY, Steven D; Sullivan HS; Sullivan, IL; ALBoysSt; Band; Chrs; ChrhWkr; HospAde; SctActv; YthFlsp; 4-H; FFA; College; Veterinarian.

EMAMI, Iraj; C C HS; Carbondale, IL; SciCl; Univ Of Oklahoma; Medicine.

EMAN, Todd B; Bishop Ryan HS; Minot, ND; 13/82 TrsSrCls; ALBoysSt; HonRl; NHS; StuCncl; KeyCl; GerCl; LetterBsktbl; PresAwd; Minot St Col; Bus Administration.

EMANUEL, Ezekiel J; New Trier West HS; Wilmette, IL; Band; HonRl; NatlFornLg; NatlMeritCmnd; PolWkr; TchrAde; SchPpr; Amherst College; Medicine.

EMANUEL, Matt; North Bend Central HS; North Bend, NE; Chrl; Chrs; SchMus; SchPl; StuCncl; Yrbk; FFA; CaptFtbl; CaptTrk; LetterWrstlng;.

EMANUEL, Sharon M; West Point Central Cath HS; West Point, NE; 6/67 HonRl; NHS; RptrYrbk; RptrSchPpr; Pres4-H; MthCl; PpCl; SciCl; Trk; Chrldr; College.

EMBERTON, Teresa R; Newman HS; Oakland, IL; TrsSophCls; Chrs; ChrhWkr; HonRl; FFA; PresFHA; PpCl; Bsktbl; GAA; AmLegAwd; College; Secretarial Science.

EMBLOM, Katherine; Alton Senior HS; Godfrey, IL; AFS; HonRl; NatlThespSoc; OffAde; Orch; SchMus; SchPl; Yrbk; College; Music.

EMBREE, Gail A; Smithton Rvi HS; Sedailia, MO; 4/47 PresJrCls; PresSophCls; ChrhWkr; HonRl; NHS; SchMus; SchPl; TreasStuCncl; PresFHA; CaptChrldr; Csmu; Social Worker.

EMBRY, Janice M; Ft Scott Sr HS; Ft Scott, KS; Chrs; ChrhWkr; HonRl; LbryAde; PolWkr; 4-H; Ft Scott Jr College; Veterinarian.

EMBRY, Patrick S; Deer Creek Mackinaw HS; Mackinaw, IL; 7/60 PresFrshCls; ALBoysSt; HonRl; Mdrgl; NatlMeritCmnd; StuCncl; SptEdYrbk; LetterBsbl; LetterBsktbl; LetterFtbl; Univ Of Il; Journalism.

EMCH, Fred; Lakeland HS; Lagrange, IN; HonRl; NHS; LatCl; MthCl; University; Engineering.

EMENS, Loraine M; Waldron Area HS; Hudson, MI; 3/51 SecBand; ChrhWkr; CmntyWkr; CncrtBnd; HonRl; NHS; SecStuCncl; TchrAde; RptrSchPpr; GAA; Mi St Univ; Physician.

EMERICK, Laura; East Noble HS; Kendallville, IN; 10/274 CncrtBnd; SecJA; VPNatlFornLg; SecNHS; PepBnd; EdSchPpr; VPSpnCl; JAAwd; Indiana Univ; Journ.

EMERICK, Lois J; East Grand Rapids Sr HS; Grand Rapids, MI; 32/330 ChrhWkr; NHS; PolWkr; FrCl; SpnCl; Aquinas College; Translator.

EMERSON, Kirk W; Sand Creek HS; Sand Creek, MI; VPSrCls; ChrhWkr; PolWkr; RptrSchPpr; SchPpr; Bsktbl; LetterFtbl; Trk; Jackson Comm College; Animal Science.

EMERSON, Mark S; Minnehaha Academy; Edina, MN; Band; ChrhWkr; CncrtBnd; HonRl; SchMus; SctActv; LetterSocr; LetterWrstlng; Olivet Nazarene Col; Engineering.

EMERSON, Paul H; Riverview Comm HS; Riverview, MI; Chr; HonRl; HospAde; SchPl; SptEdSchPpr; Ftbl; Swmmng; LetterTrk; Wrstlng; IMSpt; MasAwd; Univ Of Michigan; Medicine.

EMERY, Joy L; Turner HS; Kansas City, KS; HonRl; JrNHS; SchPl; StuCncl; EdSchPpr; PpCl; LetterGlf; Business School.

EMERY, Linden A; Fairfield Jr Sr HS; Millersburg, IN; 11/110 TreasFFA; Bsktbl; Ftbl; IMSpt; Purdue University; Animal Science.

EMERY, Richard J; Merrill HS; Merrill, MI; 10/115 HonRl; SctActv; PpCl; Bsbl; Michigan State; Electrical Technology.

EMERY, Robin K; Shawnee Heights HS; Berryton, KS; 10/183 TrsJrCls; PresAFS; Chrl; ChrhWkr; HonRl; ModUN; NatlMeritSF; SecNatlThespSoc; StuCncl; EdSchPpr; Louisiana State Univ; Journalism.

EMERY, Sue A; William Freund HS; Palatine, IL; 57/575 Chr; Chrs; HonRl; NatlMeritCmnd; PolWkr; StuCncl; Univ Of Illinois.

EMHOFF, Guy E; Subiaco Academy; Aurora, MO; Chrs; Yrbk; Ftbl; Trk; IMSpt;.

EMIG, Tina G; Wheatland HS; Kansas, KS; Chrs; HonRl; OffAde; SchPl; TchrAde; RptrYrbk; RptrSchPpr; EdSchPpr; PpCl; Chrldr; College.

EMIGH, Kim L; Brookville HS; Brookville, IN; 1/175 TrsFrshCls; PresSophCls; PresJrCls; HonRl; NHS; StuCncl; LetterBsbl; LetterGlf; LetterTennis; College; Math.

EMIGH, Randy E; Oregon Davis HS; Walkerton, IN; 25/65 PresFrshCls; HonRl; NHS; SciCl; LetterBsbl; LetterBsktbl; LetterTrk; College; Major Study.

EMILY, Dennis; Potosi R 3 HS; Potosi, MO; 2/212 HonRl; JrNHS; NHS; Quill&Scroll; StuCncl; RptrYrbk; SpnCl; Trk; IMSpt; DARAwd; Univ Of Mo At Rolla; Ceramic Engineering.

EMILY, Regina T; Notre Dame De Sion HS; Kansas City, MO; Aud/Vis; CmntyWkr; LitMag; NHS; NatlMeritCmnd; SchPl; StuCncl; RptrSchPpr; SciCl; Swmmng; Oberlin College.

EMKEN, Michele L; Yates City HS; Ma Quon, IL; 10/30 Band; Chrs; HonRl; IntrClCncl; TchrAde; SchPpr; FHA; PpCl; Bsbl; Trk; Chrldr; PresGAA; IMSpt; Carl Sandburg College; Secretary.

EMLER, Charles L; Valley Center HS; Valley Center, KS; HonRl; NatlThespSoc; SchPl; StuCncl; Wichita State Univ; Business.

EMLER, Claude R; Lansing HS; Lansing, KS; PresSrCls; CtyCnl; CAP; CmntyWkr; PolWkr; ROTC; StuGov; YthFlsp; MthCl; Bsktbl; IMSpt; Air Force Adad; Air Force.

EMLY, Alison R; Herbert Hoover HS; Des Moines, IA; ChrhWkr; CmntyWkr; NatlMeritCmnd; Orch; SchMus; Concordia College; Music.

EMME, Scott; Hays HS; Hays, KS; HonRl; StuCncl; TchrAde; Fort Hays State; Industrial Arts Teacher.

EMMENDORFER, Albert C; Durand HS; Durand, MI; Band; CncrtBnd; HonRl; Central Michigan Univ; Psychology.

EMMERT, David G; Gage Park HS; Chicago, IL; Band; CncrtBnd; SctActv; RptrSchPpr; University; Archaeology.

EMMERT, Michael A; Bolingbrook HS; Bolingbrook, IL; 32/220 HonRl; NHS; Bsbl; College; Political Science.

EMMERT, Wesley H; Dixon HS; Dixon, IL; 39/337 ALBoysSt; HonRl; NHS; SptEdSchPpr; PresPpCl; Ftbl; College; Teacher.

EMMES, Susan M; Menominee HS; Menominee, MI; 1/276 Chr; HonRl; JrNHS; NHS; SchMus; AmLegAwd; College; Nursing.

EMMETT, Lyn J; Fairbury Cropsey HS; Fairbury, IL; AFS; Chrs; HonRl; StuCncl; MthCl; PpCl; Business School; Public Relations.

EMMONS, Cheryl L; Manteno HS; Manteno, IL; 1/80 ALAGirlsSt; SecBand; Mdrgl; NHS; NatlMeritCmnd; SctActv; Yrbk; VPSpnCl; PresSciCl; BauchLmbAwd; U Of Il; Research Biology Or Medicine.

EMMONS, Daniel L; Monsignor Hackett HS; Galesburg, MI; 20/150 VPSrCls; HonRl; NatlMeritFnl; ROTC; StuCncl; StuGov; Yrbk; RptrSchPpr; GerCl; Ftbl; Trk; CchngActv; Michigan St Univ; Law.

EMMONS, Mark A; Waterford Mots HS; Pontiac, MI; 60/450 Chr; HonRl; SchAde; SchMus; SchPl; Trk; College; Professional.

EMMONS, Maureen A; Benet Academy; Glen Ellyn, IL; 89/251 HonRl; LbryAde; RptrYrbk; St Marys; Nursing.

EMOND, Susan A; Divine Savior Holy Angels HS; Milwaukee, WI; LitMag; LbryAde; Orch; SchMus; SchPl; SchPpr; GerCl; Univ Of Wisconsin; Agriculture.

EMORY, Tracy A; East Prairie HS; East Prairie, MO; HospAde; MrchBnd; NHS; SchPl; SctActv; YthFlsp; RptrSchPpr; CitAwd; Memphis State Univ; Nursing.

EMRICH, Terri L; Northwestern R 1 HS; Mendon, MO; PresJrCls; ALAGirlsSt; Band; ChrhWkr; CncrtBnd; HonRl; NHS; PepBnd; SchMus; Univ Of Missouri; Journalism.

EMRICK, Brenda D; Griggsville HS; Griggsville, IL; 9/24 SecFrshCls; TrsSophCls; PresJrCls; SecBand; CncrtBnd; HonRl; MrchBnd; PepBnd; StuCncl; SecFHA; Col; Art Education.

EMRICK, Stephan; Bishop Noll Institute; E Chicago, IN; ChrhWkr; CmntyWkr; HonRl; IMSpt; Purdue University; Engineering.

EMSWELLER, Richard E; North Decatur HS; Rushville, IN; Band; CncrtBnd; MrchBnd; PepBnd; SctActv; 4-H; VPKeyCl; PpCl; Trade School; Vocation.

ENDEAN, Debra J; Deerfield HS; Highland Park, IL; HonRl; HospAde; NatlMeritCmnd; Lake Forest College; Liberal Arts.

ENDEAN, Debra J; Deerfield HS; Highland Pk, IL; HonRl; NatlMeritCmnd; University; Health.

ENDEMAN, Debra D; Ash Grove Public R Iv HS; Bois D Arc, MO; CncrtBnd; HonRl; LbryAde; MrchBnd; ModUN; NHS; SchPl; TreasFBLA; MthCl; PPFtbl; University; Mathematics.

ENDER, Mary; West Salem HS; West Salem, WI; Chr; CncrtBnd; HonRl; MrchBnd; PepBnd; SchMus; SchPl; StuGov; PpCl; GAA; Univ; History Art.

ENDERBY, Cynthia A; West De Pere Shs; De Pere, WI; Band; CncrtBnd; HonRl; MrchBnd; NatlFornLg; PepBnd; SctActv; RptrYrbk; Yrbk; FrCl; PpCl; LetterTrk; CaptChrldr; Ne Wisconsin Tech Institute; Dental Asst.

ENDERLE, Karen J; Winnebago Lutheran Academy; West Bend, WI; Chrs; RptrSchPpr; PpCl;.

ENDERSON, Mary T; Normandy Sr HS; St Louis, MO; 6/514 HonRl; JrNHS; NHS; Quill&Scroll; EdSchPpr; FrCl; University Of Missouri.

ENDICOTT, Brian E; Carrollton HS; Carrollton, MO; Chr; Chrs; HonRl; NatlThespSoc; SchMus; SchPl; StuCncl; TchrAde; GerCl; Missouri Univ; Aviation.

ENDRES, Kathleen M; Chamberlain HS; Chamberlain, SD; 4/97 SecSrCls; Band; Chrs; HonRl; NHS; SchMus; SchPl; SciCl; AmLegAwd; BttyCrckrAwd; College; History.

ENDRESS, Denise; Pearl City Hs; Pearl City, IL; 1/49 TrsSophCls; TrsJrCls; TrsSrCls; DrlTm; NHS; 4-H; Bsbl; Tennis; Trk; DARAwd; U; Cetrified Public Accountant.

ENDRESS, Mike F; Tremont HS; Tremont, IL; HonRl; StuCncl; 4-H; FFA; Ftbl; Wrstlng; Coll; Agriculture.

ENDRULAT, Robin C; Holstein HS; Holstein, IA; Band; Chrs; CncrtBnd; HonRl; MrchBnd; RptrSchPpr; Sec4-H; PresPpCl; CaptChrldr; 4-HAwd; Trade School ;cosmet.

ENDSLEY, Dianna L; Mahomet Seymour HS; Mahomet, IL; Chr; Chrs; ChrhWkr; HonRl; LbryAde; SctActv; YthFlsp; FFA; FTA; SpnCl;.

ENERLICH, William J; Highland Senior HS; Highland, IN; 271/546 CmntyWkr; HonRl; JA; JrNHS; NHS; PepBnd; YthFlsp; FBLA; FTA; LetterFtbl; IMSpt; GodCntryAwd; CitAwd; College; Teaching.

ENESS, Nora J; Maine Twp South HS; Park Ridge, IL; 96/849 Chr; ChrhWkr; HonRl; Northwestern Univ; Special Education.

ENGBERS, Becky J; Pella Christian HS; Pella, IA; Band; CncrtBnd; MrchBnd; PepBnd; Twrl; PpCl; LetterBsbl; CaptBsktbl; Trk; IMSpt; Trade Schl; Dental Assistant.

ENGBRETSON, Paul; Fenwick Hs; Oak Park, IL; 60 ChrhWkr; CmntyWkr; HonRl; LitMag; NatlMeritFnl; SchMus; SchPl; RptrSchPpr; GerCl; De Paul U;music.

ENGEBRETSON, Celeste M; Milbank HS; Milbank, SD; 9/120 AFS; Chrs; HonRl; HospAde; NatlFornLg; NatlMeritSF; PolWkr; SchPl; PpCl; Coll; Nursing.

ENGEBRETSON, Luann; Sheffield Chapin Comm Hs; Sheffield, IA; 5/51 CncrtBnd; HonRl; LbryAde; TreasStuCncl; YthFlsp; RptrSchPpr; FBLA; LetterBsktbl; Swmmng; LetterChrldr; College; Teacher.

ENGEBRETSON, Matt F; Sturgeon Bay HS; Sturgeon Bay, WI; Chrs; ChrhWkr; CncrtBnd; HonRl; PepBnd; SchMus; Trk; College; Business Admin.

ENGEBRETSON, Warren L; Garretson HS; Sherman, SD; 8/50 CncrtBnd; HonRl; MrchBnd; PepBnd; SchMus; StuCncl; RptrYrbk; 4-H; LetterTrk; Sd State Univ; Eng.

ENGEL, Charles W; Perkins County HS; Ogallala, NE; 9/42 Chr; Chrs; HonRl; StuCncl; YthFlsp; 4-H; FFA; Glf; 4-HAwd; Chadron State Coll; Pre Vet.

ENGEL, Deborah A; El Paso HS; El Paso, IL; Band; CncrtBnd; HonRl; LbryAde; MrchBnd; PepBnd; SctActv; TchrAde; SchPpr; Jr College; Library.

ENGEL, Jacquelyn M; Owen Withee HS; Withee, WI; PresJrCls; ALAGirlsSt; CncrtBnd; HonRl; PresNHS; Pres4-H; Trk; Chrldr; GAA; William Woods Coll; Equestrian Studies.

ENGEL, Larae; Oakley HS; Oakley, KS; Chr; Chrs; ChrhWkr; HonRl; StuCncl; SchPpr; FFA; PpCl; Vo Tech School.

ENGEL, Maria A; Milam HS; Azalia, MI; Band; CncrtBnd; HonRl; LbryAde; MrchBnd; NHS; PepBnd; 4-H; Monroe Comm Clg; Accounting.

ENGEL, Pamela J; Crothersville HS; Seymour, IN; SecSophCls; ChrhWkr; CncrtBnd; HonRl; MrchBnd; NHS; PepBnd; PpCl; Bsktbl; LetterTrk; GAA; College; Physical Educ Instructor.

ENGEL, Paul; St Mary Central HS; Menasha, WI; Band; HonRl; JA; SchMus; SchPl; SpnCl; MthCl; JAAwd; OptClAwd; St Norberts College; Medical Doctor.

ENGEL, Shirley J; Mehlville Sr HS; St Louis, MO; HonRl; SchAde; FrCl; GerCl; College; Data Processing.

ENGELAND, Sandra K; Alma HS; Alma, MI; 7/266 HonRl; NatlFornLg; NHS; SchMus; SchPl; College; Music.

ENGELBART, Carol A; Newton HS; Montrose, IL; 4/206 Chrs; HonRl; NHS; University; Pharmacy.

ENGELBART, Janet M; Lutheran North HS; Ferguson, MO; 3/150 HonRl; JA; NHS; StuCncl; LetterTennis; GAA; IMSpt; PPFtbl; JAAwd; Purdue Univ; Chem Engineering.

ENGELBERT, Virginia A; Bennett County HS; Martin, SD; Band; Chrs; CncrtBnd; HonRl; HospAde; MrchBnd; NHS; PepBnd; 4-H; SpnCl; 4-HAwd; So Dakota State University; Nursing.

ENGELBRECHT, Craig L; Beaver Dam HS; Beaver Dam, WI; StuCncl; Bsbl; Bsktbl; Ftbl; Glf; IMSpt; College; Major Study.

ENGELBRIGHT, Lori J; Auburndale HS; Auburndale, WI; TrsSophCls; TreasBand; CncrtBnd; HonRl; MrchBnd; PepBnd; SchPl; FBLA; GerCl; PpCl; LetterTrk; Chrldr; GAA; College; Professional.

ENGELE, Joan; North Chicago Community HS; Great Lakes, IL; HonRl;.

ENGELHARD, Kimberley A; Carpio Public HS; Foxholm, ND; Band; Chr; Chrs; CncrtBnd; HonRl; MrchBnd; PepBnd; SchPl; SchPpr; PpCl; Business School.

ENGELHARDT, John G; New Trier East HS; Wilmette, IL; 127/850 AFS; NatlMeritSF; PolWkr; StuGov; Univ; Law.

ENGELHARDT, Linda C; Barrington HS; Barrington, IL; 62/641 ChrhWkr; DrlTm; HonRl; HospAde; NHS; TchrAde; YthFlsp; RptrSchPpr; SpnCl; IMSpt; Univ; Journalism.

ENGELHART, Steven L; Frederick HS; Barnard, SD; ChrhWkr; CmntyWkr; HonRl; MrchBnd; OffAde; StuCncl; TchrAde; YthFlsp; 4-H; Bsbl;.

ENGELKEN, Elaine; Centralia HS; Goff, KS; 4/40 PresJrCls; Band; Chrs; HonRl; StuCncl; RptrYrbk; 4-H; Chrldr; College.

ENGELKEN, Jean A; Nemaha Valley HS; Seneca, KS; Chrs; HonRl; PpCl; College; Nurse.

ENGELKEN, Rose; Beckman HS; New Vienna, IA; LbryAde; OffAde; TchrAde; College; Teaching.

ENGELKING, Karen S; Crothersville HS; Seymour, IN; 38/75 ChrhWkr; HonRl; NHS; RedCrAde; StuCncl; FFA; FTA; Bsbl; Bsktbl; Indiana Univ; Elem Education.

ENGELMAN, Harley D; St Marys Central HS; Bismarck, ND; YthFlsp; SchPpr; Bsktbl; Ftbl; LetterTrk; CchngActv; College; English.

ENGELMAN, Lynn A; Roxana HS; East Alton, IL; 20/275 Chrs; HonRl; JA; NHS; NatlThespSoc; OffAde; SchPl; FNA; PresGerCl; PpCl; Southern Ill Univ.

ENGELS, Christine D; Alleman HS; East Moline, IL; 1/220 HonRl; NHS; StuCncl; EdYrBk; FrCl; Univ Of Ill; Engineering.

ENGELSGAARD, David J; Fosston HS; Fosston, MN; 9/98 Band; Chr; CncrtBnd; HonRl; MrchBnd; NHS; PepBnd; SchPl; Glf; Univ Of Mn Duluth; Bus Admin.

ENGELSTAD, Maureen G; Carrington Public HS; Carrington, ND; 4/70 ALAGirlsSt; Chr; ChrhWkr; CncrtBnd; HonRl; SchMus; SchPl; RptrSchPpr; 4-H; FHA; U Of Nd; Guidance & Counseling.

ENGELTJES, Brenda J; Edgerton HS; Edgerton, MN; Chrs; CmntyWkr; HonRl; LbryAde; PolWkr; YthFlsp; 4-H; TrsSophCls; CchngActv;.

ENGEN, Margie J; Lamberton Public HS; Lamberton, MN; 12/44 SecTrsSrCls; Band; PresQuill&Scroll; SchPl; Twrl; EdYrBk; Pres4-H; FHA; FTA; 4-HAwd; College; Home Economist.

ENGEN, Mary D; Warren HS; Warren, MN; Chr; ChrhWkr; HonRl; SchPl; GerCl; Cov Bible Coll.

ENGEN, Paul D; Yankton Sr HS; Yankton, SD; HonRl; NHS; Univ Of So Dakota; Medicine.

ENGET, Lola G; Powers Lake HS; Powers Lake, ND; TrsFrshCls; YthFlsp; RptrYrbk; RptrSchPpr; 4-H; FHA; PpCl; LetterBsktbl; LetterTrk; IMSpt; Coll; Spec Ed.

ENGHAUSEN, James R; Melvin Sibley HS; Sibley, IL; 3/32 Band; ChrhWkr; CmntyWkr; CncrtBnd; HonRl; MrchBnd; PepBnd; SchMus; SchPl; SctActv; YthFlsp; LetterBsbl; LetterBsktbl; LetterTrk; College; Vocation.

ENGLAND, Beth A; Queen Of Peace HS; Oak Lawn, IL; 84/469 HonRl; SchAde; RptrYrbk; SpnCl; Western Ill Univ; Veterinarian.

ENGLAND, Greggory N; West Plains HS; West Plains, MO; HonRl; NatlFornLg; OffAde; StuCncl; TchrAde; LetterFtbl; LetterTrk; LetterWrstlng; IMSpt; Sw Missouri St Univ; Ecology.

ENGLAND, John J; Alma HS; Saginaw, MI; 40/260 Band; CncrtBnd; HonRl; JrNHS; MrchBnd; PepBnd; SchMus; Bsbl; Ftbl; Albion Coll; Business.

ENGLAND, Michael D; Ramsey Comm HS; Ramsey, IL; Chrs; HonRl; SchPl; SctActv; StuCncl; ChmnYrbk; RptrSchPpr; SptEdSchPpr; FTA; PpCl;.

ENGLAND, Michael D; Highland Park HS; St Paul, MN; Aud/Vis; SctActv; Ftbl; Trk; College; Professnl.

ENGLAND, Michelle R; Grundy Center HS; Grundy Center, IA; LetterChrs; ChrhWkr; HonRl; SchPpr; TreasPpCl; PPFtbl; Univ Northern Ia; Science.

ENGLAND, Norman G; Red Oak Community HS; Red Oak, IA; Chr; Chrs; CmntyWkr; SchMus; TchrAde; SpnCl; Ftbl; Trk; CchngActv; IMSpt; LbryAde;.

ENGLAND, Steve S; East HS; Wausau, WI; Chrs; SctActv; Bsbl; Bsktbl; Ftbl; Trk; Wrstlng; IMSpt; PPFtbl; AmLegAwd; Notre Dame Univ; Pro Football.

ENGLAND, Tracy E; Cassville HS; Cassville, MO; 9/108 PresJrCls; CaptDrlTm; NHS; Quill&Scroll; StuCncl; EdYrBk; TreasFBLA; PresFTA; PresPpCl; DanFAwd; 4-HAwd; College; Teach Mentally Handicapped.

ENGLE, Brenda K; W Burlington Arnold HS; W Burlington, IA; 5/48 Band; Chrs; ChrhWkr; HonRl; NHS; NatlMeritSchl; Twrl; YthFlsp; 4-H; Mount Mercy College; Nursing.

ENGLE, Dorla D; Ipswich HS; Ipswich, SD; 2/50 TrsJrCls; ALAGirlsSt; Band; Chrs; HonRl; NHS; SchMus; StuCncl; YthFlsp; VPSd St Univ ; Medical.

ENGLE, Michael R; Elmhurst HS; Ft Wayne, IN; 53/381 Aud/Vis; Band; ChrhWkr; CAP; DrlTm; HonRl; NatlFornLg; PolWkr; TchrAde; University; Osteopathy.

ENGLE, Rene J; Blue Springs HS; Blue Springs, MO; Chr; Chrs; ChrhWkr; SctActv; StuCncl; FrCl; PpCl; Missouri St Univ; Accounting.

ENGLE, Susan M; Geneva Public HS; Geneva, NE; 1/57 SecJrCls; PresSrCls; ALAGirlsSt; NHS; PresStuCncl; Pres4-H; FBLA; PpCl; CaptChrldr; 4-HAwd; Univ Of Nebraska; Home Economics.

ENGLE, Tracy M; Quincy Sr HS; Quincy, IL; AFS; Chr; Chrl; Chrs; ChrhWkr; CmntyWkr; HonRl; HospAde; NHS; NatlMeritCmnd; CchngActv; AmLegAwd; DARAwd; Univ Of Iowa; Physical Therapy.

ENGLEBERT, Jeffrey; Southern Door HS; Forestville, WI; NHS; RptrSchPpr; SchPpr; Trk; IMSpt; Design.

ENGLEHARDT, Jaye E; Central HS; Kansasville, WI; Aud/Vis; ChrhWkr; HonRl; 4-H; SecFFA; Bsbl; College; Data Processing.

ENGLEKING, Pamela J; Grant Park HS; Grant Park, IL; 1/54 VPFrshCls; TrsSophCls; ALAGirlsSt; VPChrs; HonRl; NHS; TreasStuGov; MthCl; Chrldr; Kankakee Jr College; Airlines.

ENGLEMAN, Connie J; Stapleton HS; Stapleton, NE; 4/30 Band; Chrs; ChrhWkr; CncrtBnd; HonRl; MrchBnd; NHS; PepBnd; SchPl; TchrAde; 4-H; Jr College; Police Force.

ENGLER, Debra J; Odin HS; Odin, IL; HonRl; JA; NHS; NatlMeritSchl; SchPl; TchrAde; FHA; FTA; PpCl; BttyCrckrAwd; DARAwd; Eastern Il Univ; History.

ENGLER, Frederick; Maine South HS; Park Ridge, IL; Band; Chr; HonRl; NHS; NatlThespSoc; Orch; SchMus; Northwestern Univ; Biological Sciences.

ENGLER, Frederick; Maine South HS; Park Ridge, IL; Band; Chr; Chrs; HonRl; LitMag; NHS; NatlThespSoc; SchMus; Northwestern University; Biological Science.

ENGLER, Pamela K; Randolph HS; Randolph, MN; Band; Chr; ChrhWkr; HonRl; MrchBnd; PresNHS; PepBnd; Sec4-H; SciCl; University Of Minnesota; Medicine.

ENGLER, Rachel; Parkview Hs; Beloit, WI; 9/157 SecFrshCls; HonRl; NHS; StuGov; 4-H;.

ENGLERT, Michael J; Haworth HS; Kokomo, IN; 56/425 PresJrCls; PresSrCls; HonRl; NHS; StuCncl; LatCl; LetterBsbl; LetterBsktbl; LetterFtbl; RotaryAwd; Wabash Coll; Medicine.

ENGLIN, Gregory D; Batavia HS; Batavia, IL; 20/225 HonRl; NHS; Bsktbl; College; Mathmatics.

ENGLISH, Charles L; Southeast HS; Springfield, IL; ChrhWkr; SctActv; Bsktbl; Trk; College; Professional.

ENGLISH, Jean C; Central Catholic HS; Bloomington, IL; CmntyWkr; HonRl; LbryAde; OffAde; StuGov; Yrbk; RptrSchPpr; PpCl; Bsktbl; College.

ENGLISH, La Valarie; Academy Of Our Lady; Chicago, IL; Chr; ChrhWkr; HonRl; LbryAde; Orch; PolWkr; Quill&Scroll; EdSchPpr; FNA; SpnCl; PpCl; Trk; Northwestern Univ; Physician.

ENGLISH, Margaret; Hackett HS; Kalamazoo, MI; HonRl; SchMus; SchPl; StuCncl; SpnCl; Michigan St Univ; Business.

ENGLUND, Kay L; Grant Deuel HS; La Bolt, SD; 4/44 SecJrCls; SecSrCls; ChrhWkr; HonRl; NHS; StuCncl; TchrAde;.

ENGSTLER, James R; Houston HS; Houston, MN; 3/60 Band; CncrtBnd; HonRl; MrchBnd; PepBnd; SchMus; Yrbk; LetterGlf; University; Professional.

ENGSTROM, Barbara L; St Xaviers HS; Junction City, KS; SecFrshCls; SecSophCls; VPSrCls; Chr; Chrs; ChrhWkr; HonRl; SchMus; SctActv; LetterBsktbl; Swmmng; LetterTrk; Chrldr; IMSpt; Kansas Univ; Physical Ed.

ENGSTROM, Mary K; Dist 17 HS; St Edward, NE; 12/30 TrsFrshCls; HonRl; SchPl; Twrl; FHA; Nursing School; Nurse.

ENKE, Deborah K; Parker Sr HS; Janesville, WI; SecSophCls; SecJrCls; SecSrCls; Band; HonRl; NHS; StuCncl; TchrAde; 4-H; GAA; Univ Of Wisc Madison; Dietetics.

ENLOE, Mark S; Niel Armstrong HS; Neenah, WI; PresSrCls; ALBoysSt; LitMag; NHS; NatlMeritFnl; NatlMeritSF; SchPl; StuGov; EdYrBk; RotaryAwd; College; Psychiatry.

ENLOW, Sarah A; Grayville HS; Grayville, IL; 6/42 HstSophCls; HonRl; NHS; TchrAde; RptrSchPpr; Treas4-H; TreasFHA; FrCl; GAA; 4-HAwd; College; Nursing.

ENLOW, Vickie J; Cisne HS; Cisne, IL; 2/60 SecTrsSrCls; StuCncl; Pres4-H; VPFHA; SpnCl; MthCl; TreasPpCl; BttyCrckrAwd; DARAwd; 4-HAwd; Olney Central College.

ENNEN, Gregory A; Buckley Loda HS; Loda, IL; HstFrshCls; ALBoysSt; Chr; Chrs; ChrhWkr; CmntyWkr; HonRl; LbryAde; SchPl; SctActv; Bsbl; Bsktbl; Trk; Parkland Jr College; Radiology.

ENNIS, Thomas; Danville Hs; Danvelle, IL; 72 Band; ChrhWkr; CncrtBnd; HonRl; MrchBnd; Orch; SctActv; U Illinois ; Electronic Engineer.

ENNS, Christine; Hillsboro HS; Hillsboro, KS; HonRl; NatlFornLg; CivCl; 4-H; FHA; PpCl; AmLegAwd; 4-HAwd; CitAwd; Bethel Col; Home Economics.

ENOCHS, Wanda J; Central HS; Worthington, IN; HonRl; NHS; PresYthFlsp; EdYrBk; 4-H; FHA; PpCl; Bsktbl; 4-HAwd; PresAwd; CitAwd; College; Teacher.

ENOKSEN, Diane M; Morton Sr HS; Hammond, IN; 26/529 HonRl; TchrAde; College; Social Worker.

ENQUIST, Patrick J; Horace Mann HS; Biwabik, MN; HonRl; Trk; Clg; Aviation.

ENRIQUEZ, Ricardo F; Loyola Academy; Park Ridge, IL; 116/442 HonRl; YthFlsp; Ftbl; Swmmng; University Of Illinois; Medicine.

ENSALACO, Gina; Andrean HS; Merrillville, IN; 15/250 CmntyWkr; HonRl; Quill&Scroll; RptrYrbk; MthCl; Univ Of Notre Dame; Engineer.

ENSBERG, Bruce T; Doubrook HS; Toronto, SD; Chrs; NatlMeritCmnd; SchMus; RptrYrbk; SptEdYrbk; IMSpt; Univ; Mechanized Agriculture.

ENSINGER, Beth A; F J Reitz HS; Evansville, IN; 62/432 HonRl; HospAde; VPJA; SecTeen; FFA; GAA; JAAwd; College; Agriculture.

ENSLEY, Holly A; Kewanee HS; Kewanee, IL; 21/217 ChrhWkr; HonRl; MrchBnd; NatlMeritSF; SchPl; TchrAde; Twrl; VPFTA; PresLatCl; GAA; Blackhawk Col; Psychology.

ENSMINGER, Lindi A; Marmaton Valley HS; Moran, KS; Band; Chr; Chrs; CncrtBnd; HonRl; MrchBnd; PepBnd; SecFHA; PpCl; CitAwd; University; Pianist.

ENSRUD, Mary B; Tolna Public HS; Pekin, ND; TrsFrshCls; Band; Chrs; CncrtBnd; HonRl; LbryAde; MrchBnd; PepBnd; LetterBsktbl; LetterTrk; Mayville Teachers College; Business.

ENSTROM, Marsha J; Sault Area HS; Sault Ste Marie, MI; HonRl; JrNHS; NHS; Quill&Scroll; TchrAde; RptrSchPpr; SchPpr; PpCl; Trk; CaptChrldr; IMSpt; College; Secretary.

ENSZER, Mark R; Douglas Macarthur HS; Saginaw, MI; Band; CncrtBnd; HonRl; MrchBnd; PepBnd; SctActv; Michigan Tech; Mechanical Eng.

ENSZER, Richard A; Midland HS; Midland, MI; ChrhWkr; CncrtBnd; HonRl; JA; MrchBnd; Orch; SchMus; SctActv; YthFlsp; Central Michigan Univ; Engineering.

ENTWISLE, John D; Huron Bendor HS; Huron, SD; NatlFornLg; NatlMeritSF; SpnCl; Tennis; University; Medicine.

ENTZI, Elvirta K; Lehr Public HS; Lehr, ND; Chr; Chrs; LbryAde; SchPl; YthFlsp; SchPpr; Nd State Univ; Interior Decoration.

ENYARD, Richard K; Glasgow Rii HS; Glasgow, MO; ALBoysSt; ALAGirlsSt; HonRl; NHS; NatlMeritSchl; PolWkr; ROTC; StuCncl; StuGov; YthFlsp; College; Professional.

ENZINGER, Lauren; Orangeville HS; Dakota, IL; 9/56 PresSrCls; HonRl; NHS; StuCncl; SptEdYrbk; FFA; PpCl; Bsbl; Bsktbl; Ftbl; North Central College; Recreation Major.

EOFF, David G; Heritage Christian HS; Indianapolis, IN; PresJrCls; Band; Chr; PepBnd; SchMus; YthFlsp; Tennis; Iupui; Fed Law Enforcement.

EORIATTI, Mary F; Central Catholic HS; Grand Island, NE; ChrhWkr; HonRl; NHS; SchMus; StuCncl; SchPpr; Trk; Chrldr; OptClAwd;.

EPLEY, John; Manmouth HS; Monmouth, IL; Aud/Vis; HonRl; LbryAde; YthFlsp; RptrSchPpr; LatCl; Ftbl; Swmmng; CchngActv; Vetenarian Medicine.

EPLEY, Tammy; Nokomis HS; Nokomis, IL; /100 Chrs; HonRl; PpCl; Trk; Chrldr; GAA; ;professional.

EPOLITE, Mary K; Pius X HS; Lincoln, NE; ChrhWkr; CmntyWkr; HospAde; ModUN; SchPl; RptrYrbk; 4-H; PpCl; 4-HAwd; Univ; Special Ed Teacher.

EPP, Beth E; Buhler HS; Buhler, KS; SecJrCls; HonRl; TchrAde; YthFlsp; SpnCl; CaptBsktbl; CaptTennis; CaptTrk; PresAwd; College; Social Work.

EPP, Donald R; Buhler HS; Buhler, KS; VPJrCls; Aud/Vis; HonRl; NHS; TchrAde; GerCl; LetterTrk; Bethel Clge North Newton Ks; Math Sciences.

EPP, Nancy; Central Christian HS; Buhler, KS; /23 Chr; Chrl; ChrhWkr; SchPl; EdYrBk; SpnCl; PpCl; Bsktbl; Trk; IMSpt; Grace Missions Ins;journalism.

EPPELHEIMER, William L; Tinley Park HS; Tinley Park, IL; 11/305 ChrhWkr; CmntyWkr; HonRl; NHS; Bsktbl; LetterGlf; Univ Of Illinois; Chemical Eng.

EPPERLY, Dianne C; Wayne Memorial HS; Wayne, MI; TreasBand; CncrtBnd; HonRl; MrchBnd; VPNHS; Orch; PepBnd; SchMus; FrCl; MthCl; College; Music Education.

EPPERSON, Gayla C; Marion C Early HS; Walnut Grv, MO; SecFrshCls; SecSophCls; PresSrCls; Chr; ChrhWkr; HonRl; SchPl; SecStuCncl; Yrbk; SptEdSchPpr; PresFBLA; College; Teacher.

EPPERSON, John A; Orchard Farm HS; St Charles, MO; HonRl; SchMus; SchPl; LetterBsbl; LetterFtbl; CaptSocr; IMSpt; College Or Univ; Marine Zoology & Research.

EPPERSON, Lori B; Carthage Sr HS; Carthage, MO; AFS; Chr; CmntyWkr; DrlTm; ModUN; RedCrAde; StuCncl; SpnCl; Chrldr; DARAwd; College; Public Relations Travel.

EPPERSON, Mary; Hauser HS; Hope, IN; 10/84 HstJrCls; ChrhWkr; CncrtBnd; HonRl; NHS; Quill&Scroll; SchMus; SchPl; YthFlsp; RptrYrbk; Purdue; Undecided.

EPPINETTE, Elizabeth C; Charleston HS; Charlston, IL; AFS; ChrhWkr; HonRl; FrCl; SpnCl; College.

EPPING, Cheri K; Ofallon Township HS; Ofallon, IL; Chr; Chrs; HonRl; Mdrgl; NatlFornLg; NatlThespSoc; SchMus; SchPl; College; Theatre.

EPPINGER, Tamra K; Norton Comm HS; Norton, KS; 19/80 CncrtBnd; HonRl; MrchBnd; PepBnd; SchMus; TchrAde; FHA; PpCl; College; Elem Educ.

EPPLE, Debra L; Hermitage HS; Hermitage, MO; SecTrsFrshCls; Chrs; ChrhWkr; HonRl; SchPl; SctActv; Yrbk; SchPpr; Chrldr; College; Professional.

EPPLETT, David E; Spring Lake Sr HS; Spring Lake, MI; 2/180 Band; Chr; ChrhWkr; HonRl; Mdrgl; NHS; NatlMeritCmnd; SchMus; SchPl; College; Business.

EPPLEY, Linda; Dundee Community Hs; Dundee, IL; VPJrCls; HonRl; NatlMeritCmnd; StuCncl; Tennis; GAA; College;law.

EPPS, Marcy L; Paxton HS; Paxton, IL; 5/137 AFS; ALAGirlsSt; SecBand; Chrs; SecChrhWkr; CncrtBnd; HonRl; Mdrgl; MrchBnd; NHS; NatlThespSoc; LetterTennis; TreasGAA; College; Radio Tv Broadcasting.

EPSTEIN, Cynthia; Central HS; Omaha, NE; 37/576 CmntyWkr; HonRl; IntrClCncl; JrNHS; NHS; Teen; RptrYrbk; Yrbk; SpnCl; MthCl; College; Law.

EPSTEIN, Sharon; Von Steuben HS; Chicago, IL; 34/234 HonRl; NHS; OffAde; SctActv; TchrAde; SchPpr; GAA; Northeastern Il U; Special Education.

EPSTEIN, Steven J; James B Conant HS; Hoffman Estates, IL; Band; ChrhWkr; CncrtBnd; HonRl; MrchBnd; NHS; SciCl; Southern Ill;computer Sci.

ERAZO, Anita; Immaculata Hs; Chicago, IL; 16/201 VPSrCls; HonRl; NHS; SchPl; StuCncl; Yrbk; SpnCl; PpCl; Chrldr; GAA; U Of Illinois; Psychology.

ERB, Cindy; Marissa HS; Marissa, IL; 17/74 ALAGirlsSt; Band; Chrs; ChrhWkr; CncrtBnd; HonRl; MrchBnd; PepBnd; Yrbk; SptEdSchPpr; Belleville Area Coll;journal.

ERBE, Julie; Cedarburg HS; Cedarburg, WI; ChrhWkr; HonRl; NatlMeritCmnd; StuGov; YthFlsp; EdYrBk; PpCl; ChmbCommrsAwd; Stout Univ; Fash Merchandising Textile Des.

ERBELE, Gregory; Lehr Public HS; Lehr, ND; 16/221 VPSophCls; PresJrCls; PresSrCls; Chr; Chrs; SchPl; StuGov; Bsbl; Mary College.

ERBES, Daniel F; Wyndmere HS; Barney, ND; 7/45 Band; CncrtBnd; HonRl; NHS; SchPl; StuCncl; RptrYrbk; FFA; Bsbl; Bsktbl; North Dakota State Univ; Agriculture.

ERBES, David J; Mendota HS; Mendota, IL; 38/189 Band; Chr; CncrtBnd; HonRl; Mdrgl; MrchBnd; PepBnd; SchPl; LatCl; Univ Of Illinois; Law.

ERBES, Douglas J; Wyndmere Public HS; Barney, ND; PresJrCls; CncrtBnd; HonRl; NHS; StuCncl; FFA; Bsbl; Bsktbl; Ftbl; Trk; North Dakota State Univ; Agriculture.

ERBSTOESSER, Toni; Little Falls Community HS; Little Falls, MN; HonRl; PepBnd; SchPl; StuGov; YthLg; RptrYrbk; 4-H; PpCl; LetterChrldr; IMSpt; Bemidji Coll; Criminology.

ERCHUL, William P; Xavier HS; Appleton, WI; 1/108 TrsFrshCls; TrsSophCls; TrsJrCls; HonRl; PresNHS; SchPl; SptEdYrbk; SpnCl; KiwanAwd; Univ Of Wisconsin; Psychology.

ERDELYI, Peter G; Gordon Technical HS; Chicago, IL; 30/645 HonRl; NHS; SctActv; MthCl; SciCl; Il Inst Of Technology; Architecture.

ERDENBERGER, Brenda A; Mason City HS; Mason City, IA; ALAGirlsSt; DrlTm; HonRl; SchPl; SctActv; RptrYrbk; Yrbk; RptrSchPpr; PpCl; Swmmng; Chrldr; GAA; IMSpt; Utah St Univ; Geology.

ERDKAMP, Peggy A; Exeter Public HS; Exeter, NE; PresJrCls; ALAGirlsSt; Chr; HonRl; SchPl; VPStuCncl; Yrbk; PpCl; Trk; Chrldr; U Of Ne; Nursing.

ERDLE, Karen; Richardton Public HS; Richardton, ND; DrlTm; HonRl; RptrSchPpr; SchPpr; 4-H; FBLA; 4-HAwd; Ndsu;desigh.

ERDMAN, Allan A; Catholic Memorial HS; Waukesha, WI; Band; Mdrgl; MrchBnd; PepBnd; Univ Of Wisconsin; Science.

ERDMAN, Arthur W; Chisago Lakes HS; Stacy, MN; SecFrshCls; TrsJrCls; HonRl; StuCncl; StuGov; RptrSchPpr; LetterTrk; University Of Minnesota; Medicine.

ERDMAN, Carey D; St Charles HS; St Charles, IL; 27/432 Band; Chr; Chrl; CncrtBnd; HonRl; MrchBnd; NHS; NatlMeritCmnd; Orch; PepBnd; Iowa State University; Biology.

ERDMAN, Kenneth D; J D Darnall HS; Geneseo, IL; 4/212 Chrs; ChrhWkr; HonRl; NatlFornLg; NHS; NatlMeritSF; NatlThespSoc; SchMus; SchPl; YthFlsp; Univ Of Ill; Engineering.

ERDMAN, Pamela; Adrian Public HS; Lismore, MN; Chrl; HonRl; MrchBnd; NHS; SchPl; TchrAde; Yrbk; FTA; Trk; GAA; Granite Falls Area Voc Sch; Legal Sec.

ERDMANN, Debra S; Wausau West HS; Wausau, WI; 3/442 VPSrCls; AFS; Band; NatlSciFnd; StuCncl; RptrSchPpr; PresGerCl; MthCl; PresSciCl; U Of Wis; Chemistry.

ERDMANN, Michael A; Greendale HS; Greendale, WI; VPSrCls; ChrhWkr; CmntyWkr; NHS; Ftbl; Tennis; LetterWrstlng;.

ERHARDT, Dorla; Mehlville Sr HS; St Louis, MO; 103/592 CmntyWkr; HonRl; Business School; Receptionist.

ERHART, Charles; Lemmon HS; Lemmon, SD; 9/72 ALBoysSt; HonRl; SchPl; RptrYrbk; Yrbk; RptrSchPpr; SchPpr; GerCl; SciCl; Trk; College; Actor.

ERHART, Debra L; West Aurora HS; Aurora, IL; 47/590 Band; ChrhWkr; CncrtBnd; HonRl; MrchBnd; NHS; PepBnd; RedCrAde; SchPl; Augustana; Mathematics.

ERICH, Jean; Divine Savior Holy Angels HS; Milwaukee, WI; SecTrsFrshCls; HonRl; Bsbl; CchngActv; Univ; Medical Technologist.

ERICKSEN, Dawn M; Joliet West HS; Joliet, IL; 60/500 Chr; HonRl; NHS; RptrSchPpr; Bsktbl; Tennis; Trk; Univ Of Il; Medical Tech.

ERICKSEN, George E; Maine West Twp HS; Des Plaines, IL; 158/750 Aud/Vis; HonRl; IntrClCncl; NHS; Quill&Scroll; StuCncl; RptrSchPpr; So Illinois Univ; Dentistry.

ERICKSEN, Karen; Garretson HS; Garretson, SD; 2/50 Band; Chr; Chrs; CncrtBnd; HonRl; MrchBnd; NHS; FHA; BttyCrckrAwd; DARAwd; Sd St Univ; Engr.

ERICKSON, Alan K; Essex Community HS; Essex, IA; 5/35 Band; ChrhWkr; HonRl; NHS; Pres4-H; MthCl; 4-HAwd; Iowa Western Comm College; Science.

ERICKSON, Belua L; Dumont Comm HS; Dumont, IA; 2/25 NHS; NatlMeritSchl; NatlMeritSF; PolWkr; SchPpr; FBLA; FDA; FNA; FSA; BttyCrckrAwd; CitAwd; College; Nurses Training.

ERICKSON, Betty J; Anoka Sr HS; Andover, MN; Band; HonRl; MrchBnd; PepBnd; Yrbk; SchPpr; Pres4-H; PpCl; Trk; 4-HAwd; Suburban Hennepin Vo Tech; Photographer.

ERICKSON, Bonnie J; Sacred Heart Public HS; Sacred Heart, MN; 2/29 SecFrshCls; PresSrCls; ALAGirlsSt; PresBand; PresChr; HonRl; PresNHS; NatlMeritCmnd; StuCncl; Yrbk; PresFHA; LetterBsktbl; AmLegAwd; St Cloud St College.

ERICKSON, Brad G; Marathon Consolidated HS; Marathon, IA; VPJrCls; HonRl; SchMus; SctActv; StuCncl; LetterBsbl; LetterBsktbl; LetterFtbl; IMSpt; College; Conservation.

ERICKSON, Brian D; Lakeville HS; Lakeville, MN; 11/190 PresSrCls; HonRl; NHS; SctActv; StuCncl; LetterBsktbl; LetterFtbl; DanFAwd; LionAwd; CitAwd; St Cloud State Clge; Accounting.

ERICKSON, Bruce A; Pipestone HS; Pipestone, MN; 2/127 Band; Chrs; ChrhWkr; HonRl; NHS; SctActv; YthFlsp; LetterBsbl; CaptBsktbl; LetterTrk; Univ Of Minnesota; Engineering.

ERICKSON, Bruce D; Calamus Comm HS; Calamus, IA; VPFrshCls; PresSophCls; TrsJrCls; Band; Chrl; Chrs; HonRl; NHS; PepBnd; SchMus; College; Math.

ERICKSON, Carolyn K; Marathon Consolidated HS; Marathon, IA; Band; Chr; HonRl; LbryAde; SchPl; YthFlsp; 4-H; LetterBsbl; LetterTrk; VP4-HAwd; College; Education Or Art.

ERICKSON, Caryl L; Beaver Dam Sr HS; Beaver Dam, WI; ALAGirlsSt; Chrs; ChrhWkr; Orch; PolWkr; SchMus; SctActv; University; Engineering.

ERICKSON, Dale R; Unified District #426 HS; Courtland, KS; HstFrshCls; VPSophCls; SecJrCls; TrsSrCls; HonRl; RptrYrbk; FFA; Bsktbl; Ftbl; Trk; Nck Voc Tech, Beloit, Ks; Production Ag.

ERICKSON, Darol J; Powers Lake HS; Powers Lake, ND; ChrhWkr; HonRl; SchPl; Teen; FFA; State Sch Of Sci; Carpenter.

ERICKSON, David A; Roseau HS; Roseau, MN; Chrs; HonRl; OffAde; PolWkr; SchMus; StuCncl; 4-H; FFA; LetterBsbl; LetterFtbl; VoiceDemAwd; College; Law.

ERICKSON, David A; Joliet Township HS; Joliet, IL; Band; CncrtBnd; HonRl; MrchBnd; PepBnd; Glf; Trk; PresAwd;.

ERICKSON, Deborah R; Sycamore HS; Sycamore, IL; 1/225 Chr; Chrs; ChrhWkr; NHS; NatlThespSoc; SchPl; SctActv; SpnCl; Tennis; GAA; University; Biology.

ERICKSON, Debra K; Richwoods HS; Peoria, IL; 63/474 ChrhWkr; HonRl; JA; LbryAde; NatlMeritSF; 4-H; College.

ERICKSON, Donna J; Clifford Galesburg HS; Galesburg, ND; Band; Chrs; HonRl; PepBnd; SchPl; YthFlsp; RptrSchPpr; FHA; LetterBsktbl; GAA; Mayville St Clg; Child Care Spec.

ERICKSON, Earl; Roseau HS; Salol, MN; 34/127 ChrhWkr; HonRl; TchrAde; 4-H; FFA; Bsbl; Tennis; College; Physical Therapy.

ERICKSON, Jan; Lakota HS; Brocket, ND; SecFrshCls; SecJrCls; ALAGirlsSt; Chrs; HonRl; EdSchPpr; Coll.

ERICKSON, Joan L; Burke Central HS; Lignite, ND; Band; CncrtBnd; HonRl; MrchBnd; PepBnd; SchPl; SctActv; PpCl; Bsktbl; Trk; College.

ERICKSON, Jon J; Truesdale HS; Albert City, IA; 2/50 PresJrCls; ALBoysSt; Chr; Chrs; ChrhWkr; HonRl; Mdrgl; NHS; StuCncl; YthFlsp; Ftbl; Trk; University; Engineering.

ERICKSON, Karen A; Madison HS; Mdison, KS; 1/33 SecJrCls; Band; Chrs; HonRl; NHS; SchPl; GerCl; PpCl; LetterBsbl; LetterTrk; University; Social Worker.

ERICKSON, Karlyle A; Glenburn HS; Maxbass, ND; Band; Chrs; ChrhWkr; CncrtBnd; MrchBnd; PepBnd; SchPl; Ndsu Botlineau; Forestry.

ERICKSON, Kevin J; Grand Rapids HS; Grand Rapids, MN; 20/370 CAP; OptClAwd; Northwestern Elec Inst; Elec Design.

ERICKSON, Kim M; Cleveland HS; St Louis, MO; HstJrCls; HstSrCls; HonRl; PolWkr; PpCl; LetterBsbl; GAA; IMSpt; College; Management.

ERICKSON, Laurie L; Mc Henry Public HS; Mc Henry, ND; SecJrCls; PresSrCls; ALAGirlsSt; Band; Chrs; CncrtBnd; HonRl; MrchBnd; StuGov; RptrYrbk; CaptBsktbl; LetterTrk; College.

ERICKSON, Lori; Adams Public HS; Adams, ND; SecFrshCls; ALAGirlsSt; Chrs; HonRl; LbryAde; SchPl; TchrAde; Yrbk; RptrSchPpr; AmLegAwd; Bus School; Vocational.

ERICKSON, Lynn; Fisher HS; Fisher, MN; VPSophCls; Band; CncrtBnd; MrchBnd; PepBnd; SchPl; RptrYrbk; FHA; Bsktbl; Ftbl; College; Nursing Rn.

ERICKSON, Marie J; Galesburg Sr HS; Galesburg, IL; 22/675 Chr; HonRl; JrNHS; NHS; SchMus; SctActv; YthFlsp; Yrbk; GerCl; LatCl; LetterTennis; Knox College.

ERICKSON, Marilyn J; Urbana HS; Urbana, IL; 1/350 SecSophCls; HstJrCls; Band; HospAde; MrchBnd; NHS; PepBnd; 4-H; LetterChrldr; IMSpt; Univ; Architecture.

ERICKSON, Mark; Northwestern HS; Poplar, WI; HonRl; SctActv; Trk; Uw Superior; Phy Ed.

ERICKSON, Melody A; Superior HS; Superior, NE; 2/74 TrsFrshCls; Chrs; HonRl; NHS; 4-H; FHA; PpCl; State College.

ERICKSON, Michelle J; Carrington HS; Carrington, ND; VPSophCls; SecSrCls; ALAGirlsSt; Band; Chr; ChrhWkr; HonRl; StuCncl; LetterBsktbl; LetterGAA; Unif Of Nd; Medicine.

ERICKSON, Nancy A; Sacred Heart HS; Sacred Heart, MN; PresJrCls; Band; Chr; ChrhWkr; DrmMjrt; SchPl; YthFlsp; FHA; LetterBsktbl; LetterChrldr; College.

ERICKSON, Pamela K; Mitchell Senior HS; Mitchell, SD; Chr; ChrhWkr; HonRl; SchMus; KeyCl; PpCl; Trk; Chrldr; IMSpt; South Dakota State Univ.

ERICKSON, Patrick J; Council Grove HS; Council Grove, KS; Band; Chrs; CncrtBnd; HonRl; MrchBnd; PepBnd; SchMus; Bsbl; Glf; IMSpt; College; Radio & Tv.

ERICKSON, Randal V; Gobles HS; Gobles, MI; 8/66 NHS; SchPl; EdYrBk; FrCl; MthCl; PpCl; SciCl; LetterBsbl; LetterBsktbl; CaptFtbl; LetterWrstlng; W Michigan Univ; Elec Engineer.

ERICKSON, Rhonda K; Slayton HS; Slayton, MN; ALAGirlsSt; CmntyWkr; HonRl; LetterTennis; IMSpt; College; Professional.

ERICKSON, Robert D; Canby HS; Canby, MN; SecSrCls; SchPl; StuCncl; Univ; Prof.

ERICKSON, Robert T; Mishicot HS; Mishicot, WI; HonRl; TchrAde; Air Force; Prof.

ERICKSON, Sally A; St Clair HS; St Clair, MI; 2/191 PresSrCls; HonRl; StuCncl; EdSchPpr; CaptBsktbl; CaptChrldr; U Of Mi; Languages.

ERICKSON, Sharon E; Roseau HS; Roseau, MN; ALAGirlsSt; ChrhWkr; HonRl; OffAde; SchPl; PresStuCncl; TchrAde; 4-H; FHA; CaptChrldr; Bemidji State Coll.

ERICKSON, Shirley; Boone Jr Sr HS; Boone, IA; 1/215 SecSrCls; Band; CncrtBnd; HonRl; NHS; Orch; LatCl;.

ERICKSON, Stephen T; Escanaba Sr HS; Escanaba, MI; 146/392 HonRl; SchPpr; LetterBsktbl; IMSpt; College; Business.

ERICKSON, Susan; Mead Jr Sr HS; Mead, NE; Chrs; LbryAde; NHS; NatlThespSoc; SchPl; MthCl; PpCl; Chrldr; Midland Lutheran College; Nursing.

ERICKSON, Thomas W; East Greene HS; Grand Jct, IA; 17/43 TrsSrCls; Chr; HonRl; SchPl; SctActv; LetterBsktbl; LetterFtbl; LetterTrk; IMSpt; GodCntryAwd; PresAwd; College; Electronics.

ERICKSON, Wanda J; Wittenberg Birnamwood HS; Tigerton, WI; Chr; Chrs; ChrhWkr; HonRl; NatlFornLg; NHS; SchPl; YthFlsp; EdSchPpr; SpnCl; Concordia College; Medical Technologist.

ERICKSON, William E; Plano HS; Plano, IL; 3/94 HonRl; NatlMeritCmnd; SpnCl; MthCl; Wrstlng; U Of Il; Business Mngm.

ERICSON, James; Whitefish Bay HS; Whitefish Bay, WI; 23/351 ALBoysSt; CncrtBnd; MrchBnd; NatlFornLg; NHS; PepBnd; StuCncl; MthCl; Trk; Coll; Professional Law.

ERICSON, Kevin C; Holdrege HS; Funk, NE; 17/119 VPBand; Chr; ChrhWkr; CncrtBnd; HonRl; MrchBnd; SchMus; SchPl; Trk; EldAwd; Ks State U; Veterinary.

ERICSON, Steven C; Downers Grove South HS; Downers Grove, IL; 123/830 Univ Of Illinois; Law.

ERIKSEN, Michael C; Maine Township South HS; Park Ridge, IL; VPChrhWkr; CtyCnl; HonRl; MrchBnd; PolWkr; SchMus; SchPl; VPYthFlsp; Ftbl; Trk; College; Oceanography.

ERIKSEN, Scott D; Carbondale Comm HS; Carbondale, IL; 46/323 HonRl; YthLg; CaptBsktbl; Ftbl; Trk; Vanderbilt Univ; Business.

ERIKSEN, Sue M; Clay Central Comm HS; Peterson, IA; SecJrCls; Band; Chrs; CncrtBnd; HonRl; MrchBnd; PepBnd; SchPl; EdYrBk; Chrldr; College; Marine Biologist.

ERIKSON, Barbara A; Canova Public HS; Canova, SD; ALAGirlsSt; Band; Chrs; CncrtBnd; HonRl; MrchBnd; PepBnd; SchPl; RptrYrbk; EdSchPpr; PpCl; LetterBsktbl; AmLegAwd;.

ERIKSON, Bing; Bentley HS; Burton, MI; ALBoysSt; HonRl; NHS; SctActv; YthFlsp; College; Law.

ERIKSON, Hollis J; Libertyville HS; Libertyville, IL; Chrs; HonRl; HospAde; NHS; GerCl; SciCl; Univ Of Ill; Animal Science.

ERISMAN, Anne K; University HS; Warrensburg, MO; 1/51 Chrs; CncrtBnd; HonRl; PresNatlFornLg; SecNatlThespSoc; SchMus; SchPl; RptrYrbk; PresFrCl; PresSpnCl; IMSpt; OptClAwd; Univ Of Missouri; Theatre.

ERK, Henry; St Marys HS; St Louis, MO; 9/184 HonRl; JrNHS; NHS; OffAde; SchPpr; SciCl; IMSpt; Washington Univ; Chemical Engineering.

ERKFITZ, John W; Alpena HS; Alpena, MI; CAP; SctActv; SptEdSchPpr; Comm College; Communications.

ERLAND, Kathleen M; Walther Lutheran HS; Lombard, IL; Chr; HonRl; YthLg; RptrSchPpr; Augustana Coll; Music.

ERLANDSON, David E; North Senior HS; N S Paul, MN; TrsSrCls; ALBoysSt; HonRl; NHS; StuCncl; StuGov; FrCl; LetterBsktbl; Ftbl; College; Engineering.

ERLANDSON, Janis K; Hillsboro HS; Hillsboro, WI; 7/65 TrsSophCls; TrsJrCls; Band; Chrs; DrmMjrt; NHS; PepBnd; SchMus; Chrldr; IMSpt; U W Stout; Childhood Educ.

ERLENBUSH, Bertha M; Portage Northern HS; Portage, MI; ChrhWkr; HonRl; NHS; SctActv; Michigan St University; Medicine.

ERMER, Michael G; Chaminade College Prep; St Louis, MO; 1/120 Band; CncrtBnd; HonRl; JrNHS; PresNatlFornLg; NHS; SchPl; StuCncl; IMSpt; OptClAwd; College; Law.

ERNEST, Diane C; La Salle HS; Cedar Rapids, IA; Chr; HonRl; ModUN; NatlFornLg; NHS; RptrYrbk; RptrSchPpr; Univ; Business Management.

ERNESTI, Donna; Howells HS; Dodge, NE; ALAGirlsSt; DrlTm; JA; NHS; ROTC; SchPl; StuGov; YthLg; 4-H; FBLA; Business School.

ERNESTI, Sandy; Central Catholic HS; West Point, NE; Chrs; HonRl; NHS; SchPl; LatCl; SciCl; College; Lab Technician.

ERNST, Betty L; Schleswig Comm HS; Danbury, IA; 3/51 Band; ChrhWkr; CncrtBnd; HonRl; LbryAde; MrchBnd; NHS; RptrSchPpr; FHA; PPFtbl; College; Professional.

ERNST, Craig W; Falls City HS; Rulo, NE; HonRl; FFA; College; Vocation.

ERNST, Dave; Lincoln Northeast Hs; Lincoln, NE; Chr; HonRl; Mdrgl; SchMus; LetterBsbl; LetterFtbl; Nebraska U; Engineering.

ERNST, Diane S; Humboldt HS; Hardy, IA; Band; Chr; Chrs; ChrhWkr; CncrtBnd; HonRl; MrchBnd; PepBnd; SchMus; StuCncl; TchrAde; YthFlsp; Chrldr; GAA; Iowa State Univ; Music.

ERNST, Mary; Lagrove HS; Farina, IL; Band; Chrs; CncrtBnd; LbryAde; MrchBnd; SchMus; Yrbk; FHA; FrCl; SciCl; Unicersity; Business.

ERNST, Mary K; Adair Casey Community HS; Adair, IA; 6/48 TrsJrCls; TrsSrCls; ChrhWkr; HonRl; NHS; PpCl; CaptBsktbl; CaptTrk; Nw Mo State U; Phy Ed.

ERNST, Monica L; Warren HS; Apple River, IL; Band; CncrtBnd; HonRl; MrchBnd; Orch; PepBnd; FHA; PpCl; College.

ERNST, Robert J; Norfolk Sr HS; Norfolk, NE; Band; CncrtBnd; HonRl; MrchBnd; Univ Of Nebraska; Computer Design.

ERNST, Sandra R; Gering HS; Gering, NE; ChrhWkr; HonRl; HospAde; JrNHS; StuCncl; YthFlsp; 4-H; PpCl; Trk; Chrldr; 4-HAwd; College; Major Study.

ERNST, Stephen A; Hillsboro HS; Hillsboro, IL; HonRl; NatlMeritCmnd; SctActv; Univ Of Ill; Engineering.

ERNST, Steven K; Univ Of Detroit HS; Detroit, MI; CmntyWkr; HonRl; NatlMeritCmnd; PolWkr; Trk; Univ Of Michigan; Medicine.

ERNST, Thomas G; Richland Center HS; Richland Center, WI; HonRl; ModUN; StuCncl; KeyCl; LetterBsktbl; Ftbl; LetterTrk; LionAwd; College; Science.

ERNST, Vicky L; Cochrane Fountain City HS; Fountain City, WI; 3/90 ChrhWkr; DrlTm; LbryAde; NHS; OffAde; TchrAde; RptrSchPpr; SchPpr; Pres4-H; FHA; PpCl; SciCl; GAA; 4-HAwd; Winona Area Vocational College; Nurse.

ERPELDING, Sandi J; Garrigan HS; Bode, IA; ChrhWkr; HonRl; SchPpr; 4-H; PpCl; Bsbl; Trk; IMSpt; Business Schl; Secretary.

ERPENBACH, Carol M; Hibbing HS; Hibbing, MN; Band; Chr; Chrs; ChrhWkr; CmntyWkr; HonRl; SchMus; SchPl; 4-H; FBLA; Chrldr; IMSpt; Hibbing Comm College; Special Educ.

ERPENBACH, Michael L; Bethlehem Academy; Faribault, MN; 7/93 PresFrshCls; ALBoysSt; HonRl; NHS; SchPl; SctActv; StuCncl; StuGov; SchPpr; SecSophCls; College; Math.

ERSKIN, David R; Vestaburg HS; Vestaburg, MI; Band; ChrhWkr; CncrtBnd; HonRl; MrchBnd; PepBnd; SchAde; SctActv; StuCncl; YthLg; Northwestern Mich Clg; Airlines Pilot.

ERVA, Karen T; Hancock Central HS; Hancock, MI; 7/90 Chr; CncrtBnd; HonRl; MrchBnd; PepBnd; SchPl; TchrAde; RptrYrbk; FTA; AmLegAwd; Coll; Elementary Teacher.

ERVIN, Beth M; Weeping Water Public HS; Nehawka, NE; HstFrshCls; SecSophCls; SecJrCls; HonRl; TreasNHS; OffAde; TreasStuGov; TchrAde; SecFBLA; TreasFHA; Lincoln Sch Of Comm; Bus.

ERVIN, Kent M; Parsons Sr HS; Parsons, KS; CncrtBnd; VPNatlMeritFnl; NatlSciFnd; Orch; SctActv; PresYthFlsp; Univ; Science.

ERVIN, Lissa A; Pike HS; Indianapolis, IN; 7/230 Chr; HonRl; JrNHS; NHS; NatlThespSoc; SchMus; StuCncl; TchrAde; Ball State University; Home Economics.

ERVIN, Ronald; St Louis Priory HS; St Louis, MO; 20/34 ChrhWkr; CmntyWkr; LitMag; PolWkr; SctActv; StuGov; RptrYrbk; CaptBsktbl; CaptFtbl; CaptTrk; Princeton Univ; Law.

ERVIN, Sharon S; Hoopeston East Lynn HS; Hoopeston, IL; Chrs; ChrhWkr; CncrtBnd; HonRl; MrchBnd; NatlThespSoc; PepBnd; SchMus; SchPl; GAA; Eastern Il U; Field Of Art.

ERVITI, Manuel G; John F Kennedy HS; Chicago, IL; Aud/Vis; Chrs; HonRl; NHS; Orch; SchMus; StuCncl; RptrYrbk; IMSpt; Univ.

ERWAY, Ricky; Oregon HS; Oregon, WI; SecSophCls; PresSrCls; Aud/Vis; HonRl; NHS; SctActv; StuCncl; Yrbk; Univ Of Wisconsin; English.

ERWIN, James H; Clarksville HS; Clarksville, IN; HonRl; NHS; SchPl; FTA; KeyCl; GerCl; PpCl; Trk; IMSpt; Indiana Univ Southeast; Chemical Engineer.

ERWIN, Luduska L; Little Falls Comm HS; Little Falls, MN; Chrldr; College; Professional.

ERWIN, Tim; Spencer HS; Spencer, IA; HstFrshCls; Band; CncrtBnd; HonRl; JrNHS; StuCncl; YthFlsp; Bsktbl; Glf; Trk; Univ; Journalism.

ERXLEBEN, Janice M; Bellmont HS; Decatur, IN; ChrhWkr; HonRl; College; Psychology.

ESAREY, Lynne R; Glenwood HS; Chatham, IL; 17/143 AFS; Chrl; LbryAde; SchMus; SctActv; TchrAde; GerCl; GAA; U Of Ill; Psychology.

ESAREY, Neal B; Heritage Hills HS; Evanston, IN; Aud/Vis; SctActv; Univ Of Evansville.

ESCH, Lawrence K; Gordon Tech HS; Chicago, IL; 28/647 CncrtBnd; HonRl; MrchBnd; NHS; StuCncl; StuGov; RptrSchPpr; VPGerCl; MthCl; Univ; Economics.

ESCH, Vicki; Caledonia HS; Caledonia, MN; Band; ChrhWkr; HonRl; PepBnd; SchPl; StuGov; RptrYrbk; Bsktbl; Nurse.

ESCHBACH, Sharon A; Ottawa Twp HS; Ottawa, IL; 25/425 HonRl; NHS; Ill State Univ; Psychology.

ESCHENBURG, Richard J; L Anse Creuse HS; Mt Clemens, MI; Chr; HonRl; JrNHS; NHS; SctActv; Coll; Art.

ESCHER, Deborah L; Bloomer HS; Bloomer, WI; 3/122 AFS; CncrtBnd; HonRl; HospAde; MrchBnd; NHS; SchPl; Yrbk; FFA; SciCl; U Of Wis; Environmental Science.

ESCHER, Jill; Manning Community HS; Manning, IA; CncrtBnd; HonRl; MrchBnd; NHS; Quill&Scroll; SchMus; StuCncl; EdYrBk; 4-H; BttyCrckrAwd; Creighton U; Bs In Nursing.

ESCHLIMAN, Rosemarie J; Spalding Academy; Spalding, NE; Chr; Chrs; ChrhWkr; HonRl; NHS; OffAde; SchAde; SchMus; SchPl; StuCncl; LetterTrk; Chrldr; CchngActv; IMSpt; Univ Of Ne; Home Economics.

ESCHMANN, Margaret M; Dupo Comm HS; Dupo, IL; Chrs; ChrhWkr; HonRl; ModUN; NHS; SchMus; SctActv; TchrAde; RptrYrbk; EdYrBk; College; Psychology.

ESCKELSON, Clifford; Vassar HS; Vasar, MI; 42/153 HonRl; YthFlsp; Bsbl; Ftbl; Saginaw Valley St Col; Computer Programming.

ESCOBEDO, Anthony P; Bths West HS; Belleville, IL; 1/700 HonRl; ModUN; NatlFornLg; NHS; PolWkr; TreasCivCl; CaptIMSpt; CitAwd; Univ Of Illinois; Law.

ESCONTRIAS, Juan J; E Moline United Twsp HS; East Moline, IL; 92/787 HonRl; SpnCl; LetterBsbl; IMSpt; College; Accountant.

ESCOTT, Elaine V; Lindbergh HS; Crestwood, MO; Chr; HonRl; NHS; NatlMeritSF; Orch; SchMus; RptrSchPpr; FrCl; PpCl; PPFtbl; University.

ESHELBRENNER, Rama J; Fort Scott HS; Fort Scott, KS; 1/160 VPJrCls; ChrhWkr; DrlTm; HonRl; HospAde; SchPl; StuCncl; TchrAde; RptrYrbk; RptrSchPpr; College.

ESHELMAN, Dennis K; Rochester Comm HS; Rochester, IN; 45/154 Aud/Vis; CAP; LbryAde; NatlFornLg; SchPl; CivCl; GerCl; Us Marines; Elec Technology.

ESHELMAN, Linda; Highland Pk Sr HS; St Paul, MN; Band; CncrtBnd; HospAde; SchAde; TchrAde; Glf; College;physical Education.

ESHLEMAN, Dirk E; Fisher HS; Fisher, IL; 1/59 VPFrshCls; VPSophCls; VPJrCls; PresSrCls; AFS; HonRl; NHS; SchMus; SchPl; StuCncl; Tennis; Wrstlng; Illinois State Univ; Author.

ESHLEMAN, Marietta S; Carrollton HS; Carrollton, MO; Chr; HonRl; HospAde; SchMus; SchPl; SctActv; YthFlsp; RptrYrbk; RptrSchPpr; Kansas City College; Dental Asst.

ESHOM, Gail; Warsaw HS; Sutter, IL; 14/66 SecSrCls; Band; Chr; MrchBnd; PolWkr; 4-H; FBLA; DanFAwd; 4-HAwd; USJCAwd; Quincy Coll; English.

ESKER, Alan E; St Anthony HS; Effingham, IL; 8/63 ChrhWkr; HonRl; JA; NHS; Quincy College; Medicine.

ESKURI, Lynne M; Moose Lake HS; Moose Lake, MN; 14/71 VPJrCls; HonRl; HospAde; NHS; SchPl; TchrAde; PpCl; Navy; Archetect.

ESLER, John A; Goldfield Community HS; Goldfield, IA; TrsFrshCls; ALBoysSt; Band; ChrhWkr; CncrtBnd; HonRl; MrchBnd; PepBnd; SchMus; SchPl; SctActv; Bsbl; CaptBsktbl; DanFAwd;.

ESLINGER, Kathy; Minot HS; Minot, ND; Chrs; CmntyWkr; HonRl; LbryAde; NHS; GerCl; Col; Spec Ed.

ESLINGER, Lillie D; Sullivan HS; Merom, IN; 13/139 Band; CncrtBnd; HonRl; JrNHS; MrchBnd; NHS; PepBnd; StuCncl; TchrAde; YthFlsp; LetterBsktbl; LetterTennis; CaptTrk; Indiana Univ; Physical Ed.

ESLINGER, Patricia; Reeder HS; Reeder, ND; 2/16 VPJrCls; SecSrCls; ALAGirlsSt; Band; ChrhWkr; HonRl; SchPl; StuCncl; Bsktbl; Trk; College; Social Service.

ESMANN, Mary; Guttenberg Community HS; Guttenberg, IA; Band; Chrs; CncrtBnd; HonRl; MrchBnd; NHS; PepBnd; Yrbk; FHA;.

ESPEL, Timothy G; Geneva Comm HS; Geneva, IL; 13/218 Chrs; CncrtBnd; Mdrgl; MrchBnd; NHS; PepBnd; SchMus; 4-H; FFA; Wrstlng; U Of Ill; Agricture.

ESPELAND, Ricky L; Forest City Comm HS; Forest City, IA; 35/135 ALBoysSt; Band; MrchBnd; PepBnd; PolWkr; SchMus; StuCncl; EdSchPpr; SciCl; Bsbl; Iowa State U; Politcal Sci.

ESPENSCHIED, Cindy K; Fremont Sr HS; Fremont, NE; 4-H; GerCl; MasAwd; Doane; Math.

ESPER, Theresa M; Adlai Stevenson HS; Sterling Hts, MI; Chrl; Chrs; ChrhWkr; HonRl; LbryAde; StuGov; GerCl; Msu; Teacher.

ESPER, Thomas J; Romeo HS; Romeo, MI; HonRl; RptrSchPpr; Eastern Michigan Univ; Accounting.

ESPESETH, Arlan E; Noonan HS; Noonan, ND; SecTrsJrCls; Chr; Chrs; ChrhWkr; HonRl; SchMus; 4-H; Bsbl; LetterBsktbl; LetterFtbl; University; Teacher.

ESPESETH, Sharon K; Erskine Public HS; Erskine, MN; 6/29 VPFrshCls; VPSophCls; TrsJrCls; Band; Chr; NHS; RptrYrbk; RptrSchPpr; Bsktbl; Chrldr; College; Journalism Or English Major.

ESPINOSA, Nancy G; Thornton Twp HS; Riverdale, IL; Band; HonRl; NHS; OffAde; Thornton Comm College; Special Educ.

ESPOSITO, Constance; North Shore Country Day HS; Northbrook, IL; HonRl; LatCl; Northwestern University; Doctor.

ESSAR, David W; Gull Lake HS; Richland, MI; 5/235 ChrhWkr; CncrtBnd; HonRl; NHS; SctActv; FrCl; SciCl; College; Medicine.

ESSAY, Cheryl A; St Agnes Academy; Alliance, NE; HonRl; NatlMeritCmnd; SchPl; StuGov; 4-H; FSA; FrCl; SpnCl; PpCl; LetterTrk; VoiceDemAwd; College; Nursing.

ESSELMAN, Jolie; Athens HS; Athens, WI; Band; HonRl; MrchBnd; SchPl; StuCncl; YthLg; SchPpr; University; Biology Research.

ESSELSTROM, Adrian R; Carl Sandburg HS; Palos Heights, IL; CncrtBnd; HonRl; MrchBnd; Orch; SchMus; SchPl; YthFlsp; Indiana University; Music Professor.

ESSELSTROM, Daniel; Northwestern HS; Wentworth, WI; ChrhWkr; HonRl; IMSpt; College.

ESSENBURG, Jodi K; Holland Christian HS; Holland, MI; HonRl; SpnCl; IMSpt; Hope College; Sociology.

ESSENDRUP, William J; Raymond HS; Raymond, MN; SecSophCls; Band; Chr; HonRl; PepBnd; StuCncl; TchrAde; LetterBsbl; LetterBsktbl; LetterFtbl; Alexandria Mn Vo Tech; Computer Programmer.

ESSENMACHER, Mary K; Harbor Beach Comm HS; Harbor Beach, MI; 19/136 Band; CncrtBnd; HonRl; HospAde; MrchBnd; NHS; PepBnd; FNA; FTA; Bus Sch; Office Worker.

ESSENMACHER, Sharon M; Harbor Beach Community HS; Harbor Beach, MI; 3/136 VPFrshCls; HonRl; ModUN; NHS; StuCncl; TrsSophCls; IMSpt; PPFtbl; Univ; Spec Educ.

ESSER, Joyce M; Highland HS; Highland, WI; 1/51 Chrs; HonRl; EdYrBk; RptrSchPpr; PpCl; LetterBsbl; LetterTrk; GAA; Vocational.

ESSER, Susan A; Wauwatosa East HS; Wauwatosa, WI; 3/400 HonRl; NHS; NatlMeritSchl; PolWkr; PresMthCl; SciCl; DARAwd; NCTE; Radcliffe College; Corporate Law.

ESSERMAN, Victoria L; Valparaiso Sr HS; Valparaiso, IN; 15/422 Band; CncrtBnd; MrchBnd; PepBnd; College; Business.

ESSEX, Kathy A; Columbia Central HS; Cement City, MI; ChrhWkr; LbryAde; 4-H; FHA; KeyCl; Jackson Comm College; Home Economics.

ESSIG, Mark A; Godwin Heights HS; Wyoming, MI; 2/202 PresFrshCls; TrsSophCls; PresJrCls; PresSrCls; ALBoysSt; HonRl; NHS; StuCncl; EdYrBk; FDA; College; Doctor.

ESSIG, Michael J; Washington Catholic HS; Washington, IN; 6/40 ALBoysSt; ChrhWkr; HonRl; NHS; SchPl; Yrbk; RptrSchPpr; KeyCl; PpCl; LetterBsbl; Univ Of Evansville; Business Administration.

ESSLINGER, Perry; Griffin HS; Springfield, IL; HstSophCls; HonRl; JA; PolWkr; StuCncl; StuGov; PpCl; Bsbl; Ftbl; Trk; Univ; Construction Tech.

ESSMANN, Debra J; East HS; Waterloo, IA; SecJrCls; HonRl; SchMus; SchPl; StuCncl; StuGov; SpnCl; PpCl; LetterSwmmng; MasAwd; Coll; Child Psychologist.

ESSMYER, Tom M; Vianney HS; St Louis, MO; HonRl; PresJA; NHS; Quill&Scroll; SctActv; EdSchPpr; LetterTrk; Chrldr; IMSpt; JAAwd; Univ; Business Law.

ESSNER, James L; Notre Dame HS; Cape Girardeau, MO; 9/78 Chrs; HonRl; NHS; SchMus; SctActv; IMSpt; Semo Univ; Accounting.

ESSON, Scott A; Sault Area HS; Sault St Marie, MI; HonRl; TchrAde; LetterBsbl; LetterFtbl; IMSpt; Trade School ; Vocation.

ESTABROOK, Mari; Breckenridge HS; Breckenridge, MO; 3/12 TrsFrshCls; VPSophCls; SecJrCls; SecSrCls; Band; CmntyWkr; CncrtBnd; HonRl; NHS; Missouri Western Coll; Bus.

ESTELA, Raul R; Roberto Clemente HS; Chicago, IL; Chr; ChrhWkr; HonRl; NHS; StuGov; YthFlsp; RptrSchPpr; SchPpr; PresKeyCl; FrCl; LetterFtbl; CaptTennis; CchngActv; Univ; Doctor.

ESTELL, Stephanie J; Lincoln Way Comm H S HS; Mokena, IL; 21/566 HonRl; NHS; TchrAde; RptrSchPpr; PresFHA; FTA; FrCl; Joliet Junior College; Elementary Educ Teac.

ESTERS, Crystal E; Soldan HS; St Louis, MO; HonRl; NHS; SctActv; StuCncl; Trk; GAA; Univ; Nursing.

ESTERS, Daniel W; Yorkwood HS; Kirkwood, IL; TrsFrshCls; TrsSophCls; TrsJrCls; TrsSrCls; Band; CncrtBnd; HonRl; MrchBnd; NHS; PepBnd; YthFlsp; Ftbl; Trk; College; Elec Engineer.

ESTES, Debra J; Frederic Remington HS; Potwin, KS; VPBand; CmntyWkr; SecNatlThespSoc; StuCncl; FHA; PpCl; SciCl; Chrldr; GAA; PPFtbl; Wichita St Univ; Dental Technology.

ESTES, Steven R; Pontiac Twp HS; Graymont, IL; CncrtBnd; HonRl; PresNatlThespSoc; Quill&Scroll; SchMus; SchPl; SchPpr; PresLatCl; Isu; Ministry.

ESTHER, Julie L; Memorial HS; Joplin, MO; TrsSrCls; ChrhWkr; HonRl; LitMag; PresNatlFornLg; NatlThespSoc; Quill&Scroll; TreasStuCncl; EdYrBk; Glf; College; Law.

ESTRADA, Denise M; Merrill HS; Merrill, MI; 8/117 HonRl; NHS; SchAde; StuCncl; FHA; PpCl; Bsktbl; LetterTrk; Chrldr; College; Accounting.

ESTRIDGE, Paul; Carmel HS; Carmel, IN; VPFrshCls; PresSophCls; PresJrCls; CmntyWkr; HonRl; Bsktbl; Ftbl; Trk; College.

ESTRIDGE, Peggy S; Carmel HS; Carmel, IN; 52/527 Chrs; HonRl; NatlThespSoc; SchMus; SchPl; 4-H; FHA; KeyCl; FrCl; DanFAwd; Purdue University; Fashion Design.

ETCHEGOYHEN, Teresita M; St Scholastica HS; Chicago, IL; Chr; Chrs; ChrhWkr; CmntyWkr; HospAde; SchMus; RptrYrbk; Yrbk; Purdue University.

ETCHESON, William; North Putnam HS; Roachpale, IN; 23/140 HonRl; NHS; SchMus; SchPl; LetterBsbl; LetterFtbl; CaptSwmmng; IMSpt; College.

ETCHISON, Carl; Western HS; Russiaville, IN; 18/153 Yrbk; SchPpr; Wrstlng; 4-HAwd; RotaryAwd; Ind Univ; Pol Sci Bus Adm.

ETCHISON, Marta L; Papillion Sr HS; Papillion, NE; 45/318 Chr; ChrhWkr; HonRl; Mdrgl; NatlMeritCmnd; SchMus; SchPl; TchrAde; 4-H; FrCl; LatCl; Swmmng; Tennis; Smith College; Medicine.

ETCHISON, Steven; Alexandria Monroe HS; Alexandria, IN; Band; CncrtBnd; HonRl; MrchBnd; Chrs; PepBnd; MasAwd; Business School; Acountant.

ETHELL, Judy A; Athens Comm HS; Athens, IL; 2/59 Band; HonRl; NHS; FHA; ChmnChrldr; Western Ill Univ; Business.

ETHELL, Renee A; Athens HS; Cantrall, IL; 6/51 PresFrshCls; Band; CncrtBnd; HonRl; NHS; PresStuCncl; StuGov; PresYthFlsp; FHA; PpCl; GAA; IMSpt; Lincoln Land Comm Col; Mathematics.

ETHERIDGE, Michael D; Mendota Township HS; Mendota, IL; Band; CncrtBnd; MrchBnd; PepBnd; FrCl; College; Engineering.

ETHRIDGE, Deborah A; Woodlawn Comm HS; Woodlawn, IL; 1/36 HstSrCls; Band; Chrs; ChrhWkr; CmntyWkr; HonRl; LbryAde; NHS; SchPl; StuCncl; TchrAde; EdYrBk; EdSchPpr; College; Professional.

ETLICHER, Jeanne; Chetek HS; Sand Creek, WI; DrlTm; HonRl; FBLA; PpCl; GAA; PPFtbl; 4-HAwd; Technical School; Vocation.

ETLING, Vicky J; Freeburg Community HS; Freeburg, IL; 18/134 Band; CncrtBnd; DrmMjrt; HonRl; NHS; SchMus; TchrAde; Twrl; RptrYrbk; Chrldr; University; Vocation.

ETTEL, Rebecca S; Hazelwood Central HS; Florissant, MO; 13/800 SecSrCls; VPChr; HonRl; NHS; SchPpr; Sec4-H; FrCl; CaptChrldr; AmLegAwd; PresAwd; Purdue U; Computer Science Or Math Teacher.

ETTEN, Kristin; Medford Sr HS; Dorchester, WI; 5/212 ALAGirlsSt; DrmBgl; HonRl; NHS; StuCncl; EdYrBk; PresFrCl; PpCl; CaptChrldr; CitAwd; Eau Claire Tech Sch; Pract Nurs.

ETZEL, Kathleen A; Hayden HS; Topeka, KS; 23/200 HonRl; NHS; SchMus; StuCncl; FTA; FrCl; PpCl; Chrldr; Kansas St Univ; Special Ed.

ETZENBACH, John W; La Salle Peru Twp HS; Peru, IL; 4/512 AFS; HonRl; NatlMeritCmnd; SctActv; PresGerCl; Swmmng; Univ Of Ill; Dentist.

EUBANK, Janet A; Josephinum HS; Chicago, IL; 3/104 HonRl; LbryAde; SchPl; Loyola University; Acting.

EUBANKS, Bobby S; West Liberty Comm HS; West Liberty, IA; 6/90 Chr; Chrs; CmntyWkr; HonRl; NHS; SctActv; SchPpr; LetterBsktbl; LetterFtbl; LetterGlf; CchngActv; College; Professional.

EUBANKS, John A; Romeoville HS; Romeoville, IL; 13/367 HonRl; NHS; TchrAde; LetterFtbl; LetterTennis; IMSpt; College.

EUBANKS, Michael P; Holton HS; Denison, KS; PresJrCls; Chr; Chrl; Chrs; ChrhWkr; HonRl; StuCncl; YthFlsp; Bsktbl; LetterTrk; College Or Trade Sch; Forrestry Carpenter.

EUBANKS, Rhonda L; Benton HS; Benton, IL; Band; CncrtBnd; MrchBnd; OffAde; PepBnd; StuGov; Twrl; FHA; GAA; John A Logan; Court Reporter.

EUERLE, Carol; Litchfield Sr HS; Litchfield, MN; Band; CncrtBnd; HonRl; MrchBnd; PepBnd; PpCl; JAAwd; Coll; Conservation.

EURICH, Joan M; Crete HS; Crete, NE; 13/116 Chrs; CncrtBnd; HonRl; MrchBnd; YthFlsp; FBLA; Chrldr; IMSpt; Business School; Secretarial.

EUSSEN, Christina J M; Trinity HS; Hutchinson, KS; TrsJrCls; ChrhWkr; HonRl; LitMag; NHS; OffAde; SchPl; StuCncl; SchPpr; PpCl; College; Art.

EVAN, Katherine S; St Pius X HS; Arnold, MO; 28/101 HonRl; SchPl; PpCl; SciCl; IMSpt; Southwest Missouri St Univ; Agriculture.

EVANCHENKO, Sally R; North Shore HS; Makoti, ND; Band; Chrs; CncrtBnd; HonRl; MrchBnd; PepBnd; PpCl; LetterBsktbl; Medicine.

EVANGELISTA, Nancy J; North Farmington HS; West Bloomfield, MI; 8/463 Chr; ChrhWkr; CmntyWkr; HonRl; NHS; NatlMeritCmnd; SctActv; TchrAde; FrCl; Western Mich U; Spec Ed.

EVANOFF, Kristopher; Ontonagon Area HS; Ontonagon, MI; 10/107 HonRl; NHS; Ftbl; Glf; BauchLmbAwd; Mich Tech Univ; Chemical Engineering.

EVANOFF, Vickilynn; Our Lady Of The Lakes HS; Pontiac, MI; 6/53 HonRl; SctActv; TchrAde; Yrbk; LetterBsbl; Oakland University; Journalism.

EVANS, Becky J; Clarke Comm HS; Weldon, IA; 14/107 Band; ChrhWkr; CncrtBnd; HonRl; HospAde; MrchBnd; NatlThespSoc; PepBnd; SchPl; 4-H; College; Fine Arts.

EVANS, Betty J; Lowell Sr HS; Hebron, IN; 7/250 VPBand; ChrhWkr; CncrtBnd; HonRl; MrchBnd; NHS; PepBnd; SctActv; EdYrBk; PresFTA; PPFtbl; Ball State University; Special Educ.

EVANS, Betty L; Adair County R 2 HS; Brashear, MO; SecJrCls; SecSrCls; ChrhWkr; HonRl; NHS; 4-H; FHA; CaptChrldr; DARAwd; 4-HAwd; University; Ministry.

EVANS, Betty Lou M; Maine Township W HS; Des Plaines, IL; AFS; Band; HonRl; JrNHS; NHS; StuCncl; TchrAde; PresYthFlsp; LetterBsbl; Swmmng; Carleton College; Science Math.

EVANS, Bryan L; Sioux Valley HS; Lake Park, IA; HonRl; StuCncl; Yrbk; LetterBsktbl; Col; Professional.

EVANS, Carol M; River Forest HS; Hobart, IN; TrsSophCls; Chr; HonRl; HospAde; SchPl; StuCncl; 4-H; Bsktbl; 4-HAwd; OptClAwd; In U; Rn Surgical.

EVANS, Carolyn A; Chicago Vocational HS; Chicago, IL; 33/897 Band; CmntyWkr; HonRl; OffAde; Orch; College; Liberal Arts.

EVANS, Connie D; Griffith HS; Griffith, IN; 11/319 CmntyWkr; HonRl; JrNHS; NHS; StuGov; PpCl; PPFtbl; Univ; Business.

EVANS, Curtis R; Hayfield Secondary HS; Fort Riley, KS; 7/451 ChrhWkr; HonRl; NHS; ROTC; LetterSwmmng; Tennis; LetterTrk; Univ Of Kansas; Science.

EVANS, Daniel J; Johnston HS; Des Moines, IA; 14/80 Chrs; HonRl; PolWkr; StuCncl; StuGov; UNYO; LetterFtbl; Trk; Wrstlng; IMSpt; Creighton Univ; Law.

EVANS, David W; Moline Sr HS; Moline, IL; Band; CncrtBnd; HonRl; MrchBnd; PepBnd; SchMus; SctActv; YthFlsp; Augustana College; Engineer.

EVANS, Debra J; Monticello HS; Monticello, IL; PresFrshCls; VPSophCls; TrsJrCls; Chrs; HonRl; NHS; SchPl; StuCncl; PpCl; Chrldr; College.

EVANS, Delores; Central HS; St Louis, MO; Chr; Chrs; CmntyWkr; DrlTm; JA; SchPl; Yrbk; SchPpr; FBLA; PpCl; St Louis Univ; Vocational Nurse.

EVANS, Denise M; Monticello HS; Monticello, IL; TrsFrshCls; SecJrCls; Chrs; HonRl; LitMag; NHS; SchPl; StuCncl; PpCl; Chrldr; College; Art.

EVANS, Diane M; Homer Comm HS; Homer, MI; 1/86 Band; CncrtBnd; HonRl; MrchBnd; NatlFornLg; SecNHS; 4-H; FHA; BttyCrckrAwd; DARAwd; 4-HAwd; Michigan State Univ; Food Science.

EVANS, Diane M; Chase County HS; Cottonwood Falls, KS; Chr; Chrs; PepBnd; SchMus; SchPl; YthFlsp; SchPpr; SpnCl; PpCl; Wichita St Univ; Flight Attendant.

EVANS, Eric G; South Lake HS; St Clair Shores, MI; 59/533 HonRl; NHS; StuGov; FrCl; Bsbl; Lawrence Institute Of Tech; Electrical Eng.

EVANS, Gary; Octavia HS; Cooksville, IL; 3/55 HonRl; NHS; YthFlsp; RptrSchPpr; FFA; SciCl; Northwest Missouri St; Engrg.

EVANS, Gary L; Council Grove HS; Dwight, KS; VPFrshCls; ALBoysSt; HonRl; NHS; Bsbl; Ftbl; Trk; IMSpt; Coll.

EVANS, Jerry; Hyannis HS; Whitman, NE; 4-H; Ftbl; Wrstlng; IMSpt; 4-HAwd; Eastern Wyoming; Cattle Business.

EVANS, John S; St Ignatius College Prep HS; Chicago, IL; 8/158 HonRl; LitMag; RedCrAde; StuCncl; FrCl; Bsbl; Northwestern Univ; Dentistry.

EVANS, Joseph A; Morristown HS; Morristown, IN; ALBoysSt; VPBand; HonRl; NHS; Yrbk; PresLatCl; PresSciCl; Bsktbl; LetterTennis; Wrstlng; CaptIMSpt; Purdue Univ; Wild Life.

EVANS, Joyce A; Council Grove HS; Dwight, KS; 24/110 HonRl; TchrAde; FFA; FHA; Bsbl; Tennis; Newmans School Of Nursing; Registered Nurse.

EVANS, Judith; Potosi HS; Potosi, MO; Chr; HonRl; SchPl; Vocation.

EVANS, June; Benton Harbor HS; Benton Harbor, MI; 86/417 CmntyWkr; HonRl; SctActv; 4-H; SpnCl; 4-HAwd; Univ; Social Service.

EVANS, Kathleen A; Maine West HS; Des Plaines, IL; Band; ChrhWkr; HonRl; NHS; FrCl; MthCl; PpCl; University Of Illinois; Doctor.

EVANS, Linda; Soldan HS; St Louis, MO; SecJrCls; ChrhWkr; HonRl; NHS; StuCncl; Hampton; Psychology.

EVANS, Lynn E; Richwoods HS; Peoria, IL; 6/456 ChrhWkr; CmntyWkr; DrlTm; HonRl; NHS; Quill&Scroll; SchPl; StuCncl; RptrYrbk; PpCl; Tennis; GAA; IMSpt; University Of Missouri; Health.

EVANS, Mary M; Shenandoah HS; Shenandoah, IA; 9/100 TrsSophCls; AFS; Band; CncrtBnd; HonRl; MrchBnd; NHS; PepBnd; StuGov; SchPpr; Univ Of Ia; Medical Field.

EVANS, Meredith R; Sully Buttes HS; Onida, SD; Band; CncrtBnd; HonRl; MrchBnd; NHS; PepBnd; Quill&Scroll; SctActv; RptrSchPpr; SpnCl; VFWAwd; College; Psychology.

EVANS, Monica M; Spring Valley HS; Spring Valley, WI; 4/80 PresFrshCls; HonRl; TchrAde; FFA; FHA; GAA; IMSpt; Clg; Pro.

EVANS, M Scott; Fennville HS; South Haven, MI; 1/88 ALBoysSt; Band; CncrtBnd; HonRl; MrchBnd; Orch; StuCncl; TchrAde; SchPpr; 4-H; KeyCl; FrCl; Bsktbl; Hope College; Lawyer.

EVANS, Nancy H; St Joseph HS; St Joseph, MI; 3/330 SchAde; FrCl; KiwanAwd; Marquette University; Nursing.

EVANS, Nancy I; Central; St Joseph, MO; Chr; Chrl; Chrs; ChrhWkr; HonRl; NHS; SchMus; 4-H; MthCl; 4-HAwd; College; Professional.

EVANS, Pamela R; Parkwood HS; Joplin, MO; Chr; ChrhWkr; HonRl; FrCl; MthCl; SciCl; Mo Southern St Coll; Med Tech.

EVANS, Pamela R; Claflin HS; Claflin, KS; Band; ChrhWkr; DrmBgl; HonRl; SecNHS; PepBnd; PresYthFlsp; TreasFHA; PresPpCl; Univ Of Kansas; Music.

EVANS, Paul M; Salem Community HS; Salem, IL; 25/213 CncrtBnd; MrchBnd; NHS; PepBnd; Yrbk; SchPpr; FrCl; Univ Of Il; Archi.

EVANS, Peggy; Benton Harbor HS; Benton Harbor, MI; 5/132 HstJrCls; ChrhWkr; CmntyWkr; JA; SchPl; SpnCl; Socr; Swmmng; Tennis; JAAwd; College; Professional.

EVANS, Prerry; Kadoka HS; Interior, SD; Band; CncrtBnd; HonRl; MrchBnd; PepBnd; YthFlsp; FHA; Trk; Trade Sch; Lpn.

EVANS, Robert M; Twin Rivers HS; Broseley, MO; 16/101 Chr; Chrs; ChrhWkr; HonRl; StuCncl; RptrSchPpr; SptEdSchPpr; 4-H; FFA; PpCl; Three Rivers Comm Clg.

EVANS, Ron E; Hyannis HS; Ashby, NE; 4/28 ALBoysSt; Band; Chrs; CncrtBnd; HonRl; NHS; SchMus; SchPl; StuCncl; 4-H; LetterFtbl; LetterTrk; LetterWrstlng; Univ Of Nebraska; Communications.

EVANS, Ruth A; Jefferson HS; Rockford, IL; 16/335 AFS; Chr; ChrhWkr; HonRl; HospAde; NHS; 4-H; LatCl; College; Medical Technologist.

EVANS, Sandra M; North Division HS; Milwaukee, WI; SecFrshCls; HonRl; JA; JrNHS; StuCncl; RptrYrbk; RptrSchPpr; PpCl; Trk; Jackson State Univ; Industry.

EVANS, Susan; Lincoln Sr HS; Sioux Falls, SD; 6/525 CncrtBnd; DrlTm; HonRl; Quill&Scroll; RptrYrbk; PpCl; IMSpt; Ia St Univ; Dietetics And Nutrition.

EVANS, Susan J; Oscoda Area HS; Wurtsmith Afb, MI; HonRl; JrNHS; NHS; OffAde; PpCl; Bsktbl; PPFtbl; Central Michigan; Sociology.

EVANSON, David D; Wildrose Public HS; Wildrose, ND; PresSophCls; VPJrCls; ALBoysSt; CncrtBnd; StuCncl; Yrbk; 4-H; LetterBsktbl; LetterTrk; College; Farming.

EVE, Sue E; New Albany Sr HS; New Albany, IN; 43/585 CmntyWkr; HonRl; PolWkr; Pres4-H; SciCl; 4-HAwd; College; Data Processing.

EVEN, Debbie; Fatima Hs; Westphalia, MO; 18/126 Chr; Chrs; ChrhWkr; CmntyWkr; HonRl; LbryAde; SchPl; FHA; SecPpCl; St Johns School Of Nursing; Nursing.

EVEN, Irene; Sargent Central HS; Cogswe, ND; ALBoysSt; ALAGirlsSt; FFA; FHA; FNA; 4-HAwd; VFWAwd; CitAwd; VoiceDemAwd; Mary College; Nursing.

EVENHOUSE, Mark; Illiana Christian Hs; So Holland, IL; Band; Chr; NatlFornLg; MrchBnd; NatlMeritCmnd; EdSchPpr; SpnCl; LetterBsktbl; LetterSocr; LetterTrk; Augustana College; Pre Med.

EVENSON, Barbara J; Central City Comm HS; Central City, IA; TrsSophCls; Band; Chrs; CncrtBnd; MrchBnd; NHS; NatlMeritCmnd; NatlThespSoc; PepBnd; SchMus; College; Music.

EVENSON, Cindy A; Valders HS; Valders, WI; AFS; Chrs; ChrhWkr; HonRl; FHA; PpCl; Trk; College.

EVENSON, Cynthia; Turtle Lake Mercer HS; Coleharbor, ND; 7/44 SecSrCls; Band; Chr; HonRl; OffAde; SchPl; StuCncl; FHA; Chrldr; DanFAwd;.

EVENSON, Douglass; Central HS; Aberdeen, SD; 71/426 ALBoysSt; Band; ChrhWkr; CncrtBnd; HonRl; MrchBnd; Orch; SchMus; SctActv; Tennis; Coll; Math.

EVENSON, Laurey; Cedar Falls HS; Cedar Falls, IA; HonRl; PepBnd; Iowa State Univ; Industial Administration.

EVENSON, Linda M; Pelican HS; Pelican Rapids, MN; Chr; CncrtBnd; HonRl; MrchBnd; PepBnd; SchMus; SchPl; LetterBsktbl; Glf; Tennis; College; Pro.

EVENSON, Mark; Chafard HS; Indianapolis, IN; 5/200 NHS; Bsbl; Bsktbl; RotaryAwd; Butler University; Premedicine.

EVENSON, Michele A; Oak Park HS; Kansas City, MO; PresSophCls; PresJrCls; Chr; HonRl; LbryAde; SchMus; PresStuCncl; FrCl; PpCl; Chrldr; Midwestern Univ; Political Science.

EVENSON, Vicki L; Valders HS; Valders, WI; Band; CncrtBnd; HonRl; MrchBnd; PepBnd; RptrYrbk; FHA; PpCl; CaptChrldr; GAA; Marquette Univ; Pre Med.

EVENSTAD, Jane M; Northwood Public HS; Northwood, ND; 25/42 SecJrCls; Chrs; HonRl; SchPl; StuCncl; Yrbk; SchPpr; FHA; Bsktbl; College; Teaching.

EVERDING, Janice; Red Bud HS; Red Bud, IL; Chr; HonRl; 4-H; FBLA; SpnCl; PpCl; 4-HAwd; College; Business.

EVERETT, Carl J; Mendel Prep HS; Chicago, IL; 63/200 Chr; ChrhWkr; CmntyWkr; HonRl; SctActv; FDA; Bsbl; CaptBsktbl; Trk; IMSpt; College; Science.

EVERETT, G Stephen; Benilde St Margarets HS; Minneapolis, MN; 15/114 VPSophCls; ChrhWkr; HonRl; JrNHS; StuCncl; GerCl; MthCl; Bsbl; Swmmng; Wrstlng; College; Teacher.

EVERETT, Nancy J; Harrisonville HS; Latour, MO; HonRl; SpnCl; Undecided; Undecided.

EVERHARD, Darlene L; Proviso West HS; Hillside, IL; 6801141 ChrhWkr; CmntyWkr; HonRl; JA; NHS; NatlMeritSchl; SchAde; StuCncl; YthFlsp; FTA; College; Prof.

EVERHART, Clark L; Harlem HS; Loves Park, IL; 101/560 VPSrCls; HonRl; StuCncl; College; Professional.

EVERHART, David W; Nodaway Holt HS; Skidmore, MO; CmntyWkr; HonRl; SctActv; StuCncl; RptrYrbk; FFA; LetterBsbl; LetterBsktbl; LetterFtbl; CchngActv; College; Agriculture.

EVERHART, William G; Gretna HS; Gretna, NE; 21/84 ChrhWkr; HonRl; NHS; SchPl; SctActv; TchrAde; RptrSchPpr; SpnCl; SciCl; Glf; Navy; Nuclear Field.

EVERITT, Brian M; West Ottawa HS; Holland, MI; 83/285 Band; Chr; Chrs; CncrtBnd; HonRl; MrchBnd; ModUN; Orch; PepBnd; PolWkr; Univ Of Michigan; Phamarcy.

EVERITT, Elizabeth; St Charles Hs; St Charles, IL; 17/500 VPFrshCls; AFS; Chrl; HonRl; NHS; NatlMeritFnl; NatlMeritCmnd; StuCncl; SpnCl; GAA; U Of Ill; Pre Veterinary Medicine.

EVERLY, Rocky R; Bloomington HS; Glen Haven, WI; VPJrCls; Band; Chrs; NHS; SchMus; SchPl; Yrbk; RptrSchPpr; Bsktbl; LetterTrk; U Of Wi Madison; Electrical Engineer.

EVERS, Janie A; Riverside HS; Dearborn Hts, MI; Chrs; LbryAde; SchMus; TchrAde; YthFlsp; RptrSchPpr; FrCl; GAA; Central Mich Univ; Home Ec.

EVERS, Jeffrey J; Guttenberg Co HS; Guttenberg, IA; 30/75 PresFrshCls; SecSrCls; Band; Chrs; HonRl; SchMus; CaptBsbl; CaptBsktbl; CaptFtbl; Trk; U Of Northern Ia; Business.

EVERS, Sandy A; Schleswig Comm HS; Schleswig, IA; SecJrCls; Band; Chrs; ChrhWkr; HonRl; NHS; SchMus; SecStuCncl; PresFHA; PresGerCl; College; Music.

EVERSOLE, Bradley K; Tower Hill HS; Tower Hill, IL; Chrs; ChrhWkr; HonRl; NHS; SchPl; StuCncl; YthFlsp; EdYrBk; SciCl; LetterBsbl; LetterBsktbl; LetterTrk; Lakeland Jr College; Physics.

EVERSOLE, Susan E; Shelbyville HS; Shelbyville, IL; 2/135 HonRl; HospAde; NHS; VPFHA; BttyCrckrAwd; College; Nursing.

EVERSON, Douglas L; Wild Rose HS; Pine River, WI; 2/60 TrsFrshCls; ALBoysSt; Band; Chrs; ChrhWkr; CncrtBnd; HonRl; MrchBnd; Trk; Wrstlng; College; Music.

EVERSON, Greg D; Rhinelander HS; Bundy, WI; ChrhWkr; CmntyWkr; HonRl; HospAde; RedCrAde; SchPl; SctActv; StuGov; YthFlsp; CchngActv; College; Vocational.

EVERSON, Synneva A; St Joseph Academy; De Pere, WI; Chr; Chrs; StuCncl; TchrAde; FrCl; PpCl; PPFtbl; College.

EVERT, Susan A; Thornton Township HS; Dolton, IL; 6/750 ChrhWkr; HonRl; NHS; PolWkr; PresGerCl; GAA; Valparaiso U; Bus Maj.

EVERTS, Patricia; Mishawaka HS; Mishawaka, IN; 20/410 VPSrCls; Band; CncrtBnd; HonRl; MrchBnd; NHS; StuCncl; DARAwd; College; Teaching.

EVEY, Connie L; Alma HS; Alma, MI; HonRl; NHS; TchrAde; 4-H; SpnCl; Central Mi Univ; Foreign Languages.

EVINS, Bretta A; Willow Springs HS; Willow Springs, MO; ChrhWkr; HonRl; LbryAde; OffAde; TchrAde; YthFlsp; FTA; Bsbl; Socr; Trk; College; Vocation.

EWALD, Cindy B; Unionville Sebewaing Area HS; Unionville, MI; 425/125 Chr; ChrhWkr; HonRl; HospAde; OffAde; SctActv; PresYthFlsp; SchPpr; 4-H; VPFrCl; PpCl; CitAwd; North Central Michigan College; Nursing.

EWALD, Daniel; Hill Murray HS; Maplewood, MN; Band; CncrtBnd; HonRl; PepBnd; SctActv; Wrstlng; Vo Tech 916; Diesel Mech.

EWALD, Jacqualine K; Durant HS; Durant, IA; 7/70 Band; Chrs; CncrtBnd; HonRl; JrNHS; MrchBnd; NHS; PepBnd; SchPl; College; Special Ed.

EWALD, Joseph J; North Side HS; Ft Wayne, IN; Itt Tech Inst; Electronics Engineer.

EWALD, Lynn A; Medicine Valley HS; Curtis, NE; Band; ChrhWkr; CncrtBnd; HonRl; MrchBnd; NHS; PepBnd; StuCncl; TchrAde; SchPpr; ChmnFtbl; Unsta; Farmer.

EWALD, Lynne E; Marquette HS; Ottawa, IL; 8/101 HonRl; NHS; PpCl; Chrldr; IMSpt; PPFtbl; ChmbCommrsAwd; St Marys College; Elementary Education.

EWALD, Merilee J; Ashton HS; Ashton, IL; 22/43 Band; ChrhWkr; HonRl; PepBnd; SchPl; 4-H; FrCl; Tennis; Trk; PresGAA; Jr Clge; Secretary.

EWALT, Clifton; Knox County Hs; Knox City, MO; 4-H; FFA; 4-HAwd; Trade School; Farming.

EWALT, John; Lake Crystal HS; Lake Crystal, MN; Band; HonRl; SchPl; Gustavus Adolphus Coll.

EWART, Brenda J; Lenox HS; Lenox, IA; 3/45 VPJrCls; PresSrCls; Band; HonRl; NHS; StuCncl; YthFlsp; RptrYrbk; Trk; Chrldr; Ia St U; Music.

EWBANK, Alice M; Dubois HS; Dubois, IN; 24/80 Band; ChrhWkr; SchPl; TchrAde; YthFlsp; RptrYrbk; 4-H; FHA; PpCl; Purdue Univ; Elem Education.

EWEN, Janet; Andrean HS; Gary, IN; CmntyWkr; HonRl; SchPl; SctActv; FshEdSchPpr; MthCl; PpCl; SciCl; Tennis; Trk; Purdue Univ; Professional Pharmacy.

EWERS, David J; St Ignatius Cp HS; Chicago, IL; 50/200 ChrhWkr; CmntyWkr; HonRl; Teen; GerCl; LatCl; SciCl; Glf; Socr; Trk; College; Doctor.

EWERS, Kevin L; Harlem HS; Rockford, IL; HonRl; Quill&Scroll; SchPpr; MthCl; LetterTrk; College; Graphic Art.

EWERS, Marie H; Queen Of Peace HS; Chicago, IL; HonRl; LatCl; SpnCl; Bsktbl; Loyola Univ; Teacher.

EWERT, Gene P; Marion HS; Marion, KS; Chr; Chrs; ChrhWkr; HonRl; SchMus; PresYthFlsp; Yrbk; GerCl; College; History.

EWERT, Mark A; Huntley HS; Huntley, IL; HonRl; NHS; NatlMeritCmnd; TchrAde; RptrYrbk; GerCl; Bsbl; Bsktbl; Concordia Teachers College; Teacher.

EWERT, May S; Marian HS; Hays, KS; HonRl; RptrSchPpr; FBLA; IMSpt; Wichita State Univ; Accounting.

EWERT, Steven R; Mountain Lake HS; Bingham Lake, MN; Chr; Chrl; ChrhWkr; HonRl; Mdrgl; SchMus; 4-H; FFA; Ftbl; College; Dairy Farmer.

EWIN, Sally A; Ryan HS; Omaha, NE; VPSrCls; Chrs; CmntyWkr; NHS; NatlThespSoc; SchMus; SchPl; StuCncl; RptrYrbk; University; Professional.

EWING, Elizabeth A; Webster Groves HS; Webster Groves, MO; Band; ChrhWkr; CncrtBnd; HonRl; MrchBnd; NatlMeritSF; PepBnd; SchPl; College; Interpreter.

EWING, Gary L; Centerville HS; Cincinnati, IA; CmntyWkr; HonRl; 4-H; PresFFA; 4-HAwd; JAAwd; College.

EWING, Ida; Soldan HS; St Louis, MO; 7/650 Chrs; HonRl; NHS; Yrbk; College; Legal Secretary.

EWING, John R; Sycamore HS; Sycamore, IL; Chr; CncrtBnd; HonRl; MrchBnd; PepBnd; Northern Il Univ; Music.

EWING, Kari L; Lanark HS; Lanark, IL; HstSophCls; Chrs; HonRl; SchMus; StuCncl; YthFlsp; FHA;

Chrldr; GAA; IMSpt; Sterling Sch Of Beauty; Cosmetologist.

EWING, Laura B; Flanagan Unit #4 HS; Flanagan, IL; PresJrCls; Band; SecChrs; CncrtBnd; DrmMjrt; HonRl; NHS; StuCncl; Chrldr; GAA; College.

EWING, Laurel E; Homestead Jr Sr HS; Fort Wayne, IN; VPFrshCls; SecSophCls; CmntyWkr; HonRl; StuCncl; TchrAde; YthFlsp; LetterBsktbl; Trk; LetterGAA; University; Science.

EWING, Lynn M; Nevada HS; Nevada, MO; 14/178 Band; CncrtBnd; MrchBnd; Orch; PepBnd; LatCl; Swmmng; Univ; Law/chem.

EWING, Patricia A; Wausau East HS; Wausau, WI; 54/324 Chr; Teen; RptrYrbk; RptrSchPpr; SpnCl; PpCl; Cnty Gen Hospital; X Ray Technology.

EWING, Simeon E; St Johns HS; St Johns, MI; HonRl; ModUN; StuCncl; Glf; LetterTennis; IMSpt; Central Michigan Univ; Law.

EWING, Susan E; Harvard Public HS; Harvard, NE; DrmMjrt; HonRl; HospAde; Mdrgl; SchPl; TreasYthFlsp; Yrbk; 4-H; SecGerCl; DARAwd; College; Music.

EXTEN, Denise J; Campbell Tintah HS; Foxhome, MN; PresJrCls; Chr; ChrhWkr; CncrtBnd; DrmMjrt; HonRl; 4-H; FBLA; CaptChrldr; GAA; Trade Sch; Secretary.

EXUM, Kenneth J; Brodhead HS; Brodhead, WI; Aud/Vis; ChrhWkr; HonRl; ModUN; SchMus; RptrYrbk; Yrbk; LetterFtbl; LetterGlf; Wrstlng; College.

EYCHANER, Judy A; Rochelle Twp HS; Esmond, IL; 16/212 CncrtBnd; HonRl; MrchBnd; OffAde; Orch; Illinois Wesleyan Univ; Nursing.

EYERLY, Donald R; Winterset Community HS; Winterset, IA; 37/115 LetterBsbl; LetterBsktbl; LetterFtbl; LetterTrk; LetterWrstlng; University; Lawyer.

EYERLY, Jeffrey; Oskaloosa HS; Oskaloosa, KS; CncrtBnd; HonRl; MrchBnd; PepBnd; SchPl; StuCncl; SptEdYrbk; FBLA; Bsktbl; Ftbl; Kansas City Ks J V C O; Architect.

EYGENHUYSEN, Henry P; Glenbard No HS; Bloomingdale, IL; 45/380 HonRl; PolWkr; GerCl; MthCl; Glf; Carleton College; Political Science.

EYMAN, Jill D; Greenville HS; Greenville, IL; 20/171 Chrs; NHS; OffAde; YthFlsp; 4-H; FHA; IMSpt; DanFAwd; 4-HAwd; CitAwd; Greenville College; Biology.

EYSENBACH, Mary; Homewood Flossmoor Hs; Homewood, IL; 149/900 Chr; Chrs; CmntyWkr; HonRl; SchMus; Bsbl; Bsktbl; LetterTennis; West Illinois U; Forestry.

EYSTAD, Thomas A; Kensington Public HS; Kensington, MN; Band; Chr; Chrs; ChrhWkr; CncrtBnd; HonRl; LbryAde; PepBnd; SchPl; EdSchPpr; Trade School; Vocation.

EYTALIS, Theresa M; Winnebago HS; Rockford, IL; 30/120 FHA; SpnCl; PpCl; GAA; College.

EZDON, Michael; Beloit Catholic HS; Beloit, WI; 12/86 Band; CncrtBnd; HonRl; JA; MrchBnd; PepBnd; SchMus; Trk; IMSpt; GovHonPrgAwd; Univ Wi;vet Med.

EZZELL, Janie L; Charleston HS; Bertrand, MO; 85/180 Band; Chr; Chrs; ChrhWkr; DrlTm; HonRl; Mdrgl; MrchBnd; SchMus; SchPl; Twrl; Jefferson Jr College; Dental Asst.

F

FAABORG, Andy M; Meservey Thornton HS; Meservey, IA; 5/27 PresJrCls; HonRl; SchPl; StuCncl; RptrSchPpr; 4-H; LetterBsbl; CaptBsktbl; LetterFtbl; CaptTrk; North Iowa Area Comm Clg; Teach Sports.

FAAST, Laurie J; High School; Osseo, WI; Aud/Vis; ChrhWkr; HonRl; JrNHS; SchPl; LetterBsktbl; LetterGAA; IMSpt; University; Vet Assistant.

FABBRI, Marisa; Acad Of Our Lady; Chicago, IL; 3/179 HonRl; JA; NHS; OffAde; SctActv; Sdlty; SpnCl; PpCl; IMSpt; College; Bus.

FABBRI, Richard T; Austin Catholic Prep; Grosse Pt Woods, MI; 45/115 OffAde; SchAde; SctActv; StuGov; UNYO; FBLA; Bsktbl; CchngActv; GodCntryAwd; GovHonPrgAwd; JAAwd; Michigan State Univ; Operations Mgmt.

FABEL, Kristi J; Oak Park River Forest HS; River Forest, IL; Chr; Chrl; Chrs; HonRl; Mdrgl; SchMus; Chrldr; Texas Christian Univ; Nursing.

FABER, Cheryl E; Princeton HS; Princeton, IL; AFS; ChrhWkr; CmntyWkr; HonRl; HospAde; YthFlsp; FrCl; PpCl; E Illinois Univ; Business Admin.

FABER, Joanna; Minden HS; Holstein, NE; TrsSrCls; ALAGirlsSt; Band; HospAde; PepBnd; SchPl; TchrAde; FHA; FTA; SpnCl; Doane College Ne; Music Ed.

FABER, Judy; Forest Lake Senior Hs; Forest Lake, MN; NatlFornLg; Trk;.

FABER, William K; Andrews Academy; Sturgis, MI; Chrl; ChrhWkr; HonRl; JA; NHS; StuCncl; StuGov; SchPpr; IMSpt; Univ; Medical Doctor Film Producer.

FABRIZI, Michael A; Southwest HS; St Louis, MO; 21/605 ChrhWkr; HonRl; JA; ModUN; NatlMeritFnl; Univ Of Missouri; Communications Admin.

FABRY, Mary L; Granite City North HS; Granite City, IL; 7/375 LitMag; NHS; VPQuill&Scroll; RptrSchPpr; EdSchPpr; SchPpr; PpCl; SciCl; Socr; Clge; Journalism.

FABRY, M Kym; Wausau E HS; Wausau, WI; ChrhWkr; Orch; TchrAde; Teen; CaptBsktbl; Trk; GAA; IMSpt; Univ Of Wis; Professional.

FACE, Dean W; Grosse Pointe South HS; Grosse Pointe Farm, MI; 32/637 HonRl; NHS; SctActv; CchngActv; Calif Inst Of Tech; Enginering.

FACHET, Lynn A; Lane Technical; Chicago, IL; 67/1209 HospAde; LitMag; LbryAde; TchrAde; GerCl; Univ Of Ill; Theater Design.

FACIONE, Antoinette; Marian HS; Sylvan Lake, MI; Chr; Chrl; Chrs; HonRl; SchMus; SchPl; Univ; Phy Ed.

FACKLER, Stephen W; Concordia Lutheran HS; Ft Wayne, IN; 1/250 Chr; ChrhWkr; CmntyWkr; DrlTm; HonRl; NHS; NatlMeritSF; Quill&Scroll; ROTC; SctActv; StuCncl; ChmnStuGov; SchPpr; PresLatCl; Tennis; University; American Studies.

FADDEN, Thomas P; St Bonaventure Prep HS; South Holland, IL; 4/25 SchAde; SchMus; SchPl; StuCncl; Yrbk; Bsbl; LetterSocr; IMSpt; AmLegAwd; Lewis Univ; Accounting.

FADDIS, James; Lincoln East HS; Lincoln, NE; ChrhWkr; HonRl; LitMag; RptrSchPpr; Ftbl; Trk; IMSpt; Coll.

FADER, Randy; Papillion Lavista HS; Omaha, NE; /376 Coll; Prof.

FADIE, Steven F; Milford HS; Milford, MI; Band; CncrtBnd; LitMag; MrchBnd; NHS; RotaryAwd; Mi St Univ; Communications.

FADLER, Evelyn M; Red Bud HS; Prairie Du Rocher, IL; 7/109 Band; HonRl; JrNHS; MrchBnd; PepBnd; SchPl; Twrl; Yrbk; Belleville Area College; Secretary.

FAEHN, Robert L; Florence HS; Wallace, SD; 1/14 TrsFrshCls; VPJrCls; ALBoysSt; Band; Chr; Chrs; ChrhWkr; HonRl; MrchBnd; PepBnd; South Dakota State Univ; Pre Law.

FAGAN, Ann E; H L Richards HS; Chicago Ridge, IL; 1/1010 PresAFS; DrlTm; HonRl; HospAde; PresNHS; VPOrch; StuCncl; MthCl; GAA; DARAwd; Ill State Univ; Accounting Psychology.

FAGAN, Christa J; Remington HS; Benton, KS; 5/50 SecTrsJrCls; ALAGirlsSt; Chrs; HonRl; NHS; TchrAde; RptrYrbk; LetterTrk; SptEdYrbk; RptrSchPpr; Kansas State Univ; Journalism.

FAGAN, Kathryn A; Carsonville Pt Sanilac HS; Carsonville, MI; 7/60 PresSrCls; HonRl; NHS; StuGov; FBLA; Bsbl; Bsktbl; CaptTrk; PresAwd; CitAwd; College; Commercial Art.

FAGEN, Lee M; Earlham Community HS; Earlham, IA; 4/41 Chrs; HonRl; OffAde; SchMus; SchPl; RptrYrbk; Iowa State Univ; Computer Science.

FAGG, Lonnie L; Polo HS; Polo, MO; Chr; Chrs; ChrhWkr; HonRl; SchPl; StuCncl; YthFlsp; 4-H; FFA; FrCl; College; Education.

FAGOT, Shane P; St Anns HS; Lexington, NE; VPFrshCls; TrsJrCls; SecTrsSrCls; HonRl; StuCncl; Yrbk; 4-H; LetterBsktbl; LetterFtbl; LetterTrk; U Of Ne; Engineering.

FAHEY, Nancy L; Andrew Jackson HS; South Bend, IN; 20/350 HonRl; NHS; Quill&Scroll; StuCncl; SchPpr; Ftbl; GAA; PPFtbl; KiwanAwd; Clg Of William & Mary; French Interpreter.

FAHLBERG, Marcia; Geneva HS; Geneva, NE; 3/57 TrsJrCls; Band; Chrs; ChrhWkr; Twrl; 4-H; FBLA; PpCl; GAA; PresAwd; Univ; Prof.

FAHLBERG, Peter N; Beresford HS; Beresford, SD; 3/68 ALBoysSt; Band; Chrs; CncrtBnd; HonRl; JrNHS; NHS; VPStuCncl; LetterFtbl; AmLegAwd; Univ Of Sd; Agriculture.

FAHRENDORFF, Don T; Marshall University HS; Minneapolis, MN; HonRl; StuCncl; University Of Minnesota; Computer Programer.

FAHRENWALD, Jeffrey W; Schaumburg HS; Schaumburg, IL; 32/546 Chr; Chrl; ChrhWkr; CmntyWkr; HonRl; Mdrgl; NHS; NatlMeritSF; SchMus; Bsktbl; Harper Jr College.

FAHRENWALD, Peter; Morgan Park HS; Chicago, IL; 38/493 CmntyWkr; HonRl; NHS; SchPl; College; Civil Engineering.

FAHSER, Cynthia S; Little Wolf HS; Manawa, WI; 2/80 HstSrCls; HonRl; NHS; RptrYrbk; 4-H; Bsktbl; GAA; 4-HAwd; JAAwd; CitAwd; U Wi Stout; Home Ec Clothing.

FAHY, Patricia K; Bismarck HS; Bismarck, ND; HonRl; HospAde; NatlFornLg; NHS; NatlMeritSF; SchPl; SctActv; SecStuCncl; StuGov; YthFlsp; RptrSchPpr; GerCl; PPFtbl; Univ; Psychology.

FAIER, Melinda B; New Trier West HS; Glencoe, IL; HonRl; NatlMeritSF; PolWkr; SchPpr; Tennis; College; Physician.

FAIKUS, Sandi A; Morton West HS; Berwyn, IL; Chr; Chrl; Chrs; HonRl; JrNHS; LitMag; NHS; NatlMeritSF; Coll; Anthropology.

FAIKUS, Sandra A; Morton West HS; Berwyn, IL; 1/755 Chr; Chrs; HonRl; JrNHS; LitMag; NHS; University; Anthropology.

FAILING, Douglas R; Grayling HS; Grayling, MI; NHS; Bsbl; Bsktbl; LetterTrk; Michigan Tech Univ; Civil Engineering.

FAIN, Tracy E; Prairie Home HS; Prairie Home, MO; 2/16 PresSophCls; VPSrCls; HonRl; Mdrgl; PepBnd; SchPl; Yrbk; SchPpr; FHA; Bsktbl; Clg; Pro.

FAIR, Marilee E; Crestwood HS; Elma, IA; ChrhWkr; HonRl; NHS; Quill&Scroll; PresStuCncl; EdSchPpr; 4-H; 4-HAwd; NCTE; Business School.

FAIR, Nancy L; Fowlerville HS; Fowlerville, MI; PresJrCls; HonRl; MrchBnd; OffAde; SecStuCncl; TchrAde; Twrl; RptrYrbk; PpCl; PPFtbl; Legal Secretary.

FAIR, Teresa L; Northwest Webster HS; Manson, IA; TrsFrshCls; Chrs; HonRl; TchrAde;.

FAIRBANKS, Jerry D; Southern HS; Wymore, NE; 13/50 Band; Chr; CncrtBnd; HonRl; Mdrgl; MrchBnd; NatlMeritSF; PepBnd; PolWkr; SchMus; SchPl; StuCncl; LetterGlf; Univ Of Nebraska; Journalism.

FAIRBANKS, Kathy E; Hudson Sr HS; Hudson, WI; 4/220 AFS; Chrs; ChrhWkr; CncrtBnd; HonRl; YthFlsp; RptrSchPpr; PpCl; Bsktbl; Chrldr; St Cloud State; Professional.

FAIRBANKS, Kevin T; Spalding Academy; Spalding, NE; 5/26 PresSophCls; ChrhWkr; HonRl; TreasNHS; SchPl; TreasStuCncl; EngCl; SpnCl; MthCl; SciCl; Bsbl; LetterBsktbl; LetterFtbl; College; Engineering.

FAIRBANKS, Yvonne L; Britton Macon Area HS; Britton, MI; 5/45 PresSophCls; HonRl; JrNHS; LbryAde; TreasNHS; RptrYrbk; RptrSchPpr; VPFHA; SpnCl; DARAwd; Secretarial Work.

FAIRBURN, Nancy E; Guilford HS; Rockford, IL; VPAFS; HonRl; Orch; SchPpr; VP4-H; PpCl; 4-HAwd; Univ; Journalism.

FAIRCHILD, James E; Bellflower Township HS; Fisher, IL; 16/19 Band; Chr; Chrs; ChrhWkr; CncrtBnd; HonRl; SchPl; YthFlsp; Yrbk; SptEdSchPpr; Mt Vernon Bbl Clg; Minister.

FAIRCHILD, Mark J; Boylan Catholic HS; Rockford, IL; 20/358 Chr; Chrl; Chrs; HonRl; Mdrgl; PresNHS; NatlMeritCmnd; SchMus; Univ Of Illinois; Electrical Engineer.

FAIRCHILD, Mary E; Bismarck Henning HS; Danville, IL; Chrs; CncrtBnd; HonRl; NHS; NatlMeritCmnd; PolWkr; StuCncl; EdSchPpr; 4-HAwd; VoiceDemAwd; Univ Ill; Physics.

FAIRCHILD, Tim J; Sioux Rapids Comm HS; Sioux Rapids, IA; VPFrshCls; PresSophCls; Chr; Chrs; HonRl; NHS; SchPl; YthFlsp; 4-H; LetterBsbl; CaptFtbl; LetterTrk; University; Accountant.

FAIRFAX, Robert T; Kirksville HS; Kirksville, MO; SecTrsSophCls; HonRl; StuCncl; SciCl; Bsbl; Bsktbl; Ftbl; Trk; CchngActv; IMSpt; Univ; Pro.

FAIRLESS, Kevin M; Southwestern HS; Medora, IL; 41/180 PresJA; NHS; NatlMeritCmnd; FTA; LetterTrk; SARAwd; Univ Of Illinois; Mechanical Eng.

FAIRLESS, Mark D; G Pte North HS; Grosse Pte Woods, MI; Band; CncrtBnd; HonRl; SctActv; Univ Of Mi; Banking.

FAIRLEY, Tim J; Fairbury HS; Fairbury, NE; ChrhWkr; StuCncl; YthFlsp; Pres4-H; SecFFA; Ftbl; Wrstlng; IMSpt; DanFAwd; 4-HAwd; Univ Of Nebraska; Animal Science.

FAIRMAN, Colleen R; Mt Assisi Acad; Oak Lawn, IL; HonRl; LitMag; NatlFornLg; NHS; StuCncl; RptrYrbk; RptrSchPpr;.

FAIT, Gary P; St Marys HS; Burlington, WI; 13/72 SecTrsSophCls; VPJrCls; HonRl; SchPl; StuCncl; RptrSchPpr; SptEdSchPpr; PpCl; SciCl; Marquette Univ; Medicine.

FAJA, Mary Ann; Greenfield HS; Greenfield, WI; 2/390 ALBoysSt; Band; CncrtBnd; HonRl; NHS; NatlMeritCmnd; PepBnd; EdYrBk; GAA; Marquette Univ; Pre Medical.

FAKLER, James M; Oak Creek HS; Oak Creek, WI; 1/364 ALBoysSt; HonRl; NHS; NatlMeritSF; SchAde; StuCncl; LetterFtbl; LetterWrstlng; IMSpt; BauchLmbAwd; Us Military Acad ;army Officer.

FALADA, Gayle L; Glenbard North HS; Addison, IL; NatlMeritSF; JCAwd; University; Child Psychologist.

FALCH, Bonnie M; Regis HS; Chippewa Falls, WI; 6/128 Chr; Chrs; HonRl; SchMus; 4-H; SpnCl; Stout; Home Economics.

FALCK, Linda; Melvin Sibley HS; Melvin, IL; 5/25 HonRl; Mdrgl; NHS; OffAde; Quill&Scroll; SchPl; Yrbk; FHA; Trk;.

FALCK, Nancy; Buchanan Public HS; Jamestown, ND; 1/8 ALAGirlsSt; Chrs; HonRl; StuCncl; RptrSchPpr; 4-H; VoiceDemAwd; College; Professional.

FALCONE, Debera A; Downers Grove Comm HS; Downers Grove, IL; 11/827 HonRl; College Of Du Page; Accounting.

FALDE, Paul G; Spring Valley HS; Baldwin, WI; Aud/Vis; Chrs; HonRl; SchAde; RptrYrbk; FFA; 4-HAwd; College.

FALEN, Julie D; Hinsdale Central HS; Hinsdale, IL; 214/583 HonRl; Orch; SchMus; SchPl; StuGov; TchrAde; FrCl; W Illinois Univ; Music.

FALEVSKY, Alan J; West Bend East HS; West Bend, WI; VPSpnCl; LetterBsbl; LetterBsktbl; LetterFtbl; Glf; LetterTennis; IMSpt; University; Law.

FALGE, Robert N; Anderson HS; Anderson, IN; 14/612 Band; CncrtBnd; DrmBgl; MrchBnd; NHS; SctActv; LatCl; SciCl; DARAwd; OptClAwd; Indiana Univ; Medical Dr.

FALISZEK, James E; Loyola Academy; Chicago, IL; 100/442 HonRl; LitMag; Northwestern Univ; Medicine.

FALK, David A; Minonk Dana Rutland HS; Minonk, IL; VPSrCls; HonRl; YthFlsp;.

FALK, Janice A; Osseo Fairchild HS; Fairchild, WI; Aud/Vis; ChrhWkr; HonRl; JrNHS; YthFlsp; GerCl; CaptChrldr; GAA; IMSpt; Clge; Cpa.

FALK, Sharon E; Stevenson HS; Livonia, MI; Chr; ChrhWkr; PolWkr; SchMus; SchPl; TchrAde; Swmmng; GAA; Michigan State Univ; Accounting.

FALKENBERG, Mary E; Mar Catholic Central HS; Marinette, WI; HonRl; LbryAde; OffAde; Business School; Accountant.

FALKNER, Edward W; Preston Fountain HS; Preston, MN; 1/50 HonRl; NHS; NatlMeritFnl; SecSpnCl; LetterBsbl; LetterBsktbl; LetterFtbl; Wrstlng; BauchLmbAwd; VoiceDemAwd; U Of Wisconsin; Lawyer.

FALL, Lon R; Lake Orion HS; Oxford, MI; 4/350 HonRl; NHS; Ftbl; CaptTennis; Michigan Tech Univ; Civil Engineer.

FALLER, David E; Charles City Comm HS; Charles City, IA; 63/227 Band; CncrtBnd; MrchBnd; Orch; PepBnd; GerCl; Tennis; U Of Ia; Pharmacy.

FALLER, Gerard R; Catholic Central HS; Marinette, WI; Chrs; HonRl; LetterBsktbl; LetterFtbl; LetterGlf; Tennis; Trk; CchngActv; IMSpt; PPFtbl; Marquette U; Business.

FALLESEN, Jan L; Viburnum C 4 HS; Viburnum, MO; 18/64 VPJrCls; Band; ChrhWkr; CmntyWkr; CncrtBnd; HonRl; StuCncl; YthFlsp; FHA; PpCl; University; Business.

FALLGATTER, Juleann; Dunlap Comm HS; Dunlap, IA; 1/56 Chr; ChrhWkr; CncrtBnd; HonRl; Mdrgl; MrchBnd; NHS; NatlMeritCmnd; SchMus; SchPl; Coll; Piano.

FALLON, Mike T; Northrop HS; Ft Wayne, IN; 13/568 CncrtBnd; DrmMjrt; HonRl; MrchBnd; Purdue Univ; Veterinary Medicine.

FALLON, Nancy M; Resurrection HS; Chicago, IL; 25/261 PresSrCls; HonRl; NHS; StuCncl; TchrAde; Yrbk; St Norbert College; Business.

FALLOON, Dawn G; Sullivan HS; Bourbon, MO; 23/159 ChrhWkr; HonRl; NHS; SancSoc; Southwest Baptist College; Psychology.

FALLS, Patricia K; Slater HS; Slater, MO; SecJrCls; TchrAde; FBLA; FHA; FTA; PpCl; Bsktbl; Trk; GAA; LetterIMSpt; College; Liberal Arts.

FALSEY, Jerry M; Brother Rice HS; Chicago, IL; 23/416 HonRl; NHS; StuCncl; Depaul Univ; Banking.

FALSTEIN, Noah; Stephen T Mather HS; Chicago, IL; NatlFornLg; NHS; NatlMeritSF; SchPl; TreasMthCl; Haverford College;.

FALTA, Patricia A; Garden City E HS; Garden City, MI; 10/487 ChrhWkr; HonRl; NHS; Univ Of Michigan; Nursing.

FALTIS, Joyce A; Prairie HS; Fairfax, IA; Chr; Chrs; DrlTm; HonRl; JA; JrNHS; NatlFornLg; SchMus; SecYthFlsp; VP4-H; JAAwd; College; Business Management.

FALVEY, Elizabeth J; Garber HS; Essexville, MI; 8/180 Chr; HonRl; PolWkr; SchPl; TchrAde; RptrSchPpr; PpCl; College; Journalism.

FAMULINER, James N; Carrollton HS; Carrollton, MO; HonRl; NHS; SchMus; StuCncl; 4-H; KeyCl; SpnCl; Bsbl; Bsktbl; Ftbl; College; Agricultural Engineering.

FANALE, Robert J; Griffin HS; Springfield, IL; 11/175 ChrhWkr; HonRl; College.

FANDREY, Colleen E; Wausau East HS; Wausau, WI; CmntyWkr; NHS; Orch; TchrAde; GerCl; MthCl; Univ; Teaching.

FANDRICH, Larry L; Campion Academy; Lehr, ND; PresFrshCls; VPJrCls; Chrl; HonRl; StuGov; YthFlsp; SptEdSchPpr; Bsktbl; Trk; Union Coll; Automotive Tech.

FANE, Edward R; Dixon HS; Dixon, IL; 33/333 ALBoysSt; HonRl; JrNHS; NHS; StuCncl; Bsktbl; Univ Of Illinois; Engineering.

FANGMAN, Barbara J; East Buchanan HS; Masonville, IA; PresSrCls; ChrhWkr; HonRl; NHS; TchrAde; Bsktbl; LetterTrk; IMSpt; Nurse.

FANGMAN, Jann M; Mercy HS; Omaha, NE; 1/69 ALAGirlsSt; NatlFornLg; NHS; NatlThespSoc; PolWkr; SchMus; Sdlty; University; Law.

FANGOHR, Patricia A; Sacred Heart HS; Sedalia, MO; 1/28 VPFrshCls; PresSophCls; HonRl; NHS; StuCncl; RptrSchPpr; PpCl; Chrldr; Creighton U; Premed, Medical Sch.

FANKO, Andrew P; Perry HS; Perry, MI; 62/126 Aud/Vis; HonRl; JA; SctActv; TreasStuCncl; StuGov; TchrAde; Pres4-H; VPFFA; PpCl; CaptFtbl; 4-HAwd; Lansing Comm College; Veterinarian.

FANNING, Del T; Bowling Green Ri HS; Bowling Green, MO; 10/122 Chr; CncrtBnd; HonRl; MrchBnd; NHS; PepBnd; SchMus; FBLA; MthCl; SciCl; St Louis Col Of Pharmacy; Pharmacist.

FANNING, Donald G; Larimore HS; Larimore, ND; ALBoysSt; HonRl; NatlMeritCmnd; RptrSchPpr; LetterFtbl; LetterWrstlng; College.

FANSEL, Norma M; Columbus HS; Columbus, WI; NHS; RedCrAde; TchrAde; FBLA; FHA; LatCl; Business College; Accountant.

FANSLAU, Michael J; Washington HS; Two Rivers, WI; HonRl; LetterFtbl; Glf; LetterTrk; College; Biology.

FANSLER, Judy K; Fairfield Comm HS; Fairfield, IL; Band; Chr; CncrtBnd; HonRl; NHS; SchMus; SchPl; 4-H; FBLA; AmLegAwd; Eastern Illinois U.

FANSLER, Susan J; Fairfield Comm HS; Fairfield, IL; Chr; ChrhWkr; CmntyWkr; HonRl; YthFlsp; 4-H; FHA; SpnCl; GodCntryAwd; Eastern Illinois U.

FANTA, Charlie; Lyons Township Hs; Western Springs, IL; 64/1200 Band; HonRl; NHS; Oregon College; Fisheries Science.

FANTA, Joan M; Hillsboro HS; Yuba, WI; 2/65 Chrs; HonRl; LbryAde; NHS; SchMus; Yrbk; 4-H; FHA; GAA; IMSpt; Western Wi Tech Inst; Med Lab Technician.

FANTASKI, Mike F; Papillion Lavista HS; Papillion, NE; 76/317 PresSophCls; HonRl; JrNHS; SptEdYrbk; SpnCl; CaptBsbl; LetterBsktbl; CaptFtbl; CchngActv; IMSpt; PresAwd; College; Sports.

FARAGHER, David C; O Gorman HS; Sioux Falls, SD; ALBoysSt; Band; CncrtBnd; MrchBnd; NHS; Orch; Quill&Scroll; Yrbk; RptrSchPpr; College; Health.

FARAH, Michael C; Brother Rice HS; Bloomfield Hills, MI; 59/210 HonRl; CaptTennis; Albion College; Professional.

FARAONE, Theresann; Coloma HS; Coloma, MI; HonRl; NHS; OffAde; TchrAde; Yrbk; PpCl; Bsktbl; Michigan State Univ; Biology.

FARBACH, Linda S; Edmore Public HS; Edmore, ND; HonRl; SchPl; TchrAde; Trk; GAA; College; Professional.

FARBER, Jacob E; Mather HS; Chicago, IL; Aud/Vis; CncrtBnd; NatlMeritFnl; NatlMeritSF; Orch; Yrbk; Univ Of Chicago; Medical.

FARBOTA, Leo; Willowbrook Hs; Villa Park, IL; 1/803 Band; CncrtBnd; HonRl; PepBnd; SchMus; LetterTennis; University; Pre Med.

FARBSTEIN, Kenneth M; Parkway Central HS; Chesterfield, MO; 27/450 JrNHS; NatlFornLg; NHS; NatlMeritSF; College; Politics.

FARINA, Donna M; York Community HS; Elmhurst, IL; 6/912 HonRl; NHS; NatlMeritCmnd; Quill&Scroll; RptrYrbk; TreasFrCl; GAA; George Washington Univ; Law.

FARIS, Martha L; Dondero HS; Berkley, MI; 69/540 Band; Chr; HonRl; MrchBnd; NHS; SchPl; Univ Of Mi; Naturalist.

FARIS, Michael W; East Richland HS; Olney, IL; RptrSchPpr; College.

FARIS, Tom A; West Platte HS; Weston, MO; Chr; HonRl; YthFlsp; RptrYrbk; FrCl; SciCl; LetterBsbl; LetterBsktbl; LetterTrk; College.

FARKAS, Geraldine A; Byron Area HS; Byron, MI; 1/76 PresSrCls; Band; HonRl; NHS; SecTrsFrshCls; SchPl; StuCncl; FTA; Trk; 4-HAwd; Coll; Teacher.

FARLESS, Carl R; Valley Comm HS; Arlington, IA; 10/52 HonRl; NHS; NatlThespSoc; SchPl; StuCncl; RptrYrbk; Yrbk; SciCl; OptClAwd; Upper Ia Univ; Dental Surgeon.

FARLEY, Brian; Quigley South Hs; Chicago, IL; 23/170 CmntyWkr; CncrtBnd; MrchBnd; NatlMeritCmnd; PepBnd; TchrAde; RptrSchPpr; SchPpr; LetterSwmmng; Purdue U; Chemical Engineer.

FARLEY, Dea A; Putnam Co R 1 HS; Lucerne, MO; HonRl; NHS; SchPl; 4-H; Coll; Pro.

FARLEY, Debra M; Auburn Senior HS; Rockford, IL; 18/350 HonRl; NHS; NatlMeritFnl; NatlMeritSchl; OffAde; College; Stenography.

FARLEY, James H; Geneseo HS; Geneseo, KS; VPFrshCls; PresSophCls; Band; Chrs; HonRl; MrchBnd; PepBnd; SchPl; YthFlsp; Bsktbl; University; Professional.

FARLEY, Mari E; East Peoria Comm HS; East Peoria, IL; 4/500 Band; Chr; ChrhWkr; CmntyWkr; HonRl; LitMag; Mdrgl; MrchBnd; NatlFornLg; NHS; SchMus; SchPl; YthFlsp; RptrSchPpr; John Brown Univ; Broadcasting.

FARLEY, Wanda G; Crete Monee HS; Park Forest S, IL; 4/382 HonRl; JrNHS; NHS; SchPpr; SpnCl; MthCl;.

FARLIN, Lesa; Milford Public HS; Milford, NE; 9/60 PresSophCls; ChrhWkr; CncrtBnd; NHS; SchPl; StuCncl; GerCl; Chrldr; DARAwd; Univ; Literature Related.

FARLIN, Lynne; Big Springs HS; Big Springs, NE; 1/23 VPFrshCls; PresJrCls; ALAGirlsSt; Band; Chrs; NHS; SecStuCncl; TreasFHA; PresPpCl; LetterTrk; Univ Of Ne; Business.

FARMER, Charles W; Pittsburg HS; Pittsburg, KS; CmntyWkr; LitMag; NatlFornLg; SchMus; SchPl; TchrAde; College; Professional.

FARMER, James; Falls City HS; Falls City, NE; SpnCl; Bsktbl; Arizona Sate; Architecture.

FARMER, Julie A; St Charles HS; St Charles, MI; 32/135 HonRl; MrchBnd; OffAde; 4-H; LetterTrk; Chrldr; GAA; IMSpt; PresAwd; Clge; Legal Secretary.

FARMER, Kathryn J; Jackson Hts HS; Circleville, KS; 2/39 SecTrsSophCls; VPJrCls; HonRl; LbryAde; EdYrBk; SchPpr; PpCl; LetterBsktbl; LetterTrk; Chrldr;.

FARMER, Kristy A; West Vigo HS; West Terre Haute, IN; Chr; ChrhWkr; HonRl; OffAde; RedCrAde; SchMus; TchrAde; YthFlsp; PpCl; LetterSwmmng; Clerk; Prof.

FARMER, Michael; Tamaroa HS; Tamaroa, IL; ChrhWkr; CmntyWkr; HonRl; RedCrAde; YthFlsp; SptEdSchPpr; FBLA; Bsbl; Bsktbl; Trk; College; Minning Tech.

FARMER, Pamela M; Marseilles HS; Marseilles, IL; Band; Chrs; HonRl; Mdrgl; MrchBnd; NatlThespSoc; SchMus; SchPl; StuCncl; RptrSchPpr; Trade Or Business Sch; Voation.

FARMER, Renee; Cheboygan Area HS; Cheboygan, MI; 4/209 HonRl; LetterBsktbl; Tennis; IMSpt; PresAwd; Business School; Exec Sec.

FARMER, Rhonda L; Metropolis Comm HS; Metropolis, IL; Chrs; ChrhWkr; OffAde; SchMus; SchPl; SctActv; SpnCl; PpCl; Chrldr; AmLegAwd; College; Nurse Or Fashion Merchandising.

FARMER, Sarah T; North Pemiscot HS; Wardell, MO; 4/56 Chr; HonRl; FHA; College; Professional.

FARMER, Timothy; North Muskegon HS; North Muskegon, MI; 6/87 Band; Chr; CncrtBnd; HonRl; MrchBnd; NHS; Orch; TchrAde; RptrYrbk; RotaryAwd; Lake Superior State College; Accounting.

FARMER, Vickey; Bloomfield HS; Bloomfield, MO; Chr; HonRl; LbryAde; FHA; PpCl; College.

FARNELL, Thomas S; Garden City West HS; Garden City, MI; AFS; Chr; CtyCnl; CncrtBnd; HonRl; NHS; NatlThespSoc; SchMus; StuGov; EdSchPpr; U Of Mi; Engineer.

FARNEN, Caroline A; St Teresa Acad; Kansas City, MO; Chrs; HonRl; Mdrgl; NatlMeritSF; RedCrAde; SchPl; SctActv; StuGov; FrCl; LatCl; Med Sch; Physician.

FARNEN, Mark E; Mexico HS; Mexico, MO; ALBoysSt; HonRl; NatlFornLg; NatlMeritCmnd; SchPl; StuCncl; KeyCl; LatCl; Trk; Wrstlng; Univ Of Mo; Lawyer Or Politician.

FARNER, Kathleen A; Arlington HS; Inianapolic, IN; 37/465 HonRl; NHS; TchrAde; GAA; IMSpt; PPFtbl; University.

FARNER, Susan M; Cochrane Fountain City HS; Cochrane, WI; 8/98 ALAGirlsSt; Band; Chrs; SecTrsFrshCls; JrNHS; PpCl; Coll.

FARNHAM, Cynthia M; North HS; Fargo, ND; AFS; Chr; HonRl; NatlFornLg; Orch; PresFrCl; LatCl; CitAwd; University.

FARNHAM, Dale E; Prairie Community HS; Gowrie, IA; PresFrshCls; PresSophCls; Chrs; ChrhWkr; CmntyWkr; HonRl; Mdrgl; NatlThespSoc; SchMus; SchPl; LetterBsktbl; LetterFtbl; Swmmng; LetterTrk; College; Law.

FARNSWORTH, Jodeen N; Benson HS; Omaha, NE; Band; CncrtBnd; HonRl; LbryAde; MrchBnd; NHS; Orch; PepBnd; SctActv; EdYrBk; U Of Ne; Phys Therapy.

FARQUHAR, Patricia J; Harrisburg HS; Harrisburg, IL; 3/185 Chr; ChrhWkr; CmntyWkr; HonRl; LbryAde; NHS; SecYthFlsp; PresFBLA; PresLatCl; DARAwd; College; Business.

FARR, Cathy E; Hartford HS; Emporia, KS; 4/33 HonRl; OffAde; SchPl; RptrYrbk; Yrbk; RptrSchPpr; SchPpr; FBLA; LetterBsktbl; LetterTrk;.

FARR, Daniel T; Northern HS; Pontiac, MI; Aud/Vis; Chr; Chrs; ChrhWkr; HonRl; JrNHS; LbryAde; Mdrgl; NHS; StuGov; RptrSchPpr; SchPpr; GerCl; College; Doctor.

FARR, Diana L; Pleasant Valley HS; Le Claire, IA; Band; Chrs; MrchBnd; SchMus; SctActv; TchrAde; YthFlsp; Bsbl; IMSpt; PresAwd; Coll.

FARR, Jack K; West Holt HS; Atkinson, NE; PresJrCls; Chr; Chrl; Chrs; ChrhWkr; CmntyWkr; HonRl; SchMus; SchPl; College; Physical Therapy.

FARR, Ruth A; East Buchanan C 1 HS; Gower, MO; 15/63 Band; Chr; Chrs; ChrhWkr; CncrtBnd; HonRl; MrchBnd; OffAde; PepBnd; SchAde; Mo Western State College; Elem Educ.

FARRAH, Sharon A; Mexico HS; Mexico, MO; VPSophCls; VPJrCls; Band; CncrtBnd; PepBnd; StuCncl; Bsbl; LetterBsktbl; LetterTennis; CaptTrk; College Or Univ; Science.

FARRAR, Gerard; Lakeview HS; St Clair Shores, MI; /600 ChrhWkr; HonRl; NHS; NatlMeritSchl; StuCncl; FBLA; FDA; GovHonPrgAwd; JETSAwd; Coll; Professional.

FARRAR, John P; Mt Carmel HS; Mt Carmel, IL; 15/185 HonRl; NHS; Bsbl; LetterGlf; CchngActv; Univ Of Illinois; Law.

FARRAR, Kathleen J; Brookfield R Iii HS; Brookfield, MO; Band; Chrl; ChrhWkr; CncrtBnd; HonRl; MrchBnd; SchMus; SctActv; YthFlsp; Chrldr; College; Professional.

FARRAR, Sandra A; Maywood HS; Maywood, NE; 5/22 Band; Chrs; ChrhWkr; HonRl; NHS; Bsktbl; Trk; Chrldr; 4-HAwd; VoiceDemAwd; Univ Of Nebr Lincoln; Social Work.

FARRAR, Toya A; North Senior HS; St Paul, MN; Chr; JA; Quill&Scroll; RedCrAde; SchMus; SchPl; FshEdSchPpr; Trk; Chrldr; GAA; Golden Valley Lutheran; Rec Director.

FARRELL, Cindy; Appleton West HS; Appleton, WI; Band; CmntyWkr; CncrtBnd; MrchBnd; StuGov; Chrldr; College; Professional.

FARRELL, Edward J; Marquette HS; Michigan City, IN; Chr; HonRl; SchMus; SchPl; MthCl; LetterBsktbl; RotaryAwd; Coll.

FARRELL, Elizabeth A; Bagley HS; Bagley, MN; 20/111 TrsFrshCls; VPSophCls; HonRl; SchPl; StuCncl; RptrSchPpr; 4-H; FHA; FTA; SciCl; U Of Nd; Rn.

FARRELL, Janice M; Wamego HS; Wamego, KS; 16/96 Chrs; HonRl; Yrbk; SchPpr; 4-H; FHA; Emporia State College; Business.

FARRELL, Jean M; Fonda Community HS; Fonda, IA; 2/31 TrsJrCls; ALAGirlsSt; Chr; Chrs; HonRl; JrNHS; NHS; NatlMeritSF; SchPl; RptrSchPpr; 4-H; GerCl; Univ; Physical Therapy.

FARRELL, Kathleen A; Burlington Comm HS; Burlington, IA; 13/500 HonRl; JA; LitMag; ModUN; NHS; SchMus; SchPl; Iowa State Univ; Sociology.

FARRELL, Kathleen D; Jefferson HS; Rockford, IL; AFS; ChrhWkr; HonRl; HospAde; SchMus; StuCncl; RptrSchPpr; 4-H; CaptBsktbl; Tennis; 4-HAwd; Rock Valley College; Dental Assistant.

FARRELL, Kimberly K; Grand Island Central Cath S; Grand Island, NE; SecTrsFrshCls; SecTrsSophCls; HonRl; StuCncl; StuGov; PpCl; Chrldr; PPFtbl; Kearney College.

FARRELL, Mary Jane; Wamego HS; Wamego, KS; Chr; Chrs; ChrhWkr; CmntyWkr; HonRl; FHA; TreasSpnCl; PpCl; BttyCrckrAwd; Emporia Kansas State College; Music.

FARRELL, Mary P; Schlarman HS; Danville, IL; 2/70 TrsFrshCls; TrsSophCls; HonRl; NHS; NatlMeritCmnd; SchMus; SchPl; StuCncl; Yrbk; Chrldr; Univ; Engin & Law.

FARRELL, Michael J; Ashwaubenon HS; Green Bay, WI; LetterBsbl; LetterBsktbl; LetterFtbl; Coll; Dentist.

FARRELL, Sherrie L; Cass Tech HS; Detroit, MI; NatlMeritCmnd; NatlMeritSF; College; Law.

FARRELL, Thomas A; Downers Grove North HS; Downers Grove, IL; 49/524 HonRl; JrNHS; NHS; NatlMeritCmnd; Bsktbl; LetterFtbl; Trk; Univ Of Il; Law.

FARRELL, Tim J; Larimore HS; Larimore, ND; HonRl; 4-H; College; Professional.

FARRELL, Virginia L; Argo Community HS; Willow Springs, IL; 19/432 CmntyWkr; HonRl; LitMag; NHS; StuGov; TchrAde; SciCl; Loyola Univ Of Chicago; Biology Theology.

FARREN, Cheryl; United Township HS; East Moline, IL; 79/672 Band; ChrhWkr; CncrtBnd; HonRl; JA; MrchBnd; Orch; PepBnd; SchPpr; PresAwd; College; Nursing.

FARREN, Mark S; Colo Comm HS; Colo, IA; PresFrshCls; PresSrCls; CmntyWkr; SctActv; StuCncl; StuGov; YthFlsp; FFA; PpCl; CaptBsbl; CaptBsktbl; CaptFtbl; CchngActv; College; Vocation.

FARRIS, Julie M; Galena HS; Galena, KS; ChrhWkr; HonRl; NHS; College; Journalism.

FARRIS, Kay A; Southridge HS; Huntingburg, IN; 38/167 Chr; Chrl; Chrs; ChrhWkr; HonRl; SchMus; SctActv; YthFlsp; 4-H; FHA; Trade Schl; Speech & Hearing Therapist.

FARRIS, Keith E; Ridgway HS; Ridgway, IL; 10/50 HstSrCls; Band; CncrtBnd; HonRl; MrchBnd; StuCncl; SptEdSchPpr; SpnCl; LetterBsbl; LetterBsktbl; College; Accountant.

FARRIS, Phillip A; Langdon HS; Langdon, ND; HonRl; StuGov; GerCl; PpCl; LetterBsktbl; LetterFtbl; LetterTrk; CchngActv; PresAwd; University; Athletics.

FARRISS, Janice M; Elmhurst HS; Fort Wayne, IN; HonRl; HospAde; JA; SctActv; RptrSchPpr; 4-H; Socr; GAA; Williamwoods Girls College; Liberal Arts.

FARRITOR, Rodney I; St Agnes Academy; Alliance, NE; 6/22 VPSophCls; Chrs; ChrhWkr; HonRl; SecStuCncl; SchPl; Ftbl; Trk; College; Business.

FARRO, Carol Y; Port Huron HS; Port Huron, MI; Band; CncrtBnd; HonRl; MrchBnd; PepBnd; TchrAde; FrCl; St Clair Co Com Col; Registred Nurse.

FARROW, Barbara L; Adel Community HS; Adel, IA; Band; CncrtBnd; HonRl; LbryAde; MrchBnd; PepBnd; 4-H; LetterGlf; 4-HAwd; Bus School; Professional.

FARROW, Stephen L; Cass Technical HS; Detroit, MI; Chr; ChrhWkr; DrlTm; HonRl; NatlMeritSF; ROTC; SchAde; SctActv; RptrSchPpr; Ftbl; Clge; Medicine.

FARROW, Timothy O; Lakeshore HS; St Joseph, MI; LetterBand; CncrtBnd; MrchBnd; SchPl; KeyCl; SpnCl; LetterBsbl; LetterBsktbl; LetterTrk; Western Mi.

FARRUGIA, Georgina; Crestwood HS; Dearborn Heights, MI; 28/436 JrNHS; NHS; RptrYrbk; College; Special Ed.

FARTHING, Linda S; Carrier Mills HS; Carrier Mills, IL; 2/33 Chrs; ChrhWkr; HonRl; StuCncl; YthFlsp; MthCl; PpCl; SciCl; College; Mathematics.

FARVOUR, Dennis; Custer HS; Milwaukee, WI; Bsbl; Trk; Milton Coll; Phy Ed.

FARWELL, Gary L; Pawnee City HS; Dubois, NE; SecTrsFrshCls; SecTrsSophCls; TrsJrCls; VPSrCls; HonRl; YthFlsp; FFA; LetterBsktbl; LetterFtbl; LetterTrk; Doane Col.

FASCHINGBAUER, Daniel J; Bloomer HS; Bloomer, WI; VPSrCls; ChrhWkr; NHS; SchPl; LetterBsktbl; LetterFtbl; LetterTrk; IMSpt; Trade School; Vocation.

FASCHINGBAUER, Denise L; Mc Donell Central HS; Chippewa Falls, WI; 3/95 HonRl; ModUN; SpnCl; PpCl; LetterBsktbl; Trk; LetterChrldr; College; Professional.

FASHACHT, Jaclynne M; Loyola HS; Mankato, MN; ALAGirlsSt; Chr; Chrs; ChrhWkr; CmntyWkr; HonRl; OffAde; SchAde; TchrAde; Mankato Comm College; Fashion Mdse.

FASIANG, Linda M; Thornwood HS; Calumet, IL; 33/967 HonRl; NHS; SptEdSchPpr; GerCl; Univ Of Illinois; Veterinarian Medicine.

FASKE, Carol J; Borden HS; Borden, IN; 4/74 Band; CncrtBnd; HonRl; MrchBnd; NHS; PepBnd; FHA;.

FASKO, Susanne; Elizabeth HS; Elizabeth, IL; 1/28 PresFrshCls; DrmMjrt; NHS; Quill&Scroll; StuGov; EdYrBk; SchPpr; GAA; IMSpt; BauchLmbAwd; Highland Comm Coll;prim Sch Teach.

FASS, Ruth A; Auburn HS; Auburn, NE; SecFrshCls; TrsSophCls; SecJrCls; SecSrCls; Band; ChrhWkr; HonRl; Quill&Scroll; RptrYrbk; Chrldr; Vocational Sch; Nursing.

FASSERO, James R; Gillespie HS; Gillespie, IL; 6/132 HonRl; LbryAde; NHS; LetterBsbl; LetterBsktbl; LetterTrk; Illinois State Univ; Business.

FASSNACHT, Lori; Parkway Central Sr HS; Chesterfield, MO; 3/373 SecSrCls; AFS; Chr; HonRl; NHS; StuCncl; PPFtbl; Univ Of Ind; Spanish And Business.

FAST, Kathy; Liberal HS; Iantha, MO; Band; MrchBnd; PepBnd; SctActv; Twrl; YthFlsp; FHA; PpCl; Chrldr; IMSpt; Coll.

FAST, Kim L; Winner HS; Winner, SD; Chr; Chrl; Chrs; Mdrgl; VPPpCl; College; Secretary.

FAST, Loretta; Mt Lake Hs; Mt Lake, MN; 6/80 Band; Chrs; HonRl; ModUN; PepBnd; PresYthFlsp; RptrYrbk; VP4-H; TreasFHA; PpCl; St Olaf College; Nursing.

FAST, Mary E; Columbus Unified HS; Columbus, KS; SecFrshCls; HstSophCls; TrsJrCls; ChrhWkr; HonRl; StuCncl; FHA; PpCl; Chrldr; PPFtbl; College; Professional.

FAST, Roxie A; Butterfield Odin HS; Butterfield, MN; Chr; ChrhWkr; HonRl; GerCl; Trade School; Secretary.

FATELEY, Sharon D; Dixon HS; Dixon, MO; 8/89 Chr; Chrs; DrlTm; HonRl; MrchBnd; TchrAde; VPFHA; FTA; PpCl; College; Home Economics.

FATER, Rodney D; Flat Rock HS; Flat Rock, MI; 25/130 NatlMeritFnl; NatlMeritSchl; StuCncl; PpCl; LetterFtbl; LetterTennis; LetterTrk; DARAwd; SARAwd; VoiceDemAwd; Adrian Coll; Phy Ed Teach.

FATLAND, Sandra G; Kindred Public HS; Kindred, ND; 2/46 ALAGirlsSt; Chr; CncrtBnd; HonRl; LbryAde; NHS; YthFlsp; RptrSchPpr; FBLA; FHA; Loma Courses; Accounting.

FATZINGER, Curt D; Platteville HS; Platteville, WI; 20/197 PresSrCls; Chr; HonRl; StuCncl; StuGov; RptrYrbk; RptrSchPpr; SpnCl; LetterBsbl; LetterBsktbl; LetterFtbl; College; Psychologist.

FAUBION, Teresa D; Chanute HS; Chanute, KS; Band; CncrtBnd; HonRl; MrchBnd; OffAde; PepBnd; Chrldr; IMSpt; College; Professional.

FAUCETT, Cande L; Frankfort Sr HS; Frankfort, IN; 27/250 Band; Chr; CncrtBnd; DrmMjrt; MrchBnd; NHS; Orch; SchMus; StuCncl; Twrl; YthFlsp; FTA; FrCl; Indiana Univ; Dental Hygiene.

FAUCETT, Mark A; Pembine HS; Pembine, WI; 15/35 HonRl; Yrbk; Bsktbl; LetterFtbl; Glf; CchngActv; Clge; Ocean Research.

FAUCHER, Thomas J; Loyola Academy; Park Ridge, IL; 23/442 ChrhWkr; HonRl; JrNHS; NHS; Sdlty; LetterBsktbl; IMSpt; Univ Of Notre Dame; Dentistry.

FAUGHT, Gary R; Whiting HS; Whiting, IN; 18/100 ALBoysSt; ROTC; TchrAde; MthCl; SciCl; AmLegAwd;.

FAUGHT, Mary M; Oblong HS; Oblong, IL; 13/72 Chrs; HonRl; RptrYrbk; RptrSchPpr; EdSchPpr; FTA; Mac Murray College; Special Education.

FAUL, David G; Eastbrook HS; Upland, IN; TrsSophCls; Chr; HonRl; NHS; SchPl; YthFlsp; SpnCl; College.

FAUL, Monte L; Harvey HS; Harvey, ND; PresFrshCls; Band; Chr; Chrs; ChrhWkr; CncrtBnd; HonRl; Mdrgl; MrchBnd; StuCncl; Coll;eng.

FAUL, Susan G; Sawyer HS; Sawyer, ND; 4/22 PresSrCls; Chrs; HonRl; Mdrgl; MrchBnd; SchMus; StuCncl; EdYrBk; BttyCrckrAwd; Minot State College; Medical Technologist.

FAULDS, Patrick G; Abbot Pennings HS; De Pere, WI; 6/90 TrsSrCls; Band; CncrtBnd; HonRl; MrchBnd; NHS; StuGov; RptrSchPpr; IMSpt; College; Law.

FAULKENBURG, Kim R; Leavenworth HS; Leavenworth, IN; 2/26 Band; HonRl; LbryAde; NHS; EdYrBk; SchPpr; 4-H; PresFHA; Chrldr; BttyCrckrAwd; Indiana U.

FAULKNER, Gloria L; Downers Grove Comm HS; Downers Grove, IL; 1/827 Chr; DrlTm; HonRl; NatlThespSoc; SchMus; SchPl; SctActv; Univ Of Ill; Interior Design.

FAULKNER, Jayne E; Triton HS; Bourbon, IN; Band; Chr; CncrtBnd; HonRl; MrchBnd; PepBnd; EdYrBk; FTA; PpCl; DARAwd; International Jr Col; Executive Secretarial.

FAULKNER, Jill; Brigh HS; Brighton, MI; ChrhWkr; HonRl; NHS; GerCl; PPFtbl; Michigan State.

FAULKNER, Kris; Lyons Township HS; Western Srings, IL; CncrtBnd; HonRl; NHS; OffAde; Orch; Quill&Scroll; FshEdYrbk; Purdue U; Medical Tech.

FAULKNER, Lee A; Warren Township HS; Gurnee, IL; 14/301 Chr; HonRl; SecNHS; SchMus; StuCncl; TchrAde; RptrSchPpr; SchPpr; SpnCl; Private College; Music.

FAULKNER, Patricia L; Lesterville R 4 HS; Black, MO; Band; Chr; ChrhWkr; CmntyWkr; HonRl; HospAde; LbryAde; SchMus; PpCl; IMSpt; Nursing Sch; Rn.

FAULKNER, William M; Vienna HS; Vienna, IL; Band; ChrhWkr; HonRl; MrchBnd; TchrAde; SptEdSchPpr; LetterBsbl; LetterBsktbl; Trk; ChmbCommrsAwd; Univ; Professional.

FAUSONE, William M; Austin Catholic Prep; Grosse Pt Woods, MI; 20/119 HonRl; SchPl; StuGov; Yrbk; LetterTennis; Chrldr; Univ Of Michigan; Accounting.

FAUST, Christine K; East HS; Waterloo, IA; 25/330 HonRl; HospAde; JrNHS; LbryAde; ModUN; NHS; Teen; College; Nursing.

FAUST, Christopher R; Boys Town HS; Boys Town, NE; 4/75 JA; JCC; StuGov; FrCl; CaptFtbl; Trk; College.

FAUST, Douglas A; Wilson HS; Mankato, MN; PresSrCls; ALBoysSt; Chr; SchPl; YthFlsp; EdYrBk; LetterBsktbl; CaptFtbl; LetterTrk; RotaryAwd; Mankato State Univ; Theatre Arts.

FAUST, Jeanette E; Armada Area HS; Allenton, MI; 3/140 Band; Chr; CncrtBnd; HonRl; MrchBnd; NHS; PepBnd; SchMus; PresYthFlsp; IMSpt; Oakland U; English.

FAUST, Karen L; Nazareth Academy; Riverside, IL; ChrhWkr; CmntyWkr; HonRl; OffAde; SchAde; SchMus; TchrAde; RptrSchPpr; FrCl; Purdue Univ; Architecture.

FAUST, Kathleen A; Hill Murray HS; St Paul, MN; ChrhWkr; CmntyWkr; HonRl; HospAde; NHS; OffAde; PolWkr; FrCl; IMSpt; St Catherines; Nurse.

FAUST, Linda M; Healy HS; Pierz, MN; 17/115 Aud/Vis; Chr; Chrs; HonRl; SchPl; Yrbk; 4-H; Bsktbl; Trade Schl; Photography.

FAUST, Lynn; Aurora Hoyt Lakes HS; Hoyt Lakes, MN; 6/233 Chr; ChrhWkr; HonRl; LbryAde; NatlMeritCmnd; RptrYrbk; FTA; FrCl; MthCl; Univ Of Mn; Accountant.

FAUST, Marco P; Litchville Public HS; Kathryn, ND; Band; Chrs; MrchBnd; PepBnd; SchMus; LetterBsbl; LetterBsktbl; LetterTrk; College; Science Or Math.

FAUST, Mary R; Charleston HS; Charleston, IL; 8/245 Band; Chrs; ChrhWkr; CmntyWkr; HonRl; MrchBnd; NHS; Orch; SchMus; Nursing.

FAUST, Melissa J; East HS; Waterloo, IA; 8/330 Chr; ChrhWkr; HonRl; JrNHS; LbryAde; NHS; RptrSchPpr; EdSchPpr; FshEdSchPpr; U Of No Ia; Special Elementary Education.

FAUST, Richard J; Ladysmith HS; Ladysmith, WI; AFS; Band; Chr; HonRl; NHS; SchMus; StuCncl; CaptBsbl; LetterBsktbl; LetterFtbl; Coll; Math & Musc.

FAUST, Sherry; Windsor HS; Windsor, MO; 7/51 DrlTm; HonRl; NHS; Quill&Scroll; Yrbk; RptrSchPpr; PpCl; Southwest Missouri State Univ; Journalism.

FAVA, Christopher; St Louis University HS; St Louis, MO; 95/191 Chr; HonRl; Sacrstn; SchMus; StuCncl; Ftbl; Trk; Wrstlng; Chrldr; St Louis Univ; Mathematics.

FAVERO, Brian V; Omaha Central HS; Omaha, NE; 35/527 Chr; HonRl; NHS; ROTC; SchMus; University; Professional.

FAVERO, Scott A; Reed Custer HS; Braidwood, IL; 5/53 HonRl; NHS; Bsktbl; Wrstlng; Western Il Univ; Law.

FAVISH, Pamela E; Niles East HS; Skokie, IL; HospAde; NHS; SchPl; StuGov; Chrldr; Beloit College.

FAW, Sandra M; Toluca HS; Toluca, IL; 5/23 Band; Chrs; DrmMjrt; NHS; SecFHA; VPSpnCl; Bsktbl; LetterGlf; Chrldr; TreasGAA; 4-HAwd; Illinois St University.

FAWCETT, Candice K; Miller HS; Ree Heights, SD; HonRl; JA; Mdrgl; NHS; SchPl; 4-H; FHA; Chrldr; 4-HAwd; University; Music.

FAWCETT, Peggy L; Miller HS; Ree Heights, SD; 43/99 AFS; Band; Chrs; HonRl; Yrbk; SchPpr; 4-H; FFA; FHA; 4-HAwd; Univ; Agricultural Economics.

FAWNS, Jody L; Williamsville HS; Williamsville, IL; 16/65 SecFrshCls; Chr; Chrl; Chrs; CmntyWkr; HonRl; LbryAde; Mdrgl; NatlFornLg; NatlThespSoc; College; Professional.

FAY, Barbara J; Winchester HS; Winchester, IL; 7/76 HonRl; SchPl; 4-H; FHA; Bsktbl; 4-HAwd; Kansas State Or U Of I; Vetrinarian.

FAY, Daniel B; Anita Community HS; Anita, IA; VPBand; CncrtBnd; HonRl; MrchBnd; NatlFornLg; NHS; PepBnd; Quill&Scroll; StuCncl; EdYrBk; PresFTA; DanFAwd; Central College.

FAY, Linda R; Almond HS; Almond, WI; 7/28 HonRl; JrNHS; NHS; RptrYrbk; RptrSchPpr; LetterBsktbl; LetterTrk; GAA; IMSpt; AmLegAwd; Uw La Crosse; Social Work.

FAY, Marlin L; Kasson Mantorville HS; Byron, MN; 4/92 ALBoysSt; PresChrs; CncrtBnd; NHS; TreasFFA; LetterBsktbl; LetterFtbl; LetterTrk; Univ Of Wisc; Agriculture.

FAY, Steven R; Herbert Henry Dow HS; Midland, MI; 7/430 Band; HonRl; NHS; NatlMeritCmnd; SctActv; RptrSchPpr; EngCl; College; Journalism.

FAYE, Eileen S; Bayfield HS; Bayfield, WI; LetterBand; Chr; CncrtBnd; MrchBnd; NatlFornLg; PepBnd; EdYrBk; Bsktbl; LetterTrk; College; Home Economics.

FAZER, William G; North Central HS; Powers, MI; 7/52 SecJrCls; VPSrCls; ALBoysSt; CmntyWkr; HonRl; LbryAde; SchPl; StuGov; EngCl; LetterFtbl; Coll; Water Quality Tech.

FAZZARI, Michael F; St Paul & Kennedy HS; Chicago, IL; 21/610 Band; CmntyWkr; HonRl; NHS; SctActv; MthCl; LetterBsbl; Univ Of Ill; Civil Engineer.

FEAGANS, Frank; Porta HS; Petersburg, IL; 12/131 Band; CncrtBnd; HonRl; MrchBnd; NHS; NatlThespSoc; PepBnd; SchMus; FrCl; College; Computer Science.

FEAK, Glen A; Addison Trail HS; Addison, IL; 2/567 HonRl; JrNHS; NHS; College; Physics.

FEALA, Jay F; North Bend Central HS; North Bend, NE; 36/56 StuGov; RptrSchPpr; CaptBsktbl; CaptFtbl; CaptTrk; Midland College; Business.

FEARING, Gary D; Weston HS; Lime Ridge, WI; TrsFrshCls; HstSophCls; HstJrCls; CmntyWkr; HonRl; RptrYrbk; SptEdYrbk; LetterBsbl; LetterBsktbl; LetterFtbl; Univ; Vocation.

FEARNOW, Mark A; Wabash HS; Wabash, IN; 14/203 Chr; HonRl; NatlFornLg; NHS; NatlThespSoc; SchMus; SchPl; FrCl; University; Speech.

FEATHERS, Tambra D; Crispus Attucks HS; Indianapolis, IN; 7/326 Aud/Vis; ChrhWkr; CmntyWkr; HonRl; JA; LbryAde; NHS; OffAde; SchAde; StuCncl; SchPpr; JAAwd; College; Business.

FECHER, Diana L; Hamilton Hts HS; Atlanta, IN; 19/125 SecChrhWkr; HonRl; LbryAde; PresYthFlsp; EdYrBk; Pres4-H; SecFHA; Ball St Univ; Home Ec.

FECHT, Susan D; Dalton Public HS; Dalton, NE; 1/20 PresJrCls; Chrs; ChrhWkr; DrlTm; HonRl; Mdrgl; SchPl; Bsktbl; Trk; AmLegAwd;.

FECHTELKOTTER, Gregg L; Northwestern HS; Poplar, WI; 4/126 ALBoysSt; Band; HonRl; Mdrgl; NatlMeritCmnd; SctActv; LetterBsktbl; LetterFtbl; LetterTrk; ChmbCommrsAwd; 4-HAwd; Univ Of Wisconsin; Architecture.

FECHTELKOTTER, Joan M; Northwestern HS; Poplar, WI; VPJrCls; Band; HonRl; SctActv; RptrSchPpr; 4-H; Bsktbl; LetterTrk; Chrldr; GAA; 4-HAwd; CitAwd; College; Music.

FEDA, Robert; Osseo HS; Brooklyn Park, MN; 17/358 HonRl; NHS; Univ; Accounting.

FEDDE, Peggy A; Balaton HS; Balaton, MN; ChrhWkr; SchPl; RptrYrbk; RptrSchPpr; 4-H; FHA; Bsktbl; Trk; CaptChrldr; GAA; Trade Sch; Vocational.

FEDDER, Judith A; Manistee Catholic Central HS; Manistee, MI; 4/76 TrsSophCls; Chr; CncrtBnd; HonRl; MrchBnd; NHS; PepBnd; RptrSchPpr; PpCl; Chrldr; College.

FEDDERSEN, Jan A; Lost Nation Comm HS; Lost Nation, IA; ALBoysSt; Chr; HonRl; SchMus; YthFlsp; SchPpr; PpCl; Bsktbl; Glf; College; Vocation.

FEDDERSEN, Mavis D; Zap Public HS; Zap, ND; SecTrsFrshCls; SecTrsSophCls; SecTrsJrCls; Chrs; HonRl; LbryAde; SchPl; TchrAde; College; Nurse.

FEDDERSEN, Robin; Proviso West Hs; Berkeley, IL; HonRl; NHS; GerCl; Northern Illinois U; Business Administratio.

FEDER, Susannah; Beloit Memorial HS; Beloit, WI; HonRl; LitMag; NHS; PolWkr; Quill&Scroll; RptrSchPpr; Rutgers Univ; Journ.

FEDERIUK, John R; North HS; Eau Claire, WI; 64/400 Aud/Vis; NatlFornLg; NatlThespSoc; Orch; SchMus; SchPl; PresSctActv; SecEngCl; PresGerCl; PresSciCl; LetterTennis; LetterTrk; University; Electronics Technology.

FEDEROWSKI, Dora; Cassopolis HS; Vandalia, MI; 2/125 Band; CncrtBnd; HonRl; MrchBnd; NHS; DrlTm; RptrYrbk; Bsbl; Univ; Lawyer Juvenile.

FEDERS, Jerry; Hill Murray HS; St Paul, MN; 1/246 HonRl; JrNHS; LbryAde; NHS; TchrAde; RptrYrbk; SchPpr; Coll St Thomas; Business French.

FEDEWA, Debra K; Maple Valley HS; Nashville, MI; 17/116 SecSrCls; Band; Chr; HonRl; SchMus; SchPl; StuCncl; SptEdYrbk; Chrldr; GAA; College; Voice.

FEDEWA, Sharon E; St Patrick HS; Portland, MI; 3/43 VPSophCls; Chr; ChrhWkr; CmntyWkr; HonRl; NatlMeritCmnd; SchPl; Yrbk; SciCl; IMSpt; Mi Tech U; Chemical Engineer.

FEDIE, Scott; Durand HS; Durand, WI; SecFrshCls; Aud/Vis; Band; HonRl; SctActv; StuCncl; VPFFA; LetterFtbl; LetterTrk; Wrstlng; School; Vocation.

FEDINETS, Gary W; Gordon Technical HS; Chicago, IL; 12/575 HonRl; NHS; OffAde; EdYrBk; KeyCl; SpnCl; MthCl; PpCl; Northwestern University; Dentistry.

FEDO, Diane M; St Francis Academy; Joliet, IL; 9/178 HonRl; NHS; SpnCl; Bsbl; Bsktbl; Northern Illinois Univ;medicine.

FEDO, Robert; Joliet Catholic HS; Joliet, IL; 70/165 ALBoysSt; HonRl; SancSoc; College; Accounting.

FEDOLAK, Doris O; Frank Cody HS; Detroit, MI; 1/700 HonRl; JrNHS; NHS; NatlMeritFnl; NatlMeritSchl; NatlMeritSF; Twrl; FSA; FrCl; Michigan St University.

FEDOR, David W; Virden HS; Thayer, IL; Aud/Vis; HonRl; PpCl; SciCl; Ftbl; LetterGlf; College; Professional.

FEDOR, Helen R; George Washington HS; Chicago, IL; HonRl; JrNHS; LbryAde; NHS; NatlMeritCmnd; NatlSciFnd; SchAde; TchrAde; Tennis; College; Science.

FEDRO, Randall C; Wheeling HS; Wheeling, IL; 21/487 HonRl; NHS; StuGov; LetterBsbl; College; Doctor.

FEE, Julie; Barry HS; Barry, IL; 14/46 SecJrCls; HonRl; OffAde; Twrl; SptEdSchPpr; 4-H; FHA; FrCl; Bsktbl; Chrldr; Business College; Business.

FEEHAN, Thomas M; Joliet Catholic HS; Joliet, IL; HstJrCls; HonRl; PolWkr; TchrAde; Ftbl; Trk; IMSpt; College; Business.

FEEKES, Gary A; Sheldon Comm HS; Sheldon, IA; Chr; Chrs; HonRl; SchMus; LetterBsbl; LetterBsktbl; CaptGlf; LetterTrk; College.

FEENEY, Ann M; Naper Central HS; Naperville, IL; HonRl; Mdrgl; NHS; NatlMeritSF; NatlThespSoc; SchAde; SchMus; SchPl; 4-H; University Of Illinois; Economics.

FEENEY, Colleen A; Edgewood HS; Madison, WI; Chrs; NHS; SchPl; StuCncl; PpCl; Chrldr; Univ; Business.

FEENEY, Daniel J; Joliet West HS; Joliet, IL; 123/492 HonRl; TchrAde; KeyCl; Oregon State Univ; Forestry.

FEENEY, Jane A; Romeoville HS; Lockport, IL; 15/293 HonRl; NHS; OffAde; TreasStuGov; RptrSchPpr; GAA; College; Business.

FEENSTRA, Jeffrey; Holland HS; Holland, MI; 21 317 Band; ChrhWkr; CncrtBnd; HonRl; MrchBnd; SciCl; Hope College; Science.

FEEZEL, Laura; Marquette HS; Wood River, IL; 5/300 ChrhWkr; DrlTm; HonRl; HospAde; OffAde; FNA; SpnCl; GAA; IMSpt; AmLegAwd; Univ; Professional.

FEGER, Debra J; E P Community HS; E Peoria, IL; Band; CmntyWkr; HonRl; MrchBnd; PepBnd; RptrSchPpr; 4-H; SciCl; Illinois Wesleyn; Medicine.

FEHER, Elaine D; Belleville East HS; Belleville, IL; ChrhWkr; CmntyWkr; HonRl; LitMag; NatlFornLg; NatlThespSoc; SchMus; SchPl; EdSchPpr; SpnCl; Nursing Sch; Nursing.

FEHLER, Sheri E; Harlem North Campus HS; Loves Park, IL; VPFrshCls; Chr; Chrs; HonRl; RedCrAde; SchPl; StuCncl; PpCl; LetterTrk; CaptChrldr; LetterGAA; IMSpt; College; Vet.

FEHLING, John; Menomonee Falls East HS; Menomonee Falls, WI; 13/346 AFS; HonRl; NHS; EdYrBk; FrCl; MthCl; Uw Eauclaire.

FEHR, Walton L; Normal Community HS; Hudson, IL; HonRl; SchAde; 4-H; Il Univ; Engr.

FEHRENBACHER, Susan E; Newton HS; Ingraham, IL; HonRl; JrNHS; College; Business.

FEHRIBACH, Tanya M; Forest Park HS; Ferdinand, IN; 1/120 ALAGirlsSt; Band; HonRl; LbryAde; MrchBnd; NHS; NatlMeritCmnd; PepBnd; 4-H; Indiana University.

FEICHTENBINER, Marla S; Ithaca HS; Ithaca, MI; Band; CncrtBnd; HonRl; MrchBnd; TchrAde; School Of Radiologic Tech; X Ray Tech.

FEICHTNER, Katherine S; William Horlick HS; Racine, WI; 17/554 Band; HonRl; LbryAde; PepBnd; SctActv; Swmmng; LetterTennis; Trk; GAA; GovHonPrgAwd; U Of Wi Parkside; Math.

FEIDER, Christine; New Holstein Senior HS; New Holstein, WI; 30/200 AFS; Chr; Chrs; HonRl; IntrClCncl; LbryAde; NHS; SchAde; FHA; GAA; Lakeshore Tech Institute; Professional.

FEIDER, Doris M; Random Lake HS; Cedar Grove, WI; 2/100 AFS; ALAGirlsSt; Chrs; DrlTm; HonRl; Mdrgl; SchMus; EdYrBk; FHA; Bsktbl; Lakeshore Tech Ins; Medical Secretary.

FEIGE, Kim C; John Hersey HS; Mount Prospect, IL; 27/776 JA; NatlFornLg; NHS; SchMus; LetterBsktbl; Trk; GAA; JCAwd; College; Medical Technologist.

FEIGENBAUM, Edward D; Evanston Twp HS; Skokie, IL; LbryAde; NatlFornLg; PolWkr; YthLg; University; Government.

FEIGHNER, Jon L; Turner HS; Kansas City, KS; 4/300 ALBoysSt; CncrtBnd; NHS; StuGov; FrCl; PresSpnCl; U Of Ks; Spanish Latin American Business.

FEIKES, Ralph A; Laporte HS; Laporte, IN; 12/528 ALBoysSt; HonRl; NHS; StuCncl; LetterFtbl; Trk; IMSpt; JCAwd; Ball St; Arch.

FEIL, Cindy L; Caledonia HS; Caledonia, MN; 8/159 HonRl; NHS; RptrSchPpr; 4-H; KeyCl; Chrldr; Univ Of Minn; Veterinary Med.

FEILD, Marla K; Traverse City Sr HS; Traverse City, MI; Chrs; ChrhWkr; HonRl; NHS; NatlThespSoc; SchMus; PpCl; LetterTennis; Chrldr; IMSpt; College; Science.

FEINGOLD, Jack; Midland HS; Midland, MI; 110/433 HonRl; JA; NHS; NatlMeritSF; LetterSwmmng; JAAwd; Ferris State Clge; Bus Admin.

FEIRICH, John C; Carbondale Community HS; Carbondale, IL; NatlMeritCmnd; GerCl; SciCl; LetterFtbl; Trk; Univ; Medicine.

FEIST, Beth R; Velva HS; Velva, ND; 4/48 Band; HonRl; MrchBnd; TreasNHS; StuCncl; YthFlsp; FHA; PresPpCl; Trk; CaptChrldr; College.

FEIST, Jeffrey A; Downs HS; Downs, KS; 2/26 ChrhWkr; HonRl; SchPl; StuCncl; EdYrBk; RptrSchPpr; LetterBsktbl; LetterTrk; CitAwd; Fort Hays Kansas St College; Accounting.

FEIST, Nita; Velva Public HS; Velva, ND; Chr; Chrs; HonRl; NHS; YthFlsp; 4-H; Trk; Chrldr; IMSpt; PPFtbl; Trade School; Assistant Veterinarian.

FEIST, Roman; Emmons Central HS; Strasburg, ND; 4/36 PresSophCls; HonRl; JrNHS; NHS; Bsktbl; Ftbl; Trk; Univ; Agriculture.

FEKARIS, George N; Henry Ford HS; Detroit, MI; 9/500 HonRl; RedCrAde; SchMus; StuGov; PresFrCl; PresSpnCl; Bsbl; Bsktbl; AmLegAwd; Wayne St Univ; Civil Enginer.

FEKETY, Susan E; Huron HS; Ann Arbor, MI; 133/570 VPSrCls; Chr; LitMag; NatlMeritCmnd; PolWkr; SchMus; SchPl; StuGov; NCTE; Univ.

FELAND, Debbie D; Coon Rapids Senior HS; Coon Rapids, MN; 1/850 HonRl; JrNHS; NatlFornLg; NHS; NatlMeritSF; TchrAde; College; Environmental Studies.

FELDHAKE, David J; St Anthony HS; Effingham, IL; PpCl; LetterTrk; College; Coaching.

FELDKAMP, Beth; Manchester Hs; Manchester, MI; 9/105 Chrs; HonRl; YthFlsp; FHA; KeyCl; GerCl; GAA; 4-HAwd; Michigan State U; Commercial Floriculture.

FELDKAMP, Marilyn S; Hanover HS; Breman, KS; MrchBnd; NHS; PepBnd; SchPl; TchrAde; FHA; PpCl; SciCl; Bsktbl; Swmmng; Fort Hays Coll; Nursing.

FELDMAN, Julie; James Madison Mem HS; Madison, WI; AFS; CmntyWkr; HonRl; NatlMeritSF; Yrbk; University Of Wisconsin; Broadcasting.

FELDMAN, Randy M; Hibbing HS; Hibbing, MN; 27/432 Chr; HonRl; JA; NHS; SchMus; SchPl; SpnCl; SciCl; LetterTennis; IMSpt; Univ Of Wisconsin; Meteorology.

FELDMAN, Ronald E; Tomah Sr HS; Tomah, WI; SecFrshCls; CmntyWkr; StuCncl; SchPpr; SpnCl; LetterBsbl; LetterBsktbl; Military Academy; Engineer.

FELDMANN, Lori J; Boone HS; Boone, IA; Band; ChrhWkr; CncrtBnd; HonRl; MrchBnd; Orch; PepBnd; SchPl; IMSpt; PresAwd; College; Psychologist.

FELDMEYER, Sharon M; Waubay Public HS; Waubay, SD; PresSrCls; ALAGirlsSt; ChrhWkr; HonRl; RptrYrbk; EdSchPpr; PpCl; LetterTrk; AmLegAwd; DARAwd; Northern State Coll; Business.

FELDT, Scott W; Monticello Public HS; Monticello, WI; ALBoysSt; ChrhWkr; CmntyWkr; HonRl; ModUN; StuCncl; TchrAde; Yrbk; FFA; SpnCl; Blackhawk Tech; Farming.

FELFLE, Mary A; Resurrection HS; Chicago, IL; Chr; NatlCathMusEdAsoc; YthFlsp; FDA; FFA; FHA; FNA; FSA; GodCntryAwd; VoiceDemAwd; Coll; Music.

FELICIANO, Mary; Emerson HS; Gary, IN; Band; Chr; CmntyWkr; HonRl; NHS; OffAde; TchrAde; FBLA; SpnCl; MthCl; College; Computer Programmer.

FELIX, Alan R; L F Community HS; Little Falls, MN; ChrhWkr; HonRl; Bsktbl; IMSpt; Col; Professional.

FELIX, Valerie; Fairfield Community HS; Barnhill, IL; 9/165 Chr; ChrhWkr; HonRl; NHS; SchMus; 4-H; LatCl; GAA; DanFAwd; DARAwd; Business School; Legal Secretary.

FELKER, David E; Hayes County HS; Hayes Center, NE; 6/24 College; Math.

FELKER, Vicki L; Campbell HS; Campbell, MO; Chr; ChrhWkr; HonRl; TreasNHS; OffAde; SchPl; StuCncl; FHA; PpCl; IMSpt; Arkansas State Univ; Journalism.

FELKNER, William E; Centerville HS; Centerville, IA; Band; Chr; CncrtBnd; HonRl; MrchBnd; PepBnd; YthFlsp; Yrbk; SchPpr; 4-H; SciCl; LetterGlf; University; Photography.

FELL, Bert H; Bloomington South HS; Bloomington, IN; Band; HonRl; NHS; SctActv; TchrAde; Socr; Purdue Univ; Meteorology.

FELL, Cydne A; Winfield HS; Winfield, KS; CmntyWkr; HonRl; HospAde; StuCncl; TchrAde; PpCl; College ;education.

FELL, Thomas L; Dexter HS; Dexter, KS; 2/16 PresFrshCls; VPSophCls; PresSrCls; Band; NHS; SchPl; VPStuCncl; Bsktbl; Ftbl; Trk; Southwestern Coll.

FELLENZ, David A; West Bend East HS; West Bend, WI; 11/322 Bsbl; Bsktbl; CaptFtbl; IMSpt; College; Professional.

FELLER, Diane L; Winnebago Lutheran Academy; Mayville, WI; 1/44 SecJrCls; Chrs; ChrhWkr; SchPl; YthFlsp; PpCl; College; Rn.

FELLER, Grady K; Brookville HS; Brookville, IN; 3/173 PresFrshCls; VPJrCls; HonRl; JrNHS; NHS; StuCncl; RptrSchPpr; KeyCl; SpnCl; PpCl; LetterBsbl; LetterBsktbl; Ftbl; Purdue Univ; Chemical Engineer.

FELLER, Jon F; John F Kennedy HS; Marion, IA; Band; CncrtBnd; LitMag; MrchBnd; NatlMeritSF; Orch; PepBnd; FrCl; College; Mathematics.

FELLER, Lori J; Hartford Union HS; Iron Ridge, WI; ChrhWkr; CmntyWkr; DrlTm; LbryAde; StuCncl; 4-H; GAA; Tech School; Med Lab Tech.

FELLER, Marilyn A; Wisner Pilger HS; Wisner, NE; Band; Chrs; CncrtBnd; HonRl; NHS; SchMus; Twrl; 4-H; FHA; PpCl; Univ Of Ne; Dental Hygienist.

FELLER, Mark; Blair HS; Blair, NE; Band; CmntyWkr; LitMag; NatlThespSoc; StuCncl; YthFlsp; SchPpr; FSA; IMSpt; PresAwd; Univ Of Ne; Journalism.

FELLER, Sherry; Onsted HS; Onsted, MI; Band; CncrtBnd; MrchBnd; PepBnd; FHA; Business School.

FELLINGER, Mariann; Huntington Catholic HS; Huntington, IN; ALAGirlsSt; Chrs; HonRl; OffAde; SchPl; StuCncl; Yrbk; FBLA; PpCl; LetterTrk; University; Professional.

FELLOWS, Lori J; Western HS; Buda, IL; CmntyWkr; TchrAde; RptrYrbk;.

FELLOWS, Patti; North Knox HS; Bicknell, IN; DrlTm; FHA; LatCl; PpCl; Trk; University; Professional.

FELLS, Dennis; Gresham Public HS; Gresham, NE; SchPpr; Bsbl; Bsktbl; Ftbl; Trk; Coll; Teaching.

FELLWOCK, M Alan; Monett HS; Monett, MO; 1/125 ALBoysSt; Chrl; ChrhWkr; HonRl; NatlMeritSF; PresStuGov; SecKeyCl; CaptLetterFtbl; LetterTrk; University; Military Engineering.

FELLWOCK, Peter E; St Joseph HS; St Joseph, MI; Band; CncrtBnd; NHS; PepBnd; SchPpr; Ftbl; College; Professional.

FELT, Brian H; Stanton HS; Stanton, NE; PresSophCls; VPSrCls; ALBoysSt; Band; SchPl; StuGov; Yrbk; LetterBsktbl; LetterFtbl; LetterTrk; College; Electronics.

FELTEN, Elaine M; Pilot Grove HS; Pilot Grove, MO; 2/37 LbryAde; OffAde; SchMus; SchPl; Sdlty; StuCncl; SchPpr; FHA; PpCl; CaptChrldr; Central Missouri State Univ; Business.

FELTES, Jeffry E; Aurora Central Catholic HS; Aurora, IL; 4/180 HonRl; NHS; Ftbl; Univ Of Illinois; Agriculture.

FELTES, Jeffry E; Aorora Central HS; Aurora, IL; 4/190 HonRl; NHS; NatlMeritSchl; LetterFtbl; LetterWrstlng; Univ Of Il; Agriculture.

FELTES, Nancy J; Arcadia HS; Arcadia, WI; CncrtBnd; DrmMjrt; HonRl; MrchBnd; TrsFrshCls; PepBnd; PolWkr; SctActv; EdSchPpr; IMSpt; U Of Wi Madison; Engineering.

FELTMAN, Sandra A; Ladywood HS; Livonia, MI; ChrhWkr; HonRl; LitMag; Orch; PolWkr; RedCrAde; SchMus; SctActv; StuCncl; AmLegAwd; Michigan State Unvi; Animal Tech.

FELTON, Christina; Green Lake HS; Green Lake, WI; TrsFrshCls; Band; Chrs; ChrhWkr; HonRl; SctActv; RptrYrbk; RptrSchPpr; 4-H; Chrldr;.

FELTON, Lori I; New Trier West HS; Glenview, IL; 67/694 CmntyWkr; HonRl; Univ Of Michigan.

FELTON, Melanie K; Tri Center HS; Neola, IA; LetterBand; LetterChrs; CncrtBnd; HonRl; MrchBnd; NHS; Twrl; LetterPpCl; LetterChrldr; GAA; University; Law.

FELTON, Rita; Chicago Vocational HS; Chicago, IL; 3/778 VPSophCls; SecSrCls; ChrhWkr; HonRl; NHS; MthCl; Southern Il; Medicine.

FELTS, Danny G; Hillcrest HS; Springfield, MO; 73/302 NatlMeritCmnd; Sw Mo State Univ; Marine Biologist.

FELZKE, Harvey L; Pleasant Ridge HS; Leavenworth, KS; 2/43 VPFrshCls; VPSophCls; TrsJrCls; Band; Chrs; ChrhWkr; CncrtBnd; HonRl; LbryAde; MrchBnd; NatlFornLg; Bsktbl; Univ; Accounting.

FELZKE, Ronald E; De Witt HS; Lansing, MI; 9/124 CmntyWkr; HonRl; NHS; Coll; Acctng.

FEMAL, Glen L; Appleton West HS; Appleton, WI; AFS; KeyCl; LetterTrk; IMSpt; Coll; Phy Therapy.

FENCL, Wendy C; Nazareth Academy; Westchester, IL; 11/158 PresJrCls; LitMag; NHS; SchMus; StuGov; SchPpr; University; Psychiatry.

FENDER, Gregory T; Salem Community HS; Salem, IL; 60/200 HonRl; SchPl; SctActv; SpnCl; LetterBsktbl; LetterTrk; Univ Of Illinois; P E.

FENDER, Louis A; Benton Central HS; Fowler, IN; 2/260 ALBoysSt; HonRl; FrCl; LetterFtbl; Swmmng; LetterTrk; IMSpt; Clge; Bus Adm.

FENGLER, Kathy S; Bronaugh HS; Moundville, MO; 6/23 ChrhWkr; CncrtBnd; HonRl; SchPl; Yrbk; FHA; EngCl; OptClAwd; Bus Sch; Pro.

FENLON, Mark L; Appleton West HS; Appleton, WI; ALBoysSt; Band; CncrtBnd; MrchBnd; PepBnd; KeyCl; Ftbl; College; Medicine.

FENLON, Michael J; Our Lady Of Lakes HS; Pontiac, MI; 13/51 HonRl; NHS; SchPl; Bsbl; Oakland University; Environmental Engineer.

FENNELL, Carla J; The Principia HS; Elsah, IL; TrsFrshCls; NatlMeritSF; Swmmng; IMSpt; College; Major Study.

FENNEMA, Debra J; Illiana Christian HS; Dolton, IL; 34/180 ChrhWkr; HospAde; LbryAde; FNA; Evangelical School Of Nursing; Nurse.

FENNER, John M; Usd 279 Jewell HS; Jewell, KS; Band; Chrs; CncrtBnd; MrchBnd; PepBnd; StuCncl; YthFlsp; FFA; LetterFtbl; LetterTrk; Junior College.

FENNER, Louise J; Martin HS; Plainwell, MI; 1/67 TrsJrCls; Band; CncrtBnd; HonRl; MrchBnd; NHS; PepBnd; PresStuCncl; TchrAde; Western Mich Univ; Music.

FENNER, Pamela J; Cambridge Sr HS; Isanti, MN; Chr; TreasCncrtBnd; NHS; SecNatlThespSoc; SchMus; SchPl; StuCncl; 4-H; SecFHA; CaptChrldr; College.

FENOGLIO, Cheryl A; Marseilles HS; Marseilles, IL; Chrs; HonRl; NatlThespSoc; SchMus; SchPl; StuCncl; YthFlsp; Yrbk; PpCl; Trade School; Secretary.

FENSEL, Frederick A; Madison Consolidated HS; Madison, IN; ChrhWkr; HonRl; RptrSchPpr; KeyCl; PpCl; Bsbl; Bsktbl; Ftbl; Glf; Swmmng; College; Professional.

FENSKE, Beth A; Frost Public HS; Bricelyn, MN; 5/17 Band; Chrs; HonRl; NHS; SchMus; YthFlsp; Yrbk; Bsktbl; Trk; GAA; College; Art.

FENSKE, Bruce; Edgerton HS; Edgerton, WI; NatlMeritCmnd; StuGov; FrCl; GovHonPrgAwd; Univ Of Wi; Applied Math, Engineering.

FENSKE, Douglas M; Sargent Pub HS; Sargent, NE; PresFrshCls; VPSophCls; HonRl; NatlThespSoc; SchPl; StuGov; Bsktbl; Ftbl; Trk; LetterWrstlng; Farmer.

FENSKE, Douglas M; Sargent Public HS; Sargent, NE; PresFrshCls; VPFrshCls; VPSophCls; Chrs; HonRl; NHS; NatlThespSoc; SchPl; StuGov; CivCl; FFA; LetterBsktbl; Ftbl; Trk; LetterWrstlng; Curtis Agricultural College; Farmer.

FENSKE, Jeffrey J; Cathedral HS; New Ulm, MN; 10/96 ChrhWkr; HonRl; NHS; SchPl; Yrbk; LetterBsktbl; LetterGlf; BauchLmbAwd; RotaryAwd; St Johns Univ; Pre Law.

FENSKE, Michael A; Pierce City R6 HS; Pierce City, MO; HonRl; VPFFA; LetterFtbl; Trade School; Vocational.

FENSKE, Mike M; New London HS; New London, WI; Univ; Funeral Director.

FENSLER, Ruth A; Warsaw Community HS; Winona Lake, IN; Band; Chr; ChrhWkr; CmntyWkr; HonRl; NHS; EngCl; GAA; NCTE; CitAwd; College; Professional.

FENTON, Craig A; Centerville HS; Centerville, IA; Chr; Chrs; ChrhWkr; HonRl; ModUN; NHS; PolWkr; RedCrAde; SchMus; SctActv; StuCncl; YthFlsp; FrCl; LetterFtbl; College; Professional.

FENTON, Linda J; Centerville HS; Centerville, IA; Band; ChrhWkr; CncrtBnd; MrchBnd; PepBnd; VPFHA; PpCl; College; Professional.

FENTON, Ricky L; Litchfield Comm HS; Litchfield, IL; 29/148 HonRl; JrNHS; NHS; SpnCl; SciCl; LetterBsktbl; LetterTrk; IMSpt; Univ Of Illinois; Dentist.

FENTON, Susie L; Siren HS; Siren, WI; 43 Band; Chrs; HonRl; MrchBnd; SchPl; StuCncl; 4-H; PpCl; Trk; DARAwd; Superior Voc; Lpn.

FERANEC, Joan; Mercy Hs; St Louis, MO; 10/170 HonRl; NHS; OffAde; StuCncl; TchrAde; EdYrBk; Trk; GAA; IMSpt; CitAwd; Um St Louis;elementary Or Special Education.

FERBER, Leonard A; Highland Park HS; Highland Park, IL; 38/643 NHS; PolWkr; SchPl; StuCncl; StuGov; RptrSchPpr; LetterBsbl; College; Government.

FERCH, David W; Oregon Davis HS; Hamlet, IN; Aud/Vis; CncrtBnd; HonRl; TreasStuCncl; YthFlsp; 4-H; SciCl; LetterBsbl; Bsktbl; 4-HAwd; Purdue; Agriculture.

FERCH, Thomas H; Ripon Sr HS; Ripon, WI; ChrhWkr; CmntyWkr; SchPl; Bsbl; Ftbl; University; Professional.

FERDEN, Debra J; St Charles HS; Utica, MN; 1/84 Chrs; OffAde; SchMus; TchrAde; Letter4-H; 4-HAwd; College; Rn.

FERDERER, Linda M; New Salem HS; New Salem, ND; 7/51 ALAGirlsSt; Chrs; HonRl; Yrbk; RptrSchPpr; FHA; Mary Clge.

FERENC, Thomas J; De La Salle Collegiate HS; Detroit, MI; 3/135 HonRl; NHS; NatlMeritCmnd; SctActv; SchPpr; FrCl; Ftbl; LetterTrk; IMSpt; U Of Notre Dame; Accounting.

FERGEN, Jeffrey; Tekamah Herman HS; Tekamah, NE; Band; ChrhWkr; CncrtBnd; HonRl; SctActv; Bsbl; Bsktbl; Ftbl; Trk; CchngActv; Univ Of Neb; Chemical Engineer.

FERGUSON, Ann L; Minot HS; Minot, ND; 20/656 CncrtBnd; HonRl; JrNHS; MrchBnd; NHS; PolWkr; StuCncl; RptrSchPpr; GerCl; Univ Of N Dakota; Medicine.

FERGUSON, Ann R; Savannah Riii HS; Savannah, MO; Band; Chr; CncrtBnd; HonRl; MrchBnd; NHS; PepBnd; SchMus; PpCl; LetterBsktbl; Coll; Curr Of Major Study.

FERGUSON, Calvin; Naylor R Ii HS; Naylor, MO; 1/28 HonRl; 4-H; FFA; Bsbl; VoiceDemAwd; Arkansas State U; Career Officer.

FERGUSON, Catherine T; Tipton HS; Tipton, IN; 20/172 HonRl; JA; NHS; NatlThespSoc; SchPl; 4-H; PpCl; Ball St Univ; Art.

FERGUSON, Charles L; Northloup Scotia HS; Scotia, NE; PresJrCls; Band; Chr; HonRl; SchPl; StuGov; YthFlsp; LetterBsktbl; LetterFtbl; LetterGlf; Univ.

FERGUSON, David E; Vassar HS; Vassar, MI; MrchBnd; IMSpt; College; Professional.

FERGUSON, David S; Poplar Bluff HS; Poplar Bluff, MO; 7/380 ChrhWkr; NHS; SctActv; KeyCl; FrCl; MthCl; SciCl; U Of Mo; Elec Eng.

FERGUSON, Desiree M; Cass Technical HS; Detroit, MI; HonRl; LitMag; LbryAde; NHS; PolWkr; SchPl; StuGov; TchrAde; RptrYrbk; FBLA; Univ Of Michigan; Law.

FERGUSON, Elizabeth M; Nicolet HS; Milwaukee, WI; 35/477 CmntyWkr; HonRl; NHS; StuCncl; PpCl; Bsktbl; LetterSwmmng; LetterChrldr; GAA; IMSpt; College; Chemistry.

FERGUSON, Genevieve L; St Charles HS; St Charles, IL; Chr; HospAde; IntrClCncl; Teen; RptrYrbk; Yrbk; FDA; PpCl; Bsbl; Bsktbl; Swmmng; Trk; College; Professional.

FERGUSON, Harold E; Union HS; Union, MO; 14/165 Chr; Chrs; ChrhWkr; HonRl; JA; LitMag; NatlFornLg; NHS; Quill&Scroll; RptrSchPpr; Gateway College; Minister.

FERGUSON, John; Maconaquah HS; Bunker Hill, IN; 49/243 ChrhWkr; HonRl; TchrAde; YthFlsp; Bsktbl; Ftbl; Wrstlng; IMSpt; PresAwd; College; Professional.

FERGUSON, Joleen R; Grafton HS; Grafton, ND; 47/125 HonRl; HospAde; RptrSchPpr; FHA; PpCl; Lake Region Jr College; Nursing.

FERGUSON, Josline K; Forestburg HS; Forestburg, SD; PresFrshCls; PresSophCls; VPJrCls; PresSrCls; ALAGirlsSt; ChrhWkr; HonRl; EdYrBk; EdSchPpr; Pres4-H; PresFNA; LetterBsktbl; DARAwd; 4-HAwd; College; Sociology.

FERGUSON, Kathleen P; Saint Alphonsus HS; Detroit, MI; 27/108 Chrl; CmntyWkr; HonRl; HospAde; IntrClCncl; SchPl; TchrAde; RptrYrbk; FNA; IMSpt; Henry Ford Comm; Nursing.

FERGUSON, Keith W; Savannah HS; Cosby, MO; Band; CncrtBnd; HonRl; MrchBnd; PepBnd; PresYthFlsp; TreasFrCl; LetterBsktbl; College.

FERGUSON, Lee E; Hyannis HS; Hyannis, NE; 6/24 PresJrCls; ALBoysSt; HonRl; NHS; StuCncl; FFA; Bsktbl; CaptFtbl; Trk; EldAwd; Univ Of Nebraska; Agriculture.

FERGUSON, Leonard R; Highland HS; Highland, IN; 12/573 ChrhWkr; TchrAde; SptEdYrbk; SpnCl; Wrstlng; Indiana Univ; Medicine.

FERGUSON, Linda P; Mt Vernon Sr HS; Aurora, MO; 1/100 HonRl; OffAde; SchAde; StuGov; SchPpr; FFA; Mo Univ; Medicine.

FERGUSON, Nancy; Goodridge HS; Goodridge, MN; HonRl; NHS; StuCncl; RptrYrbk; FHA; PpCl; GAA; MasAwd; Horry Georgetown Tec; Bus Adm.

FERGUSON, Paula; Holly HS; Holly, MI; HonRl; StuCncl; College; Commercial Artist.

FERGUSON, Randy S; Ben Davis HS; Indianapolis, IN; 83/816 Band; HonRl; SchAde; StuCncl; 4-H; LatCl; LetterBsktbl; LetterFtbl; LetterTrk; 4-HAwd; Ball State U; Architecture.

FERGUSON, Ricky L; Broken Bow HS; Broken Bow, NE; Chr; HonRl; NHS; NatlThespSoc; SchMus; SchPl; Univ.

FERGUSON, Roxann M; Mount St Benedict HS; New Rockford, ND; SecFrshCls; SecSophCls; ChrhWkr; LbryAde; 4-H; PpCl; Trk; Chrldr; GAA; PPFtbl; College; Professional.

FERGUSON, Stanley M; Greenville Unit 2 HS; Greenville, IL; PresSrCls; Band; Chr; Chrs; ChrhWkr; CncrtBnd; PepBnd; SchMus; Bsbl; Ftbl; Greenville College; Veterinarian.

FERGUSON, Thomas L; Dwight HS; Emington, IL; ChrhWkr; CmntyWkr; SchPl; SctActv; RptrSchPpr; SchPpr; 4-H; FFA; Ftbl; 4-HAwd; College; Agriculture.

FERIERA, Regina M; Oak Park River Forest HS; Oak Park, IL; 40/1107 Band; CncrtBnd; HonRl; MrchBnd; NatlMeritCmnd; Orch; PepBnd; PolWkr; SchMus; MthCl; U Of In; Ba In Music.

FERLAND, Deborah A; Palco HS; Zurich, KS; 9/25 SecTrsFrshCls; Chrl; HonRl; JrNHS; NHS; SchPl; FHA; LetterGlf; Chrldr; CitAwd; College; Registered Nurse.

FERLEY, Pamela D; Emmons Public HS; Emmons, MN; ChrhWkr; CmntyWkr; NatlMeritFnl; FHA; CaptBsktbl; CaptTrk; GAA; IMSpt; BttyCrckrAwd; PresAwd; Coll; Nurse.

FERMAN, Toni F; Laurel HS; Laurel, IN; 4/44 SecTrsJrCls; SecTrsSrCls; NHS; OffAde; TchrAde; RptrYrbk; SptEdSchPpr; LatCl; CaptChrldr; 4-HAwd; Business Sch; Office Job.

FERNANDES, Donald L; Jacksonville HS; Jacksonville, IL; HonRl; Ill State U; Business.

FERNANDEZ, Samuel D; Marian Catholic HS; Chicago Heights, IL; HonRl; Trk; Ill Inst Of Tech; Electrical Eng.

FERNEAU, Ronald G; Ldf Community HS; Marshalltown, IA; 5/43 Band; CncrtBnd; HonRl; MrchBnd; NHS; PepBnd; StuCncl; Yrbk; SciCl; OptClAwd; Drake Univ; Music Education.

FERNHOLZ, Jean M; Arcadia HS; Arcadia, WI; Band; Chrs; CncrtBnd; HonRl; NHS; NatlThespSoc; PepBnd; SchMus; FHA; GAA;.

FERRANTE, Mark V; Saint Patricks HS; Chicago, IL; 36/377 PresSrCls; HonRl; PresNHS; StuCncl; StuGov; Swmmng; Tennis; IMSpt; Univ; Lawyer.

FERRARA, Anthony A; Carl Sandburg HS; Palos Hts, IL; Band; CncrtBnd; HonRl; LbryAde; MrchBnd; NHS; PepBnd; RptrSchPpr; GerCl; Univ Of Illinois; Accountant.

FERRARI, Ann L; Adelphian Acad; Westland, MI; VPSophCls; Band; Chr; Chrs; ChrhWkr; CmntyWkr; CncrtBnd; DrlTm; HonRl; LitMag; Univ; Med.

FERRARI, Gary J; La Salle Peru HS; Oglesby, IL; 31/511 ALBoysSt; HonRl; College; Lawyer.

FERRARO, John P; Clay HS; South Bend, IN; 41/419 PresSrCls; Band; HonRl; HospAde; SpnCl; Bsbl; Bsktbl; College; Psychiatry.

FERRELL, Karoline J; Crete Monee HS; Crete, IL; PresSrCls; HonRl; College; Social Work.

FERRELL, Kimberly G; Thomas W Kelly HS; Benton, MO; 5/51 VPBand; CncrtBnd; HonRl; MrchBnd; StuCncl; Yrbk; EdSchPpr; VPFHA; PpCl; Chrldr; Coll; Marine Bio.

FERRELL, Lawrence R; Lillis HS; Kansas City, MO; Aud/Vis; ChrhWkr; CmntyWkr; JA; LbryAde; StuCncl; StuGov; RptrYrbk; EdYrBk; College; Professional.

FERRELL, Paul K; Huntington North HS; Andrews, IN; Indiana Univ; Journalism.

FERRELL, Steven J; Peoria HS; Peoria, IL; 62/487 HonRl; JrNHS; ModUN; SchPl; Illinois Central College; Business Admin.

FERRER, Marcos S; Knoxville HS; Knoxville, IL; 6/63 Chrs; HonRl; LbryAde; NHS; NatlMeritSF; SchPl; SctActv; RptrSchPpr; FTA; FrCl; SpnCl; Ftbl; Trk; University Of Chicago; Mathematics.

FERRETT, Allan L; Dryden Comm HS; Imlay City, MI; PresFrshCls; PresSophCls; PresJrCls; PresSrCls; CAP; CmntyWkr; HonRl; JA; NHS; NatlMeritSchl; StuCncl; Yrbk; FFA; RotaryAwd; College.

FERRETTA, Esie; Corunna HS; Corunna, MI; 2/239 PresSophCls; PresJrCls; ALBoysSt; NHS; YthLg; EdYrBk; RusCl; MthCl; Glf; JCAwd; Harvard Univ;corp Law.

FERRICK, Joseph T; Brother Rice HS; Chicago, IL; PresCncrtBnd; TreasJA; PresMrchBnd; NHS; PepBnd; SchMus; SecStuCncl; LetterSwmmng; Trk;.

FERRIN, Marilyn J; Marcus Comm HS; Marcus, IA; 10/62 Band; Chrs; ChrhWkr; CncrtBnd; HonRl; Mdrgl; MrchBnd; NHS; PepBnd; SchMus; PPFtbl; 4-HAwd; College; Vocation.

FERRING, Mark J; Wahlert HS; Dubuque, IA; 10/480 Chr; HonRl; Mdrgl; NHS; SchMus; StuCncl; MthCl; LetterBsktbl; LetterTrk; ChmbCommrsAwd; Univ Of Notre Dame; Pro Engineering.

FERRIS, Don; Homewood Flossmoor HS; Homewood, IL; 180/900 Chrl; Chrs; ChrhWkr; SchMus; FrCl; CchngActv; IMSpt; PresAwd;.

FERRIS, Elizabeth G; Shawnee Mission South HS; Leawood, KS; 41#71#84 PpCl; Univ; Nutrition.

FERRIS, Kimberly; Addison HS; Cement City, MI; 6/106 Band; HonRl; NHS; TchrAde; EdYrBk; Chrldr; GAA; Siena Heights Coll; Child Psychology.

FERRIS, T; Lincoln Senior HS; Wis Rapids, WI; HonRl; StuCncl; SpnCl; College; Professional.

FERRO, Christi L; Lewistown Comm HS; St David, IL; 6/85 PresSophCls; HonRl; NHS; NatlMeritCmnd; SchPl; StuCncl; Yrbk; SecFrCl; Chrldr; TreasGAA; Western Univ; Nurse.

FERRO, Deborah M; Dominican HS; Detroit, MI; SecSophCls; Band; CncrtBnd; HonRl; NHS; Orch; SchMus; Collge; Art.

FERRO, Michael P; Grayslake Community HS; Lindenhurst, IL; 14/219 HonRl; NHS; NatlThespSoc; SchPl; Yrbk; LetterBsktbl; LetterFtbl; Glf; Univ; Law.

FERRY, Barbara A; Rice Lake HS; Rice Lake, WI; Chrs; HonRl; SchAde; TchrAde; IMSpt; Business School; Vocation.

FERRY, Nancy A; Linton Stockton HS; Linton, IN; HonRl; HospAde; SchPl; SctActv; CivCl; SpnCl; PpCl; Swmmng; LetterChrldr; CitAwd; Ind St Univ; Journalism.

FERRY, Paul R; Waukegan East HS; Waukegan, IL; 3/886 CmntyWkr; HonRl; JrNHS; NHS; NatlMeritFnl; NatlMeritCmnd; ROTC; Ftbl; Wrstlng; AmLegAwd; Utah St Univ; Forestry.

FERRY, Peggy M; Eau Claire HS; Eau Claire, MI; VPBand; CncrtBnd; HonRl; HospAde; MrchBnd; NHS; PepBnd; TchrAde; EdYrBk; DARAwd; University; Physical Therapy.

FESENMAIER, Kathryn A; North HS; Eau Claire, WI; Chr; CmntyWkr; HonRl; HospAde; StuCncl; StuGov; Yrbk; FHA; PpCl; Chrldr; GAA; IMSpt; College; Law.

FESSLER, Brenda L; East Greene HS; Perry, IA; 1/43 PresJrCls; Band; Chr; NHS; NatlMeritCmnd; SchMus; SchPl; EdYrBk; RptrSchPpr; 4-H; LetterBsktbl; BttyCrckrAwd; 4-HAwd; University; Home Economics.

FESSLER, Clark J; East Greene HS; Perry, IA; Band; Chr; HonRl; ModUN; NHS; SchMus; SchPl; FFA; LetterBsbl; Bsktbl; Trk;.

FESSLER, Marilyn; Marseilles HS; Marseilles, IL; HonRl; HospAde; SctActv; RptrYrbk; FHA; PpCl; Military Service;.

FESSLER, Rodney M; Hartford HS; Neosho Rapids, KS; Chr; Chrs; HonRl; JA; ROTC; SchMus; SchPl; LetterFtbl; LetterTrk; Wrstlng; Rotc.

FESTE, Connie D; Central U S D 462 HS; Burden, KS; 11/34 Band; Chr; Chrs; ChrhWkr; HonRl; MrchBnd; NatlMeritCmnd; PepBnd; SchPl; SctActv; Bsktbl; Trk; Central College; Minister.

FESTER, Karin S; South HS; Sheboygan, WI; College; Commercial Art.

FESTER, Thomas W; Bridgman HS; Bridgman, MI; HonRl; NHS; PresStuCncl; SciCl; LetterBsbl; LetterBsktbl; AmLegAwd; Univ Of Mi; Architecture.

FESTOG, Randall T; Naperville Central HS; Naperville, IL; 40/880 Chrs; HonRl; NatlMeritCmnd; SctActv; Univ Il; Dentist.

FETCH, Deborah A; Pekin Comm HS; Pekin, IL; 25/830 HonRl; JrNHS; NHS; TchrAde; 4-H; LatCl; Univ Of Illinois; Anthropologist.

FETE, Kevin; St John Vianney HS; St Louis, MO; 13/170 HonRl; JrNHS; NHS; Univ; Veterinarian.

FETHER, Brian K; Sand Creek HS; Sand Creek, MI; ChrhWkr; SchPl; RptrSchPpr; Coll; Pro.

FETHERSTON, Lisa D; West Holt HS; Atkinson, NE; 10/71 Chr; Chrs; HonRl; HospAde; RptrYrbk; RptrSchPpr; PpCl; U Of Neb; Nurse.

FETSCH, John F; Langdon HS; Langdon, ND; 2/109 Chr; Chrs; HonRl; NHS; SchMus; SchPl; PpCl; LetterFtbl; Glf; University Of North Dakota; Microbiology.

FETT, Chris E; Pattonville HS; Bridgeton, MO; HonRl; JA; JrNHS; NHS; OffAde; PpCl; Chrldr; GAA; IMSpt; PPFtbl; College; Professnl.

FETTERMAN, James P; Frankton HS; Anderson, IN; 38/173 ChrhWkr; HonRl; YthFlsp; Bsktbl; Trk; College; Medical.

FETTERS, James S; Indianaola HS; Indianola, IA; ChrhWkr; HonRl; NHS; GerCl; Bsbl; LetterBsktbl; LetterFtbl; LetterTrk; College.

FETTERS, Michelle; Schlarman HS; Danville, IL; 7/67 SecJrCls; SecSrCls; HonRl; NHS; StuCncl; Yrbk; SchPpr; SciCl; College; Nurse Training.

FETTERS, Theresa L; Mt St Scholastica Academy; Excelsior Springs, MO; Chrs; SchPl; Yrbk; FHA; SpnCl; College; Professional Soloist.

FETTIG, Deborah L; Steele Public HS; Driscoll, ND; Chrs; HonRl; SchPl; Sdlty; FHA; Col; Vocation.

FETTY, Craig B; Woodstock HS; Woodstock, IL; 15/264 ChrhWkr; HonRl; NHS; Bsktbl; Ftbl; College; Professional.

FETZER, Kevin; Williamsburg Comm HS; Williamsburg, IA; 10/95 Band; Chrs; CncrtBnd; NHS; StuCncl; FFA; KiwanAwd; CitAwd; College; Engineering.

FETZER, Laura E; Whiteford HS; Ottawa Lake, MI; SecJrCls; Band; Chr; Chrs; CncrtBnd; HonRl; MrchBnd; NHS; NatlMeritCmnd; NatlMeritSchl; Monroe County Comm College; Journalist.

FEUERBORN, Sandra A; Council Grove HS; Eskridge, KS; Chrs; HonRl; NHS; 4-H; College; Professional.

FEUQUAY, Robyn; Burlington Comm HS; Burlington, IA; 5/430 Chrs; ChrhWkr; HonRl; NatlMeritSF; SpnCl; IMSpt; Lee College;accounting.

FEUQUAY, Robyn G; Burlington Comm HS; Burlington, IA; 7/500 Chrs; ChrhWkr; HonRl; NatlMeritSF; RptrSchPpr; Lee College; Accounting.

FEWKES, David A; Oak Lawn Community HS; Oak Lawn, IL; 30/667 HonRl; NHS; MthCl; LetterBsbl; LetterBsktbl; Univ Of Il; Political Science.

FEY, Dennis A; Richwoods HS; Peoria, IL; 1/519 CncrtBnd; HonRl; MrchBnd; TchrAde; LatCl; Premedical Clg; Doctor.

FIALA, Joe L; North Linn HS; Walker, IA; ALBoysSt; Chrs; RptrSchPpr; 4-H; FFA; Bsktbl; Ftbl; Trk; College; Agriculture.

FIALA, Joseph J; Chaminade College Prep; Bridgeton, MO; 5/113 VPSrCls; HonRl; NHS; NatlMeritFnl; StuCncl; Ftbl; Socr; Chrldr; IMSpt; OptClAwd; College; Md.

FIALA, Joseph L; North Linn Comm HS; Walker, IA; ALBoysSt; Chr; Chrs; SchMus; RptrSchPpr; 4-H; FFA; LetterBsktbl; LetterFtbl; LetterTrk; AmLegAwd; 4-HAwd; College; Livestock.

FIALA, Richard J; St John Vianney HS; Crestwood, MO; 47/186 HonRl; StuCncl; StuGov; RptrSchPpr; LetterBsbl; LetterBsktbl; LetterFtbl; University.

FIALA, Steven R; David City Public HS; David City, NE; Band; HonRl; NatlThespSoc; PepBnd; Quill&Scroll; SchPl; RptrSchPpr; PresFFA; IMSpt; RotaryAwd; U Of Ne; Farming & Ag.

FIALA, Timothy J; Riverside Brookfield HS; No Riverside, IL; 5/489 Chr; ChrhWkr; HonRl; NatlMeritCmnd; RptrSchPpr; Trk; Us Military Academy.

FIALKOWSKI, David; Marist HS; Chicago, IL; 70/365 Aud/Vis; Chrs; NatlMeritCmnd; SchPl; RptrSchPpr; SpnCl; PpCl; SciCl; LetterFtbl; Swmmng; Trk; College; Civil Engineering.

FIALKOWSKI, Mary Ann M; Resurrection HS; Chicago, IL; 1/270 HonRl; HospAde; LbryAde; NHS; NatlMeritCmnd; SctActv; GerCl; MthCl; Northwestern Univ; Engineering.

FICHTENMAYER, Patricia L; Southwest HS; St Louis, MO; Chr; HonRl; Mdrgl; PolWkr; SchMus; PresSctActv; PpCl; GAA; Fontbonne College; Medical Technology.

FICHTNER, Beth L; Hayes Cnty HS; Maywood, NE; Band; Chr; Chrl; Chrs; CncrtBnd; HonRl; MrchBnd; ModUN; NHS; PepBnd; LetterTrk; GAA; AmLegAwd; 4-HAwd; Univ; Medicine.

FICHTNER, Terry L; Larimore HS; Emerado, ND; 35/75 ALBoysSt; HonRl; JA; TchrAde; YthFlsp; 4-H; PpCl; Bsbl; Bsktbl; Ftbl; College; Vocation.

FICK, Cynthia L; South Shore HS; Cornucopia, WI; Chr; ChrhWkr; CmntyWkr; HonRl; JrNHS; LbryAde; OffAde; SctActv; Yrbk; FHA; Trade Or Bus Sch.

FICK, George F; St Agatha HS; Detroit, MI; VPSophCls; HonRl; StuCncl; CaptFtbl; LetterTrk; Univ Of Detroit; Dentistry.

FICKE, Shirley M; Milford Jr Sr HS; Milford, NE; 19/59 Band; Chrs; CncrtBnd; HospAde; MrchBnd; RedCrAde; SchPl; 4-H; FHA; LetterBsktbl; Registered Nurse.

FICKEISEN, Susan J; Downers Grove South HS; Woodridge, IL; Chrs; HonRl; JA; 4-H; College; Business.

FICKEN, Christine A; Williamsburg HS; Williamsburg, IA; VPSrCls; Chr; ChrhWkr; HonRl; NHS; StuCncl; SchPpr; Bsktbl; Drake University; Mathematics.

FICKEN, Jody A; Davenport Community HS; Davenport, NE; 2/23 CncrtBnd; HonRl; LbryAde; SecTeen; PresYthFlsp; 4-H; TreasPpCl; Trk; BttyCrckrAwd; 4-HAwd; Univ Of Nebraska.

FICKER, Joann R; Berkeley Sr HS; Berkeley, MO; 11/324 ChrhWkr; College; Legal Secretary.

FICKES, Ciyoe; Truro HS; St Charles, IA; ALBoysSt; Band; CmntyWkr; CncrtBnd; SecFrshCls; YthFlsp; TrsFrshCls; RptrSchPpr; Trade Sch; Vocation.

FICKLE, Nancy E; Huntington North HS; Huntington, IN; ALAGirlsSt; Band; ChrhWkr; CncrtBnd; HonRl; MrchBnd; SchMus; VPYthFlsp; 4-H; 4-HAwd; Purdue Univ; Guidance Counseling.

FIDANZE, Daniel M; Fenwick HS; Cicero, IL; 25/230 Band; HonRl; NatlMeritFnl; NatlMeritSF; IMSpt; Univ; Biology.

FIDDER, Timothy W; Belvidere HS; Belvidere, IL; 119/336 CmntyWkr; PresSctActv; Pres4-H; VPFFA; KeyCl; GerCl; PpCl; LetterFtbl; LetterTrk; DanFAwd; 4-HAwd; Woodward Gov Eng Academy; Engineering.

FIDLER, Dianne; Arthur HS; Arthur, IL; Chr; Chrs; ChrhWkr; HonRl; JA; SchPl; YthFlsp; RptrYrbk; 4-H; FHA; KeyCl; GAA; Eastern Illinois University; Home Economics.

FIDUCCIA, Frank F; Loyola Academy; Lincolnwood, IL; 8/442 HonRl; NHS; RptrSchPpr; EdSchPpr; RusCl; SciCl; College; Chemistry.

FIEBELKORN, Beth M; Holy Trinity HS; Chaska, MN; PresJrCls; PresSrCls; CncrtBnd; HonRl; NHS; StuCncl; RptrYrbk; RptrSchPpr; LetterBsktbl; IMSpt; College; Nursing.

FIEBER, Audrey L; Grayville Community HS; Grayville, IL; VPFrshCls; Chr; ChrhWkr; HonRl; StuCncl; EdSchPpr; 4-H; GAA; 4-HAwd; U Of Ill; Design.

FIEBIGER, John F; Montpelier Public HS; Montpelier, ND; CncrtBnd; HonRl; SchPl; LetterTrk; IMSpt;.

FIECHTL, Mary J; Notre Dame HS; Quincy, IL; Chr; NHS; StuCncl; RptrSchPpr; FrCl; Univ; Spec Educ.

FIEDLER, Gayla S; Civic Memorial HS; Bethalto, IL; 8/224 SecSecDrlTm; DrmMjrt; HonRl; JrNHS; SecVPNHS; FrCl; GAA; University Of Il; Special Education.

FIEDLER, James M; Putnam County HS; Hennepin, IL; College.

FIEDLER, Jill C; Calhoun HS; Batchtown, IL; Band; ChrhWkr; CncrtBnd; VPStuCncl; Chrldr; GAA; 4-HAwd; PresAwd;.

FIEDLER, Lisa; Charlevoix HS; Charlevoix, MI; Band; ChrhWkr; CncrtBnd; HonRl; LbryAde; MrchBnd; PepBnd; TchrAde; Yrbk; Olivet Nazarene Coll; Humanities.

FIEDLER, Michael T; Beloit Memorial HS; Beloit, WI; HonRl; College; Police Officer.

FIEGEN, Mark D; La Crescent HS; La Crescent, MN; 20/140 PresFrshCls; PresSrCls; HonRl; StuCncl; SptEdYrbk; LetterBsktbl; LetterFtbl; LetterTrk; Sd Sch Of Mines & Tech; Chemical Engineer.

FIELD, Barbara J; Westfield HS; Westfield, WI; TrsFrshCls; TrsSophCls; Band; CncrtBnd; MrchBnd; PepBnd; Twrl; RptrSchPpr; FHA; MthCl; College; Stewardess.

FIELD, Daniel V; Northern Valley HS; Almena, KS; PresJrCls; Band; CncrtBnd; HonRl; MrchBnd; SchPl; 4-H; FFA; LetterFtbl; 4-HAwd;.

FIELD, Esther E; Hillcrest HS; Hazel Crest, IL; 17/474 ChrhWkr; HonRl; NHS; SctActv; RptrSchPpr; LetterTennis; Trk; BttyCrckrAwd; Northern Ill Univ; Nursing.

FIELD, Janine M; Brighton HS; Brighton, MI; 5/278 Chrs; ChrhWkr; HonRl; LitMag; LbryAde; NHS; RptrYrbk; GerCl; LatCl; IMSpt; Clge; Missionary Teacher.

FIELD, Joseph T; Hackett HS; Kalamazoo, MI; Band; CncrtBnd; HonRl; MrchBnd; PepBnd; SchMus; SchPl; SctActv; Yrbk; LatCl; IMSpt; College; Medicine.

FIELD, Mary P; Edgewood HS; Madison, WI; 24/138 Chrs; CmntyWkr; HonRl; ModUN; NatlFornLg; OffAde; PolWkr; College; Law.

FIELD, Rhonda J; Logan Magnolia HS; Logan, IA; 9/50 Chrs; ChrhWkr; NHS; SchPl; Pres4-H; SecFHA; LetterBsktbl; LetterTrk; 4-HAwd; PresAwd; Col; Pro.

FIELD, Richard G; Breck HS; Minneapolis, MN; ChrhWkr; HonRl; HospAde; NatlSciFnd; TchrAde; SchPpr; LetterSocr; CaptWrstlng; Univ; Doctor.

FIELDER, Nancy L; Manchester HS; Manchester, MI; HonRl; VPStuCncl; 4-H; GerCl; PpCl; Chrldr; OptClAwd; Univ Of Michigan; German.

FIELDS, Bobby L; Cave In Rock HS; Cave In Rock, IL; 2/40 HonRl; LbryAde; NHS; StuCncl; RptrSchPpr; SpnCl; LetterBsbl; Univ Of Ill; Anthropology.

FIELDS, Darlene; Carl Schurz; Chicago, IL; ChrhWkr; CncrtBnd; HonRl; OffAde; TchrAde; FBLA; Chicago Circle; Business Major.

FIELDS, Dennis W; Hinckley Big Rock HS; Hinckley, IL; 25/77 Chrl; Chrs; ChrhWkr; CmntyWkr; HonRl; SchMus; SchPl; PresLatCl; LetterBsbl; LetterBsktbl; LetterSocr; LetterTrk;.

FIELDS, Gloria J; Manual HS; Indianapolis, IN; Chr; ChrhWkr; HospAde; SchMus; FrCl; SpnCl; College; Nurse.

FIELDS, Janet; Laurel HS; Laurel, IN; ChrhWkr; HonRl; LbryAde; SchAde; StuCncl; TchrAde; SchPpr; 4-H; PpCl; 4-HAwd;.

FIELDS, Jenifer W; Clinton Community HS; Clinton, IL; 8/181 Chr; ChrhWkr; CmntyWkr; HonRl; NHS; SchAde; YthFlsp; RptrSchPpr; 4-H; FNA; Clge; Social Work.

FIELDS, Jody E; Morrill HS; Henry, NE; 5/45 TrsFrshCls; Chrs; NHS; SchPl; TchrAde; RptrYrbk; EdYrBk; 4-H; Chrldr; 4-HAwd; College; Vet Technology.

FIELDS, Lana S; Southeast HS; Kansas City, MO; Chr; Chrs; HonRl; LbryAde; StuCncl; PpCl; IMSpt; PresAwd; CitAwd; College; Prof.

FIELDS, Leslie D; Deerfield HS; Deerfield, IL; 10/561 HonRl; TreasSctActv; SecFrCl; University; Biological Research.

FIELDS, Pamela D; St Thomas Apostle HS; Chicago, IL; 5/45 VPSophCls; ChrhWkr; HonRl; RedCrAde; StuCncl; TchrAde; RptrYrbk; Yrbk; College; Lawyer.

FIELDS, Peggy A; North Knox HS; Sandborn, IN; 15/125 PresBand; Chr; ChrhWkr; CncrtBnd; HonRl; MrchBnd; NHS; OffAde; VPPepBnd; YthFlsp; 4-H; FHA; Univ.

FIELDS, Wendy L; Northern HS; Flint, MI; HonRl; HospAde; FNA; SpnCl; Calvin College; Physical Therapist.

FIELDSETH, David; Lake Of The Woods HS; Baudette, MN; 5/58 HonRl; LbryAde; NHS; NatlMeritCmnd; StuCncl; Yrbk; RptrSchPpr; EdSchPpr; IMSpt; Univ Of Minnesota; Chemical Engineering.

FIELSTRA, Sally A; Traverse City HS; Traverse City, MI; ChrhWkr; HonRl; JA; NHS; NatlMeritSchl; PresYthFlsp; PpCl; LetterBsktbl; 4-HAwd; Northwestern College; Business Admin.

FIEMAN, Barbara A; East Grand Forks Sr HS; East Grand Forks, MN; 13/195 ALAGirlsSt; HonRl; NHS; SpnCl; Bsktbl; GAA; College; Vocation.

FIENE, Kevin W; Orangeville HS; Orangeville, IL; 14/60 PresJrCls; ALBoysSt; HonRl; NHS; SchMus; PresStuCncl; FrCl; PpCl; Bsbl; Bsktbl; Ftbl; Glf; Central College; Teacher.

FIENHOLD, Mildred R; Lincoln Way HS; Mokena, IL; 96/498 HonRl; NHS; OffAde; Univ Of Ill; Architecture.

FIERRO, Pedro; William A Wirt HS; Gary, IN; 5/237 ALBoysSt; ChrhWkr; HonRl; JrNHS; NHS; StuGov; RptrYrbk; PresSciCl; BauchLmbAwd; CitAwd; Univ Of Rochester; Biology.

FIESER, Elaine M; Campbell HS; Campbell, MO; Chr; ChrhWkr; HonRl; Pres4-H; FHA; PpCl; Itt Tech; Computer Programmer.

FIESTERMAN, Jody L; Lewellen Rural HS; Lewellen, NE; 3/15 TrsSophCls; VPJrCls; PresSrCls; ALAGirlsSt; Band; Chrs; ChrhWkr; CncrtBnd; HonRl; LbryAde; MrchBnd; Trk; IMSpt; College; Nursing.

FIET, Julie; Postville Community HS; Postville, IA; 15/90 PresSrCls; Chrs; ChrhWkr; HonRl; NHS; SchPl; StuCncl; RptrYrbk; 4-H; PpCl; CitAwd; Area 1 Voc Tech; Bookkeeping.

FIETZEK, Rhonda J; Montpelier HS; Millaton, ND; SecSophCls; TrsJrCls; HonRl; EdYrBk; SchPpr; Wahpetor State Sch Of Sci; Airline Stewarde.

FIFE, Sylvia A; Saginaw HS; Saginow, MI; 3/435 Chr; ChrhWkr; HonRl; JrNHS; NHS; StuGov; EdAwd; Ferris State College; Business Admin.

FIFER, Greg; Marist HS; Oak Lawn, IL; HonRl; SchPpr; LatCl; CaptTennis; IMSpt; College; Professional Law.

FIFER, Theodore D; Campion Jesuit HS; Saginaw, MI; 8/70 HonRl; TchrAde; Univ Of Michigan; Doctor.

FIFI, Dominique G; Assumption HS; Wis Rapids, WI; 10/117 CncrtBnd; PresDrlTm; HonRl; MrchBnd; NHS; PepBnd; SchMus; SctActv; StuCncl; YthFnd; GAA; Univ Of Marquette; Professional.

FIFI, Dominique G; Assumption HS; Wisconsin Rapids, WI; 10/117 Band; ChrhWkr; HonRl; NHS; PepBnd; SctActv; StuCncl; TchrAde; SecFDA; PresFrCl; U Of Madison; Medical Doctor.

FIGG, Janet L; North Shore Country Day HS; Palatine, IL; Chrs; TchrAde; College; Nurserly School Teacher.

FIGGE, Annette L; Valle HS; Ste Genevieve, MO; 11/81 DrlTm; HonRl; NHS; StuCncl; TchrAde; 4-H; PpCl; LetterTrk; IMSpt; PPFtbl; College.

FIGLIOLI, John; Luther North HS; Chicago, IL; CaptFtbl; Trk; LetterWrstlng; IMSpt; Augustana College; Business.

FIGUEREA, Jesue; Presser Vocational HS; Chicago, IL; HonRl; TchrAde; RptrSchPpr; SchPpr; IMSpt; Univ; Engineering.

FIJOLEK, Richard M; Morgan Park HS; Chicago, IL; 1/559 PresSrCls; Chr; Chrs; ChrhWkr; CmntyWkr; HonRl; JrNHS; NHS; NatlMeritCmnd; OffAde; SchAde; SchMus; SchPl; Harvard College; Mathematics.

FIKAR, David J; Wilber Clatonia Public HS; Wilber, NE; TrsSophCls; Chrs; HonRl; SchPl; StuCncl; RptrSchPpr; LetterBsktbl; Ftbl; LetterTrk; CchngActv; Clge; Pro.

FIKE, Herbert L; Coleman HS; Coleman, MI; 41#1115# Central Mich Univ; Math.

FIKE, Lisa J; Caruthersville HS; Caruthersville, MO; Band; ChrhWkr; CncrtBnd; HonRl; HospAde; NHS; TreasNatlThespSoc; SchPl; SctActv; StuCncl; IMSpt; College.

FILARSKI, Steven E; Pekin Community HS; Pekin, IL; HonRl; TchrAde; Univ Of Illinois.

FILBY, Rose; Northeaster HS; Richmond, IN; 8/122 Aud/Vis; HonRl; LbryAde; NHS;.

FILCEK, Cindy P; Pinconning Area HS; Linwood, MI; Band; DrmMjrt; HonRl; MrchBnd; SecNHS; PepBnd; TchrAde; Pres4-H; PPFtbl; 4-HAwd; U Of Mi; Medical Tech.

FILE, Allan E; Greenville HS; Pocahontas, IL; Band; Chrs; CncrtBnd; NHS; PepBnd; SchMus; StuCncl; YthLg; 4-H; SpnCl; PpCl; LetterBsbl; LetterBsktbl; Millikin University; Doctor.

FILE, Teresa M; La Moille HS; La Moille, IL; 9/41 VPChrs; DrmMjrt; HonRl; SchMus; StuCncl; Twrl; Yrbk; RptrSchPpr; PpCl; Trk; PresGAA; College; Secretary.

FILEMYR, Ann E; Jfk Prep; Adell, WI; HonRl; SchPl; Yrbk; 4-H; College; Photo Journalism.

FILICE, Cynthia A; Mother Of Sorrows HS; Palos Heights, IL; HonRl; RptrSchPpr; St Xavier College; Teaching.

FILIPCZAK, David; Marist Hs; Chicago, IL; 32/364 HonRl; PolWkr; StuGov; SchPpr; St Marys College; Broadcasting.

FILIPIAK, Carol A; Kennedy; Chicago, IL; HonRl; FrCl; Bsktbl; Trk; GAA; IMSpt; KiwanAwd; PresAwd; Univ; Pharmacy.

FILIPIAK, Marlene; Mosinee HS; Junction City, WI; Chrs; HonRl; LbryAde; NatlFornLg; FHA; College; Nursing.

FILIPIAK, Michael E; Sheboygan South HS; Sheboygan, WI; Aud/Vis; ChrhWkr; Orch; YthFlsp; Yrbk; SchPpr; SciCl; Univ Of Wi; Major In Physics.

FILIPIAK, Scott P; Ladysmith HS; Hawkins, WI; HonRl; NHS; SctActv; FFA; Bsktbl; LetterFtbl; Trk; Wrstlng; Univ; Agriculture.

FILIPOWICZ, Stephen J; Bryn HS; Omaha, NE; 43/416 Chr; HonRl; NHS; ROTC; SctActv; GerCl; Swmmng; LetterTennis; IMSpt; AmLegAwd; College; Naval Officer.

FILIPS, Kim M; Troy HS; Troy, MI; 79/566 CmntyWkr; HonRl; SecJA; LitMag; NHS; NatlThespSoc; SchPl; TchrAde; RptrSchPpr; SchPpr; Northern Mi Univ; Photographer.

FILKINS, Ellen M; Ann Arbor Huron HS; Ann Arbor, MI; 13/570 ChrhWkr; HonRl; HospAde; NatlMeritCmnd; Orch; RedCrAde; SchMus; Univ Of Michigan; Medicine.

FILKINS, Ken; North Branch Area HS; North Branch, MI; 17/141 ChrhWkr; HonRl; ModUN; TchrAde; CivCl; Ferris State College; Pharmocology.

FILLBRANDT, Susan M; Windom Area HS; Windom, MN; 15/140 SecTrsSrCls; ChrhWkr; DrmMjrt; HonRl; NHS; StuCncl; SchPpr; PpCl; Chrldr; GAA; PPFtbl; Col; Elem Education.

FILLINGSNESS, Renee; Beresford HS; Beresford, SD; ALAGirlsSt; Chrs; ChrhWkr; CncrtBnd; HonRl; NHS; PolWkr; SchMus; SchPl; SctActv; Coll; Music.

FILLMORE, Cynthia; Lindblom Tech HS; Chicago, IL; Chr; ChrhWkr; HospAde; LbryAde; OffAde; SchMus; SchPl; TchrAde; YthFlsp; GAA; Ill State Univ; Physical Therapy.

FILLWOCK, Annette E; Webberville HS; Williamston, MI; 3/60 HonRl; LbryAde; OffAde; TchrAde; RptrSchPpr; EdSchPpr; SptEdSchPpr; SchPpr; Computer Operator.

FILPUS, Paul E; Alpena HS; Alpena, MI; ALBoysSt; Band; Chr; ChrhWkr; CncrtBnd; MrchBnd; NatlMeritSF; PepBnd; SchMus; SctActv; Lake Superior State Clge; Chemistry.

FILSON, Durenda L; Girard HS; Girard, IL; Chrs; HonRl; LbryAde; FNA; FrCl; SciCl; Trk;.

FINAN, William W; Leavenworth HS; Leavenworth, KS; Chrs; ChrhWkr; HonRl; ModUN; PolWkr; SchMus; StuGov; College; Professional Lawyer.

FINATO, Julianne M; Maine East HS; Morton Grove, IL; ChrhWkr; HonRl; OffAde; StuCncl; U Of Il; Teach Music Ed.

FINCH, Cheryl R; Tomah Sr HS; Camp Douglas, WI; 1/283 ALAGirlsSt; Band; CncrtBnd; HonRl; MrchBnd; VPNHS; PepBnd; SchMus; SciCl; GAA; IMSpt; University; Medicine.

FINCH, Cynthia M; Lakeview HS; Columbus, NE; Band; Chrs; ChrhWkr; CncrtBnd; HonRl; MrchBnd; SchPl; TchrAde; Trk; Wrstlng; Army;.

FINCK, Rebecca L; Hillcrest HS; Markham, IL; HonRl; NHS; NatlMeritCmnd; MthCl; U Of I; Pharmacy.

FINDLAY, Bryan P; Oak Park & River Forest HS; Oak Park, IL; 101/1012 HonRl; NHS; NatlSciFnd; PolWkr; RptrSchPpr; Univ Of Chicago; Lawyer.

FINDLEY, Diana L; Worth Co HS; Grant City, MO; 1/41 TrsJrCls; Band; CncrtBnd; HonRl; SchPl; TchrAde; YthFlsp; 4-H; FTA; Bsktbl; IMSpt; PPFtbl; Nw Missouri St Univ; Nursing.

FINDLEY, Julie A; Dekalb HS; Dekalb, IL; 14/350 Chr; Chrs; DrlTm; HonRl; NHS; SchMus; SctActv; StuCncl; YthFlsp; SpnCl; College; Span.

FINDLEY, Susan; Port Huron HS; Port Huron, MI; 12/350 Band; CncrtBnd; HonRl; MrchBnd; NHS; StuCncl; TchrAde; MthCl; Tennis; Chrldr; College; Pharmacy.

FINDLEY, Tara S; Oak Park HS; Gladstone, MO; Chr; ChrhWkr; HonRl; SchMus; StuCncl; TchrAde; SpnCl; College.

FINE, Evelyn; Oak Park River Forest HS; Oak Park, IL; ChrhWkr; HonRl; NatlFornLg; SchPl; YthFnd; SchPpr; GovHonPrgAwd; Univ; Med Or Biol.

FINE, Jack D; Quenemo HS; Quenemo, KS; VPFrshCls; TrsJrCls; HonRl; SchPl; SctActv; StuCncl; TchrAde; Yrbk; Bsbl; Bsktbl; Ftbl;.

FINE, Jennifer M; Deerfield HS; Highland Park, IL; HonRl; OffAde; SchPl; Goucher College; Medicine.

FINE, Roy N; Waukesha North HS; Waukesha, WI; 27/326 PresBand; HonRl; MrchBnd; NHS; Orch; PepBnd; StuCncl; CaptSwmmng; Trk; Clge; Law.

FINEGAN, Elizabeth A; St Ann HS; Lincoln, NE; TrsSrCls; HonRl; NHS; StuCncl; TchrAde; RptrYrbk; FTA; PpCl; Chrldr; VoiceDemAwd; U Of Ne; Elementary Ed.

FINEGAN, Elizabeth A; St Ann HS; Lexington, NE; SecTrsSophCls; TrsSrCls; CtyCnl; HonRl; NHS; TchrAde; RptrYrbk; PpCl; Chrldr; VoiceDemAwd; U Of Nebraska; Guidance Counseling.

FINERAN, Thomas G; William Horlick HS; Racine, WI; ChrhWkr; CmntyWkr; ModUN; PolWkr; UNYO; RptrSchPpr; LetterTrk; CchngActv; IMSpt; PresAwd; U O Wi; Political Science.

FINET, Arthur S; Westville HS; Westville, IL; 2/100 Band; CncrtBnd; HonRl; NHS; SpnCl; SciCl; LetterBsktbl; College; Engineering.

FINGER, Mary C; Good Counsel HS; Chicago, IL; 63/287 Chr; ChrhWkr; CmntyWkr; HonRl; RptrSchPpr; Northwestern Univ; Journalism.

FINGER, Terry E; Powhattan HS; Powhattan, KS; 4/19 VPSophCls; TrsJrCls; VPSrCls; ALBoysSt; HonRl; NHS; StuCncl; FFA; Bsktbl; Washburn Univ Of Topeka; Liberal Arts.

FINGER, Thomas C; Brentwood HS; Brentwood, MO; ChrhWkr; CncrtBnd; HonRl; ModUN; NHS; NatlThespSoc; SchMus; SchPl; SctActv; Univ Of Missouri; Music.

FINGERSON, Bruce; Glenwood HS; Glenwood, MN; 30/132 HonRl; TchrAde; Yrbk; GerCl; Nd State Univ; Pharmacy.

FINGERSON, Luann; Lanesboro HS; Fountain, MN; 2/53 Band; Chr; Chrs; LbryAde; NHS; EdYrBk; SchPpr; FHA; PpCl; Rochester Comm Coll; Gen Sec.

FINIC, Ronald K; Thornridge HS; S Holland, IL; 31/670 HonRl; College; Marketing.

FINK, Brian B; Bolingbrook HS; Bolingbrook, IL; CAP; ROTC; Ftbl; Northern Illinois Univ; Law.

FINK, Debra J; Colby HS; Colby, WI; Chr; HonRl; HospAde; LbryAde; NHS; SchMus; RptrSchPpr; 4-H; FHA; SpnCl; General Laborer.

FINK, Gary L; Central HS; Waterloo, IA; 5/354 HonRl; LitMag; NHS; PolWkr; RedCrAde; Yrbk; RptrSchPpr; SchPpr; GovHonPrgAwd; Univ Of Iowa; Medicine.

FINK, Gordon G; North HS; Evansville, IN; 29/450 HonRl; NatlFornLg; NatlMeritSF; Trk; IMSpt; OptClAwd; U Of In; Music Or Semantics.

FINK, Judy L; Cal Comm HS; Latimer, IA; ChrhWkr; HonRl; NHS; SchPl; 4-H; TreasFHA; Glf; Trk; LetterChrldr; IMSpt; College; Elem Education.

FINK, Julia K; Alma HS; Lansing, MI; HonRl; NatlFornLg; NatlMeritFnl; NatlMeritCmnd; Natl-

MeritSchl; SchPl; StuGov; TchrAde; PresYthLg; RptrSchPpr; Alma College; Elementary Education.

FINK, Kathleen A; Mercy HS; St Ann, MO; 1/172 Chr; HonRl; NHS; NatlMeritCmnd; SchAde; SchMus; TchrAde; RptrYrbk; GerCl; MthCl; Wa U; Linguistics.

FINK, Linda G; Pekin Community HS; Pekin, IL; 78/731 HonRl; Chrldr; CchngActv; Univ; Elementary Teacher.

FINK, Mark S; Uniontown HS; Redfield, KS; HonRl; 4-H; FFA; LetterBsktbl; LetterFtbl; IMSpt; 4-HAwd; Kansas State Univ; Rancher.

FINK, Mary Ann; Divine Savior Holy Angels HS; Milwaukee, WI; 4 HonRl; IntrClCncl; JA; NHS; Quill&Scroll; TchrAde; EdSchPpr; IMSpt; DARAwd; CitAwd; Marquette Univ; Medical Technology.

FINK, Monica J; Bloomfield Jr/sr HS; Bloomfield, NE; 15/66 SecSrCls; Band; Chrs; DrlTm; HonRl; MrchBnd; OffAde; 4-H; FHA; PpCl; Clge; Home Ec.

FINK, Nathan; Bellmont HS; Decatur, IN; 18/351 ALBoysSt; ChrhWkr; HonRl; NHS; SctActv; Valparaiso Univ; Engineering.

FINK, Robin T; John Hersey HS; Mt Prospect, IL; 1/783 AFS; CncrtBnd; HonRl; MrchBnd; NHS; PepBnd; PolWkr; FTA; KeyCl; Univ Of Illinois; Accounting.

FINK, Tim L; Darlington HS; Darlington, WI; ChrhWkr; 4-H; Bsbl; Bsktbl; Ftbl; Madison Area Tech; Restaurant Mgmt.

FINKBEINER, Janice M; Central HS; Bay City, MI; 8/575 ChrhWkr; CtyCnl; HonRl; LbryAde; NHS; StuCncl; StuGov; VPCivCl; IMSpt; PPFtbl; CitAwd; Ferris St Clg; Nuclear Medicine.

FINKBEINER, Martin W; Warren HS; Grayslake, IL; Band; CncrtBnd; HonRl; MrchBnd; NHS; GerCl; LetterFtbl; LetterTennis; CchngActv; University; Medicine.

FINKE, Barbara; Hauser Jr Sr HS; Hope, IN; 33/83 HonRl; ModUN; OffAde; StuCncl; StuGov; RptrYrbk; 4-H; FFA; PpCl; Purdue; Vet Med.

FINKE, Laura A; Castle HS; Newburgh, IN; Chr; HonRl; NHS; NatlThespSoc; LatCl; Swmmng; Indiana University; English.

FINKE, Lois A; Tecumseh HS; Tecumseh, NE; 7/58 Chr; HonRl; NHS; Teen; YthFlsp; PpCl; Univ; Professional.

FINKE, Mary A; Nerinx Hall HS; St Louis, MO; 5/97 Aud/Vis; CmntyWkr; HonRl; SchMus; TchrAde; PpCl; GAA; St Louis Univ; Medicine.

FINKEL, Holly J; Niles North HS; Skokie, IL; HonRl; JrNHS; NHS; PolWkr; SchMus; StuCncl; StuGov; University Of Illinois.

FINKELSTEIN, Mark D; George Rogers Clark HS; Whiting, IN; 96/260 Band; CncrtBnd; MrchBnd; Orch; PepBnd; StuCncl; TchrAde; SpnCl; SciCl; Bsbl; College; Pharmacy.

FINKEN, Teresa C; Mo Valley HS; Missouri Valley, IA; Chr; Chrs; ChrhWkr; HonRl; Mdrgl; SchMus; TchrAde; FHA; FTA; PpCl; College; Music.

FINKLE, Charles D; Pembroke Country Day HS; Independence, MO; 12/50 VPFrshCls; VPSophCls; VPJrCls; VPSrCls; Chrl; HonRl; StuGov; SchPpr; Socr; CaptTrk; Stanford Univ; Architecture.

FINKLE, Gesala; Polo Community HS; Polo, IL; ALBoysSt; CmntyWkr; HonRl; SchAde; SchPl; TchrAde; Bsktbl; Ftbl; Trk; CchngActv; Western Ill Univ; Coach.

FINKLE, Lester W; Mather HS; Chicago, IL; 28/411 HonRl; NHS; StuCncl; StuGov; FrCl; Univ Of Illinois; Attorney.

FINKLE, Rodney L; Buhler HS; Hutchinson, KS; Band; CncrtBnd; HonRl; JrNHS; MrchBnd; ModUN; PepBnd; SctActv; StuCncl; YthFlsp; Unknown; Undecided.

FINLAYSON, James W; Marshall HS; Marshall, MI; NHS; SchPl; RptrSchPpr; Tennis; W Michigan Univ; Law.

FINLAYSON, Rocky A; Central City Senior HS; Central City, NE; 13/92 Band; ChrhWkr; CncrtBnd; HonRl; MrchBnd; PepBnd; Glf; Trk; College; Professional.

FINLEY, Carol G; Evanston Twp HS; Evanston, IL; University; Natural Science.

FINLEY, Catherine; Scattergood HS; Evansville, IN; TrsFrshCls; TrsSrCls; Chrs; SchPl; StuCncl; StuGov; RptrSchPpr; SchPpr; Coll; Dentistry.

FINLEY, Daniel J; St Thomas Acad; St Paul, MN; 1/96 VPJrCls; HonRl; NatlFornLg; NatlMeritSF; StuGov; RptrYrbk; RptrSchPpr; GerCl; LetterSocr; LetterTennis; College; Professional.

FINLEY, Diane E; Jefferson HS; Rockford, IL; 8/335 ChrhWkr; HonRl; JrNHS; NHS; NatlMeritCmnd; Orch; SchMus; SchPl; 4-H; LatCl;.

FINLEY, Gail M; Williamsville HS; Williamsville, IL; 10/43 SecFrshCls; VPJrCls; Band; ChrhWkr; CncrtBnd; HonRl; MrchBnd; PepBnd; SchPl; 4-H; FHA; EngCl; Swmmng; GAA; University; Professional.

FINLEY, Michael; Prospect Hs; Arlington Heights, IL; 27/625 HonRl; NHS; LetterBsbl; LetterBsktbl; University; Business.

FINLEY, Sue A; Normandy Senior HS; St Louis, MO; 11/500 VPJrCls; Band; CmntyWkr; HonRl; JrNHS; MrchBnd; NHS; SchMus; StuCncl; LatCl; Hiram College; Classics.

FINLEY, Sydney C; Wheaton Central HS; Wheaton, IL; ChrhWkr; CmntyWkr; NatlMeritCmnd; StuGov; Bsktbl; Ftbl; College; Pre Law.

FINLEY, Tammy S; Chosen Valley HS; Chatfield, MN; Chrs; ChrhWkr; CncrtBnd; HonRl; MrchBnd; NHS; Yrbk; Chrldr; College; Nursing.

FINLEY, Thomas J; Beloit Memorial HS; Beloit, WI; PresSophCls; ALBoysSt; Band; CncrtBnd; HonRl; MrchBnd; NHS; StuCncl; StuGov; RotaryAwd; University Of Wisc; Solar Energy Tech.

FINN, David; Mason Consolidated HS; Erie, MI; 12/120 Band; HonRl; NHS; SchPl; 4-H; EngCl; Monroe County Comm Coll; Architect.

FINN, Duane; Chosen Valley HS; Charfield, MN; Aud/Vis; ChrhWkr; HonRl; Trade School; Electronics Tech.

FINN, Eileen; Chosen Valley HS; Chatfield, MN; AFS; HonRl; NHS; TchrAde; FTA; SpnCl; Col; Professional.

FINN, Eileen S; Laurel Public HS; Carroll, NE; 4/63 Chrs; HonRl; TchrAde; SchPpr; 4-H; FHA; PpCl; College; Elementary Education.

FINN, John M; Borden HS; Floyds Knobs, IN; HonRl; NHS; LetterTrk;.

FINN, Linda S; Good Counsel HS; Chicago, IL; 47/247 HonRl; HospAde; SctActv; SchPpr; FNA; Northeastern Ill University.

FINN, Rory F; Alton Sr HS; Alton, IL; 63/858 NHS; TchrAde; SecLatCl; LetterSocr; College Of St Francis.

FINN, Scott R; Greenview HS; Greenview, IL; 4/49 HonRl; NHS; SchPl; SpnCl; SciCl; Bsktbl; U S Air Force Academy; Aeronautical Enginee.

FINNEGAN, James K; Holy Cross HS; Elmwood Park, IL; Triton; Architecture.

FINNEGAN, Michael E; Fenwick HS; Chicago, IL; HstJrCls; HstSrCls; HonRl; SchPl; StuCncl; StuGov; Yrbk; MthCl; Swmmng; Trk; Notre Dame Univ; Law Or Accounting.

FINNELL, Shauna K; Park Hill HS; Kansas City, MO; HstFrshCls; HstSophCls; ALAGirlsSt; HonRl; OffAde; SchPl; YthFlsp; PpCl; Bsktbl; Chrldr; College; Teacher.

FINNER, Carolyn M; Lindblom Technical HS; Chicago, IL; 24/657 HonRl; NatlMeritCmnd; SchAde; SctActv; TchrAde; FrCl; Southern Ill Univ; Pre Medicine.

FINNEREN, Diane M; Our Lady Of Mercy HS; Detroit, MI; Chrl; NHS; StuCncl; RptrYrbk; FrCl; Bsktbl; U Of Michigan.

FINNEY, June C; Winfield HS; Winfield, KS; ALAGirlsSt; HonRl; StuCncl; 4-H; 4-HAwd; CitAwd; Business School; Secretarial.

FINNEY, Marilyn E; Winfield HS; Winfield, KS; 5/187 AFS; ChrhWkr; HonRl; IntrClCncl; StuCncl; CivCl; FrCl; PpCl; LetterTrk; DARAwd; Oral Roberts Univ; Account.

FINNEY, Richard W; White Lake Public HS; White Lake, SD; 3/27 HonRl; NatlFornLg; SchPl; YthFlsp; Ftbl; VoiceDemAwd; S D Sch Of Mines & Tech.

FINNICUM, Thomas; Prophetstown HS; Prophetstown, IL; 40/100 ALBoysSt; Chr; Chrs; HonRl; JA; SchPl; SptEdSchPpr; FrCl; Bsbl; Bsktbl; Univ; Mass Communication Major.

FINNIE, Kim L; Soldan HS; St Louis, MO; 96/684 Chr; ChrhWkr; JA; ModUN; SchPl; StuCncl; PpCl; GAA; IMSpt; CitAwd; College; Medicine.

FINNIGAN, Michael D; East HS; Rockford, IL; 7/650 HonRl; NHS; NatlMeritCmnd; Orch; SctActv; Glf; Rockford College; Medicine.

FINSETH, Aleta K; Chosen Valley HS; Fountain, MN; ChrhWkr; LbryAde; YthFlsp; RptrSchPpr; SchPpr; 4-H; FHA; FTA; GAA; Mn School Of Business ;court Reporting.

FINSTROM, Debra J; Central Valley HS; Buxton, ND; 3/24 HstSrCls; SecBand; Chrs; HonRl; Yrbk; RptrSchPpr; FHA; PpCl; Chrldr;.

FINUCANE, Hallie A; Lawrence HS; Lawrence, KS; 3/537 Band; CmntyWkr; HospAde; NatlSciFnd; PolWkr; SchPl; TchrAde; PresFrCl; MthCl; SciCl; Univ Of Kansas; Medicine.

FINZEL, Barry; Monroe HS; Monroe, MI; 36/523 Band; CncrtBnd; HonRl; MrchBnd; NHS; Orch; PepBnd; SctActv; StuCncl; Trk; E Michi Univ; Chemistry.

FIORENTINI, Henry; Gordon Technical Hs; Chicago, IL; 7/620 HonRl; NHS; PolWkr; EdSchPpr; PresMthCl; College; Science.

FIORITO, Robert E; Holy Cross HS; Chicago, IL; 41/302 Northwestern University; Law.

FIRACK, Rhonda P; Les Cheneaux HS; Cedarville, MI; ChrhWkr; HonRl; LbryAde; SchPl;.

FIRCHOW, Cheryl L; Muskego HS; Hales Corners, WI; 19/325 HonRl; NHS; StuCncl; TchrAde; Yrbk; EdSchPpr; Univ Of Wisconsin; Accounting.

FIRESTONE, John D; Fenwick HS; Lagrange Park, IL; HonRl; OffAde; Univ; Professional.

FIRKINS, Lawrence D; Sycamore HS; Sycamore, IL; 22/201 ChrhWkr; HonRl; NHS; 4-H; PresFFA; LetterBsktbl; LetterTrk; 4-HAwd; University; Veterinarian.

FIRKUS, Marcia A; Pacelli HS; Stevens Point, WI; 12/116 ChrhWkr; HonRl; JrNHS; NHS; SchPl; SctActv; SecStuCncl; EdYrBk; GAA; DARAwd; EldAwd; Univ Of Wisconsin; Nursing.

FIRL, David M; Stewartville HS; Stewartville, MN; 6/98 PresBand; CncrtBnd; HonRl; MrchBnd; NHS; PepBnd; SchMus; GerCl; LetterBsbl; CaptTrk; Golden Valley Lutheran Col; Science Or Math.

FIRLE, Ronald K; Festus Sr HS; Festus, MO; ChrhWkr; CmntyWkr; HonRl; YthFlsp; LetterFtbl; College; Electronics.

FIRST, Jean; Ionia HS; Ionia, MI; Chr; ChrhWkr; OffAde; SchMus; TchrAde; 4-H; FrCl; Andrews Univ; Clothing & Textiles.

FISCHBACH, Cindy S; Paynesville HS; Paynesville, MN; Band; HonRl; MrchBnd; PepBnd; StuCncl; StuGov; FHA; Bsktbl; Trk; GAA; College; Professional.

FISCHBACH, Frances L; Warner HS; Warner, SD; TrsJrCls; Chrs; CncrtBnd; HonRl; MrchBnd; PepBnd; StuCncl; EdSchPpr; BttyCrckrAwd; EldAwd; Sioux Valley Sch; Degree In Nursing.

FISCHBEIN, Franklin S; Lawrence HS; Lawrence, KS; 3/550 VPSrCls; CncrtBnd; HospAde; NatlMeritSF; ROTC; FNA; LatCl; Wrstlng; BttyCrckrAwd; CitAwd; Harvard/yale; Rn.

FISCHER, Barbara J; Maine East HS; Niles, IL; Chrs; HonRl; JrNHS; NHS; SchMus; Teen; GerCl; University; Mathematics.

FISCHER, Becky L; Forman HS; Manito, IL; 6/70 PresSrCls; ChrhWkr; HonRl; LbryAde; NHS; SchPl; StuCncl; StuGov; TchrAde; EdYrBk; Yrbk; SchPpr; 4-H; PpCl; Western Ill University; Business.

FISCHER, Brady; Gibault HS; Waterloo, IL; HonRl; LitMag; PepBnd; StuCncl; RptrYrbk; Ranken Tech Inst; Plumber.

FISCHER, Carmen E; Heritage Hills HS; St Meinard, IN; PresSophCls; Band; CncrtBnd; HonRl; MrchBnd; NHS; PepBnd; StuCncl; FrCl; Bsktbl; Purdue U; Pro.

FISCHER, Carol L; Cornell HS; Cornell, WI; 2/48 VPSophCls; Band; Chrs; HonRl; Mdrgl; PepBnd; RptrYrbk; RptrSchPpr; PpCl; Trk; Univ; Med Tech.

FISCHER, Carolyn J; Wall Lake Community HS; Carnarvon, IA; HonRl; SchPl; College; Dental Asst.

FISCHER, Cindy K; Forest Park HS; Birdseye, IN; 60123 ALAGirlsSt; Band; HonRl; MrchBnd; NHS; StuCncl; 4-H; Chrldr; GAA; IMSpt; U Of Evansville; Nurse.

FISCHER, Denise A; South Division HS; Milwaukee, WI; Chr; HonRl; JrNHS; NHS; Business School; Secretary.

FISCHER, Douglas; Parkway West Sr HS; Ballwin, MO; 4/742 ChrhWkr; JrNHS; NHS; NatlMeritCmnd; KeyCl; Trk; Bethel Col; Christian Service.

FISCHER, Elizabeth M; Hutchinson HS; Hutchinson, MN; 20/215 AFS; Chr; ChrhWkr; CncrtBnd; HonRl; MrchBnd; SchMus; SchPl; SpnCl; Bsktbl; College; Medicine.

FISCHER, Eric D; Langdon HS; Langdon, ND; 2/159 VPSrCls; ALBoysSt; HonRl; Bsktbl; LetterTrk; PresAwd; Coll; Engi.

FISCHER, Gary F; Axtell HS; Beattie, KS; HonRl; SchPl; StuCncl; Trade Sch; Vocation.

FISCHER, Grace R; Jefferson City Sr HS; Jefferson City, MO; 75/475 HstSophCls; SecTrsJrCls; TrsSrCls; Band; NHS; StuCncl; EdSchPpr; Chrldr; AmLegAwd; University; Business Admin.

FISCHER, James; Tri Center HS; Neola, IA; 4-H; FFA; Bsbl; Bsktbl; Glf; 4-HAwd; Trade School.

FISCHER, James A; St Benedicts HS; Chicago, IL; 32/183 HonRl; SctActv; LetterBsktbl; IMSpt; Northern Univ; Lawyer.

FISCHER, Janell J; Platte HS; Platte, SD; Chrs; HonRl; LbryAde; Mdrgl; TchrAde; Yrbk; SchPpr; FHA; PpCl; College.

FISCHER, Jean M; Mater Dei HS; Breese, IL; 16/197 Chrs; HonRl; LbryAde; SchMus; TchrAde; College; Political Science.

FISCHER, Jennifer L; Rib Lake HS; Rib Lake, WI; 6/59 Band; Chr; Chrs; CncrtBnd; HonRl; LbryAde; MrchBnd; PepBnd; PpCl; LetterChrldr; North Central Tech Inst; Medical Sec.

FISCHER, John R; Scotus HS; Columbus, NE; 22/88 PresSophCls; HonRl; LetterBsbl; LetterBsktbl; LetterFtbl;.

FISCHER, Julie A; St Marys HS; Bismarck, ND; NatlMeritSF; EdSchPpr; College.

FISCHER, Kathleen; Whitehall Memorial HS; Whitehall, WI; Chr; CncrtBnd; HonRl; MrchBnd; NHS; PepBnd; SchPl; SctActv; 4-H; Hood College, Biochemistry.

FISCHER, Kathryn R; Merrill Senior HS; Merrill, WI; 38/334 TreasBand; CncrtBnd; HonRl; MrchBnd; SecFrshCls; VPGerCl; GAA; North Central Tech Inst; Radiologic Tech.

FISCHER, Kurt F; Carbondale Community HS; Carbondale, IL; 30/320 HonRl; ModUN; NHS; SctActv; StuCncl; StuGov; YthLg; IMSpt; Univ Of Il; Eng.

FISCHER, Marlin S; Eagle Grove HS; Thor, IA; PresSrCls; Band; HonRl; NHS; NatlThespSoc; SchMus; StuGov; LetterFtbl; CaptTrk; DanFAwd; Iccc Ft Dodge.

FISCHER, Martha F; Mason City HS; Mason City, IA; 15/101 Band; ChrhWkr; CncrtBnd; HonRl; HospAde; LbryAde; MrchBnd; OffAde; Orch; PepBnd; Concordia Clg; Special Ed Teacher.

FISCHER, Matthew P; Walther Lutheran HS; Cicero, IL; 4/90 Band; ChrhWkr; CncrtBnd; HonRl; MrchBnd; NHS; Orch; PepBnd; LetterBsbl; CaptBsktbl; St Olaf College; Medicine.

FISCHER, Michael C; Osseo Fairchild HS; Fairchild, WI; ALBoysSt; ChrhWkr; HonRl; NHS; TchrAde; GerCl; Bsktbl; Trk; College; Physics.

FISCHER, Michael H; Sturgis HS; Sturgis, MI; PresSrCls; SchPl; StuGov; TchrAde; KeyCl; Trade Sch; Auto Engineering.

FISCHER, Michael P; Northwest HS; High Ridge, MO; Band; Chr; ChrhWkr; HonRl; Mdrgl; NHS; RptrYrbk; SciCl; CitAwd; Oral Roberts Univ; Major Music.

FISCHER, Pamela; Lexington HS; Dover, MO; Band; ChrhWkr; CncrtBnd; HonRl; MrchBnd; NHS; PepBnd; 4-H; PpCl; GAA; Cent Mo State Univ; Elementary Ed.

FISCHER, Patricia A; Deerfield HS; Deerfield, IL; AFS; CmntyWkr; HonRl; LitMag; ModUN; PolWkr; SctActv; StuGov; SecYthFlsp; SptEdYrbk;.

FISCHER, Paul F; Marmon Military Academy; Westchester, IL; 8/87 ChrhWkr; HonRl; ROTC; SchAde; SptEdSchPpr; MthCl; PpCl; SciCl; Bsktbl; LetterTrk; IMSpt; College; Law.

FISCHER, Robert L; Lincolnway HS; New Lenox, IL; 20/498 HonRl; NHS; NatlMeritCmnd; TchrAde; MthCl; LetterTrk; College; Chemistry.

FISCHER, Sheri M; Rice Lake HS; Rice Lake, WI; HonRl; 4-H; College; Dentistry.

FISCHER, Thomas F; Franklin HS; Westland, MI; 15/775 Band; MrchBnd; NatlMeritSF; PepBnd; Ftbl; Tennis; Coll; Social Work.

FISCHER, Laurence F; Sevastopol HS; Egg Harbor, WI; 2/85 Band; Chrl; CncrtBnd; NHS; SchMus; SchPl; StuGov; LetterTrk; IMSpt;.

FISCHER, William C; Columbus HS; Marshfield, WI; Chr; Chrl; SchMus; SchPl; FrCl; EldAwd; Mount Senario Coll; Music.

FISCHER, William K; Mendota HS; Mendota, IL; 3/187 HonRl; NatlFornLg; NHS; StuGov; PresLatCl; Univ Of Illinois; Business Administration.

FISCHMAN, Leonard F; Bryan Sr HS; Omaha, NE; HonRl; Ftbl; Wrstlng; U Of Az; Aeronautical Engr.

FISCUS, Colleen M; Allegan HS; Allegan, MI; Chr; ChrhWkr; HonRl; HospAde; NHS; OffAde; LatCl; Clge; Nurse.

FISCUS, Rhonda K; Crescent Iroquois HS; Crescent City, IL; 2/25 SecBand; PresChrs; CncrtBnd; HonRl; NHS; SchPl; TreasYthFlsp; LetterBsktbl; Chrldr; Il State U; Music Therapy.

FISEL, Grace S; Lakeland HS; La Grange, IN; AFS; HonRl; Quill&Scroll; SchAde; SchPl; TchrAde; Teen; EdYrBk; PpCl; PPFtbl; Indiana Univ; Secretary.

FISEL, Grace S; Lakeland HS; Lagrange, IN; AFS; HonRl; Quill&Scroll; SchPl; Teen; EdYrBk; FTA; PPFtbl; MasAwd; Indiana Univ; Secretarial.

FISER, Frank B; North Central HS; Narka, KS; PresFrshCls; TrsJrCls; StuCncl; YthFlsp; 4-H; FFA; Bsktbl; Ftbl; AmLegAwd; College ;professional.

FISER, Marty J; North Central HS; Narka, KS; 6/26 PresFrshCls; ALBoysSt; Chr; ChrhWkr; CmntyWkr; HonRl; StuCncl; YthFlsp; SptEdYrbk; SptEdSchPpr; FFA; Bsbl; CaptBsktbl; CaptFtbl; Doane College.

FISH, Diane M; Remington HS; Whitewater, KS; Chr; Chrs; SchMus; TchrAde; FHA; Bsbl; Bsktbl; GAA; 4-HAwd; Fashion College; Interior Design.

FISH, Donald J; Sturgis HS; Sturgis, MI; Band; HonRl; NHS; StuCncl; Wester Mi Univ; Elect Engineer.

FISH, Douglas D; Martinsville R Vi HS; Martinsville, MO; PresFrshCls; ALBoysSt; HonRl; ModUN; SchPl; StuCncl; SptEdSchPpr; Bsktbl; Trk; College; Vocation.

FISH, Jon K; Milton HS; Milton, WI; HonRl; JA; NatlSciFnd; UNYO; YthFlsp; YthFnd; YthLg; FSA; SciCl; Bsktbl; Ftbl; College.

FISH, Roger J; Rockford Sr HS; Marble Rock, IA; HonRl; SchPl; StuCncl; RptrSchPpr; 4-H; FFA; LetterFtbl; IMSpt; 4-HAwd; Univ Of Northern Iowa; Business Mgmt.

FISH, Sandra; Collins Community HS; Collins, IA; 2/15 ALAGirlsSt; Band; Chr; HonRl; NHS; StuCncl; TchrAde; YthFlsp; 4-H; Chrldr; Univ Of Iowa State; Journalism.

FISHBACH, Robert J; Duchesne HS; St Charles, MO; 30/200 Band; Chrs; HonRl; TreasJrNHS; PresNHS; SchMus; StuCncl; EdYrBk; FrCl; Ftbl; University; Professional.

FISHBURN, Arlon M; Lawrence HS; Lawrence, KS; 157/540 ALBoysSt; Band; Chr; Chrs; ChrhWkr; CncrtBnd; HonRl; LbryAde; MrchBnd; 4-H; Mc Pherson Coll; Audio Visual.

FISHBURN, Susan K; Moweaqua HS; Moweaqua, IL; 17/55 PresJrCls; Chrs; ChrhWkr; HonRl; HospAde; LbryAde; SchMus; SctActv; StuCncl; Yrbk; Sec4-H; Bsbl; Tennis; Chrldr;.

FISHEL, Jo Ann; Edwards County Sr HS; West Salem, IL; Band; Chr; SecChrs; ChrhWkr; CncrtBnd; HonRl; HospAde; MrchBnd; TreasNHS; PepBnd; SchMus; StuCncl; TchrAde; Nursing School; Nursing.

FISHEL, Mark S; Storden Jeffers HS; Westbrook, MN; Band; Chrs; HonRl; SchPl; GerCl; Bsktbl; LetterFtbl; LetterTrk; PresAwd; College; Engineering.

FISHELL, Kathryn A; Roscommon HS; Roscommon, MI; Band; ChrhWkr; CncrtBnd; LbryAde; MrchBnd; PepBnd; SchAde; StuCncl; TchrAde; Trade School; Computer Programming.

FISHELL, Valerie K; Carson City Chrystal HS; Sheridan, MI; SecSophCls; HonRl; NHS; NatlMeritSchl; StuCncl; TchrAde; CaptBsktbl; Trk; CchngActv; IMSpt; College; Vetrenarian Medicine.

FISHER, Barbara; Riceville Community HS; Riceville, IA; 2/79 Band; Chrs; CncrtBnd; HonRl; Mdrgl; MrchBnd; NatlMeritCmnd; Orch; PepBnd;.

FISHER, Charles A; West HS; Wichita, KS; Chrl; ChrhWkr; HonRl; NHS; Quill&Scroll; SchPpr; Trk; College; Architectural Engineering.

FISHER, Craig; Carrollton HS; Saginaw, MI; 3/151 CmntyWkr; HonRl; NHS; NatlMeritCmnd;

PepBnd; SptEdSchPpr; Univ; Professional Engineering.

FISHER, Darla M; Triton HS; Bourbon, IN; CmntyWkr; HonRl; Yrbk; SecGAA; Air Force.

FISHER, Darrell E; Arapahoe HS; Arapahoe, NE; 15/35 VPFrshCls; TrsSophCls; Band; ChrhWkr; CmntyWkr; CncrtBnd; MrchBnd; OffAde; PepBnd; SchAde; SchPl; Bsktbl; Ftbl; Trk; Kearney State College; Politics.

FISHER, Daryl D; Holton HS; Holton, KS; TrsSophCls; ALBoysSt; Band; Chrs; HonRl; MrchBnd; TreasNHS; StuCncl; 4-H; Trk; University; Wildlife Management.

FISHER, David; Davenport Community HS; Davenport, NE; PresFrshCls; Chr; HonRl; MrchBnd; PepBnd; StuCncl; YthFlsp; 4-H; Wrstlng; 4-HAwd; Univ; Vocation.

FISHER, Deanne L; Stewartsville HS; Stewartsville, MO; SecSophCls; TrsJrCls; Chrs; HonRl; NHS; PpCl; LetterTrk; Chrldr; PPFtbl; College; Aeronautics.

FISHER, Dennis A; Charles City Community HS; Charles City, IA; ALBoysSt; LetterBsktbl; LetterGlf; College.

FISHER, Don A; Bronson HS; Bronson, MI; TchrAde; SptEdYrbk; SptEdSchPpr; LetterBsktbl; Ftbl; Tennis; Trk; CchngActv; College; State Police.

FISHER, Edward A; Adams Central HS; Decatur, IN; 3/121 PresJrCls; SecSrCls; ALBoysSt; HonRl; NHS; SchPl; StuCncl; YthFlsp; Bsbl; Bsktbl; Ftbl; Trk; Ball St Univ; Dentist.

FISHER, Edwin T; Madison Consolidated HS; Madison, IN; 7/285 ALBoysSt; Chr; HonRl; NHS; Sdlty; StuCncl; 4-H; LatCl; Bsbl; IMSpt; College; Mathematics.

FISHER, Gary; Moores Hill HS; Moores Hill, IN; 3/30 VPSophCls; TrsJrCls; ALBoysSt; HonRl; NHS; MthCl; SciCl; Bsbl; Bsktbl; University; Computer Tech.

FISHER, Gary R; Minneapolic Lutheran HS; Minneapolis, MN; 13/37 Band; HonRl; TchrAde; Bsbl; Bsktbl; Ftbl; Clge; Construction.

FISHER, Geff L; Northridge HS; Middlebury, IN; 62/134 Chr; SchMus; YthFlsp; KeyCl; PpCl; LetterFtbl; Trk; LetterWrstlng; IMSpt; College.

FISHER, Gordon L; Odin HS; Odin, IL; Band; Chrs; HonRl; PepBnd; SchPl; SptEdYrbk; Yrbk; LetterBsktbl; Trk; College; Engineering.

FISHER, James; Casey HS; Casey, IL; 50/100 PpCl; University; General.

FISHER, James H; Thornton Township Fractnl HS; Calumet City, IL; 410/474 Band; CncrtBnd; HonRl; MrchBnd; NHS; NatlMeritCmnd; Orch; PepBnd; SctActv; YthFlsp; Ftbl; Wrstlng; CchngActv; Purdue Univ; Chemical Engineering.

FISHER, James W; Conway HS; Philipsburg, MO; 4/64 HonRl; NHS; TreasFFA; FTA; Col; Doctor Of Beterinary Medicine.

FISHER, Jean M; Dexter HS; Dexter, MI; ALAGirlsSt; Band; ChrhWkr; CncrtBnd; HonRl; MrchBnd; NHS; PepBnd; TchrAde; Yrbk; 4-H; FHA; SpnCl; E Michigan Univ; Special Education.

FISHER, Jeffrey; Doniphan HS; Douiphan, NE; ALBoysSt; HonRl; SctActv; StuCncl; Bsbl; College; Anthropology.

FISHER, Julie A; Lanark HS; Lanark, IL; 1/55 PresSophCls; Band; Chr; Chrs; ChrhWkr; CncrtBnd; HonRl; Mdrgl; MrchBnd; PepBnd; SchMus; SchPl; StuCncl; Chrldr; Ill State Univ; Spec Education.

FISHER, Kay E; Heyworth HS; Heyworth, IL; 1/50 Chrs; HonRl; JrNHS; NHS; SchMus; SchPl; StuCncl; RptrYrbk; RptrSchPpr; FHA; SciCl; Trk; IMSpt; Univ Of Illinois; Special Educ.

FISHER, Kimberly D; Willow Springs HS; Willowsprings, MO; 7/91 ChrhWkr; CmntyWkr; SchPl; PresStuCncl; VPFFA; PresSciCl; Chrldr; College; Animal Science.

FISHER, Laura S; Lew Wallace HS; Gary, IN; ALAGirlsSt; HonRl; NHS; SchPl; TchrAde; RptrSchPpr; TreasEngCl; PresFrCl; PresSciCl; Purdue Univ; Geophysics.

FISHER, Madelyn A; Mother Of Sorrows HS; Chicago, IL; 52/143 HonRl; SchPl; FrCl; PpCl; GAA; VFWAwd; CitAwd; VoiceDemAwd; College; Fashions.

FISHER, Mark; Jackson HS; Jackson, MI; 119/373 Chrs; HonRl; YthFlsp; Jackson Community College; Engineering.

FISHER, Mark L; John Adams HS; South Bend, IN; 48/442 HonRl; College; Elec Engineering.

FISHER, Martin L; Niles Township East HS; Skokie, IL; 9/581 NHS; NatlMeritSF; KeyCl; LetterFtbl; Northwestern Univ; Doctor.

FISHER, Martin L; Niles Twp East HS; Skokie, IL; 9/583 HonRl; NHS; NatlMeritFnl; NatlMeritSF; KeyCl; LetterFtbl; College; Medicine.

FISHER, Mary J; Anthon Oto HS; Anthon, IA; Band; Chrs; ChrhWkr; DrlTm; HonRl; SchPl; Yrbk; PpCl; LetterBsktbl; IMSpt;.

FISHER, Nancy S; Dawson Verdon Consl HS; Dawson, NE; 5/22 Band; Chr; Chrl; ChrhWkr; CmntyWkr; CncrtBnd; HonRl; NHS; 4-H; 4-HAwd; Univ; Law.

FISHER, Paula S; La Salle HS; South Bend, IN; Band; CncrtBnd; HonRl; MrchBnd; OffAde; PepBnd; TchrAde; PresFTA; LetterSwmmng; IMSpt; Ball State University; Special Education.

FISHER, Rhonda D; Mehlville HS; St Louis, MO; CmntyWkr; HonRl; JA; OffAde; PolWkr; SchMus; StuCncl; PpCl; Chrldr; U Of Mo Columbia; Eng Teach.

FISHER, Richard J; Lake Mich Cath HS; Benton Harbor, MI; HonRl; NatlMeritSF; SchAde; TchrAde; RptrSchPpr; KeyCl; Ftbl; Trk; Wrstlng; Col; Engineering.

FISHER, Richard P; Regis HS; Eau Claire, WI; VPFrshCls; HonRl; NHS; StuCncl; Yrbk; GerCl; Bsktbl; LetterTrk; OptClAwd; Uw Eau Claire; Medicine.

FISHER, Ruth E; Tawas Area HS; Tawas City, MI; DrlTm; HonRl; FBLA; PpCl; LetterTrk; Chrldr; PresAwd; Trade Sch; Prof.

FISHER, Sheri L; Anderson HS; Anderson, IN; Chr; ChrhWkr; CmntyWkr; HonRl; HospAde; OffAde; SchAde; SctActv; TchrAde; YthFlsp; FHA; LatCl; PpCl; College; Nursing.

FISHER, Stephen R; South Hamilton HS; Story City, IA; Band; CncrtBnd; HonRl; MrchBnd; Trk; Iowa St Univ; Medicine.

FISHER, Susan A; Goshen HS; Goshen, IN; 3/250 Chr; ChrhWkr; HonRl; NHS; Orch; StuCncl; FrCl; Goshen College; English.

FISHER, Susan E; Sigourney Comm HS; Sigourney, IA; LetterChrs; HonRl; SchMus; SchPl; YthFlsp; FHA; LetterTrk; BttyCrckrAwd; Goshen Col ;nurse.

FISHER, Terrance; Spencer HS; Spencer, IA; VPFrshCls; ChrhWkr; StuCncl; FBLA; Bsbl; Ftbl; Univ Of Northern Ia; Bus Ed.

FISHMAN, Bradley J; Watertown HS; Watertown, SD; 46/301 ALBoysSt; HonRl; NHS; StuCncl; SpnCl; IMSpt; Co State U; Pre Med.

FISK, Joseph; Manistee HS; Manistee, MI; 39/169 Chr; Chrs; ChrhWkr; HonRl; Mdrgl; NatlMeritCmnd; YthFlsp; Bsbl; Tennis; IMSpt; Michigan Tech; Electrical.

FISK, Laura J; Sunnydale Academy; Rolla, MO; VPFrshCls; Band; Chr; Chrl; ChrhWkr; HonRl; NHS; Yrbk; College; Teacher.

FISK, Teresa A; Hamd Baptist HS; Munster, IN; Chr; ChrhWkr; HonRl; NHS; OffAde; SchMus; Hyles Anderson College; Secondary Ed.

FISK, Teresa A; Hammond Baptist HS; Munster, IN; Chr; ChrhWkr; HonRl; NHS; OffAde; TchrAde; Teen; SchPpr; College; High School Teacher.

FITCH, Bradley D; Casey HS; Casey, IL; Band; ChrhWkr; CncrtBnd; HonRl; MrchBnd; NHS; PepBnd; 4-H; FFA; Tennis; University; Vocational.

FITCH, Bryan C; Casey HS; Casey, IL; Band; ChrhWkr; CncrtBnd; HonRl; MrchBnd; NHS; PepBnd; 4-H; FFA; College; Vocation.

FITCH, David; Flosthing Sr HS; Flushing, MI; 61/450 HonRl; NHS; Ftbl; Univ Of Detroit; Architecture.

FITCH, Julia A; Clayton HS; Clayton, MO; Chr; ChrhWkr; DrlTm; ModUN; NHS; NatlMeritFnl; VPYthFlsp; PresFrCl; MthCl; PpCl; Dartmouth College; Medicine.

FITCH, Linda L; Arthur Hill HS; Saginaw, MI; HonRl; NHS; Saginaw Valley State College; Elem Educ.

FITCH, Rebecca A; Whitehall HS; Whitehall, MI; Chr; LitMag; TchrAde; EdSchPpr; Western Mi Univ; Elementary Ed.

FITCH, Sidney D; Battle Creek Comm HS; Battle Creek, IA; 1/23 Chrs; HonRl; SchPl; StuCncl; SptEdSchPpr; 4-H; LetterFtbl; LetterTrk; University; Cpa.

FITTANTE, Mary; Escanaba Public HS; Escanaba, MI; 76/382 Trk; IMSpt; College; Med Lab Technology.

FITTON, Alice A; Rantoul Township HS; Rantoul, IL; Chrs; HonRl; SchMus; SchPl; Eastern Ill University.

FITTON, Carol L; Davison HS; Davison, MI; 14/466 Chr; JA; NatlMeritCmnd; SchMus; SctActv; StuCncl; TchrAde; RptrYrbk; AmLegAwd; DARAwd; Mount Holyoke College; Translator Interprtr.

FITTVE, Vern; Lakeview HS; Humphrey, NE; 26/68 TrsSrCls; Chr; HonRl; StuGov; TchrAde; Bsktbl; Ftbl; IMSpt; Trade School; Vocation.

FITUCH, Catherine M; Garden City East HS; Garden City, MI; 15/485 ChrhWkr; CmntyWkr; HonRl; JrNHS; NHS; NatlThespSoc; SctActv; SchPpr; FrCl; GAA; Wayne St U; Accounting & Law.

FITUCH, Nina E; Garden City East HS; Garden City, MI; 6/485 ChrhWkr; CmntyWkr; HonRl; JrNHS; NHS; SctActv; RptrSchPpr; FrCl; GAA; Wayne St Univ; Rn.

FITZ, Debra A; Cal Community HS; Alexander, IA; Band; Chr; Chrl; Chrs; ChrhWkr; CmntyWkr; CncrtBnd; DrmMjrt; HonRl; Mdrgl; Bsktbl; Glf; Trk; Niacc; Nursing.

FITZGERALD, Alexandria L; Beloit Catholic HS; Beloit, WI; VPJrCls; Chr; HonRl; HospAde; NHS; SchMus; StuCncl; Yrbk; 4-H; Chrldr; U Of Wi; Ba In Communication Arts.

FITZGERALD, Cynthia I; Central HS; Omaha, NE; Chr; ChrhWkr; CmntyWkr; JA; NatlMeritCmnd; ROTC; StuCncl; StuGov; YthFnd; Trk; Coll; Engineer.

FITZGERALD, Daniel; Lincoln HS; Vincennes, IN; 22/343 VPSophCls; HonRl; Bsbl; Bsktbl; Glf; Tennis; PPFtbl; DanFAwd; SARAwd; MasAwd; Indiana U; Doctor.

FITZGERALD, Daniel L; Blue Mound HS; Decatur, IL; 4/50 TrsFrshCls; PresJrCls; HonRl; VPNHS; PresStuCncl; RptrSchPpr; SptEdSchPpr; Bsbl; Bsktbl; LetterTrk; IMSpt; Military Academy; Science.

FITZGERALD, David P; Griffith HS; Griffith, IN; 30/310 HonRl; NHS; LetterSwmmng; Johns Hopkins U; Engineering.

FITZGERALD, Fonda; Hinckley Big Rock Hs; Hinckley, IL; 1/77 SecNHS; SchMus; SchPl; SctActv; EdSchPpr; TreasLatCl; SecLetterSocr; BttyCrckrAwd; University Of Ill; Science.

FITZGERALD, Jonny E; La Grove HS; Farina, IL; Band; Chrs; ChrhWkr; SchMus; StuCncl; YthFlsp; FFA; LetterBsbl; LetterBsktbl; Jr College; Vocation.

FITZGERALD, Judith E; New Trier East HS; Wilmette, IL; 11/874 HonRl; LbryAde; NatlMeritSF; OffAde; SchPl; SctActv; StuGov; SpnCl; PpCl; SciCl; Univ; Medicine.

FITZGERALD, Julia L; Rosati Kain HS; St Louis, MO; HonRl; NatlMeritSF; SchPl; PresSciCl; LetterBsktbl; IMSpt; College.

FITZGERALD, Kathleen M; Lourdes Academy; Oshkosh, WI; CncrtBnd; DrmBgl; HonRl; NHS; StuCncl; EdSchPpr; 4-H; LetterBsktbl; LetterTennis; LetterWrstlng; Edgewood Clg; Pre Med.

FITZGERALD, Kathleen R; Mahtomedi HS; Stillwater, MN; 6/150 HonRl; LitMag; NatlFornLg; NHS; SchPl; TchrAde; RptrSchPpr; SchPpr; SpnCl; BttyCrckrAwd; Concordia Col; Writer.

FITZGERALD, Kelly S; Dallas City HS; Dallas City, IL; 9/46 TrsFrshCls; PresSophCls; Band; Chrs; HonRl; NHS; SchMus; StuCncl; Chrldr; GAA; Univ; Dental Tech.

FITZGERALD, Kevin T; Mt Carmel HS; Harvey, IL; 4/197 HonRl; ModUN; NHS; NatlMeritCmnd; StuCncl; TchrAde; RusCl; MthCl; Bsbl; LetterBsktbl; University; Engineering.

FITZGERALD, Marie L; St Elizabeth Academy; St Louis, MO; 10/116 HonRl; GerCl; VPSciCl; GAA; IMSpt; CitAwd; University Of Missouri; Medicine.

FITZGERALD, Mark H; Ogemaw Heights HS; West Branch, MI; 55/180 StuCncl; University; Liberal Arts.

FITZGERALD, Mark T; Highland HS; Highland, IN; 14/538 AFS; Band; CncrtBnd; MrchBnd; StuCncl; KeyCl; FrCl; College; Doctor.

FITZGERALD, Marla J; Craig R Iii HS; Craig, MO; TrsSophCls; Band; Chr; Chrs; CncrtBnd; HonRl; StuCncl; PresFHA; School; Nursing.

FITZGERALD, Mary P; Academy Of Mt St Scholastica; Atchison, KS; Chrs; HonRl; NHS; Quill&Scroll; SchPl; RptrYrbk; RptrSchPpr; EdSchPpr; College; Banking.

FITZGERALD, Mary R; Maria HS; Chicago, IL; 35/301 PresSophCls; NHS; SctActv; StuCncl; RptrYrbk; SpnCl; LetterBsktbl; GAA; St Xavier College; Nursing.

FITZGERALD, Michael; Dekalb Senior Hs; Dekalb, IL; 1/358 ChrhWkr; CmntyWkr; HonRl; NHS; SchAde; StuCncl; TchrAde; SciCl; LetterBsktbl; LetterGlf; University; Doctor Of Medicine.

FITZGERALD, Michael E; Marquette HS; Alton, IL; 20/119 HonRl; JrNHS; PresNHS; SptEdYrbk; RptrSchPpr; LetterBsbl; LetterFtbl; LetterTrk; IMSpt; AmLegAwd; DARAwd; University Of Notre Dame; Professional.

FITZGERALD, Michele M; Regina HS; Detroit, MI; ChrhWkr; HonRl; StuCncl; Med Office Assistant.

FITZGERALD, Patrick M; Lumen Christi HS; Jackson, MI; Band; HonRl; NHS; Trk; IMSpt; Jackson Comm Clg; Engineering.

FITZGERALD, Richard G; Springlake HS; Springlake, MI; PresFrshCls; PresSrCls; Chr; HonRl; Mdrgl; NHS; SchMus; SchPl; StuCncl; LetterFtbl; RotaryAwd; College; Professional.

FITZGERALD, Ruth A; Ogemaw Heights HS; West Branch, MI; VPJrCls; HonRl; NHS; StuCncl; RptrSchPpr; SchPpr; Bsktbl; University; Journalism.

FITZGERALD, Sue M; Glenbard West HS; Glen Ellyn, IL; Band; CncrtBnd; HonRl; MrchBnd; NHS; PepBnd; TchrAde; RptrYrbk; Tennis; GAA; College; French & Economics.

FITZGERALD, Susan M; Glenbard West HS; Glen Ellyn, IL; CncrtBnd; HonRl; MrchBnd; PepBnd; TchrAde; RptrYrbk; Tennis; College; French.

FITZGERALD, Terry; Humboldt HS; Clare, IA; 34/147 HonRl; NHS; College; Accounting.

FITZGERALD, Terry; Forest View HS; Des Plaines, IL; Chr; SchMus; SchPl; TchrAde; Harper Jr College; Art.

FITZGERALD, Thomas P; Brother Rice HS; Chicago, IL; 22/481 HonRl; Bsbl; Bsktbl; Univ Of Illinois; Elec Engineer.

FITZHUGH, Walter D; Western HS; Bay City, MI; PresJrCls; Band; ChrhWkr; CncrtBnd; HonRl; MrchBnd; Orch; PepBnd; SchMus; StuCncl; StuGov; RotaryAwd; Univ Of Michigan; Dentistry.

FITZJARRELL, David D; Schaumburg HS; Schaumburg, IL; 42/550 HonRl; NatlMeritCmnd; Harper College; Chemical Engineer.

FITZMAURICE, Laura S; Mercy HS; Omaha, NE; 1/75 Chr; HonRl; NatlCathMusEdAsoc; NHS; SchMus; 4-H; LatCl; Swmmng; Trk; GAA; Creighton U; Md.

FITZNER, Nancy E; Nicollet HS; Nicollet, MN; ChrhWkr; HonRl; TchrAde; YthFlsp; Yrbk; Treas4-H; FHA; LetterTrk; 4-HAwd; Trade School; Vocation.

FITZPATRICK, Deia E; Edinburg HS; Edinburg, IN; 17/82 SecSrCls; ALAGirlsSt; ChrhWkr; HonRl; NHS; OffAde; StuCncl; SpnCl; PpCl; GAA; Work At Newspaper.

FITZPATRICK, James W; Oak Forest HS; Oak Forest, IL; 82/350 Band; CncrtBnd; MrchBnd; Orch; PepBnd; PolWkr; FrCl; MthCl; Ftbl;.

FITZPATRICK, Kathleen A; St Francis Academy; Joliet, IL; 27/186 HonRl; IntrClCncl; JrNHS; NHS; Quill&Scroll; RptrYrbk; EdSchPpr; FrCl; MthCl; St Josephs College.

FITZPATRICK, Kathleen A; St Barbara HS; Chicago, IL; Band; Chr; Chrs; HonRl; PolWkr; RptrYrbk; RptrSchPpr; Pres4-H; 4-HAwd; College; Sociology.

FITZPATRICK, Kevin R; North Miami HS; Macy, IN; 36/129 Band; ChrhWkr; CncrtBnd; MrchBnd; SchMus; PresYthFlsp; GerCl; Ftbl; Trk;.

FITZPATRICK, Pete M; Bergan HS; Peoria, IL; Band; Chrs; HonRl; GerCl; Southern Illinois Univ; Journalism.

FITZPATRICK, William J; Oak Park River Forest HS; Oak Park, IL; HonRl; NatlMeritCmnd; NatlThespSoc; Univ; Electrical Engineer.

FITZSIMMONS, Janet M; Carl Sandburg HS; Palos Hts, IL; 189/815 HonRl; SctActv; TchrAde; PpCl; Chrldr; GAA; University; Professional.

FITZSIMMONS, Terri J; Center Senior HS; Kansas City, MO; Chr; DrlTm; HonRl; PpCl; College; Science.

FITZSIMONS, Barbara L; Garden City East HS; Garden City, MI; 101/500 HonRl; StuCncl; GAA; College.

FITZSIMONS, James M; Goodland HS; Goodland, KS; AFS; Bsktbl; Sydney Univ; Psychology.

FITZWATER, Debra A; Moulton Community HS; Moulton, IA; 3/40 PresFrshCls; Band; ChrhWkr; CmntyWkr; CncrtBnd; HonRl; MrchBnd; PepBnd; LetterBsktbl; Col; Musician Or Artist.

FITZWATER, Melody J; Van Buren Community HS; Birmingham, IA; Band; Chr; Chrs; ChrhWkr; HonRl; NHS; TchrAde; RptrSchPpr; 4-H; FHA; Jr College.

FITZWATER, Roy J; Highland HS; Highland, IN; 40/585 NatlFornLg; NatlMeritSF; NatlThespSoc; SchPl; TchrAde; SptEdYrbk; 4-H; MthCl; Purdue Univ; Vet.

FITZWATER, Terry J; Rogers HS; Wyoming, MI; 21/383 VPFrshCls; SecTrsSophCls; SecJrCls; CmntyWkr; NHS; NatlMeritSchl; PresStuCncl; FTA; KeyCl; Ftbl; Central Michigan Univ; Law.

FIXELL, Daniel R; Camb Sr HS; Cambridge, MN; TrsFrshCls; PresSophCls; Band; Chr; SchMus; StuCncl; YthFlsp; LetterBsktbl; LetterFtbl; LetterTrk; College; Vocation.

FLAA, Lauren K; Negaunee HS; Negaunee, MI; Chrs; ChrhWkr; HonRl; University.

FLAAGAN, Rita R; Tolna HS; Pekin, ND; Chr; Chrs; ChrhWkr; HonRl; NHS; SchPl; RptrYrbk; EdYrBk; RptrSchPpr;.

FLACH, Barbara E; St Anthony HS; Effingham, IL; SecJrCls; Band; CncrtBnd; HonRl; MrchBnd; PepBnd; SchPl; StuCncl; Eastern Ill Univ; Math.

FLACK, Cynthia G; Civic Memorial HS; Bethalto, IL; 2/214 ChrhWkr; HonRl; NHS; NatlThespSoc; PresStuCncl; EdYrBk; VPFTA; FrCl; PpCl; VPGAA; DARAwd; So Illinois Univ; Teach.

FLACKSBARTH, Richard R; Tartan HS; Maplewood, MN; 124/333 Aud/Vis; HonRl; TchrAde; YthFlsp; LetterBsktbl; LetterTennis; College; Radio Broadcasting.

FLADHAMMER, Patricia K; Mentor Public HS; Mentor, MN; SecFrshCls; PresJrCls; Band; HonRl; SchPl; RptrSchPpr; Bsbl; LetterBsktbl; GAA; PresAwd; University; Professional.

FLADLAND, Vicki L; Forest Lake Sr HS; Forest Lake, MN; PresFrshCls; VPSophCls; CncrtBnd; HonRl; MrchBnd; PepBnd; StuCncl; LetterTrk; CchngActv; GAA; PPFtbl; College.

FLAGEL, Douglas; Maquoketa Community HS; Maquoketa, IA; Aud/Vis; SchMus; FBLA; Ftbl; Trk; IMSpt; Saint Ambrose; Bus Admin.

FLAGG, David; Whitefish Bay HS; Milwaukee, WI; 1/330 HonRl; NHS; NatlSciFnd; Quill&Scroll; SptEdSchPpr; FSA; MthCl; Swmmng; Univ Of Wisc; Actuary.

FLAGG, Robert M; Elk Grove HS; Elk Grove, IL; 31/505 Bsktbl; LetterFtbl; Wrstlng; Coll; Physicist.

FLAGSTAD, Lois; Central HS; Aberdeen, SD; AFS; Band; DrlTm; HonRl; Mdrgl; RedCrAde; YthFlsp; SpnCl; Concordia Col; Minister.

FLAHARTY, Kathryn A; Derby HS; Wichita, KS; Chr; ChrhWkr; HonRl; HospAde; Mdrgl; Orch; VP4-H; FNA; PresPpCl; 4-HAwd; College; Nursing.

FLAHAVEN, Timothy R; Central HS; Aberdeen, SD; Chrs; ChrhWkr; HonRl; PolWkr; SptEdSchPpr; Ftbl; LetterTrk; Wrstlng; College; Architect.

FLAHERTY, Kevin J; Sioux County HS; Hemingford, NE; PresFrshCls; VPSophCls; VPJrCls; PresSrCls; NHS; StuCncl; FFA; Ftbl; Trk; E Wyoming College; Agriculture.

FLAHERTY, Margaret J; St Edmond HS; Fort Dodge, IA; HonRl; NHS; NatlMeritSF; StuCncl; SecSpnCl; PpCl; LetterGlf; KiwanAwd; Clg; Profes.

FLAHERTY, Winifred P; Maria HS; Chicago, IL; 115/365 RedCrAde; RptrYrbk; RptrSchPpr; College.

FLAIG, Sharon K; Sparta Senior HS; Sparta, WI; Band; CmntyWkr; NatlFornLg; PepBnd; SchPl; SctActv; Yrbk; PresSpnCl; PpCl; University; Social Worker.

FLAK, Jonathan J; Sacred Heart Public HS; Sacred Heart, MN; Chr; ChrhWkr; CmntyWkr; HonRl; NHS; SchPl; StuCncl; YthFlsp; LetterFtbl; LetterWrstlng; College; Pro.

FLAK, Karen A; Rockford HS; Rockford, MI; 25/279 HstFrshCls; HonRl; NHS; NatlMeritSF; PolWkr; StuCncl; Grand Rapids Jr Coll; Business Admin.

FLAK, Michael W; Paul Schulte HS; Terre Haute, IN; 33/91 ChrhWkr; CmntyWkr; HonRl; YthFlsp; CaptBsbl; LetterBsktbl; LetterFtbl; Indiana St Univ; Accounting.

FLAKE, Harvey; Romulus Sr HS; Romulus, MI; 28/297 ALBoysSt; PresBand; ChrhWkr; PresCncrtBnd; HonRl; LbryAde; PresMrchBnd; PresNHS; StuCncl; StuGov; U Of Michigan; Physician.

FLAKOLL, Paul J; Forbes Public HS; Forbes, ND; PresFrshCls; TrsJrCls; VPSrCls; ALBoysSt; Chr; Chrl; Chrs; ChrhWkr; CmntyWkr; HonRl; CaptBsktbl; Trk; IMSpt; 4-HAwd; Concordia College; Music.

FLAMIG, Bryan L; Dalton HS; Dalton, NE; Band; Chrs; CncrtBnd; HonRl; MrchBnd; PepBnd; SchPl; MthCl; College.

FLAMING, John; Inman HS; Inman, KS; HonRl; SchPl; YthFlsp; RptrSchPpr; FFA; College; Math Science.

FLAMM, Charles T; Cobden Unit HS; Cobden, IL; PresJrCls; TrsSrCls; HonRl; PpCl; VPSciCl; Bsbl; Southern Il Univ; Professional.

FLAMM, Linda S; Cobden HS; Cobden, IL; 6/50 SecSophCls; Band; HonRl; SchMus; Sdlty; RptrYrbk; Pres4-H; FHA; SecSciCl; CaptChrldr; Southern Illinois Univ; Early Cild Develpmt.

FLAMM, Linda S; Obden HS; Cobden, IL; 6/50 SecSophCls; Band; HonRl; SchMus; RptrYrbk; 4-H; FHA; SciCl; Chrldr; Southern Illinois Univ; Childhood Developmn.

FLAMM, Ronald A; Cobden HS; Cobden, IL; 9/48 PresFrshCls; PresSrCls; Band; HonRl; SchPl; PresStuCncl; Yrbk; PpCl; VPSciCl; Bsktbl; S Ill U;engineer.

FLAMMANG, Kerry; Lawton Bronson HS; Lawton, IA; 3 SecJrCls; Chrs; DrlTm; HonRl; NHS; StuCncl; Chrldr; Univ; Prof.

FLAMME, Theresa D; North Bend Central HS; North Bend, NE; TrsSophCls; HonRl; RptrYrbk; RptrSchPpr; FHA; FTA; PpCl; Chrldr; PPFtbl; College; Professional Nursing.

FLANAGAN, Anne M; Bishop Gallagher HS; Detroit, MI; CmntyWkr; HonRl; NatlMeritCmnd; NatlMeritSF; PolWkr; Marygrove College; Elem Education.

FLANAGAN, Jayne P; St Marys Academy; Chicago, IL; SecTrsSrCls; Chrs; OffAde; SchPl; College.

FLANAGAN, Joseph E; Springfield HS; Springfield, IL; 81/583 Ftbl; Swmmng; Tennis; Western Il U; Optician.

FLANAGAN, Maureen P; Providence HS; New Lenox, IL; 7/121 Chrs; HonRl; NHS; PolWkr; RptrYrbk; SpnCl; MthCl; SciCl; GAA; Lewis Univ; Medicine.

FLANAGAN, Michael M; Dixon HS; Dixon, IL; 5/337 HonRl; NHS; NatlMeritCmnd; RptrYrbk; LetterBsktbl; CaptTennis; CaptIMSpt; U Of Illinois; Data Processing.

FLANAGAN, Rebecca; Kirksville Senior HS; Kirksville, MO; 4/174 ChrhWkr; HonRl; YthFlsp; YthLg; EdSchPpr; CivCl; FrCl; Univ Of Missouri; Journalism.

FLANAGAN, Terence D; Rockhurst HS; Kansas City, MO; CmntyWkr; HonRl; LbryAde; NHS; PolWkr; StuCncl; LetterFtbl; LetterSocr; LetterTrk; IMSpt; Kansas Univ; Engineer.

FLANARY, Janice L; St Marys HS; St Marys, KS; 3/61 VPJrCls; ALAGirlsSt; Chrs; CmntyWkr; HonRl; SctActv; TchrAde; SchPpr; FHA; SpnCl; Kansas State Univ.

FLANARY, Suzanna; Riverview HS; Riverview, MI; 76/286 OffAde; StuGov; TchrAde; CchngActv; College; Physical Education.

FLANDERS, Dorian; Batavia HS; Batavia, IL; 12/221 HonRl; LbryAde; NatlFornLg; NHS; NatlMeritCmnd; PolWkr; SchMus; SchPl; FTA; De Paul Univ; Theater.

FLANDERS, Joan H; North Boone HS; Poplar Grove, IL; Chr; Chrs; ChrhWkr; RptrYrbk; 4-H; FHA; PpCl; Chrldr; GAA; College; Professional.

FLANEGIN, Timothy S; Yates City HS; Yates City, IL; 2/22 HonRl; LitMag; StuCncl; StuGov; TchrAde; EdYrBk;.

FLANIGAN, Carol A; Holly HS; Holly, MI; SecJrCls; SecSrCls; Chr; ChrhWkr; DrlTm; JrNHS; OffAde; SctActv; TchrAde; College; Teacher.

FLANIGAN, James J; Proviso West HS; Westchester, IL; 24/1086 ChrhWkr; HonRl; NHS; NatlMeritCmnd; Elmhurst College; Math.

FLANIGAN, Loretta A; St Clement HS; Center Line, MI; Chrs; HonRl; PolWkr; Bsbl; Bsktbl; CchngActv; CitAwd; Macomb County Com Col.

FLANIGAN, Martin; Maple Valley HS; Mapleton, IA; VPSophCls; SecJrCls; Bsbl; Bsktbl; Ftbl; Trk; Trade School; Agriculture.

FLANIGAN, Mike K; Cresbard HS; Wescota, SD; Chr; Chrs; CmntyWkr; HonRl; SchPl; Yrbk; 4-H; Bsbl; LetterBsktbl; Ftbl; Univ; Conservation.

FLANINGAM, Karen R; York HS; Elmhurst, IL; 170/925 TrsSophCls; Chr; HonRl; NHS; StuCncl; Univ Of Illinois; Professional.

FLANNERY, Joan E; Rich Central HS; Olympia Fields, IL; 10/400 PresAFS; Chr; HonRl; IntrClCncl; TreasSctActv; SchPpr; SecGerCl; PpCl; College; Science.

FLANNIGAN, Kathleen M; Auburn HS; Auburn, IL; VPSophCls; ChrhWkr; HonRl; OffAde; PolWkr; SctActv; VPStuCncl; 4-H; TreasFHA; PpCl; Bsktbl; Trk; GAA; AmLegAwd; College; Physical Ed.

FLANSBURG, Gail; Sully Buttes HS; Blunt, SD; HonRl; Bsktbl; Trk; Sd State Univ; English Major.

FLASPOHLER, Mary J; Kirksville Sr HS; Kirksville, MO; Chrs; HonRl; OffAde; SctActv; StuCncl; TchrAde; SpnCl; PpCl; LetterBsktbl; LetterTrk; LetterGAA; LetterIMSpt; College.

FLATA, Maryann; Franklin Center HS; Franklin Grove, IL; 22/50 Chrs; DrlTm; DrmMjrt; HonRl; LbryAde; SchPl; RptrYrbk; FHA; GAA; Sauk Valle Coll; Nurse.

FLATEN, Doris; Warren HS; Warren, MN; 21/61 Band; ChrhWkr; HonRl; MrchBnd; PepBnd; 4-H; FHA; GerCl; 4-HAwd; Moorhead State U And Ndsu; Home Economics.

FLATH, Ervin; Garrison HS; Garrison, ND; 3/58 VPJrCls; ALBoysSt; HonRl; NHS; StuCncl; FFA; Univ Of Nd; Engrg.

FLATHAU, Jamie A; Saginaw HS; Saginaw, MI; ChrhWkr; HonRl; NHS; OffAde; SchPl; RptrSchPpr; SchPpr; CaptChrldr; College; Police Work.

FLATT, Brenda S; Salem Sr HS; Salem, MO; 15/173 Band; CmntyWkr; CncrtBnd; HonRl; HospAde; MrchBnd; PepBnd; FHA; PpCl; Burge School; Nursing.

FLAVIN, Catherine M; Benet Academy; Downers Grove, IL; HonRl; NHS; SchPl; VPStuCncl; VPStuGov; RptrYrbk; SpnCl; PpCl; Chrldr; Illinois Benedictine College; Medicine.

FLAX, Gladys M; Jennings HS; Clayton, KS; 3/22 Band; Chr; Chrs; CncrtBnd; HonRl; MrchBnd; PepBnd; Teen; RptrYrbk; EdYrBk; 4-H; FHA; PpCl; Chrldr; Brown College; Court Reporting.

FLAXMAN, Jon E; Deerfield HS; Deerfield, IL; 53/561 HonRl; NHS; CaptBsktbl; LetterFtbl; Trk; College; Medicine.

FLEAGLE, Sharon K; Abilene HS; Abilene, KS; HonRl; TchrAde; PpCl; IMSpt; Business School; Accounting.

FLEAGLE, Timothy J; Triton HS; Etna Green, IN; Chr; HonRl; PpCl; SciCl; LetterBsbl; LetterFtbl; Wrstlng; Clge; Wildlife Management & Conservation.

FLECK, Deanna M; South Division HS; Milwaukee, WI; HonRl; FBLA; FTA; GerCl; PpCl; Whitewater Uw; Busiess Ed.

FLECK, Susan B; North White HS; Reynolds, IN; VPFrshCls; VPSophCls; PresSrCls; Band; ChrhWkr; HonRl; NatlThespSoc; SchMus; RptrYrbk; 4-H; Ball State U; Photojournalism.

FLECK, Terry L; Stromsburg HS; Stromsbrugh, NE; 1/40 PresSrCls; HonRl; NHS; NatlMeritCmnd; OffAde; TchrAde; Bsktbl; Ftbl; Trk; DanFAwd; U Of Nebraska; Civil Eng.

FLECKY, Kevin G; Saint Albert HS; Council Bluffs, IA; 6/94 HonRl; NHS; NatlMeritFnl; SchMus; StuCncl; EdYrBk; Tennis; IMSpt; OptClAwd; Creighton U; Architecture Eng.

FLEEMAN, Robert A; Greenfield R4 HS; Greenfield, MO; 10/36 PresJrCls; HonRl; SchPl; PresStuCncl; StuGov; RptrYrbk; RptrSchPpr; FTA; Col; Dramatics.

FLEENER, Brenda L; North Posey HS; Poseyville, IN; Band; HonRl; HospAde; LbryAde; NHS; TchrAde; EdYrBk; GAA; AFS; VoiceDemAwd; U Of Evansville; Special Education.

FLEENER, Kathryn; Atwood Hammond HS; Hammond, IL; 8/52 ALAGirlsSt; Chrs; ChrhWkr; CmntyWkr; HonRl; NHS; SchAde; SchPpr; 4-H; Jr College; Vocation.

FLEENOR, Carol E; Mitchell HS; Mitchell, IN; 3/141 DrlTm; HonRl; JrNHS; SchMus; PpCl; Chrldr; Stewardess School; Stewardess.

FLEENOR, Cindy L; Covington HS; Covington, IN; 13/93 SecJrCls; Chrs; NHS; OffAde; Quill&Scroll; SchPl; StuCncl; EdSchPpr; PpCl; Tennis; Taylor U; Psychology.

FLEENOR, Gordon L; Lyman HS; Lyman, NE; 7/19 Chrs; HonRl; SchMus; SchPl; SctActv; SptEdYrbk; SecFFA; Bsbl; Bsktbl; Trk; Nebraska Western Jr College; Agriculture.

FLEER, Monica E; Highland HS; Lewistown, MO; 10/120 ChrhWkr; CmntyWkr; HonRl; JrNHS; NHS; SecStuCncl; 4-H; SecFSA; PpCl; Bsktbl; IMSpt; College; Artist.

FLEES, Cynthia A; Rosholt HS; Rosholt, WI; 3/58 HonRl; NHS; FHA; MthCl; LetterBsktbl; SecGAA; N Central Tech; Acctng.

FLEGEL, Cheryl L; Hinsdale South HS; Darien, IL; 60/500 HonRl; SchAde; StuCncl; Yrbk; FrCl; GAA; Dupage College; Computer Operator.

FLEGEL, Constance L; Hazelton Public HS; Hazelton, ND; 5/32 SecSophCls; SecSrCls; Band; Chrs; ChrhWkr; HonRl; LbryAde; PepBnd; SchMus; SchPpr; Westmar Clge; Music Tchr.

FLEGEL, Eric R; Coleman HS; N Bradley, MI; Band; CncrtBnd; HonRl; MrchBnd; NHS; PepBnd; TchrAde; FTA; Coll; Math.

FLEGEL, Melinda; Leroy HS; Leroy, IL; VPFrshCls; PresSophCls; ALAGirlsSt; HonRl; StuCncl; TchrAde; SchPpr; 4-H; PpCl; GAA; Az Univ; Physical Ed.

FLEGEL, Nadine K; New Salem HS; New Salem, ND; 4/51 ALAGirlsSt; Band; Chrs; HonRl; YthFlsp; Yrbk; Sec4-H; SecFHA; SciCl; LetterChrldr; College.

FLEHARTY, Debbie S; Hays HS; Hayes, KS; ChrhWkr; HonRl; HospAde; TchrAde; Col.

FLEISCHFRESSER, Julie A; Maria HS; Chicago, IL; 29/301 HonRl; NHS; Sdlty; Univ Of Ill; Pharmacy.

FLEISCHMAN, Mary E; Crivitz HS; Wausaukee, WI; 1/69 SecJrCls; Band; HonRl; NatlFornLg; NHS; StuCncl; RptrYrbk; Univ Of Wisconsin; English.

FLEISCHMAN, Teresa A; Antigo HS; Antigo, WI; Band; Chr; ChrhWkr; CncrtBnd; LitMag; MrchBnd; PepBnd; SchMus; StuCncl; TchrAde; AmLegAwd; Univ Of Wis; Music.

FLEMING, Carol A; Northwest HS; Pleasant Lake, MI; 62/265 SecSrCls; HonRl; LbryAde; StuGov; RptrSchPpr; SchPpr; Jackson Comm Clge; Rn.

FLEMING, Christine D; Roxana Sr HS; East Alton, IL; 5/280 Chr; ChrhWkr; HonRl; NHS; Quill&Scroll; SctActv; SecYthFlsp; RptrSchPpr; SchPpr; GerCl; College; Ministry.

FLEMING, Debra L; Plattsmouth HS; Plattsmouth, NE; 7/139 Band; Chr; Chrs; CmntyWkr; CncrtBnd; HonRl; NHS; Orch; SchMus; TreasMthCl; Chrldr; PPFtbl; Univ Of Ne; Dental Hygiene.

FLEMING, Jamie H; Ewin Trout Creek HS; Ewen, MI; 10/70 Band; HonRl; NHS; SchPl; StuCncl; Yrbk; LetterBsktbl; LetterTrk; Lake Superior St College.

FLEMING, John; Lindblom Tech HS; Chicago, IL; 21/599 HonRl; SchAde; Sdlty; TchrAde; Bsbl; Mi St Univ; Veterinarian.

FLEMING, John L; Copeland HS; Copeland, KS; ALBoysSt; HonRl; NatlMeritCmnd; SchPl; StuCncl; RptrYrbk; SchPpr; Ftbl; Trk; Dodge City Jr College; Farming.

FLEMING, Jon W; Thorp Public HS; Thorp, WI; 30/98 VPSophCls; HonRl; SchMus; SchPl; StuCncl; RptrSchPpr; SptEdSchPpr; Bsktbl; Ftbl; Trk; Coll; Prof.

FLEMING, Judith M; Duchesne HS; St Charles, MO; SecJrCls; Chrs; HonRl; HospAde; SecNHS; SchMus; StuCncl; PpCl; CaptChrldr; PPFtbl; University.

FLEMING, Kathleen M; Hillsdale HS; Hillsdale, MI; Pres4-H; PresPpCl; Orch; 4-HAwd; Hillsdale College; Law.

FLEMING, Kim A; South Shore HS; Iron River, WI; SecFrshCls; SecTrsSophCls; SecTrsJrCls; Band; Chr; HonRl; StuCncl; Bsktbl; Trk; LetterChrldr; College; Law.

FLEMING, Laura E; Evanston Township HS; Evanston, IL; PresSrCls; HonRl; MrchBnd; GerCl; CaptChrldr; GAA; West Mich Univ; Dist Ed Teacher.

FLEMING, Mark; Bradley Bourbonnais Comm HS; Bourbonnais, IL; HonRl; Bsktbl; Tennis; CchngActv; College.

FLEMING, Mark M; Lawrenceville HS; Lawrenceville, IL; 25/177 ALBoysSt; CmntyWkr; NHS; StuCncl; SptEdYrbk; SptEdSchPpr; TreasKeyCl; TreasSpnCl; CaptTrk; IMSpt; EldAwd; Northwestern Univ; Journalism.

FLEMING, Pamela D; New Trier East HS; Wilmette, IL; HonRl; College; Art.

FLEMING, Patrick; Wencom Memorial HS; Garden City, MN; HonRl; SchPl; TchrAde; RptrYrbk; SchPpr; Mankato State; Science.

FLEMING, Robert E; Duchesne HS; St Charles, MO; 14/180 VPFrshCls; VPSophCls; PresJrCls; HonRl; NHS; PresStuCncl; KeyCl; VPSpnCl; LetterTennis; CitAwd; Univ; Prof.

FLEMING, Teri L; Pinckneyville HS; Pinckneyville, IL; Band; ChrhWkr; CncrtBnd; HonRl; HospAde; JrNHS; MrchBnd; NHS; PepBnd; FHA; SpnCl; PpCl; College; Special Education.

FLEMING, Thomas; Heelan HS; Sioux City, IA; HonRl; NHS; ROTC; Bsbl; Bsktbl; Wrstlng; AmLegAwd; CitAwd; Us Air Force Academy.

FLEMING, William R; Milton HS; Milton, WI; 12/173 HonRl; NHS; TchrAde; FFA; Ftbl; Voc Tech Sch; Auto & Truck Mechanic.

FLEMMER, Darcy M; Hazen HS; Beulah, ND; Chr; HonRl; HospAde; MrchBnd; SchPl; StuCncl; YthFlsp; Yrbk; 4-H; College; Professional.

FLEMMING, Dave G; Bird City HS; Bird City, KS; TrsFrshCls; Band; Chr; PepBnd; SchPl; StuCncl; FFA; LetterBsktbl; LetterFtbl; Glf; LetterTrk; IMSpt; Dodge City Comm College; Mechanic.

FLEMMING, Shannon; New Buffalo Consolidated HS; New Buffalo, MI; SecJrCls; Chr; ChrhWkr; CncrtBnd; HonRl; MrchBnd; NHS; NatlMeritCmnd; SchPl; StuCncl; Mich State Univ; Horticulture.

FLEMMING, Therese A; Mother Mc Auley HS; Chicago, IL; 11/474 Chrs; HonRl; NHS; SctActv; TchrAde; Yrbk; FTA; SpnCl; Univ Of Illinois; Psychology.

FLENAR, Teresa A; Triton Shaffer Rd HS; Etna Green, IN; Band; ChrhWkr; CncrtBnd; HonRl; MrchBnd; SecNHS; OffAde; PepBnd; TchrAde; YthFlsp; Ball State Univ; Physical Education.

FLENTJE, Sandra R; Virden HS; Auburn, IL; ChrhWkr; HonRl; LbryAde; SchMus; SchPl; PresF-HA; PPFtbl; College; Major Study.

FLESCH, Joette A; Mc Donell Central HS; Chippewa Falls, WI; 2/93 HonRl; ModUN; StuCncl; RptrSchPpr; Tennis; Trk; Eau Claire University.

FLESCH, William E; Warren County R Ii HS; Wright City, MO; 1/51 VPFrshCls; PresSophCls; ChrhWkr; HonRl; NHS; StuCncl; TchrAde; YthFlsp; RptrYrbk; AmLegAwd; Univ; Accounting.

FLESHER, Michael N; Thomas More Prep; Mc Pherson, KS; Band; Chrs; CncrtBnd; MrchBnd; PepBnd; RedCrAde; SchPl; StuCncl; Yrbk; 4-H; Coll;vocation.

FLESHER, Michele F; Minnetonka HS; Excelsior, MN; 90/600 Chr; HospAde; SchPl; Chrldr; Univ Of Minn.

FLESHMAN, James B; Putnam Co R1 HS; Unionville, MO; ChrhWkr; HonRl; MrchBnd; NHS; StuCncl; 4-H; FFA; Bsktbl; Ftbl; Trk; Univ Of Ms.

FLESSNER, Peggy L; Ford Central HS; Thawville, IL; 7/63 TrsSrCls; ALAGirlsSt; Band; CncrtBnd; HospAde; MrchBnd; LetterBsbl; LetterTrk; VPGAA; Parkland Comm Col; Nursing.

FLESSNER, Susan J; Chatsworth HS; Chatsworth, IL; 9/46 AFS; Band; Chrs; CncrtBnd; HonRl; Mdrgl; MrchBnd; PepBnd; SchMus; SchPl; SctActv; College; Nursing.

FLETCHER, Barbara; Beaver Dam Senior HS; Beaver Dam, WI; 31/350 AFS; HonRl; StuCncl; TchrAde; PpCl; Tennis; GAA; IMSpt; Univ Wisc; Accountant.

FLETCHER, Cecilia A; Lindblom HS; Chicago, IL; 47/659 HonRl; NHS; OffAde; SchPl; Univ Of Illinois; Psychologist.

FLETCHER, Daniel H; Swanville HS; Swanville, MN; PresBand; Chr; ChrhWkr; CncrtBnd; HonRl; MrchBnd; PresNatlThespSoc; SchPl; EdYrBk; RptrSchPpr; SecFFA; Ftbl; Trk; LionAwd; Anoka Voc Tech Univ; Farrier.

FLETCHER, Frank T; St Johns HS; St Louis, MO; 8/100 HonRl; NHS; LetterBsbl; LetterBsktbl; IMSpt; University.

FLETCHER, John G; Lasalle Peru Twp HS; Peru, IL; 100/517 HonRl; LetterBsktbl; LetterFtbl; LetterTrk; College; Biology.

FLETCHER, Kimberlee S; Clay Central HS; Royal, IA; PresSophCls; CmntyWkr; HonRl; SchPl; StuCncl; YthFlsp; FTA; SpnCl; PpCl; Bsktbl; Coll; Recreation.

FLETCHER, Mary K; St Johns HS; St Louis, MO; Chr; HonRl; HospAde; NHS; SchMus; SchPl; SctActv; StuCncl; RptrYrbk; Univ Of Missouri; Special Educ.

FLETCHER, Sallie A; Moores Hill HS; Moores Hill, IN; 1/23 SecJrCls; Band; CncrtBnd; MrchBnd; NHS; SchPl; TchrAde; Twrl; College; Business.

FLICK, Gary A; West Milwaukee HS; West Allis, WI; 7/177 Band; CncrtBnd; HonRl; MrchBnd; NHS; Orch; PepBnd; SchMus; StuCncl; Univ Of Wisconsin; Accounting.

FLICK, Louise A; Wauwatosa East HS; Wauwatosa, WI; HonRl; LitMag; SchPl; MthCl; OptClAwd; Univ Of Hawaii; Jeweler.

FLICK, Mary J; New Hampton Comm HS; Ionia, IA; HonRl; HospAde; Mdrgl; NHS; Quill&Scroll; TchrAde; RptrYrbk; 4-H; GAA; IMSpt; Trade Sch; Voc.

FLICKNER, Gwenda; Moundridge HS; Moundridge, KS; ChrhWkr; HonRl; NHS; PepBnd; SchMus; Trk; Chrldr; IMSpt; PresAwd; Bethel College; Professional.

FLIEGEL, Ruth E; Champaign Central HS; Champaign, IL; 1/411 Band; CncrtBnd; MrchBnd; NHS; NatlMeritSF; StuCncl; RptrYrbk; SpnCl; GAA; U Of Il.

FLIEHS, Harvey; Groton Central HS; Groton, SD; 5/55 SecSrCls; ALBoysSt; ChrhWkr; HonRl; JrNHS; LbryAde; Univ Of South Dakota; Law.

FLINCK, Laura L; Greenway HS; Boucy, MN; 9/155 Band; HonRl; NHS; RptrYrbk; RptrSchPpr; Chrldr; GAA; Itasca Comm Clg; Optimetiric Assistant.

FLINN, Donald R; De Smet Jesuit HS; Creve Coeur, MO; 24/168 HonRl; SctActv; LetterFtbl; LetterSocr; LetterTrk; IMSpt; Dayton Univ; Engineering.

FLINN, Shirleen M; Ellis HS; Ellis, KS; HonRl; NatlFornLg; SchPl; StuCncl; Pres4-H; FHA; PpCl; Trk; Chrldr; DanFAwd; 4-HAwd; Jr Comm College; Nursing.

FLINT, Colleen D; Cambridge HS; Cambridge, NE; Band; Chrs; DrmMjrt; SchPl; Yrbk; FBLA; FHA; PpCl; LetterTrk; College; Secretary.

FLINT, Roger D; Schell City HS; Harwood, MO; 1/14 SecTrsFrshCls; SecTrsSophCls; SecTrsSrCls; HonRl; SchPl; TchrAde; Yrbk; EdSchPpr; Bsktbl; Sw Baptist Col; Teaching Bus Ed English.

FLINT, Theodore W; Galesburg Sr HS; Galesburg, IL; PresSophCls; PresJrCls; StuGov; TchrAde; SchPpr; Iowa St Univ; Veterinarian.

FLINT, Timothy E; Northwestern HS; Good Hope, IL; Chrs; HonRl; StuCncl; Yrbk; SpnCl; MthCl; SciCl; Bsbl; Bsktbl; Ftbl; CchngActv; College; Professional.

FLINTROP, William J; Waseca HS; Waseca, MN; HonRl; NatlMeritCmnd; FFA; St Johns Univ.

FLIPPIN, Sharon E; Truman HS; Independence, MO; Chrs; ChrhWkr; HonRl; LbryAde; OffAde; PolWkr; Central State U; Law.

FLITTNER, Anne E; Reitz Memorial HS; Evansville, IN; 24/228 CmntyWkr; HonRl; HospAde; StuCncl; 4-H; GerCl; PresAwd; College.

FLOCK, Thomas M; Cashton HS; Cashton, WI; 4/66 Band; PresChrs; HonRl; LbryAde; RptrSchPpr; PresNHS; SchPl; EdYrBk; Yrbk; SpnCl; Viterbo Clg; Music.

FLOERCHINGER, Kim D; Underwood Comm HS; Underwood, IA; 2/59 Band; Chr; CncrtBnd; HonRl; MrchBnd; NHS; NatlMeritSF; PepBnd; SchMus; Univ; Medical Science.

FLOERCHINGER, Linda L; Tri Center HS; Neola, IA; Band; Chrs; PolWkr; 4-H; Bsktbl; Chrldr; IMSpt; 4-HAwd; University Of Iowa; Psychology.

FLOHR, Douglas G; Byron HS; Byron, IL; 5/63 PresSrCls; HonRl; JrNHS; NHS; LetterFtbl; College.

FLOHR, Pamela J; Dickinson HS; Dickinson, ND; Chr; CAP; HonRl; HospAde; NatlThespSoc; OffAde; SchMus; SchPl; RptrYrbk; College; Medicine.

FLOHRSCHUTZ, Ellen S; Shawnee Heights HS; Topeka, KS; 1/210 SecFrshCls; TrsJrCls; ALAGirlsSt; Chr; ChrhWkr; SecYthFlsp; RptrSchPpr; PpCl; LetterBsktbl; PPFtbl; College; Math.

FLOOD, Aunita; Lake Orion HS; Pontiac, MI; 16/320 HonRl; NHS; StuGov; TchrAde; RptrYrbk; RptrSchPpr; Univ Of Mi; Pre Law.

FLOOD, Donald W; Jefferson West HS; Meriden, KS; 4/60 TrsSrCls; CmntyWkr; HonRl; LbryAde; SchAde; StuCncl; RptrSchPpr; SchPpr; FFA; LetterBsbl; CaptFtbl; LetterTrk; KiwanAwd; Washburn Univ; Industrial Engineer.

FLOOD, Don W; Jefferson West HS; Meriden, KS; 4/60 TrsSrCls; CmntyWkr; HonRl; LbryAde; StuCncl; RptrSchPpr; SchPpr; LetterBsbl; LetterFtbl; LetterTrk; U Of Ks; Engineering.

FLOOD, Kim D; Clever HS; Clever, MO; 1/26 SecBand; HonRl; StuCncl; Twrl; RptrYrbk; FHA; MthCl; SciCl; Chrldr; DanFAwd; CitAwd; Southwest Mo State Univ; Home Ec Teacher.

FLOOD, Megan M; Mother Of Sorrows HS; Chicago, IL; 10/131 VPSophCls; HonRl; NHS; VPStuCncl; TchrAde; PpCl; GAA; Univ Of Illinois; Psychology.

FLOOD, Roger J; Albany HS; Brooklyn, WI; 3/34 ALBoysSt; Chrs; CncrtBnd; MrchBnd; NHS; SchMus; StuCncl; SptEdYrbk; VP4-H; LetterBsktbl; Wisconsin School Of Electronics; Engineerin.

FLOOD, Steven P; Sibley Comm HS; Sibley, IA; ALBoysSt; Aud/Vis; HonRl; NatlMeritSchl; AmLegAwd; Clg; Elec Engineering.

FLORA, Benjamin L; Hauser HS; Hope, IN; 7/84 Band; NHS; YthFlsp; LetterBsbl; LetterBsktbl; CaptTrk; GodCntryAwd; OptClAwd; Bob James Univ; Medicine.

FLOREANI, Derek A; Lakeshore HS; Stevensville, MI; HonRl; NatlMeritSchl; Univ; Professional.

FLOREK, Gregory J; Quigley South HS; Chicago, IL; 2/165 Chrs; HonRl; NHS; NatlMeritCmnd; Sacrstn; StuGov; TchrAde; EdYrBk; Northwestern Illinois Univ; Law.

FLOREK, Karen M; Lourdes HS; Chicago, IL; 18/299 HonRl; NatlFornLg; NHS; RptrYrbk; CchngActv; IMSpt; Coll.

FLORENCE, Donna E; Lincoln East HS; Lincoln, NE; PresSrCls; HonRl; NHS; NatlMeritSchl; PresQuill&Scroll; SctActv; TchrAde; YthLg; EdSchPpr; PpCl; Fl St Univ; Law.

FLORENCE, Isabell J; Lutheran West HS; Detroit, MI; Band; ChrhWkr; CncrtBnd; DrlTm; HonRl; MrchBnd; OffAde; Orch; PepBnd; LatCl; College; Liberal Arts.

FLORENCE, Kari A; Velva Public HS; Velva, ND; 11/47 PresBand; HonRl; NHS; PresStuCncl; TchrAde; Yrbk; PresFHA; PpCl; LetterBsktbl; LetterTrk; Nd State University; Phy Ed & Spec Ed.

FLORENCE, Kenneth L; Southeast HS; Wichita, KS; HonRl; LbryAde; NatlMeritCmnd; NatlThespSoc; SchPl; College; Business Admn.

FLORENCE, Martha E; Dowling HS; Des Moines, IA; 99/368 DrlTm; JA; NatlFornLg; SctActv; UNYO; EdYrBk; CaptBsktbl; LetterTrk; IMSpt; PPFtbl; Univ Of Mebraska Lincoln; Journalism.

FLORER, Timothy M; Newark HS; Newark, IL; Band; CncrtBnd; DrlTm; HonRl; MrchBnd; 4-H; FrCl; LetterBsbl; LetterTrk; U Of Ill; Radio.

FLORES, Antonio; Calumet HS; Gary, IN; Purdue Univ; Elec Tech.

FLORES, Elizabeth C; Roosevelt HS; East Chicago, IN; 23/257 TreasFrCl; MthCl; SciCl; PPFtbl; Purdue Univ; Physicist.

FLOREY, Gregory L; Bethany HS; Bethany, IL; ChrhWkr; CmntyWkr; HonRl; StuCncl; YthFlsp; FHA; Bsktbl; Ftbl; IMSpt;.

FLOREY, Michael F; Clark HS; Clark, SD; VPSophCls; ALBoysSt; HonRl; SchMus; VPStuCncl; 4-H; FFA; PpCl; Bsktbl; Trk; College.

FLORIDA, Daniel; Bernie HS; Bernie, MO; ChrhWkr; HonRl; SchPl; College.

FLORSCHUETZ, Deborah A; Alma HS; Alma, MI; 1/267 Band; ChrhWkr; HospAde; NHS; StuGov; PpCl; Bsktbl; LetterTrk; Valparaiso Univ; Medical.

FLORY, Cheryl D; St Charles HS; St Charles, MI; CncrtBnd; DrlTm; HonRl; MrchBnd; NHS; StuGov; LetterBsktbl; Chrldr; GAA; PPFtbl; Univ; Psychology.

FLOURNOY, Jeffrey E; St Anne Community HS; Momence, IL; 55/160 HonRl; JA; NHS; ROTC; SchPl; RptrYrbk; RptrSchPpr; FBLA; Bsbl; LetterFtbl; Coll; Prof.

FLOW, Michael; Yankton Sr HS; Yankton, SD; 2/233 PresFrshCls; Band; HonRl; NHS; NatlThespSoc; PepBnd; Univ Of South Dakato; Medicine.

FLOWERS, Betsy J; Berkley HS; Huntington Woods, MI; JrNHS; LetterBsbl; LetterBsktbl; VPGAA; IMSpt; College.

FLOWERS, Carol J; Centerville Community HS; Centerville, IA; Band; Chrs; DrlTm; HonRl; MrchBnd; NHS; SchMus; FBLA; SpnCl; College; Vocation.

FLOWERS, Gregory D; Houston HS; Houston, MO; HonRl; NHS; PpCl; LetterFtbl; Univ Of Missouri; Conservation.

FLOWERS, Mary A; St Elmo HS; St Elma, IL; 10/54 SecSophCls; Band; Chr; Chrs; HonRl; PepBnd; SchMus; SchPl; PpCl; GAA; College; Pharmacy.

FLOWERS, Tammy L; West Vigo HS; West Terre Haute, IN; Band; ChrhWkr; CncrtBnd; HonRl; SchAde; TchrAde; Teen; Business School; Professional.

FLOWERS, Vickie; Mark Twain HS; Perry, MO; Chrs; HonRl; HospAde; LbryAde; SchPl; FHA; FNA; PpCl; Bsktbl; Nursing School.

FLOYD, Malcolm V; Port Huron HS; Port Huron, MI; Band; CncrtBnd; HonRl; MrchBnd; StuCncl; Ftbl; Michigan State Univ; Business.

FLOYD, Sandra J; El Dorado Springs R 2 HS; El Dorado Springs, MO; 9/109 Chr; HonRl; ModUN; NHS; OffAde; Yrbk; RptrSchPpr; FHA; SecFTA; PPFtbl; Sch Of The Ozarks; English Major.

FLUEGEL, Mary J; Thomas Jefferson HS; Rockford, IL; 1/335 Band; Chr; CncrtBnd; HonRl; MrchBnd; NHS; PepBnd; Univ Of Ill; Veterinarian.

FLUGA, Eric C; Stewardson Strasburg HS; Stewardson, IL; 2/53 Band; HonRl; NHS; NatlMeritCmnd; Univ Of Illinois; Mechanical Engineer.

FLUGAUR, Linda G; John Edwards HS; Port Edwards, WI; 5/68 StuGov; TchrAde; MthCl; LetterBsktbl; LetterTrk; GAA; PPFtbl; AmLegAwd; DARAwd; CitAwd; Uw Stevens Point; Pro Jr High School Ed.

FLY, Elaine C; Niles HS; Niles, MI; 9/369 Chr; HonRl; HospAde; NHS; NatlThespSoc; SchMus; SchPl; RptrYrbk; LetterTennis; IMSpt; Univ Of Mi; Medical Tech.

FLYNN, Bruce M; Hillsdale HS; Hillsdale, MI; Chr; Chrl; HonRl; SchMus; SchPl; SctActv; RptrYrbk; 4-H; College.

FLYNN, Colleen A; Rapid City Central HS; Rapid City, SD; 1/539 PresFrshCls; AFS; ALAGirlsSt; HonRl; HospAde; LitMag; SchPl; StuCncl; PresYthFlsp; GAA; College; Nursing.

FLYNN, Daniel A; Hillsdale HS; Hillsdale, MI; Chr; Chrl; Chrs; LitMag; SchPl; RptrYrbk; EdYrBk; SptEdYrbk; Yrbk; FrCl; College; Dentistry Or Law.

FLYNN, Daniel P; Evergreen Pk Community HS; Evergreen Pk, IL; 10/439 VPFrshCls; PresSophCls; PresSrCls; ChrhWkr; HonRl; StuGov; MthCl; SciCl; Bsktbl; LetterFtbl; LetterTrk; CchngActv; AmLegAwd; Us Coast Guard Academy; Oceanography.

FLYNN, David W; Taylor Center HS; Taylor, MI; 18/417 Chr; NHS; NatlThespSoc; SchPl; SchPpr; IMSpt; College; Art.

FLYNN, Deanna C; Adrian HS; Adrian, MI; 42/404 Chr; DrmMjrt; NatlFornLg; NHS; SchMus; TchrAde; YthFlsp; FBLA; GerCl; PpCl; Central Michigan Univ; Speech Therapist.

FLYNN, James P; Routt; Jacksonville, IL; Band; HonRl; MrchBnd; NHS; LatCl; Ftbl; Glf; Univ Of Illinois; Pharmacist.

FLYNN, Jeanne E; Madrid Comm HS; Madrid, IA; 6/68 Band; HonRl; NHS; SchPl; SctActv; StuCncl; SciCl; Bsbl; Bsktbl; Trk; 4-HAwd; JCAwd; Iowa State Univ; Interior Design.

FLYNN, Kathleen M; Aurora Central Catholic HS; Aurora, IL; 5/165 HonRl; HospAde; JA; NHS; RedCrAde; Interior Decorator.

FLYNN, Kelly E; Lake Fenton HS; Fenton, MI; 31/162 Chr; CmntyWkr; HonRl; SchPl; StuCncl; TchrAde; RptrYrbk; SchPpr; Trk; Chrldr; PPFtbl; College; Art.

FLYNN, Matthew P; Chosen Valley HS; Stewartville, MN; Aud/Vis; HonRl; LetterFtbl; College; Teaching.

FLYNN, Michael K; Ogorman HS; Sioux Falls, SD; ALBoysSt; NatlFornLg; NHS; NatlMeritCmnd; SchMus; LetterTrk; S Dakota St Univ; Dentist.

FLYNN, Michael N; Community R Vi HS; Martinsburg, MO; Band; ChrhWkr; CncrtBnd; MrchBnd; PepBnd; SctActv; TchrAde; RptrYrbk; Trk; IMSpt; Northeast Missouri St U; Physcology.

FLYNN, Pamela J; Highland HS; Riverside, IA; Chrs; ChrhWkr; HonRl; YthFlsp; Yrbk; 4-H; PpCl; Bsbl; Bsktbl; Trk; Bus Sch; Secretary Medical.

FLYNN, Rebecca R; Central HS; Switz City, IN; Band; ChrhWkr; DrlTm; HonRl; MrchBnd; PepBnd; EdYrBk; SptEdYrbk; Yrbk; SchPpr; PpCl; LetterBsbl; LetterBsktbl; GAA; College; Secretary.

FLYNN, Teresa A; East Chas Mix #102 HS; Wagner, SD; HonRl; RptrSchPpr; Col; Psychologist.

FLYNN, Teresa S; Owosso HS; Owosso, MI; 6/452 NHS; SpnCl; GAA; IMSpt; EldAwd; U Of Notre Dame; Architecture.

FLYNN, Tom J; Scranton Public HS; Scranton, ND; 7/27 Band; Chrs; CncrtBnd; HonRl; NHS; SchPl; SctActv; StuCncl; FBLA; GerCl;.

FLYNN, William; R C Central HS; Rapids City, SD; 172/552 Aud/Vis; HonRl; LbryAde; NatlFornLg; SctActv; StuCncl; RptrSchPpr; KeyCl; Trk; Univ Of Sc; Broadcast Journalism.

FOCHEK, Mary A; Mercy HS; Omaha, NE; NatlFornLg; SchMus; SchPl; Sdlty; FrCl; SciCl; Swmmng; College.

FOCKEN, Joyce E; Douglas Community HS; Douglas, NE; 1/10 TrsFrshCls; TrsSophCls; PresJrCls; Band; Chr; HonRl; RptrYrbk; LetterTrk; Chrldr; 4-HAwd; Armed Forces; Math.

FODNESS, Bruce; Huron HS; Huron, SD; 8/305 Band; ChrhWkr; CncrtBnd; MrchBnd; NHS; 4-H; Bsktbl; IMSpt; South Dakota St U; Curriculum Of Major Stdy.

FODNESS, Grace A; Canton HS; Lennox, SD; Band; Chr; ChrhWkr; CmntyWkr; HonRl; Orch; SchPl; RptrSchPpr; 4-H; SciCl; University; Professional.

FOE, Darryl V; Aosiclare HS; Golconda, IL; Band; CncrtBnd; HonRl; MrchBnd; Univ Of Illinois; Dentist.

FOEGEN, Darlene; Cochrane Fountain City HS; Cochrane, WI; Band; DrmMjrt; NHS; PepBnd; SchMus; TchrAde; Yrbk; FBLA; PpCl; Business School, Accountant.

FOELSING, Maleah S; Stewardson Strasburg HS; Strasburb, IL; 3/50 SecJrCls; HonRl; NatlMeritCmnd; TchrAde; Yrbk; FHA; PpCl; College; Respiratory Therapy.

FOERSTER, Jeffery S; Woodstock HS; Woodstock, IL; 36/270 HonRl; NHS; NatlThespSoc; SchMus; SchPl; TchrAde; Yrbk; RptrSchPpr; Western Illinois Univ; Law Enforcement.

FOERSTER, Julie A; Midland HS; Midland, MI; 7/433 CncrtBnd; HonRl; MrchBnd; NHS; NatlMeritCmnd; SctActv; YthFlsp; Bsktbl; LetterGlf; Tennis; College; Nursing.

FOERTSCH, Daniel J; Leo HS; Chicago, IL; 41/200 CtyCnl; HonRl; PolWkr; StuGov; LetterTrk; CaptIMSpt; Loyola Univ; Biology.

FOERTSCH, Linda M; Wyndmere Public HS; Wyndmere, ND; VPJrCls; Chr; HonRl; NHS; SchPl; RptrSchPpr; 4-H; FHA; GAA; 4-HAwd; College; Lab Tech.

FOERY, Mary F; Immaculata HS; Detroit, MI; ChrhWkr; HonRl; NHS; NatlMeritSF; OffAde; SchAde; SchPl; StuGov; FrCl; LatCl; Western Mich Univ.

FOG, Susan G; Homewood Flossmoor HS; Homewood, IL; 79/1000 PresFrshCls; PresJrCls; ALAGirlsSt; Chr; ChrhWkr; HospAde; NatlThespSoc; Orch; SchPl; CaptChrldr; College; Nursing.

FOGARTY, Anne E; Lidgerwood Public HS; Lidgerwood, ND; 25/50 SecJrCls; Band; CncrtBnd; MrchBnd; SchPl; SchPpr; 4-H; GerCl; PpCl; LetterBsktbl; College; Teach Special Ed.

FOGARTY, Susan E; Carroll HS; Flora, IN; 9/131 Chrs; HonRl; NHS; NatlThespSoc; SchMus; SchPl; TchrAde; FTA; SpnCl; PpCl; Coll; Pro.

FOGEL, William H; South Vigo HS; Terre Haute, IN; 5/586 ALBoysSt; ChrhWkr; HonRl; NatlFornLg; NatlMeritSF; StuCncl; StuGov; YthFlsp; KeyCl; GerCl; Rose Hulman Inst Of Tech; Civil Engineering.

FOGERTY, Frances J; Herrin HS; Herrin, IL; 11/210 DrlTm; NHS; RptrYrbk; RptrSchPpr; PpCl; Siu; Physical Therapist.

FOGLE, Elizabeth A; York Community HS; Elmhurst, IL; 37/892 HonRl; JrNHS; NHS; NatlThespSoc; Quill&Scroll; SchMus; SchPpr; PresPpCl; CitAwd; Miami University; Applied Science.

FOGLEMAN, Mary B; Lanphier HS; Springfield, IL; 50/560 ChrhWkr; SctActv; TchrAde; Yrbk; RptrSchPpr; Bsbl;.

FOGLESONG, Betty S; Kirksville Sr HS; Kirksville, MO; PresSrCls; ALAGirlsSt; HonRl; NHS; NatlMeritCmnd; OffAde; SchAde; StuCncl; StuGov; TchrAde; SpnCl; DanFAwd; GovHonPrgAwd; Northeast Missouri State Univ; Special Educ.

FOGLESONG, William S; Toulon La Fayette HS; Toulon, IL; VPSophCls; Chrs; HonRl; 4-H; FFA; Bsktbl; Ftbl; Black Hawk E Jr College.

FOGT, Annette; Bishop Dubourg HS; St Louis, MO; SchPpr; Us Air Force.

FOHL, Nicholas E; Brookville HS; Cedar Grove, IN; 12/169 Aud/Vis; ChrhWkr; HonRl; NHS; StuCncl; PresSpnCl; SciCl; LetterGlf; LetterTennis; College; Computer Sciences.

FOHS, Maria L; Wateruliet HS; Wateruliet, MI; 12/100 Band; CncrtBnd; HonRl; JA; MrchBnd; NHS; PepBnd; SchAde; SchMus; SctActv; StuCncl; TchrAde; 4-H; 4-HAwd; University; Accounting.

FOILES, Gary L; Parsons HS; Parsons, KS; NatlMeritSF; KeyCl; Clge; Mathematician.

FOIST, Jill A; Jennings County HS; Scipio, IN; ChrhWkr; CmntyWkr; DrlTm; HospAde; 4-H; SpnCl; PpCl; 4-HAwd; Marion County Hospital; Nursing.

FOLAND, Laura L; South Side HS; Fort Wayne, IN; NatlFornLg; SchPl; GAA; College; Chemist.

FOLEY, Barbara J; Akron Community HS; Akron, IA; ChrhWkr; HonRl; HospAde; LbryAde; 4-H; 4-HAwd; College; Professional.

FOLEY, Bruce L; Hemingford HS; Hemingford, NE; ALBoysSt; Band; CncrtBnd; HonRl; MrchBnd; NHS; Quill&Scroll; SctActv; StuCncl; RptrSchPpr; SciCl; LetterFtbl; Glf; Wrstlng; College; Drafting.

FOLEY, Charles M; Halstad HS; Halstad, MN; 1/22 VPFrshCls; VPSophCls; ALBoysSt; Band; Chr; Chrs; HonRl; StuGov; EdSchPpr; FFA; Moorhead State Clg; Business Admin.

FOLEY, Debra D; Odell Comm HS; Odell, IL; 6/33 Chr; HonRl; SchPl; YthFlsp; RptrYrbk; FrCl; PpCl; Chrldr; Southern Illinois Univ; Social Welfare.

FOLEY, Evan J; Morton West HS; Berwyn, IL; HonRl; JrNHS; NHS; Clge; Math & Science.

FOLEY, Frances A; Mercy HS; Richmond Hts, MO; 14/170 Chr; HonRl; NHS; OffAde; St Louis U; Accounting.

FOLEY, Jane S; St Paul/kennedy HS; Chicago, IL; 43/544 HonRl; SctActv; Teen; 4-H; FrCl; De Paul Univ; Sociology.

FOLEY, Jeffrey; Tyndall HS; Tyndall, SD; PresFrshCls; ChrhWkr; SchPl; SctActv; StuCncl; Bsbl; Bsktbl; Ftbl; Swmmng; Trk;.

FOLEY, Kerry J; Jasper HS; Jasper, IN; 16/290 Chr; Chrs; CmntyWkr; HonRl; NHS; SchMus; SchPl; StuCncl; TreasKeyCl; KiwanAwd; U Of Notre Dame; Business Admin.

FOLEY, Linda M; Northwestern HS; Blandinsville, IL; 4/55 TrsJrCls; SecBand; CncrtBnd; HonRl; LbryAde; MrchBnd; VPNHS; PepBnd; VPGAA; DARAwd; Western Illinois Univ; Home Economics.

FOLEY, Mary C; Blair HS; Blair, NE; ALAGirlsSt; Chr; DrlTm; HonRl; NatlThespSoc; SchMus; 4-H; FHA; 4-HAwd; PresAwd; Un Of Ne; Dental Hygenist.

FOLEY, Patti A; Le Sueur HS; Le Sueur, MN; 2/112 TrsSophCls; Band; Chr; HonRl; JA; NHS; EdSchPpr; Bsktbl; PPFtbl; JAAwd; Univ Of Mn; Math.

FOLEY, Philip L; Southport HS; Indianapolis, IN; 40/419 Band; Chr; HonRl; NHS; SchMus; YthFlsp; VPYthLg; KeyCl; PpCl; CaptIMSpt; Anderson Coll; Music.

FOLEY, Randy; Milan HS; Milaw, IN; SecTrsFrshCls; HonRl; OffAde; RptrSchPpr; Trk; Isu In St Univ; Physical Ed Coaching.

FOLEY, Steven A; Monroe HS; La Salle, MI; 31/523 Chr; ChrhWkr; CncrtBnd; HonRl; NHS; SctActv; YthFlsp; Ftbl; CchngActv; IMSpt; College; Doctor.

FOLEY, William P; Benet Academy; Lisle, IL; HonRl; NHS; Illinois Benedictine College; Mathematics.

FOLEY, Yvonne; Parkside HS; Jackson, MI; CmntyWkr; HonRl; NatlFornLg; SchPl; FrCl; GerCl; PpCl; CchngActv; Central Michigan Univ; Law.

FOLK, Cathy J; Warsaw Senior HS; Warsaw, IN; 62/380 Band; HospAde; SchPl; YthFlsp; 4-H; Bsktbl; GAA; 4-HAwd; Purdue Univ; Vet.

FOLKENS, Luann; Central Lyon HS; Rock Rapids, IA; Chrs; HonRl; NHS; OffAde; RptrYrbk; FTA; FrCl; Business School; Vocation.

FOLKERS, Carolyn K; Minonk Dana Rutland HS; Minonk, IL; AFS; Band; CncrtBnd; HonRl; MrchBnd; PepBnd; YthFlsp; FrCl; College; Nursing.

FOLKERS, Karen L; Marion Independent HS; Marion, IA; HonRl; LbryAde; NatlMeritCmnd; SctActv; TchrAde; RptrSchPpr; LetterBsktbl; Trk; PPFtbl; William Penn Col; Elementary Ed.

FOLKERS, Rick J; B R F HS; Blackriver Falls, WI; Band; CncrtBnd; HonRl; LetterBsbl; LetterFtbl; Western Wi Tech; Elec.

FOLKERT, Bernie W; Staples HS; Staples, MN; 12/157 HonRl; YthFlsp; LetterFtbl; LetterWrstlng; Bemidii State Coll; Doctor.

FOLKERTS, Debra S; Steamboat Rock Comm HS; Steamboat Rock, IA; Chrs; ChrhWkr; HonRl; SchMus; SchPl; YthFlsp; LetterBsbl; Bsktbl; LetterTrk; LetterChrldr; 4-HAwd; Hawkeye Insitute; Commercial Art.

FOLKES, Michelle J; Coon Rapids Sr HS; Blaine, MN; 12/761 HonRl; JrNHS; NHS; SchPl; Univ Of Minn; Art.

FOLKNER, Patricia; University HS; Warrensburg, MO; 8/50 Band; Chr; HonRl; NHS; SchMus; StuCncl; EdYrBk; SpnCl; IMSpt; AmLegAwd; College; Paraprofessional Legal Assistant.

FOLKS, Sandra; Hanover Horton HS; Hanover, MI; TrsSrCls; Band; HonRl; OffAde; StuCncl; 4-H; Bsktbl; Trk; AmLegAwd; Jackson Comm; Secretarial.

FOLL, Gary R; West Richland Comm HS; Noble, IL; Chr; HonRl; LbryAde; SchPl; StuGov; SchPpr; LetterBsbl; LetterBsktbl; HstJrCls; AmLegAwd; College; Professional.

FOLLEN, Sandra L; Auburndale HS; Arpin, WI; HonRl; FBLA; FHA; PpCl; Sch; Sec Or Clerical.

FOLLETT, Kenneth G; Sycamore HS; Sycamore, IL; 20/222 Aud/Vis; HonRl; LbryAde; PolWkr; SchPl; TchrAde; RptrYrbk; EdYrBk; N Illinois Univ; Business.

FOLLMAN, Duane; Central Hs; Hampshire, IL; 1/75 VPSophCls; ChrhWkr; HonRl; NHS; PresStuCncl; PpCl; Bsbl; Bsktbl; CaptFtbl; Augustana College;doctor Of Medicine Or Pe.

FOLLOW, Dana E; East Gary Edison HS; East Gary, IN; 46/203 Band; CncrtBnd; HospAde; MrchBnd; PepBnd; SpnCl; Indiana Univ; Radiology.

FOLSOM, Robin G; Benkelman HS; Benkelman, NE; Band; Chrs; CncrtBnd; HonRl; MrchBnd; PepBnd; SchPl; StuCncl; FHA; SciCl; Univ Of Texas; Nurse.

FOLSTAD, Carolyn D; Mabel Canton HS; Mabel, MN; 8/57 Band; Chr; CncrtBnd; HonRl; MrchBnd; PepBnd; Pres4-H; FHA; 4-HAwd; Vocational Tech Schl; Nursing.

FOLTMAN, Richard A; Escanaba Area Public HS; Escanaba, MI; 24/383 Band; CtyCnl; JA; NHS; SchMus; YthLg; EdYrBk; SchPpr; FTA; JAAwd; Univ Of Michigan; Meteorology.

FOLTZ, Lisa M; Central Lyon HS; Rock Rapids, IA; PresSophCls; TrsJrCls; ALAGirlsSt; CncrtBnd; Mdrgl; NHS; SchPl; SchPpr; PpCl; Chrldr; Clge; Ed.

FOLTZ, Lois E; Hoxie HS; Hoxie, KS; 7/72 SecSrCls; Band; Chr; HonRl; HospAde; NHS; PepBnd; FHA; PpCl; York College; Nursing.

FOLTZ, Michael C; Maine East HS; Niles, IL; 85/890 HonRl; LetterBsbl; LetterSocr; Ill State Univ; Lawyer.

FOMBELLE, Lisa L; Warrensburg Latham HS; Decatur, IL; 5/105 AFS; Chr; CmntyWkr; HonRl; Mdrgl; SchMus; StuCncl; Pres4-H; FHA; KeyCl; GAA; DanFAwd; 4-HAwd; Univ Of Illinois.

FONDELL, Michelle M; Roosevelt HS; Minneapolis, MN; Chr; HonRl; HospAde; NHS; RptrSchPpr; U Of Mn; Math Acct.

FONG, Nancy; Lindblom Hs; Chicago, IL; 19 DrmMjrt; SecHonRl; LitMag; NHS; TchrAde; RptrSchPpr; MthCl; SciCl; U Of Ill;chemistry And Art.

FONG, Robert T; Weber HS; Chicago, IL; 3/193 VPFrshCls; PresSophCls; VPJrCls; DrlTm; HonRl; LbryAde; NHS; Sacrstn; SctActv; StuCncl; Yrbk; MthCl; Northwestern Univ; Doctor.

FONNER, Patricia; Urbana Sr Hs; Urbana, IL; 22/429 ChrhWkr; HonRl; U Of Illinois; Art.

FONS, Anne Marie; St Marys Acad; West Allis, WI; Chrs; HospAde; JA; NatlMeritCmnd; SchMus; RptrSchPpr; College; Nursing.

FOO, Barbara C; Niles West HS; Skokie, IL; 42/648 Chr; CmntyWkr; HonRl; LitMag; NHS; NatlMeritCmnd; SchPl; StuGov; Chrldr; College; Psychology.

FOOK, Richard D; Clayton HS; Clayton, MO; ChrhWkr; Teen; YthFlsp; SchPpr; PpCl; Bsktbl; LetterFtbl; LetterTrk; IMSpt; PPFtbl; St Louis Coll Of Pharmacy; Pharmacy.

FOOS, Richard; Kalamazoo Central HS; Kalamazoo, MI; NatlMeritCmnd; TchrAde; Univ; Computer Science.

FOOTE, Douglas E; Chariton Community HS; Chariton, IA; ALBoysSt; ChrhWkr; PresStuCncl; StuGov; Bsbl; Bsktbl; Glf; College; Professional.

FOOTE, Rita A; Shelby HS; Montague, MI; 31/125 SecSrCls; Band; CncrtBnd; HospAde; NHS; RedCrAde; SchPl; StuCncl; TchrAde; FNA; GAA; PPFtbl; CitAwd; Mich State U; Nursing.

FORAL, Joseph J; Fort Calhoun HS; Fort Calhoun, NE; PresFrshCls; PresJrCls; Chr; HonRl; NHS; StuCncl; FBLA; LetterBsktbl; LetterFtbl; LetterTrk;.

FORAN, Helen M; Ancilla Domini HS; Oak Park, IL; 1/17 Chrl; DrlTm; HonRl; HospAde; LbryAde; SchMus; SchPl; PresStuGov; IMSpt; Univ Of Ill Cahmpaign; Veterinary Med.

FORAN, Mary C; Thornwood HS; South Holland, IL; 45/846 ChrhWkr; HonRl; JrNHS; NHS; De Paul University; Accounting.

FORARE, Lester; Annandale HS; Annandale, MN; HonRl; NHS; St Cloud State College; Engineering.

FORBECK, Gerald P; Okawville HS; Okawville, IL; 1/67 TrsSophCls; HonRl; NHS; StuCncl; RptrYrbk; Pres4-H; PresFFA; Bsbl; IMSpt; 4-HAwd; Mechanic Schl; Mechanic.

FORBES, John J; Eagle Grove HS; Eagle Grove, IA; 25/135 HonRl; NHS; NatlThespSoc; SchMus; SchPl; StuCncl; YthFlsp; RptrYrbk; EdSchPpr; Trk; Univ; Pharmacist.

FORBES, Larry A; Westview HS; Kankakee, IL; 25/223 Chr; ChrhWkr; HonRl; NHS; SchMus; SctActv; LetterTrk; LetterWrstlng; GodCntryAwd; Trade Sch; Vocation.

FORBES, Laurie J; United Twp HS; Moline, IL; 7/490 TreasNHS; LetterBsktbl; LetterTrk; GAA; Illinois State Univ; Physical Education.

FORBES, Mark M; Normal Community HS; Normal, IL; 65/490 Band; HonRl; NHS; NatlMeritCmnd; Yrbk; SchPpr; Ftbl; LetterTrk; IMSpt; Bradley University; Electrical Engineer.

FORBES, Patricia A; Mother Of Sorrows HS; Chicago, IL; HospAde; SchAde; SchMus; SchPl; TchrAde; Bsbl; Bsktbl; LetterGAA; IMSpt; VoiceDemAwd; Business Schl; Professional.

FORBES, Scotty R; Riverton HS; Galena, KS; Band; Chr; Chrs; ChrhWkr; CncrtBnd; HonRl; MrchBnd; Orch; PepBnd; SchPl; StuCncl; Bsbl; Bsktbl; University; Professional.

FORBIS, Bryan L; Jeff City Senior HS; Jefferson City, MO; 8/476 ChrhWkr; HonRl; JrNHS; NHS; Quill&Scroll; SchPpr; MthCl; Univ Of Mo; Law Or Journalism.

FORBY, Daniel P; Benilde St Margarets HS; Bloomington, MN; 34/189 Chrs; ChrhWkr; HonRl; NHS; NatlMeritCmnd; Sacrstn; SancSoc; GerCl; Ftbl; CchngActv; IMSpt; St Johns University.

FORCK, Joan M; Helias HS; Jefferson City, MO; 9/174 Band; ChrhWkr; CncrtBnd; HonRl; MrchBnd; NHS; PepBnd; SchMus; SchPl; PpCl; Univ; Lab Technician.

FORD, Amy L; Hortonville HS; Appleton, WI; 11/154 Chrs; HonRl; NHS; RptrYrbk; RptrSchPpr; SchPpr; PpCl; Trk; GAA; Uw La Crosse; Phys Ther.

FORD, Anna Marie; Oak Creek Sr HS; Oak Creek, WI; Band; ChrhWkr; CncrtBnd; HonRl; NatlFornLg; PepBnd; Pres4-H; GerCl; DanFAwd; 4-HAwd; Univ Of Wis; Television Broadcaster.

FORD, Brian; Wabash HS; Wabash, IN; 5/204 VPFrshCls; PresSophCls; PresSrCls; ALBoysSt; HonRl; JA; NHS; N C State; Male Nurse Or Doctor.

FORD, Bryce L; Lebanon HS; Lebanon, IL; 18/95 Band; Chrs; ChrhWkr; CncrtBnd; HonRl; NHS; StuCncl; YthFlsp; SciCl; Trk; Univ; Physics & Music.

FORD, Dana D; Nora Springs Rock Fls Com HS; Nora Springs, IA; ALBoysSt; Chr; Chrs; ChrhWkr; CmntyWkr; HonRl; JrNHS; NHS; SchMus; SchPl; Northwestern Orange City.

FORD, Daniel L; Parkside HS; Jackson, MI; 25/435 ChrhWkr; NatlMeritCmnd; NatlMeritSF; SchPpr; Trk; Wrstlng; Spring Arbor Clge; Pastor.

FORD, David A; Southwest HS; St Louis, MO; 9/576 ChrhWkr; CncrtBnd; HonRl; YthFlsp; Bsktbl; CaptTrk; Univ; Ecological Engr.

FORD, David R; Elkhart Lake Glenbeulah HS; Glenbeulah, WI; 18/60 HonRl; SpnCl; CaptFtbl; CaptTrk; CaptWrstlng; CchngActv; GovHonPrgAwd;.

FORD, Donald A; Frankfort Sr HS; Frankfort, IN; 47/260 OffAde; StuCncl; StuGov; KeyCl; Ftbl; Wrstlng; University; Electronics.

FORD, Fred L; Wichita North HS; Columbine, KS; 9/502 Chr; HonRl; LitMag; Mdrgl; OffAde; YthFlsp; PpCl; LetterFtbl; LetterTrk; CchngActv; Ks State Univ; Nuclear Eng.

FORD, Isaac; Cass Tech HS; Detroit, MI; Chr; HonRl; OffAde; TchrAde; Tennis; IMSpt; CitAwd; V Of M Lawrence Tech; Architecture.

FORD, James; Adrian R 3 HS; Adrian, MO; ChrhWkr; FFA; Bsktbl; Ftbl; Trk; IMSpt; College; Coaching.

FORD, Jeffery L; Southern HS; Stronghurst, IL; 6/52 VPSrCls; ALBoysSt; Aud/Vis; ChrhWkr; HonRl; LbryAde; YthFlsp; SptEdSchPpr; Bsktbl; Ftbl; Illinois Weslyen Univ; Veterinarian.

FORD, John B; Peru Sr HS; Peru, IN; Band; Chr; ChrhWkr; CncrtBnd; HonRl; MrchBnd; NHS; Orch; PepBnd; SchMus; Professional.

FORD, Karla D; Romeoville HS; Bolingbrook, IL; 65/219 ChrhWkr; DrlTm; HonRl; VPSctActv; VPFNA; Ill Weselyan Univ; Nursing.

FORD, Kathleen; Campus HS; Haysville, KS; 3/256 HonRl; JA; OffAde; TchrAde; FHA; Business School; Secretarial Studies.

FORD, Kimberley A; Oak Park & River Forest HS; River Forest, IL; 140/1200 Band; Chrs; HonRl; MrchBnd; SctActv; StuCncl; StuGov; Twrl; FrCl; Trk; U Of Il; Cpa.

FORD, La Donna; Mcdonald HS; Jane, MO; Band; ChrhWkr; DrlTm; HonRl; MrchBnd; ModUN; NHS; NatlThespSoc; PepBnd; SchPl; Coll; Medical.

FORD, Lawrence R; Marion HS; Marion, KS; PresSophCls; VPSrCls; HonRl; HospAde; TchrAde; GerCl; Bsktbl; Ftbl; Trk; Kansas St University; Accounting.

FORD, Marc A; Turner HS; Kansas City, KS; PresSrCls; ALBoysSt; Band; HonRl; MrchBnd; NHS; PepBnd; StuCncl; SchPpr; Ftbl; U Of Kansas; Journalism.

FORD, Martin L; Harper Creek HS; Battle Creek, MI; HonRl; TchrAde; Yrbk; VPSpnCl; Kendall Schl Of Design; Commercial Art.

FORD, Pamela S; Waldron HS; Waldron, MI; 2/50 Band; CncrtBnd; HonRl; MrchBnd; PepBnd; TchrAde; College; Mathematics.

FORD, Richard C; Liberty HS; Mountain View, MO; ChrhWkr; CmntyWkr; HonRl; JA; SchPl; SptEdSchPpr; 4-H; Bsktbl; Ftbl; Trk; School Of The Ozarks Athletic Coach.

FORD, Ronald D; Milw Lutheran HS; Milwaukee, WI; 40/260 Aud/Vis; HonRl; HospAde; JA; LetterFtbl; LetterTrk; Wrstlng; CchngActv; IMSpt; JAAwd; Georgia Tech; Architecture.

FORD, Ronald P; Swartz Creek HS; Swartz Creek, MI; 17/370 Band; Chr; ChrhWkr; HonRl; NHS; MthCl; Spring Arbor College.

FORD, Steven R; Wabash HS; Wabash, IN; 2/200 Chr; CncrtBnd; HonRl; MrchBnd; NHS; SchMus; SecSciCl; Glf; LetterTennis; IMSpt; University; Business Man.

FORD, Tracy L; Melvin Sibley HS; Melvin, IL; 10/35 VPFrshCls; Chr; HonRl; StuCncl; StuGov; YthFlsp; RptrSchPpr; LetterBsbl; LetterBsktbl; IMSpt; College; Business Management.

FORD, Valerie; Southern Hs; Carman, IL; SecSrCls; ChrhWkr; HonRl; HospAde; PresLbryAde; StuCncl; YthFlsp; PpCl; Bsktbl; GAA; College; Associate Degree Nurse.

FORD, Warren; Forest View Hs; Mt Prospect, IL; ChrhWkr; CncrtBnd; HonRl; MrchBnd; PepBnd; SchMus; Concordia Teachers College; Teaching.

FORDHAM, Debra L; Coopersville HS; Nunica, MI; HonRl; LbryAde; ModUN; 4-H; FTA; GerCl; LatCl; LetterTrk; PPFtbl; 4-HAwd; Concordia Luth Jr Coll; Elem Teaching.

FORDYCE, Christine M; York Community HS; Elmhurst, IL; SecJrCls; ALAGirlsSt; HonRl; NHS; PresQuill&Scroll; SchPl; StuCncl; RptrSchPpr; SchPpr; AmLegAwd; University Of Minn; Communications.

FOREE, Valerie A; Van Far HS; Farber, MO; Band; ChrhWkr; CmntyWkr; CncrtBnd; HonRl; JrNHS; MrchBnd; SctActv; FHA; College.

FORELL, Sandra K; Eastern Heights HS; Phillipsburg, KS; SecFrshCls; SecSophCls; SecJrCls; ChrhWkr; HonRl; OffAde; TchrAde; CaptBsktbl; Trk; Chrldr; Jr Col; Vocational.

FOREMAN, Carolyn D; Crown Point HS; Crown Point, IN; 24/450 HonRl; JrNHS; NHS; LetterTrk; GAA; IMSpt; PPFtbl; Ball State University; Psychologist.

FOREMAN, Charles E; Walker HS; Walker, MO; Chrs; ChrhWkr; CmntyWkr; HonRl; YthFlsp; CivCl; 4-H; PpCl; Bsktbl; Trk; ChmbCommrsAwd; 4-HAwd; Southwest Baptist College; Theology.

FOREMAN, Nancy E; Metropolis Comm HS; Metropolis, IL; 1/161 VPFrshCls; HonRl; NHS; YthFlsp; RptrYrbk; SptEdYrbk; SchPpr; 4-H; SpnCl; MthCl; SciCl; LetterBsktbl; LetterTennis; Univ Of Ill; Medicine.

FORESMAN, Kim S; Derby HS; Wichita, KS; 30/371 ChrhWkr; JrNHS; NatlFornLg; NHS; TchrAde; RptrYrbk; PpCl; Bsbl; LetterTrk; Tex Woman Univ; Nursing.

FORFANG, Kelly D; Hallock HS; Hallock, MN; 3/40 Chrs; HonRl; SchPl; YthFlsp; 4-H; FHA; GAA; IMSpt; Comm Coll; Inhalation Therapy.

FORGACS, William; Divine Child HS; Dearborn Hts, MI; 1/170 PresFrshCls; VPBand; HonRl; MrchBnd; NatlMeritCmnd; NatlThespSoc; Univ Of Mi; Science Oriented.

FORGALA, Pamela A; Immaculate Heart Of Mary HS; Chicago, IL; College; Biology.

FORGE, Mary J; St Marys HS; Independence, MO; 6/75 Chr; Chrl; Chrs; DrlTm; HonRl; ModUN; SchMus; SchPl; GerCl; PpCl; College.

FORGEY, Dean R; Keya Paha Co HS; Springview, NE; 2/26 Band; Chrs; CncrtBnd; HonRl; MrchBnd; PepBnd; SchPl; Bsktbl; Ftbl; Univ Of Ne ; Pre Opt.

FORGEY, Jeffrey; Moberly HS; Moberly, MO; HonRl; Bsktbl; Ftbl; IMSpt; Moberly Jr Coll; Vocation.

FORGEY, Shirley R; Colome HS; Colome, SD; Band; Chrs; CncrtBnd; HonRl; PepBnd; SchPl; Yrbk; FHA; PpCl; Chrldr;.

FORHAN, Gary D; Frank Cody HS; Detroit, MI; 11/640 PresSrCls; HonRl; NHS; StuGov; KeyCl; MthCl; PpCl; SciCl; Bsbl; Ftbl; U Of M; Ls & A.

FORMAN, Betty J; Verdigre Public HS; Verdigre, NE; 8/38 HstFrshCls; HstJrCls; ALAGirlsSt; Chrs; HonRl; NHS; SchPl; SchPpr; SpnCl; LetterTrk; Lincoln School Of Commerce; Secretarial.

FORMAN, Diane S; Bryan HS; Omaha, NE; HonRl; NatlSciFnd; College; Geology.

FORMAN, Peggy J; Milbank HS; Marvin, SD; Band; CncrtBnd; DrlTm; HonRl; MrchBnd; 4-H; FHA; LetterTrk; Chrldr; Augustana College; Nursing.

FORMISANO, Robert A; Trenton HS; Trenton, MI; ChrhWkr; HonRl; LitMag; NatlThespSoc; SchPl; SctActv; SchPpr; IMSpt; DARAwd; Clg; Prof.

FORNAL, Mary E; Harrison HS; Chicago, IL; HonRl; SecNHS; TchrAde; Ne Illinois Univ; Math.

FORNEK, Kimberly J; Queen Of Peace HS; Chicago, IL; 13/417 LitMag; NHS; NatlMeritCmnd; FrCl; U Of Northern Illinois.

FORNENGO, John D; Farmington East HS; Farmington, IL; 1/137 Chrs; CncrtBnd; HonRl; MrchBnd; NHS; Orch; PepBnd; SchMus; SchPl; PresFrCl; Lake Forest Univ; Music.

FORNERO, Joanne M; Wilmot Union HS; Camp Lake, WI; VPFrshCls; DrlTm; HonRl; Quill&Scroll; SchPl; StuCncl; RptrYrbk; PpCl; Chrldr; GAA; Practical Nursing.

FORNEY, Wesley; Frankfort Sr HS; Frankfort, IN; Band; ChrhWkr; CncrtBnd; MrchBnd; Orch; SchMus; SchPl; MthCl; SciCl; Purdue U; Pharmacy.

FORRER, Donald B; Lapel HS; Lapel, IN; Aud/Vis; StuCncl; YthFlsp; 4-H; SpnCl; LetterBsbl; LetterBsktbl; CaptFtbl; Glf; Trk; 4-HAwd; College; Professional.

FORREST, Kevin R; Bishop Noll Institute HS; South Holland, IL; HonRl; LetterFtbl; LetterSocr; LetterWrstlng; IMSpt; College; Professional.

FORREST, Kimberly A; Mexico HS; Mexico, MO; Band; CncrtBnd; DrmMjrt; JA; MrchBnd; PepBnd; SchMus; SchPl; Twrl; College; Dramatics.

FORREST, Mary; Wenona HS; Wenona, IL; 1/43 PresJrCls; Aud/Vis; Band; HonRl; NHS; RptrSchPpr; BauchLmbAwd; DARAwd; Univ Of Illinois; Professional.

FORRESTER, Cindy A; Corunna HS; Owosso, MI; PresJrCls; VPSrCls; HonRl; StuCncl; Swmmng; Chrldr; GAA;.

FORRESTER, Kevin L; Saline HS; Saline, MI; PresFrshCls; PresSophCls; ALBoysSt; Chr; ChrhWkr; HonRl; SchMus; SctActv; StuCncl; GerCl; Bsktbl; College Seminary; Priesthood.

FORRET, Deb D; Van Meter Comm HS; Booneville, IA; PresSophCls; ALAGirlsSt; Band; HonRl; NHS; RptrSchPpr; LetterBsktbl; LetterTrk; CchngActv; 4-HAwd; Iowa St Univ.

FORRET, Mary T; Calamus Community HS; Calamas, IA; VPJrCls; JrNHS; StuCncl; GerCl; LetterBsbl; LetterBsktbl; LetterTrk; College; Professional.

FORRISTALL, Susan M; Malden HS; Malden, IL; 4/15 TrsFrshCls; TrsSophCls; PresJrCls; Chrs; ChrhWkr; SchPl; YthFlsp; Yrbk; 4-H; FHA; FrCl; Trk; Chrldr; Jr College; Secretary.

FORS, Hans G; Warren T HS; Grayslake, IL; AFS; HonRl; PolWkr; SctActv; StuCncl; StuGov; University; Science.

FORSBERG, Diane M; Kingsford HS; Iron Mountain, MI; HonRl; OffAde; RptrSchPpr; 4-H; FTA; College; Interior Decorator.

FORSBERG, Randi B; Minot HS; Minot, ND; CncrtBnd; HonRl; MrchBnd; NHS; PepBnd; SchPl; RptrSchPpr; GerCl; Univ; Professional.

FORSCH, Ann E; Dell Rapids Public HS; Dell Rapids, SD; 5/56 Band; HospAde; NHS; NatlThespSoc; SchMus; SchPl; Yrbk; FHA; PpCl; Swmmng; Chrldr; College; Physical Therapy.

FORSHEY, Bonnie S; Barry HS; Barry, IL; 7/44 Band; HonRl; NHS; StuCncl; RptrSchPpr; VP4-H; VPFHA; SciCl; Chrldr; 4-HAwd; Coll.

FORSS, Sue M; Wanamingo HS; Zumbrota, MN; 3/44 Band; ChrhWkr; HonRl; PolWkr; YthFlsp; LetterBsktbl; Chrldr; GAA; IMSpt; PresAwd;.

FORST, Kenneth E; Swartz Creek HS; Swartz Creek, MI; HonRl; JrNHS; College; Police Admin.

FORST, Richard J; St Laurence HS; Chicago, IL; 111/380 HonRl; IMSpt; U Of Il; Economics.

FORSTER, Joseph P; Illiopolis HS; Illiopolis, IL; HonRl; SchPl; TchrAde; Univ; Teaching.

FORSTER, Lois A; Lidgerwood Public HS; Lidgerwood, ND; Band; CmntyWkr; HonRl; SchPl; FHA; SpnCl; Swmmng; LetterTrk; GAA; Home Ec.

FORSTER, Stefani M; Norfolk HS; Norfolk, NE; Chr; ChrhWkr; HonRl; NatlFornLg; NatlThespSoc; Orch; SchMus; SchPl; FrCl; IMSpt; College; Psychiatry Music Recreation.

FORSTNER, Barbara; Gibbon Public HS; Gibbon, MN; 16/42 SecFrshCls; Band; Chr; CncrtBnd; HonRl; NHS; SchPpr; 4-H; FHA; Hutchinson Voc; Business.

FORSTNER, Deborah A; Shanley HS; Fargo, ND; 1/122 ALAGirlsSt; PresBand; LitMag; NHS; NatlMeritCmnd; SchMus; StuCncl; EdYrBk; RptrSchPpr; Clg Of St Benedict; Ed Psy/spe Ed.

FORSYTH, Amy V; Morton HS; Morton, IL; 13/290 SecTrsSophCls; VPJrCls; CmntyWkr; CaptDrlTm; HonRl; NHS; TreasStuCncl; 4-H; GAA; DanFAwd; Univ Of Ill; Psychology.

FORSYTHE, Kathlene L; Raymore Peculiar HS; Peculiar, MO; 2/120 PresChr; CncrtBnd; DrmMjrt; HonRl; NHS; SchMus; Twrl; FTA; SecGerCl; LionAwd; College; Social Work.

FORSYTHE, Sheryllynn K; Corunna HS; Corunna, MI; 60/220 Band; Chr; ChrhWkr; CncrtBnd; HonRl; HospAde; John Wesley College; Music.

FORT, Lewis C; Rushford Public HS; Houston, MN; ChrhWkr; HonRl; 4-H; FFA; Wrstlng;.

FORT, Marsheila R; Morton HS; Morton, IL; 47/287 Band; ChrhWkr; CmntyWkr; CncrtBnd; HonRl; MrchBnd; NatlMeritCmnd; PepBnd; Yrbk; FHA; Us Navy; Communications Technician.

FORT, Timothy L; Southern HS; Stronghurst, IL; 5/55 PresSophCls; VPJrCls; Band; Chr; Chrs; ChrhWkr; CncrtBnd; HonRl; MrchBnd; NHS; PepBnd; Bsbl; LetterFtbl; CaptTrk; College; Professional.

FORTADO, Cindy M; Jacksonville HS; Jacksonville, IL; 1/364 Band; ChrhWkr; CncrtBnd; HonRl; HospAde; LitMag; MrchBnd; NHS; GerCl; LatCl; Illinois College; Medicine.

FORTE, Nancy; Our Lady Star Of The Sea HS; Grosse Pte Woods, MI; SecTrsFrshCls; PresSrCls; HonRl; IntrClCncl; NatlFornLg; NHS; SchPl; TchrAde; GAA; IMSpt; Univ; Prof.

FORTE, Theodore; John Marshall HS; Indianapolis, IN; 40/444 ChrhWkr; CAP; CmntyWkr; HonRl; JA; NHS; PolWkr; StuCncl; StuGov; TchrAde; MthCl; Trk; JAAwd; Purdue University; Engineering.

FORTHOFER, Annette; East Central HS; Sunman, IN; ALAGirlsSt; Band; CmntyWkr; HonRl; NHS; PepBnd; 4-H; SpnCl; PpCl; College; Social Worker.

FORTIER, Glen T; Hubbard HS; Chicago, IL; 35/500 ChrhWkr; NatlMeritCmnd; Loyola Univ; Medicine.

FORTIER, Sara L; Manistee Catholic Central HS; Manistee, MI; 36/76 SecJrCls; Band; CncrtBnd; HonRl; JrNHS; MrchBnd; NHS; TchrAde; College; Computer Technology.

FORTIN, Claude J; Marmion Mil Acad; Oak Lawn, IL; 4/69 Band; HonRl; NHS; ROTC; RptrSchPpr; FSA; SciCl; LetterFtbl; LetterTrk; Loyola U Of Chicago; Pre Med.

FORTIN, Sherry K; Doland Public HS; Turton, SD; DrlTm; HonRl; SchPl; FHA; PpCl; Busi Sch; Voc.

FORTINO, Diane M; Charlotte HS; Charlotte, MI; 39/266 TrsSophCls; StuCncl; TchrAde; PpCl; Chrldr; GAA; PPFtbl; Ferris St Coll; Secretary.

FORTMEYER, Carla; Centrailia Hs; Irvington, IL; Band; DrlTm; HospAde; JrNHS; MrchBnd; NHS; OffAde; YthFlsp; 4-H; Trk; Nursing School; Nurse.

FORTMEYER, Virginia A; Hiawatha Usd #415 HS; Fairview, KS; 2/99 HonRl; NHS; OffAde; StuCncl; YthFlsp; PpCl; Bsktbl; Trk; GAA; CitAwd; Highland Junior College; Forestry.

FORTNER, Connie S; Jasper R #5 HS; Carthage, MO; 2/61 TrsJrCls; TrsSrCls; ChrhWkr; HonRl; MrchBnd; TreasNHS; RedCrAde; SchPl; FHA; PpCl; PPFtbl; Drury College; Law.

FORTNER, Karen A; Central HS; La Crosse, WI; CncrtBnd; MrchBnd; NHS; Orch; PepBnd; RptrSchPpr; BauchLmbAwd; U Of Wi Madison; Chemistry.

FORTNER, Stephen P; Quigley North HS; Chicago, IL; 8/66 TrsSrCls; ChrhWkr; CmntyWkr; HonRl; JA; SctActv; FDA; FSA; MthCl; SciCl; Bsktbl; Tennis; Univ Of Illinois; Medicine.

FORTRESS, Kenneth G; Bishop Dwenger HS; Ft Wayne, IN; 21/245 HonRl; JA; KeyCl; LetterGlf; IMSpt; Purdue U; Pharmacy.

FORTUNE, Mitchell R; Melcher Dallas HS; Belcher, IA; VPFrshCls; ALBoysSt; Aud/Vis; HonRl; StuCncl; FrCl; Bsktbl; LetterFtbl; Trk; IMSpt; Coll.

FOSHA, Patsy L; Junction City Sr HS; Junction City, KS; 36/303 Band; CncrtBnd; HonRl; MrchBnd; NHS; PepBnd; SchMus; TchrAde; PpCl; Wichita State University; Biology.

FOSHEE, Edith L; St Thomas Apostle HS; Chicago, IL; 9/36 SecFrshCls; Chr; ChrhWkr; HonRl; MrchBnd; NHS; SctActv; StuCncl; YthFlsp; Bsktbl; Chicago State Univ; Music.

FOSS, Carolyn R; Waukesha HS; Waukesha, WI; AFS; HonRl; JrNHS; NHS; SpnCl; MthCl; SciCl; College; Medicad Technology.

FOSS, Cherie L; Gull Lake HS; Richland, MI; 9/216 Band; CncrtBnd; HonRl; JrNHS; LbryAde; MrchBnd; NHS; PepBnd; TchrAde; FTA; W Mi Univ; Spec Education.

FOSS, Janice M; Lenora HS; Edmond, KS; Band; Chrs; HonRl; NatlFornLg; OffAde; YthFlsp; 4-H; PpCl; 4-HAwd; Univ; Psychology.

FOSS, Karen M; Belding HS; Belding, MI; Band; CncrtBnd; HonRl; MrchBnd; NHS; PepBnd; SchMus; YthFlsp; PPFtbl; 4-HAwd; Montcalm Comm Col; Lpn.

FOSS, Kim; Watertown Senior HS; Watertown, SD; 21/291 HonRl; NHS; GerCl; College; Nursing.

FOSS, Petria; Harlem HS; Rockford, IL; Band; ChrhWkr; CncrtBnd; HonRl; MrchBnd; NatlThespSoc; PepBnd; SchPl; SctActv; YthFlsp; Univ; Professional Ballet Dancer.

FOSS, Sherry L; Sullivan HS; Chicago, IL; HonRl; JA; SchAde; StuGov; TchrAde; RptrSchPpr; SchPpr; Swmmng; JAAwd; Writer.

FOSS, Wade O; Humboldt HS; St Paul, MN; TchrAde; CitAwd;.

FOSSEDAL, Leselie A; Hinsdale South HS; Westmont, IL; Chrs; HonRl; NHS; OffAde; YthFlsp; RptrYrbk; Yrbk; SchPpr; GerCl; Swmmng; U Od Miss; Journalism.

FOSSOY, Karla K; Rapid City Cntrl HS; Rapid City, SD; 1/580 AFS; ChrhWkr; HonRl; NHS; NatlMeritSF; SctActv; StuCncl; Tennis; LetterTrk; IMSpt; AmLegAwd; Sd Schl Of Mines & Tech; Chem Engineering.

FOSSUM, Brenda S; Lennox HS; Worthing, SD; Band; Chr; Chrl; Chrs; ChrhWkr; CncrtBnd; HonRl; Mdrgl; MrchBnd; PepBnd; SchPl; LetterBsktbl; IMSpt; 4-HAwd; College; Nurse.

FOSSUM, Burdell E; Magic City HS; Minot, ND; 3/650 CncrtBnd; HonRl; Mdrgl; MrchBnd; NHS; NatlThespSoc; Orch; PepBnd; SchMus;.

FOSTER, Barbara S; New Town Harris HS; New Town, MO; 2/24 ALAGirlsSt; PresBand; ChrhWkr; HonRl; NHS; Quill&Scroll; EdSchPpr; TreasFBLA; PresFHA; CaptBsktbl; Trk; AmLegAwd; DARAwd; Ne Mo State Univ; Accounting.

FOSTER, Brian; Crystal Lake Comm Hs; Crystal Lake, IL; NHS; EdYrBk; College Or University;law.

FOSTER, Carolyn; Marion C Early Hs; Morrisville, MO; 2/45 Chr; Chrs; ChrhWkr; HonRl; SchPl; RptrSchPpr; FBLA; FHA; FrCl;.

FOSTER, Charles L; Kirksville Sr HS; Kirksville, MO; 21/174 Band; Chrs; DrmMjrt; HonRl; NHS; PepBnd; SchMus; Ne Missouri University.

FOSTER, Christine L; Athens HS; East Leroy, MI; 2/62 HonRl; HospAde; JrNHS; NHS; OffAde; Quill&Scroll; SecStuCncl; Yrbk; 4-H; PpCl; Kellogg Comm Clg; Rn.

FOSTER, Dana W; Shawnee Mission East HS; Prairie Village, KS; ChrhWkr; HonRl; NatlFornLg; SctActv; Kansas St University.

FOSTER, Daniel G; York Comm HS; Elmhurst, IL; Band; CncrtBnd; HonRl; MrchBnd; PepBnd; Quill&Scroll; SchMus; RptrSchPpr; Illinois St Univ; Communications.

FOSTER, Debra J; Northwest HS; House Springs, MO; HonRl; College; Accounting.

FOSTER, Debra J; Mc Kinley HS; St Louis, MO; 3/170 Chr; Chrs; HonRl; OffAde; SchAde; SchMus; TchrAde; SchPpr; FBLA; KiwanAwd; Secretarial Work; Secretary.

FOSTER, Diane L; Merrill HS; Wheeler, MI; Band; HonRl; 4-H; College; Nursing.

FOSTER, Donald; Prescott Comm Hs; Prescott, IA; 2 PresJrCls; HonRl; SchPl; StuCncl; 4-H; LetterBsbl; CaptBsktbl; LetterGlf; LetterTrk; 4-HAwd; College ; Professional.

FOSTER, Gary H; Neillsville HS; Neillsville, WI; PresJrCls; ALBoysSt; ChrhWkr; HonRl; NHS; SctActv; StuCncl; RptrYrbk; SptEdYrbk; GodCntryAwd; Rotc Navy; Us Navy.

FOSTER, Glenn K; South Haven HS; South Haven, MI; 40/218 Band; CncrtBnd; HonRl; MrchBnd; PepBnd; TchrAde; Swmmng; Tennis; IMSpt; Michigan State; Electrical.

FOSTER, James J; Joliet Catholic HS; Joliet, IL; 24/170 HonRl; PresJA; RptrYrbk; RptrSchPpr; Ftbl; Trk; Wrstlng; Loyola Univ; Chemistry.

FOSTER, Janis K; Marion Co Early HS; Morrisville, MO; Chrs; ChrhWkr; HonRl; SchPl; FBLA; FHA; FrCl; PpCl; LetterBsktbl; Chrldr; Baptist Bible Clg; Missionary.

FOSTER, Jenise G; Cass Technical HS; Detroit, MI; Band; ChrhWkr; HonRl; NHS; NatlSciFnd; SpnCl; SciCl; LetterTennis; Univ Of Michigan; Biochemistry.

FOSTER, John K; Metropolis Community HS; Metropolis, IL; PresSophCls; CmntyWkr; StuCncl; CivCl; Bsbl; Trk; AmLegAwd; Southern Ill Univ; Teacher.

FOSTER, Kathleen H; Acadof The Sacred Heart; Bloomfield Hills, MI; TrsSrCls; ChrhWkr; HonRl; NHS; NatlMeritSF; StuCncl; TchrAde; CitAwd; Coll; Bus Admin.

FOSTER, Kay; Clare HS; Clare, MI; 2/147 HonRl; MthCl; PpCl; Bsbl; GAA; PPFtbl; Northwood Inst; Accounting.

FOSTER, Kendall L; Trenton Sr HS; Laredo, MO; Band; CncrtBnd; 4-H; Vo Tech; Electronics.

FOSTER, Kevin L; Zionsville Community HS; Zionsville, IN; VPJrCls; HonRl; NHS; LatCl; LetterFtbl; Univ; Pharmacist.

FOSTER, Larry G; School Of The Osage HS; Osage Beach, MO; Band; Chrs; ChrhWkr; CmntyWkr; CncrtBnd; HonRl; MrchBnd; PepBnd; SctActv; PpCl; Bsbl; Oral Roberts University; Chiropractor.

FOSTER, Louis A; Deer Creek Mackinaw HS; Mackinaw, IL; 5/67 NHS; VPStuCncl; RptrSchPpr; Pres4-H; CaptBsktbl; LetterFtbl; CaptTrk; DanFAwd; 4-HAwd; Univ Of Illinois; Veterinarian.

FOSTER, Lynn; R 1 North Callaway HS; Auxuasse, MO; 12/80 Band; CncrtBnd; DrlTm; HonRl; MrchBnd; PepBnd; SchMus; StuCncl; Trk; Chrldr; William Woods Coll; Bus Ed.

FOSTER, Lynn M; R 1 North Callaway HS; Auxuasse, MO; 12/76 MrchBnd; PepBnd; StuCncl; Twrl; Yrbk; Sec4-H; FHA; FrCl; Trk; Chrldr; Williamwoods Coll.

FOSTER, Martha A; Union Star Rii HS; Union Star, MO; Band; Chrs; ChrhWkr; CncrtBnd; HonRl; MrchBnd; NatlMeritSchl; SchPl; SctActv; College; Biology.

FOSTER, Mathew M; Wisconsin Dells HS; Wisconsin Dells, WI; 16/145 TrsSrCls; CncrtBnd; HonRl; NHS; SchPl; RptrYrbk; RptrSchPpr; KeyCl; LetterFtbl; LetterTrk; Univ Of Wi Stevens Point; Forestry.

FOSTER, Nadine J; Cal Comm HS; Alexander, IA; 4/34 SecFrshCls; SecTrsJrCls; Chrs; CmntyWkr; LbryAde; NHS; SecStuCncl; EdYrBk; RptrSchPpr; VPFHA; Waldorf Clge; Social Work.

FOSTER, Nancy L; Mendota HS; Mendota, IL; CmntyWkr; HonRl; RptrYrbk; LatCl; Trk; GAA; IMSpt; Coll; Work With Mentally Il.

FOSTER, Randall W; Albert City Truesdale HS; Albert City, IA; 3/50 PresSrCls; ChrhWkr; HonRl; NHS; SchPl; StuCncl; RptrYrbk; LetterBsbl; LetterBsktbl; LetterTrk; College; Accountin.

FOSTER, Renee E; Minneapolis Lutheran HS; Minneapolis, MN; 1/37 TrsJrCls; TrsSrCls; ALAGirlsSt; HonRl; NHS; StuCncl; Bsktbl; CaptTrk; Chrldr; College; Physical Educ.

FOSTER, Richard H; Washington HS; Washington, KS; 3/42 TrsFrshCls; CncrtBnd; HonRl; NatlMeritCmnd; Orch; SctActv; StuGov; LetterBsktbl; U Of Kansas; Business Education.

FOSTER, Rodney A; Waynesville Sr HS; Ft Leonard Wd, MO; Band; HonRl; MrchBnd; NHS; College.

FOSTER, Russell W; Dadeville HS; Dadeville, MO; HstFrshCls; HstJrCls; ALBoysSt; ChrhWkr; HonRl; SchPl; RptrSchPpr; FFA; Bsbl; CaptBsktbl; University; Vocation.

FOSTER, Scott J; Willmar Sr 'S; Willmar, MN; ChrhWkr; HonRl; NatlMeritCmnd; YthFlsp; KeyCl; LetterBsbl; LetterBsktbl; LetterWrstlng; 4-HAwd; KiwanAwd; PresAwd; St Olaf College; Doctor.

FOSTER, William; Windsor HS; Windsor, MO; ALBoysSt; HonRl; Quill&Scroll; StuCncl; SptEdSchPpr; FTA; University; Physical Education.

FOSTER, William J; St Patrick HS; Chicago, IL; 36/450 TrsSrCls; Chrs; HonRl; JrNHS; NHS; SchMus; SchPl; SctActv; StuCncl; StuGov; SptEdSchPpr; PpCl; Ftbl; LetterSwmmng; College.

FOSZCZ, Paul J; Lane Tech HS; Chicag, IL; 63/1200 Aud/Vis; ChrhWkr; CmntyWkr; StuCncl; SciCl; College; Physics.

FOTH, Brent D; Twin Rivers HS; Livermore, IA; 17/40 TrsSophCls; PresJrCls; ChrhWkr; CmntyWkr; SchPl; SctActv; StuCncl; YthFlsp; SptEdYrbk; RptrSchPpr; SptEdSchPpr; 4-H;.

FOUBERG, Debra; Forestburg HS; Forestburg, SD; 2/7 SecTrsJrCls; SecTrsSrCls; Band; Chrs; SchPl; EdYrBk; EdSchPpr; Bsktbl; Trk; AmLegAwd; College; Biology.

FOUCHE, Joy S; Clarke Comm Jr Sr HS; Osceola, IA; Band; CncrtBnd; HonRl; MrchBnd; 4-H; FFA; Bsktbl; CchngActv; PPFtbl; Trade School; Animal Tech.

FOUGEROUSSE, Mark J; Our Lady Of Providence HS; New Albany, IN; HonRl; YthFlsp; RptrSchPpr; SptEdSchPpr; SchPpr; Indiana University; Business Administration.

FOUKS, Betsy L; New Richmond HS; Deer Park, WI; Band; CncrtBnd; HonRl; Orch; SchMus; 4-H; Voc Sch; Secretary.

FOULKE, Jacqueline D; Brimfield HS; Brimfield, IL; Chrs; CncrtBnd; HonRl; NHS; StuCncl; EdYrBk; RptrSchPpr; FHA; SciCl; Chrldr; University; Professional.

FOUNTAIN, Julia; Centralia HS; Thompson, MO; 9/89 HonRl; HospAde; NHS; OffAde; SchPl; FHA; FSA; SciCl; Central Mo State Univ; Physical Therapy.

FOUNTAIN, Karen J; Immaculata HS; Detroit, MI; PresSrCls; HonRl; JA; JrNHS; NatlMeritSchl; PepBnd; PolWkr; SchAde; EdYrBk; JAAwd; Mercy College; Merchandising.

FOUNTAINE, Gerard C; Hillsboro HS; Cedar Hill, MO; Band; CncrtBnd; HonRl; MrchBnd; SctActv; StuCncl; SciCl; LetterFtbl; LetterTrk; PresAwd; College; Professional.

FOURMAN, Judith M; Garrett HS; Garrett, IN; ChrhWkr; HonRl; SecNHS; SchMus; StuCncl; PpCl; GAA; PPFtbl; Manchestr College; Stud Guiance Counselor.

FOURNIE, Eve M; Assumption HS; E St Louis, IL; HospAde; LbryAde; NatlMeritCmnd; RedCrAde; StuCncl; 4-H; Jewish Hosp Schl; Nursing.

FOURNIE, Mary A; Academy Of The Visitation; St Louis, MO; Chr; HospAde; JrNHS; NHS; SchPl; TchrAde; RptrYrbk; RptrSchPpr; SchPpr; LetterTennis; GAA; IMSpt; College.

FOURNIER, Cynthia J; Bay City Western HS; Auburn, MI; HonRl; College.

FOUST, Debra M; Conway HS; Conway, MO; 7/63 TrsJrCls; SecSrCls; ChrhWkr; HonRl; NHS; TchrAde; RptrSchPpr; FTA; SpnCl; School Of Ozarks; Social Work.

FOUST, Delbert W; North Adams HS; Hillsdale, MI; 5/52 PresSophCls; PresJrCls; PresSrCls; HonRl; NHS; SchPl; StuCncl; TchrAde; FTA; LetterGlf; Ferris St College; Optometry.

FOUST, Mary S; Dubuque Sr HS; Dubuque, IA; 20/435 Band; SecFrshCls; MrchBnd; Orch; PepBnd; 4-H; SpnCl; AmLegAwd; 4-HAwd; Univ; Medicine.

FOUT, Katherine L; Alleman HS; Rock Island, IL; SecTrsSrCls; CmntyWkr; HonRl; NHS; SecStuCncl; RptrYrbk; EdSchPpr; FrCl; PpCl; GAA; Univ Of Il; Social Work.

FOUTCH, Bradley; Waukegan East Hs; Waukegan, IL; 106/1004 Band; ChrhWkr; HonRl; LbryAde; NHS; NatlThespSoc; OffAde; SchMus; GerCl; Swmmng; U Of Ill; Wood Science.

FOUTS, Debra L; Woodbine Comm HS; Woodbine, IA; 8/60 Band; Chrs; CncrtBnd; HospAde; MrchBnd; PepBnd; TchrAde; FHA; FrCl; College; Rn.

FOUTS, Mary E; West HS; Indianola, IA; Chrs; ChrhWkr; HonRl; NatlFornLg; NatlMeritCmnd; NatlThespSoc; SchMus; SchPl; StuCncl; SpnCl; U Of Ia; Vocal Music.

FOVELL, Terese M; Mother Mc Auley HS; Oak Lawn, IL; 11/484 Chrs; HonRl; NatlMeritCmnd; SchMus; FrCl; MthCl; St Josephs Clge; Bus.

FOWL, Gregory; Richmond Sr HS; Richmond, IN; CAP; HonRl; YthFnd; Wrstlng; Purdue U; Elect Eng.

FOWLE, Brad; Onsted Community HS; Manitou Beach, MI; HonRl; SchPl; StuCncl; CchngActv; College; Business Office.

FOWLER, Anna E; Berkeley HS; Berkeley, MO; 6/289 HonRl; NHS; StuCncl; EdYrBk; SecPpCl; College.

FOWLER, Christopher G; St Joseph HS; St Joseph, MI; Chr; NatlMeritFnl; NatlMeritSF; SctActv; StuGov; SpnCl; SciCl; IMSpt; Central Michigan U; Elementary Education.

FOWLER, David M; Milford HS; Milford, NE; Chrl; Chrs; ChrhWkr; NHS; SchMus; SchPl; RptrYrbk; RptrSchPpr; PresFBLA; GerCl; Clge; Pro Teaching Music Or Math.

FOWLER, Douglas N; Williamsville HS; Sherman, IL; 2/42 HonRl; JA; JrNHS; StuCncl; 4-H; FFA; FTA; Bsktbl; Univ; Civil Engineer.

FOWLER, Joyia M; Industry HS; Plymouth, IL; 2/35 SecJrCls; VPSrCls; HonRl; PresYthFlsp; RptrYrbk; RptrSchPpr; VPFHA; FrCl; PpCl; SciCl; Chrldr; Western Ill Univ; Math Teacher.

FOWLER, Julie E; Hudson Area HS; Hudson, MI; 2/127 VPJrCls; ALAGirlsSt; Band; HonRl; NatlFornLg; NHS; EdYrBk; FHA; LatCl; DanFAwd; Mi Tech U; Math.

FOWLER, Julie G; Oak Park HS; Gladstone, MO; HonRl; HospAde; SctActv; TchrAde; YthFlsp; PpCl; LetterTrk; Smsu; Nursing.

FOWLER, Linda L; Kirksville Sr HS; Kirksville, MO; CmntyWkr; HonRl; Orch; SctActv; Nemo Univ; Architecture.

FOWLER, Mary A; Morton Sr HS; Hammond, IN; 7/499 SecSophCls; HonRl; NHS; Quill&Scroll; StuGov; RptrSchPpr; LetterBsktbl; GAA;.

FOWLER, Randy; Tri County HS; Hancock, WI; 7/50 HonRl; NHS; Bsktbl; College Uw Of Platteville; Construction.

FOWLER, Sherri L; Central Comm HS; West Point, IA; Band; Chrs; HonRl; NHS; OffAde; TchrAde; YthFlsp; RptrYrbk; RptrSchPpr; FTA;.

FOWLER, Terri; Atchison HS; Atchison, KS; HonRl; ModUN; NHS; NatlThespSoc; SchPl; College; Vocation.

FOWLOW, Dawn A; Onsted HS; Onsted, MI; Band; CncrtBnd; DrmBgl; HonRl; LitMag; NHS; SchPl; RptrSchPpr; EdSchPpr; Central Michigan Univ; Journalism.

FOX, Alice M; Edwardsville Sr HS; Edwardsville, IL; HonRl; LbryAde; NHS; SctActv; SecFHA; PpCl; College; Accountant.

FOX, Arlene J; Stafford HS; Stafford, KS; SecSrCls; Band; Chr; Chrl; Chrs; HonRl; MrchBnd; PolWkr; PpCl; Chrldr; Fort Hayes St Clg; Art Instr.

FOX, Carla J; Effingham HS; Effingham, IL; 1/230 ChrhWkr; HonRl; LbryAde; NHS; SchPl; Univ Of Washington; Law.

FOX, Carl E; Frankfort HS; Frankfort, IN; 1/242 PresChrhWkr; HonRl; NHS; StuCncl; Pres4-H; MthCl; SciCl; AmLegAwd; BauchLmbAwd; 4-HAwd; PresAwd; Purdue Univ; Engineer.

FOX, Carol E; Canton HS; Canton, SD; 37/93 Band; Chr; Chrl; Chrs; ChrhWkr; CmntyWkr; CncrtBnd; HonRl; MrchBnd; PepBnd; PolWkr; Quill&Scroll; Trk; IMSpt; South Dakota State Univ; Nursing.

FOX, Charles D; John Marshall HS; Milwaukee, WI; ALBoysSt; ChrhWkr; HonRl; JA; SchMus; SchPl; SctActv; LatCl; Swmmng; MasAwd;.

FOX, Cynthia A; Regis HS; Cedar Rapids, IA; ChrhWkr; TreasJA; Quill&Scroll; SchPl; StuCncl; RptrSchPpr; EdSchPpr; JAAwd; U Of Ia; Sociology/psychology.

FOX, Cynthia L; Marion Adams HS; Sheridan, IN; SecFrshCls; Band; HonRl; MrchBnd; NHS; SecStuCncl; FBLA; FHA; Swmmng; DanFAwd; Teller.

FOX, Daniel L; Highland HS; Ainsworth, IA; 6/58 PresSophCls; PresJrCls; Band; Chrs; CncrtBnd; HonRl; MrchBnd; NHS; PepBnd; SchMus; SchPl; StuCncl; YthFlsp; Bsktbl; College; Professional.

FOX, Danny R; Galena HS; Galena, MO; PresSophCls; VPSrCls; ChrhWkr; HonRl; StuCncl; Yrbk; LetterBsbl; Bsktbl; College.

FOX, Darryl H; Anderson HS; Anderson, IN; VPJrCls; CmntyWkr; HonRl; Mdrgl; PolWkr; SchMus; StuCncl; SpnCl; CaptFtbl; Wrstlng; PresAwd; Purdue Univ; Forestry & Music.

FOX, Deborah J; Wyanet HS; Wyanet, IL; 3/29 HonRl; LbryAde; NHS; NatlMeritCmnd; VPNatlThespSoc; OffAde; SchPl; EdYrBk; SecPpCl; AmLegAwd; Il State U; Teaching English & Speech.

FOX, Diane M; Stevenson HS; Livonia, MI; Chr; LitMag; NatlMeritCmnd; OffAde; College.

FOX, Don W; Culver Military Acad; Greensburg, IN; HonRl; NatlMeritSF; StuGov; Glf; Swmmng; IMSpt; Coll; Law.

FOX, Douglas L; Slayton HS; Slayton, MN; 38/103 HstFrshCls; HstSophCls; HstJrCls; HstSrCls; ChrhWkr; DrlTm; HonRl; GerCl; Swmmng; IMSpt; Univ Of Mn; Architect.

FOX, Edd; Edinburg; Franklin, IN; Band; CncrtBnd; MrchBnd; NHS; PepBnd; SchPpr; SpnCl; University;tv Radio Film.

FOX, Edward C; Brother Rice HS; Birmingham, MI; SecFrshCls; VPSophCls; HstSrCls; HonRl; SchPl; StuCncl; StuGov; Bsbl; Ftbl; IMSpt; Princeton U; History.

FOX, James M; Virginia HS; Virginia, IL; 19/44 ChrhWkr; CmntyWkr; SchPpr; 4-H; FFA; LetterBsktbl; 4-HAwd; Eastern Il Univ; Vocational.

FOX, Jay J; Elmhurst HS; Fort Wayne, IN; 10/492 Aud/Vis; Chr; HonRl; NHS; CitAwd; University; Professional Musician.

FOX, Jeffrey E; Hinckley Big Rock HS; Big Rock, IL; 9/77 Chrs; HonRl; NHS; SchMus; SchPl; SchPpr; Trade Sch; Building Trade.

FOX, Jerrald M; Sullivan HS; Sullivan, IL; 16/105 ChrhWkr; HonRl; FTA; FrCl; Bsktbl; LetterFtbl; Glf; Trk; Anderson College; Business.

FOX, Jon A; Robinson HS; Robinson, IL; 10/180 Band; CmntyWkr; CncrtBnd; HonRl; MrchBnd; PepBnd; SchPl; SctActv; College; Chemical Engineer.

FOX, Judith R; Carl Sandburg HS; Palos Heights, IL; CmntyWkr; HonRl; HospAde; Univ Of Illinois; Law.

FOX, Laurie; Watertown Senior HS; Watertown, SD; Band; CncrtBnd; HonRl; MrchBnd; PepBnd; YthFlsp; 4-H; GerCl; 4-HAwd; PresAwd; Coll;.

FOX, Lizabeth A; Maple Valley HS; Vermontville, MI; 5/105 TrsJrCls; Band; Chr; CncrtBnd; HonRl; MrchBnd; NHS; RptrSchPpr; Tennis; GAA; Mi State U; History.

FOX, Malinda K; Norton Community HS; Norton, KS; ChrhWkr; CmntyWkr; CncrtBnd; HonRl; MrchBnd; PepBnd; SecSctActv; SecYthFlsp; FHA; PpCl; Coll; Math.

FOX, Mary E; Corunna HS; Corunna, MI; ChrhWkr; CncrtBnd; HonRl; JA; MrchBnd; Yrbk; SpnCl; PpCl; Trk; GAA; Msu; Business Admin.

FOX, Mary L; Southmont HS; Crawfordsville, IN; ChrhWkr; HonRl; JA; NHS; OffAde; YthFlsp; SpnCl; Vocational.

FOX, Michael D; Lathrop HS; Lathrop, MO; TrsFrshCls; PresSrCls; ALBoysSt; LbryAde; SchPl; StuCncl; EdSchPpr; PresFrCl; LetterBsktbl; LetterFtbl; Univ;law.

FOX, Pamela K; J W Sexton HS; Lansing, MI; 10/499 Band; CncrtBnd; DrmMjrt; HonRl; MrchBnd; NHS; NatlMeritFnl; Orch; PepBnd; EdSchPpr; Lansing Comm Coll; Genetics.

FOX, Paulette; Black River Falls Sr HS; Hixton, WI; HonRl; OffAde; SchAde; SchMus; SchPl; EdSchPpr; 4-H; PpCl; 4-HAwd; Writing.

FOX, Stephen P; Antigo HS; Antigo, WI; 21/370 HonRl; GerCl; LetterFtbl; CaptWrstlng; College; Medicine.

FOX, Victoria E; Culver Community HS; Monterey, IN; Band; CncrtBnd; MrchBnd; SchPl; StuCncl; TchrAde; RptrSchPpr; FHA; FTA; PpCl; College; Professional.

FOX, Victoria H; Falls City HS; Falls City, NE; Band; DrlTm; HonRl; MrchBnd; GerCl; PpCl; GAA; IMSpt; PresAwd; Univ; Professional.

FOX, William; Maine Twsp East HS; Park Ridge, IL; HonRl; SchAde; YthFlsp; MthCl; CchngActv; Cornell U; Med Doc.

FOY, Margaret M; Sacred Heart Of Mary HS; Palatine, IL; HonRl; StuGov; CaptBsktbl; IMSpt; Marquette U; Health.

FOY, Patrick; Archbishop Bergan HS; Fremont, NE; 1/50 HonRl; NHS; NatlMeritCmnd; SchAde; SchPl; SctActv; StuGov; Yrbk; Trk; EldAwd; Univ Of Nebr; Accounting.

FOY, Patrick B; Archbishop Bergan HS; Fremont, NE; 1/52 HonRl; JA; NHS; SchAde; SctActv; StuCncl; StuGov; TchrAde; Yrbk; Bsktbl; Ftbl; Trk; Univ Of Nebr; Accounting.

FOY, Peter J; Lourdes Acad; Oshkosh, WI; 6/126 PresSophCls; PresJrCls; VPSrCls; ChrhWkr; HonRl; NHS; NatlMeritCmnd; StuGov; LetterTrk; AmLegAwd; Eastern Mi Univ; Engineering.

FOY, Rommel; Moline Senior HS; Moline, IL; PresFrshCls; Chr; HonRl; StuCncl; StuGov; YthFlsp; SptEdSchPpr; KeyCl; SpnCl; SciCl; Coll; Pro.

FOY, Sheila J; West HS; Davenport, IA; HonRl; SchPl; StuGov; RptrYrbk; SecGerCl; SecPpCl; Swmmng; GAA; PresAwd; University; Professional.

FOY, Terry A; Brown County HS; Morgantown, IN; 10/207 Band; ChrhWkr; DrmMjrt; NHS; Twrl; 4-H; FrCl; PpCl; 4-HAwd; OptClAwd; College; Missionary.

FOYER, Miriam; Heritage Christian Hs; Indianapolis, IN; 4/54 ALAGirlsSt; Chr; HonRl; NHS; PolWkr; SchMus; SchPl; TchrAde; CaptBsktbl; LetterTrk; College; Dental Hygiene.

FRACARO, Pamela R; St Francis Academy; Lockport, IL; 50/179 HonRl; SciCl; KiwanAwd; Joliet Junior College; Accounting.

FRACZKOWSKI, Rita; Madonna HS; Chicago, IL; 1/265 HonRl; NHS; StuCncl; SchPpr; CaptSpnCl; MthCl; SciCl; Coll.

FRAGODT, Jean; Leeds Public HS; York, ND; Band; Chrs; HonRl; MrchBnd; PepBnd; SchPl; StuCncl; EdYrBk; Trk; North Dakota State Univ; Elem Educ.

FRAISE, Martin J; Aquinas HS; Donnellson, IA; ALBoysSt; CmntyWkr; HonRl; SchPl; StuCncl; StuGov; 4-H; AmLegAwd; 4-HAwd; CitAwd; College; Professional.

FRAISE, Thomas; Mt Pleasant HS; Salem, IA; LbryAde; 4-H; FFA; 4-HAwd; Coll; Agriculture Career.

FRAKER, Douglas L; Brookfield Central HS; Brookfield, WI; 2/496 JrNHS; NHS; NatlMeritFnl; NatlMeritSF; Yrbk; KeyCl; FrCl; MthCl; LetterBsktbl; LetterGlf; Duke Univ; Pre Med.

FRAKER, Steven R; D C HS; Oberlin, KS; PresFrshCls; VPSophCls; VPJrCls; Band; Chr; HonRl; NHS; SchMus; LetterBsbl; LetterBsktbl; LetterFtbl; LetterGlf; Trk; College; Auditor.

FRAKES, Charlie W; Schell City Public HS; Schell City, MO; 5/13 Chrs; CmntyWkr; HonRl; SchPl; TchrAde; Bsktbl; Socr; LetterTrk; IMSpt; Trade School.

FRAKES, Roy; Goldfield HS; Goldfield, IA; 6/25 ALBoysSt; CmntyWkr; SchPl; SctActv; Bsbl; Trk; Militory Officer.

FRAKES, Sandra K; Dekalb HS; Rushville, MO; Chr; ChrhWkr; HonRl; RptrSchPpr; SpnCl; PpCl; College; Secretary.

FRALEY, Bernard; Carrollton HS; Carrollton, IL; 7/88 ChrhWkr; HonRl; NHS; 4-H; FBLA; FFA; FSA; AmLegAwd; DanFAwd; 4-HAwd; Univ Of Ill; Civil Engineering.

FRALEY, Bernard L; Carrollton HS; Carrollton, IL; 7/89 HonRl; NHS; Pres4-H; FBLA; PresFFA; FSA; SpnCl; AmLegAwd; DanFAwd; 4-HAwd; University Of Illinois; Civil Engineer.

FRALEY, Douglas B; Carrollton HS; Carrollton, IL; 10/88 Band; HonRl; NHS; StuCncl; FBLA; VPFFA; PpCl; SciCl; BttyCrckrAwd; Farming.

FRALEY, Linda L; Alpena HS; Alpena, MI; 75/723 ChrhWkr; TchrAde; YthFlsp; LatCl; Mich Tech; Med Tech.

FRALEY, Scotti A; Salem HS; Salem, MO; 6/170 TrsJrCls; PresBand; HonRl; OffAde; SchPl; StuCncl; TchrAde; PpCl; Chrldr; PPFtbl; Drury Coll; Insttrumental Music Education.

FRALEY, Scotti A; Salem Sr HS; Salem, MO; 7/175 TrsJrCls; PresBand; CncrtBnd; HonRl; MrchBnd; StuCncl; StuGov; TchrAde; Chrldr; PPFtbl; Drury Col; Music.

FRALEY, Stanley L; Carroll HS; Flora, IN; 1/112 Band; HonRl; MrchBnd; NHS; PepBnd; YthFlsp; FrCl; Bsbl; Tennis; IMSpt; AmLegAwd; Col; Mathematics.

FRAMARIN, Gregory M; Marian Catholic HS; Homewood, IL; ChrhWkr; HonRl; VPNHS; NatlMeritCmnd; SctActv; LatCl; Wrstlng; Ill; Vet.

FRAMBACH, John H; River Valley HS; Sawyer, MI; HonRl; SchPl; SctActv; TchrAde; College; Forest Fire Div.

FRAME, Dana L; Bronaugh R 7 HS; Garland, KS; HstFrshCls; PresJrCls; Chr; HonRl; VPNHS; OffAde; Yrbk; FHA; PpCl; Secretarial.

FRAME, Kelly K; Mt Horeb HS; Blue Mounds, WI; ALBoysSt; Band; ChrhWkr; CncrtBnd; HonRl; MrchBnd; NHS; NatlMeritSF; Orch; PepBnd; SchMus; LetterTrk; IMSpt; Univ Of Wisconsin; Chem Engineering.

FRANA, Joel A; Northfield Sr HS; Northfield, MN; Aud/Vis; Chr; HonRl; LbryAde; SctActv; Bsktbl; LetterFtbl; Swmmng; LetterTrk; LetterWrstlng; College.

FRANA, Joseph C; Ottumwa HS; Ottumwa, IA; ALBoysSt; HonRl; StuCncl; LetterFtbl; LetterTrk; LetterWrstlng; CchngActv; IMSpt; AmLegAwd; College; Math.

FRANCE, Faye F; Gothenburg Public HS; Gothenburg, NE; Chrs; HonRl; SchPl; 4-H; PpCl; Nursing School; Nursing.

FRANCE, Mary L; Astoria HS; Astoria, IL; 1/50 Band; ChrhWkr; HonRl; LbryAde; NHS; YthFlsp; Sec4-H; SecSpnCl; LetterChrldr; GAA; Illinois Central College; Physical Therapis.

FRANCESCHI, Nannette; Holy Family Academy; Chicago, IL; PresBand; Chrs; CncrtBnd; HonRl; TreasRedCrAde; StuCncl; Yrbk; SpnCl; VPMthCl; Depaul Univ; Pre Med.

FRANCIS, Alan L; Palmer HS; Pocahontas, IA; 4/14 ALBoysSt; HonRl; VPStuCncl; YthFlsp; RptrSchPpr; FFA; LetterBsbl; LetterBsktbl; IMSpt;.

FRANCIS, Artie J; Clintondale HS; Mt Clemens, MI; Chr; HonRl; NHS; RedCrAde; SchPl; TchrAde; RptrSchPpr; 4-H; LatCl; Gm Inst; Engi.

FRANCIS, Dean A; Libertyville HS; Libertyville, IL; 23/458 HonRl; Univ Of Illinois; Dentist.

FRANCIS, James D; Parker Sr HS; Janesville, WI; 9/517 Band; Chr; ChrhWkr; HonRl; Mdrgl; NHS; SchPl; StuGov; MasAwd; Coll.

FRANCIS, Jill; North County HS; Desloge, MO; 7/180 CncrtBnd; HonRl; JrNHS; MrchBnd; NHS; FBLA; FHA; PpCl; Missouri University; Journalism.

FRANCIS, Judy A; Wilsonville HS; Wilsonville, NE; SecFrshCls; PresSophCls; SecJrCls; Band; Chr; Chrs; CncrtBnd; HonRl; MrchBnd; OffAde; PepBnd; SchPl; SctActv; StuCncl; Trk; Trade School.

FRANCIS, Judy A; Wilsonville Public HS; Wilsonville, NE; SecFrshCls; PresSophCls; SecJrCls; Band; Chrs; CncrtBnd; HonRl; MrchBnd; LetterTrk; Chrldr; Coll; Voc.

FRANCIS, Leslie A; Dallas City HS; Lomax, IL; 8/40 Band; Chr; Chrs; CncrtBnd; DrlTm; HonRl; MrchBnd; PepBnd; SchMus; SchPl; Jr Col; Business.

FRANCIS, Patricia; Rolla HS; Rolla, MO; Chr; Chrl; CmntyWkr; LbryAde; NatlFornLg; SchPl; TchrAde; 4-H; GerCl; College; Profesional.

FRANCIS, Patricia A; Roncalli HS; Indianapolis, IN; 3/140 SecJrCls; PresSrCls; ALAGirlsSt; ChrhWkr; CmntyWkr; HonRl; NatlMeritCmnd; SctActv; StuGov; DARAwd; Catholic U Wash Dc; Pol Sci.

FRANCIS, Patricia K; Waterford Mott HS; Pontiac, MI; 47/375 Chr; HonRl; OffAde; YthFlsp; Univ; Nurse.

FRANCIS, Sharon A; Woodland R 4 HS; Glen Allen, MO; HonRl; FHA; Trade School; Professional.

FRANCIS, Veronica J; Eddyville HS; Eddyville, IA; SecJrCls; CncrtBnd; HonRl; MrchBnd; PepBnd; YthFlsp; Yrbk; SpnCl; PpCl; College.

FRANCISCO, Dona K; Mormon Trail HS; Humeston, IA; Band; CncrtBnd; MrchBnd; PepBnd; Yrbk;.

FRANCISCO, Todd C; Harper Creek HS; Battle Creed, MI; 1/271 HonRl; NHS; SptEdYrbk; SptEdSchPpr; Bsbl; ChmnBsktbl; Glf; Trk;.

FRANCK, Landee J; Rock Island HS; Rock Island, IL; Band; Chrs; ChrhWkr; DrlTm; Mdrgl; MrchBnd; PepBnd; SchMus; SchPl; Lutheran Hospital; Radiology Technician.

FRANCKE, Bradley J; Garber HS; Essexville, MI; 18/190 HonRl; OffAde; 4-H; LetterBsbl; Ftbl; Univ; Veterinary Med.

FRANCKOWIAK, Michael A; Gaylord HS; Elmira, MI; SecTrsFrshCls; Band; CncrtBnd; HonRl; MrchBnd; NHS; RptrSchPpr; SchPpr; Bsbl; Bsktbl; College; Social Work.

FRANCKOWIAK, Pamela M; Franklin HS; Livonia, MI; HonRl; TchrAde; Art Inst Of Pittsburgh; Visual Communicatio.

FRANCO, Joseph V; Creighton Prep School; Omaha, NE; ChrhWkr; CmntyWkr; HonRl; Sdlty; LatCl; LetterBsbl; Creighton Univ; Dentistry.

FRANCO, Philip E; Creighton Prepatory; Omaha, NE; ChrhWkr; HonRl; Sdlty; CchngActv; IMSpt; Creighton U.

FRANCO, Rodrigo; Andover HS; Orchard Lake, MI; 21/420 HonRl; ModUN; NatlMeritSF; TchrAde; U Of Mi; Bio.

FRANCOEUR, Dorothy A; Southeast HS; Wichita, KS; 1/670 PresFrshCls; ChrhWkr; HonRl; HospAde; LitMag; NatlSciFnd; SctActv; SpnCl; SciCl; IMSpt; University; Md.

FRANCOEUR, Kim; Adrian Senior HS; Adrian, MI; Aud/Vis; ChrhWkr; HonRl; TchrAde; 4-H; FrCl; SciCl; 4-HAwd; Univ; Agriculture.

FRANCOIS, Edward J; Belleville HS; Belleville, WI; VPJrCls; CmntyWkr; HonRl; OffAde; StuCncl; Yrbk; 4-H; SciCl; ChmnFtbl; ChmnWrstlng;.

FRANCOUR, David R; Marinette Sr HS; Marinette, WI; 42/250 TrsSophCls; CmntyWkr; Bsbl; Bsktbl; Ftbl; College; Computer Science.

FRANCUCK, Mark C; Troy HS; Troy, MI; 18/567 Band; HonRl; JrNHS; NHS; TchrAde; GerCl; LetterBsktbl; Michigan State Univ; Dentistry.

FRANDSEN, Jerilynn R; Pembine HS; Pembine, WI; Band; HonRl; SchPl; StuCncl; RptrYrbk; PpCl; Trk; Chrldr; GAA; 4-HAwd; College ; Vocation.

FRANDSEN, Kay; Roland Story Comm HS; Roland, IA; 7/81 Band; CncrtBnd; HonRl; MrchBnd; NHS; PepBnd; SchPl; StuCncl; 4-H; Glf; Iowa State U; Interior Designer.

FRANER, Robert F; Tartan HS; St Paul, MN; Band; ChrhWkr; CmntyWkr; CncrtBnd; MrchBnd; PepBnd; SchMus; SchPl; YthFlsp; Bsktbl; Tennis; Trade; Professional Music.

FRANGENBERG, Colleen K; Primghar Community HS; Primghar, IA; Band; ChrhWkr; CmntyWkr; CncrtBnd; HonRl; MrchBnd; NHS; PepBnd; SctActv; PpCl; Univ; Biology.

FRANK, Ann M; Queen Of Apostles HS; Madison, WI; 2/61 HonRl; OffAde; SchPl; TchrAde; Yrbk; RptrSchPpr; Bsktbl; Chrldr; PPFtbl; GovHonPrgAwd; Edgewood College; Journalism.

FRANK, Bryan A; Oscobel HS; Boscobel, WI; Band; CncrtBnd; HonRl; MrchBnd; NHS; PepBnd; TchrAde; FrCl; Univ Of Wi; Engr.

FRAÑK, Cletus J; Morton Public HS; Morton, MN; 2/40 HstJrCls; Band; Chr; Chrs; ChrhWkr; StuGov; RptrSchPpr; FSA; SciCl; CaptFtbl; U Of Mn; Secondary Teaching.

FRANK, Connie J; Osceola HS; Osceola, WI; Band; Chr; CncrtBnd; MrchBnd; NatlMeritFnl; SchPl; TchrAde; RptrYrbk; FHA; College; Professional.

FRANK, Cynthia K; Crawford HS; Crawford, NE; 3/40 TrsJrCls; Chrs; HonRl; SchPl; RptrSchPpr; TreasPpCl; LetterTrk; College.

FRANK, Debbie G; Bigfork HS; Bigfork, MN; HospAde; RedCrAde; RptrSchPpr; LetterChrldr; College; Nursing.

FRANK, Debora A; Bloomington HS; Bloomington, IL; 15/391 Chr; DrlTm; NHS; Sdlty; StuCncl; StuGov; FrCl; MthCl; PpCl; CchngActv; University; Professional.

FRANK, Donna M; Cathedral HS; St Cloud, MN; 5/155 Chr; Chrs; CncrtBnd; HonRl; Mdrgl; MrchBnd; NHS; PepBnd; SchMus; SptEdYrbk; Col; Nurse.

FRANK, Duane J; Flasher Public HS; Freda, ND; Chrs; HonRl; 4-H; LetterFtbl; Wrstlng; 4-HAwd; Trade Schl; Welding.

FRANK, Jody R; Cedarburg HS; Cedarburg, WI; AFS; Chr; HonRl; NHS; NatlMeritSchl; RedCrAde; Bsbl; CaptBsktbl; Ftbl; PresAwd; Univ Of Wis Oshkosh; Nursing.

FRANK, Joseph C; Lake Shore HS; St Clair Shores, MI; 25/820 ALBoysSt; Band; Chr; ChrhWkr; MrchBnd; NHS; NatlMeritSchl; SchMus; Wrstlng; Univ Of Michigan; Dentist.

FRANK, Kevin C; Lidgerwood Public HS; Lidgerwood, ND; SchPl; SctActv; YthFlsp; PpCl; Bsbl; LetterFtbl; College; Professional.

FRANK, Lisa A; Mt Carroll HS; Mt Carroll, IL; 7/69 Chr; ChrhWkr; CmntyWkr; HonRl; LbryAde; Mdrgl; NHS; SchMus; SchPl; SctActv; PresStuCncl; RptrSchPpr; FrCl; DARAwd; College; Psychology.

FRANK, Lori A; Freeport HS; Freeport, IL; 60/494 HonRl; HospAde; 4-H; U Of New Mexico;.

FRANK, Lynette M; Trinity HS; Dickinson, ND; ALAGirlsSt; Chr; Chrs; ChrhWkr; CmntyWkr; PresFrshCls; SchPl; Bsktbl; Trk; GAA; Dickinson Col; Education.

FRANK, Patricia A; Webster Groves HS; Webster Groves, MO; Chr; HonRl; SchMus; SchPl; YthFlsp; RptrSchPpr; SpnCl; Central College; Medicine.

FRANK, Russell M; Hammond Baptist HS; Valparaiso, IN; 3/88 VPSrCls; Aud/Vis; ChrhWkr; HonRl; NHS; SctActv; TchrAde; RptrYrbk; Yrbk; EdSchPpr; GerCl; LetterTrk; Le Tourneau College; Physics.

FRANK, Scott; Lake View Auburn HS; Auburn, IA; PresSophCls; PresJrCls; HonRl; NatlThespSoc; SchPl; StuCncl; RptrYrbk; Bsktbl; Ia State Univ; Ag Teacher.

FRANK, Scott B; Madison East HS; Madison, WI; Bsktbl; LetterWrstlng; LetterWrstlng; IMSpt; PresAwd;.

FRANK, Sherri L; Pittsburg HS; Pittsburg, KS; Band; HospAde; MrchBnd; NatlMeritSF; Quill&Scroll; SchPl; StuCncl; Twrl; EdSchPpr; FrCl; Kansas U; Journalism.

FRANKE, Carolyn J; New Hampton Community HS; New Hampton, IA; Band; Chrs; CncrtBnd; HospAde; MrchBnd; PepBnd; SpnCl; PpCl; LetterBsktbl; LetterTrk; Trade School; Nursing.

FRANKE, Deborah K; Oakfield HS; Oakfield, WI; Band; ChrhWkr; CncrtBnd; HonRl; MrchBnd; PepBnd; FHA; University; Professional.

FRANKE, Douglas R; Detroit Catholic Central HS; Detroit, MI; 62/203 VPSrCls; HonRl; JA; StuGov; RptrYrbk; FBLA; FrCl; PpCl; CaptTennis; Wrstlng; Univ Of Michigan; Business Administration.

FRANKE, Judy A; Dupo Comm HS; East Carondelet, IL; 4/110 HonRl; JCC; PolWkr; StuCncl; TchrAde; RptrYrbk; TreasMthCl; PPFtbl; College; Accounting.

FRANKE, Randy; West Bend West HS; West Bend, WI; HonRl; PolWkr; MthCl; Bsbl; Univ; Accounting.

FRANKE, Rebecca L; South Decatur HS; Greensburg, IN; ChrhWkr; CtyCnl; CmntyWkr; HonRl; HospAde; RedCrAde; 4-H; FHA; MasAwd; OptClAwd; Sociology.

FRANKENBURGER, Elizabeth A; Homewood Flossmoor HS; Flossmoor, IL; AFS; Chr; ChrhWkr; CmntyWkr; HonRl; SchAde; SchMus; TchrAde; CivCl; LatCl; Nw U Evanston.

FRANKHAUSER, Amy J; Avon HS; Avon, IL; SecJrCls; Chrs; HonRl; Mdrgl; NHS; SchPl; StuCncl; FrCl; GAA; IMSpt; College.

FRANKLIN, Arlene A; Midway Usd #433 HS; Denton, KS; SecSophCls; Aud/Vis; Band; Chrs; CncrtBnd; DrmMjrt; HonRl; MrchBnd; PepBnd; Twrl; YthFlsp; 4-H; PpCl; Vocational Tech School.

FRANKLIN, Cheryl M; Hazelwood West Sr HS; Hazelwood, MO; ChrhWkr; HonRl; JA; SchPl; Yrbk; CaptChrldr; GAA; IMSpt; PPFtbl; Sw Missouri St Univ; Journalism.

FRANKLIN, David A; Belle HS; Vichy, MO; 3/53 ChrhWkr; HonRl; NHS; StuCncl; StuGov; FFA; Bsbl; Trk; Univ Of Missouri; Nuclear Engineer.

FRANKLIN, Doris K; Adams Central HS; Ayr, NE; ChrhWkr; HonRl; SchPl; YthFlsp; PpCl; Central Tech Comm College; Business Admin.

FRANKLIN, Karen L; Chicago Vocational HS; Chicago, IL; HonRl; JA; RedCrAde; StuCncl; TchrAde; MthCl; College.

FRANKLIN, Larry J; Milan C 2 HS; Milan, MO; 1/49 TrsSophCls; PresBand; HonRl; PresNHS; NatlMeritCmnd; NatlSciFnd; SchPl; StuCncl; PresYthFlsp; EdYrBk; Bsktbl; College; Biochemistry.

FRANKLIN, Lorna R; Cass Technical HS; Detroit, MI; CmntyWkr; HonRl; NHS; NatlMeritCmnd; SchMus; SchPl; TchrAde; RptrSchPpr; Brown Univ; Research Psychologist.

FRANKLIN, Michael W; John F Kennedy HS; Bloominton, MN; Band; Chr; ChrhWkr; CncrtBnd; HonRl; MrchBnd; Orch; PepBnd; YthFlsp; Trk; Normandale Jr Coll U Of Eau Claire; Music.

FRANKLIN, Susan J; Franklin Central HS; Indianapolis, IN; VPSophCls; ChrhWkr; ModUN; SchPl; SctActv; StuCncl; EdYrBk; Bsbl; Bsktbl; LetterTrk; GAA; PresAwd; College; Missionary.

FRANKLIN, Susan K; Lincoln Community HS; Lincoln, IL; 25/272 PresSrCls; Chr; DrlTm; HonRl; LitMag; NatlThespSoc; SchMus; StuCncl; StuGov; SchPpr; Illinois State Univ; Elementary Education.

FRANKLIN, Terri; Wellington HS; Wellington, IL; SecJrCls; Chrs; HonRl; LbryAde; YthFlsp; Bsktbl; Trk; Chrldr; GAA; IMSpt;.

FRANKLIN, Terri E; Paseo HS; Kansas City, MO; 7/290 SecChr; HonRl; JA; SecNHS; SecStuCncl; RptrYrbk; SciCl; Ne Missouri State Univ; C P A Organist.

FRANKLIN, Terry L; George Rogers Clark HS; Whiting, IN; ChrhWkr; HonRl; JrNHS; NHS; OffAde; RedCrAde; StuCncl; YthFlsp; FrCl; Purdue Univ; Business Management.

FRANKLYN, Paul N; Wheeling HS; Arlington Hts, IL; 16/490 Chr; ChrhWkr; HonRl; NatlFornLg; NHS; NatlMeritCmnd; RptrSchPpr; Evangel College; Biblical Studies.

FRANKO, Marjorie K; Herbert Henry Dow HS; Midland, MI; 41/433 PresChrhWkr; HonRl; NHS; SchPpr; GerCl; PPFtbl; John Wesley College; Sociology.

FRANKOVICH, Ann E; Mona Shores HS; Muskegon, MI; HonRl; NHS; Hackley Hosp Sch Of Nursing; Nursing.

FRANKS, Cheryl J; Huron HS; Huron, SD; ALAGirlsSt; Chrs; ChrhWkr; HonRl; LbryAde; SctActv; YthFlsp; SchPpr; 4-H; GerCl; Clge; Interior Decorator.

FRANKSAIN, Roger; Marathon Consolidated HS; Marathon, IA; ChrhWkr; CmntyWkr; HonRl; LbryAde; Vocational; Electronics.

FRANKSON, Jane L; West HS; Green Bay, WI; 11/390 SecBand; CncrtBnd; NHS; Orch; RptrYrbk; EdSchPpr; SciCl; Tennis; GAA; OptClAwd; Coll; Nursing.

FRANKWICK, Diana M; Muskego HS; Muskego, WI; 47/324 AFS; Band; HonRl; NHS; YthFlsp; RptrYrbk; Yrbk; GerCl; Univ Wi Stevens Pt; Conservation.

FRANSEN, Charlotte A; Newton HS; Newton, KS; 21/295 SecTrsSrCls; Chrs; ChrhWkr; HonRl; LbryAde; StuCncl; YthFlsp; ChmnPpCl; PPFtbl; Bethel Col.

FRANSEN, Jane A; Argyle HS; Argyle, WI; 9/44 SecSophCls; Band; Chr; Chrs; CncrtBnd; HonRl; Mdrgl; MrchBnd; PepBnd; SchMus; Trk; University; Elem Education.

FRANSEN, Wendell R; Shannon HS; Shannon, IL; VPFrshCls; VPSophCls; ALBoysSt; Band; Chrs; CncrtBnd; HonRl; MrchBnd; StuCncl; YthFlsp; PpCl; CaptBsbl; Bsktbl; Glf; No Illinois Univ; Accounting.

FRANSON, Deborah; Raymore Peculiar HS; Raymore, MO; ChrhWkr; HonRl; SctActv; 4-H; PpCl; Bsbl; Trk; Chrldr; Univ; Major Study.

FRANSON, Gary; Licoln HS; Thief River Falls, MN; 8/250 Band; CncrtBnd; HonRl; NHS; Orch; PepBnd; SchMus; Augsburg Coll; Cpa.

FRANSON, Karen L; Walther Lutheran HS; Chicago, IL; 8/92 Chr; HonRl; NHS; StuGov; Yrbk; RptrSchPpr; Univ Of Illinois; Accounting.

FRANSON, Nancy M; South Newton HS; Goodland, IN; Band; CncrtBnd; HonRl; MrchBnd; PepBnd; SchMus; 4-H; GerCl; PresSciCl; Purdue Univ; Pro Chemist.

FRANSSEN, Pamela S; Portage Northern HS; Portage, MI; DrlTm; HonRl; NHS; SpnCl; Bsktbl; LetterTrk; GAA; IMSpt; PresAwd; Western Mi U; Psychology.

FRANTA, Karen M; Wabasso Public HS; Wabasso, MN; HonRl; NHS; SchPl; TchrAde; RptrSchPpr; PpCl; LetterTrk; Chrldr; GAA; PPFtbl; College.

FRANTSEN, Jil M; Chaska Senior HS; Chaska, MN; 29/210 Chr; CtyCnl; DrmBgl; HonRl; JA; NatlMeritSchl; RedCrAde; SchPl; StuCncl; YthFnd; Bus School; Real Estate.

FRANTZ, Suzanne M; La Salle HS; St Ignace, MI; TrsJrCls; ALAGirlsSt; HonRl; HospAde; NHS; Sdlty; StuCncl; RptrYrbk; EdSchPpr; SpnCl; Lake Superior St Coll; Nursing.

FRANTZEN, Peggy A; Aurora Central Catholic HS; Aurora, IL; 36/163 ChrhWkr; HonRl; NHS; NatlMeritFnl; RedCrAde; FBLA; FNA; FTA; LetterGAA; IMSpt;.

FRANTZEN, Susan A; Marquette HS; Bellevue, IA; 13/68 Chrs; HonRl; LbryAde; NHS; TchrAde; Yrbk;.

FRANZ, Cheryl A; Mishicot HS; Mishicot, WI; 5/130 Band; Chrs; CncrtBnd; HonRl; MrchBnd; NatlFornLg; OffAde; RptrYrbk; SchPpr; GAA; VoiceDemAwd; Univ; Special Ed Instructor.

FRANZ, Eileen; All Saints Central HS; Bay City, MI; 3/143 Chrs; HonRl; SchMus; PpCl; Saginaw Valley State Coll; Medical Tech.

FRANZ, Janet C; Maine South HS; Park Ridge, IL; HonRl; LitMag; NHS; Quill&Scroll; SchPpr; Univ Of Illinois.

FRANZ, Robert G; Leland Community HS; Leland, IL; AFS; ALBoysSt; HonRl; NHS; StuCncl; Bsbl; LetterBsktbl; LetterSocr; LetterTrk;.

FRANZEL, Joy L; Parkway Central HS; Chesterfield, MO; JrNHS; NatlFornLg; TreasNHS; VPNatlThespSoc; OffAde; SchPl; StuCncl; TchrAde; RptrYrbk; University.

FRANZEN, Barry R; Crivitz HS; Crivitz, WI; 2/75 PresFrshCls; ALBoysSt; HonRl; PresNHS; SchPl; SctActv; StuCncl; StuGov; SptEdSchPpr; CaptBsktbl; CaptFtbl; Trk; Marquette Univ; Dentistry.

FRANZEN, Cindy A; Stanton Community HS; Stanton, IA; 3/35 PresFrshCls; Band; HonRl; NHS; SchPl; TchrAde; Bsbl; Bsktbl; Trk; PPFtbl; Trade; Beautician.

FRANZEN, Debbie L; Flanagan HS; Flanagan, IL; SecSophCls; SecJrCls; Band; HonRl; MrchBnd; RptrYrbk; GerCl; PpCl; GAA; College.

FRANZEN, Diane M; Turkey Valley Comm HS; Waucoma, IA; 18/112 Chr; HonRl; SchMus; Sdlty; Chrldr; IMSpt; Bus Schl; Vocation.

FRANZEN, James N; Turkey Valley HS; Ft Atkinson, IA; Chr; SchMus; SchPl; PpCl; LetterBsbl; CaptFtbl; College.

FRANZKE, Beth E; Appleton East HS; Appleton, WI; 23/523 Chrl; ChrhWkr; NatlFornLg; NatlMeritCmnd; College; Medicine.

FRASCAFI, Joseph; Gordon Tech Hs; Chicago, IL; HonRl; LetterWrstlng; Loyola U; Law Enforcement.

FRASCONA, James E; Oak Park River Forest HS; Oak Park, IL; HonRl; Bsktbl; Univ Of Ill; Psychology.

FRASE, Sylvia K; Montabella HS; Edmore, MI; Band; Chr; ChrhWkr; HonRl; NHS; SchPl; EdYrBk; FTA;

SpnCl; PPFtbl; Michigan State Univ; Elementary Education.

FRASER, Barbara L; Cedar Lake Academy; St Charles, MI; PresSophCls; Chr; ChrhWkr; HonRl; Mdrgl; NHS; OffAde; StuCncl; 4-H; Andrews University.

FRASEUR, James N; Spencer HS; Spencer, IA; ChrhWkr; CmntyWkr; HonRl; NatlFornLg; NatlThespSoc; YthFlsp; Yrbk; LetterTrk; IMSpt; MasAwd; Univ Of Wyoming; Business Admin.

FRATTARELLI, Concetta; East Detroit HS; Warren, MI; SecSophCls; HonRl; NHS; OffAde; StuCncl; PpCl; Bsktbl; Ftbl; CchngActv; IMSpt; Wayne State Univ; Physical Theraphy.

FRATZKE, Jayne R; E Peo Comm HS; E Peoria, IL; 8/500 TreasChrhWkr; CncrtBnd; HonRl; MrchBnd; NHS; Orch; PepBnd; Quill&Scroll; SchPl; EdYrBk; Pres4-H; PresMthCl; PpCl; SciCl; College; Secretary.

FRAUTSCHI, Richard J; Wishek HS; Wishek, ND; Band; CmntyWkr; CncrtBnd; MrchBnd; PepBnd; SchPl; RptrSchPpr; FFA; LetterFtbl; Coll; Elect.

FRAY, Mary D; Connersville Sr HS; Connersville, IN; 3/380 Chr; ChrhWkr; HonRl; NHS; NatlThespSoc; SchMus; SchPl; YthFlsp; 4-H; SpnCl; DARAwd; KiwanAwd; Indiana Univ; Doctor.

FRAZEE, Barbara; Marshall HS; Marshall, MO; 17/155 Band; Chrs; ChrhWkr; HonRl; MrchBnd; Orch; SchMus; SctActv; YthFlsp; PpCl; Central Mo State; Accountant.

FRAZEE, Karen K; Summerfield HS; Summerfield, KS; 1/15 PresJrCls; Band; Chrs; HonRl; SchPl; StuCncl; TchrAde; 4-H; CaptBsktbl; Chrldr; College.

FRAZEE, Mark A; Lake Michigan Catholic HS; St Joseph, MI; Chrl; CmntyWkr; HonRl; KeyCl; LetterFtbl; Trk; IMSpt; College; Professional.

FRAZER, Larry D; Anderson HS; Anderson, IN; 17/580 ChrhWkr; HonRl; NHS; FrCl; SciCl; ChmbCommrsAwd; General Motors Inst; Mechanical Engineer.

FRAZHO, Renee E; Regina HS; St Clair Shores, MI; Chr; Chrl; HonRl; LbryAde; NatlFornLg; RedCrAde; SchMus; SchPl; TchrAde; RptrYrbk; RptrSchPpr; LetterTennis; GAA; IMSpt; College.

FRAZIER, Barry W; Althoff Catholic HS; Fairview, IL; 48/354 HonRl; Bsbl; Bsktbl; CaptFtbl; College; Psychology.

FRAZIER, Bradley J; Belleville Twp W HS; Belleville, IL; Chr; ChrhWkr; CAP; JrNHS; NatlFornLg; NatlThespSoc; ROTC; SchMus; SchPl; SctActv; Wrstlng; IMSpt; Univ Of Illinois; Physicist.

FRAZIER, Bret M; Bradley Bour HS; Bourbonnais, IL; CtyCnl; CmntyWkr; Sdlty; StuGov; YthFlsp; SchPpr; Glf; GodCntryAwd; CitAwd; VoiceDemAwd; College; Achitect.

FRAZIER, Deborah J; Sarcoxie HS; Sarcoxie, MO; PresJrCls; HonRl; NHS; SchPl; StuCncl; FHA; FTA; PpCl; College; Teaching.

FRAZIER, Dennis G; Evansville North HS; Evansville, IN; 1/445 HonRl; NatlFornLg; NHS; NatlMeritSF; StuCncl; StuGov; Southern Illinois Univ; Math.

FRAZIER, Gina; Pittsfield HS; Pittsfield, IL; 22/130 HonRl; FFA; PpCl; Trk; Chrldr; GAA; IMSpt; Northeast Miss State.

FRAZIER, Julie A; Pittsfield HS; Pittsfield, IL; HonRl; SchPl; PpCl; LetterBsktbl; Glf; LetterTennis; LetterTrk; Chrldr; GAA; IMSpt; College; Physical Ed.

FRAZIER, Laura; Truman HS; Independence, MO; Chr; NatlFornLg; NHS; NatlThespSoc; SchMus; SchPl;.

FRAZIER, Marjorie J; Hannibal Senior HS; Hannibal, MO; 64/266 ChrhWkr; HonRl; FBLA; Bsktbl; IMSpt; PPFtbl; University Of Columbia.

FRAZIER, Mary J; English Valleys HS; South English, IA; 10/65 Band; Chrs; HonRl; CaptBsktbl; LetterTrk; 4-HAwd; CitAwd; Iowa St Univ; Science.

FRAZIER, Richard L; River Valley HS; Harbert, MI; 5/160 HonRl; NHS; TchrAde; GerCl; Bsktbl; Glf; Trk; IMSpt; Kalamazoo Coll; Medicine.

FRAZIER, Steven K; Merrillville HS; Merrillville, IN; 110/564 Band; ChrhWkr; CncrtBnd; HonRl; MrchBnd; SchMus; YthFlsp; RptrSchPpr; FrCl; Olivet Nazarene College; Law.

FREAS, Betsy M; Fountain Central HS; Veedersburg, IN; Band; Chrs; DrlTm; HonRl; Mdrgl; MrchBnd; NHS; SchMus; SchPl; YthFlsp; 4-H; FHA; GAA; Purdue Univ; Humanities.

FREBERG, Leland L; Cambridge HS; Cambridge, IL; 6/59 PresFrshCls; AFS; ALBoysSt; Chrs; ChrhWkr; CncrtBnd; PresNHS; PresStuCncl; VPSpnCl; LetterBsktbl; LetterTrk; SARAwd; Eastern Ill Univ; Accounting.

FRECH, Mary C; Wichita South HS; Wichita, KS; Chr; Chrl; HonRl; HospAde; NHS; OffAde; RedCrAde; SctActv; StuCncl; FNA; GerCl; Texas Womens Univ; Nursing.

FRED, Donald; Willow City Public HS; Willow City, ND; VPFrshCls; Band; Chrs; ChrhWkr; PepBnd; SchPpr; 4-H; FFA; Bsktbl; College; Vocation.

FREDBLOOM, Richard; Northrop HS; Ft Wayne, IN; 38/588 ChrhWkr; JA; Quill&Scroll; SchAde; StuGov; GerCl; PpCl; Bsbl; Bsktbl; Trk; Indiana Univ; Accountant.

FREDDE, Kari B; Winterset Community HS; Winterset, IA; 6/103 AFS; ChrhWkr; HonRl; PresSpnCl; Bsbl; Bsktbl; VoiceDemAwd; College; Bi Lingual Business.

FREDELL, James E; Woodruff HS; Peoria, IL; 47/381 AFS; Chr; YthFlsp; SptEdSchPpr; KeyCl; LatCl; Bsbl; Ftbl; University Of Illinois; Mechanical Engineer.

FREDERICK, Catherine J; Lake Orion HS; Lake Orion, MI; 37/350 HonRl; LbryAde; NatlMeritCmnd; SchPl; TchrAde; FTA; Central Mi Univ; Teaching.

FREDERICK, David; Ayrshire Consolidated HS; Ruthven, IA; VPJrCls; ChrhWkr; HonRl; SchPl; Glf; College.

FREDERICK, Gerald L; Orchard Farm HS; West Alton, MO; 4/160 PresChrhWkr; HonRl; JA; VPNHS; PresKeyCl; Trk; University Of Missouri; Engineering.

FREDERICK, Jerry L; Cass City HS; Decker, MI; 42/130 CmntyWkr; HonRl; JA; 4-H; 4-HAwd; CitAwd; Mi State Univ; Dairy Farming.

FREDERICK, Kathy M; Watertown Sr HS; Watertown, SD; HonRl; HospAde;.

FREDERICK, Ruth E; Prairie Home HS; Boonville, MO; TrsJrCls; Band; Chrs; ChrhWkr; HonRl; SchPl; FHA; Bsbl; Bsktbl; Trade Schl; Beautician.

FREDERICK, Shirley; Green Lake Hs; Ripon, WI; 4/36 HonRl; LbryAde; MrchBnd; NHS; PepBnd; 4-H; LatCl; PpCl; Bsktbl; GAA; College; Physician.

FREDERICKS, Donna M; Lee M Thurston HS; Detroit, MI; 98/633 Chrs; PresChrhWkr; HonRl; NHS; SchMus; SchPl; SciCl; LetterTrk; Wayne State Univ; Health Profession.

FREDERICKS, Victoria L; Jacksonville HS; Jacksonville, IL; PresAFS; HonRl; NHS; StuGov; Swmmng; LetterTrk; College; Recreation.

FREDERICKSEN, Debbie S; Manistee HS; Manistee, MI; HonRl; JrNHS; NHS; StuCncl; Teen; Twrl; RptrSchPpr; GAA; IMSpt; PPFtbl; CitAwd;.

FREDERICKSEN, Shelley K; Frontenac HS; Frontenac, KS; 3/41 SecFrshCls; Chrs; HonRl; StuCncl; RptrYrbk; RptrSchPpr; FHA; SpnCl; MthCl; PpCl; College; Accounting.

FREDERICKSON, Karl D; Malvern Comm HS; Malvern, IA; 23/31 ALBoysSt; Band; CncrtBnd; MrchBnd; SchPl; LetterBsbl; LetterBsktbl; LetterFtbl; CaptTrk; Peru St Clg; Carpentry.

FREDIN, Tracy; Comfrey Public HS; Comfrey, MN; CncrtBnd; HonRl; MrchBnd; NatlSciFnd; PepBnd; SchPl; StuCncl; SciCl; Univ; Professional.

FREDMAN, Leland G; Jefferson Senior HS; Eagle Bend, MN; 10/330 ChrhWkr; CmntyWkr; HonRl; NHS; RptrSchPpr; Tech Sch; Prof.

FREDRICH, Michael J; Wagner Community HS; Wagner, SD; ALBoysSt; ChrhWkr; HonRl; SchPl; Bsktbl;.

FREDRICK, Catherine J; Nerinx Hall HS; Des Peres, MO; 10/99 Chrl; HonRl; LitMag; NatlThespSoc; PolWkr; SchMus; PpCl; IMSpt; University; Teacher.

FREDRICK, Guy L; Palmyra HS; Eagle, WI; ALBoysSt; Band; CmntyWkr; CncrtBnd; HonRl; LbryAde; MrchBnd; PolWkr; SchMus; LetterBsbl; LetterFtbl; LetterWrstlng; Technical Schl; Drafting.

FREDRICK, Robert S; Bedford HS; Temperance, MI; 16/435 ALBoysSt; Band; Chr; ChrhWkr; HonRl; MrchBnd; NHS; YthFlsp; IMSpt; Adrian Coll; Pre Med.

FREDRICKSON, Brian T; Glenville HS; Glenville, MN; Chrs; HonRl; OffAde; SchPl; TchrAde; Bus Sch; Vocation.

FREDRICKSON, Cynthia; Davis Co Comm HS; Bloomfield, IA; Band; CncrtBnd; HonRl; MrchBnd; PepBnd; 4-H; FTA; 4-HAwd; Univ Of Iowa; Economics.

FREDRICKSON, Dana S; Hastings Sr HS; Hastings, MN; 7/428 ALAGirlsSt; Band; Chr; CncrtBnd; HonRl; MrchBnd; NHS; SchMus; StuCncl; PpCl; LetterChrldr; St Olaf College; Med Technology.

FREDRICKSON, Mark; Pingree HS; Edmunds, ND; Band; Chr; Chrs; SchPl; Yrbk; SchPpr; 4-H; Bsbl; College; Farming.

FREDRICKSON, Mark D; New Richmond Senior HS; New Richmond, WI; Orch; StuCncl; University; Biology.

FREDRICKSON, Rhonda J; Wanamingo Ind HS; Wanamingo, MN; Chr; Chrs; ChrhWkr; HonRl; RptrSchPpr; LetterTrk; Armed Forces; Administration.

FREDRICKSON, Rodney A; Menasa HS; Menasha, WI; 50/333 HonRl; SchMus; LetterBsbl; LetterBsktbl; CaptFtbl; AmLegAwd; Usaf Acad.

FREE, Marvin K; Truman HS; Agency, MO; 383/604 AFS; DrlTm; MrchBnd; StuCncl; YthFlsp; SptEdSchPpr; CaptFtbl; Wrstlng; Nwmsu; Farmer.

FREEBERG, Jeffery; Holdrege HS; Holdrege, NE; 19 Band; Chrs; CncrtBnd; MrchBnd; Orch; PepBnd; SchMus; LetterFtbl; IMSpt;.

FREEBERG, Steven L; Lisbon HS; Lisbon, ND; 16/73 HonRl; Trade Sch; Cpa.

FREEBERG, Steven W; Parsons HS; Parsons, KS; ALBoysSt; KeyCl; College; Business.

FREEBURG, Teresa A; Plattsmouth HS; Plattsmouth, NE; Band; Chrs; ChrhWkr; CmntyWkr; CncrtBnd; DrmMjrt; MrchBnd; SchMus; SchPl; Twrl; PpCl; CaptChrldr; PPFtbl; Univ Of Nebraska; Business.

FREEBURG, Theodore A; Plattsmouth HS; Plattsmouth, NE; 10/163 Band; Chrs; CncrtBnd; HonRl; NHS; SctActv; YthFlsp; MthCl; Bsbl; Bsktbl; LetterTrk; College; Medical Field.

FREEBY, Leslie L; Appleton West HS; Appleton, WI; AFS; Chr; ChrhWkr; CmntyWkr; LbryAde; Mdrgl; NHS; NatlThespSoc; SchMus; SchPl; Depauw Univ; Medicine.

FREEBY, Sharyl M; St Marys HS; St Marys, KS; Chrs; HonRl; NHS; Quill&Scroll; TchrAde; Kansas State Univ; Engineering.

FREED, David; Lansing HS; Kansas City, KS; ALBoysSt; NatlThespSoc; NHS; YthFlsp; 4-H; SciCl; Bsktbl; Ftbl; Swmmng; 4-HAwd; Ks State Univ; Engineering.

FREED, Richard A; Bellmont HS; Decatur, IN; 29/250 ChrhWkr; HonRl; NHS; LatCl; SciCl; Ftbl; IMSpt; In U; Chemistry.

FREEDMAN, Winifred D; Granite South HS; Granite City, IL; 2/630 Chrs; ChrhWkr; CtyCnl; LitMag; NatlFornLg; PresNHS; NatlMeritCmnd; PolWkr; SchMus; SchPl; StuGov; YthFlsp; EdSchPpr; EldAwd; College; Drama.

FREELAND, Amy L; John Hersey HS; Hoffman Est, IL; 102/739 AFS; CmntyWkr; HonRl; NHS; PolWkr; SchMus; SchPl; Ill State Univ; Medical Technologist.

FREELAND, Dorothy A; Kirksville HS; Kirksville, MO; Chrs; ChrhWkr; LbryAde; OffAde; SchPl; YthFlsp; Tennis; Trk; Secretary.

FREELAND, John L; Marquette HS; Michigan City, IN; HonRl; Quill&Scroll; RedCrAde; RptrSchPpr; Bsktbl; Swmmng; Tennis; Trk; University; Radio.

FREELAND, Rusty W; Unity HS; Philo, IL; VPJrCls; PresSrCls; Chrs; HonRl; NHS; NatlThespSoc; SchMus; LetterBsbl; LetterBsktbl; LetterFtbl; University Of Illinois; Law.

FREELEND, Nicholas R; Central City Sr HS; Central City, NE; 5/74 TrsSophCls; TrsJrCls; Band; ChrhWkr; CncrtBnd; MrchBnd; NHS; PepBnd; SchMus; College; Music.

FREELON, Leroy; Cass Technical HS; Detroit, MI; NatlMeritCmnd; LetterTrk; IMSpt; Coll; Engr.

FREEMAN, Beverly J; Roosevelt HS; Gary, IN; Chr; Chrs; ROTC; Chrldr; EldAwd; College; Professional.

FREEMAN, Brenda B; Mansfield HS; Mansfield, MO; 13/45 Chr; ChrhWkr; HonRl; HospAde; LbryAde; NHS; FHA; LatCl; PpCl;.

FREEMAN, Chris D; Gideon HS; Gideon, MO; 3/41 HstJrCls; Band; Chr; ChrhWkr; CncrtBnd; HonRl; MrchBnd; PepBnd; SchPl; SctActv; StuCncl; Bsbl; Trk; Union University.

FREEMAN, Daniel J; Spring Valley HS; Spring Valley, MN; Band; CncrtBnd; MrchBnd; NHS; PepBnd; SchMus; SchPl; RptrYrbk; TreasSpnCl; LetterFtbl; AmLegAwd; Drake Univ; Accounting.

FREEMAN, Debra A; East Noble HS; Kendallville, IN; 17/278 VPSophCls; PresJrCls; Chr; DrlTm; HonRl; NHS; NatlThespSoc; SchMus; StuCncl; SchPpr; Ball State Univ; Performing Arts.

FREEMAN, Diana M; Gwinn HS; Ki Sawyer Afb, MI; HonRl; NHS; RedCrAde; StuGov; PpCl; Northern Michigan Univ; Medical Lab Tech.

FREEMAN, Jack; Riley HS; South Bend, IN; Band; HonRl; JA; Trk; IMSpt; JCAwd; College; Professional.

FREEMAN, Janice S; Pierce City HS; Pierce City, MO; HonRl; FHA; VPPpCl; College.

FREEMAN, Jeff; Osawatomie HS; Pooala, KS; Band; CncrtBnd; HonRl; MrchBnd; College Or Univ; Professional.

FREEMAN, Marilyn J; Grand Community HS; Ogden, IA; 2/23 Band; Chrs; NHS; PolWkr; SchMus; SchPl; TreasStuCncl; EdYrBk; 4-H; SciCl; Iowa Methodist Sch; Nursing.

FREEMAN, Michael; Freeman Public HS; Freeman, SD; ALBoysSt; CmntyWkr; HonRl; NHS; PolWkr; StuCncl; SptEdYrbk; EdSchPpr; CchngActv; IMSpt; Sd Univ; Journalism.

FREEMAN, Michael S; Hillsboro HS; Irving, IL; 33/185 ChrhWkr; HonRl; StuCncl; LetterBsbl; LetterFtbl; LetterWrstlng; IMSpt; College.

FREEMAN, Mike; Kennedy HS; Cedar Rapids, IA; YthFlsp; Wrstlng; IMSpt; U Of Ia; Cpa.

FREEMAN, Paula; Center Point Cons HS; Center Point, IA; Band; Chrl; HonRl; NHS; NatlThespSoc; StuCncl; EdSchPpr; 4-H; Bsbl; College; Journalism.

FREEMAN, Ray M; Smithville HS; Smithville, MO; ChrhWkr; HonRl; SctActv; YthFlsp; FFA; Ftbl; Trk; Trenton Jr College; Agriculture.

FREEMAN, Renita G; Harper HS; Chicago, IL; Chrl; Chrs; ChrhWkr; CncrtBnd; HonRl; MrchBnd; NHS; PepBnd; RptrSchPpr; GerCl; College; Nursing.

FREEMAN, Rita E; Lincoln Comm HS; Stanwood, IA; 8/64 VPSrCls; HonRl; NHS; OffAde; SctActv; YthFlsp; EngCl; PpCl; Glf; LetterChrldr;.

FREEMAN, Sara L; Beloit Memorial HS; Beloit, WI; AFS; HonRl; JrNHS; StuGov; Yrbk; VPSpnCl; Bsbl; LetterSwmmng; GAA; PresAwd; Coll; Elem Ed.

FREEMAN, Sharon B; Chicago Vocational HS; Chicago, IL; Chr; Chrs; ChrhWkr; Mdrgl; College; Professional.

FREEMAN, Theresa A; Aurora Hoyt Lakes HS; Aurora, MN; HonRl; 4-H; FrCl; MthCl; Clg; Med Tech.

FREEMAN, Walter D; Baldwin HS; Overbrook, KS; ChrhWkr; LbryAde; SctActv; YthFlsp; Bsbl; Bsktbl; Ftbl; Tennis; Trk; IMSpt; Trade; Major Study.

FREER, Lisa A; Union HS; Losantville, IN; 10/80 Band; CncrtBnd; HonRl; HospAde; MrchBnd; NHS; PepBnd; VP4-H; FHA; 4-HAwd; Indiana Univ; Dr Of Med.

FREES, Diana; Hesperia HS; Hesperia, MI; SecSrCls; Band; Chr; ChrhWkr; HonRl; IntrClCncl; NatlFornLg; OffAde; FTA; Executive Secretary.

FREESE, Henry W; Berkeley Sr HS; Berkeley, MO; HonRl; LbryAde; NHS; StuCncl; SciCl; LetterSwmmng; LetterTennis; College; Biology.

FREESE, Julie M; Streator Township HS; Streator, IL; 29/372 CmntyWkr; HonRl; LbryAde; TchrAde; PpCl; Illinois Valley Comm Coll; Librarian.

FREESE, Roxene C; Maynard HS; Montevideo, MN; 2/26 Band; Chrl; Chrs; HonRl; MrchBnd; NHS; SchPl; TchrAde; EdYrBk; GAA; Inter Fine Arts College; Merchandising.

FREESEMAN, De Laine H; Greene Community HS; Greene, IA; Chrs; HonRl; SctActv; YthFlsp; Sec4-H; LetterFtbl; N I A C C; Agriculture Busines.

FREESEMANN, Lois J; Allison Bristow Comm HS; Allison, IA; ChrhWkr; HospAde; SchAde; Yrbk; 4-H; FHA; FNA; PpCl; CaptBsktbl; 4-HAwd; Marshalltown Comm School; Nursing.

FREGO, Nancy J; Lourdes HS; Rochester, MN; Chr; HonRl; FrCl; LetterTrk; College; Accounting.

FREI, Jason L; Potter Public HS; Potter, NE; TrsFrshCls; TrsSophCls; Ftbl; Wrstlng; Trade School; Building Construction.

FREI, Jennifer L; Red Wing Central HS; Red Wing, MN; 23/328 AFS; HonRl; NHS; NatlMeritSF; NatlThespSoc; RptrYrbk; IMSpt; VoiceDemAwd; St Catherine; Library Science.

FREI, Steven; Goodrich HS; Fond Du Lac, WI; ChrhWkr; HonRl; SctActv; GodCntryAwd; College; Engineering Degree.

FREIBERG, Phyllis M; Wausau East HS; Wausau, WI; Band; ChrhWkr; CmntyWkr; MrchBnd; NHS; PepBnd; PpCl; Univ Of Wis; Behavioral Disabilities.

FREIBERGER, Michael A; St Thomas Aquinas HS; Hazelwood, MO; 13/332 HonRl; NHS; Orch; SchPl; CitAwd; St Louis University; Medicine.

FREIBURG, Jeanne E; Jacksonville HS; Jacksonville, IL; AFS; HonRl; LitMag; ModUN; NatlThespSoc; Orch; PolWkr; SchMus; SchPl; SchPpr; Mac Murray College.

FREID, Eugene; Niles East HS; Skokie, IL; 179/564 LetterSocr; Univ; Medicine.

FREIER, Merritt T; Flora HS; Flora, IL; 28/160 Band; HonRl; SchMus; SchPl; SptEdSchPpr; GerCl; MthCl; Bsbl; LetterFtbl; LetterTrk; Univ; Engineering.

FREIMUTH, Colleen L; St Agnes Academy; Alliance, NE; Chr; Chrs; ChrhWkr; HonRl; LbryAde; 4-H; FrCl; Trk; CchngActv; Chadron St; Professional.

FREIMUTH, Sandra J; Columbus HS; Columbus, WI; 14/125 Chrs; CncrtBnd; HospAde; MrchBnd; NHS; SctActv; SecYthFlsp; SecSpnCl; GAA; Univ Of Wisconsin; Nursing.

FREIS, Richard J; Lockport Central HS; Crest Hill, IL; 28/550 HonRl; College Augustana; Chemical Eng.

FREISE, Jennifer A; Waukegan HS East; Waukegan, IL; Chr; PresChrhWkr; HonRl; JA; NatlMeritCmnd; GAA; Valparaiso Univ; Social Work.

FREISE, Pamela S; Dundee Comm HS; Dundee, IL; Chr; Chrs; DrlTm; HonRl; StuCncl; StuGov; PpCl; LetterChrldr; Winona St College; Nurse.

FREITAG, Julia L; Olympia HS; Minier, IL; 20/200 AFS; ALAGirlsSt; Chr; ChrhWkr; NHS; SchMus; Treas4-H; VPGerCl; MthCl; SecSciCl; GAA; Ill State Univ; Sociology.

FREITAG, Peggy; Wahpeton Senior HS; Wahpeton, ND; 9/144 ALAGirlsSt; Band; HonRl; NHS; StuCncl; Chrldr; IMSpt; PPFtbl; Trade School; Architectural Drafting & Est.

FREIVALDS, Zaiga; Dwigt D Eisenhower HS; Saginaw, MI; 3/365 HonRl; NHS; SctActv; GerCl; LetterTrk; Univ Of Mi; Biology.

FREIVOGEL, Vicky L; Riverview Gardens HS; St Louis, MO; 3/779 ChrhWkr; HonRl; JA; NHS; StuCncl; PpCl; Univ Of Missouri; Pre Vet.

FREKING, Dennis; St Marys HS; Remsen, IA; 10/47 Band; Chr; Chrs; CncrtBnd; HonRl; PepBnd; SchMus; Trk; Univ Of Sd; Music.

FREKO, Deborah L; Forest View HS; Mt Prospect, IL; 23/600 HonRl; NHS; NatlMeritCmnd; Quill&Scroll; RptrSchPpr; SchPpr; Lewis U; Psychology.

FRENCH, Carol J; Collinsville HS; Collinsville, IL; 34/650 HonRl; NHS; OffAde; Quill&Scroll; StuCncl; EdYrBk; College; Accounting.

FRENCH, Colin V; Roosevelt HS; Des Moines, IA; 12/445 Band; ChrhWkr; HonRl; IntrClCncl; NatlFornLg; NHS; StuCncl; RptrSchPpr; LetterGlf; Socr; Swmmng; Tennis; Graceland College; Medicine.

FRENCH, Gregory W; Hillsdale HS; Hillsdale, MI; Band; HonRl; NHS; PepBnd; YthFlsp; KeyCl; Ftbl; College.

FRENCH, Judy; Bedford Comm HS; Bedford, IA; SecTrsFrshCls; Band; ChrhWkr; HonRl; TchrAde; Teen; YthFlsp; FTA; Chrldr; PPFtbl; College Or Trade School; Vocation.

FRENCH, Kimberly K; West HS; Minneapolis, MN; Chr; HonRl; StuCncl; TchrAde; Chrldr; College; Lawyer.

FRENCH, Marie E; Rosemount HS; Apple Valley, MN; 8/347 Band; Chr; CncrtBnd; MrchBnd; SpnCl; Clg Of St Catherine; Mathematics.

FRENCH, Michael R; North Greene HS; White Hall, IL; 2/123 Chrs; ChrhWkr; HonRl; Mdrgl; TreasNHS; SchMus; SchPl; EdYrBk; EdSchPpr; Bsbl; Ftbl; Glf; Wrstlng; St Louis College; Pharmacist.

FRENCHER, Stanley K; Cass Tech HS; Detroit, MI;

CncrtBnd; HonRl; NatlMeritCmnd; Univ Of Michigan; Medicine.

FRENETTE, Michael R; Hancock Central HS; Hancock, MI; HonRl; SchPpr; Ftbl; LetterGlf;.

FRERICHS, Mark L; Superior HS; Superior, NE; 27/80 PresSrCls; Chr; HonRl; StuCncl; 4-H; KeyCl; LetterBsbl; LetterBsktbl; LetterFtbl; LetterTrk; Morningside Coll; Busi Admin.

FRESCH, Joseph A; Brother Rice HS; Birmingham, MI; 1/222 HonRl; ModUN; NHS; Ftbl; LetterGlf; IMSpt; Univ; Medicine.

FRESCURA, Barbara A; Our Lady Of Mt Carmel HS; Lincoln Park, MI; 11/58 Chr; HonRl; LbryAde; OffAde; SchMus; PpCl; Bsbl; CaptBsktbl; GAA; IMSpt;.

FRESE, Richard A; Francis Howell HS; St Charles, MO; JA; SctActv; RptrYrbk; RptrSchPpr; SchPpr; SpnCl; Bsbl; Univ; Journalism.

FRESKE, Nancy M; Greenfield HS; Greenfield, WI; HonRl; TchrAde; PpCl; School Of Nursing; Nursing Rn.

FRETS, Julia L; Marshall HS; Marshall, IL; 15/115 ALAGirlsSt; Band; Chrs; CncrtBnd; MrchBnd; NHS; PepBnd; SpnCl; SciCl; U Of Il; Veterinary Medicine.

FRETT, Donna; Proviso West HS; Westchester, IL; 23/948 CmntyWkr; HonRl; JA; NHS; SchMus; MthCl; JAAwd; College.

FRETZ, Harry T; Holcomb HS; Holcomb, MO; Chr; ChrhWkr; Mdrgl; SchPl; PpCl; Bsbl; LetterTennis; Trk; Chrldr; IMSpt; Air Force.

FREUDE, Jeffrey L; Erie HS; Erie, IL; 5/81 PresJrCls; HonRl; SctActv; PresStuCncl; EdYrBk; SciCl; LetterBsktbl; LetterTrk; College; Business Admin.

FREUDENBURG, Debra L; Madison HS; Madison, NE; 13/59 Chr; Chrl; ChrhWkr; HonRl; LbryAde; SpnCl; PpCl; Coll; Nurse.

FREUDENBURG, Diane L; Madison HS; Madison, NE; TrsJrCls; Chr; Chrl; HonRl; StuGov; PpCl; AmLegAwd; Trade Sch; Vocation.

FREUDENBURG, Gregory; Madison HS; Madison, NE; ALBoysSt; Chr; HonRl; LbryAde; NHS; RptrYrbk; RptrSchPpr; Bsktbl; Ftbl; IMSpt; Trade Sch; Vocation.

FREUDENHEIM, Eric J; Rich Central HS; Park Forest, IL; 70/400 VPJrCls; PresSrCls; HonRl; StuCncl; TchrAde; KeyCl; FrCl; LetterWrstlng; IMSpt; Univ Of Illinois; Medicine.

FREUND, Cynthia M; Grant HS; Mc Henry, IL; 45/202 Band; Chr; HonRl; HospAde; LbryAde; MrchBnd; PepBnd; SchMus; 4-H; GAA; College; Medical Technology.

FREUND, Deborah J; Mchenry Comm West HS; Mchenry, IL; 4/466 AFS; Chrs; HonRl; SecNHS; PpCl; VPGAA; College; Phys Therapy.

FREUND, Galen D; Lebo HS; Lebo, KS; TrsSrCls; ALBoysSt; Chr; HonRl; MrchBnd; PepBnd; SchPl; FBLA; FFA; LetterBsktbl; Vocational Tech School; Electronics.

FREUND, Jeanne K; Mc Pherson HS; Mc Pherson, KS; ALAGirlsSt; OffAde; Jr Col; Home Ec.

FREUND, Marian; St Marys Springs HS; Fonddulac, WI; 1/120 ALAGirlsSt; HonRl; SchPl; StuCncl; Yrbk; PpCl; KiwanAwd; Marian College; Pre Med.

FREUND, Mark; Neosho HS; Neosho, MO; 23/243 ALBoysSt; Chr; ChrhWkr; HonRl; JrNHS; NHS; StuCncl; YthFlsp; EdYrBk; College And Univ; Geo.

FREUND, Susan M; Lyons Township HS; La Grange Park, IL; HospAde; JrNHS; LitMag; LbryAde; NHS; NatlMeritCmnd; SchMus; StuCncl; StuGov; Univ Of Dayton; Accounting.

FREVERT, Charles; Audubon HS; Audubon, IA; AFS; ALBoysSt; ChrhWkr; JCC; Orch; SctActv; RptrYrbk; GerCl; Ftbl; Tennis; College; Wildlife Biology.

FREVERT, Kathy A; Watertown HS; Maple Plain, MN; Band; HonRl; NHS; PolWkr; SchPl; RptrYrbk; 4-H;.

FREY, Catherine; Tri City Hs; Riverton, IL; 4/62 HonRl; SchMus; SchPpr; 4-H; SpnCl; GAA; 4-HAwd; University Of Ill; Art.

FREY, Christine M; Lourdes HS; Rochester, MN; Band; Chr; Chrs; ChrhWkr; HonRl; NHS; LetterBsktbl; LetterTrk; IMSpt; College; General Major.

FREY, Christine; Forest View HS; Mt Prospect, IL; 45/645 HonRl; NHS; TchrAde; GerCl; Western Illinois Univ; German.

FREY, Connie; Brown City HS; Brown City, MI; 6/96 Band; CncrtBnd; Orch; PepBnd; SchMus; 4-H; Chrldr; GAA; 4-HAwd; College; Mathematician.

FREY, David; Riverside Brookfield Hs; Brookfield, IL; 6 Chr; Chrs; HonRl; JrNHS; NHS; NatlThespSoc; SchMus; RptrYrbk; Yrbk; PresGerCl; Illinois Technology;economics.

FREY, Dayton J; Elmhurst HS; Fort Wayne, IN; AFS; Chr; Chrl; ChrhWkr; CncrtBnd; HonRl; JA; JrNHS; NHS; NatlSciFnd; PepBnd; Goshen College; Computer Science.

FREY, Debbie S; Brookville HS; Cedar Grove, IN; TrsFrshCls; Chr; ChrhWkr; CmntyWkr; HonRl; SchMus; 4-H; SecSpnCl; PpCl; Bsktbl; LetterTrk; Chrldr; LetterGAA; Indiana Univ; Physical Educ.

FREY, Di Ann R; Grundy Center HS; Holland, IA; ChrhWkr; CmntyWkr; HonRl; RptrSchPpr; SchPpr; Pres4-H; FHA; SpnCl; PpCl; 4-HAwd; Hawkeye Tech; Sten.

FREY, Edward; Brookville HS; Cedar Grove, IN; 5/20 HonRl; NHS; 4-H; College.

FREY, Ernest J; Rushville HS; Hay Springs, NE; VPFrshCls; VPSophCls; ALBoysSt; HonRl; NHS; SchMus; 4-H; GerCl; Bsktbl; LetterFtbl; LetterTrk; LetterWrstlng; 4-HAwd; Univ Of Nebraska; Engineer.

FREY, Frank J; Brookville HS; Cedar Grove, IN; Band; HonRl; 4-H; FFA; Bsktbl; Trk; 4-HAwd; Univ; Ag.

FREY, Kenneth; Frankfort Senior HS; Frankfort, IN; 21/242 ALBoysSt; HonRl; JrNHS; NHS; SchMus; SchPl; SptEdYrbk; Yrbk; Ftbl; EldAwd; Purdue Univ; Engin.

FREY, Michael J; John Hersey HS; Mt Prospect, IL; 73/740 ChrhWkr; CmntyWkr; HonRl; NHS; SctActv; TchrAde; North Ill Univ; Psychology.

FREY, Patricia A; Brown City Comm HS; Brown City, MI; 2/98 TrsSrCls; Band; SecChrs; LetterTrk; Hope College.

FREY, Richard J; West Platte R2 HS; Weston, MO; PresSophCls; AFS; Band; ChrhWkr; CmntyWkr; HonRl; ModUN; NHS; SctActv; StuCncl; YthFlsp; LetterFtbl; LetterTrk; LetterWrstlng; Col; Accounting.

FREY, Samuel V; Mt Morris HS; Mt Morris, IL; Band; ChrhWkr; CncrtBnd; HonRl; MrchBnd; SctActv; YthFlsp; Tennis; Clge.

FREY, Sharon; Sauk Prairie HS; Suak City, WI; 18/221 HonRl; NHS; PPFtbl; BttyCrckrAwd; OptClAwd; Univ; Curr Of Major Study.

FREY, Terry A; Lane Technical HS; Chicago, IL; 292/1213 Chrs; DrmBgl; PolWkr; ROTC; StuCncl; SchPpr;.

FREY, Tommy; Kiester HS; Kiester, MN; 10/30 Band; CncrtBnd; HonRl; MrchBnd; SchPl; RptrSchPpr; FFA; Mankato State College; Accountant.

FREY, Vicki S; Columbia City Joint HS; Roanoke, IN; CmntyWkr; HonRl; PresFBLA; FrCl; PpCl; Chrldr; GAA; Purdue Extension; Dietitian.

FREYBERG, Gerald W; Rochester HS; Rochester, IN; SchPl; SctActv; College; Graphic Art.

FREYER, Pamela; Wj Bryan HS; Omaha, NE; Chrs; HonRl; ModUN; RedCrAde; 4-H; PpCl; Swmmng; Tennis; Chrldr; IMSpt; 4-HAwd; Univ; Pe Ed.

FREYER, Russell W; Ashland HS; Ashland, NE; 19/60 PresSrCls; Band; CncrtBnd; MrchBnd; PepBnd; SctActv; Ftbl; Trk;.

FREYGANG, Mike G; High School; Fort Wayne, IN; 61/386 HonRl; JA; Quill&Scroll; RptrYrbk; Glf; Wrstlng; Army; Electronics.

FREYMILLER, Deanna D; Boscobel HS; Woodman, WI; Chr; Chrs; ChrhWkr; HonRl; NatlFornLg; PresYthFlsp; College; Nursing.

FRIBERG, Steven; Florence Hs; Florence, WI; .

FRICE, Randal C; Dallas City HS; Dallas City, IL; 7 47 Band; Chrl; CncrtBnd; HonRl; NHS; PepBnd; SchPl; TchrAde; FBLA; AmLegAwd; U Of Ill; Elec Eng.

FRICHTL, Duane M; Paxton HS; Paxton, IL; 1/137 Band; CncrtBnd; HonRl; MrchBnd; SciCl; Bsktbl; CaptFtbl; Trk; IMSpt; Univ Of Illinois; Veterinarian.

FRICHTL, Melanie M; Paxton HS; Paxton, IL; VPFrshCls; Band; CncrtBnd; HonRl; MrchBnd; NHS; PepBnd; SchPl; StuCncl; Chrldr; Ill State Univ; Accounting.

FRICK, Catherine L; New Trier East HS; Kenilworth, IL; 7/847 VPAFS; CmntyWkr; HonRl; LbryAde; NatlMeritSF; RedCrAde; VPSctActv; StuCncl; StuGov; LatCl; NCTE; College; Teach.

FRICK, Cathy J; Laville HS; Lakeville, IN; 17/160 VPFrshCls; VPSophCls; VPJrCls; Chr; NHS; 4-H; SpnCl; PpCl; Chrldr; Purdue U; Child Deve.

FRICK, Danny A; Kearney HS; Kansas, MO; 30/92 Chr; Chrs; LetterBsbl; Ftbl; Trade School.

FRICK, Dennis B; Kearney HS; Kansas City, MO; ChrhWkr; HonRl; JA; NHS; PolWkr; SchPl; StuCncl; RptrSchPpr; FFA; SciCl; Bsbl; Bsktbl; Swmmng; University; Professional.

FRICK, Janice A; Proviso West HS; Westchester, IL; 190/1200 Chrl; Chrs; HonRl; NatlMeritCmnd; VPKeyCl; PpCl; GAA; Univ; Psychology.

FRICK, Mark A; Traverse City HS; Traverse City, MI; 1/600 HonRl; ModUN; PresNHS; NatlMeritCmnd; SchMus; SctActv; StuCncl; RptrSchPpr; PresKeyCl; SciCl; Univ Mi; Medicine.

FRICK, Paula M; Luther HS; Hokah, MN; 2/75 Band; Chr; Chrs; ChrhWkr; CncrtBnd; HonRl; MrchBnd; NatlMeritCmnd; Orch; PepBnd; RptrYrbk; Yrbk; 4-H; ChmbCommrsAwd; University; Nursing.

FRICK, Phyllis J; Union HS; Union, MO; 6/165 Band; Chr; HonRl; PepBnd; SchMus; SchPl; TchrAde; Twrl; SpnCl; College; Professional.

FRICK, Robyn W; Jamaica HS; Sidell, IL; 8/50 TrsSophCls; VPSrCls; CncrtBnd; HonRl; SchMus; SchPl; SctActv; Bsktbl; Ftbl; Trk; Trade Sch; Drafting.

FRICKE, Craig E; Prairie Community HS; Harcourt, IA; 7/78 Band; ChrhWkr; MrchBnd; NHS; PepBnd; FFA; IMSpt; Iowa St U; Engineering.

FRICKE, Katherine E; Loy Norrix HS; Kalamazoo, MI; 1/512 ChrhWkr; CmntyWkr; HonRl; NatlMeritSF; Orch; SchMus; StuCncl; SchPpr; GerCl; OptClAwd; U Of Michigan; Engineering.

FRICKEL, Kurtis; Atkinson West Holt HS; Atkinson, NE; 2/70 TrsSophCls; HonRl; NHS; SchPl; VPStuCncl; 4-H; FFA; LetterBsktbl; LetterFtbl; LetterTrk; College;computer Science.

FRIDAY, Karl; New Richmond HS; New Richmond, WI; 12/180 PresSophCls; VPJrCls; Band; SchPl; VPStuCncl; StuGov; Yrbk; SchPpr; LetterTrk; Ottawa Univ; Teaching.

FRIEB, Danny L; Otis Bison HS; Olmitz, KS; Band; Chrs; CncrtBnd; DrlTm; HonRl; JrNHS; PepBnd; Yrbk; Bsbl; LetterTrk; Coll; Curr Of Maj Stud.

FRIEBE, Alan F; Denfeld HS; Duluth, MN; HonRl; NatlMeritSF; SctActv; IMSpt; University; Electronics.

FRIEBERG, Nancy J; Fairfield HS; Fairfield, IA; Band; HonRl; SecNatlThespSoc; PolWkr; SchPl; PresYthFlsp; RptrYrbk; Pres4-H; FrCl; 4-HAwd; Nursing School; Nursing.

FRIED, Jonathan S; South Side HS; Ft Wayne, IN; 8/438 AFS; HonRl; PolWkr; StuCncl; YthLg; RptrSchPpr; VPLatCl; LetterBsbl; Ftbl; IMSpt; Indiana University; Biological Science.

FRIED, Michael E; Cretin HS; St Paul, MN; HonRl; RptrSchPpr; IMSpt; College Of St Thomas; Doctor.

FRIED, Paula A; Shawnee Mission East HS; Shawnee Mission, KS; 10/600 Aud/Vis; ChrhWkr; HonRl; HospAde; NatlMeritFnl; StuCncl; StuGov; YthFlsp; PpCl; Swmmng; Col ; Dance.

FRIEDBERG, Mary; Mexico HS; Mexico, MO; Chr; CmntyWkr; HospAde; TchrAde; Yrbk; FrCl; LatCl; PpCl; Chrldr; Univ; Forestry.

FRIEDE, Roger A; Webb HS; Reedsburg, WI; CncrtBnd; HonRl; NatlThespSoc; SchMus; SchPl; SctActv; KeyCl; LatCl; Bsktbl; Trk; College; Civil Engineering.

FRIEDERICHS, Elizabeth A; Lourdes HS; Rochester, MN; 35/134 Chr; Chrs; ChrhWkr; CmntyWkr; RedCrAde; 4-H; 4-HAwd; College; Textiles & Clothing.

FRIEDERICK, James V; Lancaster HS; Lancaster, WI; VPSophCls; HonRl; SchPpr; 4-H; SpnCl; LetterFtbl; LetterTrk; LetterWrstlng; Coll; Engr.

FRIEDHOFF, John H; University HS; Normal, IL; Chrs; HonRl; NatlFornLg; NatlThespSoc; SchPl; LetterTennis; College; Law.

FRIEDL, Elizabeth C; Brookfield East HS; Elm Grove, WI; Chr; Chrs; HonRl; HospAde; LbryAde; Mdrgl; NHS; SchMus; SchPl; StuCncl; FrCl; W Madison Univ; Physician.

FRIEDL, Margy A; Moline Sr HS; Moline, IL; Aud/Vis; HonRl; LitMag; NHS; NatlMeritCmnd; Quill&Scroll; CaptTennis; College; Creative Writing.

FRIEDLEIN, Christopher E; Leroy HS; Leroy, IL; PresSrCls; AFS; ChrhWkr; SchMus; SchPl; SecFrshCls; PpCl; LetterFtbl; CaptWrstlng; Coll; Forestry.

FRIEDLUND, Michelle A; Dekalb HS; Dekalb, IL; Band; CncrtBnd; LbryAde; MrchBnd; PepBnd; 4-H; FFA; LetterTrk; AmLegAwd; Junior College; Veterinarian.

FRIEDMAN, David L; Central HS; La Crosse, WI; 15/530 Band; Chr; Chrs; CncrtBnd; HonRl; JrNHS; MrchBnd; NHS; NatlMeritCmnd; SctActv; StuCncl; TchrAde; SchPpr; LetterTennis; IMSpt; Indiana Univ.

FRIEDMAN, Diana; Dubois HS; Dubois, IN; Chrs; PpCl; Drama School; Actress.

FRIEDMAN, Gary J; Highland Park HS; Highland Park, IL; JrNHS; LbryAde; NatlFornLg; NHS; Clge; Law.

FRIEDMAN, Jean A; Fairbury Cropsey HS; Fairbury, IL; 14/103 Chrs; CmntyWkr; HonRl; YthFlsp; FHA; Trk; Methodist Hosp Sch Of Nursing; Rn.

FRIEDMAN, Marc J; Roeper City & Country HS; Farmington Hills, MI; NatlMeritSF; StuGov; RptrYrbk; Ftbl; Univ; Professional.

FRIEDMAN, Mark L; St Louis U HS; St Louis, MO; 30/205 CmntyWkr; HonRl; NatlMeritCmnd; SchPl; TchrAde; Ftbl; Oberlin College.

FRIEDMAN, Nancy G; Turkey Valley HS; Lawler, IA; Chr; HonRl; SchMus; IMSpt; Homemaker.

FRIEDMAN, Scott; Parkway North Sr HS; Creve Coeur, MO; 22/461 Band; CncrtBnd; HonRl; JrNHS; MrchBnd; Orch; PepBnd; SchMus; SctActv; Univ Of Mo; Medichine.

FRIEDRICH, Barbara A; Oak Ridge HS; Jackson, MO; PresFrshCls; Band; CncrtBnd; HonRl; MrchBnd; PepBnd; SchPl; StuCncl; SecFHA; PpCl; Semo Clge.

FRIEDRICH, Lu A; Harrisonville Sr HS; Harrisonville, MO; 18/164 AFS; Band; ChrhWkr; CncrtBnd; HonRl; MrchBnd; NatlFornLg; PepBnd; SchPl; StuCncl; SpnCl; PpCl; IMSpt; College; Sociology.

FRIEDRICH, Paula S; Sceciha Memorial HS; Indianapolis, IN; Band; Chrs; CncrtBnd; HonRl; MrchBnd; NHS; PepBnd; SchMus; Ball State Univ; Music Educator.

FRIEDRICH, Ronald; Williamsville HS; Williamsville, IL; Band; CncrtBnd; HonRl; MrchBnd; Orch; PepBnd; EngCl; FrCl; MthCl; Il St College; Business Manage Ment.

FRIEDRICHS, Beverly S; Marysville Senior HS; Bremen, KS; HonRl; YthFlsp; FHA; PpCl; Trk; College ;home Ec.

FRIEDRICHSEN, Barbara; Central Lyon HS; Rock Rapids, IA; 4/91 HonRl; Mdrgl; NHS; SchMus; Yrbk; SchPpr; 4-H; FTA; 4-HAwd; VoiceDemAwd; College; Art.

FRIEDRICHSEN, Cynthia; Holstein Comm Hs; Holstein, IA; Chr; HonRl; OffAde; TchrAde; SchPpr; 4-H; PpCl; LetterBsktbl; Glf; 4-HAwd; Collge; Elementary Teacher.

FRIEDRICHSEN, Timothy A; Schleswig Community HS; Danbury, IA; 1/50 PresJrCls; ChrhWkr; CncrtBnd; HonRl; NHS; SchPl; StuGov; SchPpr; Glf; Divine Word Coll; Priest & Math Teacher.

FRIEDRICK, Phillip J; Concord HS; Concord, MI; VPSophCls; Chr; ChrhWkr; MrchBnd; NHS; PresStuCncl; PresYthFlsp; SchPpr; Trk; GodCntryAwd; College.

FRIEL, Lori E; Maine North HS; Glenview, IL; CmntyWkr; HonRl; College; Biology.

FRIEND, Dean; Norwich HS; Norwich, KS; 2/25 ChrhWkr; HonRl; PolWkr; SchPl; StuCncl; TchrAde; YthFlsp; MthCl; SciCl; PresAwd; Ohio St U; Commercial Beekeeper.

FRIEND, Joe L; Christopher Comm HS; Royalton, IL; 13/87 ChrhWkr; HonRl; JrNHS; NHS; 4-H; PresFFA; Rend Jr College; Agriculture.

FRIEND, Laura A; Arrowhead HS; Hartland, WI; 1/310 ALAGirlsSt; HonRl; HospAde; NHS; FrCl; MthCl; PpCl; LetterBsktbl; LetterTennis; CchngActv; Univ; Engineering.

FRIEND, Michael C; Gibson City HS; Gibson City, IL; 7/89 ALBoysSt; ChrhWkr; CncrtBnd; HonRl; Mdrgl; NHS; SchPl; StuCncl; SpnCl; PpCl; LetterFtbl; CaptWrstlng; CchngActv; Eastern Ill Univ; Engineering.

FRIEND, Michael R; North Salem HS; North Salem, IN; HonRl; NHS; 4-H; VPFrCl; Bsktbl; LetterTrk; GovHonPrgAwd; Ball State Univ; Public Accountant.

FRIES, Martha K; Greenville HS; Greenville, MI; TrsSophCls; ALAGirlsSt; HonRl; SchAde; StuCncl; TchrAde; SchPpr; FrCl; SpnCl; IMSpt; Central Mich; English.

FRIES, Norman F; Mott Lincoln HS; Mott, ND; SchPl; SctActv; StuCncl; Bsktbl; Ftbl; Trk; IMSpt; Math Major.

FRIESE, Patricia; Wanamingo HS; Wanamingo, MN; Band; Chrs; ChrhWkr; CncrtBnd; HonRl; MrchBnd; PepBnd; CchngActv; 4-HAwd; Assoc Free Luthern Bible School; Phy Ed Te.

FRIESEMA, Michael J; Lake Shore HS; St Clair Shores, MI; NHS; CaptSwmmng; Michigan Tech Univ; Engineering.

FRIESEN, Marilyn; Berean Acad; Elbing, KS; 1/47 SecJrCls; SecSrCls; Chr; ChrhWkr; HonRl; NHS; SchMus; SchPl; PpCl; Bsktbl; Coll.

FRIESEN, Paul; Westmoreland HS; Westmoreland, KS; Band; Chr; Chrs; CncrtBnd; MrchBnd; Orch; PepBnd; SchPl; SchPpr; Service; Grafic Arts.

FRIESEN, Stanley W; Lawrence HS; Lawrence, KS; NatlFornLg; NatlMeritSF; YthFlsp; GerCl; Univ Of Ks; Biology.

FRIESZ, Karen; Keytesville Riii HS; Keytesville, MO; 1/21 ALAGirlsSt; Band; Chr; Chrs; ChrhWkr; CncrtBnd; HonRl; LbryAde; MrchBnd; NHS; Domestic Engr.

FRIEZE, Vonda J; Reeds Spring HS; Galena, MO; Chr; ChrhWkr; CmntyWkr; HonRl; SchAde; SctActv; 4-H; FHA; DanFAwd; The Ozarks College; State Dept.

FRIMML, Cynthia J; Williamsburg HS; S Amana, IA; Band; CncrtBnd; MrchBnd; Orch; PepBnd; Quill&Scroll; Yrbk; SchPpr; 4-H; FHA; Vocational Study.

FRINK, Daniel T; Bishop Mc Namara HS; Kankakee, IL; 72/162 RptrSchPpr; Jr Coll; Bus.

FRINK, Dianne J; Nishna Valley HS; Henderson, IA; 14/33 Band; Chr; Chrs; ChrhWkr; HonRl; NHS; TchrAde; LetterBsbl; LetterBsktbl; LetterTrk;.

FRISBIE, Kathy E; Portage Central HS; Portage, MI; Chr; HonRl; NatlMeritSF; TchrAde; EdSchPpr; GerCl; PpCl; LetterChrldr; CchngActv; IMSpt; Western Mi Univ; Bus & Ed.

FRISBY, Douglas A; Heritage HS; New Haven, IN; 21/160 HonRl; NHS; TchrAde; LetterFtbl; LetterTrk; Ball State Univ.

FRISCH, Holly G; Cary Grove HS; Cary, IL; 20/295 ChrhWkr; HonRl; NHS; StuCncl; TchrAde; College; Business.

FRISELLA, Laurie; St Dominic HS; Lake St Louis, MO; HonRl; NHS; FrCl; Col.

FRISK, Michael D; Pekin HS; Pekin, IL; 53/803 PresJrCls; PresSrCls; ALBoysSt; HonRl; JrNHS; NHS; StuGov; GerCl; Bsktbl; LetterFtbl; LetterTennis; Wrstlng; University; Law.

FRISKEY, Meri De Lee; Comstock Park HS; Comstock Park, MI; HonRl; NHS; RptrYrbk; PpCl; Bsbl; Bsktbl; Tennis; Univ Of Michigan; Pediatrician.

FRISKOP, Gary A; Wahpeton Sr HS; Wahpeton, ND; Band; ChrhWkr; CncrtBnd; HonRl; MrchBnd; 4-H; FFA; LetterBsktbl; Ftbl; 4-HAwd; Nd S; Voc Agr.

FRISSORA, Henry A; Brookfield Central HS; Brookfield, WI; CmntyWkr; LitMag; NatlFornLg; Quill&Scroll; VPStuCncl; RptrYrbk; Yrbk; SchPpr; Ftbl; Tennis; Purdue Univ; Medical Doctor.

FRITSCH, Michael; St Frances Seninary; Batesville, IN; 1/13 Chrs; HonRl; EdSchPpr; IMSpt; Univ; Unsure.

FRITSCHE, Colette R; Trico HS; Percy, IL; PresFrshCls; Chrs; ChrhWkr; HonRl; OffAde; SchMus; FBLA; FHA; Chrldr; GAA; College.

FRITSCHE, James G; Abbot Pennings HS; Green Bay, WI; 18/91 HonRl; NHS; NatlMeritCmnd; EdYrBk; Yrbk; RptrSchPpr; LetterTrk; Chrldr; IMSpt; Marquette; Dentist.

FRITSCHE, Sue A; Glenbrook South HS; Glenview, IL; 8/579 HonRl; IntrClCncl; LitMag; SecNHS; TchrAde; PresFTA; St Josephs College; English.

FRITSCHLE, Pamela J; East Richland HS; Olney, IL; ChrhWkr; NHS; SctActv; 4-H; LetterTrk; VPGAA; DanFAwd; DARAwd; 4-HAwd; Eastern Ill Univ; Phy Ed Tchr.

FRITSCHLER, Lance; Assumption HS; Wisconsin Rapids, WI; 28/120 HonRl; StuCncl; Bsktbl; Uw Madison; Doctor.

FRITSON, Diana L; Franklin Public HS; Franklin, NE; SecSophCls; Chr; Chrs; ChrhWkr; CmntyWkr; PepBnd; SchPl; StuGov; FHA; Chrldr; Trade Or Bus School; Dental Asst.

FRITZ, Barbara A; Lakeland HS; Wolcottville, IN; HonRl; NHS; PolWkr; SchPl; TchrAde; MthCl; PpCl; Trk; GAA; PPFtbl; Col; Professional.

FRITZ, Brenda L; Monett HS; Monett, MO; ALAGirlsSt; ChrhWkr; CmntyWkr; HonRl; TreasNHS; SctActv; CivCl; FHA; FTA; PpCl; Burge School Of Nursing; Nursing.

FRITZ, Cheri L; Wilber Clatonia HS; Wilber, NE; Band; HospAde; MrchBnd; SchPl; TchrAde; YthFlsp; Pres4-H; FHA; PresPpCl; LetterTrk; Doane College; Elem Education.

FRITZ, Jayne L; Delton Kellogg HS; Plainwell, MI; 1/150 HospAde; TchrAde; FNA; SpnCl; Univ; Math.

FRITZ, Jeffrey H; Kouts HS; Kouts, IN; 4/55 ALBoysSt; Aud/Vis; Band; HonRl; NHS; Yrbk; TreasFTA; University; Business Law.

FRITZ, John E; Immaculate Conception HS; Elmhurst, IL; 28/166 PresSophCls; PresJrCls; ChrhWkr; CmntyWkr; NHS; SchPl; StuCncl; SpnCl; LetterBsktbl; IMSpt; University; Professional.

FRITZ, Joseph; St Marys HS; Belfield, ND; TrsJrCls; HonRl; StuCncl; 4-H; Bsktbl; Ftbl; Trk; 4-HAwd; Coll; Rancher.

FRITZ, Joseph L; Maine Twp South HS; Park Ridge, IL; HonRl; NHS; NatlMeritSF; FDA; IMSpt; DARAwd; U Of I; Medical Field.

FRITZ, Kay M; Newton HS; Newton, KS; SecTrsJrCls; Chr; ChrhWkr; HonRl; Orch; StuCncl; TchrAde; FrCl; PpCl; LetterTennis; Sw College.

FRITZ, Lester D; Petersburg Porta HS; Tallula, IL; JA; Mdrgl; NHS; SchMus; SchPl; StuGov; TchrAde; 4-H; FFA; FHA; Prof.

FRITZ, Linda; Knightstown Hs; Shirley, IN; 12/132 ChrhWkr; HonRl; Pres4-H; FBLA; FrCl; GAA; 4-HAwd; College; Fashion Merchandising.

FRITZ, Louise E; Lansing Eastern HS; Lansing, MI; Chr; Chrs; HonRl; U Of Michigan St; Civil Engineering.

FRITZ, Martin; Clay Center Community HS; Clay Center, KS; Band; CncrtBnd; HonRl; MrchBnd; SchPl; SctActv; FTA; SciCl; Emporia Kans St Coll; Cpa.

FRITZ, Mikel; Potos HS; Potos, WI; PresFrshCls; ALBoysSt; HonRl; LbryAde; NHS; FFA; Ftbl; College; Agriculture.

FRITZ, Robert C; Louisiana HS; Louisiana, MO; Chr; HonRl; LitMag; SchMus; SpnCl; LetterTrk; University; Professional.

FRITZ, Russell N; Wilber Clatonia HS; Wilber, NE; 14/44 CncrtBnd; HonRl; MrchBnd; PepBnd; TchrAde; YthFlsp; 4-H; FFA; Ftbl; 4-HAwd; Trade Sch; Vocational.

FRITZ, Susan K; Lancaster HS; Lancaster, WI; AFS; Band; Chrs; CncrtBnd; HonRl; MrchBnd; PepBnd; SctActv; PpCl; University.

FRITZINGER, Lisa L; Harrison HS; Harrison, MI; HonRl; StuCncl; Central Michigan College; Pharmicist.

FRITZSCHE, Catherine L; Mt Olive Community HS; Mt Olive, IL; 14/56 Band; CncrtBnd; HonRl; MrchBnd; Yrbk; VPFHA; PpCl; Trk; CaptChrldr; GAA; S Il U; Music.

FRITZSCHE, Sue A; Marian Catholic HS; Chicago Hts, IL; 57/335 HonRl; NHS; SchMus; SchPl; College; Science.

FRODERMANN, Nancy; Round Lake HS; Round Lake, MN; 1/29 Band; Chrs; ChrhWkr; HonRl; SchPl; EdYrBk; EdSchPpr; AmLegAwd; BttyCrckrAwd; CitAwd; Sioux Valley Hosp Sch Of Nurs; Rn.

FRODEY, Michelle; Fremont HS; Fremont, MI; VPSophCls; HonRl; NHS; StuCncl; RptrYrbk; Yrbk; Trk; Univ Of Montana; Forestry.

FROEHLICH, Danny M; Lu Verne Comm HS; Lu Verne, IA; PresSophCls; VPSrCls; Chrs; HonRl; PepBnd; SchAde; TchrAde; RptrYrbk; 4-H; Bsbl; Clg; Agronomy.

FROEHLICH, James A; Crystal Lake Community HS; Crystal Lake, IL; 50/500 Band; HonRl; NHS; Orch; LatCl; LetterBsktbl; Glf; University; Medicine.

FROEHLY, Mary K; Jennings Senior HS; St Louis, MO; 1/248 HonRl; HospAde; FrCl; GAA; IMSpt; Univ; Physician.

FROELICH, Charlene L; Oak Creek Sr HS; Oak Creek, WI; VPAFS; ChrhWkr; NatlFornLg; TchrAde; RptrYrbk; GerCl; PPFtbl; Bryant & Stratton Bus Sch; Accountant.

FROELICH, Susanne; St Joseph Acad; Green Bay, WI; 28/150 VPJrCls; Chrs; CmntyWkr; TrsFrshCls; SchMus; RptrYrbk; 4-H; LatCl; DARAwd; State U; Speech Communications.

FROEMMING, David A; Tomahawk HS; Tomahawk, WI; Band; HonRl; NHS; PepBnd; SchMus; SchPl; RptrSchPpr; SpnCl; SciCl; Trade School; Vocation.

FROEMMING, Donna; Tomahawk HS; Tomahawk, WI; TrsFrshCls; Band; HonRl; PepBnd; SchPl; SpnCl; SciCl; Chrldr; College; Vocation.

FROESEL, Linda M; Brentwood HS; St Louis, MO; Chr; HonRl; NHS; Yrbk; SchPpr; SpnCl; PpCl; College; Journalism.

FROHAN, Nancy; Dundee Community Hs; West Dundee, IL; 25/362 SecTrsFrshCls; ChrhWkr; HonRl; StuCncl; RptrYrbk; FrCl; PpCl; Chrldr; U Of Illinois; Pharmacist.

FROHLING, Cheryl A; Sterling HS; Sterling, IL; 67/390 Chrs; ChrhWkr; HonRl; HospAde; NHS; Teen; Nursing School; Nurse.

FROHLING, Daniel D; Howell HS; Howell, MI; Chr; IntrClCncl; HonRl; NHS; Tennis; Univ Of Michigan.

FROHLING, Richard H; Forman HS; Forest City, IL; 2/68 ALBoysSt; Band; HonRl; NHS; SchPl; StuCncl; PresYthFlsp; EdSchPpr; Sec4-H; SpnCl; College; Business Administration.

FROHMADER, Mary A; Michigan Lutheran Seminary; Sault Ste Marie, MI; 7/81 Chr; Chrs; ChrhWkr; DrmMjrt; Mdrgl; Dr Martin Luther Col; Teacher.

FROHMAN, Michael A; Evanston Township HS; Evanston, IL; CmntyWkr; HonRl; NatlMeritSF; RptrYrbk; EdSchPpr; College; Bio Medical Research.

FROHRIB, Ellen M; Concordia Academy; St Paul, MN; 7/50 Chr; DrlTm; HonRl; JrNHS; NHS; NatlMeritSF; SchPl; LatCl; SpnCl; PpCl; U Of Mn; Oceanographer.

FROILAND, Kathryn; Rushford HS; Rushford, MN; /62 PresSophCls; TrsJrCls; AFS; ALAGirlsSt; Chr; Chrs; ChrhWkr; CmntyWkr; HonRl; JrNHS; Coll;pre Med.

FROKE, Thomas E; Rutland HS; Colman, SD; 2/15 ALBoysSt; Band; HonRl; NHS; TreasStuCncl; TchrAde; LetterBsktbl; ChmnFtbl; ChmnTrk; CitAwd; South Dakota State Univ; Chemistry.

FROLAND, Steven J; Clarkfield HS; Clarkfield, MN; PresSrCls; CncrtBnd; HonRl; SchPl; StuCncl; SptEdYrbk; SchPpr; FFA; LetterBsktbl; LetterFtbl; Moorhead St Univ; Mech Engineering.

FROMAN, Bonnie; Warsaw HS; Suter, IL; TrsSrCls; AFS; Band; Chrs; ChrhWkr; MrchBnd; OffAde; PepBnd; GAA; 4-HAwd; College.

FROMM, Robert E; Park HS; Cottage Grove, MN; 3/664 Band; HonRl; PresNHS; NatlMeritSF; SctActv; LetterSwmmng; Trk; Clge; Med.

FROONINCKX, Beth; Central Hs; Clifton, IL; 7/129 ALAGirlsSt; HonRl; Mdrgl; NatlFornLg; NHS; NatlThespSoc; SchMus; Yrbk; Chrldr; AmLegAwd; Universtiy; Professional Cpa.

FROSETH, Terry A; Kenmare HS; Kenmare, ND; PresJrCls; ALBoysSt; HonRl; StuCncl; FFA; Bsbl; Bsktbl; Ftbl; Glf; College; Professional.

FROSLIE, Wendy B; Rothsay HS; Rothsay, MN; SecTrsFrshCls; SecTrsSophCls; Band; HospAde; RptrYrbk; RptrSchPpr; 4-H; 4-HAwd; College; Registered Nurse.

FROSS, Teresa M; Marian HS; Hays, KS; ChrhWkr; CmntyWkr; HonRl; RedCrAde; SchPl; StuCncl; StuGov; 4-H; FBLA; FHA; College;.

FROST, Bonnie J; Marion HS; Ewing, MO; TrsJrCls; Chrs; SchPl; LetterBsbl; Trade Sch; Major Study.

FROST, Cheryl A; Grand Haven HS; Grand Haven, MI; 14/371 HonRl; NHS; LetterBsbl; LetterBsktbl; GAA; EldAwd; Muskegon Bus Coll; Legal Secretary.

FROST, Karla J; Sparta HS; Sparta, WI; 8/208 Band; ChrhWkr; HonRl; MrchBnd; ModUN; NHS; Orch; PepBnd; Yrbk; Pres4-H; College; Instrumental Music Ed.

FROST, Mark L; Dakota HS; Hunter, ND; 1/25 TrsSophCls; TrsJrCls; HonRl; NHS; SchPl; StuCncl; PpCl; Bsbl; LetterBsktbl; LetterFtbl; College; Professional.

FROST, Mike G; Bishop Ryan HS; Minot, ND; ALBoysSt; CmntyWkr; HonRl; JrNHS; NHS; GerCl; Bsktbl; LetterFtbl; Trk; IMSpt; College.

FROST, Ronald A; Overton Public HS; Overton, NE; Band; Chr; Chrs; ChrhWkr; CmntyWkr; CncrtBnd; HonRl; MrchBnd; NatlMeritCmnd; PepBnd; SchPl; YthFlsp; 4-H; LetterBsktbl; Kearney State College; Law.

FROST, Rosemary J; Hibbing HS; Hibbing, MN; Chr; CmntyWkr; HonRl; LbryAde; NatlFornLg; NatlThespSoc; PolWkr; SchAde; SchMus; SchPl; Hibbing Comm College; Theatre.

FROST, Scott F; Perry HS; Perry, MI; 8/129 HonRl; NHS; NatlMeritCmnd; 4-H; Ftbl; 4-HAwd; General Motors Inst; Industrial Administrat.

FROST, Thomas J; Dixon HS; Dixon, IL; JA; Ftbl; IMSpt; JAAwd; OptClAwd; Sauk Valley Clg; Computer Programming.

FROSTMAN, Connie J; Bayfield HS; Bayfield, WI; 1/47 Band; CncrtBnd; HonRl; PepBnd; Quill&Scroll; SptEdYrbk; RptrSchPpr; Bsktbl; LetterTrk; U W Stevens Point; Natural Resources.

FRUCHEY, Karen R; Elkhart Central HS; Elkhart, IN; HonRl; JA; NatlThespSoc; SchMus; SchPl; RptrYrbk; 4-H; In University; Medicine.

FRUCHTL, Jeffrey B; Effingham HS; Effingham, IL; 33/220 SpnCl; Bsktbl; Ftbl; U S Naval Academy; Naval Officer.

FRUCHTMAN, Brian L; Southwest HS; Minneapolis, MN; NatlMeritSF; SchPl; GerCl; Trk; Carleton College; Doctor.

FRUEHE, Jean M; Glenbard East HS; Lombard, IL; 15/653 Band; HonRl; NHS; PepBnd; Sacrstn; RptrYrbk; GerCl; PpCl; Quincy College; Accountant.

FRUEHLING, Peggy L; Maple Valley Comm HS; Castana, IA; 2/99 Band; Chrs; CncrtBnd; HonRl; MrchBnd; ModUN; NHS; PepBnd; LetterTrk; PresAwd; Olivet Nazarene College; Phd In Music.

FRUENDT, Roger A; Prairie HS; Fairfax, IA; Band; CncrtBnd; MrchBnd; Orch; PepBnd; RptrSchPpr; SpnCl; Bsktbl; Trk; Iowa State U; Engineering.

FRUETEL, Laurie A; Long Prairie HS; Long Prairie, MN; 11/113 TrsJrCls; TrsSrCls; AFS; Band; CncrtBnd; MrchBnd; NHS; PepBnd; SchMus; StuCncl; RptrYrbk; RptrSchPpr; St Cloud State Clg; Speech Pathology.

FRUGE, Marian; Covert HS; Covert, MI; SecJrCls; Band; HonRl; MrchBnd; NHS; TchrAde; FHA; Trk; Chrldr; DanFAwd; Ferris College; Medicine.

FRUHSTORFER, Catherine A; J D Darnall HS; Geneseo, IL; 10/207 SecFrshCls; ALAGirlsSt; HonRl; JrNHS; NHS; StuCncl; StuGov; FTA; FrCl; Drake University.

FRUHWIRTH, Gregory W; Larimore HS; Larimore, ND; TrsFrshCls; ALBoysSt; HonRl; StuCncl; LetterBsktbl; LetterFtbl; LetterTrk; College; Professional.

FRUIT, Kim; Hudson Senior Hs; Hudson, WI; Chr; JA; LbryAde; SctActv; YthFlsp; GerCl; Swmmng; LetterTrk; Trade School; Professional.

FRULAND, Deanne L; Newark HS; Sheridan, IL; 2/51 Chrs; HonRl; LbryAde; NHS; Yrbk; FHA; PresFrCl; PpCl; GAA; College; Art.

FRULAND, Di Ann M; Morris Community HS; Morris, IL; 20/264 VPFrshCls; HonRl; NHS; FrCl; PpCl; Trk; Chrldr; Augustana College; Law.

FRUSTERE, Nancy J; Milwaukee Lutheran HS; Wauwatosa, WI; 99/231 Chr; Chrs; ChrhWkr; OffAde; Uwm Or Mount Mary; Arts Or Law Enforcement.

FRUTIGER, Farron; Clay City Hs; Clay City, IL; Band; CncrtBnd; DrmBgl; PepBnd; SchMus; SchPpr; 4-H; FFA; 4-HAwd; Trade; Vocational.

FRVIN, Kevin R; St Ignatius HS; Hines, IL; 32/170 ChrhWkr; CncrtBnd; LitMag; PolWkr; SptEdYrbk; LetterGlf; LetterTrk; U Of Il At Cham; Medicine.

FRY, Barb J; Marcus Community HS; Marcus, IA; 7/64 Band; ChrhWkr; CncrtBnd; DrmMjrt; HonRl; MrchBnd; PepBnd; SchPl; TchrAde; LetterGlf; Coll; Elementary Teacher.

FRY, Clark A; White Cloud HS; White Cloud, MI; 7/98 Chr; Chrl; HonRl; Mdrgl; PresNHS; NatlMeritCmnd; SchPl; YthFlsp; RptrYrbk; GodCntryAwd; Coll; Pharmacy.

FRY, Cynthia; Pinckney HS; Pinckney, MI; Band; CncrtBnd; HonRl; MrchBnd; PolWkr; SctActv; YthFlsp; Bsktbl; GAA; PresAwd; Wayne State U;physical Therapy.

FRY, Daniel L; Hamilton HS; Butler, IN; 20/60 TchrAde; YthFlsp; 4-H; FFA; College; Farming.

FRY, Desiree J; Northrop HS; Fort Wayne, IN; DrlTm; HonRl; HospAde; MrchBnd; TchrAde; RptrYrbk; LatCl; PpCl; PPFtbl; Indiana Univ; Nursing Bs.

FRY, Diana L; Lead HS; Terraville, SD; ChrhWkr; CmntyWkr; HonRl; FDA; FFA; FHA; FNA; FSA; FTA; CitAwd; VoiceDemAwd; School; Model.

FRY, Edward Ta; Downers Grove North HS; Downers Grove, IL; 12/509 HonRl; LitMag; NHS; Bsktbl; Tennis; Knox Coll; Med.

FRY, Elaine L; Tipton HS; Tipton, MO; 12/87 Chrs; HonRl; Mdrgl; NHS; RptrYrbk; Yrbk; RptrSchPpr; SchPpr; FHA; FrCl; Cmsu Warrensburg Mo; Geologist.

FRY, Heidi M; Downers Grove South HS; Downers Grove, IL; 256/887 Chr; Chrs; ChrhWkr; LbryAde; YthFlsp; IMSpt; Michigan State Univ; Nursing.

FRY, Hope M; East Alton Wood River HS; East Alton, IL; Chrs; HonRl; NHS; OffAde; Univ; Professional.

FRY, Kathryn M; Park Hill HS; Kansas City, MO; 18/406 Band; CncrtBnd; HonRl; MrchBnd; ModUN; NatlMeritCmnd; Orch; PepBnd; SchMus; SchPl; Cmsu; History.

FRY, Kevin W; Ewing Public HS; Ewing, NE; Chr; Chrs; ChrhWkr; HonRl; SchMus; SchPl; TchrAde; 4-H; FFA; CaptBsktbl; CaptFtbl; LetterTrk; IMSpt; Univ Of Nebraska; Agriculture.

FRY, Lawrence A; West Chicago Comm HS; West Chicago, IL; 25/311 VPJrCls; HonRl; NHS; RptrSchPpr; LetterFtbl; CaptWrstlng; College; Communications.

FRY, Mary Lou; Winnebago HS; Seward, IL; 1/120 VPSophCls; VPBand; HonRl; NHS; OffAde; CaptBsktbl; VPGAA; Business School; Dental Asst.

FRY, Michael; Baxter HS; Chetopa, KS; Band; CncrtBnd; MrchBnd; PepBnd; SchMus; SchPl; Ftbl; JCAwd; Univ; Music & Gunsmith.

FRY, Michael J; Northridge HS; Bristol, IN; 14/116 HonRl; NatlMeritSF; SchPpr; SpnCl; PpCl; Ftbl; Purdue Univ.

FRY, Randy M; Iowa Valley Community HS; Marengo, IA; ALBoysSt; Band; CncrtBnd; HonRl; MrchBnd; SctActv; StuCncl; LetterBsbl; LetterWrstlng; Ia State U; Architectural Engr.

FRY, Rebecca; North Side HS; Ft Wayne, IN; 19/467 ChrhWkr; HonRl; NHS; SchMus; SchPl; 4-H; CitAwd; College; Church Work.

FRY, Sally K; Terre Haute North Vigo HS; Terre Haute, IN; HonRl; JA; Teen; 4-H; GerCl; PpCl; GAA; 4-HAwd; Indiana State University; Business.

FRYBARGER, Saundra L; Moline Sr HS; Moline, IL; 22/845 Chrs; NHS; SctActv; TchrAde; UNYO; RptrYrbk; Sec4-H; SpnCl; SciCl; GAA; 4-HAwd; GovHonPrgAwd; S Illinois Univ; Veterinarian.

FRYE, Denise L; Portland HS; Portland, MI; 7/126 Chr; Chrs; ChrhWkr; HonRl; NHS; StuCncl; YthFlsp; CivCl; Bus School Or Jr College; Legal-secrtary.

FRYE, Dorene K; Donald S Gauit HS; Hammond, IN; 8/311 Band; DrlTm; HonRl; NHS; PepBnd; SchPl; PpCl; ChmnChrldr; GAA; PPFtbl; Ind State Univ; Mathematics.

FRYE, Jo Ann; Alpena Public HS; Alpena, SD; 2 16 ALAGirlsSt; ChrhWkr; HonRl; LbryAde; PepBnd; TchrAde; RptrSchPpr; FHA; SpnCl; University; Nursing Air Force Rotc.

FRYE, John; Lakeview Sr HS; St Clair Shores, MI; 11/680 Chr; ChrhWkr; HonRl; JA; NHS; SpnCl; Univ Of Michigan; Dentistry.

FRYE, John J; Pontiac Catholic HS; Pontiac, MI; HonRl; PolWkr; SctActv; SpnCl; Bsbl; Univ Of Detroit; Business Management.

FRYE, Kevin S; Overland Christian HS; Kansas City, KS; 1/12 PresJrCls; Chr; HonRl; NHS; Bsbl; LetterBsktbl; Trk; IMSpt; CitAwd; University; Professional.

FRYE, Lisa M; Mo Valley HS; Missouri Valley, IA; VPFrshCls; TrsSophCls; Band; CncrtBnd; HonRl; MrchBnd; NHS; StuCncl; Yrbk; PpCl; Business; Vocational.

FRYE, Lorene G; Donald E Gavit HS; Hammond, IN; 23/311 TrsSrCls; Band; HonRl; JrNHS; NHS; PepBnd; PpCl; CaptChrldr; GAA; PPFtbl; Olivet Nazarene College; Language.

FRYE, Ronald E; Overland Christian HS; Kansas City, KS; 3/9 TrsJrCls; PresSrCls; ALBoysSt; Chr; Chrl; Chrs; ChrhWkr; HonRl; NHS; SchPl; Univ; Professional.

FRYKLIND, Karl; Brainerd HS; Brainerd, MN; HonRl; NatlMeritCmnd; College; Engineering.

FRYLING, Robert; Kelloggsville HS; Kentwood, MI; HonRl; JA; NHS; SctActv; StuGov;.

FRYMAN, Douglas F; Warrensburg Latham HS; Decatur, IL; Band; CncrtBnd; HonRl; JrNHS; MrchBnd; PepBnd; LetterBsktbl; LetterTrk; Univ; Mechanical Engineer.

FRYZA, Jeffrey A; Gilman HS; Lublin, WI; Band; ChrhWkr; CncrtBnd; HonRl; Trade School; Vocation.

FUCHS, Beckie G; Webb City HS; Webb City, MO; 96/196 ChrhWkr; OffAde; TchrAde; FHA; FTA; Bible Clge; Office Work.

FUCHS, David W; Athens HS; Cantrall, IL; PresFrshCls; PresSophCls; SecJrCls; Band; HonRl; NHS; SctActv; SecKeyCl; LetterGlf; LetterWrstlng; U Of Business; Business.

FUCHS, Karen J; Lutheran Mayer HS; Young America, MN; SecSrCls; Chrs; HonRl; JrNHS; NHS; YthFlsp; SchPpr; 4-H; FTA; Bsktbl; Vocational Sch; Accounting.

FUCHS, Nancy J; St Francis HS; Humphrey, NE; 4/35 PresSophCls; Chrs; HonRl; NHS; Quill&Scroll; SchPl; TchrAde; EdSchPpr; 4-H; IMSpt; Nce Sch Of Bus; Medical Assistant.

FUCHS, Patricia; John Hersey HS; Mt Prospect, IL; 8/600 Univ; Education.

FUCHS, Robert C; Edgerton Senior HS; Edgerton, WI; AFS; ModUN; StuCncl; Yrbk; Uw Madison; Physical Therapy.

FUCHS, Steven; St Pauls College HS; Concordia, MO; PresSophCls; ALBoysSt; Band; Chr; HonRl; NHS; 4-HAwd; St Pauls College; Teacher.

FUDALA, Carol A; Good Counsel HS; Chicago, IL; 1/248 HonRl; NatlFornLg; NHS; NatlMeritCmnd; SctActv; StuCncl; Yrbk; RptrSchPpr; Lewis Univ; Chemistry.

FUDALA, Doreen T; Lourdes HS; Chicago, IL; HonRl; SchPl; 4-H; Soutwest; Technician.

FUDGE, Craig A; Alburnett HS; Alburnett, IA; 3/45 PresSophCls; TrsSrCls; Band; NHS; EdYrBk; RptrSchPpr; FTA; Bsbl; Bsktbl; CaptGlf; Univ Of Ia; Business.

FUEHRER, Lynn; Peetz Plateau Re 5 HS; Sidney, NE; MrchBnd; OffAde; SchPl; StuCncl; Twrl; RptrYrbk; EdSchPpr; FHA; FTA; BttyCrckrAwd; Grand Island Business School; Medical Secre.

FUELBERTH, David; Osmond HS; Osmond, NE; 2/43 PresFrshCls; Band; Chr; NHS; StuCncl; YthFlsp; FBLA; Univ; Professional.

FUELLING, Martin K; Bellmont HS; Decatur, IN; 35/260 PresJrCls; HonRl; YthFlsp; Pres4-H; GerCl; LetterBsbl; Bsktbl; Ftbl; CchngActv; IMSpt; 4-HAwd;.

FUEMMELER, Carl D; Mexico HS; Mexico, MO; ALBoysSt; ChrhWkr; CmntyWkr; PresJA; NatlFornLg; Ftbl; LetterTrk; GodCntryAwd; PresAwd; Univ Of Mo; Business Management.

FUERST, Carrie L; Sevastopol HS; Sturgeon Bay, WI; ChrhWkr; LbryAde; SchPl; TchrAde; Twrl; 4-H; FTA; 4-HAwd; Martin Luther Coll; Elem Teacher.

FUERST, Jodi P; Holdrege HS; Holdrege, NE; Band; Chrs; ChrhWkr; HonRl; StuCncl; RptrSchPpr; 4-H; FBLA; PpCl; Chrldr; 4-HAwd; College.

FUESLEIN, Diane; Charlotte HS; Charlotte, MI; 11/260 Band; ChrhWkr; CncrtBnd; MrchBnd; NHS; PpCl; College; Exec Secretary.

FUESTING, Gregory M; St Anthony HS; Effingham, IL; 14/75 StuCncl; PpCl; Bsbl; Bsktbl; IMSpt; Southern Il Univ; Athletics.

FUESTING, Kathy; St Anthony HS; Effingham, IL; Band; DrmMjrt; HonRl; NHS; PepBnd; SchMus; RptrSchPpr; EdSchPpr; PpCl; Lake Land College; Comercial Art.

FUESTING, Michael L; Teutopolis HS; Teutopolis, IL; 3/116 VPSophCls; VPJrCls; VPSrCls; HonRl; SctActv; StuCncl; StuGov; TchrAde; RptrYrbk; Yrbk; CivCl; Bsbl; Bsktbl; Trk; Eastern Illinois Univ; Medicine.

FUGATE, Cheryl D; Oak Park HS; Gladstone, MO; 60/602 ALAGirlsSt; HonRl; NHS; SctActv; StuCncl; TchrAde; RptrSchPpr; EdSchPpr; FTA; Cntrl Missouri St Univ; Journalism.

FUGATE, Judy A; Divernon HS; Divernon, IL; PresJrCls; Band; Chrs; HonRl; OffAde; StuCncl; StuGov; EdYrBk; FHA; SpnCl; College; English Major.

FUGATE, Tammy J; Meadville R Iv HS; Meadville, MO; ChrhWkr; Twrl; RptrYrbk; FHA; PpCl; Bsbl; Bsktbl; Trk; Chrldr; 4-HAwd; Vo Tech Sch; Sec Steno.

FUGLEBERG, Gail L; Roseau HS; Roseau, MN; 22/129 Band; Chr; HonRl; MrchBnd; PepBnd; StuCncl; RptrYrbk; Pres4-H; PresGAA; 4-HAwd; Univ; Dental Hygiene.

FUHLER, Richard A; Crystal Lake Comm HS; Crystal Lake, IL; Chr; Chrs; NatlThespSoc; LitMag; Quill&Scroll; SchMus; SchPl; FrCl; GerCl; Mc Henry Ct Col.

FUHR, Pamela F; Leigh Comm HS; Clarkson, NE; 4/40 Band; Chrs; HonRl; Mdrgl; SchMus; SchPl; EdYrBk; 4-H; FHA; PresPpCl; Midland College; Elem Educ.

FUHRER, Catherine M; O Neill Public HS; O Neill, NE; Chr; ChrhWkr; HonRl; NHS; SctActv; EdSchPpr; PpCl; Secretary.

FUHRER, Joan; Lincoln Park HS; Lincoln Park, MI; 53/578 HonRl; NHS; NatlMeritFnl; NatlMeritSchl; Bsktbl; Chrldr; Michigan State Univ; Medicine.

FUHRHOP, Linda D; Steeleville C HS; Steeleville, IL; SecBand; Chrs; ChrhWkr; MrchBnd; SchPl; FBLA; FHA; PpCl; GAA; Eastern Illinois Univ; Physical Educ.

FUHRMAN, Clark E; Nodaway Holt HS; Mound City, MO; VPFrshCls; VPSrCls; ChrhWkr; HonRl; PepBnd; StuCncl; 4-H; FFA; LetterBsbl; LetterBsktbl; CaptFtbl; LetterTrk; IMSpt; Univ Of Missouri; Agriculture.

FUHRMAN, Daryl K; Frederick HS; Frederick, SD; VPFrshCls; Chrs; SctActv; CivCl; Bsbl; Bsktbl; LetterFtbl; LetterTrk; CchngActv; IMSpt; Clg; Prof.

FUHRMAN, Jeffrey A; Graceville HS; Graceville, MN; VPSrCls; Chrs; ChrhWkr; SchPl; 4-H; FFA; Ftbl; Wrstlng; 4-HAwd; Moorhead Vo Tec; Diesel Mech.

FUHRMAN, Susan C; Mounds View HS; New Brighton, MN; Chr; JrNHS; NHS; NatlMeritSF; Orch; TchrAde; Yrbk; St Olaf College; Music Ed.

FUHRMANN, John J; St Patrick HS; Chicago, IL; HonRl; JA; SctActv; Univ; Pro.

FUHRMANN, Timothy A; Southeast HS; Springfield, IL; HonRl; TchrAde; Springfield College.

FUHRY, Charles P; St Louis Univ HS; Glendale, MO; Chr; NatlMeritSF; PolWkr; StuCncl; StuGov; Chrldr; IMSpt; U Of Mo; Medical Doctor.

FUJII, Keri T; C S Mott HS; Warren, MI; HonRl; HospAde; LitMag; NHS; PolWkr; StuGov; TchrAde; FrCl; Univ; Md.

FUJIMOTO, James G; Lane Technical HS; Chicago, IL; 14/1200 JA; NHS; NatlMeritSF; Yrbk; GerCl; College; Computer Math.

FUJIMURA, Sheryl S; D D Eisenhower HS; Crestwood, IL; SecSophCls; VPSrCls; SecChr; Chrl; HonRl; VPNHS; VPStuCncl; PresMthCl; Univ Of Illinois; Veterinarian.

FUKAMI, Claudia M; John Hersey HS; Prospect Hts, IL; 37/786 DrlTm; HonRl; University.

FUKUYA, Penny S; Forest View HS; Des Plaines, IL; 13/640 Band; CncrtBnd; HonRl; JrNHS; LbryAde; MrchBnd; NHS; OffAde; PepBnd; Quill&Scroll; RptrSchPpr; SptEdSchPpr; GAA; Univ Of Illinois; Accounting.

FULBRIGHT, Marsha L; Meadow Heights HS; Lutesville, MO; Band; ChrhWkr; CmntyWkr; HospAde; RedCrAde; StuCncl; YthFlsp; YthLg; 4-H; FHA; Semo U; Computer Science.

FULFORD, Steven B; Marshall HS; Marshall, IL; ALBoysSt; GerCl; LetterBsbl; LetterBsktbl; LetterFtbl; AmLegAwd; College; Professional.

FULK, Steve W; West Platte HS; Platte City, MO; AFS; Band; Chr; CncrtBnd; HonRl; MrchBnd; ModUN; SchMus; StuCncl; StuGov; YthFlsp; LetterBsbl; Bsktbl; LetterFtbl; K State; Teacher.

FULK, Tia L; Morrill HS; Morrill, NE; LbryAde; NHS; NatlThespSoc; SchPl; StuGov; YthFlsp; 4-H; PpCl; 4-HAwd; Curtis Tech; Veterinary Science.

FULKER, Kristi L; Aberdeen Central HS; Aberdeen, SD; ChrhWkr; CmntyWkr; HonRl; PpCl; Tennis; College; Professional.

FULKER, Ronald A; Central HS; Aberdeen, SD; 12/402 ALBoysSt; Band; ChrhWkr; HonRl; MrchBnd; NatlFornLg; NHS; Orch; PepBnd; Bsktbl; Tennis; Trk; IMSpt; College; Engineering.

FULKERSON, Diana L; Charleston HS; Otisco, IN; 9/213 PresJrCls; MrchBnd; NHS; Yrbk; PresFHA; Chrldr; SecGAA; AmLegAwd; College; Law.

FULLENKAMP, Dan J; Marquette HS; West Point, IA; Chr; Chrs; SchPl; 4-H; FTA; Bsktbl; Trk; IMSpt; PPFtbl; 4-HAwd; College.

FULLENKAMP, Dorothy M; Marquette Inc HS; West Point, IA; 3/49 Band; Chr; HonRl; LbryAde; NHS; NatlMeritSF; SchPl; TchrAde; RptrYrbk; RptrSchPpr; IMSpt; College; Biochemistry.

FULLENWORTH, Betty J; Storm Lake Sr HS; Storm Lake, IA; 15/135 ChrhWkr; NHS; SchMus; SctActv; StuCncl; EdYrBk; FTA; GerCl; PPFtbl; AmLegAwd; Iowa St Univ; Mathematics.

FULLER, Beverly J; Liberal HS; Liberal, KS; Band; ChrhWkr; CncrtBnd; HonRl; MrchBnd; SpnCl; Seward County Comm; Business.

FULLER, Brian K; Naperville Central HS; Naperville, IL; HonRl; NatlSciFnd; SctActv; SciCl; LetterTrk; Us Naval Academy; Electrical Engineer.

FULLER, Daniel; Shelbyville HS; Shelbyville, IN; HstFrshCls; HstJrCls; HstSrCls; CmntyWkr; SciCl; Trk; Trade Or Bus; Professional.

FULLER, Esther R; Lincoln Sr HS; E St Louis, IL; 40/132 SecJrCls; SecSrCls; StuCncl; Illinois State Univ; Business Education.

FULLER, Gloria; Northern HS; Detroit, MI; 9/169 ChrhWkr; CncrtBnd; HonRl; MrchBnd; SctActv; CitAwd; Wayne St Univ, Nursing.

FULLER, Karen S; Olivet HS; Oliet, MI; 11/58 PresSrCls; ALAGirlsSt; CncrtBnd; HonRl; NHS; SchMus; StuCncl; Bsktbl; Trk; Olivet Col.

FULLER, Laine; Waterford Mott Hs; Pontiac, MI; Bsbl; Ftbl; CchngActv; College; Business.

FULLER, Leslie R; Moline Sr HS; Moline, IL; 112/845 Chr; HonRl; NHS; NatlThespSoc; PolWkr; SchMus; SchPl; RptrSchPpr; College; Broadcasting.

FULLER, Nancy; Holcomb HS; Kennett, MO; 2/35 ChrhWkr; HonRl; SchPl; StuGov; RptrYrbk; RptrSchPpr; SchPpr; PpCl; IMSpt; Univ; Journalism.

FULLER, Randy D; De Forest HS; De Forest, WI; PresSophCls; PresJrCls; HonRl; StuCncl; FrCl; Ftbl; LetterTrk; University; Chemistry.

FULLER, Rex A; Eastside Jr Sr HS; Butler, IN; 39/137 PresSophCls; HonRl; YthFlsp; VP4-H; PresFFA; LetterFtbl; Wrstlng; 4-HAwd;.

FULLER, Robin G; Rockford Sr HS; Kentwood, MI; LatCl; SecPpCl; SciCl; Grand Vally State Col; B S Nursing.

FULLER, Robin L; Erie HS; Erie, IL; 1/80 TrsJrCls; AFS; HonRl; MrchBnd; StuCncl; Twrl; Yrbk; SchPpr; Chrldr; Augustana College.

FULLER, Ruth; Dallas Community HS; Dallas Center, IA; Chrs; ChrhWkr; DrlTm; SchMus; YthFlsp; RptrSchPpr; PpCl; Bsbl; Bsktbl; Trk; Grace College; Missionary.

FULLER, Steven R; E C Memorial HS; Eau Claire, WI; Glf; LetterSwmmng; University Of Minnesota; Architecture.

FULLER, Timothy; Antigo HS; Birnamwood, WI; /700 Electonics Or Army; Technical.

FULLERTON, Douglas J; Marshfield HS; Marshfield, WI; Chr; HonRl; NHS; NatlMeritCmnd; PolWkr; SchMus; SchPl; SctActv; LetterTennis; Lawrence Univ; Physics.

FULLERTON, Faye E; Marissa HS; Marissa, IL; 3/74 VPSrCls; Band; HonRl; NHS; NatlMeritCmnd; Quill&Scroll; SctActv; TreasStuCncl; EdYrBk; EdSchPpr; University; Journalism.

FULLERTON, Mary; Rockford Sr HS; Rockford, IA; 4/70 Band; Chr; HonRl; NHS; TchrAde; EdYrBk; Glf; Trk; Niacc; Elementary Education.

FULLING, Eric V; Palestine HS; Palestine, IL; 3/47 SchMus; PresStuCncl; YthFlsp; PresFFA; LetterBsbl; LetterBsktbl; LetterFtbl; LetterTrk; AmLegAwd; 4-HAwd; SARAwd; Univ Of Il; Agriculture.

FULLINGTON, Loretta G; Irving Crown HS; Lake In The Hills, IL; 35/355 HonRl; NHS; StuCncl; TchrAde; RptrSchPpr; SptEdSchPpr; SchPpr; SciCl; LetterBsktbl; Trk; GAA; South Ill Univ; Journalism.

FULTNER, Sharon K; Alton HS; Couch, MO; HonRl; LbryAde;.

FULTON, Cynthia L; John Marshall HS; Indiannapolis, IN; 60/450 Chr; HonRl; JA; YthFlsp; RptrYrbk; Purdue U; Engineering.

FULTON, Dwight D; Kearney R 1 HS; Kearney, MO; Chrs; HonRl; NHS; TchrAde; Yrbk; SchPpr; 4-H; LetterBsktbl; LetterFtbl; LetterTrk; University; Engineering.

FULTON, Jay A; Pittsburg HS; Pittsburg, KS; 1/226 ALBoysSt; SctActv; StuCncl; CaptFtbl; Tennis; IMSpt; KiwanAwd; RotaryAwd; Wichita State Univ; Electrical Engineering.

FULTON, John A; John M Harlan HS; Chicago, IL; 68/714 HonRl; SchAde; StuCncl; StuGov; RptrYrbk; CaptBsktbl; CchngActv; PPFtbl; Illinois State Univ; Accounting.

FULTON, Julia; Union Bible Seminary; Cicero, IN; Chr; HonRl; Orch; TreasStuCncl; Yrbk; Theological Seminary;missionary.

FULTON, Karen; Melvin Sibley HS; Sibley, IL; 4/25 Chrs; Mdrgl; Quill&Scroll; SchPl; PresStuCncl; TreasYthFlsp; EdYrBk; FTA; LetterBsktbl; PresGAA; Univ; Computer Science.

FULTON, Lulu; Leeton HS; Leeton, MO; SecFrshCls; Chrs; HonRl; StuCncl; Yrbk; SchPpr; FHA; PpCl; Bsbl; Bsktbl; College; Accounting.

FULTON, Mark G; Lakeview HS; St Clair Shores, MI; CmntyWkr; SchAde; LetterTrk; IMSpt; Ferris St Col; Pre Pharmacy.

FULTON, Matthew S; Grand Rapids HS; Grand Rapids, MN; 69/377 PresJrCls; PresSrCls; ALBoysSt; Band; Chr; CncrtBnd; Mdrgl; SchAde; StuCncl; LetterFtbl; St Scholastica College; Music.

FULTON, Sandra F; Faulkner HS; Chicago, IL; Chrs; CmntyWkr; LbryAde; NatlThespSoc; PolWkr; SchMus; EdYrBk; FrCl; Chrldr; University; Professional.

FULTZ, Nathaniel W; Prairie Heights HS; Hudson, IN; 33/125 Aud/Vis; Chr; Chrs; ChrhWkr; HonRl; SchPl; IMSpt; College; History.

FULTZ, Yvonne L; Bedford Sr HS; Temperance, MI; 8/418 ChrhWkr; CncrtBnd; MrchBnd; NHS; PepBnd; TchrAde; University Of Toledo; Special Educ.

FUMAGALLI, Daniel; Joliet Catholic Hs; Joliet, IL; 5/170 HonRl; LitMag; NHS; StuCncl; RptrYrbk; RptrSchPpr; EdSchPpr; MthCl; LetterFtbl; CaptTrk; Northwestern; Political Science.

FUMICH, Karen; Gabriel Richard HS; Riverview, MI; 8/155 Chr; HonRl; HospAde; SchPl; StuCncl; StuGov; FNA; Mecy College Detroit; Nursing.

FUMO, David E; Forest View HS; Mt Prospect, IL; 64/640 HstJrCls; HstSrCls; Chr; HonRl; NHS; NatlMeritSchl; StuCncl; SciCl; Univ; Professional.

FUNCIK, Thomas E; Montini HS; Villa Park, IL; RptrSchPpr; SptEdSchPpr; Bsktbl; Clg Of Du Page; Accountant.

FUNCK, Linda A; Aquinas HS; Ft Madison, IA; 4/46 ChrhWkr; CmntyWkr; HonRl; NHS; SchPl; TchrAde; YthFlsp; EdYrBk; FHA; PpCl; Clge; Elem Tchr.

FUNDAREK, Dyane M; Maria HS; Chicago, IL; GerCl; SciCl; College; Marine Biology.

FUNESTI, Deborah A; Duchesne HS; St Charles, MO; 83/182 CmntyWkr; HonRl; JrNHS; NHS; NatlMeritSchl; PolWkr; StuGov; KeyCl; PpCl; Coll; Special Ed.

FUNFSINN, Cynthia A; Lasalle Peru Twp HS; Peru, IL; 62/517 Aud/Vis; HonRl; NHS; FrCl; PpCl; LetterBsktbl; Tennis; LetterTrk; CchngActv; GAA; IMSpt; PresAwd; Illinois St Univ; Physical Educ.

FUNK, Angela M; Lawrenceville HS; Lawrenceville, IL; HonRl; SchPl; SchPl; VPEngCl; LatCl; PpCl; SciCl; Vicennes U ; Resp Therapy.

FUNK, Beverly; Ewing Public HS; Ewing, NE; TrsJrCls; SecSrCls; Chr; ChrhWkr; HonRl; SchPl; SctActv; StuCncl; Yrbk; CitAwd;.

FUNK, Brian T; Paxton HS; Paxton, IL; 15/140 Chrs; CncrtBnd; HonRl; MrchBnd; NHS; SchPl; FFA; Bsbl; Bsktbl; AmLegAwd; Univ Of Il; Agriculture.

FUNK, Christi G; Luther South HS; Chicago, IL; 57/211 Chr; LbryAde; College; Fashion Marketing.

FUNK, David; Tremont HS; Tremont, IL; TrsFrshCls; HonRl; Illinois Central College; Draftsman.

FUNK, Debra D; Cascade HS; Stilesville, IN; 37/130 Chr; ChrhWkr; HonRl; NHS; OffAde; SchMus; StuCncl; TchrAde; FBLA; PpCl; Army.

FUNK, Elizabeth K; Monrovia HS; Mooresville, IN; Band; HonRl; HospAde; SctActv; TchrAde; 4-H; KeyCl; DARAwd; 4-HAwd; KiwanAwd; LionAwd; Iupui; Nursing.

FUNK, Gregory G; James Madison HS; Milwaukee, WI; 73/850 ChrhWkr; CmntyWkr; HonRl; SctActv; StuGov; RptrSchPpr; SchPpr; SpnCl; MthCl; Univ Of Wisconsin; Bio Medical Engineer.

FUNK, James; Edgewood Colesburg HS; Edgewood, IA; Band; Chr; CncrtBnd; HonRl; SchMus; StuCncl; RptrYrbk; Bsktbl; Ftbl; Wrstlng; Iowa State Univ; Doctor Of Veterinary Med.

FUNK, John A; St Thomas Acad; Minneapolis, MN; 42/96 DrlTm; ROTC; StuGov; SpnCl; LetterFtbl; LetterTrk; LetterWrstlng; IMSpt; Inst Of Tech; Architect.

FUNK, Mark; Troy HS; Troy, MI; 62/550 Aud/Vis; HonRl; LbryAde; SctActv; TchrAde; 4-H; 4-HAwd; Univ;pharmacy.

FUNK, Nancy S; Ewing Public HS; Ewing, NE; Chrs; HonRl; NHS; SchPl; StuGov; RptrSchPpr; FHA; PpCl; Chrldr; IMSpt; College; Major Study.

FUNK, Norma J; Lawrenceville HS; Lawrenceville, IL; School Of Nursing; Nursing.

FUNK, Raynee L; Ellsworth Sr HS; Bay City, WI; 26/195 Chr; HonRl; Mdrgl; NHS; Yrbk; SchPpr; FTA; PpCl; Chrldr; 4-HAwd; College; Early Childhood Education.

FUNK, Susan E; Topeka West HS; Topeka, KS; 1/446 Band; HonRl; MrchBnd; NatlMeritSF; Orch; PepBnd; SchMus; StuCncl; YthFlsp; PPFtbl; University; Professional Music.

FUNK, Teresa A; Sibley Community HS; Sibley, IA; 19/95 Chr; HonRl; RptrYrbk; RptrSchPpr; 4-H; FrCl; PpCl; GAA; DanFAwd; Nettleton College; Medical Secretary.

FUNK, Terri A; South Iron HS; Annapolis, MO; Band; ChrhWkr; CmntyWkr; HonRl; StuCncl; VPFHA; PpCl; Bsktbl; CaptChrldr; College;.

FUNKE, James F; Edgewood Colesburg HS; Edgewood, IA; 10/65 PresSrCls; ModUN; SchPl; SchPl; StuCncl; StuGov; FFA; LetterBsktbl; LetterFtbl; IMSpt; College; Business.

FUNKENBUSH, Paul D; Houghton HS; Houghton, MI; Band; HonRl; College; Professional.

FUNKHOUSER, Anna; Pleasant Hill HS; Pleasant Hill, MO; 6/112 ALAGirlsSt; HonRl; NHS; TchrAde; Yrbk; SptEdSchPpr; 4-H; SpnCl; PpCl; SciCl; Research Hospital Medical Center; Rn.

FUNKHOUSER, Betty J; Peru HS; Peru, IN; 38/190 CaptBand; CncrtBnd; HonRl; MrchBnd; VPNatlFornLg; PepBnd; 4-H; CaptGAA; PresAwd; CitAwd; Marion College; Physical Education.

FUNKHOUSER, Ellen M; Princeton Community HS; Princeton, IN; 2/204 PresHospAde; SecNHS; NatlMeritCmnd; 4-H; LatCl; PresMthCl; Ball State University; Engineering.

FUOG, Julia R; Glenbrook North HS; Northbrook, IL; HonRl; NatlMeritSchl; SchPl; Tennis; Univ Of Illinois; Business Admin.

FUREY, John W; Roncalli HS; Omaha, NE; HonRl; StuGov; RptrSchPpr; IMSpt; Creighton U; Medicine.

FURFARO, Tina M; Triad HS; Troy, IL; Chrs; DrlTm; HonRl; MrchBnd; NHS; SchPpr; FFA; GerCl; PpCl; SciCl; AmLegAwd; DARAwd; College; Doctor.

FURIMSKY, Amy A; Gage Park HS; Chicago, IL; 3/300 HonRl; LbryAde; OffAde; SchAde; StuCncl; Chrldr; GAA; IMSpt; University; Business Administration.

FURJANIC, Pamela J; St Francis De Sales HS; Chicago, IL; HonRl; JrNHS; NHS; StuCncl; Yrbk; SchPpr; Illinois State University; Medicine.

FURLANO, Jeanne M; Desoto HS; Stoddard, WI; 7/75 HonRl; SchPl; StuCncl; TchrAde; Yrbk; RptrSchPpr; Trade School; Professional.

FURLETTE, Debra L; Davison HS; Davison, MI; 13/434 Chr; CmntyWkr; HospAde; JA; NHS; TchrAde; RptrSchPpr; SecIMSpt; Univ Mi; Nurse.

FURLONG, Lynn M; Heelan HS; Sioux City, IA; Chrs; HonRl; RedCrAde; SchMus; SctActv; StuCncl; StuGov; TchrAde; PpCl; Chrldr; College; Professional.

FURLONG, Susette M; Galena HS; Galena, IL; 4/107 AFS; ChrhWkr; HonRl; HospAde; LbryAde; MrchBnd; ModUN; SchMus; SchPl; SchPpr; SpnCl; PpCl; Tennis; College; Medicine.

FURLONG, Teresa L; Malden HS; Malden, MO; Band; ChrhWkr; CncrtBnd; HonRl; MrchBnd; PepBnd; TchrAde; YthFlsp; PpCl; GodCntryAwd; College; Accountant.

FURMAN, David A; Highland HS; Highland, IN; Chr; Chrl; Chrs; HonRl; SchMus; Indiana Univ; Medicine.

FURMANEK, Peggi M; Thomas Jefferson HS; Rockford, IL; 9/420 CmntyWkr; HonRl; SctActv; StuCncl; TchrAde; 4-H; SpnCl; Bsbl; CchngActv; GAA; College; Professional.

FURMANIAK, Jeanette M; Lourdes HS; Chicago, IL; 8/299 HonRl; NHS; RptrSchPpr; IMSpt; PPFtbl; Coll; Journalist.

FURNAL, Kevin D; Pleasantville Comm HS; Ackworth, IA; 17/50 HonRl; YthFlsp; 4-H; FFA; Bsbl; CaptBsktbl; CaptFtbl; CaptTrk; CchngActv; 4-HAwd; Iowa State Univ; Agriculture.

FURNESS, Terri S; Hillsboro HS; Nokomis, IL; Band; Chr; Chrs; HonRl; SchMus; SctActv; VP4-H; FrCl; CaptChrldr; MasAwd; Trade; Vocation.

FURNIVAL, Ronald A; Buffalo HS; Montrose, MN; ALBoysSt; CtyCnl; HonRl; NatlMeritCmnd; StuCncl; GerCl; Gustavus Adolphus College; Medicine.

FURRER, Daniel J; St John The Baptist HS; St Louis, MO; 28/89 SchMus; SchPl; StuCncl; LetterSocr; IMSpt; Meramac Comm Coll; Drafting.

FURRER, Diane L; Darlington HS; Darlington, WI; ALAGirlsSt; Band; HonRl; NatlFornLg; SchPl; Twrl; KeyCl; SpnCl; PpCl; Trk; Chrldr; CchngActv; College; Physical Education.

FURROW, Brian K; Joliet Central HS; Joliet, IL; 46/491 ChrhWkr; HonRl; NHS; YthFlsp; Bsbl; LetterGlf; College; Professional.

FURRY, Brian L; Charleston HS; Charleston, IL; ChrhWkr; HonRl; PolWkr; YthFlsp; College; Businessman.

FURST, J P; Wahpeton Senior HS; Wahpeton, ND; ALBoysSt; Band; Chr; HonRl; NHS; NatlMeritFnl; SchPpr; Glf; Princeton U; Liberal Arts/creative Writing.

FUS, Julie M; Thorton Fractional HS; Lansing, IL; 18/563 AFS; Band; CncrtBnd; HonRl; MrchBnd; NHS; LatCl; PpCl; Univ Of Ill; Physical Therapy.

FUSSELMAN, Timothy J; Moberly HS; Moberly, MO; 8/215 HonRl; NHS; FBLA; MthCl; U Of Ms Rolla; Geophysics.

FUSSY, Caroline L; L F Community HS; Bowlus, MN; College.

FUSTIN, John M; Norris City HS; Omaha, IL; HstSophCls; VPJrCls; HstSrCls; Chrs; ChrhWkr; SchPl; StuCncl; YthFlsp; College; Social Work.

FUXD, Jacquelyn A; Louisville HS; Cedar Creek, NE; DrmMjrt; HonRl; LbryAde; SchPl; StuCncl; RptrYrbk; FHA; PpCl; Trk; GAA; College; Marine Biologist.

FYE, Bobbie N; Wauneta HS; Wauneta, NE; Chr; RedCrAde; SctActv; FFA; Ftbl; Trade School; Machinist.

FYE, Bobbie N; Wauneta Public HS; Wauneta, NE; .

FYFE, Linda K; Bayard HS; Bayard, NE; 3/43 TrsSrCls; ALAGirlsSt; Chrs; HonRl; NHS; SchMus; StuCncl; EdYrBk; RptrSchPpr; FHA; Nebraska Western College; General Courses.

FYKSEN, Laurie; Hudson HS; Hudson, WI; Band; DrmMjrt; HonRl; MrchBnd; NatlFornLg; PepBnd; SchMus; StuCncl; GerCl; GAA; College; Professional Acting.

FYLLING, Arlin J; Turtle Lake Public HS; Ruso, ND; 17/44 TrsSrCls; ALBoysSt; Band; Chr; Chrl; SchPl; Yrbk; FFA; LetterFtbl; AmLegAwd; North Dakota St Univ; Chemistry.

FYNEWEVER, Susan J; Holland Christian HS; Holland, MI; Band; CncrtBnd; MrchBnd; NatlFornLg; Orch; SchPl; Kalamazoo Valley Comm College; Nursing.

G

GAAL, Margaret A; South County Tech HS; St Louis, MO; 77/409 ALAGirlsSt; HonRl; StuCncl; VPFHA; FTA; IMSpt; Univ; Medical Studies.

GAARE, Dennis S; Arlington HS; Arlington Hts, IL; 92/585 HonRl; NHS; Bsktbl; College; Engineering.

GAB, Joyce V; Morton West HS; Stickney, IL; 4/750 Chr; CncrtBnd; HonRl; ModUN; NHS; StuCncl; RptrYrbk; Swmmng; Northwestern University.

GABALDO, Maria M; Bloomington HS; Bloomington, IL; 28/290 HonRl; NHS; SchAde; SctActv; StuCncl; GerCl; SpnCl; PresPpCl; Trk; GAA; Illinois State Univ; Interpreter.

GABBERT, Nancy; Wells HS; Wells, MN; 2/113 TrsSophCls; RptrYrbk; SchPpr; 4-H; GAA; BttyCrckrAwd; 4-HAwd; St Cloud State College; Med Tech.

GABEL, Penny A; Ness City HS; Ness, KS; Band; ChrhWkr; HonRl; MrchBnd; SchMus; Yrbk; FHA; Fort Hays Kansas St Univ; Secretary.

GABER, Tom; Rhinelander HS; Rhinelander, WI; VPSrCls; HonRl; OffAde; StuCncl; StuGov; College; Curriculum Of Study.

GABIER, Julianne; Traverse City HS; Traverse City, MI; HonRl; Sacrstn; Orch; LetterBsktbl; LetterTrk; Coll; Prof English.

GABLE, Laura D; Sidney HS; Sidney, NE; Band; CncrtBnd; HonRl; JrNHS; MrchBnd; NHS; PepBnd; FHA; MthCl; PpCl; College; Professional.

GABLER, Gregory A; Savannah HS; Savannah, MO; Band; Chr; CncrtBnd; Mdrgl; MrchBnd; Orch; PepBnd; YthFlsp; LetterFtbl; LetterTennis; University; Physical Ed.

GABRIEL, Donna L; Lyons Township HS; La Grange, IL; CmntyWkr; HonRl; LitMag; NHS; OffAde; Quill&Scroll; EdYrBk; SchPpr; SpnCl; Bradley College; Law.

GABRIEL, Helen M; Mother Mcauley HS; Chicago, IL; 15/474 Chrs; ChrhWkr; HonRl; JA; NHS; TchrAde; RptrSchPpr; FTA; MthCl; Univ Of Illinois; Med Lab Technician.

GABRIEL, Julie A; Salem Central HS; Salem, WI; HonRl; Mdrgl; NatlThespSoc; SchMus; SchPl; StuCncl; Yrbk; RptrSchPpr; GAA; 4-HAwd; Wi Univ Madison; Pro Public Relations.

GABRIEL, Mark J; Menomonie HS; Elk Mound, WI; 8/236 NHS; SciCl; LetterTrk; IMSpt; ChmbCommrsAwd; U Of Wi River Falls; Medicine.

GABRIEL, Theresa R; Immaculate Heart Of Mary HS; Westchester, IL; Chrl; ChrhWkr; SctActv; TchrAde; Yrbk; GerCl; Illinois State Univ; Dentistry.

GABRIELSON, James G; Hoven HS; Hoven, SD; 1/45 ALBoysSt; CmntyWkr; HonRl; PolWkr; PresStuCncl; StuGov; Bsbl; LetterBsktbl; LetterFtbl; LetterTrk; CchngActv; IMSpt; College; Computer Science.

GABRIELSON, Stephen D; Litchfield HS; Litchfield, MN; TrsJrCls; Band; CncrtBnd; HonRl; MrchBnd; NatlMeritSF; PepBnd; PolWkr; StuCncl; LetterTennis; Coll;medicine.

GABRYSIAK, Thomas; Mount Carmel Hs; Chicago, IL; 29/204 ChrhWkr; CmntyWkr; HonRl; SctActv; StuGov; RusCl; CaptBsktbl; Purdue University; Electrical Engineer.

GABY, Niki R; East Noble HS; Wawaka, IN; 8/274 ALAGirlsSt; HonRl; JA; MrchBnd; NHS; PepBnd; 4-H; SciCl; AmLegAwd; CitAwd; University; Special Education.

GADBERRY, Karen L; Shawnee Mission South HS; Shawnee Mission, KS; HonRl; NHS; Orch; SchMus; LetterTrk; IMSpt; College; Forestry.

GADBOIS, Virginia M; Cathedral HS; St Cloud, MN; 6/53 Mdrgl; NHS; SchMus; SchPl; CaptTennis; College Of St Benedict S; Music Therapy.

GADDIS, Beth A; Marion HS; Marion, IA; 16/179 Band; Chr; ChrhWkr; CncrtBnd; HonRl; NHS; SchMus; SchPl; SctActv; FTA; Univ; Education.

GADDIS, Gary M; Haworth HS; Kokomo, IN; 5/450 ALBoysSt; HonRl; JrNHS; NHS; NatlMeritFnl; SctActv; SptEdYrbk; LetterTennis; LetterTrk; IMSpt; U Of In; Medicine.

GADDIS, Robert D; Tri Valley HS; Ellsworth, IL; 20/40 Band; HonRl; TreasFFA; Bsbl; Bsktbl; Trk; East Iu; Accounting.

GADDY, Debra K; Northwest HS; Rives Junction, MI; 10/270 VPSrCls; TreasBand; ChrhWkr; CncrtBnd; HonRl; MrchBnd; SecNHS; StuGov; 4-H; 4-HAwd; Grand Rapids Baptist Clge; Rn.

GADDY, Garry D; Salem HS; Salem, MO; HonRl; SchPl; FFA; Bsktbl; Trk; CitAwd; College.

GADE, Susan K; Webb HS; Rock Springs, WI; 4/206 Band; CncrtBnd; HonRl; HospAde; MrchBnd; PepBnd; StuCncl; 4-H; PpCl; 4-HAwd; College; Horticulture.

GADEKEN, Arlys; West Point Public HS; West Point, NE; 4/59 Chr; Chrs; HonRl; SchPl; SchPpr; FHA; PpCl; Lincoln School Of Commerce; Accounting.

GADES, Julie B; Hancock HS; Hancock, MI; 2/90 Band; Chr; HonRl; HospAde; TchrAde; RptrYrbk; PresFTA; Mich Tech Univ; Elementary.

GADZINSKI, James G; St Ladislaus HS; Detroit, MI; 35/137 VPJrCls; SecSrCls; CmntyWkr; HonRl; Quill&Scroll; StuGov; RptrSchPpr; SchPpr; LetterBsbl; LetterBsktbl; CchngActv; Univ; Professional.

GADZINSKI, John T; Lincoln HS; Manitowoc, WI; HonRl; CaptFtbl; CaptTrk; Machinist.

GAEBEL, Jody R; Murdock HS; Murdock, NE; 7/17 Chrs; ChrhWkr; HonRl; YthFlsp; SchPpr; PpCl; Bsktbl; Chrldr; Beauty Sch; Beautician.

GAEBLER, Charlene L; Joliet West HS; Joliet, IL; 15/421 SecJrCls; JrNHS; NHS; Quill&Scroll; EdSchPpr; Tennis; Trk; Chrldr; Univ Of Illinois.

GAERTE, Kathy S; Central Noble HS; Albion, IN; Band; Chr; ChrhWkr; DrlTm; HospAde; MrchBnd; SchMus; Trk; Goshen College; Nursing.

GAERTE, Marilyn A; Central Noble HS; Albion, IN; Indiana Univ; Medicine.

GAERTNER, Patricia A; Hill Murray HS; St Paul, MN; Chrs; HonRl; TchrAde; Teen; LetterTrk; Chrldr; GAA; St Teresa; Nursing.

GAETZ, Debra E; Prairie Heights Jr Sr HS; La Grange, IN; 9/105 VPJrCls; ALAGirlsSt; NHS; SecStuCncl; RptrYrbk; FFA; Purdue U; Pre Medicine.

GAFFNEY, Cary B; L C HS; Lincoln, IL; Aud/Vis; CmntyWkr; CncrtBnd; HonRl; LitMag; NHS; Orch; PolWkr; SchMus; SctActv; TchrAde; SchPpr; SpnCl; PresSciCl; So Illinois Univ; Communication.

GAFFNEY, Cindy J; Arthur HS; Arthur, IL; 1/44 HstFrshCls; VPSrCls; Chr; Chrs; HonRl; JrNHS; NHS; SchPl; StuCncl; RptrYrbk; EdYrBk; FHA; Chrldr; GAA; Lakeland Jr College; Education.

GAFFNEY, John F; Central HS; Davenport, IA; 1/600 ALBoysSt; ChrhWkr; HonRl; NatlFornLg; StuCncl; SpnCl; SciCl; NCTE; College; Science.

GAFFNEY, Michael G; De Forest HS; De Forest, WI; 1/132 SecTrsSophCls; SecTrsJrCls; AFS; ChrhWkr; HonRl; VPNHS; RptrYrbk; FrCl; Univ Of Wisconsin; Law.

GAFFORD, Meredith L; Anderson HS; Anderson, IN; 5/621 ChrhWkr; HonRl; NHS; TchrAde; College; Engineering.

GAFRICK, David; Maine West Hs; Des Plaines, IL; HonRl; RptrSchPpr; SchPpr; CaptSwmmng; College;communications Radio & Tv.

GAGE, Duane T; Fort Calhoun Comm HS; Fort Calhoun, NE; Band; CncrtBnd; HonRl; MrchBnd; PepBnd; LetterBsbl; LetterBsktbl; LetterFtbl; Trk; College; Electronic Engineering.

GAGE, Gregory T; Border Central HS; Calvin, ND; 5/9 VPFrshCls; SecTrsSophCls; HonRl; SchPl; StuCncl; SchPpr; PpCl; CaptBsktbl; Wahpeton Trade School; Mechanical Eng.

GAGE, Kenneth L; Mc Cook Sr HS; Mc Cook, NE; Band; ChrhWkr; CmntyWkr; HonRl; NHS; PepBnd; SctActv; MthCl; SciCl; IMSpt; University; Medicine.

GAGE, Mindy; Central Noble HS; Albion, IN; VPSrCls; HonRl; MrchBnd; NHS; 4-H; PpCl; Bsktbl; Trk; GAA;.

GAGE, Pete; Meridian HS; Mounds, IL; Band; CncrtBnd; HonRl; MrchBnd; SctActv; SpnCl; SciCl; Shawnee Jr Clg; Electronics.

GAGE, Ronald R; St Laurence HS; Willow Springs, IL; 22/380 HonRl; NatlMeritCmnd; StuCncl; Bradley Univ; International Finance.

GAGE, Terry L; Saline HS; Saline, MI; ALBoysSt; Aud/Vis; Chr; HonRl; MrchBnd; SchMus; LetterFtbl; LetterTrk; IMSpt; JCAwd; College; Engineering.

GAGLIARDI, Mary J; St Joseph HS; Kenosha, WI; 1/136 Chrs; ChrhWkr; HonRl; NHS; StuCncl; RptrSchPpr; LetterTennis; Carroll College; Childhood Educ.

GAGLIARDI, William; Midland HS; Midland, MI; HonRl; JA; CivCl; Bsbl; Ftbl; Trk; IMSpt; JAAwd; College; Business Management.

GAGLIARDO, Mary Jo S; Villa Duchesne HS; St Louis, MO; CmntyWkr; HonRl; ModUN; NHS; Sdlty; University; Foreign Service.

GAGNON, Charles L; Springfield Southeast HS; Springfield, IL; ChrhWkr; OffAde; StuCncl; Bsbl; Bsktbl; Ftbl; Trk; Western Illinois Univ; Law Enforcement.

GAGNON, James; Beaver Dam Senior HS; Beaver Dam, WI; 49/296 Band; CncrtBnd; HonRl; MrchBnd; PepBnd; Glf; Univ Of Wis; Bus Adm.

GAGNON, James E; Beaver Dam Sr HS; Beaver Dam, WI; 44/310 Band; CncrtBnd; HonRl; MrchBnd; PepBnd; Univ Of Wisconsin; Business Admin.

GAGNON, Lynn M; Willow River HS; Sturgeon Lake, MN; 1/41 Band; Chr; CncrtBnd; HonRl; NatlMeritCmnd; SchMus; SchPl; Univ; Professional.

GAGNON, Paula R; Beaver Dam Sr HS; Beaver Dam, WI; 24/310 Band; HonRl; MrchBnd; StuCncl; RptrYrbk; RptrSchPpr; PpCl; Bsktbl; Trk; CaptChrldr; GAA; College; Recreation.

GAHAGAN, Teresa; Ottawa Hs; Ottawa, KS; ALAGirlsSt; DrlTm; HonRl; NHS; RptrYrbk; RptrSchPpr; 4-H; PpCl; GAA; 4-HAwd; College; Professional.

GAHLER, Cindy A; Lakeland Union HS; Woodruff, WI; Band; Chr; ChrhWkr; CncrtBnd; HonRl; MrchBnd; PepBnd; SchMus; PresGAA; CitAwd; College; Ministry.

GAHLON, Thomas L; 4436 Main St HS; Oak Brook, IL; 30/509 Chr; Chrs; NHS; NatlThespSoc; SchMus; SchPl; SARAwd; Univ Of Il.

GAHNZ, Kathy J; Newman HS; Wausau, WI; 19/134 TrsJrCls; Band; ChrhWkr; CncrtBnd; HonRl; MrchBnd; PepBnd; SpnCl; Bsktbl; College; Spanish.

GAIBRECHT, Steve P; Wentworth Military Acad; Kansas City, MO; HonRl; NHS; ROTC; Socr; Trk; Wrstlng;.

GAIER, Karen; Marshfield Senior HS; Marshfield, WI; TrsSrCls; AFS; Chrs; HonRl; StuCncl; 4-H; FrCl; PpCl; 4-HAwd; Uw Marshfield; Fashion Merchan.

GAINER, Karen S; Academy Of Our Lady; Chicago, IL; 13/188 Chrs; CmntyWkr; HonRl; LbryAde; OffAde; TchrAde; FTA; SpnCl; MthCl; PpCl; Quincy College; Sociology.

GAINES, Jan C; East Altom Wood River HS; Wood River, IL; 17/285 Chr; ChrhWkr; HonRl; NHS; StuCncl; Tennis; IMSpt; Sw Baptist Col; Music Teacher.

GAINES, Joe; Gary Emerson HS; Gary, IN; 73/223 HonRl; LbryAde; SchPl; StuCncl; StuGov; EdYrBk; PpCl; Ball State; Photographer.

GAINES, Karen J; Southport HS; Indianapolis, IN; 13/450 Band; HonRl; NHS; OffAde; LatCl; Purdue University; Food Science.

GAINES, Mark A; East Alton Wood River HS; Wood River, IL; 21/350 HonRl; JrNHS; NHS; StuCncl; LetterTrk; College; Meteorology.

GAINES, Michael; Potosi R Iii HS; Potosi, MO; 31/185 TrsSrCls; HonRl; SctActv; StuGov; YthFlsp; SpnCl; College; Bus Admin.

GAINEY, Linda K; Bergan HS; Peoria, IL; 20/208 ChrhWkr; CmntyWkr; HonRl; NatlMeritCmnd; Yrbk; SpnCl; Bsktbl; Univ Of Illinois; Law.

GAINFORTH, Mark R; Unionville Sebewaing Area HS; Unionville, MI; ALBoysSt; Band; Chrs; HonRl; StuCncl; LatCl; Bsbl; CaptBsktbl; CaptFtbl; Trk; Coll; Phy Ed.

GAITHER, Renoir W; Emmerich Manual HS; Indianapolis, IN; 38/479 ALBoysSt; HonRl; LitMag; NatlMeritCmnd; SctActv; KeyCl; Univ Of Illinois; Liberal Arts.

GAITROS, Carolyn E; Cerro Gordo HS; Cerro Gordo, IL; Band; Chrs; CncrtBnd; MrchBnd; OffAde; PepBnd; SchPl; TchrAde; FHA; FTA; Southern Il Univ.

GALASKE, James W; Cleveland HS; St Louis, MO; 24/560 HonRl; LetterTrk; Univ Mo Rolla; Eng.

GALAVIZ, David E; Lakewood HS; Lake Odessa, MI; 23/210 Band; CncrtBnd; HonRl; MrchBnd; NHS; Orch; PepBnd; SchMus; SchPl; Bsbl; College.

GALBRAITH, Cynthia A; Iron Mountain Sr HS; Iron Mountain, MI; Band; CncrtBnd; MrchBnd; PepBnd; StuCncl; FrCl; LetterTennis; GAA; Michigan Tech Univ; Med Tech.

GALBRAITH, Elizabeth E; Rich Central HS; Olympia Fields, IL; 31/364 ChrhWkr; HonRl; University.

GALBRAITH, John G; Stephenson HS; Stephenson, MI; PresFrshCls; ALBoysSt; Chrs; ChrhWkr; SchPl; StuCncl; StuGov; PpCl; Ftbl; Trk; Univ; Professional.

GALBRAITH, William A; Roxana Sr HS; Wood River, IL; 47/275 HonRl; SctActv; MthCl; Ftbl; Trk; Univ Of Ill; Architecture.

GALBREATH, Robert E; St Ignatius HS; Chicago, IL; Chrs; ChrhWkr; CmntyWkr; HonRl; HospAde; SchPl; SctActv; Drake Univ; Communication.

GALE, Andrew; Yorktown HS; Daleville, IN; 13/173 VPFrshCls; HonRl; NHS; 4-H; SpnCl; U S Militay Acad; Military.

GALE, Geoffrey L; Southwestern HS; Flint, MI; HonRl; SctActv; Socr; IMSpt; Chas Stewart Mott Com Col ;nat Resoursces.

GALE, Mark R; Decatur HS; Decatur, MI; 23/76 PresFrshCls; ALBoysSt; HonRl; SchPl; LetterBsbl; LetterBsktbl; LetterTrk; LionAwd; Central Michigan Univ; Business Admin.

GALE, Teresa A; Summersville HS; Eunice, MO; Chrs; HonRl; NHS; RptrYrbk; RptrSchPpr; FHA; PpCl; College; Teaching.

GALECKI, Mary L; Catholic Memorial HS; Brookfield, WI; Chr; ChrhWkr; YthFlsp; 4-H; GAA; College; Special Education.

GALEGHER, Charlotte A; Thompson Public HS; Thompson, ND; 1/19 SecTrsJrCls; Band; Chrs; ChrhWkr; HonRl; SchPl; StuCncl; 4-H; LetterTrk; DanFAwd; Univ Of Colorado; Physical Therapist.

GALER, Anne L; Hillsboro HS; Hillsboro, IL; Band; Chr; ChrhWkr; HonRl; NHS; RptrYrbk; RptrSchPpr; 4-H; GAA; DanFAwd; S Il Univ.

GALES, Lynn P; Wabasso Public HS; Seaforth, MN; ChrhWkr; CmntyWkr; HonRl; IntrClCncl; NatlMeritSchl; RedCrAde; StuGov; YthFlsp; RptrSchPpr; FHA;.

GALES, Patricia J; Maine North HS; Glenview, IL; HonRl; NatlFornLg; NHS; NatlMeritCmnd; NatlThespSoc; Orch; SchMus; SptEdSchPpr; Bsbl; Bsktbl; St Catherine College; Liberal Arts.

GALES, Robert H; Proctor HS; Duluth, MN; 1/200 PresSophCls; ALBoysSt; HonRl; JrNHS; NHS; Quill&Scroll; PresStuCncl; RptrSchPpr; LetterBsbl; RotaryAwd; West Point; Engineering.

GALEX, Audrey I; Rock Island HS; Rock Island, IL; VPFrshCls; HonRl; JrNHS; PolWkr; StuGov; RptrSchPpr; SpnCl; PpCl; Tennis; University; Psychology.

GALEY, Allan D; Dexter HS; Dudley, MO; 24/139 VPSrCls; Band; CncrtBnd; HonRl; SchPl; EdYrBk; PpCl; CaptBsbl; CaptFtbl; CaptTrk; Univ; Professional.

GALIARDI, Cheryl; St Charles HS; St Charles, MI; Band; CncrtBnd; NHS; SchPl; SctActv; StuCncl; Chrldr; GAA; IMSpt; PPFtbl; Univ Of Mi; Physical Therapist.

GALICA, Catherine J; Ripon HS; Ripon, WI; Chrs; ChrhWkr; HonRl; NHS; PepBnd; RedCrAde; SchMus; MthCl; LetterBsbl; Clge; Occupational Therapy.

GALIK, Barbara A; Riverview Gardens Sr HS; St Louis, MO; 14/733 CmntyWkr; HonRl; NHS; StuGov; PpCl; GAA; IMSpt; PPFtbl; JAAwd; Univ Of Mo Columbia; Professional.

GALINDO, David P; Stevenson HS; Livonia, MI; 3/700 Chr; HonRl; LetterBsktbl; CaptFtbl; LetterTrk; Kalamozaa Clg.

GALINIS, Karen R; Coldwater HS; Quincy, MI; Chr; ChrhWkr; LbryAde; NHS; YthLg; 4-H; College; Conservation.

GALITZ, Brian J; Hastings HS; Hastings, NE; Chr; CmntyWkr; HonRl; YthFlsp; Glf; IMSpt; MasAwd; Hastings College; Science Major.

GALL, David W; Humboldt HS; St Paul, MN; 32/223 ChrhWkr; CmntyWkr; HonRl; LbryAde; NHS; SchMus; SctActv; StuCncl; TchrAde; LetterBsbl; CchngActv; IMSpt; Inver Hills Comm Jr College; Business Admin.

GALL, Debra A; Bucklin HS; New Boston, MO; 2/23 VPFrshCls; PresJrCls; ALAGirlsSt; Band; CmntyWkr; EdYrBk; 4-H; FHA; LetterBsktbl; LetterTrk; BttyCrckrAwd; DanFAwd; 4-HAwd; Nw Mo Univ; Medicine.

GALL, Diane P; Morton West HS; Berwyn, IL; Chr; Chrs; ChrhWkr; HonRl; HospAde; SctActv; Loyolla U; Registerd Nurse.

GALL, Duane R; Madison HS; Madison, NE; Band; Chr; Chrl; Chrs; CncrtBnd; DrlTm; MrchBnd; PepBnd; Trade Sch; Vocation.

GALL, Kenneth M; Morrill HS; Morrill, NE; Chr; Chrs; SchAde; SchPl; SctActv; StuCncl; TchrAde; PpCl; Ftbl; Trk; Trade; Vocation.

GALL, Laurie L; Tartan HS; St Paul, MN; 8/427 CncrtBnd; HonRl; HospAde; MrchBnd; PepBnd; 4-H; Tennis; 4-HAwd; Coll; Medicine.

GALL, Lynnette D; Humboldt HS; St Paul, MN; Chr; CmntyWkr; DrlTm; HonRl; HospAde; SchAde; StuCncl; TchrAde; Trade School; Nurse.

GALL, Mary M; Derham Hall HS; St Paul, MN; Chr; Chrs; HospAde; LbryAde; SctActv; StuCncl; College; Medicine.

GALL, Rodger; Morgan Park HS; Chicago, IL; 54/493 ChrhWkr; NHS; SctActv; TchrAde; MthCl; LetterBsbl; Siuc.

GALLAGHER, Barbara L; Manhattan HS; Manhattan, KS; Chr; ChrhWkr; HonRl; HospAde; IntrClCncl; College; Counseling.

GALLAGHER, John G; St Laurence HS; Burbank, IL; 7/380 HonRl; SpnCl; LetterWrstlng; Writing.

GALLAGHER, John G; St Laurence HS; Oak Lawn, IL; 9/400 HonRl; Wrstlng; U Of Chicago.

GALLAGHER, Kerry A; Papillion HS; Papillion, NE; ALAGirlsSt; Chrs; NHS; SchMus; SchPl; StuCncl; StuGov; VPYthFlsp; PresSpnCl; PresPpCl; Theatre & Television.

GALLAGHER, Leslie R; Rock Island Sr HS; Rock Island, IL; HonRl; NHS; NatlMeritCmnd; Teen; Yrbk; GerCl; Iowa State University.

GALLAGHER, Mark J; Gordon Tech HS; Chicago, IL; 47/618 HonRl; NatlMeritCmnd; LetterFtbl; Knox College; Psychology.

GALLAGHER, Michael G; Austin Catholic Prep; St Clair Shores, MI; 17/115 HonRl; SchMus; SchPl; RptrYrbk; Bsktbl; LetterTrk; Michigan State Univ; Dentistry.

GALLAGHER, Mike J; Belding HS; Belding, MI; HonRl; FFA; Trk; College; Aviation Maintenance Mgmnt.

GALLAGHER, Pamela A; Cass City HS; Cass City, MI; ChrhWkr; HonRl; NHS; SchPl; TchrAde; YthFlsp; GerCl; Alma Col; Soc Worker.

GALLAGHER, Patricia M; Edgewood HS; Monona, WI; 27/180 HonRl; NHS; SchPl; EdSchPpr; 4-H; Trk; 4-HAwd; Uw Madison; Accounting.

GALLAGHER, Shawn G; Memorial HS; Evansville, IN; ALBoysSt; HonRl; SctActv; Ftbl; CchngActv; IMSpt; College; Geologist.

GALLAGHER, Sue A; J F Kennedy Senior HS; Bloomington, MN; Chr; CmntyWkr; HonRl; NHS; RedCrAde; SchPl; StuGov; RptrSchPpr; Chrldr; OptClAwd; Clg Of St Catherines; Public Relations.

GALLAGHER, Timothy J; Clarence Lowden Community HS; Clarence, IA; 3/45 PresSophCls; TrsSrCls; Band; Chrs; HonRl; NHS; SchMus; StuCncl; EdYrBk; Tennis; U Of Ia; Pharmacy.

GALLAHUE, Terri A; Wabash HS; Wabash, IN; 5/201 CncrtBnd; HonRl; MrchBnd; NHS; Quill&Scroll; VPStuCncl; RptrYrbk; RptrSchPpr; GerCl; PpCl; Univ; Journalism.

GALLALEE, James; Roger C Sullivan Hs; Chicago, IL; 8 HonRl; NHS; NatlMeritCmnd; NatlSciFnd;.

GALLAP, Clayton H; Union City HS; Coldwater, MI; 18/80 LbryAde; RptrSchPpr; SptEdSchPpr; Ftbl; College; Science.

GALLAS, John S; Lake Park HS; Roselle, IL; 15/537 PresJrCls; ALBoysSt; HonRl; StuCncl; StuGov; RptrSchPpr; SciCl; Bsktbl; Tennis; Univ Of Illinois; Dentistry.

GALLAS, Kathy M; Grass Lake Jr Sr HS; Grass Lake, MI; SecSrCls; OffAde; TchrAde; 4-H; Business School; Secretary.

GALLAS, Pattijo; Lake Central HS; Schererville, IN; 67/453 HonRl; Quill&Scroll; FTA; SpnCl; PpCl; PPFtbl;.

GALLATIN, Kevin D; Greenville HS; Greenville, IL; 20/177 JrNHS; MrchBnd; NHS; PepBnd; SctActv;

SpnCl; PpCl; LetterBsktbl; LetterFtbl; Trk; Univ Of Mo Rolla; Mining Eng.

GALLAWAY, Brian D; Leslie HS; Leslie, MI; Band; CncrtBnd; MrchBnd; PepBnd; Mi State Univ; Systems Analists.

GALLE, Mary B; Elk Mound HS; Eauclaire, WI; 5/43 Chrs; ChrhWkr; HonRl; Yrbk; 4-H; EngCl; SpnCl; PpCl; GAA; 4-HAwd; Univ Of Wi ; Med.

GALLEHER, Mary A; Three Rivers HS; Three Rivers, MI; 1/209 HonRl; HospAde; NHS; NatlMeritSchl; SctActv; TchrAde; RptrYrbk; LatCl; Glen Oaks Comm College; Education.

GALLEMORE, Kimberly A; Seneca HS; Seneca, MO; VPAFS; SecChrhWkr; HonRl; LbryAde; NHS; NatlThespSoc; RptrYrbk; SecFTA; SecMthCl; PresPpCl; GAA; College; Computer Analysis.

GALLENBERG, Dennis J; Antigo HS; Bryant, WI; Band; ChrhWkr; MrchBnd; NatlFornLg; SchPl; FFA; MthCl; IMSpt; EldAwd; CitAwd; U Of Wi River Falls; Doctor Of Vet Med.

GALLENBERG, Loretta A; Waupun HS; Fox Lake, WI; 17/262 SecSrCls; AFS; ALAGirlsSt; CmntyWkr; LitMag; NHS; Quill&Scroll; SchMus; StuCncl; Yrbk; U Of Wi Madison; Science Professional.

GALLER, Elaine B; Pioneer HS; Ann Arbor, MI; 5/617 Band; CncrtBnd; HonRl; MrchBnd; NatlFornLg; NatlMeritSF; Orch; SchMus; TchrAde; MthCl; Univ; Lawyer.

GALLERY, Cathy A; Morton Public HS; Morton, MN; Band; StuGov; RptrYrbk; SptEdYrbk; RptrSchPpr; SptEdSchPpr; FHA; PpCl; SciCl; CaptBsktbl; North Heangin Comm Col; Nursing.

GALLES, Julie; Lincoln HS; Wis Rapids, WI; Band; ChrhWkr; CncrtBnd; HonRl; MrchBnd; PepBnd; TchrAde; College; Nursing.

GALLETT, Jill; Lake Central Hs; St John, IN; CmntyWkr; CncrtBnd; MrchBnd; SchMus; SctActv; StuGov; TchrAde; TreasTeen; Pres4-H; Bsktbl;.

GALLETTI, Beverly A; Algonac HS; Fair Haven, MI; HstJrCls; HstSrCls; ChrhWkr; NHS; SchPl; StuCncl; TchrAde; EdYrBk; PpCl; Chrldr; College; Executive Secretary.

GALLIANI, Susan M; St Louise De Marillac HS; Lincolnwood, IL; 95/257 SecFrshCls; VPJrCls; StuCncl; StuGov; PpCl; CaptAmLegAwd; OptClAwd; PresAwd; College; Economics Or Art.

GALLIART, Gay L; Larned HS; Larned, KS; 4/91 Band; CncrtBnd; HonRl; MrchBnd; SecNHS; NatlMeritCmnd; FHA; SpnCl; Hutchinson Jr Coll.

GALLICK, Randy G; Streator Twp HS; Streator, IL; PresSophCls; ALBoysSt; CmntyWkr; HonRl; NHS; College; Mathematics.

GALLIGAN, Linda M; Campbellsport HS; Campbellsport, WI; 24/147 Chrs; HonRl; NHS; FHA; SpnCl;.

GALLIGAN, Timothy C; Griffin HS; Springfield, IL; ChrhWkr; CmntyWkr; Sdlty; StuCncl; StuGov; CivCl; FDA; KeyCl; FrCl; Bailey Technical School; Technician.

GALLINGER, Bill H; Huron HS; Ann Arbor, MI; PolWkr; StuCncl; EdSchPpr; FrCl; IMSpt; U Of Mi.

GALLINGER, William H; Huron HS; Ann Arbor, MI; CmntyWkr; HonRl; PolWkr; EdSchPpr; IMSpt; Univ Of Mich; Engr.

GALLIVAN, Kyle A; St Joseph HS; Brookfield, IL; HonRl; TchrAde; GerCl; MthCl; Bsktbl; Lewis University; Computer Programming.

GALLO, Anne P; Cor Jesu Academy; St Louis, MO; 1/101 HonRl; LitMag; PresNHS; SchMus; SchPl; RptrSchPpr; PresFNA; IMSpt; St Louis U; Physical Therapy.

GALLO, Teresa M; Parkway North HS; St Louis, MO; HonRl; HospAde; JrNHS; NHS; NatlMeritSF; SchAde; SctActv; Yrbk; 4-H; 4-HAwd; University.

GALLOGLY, Ann E; Lincoln Sr HS; Bloomington, MN; HonRl; LitMag; MrchBnd; StuCncl; PpCl; U Of Min; Marine Biology.

GALLOGLY, Myrna A; Adams Central HS; Decatur, IN; 12/125 Band; CncrtBnd; HonRl; MrchBnd; NHS; TchrAde; YthFlsp; Yrbk; SpnCl; PpCl; Modeling School; Dental Assistant & Model.

GALLOWAY, Bruce E; H H Dow HS; Midland, MI; 24/440 Aud/Vis; Band; HonRl; LbryAde; NHS; Univ Of Detroit; Architecture.

GALLOWAY, Cheryl; Unionville HS; Unionville, MO; 17/83 Band; ChrhWkr; CmntyWkr; CncrtBnd; HonRl; MrchBnd; PepBnd; SchPl; 4-H; 4-HAwd; Nebraska Christian College; Youth Work.

GALLOWAY, Gail L; Marseilles HS; Marseilles, IL; HonRl; LbryAde; RptrYrbk; FshEdYrbk; SptEdYrbk; Yrbk; RptrSchPpr; SptEdSchPpr; SchPpr; GAA; Academy; Policewomen.

GALLOWAY, Lee A; Central HS; Waterloo, IA; PresSophCls; StuGov; Ftbl; Trk; College; Pro Football.

GALLOWAY, Michelle L; Sac Community HS; Sac City, IA; HonRl; SchPl; TchrAde; UNYO; YthFlsp; SchPpr; 4-H; LetterTrk; LetterGAA; Naval Acad For Women.

GALLUCCI, Glory A; Maine West HS; Des Plaines, IL; HonRl; JrNHS; SpnCl; Univ Of Ill; Social Work.

GALLUP, Laura D; Mason City Senior HS; Mason City, IA; 16/448 Band; CncrtBnd; HonRl; MrchBnd; PepBnd; SchPl; PpCl; Niacc; Accounting.

GALLUP, Phillip C; East Noble HS; Wolcottville, IN; 59/274 Chr; ChrhWkr; HonRl; NatlThespSoc; SchMus; SchPl; 4-H; LetterFtbl; LetterWrstlng; 4-HAwd; Indiana Univ; Business.

GALLUS, Robert J; Maysville R 1 HS; Maysville, MO; Chrs; ChrhWkr; HonRl; NHS; Sacrstn; FFA; LetterFtbl;.

GALLUZZIO, Elizabeth A; Hannibal HS; Hannibal, MO; Chr; Chrs; ChrhWkr; HonRl; HospAde; SchMus; SctActv; SpnCl; GAA; Warrensberg Coll.

GALONSKY, Marc W; East Lansing HS; East Lansing, MI; 5/350 Chr; Chrl; HonRl; NHS; SchMus; U Of Mi.

GALOSKOWSKY, Gina; Ritenour Senior HS; St Louis, MO; Chr; ChrhWkr; HonRl; JrNHS; SchMus; StuCncl; Southwest Baptist Coll; Medical Receptionst.

GALT, Elizabeth J; Shawneetown HS; Shawneetown, IL; Band; Chr; ChrhWkr; CncrtBnd; HonRl; MrchBnd; PepBnd; SchMus; StuCncl; Clge; Vocation.

GALT, Fritz M; Homewood Flossmoor HS; Homewood, IL; 57/930 HonRl; LitMag; NHS; Orch; SchMus; LetterBsktbl; U Or Col; English.

GALUSKA, Annie; Lourdes HS; Rochester, MN; Band; ChrhWkr; CncrtBnd; MrchBnd; Orch; PepBnd; SchPl; TchrAde; Trk; CchngActv; Coll; Pharm.

GALUSKA, Lynn A; Mt Assisi Academy; Oak Lawn, IL; 7/189 Chr; ChrhWkr; HonRl; LbryAde; ModUN; PresNHS; SchMus; SchPl; SctActv; StuCncl; StuGov; Yrbk; FrCl; LatCl; Univ Of Ill; Medicine.

GALUSKA, Lynn A; Mount Assisi HS; Oak Lawn, IL; 10/194 Chr; ChrhWkr; HonRl; LbryAde; ModUN; PresNHS; SctActv; StuCncl; TchrAde; Yrbk; FrCl; LatCl; Univ Of Illinois; Medicine.

GALVAN, Thomas G; Mendel HS; Chicago, IL; 10/169 ChrhWkr; HonRl; NHS; NatlMeritSF; Yrbk; SchPpr; KeyCl; MthCl; PpCl; De Paul Univ; Accounting.

GALVIN, Cindi M; Marian HS; Omaha, NE; DrlTm; HonRl; HospAde; JA; SecSdlty; SchPpr; Chrldr;.

GALVIN, Joseph; Bloomington HS; Bloomington, IL; Band; CncrtBnd; HospAde; RptrYrbk; SciCl; College; Pre Law.

GALVIN, Leo E; Holstein Community HS; Ida Grove, IA; SecSrCls; Band; CncrtBnd; MrchBnd; PepBnd; SchPl; 4-H; Ftbl; Wrstlng; College; Professional.

GALVIN, Mary K; Mauston Area HS; Mauston, WI; 11/133 Band; Chrs; CncrtBnd; HonRl; MrchBnd; NHS; PepBnd; SchMus; SchPl; RptrYrbk; College; Nursing.

GAMBACH, Susan M; Chenoa HS; Chenoa, IL; 9/60 SecFrshCls; AFS; Band; Chrs; CncrtBnd; HonRl; NHS; SchPl; SpnCl; Trk; College; Communications.

GAMBILL, Alice D; Sullivan HS; Sullivan, IN; 1/140 Band; Chr; Chrs; DrlTm; HonRl; NHS; SchMus; Twrl; SecMthCl; PpCl; Chrldr; GAA; 4-HAwd; Purdue Univ; Veterinarian.

GAMBILL, Donald; Hillsdale HS; Hillsdale, MI; 25/180 Band; CncrtBnd; JrNHS; Orch; KeyCl; Bsbl; Bsktbl; Ftbl; Tennis; Trk; Air Force.

GAMBILL, Donald W; Rosedale HS; Rosedale, IN; ALBoysSt; Aud/Vis; ChrhWkr; HonRl; TchrAde; Treas4-H; TreasLatCl; LetterBsbl; CaptBsktbl; 4-HAwd; Purdue Univ; Agriculture.

GAMBILL, Donna R; Sandoval HS; Sandoval, IL; Band; CncrtBnd; HonRl; TreasLbryAde; SchPl; TchrAde; Yrbk; PresFTA; SpnCl; BttyCrckrAwd; Eastern Ill Univ; Psychology.

GAMBINI, Marianna; Whiting HS; Whiting, IN; ALAGirlsSt; ChrhWkr; DrlTm; HonRl; HospAde; NHS; SchPpr; FTA; SpnCl; College; Cpa.

GAMBINO, Valerie C; Thornton Fractional North HS; Calumet City, IL; 426/447 CmntyWkr; HonRl; JrNHS; NHS; Quill&Scroll; SctActv; Yrbk; SpnCl; MthCl; College Of St Francis; Art.

GAMBLE, Dana M; Harrison HS; Harrison, MI; SecFrshCls; SecSophCls; HonRl; StuCncl; LetterBsktbl; Chrldr; PresAwd;.

GAMBLE, Gisele A; Archie Public HS; Archie, MO; Chrs; CncrtBnd; DrlTm; HonRl; MrchBnd; SchPl; TchrAde; 4-H; FHA; Bsktbl; Receptionist.

GAMBLE, Karyn R; Hutsonville HS; Marshall, IL; 4/27 SecTrsFrshCls; Band; Chr; Chrl; Chrs; ChrhWkr; CmntyWkr; HonRl; LbryAde; OffAde; IMSpt; College; Psychology.

GAMBLE, Richard W; Columbus North HS; Columbus, IN; 64/462 Chr; HonRl; IntrClCncl; ModUN; NatlThespSoc; SchMus; StuGov; Ftbl; DARAwd; OptClAwd; Indiana Univ; Music.

GAMM, Mary E; Freeland HS; Freeland, MI; 4/115 Chr; HonRl; JA; JCC; StuCncl; StuGov; Yrbk; KeyCl; Bsktbl; PPFtbl;.

GAMMELL, Philip; Cathedral HS; St Cloud, MN; LbryAde; NHS; Ftbl; IMSpt; RotaryAwd; College; Medicine.

GAMMILL, Cheri R; Glendale HS; Springfield, MO; AFS; HonRl; ModUN; Quill&Scroll; SecStuCncl; StuGov; YthLg; SchPpr; PpCl; SciCl; Sw Missouri St Univ; Journalism.

GAMMON, Michael D; Marshall HS; Marshall, MI; 11/262 VPSrCls; HonRl; TreasJA; NatlFornLg; NHS; SctActv; PresStuGov; YthLg; LetterTennis; LetterWrstlng; AmLegAwd; DARAwd; JAAwd; Michigan St Univ; Hotel Restaurant Mgmt.

GAMMON, Patrick C; Marshall HS; Marshall, MI; Band; JA; NHS; PolWkr; SchPl; SctActv; VPStuGov; YthLg; PresLatCl; CaptSwmmng; LetterTennis; Purdue Univ; Engineer.

GAMMON, Sandra L; Adlai E Stevenson HS; Mundelein, IL; 9/235 CncrtBnd; HonRl; MrchBnd; NHS; PepBnd; SchMus; TchrAde; LetterTrk; Chrldr; College; Accounting.

GAMMON, Wendy M; Adlai E Stevenson HS; Mundelein, IL; 23/245 Band; CncrtBnd; HonRl; HospAde; JrNHS; MrchBnd; PepBnd; Evanston Hospital; Nursing.

GANA, Margaret M; St Paul Kennedy HS; Chicago, IL; HonRl; LbryAde; Yrbk; SchPpr; FTA; FrCl; GAA; Coll; Sec Educ.

GANAWAY, Robert L; Emerson HS; Gary, IN; 29/223 Band; CmntyWkr; CncrtBnd; HonRl; MrchBnd; PepBnd; SchMus; SchPl; Purdue Univ; Business.

GANDHI, Madhu M; Macomb HS; Macomb, IL; HonRl; NHS; FrCl; SpnCl; IMSpt; PresAwd; Univ; Math.

GANDRUD, Erick A; Glenwood HS; Glenwood, MN; Band; ChrhWkr; CncrtBnd; HonRl; MrchBnd; PepBnd; SchPl; LetterFtbl; Glf; College.

GANEY, Heather E; Taylorville Sr HS; Taylorville, IL; 18/271 VPSophCls; PresJrCls; VPSrCls; Chr; NHS; NatlThespSoc; SchMus; StuCncl; RptrSchPpr; FrCl; Trk; Univ Of Il; Business Admin.

GANEY, Thomas P; Lane Technical HS; Chicago, IL; 301/1213 LbryAde; PolWkr; SctActv; Univ Of Illinois; Architecture.

GANGER, Janeen K; Northwood HS; Wakarusa, IN; Chr; HonRl; NatlThespSoc; SchMus; SchPl; SpnCl; GAA; College; Business.

GANGWISH, Karla; Shelton Public HS; Shelton, NE; 1/32 SecTrsJrCls; Band; Chrs; ChrhWkr; CncrtBnd; HonRl; Mdrgl; NHS; FrCl; BttyCrckrAwd; Ottawa Univ; Sociology.

GANN, Catherine S; Lafayette HS; St Joseph, MO; CmntyWkr; JA; LitMag; PresFTA; JAAwd; College; Elementary School Teacher.

GANN, Victor E; Marshfield HS; Marshfield, MO; 20/135 Chrl; ChrhWkr; CncrtBnd; HonRl; NHS; SchPl; AmLegAwd; GodCntryAwd; Seminary; Minister Of Music.

GANNON, Anne M; Lourdes HS; Chicago, IL; 99/299 HonRl; SchPl; PpCl; Bsktbl; Ftbl; IMSpt; PresAwd; College; Pharmacy.

GANNON, Dorothy I; Beloit Catholic HS; Beloit, WI; ALAGirlsSt; HonRl; LbryAde; PresNHS; RptrSchPpr; EdSchPpr; Chrldr; GAA; Univ Of Wis; Journalism.

GANNON, Kathryn A; Laurens HS; Laurens, IA; NatlFornLg; PolWkr; SchPl; TreasTeen; Yrbk; RptrSchPpr; Bsktbl; U Of Co Boulder; Lawyer.

GANNON, Mary R; York Community HS; Elmhurst, IL; 65/950 HonRl; NHS; Quill&Scroll; SchMus; RptrSchPpr; SchPpr; Univ Of Illinois; Journalism.

GANNON, Maureen; Chippewa Hills HS; Chippewa Lake, MI; 6/160 ChrhWkr; HonRl; JA; NatlFornLg; NHS; 4-H; SciCl; Chrldr; DARAwd; Ferris State College; Respirtory Therapist.

GANNON, Patrick J; Marist HS; Oak Lawn, IL; 15/375 HonRl; NHS; SpnCl; LetterTrk; IMSpt; Loyola Univ; Pre Dental.

GANONG, Fawn M; Parkside HS; Jackson, MI; HonRl; FrCl; Jackson Comm College; Biology.

GANS, John N; Sauk Centre HS; Sauk Centre, MN; 10/156 ALBoysSt; Band; Chr; HonRl; SctActv; StuCncl; RptrYrbk; RptrSchPpr; CaptSwmmng; Trk; St Johns Univ; Physics.

GANSCHOW, Helen A; Buena Vista HS; Saginaw, MI; 1/200 SecSrCls; ChrhWkr; HonRl; NHS; OffAde; SchPl; 4-H; PresGerCl; Bsbl; 4-HAwd; Mi St U; Nurse.

GANSEL, Julie A; Hill City HS; Hill City, KS; Chrl; Chrs; DrlTm; HonRl; SchMus; FHA; PpCl; LetterTrk; IMSpt; DanFAwd; Coll; Interior Decorating.

GANSEN, Regina M; New Hampton HS; Elma, IA; 3/180 SecSophCls; Chr; Chrs; ChrhWkr; NHS; NatlThespSoc; SchMus; 4-H; FrCl; 4-HAwd; Iowa State U; Home Ec.

GANSER, Elizabeth; John Adams HS; South Bend, IN; 15/425 NatlMeritSF; RptrYrbk; Stanford Univ.

GANT, Gaye H; Bunker R 3 HS; Bunker, MO; 3/28 ChrhWkr; HonRl; MrchBnd; PepBnd; SchMus; EdYrBk; EdSchPpr; SchPpr; Chrldr; CchngActv; Clge; Music Ed.

GANT, Rita C; Gibault HS; Waterloo, IL; HonRl; NHS; SchMus; CivCl; PpCl;.

GANTEBEIN, Vicki R; Lawrence HS; Lawrence, KS; Band; CncrtBnd; HonRl; MrchBnd; Orch; PepBnd; SchPl; StuCncl; StuGov; PpCl; Univ Of Ks; Bo Sci.

GAPSKE, Jane E; Roanoke Benson HS; Roanoke, IL; 5/93 ChrhWkr; CmntyWkr; HonRl; NHS; NatlMeritFnl; NatlMeritCmnd; YthFlsp; FHA; FNA; SpnCl; Ill Central Coll; Accounting.

GAPSKI, Leann; Lasalle Peru Twp HS; Oglesby, IL; HonRl; OffAde; College; Photographer.

GARA, Aubyn; Milton Sr HS; Milton Jct, WI; Chr; ChrhWkr; SchMus; SchPl; SctActv; YthFlsp; 4-H; FrCl; Swmmng; Tennis; University.

GARBARINO, Janice; Denby HS; Detroit, MI; ChrhWkr; HonRl; JrNHS; NHS; PolWkr; SctActv; TchrAde; SciCl; Wayne St Univ; Pharmacy.

GARBE, William W; Milton HS; Milton, WI; 46/185 HonRl; VP4-H; FFA; LatCl; Ftbl; Trk; 4-HAwd; Univ Of Wisconsin; Agriculture.

GARBER, Amy B; Southfield Lathrup HS; Southfield, MI; CmntyWkr; StuCncl; College.

GARBER, Beverly J; Hale Ri HS; Hale, MO; 3/22 SecJrCls; Chr; Chrs; CncrtBnd; HonRl; OffAde; SptEdYrbk; PpCl; LetterBsktbl; LetterTrk; College; Pro Secretary.

GARBER, Michael J; Cedar Falls HS; Cedar Falls, IA; 19/434 Band; CncrtBnd; HonRl; MrchBnd; Orch; PepBnd; RptrYrbk; RptrSchPpr; Clg; Engineering.

GARBER, Robert J; Lowpoint Washburn HS; Washburn, IL; 7/60 Band; Chrs; HonRl; MrchBnd; SchMus; StuCncl; 4-H; FFA; Bsktbl; Trk; Agriculture.

GARBER, Susan T; Roncalli HS; Manitowoc, WI; 8/141 AFS; HonRl; LbryAde; SctActv; RptrYrbk; FrCl; MthCl; Univ Wi Oshkosh.

GARBERICH, Brenda J; Cosmos Public HS; Grove City, MN; 9/35 HonRl; Hutchinson Vo Tech; Office Clerk.

GARBERS, Dawn; Lake Benton Public HS; Lake Benton, MN; 8/38 Band; Chr; Chrs; CncrtBnd; HonRl; JrNHS; MrchBnd; Trk; GAA; College; Professional.

GARBERS, Robert C; Gubson Southern HS; Fort Branch, IN; 60/260 ChrhWkr; SctActv; YthFlsp; 4-H; FFA; LatCl; PpCl; SciCl; Ftbl; Purdue; Veterinary.

GARBERSON, Cheryl L; Bedford HS; Lambertville, MI; 82/420 HonRl; NatlMeritCmnd; PolWkr; StuCncl; RptrYrbk; 4-H; Chrldr; IMSpt; Toledo Hospital School Of Nursing; Nurse.

GARBISCH, Vida J; Granton HS; Granton, WI; VPJrCls; SecSrCls; Chr; Chrs; LbryAde; SchMus; SchPl; StuCncl; PresFHA; Chrldr; Univ Of Wis Stout.

GARBO, Rod M; Mercy HS; St Louis, MO; 17/200 HonRl; SctActv; VoiceDemAwd;.

GARCIA, Estella; Wellcome Memorial HS; Garden City, MN; Aud/Vis; DrlTm; HonRl; LbryAde; OffAde; SchPl; SchPpr; FHA; Us Air Force.

GARCIA, Juan; Harrison HS; Chicago, IL; 27/388 College; Profession.

GARCIA, Maggie; Holy Family Academy; Chicago, IL; Chrs; HospAde; OffAde; TchrAde; Yrbk;.

GARCIA, Patricia M; Assumption HS; Fairmont City, IL; PresSrCls; ChrhWkr; ModUN; PolWkr; SchPl; StuGov; EdYrBk; GAA; Loyola Univ; Social Work.

GARCIA, Ralph H; Waukesha North HS; Waukesha, WI; Chr; HonRl; PolWkr; SchMus; StuCncl; StuGov; TchrAde; SpnCl; Wrstlng; Uw Madison; Medicine.

GARCIA, Sofia A; Ladywood St Agnes HS; Indianapolis, IN; Chrs; CmntyWkr; HonRl; TreasJA; RedCrAde; SchMus; SchPl; StuCncl; TchrAde; RptrYrbk; FrCl; Butler Univ; Medicine.

GARD, Dan M; Maryville R Ii HS; Maryville, MO; 33/149 NHS; StuCncl; RptrYrbk; FrCl; Ftbl; College.

GARDALEN, Linda; Cal HS; Alexander, IA; Chrs; HonRl; Mdrgl; SchMus; SchPl; FTA; Trk; Account.

GARDINER, Kay K; Omaha North HS; Omaha, NE; ALAGirlsSt; Chrl; HonRl; JrNHS; Orch; SchMus; SchPl; RptrSchPpr; FrCl; NCTE; College; Law.

GARDINER, Thomas G; Homewood Flossmoor HS; Glenwood, IL; 53/917 PresSrCls; HonRl; LitMag; StuGov; KeyCl; Univ Of Illinois; Law.

GARDNER, Craig M; St Ignatius College Prep HS; Chicago, IL; 3/155 HonRl; NHS; NatlMeritCmnd; Yrbk; RptrSchPpr; LetterBsktbl; IMSpt; College; Medicine.

GARDNER, Daniel L; Beaver City HS; Beaver City We, NE; 1/26 TrsJrCls; Band; Chrs; CncrtBnd; HonRl; SchPl; EdYrBk; LetterBsktbl; LetterFtbl; LetterTrk; Univ; Pharmacy.

GARDNER, David D; Millington HS; Millington, MI; 2/168 ALBoysSt; LitMag; NHS; NatlMeritCmnd; Yrbk; Mich Tech Univ; Engineering.

GARDNER, Diane; Dondero HS; Royal Oak, MI; Band; Chr; ChrhWkr; NatlMeritCmnd; NatlMeritSF; TchrAde; FrCl; Col; Computer Analyst.

GARDNER, Donna G; Ridgewood HS; Norridge, IL; 64/369 Aud/Vis; HonRl; MrchBnd; SctActv; Bradley Univ; Interior Designer.

GARDNER, Doris J; Ridgewood HS; Norridge, IL; 65/362 William Woods College; Equestrian Studies.

GARDNER, Eric; Crestwood HS; Ridgeway, IA; HonRl; NHS; 4-H; FFA; Ftbl; Wrstlng; IMSpt; College.

GARDNER, Jeffrey L; Morton HS; Morton, IL; ALBoysSt; HonRl; JA; Bsktbl; College; Business.

GARDNER, Jonathan D; Clawson HS; Clawson, MI; 2/380 AFS; Band; ChrhWkr; NHS; NatlMeritCmnd; SchPl; RptrYrbk; Tennis; BauchLmbAwd; EldAwd; Univ Of Mi; Science.

GARDNER, Julie E; Eddyville HS; Ottumun, IA; SecBand; VPChr; HonRl; Quill&Scroll; VPStuCncl; SptEdYrbk; 4-H; PpCl; LetterBsbl; LetterBsktbl; LetterTrk; LetterWrstlng; Univ Of Iowa; Physical Therapy.

GARDNER, Kathryn; Charlotte HS; Charlotte, MI; 31/275 Band; CncrtBnd; HonRl; MrchBnd; PepBnd; YthFlsp; PpCl; Bsbl; GAA; PPFtbl; College; Professional.

GARDNER, Kim; Catholic HS; Kearney, NE; 3/28 Chrs; HonRl; SctActv; StuCncl; RptrYrbk; Trk; IMSpt; BttyCrckrAwd; Creighton Univ; Pharmacy.

GARDNER, Leah L; Lincoln HS; Vincennes, IN; 14/316 Chr; ChrhWkr; LbryAde; NatlMeritCmnd; StuCncl; LetterTrk; KiwanAwd; De Paun; Chemistry.

GARDNER, Mark S; Ashland HS; Ashland, IL; 20/36 Chrs; HonRl; SchPl; StuCncl; 4-H; FFA; SciCl; Bsktbl; AmLegAwd; College; Professional.

GARDNER, Marlea J; Harrison HS; Harrison, MI; 8/120 Chrs; ChrhWkr; LbryAde; NHS; StuCncl; TchrAde; Twrl; College; French Teacher.

GARDNER, Michael C; Farmer City Mansfield HS; Farmer City, IL; 9/73 HonRl; LetterBsbl; LetterFtbl; LetterTrk; Southern Illinois Univ; Forestry.

GARDNER, Nancy K; Heritage Christian HS; Indianapolis, IN; Chr; ChrhWkr; HonRl; JA; JrNHS; NHS; SchMus; Indiana Central Univ; Accounting.

GARDNER, Patricia A; Waukegan HS; Waukegan, IL; Chr; Chrs; ChrhWkr; CmntyWkr; HonRl; JrNHS; NHS; SecYthFlsp; CaptChrldr; AmLegAwd; University; Accounting.

GARDNER, Rebecca; Otterville HS; Otterville, MO; Chr; Chrs; ChrhWkr; CmntyWkr; HonRl; HospAde; RptrSchPpr; SchPpr; FHA; BttyCrckrAwd; Nursing School; Practical Nursing.

GARDNER, Rene C; Holton HS; Twin Lake, MI; VPFrshCls; Band; CncrtBnd; HonRl; MrchBnd; PepBnd; SchPl; StuCncl; EdYrBk; SpnCl; Clge; Psychologist.

GARDNER, Rodney J; Dighton HS; Dighton, KS; TrsFrshCls; Band; Chr; CncrtBnd; HonRl; MrchBnd; PepBnd; LetterBsktbl; LetterFtbl; LetterTrk; College Juco; Marketing.

GARDNER, Ronald; Arapahoe HS; Edison, NE; 12 VPJrCls; PresSrCls; ALBoysSt; Chr; Chrs; SchPl; YthLg; SptEdYrBk; 4-H; Bsbl; College; Business Admin.

GARDNER, Rose M; Morgan Park HS; Chicago, IL; 30/559 ChrhWkr; HonRl; OffAde; TchrAde; Chicago State Univ; Elementary Education.

GARDNER, Teresa M; St Philip Catholic Ctrl HS; Battle Creek, MI; 3/98 HonRl; NHS; NatlMeritCmnd; SpnCl; LetterTrk; VoiceDemAwd; Us Air Force.

GARDNER, Theresa A; Boscobel HS; Boscobel, WI; SecFrshCls; SecSophCls; SecJrCls; Chrs; ChrhWkr; StuCncl; YthFlsp; Technical School; Medical Assistant.

GARDNER, Vickie L; Wall Lake Comm HS; Wall Lake, IA; TrsFrshCls; TrsJrCls; TrsSrCls; ALAGirlsSt; Band; CncrtBnd; HonRl; MrchBnd; PepBnd; SchPl; Yrbk; Bsbl; Bsktbl; College; Physical Educ.

GARDNER, William P; Glenbrook South HS; Glenview, IL; 23/2581 HonRl; University Of Illinois; Physics.

GARDOCKI, Theresa A; Port Huron Northern HS; Port Huron, MI; 25/432 MrchBnd; NHS; StuCncl; CaptBsbl; CaptBsktbl; PresGAA; College; Biology.

GARDSTROM, Susan C; Arthur Hill HS; Saginaw, MI; Band; HonRl; Mdrgl; Orch; SchMus; SecTrsFrshCls; PpCl; Trk; Chrldr; Univ; Music.

GARDY, Peggy S; Elkton Pigeon Bay Port HS; Bay Port, MI; 20/146 Band; HonRl; NHS; SchMus; YthFlsp; FTA; PpCl; Chrldr; Michigan State Univ; Education.

GARIGAN, Qullian M; Immaculata HS; Highland Park, MI; 30/104 PresFrshCls; PresSophCls; PresJrCls; Chr; HonRl; NHS; SchPl; StuGov; SpnCl; Spelman College; Law.

GARKEY, Janet R; Polo Community HS; Polo, IL; 13/93 VPSophCls; Band; NHS; SchPl; Yrbk; Pres4-H; Bsbl; Trk; PresGAA; IMSpt; Madison Business Clg; Secretarial Scinece.

GARLAND, Linda J; Homewood Flossmoor HS; Homewood, IL; 7/940 Chrs; HonRl; NHS; SecFBLA; Southern Illinois Univ; Secretarial.

GARLAND, M Kathleen; Alleman HS; Moline, IL; HonRl; NHS; Yrbk; SpnCl; PpCl; College; Medical Technology.

GARLAND, Nancy; Dekalb Sr HS; Dekalb, IL; 130 316 Band; CncrtBnd; HonRl; MrchBnd; SchMus; StuCncl; 4-H; FrCl; PpCl; BauchLmbAwd; College; Nursing.

GARLAND, Susan; Lane Tech HS; Chicago, IL; 5/1200 NatlMeritCmnd; OffAde; TchrAde; SecLatCl; MthCl; Univ Of Chicago; Mathematics.

GARLICK, Sara D; Guilford HS; Rockford, IL; 20/656 ChrhWkr; HonRl; HospAde; NHS; Orch; SchMus; Northern Il Univ; Accounting.

GARLIN, Milton J; Roosevelt HS; Gary, IN; VPChrhWkr; HonRl; NatlMeritCmnd; FTA; LetterGlf; CitAwd; Engineering.

GARMAN, Cindy L; Phillipsburg HS; Manhattan, KS; Band; CncrtBnd; HonRl; LbryAde; MrchBnd; PepBnd; TchrAde; FHA; PpCl; College; Secretarial.

GARMAN, Gayle D; Pekin Community HS; Pekin, IL; Band; Chrs; CncrtBnd; HonRl; SctActv; 4-H; FrCl; GAA; IMSpt; Il State Univ; Biologist.

GARMAN, Steve; Eureka Hs; Eureka, IL; 26/99 Band; Chrl; ChrhWkr; HonRl; Mdrgl; MrchBnd; NHS; SchMus; LetterBsbl; LetterTrk; Icc College; Mechinical Engineering.

GARNER, Bryan S; Anderson Sr HS; Anderson, IN; 11/569 ALBoysSt; Band; CncrtBnd; DrmBgl; HonRl; MrchBnd; NHS; Orch; PepBnd; LatCl; Computers.

GARNER, Delores D; Halter HS; Wellston, MO; ChrhWkr; HonRl; JA; FTA; PpCl; Bsbl; Bsktbl; Ftbl; JETSAwd; Fpcc & Harris Teacher; Teacher & Auto Mech.

GARNER, Deniesa A; Tri HS; New Castle, IN; 14/90 Band; ChrhWkr; HonRl; LbryAde; NHS; EdYrBk; SpnCl; Trk; GAA; Anderson College; Registered Nursing.

GARNER, Donald R; Viola HS; Bakersfield, MO; TrsJrCls; HonRl; RptrSchPpr; FFA; Bsbl; Arizona State University.

GARNER, Leta J; South Barber HS; Kiowa, KS; Band; CncrtBnd; HonRl; MrchBnd; PepBnd; SecFHA; CitAwd; Wichita St Univ; History.

GARNER, Lorraine E; Oskaloosa Sr HS; Oskaloosa, IA; Band; CncrtBnd; HonRl; MrchBnd; StuCncl; Bsktbl; Ftbl; Glf; Trk; College; Dental Assistant.

GARNER, Mark M; Dearborn HS; Dearborn, MI; ALBoysSt; Chr; Chrs; HonRl; LitMag; Mdrgl; NHS; GerCl; Univ Of Mi; Professional Biochemistry.

GARNER, Michael D; Lindbergh HS; St Louis, MO; CncrtBnd; HonRl; SchMus; SchPl; SctActv; RusCl; LetterFtbl; LetterTrk; William Jewel College; Lawyer.

GARNER, Patrick; Catholic Central HS; Dearborn, MI; HonRl; NHS; StuCncl; RptrSchPpr; LatCl; University Of Michigan, Biology.

GARNER, Peggy; Caruthersville HS; Caruthersville, MO; HonRl; HospAde; NatlThespSoc; SchMus; SchPl; TchrAde; YthFlsp; 4-H; FTA; IMSpt; College; Teach.

GARNER, Timothy L; Elwood Comm HS; Elwood, IN; HonRl; NHS; OffAde; SchAde; TchrAde; SpnCl; Bsktbl; LionAwd; Franklin College; Psychology.

GARNETT, Dianna L; Elk Mound HS; Eau Claire, WI; 9/47 VPSrCls; HonRl; RptrSchPpr; FHA; PpCl; Bsktbl; Trk; VPGAA; IMSpt; Eau Claire Voc School; Med Record Tech.

GARNETT, Timothy A; Neosho Sr HS; Neosho, MO; 13/243 HonRl; NatlFornLg; NHS; SecStuCncl; Yrbk; SchPpr; KeyCl; MthCl; LetterTrk; Univ Of Missouri; Photo Journalism.

GARNETTE, Sandra K; Papillion Sr HS; Gibbon, NE; 29/315 SecBand; Chr; CncrtBnd; HonRl; MrchBnd; NHS; PepBnd; TchrAde; 4-H; PresFTA; Kearney St College; Music.

GARNIER, Marianne; Westview HS; Kankakee, IL; 8/223 Band; CncrtBnd; HonRl; LbryAde; MrchBnd; NHS; OffAde; SchMus; College; Psychology.

GARNIER, Maribeth; Westview HS; Kankakee, IL; 4/223 HonRl; NHS; OffAde; SchMus; Univ Of Illinois; Medicine.

GARNOS, William C; Watertown Sr HS; Watertown, SD; ALBoysSt; Band; Chr; CncrtBnd; HonRl; MrchBnd; NatlFornLg; PepBnd; SchMus; University; Professional.

GAROT, Julie A; Green Bay Southwest HS; Green Bay, WI; 15/420 Band; Chrs; ChrhWkr; HonRl; Mdrgl; MrchBnd; NHS; PepBnd; SptEdSchPpr; PresPpCl; College; Music.

GAROT, Sarah C; St Joseph Academy; Green Bay, WI; PresJrCls; JA; NHS; SchMus; StuCncl; FrCl; St Catherine Clg; Major In Business.

GARRABRANT, Mary K; Marquette HS; Michigan City, IN; JA; NHS; SchMus; TchrAde; SpnCl; College.

GARRAHY, Joan M; Oriska HS; Oriska, ND; SecTrsFrshCls; VPJrCls; Band; Chr; HonRl; HospAde; Twrl; EdYrBk; RptrSchPpr; CaptBsktbl; Trade Wahpeton Science; Reg Nurse.

GARRELTS, Luann S; Hamilton HS; Hamilton, IL; TrsJrCls; Chrs; CncrtBnd; HonRl; PepBnd; StuCncl; FrCl; LetterTrk; Chrldr; GAA; U Of Ia; Pharmacy.

GARRELTS, Susan M; St John HS; Independence, IA; 1/27 Chr; Chrs; HonRl; NHS; SchMus; StuCncl; RptrYrbk; RptrSchPpr; PpCl; Clge; Piano.

GARRETSON, Stacy L; Lanphier HS; Springfield, IL; Band; CncrtBnd; PpCl; Trk; Chrldr; GAA; IMSpt; College.

GARRETT, Billie D; Fairfield Comm HS; Fairfield, IL; PolWkr; SctActv; CivCl; SpnCl; Bsktbl; SciCl; LetterColl; Pro.

GARRETT, Bobbi K; Murphysboro Township HS; Murphysburo, IL; Band; ChrhWkr; CncrtBnd; MrchBnd; Orch; SchMus; SchPl; LetterBsktbl; LetterGAA; LetterIMSpt; Olivet Nazarene Col; Business.

GARRETT, Christine A; Sarcoxie HS; Sarcoxie, MO; 2/63 Band; CncrtBnd; HonRl; MrchBnd; NHS; PepBnd; EdYrBk; FHA; MthCl; Coll; Accounting.

GARRETT, Dana L; South Pemiscot HS; Steele, MO; 2/67 Band; CmntyWkr; CncrtBnd; HonRl; JrNHS; MrchBnd; NHS; OffAde; PepBnd; SchPl; SctActv; CchngActv; DARAwd; Arkansas State Univ; Pharmacy.

GARRETT, David; Jackson HS; Jackson, MI; VPFrshCls; ChrhWkr; CmntyWkr; HonRl; SctActv; StuGov; YthFlsp; GerCl; CaptSwmmng; Trk; College; Prof.

GARRETT, David; Lane Tech HS; Chicago, IL; 750/1213 NatlMeritCmnd; StuCncl; RptrYrbk; RusCl; U Of I; Writer.

GARRETT, Debra J; Herbert Hoover HS; Des Moines, IA; 1/355 Chr; HonRl; ModUN; SecRusCl; SciCl; LetterGlf; Iowa State Univ; Botanist.

GARRETT, Heidi; Stuart Menlo HS; Stuart, IA; Band; Chr; Chrs; CncrtBnd; HonRl; MrchBnd; SchPl; 4-H; FHA; Ia Univ; Veterinary Study.

GARRETT, Jamison J; Lake Forest Academy; Libertyville, IL; HospAde; LitMag; SchPl; EdYrBk; Bsbl; Chrldr; Bennington College; Literary Field.

GARRETT, Jeffery E; Rockkridge HS; Milan, IL; FFA; Trk; Wrstlng; Farmer.

GARRETT, Karen; Memorial HS; Joplin, MO; 6/255 AFS; ChrhWkr; NatlFornLg; NHS; NatlMeritCmnd; NatlThespSoc; SchPl; StuCncl; RptrYrbk; DARAwd; Univ Mo; Professional.

GARRETT, Karen L; Memorial HS; Joplin, MO; 6/244 AFS; HonRl; MrchBnd; NatlFornLg; NHS; NatlMeritCmnd; NatlThespSoc; StuCncl; RptrYrbk; Univ Of Missouri; Professional.

GARRETT, Karen L; Central HS; Evansville, IN; 16/601 ChrhWkr; HonRl; MrchBnd; NHS; Orch; PolWkr; SchMus; Twrl; U Of Evansville; Nursing.

GARRETT, Kevin O; Maryville R Ii HS; Maryville, MO; Band; CncrtBnd; MrchBnd; NHS; PepBnd; SchMus; PresKeyCl; SciCl; LetterTennis; Nw Missouri St Univ; Accounting.

GARRETT, Linda L; Wentzville HS; Foristell, MO; 15/233 CncrtBnd; HonRl; MrchBnd; NHS; YthFlsp; PpCl; GAA; PPFtbl; State Univ; Journalism.

GARRETT, Lisa A; Windsor HS; Gays, IL; 4/56 ALAGirlsSt; Chrs; ChrhWkr; CncrtBnd; NHS; NatlThespSoc; VPFHA; GAA; 4-HAwd; Eastern Illinois Univ; Music.

GARRETT, Marjorie J; Bullock Creek HS; Midland, MI; PresSophCls; Band; ChrhWkr; HonRl; SecStuCncl; PresYthFlsp; PpCl; CaptChrldr; Coll; Social Work.

GARRETT, Mary A; St Thomas Aquinas HS; Florissant, MO; 2/350 ChrhWkr; HonRl; NHS; NatlMeritCmnd; SctActv; RptrYrbk; U Of Mo Rolla; Computer Science.

GARRETT, Patrick; Farwell HS; Farwell, MI; ChrhWkr; StuCncl; Bsbl; Central Mi Univ; Architect.

GARRETT, Roy L; North Greene HS; Roodhouse, IL; HonRl; Trade School; Vocation.

GARRETT, Scott A; Central HS; Waterloo, IA; ALBoysSt; HonRl; NHS; StuGov; Ftbl; Iowa State; Electrical Engineering.

GARRETT, Steven; Virden Comm HS; Vinden, IL; PresFrshCls; Aud/Vis; Band; Chr; Chrs; CncrtBnd; HonRl; LbryAde; Ftbl; IMSpt; Univ; Surgeon.

GARRETT, Sue E; Benton Central HS; Otterbein, IN; HonRl; OffAde; SchMus; SchPl; StuCncl; YthFlsp; RptrYrbk; FNA; PpCl; CchngActv; GAA; Ball State University; Nursing.

GARRETT, Susan M; Owosso HS; Owosso, MI; 138/452 Band; ChrhWkr; CncrtBnd; LbryAde; MrchBnd; PepBnd; SctActv; TchrAde; YthFlsp; Ferris St College; Pharmacy.

GARRETT, Theresa A; Gillespie HS; Gillespie, IL; Band; HonRl; HospAde; NatlMeritSF; RptrYrbk; RptrSchPpr; FrCl; SciCl; Bsbl; S I U; Doctor.

GARRETT, Theresa A; La Grove HS; St Peter, IL; 3/34 VPFrshCls; Chrs; HonRl; LbryAde; SchMus; StuCncl; EdYrBk; 4-H; FBLA; FHA; LetterTrk; Chrldr; LetterGAA; IMSpt; Eastern Illinois University.

GARRETT, Timothy F; Southeast HS; Kansas City, MO; 13/350 Aud/Vis; Band; ChrhWkr; CncrtBnd; HonRl; HospAde; MrchBnd; NatlMeritCmnd; Orch; PolWkr; RedCrAde; SctActv; StuGov; CaptSwmmng; GodCntryAwd; Baker Univ; Professional.

GARRETT, William; Hordville Public HS; Hordville, NE; TrsFrshCls; Band; Chr; MrchBnd; SchPl; 4-H; VoiceDemAwd; Trade School.

GARRETT, William E; Madison HS; Madison, IL; CmntyWkr; HonRl; JA; PolWkr; SctActv; MthCl; PpCl; SciCl; LetterTennis; Trk; College; Lawyer.

GARRINGER, Marianne; Ansley HS; Ansley, NE; 3/31 PresJrCls; Band; HonRl; Mdrgl; SchMus; SchPl; TchrAde; EdYrBk; PresPpCl; Trk; Central Tech Comm Col; Practical Nurse.

GARRIOTT, Dennis L; New Palestine HS; New Palestine, IN; Chr; HonRl; StuCncl; 4-H; FFA; SpnCl; Bsbl; Wrstlng;.

GARRIOTT, Grace; Hortonville HS; Hortonville, WI; 3/153 Band; Chrs; HonRl; MrchBnd; NHS; TchrAde; Bsktbl; Tennis; Trk; IMSpt; College.

GARRIOTT, James W; Beech Grove HS; Indianapolis, IN; 12/280 HonRl; JA; NHS; SctActv; SciCl; Purdue Univ; Microbiology.

GARRISON, Frances E; Trenton HS; Trenton, MO; 19/127 Chr; Chrs; NHS; SchPl; Yrbk; RptrSchPpr; SecSciCl; GAA; University; Psychology.

GARRISON, James M; Mid County Jr Sr HS; Varna, IL; 3/63 ALBoysSt; CncrtBnd; HonRl; MrchBnd; NatlMeritSchl; TreasStuCncl; 4-H; PresFFA; LetterBsbl; LetterBsktbl; Bradley Univ; Technology.

GARRISON, Joseph; Western HS; Russiaville, IN; 7/160 Band; Chr; NHS; SchPl; StuCncl; RptrSchPpr; 4-H; SciCl; 4-HAwd; RotaryAwd; Purdue Univ; Vet.

GARRISON, Michael H; Ozark HS; Ozark, MO; ChrhWkr; CmntyWkr; HonRl; HospAde; YthFlsp; 4-H; SpnCl; Bsktbl; 4-HAwd; Westminster College; Medicine.

GARRISON, Wendy A; Cambridge HS; Cambridge, IL; 5/59 ALAGirlsSt; Band; Chrs; HonRl; VPNHS; SctActv; Pres4-H; GAA; 4-HAwd; College; Mathematics.

GARRISON, William L; Grand Haven Sr HS; Grand Haven, MI; HonRl; JrNHS; NHS; StuCncl; LetterTennis; College; Science.

GARRITY, Brian L; Waukegan HS; Waukegan, IL; NHS; SctActv; Ftbl; Glf; Ill Univ; Bus Admin.

GARRITY, Michael P; St Agatha HS; Detroit, MI; HonRl; Coll; Forester.

GARRY, Joseph L; Momence HS; Momence, IL; 44/123 Quill&Scroll; RptrSchPpr; LetterFtbl; College; Professional.

GARRY, Patricia A; Wm Fremd HS; Palatine, IL; 57/607 HonRl; NHS; Quill&Scroll; PresStuCncl; Yrbk; PpCl; University Of Illinois; Accounting.

GARRY, Ronald B; Webster HS; Webster, SD; 1/75 VPFrshCls; PresJrCls; ALBoysSt; Mdrgl; NHS; NatlMeritSF; SctActv; StuCncl; Bsktbl; Ftbl; St Marys Coll; Roman Catholic Priest.

GARSKE, James; St Marys HS; Sleepy Eye, MN; CmntyWkr; StuCncl; StuGov; GerCl; Bsbl; IMSpt; PresAwd; College; Aviation.

GARSON, David F; Parkway West Sr HS; St Louis, MO; ALBoysSt; StuGov; LetterBsktbl; LetterSocr; LetterTrk; IMSpt; University; Architecture.

GARSON, Paul J; Sts Peter & Paul HS; Saginaw, MI; Chrs; HonRl; SchPl; StuCncl; LetterBsktbl; CaptFtbl; Trk; IMSpt; West Point Academy; Science.

GARST, Tammy L; Rock Port R2 HS; Watson, MO; VPSophCls; TrsJrCls; Band; CncrtBnd; HonRl; MrchBnd; NHS; PepBnd; 4-H; Chrldr; College; Vocation.

GARSTKA, Kenneth E; Brother Rice HS; Chicago, IL; 24/470 HonRl; HospAde; NHS; SctActv; StuCncl; De Paul Univ; Lawyer.

GARTEN, Mark L; Raymore Peculiar HS; Peculiar, MO; ALBoysSt; Band; CncrtBnd; HonRl; NHS; PepBnd; SchMus; CaptBsktbl; Trk; CchngActv; LionAwd; University.

GARTLAND, Eileen J; Lourdes HS; Chicago, IL; Band; CncrtBnd; HonRl; MrchBnd; 4-H; FrCl; Bsbl; Ftbl; CaptChrldr; CaptGAA; College.

GARTLAND, Richard; Catholic Central HS; Pbn Hgts, MI; NatlMeritCmnd; SctActv; Yrbk; SciCl; Mi State U; Hotel Management.

GARTNER, Bill E; Clay Center HS; Clay Center, NE; Band; CmntyWkr; CncrtBnd; HonRl; SchPl; TchrAde; SchPpr; Bsbl; Ftbl; College.

GARTNER, Bruce A; Maine East HS; Morton Grove, IL; 18/890 HonRl; NHS; MthCl; LetterFtbl; College; Medicine.

GARTNER, Gregory; New Richmond HS; New Richmond, WI; 19/170 Band; ChrhWkr; CmntyWkr; HonRl; RedCrAde; Ftbl; PresAwd; St Marys Junior College; Professional.

GARTNER, Kyna K; Princeton HS; Princeton, IL; 8/178 AFS; ChrhWkr; HonRl; HospAde; NHS; NatlThespSoc; SchPl; SctActv; Yrbk; VPFrCl; Univ Of Illinois; Nursing.

GARTON, Bradford G; Columbus North HS; Columbus, IN; 11/638 TrsFrshCls; TrsSophCls; TrsJrCls; ALBoysSt; Band; HonRl; NatlMeritFnl; NatlMeritSchl; FDA; Tennis; Purdue U; Neurophys Or Psychoacoustical Eng.

GARTON, Harry E; Garden County HS; Oshkosh, NE; TrsSophCls; CncrtBnd; HonRl; MrchBnd; PepBnd; StuCncl; Ftbl; Trk; Wrstlng; College; Liberal Arts.

GARTON, Patricia L; Ozark HS; Ozark, MO; 3/97 VPBand; CncrtBnd; HonRl; MrchBnd; RptrSchPpr; SciCl; Univ Of Mo.

GARTUNG, William E; Liberal HS; Liberal, KS; 56/212 ALBoysSt; Chr; Chr; Chrl; Chrs; ChrhWkr; Mdrgl; NatlThespSoc; RedCrAde; SchMus; College; Music.

GARVER, Laura; Richmond Burton HS; Spring Grove, IL; Chr; Chrs; CncrtBnd; HonRl; MrchBnd; PepBnd; SchMus; SchPl; TchrAde; GAA; College; Elementary Music Teach.

GARVERICK, Kris; Marysville HS; Marysville, MI; HonRl; SchPl; SctActv; StuGov; SciCl; College; Forestry.

GARVEY, Ann L; Regis HS; Eau Claire, WI; Band; Chr; Chrs; ChrhWkr; CncrtBnd; DrmBgl; HonRl; HospAde; MrchBnd; Orch; Chrldr; GAA; College; Psychology.

GARVEY, Donald J; York Comm HS; Elmhurst, IL; 200/900 Band; CncrtBnd; HonRl; MrchBnd; Orch; PepBnd; SchMus; SctActv;.

GARVEY, Lisa; Benjamin Franklin HS; Livonia, MI; HonRl; OffAde; GerCl; Bsktbl; Chrldr; AmLegAwd; Coll; Interpretor.

GARVEY, Martin C; Waterloo West HS; Waterloo, IA; HonRl; PolWkr; SchPl; StuCncl; StuGov; RptrSchPpr; IMSpt; TIMEAwd; Us Navy; Medicine.

GARVEY, Thomas J; Marist HS; Chicago, IL; 3/365 TrsFrshCls; TrsSophCls; CmntyWkr; HonRl; JrNHS; NHS; StuCncl; TchrAde; SpnCl; MthCl; Bsktbl; Trk; University Of Illinois.

GARWOOD, Thomas J; St Charles HS; St Charles, MO; CmntyWkr; HonRl; PolWkr; SctActv; Bsktbl; CaptGlf; Sw Missouri State Univ; Bio Med Engineer.

GARY, Elizabeth A; Holly HS; Davisburg, MI; 2/232 SecSrCls; HonRl; NHS; NatlMeritFnl; OffAde; 4-H; PpCl; IMSpt; Central Mich Univ; Special Ed.

GARY, Joleen M; Graceville Public HS; Graceville, MN; Chrs; NHS; SchMus; SchPl; Yrbk; SchPpr; FrCl; Chrldr; GAA; Alexandria Tech Univ; Clerical.

GARY, Rodney L; Ralph Waldo Emerson HS; Gary, IN; Chr; HonRl; JCC; NHS; NatlMeritSF; SctActv; CivCl; Bsbl; CaptFtbl; Trk; Univ Az; Computer Etch.

GASBARRA, Shane S; Guilford HS; Rockford, IL; ChrhWkr; HonRl; LitMag; NHS; NatlMeritSF; VPOrch; PolWkr; SchMus; SchPpr; LatCl; College; Teaching.

GASCHO, Bruce; Noblesville HS; Noblesville, IN; HonRl; NatlThespSoc; SchPl; SpnCl; MthCl; Tennis; Iupui; Electrical Engineer.

GASCHO, Marlys W; Fairview HS; Fairview, MI; 1/45 PresFrshCls; PresSophCls; ChrhWkr; HonRl; NatlFornLg; NatlMeritFnl; RptrYrbk; Alma College.

GASKILL, Byron J; North Bend Central HS; Morse Bluff, NE; Band; Chrs; HonRl; PepBnd; PresYthFlsp; SchPpr; LetterFtbl; CaptTrk; Trade Sch; Mechanical Tech.

GASKIN, Ronald W; Rushford HS; Rushford, MN; Band; CncrtBnd; HonRl; MrchBnd; NHS; TchrAde; 4-H; FTA; CaptWrstlng; PresAwd; St Marys College Winona; Pre Med.

GASLIN, Barbara J; Owen Gage HS; Unionville, MI; 1/52 ALAGirlsSt; HonRl; NHS; OffAde; SchAde; SchPl; SpnCl; PpCl; Bsktbl; College; Nursing.

GASNER, Donn; Oregon HS; Oregon, WI; ALBoysSt; Band; Chrs; CncrtBnd; HonRl; MrchBnd; NHS; SchMus; SchPl; IMSpt; Univ Of Wi; Law, Music, Theatre Arts.

GASPAR, David L; Waterford Union HS; Waterford, WI; Band; ChrhWkr; HonRl; SchPl; YthFlsp; Bsktbl; Tennis; Stout Univ; Industrial Arts.

GASPAR, James M; Waterford HS; Waterford, WI; Band; Chr; ChrhWkr; CncrtBnd; HonRl; NHS; YthFlsp; Bsktbl; Coll; Science.

GASPARICH, Christine; Joliet West HS; Joliet, IL; SecSophCls; Chr; Chrl; Chrs; HonRl; Mdrgl; NHS; SchMus; StuCncl; LatCl; Illinois State Univ; Medical Records Admn.

GASPAROVIC, Claudia S; Granite City South HS; Granite City, IL; LbryAde; NatlMeritCmnd; PolWkr; Quill&Scroll; RptrSchPpr; SciCl; University; Communication.

GASPER, Denise L; Andes Central HS; Lake Andes, SD; 11/45 ALAGirlsSt; HonRl; NHS; SchPl; StuCncl; TchrAde; YthFlsp; RptrYrbk; EdYrBk; EdSchPpr; S Dakota State Univ.

GASS, Lee A; Sandy Creek HS; Edgar, NE; HonRl; NHS; Bsbl; LetterFtbl; LetterTrk; LetterWrstlng; College; Cpa.

GASS, Marvin D; Montezuma Comm HS; Montezuma, IA; ALBoysSt; NHS; StuCncl; StuGov; CaptBsbl; LetterBsktbl; CaptFtbl; Central College; Business Mgmt.

GASSER, Joanne; Incarnate Word HS; St Louis, MO; HonRl; LbryAde; SchMus; SchPl; StuCncl; IMSpt; Coll;.

GASSER, Patricia L; Weston HS; Lavalle, WI; 12/54 SecBand; HonRl; MrchBnd; SecNHS; NatlMeritFnl; StuCncl; RptrSchPpr; FBLA; FHA; GAA;.

GASSER, Randy G; Pierce City R6 HS; Pierce City, MO; PresJrCls; HonRl; StuCncl; FFA; KeyCl; SciCl; Ftbl; Trk; Trade School; Professional.

GASSMAN, Ann M; St Clement HS; Warren, MI; 7/97 HonRl; JrNHS; TreasNatlMeritCmnd; Teen; FHA; PpCl; SecSciCl; E Mic U.

GASSMANN, Marchelle; Leo HS; Holy Cross, IA; ChrhWkr; HonRl; LbryAde; SchMus; SchPl; TchrAde; RptrYrbk; RptrSchPpr; 4-H; College, Social Work.

GASSMANN, Mary; Prairie Heights HS; Dresden, KS; 9/22 HonRl; StuGov; Teen; YthFlsp; YthLg; SchPpr; FHA; PpCl; Coll;busi Adm.

GASSNER, Steve J; Newman HS; Wausau, WI; 30/130 ChrhWkr; HonRl; NHS; StuGov; SptEdYrbk; CaptFtbl; Trk; Wrstlng; IMSpt; RotaryAwd; Uw Marathon County; Accounting.

GASSWINT, Danny R; Pratt HS; Pratt, KS; 14/157 Aud/Vis; HonRl; SchMus; SchPl; TchrAde; Yrbk; Trk; Brooks Inst; Photography.

GAST, Vel L; Eldora HS; Eldora, IA; 2/62 HonRl; FrCl; Glf; LetterTrk; University; Medicine.

GASTINEAU, Cynthia L; Reynolds R 2 HS; Ellington, MO; Band; ChrhWkr; CmntyWkr; CncrtBnd; HonRl; MrchBnd; 4-H; Chrldr; IMSpt; 4-HAwd; Ark St U; Nursing.

GASTINEAU, Wanda J; Polo HS; Polo, MO; Chr; Chrs; ChrhWkr; HonRl; SchPl; YthFlsp; FHA; Sw Baptist College; Home Economics.

GASTMANN, Paula; Phillips HS; Phillups, WI; HonRl; SpnCl; SecTrsSophCls; SciCl; CaptSciCl; GAA; Ncti Waudau; Vocational.

GASTON, Arlene A; Potter Public HS; Potter, NE; 5/20 Chr; Chrs; ChrhWkr; HonRl; JrNHS; SchPl; Yrbk; SchPpr; PpCl; College; Professional.

GASTON, Dianne K; Lexington Public HS; Lexington, NE; 10/42 Band; CtyCnl; CmntyWkr; HonRl; NHS; NatlThespSoc; SchPl; FTA; CchngActv; VoiceDemAwd; College; Mental Therapist.

GASTON, Taffy A; St Ann HS; Chicago, IL; Chrs; CmntyWkr; HonRl; SchAde; SchMus; TchrAde; College; Drama Instructor.

GASWICK, Elna; Hay Springs Public HS; Hay Springs, NE; 6/40 TrsSophCls; PresSrCls; ALAGirlsSt; Band; ChrhWkr; HonRl; NHS; SchPl; TchrAde; Wesleyan Univ; Music Major.

GATELY, Denise L; Bishop Foley HS; Madison Heights, MI; HstFrshCls; HonRl; NHS; SchPl; EdYrBk; PpCl; Henry Ford Comm Clge; Rn.

GATES, Brian K; Du Quoin HS; Tamaroa, IL; 1/150 CmntyWkr; HonRl; SctActv; YthFlsp; SciCl; Bsktbl; Trk; University; Mathematics.

GATES, Camilla; Coldwater HS; Coldwater, MI; 20/320 Band; CmntyWkr; HonRl; OffAde; RedCrAde; TchrAde; RptrSchPpr; IMSpt; College; Teach Math.

GATES, Robin L; East Detroit HS; East Detroit, MI; HonRl; NHS; NatlMeritFnl; NatlMeritSchl; NatlMeritSF; TchrAde; Swmmng; Wrstlng; Michigan State; Professional.

GATES, Ronald L; Anderson HS; Anderson, IN; CncrtBnd; DrlTm; DrmBgl; HonRl; JA; MrchBnd; Orch; PepBnd; GerCl; JAAwd; Ball St Univ; Radio Sta Tech.

GATES, Trauce E; Melvern HS; Topeka, KS; TrsJrCls; Band; DrlTm; HonRl; HospAde; SchPl; YthFlsp; PpCl; LetterBsktbl; LetterTrk; Emporia Kansas State College; Secondary Ed.

GATHEMAN, James G; Southwest HS; St Louis, MO; 30/597 HonRl; ModUN; GerCl; MthCl; SciCl; College; Scientist In Physics.

GATHJE, Peter R; Lourdes HS; Rochester, MN; 14/122 HonRl; JrNHS; NHS; PolWkr; EdYrBk; RptrSchPpr; LatCl; CaptTrk; CchngActv; St Johns Univ.

GATHMAN, Tracy B; Everly Community HS; Everly, IA; 12/34 Band; ChrhWkr; CncrtBnd; HonRl; MrchBnd; NatlThespSoc; PepBnd; SchPl; Yrbk; LetterBsktbl; Iowa Lakes Comm Coll; Bus Management.

GATHMANN, Sheryl A; Forman HS; Forest City, IL; Band; Chrs; ChrhWkr; HonRl; MrchBnd; OffAde; SchPl; RptrSchPpr; FHA; GAA; Business.

GATLIN, Janet M; Duluth East HS; Duluth, MN; 1/525 HonRl; HospAde; NatlMeritSF; SchAde; TchrAde; RptrSchPpr; IMSpt; College; Medicine.

GATMAITAN, Ann W; Knightstown HS; Knightstown, IN; 6/131 VPSophCls; TrsJrCls; TrsSrCls; HonRl; LitMag; NHS; StuCncl; StuGov; YthFlsp; LatCl; SpnCl; PpCl; CaptBsktbl; LetterTennis; St Marys College; Nursing.

GATREL, Lester L; Indianaola Comm HS; Indianola, IA; 49/210 HonRl; JrNHS; NHS; Quill&Scroll; SptEdSchPpr; Bsbl; Ftbl; Trk; CaptWrstlng; CchngActv; University; Architecture.

GATTI, Keith B; Ritenour Sr HS; St Ann, MO; 57/873 Chr; HonRl; JA; JrNHS; NHS; StuCncl; TchrAde; RptrSchPpr; Trk; Wrstlng; Florissant Valley College; Journalism.

GATTO, Cynthia; Elizabeth Seton Hs; Chicago, IL; 36/252 HonRl; NHS; SchPl; StuCncl; RptrYrbk; RptrSchPpr; LatCl; U Of Illinois; Engineering.

GATZKE, Stephen L; Culver Military Academy; Muscatine, IA; 35/166 ChrhWkr; DrlTm; NatlMeritCmnd; ROTC; Socr; Swmmng; Tennis; Drake University; Dentist.

GAU, William J; Newman HS; Wausau, WI; Band; ChrhWkr; HonRl; Sacrstn; SctActv; Bsktbl; Ftbl; Col; Social Work.

GAUDA, Estelle B; Normandy HS; St Louis, MO; HonRl; JrNHS; NHS; NatlThespSoc; Univ; Professional.

GAUDARD, Steven M; Bay City Western HS; Midland, MI; HonRl; NatlMeritSF; Central Michigan Univ; Elementary Teacher.

GAUDERMAN, Terra K; Grace City Public HS; Juanita, ND; 2/9 ALAGirlsSt; Chrl; Chrs; ChrhWkr; HonRl; PepBnd; SchPl; YthFlsp; EdSchPpr; LetterBsktbl; St Paul Bible Col; Music.

GAUDRY, Robert W; St Joseph HS; Broadview, IL; 12/175 VPSrCls; HonRl; NHS; PolWkr; StuCncl; StuGov; PresPpCl; LetterFtbl; LetterWrstlng; IMSpt; GovHonPrgAwd; State College; Law.

GAUEN, Mark L; Wheaton Central HS; Wheaton, IL; 4/324 TrsSophCls; TrsJrCls; HonRl; NHS; StuCncl; SptEdSchPpr; LetterTrk; Purdue University; Engineering.

GAUER, Diane S; Sullivan HS; Sullivan, MO; Band; ChrhWkr; CncrtBnd; MrchBnd; PepBnd; SchMus; SchPl; FHA; Mid America Nazerene College; Music.

GAUER, Scott P; Anoka HS; Anoka, MN; Univ; Physician.

GAUERKE, Thomas; Athens HS; Athens, WI; TrsFrshCls; Band; HonRl; NHS; PolWkr; StuCncl; YthLg; SptEdSchPpr; PpCl; University.

GAUF, Mark A; Peoria Heights HS; Peoria Heights, IL; 18/104 SchPpr; FrCl; GerCl; LetterGlf; CaptTrk; College; Elec Engr.

GAUGER, David K; Geneva HS; Geneva, IL; HonRl; LbryAde; SchPl; StuGov; Yrbk; SchPpr; Univ Of Wisconsin; Chef.

GAUGER, Janette; Maine West Hs; Des Plaines, IL; ChrhWkr; HonRl; JrNHS; TchrAde; FHA; SpnCl; College Of St Theresa; Nursing.

GAUL, Sharon L; Beckman HS; Earlville, IA; Chrs; SecLbryAde; NatlMeritSF; SchPl; RptrSchPpr; CivCl; 4-H; GerCl; GAA; IMSpt; Univ; Behavior Sciences.

GAULEY, Elizabeth A; Rockridge HS; Reynolds, IL; AFS; RptrSchPpr; SptEdSchPpr; FTA; LatCl; IMSpt; College; Pro.

GAULKE, Guy C; Sun Prairie Senior HS; Sun Prairie, WI; 26/329 Band; CncrtBnd; HonRl; MrchBnd; NHS; PepBnd; SchMus; Univ Of Wis Madison; Chemica Engineer.

GAULT, Jim D; South Decatur HS; Greensburg, IN; PresJrCls; PresSrCls; ALBoysSt; CmntyWkr; HonRl; StuCncl; SptEdSchPpr; FFA; LetterBsbl; CchngActv; Coll;.

GAUME, Ralph A; Kapaun Mt Carmel HS; Wichita, KS; Band; Chrs; CncrtBnd; HonRl; NHS; NatlMeritCmnd; Orch; PepBnd; SchMus; StuGov; Wichita State Univ; Astronomer.

GAUNT, Sharon K; Aurora HS; Aurora, MO; SecTrsFrshCls; SecTrsSophCls; SecTrsJrCls; Band; DrlTm; HonRl; MrchBnd; NHS; StuCncl; YthFlsp; College; High School Teacher.

GAUSE, Linda M; Edison HS; Minneapolis, MN; 10/532 HonRl; NHS; SchPl; GerCl; College Of St Catherines; Pre Med.

GAUSS, Mark C; O Fallon Twp HS; O Fallon, IL; HonRl; ModUN; Southern Illinois University.

GAUTNEY, Pamela L; John Marshall HS; Chicago, IL; 13/510 HonRl; NHS; OffAde; SchPl; StuCncl; RptrSchPpr; SchPpr; Univ Of Illinois; Pharmacy.

GAUVREAU, Edmond G; De Lasalle Collegiate HS; Mt Clemens, MI; 3/125 Band; CncrtBnd; HonRl; MrchBnd; NHS; LetterTrk; Univ Of Notre Dame; Architecture.

GAVDIA, Anita L; Reavis HS; Burbank, IL; HonRl; JrNHS; LbryAde; NHS; NatlThespSoc; SchMus; SchPl; University; Data Processing.

GAVIN, Connie K; St Marys Academy; Monmouth, IL; 2/26 HonRl; NHS; OffAde; PolWkr; SecStuGov; TchrAde; Yrbk; EdSchPpr; SecFrCl; SciCl; Marquette Univ; Law.

GAVIN, Gary R; Martensdale St Marys HS; St Charles, IA; 2/35 VPJrCls; HonRl; NHS; StuCncl; 4-H; PpCl; SecTrsSophCls; 4-HAwd; Ia St Univ; Vet Med.

GAVIN, Javan; Lindblom Tech HS; Chicago, IL; 15/657 Chr; DrlTm; HonRl; NHS; ROTC; YthFlsp; Univ Of Chicago; Physician.

GAVIN, John R; Big Foot HS; Lk Geneva, WI; ALBoysSt; NatlMeritSF; VPNatlThespSoc; SchMus; SchPl; LetterTrk; College; Engineering.

GAVIN, Michael K; Big Foot HS; Lk Geneva, WI; 10/142 ALBoysSt; HonRl; NHS; NatlMeritSF; NatlThespSoc; Orch; SchPl; Trk; College; Engineer.

GAVIN, Patrick J; Kee HS; Lansing, IA; 11/67 ALBoysSt; HonRl; NHS; College.

GAVIN, Rose M; Unity HS; Chicago, IL; Chr; StuCncl; FHA; SpnCl; College; Childhood Education.

GAVINSKI, Nana A; Wisconsin Dells HS; Wisconsin Dells, WI; 3/145 Band; HonRl; NHS; SpnCl; PpCl; Chrldr; GAA; AmLegAwd; Univ Of Wisconsin; Optometry.

GAVRON, Ronald M; St Laurence HS; Chicago, IL; 5/384 HonRl; NHS; FrCl; Univ Of Il; Law.

GAW, Robert S; Moberly HS; Moberly, MO; 1/220 VPSrCls; Chr; Chrs; CmntyWkr; HonRl; Mdrgl; NHS; PolWkr; SchMus; StuCncl; StuGov; YthLg; KeyCl; SpnCl; College; Law.

GAWALUCK, Cynthia M; Mother Theodore Guerin HS; Chicago, IL; 34/407 ChrhWkr; HonRl; HospAde; LbryAde; NHS; StuGov; PresLatCl; SpnCl; MthCl; De Paul Univ; Radiologic Technology.

GAWEL, Gail V; Maine West HS; Des Plaines, IL; HonRl; NHS; Quill&Scroll; StuCncl; StuGov; TchrAde; Yrbk; Illinois St Univ; Special Education.

GAWITH, William D; Prairie Heights #295 HS; Dresden, KS; ALBoysSt; LbryAde; RptrYrbk; SchPpr; FFA; Vo Tech; Farm Salvage Yard.

GAWNE, James M; St Viator HS; Prospect Hts, IL; 2/257 ChrhWkr; HonRl; NHS; NatlMeritSF; SciCl; Purdue Univ; Mechanical Engineering.

GAY, Carolyn D; Rainee Harper HS; Chicago, IL; Chr; Chrs; ChrhWkr; SpnCl; Bsktbl; Univ; Phd In Doctrine.

GAY, Debbie L; North Mahaska HS; Rose Hill, IA; 1/62 CncrtBnd; DrlTm; NHS; OffAde; SchMus; SchPl; StuCncl; RptrSchPpr; 4-H; CaptChrldr; Northeast Missouri State Univ; Accounting.

GAY, James O; Benilde St Margarets HS; Hopkins, MN; 4/114 ALBoysSt; HonRl; NHS; NatlMeritSF; StuCncl; RptrSchPpr; LetterBsbl; LetterFtbl; IMSpt; Mich State Univ; Civil Engineer.

GAY, Katherine; Glenbard West Hs; Glen Ellyn, IL; Chrs; ChrhWkr; CmntyWkr; HonRl; StuCncl; Teen; YthFlsp; YthLg; PpCl; CaptChrldr; College; Business Math.

GAY, Kenneth W; Pekin HS; Pekin, IL; 50/850 Band; 4-H; LetterTrk; IMSpt; 4-HAwd; College; Psychology.

GAY, Penny; St Joseph HS; St Joseph, MI; 133/233 CmntyWkr; TchrAde; FrCl; SciCl; Lake Mich Coll; Special Education.

GAY, Randal S; Troy HS; Troy, MI; Band; ChrhWkr; HonRl; NHS; Oakland U; Physicist.

GAY, Robert; Dwight Township HS; Dwight, IL; VPFrshCls; Band; HonRl; NHS; PepBnd; SchMus; SchPl; SctActv; RptrYrbk; AmLegAwd; Univ; Veterinarian.

GAY, Robert L; Staunton HS; Staunton, IL; 1/102 PresSrCls; CncrtBnd; NHS; LetterBsbl; VoiceDemAwd; Univ Of Illinois; Engineering.

GAY, Teresa M; Morton HS; Pekin, IL; HonRl; Treas4-H; PresFBLA; 4-HAwd; Illinois Central College; Secretary.

GAY, Wanda; Roosevelt HS; Gary, IN; SecSophCls; HonRl; OffAde; Teen; LatCl; Ind St Univ; Surg Nurse.

GAYDOS, Carol M; Rockford East HS; Rockford, IL; 79/665 ChrhWkr; CmntyWkr; HonRl; TchrAde; FrCl; SpnCl; Ill State Univ; Special Education.

GAYLE, Jane K; Marquette HS; Alton, IL; 6/117 HonRl; JrNHS; TreasNHS; SchPl; SchPpr; St Louis University; Physical Therapy.

GAYLORD, Randy K; Richland HS; Essex, MO; StuCncl; Yrbk; LetterBsktbl; DanFAwd; Univ.

GAYLORD, Tammy M; Malden Community HS; Malden, IL; 3/15 SecSophCls; VPJrCls; Chrs; HonRl; LbryAde; SchPl; RptrYrbk; RptrSchPpr; FHA; FrCl; PpCl; Chrldr; GAA; College; Music.

GAYNES, Mary R; H L Richards HS; Oak Lawn, IL; 15/1034 CncrtBnd; HonRl; MrchBnd; NHS; Orch; PepBnd; Ohio St Univ; Engineering.

GAZZANO, Sebastian; Lake Park HS; Wooddale, IL; HonRl;.

GDOWSKI, Pamela A; Regina Dominican HS; Chicago, IL; HonRl; LitMag; SecSdlty; EdYrBk; N Ill U; Teacher.

GEAR, Gary R; West Lafayette HS; West Lafayette, IN; 67/213 Aud/Vis; HonRl; LitMag; NatlMeritCmnd; SchPl; SctActv; StuGov; SchPpr; 4-H; SpnCl; Bsktbl; LetterFtbl; LetterTrk; Purdue Univ; Anthropologist.

GEARHART, Debra A; Huntington North HS; Markle, IN; JrNHS; Bsktbl; Purdue University; Pharmacy.

GEARRING, David S; Kenwood HS; Chicago, IL; 104/413 Aud/Vis; Band; SctActv; StuCncl; StuGov; YthLg; RptrYrbk; FrCl; SciCl; IMSpt; Univ Of Fl ; Engng Or Dr.

GEARY, Margaret A; South Central HS; Elizabeth, IN; 5/58 Chrs; HonRl; NHS; SchPl; SctActv; College; Accounting.

GEARY, Peter; Palatine Hs; Palatine, IL; 42/420 Bradly; Engineering.

GEBAVI, Christel M; Immaculata HS; Skokie, IL; 4/202 Chrs; HonRl; NHS; NatlMeritCmnd; RptrYrbk; PresGerCl; GAA; College; Science.

GEBBEN, Mark A; Teutopolis HS; Teutopolis, IL; 24/113 FFA; Univ Of Ill; Animal Science.

GEBEL, David R; New Hampton Comm HS; New Hampton, IA; 3/170 ChrhWkr; HonRl; NHS;.

GEBEL, Matthew A; Bettendorf HS; Bettendorf, IA; 17/527 AFS; HonRl; Quill&Scroll; RptrSchPpr; SchPpr; Ftbl; Swmmng; CchngActv; IMSpt; LionAwd; Us Naval Acad; Internation Security Major.

GEBERS, Gary W; Holstein Comm HS; Holstein, IA; Chrs; HonRl; SchMus; SchPl; SctActv; StuGov; RptrYrbk; 4-H; Bsktbl; Ftbl; Univ; Vocation.

GEBERT, Sherri A; Wausau West HS; Wausau, WI; 17/442 SecTrsJrCls; Band; Chr; NHS; StuCncl; TchrAde; Twrl; SchPpr; GerCl; IMSpt; KiwanAwd; Univ Of Wisconsin; History.

GEBHARD, Camela F; Northern Valley HS; Alma, NE; 7/25 Band; HonRl; StuCncl; StuGov; Yrbk; SchPpr; LetterBsktbl; LetterChrldr; BttyCrckrAwd; CitAwd; Coll; Voc.

GEBHARD, Henry D; Northern Valley HS; Long Island, KS; Band; SecStuCncl; PresFFA; CaptFtbl; Colby Comm Col; Cow Calf Management.

GEBHARD, Reta A; Boscobel HS; Wauzeka, WI; HonRl; NHS; OffAde; RptrYrbk; Yrbk; RptrSchPpr; SchPpr; FHA; GAA; Foreign Exchange Student; Secretarial.

GEBHARD, Rose M; Lakeshore HS; Stevensville, MI; 15/250 ChrhWkr; HonRl; SchAde; TchrAde; Jr College; Commercial Art.

GEBHARDS, Karen E; Rock Port R 2 HS; Tarkio, MO; HonRl; HospAde; SchPl; SctActv; StuCncl; 4-H; VPFHA; MthCl; SecPpCl; 4-HAwd; Univ Of Missouri; Nurse.

GEBHARDT, Kathi; Fort Atkinson Senior Hs; Ft Atkinson, WI; Chrs; HospAde; Mdrgl; SchMus; SctActv; PresYthFlsp; Bsbl; Swmmng; College; Nursing.

GEBHARDT, Mary M; Alvernia HS; Chicago, IL; ChrhWkr; HonRl; NHS; SctActv; Wright College; Business Admin.

GEBHARDT, Sherrie L; Maine South HS; Norridge, IL; Chr; CncrtBnd; HonRl; MrchBnd; NHS; Orch; PepBnd; StuGov; YthFlsp; TreasFTA; Trinity College; Teacher.

GEBHART, Judy L; Beckman HS; Dyersville, IA; ModUN; SchPl; SctActv; StuCncl; RptrYrbk; RptrSchPpr; PpCl; Glf; GAA; IMSpt; College; English Teacher.

GEBHART, Rebecca J; Stonington HS; Stonington, IL; 4/31 Band; Chr; Chrs; HonRl; YthFlsp; RptrSchPpr; Pres4-H; PresFHA; AmLegAwd; 4-HAwd; Eastern Il Univ.

GEBKE, Mary E; Mater Dei HS; Bartelso, IL; 9/196 HonRl; SchMus; SchPl;.

GEDDES, Howard H; O Fallon Township HS; O Fallon, IL; HonRl; RptrSchPpr; SchPpr; LetterFtbl; LetterGlf; College.

GEDEIT, Rainer G; Proviso East HS; Forest Park, IL; Chrs; HonRl; GerCl; Ftbl; College; Medical Tech.

GEDO, Andrew L; New Trier East HS; Wilmette, IL; 21/847 AFS; Band; CmntyWkr; NatlMeritSF; Orch; College.

GEE, Cara D; Farmer City Mansfield HS; Farmer City, IL; 2/80 SecSrCls; AFS; CncrtBnd; HonRl; SchPl; StuCncl; YthFlsp; Sec4-H; SciCl; GAA; Ill Wesleyan Univ; Medical Tech.

GEE, Carrie; Jennings County HS; North Vernon, IN; 1/390 ChrhWkr; CncrtBnd; HonRl; MrchBnd; NHS; PepBnd; SchMus; RptrYrbk; Indiana Univ, Microbiology.

GEE, Kimberly K; Wichita Southeast HS; Wichita, KS; HonRl; NatlMeritCmnd; NatlThespSoc; SchMus; SchPl; FrCl; PpCl; Kansas State University; Foreign Languages.

GEE, Linda M; Edison Sr HS; East Gary, IN; Band; HonRl; RptrYrbk; PpCl; Business School.

GEE, Wendy; Grayling HS; Grayling, MI; 2/147 VPSrCls; NHS; NatlMeritSchl; SchMus; StuCncl; PresAwd; Univ Mich; Doctor.

GEEDING, Curtis T; Menasha HS; Menasha, WI; Band; CncrtBnd; HonRl; MrchBnd; PepBnd; SchMus; Wrstlng; University; Pre Law.

GEENE, Susan L; Eastern HS; Bloomfield, IN; SecFrshCls; PresJrCls; ALAGirlsSt; DrlTm; HonRl; TreasNHS; Quill&Scroll; EdSchPpr; PpCl; GAA; University; Pre Med.

GEESMAN, Diane J; Jackson HS; Jackson, MN; Chr; SchAde; PresStuCncl; Pres4-H; FHA; Chrldr; GAA; PPFtbl; 4-HAwd; PresAwd; S Dakota St Univ; Clothing.

GEFFE, Kent L; Nashua Comm HS; Nashua, IA; 2/70 CncrtBnd; PresNHS; NatlMeritCmnd; PolWkr; PresStuCncl; PresFrCl; PresSciCl; LetterFtbl; LetterWrstlng; Cornell College; Law.

GEFFERTH, John A; East Alton HS; Wood River, IL; 50/312 StuCncl; TchrAde; Bsktbl; Univ Of Mo; Mining Engineer.

GEFFRE, Cynthia L; Lead HS; Lead, SD; 44/160 Band; Chr; CncrtBnd; HonRl; HospAde; MrchBnd; PepBnd; SchPl; SctActv; GerCl; St Johns School; Nurse.

GEHL, Mary C; Marillac HS; Park Ridge, IL; PresJrCls; Chr; SchPl; StuCncl; StuGov; PpCl; College; Bba.

GEHL, Thomas W; George S Parker Sr HS; Janesville, WI; 14/387 HonRl; ModUN; NHS; NatlMeritCmnd; Quill&Scroll; TchrAde; Yrbk; LatCl; Bsktbl; Trk; Nw Univ; Professional Med.

GEHLBACH, Dan L; Shawnee Mission Nw HS; Shawnee, KS; 10/630 ALBoysSt; PresNHS; NatlMeritSF; NatlSciFnd; SctActv; StuGov; PresYthFlsp; SchPpr; PresSpnCl; MthCl; LetterFtbl; Tennis; OptClAwd; College; Math.

GEHLBACH, Michael W; Lincoln Comm HS; Lincoln, IL; 23/255 ChrhWkr; HonRl; Trade School; Vocation.

GEHLBACH, Philip E; Lincoln Comm HS; Lincoln, IL; CmntyWkr; HonRl; NatlMeritSF; NatlThespSoc; SchPl; RptrSchPpr; SchPpr; SpnCl; Tennis; Illinois St Univ; Special Education.

GEHLEN, Margaret E; New Prague HS; New Prague, MN; 59/194 Band; CncrtBnd; HonRl; MrchBnd; PresStuCncl; VPSpnCl; TreasPpCl; Chrldr; St Cloud State College; Elementary Educ.

GEHRING, Cindy M; Bloomer HS; Bloomer, WI; SecSophCls; SecJrCls; SecSrCls; AFS; DrlTm; HonRl; MrchBnd; OffAde; SchAde; RptrYrbk; Col; Elementary Tchr.

GEHRING, Dwight; Buhler HS; Buhler, KS; Chr; Chrs; ChrhWkr; HonRl; SchAde; SctActv; TchrAde; YthFlsp; GerCl; Ftbl; Coll; History.

GEHRING, Jay E; Batesville HS; Batesville, IN; 5/146 ALBoysSt; HonRl; NHS; SchPl; SpnCl; Bsbl; College.

GEHRING, Julie A; Bloomer HS; Bloomer, WI; AFS; DrlTm; HonRl; HospAde; MrchBnd; SchPl; Yrbk; PpCl; GAA;.

GEHRING, Peggy J; Moundridge HS; Moundridge, KS; Band; Chr; Chrs; ChrhWkr; CmntyWkr; CncrtBnd; HonRl; Mdrgl; MrchBnd; PepBnd; Bsbl; Bsktbl; LetterTrk; Chrldr; Ft Hays State.

GEHRINGER, Charles E; Martensdale St Marys Comm HS; St Marys, IA; 4/44 PresJrCls; ChrhWkr; HonRl; LetterBsbl; LetterBsktbl; LetterTrk;.

GEHRINGER, Connie E; Macon County R 1 HS; Macon, MO; Band; CncrtBnd; HonRl; MrchBnd; PepBnd; SchPl; SctActv; StuCncl; MthCl; University; Medical Technician.

GEHRINGER, John D; Durand Area HS; Durand, MI; 6/189 Band; Chr; ChrhWkr; DrmMjrt; Mdrgl; MrchBnd; PresNHS; SchPl; StuCncl; Pres4-H; LetterTrk; Michigan State University; Business Admin.

GEHRKE, Donna A; Maysville R I HS; Clarksdale, MO; 5/58 HonRl; LbryAde; TreasNHS; SctActv; RptrYrbk; EdSchPpr; SpnCl; SciCl; College; Journalism.

GEHRKE, John R; Walther Lutheran HS; Melrose Park, IL; 12/95 TrsFrshCls; HonRl; NHS; SchAde; Yrbk; College; Professional.

GEHRKE, Vickie L; Willow Lake HS; Willow Lake, SD; SecTrsSophCls; ALAGirlsSt; Band; Chrs; CncrtBnd; HonRl; PepBnd; SchPl; RptrYrbk; PresFHA; Working.

GEHRS, Barbara G; Mater Dei HS; Breese, IL; 2/182 Chrs; HonRl; NHS; Yrbk; FBLA; FrCl; Univ Of Ill; Business Management.

GEIDEL, Kathy K; Delmont Public HS; Delmont, SD; SecSrCls; TrsSrCls; Chr; Chrs; DrlTm; HonRl; SchAde; SchPl; EdYrBk; SchPpr; Mitchell Area Vo Tech; Sec.

GEIERMANN, Steven P; Catholic Central HS; Carleton, MI; 1/106 VPJrCls; Chr; ChrhWkr; HonRl; ModUN; NHS; NatlMeritFnl; NatlMeritSF; SctActv; StuCncl; StuGov; 4-H; College; Science.

GEIGER, Cynthia; Smith Green Hs; Churubusen, IN; HonRl; 4-H; KeyCl; PpCl; 4-HAwd;.

GEIGER, Janice M; La Moille Community HS; La Moille, IL; 2/40 PresBand; Chrs; CncrtBnd; SecNHS; VPYthFlsp; Yrbk; EdSchPpr; PresGAA; AmLegAwd; Ill Southern Univ; Elementary Education.

GEIGER, Raymond H; Quigley Prep North HS; Morton Grove, IL; 8/61 HstSrCls; HonRl; NHS; PresStuCncl; PresStuGov; SptEdYrbk; Yrbk; CaptBsbl; LetterSwmmng; CaptTrk; IMSpt; St Marys College; Medicine.

GEIGER, Rena K; Coon Rapids Comm HS; Coon Rapids, IA; Chrs; ChrhWkr; HonRl; ModUN; SchMus; TchrAde; RptrYrbk; RptrSchPpr; 4-H; FHA; U Of Northern Ia; Math.

GEIGER, Renee L; Manitowoc Lutheran HS; De Pere, WI; Chr; ChrhWkr; SchPpr; PpCl; IMSpt; Dr Martin Luther College; Elem Ed.

GEIGER, Steve; Uniontown HS; Uniontown, KS; Band; CmntyWkr; CncrtBnd; HonRl; MrchBnd; Teen; Bsbl; Bsktbl; Ftbl; Trk;.

GEIGER, Susan L; St Paul HS; Alhambra, IL; 5/56 VPSophCls; PresJrCls; Band; Chrs; HonRl; StuCncl; 4-HAwd; CitAwd; Univ Of Illinois; Music.

GEIGER, Susan L; St Pauls HS; Alhambra, IL; VPSophCls; PresJrCls; Chrs; CncrtBnd; HonRl; SchMus; StuCncl; SciCl; 4-HAwd; VoiceDemAwd; University; Music.

GEIGER, Thaddeus G; Bishop Le Blond HS; St Joseph, MO; ALBoysSt; HonRl; VPStuCncl; RptrSchPpr; Bsbl; Bsktbl; CaptFtbl; IMSpt; AmLegAwd; Benedictine Coll; Lawyer.

GEIK, Sharon K; Galien Twp HS; Galien, MI; SecFrshCls; SecSophCls; TrsJrCls; Band; DrlTm; HonRl; Yrbk; Chrldr; PresAwd; CitAwd; Coll; Prof.

GEIS, Becky J; Seward Senior HS; Seward, NE; Chr; Chrs; HonRl; Mdrgl; SchMus; 4-H; FHA; PpCl; College; Liberal Arts.

GEIS, Letitia M; Union Co HS; Liberty, IN; SecSophCls; SecBand; DrmMjrt; HonRl; SchMus; StuCncl; Pres4-H; SpnCl; Tennis; Clg; Musical Therapy.

GEIS, Pamela K; L P Goodrich HS; Fond Du Lac, WI; Chrs; HonRl; StuCncl; FrCl; GerCl; SpnCl; IMSpt; U W Mad; Foreign Lang.

GEISEN, Diane M; Hill Murray HS; St Paul, MN; ALAGirlsSt; HonRl; HospAde; JrNHS; NHS; NatlMeritCmnd; SchPl; SctActv; Yrbk; College Of St Catherine; Spanish.

GEISENHOF, Beverly J; Long Prairie HS; Long Prairie, MN; 1/118 HonRl; LbryAde; NHS; StuCncl; 4-H; Bsktbl; Trk; GAA; PPFtbl; 4-HAwd; St Cloud State Col; Recreation & Counceling.

GEISER, Colleen R; Anselmo Merna HS; Merna, NE; 4/25 TrsSophCls; TrsJrCls; Band; Chr; Chrs; ChrhWkr; CmntyWkr; CncrtBnd; HonRl; MrchBnd; Univ Of Nebraska; Veterinary.

GEISER, Darlene; Hilbert HS; Hilbert, WI; 4/68 ChrhWkr; CmntyWkr; HonRl; Mdrgl; NHS; SchAde; TchrAde; 4-H; Chrldr; GAA; Technical School; Child Aide & Devel.

GEISER, Robert D; North Platte HS; North Platte, NE; 34/400 HonRl; NatlMeritSchl; TchrAde; Bsbl; Bsktbl; Ftbl; Trk; CchngActv; IMSpt; College; Law.

GEISLER, Barbara J; Hastings HS; Hastings, MI; 10/286 Band; CncrtBnd; HonRl; MrchBnd; ModUN; NHS; Orch; PepBnd; SpnCl; Univ Of Mi; Free Lance Writer.

GEISLER, Dorothy M; Ladywood St Agnes HS; Indianapolis, IN; 4/96 HonRl; PolWkr; StuGov; Yrbk; SchPpr; FrCl; LatCl; Tennis; College; Special Education.

GEISLER, Sally A; Lawrenceburg HS; Lawrenceburg, IN; Band; CncrtBnd; HonRl; NHS; NatlThespSoc; SchPl; Twrl; SpnCl; PpCl; GAA; Coll; Business.

GEISLER, Steve D; Concordia HS; Concordia, KS; CmntyWkr; YthFlsp; FFA; Bsbl; LetterBsktbl; LetterFtbl; LetterTrk; IMSpt; College.

GEISLER, Susan J; Carl Schurz HS; Chicago, IL; 17/753 SecChrs; HonRl; LbryAde; NHS; OffAde; Tennis; LetterGAA; Coll; Professional.

GEISS, Paul B; Solen HS; Solen, ND; PresJrCls; CncrtBnd; HonRl; StuCncl; RptrYrbk; RptrSchPpr; FFA; Bsktbl; Ftbl; Trk; Clge; Prof.

GEISSERT, Joyce A; Central Comm HS; Breese, IL; VPSrCls; HonRl; ModUN; NHS; Quill&Scroll; SchPl; Yrbk; RptrSchPpr; FHA; Chrldr; Siu Edwardsville; Psychology.

GEISSINGER, Julie; Riverdale HS; Riverdale, ND; VPSophCls; Band; Chr; CncrtBnd; HonRl; MrchBnd; PepBnd; StuCncl; EdSchPpr; FHA; Trade School; Vocation.

GEISSLER, Jeffrey; Bloomer HS; Bloomer, WI; Aud/Vis; ChrhWkr; HonRl; NHS; RptrYrbk; PpCl; Ftbl; College; Dentist.

GEIST, Abbe S; Columbia City Joint HS; Columbia City, IN; PpCl; Chrldr; GAA; College; Pe Teacher.

GEIST, Charles G; North Scott HS; Eldridge, IA; Chr; Chrl; Chrs; HonRl; VPJA; SchMus; SctActv; RptrSchPpr; SciCl; Ftbl; U Of Iowa; Botany.

GEIST, Kurt; Roscoe HS; Roscoe, SD; Chr; Chrs; NatlMeritCmnd; YthFnd; RptrYrbk; Wrstlng; Northern State Col; Sociology.

GEIST, Marisa L; Highland Park HS; Highland Park, IL; Chr; JrNHS; NatlFornLg; NHS; NatlThespSoc; SchMus; SchPl; StuGov; EdYrBk; College; Theatre.

GEIST, Ronald; Britton HS; Amherst, SD; 5/75 Aud/Vis; Chr; Chrs; ChrhWkr; NHS; Ftbl; Trk; Wrstlng; AmLegAwd; CitAwd; College.

GEISZ, Julia; Horton Watkins HS; St Louis, MO; Chrl; Mdrgl; NatlMeritFnl; SchMus; TchrAde; IMSpt; Northwestern Univ.

GEKAS, Canella; Luther North HS; Chicago, IL; 1/222 ChrhWkr; CmntyWkr; HonRl; LitMag; NHS; PolWkr; Quill&Scroll; EdSchPpr; LatCl; Loyola University; Law.

GEKIERE, Michael A; Denby HS; Detroit, MI; 81/620 Aud/Vis; ChrhWkr; HonRl; NatlThespSoc; SchMus; SchPl; StuCncl; StuGov; YthFlsp; Mi State U; Vet Med.

GELARDI, Thomas E; Roseville HS; Roseville, MI; 16/534 HonRl; JrNHS; NHS; Ftbl; Trk; Wayne St; Business Admn.

GELBMANN, John W; St Bernards HS; St Paul, MN; 23/158 HonRl; JrNHS; NHS; Univ Of Minnesota; English.

GELDERT, Cindy; Annandale HS; Annandale, MN; Chr; HonRl; TchrAde; SchPpr; GAA; Voc Tech; Graphics Technician.

GELDNER, Peter D; Compion Jesuit HS; Neenah, WI; 7/98 SchPl; StuGov; EdYrBk; BauchLmbAwd; Univ; Med.

GELDNER, Peter D; Campion Jesuit HS; Neenah, WI; 7/98 HonRl; StuGov; Yrbk; Medical School; Medicine.

GELESKE, Cynthia J; Goshen HS; Goshen, IN; 26/250 Chr; ChrhWkr; HonRl; HospAde; NHS; SchAde; SchMus; YthFlsp; LatCl; Indiana Central University; Nursing.

GELHAR, Nancy J; Markesan HS; Markesan, WI; PresSophCls; Band; NHS; SpnCl; PpCl; LetterBsktbl; LetterTrk; Chrldr; GAA; IMSpt; College; Professional.

GELHAUS, John D; Radcliffe HS; Radcliffe, IA; ALBoysSt; Band; Chrs; HonRl; SecNHS; PresPolWkr; EdSchPpr; 4-H; Bsktbl; LetterTrk; Elmhurst College.

GELINNE, Thomas G; Redwood Falls HS; Redwood Falls, MN; 3/130 HonRl; NHS; SchPl; SchPpr; FSA; GerCl; SecSciCl; Univ Of Wi; Math.

GELLER, Evan R; Southfield HS; Southfield, MI; 10/600 HonRl; NatlFornLg; NHS; NatlMeritSF; SchMus; SchPl; StuGov; SchPpr; Tennis; Mich St Univ; Medical.

GELLERMAN, Wendell L; Lincoln Sr HS; Wisconsin Rapids, WI; ChrhWkr; CmntyWkr; HonRl; Bsbl; LetterBsktbl; Univ Of Wisconsin; Business.

GELLINGS, Lynn M; Waterford HS; Franksville, WI; 19/207 AFS; Chr; ChrhWkr; NatlFornLg; NHS; SchPl; RptrYrbk; 4-H; LatCl; Carthage College; Sociology.

GELSTON, Kay; Watertown Sr HS; Watertown, SD; Band; CncrtBnd; HonRl; MrchBnd; NatlFornLg; PolWkr; SchPl; YthFlsp; 4-H; Univ; Animals.

GELTZ, Patsy A; Newton Community HS; Willow Hill, IL; 44/187 Aud/Vis; LbryAde; FHA; LetterTrk; College; Teacher.

GEMBARA, Janice M; Lourdes HS; Chicago, IL; 36/299 HonRl; NHS; SchMus; TchrAde; Yrbk; SpnCl; College; Business Economics.

GEMMILL, Corinne A; Tri Mont HS; Trimont, MN; Chrs; ChrhWkr; SchPl; StuCncl; RptrYrbk; Yrbk; RptrSchPpr; FFA; CchngActv; GAA; Granite Falls Vocational Inst; Medical Sec.

GEMPELER, Reyne C; Monticello Public HS; Monticello, WI; ALAGirlsSt; ChrhWkr; LbryAde; ModUN; PolWkr; TchrAde; YthFlsp; RptrSchPpr; Madison Area Tech College; Police Science.

GENANDT, Dennis R; Lanark HS; Lanark, IL; SctActv; Ftbl; CitAwd; Trade School; Mech Eng.

GENDREAU, Dennis M; Langdon HS; Langdon, ND; PresSophCls; ALBoysSt; CmntyWkr; HonRl; NHS; StuCncl; Bsbl; Bsktbl; Ftbl; Univ Of North Dakota; Mortuary Science.

GENDRON, Jay W; Appleton West HS; Appleton, WI; 1/640 VPFrshCls; AFS; Band; ChrhWkr; CmntyWkr; CncrtBnd; HonRl; IntrClCncl; JrNHS; Ftbl; Univ Of Notre Dame; Law.

GENEREUX, Robert; Mentor Public HS; Red Lake Falls, MN; 5/15 Band; Chr; Chrs; CncrtBnd; HonRl; Mdrgl; MrchBnd; PepBnd; PpCl;.

GENGENBACH, Linda M; Murphysboro Twp HS; Murphysboro, IL; Chr; Chrs; ChrhWkr; HospAde; SctActv; YthFlsp; YthFnd; FHA; Bsktbl; John A Logan Jr College; Business.

GENGLER, Kara L; Carroll HS; Derby, KS; 24/258 HonRl; HospAde; SctActv; FrCl; College; Medicine.

GENGLER, Michele C; Ogorman HS; Sioux Falls, SD; ALAGirlsSt; SctActv; SchPpr; Bsktbl; Trk; College; Archaeology.

GENGLER, Nancy A; St Marys HS; Le Mars, IA; Chrs; ChrhWkr; HonRl; SchMus; SchPpr; Business School; Vocation.

GENIESSE, Catherine H; St Joseph Acad; Green Bay, WI; Chrs; ChrhWkr; CmntyWkr; JA; Mdrgl; SctActv; EdSchPpr; SchPpr; IMSpt; JAAwd; College.

GENNARA, Thomas S; Waterford HS; Franksville, WI; VPSophCls; HonRl; SchPl; StuCncl; StuGov; Ftbl; LetterTrk; IMSpt; Marquette Univ; Medicine.

GENNETT, Greg P; Richmond HS; Richmond, IN; CmntyWkr; HonRl; Univ; Doctor.

GENOVESE, Christine M; Bremen HS; Midlothian, IL; 41/510 Chr; ChrhWkr; HonRl; NHS; NatlThespSoc; SptEdYrbk; Yrbk; SchPpr; CaptBsbl; LetterChrldr; College; Nurse.

GENOVESE, Gasper; Osborn HS; Detroit, MI; VPFrshCls; HonRl; IntrClCncl; NHS; SchMus; SchPl; StuCncl; VPKeyCl; Eastern Michigan Univ; Business Admin.

GENOW, Steven M; Unionville Sebewaing Area HS; Sebewaing, MI; 22/125 TrsFrshCls; HstSophCls; TrsJrCls; HstJrCls; Chrs; HonRl; StuGov; FrCl; LetterBsbl; CaptBsktbl; LetterFtbl; Saginaw Vly State Col; Banking Bus Admin.

GENRICH, Terri L; North Boone HS; Poplar Grove, IL; 4/78 TrsSrCls; HonRl; NHS; SchPl; Yrbk; FHA; FTA; GerCl; PpCl; LetterBsktbl; LetterTrk; Chrldr; GAA; Northern Ill Univ; C P A.

GENS, Dena M; Madison Public HS; Madison, MN; 7/86 SecAFS; Band; Chr; HonRl; NHS; TchrAde; Yrbk; SchPpr; GAA; Univ Of Wisconsin; Forestry.

GENSE, David J; Minto HS; Minto, ND; 2/24 ALBoysSt; PresBand; PresCncrtBnd; HonRl; SchPl; StuCncl; EdYrBk; EngCl; SpnCl; MthCl; Univ Of Nd; Music.

GENSE, D Jay; Minto HS; Minto, ND; 2/23 ALBoysSt; PresBand; Chrs; ChrhWkr; CncrtBnd; HonRl; MrchBnd; PepBnd; SchPl; EdYrBk; EngCl; LetterBsktbl; LetterFtbl; Univ Of No Dakota; Optometry.

GENSLEY, Chris A; Hlv Community HS; Victor, IA; HonRl; SctActv; TchrAde; FTA; PpCl; Chrldr;.

GENTES, Carol L; Forrest Strawn Wing HS; Strawn, IL; 1/43 SecTrsSophCls; SecTrsJrCls; PresBand; Chrs; HonRl; NHS; RptrYrbk; PresSpnCl; GAA; DARAwd; Illinois Wesleyan Univ; Music.

GENTHE, Victoria J; E Dubuque HS; E Dubuque, IL; HonRl; ModUN; SchPl; StuCncl; StuGov; TchrAde; Yrbk; FHA; Chrldr; Clge; Secretarial.

GENTILE, Bette Lou; Proviso West HS; Westchester, IL; 69/948 Band; CncrtBnd; HonRl; MrchBnd; NHS; NatlThespSoc; Orch; PepBnd; SchMus; GAA; Eastern Il Univ; Math & Computer Science.

GENTIS, Rick D; Southern Wells HS; Bluffton, IN; 10/90 VPSrCls; ALBoysSt; ChrhWkr; HonRl; LbryAde; NHS; StuCncl; YthFlsp; 4-H; Trk; Purdue U; Agriculture.

GENTLEMAN, Sylvia B; Silver Creek Public HS; Silver Creek, NE; 2/29 SecFrshCls; Band; Chr; HonRl; PepBnd; SchPl; StuCncl; Sec4-H; TreasPpCl; Bsktbl; LetterTrk; College.

GENTNER, Karen S; Harbor Beach Comm HS; Harbor Beach, MI; 18/138 SecJrCls; HonRl; HospAde; NHS; SchPl; CivCl; FTA; PpCl; Chrldr; PPFtbl; Western Mi Univ; Occupational Theropy.

GENTRY, Gregory R; Polo HS; Polo, MO; SecFrshCls; SecSophCls; HonRl; SchPl; StuCncl; EdSchPpr; Pres4-H; PresFFA; Bsktbl; CaptFtbl; U Of Missouri; Agriculture.

GENTRY, Joyce E; Princeton HS; Princeton, MO; 6/52 PresBand; CncrtBnd; HonRl; MrchBnd; NHS; OffAde; RptrYrbk; FHA; PpCl; Bsktbl; LetterGlf; CaptChrldr; IMSpt; William Jewell College; Nursing.

GENTRY, Tina E; Hallsville Riv HS; Hallsville, MO; PresJrCls; HonRl; OffAde; StuCncl; EdYrBk; PpCl; Trk; Chrldr; IMSpt; AmLegAwd; College; Med Secretary.

GENTZ, Shirley; Beaver Dam Senior Hs; Juneau, WI; 105/314 Chrs; SchMus; VP4-H; FBLA; GAA;.

GENUALDI, John M; Gordon Technical HS; Chicago, IL; HonRl; StuCncl; PpCl; Univ Of Ill; Accounting.

GENZINK, Gail; Holland Chr HS; Holland, MI; ChrhWkr; LbryAde; SchPl; TchrAde; 4-H; FNA; SpnCl; 4-HAwd;.

GEOGHEGAN, Patrick G; Baraboo HS; Baraboo, WI; ChrhWkr; IntrClCncl; PolWkr; SchPl; SptEdSchPpr; PresKeyCl; LetterBsbl; Bsktbl; LetterFtbl; College; Professional.

GEORG, Clinton; Porta HS; Petersburg, IL; 23/122 LbryAde; NatlThespSoc; SchMus; SchPl; SctActv; StuCncl; KeyCl; University Of Illinois; Law.

GEORGE, Bert A; Lincoln Park HS; Lincoln Park, MI; NHS; FDA; College; Med Dr.

GEORGE, Carol R; Homewood Flossmoor HS; Hazel Crest, IL; 50/910 ChrhWkr; HonRl; RedCrAde; PresSctActv; VPYthFlsp; SchPpr; SpnCl; PresMthCl; Bsktbl; Swmmng; Valparaiso Univ Ind; Engineer.

GEORGE, Catherine; Huron HS; New Boston, MI; Chr; CmntyWkr; HonRl; HospAde; SchMus; TchrAde; 4-H; FNA; SpnCl; 4-HAwd; College; Nursing.

GEORGE, Christopher A; Northeastern Wayne HS; Williamsburg, IN; 20/150 Band; ChrhWkr; CncrtBnd; MrchBnd; PepBnd; SchMus; SchPl; FFA; SciCl; University; Professional.

GEORGE, Cindi K; Harrison HS; W Bloomfield, MI; VPFrshCls; HonRl; OffAde; StuCncl; TchrAde; SchPpr; PpCl; Bsbl; GAA; University Of Michigan; Teacher.

GEORGE, Cindy L; Saunemin HS; Saunemin, IL; 2/24 TrsFrshCls; Band; Chrs; CncrtBnd; HonRl; LitMag; MrchBnd; NHS; PepBnd; SchAde; SchPl; Chrldr; GAA; Illinois State University; Special Educ.

GEORGE, Darlene M; Unity HS; Sidney, IL; 2/140 Band; Chrs; CncrtBnd; HonRl; NHS; NatlThespSoc; Orch; SchMus; SchPpr; Bsbl; Univ Of Il; Med Tech.

GEORGE, David S; Ozark HS; Ozark, MO; ALBoysSt; HonRl; VPNatlFornLg; SchPl; StuCncl; LetterFtbl; LetterTrk; CchngActv; Smsu; Law.

GEORGE, Dean A; Indian Creek HS; Nineveh, IN; ChrhWkr; CncrtBnd; MrchBnd; Orch; PepBnd; SchMus; SptEdYrbk; SptEdSchPpr; PpCl; Franklin College; Journalism.

GEORGE, Debbi; Jamaica HS; Sidell, IL; VPJrCls; ChrhWkr; HonRl; NHS; StuCncl; SpnCl; Bsbl; Bsktbl; Trk; College.

GEORGE, Donald J; Central HS; St Louis, MO; HonRl; StuCncl; RptrSchPpr; EdSchPpr; College; Pharmacist.

GEORGE, Geniece; Gresham Public HS; Waco, NE; 2/13 TrsFrshCls; TrsJrCls; SecSrCls; Band; Chrs; HonRl; PepBnd; EdYrBk; 4-H; EldAwd; Univ Ne; Home Economics.

GEORGE, Jill; Otis Bison HS; Albert, KS; TrsJrCls; Band; Chrs; CncrtBnd; HonRl; MrchBnd; SchPl; SctActv; PpCl; College; Professional.

GEORGE, Joy S; Hallsville R Iv HS; Columbia, MO; TrsFrshCls; Band; ChrhWkr; HonRl; RedCrAde; Yrbk; FHA; PpCl; Chrldr; AmLegAwd; Clge; Rn.

GEORGE, Judith; Hallsville HS; Columbia, MO; 1/50 SecSophCls; PresSrCls; Band; Chr; HonRl; StuCncl; RptrYrbk; IMSpt; N W Missouri State Univ;.

GEORGE, Judith K; Hallsville HS; Columbia, MO; 1/47 SecSophCls; PresSrCls; Band; HonRl; Orch; StuCncl; RptrYrbk; LetterTrk; CaptChrldr; PresAwd; Northeast Mo State U; Business.

GEORGE, Judith L; St Marys Acad; South Bend, IN; GAA; Univ; Photographt.

GEORGE, Judy L; Lesterville R 4 HS; Lesterville, MO; Band; Chrs; HonRl; 4-H; PpCl; Business Schl; Professional.

GEORGE, Kenny E; Penney HS; Kingston, MO; ChrhWkr; HonRl; NHS; SctActv; Treas4-H; Bsbl; Bsktbl; LetterFtbl; LetterTrk; LetterWrstlng; IMSpt; College; Drafting.

GEORGE, Louis E; Hardin Central HS; Hardin, MO; FFA; Bsbl; LetterFtbl;.

GEORGE, Pamela M; St Francis HS; Anoka, MN; 18/210 Chr; ChrhWkr; CncrtBnd; HonRl; NHS;

StuCncl; RptrSchPpr; SciCl; GAA; 4-HAwd; Homemaker; Fashion.

GEORGE, Rick; Lawrence Central HS; Indianapolis, IN; CncrtBnd; Wrstlng; IMSpt; Trade; Vocation.

GEORGE, Rita R; Fairfield Comm HS; Fairfield, IL; Chr; ChrhWkr; Quill&Scroll; SctActv; RptrYrbk; EdYrBk; FshEdYrbk; SptEdYrbk; FHA; PpCl; Tennis; Olney Cntrl College; Dental Asst.

GEORGE, Rodney L; Chaparral HS; Anthony, KS; ChrhWkr; CmntyWkr; StuCncl; TchrAde; FFA; KeyCl; College; Farming.

GEORGE, Roger; Foutain Central HS; Veeedersburg, IN; JA; SctActv; 4-H; FFA; FHA; FSA; FTA; 4-HAwd; JAAwd; SARAwd; College; Ministry.

GEORGE, Sharla R; Lafayette HS; St Joseph, MO; 34/256 ChrhWkr; HonRl; TreasJA; StuCncl; LatCl; PpCl; Univ Of Mo; Lawyer.

GEORGE, Sheila; Glendale HS; Springfield, MO; AFS; HonRl; HospAde; OffAde; TchrAde; FHA; SpnCl; SciCl; St Johns Sch Of Nursing; Anesthesiology.

GEORGE, Stanley L; Oregon Davis HS; Walkerton, IN; 12/65 Band; ChrhWkr; HonRl; JrNHS; NHS; PepBnd; SciCl; IMSpt; LionAwd; Bethel Col; Bibical Lit.

GEORGE, Thomas; Luke M Powers HS; Flint, MI; NHS; NatlMeritSF; SchMus; SchPl; U Of M; Pre Med.

GEORGE, Vern W; Lebo HS; Lebo, KS; 2/21 VPJrCls; ALBoysSt; ChrhWkr; HonRl; PolWkr; StuCncl; Pres4-H; PresFFA; LetterBskbtl; 4-HAwd; Kansas State Univ; Pre Vet, Ag. Econ..

GEORGEOFF, Sharon M; Ridgewood HS; Norridge, IL; 25/369 DrmBgl; HonRl; JrNHS; MrchBnd; NHS; StuCncl; TchrAde; Twrl; Swmmng; CaptChrldr; Illinois St Univ; Elem Educ.

GERACE, Joan M; Wesclin Jr Sr HS; Trenton, IL; 6/100 ALAGirlsSt; Band; Chrs; NHS; OffAde; SchMus; YthFlsp; RptrSchPpr; LatCl; PpCl; College; Music.

GERACI, Patricia L; Quincy Sr HS; Quincy, IL; 83/816 Band; CncrtBnd; MrchBnd; Orch; PepBnd; SchMus; SctActv; Univ Of Illinois; Aeronautical Engineer.

GERARD, Gregory S; Eureka HS; Eureka, IL; 1/106 HstSrCls; ChrhWkr; HonRl; JrNHS; NHS; NatlMeritCmnd; StuCncl; SptEdSchPpr; Bsktbl; Olivet Nazarene College; Mathematics.

GERARD, Timothy G; Dondero HS; Royal Oak, MI; Central Mi Univ; Journalism.

GERARD, William J; Charleston HS; Charleston, IL; 59/259 Band; CncrtBnd; HonRl; MrchBnd; Orch; Univ Of Ill; Engineering.

GERARDO, Jamie L; Shawnee HS; Jonesboro, IL; 10/64 PresJrCls; SecSrCls; DrmMjrt; Mdrgl; SchMus; SctActv; FHA; FTA; Chrldr; GAA; Murray State U; Physical Therapist.

GERAUGHTY, Jim; Santa Fe HS; Waverly, MO; 3/47 PresFrshCls; ALBoysSt; CncrtBnd; HonRl; MrchBnd; NHS; StuCncl; LetterBsbl; Ftbl; DARAwd; U Of Missouri; Medical Prof.

GERBER, Darryl G; Adams Central HS; Decatur, IN; 21/121 Aud/Vis; Band; CncrtBnd; HonRl; MrchBnd; PepBnd; SpnCl; LetterTrk; Purdue Univ; Elec Engineering.

GERBER, David L; Drake HS; Drake, ND; Band; ChrhWkr; CncrtBnd; HonRl; MrchBnd; PepBnd; PresYthFlsp; VPFFA; College; Christian Ministry.

GERBER, Elizabeth; Algonac HS; Algonac, MI; 49/209 SecJrCls; SecSrCls; HonRl; NHS; StuCncl; TchrAde; RptrYrbk; 4-H;.

GERBER, Fritz W; Scotus Central Catholic HS; Columbus, NE; SctActv; IMSpt; U Of Ne; Engineering.

GERBER, Jacqueline J; Adams Central HS; Decatur, IN; 6/121 Band; Chr; CncrtBnd; HonRl; HospAde; MrchBnd; NHS; PepBnd; TchrAde; GAA; IMSpt; Bluffton Clinic; Lab Assistant.

GERBER, Joseph; Bellmont HS; Decalur, IN; 111/250 PolWkr; SctActv; PpCl; College; Accounting Cpa.

GERBER, Richard L; Precious Blood Sem HS; Garden City, KS; TrsSrCls; Chrs; ChrhWkr; Sacrstn; SchPl; StuCncl; SchPpr; 4-H; Bsktbl; IMSpt;.

GERBER, Ruth A; Fairview HS; Fairview, MI; 8/44 TrsSrCls; Chr; HonRl; YthFlsp; College.

GERBER, Sharon A; Watertown Sr HS; Watertown, WI; ChrhWkr; CmntyWkr; CncrtBnd; HonRl; HospAde; MrchBnd; Orch; SchMus; YthFlsp; LatCl; Trk; University; Psychiatric Nursing.

GERBERS, Shirley J; Concordia Lutheran HS; Fort Wayne, IN; 56/218 HospAde; SecJA; NatlThespSoc; StuCncl; TchrAde; YthFlsp; GAA; JAAwd; Lutheran Hospital; Nurse.

GERBERT, Cynthia A; Northview HS; Grand Rapids, MI; 9/221 TrsSophCls; TrsJrCls; TrsSrCls; Chr; HonRl; NHS; SchMus; SchPl; StuCncl; SpnCl; Grand Valley State Coll; Spanish.

GERDES, Bradley; Chokio Alberta HS; Chokio, MN; Band; ChrhWkr; HonRl; MrchBnd; PepBnd; SctActv; 4-H; Bsbl; Bsktbl; Ftbl; College; Psychology.

GERDES, Constance S; Dixon HS; Dixon, IL; 23/337 Chrs; HonRl; JA; LbryAde; YthFlsp; Sauk Valley Col; Computer Data Proc.

GERDES, James; Bayard HS; Bayard, NE; 1/43 SecFrshCls; ChrhWkr; HonRl; NHS; NatlMeritFnl; NatlMeritSchl; NatlMeritSF; SchPl; 4-HAwd; Calif Inst Of Tech; Astrophysics.

GERDES, Julie A; Roanoke Benson HS; Benson, IL; 6/86 ALAGirlsSt; HonRl; SchPl; PresYthFlsp; IMSpt; College; Professional.

GERDES, Marilyn F; Cresbard HS; Wecota, SD; 1/30 ALAGirlsSt; Band; Chrs; DrlTm; HonRl; SchPl; TchrAde; EdSchPpr; BttyCrckrAwd; VoiceDemAwd; U Of Sd; Nursing.

GERDES, Nancy J; Goodhue HS; Goodhue, MN; 1/76 Chr; ChrhWkr; HonRl; NHS; TchrAde; FHA; GerCl; BttyCrckrAwd; College; Ele Teacher.

GERDING, Jeri A; Ottawa Twp HS; Ottawa, IL; Aud/Vis; HonRl; JrNHS; LitMag; NatlThespSoc; SchMus; SchPl; TchrAde; RptrYrbk; University; Art.

GERDING, Paul A; Ottawa Township HS; Ottawa, IL; CmntyWkr; HonRl; SctActv; PresKeyCl; SciCl; LetterFtbl; LetterTennis; College; Veterinary Med.

GERDOW, George R; Gordon Technical HS; Chicago, IL; 58/618 College; Math.

GERE, Kathleen S; Gaylord HS; Gaylord, MI; HonRl; NHS; SctActv; StuCncl; StuGov; CivCl; 4-H; FrCl; SpnCl; College; Biology.

GEREAUX, Kathleen; Bradley Bourbonais HS; Bourbonnais, IL; 50/360 DrmBgl; HonRl; MrchBnd; NHS; SpnCl; PpCl; GAA; Il Benedictine Coll; Veter Med.

GERECKE, Melissa A; Calhoun HS; Kampsville, IL; Chr; ChrhWkr; HonRl; PepBnd; LetterBsbl; CaptBsktbl; LetterTrk; GAA; IMSpt; College; Accountant.

GERGELY, Lisa R; Highlands Sr HS; Highland, IN; ChrhWkr; OffAde; TchrAde; YthFlsp; 4-H; FHA; Swmmng; 4-HAwd; College; Airline Stewardess.

GERGELY, Margaret A; Our Lady Of The Lakes HS; Drayton Plains, MI; 1/53 PresSophCls; StuCncl; Yrbk; Chrldr; Univ; Physical Therapist.

GERGEN, Joan M; Shickley Public HS; Shickley, NE; 3/29 Band; HonRl; SchPl; TchrAde; SptEdYrbk; Sec4-H; PpCl; Trk; 4-HAwd; Doane College; Interior Design.

GERGER, Daniel J; Birch Run HS; Birch Run, MI; VPSophCls; Band; ChrhWkr; CncrtBnd; HonRl; MrchBnd; StuCncl; StuGov; RptrSchPpr; SciCl; LetterFtbl; LetterTrk; University.

GERGICK, Mary C; Tonganoxie HS; Tonganoxie, KS; 11/111 Band; ChrhWkr; CncrtBnd; HonRl; MrchBnd; NHS; PepBnd; TchrAde; 4-H; SciCl; Kansas City Jr College; Biology.

GERHARDT, Kathleen; Clark HS; Clark, SD; 3/50 ALAGirlsSt; Band; Chr; Chrs; HonRl; Quill&Scroll; StuCncl; Yrbk; FHA; Chrldr; Univ Of Sd; Business.

GERHART, Randall L; Wm Henry Harrison HS; Battle Ground, IN; 31/287 CmntyWkr; HonRl; NHS; PolWkr; KeyCl; SpnCl; SciCl; LetterBsktbl; LetterGlf; LetterTrk; Purdue U; Pharmacy/law.

GERIK, Michael D; Saline HS; Saline, MI; TchrAde; Wrstlng; U Of Mi; Oceanography.

GERING, Carol L; Prospect HS; Mt Prospect, IL; 5/614 SecJrCls; Chrs; CAP; NHS; NatlMeritFnl; Quill&Scroll; SchMus; StuCncl; YthFlsp; EdSchPpr; IMSpt; DanFAwd; 4-HAwd; University; Law.

GERINGER, Bernadette M; Duchesne HS; St Charles, MO; Chr; Chrl; Chrs; HonRl; JA; SchPpr; PpCl; CchngActv; LetterIMSpt; JAAwd; Coll; Journalism.

GERKE, Elaine I; Otterville HS; Otterville, MO; Chrs; HonRl; FHA; LetterBsktbl; College; Accounting.

GERKEN, Leroy; Benton Co HS; Cole Camp, MO; TrsSophCls; Band; Chr; Chrs; MrchBnd; PepBnd; SchPl; College; Dentistry.

GERKIN, Dixie J; Newell HS; Nisland, SD; 3/50 ALAGirlsSt; Chr; Chrs; HonRl; NHS; RptrSchPpr; SchPpr; 4-H; FHA; SpnCl; PpCl; Bsktbl; GAA; College; Vocational.

GERKINS, Dal R; Randolph HS; Randolph, NE; 5/69 SecTrsJrCls; TreasBand; HonRl; VPNatlThespSoc; SchPl; RptrYrbk; FHA; PresSpnCl; IMSpt; BttyCrckrAwd; 4-HAwd; Univ Of Nebraska; Journalist.

GERL, Vicky A; Valders HS; Valders, WI; 8/113 CmntyWkr; HonRl; JrNHS; LbryAde; NatlFornLg; NHS; FHA; PpCl; GAA; DARAwd; Uw Oshkosh; Professional, Speech Therapy.

GERLACH, Charles H; Barrington HS; Barrington, IL; HonRl; NatlMeritCmnd; StuCncl; GerCl; College; Business.

GERLACH, Diane T; William Howard Taft HS; Chicago, IL; 17/800 CmntyWkr; HonRl; HospAde; JrNHS; NHS; PolWkr; SchAde; EdYrBk; FNA; SciCl; University; Medicine.

GERLACH, Doreen D; Clearwater HS; Clearwater, KS; 2/75 Band; ChrhWkr; HonRl; LbryAde; NHS; StuCncl; Yrbk; PpCl; Chrldr; MasAwd; Univ; Legal Sec Or Bus Field.

GERLACH, Elaine B; Lincolnwood HS; Waggoner, IL; 20/63 Band; CncrtBnd; DrlTm; HonRl; MrchBnd; PepBnd; TchrAde; FHA; FTA; SciCl; Lincolnland Comm College; Accounting.

GERLACH, Glenn G; Parkston HS; Dimock, SD; ChrhWkr; HonRl; Trade School; Ag.

GERLACH, Laurie; Carl Sandburg Hs; Tinley Park, IL; 6/680 HonRl; NHS; SctActv; GerCl; MthCl; PpCl; Bsbl; GAA; GodCntryAwd; Doane College; Business Administration.

GERLACH, Stephanie D; Sparta HS; Sparta, IL; 1/164 ALAGirlsSt; Chrs; ChrhWkr; HonRl; NatlMeritCmnd; Quill&Scroll; SchMus; EdSchPpr; VPFBLA; GAA; DARAwd; Univ Of Ill; Business Administration.

GERLEMAN, Thomas G; Brookfield Academy; Waukesha, WI; 1/11 TrsFrshCls; TrsSophCls; TrsSrCls; Chrs; HonRl; LitMag; LbryAde; NatlMeritSF; NatlThespSoc; PolWkr; SchMus; SchPl; RptrYrbk; EdYrBk; LetterWrstlng; Univ; Educator.

GERLEVE, Russell J; Glenbard West HS; Carol Stream, IL; 5/508 HonRl; NatlMeritCmnd; Quill&Scroll; StuCncl; RptrYrbk; RptrSchPpr; Northwestern Univ; Communications.

GERLING, Mary F; Mater Dei HS; Carlyle, IL; 2/200 Chr; Chrs; HonRl; LbryAde; VPNHS; SchMus; SchPl; SchPpr; PresFrCl; U Of Illinois.

GERLT, Pamela S; Moniteu County R Vi HS; Latham, MO; 14/83 SecSrCls; HonRl; LbryAde; NHS; OffAde; RptrYrbk; RptrSchPpr; SpnCl; BttyCrckrAwd; DARAwd; College.

GERMAIN, Michael J; New Richmond Public HS; New Richmond, WI; Band; Chr; CncrtBnd; HonRl; MrchBnd; Orch; PepBnd; TchrAde; RptrYrbk; Yrbk; College; Professional.

GERMAIN, Suzanne C; Somerset Public HS; Somerset, WI; Chr; MrchBnd; RptrSchPpr; 4-H; Bsbl; Business School; Secretary.

GERMAN, Erling S; Chase County HS; Imperial, NE; 19/56 TrsJrCls; Chrs; ChrhWkr; SchMus; 4-H; PresFFA; Bsbl; LetterBsktbl; LetterFtbl; LetterGlf; Military Academy; Agriculture.

GERMAN, Gary A; Rantoul Twp HS; Rantoul, IL; SchMus; SctActv; FSA; SciCl; LetterTrk; LetterWrstlng; AmLegAwd; Eastern Il U; Phy Ed.

GERMAN, Joann M; St Francis HS; Humphrey, NE; 3/34 TrsJrCls; Chrs; HonRl; NHS; TchrAde; RptrSchPpr; SchPpr; 4-H; PpCl; LetterTrk; IMSpt; Univ Of Nebraska; Teaching.

GERMAN, Kathy A; Owen Withee HS; Owen, WI; 10/98 DrlTm; HonRl; LbryAde; NHS; SchPl; RptrSchPpr; FBLA; FrCl; MthCl; Business Field.

GERMANN, Gail M; Whitko HS; South Whitley, IN; 3/15 ChrhWkr; CmntyWkr; CncrtBnd; HonRl; NatlFornLg; NHS; EdYrBk; PpCl; SciCl; CaptTennis; Valparaiso Univ.

GERMANN, Roger L; Belleville Township West HS; Belleville, IL; 100/802 Band; MrchBnd; NatlMeritSF; SctActv; LetterTrk; IMSpt; College; Physics.

GERMANO, Gregory; Houston Sr HS; Bucyrus, MO; Band; CncrtBnd; HonRl; MrchBnd; PepBnd; SchPl; SctActv; SciCl; Ftbl; CchngActv; Us Air Force; Bs.

GERMIC, Dan R; Kingsford HS; Kingsford, MI; HonRl; LetterBsktbl; LetterFtbl; Tennis; LetterTrk; Michigan Tech; Medical Tech.

GERMINDER, Steven L; Galien HS; Galien, MI; 3/54 PresSrCls; ALBoysSt; Band; CncrtBnd; HonRl; MrchBnd; NatlFornLg; NHS; NatlMeritFnl; NatlMeritSchl; Lake Michigan Clg; Music.

GERMINO, Gregory G; Marist HS; Palos Park, IL; 2/368 HonRl; LitMag; PresNHS; NatlMeritCmnd; SctActv; SecStuCncl; TreasLatCl; Trk; IMSpt; Loyola Univ; Medicine.

GERNAT, Donna M; Oxford Area Comm HS; Oxford, MI; 5/200 NHS; NatlMeritCmnd; PolWkr; PpCl; LetterBsbl; LetterBsktbl; CaptPPFtbl; Mi State; Nutritionist.

GERO, Margaret A; Columbus HS; Columbus, WI; Band; HospAde; MrchBnd; PepBnd; SchPl; SctActv; RptrYrbk; 4-H; Trk; GAA; IMSpt; PPFtbl; Ohio State Univ; Veterinarian.

GEROT, Joe; Highland HS; Riverside, IA; 5/50 Band; HonRl; MrchBnd; PepBnd; University; Professional.

GEROT, Joseph L; Highland Comm HS; Riverside, IA; 5/50 Band; CncrtBnd; MrchBnd; Univ Of Iowa; Professional.

GERRITSON, Kathleen A; Waupun HS; Waupun, WI; 23/249 HonRl; NatlFornLg; NHS; Quill&Scroll; StuCncl; RptrSchPpr; Chrldr; Vocation.

GERRITY, Cindy L; Sheldon Comm HS; Sheldon, IL; Trade; Day Are Center.

GERRITY, Patrick M; St Anne Comm HS; Papineau, IL; SpnCl; LetterBsbl; IMSpt;.

GERROND, Richard; Atkinson HS; Atkinson, IL; 3/41 ChrhWkr; HonRl; NHS; SchPl; RptrSchPpr; MthCl; Bsktbl; Trk; IMSpt; Il St Univ; Accounting.

GERROND, Richard A; Atkinson HS; Atkinson, IL; 3/40 HonRl; NHS; SchPl; Yrbk; RptrSchPpr; 4-H; FFA; SpnCl; LetterBsktbl; LetterFtbl; LetterTrk; Illinois State Univ; Accounting.

GERSCHEFSKE, Anita; Owensville R2 HS; Rosebud, MO; TrsFrshCls; SecJrCls; ALAGirlsSt; Chrl; HospAde; NatlMeritSchl; 4-H; FNA; SpnCl; 4-HAwd; College; Professional.

GERSCHICK, Julie A; North Farmington HS; Farmington Hills, MI; 17/449 ChrhWkr; CmntyWkr; HonRl; NHS; SctActv; StuCncl; StuGov; SpnCl; Chrldr; PPFtbl; Univ Of Mich; Acct.

GERSHUNY, Barry M; Evanston Township HS; Evanston, IL; 10/1100 HonRl; SctActv; StuCncl; StuGov; YthLg; MthCl; SciCl; Bsktbl; Trk; IMSpt; Northwestern University; Medicine.

GERSHUNY, Eric S; Evanston Township HS; Evanston, IL; HonRl; PolWkr; SctActv; StuCncl; StuGov; YthLg; MthCl; SciCl; IMSpt; U Of Illinois; Law School.

GERSPACH, David H; James Madison HS; Milwaukee, WI; 11/850 HonRl; NHS; StuCncl; GerCl; MthCl; Bsbl; College; Chemical Engineering.

GERSTEIN, Loren S; James B Conant HS; Hoffman Est, IL; 3/600 HonRl; NHS; PresSciCl; College; Physics.

GERSTENBERGER, Diana; Port Huron HS; Port Huron, MI; DrlTm; HonRl; NatlMeritSchl; Chrldr; GAA; St Clair Cnty Comm Col; Bus Admin.

GERSTNER, Mark J; Thomas More Prep; Hays, KS; Band; CncrtBnd; HonRl; MrchBnd; PepBnd; StuCncl; SpnCl; LetterBsbl; LetterBsktbl; LetterFtbl; University; Professional.

GERSZEWSKI, Julie A; E Lansing HS; E Lansing, MI; 89/347 NatlMeritCmnd; SctActv; TchrAde; Teen; RptrYrbk; Yrbk; LetterBsktbl; Msu; Math/sci.

GERTEN, Betty R; Hastings Sr HS; Welch, MN; 1/434 Band; ChrhWkr; CncrtBnd; HonRl; MrchBnd; NHS; College; Accountant.

GERTH, Debra Y; Dieterich HS; Dieterich, IL; 5/37 VPSophCls; SecSrCls; Band; HonRl; PresStuCncl; Yrbk; FHA; Chrldr; GAA; DARAwd; Lakeland Jr College; Elementary Education.

GERTH, Paul K; Avon Community HS; Indianapolis, IN; 3/156 ALBoysSt; ChrhWkr; HonRl; NHS; LetterBsktbl; Trk; OptClAwd; University; Veterinarian.

GERTH, Teresa A; Ladywood St Agnes HS; Greenwood, IN; 3/125 VPFrshCls; JA; NatlMeritCmnd; SchMus; StuCncl; Yrbk; FrCl; Notre Dame; Medicine.

GERTHS, Jon C; Farmington Sr HS; Farmington, MN; HonRl; NHS; GerCl; LetterBsbl; LetterFtbl; College; Biology.

GERTISER, Anne; Davison HS; Davison, MI; 15/420 Band; Chr; CncrtBnd; HonRl; MrchBnd; NHS; SctActv; Yrbk; GerCl;.

GERTSCH, Melva R; Monroe Public HS; Monroe, NE; 1/15 TrsFrshCls; SecSophCls; TrsJrCls; PresSrCls; Chr; Chrs; ChrhWkr; HonRl; SchMus; SchPl; SctActv; StuCncl; LetterBsktbl; LetterTrk; Chrldr; College; Mathematics.

GERTSEN, Gerri L; Watertown Sr HS; Watertown, SD; 19/325 Band; Chrs; CncrtBnd; HonRl; MrchBnd; PepBnd; SctActv; University; Professional.

GESAMAN, Elizabeth C; Waterford Mott HS; Pontiac, MI; HonRl; LitMag; RedCrAde; StuCncl; LetterTennis; Oakland Univ; Elem Education.

GESCH, Donna J; Milwaukee Lutheran HS; Milwaukee, WI; 34/259 Chr; DrlTm; TchrAde; YthFlsp; RptrSchPpr; FDA; LetterSwmmng; LetterTennis; LetterTrk; College; Medical Assistant.

GESCHYVIND, Carol M; Dwight Twp HS; Dwight, IL; SecBand; DrlTm; NHS; SchPl; YthFlsp; LatCl; SpnCl; PresGAA; VFWAwd; Junior College; Nursing.

GESELL, Fred; Manistee HS; Manistee, MI; Aud/Vis; Chr; ChrhWkr; HonRl; Orch; FSA; SpnCl; Bsbl; Tennis; JETSAwd; College.

GESHAY, David J; J I Case HS; Racine, WI; 15/642 ALBoysSt; Band; ChrhWkr; CncrtBnd; HonRl; NHS; SchMus; SecFBLA; LetterGlf; OptClAwd; Dordt Coll; Engin.

GESHE, Rosemary K; Milton HS; Milton Jct, WI; 17/179 ChrhWkr; HonRl; NHS; OffAde; Quill&Scroll; TchrAde; PresYthFlsp; RptrSchPpr; Bsktbl; CaptSwmmng; Univ Of Wi; Computer Systems Analyst.

GESKEY, Michael C; Lincoln Community HS; Lincoln, IL; 35/273 PresChrhWkr; HonRl; NatlFornLg; NHS; NatlMeritSF; PolWkr; SctActv; FSA; SpnCl; SciCl; Bsbl; Tennis; Eastern Ill Univ; Industrial Chemistry.

GESSEL, Michael H; Northwest HS; House Spgs, MO; 27/372 PresFrshCls; ChrhWkr; HonRl; SctActv; StuCncl; Yrbk; Bsbl; Bsktbl; Ftbl; Univ Of Mo; Engineering.

GESSERT, Robert J; Cape Central HS; Cape Girardeau, MO; 110/423 Aud/Vis; HonRl; StuCncl; YthFlsp; Bsbl; Ftbl; Trk; Wrstlng; IMSpt; College; Doctor.

GESSFORD, Julie M; Lincoln Northeast HS; Lincoln, NE; 52/555 Chr; ChrhWkr; CncrtBnd; HonRl; MrchBnd; SchMus; YthFlsp; FrCl; PpCl; Univ Of Ne; Music.

GESSLER, Gary C; Johannesburg HS; Lewiston, MI; Aud/Vis; Band; HonRl; PepBnd; TchrAde; LetterBsbl; LetterFtbl; College; Teaching.

GESSLER, Robert N; Kapavn Mt Carmel HS; Wichita, KS; NHS; NatlThespSoc; SchMus; SchPl; Trk; IMSpt; College; Pharmacy.

GETCHEL, Jon M; Farwell Area HS; Farwell, MI; 3/93 Band; CncrtBnd; DrmMjrt; HonRl; MrchBnd; PresNHS; NatlThespSoc; SchMus; LetterBsktbl; LetterTrk; Great Lakes Bible College; Music.

GETHA, Becky S; Laville HS; Lakeville, IN; 6/127 Band; MrchBnd; NHS; StuCncl; EdYrBk; GerCl; PpCl; SciCl; LetterBsktbl; LetterTennis;.

GETSINGER, Kenneth K; Bentley HS; Livonia, MI; HonRl; PolWkr; PresStuCncl; StuGov; SchPpr; LetterGlf; OptClAwd; Univ; Law.

GETTEL, Helen D; Mahnomen HS; Lengby, MN; ChrhWkr; HonRl; LbryAde; RptrSchPpr; PpCl; Trade Schl; Fashion Merchandising.

GETTELMAN, Barbara; Brookfield Central HS; Brookfield, WI; Chr; LitMag; NHS; NatlMeritCmnd; Quill&Scroll; RptrYrbk; SchPpr; LatCl; SpnCl; IMSpt; Michigan St Univ; Interpreting.

GETTING, Gregory A; Sheldon HS; Sheldon, IA; Band; CncrtBnd; MrchBnd; SchMus; FFA; SciCl; Glf; Univ; Vocational.

GETTY, Dale L; Lisle Sr HS; Lisle, IL; Ftbl; Univ Of Illinois; Chemistry.

GETZ, Carol J; Morton HS; Morton, IL; VPSophCls; Chrs; CmntyWkr; DrlTm; HonRl; HospAde; Mdrgl; Quill&Scroll; PresStuCncl; SchPpr; Univ Of Iowa; Nursing.

GETZ, Sherry L; Madison Consolidated HS; Madison, IN; 16/286 HonRl; NHS; TchrAde; YthFlsp; FrCl; PpCl; College; Fashion Design.

GEURIN, Melinda J; West Fargo HS; West Fargo, ND; Chr; HonRl; LbryAde; SchMus; TchrAde; FHA; FTA; PpCl; SciCl; Trade Or Busness Sch; Vocation.

GEURINK, Sandra K; Hamilton HS; Holland, MI; 23/125 TrsFrshCls; TrsSophCls; Band; DrmMjrt; HonRl; NHS; OffAde; RptrSchPpr; LetterBsbl; 4-HAwd; Muskegon Comm College; Law Enforcement.

GEURKINK, Linda J; Hinsdale Central Township HS; Hinsdale, IL; Band; Chr; ChrhWkr; CmntyWkr; CncrtBnd; HonRl; HospAde; MrchBnd; College; Nursing.

GEURTS, Joan K; North HS; Eau Claire, WI; 36/350 SecSrCls; HonRl; LbryAde; StuCncl; RptrYrbk; Yrbk; SpnCl; PpCl; Chrldr;.

GEURTS, Nancy R; St Joseph Acad; Green Bay, WI; Chrs; ChrhWkr; Trade School; Clerical.

GEVELINGER, Cynthia M; Dodgeville HS; Dodgeville, WI; VPAFS; SecBand; Chrs; DrmMjrt; HonRl; NatlMeritSF; SchMus; Twrl; 4-H; Chrldr; Univ; Professional.

GEWECKE, Richard T; Stapleton HS; Stapleton, NE; HstFrshCls; HonRl; NHS; LetterBsktbl; LetterFtbl; LetterTrk;.

GEWECKE, William K; Stapleton HS; Stapleton, NE; Band; Chrs; HonRl; SchPl; StuCncl; Yrbk; Bsktbl; LetterFtbl; LetterTrk; Kearney State College.

GEX, Bill; Boys Town HS; Boys Town, NE; 26/72 JA; FrCl; Ftbl; Trk; IMSpt; JAAwd; College; Broadcasting.

GEYER, Audrey L; Clear Creek Comm HS; Oxford, IA; HonRl; LbryAde; TrsFrshCls; NatlMeritCmnd; NatlThespSoc; SchMus; SchPl; SpnCl; College.

GEYER, Doyle G; Williamsburg Comm HS; Oxford, IA; VPFrshCls; Chr; HonRl; JrNHS; NHS; StuCncl; StuGov; YthFlsp; Univ Of Iowa; Astronomy.

GEYER, Estelle A; St Scholastica HS; Chicago, IL; PresJrCls; Chrl; HospAde; StuCncl; StuGov; Teen; PpCl; CaptBsktbl; AmLegAwd; University; Law Polictical Science.

GEYER, Gregory S; Osborn HS; Detroit, MI; 17/606 JrNHS; NHS; StuCncl; PresKeyCl; PresGerCl; LetterFtbl; LetterSwmmng; Trk; AmLegAwd; Mi St Univ; Engr.

GEYER, Joni L; West Central HS; Francesville, IN; Band; HonRl; MrchBnd; TreasNHS; SctActv; StuCncl; YthFlsp; SecFHA; PpCl; Chrldr; Purdue University; Psofessional Science.

GEYER, Sandra L; St Joseph Academy; Green Bay, WI; Chrs; CmntyWkr; HospAde; LbryAde; Yrbk; SpnCl;.

GEZELLA, Terri L; Denmark HS; Green Bay, WI; SptEdYrbk; CaptBsktbl; Trk; CchngActv;.

GHANAYEM, Jawad; Downers Grove North Hs; Downers Grove, IL; TchrAde;.

GHEENS, Susan K; Keytesville R Iii HS; Keytesville, MO; 2/21 TrsFrshCls; TrsSophCls; SecJrCls; Band; Chrl; CncrtBnd; LbryAde; NHS; StuCncl; RptrSchPpr; College; Teach.

GHEI, Kiren E; Oshkosh North HS; Oshkosh, WI; 3/365 LitMag; NHS; SchPl; StuGov; YthLg; SchPpr; MthCl; College; Law.

GHER, Bill M; Richland Ctr HS; Richland Ctr, WI; ALBoysSt; Band; Chr; ChrhWkr; CncrtBnd; HonRl; NHS; PepBnd; TreasYthFlsp; Treas4-H; FFA; AmLegAwd; 4-HAwd; LionAwd; College; Vocation.

GHERTY, Maureen R; Hudson HS; Hudson, WI; AFS; Chr; ModUN; EdSchPpr; GerCl; AmLegAwd; Univ Of Wis Madison.

GHIDINA, Michael S; Richwoods HS; Peoria, IL; 47/449 HonRl; NHS; StuCncl; LetterBsbl; LetterFtbl; IMSpt; Northwestern Univ; Pre Law.

GIACALONE, Petrina; Proviso West HS; Bellwood, IL; HonRl; HospAde; YthLg; Elmhurst College;social Work Or Teaching.

GIACOLETTI, Tina M; Swan Valley HS; Saginaw, MI; 7/164 Band; CmntyWkr; HonRl; JrNHS; NHS; NatlMeritSF; SchPl; StuCncl; SpnCl; JCAwd; Mich St U; Pre Law.

GIAGNORIO, Corinne E; Willowbrook HS; Villa Park, IL; TrsFrshCls; HonRl; NHS; StuGov; Elmhurst College.

GIAGNORIO, Laurene; Willowbrook HS; Villa Park, IL; HonRl; StuCncl; TchrAde; PpCl; College; Professional, Science.

GIAMBALVO, Leo P; Cleveland HS; St Louis, MO; DrlTm; PolWkr; StuCncl; SptEdYrbk; SptEdSchPpr; CaptFtbl; Trk; Wrstlng; MasAwd; CitAwd; Trade.

GIANNETTI, Lawrence P; Bloom Township HS; Chicago Heights, IL; 240/1080 LetterFtbl; Il State U; Dentistry.

GIANNINI, Michael J; Bishop Noll Inst; Hammond, IN; 99/370 HonRl; SptEdSchPpr; MthCl; CchngActv; IMSpt; Purdue Univ; Industrial Management.

GIANNONATTI, Mark A; Delavan Darien HS; Delavan, WI; AFS; ALBoysSt; HonRl; TchrAde; SptEdSchPpr; LetterBsktbl; LetterFtbl; LetterTrk; IMSpt; Univ Of Kentucky; Conservation.

GIANOPULOS, Robin I; Baxter HS; Lawrence, KS; 12/75 Chr; ChrhWkr; HonRl; LbryAde; SchMus; RptrYrbk; SchPpr; FHA; PpCl; Evangel Clg; Sociology.

GIANUKOS, Flora; Niles West HS; Morton Grove, IL; ChrhWkr; CmntyWkr; HonRl; University; Undecided.

GIASOE, Mark J; Wild Rose Public HS; Wild Rose, ND; HonRl; PepBnd; SchPl; StuCncl; StuGov; EdYrBk; LetterBsbl; CaptBsktbl; LetterTrk; College.

GIBBARD, Theresa A; Cass City HS; Cass City, MI; HonRl; FHA; College; Vocational.

GIBBENS, Beth M; Lowpoint Washburn HS; Washburn, IL; 9/68 AFS; Band; Chrs; Mdrgl; SchMus; SchPl; YthFlsp; Yrbk; SchPpr; Ill State Univ; Special Education.

GIBBENS, Joni; Border Central HS; Calvin, ND; PresSophCls; Band; Chrs; HonRl; PepBnd; StuCncl; EdYrBk; Trk; Chrldr; Coll; Professinal.

GIBBON, Cynthia; Milnor Public HS; Milnor, ND; ALAGirlsSt; Band; Chrs; HonRl; PepBnd; PpCl; Trk; Chrldr; College; Teacher.

GIBBONS, Carol J; Albany HS; Albany, WI; 1/36 VPJrCls; Band; NHS; NatlMeritCmnd; SchPl; PresStuCncl; EdYrBk; PresFrCl; Chrldr; BttyCrckrAwd; College; Med Tech.

GIBBONS, Donna R; Monette HS; Cardwell, MO; 4/53 SecTrsFrshCls; Chr; ChrhWkr; HonRl; SchPl; TchrAde; Yrbk; FHA; FTA; FrCl; PpCl; SciCl; College; Medicine.

GIBBONS, Jane A; Johnston HS; Des Moines, IA; Band; Chr; Chrs; CncrtBnd; HonRl; HospAde; SchMus; SchPl; FTA; PpCl; Tennis; DARAwd; Iowa State Univ; Elementary Education.

GIBBONS, Kevin; Riverside HS; Dearborn Heights, MI; PresSrCls; CtyCnl; HonRl; NHS; StuGov; FBLA; Ftbl; IMSpt; CitAwd; VoiceDemAwd; Univ Of Mi; Professional.

GIBBONS, Marie T; Queen Of Peace HS; Evergreen Park, IL; CmntyWkr; HonRl; LbryAde; PolWkr; StuCncl; Yrbk; SpnCl; GAA; IMSpt; Loyola Univ; Nursing.

GIBBS, Brian L; Waupaca HS; Waupaca, WI; Chr; HonRl; CaptFtbl; College; Engineering.

GIBBS, Cindy M; Mound Westonka HS; Spring Park, MN; /280 ChrhWkr; HonRl; PpCl; LetterBsktbl; LetterTrk; CchngActv; GAA; IMSpt; College.

GIBBS, Clarice A; Ponca Public HS; Ponca, NE; SecJrCls; ChrhWkr; CmntyWkr; HonRl; NHS; Yrbk; PpCl; Trk; Trade School; Store Management.

GIBBS, Clyde H; B C HS; Benton, IL; College; Professional.

GIBBS, David E; Henry Senachwine HS; Henry, IL; 6/77 AFS; HonRl; ModUN; NHS; SchPl; PresStuCncl; EdYrBk; AmLegAwd; Univ Of Ill; Medicine.

GIBBS, Dianna L; Dekalb HS; Dekalb, IL; HonRl; LitMag; FrCl; College.

GIBBS, Jacquelyn J; Il Valley Central HS; Chillicothe, IL; 14/224 Chrs; HonRl; NHS; StuCncl; Yrbk; FrCl; College; Language.

GIBBS, James A; Clinton Prairie HS; Frankfort, IN; 8/95 Band; ChrhWkr; CncrtBnd; DrmMjrt; MrchBnd; NHS; PepBnd; TchrAde; YthFlsp; SpnCl; Purdue Univ; Industrial Mgmt.

GIBBS, Patricia A; West Delaware HS; Manchester, IA; HonRl; FHA; Chrldr;.

GIBBS, Pierce; Andrean HS; Gary, IN; HonRl; MrchBnd; NatlMeritCmnd; PepBnd; MthCl; SciCl; Ftbl; Tennis; Purdue Univ; Pharmacist.

GIBBS, Pierce M; Andrean HS; Gary, IN; Band; CncrtBnd; HonRl; PepBnd; SctActv; MthCl; LetterBsbl; CaptBsktbl; LetterFtbl; LetterTrk; BauchLmbAwd; CitAwd; Howard Univ; Dentistry.

GIBBS, Ray E; Oscoda HS; Wortsmith Afb, MI; 5/300 HonRl; JrNHS; NHS; SctActv; RptrSchPpr; SchPpr; Univ Of Texas; Engineer.

GIBBS, Robert J; Burlington Comm HS; Burlington, IA; AFS; Band; CmntyWkr; CncrtBnd; MrchBnd; StuCncl; PresKeyCl; Bsbl; Bsktbl; IMSpt; Univ Of Ia; Business Admin.

GIBBS, Sandra; Shawnee HS; Jonesboro, IL; TrsSophCls; Yrbk; SchPpr; FBLA; FHA; FTA; PpCl; Chrldr; GAA; PresAwd;.

GIBBS, Sandra K; Warren HS; Gurnee, IL; TrsSrCls; Chr; HonRl; JrNHS; NHS; OffAde; StuCncl; RptrSchPpr; GAA; Univ; Veterinarian.

GIBBS, Susan C; Kenmare HS; Kenmare, ND; 2/63 Chrs; HonRl; Mdrgl; SchMus; RptrYrbk; SchPpr; SecFHA; SpnCl; PpCl; Glf; VoiceDemAwd; University; News Media.

GIBERSON, Lorrie J; Harmony HS; Hillsboro, IA; 4/40 Chrs; ChrhWkr; HonRl; NHS; SchPl; FHA; University; Home Economics.

GIBLER, Mary E; Grandview HS; Grandview, MO; HonRl; StuCncl; FHA; FrCl; PpCl; University Of Missouri; Teacher.

GIBLIN, Michael W; St Viator HS; Mt Prospect, IL; 16/245 HonRl; PolWkr; StuCncl; RptrYrbk; University; Mathematics.

GIBNEY, Bart W; Prairie HS; Fairfax, IA; ALBoysSt; Aud/Vis; HonRl; RptrSchPpr; Bsbl; College; Medicine.

GIBNEY, Thomas J; Stockbridge HS; Gregory, MI; Band; ChrhWkr; CmntyWkr; CncrtBnd; DrmBgl; HonRl; MrchBnd; Orch; PepBnd; SchMus; Lansing Comm College; Bank Management.

GIBSON, Anita M; Princeton HS; Princeton, IL; 25/165 ChrhWkr; HonRl; YthFlsp; GerCl; Ill Valley Comm Coll; Medical Technology.

GIBSON, Charles C; Goshen HS; Goshen, IN; HonRl; Orch; Goshen College; Meteorology.

GIBSON, Connie K; Gallatin HS; Gallatin, MO; Band; Chr; CncrtBnd; HonRl; LbryAde; MrchBnd; FFA; PpCl; Bsktbl; Coll.

GIBSON, Diane L; Wall Lake Comm HS; Wall Lake, IA; Band; HonRl; MrchBnd; NHS; PepBnd; YthFlsp; RptrSchPpr; SchPpr; Bsbl; Trk; Sterling Coll.

GIBSON, George H; Lees Summit HS; Greenwood, MO; Chrs; RptrYrbk; SptEdSchPpr;.

GIBSON, Glenn E; Flint Central HS; Flint, MI; HonRl; NHS; NatlMeritCmnd; LetterFtbl; LetterTrk; IMSpt; Michigan State Univ; Veterinary Medicine.

GIBSON, Julie A; Tremont HS; Tremont, IL; 7/78 ALAGirlsSt; Band; ChrhWkr; CmntyWkr; HonRl; Coll; Major Study.

GIBSON, Karen J; Waverly Shell Rock HS; Shell Rock, IA; 5/191 Band; CncrtBnd; HonRl; MrchBnd; OffAde; Trk; College.

GIBSON, Kathryn M; Springfield Catholic HS; Springfield, MO; VPBand; Chrs; ChrhWkr; CncrtBnd; HonRl; LitMag; Orch; PepBnd; SchPl; LatCl; PpCl; Bsktbl; Trk; GAA; Univ Of Mo; Veterinary Medicine.

GIBSON, Kenneth S; Hammond HS; Hammond, IN; Chr; ChrhWkr; JA; StuCncl; TchrAde; 4-H; Bsktbl; LetterFtbl; LetterTrk; College; Professional.

GIBSON, Marie E; Leadwood HS; Leadwood, MO; 3/42 ChrhWkr; CmntyWkr; HonRl; TrsFrshCls; TchrAde; Twrl; FHA; PpCl; DanFAwd; Coll; Nursing.

GIBSON, Mark D; Bradley Bourbonnois Co HS; Bourbonnais, IL; 13/360 HonRl; NHS; Ill Wesleyan Univ; History.

GIBSON, Michael T; Ryan HS; Omaha, NE; 1/200 ModUN; NatlFornLg; NHS; NatlMeritSF; SctActv; StuCncl; Mi St U; Computer Science.

GIBSON, Peter R; Lincoln HS; Wisconsin Rapids, WI; 6/532 PresSrCls; ALBoysSt; ChrhWkr; CmntyWkr; HonRl; NHS; StuCncl; StuGov; KeyCl; DARAwd; West Point.

GIBSON, Philip A; Washington Comm HS; Washington, IL; 10/316 AFS; CtyCnl; HonRl; NHS; NatlMeritCmnd; StuCncl; Indiana Univ; Law.

GIBSON, Randy D; Eldorado HS; Eldorado, KS; Band; ChrhWkr; CncrtBnd; HonRl; MrchBnd; NatlFornLg; NatlMeritCmnd; PepBnd; StuCncl; Glf; Ottawa Univ;engineer.

GIBSON, Reginald J; Westport HS; Kansas City, MO; 35/170 Aud/Vis; HonRl; SctActv; StuCncl; TchrAde; Bsbl; Bsktbl; CaptFtbl; LetterTrk; CaptWrstlng; College; Professional.

GIBSON, Rhonda L; Leadwood HS; Leadwood, MO; 6/52 Band; Chr; DrmMjrt; HonRl; NHS; OffAde; SchPl; RptrSchPpr; FHA; PpCl; Legal Secretary; Legal Secretary.

GIBSON, Richard H; New Trier East HS; Wilmette, IL; LitMag; NatlFornLg; NatlMeritFnl; PolWkr; SchMus; SctActv; StuCncl; StuGov; RptrSchPpr; SchPpr; College; Politics.

GIBSON, Rosalie; Dundee Community HS; Dundee, MI; Chr; Chrs; ChrhWkr; HonRl; SchMus; TchrAde; FHA; FTA; SpnCl; College; Physical Therapist.

GIBSON, Susan O; Tuscola HS; Tuscola, IL; Band; ChrhWkr; CmntyWkr; CaptCncrtBnd; DrlTm; SecStuCncl; SchPpr; 4-H; SecGAA; 4-HAwd; U Of E Il; Wildlife Biology.

GIBSON, Terry E; Kewanee HS; Kewanee, IL; Chr; HonRl; PepBnd; SctActv; StuGov; FrCl; PpCl; Vocation.

GICK, Daniel J; Benton Central HS; Otterbein, IN; 3/270 TrsSophCls; PresJrCls; ALBoysSt; HonRl; NHS; 4-H; FFA; 4-HAwd; Purdue; Farming.

GICZEWSKI, Norbert G; Cabrini HS; Allen Park, MI; 17/167 PresSrCls; CmntyWkr; RedCrAde; StuCncl; StuGov; FBLA; Bsbl; Ftbl; Glf; IMSpt; Coll; Engr.

GIDDINGS, Carol J; Baraga HS; Baraga, MI; Band; CncrtBnd; HonRl; MrchBnd; PepBnd; TchrAde; Teen; PpCl; Bsktbl; College; Teacher.

GIDDINGS, Jeanne M; Humboldt HS; Humboldt, IA; 3/132 PresSophCls; PresJrCls; PresSrCls; Band; CncrtBnd; HonRl; MrchBnd; NHS; StuGov; Chrldr; University; Pre Med.

GIDDINGS, Steven L; Bettendorf HS; Bettendorf, IA; Band; Chr; ChrhWkr; CncrtBnd; JA; MrchBnd; SchMus; SchPl; SciCl; Swmmng; Univ; Sci.

GIDEON, Jack; Wayne HS; Fort Wayne, IN; 11/326 HonRl; Purdue Univ; Engineer.

GIDEON, Karen S; Ozark HS; Ozark, MO; 4/92 HonRl; YthFlsp; RptrYrbk; Yrbk; RptrSchPpr; SchPpr; 4-H; FHA; PpCl; Bsktbl; Trk; GAA; IMSpt; Trade Schl; Secretary.

GIEBELSTEIN, Sally; Bennett Comm HS; Bennett, IA; Band; HonRl; NHS; PepBnd; SchPl; RptrYrbk; 4-H; FHA; Bsktbl; 4-HAwd; Bus Sch.

GIEBER, Debra E; Centreville HS; Centreville, MI; 21/55 TrsJrCls; Chr; HonRl; PolWkr; StuCncl; TchrAde; Yrbk; FHA; SpnCl; PpCl; LetterBsktbl; IMSpt; PPFtbl; Glen Oaks Comm College; Physical Education.

GIEBINK, Bruce L; Waupun HS; Waupan, WI; NHS; TchrAde; SpnCl; Wrstlng; RotaryAwd; College; Vocation.

GIEDD, Susan E; Henry HS; Henry, SD; Chrs; CmntyWkr; HonRl; SchAde; SchPl; StuCncl; YthFlsp; RptrSchPpr; SchPpr; Sec4-H; College; Professional.

GIEDT, Randy; Bowdle Public HS; Bowdle, SD; TrsFrshCls; Band; HonRl; SchPl; StuCncl; TchrAde; SchPpr; 4-H; College; Vocation.

GIEGLER, Jeanette K; Howell HS; Howell, MI; 9/372 PresSophCls; VPSrCls; DrlTm; HonRl; LbryAde; NHS; OffAde; TchrAde; 4-H; Central Mich U; Media Specialist.

GIELNIAK, Cary F; Lake Central HS; Crn Pt, IN; 41/433 HonRl; TreasNHS; TchrAde; GerCl; PresSciCl; LetterGlf; Tennis; Rose Hulman Inst; Elec Engineering.

GIELOW, Robert D; Pinckneyville Community HS; Pinckneyville, IL; ChrhWkr; HonRl; Rend Lake Jr College; Draftsman.

GIENGER, Laure J; Luverne HS; Luverne, ND; SecFrshCls; PresJrCls; Band; ChrhWkr; HonRl; MrchBnd; SchPl; FrCl; LetterBsktbl; LetterTrk; U Of Nd; Medicine.

GIENGER, Tonya M; St Francis Comm HS; St Francis, KS; 4/29 Chr; Chrs; ChrhWkr; HonRl; Teen; YthFlsp; 4-H; FHA; PPFtbl; 4-HAwd; College; Prof.

GIERAK, Amy K; Redford Union HS; Detroit, MI; 8/750 Chr; HonRl; NHS; NatlMeritCmnd; NatlMeritSF; Bsbl; Bsktbl; GAA; University; Math Education.

GIERHART, Brian; Mauston HS; Mauston, WI; 6/130 ALBoysSt; ChrhWkr; CncrtBnd; HonRl; MrchBnd; SptEdYrbk; LatCl; Univ Of Wis; Pharmacy.

GIERL, Ann M; Tigerton HS; Tigerton, WI; 3/53 VPSophCls; Band; ChrhWkr; HonRl; NHS; NatlMeritSchl; SctActv; EdYrBk; EdSchPpr; Bsktbl; Col ;nursing.

GIERSBACH, Susan; Clintonville Sr HS; Clintonville, WI; 6/194 AFS; Band; ChrhWkr; CncrtBnd; HonRl; MrchBnd; NatlMeritFnl; NatlMeritSF; PepBnd; YthFlsp; De Paus Univ; Music.

GIERSZEWSKI, Isabel T; Taft HS; Chicago, IL; 35/792 Chrs; JrNHS; NHS; NatlMeritCmnd; OffAde; SchMus; SchPl; StuCncl; KeyCl; CaptChrldr; Loyola Univ; Pharmaceutical Science.

GIERTYCH, Theresa L; Thornwood HS; South Holland, IL; 26/900 HonRl; JrNHS; NatlFornLg; NHS; NatlThespSoc; SchPl; Butler Univ; Pharmacy.

GIERTZ, Sharon K; Marengo Community HS; Marengo, IL; 1/160 Chr; ChrhWkr; HonRl; HospAde; GerCl; PpCl; College;.

GIERYMSKI, Ivone I; George Rogers Clark HS; Hammond, IN; 15/260 ChrhWkr; HonRl; NHS; NatlThespSoc; SchPl; GAA; Business School; Professional.

GIERYN, Richard T; Brother Rice HS; Bloomfield Hills, MI; 5/230 HonRl; NatlFornLg; NHS; SecStuCncl; EdYrBk; RptrSchPpr; CaptSwmmng; IMSpt; Univ; Law.

GIERYN, Stefan; Port Washington HS; Port Washington, WI; Band; CncrtBnd; DrlTm; HonRl; HospAde; MrchBnd; Orch; PepBnd; SchMus; Bsbl; Uwm; Anesthetist.

GIES, Jerry P; Rochester HS; Rochester, IL; TrsJrCls; HonRl; VPNHS; PresStuCncl; Bsktbl; VPGlf; College; Dentistry.

GIESE, Larry J; Elgin Public HS; Elgin, ND; 2/35 ALBoysSt; HonRl; SchPl; Yrbk; FFA; PpCl; SciCl; Bsktbl; Ftbl; Trk; Nd State Univ; Engineering.

GIESE, Lori; Athens HS; Athens, WI; 2/94 ALAGirlsSt; HonRl; NatlFornLg; NHS; SchPl; EdYrBk; EdSchPpr; AmLegAwd; College; Nurse.

GIESEKE, Cheryl A; Harvard HS; Harvard, IL; 1/160 Chr; Chrs; ChrhWkr; HonRl; TreasNHS; U Of Il; Physics Teacher.

GIESELMAN, Grant; Bloomfield Community HS; Bloomfield, NE; Band; ModUN; SchPl; StuCncl; RptrYrbk; 4-H; Glf; IMSpt; Kearney St Coll.

GIESEMAN, Timothy W; Rockridge HS; Milan, IL; 24/144 HonRl; SptEdYrbk; FTA; SpnCl; Bsbl; Bsktbl; Ftbl; College.

GIESEN, Andrea S; New Prague HS; New Prague, MN; 17/194 Chr; HonRl; NHS; NatlMeritCmnd; OffAde; SchPl; StuCncl; EdYrBk; PpCl; IMSpt; University Of Minnesota; Elem Education.

GIESEN, Brad; Milbank HS; Milbank, SD; HonRl; NHS; NatlMeritCmnd; StuCncl; Sd State Univ; Engineering.

GIESEN, Doris E; Barrington HS; Barrington, IL; 24/652 Chr; Chrs; HonRl; VPNHS; NatlThespSoc; SchMus; SchPl; PresLatCl; CchngActv; AmLegAwd; Rosary College.

GIESER, Craig A; Minnehaha Acad; St Paul, MN; 28/125 Chr; ChrhWkr; CncrtBnd; DrmBgl; HonRl; Orch; SctActv; YthFlsp; EdSchPpr; GerCl; Morningside Clge Sioux City Ia; Music.

GIESKE, Patrick S; George E Thompson HS; So Elgin, IL; Aud/Vis; ChrhWkr; HonRl; LbryAde; OffAde; TreasLatCl; Ftbl; Wrstlng; University; Doctor.

GIESKEN, Mary J; Maryville Rii HS; Maryville, MO; 18/129 Chr; HospAde; NHS; StuCncl; TreasFBLA; FHA; PresPpCl; Tennis; College.

GIESKING, Kay; Titonka HS; Titonka, IA; Chrs; ChrhWkr; Yrbk; FHA; PpCl; Bsbl; Bsktbl; Trk; Northern Iowa U; Elementary Ed.

GIESLER, Kurt L; Proviso West HS; Hinsdale, IL; NHS; NatlMeritFnl; KeyCl;.

GIESSELMANN, Ruth A; Fremont Senior HS; Fremont, NE; Chrs; CmntyWkr; HospAde; SctActv; Business School; Secretary.

GIETZEL, Rick; Waupun Senior Hs; Waupun, WI; 146/264 Pres4-H; FFA; Bsbl; 4-HAwd; Tech School;agriculture Wildlife Management.

GIETZEN, Cindy M; New Haven HS; New Haven, MI; 6/100 DrlTm; HonRl; OffAde; ROTC; TchrAde; FBLA;.

GIETZEN, Debra L; Chippewa Hills HS; Remus, MI; 15/200 TrsJrCls; TrsSrCls; Band; CncrtBnd; HonRl; MrchBnd; OffAde; SctActv; TreasStuCncl; YthFlsp; PpCl; College; Professional.

GIFFHORN, Linda S; Tremont HS; Tremont, IL; Band; ChrhWkr; CmntyWkr; DrmMjrt; HonRl;

MrchBnd; SecNHS; PepBnd; Twrl; Yrbk; Pres-GAA; AmLegAwd; DARAwd;.

GIFFIN, Debra M; Southeast HS; Pittsburg, KS; HstSophCls; Band; Chr; HonRl; JA; MrchBnd; NHS; PepBnd; FrCl; PpCl; Kansas State Clg; Nursing.

GIFFORD, Carole; Spencer Hs; Spencer, IA; Band; CncrtBnd; HonRl; HospAde; MrchBnd; PepBnd; SchMus; SpnCl; University; Professional.

GIGAC, Arlene D; Whiting HS; Whiting, IN; 38/93 HonRl; StuGov; TchrAde; RptrSchPpr; EdSchPpr; FTA; GerCl; PpCl; Bsktbl; Trk; Indiana Univ; Journalism.

GIGANTE, Carl A; Fenwick HS; Chicago, IL; 13/230 PresJrCls; HonRl; IntrClCncl; NHS; SchPl; PresStuCncl; LetterBsbl; Chrldr; IMSpt; OptClAwd; Northwestern University; Biology.

GIGER, Roger B; Guide Rock HS; Guide Rock, NE; VPFrshCls; PresSophCls; Band; Chr; Chrs; MrchBnd; SchMus; SchPl; StuCncl; RptrSchPpr; 4-H; LetterBsktbl; LetterFtbl; LetterTrk; College; Teacher.

GIGLIOTTI, Anthony J; Paul Vi HS; Omaha, NE; Chrs; CmntyWkr; SchMus; SchPpr; SpnCl; Creigmton U; Business Admin.

GIGUERE, Susan P; Avon HS; Indianapolis, IN; 2/155 SecFrshCls; SecSophCls; SecSrCls; ALAGirlsSt; HonRl; LbryAde; NHS; NatlMeritCmnd; StuGov; TchrAde; Yrbk; 4-H; FrCl; GerCl; Butler Univ; Math.

GIHL, Nicholas T; Springfield HS; Springfield, IL; 50/590 SecFrshCls; HonRl; JrNHS; NHS; NatlMeritCmnd; StuCncl; Purdue Univ; Elec Engineer.

GILATY, Mitchell; Loyola Acad; Chicago, IL; 15/442 HonRl; NHS; RptrSchPpr; SciCl; Tennis; IMSpt; Cornell Univ; Law.

GILATY, Mitchell P; Loyola Academy; Chicago, IL; 15/442 HonRl; LitMag; NHS; RptrSchPpr; SciCl; Tennis; Cornell University; Lawyer.

GILB, Linda; Adrian Public HS; Adrian, MN; 4/89 CncrtBnd; HonRl; MrchBnd; ModUN; NHS; PepBnd; TchrAde; Bsktbl; GAA; IMSpt; Mankato State; Computer Programming.

GILBERT, Annette M; Garner Hayfield HS; Garner, IA; Band; CncrtBnd; HonRl; MrchBnd; NHS; PepBnd; FHA; U Of N Ia; History Teacher.

GILBERT, Arthur L; New Trier West HS; Wilmette, IL; 61/694 HonRl; Northwestern Univ; Psychology.

GILBERT, Charlotte M; Lincoln County R Ii HS; Elsberry, MO; 12/63 TrsSophCls; PresJrCls; ChrhWkr; CmntyWkr; HonRl; NHS; RptrYrbk; RptrSchPpr; SchPpr; FHA; FSA; PpCl; College; Professional.

GILBERT, Cheryl A; Antigo HS; Antigo, WI; 4-H; FBLA; LatCl; PpCl; College; Professional.

GILBERT, Cynthia; Sevastopol HS; Sturgeon Bay, WI; Band; CncrtBnd; MrchBnd; SchAde; SchMus; SchPl; LatCl; SpnCl; Trk; GAA; College.

GILBERT, Daniel W; Green Bay West HS; Green Bay, WI; Band; RptrYrbk; SptEdSchPpr; GerCl; IMSpt; Uw Mad; Engineer.

GILBERT, Denise J; Prairie City Comm HS; Prairie City, IA; 9/50 SecSrCls; Chrs; HonRl; Twrl; CaptBsktbl; PPFtbl;.

GILBERT, Duane L; Lafayette HS; St Joseph, MO; Chr; ChrhWkr; HonRl; StuCncl; LetterBsbl; Bsktbl; Ftbl; IMSpt; Col; Conservation.

GILBERT, Gary; Northern HS; Flint, MI; ChrhWkr; HonRl; NHS; FDA; FSA; SciCl; Swmmng; Tennis; IMSpt; College; Physician.

GILBERT, Gayla S; Paris HS; Paris, IL; 1/256 Band; Chr; HonRl; NHS; SecYthFlsp; 4-H; FrCl; LetterBsktbl; 4-HAwd; University Of Illinois; Professional.

GILBERT, Joyce A; St Charles HS; St Charles, IL; 32/465 HonRl; LbryAde; NHS; NatlMeritCmnd; OffAde; StuGov; TchrAde; FrCl; U Of Ia; Pediatrician.

GILBERT, Kathy J; Kent City HS; Kent City, MI; 48/90 HonRl; Ferris St College; Dental Asst.

GILBERT, Kila A; Kewaunee HS; Kewaunee, WI; 3/141 HonRl; NHS; SctActv; 4-H; FrCl; PpCl; SciCl; GAA; Univ Of Wi; Nursing.

GILBERT, Laura; East HS; Lincoln, NE; NHS; PpCl; IMSpt; PPFtbl; U Of Nebr Lincoln; Accountant.

GILBERT, Lisa C; Granite City South HS; Granite City, IL; NHS; SctActv; SpnCl; S Illinois Univ; Special Ed.

GILBERT, Mary A; Park River HS; Park River, ND; StuCncl; RptrSchPpr; 4-H; FFA; FrCl; PpCl; GAA; 4-HAwd; Jr College; Practical Nursing.

GILBERT, Pamela A; Waltonville HS; Waltonville, IL; 10/38 ChrhWkr; HonRl; GerCl; PpCl; Rend Lake College; English Teacher.

GILBERT, Raymond B; Franklin HS; Livonia, MI; PresBand; CncrtBnd; MrchBnd; Orch; PepBnd; SchMus; Univ Of Michigan; Engineer.

GILBERT, Rita M; Earlham Community HS; Earlham, IA; HonRl; Grandview Jr College; Chemistry.

GILBERT, Steven L; Moline Sr HS; Moline, IL; Chr; CncrtBnd; Mdrgl; MrchBnd; PepBnd; SchMus; SchPl; YthFlsp; SchPpr; Black Hawk Jr College; Elec Engineering.

GILBERT, Terry A; Lawrence HS; Lawrence, KS; 124/548 NatlMeritSF; SchMus; SchPl; TchrAde; LatCl; Univ; Biology.

GILBERT, Thomas A; Hershey HS; Hershey, NE; StuCncl; LetterFtbl; Trk; IMSpt;.

GILBERTSON, Beverly A; Monticello HS; Monticello, WI; HonRl; HospAde; JA; LbryAde; PepBnd; RedCrAde; TchrAde; RptrSchPpr; SpnCl; PpCl; College; Medical Tech.

GILBERTSON, Carol; Harrisburg HS; Canton, SD; 6/36 Band; CncrtBnd; DrlTm; HonRl; PepBnd; SchMus; 4-H; PpCl; BttyCrckrAwd; 4-HAwd; Mitchel Vo Tech.

GILBERTSON, De Ann R; Ellsworth Public HS; Ellsworth, MN; MrchBnd; SchPl; EdYrBk; Trade Sch; Cosmotology.

GILBERTSON, Deborah A; Huron Sr HS; Huron, SD; Band; Chr; CncrtBnd; HospAde; Mdrgl; MrchBnd; SchMus; SchPl; TchrAde; Pres4-H; 4-HAwd; University; Nursing.

GILBERTSON, Hunter J; Glenbrook North HS; Northbrook, IL; 27/640 HonRl; NatlFornLg; NHS; EdSchPpr; College; Law.

GILBERTSON, Kathleen R; Sterling HS; Sterling, IL; HonRl; Augustana College; Veterinarian.

GILBERTSON, Linda M; Albert Lea Sr HS; Albert Lea, MN; 98/526 TrsFrshCls; HonRl; HospAde; StuCncl; PpCl; LetterBsktbl; Swmmng; Trk; GAA; IMSpt; KiwanAwd; College; Physical Educ.

GILBERTSON, Mark W; Amery HS; Amery, WI; 2/135 ChrhWkr; NHS; PresPolWkr; SchPl; PresStuCncl; RptrSchPpr; PpCl; Bsbl; Bsktbl; GovHonPrgAwd; CitAwd; University; Doctor.

GILBRAITH, Sara J; Sherwood HS; Sherwood, ND; SecTrsSrCls; Chr; Chrs; CncrtBnd; HonRl; MrchBnd; PepBnd; SchPl; EdSchPpr; BttyCrckrAwd; Ndsu, Fargo; Vet Med.

GILCHREST, Sally; Quincy HS; Quincy, MI; 300118 Band; CncrtBnd; HonRl; MrchBnd; PepBnd; SctActv; TchrAde; 4-H; FTA; Tir.

GILCHRIST, Lawrence; Hampton HS; Hampton, IA; ALBoysSt; Chrs; HonRl; ModUN; SchMus; SctActv; Bsktbl; IMSpt; Univ Of Colorado; Professional.

GILDEMEISTER, Cynthia; Oggeo Fairchild HS; Fairchild, WI; Aud/Vis; Chr; HonRl; YthFlsp; 4-H; Chrldr; GAA; College; Major Study.

GILDEMEISTER, Linda K; Arlington HS; Arlington Hts, IL; HonRl; Business School; Professional.

GILDERSLEEVE, Rhonda R; Fennimore HS; Fennimore, WI; 3/113 Band; ChrhWkr; HonRl; NHS; NatlMeritSF; StuCncl; VP4-H; FFA; TreasFHA; Bsktbl; GAA; IMSpt; 4-HAwd; Uw River Falls; Animal Science.

GILE, Michelle D; Scandia HS; Scandia, KS; Chrs; ChrhWkr; CmntyWkr; HonRl; MrchBnd; SchPl; Teen; Twrl; RptrYrbk; PpCl; Brown Mackie; Fashion Merchandising.

GILES, Craig S; Downers Grove North HS; Downers Grove, IL; Band; CncrtBnd; MrchBnd; College; Business.

GILES, Franklin D; New Palestine HS; New Palestine, IN; Band; CncrtBnd; HonRl; MrchBnd; PepBnd; SptEdYrbk; PresLatCl; Bsbl; CaptFtbl; Indiana St Univ; Medicine.

GILES, Julia; Westmer HS; New Boston, IL; 14/61 ChrhWkr; CmntyWkr; HonRl; Yrbk; 4-H; FBLA; PresAwd;.

GILES, Lucinda J; Southridge HS; Holland, IN; Band; ChrhWkr; CmntyWkr; HonRl; HospAde; SctActv; YthFlsp; Trk; HstSrCls; OptClAwd; Cl;.

GILES, Mark E; High School; Haviland, KS; ALBoysSt; ChrhWkr; HonRl; PresJrNHS; StuCncl; 4-H; College; Major Study.

GILES, Michele M; Sacred Heart Of Mary HS; Arlington Hts, IL; Chrs; HonRl; LitMag; NHS; PolWkr; SchPl; StuGov; FrCl; Rosary College; Foreign Language.

GILFORD, Michael T; Grosse Pointe North HS; Harper Woods, MI; HonRl; LbryAde; NHS; YthFlsp; Ftbl; U Of Mi Ann Arbor; Engineering.

GILGALLON, Susan M; Marian Catholic HS; Dalton, IL; 5/335 ChrhWkr; CmntyWkr; HonRl; NHS; SpnCl; College; Vet.

GILGENBACH, Linda L; Prairie Heights HS; Clayton, KS; Band; CncrtBnd; HonRl; MrchBnd; PepBnd; SchPl; SchPpr; FHA; PpCl; Coll; Prof.

GILGENBACH, Mary J; Hillcrest HS; Hazel Crest, IL; 5/349 PresSrCls; CmntyWkr; HonRl; NHS; SpnCl; MthCl; CaptSciCl; GAA; IMSpt; PPFtbl; College; Foreign Languages.

GILHOOLY, Karen L; Our Lady Of Mercy HS; Farmington Hills, MI; HonRl; NHS; PolWkr; SchAde; TchrAde; SchPpr; PresFrCl; Bsbl; Bsktbl; IMSpt; University; Medicine.

GILKEY, Cary L; Downers Grove HS; Darien, IL; 97/830 ChrhWkr; HonRl; YthFlsp; Univ Of Ill; Study Architecture.

GILL, David; Huntington North HS; Huntington, IN; 51/512 NHS; Quill&Scroll; SchPl; StuCncl; SptEdSchPpr; Bsbl; CchngActv; IMSpt; Notre Dame Univ; Communications.

GILL, Dianna L; Bryant HS; Rich Hill, MO; 7/45 SecSophCls; Chrs; ChrhWkr; HonRl; Yrbk; FBLA; TreasFHA; PPFtbl; BttyCrckrAwd; Univ.

GILL, James F; Freeport Senior HS; Freeport, IL; AFS; CncrtBnd; HonRl; PolWkr; SchMus; StuCncl; RptrSchPpr; FrCl; Western Ill Univ; Pharmacy.

GILL, Jo E; Creston HS; Creston, IA; Band; CncrtBnd; HonRl; MrchBnd; NatlThespSoc; PepBnd; Nebraska Methodist Schl; Nursing.

GILL, Mary A; Friend Public HS; Friend, NE; TrsFrshCls; Chrs; ChrhWkr; HonRl; HospAde; LbryAde; TchrAde; PpCl; LetterTrk; Chrldr; Lpn Coll; Pro.

GILL, Nancy J; Academy Of Our Lady; Chicago, IL; 4/180 HonRl; LitMag; NHS; SchAde; StuCncl; StuGov; SpnCl; MthCl; PpCl; GAA; Dental Hygiene.

GILL, Toni S; La Monte HS; La Monte, MO; TrsFrshCls; TrsSophCls; SecJrCls; SecSrCls; HonRl; SchPl; Yrbk;.

GILLAN, Brian P; Central HS; Omaha, NE; 11/742 ALBoysSt; HonRl; NHS; NatlMeritFnl; NatlMeritSF; SctActv; FrCl; CaptSwmmng; Univ Of Calif; Lawyer.

GILLAN, Darcia R; Octavia HS; Colfax, IL; 3/48 SecSophCls; ALAGirlsSt; Chrs; HonRl; NHS; StuCncl; PresYthFlsp; RptrYrbk; RptrSchPpr; Pres4-H; SpnCl; MthCl; SciCl; GAA; College.

GILLAN, Deanna L; Central City HS; Central City, NE; 8/74 HonRl; SchAde; TchrAde; Teen; 4-H; FHA; 4-HAwd; MasAwd; College; Professional.

GILLAND, Kim L; Eddyville HS; Albia, IA; 1/52 Band; Chrs; ChrhWkr; NatlMeritCmnd; Quill&Scroll; EdSchPpr; SpnCl; PpCl; LetterBsbl; LetterBsktbl; LetterTrk; DARAwd; Univ Of No Iowa; Med Technology.

GILLAND, Rhonda; Cowan HS; Muncie, IN; ChrhWkr; HonRl; OffAde; TchrAde; YthFlsp; 4-H; FBLA; FHA; FTA; SpnCl; Purdue; Business.

GILLARD, J Dean; Edwards Co Sr HS; Albion, IL; VPFrshCls; VPJrCls; HonRl; StuCncl; StuGov; FrCl; PpCl; Bsbl; Bsktbl; Univ; Professional.

GILLASPEY, David C; Lamoni Community HS; Lamoni, IA; 2/39 SchPl; Yrbk; Bsktbl; Graceland College; Frelance Photography.

GILLASPIE, Kenneth; Midland Ind HS; Midland, SD; 4/16 SecSophCls; Band; Chrs; HonRl; SchMus; SchPl; Yrbk; SchPpr;.

GILLEN, Dane; White Lake Public HS; White Lake, SD; HonRl; StuCncl; StuGov; RptrYrbk; SptEdSchPpr; PpCl; Bsbl; Ftbl; Wrstlng; CitAwd; Trade School; Vocational.

GILLEN, Daniel L; East HS; Waterloo, IA; PresFrshCls; HonRl; StuCncl; MthCl; Bsbl; Ftbl; Wrstlng; IMSpt; Eastern Ky; Engineering.

GILLES, Bruce A; Stanley Boyd HS; Stanley, WI; HonRl; Ftbl; Trk; Wrstlng;.

GILLES, Jeffrey P; Elmwood HS; Elmwood, WI; ChrhWkr; HonRl; PolWkr; SptEdYrbk; Yrbk; Bsbl; Ftbl; IMSpt; College; Nurse.

GILLES, Mark R; St Edward HS; Elgin, IL; 21/123 HonRl; 4-H; LetterBsktbl; LetterGlf; 4-HAwd; Illinois Inst Of Tech; Mech Engineering.

GILLESPIE, Denise K; Alton Sr HS; Alton, IL; Chrs; ChrhWkr; CncrtBnd; HonRl; NHS; NatlThespSoc; SchMus; Yrbk; GerCl; Carthage College; Business Admin.

GILLESPIE, Gloria G; Rich East Twp HS; Park Forest, IL; LitMag; NatlFornLg; NHS; NatlMeritFnl; NatlThespSoc; Quill&Scroll; SchPl; Oberlin College.

GILLESPIE, Jan L; Canton Ind HS; Hudson, SD; Chr; DrlTm; HonRl; StuGov; RptrYrbk; Yrbk; RptrSchPpr; 4-H; FHA; Trk; IMSpt; College; Dental Hygiene.

GILLESPIE, Lawrence G; De Smet Jesuit HS; Crystal Lake Pk, MO; 38/171 HonRl; NHS; NatlMeritSF; NatlThespSoc; SchPl; Bsbl; Wrstlng; St Louis Univ; Attorney.

GILLESPIE, Roselyn; Beaumont HS; St Louis, MO; HonRl; Coll; Clinical Psychologist.

GILLESPIE, Tain; Batesville HS; Batesville, IN; SecFrshCls; Chrs; CmntyWkr; HonRl; HospAde; NatlThespSoc; Bsktbl; Trk; GAA; PresAwd; College; Professional.

GILLESPIE, Thomas G; Glenband East HS; Lombard, IL; 122/676 HonRl; SctActv; SpnCl; LetterTrk; U Of Ill; Civil Eng.

GILLESPIE, Timothy P; Aquin HS; Freeport, IL; PresJrCls; HonRl; StuCncl; Bsktbl; Ftbl; Glf; Col; Business.

GILLET, Nicole M; Edina East HS; Edina, MN; 82/530 Chr; HonRl; SchPl; TchrAde; YthFlsp; FrCl; St Marys College.

GILLETT, Carol S; Parkside HS; Jackson, MI; 3/415 SpnCl; Jackson Comm Coll; Professional.

GILLETT, Margo L; Esbon Rural HS; Red Cloud, NE; Band; Chr; Chrs; ChrhWkr; CncrtBnd; HonRl; MrchBnd; PepBnd; SchMus; StuCncl; CaptBsktbl; Ftbl; Socr; Trk; College; Vocation.

GILLETT, Rebecca R; Unity HS; Tolono, IL; 11/123 Band; Chr; Chrs; ChrhWkr; CncrtBnd; DrlTm; HonRl; MrchBnd; PepBnd; FNA; Olivet Nazarene College; Home Economics.

GILLETTE, Emily J; Chatsworth HS; Chatsworth, IL; 1/46 AFS; HonRl; Mdrgl; NHS; SchMus; SchPl; Yrbk; FFA; SpnCl; Univ Of Illinois; Conservation.

GILLEY, Debra A; Burke HS; Omaha, NE; Chr; Chrs; HonRl; SchAde; StuCncl; StuGov; GerCl; PpCl; Chrldr; College; Business.

GILLEY, Tom D; Brewster HS; Levant, KS; PresSrCls; Band; Chrl; Chrs; ChrhWkr; HonRl; YthFlsp; LetterFtbl; LetterTrk; CitAwd; Oral Roberts U; Ministry.

GILLHAM, Grant; St Paul HS; Edwardsville, IL; 15/50 Chr; HonRl; SchMus; SchPl; Bsbl; Bsktbl; Trk; IMSpt; Tulane Univ; Undecided.

GILLIAM, Gregg E; United Township HS; East Moline, IL; ChrhWkr; CmntyWkr; HonRl; HospAde; LatCl; SciCl; Trk; JCAwd; OptClAwd; Coll; Medical.

GILLICK, Timothy J; Ipswich Public HS; Ipswich, SD; PresFrshCls; TrsSophCls; Aud/Vis; Chr; Chrs; DrmMjrt; HonRl; IntrClCncl; SchMus; StuCncl; 4-H; LetterBsbl; LetterBsktbl; CaptFtbl; College; Lawyer.

GILLIGAN, Kevin L; Allegan HS; Allegan, MI; JCC; LetterBsbl; CaptBsktbl; LetterFtbl; Swmmng; Tennis; LetterTrk; CchngActv; Ferris St College; Business.

GILLILAND, David D; Mt Carroll Comm HS; Mt Carroll, IL; 4/60 PresJrCls; HonRl; PolWkr; SchMus; SchPl; StuCncl; StuGov; Pres4-H; KeyCl; LetterBsbl; LetterBsktbl; GodCntryAwd; College; Teacher.

GILLILAND, Michael V; Okemos HS; Okemos, MI; LitMag; NHS; PolWkr; LatCl; Socr; Mich State; Law.

GILLILAND, Patricia M; Deerfield HS; Deerfield, IL; 8/650 Chr; Chrs; HonRl; College; Music.

GILLILAND, Timothy W; Kennedy HS; Cedar Rapids, IA; VPFrshCls; ALBoysSt; ChrhWkr; StuCncl; AmLegAwd; KiwanAwd; College; Machine Designer.

GILLIN, Paul; Pipestone HS; Pipestone, MN; 7/135 PresJrCls; PresSrCls; Band; CncrtBnd; HonRl; NatlFornLg; NHS; NatlThespSoc; PolWkr; SchPl; College; Theatre Arts.

GILLINGHAM, Sandra K; Richland Center HS; Muscoda, WI; HonRl; 4-H; LetterTrk; GAA; IMSpt; 4-HAwd; Bus Sch; Secretary.

GILLIOM, Greg L; St Charles HS; St Charles, MO; 20/550 Band; CncrtBnd; HonRl; MrchBnd; NHS; PepBnd; MthCl; Tennis; Univ; Bioengineering.

GILLIS, Anne T; Grosse Pointe No HS; Harper Woods, MI; HonRl; Adrian College; English.

GILLIS, Robert; Rossville Alvin HS; Rossville, IL; VPSophCls; HonRl; StuCncl; RptrYrbk; SciCl; Bsbl; Bsktbl; Ftbl; Trk; IMSpt; Danville Jr Col; Accountant.

GILLISPIE, Aaron D; Moberly HS; Moberly, MO; AFS; HonRl; StuCncl; KeyCl; Bsbl; LetterBsktbl; LetterFtbl; College;architectural Engineering.

GILLISPIE, Gloria G; Rich Twp E HS; Park Forest, IL; 16/358 LitMag; NatlFornLg; NHS; NatlMeritSF; NatlThespSoc; PolWkr; Quill&Scroll; SchPl; RptrSchPpr; SchPpr; Oberlin College; Satirist.

GILLMAN, Catherine A; I C A HS; Brookville, IN; VPFrshCls; Chrs; CncrtBnd; HonRl; HospAde; NHS; Orch; SchMus; SctActv; Yrbk; SpnCl; Bsktbl; Tennis; Mt St Joseph College; Nurse.

GILLMAN, Deborah A; Acad Of The Immac Conc; Brookville, IN; 11/69 PresJrCls; NHS; Orch; Quill&Scroll; SchMus; SctActv; VPStuCncl; StuGov; Yrbk; GAA; College; Music And Acct.

GILLMAN, Stephen C; Brookville HS; Brookville, IN; 1/200 NHS; StuCncl; TchrAde; KeyCl; GerCl; LetterBsbl; Bsktbl; LetterFtbl; LetterWrstlng; BauchLmbAwd; College; Chemical Engineer.

GILLMORE, Barbara A; Lawrence HS; Indianapolis, IN; 4-H; 4-HAwd; Univ; Art Degree.

GILLMORE, Bryan H; Moundridge HS; Moundridge, KS; HonRl; NatlMeritSF; 4-H; FFA; Bsktbl; Ftbl; Univ; Profession.

GILLMORE, Dale G; Central HS; Bristol, WI; Aud/Vis; Band; CncrtBnd; MrchBnd; PepBnd; MthCl; SciCl; AmLegAwd;.

GILLOGLY, Kathleen A; Sacred Heart Of Mary HS; Mt Prospect, IL; NatlMeritSF; StuGov; Univ; Anthropology.

GILLOGLY, Laurie; Oneill Public HS; Page, NE; SchMus; SchPl; 4-H; PpCl; GAA; 4-HAwd; Coll; Pychology.

GILLOGLY, R; North Putnam HS; Roachdale, IN; ALBoysSt; Aud/Vis; Band; LbryAde; NHS; NatlThespSoc; PepBnd; SchMus; SchPl; SpnCl; Mayby Trade School; Work After School.

GILLOM, Cheryl; Swan Valley HS; Saginow, MI; 2/160 ChrhWkr; CncrtBnd; HonRl; MrchBnd; NHS; PepBnd; SchMus; RptrSchPpr; Michigan State Univ; Instrumental Music.

GILLUM, Debra K; Unionville HS; Green Castle, MO; 1/83 SecTrsFrshCls; TrsSrCls; ALAGirlsSt; SecBand; CncrtBnd; HonRl; MrchBnd; NHS; PepBnd; SchPl; VP4-H; VPPpCl; CitAwd; Univ Of Missouri; Law.

GILLUM, Jenny L; Winchester Community HS; Winchester, IN; Chr; Chrs; HonRl; LbryAde; SchMus; SchPl; TchrAde; FHA; FrCl; College; Business.

GILLUND, David L; Wildrose Public HS; Wildrose, ND; Band; CncrtBnd; SchPl; StuCncl; RptrYrbk; RptrSchPpr; Bsbl; Bsktbl; Trk; Nd St Bottineau; Wildlife Management.

GILMAN, Anita L; Marquette Manor Christian HS; Westmont, IL; PresJrCls; Band; Chr; CncrtBnd; HonRl; StuGov; RptrYrbk; SchPpr; Chrldr; IMSpt; Bob Jones Univ; Home Econ.

GILMAN, Gail A; Lake Crystal HS; Lake Crystal, MN; VPFrshCls; PepBnd; SchMus; SchPl; StuCncl; 4-H; FHA; FrCl; PpCl; Trk; Univ Mn; Economics.

GILMAN, Gaylene; Lyman Independence HS; Kennebec, SD; PresJrCls; ALAGirlsSt; CmntyWkr; HonRl; JrNHS; TchrAde; PpCl; 4-HAwd; Clge; Psychiatry.

GILMAN, Julie M; Mineral Point HS; Mineral Point, WI; Band; HonRl; MrchBnd; SchMus; YthFlsp; FHA; LetterBsktbl; LetterTrk; GAA; PresAwd; Technical School; Dental Hygiene.

GILMER, Toni A; Southwestern HS; Flint, MI; 5/600 HonRl; JrNHS; TreasNHS; SchPl; TchrAde; PpCl; Coll; History Teacher.

GILMORE, Ann L; Underwood Community HS; Underwood, IA; TrsSophCls; AFS; Band; ChrhWkr; CncrtBnd; HonRl; MrchBnd; PepBnd; Yrbk; College; Medical Technician.

GILMORE, Brenda; Assumption Jr Sr HS; Pana, IL; Chrs; RptrSchPpr; SptEdSchPpr; FHA; GAA;.

GILMORE, Michael A; Greenwood Lab HS; Springfield, MO; 3/30 HonRl; ModUN; StuCncl; Yrbk; SchPpr; Pa State Univ; Anthropology Archaeology.

GILMORE, Pammy K; Emerson HS; Gary, IN; ChrhWkr; HonRl; NHS; TchrAde; Purdue; Radiologist.

GILMORE, Rebecca J; Corunna HS; Corunna, MI; 12/200 Band; CncrtBnd; MrchBnd; NHS; PepBnd; Twrl; Yrbk; SpnCl; PpCl; GAA; Central Mich University; Counseling.

GILMORE, Steven J; Limestone HS; Bartonville, IL; 99/403 Band; ChrhWkr; CmntyWkr; CncrtBnd; MrchBnd; YthFlsp; Trade School; Electronics.

GILMORE, Tracy L; North Greene HS; Roodhouse, IL; HonRl; Orch; PepBnd; RptrYrbk; FTA; Chrldr; CchngActv; GAA; IMSpt; 4-HAwd; Southeast Missouri State U; Nursing.

GILPIN, Steven N; Southern Boone County R 1 HS; Ashland, MO; ALBoysSt; HonRl; MrchBnd; Quill&Scroll; SchPl; StuCncl; StuGov; AmLegAwd; 4-HAwd; CitAwd; University; Psychology.

GILRAY, Patricia R; Warren T HS; Wadsworth, IL; 33/330 NatlMeritSF; TchrAde; Univ Of Illinois; Recreation.

GILSON, Craig; Havana HS; Havana, IL; 10/96 ChrhWkr; HonRl; NHS; PresStuCncl; LetterBsbl; LetterBsktbl; U Of Il; Engineering.

GILSON, Sharon M; Brainerd HS; Fort Ripley, MN; Chr; HonRl; TchrAde; 4-H; SecFFA; 4-HAwd; Brainerd Vo Tech; Vocation.

GILTNER, Eric T; Minot HS; Minot, ND; ALBoysSt; Band; ChrhWkr; CncrtBnd; HonRl; JrNHS; MrchBnd; SchMus; SctActv; StuCncl; FFA; LetterGlf; Swmmng; Wrstlng; University; Medicine.

GILZOW, Teresa L; Glendale HS; Springfield, MO; Chr; Chrl; Chrs; ChrhWkr; HonRl; HospAde; Mdrgl; SchMus; YthFlsp; LatCl; College; Music Major.

GIMLIN, Debra K; Hannibal HS; Hannibal, MO; HonRl; SchPpr; FDA; SpnCl; PpCl; GAA; IMSpt; PPFtbl; Northeast Mo St Univ; Biology.

GIN, Catherine; St Mary Acad; Indianapolis, IN; 9/33 Chr; Chrl; CmntyWkr; HonRl; JA; LbryAde; NHS; OffAde; PolWkr; SchPl; Indiana Central Iniv; Cpa.

GIN, Virginia H; St Mary Acad; Indianapolis, IN; 1/44 Chr; CmntyWkr; HonRl; HospAde; RedCrAde; SchAde; YthFlsp; 4-H; FNA; PresLatCl; Iupi; Nursing.

GINCHOFF, Nona J; Beloit Memorial HS; Beloit, WI; HonRl; NHS; Quill&Scroll; StuCncl; RptrYrbk; SptEdYrbk; Yrbk; SchPpr; Chrldr; IMSpt; Patricia Stevens Career Coll; Fashion.

GINDER, Joseph R; Anderson HS; Anderson, IN; ALBoysSt; ChrhWkr; CncrtBnd; HonRl; MrchBnd; NHS; StuCncl; VPSptEdYrbk; FrCl; DARAwd; In Univ; Med.

GINDER, Judy M; East Richland HS; Olney, IL; HospAde; Quill&Scroll; EdYrBk; RptrSchPpr; Tennis; Olney Central College.

GINGER, Paul R; Notre Dame For Boys HS; Park Ridge, IL; 59/264 HonRl; PolWkr; EdSehPpr; Wrstlng; Northern Il Univ; History.

GINGERICH, Brenda S; Iowa Mennonite HS; Wellman, IA; Chr; Chrs; LbryAde; OffAde; SchPl; YthFlsp; SchPpr; Clge.

GINGERICH, Clinton H; Winola HS; Aledo, IL; 12/78 HonRl; NatlMeritCmnd; SchPl; FFA; SpnCl; Bsktbl; Western Ill; Farm Management Consultent.

GINGERICH, Kaye M; John Glenn HS; Bay City, MI; 23/365 SecSrCls; HonRl; SchMus; StuCncl; TchrAde; RptrYrbk; FrCl; PpCl; LetterBsktbl; PPFtbl; Michigan State Univ; Social Work.

GINGERICH, Phillip W; Wawasee HS; Milford, IN; 46/217 Chrs; ChrhWkr; HonRl; NatlMeritCmnd; FFA; SpnCl; Bsbl;.

GINGERY, Rose M; Garrett HS; Garrett, IN; HonRl; OffAde; RptrYrbk; LatCl; PpCl; Trk; SecGAA; Univ; Nursing.

GINGRAS, Robert B; Newberry HS; Marquette, MI; 14/129 PresFrshCls; PresSophCls; HonRl; NHS; RptrYrbk; CaptBsktbl; CaptFtbl; Univ; Curr Of Major Study.

GINGREY, Kathy J; West Fargo HS; Harwood, ND; 1/137 AFS; Band; Chr; ChrhWkr; HonRl; Mdrgl; NatlThespSoc; Orch; 4-H; Chrldr; College.

GINGRICH, Annette D; Pine River HS; Leroy, MI; VPSrCls; Band; HonRl; MrchBnd; SecTrsFrshCls; OffAde; SchPl;.

GINGRICH, Paula K; Chanute HS; Chanute, KS; 1/181 Band; CncrtBnd; HonRl; MrchBnd; NatlMeritCmnd; TchrAde; VPYthFlsp; SchPpr; SecFBLA; SpnCl; MthCl; College; Lawyer.

GINGRICH, Randall W; Western HS; Sheffield, IL; 1/54 PresJrCls; HonRl; StuCncl; YthFlsp; Yrbk; Pres4-H; FFA; FrCl; LatCl; LetterFtbl; Univ Of Ill; Engineering.

GINN, Rebecca A; Capac Comm HS; Capac, MI; 10/110 HstSrCls; Band; DrlTm; HonRl; HospAde; NHS; OffAde; StuCncl; 4-H; PpCl; St Clair County Comm; Accounting.

GINSBERG, Joni R; Rolling Meadows HS; Arlington Hts, IL; 75/581 HonRl; Chrldr; Univ Of Col; Pharmacy.

GINTHER, Laura J; Highland HS; Highland, IN; 15/587 PresJrCls; ChrhWkr; CmntyWkr; OffAde; SchMus; SchPl; StuCncl; RptrSchPpr; SptEdSchPpr; PpCl; College; Physical Ed.

GINTHER, Patricia; Jefferson HS; Stanberry, MO; 7/28 SecFrshCls; PresSrCls; Band; HonRl; StuCncl; 4-H; FHA; 4-HAwd; PresAwd; College.

GINTHER, Sharon L; Harbor Beach Comm HS; Ruth, MI; HonRl; HospAde; LbryAde; TchrAde; 4-H; FHA; Chrldr; College.

GINTHER, Theresa A; Jefferson C 123 HS; Stanberry, MO; 5/28 Band; Chrs; HonRl; SchPl; 4-H; FHA; PpCl; Northwest Mo St Coll; Home Ec.

GINTNER, Jane M; Valders HS; Cato, WI; Aud/Vis; Chrs; HonRl; SchPl; 4-H; FHA; IMSpt; PPFtbl; Technical School; Medical Assistant.

GIPE, Carolyn D; West Nodaway Ri HS; Elmo, MO; 2/45 Chrs; HonRl; NHS; SchPl; RptrSchPpr; SchPpr; Bsktbl; Trk; Coll; Business.

GIPPRICH, Julie A; East Detroit HS; Warren, MI; PresSrCls; CmntyWkr; LbryAde; NHS; NatlMeritCmnd; NatlMeritSchl; StuCncl; JAAwd; PresAwd; College; Library Technician.

GIRARD, Lori E; Northeast HS; Arma, KS; 5/50 ALAGirlsSt; Band; HonRl; NatlThespSoc; Quill&Scroll; SchPl; Twrl; RptrYrbk; RptrSchPpr; PpCl; College.

GIRARD, Yvonne M; Proviso West HS; Bellwood, IL; 130/866 Chrs; HonRl; Univ Of Arizona.

GIRBACH, Juanita J; Saline HS; Saline, MI; ALAGirlsSt; Band; CmntyWkr; HospAde; JA; NHS; NatlMeritSchl; PolWkr; StuGov; 4-H; College; History.

GIRCH, Linda; Arapahoe HS; Arapahoe, NE; 5/34 SecSophCls; SecSrCls; Band; Chrs; ChrhWkr; CncrtBnd; HonRl; LbryAde; MrchBnd; Nursing School; Rn Degree In Nursing.

GIRMAN, Karen L; George Rogers Clark HS; Whiting, IN; 64/260 Chr; StuCncl; TchrAde; SpnCl; PpCl; Indiana Univ.

GIRMAN, Marisa L; Lake Central HS; St John, IN; Chrs; HonRl; NHS; NatlThespSoc; SchMus; SchPl; StuGov; TchrAde; Teen; RptrYrbk; Chrldr; PPFtbl; Purdue Univ; Nursing.

GIROUX, Pamela M; Marian HS; Omaha, NE; DrlTm; HonRl; LbryAde; NHS; PresLatCl; Chrldr; IMSpt; Creighton Univ; Pharmacy.

GIROUX, Timothy G; Marmion Military Acad; Aurora, IL; 3/100 TrsJrCls; VPSrCls; HonRl; JrNHS; NHS; ROTC; StuCncl; StuGov; RptrYrbk; HstJrCls; Tennis; Univ Il; Dentistry.

GIRTON, Charles B; Randolph Southern HS; Lynn, IN; 1/55 ChrhWkr; HonRl; NHS; StuCncl; RptrYrbk; 4-H; Purdue Univ; Civil Eng.

GIRTON, Stephen W; Delta HS; Muncie, IN; 90/250 JA; TchrAde; JAAwd; Navy;.

GIRTZ, Rebecca; Hinckley HS; Hinckley, MN; SecSrCls; ALAGirlsSt; Chr; HonRl; SchMus; SchPl; StuCncl; RptrYrbk; RptrSchPpr; Us Air Force; Occupational Therapy.

GISE, Debra A; Lindblom Technical HS; Chicago, IL; 68/652 Chr; ChrhWkr; HonRl; NatlMeritCmnd; SctActv; RptrYrbk; FrCl; SpnCl; Swmmng; IMSpt; U Of Ill;lawyer.

GISH, Deborah S; Bushton HS; Bushton, KS; Band; HonRl; NHS; PepBnd; SchPl; TchrAde; RptrYrbk; Chrldr; AmLegAwd; College.

GISH, Teresa A; Jacksonville HS; Jacksonville, IL; 82/328 ChrhWkr; HospAde; MrchBnd; SchPl; Twrl; YthFlsp; 4-H; FrCl; Passavant School Of Nursing; Nurse.

GISKA, Cynthia; Aquinas HS; Lincoln Park, MI; 5/216 HonRl; JrNHS; NHS; SchAde; StuCncl; FNA; Univ Of Mich; Biophysical Sci.

GISSE, Mark R; Waterford Mott HS; Drayton Plains, MI; 3/420 HonRl; NatlMeritFnl; NatlMeritSchl; CaptBsktbl;.

GIST, Amron L; Highland Park HS; St Paul, MN; Band; CncrtBnd; HonRl; MrchBnd; PepBnd; SchPl; YthFlsp; FHA; University.

GIST, Roger B; Raymore Peculiar HS; Raymore, MO; 12/87 ChrhWkr; CncrtBnd; HonRl; NHS; PepBnd; PresSpnCl; LetterTrk; Univ Of Missouri; Mech Engineering.

GIST, William L; Beardstown HS; Beardstown, IL; 3/130 Band; CncrtBnd; HonRl; MrchBnd; TreasNHS; SchPl; VPStuCncl; Bsktbl; LetterGlf; Trk; Univ; Accounting.

GITLIN, Susan; Bluffton HS; Bluffton, IN; HonRl; LbryAde; SchPl; SpnCl; Bsktbl; GAA; Purdue Univ; Pre Vet Med.

GITTENS, Steven G; Wheaton Central HS; Wheaton, IL; HonRl; JrNHS; OffAde; RptrSchPpr; LatCl; Trk; Northern Illinois Univ; Business.

GITZEN, Sharon M; St Agnes HS; St Paul, MN; 5/130 Chr; HonRl; HospAde; NHS; SctActv; GAA; Coll; Elem Educ.

GIUDICI, Doreen M; Farmington HS; Northville, MI; SecFrshCls; Chrs; DrlTm; HonRl; JrNHS; SchMus; TchrAde; Bsktbl; Chrldr; PPFtbl; University; Pre Law.

GIUGLER, Mary Ellen; Lockport Township HS; Lockport, IL; 13/550 CmntyWkr; HonRl; LbryAde; NHS; SchPl; Univ Of Chicago; Foreign Language.

GIUS, Richard J; St Patrick HS; River Forest, IL; 27/427 HonRl; SctActv; LetterFtbl; CchngActv; Northern Ill Univ; Meterology.

GIUSTI, Lorraine M; Bradley Bourbonnais HS; Bradley, IL; 1/360 ChrhWkr; HonRl; NHS; Yrbk; SpnCl; LetterTrk; GAA; Univ Of Illinois; Medicine.

GIVENS, Gregory; West Side HS; Gary, IN; Chr; ChrhWkr; HonRl; JrNHS; NHS; SctActv; Bsbl; Bsktbl; IMSpt; College; Elec Engineering.

GIVENS, James A; Hickman HS; Columbia, MO; ALBoysSt; CncrtBnd; HonRl; LbryAde; NHS; NatlMeritSF; PolWkr; FrCl; SciCl; U Of Mo; Law.

GIVENS, Mike L; Central HS; Cape Girardeau, MO; JA; Ftbl; LetterTrk; Wrstlng; IMSpt; JAAwd; Coll; Bus Mgmt.

GIVINS, Michael; Highland Sr HS; St Paul, MN; Band; Chr; Chrs; ChrhWkr; CmntyWkr; DrlTm; DrmBgl; MrchBnd; RptrYrbk; Trk; Coll; Bus.

GJELSVIK, David B; Vienna Township HS; Simpson, IL; Band; ChrhWkr; CmntyWkr; LitMag; TchrAde; YthFnd; CchngActv; IMSpt; PresAwd; Trade School; Professional.

GJEMSE, Susan L; Fridley HS; Fridley, MN; Chrs; DrlTm; HonRl; MrchBnd; NatlMeritSF; FFA; Univ; Veterinarian.

GJERE, Steven A; North Winneshiek HS; Decorah, IA; 18/33 TrsSrCls; Chrs; HonRl; LbryAde; StuCncl; 4-H; FFA; PpCl; CaptBsktbl;.

GJERNES, Marvin J; Cresbard HS; Chelsea, SD; PresSrCls; ALBoysSt; Band; LetterCncrtBnd; HonRl; MrchBnd; SchPl; LetterBsktbl; LetterFtbl; AmLegAwd; Sdsu Brookins; Agri & Bio Sci.

GJERNING, Carma C; Frederic HS; Frederic, WI; ALAGirlsSt; Chr; Chrs; ChrhWkr; CmntyWkr; HonRl; Mdrgl; SchPl; FHA; Bsktbl; Nursing School; Registered Nurse.

GLADBACH, Joseph G; Bishop Miege HS; Overland Park, KS; 32/202 ALBoysSt; HonRl; NHS; LetterBsktbl; Chrldr; Univ Of Missouri; Geological Engineer.

GLADBACK, Mary L; Magic City Campus HS; Minot, ND; Band; Chr; ChrhWkr; CncrtBnd; HonRl; MrchBnd; Orch; PepBnd; SctActv; TchrAde; Minot State College; Music.

GLADE, Cindy A; Wauconda HS; Harvard, IL; ChrhWkr; CmntyWkr; HonRl; NHS; SchPl; StuCncl; FTA; College.

GLANTZ, Lucinda A; Adams Central HS; Hastings, NE; 3/54 PresFrshCls; Chr; HonRl; NHS; SchMus; SchPl; RptrYrbk; LetterTrk; BauchLmbAwd; DARAwd; College; Pharmacy.

GLANVILLE, Denise R; Paola HS; Paola, KS; 3/130 ChrhWkr; CncrtBnd; HonRl; Quill&Scroll; PresYthFlsp; RptrYrbk; RptrSchPpr; SchPpr; GerCl; PpCl; Oral Roberts Univ; Physical Therapy.

GLANZER, Patricia A; Freeman Public HS; Dolton, SD; 16/65 Chr; Chrs; HonRl; SchMus; SchPl; PresYthFlsp; Yrbk; 4-H; FHA; PpCl; Goshen Coll; Maj Study.

GLASCO, Gerald; Crab Or Chard HS; Marion, IL; VPJrCls; HonRl; YthFlsp; SchPpr; PpCl; Bsbl; Bsktbl; Trk; DanFAwd; 4-HAwd; S Ill Univ; Argriculture.

GLASCOCK, Jeffrey G; Melvin Sibley HS; Sibley, IL; 2/32 ALBoysSt; Band; Chrs; ChrhWkr; HonRl; NHS; SchPl; LetterBsbl; LetterBsktbl; LetterTrk; Coll; Engr.

GLASCOCK, Sally D; Brookville HS; Cedar Grove, IN; PresFrshCls; ALAGirlsSt; HonRl; NHS; StuCncl; Treas4-H; TreasSpnCl; LetterTrk; GAA; Univ; Professional.

GLASER, Debra C; Spalding Acad; Spalding, NE; TrsJrCls; Chr; Chrs; HonRl; HospAde; SchPl; StuCncl; RptrYrbk; Yrbk; SpnCl; College; Vocational Health Field.

GLASER, Diane M; Spalding Public HS; Spalding, NE; PresFrshCls; VPSophCls; VPJrCls; Chrs; OffAde; SchPl; RptrYrbk; Bsktbl; Trk; Chrldr; Trade School; Vocation.

GLASER, Renee C; Southwest HS; Green Bay, WI; 8/420 Band; ChrhWkr; HonRl; SctActv; 4-H; FTA; GerCl; LetterTrk; GAA; Sec4-HAwd; U Of Green Bay; Acturial Sci.

GLASER, Ronald F; Spalding Academy; Spalding, NE; 4/16 PresJrCls; Band; Chrs; HonRl; StuGov; RptrYrbk; 4-H; LetterBsktbl; LetterFtbl; LetterTrk; University; Professional.

GLASGOW, Mark J; Roseville HS; Roseville, IL; Band; CncrtBnd; MrchBnd; PepBnd; 4-H; PpCl; SciCl; Ftbl; IMSpt; College Siu; Radio Tv Repair.

GLASGOW, Stephen W; Knox County HS; Rutledge, MO; Band; Chrs; ChrhWkr; CncrtBnd; HonRl; MrchBnd; PepBnd; FFA; Bsktbl; Farming.

GLASNAPP, Robin; Lytton HS; Lytton, IA; SecFrshCls; TrsJrCls; Chr; HonRl; NHS; StuCncl; YthLg; FHA;.

GLASS, Allen B; Niles East HS; Skokie, IL; HonRl; RptrSchPpr; FBLA; KeyCl; Univ Of Illinois.

GLASS, Christopher J; Mngr John R Hackett HS; Kalamazoo, MI; HonRl; LetterTrk; Kalamazoo Coll; Physics.

GLASS, Gary R; Quigley South HS; Chicago, IL; 15/170 CmntyWkr; HonRl; NatlMeritCmnd; CaptGlf; College; Accounting.

GLASS, James M; Gobles HS; Gobles, MI; 2/65 VPJrCls; HonRl; NHS; NatlMeritSchl; EdYrBk; MthCl; SciCl; Bsbl; Ftbl; Trk; Adrian Col; Electrical Eng.

GLASS, Janice M; Linton HS; Linton, ND; 1/60 Chrs; ChrhWkr; DrlTm; HonRl; HospAde; LbryAde; NHS; Bsktbl; Chrldr; HstSrCls; Univ; Nurse.

GLASS, Kathryn K; Remington HS; Benton, KS; 5/55 Band; CmntyWkr; HonRl; NHS; StuCncl; TchrAde; EdYrBk; RptrSchPpr; PpCl; 4-HAwd; Business School; Vocation.

GLASS, Lisa M; Ash Grove HS; Bois D Arc, MO; PresSophCls; Band; Chrs; ChrhWkr; CncrtBnd; HonRl; FBLA; PpCl; SciCl; CaptChrldr; Sw Mo St Univ; Theatre And Teaching.

GLASS, Mary; Bgm Community HS; Brooklyn, IA; 8/46 VPJrCls; HonRl; NHS; StuCncl; Bsktbl; Trk; GAA; 4-HAwd; KiwanAwd; PresAwd; Univ; Farmer.

GLASS, Paula; Central Noble HS; Kendallville, IN; 5/113 Chr; HonRl; Mdrgl; NHS; PepBnd; 4-H; 4-HAwd; Univ.

GLASS, Reuben J; Kickapoo HS; Readstown, WI; 13/52 VPFrshCls; PresSophCls; CncrtBnd; HonRl; StuCncl; Bsktbl; Ftbl; CaptTrk; AmLegAwd; PresAwd; Eau Claire Clg; Business.

GLASSBURN, Earl K; Maconaquah HS; Kokomo, IN; 22/225 ALBoysSt; Chr; Chrs; HonRl; JrNHS; LbryAde; NHS; SchMus; SchPl; TchrAde; Purdue Univ; Industrial Mgmnt.

GLASSCOCK, Carol L; Athens HS; Springfield, IL; 7/51 Band; Chr; Chrs; ChrhWkr; CmntyWkr; HonRl; NHS; SchAde; SchPl; SctActv; TchrAde; RptrSchPpr; CaptBsktbl; GAA; Illinois College; Education.

GLASSEL, Becky H; Forest Lake HS; Forest Lake, MN; HonRl; NHS; NatlMeritCmnd; Quill&Scroll; Yrbk; Clge; Christian Education.

GLASSEL, Linda; I G Comm HS; Ida Grove, IA; 14/61 SecSophCls; VPJrCls; Chrs; HonRl; NHS; NatlThespSoc; SchMus; StuCncl; TchrAde; FHA; Univ Of Iowa; Nursing.

GLASSER, Kenneth R; Gaylord HS; Gaylord, MI; PresJrCls; ChrhWkr; CmntyWkr; HonRl; NHS; PolWkr; StuCncl; StuGov; YthLg; LetterBsktbl; College; Architecture.

GLATT, Christopher G; Chapman HS; Chapman, KS; ALBoysSt; Band; Chr; Chrs; CncrtBnd; HonRl; MrchBnd; NatlMeritSF; PepBnd; StuGov; YthLg; LetterGlf; LetterWrstlng; IMSpt; College; Engineer.

GLATT, Debra; Steele HS; Driscoll, ND; 3/30 SecTrsFrshCls; SecTrsSophCls; Chrs; HonRl; LbryAde; PolWkr; SchPl; Sdlty; FHA; PpCl; State Teachers Coll; Sec Education.

GLATTHAAR, Mary; Belleville Township HS; Belleville, IL; 130/835 AFS; GerCl; Univ Of Illinois; School Of Commerce.

GLATZ, Nancy E; Schaumburg HS; Hanover Park, IL; 34/539 HonRl; HospAde; RptrSchPpr; SpnCl; PpCl; St Anthony School Of Nursing; Rn.

GLAVAN, Robert A; Aurora Central Catholic HS; Aurora, IL; ChrhWkr; HonRl; JA; LitMag; SchMus; StuGov; RptrSchPpr; FBLA; LetterGlf; JAAwd; North Illinois Univ; Business Admin.

GLAVICH, Tom J; Wausau East HS; Merrill, WI; KeyCl; PpCl; Bsbl; Ftbl; CchngActv; IMSpt; Coll.

GLAZE, Robert D; Plattsmouth HS; Plattsmouth, NE; 11/163 Chrs; CmntyWkr; CncrtBnd; HonRl; Mdrgl; MrchBnd; SchMus; YthFlsp; SpnCl; Hastings Col; Business Admini.

GLAZE, Scott A; Huntington N HS; Roanoke, IN; NHS; StuCncl; 4-H; Bsbl; Ftbl; Purdue Univ; Metallurgy.

GLAZER, Barry; Mather HS; Chicago, IL; 58/421 HonRl; NHS; StuCncl; TchrAde; RptrSchPpr; Bsbl; Bsktbl; Univ Of Illinois; Law.

GLAZEWSKI, Nancy M; St Ladislaus HS; Hamtramck, MI; 6/112 HonRl; FNA; FrCl; MthCl; PpCl; Chrldr; GAA; Michigan State U; Medical Technology.

GLAZIER, Karen L; Salem HS; Salem, MO; SecJrCls; Band; Chrs; CncrtBnd; HonRl; MrchBnd; SctActv; StuCncl; Chrldr; MasAwd; Education.

GLAZIER, Martha J; Salem HS; Salem, MO; 5/179 SecFrshCls; SecSrCls; Band; Chr; Chrs; ChrhWkr; CncrtBnd; DrlTm; HonRl; Chrldr; CchngActv; IMSpt; PPFtbl; Smsu; Education.

GLAZIER, Martha J; Salem Sr HS; Salem, MO; 5/180 VPFrshCls; SecSrCls; Band; Chr; CncrtBnd; HonRl; StuGov; Chrldr; IMSpt; PPFtbl; Smsu; Elementary Ed.

GLEASON, Colleen M; St Marys HS; Berkley, MI; 2/75 NHS; SchMus; VPStuCncl; VP4-H; LetterBsbl; CaptChrldr; CchngActv; 4-HAwd; OptClAwd; Univ; Doctor.

GLEASON, George R; Greenwood HS; Springfield, MO; 10/30 ALBoysSt; Chrs; ChrhWkr; HonRl; ModUN; YthFlsp; RptrSchPpr; LatCl; Ftbl; Smsu; Bus Manager.

GLEASON, John S; Logan Sr HS; La Crosse, WI; 108/225 HonRl; Western Wisconsin Tech Institute; Welding.

GLEASON, Kathryn L; Lyons Township HS; La Grange Park, IL; ChmnAFS; HonRl; PresSctActv; StuCncl; StuGov; YthFlsp; Yrbk; FrCl; Trk; Chrldr; Univ; Arch.

GLEASON, Marilou E; Nazareth Academy; Brookfield, IL; 12/164 HonRl; NHS; Orch; SchMus; TchrAde; RptrYrbk; Loyola Univ; Psychology.

GLEASON, Robert A; Creighton Prep; Omaha, NE; HonRl; PolWkr; StuCncl; StuGov; TchrAde; MthCl; IMSpt; Univ; Law.

GLEASON, Sandra; Lyle Public HS; Lyle, MN; 2/27 VPFrshCls; Chr; HonRl; NHS; StuCncl; Yrbk; FHA; Bsktbl; Vocational & College; Child Development.

GLEASON, Shannon L; New Haven HS; New Haven, MI; TrsSophCls; Band; MrchBnd; TreasNHS; PepBnd; University Of Michigan; Medicine.

GLEASON, Sheri A; Manson Comm HS; Manson, IA; 17/81 TrsSophCls; Band; Chr; HonRl; Mdrgl; Orch; YthFlsp; 4-H; 4-HAwd; Northwestern College; Elementary Education.

GLECKLER, Mary L; Griggsville HS; New Salem, IL; 2/29 TrsFrshCls; PresJrCls; PresSrCls; Chrs; HonRl; VPNHS; NatlThespSoc; PresStuCncl; Yrbk; GAA; College; Medical Doctor.

GLEISNER, Robert A; Harper HS; Chicago, IL; 1/480 Chr; DrlTm; HonRl; JrNHS; NHS; OffAde; ROTC; MthCl; Northern Il Univ; Professional.

GLEISNER, Steve W; Custer HS; Milwaukee, WI; HonRl; College; Capentry.

GLEISNER, Veronica M; Jefferson Sr HS; Jefferson, WI; 1/175 Band; Chr; HonRl; PresLbryAde; NHS; Orch; PepBnd; SchMus; GovHonPrgAwd; JCAwd; University; Music.

GLENN, Barbara J; Wheaton Central HS; Wheaton, IL; Band; HonRl; LitMag; RptrSchPpr; Tennis; Illinois Benedictine Clg; English.

GLENN, Jaymee L; Olin HS; Olin, IA; 1/23 SecJrCls; Band; HonRl; PresNHS; SecNatlThespSoc; SchPl; SecStuCncl; 4-H; CaptChrldr; 4-HAwd; College.

GLENN, Kandy J; Rossville Alvin HS; Rossville, IL; 4/40 ALAGirlsSt; ChrhWkr; HonRl; NHS; StuCncl; EdYrBk; SecFTA; CaptChrldr; DARAwd; CitAwd; Eastern Ill Univ; Spe Educ Teach.

GLENN, Kathy L; Carrollton Sr HS; Carrollton, MO; Chrs; DrlTm; HonRl; MrchBnd; NHS; FHA; SpnCl; Maryville Clg; Kindergarten Teacher.

GLENN, Pamela D; South Harrison HS; Bethany, MO; 2/79 LbryAde; FHA; TreasFTA; Nw Mo St Univ; Acct.

GLENN, Peggy E; Franklin Center HS; Franklin Grove, IL; 9/47 Chr; Chrs; HonRl; NHS; YthFlsp; 4-H; College.

GLENN, Richard A; Olin Cons HS; Olin, IA; ALBoysSt; CAP; HstFrshCls; HonRl; JA; NHS; PolWkr; RedCrAde; ROTC; LetterBsktbl;.

GLENN, Rodney; Hermitage HS; Pittsburg, MO; Band; HonRl; MrchBnd; PolWkr; SchPl; StuGov; YthFlsp; CivCl; FSA; Bsbl; Trade School; Vocation.

GLENN, Tama D; Marquette HS; Marquette, MI; 6/384 PresBand; CncrtBnd; HonRl; MrchBnd; NHS; Orch; PepBnd; SchMus; SciCl; LetterBsktbl; U Of Mi Ann Arbor; Physician.

GLENN, Thomas L; Collinsville HS; Edwardsville, IL; 47/660 HonRl; NHS; YthFlsp; GerCl; Southern Ill Univ; Accounting.

GLENZ, Brad S; Paynesville HS; Paynesville, MN; Chr; ChrhWkr; HonRl; SchMus; YthFlsp; RptrSchPpr; LetterBsbl; Ftbl; LetterWrstlng; IMSpt; Tech Inst; Agriculture.

GLESENER, Peggy J; Bird Island Public HS; Bird Island, MN; 7/65 Band; HonRl; NatlFornLg; NHS; StuGov; Chrldr; GAA; IMSpt; Univ Of Minnesota; Music.

GLESINGER, Michael E; Spalding Academy; Spalding, NE; ALBoysSt; OffAde; SchAde; SchPl; StuCncl; RptrSchPpr; LetterBsbl; LetterBsktbl; LetterFtbl; LetterTrk; Univ; Broadcasting.

GLESINGER, Michael E; Spalding Acad; Spalding, NE; SchAde; SchPl; PresStuCncl; StuGov; TchrAde; LetterBsbl; Bsktbl; LetterFtbl; Tennis; Entertainer.

GLESSNER, Paul W; Dixon HS; Dixon, IL; 12/333 JA; NHS; College; Chemical Eng.

GLEWEN, Matthew J; Goodrich HS; Fond Du Lac, WI; 29/673 Band; CmntyWkr; CncrtBnd; HonRl; MrchBnd; NHS; PepBnd; SptEdSchPpr; Pres4-H; EldAwd; 4-HAwd; Univ Of Wisconsin; Biology.

GLICK, David A; Tower Hill HS; Tower Hill, IL; VPJrCls; VPSrCls; HonRl; Lakeland Coll; Arch.

GLIDEWELL, Kathleen S; Casey HS; Greenup, IL; SecFrshCls; TrsSophCls; HonRl; OffAde; RptrSchPpr; 4-H; FHA; FTA; U Of Fl.

GLIDEWELL, Robert W; Casey HS; Casey, IL; PresSrCls; Chr; HonRl; JA; NHS; SchPl; SctActv; FFA; LetterTrk; IMSpt; College; Professional.

GLIEBERMAN, Scott; Sullivan Hs; Chicago, IL; 6/276 PresNHS; SchPl; SchPpr; KeyCl; LetterSwmmng; LetterTennis; College; Professional.

GLIEGE, Shirley E; Prospect HS; Arlington Hts, IL; 28/620 ChrhWkr; CmntyWkr; HonRl; NatlFornLg; NHS; StuGov; LatCl; SciCl; IMSpt; University Of Illinois; Lawyer.

GLIMM, Cindy L; Heelan HS; Sioux City, IA; 1/249 HonRl; JA; LbryAde; SctActv; PpCl; JAAwd; College; English Teacher.

GLINIECKI, Peter J; Stratford HS; Stratford, WI; Band; CncrtBnd; HonRl; MrchBnd; NHS; PepBnd; FHA; SciCl; LionAwd; Coll; Nurse.

GLINIECKI, Phillip G; Stratford HS; Stratford, WI; HonRl; Ftbl; Wrstlng; CchngActv; IMSpt; Schl; Farmer Or Mechanic.

GLISAN, Renee J; Notre Dame HS; Quincy, IL; Band; Chr; CmntyWkr; HonRl; SchMus; StuGov; YthLg; SptEdSchPpr; FNA; Tennis; St Johns Sch Of Nurs; Registered Nurse.

GLISAR, Paula M; Northeast HS; Mulberry, KS; 10/51 Chrs; HonRl; SpnCl; PpCl; Bsktbl; College; Lawyer.

GLISE, Tamara S; Central HS; St Joseph, MO; Chr; Chrs; HonRl; ModUN; StuGov; College; English Major.

GLISSMAN, Denise D; Ancilla Domini HS; Plymouth, IN; 1/15 ALAGirlsSt; Chrs; CmntyWkr; HonRl; LitMag; PolWkr; SchPpr; 4-H; 4-HAwd; Coll; Pharmacy.

GLISSMAN, Denise G; Pender Public HS; Pender, NE; 6/57 HonRl; NHS; OffAde; RedCrAde; SchPl; RptrYrbk; Pres4-H; FHA; PpCl; 4-HAwd; Univ Of Ne ; Acct.

GLISSMAN, Todd; Garden County HS; Oshkosh, NE; Aud/Vis; HonRl; LbryAde; NHS; SchPl; YthFlsp; Yrbk; SpnCl; Bsktbl; College; Pre Law.

GLOCKNER, Kathleen A; Ann Arbor Pioneer HS; Ann Arbor, MI; ChrhWkr; CmntyWkr; HonRl; Orch; PolWkr; TchrAde; GerCl; LetterSwmmng; BttyCrckrAwd; Mount Holyoke College; Medicine.

GLODOWSKI, Julie A; Madison HS; Madison, KS; 6/23 ALAGirlsSt; Band; CncrtBnd; HonRl; MrchBnd; NHS; PepBnd; SchPl; 4-H; PpCl; Butler Co Jr College; Data Processing.

GLOFF, William E; Glenbard East HS; Lombard, IL; HonRl; Ball State University; Architecture.

GLOOD, Diana; Brookings HS; Brooklings, SD; 46/187 NHS; SpnCl;.

GLOS, Donna J; H L Richards HS; Oak Lawn, IL; HonRl; LbryAde; TchrAde; St Xavier College; Business Adm.

GLOTZBACH, Susan E; Hayden HS; Topeka, KS; ALAGirlsSt; HonRl; HospAde; JA; NatlMeritSchl; VPFrCl; PpCl; Trk; AmLegAwd; College; Mathematics.

GLOVER, Angela; Northwest HS; Saint Louis, MO; 5/318 HonRl; JA; MrchBnd; NHS; PolWkr; StuCncl; Twrl; FshEdSchPpr; MthCl; BttyCrckrAwd; CitAwd; Northwestern Univ; Biology Major.

GLOVER, Betty A; Serena HS; Sheridan, IL; 1/72 CncrtBnd; HonRl; MrchBnd; NHS; OffAde; PepBnd; SchPl; 4-H; FHA; PpCl; Ill Valley Comm College; Business Admin.

GLOVER, Brenda; Harbor Beach Community HS; Harbor Beach, MI; 20u134 SecSophCls; ChrhWkr; HonRl; ModUN; NHS; OffAde; SchMus; TchrAde; FTA; PpCl; Western Mich Univ; Med Tech.

GLOVER, Dana L; Salina HS; Salina, KS; 13/350 PresJrCls; CncrtBnd; DrmBgl; HonRl; MrchBnd; Orch; PepBnd; SchMus; StuCncl; OptClAwd; U Of Ks; Fine Arts.

GLOVER, Elma R; Ankeny HS; Ankeny, IA; HonRl; JrNHS; LitMag; NHS; NatlMeritSF; SchPl; EdYrBk; FrCl; IMSpt; Coll; Printing & Graphic Arts.

GLOVER, Enis; Crispus Attucks HS; Indianapolis, IN; HonRl; StuCncl; Bsktbl; Ftbl; Trk; Wrstlng; IMSpt; KiwanAwd; Bishop College; Engineering.

GLOVER, James M; Hart HS; Hart, MI; HonRl; SchPl; IMSpt; Ferris Coll; Civil Eng.

GLOVER, James S; Superior HS; Superior, WI; 46/527 HonRl; FBLA; LetterGlf; College; Accounting.

GLOVER, Janice A; Immaculata HS; Detroit, MI; HospAde; StuGov; Eastern Univ; Nursing.

GLOVER, Jeffrey A; Hamilton Southeastern HS; Noblesville, IN; 25/132 Band; ChrhWkr; DrmMjrt; HonRl; NHS; SchMus; TchrAde; PresYthFlsp; 4-H; Bsbl; Bsktbl; Trk; IMSpt; 4-HAwd; Purdue Univ; Pharmacy.

GLOVER, Letha K; Borden HS; Borden, IN; 2/74 Band; ChrhWkr; HonRl; HospAde; Asbury College; Reg Nurse.

GLOVER, Margaret A; Lafayette Co HS; Lexington, MO; VPJrCls; AFS; ALAGirlsSt; Band; Chr; DrlTm; HonRl; MrchBnd; NHS; Orch; College; Professional.

GLOVER, Martha A; Seeger HS; Williamsport, IN; 6/128 SecSophCls; CmntyWkr; NHS; StuCncl; SecYthFlsp; Yrbk; Pres4-H; PresFHA; SpnCl; 4-HAwd; Depaum Univ; Spanish.

GLOVER, Richard E; South Side HS; Ft Wayne, IN; 117/438 ChrhWkr; JA; OffAde; Baptist Bible College; Christian Service.

GLOVER, Robert P; Whitehall HS; Whitehall, MI; 42/165 Band; HonRl; NHS; StuCncl; GerCl; Bsbl; Ftbl; AmLegAwd; RotaryAwd;.

GLOVER, Steven R; Niles North HS; Skokie, IL; 50/641 Chrs; HonRl; NatlMeritSF; LetterFtbl; Univ Of Illinois.

GLOWIAK, Pamela L; Marquette Manor Christian HS; Chicago, IL; Chr; ChrhWkr; HonRl; OffAde; PolWkr; SchPl; SctActv; StuGov; YthFlsp; RptrSchPpr; SchPpr; College; Law.

GLOYD, Sheryl J; Guilford HS; Rockford, IL; ChrhWkr; CmntyWkr; HonRl; HospAde; SctActv; TchrAde; 4-H; PpCl; Pres4-HAwd; College; Fashion Merchandising.

GLUCK, Rachel L; Ida Crown Jewish Academy; Chicago, IL; 3/71 VPJrCls; Band; Chrs; HonRl; NHS; Orch; SchMus; SchPl; StuCncl; University; Music.

GLUDOVATZ, Lynne; Caro HS; Caro, MI; HonRl; SchPl; TchrAde; RptrYrbk; Yrbk; RptrSchPpr; PpCl; Bsktbl; Trk; College; Professional Music.

GLUECK, Roger W; Notre Dame HS; Illmo, MO; PresJrCls; HonRl; SchPl; StuCncl; Bsbl; Bsktbl; CchngActv; IMSpt; Univ; Law.

GLYNN, Devin L; Summerfield HS; Summerfield, KS; TrsSophCls; SecJrCls; Band; Chrs; CncrtBnd; HonRl; SchPl; StuCncl; SptEdYrbk; LetterFtbl; Col; Architecture And Design.

GLYNN, John A; Millington HS; Millington, MI; VPJrCls; HonRl; StuGov; TchrAde; LetterBsktbl; LetterFtbl; LetterTrk; College; Professional.

GLYNN, Rebecca J; St Charles HS; St Charles, MI; HonRl; RedCrAde; Twrl; 4-H; GAA; University; Law.

GNAT, Barbara L; West Allis Central HS; West Allis, WI; 1/460 ChrhWkr; HonRl; LbryAde; NHS; Alverno Col; English.

GNERER, Mary K; Lakeville Jr Sr HS; Lakeville, MN; HonRl; NatlFornLg; SchAde; TchrAde; Yrbk; PpCl; St Marys Jr Coll; Occupational Therаist.

GNEWUCH, Cindy; Oconomowoc Senior Hs; Oconomowoc, WI; 27/223 AFS; ChrhWkr; HonRl; LbryAde; NHS; FHA; GerCl; PpCl; Trade School Of Nursing.

GNIEWEK, Paul; Catholic Central HS; Detroit, MI; HstJrCls; Chrl; HonRl; TchrAde; FrCl; SciCl; IMSpt; University; Professional.

GOACHER, Brenda S; Waverly HS; Waverly, IL; PresSrCls; ChrhWkr; HonRl; NHS; NatlThespSoc; Yrbk; 4-H; FHA; Trk; College; Child Care.

GOADE, Courtney A; Baxter Springs HS; Baxter Springs, KS; Band; HonRl; NatlFornLg; NatlThespSoc; OffAde; SchMus; StuCncl; RptrYrbk; Bsbl; LetterBsktbl; Trk; LetterChrldr; CchngActv;.

GOAR, Ann E; United Township HS; East Moline, IL; 13/680 SecSophCls; ChrhWkr; HospAde; NHS; StuCncl; LetterTrk; GAA; Illinois Wesleyan Univ; Biology.

GOBEN, Mercy; Glenham HS; Graham, SD; HonRl; RptrYrbk; RptrSchPpr; GerCl; BttyCrckrAwd; Christopher Newport Coll.

GOBEN, Sally J; Balyki HS; Kilbourne, IL; 3/28 Band; CncrtBnd; HonRl; MrchBnd; NHS; PepBnd; SchAde; SchMus; SchPl; TchrAde; Yrbk; RptrSchPpr; PpCl; Bsktbl;.

GOBLIRSCH, Gregory J; Wabasso Public HS; Tyler, MN; Chrs; HonRl; TchrAde; LetterBsbl; Bsktbl; LetterFtbl; Trk; Trade School; Accountant.

GOCHEE, Angel V; Shabbona HS; Shabbona, IL; 1/44 ChrhWkr; CmntyWkr; LbryAde; SchPl; YthFlsp; Yrbk; 4-H; FHA; FrCl; SciCl; Northern Ill Univ; Medicine Pediatrics.

GOCHENOUR, Anita F; Logan Magnolia Comm HS; Logan, IA; 2/50 SecTrsFrshCls; Chrs; HonRl; LbryAde; NHS; SchMus; SchPl; Pres4-H; LetterTrk; 4-HAwd; Univ; Doctor.

GOCKE, Joan K; Centennial HS; Waco, NE; 3/58 Chrs; ChrhWkr; NHS; YthFlsp; Business School; Secretary.

GOCKEN, Beverly A; Stillman Valley HS; Stillman Valley, IL; TrsFrshCls; Band; ChrhWkr; CncrtBnd; HonRl; LbryAde; MrchBnd; PepBnd; SchMus; SchPl; StuCncl; Bsbl; Chrldr; PPFtbl; Madison Bus Col; Legal Secretary.

GOCKEN, Jeffrey L; Stillman Valley HS; Davis Junction, IL; 23/99 HonRl; NHS; NatlMeritCmnd; SctActv; FFA; Bsbl; Bsktbl;.

GOCKOWSKI, Ronald E; St Bernards HS; St Paul, MN; 25/157 HonRl; Ftbl; LetterWrstlng; U Of Mn; Forester.

GODBEY, Nicholas R; Mt Carmel HS; Chicago, IL; 3/197 CmntyWkr; HonRl; ModUN; NHS; NatlMeritCmnd; SctActv; StuGov; TchrAde; MthCl; SciCl; LetterSwmmng; College; Physical Sciences.

GODBOLD, Gilbert S; Andover HS; Birmingham, MI; 9/400 Chr; ChrhWkr; IntrClCncl; NHS; NatlMeritFnl; Orch; SctActv; StuGov; YthFlsp; GodCntryAwd; Univ; Mech Engr.

GODBOUT, Vickie S; Phillipsburg HS; Seward, NE; 27/86 Band; ChrhWkr; CncrtBnd; HonRl; LbryAde; MrchBnd; PepBnd; TchrAde; Trk; PPFtbl; College.

GODBY, Michael D; Moravia Comm HS; Moravia, IA; Band; CncrtBnd; HonRl; MrchBnd; SchMus; StuCncl; YthFlsp; FTA; SciCl; Wrstlng; U Of Northern Ia; Teaching Music.

GODDARD, Ann M; Cedar Rapids Prairie HS; Fairfax, IA; ALAGirlsSt; Band; Chr; Chrs; CncrtBnd; HonRl; JrNHS; Mdrgl; MrchBnd; Univ Of N Iowa; Music.

GODDARD, Cindy R; Wayne Memorial HS; Westland, MI; Chr; CmntyWkr; HonRl; NatlFornLg; NHS; NatlThespSoc; SchMus; SchPl; Chrldr; JCAwd; Univ; Pre Law.

GODDARD, Freeland N; Marine City HS; Marine City, MI; PresSrCls; HonRl; NHS; NatlMeritSF; SchPl; PresStuGov; Univ Of Mich; Physician.

GODDARD, Jay; Macksville HS; Pawnee Rock, KS; TrsJrCls; Band; CncrtBnd; HonRl; LbryAde; NHS; PepBnd; SchPl; TchrAde; LetterBsktbl; Ks State Univ.

GODDARD, Johna J; Lowpoint Washburn HS; Washburn, IL; Band; ChrhWkr; CncrtBnd; MrchBnd; Orch; PepBnd; SchMus; SchPl; StuCncl; Chrldr; Coll; Phy Ed.

GODDARD, Mary B; Washington Community HS; Washington, IL; Band; TreasCncrtBnd; MrchBnd; Orch; PepBnd; PpCl; Bryan College; Accountant.

GODDE, Steve J; Plano HS; Plano, IL; HonRl; NHS; LetterBsktbl; LetterFtbl; LetterGlf; University; Professional.

GODFREDSON, Lori L; Westwood HS; Sloan, IA; 14/71 DrlTm; MrchBnd; Chrldr; Colelge; Art.

GODFREY, Donald; Monrovia HS; Martinsville, IN; Aud/Vis; HonRl; TchrAde; IMSpt; LionAwd;.

GODFREY, Kim A; Argyle HS; Argyle, WI; HonRl; FFA; LetterFtbl; Vocational School; Vocation.

GODFROY, Christi L; Peru HS; Peru, IN; ALAGirlsSt; MrchBnd; NHS; OffAde; Quill&Scroll; TreasStuCncl; EdYrBk; DARAwd; Univ; Nurse.

GODFROY, Rainette D; North Miami HS; Mexico, IN; 10/120 HonRl; NHS; PpCl; LetterBsktbl; LetterTrk; GAA; IMSpt; PPFtbl; College; Cpa Accounting.

GODFROY, Steven J; Huntington Catholic HS; Huntington, IN; 4/38 HonRl; SchMus; SchPl; StuCncl; SptEdYrbk; Bsbl; Bsktbl; CchngActv; IMSpt; College; Cpa.

GODIN, Phillip R; St Marys HS; Burlington, WI; 6/72 SecTrsSophCls; Band; CncrtBnd; HonRl; MrchBnd; PepBnd; Sacrstn; SchMus; SchPl; StuCncl; LetterTrk; IMSpt; Univ Of Wi; Political Science.

GODINEZ, Belle M; St Mary Of Perpetual Help HS; Chicago, IL; 43/97 TrsJrCls; HonRl; StuCncl; TchrAde; SpnCl; PpCl; GAA; Chicago Col Of Commerce; Court Reporting.

GODKE, Julie A; Kewanee HS; Kewanee, IL; Aud/Vis; ChrhWkr; JA; StuCncl; YthFlsp; Pres4-H; FHA; LetterTennis; GAA; 4-HAwd; College.

GODLEWSKI, Edward A; Bishop Noll Institute; Calumet City, IL; 20/360 HonRl; NatlFornLg; StuCncl; StuGov; RptrSchPpr; College.

GODLEWSKI, Harry; Osborn HS; Detroit, MI; HonRl; SchAde; SctActv; TchrAde; Bsbl; Wayne State Univ; Pharmacy.

GODLEY, Paul A; Friends School In Dect; Detroit, MI; Chr; Yrbk; CaptBsktbl; Yale; Med.

GODMAN, Teresa L; Quincy HS; Quincy, IL; Band; Chr; Chrs; ChrhWkr; CncrtBnd; HonRl; MrchBnd; Orch; PepBnd; SchMus; SchPl; SctActv; FrCl; KiwanAwd; College; Professional.

GODTLAND, Julie D; Albert Lea HS; Albert Lea, MN; Band; DrmMjrt; MrchBnd; NatlThespSoc; PepBnd; Quill&Scroll; SchMus; SchPl; EdYrBk; Trk; Travel Work School; Forestry.

GODWIN, Richard A; Rosary HS; St Louis, MO; 17/350 Aud/Vis; HonRl; NHS; NatlMeritCmnd; SchMus; SchPl; University; Commercial Art.

GOEBEL, Diane S; Pacific HS; Labadie, MO; Band; CncrtBnd; DrmMjrt; HonRl; LitMag; MrchBnd; PepBnd; SchPl; Yrbk; EdSchPpr; PpCl; Chrldr; GAA; University; Professional.

GOEBEL, Janice M; Homestead HS; Ft Wayne, IN; VPJrCls; Quill&Scroll; SchMus; SchPl; Teen; RptrYrbk; EdYrBk; Yrbk; GerCl; Purdue Univ; Vet Medicine.

GOEBEL, William J; Charles City Comm HS; Ionia, IA; 34/240 HonRl; 4-H; LetterTrk; 4-HAwd; Ia St Univ; Engineering.

GOECKE, Laura L; Estherville Sr HS; Estherville, IA; Chrs; HonRl; NatlFornLg; NHS; RptrYrbk; LetterBsktbl; LetterTrk; IMSpt; PresAwd; Drake Univ; Law.

GOECKER, Kathy D; Seymour HS; Seymour, IN; Chr; ChrhWkr; HonRl; OffAde; SchPl; FrCl; Auto Machine Training Center; Comp Prog.

GOEDDE, Elaine C; Random Lake HS; Random Lake, WI; Chr; Chrs; ChrhWkr; HonRl; SchMus; RptrSchPpr; 4-H; PpCl; Lakeshore Tech Inst; Child Care Assistant.

GOEDDEL, James P; St Louis U HS; St Louis, MO; CncrtBnd; HonRl; JA; NatlMeritFnl; SctActv; JAAwd; U Of Chicago; Math.

GOEDDERZ, James F; L P Goodrich HS; Fond Du Lac, WI; 22/700 Band; HonRl; NHS; SchPl; Tech School; Electrical Technician.

GOEDEKE, Todd L; Howards Grove HS; Howards Grove, WI; 2/75 PresSophCls; PresJrCls; Chrs; HonRl; NHS; StuCncl; Yrbk; SptEdSchPpr; 4-H; LetterBsbl; CaptBsktbl; LetterTrk; CitAwd; Univ Of Wisc; Engineering.

GOEDEN, Deborah E; Central Catholic HS; West Point, NE; Band; Chr; Chrs; CncrtBnd; HonRl; MrchBnd; NHS; SchMus; SchPl; 4-H; Univ; Music.

GOEDEN, Michael J; Bloomfield Community HS; Wausa, NE; 34/67 ChrhWkr; StuGov; LetterBsbl; LetterBsktbl; IMSpt;.

GOEDKEN, Marjorie A; Starmont HS; Lamont, IA; 26/108 HonRl; SchMus; SchPl; SchPpr; Trade; Voc.

GOEDLAND, Holly; St Marys Acad; Greenfield, WI; PresJrCls; Aud/Vis; Band; CncrtBnd; DrmBgl; NHS; StuGov; RptrSchPpr; LatCl; IMSpt; Univ Wisc; Med Tech.

GOEHRING, Duane A; Marion Independent HS; Marion, IA; 16/161 CaptBand; Chr; CncrtBnd; DrmMjrt; HonRl; MrchBnd; NHS; PepBnd; LetterTrk; Iowa St Univ; Engineering.

GOEHRING, Marie S; Herreid HS; Mound City, SD; 1/29 SecFrshCls; PresJrCls; PresSrCls; SchPl; StuCncl; EdYrBk; PresPpCl; LetterTrk; IMSpt; CitAwd; 2 Yrs Coll; Rn.

GOEHRING, Ruth A; Burwell Jr Sr HS; Burwell, NE; Chr; Chrs; ChrhWkr; HonRl; SchMus; SchPl; StuGov; YthFlsp; Yrbk; 4-H; Bsktbl; LetterTrk; GAA; 4-HAwd; Grace Bible Inst; Music.

GOEKE, Geri A; Orchard Farm HS; St Charles, MO; SecSophCls; SchPl; StuCncl; TchrAde; RptrYrbk; Yrbk; FrCl; Chrldr; Col; Med Tech Or Journalism.

GOEKE, James E; Elmore HS; Elmore, MN; 7/28 PresSophCls; Chr; ChrhWkr; HonRl; NHS; SctActv; YthFlsp; RptrSchPpr; LetterFtbl; LetterWrstlng; College; Professional.

GOEKE, Sally A; Dakota HS; Davis, IL; 9/76 TrsSrCls; Band; HonRl; VPStuCncl; SecYthFlsp; EdYrBk; Pres4-H; PresFHA; BttyCrckrAwd; DARAwd; 4-HAwd; Sauk Valley College; Beautician.

GOEKEN, Lisa E; Delavan HS; Delavan, IL; 1/53 Band; Chrs; HonRl; NHS; PresNatlThespSoc; Bsktbl; Trk; ChmnChrldr; SecGAA; DARAwd; Coll; Physical Education.

GOEKEN, Nancy K; Delavan HS; Delavan, IL; Chrs; HonRl; EdYrBk; PpCl; Cosmetology School; Porcessional.

GOEKER, Rita A; Scotland HS; Scotland, SD; 4/45 ALAGirlsSt; Chrs; ChrhWkr; HonRl; HospAde; FHA; PpCl; Mitchell Area Voc Tech; Accounting.

GOEMER, Lori J; Litchfield HS; Darwin, MN; ChrhWkr; HonRl; PepBnd; SchPl; StuCncl; RptrSchPpr; 4-H; FHA; GerCl; 4-HAwd; College.

GOEN, Terri E; Sidney HS; Sidney, NE; 34/111 HonRl; LbryAde; FHA; Eastern Wyoming College; Veterinarian.

GOEPPNER, Michael T; Mendel Catholic HS; Chicago, IL; 17/289 SecFrshCls; SecSophCls; ChrhWkr; CtyCnl; CmntyWkr; HonRl; JrNHS; StuCncl; StuGov; GerCl; Bsktbl; Glf; Marquette University; Business Admn.

GOERG, Nancy B; Reavis HS; Burbank, IL; 1/700 HonRl; JrNHS; NHS; NatlMeritCmnd; NatlMeritSF; TchrAde; RptrYrbk; EdYrBk; Yrbk; RptrSchPpr; RusCl; MthCl; Loyola Univ.

GOERING, Jim H; Moundridge HS; Galva, KS; ChrhWkr; NatlFornLg; StuCncl; YthFlsp; YthLg; Ftbl; Trk; Kansas Univ; Law.

GOERING, Kevin J; Moundridge HS; Moundridge, KS; Chrs; HonRl; SchMus; StuCncl; YthFlsp; 4-H; LetterBsktbl; LetterFtbl; LetterTrk; 4-HAwd; College; Business Admin.

GOERING, Robert A; South Luther HS; Lagrange, IL; 39/215 PresSophCls; CmntyWkr; HonRl; HospAde; PolWkr; RedCrAde; StuCncl; StuGov; YthFlsp; SciCl; Bsbl; Ftbl; Wrstlng; College; Medicine.

GOERL, Heidi J; Seymour Community HS; Black Creek, WI; 1/185 ALAGirlsSt; ChrhWkr; HonRl; HospAde; TrsFrshCls; TchrAde; SecTrsFrshCls; FNA; GAA; IMSpt; Milwaukee Co Hosp For Nur; Registered Nurse.

GOERL, Tammy J; Seymour Community HS; Black Creek, WI; Band; ChrhWkr; HonRl; HospAde; 4-H; FNA; Bsktbl; Trk; GAA; IMSpt;.

GOERS, Connie E; St Agatha HS; Detroit, MI; SecJrCls; HonRl; OffAde; PpCl; CaptBsktbl; Business Col; Secretarial.

GOERS, Doretta J; Bloom Twp HS; Steger, IL; 82/1056 HonRl; JrNHS; Eastern Illinois Univ; Medical Tech.

GOERS, Peggy L; Jennings HS; St Louis, MO; 25/247 ChrhWkr; HonRl; LbryAde; GerCl; Tennis; GAA; Coll; Religious Edu.

GOERTZ, Lori G; Hillsboro HS; Hillsboro, KS; 2/70 VPJrCls; Band; Chrs; HonRl; Mdrgl; SchMus; SchPl; StuCncl; TchrAde; YthFlsp; Bethel Col; Music.

GOERTZ, Timothy M; Centennial HS; Circle Pines, MN; HonRl; NHS; LetterBsbl; LetterFtbl; St Cloud State Minn.

GOERZEN, Shelley R; Goessel HS; Newton, KS; 7/26 Band; Chrs; CncrtBnd; HonRl; Mdrgl; MrchBnd; Teen; PresYthFlsp; LetterBsktbl; LetterTrk; Tabor Coll; Social Work.

GOESTENKORS, Cathie A; Central HS; Trenton, IL; HonRl; PresFHA; Patricia Stevens; Secretarial.

GOESTENKORS, Diane T; Mater Dei HS; Trenton, IL; 2/182 Chrs; HonRl; Mdrgl; NHS; SchPl; StuCncl; Airlines.

GOETHE, Dennis L; Rolla Senior HS; Rolla, MO; 130/310 Band; ChrhWkr; CmntyWkr; CncrtBnd; LbryAde; MrchBnd; TchrAde; FDA; Forest Park Clg; Mortuary Science.

GOETSCH, Cindy K; Mitchell HS; Mitchell, SD; 30/300 Band; Chr; Chrs; HonRl; NHS; StuCncl; FBLA; SpnCl; PpCl; CaptChrldr; College; Music Educ.

GOETSCH, Greg H; Bellingham HS; Bellingham, MN; 6/28 PresSophCls; Band; Chrs; HonRl; StuCncl; TchrAde; CaptBsbl; LetterBsktbl; LetterFtbl; CitAwd; Col; Acct.

GOETTEN, Edward E; Jersey Comm HS; Jerseyville, IL; 9/277 HonRl; NHS; SpnCl; MthCl; Western Ill Univ; Physician.

GOETTING, Jody L; Steeleville Comm Unit HS; Steeleville, IL; 10/56 PresSophCls; ALBoysSt; HonRl; NHS; RptrYrbk; PpCl; LetterBsbl; LetterBsktbl; Glf; AmLegAwd; Eastern Il U; Bus Mgmt.

GOETTING, Mary P; Norborne Public HS; Norborne, MO; ChrhWkr; CmntyWkr; HonRl; NHS; SchPl; VPStuCncl; Yrbk; Pres4-H; PresFrCl; 4-HAwd; College; Medicine.

GOETTL, Leonard J; Jefferson Sr HS; Jefferson, WI; 15/180 VPSophCls; Chr; CncrtBnd; HonRl; MrchBnd; SchMus; StuCncl; StuGov; SchPpr; TreasFTA; VoiceDemAwd; Univ Of Wisconsin; Teacher.

GOETZ, Brent; Heelan HS; Sioux City, IA; PresSrCls; ChrhWkr; HonRl; Quill&Scroll; RptrYrbk; SchPpr; FrCl; Chrldr; Premed College; Medicine.

GOETZ, Catherine L; Hays HS; Hays, KS; SecFrshCls; CmntyWkr; IntrClCncl; JA; OffAde; SancSoc; StuCncl; StuGov; PpCl; Vo Tech Sch.

GOETZ, Donald K; University HS; Warrensburg, MO; TrsFrshCls; VPSophCls; TrsJrCls; ChrhWkr; HonRl; NHS; Bsktbl; Ftbl; CchngActv; GodCntryAwd; Univ;computer Prog Or Journalism.

GOETZ, Gregory; Aquinas HS; Southgate, MI; 108/245 CmntyWkr; HonRl; SctActv; IMSpt; Vofm Dearborn; Metdrology.

GOETZ, John P; Marshfield HS; Marshfield, WI; 7/327 Band; Chr; CncrtBnd; HonRl; Mdrgl; NHS; PepBnd; StuCncl; LetterFtbl; Tennis; Bryan Coll; Bus Admins.

GOETZ, Linda M; St Francis HS; Wheaton, IL; 12/127 Knox College; Mathematics.

GOETZ, Paula M; Heelan HS; Sioux City, IA; CtyCnl; HonRl; StuCncl; PpCl; Chrldr; IMSpt; CitAwd; College; Social Worker.

GOETZELMANN, Carol L; John Hersey HS; Barrington, IL; Band; CncrtBnd; HonRl; MrchBnd; NHS; SctActv; College; Environmental Research.

GOETZINGER, Craig A; Eldora HS; Eldora, IA; HonRl; Bsktbl; Iowa State U; Engineer.

GOETZMANN, Thomas J; Alleman HS; Rock Island, IL; HonRl; NHS; SchPpr; Univ Of Illinois; Civil Engineer.

GOFF, Gregory T; Ogemaw Hts HS; West Branch, MI; 28/165 LbryAde; RptrSchPpr; Ftbl; Central Michigan University.

GOFF, Margaret M; Marland HS; Marland, KS; 1/21 TrsSophCls; TrsSrCls; Band; Chr; HonRl; SchMus; SchPl; StuCncl; RptrYrbk; PresPpCl; PPFtbl; Ft Hays St College.

GOFF, Robin K; Oblong HS; Oblong, IL; TrsSophCls; StuCncl; YthFlsp; RptrYrbk; RptrSchPpr; TrsSophCls; GAA; IMSpt; Univ; Med Tech.

GOFORTH, Debbie L; Hillsboro HS; Hillsboro, MO; 1/180 HonRl; PresJrNHS; NHS; NatlMeritCmnd; StuCncl; EdYrBk; RptrSchPpr; Jefferson Jr Col.; Magazine Jo Urnalism.

GOFORTH, Glenn A; Sparta HS; Tilden, IL; 59/160 Band; CncrtBnd; HonRl; MrchBnd; NatlThespSoc; PepBnd; SchMus; SchPl; LatCl; Ftbl; Mc Kendree College; Teacher.

GOHDES, Stephen; Mapleton Public HS; Mapleton, ND; 3/10 Coll; Farmer.

GOHL, Dewayne F; Hayes Center HS; Palisade, NE; PresFrshCls; VPSophCls; PresJrCls; PresSrCls; HonRl; StuCncl; LetterBsktbl; CaptFtbl; LetterTrk; IMSpt; AmLegAwd; Kearney State Col; Physical Ed.

GOHN, Margaret A; Normandy Sr HS; St Louis, MO; HonRl; MrchBnd; NHS; StuCncl; SptEdYrbk; PresFrCl; CaptChrldr; Coll; French.

GOHR, Gale A; Pulaski HS; Sobieski, WI; 2/193 SecSophCls; ALAGirlsSt; ChrhWkr; HospAde; JrNHS; NHS; SpnCl; MthCl; AmLegAwd; JETSAwd; Clge; Rn.

GOI, Frances S; Immaculata HS; Chicago, IL; 21/198 ChrhWkr; HonRl; NHS; AmLegAwd; Loyola Univ; Nursing.

GOINES, Donald M; William A Wirt HS; Gary, IN; ChrhWkr; LbryAde; SctActv; SptEdSchPpr; LetterFtbl; Bsktbl; Trk; CchngActv; IMSpt; Briham Youn Univ; Vet.

GOINES, Ladonna S; Vienna HS; Cypress, IL; DrlTm; 4-H; FHA; FNA; FTA; PpCl; LetterChrldr; IMSpt; 4-HAwd; College; Teacher.

GOINES, Sharon C; Arthur Hill HS; Saginaw, MI; SecFrshCls; Chr; ChrhWkr; CmntyWkr; HonRl; JA; PolWkr; StuCncl; 4-H; Bsbl; College; Professional.

GOING, Deborah E; Okawville HS; Okawville, IL; 2/65 PresSrCls; Band; ChrhWkr; CncrtBnd; HonRl; MrchBnd; NHS; NatlMeritCmnd; PolWkr; RptrYrbk; Bsktbl; DanFAwd; Univ Of Ill.

GOING, Kathy F; Okawville HS; Addieville, IL; 15/67 SecSrCls; Band; Chrs; CncrtBnd; HonRl; LbryAde; MrchBnd; PresNHS; PepBnd; PresYthFlsp; Yrbk; CaptBsktbl; CaptTrk; Siu Edwardsville; Physical Ed.

GOINS, Inez; Lindblom Tech HS; Chicago, IL; 51/977 HonRl; NHS; SchAde; TchrAde; RptrYrbk; Mayfair College; Computer Programming.

GOINS, Randall E; Harper HS; Chicago, IL; HonRl; NHS; NatlMeritCmnd; NatlMeritSchl; JAAwd; Ill Institute Of Tech; Prof Architect.

GOKEE, Delores E; Bayfield HS; Bayfield, WI; VPSophCls; Band; Chr; Chrl; CncrtBnd; HonRl; MrchBnd; NHS; PepBnd; SchMus; LetterBsbl; LetterBsktbl; CaptTennis; Trk; College.

GOLASZEWSKI, Diane M; Fraser HS; Fraser, MI; 8/563 Band; ChrhWkr; DrmMjrt; HonRl; HospAde; MrchBnd; NHS; SchMus; EdSchPpr; PPFtbl; U Of Mich; Phy Therapy.

GOLASZEWSKI, James; Thornwood HS; South Holland, IL; 31/650 HonRl; JrNHS; NHS; GerCl; Univ Of Ill; Archetecture.

GOLBERG, Susan L; Evanston Twp HS; Evanston, IL; CmntyWkr; HonRl; SchMus; SchPl; TchrAde; RptrYrbk; Drake University; Business Admin.

GOLBRICHT, Jacqueline A; Gorin HS; Gorin, MO; 5/7 VPSophCls; Chrs; ChrhWkr; SchMus; StuCncl; Bsbl; Bsktbl; Factory Work.

GOLBUFF, Thomas; Mason City HS; Mason City, IA; PresFrshCls; HonRl; NHS; Quill&Scroll; EdSchPpr; PpCl; IMSpt; KiwanAwd; Univ Of Iowa; Pharmacy.

GOLD, Alan J; Mather HS; Chicago, IL; 3/421 HonRl; TreasNHS; OffAde; PolWkr; RedCrAde; SchMus; StuGov; RptrSchPpr; KeyCl; CaptMthCl; Cornell University; Medicine.

GOLD, Carl G; Parkwood HS; Joplin, MO; TrsSrCls; HonRl; NHS; SctActv; StuCncl; SptEdSchPpr; KeyCl; Bsktbl; LetterFtbl; LetterTrk; Med Sch; Md.

GOLDASICH, Vanessa L; Litchfield Senior HS; Litchfield, IL; 41/148 ChrhWkr; HonRl; Quill&Scroll; SchMus; SchPl; YthFlsp; Yrbk; RptrSchPpr; College; Psychology Major.

GOLDBACH, Cynthia M; Marathon HS; Marathon, WI; 2/100 CncrtBnd; DrmMjrt; HonRl; MrchBnd; PepBnd; SchPl; TchrAde; Univ Of Wi La Crosse; Physical Therapt.

GOLDBERG, Edward J; Niles North HS; Skokie, IL; 32/650 HonRl; NHS; StuCncl; KeyCl; LetterTennis; Tulane University; Medicine.

GOLDBERG, Silvia L; Niles West HS; Morton Grove, IL; 136/666 TrsJrCls; PresSrCls; Chr; HonRl; PresNatlThespSoc; SchMus; GAA; Univ Of Illinois; Occup Therapist.

GOLDEN, Douglas C; White Pine HS; White Pine, MI; VPFrshCls; CmntyWkr; HonRl; FrCl; Bsktbl; Glf; Trk; Michigan Tech Univ; Arch Engineer.

GOLDEN, Gary D; Wethersfield HS; Kewanee, IL; Band; CncrtBnd; HonRl; MrchBnd; VPStuCncl; ChmnSwmmng; LetterTrk; University.

GOLDEN, John R; Hinsdale Central HS; Hinsdale, IL; Chr; HonRl; Mdrgl; NHS; SchPl; StuGov; RptrSchPpr; Ftbl; Socr; University Of Illinois; Law.

GOLDEN, Nancy D; Sarcoxie HS; Sarcoxie, MO; Band; Chr; CncrtBnd; HonRl; MrchBnd; NHS; Yrbk; PresFHA; FTA; Chrldr; College; Professional.

GOLDEN, Nancy L; New Trier East HS; Wilmette, IL; 68/847 AFS; Chrs; HonRl; NatlMeritSF; SchMus; SctActv; SchPpr; Wa U; Fine Arts.

GOLDEN, Roberta P; Irving Crown HS; Carpentersville, IL; 27/351 HonRl; NHS; SctActv; TchrAde; SciCl; Elgin Comm Col; Nursing.

GOLDENCROWN, Peggy; Trimont HS; Trimont, MN; 4/30 Chrs; HonRl; LitMag; LbryAde; NHS; Quill&Scroll; SchPl; RptrSchPpr; FFA; GAA; Mounds Midway Sch Of Nurs; Nurse.

GOLDHORN, Stephen J; Castlewood HS; Castlewood, SD; 13/32 VPFrshCls; PresJrCls; PresSrCls; HonRl; SctActv; PpCl; Bsbl; Bsktbl; Trk; IMSpt;.

GOLDMAN, Arnold G; Clarenceville HS; Livonia, MI; 4/250 Band; HonRl; JrNHS; MrchBnd; NHS; Wayne State U; English.

GOLDMAN, Deborah F; Niles North HS; Skokie, IL; 30/641 Univ Of Wisconsin; Accounting.

GOLDMAN, Robin A; Jordan HS; Jordan, MN; VPFrshCls; PresSophCls; Chr; HonRl; SchPl; StuCncl; RptrSchPpr; 4-H; Chrldr; GAA; Col Of St Catherines; Social Psychology.

GOLDNER, Terry A; Corunna HS; Corunna, MI; SecFrshCls; SecSophCls; HonRl; NHS; SchPl; UNYO; Yrbk; FFA; PpCl; Bsktbl; Trk; Univ Of Mi; Medicine.

GOLDSBY, Nancy L; Lenora HS; Norton, KS; 3/15 Band; ChrhWkr; DrlTm; HonRl; StuCncl; RptrYrbk; EdSchPpr; 4-H; PpCl; Fort Hays State College; Nursing.

GOLEMAN, Melinda M; Divernon HS; Divernon, IL; 7/30 PresFrshCls; PresBand; CncrtBnd; HonRl; MrchBnd; PepBnd; SchPl; StuGov; VPYthFlsp; Yrbk; PresFHA; LetterGAA; College; Professional.

GOLEMBIEWSKI, Mark; Marquette Hs; Milwaukee, WI; 10/250 Aud/Vis; HonRl; HospAde; RptrSchPpr; LatCl; MthCl; CchngActv; Madison Uw; Acct Cpa.

GOLEMBIEWSKI, Richard; Notre Dame HS; Milwaukee, WI; HonRl; SciCl; IMSpt; Mil School Of Engineering; Mechengineering.

GOLEMBIEWSKI, Susan; Crandon HS; Crandon, WI; HonRl; Technical.

GOLEVICZ, Suzanne E; Maine Twp HS South; Park Ridge, IL; HonRl; NHS; TchrAde; FrCl; College; Teaching.

GOLIAK, Jean M; Lourdes HS; Chicago, IL; 69/276 ChrhWkr; CmntyWkr; DrlTm; HonRl; JA; PolWkr; SchAde; SctActv; Twrl; CivCl; SpnCl; College; Biology.

GOLIBER, Thomas E; Shrine HS; Royal Oak, MI; 5/180 HonRl; NHS; NatlMeritSF; Yrbk; RptrSchPpr; SchPpr; College; Physics.

GOLIGHTLY, Bradley D; Van Meter Comm HS; Booneville, IA; 11/26 CncrtBnd; SchPl; StuCncl; LetterBsbl; LetterBsktbl; LetterTrk; DanFAwd; 4-HAwd; Iowa St Univ; Animal Science.

GOLIGOWSKI, Steven P; Staples HS; Browerville, MN; 2/156 HonRl; NHS; NatlMeritCmnd; TchrAde; Yrbk; Pres4-H; BauchLmbAwd; 4-HAwd; St Johns University; Professional Army Offi.

GOLIN, Gail B; Schurz HS; Chicago, IL; HonRl; NHS; NatlMeritCmnd; OffAde; SchAde; TchrAde; RptrSchPpr; SchPpr; FrCl; Northwestern Univ; Math.

GOLLIHER, Patricia A; Murphysboro Twp HS; Murphysboro, IL; SchPl; SctActv; RptrYrbk; SciCl; Bsktbl; Swmmng; College; Home Economics.

GOLLIHER, Sally; Union HS; Losantville, IN; 2/58 Band; CncrtBnd; HonRl; LbryAde; NHS; SchPl; TchrAde; RptrYrbk; 4-H; Indiana Univ; Med Tech.

GOLLONIK, Debra M; Stevens Point Area Senior HS; Stevens Point, WI; 15/525 ALAGirlsSt; Chr; MrchBnd; NHS; Quill&Scroll; EdSchPpr; FBLA; LetterTennis; GAA; AmLegAwd; Univ Of Wi; Communicative Disorders.

GOLT, Juliann M; Rochelle Township HS; Rochelle, IL; 1/256 SecSophCls; TrsSophCls; ALAGirlsSt; HonRl; NatlThespSoc; Orch; SchPl; GAA; DARAwd; College; Pharmacist.

GOLTER, Gretchen; Orchard Public HS; Orchard, NE; 2/30 Chrs; DrmMjrt; LbryAde; NHS; StuCncl; StuGov; TchrAde; SpnCl; CaptChrldr; BttyCrckrAwd; Clge; Pro.

GOLZ, Rhonda L; Ashley HS; Ashley, ND; HonRl; RptrYrbk; 4-H; Bsktbl; Chrldr; 4-HAwd; College; Vocation.

GOMBAR, Jeanne M; St Josephs HS; Kenosha, WI; 6/138 Chrs; HonRl; SecNHS; StuCncl; PpCl; LetterTennis; Coll;medicine.

GOMBERG, Joan S; Evanston Twp HS; Skokie, IL; 9/1100 ChrhWkr; HonRl; NatlMeritCmnd; PolWkr; RedCrAde; StuGov; TchrAde; University; Science.

GOMES, Patricia A; Elmwood HS; Elmwood, IL; 38/56 Band; Chrs; ChrhWkr; HonRl; JA; MrchBnd; OffAde; PepBnd; SchPl; TchrAde; 4-H; SpnCl; 4-HAwd; Huntler Horse Center; Trainer.

GOMEZ, Alfred; St John Cathedral HS; Milwaukee, WI; PresJrCls; Band; MrchBnd; StuCncl; RptrSchPpr; Bsktbl; Socr; College; Law.

GOMEZ, Raymond; Lane Technical Hs; Chicago, IL; 267/1300 HonRl; TchrAde; YthLg; SpnCl; AmLegAwd; U Of Illinois; Medicine.

GONDEK, Susan M; Lourdes HS; Chicago, IL; 45/299 HonRl; HospAde; Univ Of Illinois.

GONDEK, Valerie A; Menominee HS; Menominee, MI; 19/280 VPAFS; ChrhWkr; HonRl; LbryAde; NHS; NatlMeritSchl; TchrAde; YthLg; Northern Michigan Univ; Professional.

GONDERINGER, Robert M; St Marys HS; Oneill, NE; 1/30 PresJrCls; Chr; Chrl; Chrs; ChrhWkr; SchMus; SchPl; PresStuCncl; StuGov; RptrYrbk; St Johns Univ; Lawyer.

GONDRO, Lesley M; Mehlville HS; St Louis, MO; RedCrAde; StuCncl; PpCl; Swmmng; Chrldr; College; Professional.

GONET, Michael V; Putnam County HS; Granville, IL; 20/78 CaptBsbl; CaptBsktbl; AmLegAwd; College; Business.

GONGAWARE, Maria T A; Reeds Spring HS; Reeds Spring, MO; 1/75 VPNHS; PresMthCl; SecSciCl; Bsktbl; Trk; BttyCrckrAwd; Culver Stockton College; Biology.

GONGWER, Geoffrey S; Bloomington HS; Bloomington, IL; 6/391 HonRl; NHS; StuCncl; FrCl; MthCl; SciCl; LetterFtbl; Trk; Univ Of Ill; Engineering.

GONIWIECHA, Ann; Harbor Beach HS; Habor Beach, MI; 4/135 ChrhWkr; CmntyWkr; HonRl; HospAde; LbryAde; NHS; NatlMeritSF; OffAde; FNA; IMSpt; St Clair County Community College; Nurse.

GONNER, Jeffrey L; Marquette HS; Bellevue, IA; 11/56 ALBoysSt; HonRl; NHS; Sacrstn; SchMus; RptrSchPpr; SpnCl; PpCl; Bsbl; Bsktbl; Glf; College; Professional.

GONSHOLT, Bruce O; Bergan HS; Peroria, IL; 12/230 HonRl; Yrbk; Bsktbl; Tennis; IMSpt; Univ Of Il; Engineering.

GONSIOR, Gayle; Thomas L Grace HS; New Brighton, MN; 14/210 Band; ChrhWkr; CncrtBnd; MrchBnd; SchPl; SchPpr; GAA; PresAwd; Collefe Of St Catherines; Pediatrician.

GONTO, Steve; Ferndale HS; Oak Park, MI; HonRl; NatlFornLg; NHS; StuGov; LatCl; Trk; OptClAwd; RotaryAwd; VFWAwd; VoiceDemAwd; College; Medicine.

GONYER, Lynn M; Manchester HS; Manchester, MI; 14/102 Band; CncrtBnd; MrchBnd; PepBnd; GAA; Mi Coll; Science.

GONZALEZ, Alma; Proviso East HS; Maywood, IL; 28/1001 HonRl; LbryAde; NHS; College; Professional.

GONZALEZ, Madeline S; Josephinum HS; Chicago, IL; 14/100 HonRl; LbryAde; SpnCl; U Of Chicago Cirle; Psycology.

GONZALEZ, Mary A; East Lansing HS; East Lansing, MI; ChmnHospAde; NatlFornLg; NHS; Orch; SchPl; TchrAde; U Of Mi; Pre Professional.

GONZALEZ, Patricia I; St Mary Of P H HS; Chicago, IL; SecJrCls; Chrs; HonRl; StuCncl; TchrAde; FTA; FrCl; PpCl; GAA; De Paul Univ.

GOOCH, Denise; North Chicago HS; North Chicago, IL; ChrhWkr; CmntyWkr; HonRl; MrchBnd; SchPl; StuGov; SciCl; LetterChrldr; IMSpt; Louisiana State; Medicine.

GOOCH, Susan E; Clinton HS; Clinton, IA; Band; Chr; DrmMjrt; HonRl; NHS; SchMus; SctActv; StuCncl; LetterTrk; Coll; Prof.

GOOD, Catherine A; Glenbard East HS; Lombard, IL; 50/646 PresJrCls; HonRl; IntrClCncl; SecNHS; StuCncl; SpnCl; PpCl; Chrldr; Millikin Univ; Secondary Educ.

GOOD, Cynthia A; Penn HS; Osceola, IN; 24/460 Band; HonRl; TreasStuGov; 4-H; FSA; SecGerCl; MthCl; Manchester College; Computer Programmer.

GOOD, George B; Lane Technical HS; Chicago, IL; VPSrCls; ChrhWkr; HonRl; NHS; OffAde; RptrSchPpr; SchPpr; Ftbl; Glf; Northwestern University; Law.

GOOD, Janis C; Lincoln HS; Wisconsin Rapids, WI; ChrhWkr; CmntyWkr; HonRl; NHS; SctActv; College.

GOOD, Joanne K; Olympia HS; Armington, IL; Chrs; CmntyWkr; CncrtBnd; HonRl; NHS; YthFlsp; 4-H; FNA; MthCl; 4-HAwd; Collge.

GOOD, Makayla M; St Johns HS; St Johns, MI; ChrhWkr; HonRl; LitMag; ModUN; NHS; NatlMeritSF; RusCl; Trk; GAA; IMSpt; Michigan St Univ; English.

GOOD, Michael D; Berkley HS; Huntington Woods, MI; 4/600 TreasBand; CncrtBnd; IntrClCncl; MrchBnd; NHS; NatlMeritSF; Orch; PepBnd; FrCl; SciCl; NCTE; Univ; Math.

GOOD, Timothy W; Danville HS; Danville, IL; HonRl; NHS; FrCl; TreasLatCl; Southern Illinois Univ; Zoology.

GOODAKER, David M; Calumet HS; Gary, IN; 26/315 HonRl; JrNHS; NHS; RptrSchPpr; SpnCl; Purdue Univ; Computer Tech.

GOODALL, Debora A; Central Community HS; De Witt, IA; AFS; LetterChrs; ChrhWkr; HonRl; Yrbk; SciCl; Trk; College; Secretary.

GOODE, Katherine M; Avon HS; Plainfield, IN; 37/159 Chr; HonRl; LbryAde; SchMus; SchPl; TchrAde; FrCl; SpnCl; GAA; IMSpt; College; Special Education.

GOODELL, Gary; Harris Lake Park HS; Lake Park, IA; Band; HonRl; Mdrgl; MrchBnd; NHS; StuGov; Ftbl; Trk; Mankato State Coll; Phy Ed.

GOODENBERGER, Debra; Mc Cook Senior HS; Mc Cook, NE; 2/162 HonRl; VPNHS; SecFBLA; MthCl; PpCl; Univ Of Neb; Bus Admin.

GOODENOW, Grant R; Ida Grove Comm HS; Ida Grove, IA; PresSophCls; VPJrCls; ALBoysSt; CncrtBnd; HonRl; NHS; LetterBsbl; LetterBsktbl; LetterFtbl; LetterGlf; Iowa St Univ; Art.

GOODER, Michael R; Crestwood HS; Cresco, IA; PresFrshCls; PresSophCls; VPJrCls; ChrhWkr; HonRl; SchMus; SctActv; StuCncl; StuGov; FFA; College; Forestry.

GOODES, Pamela A; Lew Wallace HS; Gary, IN; 75/514 ChrhWkr; HonRl; LbryAde; Quill&Scroll;

SchPl; StuCncl; RptrSchPpr; FrCl; SecSciCl; Drake Univ; Journalism.

GOODFELLOW, Kathy L; Pratt HS; Pratt, KS; ALAGirlsSt; Chr; HonRl; Twrl; YthFlsp; 4-H; FHA; SpnCl; PpCl; LetterTennis;.

GOODHEART, Gregory; Swartz Creek HS; Swartz Creek, MI; 8/416 HonRl; NHS; NatlMeritSchl; YthFlsp; FSA; MthCl; Bsbl; Ftbl; Wrstlng; IMSpt; Univ Of Mich; Engineering.

GOODIN, Judy A; Jennings County HS; Deputy, IN; 6/269 JrNHS; NHS; RptrSchPpr; SecSpnCl; PpCl; College; Business Management.

GOODIN, Michael L; Jennings County HS; Deputy, IN; JrNHS; NHS; TreasFFA; SpnCl; College; Agriculture.

GOODIN, Peter J; Carbondale Comm HS; Carbondale, IL; 20/324 HonRl; NHS; NatlMeritSF; NatlThespSoc; Orch; SchMus; SchPl; YthLg; SciCl; IMSpt; U Of Ill; Instruct Environment.

GOODING, Denise S; Corunna HS; Corunna, MI; 17/209 HonRl; JA; SchPl; TchrAde; Baker Jr College; Exec Secretary.

GOODING, Kimberly L; Fountain Central HS; Wallace, IN; 1/124 Band; Chrs; CncrtBnd; DrmMjrt; HonRl; MrchBnd; NHS; SchMus; FHA; FSA; FrCl; PpCl; SciCl; Indiana Univ; Medical Technologist.

GOODLOCK, Craig M; Stockbridge HS; Stockbridge, MI; 2/128 PresCncrtBnd; PresMrchBnd; PresNHS; YthFlsp; LetterBsbl; LetterBsktbl; Adrian College.

GOODMAN, Ann P; New Trier West HS; Wilmette, IL; 18/694 Chrs; HonRl; OffAde; RedCrAde; Yrbk; FrCl; College; Professional.

GOODMAN, Beverly A; Pontiac Central HS; Pontiac, MI; Chrs; ChrhWkr; HonRl; NHS; StuCncl; GAA; U Of Mi; Dentistry Pharmacy Med.

GOODMAN, Brenda; Garrigan HS; Algona, IA; 2/105 Chr; Chrs; DrlTm; HonRl; NHS; SchMus; 4-H; LatCl; PpCl; Chrldr; Saint Catherines College; Elementare Ed.

GOODMAN, Lisa L; Warsaw Comm HS; Warsaw, IN; Band; CncrtBnd; DrlTm; HonRl; PepBnd; College; Teaching.

GOODMAN, Marsha A; New Trier East HS; Glencoe, IL; 66/847 Chr; Chrs; HonRl; NatlFornLg; NatlMeritFnl; SchMus; Northwestern Univ; Theatre.

GOODMAN, Mary A; Burke HS; Burke, SD; HonRl; JCC; OffAde; Quill&Scroll; SchAde; StuCncl; StuGov; YthFlsp; 4-H; FHA; Mitchell Vo Tech; Secretary.

GOODMAN, Steven B; New Trier West HS; Glenview, IL; HonRl; LetterFtbl; LetterTrk; College; Medicine.

GOODMAN, Walter K; Roseville HS; Roseville, MI; CmntyWkr; HonRl; JA; NHS; SchAde; EdSchPpr; FrCl; CitAwd; College; Medicine.

GOODREAU, Susan M; Negaunee HS; Negaunee, MI; Chrl; Chrs; SchMus; PpCl; Clge; Pro Music.

GOODRICH, Barry F; Pioneer HS; Royal Center, IN; HstFrshCls; VPJrCls; VPSrCls; Band; DrmMjrt; HonRl; SchMus; VP4-H; LetterTrk; LetterWrstlng; IMSpt; 4-HAwd; Purdue University; Industrial Engineering.

GOODRICH, Cynthia L; Carthage Community HS; Basco, IL; ChrhWkr; HonRl; HospAde; LbryAde; NHS; SchPl; 4-H; Bsbl; Bsktbl; Iowa Wesleyan College; Registered Nurse.

GOODRICH, Janice R; Pecatonica HS; Pecatonica, IL; SecFrshCls; Chrs; HonRl; JrNHS; Mdrgl; NHS; Quill&Scroll; SchMus; TchrAde; RptrSchPpr; EdSchPpr; PresFHA; TreasFTA; JCAwd; W Illinois Univ; Business Admin.

GOODRICH, Jay S; Mendel Catholic HS; Chicago, IL; ALBoysSt; ChrhWkr; LbryAde; PolWkr; SchPl; StuCncl; Teen; CivCl; KeyCl; PpCl; Bsktbl; Swmmng; IMSpt; College; Law.

GOODRICH, Mara; Wells Easton HS; Wells, MN; 6/111 Chr; Chrl; Chrs; ChrhWkr; DrmMjrt; HonRl; SchMus; SchPl; GAA; IMSpt; Mankato St; Bus Admin.

GOODS, Carl D; Muskegon HS; Muskegon, MI; 54/484 ALBoysSt; CmntyWkr; HonRl; NHS; NatlMeritFnl; StuCncl; IMSpt; Michigan St Univ; Mech Engineer.

GOODSON, John E; Fort Scott HS; Fortscott, KS; SchAde; TchrAde; PpCl; Ftbl; Trk; Wrstlng; Trade School; Professional.

GOODSON, Kathleen S; Central R Iii HS; Flat River, MO; Band; Chr; Chrs; CncrtBnd; HonRl; Mdrgl; MrchBnd; OffAde; PepBnd; StuCncl; TchrAde; FBLA; FHA; FTA; Se Missouri State; Home Economics.

GOODSON, Nancy; Carrolhon HS; Carrollton, MO; 36/102 HonRl; FHA; GerCl; PpCl; College; Secretarial.

GOODWICK, Sherri L; Leland HS; Leland, IL; 3/32 PresFrshCls; SecSophCls; ALAGirlsSt; HonRl; SecJrNHS; SecStuCncl; FHA; VPSpnCl; VPPpCl; LetterSocr; Chrldr; College; Medicine.

GOODWIN, Carolynn L; Lincoln HS; Lincoln, NE; 6/484 HonRl; NatlMeritCmnd; EdYrBk; PpCl; College; Journalism.

GOODWIN, Cherie A; Dekalb HS; Dekalb, IL; 9/380 VPSrCls; ChmnNatlFornLg; NHS; NatlMeritCmnd; StuCncl; PresYthFlsp; DanFAwd; DARAwd; EldAwd; 4-HAwd; Univ Of Il; Home Ec Extension Adviser.

GOODWIN, Jim W; Minonk Dana Rutland HS; Minonk, IL; 8/75 PresFrshCls; Chr; HonRl; SchPl; StuCncl; YthFlsp; FrCl; LetterBsktbl; CaptFtbl; LetterTrk; CitAwd; College; Law.

GOODWIN, Peggy L; Langdon HS; Langdon, ND; 2/107 HstFrshCls; HonRl; LbryAde; NHS; SctActv; RptrYrbk; FBLA; PpCl; Univ Of Nd; Law.

GOODWIN, Robert L; West Catholic HS; Marne, MI; HonRl; SchPl; TchrAde; YthFlsp; Bsktbl; LetterFtbl; LetterTrk; Wrstlng; IMSpt; Grand Rapids Jr College; Architecture.

GOODWIN, Robert M; Bath HS; Bath, MI; 24/80 VPSrCls; ALBoysSt; Band; CncrtBnd; HonRl; MrchBnd; StuCncl; LetterBsbl; LetterFtbl; Col; Vocaton.

GOODYEAR, Jeffery A; Tremont HS; Morton, IL; 3/75 HonRl; Bsbl; Col; Pro.

GOOKIN, Myron L; Fairfield HS; Fairfield, IA; VPFrshCls; PresJrCls; Band; Chr; HonRl; NatlFornLg; NHS; StuCncl; LetterFtbl; LionAwd; Iowa Univ; Telecommunicative Arts.

GOOLSBY, Amy; Platteview HS; Omaha, NE; 7/75 SecSophCls; Band; DrlTm; HonRl; MrchBnd; NHS; SchPl; Twrl; PpCl; Chrldr; Undecided; Possibly High Schoolteaching.

GOOLSBY, Jerome; Lafayette HS; St Joseph, MO; 65/263 Chr; Chrl; JA; ModUN; SctActv; MthCl; CchngActv; IMSpt; Northwest Missouri State Univ; Broadcastin.

GOON, Carol A; Potomac HS; Potomac, IL; Chrs; SchMus; StuCncl; SecYthFlsp; SecPpCl; LetterBsktbl; LetterTrk; Chrldr; GAA; 4-HAwd; Olivet Coll; Nurse.

GOON, Wanda; Lindblom Tech Hs; Chicago, IL; 36/722 HonRl; NHS; TchrAde; College; Computer Programming.

GOONE, Michael A; Niles West HS; Lincolnwood, IL; 111/666 CmntyWkr; HonRl;.

GOOSEY, Gary A; Harrisburg R V Iii HS; Columbia, MO; ALBoysSt; ChrhWkr; HonRl; JrNHS; NHS; ROTC; StuCncl; StuGov; YthFlsp; YthFnd; College; Professional.

GOOSEY, Larry; Novinger Ri HS; Noringer, MO; SpnCl; IMSpt; Armed Forces.

GOOSTREE, Gregory A; Salem Community HS; Salem, IL; HonRl; FrCl; PpCl; Bsbl; LetterFtbl; Trk; IMSpt; Lakeland Clge; Radio Broadcasting.

GORA, Robert A; St Ignatius College Prep HS; Chicago, IL; HonRl; LetterBsktbl; Tennis; Univ Of Illinois; Metallurgical Engineer.

GORACKE, Cynthia A; Weeping Water HS; Weeping Water, NE; ALAGirlsSt; SecBand; Chrs; DrmMjrt; NHS; 4-H; FHA; SecPpCl; LetterTrk; GAA; College; Professional.

GORAK, Georjean M; Oak Forest HS; Oak Forest, IL; 10/326 HonRl; NHS; Univ Of Illinois; Physical Therapy.

GORALSKI, Sandra; North HS; Waukesha, WI; Chrs; HospAde; OffAde; SchPl; TchrAde; Teen; Trk; GAA; Sch; Voc.

GORANSON, Wayne L; Lake Mills Community HS; Luke Mills, IA; 10/83 CncrtBnd; HonRl; MrchBnd; Orch; PepBnd; SchPl; Ftbl; Wrstlng; CchngActv; IMSpt; College; Professional.

GORD, Connie M; Leland HS; Leland, IL; 1/33 VPFrshCls; Band; Chr; HonRl; NHS; SchPl; StuCncl; EdSchPpr; SpnCl; Chrldr; Univ; Major Study.

GORDEN, Betty J; Cambridge Comm HS; Cambridge, IL; 5#41#54# SchPl; StuCncl; StuGov; SciCl; GAA; IMSpt; JCAwd; Coll; Spec Educ.

GORDEN, Daniel W; Hawley HS; Hawley, MN; 6/65 ChrhWkr; CmntyWkr; HonRl; NHS; SchPl; MthCl; SciCl; CaptBsbl; LetterBsktbl; LetterFtbl; Trk; Wrstlng; College; Finance.

GORDON, Brenda C; Eastern HS; Lansing, MI; HonRl; JrNHS; Michigan St Univ; Pre Law.

GORDON, Brenda S; Coleman HS; Coleman, MI; SecFrshCls; SecSrCls; SchPl; 4-H; CaptBsktbl; PPFtbl; Col; Rn.

GORDON, Brock R; Northside HS; Muncie, IN; 65/310 CmntyWkr; YthFlsp; Bsbl; Bsktbl; Tennis; IMSpt; Univ; Pro.

GORDON, Bruce B; Cass Technical HS; Detroit, MI; Band; ChrhWkr; HonRl; LbryAde; OffAde; SchMus; IMSpt; College; Medica Research.

GORDON, Cathy L; Holmen HS; Onalaska, WI; 14/113 SecJrCls; Band; Chr; ChrhWkr; HonRl; NHS; RptrYrbk; FHA; PpCl; Chrldr; Univ; Professional.

GORDON, Charla J; Coleman HS; Coleman, MI; SecJrCls; PresSrCls; SchPl; StuCncl; TchrAde; Yrbk; 4-H; FHA; 4-HAwd; Michigan State Univ.

GORDON, David; Carlinville Hs; Carlinville, IL; ChrhWkr; HonRl; NHS; SchPl; SctActv; FrCl; Bsktbl; LetterFtbl; LetterGlf; LetterWrstlng; College; Biology.

GORDON, Douglas L; Marquette HS; Michigan City, IN; ChrhWkr; CmntyWkr; HonRl; Baughmans Decorating School; Decorator.

GORDON, Gail M; Harlan HS; Chicago, IL; 2/525 ChrhWkr; CmntyWkr; HonRl; JrNHS; NHS; NatlMeritCmnd; SchAde; SchPl; SctActv; StuGov; TchrAde; Swmmng; GAA; Univ; Engineer.

GORDON, Gloria L; Central HS; Atlanta, KS; Chrs; HonRl; LbryAde; SchPl; RptrSchPpr; SchPpr; College; Business.

GORDON, Glovenia A; Lindblom Tech HS; Chicago, IL; 290/637 Chr; ChrhWkr; CmntyWkr; Mdrgl; OffAde; SchAde; SchMus; TchrAde; GAA; Southern Ill University; Physical Therapist.

GORDON, Jack D; Galena HS; Galena, MO; 10/34 Band; CncrtBnd; HonRl; PolWkr; PresStuCncl; PresStuGov; Pres4-H; TreasFFA; PpCl; 4-HAwd; Southwest Mo State Univ; Law.

GORDON, Karen A; Bronaugh R 7 HS; Moundville, MO; PresSrCls; Band; HonRl; StuCncl; TchrAde; EdYrBk; SptEdSchPpr; PpCl; Bsktbl; Trk; College.

GORDON, Kathy; South Newton HS; Earl Park, IN; 11/99 SchPl; Yrbk; 4-H; PpCl; PPFtbl; Ball State Univ; Art.

GORDON, Linda J; Bremen HS; Posen, IL; 10/430 HonRl; NHS; SchAde; PpCl; GAA; Work; Secretarial Duties.

GORDON, Lori B; Lawrence HS; Lawrence, KS; 42/550 HonRl; SctActv; PpCl; LetterBsbl; LetterBsktbl; Ks U; Adaptive Physical Education.

GORDON, Mark S; Riverside HS; Dearborn Heights, MI; 12/275 Chrs; ChrhWkr; CncrtBnd; HonRl; JrNHS; MrchBnd; NHS; PepBnd; SchMus; SpnCl; U Of Mi Dearborn; Pre Dentistry Orthodontis.

GORDON, Nancy E; Bronaugh R 7 HS; Moundville, MO; TrsSophCls; TreasBand; ChrhWkr; HonRl; NatlThespSoc; StuCncl; Twrl; PpCl; Bsktbl; Trk; Business Coll; Vocation.

GORDON, Pamala; Cambridge Senior HS; Cambridge, MN; 4/209 HonRl; NHS; Brainerd Voc; Dental Assist.

GORDON, Pamela S; Albia Community HS; Lovilia, IA; 12/153 Band; Chr; Chrs; ChrhWkr; CmntyWkr; CncrtBnd; HonRl; MrchBnd; NHS; PepBnd; Humbolt Inst; Travel & Airlines.

GORDON, Rebecca M; Mather HS; Chicago, IL; CmntyWkr; HonRl; NatlMeritCmnd; PolWkr; SchAde; SchMus; SchPl; StuCncl; University; Theatre.

GORDON, Robert K; Spalding Institute; Peoria, IL; 1#7#19#4 PresSophCls; Quill&Scroll; StuCncl; StuGov; SptEdSchPpr; LetterTennis; IMSpt; Law.

GORDON, Sarah L; Smithton R Vi HS; Sedalia, MO; Chrs; HonRl; NHS; PolWkr; SchPl; 4-H; PresFHA; GAA; 4-HAwd; College; Medicine.

GORDON, Susan K; Yates Center HS; Yates Center, KS; 2/60 ALBoysSt; ALAGirlsSt; Band; ChrhWkr; CncrtBnd; DrmMjrt; HonRl; MrchBnd; NHS; OffAde; PepBnd; PolWkr; Trk; BttyCrckrAwd; Emporia College; Home Economics.

GORDON, Valerie D; Paseo HS; Kansas City, MO; ChrhWkr; HonRl; NHS; SchPl; SctActv; PresYthFlsp; PpCl; CaptBsbl; CaptBsktbl; University; Law.

GORDY, Brenda K; Wyaconda C1 HS; Granger, MO; 1/18 TrsSrCls; Chr; Chrs; HonRl; LbryAde; SchMus; SchPl; EdYrBk; 4-H; LetterBsktbl;.

GORE, Carol L; Downers Grove North HS; Downers Grove, IL; 40/509 VPSrCls; Chrs; HonRl; NHS; Eastern Illinois Univ.

GORE, Patrick L; Ashwaubenon HS; Green Bay, WI; HonRl; Bsbl; Bsktbl; Ftbl; IMSpt; College; Accounting.

GORECKI, Audrey L; Evergreen Park Comm HS; Evergreen Park, IL; 1/442 HonRl; NHS; FrCl; GerCl; MthCl; IMSpt; ChmbCommrsAwd; Mundelein Coll; Busi Management.

GORECKI, Curtis; Messmer HS; Milwaukee, WI; 10/212 ChrhWkr; CmntyWkr; HonRl; JrNHS; NHS; NatlMeritCmnd; SchAde; SctActv; TchrAde; IMSpt; College; Engineering.

GORECKI, Mark C; Douglas Macarthur HS; Decatur, IL; 15/400 Band; HonRl; NHS; SpnCl; East Ill Univ; Business.

GORECKI, Michael S; Center Line HS; Warren, MI; HonRl; Bsbl; IMSpt; Wayne State Univ; Cpa.

GOREN, Paul D; Metro HS; Chicago, IL; NatlSciFnd; PolWkr; SchAde; StuGov; TchrAde; RptrSchPpr; SptEdSchPpr; MthCl; LetterBsktbl; Tennis; College; Political Science.

GORENCE, Robert J; Prospect HS; Arlington Hts, IL; 21/625 VPFrshCls; HonRl; NHS; Ftbl; Univ Of Virginia; Law.

GORENTZ, Anthony J; Northeast HS; Arma, KS; 18/51 TrsFrshCls; TrsJrCls; ALBoysSt; HonRl; NHS; NatlThespSoc; Quill&Scroll; SchPl; RptrYrbk; RptrSchPpr; College; Furniture Design.

GORGAN, Michael W; Hartford Union HS; Hartforf, WI; AFS; Chr; Chrs; ChrhWkr; CmntyWkr; HonRl; JA; JrNHS; SpnCl; Tennis; Uw Madison; Phy Therapy.

GORHAM, Anne; Marshall Universtiy HS; Minneapolis, MN; SecSrCls; CmntyWkr; HospAde; NatlMeritFnl; SchPl; StuGov; TchrAde; BauchLmbAwd; RotaryAwd; VoiceDemAwd; Radcliffe Coll; Biology.

GORHAM, Karen M; Paul Iii HS; Omaha, NE; 24/97 HonRl; LbryAde; OffAde; TchrAde; SecPpCl; College; Professional.

GORHAM, Kerstin A; Marshall Univ HS; Minneapolis, MN; SecSrCls; ChrhWkr; CmntyWkr; HospAde; NatlMeritSF; SchPl; StuCncl; StuGov; Univ; Biology.

GORHAM, Vaughn R; Excelsior Spring HS; Excelsior Spring, MO; HonRl; JrNHS; NHS; OffAde; PpCl; Bsbl; Swmmng; Tennis; OptClAwd; CitAwd;.

GORIS, Carolyn; Little Wolf HS; Manawa, WI; TrsSophCls; ChrhWkr; HonRl; 4-H; PpCl; Chrldr; GAA; IMSpt; PPFtbl; Coll; Professional.

GORKA, Cathy A; Mahtomedi HS; Stillwater, MN; Chr; HonRl; SctActv; TchrAde; Yrbk; College.

GORMAN, Daniel S; Roger C Sullivan HS; Chicago, IL; HonRl; NatlMeritCmnd; PolWkr; SchPl; Yrbk; RptrSchPpr; SchPpr; KeyCl; Lake Forest College; Law.

GORMAN, Ellen L; Crete Monee HS; Monee, IL; 46/382 HonRl; NHS; RptrSchPpr; 4-H; Univ; Medicine.

GORMAN, Erin K; Lincolnwood HS; Farmersville, IL; 19/57 HonRl; LbryAde; RptrYrbk; RptrSchPpr; 4-H; SecSpnCl; PpCl; SciCl; College; Lawyer.

GORMAN, James G; Chaminade College; St Louis, MO; 60/112 ChrhWkr; CmntyWkr; HonRl; LitMag; StuCncl; RptrSchPpr; Bsktbl; Ftbl; Trk; IMSpt; College; Law.

GORMAN, Julie A; Trinity HS; Chicago, IL; 1/204 HonRl; PresNHS; NatlMeritSF; StuCncl; StuGov; EdYrBk; FrCl; Loyola Univ; Psychology.

GORMAN, Lisa M; Sullivan HS; Chicago, IL; VPJrCls; PresSrCls; CtyCnl; HonRl; NHS; StuGov; FrCl; GAA; University; Veterinary Medicine.

GORMAN, Michael J; Arthur Mill HS; Saginaw, MI; Band; CmntyWkr; HonRl; IMSpt; Western Michigan; Recreaton Ymca Work.

GORMAN, Michelle J; Sacred Heart Acad; Springfield, IL; HonRl; RptrYrbk; MthCl; PpCl; SciCl; Lincolnland Comm Coll; Real Estate.

GORMAN, Richard; Spalding Institute; Peoria, IL; 17/102 NHS; RptrYrbk; RptrSchPpr; KeyCl; Bsbl; IMSpt; Eastern Illinois U; Business Management.

GORMAN, Richard A; Appleton West HS; Appleton, WI; Band; CncrtBnd; SchPl; StuCncl; LetterBsbl; Bsktbl; Wrstlng; IMSpt; University Of Wisconsin; Pharmacy.

GORMAN, Thomas P; Brother Rice HS; Birmingham, MI; 1/210 Chrl; HonRl; JrNHS; NHS; NatlMeritSF; RptrYrbk; CaptFtbl; LetterTrk; IMSpt; College.

GORMICAN, Michael; Wisconsin HS; Black Earth, WI; TrsJrCls; StuCncl; FBLA; Univ Of Eau Claire; Certified Public Acct.

GORNEY, John; Osborn HS; Detroit, MI; NatlMeritFnl; NatlMeritCmnd; NatlMeritSchl; Oakland Univ; Research Chemist.

GORNEY, Kevin G; All Saints Central HS; Bay City, MI; 31/143 Band; HonRl; Sacrstn; SchAde; SctActv; Bsktbl; Trk; U Of Detroit; Socal Sci.

GORRELL, Greg D; Wichita West HS; Wichita, KS; HonRl; ROTC; Ftbl; Wrstlng; CchngActv; PPFtbl; College; Rotclor Med Sch.

GORRELL, Norma J; Laboure HS; St Louis, MO; 4/64 ChrhWkr; CmntyWkr; HonRl; HospAde; RptrSchPpr; College; Pharmacy.

GORRELL, Patty S; Tescott HS; Culver, KS; 2/19 Band; HonRl; PepBnd; SchPl; 4-H; PpCl; Bsktbl; Chrldr; Cloud Co Comm College; Home Economics.

GORRELL, Sheryl F; Newton HS; Newton, IL; 28/180 Band; CncrtBnd; HonRl; LbryAde; MrchBnd; NHS; 4-H; FNA; St Johns Hosp; Nurse.

GORSKE, Paula S; Winnebago Luth Acad; Fond Du Lac, WI; Band; Chr; ChrhWkr; CncrtBnd; JA; PepBnd; SchPl; PpCl; Bsktbl; Trk; Dr Martin Luther King Col; Teaching Math.

GORSKI, Carla; St Mary Central HS; Menasha, WI; SecJrCls; ALAGirlsSt; Band; HonRl; SchPl; SctActv; StuGov; RptrYrbk; 4-H; SpnCl; Univ Of Wisc; Pharm.

GORSKI, Dana B; Springfield Public HS; Springfield, MN; SchPl; SctActv; 4-H; Bsktbl; Glf; Trk; College.

GORSKI, Gregory F; Benet Academy; Clarendon Hills, IL; Band; ChrhWkr; CncrtBnd; HonRl; MrchBnd; NatlMeritSF; PepBnd; LetterFtbl; LetterTrk; IMSpt; College; Medicine.

GORSKI, John G; Glenbard East HS; Lombard, IL; Band; CncrtBnd; HonRl; MrchBnd; Orch; PepBnd; College; Math.

GORSKI, Karen A; Ladywood HS; Livonia, MI; 8/100 Chr; HonRl; LitMag; NatlFornLg; NHS; Orch; SchMus; StuCncl; Yrbk; Wayne State University; Art.

GORSKI, Mary B; Lourdes HS; Chicago, IL; 15/277 HonRl; HospAde; Yrbk; SpnCl; College.

GORSKI, Michael E; Thornridge HS; S Holland, IL; 3/649 VPSrCls; HonRl; JrNHS; NHS; StuCncl; MthCl; LetterBsbl; LetterFtbl; SARAwd; Univ; Doctor.

GORSKI, Sandra M; Notre Dame HS; West Allis, WI; 18/117 SecJrCls; Chrs; HonRl; SchMus; SchPl; StuGov; RptrYrbk; Yrbk; PpCl; Univ Of Wisconsin; Accounting.

GORSKI, Susan E; Notre Dame HS; Chicago, IL; 10/262 HonRl; FrCl; MthCl; U Of Il; Law.

GORSUCH, Jill A; Pattonville Sr HS; Bridgeton, MO; Chr; Chrs; HonRl; Mdrgl; SchMus; SchPl; PpCl; Chrldr; IMSpt; College; Actress.

GORTER, Peter L; Lake Benton Public HS; Lake Benton, MN; VPFrshCls; Band; Chr; Chrs; HonRl; JrNHS; NHS; 4-H; SpnCl; PpCl; Bsktbl; LetterFtbl; Trk; Wrstlng;.

GORTER, Ruth E; Zeeland HS; Zeeland, MI; ALAGirlsSt; HonRl; NHS; LatCl; Butterworth Hosp; Nurse.

GORTON, Douglas; Pine City HS; Grasston, MN; 14/117 Band; Chr; Chrs; CncrtBnd; HonRl; MrchBnd; PepBnd; SchPl; StuGov; EdSchPpr;.

GORTON, Lauri J; Niles HS; Niles, MI; Chr; Chrs; ChrhWkr; HonRl; NHS; OffAde; StuCncl; Yrbk; LetterBsktbl; LetterTennis; College; Engineering Professional.

GORTON, Robyn K; Kelloggsville HS; Wyoming, MI; HonRl; NHS; NatlMeritSF; SchPl; TchrAde; CaptBsbl; LetterBsktbl; GAA; Grand Rapids Jr College; Secretary.

GORTOWSKI, Ronald E; St Ignatius HS; Chicago, IL; Loyola Univ; Law Enforcement.

GORZEN, Kim M; St Clair HS; St Clair, MI; 6/191 ChrhWkr; HonRl; PolWkr; SchMus; SchPl; StuGov;

Yrbk; SpnCl; Swmmng; St Clair County Comm College; Education.

GOSCH, Jackie L; Lineville Clio HS; Lineville, IA; 1/10 SecFrshCls; Chrs; HonRl; 4-H; LetterBsktbl; 4-HAwd; Air Force; Pilot.

GOSCH, Thresa; Lake View Auburn HS; Auburn, IA; 9/45 SecTrsSrCls; Chrs; MrchBnd; Twrl; FHA; Bsktbl; Trk; IMSpt; BttyCrckrAwd; PresAwd; Des Moines Area Comm; Practical Nurse.

GOSCHKE, Julie M; Border Central HS; Munich, ND; VPJrCls; Band; Chrs; HonRl; SchPl; StuCncl; SchPpr; Bsbl; College; Medical Tech.

GOSCHKE, Lori J; Langdon HS; Munich, ND; Band; HonRl; PepBnd; PresYthFlsp; 4-H; FHA; GerCl; PpCl; Nd State U; Vet Tech.

GOSETTI, Gregory J; Cudahy Senior HS; Cudahy, WI; 9/360 CncrtBnd; VPNHS; PepBnd; PresStuCncl; Bsktbl; LetterFtbl; CaptTrk; LionAwd; VFWAwd; Brown Univ; Interl Relatins.

GOSH, Gail M; Carmel HS; Mundelein, IL; 19/200 Chrs; ChrhWkr; HonRl; NHS; PolWkr; RptrYrbk; RptrSchPpr; FTA; SpnCl; MthCl; Univ; Engineering.

GOSIK, Andrew C; Weber HS; Chicago, IL; 54/193 Band; Chrs; SchPl; Loyola University; Accounting.

GOSIK, Cynthia M; Hamtramck HS; Hamtramck, MI; HstJrCls; HstSrCls; HonRl; JA; NHS; OffAde; Quill&Scroll; SchPl; RptrSchPpr; SchPpr; Univ Of De; Communications.

GOSKO, Linda; Buena Vista Hs; Saginaw, MI; 6/259 Band; ChrhWkr; CncrtBnd; HonRl; MrchBnd; OffAde; SchPl; PpCl; College; Business.

GOSLIN, Carol J; Clinton HS; Clinton, MO; 49/156 ALAGirlsSt; Chrs; ChrhWkr; HonRl; NatlFornLg; NatlThespSoc; SchPl; YthFlsp; SpnCl; PpCl; Cent Mo St U; Special Education Teacher.

GOSLIN, Lura A; Mexico HS; Mexico, MO; Chr; NatlFornLg; SchPl; TchrAde; YthFnd; RptrSchPpr; LatCl; PpCl; Sms Springfield Mo; Journalism.

GOSNEY, David B; Monroe City R 1 HS; Monroe City, MO; 12/92 HonRl; NHS; StuCncl; SciCl; CaptBsktbl; LetterTrk; St Louis College; Pharmacy.

GOSS, Drew D; Park Tudor HS; Indianapolis, IN; HonRl; StuCncl; StuGov; Glf; LetterSocr; Univ; Pro.

GOSS, Luevon; Saginaw HS; Saginaw, MI; ChrhWkr; HonRl; JrNHS; RptrYrbk; Central Michigan Univ; Data Processing.

GOSS, Michael P; Whitefish Bay HS; Whitefish Bay, WI; 25/340 VPSrCls; ALBoysSt; ChrhWkr; HonRl; StuCncl; StuGov; LatCl; Bsktbl; Swmmng; Trk; Marquette; Med.

GOSS, Tommie G; Saint Anne Community HS; Saint Anne, IL; Band; Chr; CmntyWkr; CncrtBnd; DrmBgl; HonRl; Mdrgl; MrchBnd; PepBnd; StuCncl; University Of Illinois; Computer Service.

GOSS, William F; Marian Catholic HS; Chicago Hts, IL; 51/338 HonRl; RptrYrbk; LatCl; Ftbl; Univ Of Il; Law.

GOSSAGE, Margaret E; Pope County HS; Stonefort, IL; 2/54 TrsSophCls; HonRl; SchPl; Yrbk; 4-H; PresFHA; SpnCl; PpCl; GAA; Southern Illinois Univ; Psychology.

GOSSAGE, Teresa L; Oak Park HS; Kansas City, MO; 10/602 ChrhWkr; HonRl; HospAde; NatlFornLg; StuCncl; YthFlsp; RptrYrbk; PpCl; GAA; IMSpt; Univ Of Missouri; Psychology.

GOSSE, William; Colby HS; Curtiss, WI; Aud/Vis; ChrhWkr; HonRl; SchPl; YthFlsp; FFA; Trade Or Business; Vocation.

GOSSEN, Debbie M; East De Pere HS; De Pere, WI; Chrl; ChrhWkr; HonRl; NHS; 4-H; 4-HAwd; Tech Inst; Nursing.

GOSSETT, Glenna; St Elmo Comm HS; St Elmo, IL; 14/56 VPSrCls; HonRl; LbryAde; RptrYrbk; Yrbk; Siu Carbondale; Psychology.

GOSSETT, Kathryn; Udall 463 HS; Udall, KS; 1/30 VPJrCls; Band; Chrs; CncrtBnd; HonRl; SctActv; TchrAde; PpCl; Brown Mackie,saina; Law Secry.

GOSSICK, Kerry L; Winnetonka HS; Kansas City, MO; AFS; HonRl; PolWkr; SchMus; PpCl; Chrldr; College; Mathematics.

GOSSLING, Janet M; Turkey Valley HS; Waucoma, IA; 21/110 Chr; ChrhWkr; HonRl; HospAde; JA; Pres4-H; PresFHA; 4-HAwd; GodCntryAwd; College; Nursing.

GOSSLING, Steven J; Turkey Valley HS; Waucoma, IA; HonRl; FFA; Bsktbl; Trade School; Farm Implement Mechanics.

GOSSMAN, Belinda; Dieterich HS; Dietrich, IL; 2 Chrs; ChrhWkr; HonRl; LbryAde; VPFBLA; FHA; SpnCl; GAA; Lakeland College;music Education.

GOSSMAN, Patricia A; Immaculata HS; Detroit, MI; 2/108 HonRl; NHS; NatlMeritFnl; NatlMeritSF; PolWkr; StuGov; FrCl; Kalamazoo College; Foreign Languages.

GOSSMAN, Robin W; North Winneshiek HS; Decorah, IA; 23/52 Chrs; SchPl; StuCncl; EngCl; PpCl; CaptBsktbl; Trk; IMSpt; PresAwd; Iowa State University; Coach.

GOSWICK, Randolph J; Seneca HS; Racine, MO; PresFrshCls; PresAFS; ChrhWkr; NHS; NatlThespSoc; SchPl; StuCncl; RptrYrbk; SecSpnCl; MthCl; College; Math.

GOTHAM, David A; Bloomer HS; Bloomer, WI; PresJrCls; ALBoysSt; CtyCnl; CmntyWkr; HonRl; JrNHS; StuCncl; Ftbl; Trk; College; Engineering.

GOTHAM, Deborah M; Buena Vista HS; Saginaw, MI; SecSophCls; HonRl; SecNHS; SchPl; StuGov; SptEdYrbk; FTA; SpnCl; IMSpt; PPFtbl; University; Professional.

GOTHMANN, Steven; Waconia HS; St Bonifacins, MN; 10/140 VPJrCls; PresSrCls; Chr; HonRl; Mdrgl; NHS; SchMus; SptEdSchPpr; College Of St Thomas; Professional.

GOTSCHALL, Audrey J; West Holt HS; Atkinson, NE; 6/80 Chr; Chrs; ChrhWkr; DrlTm; HonRl; NHS; SchMus; SchPl; YthFlsp; SchPpr; Univ Of Nebraska; Elementary Education.

GOTSCHALL, Thomas L; Jacksonville HS; Jacksonville, IL; 45/363 HonRl; NatlMeritCmnd; LetterBsktbl; Glf; CchngActv; Eastern Il Univ;.

GOTT, Jack L; Wichita HS; Wichita, KS; Band; CncrtBnd; MrchBnd; University; Aeronautical Engineering.

GOTTBREHT, William M; Bishop Ryan HS; Minot, ND; KeyCl; GerCl; LetterBsktbl; Ftbl; Wrstlng; College; Elec Engineer.

GOTTLIEB, Malorie L; Whitefish Bay HS; Milwaukee, WI; 10/320 HonRl; NatlFornLg; NatlMeritCmnd; NatlThespSoc; SchMus; SchPl; RptrSchPpr; SchPpr; SecFrCl; Chrldr; Yale; Law Or Theatre.

GOTTLIEB, Susan L; Ida Crown Jewish Acad; Chicago, IL; Yrbk; Coll; Social Worker.

GOTTLIEB, Thomas J; Mercy HS; St Louis, MO; HonRl; NHS; TchrAde; EdSchPpr; SpnCl; SciCl; Coll; Law.

GOTTMAN, Cassandra L; Cardinal HS; Batavia, IA; 5/72 NHS; LetterBsktbl; LetterTrk; Ottumwa Heights Coll; Medical Record Tech.

GOTTSCHALK, Sharon K; Octavia HS; Anchor, IL; 5/50 ChrhWkr; CncrtBnd; HonRl; MrchBnd; NHS; PresYthFlsp; RptrYrbk; RptrSchPpr; SpnCl; SciCl; Trk; GAA; PPFtbl; Univ Of Illinois; Chemistry.

GOTTSCHALK, Steve L; Hillsboro HS; Hillsboro, MO; 1/200 ALBoysSt; Chr; HonRl; NHS; MthCl; Ftbl; Military Acad; Pro.

GOTTSCHALL, Brian A; Highland Public HS; Highland, WI; 2/51 PresJrCls; Band; Chr; ChrhWkr; CncrtBnd; HonRl; MrchBnd; SchMus; FFA; LetterTrk; Bob Jones Univ; Teach Biology.

GOTTSELIG, Gerald W; Bloomington HS; Bloomington, IL; HonRl; NHS; GerCl; MthCl; PpCl; SciCl; CaptSwmmng; Univ Of Illinois; Engineering.

GOTTULA, Bradley S; Table Rock HS; Table Rock, NE; PresFrshCls; VPJrCls; SptEdYrbk; Bsbl; Bsktbl; Ftbl; Trk; College.

GOTTULA, Deborah L; Elk Creek Public HS; Stenauer, NE; 1/13 SecJrCls; Chrs; HonRl; Mdrgl; SchPl; TchrAde; PpCl; Chrldr; Trade Sch; Secretary.

GOTTULA, Karen; Table Rock Public HS; Steinauer, NE; TrsFrshCls; Chrs; HonRl; RptrYrbk; PpCl;.

GOTZ, Robert R; Waterford Mott HS; Pontiac, MI; Chr; Chrs; NatlFornLg; Sacrstn; SchAde; SchPl; SctActv; StuCncl; StuGov; TchrAde; St Marys College; Journalism.

GOUDIE, Douglas E; Southfield Lathrup HS; Southfield, MI; HonRl; NHS; SchPl; Yrbk; SchPpr; Central Michigan University; Artist.

GOUDY, Clay F; Nicolet HS; Bayside, WI; 73/500 JrNHS; NHS; SctActv; SciCl; Glf; Swmmng; Trk; IMSpt; Univ; Attorney At Law.

GOUDY, Teresa L; Macksville HS; Macksville, KS; VPFrshCls; Band; Chrs; ChrhWkr; HonRl; MrchBnd; NHS; PepBnd; TchrAde; Yrbk; PpCl; Trk; Fort Hays St College; Elementary Educ.

GOUGEON, Martin; Alpena HS; Alpena, MI; HonRl; LatCl; Trk; Alpena Community Coll; Architectural.

GOUGER, Mary K; Marian HS; Omaha, NE; 2/162 CaptDrlTm; HonRl; NHS; Sdlty; 4-H; FTA; SpnCl; Chrldr; 4-HAwd; College; Pediatrician.

GOUGH, Gale I; Kansas HS; Kansas, IL; 2/26 PresFrshCls; VPSophCls; HonRl; NHS; StuCncl; EdYrBk; SptEdSchPpr; FrCl; PpCl; Chrldr; College; Professional.

GOUGH, Terrance A; Mc Henry Community HS; Mchenry, IL; 9/466 HonRl; NHS; PpCl; LetterBsbl; De Paul Univ; Lawyer.

GOULD, David W; North Clay HS; Louisville, IL; HonRl; SchPl; Yrbk; College; Professional.

GOULD, Judy M; Charleuoix HS; Charleuoix, MI; 2/147 HonRl; FHA; LatCl; SpnCl; BauchLmbAwd; Western Mich Univ; Spec Ed.

GOULD, Kim S; Charlevoix HS; Charlevoix, MI; StuCncl; Yrbk; LatCl; SpnCl; U Of Mi; Pre Dentistry.

GOULD, Mickey L; St Francis Acad; Joliet, IL; ChrhWkr; CmntyWkr; HospAde; StuCncl; StuGov; Yrbk; Trk; Chrldr; GAA; IMSpt; University; Professional.

GOULD, Thomas B; Ottawa Hills HS; Grand Rapids, MI; HonRl; NHS; Grand Rpds Jr College; Math Or Engineer.

GOULDIE, Connie; Osborne HS; Osborne, KS; 1/69 SecTrsFrshCls; TrsSophCls; ALAGirlsSt; Band; Chr; ChrhWkr; CncrtBnd; PPFtbl; College; Journalism.

GOULDSMITH, Kathryn; Fort Osage Senior HS; Buckner, MO; 16/312 CncrtBnd; HonRl; NHS; PepBnd; SchMus; MthCl; VPSrCls; PPFtbl; Northwest Missouri State Univ.;secondary Pe.

GOULET, Mary Jo R; Rosemount Sr HS; Rosemount, MN; 11/423 Aud/Vis; CmntyWkr; HonRl; Yrbk; PpCl; Vocational School; Art.

GOUNTANIS, Anne D; New Hartford Central HS; Mendota Heights, MN; 40/400 CncrtBnd; HonRl; MrchBnd; NHS; NatlMeritCmnd; PepBnd; StuCncl; YthFlsp; FrCl; PpCl; LetterTrk; GAA; IMSpt; University Of Minnesota; Business Admin.

GOURD, Jody C; Chanute Senior HS; Chanute, KS; Band; LitMag; NatlMeritCmnd; TchrAde; FrCl; Tennis; University; Political Science.

GOURLEY, Dennis J; Lenox Community HS; Lenox, IA; 2/33 Band; CncrtBnd; HonRl; MrchBnd; YthFlsp; Bsktbl; College.

GOURLEY, Laura S; De Kalb Sr HS; De Kalb, IL; 3/370 Chrs; NHS; Ill State Univ; Special Education.

GOUVERNEUR, Curtis J; Lincoln HS; Vincennes, IN; 190/450 ALBoysSt; CmntyWkr; YthFlsp; PpCl; Trk; IMSpt; Vincennes U; Electronics Tech.

GOVAKER, David A; Pittsburg HS; Pittsburg, KS; 8/230 JA; NatlFornLg; NatlMeritCmnd; SchMus; SchPl; StuCncl; LatCl; Kscp; Medicine.

GOVEN, Ione R; Turtle Lake Mercer HS; Turtle Lake, ND; PresFrshCls; ALAGirlsSt; Band; Chrl; HonRl; SchPl; RptrYrbk; PresFHA; LetterTrk; JETSAwd; Univ Of No Dakota; Physical Therapist.

GOVIER, Reba; Broken Bow HS; Broken Bow, NE; HonRl; LbryAde; MrchBnd; Quill&Scroll; RptrYrbk; RptrSchPpr; 4-H; Chrldr; GAA; College; Medical Field.

GOVONI, Cheryl A; Plainfield HS; Joliet, IL; 25/301 HonRl; MrchBnd; StuCncl; Bsbl; Bsktbl; Chrldr; GAA; IMSpt; PresAwd; College; Physical Education.

GOWAN, Mary J; Oslo Public HS; Oslo, MN; Band; Chr; ChrhWkr; CncrtBnd; HonRl; MrchBnd; PepBnd; StuCncl; SchPpr; FHA; PpCl; Chrldr; Moorhead St College; Accounting.

GOWEN, Beverly L; Aurora HS; Aurora, NE; VPFrshCls; CncrtBnd; HonRl; MrchBnd; NHS; 4-H; FHA; SecPpCl; 4-HAwd; Cott Univ; Dental Assistant.

GOWER, Jeffrey R; Quincy Senior HS; Quincy, IL; HonRl; JrNHS; NHS; SctActv; PresKeyCl; FrCl; TreasPpCl; LetterGlf; IMSpt; DARAwd; Bradley University; Electrical Eng.

GOWINGS, Bruce A; Burris HS; Muncie, IN; Orch; SctActv; Bsbl; Bsktbl; Trk; Ball State Univ; Musician.

GOWLER, James L; Effingham HS; Effingham, IL; Band; Chr; ChrhWkr; CmntyWkr; CncrtBnd; DrlTm; MrchBnd; PepBnd; SpnCl; Lakeland Coll; Electronics.

GOYSICH, Michael J; Morton Sr HS; Hammond, IN; 10/495 HonRl; NHS; TchrAde; PresSciCl; KiwanAwd; Purdue Univ; Marine Biology.

GRAALUM, Renae O; Litchville Public HS; Kathryn, ND; Band; Chrs; HonRl; NHS; PepBnd; FHA; PpCl; Business School.

GRABAU, Ann M; Robbinsdale Senior HS; Brooklyn Center, MN; Band; Chr; ChrhWkr; Chrldr; ChmbCommrsAwd; Concordia College; Medical Technology.

GRABAU, Teresa A; Wykoff Public HS; Wykoff, MN; 7/33 Band; Chr; Chrs; HonRl; PepBnd; StuGov; SecYthFlsp; Pres4-H; LetterTrk; 4-HAwd; Vocat Tech Inst; Medical Secretary.

GRABER, Betty; Viborg Public HS; Viborg, SD; 3/40 Band; HonRl; HospAde; SchPl; TchrAde; FrCl; SciCl; DARAwd; Sd State Univ; Child Development.

GRABER, Christine J; Parkway Central HS; St Louis, MO; ChrhWkr; HonRl; NatlMeritSF; NatlThespSoc; SchMus; Bethel College; Liberal Arts.

GRABER, Curtis H; Emerson Hubbard HS; Emerson, NE; 10/56 Band; ChrhWkr; CncrtBnd; HonRl; MrchBnd; PepBnd; College.

GRABER, Gary; Thompson Comm HS; Forest City, IA; TrsJrCls; TrsSrCls; HonRl; NHS; SchPl; YthFlsp; 4-H; FFA; Iowa Lakes Comm Coll; Farm Equipment Mechan.

GRABER, Jacelyn N; Mt Pleasant HS; Wayland, IA; AFS; Band; Chr; ChrhWkr; CmntyWkr; NHS; StuCncl; StuCncl; StuGov; Tabor College; Elementary Educ.

GRABER, Jann G; Haven HS; Burrton, KS; Chr; CncrtBnd; DrlTm; MrchBnd; Twrl; Bsktbl; College; Business Management.

GRABER, Jo A; Larned HS; Larnes, KS; Band; Chrs; CncrtBnd; MrchBnd; SchMus; FHA; PpCl; PPFtbl; Dodge City Juco; Fashion Merchandising.

GRABER, Mark S; Crete Monee HS; Park Forest So, IL; 32/382 ChrhWkr; HonRl; JrNHS; NHS; NatlMeritCmnd; NatlMeritSchl; YthFlsp; LetterBsbl; Univ Of Ill; Architecture.

GRABER, Mary L; Fairfield HS; Lockridge, IA; Band; CncrtBnd; HonRl; MrchBnd; VPNHS; PepBnd; SecYthFlsp; LetterBsbl; Bsktbl; PPFtbl; Trade Sch; Comp Programming.

GRABER, Nancy L; Southern Door HS; Sturgeon Bay, WI; ChrhWkr; HonRl; FFA; Bsbl; Trk; College; Conservation.

GRABER, Teresa A; Freeman HS; Freeman, SD; VPJrCls; VPSrCls; SecBand; HonRl; HospAde; SchMus; RptrYrbk; SecFHA; VPPpCl; LetterBsktbl; IMSpt; W Iowa Tech Comm College; Data Processing.

GRABIEL, Barbara J; H H Dow HS; Midland, MI; Chr; CncrtBnd; HonRl; HospAde; MrchBnd; NHS; Orch; PepBnd; SchMus; SchPl; GerCl; Ferris State College; Accounting.

GRABINSKI, Anthony S; Muskegon Catholic Central HS; Muskegon, MI; 23/191 HonRl; NHS; SchPl; Bsktbl; LetterTrk; Wrstlng; College; Vocation.

GRABINSKI, Eugene L; St Viator HS; Mt Prospect, IL; 1/288 HonRl; RptrSchPpr; SchPpr; GerCl; IMSpt; College; Science.

GRABLE, Karen S; Caston HS; Twelve Mile, IN; Band; Chrs; NHS; SchMus; PresYthFlsp; 4-H; PresGerCl; LetterTrk; GAA; PPFtbl; 4-HAwd; Marion College; Nursing.

GRABLE, Pamela D; Warsaw HS; Warsaw, MO; 2/61 ALAGirlsSt; SecChr; ChrhWkr; HonRl; PresNHS; SchMus; SecStuCncl; YthFlsp; VPFHA; CaptChrldr; College; Home Economics.

GRABLE, Tim D; Central Noble HS; Columbia City, IN; HonRl; StuCncl; Bsktbl; Ftbl; Glf; IMSpt; Indiana Purdue U Extension; Public Rel.

GRABNER, Kathryn A; S HS; Sheboygan, WI; 35/500 HonRl; NHS; Quill&Scroll; RptrYrbk; Yrbk; St Norbert College; Medical Technology.

GRABOUSKI, Jody M; North Platte Sr HS; North Platte, NE; SecJrCls; ALAGirlsSt; DrlTm; HonRl; HospAde; Quill&Scroll; YthFlsp; YthLg; SchPpr; GAA; Univ Of Nebraska; Nursing.

GRABOW, Carol; Stephen T Mather Hs; Chicago, IL; 65/430 Chrs; CmntyWkr; HonRl; TchrAde; Yrbk; FTA; SpnCl; GAA; University Of Ill; Teacher Of Mentally Ret.

GRABOW, Dennie E; New Haven HS; Mt Cleniens, MI; HstJrCls; HonRl; NHS; StuCncl; StuGov; TchrAde; 4-H; FrCl; 4-HAwd; University; Professional Medicine.

GRABOWSKI, Linda S; Pittsford HS; Pittsford, MI; PresFrshCls; Chr; ChrhWkr; HonRl; LbryAde; SpnCl; Bsktbl; Trk; GAA; DARAwd; Bible College; Missionary Work.

GRABOWSKI, Mark A; St Viator HS; Arlington Hts, IL; LetterTrk; IMSpt; Univ Of Ill; Engineering.

GRABOWSKI, Rebecca L; Downers Grove South HS; Darien, IL; 1/820 Band; ChrhWkr; CncrtBnd; HonRl; MrchBnd; NHS; College; Education.

GRACE, Anthony R; Michigan Ctr HS; Michigan Ctr, MI; 17/165 Aud/Vis; JA; NHS; RptrYrbk; RptrSchPpr; SpnCl; SciCl; LetterTrk; JAAwd;.

GRACE, Cindy K; St Francis HS; St Francis, KS; 1/30 SecSophCls; SecJrCls; ALAGirlsSt; Band; HonRl; SchPl; StuCncl; LetterBsktbl; Chrldr; IMSpt; Kansas State; Optometry.

GRACE, James N; Abbot Pennings HS; De Pere, WI; 6/100 SecSophCls; SecJrCls; VPSrCls; HonRl; NHS; StuGov; KeyCl; LetterSocr; CaptTrk; LetterWrstlng; U Of Notre Dame; Pre Med.

GRACE, Jerilyn J; Valentine HS; Valentine, NE; 6/90 TrsSrCls; CmntyWkr; HonRl; NHS; SctActv; StuCncl; RptrYrbk; EdYrBk; FHA; PpCl; Se Tech Comm Coll; Environmental Tech.

GRACE, Kellye V; Heelan HS; Sioux City, IA; Chrs; HonRl; RedCrAde; SchMus; StuCncl; FrCl; PpCl; LetterTrk; IMSpt; PPFtbl; St Joseph Nursing School; Nursing.

GRACE, Melanie L; Lake Forest Academy; Lake Bluff, IL; SecChr; ChrhWkr; NatlThespSoc; SchMus; SchPl; StuCncl; StuGov; YthFlsp; RptrSchPpr; PpCl; Chrldr; IMSpt; College; Medical.

GRACE, Pamela J; Luther South HS; Chicago, IL; 43/205 TrsSrCls; ChrhWkr; HonRl; NatlMeritCmnd; Yrbk; RptrSchPpr; Mac Murray College; Special Education.

GRACEY, Karen M; Dominican HS; Detroit, MI; CmntyWkr; HonRl; Mdrgl; ModUN; NHS; SchMus; SchPl; SctActv; StuGov; LetterSwmmng; Univ; Actress.

GRACYALNY, Randal D; Clinton HS; Beloit, WI; 5/96 AFS; ALBoysSt; Chrs; CncrtBnd; HonRl; NHS; GerCl; CaptBsktbl; LetterTennis; LetterTrk; Milton Coll; Music.

GRACZYK, Sylvia; Madonna Hs; Chicago, IL; HonRl; NatlMeritSF; FrCl; MthCl; Maccormac Jr Coll;field Of Travel Tourism.

GRADDY, Richard L; Bourbon R 1 HS; Bourbon, MO; ChrhWkr; HonRl; NHS; RptrSchPpr; SpnCl; Technical School; Vocation.

GRADOLF, Mark J; Morgan Park HS; Chicago, IL; 20/659 ChrhWkr; HonRl; NHS; SctActv; YthFlsp; KeyCl; GerCl; MthCl; Swmmng; Univ Of Ill; Dentistry.

GRADOVILLE, Judith A; Plattsmouth HS; Plattsmouth, NE; 4/163 HonRl; NHS; PresFBLA; PresFHA; MthCl; PpCl; Business School; Sec.

GRADY, Barbara; Mcdonell Central HS; Chippewa Falls, WI; HonRl; ModUN; SchPl; Yrbk; PpCl; Trk; Chrldr; GAA; Univ Of Wi Eau Claire.

GRADY, Jane L; Boone HS; Boone, IA; Chrs; HonRl; YthFlsp; SpnCl; PpCl; University; Major Study.

GRADY, Joan; Sacred Heart Of Mary HS; Rolling Meadows, IL; 2/135 VPSophCls; HonRl; NatlFornLg; NHS; NatlMeritCmnd; StuGov; RptrSchPpr; EdSchPpr; Washington Univ; Environmental Engineering.

GRADY, Joan M; Sacred Heart Of Mary HS; Rolling Meadows, IL; 2/134 VPSophCls; HonRl; NHS; NatlMeritCmnd; StuGov; RptrSchPpr; EdSchPpr; Washington Univ; Environmental Engineer.

GRADY, Joseph E; Msgr Hacker HS; Kalamazoo, MI; Band; CncrtBnd; HonRl; MrchBnd; NHS; Orch; PepBnd; SchMus; IMSpt; College; Music.

GRADY, Mark A; Davenport West HS; Davenport, IA; 11/655 ALBoysSt; ChrhWkr; CmntyWkr; HonRl; PolWkr; SctActv; StuGov; Bsktbl; IMSpt; LetterAmLegAwd; Univ; Law.

GRADY, Mary A; Duchesne HS; St Ann, MO; Chr; HonRl; HospAde; SchMus; RptrYrbk; EdYrBk; PresFrCl; PpCl; SciCl; IMSpt; Univ Of Mo; Home Ec & Dietetics.

GRAEBNER, Steven M; Arthur Hill HS; Saginaw, MI; ChrhWkr; HonRl; NHS; NatlMeritFnl; NatlMeritSF; StuGov; RptrSchPpr; SchPpr; Wrstlng; BauchLmbAwd; Univ; Marine Bio.

GRAEF, Russell P; Poynette HS; Poynette, WI; 50/102 Band; ChrhWkr; HonRl; SchPl; StuCncl; Trk; St Olaf Coll; Ministry.

GRAESSLE, Marion C; Stephen Decatur HS; Decatur, IL; PresJrCls; Chr; StuCncl; GerCl; Chrldr; Stewardess.

GRAEVE, Eric G; Harlan Comm HS; Earling, IA; ALBoysSt; HonRl; JrNHS; NHS; SctActv; StuCncl; StuGov; GerCl; SciCl; LetterBsktbl; College; Professional.

GRAF, David W; Tomah HS; Tomah, WI; TrsFrshCls; PresSophCls; ALBoysSt; SctActv; StuCncl; SpnCl; LetterBsbl; University.

GRAF, Donna; Tipion HS; Atlanta, IN; 5/180 HonRl; JrNHS; LbryAde; NHS; NatlMeritCmnd; NatlThespSoc; SchPl; Yrbk; SciCl; Hanover Coll; Biology.

GRAF, Donny L; Des Lacs HS; Burlington, ND; CmntyWkr; SctActv; FFA; SciCl; Bsktbl; Ftbl; Trade Schl; Trucking.

GRAF, James E; Caledonia HS; Caledonia, MN; 7/152 Aud/Vis; ChrhWkr; HonRl; LbryAde; NatlMeritSF; SchPl; TchrAde; Yrbk; RptrSchPpr; SchPpr; Coll; Gen Science Major.

GRAF, Jan R; Charlevoix HS; Charlevoix, MI; 3/150 SecSrCls; Band; CncrtBnd; DrlTm; HonRl; MrchBnd; LatCl; PpCl; Trk; GAA; Univ Mi; Chem Engr.

GRAF, Joe L; Lockwood HS; Lockwood, MO; PresSophCls; ALBoysSt; ChrhWkr; HonRl; PresStuCncl; StuGov; Bsktbl; LetterFtbl; Trk; Trade School; Vocation.

GRAF, Linda S; Saline HS; Saline, MI; HonRl; NHS; SctActv; TchrAde; FHA; SpnCl; LetterBsktbl; GAA; Law.

GRAF, Marilyn A; Momence HS; Momence, IL; 1/115 NHS; Secretary.

GRAF, Mark R; Arapahoe Public HS; Arapahoe, NE; Aud/Vis; Band; Chr; CncrtBnd; HonRl; MrchBnd; PepBnd; SchPl; 4-H; Univ; Farmer.

GRAF, Michael P; De Smet Jesuit HS; St Louis, MO; 7/188 Band; ChrhWkr; HonRl; NHS; NatlMeritSF; RptrSchPpr; LetterTrk; College; Elec Engineering.

GRAF, Peggy A; Streeter HS; Streeter, ND; 1/21 PresFrshCls; TrsSophCls; Chr; ChrhWkr; HonRl; StuCncl; YthFlsp; VPSophCls; PpCl; LetterBsktbl; Coll; Legal Secretary.

GRAF, Peter L; Tecumseh HS; Tecumseh, MI; 14/240 Band; CncrtBnd; MrchBnd; NHS; Glf; Wrstlng; IMSpt; Mich State Univ; Engineering.

GRAFE, Pamela S; Fatima HS; Westphalia, MO; 17/126 SecTrsJrCls; Band; ChrhWkr; CmntyWkr; NHS; OffAde; FHA; PpCl; Bsbl; Central Missouri State Univ; Home Economics.

GRAFF, Daniel A; Evanston Township HS; Evanston, IL; CncrtBnd; HonRl; MrchBnd; NatlMeritSF; Orch; PolWkr; SchMus; SctActv; StuGov; LetterSocr; Clge; Environmental Law.

GRAFF, David J; Marquette U HS; Elm Grove, WI; CmntyWkr; HonRl; NatlFornLg; NatlMeritSF; SchPpr; MthCl; Marquette Univ; Accounting.

GRAFF, Ellen S; Delavan HS; Delevan, IL; 2/70 Chrs; CmntyWkr; HonRl; LbryAde; TchrAde; 4-H; SciCl; GAA; DanFAwd; 4-HAwd; University; Psychology.

GRAFF, John W; Forman HS; Manito, IL; 1/51 TrsSophCls; TrsSrCls; HonRl; NHS; SchPl; StuCncl; 4-H; SpnCl; Bsbl; Bsktbl; Illinois State University; Accounting.

GRAFF, Wendy L; Huron HS; Ann Arbor, MI; CmntyWkr; CncrtBnd; HonRl; MrchBnd; PepBnd; FrCl; Univ; Med Tech.

GRAFFEO, Rosemarie; Evergreen Park Comm HS; Evergreen Pk, IL; VPAFS; StuCncl; PpCl; IMSpt; University Of Wisconsin; Marine Biology.

GRAFFIS, Kevin A; Naperville Central HS; Naperville, IL; Band; Chrs; HonRl; LitMag; NatlFornLg; NHS; NatlMeritSchl; NatlMeritSF; NatlThespSoc; SchPl; College; Journalism.

GRAFFORD, Deborah A; Lovington HS; Lovington, IL; Chrs; CncrtBnd; HonRl; MrchBnd; SchMus; EdYrBk; RptrSchPpr; FDA; Illinois St Univ; Medicine.

GRAFT, Gary L; Northrop HS; Fort Wayne, IN; Aud/Vis; HonRl; NatlMeritCmnd; TchrAde; LatCl; LetterBsbl; Bsktbl; LetterFtbl; IMSpt; Valparaiso Univ; Prof.

GRAFTON, Rose M; Seymour HS; Hull, IL; Band; Chrs; ChrhWkr; CncrtBnd; HonRl; MrchBnd; PepBnd; SchPl; StuCncl; TchrAde; College ; Professional.

GRAGE, Kurtis; 11th Street North HS; Wahpeton, ND; VPJrCls; HonRl; JrNHS; NHS; TchrAde; Trk; Univ; Physical Educ.

GRAGER, Joan M; Slinger HS; West Bend, WI; NatlMeritSchl; SchAde; TchrAde; FDA; FFA; FNA; FSA; FTA; Trk; GAA; 4-HAwd; College; Dentist.

GRAHAM, Barbara; Chippewa Hills HS; Weidman, MI; 1/151 Band; NHS; NatlMeritCmnd; YthFlsp; FTA; SciCl; BttyCrckrAwd; DanFAwd; VoiceDemAwd; Central Mich Univ; Mathematics.

GRAHAM, Barbara L; Dekalb HS; Dekalb, IL; ChrhWkr; CmntyWkr; HonRl; IntrClCncl; SchMus; SchPl; TchrAde; EdYrBk; EdSchPpr; FrCl; College; Elementary Education.

GRAHAM, Becky S; Winola HS; Viola, IL; 5/68 Band; ChrhWkr; HonRl; NHS; StuGov; Yrbk; 4-H; SpnCl; Bsbl; Bsktbl; Blackhawk Clg; Dental Asst.

GRAHAM, Carol L; Fenton HS; Fenton, MI; 7/283 HonRl; LbryAde; SecNHS; SchPl; FrCl; North Central Mi Col; Registered Nursing.

GRAHAM, Charles T; Moline Sr HS; Moline, IL; 53/845 Band; ChrhWkr; CncrtBnd; HonRl; LitMag; MrchBnd; NHS; Orch; PepBnd; Univ Of Illinois; Engineering.

GRAHAM, Cheryl L; Mark Twain HS; New London, MO; Band; DrlTm; HonRl; HospAde; LbryAde; SchPl; EdYrBk; Yrbk; PpCl; Chrldr;.

GRAHAM, Cindy L; Sullivan HS; Sullivan, IN; Chrs; HonRl; JrNHS; Mdrgl; NHS; SchPl; LatCl; MthCl; Chrldr; GAA; Col; Mathematics.

GRAHAM, Debra; Shullsburg HS; Shullsburg, WI; Chrs; HonRl; LbryAde; Twrl; RptrSchPpr; PpCl; GAA; College; Elementary Teacher.

GRAHAM, Diann L; Ida Grove HS; Ida Grove, IA; Chr; Chrs; HonRl; NatlThespSoc; SchMus; StuCncl; EdSchPpr; Pres4-H; Chrldr; 4-HAwd; Iowa State Univ; Textiles.

GRAHAM, Glenda L; Southern Reynolds R 2 HS; Ellington, MO; Chr; ChrhWkr; HonRl; PpCl; College; Medicine.

GRAHAM, Jeanne P; A D Johnston HS; Bessemer, MI; 24/104 Band; Chrs; NatlFornLg; NatlThespSoc; SchPl; EdYrBk; LetterChrldr; VoiceDemAwd; Northern Michigan Univ; Music.

GRAHAM, Joanne M; Gull Lake HS; Hickory Corners, MI; Bsktbl; Swmmng; GAA; IMSpt; PPFtbl; Mi St Univ; Airline Stewardess.

GRAHAM, Joel; Quinter HS; Quinter, KS; HonRl; LbryAde; OffAde; SchAde; TchrAde; RptrYrbk; RptrSchPpr; College.

GRAHAM, Kathryn A; Darlington HS; Darlington, WI; 32/130 Chrs; ChrhWkr; CmntyWkr; HospAde; SchMus; StuCncl; YthFlsp; EdSchPpr; FHA; PpCl; White Water College; Elem Educ.

GRAHAM, Kenneth W; Havelock Plover HS; Plover, IA; 1/18 ALBoysSt; Band; Chrs; HonRl; SchPl; PresYthFlsp; LetterBsbl; LetterBsktbl; Iowa State Univ.

GRAHAM, Kristine B; Unity HS; Ursa, IL; ALAGirlsSt; Chrs; ChrhWkr; CmntyWkr; LbryAde; MrchBnd; SchMus; YthFlsp; 4-H; GAA; College; Nursing.

GRAHAM, Larry R; Arthur Hill HS; Saginaw, MI; General Motors Inst; Engineering.

GRAHAM, Laurie E; Brown County HS; Nashville, IN; 4/176 VPSophCls; SecJrCls; VPSrCls; ALAGirlsSt; HonRl; VPJrNHS; NHS; Quill&Scroll; TchrAde; EdYrBk; LetterTrk; Ball St Univ; Special Educ.

GRAHAM, Marilyn S; Lincolnwood HS; Raymond, IL; TrsSophCls; Chr; ChrhWkr; CmntyWkr; HonRl; 4-H; FHA; FTA; PpCl; Junior College; Teacher.

GRAHAM, Mary B; Arthur HS; Arthur, IL; 1/49 Band; ChrhWkr; DrlTm; HonRl; NHS; YthFlsp; FNA; FTA; MthCl; GAA; AmLegAwd; Millikin Univ; Pre Medicine.

GRAHAM, Mary C; Wyoming Park HS; Wyoming, MI; 4/238 SecTrsJrCls; JA; NHS; SchPl; StuGov; FrCl; GerCl; LatCl; GAA; DARAwd; U Of Mi; Engineering.

GRAHAM, Robert L; Glenwood HS; Glenwood, IA; 1/117 Band; CncrtBnd; HonRl; NHS; NatlSciFnd; NatlThespSoc; PepBnd; TchrAde; FrCl; MthCl; SciCl; Bsktbl; Glf; University Of Iowa; Physics.

GRAHAM, Sandra L; H H Dow HS; Midland, MI; VPSophCls; PresJrCls; Chr; HonRl; NHS; PolWkr; SchAde; StuGov; TchrAde; Coll; Nursing.

GRAHAM, Starr K; Academy Of Our Lady; Chicago, IL; HonRl; NHS; Sdlty; FNA; St Xavier College; Nursing.

GRAHAM, Susan J; University HS; Urbana, IL; .

GRAHAM, Teresa J; Durant Comm HS; Stockton, IA; Chrs; HonRl; Yrbk; FHA; Chrldr; Marriage.

GRAHAM, Tim A; Kewanna HS; Kewanna, IN; 1/30 TrsFrshCls; Band; CncrtBnd; HonRl; PepBnd; StuCncl; StuGov; Bsbl; Oregon State Univ; Oceanography.

GRAHEK, Mary; Memorial Sr HS; Ely, MN; 6/125 Band; CncrtBnd; HonRl; MrchBnd; NHS; NatlMeritCmnd; PepBnd; StuCncl; PPFtbl; College; Music.

GRAHL, Jeff E; Plymouth HS; Cascade, WI; 2/234 ALBoysSt; Chr; Chrs; HonRl; PresNHS; SchMus; SchPl; Yrbk; LetterBsbl; U Of Wisconsin Millwaukee; Structural Engin.

GRAHLMAN, Mary A; Jefferson Sr HS; Jefferson, WI; 8/175 Chr; CncrtBnd; HonRl; NHS; PepBnd; EdYrBk; TreasFNA; Tennis; GAA; PPFtbl; U Of Wis; Nursing.

GRAHN, Ronald D; Carmel HS; Carmel, IN; 75/580 ALBoysSt; HonRl; NHS; OffAde; SctActv; StuGov; YthFlsp; LetterFtbl; LetterTrk; LetterWrstlng; Coll; Bus Admin.

GRAHN, Suzanne E; Coloma HS; Coloma, MI; 5/187 HonRl; HospAde; NHS; NatlMeritSF; Trk; College; Languages.

GRAIN, Kathleen M; St Agatha HS; Detroit, MI; SecFrshCls; HonRl; OffAde; PolWkr; StuCncl; TchrAde; RptrSchPpr; PpCl; Bsktbl; PPFtbl; College.

GRAJCZYK, Lynn M; Notre Dame HS; Milwaukee, WI; 5/117 Chrs; HonRl; SchMus; SchPl; RptrSchPpr; SpnCl; Univ Of Wisconsin; Special Education.

GRAJEWSKI, Michael A; Marquette University HS; Milwaukee, WI; Chrs; CmntyWkr; HonRl; NatlMeritFnl; NatlMeritSF; University Of Wisconsin; Medicine.

GRALAK, Glenn R; Hinsdale Central HS; Hinsdale, IL; 131/583 HonRl; SchAde; College Of Dupage; Science Teacher.

GRALHEER, Brad D; Wisner Pilger HS; Wisner, NE; 11/80 VPFrshCls; Band; ChrhWkr; CncrtBnd; HonRl; MrchBnd; NHS; PepBnd; StuCncl; SpnCl; Univ; Professional.

GRAMES, Michael P; Aurora Hoyt Lakes HS; Aurora, MN; NatlMeritCmnd; MthCl; Univ; Mineral Engin.

GRAMKE, Janice M; Liberty HS; Quincy, IL; 1/58 SecFrshCls; HstSophCls; VPJrCls; HonRl; SecNHS; SchPl; StuCncl; Yrbk; 4-H; FHA; SecSpnCl; PpCl; CaptChrldr; DARAwd; Blessing Hosp; Nursing.

GRAMM, Bradley R; Gridley HS; Gridley, IL; 5/40 VPSrCls; PresAFS; Band; ChrhWkr; HonRl; NHS; StuCncl; Pres4-H; VPFFA; PresFTA; University Of Illinois; Veterinarian.

GRAMM, David A; Gridley HS; Gridley, IL; Chrs; HonRl; SchMus; SchPl; YthFlsp; FFA; College; Vocation.

GRAMM, Gail J; Gridley HS; Gridley, IL; 3/42 SecFrshCls; AFS; HonRl; SchMus; RptrSchPpr; PpCl; Ftbl; Illinois State Univ.

GRAMS, Kathleen S; Mona Shores HS; Muskegon, MI; Band; Chr; MrchBnd; NHS; NatlMeritSF; PepBnd; TchrAde; SciCl; Bsktbl; College; Veterinary Medicine.

GRAMS, Mary; Shanley HS; Moorhead, MN; 2/122 Chrs; ChrhWkr; HonRl; JrNHS; NHS; RptrYrbk; Marquette Univ; Nursing.

GRAMSTAD, Mark G; Worthington HS; Worthington, MN; 30/272 Band; Chr; CncrtBnd; JrNHS; MrchBnd; NHS; PepBnd; SchMus; SctActv; LetterFtbl; Tennis; Wrstlng; West Point Academy; Military.

GRAN, William H; Maquoketa Comm HS; Maquoketa, IA; ALBoysSt; Band; CncrtBnd; HonRl; MrchBnd; ModUN; PepBnd; Iowa State Univ; Mechanical Engineer.

GRANAHAN, Edward; Richmond Burton Comm HS; Richmond, IL; VPFrshCls; PresSophCls; HonRl; NHS; SchAde; StuCncl; CchngActv; United States Navy; Personelman.

GRANBERG, Susan M; Darlington Comm HS; Darlington, WI; HonRl; FHA; PpCl;.

GRANDALEN, Joanne M; Mayville Portland HS; Portland, ND; 6/81 ChrhWkr; HonRl; YthFlsp; 4-H; PpCl; SciCl; GAA; IMSpt; 4-HAwd; VoiceDemAwd; College; Vocation.

GRANDBERRY, Lomas; Cregier Vocational HS; Chicago, IL; Band; HonRl; OffAde; StuCncl; CaptWrstlng; Trade School; Electrician.

GRANDE, Rosemarie; St Mary Acad; Indianapolis, IN; Chrl; JrNHS; RptrSchPpr; College; Curriculum Of Major Sutdy.

GRANDFIELD, Janice K; East Union HS; Lorimor, IA; 9/51 PresSophCls; Band; Chrs; CncrtBnd; HonRl; SchMus; SchPl; 4-H; Glf; LetterChrldr; Iowa State U; Nursing.

GRANDON, Valla G; Fairbury Cropsey HS; Fairbury, IL; Chrs; ChrhWkr; DrlTm; HonRl; HospAde; LitMag; NHS; SchMus; SchPl; College; Music.

GRANDY, Ann M; Spalding HS; Chicago, IL; .

GRANDY, Cheryl A; North HS; Fargo, ND; 1/360 AFS; HonRl; JrNHS; NHS; NatlMeritSF; NatlThespSoc; SchMus; SchPl; FrCl; College; Biochemistry.

GRANDYS, Elizabeth F; Badger HS; Lake Geneva, WI; Band; Chr; Chrs; ChrhWkr; DrmBgl; Mdrgl; MrchBnd; NatlThespSoc; SchMus; SchPl; University; Professional.

GRANER, Anne M; Mandan Sr HS; Huff, ND; PresJrCls; PresSrCls; ChrhWkr; HonRl; SecNHS; SchPl; RptrYrbk; RptrSchPpr; LatCl; EldAwd; N Dakota State Univ; Vet.

GRANEY, Marcia E; Lancaster Sr HS; Lancaster, WI; 10/158 AFS; Band; Chrs; HonRl; HospAde; Mdrgl; MrchBnd; ModUN; NHS; 4-H; LetterTrk; IMSpt; 4-HAwd; Univ Of Wi; Teaching.

GRANGER, Jay; Anderson HS; Anderson, IN; 18/562 HonRl; NHS; CitAwd; Purdue Univ; Engineering.

GRANGER, Lorri S; Cadillac HS; Cadilla, MI; 6/287 PresSrCls; ChrhWkr; DrmMjrt; HonRl; NatlFornLg; NHS; SchPl; StuCncl; MthCl; PpCl; Coll; Registered Pharmacist.

GRANGER, Marie K; Morrice Area HS; Owosso, MI; 9/50 HonRl; LbryAde; NHS; OffAde; RptrYrbk; RptrSchPpr; BttyCrckrAwd; Mi St Univ.

GRANGER, Schawnn M; Larimore HS; Emerado, ND; SecFrshCls; SecChrhWkr; HonRl; SchPpr; FHA; SpnCl; PpCl; LetterBsktbl; Chrldr; IMSpt; Univ Of Nd; Electrician.

GRANGER, Thomas D; North Bend Central HS; Ames, NE; 4-H; FFA; Ftbl; LetterTrk;.

GRANLUND, Tammy; Republic Michigamme HS; Republic, MI; Band; Chr; ChrhWkr; CncrtBnd; MrchBnd; NatlFornLg; PepBnd; FrCl; Norhtern Michigan Univ; Banking.

GRANNEMANN, Laura K; Girard HS; Hepler, KS; 6/96 TrsJrCls; ALAGirlsSt; ChrhWkr; DrlTm; HonRl; NHS; SchPl; SecStuCncl; 4-H; PpCl; Bsktbl; LetterTrk; PPFtbl; Ks State College; Business.

GRANNIS, Diane E; Belle Plaine HS; Belle Plaine, MN; 5/93 SecTrsSrCls; HonRl; NHS; Quill&Scroll; SchMus; StuCncl; RptrYrbk; RptrSchPpr; FHA; AmLegAwd; St Olaf Coll; Nursing.

GRANNON, James R; Barr Reeve HS; Montgomery, IN; 1/67 HonRl; NHS; SchPl; Yrbk; LatCl; PpCl; Rose Hulman; Engi.

GRANNON, Stephen J; Barr Reeve HS; Montgomery, IN; NHS; PpCl; Navy.

GRANQUIST, Gary A; Kingsford HS; Iron Mountain, MI; ChrhWkr; CmntyWkr; HonRl; LbryAde; OffAde; SchAde; LetterFtbl; LetterTennis; CaptIMSpt; CitAwd; College.

GRANQUIST, Mark A; John Hersey HS; Mt Prospect, IL; 119/770 Chrs; ChrhWkr; CncrtBnd; HonRl; Mdrgl; MrchBnd; NHS; NatlMeritSF; PepBnd; LetterFtbl; Coll; Anthropology.

GRANSEE, Dennis D; Sanborn Public HS; Sanborn, MN; 1/29 PresSophCls; Band; Chr; HonRl; SchMus; SchPl; StuCncl; YthFlsp; RptrSchPpr; SptEdSchPpr; Pres4-H; CaptFtbl; CaptTrk; Wrstlng; Univ Of Minnesota; Horticulture.

GRANT, Barbara; Sullivan HS; Sullivan, MO; Band; Chrs; ChrhWkr; CncrtBnd; HonRl; MrchBnd; SchMus; FHA; SpnCl; Business School; Office Work.

GRANT, Elise Y; North Division HS; Milwaukee, WI; HonRl; JrNHS; NHS; SchPl; Yrbk; SpnCl; SciCl; JAAwd; Coll; Journalism.

GRANT, Jeri A; Calumet HS; Gary, IN; 7/308 DrmMjrt; HonRl; JrNHS; NHS; PpCl; GAA; IMSpt; PPFtbl; Work ;secretary.

GRANT, Jo Ann; Moberly HS; Moberly, MO; Chr; Chrs; ChrhWkr; DrlTm; HonRl; NHS; StuCncl; FTA; LetterTrk; PPFtbl; College;.

GRANT, Joyce A; Lewis Cass Jr Sr HS; Walton, IN; 6/136 ALAGirlsSt; Band; NHS; ROTC; SchMus; PresStuCncl; 4-H; VPPpCl; GAA; PPFtbl; AmLegAwd; EldAwd; 4-HAwd; College; Communications.

GRANT, Julia E; Mattoon HS; Charleston, IL; 16/397 Band; MrchBnd; VPNatlFornLg; NHS; NatlThespSoc; SchPl; 4-H; GAA; 4-HAwd; VoiceDemAwd; Eastern Illinois University; Drama.

GRANT, Lawrence; Plattsburg HS; Plattsburg, MO; 7/62 VPSophCls; Band; NHS; StuCncl; Coll Vmkc; Engineering.

GRANT, Lenise Y; North Division HS; Milwaukee, WI; Chrs; CmntyWkr; HonRl; JA; NHS; RptrYrbk; FrCl; MthCl; Whitewater Univ; Journalism.

GRANT, Matthew R; Wheaton North HS; Wheaton, IL; 30/308 HonRl; MrchBnd; NHS; NatlMeritSF; YthFlsp; LetterBsktbl; Tennis; Bob Jones Univ; Phys Ed Teacher.

GRANT, Michael D; Johnston City HS; Johnston City, IL; CncrtBnd; HonRl; MrchBnd; NHS; StuCncl; TchrAde; 4-H; MthCl; PpCl; Southern Ill Univ; Mech Engineering.

GRANT, Patrick A; Aquin Central Catholic HS; Freeport, IL; 9/46 HonRl; NHS; SchMus; SchPl; SchPpr; MthCl; SciCl; Trk; Univ; Art.

GRANT, Richard; Gale Ettrick Trempealeau HS; Galesville, WI; 3/111 HonRl; LbryAde; NHS; StuCncl; FrCl; College.

GRANT, Robert T; Bishop Dwenger HS; Fort Wayne, IN; 13/249 Univ; Chemist.

GRANT, Sharon L; Morgan Park HS; Chicago, IL; 136/686 ChrhWkr; TchrAde; PresYthFlsp; PresFrCl; Fisk Univ; Psychology.

GRANT, Steven M; Penney HS; Hamilton, MO; 5/75 PresJrCls; ALBoysSt; HonRl; StuGov; EdSchPpr; Bsbl; LetterBsktbl; CaptFtbl; LetterTrk; CchngActv; Chillicothe Trade Sch; Electronics.

GRANT, Susan J; Chaffee HS; Chaffee, MO; ALAGirlsSt; Band; Chr; CncrtBnd; HonRl; SchPl; FHA; PpCl; SciCl; Chrldr; University; Veteranarian.

GRAPER, Pamela L; J A Craig HS; Janesville, WI; 12/470 VPAFS; PresChr; HonRl; NHS; Quill&Scroll; SchMus; EdYrBk; FrCl; Uw Eau Claire; Nursing.

GRAPP, Colleen; Wheaton North Hs; Wheaton, IL; AFS; HonRl; NHS; NatlThespSoc; SchPl; StuCncl; StuGov; Chrldr; New College; Commercial Art.

GRAPP, Janell R; Allison Bristow HS; Bristow, IA; Chr; Chrs; ChrhWkr; HonRl; 4-H; College; Professional.

GRASBERGER, Laura L; Heritage HS; Fort Wayne, IN; NatlFornLg; NatlMeritCmnd; SchMus; SchPl; Indiana Univ; Law.

GRASKE, Jerome; Hill Murray HS; White Bear Lake, MN; HonRl; NHS; StuCncl; Ftbl; IMSpt; Coll.

GRASS, Dennis; Mattoon HS; Mattoon, IL; Band; ChrhWkr; HonRl; PresJA; MrchBnd; NHS; SctActv; StuCncl; LetterTrk; GodCntryAwd; U Of Illinois; Chemical Engineer.

GRASSI, David; Hillsdale HS; Hillsdale, MI; ALBoysSt; ChrhWkr; CmntyWkr; HonRl; MrchBnd; PolWkr; SchMus; SchPl; StuGov; TchrAde; College; Law.

GRASSI, James; Msgr Hackett Catholic HS; Kalamazoo, MI; AFS; CmntyWkr; HonRl; Quill&Scroll; StuGov; EdSchPpr; Trk; College; Biology.

GRASSICK, David A; Clay City HS; Clay City, IN; 38/65 HonRl; JrNHS; ModUN; NHS; RedCrAde; StuCncl; StuGov; YthFlsp; YthFnd; VPKeyCl; Bsktbl; Glf; CaptTrk; Trade School; Engineer.

GRASSINGER, Laura; Mt Carmel HS; Mt Carmel, IL; 20/185 Chrs; HonRl; NHS; SchMus; TchrAde; SchPpr; TreasFNA; FTA; SpnCl; LetterGAA; Junior College; Retailing.

GRATE, Philip E; Peru HS; Peru, IN; 13/220 PresSrCls; Band; ChrhWkr; CncrtBnd; NHS; PepBnd; SctActv; StuCncl; YthFlsp; LatCl; In U; Dentistry.

GRATHWOHL, Linda S; Cathedral HS; New Ulm, MN; 2/95 ChrhWkr; HonRl; LbryAde; NHS; NatlMeritCmnd; SchPl; RptrYrbk; RptrSchPpr; SchPpr; 4-H; GAA; Coll; Teacher.

GRATTON, Susan E; Blue Valley HS; Leawood, KS; VPJrCls; VPSrCls; Band; CncrtBnd; HonRl; MrchBnd; PepBnd; SchPl; U Of Mo; Broadcast.

GRATZA, Bonnie; Washington Hs; Marthasville, MO; 22/276 ALAGirlsSt; HonRl; FBLA; College; Vocational.

GRAUBE, Davids V; Union HS; Grand Rapids, MI; HonRl; ModUN; PresNHS; SchMus; SchPl; LetterTennis; CchngActv; Grand Rapids Jr College; Engineering.

GRAUERHOLZ, Melinda A; West Smith County HS; Kensington, KS; Chr; CncrtBnd; Mdrgl; MrchBnd; PepBnd; SchMus; StuCncl; RptrYrbk; RptrSchPpr; College; Interior Designer.

GRAUMANN, Donell J; Harvey HS; Harvey, ND; 1/83 TrsJrCls; PresSrCls; Chr; Chrs; ChrhWkr; HonRl; StuCncl; StuGov; YthFlsp; PpCl; Tabor Clge; Medical.

GRAUPERA, Rosa E; Ames Senior HS; Ames, IA; 105/381 Chr; HonRl; Orch; Pres4-H; 4-HAwd; Iowa State University; Physician.

GRAUPMAN, Kathy; Southwest HS; Green Bay, WI; Chrs; ChrhWkr; Yrbk; PpCl; College; Criminology.

GRAVEL, David; Trenton HS; Trenton, MI; 86/571 ChrhWkr; HonRl; SchMus; SchPl; YthFlsp; Tennis; Mich Technological Univ; Physicist.

GRAVEL, Gail; Beckman HS; Cascade, IA; CncrtBnd; MrchBnd; NHS; PepBnd; GAA; Area One Voch Tech, Nursing.

GRAVEL, Vicki I; Isle HS; Isle, MN; 4/60 CncrtBnd; HonRl; JrNHS; MrchBnd; NHS; SchPl; StuCncl; RptrYrbk; SptEdSchPpr; SecFHA; Glf; College; Professional.

GRAVELY, Karen A; Southwestern HS; Shelbyville, IN; 1/70 ALAGirlsSt; Aud/Vis; Chrs; ChrhWkr; CncrtBnd; HonRl; MrchBnd; NHS; 4-H; Chrldr; College; Biology.

GRAVEN, Danny; Cabool HS; Cabool, MO; Aud/Vis; HonRl; NHS; CchngActv; Electronics.

GRAVEN, Rhonda D; Moweaqua HS; Moweaqua, IL; 2/55 ChrhWkr; HonRl; Yrbk; College; Business.

GRAVEN, Timothy G; Normandy HS; St Louis, MO; 33/500 CncrtBnd; HonRl; NHS; GerCl; LetterFtbl; LetterWrstlng; St Louis Univ; Doctor.

GRAVES, Beverly J; Wabeno HS; Wabeno, WI; 9/33 SecTrsSrCls; Chr; Chrs; HonRl; JrNHS; LbryAde; OffAde; SchMus; SchPl; PPFtbl; Ne Wi Tech Inst; Oprtng Rm Asst.

GRAVES, Cheryl M; Charlestown HS; Charlestown, IN; ChrhWkr; CmntyWkr; HonRl; MrchBnd; NHS; TchrAde; EdSchPpr; 4-H; FHA; GAA; Coll; Earth Sci.

GRAVES, David J; Bonner Springs HS; Bonner Spgs, KS; Band; Chr; CncrtBnd; HonRl; MrchBnd; PepBnd; SchMus; TchrAde; FrCl; University Of Kansas; Law.

GRAVES, John C; Lane Tech HS; Chicago, IL; 147/1210 Univ Of Illinois; Mechanical Engineer.

GRAVES, Keith H; Ypsilanti HS; Ypsilanti, MI; NHS; NatlMeritSF; Orch; SchMus; SchPl; FrCl; Tennis; College.

GRAVES, Laura; South Barber HS; Hardtner, KS; 10/36 Band; DrmMjrt; HonRl; LbryAde; OffAde; PepBnd; Bsktbl; Tennis; Trk; PPFtbl; Coll; Pe Teacher.

GRAVES, Lynn; Sarcoxie HS; Carthage, MO; 23/104 ChrhWkr; CmntyWkr; HonRl; LbryAde; SchPl; TchrAde; Yrbk; SchPpr; FHA; BttyCrckrAwd; Univ Of Mo; Occup Ther.

GRAVES, Michael P; Carmel HS; Carmel, IN; 20/535 Band; ChrhWkr; CncrtBnd; HonRl; PepBnd; SchMus; SctActv; YthFlsp; Purdue U; Vet.

GRAVES, Michael R; South Sioux Sr HS; South Sioux City, NE; 12/225 HonRl; JrNHS; NHS; SpnCl; Trk; Wrstlng; College; Business.

GRAVES, Paul A; Edwardsville Sr HS; Edwardsville, IL; 34/437 HonRl; NHS; SchMus; Univ Of Missouri; Engineering.

GRAVES, Roberta; South Barber HS; Hardtner, KS; Band; HonRl; HospAde; PepBnd; Sdlty; StuCncl; 4-H; PpCl; 4-HAwd; College; Professional.

GRAVES, Roxanna; Marion C Early HS; Morrisville, MO; 4/42 VPSrCls; HonRl; PresStuCncl; Yrbk; SchPpr; FBLA; TreasFHA; CaptBsktbl; Chrldr; CchngActv;.

GRAVES, Sheila M; Vienna Township HS; Vienna, IL; Chrs; HonRl; SctActv; FNA; Shawnee College; Medical Secretary.

GRAVES, Teresa D; Seymour HS; Payson, IL; 7/68 PresFrshCls; Band; CncrtBnd; HonRl; LbryAde; PepBnd; StuCncl; SecYthFlsp; Treas4-H; VPFHA; College; Library Science.

GRAVES, Thomas; Tuscumbia R Iii HS; Iberia, MO; 1/19 ChrhWkr; HonRl; SchPl; StuCncl; FFA; Bsbl; Bsktbl; Nmsu; Biology.

GRAVES, William D; Greensburg HS; Greensburg, KS; ALBoysSt; Band; Chr; HonRl; NatlFornLg; NHS; SchMus; SchPl; Glf; LetterWrstlng; Univ; Professional.

GRAVESEN, Mark A; Kenmare HS; Kenmare, ND; 20/53 Band; Chr; ChrhWkr; CncrtBnd; HonRl; MrchBnd; PepBnd; FFA; LetterFtbl; CaptWrstlng; Univ Of No Dakota; Aviation.

GRAWCOCK, Peggy K; Churubusco HS; Columbia City, IN; DrlTm; 4-H; FHA; PpCl; IMSpt; 4-HAwd; Business School; Secretary.

GRAWE, Roger A; St Josephs Seminary HS; Quincy, IL; 5/18 Chr; Chrl; ChrhWkr; CmntyWkr; Yrbk; RptrSchPpr; 4-H; Socr; IMSpt; Quincy Clg; Psycology.

GRAY, Amy L; Charlotte HS; Charlotte, MI; 8/256 TrsSrCls; ChrhWkr; HonRl; HospAde; NHS; TchrAde; DanFAwd; KiwanAwd; Northern Mich Univ; Nursing.

GRAY, Andrew D; Redford Union HS; Redford Twp, MI; ALBoysSt; NHS; GerCl; Trk; Lake Superior State Col; Biology.

GRAY, Becky L; West Marshall HS; State Center, IA; 14/90 Band; Chrs; ChrhWkr; HonRl; NHS; SchPl; StuCncl; Bsktbl; Trk; CchngActv; Coll; Nuring.

GRAY, Brent D; Red Hill HS; Bridgeport, IL; 4/125 PresFrshCls; ALBoysSt; Chrs; ChrhWkr; HonRl; NHS; SchMus; StuCncl; PpCl; LetterBsbl; LetterBsktbl; LetterFtbl; CchngActv; Univ Of Illinois; Chemical Engineer.

GRAY, Carla R; Platteville HS; Platteville, WI; HstFrshCls; AFS; ChrhWkr; CncrtBnd; MrchBnd; NatlFornLg; PepBnd; YthFlsp; SpnCl; U W Platteville; Art.

GRAY, Carmen; High School; Bloomington, IL; Chrs; ChrhWkr; JA; LbryAde; SchPl;.

GRAY, Carolyn D; Rockford East HS; Rockford, IL; Chr; ChrhWkr; HonRl; TchrAde; LetterTrk; GAA; IMSpt; Coll; Nursing.

GRAY, Charlotte R; Lincoln Sr HS; E St Louis, IL; 32/132 TrsSrCls; SchMus; StuCncl; RptrYrbk; 4-H; Bsbl; S I U Edwarville; Business Secretary.

GRAY, Cheryl A; Belton HS; Belton, MO; Chr; HonRl; NHS; StuCncl; TchrAde; FHA; SpnCl; PpCl; Nursing School; Nursing.

GRAY, Clayton L; Macon HS; Decatur, IL; HonRl; NHS; YthFlsp; PpCl; LetterBsktbl; LetterFtbl; LetterTrk; IMSpt; College; Business.

GRAY, Diana M; Alvernia HS; Chicago, IL; 5/226 JA; NHS; TchrAde; College; Mathematics.

GRAY, Donald R; Pioneer Jr Sr HS; Lake Cicott, IN; Band; CncrtBnd; DrmMjrt; MrchBnd; 4-H; Glf; Trk; Purdue Univ; Engineering.

GRAY, Donna L; Downers Grove North HS; Downers Grove, IL; 31/524 Band; CncrtBnd; HonRl; MrchBnd; NHS; Orch; PepBnd; SchMus; College; Home Economics.

GRAY, Donna M; Lawson HS; Lawson, MO; Band; Chr; Chrs; ChrhWkr; HonRl; MrchBnd; SchMus; SchPl; 4-H; FHA; College; Business.

GRAY, Karen F; Diamond R 4 HS; Diamond, MO; Chr; ChrhWkr; MrchBnd; SctActv; TchrAde; 4-H; FHA; Bsbl; Bsktbl; Trk; Crowder College; Home Economics.

GRAY, Karen M; Polo Comm HS; Polo, IL; Band; Chr; ChrhWkr; CmntyWkr; CncrtBnd; DrmMjrt; HonRl; MrchBnd; SchPl; StuCncl; Northern Il; Theatre.

GRAY, Kevin L; Tri Point HS; Cullom, IL; 3/37 HonRl; SchPl; RptrYrbk; SpnCl; LetterBsktbl; Ftbl; AmLegAwd; University Of Illinois; Pharmacy.

GRAY, Lauri; Rockwell City HS; Rockwell City, IA; 17/62 TrsJrCls; ChrhWkr; HonRl; Mdrgl; MrchBnd; SchMus; TchrAde; YthFlsp; RptrSchPpr; FHA; Ia Cent Comm Coll; Agri Banking.

GRAY, Laurie A; Healy HS; Pierz, MN; 1/117 VPJrCls; Band; CncrtBnd; HonRl; PepBnd; SchPl; SecStuCncl; SciCl; Trk; CaptChrldr; St Cloud St Univ; Accounting.

GRAY, Leanna J; Du Quoin HS; Du Quoin, IL; 33/136 Chrs; DrlTm; SchMus; FHA;.

GRAY, Neil; West Richland HS; Noble, IL; ALBoysSt; YthFlsp; CchngActv; IMSpt; 4-HAwd; Col; Professional.

GRAY, Norman J; Connersville HS; Connersville, IN; 29#33#37 HonRl; NatlMeritCmnd; Orch; StuCncl; SpnCl; LetterWrstlng; IMSpt; Ball State U; Med Tech.

GRAY, Patricia; East Alton Wood River HS; East Alton, IL; 5/331 HonRl; NatlMeritCmnd; Yrbk; EdSchPpr; FNA; LatCl; IMSpt; Northwestern Univ; Medical Doctor.

GRAY, Patricia A; East Alton Wood River HS; East Alton, IL; 3/312 HonRl; SecHospAde; NHS; NatlMeritCmnd; StuCncl; Yrbk; VPFNA; LatCl; University; Medical Doctor.

GRAY, Patrick J; Central HS; St Joseph, MO; HonRl; StuGov; YthLg; SpnCl; Trk; IMSpt; Univ; Engr.

GRAY, Rebecca L; Harrisburg R Viii HS; Harrisburg, MO; 1/20 PresJrCls; SecSrCls; ALAGirlsSt; Band; ChrhWkr; HonRl; PepBnd; SchPl; TchrAde; EdYrBk; Univ Of Mo Columbia; Veteriary.

GRAY, Richard E; Rockford HS; Belmont, MI; 21/289 HonRl; NHS; PolWkr; Jr College; Journalism.

GRAY, Robert E; Carlisle Comm HS; Carlisle, IA; ALBoysSt; Band; Chr; Chrs; ChrhWkr; CmntyWkr; CncrtBnd; HonRl; MrchBnd; SchAde; LetterBsbl; CaptBsktbl; LetterGlf; College; Physical Educ.

GRAY, Robin; Stevens HS; Rapid City, SD; ALAGirlsSt; Chr; ChrhWkr; HonRl; NatlFornLg; PolWkr; StuCncl; StuGov; College; Law.

GRAY, Ronald D; Parderville HS; Pardeeville, WI; ChrhWkr; CmntyWkr; HonRl; NHS; IMSpt;.

GRAY, Stephen K; Alexandria Monroe HS; Alexandria, IN; 2/199 Band; CncrtBnd; HonRl; MrchBnd; NHS; SpnCl; LetterTrk; IMSpt; Indiana Univ; Accountant.

GRAY, Steven M; Bethlehem Academy; Faribault, MN; Aud/Vis; HonRl; SchPl; SctActv; RptrSchPpr; LatCl; College; Professional.

GRAY, Susan; Coldwater HS; Coldwater, MI; 82/300 CaptBsktbl; Trk; IMSpt; Retailing.

GRAY, Terry M; Pioneer HS; Royal Center, IN; 1/115 ALBoysSt; Band; ChrhWkr; HonRl; VPNatlFornLg; NHS; YthFlsp; PresSpnCl; Bsktbl; LetterGlf; Purdue Univ; Science Teacher.

GRAY, Thaddeus; Hales Franciscan HS; Chicago, IL; 3/71 CncrtBnd; HonRl; MrchBnd; IMSpt; Depaul Univ; Radiology.

GRAY, Thomas G; Bayless HS; St Louis, MO; College.

GRAY, Vanna L; Sweet Springs R 7 HS; Sweet Springs, MO; 5/62 SecSophCls; PresJrCls; TrsJrCls; Chr; HonRl; LbryAde; SptEdYrbk; Yrbk; FHA; FTA; U Of Mo Columbia; Archaeology.

GRAYBILL, Brian D; Lytton Community HS; Lytton, IA; PresFrshCls; TrsSophCls; Aud/Vis; HonRl; NHS; LetterBsbl; LetterBsktbl; LetterFtbl; IMSpt; College; Major Study.

GRAYSON, Charles R; Lathrop HS; Lathrop, MO; PresFrshCls; PresSophCls; ModUN; SchPl; PresStuCncl; LetterBsktbl; LetterFtbl; Trk; IMSpt; Nw Missouri State Univ; Accounting.

GRAZIAN, Robert L; Maine Twp East HS; Morton Grove, IL; HonRl; JrNHS; NHS; Orch; PolWkr; SctActv; RusCl; MthCl; LetterSwmmng; Tennis; U Of Il; Med.

GRAZIANO, Nancy R; Andover HS; Bloomfield Hills, MI; ChrhWkr; CmntyWkr; HonRl; HospAde; IntrClCncl; NHS; NatlMeritSF; OffAde; SchAde; StuCncl; TchrAde; Teen; SchPpr; GAA; Central Michigan Univ; Spec Educ.

GRBCICH, Patricia A; Rosati Kain HS; Florissant, MO; PresJrCls; SecChrs; HospAde; JrNHS; NHS; NatlMeritFnl; SctActv; StuCncl; EdSchPpr; GAA; CaptIMSpt; St Louis U; Medicine.

GREATHOUSE, Darlene J; Oakland HS; Hindsboro, IL; 4/38 Band; Chrs; ChrhWkr; HonRl; MrchBnd; NHS; Yrbk; 4-H; Chrldr; GAA; Eastern Illinois Univ; Teach.

GREATHOUSE, Elaine C; Arcola HS; Hindsboro, IL; 4/67 SecFrshCls; SecSophCls; Chrs; ChrhWkr; HonRl; JrNHS; NHS; SchPl; 4-H; SpnCl; Clge; Math.

GREAVU, Susan J; Cedar Lake Acad; North Branch, MI; 10/72 VPJrCls; Chr; ChrhWkr; CncrtBnd; HonRl; Mdrgl; NHS; StuGov; RptrSchPpr;.

GREB, Mary C; Kapaun Mt Carmel HS; Wichita, KS; 7/134 ChrhWkr; CmntyWkr; HonRl; LitMag; NatlMeritCmnd; OffAde; SchAde; Yrbk; SchPpr; FrCl; Univ; French.

GREBE, Jane E; Limestone Comm HS; Peoria, IL; 5/400 Chr; ChrhWkr; HonRl; NHS; SecNatlThespSoc; SchMus; SchPl; StuCncl; FrCl; DARAwd; College.

GREBIN, Catherine; Pacelli HS; Austin, MN; Chrl; Chrs; ChrhWkr; HonRl; HospAde; RptrSchPpr; PpCl; IMSpt; Coll; Med.

GREBNER, Gail T; Farmington East HS; Glasford, IL; 26/131 HonRl; Pres4-H; FTA; SpnCl; Bsktbl; Trk; SecGAA; College; Business Admin.

GRECH, Nancy I; Holy Redeemer HS; Detroit, MI; 9/186 ChrhWkr; CmntyWkr; HonRl; NHS; SchPl; Yrbk; U Of Mi.

GRECHUS, Maribeth A; Butler R 5 HS; Butler, MO; 1/83 ALAGirlsSt; TreasChrs; ChrhWkr; HonRl; HospAde; SecNHS; NatlMeritCmnd; SchPl; SpnCl; IMSpt; Univ Of Mo; Engineering.

GRECO, Adele E; Spalding HS; Chicago, IL; 4/47 NHS; OffAde; Univ; Liberal Arts.

GRECO, Barbara R; St Joseph HS; Kenosha, WI; HstSrCls; Chrs; ChrhWkr; HonRl; Mdrgl; TchrAde; PpCl; Coll; Med Tech.

GRECO, Mary Jo; Sacred Heart Of Mary HS; Palatine, IL; 12/134 HonRl; NHS; SchPl; StuGov; Yrbk; Creighton Univ; Dentistry.

GRECULA, Marie L; Harlem HS; Rockford, IL; 19/594 ALAGirlsSt; Chr; SecChrs; HonRl; NHS; SchMus; StuCncl; TchrAde; RptrYrbk; SchPpr; PresMthCl; GAA; Mac Murray College; English.

GREEK, Ellen A; Benet Academy; Naperville, IL; 4/240 SecChrs; HonRl; NHS; SchMus; SecStuGov; Swmmng; Tennis; Trk; Univ Of Notre Dame.

GREELEY, Jane E; Wisconsin Heights HS; Mazomanie, WI; Coll; Ari Bus.

GREELEY, Susan V; Elbow Lake HS; Elbow Lake, MN; 3/68 ALAGirlsSt; Band; ChrhWkr; CncrtBnd; HonRl; NHS; NatlMeritCmnd; PolWkr; StuCncl; GAA; Augustana Coll Sioux Falls; Spec Educ.

GREELING, Rodney L; Jersey Community HS; Jerseyville, IL; 17/300 CncrtBnd; HonRl; MrchBnd; NHS; SchMus; SchPl; StuCncl; MthCl; Bsktbl; Trk; Western Ill Univ; Medicine.

GREEN, Amy S; Wausau East HS; Wausau, WI; AFS; ChrhWkr; CmntyWkr; NatlFornLg; OffAde; PolWkr; SchPl; RptrYrbk; RptrSchPpr; Carroll College; Speech Pathology.

GREEN, Andrew J; Loy Norrix HS; Kalamazoo, MI; NatlMeritFnl; NatlMeritSF; LetterTennis; NCTE;.

GREEN, Barbara A; Mother Mcauley HS; Chicago, IL; 76/474 HonRl; College; Dental Hygiene.

GREEN, Beth E; Lapeer Senior HS; Metamora, MI; TrsJrCls; HonRl; NHS; SpnCl; PpCl; Bsktbl; GAA; Northeastern Univ; Engineer.

GREEN, Brenda Jo; Oxford Area Comm HS; Oxford, MI; 11/220 Band; Chr; CmntyWkr; HonRl; NHS; Orch; StuGov; TchrAde; TreasSciCl; PPFtbl; Univ Of Mich; Business Admn.

GREEN, Brian S; Rantool Township HS; Rantoul, IL; CncrtBnd; HonRl; SecTrsFrshCls; HstFrshCls; PepBnd; SchMus; Coll; Acctng/music.

GREEN, Carter B; Lincoln HS; Thief River Falls, MN; ChrhWkr; HonRl; YthFlsp; LetterSwmmng; College; Major Study.

GREEN, Celesta E; Monrovia HS; Mooresville, IN; 4/120 Band; HonRl; NHS; StuCncl; RptrYrbk; FrCl; LetterBsktbl; LetterFtbl; LetterTrk; DARAwd; University; Education.

GREEN, Charles A; Alton Senior HS; Alton, IL; AFS; ALBoysSt; Band; HonRl; MrchBnd; Orch; SchMus; StuCncl; Bradley University; Accounting.

GREEN, Cheryl; Lindblom HS; Chicago, IL; 136/637 Chr; ChrhWkr; JA; NatlMeritCmnd; SchAde; StuCncl; StuGov; TchrAde; YthFlsp; CivCl; Howard Univ; Journalism.

GREEN, Danny L; West Washington HS; Salem, IN; CncrtBnd; HonRl; JrNHS; NHS; PepBnd; 4-H; FFA; Undecided; Agribusiness.

GREEN, Dave A; Davison HS; Davison, MI; 2/433 ALBoysSt; Band; CncrtBnd; HonRl; NHS; Bsktbl; LetterFtbl; CaptTennis; IMSpt; AmLegAwd; Spring Arbor Clge; Accounting.

GREEN, David M; Edwards County HS; Ellery, IL; 3/104 PresFrshCls; PresSophCls; ChrhWkr; NHS; NatlMeritCmnd; StuCncl; 4-H; PpCl; Trk; DanFAwd; Univ Of Ill; Mechanical Engineering.

GREEN, David M; Edwards County Sr HS; Ellery, IL; 3/110 ChrhWkr; HonRl; NHS; NatlMeritCmnd; StuCncl; 4-H; LetterTrk; DanFAwd; 4-HAwd; Univ Of Illinois; Mechanical Engineer.

GREEN, David M; Mason HS; Mason, MI; 29/235 ALBoysSt; ChrhWkr; CncrtBnd; NHS; StuCncl; RptrSchPpr; Bsbl; Bsktbl; IMSpt; 4-HAwd; Lansing Comm Col.

GREEN, Debbie L; Mc Auley Regional HS; Joplin, MO; 4/34 ChrhWkr; HonRl; HospAde; VPNHS; RptrYrbk; RptrSchPpr; PpCl; Chrldr; Mo S St Clge.

GREEN, Debora; Greenville R Ii HS; Silva, MO; PresFrshCls; TrsJrCls; Band; CncrtBnd; DrmMjrt; SchPl; SpnCl; PpCl; PresAwd; Coll; Art.

GREEN, Deborah A; Northrop HS; Fort Wayne, IN; 130/643 ChrhWkr; CtyCnl; CmntyWkr; TchrAde; FBLA; FHA; FNA; FSA; FTA; College.

GREEN, Deborah S; Richmond Sr HS; Richmond, IN; 34/630 HonRl; JrNHS; NHS; Teen; College; Science.

GREEN, Elizabeth A; Monticello HS; Hopkinton, IA; 3/121 ChrhWkr; HonRl; NHS; StuCncl; SecFFA; U Of Ia; Landscape Architecture.

GREEN, Freddie L; Laboure HS; St Louis, MO; PresSrCls; Chr; Chrs; HospAde; JA; StuCncl; TchrAde; College; Nursing.

GREEN, Henzy; Crispus Attucks HS; Indianapolis, IN; PresFrshCls; Band; ChrhWkr; HonRl; MrchBnd; NHS; Orch; PepBnd; SctActv; FBLA; Trk; IMSpt; Indiana Univ; Business Admin.

GREEN, Jill T; Immaculate Heart Of Mary HS; Westchester, IL; Chr; HospAde; SctActv; FHA; SpnCl; Tennis; Triton; Business.

GREEN, Juli A; Saunemin HS; Pontiac, IL; 3/27 ALAGirlsSt; Band; Chrs; CncrtBnd; JA; MrchBnd; StuCncl; Yrbk; 4-H; FHA; Ill State Univ; Art.

GREEN, Karolyn L; Grant Deuel HS; Strandburg, SD; 5/44 VPSrCls; Chr; HonRl; VPNHS; SchMus; SecStuCncl; YthFlsp; SpnCl; PpCl; South Dakota St University.

GREEN, Katherine; Santa Fetrail HS; Carbondale, KS; ChrhWkr; HonRl; LbryAde; StuGov; Yrbk; FrCl; College; Forest Service.

GREEN, Kimberly; Calamus Community HS; Calamas, IA; 2/28 SecJrCls; ALAGirlsSt; Chrl; PepBnd; SchMus; SchPl; YthFlsp; RptrSchPpr; 4-H; Bsktbl; Community College; Business.

GREEN, Leslie D; Franklin Comm HS; Franklin, IN; 25/232 HospAde; HonRl; SchPl; FTA; PpCl; In St Un ; Elem Educ.

GREEN, Leslie K; Norris City HS; Norris City, IL; Band; Chrs; CncrtBnd; HonRl; MrchBnd; PepBnd; Illinois State Univ; Special Educ.

GREEN, Martin R; Bismarck HS; Bismarck, ND; HonRl; NHS; NatlMeritCmnd; Ftbl; College.

GREEN, Mary J; De Witt Central Comm HS; Grand Mound, IA; ChrhWkr; CmntyWkr; HonRl; OffAde; PolWkr; Univ Of Iowa; Dental Hygiene.

GREEN, Mary L; Rolla HS; Rolla, MO; 21/274 TrsSophCls; ALAGirlsSt; Chr; HonRl; Yrbk; FHA; FrCl; PresAwd; Univ; Nursing.

GREEN, Merle L; Lockport Central HS; Crest Hill, IL; HonRl; NHS; SctActv; College; Engineering.

GREEN, Michelle E; Mother Mc Auley HS; Chicago, IL; CmntyWkr; NatlMeritCmnd; SchMus; Bradley Univ; Psychiatrist.

GREEN, Nancy A; Larkin HS; Elgin, IL; 132/515 CmntyWkr; HonRl; SchAde; PpCl; College; Special Ed.

GREEN, Nancy L; Greenville HS; Greenville, MI; 18/225 SecSrCls; HonRl; Quill&Scroll; RptrSchPpr; FrCl; Albion Clg; Comm/english.

GREEN, Ola L; Thayer R 2 HS; Thayer, MO; Chr; HonRl; SchPl; Christian Art College; Secretary.

GREEN, Pamela A; Christian Fenger HS; Chicago, IL; Chr; ChrhWkr; CmntyWkr; OffAde; PolWkr; SchPl; StuCncl; TchrAde; YthFlsp; Yrbk; FrCl; College; Architecture.

GREEN, Rhonda S; Dwight D Eisenhower HS; Saginaw, MI; Chr; ChrhWkr; HonRl; LbryAde; NatlFornLg; NHS; SchMus; Saginaw Valley St Coll; History.

GREEN, Richard; Maysville HS; Maysville, MO; 2/70 PresFrshCls; ALBoysSt; Chrs; HonRl; ModUN; NHS; Univ Of Mo; Cpa.

GREEN, Russell W; L C Mohr HS; South Haven, MI; Band; CncrtBnd; HonRl; MrchBnd; PepBnd; TchrAde; FTA; Trade School; Draftsman.

GREEN, Sandra L; Springfield HS; Springfield, MI; HonRl; NHS; Orch; SctActv; LetterBsktbl; LetterTrk; College; Forestry.

GREEN, Shannon L; Gallatin R V HS; Jamesport, MO; 4/52 VPJrCls; Chr; HonRl; LbryAde;

ModUN; NHS; SctActv; FFA; LetterFtbl; Dan-FAwd; Nw Mo St Univ; Accounting.

GREEN, Shawna R; Lathrop HS; Lathrop, MO; HonRl; SchPl; SecStuCncl; TchrAde; YthFlsp; PresFHA; PresFTA; PpCl; Chrldr; Coll; Elem Teacher.

GREEN, Starnetta A; Acad Of Our Lady; Chicago, IL; HonRl; LitMag; LbryAde; NatlMeritCmnd; SchPl; RptrYrbk; RptrSchPpr; Blackburn College; Pre Law.

GREEN, Susan L; St Anthony HS; Effingham, IL; 9/83 ChrhWkr; CmntyWkr; NHS; SchMus; SctActv; StuGov; RptrYrbk; GAA; ChmbCommrsAwd; CitAwd; Col; Medical Technology.

GREEN, Theresa J; Pontiac Central HS; W Bloomfield, MI; ChrhWkr; HonRl; NHS; SchPl; EdYrBk; FrCl; Oakland Univ; Teacher.

GREEN, Thomas H; Waverly HS; Lansing, MI; 15/378 CncrtBnd; MrchBnd; NatlFornLg; NHS; NatlMeritSchl; PolWkr; SchMus; SchPl; TchrAde; GerCl; Msu.

GREEN, Timothy M; Cretin HS; St Paul, MN; 15/213 VPSophCls; TrsJrCls; HonRl; ROTC; SchAde; StuGov; TchrAde; LetterSocr; LetterTrk; IMSpt; Coll St Thomas; Major Study.

GREEN, Todd C; Evergreen Park Comm HS; Evergreen Park, IL; 6/440 CncrtBnd; HonRl; MrchBnd; NHS; SchPl; TchrAde; MthCl; Univ Of Il; Engineering.

GREEN, Troxel D; Chambers Public HS; Ewing, NE; TrsFrshCls; VPSophCls; PresJrCls; Band; ChrhWkr; CncrtBnd; HonRl; LbryAde; NHS; PolWkr; StuCncl; Bsktbl; LetterFtbl; LetterTrk; College; Photography.

GREEN, William; Girard HS; Girard, IL; Band; HonRl; Il St Univ; Accounting.

GREENAMYER, Diann L; Reading HS; Montgomery, MI; HonRl; OffAde; TchrAde; RptrSchPpr; 4-H; FTA; College; Drafting.

GREENAN, Kathleen; Resurrection Hs; Chicago, IL; 59/261 DrmBgl; HonRl; HospAde; PolWkr; SctActv; Teen; FNA; SecFrCl; GAA; College; Business Economics.

GREENAWALT, Deborah; Oregon Davis HS; Walkerton, IN; 4/64 TrsJrCls; Band; Chrl; HonRl; NHS; OffAde; RptrYrbk; EdSchPpr; 4-H; Chrldr; Business.

GREENBERG, Kenneth; Rich Central Hs; Park Forest, IL; 3/414 HonRl; MthCl; U Of Illinois; Engineering.

GREENBERG, Lawrence D; Highland Park HS; Highland Park, IL; NHS; NatlMeritCmnd; LetterTrk;.

GREENBLATT, Ann M; Boylan Central Catholic HS; Loves Park, IL; 27/345 Chrs; ChrhWkr; HonRl; HospAde; Mdrgl; NHS; NatlMeritCmnd; SchMus; TchrAde; RptrYrbk; College; Teaching.

GREENE, Beth; Homewood Flossmoor HS; Flossmoor, IL; 2/965 Chr; HonRl; LitMag; NatlFornLg; Quill&Scroll; SchMus; StuGov; PresAwd; Washington Univ; Pre Med.

GREENE, Junius J; Mendel Catholic HS; Chicago, IL; Aud/Vis; HonRl; NatlMeritCmnd; PolWkr; TchrAde; IMSpt; Col; Med.

GREENE, Linda; Lindblom Technical Hs; Chicago, IL; 22/722 HonRl; SchAde; GAA; U; Psychology.

GREENE, Linda L; Underwood HS; Underwood, MN; PresJrCls; Chrs; HonRl; StuCncl; Yrbk; Fergus Falls Jc.

GREENE, Mark; West Washington HS; Campbellsburg, IN; 30/80 Band; Chrs; ChrhWkr; CncrtBnd; MrchBnd; PepBnd; RptrSchPpr; Indiana Univ; Teacher.

GREENE, Michael J; Glenbrook South HS; Glenview, IL; 23/582 PresSophCls; HonRl; LitMag; NatlFornLg; NHS; SchPl; StuCncl; Univ Of Michigan; Chemical Research.

GREENE, Shepard J; Mt Vernon Township HS; Mt Vernon, IL; 101/450 ChrhWkr; TreasCtyCnl; CmntyWkr; RedCrAde; SchAde; SctActv; Ftbl; Swmmng; Tennis; LetterTrk; GodCntryAwd; Us Military Academy; Medicine.

GREENE, Sylvia K; Chase County HS; Imperial, NE; 20/60 HonRl; StuCncl; TchrAde; YthFlsp; Sec4-H; FHA; Bsktbl; 4-HAwd; JAAwd; College; Art.

GREENFIELD, Cathleen A; Forreston HS; Forreston, IL; 5/68 Band; Chrs; HonRl; Mdrgl; NHS; SchMus; SchPl; StuCncl; YthFlsp; RptrYrbk; Northwestern College; Elem Education.

GREENIA, Arthur F; Dela Salle Collegiate HS; Detroit, MI; Aud/Vis; Band; HonRl; JA; NatlMeritCmnd; SchAde; SchPl; StuCncl; TchrAde; RptrSchPpr; Trk; Electronics.

GREENING, David; Antigo HS; Antigo, WI; 16/374 ChrhWkr; HonRl; StuCncl; GerCl; College.

GREENLEAF, Roger; Warrensburg Latham HS; Decatur, IL; 20/70 HonRl; Quill&Scroll; TchrAde; RptrYrbk; Bsktbl; Univ Of Illinois; Physical Education.

GREENLEE, Craig; Chosen Valley HS; Chatfield, MN; Aud/Vis; Chr; HonRl; JrNHS; LbryAde; Mdrgl; NHS; SchPl; Ftbl; IMSpt; College; Vocation.

GREENLEE, Daniel L; Herculaneum HS; Herculaneum, MO; Band; HonRl; NatlThespSoc; StuCncl; LetterFtbl; Trk; Us Navy.

GREENLEE, Herbert B; Oak Park River Forest HS; River Forest, IL; 3/91 CncrtBnd; HonRl; MrchBnd; NatlMeritSF; PepBnd; MthCl; Univ; Mathematics.

GREENLEE, Rae A; Brown City HS; Brown City, MI; 1/90 Band; Chr; PresNHS; StuCncl; SecFHA; BttyCrckrAwd; DARAwd; Mich St Univ; Med Tech.

GREENLEE, William M; Oak Park River Forest HS; River Forest, IL; 18/1000 Chr; ChrhWkr; HonRl; NHS; Orch; SchMus; SchPl; CivCl; MthCl; University; Medicine.

GREENLEY, Leslie E; Visitation Acad; St Louis, MO; Chrs; HonRl; NHS; SchAde; SchPl; RptrYrbk; EdSchPpr; IMSpt; Univ; Professional.

GREENLY, Richard L; Cotton HS; Eveleth, MN; PresSrCls; HonRl; StuCncl; SptEdYrbk; Yrbk; SptEdSchPpr; CaptBsktbl; CaptFtbl; LetterTrk; CchngActv;.

GREENMAN, Timothy; South Haven HS; South Haven, MI; Chr; Chrs; NHS; SchMus; SchMus; RptrYrbk; 4-H; Glf; 4-HAwd; College; Performing Arts.

GREENOUGH, Ronald E; Lincoln Park HS; Lincoln Park, MI; NHS; RptrYrbk; Yrbk; SciCl; Univf Science.

GREENSLAUGH, Bradley W; Hamilton HS; Hamilton, IL; AFS; ALBoysSt; ChrhWkr; HonRl; PresStuCncl; FTA; CaptFtbl; CaptGlf; LetterWrstlng; AmLegAwd; Ill State Univ; C P A.

GREENSTEIN, Marla N; Sullivan HS; Chicago, IL; 11/276 HonRl; TreasJA; TreasNHS; SchPl; TchrAde; Yrbk; SchPpr; SpnCl; JAAwd; Georgetown Univ; Political Science.

GREENSTREET, Cheri L; Spearville HS; Spearville, KS; 4/36 Chrs; DrmMjrt; HonRl; MrchBnd; SchPl; FrCl; PpCl; LetterBsktbl; LetterTrk; Chrldr; Dodge City Juco; Phy Education.

GREENSTREET, Kenneth L; Clay Center Public HS; Clay Center, NE; 4/26 VPSophCls; PresSrCls; HonRl; PresNHS; SchAde; SchPl; RptrSchPpr; SptEdSchPpr; LetterBsktbl; LetterFtbl; LetterTrk; Kearney State College; Education.

GREENSTREET, Kirk; Clay Center HS; Clay Center, NE; 10/29 VPFrshCls; PresSophCls; Band; ChrhWkr; CncrtBnd; MrchBnd; PepBnd; SchPl; RptrYrbk; College; Teacher Coach.

GREENUP, Patricia A; Dearborn HS; Dearborn, MI; HonRl; StuCncl; SptEdSchPpr; CaptChrldr; GAA; LetterIMSpt; College.

GREENWALD, Bruce; Clayton HS; Clayton, MO; Band; CncrtBnd; ModUN; Orch; PepBnd; SchMus; SchPl; StuGov; St Louis Coll Of Pharm; Phar.

GREENWALT, Steven; Marion Jr Hs; Marion, IL; 10 Band; ChrhWkr; CncrtBnd; HonRl; NHS; Orch; PepBnd; LatCl; PresSpnCl; PpCl; So Illinois U;biological Science.

GREENWELL, Cecilia M; Concordia Acad; St Paul, MN; Chr; ChrhWkr; CmntyWkr; NHS; SchMus; LatCl; Trk; Gustavus Adolphus; Vet Med.

GREENWELL, Donna M; Reitz Memorial HS; Evansville, IN; VPSophCls; Band; HonRl; NatlFornLg; PepBnd; PresStuCncl; Twrl; RptrSchPpr; PPFtbl; OptClAwd; College; English.

GREENWELL, George P; South Shelby HS; Shelbina, MO; Chr; Chrl; Chrs; HonRl; SchMus; StuCncl; RptrSchPpr; FFA; LetterFtbl; LetterGlf; U Of Mo.

GREENWELL, Jaqueline; John H Castle HS; Newburgh, IN; TchrAde; FHA; Coll; Professiona Aviation.

GREENWELL, Mary; Memorial HS; Evansville, IN; DrlTm; HonRl; HospAde; JA; SchMus; SchPl; SctActv; Chrldr; IMSpt; JAAwd; College.

GREENWOOD, Brian W; Ann Arbor Pioneer HS; Ann Arbor, MI; MthCl; IMSpt; Univ Of Michigan; Engineer.

GREENWOOD, Gay M; Glenwood HS; Chatham, IL; 2/143 SecJrCls; PresChr; SecLbryAde; PresNHS; PresNatlThespSoc; SchPl; 4-H; SecGerCl; DARAwd; 4-HAwd; Il Univ; Theatre.

GREENWOOD, Jo A; Santa Fe Trail HS; Overbrook, KS; Chr; Chrl; Chrs; HonRl; NHS; SchMus; SchPl; TchrAde; Yrbk; PpCl; Kansas Univ; Psychology.

GREENWOOD, Kent E; Diamond R 4 HS; Diamond, MO; VPSophCls; ChrhWkr; HonRl; SchPl; 4-H; FFA; LetterBsbl; LetterBsktbl; CchngActv; 4-HAwd; College; Ag Business.

GREENWOOD, Linda M; Columbus HS; Marshfield, WI; 6/100 Band; Chrs; CncrtBnd; HonRl; HospAde; MrchBnd; PepBnd; SchMus; SchPl; FrCl; St Josephs School; Physicians Asst.

GREENWOOD, Patricia; Breckenridge HS; Breckenridge, MO; 1/12 ALAGirlsSt; Band; HonRl; NHS; SchPl; RptrYrbk; Chrldr; DanFAwd; DARAwd; Univ Of Missouri; Elem Education.

GREENWOOD, Robert P; Chaminade Prep; Webster Groves, MO; 19/105 HonRl; NatlMeritSchl; LetterFtbl; LetterSocr; U Of Mo; Broadcasting Communication.

GREER, Betty J; University Of Chicago HS; Chicago, IL; Chr; Chrs; ChrhWkr; SchMus; TchrAde; YthFlsp;.

GREER, Debbie A; St Charles HS; St Charles, MO; HonRl; HospAde; IMSpt; College; Travel.

GREER, James A; Deer Creek Mackinaw HS; Mackinaw, IL; 5/56 TrsSophCls; ALBoysSt; Band; CncrtBnd; HonRl; Mdrgl; MrchBnd; NatlMeritCmnd; NatlMeritSF; PepBnd; SchPl; LetterTrk; Univ Of Ill; Elec Engineering.

GREER, Joanna; Franklin Comm HS; Franklin, IN; 50/297 ChrhWkr; CmntyWkr; NHS; PolWkr; YthFlsp; FHA; FTA; PpCl; Glf; Socr; Swmmng; CchngActv; Indianapolis Schl; Nursing.

GREER, Joseph E; Morton Sr HS; Hammond, IN; 17/525 ChrhWkr; HonRl; PresNatlFornLg; NHS; TchrAde; SciCl; Purdue; Doctor.

GREER, Keith G; Lutheran West HS; Detroit, MI; Aud/Vis; ChrhWkr; CmntyWkr; Univ Of Detroit; Broadcasting.

GREER, Louis M; Collinsville HS; Collinsville, IL; PresSrCls; HonRl; StuCncl; YthFlsp; YthFnd; LetterBsbl; CaptFtbl; AmLegAwd; SARAwd; Univ Of Missouri; Engineering.

GREER, Melvin B; Cass Technical HS; Detroit, MI; HonRl; JA; OffAde; SchAde; StuCncl; EdSchPpr; FDA; FTA; Trk; U Of Mi; Doctor Or Lawyer.

GREER, Randy J; Virginia HS; Virginia, IL; StuCncl; StuGov; TchrAde; FFA; CaptFtbl; LetterTrk; IMSpt; Lincoln Land Comm Clg; Wildlife.

GREESON, Cynthia S; Logan Magnolia Comm HS; Logan, IA; Chrs; HonRl; SchPl; SecFHA; LetterPpCl; LetterBsktbl; LetterTrk; LetterChrldr; Bus School; Vocation.

GREESON, Richard W; Ben Davis Sr HS; Indianapolis, IN; 42/712 Chr; HonRl; ModUN; NatlFornLg; NHS; NatlThespSoc; SchMus; SchPl; SctActv; AmLegAwd; SARAwd; Indiana Univ; Political Science.

GREFF, Raymond N; Mott Public HS; Mott, ND; DrlTm; FFA; PpCl; Bismark Jr Col; Auto Mech Then Farmer.

GREGERSON, Cathy E; Albert Lea HS; Albert Lea, MN; NatlThespSoc; SchPl; 4-H; GerCl;.

GREGG, Alisa J; Mark Twain HS; New London, MO; Band; CncrtBnd; MrchBnd; PepBnd; Bsbl; Bsktbl; Trk; GAA; IMSpt; College; Physical Educ.

GREGG, Amy S; Harry A Burke HS; Omaha, NE; AFS; ALAGirlsSt; HonRl; NHS; SchMus; StuGov; YthFlsp; SchPpr; FrCl; Chrldr; College; Television.

GREGG, John R; Manistee HS; Manistee, MI; 13/171 Band; JrNHS; MrchBnd; NatlFornLg; NHS; NatlMeritSF; NatlThespSoc; PepBnd; PolWkr; SchPl; Trk; IMSpt; Mi State Univ; Computer Designer.

GREGG, Michael L; Jackson HS; Jackson, MO; 2/225 HonRl; PresNHS; NatlMeritCmnd; SctActv; StuCncl; FrCl; LetterBsktbl; AmLegAwd; RotaryAwd; CitAwd; U Of Mo; Engineer.

GREGG, Michael W; Hamburg HS; Hamburg, IA; 7/37 Aud/Vis; HonRl; NHS; SctActv; StuCncl; Univ Of Missouri; Geology.

GREGG, Nancy J; Lanse HS; Lanse, MI; Band; ChrhWkr; CncrtBnd; HonRl; PepBnd; RptrYrbk; Yrbk; VP4-H; VPIMSpt; Central Mich; Interior Design.

GREGG, Nancy T; Woodstock HS; Woodstock, IL; HonRl; NHS; TchrAde; 4-H;.

GREGO, Julie; Maine Township South Hs; Park Ridge, IL; 95 Chrs; HonRl; NHS; SchMus; StuGov; PpCl; DARAwd; U Of Illinois;biology.

GREGOIRE, Paul J; Marshall Sr HS; Marshall, MN; 33/225 Band; HonRl; College Of St Thomas; Accounting.

GREGOIRE, Todd K; Northland Pines HS; Eagle River, WI; ChrhWkr; CmntyWkr; PolWkr; YthFlsp; Yrbk; GerCl; MthCl; Ftbl; Glf; Tennis; Wrstlng; Bethany Fellowship Bible Coll; Liberal Arts.

GREGOR, Kathleen; West Catholic HS; Grand Rapids, MI; CmntyWkr; HonRl; HospAde; JA; NHS; NatlMeritFnl; NatlMeritSchl; PolWkr; StuCncl; StuGov; Univ; Special Education.

GREGOR, Mary; Whiting HS; Whiting, IN; 2/105 HonRl; JA; NHS; SchPl; SctActv; EdYrBk; FTA; GerCl; MthCl; JAAwd; Business School; Secretarial.

GREGORASH, Joleen M; St Francis Academy; Joliet, IL; 14/176 HonRl; LbryAde; NHS; SpnCl; IMSpt; College; Math.

GREGORICH, Linda J; Morton West HS; Lyons, IL; Chr; HonRl; JrNHS; NHS; College; Accounting.

GREGORICH, Thomas M; Boylan HS; Rockford, IL; HonRl; PolWkr; Bradley Univ; Business.

GREGORY, Carol A; Chester HS; Chester, IL; 7/122 Chrs; HonRl; LbryAde; NHS; SchMus; StuCncl; Eastern Illinois Univ; Elem Education.

GREGORY, Connie L; Bloom Township HS; Chicago Heights, IL; 51/1018 NHS; Northwestern Univ; Medical Technology.

GREGORY, David K; Flora HS; Flora, IL; 30/137 ALBoysSt; HonRl; SctActv; FHA; FTA; SpnCl; MthCl; Tennis; IMSpt; College; Professional.

GREGORY, Henry T; Central Sr HS; Kansas City, MO; 43/367 Aud/Vis; CmntyWkr; HonRl; LitMag; NHS; NatlMeritSchl; PresUNYO; RptrYrbk; FDA; LatCl; IMSpt; Penn Valley; Business Admin.

GREGORY, Joan M; Midland HS; Midland, MI; 36/432 Band; CncrtBnd; HonRl; JA; PepBnd; College; Forestry.

GREGORY, Joann; Clark County R 7 HS; Kahoka, MO; HonRl; LbryAde; MrchBnd; NHS; OffAde; PepBnd; SchPl; YthFlsp; PpCl; Chrldr; U Of Mo Columbia; Library Science.

GREGORY, Marcia J; Thornton Township HS; Riverdale, IL; 27/727 Band; Chr; ChrhWkr; HonRl; NHS; SchMus; SchPl; SctActv; TchrAde; YthFlsp; RptrYrbk; PpCl; Ill Wesleyan Univ; Special Education.

GREGORY, Marshal K; Centralia HS; Centralia, IL; 8/360 CncrtBnd; HonRl; NHS; StuCncl; PresKeyCl; LetterTennis; LetterTrk; Millikin Univ; Music.

GREGORY, Michael L; Parkway West HS; Manchester, MO; ALBoysSt; CmntyWkr; CaptBsbl; LetterBsktbl; IMSpt; AmLegAwd; KiwanAwd; PresAwd; U Of Mo; Acctg.

GREGORY, Nanette S; Breckenridge Jr Sr HS; Breckenridge, MI; HonRl; SchPl; TchrAde; 4-H; IMSpt; PPFtbl; Business School; Secretary.

GREGORY, Raymond E; Southeastern HS; Detroit, MI; ChrhWkr; CmntyWkr; HonRl; NHS; TchrAde; MthCl; Univ; Prof.

GREGORY, Rosemary A; Pine River Public HS; Pine River, MN; 3/61 SecTrsJrCls; SecTrsSrCls; SecBand; CaptDrlTm; NHS; SecStuCncl; Yrbk; RptrSchPpr; LetterBsktbl; GAA; AmLegAwd; College; Art.

GREGORY, Susan; Lebanon Hs; Lebanon, MO; Chrs; HospAde; 4-H; FFA; FNA; Bsbl; Bsktbl; 4-HAwd;.

GREGORY, Susan L; Northwest HS; Eureka, MO; SecChr; CmntyWkr; HonRl; Mdrgl; NHS; NatlMeritFnl; NatlMeritSchl; Yrbk; FTA; PpCl; College.

GREGSON, Terry L; Highland HS; Highland, IN; 84/538 Indiana Univ; Econ.

GREICUS, Laura A; Mid Pacific Institute; Muncie, IN; ChrhWkr; CmntyWkr; HonRl; IntrClCncl; LbryAde; PolWkr; YthFlsp; FrCl; Socr; Swmmng; University.

GREIF, Carol; Pius Xi HS; West Allis, WI; Chr; HonRl; NHS; NatlThespSoc; SchMus; StuGov; TchrAde; YthLg; FTA; Chrldr; Univ Of Indianna; Pre Medicine.

GREIF, Joyce A; Osborne HS; Osborne, KS; 4/69 ALAGirlsSt; Band; CncrtBnd; HonRl; MrchBnd; NHS; OffAde; PepBnd; SchPl; SctActv; StuCncl; PpCl; LetterBsktbl; LetterTrk; Fort Hays State Col; Physical Education.

GREIM, James R; R Nelson Snider HS; Fort Wayne, IN; 38/515 HonRl; NatlMeritSchl; GerCl; LatCl; SciCl; Depauw University; Math.

GREIMAN, Karen A; Garner Hayfield HS; Garner, IA; 33/83 Chr; ChrhWkr; HonRl; SchAde; TreasYthFlsp; Sec4-H; SecFHA; 4-HAwd; College; Fashion Merchandising.

GREINER, Barbara A; Saint Joseph Sr HS; Saint Joseph, MI; 54/340 LitMag; NHS; OffAde; Quill&Scroll; SchAde; SctActv; StuCncl; Yrbk; RptrSchPpr; Trk; Mich St U; Attorney.

GREINER, Lisa; Woodruff HS; Peoria, IL; 10/273 ChrhWkr; CmntyWkr; HonRl; JA; JCC; NHS; OffAde; PolWkr; RedCrAde; KeyCl; Il St Univ; Accounting.

GREINER, Lori D; John Marshall HS; Rochester, MN; 2/618 Band; CncrtBnd; MrchBnd; NHS; Orch; PepBnd; SchMus; SciCl; MasAwd; Univ; Math.

GREINER, Sandra L; Harrison HS; Harrison, MI; HonRl; VPNHS; EdYrBk; AmLegAwd; CitAwd; Central Mi Univ; Journalism.

GREIVE, Julie A; Macarthur HS; Decatur, IL; 7/410 TrsSrCls; Chrs; HonRl; LbryAde; NHS; StuCncl; TreasGerCl; DARAwd; Ill St Univ; Elem Ed.

GREIWE, Beverly; Immaculate Conception Acad; Batesville, IN; Chrs; CmntyWkr; HonRl; SchMus; SchPl; SctActv; Teen; SpnCl; Bus School; Major Study.

GRELL, Larry; Technical HS; St Cloud, MN; 70/475 HonRl; TchrAde; Bsbl; Bsktbl; Ftbl; Univ; Professional.

GRELLNER, Eugene; Fatima HS; Bonnots Mill, MO; Chr; HonRl; 4-H; FFA; Universty; Agriculture.

GRELLNER, Eugene F; Fatima HS; Bonnots Mill, MO; Chr; HonRl; 4-H; College; Vocation.

GREMINGER, Keith G; Valle HS; St Genevieve, MO; PresFrshCls; SecJrCls; HonRl; SchMus; PpCl; LetterBsktbl; LetterFtbl; Trk; IMSpt; PPFtbl; University Of Missouri; Art.

GREMINGER, Richard J; Valle HS; Ste Genevieve, MO; 15/82 PresFrshCls; PresSophCls; VPJrCls; NHS; PresStuCncl; Yrbk; MthCl; Ftbl; Trk; RotaryAwd; Southeast No State Univ; Industrial Tech Ed.

GREMMELS, Stephen K; Du Quoin HS; Du Quoin, IL; 5/118 VPFrshCls; Band; CncrtBnd; HonRl; MrchBnd; PepBnd; SchMus; SchPl; PresStuCncl; SchPpr; PpCl; Bsbl; Trk; Southern Ill Univ.

GRENELL, Virginia L; Manistee HS; Manistee, MI; HonRl; VoiceDemAwd; Business Schl; Vocation.

GRENIER, David P; East Grand Forks Senior HS; E Grand Forks, MN; CmntyWkr; HonRl; SciCl; Ftbl; College; Computer Science Math.

GRENINGER, Gayle L; Neosho HS; Neosho, MO; 36/253 Chr; HonRl; Mdrgl; NHS; OffAde; TchrAde; FHA; PpCl; Sw Missouri St Univ; Acctng.

GRENISEN, Margie M; Aquinas HS; La Crosse, WI; 3/211 ALAGirlsSt; Band; NHS; StuCncl; LetterBsktbl; LetterTennis; LetterTrk; CchngActv; PresGAA; IMSpt; KiwanAwd; College; Law.

GRENNAN, Martin J; Concordia HS; Jamestown, KS; SciCl; Bsktbl; Ftbl; College; Professional.

GRENTZ, Dietmar J; Adelphian Academy; Warren, MI; 1/58 Chr; ChrhWkr; HonRl; NHS; StuCncl; PresStuGov; EdYrBk; IMSpt; Andrews Univ; Doctor.

GRENTZ, Renee R; Sunflower HS; Mitchell, NE; HstFrshCls; PresJrCls; Band; Chr; Chrs; ChrhWkr; HonRl; HospAde; Mdrgl; SchPl; University; Medicine.

GRENZ, Mary; Eureka HS; Eureka, SD; VPSrCls; Chrs; ChrhWkr; DrlTm; SchMus; StuCncl; RptrYrbk; RptrSchPpr; GAA; Oberlin College; Prof Law.

GRESKI, Nancy M; Bishop Noll HS; Schererville, IN; 126/360 Chrs; HonRl; 4-H; 4-HAwd; College; Social Work.

GRESS, Margaret F; Jasper HS; Velpen, IN; 49/286 Chr; Chrs; HonRl; NHS; OffAde; SchPpr; 4-H; PpCl; 4-HAwd; Univ Of Evansville; Respiratory Therapy.

GRESS, Mike N; Jasper HS; Jasper, IN; 29/286 PresSrCls; Band; ChrhWkr; CncrtBnd; HonRl; MrchBnd; PepBnd; StuCncl; 4-H; Wrstlng; Purdue Univ; Pre Veterinary.

GRESSLY, Janet G; Nodaway Holt HS; Bolckow, MO; Band; CncrtBnd; MrchBnd; SchMus; SchPl; FHA; PpCl; LetterTrk; Chrldr; PPFtbl; Univ Of Missouri; Forestry.

GRETEBECK, Todd; Merrill Sr HS; Merrill, WI; 13/354 NatlFornLg; SctActv; Univ Wis Madison; Engineering.

GRETEMAN, Susan; Kuemper HS; Carroll, IA; 4/290 HonRl; LbryAde; Orch; Quill&Scroll; SchMus; TchrAde; RptrSchPpr; FrCl; SciCl; Chrldr; College; Professional.

GRETSCHMANN, Debra K; Glenwood City HS; Glenwood City, WI; ALAGirlsSt; Chrs; DrmMjrt; HonRl; NHS; FHA; PpCl; LetterTrk; CaptChrldr; GAA; School Of Nursing; Nursing.

GRETZINGER, Beth K; Marion HS; Marion, WI; HonRl; TchrAde; SpnCl; LetterBsbl; CaptBsktbl; Ftbl; VPGAA; Trade Sch.

GREUFE, Denise A; Spring Hill HS; Spring Hill, KS; Band; HonRl; Mdrgl; NatlFornLg; NHS; SchMus; SchPl; StuCncl; PresFHA; SecPpCl;.

GREUTMAN, Theresa A; Williston HS; Williston, ND; Band; ChrhWkr; CncrtBnd; HonRl; MrchBnd; PepBnd; PpCl; Trk; Chrldr; College; Major Study.

GREVE, Ann T; Manistee Catholic Central HS; Manistee, MI; 412/68 Chr; CncrtBnd; HonRl; MrchBnd; NatlFornLg; NHS; PepBnd; StuCncl; RptrYrbk; PpCl; Chrldr; College; French.

GREVE, Jeffrey A; Wisner Pilger HS; Wisner, NE; PresSophCls; HonRl; StuCncl; StuGov; 4-H; FFA; Ftbl; Swmmng; Trk; IMSpt; Trade School; Vocation.

GREVER, Pamela S; Concordia Lutheran HS; Fort Wayne, IN; 5/220 Band; ChrhWkr; NHS; PolWkr; StuGov; PpCl; Trk; GAA; IMSpt; ChmbCommrsAwd; Concordia Clg; Med Tech/microbiology.

GREWE, Tracey A; Prospect HS; Mt Prospect, IL; 110/625 Band; ChrhWkr; HonRl; NHS; SctActv; TchrAde; FrCl; PpCl; University; Business.

GREWE, Vicki L; Roosevelt HS; Fergus Falls, MN; 54/306 Band; ChrhWkr; CncrtBnd; DrmMjrt; HonRl; MrchBnd; PepBnd; SchMus; CchngActv; Jr Coll; Prof.

GREY, Carole G; Earlville HS; Earlville, IL; Band; Chrs; ChrhWkr; CncrtBnd; DrmMjrt; LbryAde; MrchBnd; ModUN; OffAde; PepBnd; StuCncl; RptrYrbk; RptrSchPpr; GAA; College; Professional.

GREY, Edward; Lane Technical HS; Chicago, IL; DrlTm; HonRl; LbryAde; NHS; NatlMeritCmnd; ROTC; StuCncl; University Of Illinois; Medicine.

GREZESZAK, Douglas B; Whittemore Prescott HS; Whittemore, MI; 4/75 Band; CncrtBnd; DrlTm; HonRl; MrchBnd; PepBnd; SchPl; TchrAde; LetterBsktbl; LetterTrk; Michigan St; Science Teach.

GRIBBLE, Susan K; Edgewood HS; Madison, WI; 4-H; Uw La Crosse; Psychology.

GRICUS, Mary; Dwight D Eisenhower HS; Calumet Park, IL; 3/679 Chr; Chrs; HonRl; LitMag; Mdrgl; NHS; OffAde; SchPl; TchrAde; SpnCl; Univ Of I Circle Campus; Special Education.

GRIDLEY, Bobbie J; Carrollton Comm Unit HS; Carrollton, IL; Chrs; ChrhWkr; HonRl; HospAde; NHS; SchMus; SctActv; YthFlsp; FBLA; FHA; FSA; GAA; Drury College; Home Ec.

GRIEB, Michael C; Forest View HS; Des Plaines, IL; 4/600 ChrhWkr; CtyCnl; HonRl; NHS; NatlMeritCmnd; FDA; GerCl; SciCl; LetterFtbl; IMSpt; Northwestern University; Physician.

GRIEBEL, Elisa; Bellevue Community HS; Bellevue, IA; 15/45 ChrhWkr; HonRl; SchMus; RptrYrbk; RptrSchPpr; SchPpr; 4-H; FHA; 4-HAwd; MasAwd; Kirkwood Comm College; Art Instructtor.

GRIEBEL, Kirk E; Browns Valley HS; Browns Valley, MN; 5/38 VPFrshCls; PresSrCls; Chrs; ChrhWkr; HonRl; MrchBnd; NHS; LetterBsktbl; LetterTrk; Coll; Professional.

GRIEBENOW, Leon B; Valley HS; Clermont, IA; ALBoysSt; Band; Chrs; MrchBnd; NatlThespSoc; SchPl; YthFnd; PpCl; Bsbl;.

GRIEGER, Doris E; Buffalo HS; Buffalo, ND; 4/15 TrsSophCls; ALAGirlsSt; Band; Chr; Chrs; ChrhWkr; CncrtBnd; HonRl; Mdrgl; PepBnd; College; Home Ec.

GRIEGER, Marvin C; Morgan Twp HS; Valparaiso, IN; ALBoysSt; Chrs; HonRl; NHS; SecFFA; LetterBsbl; LetterBsktbl;.

GRIEPENSTROH, Dean H; Nebraska City HS; Dunbar, NE; Chr; HonRl; NHS; SchPl; SecYthFlsp; Pres4-H; PresFFA; LetterTrk; 4-HAwd; U Of Nebraska; General Agriculture.

GRIEPENSTROH, Mark S; Heritage Hills HS; Lamar, IN; 23/145 SecSophCls; ALBoysSt; Band; HonRl; NHS; NatlMeritSchl; SchMus; PresStuCncl; EdSchPpr; FrCl; Univ Of Evansville; Business Admin.

GRIEPENTROG, Ronald D; Pardeeville Sr HS; Pardeeville, WI; ChrhWkr; HonRl; Teen; 4-H; TreasFFA; Ftbl; Trk; LetterWrstlng; Madison Area Tech Clg; Hotel Cookery.

GRIER, Gary E; Bgm Community HS; Guernsey, IA; 18/48 HonRl; StuCncl; 4-H; FFA; PpCl; Bsktbl; College; Vocation.

GRIER, Kendall; Haven HS; Mt Hope, KS; Chrl; Chrs; ChrhWkr; HonRl; SchPl; SctActv; YthFlsp; Bsktbl; Univ; Nuclar Eng.

GRIER, Peter S; The Principia HS; Birmingham, MI; TrsSophCls; JrNHS; LbryAde; NatlMeritSF; SchPpr; LetterSocr; LetterTennis; Writer.

GRIES, Karen E; Charter Oak Ute Comm HS; Charter Oak, IA; 8/45 TrsSrCls; Band; Chr; Chrs; CncrtBnd; HonRl; HospAde; Mdrgl; MrchBnd; Univ; Nursing.

GRIESBAUM, Catherine; Glendale HS; Springfeld, MO; 24/428 AFS; DrmBgl; HonRl; OffAde; FrCl; University.

GRIESEDIECK, Susan E; Berkeley HS; St Louis, MO; 4/287 Band; CncrtBnd; HonRl; MrchBnd; NHS; SchPl; SctActv; StuCncl; StuGov; YthFlsp; PpCl; Bsktbl; LetterSwmmng; LetterTennis; Univ Of Missouri.

GRIESEDIECK, Susan E; Berkeley HS; Berkeley, MO; 7/287 Band; CncrtBnd; HonRl; MrchBnd; NHS; SchPl; SctActv; StuCncl; StuGov; YthFlsp; PpCl; Bsktbl; LetterSwmmng; LetterTennis; College.

GRIESENAUER, Lori A; Duchesne HS; St Charles, MO; SchPl; SctActv; TreasPpCl; LetterBsbl; LetterBsktbl; Chrldr; GAA; IMSpt; PPFtbl; College; Commercial Art.

GRIEVES, Scot E; La Fayette HS; St Joseph, MO; 20/262 Band; CmntyWkr; CncrtBnd; HonRl; JrNHS; MrchBnd; Orch; PepBnd; SchMus; SchPl; Coll; Professional.

GRIFFEE, Marlene; Marysville HS; Beattie, KS; Chrs; HonRl; YthFlsp; 4-H; Work; Secretarial.

GRIFFEL, Donna M; Gillespie HS; Gillespie, IL; 16/132 HonRl; NHS; StuCncl; EdYrBk; Chrldr; PresGAA; BttyCrckrAwd; Southern Illinois Univ; Nursing.

GRIFFEN, Judith A; Bowling Green HS; Bowling Green, MO; 4/139 Band; ChrhWkr; HonRl; HospAde; NHS; Quill&Scroll; PresSctActv; Yrbk; FHA; Chrldr; IMSpt; Ne Missouri St Univ; Med Secretary.

GRIFFIN, Ann; Cloquet Sr HS; Cloquet, MN; Band; CncrtBnd; HonRl; NHS; Orch; PepBnd; SchMus; PpCl; Chrldr; St Scholastica Col; Profession.

GRIFFIN, Belinda C; St Thomas Aquinas HS; Detroit, MI; 51/249 CncrtBnd; JrNHS; NHS; SchPl; U Of Mi; Psychology.

GRIFFIN, Boyd E; Richwoods HS; Peoria, IL; 97/449 Chr; Chrs; ChrhWkr; CmntyWkr; HonRl; NatlFornLg; NHS; NatlThespSoc; SchMus; SchPl; SctActv; YthFlsp; Knox College; Law.

GRIFFIN, Brenda M; Belton HS; Belton, MO; Band; Chrs; CncrtBnd; DrlTm; HonRl; NHS; StuCncl; PpCl; Chrldr; PPFtbl; Smsu Springfield; Phy Ed.

GRIFFIN, Carol; Munster HS; Munster, IN; HonRl; NatlThespSoc; PolWkr; SchMus; SchPl; StuGov; Yrbk; SchPpr; FNA; Valparaiso Univ; Lawyer.

GRIFFIN, Curtis D; Brother Rice HS; Southfield, MI; VPFrshCls; VPSophCls; HonRl; StuCncl; LetterBsktbl; LetterFtbl; LetterTrk; GodCntryAwd; CitAwd; U; Professional.

GRIFFIN, Darrick C; Harvard St George HS; Chicago, IL; 4/19 TrsJrCls; TrsSrCls; OffAde; Bsbl; Elmhurst College; Psychiatry.

GRIFFIN, Debra A; Twin Rivers HS; Broseley, MO; Aud/Vis; Chr; HonRl; JrNHS; OffAde; SchAde; TchrAde; KeyCl; College; Vet.

GRIFFIN, Ed T; Moline HS; Moline, IL; HonRl; CaptFtbl; Wrstlng; AmLegAwd; College; Vocation.

GRIFFIN, Judith A; Chadsey HS; Detroit, MI; HonRl; LitMag; SchAde; SctActv; TchrAde; CitAwd; College; Professional.

GRIFFIN, Kathryn A; Marian HS; Omaha, NE; HonRl; JA; TreasNHS; PresFrCl; MthCl; IMSpt; JAAwd; Kearney State College; Medical Technologist.

GRIFFIN, Kayla; Northwest HS; Fenton, MO; Chr; ChrhWkr; HonRl; NHS; SchPl; SctActv; FBLA; Trade; Bus.

GRIFFIN, Kerry A; Rantoul Tonwship HS; Rantoul, IL; Chrs; HonRl; JrNHS; NHS; StuCncl; LatCl; Trk; U Of Il; Medicine.

GRIFFIN, Kevin M; Mendel Catholic Prep; Dolton, IL; ChrhWkr; HonRl; SctActv; Yrbk; SchPpr; KeyCl; SpnCl; PpCl; IMSpt; CitAwd; Pre Med Study.

GRIFFIN, Mary E; Mancelona HS; Mancelona, MI; TrsJrCls; ChrhWkr; HonRl; NHS; SchPl; StuCncl; YthFlsp; John Wesley Clge Owosso; Int Relations.

GRIFFIN, Michael J; Proviso West HS; Berkeley, IL; 219/1100 College.

GRIFFIN, Patricia A; Roger C Sullivan HS; Chicago, IL; HonRl; JA; LitMag; NHS; NatlMeritFnl; StuCncl; Yrbk; SchPpr; Univ Of Illinois.

GRIFFIN, Patricia A; Sullivan HS; Chicago, IL; HonRl; JA; LbryAde; NHS; NatlMeritFnl; TreasStuCncl; RptrYrbk; SchPpr; KeyCl;.

GRIFFIN, Pat W; Carlisle Commuinty HS; Carlisle, IA; PresFrshCls; ALBoysSt; Band; Chr; ChrhWkr; CncrtBnd; HonRl; NHS; SchMus; StuCncl; College; Music.

GRIFFIN, Rachel L; Lane HS; Chicago, IL; Aud/Vis; Chr; ChrhWkr; NatlMeritCmnd; Orch; ROTC; SchMus; Lib Arts Col; Pre Veterinary.

GRIFFIN, Robin E; Noblesville HS; Noblesville, IN; 23/250 HonRl; JrNHS; NHS; StuCncl; PresYthFlsp; FHA; FTA; SpnCl; LionAwd; College; Chemistry.

GRIFFIN, Steven B; Fairfield Comm HS; Fairfield, IL; 1/165 PresFrshCls; Band; CncrtBnd; HonRl; JrNHS; PresNHS; Orch; PepBnd; StuCncl; Bsktbl; Ftbl; EldAwd; Univ Of Illinois; Chemical Engineer.

GRIFFIN, Teena M; Octavia HS; Saybrook, IL; 5/49 Band; CncrtBnd; HonRl; MrchBnd; NHS; RptrSchPpr; 4-H; FHA; PpCl; Trk; Chrldr; PPFtbl; College; Law Enforcement.

GRIFFIN, Tim E; Vlanney HS; Kirkwood, MO; 70/185 ChrhWkr; CmntyWkr; PolWkr; SchMus; SchPl; StuCncl; FrCl; Bsbl; CchngActv; IMSpt; University; Law Enforcement.

GRIFFIN, Timothy P; Lake Linden Hubbell HS; Lake Linden, MI; PresSrCls; HonRl; SchPl; SctActv; StuCncl; EdYrBk; Ftbl; Michigan Tech Univ; Engineering.

GRIFFIN, Tracie L; Washington Community HS; Washington, IL; 23/315 HonRl; NHS; NatlMeritCmnd; FrCl; College; Spec Educ Teach.

GRIFFIS, Janine E; Northrop HS; Ft Wayne, IN; Chr; HonRl; SchPl; Princeton Univ; Lawyer.

GRIFFITH, Brenda M; St Mary Acad; Monroe, MI; ChrhWkr; CmntyWkr; HonRl; NHS; SchMus; FrCl; PpCl; Monroe Comm Coll; Medicine.

GRIFFITH, Christy E; John Hersey HS; Arlington Hts, IL; 40/770 AFS; HonRl; JrNHS; NHS; NatlMeritCmnd; StuCncl; Univ Of Illinois; Communications.

GRIFFITH, Ellis E; East Richland HS; Olney, IL; LetterFtbl; LetterTrk; St Louis College; Pharmacy.

GRIFFITH, John; Castlewood Ind HS; Castlewood, SD; 15/31 ChrhWkr; HonRl; SchPl; SctActv; SptEdYrbk; PpCl; Bsbl; Bsktbl; Ftbl; Trk; Us Army;teletype Repairman.

GRIFFITH, Julia L; Sherwood HS; Garden City, MO; 2/63 PresSophCls; TrsJrCls; Chrs; HonRl; Mdrgl; NHS; SchMus; SchPl; StuCncl; CaptChrldr; DARAwd; VoiceDemAwd; Univ Of Missouri; Music.

GRIFFITH, Kean D; Frankfort Community HS; West Frankfort, IL; 3/172 Band; NHS; KeyCl; LatCl; BttyCrckrAwd; Knox College; Medicine.

GRIFFITH, Laurie M; Little Falls Community HS; Little Falls, MN; SecTrsSrCls; Band; Chr; CncrtBnd; HonRl; MrchBnd; SchMus; StuCncl; Bsktbl; PPFtbl; College; Major Study.

GRIFFITH, Linda S; Shawnee Mission E HS; Shawnee Mission, KS; HonRl; JrNHS; NHS; LatCl; PpCl; College; Art.

GRIFFITH, Lynn; Madelia HS; Madelia, MN; 1 85 Band; NHS; NatlMeritSchl; LetterBsktbl; LetterTrk; IMSpt; Gustavus A Adolhus; Math.

GRIFFITH, Nancy; Buffalo Grove Hs; Arlington Hts, IL; 13 CmntyWkr; HonRl; NHS; SctActv; PpCl; Illinois State U;business Administration.

GRIFFITH, Susan H; Roycemore HS; Evanston, IL; ChrhWkr; CmntyWkr; HonRl; HospAde; PolWkr; SctActv; StuCncl; StuGov; UNYO; Virginia Wesleyan; Psychology.

GRIFFITH, Twyla L; Benton County HS; Lincoln, MO; 8/39 SecTrsFrshCls; SecTrsJrCls; VPSrCls; Chr; Chrs; HonRl; SchPl; EdSchPpr; PpCl; Central Missouri State Univ; Teacher.

GRIFFITH, William B; Fairfield Community HS; Fairfield, IL; PresFrshCls; HonRl;.

GRIFFITHS, Dennis; Loup City HS; Loup City, NE; 33/67 4-H; FFA; Bsktbl; Ftbl; IMSpt; 4-HAwd; Trade School; Mechanic.

GRIFFITHS, John R; North HS; Sheboygan, WI; HonRl; SctActv; Swmmng; Tennis; LetterTrk; U Of Wi; Law.

GRIFFITHS, Larry L; Wallace 65r HS; Wallace, NE; PresSophCls; Band; Chr; Chrs; SchPl; StuCncl; 4-H; LetterBsktbl; LetterFtbl; ChmnTrk; Mid Plains; Electronics.

GRIFFITHS, Nancy; Wheaton Christian HS; Wheaton, IL; 10/ Chr; HonRl; NHS; StuCncl; StuGov; PpCl; West Sub School Of Nursing; Nursing.

GRIFFY, Beverly E; Northclay Comm HS; Louisville, IL; SpnCl; GAA; College.

GRIGALAUSKI, Karen; Winnebago HS; Rockford, IL; 5/107 VPSophCls; VPSrCls; HonRl; NHS; RptrYrbk; SchPpr; CitAwd; Univ Of Illinois; Business Admin.

GRIGAS, Stephen A; Zion Benton Township HS; Zion, IL; 34/403 HonRl; Bsbl; Butler Univ; Mathematics.

GRIGGS, Debra L; Newton Senior HS; Newton, IA; Band; Chrs; CmntyWkr; HonRl; PpCl; Secretarial Work.

GRIGGS, Gregory W; Cass Tech HS; Detroit, MI; PresSrCls; CmntyWkr; HonRl; NatlMeritCmnd; Quill&Scroll; SchMus; SchPl; TchrAde; EdSchPpr; Univ; Journalism.

GRIGGS, Jamey S; St Pius X HS; Kansas City, MO; 88/136 TrsFrshCls; TrsSophCls; Chrs; SchMus; Bsktbl; Ftbl; Trk; Coll; Major Study.

GRIGGS, Richard; Cowan HS; Muncie, IN; HonRl; HospAde; JA; JrNHS; NHS; RedCrAde; YthFlsp; 4-H; FFA; Bsktbl; College; Professional.

GRIGSBY, Deborah J; Westfield HS; Neshkoro, WI; Chr; Chrs; HonRl; OffAde; SchMus; SchPpr; LetterTrk; GAA; Business Sch; Legal Secretary.

GRIGSBY, James A; Springfield HS; Springfield, IL; 142/585 CmntyWkr; PolWkr; SchPl; College; Business Administration.

GRIGSBY, Mary; Hamilton HS; Hamilton, IL; SecJrCls; HonRl; RedCrAde; TchrAde; FrCl; Chrldr; College; Biology Major P E Minor.

GRILL, Raymond A; Fenwick HS; Westchester, IL; ChrhWkr; HonRl; SchMus; Bsktbl; Ill Institute Technology; Engineering.

GRIMBERG, Karan; Highland HS; Highland, IN; 175/585 OffAde; SctActv; GAA; PPFtbl; College; Pharmacy.

GRIMES, Austin W; Bristol Independent HS; Lily, SD; 20/30 ALBoysSt; Bsktbl; Ftbl; CchngActv; Northern; Teaching.

GRIMES, Cynthia; Madison Consolidated HS; Madison, IN; HonRl; SchAde; SchMus; TchrAde; GerCl; PpCl; GAA;.

GRIMES, Cynthia; Sandusky HS; Sandusky, MI; 5/114 TrsSophCls; NHS; 4-H; FBLA; FNA; FTA; PpCl; Chrldr; BttyCrckrAwd; Bronson Meth Hosp; Reg Nurse.

GRIMES, Daniel W; Logan Rogersville HS; Rogersville, MO; Band; Chrs; ChrhWkr; CmntyWkr; CncrtBnd; HonRl; IntrClCncl; MrchBnd; StuCncl; Bsbl; Ftbl; Trk; Business School; Computer Programming.

GRIMES, David A; Terre Haute Schulte HS; Terre Haute, IN; HonRl; ModUN; KeyCl; Trk;.

GRIMES, Donna M; Rochester Community HS; Rochester, IN; 3/152 HonRl; NHS; FHA; GerCl; BttyCrckrAwd; In Central U; Acct.

GRIMES, Gregory; Hirsch Hs; Chicago, IL; 3/335 HonRl; JrNHS; LitMag; NHS; NatlMeritCmnd; SpnCl; MthCl;.

GRIMES, Gregory; Hirsch Hs; Chiago, IL; 3/335 HonRl; JrNHS; LitMag; NHS; NatlMeritSchl; SpnCl; MthCl; Univ Of Illinois; Professional Doctor.

GRIMES, John A; Balaton HS; Balaton, MN; Aud/Vis; Chrs; StuGov; 4-H; FFA; Ftbl; Trk; Trade School; Industrial Electronic.

GRIMES, Kay D; Mahomet Seymour HS; Mahomet, IL; Band; CncrtBnd; HonRl; HospAde; NHS; NatlMeritCmnd; SchPl; StuGov; TchrAde; Yrbk; FSA; FTA; Bsktbl; Univ Of Ill; Biochemistry.

GRIMES, Loretta L; Sullivan HS; Sullivan, IN; 14/139 HonRl; NHS; TchrAde; FHA;.

GRIMES, Randy L; Huntley HS; Huntley, IL; 3/51 TrsFrshCls; VPSophCls; HonRl; NHS; GerCl; LatCl; Univ Of Ill; Electrical Engineering.

GRIMES, Rita L; Unity HS; Ursa, IL; 2/77 Band; Chrs; CncrtBnd; HonRl; MrchBnd; PepBnd; SchMus; SchPl; PresYthFlsp; RptrYrbk; RptrSchPpr; Pres4-H; 4-HAwd; Culver Stockton; History.

GRIMES, Sharon K; Northrop HS; Fort Wayne, IN; ChrhWkr; CmntyWkr; LbryAde; OffAde; PolWkr; SchAde; SchPl; TchrAde; PpCl; CitAwd; College; Teaching.

GRIMLEY, Jeffrey M; Naperville Central HS; Naperville, IL; 57/844 HonRl; NHS; Bsbl; Trk; Univ Of Iowa; Chem Engineer.

GRIMM, Celine; Bloomfield HS; Bloomfield, NE; TrsJrCls; SchAde; TchrAde; Yrbk; 4-H; FFA; FHA; PpCl; Trk; 4-HAwd; College; Nursing.

GRIMM, Corrine K; Rolla HS; Rolla, MO; 9/217 TchrAde; PresLatCl; PpCl; Univ; Accounting.

GRIMM, Ilene P; Hazen HS; Hazen, ND; Band; Chrs; CncrtBnd; HonRl; MrchBnd; PepBnd; FHA; PpCl; LetterBsktbl; IMSpt; Clg; Bus Admn Or Legal Sec.

GRIMM, Jamie S; Hinckley Big Rock HS; Hinckley, IL; 12/65 Chr; Chrs; ChrhWkr; HonRl; SchMus; SchPl; Yrbk; RptrSchPpr; 4-H; FHA; LatCl; SciCl; LetterSocr; 4-HAwd; College; Law.

GRIMM, Lora J; Sabetha HS; Sabetha, KS; Chr; Chrs; CncrtBnd; HonRl; SctActv; StuCncl; FFA; FHA; College; Nursing.

GRIMM, Robert L; Mt Vernon HS; Mt Vernon, IL; 39/388 ChrhWkr; CmntyWkr; HonRl; NHS; SchAde; TchrAde; SpnCl; CaptFtbl; Tennis; Trk; Univ; Business Ad.

GRIMM, Sheila S; Craig Riii HS; Craig, MO; Band; Chrs; CmntyWkr; CncrtBnd; LbryAde; MrchBnd; PepBnd; PolWkr; SchPpr; PpCl; Coll; Music & Drama.

GRIMMELL, Derek W; Elk River Sr HS; Elk River, MN; Band; ChrhWkr; CncrtBnd; HonRl; MrchBnd; NatlMeritSF; Univ; Medical Research.

GRIMMER, Gregory; New Haven HS; New Haven, IN; /250 YthFlsp; SciCl; Bsbl; IMSpt; Coll; Prof.

GRIMSBY, Faye; Marquette Senior HS; Marquette, MI; ALAGirlsSt; DrlTm; HonRl; JA; StuCncl; FHA; GerCl; Univ; Professional.

GRIMSHAW, Jerry A; Tomah HS; Camp Douglas, WI; Chr; Mdrgl; SchMus; SctActv; TchrAde; EdSchPpr; SptEdSchPpr; Bsbl; Univ Of Wisconsin; Broadcasting Tv.

GRIMSKE, Karen M; Lakeview HS; St Clair Shores, MI; 50/650 HonRl; HospAde; NHS; OffAde; TchrAde; RptrSchPpr; Business School; Business Trade.

GRIMSTAD, Gregory G; Stephen Decatur HS; Decatur, IL; 48/300 ChrhWkr; RedCrAde; StuCncl; StuGov; RptrSchPpr; Ftbl; LetterTrk; Il St Univ.

GRINBLATT, Arnold; Berkley HS; Oak Park, MI; ALBoysSt; JA; NHS; RptrYrbk; Yrbk; SciCl; JAAwd; Coll.

GRINDATTI, Catherine A; West Iron County HS; Stambaugh, MI; TrsSophCls; VPJrCls; VPSrCls; CmntyWkr; HonRl; StuCncl; RptrYrbk; RptrSchPpr; 4-H; FrCl; LetterTennis; Trk; GAA; IMSpt; College; Special Education.

GRINDEY, Betty J; Lanark HS; Lanark, IL; 7/60 Band; CncrtBnd; HonRl; NHS; FHA; LetterTrk; PresGAA; CitAwd; Western Il Univ; Physical Education.

GRINDLE, Elaine; Wabash HS; Wabash, IN; 36/210 HonRl; NHS; OffAde; YthFlsp; FTA; PpCl; Chrldr; College; Med Tech.

GRINOLDS, Kim G; Palermo HS; Palermo, ND; PresSrCls; Band; CmntyWkr; HonRl; SchPl; SctActv; StuCncl; YthFlsp; CaptBsktbl; LetterFtbl; Trade School; Vocation.

GRINSTEAD, Cody L; Davis County HS; Floris, IA; HonRl; NHS; OffAde; StuCncl; TchrAde; RptrSchPpr; 4-H; Glf; Trk; 4-HAwd; College; Social Work.

GRINT, Jerald E; Sargent Public HS; Sargent, NE; Band; Chrs; CncrtBnd; HonRl; Mdrgl; MrchBnd; NHS; FBLA; LetterBsktbl; LetterTrk;.

GRINVALDS, Arnolds; Yutan HS; Yutan, NE; 1/25 HonRl; NatlMeritFnl; RptrYrbk; EdSchPpr; 4-H; Ftbl; University Of Ne; Nuclear Physicist.

GRIPE, Cecilia; Macon County R I HS; Macon, MO; 28/117 Chrl; Chrs; DrlTm; HonRl; Mdrgl; OffAde; SchMus; SpnCl; PpCl;.

GRIPKA, Douglas A; Pierce City HS; Pierce City, MO; PresSophCls; Band; HonRl; PepBnd; StuCncl; KeyCl; SciCl; Bsktbl; Trk; College.

GRIPKA, Regina L; Aurora HS; Aurora, MO; SecChrhWkr; Pres4-H; SecFFA; PresFHA; 4-HAwd; College.

GRIPMAN, Lynn; Sacred Heart Of Mary HS; Arlington Hts, IL; ChrhWkr; HonRl; NHS; SchAde; StuGov; TchrAde;.

GRIPP, Steven C; New Trier West HS; Wilmette, IL; 142/694 Band; CncrtBnd; PepBnd; SchPpr; LatCl; LetterFtbl; LetterGlf; Univ Of Kansas; Business Admin.

GRISA, John A; Brookfield East HS; Brookfield, WI; CncrtBnd; HonRl; MrchBnd; RedCrAde; FDA; MthCl; Ftbl; Tennis; Trk; IMSpt; Uw Madison; Pre Med.

GRISE, Lauren L; N Nelson Snider HS; Fort Wayne, IN; 3/506 ChrhWkr; Quill&Scroll; EdSchPpr; SpnCl; ChmbCommrsAwd; Indiana Univ; Accounting.

GRISHAM, Deborah K; Morton HS; Morton, IL; Chr; Chrs; HonRl; Mdrgl; RptrYrbk; 4-H; College; Elem Teacher.

GRISHAM, Kimberly A; East HS; Wichita, KS; VPFrshCls; HonRl; PolWkr; SctActv; StuCncl; StuGov; RptrYrbk; RptrSchPpr; PpCl; MasAwd; Wichita St Univ; Business Admin.

GRISK, Mary; Central HS; Kenosha, WI; Band; DrmBgl; MrchBnd; NatlThespSoc; SchPl; 4-H; SpnCl; Swmmng; Tennis; Trk; College; Vocational.

GRISMER, Mary J; Burnsville Sr HS; Burnsville, MN; 40/613 HonRl; NHS; TchrAde; Yrbk; CaptSwmmng; IMSpt; Univ Of Wisconsin; Nursing.

GRISSETT, Mary L; Portage Central HS; Portage, MI; 2/330 Kalamazoo Valley Comm College; Teacher.

GRISSOM, Jane C; Shawnee Mission South HS; Overland Park, KS; 249/754 HonRl; SchAde; TchrAde; LetterTrk; Coll; Dentistry.

GRISSUM, Roberta A; Union HS; Union, MO; Band; CncrtBnd; HonRl; JA; MrchBnd; PepBnd; SchMus; TchrAde; Twrl; PPFtbl; East Central Jr Coll; Computer Science.

GRIST, Jennifer T; Blue Springs HS; Independence, MO; 106/293 AFS; Chrs; PolWkr; FTA; SpnCl; MthCl; SciCl; GAA; Univ Of Missouri; Engineering.

GRISWOLD, Barbara; Warsaw HS; Warsaw, IN; 38/380 Chrs; ChrhWkr; HonRl; HospAde; 4-H; FHA; Nursing.

GRISWOLD, David L; Greenfield Comm HS; Rockbridge, IL; Band; ChrhWkr; CmntyWkr; CncrtBnd; HonRl; MrchBnd; 4-H; FrCl; PpCl; LetterWrstlng; DanFAwd; 4-HAwd; Purdue Univ; Computer Science.

GRISWOLD, Jacqueline A; Tri Central HS; Windfall, IN; 1/88 VPSrCls; ALAGirlsSt; PresNHS; RedCrAde; EdYrBk; PresPpCl; HstSrCls; AmLegAwd; DARAwd; EldAwd; Indina U; Medicine.

GRISWOLD, Michael R; Wichita West HS; Wichita, KS; CtyCnl; HonRl; JA; ModUN; NHS; PolWkr; Univ Of Kansas; Engineer.

GRISWOLD, Pamela K; Carrollton HS; Carrollton, MO; SecTrsJrCls; Band; DrlTm; HonRl; HospAde; NHS; TchrAde; YthFlsp; FHA; College; Secretary.

GRISWOLD, Patti J; Benson HS; Omaha, NE; 1/410 ALAGirlsSt; DrlTm; HonRl; NHS; Quill&Scroll; RptrYrbk; SptEdSchPpr; MthCl; PpCl; GAA; IMSpt; Univ Of Nebraska; Maj In Computer Science.

GRISWOLD, Rodney L; Grand Haven Sr HS; Grand Haven, MI; 79/388 ChrhWkr; CmntyWkr; HonRl; SchMus; SctActv; StuCncl; PresYthFlsp; Swmmng; College; Medicine.

GRISWOLD, Stan R; Fremont HS; Fremont, MI; 8/260 Band; Chr; ChrhWkr; CncrtBnd; HonRl; MrchBnd; Orch; PepBnd; GerCl; Calvin Col; Engineering.

GRISWOLD, Stephen D; Tri Central HS; Windfall, IN; 5/112 ALBoysSt; HonRl; NHS; FrCl; LetterBsbl; LetterBsktbl; LetterFtbl; College; Engr.

GRISWOLD, Susan R; Davison HS; Davison, MI; Chrs; NatlMeritCmnd; 4-H; Bsktbl; Swmmng; CaptTrk; CchngActv; GAA; Grand Vally & Central Mi Univ; Phy Educ.

GRISWOLD, Victor D; Fairfield Comm HS; Fairfield, IL; 1/165 ALBoysSt; HonRl; LatCl; SciCl; LetterFtbl; AmLegAwd; Univ Of Illinois; Mathematics.

GRITHER, Janet L; Blue Mound HS; Blue Mound, IL; 2/40 TrsSophCls; PresJrCls; PresSrCls; SecAFS; SecNHS; SchPl; EdYrBk; Chrldr; GAA; Univ Of Illinois; Nurse.

GRITIS, Cynthia A; Morton West HS; Berwyn, IL; Chrs; HonRl; JrNHS; Chrldr; Coll; Acct.

GRITMAN, Beth J; Saline HS; Ann Arbor, MI; CncrtBnd; HonRl; HospAde; MrchBnd; RedCrAde; Yrbk; RptrSchPpr; FTA; PpCl; LetterTrk; College; Physical Therapy.

GRITTEN, Bruce E; Covington HS; Kingman, IN; CmntyWkr; SctActv; YthFlsp; Bsktbl; CaptTrk;.

GRITTI, Nick E; Mattoon Sr HS; Mattoon, IL; HonRl; YthFlsp; Bsbl; LetterFtbl; College; Medicine.

GRIZZLE, Jessy W; Jay HS; Southwest City, MO; 1/89 ALBoysSt; HonRl; NHS; SchPl; StuCncl; TchrAde; SchPpr; FFA; GovHonPrgAwd; MasAwd; Oklahoma State; Electrical Engineer.

GROAT, Marta J; Maconaquah HS; Peru, IN; 28/217 Chr; ChrhWkr; HonRl; MrchBnd; NHS; SchPl; Twrl; SpnCl; Glf; GAA; Vocational Tech; Accounting.

GROB, Shari M; Glenbard West HS; Glen Ellyn, IL; Chr; Chrs; HonRl; Quill&Scroll; RptrSchPpr; SchPpr; Indiana Univ; Undecided.

GROB, Sheila; University HS; Urbana, IL; HospAde; LitMag; Univ Of Ill; Nursing.

GROBER, Tisa K; Dondero HS; Royal Oak, MI; Chr; HonRl; NHS; NatlMeritSchl; OffAde; KiwanAwd; Wayne State U; Pre Medicine.

GROBLE, Thomas J; Quigley South HS; Chicago, IL; Chrs; SecCncrtBnd; HonRl; StuGov; LetterGlf; CaptSocr; LetterTennis; Univ Of Illinois; Accountant.

GROCE, Michele T; Dupo Comm HS; Dupo, IL; Chrs; HonRl; SchPl; StuCncl; Yrbk; FNA; SciCl; GAA; PPFtbl; Eastern Illinois Univ; Science.

GROCHOWSKY, Janet L; Carroll HS; Wichita, KS; ChrhWkr; CmntyWkr; HonRl; OffAde; Sdlty; TchrAde; PpCl; Bsbl; Bsktbl; LetterTennis; CchngActv; Wichita State Univ; Human Relations.

GRODE, Alice J; Bristol HS; Andover, SD; 3/30 Chr; Chrs; ChrhWkr; HonRl; LbryAde; Yrbk; VPFHA; PpCl; VoiceDemAwd; Work At 1st Natl Bank Bristol Sd.

GRODE, Susanne R; Bristol Independent HS; Bristol, SD; Chr; Chrs; HospAde; LbryAde; SctActv; RptrYrbk; FNA; PpCl; Bsktbl; Trk; Mc Connell Airline Sch; Airport Employee.

GRODI, Cathy S; Ida HS; Ida, MI; HonRl; SchPl; SchPpr; PpCl; GAA; IMSpt; Coll; Data Proc.

GRODIE, Jerry J; Meramec Valley R Iii HS; Pacific, MO; 9/200 Chr; ChrhWkr; HonRl; Mdrgl; SctActv; VPYthFlsp; 4-H; PpCl; SciCl; LetterBsktbl; LetterFtbl; Trk; College; Liberal Arts.

GRODZICKI, John A; Edsel Ford HS; Dearborn, MI; NatlMeritSchl; GerCl; LetterTrk; Hillsdale Coll; Engr Or Med.

GROEBER, Jean; Plankinton Independent HS; Plankinton, SD; 27#41#54 SchPl; StuCncl; Yrbk; FHA; Bsktbl; DARAwd; VoiceDemAwd; U Of South Dakota; Music Education.

GROEBER, Jean L; Plankinton Independent HS; Plankinton, SD; 3/22 ALAGirlsSt; Band; Chrs; SecNHS; SchPl; VPStuCncl; Yrbk; FHA; CaptBsktbl; DARAwd; VoiceDemAwd; Univ Of South Dakota; Music.

GROEN, Curt F; Hubbard Community HS; Hubbard, IA; ALBoysSt; Chr; Chrl; Chrs; SchMus; SchPl; YthFlsp; Yrbk; Iowa State Univ; Wildlife Biology.

GROEN, Kathy A; Polo Comm HS; Polo, IL; 35/92 Aud/Vis; ChrhWkr; HonRl; LbryAde; OffAde; SchPl; YthFlsp; RptrYrbk; FHA; College; Library Tech.

GROENE, Gregory A; Streator Twp HS; Streator, IL; ChrhWkr; HonRl; StuCncl; FFA; Bsbl; Ftbl; University; Professional.

GROENENDYK, Bruce; Pella Christian HS; Leighton, IA; Chr; Chrs; ChrhWkr; HonRl; SchMus; SciCl; IMSpt; Trade Sch; Vocation.

GROENENDYK, Kathy L; Oskaloosa Sr HS; Oskaloosa, IA; Chr; CncrtBnd; DrlTm; MrchBnd; NHS; NatlThespSoc; StuCncl; PresYthFlsp; TreasPpCl; Trk; IMSpt; PPFtbl; Central College; Vocation.

GROENENDYK, Sharon A; Pella Community HS; Pella, IA; 11/126 AFS; ChrhWkr; DrlTm; HonRl; NHS; NatlThespSoc; SchMus; SchPl; StuCncl; PpCl; Central College; Christian Education.

GROENEVELD, Lorri J; Oshkosh West HS; Oshkosh, WI; 140/405 Band; Chr; ChrhWkr; CncrtBnd; DrmBgl; HonRl; SchMus; SchPl; RptrYrbk; PpCl; GAA; College; Liberal Arts.

GROENEWEG, Gail J; Albert Lea Senior HS; Clarks Grove, MN; ChrhWkr; HonRl; 4-H; Dordt College.

GROENEWEG, Sharla F; Rock Valley Community HS; Rock Valley, IA; 9/62 HonRl; Yrbk; RptrSchPpr; FHA;.

GROENEWOLD, Gary; Timothy Christian HS; Westcheseter, IL; 8/90 ChrhWkr; NHS; SchPl; RptrYrbk; EdSchPpr; SptEdSchPpr; LetterBsktbl; CaptWrstlng; Calvin Coll; History.

GROENKE, Dale R; Union HS; Beaufort, MO; HonRl; LetterFtbl; Trk; College.

GROENKE, Karen A; Union HS; Beaufort, MO; 23/167 TrsFrshCls; Chrs; ChrhWkr; HonRl; JA; OffAde; 4-H; FHA; PPFtbl; East Central Jr Clg; Executive Sec.

GROEPPER, Peter S; Evanston Township HS; Evanston, IL; Band; CncrtBnd; HonRl; MrchBnd; NatlMeritCmnd; Orch; PepBnd; SchMus; RptrSchPpr; SchPpr; Harvard Univ; Journalism.

GROESBECK, Rolf A; Ann Arbor Pioneer HS; Ann Arbor, MI; 11/620 Chr; HonRl; LitMag; MrchBnd; Orch; PolWkr; SchMus; RusCl; MthCl; IMSpt; Oberlm Coll; Music.

GROFF, Kimberlee K; Grand Comm HS; Boxholm, IA; 6/23 SecFrshCls; SecSophCls; SecTrsJrCls; SecSrCls; HonRl; SptEdYrbk; SciCl; LetterBsktbl; LetterTrk; LetterChrldr; U Of Arkansas; Biological Science.

GROFF, Kimberlee K; Grand Community HS; Boxholm, IA; 8/23 SecTrsFrshCls; SecJrCls; SecSrCls; Band; Chrs; CncrtBnd; MrchBnd; PepBnd; SchMus; SchPl; Twrl; SptEdYrbk; SchPpr; EngCl; Univ Of Arkansas; Biology.

GROGAN, Debra L; Pardeeville HS; Pardeeville, WI; TrsFrshCls; SecJrCls; Band; Chrs; ChrhWkr; CmntyWkr; NatlFornLg; PepBnd; SchPl; Chrldr; Brigham Young Univ; Theatre.

GROGAN, Kay C; Billings HS; Springfield, MO; VPJrCls; TrsSrCls; HonRl; SchPl; RptrYrbk; FFA; FHA; PpCl; IMSpt; PresAwd; Smsu.

GROGAN, Laurie J; Ogorman HS; Sioux Falls, SD; Chrs; PolWkr; SchMus; TchrAde; Chrldr; IMSpt; College; Elementary Education.

GROGAN, Sherry L; Summersville HS; Summersville, MO; PresJrCls; SecSrCls; Chrs; ChrhWkr; CtyCnl; CmntyWkr; StuCncl; 4-H; FHA; PpCl; Receptionist.

GROH, Frank J; Appleton West HS; Appleton, WI; SptEdSchPpr; LetterTrk; IMSpt; College; Professional.

GROH, Karen J; New Holstein HS; New Holstein, WI; 18/196 Chrs; HonRl; NatlFornLg; NHS; PolWkr; SchPl; GAA; Fox Valley Tech Appleton; Occupational Ther.

GROHLER, Kent B; Sullivan HS; Sullivan, IL; ChrhWkr; NatlMeritSchl; StuCncl; StuGov; YthFlsp; 4-H; FTA; SciCl; LetterBsktbl; LetterFtbl; Glf; IMSpt; 4-HAwd; Danville Jr College; Landscaping.

GROHS, Jeffrey M; Pinckney HS; Pinckney, MI; Band; Chr; ChrhWkr; CncrtBnd; HonRl; MrchBnd; Orch; PepBnd; Sacred Heart Seminary; Priest.

GROHS, Natalie L; Scotus Central Catholic HS; Columbus, NE; 2/60 VPSophCls; Chrs; HonRl; NHS; NatlMeritCmnd; StuCncl; TchrAde; RptrYrbk; PresPpCl; EldAwd; Mt Marty Coll ; Nurse Aresthetist.

GROLEAU, Daniel G; Catholic Central HS; Marinette, WI; 24/90 Band; ChrhWkr; CncrtBnd; DrmBgl; HonRl; PepBnd; 4-H; PpCl; Bsktbl; Ftbl; Coll; Med Tech.

GROLMUS, Michael D; Williamsburg Comm HS; Williamsburg, IA; HonRl; JrNHS; NHS; LetterBsbl; LetterBsktbl; Ftbl; LetterGlf; U Of Ia; Business.

GROM, Rodney L; Peshtigo HS; Peshtigo, WI; 17/78 HonRl; TchrAde; LetterBsktbl; LetterFtbl; Trk; U W Marinette; Architectural Field.

GROMALA, Edward; Antioch Comm HS; Antioch, IL; 17/321 HonRl; NHS; StuCncl; StuGov; Trk; College; Engineering Degree.

GROMKE, George D; Niles West HS; Morton Grove, IL; 87/666 HonRl; LbryAde; University Of Champaign; Liberal Arts.

GRONBACH, Steven; Luverne Community HS; Luverne, IA; VPSrCls; ChrhWkr; CmntyWkr; HonRl; SctActv; YthFlsp; Bsbl; Bsktbl; IMSpt;.

GRONBACH, Vicki; Lu Verne Community HS; Luverne, IA; PresJrCls; Band; Chrs; CmntyWkr; HonRl; PepBnd; SchPl; RptrYrbk; Bsktbl; Trk; Guena Vista College;sociology.

GRONDAHL, Karen; Granville HS; Granville, ND; 3/16 Chrs; DrlTm; HonRl; SchPl; TchrAde; Yrbk; EdSchPpr; TreasPpCl; GAA; DARAwd; Minot Bus Coll; Bus Admin.

GRONECK, Timothy; Chaminade HS; St Louis, MO; ChrhWkr; HonRl; LitMag; LbryAde; SchPl; SchPpr; SpnCl; Bsbl; St Louis Univ; Accounting.

GRONEMEYER, Robert J; Paxton HS; Paxton, IL; 6/140 Univ Of Illinois; Architecture.

GRONENTHAL, Donald G; Lindsay Holy Family HS; Lindsay, NE; ChrhWkr; CmntyWkr; HonRl; SchPl; 4-H; LetterBsktbl; LetterFtbl; 4-HAwd; JAAwd; Trade School.

GRONER, Judy P; Highland Park HS; Highland Park, IL; HospAde; JrNHS; NHS; NatlMeritCmnd; SecStuGov; Swmmng; GAA; Branders Univ; Hebrew Education.

GRONER, Sarah; Ida Crown Jewish Acad; Chicago, IL; VPSophCls; Band; HonRl; NHS; NatlMeritSF; StuCncl; Yrbk; SchPpr; Clg; Math.

GRONERT, Jill; Alburnett Community Hs; Marion, IA; 4/40 VPFrshCls; Chr; Chrs; SchMus; RptrSchPpr; SchPpr; FTA; LetterBsbl; LetterBsktbl;.

GRONEWOLD, Carmer; Buckley Loda Hs; Buckley, IL; VPJrCls; Chr; Chrs; HonRl; NHS; VPFHA; TreasMthCl; VPPpCl; Bsbl; Bsktbl; St Paul Concordia; Special Ed.

GRONEWOLD, Nancy L; Unity HS; Quincy, IL; 39/78 Chrs; HospAde; LbryAde; MrchBnd; PepBnd; SchMus; SchPl; TchrAde; PpCl; Black Hawk College; Respiratory Therapist.

GRONINGER, Kim V; Norfolk Senior HS; Norfolk, NE; Chrs; DrlTm; HonRl; SchPl; TchrAde; PpCl; Chrldr; College; Psychiatric Technician.

GROOM, Justin M; Usd 463 HS; Rock, KS; VPSophCls; PresJrCls; HonRl; StuCncl; FFA; Bsktbl; Cowley County Comm Clge; Farmer.

GROOM, Sandy L; West Sioux HS; Ireton, IA; Chrs; HonRl; SchMus; SchPl; StuCncl; RptrYrbk; 4-H; PpCl; Trk; LetterChrldr; IMSpt; 4-HAwd; South Dakota State University.

GROOMS, Tanya K; Wapello Comm HS; Oakville, IA; PresJrCls; ALAGirlsSt; Chrs; HonRl; NatlThespSoc; SchMus; SchPl; StuCncl; FHA; College; Art.

GROOTHUIS, Lisa M; Granite City N HS; Granite City, IL; Band; Chr; Chrs; ChrhWkr; CncrtBnd; HonRl; MrchBnd; NatlFornLg; NHS; NatlMeritSF; OffAde; Washington Univ; Engineering.

GROOVER, Kent; Dexfield Comm HS; Redfield, IA; 5/40 TrsSophCls; Band; Chrs; HonRl; JrNHS; SchPl; YthFlsp; FFA; Ftbl; Univ; Mus.

GROSE, Larry; Bern HS; Bern, KS; HonRl; JA; LitMag; NatlMeritCmnd; NatlMeritSchl; PolWkr; SchPl; StuGov; Teen; YthFlsp; Bsbl; Bsktbl; Ftbl; College; Business.

GROSE, Randy; Indian Creek HS; Trafalgar, IN; 14/115 CncrtBnd; HonRl; MrchBnd; NHS; PepBnd; 4-H; FFA; Bsktbl; Univ; Engineering.

GROSHAN, Edward H; J A Craig HS; Janesville, WI; 2/474 CncrtBnd; HonRl; NHS; NatlMeritCmnd; Quill&Scroll; Yrbk; RptrSchPpr; Univ Wi; Pre Med.

GROSHANS, Michael J; Marquette HS; Godfrey, IL; 7/143 ChrhWkr; HonRl; RptrSchPpr; SchPpr; Wrstlng; IMSpt; University; Physics Research.

GROSKOPP, Kristine A; Pacelli HS; Stevens Point, WI; ChrhWkr; NatlMeritSF; StuCncl; StuGov; FrCl; PpCl; LetterTennis; GAA; IMSpt; PPFtbl; College; Pre Med.

GROSS, Charlene M; St Marys Central HS; Bismarck, ND; ALAGirlsSt; Chr; ChrhWkr; HonRl; OffAde; PolWkr; College; Legal Secretary.

GROSS, Cindy D; Hays HS; Hays, KS; Chr; Chrs; HonRl; TchrAde;.

GROSS, Deborah K; Ladywood HS; Livonia, MI; Band; CncrtBnd; HonRl; NHS; FNA; SpnCl; Mich State U; Nursing.

GROSS, Donna; Union County HS; Liberty, IN; HonRl; 4-H; SpnCl; 4-HAwd; Arm Services; Secretary.

GROSS, Gerry L; New Lothrop HS; New Lothrop, MI; 11/80 VPSophCls; HonRl; LbryAde; NHS; SchPl; TchrAde; Twrl; SpnCl; Trk; CaptChrldr; College.

GROSSE, Kathleen; Marian HS; Hays, KS; 3/61 HonRl; LbryAde; ModUN; SchMus; StuCncl; PpCl; Trk; GAA; Ft Hays St Coll; Commercial Art.

GROSS, Margaret B; Marian HS; Omaha, NE; VPSophCls; VPJrCls; VPSrCls; HonRl; Quill&Scroll; VPStuCncl; TchrAde; Yrbk; Bsbl; Bsktbl; Glf; LetterTennis; CaptIMSpt; College; Liberal Arts.

GROSS, Marti E; Elmhurst HS; Ft Wayne, IN; 22/381 AFS; Chr; CmntyWkr; HonRl; JA; LbryAde; NHS; PolWkr; RptrSchPpr; TreasPpCl; Univ; Chemical Engineer.

GROSS, Mary E; Peotone HS; Monee, IL; 1/102 ChrhWkr; HonRl; NHS; Quill&Scroll; EdSchPpr; SpnCl; MthCl; SciCl; LetterBsktbl; LetterGlf; GAA; 4-HAwd; Drake Col; Pharmacy.

GROSS, Patty L; Alma HS; Alma, WI; 4/39 VPFrshCls; VPJrCls; TrsSrCls; ALAGirlsSt; Chrs; ChrhWkr; HonRl; NatlFornLg; NHS; SchMus; EdYrBk; Univ Of Wisc; Special Ed.

GROSS, Rachel D; Columbus HS; Columbus, WI; 10/130 SecJrCls; SecSrCls; HonRl; NHS; StuCncl; FHA; AmLegAwd; DARAwd; GovHonPrgAwd; KiwanAwd; Uw Oshkosh; Guidance Counselor.

GROSS, Randy L; Sioux Valley HS; Volga, SD; 19/67 TrsSophCls; TrsJrCls; ChrhWkr; HonRl; MrchBnd; StuGov; SptEdSchPpr; Bsktbl; Ftbl; Trk; Dordt College; Electronical Engineer.

GROSS, Sally A; Jefferson Sr HS; Jefferson, WI; 2/170 Band; Chr; Chrs; CncrtBnd; HonRl; MrchBnd; SchPl; FFA; IMSpt; PPFtbl; Tech School; Zoology.

GROSS, Sally J; Libertyville HS; Libertyville, IL; 30/431 Orch; Univ; Music.

GROSS, Stacey L; Marian HS; Hays, KS; CmntyWkr; HonRl; StuCncl; LatCl; College; Nursing.

GROSSE, Randy; Middleton HS; Middleton, WI; 64/291 HonRl; Yrbk; SchPpr; Trk; Photography College; Professional Photograp.

GROSSE, Timothy G; Octavia HS; Anchor, IL; 17/46 HonRl; SchPl; SctActv; MthCl; SciCl; Col; Marketing Agent.

GROSSENBURG, Jolenne K; Winner Sr HS; Winner, SD; 12/140 Band; DrlTm; HonRl; MrchBnd; PpCl; LetterTrk; Chrldr; IMSpt; College; Medical Lab Technician.

GROSSKOPF, Jay; Bowler Hs; Bowler, WI; VPFrshCls; HonRl; StuCncl; SptEdSchPpr; 4-H; FFA; Bsbl; Bsktbl; Ftbl; College; Contractor.

GROSSMAN, Elaine M; Ohio Comm HS; Ohio, IL; 2/24 VPFrshCls; VPSophCls; PresBand; Chrs; ChrhWkr; VPNHS; OffAde; PepBnd; SchMus; SchPl; SecStuCncl; CaptChrldr; PresSciCl; GAA; College; Recreation.

GROSSMAN, Jeanne L; Horton Watkins HS; Creve Coeur, MO; AFS; StuGov; FHA; RusCl; Univ Of Mo; Psychology Or Law.

GROSSMAN, Randall W; Northfield HS; Urbana, IN; 34/111 Band; StuCncl; TchrAde; YthFlsp; 4-H; FFA; CaptFtbl; Trk; CaptWrstlng; IMSpt; Farmer.

GROSULAK, Patrick J; Belfield HS; Belfield, ND; 4/62 PresSophCls; CncrtBnd; HonRl; MrchBnd; ModUN; NHS; Sacrstn; StuCncl; LetterBsktbl; LetterFtbl; Trade Sch; Wildlife Mgr.

GROSVENOR, Susan K; Lansing Harry Hill HS; Lansing, MI; 1/315 JrNHS; NHS; PresSctActv; StuGov; YthFlsp; LetterBsktbl; LetterTennis; IMSpt; JAAwd; Mich Tech Univ; Chem Engr.

GROSZ, Chris G; Breckenridge HS; Breckenridge, MN; CmntyWkr; HonRl; Col; Curriculum Of Major Study.

GROTE, Mark D; De Soto HS; Shawnee, KS; Band; Chr; CncrtBnd; MrchBnd; PepBnd; SchPl; 4-H; Bsktbl; Ftbl; Kansas Univ; Law.

GROTELUESCHEN, Karmen L; Oalces Public HS; Ludden, ND; 3/80 HonRl; 4-H; GAA; 4-HAwd; College.

GROTENHUIS, Kim M; Zeeland HS; Zeeland, MI; Band; HonRl; MrchBnd; PepBnd; TchrAde; LetterFtbl; Trade Sch; Elec.

GROTENHUIS, Laura M; Marshall HS; Marshall, IL; 14/126 Band; NHS; NatlThespSoc; YthFlsp; Pres4-H; PresFHA; LatCl; Trk; GAA; 4-HAwd; Iowa State; Veterinary.

GROTEWOLD, Brad E; Lake Mills Community HS; Lake Mills, IA; ALBoysSt; Chr; Chrs; ChrhWkr; HonRl; LetterBsktbl; LetterFtbl; LetterGlf; Trk; IMSpt; University.

GROTH, Julie A; Postville Community HS; Postville, IA; Chr; Chrs; HonRl; RptrYrbk; Yrbk; PpCl; LetterChrldr; GAA; IMSpt; PPFtbl; Amer Inst Of Bus ;secretary.

GROTH, Kristi L; Enderlin Public HS; Enderlin, ND; 1/44 SecTrsSophCls; AFS; ALAGirlsSt; SecCncrtBnd; HonRl; MrchBnd; SecStuCncl; TreasFHA; Chrldr; BttyCrckrAwd; Univ Nd; Teach Visually Handicapped.

GROTH, Stephen M; Marquette HS; Shorewood, WI; HonRl; StuCncl; YthFlsp; SpnCl; LetterBsbl; IMSpt; George Washington University; Accountant.

GROTHAUS, Ann E; Kingsley Pierson HS; Kingsley, IA; 5/64 Chr; Chrs; HonRl; SecNHS; SchMus; RptrYrbk; VPFTA; MthCl; PpCl; LetterGlf; College; Home Economics.

GROTHE, Jean M; St Piux X HS; Arnold, MO; 9/115 HonRl; NHS; StuCncl; IMSpt; College; Law.

GROTHEN, Brenda S; Mendota HS; Mendota, IL; 25/187 ChrhWkr; CmntyWkr; HonRl; HospAde; LatCl; SciCl; Trk; Northern Il Univ; Special Ed Teacher.

GROTHEN, Thelma M; Moille Community HS; Lamoille, IL; 1/45 VPFrshCls; CncrtBnd; HonRl; MrchBnd; SecNHS; Yrbk; RptrSchPpr; 4-H; FrCl; College; Life Science.

GROTJAN, Lori D; Brunswick Rii HS; Brunswick, MO; 5/50 DrmMjrt; HonRl; NHS; OffAde; Twrl; RptrSchPpr; FHA; Trk; CaptChrldr; IMSpt; Clg Or Business School; Computer Programing.

GROTJOHN, Carolee M; Schaller Comm HS; Schaller, IA; 3/34 Chr; Chrs; ChrhWkr; CmntyWkr; CncrtBnd; HonRl; Mdrgl; SchPl; StuCncl; 4-H; Chrldr; College; Vocation.

GROTJOHN, Shirley R; Schaller Comm HS; Schaller, IA; Band; Chrs; CncrtBnd; HonRl; MrchBnd; PepBnd; YthFlsp; EdYrBk; RptrSchPpr; 4-H; Bsktbl; LetterTrk; DanFAwd; 4-HAwd; Business School; Secretarial.

GROTRIAN, Kimberly A; Northridge HS; Goshen, IN; 6/117 HonRl; LbryAde; OffAde; YthFlsp; SchPpr; FHA; College.

GROTT, Deborah K; Chester HS; Chester, IL; 13/120 Chrs; HonRl; HospAde; OffAde; RptrYrbk; Yrbk; PpCl; CaptChrldr; GAA;.

GROTZINGER, John E; Pilot Grove HS; Pilot Grove, MO; 1/37 SecFrshCls; PresSophCls; ALBoysSt; Chrs; HonRl; SchPl; FFA; LetterBsbl; LetterBsktbl; LetterTrk; Univ Of Missouri; Electrical Engineering.

GROVE, Cheryl; Bethany HS; Bethany, IL; CncrtBnd; HonRl; PepBnd; SchMus; SctActv; YthFlsp; FHA; 4-HAwd;.

GROVE, Jean; Harding HS; St Paul, MN; 15/725 HonRl; HospAde; NHS; TchrAde; SpnCl; Chrldr; GAA; Augustana Coll; Nursing.

GROVE, Jeffrey A; Fenton Senior HS; Fenton, MI; PresFrshCls; VPJrCls; ALBoysSt; Aud/Vis; HonRl; NHS; StuCncl; FTA; LatCl; Bsktbl; Ftbl; College.

GROVE, Kevin A; Lew Wallace HS; Gary, IN; 17/519 HonRl; JA; JrNHS; Indiana Univ; Medicine.

GROVE, Mary E; Grand Ledge HS; Grand Ledge, MI; 2/400 SecBand; HonRl; MrchBnd; NHS; PepBnd; SchMus; StuCncl; TchrAde; LatCl; LetterTennis; Mich St Univ; Music.

GROVE, Meg; Shanley HS; Fargo, ND; 18/122 CmntyWkr; HospAde; NHS; SchMus; SchPl; StuCncl; StuGov; RptrYrbk; RptrSchPpr; Univ; Advertising.

GROVE, Willard L; Prospect HS; Britt, IA; 9/67 ALBoysSt; CncrtBnd; HonRl; SchPl; StuCncl; Yrbk; SchPpr; 4-H; Wrstlng; 4-HAwd; College; Law.

GROVE, Yolanda; Moulton Udell HS; Unionville, IA; Band; Chr; DrmMjrt; HonRl; SchMus; YthFlsp; 4-H; Bsktbl; Trk; 4-HAwd; Macpherson Col; Trainer Of Animals.

GROVENBURG, Douglas A; Milbank HS; Milbank, SD; ALBoysSt; Band; ChrhWkr; CAP; CncrtBnd; HonRl; MrchBnd; NHS; Orch; PepBnd; TchrAde; KeyCl; LetterFtbl; LetterTennis; College.

GROVER, Joan; Rushford Public HS; Rushford, MN; VPFrshCls; SecSophCls; Chrs; DrlTm; HonRl; JrNHS; LbryAde; SchPpr; FHA; FTA; Coll; Bio.

GROVER, Marsha I; Gordon HS; Gordon, NE; 14/67 Band; Chr; CncrtBnd; HospAde; MrchBnd; SchPl; TchrAde; YthFlsp; 4-H; College; Professional.

GROVER, Timothy G; Independence HS; Rowley, IA; ChrhWkr; HonRl; LitMag; StuCncl; YthFlsp; Yrbk; RptrSchPpr; LetterFtbl; Iowa Central Comm College; Broadcasting.

GROVES, Jada A; Southern Boone County R I HS; Hartsburg, MO; Chrs; HonRl; SchPl; YthFlsp; Yrbk; SchPpr; 4-H; FHA; PpCl; College.

GROVIJOHN, Theresa M; Dodge Public HS; Dodge, NE; Band; Chrs; CncrtBnd; HonRl; ModUN; PepBnd; SchPl; SchPpr; PpCl; Lincoln Sch Of Commerce; Secretary.

GROW, Lewis E; Washington Catholic HS; Washington, IN; 1/40 PresSophCls; ALBoysSt; HonRl; NHS; Yrbk; KeyCl; LatCl; PpCl; Bsktbl; Rose Hulman Inst Of Tech; Engineer.

GRUBAUGH, Rick C; David City Aquinas HS; Rising City, NE; 20/100 ALBoysSt; HonRl; NHS; NatlMeritFnl; SchMus; SchPl; PresStuCncl; StuGov; LetterBsktbl; LetterFtbl; University Of Nebraska; Medicine.

GRUBB, Brent A; Washington Comm HS; Washington, IL; AFS; Band; CncrtBnd; HonRl; JrNHS; MrchBnd; NHS; PepBnd; FrCl; Univ Of Illinois; Architecture.

GRUBB, Brian T; Homer HS; Homer, IL; TrsFrshCls; VPSophCls; Chrs; LbryAde; NatlMeritSF; SchMus; StuCncl; StuGov; Yrbk; PpCl; Swmmng; College; Psychology.

GRUBB, Cathleen S; St Elizabeth Academy; St Louis, MO; 5/110 SecFrshCls; HonRl; NHS; Orch; SchMus; StuCncl; LatCl; CaptBsktbl; GAA; IMSpt; Washington U; Science.

GRUBB, Colin M; Rockridge HS; Andalusia, IL; HonRl; Yrbk; Glf; Wrstlng; Col; Pro.

GRUBB, Debra K; Mcgregor HS; Mc Gregor, MN; 1/57 Band; Chr; HonRl; JrNHS; NHS; NatlMeritSF; SchPl; 4-H; KeyCl; 4-HAwd; Carleton Coll; Psych.

GRUBB, Ellen W; Prospect HS; Arlington Hts, IL; ChrhWkr; HonRl; SchMus; College; Home Economics.

GRUBB, Pamela A; Western Comm Unit HS; Buda, IL; Band; Chrs; HonRl; SchPl; 4-H; FHA; PpCl; GAA; Coll; Fashion Retailing.

GRUBB, Stanton E; Powers Lake HS; Powers Lake, ND; ALBoysSt; ChrhWkr; DrlTm; MrchBnd; SchPl; SctActv; RptrSchPpr; LetterBsktbl; LetterFtbl; LetterTrk; Natl Clg Of Bus Rapid City; Ranch Manager.

GRUBB, Thomas R; El Paso HS; El Paso, IL; AFS; Band; ChrhWkr; CncrtBnd; LbryAde; MrchBnd; SchPl; YthFlsp; SchPpr; SpnCl; Col; Mucis Education.

GRUBBS, Joyce L; East Central HS; Lawrenceburg, IN; Band; CncrtBnd; HonRl; NatlMeritCmnd; TchrAde; 4-H; SpnCl; PpCl; SciCl; Bsbl; Purdue U; Medical Tech.

GRUBBS, Karla J; Wes Del HS; Muncie, IN; 2/110 SecBand; CncrtBnd; MrchBnd; NHS; PepBnd; TchrAde; FTA; VPGerCl; PresSciCl; Univ Of Evansville; Nursing.

GRUBE, Doug M; Auburndale HS; Auburndale, WI; 4/100 TrsSophCls; VPJrCls; ALBoysSt; ChrhWkr; HonRl; NHS; SchPl; RptrSchPpr; FBLA; Bsbl; LetterBsktbl; Ftbl; College; Professional.

GRUBER, Anthony; Lincoln HS; Manitowoc, WI; CmntyWkr; SptEdYrbk; RptrSchPpr; Bsktbl; Ftbl; Coll; Soc Serv.

GRUBER, John J; Assumption HS; Wis Rapids, WI; 19/117 HonRl; Bsktbl; Trk; Uw Madison; Phd Physics.

GRUBER, John W; Monroe HS; Monroe, MI; 1/530 ChrhWkr; HonRl; NHS; StuCncl; GerCl; Bsktbl; Univ Michigan; Accounting.

GRUBER, Michael T; Cass City HS; Cass City, MI; PresSrCls; CmntyWkr; NatlSciFnd; PolWkr; ROTC; YthFnd; EdYrBk; FBLA; FSA; PresAwd; Armed Services; Railroad.

GRUBER, Pamela S; Marshall HS; Marshall, MI; Chr; ChrhWkr; HonRl; NHS; SchPl; Western Mich U; Education.

GRUBER, Ramona J; Sabetha HS; Morrill, KS; 1/72 Band; CncrtBnd; HonRl; JrNHS; MrchBnd; PepBnd; EdYrBk; Bsbl;.

GRUBER, Rosalie A; St Josephs Acad; Green Bay, WI; Chrs; LbryAde; SpnCl; Voc Schl;.

GRUBER, Scott F; Lake Benton Public HS; Lake Benton, MN; 1/36 Chr; Chrs; HonRl; NHS; SchPl; Ftbl; College; Professional.

GRUBER, Susan A; Healy HS; Genola, MN; Band; HonRl; MrchBnd; PepBnd; RptrYrbk; 4-H; CaptTrk; GAA; 4-HAwd; JAAwd; College; Major Study.

GRUDZIEN, Robert A; Notre Dame HS; Chicago, IL; Band; CAP; HonRl; PolWkr; SchPl; StuGov; Trk; De Paul Univ; Accounting.

GRUDZINSKI, Debby A; Loup City HS; Loup City, NE; 8/70 Chrs; HonRl; NHS; SchMus; TchrAde; PpCl; Chrldr; Hastings College; Biology Major.

GRUDZINSKI, Timothy L; Aurora Sr HS; Phillips, NE; Aud/Vis; ChrhWkr; CmntyWkr; LbryAde; SchAde; SchPl; SctActv; YthFlsp; SptEdYrbk; SptEdSchPpr; CaptBsbl; Trk; IMSpt; Trade School; Professional.

GRUEBMEYER, Lisa A; Richwoods HS; Peoria, IL; 91/411 Chr; Chrs; CmntyWkr; HonRl; LbryAde; NHS; SchPl; SctActv; YthFlsp; Univ Of Iowa; Nurse.

GRUEN, Harold A; Wi Heights HS; Black Earth, WI; 7/110 CncrtBnd; HonRl; MrchBnd; NHS; PepBnd; SchMus; StuCncl; EdSchPpr; LetterTrk; LetterWrstlng; Nw Madisn ;engineer.

GRUEN, Michele; Turner HS; Kansas City, KS; 7/288 Chr; ChrhWkr; HospAde; NHS; PolWkr; SchMus; SciCl;.

GRUENEICH, Kathy L; Turtle Lake Mercer HS; Turtle Lake, ND; 5/30 SecSrCls; ALAGirlsSt; HonRl; HospAde; SecTrsFrshCls; VPYthFlsp; Pres4-H; FFA; LetterBsktbl; 4-HAwd; Coll; Teach.

GRUENENFELDER, Glenda M; Southeast HS; Springfield, IL; 33/464 VPSophCls; AFS; HospAde; SecStuCncl; YthFlsp; EdYrBk; GAA; BttyCrckrAwd; College; Journalism.

GRUENLOH, Mary A; R 1 North Callaway HS; Williamsburg, MO; HonRl; LbryAde; TchrAde; SpnCl; Business School; Vocation.

GRUENSTERN, Cheryl; Marion HS; Marion, WI; Chr; Chrs; NatlFornLg; OffAde; TchrAde; Yrbk; SchPpr; Chrldr; Vocational.

GRUGEL, Cynthia L; Waukesha South HS; Waukesha, WI; ALAGirlsSt; CaptDrlTm; HonRl; NHS; PpCl; GAA; Univ Of Wisconsin; Interior Design.

GRUHLKE, Richard E; Hillcrest HS; Markham, IL; HonRl; SctActv; MthCl; Valparaiso Univ; Electrical Engineering.

GRUIS, Bradford D; Meservey Thornton HS; Thornton, IA; PresSophCls; TrsJrCls; SchPl; LetterBsktbl; CaptFtbl; CaptTrk; BauchLmbAwd; DanFAwd; Central College; Physics.

GRULKE, Darlyn K; Ballard Community HS; Kelley, IA; Chrs; CncrtBnd; HonRl; MrchBnd; NatlThespSoc; PepBnd; SchMus; SchPl; EdYrBk; FrCl; Grandview Coll; Nursing.

GRULKE, David H; Corunna HS; Owosso, MI; ChrhWkr; HonRl; 4-H; MthCl; Bsbl; Bsktbl; LetterWrstlng; PresAwd; Trade School; Professional.

GRUMISH, Nancy J; Bishop Mc Namara HS; Kankakee, IL; 13/162 HonRl; NHS; NatlThespSoc; SchMus; SchPl; TchrAde; SecFrCl; SpnCl; PPFtbl; AmLegAwd; University Of Illinois; Linguist.

GRUNDEN, David W; Reading HS; Reading, MI; HonRl; LetterBsktbl; CaptFtbl; CaptIMSpt; Jackson Comm Clg; Dentist.

GRUNDER, Ann E; Fennimore HS; Fennimore, WI; Chrs; ChrhWkr; HonRl; OffAde; 4-H; Trk; GAA; College; Phy Ed Teacher.

GRUNDER, Richard W; Wilton HS; Wilton, IA; ALBoysSt; HonRl; NHS; StuCncl; Yrbk; SchPpr; LetterBsbl; Bsktbl; LetterFtbl; LetterTrk; Iowa State; Architecture.

GRUNDHAUSER, Deborah A; Lefor Public HS; Lefor, ND; 1/7 PresSophCls; Chrs; HonRl; LbryAde; NHS; SchPl; StuCncl; Yrbk; EdSchPpr; LetterBsktbl; Trk; Chrldr; GAA; Mary College; Accounting.

GRUNDHOEFER, Thomas L; Northfield Sr HS; Northfield, MN; 30/250 HonRl; NHS; Bsbl; Bsktbl; Ftbl; College; Law.

GRUNDMAN, Richard R; Nemaha Valley HS; Talmage, NE; 3/33 Band; CncrtBnd; HonRl; MrchBnd; NHS; YthFlsp; MthCl; Bsktbl; LetterFtbl; LetterTrk; Trade School; Draftsman.

GRUNDMEIER, Scott M; Kelliher HS; Kelliher, MN; 2/37 CmntyWkr; CncrtBnd; HonRl; MrchBnd; SchPl; SciCl; CaptBsktbl; LetterFtbl; Trk; IMSpt; CitAwd; Us Naval Academy; Ocean Engineering.

GRUNDY, Allison; Lakeland Union HS; Minocqua, WI; 10/182 Band; ChrhWkr; CmntyWkr; CncrtBnd; HonRl; NHS; SchMus; TchrAde; FTA; AmLegAwd; Univ Of Wis Eua Claire; Music Therapy.

GRUNEICH, Kevin R; Montezuma Comm HS; Montezuma, IA; 3/43 ChrhWkr; HonRl; NHS; YthFlsp; RptrYrbk; RptrSchPpr; MthCl; SciCl; LetterBsktbl; LetterTrk; College; Law Banking & Finance.

GRUNEICH, Sandra; Graceville HS; Dumont, MN; Band; HonRl; MrchBnd; NHS; YthFlsp; Yrbk; SptEdSchPpr; FrCl; GAA; Brown Inst; Broadcasting.

GRUNER, Colleen M; Coldwater HS; Coldwater, MI; 24/270 Band; ChrhWkr; CncrtBnd; HonRl; LbryAde; MrchBnd; NHS; PolWkr; StuGov; 4-H; DARAwd; Mich State Univ; Home Economics.

GRUNEWALD, Alan G; Warsaw HS; Warsaw, IL; TrsFrshCls; TrsSophCls; PresJrCls; HstSrCls; HonRl; NHS; StuCncl; FFA; Bsktbl; College; Farming.

GRUNSKE, Gloria J; Slinger HS; Slinger, WI; Band; CncrtBnd; MrchBnd; PepBnd; 4-H; FBLA; FHA; SpnCl; Moraine Park Tech Inst; Ward Clerk.

GRUNWELL, Howard R; Saginaw Douglas Macarthur HS; Saginaw, MI; CncrtBnd; HonRl; MrchBnd; NHS; NatlMeritSchl; Orch; PolWkr; SchPl; TchrAde; Tennis; Delta College; Optometry.

GRUWELL, Polly; Franklin Public HS; Naponee, NE; /50 TrsFrshCls; ALAGirlsSt; Band; Chrs; HonRl; NHS; SchPl; FHA; SciCl; AmLegAwd; College;.

GRZECA, Jeff G; Plymouth HS; Plymouth, WI; ChrhWkr; HonRl; KeyCl; U Of Wi; Industrial Arts.

GRZECHOWIAK, Mary; Messmer HS; Milwaukee, WI; 3/209 ChrhWkr; HonRl; HospAde; VPSophCls; NHS; SctActv; RptrYrbk; RptrSchPpr; SecFTA; GovHonPrgAwd; Mt Mary Col; Lw.

GRZESIAK, Diane M; Freeland HS; Saginaw, MI; TrsJrCls; HonRl; NHS; GerCl; PpCl; CaptBsktbl; Chrldr; Univ.

GRZESIAK, Thomas; Marmion Military Acad; Dolton, IL; 7/90 HonRl; ROTC; SciCl; IMSpt; U Of Il Urbana; Doctor.

GRZESIOWSKI, Matthew J; St Louis University HS; St Louis, MO; 45/196 Band; CncrtBnd; HonRl; LetterSwmmng; College; Accountant.

GUARD, Lucinda; Chicago Public HS; Chicago, IL; CmntyWkr; OffAde; PolWkr; TchrAde; SchPpr; CchngActv; College; Videotape.

GUBBELS, Joann; Randolph HS; Randolph, NE; Chr; Chrs; HonRl; OffAde; College; Vocation.

GUBBELS, Maryann; Randolph HS; Randolph, NE; 2/69 Chr; Chrs; HonRl; NHS; OffAde; 4-H; FBLA; SpnCl; PpCl; Wayne Statea College; Teaching Elem Ed Musi.

GUCCIARDO, V J; Rockford East HS; Rockford, IL; Bsbl; Rock Valley Clg; Business Administration.

GUCKELBERG, Frederich A; Greenwood Comm HS; Greenwood, IN; Band; ChrhWkr; CncrtBnd; HonRl; MrchBnd; NHS; PepBnd; SchMus; SctActv; KeyCl; PpCl; LetterBsktbl; LetterGlf; University; Law.

GUDAHL, Kevin; Salem HS; Salem, SD; SecTrsJrCls; Band; HonRl; SchMus; StuCncl; AmLegAwd; So Dakota State Univ; Speech Teaching.

GUDAS, Carol J; Winamac Community HS; Winamac, IN; SecFrshCls; HonRl; NHS; OffAde; FTA; SpnCl; IMSpt; College; Teaching.

GUDE, Glen D; Elk Horn Kimballton HS; Exira, IA; SctActv; PresStuCncl; FFA; LetterFtbl; LetterWrstlng; University.

GUDEMAN, Donna; St Elizabeth HS; Tuscumbia, MO; Chrs; SchMus; Yrbk; 4-H; PpCl; 4-HAwd; U Of Missouri; Medical Technology.

GUDEMAN, Timothy A; West Central HS; Francesville, IN; 6/80 ALBoysSt; SchPl; RptrSchPpr; SchPpr; SpnCl; MthCl; Trade; Owner Of Sm Grocery Store.

GUDENKAUF, Jamie S; Nemaha Valley HS; Seneca, KS; TrsFrshCls; Aud/Vis; Chr; HonRl; ModUN; SpnCl; PpCl; LetterBsktbl; LetterTrk; GAA; College.

GUDSEN, Neil A; Austin Catholic Prep; Grosse Pt Woods, MI; 7/135 HonRl; NHS; Trk; University; Professional.

GUE, Sheryl; Cass City HS; Cass City, MI; 7/130 VPFrshCls; CmntyWkr; HonRl; JrNHS; NHS; OffAde; StuCncl; Chrldr; GAA; PPFtbl; St Clair County Comm College; Rn.

GUEBERT, Stephen C; Red Bud Comm Unit HS; Red Bud, IL; Band; Chrs; NHS; NatlThespSoc; SchMus; VPYthFlsp; SptEdSchPpr; CivCl; PresSpnCl; CitAwd; Belleville Area College; Business Admin.

GUEHLSTORF, John K; Roncalli HS; Two Rivers, WI; 23/143 TrsSrCls; Aud/Vis; ChrhWkr; HonRl; NHS; StuGov; SptEdSchPpr; KeyCl; MthCl; Trk; Uw Milwaukee; Biology Or Pre Med.

GUENDERT, Cynthia; Wauwatosa West HS; Wauwatosa, WI; 18/436 Chr; HonRl; LitMag; NHS; NatlMeritFnl; NatlMeritSchl; NatlMeritSF; SchPl; Swmmng; Beloit College; Internatonal Relatons Spani.

GUENETTE, Francis J; Escanaba Area Public HS; Escanaba, MI; 32/387 SecJrCls; Band; Chrs; ChrhWkr; CncrtBnd; MrchBnd; NatlMeritCmnd; PepBnd; SchMus; Northwestern University.

GUENGERICH, Gene A; Pekin Community HS; Manito, IL; 15/800 ChrhWkr; HonRl;.

GUENSBURG, Carol A; Columbus HS; Marshfield, WI; 37/114 SecTrsFrshCls; VPJrCls; PresSrCls; Chrs; HonRl; StuCncl; RptrSchPpr; FrCl; PpCl; Univ.

GUENTHER, David J; Waubun Public HS; Waubun, MN; ChrhWkr; CmntyWkr; HonRl; SchPl; RptrSchPpr; SptEdSchPpr; 4-H; LetterTrk; LetterWrstlng; 4-HAwd; JAAwd; PresAwd; College; Commercial Artist.

GUENTHER, Glen W; Central HS; St Joseph, MO; LitMag; YthFlsp; FTA; LatCl; MthCl; SciCl; College; Photography.

GUENTHER, Jeffrey R; Woodstock HS; Woodstock, IL; HonRl; NatlFornLg; NHS; NatlMeritCmnd; TchrAde; Yrbk; SchPpr; TreasFTA; College; Accounting.

GUENTHER, Jerry N; Columbus HS; Columbus, WI; 13/130 PresFrshCls; ALBoysSt; Aud/Vis; ChrhWkr; HonRl; SchAde; RptrSchPpr; 4-H; SpnCl; Bsktbl; CchngActv; Univ Of Wisc; Political Science.

GUENTHER, Sharon; Okemos HS; Okemos, MI; ChrhWkr; NHS; YthFlsp; LatCl; Grand Valley St Coll.

GUENZLER, Sharon M; Elizabeth HS; Elizabeth, IL; 10/28 TrsFrshCls; TrsSophCls; SecSrCls; Chrs; ChrhWkr; DrmMjrt; SchAde; SchMus; SchPl; Bsktbl; Trk; Col; Pro.

GUERICKE, Daniel M; Hanson Ind #40 HS; Alexandria, SD; PresSrCls; ALBoysSt; Teen; Band; Chr; Chrs; Bsktbl; Trk; Chrldr; IMSpt; College; Medecine.

GUERIN, Deborah A; Weselin Sr HS; New Baden, IL; 16/100 ChrhWkr; HonRl; JrNHS; SchPl; YthFlsp; RptrSchPpr; FBLA; FHA; PpCl; GAA; Kaskaskia Jr College; Nursing Major.

GUERIN, James B; Menasha HS; Menasha, WI; ChrhWkr; CmntyWkr; HonRl; SctActv; LetterTrk; Stevens Point; Natural Resourcer.

GUERIN, Robert M; Creighton Prep HS; Omaha, NE; PresFrshCls; PresSophCls; PresJrCls; ChrhWkr; HonRl; RedCrAde; Sdlty; StuCncl; StuGov; LetterSwmmng; CchngActv; IMSpt; OptClAwd; Univ; Vocation.

GUERRA, Donald J; Lyons Township HS; La Grange Park, IL; 200/1229 HonRl; Valparaiso Univ; Accounting.

GUERRERA, Gloria; Oak Forest HS; Oak Forest, IL; HospAde; JA; SchMus; SchPl; TchrAde; YthFnd; FshEdSchPpr; FDA; FNA; FTA; LetterBsktbl; LetterSwmmng; LetterTrk; Arizona State Univ; Physical Education.

GUERRERO, Eugene J; Niles East HS; Skokie, IL; 1/581 VPCncrtBnd; HonRl; JrNHS; NHS; NatlMeritCmnd; Orch; SctActv; KeyCl; LetterSocr; CaptTennis; Univ; Doctor.

GUERRERO, Julie S; St Casimir HS; Chicago, IL; 2/30 PresSrCls; HonRl; SchPl; Coll; Journalism.

GUERRIERI, Michaelene M; Resurrection HS; Chicago, IL; SecSrCls; SchPl; StuCncl;.

GUERRIERO, Anne M; St Stephen HS; Saginaw, MI; ALAGirlsSt; Band; ChrhWkr; HospAde; NHS; NatlMeritSF; SchPl; SctActv; LetterBsktbl; LetterTennis; Michigan State Univ.

GUERRIERO, Mary J; Mason HS; Mason, MI; 2/233 VPSophCls; PresJrCls; Chrl; NHS; NatlMeritCmnd; PresStuCncl; Yrbk; Bsktbl; CaptSwmmng; Trk; U Of Michigan.

GUERRIERO, Mary Jo; St Stephens HS; Saginaw, MI; HonRl; HospAde; SchAde; SctActv; EdSchPpr; Bsktbl; Tennis; PPFtbl; Univ; Professional.

GUERTLER, Bruce D; Simley Sr HS; Inver Grove Hts, MN; HonRl; NatlMeritSchl; NatlMeritSF; SctActv; LetterFtbl; Univ Of Minnesota.

GUEST, Lizabeth A; Harry A Burke HS; Omaha, NE; PresAFS; PresChrhWkr; HonRl; TreasNHS; StuCncl; TchrAde; VPFrCl; LetterTennis; IMSpt; Tech Inst; Marine Biology.

GUEST, Rosemarie; Bogan HS; Chicago, IL; 18/704 HonRl; JrNHS; LbryAde; NHS; OffAde; SchAde; TchrAde; PresFNA; SpnCl; MthCl; College; Nursing.

GUESTE, Shirley U; Visitation Convent HS; S St Paul, MN; PresFrshCls; VPSrCls; Chr; DrlTm; DrmMjrt; Mdrgl; NatlThespSoc; PepBnd; SctActv; Wrstlng;.

GUETSCHOW, Deborah K; Beloit Memorial HS; Beloit, WI; HonRl; LbryAde; College; Teacher.

GUETTER, Benedict; Wabasso Public HS; Wabasso, MN; Chrs; ChrhWkr; HonRl; TchrAde; FFA; Canby Vo Tech; Agriculture.

GUETZKE, Hal H; Menomonee Falls East HS; Menomonee Falls, WI; RptrSchPpr; SptEdSchPpr; Bsbl; LetterTrk; CchngActv; Collge; Vocational.

GUEVEL, Eugene L; Lexington HS; Lexington, MO; Band; Chr; CncrtBnd; HonRl; MrchBnd; NHS; NatlThespSoc; SchMus; EdYrBk; FrCl; College; Accounting Music.

GUGGEMOS, Debra A; Holy Trinity HS; Winstead, MN; PresSrCls; HonRl; SchMus; SchPl; StuCncl; TchrAde; PpCl; CaptTrk; Chrldr; IMSpt; College; Biology.

GUGGEMOS, Patricia L; Schlarman HS; Danville, IL; 9/70 TrsSrCls; Chrs; HonRl; JA; SchMus; SchPl; SctActv; StuCncl; YthFlsp; EdYrBk; Yrbk; Eastern Ill Univ; Med Technologist.

GUGGENMOS, Janet; Sidney HS; Sidney, NE; Band; Chrs; ChrhWkr; CncrtBnd; HonRl; JrNHS; LbryAde; Mdrgl; MrchBnd; PepBnd; Bible Coll; Nurse.

GUHL, Steven W; Huntington North HS; Huntington, IN; ChrhWkr; JA; YthFlsp; GerCl; LetterFtbl; LetterWrstlng; CchngActv; IMSpt; Coll; Law/teaching.

GUHR, Carol A; Hillsboro HS; Hillsboro, KS; Chrs; ChrhWkr; HonRl; HospAde; Mdrgl; SchAde; SchPl; TchrAde; RptrYrbk; RptrSchPpr; Sterling Clg; Counseling Or Theat Arts.

GUHSE, Lisa K; Arcadia Valley HS; Ironton, MO; 3/90 HonRl; NHS; Yrbk; SchPpr; FBLA; FHA; VPSpnCl; AmLegAwd; EldAwd; PresAwd; Se Mo St Univ; Elem Ed.

GUIANG, Maria R; Notre Dame HS; Burlington, IA; 15/79 CmntyWkr; DrlTm; HonRl; SctActv; YthFlsp; RptrYrbk; SpnCl; PpCl; Glf; Trk; CchngActv; U Of Wi Madison.

GUICE, Karen N; Englewood HS; Chicago, IL; 2/345 DrlTm; HonRl; JrNHS; ROTC; SchPl; StuCncl; SptEdSchPpr; SciCl; Ucla; Lawyer.

GUICHARD, Gary G; Mendel HS; Chicago, IL; 41/191 HonRl; NatlFornLg; Ftbl; Trk; Univ; Law.

GUICHARD, Peggy J; Normal Community HS; Normal, IL; 1/400 HonRl; NHS; SchMus; StuCncl; TchrAde; RptrYrbk; MthCl; PpCl; Chrldr; College; Environmental Health.

GUIDA, Bernard; Warren Woods HS; Warren, MI; 100/300 Inacomb Cnty Comm Col; Optometry Do.

GUIDA, Cathie J; Lewiston Consolidated HS; Burchard, NE; TrsJrCls; Chrs; HonRl; LbryAde; SchPl; Yrbk; 4-H; FHA; PpCl; College; Professional.

GUIDEN, Robert G; Morton HS; Hammond, IN; 23/500 HonRl; JrNHS; NHS; StuCncl; StuGov; TchrAde; YthLg; LetterGlf; Purdue Univ; Business.

GUIER, Kathryn L; Sweet Springs HS R 7; Sweet Springs, MO; ALAGirlsSt; Band; Chr; Chrs; ChrhWkr; OffAde; FHA; FTA; PpCl; Chrldr; Central Mo State Univ; Business.

GUIGAR, Marilyn R; Peck Community HS; Peck, MI; 4/65 ChrhWkr; CmntyWkr; HonRl; NHS; SctActv; TchrAde; FHA; College; Professional.

GUIHEA, William E; Brother Rice HS; Chicago, IL; HonRl; NatlMeritFnl; Ftbl; Wrstlng; Ripon College; Medicine.

GUILD, Bonnie J; Central Lake Public HS; Central Lake, MI; CncrtBnd; HonRl; MrchBnd; NHS; PepBnd; SchPl; StuCncl; Trk; 4-HAwd; VoiceDeMAwd; Western Mich U; Dr Of Aquatic Biology.

GUILD, Robert B; Big Foot HS; Lake Geneva, WI; 9/125 ALBoysSt; HonRl; NHS; NatlThespSoc; SchMus; SchPl; MthCl; Bsktbl; LetterTrk; IMSpt; West Point Military Academy; Doctor.

GUILDNER, Gayle B; Perkins Co HS; Grant, NE; 2/40 HonRl; NHS; SchMus; SecStuCncl; Yrbk; SecFHA; PpCl; LetterTrk; EldAwd; CitAwd; College; Criminal Justice.

GUILFOYLE, Timothy P; Wheaton Warrenville HS; Wheaton, IL; HonRl; LitMag; VPNHS; Yrbk; SchPpr; Bsktbl; Ftbl; LetterSwmmng; LetterTennis; Trk; Wrstlng; DARAwd; College; Dentistry.

GUILL, Dawn R; Sunnydale Academy; Centralia, MO; ChrhWkr; HonRl; SchPl; College; Vocation.

GUILLORY, Kathleen T; Rosarian Acad; Ft Wayne, IN; Chrl; HonRl; SchMus; SpnCl; College; Professional.

GUINAN, Dan F; Missouri Valley HS; Missouri Valley, IA; ALBoysSt; ChrhWkr; HonRl; KeyCl; LetterBsktbl; LetterFtbl; LetterSwmmng; LetterTrk; AmLegAwd; College; Vocation.

GUINAN, Michael D; Petersburg Porta HS; Petersburg, IL; VPSophCls; PresJrCls; StuCncl; StuGov; Yrbk; RptrSchPpr; KeyCl; SpnCl; LetterBsktbl; LetterFtbl; LetterTrk; College; Professional.

GUINN, Catherine; St Charles HS; St Charles, MO; Chr; Chrs; ChrhWkr; HospAde; SchMus; SctActv; TchrAde; FNA; PpCl; Nursing.

GUINN, Michael H; Raytown South HS; Raytown, MO; CmntyWkr; HonRl; NHS; PolWkr; PresKeyCl; LetterTrk; IMSpt; Central Mo St Univ; Law Enf.

GUINN, Stuart N; Washburn Rural HS; Topeka, KS; 16/199 HonRl; RedCrAde; Yrbk; SciCl; Gordon College; Ministry.

GUION, Michael R; Park Tudor HS; Indpls, IN; Aud/Vis; Chr; ChrhWkr; CncrtBnd; HonRl; NatlMeritSF; StuCncl; YthFlsp; SciCl; CaptTennis; U Of Wa; Ocean Engineering.

GUISE, Jacqueline A; Delwood HS; Delmar, IA; 2/29 Chr; HonRl; SchPl; StuCncl; 4-H; FNA; Bsktbl; Trk; 4-HAwd; Marycrest C; B S Nursing.

GUISE, Vicky L; Hayti HS; Hayti, MO; 16/87 HstJrCls; ChrhWkr; HonRl; NHS; StuCncl; YthFlsp; Yrbk; Univ Of Missouri; Dental Hygienist.

GUITER, Steven M; Comstock HS; Kalamazoo, MI; 4/250 HonRl; NHS; SctActv; TreasSpnCl; Western Michigan Univ; Physics.

GUITORD, Roberta; Bishop Dwenger HS; Ft Wayne, IN; SecJA; Coll; Writinhg.

GUIU, Ana E; West Leyden HS; Melrose Park, IL; 18/417 Chr; HonRl; LitMag; TchrAde; College; Accounting.

GULA, Jo; Negaunee HS; Negaunee, MI; JrNHS; NHS; RptrYrbk; EdYrBk; IMSpt; College; Fine Arts.

GULBERSON, Gloria J; Harrison HS; Chicago, IL; HstFrshCls; HstSophCls; HstJrCls; HstSrCls; Chrs; ChrhWkr; CmntyWkr; StuGov; TchrAde; UNYO; Yrbk; FrCl;.

GULBRANSON, Laurie S; Chisago Lakes Area HS; Lindstrom, MN; Chr; ChrhWkr; DrlTm; HonRl; SchMus; 4-H; LetterTrk; GAA; 4-HAwd; Col; Ed.

GULDAN, Debbie L; Columbus HS; Marshfield, WI; Chrs; HonRl; LitMag; SchPl; RptrYrbk; Yrbk; RptrSchPpr; SchPpr; FrCl; Eau Claire College; Spec Education.

GULDEN, Michael U; Community HS; Detroit Lakes, MN; 1/260 ALBoysSt; ChrhWkr; HonRl; NatlFornLg; TreasNHS; NatlMeritSF; GerCl; MthCl; Tennis; IMSpt; Univ; Elec Engr.

GULER, Gregory T; New Rockford Central HS; New Rockford, ND; PresJrCls; Chrs; ChrhWkr; SchMus; SchPl; SchPpr; Bsbl; Ftbl; AmLegAwd; 4-HAwd; Mayville Clg; Commercial Art.

GULER, Jeanne M; New Rockford Central HS; New Rockford, ND; ALAGirlsSt; Band; CncrtBnd; Orch; PepBnd; SchPl; VPStuCncl; YthFlsp; RptrYrbk; MthCl; CaptBsktbl; Trk; PresGAA; College; Nursing.

GULICK, Craig L; Wm Chrisman HS; Independence, MO; 180/400 ChrhWkr; CmntyWkr; SctActv; StuCncl; YthFlsp; Yrbk; KeyCl; LetterBsktbl; LetterTrk; College; Public Relations.

GULICK, Nancy C; Durand Area HS; Bancroft, MI; Band; Chr; ChrhWkr; CncrtBnd; HonRl; Mdrgl; NHS; TchrAde; Twrl; 4-H; Bsbl; Bsktbl; College; Professional.

GULICK, Patricia L; Breckenridge HS; Merrill, MI; 16/91 TrsSrCls; HonRl; NHS; OffAde; RptrYrbk; Yrbk; RptrSchPpr; PpCl; Chrldr; PPFtbl; Central Mich U; Elem Ed.

GULIK, Janet M; Proviso West HS; Bellwood, IL; 40/1100 Band; CncrtBnd; HonRl; HospAde; NHS; VPStuCncl; StuGov; YthLg; Swmmng; GAA; Triton Jr College; Adm In Criminal Justice.

GULLEDGE, Joanie; Malden HS; Malden, MO; 9/107 Band; Chr; CncrtBnd; HonRl; OffAde; StuCncl; Yrbk; SchPpr; FHA; PpCl; Patricia Stevens; Fashion Merchandising.

GULLETT, Jane; Macksville HS; Macksville, KS; 37 SecSrCls; Band; Chrs; HonRl; MrchBnd; PepBnd; SchMus; SchPl; TchrAde; PpCl; College;medicalsec Recep.

GULLETT, Robert S; St Charles Bor HS; Romeoville, IL; 3/19 HonRl; SchPl; LetterSocr; College; Mathematics.

GULLEY, Marilyn S; Paxton HS; Paxton, IL; 38/150 HonRl; TchrAde; Bsbl; Trk; CchngActv; GAA; Illinois St Univ; Physical Educ.

GULLEY, Tina L; Vienna Township HS; Grantsburg, IL; VPFrshCls; VPSophCls; PresJrCls; SchPpr; VPFHA; FTA; SecSpnCl; MthCl; PpCl; Chrldr;.

GULLEY, Tina L; Vienna HS; Grantsburg, IL; VPFrshCls; VPSophCls; PresJrCls; RptrSchPpr; FHA; FTA; SpnCl; MthCl; PpCl; Chrldr;.

GULLICKSON, Gregory L; Walhalla Public HS; Walhalla, ND; 1/60 VPSophCls; ALBoysSt; Band; HonRl; NatlMeritCmnd; GerCl; Glf; St John S Univ;.

GULLICKSON, Lynne J; Lanesboro HS; Whalan, MN; Chr; ChrhWkr; CmntyWkr; HospAde; NatlSciFnd; RedCrAde; StuGov; YthFlsp; Yrbk; FDA; College; Nursing.

GULLICKSON, Mary M; Memorial HS; Milwaukee, WI; HonRl; NHS; Orch; SchMus; Technical School; Nursing.

GULLICKSON, Sheryl A; Freeman Public HS; Freeman, SD; Band; Chrs; HonRl; SchMus; SchPl; StuCncl; RptrYrbk; EdYrBk; RptrSchPpr; Univ Of South Dakota; Nurse.

GULLIKSON, Vonnie J; White Shield HS; Roseglen, ND; 2/13 PresJrCls; PresSrCls; ALAGirlsSt; HonRl; HospAde; StuCncl; StuGov; EdYrBk; MasAwd; Mary College; Nursing.

GULLION, Kathy L; Marshall HS; Marshall, IL; 51/130 Chr; ChrhWkr; HospAde; YthFlsp; FHA; AmLegAwd;.

GULSVIG, Dean C; Oakes Public HS; Oakes, ND; PresFrshCls; Chrs; HonRl; StuCncl; FFA; Bsktbl; Ftbl; Glf; Trk; Univ; Business.

GUMERINGER, Kathy; Esmond HS; Esmond, ND; SecTrsFrshCls; Chrs; HonRl; LbryAde; PpCl; College; Professional Nurse.

GUMHOLD, Linda J; St Benedict HS; Chicago, IL; CncrtBnd; HonRl; LbryAde; MrchBnd; Orch; EdYrBk; GerCl; Loyola Univ Of Chicago; Biology.

GUMM, Ed L; Maryville R Ii HS; Maryville, MO; PresJrCls; StuCncl; Bsbl; LetterBsktbl; CaptFtbl; College; Business.

GUMM, Jeffrey R; Prairie City HS; Prairie City, IA; 6/41 Chrs; HonRl; LbryAde; Mdrgl; SchMus; SchPl; Yrbk; Mc Pherson Coll; Accountant.

GUMMERSHEIMER, Robert; Dupo HS; East Carondelet, IL; 15/110 Band; HonRl; JA; MrchBnd; PepBnd; SctActv; SptEdYrbk; MthCl; College; Engineer.

GUMOS, Sandra J; Maria HS; Chicago, IL; 44/335 HonRl; JA; SchMus; StuCncl; SpnCl; Trk; Chrldr; College; Elem Education.

GUND, Barbara K; St Josephs Academy; St Louis, MO; HonRl; PpCl; LetterBsktbl; CchngActv; GAA; IMSpt; St Louis University; Business.

GUNDER, Colleen D; Northrop HS; Fort Wayne, IN; 34/647 Chr; ChrhWkr; HonRl; JA; Orch; SctActv; RptrSchPpr; SchPpr; LatCl; Chrldr; University; Journalism.

GUNDERSON, Bruce D; Lincoln Sr HS; Bloomington, MN; 46/556 Band; CncrtBnd; HonRl; MrchBnd; NHS; Orch; PepBnd; SctActv; LetterTennis; IMSpt; Univ Of Mn; Medicine.

GUNDERSON, Cheryl D; Henning Public HS; Vining, MN; Band; Chr; CncrtBnd; HonRl; MrchBnd; PepBnd; SchMus; SchPl; EdSchPpr; FTA; Trade School; Vocation.

GUNDERSON, Diane M; Academy Of The Holy Angels; Richfield, MN; Chrl; Chrs; SchPl; TchrAde; U Of Minn; Physical Therapy.

GUNDERSON, Jan M; Forest Lake HS; Wyoming, MN; PresFrshCls; PresSophCls; PresJrCls; Band; HonRl; PepBnd; SchMus; StuCncl; Swmmng; LetterTennis; GAA; PresAwd; College; Law.

GUNDERSON, Jeffery L; Garnavillo Comm HS; Garnavillo, IA; 15/42 ALBoysSt; Band; Chrs; HonRl; MrchBnd; PepBnd; LetterBsktbl; CaptGlf; Luther College; Accounting.

GUNDERSON, Jon E; Lakeville HS; Lakeville, MN; 17/198 ChrhWkr; HonRl; NHS; StuCncl; YthFlsp; SptEdSchPpr; Bsbl; Glf; CaptWrstlng; CchngActv; Univf Accounting Law.

GUNDERSON, Kathleen M; Mahtomedi HS; White Bear Lake, MN; 2/141 Band; Chr; ChrhWkr; HonRl; NHS; SchPl; StuCncl; Tennis; St Catherine College; Music Mj.

GUNDERSON, Laura; Niles East Hs; Skokie, IL; 50/567 HonRl; NatlMeritCmnd; Trk; GAA; College; Pre Law.

GUNDERSON, Renae D; Leeds Public HS; York, ND; VPJrCls; ALAGirlsSt; HonRl; SchPl; StuCncl; TchrAde; 4-H; FHA; 4-HAwd;.

GUNDLACH, Kurt E; Iowa Grant HS; Montfort, WI; 43/122 HonRl; RptrYrbk; RptrSchPpr; CaptBsbl; CaptBsktbl; LetterFtbl; CaptTrk; University; Business.

GUNDRUM, Daniel J; Grafton HS; Grafton, WI; HonRl; Bsbl; Swmmng; CaptTrk; Marquette U; Architect.

GUNDRUM, Robert R; Kewaskum HS; Kewaskum, WI; CmntyWkr; FFA; Ftbl; Trk; Univ Of Wisconsin; Accounting.

GUNDY, Gregg A; Flanagan Unit #4 HS; Flanagan, IL; 4/59 PresJrCls; PresSrCls; Band; CncrtBnd; Mdrgl; NHS; SchMus; LetterBsktbl; LetterFtbl; LetterTrk; Clge; Sci.

GUNDY, Janice R; Burrton HS; Burrton, KS; 4/38 Chr; HonRl; NatlFornLg; SchPl; YthFlsp; PpCl; LetterBsktbl; LetterFtbl; LetterTrk; GAA; PPFtbl; Bethel College.

GUNDY, Kathryn J; Flanagan HS; Flanagan, IL; HonRl; Mdrgl; MrchBnd; NHS; SchMus; SchPl; StuCncl; YthFlsp; Yrbk; IMSpt; Coll; Major Study.

GUNLOCK, Jody; Noonan Public HS; Noonan, ND; Band; Chrs; ChrhWkr; HonRl; SchMus; 4-H; Bsktbl; Ftbl; Trk; 4-HAwd;.

GUNN, Helen L; Downers Grove North HS; Downers Grove, IL; Band; Chr; HonRl; MrchBnd; NatlFornLg; NHS; NatlThespSoc; PolWkr; SchPl; College; Law.

GUNN, Mary J; Union HS; Union, MO; 51/174 HonRl; HospAde; JA; OffAde; YthFlsp; SpnCl; PpCl; LetterBsbl; GAA; IMSpt; PPFtbl; PresAwd; College; Professional.

GUNN, Michael T; Harmony Community HS; Bonaparte, IA; 1/41 PresFrshCls; PresSophCls; PresJrCls; HonRl; JrNHS; NHS; SctActv; StuCncl; Bsktbl; Ftbl; Prof.

GUNN, Robert; Tri Valley HS; Baltic, SD; 13/63 ALBoysSt; Band; Chrs; HonRl; NHS; SchPl; SptEdSchPpr; 4-H; Sdsm&t; Chemical Engineer.

GUNN, Robert C; Waukegan East HS; Waukegan, IL; ChrhWkr; HonRl; LitMag; PolWkr; StuCncl; YthFlsp; FDA; Northern Ill University; Elementary Educ.

GUNNAR, William P; Riverside Brookfield HS; Riverside, IL; 97/488 HonRl; LetterTennis; Northwestern Univ; Medical Field.

GUNNER, Lorie; Atwater Public HS; Atwater, MN; 1/63 ALAGirlsSt; Band; ChrhWkr; HonRl; NHS; PepBnd; SchPl; StuCncl; Coll; Phy Ed.

GUNNER, Lorie J; Atwater Public HS; Atwater, MN; 1/63 ALAGirlsSt; Band; ChrhWkr; HonRl; NHS; SchPl; StuCncl; LetterBsktbl; CaptTrk; LetterGAA; College; Physical Education.

GUNNESS, Julie S; Craig HS; Janesville, WI; 48/474 Band; CncrtBnd; DrlTm; HonRl; MrchBnd; Orch; StuCncl; FrCl; Trk; University Of Wisc; Medicine.

GUNNESS, Peter D; Richland #44 HS; Abercrombie, ND; 11/28 ALBoysSt; Chrs; HonRl; YthFlsp; SciCl; LetterBsktbl; LetterFtbl; LetterTrk; IMSpt; 4-HAwd; College; Engr Or Flying.

GUNNLAUGSSON, Patricia L; Washington Island HS; Washington Island, WI; PresFrshCls; PresSophCls; Chr; ChrhWkr; CmntyWkr; HonRl; NatlFornLg; TchrAde; 4-H; Coll.

GUNTER, April A; Okawville Community 'S; Addieville, IL; Band; HonRl; LbryAde; PepBnd; YthFlsp; FHA; CaptChrldr; Army; Doctor.

GUNTER, Diane J; Josephinum HS; Chicago, IL; 1/88 HonRl; De Paul Univ; Foreign Languages.

GUNTER, Marcia K; Sacred Heart Public HS; Sacred Heart, MN; 6/29 VPJrCls; Band; Chr; CncrtBnd; HonRl; NHS; SchPl; RptrYrbk; FHA; Chrldr; Anoka Ramsey Comm Clge; Registered Nurse.

GUNTER, Mark R; Conway HS; Conway, MO; PresFrshCls; PresSophCls; Chrs; ChrhWkr; HonRl; SchMus; YthFlsp; FFA; FTA; ChmnBsktbl; College; Physical Education.

GUNTER, Robert W; Rock Island HS; Milan, IL; HonRl; LetterBsbl; Univ; Commercial Art.

GUNTER, Sandra R; Pierce HS; Hoskins, NE; ChrhWkr; HonRl; StuGov; TchrAde; YthFnd; GerCl; Business School; Vocation.

GUNTERN, Ursula; Belding HS; Belding, MI; HonRl; HospAde; NatlMeritSchl; StuCncl; PpCl; Trk; Univ; Psychology.

GUNTHER, Cheryl A; Immaculate HS; Leavenworth, KS; CmntyWkr; HonRl; HospAde; NatlCathMusEdAsoc; NHS; PolWkr; RedCrAde; SchMus; StuCncl; StuGov; Univrsity; Professional.

GUNTHER, Monica C; Downers Grove North HS; Downers Grove, IL; 102/575 AFS; HonRl; HospAde; StuCncl; Teen; FNA; PresGerCl; College; Nursing.

GUNTHER, Pamela L; Somonauk HS; Somonauk, IL; 15/52 Chrs; HonRl; SchAde; GerCl; PpCl; Bsbl; LetterBsktbl; Trk; Chrldr; GAA; Univ; Phyed.

GUNTY, John; Quigley South HS; Hometown, IL; 5/170 PresJrCls; VPSrCls; HonRl; NHS; SchMus; StuCncl; TchrAde; SchPpr; LetterSocr; LetterTrk; 4 Yr College; Education.

GUNTY, Mary C; Romeoville HS; Romeoville, IL; 11/293 Chr; Chrs; ChrhWkr; CmntyWkr; DrlTm; HonRl; ROTC; SchAde; SchPl; SctActv; TchrAde; College; Professional.

GUOKAS, Charles R; St Francis HS; St Francis, WI; 5/195 Chrs; HonRl; Mdrgl; NHS; SchMus; SchPl; GerCl; SpnCl; College; Law.

GUPTA, Ratnamala; Westport HS; Kansas City, MO; 3/170 PresAFS; CmntyWkr; VPJA; NHS; TreasStuCncl; PresSpnCl; BttyCrckrAwd; DARAwd; JAAwd; CitAwd; Univ Of Missouri; Medicine.

GURA, Nancy C; Streator Township HS; Streator, IL; 22/330 HonRl; HospAde; NHS; StuCncl; GerCl; PpCl; LetterTennis; Northern Ill Univ; Nursing.

GURA, Nancy C; Streator Twp HS; Streator, IL; HonRl; HospAde; NHS; StuCncl; GerCl; PpCl; LetterTennis; IMSpt; No Illinois Univ; Nurse.

GURCHE, Carolyn; Shawnee Mission South HS; Overland Park, KS; /818 Band; CncrtBnd;.

GURDIAN, Maria D; Bergan HS; Peoria, IL; 50/200 ChrhWkr; HonRl; LbryAde; SchPl; 4-H; SpnCl; College; Psychology.

GURKA, David C; Rolling Meadows HS; Rolling Meadows, IL; 4/532 ChrhWkr; HonRl; NHS; AmLegAwd; NCTE; U Of Ill; Scientific Research.

GURSKI, Jeanne M; Franklin HS; Westland, MI; Aud/Vis; Chr; Chrl; Chrs; ChrhWkr; JA; SchMus; SchPl; E Mi Univ; Voice Tchr.

GURTLER, Cynthia K; Marysville HS; Beattie, KS; TrsSrCls; HonRl; 4-H; PpCl; Jr Coll; Vet Asst.

GURUNIAN, Jeffrey S; Lincoln Park HS; Lincoln Park, MI; 9/129 AFS; HonRl; TreasJA; NHS; RptrSchPpr; JAAwd; U Of Mi; Medical.

GUSE, Craig A; Sparta Sr HS; Sparta, WI; Band; CncrtBnd; HonRl; MrchBnd; NHS; PepBnd; SchPl; SctActv; YthFlsp; LetterWrstlng; Trade School; Vocation.

GUSE, Roy J; Brookfield East HS; Brookfield, WI; TrsFrshCls; JrNHS; NatlMeritSF; HstFrshCls; SchAde; KeyCl; MthCl; LetterBsktbl; LetterGlf; LetterTrk; Univ; Bio Engr.

GUSICH, Margaret M; Naperville Central HS; Naperville, IL; SecBand; CncrtBnd; HonRl; MrchBnd; NHS; Orch; PepBnd; SchMus; SpnCl; Eastern Illinois Univ; Music.

GUSS, Sherry A; Kennedy HS; Chicago, IL; 213/544 Band; CncrtBnd; HonRl; MrchBnd; Orch; PepBnd; StuCncl; StuGov; PpCl; GAA; Clge; Special Ed.

GUSSE, Sherry M; Highmore HS; Highmore, SD; 1/54 HonRl; LetterBsktbl; DARAwd; Univ Of South Dakota; Computer Programmer.

GUSSIN, Michael H; Roosevelt HS; Chicago, IL; Chr; HonRl; LbryAde; NHS; TchrAde; LatCl; IMSpt; U Of Ill Urbana; Physician.

GUST, Cynthia A; Central HS; Grand Forks, ND; HonRl; Yrbk; College.

GUST, Gregory J; Sacred Heart HS; East Grand Forks, MN; 2/52 PresFrshCls; TrsSophCls; ALBoysSt; Chr; HonRl; NatlMeritCmnd; SptEdYrbk; LetterBsktbl; LetterFtbl; AmLegAwd; St John U.

GUST, Karyn A; Chaska Senior HS; Chaska, MN; 3/200 VPFrshCls; VPSophCls; TrsJrCls; Band; HonRl; NHS; PpCl; Trk; LetterChrldr; University Of Minnesota; Professional Med.

GUST, Loretta L; L L Wright HS; Ironwood, MI; 28/201 Chr; Chrs; ChrhWkr; HonRl; NatlThespSoc; SchMus; SchPl; RptrYrbk; SecYrbk; PpCl; Michigan Tech Univ; Chemical Engineering.

GUSTAD, Jeanine S; Gayville Volin HS; Volin, SD; 1/27 PresSophCls; PresJrCls; Chrs; HonRl; StuCncl; Yrbk; PpCl; Bsktbl; Bus School; Business.

GUSTAFSON, Catherine A; St John Public HS; St John, ND; 1/19 PresSophCls; Band; Chrs; ChrhWkr; HonRl; SchMus; SchPl; StuCncl; Yrbk; LetterBsktbl; Ndsu Fargo; Law.

GUSTAFSON, Dianne M; Richwoods HS; Peoria, IL; 26/442 Chr; Chrs; ChrhWkr; HonRl; LbryAde; NHS; SchMus; RptrYrbk; FNA; St Olaf College; Nursing.

GUSTAFSON, Ella I; Three Rivers HS; Three Rivers, MI; 32/210 ChrhWkr; NatlFornLg; NHS; StuCncl; TchrAde; RptrYrbk; RptrSchPpr; SpnCl; PpCl; Tennis; Ferris St Col; Dental Lab.

GUSTAFSON, Jeffrey S; Wayne Comm HS; Corydon, IA; Band; CncrtBnd; HonRl; NHS; SctActv; StuCncl; YthFlsp; Bsbl; Ftbl; Wrstlng; Col; Criminalogy.

GUSTAFSON, Jill L; Harvard HS; Harvard, IL; Band; Chrs; CncrtBnd; HonRl; MrchBnd; PepBnd; SchMus; SchPl; SecStuCncl; StuGov; Univ; Engr.

GUSTAFSON, Joelene B; Scribner Public HS; Scribner, NE; ALAGirlsSt; Band; ChrhWkr; HonRl; Mdrgl; NHS; YthFlsp; RptrSchPpr; 4-H; LetterTrk; College; Major Study.

GUSTAFSON, John R; Negaunee HS; Palmer, MI; Band; Chrs; CncrtBnd; HonRl; MrchBnd; PepBnd; Bsbl; Univ; Professional.

GUSTAFSON, Lisa L; J D Darnall HS; Geneseo, IL; 28/207 Band; Chr; HonRl; Orch; Univ Of Iowa; Music.

GUSTAFSON, Mary; Frankfort HS; Frankfort, MI; HonRl; HospAde; LbryAde; NHS; StuCncl; TchrAde; Trk; KiwanAwd; Northwestern Michigan College; Surgical Nur.

GUSTAFSON, Michael L; Public HS; Lyons, NE; 3/29 ALBoysSt; HonRl; NHS; StuCncl; Pres4-H; SecBsbl; LetterBsktbl; LetterFtbl; 4-HAwd; College; Veterinary Medicine.

GUSTAFSON, Norman; Denison HS; Kiron, IA; 5/150 ALBoysSt; Chr; ChrhWkr; HonRl; NHS; Quill&Scroll; YthFlsp; SptEdSchPpr; FFA; IMSpt; Coll; Vocation.

GUSTAFSON, Pamela; Prairie Community HS; Paton, IA; SecTrsSrCls; Chrs; PresChrhWkr; SchMus; StuGov; Yrbk; PresFHA; Des Moines Area Comm Coll; Child Care.

GUSTAFSON, Paula A; Hibbing HS; Hibbing, MN; 12/432 Band; CncrtBnd; DrmMjrt; HonRl; MrchBnd; NHS; Orch; PepBnd; SpnCl; PpCl; Trk; Hibbing Comm College; Medical Technology.

GUSTAFSON, Richard D; Marshall HS; Marshall, IL; 21/157 Band; Chr; CncrtBnd; MrchBnd; NHS; PepBnd; University Of Illinois; Farm Mgmt.

GUSTAFSON, Robert W; Van Buren Comm HS; Keosauqua, IA; TrsFrshCls; PresJrCls; VPBand; CncrtBnd; HonRl; MrchBnd; PepBnd; PolWkr; SchMus; 4-H; College; Criminal Justice.

GUSTAFSON, Sherry L; Magic City Campus HS; Minot, ND; Chr; ChrhWkr; SchPl; StuCncl; TchrAde; PpCl; Chrldr; PPFtbl; College; Psychology.

GUSTAFSON, William T; Hallock HS; Hallock, MN; Band; Chrs; CmntyWkr; HonRl; PepBnd; StuCncl; Ftbl; College.

GUSTIN, Virginia R; Mapleton Public HS; Mapleton, ND; VPFrshCls; PresSophCls; Band; Chrs; CncrtBnd; HonRl; PepBnd; SchPl; Yrbk; SptEdSchPpr; Trade School; Management.

GUSTKE, Martha K; Gull Lake Comm HS; Hickory Corners, MI; 12/250 HonRl; SecFrCl; SciCl; IMSpt; College; Medicine.

GUT, George M; Weber HS; Chicago, IL; 9/197 ChrhWkr; HonRl; NHS; NatlMeritCmnd; SancSoc; TchrAde; SciCl; LetterTrk; Illinois Inst Of Tech; Mechanical Engineer.

GUTH, John C; Washington Comm HS; Eureka, IL; Chrs; HonRl; NHS; StuCncl; YthFlsp; Pres4-H; PresFFA; IMSpt; 4-HAwd; College; Agriculture.

GUTHALS, Louise A; Mt Olive HS; Walshville, IL; 2/60 Band; Chrs; ChrhWkr; HonRl; RptrYrbk; CivCl; 4-H; FBLA; IMSpt; VoiceDemAwd; Siu; Music.

GUTHERLESS, William; Maxwell Dist 7 HS; Maxwell, NE; 4/16 HonRl; NHS; SchPl; TchrAde; Bsktbl; Ftbl; Voc Tech College; Mechanic.

GUTHIER, Martha R; St Elizabeths Academy; St Louis, MO; SecTrsJrCls; ChrhWkr; CmntyWkr; HonRl; LbryAde; OffAde; PolWkr; SchPl; StuCncl; StuGov; TchrAde; GAA; Notre Dame College; Medical Tech.

GUTHMILLER, Cynthia M; Leola HS; Leola, SD; 6/50 ChrhWkr; CmntyWkr; HonRl; SchPl; FHA; PpCl; Trk; U Sd; Med Tech.

GUTHRIE, Gara L; Mexico HS; Mexico, MO; ChrhWkr; CmntyWkr; NatlFornLg; SchAde; SchMus; SchPl; SctActv; StuCncl; TchrAde; SchPpr; College; Public Relations Advertising.

GUTHRIE, Gary A; Nevada Community HS; Nevada, IA; 1/117 CncrtBnd; MrchBnd; PresNHS; PepBnd; FSA; VPSciCl; LetterBsbl; LetterBsktbl; CaptTrk; Wrstlng; Iowa Stat U; Priesthood.

GUTHRIE, Timothy F; Vienna HS; Vienna, IL; 13/104 HonRl; StuCncl; TchrAde; PpCl; College; Professional.

GUTHRIE, Walker L; Marlette HS; Marlette, MI; Band; ChrhWkr; CncrtBnd; MrchBnd; PepBnd; LetterBsbl; Univ Of Michigan; Pilot.

GUTIERREZ, Mario V; Russell HS; Russell, KS; PresJrCls; VPBand; Chr; HonRl; StuCncl; KeyCl; SpnCl; PpCl; LetterTrk; Fort Hays State Clg; Business Administratn.

GUTKNECHT, Julie A; Milwaukee Lutheran HS; Wauwatosa, WI; 1/231 Chr; NHS; RptrSchPpr; College; Reg Nurse.

GUTMANN, Donald J; Griffin HS; Springfield, IL; 21/175 ChrhWkr; CmntyWkr; HonRl; NHS; SctActv; TchrAde; Ill State Univ; Business Admin.

GUTOWSKI, Karen A; Bishop Foley HS; Madison Heights, MI; Chrl; ChrhWkr; HospAde; PolWkr; RptrYrbk; RptrSchPpr; PpCl; BauchLmbAwd; BttyCrckrAwd; EldAwd; U Of Mi; Pre Med.

GUTOWSKI, Margaret A; Roncalli HS; Omaha, NE; HonRl; NHS; SchPl; FrCl; Univ; Nurse.

GUTSCH, Catherine T; Regis HS; Altoona, WI; 1/140 Chr; Chrs; HonRl; NHS; SchMus; SctActv; FrCl; PpCl; GAA; IMSpt; Univ; Home Econ.

GUTSCHENRIHER, E J; Neodesha HS; Neodesha, KS; 1/57 ALBoysSt; HonRl; NatlMeritFnl; SchPl; Pres4-H; PresFFA; LetterBsktbl; Ftbl; BauchLmbAwd; 4-HAwd;.

GUTSCHENRITTER, David J; Niles Senior HS; Niles, MI; 14/365 ALBoysSt; CtyCnl; HonRl; NHS; NatlMeritSF; SctActv; StuCncl; StuGov; RptrYrbk; University; Engineering.

GUTSTEIN, Howard B; Interlochen Arts Acad; Kalamazoo, MI; AFS; Chr; CncrtBnd; LitMag; NatlMeritFnl; Orch; SchPpr; LatCl; Trk; Col;.

GUTT, Raymond T; St Mary Of Ph HS; Chicago, IL; 5/100 HonRl; SchMus; SchPl; SpnCl; LetterBsktbl; LetterTrk; IMSpt; Ill Inst Of Tech; Chemical Engineering.

GUTWEIN, Roger W; West Central HS; Medaryville, IN; 9/85 VPJrCls; Band; CncrtBnd; MrchBnd; NHS; PepBnd; PresStuCncl; LetterFtbl; Wrstlng; Univ; Professional.

GUTZ, Barbara A; Osmond HS; Osmond, NE; 24/44 PresJrCls; Chr; HonRl; SchMus; SchPl; StuCncl; PpCl; LetterTrk; TrsSrCls; 4-HAwd; Bus Sch; Bookkeeper.

GUTZ, Kristina M; Osmond Community HS; Osmond, NE; 9/44 Band; Chr; Chrs; ChrhWkr; CncrtBnd; HonRl; MrchBnd; PepBnd; SchPl; GAA; Air National Guard; Photographer.

GUTZEIT, Michael F; Marist HS; Palos Heights, IL; 19/365 CmntyWkr; HonRl; NHS; HstFrshCls; StuCncl; LetterTrk; Loyola Univ; Pre Medical.

GUTZWILLER, Catherine A; Lawrenceburg HS; Lawrenceburg, IN; 10/150 ALAGirlsSt; DrlTm; HonRl; JrNHS; MrchBnd; NHS; SchPl; FHA; LetterTrk; LetterGAA; Indiana State U; Scretary.

GUY, Debbie L; Dora HS; West Plains, MO; 3/35 SecFrshCls; VPJrCls; HonRl; LbryAde; SchPl; 4-H; FFA; PpCl; SciCl; 4-HAwd; U Of Mo; Vet Med.

GUY, Jeffrey O; Grinnell HS; Grinnell, IA; 25/200 PresSophCls; PresJrCls; PresSrCls; HonRl; NHS; RptrSchPpr; KeyCl; LetterFtbl; LetterTrk; IMSpt; University; Engineering.

GUY, Joel A; Kalkaska HS; Rapid City, MI; Band; ChrhWkr; CncrtBnd; HonRl; MrchBnd; PepBnd; StuCncl; Bsbl; CaptBsktbl; CaptFtbl; CchngActv; IMSpt; 4-HAwd; College; Professional.

GUY, Johanna L; Washington Catholic HS; Washington, IN; SecFrshCls; Chrs; HonRl; NHS; SchPl; RptrSchPpr; PpCl; Bsktbl; College; Journalism.

GUY, Larry G; Guide Rock Public HS; Guide Rock, NE; Chrs; SchPl; EdYrBk; EdSchPpr; SptEdSchPpr; Bsbl; LetterBsktbl; LetterFtbl; IMSpt; 4-HAwd; College; Journalism.

GUY, Scott; St Charles HS; Saginaw, MI; 41#54#72 TchrAde; LetterFtbl; LetterTrk; CaptIMSpt; University.

GUYER, Dawson D; North Miami HS; Denver, IN; Aud/Vis; Band; Chr; Chrs; ChrhWkr; CncrtBnd; HonRl; Mdrgl; MrchBnd; NHS; PepBnd; SchMus; Trade Sch; Mechanic.

GUYER, Evan D; Jefferson Sr HS; Cedar Rapids, IA; 47/530 ALBoysSt; Band; MrchBnd; NatlThespSoc; Orch; SchMus; College; Law.

GUYER, John F; Lake Central HS; Schererville, IN; 10/463 HonRl; NHS; Rose Hulmar Inst; Engineer.

GUYER, Paul S; East HS; Lincoln, NE; Band; Chr; CncrtBnd; HonRl; PepBnd; SchMus; 4-H; LetterFtbl; Trk; IMSpt; College; Forestry.

GUYERSON, Michael J; Thornton Frac South HS; Lansing, IL; HonRl; PresNatlFornLg; NHS; GerCl; AmLegAwd; Univ Of Il; Political Science.

GUYETT, Debra; Woodbine Community HS; Woodbine, IA; DrlTm; HonRl; NHS; Twrl; YthFlsp; 4-H; FrCl; PpCl; Bsktbl; Trade School; Art.

GUYETTE, Nancy A; St Francis HS; Traverse City, MI; 10/83 Chr; HonRl; NHS; NatlMeritFnl; NatlMeritCmnd; OffAde; TchrAde; RptrSchPpr; PpCl; Coll; Dental Hygiene.

GUYMON, James P; Paris HS; Paris, IL; 22/226 ChrhWkr; HonRl; NHS; SctActv; StuCncl; CaptTrk; 4-HAwd; CitAwd; In St U; Optometry.

GUYNAN, Mary E; Schuyler HS; Schuyler, NE; Chrs; HonRl; SchPl; StuGov; 4-H; 4-HAwd; RotaryAwd; Creighton University.

GUZDZIOL, Loretta A; St Barbara HS; Chicago, IL; PresSophCls; HonRl; StuCncl; RptrSchPpr; Chicago Cir; Pharmacist.

GUZIAK, Joyce A; Chesaning Union HS; Oakley, MI; PresJrCls; PresSrCls; ALAGirlsSt; Aud/Vis; HonRl; NHS; RptrYrbk; 4-H; FrCl; AmLegAwd; College; Nursing.

GUZMAN, Linda; St Francis HS; St Francis, WI; 3/197 SecAFS; HonRl; NHS; SpnCl; LetterGAA; Univ Of Wisc; Spanish.

GUZOLEK, Catherine E; Maine South HS; Park Ridge, IL; 60/849 HonRl; NatlMeritCmnd; PolWkr; Univ Of Illinois; Biological Sciences.

GUZZY, Catherine A; Metropolis Comm HS; Metropolis, IL; 1/161 Band; CmntyWkr; CncrtBnd; HonRl; HospAde; MrchBnd; NHS; NatlThespSoc; PepBnd; PolWkr; Univ Of Il; Journalism.

GWALTNEY, Brenda K; Mills Prairie HS; Mill Shoals, IL; 1/15 SecFrshCls; TrsSophCls; PresJrCls; SecSrCls; HonRl; NHS; OffAde; RptrYrbk; EdSchPpr; 4-H; Wabash Vly Clg; Secretary.

GWIDT, Lisa; Lakeland Union HS; Woodruff, WI; 12/172 Chr; HonRl; HospAde; NHS; GerCl; Trk; Navy Hosp Corpsman; Lpn.

GWIN, Nancy S; Nashville Comm Cons HS; Nashville, IL; 27/137 FBLA; Bookkeeper.

GWINN, Daniel A; Waterford Mott HS; Pontiac, MI; Band; ChrhWkr; CncrtBnd; HonRl; MrchBnd; SchPl; StuCncl; RptrYrbk; Yrbk; Univ; Education.

GWYN, Julie A; Lake Fenton HS; Fenton, MI; 6/162 Chr; HonRl; SchPl; Yrbk; RptrSchPpr; 4-H; Chrldr; PPFtbl; 4-HAwd; University; Business.

GYLDENVAND, Mary A; Milnor Public HS; Milnor, ND; SecJrCls; Chrs; SchPl; SchPpr; SecFHA; VPPpCl; SecSciCl; Trk; Chrldr; Nd S U; Nursing.

GYSIN, Kathy L; Peru HS; Peru, IN; 41/221 HonRl; TchrAde; Chrldr; GAA; Ball State Univ; Physical Education.

H

H DOUBLER, Scott W; Greenwood Lab HS; Springfield, MO; 3/30 PresJrCls; ChrhWkr; HonRl; ModUN; StuCncl; EdSchPpr; LatCl; SpnCl; LetterFtbl; LetterGlf; Uni Of Mo; Medicine.

HAAB, Robert K; Forrest Strawn Wing HS; Forrest, IL; 4/42 PresSrCls; Chrs; NHS; SchPl; FFA; Bsbl; University; Education.

HAAG, Jeffery E; Plattsmouth HS; Plattsmouth, NE; Band; ChrhWkr; CncrtBnd; HonRl; MrchBnd; PepBnd; YthFlsp; LetterTrk; LetterWrstlng; GodCntryAwd; Kansas State Univ; Veterinarian.

HAAG, Joann M; St Marys HS; Fairfield, ND; 5/44 Chrs; HonRl; NHS; OffAde; SchAde; TchrAde; College; Rn.

HAAG, Judy R; Orient Macksburg HS; Orient, IA; Band; Chrs; HonRl; MrchBnd; PepBnd; SchMus; SchPl; StuCncl; Chrldr; Iowa State; Professional.

HAAG, Lorraine A; Taylors Falls HS; Cenyer City, MN; HonRl; OffAde; FHA; College; Business.

HAAG, Michael J; Fenwick HS; Winfield, IL; 14/223 NatlMeritCmnd; CaptSwmmng; IMSpt; University Of Illinois; Architecture.

HAAG, Monica M; Swea City Comm HS; Ledyard, IA; Band; HonRl; JrNHS; NHS; PepBnd; RptrYrbk; RptrSchPpr; FHA; Trk; Chrldr; U Of Northern Iowa; Accounting.

HAAG, Susan E; Belfield HS; Fairfield, ND; 3/64 Chr; Chrs; HonRl; NHS; SchMus; RptrSchPpr; 4-H; FBLA; PpCl; College; Nurse.

HAAGENSON, Kathryn; Baltic HS; Baltic, SD; 4/19 SecFrshCls; SecSophCls; VPJrCls; Band; College.

HAAK, Lee; Moberly HS; Moberly, MO; PresFrshCls; HstSophCls; HstJrCls; Chrs; CncrtBnd; PresJA; MrchBnd; StuCncl; StuGov; LetterFtbl; Arizona State Univ; Business Mgmt.

HAAK, Martin E; Sterling HS; Polo, IL; Chr; JA; SchMus; YthFlsp; FFA; GerCl; Tennis; College; Agriculture.

HAAKE, Joan; Duchesne HS; St Charles, MO; 18/135 HonRl; NHS; PolWkr; StuCncl; SchPpr; Col; Prof.

HAAKENSON, Jane L; Clifford Galesburg HS; Galesburg, ND; PresFrshCls; VPJrCls; Band; SchMus; StuCncl; EdYrBk; RptrSchPpr; FHA; CaptBsktbl; Trk; N D State Sch Of Sci.

HAAKENSON, Mark C; Oslo Public HS; Oslo, MN; Band; Chrs; SchPl; SptEdSchPpr; LetterFtbl; Vocational Sch; Farming.

HAAKENSTAD, Amy L; Souris Public HS; Souris, ND; 3/14 VPSophCls; ALAGirlsSt; Band; Chr; CncrtBnd; HonRl; PepBnd; SchMus; SchPl; YthFlsp; U Of Nd Grand Forks; Biology/chem.

HAAKONSEN, Kevin L; Cary Grove HS; Fox River Grove, IL; 1/263 ALBoysSt; CncrtBnd; HonRl; MrchBnd; NHS; PepBnd; RptrYrbk; SchPpr; Bsbl; IMSpt; Northwestern Univ; Math.

HAALAND, Robin; Lidgerwood Public HS; Lidgerwood, ND; VPFrshCls; TrsSophCls; PresJrCls; ALBoysSt; HonRl; NHS; SchPl; Ftbl; Trk; CitAwd; U Nd; Medical Doctor.

HAAPALAINEN, Vicki L; Newberry HS; New Berry, MI; PresSrCls; ChrhWkr; JrNHS; MrchBnd; NHS; OffAde; StuCncl; StuGov; YthFlsp; Yrbk; College; Medical Profession.

HAAPOJA, Jeffrey D; A D Johnston HS; Bessemer, MI; 24/104 TrsFrshCls; StuCncl; RptrYrbk; LetterBsbl; CaptBsktbl; CaptFtbl; LetterTrk; MrchBnd; College; Coaching.

HAAR, Kevin J; Chaminade HS; St Louis, MO; 8/107 ChrhWkr; HonRl; NHS; PresStuCncl; RptrYrbk; SchPpr; LetterBsbl; LetterBsktbl; LetterFtbl; Univ; Bs Engineering.

HAARER, Mark A; Elkton Pigeon Bay Port HS; Pigeon, MI; 3/146 ChrhWkr; HonRl; NHS; NatlMeritCmnd; GerCl; Goshen College; Mathematics Major.

HAARSTICK, Joseph P; Lincolnwood HS; Waggoner, IL; 10/63 Band; Chrs; CncrtBnd; HonRl; MrchBnd; Orch; PepBnd; SctActv; FTA; SpnCl; Siu; Auo.

HAAS, Andrea L; Owosso HS; Owosso, MI; CmntyWkr; NHS; RedCrAde; GAA;.

HAAS, Beverly A; Valders HS; Valders, WI; Chr; Chrs; HonRl; FHA; Trk; Univ; X Ray Tech.

HAAS, Bruce; Assumption HS; Wis Rapids, WI; 1/117 CncrtBnd; NHS; NatlMeritCmnd; PepBnd; SchMus; Marquette Univ; Law.

HAAS, Bruce R; Assumption HS; Wis Rapids, WI; 1/119 Chr; Chrs; CncrtBnd; MrchBnd; NHS; NatlMeritCmnd; PepBnd; SchMus; PresStuCncl; KeyCl; PresMthCl; LetterBsktbl; LetterFtbl; Univ Of Wis; Math.

HAAS, Cindy L; Markesan HS; Kingston, WI; 2/112 PresFrshCls; Band; CncrtBnd; HonRl; MrchBnd; NHS; PepBnd; RptrYrbk; VPSpnCl; GAA; University Of Wisconsin; Business.

HAAS, Cynthia K; Riverdale HS; Riverdale, ND; HonRl; NHS; SchPl; Yrbk; SchPpr; SecFHA; PpCl; LetterTrk; Chrldr; Trade; Secretarial.

HAAS, Danny A; Savanna HS; Savanna, IL; 13/65 PresSrCls; ChrhWkr; HonRl; NHS; TreasStuCncl; Pres4-H; Ftbl; Univ Of Illinois; Agriculture.

HAAS, Donna R; Forest Park HS; Birdseye, IN; HonRl; Quill&Scroll; RptrYrbk; Yrbk; RptrSchPpr; SchPpr; 4-H; FHA; PpCl; GAA;.

HAAS, Jaime L; Morgan Park HS; Chicago, IL; 11/550 Chrs; HonRl; NHS; NatlMeritCmnd; TreasQuill&Scroll; SchPl; SchPpr; KeyCl; Swmmng; JCAwd; Northwestern Univ; Journalism.

HAAS, Jeffrey L; Jefferson Sr HS; Jefferson, WI; CncrtBnd; HonRl; MrchBnd; NHS; NatlMeritCmnd; PepBnd; SchMus; SchPl; KeyCl; Bsktbl; LetterTennis; IMSpt; Univ Of Wis; Pharmacy.

HAAS, John P; John Marshall Jr Sr HS; Milwaukee, WI; 98/674 HonRl; NHS; NatlMeritCmnd; GerCl; MthCl; Univ Of Wi; Medical Tech.

HAAS, Laura J; Rich Central HS; Olympia Fields, IL; HonRl; SchAde; RptrYrbk; PpCl; CaptChrldr; GAA; PresAwd; University Of Arizona; Home Economics.

HAAS, Mary B; Hutchinson Sr HS; Hutchinson, MN; Band; Chr; HonRl; OffAde; PepBnd; TchrAde; 4-H; FHA; Business School; Secretary.

HAAS, Michael G; Sparta HS; Casnovia, MI; 82/209 ChrhWkr; CncrtBnd; HonRl; MrchBnd; FTA; Lawrence Inst Of Tech; Architecture.

HAAS, Nancy A; Southridge HS; Huntingburg, IN; 14/160 Band; ChrhWkr; CncrtBnd; HonRl; MrchBnd; PepBnd; SchMus; SctActv; YthFlsp; 4-HAwd;.

HAAS, Pamela S; Deland Weldon HS; Deland, IL; 3/38 TrsFrshCls; TrsSophCls; TrsJrCls; TrsSrCls; AFS; ALAGirlsSt; Chrs; ChrhWkr; HonRl; NHS; Eastern Il U; Elem & Spec Ed.

HAAS, Roberta L; Lidgerwood HS; Lidgerwood, ND; 3/49 ALAGirlsSt; ChrhWkr; HonRl; NHS; SchMus; SchPl; TchrAde; Yrbk; SchPpr; GerCl; Und; Elem Ed.

HAASE, Charles E; Beaver City HS; Beaver City, NE; 5/26 Aud/Vis; Chr; Chrs; HonRl; SchMus; SchPl; RptrYrbk; RptrSchPpr; LetterBsktbl; VoiceDemAwd; Univ Of Nebraska; Accounting.

HAASE, Kathie J; Friend HS; Friend, NE; Chrs; HonRl; LbryAde; College; Sociology.

HAASE, Kathryn; Parkers Prairie HS; Eagle Bend, MN; Band; Chr; HonRl; Mdrgl; NHS; BttyCrckrAwd; Bemidji State; Teach.

HAASE, Loraine M; Dodgeland HS; Juneau, WI; 5/76 AFS; Chr; Chrs; HonRl; NatlFornLg; NHS; TchrAde; RptrSchPpr; SchPpr; SpnCl; Uv Platteville; Criminal Justice.

HAASE, Mitchell P; Plainfield HS; Plainfield, IN; 54/260 ALBoysSt; HonRl; JrNHS; StuCncl; CaptFtbl; LetterTrk; Purdue University; Business.

HAASE, Yvonne A; New Haven HS; New Haven, MI; Band; ChrhWkr; CncrtBnd; HonRl; JA; LbryAde; MrchBnd; NHS; PepBnd; SctActv;.

HAASL, Dolores M; J F Kennedy HS; Babbitt, MN; 5/145 TrsJrCls; Chr; DrmBgl; HonRl; Mdrgl; NHS; SchMus; Yrbk; LetterTrk; Chrldr; College Of St Scholastica; Med Tech.

HAATAJA, Nancy E; Calumet HS; Calumet, MI; HonRl; NHS; 4-H; 4-HAwd;.

HAATAJA, Ranae; Eveleth Senior HS; Eveleth, MN; 25/166 Chr; Chrs; NHS; OffAde; Yrbk; 4-H; FHA; SecTrsSophCls; Trk; 4-HAwd; Hibbing Comm College; Nursing.

HAAVISTO, Mary E; Menahga Public HS; Menagha, MN; 19/53 Chr; HonRl; LbryAde; PpCl; LetterBsktbl; LetterTrk; Fergus Falls Comm Clg; Educational Aide.

HABERER, Beth R; Greenville HS; Greenville, IL; NHS; Quill&Scroll; SchMus; SchPl; RptrYrbk; EdYrBk; FTA; University; Accounting.

HABERER, Jeffery E; Perry Comm HS; Woodward, IA; HonRl; NHS; NatlThespSoc; Quill&Scroll; SchMus; SchPl; RptrSchPpr; 4-H; LetterFtbl; LetterTrk; Univ Of Ia; Arts.

HABERLAND, Gail M; Glenbrook North HS; Northbrook, IL; 112/604 Chrs; HonRl; College; Professional.

HABERLAND, Mary E; Middleton HS; Middletown, WI; Chr; CncrtBnd; HonRl; MrchBnd; NHS; Orch; PepBnd; SchMus; SpnCl; SciCl; Univ Of Wisconsin Madison; Science.

HABERLAND, Todd; T L Handy HS; Bay City, MI; 15/375 PresSophCls; PresSrCls; HonRl; JA; NHS; CchngActv; IMSpt; College; Data Processing.

HABERMAN, David J; Parkview HS; Janesville, WI; 15/163 Band; HonRl; NHS; 4-H; PresFFA; Univ Of Wisc; Dairy Science.

HABERMAN, Douglas J; Aquinas HS; La Crosse, WI; 10/201 HonRl; JrNHS; NHS; University; Biomedical.

HABERMEHL, Cathy L; O Fallon Township HS; O Fallon, IL; SecJrCls; SecSrCls; HonRl; NHS; FSA; VPFrCl; PpCl; SciCl; Eastern Ill Univ; Merchandising.

HABISCH, Mark A; Central HS; Norwood, MN; 2/94 TrsSophCls; CncrtBnd; MrchBnd; NHS; StuCncl; CaptBsktbl; LetterTrk; College; Professional.

HABLER, Betty L; Marian HS; Omaha, NE; 5/162 Chr; ChrhWkr; HonRl; NatlFornLg; NHS; NatlThespSoc; SchMus; SchPl; PresFTA; MthCl; Creighton U; Doctor.

HABLUETZEL, Tracy; Clay Center Community HS; Clay Center, KS; /137 CmntyWkr; HonRl; YthFlsp; FTA; SciCl; Trk; PresAwd; RotaryAwd; Wichitee State; Engr.

HABREL, Eric J; Badger HS; Genoa, WI; Band; CmntyWkr; CncrtBnd; HonRl; NHS; LetterBsbl; Bsktbl; College.

HACHINSKY, Annette C; Bishop Ward HS; Kansas City, KS; Chrl; Chrs; ChrhWkr; HonRl; NHS; OffAde; SchMus; PpCl; Trk; College.

HACHMAN, Barbara L; Ida HS; Temperance, MI; HstSrCls; Chr; Chrs; HonRl; NatlThespSoc; SchMus; SchPl; StuGov; 4-H; IMSpt; College; Social Service Or Legal Tech.

HACHMEISTER, Vicki L; Southridge HS; Huntingburg, IN; TrsJrCls; DrlTm; MrchBnd; PepBnd; YthFlsp; FrCl; PpCl; LetterSwmmng; LetterTrk; GAA; PPFtbl; College; Professional.

HACK, Bonnie J; Mosinee Sr HS; Mosinee, WI; 40/176 SecSrCls; Chrs; CncrtBnd; HonRl; SchMus; Twrl; PpCl; LetterChrldr; University Of Wisconsin; Biology.

HACK, Jana C; Huntington North HS; South Whitley, IN; Band; ChrhWkr; CncrtBnd; DrmMjrt; MrchBnd; PepBnd; Twrl; YthFlsp; 4-H; 4-HAwd; College; Social Worker.

HACKAMACK, David L; Dekalb Sr HS; Dekalb, IL; 20/365 ChrhWkr; HonRl; College; Computers.

HACKBARDT, Kim A; Tri County HS; Howard City, MI; 14/95 PresFrshCls; VPSrCls; Band; CncrtBnd; HonRl; MrchBnd; PepBnd; StuCncl; CaptFtbl; College Msu; Teaching.

HACKBART, Dana R; Seward HS; Seward, NE; Chr; ChrhWkr; DrlTm; SchMus; 4-H; PresFHA; PpCl; Bsktbl; 4-HAwd; GovHonPrgAwd; Business School; Secretary.

HACKBARTH, Cheryl A; Merrill Sr HS; Merrill, WI; 47/354 Chr; ChrhWkr; CmntyWkr; HonRl; HospAde; 4-H; GerCl; Bsktbl; LetterTrk; GAA; IMSpt; 4-HAwd; Technical Inst; Nursing.

HACKBARTH, Paul A; Iowa Falls HS; Iowa Falls, IA; 11/145 CmntyWkr; HonRl; NHS; FFA; LetterWrstlng; Iowa State Univ; Agriculture.

HACKBARTH, Sharon D; Campbellsport HS; St Cloud, WI; 70/150 Chrs; HonRl; Trade School Accounting; Professional.

HACKBUSH, Cynthia L; Oak Park & River Forest HS; Oak Park, IL; 69/1200 ChrhWkr; CmntyWkr; HonRl; OffAde; Depaul Univ; Business Adm.

HACKENBURG, Karen S; Marshall HS; Marshall, MI; 30#41#44 OffAde; SchMus; TchrAde; SpnCl; PpCl; JAAwd; Col; Secretary.

HACKER, Jeff D; Casey HS; Martinsville, IL; 2/93 Chr; NHS; OffAde; SchMus; 4-H; Bsbl; Ftbl; IMSpt; College; Electrical Engr.

HACKER, Joseph C; Public HS; Sleepy Eye, MN; Chr; Chrs; SchPl; Trade; Professional.

HACKER, Lisa A; West Washington HS; Fredericksburg, IN; HstJrCls; Band; Chr; CmntyWkr; DrmBgl; MrchBnd; OffAde; SchPl; TchrAde; YthFlsp; RptrSchPpr; Treas4-H; FHA; PpCl; Trk; College; Psychology.

HACKER, Mary; Lawton Bronson HS; Lawton, IA; /65 SecSophCls; Band; Chrs; ChrhWkr; CmntyWkr; CncrtBnd; Bsbl; Bsktbl; Trk; PresAwd; Univ; Nursing.

HACKEROTT, Melanie G; Natoma HS; Alton, KS; 4/29 Band; Chrs; ChrhWkr; CncrtBnd; HonRl; MrchBnd; PepBnd; SchPl; StuCncl; Twrl; Chrldr; Kansas State Univ; Education.

HACKERT, Mark F; High School; Palisade, NE; 1/13 Chr; Chrs; ChrhWkr; CmntyWkr; SchPl; SctActv; StuCncl; Bsktbl; Ftbl; Trk; College; Prof.

HACKETT, Cheryl L; Charleston HS; Charleston, IL; 49/237 HonRl; LbryAde; MrchBnd; RptrSchPpr; SchPpr; Chrldr; PPFtbl; Eastern Il U; Social Work.

HACKETT, David W; Willow Springs HS; Willow Springs, MO; 18/98 ALBoysSt; Band; Chr; CmntyWkr; CncrtBnd; HonRl; MrchBnd; PepBnd; SctActv; RptrSchPpr; University Of Missouri; Aerospace Engineer.

HACKETT, Joel A; Catholic Central HS; Detroit, MI; 21/205 TrsSrCls; Band; ChrhWkr; CmntyWkr; HonRl; MrchBnd; NHS; NatlMeritCmnd; Bsbl; Bsktbl; Ftbl; Trk; Univ Of Mi; Dentist.

HACKETT, John S; Waterville Elysian HS; Kilkenny, MN; PresSophCls; HonRl; StuCncl; SptEdSchPpr; LetterBsktbl; LetterFtbl; CaptTrk; PresAwd; College;.

HACKETT, Marifaith; St Scholastica HS; Chicago, IL; 1/242 Chrs; HospAde; NHS; NatlMeritSF; Quill&Scroll; SchPl; StuCncl; RptrSchPpr; EdSchPpr; College; Biology.

HACKETT, Mary E; Notre Dame HS; Chicago, IL; 11/302 Chrl; HonRl; NHS; NatlMeritCmnd; Chrldr; College; Lawyer.

HACKI, Lynn M; Darlington HS; Darlington, WI; TrsSophCls; ALAGirlsSt; Band; Chrs; CncrtBnd; HonRl; MrchBnd; NatlFornLg; FHA; PpCl; Chrldr; Univ Of Osh Kosh; Sociology.

HACKLEY, Michael P; St Xaviers HS; Junction City, KS; PresFrshCls; TrsSophCls; TrsJrCls; HonRl; StuCncl; StuGov; TchrAde; Bsktbl; LetterFtbl; College; Chemistry.

HACKMAN, Ann; Columbus HS; Marshfield, WI; 6/104 SecTrsSophCls; Band; ChrhWkr; HonRl; NHS; SchMus; RptrYrbk; FrCl; MthCl; U Of Eau Claire; Music.

HACKMAN, Connie K; New Franklin HS; Fayette, MO; 3/50 SecFrshCls; Chr; ChrhWkr; HonRl; NHS; YthFlsp; 4-H; FHA; SpnCl; PpCl; LetterBsbl; LetterBsktbl; LetterTrk; College; Social Worker.

HACKMAN, Thomas J; Prospect HS; Arlington Hts, IL; 244/610 HonRl; SchPl; De Paul Univ; Mathematics.

HACKNEY, Peggy J; Granite City Senior HS; Granite City, IL; 116/550 Aud/Vis; ChrhWkr; JA; LbryAde; StuCncl; SpnCl; Ftbl; JAAwd; Sw Missouri State Univ; Phys Ed Of Elem.

HACKWITH, Randeen L; Plattsmouth HS; Plattsmouth, NE; 38/163 Band; Chrs; DrlTm; HonRl; Mdrgl; MrchBnd; SchPl; SctActv; PpCl; Swmmng; Univ Of Nebraska; Teacher.

HADDAS, Raymond; Sterling Heights HS; Sterling Hgts, MI; HonRl; HospAde; IMSpt; Wayne State Univ; Pre Medicine.

HADDEN, Carl D; High School; Hamlet, IN; ALBoysSt; ChrhWkr; SchAde; YthFlsp; MthCl; Bsbl; Wrstlng; IMSpt; Trade School; Professional.

HADDEN, Cynthia K; Onsted HS; Onsted, MI; PresFrshCls; Band; CncrtBnd; HonRl; MrchBnd; StuCncl; CaptBsktbl; CaptTrk; GAA; CaptIMSpt; St Vincents Sch Of Nursing; Rn.

HADDEN, Linda K; St Francis HS; Cedar, MN; 15/150 HonRl; 4-H; FFA; BttyCrckrAwd; Tech; Comp Prog.

HADDOCK, Stanley I; Solomon HS; Solomon, KS; SecFrshCls; HonRl; PolWkr; SctActv; TreasStuCncl; PresYthFlsp; VPFFA; LetterBsktbl; LetterFtbl; LetterHstSophCls; Kansas State; Electronics.

HADDOCK, Stephanie L; Solomon HS; Solomon, KS; PresFrshCls; ChrhWkr; HonRl; PolWkr; SctActv; YthFlsp; RptrSchPpr; FHA; PpCl; Chrldr; Asbury Schl Of Nursing; Rn.

HADDON, Micheal; Southwestern Heights HS; Plains, KS; HonRl; JrNHS; NHS; SctActv; TchrAde; YthFlsp; 4-H; FFA; Bsktbl; Ftbl; Coll.

HADEN, Donald; Lytton Community HS; Lytton, IA; 1/25 ALBoysSt; Chrs; NHS; StuCncl; FFA; 4-HAwd; Univ; Engineering.

HADENFELDT, David; Kenesaw Public HS; Juniata, NE; 1/30 VPFrshCls; ALBoysSt; Chrs; ChrhWkr; HonRl; YthFlsp;.

HADFIELD, Maye Beth V; El Paso HS; El Paso, IL; AFS; Band; HonRl; NHS; SchPl; StuCncl; SpnCl; MthCl; Chrldr; VPGAA; College.

HADLAND, Erik M; Eisenhower HS; Hopkins, MN; Chr; ChrhWkr; CncrtBnd; Mdrgl; MrchBnd; SchMus; SchPl; Bsktbl; Socr; LetterTrk; College; Professional.

HADLEY, Joyce A; Manlius HS; Sheffield, IL; 4/26 VPJrCls; PresSrCls; Band; Chrs; JrNHS; SchPl; StuCncl; VP4-H; TreasFHA; Chrldr; Univ Of Ill; Speech.

HADLEY, Linda S; Fairfield Community HS; Fairfield, IA; ChrhWkr; HonRl; LbryAde; SchMus; SchPl; 4-H; SpnCl; SciCl; 4-HAwd;.

HADLEY, Patricia A; Franklin HS; Westland, MI; ChrhWkr; CmntyWkr; HonRl; JA; SctActv; Northwood Inst; Merchandising.

HADLEY, Stanton W; Southwest HS; Kansas City, MO; 15/492 Chr; Chrs; HonRl; NatlFornLg; NatlMeritSF; PolWkr; SchMus; SchPl; StuCncl; RusCl; SciCl; Univ; Engineer.

HADLEY, Stuart D; Audubon HS; Audubon, IA; 8/120 ALBoysSt; Band; HonRl; ModUN; VPNHS; PresStuCncl; LetterBsbl; LetterFtbl; Glf; LetterTennis; College.

HADLOCK, Michael R; Custer HS; Pringle, SD; CmntyWkr; JA; NHS; PolWkr; YthFlsp; 4-H; Bsktbl; Ftbl; Swmmng; Trk; CchngActv;.

HADUCH, Cynthia M; Kennedy/st Paul HS; Chicago, IL; CmntyWkr; HonRl; LbryAde; StuCncl; TchrAde; RptrYrbk; RptrSchPpr; FrCl; HstSrCls; Jr Col; Dat Rpocessting.

HAEFLI, Jeanne E; Richwoods HS; Peoria, IL; 75/476 Chr; Chrs; ChrhWkr; CmntyWkr; DrlTm; HonRl; HospAde; NHS; 4-H; Methodist Hosp Schl Nursing; Rn.

HAEFNER, Carol; Pioneer HS; Ann Arbor, MI; HonRl; NatlMeritSchl; Orch; Carleton College.

HAEFNER, Jane M; St Pius HS; Imperial, MO; ALAGirlsSt; HonRl; Yrbk; RptrSchPpr; PpCl; LetterTrk; GAA; AmLegAwd; College; Doctor.

HAEFNER, Jeremy; West HS; Iowa City, IA; 1/290 Band; HonRl; JrNHS; NatlFornLg; StuCncl; StuGov;.

HAEFNER, Lee G; Loyola HS; Mankato, MN; Chrs; HonRl; NHS; NatlMeritSF; SchMus; StuCncl; LetterFtbl; LetterTrk; Texas Am Univ; Meteorology.

HAEFS, Evelyn; La Crescent Sr HS; La Crescent, MN; 6/150 Aud/Vis; Chr; CncrtBnd; HonRl; LbryAde; MrchBnd; PepBnd; TchrAde; FHA; GerCl; Univ Of Wi; Pharmacy Major.

HAEGER, Kimberly A; Rolling Meadows HS; Arlington Heights, IL; CmntyWkr; DrlTm; HonRl; HospAde; TchrAde; Western Ill Univ; Business.

HAEHLKE, Donald; Merrill HS; Hamburg, WI; 4/352 HonRl; College; Engineering.

HAESE, Kathleen M; Elgin HS; Elgin, IL; Chr; ChrhWkr; CmntyWkr; PolWkr; SchPl; StuCncl; LatCl; Bsktbl; Trk; Chrldr; GAA; College; Professional.

HAESE, William; Wrightstown HS; Greenleaf, WI; PresFrshCls; HonRl; StuCncl; StuGov; MthCl; PpCl; IMSpt; Univ; Curr Of Major Study.

HAEUSLER, Linda M; T L Handy HS; Bay City, MI; 2/365 HonRl; NHS; NatlMeritCmnd; StuCncl; SchPpr; PpCl; CaptChrldr; GAA; PresAwd; Mi U ;data Processing.

HAFELE, Cindy K; St Marys HS; Bowman, ND; Chrs; HonRl; SchPl; PpCl;.

HAFENSTEIN, Norma Lu; Wabaunsee HS; Alma, KS; 1/39 PresJrCls; ALAGirlsSt; Band; ChrhWkr; HonRl; SchPl; StuCncl; Yrbk; Sec4-H; Chrldr; 4-HAwd; College; Music.

HAFER, Susan; Geneva Public HS; Geneva, NE; 9/64 ALAGirlsSt; Chrs; CncrtBnd; HonRl; MrchBnd; NHS; PepBnd; StuCncl; 4-H; PpCl; College; Professional.

HAFERBIER, Julie E; East Central HS; Green Island, IA; CncrtBnd; Mdrgl; PepBnd; Bsktbl; Business School; Executive Secretary.

HAFERMANN, Bethel; Lincoln HS; Wisconsin Rapids, WI; Chr; Chrs; ChrhWkr; HonRl; Mdrgl; NHS; SchMus; Dr Martin Luther College; Elementary Teache.

HAFERMANN, David D; Meservey Thornton HS; Thornton, IA; PresSophCls; Band; HonRl; NHS; SchPl; StuCncl; Coll; Elec Eng.

HAFF, Cinda K; Frontier HS; Brookston, IN; Band; Chr; CncrtBnd; HonRl; LbryAde; MrchBnd; PepBnd; TchrAde; 4-H; PpCl; Purdue Univ; Physical Education.

HAFF, William A; Milan HS; Watson, MN; Band; Chr; CncrtBnd; HonRl; Orch; PepBnd; SchPl; TchrAde; SptEdSchPpr; CaptBsktbl; Trade School; Vocation.

HAFFEY, Randy L; Hale R 1 HS; Hale, MO; PresSophCls; PresJrCls; Aud/Vis; HonRl; ModUN; NatlFornLg; NatlThespSoc; StuCncl; StuGov; LetterBsktbl; Coll; Prof.

HAFFNER, Robert A; Palmyra HS; Eagle, WI; HonRl; 4-H; Wrstlng; Uw Whitewater; Vet.

HAGA, Karen S; Covington Community HS; Covington, IN; 16/93 Chr; Chrs; ChrhWkr; HonRl; LbryAde; FHA; College; History.

HAGALE, John E; Springfield Catholic HS; Springfield, MO; VPJrCls; HonRl; ModUN; PresStuCncl; StuGov; PresLatCl; Bsbl; Bsktbl; Trk; OptClAwd; Coll; Bus.

HAGALE, Thomas J; Springfield Catholic HS; Springfield, MO; Aud/Vis; Chrs; HonRl; YthLg; LatCl; TreasSciCl; Bsktbl; Tennis; IMSpt; U Of Mo;aerospace Eng.

HAGAN, Cynthia L; E R HS; Olney, IL; 10/258 VPFrshCls; Band; Chr; Chrs; CncrtBnd; JrNHS; Mdrgl; MrchBnd; NHS; PepBnd; SchMus; StuGov; Greenville College; Art.

HAGAN, Cynthia S; North Side HS; Ft Wayne, IN; StuCncl; StuGov; Yrbk; RptrSchPpr; University; Nursing.

HAGAN, Michael J; Fruitport HS; Muskegon, MI; 1/289 Band; CncrtBnd; HonRl; MrchBnd; NHS; SctActv; MthCl; Bsktbl; IMSpt; LionAwd; Michigan State U; Business Admn.

HAGAR, Kathy S; Lincoln County Rii HS; Elsberry, MO; HonRl; NHS; TchrAde; Business School; Secretary.

HAGBERG, Mark K; Monte HS; Montevideo, MN; AFS; ChrhWkr; HonRl; LetterBsktbl; LetterFtbl; LetterTennis; Concordia Coll, Moorhead; Pre Med.

HAGE, Pamela G; Gibson Southern HS; Princeton, IN; Chr; ChrhWkr; Orch; SchMus; RptrYrbk; FHA; LatCl; University Of Evansville; Social Worker.

HAGE, Sandra F; New Ulm Sr HS; Hanska, MN; 6/241 ALAGirlsSt; ChrhWkr; LbryAde; SptEdYrbk; RptrSchPpr; SpnCl; CaptBsktbl; LetterTrk; Mankato State College.

HAGEDORN, Doris; Central Catholic HS; West Point, NE; 6/67 Chrs; HonRl; NHS; SchMus; 4-H; SpnCl; MthCl; PpCl; Trk; 4-HAwd; Nursing.

HAGEDORN, John J; Spencer Community HS; Spencer, IA; ALBoysSt; Band; CncrtBnd; MrchBnd; Orch; PepBnd; RptrSchPpr; SpnCl; LetterBsktbl; Trk; Univ.

HAGEDORN, Julie A; North HS; Eau Claire, WI; 1/365 HonRl; JrNHS; NHS; SpnCl; PpCl; IMSpt; Univ; Medical Field.

HAGEDORN, Kristin J; Jefferson Community HS; Jefferson, IA; Chr; Chrs; HonRl; NHS; Quill&Scroll; SchMus; RptrSchPpr; LetterSwmmng; LetterTrk; Univ ;recreation.

HAGEDORN, La Donna J; Central Catholic HS; West Point, NE; HonRl; RedCrAde; RptrYrbk; Yrbk; RptrSchPpr; LatCl; Business School.

HAGEL, Denise A; Dunseith Public HS; San Haven, ND; 1/25 HstJrCls; ALAGirlsSt; Chr; Chrs; HonRl; JrNHS; NHS; VPStuCncl; YthFlsp; EdYrBk; Yrbk; SchPpr; 4-H; PpCl; Trk; College; Liberal Arts.

HAGEL, Odell; Rugby HS; Orrin, ND; VPSrCls; Chrs; HonRl; 4-H; FFA; Trade School; Carpentry.

HAGELE, Joseph C; Griffin HS; Springfield, IL; SecFrshCls; Sacrstn; StuCncl; RptrYrbk; PpCl; Ftbl; Wrstlng; IMSpt; Medicine.

HAGEMAN, Linda; Jamaica HS; Fairmount, IL; 3/50 Band; HonRl; SchMus; RptrYrbk; Chrldr; DARAwd; Univ Illinois; Finance.

HAGEMAN, Pamela J; Wahoo Public HS; Ithaca, NE; Chrs; HonRl; YthFlsp; 4-H; PpCl; Trk; University; Professional.

HAGEMAN, Steve J; South Newton HS; Brook, IN; 32/94 HonRl; VPFFA; 4-HAwd; Purdue Univ; Farming.

HAGEMEIER, Martha L; Lincoln HS; Elsberry, MO; 8/59 HonRl; NHS; Twrl; FBLA; FHA; PpCl; Nmsu; Business.

HAGEMEYER, Bethleen; Sandy Creek HS; Fairfield, NE; Band; CncrtBnd; MrchBnd; PepBnd; Kearney State College; Law Enforcement.

HAGEMEYER, Sandra K; Clara City HS; Clara City, MN; Band; Chr; CncrtBnd; HonRl; NHS; PepBnd; Coll; Nursing.

HAGEN, Ann M; Dixon HS; Dixon, IL; 52/350 HonRl; JA; SchAde; SchPl; 4-H; College; Social Work.

HAGEN, Arlo J; Grygla HS; Grygla, MN; VPFrshCls; VPJrCls; ChrhWkr; HonRl; YthFlsp; LetterFtbl; LetterTrk; College.

HAGEN, Coleen K; Hillsboro HS; Hillsboro, KS; ALAGirlsSt; DrmMjrt; HonRl; EdYrBk; Chrldr; College; Accounting.

HAGEN, Deborah K; Mater Dei HS; Breese, IL; Sacrstn; SchMus; SchPl; FBLA; SpnCl; Swmmng; LetterTrk; Chrldr; CchngActv;.

HAGEN, Gary A; Ingalls HS; Ingalls, KS; 3/23 SecTrsJrCls; SecTrsSrCls; VPBand; ChrhWkr; CncrtBnd; HonRl; NHS; PepBnd; SchPl; Yrbk; College; Business.

HAGEN, Jeffrey W; Northwood Public HS; Aneta, ND; ALBoysSt; HonRl; StuCncl; LetterWrstlng; University.

HAGEN, Jeffry D; Anamosa Community HS; Anamosa, IA; 8/138 ChrhWkr; CncrtBnd; HonRl; MrchBnd; PepBnd; SchMus; SchPl; SciCl; LetterFtbl; LetterTrk; Ia St Univ; Agri Business.

HAGEN, John P; Rhinelander HS; Rhinelander, WI; CmntyWkr; HonRl; RedCrAde; SctActv; 4-H; Ftbl; 4-HAwd; KiwanAwd; OptClAwd; U S Navy; Medicine.

HAGEN, Jon; Waupaca HS; Waupaca, WI; VPJrCls; HonRl; RedCrAde; StuCncl; StuGov; Bsbl; Bsktbl; Ftbl; CchngActv; IMSpt; College; Athletic Trainer.

HAGEN, Judy M; Cooperstown HS; Cooperstown, ND; Band; HonRl; NHS; EdSchPpr; 4-H; PresFHA; PpCl; CaptBsktbl; Trk; Chrldr; Lutheran Coll.

HAGEN, Linda B; West HS; Green Bay, WI; 27/390 Band; Chrs; CncrtBnd; Mdrgl; MrchBnd; PepBnd; SchMus; SpnCl; Psycholohy.

HAGEN, Mark; Charles Community HGS; Charles City, IA; VPJrCls; MthCl; Ia State; Biological Field.

HAGEN, Mark J; Kiester HS; Kiester, MN; 4/30 Band; Chrs; ChrhWkr; HonRl; SchMus; SchPl; RptrYrbk; SptEdSchPpr; LetterBsktbl; LetterFtbl; LetterTrk; Mankato State Univ; Accounting.

HAGEN, Pamela S; Clinton HS; Clinton, IL; 28/160 VPJrCls; SecTrsSrCls; ChrhWkr; HonRl; NHS; SchPl; YthFlsp; 4-H; Bsktbl; GAA; DanFAwd; Ill State Univ; Recreation.

HAGEN, Rosemary; Bayard HS; Minature, NE; 22/42 Chrs; HonRl; JA; LbryAde; SchPl; Business Schl; Business.

HAGEN, Shelley E; Riverdale HS; Muscoda, WI; AFS; Chrs; ChrhWkr; HonRl; LbryAde; NatlFornLg; NatlSciFnd; OffAde; PepBnd; SchAde; College; Nursing.

HAGENBUCH, Curtis A; Ottawa Twp HS; Utica, IL; 59/425 HonRl; NatlFornLg; NHS; NatlMeritCmnd; NatlThespSoc; SchPl; 4-H; 4-HAwd; Univ Of Illinois; Engineer.

HAGENBUSH, Elizabeth A; North Miami HS; Peru, IN; Chr; Chrs; HonRl; PolWkr; SchPl; StuCncl; Yrbk; LatCl; Ftbl; GAA; Indiana University; Interior Design.

HAGENESS, Sherry; Eleva Strum Central HS; Eleva, WI; 11/72 Band; Chr; Chrs; CncrtBnd; HonRl; MrchBnd; PepBnd; Chrldr; GAA; 4-HAwd; College; Music Maor.

HAGER, Clemans J; Towner HS; Towner, ND; Band; Chr; Chrs; CncrtBnd; HonRl; MrchBnd; SchPl; LetterBsktbl; LetterFtbl; LetterTrk; College; Teacher.

HAGER, Connie L; Wyndmere Public HS; Wyndmere, ND; ALAGirlsSt; Band; Chr; CmntyWkr; HonRl; SchPl; FHA; LetterBsktbl; LetterTrk; CchngActv; Science Sch; License Pratical Nurse.

HAGER, Cynthia S; La Porte City HS; La Porte City, IA; 4/69 SchPl; Chrs; CmntyWkr; HonRl; NHS; NatlThespSoc; StuCncl; YthFlsp; 4-H; PpCl; Iowa State U; Accounting.

HAGER, John; 11th & Douglas HS; Sioux City, IA; ChrhWkr; HonRl; ModUN; StuGov; YthFlsp; SpnCl; Univ Of Notre Dame; Business Major.

HAGER, John; Depere HS; Depere, WI; 1/210 CtyCnl; HonRl; IntrClCncl; JA; JrNHS; LitMag; NHS; PolWkr; SctActv; StuCncl; StuGov; TchrAde; SptEdYrbk; SptEdSchPpr; SchPpr; U Of Whitewater; Business Administration.

HAGER, Joseph P; Wyndmere Public HS; Wyndmere, ND; PresFrshCls; VPSophCls; VPJrCls; PresSrCls; HonRl; NHS; StuCncl; RptrSchPpr; FFA; LetterFtbl; Nd State Schl Of Science; Eng.

HAGER, Michele R; Kalkaska HS; Kalkaska, MI; 7/133 Aud/Vis; HonRl; HospAde; NHS; OffAde; SctActv; TchrAde; RptrYrbk; RptrSchPpr; GAA; BttyCrckrAwd; College; Special Education.

HAGERMAN, Ralph K; Bronaygh HS; Moundville, MO; Band; CncrtBnd; MrchBnd; PepBnd; SchPpr; FFA; Bsbl; Bsktbl; Trk; Trade Sch.

HAGERTY, Brigid M; Immaculata HS; Detroit, MI; 23/106 HonRl; U Of Detroit; Political Science.

HAGERTY, James D; Fraser HS; Fraser, MI; ChrhWkr; HonRl; PolWkr; StuCncl; YthFlsp; FBLA; Ftbl; Wrstlng; CchngActv; IMSpt; College; Professional.

HAGGITH, Pamela L; Bay View HS; Milwaukee, WI; 1/550 Band; ChrhWkr; CncrtBnd; HonRl; MrchBnd; OffAde; Orch; PepBnd; SecFNA;.

HAGLER, Jene E; Arnold HS; Arnold, NE; SecFrshCls; SecSophCls; Chr; Chrs; ChrhWkr; DrlTm; HonRl; FHA; PpCl; CaptChrldr; Univ Of Nebraska; Vocational.

HAGLUND, Eric J; Tawas Area HS; East Tawas, MI; PresFrshCls; HonRl; LitMag; SchPl; StuCncl; EdSchPpr; SptEdSchPpr; KeyCl; Trk; IMSpt; U Of Mi State; Radio Broadcasting.

HAGLUND, Robbie J; Northwestern HS; Wentworth, WI; Band; Chr; ChrhWkr; CncrtBnd; HonRl; LbryAde; MrchBnd; PepBnd; LetterBsktbl; LetterGlf; College; Mathematics.

HAGMAN, Camille J; Gladstone HS; Gladstone, MI; 1/171 HonRl; NHS; StuGov; Bay De Noc Community College; Business Admi.

HAGNESS, Janet; Durand HS; Durand, WI; Band; ChrhWkr; HonRl; NHS; SchPl; RptrYrbk; Luther College; Elementary Ed.

HAGNI, Ann M; Rolla HS; Rolla, MO; 17/307 ChrhWkr; CmntyWkr; HonRl; NatlFornLg; StuGov; VPYthFlsp; SecFTA; GerCl; IMSpt; VoiceDemAwd; Univ Mo Rolla.

HAGOPIAN, Lisa L; Fordson HS; Dearborn, MI; ChrhWkr; HospAde; NHS; Orch; SchMus; Henry Ford Comm College; Music Therapy.

HAGSTROM, Jane; Minnehaha Acad; St Paul, MN; 13/125 Chr; ChrhWkr; CncrtBnd; HonRl; PepBnd; Yrbk; SpnCl; PpCl; Northwestern Bible College.

HAGUEWOOD, James H; Ash Grove HS; Bois D Arc, MO; Chr; Chrs; ChrhWkr; CmntyWkr; ModUN; SptEdSchPpr; FBLA; FSA; SciCl; Sms Univ; Bs In Business.

HAHN, Bernice A; Keota Comm HS; Keota, IA; Band; HonRl; LbryAde; NatlMeritSF; Yrbk; SchPpr; 4-H; Bsktbl; CchngActv; BttyCrckrAwd; College; Law.

HAHN, Betty; Kingston HS; Kingston, MI; Band; HonRl; LbryAde; MrchBnd; OffAde; SchPl; TchrAde; FHA; CitAwd; Delta Coll; Drawing.

HAHN, Carol M; Lewis Central HS; Council Bluffs, IA; 3/188 HonRl; HospAde; NHS; TchrAde; Pres4-H; FHA; 4-HAwd;.

HAHN, Carolyn S; Salem Community HS; Iuka, IL; 29/208 HonRl; Yrbk; 4-H; FFA; SpnCl; Deaconess Hospital; Professional.

HAHN, Christine M; Oak Park River Forest HS; Oak Park, IL; ChrhWkr; CmntyWkr; HonRl; Trk; Univ Of Il; Biology.

HAHN, Clifford W; Mt Pulaski HS; Elkhart, IL; VPSophCls; VPJrCls; FFA; PpCl; Bsbl; Bsktbl; Trk; Trade School; Mechanic.

HAHN, Cynthia A; New Trier West HS; Winnetka, IL; 36/693 Band; CncrtBnd; HonRl; NatlMeritCmnd; Orch; PepBnd; SchMus; StuGov; FDA; University; Biology.

HAHN, Cynthia M; E Richland HS; Olney, IL; HospAde; TchrAde; RptrYrbk; Olney Central College; Accountant.

HAHN, David H; Mt Zion HS; Mt Zion, IL; 12/195 AFS; ChrhWkr; HonRl; NHS; SctActv; LetterBsktbl; Ftbl; LetterTrk; Bethany College; Chemistry.

HAHN, Deborah; Macomb Hs; Macomb, IL; Chr; HonRl; Mdrgl; NHS; NatlThespSoc; SchMus; SchPl; YthFlsp; SciCl; GAA; Taylor U; Speech Audiology.

HAHN, Deborah; Macomb HS; Macomb, IL; 22/242 Chr; Chrs; CncrtBnd; HonRl; Mdrgl; NHS; NatlThespSoc; SchMus; SchPl; YthFlsp; Taylor Univ.

HAHN, Donald; Chaffee HS; Wheatland, ND; 1/11 PresSrCls; ALBoysSt; Chr; ChrhWkr; HonRl; StuCncl; EdYrBk; 4-H; Ftbl; Trk; N D School Of Science; Farm.

HAHN, Gayle; Lawton HS; Lawton, MI; HonRl; SchMus; SchPl; SctActv; TchrAde; SpnCl; PpCl; Chrldr; College; Languages.

HAHN, Jane E; North County HS; Desloge, MO; 54/165 ChrhWkr; HospAde; TchrAde; Southeast Missouri State Univ; Nurse.

HAHN, Kison; Sullivan HS; Chicago, IL; 28/276 ChrhWkr; HonRl; NHS; ROTC; YthFnd; University Of Chicago; Economics.

HAHN, Mark S; Lincoln HS; Warren, MI; ChrhWkr; HonRl; NatlFornLg; OffAde; RptrSchPpr; SpnCl; SciCl; Tennis; Baptist Bible Clg; Christian Education.

HAHN, Michael; Solomon HS; New Cambria, KS; Band; HonRl; MrchBnd; PepBnd; FFA; GerCl; Bsktbl; Trade Sch; Vocation.

HAHN, Michael R; Newman HS; Newman, IL; 1/40 VPFrshCls; PresSophCls; HonRl; StuCncl; College; Math.

HAHN, Patrice E; Hampton Public HS; Hampton, NE; 1/18 SecJrCls; Band; ChrhWkr; CncrtBnd; HonRl; MrchBnd; SchAde; SctActv; YthFlsp; PpCl; IMSpt; College; Veterinary Technician.

HAHN, Rhoda K; Millard Sr HS; Omaha, NE; SecSrCls; Chr; DrlTm; HonRl; LitMag; NHS; NatlMeritCmnd; RptrYrbk; GerCl; PpCl; Univ Of Nebraska; Medicine.

HAHN, Rhonda L; Starmont HS; Lamont, IA; 6/108 VPSrCls; Chr; ChrhWkr; HonRl; NHS; StuCncl; RptrYrbk; RptrSchPpr; LetterTrk; GAA; Waldorf Coll; English.

HAHN, Rosalie M; Waldron HS; Waldron, MI; Jackson Bus Univ; Exec Secretary.

HAHN, Terri J; Garden County HS; Oshkosh, NE; 14/45 Chrs; ChrhWkr; HonRl; SchMus; SctActv; PresYthFlsp; RptrYrbk; SptEdSchPpr; FHA; PpCl; Nw Community College; Speech Communications.

HAHN, Todd T; Northwood HS; Nappanee, IN; Chr; HonRl; StuCncl; Sec4-H; Ftbl; Wrstlng; IMSpt; 4-HAwd; University.

HAHN, Virginia L; North County HS; Desloge, MO; Band; CncrtBnd; HonRl; JrNHS; MrchBnd; PepBnd; FHA; FTA; FrCl; CaptChrldr; College; Political Science.

HAHS, Kathy; Oak Ridge R 6 Hs; Oak Ridge, MO; 1 PresFrshCls; SecJrCls; SecBand; HonRl; SchPl; TreasStuCncl; PresYthFlsp; VP4-H; VPFHA; Chrldr;.

HAIAR, Renee S; St Francis HS; Humphrey, NE; HonRl; LbryAde; StuCncl; TchrAde; 4-H; PpCl; IMSpt; Nettleton Commercial Ext; Medical Asst.

HAIDER, Donna M; Brooklyn Center HS; Brooklyn Center, MN; 3/178 Chr; NHS; Quill&Scroll; SchMus; StuGov; Yrbk; DanFAwd; U Of Mn; Surgical Nursing.

HAIDLER, John W; Fairborn Baker HS; Ann Arbor, MI; HonRl; TchrAde; CaptSocr; CchngActv; Michigan St Univ; Agriculture.

HAIER, Katherine A; Okawville HS; Okawville, IL; PresFrshCls; Chrs; DrmMjrt; HonRl; LbryAde; NHS; SecNatlThespSoc; PolWkr; SchPl; StuCncl; Chrldr; IMSpt; DanFAwd; 4-HAwd;.

HAIGHT, Scott C; Aurelia Comm HS; Aurelia, IA; 20/50 Band; Chrs; CncrtBnd; PepBnd; SchPl; YthFlsp; Yrbk; SchPpr; FFA; Drake Univ; Political Science.

HAIKIO, Peter J; Chassell HS; Chassell, MI; Band; CncrtBnd; DrlTm; DrmBgl; HonRl; SchPl; GerCl; LetterBsktbl; LetterTrk; IMSpt; Mi Tech; Metal Engineer.

HAILE, Karen L; Lewistown HS; Lewistown, IL; HonRl; OffAde; SchPl; SpnCl; PpCl; Bsbl; LetterGAA; College; Secretary.

HAINES, Amy L; Southern Door HS; Sturgeon Bay, WI; 10/131 ALAGirlsSt; Band; Chr; NHS; PepBnd; SchMus; RptrYrbk; LetterBsktbl; CchngActv; GAA; Carthage College; Language Major.

HAINES, Craig E; James B Conant HS; Hoffman Estates, IL; 75/627 HonRl; College; Insurance Actuary.

HAINES, Elizabeth A; Arthur Hill HS; Saginaw, MI; Chr; ChrhWkr; HonRl; HospAde; OffAde; YthFlsp; KeyCl; Saginaw Valley State Clg; Geriatrics Nurse.

HAINES, Janice R; Columbus North HS; Columbus, IN; 150/470 CmntyWkr; HonRl; HospAde; RedCrAde; TchrAde; 4-H; LetterGlf; LetterTrk; Chrldr; Ball State Univ; Nursing.

HAINES, Kirk D; Millington HS; Vassar, MI; PresJrCls; HonRl; Bsbl; Bsktbl; Ftbl; College; Accounting.

HAINES, Mary L; Douglass HS; Douglass, KS; 6/45 Chrs; ChrhWkr; DrlTm; HonRl; LbryAde; NHS; SchMus; StuCncl; Yrbk; Bsktbl; Ks St U; Veterinary Medicine.

HAINES, Richard; Cadott HS; Cadott, WI; 5/95 HonRl; JA; JrNHS; NatlMeritFnl; RedCrAde; UNYO; YthFnd; GodCntryAwd; PresAwd; VFWAwd; College.

HAINES, Sandra L; Proviso West HS; Hillside, IL; 77/948 ChrhWkr; HonRl; NHS; Illinois State Univ; Psychology.

HAINS, Diana E; Rockridge HS; Taylor Ridge, IL; ChrhWkr; HospAde; MrchBnd; SchMus; Yrbk; FTA; VPSpnCl; Chrldr; GAA; IMSpt; College; Professional.

HAINSTOCK, Echo M; W G Mather HS; Munising, MI; 18/127 ChrhWkr; HonRl; HospAde; JrNHS; LbryAde; NHS; FDA; FNA; GAA; Butterworth Hosp; Rn.

HAIRE, Diane R; Anna Jonesboro HS; Anna, IL; 18/135 RptrYrbk; FTA; SpnCl; PpCl; University.

HAIRE, Pamela; Exira Comm HS; Exira, IA; 4/4689#9 FTA; MasAwd; Des Moines Area Comm Coll; Acct.

HAIRSTON, Marie Ann; Peoria HS; Peoria, IL; 152/481 NatlMeritCmnd; PolWkr; StuGov; Trk; Coll; Law.

HAIRSTON, Norman E; West Side HS; Gary, IN; ALBoysSt; HonRl; NHS; NatlMeritSF; TchrAde; LatCl; SciCl; LetterWrstlng; Univ; Engineering.

HAIST, Leesa M; Galesburg Augusta HS; Galesburg, MI; 9/115 AFS; Band; CncrtBnd; HonRl; MrchBnd; NHS; PepBnd; Olivet College; Sociology.

HAITHCO, Shari; St Stephen Area Hs; Saginaw, MI; Chr; ChrhWkr; CmntyWkr; HonRl; Mdrgl; NHS; SchPl; AmLegAwd; Michigan State Univesity; Pediatric Nurse.

HAITHCO, Shari L; St Stephen Area HS; Saginaw, MI; SecFrshCls; Chr; ChrhWkr; CmntyWkr; HonRl; LitMag; Mdrgl; NHS; University.

HAJEK, Michael L; West Fargo HS; Davenport, ND; 14/130 AFS; HonRl; ModUN; NHS; NatlMeritSchl; SchPl; RptrSchPpr; 4-H; LetterTrk; 4-HAwd; Nd St U; Civil Engin.

HAKA, Joel N; Sycamore HS; Sycamore, IL; ALBoysSt; HonRl; RptrSchPpr; KeyCl; SpnCl; LetterBsktbl; Ftbl; LetterGlf; College; Oceanography.

HAKES, Gerlann M; Bark River Harris HS; Bark River, MI; 8/47 ChrhWkr; HonRl; MrchBnd; PepBnd; SchAde; TchrAde; Twrl; 4-H; IMSpt; 4-HAwd; Business Sch; Secretary.

HAKES, Jeffery B; Dallas Community HS; Dallas Center, IA; 11/51 HonRl; SctActv; StuCncl; Ftbl; Trk; Wrstlng; Coll; Forestry.

HALAMA, Thomas J; Sacred Heart HS; Dearborn, MI; 8/117 TrsSrCls; ChrhWkr; HonRl; NHS; SchAde; SchMus; TchrAde; FrCl; IMSpt; Lawrence Inst; Architecture/city Plan.

HALAS, Natalie M; Munster HS; Munster, IN; Chr; DrlTm; HonRl; SchAde; SctActv; StuCncl; TchrAde; PpCl; GAA; Purdue Univ; Special Ed.

HALBACH, Sandra A; New Holstein Senior HS; St Cloud, WI; 12/197 HonRl; PresLbryAde; SecNHS; SchPl; SchPpr; SpnCl; PpCl; LetterTrk; GAA; College; Professional.

HALBERG, Catherine L; High School; Princeton, IL; VPSophCls; Chr; Chrl; SchMus; SchPl; StuCncl; StuGov; YthFlsp; SchPpr; LatCl; PpCl; University; Liberal Arts.

HALBERG, Constance A; Harvard Community HS; Harvard, IL; AFS; Band; Chr; Chrs; CncrtBnd; HonRl; MrchBnd; NatlMeritSF; SecNatlThespSoc; SchMus; SchPl; RptrYrbk; Yrbk; EngCl; GerCl; University; Life Sciences.

HALBERSMA, Connie J; Pipestone HS; Pipestone, MN; Band; Chrs; ChrhWkr; CncrtBnd; HonRl; MrchBnd; NHS; Orch; PepBnd; Twrl; Univ Of Mn; Math.

HALBERSTADT, Marie I; Onsted HS; Brooklyn, MI; 1/121 Band; CncrtBnd; DrmMjrt; HonRl; MrchBnd; NHS; PepBnd; SchPl; Twrl; DARAwd; Mi State U; Music Major.

HALBERT, James; Southeast HS; Springfield, IL; Band; Chr; CncrtBnd; HonRl; OffAde; SctActv; SchPpr; Trk; Wrstlng;.

HALBERT, John; Northrop HS; Fort Wane, IN; HonRl; Chemistry.

HALBIG, Mark; Cairo HS; Cairo, IL; ChrhWkr; HonRl; NHS; StuCncl; RptrYrbk; FrCl; MthCl; SciCl; CchngActv; Univ Of Ill; Computer Science.

HALBIG, Michael R; Reitz Memorial HS; Evansville, IN; 36/236 HonRl; NHS; LetterBsbl; Bsktbl; Ftbl; IMSpt; Rose Hulman Inst Tech; Computer Science.

HALBMAIER, Barbara K; Campbell HS; Campbell, NE; TrsFrshCls; Chrs; HonRl; SchPl; Yrbk; RptrSchPpr; FHA; College; Liberal Arts.

HALBROOK, Linda L; Central Riii HS; Flat River, MO; SecFrshCls; ChrhWkr; CmntyWkr; HonRl; JrNHS; NHS; StuCncl; FBLA; PpCl; Junior College; Medical Field.

HALBROOK, Susan A; Saint Joseph Academy; Green Bay, WI; Chrs; HospAde; LbryAde; NHS; RptrYrbk; LatCl; SpnCl; Coll; Nursing.

HALCIN, April M; Benilde HS; Hopkins, MN; ChrhWkr; CmntyWkr; HonRl; PolWkr; 4-H; SpnCl; Trk; Univ Of Minnesota; Commercial Art.

HALCOMB, Octava D; Edinburg HS; Edinburg, IN; Chr; HonRl; RedCrAde; FHA; FrCl; PpCl; Trade Or Bus Sch; Nurse.

HALD, Randy K; Watertown HS; Watertown, SD; 57/291 ALBoysSt; ChrhWkr; HonRl; NHS; PolWkr; TreasSpnCl; Bsbl; Bsktbl; Ftbl; Trk; JCAwd; Lake Area Voc School; Respiratory Therapist.

HALDA, Maxine R; Mayville Portland HS; Mayville, ND; Band; ChrhWkr; CmntyWkr; HonRl; YthFlsp; FHA; SciCl; LetterBsktbl; LetterTrk; GAA; College; Curr Of Maj Study.

HALDEMAN, Mary A; Carmel Girls HS; Mundelein, IL; 47/183 HonRl; NHS; SchAde; StuCncl; TchrAde; Trk; PresGAA; Arizona State Univ; Coach.

HALDER, Katherine P; Fonda Comm HS; Fonda, IA; Band; Chrs; HonRl; JA; SchPl; FHA; LetterBsktbl; LetterGlf; Chrldr; GAA; College; Nurse.

HALDERMAN, Brent L; Northern Valley HS; Long Island, KS; Band; Chr; PresStuCncl; PresStuGov; YthFlsp; RptrYrbk; RptrSchPpr; CaptBsktbl; CaptFtbl; LetterTrk; Ft Hays Ks St Col; Psychology.

HALE, Brian; St Mary Central HS; Neenah, WI; VPSrCls; HonRl; StuGov; SpnCl; Trk; IMSpt; JCAwd; College; Business Economics.

HALE, Charles R; West HS; Iowa City, IA; 9/288 NatlFornLg; PresStuGov; Tennis; Harvard.

HALE, Cordelia; Central HS; Kansas City, MO; 17/380 Chr; HonRl; JrNHS; NHS; StuCncl; SpnCl; Mo Univ; Accounting.

HALE, Denise D; Harold L Richards HS; Chicago Ridge, IL; CmntyWkr; HonRl; HospAde; JA; JrNHS; MrchBnd; NHS; Orch; TchrAde; College; Doctor.

HALE, Diana L; Lena Winslow HS; Lena, IL; 4/97 ALAGirlsSt; Band; HonRl; NHS; SchMus; Yrbk; 4-H; FHA; College; Secretary.

HALE, Floyd B; Mitchell HS; Mitchell, NE; 2/54 PresFrshCls; PresSrCls; Band; Chrs; NHS; NatlThespSoc; StuGov; RptrYrbk; CaptBsktbl; LetterFtbl; LetterTrk; CchngActv; AmLegAwd; College; Medicine.

HALE, Joseph E; Thornwood HS; Calumet City, IL; Aud/Vis; HonRl; RptrYrbk; Yrbk; RptrSchPpr; SchPpr; Thornton Comm College; Elec Engineering.

HALE, Justina M; Woodstock HS; Woodstock, IL; 10/270 Band; Chr; Chrl; Chrs; DrlTm; HonRl; Mdrgl; NatlFornLg; NHS; NatlMeritCmnd; LetterSwmmng; Chrldr; GAA; Univ Of Colorado; Psychology.

HALE, Kathryn A; Arthur HS; Arthur, IL; 2/48 PresJrCls; HonRl; HospAde; NHS; SchPl; StuCncl; FHA; FNA; Eastern Illinois Univ; Home Economics.

HALE, Lloyd E; Spokane R 7 HS; Ozark, MO; 4/32 PresFrshCls; PresSophCls; PresSrCls; Band; ChrhWkr; HonRl; PepBnd; SchPl; StuCncl; Yrbk;.

HALE, Lori J; Jenison HS; Jenison, MI; Band; CncrtBnd; HonRl; MrchBnd; Chrldr; College; Vocation.

HALE, Merrill G; Wakefield HS; Wakefield, NE; 4/35 VPJrCls; Chr; HonRl; SchPl; StuCncl; TchrAde; LetterFtbl; LetterLetterWrstlng; Collge; Professional.

HALE, Patsy; Benton HS; St Joseph, MO; ChrhWkr; HonRl; LbryAde; SchPl; StuCncl; FHA; PpCl; Coll; Nursing.

HALE, Rosemarie A; Burrton HS; Burrton, KS; 2/25 SecSrCls; Chr; HonRl; NHS; SctActv; College; Biology.

HALE, Shelley E; East HS; Kansas City, MO; VPJrCls; Band; HonRl; JA; JrNHS; MrchBnd; SchPl; StuCncl; Yrbk; College; Accounting.

HALE, Steven; Garden City East HS; Highland Park, MI; Band; DrmMjrt; HonRl; JrNHS; MrchBnd; NHS; SchPl; Twrl; PpCl; Valparaiso U; Nursing.

HALER, Patrica K; Waukon HS; Waukon, IA; 10/155 ALAGirlsSt; ChrhWkr; HonRl; HospAde; SchPl; SctActv; 4-H; FNA; SpnCl; Area I Voc Tech; Regitered Nurse.

HALES, Carolyn; Brookings HS; Brookings, SD; ChrhWkr; CmntyWkr; HonRl; NHS; SchMus; TchrAde; SpnCl; Brigham Young Univ; Humanities.

HALES, Kandi K; Penney HS; Hamilton, MO; 4/79 PresBand; CncrtBnd; DrmMjrt; HonRl; MrchBnd; PepBnd; StuCncl; PresSpnCl; VPPpCl; Glf; Chrldr; College; Bookkeeper.

HALES, Norma N; Arthur Hill HS; Saginaw, MI; 26/692 Chr; ChrhWkr; HonRl; NHS; CaptBsktbl; U Of Mi State; Registered Nurse.

HALES, Randy R; Wyaconda C 1 HS; Wyaconda, MO; 1/20 TrsFrshCls; ChrhWkr; CmntyWkr; HonRl; SchPl; MthCl; PpCl; SciCl; LetterBsbl; LetterBsktbl; IMSpt; DanFAwd; Northeast Missouri Univ; Eng.

HALES, Sharon M; Munster HS; Munster, IN; 108/424 TrsJrCls; DrlTm; HonRl; SchPl; StuCncl; PpCl; GAA; IMSpt; Univ; Professional.

HALES, Steven; Abraham Lincoln HS; Council Bluffs, IA; Chrs; HonRl; JrNHS; Mdrgl; NatlMeritFnl; NatlMeritSchl; NatlMeritSF; NatlThespSoc; SchMus; SchPl; Cornell Coll; Engineering.

HALEY, Anne L; Schulte HS; Terre Haute, IN; 1/106 SecSophCls; HonRl; RptrSchPpr; GerCl; Chrldr; St Mary Woods College; Pediatrician.

HALEY, Daniel F; Thompson Public HS; Thompson, ND; Chrs; ChrhWkr; HonRl; StuCncl; CaptBsbl; LetterBsktbl; LetterFtbl; LetterTrk; CchngActv; Trade School; Vocation.

HALEY, Doreen K; Frazee HS; Frazee, MN; 27/113 Chrs; HonRl; Mdrgl; TchrAde; YthFlsp; FHA; PPFtbl; MasAwd; VFWAwd; VoiceDemAwd; Univ; Elem Teacher.

HALEY, James F; Lincoln Way HS; Manhattan, IL; 159/498 Aud/Vis; HonRl; Glf; College; Business Computers.

HALEY, Patricia M; Ritenour HS; St Ann, MO; 27/887 JrNHS; NHS; Bsktbl; Socr; Swmmng; GAA; IMSpt; AmLegAwd; Law School; Accounting And Law.

HALEY, Robert N; Clinton Comm HS; Clinton, IL; 1/156 HonRl; NHS; PresStuCncl; RptrSchPpr; 4-H; FrCl; LetterBsktbl; Univ Of Illinois; Law.

HALEY, Susan; Don Bosco HS; Jesup, IA; 1/57 Chrs; HonRl; HospAde; NHS; NatlMeritCmnd; SchMus; SchPl; RptrYrbk; DARAwd; Loras Col Dubuque Ia; Chemistry Major.

HALEY, Tony D; Meramec Valley HS; Pacific, MO; HonRl; SpnCl; Bsbl; College; Art.

HALFACRE, Vickie L; Bluford HS; Kell, IL; ChrhWkr; HonRl; Yrbk; SchPpr; FHA; College; Secretary.

HALFERTY, Carolyn A; Smithville HS; Smithville, MO; 11/75 SecJrCls; ChrhWkr; HonRl; SchPl; SecStuCncl; RptrYrbk; RptrSchPpr; Pres4-H; PresFTA; Chrldr; Univ Of Missouri; Education.

HALFMAN, Denise L; Thomson HS; Mt Carroll, IL; 10/39 Band; Chrs; CmntyWkr; HonRl; Mdrgl; NHS; PepBnd; SchMus; TchrAde; College; Social Work.

HALFPENNY, Kathleen M; Pontiac Catholic HS; Drayton Plains, MI; 1/142 ChrhWkr; HonRl; ModUN; PresNHS; StuCncl; RptrYrbk; ChmnFrCl; Trk; GAA; VoiceDemAwd; Univ Of Mi; Med.

HALKA, Lorraine K; Swartz Creek HS; Swartz Creek, MI; SecJrCls; HonRl; HospAde; JrNHS; NHS; StuCncl; FrCl; LetterBsktbl; LetterTrk; CchngActv; U Of Mich; Pre Law.

HALKO, Mark M; St Ignatius College Prep HS; Chicago, IL; ChrhWkr; CAP; HonRl; PolWkr; SctActv; TchrAde; KeyCl; RusCl; Bsbl; Bsktbl; Socr; IMSpt; College; Medicine.

HALKYARD, Debbie A; Gibbon HS; Gibbon, NE; 8/59 Band; Chr; HonRl; Yrbk; FHA; PpCl; LetterBsktbl; LetterTrk; LetterChrldr; PPFtbl; Kearney St Coll; Major Study.

HALL, Annette Y; W Washington HS; Salem, IN; 14/98 CmntyWkr; HonRl; SctActv; RptrSchPpr; 4-H; SpnCl; DARAwd; 4-HAwd; Ind State Univ; Medicine.

HALL, Beatrice; Hayti HS; Hayti, MO; Band; Chr; Chrs; CncrtBnd; DrmMjrt; HonRl; MrchBnd; PepBnd; SchPl; StuCncl; Bsbl; Bsktbl; Socr; College.

HALL, Brenda K; Connersville Sr HS; Connersville, IN; 13/371 ChrhWkr; HonRl; NHS; NatlMeritCmnd; NatlThespSoc; SchPl; StuCncl; FTA; Anderson College; Special Educ Teacher.

HALL, Brien; Northwood HS; Nappanee, IN; HonRl; PpCl; Ftbl; Bus School; Store Manager.

HALL, Bruce W; Thornridge HS; Dolton, IL; 34/684 Band; CncrtBnd; HonRl; JrNHS; MrchBnd; NHS; Quill&Scroll; EdSchPpr; MthCl; LetterTrk; College; Journalism.

HALL, Cathy A; Galena HS; Galena, IL; 4/110 Chrs; HonRl; PresSctActv; PpCl; LetterBsbl; Univ; Medical Tech.

HALL, Charles H; Mary Persons HS; Detroit, MI; Chr; ChrhWkr; CmntyWkr; Bsbl; Ftbl; Trk; Attend Coll; Busi Ed.

HALL, Cheryl L; Taylor Center HS; Westland, MI; 40/420 CmntyWkr; JA; JCC; ModUN; NHS; NatlMeritSchl; StuGov; UNYO; YthLg; FBLA; Henry Ford Comm Coll; Secretary.

HALL, Cheryl L; Lincoln East HS; Lincoln, NE; 18/480 AFS; CmntyWkr; HonRl; SchAde; TchrAde; 4-H; PpCl; Univ Of Nebraska; Teaching.

HALL, Cindy L; So Newton HS; Kentland, IN; 7/102 ChrhWkr; SchMus; VP4-H; TreasFBLA; LatCl; PpCl; SciCl; PPFtbl; 4-HAwd; College; Business Educ.

HALL, Cynthia A; Kouts HS; Kouts, IN; 25/58 PresSophCls; Chr; ChrhWkr; HonRl; OffAde; SchPl; SecStuCncl; PresPpCl; GAA; PPFtbl; Cedarville College In Ohio; Social Work.

HALL, Cynthia L; Dixon HS; Dixon, IL; Band; Chr; Chrs; ChrhWkr; CmntyWkr; CncrtBnd; HonRl; MrchBnd; SctActv; YthFlsp; FTA; College; Professional.

HALL, David R; Greendale HS; Greendale, WI; ChrhWkr; CAP; College; Professional.

HALL, Debi L; Glenwood HS; Springfield, IL; 38/150 CmntyWkr; SecJA; OffAde; SctActv; FHA; PresFNA; Lincolnland Comm Coll; Retailing.

HALL, Debra; Dickinson HS; Dickinson, ND; Band; Chrl; CncrtBnd; HonRl; MrchBnd; NatlThespSoc; PepBnd; SchMus; GerCl; College; Music.

HALL, Debra A; University HS; Cape Girardeau, MO; 12/38 SecTrsSophCls; SecTrsSrCls; SchPl; TchrAde; Yrbk; 4-H; SpnCl; PresPpCl; IMSpt; 4-HAwd; Semo St University.

HALL, Debra K; Spring Valley HS; Spring Valley, MN; Chr; HonRl; NHS; FHA; SpnCl; College; Business.

HALL, Diana L; Butterfield Odin Public HS; Butterfield, MN; Band; Chr; ChrhWkr; HonRl; Mdrgl; SchPl; EdYrBk; Treas4-H; 4-HAwd; University.

HALL, Diane K; Exeter Public HS; Exeter, NE; Band; Chrs; CncrtBnd; HonRl; MrchBnd; PepBnd; SchPl; MthCl; PpCl; LetterTrk; Coll; Elem Ed.

HALL, Douglas R; Lawrence Central HS; Indianapolis, IN; 4/800 Band; ChrhWkr; HonRl; MrchBnd; NHS; PepBnd; SchAde; Bsktbl; Ftbl; LetterTrk; IMSpt; Purdue Univ; Engineering.

HALL, Eldon C; Oxford HS; Oxford, KS; 6/39 Band; Chr; Chrl; Chrs; ChrhWkr; CncrtBnd; DrlTm; HonRl; MrchBnd; NatlMeritCmnd; Bsbl; LetterBsktbl; LetterTrk; DanFAwd; Cowley County Jr College; Tech Drafting.

HALL, Elizabeth; Lisbon Community HS; Lisbon, IA; 4/44 DrmMjrt; Mdrgl; MrchBnd; PepBnd; SchMus; SchPl; Twrl; YthFlsp; SptEdSchPpr; FTA; Unif Of Ia; Vocal Music Teacher.

HALL, Elizabeth F; Lisbon Community HS; Lisbon, IA; 6/43 Band; Chr; Chrs; ChrhWkr; CncrtBnd; DrmMjrt; HonRl; Mdrgl; MrchBnd; NHS; PepBnd; CaptBsktbl; GAA; PPFtbl; Iowa City University; Music.

HALL, Gary D; Carbondale Comm HS; Carbondale, IL; HonRl; NHS; NatlMeritFnl; SctActv; SciCl; Southern Ill Univ; Engineering.

HALL, Georgean A; Queen Of Peace HS; Chicago, IL; 7/420 Chrl; ChrhWkr; CmntyWkr; HonRl; LitMag; LbryAde; NHS; NatlMeritCmnd; RptrYrbk; Depaul Univ; Mathematics.

HALL, Holly G; Huron HS; Ann Arbor, MI; HonRl; Univ Of Mich; Law.

HALL, Jacky R; Superior HS; Superior, NE; Chrs; OffAde; FBLA; FHA; PpCl; LetterTrk;.

HALL, Jacqueline I; Merrill HS; Merrill, MI; 6/106 PresBand; ChrhWkr; HonRl; PresNHS; SchMus; TchrAde; Pres4-H; GAA; 4-HAwd; John Wesley College; Nursing.

HALL, James G; Assumption HS; Granite City, IL; Chrs; HonRl; Univ Of Illinois; Zoology.

HALL, James W; Holden HS; Holden, MO; 18/93 VPFrshCls; Aud/Vis; HonRl; SchPl; SctActv; SptEdSchPpr; SchPpr; 4-H; SciCl; LetterBsktbl; LetterFtbl; LetterTennis; IMSpt; College; Public Relations.

HALL, Jenna L; Zionsville Comm HS; Zionsville, IN; SecTrsFrshCls; TrsJrCls; Band; ChrhWkr; NHS; 4-H; PresLatCl; LetterBsktbl; LetterTrk; GAA; 4-HAwd; College; Music.

HALL, Jon S; Gering HS; Gering, NE; LitMag; FFA; Tennis; Wrstlng; University Of Nebraska; Journalism.

HALL, Joyce E; Thomas Jefferson HS; Council Bluffs, IA; 26/460 HonRl; JA; StuCncl; FTA; Wartburg Coll; Teacher.

HALL, Judith A; Luther South HS; Chicago, IL; Chr; HonRl; RptrSchPpr; Trk; Augustana College; Law.

HALL, Julie A; Taylorville Sr HS; Taylorville, IL; 25/255 Chr; ChrhWkr; DrlTm; HonRl; OffAde; PolWkr; StuCncl; FTA; FrCl; PpCl; Chrldr; Eastern Ill Univ; Medical Tech.

HALL, Justina G; Southwestern Heights HS; Kismet, KS; 1/53 SecTrsJrCls; SecTrsSrCls; ChrhWkr; HonRl; NHS; StuCncl; YthFlsp; 4-H; DanFAwd; 4-HAwd; Seward County Comm Col; Architectural Engin.

HALL, Karen S; Galatia HS; Galatia, IL; 1/24 HstFrshCls; TrsJrCls; Band; ChrhWkr; HonRl; RptrYrbk; 4-H; FHA; PresMthCl; Chrldr; GAA; BauchLmbAwd; 4-HAwd; College.

HALL, Kenneth R; Edgar HS; Edgar, WI; 6/88 Chrs; ChrhWkr; CmntyWkr; HonRl; Sacrstn; SctActv; TchrAde; RptrYrbk; SptEdSchPpr; FrCl; Univ Wisc; Math.

HALL, Kimberly A; Granite City HS; Granite City, IL; 4/375 ChrhWkr; NatlFornLg; NHS; SchMus; SchPl; YthFlsp; PresSciCl; GAA; University; Biology.

HALL, Larry R; Bismarck Henning HS; Danville, IL; Band; Chr; Chrs; ChrhWkr; NHS; PepBnd; SchMus; SchPl; SctActv; DanFAwd; Lincoln Christian Coll; Music.

HALL, Lori; Moose Lake HS; Moose Lake, MN; Chrs; HonRl; NHS; SchPl; SctActv; RptrYrbk; FHA; PpCl; Umd;acc.

HALL, Lori A; Stet HS; Richmond, MO; Chrs; ChrhWkr; CncrtBnd; HonRl; SchPl; Yrbk; RptrSchPpr; FHA; Trk; CaptChrldr; College; Secretary.

HALL, Lori J; Roland Story HS; Roland, IA; 2/79 SecTrsSophCls; HonRl; NHS; RptrSchPpr; PpCl; LetterBsbl; Bsktbl; CchngActv; Trade Schl; Secretary.

HALL, Lori L; Central Community HS; Low Moor, IA; AFS; Band; Chrs; ChrhWkr; CncrtBnd; HonRl; HospAde; MrchBnd; PepBnd; SchMus; Kirkwood Comm Clg; Dental Assistant.

HALL, Lou A; Frankton HS; Anderson, IN; 2/175 ChrhWkr; HonRl; NHS; SchAde; 4-H; SpnCl; LetterTrk; 4-HAwd; College; Medical Technology.

HALL, Mark; Evansville Senior HS; Evansville, WI; HonRl; NHS; SchMus; StuCncl; RptrSchPpr; SptEdSchPpr; Bsktbl; Uw Eau Claire; Computer Science.

HALL, Mark E; Lincoln East HS; Lincoln, NE; 1/408 Chr; HonRl; NatlMeritSF; Orch; SchMus; YthFlsp; MthCl; LetterIMSpt; Carleton Coll; Math.

HALL, Mary; Putnam County Hs; Magnolia, IL; 6/89 CncrtBnd; DrlTm; HonRl; LbryAde; NHS; NatlMeritCmnd; SchMus; EdYrBk; SchPpr; 4-HAwd; U Of Illinois; Journalism.

HALL, Mary B; Norris City Omaha HS; Norris City, IL; TrsSophCls; SecJrCls; ALAGirlsSt; LbryAde; SchPl; YthFlsp; PresFHA; PpCl; GAA; CaptIMSpt; College; Professional.

HALL, Mary M; Gresham HS; Gresham, WI; 3/30 HospAde; NHS; StuCncl; PresFBLA; SecFHA; FTA; Trk; GAA; BttyCrckrAwd; College; Nursing.

HALL, Nancy L; Mt Olive HS; Mt Olive, IL; SecTrsFrshCls; PresBand; Chrs; CncrtBnd; HonRl; NHS; StuCncl; Yrbk; PresFHA; TreasSpnCl; VPGAA; Lutheran Med Center; Nursing.

HALL, Nanette L; Limestone Community HS; Hanna City, IL; CmntyWkr; HonRl; SchAde; SchPl; StuCncl; Icc Isu; Nurse.

HALL, Pamela S; Sunshine Bible Academy; Orchard, NE; 2/27 SecFrshCls; VPJrCls; Chrs; ChrhWkr; HonRl; HospAde; SchPl; Yrbk; PpCl; Bsktbl; Trk; IMSpt; PPFtbl; University Of Nebraska; Speech.

HALL, Patrick W; Kuemper HS; Carroll, IA; 14/298 VPSophCls; PresJrCls; ModUN; NatlMeritCmnd; PolWkr; StuCncl; RptrYrbk; Ftbl; Wrstlng; EldAwd; Creighton.

HALL, Phillip L; Central HS; Bristol, WI; ChrhWkr; HonRl; NatlThespSoc; SchMus; SchPl; Pres4-H; TreasFFA; LetterFtbl; LetterTrk; Parkside Univ; Doctor Of Veterinary Med.

HALL, Rex A; Wellington Sr HS; Wellington, KS; HonRl; SctActv; LetterBsktbl; LetterTrk; Butler Cty Comm College; Electronics.

HALL, Richard R; Bullock Creek HS; Midland, MI; 16/170 HonRl; NHS; SchPl; TchrAde; SptEdSchPpr; LetterTrk; Univ Of Michigan; Pre Med.

HALL, Ronnie J; South Spencer HS; Grandview, IN; Chr; ChrhWkr; HonRl; SancSoc; SctActv; Teen; YthFlsp; YthLg; IMSpt; Business School; Bussiness Administration.

HALL, Stephanie L; Perry Comm HS; Perry, IA; Band; Chr; ChrhWkr; CmntyWkr; HonRl; NatlFornLg; SecNatlThespSoc; SchPl; StuCncl; College; Speech Therapy.

HALL, Stephanie J; Field Kindley HS; Coffeyville, KS; 2/244 SecSrCls; TrsSrCls; Chr; HonRl; NHS; NatlThespSoc; SchPl; TchrAde; FrCl; DARAwd; Tx Christian U; Ballet.

HALL, Steven L; Park Hill HS; Parkville, MO; Band; CncrtBnd; HonRl; MrchBnd; PepBnd; SctActv; Ftbl; Swmmng; VPTrk; Usaf; Pilot.

HALL, Steven W; E Charles Mix 102 HS; Wagner, SD; ALBoysSt; Band; ChrhWkr; HonRl; NHS; LetterBsktbl; LetterFtbl; Trk;.

HALL, Vicky L; Brentwood HS; Bridgeton, MO; 12/140 Band; ChrhWkr; HonRl; ModUN; NHS; StuCncl; FrCl; Univ Of Mo St Louis; Music.

HALL, Victoria L; Mt Pleasant HS; Mt Pleasant, MI; 35/332 HonRl; NHS; LatCl; Central Mi Univ.

HALL, William E; Troy HS; Troy, MI; 7/534 ALBoysSt; HonRl; NHS; NatlMeritCmnd; SpnCl; BauchLmbAwd; U Of M; Science.

HALLA, Dennis J; Clinton HS; Clinton, WI; 21/98 VPJrCls; PresSrCls; HonRl; SctActv; StuCncl; CaptBsbl; CaptFtbl; CchngActv; KiwanAwd; University; Professional.

HALLAUER, Linda; Immanuel Luthern HS; Hancock, MN; Chr; ChrhWkr; HonRl; NatlMeritCmnd; Yrbk; LatCl; Bsktbl; Trk; GAA; IMSpt; Coll; Curricrlum Of Major Study.

HALLBECK, Jeffrey T; North HS; Eau Claire, WI; PresSophCls; VPSrCls; ALBoysSt; HonRl; JrNHS; NHS; StuCncl; StuGov; Ftbl; Swmmng; Univ; Law.

HALLEEN, Richard A; Benson HS; Omaha, NE; Band; CncrtBnd; HonRl; MrchBnd; NHS; Orch; SchMus; North Park College; Music.

HALLEMEIER, Kim E; St Charles HS; St Charles, MO; ChrhWkr; HonRl; NHS; SecFNA; FrCl; IMSpt; School; Nursing.

HALLEN, Kathryn J; Rockford East HS; Rockford, IL; 16/665 HonRl; NHS; Quill&Scroll; StuGov; Augustana College; Medicine.

HALLENBECK, Ann M; Our Lady Of Lakes HS; Drayton Plains, MI; 10/51 Chrs; HonRl; JA; NHS; StuCncl; TchrAde; Oakland U; Nursing.

HALLENBECK, Randy R; Kingsford HS; Kingsford, MI; 48/161 HonRl; CivCl; LetterTrk; College; Cpa.

HALLER, Dennis M; Creighton Prep; Omaha, NE; HonRl; Sdlty; LetterSocr; LetterSwmmng; IMSpt; Math Or Science.

HALLER, Jerry; Rockford Senior HS; Marble Rock, IA; VPJrCls; Chr; ChrhWkr; HonRl; StuCncl; FTA; Trk; Univ Cedar Falls Ia; Teaching.

HALLER, Mark S; Harding HS; St Paul, MN; 13/780 HonRl; NHS; TchrAde; FrCl; SciCl; Univ Of Mn; Chemical Engineer.

HALLER, Robert W; Notre Dame HS; Morton Grove, IL; 64/276 CmntyWkr; HonRl; PolWkr; Sacrstn; SctActv; Bsktbl; Ftbl; Univ Of Ill; Architecture.

HALLETT, Ann E; Marinette Sr HS; Marinette, WI; 11/243 TrsSrCls; ALAGirlsSt; HonRl; NHS; SchPl; FrCl; PpCl; LetterBsktbl; LetterTrk; GAA; U Of Wi Stevens Point; Elem Education.

HALLEY, Alan R; North County HS; Bonne Terre, MO; ChrhWkr; College; Vocational Teacher.

HALLEY, Donald R; Rockford West HS; Rockford, IL; 3/379 CncrtBnd; HonRl; MrchBnd; NHS; NatlMeritCmnd; PepBnd; ROTC; SctActv; Univ Of Illinois; Computer Science.

HALLFRISCH, Michael P; Stephenson HS; Stephenson, MI; HonRl; NatlMeritCmnd; LetterTrk;.

HALLGREN, Janet D; Medford Senior HS; Medford, WI; 11/215 VPJrCls; CmntyWkr; HonRl; HospAde; JrNHS; NHS; SchPl; StuCncl; StuGov; PpCl; University Of Wisconsin; Medical Technology.

HALLIDAY, Clifton; Houghton Lake Comm HS; Houghton Lake, MI; HonRl; JrNHS; NHS; SciCl; Ftbl; Gravel Businss.

HALLIGAN, James M; Draper HS; Draper, SD; 1/9 ALBoysSt; Band; ChrhWkr; HonRl; PepBnd; SchPl; StuCncl; 4-H; Bsktbl; Trk; College; Lawyer.

HALLINEN, Carrie L; Franklin HS; Livonia, MI; Col ; Major.

HALLMAN, Bruce A; Waverly Shell Rock HS; Waverly, IA; VPSophCls; VPJrCls; ChrhWkr; HonRl; JrNHS; PolWkr; SchPl; Bsktbl; LetterFtbl; Trk; College; Professional.

HALLMAN, James F; St Edward HS; Elgin, IL; 18/123 HonRl; NatlMeritFnl; NatlMeritSchl; NatlThespSoc; SchPl; SchPpr; Bsktbl; St Marys College; Medicine.

HALLMON, Carolyn D; Central HS; St Louis, MO; Aud/Vis; JA; LbryAde; SchPpr; PresSrCls; Univ; Pediatrician.

HALLO, Elizabeth R; Cass Technical HS; Detroit, MI; Aud/Vis; CmntyWkr; HonRl; PolWkr; SchMus; SchPl; Wayne State Univ; Acting.

HALLORAN, Ann B; Green Lake HS; Green Lake, WI; 8/46 TrsFrshCls; TrsSophCls; TrsJrCls; TrsSrCls; HonRl; NHS; SchPl; RptrYrbk; RptrSchPpr; SpnCl; Coll; Schl Counsoler.

HALLORAN, Edward H; Brodhead HS; Brodhead, WI; HonRl; SctActv; LetterBsktbl; CaptFtbl; Blackhawk Tech Inst; Office Machine Repair.

HALLORAN, Sheila E; New Prague HS; Belle Plaine, MN; Band; CncrtBnd; MrchBnd; NHS; SchPl; RptrSchPpr; 4-H; GerCl; PpCl; 4-HAwd; St Univ; Music Major.

HALLOWELL, Jay E; Mt Pleasant HS; Mt Pleasant, IA; 1/150 ChrhWkr; HonRl; ModUN; NatlFornLg; NHS; NatlMeritFnl; FBLA; AmLegAwd; Friends Univ; Professional.

HALLOWS, Diane M; Bowling Green R1 HS; Curryville, MO; /125 ChrhWkr; CmntyWkr; HonRl; YthFlsp; FHA; SpnCl; GAA; BttyCrckrAwd; College; Social Work.

HALLQUIST, David R; River Falls Sr HS; River Falls, WI; 62/186 Band; PresChr; Chrs; ChrhWkr; CncrtBnd; MrchBnd; PepBnd; Swmmng; University; Communications.

HALLQUIST, Kevin D; Stanton Comm HS; Stanton, IA; 14/34 Band; Chr; HonRl; StuCncl; FFA; Bsbl; Bsktbl; Ftbl; Trk; Augavstana College.

HALLQUIST, Todd; Aurelia Community HS; Aurelia, IA; PresFrshCls; ALBoysSt; HonRl; MrchBnd; PepBnd; SchPl; RptrSchPpr; MthCl; Bsbl; Swmmng; Coll; Coaching.

HALLUM, Debra; Udall HS; Udall, KS; DrlTm; HonRl; LbryAde; SchPl; StuCncl; FHA; College; Art.

HALM, Gregory; Leroy HS; Leroy, IL; 11/89 Band; HonRl; LbryAde; SchMus; SchPl; Univ Of Illinois; Accounting.

HALMA, Bruce W; West Lyon HS; Inwood, IA; LetterBsbl; LetterFtbl; LetterTrk; Vocational School.

HALOUSKA, Diane L; Sargent Public HS; Sargent, NE; Chrs; HonRl; NHS; NatlThespSoc; SchMus; SchPl; SctActv; YthFlsp; FFA; Col; Biology.

HALPIN, Patrick R; Fenwick HS; Oak Park, IL; ChrhWkr; HonRl; PolWkr; Sacrstn; SpnCl; LetterBsktbl; LetterFtbl;.

HALPIN, Stephen E; Quincy Sr Ii HS; Quincy, IL; 7/816 NHS; YthFlsp; SecKeyCl; FrCl; IMSpt; Quincy College; Medicine.

HALSEY, Clarence L; Virginia HS; Virginia, IL; CmntyWkr; IntrClCncl; YthFlsp; Ftbl; Trk; Trade Sch; Prof.

HALSEY, Mary Beth; Matoon Sr HS; Charleston, IL; PresAFS; Band; HonRl; LbryAde; NHS; RptrYrbk; Pres4-H; DanFAwd; 4-HAwd; Eastern Ill Univ; Medical Technology.

HALSEY, Mary L; Fairmont Public HS; Fairmont, NE; 5/28 Band; Chrs; HonRl; LbryAde; StuCncl; Twrl; 4-H; PpCl; LetterTrk; PresAwd; Kearney St;librarian.

HALSTEAD, Annette L; East Peoria Comm HS; East Peoria, IL; 14/446 Aud/Vis; Band; ChrhWkr; CncrtBnd; HonRl; MrchBnd; NHS; PepBnd; Quill&Scroll; SchMus; EdYrBk; Yrbk; Bsbl; Swmmng; Junior College; Dental Assistant.

HALSTEAD, Jane L; Gibault Catholic HS; Waterloo, IL; Chrs; CmntyWkr; HonRl; NHS; SchMus; SchPl; StuCncl; StuGov; SchPpr; College; Theatre.

HALT, David W; N Liberty HS; N Liberty, IN; 3/100 Band; ChrhWkr; HonRl; RptrYrbk; FrCl; SciCl; LetterBsbl; AmLegAwd; KiwanAwd; RotaryAwd; Purdue Univ; Engineering.

HALT, Jane A; Central HS; Worthington, IN; 7/48 PresBand; ChrhWkr; DrmMjrt; NHS; PepBnd; StuCncl; CaptBsbl; CaptBsktbl; CaptChrldr; JCAwd; In State Univ; Bus.

HALTER, Debbie L; Brookfield Central HS; Brookfield, WI; 77/474 HospAde; NatlThespSoc; SchMus; SchPl; College; Nursing.

HALTER, Lou A; Climax Scotts HS; Scotts, MI; SecJrCls; HonRl; Yrbk; 4-H; Bsktbl; LetterTrk; PPFtbl; Univ Mi State; Veterinarian.

HALTER, Rachel; Gaylord Community HS; Gaylord, MI; Chrs; CncrtBnd; HonRl; HospAde; MrchBnd; NHS; OffAde; RedCrAde; Yrbk; College; Engineering.

HALTERMAN, Timothy A; Anna Jonesboro Comm HS; Anna, IL; 11/137 TrsSrCls; HonRl; ModUN; NatlMeritCmnd; SchPl; Ftbl; Univ Of Illinois; Law.

HALTINER, Terry M; Hill Murray HS; St Paul, MN; HonRl; IntrClCncl; StuCncl; Univ Of Minnesota It; Science.

HALTLI, Cindy A; Central HS; Duluth, MN; 20/437 ChrhWkr; HonRl; NHS; RptrYrbk; PpCl; IMSpt; Univ Of Mn; Dental Hygiene.

HALTON, Timothy J; Bishop Natl Inst; Lansing, IL; StuGov; SpnCl; MthCl; CaptBsbl; IMSpt; JCAwd; College; Teaching.

HALUB, Kevin M; T L Handy HS; Bay City, MI; HonRl; NHS; StuCncl; GerCl; Bsbl; Ftbl; Alma College; Dentistry.

HALUB, Rodney P; T L Handy HS; Bay City, MI; ChrhWkr; HonRl; NHS; StuCncl; FrCl; LetterGlf; LetterSwmmng; LetterTrk; IMSpt; Albion Coll; Pre Med.

HALUZAK, Roger M; Wilton Public HS; Wilton, ND; PresSrCls; HonRl; SchPl; StuCncl; StuGov; FBLA; FFA; LetterBsbl; LetterBsktbl; LetterFtbl; Wahpeton State School; Professional.

HALVA, Jeanine A; Prairie HS; Amana, IA; VPSrCls; Chr; HonRl; JrNHS; SchMus; SchPl; StuCncl; TchrAde; Swmmng; University; English Major.

HALVERSON, Debra L; Sycamore HS; Sycamore, IL; 17/205 ChrhWkr; CncrtBnd; MrchBnd; NHS; PolWkr; SchMus; TchrAde; YthFlsp; SpnCl; University; Business Admin.

HALVERSON, Elaine K; Granite Falls HS; Granite Falls, MN; Chr; ChrhWkr; CncrtBnd; HonRl; MrchBnd; NHS; PepBnd; SchMus; TchrAde; RptrYrbk; Concordia College; Theology.

HALVERSON, Jill M; Springfield HS; Springfield, IL; 58/590 Chr; ChrhWkr; JA; SchMus; YthFlsp; RptrYrbk; Trk; University Of Illinois; Business Admin.

HALVERSON, Karen L; Frederic HS; Frederic, WI; Chr; ChrhWkr; LbryAde; SchMus; 4-H; SecFFA;

LetterBsktbl; Trk; GAA; 4-HAwd; Nursing School; Physical Therapy.

HALVERSON, Katherine B; Lansing HS; Lansing, KS; Band; PresDrlTm; MrchBnd; PepBnd; TchrAde; FTA; PPFtbl; College; Dancing.

HALVERSON, Kimberly K; Gladbrook Comm HS; Gladbrook, IA; CncrtBnd; HonRl; LbryAde; YthLg; SchPl; StuCncl; PresYthFlsp; FHA; BttyCrckrAwd; Nursing School.

HALVERSON, Kim G; Pius Xi HS; Milwaukee, WI; 69/386 LbryAde; OffAde; TchrAde; FTA; MthCl; Col Uw Milwaukee; Pro Pre Med.

HALVERSON, Lisa A; Malta HS; Malta, IL; 1/35 ALAGirlsSt; Chr; Chrs; HonRl; NHS; SchPl; StuCncl; 4-H; PpCl; Western Illinois Univ; Dietician.

HALVERSON, Mark A; Eagle Grove HS; Eagle Grove, IA; Band; ChrhWkr; CmntyWkr; CncrtBnd; HonRl; MrchBnd; NHS; PepBnd; Quill&Scroll; SchMus; StuCncl; RptrYrbk; EdSchPpr; LetterFtbl; 4-HAwd; Iowa St Univ; Journalism.

HALVERSON, Michael C; Cedar Falls HS; Cedar Falls, IA; 20/389 HonRl; LbryAde; Bsbl; Bsktbl; Ftbl; Glf; GovHonPrgAwd; KiwanAwd; U Of N Ia; Business Major.

HALVERSON, Patricia J; Duluth Central HS; Duluth, MN; AFS; Chr; ChrhWkr; HospAde; Mdrgl; ModUN; NHS; SchMus; SchPl; PpCl; College Of St Scholastica; Music.

HALVERSON, Robert H; Sioux Valley HS; Linn Grove, IA; VPJrCls; PresSrCls; ALBoysSt; Chrs; ChrhWkr; Mdrgl; NHS; SchMus; SchPl; Yrbk; U Of Ia; Engineering.

HALVORSEN, Rick J; Southeast Warren HS; Indianola, IA; TrsFrshCls; TrsJrCls; HonRl; RptrSchPpr; FFA; LetterFtbl; LetterWrstlng; IMSpt; JAAwd; CitAwd; Farming.

HALVORSON, Cindy A; Wolford Public HS; Mylo, ND; SecTrsSophCls; SecJrCls; PresSophCls; Band; Chrs; HonRl; StuCncl; PpCl; Bsktbl; LetterChrldr; College; Vocation.

HALVORSON, Daryl D; Northwestern; Mellette, SD; ALBoysSt; Band; ChrhWkr; HonRl; SchPl; AmLegAwd; VFWAwd; VoiceDemAwd; University; Professional.

HALVORSON, Martin N; Wilton HS; Regan, ND; HonRl; NHS; SctActv; College; Elec Engineer.

HALVORSON, Tamara K; Parkview HS; Footville, WI; 2/156 Band; CncrtBnd; HonRl; MrchBnd; NHS; NatlMeritFnl; GAA; College; Cpa.

HALVORSON, Tracey D; M F L Comm HS; Monona, IA; 23/80 Band; Chr; Chrl; Chrs; ChrhWkr; CncrtBnd; DrmMjrt; HonRl; Mdrgl; MrchBnd; I S U; Home Economics.

HAM, Floyd R; F L Schlagle HS; Kansas City, KS; 3/383 ALBoysSt; ChrhWkr; HonRl; NHS; NatlMeritSchl; PepBnd; SchPl; PresStuCncl; RptrSchPpr; BttyCrckrAwd; Univ Of Kansas; Physics.

HAMACHER, Shari; Edgewood HS; Madison, WI; Chrs; HonRl; HospAde; Yrbk; Bsktbl; IMSpt; State Univ.

HAMAN, Pauline R; Regina HS; Iowa City, IA; HonRl; SchPl; RptrSchPpr; SchPpr; 4-H; SpnCl; PpCl; Chrldr; 4-HAwd; U Of Iowa; Psychologist.

HAMAN, William G; Prairie HS; Swisher, IA; Aud/Vis; HonRl; JrNHS; TchrAde; EdYrBk; SptEdYrbk; MthCl; PresSciCl; LetterFtbl; CaptUniv Of Iowa.

HAMANN, Deborah A; Niles West HS; Morton Grove, IL; 90/666 ChrhWkr; HonRl; Swmmng; Trk; GAA; Eastern Illinois Univ; Accounting.

HAMANN, John M; Campbell Tintah HS; Tintah, MN; TrsFrshCls; Chrs; ChrhWkr; HonRl; SchPl; YthFlsp; FBLA; FFA; CaptTrk; Wrstlng; College; Professional.

HAMANN, Karen; William Chrisman HS; Independence, MO; 3/400 ALAGirlsSt; Band; CncrtBnd; HonRl; JrNHS; NHS; StuCncl; DARAwd; OptClAwd; College; Medical Tech.

HAMANN, Karen L; Appleton Public HS; Appleton, MN; Chrs; HonRl; LbryAde; SchPl; PresStuCncl; LetterBsktbl; LetterTrk; Chrldr; GAA; IMSpt; Moorhead St; Elem Ed.

HAMANN, Kathryn S; Athens HS; Hamburg, WI; 3/94 PresSophCls; PresBand; HonRl; NatlFornLg; NHS; VPSchPl; StuCncl; RptrSchPpr; FBLA; PpCl; Coll; Tchr.

HAMANN, Melissa L; Mendota Township HS; Mendota, IL; 6/187 Chr; CaptDrlTm; LbryAde; NHS; StuCncl; YthFlsp; RptrSchPpr; TreasSpnCl; PpCl; GAA; Ill Valley Comm College; Math.

HAMAR, Hamilton J; Wayland Academy; Calumet, MI; Band; Chr; Chrl; ChrhWkr; LbryAde; SchAde; SchMus; RptrSchPpr; IMSpt; College; Business.

HAMAR, Julie A; Chassell HS; Chassell, MI; ChrhWkr; CmntyWkr; HonRl; NatlFornLg; RedCrAde; SchPl; SptEdYrbk; Yrbk; FHA; Bsktbl; Col; Phy Ed.

HAMARI, Jacqueline; Marquette Senior HS; Marquette, MI; 52/386 HonRl; NatlMeritCmnd; GerCl; SpnCl; AmLegAwd; University.

HAMBEK, Steven L; Burke Public HS; Herrick, SD; 3/37 Chr; Chrl; Chrs; HonRl; SchMus; SchPl; YthFlsp; College; Agriculture.

HAMBLEN, Elaine Y; Lanesville HS; Lanesville, IN; TrsJrCls; HospAde; JA; SchPl; StuCncl; 4-H; CaptChrldr; Business School.

HAMBLET, Kris A; North HS; Fargo, ND; Chr; Chrl; ChrhWkr; HonRl; NHS; SchMus; SchPl; RptrYrbk; SpnCl; College; Law.

HAMBLIN, Pamela K; Litchfield HS; Litchfield, IL; 7/149 VPSophCls; Band; HonRl; NHS; RedCrAde; SchMus; PresFrCl; LetterTrk; Chrldr; PresAwd; University; Liberal Arts.

HAMBLY, Jane E; Industry HS; Macomb, IL; 4/36 ALAGirlsSt; HonRl; StuCncl; Yrbk; RptrSchPpr; VP4-H; PresFHA; PpCl; 4-HAwd; KiwanAwd; Western Ill Univ; Peace Corp.

HAMBRICK, Patricia A; Lindblom Tech; Chicago, IL; 79/657 Band; Chr; HonRl; LbryAde; MrchBnd; Orch; SchMus; TchrAde; LatCl; IMSpt; Univ; Teacher Spec Ed.

HAMBY, Sharon; Troy HS; Troy, MI; 1/275 PresJrCls; ALAGirlsSt; HonRl; NHS; StuGov; FrCl; PpCl; Swmmng; Tennis; Trk; Mich Univ; Engineer.

HAMBY, William H; Troy HS; Troy, MI; 10/525 ChrhWkr; CmntyWkr; HonRl; JrNHS; NHS; StuGov; FrCl; Ftbl; CaptTrk; EldAwd; U Of Mich; Physics.

HAMEL, Elizabeth E; Carlinville HS; Carlinville, IL; 5/165 ALAGirlsSt; HonRl; JrNHS; NHS; OffAde; SchPl; SctActv; FrCl; PpCl; LetterTrk; LetterChrldr; Univ Of Illinois; Biochemistry.

HAMEL, Larry R; Concordia HS; Concordia, KS; ALBoysSt; ChrhWkr; HonRl; SctActv; Bsbl; Bsktbl; Ftbl; Trk; IMSpt; AmLegAwd; College; Vocation.

HAMELIN, Joann J; Escanaba Area Public HS; Escanaba, MI; 34/392 NHS; YthLg; Univ Of Michigan; Oceanography.

HAMELINK, Mark C; Lincoln Sr HS; Wis Rapids, WI; Chr; ChrhWkr; HonRl; Mdrgl; NatlMeritCmnd; NatlThespSoc; SchMus; SchPl; SctActv; U Of Wis; Anesthetist.

HAMER, Dale; Eagle Grove HS; Eagle Grove, IA; 20/132 HonRl; NHS; Navy; Nuclear Field.

HAMER, Dawn A; Mt Clemens HS; Mt Clemens, MI; 53/386 Band; CncrtBnd; HonRl; MrchBnd; NHS; OffAde; Orch; SchPl; PresAwd; College; Nursing.

HAMER, Dean H; Eagle Grove HS; Eagle Grove, IA; HonRl; NHS; SchPl; SpnCl; Ia Central Community Clge.

HAMER, Mark J; Marinette HS; Marinette, WI; Band; CmntyWkr; CncrtBnd; MrchBnd; PepBnd; SctActv; LetterBsbl; LetterBsktbl; Ftbl; LetterSwmmng; IMSpt; College.

HAMERA, Darlene A; Morton West HS; Berwyn, IL; 14/755 Chr; Chrs; HonRl; VPJrNHS; NHS; StuGov; Tennis; CchngActv; GAA; Univ Of Illinois; Army.

HAMERLINCK, Mark E; Sherrard HS; Milan, IL; HonRl; 4-H; FFA; Blackhawk College; Agriculture.

HAMERS, Brian O; Palermo HS; Palermo, ND; PresFrshCls; VPSophCls; PresJrCls; VPSrCls; Chrs; ChrhWkr; CmntyWkr; HonRl; SchMus; SchPl; Yrbk; RptrSchPpr; Bsbl; LetterBsktbl; LetterTrk; Trade School; Vocation.

HAMES, Jackie S; Aurora Central HS; Aurora, IL; Chrs; HonRl; HospAde; NHS; NatlSciFnd; RedCrAde; StuCncl; RptrSchPpr; FNA; SpnCl; GAA; GodCntryAwd; College; Nursing.

HAMIL, Veronica A; Mauston Area HS; Mauston, WI; 51/133 CncrtBnd; HonRl; MrchBnd; PepBnd; SchMus; SchPl; Yrbk; FFA; College; Cosmetology.

HAMILL, Kimberly J; Clearwater HS; Clearwater, KS; Band; Chr; Chrs; HonRl; MrchBnd; PepBnd; SchMus; StuCncl; Twrl; RptrSchPpr; PpCl; Wichita State Univ; Professional.

HAMILTON, Ada E; Macomb HS; Macomb, IL; 21/260 Chr; HonRl; LitMag; SecNHS; SecOrch; SchMus; SchPpr; 4-H; SpnCl; SciCl; 4-HAwd; Western Illinois Univ; Accountant.

HAMILTON, Bina J; Princeton HS; Princeton, MO; PresFrshCls; TrsJrCls; VPBand; ChrhWkr; VPCncrtBnd; HonRl; MrchBnd; NHS; PepBnd; SchAde; SchPl; TchrAde; Twrl; Bsktbl; IMSpt; Trenton Jr College; Professional.

HAMILTON, Cindy L; West Washington HS; Campbellsburg, IN; Chrs; CmntyWkr; HospAde; LbryAde; FDA; FFA; FHA; FNA; FTA; Swmmng; Nursing.

HAMILTON, Connie A; Whitmore Lake HS; Ann Arbor, MI; HonRl; JrNHS; NHS; RptrYrbk; RptrSchPpr; 4-H; FrCl; Bsktbl; Chrldr; University Of Michigan.

HAMILTON, Connie L; Pine River Jr Sr HS; Luther, MI; HonRl; Trade School; Art.

HAMILTON, Cynthia; Soldan HS; St Louis, MO; 209/654 CmntyWkr; JA; LbryAde; OffAde; SchAde; StuCncl; JAAwd; Columbia College; Social Worker.

HAMILTON, Cynthia L; J D Darnall HS; Geneseo, IL; 17/225 Chr; DrmBgl; HonRl; NHS; NatlThespSoc; SchMus; SchPl; TchrAde; Yrbk; Illinois State Univ; Elem Education.

HAMILTON, David A; Hillsboro HS; Taylor Springs, IL; 11/180 ChrhWkr; HonRl; 4-H; GerCl; Ftbl; College; Math.

HAMILTON, Debra A; Morton HS; Morton, IL; 11/312 HonRl; HospAde; NHS; SctActv; Yrbk; PpCl; College; Nursing.

HAMILTON, Debra K; Danville HS; Danville, IL; SecSophCls; SecJrCls; Chr; Chrl; ChrhWkr; HonRl; Mdrgl; StuCncl; RotaryAwd; Univ Of Illinois; Business Admin.

HAMILTON, George R; Franklin HS; Franklin, IL; TrsFrshCls; TrsSophCls; Aud/Vis; ChrhWkr; SpnCl; Bsktbl; Trk; College.

HAMILTON, Gerald G; Hauser HS; Hope, IN; 3/90 Band; Chr; CncrtBnd; MrchBnd; NHS; PepBnd; SecFrshCls; YthFlsp; Bsktbl; LetterTrk; College; Music.

HAMILTON, Jeana R; Mark Twain HS; New London, MO; VPJrCls; Band; ChrhWkr; CncrtBnd; HonRl; SchMus; YthFlsp; FHA; DARAwd; CitAwd; Univ; Music Major.

HAMILTON, John C; Madison Cnty HS; Madison, IN; Band; ChrhWkr; HonRl; JA; TchrAde; SchPpr; PpCl; LetterBsbl; LetterWrstlng; IMSpt; JAAwd;.

HAMILTON, Joyce A; North Mahaska HS; Barnes City, IA; 10/63 VPFrshCls; Chr; Chrl; Chrs; ChrhWkr; CmntyWkr; HonRl; NHS; SchMus; SchPl; RptrSchPpr; 4-H; FHA; IMSpt; Oral Roberts Univ; Business.

HAMILTON, Joyce D; Switzerland County HS; Bennington, IN; HonRl; NHS; Trade; Medical Secretary.

HAMILTON, Julie; Belmont HS; Platteville, WI; 1/46 TrsSrCls; ALAGirlsSt; Band; HonRl; SchPl; 4-H; FHA; GAA; BttyCrckrAwd; U W Platteville; Nursing.

HAMILTON, Karen L; Decatur Jr Sr HS; Stevens Point, WI; 10/73 SecSophCls; HonRl; NatlFornLg; NHS; NatlMeritFnl; NatlThespSoc; SchPl; TchrAde; SptEdYrbk; PpCl; University; Ba Major In English.

HAMILTON, Kathryn A; Lewellen Rural HS; Lewellen, NE; SecSophCls; SecTrsJrCls; Band; ChrhWkr; CmntyWkr; CncrtBnd; HonRl; MrchBnd; PepBnd; SchPl; Yrbk; 4-H; LetterTrk; 4-HAwd; Univ Of Nebraska; Professional.

HAMILTON, Kay; Sun Prairie Senior HS; Sun Prairie, WI; 35/331 ChrhWkr; HonRl; NHS; RedCrAde; StuCncl; GAA; Univ Of Wis; Environmental Science.

HAMILTON, Keith L; Morning Sun Comm HS; Morning Sun, IA; 3/24 VPJrCls; HonRl; NatlThespSoc; SchMus; SchPl; StuCncl; LetterBsbl; CaptBsktbl; CaptFtbl; Trk; Trade School; Electronics.

HAMILTON, Luann M; Resurrection HS; Chicago, IL; 42/260 HonRl; LitMag; PolWkr; RptrSchPpr; De Paul University; Political Science.

HAMILTON, Mark J; Verdigre Public HS; Verdigre, NE; VPSrCls; HonRl; SctActv; StuCncl; StuGov; LetterBsktbl; LetterFtbl; LetterTrk; Trade School; Vocation.

HAMILTON, Marsha A; Decatur Comm HS; Oberlin, KS; 30/85 Chrs; CmntyWkr; Teen; RptrYrbk; 4-H; PpCl; LetterBsktbl; GAA; 4-HAwd; PresAwd; College; Dental Hygiene.

HAMILTON, Minnetta L; Gilman HS; Lafayette, IN; 7/50 Band; Chrs; DrlTm; HonRl; StuCncl; RptrYrbk; RptrSchPpr; 4-H; FFA; FHA; GAA; Purdue Univ; Agriculture.

HAMILTON, Norma L; Sesser HS; Sesser, IL; 5/43 SecSophCls; ALAGirlsSt; Band; ChrhWkr; NatlFornLg; NHS; NatlThespSoc; PresStuCncl; Yrbk; FHA; Southern Ill U; Cert Pub Accountat.

HAMILTON, Pamela L; East HS; Madison, WI; 15/563 SecTrsJrCls; ALAGirlsSt; CmntyWkr; NHS; NatlMeritSF; RedCrAde; SchPl; StuGov; RptrSchPpr; FrCl; Clge; Law.

HAMILTON, Penny L; Lafayette County C 1 HS; Higginsville, MO; 18/98 DrlTm; TreasNHS; 4-H; PpCl; SciCl; GAA;.

HAMILTON, Rebecca S; Chapman HS; Chapman, KS; Band; CncrtBnd; HonRl; MrchBnd; PepBnd; TchrAde; Teen; RptrSchPpr; SecFHA; Tech School; Secretarial Course.

HAMILTON, Robert J; West Dubuque HS; Epworth, IA; 10/243 ALBoysSt; HonRl; NHS; NatlMeritSchl; StuCncl; LetterBsbl; LetterBsktbl; Univ; Accounting.

HAMILTON, Roger D; Fenton HS; Fenton, MI; 22/285 CtyCnl; HonRl; NHS; StuGov; LatCl; Michigan State Univ; Humanities.

HAMILTON, Sarah L; Dunbar Vocational HS; Chicago, IL; 1/450 HonRl; NHS; StuCncl; GAA; Univ Of Illinois; Business Management.

HAMILTON, Scott D; Oakland Community HS; Oakland, IA; 1/37 Band; HonRl; NHS; SchMus; 4-H; FFA; LetterBsbl; LetterBsktbl; LetterFtbl; Trk; 4-HAwd; University.

HAMILTON, Shelley A; Maple Valley Jr Sr HS; Nashville, MI; 9/108 TrsFrshCls; TrsSophCls; TrsSrCls; Chrs; VPNHS; SchPl; VPStuCncl; Yrbk; RptrSchPpr; CaptChrldr; Grand Rapids Schl Of Bible & Music Architec.

HAMILTON, Susan K; North Tama Community HS; Traer, IA; Chr; HonRl; NHS; PolWkr; YthLg; FHA; PpCl; JAAwd; PresAwd; CitAwd; Univ Of Northern Ia; Kindergarten Teacher.

HAMILTON, Vicki S; North Calloway R 1 HS; Fulton, MO; 1/76 SecSophCls; Band; Chr; Chrs; ChrhWkr; CncrtBnd; HonRl; MrchBnd; OffAde; PepBnd; SchMus; TchrAde; FHA; SpnCl; Business School; Vocation.

HAMILTON, William J; North Vigo HS; Terre Haute, IN; PresFrshCls; PresSophCls; HonRl; ModUN; NHS; OffAde; PolWkr; SchAde; StuCncl; StuGov; TchrAde; LetterGlf; In State U; Law.

HAMLETT, Mary J; J M Harlan HS; Chicago, IL; 4/500 ChrhWkr; CncrtBnd; HonRl; JrNHS; MrchBnd; NHS; SchAde; FrCl; SecMthCl; SciCl; Carleton College; Mathematics.

HAMLIN, Michelle L; Plymouth Salem HS; Plymouth, MI; TchrAde; Bsktbl; Michigan St Univ; Psychology.

HAMLING, Jane; Humphrey Public HS; Creston, NE; 8/22 Chrs; HonRl; RptrYrbk; RptrSchPpr; SecTrsSophCls; Chrldr;.

HAMM, Cecilia S; South Sioux HS; South Sioux, NE; Chr; CmntyWkr; HospAde; 4-H; PpCl; Chrldr; IMSpt; 4-HAwd; Trade School; Animal Tech.

HAMM, Douglas C; Kingsley Pierson HS; Kingsley, IA; Band; Chrs; ChrhWkr; CncrtBnd; HonRl; Mdrgl; MrchBnd; ModUN; PepBnd; SchMus; Glf; Univ Of Midwest; Musician.

HAMM, John E; Wisconsin Dells HS; Wisconsin Dells, WI; 2/145 ALBoysSt; PresBand; HonRl; NHS; SchPl; RptrYrbk; RptrSchPpr; TreasKeyCl; Bsktbl; LetterFtbl; LetterTrk; CaptIMSpt; Univ Of Wisconsin.

HAMM, Susan A; Lincoln HS; Wisconsin Rapids, WI; HonRl; Yrbk; SchPpr; PpCl; SciCl; Univ Of Wis; Home Ec.

HAMM, Thomas D; W P Chrysler Memorial HS; New Castle, IN; 5/396 ALBoysSt; ChrhWkr; HonRl; NatlFornLg; NHS; NatlMeritSF; PolWkr; Northwestern Univ; History.

HAMMAC, Geraldine L; Monroe HS; Monroe, MI; ChrhWkr; HonRl; NHS; TchrAde; YthFlsp; LetterTrk; CchngActv; GAA; IMSpt; Navy; Dental Hygienist.

HAMMACK, Barbara J; Morrill HS; Morrill, NE; Band; Chrs; NHS; NatlThespSoc; SchPl; StuGov; Twrl; Yrbk; FHA; PpCl; College; Forestry Or Veterinary Assistant.

HAMMACK, Michele L; Atlanta HS; Atlanta, MO; PresSrCls; ChrhWkr; CmntyWkr; StuGov; YthLg; FFA; FHA; LetterBsktbl; LetterTrk; College; Phy Ed.

HAMMAN, James M; Libertyville HS; Libertyville, IL; Band; CncrtBnd; HonRl; MrchBnd; NHS; SchMus; SctActv; FrCl; College; Law.

HAMMAN, Phyllis F; Summit HS; Summit, SD; 1/21 SecTrsJrCls; ALAGirlsSt; Chr; Chrs; HonRl; ROTC; YthFlsp; RptrYrbk; SecFNA; PpCl; Sd State U; Dietetics.

HAMMEL, Karen A; Champaign Central HS; Champaign, IL; HonRl; SchPl; Sdlty; Yrbk; CivCl; Pres4-H; FHA; KeyCl; DanFAwd; 4-HAwd; College; Accounting.

HAMMEL, Thomas J; Manual HS; Indianapolis, IN; CmntyWkr; HonRl; Socr; College; Professional.

HAMMEN, Peggy L; Rockwell City HS; Rockwell City, IA; ChrhWkr; HonRl; Bsktbl; IMSpt; College; Business.

HAMMER, James; Farmer City Mansfield HS; Farmer City, IL; 50/85 CmntyWkr; HonRl; SchPl; StuCncl; RptrYrbk; 4-H; FFA; Ftbl; IMSpt; Southern Univ; Forestry.

HAMMER, Jamie R; Elgin HS; Elgin, IL; CmntyWkr; CncrtBnd; DrmBgl; University; Law.

HAMMER, Julie A; Stockton HS; Stockton, IL; Chr; HonRl; LbryAde; Yrbk; SchPpr; 4-H; FBLA; SecFrCl; GAA; 4-HAwd; Il St Univ; Business.

HAMMER, Kai Q; Jordan HS; Jordan, MN; 9/90 ALBoysSt; Band; CmntyWkr; HonRl; PepBnd; PolWkr; SchMus; SchPl; StuCncl; EngCl; St Johns Univ; Lawyer.

HAMMER, Mary T; St Mary Academy; Monroe, MI; CmntyWkr; HonRl; StuGov; EdYrBk; LetterTrk; SecGAA; 4-HAwd; St Vincents; Nurse.

HAMMER, Steven; Fort Atkinson HS; Ft Atkinson, WI; Chr; ChrhWkr; HonRl; NHS; NatlMeritCmnd; NatlThespSoc; SchPl; Uw Madison Med School; Medical Missionary.

HAMMER, Steven; Fort Senior Hs; Fort Atkinson, WI; Chr; ChrhWkr; HonRl; NHS; NatlMeritCmnd; SchPl; SecKeyCl; SpnCl; Uw Madison ; Pre Med Curriculum.

HAMMERAND, Colleen K; Bellevue Comm HS; Bellevue, IA; 8/44 Chrs; HonRl; ModUN; NHS; SchMus; StuCncl; StuGov; RptrSchPpr; TreasFHA; SpnCl;.

HAMMERLE, Cynthia M; Hart HS; Hart, MI; 7/126 ChrhWkr; HonRl; TchrAde; 4-H; SpnCl; PpCl; Davenport Business School; Accounting.

HAMMERSCHMIDT, Dale L; Satanta HS; Satanta, KS; Chrs; ChrhWkr; CmntyWkr; HonRl; SctActv; YthFlsp; Bsktbl; Ftbl; University; Vocation.

HAMMERSLEY, Ellen; Tomahawk HS; Heafford Jct, WI; SecSophCls; SecJrCls; ChrhWkr; HonRl; NHS; NatlSciFnd; NatlThespSoc; SchPl; StuCncl; SchPpr; College; Professional.

HAMMERSTROM, Leroy P; Omaha Benson HS; Omaha, NE; 26/460 Band; ChrhWkr; CncrtBnd; HonRl; MrchBnd; NHS; PepBnd; YthFlsp; Bsbl; Mid America Nazarene College; Computers.

HAMMES, Ted L; Tri County HS; Keswick, IA; VPFrshCls; TrsJrCls; TrsSrCls; Band; ChrhWkr; HonRl; StuCncl; CaptBsbl; CaptBsktbl; CaptFtbl; College.

HAMMIS, Marcia J; St Stephen HS; Saginaw, MI; PresJrCls; HonRl; LbryAde; NHS; OffAde; SchPl; StuGov; PpCl; Univ Of Mich; Medicine.

HAMMITT, Sandra J; Central Webster HS; Lehigh, IA; Chr; Chrs; ChrhWkr; HonRl; YthFnd; Yrbk; RptrSchPpr; SpnCl; Spencer School Of Buss; Accounting.

HAMMOND, Christine S; Ionia HS; Ionia, MI; ChrhWkr; HonRl; LitMag; NatlMeritCmnd; StuGov; TchrAde; YthFlsp; RptrYrbk; RptrSchPpr; SpnCl; Central Michigan Univ; Journalism.

HAMMOND, David; Dexfield HS; Redfield, IA; SecFrshCls; Chrs; ChrhWkr; CmntyWkr; HonRl; NHS; StuCncl; MthCl; Emmaus Bible Coll; Social Work.

HAMMOND, Deborah L; Arthur Hill HS; Saginaw, MI; HospAde; RedCrAde; Delta College; Rn.

HAMMOND, Debra J; Clay Center Public HS; Clay Center, NE; SecFrshCls; SecJrCls; Band; ChrhWkr; CmntyWkr; CncrtBnd; HonRl; MrchBnd; SecNHS; PepBnd; SchPl; PresStuCncl; Trk; Chrldr; 4-HAwd; Univ Of Nebraska; Guidance Counselor.

HAMMOND, Delores L; Stanton County HS; Johnson, KS; Band; Chr; Chrs; HonRl; NHS; RedCrAde; SctActv; TchrAde; Bsktbl; Trk;.

HAMMOND, Doug; Harrisonville Sr HS; Harrisonville, MO; 68/150 HonRl; NatlSciFnd; FFA; Ftbl; Trk; Rodeo College; Equistrian Field.

HAMMOND, Fred W; Westfield HS; Westfield, IL; 5/17 PresSophCls; TrsSrCls; Band; Chr; Chrs; ChrhWkr; CncrtBnd; HonRl; Mdrgl; MrchBnd; NHS; PepBnd; SchMus; SchPl; SctActv; Eastern Ill Univ; Science.

HAMMOND, Kathleen A; Williamston HS; Williamston, MI; 1/150 Chr; Chrl; CncrtBnd; DrmMjrt; JrNHS; MrchBnd; SchPl; 4-H; FTA; Central Michigan Univ; Music.

HAMMOND, Lisa M; Northwest HS; Rives Jct, MI; PresChr; Chrl; HonRl; NHS; SchMus; SctActv; YthFlsp; 4-H; 4-HAwd; Eastern Michigan Univ; Dramatics.

HAMMOND, Noral W; Springs Valley HS; West Baden, IN; Band; Chrs; CmntyWkr; CncrtBnd; DrmBgl; MrchBnd; PepBnd; SchPl; 4-H; FFA; PpCl; Bsbl; Bsktbl; College; Vocation.

HAMMOND, Rhonda F; Golva HS; Golva, ND; PresSophCls; Band; CmntyWkr; HonRl; PepBnd; SchPl; Bsktbl; Trk; Chrldr; 4-HAwd; Col ; Med Scre.

HAMMOND, Shari D; Fremont Sr HS; Fremont, NE; 83/424 Band; CncrtBnd; MrchBnd; PepBnd; Midland Lutheran College; Accounting.

HAMMOND, Sharon; West Washington HS; Salem, IN; Band; CncrtBnd; MrchBnd; NatlThespSoc; PepBnd; SchMus; SctActv; Twrl; YthFlsp; 4-H; Beauty College.

HAMMOND, Susan F; Reading HS; Reading, KS; SecTrsJrCls; ChrhWkr; CmntyWkr; HonRl; StuCncl; TchrAde; RptrYrbk; EdSchPpr; PpCl; Trade School; Professional.

HAMMOND, Susan K; Tremont HS; Tremont, IL; 1/66 Chr; CncrtBnd; HonRl; MrchBnd; NHS; NatlThespSoc; Orch; PepBnd; SchMus; SchPl; Il Wesleyan Univ; Music Ed.

HAMMONDS, Thomas L; Beaumont HS; St Louis, MO; 8/803 HonRl; LbryAde; NHS; StuGov; TchrAde; RptrYrbk; LetterSocr; Tennis; IMSpt; JAAwd; JETSAwd; Air Force Academy; Civil Engineer.

HAMMONS, Barbara L; Harper Creek HS; Battle Creek, MI; 18/237 Band; CncrtBnd; MrchBnd; PepBnd; SchPl; RptrYrbk; Yrbk; SpnCl; Trk; Coll; Sci Botany.

HAMMONS, Betty J; Jennings County HS; Holton, IN; ChrhWkr; NHS; RptrSchPpr; PresFHA;.

HAMNER, Patricia G; Reitz Memorial HS; Evansville, IN; 5/211 HonRl; NHS; StuCncl; GerCl; PpCl; Tennis; In U; Physical Therapy.

HAMOOD, John A; Fordson HS; Dearborn, MI; HonRl; NHS; Bsbl; College; Electrical Technology.

HAMPEL, Scott E; Kapaun Mt Carmel HS; Wichita, KS; HonRl; SctActv; Yrbk; SchPpr; Tennis; College; Engineering, Law.

HAMPLEWSKI, Cynthia M; Dominican HS; Detroit, MI; ChrhWkr; HonRl; NHS; PolWkr; SchMus; SchPl; College; Pre Law.

HAMPTON, Carl L; New Trier East HS; Glencoe, IL; CmntyWkr; SctActv; StuGov; YthFlsp; Bsbl; San Jose City College; Biology.

HAMPTON, Chris S; Chaffee HS; Chaffee, MO; 9/65 ALBoysSt; Band; Chr; CncrtBnd; HonRl; MrchBnd; SchPl; Ftbl; LetterTrk; Military Service.

HAMPTON, Debra K; Gering HS; Gering, NE; Chr; DrlTm; HonRl; JrNHS; SchMus; GerCl; PpCl; Trk; Chrldr; 4-HAwd; College; Semantics.

HAMPTON, Gail L; Salem HS; Salem, MO; 9/173 Band; CncrtBnd; HonRl; MrchBnd; PepBnd; PPFtbl; Univ.

HAMPTON, Georgena A; Ellington HS; Piedmont, MO; ChrhWkr; CmntyWkr; HonRl; HospAde; RedCrAde; StuGov; TchrAde; 4-H; FFA; VPFHA; Nursing.

HAMPTON, Jerry L; Mt Vernon Township HS; Mount Vernon, IL; 81/388 Band; ChrhWkr; CncrtBnd; HonRl; LbryAde; MrchBnd; SchMus; Rend Lake Jr Clge; Cert Pub Accountant.

HAMPTON, Kevin L; Eastern HS; Salem, IN; 10/80 Band; DrlTm; NHS; SctActv; StuGov; YthLg; RptrSchPpr; SptEdSchPpr; FBLA;.

HAMPTON, Mark J; Warsaw Community HS; Warsaw, IN; ChrhWkr; CmntyWkr; PolWkr; StuCncl; StuGov; PresYthFlsp; SptEdYrbk; 4-H; EngCl; Ftbl; Purdue Univ; Environment.

HAMPTON, Mary; Our Lady Of Grace HS; Indianapolis, IN; 14/60 PresJrCls; ALAGirlsSt; HonRl; ModUN; PolWkr; EdSchPpr; IMSpt; St Joseph Coll; Lawyer.

HAMPTON, Melanie J; Colchester HS; Colchester, IL; 6/52 SecJrCls; SecChr; Chrl; Chrs; DrlTm; HonRl; NHS; SchMus; SchPl; RptrYrbk; SpnCl; Chrldr; IMSpt; PresAwd; University; Horticulture.

HAMPTON, Pamela; Laville HS; Bremen, IN; 12/126 Band; Chr; ChrhWkr; HonRl; JrNHS; NHS; RptrSchPpr; SpnCl; AmLegAwd; 4-HAwd; Voc Coll;vocational.

HAMPTON, Theresa A; Edison HS; East Gary, IN; HonRl; JrNHS; EdSchPpr; FBLA; PpCl; SciCl; GAA; PPFtbl; College; X Ray Technician.

HAMPTON, Tina M; Christopher Comm HS; Christopher, IL; Band; ChrhWkr; HonRl; LbryAde; OffAde; SchPl; Pres4-H; VPFFA; DanFAwd; 4-HAwd; Rend Lake Jr College; Agriculture.

HAMRE, Paul; Sacred Heart Public HS; Sacred Heart, MN; Band; Chr; ChrhWkr; CmntyWkr; HonRl; 4-H; FFA; LetterBsbl; LetterFtbl; Coll; Math.

HAMRE, Timothy L; Kelly Walsh HS; Rapid City, SD; CmntyWkr; HonRl; JrNHS; LitMag; NHS; StuCncl; TchrAde; IMSpt; Sd School Of Mines; Mining Engineer.

HAMRICK, Alan; Southwest HS; St Louis, MO; CncrtBnd; HonRl; Swmmng; Univ; Vocation.

HAMS, Pierre F; Divine Heart Seminary HS; Kansas City, MO; PresSophCls; PresJrCls; CmntyWkr; HonRl; RedCrAde; SctActv; StuCncl; Yrbk; LetterBsbl; LetterBsktbl; Saint Louis Univ; Pre Law.

HAMTAK, Donna M; Bryan Sr HS; Omaha, NE; 16/400 Chr; DrlTm; HonRl; ModUN; PpCl; LetterSwmmng; Trk; GAA; IMSpt; College; Physical Ed.

HAN, Dennis P; Ishpeming HS; Ishpeming, MI; TrsFrshCls; Band; HonRl; NHS; NatlMeritSF; LetterTennis; IMSpt; Univ Of Michigan; Doctor.

HAN, Kwang K; Ypsilanti HS; Ypsilanti, MI; StuCncl; University Of Michigan; Physics.

HANACIK, Linda J; Waukesha North HS; Waukesha, WI; HonRl; NHS; StuCncl; EdYrBk; SptEdYrbk; RptrSchPpr; VPLatCl; DanFAwd; Milwaukee County Gen Hospital; Nurse.

HANAUER, Cynthia K; Dixon HS; Dixon, MO; ALAGirlsSt; HonRl; NHS; College; Home Ec.

HANCHEK, Bill J; Carney Nadeau Public HS; Carney, MI; VPSophCls; ALBoysSt; Band; CncrtBnd; HonRl; PepBnd; SchPl; StuCncl; LetterBsktbl; LetterTrk; Mi Tech Univ.

HANCHEK, Richard J; Carney Nadeau HS; Carney, MI; 2/25 VPSrCls; ALBoysSt; HonRl; NatlMeritCmnd; PpCl; CaptBsktbl; DanFAwd; Mich Tech U; Accountant Or Engineer.

HANCOCK, Charles; Nevada HS; Nevada, MO; LetterFtbl; LetterTennis; LetterWrstlng; Electronics.

HANCOCK, Edward F; Houghton Lake HS; Houghton Lake, MI; HonRl; NHS; TchrAde; LetterBsbl; LetterFtbl; IMSpt; Univ; Professional.

HANCOCK, Jeanne M; Collinsville HS; Edwardsville, IL; Chrs; ChrhWkr; HospAde; GAA; Nursing School; Nurse.

HANCOCK, Peggy A; Oak Park HS; Gladstone, MO; DrlTm; HonRl; MrchBnd; StuCncl; StuGov; Business School; Data Processing.

HANCOCK, Randall D; Dwight Township HS; Dwight, IL; CncrtBnd; HonRl; MrchBnd; NHS; NatlMeritCmnd; PepBnd; PolWkr; SctActv; LetterTennis; LetterWrstlng; Univ Of Il.

HANCOCK, Scott S; Westview HS; Kankakee, IL; 11/270 Band; ChrhWkr; CncrtBnd; HonRl; MrchBnd; NHS; Univ Of Ill; Business Adm.

HANCOCK, Tara S; Blair HS; Blair, NE; PresBand; Chr; ChrhWkr; CncrtBnd; MrchBnd; NatlThespSoc; PepBnd; SchMus; SchPl; YthFlsp; Clg; Music.

HANCOX, Denise R; Plymouth HS; Plymouth, IL; SecJrCls; SecChrhWkr; HonRl; MrchBnd; Yrbk; RptrSchPpr; 4-H; PresFHA; SecGAA; 4-HAwd; Trade School; Business.

HAND, Jeff T; Sargent HS; Sargent, NE; JA; NHS; NatlThespSoc; RptrSchPpr; FBLA; Bsbl; Bsktbl; Ftbl; Glf; Trk; Coll; Pro.

HAND, Judy L; Valley Park HS; Valley Park, MO; SecSophCls; VPJrCls; Chr; Chrs; HonRl; NHS; StuCncl; RptrYrbk; Yrbk; Chrldr;.

HAND, Lois; Munster Hs; Munster, IN; Chr; DrlTm; HonRl; StuCncl; StuGov; 4-H; PpCl; GAA; College; Forestry.

HAND, Maxine R; Union City HS; Union City, MI; HonRl; NHS; TchrAde; FHA; SpnCl; PpCl; Bsktbl; College; Science.

HANDLER, Harry H; Urbana HS; Urbana, IL; PresFrshCls; SecSophCls; ChrhWkr; HonRl; SchPl; StuCncl; RptrYrbk; RptrSchPpr; Tennis; Univ; Bus.

HANDLEY, Annette J; West Side HS; Gary, IN; HonRl; JrNHS; LbryAde; NHS; NatlMeritSF; SchPl; SctActv; Twrl; College; Journalism.

HANDLIN, Sharon; Malden HS; Malden, MO; Chr; HonRl; NatlFornLg; NHS; NatlThespSoc; StuCncl; 4-H; DARAwd; 4-HAwd; Mo Univ; Speech And Law.

HANDLY, Steven E; Perry Meridian HS; Indianapolis, IN; ChrhWkr; HonRl; StuGov; PpCl; Milligan College; Christian Ministry.

HANDRICH, Debra J; Little Wolf HS; Manawa, WI; Chrs; HonRl; SchPl; TchrAde; RptrSchPpr; 4-H; FHA; PpCl; GAA; 4-HAwd; JAAwd; Fox Valley Tech Inst; Occupational Therapy.

HANDRICH, Lynn R; Fairview HS; Fairview, MI; PresSophCls; TrsJrCls; ALBoysSt; YthFlsp; EdSchPpr; Bsbl; Bsktbl; Glf; College; Accounting.

HANDRICK, Steve G; Auburndale HS; Auburndale, WI; ALBoysSt; Band; HonRl; NHS; SchPl; SctActv; SptEdYrbk; FBLA; Bsbl; Bsktbl; Eau Claire College; Cpa.

HANDWERK, Tamey J; Raytown HS; Kansas City, MO; Chr; DrlTm; HonRl; JrNHS; NatlFornLg; SchPl; StuCncl; Yrbk; GerCl; PpCl; Col; Journalism.

HANDY, Karen S; Waverly HS; Waverly, IL; 5/33 SecSophCls; PresJrCls; Chrs; HonRl; NHS; OffAde; StuCncl; RptrYrbk; SptEdYrbk; LatCl; Bsktbl; Chrldr; Trade School; Radiology Technology.

HANDY, Patricia A; Waverly HS; Waverly, IL; 5/33 Band; Chrs; HonRl; LbryAde; NHS; NatlThespSoc; PresYthFlsp; VP4-H; 4-HAwd; University; History.

HANDY, Sylvia L; Onsted HS; Onsted, MI; Band; CncrtBnd; HonRl; MrchBnd; PepBnd; SchAde; SchPl; StuCncl; EdSchPpr; FHA; Houghton; Conservation.

HANDZIK, Leslie A; Maria HS; Chicago, IL; 48/304 Chr; Chrs; HonRl; SctActv; Twrl; Bsbl; LetterBsktbl; Ftbl; CchngActv; BttyCrckrAwd; Southwest Col; Physical Ed Teacher.

HANEGRAAF, Mary; Derham Hall HS; St Paul, MN; Band; Chrs; CncrtBnd; HonRl; MrchBnd; PepBnd; ROTC; SchPl; FrCl; SciCl; Liberal Arts Or State; Professional, Major.

HANEKE, David C; Ellis HS; Ellis, KS; PresJrCls; ALBoysSt; Chrl; ChrhWkr; HonRl; SchPl; SctActv; Ftbl; Wrstlng; College; Business.

HANEKE, Shirley A; Polo HS; Orient, SD; 1/13 SecJrCls; ALAGirlsSt; Chrs; ChrhWkr; DrlTm; HonRl; StuCncl; LetterBsktbl; LetterTrk; Chrldr; DARAwd; College; Journalism.

HANEL, Judith A; Howells HS; Howells, NE; 25/44 Band; HospAde; NatlMeritCmnd; NatlMeritSchl; PolWkr; SchPl; StuCncl; CivCl; BttyCrckrAwd; College; Forestry.

HANEN, Kathy; Mo Valley HS; Missouri Valley, IA; DrlTm; HonRl; StuCncl; RptrYrbk; PpCl; SciCl; Trk; Chrldr; PresAwd; Business School; Legal Executive Secretary.

HANERUD, Karen M; Campbell Tintah HS; Norcross, MN; 1/35 Band; Chr; HonRl; SchPl; YthFlsp; Bethel College.

HANES, Alice J; Moulton Udell Comm HS; Moulton, IA; 4/33 SecSophCls; PresJrCls; Band; Chrs; MrchBnd; PepBnd; 4-H; Bsktbl; Wrstlng; MasAwd; Ottaumwa Heights; Radiologis.

HANES, Sally J; Paxton HS; Paxton, IL; 40/125 Band; HonRl; Mdrgl; StuCncl; PresYthFlsp; LetterBsbl; LetterBsktbl; LetterTrk; PresGAA; IMSpt; Illinois State Univ; Criminology.

HANEY, Angie K; Gothenburg HS; Gothenburg, NE; SecJrCls; Band; Chrs; ChrhWkr; CmntyWkr; CncrtBnd; HonRl; MrchBnd; PepBnd; SchMus; SchPl; AmLegAwd; College; Elementary Teaching.

HANEY, Jerri L; North Vigo HS; Terre Haute, IN; 50/650 SecSophCls; Band; DrlTm; HonRl; NHS; SchPl; StuCncl; Trk; GAA; PPFtbl; Indiana St Univ; Nursing.

HANEY, Kenneth C; Seymour HS; Seymour, MO; 1/70 ChrhWkr; CmntyWkr; HonRl; StuCncl; PpCl; LetterBsktbl; CitAwd; University; Computer Programming.

HANEY, Stuart A; Topeka West HS; Topeka, KS; 10/421 ALBoysSt; ChrhWkr; HonRl; ModUN; NatlFornLg; PolWkr; StuGov; LatCl; College; Law.

HANFORD, Kathryn J; J D Darnall HS; Geneseo, IL; 46/207 Chrs; HonRl; NatlMeritCmnd; NatlThespSoc; SchMus; SchPl; Augustana College; Education.

HANFORD, Linda; Big Rapids HS; Big Rapid, MI; ChrhWkr; SctActv; TchrAde; YthFlsp; FrCl; MthCl; Mi State Univ; Psychology.

HANGEN, Janice; Marquette Sr HS; Marquette, MI; 15/400 ALAGirlsSt; Chr; ChrhWkr; CmntyWkr; PolWkr; SchPl; StuCncl; StuGov; FrCl; SciCl; Bryn Mawr Coll; Biochemistry.

HANGGI, Douglas A; John A Johnson HS; St Paul, MN; AFS; Chr; ChrhWkr; HonRl; NatlFornLg; NHS; NatlMeritSF; PolWkr; SctActv; Coll; Medicine.

HANGSLEBEN, David H; Ofallon Township HS; O Fallon, IL; Aud/Vis; Chr; Chrs; Mdrgl; SchMus; SchPl; FSA; SpnCl; SciCl; IMSpt; Belleville Area College; Physical Sciences.

HANIGAN, Brian J; Marist HS; Oak Lawn, IL; 17/393 HonRl; NHS; StuCncl; SpnCl; Trk; University; Professional.

HANIGAN, Richard; Dunlap Community HS; Dunlap, IA; 5/55 VPFrshCls; PresJrCls; HonRl; JrNHS; NHS; StuCncl; FTA; Bsbl; Bsktbl; Ftbl; Iowa State Univ; Agriculture.

HANISKO, Carolyn M; St Stephen HS; Saginaw, MI; 1/96 HonRl; HospAde; TreasNHS; PolWkr; PpCl; College.

HANKINS, Andrea L; Waverly HS; Waverly, IL; 2/31 ALAGirlsSt; HonRl; NHS; StuCncl; SecFHA; LetterTrk; Chrldr; IMSpt; Business Schl; Secretary.

HANKINS, David J; Webb HS; Reedsburg, WI; Band; CncrtBnd; HonRl; Mdrgl; MrchBnd; PepBnd; SctActv; LatCl; Ftbl; College; Clergy.

HANKINS, Deborah L; Cedar Springs Public HS; Cedar Springs, MI; ChrhWkr; HonRl; NatlFornLg; TchrAde; SchPpr; LetterTennis; Grand Rapids Baptist College; Secondary Ed.

HANKINS, Henry P; Harbor HS; Harbor Springs, MI; HonRl; LbryAde; TchrAde; Trk; IMSpt; State Police Acad; State Trooper.

HANKINS, Rhonda J; Granton HS; Granton, WI; 4/36 ChrhWkr; HonRl; HospAde; LbryAde; NHS; SchPl; EdYrBk; EdSchPpr; Med State Tech Inst; Med Asst.

HANKINS, Ronald W; Twin Rivers HS; Bode, IA; 6/40 ALBoysSt; Band; Chrs; HonRl; SptEdYrbk; 4-H; PpCl; LetterBsktbl; LetterTrk; College; Accounting.

HANKINSON, Desiree D; Pawnee HS; Pawnee, IL; SecJrCls; HonRl; JCC; NHS; StuGov; Yrbk; FSA; FrCl; LetterTrk; LetterWrstlng; U Of Tn; Phys Ed.

HANKLA, Gordon R; Marion Sr HS; Marion, IL; Chr; HonRl; SctActv; LatCl; MthCl; SciCl; Southern Illinois Univ; Civil Engineering.

HANKS, Roberta L; Ritenour HS; Overland, MO; ChrhWkr; OffAde; SctActv; StuCncl; YthFlsp; PpCl; Parks Air College; Stewardess.

HANLEY, Cindy; Schulte HS; Terre Haute, IN; Band; Bsktbl; GAA; College.

HANLEY, Jo Ann; Mt Assisi HS; Chicago, IL; 18/194 ChrhWkr; HospAde; NHS; NatlMeritCmnd; SchMus; TchrAde; FrCl; Bsktbl; Culver University.

HANLEY, John E; Cathedral HS; Indianapolis, IN; 10/140 ChrhWkr; HonRl; JrNHS; NHS; PolWkr; SctActv; SpnCl; CaptTrk; IMSpt; Indiana State Univ; Business.

HANLEY, Martin S; Ottawa Twp HS; Ottawa, IL; 42/426 HonRl; NHS; StuCncl; CivCl; LetterBsbl; LetterBsktbl; Ftbl; Creighton Univ; Optometry.

HANLEY, Mary A; Oak Forest HS; Oak Forest, IL; 9/291 ChrhWkr; HonRl; HospAde; SctActv; FrCl; SpnCl; St Xavier College; Nurse.

HANLEY, Thomas D; Lake Michigan Catholic HS; St Joseph, MI; DrmBgl; LetterGlf; CaptTennis; Mi St Univ Of W Mi Col; Accountant.

HANLEY, William J; M V K Comm Unit #2 HS; Verona, IL; 1/43 PresSrCls; HonRl; NHS; NatlMeritCmnd; Yrbk; PresFrCl; PresLatCl; PresMthCl; LetterBsktbl; Glf; TIMEAwd; NCTE; College; Math.

HANLON, Barbara A; Tigerton HS; Tigrton, WI; 4/36 PresSrCls; HonRl; NHS; SctActv; YthLg; EdSchPpr; FHA; CaptLetterTrk; Chrldr; St Norbert Coll; Med Tech.

HANLON, Barbara A; Tigerton HS; Tigerton, WI; 5/36 PresSrCls; HonRl; NatlCathMusEdAsoc; SchPl; SctActv; LetterBsktbl; LetterTrk; Chrldr; LionAwd; PresAwd; St Norbert Coll; Med Tech.

HANLON, Pamela J; Harmony HS; Harmony, MN; ALAGirlsSt; Band; Chr; CncrtBnd; DrlTm; HonRl; NHS; StuCncl; EdYrBk; Chrldr; Trade School; Cosmatology.

HANLON, Therese A; Andrean HS; Merrillville, IN; HonRl; Butler Univ; Social Work.

HANMER, Robert S; Hibbing HS; Hibbing, MN; 39/424 PresAud/Vis; HonRl; NHS; Orch; MthCl; PresSciCl; Swmmng; University; Computer Programming.

HANNA, Angela; Oakfield HS; Oakfield, WI; HonRl; NatlFornLg; OffAde; RptrSchPpr; FBLA; SpnCl; PpCl; PresAwd; College; History Or Business.

HANNA, Betsy; Winfield HS; Winfield, KS; ChrhWkr; CmntyWkr; HonRl; HospAde; RedCrAde; YthFlsp; Bsktbl; Swmmng; Tennis; CchngActv; College.

HANNA, Brenda H; Woden Crystal Lake HS; Woden, IA; SecTrsSrCls; Band; Chr; CncrtBnd; MrchBnd; Yrbk; PpCl; LetterBsbl; LetterBsktbl; LetterChrldr; Store Clerk.

HANNA, Cheryl D; Princeton HS; Princeton, IL; 5/178 VPSrCls; CncrtBnd; DrlTm; HonRl; HospAde; PepBnd; RptrSchPpr; 4-H; GerCl; Bsktbl; Univ Of Ill; Computer Science.

HANNA, Cynthia K; Liberal HS; Liberal, KS; 5/282 ChrhWkr; HonRl; NHS; NatlThespSoc; SchPl; YthFlsp; Jr Col; Vocation.

HANNA, David G; Wauneta Public HS; Wauneta, NE; 5/30 PresFrshCls; PresJrCls; Chr; HonRl; NHS; CaptFtbl; Tennis; CchngActv; IMSpt; GodCntryAwd; Univ Of Neb; Vo Ag Instruc.

HANNA, Gerald G; Manistee Catholic Central HS; Manistee, MI; Band; CncrtBnd; HonRl; MrchBnd; Yrbk; IMSpt; Northwestern Mi College; Hotel Management.

HANNA, James D; Monroe HS; Monroe, WI; PresAFS; SctActv; StuGov; TreasKeyCl; FrCl; CaptIMSpt; PresAwd; College; Medicine.

HANNA, Lisa J; Shenandoah HS; Middletown, IN; Band; ChrhWkr; CmntyWkr; CncrtBnd; MrchBnd; Orch; PepBnd; YthFlsp; 4-H; FHA; University; Business Admin.

HANNA, Melanie K; Bloomfield HS; Bloomfield, MO; 8/60 TrsJrCls; ALAGirlsSt; Chr; ChrhWkr; CmntyWkr; SctActv; IMSpt; DARAwd; 4-HAwd; CitAwd; College; Nursing.

HANNA, Michael D; Wichita North HS; Wichita, KS; 6/550 ChrhWkr; CmntyWkr; HonRl; JrNHS; TreasNHS; StuCncl; StuGov; YthFlsp; GerCl; MthCl; Tennis; LetterTrk; OptClAwd; Oral Roberts Univ; Theology.

HANNA, Myron A; Kinmundy Alma HS; Kinmundy, IL; 1/57 Band; Chr; CncrtBnd; HonRl; MrchBnd; NHS; PepBnd; SchMus; PresYthFlsp; SchPpr; Bsbl; Bsktbl; Trk; 4-HAwd; College; Law.

HANNA, Nancy J; Wauneta Public HS; Wauneta, NE; 1/34 Band; Chr; HonRl; NHS; StuCncl; YthFlsp; PpCl; Bsktbl; Ftbl; AmLegAwd; Mc Coor Jr College; Home Ec.

HANNA, Nancy M; Warren Woods HS; Warren, MI; HonRl; LitMag; OffAde; SchAde; SchMus; SchPl; TchrAde; Bsktbl; LetterSwmmng; LetterTrk; N Mi Univ; Business.

HANNA, Pam; Alexis HS; Alexis, IL; 11/47 Chr; HonRl; StuCncl; TchrAde; Bsktbl; Chrldr; GAA; 4-HAwd; Business Schl; Singer.

HANNA, Rebecca; Woden Crystal Lake HS; Woden, IA; Band; Chrs; ChrhWkr; HonRl; MrchBnd; NHS; PolWkr; Yrbk; FNA; PpCl; Luther Coll; Elementary Education.

HANNA, Sheryl J; Burke HS; Omaha, NE; VPFrshCls; Chr; Chrs; HonRl; SchMus; SchPl; StuCncl; YthFlsp; Yrbk; PpCl; Elem Education.

HANNA, Vicki L; Guttenberg Comm HS; Guttenberg, IA; 3/74 Band; Chrs; CncrtBnd; HonRl; MrchBnd; SecNHS; SchMus; Bsktbl; LetterGlf; PresGAA;.

HANNAH, Andrew S; Clarence M Kimball HS; Royal Oak, MI; Chr; ChrhWkr; HonRl; Mdrgl; NHS; SchMus; SchPl; SctActv; GerCl; Mi St U ;archivist.

HANNAH, Clinton G; Illinois Valley Central HS; Peoria, IL; PresSrCls; Chr; ChrhWkr; HonRl; YthFlsp; 4-H; Trk; DanFAwd; Jr College; Art.

HANNAH, Steven K; Polo Community HS; Polo, IL; 6/90 ChrhWkr; HonRl; NHS; SctActv; StuCncl; YthFlsp; KeyCl; SpnCl; Wrstlng; College; Engineer.

HANNAH, Victoria L; Lincoln HS; Vincennes, IN; 25/328 ChrhWkr; CmntyWkr; HonRl; JA; NatlMeritSchl; PolWkr; StuCncl; StuGov; RptrSchPpr; FBLA; Vincennes Univ; Accounting.

HANNAHS, Marguerite E; Oxford Area HS; Leonard, MI; 16/202 HonRl; 4-H; 4-HAwd; RotaryAwd; Occ; Veterinary Medicine.

HANNAN, Mark C; Mead Public HS; Fremont, NE; 1/39 PresFrshCls; PresSophCls; TrsJrCls; HonRl; NHS; NatlThespSoc; StuCncl; Bsktbl; Ftbl; 4-HAwd; Uni Of Ne; Busines Administration.

HANNAPEL, Leslie J; St Teresa HS; Decatur, IL; 11/120 VPAFS; Chr; Chrs; HonRl; HospAde; JrNHS; NHS; NatlMeritSchl; NatlThespSoc; SchAde; SchMus; SchPl; RptrYrbk; PpCl; Washington Univ; Law.

HANNEM, Wendy; Oregon Senior HS; Oregon, WI; AFS; HonRl; FHA; College.

HANNEMAN, Candace; Brunswick HS; Brunswick, NE; VPFrshCls; VPSophCls; ALAGirlsSt; Band; Chr; Chrs; Trk; Chrldr; 4-HAwd; MasAwd; College; Home Economics.

HANNEMAN, Jill P; Pembine HS; Pembine, WI; 2/18 TrsJrCls; HonRl; StuCncl; EdYrBk; Trade School; Med Asst.

HANNEMAN, Mary P; O Gorman HS; Sioux Falls, SD; HonRl; NHS; TchrAde; PpCl; Swmmng; Chrldr; IMSpt; South Dakota State Univ; Nursing.

HANNEMAN, Mary Pat; O Gorman HS; Sioux Falls, SD; NHS; TchrAde; PpCl; VPSwmmng; Chrldr; IMSpt; Sd State Univ; Bs In Nursing.

HANNEMAN, Russell E; Madison HS; Madison, SD; 6/160 ALBoysSt; HonRl; NHS; SchPl; LetterFtbl; Wrstlng; IMSpt; College; Business Mgmt.

HANNEMANN, Deanne K; Oldham HS; Ramona, SD; 3/25 ALAGirlsSt; Chr; ChrhWkr; HonRl; SchPl; TchrAde; SchPpr; FHA; IMSpt; PPFtbl; BttyCrckrAwd; DARAwd; College; Special Educ.

HANNIGAN, Michael E; St Rita HS; Chicago, IL; 7/454 VPJrCls; VPSrCls; HonRl; NHS; StuCncl; LetterFtbl; College; Engineering.

HANNINK, Barbara J; Marceline R V HS; Brookfield, MO; 7/68 ChrhWkr; CmntyWkr; HonRl; NHS; SchPl; 4-H; SpnCl; SciCl; Bsktbl; Trk; AmLegAwd; U Of Mo Columbia; Psychology.

HANNINK, Douglas J; Hudsonville HS; Hudsonville, MI; 13/151 ChrhWkr; LbryAde; NHS; SctActv; TchrAde; Northwestern College; Cpa.

HANNON, Jim; Highland Park HS; St Paul, MN; GerCl; AmLegAwd; College; Professional.

HANNON, Kristine E; Boylan Central Cath HS; Rockford, IL; 16/358 HonRl; JrNHS; NHS; Quill&Scroll; SchMus; SctActv; RptrSchPpr; SpnCl; Eastern Illinois University; Special Educ.

HANNON, Teresa; Bishop Miege HS; Shawnee Mission, KS; 6/250 Chr; Chrl; CmntyWkr; DrlTm; HonRl; NHS; SchMus; SchPl; PpCl; IMSpt; College; Home Economics Interior Decorating.

HANNUKSELA, Julie L; Cotton HS; Gilbert, MN; SecTrsSophCls; VPSrCls; HonRl; NHS; SchAde; StuCncl; RptrYrbk; EdSchPpr; 4-H; 4-HAwd; Key Punch Operator.

HANNUM, Margaret; Brazil HS; Brazil, IN; OffAde; Yrbk; 4-H; PpCl; GAA; PPFtbl;.

HANOWSKI, Jo Ann; Little Falls Community HS; Little Falls, MN; 15/295 AFS; HonRl; RptrYrbk; SptEdYrbk; RptrSchPpr; EdSchPpr; SptEdSchPpr; FrCl; Mn Univ; Biology.

HANRAHAN, Donald J; Griffin HS; Springfield, IL; 13/172 HonRl; NHS; RptrSchPpr; Springfield College; Lawyer.

HANRAHAN, Lawrence M; Griffin HS; Springfield, IL; 4/200 ChrhWkr; HonRl; RptrSchPpr; Ftbl; College; Professional.

HANS, Carolyn A; Cedar Catholic HS; St Helena, NE; 8/69 Band; Chrs; CncrtBnd; HonRl; JrNHS; MrchBnd; NHS; PepBnd; EngCl; ChmnTrk; Lincoln Sch Of Nurse; Medical.

HANS, Jerry; Blue Springs HS; Blue Springs, MO; 96/298 ChrhWkr; OffAde; Trk; College.

HANSA, Kathleen J; Proviso West HS; Westchester, IL; 15/1086 Chr; Chrs; HonRl; Mdrgl; NHS; StuGov; Purdue Univ; Clinical Dietetics.

HANSCHE, Susan; Salem Central HS; Paddock Lake Salem, WI; HonRl; NatlThespSoc; SchMus; SchPl; Yrbk; 4-H; SpnCl; PpCl; Bsktbl; Chrldr; 4-HAwd; JCAwd; College; Fashions.

HANSEL, Mary A; Pacelli HS; Austin, MN; 3/116 ALAGirlsSt; Chrs; ChrhWkr; HonRl; SchMus; SchPl; PresStuCncl; MthCl; PpCl; LetterBsktbl; St Olaf Col; Psychology.

HANSEL, Pamela I; Ridgeway R V HS; Ridgeway, MO; SecJrCls; PresSrCls; HonRl; OffAde; StuCncl; EdYrBk; EdSchPpr; 4-H; FHA; Bsbl; LetterBsktbl; Trk; Chrldr; Trade School.

HANSELMAN, Kimberly; Sturgis HS; Sturgis, MI; DrmBgl; HonRl; SchPl; TchrAde; Yrbk; EngCl; MthCl; Swmmng; IMSpt; CitAwd; Kalamazoo Valley; Acc.

HANSEN, Allan L; New Hartford HS; New Hartford, IA; Chrs; CncrtBnd; StuCncl; Bsbl; Bsktbl; Ftbl; Trk; JCAwd; PresAwd; Tech School; Police Scinece.

HANSEN, Barbara; Zionsville Comm HS; Zionsville, IN; 10/126 Chr; HonRl; LbryAde; LatCl; PpCl; Purdue Univ; Biological Sciences.

HANSEN, Barbara; Cyrus HS; Cyrus, MN; Band; Chr; CncrtBnd; HonRl; OffAde; SchPl; YthFlsp; Yrbk; FHA; Chrldr; Willmar Avti; Administrative Secretary.

HANSEN, Barbara L; Milbank HS; Millbank, SD; Band; Chr; Chrs; CmntyWkr; HonRl; LbryAde; OffAde; KeyCl; PpCl; Trk; Chrldr; GAA; Trade School; Vocation.

HANSEN, Beth E; Albert Lea Sr HS; Albert Lea, MN; 145/495 Band; CncrtBnd; HonRl; JA; MrchBnd; NatlThespSoc; Orch; PepBnd; GAA; College; Business.

HANSEN, Carl R; Lakeview HS; Lakeview, MI; 5/119 HonRl; TchrAde; FTA; FrCl; MthCl; SciCl; Ferris State College; Chemistry.

HANSEN, Carrie; Bear Lake HS; Bear Lake, MI; TrsFrshCls; TrsSophCls; HonRl; LbryAde; OffAde; StuCncl; TchrAde; 4-H; 4-HAwd;.

HANSEN, Catherine M; Brookwood HS; Norwalk, WI; 9/65 ChrhWkr; HonRl; LbryAde; NHS; PolWkr; Yrbk; SchPpr; SecFHA; LetterTrk;.

HANSEN, Cindy R; Redfield HS; Redfield, SD; SecTrsJrCls; Band; Chrs; HonRl; StuCncl; Trk; Chrldr; AmLegAwd; PresAwd; CitAwd; Presentation Col; Soc Ser Tech.

HANSEN, Connie H; Holdrege HS; Holdrege, NE; 12/120 CncrtBnd; HonRl; HospAde; MrchBnd; PepBnd; SchMus; SchPl; Teen; PpCl; BttyCrckrAwd; Midland Coll; Nursing.

HANSEN, Cristie; Exira Community HS; Exira, IA; 4/48 Chr; Chrs; HonRl; Mdrgl; NHS; SchMus; StuCncl; RptrYrbk; Univ; Law.

HANSEN, Dana R; Hale R 1 HS; Hale, MO; SecSophCls; Band; Chrs; HonRl; Mdrgl; MrchBnd; SchPl; StuGov; LetterBsktbl; LetterTrk; College.

HANSEN, Daniel; Rutland HS; Nunda, SD; IMSpt;.

HANSEN, Darlene M; Columbus HS; Columbus, WI; Band; DrmMjrt; PepBnd; LetterTrk; IMSpt; PPFtbl; Oshkosh Univ; Music.

HANSEN, David J; Ryan HS; Omaha, NE; PresSophCls; PresJrCls; Aud/Vis; ChrhWkr; NHS; SchPl; StuCncl; StuGov; Yrbk; University; Professional.

HANSEN, David W; Maine Township North HS; Des Plaines, IL; CncrtBnd; HonRl; MrchBnd; Orch; PepBnd; SchMus; SchPl; SctActv; PpCl; LetterFtbl; Tennis; Univ Of Ill; Chemistry.

HANSEN, Diane M; Sterling Public HS; Sterling, NE; 8/25 Band; Chr; Chrs; ChrhWkr; CncrtBnd; HonRl; LbryAde; MrchBnd; PepBnd; SchPl; 4-H; PpCl; College; Music.

HANSEN, Dianne; Oxford Junction Cons HS; Oxford Junction, IA; 2/20 CncrtBnd; HonRl; NHS; NatlMeritCmnd; RptrYrbk; SpnCl; SciCl; 4-HAwd; Nursing School; Registered Nurse.

HANSEN, Dianne M; Waupaca HS; Waypaca, WI; 27/154 Band; Chr; CncrtBnd; HonRl; MrchBnd; NHS; PepBnd; SchMus; FrCl; LetterChrldr; Univ; Nurse.

HANSEN, Dirk A; Woodbury Central HS; Hornick, IA; PresFrshCls; HonRl; NHS; StuCncl; 4-H; LetterBsbl; CaptBsktbl; CaptFtbl; College; Wildlife Biologist.

HANSEN, Donald N; Rockwell Swaledale HS; Rockwell, IA; ChrhWkr; HonRl; NHS; StuCncl; StuGov; SecFFA; Bsktbl; Ftbl; Trk; College; Management.

HANSEN, Ellen J; West HS; Madison, WI; 11/583 NatlMeritSF; Quill&Scroll; StuCncl; EdYrBk; RptrSchPpr; PresFrCl; RusCl; Chrldr; College; French.

HANSEN, Faye A; Storden Jeffers HS; Jeffers, MN; 11/51 Chrs; CncrtBnd; HonRl; MrchBnd; OffAde; PepBnd; TchrAde; Yrbk; Willmar Voc Tech Inst; Accountant.

HANSEN, Freda D; Irwin Comm HS; Harlan, IA; Chr; Chrs; HonRl; SchMus; RptrSchPpr; GerCl; Univ; Professnl.

HANSEN, Garry D; Lynch Public HS; Lynch, NE; VPFrshCls; PresSophCls; HonRl; NHS; SchPl; StuCncl; RptrYrbk; RptrSchPpr; Ftbl; Trk; College At Wayne State; Major In Pe.

HANSEN, George K; Washington HS; Two Rivers, WI; ALBoysSt; Band; Chr; CncrtBnd; DrmBgl; HonRl; MrchBnd; PepBnd; SchMus; SchPl; U Of Wi; Medicine.

HANSEN, Glee A; Elk Grove HS; Elk Grove Village, IL; 48/505 PresChrs; ChrhWkr; CmntyWkr; HonRl; HospAde; NatlMeritSchl; GerCl; PpCl; LetterGAA; Loyola Univ; Medicine.

HANSEN, Gregory; Chicago Christian Hs; Chicago, IL; Chr; Chrl; HonRl; Mdrgl; NHS; NatlMeritFnl; PresYthFlsp; RptrYrbk; GodCntryAwd; U Of Michigan; Mathematics.

HANSEN, James J; Milwaukee Lutheran HS; Milwaukee, WI; 18/229 AFS; HonRl; NatlFornLg; NatlMeritSF; PresStuCncl; LetterTrk; IMSpt; Marquette Univ; Lawyer.

HANSEN, Jana S; Willard HS; Springfield, MO; 4-H; FHA; Chrldr; College.

HANSEN, Jay D; Walnut Community HS; Walnut, IA; PresSophCls; PresJrCls; ChrhWkr; HonRl; NHS; SchPl; YthFlsp; FFA; PpCl; LetterFtbl; Iowa State Univ; Ag Engineering.

HANSEN, Jeanne M; Boone HS; Boone, IA; Chrs; HonRl; LbryAde; NatlThespSoc; SchMus; RptrSchPpr; FrCl; PpCl; Bsktbl; IMSpt; Afs Student; Airline Stewardess.

HANSEN, Jeffrey; Custer HS; Custer, SD; 1/56 PresSrCls; ChrhWkr; HonRl; NHS; NatlThespSoc; RptrSchPpr; Bsktbl; DARAwd; Union College; Math Maj.

HANSEN, Jenean L; Montabella HS; Stanton, MI; 6/94 Band; Chr; ChrhWkr; CncrtBnd; HonRl; NHS; StuCncl; Yrbk; SpnCl; DanFAwd; Michigan St Univ; Parks & Recreation.

HANSEN, Joy; Hudson Senior HS; Hudson, WI; Band; Chrs; ChrhWkr; CmntyWkr; HonRl; Mdrgl; MrchBnd; SchMus; TchrAde; Music.

HANSEN, Julie; Cedarburg HS; Cedarburg, WI; 60/260 LbryAde; StuGov; RptrSchPpr; Uw Stevens Point; Dietetics.

HANSEN, Julie L; Kingsley Pierson HS; Kingsley, IA; 3/52 Band; CncrtBnd; HonRl; MrchBnd; PepBnd; SecStuCncl; Twrl; YthFlsp; RptrYrbk; FTA;.

HANSEN, Julie L; Normandy Sr HS; St Louis, MO; 38/499 CncrtBnd; HonRl; JA; NatlMeritCmnd; Yrbk; College; Writer.

HANSEN, Karen I; Glenville HS; Northwood, IA; 2/50 Band; Chrs; ChrhWkr; HonRl; SchPl; FHA; LetterBsktbl; Chrldr; IMSpt; 4-HAwd; St Cloud Univ; Accounting.

HANSEN, Katherine M; Cashton HS; Cashton, WI; 9/65 TrsFrshCls; Band; Chr; CncrtBnd; HonRl; Mdrgl; MrchBnd; NHS; EdYrBk; Chrldr; Western Wi Tech Inst; Technical Nursing.

HANSEN, Kathy J; St Marys HS; Sleepy Eye, MN; Chrs; DrlTm; MrchBnd; SchPl; SchPpr; LatCl; GAA; St Cloud Sch Of Nursing; Nursing.

HANSEN, Kevin J; Redfield Public HS; Redfield, SD; Chr; HonRl; SctActv; YthFlsp; KeyCl; LetterBsktbl; LetterFtbl; LetterTrk; CchngActv; CitAwd; College; Professional.

HANSEN, Kurt W; Marshfield HS; Marshfield, WI; 1/326 Band; CncrtBnd; HonRl; MrchBnd; NHS; RptrYrbk; SchPpr; MthCl; LetterSwmmng; RotaryAwd; Uw/marshfield.

HANSEN, Laurie E; Irene HS; Irene, SD; 3/34 PresJrCls; Chr; CncrtBnd; HonRl; MrchBnd; SchPl; FHA; Bsktbl; Ftbl; Trk; Coll; Prof Music.

HANSEN, Lee; Faulkton HS; Faulkton, SD; 12/51 ALBoysSt; ChrhWkr; HonRl; SchPl; RptrYrbk; RptrSchPpr; Ftbl; Wrstlng; College; Prof.

HANSEN, Lois M; Northfield HS; Northfield, MN; Chrs; ChrhWkr; CmntyWkr; HonRl; LbryAde; FSA; GerCl; SciCl; LetterTrk; Chrldr; Coll; Med Tech.

HANSEN, Loretta A; Ohio HS; Ohio, IL; PresSophCls; Band; NHS; PepBnd; StuCncl; TchrAde; YthFlsp; SciCl; LetterTrk; VPGAA; Illinois State Univ; Special Education.

HANSEN, Lori A; Spalding HS; Granville, IA; Chrs; HonRl; SchPl; MthCl; Trk; IMSpt; College; Nursing.

HANSEN, Lori A; North Bend Central HS; Ames, NE; TrsSrCls; ChrhWkr; HonRl; RptrYrbk; 4-H; FBLA; FHA; FTA; PpCl; BttyCrckrAwd; Univ; Teach Speech.

HANSEN, Lori E; Seneca HS; Seneca, MO; SecTrsFrshCls; PresSophCls; TreasAFS; HonRl; LetterLetterBsktbl; Chrldr; GAA; IMSpt; PPFtbl; Univ; Pe Coach.

HANSEN, Lori K; Proctor HS; Duluth, MN; Band; HonRl; HospAde; NHS; NatlMeritCmnd; VPSophCls; Orch; FrCl; U Of Mn Duluth; Chemist.

HANSEN, Lorri B; Kingsley Pierson Comm HS; Kingsley, IA; 3/65 PresBand; PresChrs; HonRl; MrchBnd; PresNHS; PepBnd; SchMus; Yrbk; PresSpnCl; PresMthCl; Univ; Nurse.

HANSEN, Lyla K; Gettysburg HS; Gettysburg, SD; 4/64 Chr; HonRl; NatlFornLg; VPNHS; UNYO; LetterTrk; GAA; PPFtbl; South Dakota St Univ; Biology.

HANSEN, Lynn A; Immaculata HS; Chicago, IL; 4/220 ChrhWkr; HonRl; SecNHS; NatlThespSoc; Quill&Scroll; StuCncl; RptrYrbk; RptrSchPpr; EdSchPpr; SpnCl; Loyola Univ; Spanish.

HANSEN, Marcus L; Wichita West HS; Wichita, KS; ALBoysSt; Chr; HonRl; IntrClCncl; Orch; SchMus; Wichita State College; Education.

HANSEN, Mark; Benson HS; Omaha, NE; VPSrCls; HonRl; NHS; Quill&Scroll; StuCncl; SchPpr; College;theology.

HANSEN, Mary; Memorial HS; Eau Claire, WI; HonRl; SctActv; RptrYrbk; PpCl; College; Art Major.

HANSEN, Mary B; Wahoo Public HS; Wahoo, NE; ALAGirlsSt; Band; HonRl; HospAde; SpnCl; PpCl; LetterGlf; LetterTrk; Chrldr; CchngActv; Trade School; Dental Assistant.

HANSEN, Mary K; Columbus HS; Marshfield, WI; 3/114 HonRl; NHS; SchPl; RptrSchPpr; 4-H; 4-HAwd; College.

HANSEN, Michelle L; Oelwein Comm Sr HS; Oelwein, IA; Band; Chr; CncrtBnd; HonRl; LbryAde; MrchBnd; PepBnd; Pres4-H; University; Law.

HANSEN, Nicholas G; Sutton HS; Edgar, NE; ChrhWkr; CmntyWkr; HonRl; Sacrstn; SchMus; SchPl; StuCncl; Teen; Twrl; YthLg; Trade School; Agriculture.

HANSEN, Norma L; Medicine Valley HS; Curtis, NE; VPJrCls; Chrs; ChrhWkr; HonRl; VPNHS; StuCncl; Yrbk; RptrSchPpr; 4-H; 4-HAwd; Trade Schl; Vocation.

HANSEN, Patricia R; New Prairie HS; La Porte, IN; HonRl; YthFlsp; 4-H; FrCl; GerCl; Trk; PresAwd; Ball State Univ; Soc Worker.

HANSEN, Raymond D; Davenport Community HS; Davenport, NE; Band; ChrhWkr; CncrtBnd; MrchBnd; PepBnd; SchPl; Yrbk; SchPpr; Ftbl; Trk; Trade School; Vocation.

HANSEN, Rebecca A; Brainerd Senior HS; Brainerd, MN; Band; ChrhWkr; HonRl; MrchBnd; PepBnd; Quill&Scroll; EdYrBk; 4-H; Chrldr; 4-HAwd; Concordia Clg; Home Economics.

HANSEN, Rebecca S; Hartley HS; Hartley, IA; Band; ChrhWkr; CncrtBnd; HonRl; LbryAde; PepBnd; YthFlsp; RptrYrbk; FHA; FTA; U Of N Iowa; Elem Ed.

HANSEN, Robin S; Elk Horn Kimballton Comm HS; Elk Horn, IA; 2/43 Band; Chrs; CncrtBnd; HonRl; MrchBnd; NHS; PepBnd; Yrbk; RptrSchPpr; Fashion Merchandising.

HANSEN, Rodney; Doland HS; Turton, SD; 4/32 TrsSrCls; HonRl; 4-H; FFA; Bsktbl; AmLegAwd; 4-HAwd; Sd St Univ; Ag.

HANSEN, Rodney; Blair HS; Blair, NE; Chr; ChrhWkr; HonRl; SchMus; YthFlsp;.

HANSEN, Roger W; St Croix HS; Bennett, WI; 1/35 VPSrCls; HonRl; NHS; NatlMeritCmnd; SchPl; StuCncl; PpCl; LetterBsbl; LetterBsktbl; DanFAwd; Uw Superior.

HANSEN, Ronald; Herscher Hs; Kankakee, IL; Chrs; StuCncl; SchPl; Pres4-H; VPLetterWrstlng; DanFAwd; 4-HAwd; Junior College; Ag Commiunications.

HANSEN, Ruth; Richland Center HS; Blue River, WI; 5/185 PresFrshCls; Band; HonRl; NHS; StuCncl; 4-H; PpCl; Trk; Chrldr; GAA; Uw Lacrosse; Medical Technology.

HANSEN, Ruth A; West HS; Green Bay, WI; HonRl; NHS; SchPl; EdYrBk; DARAwd; College; Physical Therapy.

HANSEN, Sally; Papillion HS; Papillion, NE; 23/315 TrsSrCls; HonRl; NHS; SchMus; SchPl; TchrAde; 4-H; FTA; FrCl; PpCl; Univ Of Nebraska; Denistry.

HANSEN, Sandra J; Laurens Comm HS; Laurens, IA; ALAGirlsSt; Band; ChrhWkr; HospAde; SchPl; Teen; YthFlsp; RptrSchPpr; 4-H; FHA; Wilma Boyd Career School; Airlines.

HANSEN, Scott A; Ellsworth HS; Ellsworth, MN; 7/33 ALBoysSt; Band; HonRl; MrchBnd; PepBnd; SchMus; SchPl; RptrYrbk; 4-H; 4-HAwd; Augustana Coll; Pharmacy.

HANSEN, Shane B; Greenville HS; Greenville, MI; 1/230 PresSrCls; ALBoysSt; HonRl; StuCncl; PresFrCl; Albion Coll; Law.

HANSEN, Sharon K; Lewis Central HS; Council Bluffs, IA; 1/172 HonRl; HospAde; PresNHS; FNA; Iowa St Univ; Mathematics.

HANSEN, Sharon S; Hampton Public HS; Hampton, NE; 3/20 SecTrsFrshCls; SecSrCls; HonRl; StuCncl; Bsbl; LetterBsktbl; Tennis; LetterTrk; Chrldr; IMSpt; Hastings Tech; Business Legal Secretary.

HANSEN, Sheryl A; North Bend Central HS; Ames, NE; HonRl; RptrYrbk; SchPpr; FHA; PpCl; LetterBsktbl; Trk; College.

HANSEN, Susan M; Glenwood HS; Springfield, IL; 32/139 SecFrshCls; VPSrCls; AFS; Chr; ChrhWkr; HonRl; Mdrgl; SchMus; College.

HANSEN, Susie M; Pender Public HS; Pender, NE; Chr; ChrhWkr; SchMus; StuCncl; EdYrBk; FHA; PpCl; Glf; Trk; Chrldr; Univ; Bus Degree.

HANSEN, Sybel M; Litchfield Sr HS; Litchfield, MN; 16/185 Chr; CncrtBnd; HospAde; MrchBnd; SchPl; SctActv; RptrSchPpr; FHA; SpnCl; Hospital Schl; Nursing.

HANSEN, Vicki L; Stillwater HS; Lake Elmo, MN; 7/675 CmntyWkr; HonRl; NHS; SctActv; StuCncl; StuGov; Yrbk; PPFtbl; College; Medicine.

HANSEN, Wendy L; Oakland Community HS; Oakland, IA; 2/36 SecSophCls; Band; ChrhWkr; HonRl; NHS; PepBnd; YthFlsp; FHA; FNA; Glf; Nurses Training.

HANSES, Suzanne M; Waverly HS; Lansing, MI; 10/400 VPJrCls; SecNHS; SchPl; StuCncl; TchrAde; GerCl; PPFtbl; Univ Of Michigan; Medicine.

HANSFORD, Scott J; Premontre HS; Green Bay, WI; CmntyWkr; HonRl; JA; RedCrAde; SchPl; StuCncl; RptrYrbk; Yrbk; 4-H; Tennis; Trk; Chrldr; 4-HAwd; College; Architect.

HANSKALA, Sandra J; Orr HS; Orr, MN; Chr; ChrhWkr; HonRl; LbryAde; NHS; TchrAde; RptrSchPpr; FHA; PresPpCl; Trk; College; Professional.

HANSMANN, Erwin; Fredericktown HS; Fredericktown, MO; TrsSophCls; SecJrCls; PresSrCls; HonRl; FFA; Univ Of Mo; Ag Econ.

HANSMIRE, Julie A; Fairbury HS; Fairbury, NE; 2/132 VPFrshCls; SecSophCls; Band; HonRl; NHS; StuCncl; 4-H; VPSpnCl; LetterTrk; Chrldr; AmLegAwd; Univ Nebrasks.

HANSON, Angie L; Fairbury Sr HS; Fairbury, NE; Band; Chrs; MrchBnd; TreasSctActv; FBLA; PpCl; Trk; IMSpt; MasAwd; College; Lpn Nurse.

HANSON, April D; Greendale HS; Greendale, WI; Band; Chr; CmntyWkr; CncrtBnd; HospAde; MrchBnd; Orch; RedCrAde; SctActv; Forestry Tech.

HANSON, Barbara A; Lafayette HS; Red Lake Falls, MN; Band; Chrs; CncrtBnd; MrchBnd; PepBnd; SchMus; Bsbl; Bsktbl; Trk; College.

HANSON, Barbara E; Belmond Comm HS; Belmond, IA; 10/66 HonRl; HospAde; SctActv; FHA; IMSpt; BttyCrckrAwd; Morningside College; Accounting.

HANSON, Brenda; Luck Public HS; Luck, WI; 1/54 TrsSophCls; Band; Chr; HonRl; MrchBnd; NHS; PepBnd; FHA; Univ; Professional.

HANSON, Carla J; Triplains HS; Wallace, KS; 2/18 PresSophCls; Band; Chrs; DrmMjrt; HonRl; Twrl; 4-H; PpCl; PPFtbl; 4-HAwd; Concordia College; Church Work.

HANSON, Carla J; Carthage HS; Carthage, SD; Chrs; LbryAde; SchPl; RptrSchPpr; PpCl; LetterTrk; IMSpt;.

HANSON, Carol A; Fremont HS; Fremont, MI; Chr; ChrhWkr; HonRl; LbryAde; NHS; NatlMeritSF; TchrAde; YthFlsp; LetterSwmmng; CchngActv; Western Michigan Univ; Library Science.

HANSON, Carol M; Superior Sr HS; Superior, WI; 33/540 Chr; Chrl; HonRl; Mdrgl; NHS; SchMus; College; Liberal Arts.

HANSON, Carolyn A; Shawnee Mission Nw HS; Lenexa, KS; 15/600 ChrhWkr; HonRl; NHS; TchrAde; SptEdYrbk; GerCl; PpCl; LetterBsbl; Trk; GAA; Emporia St College; Data Processing.

HANSON, Chris J; Leslie HS; Leslie, MI; CAP; HonRl; NatlSciFnd; PolWkr; ROTC; FSA; Bsktbl; Swmmng; Tennis; Trk; Mi State; Archeologist.

HANSON, Cynthia E; Mormon Trail HS; Humeston, IA; 5/40 ALAGirlsSt; HonRl; NatlMeritSF; SchPl; Yrbk; Pres4-H; Bsktbl; BttyCrckrAwd; 4-HAwd; CitAwd; Mt Mercy College; Law.

HANSON, David A; St Francis Sr HS; Cedar, MN; PresJrCls; Band; ChrhWkr; CncrtBnd; HonRl; MrchBnd; NHS; LetterBsktbl; LetterFtbl; LetterTrk; College; Surgeon.

HANSON, David M; North HS; Eau Claire, WI; 82/369 ChrhWkr; HonRl; LbryAde; NHS; LetterBsktbl; LetterFtbl; LetterTennis; Univ Of Wisc; Mathematics.

HANSON, Debbie S; Brainerd Sr HS; Brainerd, MN; Chr; Chrs; HonRl; Mdrgl; SchAde; SchMus; SchPl;.

HANSON, Denise I; Moline Sr HS; Moline, IL; 31/845 HonRl; TreasJA; LitMag; NHS; LatCl; Univ Of Illinois; Business Admin.

HANSON, Drew A; Concordia Sr HS; Jamestown, KS; 15/150 VPFrshCls; VPSophCls; ALBoysSt; Band; Chr; CncrtBnd; DrmMjrt; HonRl; MrchBnd; PepBnd; Univ; Psychologist.

HANSON, Earlyn J; De Soto HS; Ferryville, WI; ALBoysSt; HonRl; StuCncl; SptEdSchPpr; 4-H; FFA; LetterBsktbl; CaptFtbl; LetterWrstlng; AmLegAwd; Uw River Falls; Mech Engr.

HANSON, Edward D; North Liberty HS; North Liberty, IN; 15/95 Chrs; ChrhWkr; HonRl; SchPl; SctActv; 4-H; Bsktbl; Trk; 4-HAwd; GovHonPrgAwd; Andrews Univ.

HANSON, Gene D; Pine City HS; Brook Park, MN; 13/117 ALBoysSt; HonRl; CaptBsbl; CaptFtbl; CaptWrstlng; CitAwd; Rochester Comm Clg.

HANSON, Henry A; Sparta HS; Sparta, WI; 17/192 Band; HonRl; NatlFornLg; PresNHS; NatlMeritCmnd; SchPl; StuCncl; Bsbl; Us Naval Acad; Engineering.

HANSON, Ilene F; Wausaukee HS; Athelstane, WI; 1/47 SecSrCls; ALAGirlsSt; HonRl; NHS; EdYrBk; LetterBsktbl; LetterTrk; LetterChrldr; TreasGAA; BttyCrckrAwd; Bellin Mem Hosp; Nurse.

HANSON, Jayne L; Heron Lake Public HS; Heron Lake, MN; 1/34 ALAGirlsSt; Band; Chrs; ChrhWkr; HonRl; NHS; PresYthFlsp; Yrbk; EdSchPpr; FHA; Willmar Area Voc Inst; Acct.

HANSON, Jean A; Lincoln HS; Wisconsin Rapids, WI; Band; Chr; ChrhWkr; CncrtBnd; HonRl; MrchBnd; NHS; NatlThespSoc; PepBnd; GerCl; U Of Wisconsin; Medicine.

HANSON, Jeffrey D; Northwood HS; Northwood, ND; 3/38 TrsFrshCls; ALBoysSt; Band; CncrtBnd; HonRl; MrchBnd; SchPl; StuCncl; RptrSchPpr; CaptBsktbl; U Of Nd; Chemical Engr.

HANSON, Jodi D; Central HS; Aberdeen, SD; Band; ChrhWkr; CncrtBnd; DrlTm; HonRl; MrchBnd; PepBnd; TchrAde; 4-H; SpnCl; College; Teaching.

HANSON, John; South Page Community HS; Bredyville, IA; 5/37 Band; CncrtBnd; HonRl; MrchBnd; Orch; PepBnd; RptrYrbk; Bsktbl; Parks Of St Louis Univ; Aerospace Engineer.

HANSON, Judith L; Brainerd HS; Brainerd, MN; Band; HonRl; MrchBnd; PepBnd; FshEdYrbk; Comm Clge; Secretarial.

HANSON, Kara L; Custer HS; Custer, SD; Band; Chr; HonRl; NHS; 4-H; LetterBsktbl; Trk; Chrldr; TreasGAA; Univ; Professional.

HANSON, Kathy; Thompson Comm HS; Thompson, IA; CncrtBnd; HonRl; NHS; YthFlsp; RptrYrbk; SptEdYrbk; FHA; Bsktbl; 4-HAwd;.

HANSON, Kathy J; Rockford E HS; Rockford, IL; 130/655 HonRl; HospAde; NHS; Rock Valley College; Law Enforcement.

HANSON, Keith G; Magic City Campus HS; Minot, ND; Band; ChrhWkr; MrchBnd; College; Professional.

HANSON, Keith W; Westville HS; Westville, IL; 12/133 PresJrCls; Band; CncrtBnd; JrNHS; MrchBnd; NHS; Orch; PepBnd; PolWkr; SchPl; StuCncl; RptrYrbk; RptrSchPpr; Macmurray College; Law.

HANSON, Kevin L; Paxton HS; Paxton, IL; Chr; ChrhWkr; CmntyWkr; HospAde; LbryAde; NatlThespSoc; OffAde; TchrAde; YthFlsp; CivCl; Appalachian Bible Inst; Rn.

HANSON, Kristine; Adrian HS; Adrian, MN; Band; Chr; Chrl; Chrs; ChrhWkr; CncrtBnd; MrchBnd; Bsktbl; Trk; GAA; College; Elementary Education.

HANSON, Kristine A; Wis Rapids Lincoln HS; Wis Rapids, WI; Band; HonRl; MrchBnd; 4-HAwd; University; Broadcast Journalism.

HANSON, Linda R; Eagle Bend HS; Eagle Bend, MN; 2/33 Chr; HonRl; TchrAde; Yrbk; VP4-H; SecFHA; TreasFTA; 4-HAwd; Moorhead State Univ; Social Work.

HANSON, Lori; Brnd Sr HS; Brainerd, MN; Coll; Teacher.

HANSON, Lorri K; Reeder Public HS; Reeder, ND; 1/16 PresSrCls; ALAGirlsSt; HonRl; EdYrBk; EdSchPpr; Dickinson State College.

HANSON, Lualan J; Minot Sr HS; Minot, ND; HonRl; StuCncl; StuGov; SpnCl; Bsbl; College; Professional.

HANSON, Lyndon B; New Rockford Central HS; New Rockford, ND; 26/67 ChrhWkr; HonRl; LetterTrk; IMSpt; College; Vocation.

HANSON, Mark A; Rosemount HS; Rosemount, MN; 50/380 ALBoysSt; Band; DrmBgl; HonRl; NHS; NatlThespSoc; SchPl; VPStuCncl; CaptTennis; IMSpt; Mankato State Univ; Recreation.

HANSON, Marsha L; Belvidere HS; Belvidere, IL; 35/343 Chrs; HonRl; JA; MrchBnd; NHS; Quill&Scroll; Twrl; EdSchPpr; 4-H; FHA; GerCl; PpCl; Rockford College; Psychology.

HANSON, Martha K; Brandon Valley HS; Valley Springs, SD; ALAGirlsSt; CncrtBnd; HonRl; HospAde; TreasJA; MrchBnd; NHS; PepBnd; SchPl; EdYrBk; College; Fashion Mdse.

HANSON, Mary; New Richland Hartland HS; New Richland, MN; 15/67 TrsSophCls; Band; CncrtBnd; HonRl; MrchBnd; NHS; PepBnd; SchPl; Chrldr; St Cloud State Univ; Physical Ed & Health.

HANSON, Mary B; Tomahawk HS; Tomahawk, WI; AFS; ALAGirlsSt; CmntyWkr; HonRl; NatlFornLg; RedCrAde; SpnCl; MthCl; PpCl; LetterTrk; Chrldr; SecGAA; IMSpt; College; Professional.

HANSON, Mary E; Hancock Central HS; Hancock, MI; HonRl; HospAde; NatlFornLg; RptrYrbk; FrCl; IMSpt; College.

HANSON, Maurice; Mc Pherson Senior HS; Mc Phersn, KS; 55/222 Chr; HonRl; NHS; StuCncl; YthFlsp; Tennis; Central College; General Drafting.

HANSON, Michael; Newman HS; Mason City, IA; ALBoysSt; Band; CncrtBnd; HonRl; Orch; PepBnd; SchMus; SchPl; Wrstlng; IMSpt; College; Pharmacy.

HANSON, Monica; Garden City East HS; Garden City, MI; TrsSophCls; PresJrCls; TrsJrCls; PresSrCls; VPSrCls; TrsSrCls; SchPl; SpnCl; PpCl; GAA; Michigan State; Law.

HANSON, Nancy J; Parkers Prairie HS; Parkers Prairie, MN; 1/73 SecSrCls; Band; Chr; CncrtBnd; HonRl; MrchBnd; PepBnd; LetterTrk; Chrldr; 4-HAwd; Mankato St Clg.

HANSON, Pamela A; Litchville HS; Litchville, ND; SecFrshCls; PresJrCls; Band; Chrs; HonRl; SchMus; RptrYrbk; RptrSchPpr; Bsktbl; Chrldr; Coll; Fashion.

HANSON, Pamela J; Windom Area HS; Windom, MN; Chr; DrmMjrt; HonRl; MrchBnd; NHS; OffAde; StuCncl; Twrl; PpCl; Chrldr; Coll; Sci.

HANSON, Paul K; Hope Public HS; Hope, ND; PresFrshCls; VPSophCls; TrsJrCls; ALBoysSt; Band; Chr; Chrs; ChrhWkr; CncrtBnd; HonRl; MrchBnd; Bsktbl; AmLegAwd; University.

HANSON, Perry W; Neodesha HS; Neodesha, KS; ALBoysSt; Band; CncrtBnd; HonRl; PepBnd; SctActv; PresStuCncl; PresYthFlsp; LetterFtbl; LetterTrk; University; Journalism.

HANSON, Rhonda J; Marcus Comm HS; Marcus, IA; 8/64 SecJrCls; Chr; HonRl; Mdrgl; MrchBnd; NHS; SchMus; Twrl; EdYrBk; FHA; Bsktbl; Bus Col; Medical Secretary.

HANSON, Robert; Tomorrow River HS; Waupaca, WI; 1/32 Band; CncrtBnd; HonRl; PepBnd; RptrYrbk; 4-H; BttyCrckrAwd; EldAwd; 4-HAwd; University Of Wis Oshkosh.

HANSON, Robert D; Edw Tilden HS; Chicago, IL; 17/368 HonRl; NHS; College; Electrical.

HANSON, Robert T; Maconaquah HS; Bunker Hill, IN; HonRl; NHS; SchAde; Indiana Univ Of Kokomo; Elec Eng.

HANSON, Roxanne R; Madison Public HS; Madison, MN; 13/87 SecJrCls; VPAFS; Band; CncrtBnd; HonRl; MrchBnd; PepBnd; SchPl; FHA; PpCl; Trade; Business.

HANSON, Royal D; Fosston HS; Fasston, MN; 3/98 Chr; CncrtBnd; HonRl; ModUN; NHS; NatlMeritCmnd; SchPl; Yrbk; LetterTrk; LetterWrstlng; Concordia Coll; Acct.

HANSON, Shauna J; Southland HS; Taopi, MN; 8/122 Band; ChrhWkr; CncrtBnd; HonRl; MrchBnd; NHS; PepBnd; YthFlsp; Yrbk; College; Art.

HANSON, Shirley; St Pauls College HS; Ottertail, MN; Chr; ChrhWkr; HonRl; NHS; SchPl; 4-H; PpCl; IMSpt; CAP; St Lukes Hospital Of Nursing; Regestered Nu.

HANSON, Sonja G; North HS; Eau Claire, WI; 48/370 ChrhWkr; HonRl; NatlFornLg; NHS; Orch; SctActv; StuCncl; YthFlsp; Tech Sch; X Ray Technology.

HANSON, Stephen M; Lockport Central HS; Lockport, IL; ChrhWkr; HonRl; NHS; Lewis Univ; Astronautical Engr.

HANSON, Steven W; Glidden Ralston Comm HS; Glidden, IA; PresJrCls; ALBoysSt; HonRl; SchMus; SchPl; StuCncl; LetterBsbl; LetterBsktbl; LetterFtbl; LetterGlf; College; Law Enforcement.

HANSON, Susan; Manilla Community HS; Manilla, IA; 3/43 Chrs; ChrhWkr; HonRl; NHS; EdYrBk; EdSchPpr; FNA; FrCl; SciCl; Bsktbl; Simpson College.

HANSON, Teresa; Westby HS; Chaseburg, WI; Band; ChrhWkr; HonRl; MrchBnd; PepBnd; TchrAde; Yrbk; 4-HAwd; Viterbo College; Registered Nurse.

HANSON, Timothy S; Henry Sibley HS; W St Paul, MN; 24/579 HonRl; NHS; NatlMeritFnl; NatlMeritSF; YthFlsp; Bsbl; LetterBsktbl; LetterFtbl; LetterTrk; Univ Of Minn; Doctor.

HANSON, Van D; Allen HS; Allen, NE; Chr; Chrs; CmntyWkr; HonRl; SchPl; SptEdSchPpr; VPFFA; Bsbl; Bsktbl; Ftbl; Trade School; Heavy Equipment Operator.

HANSON, Vicki L; Central HS; Aberdeen, SD; Chr; Chrs; ChrhWkr; DrlTm; HonRl; HospAde; TchrAde; 4-H; PpCl; 4-HAwd; U Of Sd; Social Work.

HANSON, Wyanita A; Rushford HS; Rushford, MN; AFS; Band; Chr; Chrs; ChrhWkr; CncrtBnd; DrlTm; MrchBnd; PepBnd; SchMus; SchPl; Yrbk; SchPpr; IMSpt; Minnesota Schl Of Business; Fashion Mdse.

HANSSEN, Deborah A; Emery HS; Emery, SD; 1/27 PresJrCls; Chrs; DrlTm; HonRl; SchPl; PresYthFlsp; RptrSchPpr; PresFHA; PpCl; Chrldr; College; Accounting.

HANSSEN, Patricia; Monticello Comm HS; Scotch Grove, IA; CncrtBnd; HonRl; SchMus; YthFlsp; FHA; Bsbl; Bsktbl; Glf; Trk; 4-HAwd; College; Florist.

HANTSBARGER, Brian D; Ballard HS; Cambridge, IA; 3/81 ChrhWkr; HonRl; NHS; Trk; Wrstlng; Central Col Of Pell Ia.

HANUS, Carol A; Kettle Moraine HS; Delafield, WI; 10/180 ChrhWkr; CmntyWkr; HonRl; HospAde; PresNHS; SchMus; SchPl; StuCncl; FHA; Trk; Marquette U; Nursing.

HANUS, Eileen A; Johnson Creek HS; Johnson Creek, WI; Chrs; HonRl; HospAde; LbryAde; Treas4-H; FHA; FrCl; SpnCl; 4-HAwd; Vocational Sch; Nursing.

HANUS, Kathleen M; South HS; Omaha, NE; 32/611 HonRl; VPJA; NHS; Orch; Quill&Scroll; SchMus; EdSchPpr; VPEngCl; College; Creative Writing.

HANVELT, Debbie K; Hempstead HS; Sherrill, IA; 24/455 HonRl; NHS; FrCl; Tennis; ChmbCommrsAwd; Finley Hosp Schl Nursing; Rn.

HANY, Nancy J; Normal Comm HS; Normal, IL; HonRl; HospAde; NHS; NatlThespSoc; SchPl; StuCncl; TchrAde; YthFlsp; FHA; SecMthCl; College; Mass Communications.

HANZAI, Mary E; Mayo HS; Rochester, MN; 95/456 Coll; Art.

HANZALIK, Janice M; Gull Lake Comm HS; Augusta, MI; Chr; CmntyWkr; TchrAde; RptrYrbk; FTA; FrCl; IMSpt; Michigan Tech; Forestry.

HANZE, Rodney D; Waco Community HS; Swedesburg, IA; 1/62 TrsSrCls; ALBoysSt; CncrtBnd; HonRl; NHS; NatlMeritCmnd; StuCncl; 4-H; Wrstlng; DanFAwd; Clge; Elec Eng Or Music.

HAPKA, Della M; Argyle Public HS; Argyle, MN; Band; Chrs; CncrtBnd; LbryAde; TchrAde; 4-H; FHA; CaptBsktbl; GAA; PresAwd; Uni; Tchr.

HAPNER, Linda K; Kewanee HS; Kewanee, IL; 5/220 AFS; HonRl; OffAde; StuCncl; TchrAde; EdYrBk; FHA; FTA; FrCl; Illinois State Univ; Accounting.

HAPP, Eunice H; Mendota Twp HS; Mendota, IL; 1/187 HonRl; NHS; OffAde; Augustana College; Accountant.

HAPP, Karen R; La Moille HS; La Moille, IL; Chrs; DrlTm; HonRl; MrchBnd; SchMus; StuCncl; RptrYrbk; RptrSchPpr; CaptTrk; GAA; Il State Univ; Speech Therapy.

HAPPEL, Anita J; Castle HS; Newburgh, IN; 2/298 HonRl; NHS; FTA; LatCl; PpCl; PPFtbl; NCTE; College; Physics.

HAPPEL, Dennis H; Starmont HS; Strawberry Pt, IA; ALBoysSt; Band; ChrhWkr; HonRl; MrchBnd; PepBnd; PpCl; Bsktbl; Ftbl; AmLegAwd; Trade Sch; Pro.

HAPTONSTAHL, Michael W; Galesburg Sr HS; Galesburg, IL; HonRl; SpnCl; LetterTrk; Illinois State Univ.

HARAF, John C; Amos Alonzo Stagg HS; Hickory Hills, IL; 31/468 CncrtBnd; HonRl; MrchBnd; NHS; NatlMeritCmnd; NatlMeritSchl; LetterTrk; U Of Il; Michanical Engi.

HARALDSON, Joel W; Dilworth Public HS; Dilworth, MN; Chrs; HonRl; LetterBsbl; LetterBsktbl; LetterFtbl; Glf; LetterTrk; IMSpt;.

HARANGODY, David J; Whiting HS; Whiting, IN; ALBoysSt; Chrs; SchMus; StuCncl; SpnCl; LetterBsbl; LetterBsktbl; LetterFtbl; College.

HARASYM, Heidi M; Maria HS; Chicago, IL; 19/335 HonRl; HospAde; NHS; VPMthCl; GAA; IMSpt; College; Nursing.

HARBACH, Todd P; Warren HS; Apple River, IL; 6/60 PresSophCls; HonRl; StuCncl; FFA; Bsbl; Bsktbl; Ftbl; Trk; AmLegAwd; Clge; Vet.

HARBER, Kim L; Toluca HS; Toluca, IL; 11/44 SecTrsFrshCls; PresSrCls; HonRl; PolWkr; SchPl; RptrYrbk; Bsbl; Bsktbl; Trk; CchngActv; College; Law.

HARBER, Renay A; Toluca HS; Toluca, IL; SecTrsSophCls; PresJrCls; Chrs; ChrhWkr; CmntyWkr; DrlTm; HonRl; LbryAde; PepBnd; Swmmng; College; Nursing.

HARBERS, Cheryl K; Roanoke Benson HS; Benson, IL; SecFrshCls; PresAFS; Chr; Chrs; ChrhWkr; DrlTm; HonRl; OffAde; SchPl; TchrAde; Glf; GAA; IMSpt; Midstate College; Fashion Merchandising.

HARBERS, Timothy R; Spalding Institute HS; Metamora, IL; 6/102 ALBoysSt; ChrhWkr; HonRl; NHS; Ftbl; Marquette University; Physical Therapy.

HARBERTS, Karla J; Emery HS; Emery, SD; Band; ChrhWkr; CncrtBnd; DrlTm; HonRl; MrchBnd; PepBnd; StuCncl; RptrYrbk; FHA; PpCl; Univ; Math.

HARBIN, Kathleen M; L C Mohr HS; South Haven, MI; HonRl; Twrl; College; Medicine.

HARBIN, Terri L; South Haven HS; South Haven, MI; 6/213 HonRl; Yrbk; Kalamazoo Vly Comm College; Dental Hygiene.

HARBISON, Gregory A; Turkey Run HS; Rockville, IN; 5/73 HonRl; SchPl; 4-H; FFA; SciCl; College; Agriculture.

HARBISON, Myrna E; Valley R 6 HS; Belleview, MO; 6/45 TrsSrCls; Chrs; HonRl; LbryAde; NHS; SchPl; EdYrBk; RptrSchPpr; FHA; TreasSpnCl; Mineral Area College; Business.

HARBISON, Resa L; Robinson HS; Robinson, IL; 7/180 HonRl; ModUN; SchPl; PresSpnCl; PpCl; SciCl; DARAwd; Lincoln Trail College.

HARCOURT, Tracy J; Oshkosh North HS; Oshkosh, WI; 6/370 ChrhWkr; CmntyWkr; NHS; Orch; SchMus; StuCncl; PresFrCl; MthCl; SciCl; Swmmng; DARAwd; Univ Of Wisconsin; Physical Therapy.

HARDAWAY, Michelle Y; Cass Tech HS; Detroit, MI; Chr; ChrhWkr; HonRl; NHS; SchAde; TchrAde; Univ Of Michigan; Microbiology.

HARDCASTLE, Carl A; Whitko HS; Larwill, IN; Band; Chr; ChrhWkr; CmntyWkr; HonRl; UNYO; YthFlsp; Bsktbl; Ftbl; Trk; IMSpt; Purdue Univ; Industrial Arts.

HARDCASTLE, Jay S; Columbia Central HS; Brooklyn, MI; 17/153 HonRl; LbryAde; SchMus; Yrbk; LetterTrk; Jackson Community Clg; Education.

HARDEE, Jayne E; Bedford HS; Gravity, IA; TrsSophCls; PresJrCls; AFS; Chr; Chrs; ChrhWkr; HonRl; LbryAde; NHS; StuCncl; CaptBsktbl; LetterTrk; IMSpt; PPFtbl; College; Professional.

HARDEMAN, Julia M; Immaculata HS; Detroit, MI; PresSrCls; CmntyWkr; SchPl; PresAwd; Msu; Child Psychologist.

HARDEN, Don; Lanphier Hs; Springfield, IL; 58 CncrtBnd; MrchBnd; NHS; SptEdSchPpr; Springfield College ; Game Biologist.

HARDEN, Jennifer L; Loup County Public HS; Almeria, NE; 3/15 HonRl; SchPl; StuCncl; TchrAde; Twrl; EdYrBk; RptrSchPpr; Bsktbl; LetterTrk; Chrldr; College; Fashion.

HARDEN, Katherine L; Brown County HS; Nashville, IN; Chrs; HonRl; OffAde; SctActv; TchrAde; RptrSchPpr; 4-H; Business College; Medical Asst.

HARDEN, Michael; Central HS; Detroit, MI; HonRl; JA; SctActv; CaptBsktbl; CaptFtbl; Trk; Clge; Law.

HARDEN, Richard C; St Pius X HS; Kansas City, MO; 30/129 SctActv; SchPpr; IMSpt; GodCntryAwd; Coll; Elec.

HARDEN, Vicki D; Brown County HS; Nashville, IN; 35/207 HonRl; OffAde; SpnCl; IMSpt; Coll; Nursing.

HARDEN, Vicky L; Marseilles HS; Marseilles, IL; HonRl; NatlThespSoc; SchPl; SecStuCncl; RptrYrbk; RptrSchPpr; Socr; CaptChrldr; GAA; PresAwd; Coll; Dentist Or Dental Hygienist.

HARDER, John W; Dekalb HS; Dekalb, IL; 46/380 ChrhWkr; CmntyWkr; HonRl; NHS; SctActv; StuCncl; Bsktbl; LetterFtbl; LetterTrk; Univ; Civil Engineering.

HARDER, Patricia J; Centura HS; Cairo, NE; PresFrshCls; Band; CmntyWkr; NHS; StuCncl; TchrAde; YthFlsp; FBLA; CaptBsktbl; LetterTrk; College; Professional.

HARDER, Steve; Waterloo West HS; Cedar Falls, IA; 17/475 NHS; NatlMeritCmnd; StuCncl; RptrSchPpr; Bsktbl; Iowa State Univ; Computer Science.

HARDESTY, John A; Broad Ripple HS; Indpls, IN; HonRl; NatlThespSoc; Orch; SchMus; LetterTrk; Wrstlng; Purdue; Engineering.

HARDESTY, Robin A; Morrill HS; Henry, NE; Chrs; HonRl; JrNHS; SchPl; 4-H; FHA; PpCl; GAA; Coll; Professional.

HARDESTY, Sheila L; Clifton HS; Clifton, KS; Band; Chrl; Chrs; CncrtBnd; MrchBnd; PepBnd; StuCncl; RptrYrbk; FHA; PpCl; Manhattan Votech; Nursing.

HARDIN, Carl R; Cass Technical HS; Detroit, MI; ChrhWkr; CmntyWkr; NHS; NatlMeritCmnd; SchAde; SctActv; SciCl; University; Chemistry.

HARDIN, Danny R; Hallsville R Iv HS; Columbia, MO; PresFrshCls; HonRl; LbryAde; SctActv; StuCncl; RptrSchPpr; LetterBsktbl; Electrician.

HARDIN, Deborah L; Leavenworth HS; Milltown, IN; 8/26 Chrs; ChrhWkr; LbryAde; OffAde; RptrSchPpr; Sec4-H; FHA; FTA; Trk; GAA; DARAwd; 4-HAwd; JCAwd; Indiana Voc Tech College; Medical Asst.

HARDIN, Janelle; Hudson Hs; Hudson, WI; CncrtBnd; HonRl; LbryAde; MrchBnd; ModUN; SctActv; YthFlsp; SchPpr; GerCl; GAA;.

HARDIN, Joann; Cooley HS; Detroit, MI; 3/200 Chr; ChrhWkr; HonRl; HospAde; NHS; NatlMeritCmnd; OffAde; TchrAde; Swmmng; CitAwd; Mercy Coll; Rn.

HARDIN, Mary L; N Clay Community HS; Louisville, IL; SecJrCls; Chrs; HonRl; NHS; SchPl; Twrl; RptrYrbk; RptrSchPpr; SpnCl; College; Speech Therapy.

HARDIN, Steven L; Zionsville Comm HS; Zionsville, IN; Aud/Vis; StuCncl; IMSpt; Clg; Architecture/drafting.

HARDING, Alfred D; Washington HS; Washington,

MO; Chr; HonRl; Mdrgl; Orch; SchMus; SchPl; Univ Of Mo; Medicine.

HARDING, Cindy J; Onarga HS; Onarga, IL; VPFrshCls; VPSophCls; Band; Chrs; DrmMjrt; HonRl; Yrbk; FHA; SpnCl; Bsktbl; Trk; Parkland Jr College; Registered Nurse.

HARDING, Karen M; Mullen Public HS; Mullen, NE; TrsJrCls; ALAGirlsSt; Band; Chr; Chrs; CncrtBnd; HonRl; MrchBnd; PepBnd; StuCncl; Kearney St Col; Elem Ed.

HARDINGER, Sharon A; Columbus HS; Marshfield, WI; 8/104 Chrs; HonRl; LbryAde; RptrYrbk; EdYrBk; 4-H; FrCl; GAA; 4-HAwd; College; Professnl.

HARDMAN, Elaine E; Brazil HS; Brazil, IN; Band; Chr; HonRl; NHS; NatlThespSoc; SchMus; Yrbk; FrCl; PpCl; Trk; Univ; Teacher.

HARDMAN, Mary E; Brazil HS; Brazil, IN; JrNHS; NHS; SchAde; FHA; Business School.

HARDNETT, George; Cass Technical HS; Detroit, MI; HonRl; NHS; NatlMeritCmnd; Quill&Scroll; SchMus; SchPl; StuCncl; StuGov; SchPpr; U Of Mi; Accounting.

HARDT, Julie; Northeast Hs; Lincoln, NE; 14 Band; ChrhWkr; CmntyWkr; HonRl; Orch; TchrAde; PpCl; Swmmng; Sioux Falls College;social Work.

HARDTKE, Carol M; Oconto Falls HS; Oconto Falls, WI; ALAGirlsSt; HonRl; NHS; SchPl; EdYrBk; 4-H; FBLA; GAA; IMSpt; DARAwd; Uw Madison; Bus Adm.

HARDWICK, James C; Chicago Voc HS; Chicago, IL; 90/776 LetterBsbl; Northern Ill Univ; Dentist.

HARDWICK, Pamela S; West Washington HS; Salem, IN; PresFrshCls; ChrhWkr; HonRl; NHS; SchMus; TchrAde; Yrbk; LatCl; PpCl; CaptChrldr; Indiana U; Nursing.

HARDWICK, Roger D; Fox HS; Imperial, MO; 147/500 ChrhWkr; CncrtBnd; MrchBnd; Quill&Scroll; RedCrAde; FrCl; Ftbl; Swmmng; Trk; Tennessee Temple College; Missionary.

HARDY, Ann L; West Chicago Comm HS; West Chicago, IL; 9/311 Chr; Chrl; ChrhWkr; CmntyWkr; HonRl; NHS; NatlThespSoc; SchMus; VPSctActv; PresYthFlsp; RptrYrbk; Univ Of Ill; Law.

HARDY, Daniel; Plymouth Salem HS; Plymouth, MI; HonRl; TchrAde; Eastern Mi; Busi Ad.

HARDY, James P; Bremen HS; Midlothian, IL; 21/427 HonRl; NHS; College; Accounting.

HARDY, Janice E; Worth Co HS; Grant City, MO; VPFrshCls; SecSophCls; Band; CncrtBnd; HonRl; MrchBnd; PepBnd; Trk; Chrldr; PPFtbl;.

HARDY, Jeffrey; Grandview Sr HS; Grandview, MO; 132/450 HonRl; Trk; GAA; Southwest Mo St; Phy Ed.

HARDY, Mary M; Kalkaska HS; Kalkaska, MI; ALAGirlsSt; Band; HonRl; NHS; Twrl; 4-H; Trk; Chrldr; GAA; CitAwd; Nw Michigan; Fashion Merchandising.

HARDY, Rachelle; Lindblom Technical HS; Chicago, IL; Chr; JA; LitMag; NatlMeritCmnd; NatlThespSoc; SchPl; SctActv; Yrbk; EdSchPpr; SchPpr; Univ; Liberal Arts.

HARDY, Sue L; Lakeland HS; Wolcottville, IN; SecFrshCls; AFS; Band; CncrtBnd; MrchBnd; PolWkr; Quill&Scroll; SchMus; SchPl; Trk; In St U; Clinical Psychologist.

HARDY, Susan N; Sunset Hill HS; Shawnee Mission, KS; TrsSrCls; Chrs; CmntyWkr; DrlTm; HonRl; PolWkr; TchrAde; PpCl; Swmmng; Chrldr; Vassar Coll; Teach Mentally Handicapped.

HARDY, Tad N; Scott Comm HS; Scott City, KS; 2/102 ALBoysSt; Band; Chr; Chrl; CncrtBnd; PepBnd; SchMus; Bsbl; LetterTennis; Coll; Bio Research.

HARE, Denise J; Sidney Public HS; Sidney, NE; Band; Chr; ChrhWkr; CncrtBnd; DrmMjrt; JrNHS; MrchBnd; MthCl; Chrldr; GAA; Univ; Major Study.

HARE, Gwen D; Spring Valley HS; Spring Valley, MN; 48/78 OffAde; TchrAde; YthFlsp; GerCl; PpCl; CaptBsktbl; CaptTrk; CchngActv; GAA; IMSpt; Winona State Univ; Physical Educ.

HARE, Terry M; Holy Angels Academy; Minneapolis, MN; HospAde; PolWkr; SchAde; SctActv; StuCncl; RptrYrbk; LetterTrk; Chrldr; College; Professional.

HARE, Wilbert L; Washington Comm HS; Washington, IL; 37/386 ChrhWkr; HonRl; SchPpr; Ftbl; Illinois Central College.

HAREN, Sandra L; Wellsburg Comm HS; Grundy Ctr, IA; 4/33 VPSophCls; VPJrCls; Chr; HonRl; NHS; StuCncl; EdSchPpr; 4-H; PpCl; Bsktbl; Business School; Accounting.

HARFMANN, Helen E; Thornton Township HS; Riverdale, IL; SecJrCls; PresSrCls; HonRl; NHS; OffAde; StuGov; GerCl; Valparaiso; Biology.

HARGER, Dave T; Farmington HS; Farmington, MI; HonRl; Michigan State Univ; Computer Science.

HARGER, Kendall W; Belding HS; Orleans, MI; ALBoysSt; Aud/Vis; Chr; ChrhWkr; HonRl; SchMus; SchPl; SctActv; CaptTrk; College.

HARGER, Nancy A; Leland HS; Leland, IL; Band; Chrs; HonRl; MrchBnd; NHS; PepBnd; SchPl; StuCncl; TchrAde; PresFHA; PpCl; University.

HARGROVE, Rene A; Dekalb HS; Rushville, MO; Band; ChrhWkr; CncrtBnd; DrmMjrt; HonRl; MrchBnd; NHS; PepBnd; PpCl; Chrldr; College; Interior Design.

HARIG, Janet L; Zeeland HS; Zeeland, MI; 32/170 Chr; Chrs; HonRl; SchMus; SchPl; YthFlsp; PpCl; Bsbl; Bsktbl; Chrldr; PPFtbl; College; Social Work.

HARJA, Cynthia L; Ontonagon Area HS; Mass, MI; ALAGirlsSt; HonRl; TreasNHS; YthFlsp; Yrbk; 4-H; Trk; GAA; College; Pediatric Nursing.

HARJU, Christine E; Calumet HS; Calumet, MI; Chr; DrlTm; HonRl; TchrAde; Yrbk; FTA; PpCl; Chrldr; College; Law.

HARKER, Ann D; Jasper HS; Jasper, IN; 18/286 SecBand; CncrtBnd; HonRl; MrchBnd; NHS; PepBnd; Quill&Scroll; StuCncl; Yrbk; Indiana Univ; Mathematics.

HARKER, Barbara; Clear Creek Comm HS; Oxford, IA; 8/64 SecFrshCls; SecSophCls; SecJrCls; Band; PresNHS; NatlThespSoc; SchPl; StuCncl; VPSpnCl; DARAwd; Univ Of Iowa.

HARKER, Jacalyn M; Lincoln HS; Vincennes, IN; 112/384 Band; ChrhWkr; CmntyWkr; CncrtBnd; HospAde; MrchBnd; SctActv; YthFlsp; Yrbk; FTA; Vincennes Jr Clg; Elem Educ.

HARKER, Jane A; Verona HS; Verona, WI; 12/122 Chrs; HonRl; NHS; NatlMeritFnl; GerCl; Univ; Gp Or Pediatric.

HARKESS, Christine M; Delano HS; Delano, MN; 32/109 HonRl; EdYrBk; RptrSchPpr; Coll; Nurse.

HARKEY, Carl W; Moline Sr HS; Coal Valley, IL; 69/845 Aud/Vis; HonRl; JrNHS; NHS; NatlMeritFnl; StuGov; Univ Of Illinois; Computer Science.

HARKEY, Carl W; Moline HS; Coal Valley, IL; 69/845 Aud/Vis; HonRl; NHS; NatlMeritSF; StuGov; RptrSchPpr; Univ Of Illinois; Computer Science.

HARKINS, Tracey L; Willowbrook HS; Lombard, IL; 45/821 TrsSrCls; HonRl; NHS; SchMus; SchPl; StuCncl; StuGov; TchrAde; College Of Du Page; Accounting.

HARKLESS, Thomas N; Pontiac Central HS; Pontiac, MI; LbryAde; Ferris St College; Printing Mgmt.

HARKNESS, Kathy; Westfield Washington HS; Westfield, IN; 1/89 Band; LitMag; MrchBnd; NHS; NatlMeritCmnd; SchMus; SchPl; RptrYrbk; Indiana Univ; Radio Television.

HARKNESS, Kevin M; Fenton HS; Bensenville, IL; Band; ChrhWkr; CmntyWkr; CncrtBnd; HonRl; MrchBnd; NHS; PepBnd; SchMus; YthFlsp; Glf; Depaul Univ; Musician.

HARKNESS, Michael E; Burlington HS; Burlington, IA; Bsbl; Bsktbl;.

HARKOVICH, Sandra; Evanston Township HS; Skokie, IL; ChrhWkr; HonRl; TchrAde; Yrbk; College; Science.

HARLAMERT, David J; High School; Boggstown, IN; 34/143 Band; Chr; CmntyWkr; CncrtBnd; Orch; PepBnd; Bsbl; Bsktbl; Ftbl; Glf; Purdue U; Farmer.

HARLAMERT, Edward A; Park Tudor HS; Boggstown, IN; PresFrshCls; Chr; Chrs; ChrhWkr; CmntyWkr; HonRl; PolWkr; SchMus; StuCncl; LetterBsbl; LetterBsktbl; CaptFtbl; LetterGlf; Wabash College; Medicine.

HARLAN, Debora A; Norris Dist 160 HS; Hickman, NE; Band; ChrhWkr; NHS; PolWkr; StuCncl; YthFlsp; 4-H; FHA; VPPpCl; 4-HAwd; Nursing College; Nursing.

HARLAN, Lamon D; Holy Trinity HS; Chicago, IL; 55/171 HonRl; LbryAde; MthCl; Bsktbl; Southern Illinois Univ; Medicine.

HARLAN, Linda K; Riverdale HS; Muscoda, WI; 19/90 SecJrCls; AFS; Band; Chr; HonRl; YthFlsp; 4-H; VPFHA; PpCl; Chrldr; School Of Art; Fashion Design.

HARLAN, Mary; Dunlap HS; Dunlap, IL; Chrs; ChrhWkr; HonRl; JrNHS; YthFlsp; SpnCl; PpCl; Chrldr; GAA; IMSpt; Co St College; Veterinarian.

HARLAN, Scott L; Barrington HS; Barrington, IL; HonRl; PresNHS; SchPpr; GerCl; LatCl; IMSpt; Univ; Tax Law.

HARLAND, Elaine K; Perry Community HS; Perry, IA; 2/160 ChrhWkr; CncrtBnd; HonRl; NHS; NatlThespSoc; SchMus; 4-H; 4-HAwd; KiwanAwd; CitAwd; Bible College; Math.

HARLASS, Adrian E; Shelbyville HS; Shelbyville, IL; 12/130 Aud/Vis; Band; ChrhWkr; CncrtBnd; HonRl; MrchBnd; NHS; SchMus; SchPl; SctActv; PresStuCncl; Bsktbl; Tennis; 4-HAwd; Univ Of Illinois; Communications.

HARLEY, Bruce D; Grand Blanc HS; Grand Blanc, MI; 104/705 SchPl; LetterTrk; Eastern Michigan Univ; Accounting.

HARLEY, Kathleen; West Holt HS; Atkinson, NE; 6/71 Band; CncrtBnd; HonRl; MrchBnd; PepBnd; SchPl; 4-H; FHA; GerCl; Ftbl; Business School; Accounting.

HARLEY, Suzanne L; Kalamazoo Central HS; Kalamazoo, MI; 25/450 HonRl; NatlFornLg; NatlMeritCmnd; Orch; SchMus; SchPl; StuCncl; LatCl; Ftbl; Trk; Michigan State Univ.

HARLING, Christopher; Elgin HS; Wayne, IL; ChrhWkr; SctActv; StuCncl; StuGov; YthFlsp; CaptSwmmng; LetterTennis; Southern Methodist Univ; Business.

HARLING, Claire J; Mc Donell Central HS; Chippewa Falls, WI; 1/92 HonRl; HospAde; ModUN; SchPl; EdYrBk; PpCl; BttyCrckrAwd; College; Medicine.

HARLOW, Jon; Drayton Public HS; Drayton, ND; PresJrCls; TrsJrCls; PresSrCls; TrsSrCls; ALBoysSt; ALAGirlsSt; EdYrBk; Bsktbl; Ftbl; Trk; Bismark Jr Coll; Cpa.

HARLOW, Richard J; St Pius X HS; Kansas City, MO; 1/137 VPJrCls; HonRl; JA; JrNHS; ModUN; VPNHS; SchMus; SchPl; StuCncl; UNYO; LetterBsktbl; LetterFtbl; Creighton Univ; Gen Practitioner.

HARLOW, Robin D; Baxter Comm HS; Baxter, IA; Chr; Chrs; HonRl; NatlThespSoc; SchMus; SchPl; SctActv; LetterBsbl; LetterBsktbl; LetterTrk; Des Moines Area Comm Coll; Photo Journalism.

HARLSON, Thomas J; James H Bowen HS; Chicago, IL; 58/613 Band; ChrhWkr; CmntyWkr; HonRl; StuCncl; YthFlsp; SchPpr; FrCl; MthCl; PpCl; Bsktbl; IMSpt; University Of Alabama; Business Admin.

HARM, Charles E; Stephen Decatur HS; Decatur, IL; 1/476 HonRl; NHS; NatlMeritFnl; NatlMeritSF; PolWkr; Yrbk; GerCl; RusCl; BauchLmbAwd; Mass Inst Of Tech; Research.

HARM, Linda A; Spalding Public HS; Spalding, NE; 1/15 VPSophCls; PresSrCls; Chrs; HonRl; NHS; SchPl; FHA; PpCl; Chrldr; BttyCrckrAwd; U Of Neb; Spec Ed.

HARMACEK, Susan M; Gregory Public HS; Dallas, SD; 25/56 Band; CmntyWkr; CncrtBnd; HonRl; HospAde; MrchBnd; PepBnd; RptrYrbk; Yrbk; RptrSchPpr; SchPpr; College.

HARMAN, Barbara E; Elmhurst HS; Fort Wayne, IN; 10/382 HonRl; NatlFornLg; PolWkr; Quill&Scroll; SchPl; Univ.

HARMAN, Corey J; Fort Atkinson S HS; Fort Atkinson, WI; Aud/Vis; Chr; ChrhWkr; HonRl; NatlFornLg; NatlThespSoc; SchMus; SchPl; SctActv; KeyCl; SpnCl; Bsbl; LetterBsktbl; Ftbl; College; Chem Engineering.

HARMAN, Donna S; Sacred Heart Academy; Springfield, IL; 7/148 NHS; SchPl; Sdlty; StuCncl; Yrbk; SchPpr; SpnCl; MthCl; PpCl; Univ Of Illinois; Physicians Asst.

HARMAN, Kenneth L; Northeastern HS; Richmond, IN; 20/122 Aud/Vis; Chr; Chrs; ChrhWkr; HonRl; LbryAde; SchMus; SchPl; SctActv; LetterBsbl; Trade School; Vocational.

HARMEIER, Ann L; Lincoln HS; Cambridge City, IN; 4/118 Band; Chr; Chrl; ChrhWkr; CmntyWkr; CncrtBnd; HonRl; Mdrgl; MrchBnd; NHS; Orch; PepBnd; SchMus; TchrAde; Indiana University; Theatre Arts.

HARMEIJ, Paul; Lowell Sr HS; Lowell, IN; Chr; Chrs; ChrhWkr; HonRl; NatlThespSoc; ROTC; SchMus; SchPl; StuCncl; Wrstlng; College; Professional.

HARMER, Robert W; Yale HS; Yale, MI; 8/150 Band; ChrhWkr; CncrtBnd; HonRl; MrchBnd; PepBnd; SchPl; TchrAde; SciCl; LetterTennis; IMSpt; Central Mich Univ; Music.

HARMEYER, Jan M; Marquette HS; West Point, IA; 5/51 SecFrshCls; SecSophCls; ALAGirlsSt; Chrs; ChrhWkr; CmntyWkr; HonRl; NHS; RedCrAde; StuCncl; TchrAde; RptrSchPpr; Bsbl; Bsktbl; Iowa State Univ; Science.

HARMISON, Darcy W; Rova Sr HS; Oneida, IL; 7/72 ALBoysSt; HonRl; NHS; OffAde; SctActv; StuCncl; FFA; PpCl; College; Agri Business.

HARMON, Carl R; Hugoton HS; Hugoton, KS; ALAGirlsSt; Chr; Mdrgl; SchMus; LetterFtbl; CaptWrstlng; College; Vocation.

HARMON, Darlene C; Pardeeville HS; Pardeeville, WI; TrsSrCls; HonRl; NHS; SchPl; RptrSchPpr; SchPpr; Pres4-H; GAA; 4-HAwd; University; Commercial Art.

HARMON, David A; Limestone Comm HS; Bartonville, IL; 6/403 Chr; PresChrhWkr; HonRl; NHS; NatlMeritCmnd; PresSancSoc; SctActv; StuCncl; YthFlsp; TreasKeyCl; Concordia; Minister.

HARMON, Forrest K; Gordon Technical HS; Chicago, IL; 96/594 HonRl; VPJA; Sacrstn; SctActv; StuCncl; GerCl; JAAwd; Depaul University; Accountant.

HARMON, Glenda J; Frank Cody HS; Detroit, MI; Chr; Chrl; Chrs; ChrhWkr; HonRl; HospAde; NHS; RedCrAde; FNA; Swmmng; Henry Ford Comm College; Baccauauret.

HARMON, Greg L; Brimfield HS; Brimfield, IL; 2/48 TrsSophCls; PresJrCls; HonRl; JrNHS; FFA; LetterBsbl; LetterBsktbl; LetterTrk; 4-HAwd; JCAwd; Ill Central Coll; Agriculture.

HARMON, James D; Harrisonville HS; Latour, MO; 32/148 Band; CncrtBnd; HonRl; MrchBnd; SctActv; FFA; SciCl; Ftbl; Glf; Trk; University Of Mo; Veterniary Medicine.

HARMON, Jeffrey D; West Vigo HS; West Terre Haute, IN; HonRl; LetterBsbl; LetterFtbl; LetterWrstlng; College.

HARMON, John P; Burnsville HS; Savage, MN; 32/720 Band; CncrtBnd; HonRl; JrNHS; NHS; StuCncl; StuGov; Bsktbl; LetterTrk; Univ Of Mn; Accounting.

HARMON, Pamela M; Southern Boone HS; Ashland, MO; ALAGirlsSt; Chr; Chrs; ChrhWkr; HonRl; OffAde; PolWkr; TchrAde; 4-H; FBLA; SpnCl; PpCl; Chrldr;.

HARMON, Russell; Sullivan HS; Sullivan, MO; Band; CncrtBnd; HonRl; MrchBnd; PepBnd; RotaryAwd; Univer Of Misso; Computer Science.

HARMON, Sue E; Turner HS; Kansas City, KS; Chr; Chrs; DrlTm; HonRl; SchPl; SctActv; StuCncl; PpCl; Ottawa Univ; Art.

HARMON, Teressa J; Rolla HS; Rolla, MO; Band; CncrtBnd; DrlTm; HonRl; MrchBnd; OffAde; StuGov; TchrAde; SchPpr; PpCl; College; Secretary.

HARMON, Thomas E; Cheney HS; Cheney, KS; HonRl; SchMus; RptrYrbk; RptrSchPpr; FFA; SpnCl; LetterBsbl; LetterBsktbl; LetterFtbl; LetterTrk; Butler County Comm College.

HARMON, Tom D; Brimfield HS; Brimfield, IL; 3/50 TrsFrshCls; TrsSrCls; HonRl; NHS; RptrSchPpr; SchPpr; 4-H; FFA; Univ Of Illinois; Agriculture.

HARMON, Vicky; Swartz Creek HS; Swartz Creek, MI; 20,360 ChrhWkr; HonRl; HospAde; NHS; SchMus; YthFlsp; VFWAwd; VoiceDemAwd; Attend Marion College; Nursing.

HARMON, William G; Lyons HS; Lyons, KS; StuCncl; StuGov; TchrAde; Bsbl; Bsktbl; LetterFtbl; Glf; Tennis; CaptTrk; IMSpt; Hutchinson Comm Jr College; Physical Educ.

HARMONEY, Marilyn S; Amherst HS; Amherst, NE; Band; Chrs; HonRl; NHS; SchPl; TreasStuCncl; EdYrBk; SchPpr; PpCl; LetterTrk; Kearney State Clg.

HARMS, Bruce W; Excelsior Springs HS; Excelsior Springs, MO; PresSrCls; ALBoysSt; Chr; HonRl; PolWkr; SchPl; StuCncl; Yrbk; RptrSchPpr; FTA; Columbia Coll; Travel Administration.

HARMS, Craig A; Hastings HS; Hastings, NE; 35/329 HonRl; Mdrgl; SctActv; StuCncl; YthFlsp; LetterBsbl; CaptBsktbl; ChmnTrk; Neb Wesleyan University; Medicine.

HARMS, Dean C; Polo Community HS; Dixon, IL; ALBoysSt; CncrtBnd; HonRl; MrchBnd; SecTrsFrshCls; PepBnd; SchPl; StuCncl; RptrYrbk; LetterWrstlng; Air Force Rotl; Pro Elying.

HARMS, Douglas P; Eastbrook HS; Upland, IN; 6/180 ChrhWkr; HonRl; Ftbl; IMSpt; Clge; Environmental Science.

HARMS, Elvin R; Edwardsville Sr HS; Edwardsville, IL; Chr; ChrhWkr; HonRl; Valparaiso Univ; Nuclear Physics.

HARMS, James A; Roanoke Benson HS; Benson, IL; Band; CmntyWkr; CncrtBnd; MrchBnd; PepBnd; 4-H; FFA; Bsbl; IMSpt; 4-HAwd; College; Accounting.

HARMS, Janice L; Hobart HS; Hobart, IN; 13/370 AFS; ChrhWkr; HonRl; HospAde; NHS; SctActv; TchrAde; SecFTA; SecGerCl; Manchester College; Teacher.

HARMS, Keith; Allison Bristow Comm HS; Bristow, IA; 8/40 VPSrCls; Chr; Chrs; HonRl; NHS; TchrAde; PpCl; IMSpt; Waldorf Coll; Coaching.

HARMS, Lu Ann E; Rock Island HS; Rock Island, IL; Chr; SecChrs; ChrhWkr; RedCrAde; SchMus; SchPl; StuGov; VPYthFlsp; GAA; CaptIMSpt; College; Forestry & Conserve.

HARMS, Patricia L; Brule HS; Brule, NE; Chr; ChrhWkr; HonRl; SchPl; SctActv; TchrAde; YthFlsp; 4-H; PpCl; Trk; Natl College Business; Secretary.

HARMS, Scott L; Brookfield East HS; Brookfield, WI; VPFrshCls; Chr; HonRl; LitMag; Quill&Scroll; SchMus; RptrSchPpr; SptEdSchPpr; LetterBsktbl; LetterFtbl; Coll.

HARMS, Susan; Deshler Public HS; Byron, NE; 8/26 Business School; Accounting.

HARMS, Vicki R; Holdrege HS; Holdrege, NE; Band; Chrs; ChrhWkr; CncrtBnd; HonRl; MrchBnd; SchMus; YthFlsp; Yrbk; FBLA; College; Business.

HARMSEN, Brenda L; Steeleville Comm HS; Steeleville, IL; VPSophCls; Chrs; ChrhWkr; DrlTm; HonRl; MrchBnd; StuCncl; Twrl; PresSpnCl; PpCl; AmLegAwd; Univ Of Tennessee; Cytotechnology.

HARMSEN, Ronald A; Hartsburg Emden HS; Emden, IL; TrsFrshCls; VPSophCls; HonRl; StuCncl; 4-H; Bsbl; Bsktbl;.

HARNACK, Jojean; Ralston HS; Ralston, NE; AFS; HonRl; NHS; NatlMeritCmnd; SpnCl; PpCl; Creighton University; Law.

HARNED, Linda L; Casey HS; Casey, IL; 7/90 Chr; HonRl; NHS; OffAde; SchMus; TchrAde; RptrYrbk; RptrSchPpr; SchPpr; College; Professional.

HARNER, David R; Dubois HS; French Lick, IN; 15/80 Band; Chr; CncrtBnd; StuCncl; University.

HARNER, Javonda J; Brownstown HS; St Elmo, IL; PresBand; TreasChrs; ChrhWkr; HonRl; PepBnd; YthFlsp; EdYrBk; FrCl; PpCl; Chrldr; College; Physical Education.

HARNESS, Carl S; Hales Franciscan HS; Chicago, IL; 4/73 Band; CncrtBnd; HonRl; LetterTennis; University; Medicine.

HARNESS, Debra A; Webster Groves HS; Webster Groves, MO; Chr; ChrhWkr; CmntyWkr; HonRl; SchAde; YthFlsp; GerCl; CchngActv; IMSpt; PPFtbl; Univ; Business Admin.

HARNESS, Donita; Oregon Davis HS; Hamlet, IN; Chr; ChrhWkr; HonRl; PolWkr; PpCl; Trk; Ancilla; Psychologist.

HARNETIAUX, Lester R; Bond County Comm Unit 2 HS; Greenville, IL; ChrhWkr; JA; NHS; StuGov; PpCl; Bsbl; Bsktbl; Ftbl; LetterTennis; JAAwd; University; Accounting.

HARNEY, Patrick J; St Ignatius Cp HS; Chicago, IL; HonRl; NHS; TchrAde; Swmmng; University; Professional.

HARNICA, Diane M; Dundee HS; Dundee, MI; Band; HonRl; MrchBnd; SecNHS; PepBnd; SchPl; Yrbk; 4-H; FTA; Wrstlng; U Of Mich; Dental Hygiene.

HARNICA, Kathy; Dundee HS; Dundee, MI; 8/128 HonRl; NHS; RptrYrbk; RptrSchPpr; FTA; GerCl; Trk; Community Col; Medical Secretary.

HARNICK, Kurt T; Midland HS; Midland, MI; HonRl; JA; NHS; PolWkr; StuGov; YthLg; CivCl; LetterFtbl; GovHonPrgAwd; Coll; Accountant.

HARNSBERRY, Elizabeth N; Mt Clemens HS; Mt Clemens, MI; 32/463 ChrhWkr; HonRl; NHS; OffAde; PolWkr; SctActv; GAA; University; Professional.

HAROFF, Woodrow H; Harper Creek Sr HS; Battle Creek, MI; Band; ChrhWkr; CmntyWkr; CncrtBnd; HonRl; MrchBnd; TchrAde; Bsbl; LetterFtbl; LetterWrstlng; College.

HAROLDSON, Alana; Fergus Falls HS; Fergus Falls, MN; DrmMjrt; MrchBnd; RptrYrbk; Yrbk; PpCl; Bsktbl; Swmmng; CchngActv; GAA; IMSpt; Coll; Science.

HARP, Gwendolyn S; Doniphan HS; Poynor, MO; Chr; ChrhWkr; HonRl; VPFrshCls; 4-H; FHA; Coll; Medicine.

HARP, Teresa; Catholic Central HS; Muskegon, MI; 44/215 HonRl; GovHonPrgAwd; College; Mathematics.

HARPER, Arlene M; Yankton Senior HS; Yankton, SD; Band; CncrtBnd; HonRl; MrchBnd; OffAde; 4-H; IMSpt; 4-HAwd; Vocational Technical; Vocation.

HARPER, Brian; Madison Central HS; Madison, IN; ALBoysSt; HonRl; NatlThespSoc; Quill&Scroll; SchMus; SctActv; StuCncl; RptrSchPpr; College; Child Psychology.

HARPER, Christopher L; Newton HS; Yale, IL; Chrs; HonRl; Olney Central College; Carpenter.

HARPER, Christopher A; Benton Harbor HS; Benton Harbor, MI; 8/435 HonRl; PresNHS; NatlMeritCmnd; MthCl; Bsbl; LetterFtbl; Glf; College; Business Admin.

HARPER, Debra S; Morristown HS; Fountaintown, IN; 10/77 Band; CncrtBnd; MrchBnd; NHS; RptrYrbk; EdSchPpr; SciCl; Indiana Central Univ; Band Director.

HARPER, Linda D; Colo Comm HS; Colo, IA; TrsSrCls; Band; Chrs; CncrtBnd; HonRl; MrchBnd; NHS; SchMus; SchPl; StuCncl; LetterBsbl; LetterBsktbl; LetterTrk; Iowa State Univ; Child Development.

HARPER, Pamela S; Greeley County HS; Tribune, KS; 10/40 CmntyWkr; HonRl; SchPl; StuCncl; TchrAde; Teen; EdSchPpr; 4-H; LetterTennis; 4-HAwd; Trade; Vocation.

HARPER, Patricia A; Muskegon Sr HS; Muskegon, MI; 12/550 ChrhWkr; HonRl; NHS; NatlMeritSF; OffAde; Muskegon Comm College; Accounting.

HARPER, Richard C; Kewanee HS; Kewanee, IL; 55/217 Chrs; HonRl; SchMus; SchPl; SctActv; StuCncl; VPGerCl; LetterFtbl; Glf; LetterWrstlng; U Of Iowa; Dentist.

HARPER, Teenya M; L P Goodrich HS; Fond Du Lac, WI; 18/620 SecSophCls; HonRl; JA; NHS; StuCncl; StuGov; GerCl; PpCl; BttyCrckrAwd; Uw Whitewater; Undecided.

HARPER, Wanda K; Clark County R I HS; Kohoka, MO; Band; ChrhWkr; HonRl; NHS; OffAde; YthFlsp; 4-H; FBLA; PpCl; DanFAwd; Secretary.

HARPER, Wesley E; Port Huron Northern HS; Port Huron, MI; 64/460 Band; ChrhWkr; CncrtBnd; NHS; Spring Arbor Col; Teacher.

HARPOLD, Laura K; Rosedale HS; Rosedale, IN; 10/49 HonRl; TchrAde; RptrYrbk; SchPpr; 4-H; Indiana Business College; Secretary.

HARPOLE, Pamela K; Griggsville HS; Griggsville, IL; 3/28 Chrs; HonRl; NHS; SchPl; 4-H; SpnCl; N E Missouri State Univ; Medical Lab Tech.

HARPSTER, David L; East Grand Forks Sr HS; E Grand Forks, MN; Band; Chrs; HonRl; IMSpt; University Of North Dakota.

HARR, Peggy J; Sheyenne River Academy; Jamestown, ND; Band; HonRl; StuCncl; RptrYrbk; RptrSchPpr; SptEdSchPpr; CaptBsktbl; IMSpt; CaptPPFtbl; College; Vetenary Technician.

HARRAL, Kaia L; Fairgrove HS; Fairgrove, MO; Band; Chrs; HonRl; MrchBnd; PepBnd; PolWkr; SchPl; PresStuCncl; PresYthFlsp; SecFHA; PresSpnCl; Drury Col; Music.

HARRAL, Loretta M; South Sioux City HS; Dakota City, NE; Chr; HonRl; JrNHS; NHS; SchMus; SctActv; StuGov; TchrAde; SchPpr; TreasFHA; SpnCl; PpCl; College; Teacher.

HARRAWOOD, Michelle; Marquette HS; Alton, IL; HonRl; IMSpt; College; Physical Therapy.

HARRE, Christina L; Carmi HS; Carmi, IL; 2/140 Chr; ChrhWkr; SchMus; SchPl; StuCncl; EdYrBk; FshEdSchPpr; EldAwd; KiwanAwd; RotaryAwd; Southern Illinois Univ; Theater.

HARRE, Ray; Dow City Arion HS; Dow City, IA; 4/42 SecSophCls; Chr; Chrs; CncrtBnd; HonRl; MrchBnd; NHS; Orch; IMSpt; Creighton Univ; Doctor.

HARRE, Ray G; Dow City Arion Comm HS; Dow City, IA; 5/42 SecSophCls; Band; Chr; CncrtBnd; MrchBnd; PepBnd; SchMus; SchPl; RptrSchPpr; College; Medicine.

HARRE, Sharon K; Okawville HS; Okawville, IL; 18/65 VPFrshCls; Chr; Chrs; ChrhWkr; HonRl; NHS; StuCncl; YthFlsp; 4-H; GerCl; MthCl; Bsktbl; Trk; Eastern Ill Univ; Special Ed.

HARREL, Jon M; Pratt HS; Pratt, KS; 29/147 ALBoysSt; Chr; ChrhWkr; HonRl; PresNatlFornLg; SchMus; TchrAde; FrCl; SpnCl; SciCl; Univ Of Ks; Medicine.

HARRELD, Kathy S; Hammond Baptist HS; Cedar Lake, IN; 18/88 SecSophCls; Chr; ChrhWkr; DrlTm; HonRl; NHS; OffAde; RptrSchPpr; PpCl; Coll; Music & History.

HARRELL, Anthony D; East Richland HS; Olney, IL; RptrSchPpr; LetterFtbl; Univ Of Ill; Civil Engineering.

HARRELL, Bradley W; Deer Creek Mackinaw HS; Mackinaw, IL; 7/60 PresSrCls; Band; HonRl; Mdrgl; StuCncl; RptrSchPpr; LetterBsbl; LetterBsktbl; LetterFtbl; DARAwd; Univ Of Illinois; Mechanical Engineering.

HARRELL, Charles; Meridian HS; Mounds, IL; CncrtBnd; HonRl; MrchBnd; Bsktbl; Trk; Siu Coll; Bio.

HARRELL, Jane E; Memorial HS; Joplin, MO; 1/257 ALAGirlsSt; ChrhWkr; HonRl; TreasHospAde; NHS; Orch; MthCl; Glf; College.

HARRELL, Patricia N; Macon County R 1 HS; Bevier, MO; Band; ChrhWkr; CncrtBnd; DrlTm; HonRl; MrchBnd; StuGov; RptrSchPpr; 4-H; SpnCl; Ozark Clg.

HARRELL, Wendell K; Farmington East HS; Hanna City, IL; Aud/Vis; HonRl; LbryAde; NatlSciFnd; SchAde; RptrYrbk; RptrSchPpr; EdSchPpr; SciCl; Swmmng; Trk; Illinois Central College; Accounting.

HARRELSON, Jerome L; East Dubuque HS; East Dubuque, IL; TrsFrshCls; VPSophCls; HonRl; SchPl; LetterBsbl; LetterBsktbl; PresAwd; College; Professional.

HARRELSON, Robert E; Circle HS; Towanda, KS; HonRl; TchrAde; Trade School; Vocation.

HARREN, Susan M; Lafayette HS; Red Lake Falls, MN; Band; Chr; Chrs; ChrhWkr; CmntyWkr; CncrtBnd; HonRl; MrchBnd; PepBnd; SchMus; College; Professional.

HARRER, James L; Marian Central HS; Mc Henry, IL; Band; HonRl; NHS; 4-H; Bsktbl; Trk; Univ Of Ill; Engineering.

HARRES, Susan; Columbia HS; Columbia, IL; 30/130 StuCncl; StuGov; Yrbk; EdSchPpr; FTA; GerCl; PpCl; Trk; Chrldr; Eastern Il Univ; History.

HARRI, Cheryl; Calumet HS; Kearsarge, MI; 50/187 CmntyWkr; HonRl; RptrSchPpr; 4-H; PpCl; 4-HAwd;.

HARRIMAN, Cynthia; Papillion HS; Papillion, NE; 3/325 Chrs; ChrhWkr; DrlTm; HonRl; NHS; NatlMeritCmnd; TchrAde; FHA; FTA; PpCl; Univ Of Neb Med Center; Nursing.

HARRINGA, Kathy L; North Central HS; Kensett, IA; Chrs; DrlTm; HonRl; Mdrgl; SchMus; 4-H; FrCl; PpCl; Chrldr; PresAwd; Wartburg College; Bus Admin.

HARRINGTON, Ann L; Beaver Dam Sr HS; Beaver Dam, WI; 105/349 Chrs; ChrhWkr; SchMus; SctActv; StuCncl; Bsktbl; LetterSwmmng; GAA; IMSpt; College.

HARRINGTON, Barbara A; Moulton Udell Comm HS; Unionville, IA; PresJrCls; Band; Chrs; CncrtBnd; HonRl; MrchBnd; PepBnd; StuCncl; LetterBsktbl; LetterTrk; Clge; Nursing.

HARRINGTON, Emily A; O Gorman HS; Sioux Falls, SD; SchMus; StuGov; RptrSchPpr; College; Professional.

HARRINGTON, Janice M; Port Huron Northern HS; Port Huron, MI; HonRl; NHS; PolWkr; Jr Co ;llaw.

HARRINGTON, Judith; Herscher HS; Kankakee, IL; 13/150 HonRl; NHS; PepBnd; PolWkr; SchPpr; PresPpCl; Wrstlng; GAA; AmLegAwd; 4-HAwd;.

HARRINGTON, Randal R; Tremont Community HS; Tremont, IL; TrsJrCls; ChrhWkr; StuGov; YthFlsp; LetterBsbl; LetterBsktbl; LetterFtbl; LetterTrk; DanFAwd; 4-HAwd; Ill Central College; Agriculture.

HARRIS, Carmelita; Lew Wallace HS; Gary, IN; Band; ChrhWkr; CmntyWkr; DrlTm; PolWkr; ROTC; SctActv; CivCl; 4-H; KeyCl; PpCl; GAA; Purdue Univ; Elem Education.

HARRIS, Cheryl B; John Marshall HS; Milwaukee, WI; Band; HonRl; JA; StuCncl; GAA; IMSpt; Uw Madison; Cpa & Lawyer.

HARRIS, Cheryl L; Dupo Community HS; East Carondelet, IL; Chr; ChrhWkr; HonRl; ModUN; SctActv; FTA; FrCl; Glf; Socr; GAA; Eastern Univ; Special Ed Teacher.

HARRIS, Cheryl R; Central Ymca HS; Chicago, IL; 2/215 Chrs; HonRl; JA; JrNHS; NHS; NatlMeritSchl; OffAde; TchrAde; SpnCl; Loyola Univ; Business Admin.

HARRIS, Cynthia; Waterford Mott HS; Drayton Plains, MI; 4/410 ChrhWkr; LetterCncrtBnd; HonRl; LetterMrchBnd; NatlMeritCmnd; SchPl; VPStuGov; Tennis; LetterChrldr; Wayne State; Political Lawyer.

HARRIS, Danny C; Wetmore HS; Wetmore, KS; VPSophCls; ALBoysSt; Band; Chrs; CncrtBnd; MrchBnd; StuCncl; RptrYrbk; RptrSchPpr; LetterFtbl; Professional.

HARRIS, Deborah D; Holy Redeemer HS; Detroit, MI; 66/189 ChrhWkr; CmntyWkr; HospAde; LbryAde; OffAde; Trk; Chrldr; Univ Of Detroit; Medicine.

HARRIS, Deborah L; New Trier West HS; Wilmette, IL; 28/700 HonRl; NatlMeritFnl; Radcliffe College; Medicine.

HARRIS, Deborah S; Atchison HS; Atchinson, KS; ALAGirlsSt; Chrs; ChrhWkr; HonRl; ModUN; NHS; NatlThespSoc; SchMus; SchPl; Univ; Math.

HARRIS, Denise; Fargo North HS; Fargo, ND; ChrhWkr; OffAde; 4-H; FHA; SpnCl; Bsktbl; 4-HAwd; Coll; Occ Ther.

HARRIS, Donna; Benton County R1 HS; Lincoln, MO; HonRl; HospAde; RptrYrbk; RptrSchPpr; PpCl; Us Army.

HARRIS, Doris; Naylor HS; Nyalor, MO; 1/35 PresSophCls; Chrs; HonRl; JrNHS; SchPl; SctActv; TchrAde; BttyCrckrAwd; Univ Of Mo; Vet Medical Research.

HARRIS, Frances M; Sumner HS; St Louis, MO; 14/448 DrmMjrt; HonRl; MrchBnd; NHS; Washington Univ; Psychology.

HARRIS, Francine; Dupo Community HS; East Carondelet, IL; LbryAde; ModUN; StuCncl; RptrYrbk; MthCl; Trk; GAA; IMSpt; Belleville Area College; Nursing.

HARRIS, Gregory A; Oak Park Sr HS; Kansas City, MO; 70/602 Chr; HonRl; SctActv; Ftbl; Univ Of Missouri; Elec Engineering.

HARRIS, Hobart W; Roeper City & Country HS; Flint, MI; ChrhWkr; HonRl; PolWkr; SchAde; TchrAde; Teen; CivCl; Bsbl; Ftbl; Socr; Trk; CchngActv; Univ; Physician.

HARRIS, Idajane; Homer Comm HS; Homer, NE; Chrs; ChrhWkr; IntrClCncl; LbryAde; SchPl; TchrAde; PpCl; SciCl; Trk; JAAwd; College.

HARRIS, Jackie R; Galena HS; Galena, MO; Chr; ChrhWkr; FFA; LetterBsbl; CaptBsktbl;.

HARRIS, Jamie K; Herrin HS; Herrin, IL; 20/216 DrlTm; OffAde; StuCncl; TchrAde; PpCl; Chrldr;.

HARRIS, Janet M; Regina Dominican HS; Glenview, IL; 11/206 Chrl; HonRl; LitMag; Mdrgl; Sdlty; StuCncl; FDA; FNA; FTA; GerCl; Univ Of Illinois; Medicine.

HARRIS, Jean M; Stoughton Sr HS; Stoughton, WI; AFS; Chrs; TchrAde; FTA; PpCl; Tennis; Trk; GAA; JCAwd; Univ Of Wisconsin; Occup Therapy.

HARRIS, Jeffery L; Belding Central HS; Belding, MI; ChrhWkr; HonRl; StuGov; TchrAde; FTA; MthCl; LetterFtbl; LetterTrk; College; Professional.

HARRIS, Jodi L; Cassville HS; Cassville, WI; SecJrCls; Band; CncrtBnd; HonRl; NatlFornLg; SchPl; RptrSchPpr; LetterChrldr; GAA; IMSpt; PPFtbl; University.

HARRIS, Joni L; Moberly Sr HS; Moberly, MO; SecJrCls; AFS; CmntyWkr; HonRl; NatlMeritSchl; PolWkr; SchPl; StuGov; RptrYrbk; SpnCl; College; Journalism.

HARRIS, Judith L; Williamsville HS; Williamsville, IL; 15/61 HonRl; LbryAde; SchPl; YthFlsp; FHA; FTA; PpCl;.

HARRIS, Julie; Lourdes HS; Nebraska City, NE; 10/34 DrmBgl; Chrs; CncrtBnd; HonRl; PepBnd; SchMus; RptrYrbk; SpnCl; MthCl; PpCl; Coll Saint Mary; Ele Ed.

HARRIS, Julie A; Anita HS; Anita, IA; HonRl; StuCncl; RptrYrbk; SptEdYrbk; SchPpr; SciCl; Bsbl; LetterBsktbl; LetterTrk; GAA; Nursing School; Nursing.

HARRIS, Karen K; Kirksville Sr HS; Kirksville, MO; HonRl; Orch; TchrAde; PresAwd; Coll; Elem Teacher.

HARRIS, Kelli J; Notre Dame HS; West Burlington, IA; 3/74 HonRl; SchPl; RptrSchPpr; SecSpnCl; Chrldr; American Inst; Secretary.

HARRIS, Kenneth D; Lillis HS; Kansas City, MO; 20/80 Band; Chrs; Bsktbl; LetterTrk; College; Pro Basketball.

HARRIS, Lauri D; Big Springs HS; Big Springs, NE; 3/24 Band; Chrs; CncrtBnd; HonRl; MrchBnd; NHS; SchPl; Twrl; 4-H; Chodron St Coll; Vet.

HARRIS, Lavan J; Harrison HS; Chicago, IL; Band; Chr; Chrs; CncrtBnd; HonRl; NHS; Orch; CaptROTC; EdYrBk; Wrstlng; Univ; Professional.

HARRIS, Lesa K; Senath Hornersville HS; Kennett, MO; Chrs; ChrhWkr; VPNHS; StuGov; VPFHA; SecSciCl; Arkansas St University.

HARRIS, Linda L; Galesburg Senior HS; Galesburg, IL; 2/630 ChrhWkr; CmntyWkr; HonRl; JrNHS; NHS; TchrAde; YthLg; RptrSchPpr; GerCl; KiwanAwd; Middlebury College; Political Science.

HARRIS, Linda S; West Nodaway R 1 HS; Clearmont, MO; ChrhWkr; HonRl; LbryAde; NHS; SchPl; RptrSchPpr; SptEdSchPpr; PpCl; Chrldr; Nebreska Christian Col; Librian.

HARRIS, Lois M; Oak Park HS; Kansas City, MO; ChrhWkr; HonRl; HospAde; YthFlsp; PpCl; Tennis; College; Physician.

HARRIS, Lori J; Jennings HS; Jennings, MO; 24/256 TreasChr; HonRl; Mdrgl; NHS; SchMus; StuCncl; SchPpr; EngCl; PpCl; CaptTennis; Univ Of Mo Saint Louis; Psychology.

HARRIS, Mark R; Milwaukee Lutheran HS; Wauwatosa, WI; ChrhWkr; CAP; NatlThespSoc; SchPl; SchPl; SctActv; Swmmng; Col; Aviation.

HARRIS, Mary; Central HS; Cape Girardeau, MO; 2/400 HonRl; NatlSciFnd; 4-H; College; Biological Scientist.

HARRIS, Mary B; St Edmonds HS; Fort Dodge, IA; 50/114 Chr; CmntyWkr; HonRl; PepBnd; PpCl; Bsktbl; IMSpt; Fort Dodge Tccc; Nursing.

HARRIS, Mary M; Anchor Bay HS; New Baltimore, MI; 1/230 ChrhWkr; CmntyWkr; HonRl; TreasNHS; TchrAde; TreasFrCl; Grand Valley St College; Spec Educ.

HARRIS, Merrie; Maquoketa Valley HS; Earlville, IA; HonRl; NHS; OffAde; Quill&Scroll; RptrSchPpr; Bsktbl; Tennis; Univ Of Dubuque; Special Ed.

HARRIS, Michael D; Vienna HS; Tunnel Hill, IL; 13/104 StuCncl; FFA; PpCl; Bsbl; Univ; Professional.

HARRIS, Michael V; Mendel HS; Chicago, IL; 24/191 Aud/Vis; ChrhWkr; CmntyWkr; HonRl; IntrClCncl; LbryAde; NHS; OffAde; SchAde; CaptBsbl; Trk; IMSpt; AmLegAwd; KiwanAwd; Col; Professional.

HARRIS, Monica A; Hartford HS; Hartford, MI; ChrhWkr; RedCrAde; StuGov; FBLA; FDA; FFA; FSA; FTA; SciCl; GodCntryAwd; VoiceDemAwd; Coll; Secretary.

HARRIS, Nicky; Centerville HS; Richmond, IN; 6 HonRl; JrNHS; NHS; SchPpr; Bsktbl; Glf; IMSpt; AmLegAwd; JCAwd; Purdue Univ; Engineering.

HARRIS, Peggy J; Greenway HS; Coleraine, MN; PresFrshCls; PresSophCls; PresJrCls; PresSrCls; ALBoysSt; ALAGirlsSt; HonRl; EdYrBk; EdSchPpr; PpCl; College; Nursing.

HARRIS, Phyllis J; Deer River HS; Deer River, MN; Band; HonRl; NHS; SchPl; Twrl; RptrYrbk; RptrSchPpr; GerCl; Bsktbl; Trk; University Of Ks ;medicine.

HARRIS, Rebecca A; Crete Public HS; Hallam, NE; 17/120 ALAGirlsSt; Chrs; DrlTm; HonRl; MrchBnd; SchPl; YthFlsp; FBLA; PresPpCl; Trk; 4-HAwd; PresAwd;.

HARRIS, Richard E; Hermantown HS; Duluth, MN; 27/141 Aud/Vis; HonRl; LbryAde; NHS; NatlMeritCmnd; SchPl; SctActv; Trade Schl; Electronics Engineer.

HARRIS, Richard L; Meridian HS; Sanford, MI; 42/125 HonRl; Bsbl; LetterBsktbl; Olivet College; Business Administration.

HARRIS, Rita J; Galatia HS; Galatia, IL; SecFrshCls; SecSophCls; Band; HonRl; StuCncl; RptrYrbk; EdSchPpr; FHA; MthCl; Se Ill Jr College; Business Adm.

HARRIS, Robin E; Red Cloud HS; Red Cloud, NE; TrsFrshCls; Band; Chrs; HonRl; Twrl; Yrbk; 4-H; FHA; Glf; Univ Of Nebr; Home Economics.

HARRIS, Rochelle; Wm R Harper HS; Chicago, IL; 9/300 PresSrCls; Chr; HonRl; JrNHS; NHS; OffAde; SchAde; SctActv; StuCncl; RptrYrbk; RptrSchPpr; SchPpr; SpnCl; PresGAA; University Of Illinois; Design.

HARRIS, Rochelle L; Lane Tech HS; Chicago, IL; 3/1200 VPSophCls; PresNHS; NatlMeritCmnd; OffAde; PolWkr; PresStuCncl; StuGov; SchPpr; Tennis; Chrldr; Brown Univ; Law.

HARRIS, Russell A; Cheney HS; Cheney, KS; VPFrshCls; VPSophCls; VPBand; Chr; CncrtBnd; HonRl; Mdrgl; MrchBnd; LetterFtbl; LetterTrk; College; Professional.

HARRIS, Sandra L; Maine West HS; Des Plaines, IL; Band; Chr; ChrhWkr; CncrtBnd; HonRl; MrchBnd; PepBnd; SchMus; YthFlsp; College; Musician.

HARRIS, Scott D; Rossville Alvin HS; Rossville, IL; Band; Chrs; ChrhWkr; HonRl; MrchBnd; SchMus; SchPl; SpnCl; Bsktbl; Glf; IMSpt; AmLegAwd; Eastern Illinois Univ; Accounting.

HARRIS, Susan E; Oakland HS; Oakland, IA; 2/36 Band; Chr; NHS; Twrl; RptrSchPpr; 4-H; Bsktbl; Trk; 4-HAwd; MasAwd;.

HARRIS, Susan I; Niles Township HS North; Skokie, IL; HonRl; NHS; University.

HARRIS, Susan L; Mulberry Grove HS; Greenville, IL; Band; CncrtBnd; HonRl; NHS; Yrbk; RptrSchPpr; FHA; SpnCl; GAA; CitAwd; Secretarial Work.

HARRIS, Susy; Hardin Central HS; Hardin, MO; SecJrCls; SecSrCls; ChrhWkr; HonRl; NHS; SchAde; RptrYrbk; RptrSchPpr; FHA; PpCl;.

HARRIS, Terrance L; Chicago Vocational HS; Chicago, IL; 76/765 HonRl; NatlMeritCmnd; StuCncl; LetterFtbl; U Of Dayton; Metal Engineer.

HARRIS, Terry V; South Knox HS; Monroe City, IN; 18/99 Aud/Vis; Band; ChrhWkr; HonRl; PepBnd; Tennis; CchngActv; IMSpt; U Of Evansville; Lawyer.

HARRIS, Thomas; Central HS; Lacrosse, WI; 87/534 Band; Chr; CncrtBnd; HonRl; MrchBnd; SctActv; Trk; IMSpt; KiwanAwd; College; Business Administration.

HARRIS, Thomas; River Rouge HS; River Rouge, MI; 109/214 CmntyWkr; RptrSchPpr; SptEdSchPpr; SchPpr; SciCl; Bsktbl; Coll; Bus Adm.

HARRIS, Timothy M; Woodruff HS; Peoria, IL; Aud/Vis; Chr; ChrhWkr; JA; TchrAde; Ftbl; Ill State University; Accountant.

HARRISON, Ann M; Huntington Cath HS; Huntington, IN; 4/40 ALBoysSt; Chr; Chrs; HonRl; SchPl; SecStuCncl; RptrYrbk; EdYrBk; PpCl; Univ; Foreign Service.

HARRISON, Blaine W; East Richland HS; Olney, IL; 65/265 Band; Chr; Mdrgl; SchMus; SchPl; RptrSchPpr; LetterGlf; CchngActv; University Of Illinois; Chemical Engineer.

HARRISON, Brenda L; Colfax HS; Colfax, WI; Band; Chrs; HonRl; NHS; SchPl; SctActv; EdSchPpr; FHA; PpCl; GAA; University; Voc Rehabilitation.

HARRISON, D Arcy A; Mercy HS; University City, MO; TrsFrshCls; VPSophCls; PresJrCls; ChrhWkr; CtyCnl; CmntyWkr; SchMus; SchPl; SctActv; Sdlty; Bsktbl; Swmmng; Chrldr; Univ Of Missouri; Journalism.

HARRISON, David S; Blair HS; Blair, NE; Band; CncrtBnd; HonRl; MrchBnd; PepBnd; Yrbk; SchPpr; FBLA; FSA; SciCl; College; Law.

HARRISON, Donald; Stratton HS; Stratton, NE; VPFrshCls; HonRl; JrNHS; StuCncl; LetterBsktbl; LetterFtbl; Vo Tech Coll; Vet.

HARRISON, Donald D; Eminence HS; Eminence, MO; StuCncl; Bsbl; Bsktbl; Trade School; Mchanics.

HARRISON, Gloria J; Calumet HS; Chicago, IL; 26/379 Chr; Chrs; ChrhWkr; HonRl; NHS; OffAde; SchMus; TchrAde; FrCl; Unif Of Ill; Medical Technologist.

HARRISON, Gregory E; North Brown #400 HS; Frederick, SD; ALBoysSt; ChrhWkr; CmntyWkr; HonRl; SctActv; Bsbl; Bsktbl; Trk; CchngActv; IMSpt; Sd Univ; Consevation.

HARRISON, Jerry J; Allegan HS; Allegan, MI; HonRl; StuCncl; StuGov; Michigan State; Pre Med.

HARRISON, Karen L; Paris R 2 HS; Holliday, MO; 9/76 VPJrCls; PresSrCls; ChrhWkr; CmntyWkr; HonRl; NHS; VP4-H; FHA; SpnCl; SecPpCl; LetterBsktbl; IMSpt; College; Med Secretary.

HARRISON, Kathy S; North Decatur HS; Milroy, IN; 11/84 Band; ChrhWkr; CmntyWkr; HonRl; MrchBnd; NHS; YthFlsp; 4-H; GAA; College; Lab Technician.

HARRISON, Kenneth C; Harper Creek HS; Battle Creek, MI; 22/280 HonRl; HonRl; NHS; StuGov; LetterBsktbl; LetterFtbl; Central Mi Univ; Political Science Journali.

HARRISON, Mark; Lourdes HS; Rochester, MN; Chr; Chrs; SctActv; StuCncl; SpnCl; College; Cival Field.

HARRISON, Mary B; Fountain Central HS; Kingman, IN; 17/128 Chrs; ChrhWkr; HonRl; NatlMeritCmnd; YthFlsp; FBLA; FSA; Bob Jones University; Nurse.

HARRISON, Michael D; Riverview Comm HS; Riverview, MI; 31/249 Band; HonRl; JrNHS; NHS; StuCncl; RptrSchPpr; Bsbl; LetterBsktbl; LetterTennis; Coll.

HARRISON, Montgomery A; Memorial HS; Joplin, MO; ChrhWkr; CncrtBnd; NHS; Orch; SchPl; StuCncl; RptrSchPpr; SchPpr; MthCl; Bsktbl; Univ; Medicine.

HARRISON, Pamela; Woodruff Hs; Peoria, IL; Chr; HonRl; HospAde; SchMus; SctActv; YthFlsp; KeyCl; FrCl; Swmmng; SciCl; University; Professional.

HARRISON, Pamela S; Woodruff HS; Peoria, IL; Chr; ChrhWkr; CmntyWkr; HospAde; SchMus; SctActv; KeyCl; FrCl; Swmmng; Chrldr; Univ; Professional.

HARRISON, Suzanne; U Of Chicago HS; Chicago, IL; Chr; CmntyWkr; LitMag; Quill&Scroll; SchPl; TchrAde; RptrYrbk; RusCl; IMSpt; Eastern Clg; Creative Writing.

HARRISON, Teresa J; Martinsville R Vi HS; Martinsville, MO; 2/9 SecFrshCls; SecSophCls; HonRl; RptrYrbk; RptrSchPpr; FHA; PpCl; LetterBsktbl; LetterTrk; BttyCrckrAwd; Platt Clg; Secretary.

HARRISON, Teresa L; Mexico HS; Mexico, MO; Chrs; HospAde; SctActv; StuCncl; TchrAde; EdYrBk; FrCl; LatCl; PpCl; Trk; College; Anesthetiologist.

HARRISON, Tresa A; Zeeland HS; Zeeland, MI; TrsFrshCls; PresSophCls; Band; DrmMjrt; HonRl; SecStuCncl; Twrl; PPFtbl; Hope College; Social Work.

HARRMANN, Timothy J; Menasha HS; Menasha, WI; PresFrshCls; MrchBnd; NHS; PepBnd; SchMus; StuCncl; StuGov; Bsktbl; Ftbl; OptClAwd; Univ Of Wi, Platteville; Engineer.

HARROLD, Karen S; Hagerstown Jr Sr HS; Hagerstown, IN; 24/101 HonRl; OffAde; VP4-H; SpnCl; PpCl; GAA;.

HARROM, Charleen L; College View Acad; Lincoln, NE; 1/31 TrsFrshCls; SecJrCls; Chr; CmntyWkr; HonRl; NHS; SchPl; StuGov; RptrSchPpr; CitAwd; College; Math Teacher.

HARROW, Susan A; Pinconning Area HS; Pinconning, MI; 20/244 Band; HonRl; MrchBnd; NHS; PepBnd; SchPl; FNA; Trk; PPFtbl; MasAwd; Mich St Univ; Nursing.

HARRY, Debra K; West Sioux HS; Hawarden, IA; 25/79 ChrhWkr; HonRl; YthFlsp; FHA; FTA; IMSpt; Wayne St Coll; Elem School Teacher.

HARRY, Debra L; Jeffers HS; Baltic, MI; Aud/Vis; Band; ChrhWkr; HonRl; HospAde; NHS; TchrAde; YthFlsp; FNA; GerCl; Mich Tech At Houghton; Nursing.

HARRY, Jeanine R; Clinton Comm HS; Clinton, IL; 25/180 CmntyWkr; HospAde; OffAde; YthFnd; Bsktbl; Illinois St Univ; Secretary.

HARSHAW, Gina; Oswego HS; Oswego, KS; 4/27 TrsJrCls; ALAGirlsSt; EdYrBk; Chrldr; AmLegAwd; BttyCrckrAwd; DanFAwd; CitAwd; Business Education.

HARSHBARGER, Paula H; Centralia HS; Centralia, MO; 2/88 TrsSrCls; Band; SecChrhWkr; HonRl; MrchBnd; NHS; SchMus; Pres4-H; 4-HAwd; OptClAwd; VoiceDemAwd; Univ Of Missouri; Science.

HARSHBARGER, Sandra L; Atwood Hammond HS; Atwood, IL; Band; CncrtBnd; HonRl; MrchBnd; NHS; PepBnd; StuCncl; PresYthFlsp; SchPpr; VPFHA; Eastern Illinois Univ; Elem Education.

HARSHBERGER, Kay L; Minneola HS; Minneola, KS; PresFrshCls; VPJrCls; Band; Chr; ChrhWkr; CncrtBnd; HonRl; LitMag; Mdrgl; Tennis; College; Lawyer.

HARSHMAN, Ronda D; Malcolm HS; Malcolm, NE; PresJrCls; Chrs; JA; SchPl; Yrbk; SchPpr; 4-H; PpCl; LetterBsktbl; LetterTrk; College.

HARSIN, Sharon K; Twin Cedars HS; Tracy, IA; 9/42 SecTrsSophCls; Band; Chrs; HonRl; SchPl; YthFlsp; Yrbk; 4-H; FTA; Trk; Chrldr; William Penn College; Teaching.

HARSTAD, Barbara J; Southeast HS; Kansas City, MO; HonRl; HospAde; NHS; OffAde; Yrbk; PpCl; Washington Univ St Louis; Physical Therapst.

HARSTAD, Judy R; Little Falls Community HS; Little Falls, MN; ChrhWkr; TchrAde; Trade School.

HARSTAD, Lila D; Magic City Campus HS; Minot, ND; 23/656 ChrhWkr; CncrtBnd; HonRl; MrchBnd; NHS; StuCncl; YthFlsp; FBLA; PresFHA; GerCl; No Dak State Univ; Home Econ.

HARSY, Julius S; Du Quoin HS; Du Quoin, IL; VPSophCls; HonRl; SchPl; RptrSchPpr; Bsktbl; Ftbl; Southern Ill Univ; Biology.

HART, Ann L; Irving Crown HS; Algonquin, IL; 56/351 ChrhWkr; CncrtBnd; HonRl; College; Medicine.

HART, Bruce R; Gilmanton Area HS; Gilmanton, WI; VPSrCls; ALBoysSt; Band; HonRl; PolWkr; SchMus; SchPl; YthFlsp; FFA; AmLegAwd; Univ Of Wis.

HART, Charles A; Rockford Senior HS; Rockford, MI; 3/289 Chr; HonRl; Mdrgl; SchMus; SchPl; SciCl; Calvin College; Chemist.

HART, Colleen K; Bartley Public HS; Bartley, NE; 2/15 PresSrCls; Band; Chrs; ChrhWkr; HonRl; SchPl; EdYrBk; PpCl; Trk; GAA; Clge; Secretarial Science.

HART, Crystal; Paseo Hs; Kansas City, MO; 1/402 SecFrshCls; Chr; ChrhWkr; HonRl; StuCncl; FrCl; MthCl; PpCl; Glf; Trk; College; Medicine.

HART, Cynthia; John Hersey Hs; Arlington Heights, IL; AFS; Band; HonRl; JrNHS; LbryAde; MrchBnd; NHS; SctActv; Yrbk; Bsktbl; Purdue University; Pharmacy.

HART, Debra A; Marian HS; Mishawaka, IN; DrmMjrt; HonRl; JA; MrchBnd; NHS; PolWkr; SchPl; Twrl; IMSpt; PPFtbl; St Marys Col ; Nursing.

HART, Denise E; Central Montcalm HS; Stanton, MI; 22/121 ChrhWkr; CncrtBnd; MrchBnd; NHS; SchMus; SchPl; StuCncl; TchrAde; RptrYrbk; IMSpt; Grand Rapids Baptist Clg; Social Work.

HART, Donna; Annapolis HS; Dearborn Hts, MI; 48/435 ChrhWkr; CmntyWkr; HonRl; JA; SchPl; SctActv; Swmmng; Trk; JAAwd; Spring Arbor Coll; Mdical Tech.

HART, Douglas E; Richmond HS; Richmond, IN; 5/634 CncrtBnd; DrmBgl; HonRl; MrchBnd; NatlFornLg; NHS; PepBnd; PolWkr; EdSchPpr; LatCl; Indiana Univ; Law.

HART, Garry W; Cuba HS; Cuba, IL; 1/70 ALBoysSt; PresBand; PresNHS; SchMus; StuGov; PresYthFlsp; SptEdSchPpr; VPLatCl; TreasSciCl; Glf; Univ Of Il; Civil Engineering.

HART, Julie A; Mayo HS; Rochester, MN; 16/467 AFS; LitMag; NHS; NatlMeritFnl; NatlMeritSchl; PolWkr; SchMus; FrCl; SciCl; Swmmng; Carleton Clge.

HART, Kathryn B; Richmond Burton HS; Mchenry, IL; HonRl; SchPl; GAA; Mchenry Co College; Veterinarian.

HART, Kerry M; East Peoria Comm HS; E Peoria, IL; NHS; NatlMeritFnl; SchAde; GerCl; Ftbl; Glf; Trk; College; Engineer.

HART, Kevin D; Brother Rice HS; Birmingham, MI; 30/225 PresFrshCls; PresSophCls; ChrhWkr; HonRl; NatlSciFnd; StuCncl; StuGov; SciCl; Bsktbl; CaptFtbl; KiwanAwd; OptClAwd; Notre Dame; Engineering.

HART, Linda; Virden HS; Virden, IL; SchPl; TchrAde; RptrSchPpr; FHA; FTA; PpCl; PPFtbl; Univ; Special Ed.

HART, Lori J; Hiawatha HS; Kirkland, IL; 2/50 TrsSrCls; Band; Chrs; CncrtBnd; HonRl; MrchBnd; NHS; PepBnd; SchMus; SchPl; SctActv; GAA; College; Nursing.

HART, Lorraine M; Oak Lawn Comm HS; Oak Lawn, IL; 14/600 HonRl; JrNHS; NHS; NatlMeritCmnd; OffAde; SchAde; TchrAde; Yrbk; MthCl; LetterBsktbl; LetterTennis; CchngActv; GAA; Ill State University; Physical Educ.

HART, Mary; Corunna HS; Corunna, MI; VPJrCls; HonRl; NHS; StuCncl; TchrAde; RptrYrbk; Kalamazoo College.

HART, Mary P; Barr Reeve HS; Cannelburg, IN; 7/67 ALAGirlsSt; ChrhWkr; DrlTm; HonRl; JrNHS; NHS; Chrldr; GAA; IMSpt; 4-HAwd; Indiana State Univ; Speech Hearing.

HART, Peter P; Gibraltar HS; Fish Creek, WI; 4/70 Band; CncrtBnd; HonRl; MrchBnd; NHS; PepBnd; StuCncl; StuGov; Trk; Wrstlng; IMSpt; College; Music.

HART, Rick D; Clarke Comm HS; Osceola, IA; 25/106 PresFrshCls; ChrhWkr; HonRl; 4-H; LetterBsbl; LetterBsktbl; LetterFtbl; LetterTrk; DanFAwd; 4-HAwd; Trade School; Architectural Drafting.

HART, Roxann E; North Bend Central HS; Ames, NE; HonRl; LbryAde; StuGov; FBLA; FTA; FrCl; PpCl; Midland College; Business.

HART, Sari L; New Trier East HS; Wilmette, IL; 4/847 HonRl; LitMag; NatlMeritSF; College; Psycho Biology Research.

HART, Sheila; Oscoda Area HS; Wurtsmith Afb, MI; 12/220 HonRl; JrNHS; NHS; SchPpr; FrCl; Northern Michigan U; Nursing.

HART, Stephen R; Downers Grove North HS; Downers Grove, IL; Band; HonRl; Mdrgl; MrchBnd; NHS; Orch; SchMus; RptrSchPpr; Ftbl; Wrstlng; U Of Ill; Music.

HART, Steve W; Slinger HS; Allenton, WI; ALBoysSt; CmntyWkr; HonRl; StuCncl; SchPpr; SpnCl; LetterBsktbl; Ftbl; Tennis; LetterTrk; College; History.

HART, Susan K; Elmhurst HS; Ft Wayne, IN; AFS; ChrhWkr; CmntyWkr; HonRl; JA; OffAde; SchPl; TchrAde; Chrldr; CitAwd;.

HART, Thomas; Sts Peter And Paul Area HS; Saginaw, MI; /107 TrsFrshCls; PresSophCls; ChrhWkr; CmntyWkr; SchMus; StuCncl; StuGov; YthLg; FrCl; Glf; Coll; Busi Admin And Political Science.

HART, William G; South Division HS; Milwaukee, WI; PresJrCls; PresSrCls; CmntyWkr; HonRl; PolWkr; StuGov; College; Professional.

HARTE, Virginia L; Divine Savior Holy Angels HS; Elm Grove, WI; PresJrCls; Chrs; HospAde; IntrClCncl; SchMus; StuCncl; TchrAde; Yrbk; PpCl; LetterTrk; Marquette U; Registered Nurse.

HARTEL, Mike A; Marysville HS; Marysville, MI; ChrhWkr; HonRl; SchPl; SctActv; SciCl; Bsktbl; Ftbl; St Clair Comm Col & Mich Tech; Engineering.

HARTENBERGER, Brenda K; Chester HS; Chester, IL; 13/120 Chrs; HonRl; NHS; NatlThespSoc; OffAde; SchPl; PpCl;.

HARTER, Bill; Auburndale HS; Auburndale, WI; Band; CncrtBnd; HonRl; MrchBnd; PepBnd; GerCl; College; Accountting.

HARTER, Gary S; Naperville Central HS; Naperville, IL; 3/844 HonRl; Univ Of Illinois; Business Management.

HARTER, Marcia L; Winner Sr HS; Winner, SD; 27/133 DrlTm; College; Accounting.

HARTER, Noel P; Hagerstown Jr Sr HS; Hagerstown, IN; 10/119 ALBoysSt; HonRl; NHS; StuCncl; YthLg; Pres4-H; PresFrCl; SecSciCl; 4-HAwd; Ball State Univ; Teaching.

HARTER, Patti R; West Harrison HS; Mondamin, IA; Chrs; ChrhWkr; CncrtBnd; DrmMjrt; HonRl; NHS; SchPl; YthFlsp; VP4-H; LetterBsktbl; 4-HAwd; College; Stewardess.

HARTER, Patti S; Eddyville HS; Ottumwa, IA; 24/53 CncrtBnd; LbryAde; MrchBnd; Quill&Scroll; RptrYrbk; SptEdYrbk; PpCl; Bsbl; Trk; Chrldr; Mo St Univ ;.

HARTER, Todd J; Savanna Community HS; Savanna, IL; 2/66 PresFrshCls; PresSophCls; ChrhWkr; HonRl; PresNHS; StuCncl; FrCl; SciCl; LetterBsktbl; LetterGlf; Univ Of Illinois; Optometry.

HARTFORD, Janet L; F L Schlagle HS; Kansas City, KS; Chr; PresChrhWkr; HonRl; JrNHS; NHS; OffAde; SchMus; FBLA; College; Music.

HARTFORD, Julie A; Norfolk HS; Norfolk, NE; Chrs; CmntyWkr; HospAde; Mdrgl; NatlFornLg; NHS; RedCrAde; StuCncl; StuGov; Ftbl; College; Data Processing.

HARTGERS, Debbie J; Pella Comm HS; Pella, IA; DrlTm; HonRl; MrchBnd; Twrl; VP4-H; SecFFA; Bsktbl; 4-HAwd;.

HARTH, Ava; Lindblom Hs; Chicago, IL; 3 PresJrCls; DrmMjrt; HonRl; IntrClCncl; JrNHS; MrchBnd; NHS; NatlMeritCmnd; StuGov; Twrl; Norhtwestern U;biomedical Engineer.

HARTH, Ava D; Lindblom Technical HS; Chicago, IL; 2/650 PresJrCls; DrmMjrt; HonRl; HospAde; JrNHS; MrchBnd; NHS; NatlMeritCmnd; GAA; IMSpt; Northwestern; Biomedical Engineering.

HARTH, Catherine; Acad Of Our Lady; Chicago, IL; HonRl; NHS; EdSchPpr; Purdue U; Pre Med.

HARTHAN, Debra S; L F Comm HS; Little Falls, MN; SecTrsJrCls; AFS; Chr; CncrtBnd; Orch; PepBnd; SchMus; SchPl; College; Teacher.

HARTHAN, Patricia L; Casey Sr Jr HS; Casey, IL; 34/94 YthFlsp; FHA; College; Health.

HARTIG, Paul A; Holmen HS; Onalaska, WI; 4/110 ChrhWkr; HonRl; College.

HARTING, Randall C; Laporte City HS; Laporte City, IA; TrsFrshCls; Band; ChrhWkr; CncrtBnd; HonRl; MrchBnd; NHS; PepBnd; SchPl; StuCncl; College; Psychology.

HARTLEY, Charles; Ernest W Seaholm HS; Troy, MI; Orch; SciCl; Reed College; Physics.

HARTLEY, Judith; Central HS; Springfield, MO; HonRl; LbryAde; OffAde; MthCl; Burge Nursing; Nurse.

HARTLEY, Karen L; Oak Park HS; Gladstone, MO; AFS; HonRl; NHS; SchMus; TchrAde; CivCl; KeyCl; FrCl; PpCl; Kansas Univ; Architecture.

HARTLEY, Kimberly E; Mount Academy; Atchison, KS; Chrs; HonRl; Sdlty; RptrYrbk; RptrSchPpr; Colby Comm Clg; Vet.

HARTLINE, Margaret A; Iron Mtn HS; Iron Mountain, MI; 7/156 Band; Chrs; ChrhWkr; HonRl; LbryAde; NHS; SchPl; SchPpr; FTA; FrCl; Army; Preventive Medicine Specialist.

HARTMAN, Ann; Kearney HS; Kearney, NE; 23/248 HonRl; TchrAde; 4-H; PpCl; 4-HAwd; College; Voc Home Ec.

HARTMAN, Anne E; Sac Comm HS; Sac City, IA; TrsSophCls; Band; Chr; ChrhWkr; CmntyWkr; HonRl; HospAde; MrchBnd; RptrSchPpr; FNA; Univ Of Northern Ia; Speech Pathology.

HARTMAN, Arlo R; Sheldon Comm HS; Sheldon, IA; ChrhWkr; HonRl; Bus School.

HARTMAN, Beverly A; Milbank HS; Milbank, SD; SecJrCls; HonRl; JA; SchMus; SchPl; StuCncl; 4-H; PPFtbl; 4-HAwd; JAAwd; Coll; Business.

HARTMAN, Christine L; Bishop Dwenger HS; Ft Wayne, IN; HonRl; HospAde; Yrbk; PpCl; GAA; College.

HARTMAN, Cynthia M; Richmond Sr HS; Richmond, IN; 199/600 HonRl; HospAde; Teen; Pres4-H; PresFHA; BttyCrckrAwd; 4-HAwd; Purdue U; Home Ec.

HARTMAN, David P; Gull Lake HS; Hickory Corners, MI; Band; ChrhWkr; CmntyWkr; CncrtBnd; HonRl; JrNHS; MrchBnd; NHS; Orch; PepBnd; SctActv; StuCncl; LetterBsbl; Bsktbl; College; Cpa Gen Accounting.

HARTMAN, David R; Waterman HS; Waterman, IL; Bsbl; Bsktbl; Glf; Kishwaukee College; Elec Engineering.

HARTMAN, Douglas; Lincoln Way HS; Mokema, IL; 3/566 HonRl; NHS; OffAde; YthFlsp; Ftbl; Glf; VFWAwd; College; Wildlife Management.

HARTMAN, Ellen; Rugby HS; Rugby, ND; 19/100 SecSophCls; Chr; HonRl; NHS; StuCncl; PpCl; Trk; Chrldr; Univ Of North Dakota; Professional.

HARTMAN, Eric R; New Franklin HS; New Franklin, MO; VPFrshCls; Band; Chrs; ChrhWkr; HonRl; NHS; SchPl; StuCncl; YthFlsp; SpnCl; Univ Of Mo; Music.

HARTMAN, Gary A; Thomson HS; Thomson, IL; 2/40 PresSophCls; Chr; Chrs; Mdrgl; NHS; SchMus; 4-H; FFA; 4-HAwd; College.

HARTMAN, Laurie L; Sheldon HS; Sheldon, IL; 9/24 Chrs; HonRl; Quill&Scroll; SchPl; TchrAde; Yrbk; SchPpr; 4-H; PpCl; VoiceDemAwd; Jr Coll; Specialized Nursing.

HARTMAN, Lisa; St Stephen Area HS; Saginaw, MI; 11/105 CtyCnl; CmntyWkr; HonRl; PolWkr; SchPl; YthFlsp; GAA; AmLegAwd; DARAwd; JAAwd; Green Mountain Col; Art.

HARTMAN, Marcy R; Barrett Public HS; Barrett, MN; 4/19 SecSophCls; SecSrCls; ALAGirlsSt; Band; Chr; Chrs; ChrhWkr; CmntyWkr; CncrtBnd; HonRl; MrchBnd; NHS; Chrldr; DARAwd; College.

HARTMAN, Marlin J; Mazon Verona Kinsman HS; Mazon, IL; 5/39 Chrs; HonRl; JrNHS; NHS; SchPl; SctActv; StuCncl; FrCl; MthCl; Bsbl; Western Ill Univ; Law Enforcement.

HARTMAN, Paula J; Clark HS; Garden City, SD; 1/50 ALAGirlsSt; Band; Chrs; CncrtBnd; HonRl; Mdrgl; NHS; NatlMeritSF; PepBnd; SchMus; College; Medical Technology.

HARTMAN, Peggy A; Lanark HS; Lanark, IL; Chrs; SchMus; SchPl; 4-H; LetterTrk; TrsSrCls; GAA; PPFtbl; 4-HAwd; PresAwd; Bus Sch; Public Relations.

HARTMAN, Ruth A; Bentley HS; Burton, MI; 75/170 TrsSophCls; TrsJrCls; TrsSrCls; NHS; Sacrstn; EdYrBk; AmLegAwd; DARAwd; KiwanAwd; VFWAwd; Western Michigan Univ; Geography.

HARTMAN, Sandra; Richmond Senior HS; Richmond, IN; 259/805 4-H; IMSpt; Indiana Univ; Spec Ed.

HARTMANN, Janice; Elgin Hs; Bartlett, IL; TreasGerCl; PpCl; GAA;.

HARTMANN, Karen J; Armour HS; Armour, SD; VPJrCls; PresSrCls; Chr; Chrs; ChrhWkr; HonRl; SchMus; 4-H; FHA; DARAwd; College; Social Work.

HARTMANN, Marilyn J; Trico HS; Campbell Hill, IL; 1/78 PresJrCls; ALAGirlsSt; Band; Chrs; ChrhWkr; DrmMjrt; HonRl; NHS; SchPl; EdYrBk; Clge; Spec Ed.

HARTMANN, Michael J; St Charles HS; St Charles, MO; 57/600 Chr; HonRl; NHS; SctActv; Trk; College; Chemical Geol.

HARTMANN, Robert L; Brother Rice HS; Chicago, IL; 7/416 HonRl; LbryAde; NHS; NatlMeritCmnd; SctActv; LbryAde; LetterBsktbl; Tennis; CchngActv; Northern Ill Univ; Physics.

HARTNETT, John A; Shelbyville HS; Shelbyville, IN; PresSrCls; Aud/Vis; ChrhWkr; CmntyWkr; HonRl; StuCncl; RptrSchPpr; SptEdSchPpr; SchPpr; LetterBsktbl; College; Broadcasting.

HARTNETT, Lawrence G; Proviso West HS; Hillside, IL; 207/1086 CmntyWkr; HonRl; SctActv; Coll; Law.

HARTNETT, Timothy P; Sidney Comm HS; Percival, IA; 6/33 ALBoysSt; ChrhWkr; CmntyWkr; HonRl; SchMus; SchPl; YthFlsp; RptrSchPpr; Bsbl; Ftbl; Mosu; Dramatic Arts.

HARTRANFT, Bruce W; Caro HS; Caro, MI; 39/163 SctActv; TchrAde; YthFlsp; RptrSchPpr; PpCl; Swmmng; Mi Univ; Bus.

HARTSBURG, Darlene L; Lebanon HS; Trenton, IL; 14/90 HonRl; Business School.

HARTSELL, Steven W; John Glenn HS; Walkerton, IN; HonRl; RedCrAde; SchPl; FTA; Bsbl; Bsktbl; Glf; Socr; Purdue; Foreign Lang.

HARTSFIELD, Valerie V; Lindblom Tech HS; Chicago, IL; 43/722 CmntyWkr; HonRl; NHS; NatlMeritFnl; NatlMeritCmnd; NatlMeritSchl; NatlMeritSF; RptrYrbk; Yrbk; JAAwd; College; Business Manager.

HARTSHORN, Lynda A; Riverton HS; Galena, KS; Chr; ChrhWkr; HonRl; NHS; SpnCl; MthCl; PpCl; College; Professional.

HARTSOCK, Teresa J; Moline HS; Moline, IL; 50/845 HonRl; NHS; StuCncl; Teen; RptrYrbk; Swmmng; Chrldr; GAA; IMSpt; Univ Of Kansas.

HARTSOUGH, Denise L; West Lafayette HS; W Lafayette, IN; 1/205 Band; CmntyWkr; HonRl; LitMag; NatlMeritSchl; StuCncl; Washington Univ; Social Science.

HARTTER, Roger E; Washington Comm HS; Washington, IL; College.

HARTUNG, Alvin; Hempstead HS; Dubuque, IA; 10/565 CmntyWkr; HonRl; NHS; StuGov; SciCl; Wrstlng; IMSpt; ChmbCommrsAwd; JCAwd; Univ Of Norhtern Ia; Professional.

HARTUNG, Edward; Elmwood Area HS; Elmwood, WI; 32/56 Chrs; HonRl; FFA; Farming.

HARTUNG, Marcia A; Mineral Point HS; Mineral Point, WI; 13/85 Band; ChrhWkr; CncrtBnd; HonRl; MrchBnd; ModUN; RptrSchPpr; 4-H; GAA; College; Accounting.

HARTUNG, Marian R; Granite City North HS; Granite City, IL; CncrtBnd; LitMag; MrchBnd; NHS; Southern Illinois University.

HARTUNG, Mark S; Saint Xaviers HS; Junction City, KS; VPSophCls; ALBoysSt; HonRl; TchrAde; LetterBsktbl; LetterFtbl; LetterTrk; Coll; Teach.

HARTUNG, Pamela J; Beardstown HS; Beardstown, IL; 12/126 VPSophCls; PresSrCls; Band; CmntyWkr; CncrtBnd; HonRl; MrchBnd; NHS; SchPpr; SpnCl; Univ; Music.

HARTUNG, Wanda L; Arkansaw HS; Arkansaw, WI; 4/24 Band; Chr; PresSophCls; HonRl; PepBnd; SchPl; StuCncl; FHA; GAA; Tech ;secret.

HARTWAY, Sue; Lincoln HS; Park Falls, WI; 40/117 TrsSophCls; SecSrCls; Band; CncrtBnd; MrchBnd; PepBnd; SchPl; River Falls Univ; Vet.

HARTWELL, Lynne A; Wilmington HS; Wilmington, IL; Band; CncrtBnd; HonRl; HospAde; MrchBnd; PepBnd; Yrbk; 4-H; FNA; SpnCl; PpCl; College; Physicians Asst.

HARTWIG, Barbara J; Monroe Sr HS; Browntown, WI; 49/253 ChrhWkr; HonRl; NatlFornLg; 4-H; Trk; Univ; Physical Education.

HARTWIG, David J; Johnson Creek HS; Johnson Creek, WI; 12/55 PresSophCls; PresJrCls; CncrtBnd; HonRl; NatlFornLg; SchPl; SchPpr; Bsbl; Bsktbl; Oshkosh Univ; Broadcasting.

HARTWIG, Randy A; Galena HS; Galena, IL; 43/107 HonRl; LetterBsktbl; LetterTrk; IMSpt; CitAwd; College; Medicine.

HARTWIG, Ruth A; Roseville HS; Roseville, MI; 8/485 Band; TreasCncrtBnd; MrchBnd; NHS; PepBnd; SchMus; CitAwd; Eastern Michigan Univ; Music.

HARTY, Gail J; Lourdes HS; Rochester, MN; College; Veterinary Technician.

HARTY, Mary K; Marillac HS; Northbrook, IL; 46/248 Chrl; Chrs; NHS; SchMus; Sdlty; StuCncl; College St Marys.

HARTZ, Brenton M; Mapleton HS; Mapleton, ND; ALBoysSt; Bsbl; LetterBsktbl; LetterFtbl; Glf; LetterTrk; CchngActv; NCTE; CitAwd; VoiceDemAwd; North Dakota St Univ; Law.

HARTZ, David H; Western Comm HS; Mineral, IL; Band; CncrtBnd; HonRl; MrchBnd; VPNHS; LatCl; Bsktbl; Ftbl; Trk; College; Professional.

HARTZ, Jane A; Perry HS; Perry, IA; Band; Chr; Chrs; ChrhWkr; CncrtBnd; HonRl; MrchBnd; PepBnd; Col; Pro.

HARTZ, Jerry L; Pleasantville Comm HS; Pleasantville, IA; 2/56 TrsFrshCls; ChrhWkr; HonRl; NHS; SchPl; StuCncl; 4-H; FFA; PpCl; Bsbl; LetterFtbl; 4-HAwd; College; Agriculture.

HARTZ, Nancy E; Manlius HS; Sheffield, IL; Chrs; HonRl; NHS; Twrl; RptrYrbk; RptrSchPpr; 4-H; FHA; Moline Public Hosp; Nursing.

HARTZ, Raejean; Benton Community HS; Newhall, IA; Chr; ChrhWkr; HonRl; OffAde; 4-H; FHA; 4-HAwd; College; Business Adm.

HARTZELL, Matthew H; Evanston Township HS; Evanston, IL; HonRl; LetterBsbl; LetterFtbl; Univ Of Soutern Calif; Law.

HARTZLER, Cheryl A; Yates Center HS; Yates Center, KS; 2/57 Band; HonRl; 4-H; FHA; SpnCl; College; Professional.

HARTZOLD, Joseph B; Olympia HS; Danvers, IL; 18/200 HonRl; NHS; StuCncl; VPFFA; Pres4-HAwd; Ill State Univ; Farming.

HARTZOLD, Rodney M; Olympia HS; Danvers, IL; HonRl; 4-H; FFA; FrCl; MthCl; PpCl; SciCl; CaptWrstlng; 4-HAwd; Illinois State University; Agriculture.

HARVATH, Paul; Clio HS; Clio, MI; 11/366 HonRl; JrNHS; NHS; Yrbk; Univ Of Mich Flint; Photography.

HARVEY, Charles M; Liberal HS; Liberal, MO; Band; ChrhWkr; CmntyWkr; SchPl; StuCncl; FFA; SciCl; LetterBsbl; LetterBsktbl; LetterFtbl; Trade School; Drafting.

HARVEY, Cindy K; Yorkwood HS; Kirkwood, IL; Band; CncrtBnd; MrchBnd; PepBnd; TchrAde; Yrbk; FHA; FTA; PpCl; Illinois State University; Special Educ.

HARVEY, David A; Millard Senior HS; Omaha, NE; 34/363 HonRl; LitMag; NHS; Quill&Scroll; RptrYrbk; RptrSchPpr; GerCl; MthCl; College; Astrophysics.

HARVEY, Gregg L; Sault Area HS; Sault Ste Marie, MI; HonRl; PolWkr; Quill&Scroll; ROTC; RptrSchPpr; SptEdSchPpr; 4-H; FBLA; Ftbl; IMSpt; 4-HAwd; College; Stockbroker.

HARVEY, Hal D; Greenwood HS; Springfield, MO; Band; Chrs; CmntyWkr; HonRl; PolWkr; SctActv; RptrSchPpr; PresFrCl; LatCl; SpnCl; LetterBsktbl; Glf; Tennis; Washington University.

HARVEY, Jack L; Virden Comm HS; Virden, IL; Band; Chrs; HonRl; Mdrgl; NHS; SchMus; SchPl; StuCncl; College; Professional.

HARVEY, Janet L; Greenwood HS; Springfield, MO; 4/30 Band; Chr; Chrs; ChrhWkr; CmntyWkr; DrmBgl; HonRl; HospAde; PolWkr; StuCncl; Bsktbl; Chrldr; University.

HARVEY, Julie A; Abraham Lincoln HS; Bloomington, MN; Orch; RptrYrbk; LetterBsktbl; LetterTennis; LetterTrk; IMSpt; College; Professional.

HARVEY, Maureen A; St Francis Acad; Joliet, IL; 4/178 SecFrshCls; Chrs; HonRl; LitMag; NHS; NatlMeritCmnd; StuCncl; RptrYrbk; RptrSchPpr; PresFrCl; Lewis Univ; Biology.

HARVEY, Phillip A; New Haven HS; New Haven, MI; HonRl; JA; NHS; ROTC; SctActv; TchrAde; RptrYrbk; PpCl;.

HARVEY, Randy L; Haworth HS; Kokomo, IN; Band; CncrtBnd; HonRl; JA; MrchBnd; NatlFornLg; PepBnd; PolWkr; SchMus; StuGov; University; Professional.

HARVEY, Richard R; Coloma HS; Coloma, MI; ChrhWkr; HonRl; Bsbl; Ftbl; Mi St Univ; Art Teacher.

HARVEY, Steven D; Thomas More Prep; Hays, KS; ChrhWkr; HonRl; PolWkr; SctActv; RptrSchPpr; KeyCl; LetterTrk; LetterWrstlng; CchngActv; IMSpt; University; Military.

HARVEY, Susan M; East HS; Waterloo, IA; 10/343 Chr; ChrhWkr; HonRl; NHS; SchMus; StuCncl; GerCl; PpCl; Chrldr; DARAwd; PresAwd; College; Music.

HARVEY, Thomas L; Northwestern HS; Lake Negagamon, WI; IntrClCncl; StuCncl; RptrSchPpr; PpCl; Bsbl; CaptBsktbl; Ftbl; Univ; Major Study.

HARVILLA, Ann; Althoff Catholic Hs; Ofallon, IL; 2/319 HonRl; PresNHS; Yrbk; SpnCl; CchngActv; EldAwd; University Of Chicago; Humanities.

HARWOOD, Brian K; Lake Central HS; Dyer, IN; 14/453 HonRl; LetterBsbl; Ftbl; Purdue Univ; Pharmaceutical.

HARWOOD, Charles R; Allegan HS; Allegan, MI; CncrtBnd; HonRl; MrchBnd; PepBnd; SchMus; SctActv; Central Michigan University; Business.

HARWOOD, Gregg S; Pawnee HS; Pawnee, IL; 3/53 Band; ChrhWkr; CncrtBnd; HonRl; JrNHS; MrchBnd; PepBnd; 4-H; SciCl; Bsktbl; LetterFtbl; Trk; Univ Of Illinois; Architect.

HARWOOD, Sandra E; Mc Louth HS; Mc Louth, KS; 1/39 PresSophCls; Band; NHS; SchPl; StuCncl; EdYrBk; PpCl; LetterBsktbl; LetterTrk; Chrldr; Coll;prof.

HARYU, Carol S; Moose Lake HS; Kettle River, MN; HonRl; NHS; SchPl; FHA; PpCl; Business Sch.

HASBACH, Donna L; Palatine HS; Palatine, IL; 31/440 Chr; HonRl; HospAde; Mdrgl; NatlThespSoc; SchMus; SchPl; YthFlsp; Univ Of Illinois.

HASEK, Jeri A; Egan HS; Egan, SD; 4/20 TrsFrshCls; SecSophCls; ALAGirlsSt; HonRl; LbryAde; StuCncl; StuGov; FHA; SpnCl; PpCl; Watertown Bs U; Secretarial.

HASELHORST, Gail M; Mater Dei HS; Trenton, IL; 25/190 VPFrshCls; VPSophCls; Chrs; HonRl; HospAde; NHS; SchMus; SctActv; VPStuCncl; Chrldr; Eastern Ill U; Medical.

HASELHORST, John D; Fatima HS; Westphalia, MO; Chrs; ChrhWkr; TreasFFA; University Of Missouri; Ag Mech.

HASELHUHN, Diane L; Finney HS; Detroit, MI; 15/450 Band; ChrhWkr; CmntyWkr; CncrtBnd; HonRl; MrchBnd; NHS; TchrAde; Teen; Wayne St; Pre Physical Therapy.

HASELHUHN, Lois A; Eddyville HS; Eddyville, IA; Band; Chrs; ChrhWkr; CncrtBnd; MrchBnd; PepBnd; Quill&Scroll; Teen; EdYrBk;.

HASELOW, William; Portage Central HS; Portage, MI; VPSrCls; HonRl; HospAde; SctActv; TchrAde; Bsktbl; Ftbl; Trk; IMSpt; RotaryAwd; Mich St Univ; Pre Med.

HASELRICK, Lori; Paola HS; Paola, KS; 9/130 HonRl; Quill&Scroll; SchPl; StuCncl; TchrAde; RptrYrbk; EdYrBk; RptrSchPpr; Ri Sch Of Design 2 Yrs;artist.

HASELTON, Elizabeth A; Parkway Central HS; Chesterfield, MO; Chr; SctActv; 4-H; PpCl; Chrldr; PresAwd; VoiceDemAwd; College; Veterinarian.

HASENBERG, Daniel M; Glenbrook North HS; Northbrook, IL; 25/610 Band; CncrtBnd; HonRl; MrchBnd; NHS; NatlMeritCmnd; PepBnd; SciCl; Univ Of Illinois; Chemical Engineering.

HASENBERG, David; Queen Of Apostles HS; Madison, WI; 8/60 SecFrshCls; ALBoysSt; SchPl; StuCncl; StuGov; YthFlsp; RptrYrbk; Bsbl; Wrstlng; Univ.

HASENBERG, Pamela L; Ewen Trout Creek HS; Ewen, MI; 1/70 PresSophCls; HonRl; NHS; NatlMeritSchl; NatlMeritSF; StuCncl; LetterTrk; GAA; IMSpt; CitAwd; Clge Of St Scholastica; Physical Therapy.

HASENBERG, Susan M; St Joseph HS; Kenosha, WI; 9/138 SecSrCls; Chrs; ChrhWkr; HonRl; StuCncl; PpCl; Trk; Univ Of Wisconsin; Business.

HASENBERG, Thomas C; St Josephs HS; Kenosha, WI; 1/150 ChrhWkr; HonRl; SctActv; IMSpt; U Of Notre Dame; Engng.

HASENFANG, Mary R; William J Bogan HS; Chicago, IL; 16/756 HonRl; NHS; NatlSciFnd; Treas4-H; SciCl; LetterGAA; NCTE; College; Engineering.

HASENMILLER, Diane; Central Community HS; Grand Mound, IA; 1/166 ALAGirlsSt; Chrs; HonRl; NHS; SptEdYrbk; PpCl; SciCl; Iowa State Univ; Math And Computer Science.

HASH, Daniel E; Olympia HS; Hopedale, IL; VPSrCls; StuCncl; StuGov; Yrbk; SchPpr; LetterBsbl; LetterBsktbl; Northeastern Oklahoma A & M; Pol Science.

HASKAMP, Dennis; Glasgow R Ii HS; Glasgow, MO; PresJrCls; NHS; StuCncl; SptEdSchPpr; 4-H; Bsbl; 4-HAwd;.

HASKELL, Jackie L; Davis Co Comm HS; Bloomfield, IA; HonRl; SctActv; LetterWrstlng; AmLegAwd; College; Biology.

HASKELL, Teri L; Waterford Twsp HS; Union Lake, MI; NHS; OffAde; LetterBsktbl; Trk;.

HASKER, Marjean; Solomon HS; Solomon, KS; Band; HonRl; StuCncl; 4-H; FHA; GerCl; PpCl; Bsbl; Trk; Chrldr;.

HASKETT, Sally D; Eastern Heights HS; Naponee, NE; Chrs; HonRl; SchMus; FHA; PpCl; LetterBsktbl; LetterTrk; Wrstlng; Business School.

HASKINS, David S; East Noble HS; Kendallville, IN; Band; CncrtBnd; HonRl; MrchBnd; PepBnd; SchMus; SchPl; SciCl; Indiana University; Law Enforcement.

HASKINS, Forrest P; Quincy HS; Quincy, IL; 1/650 ChrhWkr; HonRl; NHS; StuCncl; YthFlsp; TreasKeyCl; PresSpnCl; IMSpt; DanFAwd; KiwanAwd; Illinois St Univ; Business Admin.

HASKINS, John R; Battle Creek Central HS; Battle Creek, MI; 1/500 ChrhWkr; LitMag; NHS; LetterTrk; Univ; Eng.

HASKINS, Katherine G; Freeport Sr HS; Freeport, IL; 63/507 HonRl; HospAde; NatlMeritSF; Orch; SchPpr; Univ Of Il; Anthropology.

HASKINS, William; Lincoln East HS; Lincln, NE; Aud/Vis; Chr; Chrs; HonRl; PolWkr; StuCncl; YthFlsp; IMSpt; Univ Of Ne; Sci.

HASLEDALEN, Lee A; St Louis Park HS; St Louis Park, MN; 7/746 ChrhWkr; NHS; Teen; GAA; College; Professional.

HASLER, Michael G; Northwestern HS; Kokomo, IN; 5/180 Band; Chr; DrmMjrt; Mdrgl; NHS; NatlMeritCmnd; SchPl; VPYthFlsp; Yrbk; Tennis; General Motors Institute; Mechanical Engine.

HASLER, Rodney A; Richwoods HS; Peoria, IL; 60/449 PresSrCls; HonRl; HospAde; StuCncl; PpCl; LetterTrk; AmLegAwd; DARAwd; SARAwd; Eastern Illinois Univ; Veterinarian.

HASLINGER, Richard P; Pontiac Catholic Central HS; Pontiac, MI; 18/139 TrsSrCls; HonRl; NHS; NatlMeritSF; PolWkr; StuGov; LetterBsbl; Ftbl; Tennis; CaptWrstlng; IMSpt; KiwanAwd; Central Michigan Univ; Internatl Business.

HASPER, Mark D; South Christian HS; Grand Rapids, MI; RptrSchPpr; SptEdSchPpr; SchPpr; Bsktbl; Ftbl; IMSpt; Davenport Bus Coll; Accountant.

HASS, Denise L; La Salle Peru HS; La Salle, IL; 45/506 Chrs; CmntyWkr; HonRl; NHS; SpnCl; PpCl; Il Valley Comm Coll; Foreign Languages.

HASS, George; River Valley HS; Three Oaks, MI; 9/147 Band; CncrtBnd; HonRl; MrchBnd; SchAde; TchrAde; Bsktbl; Trk; IMSpt; PresAwd; Lake Michigan Coll; Law.

HASS, Melinda K; Central Noble HS; Kendallville, IN; 12/96 TrsFrshCls; NHS; TreasStuCncl; EdSchPpr; Pres4-H; FFA; Chrldr; SecGAA; 4-HAwd; Goshen Coll; Nurse.

HASSEBROOK, Dean R; Lakeview HS; Platte Center, NE; CmntyWkr; SctActv; 4-H; FFA; Platte College; Agri Business.

HASSEL, Kathi J; South Sioux City HS; Dakota City, NE; 26/200 Chr; Chrs; HonRl; HospAde; JA; JrNHS; SchPl; StuCncl; TchrAde; Yrbk; Trade School; Radiology Technician.

HASSELBRING, Robyn A; Sarcoxie HS; Sarcoxie, MO; Chr; HonRl; NHS; SchPl; StuCncl; PresFHA; FTA; PpCl; Chrldr; GAA; Coll; Dental Assistant.

HASSELER, Barbara; East De Pere HS; De Pere, WI; 11/200 HonRl; LitMag; LbryAde; NHS; PolWkr; SchPl; Yrbk; SciCl; IMSpt; CitAwd; Univ Wis Eau Claire; Professional.

HASSEMER, Kathryn M; Bloomer Sr HS; Bloomer, WI; 18/122 Chrs; ChrhWkr; CmntyWkr; DrlTm; DrmMjrt; HonRl; IntrClCncl; JA; MrchBnd; NHS; Bsbl; CaptBsktbl; LetterTrk; GAA; Technical School; Veterinary Tech.

HASSENSTAB, Gary R; St Francis HS; Humphrey, NE; TrsFrshCls; HonRl; NHS; Sacrstn; Bsktbl; Ftbl; Trk; Univ; Law.

HASSIEN, Barbara L; Van Far HS; Vandalia, MO; 6/90 TrsSrCls; ChrhWkr; HonRl; JrNHS; NHS; OffAde; SchPl; FBLA; FHA; FrCl; Northeast Mo State; Accounting.

HASSING, Barbara J; Blue Earth HS; Blue Earth, MN; 36/107 Band; Chr; CmntyWkr; Orch; SchMus; LetterTennis; PresGAA; IMSpt; College Of St Catherines; Elementary Ed.

HASSING, Cheryl G; Mankato East HS; Mankato, MN; Band; DrlTm; NHS; NatlMeritCmnd; Orch; YthFlsp; RptrYrbk; South Dakota State Univ; Pharmacy.

HASSING, Jeffrey C; Kennedy Sr HS; Bloomington, MN; HonRl; SctActv; Ftbl; Trk; College.

HASSLER, Rachel M; St Mary Central HS; Neenah, WI; ChmnDrlTm; HonRl; NatlFornLg; NHS; SchMus; RptrSchPpr; FrCl; PpCl; IMSpt; St Norbert College; Professional.

HASSLINGER, Mark J; Oconomowoc Sr HS; Oconomowoc, WI; 17/212 HonRl; JrNHS; NHS; CaptSwmmng; LetterTennis; Marquette Univ; Medicine.

HASSOUN, Rebecca A; Northrop HS; Ft Wayne, IN; 15/587 Aud/Vis; SecBand; CncrtBnd; HonRl; SecJA; MrchBnd; Orch; PepBnd; SchMus; 4-H; Univ Of Chicago; Medicine.

HASTINGS, Donald F; Charlestown HS; Charkstown, IN; CAP; HonRl; JA; RptrSchPpr; FrCl; SciCl; Univ; Ecology Enviromental Science.

HASTINGS, Jane; Waverly Shell Rock HS; Waverty, IA; 1/193 Band; Chr; HonRl; JrNHS; NHS; NatlMeritCmnd; StuCncl; RptrYrbk; GerCl; Wartburg College; Teacher Math And Chemistr.

HASTINGS, Jeanette S; Pine River HS; Luther, MI; SecFrshCls; OffAde; SecStuCncl; 4-H; PpCl; Bsktbl; Trk; Chrldr; CchngActv; 4-HAwd; College; Professional.

HASTINGS, Jeffery A; Norway Community HS; Norway, IA; Band; ChrhWkr; CmntyWkr; CncrtBnd; MrchBnd; PepBnd; SchPl; YthFlsp; RptrYrbk; LetterTrk; Wartburg College; Business Adm.

HASTINGS, Pamela R; Taylors Falls HS; Shafer, MN; Chrs; HonRl; SchPl; YthFlsp; RptrSchPpr; GerCl; SciCl; College; Journalism.

HASTINGS, Pamela S; St Paul HS; Edwardsville, IL; Chr; ChrhWkr; CmntyWkr; HonRl; OffAde; SchPl; StuCncl; Yrbk; GAA; IMSpt; Southern Il U; Psychologist.

HASTINGS, Paul S; Bishop Mc Namara HS; Kankakee, IL; 25/170 VPFrshCls; HonRl; NHS; StuCncl; TchrAde; SpnCl; CaptFtbl; Trk; Notre Dame; Lawyer.

HASTINGS, Raymond; Savanna HS; Savanna, IL; 41/66 Bsbl; Bsktbl; Ftbl; Trk; Wrstlng;.

HASTINGS, Sue M; York Comm HS; Elmhurst, IL; 12/912 HonRl; JrNHS; NHS; Univ Of Illinois; Nurse.

HASTINGS, Timothy G; Aledo HS; Aledo, IL; 6/101 VPSrCls; ChrhWkr; CmntyWkr; HonRl; RptrSchPpr; SptEdSchPpr; FDA; Bsktbl; Ftbl; LetterTrk; Augustana College; Dentist.

HASTINGS, Vicki S; Jefferson Community HS; Jefferson, IA; Chrs; HonRl; MrchBnd; SchMus; Pres4-H; FrCl; PpCl; LetterChrldr; 4-HAwd; CitAwd; University.

HASTREITER, Karen; Columbus HS; Marshfield, WI; 8/114 HonRl; LbryAde; NHS; SchMus; SchPl; FrCl; University; Medical Technology.

HASTY, Gregory S; Hudson HS; Hudson, IA; 1/65 HonRl; NHS; SpnCl; Bsbl; Ftbl; Wrstlng; Air Force Academy; Air Force.

HATCH, Shelli S; Manhattan HS; Manhattan, KS; HonRl; PpCl; CitAwd;.

HATCH, Susan L; Ash Grove HS; Ash Grove, MO; TrsFrshCls; TrsSophCls; TrsJrCls; TreasBand; CncrtBnd; HonRl; MrchBnd; SchPl; FHA; PpCl; Business School; Vocation Sec.

HATCHEL, Elizabeth; Shortridge HS; Indianapolis, IN; Chr; Chrs; HonRl; SchPl; SctActv; RptrYrbk; FrCl; Bsktbl; Ftbl; IMSpt; Coll; Musi.

HATCHER, April J; Goodland HS; Goodland, KS; SecAFS; DrlTm; SecQuill&Scroll; VPStuCncl; EdYrBk; Pres4-H; PpCl; Bsbl; LetterTrk; Pres4-HAwd; Kansas St Univ; Art.

HATCHER, Denise J; Milan C Ii HS; Milan, MO; 4/50 ChrhWkr; HonRl; NHS; SchPl; RptrSchPpr; FBLA; Ne Mo St Univ; Secretary.

HATCHER, Lisa A; Lincoln Community HS; Mechanicsville, IA; 6/65 Band; Chrs; CncrtBnd; HonRl; Mdrgl; MrchBnd; VPNHS; SecStuCncl; Bsktbl; LetterTrk; Mount Mercy College ; Nursing.

HATCHER, Lisa C; Lake Orion Sr HS; Lake Orion, MI; 35/350 PresJrCls; PresSrCls; HonRl; NHS; StuCncl; RptrYrbk; RptrSchPpr; Harding College.

HATCHER, Michael J; Richmond HS; Richmond, IN; 13/680 CAP; HonRl; JrNHS; SecNHS; PresSpnCl; AmLegAwd; Ind Univ; Intenatl Business.

HATCHER, Roberta J; Holy Angels Acad; Bloomington, MN; CmntyWkr; HonRl; SchMus; SchPl; Clge.

HATFIELD, Brent W; Peoria Hts HS; Peoria Hts, IL; 8/105 HonRl; JrNHS; NHS; NatlThespSoc; SchPl; PresStuCncl; StuGov; GerCl; MthCl; Swmmng; Trk; Univ Of Ill; Economics.

HATFIELD, Jane L; Winfield Sr HS; Winfield, KS; Band; CivCl; 4-H; FHA; Trk; IMSpt; 4-HAwd; JAAwd; College; Pharmacy.

HATFIELD, Jane R; Newton Senior HS; Newton, IA; 5/310 Band; ChrhWkr; HonRl; LitMag; LbryAde; NHS; OffAde; 4-H; 4-HAwd;.

HATFIELD, Jay P; Fairbury HS; Fairbury, NE; Chr; YthFlsp; GerCl; LetterTrk; CchngActv; IMSpt; Fairbury S Comm Coll; Bus Mngmnt.

HATFIELD, Joyce S; Wamego HS; Wamego, KS; 9/98 ChrhWkr; HonRl; SchPl; SecSec4-H; VPVPGerCl; 4-HAwd; Vocation Tech; Floriculture.

HATFIELD, Lisa M; Norfolk Sr HS; Norfolk, NE; ChrhWkr; HonRl; HospAde; JCC; StuGov; TchrAde; SpnCl; Swmmng; College; Business.

HATHAWAY, Diana; Putnam County HS; Granville, IL; Chr; HonRl; OffAde; SchMus; SchPl; FrCl; LatCl; RusCl; SpnCl; VoiceDemAwd; Ill Valley Comm Coll; English.

HATHCOCK, Bryce L; West Plains HS; West Plains, MO; 60/341 PresFrshCls; VPSophCls; PresSrCls; Band; Yrbk; Bsktbl; Ftbl; Trk; IMSpt; ChmbCommrsAwd; U Of Mo; Law.

HATLESTAD, Jay C; Glencoe HS; Glencoe, MN; 3/145 PresFrshCls; PresSophCls; Chr; CmntyWkr; HonRl; NatlSciFnd; StuCncl; SchPpr; SciCl; Tennis; Gustavus Adolphus College; Chemistry.

HATLEVIG, Rita S; Peterson HS; Peterson, MN; ALAGirlsSt; Band; Chr; HonRl; JrNHS; RptrYrbk; EdSchPpr; 4-H; Chrldr; IMSpt; College.

HATLEY, Jack R; Anderson HS; Anderson, IN; HonRl; NHS; RedCrAde; SciCl; Purdue Univ; Astronautical Engineering.

HATLEY, Sherry M; Fenton HS; Fenton, MI; SchPl; RptrSchPpr; SchPpr; 4-H; GerCl; Trk; PPFtbl; College; Law.

HATLING, Colleen A; Comfrey HS; Comfrey, MN; 1/49 Chrs; HonRl; NatlMeritCmnd; SchPl; Sdlty; StuGov; SciCl; Mankato St Univ; Accounting.

HATT, Teresa L; Lincoln Southeast HS; Lincoln, NE; Chr; Chrs; HonRl; NHS; SchAde; TchrAde; U Of Nebraska; Elementary Education.

HATTAN, Debra M; Lowpoint Washburn HS; Washburn, IL; 2/60 AFS; Chrs; CmntyWkr; HonRl; IntrClCncl; SchMus; StuCncl; Yrbk; RptrSchPpr; FHA; Coll; Graphic Designing.

HATTEBERG, Gregory A; Newark Comm HS; Newark, IL; 4/56 VPFrshCls; VPSophCls; ChrhWkr; CmntyWkr; HonRl; IntrClCncl; NHS; SchPl; StuCncl; YthFlsp; 4-H; FFA; Bsbl; LetterBsktbl; LetterSocr;.

HATTEBERG, Jeri J; Fonda Community HS; Fonda, IA; 2/30 ChrhWkr; CncrtBnd; HonRl; JrNHS; NHS; RptrYrbk; Bsbl; Bsktbl; IMSpt; PPFtbl; Clge; Accounting Or Lobbyist.

HATTEN, Cindy L; Oakland HS; Hindsboro, IL; 6/44 TrsJrCls; Chrs; DrlTm; HonRl; NHS; SchMus; Yrbk; FHA; MthCl; GAA; Eastern Il Univ; Lab Tech Or Coaching.

HATTEN, Kimberly V; Central HS; Devilslake, ND; 36/141 ALAGirlsSt; Band; Chrs; CmntyWkr; HonRl; VPSophCls; PolWkr; Twrl; EdYrBk; SchPpr; University; Pharmecy.

HATTEN, Susan M; Lakota HS; Lakota, ND; CmntyWkr; HonRl; OffAde; SctActv; FHA; PpCl; Voc School; Lpn.

HATTER, Valerie J; Ida HS; Petersburg, MI; 19/175 Band; CncrtBnd; HonRl; PepBnd; SchAde; StuCncl; Twrl; SchPpr; PpCl; Chrldr; College; Airline Stewardess.

HATTERVIG, Robin L; Carthage HS; Carthage, SD; ALBoysSt; SchPl; PresStuCncl; LetterBsbl; LetterBsktbl; LetterFtbl; LetterTrk; LetterAmLegAwd; College; Dentistry.

HATZIS, Louis; Crestwood HS; Dearborn Heights, MI; HonRl; NHS; SciCl; CaptTennis; University; Medicine.

HATZIS, Michele M; Joliet Township West HS; Joliet, IL; 55/521 AFS; TreasChr; PresChrs; CmntyWkr; HonRl; Mdrgl; NHS; SchMus; SecStuCncl; GAA; University Of Illinois; Education.

HAUAN, Kenneth; Dassel Cokato HS; Cokato, MN; 23/117 Chr; CncrtBnd; HonRl; Mdrgl; MrchBnd; NHS; PepBnd; SchMus; SchPl; TchrAde; College; Music Teacher.

HAUB, Michelle A; Franklin Center HS; Lee Center, IL; 7/33 Chrs; HonRl; NHS; SchMus; StuCncl; RptrYrbk; RptrSchPpr; FrCl; PpCl; Chrldr; Rockford Memorial Clg; Nursing.

HAUBRICH, John L; Hallock HS; Hallock, MN; VPJrCls; Band; HonRl; PepBnd; SchMus; SchPl; LetterBsktbl;.

HAUCH, Bonnie M; River Valley HS; Sawyer, MI; SecSophCls; VPJrCls; VPSrCls; ChrhWkr; HonRl; NHS; StuCncl; Trk; ChmnChrldr; DARAwd; Secretary.

HAUCH, Martha A; St Joseph HS; St Joseph, MI; 1/330 Band; CncrtBnd; HonRl; LitMag; NHS; NatlThespSoc; PepBnd; SchAde; SchPl; StuCncl; Northwestern U; Medical Dr.

HAUCK, Edmund C; Harper Woods HS; Harper Woods, MI; Ferris State; Heating & Air Conditioning.

HAUCK, Reed W; Lake Preston HS; Lake Preston, SD; Band; CncrtBnd; HonRl; MrchBnd; PepBnd; SchPl; TreasFFA; BttyCrckrAwd; Vocational School.

HAUFEK, David J; Lincoln HS; Thief River Falls, MN; VPFrshCls; VPJrCls; HonRl; StuCncl; GerCl; SciCl; LetterFtbl; LetterSwmmng; CaptTrk; AmLegAwd; Us Military Acad; Officer.

HAUG, Christine; Baileyville HS; Seneca, KS; StuCncl; 4-H; FHA; PpCl; Chrldr; GAA; 4-HAwd; College; Prof.

HAUG, Jane A; B & B HS; Vermillon, KS; 13/39 TrsFrshCls; HonRl; SchPl; RptrYrbk; SptEdSchPpr; MthCl; Cloud Co Comm.

HAUG, Kendal; Hamlin HS; Bryant, SD; 13/73 PresSophCls; Band; HonRl; SchPl; StuCncl; Yrbk; DanFAwd; Sd State Univ; College Of Art.

HAUG, Stephanie J; Brussels Comm HS; Golden Eagle, IL; 6/28 SecSrCls; HonRl; PolWkr; SchMus; SchPl; StuCncl; RptrSchPpr; Chrldr; DanFAwd; Illinois College; Reporter.

HAUGAN, Robert R; St Thomas Academy; St Paul, MN; 45/96 ChrhWkr; CmntyWkr; ROTC; YthFlsp; FBLA; Bsbl; LetterSocr; Tennis; IMSpt; VoiceDemAwd; Univ Denver; Business/pol Sci.

HAUGE, John B; Parshall HS; Parshall, ND; 12/46 TrsFrshCls; SecSophCls; ALBoysSt; HonRl; Yrbk; SptEdSchPpr; PpCl; Bsbl; Ftbl; IMSpt; College.

HAUGE, Pamela J; Emmons Public HS; Emmons, MN; Band; Chrs; HonRl; SchPl; StuCncl; SptEdYrbk; ChmnBsktbl; Trk; ChmnChrldr; PresGAA; College; Pe.

HAUGE, Stacy D; Oregon Sr HS; Madison, WI; 40/200 TrsFrshCls; CncrtBnd; HonRl; MrchBnd; GerCl; SpnCl; Stevens Point College; Engineering.

HAUGEN, Bradley A; Binford Public HS; Binford, ND; PresJrCls; Band; HonRl; StuCncl; LetterBsktbl;.

HAUGEN, David; Edmore Public HS; Edmore, ND; 3/24 CncrtBnd; HonRl; MrchBnd; PepBnd; SchPl; StuCncl; 4-H; Ftbl; Trk; 4-HAwd; Univ.

HAUGEN, Dennis A; New Hampton Comm HS; New Hampton, IA; 9/178 NHS; LetterFtbl; BauchLmbAwd; Ia State; Conservation.

HAUGEN, Douglas D; Centennial HS; Circle Pines, MN; VPSophCls; Band; CncrtBnd; MrchBnd; StuCncl; LetterFtbl; LetterTrk; Univ; Coach.

HAUGEN, Douglas E; Dekalb Sr HS; Dekalb, IL; Chrs; HonRl; JrNHS; StuGov; FrCl; LetterTrk; Univ; Professional.

HAUGEN, Glenn A; Verona Public HS; Verona, ND; 4/17 VPSophCls; ALBoysSt; Chr; SchPl; StuCncl; 4-H; PpCl; CaptBsktbl; Trk; BttyCrckrAwd; N Dakota St Univ; Agriculture.

HAUGEN, Karla R; Oslo HS; Oslo, MN; 1/50 Band; Chrs; ChrhWkr; CncrtBnd; HonRl; MrchBnd; PepBnd; RptrSchPpr;.

HAUGEN, Katherine M; Williston HS; Williston, ND; Band; Chr; CncrtBnd; HonRl; MrchBnd; PepBnd; StuCncl; PpCl; IMSpt; CaptPPFtbl; Mary College; Elementary Ed.

HAUGEN, Kevin J; Hill HS; Lansing, MI; PresSrCls; Chr; Chrs; HonRl; ROTC; SchPl; SciCl; Swmmng; LetterTennis; IMSpt; Lansing Comm Coll; Commercial Pilot.

HAUGEN, Larry D; Rockwell Swaledale HS; Rockwell, IA; ChrhWkr; HonRl; StuCncl; StuGov; College; Natural Resources Mgmt.

HAUGEN, Larry D; Parkview HS; Orfordville, WI; 1/168 ALBoysSt; HonRl; TreasNHS; SpnCl; MthCl; Glf; Univ Of Wisconsin; Accounting.

HAUGEN, Martha B; Strandquist HS; Strandquist, MN; 1/21 TrsSophCls; TrsJrCls; SecTrsSrCls; TreasBand; PresChr; Chrs; ChrhWkr; CncrtBnd; HonRl; MrchBnd; PepBnd; CaptBsktbl; Trk; Chrldr; Lutheran Bible Sch; Teaching.

HAUGEN, Rita M; Altoona HS; Altoona, WI; SecTrsFrshCls; SecTrsSophCls; ChrhWkr; CmntyWkr; NHS; RptrSchPpr; CaptBsktbl; LetterTrk; GAA; IMSpt; Coll; Pro.

HAUGEN, Shirley K; Whitehall Memorial HS; Pigeon Falls, WI; 3/73 VPChrs; ChrhWkr; HonRl; SchPl; TreasStuCncl; SchPpr; VPFHA; PresSpnCl; GAA; DARAwd; Uw La Crosse; Phy Therapy.

HAUGEN, Timothy A; Sturgeon Bay HS; Sturgeon Bay, WI; Chr; HonRl; JrNHS; SchPl; StuCncl; StuGov; LetterBsktbl; Ftbl; LetterTrk; OptClAwd; College.

HAUGEN, Vance J; Oklee Public HS; Oklee, MN; 2/36 Band; Chrs; ChrhWkr; CncrtBnd; HonRl; NatlMeritCmnd; PolWkr; SchPl; StuCncl; SchPpr; CaptBsktbl; CaptFtbl; Trk; Moorhead State College; Farmer.

HAUGENS, Claire E; Toluca HS; Toluca, IL; 6/40 PresJrCls; TrsSrCls; Band; Chrs; HonRl; NHS; SchPl; EdYrBk; GAA; 4-HAwd; Ill Valley Comm Coll; Education.

HAUGH, Terri L; Phillipsburg HS; Phillipsburg, KS; SecTrsFrshCls; Band; Chr; CncrtBnd; DrlTm; HonRl; StuCncl; FHA; PpCl; University; Med Tech.

HAUGLUND, James D; Chokio Alberta HS; Alberta, MN; Band; Chrs; ChrhWkr; SchPl; Bsbl; LetterFtbl; Trade Sch; Carpentry.

HAUGRUD, Kevin J; Pelican Rapids HS; Pelican Rapids, MN; PresSrCls; ChrhWkr; CmntyWkr; HonRl; SchMus; RptrSchPpr; 4-H; Bsktbl; LetterFtbl; 4-HAwd; College; Astronomy.

HAUGRUD, Paulette J; Lake Park HS; Lake Park, MN; 2/41 ChrhWkr; CncrtBnd; HonRl; NHS; PepBnd; SchPl; EdYrBk; 4-H; FHA; 4-HAwd; Moorhead State Clg; Home Economist.

HAUGRUD, Richard L; Pelican Rapids HS; Pelican Rapids, MN; HonRl; 4-H; FFA; Farming.

HAUGSDAL, Craig L; Lake Mills Comm HS; Emmons, MN; PresFrshCls; PresSophCls; PresJrCls; FFA; LetterFtbl; LetterWrstlng; University; Agriculture.

HAUK, Brian; Cassville HS; Cassville, WI; Ftbl; IMSpt; Vocational School.

HAUK, David M; Warsaw HS; Warsaw, IL; VPFrshCls; VPSophCls; AFS; ALBoysSt; HonRl; LetterBsktbl; Trade Sch; Voc.

HAUK, Paul L; Coranna HS; Corunna, MI; 59/209 StuCncl; Michigan Tech University; Pilot.

HAUN, Melinda; St Thomas Public HS; St Thomas, ND; 7/22 SecFrshCls; ALAGirlsSt; Band; Chrs; HonRl; SchPl; GAA; MasAwd; CitAwd; Moorehead St Coll; Childrens Theatre.

HAUNSPERGER, Blair A; Newton Sr HS; Kellogg, IA; HonRl; NHS; Iowa State Univ; Chemistry.

HAUPERT, Diane M; Tri County HS; What Cheer, IA; Band; Chrs; CncrtBnd; HonRl; MrchBnd; PepBnd; SchMus; 4-H; LetterBsbl; LetterBsktbl; Aib Des Moines; Legal Secretary.

HAUPERT, Jane; Hartford Union HS; Hartford, WI; Band; Chr; StuCncl; RptrSchPpr; EdSchPpr; SchPpr; ChmbCommrsAwd; CitAwd; Uw; English.

HAUPERT, Jeanne; Spalding HS; Alton, IA; PresJrCls; Band; CncrtBnd; DrlTm; HonRl; MrchBnd; NatlFornLg; PepBnd; SchPl; MthCl; Clarke College; Mathematics.

HAUPT, Mary J; La Salle Peru HS; Peru, IL; HstFrshCls; HstJrCls; Chrs; HonRl; FrCl; Jr College; Psychology.

HAUSAUER, Dirk P; St Marys Central HS; Bismarck, ND; ROTC; StuCncl; TchrAde; SptEdSchPpr; FDA; SciCl; Bsbl; Ftbl; LetterWrstlng; IMSpt; Clge; Psychiatrist.

HAUSER, Cheryl A; Ann Arbor Pioneer HS; Ann Arbor, MI; HonRl; NatlMeritCmnd; GAA; U Of Mi; Humanities.

HAUSER, James; Washington HS; Germantown, WI; HonRl; NHS; TchrAde; Bsktbl; Ftbl; Tennis; Trk; IMSpt; Unknown; Unknown.

HAUSER, Jeffrey J; Norfolk Catholic HS; Norfolk, NE; VPFrshCls; VPSrCls; ChrhWkr; HonRl; JrNHS; NHS; CaptBsktbl; LetterFtbl; LetterTrk; College; Professnl.

HAUSER, Laureen A; St Marys HS; Sleepy Eye, MN; 1/69 Band; CncrtBnd; HonRl; MrchBnd; PepBnd; SchPl; VP4-H; 4-HAwd; College; Nursing.

HAUSER, Lynn J; Lyons Township HS; Lagrange, IL; PresChr; ChrhWkr; CncrtBnd; HonRl; NatlSciFnd; NHS; NatlMeritCmnd; Orch; SchAde; GerCl; Coll; Music.

HAUSHEER, Jean R; Truman HS; Independence, MO; AFS; Band; CmntyWkr; DrmMjrt; MrchBnd; NatlFornLg; NHS; NatlThespSoc; SchMus; SchPl; EdSchPpr; PpCl; GAA; U M K C; Physician.

HAUSKEN, Monta A; Central HS; Glenwood, MN; 6/145 AFS; Band; CncrtBnd; HonRl; MrchBnd; PepBnd; StuCncl; RptrYrbk; FHA; GerCl; Montana St Univ; Physical Therapy.

HAUTAMAKI, David; Markesan HS; Markesan, WI; Bsktbl; Ftbl; Trk; CchngActv; IMSpt; College; Teaching.

HAUX, Jonathan C; Kindred HS; Kindred, ND; ALBoysSt; Chrs; CncrtBnd; HonRl; NHS; PepBnd; 4-H; FFA; KeyCl; 4-HAwd; Trade School; Agricultural.

HAVALDA, Renee M; Corunna HS; Owosso, MI; 57/210 HonRl; SchPl; TchrAde; RptrYrbk; 4-H; PpCl; CaptBsktbl; GAA; 4-HAwd; Lansing Com Clg; Law.

HAVEL, Debra A; Milligan Public HS; Milligan, NE; HstFrshCls; HstSophCls; SecJrCls; Band; Chrs; CncrtBnd; MrchBnd; PepBnd; SchPl; TchrAde; LetterTrk; 4-HAwd; PresAwd; Kearney State College; Home Economics.

HAVEL, George E; Riverside Brookfield HS; Brookfield, IL; 30/489 HonRl; NHS; SchAde; TchrAde; SchPpr; FBLA; Univ Of Il; Finance.

HAVEL, Nita L; Hillcrest HS; Belleville, KS; 1/16 TrsSrCls; Band; Chrs; DrmMjrt; HonRl; NHS; SecStuCncl; YthFlsp; Trk; Chrldr; Kansas State Univ; Music Education.

HAVELHORST, Mary E; Jenison HS; Jenison, MI; Band; CncrtBnd; HonRl; MrchBnd; StuCncl; LetterBsktbl; GAA; IMSpt; Grand Valley St College; Social Work.

HAVELKA, Dean J; Ithaca HS; Ithaca, MI; PresJrCls; Band; HonRl; MrchBnd; SchMus; PresStuCncl; SptEdYrbk; Yrbk; LetterBsbl; ChmnFtbl; College; Teacher.

HAVELKA, Douglas W; Owensville HS; Owensville, MO; PresFrshCls; PresSophCls; PresJrCls; HonRl; NHS; NatlThespSoc; SchMus; LetterBsktbl; CaptFtbl; CchngActv; Coll; Prof.

HAVEMAN, Daniel; Holland HS; Holland, MI; /317 Band; MrchBnd; NatlMeritSF; Orch; PepBnd; SchMus; SchPl; Tennis; IMSpt; Western Mich U; Teacher.

HAVEMAN, Julie; Weeping Water Public HS; Avoca, NE; ChrhWkr; CmntyWkr; HonRl; OffAde; StuCncl; 4-H; FBLA; FHA; Chrldr; GAA; Bus Sch; Vocation.

HAVEN, Renee M; Swan Valley HS; Saginaw, MI; 50/166 TrsSrCls; ChrhWkr; HospAde; OffAde; TchrAde; 4-H; PpCl; PPFtbl; Ferris St; Med Asst.

HAVENER, Scott; Whiteland Community HS; New Whiteland, IN; 38/183 SctActv; SchPpr; FrCl; Bsbl; IMSpt; Colorado St U.

HAVENS, Julie; Elverado HS; Elkville, IL; HonRl; SchPl; RptrSchPpr; 4-H; FBLA; FHA; FrCl; PpCl; BauchLmbAwd;.

HAVENS, Patrick J; Roncalli HS; Indianapolis, IN; 29/149 HonRl; SchPl; LetterFtbl; LetterWrstlng; Iupui; Acctng.

HAVENS, Roberta J; Yale HS; Yale, MI; 15/137 Band; Chr; Chrl; Chrs; ChrhWkr; CmntyWkr; CncrtBnd; HonRl; MrchBnd; PepBnd; DanFAwd; 4-HAwd; Trade School.

HAVENSTEIN, Rebecca; Huron HS; New Boston, MI; 3/170 Chr; ChrhWkr; StuCncl; FHA; Trk; KiwanAwd; Eastern Michigan Univ; Library Science.

HAVER, John T; Plainfield HS; Plainfield, IN; Band; CncrtBnd; HonRl; JrNHS; MrchBnd; NHS; PepBnd; 4-H; FrCl; In Univ Bloomington; Surgeon.

HAVERKAMP, Dennis J; B & B HS; Seneca, KS; 2/36 PresSophCls; ChrhWkr; HonRl; SchPl; StuCncl; StuGov; FrCl; SciCl; LetterBsktbl; LetterFtbl; Ks State U; Veterinarian.

HAVERKAMP, Rita M; Kearney Catholic HS; Kearney, NE; 7/31 PresSophCls; Chr; HonRl; SchMus; SchPl; EdYrBk; RptrSchPpr; PresPpCl; LetterWrstlng; Chrldr; Kearney St Col ; Bus.

HAVERKAMP, Tim J; Grundy Center Community HS; Holland, IA; 28/83 SecSophCls; HonRl; PresFFA; Bsbl; Bsktbl; PresAwd; Waldorf College; Pre Agriculture.

HAVERLY, Steven A; Corwith Wesley Comm HS; Wesley, IA; TrsFrshCls; Chrs; HonRl; Mdrgl; StuCncl; 4-H; LetterTrk; 4-HAwd; College; Professional.

HAVERTY, Patrick M; St Edward Catholic HS; Elgin, IL; 1/123 HonRl; NHS; FSA; LatCl; MthCl; Augustana College; Veterinary Medicine.

HAVEY, Timothy J; Springfield HS; Springfield, IL; 95/538 Aud/Vis; Chr; Chrs; HonRl; SchMus; SchPl; TchrAde; YthFlsp; Yrbk; Trk; College; Law.

HAVIAR, Peter P; University HS; Munster, IN; Aud/Vis; SchAde; CivCl; College; Engineering Tech.

HAVICE, Ronald P; Niantic Harristown HS; Decatur, IL; 1/40 PresSrCls; Band; HonRl; NHS; SchPl; StuCncl; TreasYthFlsp; RptrYrbk; RptrSchPpr; LetterFtbl; Washington Univ; Engineering.

HAVLIK, Joseph A; Campion Jesuit HS; La Crosse, WI; 10/98 ALBoysSt; ModUN; SchPl; SctActv; StuGov; RptrYrbk; College; Medicine.

HAVLIK, Linda J; Logan HS; La Crosse, WI; HonRl; NHS; Yrbk; FrCl; PpCl; Viterbo Clge; Art.

HAVLIK, Mark J; Denison Comm HS; Denison, IA; ALBoysSt; CncrtBnd; LbryAde; MrchBnd; PepBnd; RptrSchPpr; FBLA; Glf; IMSpt; PresAwd; College; Law.

HAVLIN, Brenda K; North Greene HS; Roodhouse, IL; GAA;.

HAVLIS, John T; Starkweather Public HS; Starkweather, ND; VPSophCls; Band; Chrs; CncrtBnd; HonRl; PepBnd; SchPl; StuCncl; Yrbk; Univ Of Nd; Law.

HAVLOVIC, George; Aquinas HS; Brainard, NE; ChrhWkr; SpnCl; MthCl; LetterBsktbl; LetterFtbl; LetterTrk; IMSpt; College; Accounting.

HAVNOONIAN, Rebecca A; Good Counsel HS; Chicago, IL; HonRl; SchAde; StuCncl; FrCl; PresMthCl; Illinois Wesleyan Univ; Dietician.

HAWBAKER, Jon W; South Adams HS; Geneva, IN; 43/124 Chr; YthFlsp; 4-H; FFA; LetterTrk; 4-HAwd; Air Force; Pilot.

HAWES, Barbara A; Homewood Flossmoor HS; Homewood, IL; 134/950 ChrhWkr; HonRl; YthFlsp; College; Linguist.

HAWES, Gary R; Coon Rapids Sr HS; Coon Rapids, MN; 5/756 ALBoysSt; ChrhWkr; HonRl; JrNHS; NatlFornLg; NHS; NatlMeritCmnd; TchrAde; FrCl; Augustana College; Economics.

HAWES, Jan D; New Holland Middletown HS; New Holland, IL; Chrs; CncrtBnd; HonRl; NHS; PepBnd; EdYrBk; 4-H; Chrldr; AmLegAwd; 4-HAwd; U Of Il; Interior Design Home Ec Or Music.

HAWES, Kirk W; Smith Center HS; Smith Center, KS; PresJrCls; HonRl; SchPl; StuCncl; LetterBsktbl; LetterFtbl; Univ; Aviation.

HAWES, Richard D; North HS; Omaha, NE; 2/440 ALBoysSt; Band; CncrtBnd; HonRl; MrchBnd; NHS; NatlMeritFnl; PepBnd; SctActv; EdSchPpr; GerCl; Univ Of Nebraska; Mech Engineering.

HAWF, Gail L; Allendale HS; Allendale, IL; SecFrshCls; SecSophCls; SecJrCls; SecSrCls; PresBand; SecChrhWkr; HonRl; SchPl; TreasYthFlsp; Yrbk; FHA; PpCl; Chrldr; AmLegAwd; College; Secretary.

HAWK, Lynne E; Yankton Senior HS; Yankton, SD; Chrs; HonRl; LitMag; NHS; SchMus; RptrSchPpr; College; Elementary Edu.

HAWKE, Jim D; Corad City HS; Cocad, NE; Ftbl; Trk; Wrstlng; IMSpt;.

HAWKE, Scott A; Parkview HS; Beloit, WI; 22/157 HonRl; NatlThespSoc; SctActv; SciCl; Coast Guard Academy; Nuclear Physist.

HAWKEN, James M; School Of The Osage HS; Lane Ozark, MO; PresJrCls; PresSrCls; HonRl; StuCncl; StuGov; Bsktbl; CaptFtbl; Trk; IMSpt; AmLegAwd; LionAwd; CitAwd; S Missouri St Univ; Physical Educ.

HAWKEN, Susan; Gull Lake HS; Richland, MI; TrsSrCls; Band; NHS; SchPl; FrCl; SciCl; Swmmng; Management.

HAWKES, James E; Potosi Sr HS; Cadet, MO; Band; HonRl; Wrstlng; Navy; Mechanics.

HAWKINS, Annette M; Civic Memorial HS; Cottage Hills, IL; SecTrsSophCls; VPJrCls; VPSrCls; DrlTm; HonRl; NHS; StuCncl; VPGerCl; TreasPpCl; GAA; Southern U Of Il; Nursing.

HAWKINS, Brenda G; Fairfax R Iii HS; Skidmore, MO; Band; ChrhWkr; CncrtBnd; HospAde; MrchBnd; SchPl; YthFlsp; SptEdYrbk; 4-H; FHA; Bsbl; Bsktbl; Swmmng; Business School; Medical Secretary.

HAWKINS, Carole L; Walker R 4 HS; Walker, MO; 4/12 SecSophCls; SecSrCls; Chrs; HonRl; SchPl; StuCncl; RptrYrbk; SchPpr; 4-H; Bsbl; Bsktbl; Chrldr; Missouri So St College; Dental Hygiene.

HAWKINS, Cynthia A; Sparta HS; Sparta, IL; Band; ChrhWkr; CncrtBnd; MrchBnd; Orch; PepBnd; SchMus; SchPl; LetterBsktbl; LetterTrk; Mac Murray Clge; Speech Therapist.

HAWKINS, Derrick; Brunnerdale HS; Detroit, MI; 3/12 PresFrshCls; PresSophCls; ChrhWkr; HonRl; NHS; SchPl; StuCncl; EdYrBk; FrCl; Socr; Wayne State Univ; Psychology.

HAWKINS, Derrick K; Brunnerdale Seminary; Detroit, MI; PresFrshCls; PresSophCls; HonRl; NHS; Sacrstn; SchPl; StuCncl; RptrSchPpr; FrCl; Socr; Chrldr; St Josephs College; Lawyer.

HAWKINS, Donna D; Marinette Sr HS; Marinette, WI; 47/242 TrsJrCls; PresSrCls; AFS; Band; ChrhWkr; CncrtBnd; HospAde; MrchBnd; NHS; PepBnd; StuCncl; Twrl; Deaconess Sch Of Nursing; Rn.

HAWKINS, Douglas E; Rosedale HS; Carbon, IN; ALBoysSt; Aud/Vis; Band; ChrhWkr; HonRl; SctActv; StuCncl; TchrAde; 4-H; FrCl; LatCl; Bsbl; Bsktbl; Indiana Univ.

HAWKINS, Ellyn M; Queen Of Peace HS; Burbank, IL; 198/485 Chr; HonRl; LbryAde; NHS; OffAde; SchAde; StuCncl; W Illinois Univ; Medical Tech.

HAWKINS, Heidi; Maine Twp East HS; Park Ridge, IL; 50/877 Chr; Chrs; HonRl; LbryAde; NHS; TchrAde; Wheaton College; Elem Education.

HAWKINS, Jeffrey W; Bremen HS; Midlothian, IL; Band; CncrtBnd; HonRl; JrNHS; MrchBnd; NHS; SciCl; Bsbl; LetterGlf; LetterWrstlng; Augustana Clge; Science.

HAWKINS, Kelly J; Vienna HS; Creal Springs, IL; SecTrsFrshCls; ChrhWkr; CmntyWkr; NatlThespSoc; SchPl; TchrAde; 4-H; SpnCl; PpCl; Chrldr; Se Ill Jr College; Physical Ed.

HAWKINS, Kimberley K; Newman HS; Oakland, IL; 1/36 Chrs; ChrhWkr; CmntyWkr; HonRl; LbryAde; ModUN; NHS; OffAde; YthFlsp; 4-H; Bsktbl; GAA; DanFAwd;.

HAWKINS, Linda M; Collinsville HS; Collinsville, IL; HonRl; VPSpnCl; MthCl; Southern Ill Univ; Mathematics.

HAWKINS, Michelle V; Lincoln Sr HS; E St Louis, IL; 11/132 TrsJrCls; PresSrCls; Chr; DrlTm; HonRl; JA; OffAde; SchPl; StuCncl; Twrl; 4-H; PpCl; SciCl; Texas South Univ; Fashion Designing.

HAWKINS, Pamela R; Kenwood HS; Chicago, IL; PresFrshCls; PresSophCls; PresJrCls; NatlMeritCmnd; OffAde; SecStuCncl; TchrAde; Yrbk; College; Child Psychology.

HAWKINS, Peggy A; Glenwood Comm HS; Glenwood, IA; 15/110 ChrhWkr; HonRl; Bsbl; LetterBsktbl; LetterTrk; PPFtbl; AmLegAwd; OptClAwd; CitAwd; Medical Inst Of Minnesota; Veterinarian.

HAWKINS, Phyllis A; Riverside Brookfield HS; La Grange Park, IL; Chr; Chrs; ChrhWkr; HonRl; LitMag; NHS; TchrAde; College; Commercial Art.

HAWKINS, Regina L; Lafayette HS; St Joseph, MO; JA; NHS; College; Teacher.

HAWKINS, Sharon K; Marquette HS; Alton, IL; Chrs; HonRl; JA; 4-H; GAA; IMSpt; Coll; Art.

HAWKINS, Susan C; Willow Run HS; Upsilanti, MI; Chrs; HonRl; NHS; SchMus; SchPl; FrCl; Univ Of Michigan; Nursing.

HAWKINS, Suzanne L; Coldwater HS; Coldwater, MI; Band; CncrtBnd; MrchBnd; PepBnd; SpnCl; PpCl; Michigan State Univ; Veterinary Medicine.

HAWKINS, Teresa L; Northridge HS; Middlebury, IN; ALAGirlsSt; HonRl; YthFlsp; 4-H; FHA; SpnCl; PpCl; Bsktbl; Trk; HstSrCls; Purdue Univ; Psychology Major.

HAWKINS, Terry L; Granite City South HS; Granite City, IL; ALAGirlsSt; CmntyWkr; HonRl; JA; OffAde; Orch; TchrAde; PpCl; GAA; IMSpt; College; Special Education Teacher.

HAWKINSON, Charles L; Sterling Heights HS; Sterling Heights, MI; 25/550 HonRl; NatlMeritSF; StuCncl; LetterBsbl; LetterFtbl; IMSpt; Western Mich Univ; Bus Admin.

HAWKINSON, Steven A; North HS; Sioux City, IA; 76/310 HonRl; LetterGlf; IMSpt; Technical School; Data Processing.

HAWKS, Bradley E; Sidney HS; Sidney, NE; 10/42 HstJrCls; ALBoysSt; Band; Chr; HonRl; NHS; StuCncl; LetterBsktbl; LetterFtbl; LetterTrk;.

HAWKS, Kelly M; Ft Zumwalt HS; St Peters, MO; 1/385 HonRl; PresNHS; NatlMeritSF; PolWkr; SchPl; PresSpnCl; PpCl; College.

HAWLEY, Debra; Alpena Sr HS; Alpena, MI; HospAde; LitMag; YthFnd; RptrSchPpr; FNA; LatCl; SpnCl; PpCl; GAA; PPFtbl; Alpena Community Coll; Spanish.

HAWLEY, James O; Penney HS; Hamilton, MO; 7/74 ALBoysSt; Band; ChrhWkr; CncrtBnd; HonRl; MrchBnd; SchPl; RptrSchPpr; Bsktbl; AmLegAwd; Graceland Coll; Eng.

HAWLEY, Mari Jo; Eaton Rapids HS; Onodaga, MI; 49/162 SecSrCls; Aud/Vis; ChrhWkr; HonRl; 4-H; GAA; 4-HAwd; Ferris St Coll; Library Tech.

HAWLEY, Martin R; Grosse Pointe South HS; Grosse Pointe Farm, MI; 5/580 ChrhWkr; CmntyWkr; HonRl; NHS; YthFlsp; GerCl; MthCl; Bsbl; LetterFtbl; IMSpt; Mi Tech U; Math Bus.

HAWLEY, Mary K; Pius Xi HS; Milwaukee, WI; 19/375 Chrs; NatlMeritSF; SctActv; SchPpr; FTA; Coll; Journalism Communications.

HAWN, Terrie A; Hannibal HS; Hannibal, MO; 25/266 ChrhWkr; HonRl; PpCl; Univ Of Missouri; Law.

HAWRY, Joseph R; Evanston Twp HS; Evanston, IL; HonRl; LetterFtbl; University; History.

HAWRYLUK, Marita C; Queen Of Peace HS; Evergreen Park, IL; 78/416 Chrs; HonRl; PolWkr; Univ Of Illinois; Business.

HAWRYSH, Stephen P; Fridley HS; Burnsville, MN; 39/435 Chr; HonRl; JrNHS; Mdrgl; NHS; Ftbl; College; Business Admin.

HAWS, Matthew J; Dela Salle HS; Minneapolis, MN; 4/127 SecSophCls; SecJrCls; Chrs; JrNHS; NHS; StuCncl; SchPpr; Bsktbl; Ftbl; Trk; Univ Of Notre Dame; Dentist.

HAY, Nancy L; Southeast Polk HS; Mitchellville, IA; 14/214 Chr; HonRl; HospAde; NHS; OffAde; SchMus; SctActv; StuCncl; StuGov; SptEdYrbk; LetterBsktbl; LetterTennis; LetterTrk; PPFtbl; Iowa State Univ; Education.

HAY, Patricia L; Granite City South HS; Granite City, IL; 95/630 Band; ChrhWkr; HonRl; NatlFornLg; SctActv; PpCl; GAA; St Louis U; Physical Therapy.

HAY, Richard C; William Horlick HS; Racine, WI; 31/603 VPFrshCls; PresSophCls; Aud/Vis; HonRl; NatlMeritFnl; SchPl; StuCncl; StuGov; RptrSchPpr; College; Doctor.

HAY, Ronald A; Hazel Pk HS; Hazel Pk, MI; 78/410 HonRl; SctActv; Tennis; Michigan St Univ; State Police.

HAY, Scott D; Milbank HS; Big Stone City, SD; 14/122 VPSrCls; ChrhWkr; HonRl; StuGov; TchrAde; TreasKeyCl; PpCl; LetterFtbl; LetterWrstlng; Us Air Force Academy.

HAY, Timothy G; Bishop Luers HS; Ft Wayne, IN; VPSrCls; HonRl; JA; NHS; PolWkr; SptEdYrbk; KeyCl; LetterTennis; LetterTrk; IMSpt; St Josephs College; Law.

HAY, Wesley R; Ottawa HS; Ottawa, KS; PresJrCls; ALBoysSt; ChrhWkr; HonRl; MrchBnd; SchPl; SctActv; StuCncl; RptrSchPpr; LionAwd; Ks State U;.

HAYASHI, John E; Maplewood Richmond Hts HS; Maplewood, MO; 1/185 PresSophCls; VPSrCls; ALBoysSt; CtyCnl; PresNHS; VPSctActv; StuCncl; EdSchPpr; Bsbl; Bsktbl; Trk; Massachusetts Inst Of Tech; Management.

HAYDEN, Andrea R; Emil G Hirsch HS; Chicago, IL; 29/300 Chr; ChrhWkr; CmntyWkr; HonRl; NatlMeritCmnd; PolWkr; RedCrAde; StuCncl; TchrAde; YthFlsp; RptrSchPpr; SchPpr; GAA; Howard Univ; Law.

HAYDEN, Karen M; Henry Senachwine HS; Putnam, IL; 2/73 VPSophCls; PresJrCls; ALAGirlsSt; NHS; SecPpCl; DARAwd; Ill State Univ; Psychology.

HAYDEN, Kevin P; Wentzville HS; Lake St Louis, MO; 47/211 ChrhWkr; CmntyWkr; HonRl; JA; LbryAde; NHS; SchPl; StuCncl; TchrAde; St Marys College; Medicine.

HAYDEN, Linda; Harvard HS; Harvard, IL; Band; Chr; Chrs; CncrtBnd; HospAde; MrchBnd; PepBnd; SchMus; PpCl; Trk; Business School; Vocation Secretary.

HAYDEN, Melvin B; Mark Twain HS; Center, MO; 1/70 SctActv; DARAwd; Univ Of Missouri; Teaching/geologist.

HAYDEN, Ron E; Casey HS; Casey, IL; 8/100 Chr; HonRl; Mdrgl; NHS; SchMus; SchPl; StuCncl; SpnCl; Bsbl; Ftbl; College; Pro.

HAYENGA, Dawn M; Rochelle Twp HS; Kings, IL; 6/226 Chr; Chrl; Chrs; ChrhWkr; HonRl; HospAde; LbryAde; Mdrgl; MrchBnd; NatlThespSoc; OffAde; GAA; DanFAwd; Kishwaukee College; Medicine.

HAYES, Angela R; Enierson HS; Gary, IN; Band; Chr; CncrtBnd; HonRl; MrchBnd; NHS; Orch; PepBnd; SchMus; StuCncl; College; Professional Singer.

HAYES, Barbara C; Riverside Brookfield HS; Brookfield, IL; HonRl; LitMag; NHS; NatlMeritFnl; SchAde; RptrYrbk; GerCl; Univ Of Illinois.

HAYES, Bridget M; O Gorman HS; Sioux Falls, SD; CmntyWkr; HonRl; TchrAde; LetterBsktbl; LetterTrk; College.

HAYES, Daniel G; Irving Crown HS; Carpentersville, IL; 1/360 ChrhWkr; CtyCnl; HonRl; IntrClCncl; NatlFornLg; NHS; NatlMeritCmnd; StuCncl; StuGov; RptrYrbk; Yrbk; SchPpr; AmLegAwd; Northwestern Univ; Civil Law.

HAYES, Dean E; Hamady HS; Flint, MI; Band; CncrtBnd; HonRl; MrchBnd; NHS; NatlMeritSF; SctActv; Ferris St Coll; Data Processing.

HAYES, Douglas S; Garner Hayfield Community HS; Garner, IA; VPSrCls; ALBoysSt; HonRl; PresNHS; StuCncl; Pres4-H; Ftbl; Trk; Wrstlng; AmLegAwd; Ia State Univ; Agriculture.

HAYES, James H; St Thomas Academy; St Paul, MN; 1/96 HstJrCls; SecSrCls; NatlMeritSF; PolWkr; StuCncl; RptrYrbk; Yrbk; RptrSchPpr; LatCl; LetterFtbl; IMSpt;.

HAYES, James L; Triton HS; Bourbon, IN; Band; Chr; CncrtBnd; HonRl; MrchBnd; NHS; PepBnd; SchMus; SchPl; SciCl;.

HAYES, Jane; Hillsdale HS; Hillsdale, MI; VPSophCls; Band; NHS; Orch; PepBnd; StuGov; FrCl; LetterTrk; GAA; Univ; Speech Therapy.

HAYES, Jean M; Central HS; Duluth, MN; 13/437 Band; Chr; Chrs; CncrtBnd; HonRl; HospAde; MrchBnd; ModUN; NHS; NatlMeritFnl; NatlMeritCmnd; NatlMeritSchl; NatlMeritSF; PepBnd; SchMus; Michigan St Univ; Medical Technology.

HAYES, John J; Marist HS; Oak Lawn, IL; 12/393 HonRl; NHS; Glf; LetterSocr; IMSpt; Univ Of Ill; Business Admn.

HAYES, Joseph A; Brother Rice HS; Chicago, IL; 8/416 Univ Of Notre Dame; Medicine.

HAYES, Louise A; Rochester HS; Springfield, IL; HonRl; NHS; OptClAwd; College; Zoology.

HAYES, Mark A; Palco HS; Palco, KS; Chr; Chrs; HonRl; SchPl; 4-H; FFA; Bsktbl; LetterFtbl; LetterTrk; College; Law Enforce.

HAYES, Mary B; Northwestern HS; Mendon, MO; ALAGirlsSt; Band; Chrs; ChrhWkr; CncrtBnd; HonRl; MrchBnd; NHS; PepBnd; FFA; College; Political Science.

HAYES, Matthew D; Carl Junction HS; Galena, KS; 14/99 VPSrCls; PresAFS; HonRl; NatlFornLg; NHS; VPNatlThespSoc; StuGov; EdSchPpr; PresFrCl; Trk; Univ Of Mo; Med.

HAYES, Michael J; Benton Harbor HS; Benton Harbor, MI; JA; NHS; MthCl; Ftbl; Mi State U; Cpa Business Owner.

HAYES, Michael J; Waldron HS; Shelbyville, IN; HonRl; FrCl; Bsbl; Bsktbl; College; Chemical Engineering.

HAYES, Michael W; Brother Rice HS; Southfield, MI; Chr; ChrhWkr; HonRl; PolWkr; SchMus; RptrSchPpr; IMSpt; College At Mi State; Business.

HAYES, Regina; Lindblom Technical HS; Chicago, IL; Chr; Chrs; ChrhWkr; LitMag; TchrAde; GAA; University; Interior Designer.

HAYES, Roger A; Yates City HS; Yates City, IL; ALBoysSt; SctActv; StuCncl; EdSchPpr; SpnCl; LetterTrk; BttyCrckrAwd; Ranger School; Law Enforcement.

HAYES, Sheryl; Brighton HS; Brighton, MI; HonRl; StuCncl; Bsktbl; Tennis; Chrldr; GAA; PPFtbl; College Or U; Professional And Major Study.

HAYES, Stephanie A; Montini HS; Downers Grove, IL; 33/155 Chrs; HonRl; SchPl; StuCncl; RptrYrbk; RptrSchPpr; EngCl; Trk; GAA; IMSpt; St Marys College; Medical Technology.

HAYES, Stephen K; Draper HS; Draper, SD; 2/9 VPFrshCls; PresSophCls; ChrhWkr; CmntyWkr; HonRl; MrchBnd; PepBnd; SchMus; SchPl; StuCncl; StuGov; Bsbl; Bsktbl; Univ Of South Dakota; Professional.

HAYES, Susan M; Thornton Fract South HS; Lansing, IL; 27/363 HonRl; Yrbk; RptrSchPpr; VPFrCl; PpCl; GAA; College; Language.

HAYES, Terry G; Crandon HS; Crandon, WI; 2/70 HonRl; TchrAde; Trk; Technical Inst.

HAYES, Tonya R; Concordia Lutheran HS; Ft Wayne, IN; 8/220 SecSophCls; Band; Chr; HonRl; JA; NHS; NatlThespSoc; SchMus; SchPl; StuCncl; TchrAde; EdYrBk; Chrldr; GAA; Purdue Univ; Engineering.

HAYES, William P; St Patrick HS; Chicago, IL; Trk; IMSpt; College; Political Sciences.

HAYFORD, Michele A; Melrose Mindoro HS; Melrose, WI; 14/93 SecSophCls; ALAGirlsSt; Band; ChrhWkr; CncrtBnd; MrchBnd; OffAde; PepBnd; Yrbk; SecFHA; Univ Of Wisconsin; Vocation.

HAYHOE, Jill M; Leslie HS; Onondaga, MI; 2/120 TrsFrshCls; SecJrCls; ALAGirlsSt; Band; ChrhWkr; NHS; SctActv; StuCncl; College.

HAYNER, David A; Ottawa HS; Ottawa, IL; ALBoysSt; Aud/Vis; HonRl; SchAde; TchrAde; SciCl; LetterTennis; Univ Of Ill; Computer Engineering.

HAYNES, Christine M; Central Valley HS; Reynolds, ND; 14/24 ChrhWkr; SchPl; TchrAde; RptrYrbk; RptrSchPpr; 4-H; FHA; PpCl; Aakers Bus Sch; Med Sec.

HAYNES, Cynthia K; Yorkville HS; Yorkville, IL; Band; ChrhWkr; CncrtBnd; HonRl; NHS; YthFlsp; FHA; FrCl; MasAwd; Waubonsee Clg; Accountant.

HAYNES, Dorothy A; Kewanee HS; Kewanee, IL; 1/245 Chr; ChrhWkr; HonRl; NatlFornLg; EdYrBk; SecSpnCl; LetterTennis; GAA; IMSpt; VoiceDemAwd; Univ Of Illinois; Engineering.

HAYNES, Jeffrey; Lake Benton Public HS; Lake Benton, MN; PresJrCls; ALBoysSt; Chr; HonRl; NHS; SchAde; SchPl; StuCncl; Ftbl; Glf; College; Electronic Engineer.

HAYNES, Julianne; Highland HS; Highland, IN; 169/538 DrlTm; NatlFornLg; NatlThespSoc; SchPl; TchrAde; Purdue Calumet University; Nursing.

HAYNES, Kim P; Dryden HS; Dryden, MI; 6/56 Band; HonRl; NHS; TchrAde; Bsktbl; Ftbl; Glf; IMSpt; College; Mech Engineer.

HAYNES, Marion L; Troy HS; Troy, MI; 13/540 ChrhWkr; CncrtBnd; HospAde; NHS; NatlMeritCmnd; PolWkr; StuGov; GerCl; Univ; Physicain.

HAYNES, Ricky D; Central HS; St Joseph, MO; 28/515 ChrhWkr; CmntyWkr; HonRl; NHS; Quill&Scroll; SchAde; SchMus; SchPl; SctActv; TchrAde; Missouri Western College; Political Science.

HAYNES, Sarah J; Bennett County HS; Long Valley, SD; SecFrshCls; Band; Chr; Chrs; ChrhWkr; LetterTrk; Chrldr; IMSpt; CAP; ModUN; Cl; Pro.

HAYNES, Timothy J; Notre Dame For Boys HS; Morton Grove, IL; 5/268 HonRl; NHS; NatlMeritCmnd; SctActv; TchrAde; RptrSchPpr; College; Curriculum Ofmathematics.

HAYNIE, Gregory D; Thomas Jefferson HS; Rockford, IL; 3/331 CncrtBnd; HonRl; MrchBnd; SecNHS; SctActv; TreasYthFlsp; TreasLatCl; Bsktbl; Ftbl; Trk; College; Electronics.

HAYOB, Thomas; Marshall HS; Marshall, MO; 6/150 PresSophCls; ALBoysSt; HonRl; StuCncl; SptEdSchPpr; Missouri Valley College; Mathematics.

HAYS, Andrew L; Exira Comm HS; Hamlin, IA; 4/43 PresJrCls; Chrs; HonRl; Mdrgl; NHS; SchMus; SchPl; RptrYrbk; RptrSchPpr; EdSchPpr; FFA; University; Veterinarian.

HAYS, Carol A; Monroe City R 1 HS; Monroe City, MO; ChrhWkr; CmntyWkr; SchAde; StuCncl; YthFlsp; FHA; PpCl; Chrldr; Moberly Jr Coll; English.

HAYS, Charles R; Braymer HS; Braymer, MO; ALBoysSt; Chrs; HonRl; PolWkr; SctActv; FFA; LetterTrk; CitAwd; Central Missour State Univ; Biology.

HAYS, Cynthia S; North County HS; Desloge, MO; HonRl; NHS; SchPl; PresSpnCl; LetterTrk; College; Medicine.

HAYS, Deborah; Eden Prairie HS; Eden Prairie, MN; HonRl; U Of Minn; Medical.

HAYS, Dennis G; Monroe City R 1 HS; Monroe City, MO; 1/93 HonRl; JrNHS; NHS; SecFFA; University Of Missouri; Accounting.

HAYS, Larry; Kirksville HS; Kirksville, MO; CmntyWkr; HonRl; Bsktbl; Trk; IMSpt; PresAwd; Nmsu; Business Management.

HAYS, Steven W; Ritenour HS; Overland, MO; 56/904 HonRl; JrNHS; TreasNHS; SchAde; Teen; LetterBsbl; Bsktbl; IMSpt; College; Business Admin.

HAYS, Susan K; Woodland HS; Streator, IL; 25/89 Chrs; HonRl; StuCncl; RptrSchPpr; EdSchPpr; GAA; Coll; Bus Admin.

HAYSLETT, Steven D; Bloom Township HS; Steger, IL; 118/1018 CncrtBnd; HonRl; NHS; Orch; College; Engineering.

HAYSLETT, Thomas W; Milford Twnshp HS; Milford, IL; VPJrCls; VPSrCls; VPStuCncl; StuGov; SchPpr; Bsbl; CaptBsktbl; IMSpt; Il Univ; Bus Admin.

HAYSLIP, Julie L; Carl Schurz HS; Chicago, IL; 92/750 PresChrs; LbryAde; SchAde; CivCl; FrCl; PpCl; Tennis; GAA; Eastern Ill U; Medical Technologist.

HAYTER, Suzette; Osborn HS; Osborn, MO; 2/12 Band; HonRl; MrchBnd; SchPl; StuCncl; Yrbk; 4-H; PpCl; Chrldr;.

HAYWARD, Sandra M; Mt Pleasant HS; Mt Pleasant, MI; 77/322 Band; HonRl; MrchBnd; Orch; PepBnd; SchMus; Bsktbl; Trk; IMSpt; Central Michigan Univ; Animal Husbandry.

HAYWOOD, Jan; Chicago Vocational HS; Chicago, IL; 29/778 HonRl; NHS; SchPl; TchrAde; Teen; FHA; GAA; Niu; Accountant.

HAYWORTH, Douglas E; Lenox Community HS; Lenox, IA; 9/45 CmntyWkr; HonRl; SchPl; YthFlsp; Bsbl; Bsktbl; Ftbl; Trk; College; Computer Programming.

HAYWORTH, Linda D; Anthon Oto Comm HS; Anthon, IA; 1/33 PresFrshCls; ChrhWkr; HonRl; NHS; SchPl; StuCncl; EdYrBk; PpCl; LetterBsktbl; BttyCrckrAwd; Creighton Univ; Pharmacy.

HAZEL, Bruce A; Whitko HS; Suth Whitley, IN; 10/153 VPSrCls; ALBoysSt; HonRl; NHS; StuCncl; SciCl; LetterBsktbl; Trk; IMSpt; Iupui; Pre Denistry.

HAZEL, Stephanie J; Clinton HS; Clinton, IL; 13/156 ChrhWkr; HospAde; LitMag; NHS; SchMus; SchPl; StuCncl; 4-H; FNA; FrCl; Illinois Wesleyan Univ; Nurse.

HAZELBAKER, Mark C; Mukwenago HS; Mukwenago, WI; 1/212 PresJrCls; ALBoysSt; Aud/Vis; Chrs; ChrhWkr; HonRl; NHS; NatlMeritSF; SchPl; StuCncl; LetterBsbl; CitAwd; Univ Of Wisconsin; Law.

HAZELDEAN, Mary L; Switzerland Co Jr Sr HS; Vevay, IN; Chr; ChrhWkr; DrlTm; TchrAde; 4-H; FHA; SpnCl; PpCl; College; Beautician.

HAZELETT, Jeannine M; Hartford HS; Hartford, MI; 10/83 Band; ChrhWkr; CncrtBnd; HonRl; MrchBnd; NHS; SchPl; StuCncl; PpCl; Lake Michigan College.

HAZELRIGG, Karen K; Warrensburg HS; Decatur, IL; SecSophCls; Band; Chrs; CncrtBnd; MrchBnd; PepBnd; TchrAde; College; Social Science.

HAZELTINE, Julie M; Parkview HS; Orfordville, WI; 16/163 AFS; Band; Chr; HonRl; NHS; StuCncl; Twrl; VPFFA; GAA; IMSpt;.

HAZELWOOD, Bonnie L; Girard HS; Girard, IL; 6/50 Chr; Chrs; ChrhWkr; HonRl; LbryAde; RptrSchPpr; SchPpr; FrCl; College; Teacher.

HAZELWOOD, Kanda S; Brainerd Sr HS; Brainerd, MN; TrsFrshCls; SecSophCls; ChrhWkr; HonRl; NHS; SchAde; StuCncl; StuGov; TchrAde; Swmmng; Trk; GAA; University; Science.

HAZEN, Ronny J; Wichita East HS; Wichita, KS; PresFrshCls; ALBoysSt; HonRl; Quill&Scroll; YthFlsp; RptrYrbk; CaptBsktbl; LetterFtbl; CaptTrk; IMSpt; Wichita State Univ.

HAZLETT, Joyce A; Norton Comm HS; Norton, KS; HonRl; MrchBnd; PepBnd; SchMus; StuCncl; Pres4-H; FFA; TreasFHA; 4-HAwd; College; Veterinarian.

HEACOCK, Bradley D; Lawrence HS; Lawrence, KS; Trk; CaptIMSpt; Kansas U; Geology.

HEACOCK, Timothy; Maple Valley HS; Nashvlle, MI; ChrhWkr; CncrtBnd; HonRl; MrchBnd; PepBnd; SchMus; SchPl; YthFlsp; SchPpr; Bsbl; Univ Of Fl; Electronics.

HEAD, Bobbie; Mead HS; Ashland, NE; Band; ChrhWkr; CncrtBnd; LitMag; MrchBnd; NatlThespSoc; RedCrAde; SchPl; YthFlsp; College; Professional.

HEAD, George; Savanna HS; Savanna, IL; HonRl; SctActv; Bsbl; Glf; IMSpt; College; Professional.

HEAD, James P; Northwest HS; Dittmer, MO; HonRl; Socr; IMSpt; College; Doctorate In Chemistry.

HEAD, Jennifer J; Abingdon HS; Abingdon, IL; 10/105 VPJrCls; Band; HonRl; NHS; StuCncl; PpCl; LetterBsktbl; CaptChrldr; LetterGAA; College.

HEAD, Mary K; Edwardsville Sr HS; Edwardsville, IL; Chr; HonRl; NHS; StuCncl; GerCl; Southern Ill Univ.

HEAD, Melissa G; Gaylord HS; Gaylord, MI; Band; ChrhWkr; HonRl; LbryAde; OffAde; YthFlsp; College; Social Service.

HEAD, Michael; Sullivan HS; Sullivan, MO; 7/160 HonRl; NHS; StuCncl; FTA; Tennis; Trk; RotaryAwd; U Of Miss; Actuarial Science.

HEADLEE, Thomas R; Marysville HS; Marysville, MI; ALBoysSt; Chr; ChrhWkr; HonRl; NHS; SchPl; StuCncl; PpCl; Bsktbl; Ftbl; Maranath Baptist Bible Coll; Bible Major.

HEADLEY, Margaret M; Roncalli HS; Omaha, NE; Chr; Chrs; HonRl; NHS;.

HEADRICK, Terri; Mullinville HS; Mullinville, KS; 2/13 TrsSrCls; Aud/Vis; Chrs; DrmMjrt; YthLg; RptrSchPpr; Sdodge City Comm Coll; Physical Therapy.

HEADY, Karen L; Nauvoo Colusa HS; Nauvoo, IL; Chrs; ChrhWkr; HonRl; LbryAde; NatlThespSoc; TchrAde; YthFlsp; RptrYrbk; Yrbk; SchPpr; FBLA; Graceland College; Psychology.

HEADY, Kathy D; Oakville Senior HS; St Louis, MO; TrsSrCls; AFS; ALAGirlsSt; Aud/Vis; ChrhWkr; HonRl; HospAde; JrNHS; NHS; StuCncl; Nursing School; Registered Nurse.

HEADY, Ralph; Parsons Senior HS; Parsons, KS; Band; CncrtBnd; MrchBnd; NHS; PepBnd; Trk; Wrstlng; Labethe Comm Jr Coll; Mechanical Eng.

HEALD, Edward J; Bennington HS; Bennington, KS; VPSophCls; Chrs; HonRl; SchPl; StuCncl; TchrAde; Yrbk; RptrSchPpr; Ftbl; Trk; College; Chemistry.

HEALEY, David A; Superior Public HS; Hardy, NE; SecTrsFrshCls; VPSophCls; ALBoysSt; Chr; ChrhWkr; HonRl; SchPl; SctActv; StuCncl; YthFlsp; SchPpr; KeyCl; Bsbl; LetterBsktbl; Technical College; Construction.

HEALEY, Deborah E; Adrian Riii HS; Adrian, MO; 24/55 Chr; Chrs; SchPl; StuCncl; FHA; PpCl; Trk; Chrldr; College; Teaching.

HEALEY, Ellen; Ladywood St Agnes HS; Indpls, IN; HospAde; Orch; SchMus; SchPl; Yrbk; SpnCl; GAA; College; Spanish.

HEALTON, William L; Haworth HS; Kokomo, IN;

25/450 HonRl; JA; GerCl; Ftbl; IMSpt; General Motors Inst; Automotive Engineering.

HEALY, Betsy; Lincoln HS; Lincoln, KS; 5/60 Band; CncrtBnd; HonRl; MrchBnd; NatlFornLg; NatlMeritFnl; NatlMeritSF; PolWkr; StuCncl; GerCl; Univ Of Ks; Law.

HEALY, Betsy A; Lincoln HS; Lincoln, KS; Band; CncrtBnd; HonRl; MrchBnd; NatlFornLg; NatlMeritSF; PepBnd; PolWkr; StuCncl; StuGov; Univ; Lawyer.

HEALY, Daniel P; Thomas More HS; Milwaukee, WI; CmntyWkr; Bsktbl; Ftbl; College; Social Worker.

HEALY, Eileen J; Moline HS; Moline, IL; CmntyWkr; HonRl; NHS; 4-H; LatCl; Univ Of Ill; Medicine.

HEALY, Kathy C; Lourdes HS; Chicago, IL; ChrhWkr; HonRl; SchAde; TchrAde; PpCl; Coll; Nurse.

HEALY, Mary; Mother Of Sorrows HS; Chicago, IL; 38/143 HonRl; Bsktbl; CchngActv; GAA; IMSpt; VoiceDemAwd; College; Major Study.

HEALY, Mary A; St Benedicts HS; Chicago, IL; Chr; HonRl; TchrAde; YthFlsp; RptrYrbk; EdSchPpr; Trk; GAA; Loyola U; Ba In Nursing.

HEALY, Ruth A; Hancock HS; Hancock, MN; 5/27 Band; Chr; HonRl; HospAde; TchrAde; 4-H; FNA; FTA; LetterTrk; Willmar Vocational; Nursing Lpn.

HEANEY, Kathleen M; Aukeny HS; Ankeny, IA; Chrs; HonRl; HospAde; NHS; StuCncl; PpCl; LetterTrk; Univ; Doctor.

HEARD, Jonathan S; St Ignatius HS; Chicago, IL; 46/220 HonRl; SchAde; StuGov; SchPpr; Bsbl; Bsktbl; Tennis; CchngActv; IMSpt; University; Medical Schooling.

HEARN, Jacquelyn K; Paris HS; Paris, IL; 9/256 Band; Chr; Chrs; ChrhWkr; CncrtBnd; HonRl; MrchBnd; NHS; PepBnd; SctActv; SecStuCncl; YthFlsp; 4-H; SpnCl; Univ Of Illinois; Medicine.

HEARN, Jeffrey R; Oswego HS; Aurora, IL; JA; RptrSchPpr; Bsbl; IMSpt; U Of Illinois; Computer Programing.

HEARN, Sue A; St John HS; Independence, IA; Chr; Chrs; HonRl; HospAde; NHS; StuCncl; Yrbk; RptrSchPpr; LatCl; PpCl; Allen Memorial Hospital; Registered Nursing.

HEARNE, Richard A; S Siux City HS; S Sioux City, NE; 28/168 HonRl; LitMag; NHS; NatlThespSoc; SchMus; SctActv; Yrbk; SchPpr; Wrstlng; IMSpt; Univ Of Nebr; Architecture.

HEARON, Teresa D; Baxter Spgs HS; Baxter Springs, KS; 5/69 Chrs; ChrhWkr; HonRl; NHS; OffAde; SchMus; TchrAde; FHA; FrCl; Kansas St College; Social Work.

HEASLEY, Diane D; East Kentwood HS; Grand Rapids, MI; 4/390 Chr; ChrhWkr; CncrtBnd; MrchBnd; NHS; NatlMeritSF; SchMus; StuCncl; SecSpnCl; College; Medicine.

HEATH, Andrea L; Morris Comm HS; Morris, IL; 29/250 Chr; HonRl; HospAde; RptrYrbk; 4-H; GerCl; Joliet Jr College; German.

HEATH, Cheryl L; New Palestine HS; New Palestine, IN; Chr; Chrs; HonRl; NatlThespSoc; SchPl; EdSchPpr; Coll; Speech.

HEATH, Chuck V; Lafollette HS; Madison, WI; HonRl; Bsbl; Ftbl; University.

HEATH, Cindi D; Henryville HS; Henryville, IN; VPSophCls; TrsJrCls; PresNHS; SecStuCncl; Treas4-H; PpCl; LetterTrk; Marriage; Clerical Office.

HEATH, Dan C; Siren HS; Siren, WI; 2/42 PresSrCls; Band; CncrtBnd; HonRl; NatlFornLg; PepBnd; Bsktbl; Ftbl; College; Sports Broadcaster.

HEATH, David E; Clave Public HS; Clave, MI; 7/138 CncrtBnd; HonRl; MrchBnd; NHS; PepBnd; HstSophCls; VoiceDemAwd; Clg; Elec Engr.

HEATH, Debbie A; Kimball HS; Kimball, SD; Chrs; DrlTm; HonRl; LbryAde; RptrSchPpr; FHA; PpCl; LetterBsktbl; Chrldr; College; Med Lab Technician.

HEATH, Debby J; Midland Community HS; Monmouth, IA; Chr; Chrs; ChrhWkr; CmntyWkr; HonRl; TchrAde; YthFlsp; Yrbk; FHA; FTA; U Of Northern Ia; Elem Ed.

HEATH, Gregory; La Salle Peru HS; Peru, IL; HonRl; IMSpt; College; Psycology.

HEATH, Helen; Naylor R Ii HS; Doniphan, MO; 10/38 ChrhWkr; CmntyWkr; HonRl; SchPl; YthFlsp; EdYrBk; 4-H; FHA; 4-HAwd; VoiceDemAwd; Central Baptist Coll; Professional.

HEATH, Holly M; Rogers HS; Michigan City, IN; AFS; HonRl; NHS; 4-H; SpnCl; State Owned Univ; Math Or Science.

HEATH, Lori J; Anthon Oto HS; Anthon, IA; 5/31 SecSophCls; Band; Chrs; HonRl; MrchBnd; NHS; SchPl; Yrbk; Briar Cliff.

HEATH, Susan E; King City R I HS; King City, MO; 2/42 Band; CncrtBnd; HonRl; MrchBnd; NHS; PepBnd; SchPl; StuCncl; FHA; PpCl; U Of Mo; Law.

HEATHER, Laura L; Garden City West HS; Garden City, MI; 9/425 ALAGirlsSt; HonRl; NHS; NatlMeritSchl; PpCl; PPFtbl; Univ; Occup Therapy.

HEATLY, Cathy S; Kalkaska HS; Kalkaska, MI; SecJrCls; SecSrCls; Band; ChrhWkr; LbryAde; NHS; PepBnd; SchPl; LetterBsktbl; VoiceDemAwd; College; Music Educations.

HEATON, Carl E; Lawrence Central HS; Indianapolis, IN; 160/770 Band; Chr; DrmMjrt; MrchBnd; NHS; Orch; SchMus; SchPl; 4-H; 4-HAwd; University; Elec Engineer.

HEATON, James; Corning Community HS; Brooks, IA; Chrs; HonRl; Mdrgl; SchMus; SchPl; YthFlsp; Bsbl; Bsktbl; Ftbl; Trk;.

HEATON, Ronald; V I T Jr Sr Hs; Vermont, IL; 5/56 SecSrCls; Band; CncrtBnd; HonRl; MrchBnd; NHS; PepBnd; SctActv; Yrbk; TreasSciCl; College; Engineering.

HEAVEN, Jane E; Lakewood HS; Clarksville, MI; Chrs; ChrhWkr; HonRl; LbryAde; YthFlsp; SpnCl; PpCl; Clge; Occupational Therapist.

HEAVERLO, Linda J; Thomas Jefferson HS; Council Bluffs, IA; ChrhWkr; HonRl; LbryAde; NHS; TchrAde; YthFlsp; Wayne St College; Home Ec.

HEAVIN, Jeffrey K; Seymour HS; Seymour, IN; 50/339 ALBoysSt; Band; CncrtBnd; HonRl; MrchBnd; PpCl; SciCl; Ftbl; Wrstlng; Indiana University; Medicine.

HEAZLIT, Cindy K; Clarkston Senior HS; Clarkston, MI; 42/456 Band; ChrhWkr; CncrtBnd; HonRl; MrchBnd; NHS; PepBnd; SchMus; VPYthFlsp; PPFtbl; College; Chemical Engineering.

HEBDA, Janice L; Silver Creek HS; Silver Creek, NE; 10/29 Band; CncrtBnd; HonRl; PepBnd; SchPl; 4-H; MthCl; SciCl; LetterTrk; 4-HAwd; Univ; Medicine.

HEBEKEUSER, Gerald F; Corunna HS; Corunna, MI; VPSophCls; ChrhWkr; HonRl; StuCncl; 4-H; LetterBsbl; LetterBsktbl; LetterFtbl; LetterTrk; College.

HEBEL, Laurie A; La Salle Peru HS; Peru, IL; 75/506 Chrs; HonRl; NHS; SpnCl; College; Biology.

HEBEL, Patricia; Poynette HS; Poynette, WI; Band; HonRl; JrNHS; NHS; SchPl; YthFlsp; 4-H; BauchLmbAwd; 4-HAwd; Medical Inst Of Minn; Med Lab Technician.

HEBERLEIN, Mark; Campion Jes Hs; La Crosse, WI; 34/80 Band; CncrtBnd; HonRl; PepBnd; SchAde; StuCncl; Bsbl; Bsktbl; Chrldr; 4-HAwd; College; Professional.

HEBERT, Larry; Baraga HS; Baraga, MI; 15/61 Aud/Vis; HonRl; LbryAde; OffAde; SchAde; TchrAde; PpCl; Trk; PresAwd; Trade School.

HEBERT, Marcia F; Saint Clement HS; Centerline, MI; 9/97 SecFrshCls; TrsJrCls; ChrhWkr; HonRl; NHS; SchPl; StuCncl; PresSciCl; Chrldr; OptClAwd; Univ Of Mich; Law.

HEBL, Katherine M; Kennedy HS; Cedar Rapids, IA; Chr; Chrs; SpnCl; University Of Northern Iowa; Mathematics.

HEBLE, Theresa A; Benet Acad; Lisle, IL; 49/230 Band; Chr; ChrhWkr; CncrtBnd; HonRl; NHS; SchPl; StuGov; RptrSchPpr; DARAwd; College & Med School; Doctor.

HEBRINK, Rodney W; Renville Public HS; Renville, MN; 3/53 PresSrCls; Chr; HonRl; PresNHS; NatlMeritCmnd; SchPl; StuCncl; YthFlsp; RptrYrbk; Yrbk; RptrSchPpr; PresFFA; FTA; LetterTrk; Hamline Univ; Law.

HEBRON, Mary; Incarnate Word HS; St Louis, MO; CtyCnl; StuCncl; StuGov; FNA; Socr; Swmmng; PPFtbl; ChmbCommrsAwd; PresAwd; VoiceDemAwd; Col; Rn.

HECHT, Catherine A; Jackson HS; Altenburg, MO; 38/212 Band; CncrtBnd; HonRl; MrchBnd; PepBnd; Quill&Scroll; Yrbk; Semo St Univ; Computer Programming.

HECHT, Charlene K; Hastings Senior HS; Hastings, MN; Band; CncrtBnd; MrchBnd; NatlThespSoc; SchPl; RptrSchPpr; FHA; Trade School.

HECHT, Donna J; Buena Vista HS; Saginaw, MI; 31/259 HonRl; 4-H; PpCl; SciCl; Bsbl; Busi; Sec.

HECHT, Marilyn E; Waseca HS; Waseca, MN; Band; ChrhWkr; CncrtBnd; HonRl; MrchBnd; PepBnd; SchPl; SctActv; StuGov; LetterSwmmng; GAA; College.

HECHT, Mary B; Sacred Heart HS; E Grand Forks, MN; PresFrshCls; Chr; Chrs; SchPl; StuCncl; TchrAde; 4-H; SciCl; Bsktbl; Chrldr; GAA; Business School; Vocation.

HECHT, Sandra K; Buena Vista HS; Saginaw, MI; 7/193 ChrhWkr; HonRl; OffAde; 4-H; PpCl; Business School; Secretary.

HECHTNER, Arlan R; Sac Community HS; Sac City, IA; 6/90 Chr; Chrs; HonRl; NHS; NatlThespSoc; SchMus; YthFlsp; Bsbl; Bsktbl; CaptFtbl; LetterTrk; Univ; Bus Admin.

HECIMOVICH, Diane; Geo Washington HS; Chicago, IL; 19/530 HonRl; JrNHS; NHS; NatlMeritCmnd; OffAde; Calumet College; Economics.

HECK, Bryan W; Senior HS; Shelbyville, IN; PolWkr; TchrAde; Wrstlng; Wyoming Tech; Automotive Industry.

HECK, Catherine A; Ypsilanti HS; Ypsilanti, MI; 17/507 DrmBgl; HonRl; HospAde; NHS; NatlThespSoc; OffAde; SchMus; SchPl; SecStuCncl; SpnCl; PpCl; Michigan State Univ; Social Work.

HECK, Frances E; Big Rapids HS; Big Rapids, MI; PresJrCls; Chr; ChrhWkr; NHS; OffAde; StuCncl; SecYthFlsp; SecFrCl; IMSpt; DARAwd; Grand Rapids Baptist Coll; Secretary.

HECK, Jean C; Cheney HS; Cheney, KS; HonRl; LbryAde; StuCncl; TchrAde; YthFlsp; SpnCl; PpCl; Trk; Cosmotology; Cosmotologist.

HECK, Jeffrey L; Waltonville HS; Bonnie, IL; PresFrshCls; Band; HonRl; SchPl; SptEdYrbk; SptEdSchPpr; LetterBsbl; CaptBsktbl; LetterTrk; Rend Lake College; Accounting.

HECK, Lyndee A; Kadoka Public HS; Kadoka, SD; 4/29 SecSophCls; ALAGirlsSt; SecBand; Chrs; ChrhWkr; EdYrBk; PpCl; CaptBsktbl; Chrldr; VPGAA; Sterling Clge; Bus Management Secretarial.

HECK, Marianne C; Our Lady Of Grace Academy; Indianapolis, IN; Chrs; HonRl; SchMus; SctActv; SpnCl; IMSpt; Ball State Univ; Business.

HECK, Mary E; Riverton HS; Springfield, IL; 7/72 Aud/Vis; Chr; Chrs; HonRl; HospAde; IMSpt; College; Teaching.

HECK, Virginia S; Thomas Jefferson HS; Council Bluffs, IA; 43/465 ChrhWkr; CmntyWkr; PresFrshCls; NHS; Orch; VPFrshCls; Drake U; Fine Arts.

HECKAMAN, Kathy D; Plymouth HS; Plymouth, IN; 8/221 Band; CncrtBnd; HonRl; MrchBnd; NHS; PepBnd; PresYthFlsp; EngCl; VPMthCl; Bsktbl; LetterTennis; SecGAA; Purdue Univ; Math.

HECKE, Brenda K; Spring Hill HS; Spring Hill, KS; Band; Chr; HonRl; PresNHS; NatlThespSoc; StuCncl; RptrYrbk; EdSchPpr; CaptBsktbl; PresGAA; Coll ; Bus Or Acct.

HECKEL, Joseph P; Hill Murray HS; White Bear Lake, MN; ChrhWkr; CmntyWkr; HonRl; Sacrstn; SchMus; SctActv; 4-H; IMSpt; College; Chemistry.

HECKMAN, Janet S; Northwest HS; Cedar Hill, MO; Band; CncrtBnd; MrchBnd; PepBnd; SctActv; PpCl; IMSpt; College; Professional.

HECKMAN, Merle E; Heritage Christian Acad; Clark, MO; 5/218 Chr; Chrl; ChrhWkr; HonRl; NHS; VPMthCl; Tn Temple Co ;ministry.

HECKMAN, Susan; Crete HS; Crete, NE; PresSophCls; Chrs; HonRl; NHS; Quill&Scroll; SchMus; SchPl; StuCncl; EdYrBk; IMSpt; College; Proffessional.

HECTOR, Mary A; Cambria Friesland HS; Friesland, WI; 1/51 TrsJrCls; ALAGirlsSt; Band; Chrs; HonRl; NHS; TchrAde; RptrYrbk; Bsbl; LetterTrk; LetterChrldr; GAA; Northwestern College.

HECTOR, Wayne M; Hudson Senior HS; Hudson, WI; 29/227 Band; CncrtBnd; MrchBnd; PepBnd; SctActv; College; Computer Programer.

HEDBERG, Jackie S; Marquette HS; Marquette, KS; SecFrshCls; SecJrCls; Band; Chr; Chrs; ChrhWkr; CmntyWkr; CncrtBnd; DrlTm; HonRl; MrchBnd; CaptChrldr; Kansas St Univ; Music.

HEDBLOM, Nancy K; Naperville Central HS; Naperville, IL; 229/820 HonRl; LbryAde; PresTeen; SecFFA; College; Animal Science.

HEDDENS, Helen L; Sunset Hill HS; Kansas City, MO; TrsFrshCls; Chrs; HospAde; SchMus; SchPl; SciCl; Bsktbl; College; Architecture.

HEDDINS, Steve A; Joliet East HS; Elwood, IL; Chr; CmntyWkr; HonRl; NHS; SctActv; Univ Of Illinois; Construction.

HEDGCOCK, David R; Clinton Comm HS; Clinton, IL; Band; CncrtBnd; HonRl; MrchBnd; FrCl; Univ Of Illinois; Mathematics.

HEDGE, Mary A; East Prairie HS; East Prairie, MO; Band; Chr; CmntyWkr; CncrtBnd; HonRl; MrchBnd; NHS; StuCncl; FHA; Chrldr; Coll; Pharmacist.

HEDGECORTH, Susan J; North County HS; Desloge, MO; 34/175 ChrhWkr; CmntyWkr; HonRl; NHS; OffAde; TchrAde; FTA; LionAwd; VoiceDemAwd; College.

HEDGES, David L; Mackinaw City HS; Mackinaw City, MI; 5/22 HonRl; PpCl; LetterBsktbl; LetterFtbl; LetterTrk; IMSpt; College.

HEDGES, Joe; Winfield HS; Winfield, KS; PresSrCls; HonRl; StuCncl; RptrSchPpr; Bsktbl; Glf; University.

HEDGES, John H; Gibson Southern HS; Ft Branch, IN; Quill&Scroll; YthFlsp; RptrYrbk; SchPpr; 4-H; PpCl; Bsktbl; CchngActv; Indiana St Univ; Accounting.

HEDGES, Marc S; Bishop Lvers HS; Ft Wayne, IN; 81/247 HonRl; SctActv; SchPpr; FDA; CaptFtbl; Socr; Trk; AFS; St Jsoeph ;acct.

HEDGLEY, Crystal A; Proviso East HS; Haywood, IL; 25/1000 Band; CncrtBnd; HonRl; HospAde; MrchBnd; NHS; NatlMeritCmnd; Orch; PepBnd; YthFlsp; Elmhurst Clge; Doctorate.

HEDICKE, Kenneth C; St Charles HS; St Charles, MO; 15/600 Band; ChrhWkr; CncrtBnd; HonRl; MrchBnd; NHS; LetterBsktbl; LetterFtbl; LetterTrk; College; Mathematics.

HEDIN, Judi L; Willowbrook HS; Lombard, IL; 12/823 HonRl; HospAde; IntrClCncl; JA; NHS; NatlMeritCmnd; PolWkr; Quill&Scroll; 4-H; VPFTA; 4-HAwd; Drake Univ; Journalism.

HEDIN, Nancy J; Sparta HS; Sparta, IL; 1/170 Chr; Chrs; ChrhWkr; HonRl; HospAde; NHS; SchMus; StuCncl; Yrbk; FTA; Univ Of Illinois; Accounting.

HEDIN, Sally L; Waterford Mott HS; Pontiac, MI; HonRl; LbryAde; SchPl; FrCl; Univ; Biology.

HEDINGER, Keith G; Jasper HS; Jasper, IN; 16/294 PresSophCls; HonRl; VPStuCncl; LetterFtbl; LetterTrk; OptClAwd; University; Professional.

HEDLER, Sally; Thorp HS; Thorp, WI; CncrtBnd; DrmMjrt; HonRl; Mdrgl; MrchBnd; NHS; StuCncl;.

HEDLEY, Ronald K; Salem Sr HS; Salem, MO; HonRl; SchPl; TchrAde; RptrSchPpr; SchPpr; LetterTrk; Se Missouri State Univ; Art.

HEDLUND, David J; St Louis Park HS; St Louis Park, MN; Band; HonRl; Trk; College; Oceanography, Photography.

HEDLUND, Debra L; St Cecilia HS; Hastings, NE; College; Music.

HEDLUND, Holly B; Roseau HS; Roseau, MN; TrsFrshCls; PresSophCls; VPJrCls; Chrs; HonRl; LbryAde; SchAde; StuCncl; TchrAde; SchPpr; Trk; Chrldr; GAA; College; Physical Ed.

HEDLUND, Keith A; Roseau HS; Roseau, MN; 7/128 VPSophCls; HonRl; TchrAde; Ftbl; Glf; Coll; Lawyer.

HEDLUND, Robert E; Medford HS; Medford, WI; ChrhWkr; HonRl; PolWkr; YthFlsp; Tennis; Clg; Business.

HEDMAN, Calvin D; Scranton Public HS; Scranton, ND; 1/28 PresJrCls; ALBoysSt; SecFrshCls; NHS; StuCncl; RptrYrbk; FBLA; GerCl; AmLegAwd; University Of N Dakota; Accounting.

HEDMAN, Glenn E; Gordon Technical HS; Chicago, IL; 45/591 HonRl; NHS; SchPpr; VPMthCl; College.

HEDMAN, Susan; John Edwards HS; Port Edwards, WI; 1/68 PresFrshCls; Band; Chrs; ModUN; NatlFornLg; TchrAde; EdYrBk; EdSchPpr; EldAwd; NCTE; Ripon Col; Law.

HEDMARK, Eric R; Lyons Twp HS; La Grange, IL; HonRl; JrNHS; NHS; YthFlsp; LetterFtbl; LetterTrk; IMSpt; Augustana College; Medicine.

HEDRICH, Susan P; Princeton HS; Princeton, IL; SecFrshCls; AFS; HonRl; MrchBnd; SchPl; GerCl; PpCl; Bradley Univ; Chemistry.

HEDRICK, David E; Brookfield HS; Brookfield, MO; Chr; HonRl; PpCl; LetterBsktbl; LetterFtbl; LetterTrk; IMSpt; College.

HEDRICK, Helen K; Hesston HS; Newton, KS; 6/55 Band; Chr; HonRl; TchrAde; YthFlsp; RptrYrbk; RptrSchPpr; Pres4-H; FHA; 4-HAwd; College; Psychology.

HEDRICK, Tena M; Delavan HS; Pekin, IL; 14/76 ChrhWkr; HonRl; TchrAde; RptrSchPpr; Icc; Accountant.

HEDTKE, Connie J; Grove City HS; Grove City, MN; SchPl; Yrbk; LetterBsktbl; Trk; GAA; College; Secretary.

HEDTKE, Debra L; Waconia HS; New Germany, MN; Chr; HonRl; FHA; Mankato State College; Accounting.

HEEG, Marie D; Perry HS; Perry, MI; 13/135 SecTrsSrCls; HonRl; VPNHS; SctActv; TchrAde; Twrl; RptrYrbk; 4-H; PpCl; Chrldr; Winona State U; Phy Therapist.

HEEG, Randal J; Dixon HS; Dixon, IL; HonRl; NHS; NatlMeritCmnd; SptEdSchPpr; Bsktbl; LetterGlf; LetterTennis; Western Illinois Univ; Business.

HEEGER, Pamela J; Union HS; Union, MO; ALAGirlsSt; Band; CncrtBnd; HonRl; JA; MrchBnd; NatlFornLg; NHS; OffAde; Twrl; LetterBsktbl; PPFtbl; JAAwd; College; Secretary.

HEEHN, Kenneth C; Morgan Park HS; Duluth, MN; AFS; Chr; ChrhWkr; ModUN; SptEdYrbk; Clg Of St Scholastica; Medcine.

HEEKE, Verlyn C; Jasper HS; Jasper, IN; 2/286 ALBoysSt; CtyCnl; HonRl; NHS; PresStuCncl; StuGov; LetterTennis; DanFAwd; DARAwd; Notre Dame Univ; Engineering.

HEELAN, Robin J; Downers Grove North HS; Downers Grove, IL; 10/524 HonRl; NatlMeritCmnd; PolWkr; N Ill Univ; Medicine.

HEENAN, Colleen; Pontiac Township HS; Pontiac, IL; 20/185 ChrhWkr; HonRl; NHS; Quill&Scroll; TchrAde; SptEdYrbk; PpCl; SciCl; Chrldr; GAA; Parkland Jr College; Data Processing.

HEENAN, John; Joliet Catholic HS; Joliet, IL; ChrhWkr; HonRl; GerCl; PpCl; CchngActv; IMSpt; Univ; Business.

HEEPKE, Beth E; Edwardsville HS; Edwardsville, IL; 10/460 Chr; Chrs; HonRl; NHS; StuCncl; YthFlsp; VP4-H; GerCl; GAA; 4-HAwd; College; Surgical Nursing.

HEER, Ann M; Doland HS; Doland, SD; PresFrshCls; TrsJrCls; Band; Chrs; HonRl; SchMus; SchPl; Yrbk; SchPpr; FrCl; Coll; Law.

HEERDT, Brian L; Bolingbrook HS; Bolingbrook, IL; Band; Chr; CncrtBnd; HonRl; MrchBnd; NHS; StuGov; College; Music.

HEEREN, Dennis R; West Sioux Comm HS; Hawarden, IA; Chrs; PolWkr; TchrAde; FTA; LetterBsbl; LetterFtbl; LetterTrk; LetterWrstlng; Iowa State University; Landscape Design.

HEERINGA, Benita; Central Wis Christian HS; Fox Lake, WI; 1/24 Chr; HonRl; JrNHS; NHS; OffAde; SchPl; TchrAde; 4-H; PpCl; Chrldr; Dordt College; Special Education.

HEERMAN, William; Ahs West HS; Appleton, WI; 34/640 CncrtBnd; LitMag; MrchBnd; NHS; SchPpr;.

HEERMANN, Marlene F; Sweet Springs R 7 HS; Sweet Springs, MO; 11/63 Band; Chrs; ChrhWkr; CmntyWkr; HonRl; HospAde; MrchBnd; Twrl; FHA; SecTrsSophCls; College.

HEESE, Candy R; North Bend Central HS; Dodge, NE; 37/69 LbryAde; RptrSchPpr; Sec4-H; TreasFBLA; FHA; SpnCl; Beauty College; Veterinary Study.

HEFEL, Gerard S; Leo HS; Holy Cross, IA; Chr; Chrs; ChrhWkr; SchMus; SchPl; TchrAde; TreasLatCl; Yrbk; IMSpt; Trade School; Professional.

HEFFELMIRE, Daniel L; Portland HS; Bryant, IN; 37/189 Chr; Chrs; ChrhWkr; CmntyWkr; NHS; SchPl; StuCncl; TchrAde; PresYthFlsp; PresFFA; SpnCl; PpCl; EldAwd; Purdue Univ; Computer Science.

HEFFERNAN, Steven T; Doland HS; Doland, SD; HonRl; SchPl; FFA; Bsktbl; Black Hills Area Vo Tech; Auto Mechanic.

HEFFERNAN, William P; St Viator HS; Arlington Hts, IL; 60/250 ChrhWkr; HonRl; PolWkr; Teen; Bsktbl; College; Accounting.

HEFLEY, Joy G; Baxten HS; Baxter Springs, KS; Band; CncrtBnd; HonRl; MrchBnd; NatlFornLg; NHS; NatlThespSoc; PepBnd; YthFlsp; 4-H; MthCl; College; Journalism.

HEFNER, Roma C; Seymour Community HS; Seymour, IA; SecFrshCls; VPJrCls; HonRl; PresNHS; StuCncl; SchPpr; SecFFA; SecPpCl; LetterTrk; College; Agriculture.

HEFTWER, Peter N; Sacred Heart HS; E Grand Forks, MN; 2/40 Chr; HonRl; StuCncl; Yrbk; SchPpr; College; Professional.

HEFTY, Becky K; Lu Verne Comm HS; Lu Verne, IA; TrsSrCls; Band; Chrs; HonRl; PepBnd; SchPl; Yrbk; Bsktbl; AmLegAwd; DanFAwd; Ia State U; Industrial Eng.

HEFTY, Becky K; La Verne Community HS; Lu Verne, IA; TrsJrCls; TrsSrCls; Chr; ChrhWkr; HonRl; SchPl; Yrbk; CaptBsktbl; Trk; AmLegAwd; Ia State U; Industrial Engineering.

HEFTY, Glenda K; Lu Verne Comm HS; Lu Verne, IA; PresSrCls; Band; Chr; Chrs; MrchBnd; SchAde; StuCncl; TchrAde; Fort Dodge College.

HEGEDUS, Maria B; George Rogers Clark HS; Whiting, IN; 27/260 Chr; HonRl; JrNHS; NHS; SchAde; SchMus; SchPl; TchrAde; GerCl; PpCl; Butler Univ; Dance.

HEGEMAN, Elizabeth A; Savannah Riii HS; Cosby, MO; Band; Chr; Chrs; CmntyWkr; HonRl; MrchBnd; NHS; PepBnd; SchMus; StuCncl; College; Music.

HEGENBARTH, Mary A; West Bloomfield HS; Orchard Lake, MI; 4/400 HonRl; NHS; NatlMeritCmnd; Univ Of Michigan; Medicine.

HEGER, Mark A; Mona Shores HS; Norton Shores, MI; HonRl; RptrYrbk; LetterFtbl; LetterTrk; Univ Of Michigan; Architecture.

HEGER, Mary M; Fulda HS; Fulda, MN; 6/80 LbryAde; MrchBnd; NHS; SchPl; StuCncl; RptrYrbk; 4-H; FHA; GAA; 4-HAwd; Collge Of St Catherine; Nursing.

HEGG, Kathleen L; Covington Comm HS; Covington, IN; Band; CncrtBnd; MrchBnd; PepBnd; SchPl; TchrAde; FTA; LatCl; GAA; Indiana State Univ; Teaching.

HEGG, Teresa L; Rocky HS; Rock Island, IL; Chrs; ChrhWkr; CmntyWkr; HonRl; NHS; SchPl; Teen; Swmmng; Tennis; PPFtbl; College.

HEGGE, Dawn R; Oklee Public HS; Goodridge, MN; Chrs; ChrhWkr; HonRl; SchPl; SctActv; 4-H; FHA; 4-HAwd;.

HEGGELMAN, Monique A; Mound Westonka HS; Mound, MN; Chr; HonRl; HospAde; RptrSchPpr; GerCl; SpnCl; College; Professional.

HEGI, Denise; Monett HS; Monett, MO; 2/123 Chrs; ChrhWkr; CmntyWkr; NHS; NatlMeritCmnd; FBLA; FTA; Chrldr; BttyCrckrAwd; DARAwd; Univ Mo Columbia; Industrial Eng.

HEGNA, Constance M; Granite Falls HS; Granite Falls, MN; 2/108 ALAGirlsSt; HonRl; NHS; NatlMeritFnl; NatlMeritSF; SptEdSchPpr; TreasFHA; GerCl; PpCl; BttyCrckrAwd; U Of Mn.

HEGSTAD, Pamela G; Powers Lake HS; Powers Lake, ND; 5/26 Band; HonRl; RptrYrbk; RptrSchPpr; SchPpr; 4-H; FFA; PpCl; LetterBsktbl; LetterTrk; Clge; Prof.

HEIBERGER, Cheryl M; Montrose HS; Montrose, SD; VPFrshCls; Band; DrmMjrt; HonRl; SchPl; RptrYrbk; RptrSchPpr; PpCl; LetterTrk; CaptChrldr; Mc Kennan Hospital; Radiologic Tech.

HEIBERGER, Mary K; Montini HS; Elmhurst, IL; 12/154 HonRl; NHS; StuCncl; College; Occupational Therapy.

HEICHELBECH, Terrie L; John Marshall HS; Indianapolis, IN; 4/444 NHS; Quill&Scroll; EdSchPpr; Butler University; Journalism.

HEID, Debra A; New Salem HS; New Salem, ND; 11/35 TrsJrCls; ALAGirlsSt; Band; Chr; SchPl; YthFlsp; EdYrBk; Trk; Chrldr; 4-HAwd; College; Vocational.

HEID, Jeffrey A; New Salem HS; New Salem, ND; 2/35 ALBoysSt; Band; CncrtBnd; HonRl; MrchBnd; YthFlsp; College; Accounting.

HEID, Jeri L; New Salem HS; New Salem, ND; 1/50 Band; Chr; Chrs; HonRl; NatlMeritSchl; SchPl; Yrbk; SchPpr; Bsktbl; 4-HAwd;.

HEID, Jill M; Harlem HS; Rockford, IL; StuGov; RptrYrbk; 4-H; FFA; FTA; GAA; JAAwd; College; Professional.

HEIDBREDER, Jeanie L; Hillsboro HS; Hillsboro, MO; HonRl; JrNHS; NHS; SpnCl;.

HEIDBRINK, Kristina; Union HS; Beaufort, MO; 17/168 ALAGirlsSt; HonRl; MrchBnd; SchMus; TchrAde; PPFtbl; DanFAwd; East Central Jr College; Elementary Educati.

HEIDBRINK, Kristina L; Union HS; Beaufort, MO; 18/168 ALAGirlsSt; Band; JA; MrchBnd; SchPl; TchrAde; 4-H; SpnCl; PPFtbl; East Central Jr College; Elementary Educ.

HEIDE, Kyle P; Minot HS; Minot, ND; Band; HonRl; MrchBnd; Orch; SchMus; SchPl; College; Music.

HEIDEMANN, Scott A; Clearwater R 1 HS; Patterson, MO; 4/89 HonRl; SciCl; College; Lawyer.

HEIDEN, Dana C; Greenfield Central HS; Greenfield, IN; 35/278 CncrtBnd; MrchBnd; NHS; GerCl; Ball State Univ; Education.

HEIDEN, David C; Marshalltown HS; Marshalltown, IA; ALBoysSt; Band; CncrtBnd; HonRl; MrchBnd; NatlFornLg; PepBnd; SchMus; SchPl; SctActv; StuCncl; StuGov; Ftbl; Trk; Iowa State Univ; Biochemistry.

HEIDEN, Gary L; Joliet East HS; Joliet, IL; 39/407 HonRl; NHS; Quill&Scroll; RptrSchPpr; SptEdSchPpr; LetterTrk; St Louis Clg Of Pharmacy; Pharmacist.

HEIDEN, Glen E; Maine West HS; Des Plaines, IL; 25/750 HonRl; NHS; Ftbl; Augustana College; Accounting.

HEIDEN, Jeff W; Marshalltown HS; Marshalltown, IA; ALBoysSt; HonRl; SctActv; RptrSchPpr; Bsktbl; Ftbl; Trk; IMSpt; College Iowa State; Us Air Force Pilot.

HEIDENREICH, David R; Port Huron Northern HS; Port Huron, MI; 90/437 HonRl; TchrAde; Coll; Pre Law.

HEIDENREICH, Diana C; Harlem HS; Loves Park, IL; Chr; HonRl; SchMus; PPFtbl; Univ; Special Education.

HEIDENREICH, James; Brebeuf Prep; Noblesville, IN; SecTrsJrCls; StuCncl; TchrAde; IMSpt; PPFtbl;.

HEIDENREICH, Jean L; Badger HS; Genoa City, WI; Band; HonRl; PepBnd; RptrYrbk; SchPpr; PpCl; Bsbl; LetterBsktbl; LetterTrk; LetterChrldr; College; Professional.

HEIDENREICH, Marcia A; Rich Central HS; Olympia Fields, IL; 12/400 HonRl; JrNHS; NHS; TchrAde; RusCl; Univ Of Nebraska; Health.

HEIDENREICH, Sue A; Northwestern HS; Mansfield, SD; 12/35 Band; Chr; Chrs; HonRl; LbryAde; PepBnd; RptrYrbk; Yrbk; 4-H; PpCl; Coll; Elem Educ.

HEIDER, Barbara A; Humboldt Sr HS; Humboldt, IA; 6/140 ChrhWkr; CmntyWkr; HonRl; NHS; SchPl; PpCl; Bsktbl; Glf; Des Moines Area Comm College; Secretary.

HEIDFELD, Ann L; Carl Brablec HS; Roseville, MI; ChrhWkr; CncrtBnd; HonRl; JrNHS; MrchBnd; NHS; PepBnd; SchAde; FrCl; SpnCl; Mi State U; German Consul To Immigrants.

HEIDORN, Sharon; Dakota HS; Arthur, ND; 6/26 ChrhWkr; CtyCnl; CmntyWkr; HonRl; HospAde; JCC; OffAde; PolWkr; SchPl; StuGov; PpCl; GAA; College.

HEIDRICK, Greg D; Girard Rural HS; Girard, KS; HonRl; NHS; NatlMeritSchl; SchPl; SpnCl; MthCl; LetterBsktbl; LetterFtbl; LetterTrk; PPFtbl; College; Professionl.

HEIER, Gary L; Ipswich HS; Ispwich, SD; 3/50 VPFrshCls; PresSophCls; VPSrCls; Chrs; HonRl; NHS; SchMus; SchPl;.

HEIER, Linda K; Wheatland HS; Park, KS; 5/37 TrsSrCls; Chrs; HonRl; Goodland Vo Tech; Data Processing.

HEIFETZ, Melanie L; Proviso West HS; Westchester, IL; HonRl; HospAde; NHS; Teen; Univ Of Illinois; Languages.

HEIGHWAY, Douglas E; Northeastern HS; Richmond, IN; 1/152 PresJrCls; ALBoysSt; Band; PresChr; NHS; SchPl; VPStuCncl; PresYthFlsp; SciCl; Trk; Col; Music.

HEIKENS, Janet C; Wellsburg HS; Wellsburg, IA; Band; Chr; Chrs; ChrhWkr; CncrtBnd; HonRl; Mdrgl; MrchBnd; PepBnd; Chrldr; DanFAwd; Iowa Central Comm College; Fashion Mdse.

HEIKKA, Cheryl L; Calumet HS; Laurium, MI; HonRl; LbryAde; NHS; TchrAde; PpCl; College; Actuarial Science.

HEIKKILA, Ruth A; J F Kennedy HS; Babbitt, MN; 2/140 ALAGirlsSt; HonRl; NHS; SchMus; TchrAde; Yrbk; Trk; Chrldr; CchngActv; GAA; Coll Of St Scholastica; Medical Rec Adminis.

HEIKKINEN, Gail; Wyoming Park HS; Wyoming, MI; HonRl; StuCncl; RptrYrbk; Coll; Journ.

HEIL, Debbie; Hardin Central HS; Hardin, MO; Band; ChrhWkr; CncrtBnd; DrmMjrt; HonRl; MrchBnd; PepBnd; FHA; Chrldr; OptClAwd;.

HEIL, Janice V; Ritenour Senior HS; Sycamore Hills, MO; 104/873 NHS; Orch; SchMus; PpCl; Bsktbl; Chrldr; IMSpt; Univ Of Missouri; Physical Educ.

HEILBRUNN, Robin B; Homewood Flossmoor HS; Glenwood, IL; 63/936 ChrhWkr; CmntyWkr; HonRl; NHS; SctActv; Teen; FrCl; University; Anthropology.

HEILER, Jeffrey; Jackson HS; Jackson, MI; Aud/Vis; CmntyWkr; HonRl; SchMus; SchPl; StuCncl; StuGov; EdSchPpr; SchPpr; Jackson Community College; Professional.

HEILIG, Scott A; Chicago Lakes Sr HS; Lindstrom, MN; HonRl; FFA; LetterWrstlng;.

HEILMAN, Marilyn; Rugby HS; Rugby, ND; 2/130 ALAGirlsSt; Chr; DrlTm; HonRl; NHS; StuCncl; RptrYrbk; PpCl; IMSpt; Univ; Professional.

HEILMAN, Warren; Eureka HS; Eureka, SD; 3/57 VPSophCls; SecJrCls; ALBoysSt; Chr; Chrs; HonRl; Mdrgl; CitAwd; Sd St Univ; Engrg Physics.

HEILWAGEN, Mary Jo; Scecina Memorial HS; Indianapolis, IN; 3/200 HonRl; IMSpt; Indiana Univ; Med Tech.

HEIM, Barbara L; Immaculata HS; Leavenworth, KS; TrsFrshCls; Chrs; HonRl; SctActv; 4-H; PpCl; Bsktbl; CaptTrk; GAA; IMSpt; Kansas University; Occupational Therapist.

HEIM, Kimberly; Dawson Verdon Cons HS; Dawson, NE; Chrl; Chrs; DrmMjrt; MrchBnd; SchPl; 4-H; PpCl; Bsktbl; Trk; Univ Of Nebr; Airline Stewardess.

HEIM, Maria T; Galena HS; Galena, IL; 9/105 HonRl; LbryAde; OffAde; SchAde; SchPl; StuCncl; StuGov; RptrSchPpr; Trk; PresAwd; Northern Il Univ; Med Secretary.

HEIM, Stephen E; Wheaton Warrenville HS; Wheaton, IL; ChrhWkr; HonRl; JrNHS; NHS; SchMus; SctActv; YthFlsp; RptrSchPpr; SchPpr; LetterBsbl; LetterFtbl; LetterTrk; LetterWrstlng; Univ Of Illinois; Medicine.

HEIMAN, Ellen; Eastridge Hs; Kankakee, IL; 10/280 TrsSophCls; TrsJrCls; CmntyWkr; HonRl; HospAde; NHS; OffAde; EdYrBk; FrCl; University; Professional.

HEIMAN, Frederick; Holden R HS; Holden, MO; TrsSrCls; HonRl; NHS; StuCncl; RptrSchPpr; College; Business Major.

HEIMAN, Paulette M; Dickinson HS; Dickinson, ND; 80/180 SecJrCls; HonRl; LbryAde; StuCncl; StuGov; FFA; N Dakota State Univ; Home Economics.

HEIMANN, Cynthia L; Scotus Central Catholic HS; Columbus, NE; 4/61 Chrs; HonRl; NHS; SchAde; SchPl; StuCncl; RptrYrbk; PpCl; Trk; Chrldr; Univ Of Neb; Rn.

HEIMANN, Michael H; Millard Sr HS; Omaha, NE; HonRl; SctActv; LetterFtbl; LetterSwmmng; LetterTrk; U Of Ne; Civil Engineer.

HEIMBACH, Carolyn A; Good Counsel HS; Chicago, IL; 13/285 HonRl; JA; SchPl; TchrAde; FTA; College; Accounting.

HEIMBERGER, Julie A; Earlham Community HS; Dexter, IA; 1/40 TrsFrshCls; TrsSrCls; Band; Chrs; CncrtBnd; DrlTm; HonRl; Mdrgl; MrchBnd; NHS; PepBnd; SchMus; SchPl; LetterBsktbl; PresGAA; Iowa State Univ; Elem Ed.

HEIMER, Laurie; Lexington HS; Lexington, MO; 6/94 PresSophCls; ALAGirlsSt; Band; HonRl; NHS; SchMus; StuCncl; FrCl; Trk; GAA; Central Missouri State U; Secretarial Scien.

HEIMERDINGER, Marie A; Pearl City HS; Pearl City, IL; 3/50 SecSrCls; Chr; Chrs; HonRl; JrNHS; NHS; StuCncl; EdYrBk; 4-H; Bsbl; College; Medical Tech.

HEIMERL, James; Hilbert HS; Hilbert, WI; 2/63 PresSophCls; ChrhWkr; HonRl; NHS; RptrYrbk; Moraine Park Tech Inst; Electronic Servicin.

HEIMERMAN, Kenneth J; Oconto Sr HS; Oconto, WI; 17/141 HonRl; SchPl; StuCncl; Bsktbl; Ftbl; Glf; LetterTrk; Univ Of Wisconsin; Social Work.

HEIMES, Dolores; North Branch HS; North Branch, MI; 14/147 DrlTm; HonRl; NHS; TchrAde; FrCl; Mich State Univ; General Course.

HEIMSOTH, Cheryl J; Santa Fe R 10 District HS; Alma, MO; 1/47 SecJrCls; ALAGirlsSt; HonRl; PresNHS; PresYthFlsp; 4-H; PresFHA; Univ Of Mo Columbia; Interior Design.

HEIMSOTH, Jeffrey E; Benton County R1 HS; Cole Camp, MO; PresJrCls; ALBoysSt; Band; Chr; ChrhWkr; HonRl; NHS; PepBnd; FFA; LetterBsktbl; College.

HEIN, David A; Inswich HS; Ipswich, SD; ALBoysSt; Aud/Vis; Band; Chr; Chrs; HonRl; Bsbl; CaptBsktbl; Ftbl; Trk; Univ Of South Dakota; Law.

HEIN, Harry H; Bogan HS; Chicago, IL; 42/680 NHS; TchrAde; Yrbk; RptrSchPpr; SchPpr; Univ Of Illinois; Electrical Engineering.

HEIN, James; Mcfarland HS; Mcfarland, WI; 23/90 Band; CncrtBnd; HonRl; MrchBnd; PepBnd; IMSpt; Univ; Professional.

HEIN, John J; Tomahawk HS; Tomahawk, WI; 8/156 ALBoysSt; NHS; StuGov; RptrYrbk; RptrSchPpr; SpnCl; MthCl; Bsktbl; Ftbl; Glf; Univ Of Wisc; Law.

HEIN, Robin K; Dawson HS; Dawson, MN; 4/76 AFS; Chr; HonRl; HospAde; SchMus; RptrSchPpr; 4-H; Chrldr; 4-HAwd; VoiceDemAwd; Concordia College; Luth Teacher Ed.

HEIN, Sarah E; Sacred Heart HS; Salina, KS; Chrs; HonRl; NHS; NatlMeritCmnd; StuGov; RptrYrbk; SchPpr; FHA; PpCl; Chrldr; Northwestern Univ Or Univ Of Ks; Pre Medici.

HEIN, Sharon K; Woodruff HS; Peoria, IL; 20/232 Chr; HonRl; HospAde; OffAde; SchMus; SctActv; TchrAde; CivCl; SpnCl; 4-HAwd; Icc; Elementary Teacher.

HEIN, Steven C; Calumet HS; Calumet, MI; ALBoysSt; ChrhWkr; HonRl; PresNHS; SctActv; LetterBsktbl; Bsbl; Trk; Mi Tech Univ; Forestry.

HEINDL, Daniel; Colby HS; Abbotsford, WI; ChrhWkr; HonRl; SchAde; SchPl; 4-H; FBLA; PpCl; SciCl; Bsktbl; Univ Of Wi At Marshfield;elec Engineering.

HEINDSELMAN, Natalie A; Jimtown HS; Elkhart, IN; Chr; HonRl; LbryAde; SchPl; RptrYrbk; RptrSchPpr; FTA; Chrldr; GAA; PPFtbl; Coll; Lpn.

HEINE, Mary K; Frederick HS; Barnard, SD; HonRl; StuCncl; YthFlsp; Yrbk; SchPpr; PpCl; LetterTrk; Chrldr; College; Rn.

HEINEMAN, Susan E; R N Snider HS; Fort Wayne, IN; ChrhWkr; CmntyWkr; HonRl; NatlMeritSF; PolWkr; SctActv; StuCncl; RptrSchPpr; Univ; Political Science.

HEINEMANN, James K; Parkway West Sr HS; Ballwin, MO; SchAde; TchrAde; YthFlsp; Bsktbl; Ftbl; Trk; CchngActv; IMSpt; AmLegAwd; PresAwd; Univ Of Utah.

HEINEN, Gerald W; Valley Falls HS; Valley Falls, KS; VPJrCls; PresSrCls; Chrs; ChrhWkr;.

HEINEN, John J; Marquette HS; Wauwatosa, WI; PresFrshCls; PresSophCls; PresJrCls; HonRl; LitMag; NHS; SchMus; Sdlty; StuGov; RptrSchPpr; LatCl; Trk; College; Law.

HEINEN, Karen; St Francis HS; Humphrey, NE; Chrs; HonRl; TchrAde; Yrbk; 4-H; PpCl; IMSpt; 4-HAwd;.

HEINEN, Meredith A; Downs HS; Cawker City, KS; 1/27 ChrhWkr; HonRl; VPYthFlsp; PresFHA; LetterBsktbl; LetterTrk; BttyCrckrAwd; GodCntryAwd; VFWAwd; VoiceDemAwd; Univ Of Kansas; Med Technology.

HEINEN, Michelle R; Concordia HS; Concordia, KS; SecFrshCls; Chr; Chrs; HonRl; StuCncl; FTA; VPFrCl; VPPpCl; Trk; IMSpt; Kansas St Univ; Psychology.

HEINIGER, Jim E; Niles West HS; Oakbrook, IL; HonRl; NHS; Bsktbl; Ftbl; Trk; College; Mechanical Engineering.

HEINRICH, Barbara J; Freeport HS; Freeport, IL; HonRl; JA; NatlMeritCmnd;.

HEINRICH, Carolyn S; Van Horn HS; Independence, MO; 80/471 VPJrCls; VPSrCls; Chr; HonRl; SchMus; StuCncl; PpCl; Chrldr; GAA; Concordia Teachers Coll; Elem Teacher.

HEINRICH, Deborah C; Antigo HS; Antigo, WI; 12/335 SecTrsJrCls; Chr; Chrs; NatlFornLg; StuCncl; StuGov; GerCl; MthCl; IMSpt; DARAwd; U Of Wis; Nursing.

HEINRICH, Diana; Rush City HS; Rush City, MN; 2/68 Chr; HonRl; LbryAde; TrsFrshCls; NatlMeritCmnd; SchPl; RptrYrbk; FHA; FTA; Univ Of Minnesota.

HEINRICH, Maria; Fairburt Cropset HS; Fairburt, IL; 26/103 Matbee Coll; Dental Asst.

HEINRICH, Milo J; Sheyenne River Academy; Alfred, ND; 1/15 PresSophCls; VPJrCls; Band; Chr; HonRl; NatlMeritCmnd; StuCncl; EdYrBk; IMSpt; DanFAwd; Union Col Lincoln; Music.

HEINRICHS, Kristinn I; Watertown Senior HS; Watertown, SD; 39/330 AFS; Band; Chrs; ChrhWkr; NatlFornLg; NHS; NatlThespSoc; RptrYrbk; 4-H; College; German.

HEINS, Brenda K; Wichita North HS; Wichita, KS; PresFrshCls; Chr; Chrl; ChrhWkr; HonRl; NHS; SchMus; YthFlsp; EdYrBk; Chrldr; Emporia State Col; Law.

HEINS, Donna G; Lincoln HS; Lincoln, KS; Chr; Chrs; HonRl; JA; TchrAde; 4-H; GerCl; 4-HAwd; JAAwd; College; Major Study.

HEINS, Janet L; Belmont HS; Belmont, WI; 28/56 Band; CncrtBnd; HonRl; LbryAde; MrchBnd; PepBnd; SchPl; RptrSchPpr; GAA; State U Of Wi Platteville; Criminal Justice.

HEINS, Juliana M; Central City HS; Central City, NE; Band; CncrtBnd; Mdrgl; Orch; PepBnd; Teen; YthFlsp; Glf; Swmmng; Tennis; Coll; Music Ed.

HEINS, Laura L; Amherst Public HS; Riverdale, NE; Band; Chr; ChrhWkr; CncrtBnd; HonRl; HospAde; MrchBnd; NHS; PepBnd; SchPl; RptrYrbk; Bsbl; Bsktbl; College; Phys Ed Teacher.

HEINS, Mary J; Clara City HS; Clara City, MN; PresSophCls; Band; Chr; ChrhWkr; HonRl; NHS; PepBnd; StuCncl; Bsktbl; Gustavus Adolphus Clge; Church Music.

HEINS, Stanley K; Gwinn HS; K I Sawyer Afb, MI; 26/170 HonRl; NatlFornLg; NHS; SchAde; StuCncl; StuGov; Bsbl; Glf; IMSpt; Univ Of Sc; Law.

HEINSOHN, Hugh R; Harrison HS; Evansville, IN; 10/475 CncrtBnd; HonRl; MrchBnd; NHS; NatlMeritCmnd; Orch; In U; Physics.

HEINSZ, Karen L; Duchesne HS; St Charles, MO; Chrs; HonRl; SchMus; SctActv; PpCl; Chrldr; CchngActv; IMSpt; PPFtbl; Nursing School; Major In Nursing.

HEINTZ, Jacqueline L; Ventura Community HS; Clear Lake, IA; Band; CncrtBnd; HonRl; MrchBnd; PepBnd; Bsktbl; Tennis; College; Professional.

HEINTZ, Rodney J; Joliet East HS; Joliet, IL; 49/408 Aud/Vis; HonRl; NHS; StuCncl; Bsktbl; Trk; IMSpt; Joliet Jr Clge; Pilot.

HEINTZLEMAN, E; Lansing HS; Lansing, KS; Chr; StuCncl; TchrAde; 4-H; PpCl; Trk; Chrldr; IMSpt; College.

HEINTZMAN, Jeff B; Peoria HS; Peoria, IL; TrsJrCls; PresSrCls; ChrhWkr; HonRl; GerCl; LatCl; Swmmng; College; Foreign Language.

HEINTZMAN, Terri J; Rapid City Central HS; Rapid City, SD; 11/583 Band; ChrhWkr; HonRl; LbryAde; MrchBnd; NatlFornLg; NatlMeritSF; Orch; PepBnd; TchrAde; Univ Of Colorado; Pharmacist.

HEINZ, Catherine M; Bergan HS; Edwards, IL; CmntyWkr; HonRl; OffAde; SchAde; TchrAde; Illinois Central Clg; Secretarial.

HEINZ, Janet L; Carlinville HS; Carlinville, IL; 6/160 Band; Chr; CncrtBnd; HonRl; JrNHS; NHS; OffAde; SchMus; SchPl; SctActv; StuCncl; Chrldr; TreasGAA; West Ill Univ; Primary Sch Teacher.

HEINZ, Jenny R; High School; Vincennes, IN; 1/47 Chrl; HonRl; ModUN; RptrYrbk; EdYrBk; VPFHA; MthCl; PpCl; SciCl; Trk; Purdue Univ; Chemical Engineer.

HEINZ, Julia E; Lincoln HS; Bloomington, MN; Chr; HonRl; JA; NHS; NatlMeritSF; NatlThespSoc; SchMus; SchPl; StuCncl; RptrYrbk; College; Pre Law, Majoring In Economics.

HEINZ, Patricia M; John Hersey HS; Arlington Hts, IL; 200/739 AFS; HonRl; TchrAde; Loyola Univ; Nursing.

HEINZE, Denise E; Rock Island HS; Rock Island, IL; 51/650 AFS; Chr; ChrhWkr; Mdrgl; NHS; SchMus; SchPl; YthFlsp; FrCl; GAA; College; Music.

HEINZE, Pamela; Clark Co HS; Kahoka, MO; 5/95 Band; CncrtBnd; HonRl; MrchBnd; NHS; PepBnd; SchPl; SciCl; Nmsu.

HEINZEN, Daniel J; Apollo HS; St Cloud, MN; 17 595 Band; Chr; CncrtBnd; MrchBnd; NatlMeritSF; PepBnd; PolWkr; Univ; Music.

HEINZERLING, Karl K; Chaska HS; Chaska, MN; 4/217 ALBoysSt; Band; HonRl; NHS; NatlMeritSF; SchMus; SchPl; FrCl; Trk; IMSpt; College; Medicine.

HEINZMAN, Debra S; Zionsville Comm HS; Zionsville, IN; 15/125 HonRl; NHS; NatlMeritCmnd; RptrYrbk; 4-H; SpnCl; 4-HAwd; In U; Bus.

HEINZMANN, Dean A; Centralia HS; Centralia, IL; 5/358 PresSrCls; ChrhWkr; HonRl; JrNHS; NHS; SchMus; SchPl; StuCncl; YthFlsp; KeyCl; GerCl; Kaskaskia College; Electronics.

HEIRIGS, John F; Irene HS; Irene, SD; ChrhWkr; CmntyWkr; HonRl; Sacrstn; SchPl; StuCncl; LetterFtbl; LetterTrk;.

HEISE, Catherine S; Maine South HS; Park Ridge, IL; Chr; Chrs; ChrhWkr; HonRl; NHS; PolWkr; PpCl; College; Writing Or Art.

HEISE, Judith A; Crestwood HS; Dearborn Heights, MI; ChrhWkr; CmntyWkr; HonRl; TreasJA; NatlMeritSF; SecSctActv; TreasSpnCl; JAAwd; Ferris State Col; Accountancy.

HEISE, Nancy A; Kewanee HS; Kewanee, IL; TrsFrshCls; SecAFS; PolWkr; SchPl; StuCncl; Twrl; Yrbk; PresFBLA; GerCl; PpCl; College; Legal Assistant.

HEISE, Susan; Cedar Falls HS; Cedar Falls, IA; Chrs; ChrhWkr; HonRl; SctActv; PpCl; BauchLmbAwd; Ia State Univ; Veterinary Med.

HEISEL, Amy D; Pacific HS; Labadie, MO; Chrs; HonRl; TchrAde; FBLA; FHA; PpCl; Coll; Business Education.

HEISEL, Nancy A; Pekin Comm HS; Pekin, IL; 35/700 AFS; Chr; HonRl; NHS; YthFlsp; 4-H; GerCl; GAA; IMSpt; Illinois State Univ; Elem Educ.

HEISER, Boyd L; Raymond Central HS; Ceresco, NE; SecFrshCls; HonRl; Bsktbl;.

HEISER, Kathleen J; Lowell HS; Lowell, IN; Aud/Vis; ChrhWkr; HonRl; LbryAde; NHS; OffAde; SctActv; TchrAde; FHA; GAA; Business School; Professional.

HEISER, Sharon A; O Neill Public HS; Oneill, NE; Band; Chr; Chrs; ChrhWkr; HonRl; PolWkr; SchMus; 4-H; PpCl; AmLegAwd; College; Professional.

HEISKELL, Jacqueline L; Lockwood Ri HS; Lockwood, MO; 3/42 TrsSophCls; Chr; Chrs; ChrhWkr; HonRl; SchPl; PPFtbl; College; Forrestry.

HEISLER, Rebecca J; Minnewaukan HS; Minnewaukan, ND; 5/30 SecSrCls; Band; Chrs; ChrhWkr; CmntyWkr; CncrtBnd; HonRl; SchPl; Yrbk; FHA; University; Nursing.

HEISSERER, Sherri L; Notre Dame HS; Cape Girardeau, MO; 6/78 Band; Chrs; HonRl; NHS; PepBnd; SchPpr; SecFBLA; PpCl; Univ; Secretarial Work.

HEITER, Michael L; Boone Valley HS; Goldfield, IA; 5/27 VPFrshCls; TrsSrCls; ChrhWkr; HonRl; SchPl; StuCncl; Yrbk; 4-H; PpCl; SciCl; Bsbl; Bsktbl; Ftbl; Wartburg College; Biology.

HEITING, Steven; Hay Springs Public HS; Hay Springs, NE; 5/40 NatlMeritCmnd; Coll; Math Major.

HEITMAN, Carol J; Osceola HS; Osceola, WI; Chr; PepBnd; 4-H; FHA; FrCl; PpCl; Bsktbl; Trk; GAA;.

HEITMAN, Elizabeth; John Burroughs HS; St Louis, MO; Chrs; ModUN; NatlMeritSF; SchPl; SctActv; StuGov; RptrSchPpr; Rice Univ; International Trade.

HEITMAN, Jill K; Cochrane Fountain City HS; Fountain City, WI; 4/89 Chrs; NHS; SchMus; TchrAde; YthFlsp; RptrSchPpr; GAA; Uw Stevens Point; Wildlife Manager.

HEITMAN, Kathleen A; Gladstone Ares HS; Gladstone, MI; 3/171 HonRl; NHS; Mi Tech; Comuputer Sci.

HEITMANN, Janet K; St Charles HS; St Charles, MO; ChrhWkr; CmntyWkr; HonRl; LbryAde; IMSpt; Clge; Teach Elem Or Nursery Schl.

HEITSCH, Bonnie E; Kingswood HS; Birmingham, MI; HonRl; JrNHS; TchrAde; FrCl; PpCl; Bsbl; Swmmng; IMSpt;.

HEITZ, Sandra L; Bronaugh R 7 HS; Garland, KS; 1/26 TrsJrCls; Chr; HonRl; NHS; StuCncl; 4-H; FFA; PpCl; LetterBsktbl; LetterTrk; College; Veterinarian.

HEITZ, Tammie A; Bronaugh R 7 HS; Garland, KS; 1/23 TrsJrCls; ALAGirlsSt; Band; CncrtBnd; HonRl; LbryAde; MrchBnd; NHS; LetterBsktbl; LetterTrk; College; Curr Of Maj Study.

HEITZMAN, Jeanne; Cleveland HS; St Louis, MO; 1/559 HonRl; NHS; SecGerCl; LetterBsktbl; GAA; IMSpt; OptClAwd; PresAwd; Clge; Medical Tech.

HEITZMAN, Kenneth D; St Marys HS; St Louis, MO; 4/175 Band; CncrtBnd; HonRl; JrNHS; NHS; PepBnd; SchPl; Socr; IMSpt; U Of Mo; Engineering.

HEITZMAN, Laura J; J D Darnall HS; Geneseo, IL; 8/212 Chr; HonRl; NatlFornLg; NHS; NatlThespSoc; Blackhawk Col; Accounting.

HEIZMAN, Stephen P; Northeast HS; Kansas City, MO; Band; SchMus; SctActv; Univ; Medical.

HEJLIK, Cynthia L; Garner Hayfield HS; Garner, IA; 3/65 TrsSophCls; TrsJrCls; CncrtBnd; HonRl; MrchBnd; PepBnd; PpCl; LetterBsktbl; Calmar Tech School; Dental Assistant.

HEJNA, William J; Riverside Brookfield HS; Riverside, IL; HonRl; NatlMeritSchl; Knox College; Medicine.

HEJNY, Terence; Milford HS; Pleasant Dale, NE; ALBoysSt; CncrtBnd; MrchBnd; NHS; StuCncl; GerCl; Bsktbl; Wrstlng; Univ; Hictory.

HEJZA, Donna J; Resurrection HS; Chicago, IL; 41/261 HonRl; SchMus; SchPl; StuCncl; RptrYrbk; SpnCl; MthCl; Mundelein College; Medical Tech.

HEKKING, Carol J; Morton West HS; Berwyn, IL; 133/755 HonRl; Orch; SchPpr; Eastern Illinois Univ; Zoology.

HEKTNER, Neil C; Oak Grove Luth HS; Moorhead, MN; Band; Chr; CncrtBnd; HonRl; Mdrgl; PepBnd; SctActv; LetterBsktbl; LetterFtbl; LetterTrk; Coll.

HELBERG, Jeffrey H; Harlem HS; Loves Park, IL; 6/560 ChrhWkr; HonRl; NHS; NatlThespSoc; Quill&Scroll; SchPl; SctActv; College; Commercial Art.

HELBLING, James F; Washington HS; East Chicago, IN; 4/299 Band; CncrtBnd; HonRl; MrchBnd; NHS; NatlMeritCmnd; PepBnd; KeyCl; LetterFtbl; IMSpt; Purdue Univ; Aeronautical Engr.

HELD, Kirsten L; Hinton Community HS; Hinton, IA; 2/45 Chrs; ChrhWkr; CncrtBnd; HonRl; NHS; YthFlsp; Yrbk; 4-H; AmLegAwd; 4-HAwd; Iowa State Univ; Forestry Major.

HELD, Richard J; Hartford Union HS; Colgate, WI; AFS; HonRl; HospAde; SctActv; StuCncl; StuGov; 4-H; Bsbl; Bsktbl; CaptIMSpt; Marquette Univ; Medicine.

HELD, Shelley; Ventura Community HS; Ventura, IA; 3/38 HonRl; NHS; NatlThespSoc; PepBnd; SchMus; SchPl; TchrAde; RptrYrbk; SchPpr; Western Co St Col; Elementary Education.

HELD, William; Wauwatosa West HS; Wauwatosa, WI; 76/436 Aud/Vis; Chr; DrmMjrt; NHS; NatlMeritCmnd; NatlThespSoc; SchMus; SchPl; SctActv; GodCntryAwd; Univ Of Wisc Madison; Mechanical Eng.

HELDER, Dennis L; Canton HS; Canton, SD; 2/96 VPBand; Chrs; VPCncrtBnd; HonRl; VPMrchBnd; NHS; VPPepBnd; RptrSchPpr; SciCl; BauchLmbAwd; South Dakota School Of Mines; Engineer.

HELDER, Norma J; Zeeland HS; Holland, MI; 3/180 ChrhWkr; HonRl; Davenport College; Accountant.

HELDMAN, Gregory E; Dubois HS; Jasper, IN; Band; CncrtBnd; MrchBnd; SchPl; 4-H; PpCl; LetterBsktbl; LetterTrk; Vujc; Accounting.

HELDT, Bernadette; St Philip Catholic Central; Battle Creek, MI; 10/98 Chr; Chrs; HonRl; NHS; LatCl; SpnCl; PpCl; Trk; Kellogg Community College; Undecided.

HELEBRANDT, Kay A; Morton West HS; Stickney, IL; CncrtBnd; HonRl; JrNHS; MrchBnd; ModUN; Orch; Ill State Univ.

HELENBOLT, Sherry R; Stuart HS; Stuart, NE; VPFrshCls; PresSophCls; TrsJrCls; Chr; HonRl; MrchBnd; SchPl; VPStuCncl; Twrl; College; Professional.

HELENTHAL, Teresa M; Hamilton HS; Hamilton, IL; TrsFrshCls; HonRl; LbryAde; 4-H; FrCl; LetterBsktbl; LetterTrk; Chrldr; GAA; College; Professional.

HELF, Lisa A; Kimberly HS; Combined Locks, WI; ALAGirlsSt; HonRl; MrchBnd; NHS; SchPl; StuCncl; 4-H; LetterBsktbl; LetterGlf; BttyCrckrAwd; Uw Fox Valley; Dietician.

HELFER, Cheryl D; Richwoods HS; Peoria, IL; 1/449 NHS; TchrAde; Yrbk; Trk; Univ Of Il; Veterinarian.

HELFFRICH, Jerome; Glenbrook North Hs; Northbrook, IL; 43 HonRl; NatlMeritCmnd; U Illinois ; Eng/physics.

HELFRICH, Joseph F; Mater Dei HS; Evansville, IN; ChrhWkr; HonRl; JrNHS; RedCrAde; SchPl; SctActv; SciCl; Ftbl; IMSpt; 4-HAwd; University; Engineering.

HELFTER, Mary B; Osage Community HS; Osage, IA; 1/154 PresSophCls; ModUN; VPNHS; NatlMeritCmnd; EdSchPpr; LetterBsbl; CaptBsbl; LetterTrk; JCAwd; RotaryAwd; Univ; Math Teacher.

HELGASON, Craig M; Central HS; Grand Forks, ND; HonRl; NHS; RptrSchPpr; Bsbl; IMSpt; College; Engineering Or Art.

HELGELAND, Eric T; Maine Twp West HS; Des Plaines, IL; 29/800 Aud/Vis; HonRl; IntrClCncl; JrNHS; NatlFornLg; NatlThespSoc; PolWkr; SchMus; SchPl; MthCl; SciCl; Univ; Law.

HELGELAND, Jon L; Maine Township West HS; Des Plaines, IL; 50/755 HonRl; NHS; NatlMeritCmnd; MthCl; LetterSwmmng; Trk; Univ; Physics.

HELGERSON, Kathy E; Cornell HS; Cornell, WI; Band; Chr; Chrs; HonRl; MrchBnd; TchrAde; YthFlsp; PpCl; LetterBsktbl; Chrldr; Voc Sch; Child Care Asst.

HELGESON, Kathryn; Durand Area HS; Durand, MI; 47/189 CncrtBnd; HonRl; HospAde; MrchBnd; NHS; FrCl; SpnCl; SciCl; Trk; Ferris State College; Medical Technologist.

HELGREN, Janet T; North HS; Omaha, NE; Chr; HonRl; NHS; Un Lincoln; Journalism.

HELIS, Karen S; Lyons Township HS; Western Springs, IL; Chr; HonRl; JrNHS; NHS; SchAde; StuCncl; SchPpr; Univ Of Ill; Journalism.

HELKER, Dennis; Waukesha South HS; Waukesha, WI; 77/583 Chr; HonRl; NHS; StuCncl; Bsbl; Bsktbl; IMSpt; La Crosse; Business.

HELLAND, Carolyn S; Park Center Senior HS; Brooklyn Park, MN; ChrhWkr; CmntyWkr; CncrtBnd; HospAde; JA; OffAde; Tennis; College; Doctor.

HELLAND, Rhonda L; Newark Community HS; Newark, IL; 7/60 TrsSrCls; HonRl; LbryAde; Yrbk; FHA; FrCl; GAA; Jolit Jr College; Bookkeeper.

HELLBUSCH, Veronica R; Watertown HS; Watertown, SD; 3/291 ALAGirlsSt; Chr; Chrs; Mdrgl; NHS; NatlMeritCmnd; NatlThespSoc; Orch; SchMus; SchPl; Univ; Music Teacher.

HELLEBUYCK, Cindy M; Akron Fairgrove HS; Fairgrove, MI; ChrhWkr; HonRl; LbryAde; NHS; TchrAde; VPFHA; IMSpt; Delta College; Secretarial.

HELLELAND, Judy K; Rushford HS; Rushford, MN; 1/63 PresBand; Chrs; CaptDrlTm; HonRl; NHS; SchPl; EdYrBk; FHA; AmLegAwd; DARAwd; U Of Wis; Nursing.

HELLEM, Carol M; Riverside Brookfield HS; Brookfield, IL; Chr; Chrl; VPNatlThespSoc; SchMus; SchPl; TchrAde; Illinois St Univ; Theatre.

HELLENDRUNG, Darlene J; Prairie Farm HS; Ridgeland, WI; Chrs; HonRl; 4-H; FFA; FHA; PpCl; Rice Lake Vocation School; Accounting.

HELLER, Cynthia L; Benton Comm HS; Newhall, IA; HonRl; HospAde; SchMus; SchPl; YthFlsp; SpnCl; Trk; College; Professional.

HELLER, Jeanine R; Glenbrook South HS; Glenview, IL; 4/579 Chr; ChrhWkr; HonRl; NHS; NatlMeritCmnd; FTA; GAA; Dr Martin Luther College; Elementary Ed.

HELLER, John A; University HS; Milwaukee, WI; AFS; Chrs; HonRl; NatlMeritCmnd; PolWkr; SchPpr; LetterSocr; LetterSwmmng; Dartmouth College; Engineering.

HELLER, John M; Glenbard East HS; Lombard, IL; ChrhWkr; HonRl; NatlFornLg; SchMus; SchPl; Loyola University; History.

HELLER, Joyce; Fairbury HS; Hebron, NE; 21/132 VPSrCls; Chrs; HonRl; OffAde; StuCncl; 4-H; PpCl; IMSpt; 4-HAwd; Univ Of Neb; Biology.

HELLER, Kelley A; Alexander Ramsey Sr HS; St Paul, MN; HonRl; NHS; Bsbl; LetterBsktbl; Swmmng; Trk; CchngActv; IMSpt; St Olaf College; Medicine.

HELLER, Stan E; Stockton HS; Stockton, IL; AFS; Band; CncrtBnd; HonRl; MrchBnd; PepBnd; SchPl; RptrSchPpr; 4-H; FFA; FTA; College; Engineering.

HELLER, Timothy; Wisner Pilger HS; Pilger, NE; 7/67 ALBoysSt; ChrhWkr; HonRl; NHS; NatlMeritSchl; YthFlsp; Univ; Professional Architect.

HELLING, Mary; Northwestern HS; Mansfield, SD; ALAGirlsSt; Chrs; ChrhWkr; HonRl; LbryAde; NHS; NatlThespSoc; SchPl; RptrSchPpr; Northern Stae College; Elem Education.

HELLMAN, Brent; Hartsburg Emden HS; Emden, IL; 1/37 ALBoysSt; Band; ChrhWkr; HonRl; StuCncl; 4-H; Bsktbl; LetterTrk; University; Agriculture.

HELLMAN, Michael A; Jackson HS; Jackson, MI; 33/373 Chr; Chrl; Chrs; ChrhWkr; HonRl; NHS; Univ Of Michigan; Architecture.

HELLMAN, Sharon K; Hancock Central HS; Hancock, MI; CncrtBnd; DrmMjrt; HonRl; HospAde; StuCncl; 4-H; KeyCl; PpCl; Glf; GAA; College; Orthodontist.

HELLMER, Connie R; Olpe HS; Olpe, KS; TrsJrCls; Band; Chr; DrmMjrt; HonRl; PepBnd; SchPl; SchPl; 4-H; PresPpCl; College; Radio/tv Journalism.

HELLWIG, Donald M; Custer HS; Milwaukee, WI; 7/728 Aud/Vis; HonRl; NHS; FrCl; MthCl; SciCl; CaptSwmmng; CaptTennis; LetterTrk; CchngActv; IMSpt; Carroll College; Environment.

HELLWIG, Mary Ann; Lebanon HS; Lebanon, IL; 10/40 Chrs; HonRl; SchPl; StuCncl; RptrYrbk; PpCl; SciCl; Bsktbl; PresAwd; Jr College; Nursing.

HELLYER, Brus; Lake Forest Academy HS; Northbrook, IL; CmntyWkr; HonRl; HospAde; StuCncl; StuGov; RptrSchPpr; SchPpr; PpCl; Swmmng; PPFtbl; College.

HELLYER, William A; John Hersey HS; Mt Prospect, IL; 100/800 Chr; HonRl; JrNHS; NatlFornLg; NHS; EdYrBk; RptrSchPpr; LetterTrk; LetterWrstlng; Princeton; Science.

HELM, Brett H; Munster HS; Munster, IN; 74/440 HonRl; SchAde; LetterFtbl; LetterTrk; LetterChrldr; IMSpt; Univ; Bus Admn/corporate Law.

HELM, Deanna K; Kewanee HS; Kewanee, IL; 13/213 Chrs; HonRl; SchPl;.

HELM, Douglas W; Drayton Public HS; Drayton, ND; Band; Chrs; CncrtBnd; HonRl; SchPl; SctActv; SchPpr; Ftbl; Trk; University; Vocation.

HELM, Murdeen; Platte Valley Acad; Kearney, NE; 1 TrsSophCls; PresSrCls; Chr; CncrtBnd; HonRl; NHS; OffAde; SctActv; StuGov; RptrYrbk; Union College;business Administration.

HELMA, Kathryn T; Riverdale HS; Blue Springs, MO; SecJrCls; Band; ChrhWkr; CmntyWkr; HonRl; MrchBnd; PepBnd; RptrYrbk; RptrSchPpr; VPGerCl; PpCl; LetterBsktbl; LetterChrldr; University; Liberal Arts.

HELMBOLDT, Dan; Rolling Meadows HS; Rolling Meadows, IL; HonRl; TchrAde; Bsbl; Bsktbl; CchngActv; IMSpt; BauchLmbAwd; Western State College; Psychology.

HELMBRECHT, Kay; Lytton Comm HS; Lytton, IA; Band; Chrs; DrlTm; HonRl; NHS; StuCncl; YthFlsp; FHA; 4-HAwd; College; Vocation.

HELMBRECHT, Sherry A; Lytton Comm HS; Lytton, IA; Band; Chr; Chrs; HonRl; NHS; YthFlsp; RptrSchPpr; FHA; LetterBsktbl; LetterTrk; College.

HELMER, Scott A; Lidgerwood Public HS; Lidgerwood, ND; TrsFrshCls; Band; Chrs; CncrtBnd; HonRl; MrchBnd; PepBnd; SchPl; LetterBsktbl; College; Teaching.

HELMER, Steven C; Jennings HS; Jennings, MO; 39/270 HonRl; TchrAde; Yrbk; SchPpr; EngCl; FrCl; CaptFtbl; LetterTrk; Coll; Photography.

HELMERS, James A; Kenmare Public HS; Kenmare, ND; 2/55 ALBoysSt; HonRl; TchrAde; Bsbl; Ftbl; Glf; Wrstlng; North Dakota State Univ; Optometrist.

HELMICK, Robert N; Roosevelt HS; Des Moines, IA; ModUN; NatlFornLg; StuGov; LetterSwmmng; Uni; Prof.

HELMICK, Wilbert C; Farmington HS; Hanna City, IL; KeyCl; GerCl; LetterBsbl; Bsktbl; Ftbl; Wrstlng; College.

HELMIG, Steve R; Lone Jack C 6 HS; Lone Jack, MO; PresJrCls; Band; Chr; ChrhWkr; HonRl; StuCncl; RptrYrbk; LetterBsbl; LetterBsktbl; LetterFtbl; LetterTrk; College; Physical Ed.

HELMING, Mark T; Tomah Sr HS; Tomah, WI; 27/254 HonRl; SchPpr; 4-H; FFA; Wrstlng; AmLegAwd; Univ Of Wisconsin; Veterinarian.

HELMINK, Sharon K; Newton Community HS; Montrose, IL; Chrs; NHS; Sec4-H; FHA; 4-HAwd; Lake Land Jr Col; Elem Ed.

HELMINSKI, Frank J; Austin Preparatory; Grosse Pointe, MI; 11/114 ChrhWkr; HonRl; HospAde; NatlFornLg; NHS; Quill&Scroll; RptrSchPpr; SciCl; Trk; CchngActv; Wayne St U ;med.

HELMISTO, Carol A; Ishpeming HS; Ishpeming, MI; 6/210 CmntyWkr; HonRl; HospAde; NHS; StuGov; RptrYrbk; FTA; FrCl; SpnCl; Tennis; U Of Mi; Pre Law.

HELMKAMP, Kevin J; East Noble HS; Avilla, IN; 51/271 HonRl; Bsbl; Univ; Comm.

HELMREICH, Ellen C; Northrop HS; Fort Wayne, IN; 9/568 Chr; ChrhWkr; HonRl; SchMus; StuCncl; LatCl; Swmmng; ChmbCommrsAwd; DanFAwd; DARAwd; Hillsdale Clge; Ed.

HELMS, Jace R; South Decatur HS; Westport, IN; PresFrshCls; HonRl; IntrClCncl; StuCncl; SptEdSchPpr; LetterBsbl; LetterBsktbl; LetterFtbl; 4-HAwd; KiwanAwd; PresAwd; Indiana University; Sports Writer.

HELMS, Jill A; Roosevelt HS; Minneapolis, MN; AFS; Chr; HonRl; NHS; SchMus; SchPl; CaptSwmmng; GAA;.

HELMS, Kristi K; Oxford Area Comm HS; Oxford, MI; SecAud/Vis; Chr; ChrhWkr; NHS; TchrAde; UNYO; YthFlsp; RptrYrbk; PpCl; SciCl; RotaryAwd; Oakland Univ; Business Admin.

HELMS, Lynda; Shenandoah Comm HS; Shenandoah, IA; 8/97 TrsSrCls; ALAGirlsSt; Band; Chr; HonRl; NHS; Quill&Scroll; EdSchPpr; Chrldr; Nw Mo Univ; Professional.

HELMSING, Lawrence A; Bishop Luers HS; Fort Wayne, IN; CmntyWkr; HonRl; NatlMeritSchl; StuGov; KeyCl; LetterTrk; CchngActv; IMSpt; KiwanAwd; St Francis Coll; Psychology.

HELMUTH, Margaret M; Glenbrook North HS; Northbrook, IL; Chr; Chrs; HonRl; MrchBnd; University.

HELMUTH, Robin A; Bethany Christian HS; Middlebury, IN; PresFrshCls; ChrhWkr; HonRl; SchPl; StuGov; YthFlsp; RptrSchPpr; LetterBsktbl; LetterTrk; IMSpt; College; Professional.

HELMUTH, Roy E; Northridge HS; Middleburg, IN; SecFrshCls; TrsFrshCls; Chr; ChrhWkr; HonRl; StuCncl; YthFlsp; Trade Sch.

HELPER, David L; Centennial HS; Champaign, IL; TchrAde; Swmmng; IMSpt; Siu; Forestry.

HELPLING, Karla; Anderson HS; Anderson, IN; HonRl; StuCncl; Teen; FSA; Tennis; Univ; Teacher.

HELSING, Lori J; Randolph Public HS; Randolph, NE; 2/57 TrsFrshCls; SecTrsSophCls; Chr; Chrs; ChrhWkr; CmntyWkr; HonRl; HospAde; LbryAde; College; Teaching.

HELSTEDT, Marilee P; Radcliffe Comm HS; Radcliffe, IA; Band; Chrs; HonRl; Mdrgl; NHS; NatlThespSoc; OffAde; RptrYrbk; LetterTrk; LetterChrldr; LetterPPFtbl; Iowa State Univ; Art.

HELSTEIN, Linda A; Negaunee HS; Negaunee, MI; 7/145 SecFrshCls; SecSophCls; Chrs; ChrhWkr; HonRl; HospAde; NHS; PpCl; Northern Michigan Univ; Medical Field.

HELSTROM, Jeffrey; Hibbing HS; Hibbing, MN; 20/432 HonRl; NHS; Col; Engrg.

HELTON, Barbara S; Lincoln HS; Warren, MI; Band; Chr; ChrhWkr; CncrtBnd; HonRl; MrchBnd; OffAde; SchAde; GAA; College.

HELTON, Brent M; Bishop Dwenger HS; Ft Wayne, IN; 20/243 HonRl; PolWkr; ROTC; RptrYrbk; RptrSchPpr; LatCl; PpCl; SciCl; IMSpt; Indiana U; Business.

HELTON, James; Stewardson Strasburg HS; Strasburg, IL; 8/47 Chrs; ChrhWkr; HonRl; SchPl; Yrbk; EdSchPpr; PpCl; Lakeland Jr Coll.

HELTON, Jesse; Crocker HS; Crocker, MO; 5/61 Univ Of Miss; Architectural Engineer.

HELTSLEY, Paula J; Charlestown HS; Charlestown, IN; 28/164 Chr; HonRl; OffAde; YthFlsp; Yrbk; 4-H; FHA; SpnCl; LetterTrk; GAA; 4-HAwd; Louisville Gen Hosp; X Ray Tech.

HELVATY, Kathleen A; Our Lady Of Grace Academy; Indianapolis, IN; Chrs; HonRl; RedCrAde; SchMus; SchPl; VP4-H; IMSpt; 4-HAwd; Butler Univ; Veterinarina.

HELWIG, John; St Patrick HS; Chicago, IL; 87/400 ChrhWkr; CmntyWkr; HonRl; HospAde; GerCl; Loyola University; Medicine.

HELWIG, Leonard J; Annandale HS; Annandale, MN; Band; CncrtBnd; HonRl; MrchBnd; NHS; TchrAde; Bsktbl; Ftbl; Trk; Wrstlng; Col; Professional.

HELZER, Julia D; Maryville R Ii HS; Maryville, MO; 5/129 Band; ChrhWkr; CmntyWkr; HospAde;

MrchBnd; CivCl; 4-H; FHA; FNA; FrCl; Univ; Elem Educ.

HEMBERGER, Jean R; Auburn HS; Loami, IL; ChrhWkr; CmntyWkr; HonRl; IntrClCncl; NHS; OffAde; StuCncl; Yrbk; EdSchPpr; FHA; PpCl; College; Accountant.

HEMBROUGH, Kevin L; Winchester HS; Winchester, IL; Band; 4-H; FFA; SciCl; Ftbl; DanFAwd; College; Agriculturist.

HEMBY, Jo Vonna; Anna Jonesboro Comm HS; Anna, IL; TrsSophCls; HonRl; YthFlsp; FTA; SpnCl; PpCl; Southern Illinois Univ; Teaching.

HEMERSON, Cartha L; Sheldon Community HS; Sheldon, IA; 2/164 Aud/Vis; Band; Chr; Chrs; ChrhWkr; CncrtBnd; HonRl; Mdrgl; MrchBnd; NHS; SchMus; SchPl; StuCncl; Chrldr; Iowa State Univ; Spanish.

HEMESATH, Karen J; Turkey Valley HS; Lawler, IA; Band; Chr; ChrhWkr; CncrtBnd; HonRl; MrchBnd; PepBnd; SchMus; EdYrBk; Yrbk; Area I Voc Sch; Bookkeeping.

HEMINGER, Colleen D; Sisseton HS; Peever, SD; Coll; Rn.

HEMINGWAY, Drexel; Lindblom Technical HS; Chicago, IL; 77/720 Band; HonRl; StuCncl; TchrAde; Loyola Univ; Physician.

HEMMEL, Mary; Helias HS; Jefferson City, MO; 6/180 DrmBgl; HonRl; SchMus; RptrYrbk; RptrSchPpr; Chrldr; AmLegAwd; Sw Mo State Univ; Special Education.

HEMMEN, David; Harper Woods HS; Harper Woods, MI; HonRl; CchngActv; College.

HEMMEN, Kevin; Dike Community HS; Parkersburg, IA; 7/41 PresSrCls; Band; Chr; Chrs; CncrtBnd; HonRl; MrchBnd; NHS; Bsktbl; Univ Of North Ia; Business Management.

HEMMER, Vicki; Southridge HS; Holland, IN; 1/138 SecTrsFrshCls; SecJrCls; ALAGirlsSt; Band; Chr; Chrs; HospAde; SchMus; PpCl; Purde Univ; Pharmacology.

HEMMERLEIN, Cathy J; Dubois HS; Dubois, IN; 13/80 Band; ChrhWkr; HonRl; NHS; SchPl; TchrAde; RptrSchPpr; FHA; PpCl; GAA; Ball State U; Speech.

HEMMING, Carla V; Pontiac Catholic HS; Pontiac, MI; 1/150 ALAGirlsSt; ChrhWkr; ModUN; SecNHS; SecStuCncl; SecStuGov; SchPpr; SciCl; LetterTennis; VPGAA; Michigan State University.

HEMMING, Patti M; Ewen Trout Creek HS; Bruce Crossing, MI; Chrs; ChrhWkr; OffAde; Yrbk; 4-H; RusCl; Bsktbl; Trk; GAA; 4-HAwd; College.

HEMMING, Sherre R; Cedar Falls HS; Cedar Falls, IA; Band; CncrtBnd; HonRl; MrchBnd; SchPl; Trk; U Of Northern Iowa.

HEMMINGER, Rebecca; Galien HS; Buchanan, MI; 1/50 SecSrCls; Band; HonRl; NHS; SchPl; Yrbk; Bsktbl; Trk; Chrldr; JAAwd; Coll; Accounting.

HEMMINGS, Keith W; Central Community HS; Farmington, IA; 1/98 Band; Chr; HonRl; MrchBnd; NHS; FFA; Farming.

HEMMINGSEN, Barbara L; Marion HS; Marion, IA; Chr; Chrs; CncrtBnd; HonRl; HospAde; Mdrgl; MrchBnd; NatlThespSoc; SchMus; FNA; Col; Medicine.

HEMMINGSON, Carla K; Roseau HS; Warroad, MN; 11/128 HonRl; OffAde; 4-H; EngCl; 4-HAwd; Univ Of Minnesota; Biology.

HEMMINGSON, Julie A; Alpena HS; Herron, MI; ChrhWkr; HonRl; SchAde; 4-H; RotaryAwd; Baker Jr Coll; Data Processing.

HEMMINGSON, Robin R; Bradley HS; Bradley, SD; SecTrsSophCls; SecTrsJrCls; SecTrsSrCls; ALAGirlsSt; Chrs; ChrhWkr; HonRl; SchPl; RptrYrbk; 4-H; FFA; BttyCrckrAwd; DARAwd; College; Vet Assistant.

HEMPHILL, Tanya J; Sumner HS; Sumner, NE; 1/18 TrsSophCls; TrsJrCls; ALAGirlsSt; DrmMjrt; HonRl; SchPl; EdYrBk; 4-H; LetterBsktbl; LetterFtbl; Kearnery State Col;.

HEMPHILL, Thomas C; Harris Lake Park HS; Lake Park, IA; PresFrshCls; TrsSophCls; TrsJrCls; PresSrCls; Chr; ChrhWkr; HonRl; NHS; StuCncl; LetterBsbl; LetterTrk; Iowa State U; Law.

HEMPSTEAD, Charles A; Griffin HS; Springfield, IL; HonRl; SctActv; StuCncl; RptrSchPpr; PpCl; Bsbl;.

HENAK, Robert R; Coon Rapids Comm HS; Coon Rapids, IA; 1/48 Band; CncrtBnd; HonRl; MrchBnd; ModUN; NHS; PepBnd; SctActv; Ftbl; Glf; Wartburg Coll; Law Or Music.

HENCHEN, Cheryl A; Neillsville HS; Neillsville, WI; ChrhWkr; HonRl; NHS; YthFlsp; RptrYrbk; FHA; PpCl; College; Professional.

HENDERSHOT, Karla D; Owen Vly Comm HS; Spencer, IN; 35/180 Band; CncrtBnd; HonRl; MrchBnd; TchrAde; 4-H; PpCl; Chrldr; GAA; 4-HAwd; Indiana Central Bus Sch; Professional.

HENDERSHOTT, Paul W; Riverton HS; Baxter Springs, KS; HonRl; ModUN; NHS; FFA; Kansas St Univ; Engineering.

HENDERSON, Bill A; Scottsbluff Sr HS; Scottsbluff, NE; ALBoysSt; Band; ChrhWkr; HonRl; MrchBnd; KeyCl; Glf; Tennis; University Of Arizona; Business Admin.

HENDERSON, Brenda A; Lawson HS; Lawson, MO; Band; Chrs; ChrhWkr; HonRl; NHS; SchMus; SchPl; StuCncl; Yrbk; Evangel College; Communications.

HENDERSON, Brenda A; Lawson HS; Excelsior Sprngs, MO; Band; Chrs; HonRl; NHS; SchMus; SchPl; Yrbk; EdSchPpr; PpCl; IMSpt; Evangel Clg; Broadcasting.

HENDERSON, Brent A; Flora HS; Flora, IL; 1/160 HonRl; NHS; Quill&Scroll; SptEdSchPpr; SpnCl; MthCl; Bsbl; Bsktbl; University; Professional.

HENDERSON, Bruce E; Oak Park River Forest HS; Oak Park, IL; 50/1000 HonRl; NatlFornLg; NatlMeritFnl; NatlThespSoc; Orch; SchMus; Northwestern Univ; English.

HENDERSON, Coleen E; Raymore Peculiar HS; Raymore, MO; Chrs; HonRl; LbryAde; NatlFornLg; 4-H; FTA; PresFrCl; VPPpCl; 4-HAwd; Univ; Spec Educ.

HENDERSON, Deborah J; Carrollton HS; Carrollton, MO; Chrs; HonRl; NHS; FHA; GerCl; PpCl; College; Social Work.

HENDERSON, Denise; South Hamilton HS; Story City, IA; 1/91 SecSophCls; HonRl; RptrYrbk; Ia State Univ;.

HENDERSON, Donald; Williamston HS; Williamston, MI; 17/156 VPSrCls; ALBoysSt; HonRl; StuCncl; KeyCl; Ftbl; Tennis; Wrstlng;.

HENDERSON, Elaine M; Wheaton Central HS; Wheaton, IL; 41/390 ChrhWkr; HonRl; JrNHS; NHS; RptrSchPpr; Treas4-H; PpCl; Illinois State Univ; Social Welfare.

HENDERSON, Geralyn S; Duchesne HS; St Charles, MO; 6/134 SecSrCls; Chrs; HonRl; NHS; StuCncl; LatCl; SecPpCl; Chrldr; PPFtbl; DARAwd; College.

HENDERSON, Gregory C; Sedan HS; Niotaze, KS; VPSrCls; Band; CncrtBnd; HonRl; MrchBnd; NHS; PepBnd; SchPl; SctActv; StuCncl; Coffeyville Jr Clg; Radio & Tv Broadcasting.

HENDERSON, James M; Elgin HS; Streamwood, IL; 9/783 Chr; CncrtBnd; HonRl; MrchBnd; NatlMeritFnl; NatlMeritSF; Orch; PepBnd; SchPl; StuGov; SpnCl; MthCl; LetterTrk; RotaryAwd; College; Engineering.

HENDERSON, Kathleen; Franklin Comm HS; Franklin, IN; 12/240 HonRl; HospAde; JrNHS; NHS; StuCncl; FrCl; PpCl; Chrldr;.

HENDERSON, Kathryn A; Charlestown HS; Charlestown, IN; ChrhWkr; NHS; SchPl; VPStuCncl; TchrAde; FshEdYrbk; FHA; FrCl; SciCl; Chrldr; College; Journalist.

HENDERSON, Kirk; Mediapolis HS; Mediapolis, IA; HonRl; Wrstlng;.

HENDERSON, Larry D; West Side HS; Gary, IN; ChrhWkr; CmntyWkr; HonRl; NHS; FrCl; Bsbl; JETSAwd; U Of Ill; Electrical Eng.

HENDERSON, Martha A; Rosemount HS; Inver Grove Hts, MN; Band; CncrtBnd; HonRl; MrchBnd; PepBnd; SchPl; FrCl; College.

HENDERSON, Nancy R; Tipton HS; Tipton, IN; 2/193 Chr; ChrhWkr; CmntyWkr; HonRl; PresNHS; SchMus; TchrAde; Pres4-H; PpCl; 4-HAwd; Hanover College; Science.

HENDERSON, Patricia M; New London Sr HS; New London, WI; Band; CncrtBnd; HonRl; Orch; PepBnd; SchMus; StuCncl; PpCl; LetterBsktbl; IMSpt; U W Oshkosh; Health Education.

HENDERSON, Patrick G; Escanaba Area HS; Bark River, MI; 22/382 Band; CncrtBnd; MrchBnd; NHS; NatlMeritCmnd; NatlMeritSchl; NatlMeritSF; Orch; PepBnd; Univ; Professional.

HENDERSON, Rita R; Williamsville HS; Sherman, IL; HonRl; Chrs; JrNHS; Mdrgl; NHS; OffAde; SchPl; TchrAde; FTA; FHA; PpCl; Secretariln Job.

HENDERSON, Robert K; Glenbard So HS; Glen Ellyn, IL; 2/292 ALBoysSt; HonRl; SecNHS; NatlMeritCmnd; LetterBsktbl; LetterGlf; College.

HENDERSON, Ruth A; Warren HS; Round Lake Park, IL; 68/301 SchPl;.

HENDERSON, Therena L; Flint Southwestern HS; Flint, MI; ChrhWkr; HonRl; HospAde; RedCrAde; FNA; LetterBsktbl; Mi State;.

HENDERSON, Vicki C; Kokomo HS; Kokomo, IN; Band; HonRl; SchPl; TchrAde; 4-H; FBLA; FHA; FTA; IMSpt; 4-HAwd; Business College; Seecretary.

HENDRICK, Janice; Parkside HS; Jackson Mi, MI; 70/413 ChrhWkr; CmntyWkr; HonRl; StuGov; Swmmng; Msu; Writer.

HENDRICK, Mary A; Harbor Beach HS; Harbor Beach, MI; 1/138 Band; Chr; CncrtBnd; HonRl; MrchBnd; NHS; NatlMeritSF; PepBnd; SchMus; StuGov; TchrAde; PresFTA; MthCl; PPFtbl; Michigan State Univ.

HENDRICK, Peggy J; Mosinee HS; Mosinee, WI; 24/163 Band; Chr; Chrs; CncrtBnd; HonRl; NHS; SchMus; PpCl; LetterBsktbl; GAA; Univ; Spec Learning Disabilities.

HENDRICK, Teresa F; Raymore Peculiar HS; Peculiar, MO; VPJrCls; CncrtBnd; HonRl; MrchBnd; NHS; FHA; FTA; FrCl; PpCl; GAA; Univ; Professional.

HENDRICKER, Rebecca J; Beardstown HS; Arenzville, IL; Band; ChrhWkr; CncrtBnd; MrchBnd; OffAde; YthFlsp; Pres4-H; VPFHA; IMSpt; Olivet Nazarene Clge; Home Ec.

HENDRICKS, Avila D; Immaculata HS; Detroit, MI; JA; PolWkr; SchPl; StuCncl; StuGov; EdYrBk; RptrSchPpr; Vassar College; Lawyer.

HENDRICKS, Cynthia; Reed Custer Hs; Braceville, IL; SecFrshCls; Band; Chrs; ChrhWkr; JrNHS; PepBnd; SciCl; AmLegAwd; University; Parolle Officer.

HENDRICKS, Deborah F; West Side Sr HS; Gary, IN; SecFrshCls; PresSophCls; VPJrCls; VPSrCls; Chr; ChrhWkr; CmntyWkr; HonRl; NHS; NatlMeritCmnd; Marquette Univ; Nursing.

HENDRICKS, Diane M; Taylorville Sr HS; Taylorville, IL; CmntyWkr; HonRl; NHS; NatlThespSoc; Lincoln Land Jr College; Art.

HENDRICKS, Michelle M; St Agatha HS; Detroit, MI; 20/100 SecSrCls; StuGov; FNA; SpnCl; Bsbl; Bsktbl; GAA; DARAwd; Mich State; Nursing.

HENDRICKS, Robyn E; Ofallon Township HS; Ofallon, IL; HonRl; OffAde; IMSpt; Junior College; Secretary.

HENDRICKSON, Andrew J; Pecatonica Area HS; Blanchardville, WI; TrsSrCls; ALBoysSt; HonRl; Yrbk; LetterBsktbl; LetterFtbl; LetterGlf; Univ Of Wisconsin; Business.

HENDRICKSON, Anita C; Velva Public HS; Velva, ND; Chrs; LbryAde; NHS; SctActv; FHA; GerCl; PpCl; Bsktbl; Trk; Chrldr; College; Tchr Of Psychology Phy Ed.

HENDRICKSON, Bruce A; Belle Fourche HS; Belle Fourche, SD; 11/111 Band; CncrtBnd; HonRl; JrNHS; MrchBnd; NHS; PepBnd; Ftbl; Trk; AmLegAwd; Trade School; Vocation.

HENDRICKSON, Daniel C; Memorial HS; Eau Claire, WI; Chr; HonRl; JrNHS; Mdrgl; SchMus; SchPl; LetterBsbl; LetterSwmmng; College; Pharmacy.

HENDRICKSON, David E; Rochester HS; Rochester, IL; VPFrshCls; PresJrCls; HonRl; VPNHS; SchPl; TreasStuCncl; Treas4-H; PresFFA; DanFAwd; Lincolnland Jr College; Agriculture.

HENDRICKSON, Dawn L; New Richland Hartland HS; New Richland, MN; SecSophCls; Band; ChrhWkr; CncrtBnd; HonRl; MrchBnd; NHS; SchPl; FHA; CaptChrldr; Waldorf Clg; Nursing.

HENDRICKSON, Diann M; Richland #44 HS; Colfax, ND; Chrs; CncrtBnd; HonRl; PepBnd; SchPl; StuCncl; Yrbk; SchPpr; FHA; Trk; North Dakota St Univ; Accounting.

HENDRICKSON, Jeffrey H; Fall River Public HS; Fall River, WI; 7/32 VPSrCls; AFS; ALBoysSt; Band; Chrs; CncrtBnd; HonRl; MrchBnd; OffAde; StuCncl; Technical Col; Architecture.

HENDRICKSON, Joni L; Richland 44 HS; Christine, ND; 5/25 Chrs; HonRl; StuCncl; SptEdYrbk; FHA; Bsktbl; Trade School; Vocation.

HENDRICKSON, Karen M; Pecatonica HS; Hollandale, WI; ALAGirlsSt; ChrhWkr; CmntyWkr; HonRl; TchrAde; YthFnd; SchPpr; 4-H; Trade; Vocation.

HENDRICKSON, Kenneth J; Frontier HS; Brookston, IN; 10/59 ChrhWkr; HonRl; NHS; SchAde; YthFlsp; LetterBsbl; LetterBsktbl; Ftbl; CchngActv; College; Farming.

HENDRICKSON, Lyle W; Argyle HS; Argyle, WI; SecFrshCls; PresJrCls; ALBoysSt; Band; Chr; HonRl; Mdrgl; ModUN; SchMus; RptrYrbk; College; Psychology.

HENDRICKSON, Marcia L; Danville HS; Danville, IL; Chr; HonRl; MrchBnd; Orch; Univ Of Ill; Teacher.

HENDRICKSON, Mona K; Estelline HS; Estelline, SD; 1/38 SecTrsSrCls; ALAGirlsSt; Band; NHS; SchPl; StuCncl; Yrbk; SpnCl; Bsktbl; Chrldr; Sd St U; Music.

HENDRICKSON, Nan M; Cornell HS; Cornell, WI; 1/47 ALAGirlsSt; HonRl; SchPl; StuCncl; Yrbk; EdSchPpr; PpCl; LetterBsktbl; LetterTrk; Univ Of Wisc; Pharmacy.

HENDRICKSON, Rhonda; Hanston HS; Hanston, KS; Band; ModUN; SchPl; SecFFA; Kansas State U;study Vet Medicine.

HENDRICKSON, Robert H; Armstrong HS; Plymouth, MN; 7/596 HonRl; NHS; LetterFtbl; Trk; St John Univ; Math.

HENDRIX, Kimberly J; Marshall HS; Marshall, IL; YthFlsp; 4-H; SecFHA; FTA; SciCl; GAA; 4-HAwd; Indiana State Univ; Physical Education.

HENDRIX, Leon; Lindblom Tech HS; Chicago, IL; NatlMeritCmnd; Trk; Univ Of Wisconsin; Communications.

HENDRIX, Sandra E; North Platte HS; Dearborn, MO; LetterBsktbl; LetterTrk; College; Physical Ed.

HENDRIX, Sandra L; North Andrew HS; Bolckow, MO; VPFrshCls; HonRl; ModUN; NHS; VPStuCncl; RptrSchPpr; Pres4-H; GAA; AmLegAwd; VFWAwd; Nw Mo Univ; Teacher.

HENDRON, Sally R; Bishop Mc Namara HS; Kankakee, IL; HonRl; StuCncl; StuGov; RptrSchPpr; FrCl; CaptGlf; Swmmng; KiwanAwd; VFWAwd; CitAwd; Indiana Univ; Education Admin.

HENDRY, Becky J; Cassville HS; Cassville, MO; HospAde; MrchBnd; Twrl; 4-H; FBLA; FTA; PpCl; Bsbl; Bsktbl; Chrldr; College; Law Or Medicine.

HENDRYX, Julie A; Frontier HS; Battle Ground, IN; 1/58 SecFrshCls; TrsJrCls; Band; HonRl; NHS; OffAde; PepBnd; 4-H; PpCl; Chrldr;.

HENERFAUTH, Norma T; Valmeyer HS; Priarie Du Rocher, IL; 6/56 HonRl; LbryAde; NHS; SchAde; StuCncl; TchrAde; Pres4-H; TreasFHA; PresMthCl; BttyCrckrAwd; Southern Ill U; Bus Adm.

HENGGELER, Gerald M; South Nodaway HS; Barnard, MO; PresFrshCls; ALBoysSt; HonRl; NHS; StuCncl; StuGov; 4-H; LetterBsktbl; LetterFtbl; 4-HAwd; Univ Of Mo; Agricult.

HENGGELER, Gerianne M; Jefferson HS; Stanberry, MO; 2/27 SecTrsSophCls; SecTrsSrCls; Band; CncrtBnd; HonRl; LbryAde; SchPl; StuCncl; Yrbk; PresFHA; University.

HENGY, Susan M 8; Lakers HS; Pigeon, MI; Band; HonRl; LbryAde; NHS; NatlThespSoc; Twrl; Yrbk; GerCl; Glf; Albion College; Pharmacy.

HENHAPL, Ingrid C; Adlai E Stevenson HS; Long Grove, IL; 10/240 CmntyWkr; HonRl; NHS; University; Professional.

HENIGE, Dennis L; New Lothrop HS; New Lathrop, MI; HonRl; NatlFornLg; Yrbk; Ftbl; Trk; Wrstlng; Lake Superior St Coll.

HENINGER, Ralph W; Bettendorf HS; Bettendorf, IA; 39/408 PresJrCls; HonRl; SctActv; StuCncl; StuGov; FrCl; Bsktbl; Ftbl; University; Lawyer.

HENKE, Brenda J; Keypunch W/o; Markesan, WI; SecSrCls; ChrhWkr; RptrYrbk; 4-H; FHA; GAA;.

HENKE, Cahterine D; Lincoln HS; Wisocnsin Rapids, WI; HonRl; NHS; Bsktbl; LetterTennis; College Uw Eau Claire; Medical Tech.

HENKE, Craig; Chaska Sr HS; Chaska, MN; 10/218 ChrhWkr; CmntyWkr; HonRl; NHS; StuCncl; YthFlsp; FrCl; Tennis; Trk; IMSpt; Univ Of Minn; Doctor Of Medicine.

HENKE, Debra; Milford Township HS; Milford, IL; Band; Chr; Chrs; ChrhWkr; CncrtBnd; HonRl; HospAde; MrchBnd; SciCl; School Of Nursing; Nurse.

HENKE, Jamie P; Edgewood HS; Ellettsville, IN; 12/168 SecJrCls; HonRl; PolWkr; StuCncl; TchrAde; RptrYrbk; EdYrBk; RptrSchPpr; VPFrCl; PpCl; Indiana Univ; Journalism.

HENKE, Richard L; Menasha HS; Menasha, WI; LetterBsbl; Bsktbl; LetterFtbl; College; Teacher Phyed.

HENKEL, Dean C; Dodgeland Senior HS; Juneau, WI; SecFrshCls; VPSophCls; AFS; Band; Chr; CncrtBnd; HonRl; MrchBnd; PepBnd; RptrSchPpr; U W Madison; Orthodontist.

HENKEL, Kent; Bennett Comm HS; New Liberty, IA; Band; HonRl; CitAwd; Univ Of Iowa; Commercial Artist.

HENKEL, Susan E; L P Goodrich HS; Fond Du Lac, WI; 8/658 Band; Chr; HospAde; NHS; NatlMeritCmnd; NatlMeritSF; NatlSciFnd; SctActv; SptEdSchPpr; 4-H; Washington Univ; Biomedical Eng.

HENKELS, Carmen; Heron Lake Public HS; Heron Lake, MN; 3/34 Band; HonRl; NHS; OffAde; SchPl; TchrAde; EdYrBk; RptrSchPpr; DARAwd; Univ Of Wasera; Child Care.

HENKEN, Deborah L; Golden Valley HS; Golden Valley, MN; 2/150 ChrhWkr; HonRl; NHS; NatlMeritSF; PolWkr; RptrYrbk; FrCl; PpCl; LetterTrk; CaptChrldr; Univ; Professional.

HENKEN, Mary Jo; Mater Dei HS; Carlyle, IL; 4/198 TrsJrCls; Chrs; HonRl; NHS; SchMus; StuCncl; RptrYrbk; RptrSchPpr; SecLatCl; Glf; St Louis U; Social Science.

HENKEN, Susan L; Golden Valley HS; Golden Valley, MN; 1/150 Chr; ChrhWkr; HonRl; NHS; PolWkr; SchMus; PresFrCl; PpCl; LetterTrk; Chrldr; Coll.

HENKHAUS, Richard A; Routt HS; Jacksonville, IL; StuCncl; Bsktbl; Univ Of Illinois.

HENKLE, Nancy A; Central HS; Evansville, IN; 8/665 CncrtBnd; HonRl; MrchBnd; NHS; Orch; SchMus; StuCncl; PpCl; LetterTrk; PPFtbl; University; Engineering Profession.

HENLEY, Anne; Broad Ripple HS; Indianapolis, IN; 6/230 Chr; HonRl; Mdrgl; NHS; NatlMeritCmnd; NatlThespSoc; SchMus; YthFlsp; RptrSchPpr; Indiana Univ; Physician.

HENLEY, Beth A; Elcho HS; Deerbrook, WI; CncrtBnd; HonRl; LbryAde; MrchBnd; OffAde; TchrAde; SecSecFHA; SciCl; GAA; Univ.

HENLEY, Betty L; Richland HS; Richland, MO; 3/63 SecSrCls; Chrs; ChrhWkr; HonRl; RptrYrbk; EdSchPpr; FTA; PpCl; LetterBsktbl; Business Sch; Legal Sec.

HENLEY, David S; Aberdeen Central HS; Aberdeen, SD; Band; ChrhWkr; CncrtBnd; HonRl; PolWkr; CaptWrstlng; College.

HENLEY, Philip A; Turkey Run HS; Marshall, IN; ChrhWkr; YthFlsp; Pres4-H; PresFFA; 4-HAwd; SARAwd; Purdue Univ; Agriculture.

HENLEY, William A; Edison Sr HS; East Gary, IN; Band; CncrtBnd; HonRl; JrNHS; MrchBnd; PepBnd; FrCl; College; Biology.

HENN, Marcia K; West Central HS; Hawkeye, IA; SecSrCls; DrlTm; HonRl; Mdrgl; MrchBnd; PepBnd; SchMus; FHA; PpCl; LetterTrk; College; Nursing.

HENN, Verona; Pope John Xxiii Cc HS; Elgin, NE; 10/54 Chrs; ModUN; NHS; SchMus; StuCncl; PpCl; Business School; Business Administration.

HENNE, Sheila; Arthur Hill HS; Saginaw, MI; HonRl; HospAde; LbryAde; OffAde; FDA; GerCl; Bsktbl; Swmmng; Univ;physician.

HENNEBERRY, Scott M; Central Catholic HS; Bloomington, IL; ALBoysSt; HonRl; SchPl; College; Physics.

HENNECK, Louis J; L F Community HS; Little Falls, MN; 26/303 SctActv; TchrAde; FBLA; IMSpt; Brainerd Vo Tech; Natural Resource Tech.

HENNEKE, Maureen L; Owensville HS; Owensville, MO; HonRl; NHS; PresNatlThespSoc; Quill&Scroll; SchMus; SchPl; StuCncl; EdSchPpr; PresFTA; LatCl; Univ Of Missouri Columbia; Broadcasting.

HENNEMAN, Richard L; Rock Island HS; Rock Island, IL; Band; TreasNHS; Orch; PolWkr; SchMus; StuGov; TreasKeyCl; GerCl; PpCl; U Of Ill; Engineering Or Medicine.

HENNEMAN, Susan L; Logan View HS; Hooper, NE; 3/60 PresFrshCls; VPJrCls; HonRl; NHS; SchPl; 4-H; PpCl; LetterBsktbl; LetterTrk; Chrldr; University; English.

HENNEMANN, Lana; Lindbergh HS; Crestwood, MO; /1000 CmntyWkr; HospAde; JrNHS; NHS; OffAde; SchAde; SctActv; GerCl; PpCl; Coll; Business Admin.

HENNEN, Mark J; Belle Plaine HS; Belle Plaine, MN; VPSophCls; ChrhWkr; HonRl; SchMus; SchPl; TchrAde; RptrSchPpr; LetterBsktbl; LetterFtbl; St Johns Univ; Pre Med.

HENNES, Diane; St Mary Central HS; Neenah, WI; 9/121 SctActv; SpnCl; College; Medical Tech.

HENNESSEE, Mark S; Lake Central HS; Schererville, IN; 23/453 HonRl; NHS; PresNatlThespSoc; SchMus; SchPl; StuGov; TchrAde; FrCl; LionAwd; Purdue Univ; Engineering.

HENNESSEY, Lawrence R; Churchill HS; Livonia, MI; 4/861 ModUN; NatlMeritSF; PolWkr; University; Dentistry.

HENNESSEY, Leo K; Bergan HS; Fremont, NE; Chr; Chrs; HonRl; SchPl; SchPpr; Bsbl; Bsktbl; Ftbl; LetterTrk; CchngActv; College; Professional.

HENNESSEY, Ronald J; Wm Chrisman HS; Independence, MO; AFS; SctActv; RptrSchPpr; Bsktbl; LetterSwmmng; LetterTrk; University.

HENNESSEY, Sue; Mankato West HS; Mankato, MN; HonRl; StuCncl; SpnCl; Bsktbl; Glf;.

HENNESSY, Delwyn J; Minot HS; Minot, ND; PresFrshCls; HonRl; NHS; StuCncl; YthLg; PresGerCl; Ftbl; Trk; Wrstlng; PresAwd; RotaryAwd; University.

HENNESSY, Jill N; Mother Mc Auley HS; Oak Lawn, IL; HonRl; HospAde; NatlMeritCmnd; OffAde; RedCrAde; Univ Of Illinois; Nursing.

HENNESSY, Rebecca R; Berthold Public HS; Berthold, ND; 3/15 SecJrCls; Band; Chr; Chrl; HonRl; SchPl; SctActv; SptEdYrbk; Bsktbl; Trk; Chrldr; North Dakota St U Fargo; Horticulture.

HENNICKE, Ralph; Vianney HS; St Louis, MO; 57/171 Band; CmntyWkr; HonRl; Sacrstn; Ftbl; Trk; IMSpt; Coll; Law.

HENNIG, Brad A; Garden Cnty HS; Lisco, NE; PresFrshCls; TrsJrCls; ALBoysSt; HonRl; NHS; StuCncl; StuGov; YthFlsp; LetterBsktbl; LetterTrk; College; Professional.

HENNIGS, Lowell; Lemars Community HS; Lemars, IA; 8/221 AFS; ALBoysSt; Chr; Chrl; Chrs; HonRl; BauchLmbAwd; Central College; Law.

HENNING, Bonnie L; Memorial Senior HS; Fall Creek, WI; 78/435 Band; CncrtBnd; HonRl; MrchBnd; PepBnd; 4-H; 4-HAwd; Vocational School; Accounting.

HENNING, Christine M; Plattsmouth HS; Plattsmouth, NE; 3/163 Band; Chrs; HonRl; Mdrgl; NHS; SchMus; StuCncl; YthFlsp; Univ Of Ne; Medicine.

HENNING, Holly; Dixon Hs; Dixon, IL; Chr; HonRl; HospAde; JA; Bsbl; GAA; Illinois State U; social Work.

HENNING, Inez J; Webster HS; Grenville, SD; Chr; HonRl; NHS; NatlThespSoc; SchPl; Yrbk; FHA; DARAwd; Business School; Secretary.

HENNING, Jackie J; Crete Sr HS; Crete, NE; 22/114 HospAde; YthFlsp; FBLA; FHA; PpCl; University; Nursing.

HENNING, Janet; Watseka Community HS; Watseka, IL; Kankakee Comm College; Nursing.

HENNING, Mary E; Grinnell Newburg HS; Grinnell, IA; 24/189 Band; CncrtBnd; HonRl; MrchBnd; Orch; SchMus; SchPl; RptrYrbk; College; Music.

HENNING, Patricia; Newburg Public HS; Newburg, ND; ALAGirlsSt; Band; Chr; HonRl; PepBnd; 4-H; Chrldr; College.

HENNING, Paul W; Community HS; Oakdale, IL; Band; Chr; CncrtBnd; Mdrgl; MrchBnd; NHS; PepBnd; SchPl; EdYrBk; 4-HAwd; College Geneva; Chemist.

HENNING, Richard E; Muskego HS; Hales Corners, WI; HonRl; LitMag; GerCl; IMSpt;.

HENNING, Timothy A; Churubusco HS; Churubusco, IN; 2/102 PresFrshCls; PresSophCls; PresJrCls; HonRl; NHS; NatlThespSoc; SchMus; StuCncl; LetterFtbl; NCTE; In Univ.

HENNINGER, Ann; Delavan HS; Delavan, IL; Chr; Chrl; Chrs; ChrhWkr; HonRl; NatlThespSoc; OffAde; SchPl; GAA; IMSpt; Coll;.

HENNINGER, Jane L; Pekin Comm HS; Pekin, IL; 74/803 ChrhWkr; LbryAde; PolWkr; TchrAde; FrCl; PpCl; Univ Of Illinois; Political Science.

HENNINGFIELD, Debra A; Union Grove HS; Sturtevant, WI; AFS; HonRl; University; Elementary Ed.

HENNINGSGAARD, Kari; Thomas Jefferson HS; Bloomington, MN; Band; ChrhWkr; CncrtBnd; MrchBnd; NHS; RedCrAde; College.

HENNRICH, Jacinta E; Chester HS; Chester, IL; Chrs; ChrhWkr; HonRl; HospAde; NatlThespSoc; RptrSchPpr; PpCl; GAA;.

HENRICH, Beverly; Thornton Twp Hs; Dolton, IL; 18/727 HonRl; NHS; OffAde; EdYrBk; FrCl; SecMthCl; VPPpCl; U Of Illinois; Metallurgical Engineering.

HENRICHS, Cheryl A; Columbus HS; Marshfield, WI; 24/117 SecTrsSrCls; Chrs; HonRl; NHS; SchPl; StuCncl; TchrAde; SchPpr; GerCl; PpCl; Bsbl; LetterBsktbl; Ftbl; Tech School; Lab Tech.

HENRICHS, Debra A; Medford Senior HS; Medford, WI; 56/254 HonRl; FHA;.

HENRICHS, Leslee; Athens HS; Hamburg, WI; HonRl; LbryAde; NHS; 4-H; FHA; SpnCl; PpCl; IMSpt; College; Vocation.

HENRICHS, Randy J; William Chrisman HS; Independence, MO; Ftbl; Trk; PresAwd; CitAwd; College.

HENRICHS, Ravon S; Ramona HS; Ramona, SD; 4/18 SecSrCls; Band; Chrs; HonRl; SchPl; RptrYrbk; 4-H; FHA; LetterBsktbl; GAA; 4-HAwd; College; Dental Asst.

HENRICKS, Steven C; William Fremd HS; Palatine, IL; Band; HonRl; NHS; NatlMeritCmnd; St Olaf College; Music.

HENRIKSEN, Gerry; Wakonda Public HS; Vermillion, SD; SecFrshCls; PresSophCls; Band; CncrtBnd; HonRl; SchPl; StuCncl; Bsktbl; Ftbl; Trk; College.

HENRIKSEN, Paul W; Lena Winslow HS; Lena, IL; 1/95 HonRl; LitMag; NHS; NatlMeritCmnd; Quill&Scroll; SchPl; Yrbk; EdSchPpr; SchPpr; Loras College; Biophysics.

HENRIKSON, Angela C; Academy Of Our Lady; Peoria, IL; 27/95 HonRl; NHS; OffAde; Bradley University; Intl Studies.

HENRIKSON, Diane R; Maine Township West HS; Des Plaines, IL; ChrhWkr; HonRl; NHS; StuCncl; GAA; Augustana.

HENRIKSON, Tammy; Adams HS; Rochester, MI; Band; Chr; MrchBnd; OffAde; SchMus; SctActv; TchrAde; SpnCl; Ferris St;liberal Arts.

HENRY, Amber C; Duchesne HS; St Charles, MO; 7/196 Chrs; ChrhWkr; CmntyWkr; HonRl; SchMus; SchPl; SctActv; CivCl; PpCl; University; Psychology.

HENRY, Ann M; Mother Mcauley HS; Oak Lawn, IL; 55/475 TreasChrs; ChrhWkr; HonRl; VPNHS; SchMus; SchPl; 4-H; Tennis; IMSpt; E Illinois Univ; Liberal Arts.

HENRY, Anthony R; St Clair HS; St Clair, MO; ChrhWkr; HonRl; JrNHS; VPNHS; TchrAde; KeyCl; PpCl; LetterBsbl; LetterBsktbl; LetterFtbl; Jr College; Computor Study.

HENRY, Cheryl J; Ida Public HS; Ida, MI; 7/175 TrsJrCls; ALAGirlsSt; Band; ChrhWkr; HonRl; NHS; YthFlsp; 4-H; Chrldr; IMSpt; Western Mi U; Social Work.

HENRY, Darton C; Council Grove HS; Council Grove, KS; Band; Chr; CncrtBnd; HonRl; MrchBnd; NHS; PepBnd; SchMus; Bsktbl; Ftbl; Oral Roberts U; Psychology.

HENRY, David M; Southern Reynolds R2 HS; Ellington, MO; Band; CncrtBnd; HonRl; MrchBnd; SctActv; SchPpr; IMSpt; Univ Mo Columbia; Veterinarian.

HENRY, David P; Lancaster HS; Lancaster, WI; VPFrshCls; PresSrCls; AFS; ALBoysSt; Chrs; ChrhWkr; HonRl; Mdrgl; ModUN; Bsktbl; Univ Of Wi Platville; Music Business.

HENRY, Debra K; Clio HS; Clio, MI; Chr; HonRl; LbryAde; SctActv; Yrbk; Col; Medical Assistant.

HENRY, Donna S; Liberty HS; Mtn View, MO; HonRl; NHS; FHA;.

HENRY, Elizabeth; Beloit Catholic HS; Beloit, WI; Chrs; ChrhWkr; CmntyWkr; HonRl; NHS; SchMus; Sdlty; YthFnd; Yrbk; Bsktbl; College; Nursing.

HENRY, John D; Big Rapids HS; Big Rapids, MI; TrsFrshCls; HonRl; StuCncl; TchrAde; FrCl; MthCl; Glf; CchngActv; IMSpt; Michigan Tech Univ; Civil Engineering.

HENRY, John M; James B Conant HS; Hoffman Estates, IL; CmntyWkr; HonRl; RedCrAde; SctActv; LetterFtbl; Eastern Ill Univ; Business.

HENRY, John P; Marion HS; Marion, IL; 49/277 ChrhWkr; CmntyWkr; HonRl; NatlMeritCmnd; Illinois State Univ; Special Educ.

HENRY, Julie; Fremont Senior HS; Fremont, NE; OffAde; 4-H; SpnCl; PpCl; Office Work.

HENRY, Karen L; Marshall HS; Marshall, MN; 4/219 Band; Chr; ChrhWkr; CmntyWkr; CncrtBnd; HonRl; MrchBnd; NHS; OffAde; SpnCl; Mn Univ; Math.

HENRY, Leslie J; South Vigo HS; Terre Haute, IN; 51/560 Chr; HonRl; HospAde; NHS; OffAde; SchMus; Indiana State University; Life Science.

HENRY, Lisa M; Arcadia Valley HS; Roselle, MO; 11/95 SecFrshCls; TrsFrshCls; Band; ChrhWkr; CmntyWkr; HonRl; NHS; PolWkr; StuCncl; TchrAde; Twrl; SchPpr; FHA; FTA; Rolla Area Vo Tech School; Nursing.

HENRY, Maureen; Beloit Catholic HS; Beloit, WI; AFS; Chrs; ChrhWkr; CmntyWkr; HonRl; HospAde; NHS; RptrYrbk; RptrSchPpr; GAA; Coll; Nursing.

HENRY, Michael R; Battle Creek Central HS; Battle Creek, MI; 140/675 VPFrshCls; Chr; Chrl; Chrs; Mdrgl; SctActv; Bsktbl; Ftbl; Swmmng; College; Teacher.

HENRY, Pamela; Callaway Public HS; Callaway, NE; Band; HonRl; RedCrAde; StuCncl; Twrl; FHA; Bsktbl; Swmmng; Trk; Chrldr; Trade School; Vocation.

HENRY, Peggy J; Waterman HS; Waterman, IL; 5/41 CncrtBnd; HonRl; MrchBnd; PepBnd; LetterSocr; LetterTrk; GAA; PresAwd; College; Professnl.

HENRY, Richard N; Clifford Galesburg HS; Galesburg, ND; 2/13 VPFrshCls; SecTrsSophCls; Band; CncrtBnd; HonRl; PepBnd; SchPl; StuCncl; LetterBsktbl; LetterTrk; College.

HENRY, Scott D; Larimore HS; Northwood, ND; Chr; ChrhWkr; CncrtBnd; LitMag; MrchBnd; PepBnd; SchPl; RptrYrbk; College; Professional.

HENRY, Sherry L; Ellington HS; Ellington, MO; VPFrshCls; Chrs; HonRl; LbryAde; FHA; Chrldr; IMSpt; Coll; Pro.

HENRY, Susan L; Nemaha Valley HS; Seneca, KS; PresFrshCls; SecSrCls; ALAGirlsSt; HonRl; SpnCl; PpCl; LetterBsktbl; LetterTennis; LetterTrk; GAA; College.

HENRY, Terrence L; Sherrard HS; Coal Valley, IL; 2/100 HonRl; NHS; 4-H; FrCl; Augustana College; Medicine.

HENRY, William R; Badger HS; Lake Geneva, WI; 1/219 ALBoysSt; ChrhWkr; HonRl; NHS; TchrAde; LetterGlf; Milwaukee School; Architect.

HENSCHEL, Becky J; Ogilvie Public HS; Ogilvie, MN; HonRl; LbryAde; Trade School; Cosmotoligest.

HENSCHEL, Laurie K; Ogilvie HS; Ogilvie, MN; 3/54 TrsSrCls; Band; HonRl; MrchBnd; NHS; SchMus; StuCncl; TchrAde; FHA; BttyCrckrAwd; Univ Of Mn; Music.

HENSCHEL, Lonna; Kiel HS; Cleveland, WI; Band; ChrhWkr; MrchBnd; PepBnd; YthFlsp; FFA; Technical School; Vocation.

HENSCHKE, Denise C; Buffalo Lake Public HS; Hector, MN; VPFrshCls; Band; Chr; HonRl; MrchBnd; NHS; PepBnd; SchPl; RptrYrbk; RptrSchPpr; FHA; Bsktbl; College; Biology.

HENSEL, Beth J; Merrill HS; Brant, MI; 1/107 Chr; Chrs; ChrhWkr; HonRl; NHS; SchMus; 4-H; University; Professional.

HENSEL, Geannie M; Carmel HS; Carmel, IN; ChrhWkr; CmntyWkr; OffAde; PolWkr; TchrAde; YthFlsp; 4-H; FTA; MthCl; PpCl; Bsktbl; GAA; Ball State Univ; Physical Educ Coaching.

HENSEL, James W; South Iron R 1 HS; Des Arc, MO; VPBand; VPCncrtBnd; HonRl; MrchBnd; PepBnd; VPStuCncl; Bsktbl; Clge; Architecture.

HENSEL, Karen A; George S Parker Sr HS; Janesville, WI; 10/387 ALAGirlsSt; CmntyWkr; NHS; Carthage College; Law.

HENSEL, Violet M; Lakeview Sr HS; St Clair Shores, MI; ChrhWkr; HonRl; Orch; SchMus; SchPl; Music Conservatory; Musician.

HENSELER, Dennis A; Columbus HS; Marshfield, WI; ALBoysSt; HonRl; NHS; Bsktbl; LetterTrk; Accounting.

HENSELER, Mary J; Benet Acad; Glen Ellyn, IL; HonRl; HospAde; NatlMeritSF; YthLg; RptrYrbk; Bsbl; Medical Field.

HENSELER, Susan K; Marshfield HS; Marshfield, WI; Band; CncrtBnd; HonRl; MrchBnd; NHS; Orch; RedCrAde; SchMus; SchPl; RotaryAwd; St Josephs Nur Sch; Registered Nurse.

HENSHAW, Donn A; Fort Dodge HS; Fort Dodge, IA; HonRl; JrNHS; NHS; NatlMeritSF; SchAde; GerCl; Bsktbl; LetterFtbl; Glf; IMSpt; College; Curriculum Of Major.

HENSLEY, Carolyn J; Festus R 6 HS; Festus, MO; 20/157 Chr; HonRl; NHS; SchPl; FHA; FrCl; PpCl; Trk; GAA; IMSpt; Southeast Mo State U.

HENSLEY, Debra; Seymour HS; Seymour, MO; 4/57 Band; HonRl; MrchBnd; PepBnd; SchPl; EdYrBk; PpCl; Univ; Physical Therapist.

HENSLEY, Marion P; Hamilton Southeastern HS; Fortville, IN; Aud/Vis; HonRl; LbryAde; TchrAde; Univ; Prof.

HENSLEY, Pamela F; Salem HS; Salem, IN; Chr; HonRl; HospAde; JrNHS; NHS; SchAde; TchrAde; FHA; LatCl; PpCl;.

HENSLEY, Randy D; Charlestown HS; Charlestown, IN; 12/142 HstFrshCls; TrsSrCls; HonRl; HospAde; NHS; YthFlsp; LetterBsbl; LetterFtbl; LetterTennis; GovHonPrgAwd; Air Force.

HENSLIN, Vickie L; Bird Island Public HS; Bird Island, MN; Band; ChrhWkr; DrmMjrt; NatlFornLg; SchMus; StuCncl; FHA; Trk; IMSpt; PPFtbl; Concordia Moorhead; Biology.

HENSON, Donald F; Fairfield Comm HS; Fairfield, IL; ChrhWkr; CmntyWkr; HonRl; NatlSciFnd; PolWkr; RedCrAde; StuCncl; FFA; FSA; 4-HAwd; College; Lab Technician.

HENSON, Donna D; Queen Of Peace HS; Chicago, IL; 32/421 Chrs; HonRl; JrNHS; LbryAde; NHS; College; Physical Therapy.

HENSON, Gregory E; Paris HS; Paris, IL; 17/256 HonRl; NHS; SctActv; Bsktbl; LetterFtbl; LetterGlf; CaptTennis; IMSpt; Rose Holman Inst Of Tech; Mechanical Eng.

HENSON, James B; Norris City Omaha HS; Norris City, IL; Band; Chrs; HonRl; Trade School; Motorcycle Business.

HENSON, Kim M; Galesburg Augusta HS; Galesburg, MI; 1/129 PresAFS; Band; CncrtBnd; HonRl; PresJA; MrchBnd; NHS; NatlMeritSF; PepBnd; SctActv; TchrAde; DARAwd; Mass Inst Of Tech; Engineering.

HENSON, Lynn M; Lowell Sr HS; Hebron, IN; 29/249 DrlTm; HonRl; LbryAde; OffAde; 4-H; SpnCl; PpCl; Purdue Univ At W Lafayette; Spanish Teacher.

HENSON, Nancy F; Galena HS; Galena, MO; Chr; HonRl; SchPl; FHA; Trade School.

HENSRUD, Debra K; Tolna Public HS; Pekin, ND; Chrs; ChrhWkr; HonRl; SchPl; PpCl; College; Business.

HENSS, Janet M; Lebanon HS; Trenton, IL; 1/91 VPFrshCls; SecTrsSophCls; VPJrCls; Band; Chrs; CncrtBnd; HonRl; MrchBnd; NHS; SchMus; SchPl; StuCncl; AmLegAwd; College; Nursing.

HENSTEIN, Leslie P; Montevideo Senior HS; Montevideo, MN; HonRl; LetterBsktbl; LetterTrk; KiwanAwd; Mankato State College; Accounting.

HENTRICH, Kathleen E; North Scott HS; Walcott, IA; 20/201 Band; Chr; PresChrhWkr; HonRl; NHS; SchMus; Lincoln Christian Col; Music.

HENTSCHELL, Mark S; Chaminade HS; Chesterfield, MO; 13/113 StuCncl; LetterFtbl; CaptSocr; LetterTennis; College.

HENTZ, Blase J; John Marshall HS; Zumbro Falls, MN; 51/608 Band; CncrtBnd; MrchBnd; NHS; PepBnd; GerCl; Wrstlng; Georgetown Univ; Foreign Service.

HENTZE, Janet S; Minooka Community HS; Minooka, IL; 6/106 CncrtBnd; HonRl; SecNHS; SchPl; YthFlsp; MthCl; LetterSocr; LetterTrk; PresGAA; PresAwd; Southern Il Univ; Doctor.

HENTZEN, Patrick M; Bishop Carroll HS; Goddard, KS; ALBoysSt; HonRl; StuGov; 4-H; Bsbl; LetterFtbl; Wrstlng; CchngActv; College; Professional.

HENTZEN, William R; Whitefish Bay HS; Milwaukee, WI; 99/344 ChrhWkr; HonRl; SctActv; SchPpr; GerCl; MthCl; University; Engineering.

HENZE, Charles R; West Marshall HS; State Center, IA; TrsSophCls; PresJrCls; PresSrCls; ALBoysSt; ChrhWkr; HonRl; StuCncl; YthFlsp; LetterFtbl; IMSpt; College.

HENZE, Janna R; West Marshall HS; State Center, IA; 2/109 Band; CncrtBnd; HonRl; MrchBnd; PepBnd; YthFlsp; PpCl; Bsktbl; LetterTrk; PPFtbl; College; Mathematics.

HENZE, Kay L; Shannon HS; Shannon, IL; 6/30 HonRl; StuCncl; EdSchPpr; 4-H; LetterBsbl; CaptSocr; LetterTrk; AmLegAwd; DanFAwd; 4-HAwd; College; Elementary Education.

HEPKER, Susan L; Addison HS; Pittsford, MI; 14/107 HonRl; SchMus; SchPl; 4-H; FNA; Chrldr; GAA; PPFtbl; 4-HAwd; CitAwd; Univ Of Mi; Med Surgical Rn.

HEPNER, Blake A; Ottawa HS; Ottawa, IL; 66/426 Band; HonRl; NHS; SchMus; SchPl; SctActv; CaptTrk; AmLegAwd; JETSAwd; Univ Of Il; Chemical Engineering.

HEPNER, Julie A; Kewanee HS; Kewanee, IL; Chr; HonRl; SchMus; SecYthFlsp; RptrYrbk; Pres4-H; SecFHA; GAA; AmLegAwd; 4-HAwd; College; Architectural Engineering.

HEPNER, Marcia A; Marseilles HS; Marseilles, IL; 1/67 ALAGirlsSt; VPBand; NHS; NatlThespSoc; PresStuCncl; YthFlsp; EdSchPpr; Chrldr; VPGAA; DARAwd; Drake Univ; Pharmacy.

HEPOLA, Pamela S; Lutheran West HS; Detroit, MI; ChrhWkr; HonRl; NHS; StuCncl; GerCl; PpCl; Chrldr; University; Medicine.

HEPP, Margaret A; Rich Central HS; Olympia Fields, IL; 7/400 Chr; HonRl; TrsFrshCls; SecSophCls; NHS; NatlMeritCmnd; SchMus; SchPl; Bsktbl; GAA; Michigan State U; Liberal Arts.

HEPP, Nancy; Rosary HS; Aurora, IL; HonRl; NatlMeritCmnd; StuCncl; EdYrBk; SpnCl; PpCl; GAA; BttyCrckrAwd; Univ Ill.

HEPP, Sheryl A; Trico HS; Cutler, IL; 10/75 ChrhWkr; CmntyWkr; HonRl; HospAde; JrNHS; NHS; FBLA; Chrldr; CchngActv; DARAwd;.

HEPPEARD, Gloria S; Lakeview HS; Battle Creek, MI; Chr; HonRl; Mdrgl; NHS; Quill&Scroll; TchrAde; SchPpr; FTA; SecSciCl; BttyCrckrAwd; Olivet College; Music Therapy.

HEPPNER, Glen G; Batesville HS; Oldenburg, IN; ALBoysSt; Band; CncrtBnd; HonRl; SctActv; SpnCl; LetterBsbl; LetterBsktbl; LetterFtbl; LetterTrk; Earlham College; Optometry.

HEPTIG, Debbie; Westmoreland HS; St George, KS; PresJrCls; PresSrCls; HonRl; OffAde; StuCncl; TchrAde; RptrYrbk; FHA; Bsbl; Chrldr;.

HERAUF, William A; Dickinson HS; Dickinson, ND; 35/186 HstFrshCls; PresSrCls; ALBoysSt; HonRl; ModUN; NatlFornLg; PolWkr; SctActv; StuCncl; StuGov; YthFlsp; YthFnd; YthLg; LetterFtbl; CaptWrstlng; Dickinson State Univ; Business.

HERBER, Harry A; Adelphian Acad; Holly, MI; HonRl; NHS; RptrYrbk; Yrbk; EldAwd; IMSpt; Andrews Univ; Medicine.

HERBERG, John T; Warren Central HS; Indianapolis, IN; HonRl; JrNHS; NatlMeritSF; KeyCl; MthCl; SciCl; Coll; Doctor.

HERBERGER, Evie M; Hays HS; Hays, KS; DrlTm; HonRl; SchPl; PpCl; Coll.

HERBERS, John A; St Louis HS; St Louis, MO; 20/205 Chr; CncrtBnd; HonRl; NHS; NatlMeritCmnd; SctActv; StuCncl; RptrSchPpr; LetterFtbl; Georgetown U; Education.

HERBERS, Mark A; St Charles HS; Brant, MI; HonRl; MrchBnd; TchrAde; Ftbl; Trk; Trade Sch.

HERBERT, Beverly A; Verdigre Public HS; Winnetoon, NE; VPFrshCls; PresSophCls; Band; Chr; ChrhWkr; DrmMjrt; HonRl; MrchBnd; OffAde; PepBnd; SchMus; SchPl; StuCncl; YthFlsp; PpCl; Norfolk Tech College; Exec Secretary.

HERBERT, Chris A; St Pius X HS; Festus, MO; ChrhWkr; SecCncrtBnd; HospAde; MrchBnd; PepBnd; StuCncl; RptrYrbk; Yrbk; Clge; Pro Music Therapy.

HERBERT, Eddie D; Winfield HS; Winfield, MO; 3/60 SecTrsFrshCls; PresSrCls; ALBoysSt; HonRl; PresNHS; StuCncl; TchrAde; CaptBsktbl; U Of Mo Rolla; Engineering.

HERBERT, Janine M; Glenwood HS; Glenarm, IL; 66/159 AFS; Chr; JA; RptrSchPpr; 4-H; FHA; GerCl; 4-HAwd; JAAwd; Concordia Lutheran Clg; Abnormal Psychology.

HERBERT, Lisa A; Greenfield HS; Greenfield, WI; HonRl; LbryAde; NHS; SctActv; GAA; Clge; Zoology.

HERBERT, Randy J; Greensburg HS; Greensburg, IN; 16/191 ALBoysSt; HonRl; NHS; SchMus; PresCivCl; PpCl; LetterFtbl; CaptTrk; IMSpt; OptClAwd; College; Accounting.

HERBERTZ, Julie A; Roncalli HS; Indianapolis, IN; HonRl; HospAde; JA; SchPl; GAA; School Of Nursing; Registered Nurse.

HERBST, Anna L; Brighton HS; Brighton, MI; HonRl; NHS; GerCl; College;.

HERBST, Barbara M; Milaca HS; Foreston, MN; Chrs; HospAde; MrchBnd; SchMus; RptrYrbk; 4-H; FHA; DanFAwd; Junior College; Medical Technician.

HERBST, Jeannie M; Washington Comm HS; Washington, IL; 49/345 AFS; Chrl; Chrs; HonRl; Mdrgl; Orch; SchMus; SchPl; TreasTennis; Il Wesleyan Univ; Music.

HERCHENBACH, Nancy J; St Francis HS; Lindsay, NE; Chrs; HonRl; StuCncl; TchrAde; 4-H; PpCl; 4-HAwd; College;.

HERCHENBACK, Sheri; St Francis HS; Lindsay, NE; ;35 SecSrCls; Chrs; HonRl; StuCncl; StuGov; SchPpr; 4-H; PpCl; IMSpt; Business.

HERCULES, Daryl P; Duchesne HS; St Charles, MO; HonRl; KeyCl; College; Accounting.

HERD, John; Arlington Green Isle HS; Green Isle, MN; TrsFrshCls; ALBoysSt; HonRl; JrNHS; NHS; Bsbl; Bsktbl; Ftbl; IMSpt; PresAwd; Coll.

HERD, Mark R; Fair Grove R10 HS; Fair Grove, MO; VPFrshCls; Band; StuCncl; Pres4-H; PresFFA; LetterBsbl; LetterBsktbl; 4-HAwd; Drury College.

HERDA, Penny L; Washington HS; Washington, KS; HstJrCls; DrmMjrt; HonRl; StuCncl; StuCncl; SciCl; CaptBsktbl; LetterTrk; Chrldr; GAA; College; Professional.

HERDA, Vince J; Albany HS; Albany, MN; 3/130 ChrhWkr; HonRl; SchPl; LetterFtbl; LetterTrk; University; Mathematics.

HERDINA, Anne E; Lourdes HS; Rochester, MN; Band; CncrtBnd; MrchBnd; PepBnd; SchMus; TchrAde; Coll; Eng & Mus.

HERDMAN, Tracy E; Atchison HS; Atchison, KS; SecSophCls; SecJrCls; HonRl; NHS; SchPl; RptrSchPpr; PpCl; Ks State Coll; Bus Admin.

HERFEL, Julie; Waterloo HS; Waterloo, WI; 15/76 Aud/Vis; Chrs; HonRl; NatlFornLg; SchMus; SchPl; StuCncl; EdYrBk; RptrSchPpr; Uw Madison; Communication Ats.

HERGET, Lisa L; Toulon Lafayette HS; Toulon, IL; VPSrCls; Band; Chrs; CncrtBnd; HonRl; MrchBnd; PepBnd; SchMus; SchPl; EdYrBk; Illinois Wesleyan Univ; Art.

HERHAGER, Alice; St Mary Acad; New Boston, MI; 16/131 HonRl; HospAde; ModUN; NHS; FNA; Ferris St Coll; Nuclear Med Tech.

HERHAGER, Alice M; St Mary Academy; New Boston, MI; 18/145 Chrl; HonRl; ModUN; SecNHS; FNA; Ferris St College; Nuclear Med Tech.

HERINK, Jackie J; Leigh Comm HS; Clarkson, NE; TrsJrCls; Chrs; CncrtBnd; HonRl; Mdrgl; SchPl; FHA; GerCl; Chrldr; VoiceDemAwd; College; Medical Records.

HERJE, Stephen A; Armstrong HS; Robbinsdale, MN; CmntyWkr; HonRl; NatlMeritSF; PolWkr; SctActv; SpnCl; Univ; Law.

HERKERT, Lauri J; Joliet West HS; Joliet, IL; 3/580 HonRl; NHS; OffAde; TchrAde; 4-H; GerCl; CaptChrldr; AmLegAwd; 4-HAwd; KiwanAwd; College.

HERL, Faye T; Academy Of Mt St Scholastica; Quinter, KS; Band; Chrs; HonRl; NatlMeritCmnd; PepBnd; SchMus; Sdlty; EdYrBk; SptEdSchPpr; Ft Hays Kansas St College; Law.

HERL, Jeff R; Fox HS; Arnold, MO; 165/599 Chrs; HonRl; SctActv; 4-H; Bsktbl; IMSpt; College; Teaching.

HERMAN, Catherine A; Lockport Central HS; Lockport, IL; 1 620 HonRl; LbryAde; NHS; NatlMeritFnl; NatlMeritCmnd; NatlMeritSF; SchPpr; VoiceDemAwd;.

HERMAN, Catherine; O L Of Mt Carmel HS; Wyandotte, MI; 4/61 Chr; HonRl; NHS; RedCrAde; SchMus; RptrYrbk; RptrSchPpr; SpnCl; College.

HERMAN, Chris H; Moravia Comm HS; Unionville, IA; 4/42 HonRl; SciCl; Trk; Navy; Nuclear Technician.

HERMAN, Curtis A; Tolna Public HS; Tolna, ND; ALBoysSt; HonRl; NHS; SchPl; SptEdSchPpr; PpCl; Bsbl; Bsktbl; Ftbl; EldAwd; Coll; Coach.

HERMAN, Daniel; Fonda Comm HS; Pocahontas, IA; ALBoysSt; ALAGirlsSt; HonRl; SchPl; StuCncl; StuGov; FFA; FHA; Farming.

HERMAN, Daniel; Moravia Community HS; Unionville, IA; 8/42 Band; ChrhWkr; CncrtBnd; HonRl; MrchBnd; PepBnd; SchMus; RptrSchPpr; SciCl; Bob Jones Univ; Medicine.

HERMAN, Diane B; Laker HS; Elkton, MI; 8/146 PresChrs; ChrhWkr; HonRl; NHS; TchrAde; FTA; Spring Arbor College; Math.

HERMAN, Elizabeth M; Maconaquah HS; Grissom Afb, IN; 32/240 Chrs; CAP; CmntyWkr; HonRl; SchMus; SchPl; YthFlsp; Swmmng; Trk; GAA; College; Medicine.

HERMAN, James J; Frederick HS; Westport, SD; 1/34 SecTrsJrCls; Band; Chrs; CncrtBnd; HonRl; MrchBnd; PepBnd; SchPl; U Of Sd; Dentistry.

HERMAN, Jodi J; Leeds Public HS; Brinsmade, ND; Chrl; ChrhWkr; HonRl; SchPl; TchrAde; SecYthFlsp; FHA; LetterTrk; IMSpt; AmLegAwd; Medical Field.

HERMAN, Joe; N C HS; Norton, KS; ChrhWkr; HonRl; LbryAde; TchrAde; FrCl; Bsbl; Bsktbl; CaptGlf; CchngActv; University; Professional.

HERMAN, Lori J; Carl Sandburg HS; Orland Park, IL; 18/680 HonRl; HospAde; NHS; NatlMeritCmnd; RptrSchPpr; SecSpnCl; PpCl; Swmmng; GAA; Evangelical Sch Of Nsg; Reg Nurse.

HERMAN, Mary; Lourdes HS; Byron, MN; Band; Chrs; CmntyWkr; HonRl; NHS; StuGov; TchrAde; YthFlsp; RptrYrbk; RptrSchPpr; Coll; Pro.

HERMAN, Mary C; Roncalli HS; Indianapolis, IN; CmntyWkr; HonRl; JA; SchPl; Purdue Univ; Bio Chemistry.

HERMAN, Michael A; Mo Valley HS; Mo Valley, IA; Chr; ChrhWkr; HonRl; ModUN; SchPl; KeyCl; LetterBsbl; LetterBsktbl; LetterFtbl; LetterTrk; IMSpt; College; Accounting.

HERMAN, Paul C; Maconaquah HS; Grissom Afb, IN; 60/225 Chrs; CmntyWkr; HonRl; NatlThespSoc; SchMus; SchPl; SctActv; StuCncl; LetterFtbl; CaptWrstlng; 4-HAwd; GodCntryAwd; College; Professional.

HERMAN, Russell J; Central Catholic HS; West Point, NE; TrsFrshCls; HonRl; JrNHS; NHS; SchMus; SchPl; EdYrBk; RptrSchPpr; SpnCl; IMSpt; Clg; Prof.

HERMAN, Steven C; Central HS; Grand Forks, ND; ChrhWkr; HonRl; Mdrgl; NatlThespSoc; SchPl; SctActv; 4-H; GerCl; Ftbl; Trk; Univ Nd; Spec Educ.

HERMANN, Brock G; West Delaware HS; Manchester, IA; HonRl;.

HERMANN, Deborah M; Oak Creek HS; Oak Creek, WI; 4/323 AFS; HonRl; JrNHS; ModUN; NHS; NatlMeritCmnd; Orch; SpnCl; College; Chemical Engr.

HERMANN, Jan K; Macomb Sr HS; Macomb, IL; Chr; ChrhWkr; DrlTm; HonRl; NHS; SchMus; SctActv; YthFlsp; RptrSchPpr; SpnCl; Univ Of Iowa; Pharmacist.

HERMANN, Jon M; Benton Harbor HS; Benton Harbor, MI; 11/417 HonRl; JrNHS; NHS; NatlMeritSF; MthCl; Bsbl; EldAwd; RotaryAwd; Central Mi U.

HERMANN, Peter H; Melrose Mindoro HS; Melrose, WI; 9/84 Aud/Vis; HonRl; NatlMeritSF; SchPl; StuGov; FBLA; SciCl; Bsktbl; Trk; Uw Lacrosse; Music Or Mass Communications.

HERMANS, Mark G; Premontre HS; Green Bay, WI; 4/135 ChrhWkr; HonRl; SchMus; RptrYrbk; EdSchPpr; KeyCl; LetterFtbl; IMSpt; 4-HAwd; College; Medical Career.

HERMANSEN, Margaret G; Queen Of Peace HS; Chicago, IL; 20/430 IntrClCncl; NHS; SctActv; Yrbk; Univ Of Illinois; Science.

HERMANSON, Jill M; Duluth Central HS; Duluth, MN; AFS; Band; CncrtBnd; MrchBnd; Orch; PepBnd; PpCl; IMSpt; Univ Of Mn; Physical Ed Major.

HERMANSON, Thomas C; St Viator HS; Mt Prospect, IL; 10/256 NHS; CaptGlf; Univ Of Illinois; Medicine.

HERMES, Jeffrey D; Wm Horlick HS; Racine, WI; HonRl; StuGov; RptrSchPpr; U W Parkside; Pre Med.

HERMES, Julie E; Adrian Sr HS; Adrian, MI; 141/400 Chr; HospAde; SchAde; SchMus; SchPl; TchrAde; FrCl; PpCl; Swmmng; Chrldr; GAA; Adrian College; Medicine.

HERMES, Michelle D; Routt HS; Alexander, IL; 5/63 SecSrCls; SchPpr; SpnCl; AmLegAwd; College; Math.

HERMESDORF, Timothy A; St Patrick HS; Chicago, IL; 155/441 HonRl; RedCrAde; SctActv; Ftbl; Triton College; Respiratory Therapy.

HERMS, Pamela A; Green Lake HS; Green Lake, WI; 3/45 HonRl; SecNHS; SchPl; VPStuCncl; RptrYrbk; RptrSchPpr; PresFrCl; Bsktbl; Tennis; GAA; St Norberts; Cpa.

HERMSEN, Michael L; Escanaba Area HS; Escanaba, MI; 31/392 CtyCnl; CncrtBnd; JA; MrchBnd; NHS; PepBnd; YthLg; FTA; Trk; Univ Of Wisconsin; Mathematics.

HERMUS, Maureen; St Mary Central HS; Menasha, WI; Chrs; HonRl; SchPl; SpnCl; LetterBsktbl; LetterTennis; LetterTrk; Chrldr; CchngActv; PresAwd; Coll; Curr Of Maj Study.

HERNANDEZ, Elsa; Good Counsel HS; Chicago, IL; Chrl; TreasNatlFornLg; NHS; Quill&Scroll; RptrYrbk; RptrSchPpr; SciCl; Ill Benedictine Col; Medicine.

HERNANDEZ, Fred J; Sacred Heart HS; Salina, KS; ALBoysSt; Chrl; Chrs; HonRl; JCC; StuCncl; Bsktbl; LetterFtbl; LetterTrk; CchngActv; Univ; Bus Admin.

HERNANDEZ, Maria D; Central Ymca HS; Chicago, IL; PresJrCls; StuCncl; RptrSchPpr; FrCl; Bsktbl; Swmmng; Trk; CchngActv; GAA; IMSpt; College; Rn Or Dental Assistant.

HERNANDEZ, Pamela J; Savanna HS; Savanna, IL; HonRl; TreasStuCncl; StuGov; Yrbk; Bsktbl; GAA; IMSpt;.

HERNANDEZ, Timothy L; Waterford Township HS; Union Lk, MI; PresSophCls; HonRl; NHS; StuGov; RptrSchPpr; LetterTrk; Coll.

HERNANDEZ, Victoria; Northeast Sr HS; Kansas City, MO; 8/380 TrsJrCls; TrsSrCls; Band; JrNHS; NHS; Orch; StuCncl; SpnCl; SciCl; Tennis; Rockhurst College; Medical Technology.

HERNDON, Bradley J; State HS; Terre Haute, IN; PresSrCls; ALBoysSt; Band; Chr; ChrhWkr; JrNHS; MrchBnd; NHS; StuGov; RptrSchPpr; U Of In; Music.

HERNDON, Mark E; Central HS; Springfield, MO; HonRl; NatlMeritCmnd; NatlThespSoc; OffAde; SchAde; SchMus; KeyCl; MthCl; SciCl; College; Biochemistry.

HERNLEY, Cynthia A; Goshen HS; Goshen, IN; CncrtBnd; HonRl; HospAde; JrNHS; SctActv; StuCncl; YthFlsp; FrCl; SciCl; Chrldr; College; Medical.

HERNLY, Nancy J; Shortridge HS; Indianapolis, IN; 2/560 HonRl; NHS; Quill&Scroll; StuCncl; EdYrBk; University; Psychology.

HEROLD, Amy J; Aquinas HS; Ft Madison, IA; 1/46 TrsSophCls; Band; CncrtBnd; HonRl; MrchBnd; NHS; PepBnd; SpnCl; PpCl; IMSpt; Mt Mercy Col; Medical Technologist.

HEROLD, Constance M; East Grand Forks HS; East Grand Forks, MN; Chrs; HonRl; HospAde; TchrAde; RptrYrbk; GAA; Univ; Vocational.

HEROLD, David M; Notre Dame HS; Cresco, IA; HonRl; TchrAde; Teen; RptrSchPpr; SptEdSchPpr; PpCl; CaptBsbl; Bsktbl; CchngActv; IMSpt; Ellsworth College; Physical Educ.

HEROLD, Debra A; Aquinas HS; Fort Madison, IA; 7/47 TrsJrCls; TrsSrCls; Chr; Chrs; ChrhWkr; DrlTm; HonRl; LbryAde; MrchBnd; OffAde; PolWkr; LionAwd; PresAwd; Ne Missouri St Univ; Legal Secretary.

HERON, Christopher D; Cass Technical HS; Detroit, MI; HonRl; AmLegAwd; Columbus Coll; Graphic Design.

HERPEL, Steven; Fort Zumwalt HS; Ofallon, MO; SctActv; Missouri Inst Of Tech; Bs In Electronics.

HERR, Dennis; Carl Junction HS; Asbury, MO; HonRl; NHS; FFA; MthCl; 4-HAwd; Mo Southern Coll; Sci.

HERR, Diane; Arlington HS; Arlington Hts, IL; 29/585 HonRl; TchrAde; Illinois State Univ; Special Educ.

HERR, Gaylan C; Wisc Acad; Sun Prairie, WI; VPSophCls; Chr; ChrhWkr; HonRl; Yrbk; CaptIMSpt; Univ; Theology.

HERR, Michael E; Clinton Prairie HS; Frankfort, IN; Band; CncrtBnd; HonRl; MrchBnd; RptrSchPpr; LatCl; SpnCl; LetterFtbl; Tennis; Assoc Sch Inc; Airline Personnel.

HERR, Monica L; Fairfield HS; Fairfield, IA; 3/211 Band; CncrtBnd; HonRl; MrchBnd; NHS; PepBnd; RptrSchPpr; SpnCl; LetterTrk; College.

HERR, Nancy A; Waterford Township HS; Pontiac, MI; HonRl; JrNHS; NHS; NatlMeritSchl; OffAde; TchrAde; AmLegAwd; DanFAwd; DARAwd; GovHonPrgAwd; PresAwd; College; Vocation.

HERRAN, Catherine A; Wheeling HS; Wheeling, IL; 62/488 Band; CncrtBnd; HonRl; MrchBnd; NHS; NatlMeritCmnd; College; Chemistry.

HERRAN, Steven M; Huntington North HS; Huntington, IN; GerCl; U Of In; Lawyer.

HERRBOLDT, Rebecca S; Nemaha Valley HS; Cook, NE; 4/23 Band; HonRl; MrchBnd; PepBnd; SchPl; YthFlsp; 4-H; PpCl; Trk; Chrldr; Augustana Col; Nursing.

HERREID, Steven M; Marion HS; Marion, IA; 7/179 Aud/Vis; HonRl; ModUN; Quill&Scroll; SctActv; SptEdSchPpr; University.

HERREN, Kimberly A; Sioux County HS; Harrison, NE; PresJrCls; Chrs; HonRl; HospAde; NatlFornLg; NHS; EdYrBk; FHA; LetterTrk; VoiceDemAwd; E Wy Coll; Busi.

HERRERA, William G; Lyons Township HS; La Grange, IL; 38/1214 Band; ChrhWkr; HonRl; NHS; NatlMeritFnl; SchAde; SctActv; YthFlsp; MthCl; SciCl; Medicine.

HERRICK, Debra A; Port Huron HS; Port Huron, MI; 8/390 ChrhWkr; HonRl; NHS; U Of Mi; Physical Therapy.

HERRICK, Donald W; St Thomas Acad; White Bear Lake, MN; Aud/Vis; DrlTm; ROTC; SchPl; Yrbk; SchPpr; LatCl; PpCl; Coll Of St Thomas; Banking.

HERRICK, Mary S; Independence HS; Independence, IA; 10/160 SecSophCls; SecSrCls; Chr; CncrtBnd; HonRl; MrchBnd; NatlMeritSF; PepBnd; SchMus; Iowa State Univ; Economics.

HERRICK, Melodee R; Kewanee HS; Kewanee, IL; 8/216 AFS; ChrhWkr; HonRl; Orch; TchrAde; YthFlsp; FTA; Judson College; Mathematics.

HERRICK, Timothy L; Princeton HS; Princeton, IL; 1/176 VPFrshCls; PresCncrtBnd; HonRl; Mdrgl; NHS; NatlMeritSF; NatlThespSoc; VPStuCncl; PresYthFlsp; Pres4-H; IMSpt; DanFAwd; 4-HAwd; Univ Of Ill; Medicine.

HERRICKS, Ronald T; Cashton HS; Cashton, WI; 35/65 ChrhWkr; HonRl; NatlMeritSchl; YthLg; Yrbk; 4-H; FFA; PpCl; LetterFtbl; Trk; Wrstlng; IMSpt; 4-HAwd; Univ Of Wisconsin; Teacher.

HERRIFORD, Anita M; Lewistown Comm HS; Lewistown, IL; ALAGirlsSt; HonRl; Yrbk; PresFHA; PpCl; GAA;.

HERRIFORD, David V; St Louis U HS; St Louis, MO; 60/205 SecSrCls; HonRl; JA; NHS; NatlMeritSF; SchPl; StuCncl; RptrSchPpr; IMSpt; Stanford Univ.

HERRIG, Russell L; Spalding HS; Alton, IA; 2/49 PresSophCls; PresSrCls; ALBoysSt; HonRl; NatlMeritCmnd; SchPl; MthCl; LetterBsbl; Chrldr; Iowa State Univ; Engineer.

HERRIGES, J C; Dwight D Eisenhower HS; Utica, MI; HonRl; LetterBsbl; LetterBsktbl; Lawrence Inst Of Tech; Architecture.

HERRING, Dale; Owen Valley Community HS; Spencer, IN; Band; CncrtBnd; HonRl; MrchBnd; TchrAde; 4-H; Univ; Pharmacy.

HERRING, Daniel W; Chariton Comm HS; Chariton, IA; HonRl; StuCncl; 4-H; FFA; Ftbl; DanFAwd; Des Moines Area Comm; Tool & Die.

HERRING, Dee A; Galesburg Sr HS; Galesburg, IL; Band; ChrhWkr; CmntyWkr; CncrtBnd; HonRl; MrchBnd; NHS; PepBnd; SctActv; College.

HERRING, Donald G; Meadville R Iv HS; Linneus, MO; 4/36 Band; ChrhWkr; CncrtBnd; HonRl; MrchBnd; PepBnd; StuCncl; 4-H; Bsbl; LetterBsktbl; 4-HAwd; University; Agriculture.

HERRING, Steven; Meservey Thornton HS; Meservey, IA; 2/27 PresSrCls; ALBoysSt; HonRl; NatlMeritSF; SchPl; StuCncl; StuGov; YthFlsp; Bsbl; Trk; College; Curriculum Of Major Study.

HERRIOTT, Janet L; Mahomet Seymour HS; Champaign, IL; 8/126 ChrhWkr; HonRl; NHS; EdYrBk; 4-H; FTA; MthCl; Chrldr; GAA; IMSpt; Ksu; Ag Field.

HERRIOTT, Sue A; Mahomet Seymour HS; Champaign, IL; PresFrshCls; VPSophCls; HonRl; NHS; Yrbk; FFA; LetterTrk; CaptChrldr; GAA; 4-HAwd; College.

HERRMANN, Brenda L; Central HS; Norwood, MN; 7/108 Band; CncrtBnd; HonRl; NHS; SchPl; SctActv; TchrAde; Yrbk; FNA; Chrldr; Coll; Health.

HERRMANN, Craig M; Manistee HS; Manistee, MI; ALBoysSt; HonRl; JrNHS; NHS; RptrSchPpr; SchPpr; College; Science Field.

HERRMANN, Elizabeth A; Manistee HS; Manistee, MI; 1/169 ChrhWkr; HonRl; NHS; Quill&Scroll; YthLg; EdSchPpr; 4-H; GAA; IMSpt; 4-HAwd; Michigan State; Natural Science.

HERRMANN, Joan; Pecatonica Hs; Rock City, IL; 5/60 VPSrCls; HonRl; MrchBnd; PepBnd; Quill&Scroll; StuCncl; EdYrBk; 4-H; FHA; GAA;.

HERRMANN, Laura A; Niles HS; Niles, MI; Chr; HonRl; HospAde; JA; NatlMeritSF; YthFlsp; JAAwd; U Or Mich; Med Technology.

HERRMANN, Michele R; Columbia Central HS; Brooklyn, MI; 9/143 Band; ChrhWkr; CncrtBnd; HonRl; MrchBnd; SecTrsFrshCls; SchMus; Yrbk; Coll; Musician.

HERRNSTADT, Owen; Ames HS; Ames, IA; PresSrCls; ALBoysSt; CmntyWkr; HonRl; PolWkr; SchPl; FrCl; Univ; Major Study.

HERRO, Bernard L; Messmer HS; Milwaukee, WI; 55/209 HonRl; TchrAde; SpnCl; Bsbl; LetterFtbl; LetterWrstlng; IMSpt; Univ Of Wisconsin; Lawyer.

HERRO, Melissa A; Mather HS; Wetmore, MI; HonRl; LbryAde; College; Commercial Art.

HERRON, Catherine A; Wheeling HS; Wheeling, IL; 62/488 Band; CncrtBnd; HonRl; MrchBnd; NHS; NatlMeritCmnd; PepBnd; Lake Forest College; Engineer.

HERSBERGER, Katherine; Hamilton Southeastern HS; Noblesville, IN; 15/132 HonRl; NHS; PpCl; College.

HERSCHBERGER, Tammy K; Northridge HS; Middlebury, IN; Chr; DrlTm; HonRl; StuCncl; RptrYrbk; 4-H; PpCl; LetterBsktbl; LetterTrk; Chrldr; GAA; 4-HAwd; College; Physical Therapy.

HERSCHER, Margaret A; Gilman HS; Gilman, IL; VPSophCls; ALAGirlsSt; Band; ChrhWkr; CncrtBnd; HonRl; LbryAde; MrchBnd; NHS; PepBnd;.

HERSCHLAG, Diane; North HS; Omaha, NE; ChrhWkr; HonRl; NHS; YthFlsp; Univ Of Ne At Omaha; Pre Med.

HERSCHTHAL, Mark A; Stephen Tyng Mather HS; Chicago, IL; 17/425 CncrtBnd; HonRl; JrNHS; NHS; NatlMeritSchl; Orch; StuCncl; Yrbk; KeyCl; GerCl; Univ Of Il; Nuclear Engineering.

HERSH, Cheryl S; Maryville R Ii HS; Maryville, MO; 15/129 Chr; Mdrgl; StuCncl; PpCl; Swmmng; Trk; College; Art.

HERSH, Neil K; Niles North HS; Skokie, IL; CmntyWkr; HonRl; NHS; NatlMeritFnl; NatlMeritSF; StuCncl; StuGov; LetterSwmmng; University.

HERSHMAN, Graham L; Lyons Twp HS; La Grange, IL; ChrhWkr; HonRl; JrNHS; NHS; NatlMeritCmnd; PolWkr; SchAde; TchrAde; Purdue Univ; Industrial Mgmt.

HERSHMAN, Julie K; Huron Sr HS; Huron, SD; Chrs; NatlMeritCmnd; GerCl;.

HERSTEIN, Robin D; Nevada HS; Nevada, MO; Band; CncrtBnd; MrchBnd; PepBnd; Business School.

HERTEL, Catherine A; Marian HS; Hays, KS; SecFrshCls; ChrhWkr; CmntyWkr; NHS; SchAde; StuCncl; SpnCl; PpCl; Chrldr; College; Education.

HERTEL, Deborah A; Carmel Girls HS; Grayslake, IL; 6/195 PresJrCls; Chrs; HonRl; NHS; StuCncl; 4-H; GerCl; 4-HAwd; Coll; Medicine.

HERTEL, Georgia R; Mundelein HS; Grays Lake, IL; 56/371 CmntyWkr; HonRl; Quill&Scroll; RptrYrbk; Yrbk; 4-H; PpCl; GAA; IMSpt; Trade Schl; Stewardess.

HERTEL, Lynda L; Technical HS; St Cloud, MN; CncrtBnd; HonRl; MrchBnd; NHS; Orch; PepBnd; SchMus; LetterSwmmng; LetterTrk; BttyCrckrAwd; Coll.

HERTEL, Maxine M; Victoria HS; Victoria, KS; Chr; Chrs; DrlTm; HonRl; NatlFornLg; SchPl; Yrbk; SchPpr; FHA; College.

HERTEL, Susan; Godwin Heights HS; Wyoming, MI; TrsJrCls; Chrs; HonRl; NHS; SchMus; StuCncl; PpCl; GAA; PPFtbl; Aquinas College; Psychology.

HERTSGAARD, Craig L; Kindred Public HS; Kindred, ND; ALBoysSt; Chrs; CncrtBnd; NHS; YthFlsp; 4-H; PresFFA; LetterFtbl; 4-HAwd; College.

HERTZ, Nick J; Harvey HS; Harvey, ND; VPFrshCls; PresJrCls; HonRl; StuCncl; StuGov; Ftbl; CchngActv; Univ Of North Dakota; Medicine.

HERTZ, Tom W; Flint Southwestern HS; Flint, MI; MthCl; SciCl; Mott Community College; Computer Engineer.

HERTZLER, Julia D; Elkhart Central HS; Elkhart, IN; HonRl; HospAde; LbryAde; NHS; NatlThespSoc; Orch; SchMus; SchPl; College; Medicine.

HERVEY, Carla J; Wheaton HS; Wheaton, MN; 12/88 Band; Chrs; CncrtBnd; MrchBnd; TchrAde; Pres4-H; FHA; 4-HAwd; Ndss; Food Service.

HERVEY, Michael D; Galena HS; Galena, IL; Aud/Vis; Band; SecFrshCls; CncrtBnd; HonRl; MrchBnd; PepBnd; StuGov; FrCl; LetterTennis; Electronics.

HERZ, Paul N; Lawrence Public HS; Lawrence, NE; HstFrshCls; HstSophCls; HstJrCls; HstSrCls; SchPl; TchrAde; Trk; Cntc; Carpentry.

HERZOG, Carl E; Fair Bury Cropsey HS; Fairbury, IL; 3/103 Band; Chr; Chrs; CncrtBnd; DrmMjrt; HonRl; MrchBnd; SchPl; RptrYrbk; AmLegAwd; Univ Of Il; Accounting.

HERZOG, Carl E; Fairbury Cropsey HS; Fairbury, IL; 3/103 Band; Chr; CncrtBnd; DrmMjrt; MrchBnd; NHS; SchPl; RptrYrbk; PresMthCl; AmLegAwd; Univ Of Illinois; Accounting.

HERZOG, Carl R; Barrington HS; Barrington, IL; 52/658 HonRl; NHS; Bsbl; LetterBsktbl; Univ Of Chicago; Lawyer.

HERZOG, Joseph P; Lake Michigan Catholic HS; Benton Harbor, MI; PresSrCls; Chrl; HonRl; NatlFornLg; NHS; NatlThespSoc; OffAde; SchAde; SchMus; SchPl; StuCncl; LetterFtbl; IMSpt; CitAwd; Central Michigan Univ; Theater.

HERZOG, Rebecca R; Florence HS; Iron Mtn, MI; 19/67 ALAGirlsSt; NHS; RptrYrbk; RptrSchPpr; SchPpr; FHA; PpCl; GAA; Northwest Tech; Accounting.

HERZOG, Suzanne; St Mary Acad; Rockwood, MI; HonRl; SctActv; Secretary.

HERZON, Sanford M; Elgin HS; Elgin, IL; 99/1000 TrsFrshCls; CmntyWkr; HonRl; SchAde; StuCncl; TchrAde; UNYO; SptEdSchPpr; FrCl; SpnCl; SciCl; College; Medicine.

HERZUCK, Cynthia A; Spring Lake Park HS; Minneapolis, MN; SecChr; HonRl; MrchBnd; NHS; SchMus; Yrbk; SpnCl; PpCl; Tennis; MasAwd; St Catherine Clg.

HESBY, Kyle G; Lake Preston HS #102; Lake Preston, SD; 8/37 TrsSophCls; ALBoysSt; HonRl; FFA; CaptFtbl; Trade School.

HESCH, Jeff T; Lisbon HS; Lisbon, ND; Chr; HonRl; SchPl; Yrbk; FBLA; LetterFtbl; College; Business.

HESCH, Roger K; Little Falls Comm HS; Little Falls, MN; AFS; Aud/Vis; ChrhWkr; SchPl; TchrAde; LetterBsktbl; LetterFtbl; IMSpt; College; Religion.

HESELSCHWERDT, Dorothy D; Napoleon HS; Napoleon, MI; ChrhWkr; HonRl; NHS; StuCncl; StuGov; TchrAde; Pres4-H; LetterGlf; 4-HAwd; Business School; Secretary.

HESEMANN, Joann V; Gascondade County R2 HS; Owensville, MO; Chr; Chrs; ChrhWkr; HonRl; NHS; TreasYthFlsp; VPFHA; College; Accounting.

HESH, Mary C; Wilber Clatonia HS; Crete, NE; 1/45 Band; HonRl; SchPl; TchrAde; YthFlsp; 4-H; PresFHA; SecPpCl; Chrldr; 4-HAwd; Cosmetology School; Cosmotology.

HESLER, Denise A; Charleston HS; Charleston, IL; 5/237 Band; ChrhWkr; CncrtBnd; HonRl; MrchBnd; NHS; PepBnd; RptrSchPpr; 4-H; 4-HAwd; Eastern Il U; Journalism.

HESS, Cynthia M; Ottawa HS; Grand Ridge, IL; 51/420 Chr; HonRl; NHS; 4-H; Univ Of Illinois; Medicine.

HESS, Deborah T; Rockford HS; Rockford, MI; 30/289 HonRl; NHS; NatlMeritCmnd; NatlMeritSchl; PolWkr; LetterTennis; Chrldr; CchngActv; GAA; PPFtbl; College; Law.

HESS, James E; Sterling HS; Sterling, IL; 66/400 Chr; Chrs; ChrhWkr; HonRl; NHS; LetterWrstlng; AmLegAwd; Olivet Nazarene College; Teacher.

HESS, Jane M; St Joseph HS; Kenosha, WI; 8/150 PresSophCls; HonRl; NHS; StuCncl; RptrSchPpr; OptClAwd; VFWAwd; VoiceDemAwd; Psychology.

HESS, Jeanette; Humboldt HS; Humboldt, KS; 6/57 HonRl; LbryAde; TchrAde; FHA; PpCl; GovHonPrgAwd; Hutchinson Cjc;med Rec Tech.

HESS, Joan; Delta HS; Muncie, IN; CmntyWkr; HonRl; JrNHS; NHS; NatlMeritSchl; RedCrAde; StuCncl; StuGov; YthFlsp; YthLg; Univ; Professional.

HESS, Kathleen R; Newton HS; Newton, KS; Band; ChrhWkr; CmntyWkr; HonRl; LbryAde; MrchBnd; SctActv; YthFlsp; FrCl; Bethel Clge; Med Tech.

HESS, Leia; Farmington East HS; Hanna City, IL; 15/145 Chrs; HonRl; SchMus; SchPl; Yrbk; SchPpr; FrCl; Ill Cent Coll; French Major Interpreter.

HESS, Linda; Vassar HS; Vassar, MI; 24/150 Band; Chr; HonRl; MrchBnd; NHS; Orch; PepBnd; Michigan State; Physical Therapy.

HESS, Lorraine J; Central HS; Cambridge, KS; Band; Chr; DrmMjrt; HonRl; OffAde; Orch; Bsktbl; Chrldr; PPFtbl; CitAwd; College; Professional.

HESS, Lynn; Hempstead HS; Dubuque, IA; 55/455 Chrs; CmntyWkr; HonRl; JA; NHS; OffAde; RedCrAde; StuGov; SciCl; JAAwd; Vocational Technical School; Accountin.

HESS, Mark L; Herscher HS; Kankakee, IL; 40/168 Chrs; ChrhWkr; HonRl; Mdrgl; SchPl; RptrSchPpr; Glf; Concordia College; Teaching.

HESS, Mary E; Onsted HS; Brooklyn, MI; CmntyWkr; HonRl; OffAde; StuCncl; FHA; LetterBsktbl; LetterTrk; LetterChrldr; GAA; College; X Ray Tech.

HESS, Mary M; Wautoma HS; Redgranite, WI; 5/110 SecJrCls; Band; HonRl; NHS; RptrYrbk; Bsbl; Trk; GAA; Stout College; Commercial Art.

HESS, Pamela; Mount Saint Scholastica Acad; Atchison, KS; HonRl; NHS; HstFrshCls; Sdlty; RptrYrbk; EdYrBk; RptrSchPpr; SchPpr; FshEdSchPpr; SpnCl;.

HESS, Teri K; North Central HS; Mahaska, KS; HonRl; HospAde; RptrYrbk; RptrSchPpr; 4-H; Univ Of Nebraska; Business.

HESS, Toni M; Beech Grove HS; Beech Grove, IN; HonRl; PresStuCncl; CaptBsktbl; CaptTennis; SecGAA; Franklin College; Tennis Or Music.

HESSE, Cheryl A; Denver Community HS; Denver, IA; 2/79 Chrs; HonRl; LbryAde; NHS; NatlMeritCmnd; SchPl; Yrbk; SchPpr; LetterTrk; LetterChrldr; Ia State U; Veterinary Medicine.

HESSE, David M; Academy Of The Holy Angels; Edina, MN; SecFrshCls; HonRl; RptrSchPpr; Bsbl; Ftbl; College; Accounting.

HESSE, Dean M; Pershing HS; Plummer, MN; Band; CncrtBnd; HonRl; MrchBnd; SchPl; 4-H; LetterFtbl;.

HESSE, Debra J; Belle Plaine HS; Belle Plaine, KS; Chr; ChrhWkr; HonRl; SchPl; TchrAde; RptrSchPpr; FHA; PpCl; Bsktbl; Trk; Emporia Kansas State Clg; Elem Ed.

HESSEL, Nancy; Rosemount Sr HS; Apple Valley, MN; HonRl; SchPl; Yrbk; PpCl; Tennis; Trk; Univ Of Mn; Biology.

HESSELBEIN, Teresa M; Wauwatosa West HS; Wauwatosa, WI; 11/456 ChrhWkr; HonRl; NHS; SctActv; MthCl; Purdue Univ; Agriculture.

HESSELBERG, Leah B; Bangor HS; West Salem, WI; 2/53 SecFrshCls; Chr; Chrs; ChrhWkr; DrlTm; HonRl; MrchBnd; NatlFornLg; NatlMeritCmnd; SchPl; PresStuCncl; StuGov; TchrAde; GAA; St Josephs School; Nursing.

HESSELFINE, Joellen; Clear Creek HS; Oxford, IA; SecSrCls; DrlTm; HonRl; NHS; UNYO; FBLA; Chrldr; Coll; Nursing.

HESSELINK, Jud B; Hope College HS; Holland, MI; Chr; CncrtBnd; HonRl; Mdrgl; NHS; NatlMeritFnl; StuCncl; YthFlsp; FrCl; Bsktbl; Ftbl; IMSpt; College; Criminal Psychology.

HESSELTINE, Christine G; Washington Community HS; Brighton, IA; 21/157 CmntyWkr; HonRl; HospAde; LbryAde; TchrAde; 4-H; FBLA; FHA; 4-HAwd; KiwanAwd; St Lukes Meth Sch Of Nursing; Nurse.

HESSELTINE, Rebecca E; Pekin HS; Rubio, IA; 4/46 SecFrshCls; Band; HonRl; Mdrgl; MrchBnd; NHS; EdYrBk; 4-H; FNA; 4-HAwd; School; Practical Nursing.

HESSIL, Diane K; West HS; Green Bay, WI; 15/390 Band; VPCncrtBnd; HonRl; MrchBnd; PepBnd; YthFlsp; RptrSchPpr; Swmmng; GAA; Coll; English.

HESSING, Robert B; St Charles HS; St Charles, IL; 6/450 HonRl; NHS; StuCncl; StuGov; Northern Illinois Univ; Math.

HESSLING, Catherine S; Academy Of Our Lady; Washington, IL; 22/92 Chrs; HonRl; NHS; 4-H; LatCl; St Francis Nursing School; Nurse.

HESSON, Jim; Logan View HS; Uehling, NE; HonRl; StuGov; 4-H; Bsktbl; Ftbl; Glf; 4-HAwd; Univ.

HESTER, Jim A; South Pemiscot HS; Holland, MO; 1/75 PresJrCls; Band; CncrtBnd; HonRl; JrNHS; MrchBnd; NHS; PepBnd; SchPl; StuCncl; YthFlsp; Bsktbl; Ftbl; Univ Of Miss; Pharmacy.

HESTER, Mark; Morton Senior Hs; Hammond, IN; 3/500 ALBoysSt; CncrtBnd; HonRl; MrchBnd; NHS; Orch; PepBnd; SchMus; CivCl; SciCl; College; Biology.

HESTER, Patricia L; Winchester HS; Winchester, IL; 3/73 Band; ChrhWkr; CncrtBnd; HonRl; MrchBnd; SctActv; Yrbk; FHA; FrCl; PpCl; Passavant Sch Of Nursing; Nursing.

HESTERMANN, Sharon; Norris Dist 160 HS; Firth, NE; 2/102 ALAGirlsSt; CncrtBnd; HospAde; MrchBnd; NHS; PepBnd; SchPl; EdYrBk; FNA; Nursing School; Surgical Nurse.

HESTING, Leo J; Ludington Sr HS; Ludington, MI; Chr; CmntyWkr; HonRl; NatlMeritFnl; NatlMeritSF; Michigan State Univ; Psychology.

HETH, Kathlyn R; Granite City South HS; Granite City, IL; PresFrshCls; Chrs; HonRl; NHS; Quill&Scroll; PresStuCncl; PpCl; Bsktbl; Tennis; GAA; University.

HETH, Lisa M; Ottawa Twp HS; Marseilles, IL; 24/420 ALAGirlsSt; Chr; HonRl; NHS; SchMus; TchrAde; YthFlsp; FHA; GAA; Lakeland Med Academy; Lab Tech.

HETHERINGTON, Peter A; Danville HS; Danville, IL; HonRl; NatlMeritCmnd; StuCncl; RptrSchPpr; Trk; RotaryAwd; Univ Of Illinois; Geology.

HETLAND, Dee Ann; Glenburn Public HS; Deering, ND; 1/28 ALAGirlsSt; Band; Chrs; ChrhWkr; CncrtBnd; HonRl; MrchBnd; Orch; PepBnd; SchPl; Minot State College; Chemical Eng.

HETLINGER, Theresa A; Taft HS; Chicago, IL; 67/700 HonRl; NHS; StuCncl; GAA; Loyola Univ; Nursing.

HETRICK, Cary L; Seeger HS; Williamsport, IN; 12/120 Band; Chr; ChrhWkr; CncrtBnd; HonRl; MrchBnd; NHS; PepBnd; SctActv; YthFlsp; 4-H; Bsktbl; Trk; Ivy Tech; Refrigeration.

HETRICK, Lori A; North Putnam HS; Roachdale, IN; 1/130 Band; Chr; ChrhWkr; HonRl; NatlFornLg; NHS; NatlThespSoc; StuCncl; FHA; Bsktbl; Lincoln Christian College; Voice & Speech.

HETT, Cynthia R; Bottineau HS; Gardena, ND; Chr; Chrs; ChrhWkr; 4-H; PpCl; CaptBsktbl;.

HETT, Darlene M; Northwest Webster HS; Fort Dodge, IA; ChrhWkr; HonRl; SchPl; YthFlsp; Bsktbl; College; Vocation.

HETTASCH, Joanne; J F Kennedy HS; Chicago, IL; HonRl; HospAde; LbryAde; PresNHS; OffAde; FNA; TreasSpnCl; MthCl; TreasPpCl; GAA; College; Professional.

HETTENBACH, Beverly A; Osage R 1 HS; Chamois, MO; TrsJrCls; HonRl; StuCncl; Yrbk; FHA; SpnCl; PpCl; Trk; Chrldr; IMSpt; College.

HETTER, Charles M; Aquinas HS; Lincoln Park, MI; 23/216 CmntyWkr; HonRl; LetterFtbl; LetterWrstlng; Mi Tech; Eng.

HETTINGER, Diane K; Petersburg Porta HS; Petersburg, IL; 2/140 ChrhWkr; CmntyWkr; DrlTm; HonRl; HospAde; LbryAde; MrchBnd; NHS; NatlThespSoc; SchMus; Brigham Young Univ; Communications.

HETTINGER, Glen J; Porta HS; Petersburg, IL; ChrhWkr; Mdrgl; NatlFornLg; VPNHS; NatlMeritCmnd; PresNatlThespSoc; SchMus; SchPl; StuCncl; RptrSchPpr; TreasKeyCl; Bsktbl; Ftbl; Brigham Young Univ; Law.

HETTINGER, Peter H; Bloomington HS; Bloomington, IL; HonRl; Univ Of Illinois; Business Admin.

HETTINGER, Roch S; Roncalli HS; Elkhorn, NE; ChrhWkr; HonRl; NHS; MthCl; Bsktbl; LetterFtbl; LetterTrk; Coll; Math.

HETTINGER, Sandra S; Heyworth HS; Heyworth, IL; Band; Chrs; ChrhWkr; CmntyWkr; HonRl; NHS; PepBnd; SchMus; RptrSchPpr; 4-H; College Of The Scriptures.

HETTRICH, Joyce A; Oswego Senior HS; Oswego, IL; VPSophCls; PresJrCls; Chr; NHS; StuCncl; 4-H; KeyCl; PpCl; Chrldr; DanFAwd;.

HETTRICK, Brian T; Topeka West HS; Topeka, KS; 20/422 ChrhWkr; HonRl; NHS; NatlMeritCmnd; PresFrshCls; RptrYrbk; SpnCl; MthCl; Bsktbl; Kansas State Univ; Chemical Engineering.

HETTWER, Richard J; Sacred Heart HS; E Grand Forks, MN; Chr; Chrs; RptrYrbk; FshEdYrbk; Yrbk; RptrSchPpr; SchPpr; FrCl; SciCl; Bsbl; U Of N D; Computer Programming.

HETZEL, James R; Tri County Area HS; Almond, WI; 8/71 ChrhWkr; HonRl; NHS; SctActv; 4-H; Bsbl; Bsktbl; IMSpt; 4-HAwd; University; Math.

HETZEL, Keith L; Lincoln HS; Wisconsin Rapids, WI; Band; SecChr; ChrhWkr; CmntyWkr; HonRl; MrchBnd; Orch; YthFlsp; KeyCl; GerCl; Univ; English.

HETZEL, Kim M; Brookfield Central HS; Brookfield, WI; ChrhWkr; CmntyWkr; NatlFornLg; Quill&Scroll; SchPl; TchrAde; EdSchPpr; 4-H; GerCl; LatCl;.

HETZEL, Mark L; Richland Center HS; Richland Center, WI; HonRl; NatlMeritCmnd; SecKeyCl; LetterBsbl; Coll; Pro.

HETZEL, Mary E; Hilbert HS; Menasha, WI; Chrl; CncrtBnd; HonRl; Mdrgl; PepBnd; SchMus; TchrAde; Twrl; RptrYrbk; Chrldr; Univ; Phys Therapy.

HETZNER, Jayne M; Buena Vista HS; Saginaw, MI; ChrhWkr; HonRl; HospAde; NHS; SchPl; 4-H; GerCl; University; Nursing.

HEUBER, Robin L; Hammond Baptist HS; Munster, IN; Chr; Chrl; Chrs; ChrhWkr; OffAde; SchMus; Tenn Temple; Elem Teaching.

HEUCHERT, Janet G; St Thomas Public HS; St Thomas, ND; TrsJrCls; Band; Chrs; ChrhWkr; HonRl; SchPl; EdYrBk; LetterBsktbl; LetterTrk; GAA; PPFtbl; College; Chemical Engineer.

HEUCHERT, Joan C; St Thomas Public HS; St Thomas, ND; 1/23 TrsSophCls; TrsJrCls; Band; Chr; Chrs; ChrhWkr; CncrtBnd; HonRl; MrchBnd; NatlMeritSF; LetterBsktbl; LetterTrk; GAA; PPFtbl; College; Biology.

HEUCKROTH, Brian A; Riverview Gardens Sr HS; St Louis, MO; 5/800 Aud/Vis; CncrtBnd; HonRl; NHS; NatlMeritSF; NatlThespSoc; Orch; SchMus; SchPl; LetterTennis; U Of Mo; Elec Engr.

HEUER, Gordon L; Bunker Hill HS; Plainview, IL; 3/81 VPSophCls; TrsJrCls; PresSrCls; ChrhWkr; HonRl; NHS; StuCncl; FFA; University.

HEUER, Jeffrey T; Northwestern Military Academy; Des Plaines, IL; DrlTm; HonRl; ROTC; SchPl; RptrYrbk; RptrSchPpr; Bsbl; College; Professional.

HEUERMAN, Julie I; Effingham HS; Effingham, IL; 29/223 HonRl; NatlMeritFnl;.

HEUERMANN, Karen J; Aurora HS; Phillips, NE; 7/91 SecTrsJrCls; CncrtBnd; HonRl; MrchBnd; NHS; StuCncl; Teen; 4-H; FHA; University Of Nebraska.

HEUPEL, Rebecca D; Medina Public HS; Medina, ND; 1/21 TrsJrCls; ALAGirlsSt; Band; Chr; HonRl; EdSchPpr; FHA; Bsbl; Trk; LetterChrldr; N D S U Or U N D; Doctor Vet Or R N.

HEUSINKUELT, Judy M; Crete HS; Hallam, NE; 5/98 ALAGirlsSt; ChrhWkr; CmntyWkr; HonRl; SchMus; SchPl; TchrAde; Trk; IMSpt; BauchLmbAwd; Coll; Nursing.

HEUSTED, Kimberley L; Lakeville HS; Otisville, MI; 3/185 TrsSrCls; HonRl; NHS; SchPl; StuCncl; SchPpr; LetterTrk; TreasGAA; Central Mich Univ; Teaching.

HEUTON, Dixie A; Lake City HS; Lohrville, IA; 1/61 Chrs; ChrhWkr; CncrtBnd; HonRl; MrchBnd; NHS; SchMus; UNYO; RptrYrbk; Trk; Iowa St U; English.

HEUVELMAN, John M; Marquette HS; Godfrey, IL; 2/119 HonRl; VPJA; JrNHS; VPNHS; NatlMeritFnl; NatlMeritSF; SchPl; Yrbk; SchPpr; LetterGlf; IMSpt; Univ; Business.

HEWES, Cheryl B; Maplewood Academy; Pierre, SD; Band; Chr; Chrl; ChrhWkr; HonRl; College; Nursing.

HEWETT, Mardel L; South Side HS; Fort Wayne, IN; ChrhWkr; JA; YthFlsp;.

HEWITT, David L; Catlin HS; Catlin, IL; 11/65 PresFrshCls; Aud/Vis; PresBand; Chrs; PresCncrtBnd; PresMrchBnd; PresPepBnd; SchMus; SctActv; StuCncl; Ftbl; Eastern Il Univ; Industrial Technologist.

HEWITT, Donita; New Monroe HS; Monroe, IA; TrsFrshCls; Chrs; DrlTm; HonRl; MrchBnd; SchPl; StuCncl; YthFlsp; FHA; Chrldr;.

HEWITT, Gary A; Beaver Dam HS; Beaver Dam, WI; ALBoysSt; HonRl; StuCncl; StuGov; SecTrsSophCls; IMSpt; Coll; Pharmacist.

HEWITT, Gregory L; Beloit HS; Beloit, KS; PresFrshCls; VPSophCls; Chrs; HonRl; 4-H; Wrstlng; CchngActv; AmLegAwd; Kansas State Univ; Air Force.

HEWITT, Jayne M; St Joseph HS; Kenosha, WI; Chrs; HonRl; SctActv; StuCncl; PpCl; Chrldr; IMSpt; Coll; Micro Biologist.

HEWITT, Sara A; Fredericksburg Comm HS; Fredericksburg, IA; 1/37 Chrs; ChrhWkr; CncrtBnd; HonRl; MrchBnd; PepBnd; SchPl; Pres4-H; GovHonPrgAwd; College; Arts.

HEWITT SILCOX, Cherie L; El Dorado Springs R Ii HS; El Dorado Springs, MO; HonRl; SchPl; Twrl; FHA; PpCl; PPFtbl; Southwest Mo State U; Interior Design.

HEWLETT, Donald R; Richland Public HS; Richland, MO; Chr; Chrs; SecFrshCls; LetterBsktbl; LetterTrk; Trade School; Mechaical Field.

HEWLETT, Linda G; Plainfield HS; Plainfield, IL; 34/300 TrsFrshCls; Chr; Chrs; ChrhWkr; HonRl; NatlFornLg; NatlThespSoc; SchMus; SchPl; University; Performing Arts.

HEWLETT, Roderic; Carson Long Military Inst; Troy, MI; DrlTm; HonRl; OffAde; ROTC; StuCncl; LetterFtbl; Tennis; IMSpt; Wayne State Univ; Medicine.

HEXUM, Wanda L; Hendricks HS; Hendricks, MN; SecFrshCls; ALAGirlsSt; Band; Chr; CncrtBnd; MrchBnd; PepBnd; GerCl; PpCl; Chrldr; College; German.

HEXUM, Wendy L; Hendricks HS; Hendricks, MN; TrsFrshCls; SecSophCls; Band; ChrhWkr; CmntyWkr; CncrtBnd; DrlTm; SecTrsSophCls; Trk; IMSpt; Bus Sch; Ct Reporter.

HEYDEMANN, Steven; Evanston Twp HS; Evanston, IL; CmntyWkr; HonRl; PolWkr; StuCncl; StuGov; College; Liberal Arts.

HEYDEN, Walter D; Whiting HS; Whiting, IN; PresFrshCls; PresSophCls; HonRl; NHS; SchPl; SptEdSchPpr; SpnCl; LetterBsktbl; LetterFtbl; LetterTrk; Indiana St Univ; Medicine.

HEYDON, Ann M; Lourdes HS; Rochester, MN; Band; CncrtBnd; HonRl; MrchBnd; NHS; Orch; PepBnd; FrCl; College.

HEYDT, Mary L; Moores Hill HS; Moores Hill, IN; 3/35 HonRl; College; Lawyer.

HEYEN, Kyle K; Milford Junior Senior HS; Milford, NE; SptEdSchPpr; LetterBsktbl; LetterFtbl; LetterTrk; College.

HEYEN, Neil M; Minooka HS; Joliet, IL; 1/113 HonRl; NHS; FrCl; MthCl; Shimer College; Liberal Arts.

HEYER, Kimberly; Cosmos HS; Grove City, MN; Band; Chrs; CncrtBnd; HonRl; MrchBnd; PepBnd; SchPl; YthFlsp; RptrSchPpr; Glf; Vocational School; Airline Hostess.

HEYLIN, Kevin C; Manhattan HS; Manhattan, KS; 2/480 ALBoysSt; Chrl; HonRl; Mdrgl; NatlFornLg; SchMus; SctActv; TreasStuCncl; YthFlsp; OptClAwd; University; Medical Career.

HEYMEN, Marcia E; Escanaba Area Public HS; Escanaba, MI; 33/385 NHS; Tennis; IMSpt; College; Geography Field.

HEYNEN, Mary; Wyoming Park HS; Wyoming, MI; HstFrshCls; 4-H; PpCl; Bsktbl; Glf; Tennis; Chrldr; 4-HAwd; Davenport Business School;secretary.

HEYNINCK, Kim M; United Twp HS; E Moline, IL; 9/517 HonRl; TreasJA; NHS; SchMus; StuCncl; GerCl; PpCl; LetterTennis; GAA; University; Physical Therapy.

HEYRMAN, Cynthia J; Menomonee Falls East HS; Menomonee Falls, WI; 24/335 TrsJrCls; TrsSrCls; HonRl; NHS; SchPl; FrCl; PpCl; Trk; Chrldr; Loyola University; Dental Hygienist.

HEYROTH, Jean R; Lodi HS; Dane, WI; TrsSophCls; SpnCl; PpCl; College; Physical Ed.

HEYSE, Margaret S; Joliet West HS; Joliet, IL; 60/520 Chr; Chrs; SecChrhWkr; HonRl; HospAde; NHS; OffAde; SchMus; GerCl; GAA; Valparaiso University.

HEYWOOD, David J; Battle Creek Central HS; Battle Creek, MI; 27/475 NHS; Coll; Acct.

HIATT, Charles C; Orion HS; Orion, IL; Chrs; HonRl; JA; NHS; SctActv; LatCl; LetterFtbl; JAAwd; Augustana Clg.

HIATT, Kimberly J; Monroe Central HS; Parker, IN; SecFrshCls; TrsSophCls; SecJrCls; TrsSrCls; Band; HonRl; NHS; Glf; Chrldr; GAA; Univ; Special Education.

HIATT, Linda M; Crystal Lake HS; Crystal Lake, IL;

Chr; Chrs; ChrhWkr; HonRl; JA; NHS; Ill State Univ; Accounting.

HIATT, Tony J; South Ripley HS; Versailles, IN; 5/98 ALBoysSt; Band; HonRl; PresNHS; PepBnd; Quill&Scroll; VPYthFlsp; Yrbk; SchPpr; MthCl; Purdue Univ; Biology.

HIBBERD, Don B; Fonlerville HS; Howell, MI; 5/134 ChrhWkr; HonRl; Yrbk; 4-H; LetterFtbl; 4-HAwd; Lansing Community; Electronies Tech.

HIBBERT, Barbara J; Brimfield HS; Brimfield, IL; 6/55 HonRl; NHS; SpnCl; University; Liberal Arts.

HIBBS, Deborah N; Grant HS; Grant, MI; 12/109 Band; Chr; HonRl; SchPl; StuCncl; SecYthFlsp; Sec4-H; PresFTA; SecSciCl; LetterTennis; Univ; Counseling.

HIBST, Debra S; Freeport HS; Freeport, IL; 67/507 Chr; ChrhWkr; HonRl; OffAde; SchMus; RptrSchPpr; GerCl; College; Professional.

HICK, William; East Greene HS; Rippey, IA; Chr; SchMus; YthFlsp; RptrYrbk; 4-HAwd; College; Professional.

HICKAM, Robin L; Corunna HS; Corunna, MI; 69/201 ChrhWkr; CncrtBnd; HonRl; JA; MrchBnd; Twrl; Swmmng; Tennis; Business Schl; Vocation.

HICKEN, Elizabeth A; Macomb Senior HS; Macomb, IL; HonRl; SchPpr; LetterSwmmng; IMSpt; College; Ornithology.

HICKENBOTTOM, Sandra J; Callaway HS; Callaway, NE; SecSophCls; SecJrCls; ALAGirlsSt; Band; CncrtBnd; MrchBnd; StuCncl; 4-H; FHA; PpCl; Trade; Vocation.

HICKENBOTTOM, Vicky I; Southern HS; Media, IL; TrsSrCls; Chrs; CmntyWkr; YthFlsp; Yrbk; SchPpr; 4-H; FHA; FTA; FrCl; Western Il U; Business.

HICKERSON, David B; Bedford N Lawerence HS; Bedford, IN; 16/400 ALBoysSt; ChrhWkr; CmntyWkr; HonRl; NHS; StuCncl; StuGov; KeyCl; FrCl; LetterBsbl; In Univ; Optometry.

HICKERSON, Leah; Shortridge HS; Indianapolis, IN; 3/650 HonRl; JrNHS; NHS; Quill&Scroll; StuCncl; EdYrBk; FrCl;.

HICKERSON, William J; Bowling Green Ri HS; Bowling Green, MO; 5/124 Band; Chr; ChrhWkr; CncrtBnd; HonRl; NHS; SchMus; TchrAde; PresFBLA; FTA; Ne Missouri State Univ; Business Admin.

HICKERT, Joseph S; Lenora HS; Lenora, KS; 4/28 VPJrCls; ALBoysSt; HonRl; SchPl; SctActv; Bsktbl; Ftbl; University; Engineering.

HICKEY, Doreen M; Carl Sandburg HS; Orland Park, IL; 24/680 HonRl; HospAde; LitMag; NHS; NatlMeritFnl; FNA; FrCl; MthCl; PpCl; Univ Of Ill; Nursing.

HICKEY, Jennifer A; Elizabeth Seton HS; Calumet Park, IL; 32/252 VPSophCls; Chrs; ChrhWkr; HonRl; NHS; EdYrBk; RptrSchPpr; LatCl; Loyola Univ; Law.

HICKEY, Joanne L; Lisle Senior HS; Lisle, IL; 1/195 AFS; Chr; Chrs; CncrtBnd; HonRl; Mdrgl; NHS; SecStuGov; RptrYrbk; Yrbk; College; Music Ed.

HICKEY, Karen J; Maple Valley HS; Nashville, MI; 7/108 HonRl; HospAde; SecNHS; OffAde; SchPl; FHA; PPFtbl; BttyCrckrAwd; DARAwd; 4-HAwd; Kellogg Comm College; Rn.

HICKEY, Mary Jo; St Francis Academy; Joliet, IL; 7/178 HonRl; JrNHS; NHS; NatlThespSoc; SchMus; SchPl; StuCncl; RptrYrbk; FrCl; Chrldr; IMSpt; Univ Of Illinois.

HICKEY, Maureen O; Rich Central HS; Park Forest, IL; 37/400 ChrhWkr; DrlTm; HonRl; NHS; TchrAde; College; Architecture.

HICKEY, Patrick E; De La Salle HS; Chicago, IL; 35/250 HonRl; NatlMeritCmnd; StuCncl; StuGov; University; Professional.

HICKEY, Robin L; La Crosse HS; Wanatah, IN; ChrhWkr; HonRl; OffAde; SctActv; YthFlsp; RptrYrbk; FHA; Bsbl; LetterTrk; GAA; Univ; Pro.

HICKLE, Jeanine K; Mason City HS; Clearlake, IA; Chrs; HonRl; PresLatCl; PpCl; N Ia Coll; Medical Assistant.

HICKLIN, Sherri L; Southland HS; Cardwell, MO; 1/27 HstSophCls; SecTrsJrCls; HstSrCls; PresNHS; SecSchPl; SecStuCncl; PresFHA; PresFTA; SecFrCl; DanFAwd; Baptist Memorial Hosp; Rn Nurse.

HICKMAN, Deborah K; De Soto HS; De Soto, MO; Chr; ChrhWkr; DrlTm; HonRl; Treas4-H; PpCl; 4-HAwd; College.

HICKMAN, Jeffrey B; Columbus Public HS; Columbus, ND; ALBoysSt; Band; ChrhWkr; HonRl; SchPl; RptrYrbk; Bsbl; Bsktbl; ChmnFtbl; LetterTrk; Univ; Liberal Arts.

HICKMAN, Kenneth E; Corning Community HS; Mount Etna, IA; CmntyWkr; JrNHS; NHS; NatlMeritFnl; NatlMeritCmnd; NatlMeritSchl; NatlMeritSF; StuGov; Wrstlng; JAAwd; College; Accounting.

HICKMAN, Kimberly A; Sheldon Comm HS; Sheldon, IA; Chr; CncrtBnd; HonRl; MrchBnd; NHS; SchMus; Twrl; YthFlsp; Bsktbl; Trk; Coll; Music.

HICKMAN, Mark S; Shorewood HS; Shorewood, WI; 15/195 Chrs; HonRl; Mdrgl; NHS; NatlMeritFnl; Orch; SchMus; SchPl; LetterTrk; Coll; Teacher.

HICKMAN, Michael S; Shorewood HS; Shorewood, WI; 18/200 AFS; ALBoysSt; Chr; HonRl; Mdrgl; NHS; StuCncl; Ftbl; Trk; JAAwd; College; Cirriculum Of Major Study.

HICKMAN, Randy D; Lakeview HS; Columbus, NE; ALBoysSt; HonRl; JA; RedCrAde; StuCncl; StuGov; TchrAde; YthFlsp; CaptBsktbl; LetterFtbl; LetterTrk; College; Liberal Arts.

HICKMOTT, Suzanne T; Davison HS; Davison, MI; ChrhWkr; CmntyWkr; HonRl; NatlMeritCmnd; OffAde; SctActv; 4-H; IMSpt;.

HICKROD, Steven R; Gibson Southern HS; Ft Branch, IN; 93/227 Band; Chr; CncrtBnd; MrchBnd; PepBnd; SchPpr; PpCl; Isu; Majoring In Music, Enlish, Or Nursing.

HICKS, Anthony W; Curie HS; Chicago, IL; Aud/Vis; HonRl; LbryAde; NHS; 4-H; Ftbl; LetterWrstlng; 4-HAwd; University; Elec Engineer.

HICKS, Betty J; Otis Bisons HS; Pawnee Rock, KS; Chrs; HonRl; IntrClCncl; RedCrAde; SctActv; RptrSchPpr; 4-H; SpnCl; PpCl; Swmmng; Clge; Prof.

HICKS, Carmen J; Harris HS; Chicago, IL; OffAde; StuCncl; TchrAde; SpnCl; College; Doctor.

HICKS, Carol D; El Dorado Springs HS; El Dorado Springs, MO; 5/112 HonRl; PresLbryAde; NHS; Orch; TchrAde; FTA; PPFtbl; Coll; Prof.

HICKS, Cynthia D; Valley Park HS; Valley Park, MO; TrsFrshCls; TrsSophCls; TrsJrCls; Chr; HonRl; RptrYrbk; RptrSchPpr; SptEdSchPpr; PpCl; CaptChrldr; Bus School; Secretary.

HICKS, David C; Willow Springs HS; Willow Springs, MO; VPJrCls; HonRl; StuGov; PresFTA; PpCl; SciCl; LetterBsbl; LetterBsktbl; LetterGlf; LetterTrk; U Of Mo; Law School & Govnmt.

HICKS, Donald E; Scranton HS; Scranton, IA; 10/18 VPSrCls; HonRl; YthFlsp; RptrSchPpr; SptEdSchPpr; CaptBsbl; Ftbl; Glf; CchngActv; IMSpt; Buena Vista College; Business Admin.

HICKS, Douglas G; Sturgis HS; Sturgis, MI; HonRl; NHS; LatCl; LetterTrk; Michigan St Univ; Computer Science.

HICKS, Edwin E; Lyons HS; Lyons, KS; 2/96 Band; Chr; HonRl; PepBnd; PolWkr; Quill&Scroll; SchMus; SchPl; Yrbk; SchPpr; Univ Of Ks; Organ.

HICKS, Franklin D; Bishop Noll Inst; Hammond, IN; 175/324 Chr; ChrhWkr; HonRl; HospAde; Ball State U; Nursing.

HICKS, Glen W; Bennington HS; Bennington, KS; Chrs; SchMus; SchPl; Yrbk; SciCl; Ftbl; University; Mech Engineer.

HICKS, Heidi A; Davison HS; Davison, MI; 13/433 Chr; ChrhWkr; CmntyWkr; HonRl; LbryAde; NHS; SchMus; SchPl; RptrYrbk; FrCl; Michigan State Univ; Physical Education.

HICKS, Jane E; Jefferson City HS; Jefferson City, MO; Chrl; NHS; NatlMeritCmnd; Quill&Scroll; StuCncl; RptrYrbk; EdSchPpr; GAA; AmLegAwd; VFWAwd; Miss Univ; Jounralism.

HICKS, Karen R; Lindblom HS; Chicago, IL; 10/657 Band; ChrhWkr; CncrtBnd; HonRl; HospAde; MrchBnd; SctActv; TchrAde; Yrbk; FrCl; Northern Univ; Accountant.

HICKS, Lori; West Dubuque HS; Dyersville, IA; VPFrshCls; SecSophCls; HonRl; MrchBnd; PepBnd; RusCl; PpCl; Bsktbl; Trk; IMSpt; College; Vet Assistant.

HICKS, Maureen K; St Francis Academy; Joliet, IL; 19/178 Chr; Chrs; ChrhWkr; HonRl; IntrClCncl; NHS; Sacrstn; SchMus; PresSpnCl; College; Medical Science.

HICKS, Melissa M; Owensville HS; Gerald, MO; TrsFrshCls; SecTrsJrCls; Band; HonRl; NHS; NatlMeritCmnd; NatlThespSoc; SchPl; GAA; OptClAwd; Arkansas College; Medicine.

HICKS, Nancy K; Rockford West HS; Rockford, IL; 48/390 AFS; HonRl; LitMag; NHS; Orch; Quill&Scroll; TchrAde; Yrbk; 4-H; EngCl; Clge; Veterinarian.

HICKS, Thomas L; Oakwood Twp HS; Oakwood, IL; PresSrCls; NHS; StuCncl; SpnCl; PpCl; LetterBsbl; LetterBsktbl; LetterFtbl; BauchLmbAwd; VoiceDemAwd; Illinois St Univ; Veterinarian.

HICKS, William C; Pipestone HS; Pipestone, MN; 5/140 VPFrshCls; PresSophCls; PresJrCls; PresSrCls; ALBoysSt; HonRl; NHS; LetterBsbl; CaptFtbl; Trk; Gustavus Adolphus College; Math And Economi.

HICOK, Jane A; Peoria HS; Peoria, IL; HonRl; JrNHS; LbryAde; NHS; GerCl; SciCl; U Of Illinois.

HIDDING, Mary L; Osseo HS; Brooklyn Park, MN; 64/360 AFS; HonRl; HospAde; JrNHS; NHS; PolWkr; SchPl; SctActv; SchPpr; GerCl; College Of St Catherine; Medical.

HIDEG, Laszlo M; Divine Child HS; Dearborn Hts, MI; ChrhWkr; CncrtBnd; HonRl; NHS; NatlThespSoc; PepBnd; SchMus; GerCl; MthCl; Univ Of Michigan; Mech Engineer.

HIDKIFF, Denise M; Academy Of Our Lady; Chicago, IL; 13/189 ChrhWkr; HonRl; HospAde; NHS; RedCrAde; SchAde; Sdlty; SchPpr; Lewis University; Business Admin.

HIEB, Kelcy; Madison Consolidated HS; Madison, IN; 18/290 CncrtBnd; HonRl; MrchBnd; NHS; SchMus; GerCl; GAA; College; Cpa.

HIEBERT, Becky A; Mason HS; Mason, MI; Chr; ChrhWkr; OffAde; SchMus; StuCncl; TchrAde; SchPpr; VPFHA; IMSpt; Col; Special Ed.

HIEDEMAN, Duane; Campbell Tintah HS; Campbell, MN; 3/34 Band; Chr; ChrhWkr; CmntyWkr; CncrtBnd; HonRl; Mdrgl; YthFlsp; RptrSchPpr; Ftbl; N Dak St Sch Of Sci; Diesel Mech.

HIELSCHER, Nancy J; Alliance HS; Alliance, NE; Band; CncrtBnd; HonRl; MrchBnd; NatlThespSoc; PepBnd; Quill&Scroll; SchPl; Yrbk; IMSpt; Journalism.

HIEMENZ, Tammy J; Little Fork Big Falls HS; Big Falls, MN; 10/40 Chr; Chrs; CmntyWkr; HonRl; LbryAde; FHA; PpCl; Bus Sch; Professional.

HIEMES, Alan M; Aquinas HS; Shelby, NE; 6/88 Chrs; NHS; NatlThespSoc; SchPl; TchrAde; LatCl; MthCl; LetterWrstlng; CchngActv; Farming.

HIER, Karen G; Wethersfield HS; Galva, IL; 18/87 VPFrshCls; VPSophCls; AFS; HonRl; SchAde; TchrAde; 4-H; FTA; PpCl; CaptChrldr; GAA; Black Hawk Jr Clg; Interior Decorator.

HIERONYMUS, Donna K; Farmer City Mansfield HS; Farmer City, IL; 37/73 AFS; Band; Chr; CncrtBnd; HonRl; MrchBnd; PepBnd; SchPl; StuCncl; YthFlsp; 4-H; KeyCl; Bsktbl; Eastern Ill Univ; Physical Education.

HIETIKKO, Brad L; Baraqa Townships HS; Baraqa, MI; Band; Chrs; ChrhWkr; OffAde; SchPl; SctActv; RptrSchPpr; 4-H; SpnCl; 4-HAwd; Univ; Commercial Pilot.

HIGBEE, Scott A; Spearfish HS; Spearfish, SD; 5/81 PresSophCls; HonRl; NHS; Quill&Scroll; SchPl; EdYrBk; EdSchPpr; LetterFtbl; SecSwmmng; LetterWrstlng; South Dakota State U.

HIGDON, Ray D; Pontiac Central HS; Pontiac, MI; PresJrCls; CmntyWkr; HonRl; NatlFornLg; StuCncl; StuGov; RptrSchPpr; CivCl; Bsbl; Trk; IMSpt; EldAwd; OptClAwd; Oakland University; Law.

HIGGASON, Vicki S; Eldora HS; Eldora, IA; ChrhWkr; HonRl; SctActv; SpnCl;.

HIGGERSON, Philip K; Carterville HS; Carterville, IL; Chr; Chrs; CncrtBnd; MrchBnd; SchMus; SchPl; EdYrBk; FBLA; Bsktbl; Ftbl; Ill Univ; Bus.

HIGGINBOTHAM, Bradley D; Thomas Jefferson HS; Council Bluffs, IA; 5/535 HonRl; NHS; NatlMeritCmnd; Glf; Wrstlng; IMSpt; College; Dentistry.

HIGGINS, Barbara L; Yale HS; Yale, MI; 4/137 StuCncl; StuGov; TchrAde; 4-H; SpnCl; SciCl; 4-HAwd; Scccc; Accountant.

HIGGINS, Gregory L; Tuscola HS; Tuscola, IL; 13/147 ChrhWkr; HonRl; NatlMeritCmnd; FrCl; Univ Of Ill; Law.

HIGGINS, Jayne; Mayville HS; Mayville, MI; 2/117 Band; Chr; ChrhWkr; HonRl; MrchBnd; NHS; PepBnd; Yrbk; Chrldr; Central Mi Univ; Cpa.

HIGGINS, Joan M; Mt Assisi Academy; Hometown, IL; 18/145 CAP; DrlTm; HonRl; LitMag; RptrSchPpr; SchPpr; FNA; FrCl; VFWAwd; College; Public Health Nursing.

HIGGINS, Judith; Mt Assisi Acad; Chicago, IL; 2/189 HonRl; HospAde; NHS; SchMus; SchPl; StuCncl; StuGov; SchPpr; FrCl; LatCl; Loyola U;psychology.

HIGGINS, Judith A; Mt Assisi Academy; Chicago, IL; 2/190 HonRl; HospAde; ModUN; NHS; SchAde; SchMus; SchPl; StuCncl; StuGov; TchrAde; EdSchPpr; 4-H; Loyola Univ; Psychology.

HIGGINS, Kathi; Marian Catholic HS; Chicago Hts, IL; Chr; CmntyWkr; HonRl; StuCncl; Yrbk; GAA; IMSpt; PPFtbl; College; Medicine.

HIGGINS, Kathy; Switzerland County Hs; Bennington, IN; ChrhWkr; HonRl; TchrAde; FHA; SpnCl; PpCl; Trade School;beautician.

HIGGINS, Marcia A; Garrett HS; Garrett, IN; ChrhWkr; HonRl; TchrAde; Yrbk;.

HIGGINS, Marian E; Merrill HS; Merrill, WI; HonRl; BttyCrckrAwd; Broward Comm Col; Psychology.

HIGGINS, Maryanne P; St Charles HS; St Charles, MO; Chr; ChrhWkr; CmntyWkr; HonRl; Treas4-H; SpnCl; SciCl;.

HIGGINS, Marybeth; Streator Twp HS; Streator, IL; 38/360 HonRl; GerCl; College; Elementary Education.

HIGGINS, Mary Jo; Dysart Geneseo Comm HS; Traer, IA; 15/55 Band; Chr; Chrs; ChrhWkr; CncrtBnd; HonRl; HospAde; Mdrgl; PolWkr; Glf; Iowa State Univ; Elementary Education.

HIGGINS, Maureen A; Prospect HS; Arlington Hgts, IL; HonRl; NatlMeritCmnd; SchPl; FNA; PpCl; GAA; Univ Of Iowa; Occupational Therapy.

HIGGINS, Michael J; Mahtomedi HS; Mahtomedi, MN; Aud/Vis; HonRl; NatlFornLg; TchrAde; Bsktbl; Ftbl; Socr; Trk; CchngActv; IMSpt; Collge; Professional.

HIGGINS, Penny L; Macksville HS; Macksville, KS; Band; Chr; Chrs; ChrhWkr; CncrtBnd; HonRl; MrchBnd; PepBnd; SchMus; Yrbk; College.

HIGGINS, Raymond W; Homewood Flossmoor HS; Homewood, IL; 19/932 Chr; HonRl; JrNHS; NHS; Orch; SchMus; SchPl; RusCl; SciCl; College; Meteorology.

HIGGINS, Rosalyn L; Parkview HS; Orfordville, WI; 9/163 Band; CncrtBnd; HonRl; MrchBnd; PresNHS; NatlThespSoc; PepBnd; TreasFHA; GAA; BttyCrckrAwd; U Of Wi; Home Ec.

HIGGINS, Timothy; Dekalb Senior Hs; Dekalb, IL; 37/357 VPFrshCls; VPSophCls; CncrtBnd; HonRl; NatlThespSoc; SchMus; SchPl; StuCncl; YthFlsp; LetterTennis; College; Sociology.

HIGH, Kandy L; North White HS; Reynolds, IN; 5/98 SecJrCls; Chrs; HonRl; LbryAde; NHS; Twrl; EdSchPpr; PpCl; Trade Schl; Commercial Art.

HIGHLAND, Brenda J; Lilbourn HS; Lilbourn, MO; 2/80 HonRl; FBLA; FHA; Univ Of Mo Columbia; Business.

HIGHLAND, Cindy L; Stuart Menlo Comm HS; Stuart, IA; 8/65 Chrs; HonRl; SchPl; SpnCl; PpCl; SciCl; College; Professional.

HIGHLAND, Jeffrey A; Lexington HS; Lexington, IL; 16/48 PresFrshCls; AFS; Band; CncrtBnd; HonRl; MrchBnd; PepBnd; SciCl; LetterFtbl; Trk; College; Public Relations Major.

HIGHNESS, Barbara L; Fargo South HS; Fargo, ND; Band; ChrhWkr; CncrtBnd; MrchBnd; University; Fashion Retailing.

HIGHT, Michael D; Hallsville HS; Centralia, MO; PresSophCls; HonRl; StuCncl; RptrYrbk; PpCl; Bsbl; Bsktbl; Trk; College.

HIGHTOWER, Dawna K; Colchester HS; Colchester, IL; 3/52 TrsFrshCls; PresSophCls; ChrhWkr; CmntyWkr; HonRl; JA; LbryAde; MrchBnd; NHS; GAA; Univ; Secretary.

HIGHTOWER, Debra A; Gods Bible School HS; Union City, IN; SecSrCls; Chr; ChrhWkr; HonRl; HospAde; OffAde; SchPl; FNA; FTA; College.

HIGHUM, Louise; Rushford Public HS; Rushford, MN; 7/63 Band; Chrs; HonRl; HospAde; RptrSchPpr; PpCl; Chrldr; GAA; Junior College; Registered Nurse.

HIGLEY, Michael B; Oswego HS; Oswego, IL; 13/262 Chrs; HonRl; JrNHS; NHS; SpnCl; CaptFtbl; Glf; Wrstlng; GovHonPrgAwd; College; Medicine.

HIGMAN, Debbie S; N Kansas City HS; Kansas City, MO; Chrs; HonRl; NatlFornLg; StuCncl; PpCl; Tennis; Chrldr; PresAwd; College.

HIGNITE, Mary J; Crothersville HS; Crothersville, IN; 13/75 MrchBnd; OffAde; PolWkr; SchMus; SchPl; SctActv; RptrSchPpr; 4-H; PpCl; GAA; Career Coll; Professional.

HIGUCHI, Kenneth; Huron HS; Ann Arbor, MI; HonRl; GerCl; Univ Of Mich; Medicine.

HILAND, George K; Rosedale HS; Bridgeton, IN; 2/55 PresFrshCls; PresJrCls; HonRl; ModUN; NHS; LatCl; Univ; Marketing.

HILBER, Colleen S; Wausau West HS; Wausau, WI; 1/440 ALBoysSt; LbryAde; MrchBnd; NHS; TchrAde; GerCl; MthCl; SciCl; CaptSwmmng; IMSpt; Uw Eau Claire; Chem.

HILBERG, Jeanne L; Forest Park HS; Crystal Falls, MI; HonRl; StuCncl; TchrAde; YthLg; CivCl; Chrldr; PresAwd; University; Law Enforcement.

HILBERT, Laneal E; Hagerstown Jr Sr HS; Hagerstown, IN; ChrhWkr; VPYthFlsp; Pres4-H; VPFFA; LetterBsktbl; 4-HAwd;.

HILBRANDS, Maureen K; George Community HS; George, IA; 9/47 CncrtBnd; HonRl; LbryAde; MrchBnd; NHS; PepBnd; SchPl; Sec4-H; FTA; Univ Of Northern Ia; Mathematics.

HILBRANDT, William P; Carrollton HS; Saginaw, MI; 2/180 Band; ChrhWkr; CmntyWkr; CncrtBnd; HonRl; MrchBnd; NHS; NatlMeritSF; PepBnd; LetterGlf; College; Mech Engineering.

HILBRENNER, Kevin L; Santa Fe HS; Waverly, MO; HonRl; NHS; StuCncl; StuGov; TchrAde; LetterBsbl; CaptBsktbl; CaptFtbl; AmLegAwd;.

HILD, Debra; Plattsmouth Sr HS; Plattsmouth, NE; 15/144 Band; CncrtBnd; HonRl; MrchBnd; NHS; PepBnd; StuCncl; 4-H; FHA; Univ Of Ne; Curr Of Major Study.

HILD, Steven; La Porte City HS; La Porte City, IA; Chrs; HonRl; NHS; NatlThespSoc; SchPl; SchPpr; Univ; Astrophysics.

HILDEBRAND, Becky; East Newton HS; Stark City, MO; 5/91 SecJrCls; ChrhWkr; HonRl; MrchBnd; ModUN; NHS; SchPl; Yrbk; PpCl; Missouri Southern State College; Dental Ass.

HILDEBRAND, Karol J; Bradley Bourbonnais Comm HS; Bourbonnais, IL; Aud/Vis; HonRl; NHS; Teen; PpCl; GAA; IMSpt; Kankakee Comm Coll; X Ray Technician.

HILDEBRAND, Kim D; Mitchell HS; Mitchell, SD; 64/288 Chr; HonRl; Mdrgl; NHS; PolWkr; SchMus; StuCncl; RptrYrbk; PpCl; IMSpt; AmLegAwd; Sd State U; Pre Med.

HILDEBRAND, Larry; Nickerson HS; South Hutchinson, KS; 4/107 HonRl; TchrAde; PpCl; Tennis; Kansas Univ; Political Science.

HILDEBRAND, Linda K; Bradley Bourbonnais Comm HS; Bourbonnais, IL; CmntyWkr; HonRl; JA; JrNHS; NHS; RedCrAde; StuCncl; FNA; CaptChrldr; AmLegAwd; Coll; X Ray Technology.

HILDEBRANDT, Cheryl; Western HS; Parma, MI; 5/149 HonRl; HospAde; ModUN; SchMus; SchPl; StuCncl; TchrAde; SpnCl; Hillsdale College; Frence Teacher.

HILDEBRANDT, Joseph; Lake Park HS; Itasca, IL; HonRl; Ftbl; Univ; Curriculum Of Major Study.

HILDEBRANDT, Kim M; Kenyon HS; Kenyon, MN; 2/68 PresJrCls; Band; Chr; HonRl; PresNHS; SchMus; RptrYrbk; FHA; FrCl; BttyCrckrAwd; Gustavus Adolphus; Medicine Nurse Or Dr.

HILDEBRANT, Joan M; North Central HS; Sanborn, ND; 8/30 SecTrsSrCls; Band; CncrtBnd; HonRl; ModUN; OffAde; PepBnd; Univ Of Nd; Secretary.

HILDEBRECHT, Susan M; Parkway Central HS; Chesterfield, MO; 43/470 Chr; ChrhWkr; HospAde; JrNHS; Mdrgl; NHS; PresPpCl; PPFtbl; Univ Of Mo; Nursing.

HILDENBRAND, Charles; Southridge HS; Holland, IN; 48/167 ALBoysSt; ChrhWkr; CmntyWkr; HonRl; Sacrstn; 4-H; Wrstlng; 4-HAwd; Univ; Geol.

HILDENBRAND, Jane A; Reitz Memorial HS; Evansville, IN; 10/225 HonRl; NHS; GerCl; Lock Years College; Accounting.

HILDENBRAND, Marsha D; Sullivan HS; Carlisle, IN; 6/154 HonRl; LbryAde; NHS; Teen; FHA; LatCl; College; Business.

HILDERBRAND, Cathleen M; Ogallala Sr HS; Ogallala, NE; Chrs; ChrhWkr; SchPl; TchrAde; SptEdSchPpr; 4-H; PpCl; Chrldr; IMSpt; College.

HILDRETH, Craig; Ankeny Sr HS; Ankeny, IA; 8/260 HonRl; JrNHS; NHS; Trk; Wrstlng; IMSpt; Attend Univ; Sci Math Or Psych.

HILE, Dorothy D; Mitchell HS; Mitchell, IN; ChrhWkr; HonRl; Coll; Pharmacy.

HILEMAN, Carey R; Anna Jonesboro HS; Anna, IL; HonRl; FrCl; Ftbl; Trk; Univ Of Illinois; Physician.

HILEMAN, David L; Conway HS; Niangua, MO; HonRl; TchrAde; 4-H; VPFFA; FTA; LetterBsbl; Bsktbl; 4-HAwd; Univ Of Mo; Conservation.

HILEMAN, Debbie K; Conway HS; Niangua, MO; Chrs; HonRl; HospAde; IntrClCncl; StuCncl; TchrAde; 4-H; FHA; FNA; FTA; PpCl; Waynesville Vo Tech; Nursing.

HILEMAN, Douglas E; Anna Jonesboro HS; Anna, IL; Chrs; HonRl; 4-H; FFA; LetterBsktbl; LetterFtbl; DanFAwd; 4-HAwd; Shawnee Jr College; Farmer.

HILER, Craig; Rockwell City Comm HS; Rockwell City, IA; VPJrCls; HonRl; StuCncl; FFA; Ia Central Comm Col; Agri Banking.

HILES, Joni R; Wahpeton SR; Wahpeton, ND; HonRl; FBLA; IMSpt; Ins Agent.

HILEY, Chretta A; Gallatin HS; Altamont, MO; 2/52 Band; ChrhWkr; CncrtBnd; HonRl; PresLbryAde; MrchBnd; ModUN; TreasNHS; SchPl; SecFHA; LetterTrk; University; Medicine.

HILF, James C; Vianney HS; St Louis, MO; 90/200 ChrhWkr; Sacrstn; IMSpt; College Or Univ; Electronics.

HILGEMANN, David J; Valley Comm HS; Elgin, IA; CncrtBnd; HonRl; MrchBnd; PresNatlThespSoc; SchPl; StuCncl; RptrYrbk; PresSciCl; U Of N Iowa; Industrial Tech.

HILGENBERG, Jim M; Artesian HS; Artesian, SD; 3/25 PresSrCls; ALBoysSt; HonRl; StuCncl; LetterBsktbl; LetterFtbl; CaptTrk; AmLegAwd; South Dakota St Univ; Elec Engineering.

HILGENBERG, Peggy L; West HS; Green Bay, WI; Chr; ChrhWkr; HonRl; Trk; College; Home Economics.

HILGENDORF, Scott T; Edina West HS; Edina, MN; ChrhWkr; TchrAde; College; Mathematics.

HILGENDORF, Susan M; Clifton Central HS; Chebanse, IL; 11/132 Chrs; ChrhWkr; HonRl; LbryAde; NHS; NatlThespSoc; SchPl; PresYthFlsp; FrCl; MthCl; College; Accounting.

HILGENDORF, Thomas J; Tuscola HS; Tuscola, IL; 17/128 TrsFrshCls; TrsSophCls; TrsJrCls; TrsSrCls; PresChrhWkr; HonRl; FrCl; Ftbl; LetterTrk; Univ Of Ill; Accounting.

HILGENKAMP, Deborah E; Arlington HS; Arlington, NE; 6/62 VPJrCls; ChrhWkr; HonRl; Twrl; YthFlsp; 4-H; PpCl; LetterBsktbl; LetterTrk; 4-HAwd; College; Teaching.

HILGER, Lori L; Luther South HS; Chicago, IL; 39/230 Chr; NHS; EdSchPpr; GAA; IMSpt; College; Journalism Vacation.

HILGER, Mary A; Aquinas HS; David City, NE; 11/97 SecJrCls; Chrs; ChrhWkr; CmntyWkr; OffAde; Quill&Scroll; SchPl; StuGov; LatCl; Chrldr; U Of Ne; Nursing.

HILGER, Ted L; Bishop Carroll HS; Wichita, KS; HonRl; SchPl; LetterBsbl; LetterFtbl; Liberal Jr Col; Pro Artist.

HILGERS, Gary E; Moorhead HS; Moorhead, MN; ChrhWkr; CmntyWkr; HonRl; SchPl; SctActv; KeyCl; Bsbl; Bsktbl; IMSpt; Moorhead St College; Accountant.

HILKEMANN, Aaron C; Norfolk HS; Norfolk, NE; Band; ChrhWkr; CncrtBnd; HonRl; MrchBnd; YthFlsp; SpnCl; LetterBsktbl; LetterFtbl; IMSpt; Wayne Col; Cpa.

HILL, Anne M; Woodlands Academy; Winnetka, IL; 16/75 Chrs; Orch; Vassar College; Music.

HILL, Ann M; Andrean HS; Gary, IN; ChrhWkr; CmntyWkr; YthFlsp; SpnCl; PpCl; Pudue Univ; Medical Tech.

HILL, Betty G; Winfield R Iv HS; Foley, MO; Chrs; ChrhWkr; HonRl; NHS; SchPl; College.

HILL, Beverly R; Lakeshore HS; Stevensville, MI; Chr; ChrhWkr; HonRl; OffAde; StuCncl; YthFlsp; RptrYrbk; FHA; SpnCl; PpCl; University; Science.

HILL, Brenda; Northeastern Wayne HS; Fountain City, IN; 7/130 ChrhWkr; HonRl; NHS; 4-H; SpnCl; Purdue Univ; Pharmacist.

HILL, Brent L; Newell HS; Newell, SD; PresJrCls; NatlFornLg; SchMus; SchPl; Bsktbl; Ftbl; CchngActv; IMSpt; AmLegAwd; VoiceDemAwd; Univ.

HILL, Carol; South Nodaway R Iv HS; Barnard, MO; 7/28 SecJrCls; HonRl; NHS; VPFrshCls; FHA; PpCl; Trk; CitAwd; Northwest Mo St Univ; Home Ec.

HILL, Cheryl R; Reynolds County R Ii HS; Redford, MO; Band; PpCl;.

HILL, Christopher J; Bishop Carroll HS; Wichita, KS; Chr; ChrhWkr; CmntyWkr; HonRl; NatlFornLg; SchPl; College; Public Health.

HILL, Cindy; Diagonal HS; Tingley, IA; Band; Chrs; HonRl; OffAde; Trk; College.

HILL, Corinne E; Reese HS; Reese, MI; 17/130 Band; CncrtBnd; HonRl; MrchBnd; NatlMeritCmnd; PepBnd; SctActv; Twrl; LetterBsktbl; LetterTrk; Univ; Teacher.

HILL, Craig C; Springfield HS; Springfield, IL; PresFrshCls; AFS; Chr; Chrs; ChrhWkr; CmntyWkr; PolWkr; SchMus; YthFlsp; RptrSchPpr; GerCl; Bsktbl; Ftbl; Illinois Wesleyan; Minister.

HILL, Daily S; Brown County HS; Nashville, IN; 1/168 TrsSophCls; PresJrCls; ALBoysSt; Band; CncrtBnd; HonRl; ModUN; Bsktbl; Trk; IMSpt; College; Mechanical Engineering.

HILL, Daniel C; Glenbard East HS; Lombard, IL; 120/654 Band; ChrhWkr; CncrtBnd; HonRl; MrchBnd; College; Elec Technician.

HILL, Darrel L; Medicine Valley HS; Curtis, NE; TrsSrCls; Band; Chr; Chrs; CncrtBnd; HonRl; MrchBnd; FFA; LetterBsktbl; CaptFtbl;.

HILL, David J; Maine North HS; Glenview, IL; HonRl; NHS; SctActv; YthFlsp; Northwestern Univ; Electronics.

HILL, Debra L; Fairfield HS; Plevna, KS; SecSophCls; SecJrCls; Chr; ChrhWkr; CncrtBnd; HonRl; SchPl; TchrAde; 4-H; Bsktbl; LetterTennis; 4-HAwd; JAAwd; CitAwd; Hutchinson Comm Jr College; Retail Mgmt.

HILL, Debra L; Anna Jonesboro HS; Jonesboro, IL; HonRl; FHA; FrCl; Southern Ill Univ; Social Work.

HILL, Dianna S; Humboldt HS; Humboldt, IA; 15/140 Chr; ChrhWkr; CncrtBnd; HonRl; MrchBnd; Orch; PepBnd; 4-H; GAA; College; Special Ed.

HILL, Donald L; Kenwood HS; Chicago, IL; 28/485 HonRl; NHS; NatlMeritSF; FDA; LetterFtbl; Univ Of Notre Dame; Physician.

HILL, Elizabeth A; Newman Central Catholic HS; Rockfalls, IL; 2/69 Chrs; HonRl; NHS; NatlMeritCmnd; SchMus; SchPl; EdSchPpr; GAA; AmLegAwd; DARAwd; Northern Il Univ; Pharmacy Or Science.

HILL, Elizabeth A; Bremen Comm HS; Midlothian, IL; HonRl; OffAde; SctActv; StuCncl; TchrAde; EdYrBk; SchPpr; PresFTA; SpnCl; GAA; National Col Of Educ; Elementary Teacher.

HILL, Eugene M; East Des Moines HS; Des Moines, IA; HonRl; UNYO; Bsbl; Bsktbl; LetterFtbl; University.

HILL, Gayleen D; Ainsworth HS; Ainsworth, NE; 1/65 Band; HonRl; NHS; NatlThespSoc; RptrYrbk; EdYrBk; RptrSchPpr; FrCl; Bsktbl; GAA; BttyCrckrAwd; University Of Nebraska; Classics.

HILL, Gregory J; Glenbard East HS; Lombard, IL; 24/600 ChrhWkr; NHS; NatlMeritCmnd; Sacrstn; FrCl; Trk; Univ Of Illinois; Engineering.

HILL, Herbert; Salem HS; Salem, MO; ChrhWkr; CmntyWkr; HonRl; JA; JCC; RedCrAde; YthFlsp; FFA; Bsbl; Bsktbl; Trade.

HILL, Holly B; Estherville HS; Estherville, IA; Chrs; HonRl; Mdrgl; NatlThespSoc; SchMus; SchPl; 4-H; Iowa Lakes Comm College; Interior Decorator.

HILL, Janelle D; Y J B HS; Bagley, IA; TrsJrCls; Chrs; ChrhWkr; CncrtBnd; HonRl; HospAde; SchPl; StuCncl; RptrYrbk; LetterBsktbl; College; Social Service.

HILL, Janet L; Valley Park HS; Valley Park, MO; ChrhWkr; HonRl; RptrYrbk; EdSchPpr; College; Physical Therapy.

HILL, Janice L; Rolla HS; Rolla, MO; 3/280 TrsJrCls; Band; CncrtBnd; HonRl; MrchBnd; NatlMeritSF; PepBnd; SchPl; LatCl; PresAwd; College; Anthropology.

HILL, Joy; Holly Senior HS; Holly, MI; Chr; Chrl; Chrs; ChrhWkr; HonRl; NHS; SchMus; Coll; Secretary.

HILL, Julie A; Everly HS; Everly, IA; 11/34 ChrhWkr; CmntyWkr; HonRl; SchPl; RptrYrbk; Yrbk; Iowa Lakes Comm College; Rehabilitation.

HILL, Karla K; Staples HS; Staples, MN; 13/149 Chr; HonRl; HospAde; JrNHS; YthFlsp; FHA; GAA; College; Accounting.

HILL, Kathryn M; Lake Forest HS; Lake Forest, IL; AFS; Chr; HonRl; NatlFornLg; NHS; SchMus; SchPl; Mt Holyoke College; Political Science.

HILL, Kevin N; Wyandotte Roosevelt HS; Wyandotte, MI; HonRl; VPStuCncl; LetterBsbl; LetterBsktbl; LetterFtbl; IMSpt; Wayne St Univ; Business.

HILL, Kimberlee; Vienna Hs; New Burnside, IL; 14/104 Chrs; CmntyWkr; HonRl; SchPl; StuCncl; StuGov; RptrSchPpr; FNA; SpnCl; PpCl; GAA; U; Professional.

HILL, Kimberly B; Adair County R Ii HS; Greentop, MO; Band; Chrs; HonRl; SchPl; StuCncl; 4-H; Bsktbl; Trk;.

HILL, Laura; Rochester HS; Rochester, IN; 16/160 Chr; HonRl; LbryAde; NatlFornLg; NHS; SchMus; SchPl; SctActv; StuCncl; Trk; College; Drafting.

HILL, Leah J; Crab Orchard HS; Marion, IL; 9/31 Chr; Chrs; ChrhWkr; CmntyWkr; YthFlsp; RptrSchPpr; 4-H; FHA; Chrldr; 4-HAwd; Coll; Teacher Aide Child Care.

HILL, Lorie; Chandler Lake Wilson HS; Lake Wilson, MN; 1/39 SecFrshCls; PresSrCls; Band; Chr; ChrhWkr; HonRl; MrchBnd; SchPl; EdYrBk; RptrSchPpr; Makkato St Col; Accounting.

HILL, Lucinda S; Battle Creek Acad; Battle Creek, MI; 1/22 Band; Chr; ChrhWkr; HonRl; NHS; SchPl; AmLegAwd; Andrews Univ; Md.

HILL, Lynn M; Patoka Community Unit HS; Patoka, IL; 3/25 SecTrsSophCls; PresJrCls; SecTrsSrCls; Band; Chrl; SchPl; Yrbk; SchPpr; Chrldr; Kaskaskia College; Vocation.

HILL, Mark S; Montague HS; Montague, MI; Band; CncrtBnd; MrchBnd; SctActv; StuCncl; Yrbk; GerCl; Glf; Trk; College; Chemical Engineer.

HILL, Marsha A; Thomson HS; Thomson, IL; 1/41 HonRl; PresNHS; NatlMeritFnl; SctActv; Yrbk; PresFHA; VPFTA; Bsktbl; Chrldr; DARAwd; Drake Univ; Mass Communications.

HILL, Martha; Waterman HS; Waterman, IL; 8/35 TrsJrCls; CncrtBnd; DrlTm; HonRl; MrchBnd; PepBnd; FTA; Socr; Trk; College; Business Ed.

HILL, Michael; Sherwood HS; Creighton, MO; Band; CncrtBnd; HonRl; MrchBnd; PepBnd; ROTC; SctActv; SptEdYrbk; Ftbl; Trk; College; Professional.

HILL, Nancy; Mitchell Senior HS; Mitchell, SD; HonRl; Black Hills St Coll;.

HILL, Nancy F; Columbia City Joint HS; Columbia City, IN; 33/270 CmntyWkr; HonRl; LitMag; StuCncl; SpnCl; GAA; NCTE; Manchester College; Social Work.

HILL, Nancy J; North Central HS; Indianapolis, IN; HonRl; NatlFornLg; NHS; NatlMeritSF; PolWkr; SchMus; StuGov; 4-H; FDA; GerCl; PpCl; Bsbl; LetterTrk; GAA; Mich St; Medicine.

HILL, Nina K; Tippecanoe Valley HS; Akron, IN; 7/150 PresJrCls; AFS; Chr; CncrtBnd; HonRl; ModUN; NHS; StuCncl; FTA; Bsktbl; LetterTrk; GAA; College; Music.

HILL, Patricia L; Calumet HS; Mohawk, MI; HonRl; HospAde; SchAde; SchPl; FNA; Mich Tech Univ; Medical Technology.

HILL, Randal L; Wheaton Christian HS; Algonquin, IL; Chr; LetterFtbl; LetterWrstlng; Le Tourneau College; Auto Maintenance Tech.

HILL, Randall L; Merrill Sr HS; Merrill, WI; VPJrCls; ChrhWkr; StuCncl; YthFlsp; 4-H; CaptFtbl; CaptWrstlng; AmLegAwd; Univ Of Wisconsin; Teacher.

HILL, Randy S; Forest City Comm HS; Leland, IA; Band; Chr; Chrs; ChrhWkr; CmntyWkr; CncrtBnd; MrchBnd; PepBnd; SchMus; SchPl; 4-H; Bsktbl; LetterFtbl; 4-HAwd; Waldorf Jr College; Drafting.

HILL, Richard W; Zionsville HS; Zionsville, IN; 2/160 HonRl; JrNHS; NHS; SpnCl; Bsbl; Bsktbl; Tennis; CchngActv; Univ; Comp Sci.

HILL, Robert M; Cousino Sr HS; Warren, MI; Band; CncrtBnd; HonRl; MrchBnd; PepBnd; SctActv; Swmmng; Ferris State Col; Pharmacy.

HILL, Roland S; Tri Valley HS; Bloomington, IL; PolWkr; College; Commercial Artist.

HILL, Ronald M; Quigley South HS; Chicago, IL; 21/179 PolWkr; Loyola Univ; Criminal Justice.

HILL, Rory E; Baxter Comm HS; Baxter, IA; 4/32 PresFrshCls; SecJrCls; ChrhWkr; NHS; NatlThespSoc; Orch; VPStuCncl; PresYthFlsp; VPPpCl; Bsktbl; U Of N Iowa; Accounting.

HILL, Rosa M; Villa Duchesne HS; St Louis, MO; 8/56 VPJrCls; Chrl; HonRl; NatlMeritCmnd; NatlMeritSF; SchMus; SchPl; StuCncl; LetterBsbl; LetterBsktbl; IMSpt; Univ; Doctor.

HILL, Sheryl; Adrian HS; Adrian, MI; NHS; TchrAde; LatCl; Trk; GAA; IMSpt; Cent Mich Univ.

HILL, Susan D; Gibson City HS; Gibson City, IL; 3/98 SecSophCls; SecJrCls; Chrs; NHS; SchMus; SchPl; SctActv; StuCncl; SptEdYrbk; SpnCl; PpCl; SciCl; CaptChrldr; GAA; Jr College; Dental Hygienist.

HILL, Theresa A; Iowa Grant HS; Livingston, WI; 7/118 Chrs; HonRl; NHS; SecStuCncl; RptrYrbk; RptrSchPpr; SchPpr; PresFHA; PpCl; Univ Of Wisconsin; Secretary.

HILL, Thomas J; Estherville HS; Estherville, IA; 1/200 PresFrshCls; Band; ChrhWkr; CncrtBnd; HonRl; MrchBnd; StuCncl; Pres4-H; SpnCl; LetterFtbl; LetterTrk; LetterWrstlng; CchngActv; Univ Of North Ia; Education.

HILL, Timothy; Eastbrook HS; Upland, IN; HonRl; StuCncl; StuGov; RptrSchPpr; GerCl; PpCl; Bsktbl; Ftbl; IMSpt; Col; Phsychologist.

HILL, Vanessa D; Lindblom Tech HS; Chicago, IL; 13/695 HonRl; NHS; NatlMeritSF; NatlSciFnd; SchAde; TchrAde; Yrbk; TreasFrCl; SecMthCl; GAA; JETSAwd; Ill Inst Of Tech; Engineering.

HILL, Virginia D; Murray Community HS; Murray, IA; PresSophCls; ALAGirlsSt; Band; ChrhWkr; CmntyWkr; HonRl; MrchBnd; LetterBsktbl; LetterTrk; Coll.

HILLAL, Michelle B; Normandy HS; St Louis, MO; ChrhWkr; CmntyWkr; HonRl; Orch; PolWkr; TchrAde; GerCl; IMSpt; College; Pharmacy.

HILLAN, Janet L; Rock Island Sr HS; Rock Island, IL; 6/690 TreasHospAde; NHS; RptrYrbk; SpnCl; MthCl; Illinois St Univ; Teacher.

HILLARD, Ann M; Galena HS; Galena, IL; 18/110 Band; HonRl; PepBnd; SchMus; StuCncl; Yrbk; RptrSchPpr; PpCl; Bsbl; Tennis; Trk; Chrldr; College; Counseling.

HILLARD, Nancy K; Pine River HS; Cadillac, MI; 8/85 TrsSrCls; Band; CncrtBnd; HonRl; NHS; SchPl; PresStuCncl; RptrYrbk; LetterTrk; LetterChrldr; Central Mi Univ.

HILLARY, James K; Farmer City Mansfield HS; Farmer City, IL; Band; Chr; Chrs; CncrtBnd; HonRl; MrchBnd; PepBnd; Ftbl; Glf; Trk; Eastern Il U; Music.

HILLARY, Michael T; Bishop Mc Namara HS; Kankakee, IL; 25/170 HonRl; NHS; SchPl; SpnCl; Bsbl; Ftbl; Illinois St Univ; Business.

HILLE, Kim E; Streator Twp HS; Streator, IL; 2/380 TreasChrs; ChrhWkr; CmntyWkr; HonRl; NHS; NatlThespSoc; SchMus; SchPl; StuCncl; Tennis; Concordia Tchrs Col; Deaconess.

HILLE, William L; Dakota HS; Freeport, IL; 1/78 VPFrshCls; VPJrCls; PresSrCls; HonRl; StuCncl; StuGov; TchrAde; LetterBsktbl; LetterTrk; IMSpt; Rockford College; Mathematics.

HILLEBRAND, Maureen; Hudsonville HS; Hudsonville, MI; 34/156 HonRl; OffAde; SchAde; SchMus; SchPl; TchrAde; PpCl; Swmmng; GAA; PresAwd; College Grand Valley State.

HILLEGAS, Jo A; Everly HS; Everly, IA; 1/36 PresJrCls; Aud/Vis; Chr; ChrhWkr; CmntyWkr; HonRl; SchPl; PresStuCncl; RptrYrbk; RptrSchPpr; Id State; Accounting.

HILLEN, Terry W; Ofallon Twp HS; Ofallon, IL; Chrs; HonRl; JrNHS; SchMus; LatCl; SciCl; IMSpt; College; Law Or Politics.

HILLENBRAND, Rita A; Golden Valley HS; Golden Valley, MN; Chr; StuGov; Yrbk; St Benedict Clg; Law & Accounting.

HILLENBRAND, Teresa L; Dollar Bay HS; Dollar Bay, MI; 3/23 VPFrshCls; TrsSophCls; VPJrCls; PresSrCls; HonRl; HospAde; LbryAde; SchPl; Yrbk; SchPpr; 4-H; LetterTrk; Chrldr; DanFAwd; Michigan Tech Univ; Medicine.

HILLERUD, Gary; Velva Public HS; Velva, ND; HonRl; NHS; FFA; LetterBsbl; LetterBsktbl; LetterFtbl; Coll.

HILLERUD, Laurie A; Velva Public HS; Norwich, ND; VPSophCls; Band; CncrtBnd; HonRl; MrchBnd; NHS; RedCrAde; PpCl; Chrldr; ChmnGAA; Business School.

HILLERY, Cheryl A; Lancaster HS; Lancaster, WI; 1/160 AFS; ChrhWkr; CncrtBnd; HonRl; HospAde; NHS; Orch; SchMus; YthFlsp; SpnCl; Univ; Pre Med.

HILLESTAD, Mary L; New Effington HS; Claire City, SD; 2/17 TrsJrCls; Band; Chr; CncrtBnd; HonRl; SchPl; EdYrBk; Yrbk; 4-H; CaptChrldr;.

HILLESTAD, Tamra K; Border Central HS; Calvin, ND; SecSophCls; ALAGirlsSt; Band; Chrs; HonRl; SchPl; Yrbk; RptrSchPpr; 4-H; PpCl; U S Navy; X Ray Technician.

HILLHOUSE, Lisa A; Charleston HS; Charleston, MO; TrsJrCls; Band; Chr; Chrs; CmntyWkr; HonRl; StuCncl; Twrl; Yrbk; PpCl; Stephens College.

HILLHOUSE, Ruth E; Southeast HS; Springfield, IL; 60/478 Chrs; ChrhWkr; HonRl; Chrldr; IMSpt; Business School; Secretarial.

HILLIARD, James W; Luther South HS; Chicago, IL; Band; ChrhWkr; CncrtBnd; MrchBnd; NHS; PepBnd; Col; Pro.

HILLIS, Elizabeth; Twin River R 10 HS; Broseley, MO; 1/101 TrsJrCls; HonRl; PresMthCl; PpCl; DanFAwd; PresAwd; Three Rivers Comm Coll.

HILLMAN, Ann M; Springfield Catholic HS; Springfield, MO; ChrhWkr; CmntyWkr; HonRl; SctActv; Coll; Interior Design.

HILLMAN, Arlene; Cheney HS; Cheney, KS; Chr; Chrs; ChrhWkr; CmntyWkr; SchPl; TchrAde; RptrYrbk; SchPpr; FHA; PpCl; Coll.

HILLMAN, Catherine M; Green Mountain Indep HS; Marshalltown, IA; Band; Chrs; ChrhWkr; CncrtBnd; HonRl; Mdrgl; MrchBnd; NatlThespSoc; PepBnd; SchMus; College; Social Work.

HILLMAN, James F; Forreston Comm HS; German Valley, IL; HonRl; NatlMeritCmnd; StuCncl; CaptFtbl;.

HILLMAN, Jane I; Flanagan HS; Flanagan, IL; 1/59 Band; Chrs; CncrtBnd; HonRl; TreasNHS; PepBnd; SchMus; SchPl; SecYthFlsp; Pres4-H; GAA; DanFAwd; 4-HAwd; Univ Of Illinois; Elem Education.

HILLMAN, Joan E; Tremont HS; Tremont, IL; 1/75 PresJrCls; AFS; HonRl; NHS; StuCncl; 4-H; CaptChrldr; GAA; IMSpt; 4-HAwd; Coll; Dental Hygiene.

HILLMAN, Julie M; Tremont Comm HS; Tremont, IL; 4/64 SecSrCls; AFS; Chrs; NHS; 4-H; GerCl; Trk; Chrldr; GAA; Ill Central College; Banking.

HILLMAN, Nancy J; Carl Sandburg HS; Palos Heights, IL; 2/680 HonRl; NHS; NatlMeritCmnd; FHA; VPSpnCl; SecMthCl; PpCl; U Of Il; Civil Engineering.

HILLMAN, Richard N; Flanagan HS; Flanagan, IL; 7/41 VPJrCls; VPSrCls; Band; ChrhWkr; CncrtBnd; HonRl; MrchBnd; PepBnd; YthFlsp; 4-H; FFA; SciCl; Ftbl; College; Agriculture.

HILLMER, Kristy J; Ralston HS; Ralston, NE; AFS; Chr; Chrs; ChrhWkr; HospAde; NHS; SchMus; YthFlsp; PpCl; LetterGlf; Univ Of Nebr Omaha;.

HILLQUIST, Neil A; Sycamore HS; Sycamore, IL; HonRl; NatlThespSoc; SchPl; SctActv; SchPpr; Wrstlng;.

HILLS, Thomas G; Minonk Dana Rutland HS; Minonk, IL; SecJrCls; Band; Chr; CncrtBnd; DrmMjrt; HonRl; PepBnd; SchPl; StuCncl; YthFlsp; 4-H; FrCl; LetterBsbl; 4-HAwd; Univ Of Il; Engineering.

HILLSON, Steven D; Norfolk HS; Norfolk, NE; 1/300 ALBoysSt; Band; CmntyWkr; CncrtBnd; HonRl; MrchBnd; NatlFornLg; NHS; NatlMeritSF; DARAwd; Univ; Chemistry.

HILLSTROM, Linda M; Crystal Lake Comm HS; Crystal Lake, IL; 13/490 Chr; HonRl; NHS; NatlMeritCmnd; SchMus; StuCncl; Univ Of Notre Dame; Chemistry.

HILLSTROM, Mark A; Washington HS; Sioux Falls, SD; ALBoysSt; NHS; CaptTrk; IMSpt; KiwanAwd; Univ; Mech Eng.

HILLYER, Gregg A; Nishna Valley HS; Imogene, IA; PresFrshCls; VPJrCls; PresSrCls; Band; HonRl; NHS; 4-H; LetterBsktbl; LetterFtbl; LetterTrk; Nw Missouri State Univ; Ag Journalism.

HILLYER, Jeffrey L; Dixon HS; Dixon, IL; HonRl; SchPpr; West Il U; Optometry.

HILLYER, Michael S; Flat Rock HS; Flat Rock, MI; 19/120 HonRl; NHS; SchPl; SctActv; StuCncl; PpCl; SciCl; Michigan State U; Hotel & Restaurant Mgmt.

HILMAN, James F; Forreston HS; German Valley, IL; NatlMeritCmnd; StuCncl; CaptFtbl; College.

HILMES, Thomas F; Mater Dei HS; Breese, IL; College; Accounting.

HILT, James D; Wisconsin Academy; Racine, WI; VPFrshCls; Chr; Chrs; ChrhWkr; CmntyWkr; DrlTm; HonRl; Bsbl; Bsktbl; Ftbl; Glf; Andrews Univ; Medicine.

HILT, Lorri S; Downers Grove So HS; Downers Grove, IL; Band; ChrhWkr; CmntyWkr; HonRl; MrchBnd; NHS; NatlMeritFnl; GAA; IMSpt; College; Nurse.

HILT, Terri L; Downers Grove So HS; Downers Grove, IL; Band; Chr; ChrhWkr; HonRl; MrchBnd; NHS; PepBnd; SchMus; College; Music.

HILTEN, Carol E; Southern HS; Smithshire, IL; Chrs; CmntyWkr; LbryAde; YthFlsp; FHA; Chrldr; GAA; IMSpt; 4-HAwd; Southeastern College; Social Worker.

HILTNER, Lyle A; Langdon HS; Langdon, ND; 80/729 PresFrshCls; PresSophCls; HonRl; StuCncl; RptrYrbk; Bsbl; CaptFtbl; Trk; CaptWrstlng; College.

HILTON, Beverly A; Richwoods HS; Peoria, IL; 52/449 ChrhWkr; CmntyWkr; HonRl; HospAde; ROTC; StuCncl; StuGov; YthFlsp; RptrSchPpr; LatCl; PpCl; Wheaton College; Doctor.

HILTON, David; Horton Watkins HS; Saint Louis, MO; 25/498 CncrtBnd; MrchBnd; Orch; PepBnd; SchMus; SctActv; TchrAde; LatCl; Grinnell College; Medicine.

HILTON, Deborah L; Onsted HS; Onsted, MI; Band; CncrtBnd; HonRl; HospAde; MrchBnd; OffAde; PepBnd; 4-H; FHA; 4-HAwd; Monroe Col; Rn.

HILTON, Jeffery L; Harper HS; Chicago, IL; 10/530 HonRl; IntrClCncl; JrNHS; LbryAde; ModUN; NHS; NatlMeritCmnd; OffAde; SchAde; StuCncl; TchrAde; Morehouse; Medicine.

HILTON, Michael J; Wilton Comm HS; Moscow, IA; ALBoysSt; Band; Chrs; CncrtBnd; MrchBnd; PepBnd; Bsbl; Bsktbl; LetterFtbl; College; Teaching Or Lawyer.

HILTON, Ramona D; East Prairie HS; East Prairie, MO; Band; Chr; ChrhWkr; CncrtBnd; HonRl; JrNHS; MrchBnd; NHS; SctActv; Harding College; Business Admin.

HILTON, Tina L; Franklin Central HS; Indianopolis, IN; HonRl; ModUN; NHS; SchPl; FHA; GerCl; Bsktbl; GAA; College; Med Asst.

HILTY, Luann R; Morrison Community HS; Morrison, IL; HonRl; SecYthFlsp; Pres4-H; VPFHA; LetterBsktbl; LetterTrk; PresGAA; Secretary.

HILTZ, Gail; Lincoln HS; Park Falls, WI; 4/117 ALAGirlsSt; CncrtBnd; HonRl; JrNHS; MrchBnd; NHS; NatlThespSoc; PepBnd; SchPl; YthFlsp; U Of Wi Madison; Doctor.

HILTZMAN, Kim D; Oxford HS; Oxford, KS; 17/40 Chrs; ChrhWkr; HonRl; SchPl; PresStuCncl; TchrAde; Teen; RptrYrbk; FshEdSchPpr; SchPpr; Jucco Ark City Coll; Artist & Singer.

HILYCORD, Gregory B; Columbus East HS; Columbus, IN; 57/336 Band; CncrtBnd; MrchBnd; StuGov; LetterBsbl; LetterBsktbl; LetterFtbl; Purdue Univ; Engineering.

HILZ, Carey J; Beulah HS; Beulah, ND; Band; Chr; DrlTm; PepBnd; SchPl; RptrSchPpr; 4-H; FBLA; FHA; PpCl; LetterTrk; GAA; 4-HAwd;.

HIME, Lisa A; Maine Township HS North; Glenview, IL; 2/350 Chr; ChrhWkr; HonRl; NHS; NatlThespSoc; EdSchPpr; LetterBsktbl; Glf; DARAwd; College; Chemistry Teacher.

HIME, Scott A; South Decatur HS; Greensburg, IN; 3/140 TrsSophCls; ChrhWkr; HonRl; NHS; PresStuCncl; StuGov; SptEdSchPpr; PresSpnCl; LetterBsbl; CaptBsktbl; LetterTrk; College.

HIMEBAUCH, Linda; Charlevoix HS; Charlevoix, MI; Band; ChrhWkr; CncrtBnd; HonRl; MrchBnd;.

HIMLIE, Patricia A; Rushford HS; Rushford, MN; 1/65 SecBand; CncrtBnd; DrmMjrt; HonRl; NHS; SctActv; Twrl; Yrbk; VoiceDemAwd; Winona St Col; Busness Adm.

HIMLIE, Todd D; Rushford HS; Rushford, MN; PresSrCls; ChrhWkr; CmntyWkr; NHS; SctActv; TchrAde; LetterBsbl; LetterBsktbl; LetterFtbl; LetterGlf; Job.

HIMMELBERG, Michael M; Glasgow HS; Glasgow, MO; 5/50 PresFrshCls; HonRl; NHS; StuCncl; Bsbl; Bsktbl; IMSpt; AmLegAwd; Clge; Law.

HIMMELBERG, Paul H; St Thomas Prep HS; Glasgow, MO; 1/11 HonRl; NatlMeritSF; StuCncl; RptrYrbk; EdYrBk; SchPpr; PpCl; Bsktbl; Socr; IMSpt; Seminary Coll; Priest.

HIMMELRICK, Harold W; Havana HS; Havana, IL; TrsSrCls; HonRl; CivCl; FFA; EngCl; MthCl; PpCl; SciCl; LetterBsktbl; LetterFtbl; Western Ill Univ; Phys Ed Teacher.

HIMMELSPACH, William M; Pontiac Catholic HS; Pontiac, MI; IMSpt; Oakland Comm Col; Archeologist.

HINCE, Elaine L; Pepin HS; Pepin, WI; Chrs; ChrhWkr; HonRl; LbryAde; Yrbk; FHA; PpCl; Bus Sch; Vocation.

HINCHEY, Laura; Custer HS; Milwaukee, WI; 2/650 CmntyWkr; HonRl; ModUN; NHS; NatlMeritCmnd; GerCl; GAA; VoiceDemAwd; Uw Milwaukee; Botany.

HINCK, Robert M; Minneapolis Lutheran HS; Minneapolis, MN; VPFrshCls; Band; Chr; ChrhWkr; HonRl; LitMag; SchPl; VPStuCncl; Yrbk; SchPpr; LetterWrstlng; University; Engineering.

HINCKS, Jeff R; Grosse Pte No HS; Grosse Pte Shores, MI; HonRl; LetterSwmmng; Tennis; Mich St U; Vet Med.

HINDERER, Jeana R; New Franklin HS; New Franklin, MO; 2/31 TrsSophCls; ALAGirlsSt; Chrs; ChrhWkr; HonRl; NHS; Twrl; YthFlsp; EdYrBk; RptrSchPpr; PresFHA; SpnCl; Bsktbl; Chrldr; College; Legal Secretary.

HINDERLIDER, Garry; Culver HS; Winamac, IN; Aud/Vis; ChrhWkr; CmntyWkr; HonRl; YthFlsp; IMSpt;.

HINDERLIE, Louise M; J A Craig HS; Janesville, WI; HonRl; MrchBnd; OffAde; StuCncl; TchrAde; Yrbk; SchPpr; SpnCl; LetterChrldr; College; Professional.

HINDERLITER, Carol; East HS; Wichita, KS; Chr; ChrhWkr; CmntyWkr; Mdrgl; SchAde; SchMus; StuCncl; PpCl; SciCl; IMSpt; College; Professional.

HINDERSMAN, Christie E; Carbondale Comm HS; Carbondale, IL; 1/325 Band; CmntyWkr; NHS; Orch; SchMus; SctActv; Butler University.

HINDMAN, Douglas W; Scotsbluff HS; Gering, NE; LetterTennis; IMSpt; Education.

HINDMAN, Geri L; Glenwood HS; Glenwood, IA; Chrs; HonRl; NatlThespSoc; SchPl; Bsbl; Bsktbl; Trk; IMSpt; Trade Schl; Professional.

HINDMAN, Randall C; Kirksville Senior Shs; Kirksville, MO; CmntyWkr; HospAde; RedCrAde; SctActv; LetterGlf; LetterTennis; University; Medicine.

HINDS, Mark A; Central HS; Champaign, IL; ChrhWkr; HonRl; JrNHS; Yrbk; FFA; Univ Of Illinois; Agriculture.

HINDS, Richard M; Flaxton Public HS; Flaxtn, ND; 4/13 PresFrshCls; VPSophCls; HonRl; OffAde; StuCncl; SptEdYrbk; Bsktbl; IMSpt; AmLegAwd; 4-HAwd; Trade School; Auto Mech.

HINDSLEY, Barbara L; Harvard Community HS; Harvard, IL; AFS; Chr; Chrs; ChrhWkr; CmntyWkr; HospAde; SchMus; SchPl; SctActv; TchrAde; Yrbk; College; Spanish Major.

HINEBAUGH, Paula J; Tri HS; Lewisville, IN; SecSophCls; SecJrCls; HonRl; LbryAde; StuCncl; YthFlsp; 4-H; Chrldr; GAA; University; Health.

HINEMAN, Linda; Dighton HS; Dighton, KS; 1/48 SecJrCls; ALAGirlsSt; HonRl; NHS; EdYrBk; LetterBsktbl; LetterTennis; AmLegAwd; DanFAwd; MasAwd; Univ Of Ks; Journalism.

HINER, Sharon L; Coldwater HS; Coldwater, MI; Band; MrchBnd; SchMus; SchPl; SctActv; YthFlsp; 4-H; Glf; College; Professional.

HINES, Brenda L; Chippewa Hills HS; Barryton, MI; 5/150 Band; CncrtBnd; HonRl; JrNHS; MrchBnd; NHS; PepBnd; SchMus; StuCncl; TchrAde; 4-H; LetterBsktbl; Chrldr; 4-HAwd; Ferris St College; Social Service Tech.

HINES, Catherine M; Elizabeth Seton HS; Chicago, IL; 23/239 HonRl; NHS; SctActv; TchrAde; FSA; VPMthCl; VPSciCl; GAA; Univ; Vet Med.

HINES, Chris L; Gibson City HS; Gibson City, IL; AFS; Chrs; HonRl; SchMus; SchPl; PpCl; LetterFtbl; LetterWrstlng; College; Kinesiology.

HINES, Cynthia M; Lindblom Tech HS; Chicago, IL; Chr; HospAde; RedCrAde; SchAde; TchrAde; RptrSchPpr; Loyola Univ; Medical Tech.

HINES, Deedee K; Morton HS; Morton, IL; HonRl; JA; FBLA; FHA; PpCl; GAA; JAAwd; Business School; Accounting.

HINES, James P; Fort Wayne South Side HS; Fort Wayne, IN; 33/425 HonRl; Ftbl; IMSpt; University.

HINES, John D; Indianola HS; Indianola, IA; PresSophCls; ALBoysSt; ChrhWkr; HonRl; NHS; Bsktbl; Trk; AmLegAwd; College.

HINES, Michael T; Assumption HS; Davenport, IA; 45/220 ChrhWkr; CmntyWkr; HonRl; NHS; StuCncl; LetterBsbl; LetterFtbl; LetterTrk; IMSpt; CitAwd; St Thomas College.

HINES, Patti A; Castle HS; Newburgh, IN; 25/302 ChrhWkr; HonRl; SchMus; FTA; PpCl; Cllege; Teaching.

HINES, Shelley G; Red Wing Central HS; Red Wing, MN; 5/300 Chr; HonRl; NatlMeritSF; SctActv; Col; Business Admin.

HINES, Virginia R; Central HS; Chebanse, IL; Chrs; ChrhWkr; HonRl; JrNHS; NHS; NatlMeritCmnd; MthCl; PpCl; PresAwd; Bus College; Pro Secretary.

HINES, William E; Watseka Comm HS; Watseka, IL; ALBoysSt; Band; CncrtBnd; HonRl; MrchBnd; PepBnd; StuGov; YthLg; Yrbk; Bsbl; Bsktbl; Ftbl; IMSpt; VoiceDemAwd; College Illinois; Psychologist.

HINGTGEN, James J; Wahlert HS; Dickeyville, WI; 35/450 HonRl; NHS; LetterBsktbl; LetterFtbl; Trk; IMSpt; Loras College; Accounting.

HINK, Randy R; Jefferson Senior HS; Alexandria, MN; 31/336 HonRl; SchPl; StuCncl; MthCl; LetterFtbl; LetterTrk; IMSpt; St Cloud St Univ; Electronic Engineering.

HINKELMAN, Carlyn R; Watervliet HS; Benton Harbor, MI; 21/98 ALBoysSt; HonRl; NHS; NatlMeritSF; TchrAde; 4-H; LetterBsktbl; LetterFtbl; LetterTrk; IMSpt; 4-HAwd; Western Mich U; Cpa.

HINKELMAN, Debbie A; Ottawa Township HS; Grand Ridge, IL; 23/425 TrsJrCls; Band; HonRl; NHS; PepBnd; TchrAde; 4-H; GAA; College; Biology.

HINKLE, Charles L; Advance HS; Advance, MO; Aud/Vis; ChrhWkr; CmntyWkr; HonRl; OffAde; PolWkr; YthFlsp; RptrYrbk; EdSchPpr; Se Missouri State Univ; Journalism.

HINKLE, Cindy A; Cahokia HS; Cahokia, IL; 8/529 SecSophCls; Chr; HonRl; NHS; Quill&Scroll; StuGov; Yrbk; PpCl; Chrldr; College; Professional.

HINKLE, Gerald G; S Haven HS; South Haven, MI; HonRl; SchPl; StuCncl; StuGov; TchrAde; CaptBsktbl; Ftbl; Trk; PresAwd; CitAwd; College.

HINKLE, Jack; Jackson HS; Jackson, MI; 45/373 PresSrCls; Chr; Chrs; ChrhWkr; HonRl; NHS; SchMus; StuCncl; Bsktbl; Univ.

HINKLE, Katherine L; Pacific HS; Robertsville, MO; 41/198 PresSrCls; ChrhWkr; CmntyWkr; HonRl; HospAde; StuCncl; FHA; PpCl; SciCl; Bsktbl; Tarkio College; Nursing.

HINKLE, Sally J; North Side HS; Fort Wayne, IN; 29/438 CncrtBnd; HonRl; MrchBnd; NatlFornLg; VPNHS; Orch; SchMus; VPEngCl; PresLatCl; Tennis; Univ; Music.

HINKLEY, Jane R; Mt Vernon HS; Greenfield, IN; ChrhWkr; HonRl; NHS; PpCl; GAA; Purdue Univ; Medical Technology.

HINKSON, Brian W; Centura HS; Wood River, NE; VPJrCls; Band; Chr; Chrs; MrchBnd; YthFlsp; FBLA; Bsktbl; Ftbl; Glf; University; Agriculture.

HINKSTON, David H; Shabbona HS; Shabbona, IL; Band; Chr; Chrs; CncrtBnd; HonRl; MrchBnd; PepBnd; SchPl; Yrbk; 4-H; SciCl; LetterBsbl; LetterParkland College; Construction Tech.

HINMAN, Cheryl D; Mitchell HS; Mitchell, NE; VPFrshCls; HstSophCls; Chr; Chrs; ChrhWkr; HonRl; HospAde; LbryAde; Mdrgl; OffAde; SchMus; Ne Western College.

HINMAN, David S; Mt Vernon Comm HS; Mt Vernon, IA; Band; CncrtBnd; HonRl; MrchBnd; NatlFornLg; NatlThespSoc; PepBnd; SchMus; SchPl; University; Computer Science.

HINNANT, Brenda A; O Fallon Twp HS; O Fallon, IL; HonRl; MrchBnd; NHS; Twrl; LetterTennis; JCAwd; Winthrop College.

HINNEFELD, Jon D; Seymour HS; Seymour, IN; ChrhWkr; HonRl; NatlMeritSF; SctActv; PresLatCl; SciCl; Rose Hulman Inst Of Tech; Mech Engineer.

HINNEN, Larry D; Balboa HS; Edwardsville, IL; 6/474 ALBoysSt; HonRl; JA; ROTC; SchAde; StuGov; TchrAde; SptEdSchPpr; AmLegAwd; LionAwd; Univ; Psychiatrist.

HINNERS, Neal; Spring Valley HS; Spring Valley, MN; CmntyWkr; SctActv; IMSpt; PresAwd; Austin Minn Area Vo Tech; Auto Body.

HINNONT, Brenda A; Ofallon Township HS; Ofallon, IL; Band; CncrtBnd; HonRl; MrchBnd; Twrl; Tennis; College.

HINRICH, Ann; Niles Senior HS; Niles, MI; 23/369 Chr; ChrhWkr; HonRl; Indiana Univ; Law.

HINRICH, Randy D; Pender Public HS; Pender, NE; 13/56 ALBoysSt; Band; ChrhWkr; HonRl; MrchBnd; SctActv; Bsktbl; Ftbl; Trk; College.

HINRICHS, Cristina A; Petersburg Porta HS; Petersburg, IL; 15/101 VPFrshCls; VPSophCls; Band; Chrs; ChrhWkr; HonRl; MrchBnd; Orch; TchrAde; Bsktbl; Illinois State U; Teacher.

HINRICHS, Dianne Y; Dist 2r HS; Giltner, NE; Band; Chr; Chrl; Chrs; ChrhWkr; CtyCnl; CncrtBnd; MrchBnd; PepBnd; SchMus; Airline School; Stewardess.

HINRICHS, Judy; Sandy Creek HS; Glenvil, NE; 4/51 Chr; Chrs; HonRl; NHS; SchPl; RptrYrbk; EdSchPpr; 4-H; PpCl; IMSpt; Midland Lutheran College; Business.

HINRICHS, Mark S; St Thomas Aquinas HS; Ferguson, MO; 28/360 HonRl; JA; NHS; ROTC; RptrSchPpr; LetterFtbl; JAAwd; College; Navy Aeronautics.

HINRICHS, Mary E; Alton Sr HS; Alton, IL; Chrs; HonRl; NHS; SchPl; StuGov; GerCl; College; Computer Science.

HINRICHS, Randall D; Riceville Comm HS; Riceville, IA; 1/80 Band; Chr; Chrs; ChrhWkr; CmntyWkr; CncrtBnd; HonRl; NHS; NatlMeritSF; PepBnd; SctActv; LetterBsbl; LetterBsktbl; LetterTrk; College; Elec Engineering.

HINRICHS, Randall D; Riceville Community HS; Riceville, IA; 1/79 Band; Chr; ChrhWkr; CmntyWkr; CncrtBnd; HonRl; MrchBnd; PresNHS; NatlMeritFnl; PepBnd; Mass Inst Technology; Elec Eng.

HINRICHS, Wanda M; Ellsworth Public HS; Ellsworth, MN; SecFrshCls; HonRl; MrchBnd; SchPl; StuCncl; TchrAde; EdSchPpr; FHA; PpCl; Chrldr; Air Force.

HINRICHSEN, Marvin J; E Monona HS; Moorhead, IA; Band; Chr; Chrs; ChrhWkr; CncrtBnd; MrchBnd; PepBnd; Sec4-H; SecFFA; 4-HAwd; Agricollege; Farming.

HINSDALE, Joan; Immaculate Heart Of Mary HS; Westchester, IL; PresSophCls; Chrl; ChrhWkr; CmntyWkr; SchPl; TchrAde; SpnCl; Chrldr; GAA; PPFtbl; Coll; Bio.

HINSHAW, Gary D; Emporia HS; Emporia, KS; 1/300 Band; ChrhWkr; CncrtBnd; HonRl; MrchBnd; NatlMeritFnl; NatlMeritSF; Orch; Univ; Physicist.

HINSHAW, Karen L; Chrysler HS; New Castle, IN; Chrl; ChrhWkr; HonRl; JA; NatlThespSoc; SchMus; SchPl; YthFlsp; EdSchPpr; 4-H; LatCl; PpCl; 4-HAwd; Purdue Univ; Interior Design.

HINSON, Cathy; Union HS; Union, MO; 26/165 Chr; ChrhWkr; HonRl; SchMus; SchPl; StuCncl; RptrYrbk; EdSchPpr; PPFtbl; Southeast Mo State Univ; Elementary Educati.

HINSON, Kirk A; Effingham HS; Effingham, IL; 26/220 ChrhWkr; HonRl; PresSctActv; PresYthFlsp; KeyCl; LatCl; VoiceDemAwd; Mckendree College; Psychiatry.

HINSVERK, Lorie A; Underwood HS; Erhard, MN; Chr; CncrtBnd; HonRl; PepBnd; SchPl; Yrbk; FHA; Chrldr; Trade Sch; Archit Drafting.

HINTERBERG, Helen J; Pewaukee HS; Pewaukee, WI; HonRl; NatlMeritFnl; Univ Of Wisconsin; Library Science.

HINTON, Alice L; Rockford HS; Rockford, MI; 6/290 Band; HonRl; HospAde; NatlMeritSchl; TchrAde; YthFlsp; 4-H; PPFtbl; Michigan St Univ; Medicine.

HINTON, Gregory D; Central HS; Cape Girardeau, MO; ALBoysSt; ALAGirlsSt; HonRl; JrNHS; NHS; NatlMeritSchl; StuCncl; LetterFtbl; Trk; IMSpt; PresAwd; CitAwd; Univ Of Missouri; Draftsman.

HINTON, Rhonda L; Tower Hill HS; Tower Hill, IL; 2/32 Band; Chrs; ChrhWkr; CncrtBnd; HonRl; NHS; OffAde; PepBnd; SchMus; SchPl; Trk; IMSpt; St Johns Sch; Nurse.

HINTON, Ronnie P; St Elmo HS; St Elmo, IL; 2/54 TrsJrCls; HonRl; JrNHS; NHS; PpCl; Bsktbl; College; Accounting.

HINTON, William; Orchard Farm HS; St Charles, MO; Aud/Vis; Chr; Chrs; DrlTm; HonRl; PepBnd; StuCncl; Bsktbl; College.

HINTZ, David E; Lawton HS; Lawton, IA; Chrs; ChrhWkr; SchMus; SctActv; 4-H; Bsbl; LetterFtbl; LetterTrk; LetterWrstlng; 4-HAwd; Trade School; Police Science.

HINTZ, Elizabeth M; St Agatha HS; Farmington, MI; ChrhWkr; HonRl; NHS; OffAde; StuCncl; Mich Stae Univ; Bs In Nursing.

HINTZ, Jack L; Neche Public HS; Neche, ND; VPFrshCls; ALBoysSt; Chr; Chrs; HonRl; LbryAde; NHS; LetterBsbl; CaptBsktbl; LetterTrk; Univ; Curriculum.

HINTZ, Jill A; Winamac Comm HS; Winamac, IN; Band; Chr; ChrhWkr; CncrtBnd; HonRl; MrchBnd; NHS; PepBnd; 4-H; SpnCl; PpCl; GAA; University; Pharmacy.

HINTZ, Kimberly R; Harrison HS; Gladwin, MI; DrlTm; HonRl; JA; OffAde; SctActv; Pres4-H; FHA; 4-HAwd; University; Vocational.

HINTZ, Leone L; Center HS; Center, ND; ALAGirlsSt; Chrs; HonRl; StuCncl; RptrSchPpr; SptEdSchPpr; SchPpr; GerCl; PpCl; LetterTrk; Nd U; Art.

HINTZ, Margo L; O Gorman HS; Sioux Falls, SD; VPJrCls; HonRl; NHS; SctActv; StuCncl; TchrAde; 4-H; Bsktbl; Swmmng; Trk; Navy; Nursing.

HINTZ, Michael A; Oak Creek HS; Franklin, WI; 16/323 HonRl; NHS; SctActv; SptEdYrbk; GerCl; LetterTennis; Marquette University; Business Admin.

HINTZ, Suzanne M; Carl Sandburg HS; Tinley Park, IL; 134/832 ChrhWkr; CmntyWkr; HonRl; NHS; NatlMeritFnl; NatlMeritSchl; StuCncl; YthFlsp; CitAwd; Univ; English Teacher.

HINTZMAN, Nancy A; Twin Lakes HS; Monticelo, IN; 6/202 Band; Chrs; HonRl; VPJrNHS; MrchBnd; SchMus; 4-H; PpCl; GAA; 4-HAwd; College; Math.

HINZ, Rebecca J; Crosby Ironton HS; Deerwood, MN; Chr; ChrhWkr; CAP; HospAde; Teen; LatCl; College; Biology & Religion.

HINZ, Robert F; Tinley Park HS; Tinley Park, IL; HonRl; NHS; De Paul Univ; C P A.

HINZ, Ronald; South Haven HS; South Haven, MI; ChrhWkr; HonRl; Trk; IMSpt; Coll.

HINZMANN, Denise M; Chosen Valley HS; Chatfield, MN; Chr; ChrhWkr; HonRl; LbryAde; Mdrgl; FHA; FTA; SpnCl; Trade; Vocation.

HIPKE, Earl M; Oneill Public HS; Oneill, NE; HonRl; NHS; SchMus; SchPl; 4-H; 4-HAwd; Trade Sch; Vocation.

HIPKE, Teresa A; Peshtigo HS; Peshtigo, WI; Band; Chrs; CncrtBnd; HonRl; Mdrgl; MrchBnd; LetterPepBnd; LetterBsktbl; LetterTrk; Chrldr;.

HIPP, Carol E; North Platte Senior HS; North Platte, NE; Chrl; HonRl; PpCl; College; Interior Design.

HIPPARD, John M; Shelbyville HS; Shelbyville, IL; 6/135 ChrhWkr; HonRl; NHS; LetterBsbl;.

HIPPLER, Suzanne M; Rockford East HS; Rockford, IL; 23/650 HonRl; NHS; Quill&Scroll; SchPl; Millikin Univ; Engineering.

HIRCHENT, Brian D; Allen Consolidated HS; Dixon, NE; Chrs; HonRl; OffAde; SchPl; FFA; LetterBsktbl; LetterFtbl;.

HIRE, Karen A; Bishop Dwenger HS; Fort Wayne, IN; Chrs; ChrhWkr; HonRl; SchMus; SchPl; FrCl; College.

HIRMING, Betty; Mott Lincoln HS; Mott, ND; PpCl; Univ Of Nd; Psychology.

HIRNER, Jenny; Hannibal HS; Hannibal, MO; LbryAde; NHS; GAA; U Mo.

HIROTA, Georgianne; Robert A Waller HS; Chicago, IL; 1/214 HonRl; NHS; SchMus; SctActv; SchPpr; KeyCl; PpCl; LetterSwmmng; LetterTennis; LetterChrldr; GAA; Univ Of Illinois; Education.

HIROZE, Frances E; Boylan HS; Rockford, IL; 13/345 Chrs; CmntyWkr; HonRl; NHS; NatlMeritCmnd; SpnCl; St Norbert Clg; International Bus.

HIRSCH, Ann; Sparta Sr HS; Sparta, WI; Chrs; HonRl; Trk; Uw La Crosse; Elem Ed.

HIRSCH, Bernard D; Highland Park HS; Highland Park, IL; PresChrs; HonRl; JrNHS; NatlMeritCmnd; NatlThespSoc; SchMus; SctActv; StuGov; Indiana Univ; Music.

HIRSCH, Cynthia L; Benton Consolidated HS; Benton, IL; 13/185 VPJrCls; Band; Chrs; ChrhWkr; HonRl; Mdrgl; NatlThespSoc; SchMus; SchPl; Univ Of Ill; Science.

HIRSCH, Davi L; Niles East HS; Skokie, IL; 90/583 AFS; Chr; HonRl; NatlThespSoc; SchPl; StuGov; Yrbk; KeyCl; Tennis; Univ Of Illinois; Law.

HIRSCH, Michael J; St Mary Central HS; Menasha, WI; ChrhWkr; HonRl; SpnCl; LetterBsktbl; CchngActv; College.

HIRSCH, Nancy R; Winona Junior HS; Winona, MN; DrlTm; NHS; SpnCl; Univ Of Wis Stout; Home Economics.

HIRSCH, Sara; Anderson HS; Anderson, IN; 60/657 Chr; ChrhWkr; CmntyWkr; HonRl; HospAde; LitMag; Mdrgl; NHS; NatlThespSoc; GAA; Miami Univ;speech And Hearing Therapy.

HIRSCHEL, Anthony G; Southfield Lathrup HS; Southfield, MI; 8/683 AFS; Band; NHS; NatlMeritFnl; NatlMeritSchl; NatlThespSoc; SchMus; SchPl; StuCncl; Univ Of Michigan; History.

HIRSCHENBERGER, Kathryn; New Lothrop HS; New Lothrop, MI; HonRl; TchrAde; 4-H; SpnCl; 4-HAwd; Central Mich U; Child Psychol.

HIRSCHHORN, Charles J; New Trier East HS; Glencoe, IL; 46/847 IntrClCncl; NatlMeritCmnd; StuGov; Socr; CaptWrstlng; College; Business.

HIRSCHLER, Jill; Central Comm HS; Donnellson, IA; VPSophCls; Band; Chr; CncrtBnd; HonRl; MrchBnd; PepBnd; StuCncl; YthFlsp; PpCl; College; Accounting.

HIRSCHMAN, Helen K; University City Sr HS; St Louis, MO; NatlMeritCmnd; NatlMeritSF; SchPl; SctActv; RptrSchPpr; FrCl; College Or Univ; French Art Anddesign.

HIRSCHMAN, James A; Ithaca HS; Ithaca, MI; PresSophCls; PresJrCls; ALBoysSt; HonRl; NHS; 4-H; FFA; LetterBsbl; LetterBsktbl; Ftbl; 4-HAwd;.

HIRSCHTICK, Cynde M; Sullivan HS; Chicago, IL; 21/276 Chr; HonRl; NHS; OffAde; StuGov; RptrYrbk; Univ Of Illinois; Journalism.

HIRSCHY, Colin; Adams Central HS; Monroe, IN; SctActv; TchrAde; RptrYrbk; Trk; IMSpt; Ohio Inst Of Tech; Elect Engin Tech.

HIRSHEY, Sherrill L; Carl Junction HS; Asbury, MO; Band; CncrtBnd; HonRl; MrchBnd; ModUN; SchPl; TchrAde; FFA; FHA; Business Sch; Secretary.

HIRST, Jeff L; Hutchinson HS; Hutchinson, KS; 4/485 AFS; Chr; HonRl; LitMag; Mdrgl; NatlFornLg; NatlMeritFnl; NatlMeritSF; SchMus; StuCncl; U Of Kansas; Mathematician.

HIRTES, Dani J; Webster HS; Webster, SD; 7/74 ALAGirlsSt; Chr; CncrtBnd; DrlTm; HonRl; NHS; Yrbk; FHA; FNA; Chrldr; Augustana College; Criminal Justice.

HIRTH, Robin; Eastern HS; Owensburg, IN; HonRl; NHS; Quill&Scroll; StuCncl; Yrbk; RptrSchPpr; SciCl; College; Photographer.

HISCOCK, Renee; Climax Scotts HS; Climax, MI; CncrtBnd; HonRl; NatlFornLg; NHS; SchPl; TchrAde; 4-H; LetterTrk; 4-HAwd; College Or Univ;.

HISH, Evelyn K; Virginia HS; Virginia, IL; 5/49 PresSophCls; HonRl; OffAde; TchrAde; 4-H; KeyCl; PpCl; GAA; Moser College; Secretary.

HISHAW, Chiquita R; Southeast HS; Kansas City, MO; HonRl; JrNHS; NHS; FrCl; PpCl; SciCl; Trk; Chrldr; IMSpt; PresAwd; College; Dentistry.

HISLE, Robert E; Marshall HS; Miami, MO; 8/156 ALBoysSt; StuCncl; LetterWrstlng; Coll; Computer Programming.

HISLOP, Christine L; Hazelwood Central Sr HS; Florissant, MO; 28/693 Chrl; ChrhWkr; CmntyWkr; DrlTm; HonRl; NHS; NatlMeritCmnd; Brigham Young Univ; Special Education.

HISS, Charles E; Plymouth HS; Plymouth, IN; HonRl; 4-H; FFA; LatCl; MthCl; PpCl; Ftbl; Purdue Univ; Veterinarian.

HISS, Sally J; Columbia City Joint HS; Columbia City, IN; Chr; ChrhWkr; HonRl; OffAde; RptrSchPpr; FBLA; SpnCl; GAA; International Jr College; Insurance Sec.

HISTED, Denise M; Reese HS; Munger, MI; 16/125 Band; HonRl; ModUN; NHS; SchPl; StuCncl; Twrl; AmLegAwd; 4-HAwd; Aquinas; Home Economics.

HITE, Linda K; Holden HS; Holden, MO; 11/80 VPSrCls; HonRl; ModUN; NHS; OffAde; SchPl; TchrAde; Yrbk; PpCl; College; Vocation.

HITESHEW, Tina; Holy Rosary HS; Fint, MI; 11/58 Chr; CmntyWkr; HonRl; JA; LbryAde; NHS; SchPl; SctActv; Yrbk; FNA; Nazareth Coll; Rn Nurse.

HITPAS, Terence A; Mater Dei HS; Carlyle, IL; 10/190 Chr; Chrs; HonRl; Sacrstn; SchMus; SchPl; PresStuCncl; RptrSchPpr; GerCl; PpCl; Bsbl; Bsktbl; LetterFtbl; Univ Of Il; Business.

HITT, Patricia K; Granite City HS; Granite City, IL; 5/610 HonRl; NHS; OffAde; PpCl; LetterTrk; GAA; IMSpt; AmLegAwd; PresAwd; University; Medicine.

HITZEMAN, Wynelle J; Nemaha Valley HS; Tecumseh, NE; 13/34 Chrs; CmntyWkr; HonRl; SchPl; GerCl; PpCl; University; Vocation.

HITZEMANN, Paulette E; Akron Comm HS; Akron, IA; PresSophCls; Chrs; ChrhWkr; HonRl; NHS; SchMus; TchrAde; 4-H; FHA; 4-HAwd; Trade School; Professional.

HITZEMANN, Renee J; Akron Comm HS; Akron, IA; 6/60 VPSrCls; Chr; Chrs; ChrhWkr; HonRl; SchPl; 4-H; FFA; Bsktbl; College; Agriculture.

HITZKE, Jeannine R; Luther North HS; Chicago, IL; 12/222 Chr; ChrhWkr; HonRl; NHS; OffAde; YthFlsp; GerCl; Concordia Teachers Col; Teacher.

HITZSCHKE, Nancy A; Immaculata HS; Chicago, IL; 4/200 HonRl; HospAde; NHS; College; Biology.

HIXON, Willie J; Romulus HS; Romulus, MI; CmntyWkr; HonRl; JrNHS; LetterBsbl; LetterFtbl; LetterTrk; Mi State U; Social Sci.

HIXSON, Catherin A; Mc Cook Sr HS; Mc Cook, NE; Band; CncrtBnd; HospAde; LbryAde; MrchBnd; PepBnd; SctActv; 4-H; Business School; Secretary.

HIXSON, Jeffrey S; Bedford Comm HS; Bedford, IA; 3/72 ChrhWkr; CmntyWkr; HonRl; NHS; NatlThespSoc; SchAde; SchPl; TchrAde; YthFlsp; SpnCl; Cornell Coll; Medicine.

HLAD, Cynthia C; J S Morton West HS; Berwyn, IL; 21/755 Band; CncrtBnd; HonRl; JrNHS; MrchBnd; NatlFornLg; Orch; SchMus; Univ Of Ill; Piano.

HLADIK, Judith A; Riverside Brookfield HS; Brookfield, IL; HonRl; Knox College; Art.

HLADKY, Sue G; Oak Park HS; Kansas City, MO; Chr; HonRl; RptrYrbk; SchPpr; College; Liberal Arts.

HLAS, John; Garwin Community Hs; Toledo, IA; 5 ALBoysSt; HonRl; NHS; RptrSchPpr; SptEdSchPpr; LetterBsbl; LetterBsktbl; LetterFtbl; LetterTrk; CchngActv; College ; Proffesional.

HLAS, Mike G; Lasalle HS; Cedar Rapids, IA; PresFrshCls; PresSophCls; JCAwd; Aud/Vis; Band; CtyCnl; HstFrshCls; Bsktbl; Ftbl; Trk; Harvard.

HLAVAC, Mary A; Louisville HS; Louisville, NE; 15/40 Chrs; ChrhWkr; CmntyWkr; CncrtBnd; HospAde; MrchBnd; PepBnd; YthFlsp; FHA; Midland Lutheran College; Nursing.

HLAVACH, Laura; Bradley Bourbonnais Community; Bourbonnais, IL; Chr; NHS; NatlMeritSchl; NatlThespSoc; Orch; Quill&Scroll; SchPl; VPStuCncl; SchPpr; EldAwd; U;journalism.

HLAVATY, Tammy A; Fort Zumwalt HS; Ofallon, MO; ChrhWkr; DrlTm; HonRl; StuCncl; PpCl; Chrldr; PPFtbl; Col; Med Field.

HLEBAIN, Gerri A; Sartell HS; St Joseph, MN; 2/75 VPSrCls; NHS; TreasStuCncl; PresGerCl; CaptBsktbl; LetterTrk; AmLegAwd; BauchLmbAwd; BttyCrckrAwd; ChmbCommrsAwd; DanFAwd; College.

HLINAK, Diane; Ritenour Sr HS; Overland, MO; NatlMeritCmnd; Coll; Law.

HLOUCHA, Sheryl M; Chamberlain HS; Chamberlain, SD; Chrs; ChrhWkr; CmntyWkr; HonRl; SchAde; SchPl; TchrAde; FSA; SpnCl; PpCl; College; Nursing.

HOAG, Barbara A; D D Eisenhower HS; Saginaw, MI; 31/365 CncrtBnd; HonRl; VPJA; JrNHS; MrchBnd; NHS; Orch; PepBnd; SchMus; VPLatCl; College; Engineer.

HOAG, Dean G; Manson Community HS; Manson, IA; PresJrCls; Chr; HonRl; NHS; SchMus; VPStuCncl; LetterFtbl; LetterWrstlng; U Of Ia; Pre Med.

HOAG, Rita K; Manson HS; Manson, IA; Band; CncrtBnd; HonRl; MrchBnd; PepBnd; SchPl; RptrYrbk; RptrSchPpr; 4-H; LetterTrk; Univ Of N Ia; Secondary Ed.

HOAGLAND, Gary J; Gordon HS; Gordon, NE; TrsJrCls; ALBoysSt; StuCncl; LetterBsktbl; LetterFtbl; College; Professional.

HOAGLAND, Jerry; Bishop Luers HS; Ft Wayne, IN; Aud/Vis; CmntyWkr; HonRl; SctActv; Trk; IMSpt; GovHonPrgAwd; Oh Institute Of Tech; Electronics.

HOAGLAND, Luann; Northside HS; Ft Wayne, IN; AFS; StuCncl; EngCl; Swmmng; PPFtbl; ChmbCommrsAwd; Ind Univ; Radiologist.

HOAGLAND, Mark C; Oak Lawn Community HS; Oak Lawn, IL; 131/515 HonRl; College; Gen Bus Major.

HOAN, Mary P; Elizabeth Seton HS; So Holland, IL; SecJrCls; HonRl; IntrClCncl; NHS; SchPl; StuCncl; StuGov; RptrYrbk; Yrbk; RptrSchPpr; SchPpr; College; Law.

HOARD, Tamara A; South Decatur HS; Westport, IN; Band; ChrhWkr; MrchBnd; OffAde; SpnCl; PpCl; Chrldr; Indiana Central Univ; Nursing.

HOBACK, Norman A; Clinton HS; Clinton, IL; Aud/Vis; LbryAde; SchAde; SchPl; StuCncl; StuGov; TchrAde; Yrbk; RptrSchPpr; SptEdSchPpr; SciCl; LetterBsktbl; LetterFtbl; Trk; College; Chemistry.

HOBAN, Debbie; Minden HS; Heartwell, NE; Band; Chrs; CncrtBnd; MrchBnd; PepBnd; TchrAde; YthFlsp; FHA; FTA; GAA; Kearney State College; Elementary Ed.

HOBART, Jan M; Dallas City HS; Dallas City, IL; 3/32 SecTrsSrCls; SchPl; StuCncl; RptrYrbk; RptrSchPpr; FBLA; PpCl; College.

HOBAUGH, Connie L; Braman HS; South Haven, KS; 1/17 PresSophCls; SecTrsJrCls; Chrs; ChrhWkr; HonRl; StuCncl; YthFlsp; Pres4-H; TreasPpCl; LetterBsktbl; 4-HAwd; GovHonPrgAwd; Cowley County Jr Col; Accounting.

HOBAUGH, Perry S; Seeger HS; Wes Lebanon, IN; 15/120 ChrhWkr; CmntyWkr; HonRl; LitMag; LbryAde; Bsbl; Bsktbl; LetterFtbl; LetterTrk; DanFAwd; Purdue U; Engineering.

HOBBS, Daniel R; Sault HS; Sault Ste Marie, MI; 12/350 VPJrCls; HonRl; NHS; NatlMeritFnl; NatlMeritCmnd; NatlMeritSchl; SctActv; TchrAde; RptrSchPpr; Ftbl; Univ; Law.

HOBBS, Jeene M; Yankton HS; Yankton, SD; ALAGirlsSt; ChrhWkr; HonRl; HospAde; LitMag; NHS; Orch; EdSchPpr; AmLegAwd; Sd Sch Mines And Tech; Chemical Engineer.

HOBBS, John M; University HS; Warrensburg, MO; PresSophCls; StuCncl; SpnCl; LetterFtbl; LetterTrk; College; Pre Med.

HOBBS, Karen S; Wellington HS; Wellington, KS; 1/163 ChrhWkr; CncrtBnd; DrmMjrt; HonRl; HospAde; MrchBnd; NatlFornLg; PepBnd; TchrAde; YthFlsp; Southwestern College; Park Recreation Mgmt.

HOBBS, Lisa M; Madison Consolidated HS; Madison, IN; Band; Chr; CAP; HonRl; MrchBnd; SctActv; YthFlsp; 4-H; PpCl; Bsbl; Embry Riddle Aero Univ; Aeronautics.

HOBBS, Margaret S; Bowling Green HS; Bowling Green, MO; Band; ChrhWkr; CmntyWkr; CncrtBnd; HonRl; NHS; Quill&Scroll; RptrSchPpr; FBLA; PresFHA; Ne Missouri St Univ; Accounting.

HOBBS, Mary Beth; Hartsburg Emden HS; Emden, IL; PresSophCls; Band; Chrs; ChrhWkr; HonRl; PresStuCncl; YthFlsp; RptrYrbk; RptrSchPpr;.

HOBBS, Michael H; Alexandria Monroe HS; Alexandria, IN; 40/242 HonRl; SpnCl; Bsbl; Tennis; Trk;.

HOBBS, Pamela J; Chambers HS; Ewing, NE; 4/21 Chrs; HonRl; NHS; TchrAde; EdYrBk; 4-H; PpCl; LetterTrk; Chrldr; 4-HAwd; Coll; Math.

HOBECK, Deborah K; Chester HS; Chester, IL; TrsFrshCls; TrsSophCls; TrsJrCls; Band; Chrs; HonRl; FTA; PpCl; Chrldr; AmLegAwd; Business School; Medical Secretary.

HOBERT, Ben W; Charles City Comm HS; Charles City, IA; 2/226 HonRl; NatlFornLg; NHS; NatlMeritFnl; SchPl; StuCncl; StuGov; MthCl; LetterTennis; U Of Ia; Business Admin.

HOBSON, Catherine A; Plattsmouth HS; Murray, NE; 5/163 HonRl; YthFlsp; FBLA; Business Sch; Executive Secretary.

HOBSON, Danny A; Black Hawk HS; Browntown, WI; Band; CncrtBnd; HonRl; MrchBnd; PepBnd; YthFlsp; RptrSchPpr; Bsktbl; Trk; 4-HAwd; College; Professional.

HOBSON, Donald D; Birch Run HS; Birch Run, MI; 2/155 PresSophCls; CncrtBnd; HonRl; VPNHS; NatlMeritSF; VPStuCncl; SpnCl; VPSciCl; Bsktbl; CaptTrk; Taylor Univ; Professional.

HOBSON, Eric P; Griggsville HS; Griggsville, IL; VPJrCls; StuCncl; TchrAde; RptrYrbk; FFA; SpnCl; Bsbl; Bsktbl; College.

HOBSON, Gail; Central Lyon HS; Doon, IA; Chrs; HonRl; LitMag; Trk; 4-HAwd; College.

HOBSON, Keith L; Nevada HS; Nevada, IA; ALBoysSt; Chrs; HonRl; NHS; SctActv; StuCncl; YthFlsp; Bsktbl; University; Professional.

HOBSON, Venita M; Unity HS; Chicago, IL; Chrs; ChrhWkr; StuGov; YthFlsp; 4-H; College; Special Education.

HOCH, Dawn J; Council Grove HS; Dwight, KS; HonRl; NHS; RptrYrbk; EdSchPpr; FHA; Bsktbl; AmLegAwd; DARAwd; GodCntryAwd; School Of Nursing; Reg Nurse.

HOCH, James E; Marion HS; Marion, KS; HonRl; Yrbk; GerCl; Trk; RotaryAwd;.

HOCHARD, Melvin R; West Platte HS; Farley, MO; 2/50 HonRl; ModUN; NHS; 4-H; FBLA; Nw Missouri St Univ; Chemistry.

HOCHBERG, Lee E; Carl Sandburg HS; Orland Park, IL; 16/746 HonRl; NHS; NatlMeritCmnd; Quill&Scroll; SchPl; SctActv; StuCncl; TchrAde; EdSchPpr; TreasSpnCl; Socr; Trk; Vanderbilt Univ; Law.

HOCHHALTER, Belva J; New Leipzig HS; New Leipzig, ND; 3/15 TrsFrshCls; SecSophCls; TrsJrCls; PresSrCls; HonRl; FshEdSchPpr; PpCl; Bsktbl; Trk; IMSpt; Coll; Legal Sec.

HOCHHALTER, Rosemary; Wilton HS; Regan, ND; 1/36 SecSophCls; ALAGirlsSt; Chrs; HonRl; NHS; SchPl; PpCl; Bsktbl; Trk; Chrldr; Trade Wahpeton Nd; Accountant.

HOCHNADEL, Sharon M; Argo HS; Burr Ridge, IL; 10/432 HonRl; NHS; OffAde; SchPl; SpnCl; SciCl; College; Physical Therapy.

HOCHSTATTER, Larry D; Lynd HS; Lynd, MN; PresJrCls; ALBoysSt; Chrs; HonRl; SchPl; 4-H; FFA; LetterBsbl; LetterFtbl; LetterTrk; Vo Tech; Business Management.

HOCHSTATTER, Susan E; Nevada HS; Nevada, MO; 35/174 CtyCnl; CmntyWkr; NatlFornLg; SecNatlThespSoc; SchPl; StuCncl; StuGov; SecLatCl; LetterTennis; GAA; U Of Mo; Us History.

HOCHSTEIN, Dale D; Wynot Public HS; Wynot, NE; 1/38 Band; ChrhWkr; HonRl; NHS; Yrbk; Bsktbl; Trk; EldAwd; Clg; Biology Teacher.

HOCHSTEIN, Pamela J; Cedar Catholic HS; Hartington, NE; 19/69 TrsSrCls; Band; HonRl; NHS; StuCncl; Pres4-H; PresPpCl; Trk; Chrldr; PPFtbl; Nebraska U; Business.

HOCHSTEIN, Scott J; Cedar Catholic HS; Hartington, NE; Chr; Chrl; Chrs; SchMus; SchPl; VP4-H; SecFFA; Bsktbl; LetterFtbl; Trk; IMSpt; 4-HAwd; Univ Of Nebraska; Auto Mechanic.

HOCHSTETLER, Amy; Wolford Public Hs; Mylo, ND; 1/7 SecJrCls; SecTrsSrCls; Band; Chr; HonRl; TchrAde; EdYrBk; MthCl; Bsktbl; Trk; Hesston College;nurses Training.

HOCHSTETLER, Barbara A; Northridge HS; Goshen, IN; HonRl; YthFlsp; 4-H; PpCl; GAA; 4-HAwd; Marriage; Commercial Art.

HOCHSTETLER, Gary; Enterprise Acad; Horton, KS; PresSrCls; Band; Chr; Chrs; Yrbk; FFA; Se Union College; Medicine.

HOCK, Terri S; Casey Jr Sr HS; Casey, IL; 66/94 PresJrCls; Chr; ChrhWkr; CmntyWkr; JA; NHS; RedCrAde; TchrAde; YthFlsp; FHA; College; Special Ed.

HOCKENBERRY, Darrell L; Anita HS; Wiota, IA; 6/60 TrsSophCls; VPJrCls; HonRl; NatlFornLg; VPNHS; SctActv; PresStuCncl; SciCl; LetterBsktbl; College Morningside; Accounting.

HOCKER, James R; El Paso HS; El Paso, IL; 14/92 VPSrCls; ChrhWkr; HonRl; NHS; SchPl; SpnCl; MthCl; Bsktbl; LetterFtbl; Trk; College.

HOCKER, Justin P; Canton Sr HS; Canton, IL; 22/266 ALBoysSt; HonRl; NHS; SchAde; Univ Of Illinois; Law.

HOCKERS, Patricia A; West De Pere HS; De Pere, WI; HonRl; NHS; Univ Of Wisconsin; Art.

HOCKETT, Lori J; Raymore Peculiar HS; Belton, MO; 3/116 SecSophCls; TrsJrCls; Band; CncrtBnd; HonRl; HospAde; NHS; SecStuCncl; LetterBsktbl; LetterTrk; Coll; Medical Field.

HOCKING, Mary D; Hancock Central HS; Hancock, MI; Chr; HonRl; EdYrBk; 4-H; KeyCl; Bsktbl; LetterSwmmng; Trk; GAA; PPFtbl; 4-HAwd; Trade Schl; Vocation.

HODAPP, Terry J; Collinsville Sr HS; Collinsville, IL; 91/654 Aud/Vis; HonRl; NHS; StuCncl; FBLA; PpCl; LetterBsbl; LetterGlf; Southern Il Univ; Accounting.

HODEL, Mark W; Roanoke Benson HS; Roanoke, IL; PresJrCls; ChrhWkr; HonRl; ModUN; NHS; YthFlsp; PresFFA; LetterWrstlng; IMSpt;.

HODEL, Wendy L; Atkinson HS; Erie, IL; 8/35 SecJrCls; HonRl; SchAde; SchPl; Yrbk; RptrSchPpr; FHA; SpnCl; PpCl; GAA; Business School; Professional.

HODERSPECK, Karolina; Taft Hs; Chicago, IL; 16 Band; Chr; HonRl; NHS; TchrAde; Tennis; U Of Illinois;math And Computer Science.

HODGDON, Frank W; Whitfield HS; Chesterfield, MO; HonRl; OffAde; StuCncl; Yrbk; Bsbl; Socr; Tennis; Univ; Bus Admin.

HODGE, Anne; Waterford Twp HS; Pontiac, MI; Chr; HonRl; NHS; StuGov; Yrbk; RptrSchPpr; Trk; 4-HAwd; Michigan St Univ; Veterinary Medicine.

HODGE, Cindy J; Mt Vernon Twp HS; Mt Vernon, IL; 24/388 ALAGirlsSt; Chr; ChrhWkr; HonRl; Mdrgl; NHS; NatlThespSoc; SchMus; SchPl; TchrAde; SpnCl; LetterTrk; So East University.

HODGE, Jeneasa K; Ypsilanti HS; Ypsilati, MI; Band; ChrhWkr; HonRl; MrchBnd; NHS; NatlMeritSchl; OffAde; StuCncl; FTA; PpCl; Univ Bus.

HODGE, Linda D; South Page HS; Coin, IA; Band; Chr; Chrl; Chrs; CncrtBnd; HonRl; MrchBnd; Orch; PepBnd; SchMus; SchPl; 4-H; FHA; PpCl; College; Professional.

HODGES, Cynthia L; East Prairie HS; East Prairie, MO; 5/80 Band; Chr; HonRl; NHS; SctActv; VPStuCncl; SecSpnCl; PpCl; LetterChrldr; PPFtbl; Southeast Mo State U; Accounting.

HODGES, Diane L; Auburn Sr HS; Julian, NE; 1/86 HonRl; OffAde; TchrAde; RptrYrbk; 4-H; FHA; BttyCrckrAwd; KiwanAwd; Lincoln Sch Of Comm; Legal Assistant.

HODGES, Douglas D; Evart HS; Evart, MI; CncrtBnd; HonRl; MrchBnd; TreasYthFlsp; RptrSchPpr; 4-H; LetterFtbl; Spring Arbor Coll; Biology.

HODGES, Jacqueline J; Chicago Vocational HS; Chicago, IL; 66/776 Swmmng; College; Business Adm.

HODGES, Joy; Yale Jamacia Bagley Community; Yale, IA; 5 TrsSrCls; Chrs; CncrtBnd; HonRl; MrchBnd; StuCncl; FTA; Bsbl; Bsktbl; CaptChrldr; Des Moines Area College ; Medical Secretary.

HODGES, Joy L; Y J B Community HS; Yale, IA; 5/35 TrsSrCls; Band; Chrs; CncrtBnd; HonRl; SchPl; StuCncl; Bsktbl; Trk; CaptChrldr; Des Moine Area Comm Coll; Medical Secretary.

HODGES, Mark R; Walther Lutheran HS; Forest Park, IL; Chr; CncrtBnd; PepBnd; LetterBsktbl; CaptTennis; Coll; Teacher.

HODGES, Michael G; Forest Lake HS; Hugo, MN; HonRl; SchPl; Vo Tec; Medicine.

HODGES, Nyla R; Mullen HS; Mullen, NE; 7/36 SecFrshCls; SecSophCls; SecJrCls; Band; Chr; Chrs; ChrhWkr; CncrtBnd; HonRl; MrchBnd; PepBnd; LetterTrk; Chrldr; PresAwd; E Wyoming College; Secretary.

HODGES, Oletha D; Willow Run HS; Ypsilanti, MI; Band; ChrhWkr; CncrtBnd; HonRl; MrchBnd; 4-H; Bsbl; Chrldr; CitAwd; U Of Michigan; Registered Nurse.

HODGES, Patricia L; St Pius X HS; Festus, MO; CAP; CncrtBnd; HonRl; MrchBnd; College; Nursing.

HODGES, Sharise J; Tripoli Community HS; Ionia, IA; 1/53 TrsJrCls; Band; Chr; Chrs; CncrtBnd; HonRl; MrchBnd; NHS; PepBnd; SchMus; University; Mathematics.

HODGES, Stephen S; Durand HS; Lennon, MI; HonRl; Bsktbl;.

HODGIN, Larry A; Custer HS; Custer, SD; Band; CncrtBnd; HonRl; MrchBnd; NHS; GerCl; South Dakota Schl; Chemistry.

HODGKINSON, Vicki J; St James HS; St James, MN; HonRl; SchPl; StuCncl; FHA; GerCl; CaptTrk; Chrldr; GAA; PPFtbl; PresAwd; Trade School.

HODGSON, Hilary E; Whitefish Bay HS; Milwaukee, WI; 18/330 HonRl; NHS; NatlMeritCmnd; SctActv; StuCncl; StuGov; RptrYrbk; SptEdYrbk; FrCl; LetterSwmmng; Williams College; Architecture.

HODGSON, Jerry L; Gettysburg HS; Gettysburg, SD; ALBoysSt; Band; HonRl; JrNHS; MrchBnd;

NHS; ROTC; StuCncl; YthFlsp; LetterBsktbl; Univ Of Sd; Business Law.

HODGSON, Judd; Dakota Hs; Dakota, IL; SchPl; Yrbk; RptrSchPpr; Four Years School;elec Eng Or Tech.

HODNEFIELD, Daryl W; Ray Public HS; Williston, ND; 1/27 PresSophCls; ALBoysSt; HonRl; SchPl; Yrbk; LetterBsktbl; BauchLmbAwd; Univ Nd Williston Center; Pharmacy.

HODNEFIELD, Glen I; Radcliffe Community HS; Radcliffe, IA; Band; CncrtBnd; HonRl; MrchBnd; NHS; PepBnd; CivCl; 4-H; LetterBsbl; Bsktbl; LetterTrk; Aflbs.

HODNETT, William R; Cooley HS; Detroit, MI; 48/366 HonRl; LbryAde; OffAde; RptrSchPpr; Coll; Psychology.

HODOROWSKI, Mary L; Thorp HS; Thorp, WI; 12/94 HonRl; NHS; FFA; Bsbl; LetterBsktbl; LetterTrk; Vocational School; Agri Business.

HODOUS, Linda L; Edmore Public HS; Edmore, ND; Chrs; HonRl; LbryAde; Yrbk; FHA; PpCl; Bsktbl; Trk; Chrldr; Univ Of North Dakota; Physical Therapy.

HODOUS, Patricia S; Downers Grove Comm HS; Downers Grove, IL; HonRl; SctActv; TchrAde; SciCl; GAA; PPFtbl; U Of Wi Stout; Home Economics.

HODSON, Billie J; West Washington HS; Campbellsburg, IN; Band; HonRl; FHA; SpnCl; Bus Sch; Accountant.

HODSON, Kathryn L; Anderson HS; Anderson, IN; Aud/Vis; Chr; Chrl; HonRl; NHS; LetterGlf; Swmmng; GAA; BauchLmbAwd; College; Accounting.

HODSON, Kay; Bennett County HS; Martin, SD; ALAGirlsSt; Band; ChrhWkr; HonRl; NHS; SpnCl; PpCl; Univ Of Sd; Ed Admin.

HODSON, Matthew S; Triton Central HS; Fairland, IN; 2/126 NHS; StuCncl; PresKeyCl; SpnCl; LetterBsbl; LetterBsktbl; LetterFtbl; LetterTrk; Rose Hulman Inst Tech; Engineer.

HODSON, Pamela L; Galena HS; Galena, MO; 6/35 SecJrCls; SecSrCls; Band; ChrhWkr; HonRl; NHS; FHA; PpCl; DanFAwd; Clg; Vocation.

HOEBERLING, Thomas C; Lee M Thurston HS; Milford, MI; 10/633 Band; Chr; Chrs; CncrtBnd; HonRl; JrNHS; MrchBnd; NHS; NatlMeritCmnd; PepBnd; Univ Of Michigan.

HOEBING, Lynn; Scotus Central Cath HS; Columbus, NE; 19/65 HstFrshCls; HstSrCls; Chr; HonRl; StuCncl; GerCl; IMSpt; Univ Of Nebraska; Accounting.

HOECKELBERG, Amy T; Hanover Central HS; Cedar Lake, IN; 1/127 HonRl; JrNHS; NHS; Yrbk; 4-H; GAA; Purdue Extension; Business.

HOEF, Theodore F; Assumption HS; E St Louis, IL; 2/198 Aud/Vis; Band; HonRl; ModUN; SchMus; StuGov; Yrbk; MthCl; Bsktbl; LetterGlf; BauchLmbAwd; St Louis College; Pharmacy.

HOEFAKKER, Pamela L; Muskegon HS; Muskegon, MI; Chr; ChrhWkr; HonRl; HospAde; NHS; NatlMeritSchl; SctActv; YthFlsp; SpnCl; College; Nurse.

HOEFER, Mary S; Marian HS; Omaha, NE; ChrhWkr; HospAde; SctActv; TchrAde; FNA; U Of Ne At Omaha; Special Ed.

HOEFER, Mitchell R; Lafayette Ct District C1 HS; Higginsville, MO; AFS; HonRl; NHS; RedCrAde; SpnCl; LetterFtbl; Trk; MasAwd; College; Architecture.

HOEFFLIGER, Nancy L; Princeton HS; Princeton, IL; HonRl; LbryAde; Yrbk; Treas4-H; SpnCl; PpCl; 4-HAwd; Illinois State Univ; Elem Education.

HOEFLICH, Phyllis S; Pkwy North HS; Maryland Heights, MO; 6/470 TrsFrshCls; Chr; Chrs; DrlTm; HonRl; HospAde; JrNHS; Mdrgl; PpCl; PPFtbl; College; Animal Science.

HOEFLINGER, James H; St Rita HS; Chicago, IL; 62/424 HonRl; NHS; PolWkr; LetterTrk; IMSpt; Univ Of Il Cir Campus Chicago; Law.

HOEFNER, Paula D; Dearborn HS; Dearborn, MI; Band; Chrs; CncrtBnd; HonRl; MrchBnd; NHS; U Of Mi; Medical Field.

HOEFS, Brad D; Wisner Pilger HS; Wisner, NE; Band; Chr; Chrl; Chrs; ChrhWkr; CmntyWkr; CncrtBnd; HonRl; HospAde; LbryAde; Mdrgl; MrchBnd; Bsktbl; College; Minister.

HOEFS, Danny L; Gaylord Public HS; Gaylord, MN; 20/65 HonRl; SptEdSchPpr; CaptBsbl; CaptBsktbl; CaptFtbl; LionAwd; Worthington College.

HOEFS, Susan A; Pender HS; Pender, NE; 6/58 PresJrCls; Chrs; HonRl; VPFHA; PpCl; U Of Ne; English Major.

HOEFT, David F; Sun Prairie HS; Sun Prairie, WI; 1/350 ALBoysSt; Chr; HonRl; JrNHS; LbryAde; NHS; NatlMeritFnl; NatlMeritSF; Ftbl; IMSpt; U Of W; Medical Field.

HOEFT, Kathryn A; Fairmont HS; Grafton, NE; 5/28 SecFrshCls; SecJrCls; SecSrCls; Band; Chr; HonRl; NHS; SchPl; StuCncl; 4-HAwd;.

HOEFT, Paul; Erskine Public HS; Erskine, MN; /29 PresFrshCls; ALBoysSt; Band; Chr; MrchBnd; SchMus; SchPl; StuCncl; RptrYrbk; RptrSchPpr; Univ.

HOEGEMEYER, Beth A; Lyons HS; Lyons, NE; Chrs; HonRl; JrNHS; NHS; SchMus; RptrYrbk; EdSchPpr; Pres4-H; SecFHA; PresLetterTrk; University; Professional.

HOEGGER, Elaine M; Odell Community HS; Odell, IL; 10/35 TrsFrshCls; Chr; HonRl; OffAde; RptrYrbk; FHA; SpnCl; PpCl; Chrldr; GAA; Ill State U; Sociology.

HOEHNS, Rhonda; Smithton HS; Smithton, MO; 5/41 Band; ChrhWkr; HonRl; MrchBnd; NHS; SchPl; Twrl; YthFlsp; Univ Of Mo Columbia; Law.

HOEKSEMA, Elayne J; Holland Christian HS; Zeeland, MI; 25/261 Chr; CncrtBnd; HonRl; MrchBnd; NHS; PepBnd; SchPl; RptrYrbk; FNA; CaptIMSpt; Bronson Methodist School; Rn.

HOEKSEMA, Lynne; Pella Community HS; Pella, IA; 2/116 PresBand; Chrs; CmntyWkr; CncrtBnd; HonRl; SecNHS; SchMus; YthFlsp; FrCl; CitAwd; Ia State Univ; Math Statistics.

HOEKSEMA, Pamela J; Platte Public HS; Platte, SD; ChrhWkr; HonRl; HospAde; LbryAde; NatlFornLg; TchrAde; SchPpr; FHA; FNA; Trk; IMSpt;.

HOEKSTRA, James; Unity Christian HS; Jenison, MI; 24/210 Chr; HonRl; Mdrgl; RptrSchPpr; IMSpt; Calvin College; Actvary.

HOEKSTRA, Michele; Chicago Christian Hs; Oak Lawn, IL; Chrl; ChrhWkr; HonRl; JrNHS; NHS; SchPl; PpCl; GovHonPrgAwd; College; Medicine.

HOEL, Eddie B; Liberal HS; Liberal, KS; HonRl; LitMag; NHS; EdSchPpr; SchPpr; SpnCl; Rochester Inst; Photographer.

HOELLE, David; Bishop Luers HS; Ft Wayne, IN; 44/250 HonRl; NHS; Bsktbl; Ftbl; IMSpt; Ind Univ; Acct.

HOELSCHER, Carol J; Blair Oaks HS; Jefferson City, MO; 11/51 VPSophCls; VPSrCls; Band; Yrbk; SchPpr; 4-H; FBLA; FHA; PpCl; IMSpt; College.

HOELSCHER, Sandra M; Union HS; Union, MO; 4/174 HonRl; TchrAde; SpnCl; College; Professional.

HOELTING, Debra; Lawrence HS; Lawrence, NE; 5/30 Band; CmntyWkr; HonRl; SchPl; Yrbk; Glf; Swmmng; Trk; Chrldr; PPFtbl; Patricia Stevens Fashion; Pub Relations.

HOELTING, Diane E; Duchesne HS; St Charles, MO; Chrs; HonRl; SchMus; StuCncl; PpCl; CaptChrldr; IMSpt; PPFtbl;.

HOELTING, James T; Lincolnwood HS; Farmersville, IL; ChrhWkr; CtyCnl; HonRl; NHS; PolWkr; SciCl; Lincoln Land Comm Clg.

HOELTL, Patricia A; Central HS; Devils Lake, ND; 20/140 Chrl; HonRl; SchMus; FHA; PpCl; Jur Coll; Doctor.

HOELZEL, Barbara; Hitchcock HS; Hitchcock, SD; 5/21 Chrs; HonRl; LbryAde; SchPl; TchrAde; Yrbk; RptrSchPpr; FHA; College; Business.

HOELZEL, Joan M; Kaukauna HS; Kaukauna, WI; Chrs; ChrhWkr; HonRl; JrNHS; NHS; Quill&Scroll; RptrSchPpr; SchPpr; SpnCl; DanFAwd; Univ; Occupational Therapy.

HOEMANN, Carol D; Union HS; Union, MO; Chr; ChrhWkr; CncrtBnd; HonRl; MrchBnd; OffAde; PepBnd; YthFlsp; PpCl; College.

HOENER, Teresa J; Notre Dame HS; Quincy, IL; 2/83 Chrs; HonRl; NHS; SpnCl; IMSpt; Quincy Coll;.

HOENIG, Jo A; Cudahy Sr 'S; Cudahy, WI; DrlTm; HonRl; LbryAde; NatlThespSoc; SchPl; SctActv; SchPpr; FBLA; GerCl; Bsktbl; Uw Platteville; Criminology.

HOENK, Nancy K; Elgin Millville HS; Elgin, MN; 4/49 PresJrCls; Band; Chrs; HonRl; SchPl; EdYrBk; SpnCl; Trk; Chrldr; IMSpt; College; Nurse.

HOERATH, Martin E; Lutheran HS; St Louis, MO; 19/150 Chr; HonRl; NHS; SchMus; LetterBsbl; College; Architecture.

HOERAUF, Geralyn C; Marian HS; Birmingham, MI; 7/178 TrsJrCls; ModUN; NHS; NatlMeritFnl; NatlMeritSF; SctActv; StuGov; SchPpr; Notre Dame Univ; Architecture.

HOERAUF, Sharon R; Marian HS; Birmingham, MI; ChrhWkr; HonRl; ModUN; NHS; TreasSctActv; University; Forestry Major.

HOERBERT, Karen K; Hartsburg Emden HS; Delavan, IL; PresFrshCls; PresJrCls; TrsSrCls; Band; Chr; HonRl; NHS; StuCncl; RptrSchPpr; GAA; Western Ill Univ; Medical Tech.

HOERER, Clifford M; Wauconda HS; Wauconda, IL; Aud/Vis; Band; CtyCnl; HonRl; MrchBnd; NHS; LetterFtbl; LetterTrk; Wrstlng; Palmer Chiropractor Coll; Chiropractic.

HOERNEMANN, Mary E; Lester Prairie HS; Lester Prairie, MN; Band; Chr; CncrtBnd; HonRl; MrchBnd; TchrAde; YthFlsp; RptrYrbk; LetterBsktbl; LetterTrk; Trade School; Dental Assistant.

HOERNIG, Karen A; Lake Central HS; Dyer, IN; ALAGirlsSt; HonRl; LbryAde; SchAde; TchrAde; Teen; GerCl; Indiana Col Of Bus & Tech; Med Assistant.

HOERR, Colette M; Princeville HS; Chillicothe, IL; 2/75 Chrs; HonRl; NatlMeritCmnd; SchMus; SchPl; 4-H; SpnCl; PpCl; University Of Illinois.

HOERR, Ruth; Richwoods HS; Peoria, IL; 39/449 Chr; DrlTm; HonRl; NHS; RedCrAde; StuCncl; StuGov; 4-H; PPFtbl; Methodist Sch Of Nr; Nursing.

HOESE, Pamela; Mayer Lutheran Hs; Mayer, MN; Chr; Yrbk; PpCl; Trade Or Bus School; Vocation.

HOESLY, David L; St Pius X HS; Kansas City, MO; 37/129 Band; ChrhWkr; CncrtBnd; HonRl; PepBnd; SchAde; SchMus; SchPl; TchrAde; GodCntryAwd; College; Aviation.

HOESMAN, Clay R; Sullivan HS; Sullivan, IN; 3/158 Chrs; HonRl; PresJrNHS; NHS; SpnCl; VPMthCl; Bsbl; IMSpt; PresAwd; Rose Hulman Col; Engineering.

HOEVEN, John H; Bishop Ryan; Minot, ND; 1/80 PresSophCls; TrsJrCls; PresSrCls; ALBoysSt; Band; Chr; CmntyWkr; CncrtBnd; HonRl; MrchBnd; LetterBsktbl; LetterFtbl; LetterGlf; KiwanAwd; College; Professional.

HOFBAUER, Daniel G; Wesclin HS; New Baden, IL; 15/100 ALBoysSt; ChrhWkr; NatlThespSoc; StuCncl; YthFlsp; RptrSchPpr; SchPpr; FFA; GerCl; CitAwd; College; Animal Tech.

HOFBAUER, Diane L; Meno Falls East HS; Menomonee Falls, WI; 4/350 AFS; HonRl; JrNHS; ModUN; NHS; NatlMeritSF; SchPl; PresFrCl; MthCl; PpCl; Duke Univ; Medical Research.

HOFER, Carrie J; Emery HS; Emery, SD; DrlTm; HonRl; SchPl; YthFlsp; FHA; PpCl; LetterTrk; Business Schl; Vocation.

HOFER, Denise M; Bishop Gallagher HS; Harper Woods, MI; HonRl; NHS; SchPl; StuGov; Yrbk; GAA; IMSpt; Univ Of Detroit; Business.

HOFER, Jeffery L; Cocrane Fountain City HS; Cochrane, WI; Band; Chr; Chrl; Chrs; ChrhWkr; CncrtBnd; MrchBnd; Orch; PepBnd; SchMus; PpCl; Trk; College; Engineering.

HOFER, Jennifer A; Larimore HS; Arvilla, ND; ALAGirlsSt; Band; ChrhWkr; CncrtBnd; HonRl; MrchBnd; PepBnd; SchPl; Sdlty; 4-H; Bsktbl; Trk; Chrldr; School Of Nursing; Nurse.

HOFER, Larry D; Mar Mac HS; Mc Gregor, IA; 1/36 PresSophCls; ALBoysSt; Band; HonRl; NHS; SchMus; University Of Iowa; Engineering.

HOFER, Marty D; Sully Buttes HS; Onida, SD; 9/55 HonRl; 4-H; LetterFtbl; Wrstlng; U Of Sd; Business.

HOFER, Mary P; St Paul HS; Walnut, KS; 1/30 Band; Chrs; DrlTm; DrmMjrt; HonRl; NHS; RptrYrbk; RptrSchPpr; PpCl; Chrldr; Kansas State Clg; Business.

HOFER, Preston L; Hot Springs HS; Hot Springs, SD; 1/80 ALBoysSt; Chr; CncrtBnd; HonRl; NHS; Bsbl; LetterBsktbl; LetterFtbl; LetterTrk; Univ Sd; Acctng.

HOFER, Vernon L; Rankin HS; Rankin, IL; 5/23 PresFrshCls; PresSophCls; VPSrCls; ALBoysSt; HonRl; StuCncl; RptrYrbk; LetterBsbl; LetterBsktbl; LetterTrk; AmLegAwd; College; Professional.

HOFF, Ann M; South Side HS; Ft Wayne, IN; HonRl; HospAde; NatlMeritCmnd;.

HOFF, Barbara H; Marshall HS; Marshall, MO; ChrhWkr; HonRl; OffAde; PolWkr; SctActv; StuCncl; RptrSchPpr; PpCl; LetterTrk; Chrldr; IMSpt; Business School; Major Study.

HOFF, Brenda L; Washburn HS; Washburn, ND; Band; Chrs; CncrtBnd; HonRl; MrchBnd; PepBnd; SchPl; 4-H; FHA; 4-HAwd; Jamestown Clge; Nursing.

HOFF, Carol A; Center HS; Hensler, ND; Band; Chrs; HonRl; PepBnd; SchPpr; GerCl; PpCl; Trk; Chrldr; Clg; Acct.

HOFF, Charlotte; Flasher Public HS; Flasher, ND; Chrs; HonRl; LbryAde; SchPpr; SecTrsSophCls; SciCl; Coll; Nursing.

HOFF, David J; Warren Woods HS; Warren, MI; HonRl; NHS; StuGov; LetterTrk; College Teacher.

HOFF, Deborah A; Franklin Central HS; Indianapolis, IN; 9/214 Band; CncrtBnd; HonRl; JrNHS; LbryAde; MrchBnd; NHS; College; Accounting.

HOFF, Karen R; Alvarado HS; Oslo, MN; TrsJrCls; Band; Chrs; CncrtBnd; HospAde; MrchBnd; PepBnd; RptrYrbk; FHA; Chrldr;.

HOFF, Laurie R; Pleasant Hill HS; Pleasant Hill, MO; 1/111 PresFrshCls; Chr; HonRl; NHS; StuCncl; SpnCl; PpCl; SciCl; Swmmng; LetterTrk; Chrldr; College; Designer.

HOFF, Sandra M; Leigh Community HS; Leigh, NE; 1/32 SecFrshCls; Band; HonRl; SchPl; FFA; GerCl; VPPpCl; Bsktbl; Trk; PPFtbl; Wayne State College.

HOFFA, Sandra K; Urbandale HS; Urbandale, IA; 38/245 DrlTm; HonRl; HospAde; NatlMeritSF; RptrSchPpr; FrCl; State Univ; English.

HOFFA, Sara J; Downers Grove Community HS; Downers Grove, IL; 47/830 PresJrCls; HonRl; JrNHS; NHS; NatlThespSoc; SchPl; Iowa State University; Anthropology.

HOFFART, Judith E; Plainview HS; Plainview, NE; PresSophCls; SecBand; Chrs; CncrtBnd; DrmMjrt; HonRl; HospAde; MrchBnd; PepBnd; TreasStuCncl; YthFlsp; PpCl; LetterTrk; Chrldr; College; Nursing.

HOFFARTH, Mike J; Langdon HS; Langdon, ND; 11/167 ALBoysSt; HonRl; NHS; StuGov; Bsktbl; Ftbl; Tennis; Wrstlng; Coll; Vocational.

HOFFBAUER, Russell E; Aquinas HS; David City, NE; 6/88 Band; Chrs; MrchBnd; NatlThespSoc; LatCl; MthCl; SciCl; LetterFtbl; LetterGlf; IMSpt; U Of Ne; Physical Therapy.

HOFFBECK, Randall; Mora HS; Mora, MN; 3/137 NHS; NatlMeritCmnd; NatlThespSoc; StuCncl; Bsktbl; Ftbl; Wrstlng; IMSpt; MasAwd; Univ Of Minn; Environmental Engineering.

HOFFELT, Nancy E; Willard HS; Spring Field, MO; SecTrsJrCls; Chr; HonRl; NHS; SchPl; StuCncl; PpCl; Bsktbl; Trk; Chrldr; Business School; Secretary.

HOFFER, Heidi R; Taft HS; Chicago, IL; 65/790 Chrs; HonRl; NHS; SchMus; SctActv; SecYthFlsp; FrCl; SpnCl; PpCl; GAA; Northeastern Univ; Medicine.

HOFFER, Lani K; Warsaw HS; Warsaw, IN; Band; CncrtBnd; MrchBnd; NatlFornLg; PepBnd; Bus Sch; Pro.

HOFFER, Mark C; Argo Comm HS; Justice, IL; 56/511 ChrhWkr; HonRl; YthFlsp; YthLg; RptrYrbk; SptEdYrbk; RptrSchPpr; EdSchPpr; SptEdSchPpr; CaptSwmmng; Augustana Univ; Journalism.

HOFFERBER, David A; Lexington HS; Lexington, NE; 11/142 PresSophCls; HonRl; TchrAde; 4-H; LetterFtbl; LetterWrstlng; 4-HAwd; Central Nebr Tech College; Carpentry.

HOFFERBERT, Anthony D; Lyons Township HS; La Grange, IL; Chr; ChrhWkr; CmntyWkr; HonRl; NatlFornLg; YthFlsp; Ill Inst Of Tech; Mech Engineering.

HOFFMAN, Arlene J; Dubois HS; Jasper, IN; 11/81 Band; ChrhWkr; PresSophCls; HonRl; MrchBnd; PepBnd; SchPl; RptrSchPpr; 4-H; FHA; Col; Business.

HOFFMAN, Barbara L; Mss Acad; Atchison, KS; Band; Chrs; CncrtBnd; DrlTm; HonRl; MrchBnd; SchMus; Sdlty; 4-H; GAA; Kansas State Univ; Interior Dec.

HOFFMAN, Bethany J; Pontiac Central HS; Pontiac, MI; ChrhWkr; HonRl; StuCncl; TchrAde; Yrbk; RptrSchPpr; 4-H; Chrldr; PPFtbl; 4-HAwd; Central Michigan U; Biology.

HOFFMAN, Bob D; Chadwick HS; Chadwick, IL; Band; Chr; LbryAde; PepBnd; SchMus; SchPl; TchrAde; Yrbk; FTA; PpCl; University; Teacher.

HOFFMAN, Catherine A; Arthur Hill HS; Saginaw, MI; Chr; CmntyWkr; HonRl; Mdrgl; NHS; Orch; SchMus; Bsktbl; Swmmng; Tennis; College; Business.

HOFFMAN, Danny D; Centennial HS; Beaver Crossing, NE; Band; CncrtBnd; NHS; PepBnd; TreasFFA; LetterFtbl; Univ Of Nebraska; Agricultural Business.

HOFFMAN, David L; Leola Ind HS; Long Lake, SD; 3/50 PresSrCls; ALBoysSt; HonRl; SptEdSchPpr; CaptBsktbl; CaptFtbl; Trk; Sch Of Mines & Tech; Engineering.

HOFFMAN, Diane; New Hampton Comm HS; Ionia, IA; ChrhWkr; CmntyWkr; HonRl; SctActv; TchrAde; PpCl;.

HOFFMAN, Diane L; Horicon HS; Horicon, WI; PresFrshCls; ALAGirlsSt; ChrhWkr; NatlFornLg; NHS; Quill&Scroll; StuCncl; EdSchPpr; LetterTrk; Chrldr; Iowa State Univ; Food & Nutrition.

HOFFMAN, Donna S; Lebanon HS; Lebanon, MO; 82/232 ChrhWkr; OffAde; StuGov; TchrAde; 4-H; Bsbl; CaptBsktbl; Trk; DanFAwd; 4-HAwd;.

HOFFMAN, Duane; Seneca HS; Seneca, MO; Chr; HonRl; NHS; Trade School; Vocation.

HOFFMAN, Frank A; Andrean HS; Hobart, IN; 50/326 ChrhWkr; HonRl; NHS; SctActv; CaptFtbl; Socr; Trk; IMSpt; Depauw Univ; Medicine.

HOFFMAN, Gene R; Danube HS; Blomkest, MN; Band; Chr; Chrs; ChrhWkr; CmntyWkr; TchrAde; YthFlsp; SchPpr; 4-H; LetterFtbl; Trade Or Bus; Vocation.

HOFFMAN, Herbert J; Cass HS; Cassopolis, MI; 7/140 HonRl; NHS; MthCl; Glf; Univ Of Michigan; Math.

HOFFMAN, Janet M; Jasper HS; Jasper, IN; 85/287 Chrs; ChrhWkr; HonRl; OffAde; TchrAde; SchPpr; 4-H; Purdue Univ; Home Economics.

HOFFMAN, Jean L; Laona HS; Laona, WI; 1/36 SecSrCls; Band; Chrs; NatlMeritSchl; SchPl; StuCncl; RptrSchPpr; LetterBsktbl; BttyCrckrAwd; DARAwd; Carroll College; Biology.

HOFFMAN, John A; Saline HS; Saline, MI; 6/195 HonRl; NHS; TchrAde; Bsbl; CaptFtbl; U Of Mich; Architect.

HOFFMAN, John D; Morgan Park HS; Duluth, MN; 7/134 ALBoysSt; HonRl; NHS; StuCncl; CaptBsbl; CaptBsktbl; CaptFtbl; Trk; RotaryAwd; VFWAwd; Af Academy Prep School; Engineering.

HOFFMAN, Joyce A; Clearwater Public HS; Clearwater, NE; TrsFrshCls; VPJrCls; ALAGirlsSt; HonRl; SchPl; EdYrBk; PpCl; LetterTrk; CaptChrldr; College; Professional.

HOFFMAN, Judy A; Foley HS; Foley, MN; 5/135 Chrs; HonRl; NHS; SchPl; RptrYrbk; FHA; FNA; PpCl; PPFtbl; PresAwd; Hamline Univ; For Lang.

HOFFMAN, Julie; Worthington Senior HS; Wilmont, MN; ALAGirlsSt; ChrhWkr; JrNHS; LbryAde; 4-H; FHA; 4-HAwd; College; Math.

HOFFMAN, Kevin W; Little Wolf HS; Manawa, WI; VPSophCls; PresJrCls; ChrhWkr; StuCncl; StuGov; TchrAde; RptrSchPpr; LetterBsbl; LetterBsktbl; LetterFtbl; Coll; Teacher.

HOFFMAN, Laurie A; Marquette HS; Ottawa, IL; 2/96 HonRl; NHS; NatlMeritSF; NatlThespSoc; SchMus; SchPl; StuCncl; Yrbk; RptrSchPpr; EdSchPpr; 4-H; PpCl; Trk; GAA; Univ; Law.

HOFFMAN, Lew E; Clinton Comm HS; Clinton, IL; 5/154 Band; CncrtBnd; HonRl; MrchBnd; NHS; SpnCl; LetterBsbl; Ftbl; IMSpt; E Illinois Univ; Dentist.

HOFFMAN, Linda; Marian Catholic HS; Matteson, IL; ChrhWkr; HonRl; SchMus; College; Nurse.

HOFFMAN, Louis; Roger C Sullivan HS; Chicago, IL; PresFrshCls; NHS; College; Political Science.

HOFFMAN, Lynn M; Hill Murray HS; St Paul, MN; Chrs; DrmBgl; HonRl; NHS; SchMus; SctActv; SpnCl; PpCl; Bsktbl; Trk; College; Teaching.

HOFFMAN, Marcia R; Stuart HS; Stuart, NE; Band; Chrs; CmntyWkr; CncrtBnd; HonRl; MrchBnd; PepBnd; SchPl; RptrSchPpr; FrCl; Lincoln Sch Of Commerce; Secretary.

HOFFMAN, Mark; Claflin HS; Claflin, KS; 2/50 PresFrshCls; Chrs; HonRl; NHS; SchPl; StuCncl; RptrYrbk; RptrSchPpr; FFA; KeyCl; Bsktbl; Kansas State Univ.

HOFFMAN, Mark A; Claflin HS; Claflin, KS; 3/50 PresFrshCls; Chrs; HonRl; NHS; SchPl; StuCncl; RptrYrbk; RptrSchPpr; FFA; KeyCl; Bsktbl; College; Engineering.

HOFFMAN, Mark C; Wayne HS; Fort Wayne, IN; 30/324 HonRl; StuCncl; TchrAde; CaptBsktbl; CaptGlf; College.

HOFFMAN, Mark P; Seymour HS; Black Creek, WI; 7/190 HonRl; NHS; FFA; Ftbl; College; Mathematics.

HOFFMAN, Mark S; Drake Public HS; Drake, ND; 20/29 LetterBsbl; CaptBsktbl; LetterFtbl; Ndsu; Intl Trade Or Bus.

HOFFMAN, Mary Anne; Elmwood Park Community Hs; Elmwood Park, IL; 1/365 Aud/Vis; HonRl; HospAde; NatlMeritCmnd; SchMus; SchPl; RptrYrbk; RptrSchPpr; SchPpr; FrCl; Northwestern U; Medicine.

HOFFMAN, Mary Ellen; Carmel Hs For Girls; Mundelein, IL; 22 HonRl; NHS; NatlMeritCmnd; StuCncl; RptrYrbk; RptrSchPpr; GerCl; College;elementary Education.

HOFFMAN, Melissa A; Tri Jr Sr HS; Lewisville, IN; 12/85 TrsFrshCls; Band; CaptDrlTm; LbryAde; NHS; RptrYrbk; 4-H; FBLA; Chrldr; GAA; Business Schl; Accounting.

HOFFMAN, Michael G; Homewood Flossmoor HS; Chicago Heights, IL; CmntyWkr; HonRl; SctActv; College; Dentist.

HOFFMAN, Nancy L; Bradley Bourbonnais C HS; Bourbonnais, IL; CmntyWkr; HonRl; NHS; StuGov; YthFlsp; FBLA; 4-HAwd; PresAwd; CitAwd; VoiceDemAwd; University; Law Field.

HOFFMAN, Rebecca J; Churubusco HS; Columbia City, IN; 5/102 Chr; HonRl; NHS; Pres4-H; FHA; 4-HAwd; College; Nursing.

HOFFMAN, Rhonda D; Valentine HS; Valentine, NE; TrsJrCls; Chr; ChrhWkr; HonRl; StuCncl; YthFlsp; SchPpr; 4-H; IMSpt; College; Architecture.

HOFFMAN, Richard K; High School; Wagner, SD; ALBoysSt; Band; CncrtBnd; HonRl; MrchBnd; PepBnd; SchPl; SctActv; Bsktbl; LetterFtbl; College; Professional.

HOFFMAN, Ricky E; Eastern HS; Bloomington, IN; 4/68 Band; HonRl; PresNHS; Quill&Scroll; RptrYrbk; SpnCl; SciCl; LetterBsktbl; AmLegAwd; DanFAwd; Indiana U; Math.

HOFFMAN, Rita J; Van Buren HS; Brazil, IN; 11/65 Band; PepBnd; SchPl; TchrAde; YthFlsp; 4-H; FTA; SpnCl; PpCl; Chrldr; Purdue U; Pharmacy.

HOFFMAN, Roxanne C; Benton Central HS; Otterbein, IN; 92/260 HonRl; TreasStuCncl; PresYthFlsp; 4-H; PpCl; Glf; Purdue Univ; Business.

HOFFMAN, Sandra A; Leola HS; Leola, SD; 5/50 VPFrshCls; PresSophCls; ALAGirlsSt; Band; ChrhWkr; HonRl; StuCncl; SchPpr; FHA; DARAwd; Sd Uni; Nurse.

HOFFMAN, Sharon; Warren HS; Apple River, IL; 12/59 Band; CncrtBnd; HonRl; MrchBnd; OffAde; PepBnd; SchMus; SchPpr; Highland Community College; Elem Education.

HOFFMAN, Sharon A; Tripoli Comm HS; Frederika, IA; Chrs; HonRl; VPNHS; SchMus; SecStuCncl; Yrbk; Pres4-H; Trk; PPFtbl; 4-HAwd; Wartburg College; Pre Law.

HOFFMAN, Shelby R; Jasper HS; Jasper, IN; 17/286 Chrs; HonRl; LbryAde; NHS; SchPpr; 4-H; U Of Evansville; Nursing.

HOFFMAN, Thomas; Franklin Public HS; Franklin, MN; Band; Chr; PepBnd; SchPl; StuCncl; StuGov; RptrSchPpr; FFA; Bsbl; Bsktbl; Coll.

HOFFMAN, Timothy J; Pacific HS; Robertsville, MO; 1/200 ALBoysSt; ChrhWkr; HonRl; Univ Of Missouri; Medicine.

HOFFMAN, Valinda A; Reddick HS; Essex, IL; 5/43 TrsSophCls; SecJrCls; SecSrCls; Band; Chrs; ChrhWkr; HonRl; NHS; SchPl; StuCncl; Kankakee Comm College; Secretarial.

HOFFMAN, William P; Bedford HS; Temperance, MI; ChrhWkr; HonRl; PolWkr; FrCl; Bsbl; Ftbl; Swmmng; Trk; University; Liberal Arts.

HOFFMANN, Curtis H; Washington HS; St Paul, MN; 46/267 Band; JA; SctActv; StuCncl; North Western Elec Inst; Electronic Design.

HOFFMANN, Deborah; Ogorman HS; Sioux Falls, SD; /143 DrlTm; NHS; SchMus; StuCncl; StuGov; TchrAde; IMSpt; OptClAwd; Coll/univ;bus Maj/accounting.

HOFFMANN, Deborah A; O Gorman HS; Sioux Falls, SD; DrlTm; NHS; SchMus; StuCncl; StuGov; TchrAde; College; Business.

HOFFMANN, Dennis; Little Wolf HS; Manawa, WI; /95 LetterBsktbl; LetterFtbl; CaptTrk; Coll;pro.

HOFFMANN, Robert J; Milwaukee Lutheran HS; Brookfield, WI; Band; Chr; CncrtBnd; MrchBnd; PepBnd; SchMus; Swmmng; Concordia Clg; Music.

HOFFMANN, Steve S; Omalaska HS; Onalaska, WI; PresFrshCls; VPSophCls; ALBoysSt; Band; SptEdYrbk; SptEdSchPpr; Bsktbl; Ftbl; Tennis; IMSpt; College; Professional.

HOFFMANN, Tammy G; Webb City HS; Webb City, MO; 7/284 HstSophCls; LetterHonRl; JrNHS; NHS; StuCncl; FTA; PpCl; Swmmng; LetterTrk; Chrldr; PPFtbl; College; Recreation.

HOFFMASTER, John D; Lake Central HS; Crown Point, IN; HonRl; JrNHS; SciCl; Bsbl; Bsktbl; Tennis; AmLegAwd; College; Science.

HOFFMEYER, Jill A; Joliet West HS; Joliet, IL; 2/529 TrsSophCls; TrsJrCls; HonRl; PresNHS; StuCncl; Yrbk; Trk; AmLegAwd; DARAwd; KiwanAwd; U Of I; Biochemistry.

HOFFMEYER, Mark A; Joliet Catholic HS; Joliet, IL; 15/169 ChrhWkr; CmntyWkr; HonRl; JA; JrNHS; LbryAde; NHS; RptrSchPpr; GerCl; Univ Of Illinois; Accounting.

HOFFMEYER, Rodney A; Devils Lake Central HS; Devils Lake, ND; 5/143 HonRl; LetterFtbl; IMSpt; KiwanAwd; University; Chemistry.

HOFFNER, Brenda; A D Johnston HS; Bessemer, MI; 2/104 Band; DrmBgl; HonRl; SchPl; PpCl; Bsktbl; Trk; GAA; IMSpt; EldAwd; Coll; Biology Field.

HOFFNER, Cynthia; Dongola Unit Hs; Dongola, IL; 2/23 TrsFrshCls; TrsJrCls; PresChrhWkr; HonRl; SchPl; VPStuCncl; StuGov; FHA; SpnCl; BttyCrckrAwd; Bethel College; Sociology.

HOFHERR, John F; Marinette HS; Marinette, WI; ALBoysSt; HonRl; NHS; SchPpr; FrCl; Bsktbl; LetterFtbl; Trk; Uw Stevens Point; Chemical Engineer.

HOFLAND, Connie; Newburg Public HS; Maxbass, ND; Band; Chrs; CncrtBnd; HonRl; PepBnd; RedCrAde; EdSchPpr; 4-H; Chrldr; 4-HAwd;.

HOFLEN, James; Sargent Central HS; Rutland, ND; ALBoysSt; Band; ChrhWkr; CncrtBnd; HonRl; MrchBnd; Orch; PepBnd; SchMus; SchPl; Nd State Univ; Electrical Technician.

HOFMAN, Cheryl A; Holland Christian HS; Holland, MI; VPSophCls; Band; NHS; PepBnd; RptrYrbk; RptrSchPpr; SptEdSchPpr; GerCl; LetterTennis; IMSpt; Central Mi Univ; Phys Ed Teacher Trainer.

HOFMANN, Kenneth F; Medina Public HS; Medina, ND; 8/20 ALBoysSt; Band; Chr; Chrs; ChrhWkr; CncrtBnd; HonRl; MrchBnd; SchPl; YthFlsp; LetterBsktbl; CaptTrk; Nd State Univ; Agriculture.

HOFMANN, Steve C; Edwardsville HS; Edwardsville, IL; 1/450 NHS; LetterFtbl; LetterTrk; Clg; Math.

HOFMEISTER, Helen K; Claflin HS; Claflin, KS; 2/51 SecTrsFrshCls; Band; Chrs; HonRl; VPNHS; StuCncl; FHA; PpCl; Tennis; LionAwd; U Of Ksf.

HOFMEISTER, John R; Cathdral HS; New Ulm, MN; ALBoysSt; Aud/Vis; Band; HonRl; MrchBnd; NHS; PepBnd; SchPl; Yrbk; LetterFtbl; Coll; Bus Admin.

HOFMEISTER, Karen J; J D Darnall HS; Prophetstown, IL; 5/207 ChrhWkr; HonRl; NHS; YthFlsp; 4-H; GAA; Black Hawk Jr Col; Library Aide.

HOFREITER, Cora; Green Valley HS; Green Valley, IL; PresFrshCls; TrsJrCls; Chrs; ChrhWkr; DrlTm; SctActv; EdYrBk; EdSchPpr; 4-H;.

HOFSCHILD, Lynn R; Plymouth HS; Plymouth, WI; 12/234 VPAFS; Band; ChrhWkr; CncrtBnd; HonRl; MrchBnd; NatlFornLg; NHS; PepBnd; SchMus; Clge; Elem Ed.

HOFSESS, Diane M; Farmington HS; Farmington Hills, MI; VPSrCls; ChrhWkr; HonRl; SchMus; StuCncl; StuGov; FrCl; Swmmng; Chrldr; University Of Michigan; Business Admin.

HOFSTETTER, Frederick G; Moores Hill HS; Moores Hill, IN; 2/33 PresSophCls; PresJrCls; HonRl; NHS; SchPl; StuCncl; FFA; Bsbl; Bsktbl; Purdue Univ; Veterinarian.

HOFSTETTER, Kevin H; Pacific Senior HS; Gray Summit, MO; ALBoysSt; HonRl; StuCncl; TchrAde; CaptBsbl; Bsktbl; CaptFtbl; Trk; Wrstlng; CchngActv; IMSpt;.

HOFSTROM, Mary E; Southwest HS; Minneapolis, MN; Chr; ChrhWkr; DrlTm; HonRl; HospAde; Mdrgl; YthFlsp; RptrYrbk; FHA; Chrldr; Stout; Fashion Merch.

HOFT, Julie M; St Marys HS; Storm Lake, IA; 15/44 SecFrshCls; HonRl; TchrAde; RptrYrbk; RptrSchPpr; PpCl; Trk; Mount Mercy College; Marine Biology.

HOFTIEZER, Pamela; New Monroe Comm HS; Monroe, IA; 22/54 Chrs; HonRl; NatlThespSoc; SchMus; SchPl; RptrSchPpr; 4-H; FHA; PpCl; CchngActv; Jr Coll; Physical Education.

HOFTIEZER, Scott A; Libertyville HS; Lake Bluff, IL; HonRl; NatlFornLg; NHS; NatlMeritSF; SchPl; FDA; Univ; M D.

HOGAN, Anne; Jordan HS; Jordan, MN; 6/95 Chr; SchMus; SctActv; FHA; PpCl; Rochester Community Col; R Nurse.

HOGAN, Brian J; St Edmond HS; Fort Dodge, IA; 2/120 TrsJrCls; ALBoysSt; Band; CncrtBnd; HonRl; JA; MrchBnd; NatlFornLg; NHS; NatlMeritSF; PepBnd; SctActv; StuCncl; Bsktbl; Univ Of Notre Dame; Lawyer.

HOGAN, Cecilia M; Hillsboro HS; Hillsboro, MO; 4/169 HonRl; JrNHS; TreasNHS; SchPpr; MthCl; VPSciCl; Clge.

HOGAN, Colleen M; Marian HS; Birmingham, MI; 1/180 HonRl; IntrClCncl; ModUN; NHS; SchPl; SctActv; StuGov; RptrYrbk; University Of Michigan.

HOGAN, Constance J; Arthur HS; Arthur, IL; 4/48 HstSophCls; Band; HonRl; HospAde; JrNHS; PresStuCncl; VPFHA; FNA; PresFTA; LetterBsktbl; GAA; Nurses Training; Nursing.

HOGAN, Dan R; Abraham Lincoln HS; Council Bluffs, IA; Chr; Chrs; ChrhWkr; CmntyWkr; Mdrgl; SchMus; SctActv; YthFlsp; KeyCl; DARAwd; Minnesota Bible College; Ministry.

HOGAN, Donald A; Nauvoo Colusa HS; Nauvoo, IL; Band; MrchBnd; SctActv; TchrAde; Trk; LetterWrstlng; Col; Computer Operating.

HOGAN, Jeffrey D; Boylan Central Catholic HS; Rockford, IL; CmntyWkr; HonRl; Bsbl; Bsktbl; LetterFtbl; LetterTrk; IMSpt; PresAwd; College; Law.

HOGAN, Jennifer J; Hardin Central HS; Hardin, MO; Band; Chr; Chrs; ChrhWkr; CncrtBnd; HonRl; MrchBnd; PepBnd; StuCncl; YthFlsp; RptrYrbk; LetterBsktbl; AmLegAwd; OptClAwd; Univ Of Missouri.

HOGAN, John E; Rolling Meadows HS; Arlington Hts, IL; 90/600 HonRl; StuCncl; LetterBsktbl; Lake Forest College; Teacher.

HOGAN, Julie A; Gibraltar HS; Fish Creek, WI; VPJrCls; SchPl; StuCncl; TchrAde; SchPpr; 4-H; FHA; CchngActv; Univ; Urban Studies.

HOGAN, Kurt A; Pacific HS; Pacific, MO; Band; Chr; ChrhWkr; CmntyWkr; HonRl; Mdrgl; SchMus; StuCncl; YthFlsp; LetterBsbl; LetterBsktbl; LetterFtbl; LetterTrk; College; Teach.

HOGAN, Margaret R; Bradley Bourbonnais HS; Bradley, IL; HonRl; MrchBnd; SchPl; SpnCl; Eastern Illinois University; Art Teacher.

HOGAN, Mary E; Pacific HS; Villa Ridge, MO; VPChr; Chrs; HonRl; Mdrgl; NatlFornLg; NatlThespSoc; SchMus; SchPl; FrCl; Sw M St U; Psychology.

HOGAN, Michael K; Marine Military Acad; Independence, MO; 7/32 HonRl; ROTC; LetterFtbl; LetterTrk; VoiceDemAwd; Univ Ks; Accntg.

HOGAN, Pamela; Lincoln Senior HS; E St Louis, IL; 14/132 VPSrCls; CaptDrmMjrt; StuCncl; PresPpCl; Bishop College; Interior Decorating.

HOGAN, Robert; Wabeno HS; Lakewood, WI; 8/36 PresSophCls; HonRl; SchPl; StuGov; PpCl; Glf; AmLegAwd; Fox Valley Tech Inst; Automotive Tech.

HOGAN, Robert A; Schulte HS; Terre Haute, IN; 10/95 PresFrshCls; VPJrCls; ALBoysSt; HonRl; ModUN; StuCncl; RptrYrbk; SptEdSchPpr; KeyCl; Tennis; Medical School.

HOGAN, Stephanie A; Hardin Central HS; Hardin, MO; ALAGirlsSt; Band; Chr; Chrs; ChrhWkr; CmntyWkr; CncrtBnd; HonRl; JA; MrchBnd; PepBnd; Chrldr; AmLegAwd; Univ Of Mo; Cpa.

HOGAN, Sue E; Pinckney HS; Hamburg, MI; Band; CncrtBnd; HonRl; MrchBnd; PepBnd; TchrAde;.

HOGAN, Terry; Kinsley HS; Kinsley, KS; 19/75 CncrtBnd; HonRl; EdYrBk; FBLA; FHA; KeyCl; EngCl; Chrldr; AmLegAwd; Ks State Univ; Engineering.

HOGENSON, James G; Halstad HS; Halstad, MN; SecFrshCls; PresSophCls; TrsSrCls; Band; CncrtBnd; HonRl; StuGov; EdYrBk; EdSchPpr; 4-HAwd; Univ; Electronic Engr.

HOGER, Brenda K; New Salem HS; New Salem, ND; 1/35 PresSrCls; Band; Chrs; ChrhWkr; HonRl; SchMus; SchPl; EdYrBk; 4-H; FHA; Bsktbl; Trk; Chrldr; Univ Of North Dakota; Retail Merchandising.

HOGG, Barbara C; Chippewa Hills HS; Remus, MI; 9/149 CncrtBnd; MrchBnd; NHS; PepBnd; SecStuCncl; PresPpCl; LetterBsktbl; LetterWrstlng; Michigan State Univ; Animal Husbandry.

HOGGATT, Brenda K; West Vigo HS; W Terre Haute, IN; 19/192 SecSophCls; Band; Chr; ChrhWkr; CmntyWkr; CncrtBnd; DrlTm; HonRl; JA; MrchBnd; ModUN; Swmmng; Trk; GAA; Purdue Univ; Home Economics.

HOGGINS, George W; Milford HS; Milford, NE; SecFrshCls; VPSophCls; VPJrCls; Band; CncrtBnd; IntrClCncl; SchPl; StuCncl; YthFlsp; SptEdYrbk; SptEdSchPpr; 4-H; FBLA; Bsktbl; CaptFtbl; Kearney State College; Special Education.

HOGIE, Bradley S; Hendricks Public HS; Astoria, SD; Band; Chr; Chrs; HonRl; MrchBnd; PepBnd; SchPl; 4-H; PpCl; 4-HAwd; Col; Langugages.

HOGIE, Leanne E; Sleepy Eye Public HS; Sleepy Eye, MN; 4/74 AFS; Band; Chr; Chrs; CncrtBnd; HonRl; MrchBnd; NatlFornLg; NatlMeritSF; NatlThespSoc; PepBnd; LetterBsktbl; Glf; LetterTrk; Carleton College; Professional.

HOGLAN, Cheryl L; Independence HS; Independence, IA; 17/160 Band; Chrs; CncrtBnd; HonRl; MrchBnd; GAA; Iowa State University.

HOGLUND, Becky A; Cooperstown HS; Cooperstown, ND; HonRl; LbryAde; NHS; RptrYrbk; 4-H; FHA; PpCl; Bsktbl; IMSpt; 4-HAwd; Nd St Univ;.

HOGLUND, Marguerite C; Bishop Carroll HS; Wichita, KS; 1/250 Aud/Vis; Chr; HonRl; NatlThespSoc; OffAde; PolWkr; SchMus; SchPl; SpnCl; SciCl; Clge; Journalism.

HOGRABE, John R; Dows Community HS; Dows, IA; Band; Chrs; ChrhWkr; CncrtBnd; MrchBnd; PepBnd; SchPl; StuCncl; FFA; LetterFtbl;.

HOGT, Jeffrey; Senior High Ii; Quincy, IL; Band; Chr; ChrhWkr; CncrtBnd; VPMrchBnd; Orch; PepBnd; SchMus; SctActv; YthFlsp; University Of Illinois; Engineering.

HOGUE, Carol; Bayard Community HS; Bayard, IA; 4/30 PresSrCls; Band; Chrs; HonRl; NHS; Quill&Scroll; StuCncl; RptrYrbk; RptrSchPpr; College; Music Teaching.

HOGUE, Lyle R; Wilton HS; Wilton, ND; 4-H; LetterBsbl; CaptBsktbl; CaptFtbl; College; Vocation.

HOGUE, Mark K; Harlan Community HS; Harlan, IA; 18/259 AFS; Band; HonRl; NatlFornLg; NHS; NatlThespSoc; SchPl; StuCncl; Swmmng; LetterTennis; College; Computer Science.

HOGUE, Robert D; Mission Valley HS; Eskridge, KS; 10/58 ALBoysSt; Band; SecSrCls; ChrhWkr; DrmMjrt; HonRl; NHS; SchMus; SchPl; StuCncl; College; Business Admin.

HOGUE, William E; Enfield HS; Enfield, IL; ChrhWkr; TchrAde; RptrSchPpr; EdSchPpr; SchPpr; FFA; PpCl; Mc Kendree College; Law.

HOHENSTEIN, Deborah; Divernon HS; Divernon, IL; 4/23 SecTrsSophCls; HonRl; SchPl; Yrbk; SchPpr; FHA; SciCl; Trk; Chrldr; College; Child Care.

HOHL, Daniel J; Marquette Univ HS; Milwaukee, WI; 7/230 LitMag; NHS; NatlMeritCmnd; KeyCl; Marquette Univ; Accounting.

HOHL, David J; Reeds Spring HS; Reeds Spring, MO; HonRl; NatlThespSoc; SchPl; SchPpr; FFA; SciCl; CaptFtbl; LetterTrk; OptClAwd; CitAwd; Mo St Coll; Law Enf.

HOHL, Patricia A; Wentzville Riv HS; Wentzville, MO; CmntyWkr; SctActv; TchrAde;.

HOHL, Penny S; Griswold Comm HS; Griswold, IA; TrsSophCls; Band; Chr; Chrs; CncrtBnd; HonRl; Mdrgl; MrchBnd; PresYthFlsp; Chrldr; Morningside Coll; Elem Educ.

HOHL, Ruth A; St Mary Of Redford HS; Detroit, MI; 1/163 CmntyWkr; HonRl; JA; JrNHS; LitMag; TreasNHS; SchPl; StuCncl; RptrSchPpr; IMSpt; University Of Notre Dame; Engineer.

HOHLFELD, Mark R; Adams Central HS; Roseland, NE; VPFrshCls; VPSophCls; PresSrCls; ALBoysSt; Chr; CmntyWkr; Mdrgl; Yrbk; LetterWrstlng; 4-HAwd; U Of Ne; Vet.

HOHMAN, David F; T L Handy HS; Bay City, MI; HonRl; NHS; NatlMeritCmnd; SctActv; LetterFtbl; LetterTrk; IMSpt; Michigan Tech Univ; Electrical Engineering.

HOIDA, Robert; James Madison HS; Milwaukee, WI; HonRl; GerCl; Ftbl; College; Architecture.

HOIEN, Patricia S; Estherville Sr HS; Estherville, IA; Band; HonRl; NatlFornLg; SchMus; SchPl; Twrl; 4-H; FHA; Bsktbl; Iowa State Univ; Vet Medicine.

HOIFELTZ, Jay R; West Bend East HS; West Bend, WI; LbryAde; ChmnBsbl; Bsktbl; Ftbl; Glf; U Of Wis; Health Major.

HOING, Marie F; St Thomas Aquinas HS; Florissant, MO; CncrtBnd; HonRl; HospAde; NHS; NatlMeritCmnd; SchMus; PPFtbl; 4 Yr College; Nursing.

HOINS, Bruce A; Bellevue HS; Bellevue, NE; HonRl; JrNHS; NHS; Bsktbl; Ftbl; CchngActv; Univ Of Ne; Business.

HOINS, Patricia A; Guide Rock Public HS; Guide Rock, NE; 2/14 SecSophCls; ALAGirlsSt; Chrs; LbryAde; SchPl; TchrAde; 4-H; PpCl; CaptBsktbl; LetterTrk;.

HOISINGTON, Beverly A; East HS; Rockford, IL; 35/600 ChrhWkr; HonRl; NHS; Quill&Scroll; LetterSwmmng; KiwanAwd; Wheaton College; Science.

HOISINGTON, Lisa M; University HS; Warrensburg, MO; 1/44 TrsSophCls; VPJrCls; HonRl; NHS; NatlThespSoc; StuCncl; RptrYrbk; SchPpr; SecSpnCl; IMSpt; Missouri Univ; Biology.

HOISINGTON, Stephen P; Durand HS; Durand, MI; 26/214 Band; Chr; CncrtBnd; HonRl; MrchBnd; PepBnd; StuCncl; FrCl; Coll; Pro.

HOIT, Neal G; Red Cloud HS; Guide Rock, NE; Chrs; SchMus; SchPl; YthFlsp; 4-H; FFA; LetterBsktbl; LetterTrk; 4-HAwd; College; Rancher.

HOITINK, Terry J; Cedar Grove HS; Cedar Grove, WI; 8/82 PresFrshCls; TrsJrCls; Chrs; HonRl; Mdrgl; LetterEldAwd; LetterBsktbl; LetterFtbl; U Of Sheboyan; Accountant.

HOKANA, Jean E; Oakes Public HS; Oakes, ND; ALAGirlsSt; Chr; ChrhWkr; HonRl; PolWkr; 4-H; LetterBsktbl; LetterTrk; GAA; 4-HAwd; Univ Of Nd; Nursing.

HOKANSON, Stan; River Valley HS; Three Oaks, MI; HonRl; SctActv; TchrAde; Trk; IMSpt; Lake Superior State Coll; Biology.

HOKE, Cindy; Van Buren HS; Carbon, IN; Chr; Chrs; ChrhWkr; HonRl; SchMus; YthFlsp; 4-H; FHA; Bsbl;.

HOKENSON, Cheryl A; Wahpeton HS; Wahpeton, ND; ALAGirlsSt; Chr; LetterTrk; GAA; PPFtbl; College; Light Horse Management.

HOKSBERGEN, Michael G; Lynnville Sully Comm HS; Lynnville, IA; 20/57 Band; CncrtBnd; MrchBnd; PepBnd; SchMus; SchPl; YthFlsp; Iowa Central Comm College; Farm Supply.

HOL, Marlene A; Pella Christian HS; Cedar, IA; Chr; HonRl; LbryAde; PpCl; LetterTrk; IMSpt; Indian Hills Comm Col; Rn.

HOLADAY, Leann M; Anita HS; Anita, IA; 3/45 TrsSophCls; Band; Chrs; CncrtBnd; HonRl; MrchBnd; TreasNatlFornLg; PepBnd; Quill&Scroll; SchPl; Bsktbl; LetterTrk; LetterChrldr; Business School; Accounting.

HOLAHAN, Patricia S; Ripon HS; Ripon, WI; 35/185 SecJrCls; ChrhWkr; HonRl; RptrSchPpr; FHA; Trk; GAA; Uw Madison; Eng.

HOLAN, Danny J; Madison Public HS; Madison, MN; 2/86 Band; CncrtBnd; HonRl; MrchBnd; NHS; PepBnd; TchrAde; LetterBsbl; College; Accounting.

HOLANDA, Scott B; Anderson Senior HS; Anderson, IN; CAP; HonRl; OffAde; 4-H; Air Force Acad; Airline Pilot.

HOLBROOK, Diane L; Walkerville HS; Walkerville, MI; 1/26 VPSophCls; TrsSrCls; HonRl; LbryAde; Yrbk; SchPpr; LetterTrk; Chrldr; IMSpt; PresAwd; Muskegon Bus Clge; Accountant.

HOLCOMB, Brenda L; Springfield HS; Springfield, MI; 5/84 SecJrCls; SecSrCls; ALAGirlsSt; HonRl; NHS; LetterTennis; LetterTrk; Chrldr; PPFtbl; AmLegAwd; Judson College; Human Relations.

HOLCOMB, Brian J; Springfield HS; Springfield, MI; Band; CncrtBnd; HonRl; MrchBnd; NHS; PepBnd; SctActv; YthFlsp; LetterFtbl; LetterTennis; Wrstlng;.

HOLCOMB, John C; Mt Carmel HS; Mt Carmel, IL; Chrs; NHS; SchPl; LetterGlf; Wabash Valley College.

HOLCOMB, Miki L; Stevenson HS; Livonia, MI; Band; Chr; Chrl; CncrtBnd; MrchBnd; SchMus; StuCncl; CaptBsktbl; LetterTrk; Chrldr; Univ Of Mi; Music Therapy.

HOLCOMB, Robert A; North Muskegon HS; North Muskegon, MI; 24/89 HonRl; SchPl; PpCl; Bsbl; Bsktbl; Ftbl; Wrstlng; IMSpt; Col; Police Science.

HOLDA, Michael A; Reavis HS; Burbank, IL; 50/676 HonRl; JrNHS; NHS; SciCl; Ftbl; Univ Of Illinois; Electrical Engineer.

HOLDEN, Connie S; Caruthersville HS; Caruthersville, MO; Band; CncrtBnd; HonRl; MrchBnd; SctActv; Twrl; RptrSchPpr; SchPpr; PpCl; Trk; Business Schl; Professional.

HOLDEN, Dennis; Buena Vista Hs; Saginaw, MI; 8/230 HonRl; NHS; PolWkr; Quill&Scroll; EdSchPpr; GerCl; LetterGlf; Michigan State U; Journalism.

HOLDEN, James K; Peddie HS; Kansas City, KS; SecTrsFrshCls; HonRl; NatlMeritCmnd; NatlMeritSchl; Quill&Scroll; SchPl; StuCncl; StuGov; Yrbk; SchPpr; College; Law.

HOLDEN, Jeffery R; Lapeer Senior HS; Metamora, MI; 13/425 CtyCnl; HonRl; NHS; StuCncl; StuGov; FrCl; Tennis; IMSpt; KiwanAwd; RotaryAwd; U Of Mi; Physician.

HOLDEN, Julie M; Mercy HS; St Ann, MO; 8/193 HonRl; NHS; StuCncl; Coll; Professional.

HOLDEN, Mary; Liberty HS; Mountain View, MO; Band; CncrtBnd; HonRl; HospAde; MrchBnd; NHS; FHA; SpnCl; PpCl; Trk; Coll; Profession.

HOLDEN, Otis T; Mendel HS; Chicago, IL; 39/143 SecJrCls; VPSrCls; HonRl; StuCncl; SpnCl; MthCl; Bsbl; University; Professional.

HOLDEN, Patricia L; Northwestern HS; Iron River, WI; PresSrCls; ChrhWkr; HonRl; SchPl; SctActv; StuCncl; EdYrBk; RptrSchPpr; GAA; University; Mathematics.

HOLDEN, Paul C; John Marshall HS; Indianapolis, IN; HonRl; IntrClCncl; NHS; StuCncl; KeyCl; CaptFtbl; LetterTrk; LetterWrstlng; KiwanAwd; Purdue Univ; Veterinarian.

HOLDER, Larry W; North Posey HS; Wadesville, IN; 2/172 HonRl; JrNHS; NHS; SctActv; 4-H; PresPpCl; SciCl; Bsktbl; LetterFtbl; LetterTrk; U Of In; Veternarian.

HOLDER, Paula L; Trico HS; Cutler, IL; Band; Chr; ChrhWkr; CncrtBnd; HonRl; MrchBnd; SecYthFlsp; 4-H; FBLA; FHA;.

HOLDER, Renee A; North Central HS; Indianapolis, IN; Band; JA; NatlMeritSF; OffAde; SchMus; StuCncl; College; Psychology.

HOLDERFIELD, Timothy R; Marion Sr HS; Marion, IL; ChrhWkr; HonRl; TreasNHS; SpnCl; TreasSciCl; Illinois State University; Biology.

HOLDFORD, David A; New Trier East HS; Wilmette, IL; HonRl; PolWkr; YthFlsp; LetterSwmmng; College; Pharmacy.

HOLDING, Brenda R; Auburn Sr HS; Auburn, NE; 19/90 NHS; Quill&Scroll; LetterBsktbl; LetterTrk; Chrldr; PresGAA; IMSpt; Southeast Comm College; Dental Asst.

HOLDMAN, Mark C; Mercy HS; St Louis, MO; HonRl; NHS; RedCrAde; SchAde; SctActv; TchrAde; SchPpr; SciCl; Col; Medicine.

HOLDMEYER, Peggy M; St Francis Borgia HS; Washington, MO; 5/95 Chrl; HonRl; VPNHS; SchPl; RptrSchPpr; Lab Technology.

HOLDSWORTH, John E; Pontiac Catholic HS; Pontiac, MI; ChrhWkr; PolWkr; SchPl; Ferris State Clg; Auto Mechanic.

HOLDT, Cindy R; Kearney HS; Kearney, NE; OffAde; SchAde; TchrAde; FBLA; FHA; PpCl; LetterTrk; IMSpt; College.

HOLDWICK, Kathy A; Ubly Community HS; Ruth, MI; 2/113 HonRl; NatlFornLg; NHS; NatlMeritCmnd; NatlMeritSF; 4-H; BttyCrckrAwd; 4-HAwd; Ferris State College; Higher Accounting.

HOLE, Eric B; Creighton Prep HS; Omaha, NE; Band; CncrtBnd; MrchBnd; Orch; PepBnd; SchPl; Sdlty; University; Medicine.

HOLEMAN, Ann E; Centerville HS; Centerville, IA; TrsJrCls; SecSrCls; Band; Chrs; ChrhWkr; HonRl; NHS; SchPl; StuCncl; Univ Of N Iowa; Social Work.

HOLEMAN, Hilbert; King City HS; King City, MO; VPSophCls; VPJrCls; FFA; Col.

HOLEMAN, Jeff L; Frontier HS; Chalmers, IN; TrsSophCls; HonRl; FFA; PpCl; Bsbl; Ftbl; IMSpt; Business College; Public Accountant.

HOLEMAN, Robin D; Hanover Central HS; Cedar Lake, IN; HonRl; LetterBsktbl; LetterTrk; College; Elec Engineer.

HOLEN, Gina A; La Moure HS; La Moure, ND; 2/48 SecTrsJrCls; Chr; Chrs; HonRl; SecStuCncl; PpCl; CaptChrldr; Nd State Univ; Nursing.

HOLES, Sandra R; Fairbury HS; Fairbury, NE; Chr; Chrs; ChrhWkr; HonRl; SchMus; StuCncl; 4-H; PpCl; LetterTrk; IMSpt; Nursing; Rn.

HOLESHA, Carol A; Lourdes HS; Chicago, IL; HonRl; HospAde; NHS; SchMus; SchPl; FrCl; IMSpt; U Of Illinois; Teaching.

HOLESINGER, Kent B; Thomson Comm HS; Mt Carroll, IL; Band; Chr; Chrl; Chrs; CncrtBnd; HonRl; JrNHS; MrchBnd; NHS; PepBnd; SchMus; Knox College; Lawyer.

HOLETON, Rhonda R; Ogemaw Heights HS; West Branch, MI; Chr; Chrl; Chrs; ChrhWkr; CmntyWkr; Mdrgl; NatlFornLg; Orch; SchMus; Cedarville College; Music.

HOLFELTZ, Jed A; West Bend East HS; West Bend, WI; KeyCl; GerCl; CaptBsbl; CaptBsktbl; CaptFtbl; LetterGlf; College.

HOLIEN, Christopher; Maynard Public HS; Maynard, MN; 7/26 VPSophCls; PresJrCls; TrsSrCls; ALBoysSt; Band; NHS; SchPl; AmLegAwd; Southwest State College; Geology.

HOLLAN, William P; Northeast HS; Kansas City, MO; 5/370 HonRl; NHS; NatlMeritCmnd; Orch; SctActv; KeyCl; University Of Mo Kansas City.

HOLLAND, Bradley; Wisner Pilger HS; Wisner, NE; 3/74 Band; CncrtBnd; HonRl; MrchBnd; SchMus; YthFlsp; RptrYrbk; SpnCl; Wrstlng; DanFAwd; Co St; Law.

HOLLAND, Brenda K; Blue River HS; Springport, IN; Chr; Chrs; ChrhWkr; CmntyWkr; HonRl; Chrldr; DARAwd; Maranatha Baptist Bible; Missionary.

HOLLAND, Brian K; O Fallon Twnsp HS; O Fallon, IL; HonRl; NHS; SctActv; YthFlsp; SchPpr; LetterBsbl; LetterBsktbl; LetterFtbl; GodCntryAwd; College; Professional.

HOLLAND, Heidi A; Newton HS; Newton, IL; Aud/Vis; Chrs; HonRl; HospAde; LbryAde; Mdrgl; SchMus; CivCl; LatCl; Nursing School; Professional.

HOLLAND, James M; Warren HS; Warren, IL; 4/66 PresFrshCls; VPJrCls; HonRl; SctActv; 4-H; LetterBsbl; LetterBsktbl; Trk; 4-HAwd; College.

HOLLAND, Jolie; Buffalo Sr HS; Buffalo, MN; 65/225 Band; Chr; Chrs; ChrhWkr; HonRl; HospAde; Orch; YthFlsp; RptrSchPpr; 4-H; Gustavas Adolphus Coll.

HOLLAND, Kim; Archbishop O Hara HS; Raytown, MO; 28/179 HonRl; NHS; FshEdYrbk; PpCl; Chrldr; PPFtbl; University; Nursing.

HOLLAND, Kimberly A; Sycamore HS; Sycamore, IL; HonRl; TchrAde; 4-H; FHA; PpCl; Kishwaukee Jr College; Elem Education.

HOLLAND, Lane A; Norris City Omaha HS; Norris City, IL; ALBoysSt; HonRl; CaptIMSpt; Southeastern Illinois Clg; Physician.

HOLLAND, Larry J; Prairie HS; Cedar Rapids, IA; PresFrshCls; PresSophCls; HonRl; JrNHS; StuCncl; CaptFtbl; LetterTrk; College; Dentist.

HOLLAND, Lu Anne R; Oregon HS; Oregon, IL; 4/112 DrlTm; HonRl; NHS; TreasStuCncl; SecStuGov; EdYrBk; PresFrCl; TreasPpCl; Eastern Ill Univ; Computational Mathematics.

HOLLAND, Mary J; Earlham Comm HS; Earlham, IA; 1/45 HonRl; TreasFHA; Iowa St Univ; Architecture.

HOLLAND, Pamela N; Comstock Park HS; Comstock Park, MI; 9/147 SecJrCls; SecSrCls; HonRl; PolWkr; Yrbk; PpCl; Bsktbl; Trk; CchngActv; GAA; Michigan State; Goverment.

HOLLAND, Pat; Moores Hill HS; Moores Hill, IN; PresFrshCls; VPSrCls; ALBoysSt; Band; Chr; Chrs; CncrtBnd; HonRl; MrchBnd; NHS; PepBnd; SchAde; Trk; Purdue Univ; Vet.

HOLLAND, Paul E; Diamond HS; Joplin, MO; 16/68 PresSophCls; Band; HonRl; MrchBnd; SchPl; StuCncl; FFA; MthCl; LetterBsktbl; LetterTrk; Missouri Southern State Clg; Phys Therapist.

HOLLAND, Theresa L; Trenton HS; Trenton, MI; HonRl; NHS; TchrAde; PpCl; GAA; Ferris State Col; Respiratory Therapist.

HOLLANDER, Dennis C; Markesan HS; Markesan, WI; NHS; YthFlsp; 4-H; FFA; Bsbl; Bsktbl; Ftbl; Trk; LetterWrstlng; Univ Of Wisconsin; Agriculture.

HOLLANDER, John K; No Mahaska HS; New Sharon, IA; HonRl; NHS; Sec4-H; FFA; SecSciCl; LetterBsktbl; Indian Hills Comm College; Agri Business.

HOLLANDER, John K; North Mahaska HS; New Sharon, IA; HonRl; NHS; Pres4-H; FFA; SciCl; LetterBsktbl; Indian Hills Comm College; Agri Business.

HOLLANDER, Rhonda; Owensville Rt 2 HS; Rosebud, MO; ChrhWkr; CmntyWkr; HonRl; YthFlsp; LatCl; College; Professional.

HOLLANDER, Steve J; Duchesne HS; St Charles, MO; 56/136 CaptTennis; Clge; Architecture.

HOLLAR, Robert C; Yorkville HS; Yorkville, IL; NHS; SchPl; TchrAde; Glf; Tennis; College; Professional.

HOLLATZ, Cathy A; Ridgewood HS; Norridge, IL; 14/369 ChrhWkr; CmntyWkr; HonRl; HospAde; NHS; OffAde; Rosary College; English.

HOLLATZ, Joan; Leigh Community HS; Creston, NE; HonRl; Yrbk; GerCl; PpCl; PPFtbl; College.

HOLLE, Cindy L; New Salem HS; New Salem, ND; 6/51 Chr; Chrs; HonRl; SchAde; FHA; SciCl; Trk; College.

HOLLE, Lynn T; Marysville HS; Marysville, KS; Band; CncrtBnd; DrlTm; HonRl; MrchBnd; Bsktbl; College; Medicine.

HOLLEMAN, Peter J; Hancock HS; Hancock, MN; ChrhWkr; HonRl; SchPl; RptrSchPpr; LetterWrstlng; Trade School; Agri Business.

HOLLENBACH, Tim J; St Thomas Aquinas HS; Ballwin, MO; IMSpt; CitAwd; VoiceDemAwd; Univ Mo St Louis; Journalism.

HOLLENBECK, Joan E; Madison Sr HS; Madison, IL; 2/119 PresJrCls; TrsSrCls; ALAGirlsSt; Band; VPNHS; PresStuCncl; Yrbk; 4-H; PresLatCl; DARAwd; Univ Of Illinois.

HOLLER, Keitha; Northeast Sr HS; Kansas City, MO; 14/385 HonRl; NHS; NatlThespSoc; KeyCl; FrCl; Univ Of Mo; Accountant.

HOLLER, Kristi L; Northeast Sr HS; Kansas City, MO; 13/385 Chr; ChrhWkr; LbryAde; PresNHS; TchrAde; RptrYrbk; FrCl; College; Nursing.

HOLLERICH, Helen M; St Bede Academy; Peru, IL; HonRl; LbryAde; OffAde; TchrAde; RptrYrbk; RptrSchPpr; SpnCl; Rosary Coll; Bus.

HOLLERICH, Teresa L; Wellcome Memorial HS; Good Thunder, MN; 16/45 Chr; Chrs; OffAde; StuCncl; RptrYrbk; 4-H; 4-HAwd; Clge.

HOLLEY, Connie R; West HS; Rockford, IL; 37/335 Chrs; ChrhWkr; HonRl; College; English.

HOLLEY, Marna M; Holmen HS; Holmen, WI; 2/118 TrsSophCls; ALAGirlsSt; Chr; NHS; EdYrBk; SchPpr; VPFHA; PpCl; DARAwd; Univ Of Wis; Mass Communications.

HOLLEY, Mike A; Kirkwood HS; Huntleigh, MO; 29/700 ALBoysSt; HonRl; NatlMeritSF; TchrAde; RptrSchPpr; GerCl; PpCl; Bsktbl; Ftbl; Miami Univ.

HOLLICK, Maryann; St Benedict HS; Chicago, IL; 1/186 TrsFrshCls; Chrs; HonRl; NHS; NatlMeritSchl; SchPl; TchrAde; Yrbk; SpnCl; GAA; Northern Il Univ; Pro Pre Vet.

HOLLIDA, Martha; Greenville HS; Silva, MO; Band; HonRl; SchPl; RptrYrbk; RptrSchPpr; FHA; SpnCl; Chrldr; IMSpt; 4-HAwd; Univ; Journalism.

HOLLIDAY, Christi C; Anderson HS; Anderson, IN; HonRl; NatlThespSoc; Quill&Scroll; SchPl; SchPpr; 4-H; SpnCl; College; Physical Therapy.

HOLLIDAY, Karen Y; Holy Name Cathedral HS; Chicago, IL; ChrhWkr; HonRl; HospAde; Tennis; Univ; Major Study.

HOLLIDAY, William J; Zion Benton HS; Zion, IL; 4/431 ChrhWkr; LitMag; VPNHS; College; Professiona.

HOLLING, Sherrie L; Sweet Springs R 7 HS; Sweet Springs, MO; 2/42 TrsFrshCls; TrsSophCls; VPJrCls; ALAGirlsSt; HonRl; NHS; Yrbk; FHA; FTA; SciCl; Cmsu; Acctng.

HOLLINGER, Lynn G; Glen Ullin HS; Beach, ND; 4/40 SecSophCls; Band; HonRl; FHA; GerCl; PpCl; SciCl; SecBsktbl; Ftbl; Trk; Dickinson St Coll; Legal Secretary.

HOLLINGS, Jeffrey J; Lawrence Central HS; Indianapolis, IN; 22/700 Chr; Chrl; HonRl; Mdrgl; NHS; SchMus; SctActv; SciCl; LetterGlf; IMSpt; Purdue U; Eng.

HOLLINGSHEAD, Carolyn D; Princeton R 5 HS; Cainsville, MO; 2/48 CmntyWkr; HonRl; NHS; TchrAde; RptrYrbk; Yrbk; 4-H; SpnCl; LetterBsktbl; 4-HAwd; PresAwd; University; Art.

HOLLINGSHEAD, Daniel K; Salem HS; Salem, MO; ChrhWkr; CmntyWkr; HonRl; UNYO; 4-H; SpnCl; PpCl; SciCl; DanFAwd; 4-HAwd; U Of Miss; Science.

HOLLINGSWORTH, David D; Mediapolis Community HS; Mediapolis, IA; PresFrshCls; PresSophCls; ALBoysSt; StuCncl; PpCl; Ftbl; IMSpt; College; Vocation.

HOLLINGSWORTH, David M; Paris R Ii HS; Paris, MO; PresFrshCls; HstSophCls; ALBoysSt; HonRl; NHS; CaptBsktbl; Ftbl; Glf; Trk; Northeast Mo U; Bus Adm.

HOLLINGSWORTH, Kim A; Marion Adams HS; Sheridan, IN; 4/99 HonRl; JrNHS; StuCncl; TchrAde; 4-H; SpnCl; SciCl; Bsktbl; LetterGlf; 4-HAwd; College; Cpa.

HOLLINGSWORTH, Mary A; Princeton HS; Princeton, IL; 21/165 CncrtBnd; HonRl; NHS; PolWkr; SchMus; StuCncl; StuGov; TchrAde; FshEdYrbk; GAA; Illinois State University; Geology.

HOLLINGSWORTH, Michael H; Buhley HS; Hutchinson, KS; Chr; StuCncl; SpnCl; PpCl; LetterGlf; College; Medicine.

HOLLINGWORTH, Steven L; Elgin HS; Elgin, IL; 32/825 SecChr; HonRl; Mdrgl; LatCl; LetterBsbl; LetterBsktbl; RotaryAwd; University; Law.

HOLLINRAKE, Janice M; Albia Comm HS; Lovilia, IA; 16/165 SecFrshCls; Band; Chrs; HonRl; MrchBnd; StuCncl; Yrbk; Pres4-H; LetterBsktbl; GAA; Coll; Nursing.

HOLLIS, Nelwyn; Litchfield HS; Litchfield, IL; 5/137 Chrs; ChrhWkr; HonRl; JrNHS; NHS; SchMus; SchPl; FrCl; PpCl; SciCl; Illinois State Univ; Business Admin.

HOLLISTER, Jeri S; Portage Northern HS; Portage, MI; ChrhWkr; HonRl; NatlMeritSF; StuGov; LatCl; Univ Of Michigan; Law.

HOLLON, Donna E; Baraga Twp HS; Baraga, MI; CncrtBnd; HonRl; PepBnd; StuCncl; PresPpCl; IMSpt; College; Nursing.

HOLLON, Vickie L; Sullivan HS; Sullivan, IN; Chrs; HonRl; LbryAde; SchMus; SpnCl; MthCl; PpCl; I V Tech; Nurse.

HOLLOW, Karen D; Charlevoix HS; Charlevoix, MI; PresSrCls; ALAGirlsSt; HonRl; JA; NHS; ROTC; SchPl; StuCncl; PpCl; PresAwd; Univ; Rn.

HOLLOWAY, Donald D; Irwin HS; Defiance, IA; HonRl; StuCncl; Bsktbl; CaptFtbl; Trk; IMSpt; College.

HOLLOWAY, Nathaniel O; Cass Technical HS; Detroit, MI; HonRl; HospAde; NatlMeritCmnd; StuCncl; StuGov; Yrbk; FDA; Tennis; Trk; College; Doctor.

HOLLOWAY, Robert W; Sparta HS; Sparta, IL; 1/170 HonRl; NHS; NatlMeritSF; NatlThespSoc; PolWkr; SchMus; VPStuCncl; Ftbl; Trk; AmLegAwd; SARAwd; Univ Of Il; Medicine.

HOLLOWELL, Bryan C; Elgin HS; Elgin, IL; Aud/Vis; Band; ChrhWkr; CmntyWkr; CncrtBnd; MrchBnd; PepBnd; SchMus; Yrbk; SchPpr; Clge; Communications.

HOLLSTEIN, Kristen L; Rushville HS; Rushville, NE; Band; Chrs; HonRl; Mdrgl; SchMus; StuCncl; YthFlsp; FTA; PpCl; College; Elementary Education.

HOLM, Eileen M; Oregon Davis HS; Grovertown, IN; 9/63 PresJrCls; ALAGirlsSt; Band; NHS; NatlThespSoc; SchMus; SecStuCncl; EdYrBk; LatCl; PpCl; Ball State; Elem Educ.

HOLM, Nancy A; Oregon HS; Oregon, IL; 10/136 Band; VPChrhWkr; CncrtBnd; HonRl; MrchBnd; NHS; PepBnd; SchMus; SctActv; RptrSchPpr; FrCl; GAA; IMSpt; PPFtbl; University; Law Enforcement.

HOLM, Susan C; John F Kennedy HS; Babbitt, MN; TreasChr; HonRl; Mdrgl; NHS; SchMus; Yrbk; PpCl; Trk; LetterChrldr; GAA; Umd; Pharmacy.

HOLM, Theresa L; North Fayette HS; West Union, IA; HonRl; OffAde; PpCl; SciCl; CaptBsktbl; Swmmng; LetterTrk; CchngActv; 4-HAwd; JAAwd; PresAwd; RotaryAwd; Central College; Recreation.

HOLMAAS, Wanda L; Marshall County Central HS; Newfolden, MN; 4/39 Chr; ChrhWkr; HonRl; NHS; SchPl; YthFlsp; RptrSchPpr; FHA; GerCl; Trk; Bible School.

HOLMAN, Jeffrey N; Cass Tech HS; Detroit, MI; Band; Chr; CncrtBnd; HonRl; NHS; Orch; SchMus; Univ Of Mi; English Literature.

HOLMAN, Kari A; Fargo North HS; Fargo, ND; ChrhWkr; CncrtBnd; HonRl; NHS; PepBnd; StuCncl; FrCl; PpCl; CaptChrldr; Corcordia College.

HOLMAN, Kimber; Northeast Sr HS; Kansan City, MO; 4/380 ChrhWkr; HonRl; JrNHS; NHS; OffAde; StuCncl; RptrSchPpr; KeyCl; Bsktbl; IMSpt; Univ Of Mo Columbia; Dr Of Veterinary Med.

HOLMAN, Leah S; Danville HS; Danville, IL; 61/680 HonRl; HospAde; JA; OffAde; SchPl; SctActv; SchPpr; College; Medical Technologist.

HOLMAN, Liz A; Clio HS; Clio, MI; ChrhWkr; HonRl; NatlFornLg; OffAde; StuCncl; YthFlsp; Chrldr; Gmi; Cumputer Program Engineer.

HOLMBERG, Beth E; Batavia HS; Batavia, IL; ChrhWkr; HonRl; Orch; RedCrAde; SchPl; PpCl; Trk; GAA; IMSpt; AmLegAwd; North Park College.

HOLMBERG, Donald A; Stromsburg HS; Stromsburg, NE; VPSrCls; Band; CncrtBnd; HonRl; MrchBnd; NHS; PepBnd; LetterBsktbl; LetterFtbl; LetterTrk; Univ Of Ne; Lincoln; Accounting.

HOLMBERG, Mark J; Scotus Central Catholic HS; Columbus, NE; ChrhWkr; HonRl; NHS; TchrAde; SciCl; LetterGlf; IMSpt; EldAwd; JETSAwd; U Notre Dame; Architect.

HOLMEN, Shelly A; Powers Lake HS; Powers Lake, ND; TrsSrCls; HonRl; LbryAde; SchAde; SchPpr; Und Williston HS.

HOLMER, Bruce K; Wichita Heights HS; Wichita, KS; 8/450 HonRl; NHS; CaptSwmmng; Univ; Professional.

HOLMES, Barbara; Marian Heights Acad; Datoka, IN; PresFrshCls; TrsSophCls; PresJrCls; Chrs; HonRl; Orch; EdSchPpr; FrCl; Trk; Unif.

HOLMES, Brian J; Savannah Sr HS; St Joseph, MO; 4-H; FFA; Ftbl;.

HOLMES, Connie I; Battle Creek Central HS; Battle Creek, MI; Chrs; HonRl; LbryAde; OffAde; SchPl; TchrAde; FBLA; PpCl; Chrldr; Col; Secretariel.

HOLMES, Diane M; Rantoul Twp HS; Rantoul, IL; RptrSchPpr; SchPpr; Swmmng; College; Psyc Of Anthropology.

HOLMES, H Brennon; Brother Rice HS; Oak Lawn, IL; 54/416 HonRl; JrNHS; NHS; PolWkr; StuCncl; LetterSocr; LetterTrk; Loyola Univ; Physician.

HOLMES, James; Chester Hubbell HS; Chester, NE; 4/24 PresFrshCls; VPSrCls; Band; Chrs; HonRl; SchPl; SptEdYrbk; Bsbl; Bsktbl; Ftbl; College;.

HOLMES, Jean; Kewaskum HS; West Bend, WI; VPJrCls; VPSrCls; HonRl; StuGov; EdYrBk; Trk; GAA; DARAwd; KiwanAwd; PresAwd; U Of Wis, Wash Cnty; Rn.

HOLMES, Joan; Kewaskum HS; West Bend, WI; /176 TrsSophCls; TrsJrCls; TrsSrCls; HonRl; EdYrBk; FHA; Trk; GAA; DARAwd; KiwanAwd; PresAwd; University Of Wis; Rn.

HOLMES, John; Chester Hubbell HS; Chester, NE; PresFrshCls; VPJrCls; Band; HonRl; SchPl; SptEdYrbk; Bsbl; Bsktbl; Ftbl; Glf; College.

HOLMES, John M; Waukegan East HS; Waukegan, IL; 135/1004 DrlTm; HonRl; ROTC; StuCncl; PresLatCl; Bsbl; South Dakota State Univ; Pharmacist.

HOLMES, Karen M; Green Bay West HS; Green Bay, WI; 1/390 Chr; Chrl; Chrs; ChrhWkr; PolWkr; SchMus; TchrAde; FNA; FTA; FrCl; X Ray Technology.

HOLMES, Kenneth; North Greene HS; White Hall, IL; 4/120 Band; ChrhWkr; CncrtBnd; HonRl; MrchBnd; NHS; SchMus; SchPl; Bsktbl; AmLegAwd; Univ Of Illinois; Medical Doctor.

HOLMES, Kenneth R; Frankenmuth HS; Frankenmuth, MI; ALBoysSt; SchPl; VPStuCncl; TchrAde; LetterTrk; IMSpt; College Mich State; Veterinary Medicine.

HOLMES, Kevin D; Holy Name Seminary; Janesville, WI; 1/15 HonRl; NatlFornLg; NHS; NatlMeritSF; PresStuCncl; RptrYrbk; EdYrBk; Chrldr; IMSpt; OptClAwd; St Francis De Sales; Philosophy.

HOLMES, Kim B; Thornwood HS; Markham, IL; 103/852 JrNHS; PresNHS; NatlMeritSF; PolWkr; SchPl; StuCncl; StuGov; RptrSchPpr; EdSchPpr; AmLegAwd; VoiceDemAwd; Shimer Col; Attorney.

HOLMES, Lela; Paseo Hs; Kansas City, MO; 2/402 Chr; HonRl; SctActv; StuCncl; PpCl; College; Psychologist.

HOLMES, Michael R; Berkeley Sr HS; Berkeley, MO; VPFrshCls; Aud/Vis; CmntyWkr; HonRl; JA;

NHS; PolWkr; StuCncl; StuGov; RptrSchPpr; FrCl; LetterFtbl; LetterTrk; College; Lawyer.

HOLMES, Pamela S; Monroe HS; Monroe, WI; ALAGirlsSt; Chr; Chrl; HonRl; PresLbryAde; SchMus; SctActv; YthFlsp; RptrYrbk; Swmmng; State Univ; Business.

HOLMES, Paul B; Ogemaw Heights HS; West Branch, MI; StuCncl; SptEdSchPpr; Bsbl; CaptBsktbl; Ftbl; Glf; Central Michigan Univ; Recreational.

HOLMES, Peggy A; Miller HS; S Greenfield, MO; VPSophCls; HonRl; NHS; OffAde; StuCncl; PresFHA; FTA; SpnCl; MthCl; PpCl; SciCl; Univ; Teacher.

HOLMES, Rhonda M; Eastern HS; Springville, IN; 10/78 HonRl; LitMag; NHS; Quill&Scroll; TchrAde; RptrYrbk; SciCl; Bsktbl; Indiana University; Registered Nurse.

HOLMES, Robyn; Gieneseo HS; Cieneseo, KS; 4/19 HonRl; OffAde; SchPl; TchrAde; Bsktbl; Trk; BttyCrckrAwd; PresAwd; Nw Okla State Univ; Elementary Education.

HOLMES, Rodney W; Platteville HS; Platteville, WI; 7/200 Aud/Vis; HonRl; VPSctActv; FSA; MthCl; VPSciCl; LetterWrstlng; KiwanAwd; Univ Of Wisconsin; Computer Programming.

HOLMES, Sheryl L; Flint Central HS; Flint, MI; ChrhWkr; HonRl; TchrAde; Mi State U; Journalism.

HOLMES, Stephanie N; Peoria HS; Peoria, IL; 24/450 Chr; Chrs; ChrhWkr; HonRl; TreasJA; JrNHS; NHS; YthFlsp; RptrSchPpr; JAAwd; Ill State Univ; Teacher.

HOLMES, Terri S; Jennings County HS; Butlerville, IN; TreasNHS; Sec4-H; FNA; LetterGAA; 4-HAwd; JCAwd; CitAwd; Fort Wayne University; Paramedic.

HOLMES, Terry; Flint Northern HS; Flint, MI; GerCl; Univ Of Mi; Business Career.

HOLMGREN, Laura A; Manistee HS; Manistee, MI; ChrhWkr; HonRl; SchPl; StuCncl; Bsbl; Bsktbl; Trk; Chrldr; CchngActv; GAA; VoiceDemAwd; Coll; Ecology Or Science.

HOLMQUIST, Ann L; West Bend East HS; West Bend, WI; 1/320 Chr; HonRl; Mdrgl; NatlFornLg; NHS; SchMus; SchPl; StuGov; RptrYrbk; College; Medicine.

HOLMQUIST, Penny; Thomson Comm HS; Mt Carroll, IL; TrsFrshCls; SecJrCls; HonRl; TchrAde;.

HOLMQUIST, Richard A; Ladysmith HS; Ladysmith, WI; HonRl; LetterBsktbl; LetterGlf; Tech School; Electronics.

HOLMQUIST, Thomas C; Central HS; Saint Joseph, MO; Aud/Vis; ChrhWkr; CmntyWkr; JA; SchMus; SchPl; YthFlsp; YthLg; GerCl; College; Forestry.

HOLMSTROM, Martin L; Waukegan East HS; Waukegan, IL; Band; CncrtBnd; HonRl; JrNHS; MrchBnd; NHS; SchMus; Swmmng; Tennis; PresAwd; U Of Illinois; Journalism.

HOLMSTROM, Murry L; Waukegan HS; Waukegan, IL; 59/1004 CncrtBnd; HonRl; JrNHS; NHS; NatlThespSoc; SchMus; SchPl; YthFlsp; LetterSwmmng; College; Special Education.

HOLMSTROM, Susan G; Gladstone Area HS; Gladstone, MI; 15/171 ChrhWkr; CncrtBnd; HonRl; MrchBnd; NHS; OffAde; RptrYrbk; RptrSchPpr; FNA; FTA; Noc Comm College; Secretarial.

HOLOBAUGH, Susan; Lakeshore HS; Baroda, MI; Chr; HonRl; JA; LbryAde; TchrAde; YthFlsp; 4-H; SpnCl; 4-HAwd; JAAwd; College; Nursing.

HOLODAY, Marcia M; Fraser HS; Fraser, MI; 66/675 HonRl; HospAde; TreasNHS; FrCl; University; Rn.

HOLODNICK, Steven E; Lakers HS; Caseville, MI; ALBoysSt; HonRl; NHS; 4-H; GerCl; LetterFtbl; LetterTrk; 4-HAwd; CitAwd; VoiceDemAwd; University; Major Study.

HOLOUBECK, Edith A; Kearney HS; Kearney, NE; 13/232 HonRl; TchrAde; 4-H; FrCl; College; Teacher.

HOLOUBEK, Mark R; Clarkson HS; Clarkson, NE; HonRl; MrchBnd; NHS; PepBnd; Bsbl; LetterBsktbl; LetterFtbl; Trk; AmLegAwd; 4-HAwd; U Of Neb; Ag Engineer.

HOLOUBEK, Michael J; Plattsmouth HS; Plattsmouth, NE; 20/133 TrsJrCls; HonRl; NHS; StuCncl; 4-H; MthCl; LetterBsbl; LetterBsktbl; ChmnWrstlng; 4-HAwd; Us Naval Acad ; Math.

HOLOUBEK, Roland A; Clarkson HS; Clarkson, NE; TrsSophCls; PresJrCls; PresSrCls; Chr; ChrhWkr; HonRl; NHS; StuCncl; RptrYrbk; 4-H; U Of Nebraska; Ag Journalism.

HOLOVACH, Kevin D; Sublette HS; Sublette, KS; Band; Chr; Chrs; CncrtBnd; HonRl; MrchBnd; PepBnd; SchPl; TchrAde; SptEdSchPpr; 4-H; Bsbl; Bsktbl; University; Accounting.

HOLQUIST, Gary W; Marinette Cath Central HS; Marinette, WI; 15/90 Chrs; ChrhWkr; CmntyWkr; Quill&Scroll; SchAde; SctActv; TchrAde; Bsktbl; CchngActv; AmLegAwd; Milton Coll; Tchr.

HOLSAPPLE, Brad L; Newton HS; Jewett, IL; NHS; FFA; LetterBsbl; IMSpt; Univ; Agriculture.

HOLSCHBACH, Julie K; Roncalli HS; Manitowoc, WI; 25/141 AFS; Chrs; HonRl; JA; NHS; StuCncl; FrCl; MthCl; GAA; Sch Of Nursing; Rn.

HOLSCHEN, Patricia K; Laboure HS; St Louis, MO; Chrs; HonRl; SchMus; SchPl; StuCncl; IMSpt; College; Social Worker.

HOLSCHER, Kathy J; Noblesville HS; Noblesville, IN; 3/249 CncrtBnd; DrlTm; HonRl; MrchBnd; NHS; NatlThespSoc; FHA; FTA; SciCl; Butler U; Accounting.

HOLSCHER, Vicky L; Nemaha Valley HS; Cook, NE; 1/33 VPJrCls; Band; Chrs; NHS; VP4-H; GerCl; MthCl; Bsktbl; Chrldr; DanFAwd; College; Mathematics.

HOLSCHUH, Karen M; St Josephs Acad; Green Bay, WI; Chrs; SchMus; StuCncl; TchrAde; 4-H; SpnCl; Chrldr; College.

HOLSCHUH, Marianne; St Joseph Academy; Green Bay, WI; 7/156 VPFrshCls; Chr; Chrs; NHS; SchMus; StuCncl; Yrbk; Pres4-H; PresSpnCl; 4-HAwd; College.

HOLSCLAW, Jeanne M; Oneill HS; Oneill, NE; VPSophCls; Band; Chr; Chrs; ChrhWkr; CncrtBnd; HonRl; MrchBnd; OffAde; PepBnd; College; Professional.

HOLSING, Linda L; Ipswich Public HS; Loyalton, SD; 7/50 CncrtBnd; HonRl; NHS; SchMus; StuCncl; YthFlsp; RptrYrbk; FHA; LetterBsktbl; LetterTrk; Marion Coll; Nursng.

HOLSINGER, Coradella E; Glendale HS; Springfield, MO; ChrhWkr; CmntyWkr; HonRl; HospAde; NatlFornLg; Orch; PolWkr; SchMus; SecSctActv; TreasLatCl; PPFtbl; CitAwd; Evangel College; Education.

HOLSINGER, Terry D; Prairie Heights HS; Howe, IN; 12/103 Band; CncrtBnd; HonRl; MrchBnd; PepBnd; FFA; Bsbl; Bsktbl; Trk; Coll.

HOLST, Grant P; Southeastern HS; Augusta, IL; 2/50 ChrhWkr; HonRl; IntrClCncl; NHS; SchAde; SchMus; SchPl; StuCncl; TchrAde; 4-H; LetterBsktbl; LetterGlf; LetterTrk; Univ Of Illinois; Veterinarian.

HOLST, Gregg A; Warren Twp HS; Gurnee, IL; Band; HonRl; MrchBnd; Bsbl; Bsktbl; Ftbl; College.

HOLST, Gregory M; Culertson HS; Culbertson, NE; 5/26 TrsSophCls; TrsJrCls; CncrtBnd; HonRl; MrchBnd; NHS; PepBnd; SchMus; RptrYrbk; Bsktbl; Embry Riddle Aeron Univ; Aeronautical Sci.

HOLST, Valerie A; Murphysboro HS; Murphysboro, IL; Band; ChrhWkr; HonRl; NHS; StuCncl; Univ Of Missouri; Doctor.

HOLSTE, Craig A; Hays HS; Hays, KS; 25/188 ChrhWkr; CncrtBnd; HonRl; MrchBnd; YthFlsp; 4-H; PresSrCls; IMSpt; 4-HAwd; University; Biology.

HOLSTEEN, Stephen E; Ralston HS; Omaha, NE; Chr; CncrtBnd; HonRl; MrchBnd; NHS; NatlMeritSF; SchMus; SchPl; PresSctActv; Bsktbl; Coll; Lawyer.

HOLSTEGE, Lori J; Grand Rapids Christian HS; Grand Rapids, MI; ChrhWkr; CmntyWkr; HonRl; NHS; Orch; SchMus; IMSpt; College; Professional.

HOLSTEIN, Michael P; Rantoul Twp HS; Rantoul, IL; 9/389 HonRl; JrNHS; NatlMeritCmnd; StuCncl; Glf; Univ Of N Mex; Architecture.

HOLSTINE, Karen S; Fremont HS; Fremont, NE; VPSrCls; ChrhWkr; CmntyWkr; HonRl; NHS; StuCncl; StuGov; TchrAde; FTA; GerCl; MthCl; GAA; ChmbCommrsAwd; Col; Special Education.

HOLT, Anthony A; Elmwood Area HS; Elmwood, WI; SecJrCls; Aud/Vis; Chrl; HonRl; NHS; SchMus; StuCncl; StuGov; Bsktbl; Ftbl; Coll; Prof.

HOLT, Colette; Francis W Parker HS; Chicago, IL; VPFrshCls; VPSophCls; Chrs; LitMag; PolWkr; SchMus; StuCncl; StuGov; LatCl; College; Law.

HOLT, Dona J; Cobden HS; Alto Pass, IL; HonRl; Eastern Illinois University; Business Admin.

HOLT, Dorsey D; West Leyden HS; Northlake, IL; 5/432 HonRl; PresNHS; SecStuCncl; TchrAde; FrCl; SciCl; Loyola Univ; Nursing.

HOLT, Gregory; Jennings County HS; Butlerville, IN; ChrhWkr; CmntyWkr; Quill&Scroll; ROTC; SchAde; SctActv; StuGov; TchrAde; YthFlsp; FrCl; Ball State Univ.

HOLT, James B; University Court HS; Milwaukee, WI; HonRl; NatlMeritSF; YthLg; RptrSchPpr; College; Biology.

HOLT, Jeff T; Brookport HS; Brookport, IL; 1/34 ChrhWkr; HonRl; Yrbk; College; Professional.

HOLT, Patrice A; Lindblom Tech HS; Chicago, IL; 70/702 ChrhWkr; HonRl; Quill&Scroll; TchrAde; YthFlsp; RptrSchPpr; MthCl; SciCl; Bsktbl; Univ; Biological Science.

HOLT, Randolph; Cowan HS; Moncie, IN; ALBoysSt; HonRl; NHS; PolWkr; StuCncl; StuGov; GerCl; Trk; College; Engineering Degree.

HOLT, Rebecca A; Jasper HS; Jasper, MN; PresFrshCls; Band; HonRl; MrchBnd; NHS; StuCncl; Twrl; FHA; PpCl; CaptChrldr; Pipestone Mn Voc Sch; Secretary.

HOLT, Reggie W; Pendleton Heights HS; Fortville, IN; 137/299 LetterFtbl; LetterWrstlng; Trade School; Vocation.

HOLT, Stephen D; Haysville Campus HS; Haysville, KS; 1/260 HonRl; NHS; Orch; PolWkr; StuCncl; TreasFrCl; University; Law.

HOLT, Teresa D; Zalma HS; Zalma, MO; SecJrCls; Chr; ChrhWkr; CmntyWkr; HonRl; StuCncl; UNYO; CivCl; FHA; PpCl; IMSpt; JAAwd; Se Missouri Univ; Physical Therapy.

HOLTAN, Carole; Forest City Community Hs; Forest City, IA; Band; Chr; ChrhWkr; DrlTm; HonRl; SchMus; StuCncl; RptrSchPpr; 4-H; SpnCl; College; Musical.

HOLTE, Lorrie A; Powers Lake HS; Stanley, ND; Band; Chr; CncrtBnd; HonRl; MrchBnd; PepBnd; SchPl; Yrbk; SchPpr; Chrldr; Coll; Nurse.

HOLTER, Lesli T; Oslo HS; Oslo, MN; Aud/Vis; Chr; Chrs; ChrhWkr; HonRl; LbryAde; OffAde; SchPl; FHA; PpCl; Bemidji State College; Social Worker.

HOLTERMAN, Gerilyn M; Fatima HS; Loose Creek, MO; Chr; Chrs; ChrhWkr; CmntyWkr; HonRl; LbryAde; SchAde; TchrAde; SchPpr; FBLA; FHA; Bsbl; College; Secretarial.

HOLTGREW, Patricia A; Winside HS; Winside, NE; 1/28 TrsSrCls; Band; Chrs; CncrtBnd; MrchBnd; PepBnd; YthFlsp; Yrbk; 4-H; SpnCl; Trade Sch; Veterinary Tech.

HOLTHAUS, Darlene L; Meramec Valley HS; Gray Summit, MO; ChrhWkr; CncrtBnd; HonRl; MrchBnd; NatlFornLg; NHS; SchMus; YthFlsp; PresSciCl; OptClAwd; Coll; Nursing.

HOLTHAUS, Howard D; Band B HS; Baileyville, KS; PresFrshCls; TrsSrCls; HonRl; NatlMeritFnl; NatlMeritSchl; NatlMeritSF; SchPl; Sdlty; StuCncl; CaptFtbl; Ks Technical Institute; Computer Systems.

HOLTHAUS, John R; North Winneshiek HS; Decorah, IA; VPJrCls; CaptTrk; LetterWrstlng; Ryder Tech Ins; Mechanic.

HOLTHAUS, Ruth A; Central Community HS; Carlyle, IL; 9/129 SecFrshCls; HonRl; SchPl; FHA; SpnCl; College.

HOLTHE, Karen; Wash Community HS; Washington, IL; 2/425 JA; 4-H; GerCl; Univ; Lawyer.

HOLTHOUSE, Debra; Virden HS; Virden, IL; HonRl; NHS; SchAde; SchPpr; FHA; PPFtbl; College; Job.

HOLTKAMP, Holly L; North Decatur HS; Greensburg, IN; 3/100 VPJrCls; Band; ChrhWkr; CmntyWkr; CncrtBnd; HonRl; MrchBnd; NHS; PepBnd; Quill&Scroll; College; Accounting.

HOLTKAMP, Marlys J; Alcester Community HS; Alcester, SD; 3/38 SecSophCls; TrsSrCls; Chrs; HonRl; VPNHS; SchPl; RptrYrbk; RptrSchPpr; FHA; PpCl; Bus Schl; Vocation.

HOLTKAMP, Sandy K; Marquette Inc HS; West Point, IA; SecFrshCls; Chrs; LbryAde; StuCncl; PresStuCncl; PresFTA; PpCl; LetterTrk; Chrldr; 4-HAwd; Coll;nursing.

HOLTKAMP, Theresa; Marquette HS; Donnellson, IA; 9/50 Chrs; CmntyWkr; DrlTm; DrmMjrt; StuCncl; PpCl; IMSpt; Brier Cliff Sioux City; Social Worker.

HOLTMAN, Douglas A; Gull Lake HS; Augusta, MI; 4/230 Band; HonRl; NHS; PepBnd; 4-H; 4-HAwd; Mi State Univ; Chemistry.

HOLTMAN, Patricia A; Springfield HS; Springfield, IL; 37/585 Chr; ChrhWkr; StuCncl; St Louis College; Pharmicist.

HOLTMAN, Richard H; Limestone HS; Bartonville, IL; 28/396 HonRl; JA; NHS; SctActv; TchrAde; RptrYrbk; Bradley Univ; Mech Engineering.

HOLTMANN, Carol A; Mater Dei HS; Germantown, IL; 15/198 HonRl; OffAde; SchAde; FBLA; Junior College; Dental Hygienist.

HOLTMEIER, Michael G; Minneapolis Lutheran HS; St Louis Park, MN; 6/36 Band; Chr; HonRl; NHS; StuCncl; Bsbl; LetterBsktbl; Glf; Concordia College.

HOLTMEYER, Lynn M; Quincy Sr HS; Quincy, IL; AFS; ALBoysSt; ALAGirlsSt; ChrhWkr; CmntyWkr; HonRl; NHS; SctActv; Quincy College; Computer Programming.

HOLTON, Jeannette; St Joseph Senior HS; St Joseph, MI; NHS; NatlMeritFnl; NatlMeritSchl; NatlThespSoc; Quill&Scroll; SchPl; StuCncl; EdSchPpr; DanFAwd; DARAwd; Kalamazoo College; Law.

HOLTORF, Cynthia J; Buffalo Center HS; Britt, IA; SecTrsFrshCls; Chr; ChrhWkr; HonRl; StuCncl; YthFlsp; Yrbk; 4-H; FHA; PpCl; Bsktbl; Trk; PPFtbl;.

HOLTORP, Gary; Three Lakes HS; Clearwater Lake, WI; Band; CncrtBnd; HonRl; MrchBnd; PepBnd; College; Vocation.

HOLTSCLAW, Sherry K; Dixon HS; Dixon, MO; Chr; Chrs; DrlTm; HonRl; LbryAde; MrchBnd; SchMus; SchPl; StuCncl; TchrAde; Yrbk; FHA; College; Home Economics.

HOLTZ, Diane; Avoha Community HS; Avoca, IA; 8/46 TrsJrCls; Chrs; HonRl; MrchBnd; NHS; Quill&Scroll; SchMus; EdSchPpr; FNA; Bsbl; Bus School.

HOLTZ, Elizabeth A; Dundee Community HS; Carpentersville, IL; HonRl; NatlFornLg; NatlThespSoc; OffAde; SchPl; SctActv; RptrSchPpr; Ill State Univ; Political Science.

HOLTZ, Jeffrey A; West Central HS; Westgate, IA; Chr; Chrl; Chrs; HonRl; Mdrgl; SchMus; SchPl; StuCncl; FFA;.

HOLTZ, Keith M; Hutch Jr Sr HS; Hutchinson, MN; 25/198 Band; ChrhWkr; CncrtBnd; HonRl; MrchBnd; PepBnd; St Cloud State Clg; Accounting.

HOLTZ, Michael C; Auo Ha Comm HS; Auoca, IA; 3/48 Band; Chr; Chrs; ChrhWkr; CncrtBnd; DrmMjrt; HonRl; MrchBnd; NHS; NatlMeritCmnd; Bsktbl; Ftbl; Swmmng; Univ Of Iowa; Doctor.

HOLTZCLAW, Darrell F; Delta HS; Muncie, IN; 34/220 Band; CncrtBnd; HonRl; MrchBnd; SchMus; TchrAde; SpnCl; SciCl; LetterTrk; OptClAwd; Indiana Clg Of Mortuary Science; Mortician.

HOLTZEN, Barbara K; Deshler HS; Davenport, NE; VPSrCls; Chr; Chrs; OffAde; SchPl; StuCncl; 4-H; PpCl; Trk; PPFtbl; Bus Sch; Med Sec.

HOLUB, David W; River Valley HS; Three Oaks, MI; ALBoysSt; CncrtBnd; HonRl; MrchBnd; PepBnd; SchMus; GerCl; Bsktbl; IMSpt; Univ; Law.

HOLUB, Diane M; Beloit Memorial HS; Beloit, WI; Chr; Chrs; VP4-H; Band; ChrhWkr; NHS; SchMus; 4-HAwd; College Or Univ; Home Economics.

HOLUB, Rodney; Centre HS; Marion, KS; 2/39 Band; ChrhWkr; CncrtBnd; HonRl; MrchBnd; PepBnd; SchPl; Bsbl; Bsktbl; Glf; Ks St Univ; Wildlife Biology.

HOLUBEC, George B; T F North HS; Calumet City, IL; 6/500 HonRl; NHS; Purdue Univ; Engineering.

HOLVERSON, Christian A; Blackhawk HS; Gratiot, WI; VPSophCls; TrsSrCls; HonRl; NHS; StuCncl; 4-H; College; Professional.

HOLVEY, Renita A; Janesville Parker HS; Janesville, WI; 63/517 Chrs; HonRl; TchrAde; FFA; LatCl; Univ Of Madison; Agribusiness Ed.

HOLWEGER, Camilla J; Midway HS; Inkster, ND; PresJrCls; Band; Chrs; ChrhWkr; HonRl; SchMus; SchPl; StuCncl; TchrAde; EdYrBk; Trade School; Business.

HOLWERDA, Larry D; Danube HS; Blomkest, MN; ALBoysSt; StuCncl; Yrbk; SptEdSchPpr; FFA; LetterBsktbl; LetterFtbl; LetterTrk; AmLegAwd; PresAwd; Trade School; Professional.

HOLZ, Darrell V; Winona Sr HS; Winona, MN; 106/431 Chr; Chrl; Chrs; ChrhWkr; HonRl; Mdrgl; NHS; SchMus; SchPl; StuGov; Univ Of Wisconsin; Music.

HOLZ, David C; Toluca HS; Toluca, IL; 4/40 Band; Chrs; ChrhWkr; CncrtBnd; HonRl; MrchBnd; NHS; PepBnd; Yrbk; VPPpCl; LetterBsbl; LetterGlf; Ill St Univ; Business Management.

HOLZ, Kristi; E Greene Comm HS; Jefferson, IA; Chrs; HonRl; SchMus; SchPl; YthFlsp; Yrbk; 4-H; FFA; FHA; PpCl; Bsbl; LetterTrk; Chrldr; Iowa St Univ; Veterinarian.

HOLZ, Robert L; East Greene Comm HS; Rippey, IA; 2/46 HonRl; ModUN; NHS; SchMus; SchPl; StuCncl; 4-H; FFA; Bsktbl; CaptFtbl; Iowa State University; Business.

HOLZBACHER, Deena J; East Central HS; Lawrenceburg, IN; Band; ChrhWkr; HonRl; MrchBnd; SchPl; StuCncl; Twrl; Pres4-H; SpnCl; Chrldr; In Central U; Physical Therapy.

HOLZBERGER, Wilda C; Gordon HS; Gordon, NE; 8/67 ALAGirlsSt; Band; Chrs; CncrtBnd; HonRl; MrchBnd; PepBnd; PresFHA; BttyCrckrAwd; Chadron State College; Medicine.

HOLZEMER, Thomas C; Onamia HS; Onamia, MN; Band; Chr; CncrtBnd; HonRl; MrchBnd; PepBnd; StuCncl; LetterBsktbl; LetterGlf; LetterTrk; College; Computers.

HOLZINGER, Peggy L; Lancaster Sr HS; Lancaster, WI; 15/159 SecFrshCls; TrsSophCls; Band; Chrs; ChrhWkr; CncrtBnd; HonRl; HospAde; JrNHS; Mdrgl; CaptChrldr; IMSpt; 4-HAwd; St Lukes Meth Hosp; Nursing.

HOLZMAN, Bruno L; St Laurence HS; Chicago, IL; 19/372 ChrhWkr; HonRl; NatlMeritCmnd; University; Engineering.

HOLZNECHT, Kathleen; Craig Sr HS; Janesville, WI; 120/490 ChrhWkr; HonRl; SpnCl; College.

HOM, Gordon; Mather Hs; Chicago, IL; 24 CmntyWkr; HonRl; NHS; OffAde; Orch; PolWkr; SchAde; GerCl; CaptMthCl; SciCl; Northwestern U;biology.

HOMAN, Dennis J; Worthington HS; Worthington, MN; Band; ChrhWkr; PepBnd; SctActv; KeyCl; Bsbl; Bsktbl; Ftbl; LetterTennis; IMSpt; Col; Business Admn.

HOMAN, Kathe L; Wentzville Riv HS; Wentzville, MO; ALAGirlsSt; Band; CmntyWkr; CncrtBnd; NHS; StuCncl; SptEdSchPpr; Chrldr; AmLegAwd; PresAwd; Univ; Foreign Lang.

HOMANN, Nancy; Waverly Hs; Waverly, IL; 1/33 VPJrCls; PresNHS; NatlThespSoc; OffAde; SchPl; StuCncl; EdYrBk; Yrbk; VPFTA; SpnCl; Illinois College; English Major.

HOMANT, Cheryl; Warren Cons HS; Warren, MI; Chr; HonRl; OffAde; Swmmng; Chrldr; College; Specialized Secretary.

HOMB, Sandra J; Richland Center HS; Richland Center, WI; Band; Chr; ChrhWkr; HonRl; VPNHS; SchPl; StuCncl; FTA; VPFTA; AmLegAwd; Col; Law.

HOMBERG, Steven L; Westview HS; Kankakee, IL; 4/223 ALBoysSt; ChrhWkr; HonRl; JrNHS; NHS; SctActv; VPStuCncl; StuGov; FrCl; MthCl; PpCl; Bsktbl; Ftbl; Univ Of Ill; Business Admini.

HOMER, Daniel J; Kewanee HS; Kewanee, IL; 40/217 Band; CncrtBnd; MrchBnd; PepBnd; KeyCl; LatCl; Bsktbl; LetterFtbl; Western Il Univ; Medicine Field.

HOMER, Mark L; Brown City HS; Brown City, MI; PresFrshCls; Aud/Vis; ChrhWkr; HonRl; 4-H; 4-HAwd; Central Mich Univ; Pre Med.

HOMER, Matthew; Brown City HS; Brown City, MI; Band; ChrhWkr; HonRl; Yrbk; SchPpr; 4-H; 4-HAwd; Air Force Rotc; Nuclear Physicist.

HOMER, William E; Dexter HS; Dexter, MO; 3/139 DrmMjrt; HonRl; NHS; NatlThespSoc; StuCncl; EdSchPpr; FBLA; LetterFtbl; LetterTennis; AmLegAwd; College; Professional.

HOMES, Laurie S; Blair HS; Blair, NE; Band; Chr; CncrtBnd; HonRl; MrchBnd; NHS; VPNatlThespSoc; SchMus; SchPl; PpCl; Wayne State College.

HOMEYER, Teresa K; Wellsburg Comm HS; Wellsburg, IA; 1/33 SecTrsSophCls; TrsSrCls; ChrhWkr; PresNHS; RptrYrbk; Bsktbl; Trk; BttyCrckrAwd; GovHonPrgAwd; Hamilton Business Coll; Accountng.

HOMIC, Mary K; Roncalli HS; Omaha, NE; ALAGirlsSt; Chr; HonRl; NHS; SchPl; RptrSchPpr; GerCl; Tennis; Busi Coll; Sec.

HOMKES, Carol; Holland Chr HS; Holland, MI; 6/

361 ChrhWkr; HonRl; JrNHS; NHS; SchPl; Yrbk; RptrSchPpr; GerCl; Swmmng; College; Medicine.

HOML, Karmon K; Wauneta Public HS; Wauneta, NE; Band; ChrhWkr; CmntyWkr; HonRl; HospAde; RedCrAde; YthFlsp; 4-H; FHA; 4-HAwd; Trade School; Vocation.

HOMMES, Robert A; Lincoln Way HS; Manhattan, IL; 21/566 HonRl; NHS; OffAde; MthCl; Bsbl; ChmnFtbl; IMSpt; Univ; Professional.

HOMOKI, Albert A; Portage Northern HS; Portage, MI; HonRl; TchrAde; Ftbl; Trk; Wrstlng; Western Mi Univ; Paper Science Engineering.

HOMOLKA, Frances L; E Charles Mix #102 HS; Wagner, SD; Band; Chrs; DrlTm; HonRl; Mdrgl; RptrSchPpr; 4-H; SecFNA; PpCl; Chrldr; College; Secretarial Work.

HOMSEY, Terri A; Superior HS; Superior, WI; 8/540 SecJrCls; NHS; Orch; StuCncl; SchPpr; PresSpnCl; Bsktbl; Trk; SecGAA; PPFtbl; PresAwd; Univ Of Wisconsin; Medicine.

HOMSTAD, Laurel S; Lancaster Public HS; Lancaster, MN; ALAGirlsSt; Chr; Chrs; ChrhWkr; HonRl; SchAde; SchPl; StuCncl; TchrAde; RptrYrbk; SchPpr; FHA; College.

HON, Debbie D; Neodesha HS; Neodesha, KS; 2/60 Band; Chrs; HonRl; VPHospAde; StuCncl; CAP; SecFHA; MthCl; PpCl; ChmbCommrsAwd; Coll; Business.

HON, Jeanette L; North Platte HS; Camben Point, MO; Band; Chr; CncrtBnd; HonRl; JA; SchMus; FHA; SciCl; JAAwd; Missouri Western Univ; Music.

HON, Jerilyn S; Waterford Mott HS; Pontiac, MI; 4/410 Band; Chr; ChrhWkr; CncrtBnd; HonRl; MrchBnd; PepBnd; SchMus; StuGov; TchrAde; YthFlsp; Michigan State Univ; Elem Educ.

HONAKER, Lisa; Quincy Sr Hs Ii; Quincy, IL; 21/816 HonRl; JrNHS; NatlFornLg; NHS; NatlThespSoc; SchMus; SchPl; Bsktbl; Tennis; GAA; Indiana U; French.

HONAMAN, John M; St Charles HS; St Charles, MI; PresFrshCls; HonRl; TchrAde; Yrbk; SchPpr; CaptBsktbl; LetterGlf; IMSpt; VoiceDemAwd; Univ; Radio Television Communications.

HONAN, Marion K; West Nodaway R1 HS; Elmo, MO; VPFrshCls; VPSrCls; Band; Chr; CncrtBnd; HonRl; MrchBnd; NHS; SchPl; StuCncl; PpCl; Bsktbl; Trk;.

HONEGGER, Paul A; Forrest Strawn Wing HS; Forrest, IL; 5/60 SecTrsFrshCls; SecTrsSophCls; Chr; HonRl; StuCncl; YthFlsp; SchPpr;.

HONEK, Eddie F; Alvarado HS; Angus, MN; 9/23 HonRl; SchPl; TchrAde; FBLA; FDA; FFA; FSA; AmLegAwd; ChmbCommrsAwd; EldAwd; JCAwd; LionAwd; University; Business.

HONEYMAN, Diane L; Nemaha Valley HS; Seneca, KS; Chr; HonRl; HospAde; JrNHS; SpnCl; PpCl; Glf; Trk; GAA; TIMEAwd; College.

HONEYMAN, Diane M; Oak Lawn Comm HS; Oak Lawn, IL; ChrhWkr; HonRl; NatlFornLg; Quill&Scroll; SchPl; StuGov; TchrAde; YthLg; FshEdSchPpr; N Il Univ; Pre Law.

HONG, Jenny L; Coldwater HS; Coldwater, MI; ChrhWkr; CmntyWkr; LbryAde; PolWkr; StuGov; YthLg; RptrYrbk; 4-H; GAA; Michigan Tech Univ; Forestry.

HONG, Pamela K; Osseo Fairchild HS; Osseo, WI; ALAGirlsSt; ChrhWkr; CncrtBnd; HonRl; JrNHS; SchPl; RptrYrbk; LetterBsktbl; Chrldr; GAA; IMSpt; Univ Of Wisconsin; Medicine.

HONG, Robert; Luther South HS; Chicago, IL; 11/210 ChrhWkr; HonRl; NHS; College.

HONGERHOLT, Faye C; Peterson HS; Whalan, MN; TrsSophCls; CncrtBnd; HonRl; PepBnd; Twrl; Yrbk; RptrSchPpr; FFA; PpCl; College; Professional.

HONICAN, Tina L; Lansing HS; Lansing, KS; SecSophCls; Chrs; CmntyWkr; HonRl; FTA; PpCl; SciCl; College; Med Tech.

HONIG, John; Brentwood HS; Brentwood, MO; 2/130 SecTrsSophCls; VPJrCls; ALBoysSt; Band; CncrtBnd; HonRl; Bsbl; Bsktbl; Ftbl; Univ; Engin.

HONIG, Stephen R; Romeoville HS; Lockport, IL; HonRl; Ftbl; Tennis; IMSpt; Univ; Professional.

HONIOTES, James P; Joliet Twp West HS; Joliet, IL; 78/521 Chr; Chrl; HonRl; NatlThespSoc; SchMus; SchPl; StuCncl; StuGov; Ftbl; Wrstlng; Univ Of Ill; Optometrist.

HONISH, Maureen K; Wis Dells HS; Wis Dells, WI; 3/152 VPJrCls; PresBand; HonRl; NatlFornLg; NHS; NatlMeritSF; StuCncl; Bsktbl; Trk; PresGAA; Wi U.

HONKOMP, Dennis J; St Thomas Aquinas HS; Bridgeton, MO; 50/329 HonRl; NHS; VPLatCl; U Of Mo St Louis.

HONOLD, Carol; Cal Comm HS; Latimer, IA; 3/34 TrsFrshCls; Chrs; ChrhWkr; HonRl; NHS; EdSchPpr; FHA; BttyCrckrAwd; Ia St Univ.

HONOMICHL, Terri J; Avon HS; Wagner, SD; 20/39 Chrs; HonRl; HospAde; LbryAde; MrchBnd; FHA; FNA; PpCl; Coll; Nurse.

HONOUR, Bert W; High School; Wyandotte, MI; PresFrshCls; HonRl; RptrSchPpr; SptEdSchPpr; Bsbl; Bsktbl; CaptFtbl; Trk; CchngActv; College.

HONZLIK, Frank A; Niobrara Public HS; Verdel, NE; Aud/Vis; Band; Chr; CncrtBnd; MrchBnd; PepBnd; Yrbk; 4-H; Ftbl; Wrstlng; Trade Sch; Voc.

HOOBLER, Vernon J; Washburn Rural HS; Topeka, KS; ALBoysSt; Band; Chr; ChrhWkr; CncrtBnd; HonRl; JA; MrchBnd; PepBnd; 4-H; Trk; Kansas State University; Minister.

HOOD, David W; Gibson City HS; Gibson City, IL; 9/98 PresAFS; Band; CncrtBnd; MrchBnd; NHS; SctActv; StuCncl; PresYthFlsp; PpCl; GodCntryAwd; Univ Of Ill; Business.

HOOD, Dennis G; North Platte HS; North Platte, NE; College; Business Admin.

HOOD, Georgea L; Wood River Rural HS; Wood River, NE; 3/56 ChrhWkr; HonRl; Nebraska Wesleyan Univ; Psychology.

HOOD, Heather; Springfield Hs; Springfield, IL; 9/585 PresChr; Chrl; Chrs; ChrhWkr; NHS; YthFlsp; FrCl; Judson College; Music.

HOOD, Jamie D; Randolph Southern HS; Lynn, IN; 6/50 Band; Chrs; ChrhWkr; HonRl; MrchBnd; SchMus; Yrbk; 4-H; PpCl; 4-HAwd; Coll; Art.

HOOD, Julia E; Meadville R 4 HS; Meadville, MO; SecSophCls; Chrs; ChrhWkr; CncrtBnd; NHS; StuCncl; Yrbk; SchPpr; PresFHA; Chrldr; Northeast Mo U; Child Devel.

HOOD, Laura M; Neponset HS; Buda, IL; VPSrCls; Band; Chr; ChrhWkr; HonRl; SchPl; StuCncl; Yrbk; FHA; Chrldr; Ia St Univ; Home Ec.

HOOD, Peggy; Cabool HS; Cabool, MO; 1/72 SecTrsSophCls; VPJrCls; SchPl; Yrbk; RptrSchPpr; Univ Of Mo; Recreation Park Administration.

HOOD, Peter; West HS; Iowa City, IA; Band; Chrs; CncrtBnd; Orch; Luther College; Marine Biology.

HOOD, Susan J; Lohrville Comm HS; Lohrville, IA; 3/29 HonRl; LbryAde; TchrAde; Yrbk; GerCl; PpCl; LetterGlf; LetterTrk; Jennie Edmundson Schl Nursing; Nurse.

HOOD, Teresa I; Estherville HS; Estherville, IA; 39/186 Chrs; DrlTm; HonRl; SchPl; SpnCl; Bsktbl; Trk; CchngActv; College; Professional.

HOODLEBRINK, Lori A; Centerville HS; Centerville, IN; 7/156 VPJrCls; ChrhWkr; HonRl; JrNHS; NHS; OffAde; SchPl; StuCncl; StuGov; YthLg; Tech Sch; X Ray Tech.

HOOGENHOUS, Diane; Holmen HS; Holmen, WI; 4/98 Band; Chr; Chrs; HonRl; MrchBnd; NHS; PepBnd; FHA; PpCl; Tech Sch; Data Proc.

HOOGESTRAAT, Fran M; Lennox HS; Chancellor, SD; Chr; Chrl; HonRl; OffAde; StuCncl; VPStuGov; FHA; Trk; IMSpt; DARAwd; College; Biotechnology.

HOOGESTRAAT, Patty F; Lennox HS; Lennox, SD; 5/117 SecFrshCls; PresSophCls; Band; Chrs; HonRl; SecStuCncl; RptrYrbk; FHA, Chrldr; AmLegAwd; University; Med Technician.

HOOGEVEEN, Dean A; West Lyon Comm HS; Lester, IA; ChrhWkr; CmntyWkr; HonRl; TchrAde; YthFlsp; Bsbl; Bsktbl; Ftbl; Glf; Trk; Northwestern College; Physical Educ.

HOOGSTRATEN, Shelley; Otsego HS; Kalamazoo, MI; 15/225 Band; ChrhWkr; CncrtBnd; HonRl; MrchBnd; 4-H; LatCl; Trk; Michigan State Univ; Animal Technology.

HOOK, Carl C; Carlinville Community HS; Carlinville, IL; 1/161 Aud/Vis; HonRl; IntrClCncl; JrNHS; LbryAde; PresNHS; SchPl; RptrYrbk; Yrbk; 4-H; SpnCl; PpCl; 4-HAwd; SARAwd; Knox College.

HOOK, Debra; Stafford HS; Stafford, KS; Band; Chr; ChrhWkr; DrlTm; HonRl; NatlThespSoc; PepBnd; SchPl; YthFlsp; Bsktbl; Trade School.

HOOK, Debra E; Northeast R Iv HS; Cairo, MO; 2/24 ChrhWkr; HonRl; VPNHS; SchPl; SecStuCncl; EdYrBk; RptrSchPpr; DanFAwd; LionAwd; Ne Missouri St Univ; Communications.

HOOK, Dennis L; Effingham HS; Effingham, IL; 46/230 HonRl; JA; KeyCl; LatCl; LetterTrk; JAAwd; College; Professional Optometry.

HOOK, Donn R; Stockton HS; Stockton, IL; 2/86 AFS; Band; ChrhWkr; NHS; SchPl; RptrSchPpr; 4-H; FTA; FrCl; Drake Univ; Theatre.

HOOK, Jeffery D; Hardin Central HS; Hardin, MO; VPJrCls; Band; Chrs; ChrhWkr; HonRl; Pres4-H; VPFFA; Bsktbl; CaptFtbl; AmLegAwd; Mo U; Civil Engineering.

HOOK, Milton E; Newark Comm HS; Newark, IL; HonRl; FFA; LetterBsbl; IMSpt; University; Agricultural Mech.

HOOK, Rick D; Wayne Comm HS; Allerton, IA; HonRl; LetterBsktbl; LetterFtbl; LetterTrade; Farmer.

HOOK, Robert E; Hardin Central HS; Hardin, MO; ALBoysSt; Band; Chrs; ChrhWkr; HonRl; SctActv; LetterBsktbl; LetterFtbl; LetterTrk; AmLegAwd; Midwest Tech Inst.

HOOKER, Brenda J; Sand Creek HS; Adrian, MI; Band; Chr; ChrhWkr; HonRl; HospAde; SchMus; YthFlsp; 4-H; FHA; College; Nursing.

HOOKER, Ellen; St Joseph Acad; Green Bay, WI; 4/150 NHS; LatCl; SpnCl; MthCl; Premed School; Veterinary Science.

HOOKER, Jeffrey; West Ottawa HS; Holland, MI; 5/271 HonRl; NHS; Univ.

HOOKER, Larry E; Spalding Public HS; Primrose, NE; 1/7 PresFrshCls; PresJrCls; HonRl; NHS; SchPl; StuCncl; StuGov; LetterBsktbl; LetterFtbl; IMSpt; Univ Of Nebraska; Law.

HOOKER, Terri; Pinckney HS; Howell, MI; 13/188 ChrhWkr; CmntyWkr; HospAde; JA; NHS; RedCrAde; StuGov; YthFlsp; YthFnd; CivCl; Eastern Mi Univ; Hs Math Teacher.

HOOKS, Melissa A; Lyons Public HS; Lyons, NE; VPBand; Chr; Chrs; DrmMjrt; HonRl; NHS; 4-H; FBLA; GerCl; PpCl; Swmmng; LetterTrk; Chrldr; Bus School.

HOOKSTADT, Stephen M; Harvard HS; Harvard, IL; HonRl; GerCl; LetterFtbl; IMSpt; Coll; Bus.

HOOLEY, Beverly A; Westview HS; Shipshewana, IN; Chrs; HonRl; HospAde; NHS; SchPl; TreasYthFlsp; Sec4-H; PresFNA; FTA; 4-HAwd; College; Psychology.

HOOLEY, Charles M; Stillwater Sr HS; Stillwater, MN; Aud/Vis; Band; College; Psychology.

HOOLSEMA, Sharon; Rudyard Area HS; Rudyard, MI; ChrhWkr; CmntyWkr; HonRl; StuCncl; Yrbk; 4-H; GAA; 4-HAwd; VFWAwd; VoiceDemAwd; College; Not Certain.

HOOPER, Kathy L; North HS; Omaha, NE; 15/432 Band; CncrtBnd; HonRl; LbryAde; MrchBnd; NHS; Orch; PepBnd; TchrAde; Twrl; Mo Inst Of Tech; Physical Oceanographer.

HOOPER, Pamela R; River Valley HS; Three Oaks, MI; HonRl; OffAde; 4-H; College; Stewardess.

HOOPER, Vanessa; Rushville HS; Rushville, NE; 8/43 SecSophCls; Chrs; HonRl; SctActv; StuCncl; StuGov; FHA; PpCl; IMSpt; MasAwd; Bus School; Vocation.

HOOPINGARNER, Michael R; Bellmont HS; Decatur, IN; 4/251 VPFrshCls; VPSophCls; PresJrCls; ALBoysSt; ChrhWkr; HonRl; NHS; YthFlsp; LetterBsbl; LetterBsktbl; LetterFtbl; RotaryAwd; Univ Of Arizona; Architecture.

HOOPMAN, Nancy L; Des Lacs HS; Burlington, ND; Chrs; HonRl; SchPl; TreasYthFlsp; RptrYrbk; RptrSchPpr; PpCl; SciCl; CitAwd; Minot St Coll; Medica Field.

HOOS, Christine K; Lakeview HS; Battle Creek, MI; 15/432 ChrhWkr; CncrtBnd; HonRl; MrchBnd; NHS; Orch; SchMus; SctActv; Spring Arbor College; Psychology.

HOOTMAN, Craig J; Davis Co Comm HS; Floris, IA; HonRl; SchPl; FFA; LetterFtbl; LetterWrstlng; Agriculture School; Farming.

HOOVEN, Sharon L; Pinckney HS; Pinckney, MI; HonRl; Univ; Lawyer.

HOOVER, Barbara M; Aurora Central HS; Aurora, IL; Chrs; HonRl; OffAde;.

HOOVER, Bridget A; Falls City HS; Falls City, NE; 17/87 Peru St College; Social Work.

HOOVER, Charles K; South Decatur HS; Veedersburg, IN; 25/99 Chr; ChrhWkr; HonRl; MrchBnd; PepBnd; TchrAde; YthFlsp; Bsktbl; Glf; Wrstlng; Indiana Central Univ; Math Teacher.

HOOVER, Jeana R; Kingsville R 1 HS; Kingsville, MO; Chrs; ChrhWkr; HonRl; JrNHS; NHS; 4-H; SciCl; Bsbl; 4-HAwd; Univ; Professional.

HOOVER, Yvonne L; Paxton HS; Paxton, IL; VPSophCls; AFS; Band; HonRl; NHS; SchPl; TreasStuCncl; EdSchPpr; LatCl; SciCl; Bsktbl; IMSpt; Univ Of Il; Journalism.

HOP, Bruce; Maurice Orange City HS; Orange City, IA; Chr; Chrs; HonRl; SchMus; Bsbl; Ftbl; IMSpt;.

HOP, Rodney J; Maurice Orange City HS; Orange City, IA; PresSophCls; Band; Chr; HonRl; NHS; StuCncl; PresYthFlsp; LetterBsktbl; LetterFtbl; College; Professional.

HOPE, Mary J; Lanse Creuse HS; Mt Clement, MI; 26/567 Chr; Chrs; CmntyWkr; HonRl; JrNHS; Mdrgl; NHS; SchMus; IMSpt; CitAwd; Judson Col; Social Work.

HOPE, Sharon L; Immaculata HS; Leavenworth, KS; ALAGirlsSt; ChrhWkr; HonRl; SchPpr; LetterBsktbl; IMSpt; U; Professional.

HOPE, Vicki L; Albia Community HS; Albia, IA; Band; DrlTm; HonRl; NHS; NatlMeritSchl; StuCncl; StuGov; RptrSchPpr; Chrldr; CitAwd;.

HOPEN, Edward P; Walker Public HS; Walker, MN; HonRl; LbryAde; SchAde; TchrAde; Yrbk; Bsktbl; LetterTrk; College; Professional Teacher.

HOPFENSPERGER, Jay; Midland HS; Midland, MI; HonRl; NatlMeritCmnd; Bsktbl; Delta College; Computer Science.

HOPFNER, Danielle M; St Xaviers HS; Junction City, KS; 4/36 CmntyWkr; HonRl; HospAde; TreasStuCncl; TchrAde; EdYrBk; PresFHA; FrCl; PpCl; GAA; Jr College; Animal Tech.

HOPKEN, Karen A; Geneva HS; Geneva, NE; Band; Chrs; VPChrhWkr; CmntyWkr; HonRl; RptrSchPpr; 4-H; FBLA; FHA; PpCl; U Of Ne; Lawyer.

HOPKINS, Christine A; Cumberland HS; Cumberland, WI; 7/127 TrsFrshCls; CncrtBnd; HonRl; SctActv; StuCncl; 4-H; PpCl; Chrldr; GAA; IMSpt;.

HOPKINS, Gregory C; Warsaw HS; Warsaw, IN; 30/450 Band; CncrtBnd; HonRl; MrchBnd; SchPpr; Purdue Univ; Drafting.

HOPKINS, James; Clarkston HS; Waterford, MI; 144/450 Band; LbryAde; MrchBnd; NatlMeritCmnd; TchrAde; Mich State Univ;biochemistry Oceanography.

HOPKINS, Mark D; Gladstone HS; Gladstone, MI; 7/177 VPSophCls; CncrtBnd; HonRl; NHS; NatlMeritSchl; SchPl; StuCncl; RptrYrbk; LetterFtbl; Trk; Michigan Tech; Business Ad.

HOPKINS, Rebecca J; Fredericktown HS; Fredericktown, MO; Chrs; HonRl; NHS; StuCncl; SpnCl; PpCl; Trk; Chrldr; MasAwd; PresAwd; Southeast Mo Clge; Dental Hygienist.

HOPKINS, Richard S; Delavan HS; Delavan, IL; 26/54 Band; Chr; ChrhWkr; CncrtBnd; MrchBnd; SchMus; SchPl; CivCl; 4-H; Wrstlng; Clge; Agriculture.

HOPKINS, Sharon K; La Monte R 4 HS; La Monte, MO; 5/25 HonRl; RptrYrbk; RptrSchPpr; FBLA; PpCl; College; Teaching.

HOPKINS, Stephen F; Bunker Hill HS; Bunker Hill, IL; Band; HonRl; NHS; NatlMeritCmnd; SctActv; LetterTrk; U Of Il; Engineer.

HOPKINS, Susan D; Starberry Rii HS; Gentry, MO; TrsSophCls; Chrs; Mdrgl; NatlMeritCmnd; OffAde; StuCncl; FHA; PpCl; Chrldr;.

HOPKINS, Tammy L; Marshall HS; Marshall, MI; 7/259 ALAGirlsSt; CncrtBnd; HonRl; MrchBnd; NHS; Orch; SecCivCl; GAA; KiwanAwd; University; Veterinarian.

HOPKINS, Tammy L; Norfolk Senior HS; Norfolk, NE; Chr; ChrhWkr; DrlTm; NatlThespSoc; Quill&Scroll; SchMus; StuCncl; Yrbk; PpCl; PPFtbl; Doane College.

HOPKINS, Tony C; Southmont HS; Waveland, IN; 36/159 ALBoysSt; Chr; ChrhWkr; HonRl; JrNHS; SchPl; SctActv; YthFlsp; Wrstlng; College; Radio Broadcasting.

HOPKINS, Trent; North Putnam HS; Roachdale, IN; 8/139 Band; HonRl; NHS; SchMus; IMSpt; Ball State U; Math Masters.

HOPKINS, William E; Carrolton Community HS; Carrollton, IL; 8/78 Band; HonRl; NHS; StuCncl; FTA; SpnCl; PpCl; SciCl; LetterFtbl; LetterTrk; College; Porfessional.

HOPP, Kimberlie L; Louisville HS; Louisville, NE; ALAGirlsSt; Chrs; HonRl; NHS; OffAde; EdYrBk; FHA; PpCl;.

HOPP, Lauri S; Ypsilanti HS; Ypsilanti, MI; 1/504 Band; DrmBgl; HonRl; NHS; Orch; SchMus; YthFlsp; FrCl; PresGerCl; Chrldr; U Of Michigan; Engineering.

HOPPE, Bradley J; Primghar Comm HS; Primghar, IA; 4/40 PresJrCls; Band; Chrs; HonRl; JrNHS; Mdrgl; SchMus; SchPl; EdSchPpr; PpCl; College; Professional.

HOPPE, Darrell A; Camelot HS; Cairo, IL; 3/16 VPSrCls; Chrs; StuCncl; SptEdYrbk; SchPpr; PpCl; SciCl; LetterBsbl; LetterBsktbl; Shawnee Jr Coll.

HOPPE, Dennis J; Gordon Tech HS; Chicago, IL; 4/618 HonRl; LitMag; NHS; StuCncl; StuGov; RptrSchPpr; PresFrCl; MthCl; PpCl; Northwestern Univ; Corporation Law.

HOPPE, Louise A; Oconto Senior HS; Oconto, WI; 64/136 Chrs; HonRl; LbryAde; OffAde; RptrSchPpr; FrCl; LatCl; PpCl; DARAwd; TIMEAwd; Northeast Wisc Tech Inst; Medical.

HOPPE, Lynn E; Jennings HS; Jennings, MO; 6/249 Chr; ChrhWkr; HonRl; NHS; TreasFNA; EngCl; LetterBsktbl; LetterTennis; LetterTrk; SecGAA; U Of Mo; Journalism.

HOPPE, Peggy L; Unionville Sebewaig Area HS; Sebewaing, MI; Chr; ChrhWkr; OffAde; YthFlsp; FrCl; PpCl; Navy ;acct Or Police.

HOPPE, Rhonda; Wisconsin Acad; Hinsdale, IL; VPFrshCls; HonRl; LbryAde; NHS; StuCncl; EdSchPpr; GAA; College; Vocation.

HOPPENRATH, John C; Benet Academy; Naperville, IL; 31/230 Band; CncrtBnd; MrchBnd; RptrSchPpr; EdSchPpr; SchPpr; Bsbl; Bsktbl; Ill State Univ; Engineering.

HOPPENS, Brad J; Alliance HS; Alliance, NE; ChrhWkr; HonRl; NHS; NatlMeritCmnd; SchPl; StuCncl; TchrAde; GerCl; SciCl; LetterTrk; Univ Of Ne; Bio Chemistry.

HOPPERSTAD, Kenneth R; Emmons HS; Emmons, MN; 4/26 Band; Chrs; CncrtBnd; MrchBnd; PepBnd; SchPl; Bsktbl; Augustana Coll; Chemist.

HOPSON, Candyce L; Marion HS; Marion, IA; AFS; ChrhWkr; CmntyWkr; HonRl; RedCrAde; TchrAde; UNYO; YthFnd; FBLA; CmntyWkr; Coll; Acctng.

HOPWOOD, Rhonda E; Charlestown HS; Memphis, IN; 12/210 ChrhWkr; HonRl; MrchBnd; YthFlsp; Yrbk; 4-H; FHA; FTA; PpCl; SciCl; Ind Univ Se; Registered Nurse.

HOPWOOD, Robert M; Shelby Public HS; Shelby, NE; PresFrshCls; PresSophCls; PresJrCls; ALBoysSt; Band; Chr; Chrs; ChrhWkr; CncrtBnd; HonRl; MrchBnd; CaptBsktbl; CaptFtbl; Trk;.

HORACEK, Mark; Wilber Clatonia Hs; Wilber, NE; 4/47 PresFrshCls; Band; CncrtBnd; HonRl; MrchBnd; StuCncl; RptrSchPpr; LetterBsktbl; LetterFtbl; Trk; College; Professional.

HORAK, Jamie S; Owosso HS; Owosso, MI; 95/452 ChrhWkr; NHS; SchPl; TchrAde; LetterBsbl; LetterBsktbl; CchngActv; GAA; IMSpt; PPFtbl; Western Michigan Univ; Physical Education.

HORALEK, Susan M; Queen Of Peace HS; Chicago, IL; 51/448 Chrs; HonRl; JrNHS; NHS; Yrbk; Univ Of Ill; Anthropology.

HORAN, David M; Bryan Sr HS; Omaha, NE; 50/395 DrlTm; HonRl; NHS; ROTC; SctActv; TchrAde; LetterTennis; LetterTrk; LetterWrstlng; RotaryAwd; University; Law.

HORATH, Kevin L; Roseville HS; Roseville, IL; 8/53 CmntyWkr; HonRl; VPNHS; SchPpr; PpCl; Bsktbl; Ftbl; Trk; College; Professional.

HORCHER, Ann Marie T; Gibault HS; Columbia, IL; 1/91 SecSophCls; SecSrCls; Chrl; LitMag; NHS; NatlMeritFnl; SchPl; StuCncl; RptrYrbk; SchPpr; Univ Of Ill; Med Lib.

HORD, Christopher S; Clinton HS; Clinton, MO; 10/168 ChrhWkr; HonRl; SctActv; Univ Of Mo; Atmospheric Science.

HORD, Steven R; Kingsford HS; Iron Mountain, MI; HonRl; NHS; FTA; Univ Of Arizona; Medicine.

HORDOS, Doug L; Bad Axe HS; Bad Axe, MI; Aud/Vis; ChrhWkr; CmntyWkr; NatlFornLg; RedCrAde; StuGov; TchrAde; PresSciCl; LetterBsbl; LetterBsktbl; LetterFtbl; Glf; Central Michigan Univ; Doctor.

HORENKAMP, Ronda S; St Charles Senior HS; St Charles, MO; Chrs; ChrhWkr; HonRl; HospAde;

NHS; Pres4-H; IMSpt; 4-HAwd; St Pauls College; Teacher.

HORGAN, James T; Catholic Central HS; Grand Rapids, MI; HonRl; JA; NHS; Yrbk; LatCl; AmLegAwd; Aquinas College; Law Diplomacy.

HORGEN, Kristie; Warren HS; Warren, MN; Chrs; HospAde; SchMus; RptrYrbk; 4-H; FHA; GerCl; Trk; GAA; IMSpt; Northland Junior College; Nursing.

HORINE, Juanita; Osceola HS; Osceola, MO; Band; Chr; Chrs; CncrtBnd; HonRl; MrchBnd; YthFlsp; 4-H; SpnCl;.

HORKAN, Debra A; Webb HS; Reedsburg, WI; 1/223 AFS; Band; CncrtBnd; HonRl; NatlThespSoc; SchMus; SchPl; TchrAde; LatCl; Marquette Univ; Medicine.

HORKAN, Diane L; Webb HS; Reedsburg, WI; SecTrsJrCls; HonRl; HospAde; StuCncl; StuGov; 4-H; FHA; SpnCl; IMSpt; Madison Area Tech College; Nurse.

HORKAN, Mary J; Harold L Richards HS; Worth, IL; 168/1035 ChrhWkr; CmntyWkr; OffAde; College; Mass Communications.

HORKY, Mark M; Sargent HS; Sargent, NE; TrsSophCls; Band; Chrs; PepBnd; SchMus; StuGov; YthFlsp; Bsktbl; Ftbl; Trk; College.

HORMANN, Steven M; Bellmont HS; Ossian, IN; 17/248 ChrhWkr; HonRl; NHS; LetterBsktbl; CaptFtbl; CchngActv; Ball State University; Architecture.

HORN, Andrew J; Lane Tech HS; Chicago, IL; 4/1213 HonRl; SecNHS; TchrAde; GerCl; MthCl; SciCl; Univ Of Illinois; Chemical Engineering.

HORN, Brian H; Creighton Prep; Council Bluffs, IA; Band; ChrhWkr; HonRl; NatlMeritSF; NatlSciFnd; SctActv; Univ; Medicine.

HORN, Donelle J; Oregon Community HS; Oregon, IL; 1/112 CncrtBnd; DrlTm; HonRl; NHS; NatlMeritCmnd; StuCncl; StuGov; TchrAde; FrCl; GAA; College; Math.

HORN, Idona M; Phillipsburg HS; Phillipsburgh, KS; HonRl; LbryAde; Teen; 4-H; Bsktbl; Married.

HORN, Jenilynn; Ralston HS; Ralston, NE; Band; CncrtBnd; HonRl; MrchBnd; NHS; PepBnd; SchMus; SpnCl; PpCl; Bsktbl; College; Doctor Of Medicine.

HORN, Jerome C; Lincoln HS; Wisconsin Rapids, WI; 7/600 ALBoysSt; Band; CmntyWkr; HonRl; JrNHS; NHS; NatlMeritCmnd; StuCncl; RptrYrbk; 4-H; Univ; Civilor Environmental Engineering.

HORN, Jo A; Centerville HS; Richmond, IN; 13/164 Band; ChrhWkr; CncrtBnd; HonRl; MrchBnd; NHS; PepBnd; YthFlsp; 4-H; PresFTA; FrCl; LetterTennis; GAA; College; Professional.

HORN, John J; Centerville HS; Cincinnati, IA; Band; CncrtBnd; HonRl; NHS; StuCncl; RptrYrbk; RptrSchPpr; 4-H; SpnCl; Iowa State University; Engineering.

HORN, Lonnie; Davis Co Comm HS; Drakesville, IA; 5/137 VPJrCls; ALBoysSt; NHS; NatlThespSoc; SchMus; SchPl; RptrSchPpr; 4-H; PresFFA; DanFAwd; Coll; Pilot.

HORN, Louella L; Chilocco Indian HS; Presho, SD; Band; HonRl; OffAde; IMSpt; Coll; Voc.

HORN, Michael H; Marmion Military Academy; Chicago, IL; 9/87 VPFrshCls; VPSophCls; VPJrCls; HonRl; ROTC; VPStuCncl; PpCl; SciCl; LetterFtbl; Trk; IMSpt; University.

HORN, Patricia A; Orient Macksburg HS; Orient, IA; Chr; Chrs; SchMus; SctActv; StuCncl; Twrl; 4-H; Chrldr; College; Elementary Teacher.

HORN, Randall; Charles City Comm HS; Charles City, IA; 70/225 Band; CncrtBnd; HonRl; MrchBnd; SancSoc; PepBnd; SchPl; PpCl; Ftbl; Wrstlng; College; Computer Science.

HORN, Raymond C; Durand HS; Durand, MI; 42/202 Chrs; ChrhWkr; CmntyWkr; HonRl; SctActv; Trade School; Mechanics.

HORN, Renda L; Moweaqua HS; Moweaqua, IL; 3/49 Chrs; HonRl; NHS; SchMus; VPStuCncl; TchrAde; RptrYrbk; FHA; SpnCl; Chrldr; VPGAA; DARAwd; Illinois State Univ; Elem Educ.

HORN, Roy A; Newton HS; Newton, KS; College; Business.

HORNBACHER, Rudy C; Usa HS; Sebewaing, MI; 42/125 ChrhWkr; HonRl; YthFlsp; FFA; LatCl;.

HORNBACHER, Valerie J; Gibert Comm HS; Story City, IA; 5/30 ChrhWkr; CmntyWkr; HonRl; NHS; StuCncl; TchrAde; FHA; PpCl; CaptBsktbl; DARAwd; University Of Iowa; Nursing.

HORNBECK, Bill J; Logan Magnolia HS; Logan, IA; CmntyWkr; HonRl; SctActv; KeyCl; LetterBsbl; LetterBsktbl; LetterFtbl; LetterGlf; Swmmng; CchngActv; IMSpt; College; Professional.

HORNBROOK, Lisa A; Downers Grove North HS; Downers Grove, IL; 26/558 Chr; Chrs; HonRl; NHS; NatlThespSoc; SchPl; 4-H; U Of Il; Business Admn.

HORNBROOK, Walter A; Ferndale HS; Ferndale, MI; Oakland Univ; Aviation.

HORNE, Kathryn J; Grand Blanc HS; Grand Blanc, MI; Chr; ChrhWkr; HonRl; HospAde; NHS; NatlMeritSF; OffAde; YthFlsp; SpnCl; Univ Of Mich; Bus Admind.

HORNE, Kristine M; Oak Park HS; Kansas City, MO; Band; Chr; Chrl; ChrhWkr; CncrtBnd; HonRl; MrchBnd; NHS; PepBnd; SchMus; SchPl; TchrAde; PpCl; Chrldr; College; Law.

HORNE, Nancy L; Central Heights HS; Princeton, KS; Chrs; HonRl; NHS; YthFlsp; 4-H; FHA; PpCl; GAA; 4-HAwd; CitAwd; Jr College; Business.

HORNER, Dawn M; Randolph Southern HS; Carlos, IN; 7/61 Band; Chr; ChrhWkr; CncrtBnd; HonRl; MrchBnd; YthFlsp; Yrbk; PpCl; College; Accounting Cpa.

HORNER, James L; Lincoln East HS; Lincoln, NE; PresJrCls; HonRl; Orch; SecFrshCls; TchrAde; 4-H; CaptFtbl; LetterTrk; IMSpt; 4-HAwd; College; Professional.

HORNER, Jean; Watertown Senior HS; Watertown, SD; 23/300 Chr; Chrs; DrlTm; HonRl; JrNHS; NHS; StuCncl; SpnCl; GAA; Col; Elementary Teacher.

HORNER, Joseph W; Grosse Pointe South HS; Grosse Pointe Park, MI; 160/612 Chr; Chrs; NatlMeritSF; NatlThespSoc; SchPl; Trk; IMSpt; Michigan State Univ; Engineering.

HORNER, Paulette A; Napoleon HS; Burnstad, ND; 37/61#99 PpCl; Bsktbl; Trk; GAA; College.

HORNER, Randy L; Emmons Central HS; North Dakota, ND; PresSrCls; Chrs; SchPpr; Ftbl; Trk; Trade Schl; Vocational.

HORNER, Robert R; East Charles Mix #102 HS; Wagner, SD; 30/65 ChrhWkr; HonRl; 4-H; FFA; LetterFtbl; LetterWrstlng; AmLegAwd; DanFAwd; 4-HAwd; Trade School; Auto Mechanic.

HORNER, Shirley A; Esmond HS; Esmond, ND; 3/32 Chrs; CncrtBnd; HonRl; MrchBnd; SchAde; SchPl; SecStuCncl; RptrYrbk; EdSchPpr; PpCl; Univ Of North Dakota; Accounting.

HORNEY, Richard R; Roseville HS; Roseville, IL; Chrs; HonRl; SctActv; SptEdSchPpr; SpnCl; LetterFtbl; LetterTrk; DanFAwd; Pres4-HAwd; JAAwd; College; Professional.

HORNICKEL, Lori D; Chatsworth HS; Chatsworth, IL; 5/46 VPFrshCls; SecSophCls; AFS; Band; HonRl; StuCncl; YthFlsp; FFA; FHA; GAA; Parkland Jr Clge.

HORNICKEL, Vicki R; Chatsworth HS; Chatsworth, IL; 7/27 AFS; Band; ChrhWkr; CncrtBnd; HonRl; HospAde; MrchBnd; PepBnd; SchMus; SchPl; SecStuCncl; Yrbk; Trk; PresGAA; Nursing School; Nurse.

HORNING, Deb; Chokio Alberta HS; Chokio, MN; SecJrCls; ALAGirlsSt; Band; CncrtBnd; HonRl; PepBnd; RptrSchPpr; Bsktbl; 4-HAwd; Alexandria Voc Tech School; Clerical.

HORNING, Diane M; L P Goodrich HS; Fond Du Lac, WI; /600 ChrhWkr; SpnCl; PpCl; Techmical Shl; Secretary.

HORNING, Terese A; Divine Savior Holy Angels HS; Brookfield, WI; SctActv; TchrAde; GAA; Univ.

HORNSBY, Michael E; Chillicothe HS; Chillicothe, MO; 10/187 SecSophCls; HonRl; Quill&Scroll; StuGov; RptrSchPpr; EdSchPpr; FTA; LetterBsktbl; LetterTennis; Nemsu; Teaching.

HORNUNG, Daniel R; Lincoln HS; Manitowoc, WI; MrchBnd; NatlThespSoc; PepBnd; SchMus; SchPl; Ftbl; U Of Wi; Engineering.

HORNUNG, Jere; Ludington HS; Ludington, MI; 25/233 Band; CncrtBnd; HonRl; JrNHS; MrchBnd; NHS; NatlMeritFnl; NatlMeritCmnd; NatlMeritSchl; Trk; Michigan Technological Univ; Electrical Eng.

HORNUNG, Scott A; Walhalla Public HS; Walhalla, ND; 15/76 ALBoysSt; Chrs; HonRl; Bsbl; LetterBsktbl; LetterFtbl; LetterTrk; Dakota Aero; Mechanic.

HORNYAK, James; St Francis HS; Traverse City, MI; 13/82 HonRl; JrNHS; NHS; NatlMeritSchl; TchrAde; Yrbk; CaptGlf; Central Mi Univ; Accountant.

HORR, Bret W; Lincoln HS; Stanwood, IA; ChrhWkr; HonRl; NHS; Pres4-H; FFA; LetterBsbl; LetterFtbl; LetterWrstlng; 4-HAwd; Univ Or College; Agriculture Or Athletics.

HORRALL, Terry D; South Knox HS; Vincennes, IN; PresFrshCls; HonRl; StuCncl; TchrAde; 4-H; FFA; LetterBsbl; LetterBsktbl; Trk; IMSpt; 4-HAwd; Okland City College Tech; Agriculture.

HORRAS, Connie; Fairfield HS; Fairfield, IA; 35/211 Chr; ChrhWkr; HonRl; StuCncl; RptrYrbk; 4-H; SpnCl; PpCl; Univ; Journalism.

HORRELL, Cathy A; St Edmond HS; Fort Dodge, IA; Chr; ChrhWkr; CmntyWkr; HonRl; NHS; NatlMeritSchl; PolWkr; LetterBsbl; LetterTennis; GovHonPrgAwd; Iowa St Univ; Math & Sciecne.

HORROCKS, Teresa M; Greenville HS; Greenville, MI; Aud/Vis; HonRl; Quill&Scroll; TchrAde; RptrSchPpr; EdSchPpr; SchPpr; FrCl; Central Mi Univ.

HORSFORD, Brian; Jackson HS; Jackson, MI; Band; HonRl; MrchBnd; NHS; PepBnd; RptrSchPpr; Lawrence Inst Of Tech; Construction Eng.

HORSIC, Lori A; Benton Harbor HS; Benton Harbor, MI; 6/417 SecSrCls; SecBand; HonRl; JrNHS; LbryAde; MrchBnd; NHS; NatlMeritCmnd; OffAde; PepBnd; TreasMthCl; Michigan State Univ; Music Therapy.

HORST, Cynthia; Litchfield HS; Litchfield, IL; 1/142 Band; Chrs; HonRl; NHS; OffAde; RedCrAde; StuCncl; GAA; College; Pharmacy.

HORST, Julie A; Rockford East HS; Rockford, IL; 57/665 ChrhWkr; CmntyWkr; HonRl; JrNHS; NHS; StuCncl; StuGov; TchrAde; YthFlsp; Yrbk; College; Elem Teaching.

HORST, Kim A; Duchesne HS; St Charles, MO; Chrs; HonRl; SctActv; IMSpt; College; Art.

HORST, Petra L; Marillac HS; Park Ridge, IL; 5/263 ChrhWkr; CmntyWkr; NHS; SchAde; Sdlty; TchrAde; PresSpnCl; Tennis; Rosary College; Medicine.

HORST, Susan; Litchfield HS; Litchfield, IL; 3/142 Band; Chrs; ChrhWkr; CmntyWkr; HonRl; NHS; RedCrAde; SctActv; FrCl; College; Business Administration.

HORSTED, Daniel; Brandon Valley HS; Brandon, SD; 33/110 Chrs; ChrhWkr; HonRl; JA; NHS; Yrbk; Wrstlng; Univ Of So Dak; Bus Admin.

HORSTMAN, Patricia A; Sacred Heart Academy; Springfield, IL; 26/177 HonRl; NHS; FrCl; Purdue Univ; Interior Design.

HORSTMAN, William; Parkston HS; Parkston, SD; 4/97 ALBoysSt; Chrl; ChrhWkr; HonRl; ModUN; NatlFornLg; SctActv; FSA; GerCl; Glf; Unif Of South Dakota; Professional.

HORSTMANN, Carla D; Pleasantville Comm HS; Ackworth, IA; HonRl; NHS; OffAde; Quill&Scroll; StuCncl; TchrAde; RptrYrbk; RptrSchPpr; 4-H; FTA; Bsktbl; LetterTrk; PPFtbl; College; Math.

HORSTMANN, Rick; Verdigre Public HS; Verdigre, NE; TrsJrCls; FFA; IMSpt; Tech School.

HORSTMANN, Shirley J; Mater Dei HS; Damiansville, IL; 32/197 HonRl; OffAde; TchrAde; FBLA;.

HORT, Hope; Lyman Hs; Lyman, NE; 2/19 Chr; HonRl; NHS; OffAde; SchMus; SchPl; FHA; PpCl; Wrstlng; Chrldr; Eastern Wyoming College; Elem Education.

HORT, Hope M; Lyman HS; Lyman, NE; 2/19 SecFrshCls; Chr; Chrs; HonRl; HospAde; NHS; Trk; Chrldr; Eastern Wyo Coll; Elem Ed.

HORTENSTINE, Cecelia R; Sullivan HS; Gays, IL; 11/105 Band; CncrtBnd; HonRl; LbryAde; MrchBnd; RptrYrbk; RptrSchPpr; EdSchPpr; 4-H; FHA; FTA; FrCl; Augustana College; Journalism.

HORTON, Barbara J; Western HS; Parma, MI; HonRl; SctActv; StuCncl; TchrAde; Twrl; Yrbk; FrCl; SpnCl; LetterTrk; GAA; Central Mi U; Nutrition.

HORTON, Charles L; Oakville Sr HS; St Louis, MO; HonRl; NatlThespSoc; SchMus; SchPl; SctActv; StuCncl; RptrSchPpr; Trk; University; English.

HORTON, Cynthia K; Southwestern HS; Brighton, IL; 78/169 Chr; ChrhWkr; HonRl; SecJA; LbryAde; OffAde; PolWkr; SchAde; FDA; FHA; Lewis & Clark Community Clg; Nursing.

HORTON, David J; Lodi Sr HS; Lodi, WI; 13/136 NHS; StuCncl; RptrSchPpr; FBLA; SpnCl; SciCl; CaptBsbl; LetterBsktbl; LetterFtbl; Madison Area Tech College; Merchandising.

HORTON, Edna; Morrice HS; Morrice, MI; 5/50 Band; HonRl; NHS; PepBnd; SchPl; TchrAde; EdYrBk; EdSchPpr; Spring Arbor College; Journalism.

HORTON, Gary L; Northwest HS; Cedar Hill, MO; HonRl; College; Aerospace Field.

HORTON, Jeff L; Murphysboro Township HS; Murphysboro, IL; HonRl; Bsbl; Bsktbl; CchngActv; IMSpt; Univ.

HORTON, Laurisa M; Burlington HS; Burlington, IA; 17/450 Chr; Chrl; Chrs; HonRl; JA; LbryAde; Mdrgl; NatlMeritCmnd; Orch; SchMus; Knox College; Mathematics.

HORTON, Loralee A; Glenbard East HS; Lombard, IL; 3/653 ChrhWkr; CmntyWkr; HonRl; JrNHS; NHS; NatlMeritSF; Orch; Quill&Scroll; SchPpr; GAA; Syracuse U; Communication.

HORTON, Lynn M; Central Catholic HS; Bloomington, IL; 2/84 PresFrshCls; VPJrCls; NHS; SctActv; StuCncl; RptrYrbk; FrCl; PresPpCl; LetterTennis; University.

HORTON, Mary F; Green Mountain Indep HS; Gladbrook, IA; TrsJrCls; Chrs; DrlTm; HonRl; SchMus; SchPl; FTA; PpCl; Bsktbl; IMSpt; College.

HORTON, Timothy M; Western HS; Kokomo, IN; 21/165 HonRl; NHS; Yrbk; LatCl; College.

HORVAT, Jeanette M; St Mary HS; Sleepy Eye, MN; 40/86 Chr; ChrhWkr; HospAde; Quill&Scroll; SchPl; TchrAde; RptrSchPpr; SchPpr; 4-H; FHA; Willmar Comm Collf Interior Design.

HORVAT, Marjorie A; St Marys HS; Sleepy Eye, MN; ChrhWkr; CmntyWkr; HonRl; SchAde; TchrAde; GAA; CitAwd; VoiceDemAwd; Army; Nursin.

HORVATH, Jean E; Stephenson HS; Stephenson, MI; 3/99 ALAGirlsSt; Band; Chr; CncrtBnd; HonRl; MrchBnd; NHS; PepBnd; SchPl; RptrYrbk; Rochester Community Clg; Health Career.

HORVATH, Sylvia; Resurrection HS; Chicago, IL; 53/294 HonRl; HospAde; GerCl; SpnCl; GAA; College; Accounting.

HORWITZ, Randy J; Niles West HS; Skokie, IL; CAP; NHS; NatlSciFnd; StuGov; MthCl; College; Medicine.

HORYNA, Jonea; Otis Bison Sr HS; Bison, KS; Band; Chr; ChrhWkr; HonRl; NHS; SchPl; 4-H; PpCl; 4-HAwd; College; Math.

HOSCH, Beverly C; Aquin HS; Bernard, IA; 16/66 Chr; Chrs; ChrhWkr; CmntyWkr; LbryAde; NatlFornLg; SchMus; TchrAde; RptrSchPpr; PpCl; Mt Mercy College; Music.

HOSCH, Diane L; Hutsonville HS; West Union, IL; 1/40 PresFrshCls; SecTrsJrCls; Chr; HonRl; NHS; StuCncl; TchrAde; Yrbk; SchPpr; College; Business.

HOSCHEIT, Donald C; St Charles HS; St Charles, IL; 21/460 HonRl; LitMag; NHS; NatlMeritCmnd; RptrSchPpr; EngCl; FrCl; MthCl; SciCl; Trk; University Of Illinois; Medicine.

HOSEA, Thomas J; Rich Central HS; Matteson, IL; 66/364 HonRl; TreasKeyCl; LetterTrk; LetterWrstlng; Az State; Civil Engineering.

HOSEK, Debra; Amos Alonzo Stagg Hs; Hickory Hills, IL; 22/480 HonRl; VPNHS; NatlMeritCmnd; SchMus; SchPl; TchrAde; YthLg; RptrYrbk; FrCl; Bsbl; Carthage College; Law.

HOSICK, Cynthia; Rosiclare HS; Rosiclare, IL; 8/40 SecFrshCls; VPJrCls; Band; HonRl; MrchBnd; PolWkr; SchPl; Yrbk; 4-H; FHA; Major In Music; Performing Piano.

HOSIER, Donna M; Huntington North HS; Huntington, IN; Aud/Vis; DrmMjrt; VPFTA; College; Teacher.

HOSKER, Geoffrey B; Edsal Ford HS; Dearborn, MI; CncrtBnd; MrchBnd; NatlFornLg; NatlMeritSF; VPStuCncl; RptrSchPpr; NCTE; College; Education English Maj.

HOSKIN, Cynthia S; Davis County Comm HS; Bloomfield, IA; HonRl; NHS; StuCncl; RptrYrbk; 4-H; FBLA; PpCl; Bsktbl; 4-HAwd; CitAwd; Business School.

HOSKING, Debra J; Hancock Central HS; Hancokc, MI; 54/90 ChrhWkr; DrlTm; HonRl; LbryAde; OffAde; SchAde; PpCl; College; Interior Design.

HOSKINS, Ernie R; Brown County HS; Trafalgar, IN; VPFrshCls; VPSophCls; HonRl; StuCncl; Bsbl; Bsktbl; Ftbl; CchngActv; IMSpt; Univ.

HOSKINS, Gayla R; New Bloomfield HS; Holts Summit, MO; HonRl; TchrAde; RptrYrbk; Yrbk; CchngActv; Professional.

HOSKINS, Patricia A; Chicago Vocational HS; Chicago, IL; 13/778 Chr; ChrhWkr; HonRl; NHS; StuCncl; TchrAde; RptrYrbk; GAA; College; Psychology.

HOSKINSON, Donna A; Haven HS; Burrton, KS; 2/90 ALAGirlsSt; Band; Chr; Chrl; ChrhWkr; HonRl; NHS; OffAde; SchMus; YthFlsp; 4-H; FrCl; PpCl; Kansas Newman College; Counselor.

HOSMER, John M; Eagle Bend Public HS #790; Eagle Bend, MN; ALBoysSt; Band; Chr; ChrhWkr; HonRl; TchrAde; FFA; FTA; CaptBsktbl; AmLegAwd; Austin Jr Col; Dentistry.

HOSMER, Mark E; Charlevoix HS; Charlevoix, MI; ALBoysSt; CncrtBnd; MrchBnd; TchrAde; Bsktbl; Ftbl; Tennis; Trk; IMSpt; College; Professional.

HOSMON, Tracy K; Crab Orchard HS; Marion, IL; ChrhWkr; HonRl; LbryAde; SchPpr;.

HOSPADARUK, Suzanne; Crestwood HS; Dearborn Heights, MI; 5/400 CncrtBnd; MrchBnd; NHS; NatlMeritCmnd; RusCl; Univ Of Mi; Premedical Med Program.

HOSPERS, Susanne M; East Kentwood HS; Grand Rapids, MI; 20/475 HonRl; JA; NatlFornLg; NHS; GerCl; LatCl; JAAwd; Mich State U; Nursing.

HOSS, David A; Gehlen HS; Lemars, IA; 15/60 TrsSophCls; ALBoysSt; Band; Chr; Chrs; HonRl; MrchBnd; StuCncl; IMSpt; AmLegAwd; Ia St; Archit.

HOSS, Donna; Chandlerville HS; Chandlerville, IL; SecSophCls; Chrs; HonRl; SchMus; SchPl; StuGov; 4-H; FHA; Swmmng; Trk; Coll; Veterinarian.

HOSTE, Stephen A; St Clement HS; Center Line, MI; 1/98 PresSophCls; HonRl; NHS; SchPl; RptrYrbk; RptrSchPpr; SciCl; College; Law.

HOSTETLER, Gerald D; Glendale HS; Springfield, MO; ChrhWkr; University; Architect.

HOSTETLER, Sharee A; Westview Jr Sr HS; Topeka, IN; 2/65 TrsSophCls; TrsJrCls; TrsSrCls; Chr; ChrhWkr; HonRl; Mdrgl; NHS; NatlMeritCmnd; SchMus; SchPl; StuCncl; SchPpr; SpnCl; Goshen Col; Nursing.

HOSTETTER, Anthony W; Beech Grove HS; Beech Grove, IN; Band; CncrtBnd; HonRl; MrchBnd; PepBnd; Navy; Demolitions Expert.

HOSTETTER, Elizabeth; Beaver Dam HS; Beaver Dam, WI; 25/300 Chrs; ChrhWkr; HonRl; SchAde; SchMus; StuCncl; TchrAde; RptrYrbk; PpCl; Bsktbl; Univ; Art.

HOTLE, Tom G; Panora Linden HS; Panora, IA; 4/55 VPFrshCls; TrsSophCls; HonRl; LetterFtbl; LetterTrk; College; Electronics.

HOTMER, Donald J; Odessa HS; Odessa, MO; 19/120 HonRl; NHS; 4-H; FFA; Bsbl; Marines; Mech.

HOTSON, Ramona; Lyle Public HS; Austin, MN; 3/29 Chr; HonRl; NHS; SchPl; Twrl; EdSchPpr; PpCl; Chrldr; IMSpt; Coll; Med Tech.

HOTT, Jon M; Braymer C 4 HS; Braymer, MO; 3/31 Band; Chr; Chrs; ChrhWkr; CncrtBnd; DrmMjrt; HonRl; Mdrgl; MrchBnd; PepBnd; SctActv; StuCncl; TchrAde; YthFlsp; Central Missouri State Univ; Music.

HOTT, Timothy J; Riverton Community HS; Riverton, IL; Aud/Vis; HonRl; StuCncl; YthFlsp; CchngActv; IMSpt; PresAwd; College; History.

HOTTOVY, Terry; David City Aquinas HS; Dwight, NE; TrsSophCls; NHS; NatlMeritFnl; 4-H; SpnCl; MthCl; Trk; Wrstlng; Washington Univ; Chem Engineering.

HOTTOVY, Terry J; Aquinas HS; Dwight, NE; 6/87 TrsSophCls; ChrhWkr; NHS; NatlMeritSF; StuCncl; 4-H; VPSpnCl; PresSciCl; Bsbl; CaptFtbl; Trk; LetterWrstlng; Univ Of Ne; Chemical Engineer.

HOTVEDT, Steven W; Tartan HS; Lake Elmo, MN; Bsktbl; Ftbl; LetterTrk; Concordia Clge St Paul.

HOTZ, Donna R; Salina Central HS; Salina, KS; 23/319 HonRl; LbryAde; PolWkr; SchPl; College; Evangelism.

HOTZ, Linda R; Gregory Public HS; Gregory, SD; 3/45 Band; Chr; Chrs; ChrhWkr; CncrtBnd; HonRl; JrNHS; NHS; PepBnd; YthFlsp; FHA; PpCl; College; Biology.

HOTZE, Karla R; Teutopolis HS; Teutopolis, IL; 13/120 Band; Chrs; HonRl; HospAde; SchMus; SchPl;

Twrl; RptrSchPpr; EdSchPpr; FHA; Chrldr; Eastern Ill Univ; Special Ed.

HOUCHEN, Nancy L; Bogan HS; Chicago, IL; HonRl; JrNHS; NHS; NatlMeritCmnd; SchAde; TchrAde; MthCl; SciCl; Northwestern Univ; Law.

HOUCHIN, Kelli A; M V K Comm HS; Mazon, IL; PresFrshCls; VPSrCls; ALAGirlsSt; ChrhWkr; HonRl; HospAde; NHS; Quill&Scroll; Yrbk; Chrldr; GAA; College; Nursing.

HOUCK, Beth; Cromwell HS; Cromwell, MN; 1/30 Band; Chrs; CncrtBnd; HonRl; NHS; NatlMeritCmnd; NatlMeritCmnd; PepBnd; YthFlsp; SchPpr; Trk; VoiceDemAwd; Mercy Central School Of Nur.

HOUCK, Colleen M; Brown City HS; Brown City, MI; 1/96 Band; Chrs; CncrtBnd; HonRl; MrchBnd; OffAde; SchMus; TchrAde; FHA; FTA; College; Business Adm.

HOUCK, Gregory P; Highland HS; Highland, IN; 37/585 NatlMeritSF; FDA; KeyCl; GerCl; LetterFtbl; Univ; Physician.

HOUCK, Jane L; Lyons Township HS; Lagrange, IL; SecChrhWkr; NHS; NatlMeritCmnd; PresYthFlsp; Kalamazoo College.

HOUCK, Jean G; Princeton R V HS; Princeton, MO; SecFrshCls; VPJrCls; HonRl; PresNHS; SchPl; SecStuCncl; VPFHA; PpCl; CaptChrldr; MasAwd; College; Guidance Counselor.

HOUCK, Karen; Macomb Hs; Macomb, IL; 16/250 Chr; ChrhWkr; HonRl; NHS; Orch; SchMus; SctActv; SchPpr; SciCl; University Of Ill; Teaching.

HOUCK, Sandra K; Nokomis HS; Witt, IL; Chrl; Chrs; ChrhWkr; HonRl; SchMus; RptrYrbk; GAA; Eastern Ill U.

HOUDEK, Irene S; Proviso West HS; Hillside, IL; 68/1141 HonRl; OffAde; Bsktbl; LetterTrk; Eastern Ill Univ; Teacher.

HOUDEK, Thomas G; Cody HS; Detroit, MI; HonRl; SpnCl; LetterTennis; University; Major Study.

HOUFER, Jennifer A; Ceylon Public HS; Ceylon, MN; SecFrshCls; Band; CmntyWkr; HonRl; MrchBnd; SchPl; YthFlsp; RptrSchPpr; PpCl; GAA; Mankato Avti; Secretary.

HOUGARD, Bonny S; Lutheran HS; Racine, WI; Chr; HonRl; TchrAde; SchPpr; PpCl; GAA; Trade; Pro.

HOUGAS, James E; Morris Comm HS; Morris, IL; 1/244 PresSophCls; Band; HonRl; NHS; PresGerCl; Ftbl; Trk; Wrstlng; AmLegAwd; Creighton Univ; Chemistry.

HOUGE, Linda S; Albert Lea Central HS; Albert Lea, MN; 14/526 HonRl; NatlMeritCmnd; FrCl; College; Psychology.

HOUGH, James; Plymouth Salem HS; Plymouth, MI; HonRl; NHS; Michigan St Univ; Engineering.

HOUGH, Jeffrey; Northrop HS; Ft Wayne, IN; ChrhWkr; HonRl; SctActv; IMSpt; GodCntryAwd; CitAwd; Coll; Conserv Officer.

HOUGH, Mary; Chilhowee HS; Chilhowee, MO; 1/14 PresSophCls; TrsSrCls; Chrs; CmntyWkr; HonRl; SchPl; EdSchPpr; VPFHA; LetterPpCl; BttyCrckrAwd; College; Medical Technology.

HOUGH, Stephen J; East Richland HS; Olney, IL; RptrSchPpr; LetterFtbl; LetterTrk; Olney Central Coll; Law.

HOUGH, Steven W; Beloit Memorial HS; Beloit, WI; ChrhWkr; HonRl; TchrAde; U Of Rock Co.

HOUGHLAND, Pamela S; Pleasant Hill HS; Pleasant Hill, IL; 2/47 VPSrCls; Band; ChrhWkr; CncrtBnd; PepBnd; Yrbk; PpCl; Bsbl; Bsktbl; GAA; Eastern Illinois Univ; Speech Pathology.

HOUGHTALING, Robin A; Battle Creek Academy; Battle Creek, MI; SecJrCls; Band; ChrhWkr; CncrtBnd; HonRl; NHS; StuCncl; StuGov; Yrbk; Andrews University; Nursing.

HOUGHTON, Cheryl T; Mt Morris HS; Mt Morris, IL; TrsJrCls; HonRl; SchPl; YthFlsp; SpnCl; PpCl; College; Psychology.

HOUGHTON, George; Penney HS; Polo, MO; 1/78 CmntyWkr; HonRl; StuGov; RptrSchPpr; SchPpr; FFA; MthCl; Bsktbl; AmLegAwd; Umc; Ag Journalism.

HOUGHTON, Marsha L; Manistique HS; Manistique, MI; 12/157 ChrhWkr; DrmBgl; HonRl; SchPl; SctActv; BttyCrckrAwd; Lake Superior Coll; Nursing.

HOUGLAND, Mary A; Santa Fe Trail HS; Topeka, KS; 21/93 Band; Chr; Chrs; ChrhWkr; CncrtBnd; HonRl; MrchBnd; PepBnd; SchMus; SchPl; Washburn Univ; Music Teacher.

HOUIN, Mark A; Plymouth HS; Plymouth, IN; HonRl; 4-H; FFA; MthCl; Purdue Univ; Agricultural Science.

HOUIOUS, Timothy; Marseilles HS; Marseilles, IL; TrsFrshCls; Band; CncrtBnd; Orch; PepBnd; SchMus; SchPl; SptEdSchPpr; College; Business.

HOULE, Jennifer A; Forest Lake HS; Hugo, MN; 22/416.

HOULIHAN, Mary Jane; Elizabeth Seton HS; Dolton, IL; 48/253 Chrl; HonRl; HospAde; Mdrgl; SchMus; StuGov; TchrAde; LatCl; Tennis; North Ill Univ; Nursing.

HOULIHAN, Tim B; Roncalli HS; Omaha, NE; HonRl; JrNHS; NHS; SchPl; StuCncl; Cregton U; Med.

HOUMES, Angela D; Sheldon HS; Watseka, IL; 1/30 Chrs; ChrhWkr; CmntyWkr; PresCncrtBnd; HonRl; PepBnd; Quill&Scroll; SchPl; Yrbk; RptrSchPpr; Ill St Univ; Speech Pathologist.

HOUNSHEL, Joyce; Brownstown Central HS; Vallonia, IN; 14/143 LbryAde; NHS; SchPl; Business.

HOUSE, Barry P; Lanphier HS; Springfield, IL; 29/473 ChrhWkr; LbryAde; NHS; NatlMeritCmnd; SchPl; RptrSchPpr; KeyCl; PpCl; Ftbl; Springfield Col; Economics.

HOUSE, Gary; Kewanna HS; Kewanna, IN; VPSrCls; Aud/Vis; Chrs; ChrhWkr; HonRl; LbryAde; EdSchPpr; FrCl; Transportaion.

HOUSE, Harold V; Brazil HS; Brazil, IN; PresJrCls; CmntyWkr; HonRl; OffAde; PolWkr; StuCncl;.

HOUSE, Karen; Caruthersville HS; Caruthersville, MO; Band; CncrtBnd; LbryAde; MrchBnd; PepBnd; FHA; College; Professional.

HOUSE, Linda D; Northwest HS; St Louis, MO; 1/513 ChrhWkr; HonRl; VPJA; PresNHS; StuCncl; YthFlsp; RptrSchPpr; FrCl; PresMthCl; Tennis; PPFtbl; CitAwd; Univ Of South California; Marketing Mgmt.

HOUSE, Mary A; Wainwright HS; Lafayette, IN; 5/104 SecFrshCls; SecSophCls; ALAGirlsSt; Band; HonRl; NHS; SecYthFlsp; EdYrBk; 4-H; Ball St Univ; Business.

HOUSE, Ruth L; Bradford HS; Bradford, IL; 5/44 TrsFrshCls; TrsSrCls; Band; Chrs; HospAde; NHS; FHA; DARAwd; Methodist Hosp Schl Nursing; Rn.

HOUSE, Sam W; Gresham HS; Gresham, WI; 3/35 HonRl; NHS; SchPl; RptrSchPpr; Pres4-H; VPFBLA; FFA; FTA; Bsbl; 4-HAwd; Univ; Radio Broadcasting.

HOUSE, Terresa A; Hagerstown HS; Hagerstown, IN; 1/96 VPJrCls; HonRl; NHS; NatlMeritCmnd; TchrAde; PresYthFlsp; YthLg; PresFHA; LetterTrk; BttyCrckrAwd; In Univ; Math.

HOUSEHOLDER, Barbara J; Warsaw HS; Warsaw, IL; Chrs; HonRl; StuCncl; FHA; KiwanAwd; Trade School; Vocation.

HOUSEHOLDER, Gregory B; Delta R 5 HS; Puxico, MO; VPFrshCls; PresSophCls; TrsJrCls; NHS; Yrbk; SptEdSchPpr; FFA; VPPpCl; LetterBsbl; IMSpt; Univ; Pro Law.

HOUSEHOLDER, Robert S; Marian Catholic HS; Park Forest, IL; Aud/Vis; Band; Chr; Chrl; Chrs; HonRl; SchMus; Univ; Theatre.

HOUSER, Danny T; Hamilton HS; Pleasant Lake, IN; 26/60 ChrhWkr; HonRl; PresYthFlsp; Trk; College.

HOUSER, Jamie L; Streator Twp HS; Streator, IL; 83/400 SecFrshCls; SecSophCls; SecJrCls; SecSrCls; HonRl; RptrSchPpr; GerCl; Illinois State Univ; Special Educ Teacher.

HOUSER, Michael A; Glenwood Community HS; Glenwood, IA; HonRl; NHS; RptrSchPpr; PresFrCl; AmLegAwd; Wa U St Louis.

HOUSER, Rick; Lebo Public Hs; Lebo, KS; Chrs; HonRl; SchPl; YthFlsp; FFA; LetterTrk;.

HOUSER, Rick W; Centerville HS; Centerville, IA; CmntyWkr; LetterFtbl; LetterTrk; IMSpt; College.

HOUSER, Tania M; Homewood Flossmoor HS; Homewood, IL; 192/940 HonRl; OffAde; TchrAde; FDA; Univ; Veterinarian.

HOUSER, Terri J; Centerville HS; Centerville, IA; 17/125 Chrs; DrlTm; HonRl; SchPl; SpnCl; College; Sociology.

HOUSEWORTH, Debra L; Unity HS; Chicago, IL; 23/227 Chrs; NHS; FrCl; Mundelein Coll; Phy Therapist.

HOUSEWORTH, Rebecca S; Carrollton HS; Carrollton, MO; 10/100 Band; Chrs; HonRl; NHS; StuCncl; StuGov; EdYrBk; GerCl; PpCl; Tennis; College; Vocation.

HOUSKEN, Rhonda J; Central Webster HS; Lehigh, IA; 10/45 SecJrCls; HonRl; SchMus; SchPl; RptrYrbk; SchPpr; LetterBsktbl; LetterTrk; College; Secretarial.

HOUSNER, Randal F; Bridgeport HS; Saginaw, MI; 11/324 Band; ChrhWkr; CncrtBnd; HonRl; JrNHS; MrchBnd; NHS; PepBnd; SchMus; StuCncl; Bsktbl; LetterFtbl; LetterTrk; Univ Of Michigan; Doctor.

HOUSTON, Beverly; Roosevelt HS; Gary, IN; Chr; ChrhWkr; HonRl; StuGov; YthFlsp; FBLA; JAAwd; JETSAwd; CitAwd; College; Professional.

HOUSTON, Karen K; Truman HS; Independence, MO; StuCncl; PresFHA; FrCl; PpCl; Kansas St Univ; Interior Design.

HOUSTON, Linda J; Rochelle Twp HS; Rochelle, IL; Chr; Chrs; ChrhWkr; HonRl; YthFlsp; FHA; Central College.

HOUSTON, Margaret E; Villa Duchesne HS; St Louis, MO; Aud/Vis; CmntyWkr; HonRl; HospAde; JrNHS; NHS; SchPl; Bsktbl; Swmmng; IMSpt; Creighton Univ; Medical Field.

HOUSTON, Mary; Woodland R 4 HS; Marble Hill, MO; Chrs; CncrtBnd; MrchBnd; PepBnd; Twrl; RptrYrbk; RptrSchPpr; 4-H; FHA; PpCl;.

HOUSTON, Scott R; Rock Falls Twp HS; Rock Falls, IL; 19/250 HonRl; JrNHS; NHS; Bsktbl; LetterFtbl; LetterTrk; Univ Of Ia; Pharmacy.

HOUSTON, Sheila; Leroy HS; Leroy, KS; 2/33 ChrhWkr; HonRl; NHS; SchPl; RptrSchPpr; College; Secretarial.

HOUSTON, Velina A; Junction City HS; Junction City, KS; VPFrshCls; PresSophCls; VPJrCls; Chr; HonRl; LitMag; NatlMeritCmnd; SchMus; SchPl; StuGov; TchrAde; EdYrBk; Kansas St Univ; Journalism.

HOUTHOOFD, Tina M; Unionville Sebewaing Area HS; Unionville, MI; 17/125 ALAGirlsSt; Chr; HonRl; LbryAde; NHS; FHA; PpCl; Chrldr; Northwood Inst; Voc.

HOUTSMA, John E; Marist HS; Chicago, IL; 11/475 Aud/Vis; HonRl; NHS; NatlMeritCmnd; PolWkr; SctActv; RptrSchPpr; SpnCl; Glf; Marquette Univ; Lawyer.

HOUZENGA, Denise; Chadwick HS; Chadwick, IL; /26 SecFrshCls; TrsJrCls; Chr; Chrs; ChrhWkr; HonRl; RptrYrbk; EdYrBk; PresFHA; GAA;.

HOVDA, Dale R; Clayton HS; Clayton, MO; 30/208 Band; Chrs; NHS; SchMus; Trk; CaptWrstlng; Wheaton Clge.

HOVDA, Kathleen L; Rich South HS; Park Forest, IL; 20/273 Chrs; ChrhWkr; HonRl; YthFlsp; SpnCl; PpCl; College; Elem Teacher.

HOVE, Lerri R; North Shore HS; Ryder, ND; PresJrCls; ALAGirlsSt; Band; Chr; ChrhWkr; CncrtBnd; PepBnd; 4-H; PpCl; IMSpt; College; Special Educ.

HOVE, Scott K; Grafton Central HS; Grafton, ND; PresSophCls; ALBoysSt; NHS; PresStuCncl; SptEdSchPpr; MthCl; SciCl; Bsktbl; Ftbl; DanFAwd; Concordia Clg; History.

HOVELSON, Lyle K; Hawley HS; Hawley, MN; TrsJrCls; HonRl; SchPl; Farming.

HOVERMALE, Connie S; Anderson HS; Anderson, IN; HonRl; LitMag; Quill&Scroll; SctActv; TchrAde; FrCl; PpCl; Ball State Univ; Kindergarten Teaching.

HOVIS, Norman E; Lapeer HS; Metamora, MI; Band; CncrtBnd; MrchBnd; NatlMeritSF; PepBnd; Yrbk; 4-H; Ftbl; IMSpt; Michigan Tech Univ; Mechanical Engineering.

HOVLAND, Kevin C; Northwood HS; Northwood, ND; VPJrCls; Band; CncrtBnd; HonRl; MrchBnd; StuCncl; YthFlsp; 4-H; FFA; Bsbl; LetterBsktbl; LetterFtbl; CaptGlf; North Dakota State Univ.

HOWAR, Kathleen A; Tri County HS; Deep River, IA; SecFrshCls; TrsSophCls; PresJrCls; SecSrCls; Band; CncrtBnd; HonRl; MrchBnd; PepBnd; SchMus; SchPl; EdYrBk; FrCl; PpCl;.

HOWARD, Barbara L; Menominee HS; Menominee, MI; 5/260# Band; ChrhWkr; CmntyWkr; CncrtBnd; HonRl; MrchBnd; NHS; Orch; Univ; Professional.

HOWARD, Christopher R; Regis HS; Eau Claire, WI; 14/130 VPSophCls; PresJrCls; Chrs; HonRl; SchMus; GerCl; SpnCl; Univ Of Wisconsin; Medicine.

HOWARD, Daniel J; Morton West HS; Berwyn, IL; CmntyWkr; HonRl; Swmmng; Trk; Univ; Cpa.

HOWARD, David J; Waterford Twp HS; Pontiac, MI; 15/380 HonRl; TchrAde; RptrYrbk; RptrSchPpr; Mi Tech U; Conservation.

HOWARD, Deborah A; St Agatha HS; Detroit, MI; 18/99 Chrl; CmntyWkr; HonRl; NHS; OffAde; SchAde; SchPl; RptrYrbk; College; Art.

HOWARD, Deborah M; Mulvane HS; Mulvane, KS; ALAGirlsSt; CncrtBnd; HonRl; Mdrgl; MrchBnd; VPNatlFornLg; NHS; NatlThespSoc; SchPl; StuCncl; 4-H; PpCl; Kansas Univ; Education.

HOWARD, Diana; Douglass HS; Douglass, KS; SecTrsJrCls; Band; ChrhWkr; HonRl; NHS; SchAde; StuCncl; FHA; Trade Sch; Pro.

HOWARD, Duncan; East Jackson HS; Jackson, MI; 12/122 HstSrCls; HonRl; NatlMeritFnl; NatlMeritCmnd; NatlMeritSF; Bsbl; Bsktbl; AmLegAwd; CitAwd; Mich St Univ;vet.

HOWARD, Freda D; Mc Donald HS; Anderson, MO; 4/159 Chr; Chrs; ChrhWkr; HonRl; YthFlsp; FHA; FTA; FTA; TIMEAwd; Crowder Col; Journalism.

HOWARD, Hope D; Rolfe Community HS; Rolfe, IA; 3/30 SecFrshCls; Band; HonRl; NHS; StuCncl; YthFlsp; LetterBsbl; LetterTrk; Wartburg College; Physical Therapy.

HOWARD, John L; Fountain Central HS; Veedersburg, IN; 8/130 PresJrCls; PresSrCls; Band; ChrhWkr; HonRl; NHS; NatlMeritCmnd; StuCncl; LetterTrk; CchngActv; DanFAwd; Indiana University; Law.

HOWARD, John M; Jennings County HS; North Vernon, IN; 25/420 HonRl; LatCl; Swmmng; Trk; Wrstlng; College; Professional.

HOWARD, Julie A; Lakeview HS; Decatur, IL; 3/184 Band; SecNHS; SchMus; EdSchPpr; GerCl; LetterTennis; George Washington Univ; International Relat.

HOWARD, Kerry; Hillsboro HS; Hillsboro, IL; HonRl; TchrAde; RptrSchPpr; SciCl; Ftbl; Trk; Wrstlng; IMSpt; Col; Elementary Education.

HOWARD, Kimberly S; Central HS; La Crosse, WI; 12/507 HonRl; JrNHS; NHS; RptrSchPpr; FrCl; MthCl; Swmmng; LetterTrk; Carleton College Northfield Mn;economics.

HOWARD, Larry F; Sargent Public HS; Sargent, NE; Chr; Chrs; CmntyWkr; HonRl; NHS; StuGov; YthFlsp; SecFFA; Bsktbl; VoiceDemAwd; University; D V M.

HOWARD, Mary L; Delavan Comm HS; Delavan, IL; 4/52 TrsJrCls; Chrs; HonRl; Mdrgl; NHS; SchMus; SchPl; StuCncl; PresYthFlsp; Chrldr;.

HOWARD, Nancy L; Msgr Hackett HS; Kalamazoo, MI; HstSrCls; Chr; HonRl; SchMus; SchPl; SecTrsFrshCls; LatCl; PPFtbl; Western Mi Univ; Biology.

HOWARD, Pamela L; Oregon Davis HS; Walkerton, IN; Band; ChrhWkr; HonRl; YthFlsp; 4-H; LetterTrk; LetterChrldr; GAA; 4-HAwd; PresAwd; Ball State.

HOWARD, Rebecca; Morton HS; Morton, IL; CmntyWkr; HonRl; JA; ModUN; 4-H; FNA; PpCl; Chrldr; PresAwd; Icc; Rn.

HOWARD, Sally A; Warsaw Community HS; Winona Lake, IN; VPFrshCls; Band; ChrhWkr; CncrtBnd; HonRl; MrchBnd; SchMus; StuCncl; Chrldr; Wheaton Coll; Child Psychologist.

HOWARD, Stephanie; Beaver Dam Sr HS; Beaver Dam, WI; 20/300 Chrs; HonRl; NatlMeritCmnd; SchMus; StuCncl; PpCl; LetterTennis; LetterTrk; Chrldr; VPGAA; IMSpt; College; Liberal Arts.

HOWARD, Stephen E; Carmel HS; Carmel, IN; Chrs; HonRl; NatlMeritSF; NatlThespSoc; Orch; SchMus; SchPl; RptrSchPpr; FDA; GerCl; In U; Medical Doctor.

HOWARD, Steven L; Boys Town HS; Boys Town, NE; 3/71 ALBoysSt; HonRl; NHS; OffAde; TchrAde; RptrYrbk; Yrbk; RptrSchPpr; SchPpr; 4-H; College; Psychology.

HOWARD, Sylvia A; Worth Central HS; Indianapolis, IN; 150/1300 LetterTrk; College; Dentist.

HOWARD, Tammy S; Westville HS; Westville, IL; DrlTm; HonRl; MrchBnd; SctActv; SchPpr; 4-H; SpnCl; PpCl; Trk; GAA; College; Business.

HOWARD, Terry H; Milan Jr Sr HS; Milan, IN; VPJrCls; ALBoysSt; Band; Chr; Chrs; CmntyWkr; CncrtBnd; HonRl; MrchBnd; NHS; Orch; PepBnd; LetterBsktbl; CaptGlf; College; Professional.

HOWARD, Tim J; Barrington HS; South Barrington, IL; HonRl; IMSpt; College.

HOWARD, Vera; Montabella HS; Blanchard, MI; 2/98 SecSrCls; CncrtBnd; HonRl; NHS; NatlMeritCmnd; 4-H; SpnCl; Bsktbl; GAA; 4-HAwd; Mi State Univ; Science.

HOWARD, Vickie E; Fenton HS; Fenton, MI; HonRl; HospAde; JA; NHS; Quill&Scroll; SchPpr; LatCl; Trk; PPFtbl; JAAwd; College; Recreation.

HOWARTER, Deanna M; Princeton HS; Princeton, IL; Chrs; HonRl; NHS; SchMus; StuCncl; VPYthFlsp; GerCl; PpCl; GAA; AmLegAwd; Augustana College; Accounting.

HOWARTER, Teresa L; Lewistown Comm HS; Lewistown, IL; Band; Chrs; CncrtBnd; HonRl; MrchBnd; NHS; PepBnd; SchPl; PpCl; GAA; College; Vocation.

HOWE, Cynthia J; Sycamore HS; Sycamore, IL; 15/225 SecFrshCls; AFS; Chr; DrlTm; HonRl; Mdrgl; NHS; NatlThespSoc; StuCncl; PpCl; University; Teacher.

HOWE, Darcy A; Kirkwood HS; Kirkwood, MO; ChrhWkr; CmntyWkr; HonRl; PolWkr; SchMus; StuGov; YthFlsp; Yrbk; PresPpCl; Chrldr; PresAwd; Indiana University.

HOWE, Debbora M; Velva Public HS; Velva, ND; 1/48 Band; Chrs; CncrtBnd; HonRl; MrchBnd; NHS; PepBnd; StuCncl; EdYrBk; Yrbk; FBLA; FHA; PpCl; College; Special Ed.

HOWE, Douglas C; Owosso HS; Owosso, MI; CmntyWkr; PolWkr; SctActv; Bsktbl; Lake Superior State Clg; Teacher.

HOWE, Holly J; Central City Comm HS; Central City, IA; 4/48 Band; Chr; NHS; SchMus; PresStuCncl; Bsktbl; Chrldr; Cornell College; Art.

HOWE, Julie E; Marian Catholic HS; Chicago Heights, IL; TreasBand; CncrtBnd; HospAde; ModUN; Orch; StuCncl; Yrbk; LatCl; GAA; PresAwd; College; Medicine.

HOWE, Mary J; Fremont HS; Fremont, NE; Band; SecChr; Chrl; MrchBnd; NHS; NatlThespSoc; VPQuill&Scroll; SchMus; SchPl; Yrbk; U Of Ne; Journalism.

HOWE, Neal J; Pike HS; Indianapolis, IN; 99/267 Band; CncrtBnd; HonRl; MrchBnd; PepBnd; SchMus; StuGov; YthFlsp; Bsktbl; LetterGlf; IMSpt; University; Lawyer.

HOWE, Patricia; Milton Senior HS; Milton, WI; SecSophCls; Band; Chr; CncrtBnd; HonRl; MrchBnd; 4-H; PpCl; Technical College; Vocaional Secretary.

HOWE, Ronald D; Winnebago HS; Winnebago, MN; PresFrshCls; ChrhWkr; HonRl; LbryAde; YthFlsp; LetterBsbl; IMSpt; AmLegAwd; Voc Schl; Vocation.

HOWE, Shirley; Erskine HS; Erskine, MN; ; SecJrCls; Band; Chr; NHS; SchPl; RptrYrbk; EdSchPpr; PpCl; College.

HOWE, Susan J; Farmer City Mansfield HS; Farmer City, IL; 1/73 TrsFrshCls; TrsSophCls; TrsJrCls; TrsSrCls; AFS; Band; CncrtBnd; HonRl; MrchBnd; NHS; PepBnd; SchPl; Chrldr; GAA; Eastern Ill Univ; Geology.

HOWELL, Anthony; Vassar HS; Vassar, MI; HonRl; MrchBnd; NHS; PepBnd; SctActv; Univ; Math.

HOWELL, Carol A; Barry HS; Barry, IL; HonRl; MrchBnd; NHS; OffAde; SchAde; TchrAde; Twrl; RptrYrbk; RptrSchPpr; FTA; Business.

HOWELL, Debora K; Bradford HS; Bradford, IL; SecSophCls; TrsJrCls; SecSrCls; CncrtBnd; NHS; SecStuCncl; SchPpr; PresFHA; GAA; 4-HAwd; Bob Jones U; Missionary.

HOWELL, Debra S; Johnston City HS; Johnston City, IL; 3/78 SecTrsSophCls; VPJrCls; ChrhWkr; HonRl; NHS; Yrbk; FBLA; FHA; MthCl; PpCl; John A Logan Jr College; Child Care.

HOWELL, Douglas K; Oak Hill HS; Marion, IN; 4/180 PresFrshCls; VPSophCls; Chr; NHS; NatlMeritSF; StuCncl; Ftbl; Trk; Wrstlng; Coll; Engineering.

HOWELL, James D; Mitchell HS; Mitchell, IN; 7/141 DrmBgl; Chr; Chrl; ChrhWkr; HonRl; MrchBnd; NatlThespSoc; Quill&Scroll; SchMus; YthFlsp; Ftbl; College; Music.

HOWELL, James R; Seymour HS; Plainville, IL; 3/65 VPBand; CncrtBnd; HonRl; MrchBnd; NHS; PepBnd; StuCncl; 4-H; FTA; FrCl; University Of Illinois; Agriculture.

HOWELL, Marirose; Fennimore HS; Fennimore, WI; Band; CmntyWkr; CncrtBnd; HonRl; MrchBnd; PepBnd; 4-H; Bsbl; GAA; 4-HAwd; Vocational; Veterinarian Assistant.

HOWELL, Marjorie E; South Iron HS; Annapolis, MO; Band; ChrhWkr; CmntyWkr; CncrtBnd; HonRl; MrchBnd; PepBnd; 4-H; FHA; 4-HAwd; College; Law.

HOWELL, Mary; Northwestern HS; Blandinsville, IL; 14/58 AFS; Band; ChrhWkr; HonRl; HospAde; RptrYrbk; FHA; FTA; MthCl; GAA; W Il Univ; Med Tech.

HOWELL, Mike E; Cabool HS; Cabool, MO; Band; HonRl; RptrYrbk; RptrSchPpr; FFA; Univ; Teaching Or Bs Mgmt.

HOWELL, Nancy Jo A; Sacred Heart Academy; Mt Pleasant, MI; ChrhWkr; HonRl; LbryAde; SchAde; TchrAde; SchPpr; PpCl; ; Office Work.

HOWELL, N J; South Lyon HS; South Lyon, MI; HonRl; JrNHS; NHS; NatlMeritCmnd; NatlMeritSchl; OffAde; SchPl; TchrAde; LatCl; GAA; Mi State U; Psychiatry Or Medical Field.

HOWELL, Richard W; Yates City HS; Yates City, IL; PresJrCls; HonRl; StuCncl; StuGov; SchPpr; SpnCl; College; Banking.

HOWELL, Robert; Central HS; St Joseph, MO; HonRl; LatCl; SciCl; Coll; Med.

HOWELL, Robert G; Crocker HS; Crocker, MO; Band; HonRl; PresNHS; SctActv; LetterBsbl; LetterBsktbl; Univ Of Mo; Engi.

HOWELL, Ronald F; St Charles Comm HS; Saginaw, MI; HonRl; NHS; LetterBsbl; LetterBsktbl; LetterFtbl; College.

HOWELL, Shelly L; Truman HS; Independence, MO; DrlTm; NatlThespSoc; SchMus; SchPl; StuCncl; VPFHA; FrCl; PpCl; College; Elementary Ed.

HOWELL, Steven L; Henryville HS; Borden, IN; 1/70 HonRl; LbryAde; PresNHS; PresStuCncl; RptrSchPpr; SptEdSchPpr; 4-H; AmLegAwd; 4-HAwd; PresAwd; Coll; Teach.

HOWELL, Thomas C; Oak Lawn Community HS; Oak Lawn, IL; Chr; CmntyWkr; NatlThespSoc; RedCrAde; SchAde; SchPl; TchrAde; GerCl; SciCl; Swmmng; Elmhurst Col; Teacher.

HOWELL, Timothy R; Hillsdale HS; Hillsdale, MI; 29#33#37 MrchBnd; PepBnd; SctActv; YthFlsp; GerCl; LetterGlf; LetterTennis; IMSpt; Lake Superior State Col; Electronics.

HOWENSTEIN, Randy E; St Louis U HS; St Louis, MO; HonRl; LetterTennis; LetterTrk; LetterWrstlng; IMSpt; College; Professional.

HOWER, Judith; Gardner HS; Gardner, KS; 16/91 Chrs; HonRl; HospAde; ModUN; TchrAde; RptrSchPpr; SciCl; LetterBsktbl; Trk; IMSpt; Univ Ks; Sci.

HOWER, Matthew J; St Viator HS; Mount Prospect, IL; 50/292 ChrhWkr; HonRl; SchPl; StuCncl; StuGov; Teen; SpnCl; Bsbl; LetterFtbl; Univ Of Ill; Business.

HOWER, Michael L; Unified Dist #333 HS; Concordia, KS; PresFrshCls; ALBoysSt; HonRl; StuCncl; LetterBsktbl; LetterFtbl; LetterTrk; Coll; Professional.

HOWERTON, Cindy; Memorial HS; Joplin, MO; Chr; ChrhWkr; HonRl; NHS; TchrAde; YthFlsp; FBLA; IMSpt; Ms So State College; Business.

HOWERTON, Jamie C; Southern Boone County HS; Hartsburg, MO; Chr; ChrhWkr; DrlTm; HonRl; LitMag; University; Professional.

HOWERTON, John D; Pawnee HS; Pawnee, IL; VPSrCls; HonRl; JrNHS; StuCncl; FrCl; College; Professional.

HOWERY, Patricia A; Tipton HS; Tipton, IN; 8/199 HonRl; StuCncl; SchPpr; 4-H; GAA; 4-HAwd; College; Botany.

HOWES, Patricia J; Ithaca HS; Ithaca, MI; 5/148 SecSophCls; ALAGirlsSt; Band; CncrtBnd; HonRl; MrchBnd; NHS; SchMus; StuCncl; Twrl; Alma College; Chemistry.

HOWEY, Deborah J; Watertown Sr HS; Watertown, SD; 82/297 Chr; Chrs; ChrhWkr; HonRl; PresNatlFornLg; NatlThespSoc; PolWkr; SchMus; SchPl; South Dakota State Univ; Nurse.

HOWIE, Mary Ann E; Crystal Lake Comm HS; Crystal Lake, IL; AFS; Chr; Chrl; Chrs; ChrhWkr; DrlTm; DrmBgl; HonRl; LitMag; MrchBnd; NHS; SchMus; SchPl; SctActv; Eastern Illinois Univ; Medicine.

HOWIE, Richard R; Northwestern HS; Mellette, SD; Band; Chrs; CmntyWkr; HonRl; SchPl; YthFlsp; SchPpr; 4-H; SciCl; Ftbl; Clg; Science.

HOWK, John M; Burr Oak HS; Burr Oak, MI; PresJrCls; Band; Chrs; CncrtBnd; HonRl; MrchBnd; NHS; SchMus; SchPl; TchrAde; 4-H; College.

HOWLAND, Patricia M; Kent City HS; Ravenng, MI; 54/90 Chr; ChrhWkr; HonRl; TchrAde; SchPpr; FHA; Bsktbl; IMSpt; 4-HAwd; Coll; Nurse.

HOWLAND, Robert; East Pike HS; Milton, IL; 3/29 CmntyWkr; HonRl; NHS; SchPl; StuCncl; Yrbk; 4-H; FFA; CchngActv; Univ Of Ill; Agriculture.

HOWLETT, Ronald D; Flat River Central HS; Flat River, MO; HonRl; PolWkr; RptrSchPpr; SciCl; LetterBsktbl; LetterFtbl; LetterTrk; College.

HOXMEIER, Leslie J; Holdrege Sr HS; Holdrege, NE; Chr; Chrl; Chrs; ChrhWkr; HonRl; RedCrAde; SchMus; SchPl; RptrYrbk; Swmmng; U Of Neb; Prof.

HOXWORTH, Tamara L; O Fallon Twp HS; O Fallon, IL; TrsSophCls; TrsJrCls; Chrs; HonRl; JrNHS; SchMus; StuCncl; College; Professional.

HOXWORTH, Teresa L; Bridgeport HS; Bridgeport, NE; 9/62 ALAGirlsSt; Band; CncrtBnd; HonRl; MrchBnd; SecNHS; PepBnd; Quill&Scroll; SchMus; SchPl; VPStuCncl; Trk; VoiceDemAwd; Mounds Midway School; Nursing.

HOY, Mary B; Caseville Public HS; Caseville, MI; 1/21 TrsFrshCls; SecSophCls; SecJrCls; SecSrCls; Band; Chr; CncrtBnd; DrmMjrt; HonRl; JrNHS; Mdrgl; Bsbl; CaptBsktbl; Chrldr; DanFAwd; Central Michigan University; Secretary.

HOYER, Karen D; Beaver Dam HS; Beaver Dam, WI; 25/349 Chrs; Mdrgl; SchMus; GAA; University.

HOYER, Mitchell L; Cal Community HS; Hampton, IA; Band; HonRl; NHS; SchPl; StuCncl; SecYthFlsp; Pres4-H; FFA; LetterGlf; Pres4-HAwd; Iowa St Univ; Veterinary Med.

HOYLAND, Michele A; Traverse City HS; Traverse City, MI; 1/650 SecSrCls; HonRl; JrNHS; NHS; NatlMeritSF; SchMus; StuCncl; PpCl; PresAwd; Engineering.

HOYLE, Terri L; Polo HS; Polo, IL; 30/85 Band; CncrtBnd; HonRl; MrchBnd; PepBnd; YthFlsp; SpnCl; Swmmng; LetterTennis; GAA; College; Physical Ed.

HOYLES, Gary; Ogilvie HS; Ogilvie, MN; 4/56 Band; Chr; Mdrgl; MrchBnd; NHS; SchMus; SchPl; St Cloud St Coll; Certified Pubaccountant.

HOYME, Kenneth P; Neil A Armstrong HS; Golden Valley, MN; 18/592 Aud/Vis; Chr; TreasChrhWkr; HonRl; Mdrgl; NHS; NatlMeritCmnd; SchMus; Pres4-H; 4-HAwd; Univ; Elec Engin.

HOYOS, Sheila; Our Lady Star Of The Sea HS; Grasse Point Shore, MI; HonRl; LbryAde; NHS; SchPl; GAA; Univ; Astronomy.

HOYT, Deborah; Osceola HS; Osceola, WI; SchPl; FBLA; Coll; Home Ec.

HOYT, Jeffrey K; Quincy Sr HS; Quincy, IL; Chr; VPCncrtBnd; NHS; Orch; PepBnd; SctActv; YthFlsp; KiwanAwd; Univ Of Illinois; Engineering.

HOYT, John R; Theodore Roosevelt HS; Des Moines, IA; Chr; Chrs; HonRl; Orch; SchMus; SctActv; Ftbl; LetterWrstlng; Drake Univ; Medicine.

HOYT, Kathie R; Glenfield Sutton HS; Glenfield, ND; 3/14 SecJrCls; Band; Chrs; CncrtBnd; HonRl; MrchBnd; NHS; PepBnd; Valley City St College; English.

HOYT, Tedd J; North Sr HS; Eau Claire, WI; 1/400 HonRl; NHS; ROTC; TchrAde; GerCl; LetterTrk; IMSpt; Air Force Academy; Pilot.

HOYUM, Edward M; Jefferson HS; Cedar Rapids, IA; 106/451 Chr; HonRl; Orch; SchMus; LetterTrk; College; Mathematics.

HOZIE, Barbara L; Streator Twp HS; Streator, IL; 18/415 ChrhWkr; HonRl; NHS; StuCncl; SpnCl; LetterTennis; Ill State Univ; Medicine.

HOZMAN, Robert A; New Trier East HS; Glencoe, IL; 20/847 HonRl; NHS; Orch; PolWkr; StuGov; TchrAde; Northwestern Univ; Doctor.

HOZZIAN, Rosemary; St Ann HS; Chicago, IL; HonRl; JA; SchAde; IMSpt; Trade School; Interior Decorating.

HRABOVSKY, Eleanore S; Whiting HS; Whiting, IN; 10/104 Chrs; HonRl; LbryAde; NHS; SchPl; RptrSchPpr; FTA; SpnCl; PpCl; Chrldr; Purdue Calumet Univ; Medical Technology.

HRDLICKA, Brenda J; Crete HS; Crete, NE; TrsJrCls; Band; HonRl; Quill&Scroll; RptrSchPpr; FBLA; FHA; PpCl; SciCl; IMSpt; U Oj Ne; Microbiology.

HRESKO, Mark; Hamady HS; Flint, MI; 2/170 VPSrCls; HonRl; JrNHS; NHS; NatlMeritCmnd; NatlMeritSchl; KeyCl; Bsbl; Bsktbl; Ftbl; Gm Inst; Engr.

HRIBAL, C J; Hortonville HS; Hortonville, WI; 1/154 AFS; PresAud/Vis; NHS; StuCncl; StuGov; Yrbk; EdSchPpr; PresRusCl; CaptSwmmng; Coll; Writer.

HRIBEK, Craig M; Pineonning Area HS; Pinconning, MI; 13/260 Band; HonRl; MrchBnd; NHS; PepBnd; SchMus; SchPl; SchPpr; FTA; FrCl; Mich Univ; Prof Saxophonist.

HRIGORA, Karen; Grosse Ile HS; Grosse Ile, MI; Chr; DrlTm; CncrtBnd; HonRl; Mdrgl; NatlThespSoc; SchMus; SchPl; TchrAde; GAA; Mich State Univ; Choral Music Education.

HROVAT, Kinleigh J; Rolla Senior HS; Rolla, MO; HonRl; FDA; FNA; Univ Of Columbia; Medical Field.

HROW, David T; Deer River HS; Deer River, MN; Band; ChrhWkr; HonRl; LbryAde; 4-H; CaptBsktbl; CchngActv; Tradeb; Farmer.

HRUBAN, Judy L; Schuyler Central HS; Schuyler, NE; SecJrCls; Yrbk; 4-H; PpCl; Glf; BttyCrckrAwd; U Of Ne.

HRUBY, Christine A; Montgomery HS; Montgomery, MN; 6/92 HonRl; LbryAde; NHS; OffAde; SchPl; SctActv; StuCncl; TchrAde; GAA; PresAwd; St Marys Jr Coll; Physical Therapist Asstnt.

HRUPCIN, Catherine; So Division HS; Milwaukee, WI; HonRl; JrNHS; SctActv; PpCl; GAA; Business School; Vocaton.

HRUSKA, Dianna M; Patricks HS; Sidney, NE; 3/30 Chr; Chrs; ChrhWkr; CmntyWkr; HonRl; NHS; SchAde; SchPl; StuCncl; RptrYrbk; Nebraska Univ; Business.

HRUSKOCY, Michael J; Whiting HS; Whiting, IN; 4/100 PresFrshCls; PresSophCls; PresSrCls; ALBoysSt; Chrs; HonRl; PresNHS; SchMus; VPStuCncl; SpnCl; Bsktbl; CaptFtbl; LetterTrk; College; Veterinarian.

HRUZA, Suzanne L; North Bend Central HS; Morse Bluff, NE; 2/68 Chrs; CncrtBnd; HonRl; MrchBnd; NHS; StuCncl; 4-H; FHA; PpCl; 4-HAwd; Univ Of Nebraska; Medicine.

HRYHORYSAK, Jo Ann; Pana Sr HS; Pana, IL; 2/170 SecSophCls; SecJrCls; TrsSrCls; Band; HonRl; NHS; NatlMeritCmnd; EdSchPpr; VP4-H; GAA; Univ Of Il; Chemistry Research.

HRYNYSHYN, Alec; Pike HS; Indianapolis, IN; 55/234 HonRl; OffAde; LatCl; SciCl; Bsktbl; Trk; IMSpt; Univ Of Wyoming; Geology.

HSIUNG, Robert C; Rich Central HS; Park Forest, IL; 1/410 HonRl; NHS; NatlMeritSF; NatlSciFnd; Orch; MthCl; SciCl; Medical School; Medicine.

HSU, Khai L; Eastern HS; Lansing, MI; 5/20 HonRl; NatlFornLg; Bsktbl; Trk; Chrldr; IMSpt; DARAwd; GovHonPrgAwd; SARAwd; PresAwd; College; Professional.

HUBATCH, Kathleen M; Antigo HS; Antigo, WI; Band; CncrtBnd; JA; LbryAde; MrchBnd; 4-H; Chrldr; GAA; IMSpt; 4-HAwd; Coll; Professional.

HUBBARD, Bruce W; Fox Sr HS; Imperial, MO; 73/500 Chr; StuCncl; LetterBsbl; CaptBsktbl; LetterFtbl; Se Missouri State; Basketball Coach.

HUBBARD, David H; Jawas Area HS; Tawas, MI; Chr; College /unknown.

HUBBARD, David S; Oak Grove Lutheran HS; Fargo, ND; ALBoysSt; Chr; ChrhWkr; HonRl; SctActv; YthFlsp; Bsktbl; LetterFtbl; Glf; Trk; College.

HUBBARD, Deborah D; Highland Park HS; Highland Park, MI; ChrhWkr; HonRl; NHS; OffAde; SchAde; SchPl; TchrAde; CitAwd; Mercy Clg; Clothing Mrch.

HUBBARD, Elizabeth A; Aurora Central Catholic HS; Aurora, IL; 14/181 Chrs; HonRl; NHS; SchMus; Yrbk; PpCl; Bsbl; LetterBsktbl; LetterTennis; Trk; College; Pre Med.

HUBBARD, Jeff G; Elm Creek HS; Elm Creek, NE; 5/31 VPFrshCls; PresSophCls; HonRl; NHS; StuCncl; StuGov; TchrAde; YthFlsp; SchPpr; 4-H; LetterFtbl; LetterTrk; LetterWrstlng; 4-HAwd; Univ; Professional.

HUBBARD, Judith C; Powers Lake HS; Powers Lake, ND; SecFrshCls; SecSophCls; SecSrCls; Band; ChrhWkr; HonRl; NatlMeritCmnd; SchPl; StuCncl; RptrYrbk; RptrSchPpr; FHA; Chrldr; Duke Univ; Nursing.

HUBBARD, Leslie M; Batavia HS; Batavia, IL; 20/240 CncrtBnd; DrlTm; HospAde; NHS; StuCncl; YthFlsp; 4-H; Chrldr; GAA; 4-HAwd; Luther Coll; Med.

HUBBARD, Marlene V; Plano HS; Plano, IL; .

HUBBARD, Thomas J; St Teresa HS; Decatur, IL; 1/120 HonRl; NHS; AmLegAwd; Univ Of Notre Dame; Medicine.

HUBBARD, William A; Matthews HS; Matthews, MO; 1/43 Band; HonRl; MrchBnd; NHS; PepBnd; SchPl; StuCncl; RptrYrbk; College; Data Processing.

HUBBART, Cindy; Racine Lutheran Hs; Racine, WI; 3 ChrhWkr; HonRl; NHS; StuCncl; TchrAde; EdYrBk; 4-H; Bsktbl; LetterFtbl; VPGAA; College; Math Major.

HUBBARTH, Cindy M; Algonac HS; Fair Haven, MI; 2/209 HonRl; NHS; StuCncl; TchrAde; Twrl; Chrldr; GAA; IMSpt; VFWAwd; VoiceDemAwd; Fresno St Clg; Medical.

HUBBELING, Edwin L; Stevens HS; Rapid City, SD; ALBoysSt; NatlFornLg; StuCncl; StuGov; Bsktbl; College; Professional.

HUBBERT, Robbie D; Puxico HS; Pusico, MO; PresFrshCls; PresJrCls; CmntyWkr; CncrtBnd; HonRl; MrchBnd; SchPl; StuCncl; CivCl; SciCl; University.

HUBBLE, Melanie J; Academy Of Our Lady; Peoria, IL; 30/89 SecTrsSrCls; HonRl; NatlMeritCmnd; StuCncl; GAA; Univ; Sociology Major.

HUBBLE, Susan M; Richwoods HS; Peoria, IL; 90/149 NHS; StuCncl; LetterBsbl; LetterBsktbl; GAA; IMSpt; Ill St Univ; Phy Ed Teacher.

HUBBS, Faye J; Salem Sr HS; Salem, MO; HonRl; StuCncl; RptrSchPpr; FrCl;.

HUBER, Anne B; Crispus Attucks HS; Indianapolis, IN; ChrhWkr; HonRl; ModUN; VPNHS; StuCncl; VPYthFlsp; RptrYrbk; LetterBsktbl; LetterTrk; College.

HUBER, Brian R; Melrose Mindoro HS; Melrose, WI; 13/88 ChrhWkr; CmntyWkr; RedCrAde; SchPl; StuGov; RptrSchPpr; VP4-H; TreasFFA; 4-HAwd; College; Agriculture.

HUBER, Cindy R; Andes Central HS; Lake Andes, SD; 14/45 TrsSrCls; VPBand; CncrtBnd; HonRl; MrchBnd; NHS; PepBnd; CaptBsktbl; Trk; GAA; Mount Marty College; Medical Tech.

HUBER, Dalton D; Dodge HS; Dodge, ND; VPSophCls; PresJrCls; Band; Chrs; ChrhWkr; CncrtBnd; HonRl; SchPl; StuCncl; SchPpr; Bus School; Vocational.

HUBER, Jeannie L; Quinter HS; Quinter, KS; Chr; Chrs; ChrhWkr; DrlTm; LbryAde; SchMus; SchPl; TchrAde; FHA; Academy Of Hair Design; Cosmetologist.

HUBER, Jerene M; Pattonville HS; Maryland Heights, MO; HonRl; PpCl; SciCl; Trk; Chrldr; GAA; IMSpt; PPFtbl; University; Nursing.

HUBER, Joyce H; Arrowhead HS; Delafield, WI; 10/260 AFS; Band; NHS; PolWkr; SchPl; StuGov; RptrSchPpr; SpnCl; Swmmng; LetterTennis; College; Journalist.

HUBER, Laurel A; Friend Public HS; Friend, NE; ALAGirlsSt; Chr; HonRl; HospAde; LbryAde; SchMus; TchrAde; YthFlsp; 4-H; PpCl; Coll; Nursing.

HUBER, Mark R; Chaska HS; Chaska, MN; HonRl; FFA; Technical Schl; Vocation.

HUBER, Mary E; High School; Fremont, NE; SecFrshCls; ALAGirlsSt; Chrl; HonRl; NHS; Yrbk; PpCl; Chrldr;.

HUBER, Mary J; Fingal Public HS; Fingal, ND; SecSophCls; Band; Chrs; CncrtBnd; HonRl; LbryAde; PepBnd; SchPl; RptrYrbk; RptrSchPpr; Nd State Sch Of Sci; Lnp.

HUBER, Michael R; Champaign Central HS; Champaign, IL; 1/411 JrNHS; NatlFornLg; NHS; NatlMeritCmnd; SchMus; SchPl; TchrAde; RptrSchPpr; SpnCl; Coll; Professional.

HUBER, Nancy C; Columbus HS; Marshfield, WI; 25/117 Chrs; HonRl; PolWkr; VPStuCncl; FrCl; PpCl; GAA; IMSpt; University; Fashion Merchandizi.

HUBER, Paul D; Fatima HS; Jefferson City, MO; 17/119 Chr; HonRl; SchPl; TchrAde; RptrYrbk; EdSchPpr; College; Journalism.

HUBER, Ray; Fairbury Cropsey HS; Fairbury, IL; 8;-103 ALBoysSt; HonRl; NHS; Ftbl; Universityofillinois;business.

HUBER, Raymond S; Clintonville Sr HS; Clintonville, WI; 4/188 ChrhWkr; HonRl; NHS; NatlMeritCmnd; NatlThespSoc; PolWkr; SchPl; StuCncl; GerCl; BauchLmbAwd; GovHonPrgAwd; College; Professional.

HUBER, Robyn J; Harrison Comm HS; Harrison, MI; ALBoysSt; HonRl; TchrAde; FshEdYrbk; FFA; MthCl; Bsktbl; CitAwd;.

HUBER, Ross D; Fairbury Cropsey HS; Fairbury, IL; 18/103 ALBoysSt; Band; CncrtBnd; HonRl; MrchBnd; PepBnd; VPMthCl; LetterBsktbl; LetterGlf; Univ Of Illinois; Architecture.

HUBER, Stephen F; Columbus HS; Marshfield, WI; 9/108 HonRl; SchPl; StuCncl; RptrSchPpr; GerCl; Bsktbl; LetterFtbl; Trk; Wrstlng; IMSpt; College; Business Admin.

HUBER, Stephen M; Easton Comm HS; Easton, IL; 3/19 Chrs; CncrtBnd; HonRl; SchPl; LetterBsbl; LetterBsktbl; AmLegAwd; SARAwd; College; Mathematics.

HUBER, Susan; G C H S South; Granite City, IL; 3/630 ChrhWkr; HonRl; LitMag; NHS; SecGerCl; PpCl; LetterChrldr; AmLegAwd;.

HUBER, Susan M; Alton Sr HS; Alton, IL; 35/803 HonRl; JrNHS; NHS; StuGov; RptrYrbk; Yrbk; LatCl; PpCl; Chrldr; Quincy College; Physical Therapist.

HUBER, T Liisa; Brown Cty HS; Columbus, IN; 4/206 VPJrCls; DrmMjrt; HonRl; HospAde; ModUN; StuCncl; Yrbk; FrCl; Trk; Indiana Univ; Journalism.

HUBERT, Constance M; Reitz Memorial HS; Evansville, IN; VPFrshCls; VPSophCls; PresJrCls; VPSrCls; HonRl; NHS; VPStuCncl; PpCl; LetterTrk; CaptChrldr; Univ Of Notre Dame.

HUBERT, Richard R; Concordia HS; Concordia, KS; HonRl; IMSpt;.

HUBERT, Steven D; Charles City HS; Ionia, IA; 17/225.

HUBERT, Terry D; Mauston Area HS; Mauston, WI; 11/175 ALBoysSt; Chr; Chrs; HonRl; Mdrgl; NHS; SchMus; LatCl; LetterBsktbl; College; Chemistry.

HUBERTY, Patrick W; Wabeno HS; Wabeno, WI; Chrs; SchMus; SchPl; StuCncl; RptrSchPpr; FBLA; DanFAwd; Col;major Sutydyt.

HUBIN, Kendall R; Jetmore HS; Jetmore, KS; SptEdYrbk; 4-H; FFA; Bsbl; Bsktbl; LetterFtbl; LetterTrk; 4-HAwd; College; Vocation.

HUBL, Debra A; Lawrence Public HS; Lawrence, NE; PresFrshCls; Band; Chr; HonRl; MrchBnd; SchPl; Yrbk; PpCl; Chrldr; PPFtbl; Kearney State College; Nursing.

HUBL, Lyle W; Lawrence HS; Glenvil, NE; 1/30 VPFrshCls; PresSophCls; Band; CncrtBnd; HonRl; MrchBnd; NHS; SchPl; RptrYrbk; LetterTrk; U Of Ne; Professional.

HUBLER, Kenneth W; Vandalia Comm HS; Vandalia, IL; 29/118 University Of Illinois; Biomedical Engineer.

HUBLOU, Richard; Corona HS; Milbank, SD; 4/10 PresJrCls; TrsSrCls; HonRl; SchPl; StuCncl; College; Business.

HUBMANN, Kathleen; West Milwaukee HS; West Allis, WI; 25/172 Chrs; HonRl; NHS; Sdlty; Bsbl; Bsktbl; Trk; GAA; IMSpt; PPFtbl; Milwaukee Area Tech Coll; Accounting.

HUCHEL, Deborah C; Jamaica HS; Fairmount, IL; 1/54 PresFrshCls; VPJrCls; HonRl; PresNHS; EdSchPpr; PresFHA; PpCl; PresSciCl; DARAwd; VoiceDemAwd; Lake View School Of X Ray; X Ray Tech.

HUCHTEMAN, Jacquelyn K; Dadeville HS; Dadeville, MO; TrsJrCls; Chrs; ChrhWkr; HonRl; SchPl; RptrSchPpr; FHA; PpCl; Bsbl; Chrldr; Beauty School; Beautician.

HUCK, Kelly J; Denver Community HS; Waverly, IA; 10/78 Chr; Chrs; HonRl; JrNHS; YthFlsp; PpCl; LetterBsbl; CaptBsktbl; GAA; PPFtbl; Clge; Elem Ed.

HUCK, Linda M; Carl Brablec HS; Roseville, MI; HonRl; NHS; OffAde; ROTC; SchPl; SctActv; TchrAde; Oakland U; Elem Ed.

HUCK, Mary C; St Marys HS; Union Grove, WI; 1/76 ChrhWkr; HonRl; NatlMeritSF; TchrAde; Yrbk; SchPpr; Col; Elem Education.

HUCK, Michael; Mary D Bradford HS; Somers, WI; HonRl; KiwanAwd; Technical Inst; Auto Mechanic.

HUCK, Paul F; St Marys HS; Union Grove, WI; 4/71 HonRl; SchPl; PpCl; LetterFtbl; IMSpt; College; Engineer.

HUCKEBY, Kiki J; Gideon HS; Gideon, MO; 1/39 PresJrCls; Band; HonRl; MrchBnd; NHS; StuCncl; TchrAde; Bsktbl; GAA; IMSpt; Univ Semo; Athletic Director.

HUCKER, Kevin A; Hiawatha HS; Kirkland, IL; 14/50 Band; Chrs; CncrtBnd; HonRl; MrchBnd; NHS; PepBnd; EdSchPpr; 4-H; SpnCl; PpCl; LetterFtbl; LetterTrk; Univ Of Wisc; Accounting.

HUCKER, Michael K; La Crosse HS; Lacrosse, IN; PresFrshCls; PresJrCls; ALBoysSt; Band; HonRl; NHS; StuCncl; Yrbk; Bsbl; Bsktbl; Purdue University; Biology.

HUCKEY, Kirk A; Clark County R 1 HS; Kahoka, MO; PresSophCls; FFA; LetterBsktbl; LetterFtbl; Trk; IMSpt; Trade Schl; Vocation.

HUCKINS, Gregory S; E A Johnson Mem HS; Mt Morris, MI; 6/300 Chr; ChrhWkr; CncrtBnd; HonRl; NHS; SchMus; SchPl; StuCncl; StuGov; Ferris St College; Medicine.

HUDACHEK, Mark A; Hill Murray HS; Stillwater, MN; PresBand; HonRl; MrchBnd; NHS; Orch; PepBnd; SchMus; StuCncl; Yrbk; LetterSocr; Univ; Engineering Or Mathematics.

HUDDLE, Michael L; Woodruff HS; Peoria, IL; 25/281 Band; CncrtBnd; MrchBnd; Orch; PepBnd; SchMus; YthFlsp; Yrbk; KeyCl; Univ Of Il; Music.

HUDDLESTON, James B; Rolling Meadows HS; Rolling Meadows, IL; 180/540 Aud/Vis; CAP; HonRl; LbryAde; NHS; MthCl; SciCl; LetterTrk; William Raney Harper Jr Clge; Computer Sci.

HUDDLESTON, Shirley L; Paseo HS; K C, MO; 2/290 Chr; ChrhWkr; HonRl; NHS; NatlMeritCmnd; SctActv; StuCncl; StuGov; PresFrCl; PpCl; Univ Of Mo; Engineering.

HUDDLESTUN, Freddie G; Newton HS; Yale, IL; 6/185 Aud/Vis; HonRl; NHS; 4-H; FFA; IMSpt; Farming.

HUDDLESTUN, Susan L; Casey HS; Casey, IL; 3/94 Band; Chr; ChrhWkr; CncrtBnd; HonRl; Mdrgl; MrchBnd; SchMus; FHA; SpnCl; GAA; Eastern Ill Univ; Home Economics.

HUDECEK, Brenda J; Chesaning Union HS; Chesaning, MI; PresFrshCls; Band; CncrtBnd; DrlTm; HonRl; MrchBnd; Teen; Pres4-H; FrCl; GAA; College; Interior Design.

HUDGENS, Kerry J; Marion Sr HS; Marion, IL; 21/277 HonRl; JrNHS; NHS; Bsbl; CaptBsktbl; CaptFtbl; Trk; LionAwd; RotaryAwd; College; Accountant.

HUDGINS, Carolyn V; Sumner HS; St Lous, MO; 27/450 Band; HonRl; JA; LatCl; Coll; Prof.

HUDGINS, Kathy; Charleston R 1 HS; Caruthersville, MO; Chr; Chrs; ChrhWkr; HonRl; LbryAde; NHS; YthFlsp; FBLA; Vocation; Business.

HUDGINS, Patricia A; Elk Grove HS; Elk Grove Village, IL; HonRl; LitMag; Quill&Scroll; College; Journalism.

HUDKINS, Malinda; Manchester Hs; Manchester, MI; 2/102 VPSophCls; HonRl; StuCncl; TchrAde; GerCl; LetterBsbl; LetterBsktbl; CchngActv; GAA; Michigan State U;veterinary Mdicine.

HUDNUT, Barbara; R 1 North Callaway HS; Auxuasse, MO; Chr; ChrhWkr; HonRl; OffAde; TchrAde; College.

HUDON, Michael J; Pennfield HS; Battle Creek, MI; Band; Chr; CmntyWkr; CncrtBnd; HonRl; MrchBnd; PepBnd; SchMus; SciCl; IMSpt; Western Michigan College; Natural Science.

HUDSON, Allen L; Lena Winslow HS; Lena, IL; 2/94 Chrs; ChrhWkr; NatlMeritCmnd; StuCncl; Bsktbl; LetterTrk; College; Business.

HUDSON, Amanda M; Montello HS; Montello, WI; HonRl; NHS; SchPl; 4-H; FHA; FrCl; SpnCl; 4-HAwd; College; Physical Ed Recreation.

HUDSON, Amy E; Northwestern HS; Good Hope, IL; PresJrCls; HonRl; NHS; StuCncl; SciCl; Chrldr; Western Ill Univ; Veterinarian.

HUDSON, Barbara; Morrill Senior HS; Morrill, NE; Chrs; LbryAde; NHS; FHA; College.

HUDSON, Barbara; Oscoda Area HS; Oscoda, MI; HonRl; RptrSchPpr; Alpena Community College; Liberal Arts.

HUDSON, Beverly J; Eastern HS; Solsberry, IN; 3/80 Band; ChrhWkr; CncrtBnd; HonRl; HospAde; JrNHS; MrchBnd; NHS; PepBnd; OptClAwd; College; Nursing.

HUDSON, Brian D; Winston Churchill HS; Livonia, MI; Band; Mich Tech Univ; Electrical Engineer.

HUDSON, Dale R; Wellcome Memorial HS; Garden City, MN; 9/46 TrsSophCls; Chrs; ChrhWkr; HonRl; LbryAde; SchMus; SchPl; PresFFA; Bsbl; Ftbl; Trade School; Vacation.

HUDSON, Gerrilee; Pennville HS; Dunkirk, IN; 2/40 TrsJrCls; HonRl; NHS; StuCncl; SchPpr; PpCl; Bsktbl; GAA; AmLegAwd; 4-HAwd; Coll; Teaching.

HUDSON, Hannah M; Saybrook Arrowsmith HS; Saybrook, IL; VPJrCls; Chrs; HonRl; SchPl; StuCncl; FFA; LetterBsktbl; LetterTrk; Chrldr; GAA; IMSpt; 4-HAwd; JCAwd; College; Professional.

HUDSON, Janice K; West HS; North Liberty, IA; Chr; Chrs; ChrhWkr; HonRl; FrCl; LatCl; Trk; PresAwd; Coll; Doctor.

HUDSON, Julie M; Mt Clemens HS; Mt Clemens, MI; 18/397 Chr; CmntyWkr; CncrtBnd; CaptDrmMjrt; MrchBnd; NHS; NatlMeritSF; Orch; SchMus; KeyCl; Western Mi Univ; Music.

HUDSON, Karen M; Trego Community HS; Ellis, KS; HonRl; SchPl; FHA; PpCl; SciCl; LetterGlf; College; Professional.

HUDSON, Linda B; Farmington East HS; Hanna City, IL; 19/131 ChrhWkr; HonRl; NHS; RptrSchPpr; 4-H; KeyCl; IMSpt; AmLegAwd; DanFAwd;.

HUDSON, Linda M; Wyoming Pk HS; Wyoming, MI; ChrhWkr; College; Secretary.

HUDSON, Marsha; Homer; Litchfield, MI; 3/87 VPJrCls; HonRl; NHS; SchPl; TchrAde; LetterBsktbl; LetterTrk; Wayne State U; General Practioner.

HUDSON, Michael P; Girard HS; Girard, KS; 14/89 HonRl; NHS; SchPl; StuCncl; Pres4-H; PresSciCl; Bsbl; LetterFtbl; LetterTrk; 4-HAwd; College; Math Science.

HUDSON, Pamela G; Chicago Vocational HS; Chicago, IL; 16/778 HonRl; JrNHS; TchrAde; Univ; Business Admin.

HUDSON, Patricia C; Wahpeton HS; Wahpeton, ND; HonRl; Yrbk; SchPpr; SecKeyCl; PpCl; Chrldr; GAA; IMSpt; College; Commercial Ar.

HUDSON, Rose; Crane HS; Galena, MO; 8/26 HstJrCls; VPSrCls; HonRl; NatlThespSoc; SchPl; StuCncl; FHA; PpCl; SciCl; Southwest Missouri State;.

HUDSON, Roslyn F; Dakota HS; Hunter, ND; SecFrshCls; TrsFrshCls; VPSophCls; SecJrCls; Band; Chr; HonRl; NHS; SchPl; RptrYrbk; RptrSchPpr; 4-H; Bsktbl; Trk; College; Elem Ed.

HUDSPETH, John A; Petersburg Porta HS; Petersburg, IL; 30/122 JA; LbryAde; Trk; Wrstlng; IMSpt; College; Professional.

HUDSPETH, Mary L; Northern HS; Flint, MI; CmntyWkr; HonRl; LitMag; NatlMeritCmnd; TchrAde; EngCl; U Of Michigan; Journalism.

HUEBEL, Elizabeth A; Wonewoc Center HS; Wonewoc, WI; Band; CncrtBnd; HonRl; MrchBnd; PepBnd; StuCncl; Twrl; Yrbk; FHA; LetterBsbl; College; Nursing.

HUEBNER, Barbara A; Oakes HS; Oakes, ND; 2/68 PresSophCls; ALAGirlsSt; Band; Chrs; DrlTm; HonRl; SctActv; StuCncl; FHA; Nd State U; Dietetics.

HUEBNER, Candace L; Alma HS; Alma, WI; 2/39 TrsFrshCls; TrsJrCls; Chrs; ChrhWkr; HonRl; Mdrgl; SchMus; YthFlsp; RptrYrbk; EdSchPpr; SecFBLA; SecFTA; College; Professional.

HUEBNER, Catherine A; Puxico HS; Puxico, MO; SecSophCls; Band; Chrl; CncrtBnd; PepBnd; SchPl; PpCl; SciCl; IMSpt; University; Physical Education.

HUEBNER, Charles W; Michigan Lutheran Seminary; Saginaw, MI; 3/80 TrsJrCls; TrsSrCls; Band; Chrs; CncrtBnd; HonRl; MrchBnd; StuGov; Trk; IMSpt; Northwestern Lutheran; Minister.

HUEBNER, Deborah J; Cumberland HS; Barronett, WI; 5/105 Chrs; CmntyWkr; HonRl; SchPl; RptrYrbk; RptrSchPpr; 4-H; SpnCl; 4-HAwd; PresAwd; U Of Mn; Electrical Engineering.

HUEBNER, Richard T; Grand Island Sr HS; Grand Island, NE; 75/480 CmntyWkr; HonRl; NatlFornLg; PolWkr; LetterBsktbl; Nebraska Wes; Law.

HUEBNER, Rickie D; Wapsie Valley HS; Readlyn, IA; 5/94 Chr; HonRl; NHS; SchPl; LetterBsktbl; LetterFtbl; Hawkeye Inst Of Technology; Animal Science.

HUEBSCHMAN, Jeffery C; Heritage Hills HS; Evanston, IN; YthFlsp; Bsbl; Bsktbl;.

HUEDEPOHL, Anne K; Maine South HS; Park Ridge, IL; Chr; HonRl; LitMag; VPNHS; NatlMeritSF; StuCncl; RptrSchPpr; PresFrCl; VPPpCl; DARAwd; College; Languages Business.

HUEDEPOHL, Ann L; Williamsburg HS; Williamsburg, IA; 1/95 Chrs; HonRl; LbryAde; NatlMeritSF; StuCncl; YthFlsp; GerCl; LetterBsktbl; GAA; IMSpt; PPFtbl; College.

HUEHOLT, Diana L; Y J B Comm HS; Bagley, IA; 4/23 Band; Chr; Chrs; ChrhWkr; CncrtBnd; HonRl; MrchBnd; PepBnd; SchPl; FTA; PpCl; Bsbl; Bsktbl; College.

HUELSBECK, Michael J; St Marys HS; Menasha, WI; ALBoysSt; ALAGirlsSt; ChrhWkr; CmntyWkr; HonRl; JA; NatlMeritSchl; StuGov; YthFnd; FBLA; Trade School; Vocation.

HUELSEBUSCH, Sally; Naperville Central Hs; Naperville, IL; Chrs; HonRl; HospAde; NatlMeritCmnd; SchMus; College Of Dupage; Liberal Arts.

HUELSKAMP, Mary B; Marian HS; Omaha, NE; 2/162 TrsFrshCls; Chr; HonRl; HospAde; JrNHS; NHS; Sdlty; StuCncl; LetterBsktbl; Chrldr; IMSpt; College; Nursing.

HUELSMANN, Cynthia; Mater Dei HS; Auston, IL; 7/198 Band; Chrs; HonRl; NHS; NatlMeritCmnd; PepBnd; SchMus; RptrYrbk; SchPpr; FrCl; Univ; Curr Of Major Study.

HUELSMANN, Cynthia M; Mater Dei HS; Aviston, IL; 7/198 Band; Chrs; CncrtBnd; HonRl; MrchBnd; NatlMeritCmnd; PepBnd; SchMus; RptrYrbk; SchPpr; University.

HUELSMANN, David R; Central Community HS; Breeze, IL; 3/129 HonRl; NHS; EdYrBk; Bsbl; Bsktbl; CaptFtbl;.

HUENERGARDT, Gwen M; Ness City HS; Ness City, KS; SecJrCls; ALAGirlsSt; SecChrhWkr; HonRl; LbryAde; NHS; NatlThespSoc; FHA; PpCl; College; Home Ec.

HUERTER, Chris J; Creighton Prep; Omaha, NE; 30/210 HonRl; Sdlty; Bsbl; Ftbl; LetterSwmmng; IMSpt; Univ; Medicine.

HUESER, Mary L; Hubbard Community HS; Hubbard, IA; Chr; HonRl; PepBnd; SchMus; SchPl; YthFlsp; FHA; LetterBsbl; LetterBsktbl; LetterTrk;.

HUESMAN, Keith A; Titonka Consolidated; Titonka, IA; VPSrCls; ChrhWkr; HonRl; TchrAde; YthFlsp; LetterBsbl; LetterBsktbl; LetterTrk; CchngActv; College; Coaching & Physical Ed Health.

HUFF, Barbara K; North Nodaway R Vi HS; Hopkins, MO; 1/39 TrsSrCls; Band; Chr; HonRl; ModUN; NatlMeritSF; RedCrAde; PpCl; LetterBsktbl; LetterTrk; Coll; Psych.

HUFF, Cathy L; Wilmot HS; Twin Lakes, WI; ALAGirlsSt; HonRl; NHS; Quill&Scroll; StuCncl; EdYrBk; Trk; GAA; College; Professional.

HUFF, Charles B; South Iron HS; Annaplois, MO; PresFrshCls; HonRl; StuCncl; LetterBsbl;.

HUFF, Daniel R; Tipton HS; Clarksburg, MO; Band; CncrtBnd; HonRl; MrchBnd; NHS; PepBnd; FrCl; SpnCl; Ftbl; Univ Of Missouri; Engineer.

HUFF, David L; Clinton HS; Clinton, IL; 35/160 HonRl; SctActv; StuCncl; StuGov; TchrAde; FrCl; PpCl; Ftbl; College; Doctor.

HUFF, Jay L; Glendale HS; Springfield, MO; CmntyWkr; HonRl; NatlFornLg; SctActv; StuCncl; SciCl; Sw Missouri State Univ; Firefighting.

HUFF, Lea Ann; Sullivan HS; Sullivan, IN; 17/154 Chr; ChrhWkr; DrlTm; HonRl; OffAde; SchMus; SchPl; 4-H; SpnCl; GAA; Purdue Univ; Home Ec.

HUFF, Mark A; Anita Comm HS; Anita, IA; SecFrshCls; HonRl; NatlFornLg; NatlMeritSchl; 4-H; Bsktbl; Ftbl; Glf; Wrstlng; University; Accounting.

HUFF, Maryann; Clarkston HS; Clarkston, MI; 25/430 ALAGirlsSt; HonRl; JrNHS; NHS; Oakland Community College.

HUFF, Mary E; Woodlands Academy; Northfield, IL; ChrhWkr; HonRl; HospAde; SchMus; YthFnd; Bsktbl; College; Professional.

HUFF, Randall P; Fremont Mills Jr Sr HS; Tabor, IA; ChrhWkr; CmntyWkr; MrchBnd; SctActv; 4-H; LetterFtbl; LetterTrk; 4-HAwd; College; Professional.

HUFF, Valerie K; Dodge City Sr HS; Dodge City, KS; 5/341 Band; CncrtBnd; HonRl; MrchBnd; NHS; Orch; PepBnd; SchAde; SchMus; College; Education.

HUFFER, Dorothy; Parkside HS; Jackson, MI; 2/415 HonRl; SchMus; FrCl; Central Michigan Univ; Teaching.

HUFFINE, Laurie M; Chatard HS; Indianpolis, IN; 24/190 SecSophCls; Chrs; HonRl; JrNHS; LitMag; NHS; StuCncl; 4-H; SpnCl; PpCl; Ball St Univ; Elem Educ.

HUFFINES, Debra L; Edinburg HS; Edinburg, IL; 3/33 PresSrCls; Band; ChrhWkr; CncrtBnd; HonRl; LbryAde; MrchBnd; TchrAde;.

HUFFINGTON, Delores L; Melvin Sibley HS; Sibley, IL; 3/25 Band; HonRl; TreasNHS; RptrYrbk; RptrSchPpr; FTA; Chrldr; GAA; 4-HAwd; JAAwd; Univ Of Il; Recreational Therapist.

HUFFMAN, Carol L; Shawnee HS; Mcclure, IL; Chr; Chrs; ChrhWkr; HonRl; SchMus; SchPl; FBLA; FHA;.

HUFFMAN, Cheryl A; Arthur HS; Arcola, IL; 3/43 PresJrCls; TrsSrCls; Band; Chrs; ChrhWkr; NHS; SchPl; Yrbk; FTA; Eastern Illinois Univ; Teaching.

HUFFMAN, Joe A; Southern HS; Stronghurst, IL; SchPl; RptrSchPpr; CaptBsktbl; LetterFtbl; LetterTrk; College; Professional.

HUFFMAN, John D; Clark County Ri HS; Kahoka, MO; 6/94 ChrhWkr; NHS; PpCl; LetterBsktbl; LetterFtbl; LetterGlf; CchngActv; IMSpt; University Of Missouri; Business Admin.

HUFFMAN, Kathy; Beloit HS; Beloit, KS; 9/66 Chrl; Chrs; ChrhWkr; HonRl; NatlFornLg; Orch; SchPl; YthFlsp; 4-H; 4-HAwd; Kansas State Univ; Pre Law.

HUFFMAN, Melanie; Deep River Millersburg HS; Millersburg, IA; DrmBgl; ChrhWkr; HospAde; OffAde; PepBnd; SctActv; Yrbk; EdSchPpr; FHA; PpCl; College; Professional.

HUFFMAN, Myra G; Bismarc Henning HS; Danville, IL; 3/78 Band; Chrs; ChrhWkr; CncrtBnd; HonRl; MrchBnd; NHS; PepBnd; SchMus; EdSchPpr; 4-H; SpnCl; PpCl; Univ Of Ill; Political Science.

HUFFMAN, Myra G; Bismarck Henning HS; Danville, IL; 3/78 Chrs; ChrhWkr; CncrtBnd; HonRl; MrchBnd; NHS; NatlMeritCmnd; EdSchPpr; SpnCl; SciCl; Univ Of Illinois; Law.

HUFFMAN, Pamela L; Niagara HS; Niagara, WI; Chrs; OffAde; SctActv; Yrbk; SchPpr; FBLA;.

HUFFMAN, Patti; Richland Center HS; Richland Center, WI; Band; MrchBnd; 4-H; PpCl; Swmmng; Tennis; Chrldr;.

HUFFMAN, Raymond D; Banner County HS; Potter, NE; VPJrCls; Band; HonRl; NHS; SchPl; StuCncl; EdYrBk; EdSchPpr; LetterBsktbl; LetterFtbl; College.

HUFFMAN, Zane N; Madison Consolidated HS; Madison, IN; ChrhWkr; CmntyWkr; SchAde; VPYthFlsp; PpCl; CaptFtbl; LetterTrk; CaptWrstlng; IMSpt; College; Art.

HUFFMON, Stephen; Brookfield HS; St Catherine, MO; Airforce.

HUFFORD, Larry; Harmony HS; Farmington, IA; Yrbk; Univ.

HUFFSTUTLER, William D; Nashville Comm Conso HS; Nashville, IL; 2/138 NHS; SctActv; LetterTrk; Univ Of Illinois; Biology.

HUFNAGLE, Lorraine H; Kelliher HS; Kelliher, MN; Band; Chr; HonRl; NatlCathMusEdAsoc; StuCncl; EdYrBk; RptrSchPpr; GerCl; VFWAwd; CitAwd; Bemidji St Univ; Medicine.

HUG, Margaret E; Robert A Waller HS; Chicago, IL; 13/214 TrsSophCls; SecTrsJrCls; Chrs; HonRl; NHS; PolWkr; StuCncl; StuGov; TchrAde; Yrbk; SchPpr; Chrldr; University Of Chicago; Computer Science.

HUG, R Brian; Eisenhower HS; Decatur, IL; AFS; ChrhWkr; CncrtBnd; DrmMjrt; MrchBnd; TreasYthFlsp; Wheaton College; Professional.

HUGELEN, Denise A; Velva HS; Velva, ND; 3/48 SecJrCls; Band; Chrs; ChrhWkr; HonRl; NHS; TchrAde; Yrbk; FBLA; SecFHA; College;elem Education.

HUGENBERG, Karen A; Seymour HS; Quincy, IL; 6/65 PresSophCls; HonRl; SptEdSchPpr; Treas4-H; FHA; CaptBsbl; Trk; College.

HUGENER, Doreen E; Lake Mills HS; Lake Mills, WI; 2/113 VPFrshCls; VPSophCls; ALAGirlsSt; CncrtBnd; HonRl; MrchBnd; NHS; Yrbk; EdSchPpr; University; Law.

HUGGARD, Janet; H H Dow HS; Midland, MI; 14/433 HonRl; ModUN; NHS; SpnCl; Eastern Michigan Univ; Biology.

HUGGETT, Mark D; Gull Lake HS; Battlecreek, MI; ChrhWkr; RedCrAde; SctActv; TchrAde; 4-H; Bsbl; Bsktbl; Ftbl; Swmmng; IMSpt; College; Architect.

HUGGINS, Dale L; Goreville HS; Goreville, IL; Yrbk; 4-H; FFA; FHA; PpCl; SciCl; Bsbl; LetterBsktbl; IMSpt; VoiceDemAwd; Trade School.

HUGGINS, Karl E; Lincoln Consolidated HS; Ypsilanti, MI; 6/164 ALBoysSt; HonRl; NatlFornLg; NHS; Orch; StuCncl; 4-H; SpnCl; LetterSwmmng; LetterTrk; Univ Of Mi.

HUGHES, Barry K; Campus HS; Haysville, KS; 4/225 PresSophCls; PresJrCls; HonRl; ModUN; PresNHS; NatlMeritSF; PresStuCncl; TchrAde; SpnCl; LetterTennis; College; Political Science.

HUGHES, Beverly K; South Spencer HS; Grandview, IN; 16/126 ChrhWkr; HonRl; 4-H; GAA; Indiana State University; Dental Asst.

HUGHES, Brenda L; Floyd Central HS; Floyds Knobs, IN; Chrl; Chrs; ChrhWkr; HospAde; SchPl; TchrAde; YthFlsp; PpCl; GAA; College; Nurse.

HUGHES, Charles A; Waterford Mott HS; Drayton Plains, MI; 1/400 HonRl; SctActv; TchrAde; Mich Tech U; Physics.

HUGHES, Charles E; Chase County HS; Imperial, NE; 2/58 PresJrCls; Band; Chrs; ChrhWkr; HonRl; NHS; SchMus; SchPl; YthFlsp; Ftbl; Wrstlng; University; Music.

HUGHES, Christine; Central Comm HS; Dewitt, IA; HonRl; Yrbk; 4-H; FTA; PpCl; SciCl; 4-HAwd; St Ambrose College; Math.

HUGHES, Christopher W; South Lake HS; St Clair Shores, MI; 35/535 HonRl; ChmnBsbl; LetterFtbl; LetterWrstlng; Univ Of Detroit; Med Pro.

HUGHES, David; Plano HS; Plano, IL; Band; HonRl; NatlFornLg; SpnCl; Bsbl; Bsktbl; Trk; Wrstlng; University; Law.

HUGHES, David C; Vianney HS; Kirkwood, MO; 33/186 HonRl; OffAde; EdYrBk; Ftbl; Trk; U Of Mo; Journalism.

HUGHES, Deborah K; Girard HS; Girard, KS; Chr; ChrhWkr; CmntyWkr; DrlTm; HonRl; HospAde; NatlFornLg; NHS; YthFlsp; 4-H; P Univ ; Elem Educ.

HUGHES, Elaine; Clarke Community Hs; Osceola, IA; 10/110 HonRl; RptrYrbk; RptrSchPpr; 4-H; FHA; 4-HAwd;.

HUGHES, Frank L; Central HS; Omaha, NE; HonRl; JA; LbryAde; NatlMeritCmnd; College; Accounting.

HUGHES, Gregg; Hay Springs Public HS; Hay Springs, NE; 17/40 PresJrCls; Chrs; ChrhWkr; HonRl; NHS; SchPl; CaptBsktbl; CaptFtbl; CaptTrk; AmLegAwd; Collg.

HUGHES, Harold; Flat Rock HS; Flat Rock, MI; Band; CncrtBnd; JrNHS; Mich Tech Univ; Civil Eng.

HUGHES, Harry R; Aurora West HS; Aurora, IL; Chr; ChrhWkr; HonRl; NHS; NatlMeritSF; Orch; SchMus; College; Music Mathematic.

HUGHES, Helen E; Albia HS; Albia, IA; 7/150 HonRl; NHS; Quill&Scroll; SchPl; RptrSchPpr; FHA; PpCl; GAA; William Penn Clg; Elem Ed.

HUGHES, James A; Whitefish Bay HS; Whitefish Bay, WI; AFS; ChrhWkr; HonRl; NHS; PolWkr; Quill&Scroll; Yrbk; U Of Wi; Law.

HUGHES, James W; Bath HS; Bath, MI; HonRl; JA; SctActv; SpnCl; MthCl; SciCl; Wrstlng; JAAwd; CitAwd; Univ; Doctor.

HUGHES, Jane; Parsons Sr HS; Parsons, KS; 11/168 HonRl; IntrClCncl; NHS; SctActv; Tennis; Trk; PPFtbl; College.

HUGHES, Janet M; Williston HS; Williston, ND; HonRl; Yrbk; FFA; PpCl; LetterBsktbl; CaptTrk; PresGAA; Univ Nd Williston; Pro Coaching.

HUGHES, Jerry A; Frankton HS; Elwood, IN; 16/175 Band; CncrtBnd; HonRl; MrchBnd; NHS; PepBnd; SchMus; Itt; Electronics.

HUGHES, John; Macomb Hs; Macomb, IL; Aud/Vis; HonRl; Yrbk; SpnCl; LetterFtbl; LetterTrk; College; Environmental Health.

HUGHES, John F; Glenbard South HS; Glen Ellyn, IL; 90/292 SciCl; Ftbl; Glf; Trk; Univ Of Southern Il; Pilot.

HUGHES, Julie A; Albia Comm HS; Albia, IA; Aud/Vis; DrlTm; HonRl; SecFHA; SecFTA; Central Clg; Math.

HUGHES, Kathi J; Maple Valley HS; Nashville, MI; HonRl; NHS; StuCncl; 4-H; FFA; Chrldr; PPFtbl; 4-HAwd; Michigan State Univ; Professional.

HUGHES, Kathryn J; New Richmond HS; New Richmond, WI; HonRl; Orch; SchMus; Minn Schl Of Business; Accounting.

HUGHES, Kevin E; Sterling HS; Sterling, IL; Aud/Vis; Chr; Chrs; ChrhWkr; HonRl; LbryAde; NatlThespSoc; PolWkr; SctActv; PresGerCl; Sauk Valley Jr Clge; Photography.

HUGHES, Kimberly S; Winamac Comm HS; Star City, IN; AFS; Band; Chr; ChrhWkr; CncrtBnd; HonRl; IntrClCncl; Bsktbl; LetterTrk; Chrldr; GAA; IMSpt; College; Medicine.

HUGHES, Lawrence R; Spencer Community HS; Spencer, IA; 8/168 Chr; CmntyWkr; HonRl; JCC; NHS; NatlMeritCmnd; PolWkr; SctActv; SchPpr; FrCl; LatCl; SpnCl; Univ Of Iowa; Law.

HUGHES, Lori J; Central HS; St Joseph, MO; 151/550 HonRl; TchrAde; FTA; GerCl; MthCl; PpCl; SciCl; University; Medical And Musical.

HUGHES, Lynn; Maquoketa Comm HS; Maquoketa, IA; TrsSrCls; Chr; College; Curriculum Of Major Study.

HUGHES, Mary B; Rock Falls Twp HS; Rock Falls, IL; 5/270 ChrhWkr; HonRl; NHS; NatlThespSoc; SchPl; RptrYrbk; RptrSchPpr; FTA; SpnCl; Univ; Professional.

HUGHES, Mary B; Chatard HS; Indianapolis, IN; 5/192 CmntyWkr; HonRl; NHS; NatlMeritCmnd; SchPl; RptrYrbk; PpCl; CchngActv; IMSpt; Purdue U; Medical Tech.

HUGHES, Mary E; Okawville HS; Okawville, IL; 20/68 TrsJrCls; Chrs; HonRl; SchPl; StuCncl; RptrSchPpr; FHA; PpCl; LetterTrk; Chrldr; S Illinois Univ; Social Work.

HUGHES, Melanie G; Benton HS; Thompsonville, IL; 34/185 Chrs; ChrhWkr; HonRl; HospAde; YthFlsp; SchPpr; 4-H; FNA; LatCl; GAA; AmLegAwd; Nursing School; Nurse.

HUGHES, Michael; Catholic Central HS; Livonia, MI; /250 HonRl; PolWkr; SctActv; Bsbl; IMSpt; Univ; Law.

HUGHES, Michele M; Godwin Heights HS; Wyoming, MI; 6/186 IntrClCncl; NatlFornLg; NHS; SchPl; VPStuCncl; PresFTA; TreasGerCl; PpCl; LetterTennis; GAA; PPFtbl; AmLegAwd; College; German.

HUGHES, Richard P; Adlai E Stevenson HS; Livonia, MI; ChrhWkr; NatlMeritCmnd; LetterTrk; U S Military Academy; Mathematics.

HUGHES, Rose; Paseo Hs; Kansas City, MO; Chr; ChrhWkr; HonRl; FHA; SciCl; Trk; College; Professional.

HUGHES, Shannan C; Chosen Valley HS; Chatfield, MN; Band; Chr; Chrs; CncrtBnd; HonRl; Mdrgl; MrchBnd; NHS; PepBnd; SpnCl; College; Unknown.

HUGHES, Sharon E; Springfield Southeast HS; Springfield, IL; 17/473 ChrhWkr; HonRl; NHS; YthFlsp; FBLA; Business Sch; Private Secretary.

HUGHES, Steven H; Pem Day HS; Mission Hills, KS; PresAFS; HonRl; Mdrgl; SchMus; SchPpr; Bowdoin College; Business.

HUGHES, Susan E; Lancaster HS; Lancaster, WI; Band; Chrs; HonRl; PepBnd; SchMus; RptrSchPpr; 4-H; LetterTrk; GAA; IMSpt; 4-HAwd; Univ Of Wisconsin; Nursing.

HUGHES, Susan M; Stapleton Public HS; Stapleton, NE; 2/31 TrsJrCls; Chrs; HonRl; NHS; StuCncl; Yrbk; FHA; PpCl; Trk; PPFtbl; 4-HAwd; Trade; Vocational.

HUGHES, Theresa A; Centennial Public HS; Utica, NE; 6/57 ALAGirlsSt; Band; CncrtBnd; HonRl; MrchBnd; NHS; PepBnd; SchPl; RptrYrbk; EdYrBk; Yrbk; RptrSchPpr; FHA; PresPpCl; Trk; Nebraska Wesleyan Univ; Theatre Arts.

HUGHES, Vera L; Eisenhower HS; Decatur, IL; 21 308 AFS; ChrhWkr; NHS; NatlMeritSF; FrCl; Grinnell College.

HUGHES, William S; Parkwood HS; Joplin, MO; AFS; HonRl; NHS; LatCl; Univ Of Missouri; Medicine.

HUGHEY, Beverly A; Ottawa HS; Ottawa, KS; 2/183 ALAGirlsSt; Chrs; ChrhWkr; NHS; SchMus; SchPl; EdSchPpr; 4-H; FBLA; PpCl; College; Music.

HUGO, Nancy L; Central Catholic HS; West Point, NE; HonRl; NHS; SchMus; SctActv; SpnCl; MthCl; PpCl; SciCl; Trk; IMSpt; College; Medical Field.

HUGUELET, Robert J; Brother Rice HS; Oak Lawn, IL; 60/420 HonRl; LbryAde; NHS; SptEdSchPpr; Ftbl; Tennis; Northwestern Univ.

HUGUSTYN, Donna M; Queen Of Peace HS; Chicago, IL; 11/430 PresNHS; PresLatCl; SpnCl; GAA; University Of Illinois; Counselor.

HUHN, Beth E; William H Taft HS; Chicago, IL; 1/816 Chrs; HonRl; IntrClCncl; JrNHS; LitMag; NHS; NatlMeritSF; OffAde; PresFrCl; LetterGAA; Univ; Math.

HUHN, Laurence J; Bishop Dwenger HS; Grabill, IN; College; Conservation.

HUHN, Mary; St Patrick HS; Portland, MI; CmntyWkr; HonRl; NHS; TchrAde; SptEdYrbk; Yrbk; Bsktbl; IMSpt; Trade School; Vocation.

HUIGENS, Kevin J; Rapid City Central HS; Rapid City, SD; 8/583 AFS; Band; ChrhWkr; HonRl; LitMag; MrchBnd; NatlFornLg; NatlMeritSF; FrCl; Univ Of Chicago; Foreign Language.

HUINKER, Larry J; Garner Hayfield Comm HS; Garner, IA; 6/68 PresSophCls; PresSrCls; HonRl; NHS; College; Professional.

HUINKER, Mary J; Garner Hayfield HS; Garner, IA; 28/65 ChrhWkr; CmntyWkr; HonRl; LbryAde; PpCl; College.

HUISENGA, Kevin M; Gildden Ralsten HS; Glidden, IA; ALBoysSt; Band; Chr; CncrtBnd; MrchBnd; PepBnd; SchMus; SchPl; YthFlsp; RptrYrbk; Bsktbl; Glf; College; Accounting.

HUISINGA, Henry J; Clarion HS; Clarion, IA; Chrs; SchMus; SchPl; Yrbk; RptrSchPpr; Wartburg College; Chemistry.

HUISJEN, Nancy L; Fremont HS; Fremont, MI; 99/189 SecSrCls; Chr; ChrhWkr; HospAde; StuCncl; DanFAwd; Davenport Clg; Med Secretary.

HUISKAMP, Janne L; Keokuk HS; Keokuk, IA; 14/210 DrlTm; HonRl; LitMag; NHS; StuCncl; RptrYrbk; SptEdSchPpr; SpnCl; LetterSwmmng; LetterTennis; Clge; Phy Ed & History Teacher.

HUISMAN, James D; Wellsburg Comm HS; Grundy Center, IA; PresSophCls; HonRl; SchPl; StuCncl; Yrbk; Trade Schl; Mechanic.

HUISMAN, Lisa M; Ellsworth Public HS; Ellsworth, MN; Band; Chr; CncrtBnd; SchMus; SchPl; EdYrBk; Yrbk; 4-H; FHA; Chrldr; College; Curriculm Of Major Study.

HUITING, Tara J; Downs HS; Downs, KS; HonRl; OffAde; SchPl; 4-H; FFA; FHA; SpnCl; PpCl; Trk; Art Or Clown School; Clown.

HUITSING, Henry G; Holland Christian HS; Holland, MI; ALBoysSt; HonRl; RptrYrbk; Swmmng; Tennis; IMSpt; Calvin Coll; Medical Field.

HUIZENGA, Gary D; Morrison Comm HS; Morrison, IL; CaptBsbl; LetterBsktbl; LetterTrk; ALAGirlsSt; Univ; Teaching.

HUIZENGA, Jack A; Fulton HS; Fulton, IL; Chr; ChrhWkr; JA; NatlThespSoc; YthFlsp; Ftbl; Trk; Wrstlng; Coll.

HULET, Paul A; Gorin R Iii HS; Gorin, MO; PresSophCls; SecSrCls; SchPl; VPStuCncl; Yrbk; 4-H; LetterBsbl; CaptBsktbl; Trade Sch.

HULETT, Thomas A; Munster HS; Munster, IN; 107/440 HonRl; NatlThespSoc; SchMus; SchPl; Trk; IMSpt; Clg; Architect.

HULINSKY, Barbara J; Brule HS; Brule, NE; 5/17 Band; Chrs; CmntyWkr; HonRl; StuCncl; SchMus; TchrAde; 4-H; PpCl; GAA; Kearney State College; Home Economics.

HULL, Andrew; Our Lady Of The Lakes HS; Waterford, MI; 9/57 ChrhWkr; HonRl; NHS; NatlMeritCmnd; SctActv; Bsbl; Bsktbl; Ftbl; College; Professional.

HULL, Deborah A; Chetopa HS; Chetopa, KS; 2/34 Band; NHS; NatlThespSoc; Twrl; LetterTrk; Chrldr; IMSpt; CaptPPFtbl; Kansas St College; Elem Education.

HULL, Dennis A; Garrett HS; Garrett, IN; 1/150 ChrhWkr; HonRl; TreasNHS; NatlMeritSF; CaptTrk; Purdue Univ; Engineering.

HULL, Diane L; High School; Hill City, KS; Band; Chr; Chrl; Chrs; ChrhWkr; CmntyWkr; CncrtBnd; HonRl; MrchBnd; ModUN; Bsbl; Bsktbl; Trk; University; Science.

HULL, Genna M; Haven HS; Haven, KS; 1/91 HstFrshCls; HonRl; NHS; StuCncl; Twrl; EdSchPpr; TreasFHA; PpCl; Trk; Chrldr; Kansas Univ Lawrence; Education.

HULL, Judy; Tarkio HS; Tarkio, MO; 13/64 ChrhWkr; CncrtBnd; HonRl; MrchBnd; NHS; Twrl; EdYrBk; FHA; Bsbl; Trk; Nw Missouri State Univ.

HULL, Kevin L; Garrett HS; Garrett, IN; FFA; Bsbl; Bsktbl; Ftbl; Glf; Socr; Swmmng; Tennis; Trk; Wrstlng; CchngActv;.

HULL, Ronald L; Lapel HS; Lapel, IN; LbryAde; YthFlsp; 4-HAwd; Indiana Univ; Accounting.

HULL, Sherry; Bishop Ward HS; Kansas City, KS; Chrs; HonRl; ModUN; SchMus; TchrAde; SpnCl; Trenton Junior College; Lawyer.

HULL, Sue H; Ithaca HS; Ithaca, MI; Chr; ChrhWkr; HonRl; NHS; SchMus; StuCncl; YthFlsp; RptrYrbk; 4-H; FHA; PpCl; Chrldr; BttyCrckrAwd; Michigan State Univ; Home Economics.

HULL, Susan M; Granite City South HS; Granite, IL; Chrs; Certified Laboratory Assistant.

HULL, Terry A; Hill City HS; Hill City, KS; 3/54 Band; Chrl; Chrs; ChrhWkr; CncrtBnd; ModUN; NHS; PepBnd; SchMus; Ftbl; Kansas State Univ; Electrical Eng.

HULL, Theresa A; North Adams HS; Jonesville, MI; 1/52 Band; CncrtBnd; HonRl; MrchBnd; NHS; PepBnd; SchPl; StuCncl; StuGov; LetterTrk; College; Business Education.

HULL, Treva E; Remington HS; Whitewater, KS; 1/50 Band; Chrs; HonRl; PepBnd; SchMus; Yrbk; PpCl; CaptBsbl; Bsktbl; GAA; College; Vocation.

HULLINGER, Cheri L; Wayne Community HS; Corydon, IA; Chr; ChrhWkr; NHS; Yrbk; 4-H; FHA; FTA; SpnCl; SciCl; LetterBsktbl; 4-HAwd; JAAwd; CitAwd; Kirksville College; Teach.

HULLMAN, Lana J; Falls City HS; Falls City, NE; Band; CncrtBnd; MrchBnd; PepBnd; SchMus; StuGov; PpCl; GAA; IMSpt; Lincoln School Of Commerce; Accounting.

HULME, Patricia K; Seymour HS; Seymour, MO; 9/52 Band; Chr; ChrhWkr; CncrtBnd; HonRl; JrNHS; SchPl; StuCncl; TchrAde; PpCl; College; Music.

HULSETLER, Mark D; Kanawha HS; Kanawha, IA; 1/21 TrsJrCls; TrsSrCls; Band; Chrs; CncrtBnd; HonRl; Mdrgl; NatlMeritSF; PepBnd; SchMus; PresStuCncl; Yrbk; Bsktbl; LetterTrk; College; Music.

HULSHOF, Helen M; West Sioux Comm HS; Ireton, IA; 6/79 Chrs; ChrhWkr; HonRl; LbryAde; NHS; SchMus; SchPl; TchrAde; RptrYrbk; EdSchPpr; 4-H; FTA; Univ Of So Dakota; Computer Science.

HULSHOF, Joseph G; Notre Dame HS; Oran, MO; 10/79 Band; Chr; ChrhWkr; HonRl; VPNHS; PepBnd; FBLA; LetterTrk; IMSpt; Univ Of Mo; Ag Mechinization.

HULSHOF, Kenny C; Kelly HS; Bertrand, MO; 2/64 PresSophCls; ChrhWkr; HonRl; SchPl; SctActv; FFA; SpnCl; LetterBsbl; LetterBsktbl; GodCntryAwd; Purdue University; Professional.

HULSING, Julie; Rockwell Swaledale HS; Rockwell, IA; Band; Chrs; ChrhWkr; HonRl; HospAde; RptrYrbk; FHA; PpCl; Bsktbl; Chrldr; Capri Cosmetology Coll; Cosmetologist.

HULSLANDER, Sarah L; Ottawa Twp HS; Marselles, IL; 34/420 Chr; ChrhWkr; HonRl; NHS; NatlMeritFnl; NatlThespSoc; SchMus; PresYthFlsp; SciCl; Illinois St U; Biological Research.

HULSTEDT, Colleen; Belvidere Hs; Belvidere, IL; 2 AFS; Chrs; HonRl; NHS; YthFlsp; RptrYrbk; SecFTA; PresFrCl; PpCl; GAA; Trinity Gollege;elementary Teacher.

HULSTEIN, Leon R; Sheldon Community HS; Ashton, IA; Chrs; ChrhWkr; DARAwd; Trade; Vocation.

HULTBERG, Douglas B; East HS; Duluth, MN; 107/523 CAP; HonRl; NHS; Quill&Scroll; StuCncl; EdYrBk; Yrbk; LetterFtbl; IMSpt; CitAwd; College; Business.

HULTGREN, Donald W; York Comm HS; Elmhurst, IL; 116/900 HonRl; NatlFornLg; Augustana College.

HULTQUIST, Barry C; Belview Public HS; Belview, MN; 1/20 VPFrshCls; Chrs; ChrhWkr; HonRl; NHS; SchPl; IMSpt; College.

HULTZ, Karen K; Marion Co HS; Philadelphia, MO; TrsJrCls; PresSrCls; ChrhWkr; HonRl; SchPl; RptrYrbk; FshEdYrbk; Yrbk; EdSchPpr; FHA; Bsktbl; Trk; GAA; College; Home Economics.

HULVERSON, Cindy L; Durand HS; Durand, WI; VPSophCls; Chr; HonRl; NatlFornLg; NHS; Sacrstn; Sdlty; FrCl; Univ Of Wisconsin; English.

HULVEY, Diane K; North HS; Omaha, NE; Band; Chrl; CncrtBnd; HonRl; MrchBnd; OffAde; PepBnd; SchMus; RptrSchPpr; FFA; Coll; Professional.

HUM, Diana; Mt Pulaski; Lincoln, IL; 15/101 Band; HonRl; NHS; PepBnd; SchMus; RptrSchPpr; Pres4-H; TreasGerCl; PpCl; BttyCrckrAwd;.

HUMBERT, Michael A; Dwight Twp HS; Dwight, IL; 10/110 HonRl; LbryAde; RptrYrbk; RptrSchPpr; LetterGlf; Univ Of Illinois; Professional.

HUMBLE, Douglas P; Van Buren Comm HS; Cantril, IA; 5/61 ALBoysSt; HonRl; NHS; SchMus; SchPl; SctActv; RptrYrbk; RptrSchPpr; LetterBsbl; LetterBsktbl; LetterFtbl; PPFtbl; College; Liberal Arts.

HUMBLE, Willard A; Meridian Dist 101 HS; Pulaski, IL; Band; HonRl; SchPl; LetterBsktbl; Trk; CchngActv; Trade School; Vocational.

HUME, Melodee; Urbandale Senior Hs; Urbandale, IA; 1/250 Chr; ChrhWkr; CmntyWkr; HonRl; JA; NHS; StuCncl; YthFlsp; 4-H; MthCl; U Of Iowa; Medicine.

HUME, Starr A; Houghton HS; Houghton, MI; SecSophCls; HonRl; HospAde; StuCncl; Yrbk; RptrSchPpr; PpCl; Chrldr; Michigan Tech Univ; Accounting.

HUMERICKHOUSE, Gina R; Heritage Christian Academy; Anderson, IN; College; Christian Science.

HUML, Jeffrey P; Fenwick HS; Westchester, IL; 3/220 PresSophCls; Chrs; HonRl; SchPl; StuCncl; LetterTrk; Chrldr; Notre Dame Univ; Medicine.

HUMMEL, Beverly A; Hague Public HS; Hague, ND; 2/13 PresJrCls; Chr; HonRl; OffAde; SchAde; TchrAde; Bsktbl; Trk; Chrldr; GAA; Clge; Rn.

HUMMEL, Cheryl A; West Catholic HS; Grand Rapids, MI; 13/910 HonRl; HospAde; NHS; SchMus; Bsktbl; Trk; IMSpt; Col; History.

HUMMEL, Robert E; Bloom Township HS; Steger, IL; HonRl; JrNHS; College; Math.

HUMPAL, John J; Evanston Twp HS; Evanston, IL; HonRl; PolWkr; TchrAde; RptrSchPpr; University; Journalism.

HUMPHRES, Wesley D; Kansas HS; Ashmore, IL; Band; CncrtBnd; HonRl; PepBnd; YthFlsp; FFA; Lakeland Jr Clg; Farm.

HUMPHREVILLE, Roger G; Holy Cross HS; Chicago, IL; 2/314 HonRl; NatlFornLg; NHS; NatlMeritSF; SctActv; Univ Of Chicago; Attorney.

HUMPHREY, Bill; Seymour HS; Quincy, IL; 20/68 Band; CncrtBnd; MrchBnd; PepBnd; SchMus; YthFlsp; 4-H; FFA; PpCl; Trk; Farming.

HUMPHREY, Douglas L; Mt Pleasant HS; Mt Pleasant, IA; HonRl; LetterBsbl; LetterFtbl; Wrstlng; IMSpt; Coll; Maj Study.

HUMPHREY, Eloise; North Division Hs; Milwaukee, WI; 22#29#37 HonRl; JA; MrchBnd; StuCncl; FNA; Culveruio College ; Nursing.

HUMPHREY, Karla; Davis County Comm HS; Milton, IA; TrsSrCls; Band; CncrtBnd; DrlTm; HonRl; MrchBnd; NHS; OffAde; PepBnd;.

HUMPHREY, Lori J; Pella Community HS; Pella, IA; Band; Chr; Chrs; ChrhWkr; CncrtBnd; HonRl; MrchBnd; NHS; Quill&Scroll; StuCncl; Twrl; Bsktbl; Glf; College; Elementary Education.

HUMPHREY, Michael J; Clare HS; Clare, MI; 20/158# Band; Chrs; HonRl; MrchBnd; PepBnd; StuCncl; TchrAde; SpnCl; LetterBsbl; Ftbl; Central Mi Univ; Bach Education.

HUMPHREY, Sam J; Edwards County HS; Albion, IL; VPSophCls; SctActv; Bsbl; Ftbl; Univ; Dentistry.

HUMPHREY, Tim J; Beatrice HS; Beatrice, NE; Band; CncrtBnd; MrchBnd; PepBnd; SctActv; Yrbk; SchPpr; Bsktbl; Ftbl; Univ Of Nebraska; Business.

HUMPHREYS, Arthur D; Minooka Comm HS; Minooka, IL; Chr; Chrs; ChrhWkr; HonRl; Mdrgl; SchPl; SctActv; Bsbl; Ftbl; Trk; Wrstlng; College; Business.

HUMPHRIES, Ellen J; St Josephs Acad; Florissant, MO; SecSophCls; ChrhWkr; HospAde; RedCrAde; StuCncl; TchrAde; SchPpr; SpnCl; GAA; IMSpt; Work.

HUMPHRIES, Ruth A; Harper Creek HS; Battle Creek, MI; 5/221 Band; ChrhWkr; HonRl; MrchBnd; NHS; SchPl; Twrl; SchPpr; SpnCl; NCTE; College;.

HUMTER, Gary L; Ludington HS; Ludington, MI; HonRl; Mi Tech Univ; Mechanical Eng.

HUNCKLER, Matthew D; Huntington Catholic HS; Huntington, IN; SecSophCls; HonRl; StuCncl; SchPpr; PpCl; LetterBsktbl; LetterGlf; LetterTrk; CchngActv; IMSpt; College; Professional.

HUNCKLER, Stephen P; Joliet Township HS; Joliet, IL; CmntyWkr; HonRl; StuCncl; StuGov; IMSpt; Joliet Jr Coll; Brdcsting.

HUNCOVSKY, James J; Flasher Public HS; Flasher, ND; PresSophCls; HonRl; StuCncl; SptEdSchPpr; SchPpr; Bsktbl; Ftbl; Trk; Col; Dentistry.

HUND, Morris A; Carroll HS; Wichita, KS; 7/258 HonRl; StuCncl; LetterTennis; Wichita State Univ; Bus Or Sci.

HUNDER, Heidi; Mayo HS; Rochester, MN; 84/485 Chr; NHS; NatlMeritCmnd; LatCl; College; Pre Med.

HUNDSTAD, Kathryn; Central HS; Bath, SD; 21/423 Band; CncrtBnd; DrlTm; HonRl; HospAde; MrchBnd; YthFlsp; RptrSchPpr; TrsSophCls; SecSophCls; PpCl; Northern State Coll; Medical Technology.

HUNDT, Bruce D; Cashton HS; Cashton, WI; 10/70 ALBoysSt; Band; Chr; CncrtBnd; HonRl; Bsbl; Bsktbl; Ftbl; AmLegAwd; LionAwd; University; Teaching.

HUNGATE, Susan K; Macon HS; Macon, MO; PresSrCls; Band; CncrtBnd; HonRl; MrchBnd; SchMus; SctActv; StuCncl; Chrldr; IMSpt; College; Curriculum Of Major Study.

HUNGERFORD, Brian D; Grand Blanc HS; Flint, MI; 6/637 CncrtBnd; HonRl; MrchBnd; NHS; NatlMeritSF; PepBnd; U Of Mi; Law.

HUNGERFORD, Laura L; Loy Norrix HS; Kalamazoo, MI; NatlMeritSF; YthFlsp; FrCl; LetterBsktbl; Mich St Univ; Veterinarian.

HUNGERFORD, Teresa; Plum City HS; Maiden Rock, WI; SecFrshCls; TrsSrCls; HonRl; FHA; MthCl; Chrldr; PPFtbl; BttyCrckrAwd; PresAwd; VoiceDemAwd; Coll.

HUNGERHOLT, Darrell D; Lanesboro HS; Lanesboro, MN; ChrhWkr; SctActv; StuCncl; FFA; Bsktbl; CaptFtbl; Glf; Trk; Trade School; Auto Body.

HUNING, Elizabeth M; Girard U D #248 HS; Hepler, KS; 2/98 HonRl; NHS; PpCl; Bsktbl; LetterTrk; PPFtbl; K State College; Chemical Engineering.

HUNKE, Jacklyn S; Central Catholic HS; West Point, NE; Chrs; ChrhWkr; HonRl; JrNHS; SchMus; SchPl; MthCl; PpCl; SciCl; IMSpt; St Marys Coll; Registered Nurse.

HUNNEL, Daniel P; Leavenworth Sr HS; Leavenworth, KS; Band; CncrtBnd; MrchBnd; NHS; NatlMeritSF; ROTC; Pres4-H; SpnCl; SciCl; 4-HAwd; KiwanAwd; College; Para Physics.

HUNOTT, Philip A; Sikeston Senior HS; Sikeston, MO; 12/258 ALBoysSt; Chr; CncrtBnd; HonRl; MrchBnd; NHS; StuCncl; Southeast Mo State Univ; Business Admin.

HUNSAKER, Karen E; Southeast HS; Springfield, IL; 51/464 AFS; ChrhWkr; JA; SctActv;.

HUNSANGER, Karen S; Ubly HS; Ruth, MI; 17/111 HonRl; ModUN; TchrAde; Clge; High Schl Counselor.

HUNSICKER, William; Valley HS; West Des Moines, IA; Band; CncrtBnd; MrchBnd; NatlMeritCmnd; Orch; PepBnd; Professional Musician.

HUNSPERGER, Clarence W; Oregon Howell R 3 HS; Koshkonong, MO; PresFrshCls; HstJrCls; Chrs; HonRl; SchPl; PpCl; Bsbl; Bsktbl; Mo Univ; Mech Eng.

HUNT, Beth A; Gibson City HS; Gibson City, IL; 2/90 Chr; Chrs; ChrhWkr; HonRl; Mdrgl; NHS; Quill&Scroll; SchMus; SchPl; StuCncl; Tennis; Trk; Arizona State Univ; Advertising.

HUNT, Brenda L; Spalding HS; Granville, IA; 5/43 PresJrCls; PresSrCls; Chr; Chrs; HonRl; MrchBnd; NatlMeritFnl; MthCl; Bsbl; Tennis; LetterTrk; Chrldr; IMSpt; College; Interior Design.

HUNT, Cindy S; North Central HS; Rock Lake, ND; Chrs; HonRl; LbryAde; SchPl; SecYthFlsp; 4-H; FHA; PpCl; Bsktbl; GAA; Trade; Hairdressing.

HUNT, Daniel J; Central Catholic HS; Grand Island, NE; Chrs; HonRl; StuCncl; StuGov; RptrYrbk; Bsktbl; Ne Univ.

HUNT, Daniel W; Mcdonell Central HS; Chippewa Falls, WI; 7/95 PresFrshCls; PresSophCls; PresSrCls; ALBoysSt; HonRl; ModUN; StuCncl; LetterBsbl; LetterBsktbl; LetterFtbl; College; Computers.

HUNT, David Y; Palisade Public HS; Palisade, NE; VPFrshCls; VPSophCls; VPJrCls; Chr; HonRl; SchPl; Bsktbl; Ftbl;.

HUNT, Douglas J; Carbondale Comm HS; Carbondale, IL; 28/330 HonRl; NatlMeritCmnd; GerCl; LetterFtbl; JETSAwd; College; Engineering.

HUNT, Edward A; Carson City Crystal HS; Carson City, MI; Band; CncrtBnd; MrchBnd; PepBnd; TchrAde; FFA; College; Professional.

HUNT, Jacqueline; Harrisburg HS; Columbia, MO; 2/24 TrsJrCls; ChrhWkr; CmntyWkr; HonRl; SchPl; EdSchPpr; FHA; 4-HAwd; JAAwd; CitAwd; Northeast Missouri State U; Vocational.

HUNT, John D; Chesaning Union HS; Oakley, MI; 25/234 Chr; ChrhWkr; HonRl; NHS; NatlMeritCmnd; SchMus; SchPl; Delta College; Elementary Educ.

HUNT, Joseph M; North HS; Fargo, ND; Quill&Scroll; RptrSchPpr; EdSchPpr; IMSpt; Univ; Writer.

HUNT, Kevin C; Catholic HS; Joliet, IL; 28/180 HstFrshCls; HstSophCls; HstJrCls; VPSrCls; HonRl; JrNHS; NHS; OffAde; SchAde; StuCncl; TchrAde; SciCl; Bsktbl; Trk; Marquette College; Medicine.

HUNT, Kimela D; Carlisle Comm HS; Carlisle, IA; Band; DrlTm; HonRl; MrchBnd; Orch; PepBnd; YthFlsp; FHA; Bsktbl; Trk; Methodist Sch Of Nursing; Rn.

HUNT, Lorrie K; Osky Sr HS; Oskaloosa, IA; Band; Chr; HonRl; Orch; SchMus; StuCncl; 4-H; SpnCl; PpCl; Trk; Chrldr; Nursing School; Professional.

HUNT, Monica A; Acad Of Lady Of Good Counsel; North Mankato, MN; ChrhWkr; JA; SchPl; StuCncl; RptrSchPpr; FrCl; LetterBsktbl; Chrldr; GAA; IMSpt; Clge; Law Enforcement & French.

HUNT, Nancy K; Charleston HS; Charleston, IL; Chr; Chrl; Chrs; HonRl; NHS; SchMus; SchPl; YthFlsp; RptrSchPpr; College.

HUNT, Ohlen M; Cahokia HS; Cahokia, IL; 7/537 HonRl; NHS; Us Naval Academy; Officer.

HUNT, Patricia S; Phillipsburg HS; Phillipsburg, KS; SecTrsSophCls; Chr; CncrtBnd; HonRl; MrchBnd; PepBnd; TreasFHA; LetterTrk; PPFtbl; MasAwd; College; Professional.

HUNT, Randy J; Fergus Falls HS; Fergus Falls, MN; TrsJrCls; Band; ChrhWkr; MrchBnd; PepBnd; SctActv; StuCncl; LatCl; LetterFtbl; LetterTrk; U Of Mn; Civil Engr.

HUNT, Sharon M; Morgan Park HS; Chicago, IL; ChrhWkr; CmntyWkr; NHS; NatlMeritSchl; StuCncl; StuGov; YthFlsp; FBLA; College; Social Work.

HUNT, Shawn M; Ursuline Academy; Springfield, IL; PresFrshCls; SecSophCls; Chr; Quill&Scroll; SchPl; PresStuCncl; RptrYrbk; RptrSchPpr; SchPpr; 4-H; LatCl; PpCl; DanFAwd; DARAwd; Eastern Illinois Univ; Journalism.

HUNT, Stephen L; Churchill HS; Livonia, MI; 10/850 Univ Of Michigan; Medicine.

HUNT, Sue A; De Witt HS; De Witt, MI; 1/130 SecSophCls; HonRl; NHS; SchPl; TchrAde; RptrYrbk; RptrSchPpr; PresFrCl; Chrldr; DanFAwd; DARAwd; Michigan St Univ; Medical Tech.

HUNT, Susan M; Aol Spalding Institute; Peoria, IL; 16/90 Chrs; HonRl; SctActv; College; Veterinarian.

HUNT, Wade A; Winona HS; Winona, MO; PresFrshCls; VPFrshCls; PresSrCls; Band; CncrtBnd; HonRl; VPJrNHS; LbryAde; MrchBnd; SchPl; StuCncl; LetterBsbl; LetterBsktbl; School Of The Ozark.

HUNTER, Anne M; West Vigo HS; W Terre Haute, IN; Band; HonRl; MrchBnd; PepBnd; TchrAde; YthFlsp; Pres4-H; LetterSwmmng; Trk; GAA; 4-HAwd; Clg;.

HUNTER, Barbara A; Marshall HS; Marshall, IL; 1/127 Band; PresNHS; VPNatlThespSoc; SchPl; Yrbk; LatCl; SciCl; Swmmng; BauchLmbAwd; BttyCrckrAwd; Butler Univ; Pharmacist.

HUNTER, Carol J; Bedford North Lawrence HS; Norman, IN; 97/405 SecTrsJrCls; ALAGirlsSt; Band; ChrhWkr; CmntyWkr; MrchBnd; NHS; OffAde; RptrSchPpr; GAA; Indiana U; Business.

HUNTER, David C; Centennial HS; Champaign, IL; 101/355 ChrhWkr; CmntyWkr; College; Medicine.

HUNTER, David W; Platte Co R Iii HS; Kansas City, MO; CncrtBnd; HonRl; RptrYrbk; RptrSchPpr; EdSchPpr; SptEdSchPpr; Ftbl; Trk; Wrstlng; CchngActv; Ne Mo State Univ; Law Politics.

HUNTER, Debbie J; Y J B Community HS; Bagley, IA; ALAGirlsSt; Band; CncrtBnd; HonRl; MrchBnd; NHS; PepBnd; SchPl; Twrl; RptrYrbk; RptrSchPpr; FTA; PpCl; College; Nursing.

HUNTER, Debbie S; Manhattan HS; Manhattan, KS; Chrs; Kansas St Univ; History.

HUNTER, Diane K; Southwood HS; Lafontaine, IN; 1/110 ChrhWkr; HonRl; TreasNatlFornLg; NHS; NatlMeritSF; VPNatlThespSoc; SchPl; YthFlsp; EdSchPpr; GAA; University.

HUNTER, James; Central Community HS; Donnellson, IA; HonRl; NHS; SchPl; RptrSchPpr; Trk; Coll; Journ.

HUNTER, Jennifer R; Glenbrook North HS; Northbrook, IL; HonRl; 4-H; IMSpt; Loyola University; Medicine.

HUNTER, Jill A; Manhattan HS; Ogden, KS; ALAGirlsSt; OffAde; RptrSchPpr; PpCl; Kansas State Univ; Interior Decorator.

HUNTER, John B; Carrollton HS; Saginaw, MI; 5/151 HonRl; NHS; NatlMeritCmnd; SchAde; TchrAde; RptrSchPpr; SciCl; Bsbl; Ftbl; RotaryAwd; Mich St U; Math.

HUNTER, John J; Chadsey HS; Detroit, MI; PresSrCls; Chr; CmntyWkr; HonRl; ROTC; SchPl; StuCncl; StuGov; SpnCl; LetterBsbl; Morehouse Clge; Lawyer.

HUNTER, Kathy A; Vandercook Lake HS; Jackson, MI; 12/105 Band; CmntyWkr; CncrtBnd; HonRl; MrchBnd; PolWkr; TchrAde; LetterBsbl; LetterBsktbl; GAA; CitAwd; College.

HUNTER, Kerry; Warren Woods HS; Waren, MI; 9/289 NHS; University; Professional Medicine.

HUNTER, Lori; Edgemont HS; Ardmore, SD; TrsSophCls; Band; Chrs; HonRl; NHS; SchPl; TchrAde; FrCl; PpCl; CitAwd; Business Sch; Airline Stewardess.

HUNTER, Mark J; Alpena HS; Alpena, MI; NatlMeritFnl; Yrbk; SchPpr; FrCl; Michigan St Univ; Psychiatry.

HUNTER, Stanley W; Chicago Vocational HS; Chicago, IL; 39/781 HonRl; NHS; SchAde; RptrYrbk; Ftbl; ChmnWrstlng; IMSpt; Sheet Metalist; Voc.

HUNTER, Thomas; Greensburg Community HS; Greensburg, IN; 36/208 ALBoysSt; HonRl; LatCl; PpCl; SciCl; Trk; College; Teaching.

HUNTINGTON, Daniel L; Huron HS; Ann Arbor, MI; HonRl; SchPl; SctActv; FrCl; College; Professional.

HUNTINGTON, Jayne E; Darlington HS; Darlington, WI; 22/122 SecSophCls; SecSrCls; HospAde; NatlFornLg; StuGov; PresYthFlsp; Yrbk; 4-H; FHA; PresPpCl; 4-HAwd; Madison Area Tech Col; Dental Hygiene.

HUNTINGTON, Natalie A; Memorial HS; Eau Claire, WI; Chr; Chrs; ChrhWkr; HonRl; LbryAde; SchMus; SchPl; SctActv; FHA; Tennis; College; Interior Dec.

HUNTLEY, Debra L; Chosen Valley HS; Chatfield, MN; 24/86 Band; Chr; HonRl; Mdrgl; NHS; SchMus; EdYrBk; AmLegAwd; DARAwd; CitAwd; Viterbo College; Music.

HUNTLEY, Kristi E; Decatur Community HS; Oberlin, KS; Chrl; Chrs; ChrhWkr; CmntyWkr; HospAde; NatlFornLg; TchrAde; 4-H; FHA; FTA; SpnCl; PpCl; College; Nurse.

HUNTON, Susan G; Green Ridge HS; Windsor, MO; PresFrshCls; SecJrCls; Band; Chrs; ChrhWkr; YthFlsp; Pres4-H; FHA; PpCl; LetterChrldr; Comm Col & U; High School Music Teacher.

HUNTSMAN, Larry W; Waldron HS; Waldron, IN; VPFrshCls; PresSophCls; Band; CncrtBnd; HonRl; MrchBnd; StuCncl; KeyCl; Bsbl; Bsktbl; Trk; Trade School.

HUNTZINGER, Joseph K; Pendleton Hts HS; Pendleton, IN; ChrhWkr; OffAde; YthFlsp; CaptFtbl; Wrstlng; Purdue Univ; Engineering.

HUNZEKER, Bonnie J; Humboldt Public HS; Humboldt, NE; 3/18 Chrs; HonRl; NHS; OffAde; Nebr Univ Medical Clg; Rn.

HUNZEKER, Judy K; Pawnee Public HS; Pawnee City, NE; 2/36 PresJrCls; Band; Chrs; CncrtBnd; HonRl; MrchBnd; PepBnd; StuCncl; YthFlsp; 4-H; Univ Of Ne; Professional.

HUNZIKER, Arlene S; Sherwood HS; Creighton, MO; 5/61 Chrs; SecDrlTm; HonRl; NHS; SchMus; SchPl; EdYrBk; PpCl; Trk; PPFtbl; PresAwd;.

HUOTARI, Cindy; Cherry HS; Iron, MN; Band; Chr; HonRl; NHS; EdYrBk; RptrSchPpr; FHA; PpCl; Chrldr; BttyCrckrAwd; Hibbing Vo Tech Inst; Retail Marketing Mgnt.

HUPACH, Linda D; Plainfield HS; Joliet, IL; 77/297 Chr; ChrhWkr; CncrtBnd; HonRl; MrchBnd; PepBnd; PresYthFlsp; GerCl; PpCl; Trk; GAA; Univ Of Illinois; Veterinarian.

HUPP, Mike M; Norfolk Catholic HS; Norfolk, NE; 4/48 VPFrshCls; VPJrCls; ALBoysSt; HonRl; StuCncl; StuGov; LetterBsktbl; LetterFtbl; LetterGlf; Univ Of Nebraska.

HUPP, Nancy K; Orrick HS; Orrick, MO; Band; CncrtBnd; HonRl; MrchBnd; PepBnd; YthFlsp; FHA; PpCl; Chrldr; PPFtbl; Kcbc; Bookkeeper.

HUPPENTHAL, Jon; Marquette HS; Michigan City, IN; HonRl; JA; NHS; SchMus; SchPl; Yrbk; FSA; SciCl; Tennis; BauchLmbAwd; Purdue; Electro Medical Engin.

HUPPERICH, Elizabeth; Regina Dominican HS; Morton Grove, IL; Aud/Vis; HonRl; LitMag; SchMus; SchPl; Sdlty; GerCl; MthCl; Saint Teresa Coll; Theater.

HUPPERT, Michael; Laporte City HS; Laporte City, IA; 5/69 ALBoysSt; HonRl; NHS; NatlMeritCmnd; NatlThespSoc; SchPl; StuCncl; DanFAwd; VoiceDemAwd; Drake Univ; Lawyer.

HURD, David; Sycamore HS; Sycamore, IL; Aud/Vis; Chr; ChrhWkr; LbryAde; SctActv; YthFlsp; College; Electrical Engineer.

HURD, Lana A; Waukesha North HS; Waukesha, WI; 6/322 Band; ChrhWkr; HonRl; NatlFornLg; NatlMeritCmnd; 4-H; FrCl; U Of Mn St Paul; Vet.

HURD, Margaret A; New Hampton Comm HS; New Hampton, IA; 26/165 Chrs; HonRl; HospAde; SchPl; RptrYrbk; RptrSchPpr; SpnCl; PpCl; LetterGlf; Univ Of Ia; Pro Accounting.

HURESTON, Patricia J; St Francis De Sales HS; Chicago, IL; 15/300 Band; ChrhWkr; CmntyWkr; CncrtBnd; HonRl; LbryAde; MrchBnd; NHS; NatlMeritCmnd; Orch; SchAde; Northwestern; Lawyer.

HURLA, Joan R; Bishop Ward HS; Kansas City, KS; 25/210 HonRl; ModUN; NHS; SchPl; StuCncl; TchrAde; SchPpr; PpCl; College; Journalism.

HURLBURT, Andy L; Sentral HS; Lone Rock, IA; Band; Chr; Chrs; CncrtBnd; HonRl; MrchBnd; NHS; PepBnd; SchMus; StuCncl; College.

HURLBURT, Candyce J; Sentnal HS; Lone Rock, IA; 13/37 Band; Chr; Chrs; ChrhWkr; CncrtBnd; HonRl; MrchBnd; NHS; PepBnd; SchMus; Univ Of Northern Iowa; Secondary Education.

HURLBUT, Annette M; Nashua HS; Nashua, IA; HonRl; Yrbk; FHA;.

HURLEY, Cindy L; Mallard Community HS; Curlew, IA; 3/33 SecTrsSrCls; DrlTm; HonRl; SchPl; YthFlsp; RptrYrbk; EdSchPpr; 4-H; BttyCrckrAwd; 4-HAwd; Westmar College; Dietician.

HURLEY, Lowell D; United Community HS; Madrid, IA; Band; CncrtBnd; MrchBnd; PepBnd; SchPpr; PpCl; Bsktbl; Ftbl; Trk; IMSpt; Coll; Wildlife.

HURLEY, Mary A; Ladywood St Agnes HS; Indianapolis, IN; SchPl; CaptBsktbl; CaptTennis; Trk; CchngActv; TreasGAA; IMSpt; CaptPPFtbl; PresAwd; College; Professional.

HURON, Susan C; St Peter & Paul Area HS; Saginaw, MI; PresBand; Chrs; ChrhWkr; CncrtBnd; DrlTm; Mdrgl; MrchBnd; PepBnd; SchMus; TchrAde; Delta Clg; Elem Educ.

HURRISH, Gabe; Stevens Point Area Senior HS; Stevens Point, WI; 26/710 ChrhWkr; StuCncl; StuGov; Yrbk; Trk; IMSpt; EldAwd; Coll; Professional.

HURRY, Vanessa; Chadsey HS; Detroit, MI; PresSrCls; VPSrCls; SecSrCls; Chr; CmntyWkr; HonRl; JA; LbryAde; SchMus; TchrAde; College; Exec Secretary.

HURSELL, Clarence E; Edison Sr HS; East Gary, IN; 9/147 ALBoysSt; ChrhWkr; HonRl; LetterBsbl; BauchLmbAwd; College; Professional Baseball.

HURSEY, Richard; North Pemiscot HS; Wardell, MO; 8/60 ALBoysSt; Chr; ChrhWkr; CmntyWkr; HonRl; NHS; StuCncl; 4-H; PpCl; CaptBsktbl; School Of The Azarro; Architectt.

HURSHMAN, Terry D; Liberty HS; Fowler, IL; HonRl; SchPl; PpCl; LetterBsbl; LetterBsktbl; College.

HURST, Daniel E; Belleville East HS; Fairview Hts, IL; 32/645 ChrhWkr; CncrtBnd; HonRl; JrNHS; NHS; Orch; StuCncl; Yrbk; Wrstlng; IMSpt; Parks College; Aviation.

HURST, Diane L; Chester HS; St Marys, MO; 16/125 Band; ChrhWkr; CmntyWkr; HonRl; MrchBnd; NHS; PepBnd; RedCrAde; SchPl; TchrAde; RptrSchPpr; SchPpr; FHA; AmLegAwd; Stephens College; Fashion Designer.

HURST, Mark E; St Johns HS; St Johns, MI; Band; CncrtBnd; DrlTm; HonRl; MrchBnd; PepBnd; LetterSwmmng; Itt Tech Inst; Elec Tech.

HURST, Paula D; Charleston Sr HS; Mattoohn, IL; SecJrCls; Chrs; ChrhWkr; CncrtBnd; DrlTm; HonRl; MrchBnd; SchMus; StuCncl; 4-H; Eastern Ill Univ; Music Ed.

HURST, Robert M; Griggsville HS; Griggsville, IL; HonRl; SchPl; 4-H; TreasSpnCl; Tennis; IMSpt; 4-HAwd; College; Vocation.

HURST, Russell A; Laona HS; Laona, WI; ALBoysSt; ChrhWkr; HonRl; NatlFornLg; NatlMeritSchl; SchPl; LetterBsktbl; LetterFtbl; LetterGlf; DanFAwd; Univ Of St Paul; Ministerial.

HURT, Brent D; Excelsior Springs HS; Excelsior Springs, MO; PresFrshCls; VPSophCls; JrNHS; NHS; StuCncl; RptrSchPpr; LetterBsktbl; LetterFtbl; LetterTrk; CitAwd; Coll; Architecture.

HUSA, Christopher J; De Kalb HS; De Kalb, IL; ChrhWkr; HonRl; SctActv; StuCncl; YthFlsp; FSA; FrCl; SciCl; Ftbl; Glf; University.

HUSAIN, David D; West Vigo HS; W Terre Haute, IN; VPFrshCls; VPSophCls; VPJrCls; HonRl; FTA; KeyCl; LetterBsktbl; LetterFtbl; IMSpt; Univ; Pre Dentistry Or History.

HUSARIK, Gregory L; Valparaiso HS; Valparaiso, IN; 17/417 HonRl; NHS; NatlMeritSF; LetterSwmmng; Mi St U; Psychology.

HUSAYNU, Carmen A; Marian HS; Birmingham, MI; 12/178 HonRl; ModUN; NHS; RptrSchPpr; Oakland Univ; Special Ed.

HUSAYNU, Carol T; Marian HS; Birmingham, MI; HonRl; Oakland U; Secretary.

HUSBAND, Janet S; Tri County Comm HS; What Cheer, IA; VPJrCls; Band; Chrs; HonRl; SchPl; StuCncl; Twrl; Yrbk; Bsktbl; College; Lab Technician.

HUSBAND, Jerry L; Highmore HS; Highmore, SD; 9/54 HonRl; JrNHS; NHS; StuCncl; SptEdSchPpr; 4-H; FBLA; SecSciCl; LetterBsktbl; LetterFtbl; College.

HUSEBY, Crystal; Pelican Rapids HS; Pelican Rapids, MN; 2/124 Chr; Chrs; CncrtBnd; HonRl; PepBnd; SchMus; SchPl; TchrAde; EdYrBk; FHA; Moorehead St Univ; Elem Education.

HUSEBY, Reta J; Halstad Public HS; Halstad, MN; 5/22 SecSrCls; Chrs; CncrtBnd; HonRl; NatlThespSoc; VPStuGov; SptEdSchPpr; Bsbl; CaptBsktbl; Chrldr; GAA; IMSpt; PresAwd; Mayville State College; Music.

HUSEMAN, Christine M; Lowell Sr HS; Crown Point, IN; TrsFrshCls; Chr; HonRl; SchMus; SecStuCncl; RptrSchPpr; 4-H; FHA; PpCl; 4-HAwd; Purdue Univ; Home Economics.

HUSEMAN, Patricia A; Tri County HS; Brookston, IN; 3/86 HonRl; NHS; StuCncl; 4-H; SpnCl; PpCl; GAA; BttyCrckrAwd; 4-HAwd; Univ; Nursing.

HUSEMAN, Scott; East Dubuque HS; East Duboque, IL; VPJrCls; HonRl; SchPl; StuCncl; StuGov; EdYrBk; GerCl; SciCl; Bsktbl; Glf; Trade School; Professional Electronics.

HUSEN, Gale; North Scott HS; Dixon, IA; 30/200 Chr; Chrs; HonRl; LbryAde; SchMus; SpnCl; PpCl; Business College; Secretary.

HUSETH, Diane S; Wyndmere HS; Mcleod, ND; ALAGirlsSt; Band; Chr; Chrs; HonRl; Mdrgl; NHS; EdSchPpr; FHA; Chrldr; College; Teacher.

HUSHOUR, Loretta L; Centerville HS; Centerville, IA; Band; ChrhWkr; CncrtBnd; HonRl; MrchBnd; SctActv; Teen; TreasFHA;.

HUSK, Jacque; Tekamah Herman HS; Herman, NE; 9/72 Chr; CncrtBnd; HonRl; PepBnd; StuCncl; AmLegAwd; CitAwd; Coll; Physicians Assistant.

HUSKEY, David K; Brownell Talbor HS; Omaha, NE; PresFrshCls; Chrs; HonRl; RptrSchPpr; EngCl; MthCl; LetterBsktbl; LetterTennis; University.

HUSKEY, Robert C; Brownell Talbot HS; Omaha, NE; ALBoysSt; Band; HonRl; NHS; NatlMeritFnl; SchMus; SchPl; Yrbk; FrCl; MthCl; Bsktbl; Tennis; College; Math.

HUSMANN, Catherine S; Mater Dei HS; Breese, IL; 31/197 Chrs; HonRl; HospAde; Sacrstn; SchMus; RptrYrbk; EdYrBk; RptrSchPpr; 4-H; FrCl; Quincy College; Psychology.

HUSMANN, H Henry; Greenville HS; Greenville, IL; 10/183 Aud/Vis; MrchBnd; NHS; PepBnd; SchMus; FrCl; LetterFtbl; LetterTennis; JAAwd; Eastern Il Univ; Law.

HUSMANN, Jeanene M; Normandy HS; St Louis, MO; 60/500 Chrs; HonRl; JA; NHS; SancSoc; SchMus; SctActv; FrCl; IMSpt; Univ Of Mo St Louis; Med Pro.

HUSS, Cindy; Coleman HS; Coleman, MI; 2/84 VPSophCls; HonRl; NHS; SchPl; GerCl; Trk; PPFtbl; Delta Coll;.

HUSS, Jon B; Shawnee Mission East HS; Mission Hills, KS; AFS; ALBoysSt; HonRl; PresNHS; NatlMeritSF; SpnCl; PpCl; Tennis; IMSpt; Univ.

HUSS, Martha J; Troy HS; Troy, KS; 5/51 Band; Chrs; HonRl; NHS; SchPl; StuCncl; TchrAde; PpCl; Chrldr; BttyCrckrAwd; CitAwd; Platt Gard Clg Of Commerce; Accountant.

HUSS, Vicki R; Sykeston HS; Sykeston, ND; 2/18 Band; Chrs; ChrhWkr; HonRl; SchPl; EdSchPpr; LetterBsktbl; LetterTrk; LetterChrldr; IMSpt; Clg; Prof.

HUSSEY, Deborah; St Thomas Aquinas HS; Berkeley, MO; ChrhWkr; DrlTm; JA; SchMus; SchPl; JAAwd; College.

HUSSEY, Kelly J; Charleston HS; Charleston, IL; 56/256 Band; Chr; Chrl; Chrs; HonRl; Mdrgl; SchMus; SchPl; LetterFtbl; LetterWrstlng; Eastern Ill; Prof.

HUSSEY, Mary E; St Francis HS; Winfield, IL; 9/88 SecTrsSophCls; SecJrCls; ChrhWkr; CmntyWkr; HonRl; StuCncl; StuGov; RptrYrbk; 4-H; LetterTrk; LetterChrldr; 4-HAwd; JCAwd; Univ; Professional.

HUSSEY, Susan M; East Alton HS; East Alton, IL; 34/312 ALAGirlsSt; Band; HonRl; JrNHS; NHS; OffAde; PresFNA; LatCl; PpCl; IMSpt; Sam Houston St Univ; Pre Nursing.

HUSSLI, Mary C; Beaver Dam HS; Beaver Dam, WI; 18/317 Band; TreasChrs; MrchBnd; NatlFornLg; SchMus; StuCncl; Yrbk; PpCl; GAA; DARAwd; Uw Madison; Political Sci.

HUSTEDDE, Ralph E; Carlyle HS; Carlyle, IL; 23/137 ChrhWkr; CmntyWkr; HonRl; JA; NHS; SchPl; StuCncl; StuGov; College; Business Adm.

HUSTEDT, Mark A; Watseka HS; Watseka, IL; ChrhWkr; CmntyWkr; HonRl; YthFlsp; FFA; Ftbl; College; Agricultural Mechanic.

HUSTON, Carolyn F; Jennings HS; Jennings, MO; Band; Chr; Chrs; HonRl; PolWkr; SchPpr; FHA; SecEngCl; VPSciCl; GodCntryAwd; College; Tv & Radio.

HUSTON, Char; Litchfield Sr HS; Litchfield, MN; Band; Chr; ChrhWkr; HonRl; SchPl; StuCncl; 4-H; FHA; GAA; 4-HAwd; Northwestern Bible Coll; Exec Receptionist.

HUSTON, David L; Clarks HS; Central City, NE; 5/24 ALBoysSt; Chrs; HonRl; MrchBnd; NatlFornLg; YthFlsp; 4-H; LetterBsktbl; LetterFtbl; LetterTrk; Coll; Pro.

HUSTON, Debra; Houston HS; Houston, MO; 23/113 Chrs; HonRl; OffAde; TchrAde; EngCl; PpCl; SciCl; Swmmng; College; Business Major.

HUSTON, Debra; Beardstown HS; Beardstown, IL; 5/140 SecFrshCls; ChrhWkr; HonRl; NHS; SchMus; SecYthFlsp; SpnCl; LetterTrk; LetterChrldr; CaptIMSpt; Univ; Pharm.

HUSTON, James D; Axtell Community HS; Axtell, NE; 4/34 ChrhWkr; HonRl; SchPl; LetterBsktbl; LetterFtbl; LetterTrk; ChmbCommrsAwd; Kearney State Col; Farming.

HUSTON, James W; Ben Davis HS; Indianapolis, IN; 7/950 PresFrshCls; PresSophCls; ALBoysSt; NHS; StuCncl; LetterFtbl; LetterTrk; AmLegAwd; JETSAwd; MasAwd; College; Engineering.

HUSTON, Lori A; Benson HS; Benson, MN; 2/160 Band; HonRl; MrchBnd; NHS; NatlMeritCmnd; TchrAde; RptrYrbk; 4-H; BttyCrckrAwd; 4-HAwd; Univ Of Mn; Accounting.

HUSTON, Mary A; Marian HS; Omaha, NE; HospAde; FNA; SciCl; Creighton Univ; Nursing.

HUSTON, Mary J; Newton HS; Newton, IA; 31/310 Chrl; Chrs; CncrtBnd; HonRl; NatlThespSoc; SchMus; StuCncl; YthFlsp; LatCl; OptClAwd; Coll; Biology.

HUSTON, Michael L; Roseville HS; Roseville, IL; PresFrshCls; Chrs; CncrtBnd; SctActv; YthFlsp; FFA; LetterFtbl; LetterTrk; AmLegAwd; U Of Il; Liberal Arts.

HUSTON, Shelly K; Lake Forest Academy; Dawson, IL; 22/100 HonRl; OffAde; SchAde; Bsbl; Brigham Young Univ; Math.

HUTCHCRAFT, Douglas W; Union Star R 2 HS; Union Star, MO; VPSophCls; TrsJrCls; CncrtBnd; HonRl; SchPl; University; Vocation.

HUTCHCROFT, Ann L; Knoxville HS; Knoxville, IL; 1/95 Band; CncrtBnd; HonRl; MrchBnd; PresNHS; Orch; SchPl; FTA; SecLatCl; GAA; Knox College.

HUTCHENS, John E; Horton Watkins HS; Olivette, MO; 81/498 Band; ChrhWkr; HonRl; SctActv; YthFlsp; LetterSocr; LetterTrk; GodCntryAwd; Central Missouri; Medical Doctor.

HUTCHESON, Lori; Woodbine Community HS; Woodbine, IA; 16/60 CncrtBnd; DrlTm; HonRl; HospAde; Mdrgl; MrchBnd; NHS; YthFlsp; FHA; PpCl; Nursing; Rn.

HUTCHINGS, Jeffrey L; Excelsoir Springs HS; Excelsior Springs, MO; PresSophCls; VPJrCls; ChrhWkr; HonRl; NHS; StuCncl; FTA; Bsbl; LetterFtbl; CitAwd; Coll; Electronics.

HUTCHINGS, Susie L; Holden R 3 HS; Latour, MO; 22/85 Chrs; HonRl; College.

HUTCHINS, Kathryn J; Roseville HS; Roseville, IL; 5/53 Band; HonRl; NHS; PepBnd; StuCncl; 4-H; GAA; IMSpt; DARAwd; College; Math.

HUTCHINS, Kenneth A; Grand Ledge Academy; Lansing, MI; 1/13 PresJrCls; VPSrCls; Chrs; ChrhWkr; NHS; NatlMeritSF; SchPl; StuCncl; EdYrBk; CaptBsktbl; Andrews Univ; Medicine.

HUTCHINS, Linda A; Huron HS; Ann Arbor, MI; 1/600 Band; HonRl; LitMag; MrchBnd; NatlMeritSF; NatlSciFnd; PepBnd; FrCl; College; Computer Engineering.

HUTCHINS, Lora J; Carthage HS; Carthage, MO; AFS; Chr; CmntyWkr; Mdrgl; SchMus; PpCl; Trk; LetterChrldr; PPFtbl; Clge; Rn.

HUTCHINS, Nancy M; Highland Park HS; St Paul, MN; Band; CncrtBnd; HospAde; LitMag; StuCncl; TchrAde; RptrYrbk; Yrbk; SchPpr; PpCl; University; Nursing.

HUTCHINS, Sheryl A; Oxford HS; Geuda Springs, KS; Band; Chrs; CncrtBnd; HonRl; LbryAde; NHS; OffAde; SchPl; RptrYrbk; PPFtbl; Coll; Music.

HUTCHINSON, Constance; University HS; Bloomington, IL; Chr; Chrs; HonRl; Mdrgl; NHS; NatlThespSoc; SchMus; SchPl; StuCncl; Texas Christian Univ; Ballet.

HUTCHINSON, Dennis E; Tina Avalon HS; Dawn, MO; PresFrshCls; Band; Chrs; HonRl; StuCncl; SptEdYrbk; SchPpr; 4-H; FFA; LetterBsbl; Trenton Jr Clg; Agriculture.

HUTCHINSON, Kathryn; Beech Grove HS; Beech Grove, IN; 2/217 ALAGirlsSt; Band; Chr; ChrhWkr; NHS; SctActv; YthFlsp; BauchLmbAwd; DARAwd; GodCntryAwd; Butler Univ; Pharmacy.

HUTCHINSON, Lisa D; Lincoln Community HS; Lincoln, IL; Chr; ChrhWkr; HonRl; HospAde; StuGov; LatCl; University Of Illinois; Nursing.

HUTCHINSON, Penny J; Magic City Campus HS; Minot, ND; 2/640 AFS; ALAGirlsSt; HonRl; NHS; StuCncl; FrCl; U Of No Dak; Medicine.

HUTCHINSON, Rodney M; Cass City HS; Cass City, MI; HonRl; JrNHS; TchrAde; FrCl; LetterFtbl; CchngActv; Bus Sch; Business.

HUTCHISON, Jill L; Natoma HS; Paradise, KS; 7/29 TrsFrshCls; SecTrsJrCls; TrsSrCls; SchPl; TchrAde; SchPpr; SecTrsSophCls; Bsktbl; Chrldr; PPFtbl; Ft Hays Ks State Clg; Advertising.

HUTCHISON, Pamela; Jonesville HS; Jonesville, MI; 7/84 HonRl; NatlMeritSF; Univ; History.

HUTCHISON, Rick D; Washburn Rural HS; Topeka, KS; HonRl; TchrAde; SciCl; Trk; Trade School; Vocational Mechanic.

HUTCHISON, Steven; Polo HS; Rayville, MO; TrsFrshCls; Band; Chr; Chrs; ChrhWkr; CncrtBnd; HonRl; LetterFtbl; LetterTrk; IMSpt; Coll; Voc.

HUTCHISON, Steven J; Adelphian Academy; Flint, MI; Band; HonRl; FrCl; College; Teacher.

HUTFLESS, Maureen K; Benson HS; Omaha, NE; HonRl; NatlMeritSF; SchPpr; MthCl; PpCl; University Of Nebraska.

HUTH, Jeffrey A; Lakeland HS; Wolcottville, IN; PpCl; Bsktbl; Glf; LetterTennis; IMSpt; Trade Schl; Drafting.

HUTH, Jeffrey W; Prairie Home HS; Boonville, MO; ALBoysSt; ChrhWkr; HonRl; StuCncl; SptEdYrbk; SptEdSchPpr; 4-H; LetterBsktbl; DanFAwd; 4-HAwd; Ctrl Ms St Univ; Agriculture.

HUTJENS, Keith D; East De Pere HS; De Pere, WI; HonRl; JA; PolWkr; SchPl; 4-H; College; Business.

HUTJENS, Sandy A; East De Pere HS; De Pere, WI; 16/192 ChrhWkr; CncrtBnd; HonRl; JrNHS; MrchBnd; NatlFornLg; NHS; PolWkr; SchPl; TreasFNA; Trade School; Vocation.

HUTNIK, Gary; West Sr HS; Garden City, MI; 1/535 ALBoysSt; HonRl; NHS; StuGov; Univ Of Michigan; Dentistry.

HUTSEBAUT, John E; Lane Tech HS; Chicago, IL; 27/1200 NatlMeritFnl; NatlMeritSF; SctActv; RptrYrbk; Ill Inst Of Tech; Engineering.

HUTSON, Deborah A; Sandusky HS; Sandusky, MI; 18/114 Chr; HonRl; SctActv; SecFHA; VFWAwd; VoiceDemAwd; College; Cosmetology.

HUTSON, Randy L; Westfield HS; Westfield, IL; PresSrCls; HonRl; SchMus; StuCncl; RptrYrbk; RptrSchPpr; Bsbl; Bsktbl; Trk; Lake Land Jr Col.

HUTT, Douglas E; Maryville Rii HS; Maryville, MO; TrsJrCls; ALBoysSt; ModUN; SctActv; StuCncl; LetterFtbl; CaptTrk; Univ; Business Management.

HUTTER, Deborah A; Spencer HS; Spencer, WI; 3/60 Chrs; ChrhWkr; HonRl; LbryAde; PolWkr; SchPl; RptrYrbk; FHA; PpCl; U Of Wis Green Bay; Bus Admin.

HUTTLE, Wayne K; Munster HS; Munster, IN; ChrhWkr; HonRl; SctActv; TchrAde; RptrSchPpr; TreasSciCl; Univ; Medicine.

HUTTNER, Judith A; South Division; Milwaukee, WI; Chr; ChrhWkr; Quill&Scroll; SchPl; RptrSchPpr; SchPpr; FBLA; FTA; FrCl; Uw Whitewater; Business Teacher.

HUTTO, Rex; Haworth HS; Kokomo, IN; Aud/Vis; ChrhWkr; HonRl; LitMag; SchMus; SchPl; YthFlsp; In Cntrl Univ; Ministry.

HUTTON, Felise; Lutheran North HS; Florissant, MO; 73/158 AFS; Chr; HonRl; JA; NatlThespSoc; StuCncl; StuGov; RptrYrbk; GAA; PPFtbl; Coll; Speech Pathologist.

HUTTON, Karen S; Arkansas City HS; Arkansas City, KS; AFS; Chr; ChrhWkr; HonRl; OffAde; SchMus; TchrAde; FTA; PpCl; LetterTennis; Clge; Curr Of Major Study.

HUTTON, Lisa; Cobden Unit HS; Cobden, IL; Chrs; HonRl; Mdrgl; SchMus; SchPl; RptrYrbk; RptrSchPpr; FHA; PpCl; SciCl; Southern Ill Univ; Medical Secretary.

HUTTON, Michael; William A Wirt HS; Gary, IN; 13/267 DrlTm; HonRl; NHS; NatlMeritFnl; NatlMeritCmnd; ROTC; TchrAde; LatCl; Air Force; Electronics Eng.

HUTTON, Terry M; Mc Donell HS; Chippewa Falls, WI; CmntyWkr; HonRl; ModUN; PolWkr; Bsbl; University; Agriculture.

HUTULA, Carole A; L Anse HS; Sidnaw, MI; 10/85 PresJrCls; PresSrCls; Chr; Chrl; ChrhWkr; HonRl; SchPl; StuCncl; PpCl.

HUTZLER, Jerome A; Cambria Friesland Area HS; Cambria, WI; 2/51 PresSophCls; PresSrCls; ALBoysSt; HonRl; NHS; TreasStuCncl; StuGov; LetterBsbl; LetterFtbl; CaptWrstlng; U Of Wi Madison; Civil Or Environ Engr.

HUVAERE, Gregory G; Grosse Pointe South HS; Grosse Point Park, MI; 114/612 ChrhWkr; HonRl; ModUN; NatlMeritCmnd; PolWkr; CchngActv; IMSpt; JAAwd; KiwanAwd; Michigan State University; Hotel Mgmt.

HUWE, Christine J; Fairmont HS; Fairmont, MN; 1/250 VPJrCls; AFS; ChrhWkr; CmntyWkr; HonRl; NHS; NatlMeritSF; StuCncl; Yrbk; GerCl; CaptChrldr; IMSpt; PresAwd; St Olaf College.

HUXHOLD, David M; Shortridge HS; Indpls, IN; CmntyWkr; HonRl; Quill&Scroll; SchAde; SptEdYrbk; SptEdSchPpr; KeyCl; LetterFtbl; LetterWrstlng; KiwanAwd; Purdue Univ; Forestry.

HUXMAN, Leigh A; Morland HS; Morland, KS; DrlTm; HonRl; SchMus; StuCncl; Treas4-H; VPPpCl; LetterTrk; Chrldr; PPFtbl; 4-HAwd; Kansas State Univ.

HUXOLL, Theresa A; Holbrook HS; Holbrook, NE; 2/13 TrsJrCls; Band; Chrs; HonRl; SchPl; TchrAde; EdYrBk; RptrSchPpr; VPFHA; VPPpCl; Trk; College.

HUXTABLE, Robert L; Pinckney HS; Pinckney, MI; Aud/Vis; Band; CncrtBnd; HonRl; LbryAde; MrchBnd; SctActv; RptrYrbk; MthCl; Clge; Pro.

HUYCK, Eric T; Harrison HS; Lafayette, IN; 9/372 Chr; HonRl; JrNHS; Mdrgl; NHS; NatlMeritCmnd; NatlThespSoc; SchMus; MthCl; LetterFtbl; Univ; Professional.

HUYCKE, Peggy A; Lansing HS; Lansing, KS; HonRl; NHS; SecNatlThespSoc; SchMus; SchPl; StuCncl; FTA; PpCl; SciCl; Trk; IMSpt; PPFtbl; College; French.

HVOSTIK, George; Von Steuben HS; Chicago, IL; VPSrCls; ChrhWkr; CmntyWkr; HonRl; SctActv; StuGov; TchrAde; Bsktbl; Trk; Univ; Psychiatrist.

HVOSTIK, George R; Von Steuben HS; Chicago, IL; 13/219 VPSrCls; ChrhWkr; SctActv; TchrAde; YthFnd; EdYrBk; SptEdSchPpr; Bsktbl; Tennis; University; Medicine.

HYATTL, Deborah K; Frederick HS; Westport, SD; Chrs; HonRl; OffAde; SchPl; TchrAde; RptrYrbk; 4-H; Bsbl; Bsktbl; Trk; Northern St Col; Secretarial Business.

HYBERTSON, Sharon M; Centerville Public HS; Centerville, SD; VPSophCls; Band; Chr; Chrs; ChrhWkr; CncrtBnd; DrlTm; HonRl; MrchBnd; Orch; College; Music.

HYDE, Daria A; Cass Technical HS; Detroit, MI; Band; HonRl; NHS; PolWkr; StuGov; TchrAde; SpnCl; Mi St Univ; Special Education.

HYDE, Eric A; Loy Norrix HS; Kalamazoo, MI; 10/435 Band; CncrtBnd; LbryAde; MrchBnd; NHS; Orch; PepBnd; Michigan St Univ; Law.

HYDE, Joanne B; Yale HS; Emmett, MI; 6/146 HonRl; SchPl; 4-H; Jr Coll; Language.

HYDE, Mary L; South Barber HS; Kiowa, KS; 1/36 Band; Chrl; ChrhWkr; NHS; StuCncl; EdYrBk; PresFHA; TreasPpCl; BttyCrckrAwd; DanFAwd; Univ; Professional.

HYDE, Pamela J; Culver Girls Academy; Fort Wayne, IN; 29/163 Chr; LbryAde; StuGov; Hanover College; Psychology.

HYDE, Terry M; Port Huron Northern HS; Port Huron, MI; 18/437 CncrtBnd; HonRl; MrchBnd; NHS; PepBnd; StuCncl; LetterWrstlng; University; Physical Education.

HYDORN, Michael B; West Ottawa HS; Holland, MI; ALBoysSt; CncrtBnd; ModUN; NHS; Orch; PepBnd; PolWkr; FDA; GerCl; U Of Mich; Physician.

HYLAND, Eileen E; Immaculate Heart Of Mary HS; Cicero, IL; 33/211 HstSophCls; SecJrCls; ChrhWkr; HospAde; SctActv; Chrldr; GAA; IMSpt; Coll; Nursing.

HYLAND, Judith; Urbana Senior Hs; Urbana, IL; Chr; Chrs; HonRl; NHS; PolWkr; SchPl; Yrbk; 4-H; SpnCl; BttyCrckrAwd; U Of Illinois; Elementary Education Major.

HYLAND, Karen A; York Community HS; Elmhurst, IL; 156/881 Band; CncrtBnd; MrchBnd; Orch; PepBnd; Louisiana State Univ; Biological Science.

HYLAND, Kevin R; Delavan Public HS; Winnebago, MN; 4/19 VPFrshCls; TrsSophCls; PresJrCls; HstSrCls; HonRl; StuCncl; SptEdSchPpr; SecFFA; LetterBsktbl; LetterTrk; Coll; Vet.

HYLAND, Kimberly K; Gering HS; Gering, NE; 29/137 SecSrCls; Band; Chrs; DrlTm; HonRl; JrNHS; SecNHS; PepBnd; SecYthFlsp; KeyCl; SecPpCl; Nebraska Western College; Vocation.

HYLAND, Norma L; Guilford HS; Rockford, IL; AFS; HonRl; VPNHS; PpCl; Univ Of Illinois.

HYLDEN, Sharon E; St Francis HS; Little Falls, MN; Band; Chrs; CmntyWkr; PolWkr; StuCncl; TchrAde; SciCl; St Cloud State Coll; Musical Therapist.

HYLDEN, Steven; Holy Angles HS; Minneapolis, MN; SchPl; SctActv; LetterFtbl; Coll.

HYLES, Linda L; Hammond Baptist HS; Munster, IN; SecTrsSrCls; Chr; Chrl; ChrhWkr; HonRl; NHS; OffAde; RptrSchPpr; SchPpr; GerCl; Hyles Anderson College; Music Education.

HYMAN, Susan; Bogan Hs; Chicago, IL; 75/704 CncrtBnd; HonRl; HospAde; NHS; SchMus; SctActv; SciCl; Tennis; GAA;.

HYNEK, Emil J; Wheeling HS; Wheeling, IL; HonRl; NHS; Bradley Univ; Accounting.

HYNEK, Lennis A; Hillsboro HS; Yuba, WI; VPFrshCls; ALBoysSt; HonRl; NHS; SchPl; FFA; CaptBsbl; IMSpt; VFWAwd; Univ; Elem Teacher.

HYRY, John; Wm G Mather HS; Munising, MI; 70/142 HonRl; SctActv; Bsbl; Ftbl; IMSpt; Soumi College; Liberal Arts.

HYSTAD, Susan K; Velva Public HS; Velva, ND; SecSophCls; CmntyWkr; HonRl; OffAde; StuCncl; FBLA; FHA; CaptBsktbl; Trk; CchngActv; GAA; IMSpt; College; Business.

HYTINEN, Gail J; Rapid River HS; Rapid River, MI; 2/44 TrsFrshCls; ChrhWkr; HonRl; NatlMeritSF; SchPl; StuCncl; EdYrBk; RptrSchPpr; Bsktbl; Chrldr; Bay De Noc Comm College;.

HYVARINEN, Carol B; Brimley HS; Brimley, MI; Chr; Chrs; ChrhWkr; HonRl; College; Accounting.

I

IAFRATE, Joanne M; Regina HS; East Detroit, MI; Aud/Vis; ChrhWkr; CmntyWkr; HonRl; SchAde; SchPl; TchrAde; Teen; Wayne State Univ; Medicine.

IANNUCCI, Jacqueline M; Rich Central HS; Olympis Fields, IL; 47/420 Chr; HonRl; PpCl; CaptChrldr; GAA; IMSpt; PresAwd; Clg; Health Services.

IANNUCCI, Patricia M; Dominican HS; Detroit, MI; CmntyWkr; StuGov; Yrbk;.

IATESTA, Valerie; Maine Township HS South; Park Ridge, IL; ChrhWkr; HonRl; NatlThespSoc; SchMus; SchPl; SctActv; FrCl; Taylor Univ; French.

IBACH, Mark D; Naperville Central HS; Naperville, IL; 43/820 CmntyWkr; HonRl; NHS; Quill&Scroll; Univ; Professional.

IBBOTSON, Debra J; Pekin Comm HS; Pekin, IL; 187/700 HonRl; JA; NHS; Quill&Scroll; RptrYrbk; RptrSchPpr; Central Illinois College; Legal Secretary.

IBEN, Timothy; Champaign Centenial HS; Champaign, IL; 1/300 NHS; StuCncl; KiwanAwd; RotaryAwd; Univ Calif Berkely Med.

IBSEN, Johanne; Central Catholic HS; Bloomington, IL; CmntyWkr; HonRl; StuGov; FrCl; PpCl; Trk; IMSpt; College; Business.

IBURG, Tim; Petersburg HS; Petersburg, NE; 6/15 ChrhWkr; CmntyWkr; HonRl; LbryAde; SchPl; GerCl; Bsktbl; College; Professional.

IBURG, Tim G; Petersburg HS; Petersburg, NE; Chr; Chrs; ChrhWkr; CmntyWkr; LbryAde; SchPl; StuCncl; LetterBsktbl; ChmnFtbl; LetterTrk; College; Wildelife Management.

ICE, Linda K; Centralia HS; Centralia, KS; ChrhWkr; HonRl; SchPl; Twrl; YthFlsp; 4-H; FHA; PpCl; LetterTrk; CitAwd; Cloud County Comm Coll; Medical Secy.

ICE, Marcia; Madison Cons HS; Madison, IN; 14/292 HonRl; NHS; SchMus; TchrAde; FrCl; PpCl; Univ; Professional.

ICENOGLE, Catherine J; Roseville HS; Roseville, IL; Band; Chrs; CncrtBnd; HonRl; MrchBnd; PepBnd; SpnCl; PpCl; Loyola Univ; Medicine.

ICKES, Donna M; St Alphonsus HS; Detroit, MI; 41/109 Chrl; ChrhWkr; HonRl; NHS; SchMus; StuCncl; Yrbk; PpCl; Chrldr; GAA; Univ Of Mich; Veterinary Medicine.

ICKSTADT, William M; Memorial HS; Eau Claire, WI; HonRl; Orch; SchMus; Univ Of Wisconsin; Optometry.

ICZKOWSKI, Timothy; Mount Carmel HS; Chicago, IL; 29/205 HonRl; NHS; Sacrstn; SctActv; StuGov; Illinois Inst Of Tech; Bio Engineering.

IDEUS, Wayne L; Beatrice HS; Beatrice, NE; 8/227 ALBoysSt; HonRl; Orch; SctActv; YthFlsp; VPKeyCl; LetterFtbl; EldAwd; GodCntryAwd; College; Biology Teacher.

IFFERT, Marlene M; Mattoon Senior HS; Mattoon, IL; 33/407 HonRl; NHS; OffAde; 4-H; FHA; SpnCl; College.

IFFRIG, Kathy; St Dominic HS; St Peters, MO; TrsSrCls; Chrl; NHS; SchMus; EdYrBk; FrCl; PpCl; IMSpt; BttyCrckrAwd; 4-HAwd; Ne Mo Univ; Childrens Librarian.

IFFT, Keith H; Fairbury Cropsey HS; Fairbury, IL; 4/104 Band; HonRl; NHS; SchPl; StuCncl; 4-H; PresFFA; MthCl; University Of Illinois; Liberal Arts.

IGNACEK, Michael M; Quigley South HS; Chicago, IL; Chrs; ChrhWkr; SchMus; SctActv; TchrAde; SpnCl; LetterBsbl; Trk; Wrstlng; IMSpt; Illinois Inst Of Tech; Engineering.

IGNASZEWSKI, Nina H; Badger HS; Badger, MN; 2/23 HonRl; LbryAde; StuCncl; RptrYrbk; RptrSchPpr; EdSchPpr; FHA; PpCl; River Falls Voc Tech Inst; Clerical.

IHDE, Lee W; Menominee HS; Menominee, MI; 10/276 HonRl; NHS; StuCncl; LetterTennis; Michigan Tech Univ; Civil Engineer.

IHDE, Theresa A; Washington HS; Germantown, WI; 11/215 Band; ChrhWkr; HonRl; NHS; RptrSchPpr; SchPpr; 4-H; FrCl; LatCl; 4-HAwd; Cardinal Stritch College; Special Educ.

IHNEN, Shari L; Sanborn HS; Lamberton, MN; 7/26 ALAGirlsSt; Band; Chr; ChrhWkr; CncrtBnd; HonRl; MrchBnd; PepBnd; SchMus; SchPl; TchrAde; YthFlsp; LetterTrk; LetterChrldr; College; Music.

IHRY, Robert D; Sioux Rapids Comm HS; Sioux Rapids, IA; 1/23 PresFrshCls; Chr; HonRl; NHS; SchPl; StuGov; Bsktbl; CaptFtbl; Trk; Iowa State; Business Mgmnt.

IKENBERRY, Tracy; Quinter HS; Quinter, KS; 3/30 TrsJrCls; ModUN; NHS; StuGov; SptEdYrbk; Mcpherson College.

ILANES, Horrcio; Washington Park HS; Racine, WI; AFS; ChrhWkr; CmntyWkr; NHS; TchrAde; GerCl; SpnCl; Socr; Swmmng; Univ Uruguay; Architecture.

ILCZUK, Ida; Lyons Township HS; Labrange, IL; 86/1280 Chrs; HonRl; NHS; OffAde; Quill&Scroll; RptrSchPpr; RusCl; Univ Of Wi; Bus & Journalism.

ILER, Gary R; Bethany HS; Bethany, IL; PresSrCls; HonRl; MrchBnd; SctActv; StuCncl; YthFlsp; Yrbk; LetterBsbl; LetterFtbl; LetterTrk; Clg; Mechanic.

ILIFF, Mary Ann; Elk River Sr HS; Zimmerman, MN; 5/240 AFS; Chr; HonRl; HospAde; NHS; RptrSchPpr; SchPpr; SpnCl; GAA; IMSpt; Bemidji St Coll; Bus Admin.

ILIFF, Terry G; Portland HS; Portland, IN; 10/187 HonRl; NHS; StuCncl; Pres4-H; SecFFA; FSA; MthCl; SciCl; 4-HAwd; Purdue University; Veterinarian.

ILKOVITZ, Mary; Queen Of Peace Hs; Chicago, IL; 3/430 Chrs; HonRl; NHS; Yrbk; SpnCl; Ui Chicago Circle Campus;mathematics & Comp.

ILLIAS, Mark R; Virginia HS; Virginia, IL; 4-H; FFA; Trade Schl; Motor Mechanics.

ILLIAS, Marsha R; Virginia HS; Virginia, IL; 1/46 TrsJrCls; Band; Chrs; CncrtBnd; HonRl; NHS; PresStuCncl; Sec4-H; SecPpCl; LetterTrk; GAA; DanFAwd; Univ; Pharmacy.

ILNICKI, Dawn L; Bentley HS; Livonia, MI; 1/790 TrsJrCls; TrsSrCls; HonRl; LitMag; SchPl; StuCncl; StuGov; TchrAde; Chrldr; U Of Michigan; Engineering.

IMAN, James M; Owensville Public HS; Owensville, MO; Band; ChrhWkr; CmntyWkr; CncrtBnd; MrchBnd; PepBnd; RedCrAde; SctActv; FNA; Bsktbl; College; Emergency Med Tech.

IMAN, John N; Slater HS; Slater, MO; 6/55 ALBoysSt; Chrs; HonRl; StuCncl; 4-H; FFA; LetterFtbl; Trk; Wrstlng; 4-HAwd; University; Animal Husbandry.

IMBODEN, Alan M; Hobart HS; Hobart, IN; 8/400 HonRl; NHS; NatlMeritSF; TchrAde; SchPpr; Socr; LetterWrstlng; Coll; Art.

IMEL, Judy L; Chadwick HS; Chadwick, IL; Band; ChrhWkr; CncrtBnd; HonRl; LbryAde; PepBnd; SctActv; FHA; PpCl; GAA; Sterling School Of Beauty ;beautician.

IMEL, Lorraine C; George Washington HS; Indianapolis, IN; 30/340 Band; ChrhWkr; HonRl; HospAde; MrchBnd; SctActv; YthFlsp; YthLg; FNA; AmLegAwd; 4-HAwd; University; Nursing.

IMHOF, Christine; Southwest HS; St Louis, MO; 53/533 Chr; HonRl; JA; LbryAde; Mdrgl; SchMus; SchPl; JAAwd;.

IMHOFF, Mary A; Highland HS; Highland, WI; 5/49 TrsSrCls; Chr; Chrs; HonRl; SchPl; TchrAde; 4-H; FHA; CaptBsktbl; Ftbl; LetterTrk; GAA; College; Professional.

IMHOFF, Randy R; Laura Speed Elliot HS; Boonville, MO; PresSrCls; SchPl; StuCncl; FrCl; Bsktbl; LetterSocr; LetterTrk; Central Mo State U; Vocation.

IMHOLTE, Dorothy M; Litchfield Senior HS; Watkins, MN; ChrhWkr; HospAde; TrsFrshCls; NatlCathMusEdAsoc; ROTC; StuGov; UNYO; FFA; FHA; PpCl; College; Recreational Therapy.

IMHOLTE, Kathleen A; Leigh Community HS; Clarkson, NE; 1/40 ALAGirlsSt; HonRl; MrchBnd;

PepBnd; SchMus; SchPl; 4-H; FHA; PpCl; PPFtbl; Wayne State College; Medical Technologist.

IMLER, David C; Watervliet HS; Watervliet, MI; Aud/Vis; HonRl; LbryAde; SctActv; TchrAde; FFA; SciCl; LetterBsbl; Coll; Med.

IMLER, Steven F; Merrill Sr HS; Merrill, WI; 58/350 Aud/Vis; HonRl; NatlFornLg; SchPl; Yrbk; Tennis; Marathon Ext; Nuclear Engineering.

IMM, Ann M; Toluca HS; Toluca, IL; Band; HonRl; MrchBnd; PepBnd; RptrYrbk; PpCl; Bsktbl; Trk; LetterChrldr; GAA; College; Professional.

IMMONEN, Kenneth L; Ontonagon HS; Greenland, MI; Chrs; LbryAde; SctActv; PpCl; Bsktbl; Ftbl; Glf; IMSpt; College; Scientist.

IMPECOVEN, Elouise F; Britton Public HS; Britton, SD; 1/75 ALAGirlsSt; CncrtBnd; HonRl; NHS; PolWkr; YthFlsp; 4-H; AmLegAwd; 4-HAwd; VFWAwd; Col; Statistician.

IMPEY, Julia; Houston HS; Houston, MO; 4/110 ChrhWkr; CmntyWkr; CncrtBnd; HonRl; MrchBnd; NHS; StuCncl; YthFlsp; RptrYrbk; IMSpt; Univ Of Mo; Music.

IMSDAHL, Bradley J; Buffalo HS; Buffalo, MN; Band; CncrtBnd; HonRl; MrchBnd; PepBnd; RptrSchPpr; IMSpt; Augsburg Coll; Accounting.

INBODY, Diane E; Buhler HS; Hutchinson, KS; VPJrCls; Band; CmntyWkr; JrNHS; ModUN; NHS; StuCncl; EdSchPpr; SpnCl; PpCl; Chrldr; IMSpt; Benedictine; Photojournalism.

INDREBO, Kay L; Altoona Public HS; Altoona, WI; ALAGirlsSt; Band; Chrs; LbryAde; MrchBnd; NHS; StuCncl; PpCl; Chrldr; College; Science.

INDRELAND, David B; Centralia HS; Centralia, MO; 11/90 SecFrshCls; VPSophCls; Chr; Chrs; HonRl; NHS; SchPl; StuCncl; SchPpr; CaptFtbl; U Of Missouri; Eng.

INES, Benjamin P; St George R HS; St George, KS; VPJrCls; PresSrCls; ALBoysSt; Chrs; HonRl; SchPl; PresStuCncl; EdYrBk; RptrSchPpr; CitAwd; Ks State U; Teacher Social Sciences.

ING, Patricia M; Immaculata HS; Chicago, IL; CmntyWkr; HonRl; HospAde; NHS; EdYrBk; RptrSchPpr; Illinois Inst Of Tech; Mathematics.

INGABRAND, Jo A; Northeastern HS; Fountain City, IN; 41/145 VPFrshCls; CncrtBnd; HonRl; PepBnd; TchrAde; 4-H; Chrldr; GAA; IMSpt; 4-HAwd; In St Univ; Physical Educ.

INGEBRETSON, Mark; Meseruey Thornton HS; Thornton, IA; ALBoysSt; HonRl; LetterBsbl; LetterBsktbl; LetterGlf; Trk; College; Professional.

INGEBRIGTSEN, Nita A; Kennedy HS; Bloomington, MN; AFS; CtyCnl; HonRl; LbryAde; OffAde; StuCncl; TchrAde; Bsbl; Chrldr; IMSpt; Counseling.

INGEMANSEN, Lynnae C; Brainerd HS; Brainerd, MN; 24/460 Chr; HonRl; StuGov; RptrSchPpr; SpnCl; College; Chemical Engineering.

INGHAM, Barbara M; Addison Trail HS; Addison, IL; 12/597 HonRl; JrNHS; NatlThespSoc; OffAde; TchrAde; College; Radio.

INGHAM, Diana; Elgin HS; Elgin, IL; 131/749 TrsSrCls; Chr; ChrhWkr; Orch; SchPl; StuCncl; YthFlsp; FrCl; Socr; IMSpt; Southern Il U; Dental Hygienist.

INGHRAM, Terry H; Danville HS; Danville, IA; TrsFrshCls; CmntyWkr; HonRl; SchPl; TchrAde; LetterBsbl; LetterBsktbl; LetterFtbl; LetterTrk; CchngActv; College; Broadcasting.

INGLAND, Andy J; Liberal HS; Liberal, KS; HonRl; OffAde; StuCncl; StuGov; Ftbl; College; Dentist.

INGLEBRET, Vicki L; Greenway HS; Grand Rapids, MN; 4/157 Band; Chr; CncrtBnd; HonRl; HospAde; MrchBnd; NHS; PepBnd; MthCl; Itasca Community College; Nursing.

INGLEMAN, Joyce; Rantoul Twp Hs; Paxton, IL; 73/378 ChrhWkr; HonRl; HospAde; TreasYthFlsp; Yrbk; EdSchPpr; 4-H; KeyCl; DanFAwd; 4-HAwd; College Illinois Wesleyan;teaching English.

INGLETT, Paula A; Littlefork Big Falls HS; Litlefork, MN; 3/33 Chr; CmntyWkr; HonRl; LbryAde; NHS; SchPl; RptrYrbk; PpCl; Bsktbl; Chrldr; Concordia Col; Elem Ed.

INGOLD, Denise; Farmington East HS; Farmington, IL; 3/170 CncrtBnd; HonRl; MrchBnd; SchPl; SchPpr; 4-HAwd; CitAwd; Univ; Health Career.

INGOLD, John F; Lyons HS; Lyons, KS; StuCncl; TchrAde; LetterBsktbl; LetterTrk; Hutchinson Jr College; Electronics.

INGOLD, Kathy J; Lowpoint Washburn HS; Washburn, IL; 19/65 AFS; HonRl; MrchBnd; Orch; SchMus; SchPl; Yrbk; PresFHA; Glf; GAA; Illinois Central; Typing.

INGOLIA, Mary Jo M; Maine South HS; Park Ridge, IL; Chrs; HonRl; NHS; Orch; SchMus; Univ; Music.

INGRAM, Belinda M; Shortridge HS; Indianapolis, IN; 4-H; 4-HAwd; Clg; Vocation.

INGRAM, Beverly J; Mackenzie HS; Detroit, MI; HonRl; SchAde; StuCncl; TchrAde; MthCl; Bsktbl; Univ Of Detroit; Pro Attorney.

INGRAM, Beverly R; Daleville HS; Daleville, IN; 16/85 ChrhWkr; HonRl; 4-H; FrCl; Trk; GAA; David Lipscomb; Nursing.

INGRAM, Deborah J; Hurley HS; Crane, MO; 2/14 TrsSophCls; VPJrCls; Chrs; HonRl; SchPl; FHA; PpCl; Chrldr; College.

INGRAM, Jerri L; Charlestown HS; Charlestown, IN; 17/178 Band; CncrtBnd; DrmBgl; HonRl; MrchBnd; NHS; LetterBsktbl; LetterTrk; LetterChrldr; SecBusiness School; Legal Secretary.

INGRAM, Pamela S; Limestone Comm HS; Peoria, IL; 16/403 SecFrshCls; SecSophCls; SecJrCls; Band; ChrhWkr; CncrtBnd; HonRl; MrchBnd; PepBnd; SctActv; GerCl; PpCl; Western Ill Univ; Med Tech.

INGRUM, Becky J; Centralia HS; Centralia, MO; 7/90 TrsJrCls; AFS; Band; SecJA; TreasNHS; SchMus; SchPl; SctActv; RptrYrbk; RptrSchPpr; Central Methodist Col; English.

INGVALSON, Michael J; Caledonia HS; Caledonia, MN; Band; Chrs; CncrtBnd; HonRl; MrchBnd; NatlSciFnd; PepBnd; Sacrstn; 4-H; FFA; Bsbl; Univ Of Mn; Agriculture.

INMAN, Brad L; Clay City HS; Clay City, IN; 10/65 ALBoysSt; HonRl; NHS; SptEdSchPpr; 4-H; FFA; LetterTrk; Purdue Univ; Agriculture.

INMAN, David R; Fenwick HS; Chicago, IL; 23/223 Band; CncrtBnd; NatlMeritCmnd; SchPl; GerCl; Univ Of Ill; Engineering.

INMAN, George R; Century HS; Grand Chain, IL; 17/60 Band; CncrtBnd; HonRl; MrchBnd; PepBnd; SchPl; PresYthFlsp; SptEdYrbk; PresFFA; KeyCl; Bsktbl; DanFAwd; 4-HAwd; Shawnee Jr College; Farmer.

INMAN, Gregory; Mendota HS; Mendota, IL; Chr; Ill Univ; Plant Science.

INMAN, Laroy D; Lindblom Tech HS; Chicago, IL; CmntyWkr; HonRl; LitMag; LbryAde; NatlMeritCmnd; OffAde; SchMus; SchPl; TchrAde; RptrSchPpr; SchPpr; College; History.

INMAN, Marsha A; Anna Jonesboro CHS; Jonesboro, IL; 20/137 TrsJrCls; HonRl; NHS; TchrAde; RptrYrbk; Yrbk; FTA; LatCl; PpCl; Chrldr; U Of Ill; Spec Ed.

INMAN, Tammy J; F L Schlagle HS; Kansas City, KS; 8/389 ChrhWkr; CncrtBnd; JrNHS; MrchBnd; VPNHS; NatlMeritCmnd; SecStuCncl; Pres4-H; DanFAwd; 4-HAwd; Kansas St Univ; Veterinarian.

INNES, James E; Deckerville Community HS; Deckerville, MI; VPSophCls; PresJrCls; NatlMeritSchl; StuCncl; LetterBsbl; CaptBsktbl; LetterFtbl; LetterTrk; Houghton Tech Univ; Eng.

INNESS, Patricia A; Elkhorn Valley HS; Meadow Grove, NE; Band; Chr; Chrs; CncrtBnd; HonRl; MrchBnd; PepBnd; SchMus; SchPl; LetterChrldr; Univ; Law.

INNIS, Brian L; Virden Com HS; Thayer, IL; 21/80 Us Armed Forces; Police Officer.

INNIS, Gail M; Clarkston HS; Clarkston, MI; 21/430 Chr; ChrhWkr; HonRl; NHS; TchrAde; EdYrBk; Concordia Lthrn Clg; Education.

INNIS, Michael; Lasalle Perv Hs; Peru, IL; HonRl; NHS; FrCl; Bsktbl; Ftbl; Tennis; College; Foreign Languages.

INSKEEP, Barbara S; Hillcrest HS; Springfield, MO; Chrs; ChrhWkr; HonRl; HospAde; LbryAde; FBLA; PpCl; Business; Secretary.

INSKEEP, Kenneth H; Sullivan HS; Merom, IN; 11/139 HonRl; ModUN; NatlFornLg; NHS; PresYthFlsp; SptEdYrbk; SptEdSchPpr; PresMthCl; Bsbl; Bsktbl; College; Poli Sci.

INSKEEP, Susan K; Harlem HS; Loves Park, IL; SecChr; ChrhWkr; HonRl; HospAde; SchMus; College; Speech Pathology.

IOCCO, Gary J; Gordon Tech HS; Chicago, IL; 167/744 HstFrshCls; HstSrCls; ChrhWkr; StuCncl; StuGov; SchPpr; PpCl; Wrstlng; Univ Of Co; Accountant.

IPPOLITO, Patricia; Riverton Comm HS; Riverton, IL; TrsJrCls; SecTrsJrCls; HonRl; IMSpt; College; Business.

IPPOLITO, Rose M; Abingdon HS; Abingdon, IL; 2/93 Band; Chrs; HonRl; TreasNHS; SecStuCncl; EdYrBk; RptrSchPpr; 4-H; AmLegAwd; DARAwd; Bradley Univ; Journalism.

IRBY, Pamela S; Florence HS; Iron Mountain, MI; 5/69 Band; CncrtBnd; HonRl; MrchBnd; NatlFornLg; NHS; Orch; PepBnd; SchPl; Yrbk;.

IRELAND, Charles M; Mendel HS; Chicago, IL; 21/200 HonRl; NHS; MthCl; LetterTrk; IMSpt; Bradley Univ; Business.

IRELAND, Cliff J; Glenbard East HS; Lombard, IL; PresGerCl; LetterFtbl; LetterTrk; SARAwd; Northern Illinois Univ; Medicine.

IRELAND, Frank A; Doniphan HS; Doniphan, MO; 3/172 ChrhWkr; CmntyWkr; HonRl; Univ Of Missouri; Vet.

IRELAND, Joyce J; Bosworth R U HS; Bosworth, MO; 1/12 VPFrshCls; Band; Chr; Chrs; ChrhWkr; HonRl; PepBnd; SchAde; SchPl; TchrAde; YthFlsp; 4-H; FHA; PpCl; LetterBsbl; College; Home Economics.

IRELAND, Kevin A; Midland Community HS; Wyoming, IA; HonRl; NHS; TchrAde; YthFlsp; 4-H; SciCl; LetterFtbl; LetterTrk; 4-HAwd; College; MaTh.

IRELAND, Valerie K; Nathan Hale HS; West Allis, WI; 15/549 Band; HonRl; NHS; Orch; StuCncl; TchrAde; SptEdYrbk; LetterBsktbl; LetterTrk; College; Teacher.

IREY, Glenda D; Tipton HS; Latham, MO; 21/84 Chr; Chrs; ChrhWkr; HonRl; NHS; SchPl; RptrYrbk; RptrSchPpr; EdSchPpr; FHA; College; English.

IREY, Joan; Granville HS; Granville, ND; 4/15 SecJrCls; Band; Chr; HonRl; HospAde; LbryAde; Bsktbl; Trk; Chrldr; GAA; Work.

IRISH, Elizabeth A; North Adams HS; Jerome, MI; 3/52 CncrtBnd; HonRl; LbryAde; MrchBnd; PepBnd; SchPl; 4-H; FTA; SpnCl; GAA; Kellogg Comm Clge; X Ray Tech.

IRISH, Gary; Hamady HS; Flint, MI; HonRl; SchAde; TchrAde; IMSpt; College; Cpa.

IRISH, Janetta M; Clio Area HS; Clio, MI; Band; ChrhWkr; CncrtBnd; HonRl; JrNHS; MrchBnd; NHS; PepBnd; SchMus; SchPl; College.

IRISH, Joseph R; Mt Pulaski Twp HS; Middletown, IL; 10/105 VPFrshCls; PresSophCls; VPSrCls; Band; ChrhWkr; CncrtBnd; HonRl; JrNHS; NHS; NatlMeritSchl; SctActv; StuCncl; StuGov; Univ Of Ill; Mech Engineering.

IRISH, Melanie J; St Stephen Area HS; Saginaw, MI; 10/104 TrsFrshCls; HospAde; NHS; OffAde; SchMus; SchPl; TchrAde; EdYrBk; IMSpt; PPFtbl; Political Science.

IRISH, Phyllis; Genoa Public HS; Genoa, NE; 1/27 Chr; HonRl; NHS; EdSchPpr; DanFAwd; Doane College.

IRMITER, Michael; St Vincent De Paul Seminary; Chicago, IL; 2/9 VPJrCls; Chrs; NHS; EdYrBk; Bsktbl; Socr; Tennis; IMSpt; St Mary Of The Barrens Coll;math Teach.

IRMITER, Michael P; St Vincent De Paul HS; Chicago, IL; 2/9 VPJrCls; Chr; EdYrBk; CaptBsktbl; LetterSocr; College; Mathematics.

IRONSIDE, Marg J; North Linn Comm HS; Coggon, IA; 4/59 ALAGirlsSt; Band; Chrs; HonRl; NHS; StuGov; PresSpnCl; CaptBsktbl; CaptTrk; DARAwd; Coll; Med Tech.

IRSIK, Mark A; Cassville HS; Shell Knob, MO; 20/108 TrsFrshCls; PresSophCls; HonRl; SctActv; StuCncl; FTA; MthCl; Bsbl; LetterFtbl; LetterTrk; Military School.

IRVIN, Brian W; Dekalb HS; Dekalb, IL; Band; CncrtBnd; HonRl; MrchBnd; Knox College.

IRVIN, Charles P; Carroll HS; Ft Wayne, IN; 37/196 Chr; Chrl; ChrhWkr; JrNHS; NHS; SchMus; SchPl; StuCncl; LetterBsktbl; LetterTrk; Purdue U; Electrician.

IRVIN, Douglas W; Goodland HS; Goodland, KS; 2/132 VPJrCls; PresSrCls; ALBoysSt; Band; CncrtBnd; HonRl; MrchBnd; NHS; LetterGlf; CitAwd; Kansas State U; Chemical Engineering.

IRVIN, Joel G; Mcleansboro HS; Mcleansboro, IL; 58/159 ChrhWkr; HonRl; SchPl; Yrbk; PresMthCl; PpCl; Bsbl; Bsktbl; Ftbl; Trk; N Il Univ; Journalism.

IRVIN, Linda D; Bedford Comm HS; Bedford, IA; SecFrshCls; AFS; HonRl; NHS; Quill&Scroll; EdSchPpr; 4-H; FTA; BttyCrckrAwd; Ia State Univ; Journalism.

IRVINE, Barbara S; Quincy Sr HS; Quincy, IL; 21/694 HonRl; SecJA; JrNHS; NHS; SchAde; TchrAde; FrCl; GAA; DARAwd; Quincy College; Social Studies Teacher.

IRVINE, Delma; Ladywood HS; Plymouth, MI; Band; HonRl; NatlMeritSF; Orch; SchMus; SchPl; StuCncl; StuGov; SciCl; Bsktbl; Mich State Univ; Fisheries Wildlife.

IRVINE, Kim M; Alton Sr HS; Alton, IL; ALAGirlsSt; Chr; Chrs; HonRl; PresNHS; SchMus; PpCl; Illinois State Univ; Law.

IRVINE, Nancy J; Holden HS; Holden, MO; 21/90 ChrhWkr; HonRl; OffAde; SchPl; TchrAde; PresSpnCl;.

IRVINE, Scott R; Manistee HS; Manistee, MI; CncrtBnd; HonRl; NatlMeritFnl; College; Professional.

IRVINE, Steven M; Naperville Central HS; Naperville, IL; 62/844 Band; CncrtBnd; HonRl; MrchBnd; NatlMeritFnl; Orch; PepBnd; Univ Of Ill; Architecture.

IRVINE, Vicki D; Pittsfield HS; Rockport, IL; Chrs; HonRl; LbryAde; NHS; OffAde;.

IRVING, Barbara K; St Marys HS; Burlington, WI; 5/73 SecTrsJrCls; Chr; Chrs; HonRl; NatlMeritCmnd; SchMus; SctActv; PpCl; IMSpt; University; Psychology.

IRVING, Catherine M; Romeo HS; Romeo, MI; 21/324 HonRl; LbryAde; NHS; NatlMeritSF; SctActv; GerCl; SpnCl; IMSpt; Univ; Natural Sci.

IRVING, Kelly; Pittsfield HS; Pittsfield, IL; Band; HonRl; StuCncl; PpCl; Swmmng; GAA; IMSpt; LionAwd; S Ill Univ; Nursing.

IRWIN, Bryan J; St Louis University HS; Webster Grove, MO; CncrtBnd; RptrSchPpr; IMSpt; University; Forestry.

IRWIN, Debra L; Sterling HS; Sterling, IL; 38/400 JrNHS; NHS; NatlMeritCmnd; PresNatlThespSoc; SchPl; StuCncl; TreasFrCl; GAA; AmLegAwd; VoiceDemAwd; College; Political Science.

IRWIN, Dorothy G; St Mary Of Redford HS; Detroit, MI; 10/163 SecJA; LitMag; NHS; SchMus; SchPl; StuCncl; Yrbk; RptrSchPpr; LetterSwmmng; LetterTrk; CchngActv; Michigan St Univ.

IRWIN, James H; Pleasant Plains HS; Springfield, IL; 5/57 Band; ChrhWkr; CncrtBnd; HonRl; NHS; Orch; YthFlsp; VPSciCl; Bradley Univ; Electrical Engineering.

IRWIN, Karen E; Hume R Viii HS; Hume, MO; PresFrshCls; TrsSrCls; Band; Chrs; CncrtBnd; MrchBnd; PepBnd; Bsbl; Bsktbl; CaptChrldr;.

IRWIN, Pattie; Green Valley HS; Green Valley, IL; 5/30 Band; Chrs; HonRl; JrNHS; MrchBnd; PepBnd; SchMus; SchPl; TchrAde; PpCl; Ill Central Coll; Secretarial.

IRWIN, Scott; Yjb HS; Bagley, IA; 4/23 SecJrCls; ALBoysSt; HonRl; NHS; SchPl; StuGov; 4-H; Ftbl; Trk; Iowa St; Ag Law.

IRWIN, Scott H; Y J B HS; Bagley, IA; PresFrshCls; SecJrCls; Band; CncrtBnd; HonRl; MrchBnd; NHS; SchPl; StuCncl; 4-H; SciCl; Bsktbl; Ftbl; Iowa State Univ; Farmer.

IRWIN, Susan M; Ludington HS; Ludington, MI; 18/233 HonRl; Quill&Scroll; PresFHA; VPSpnCl; EldAwd; Alma College; Psychology.

ISAACS, Paul W; Mankato East HS; Mankato, MN; Band; Chr; HonRl; NHS; NatlThespSoc; Orch; SchMus; SchPl; Yrbk; Mankato State; Music.

ISAACS, Phillip D; Mankato East HS; Mankato, MN; 8/233 Band; Chr; HonRl; NHS; NatlThespSoc; SchPl; Yrbk; SchPpr; Ftbl; Trk; Univ Of Minnesota; Doctor.

ISAACSON, Cheryl J; Riceville HS; Leroy, MN; HonRl; 4-H; FTA; Trade School.

ISAACSON, Diane J; Barnum HS; Kettle River, MN; 9/58 ChrhWkr; HonRl; JrNHS; NHS; SchPl; TchrAde; Yrbk; SchPpr; 4-H; FTA; Duluth Area Vocational Tech Ins; Architecur.

ISAACSON, Julie A; Hancock Central HS; Hancock, MI; 17/90 Chr; CncrtBnd; HonRl; MrchBnd; PepBnd; TchrAde; RptrYrbk; FTA; Glf; GAA; Michigan Tech; Liberal Arts.

ISAACSON, Raeann K; West HS; Sioux City, IA; 19/266 Band; CncrtBnd; HonRl; MrchBnd; PepBnd; SchMus; PpCl; Bsktbl; Trk; Morningside College; Nursing.

ISAAK, Brenda K; Tyndall HS; Tyndall, SD; Band; Chr; ChrhWkr; CncrtBnd; HonRl; MrchBnd; PepBnd; Usd University; Probation Officer.

ISAAK, Wayne D; Eureka Public HS; Eureka, SD; 5/56 PresSophCls; ALBoysSt; HonRl; Orch; SchMus; SptEdYrbk; SptEdSchPpr; CaptBsktbl; CaptFtbl; Trk; Univ Of Sd;.

ISACKSON, Robert; Oak Park HS; Oak Park, MI; 60/480 ChrhWkr; HonRl; SctActv; StuGov; RptrSchPpr; FDA; Univ Of Mich;eng Elec.

ISBELL, Chris; Hutsonville HS; West York, IL; VPJrCls; HonRl; NHS; RptrSchPpr; MthCl; SciCl; Univ; Professional.

ISEBERG, Lisa; Adiai E Stevenson Hs; Deerfield, IL; LitMag; TchrAde; RptrSchPpr; EdSchPpr; FrCl; GovHonPrgAwd; U Of Ill; Humaties.

ISELER, Mark E; Taylor Center HS; Taylor, MI; HonRl; NHS; StuCncl; RptrSchPpr; SptEdSchPpr; SchPpr; Valparaiso University; Engineering.

ISELY, Mary M; St Marys Springs HS; Fond Du Lac, WI; 23/120 ChrhWkr; CmntyWkr; JA; LbryAde; SchPl; SctActv; StuCncl; TchrAde; RptrYrbk; LetterBsktbl; CchngActv; GAA; IMSpt; Univ Of Wisconsin; Pharmacy.

ISEMAN, Karen A; Raymore Peculiar HS; Raymore, MO; NHS; SchPl; StuCncl; VoiceDemAwd; College; Journalism.

ISEMINGER, Betty J; Heyworth HS; Heyworth, IL; PresSrCls; HonRl; SchPl; StuCncl; RptrYrbk; RptrSchPpr; VPFHA; PresSciCl; Chrldr; Univ.

ISENHART, Renee R; Lake Park HS; Medinah, IL; 4/520 TrsSrCls; HonRl; SchMus; SchPl; StuCncl; CaptTrk; CaptChrldr; College; Liberal Arts.

ISENHOWER, Sandra K; Fremont HS; Fremont, IN; 7/63 Chr; HonRl; LbryAde; NHS; SchPl; SchPpr; FHA; LatCl; PpCl; GAA; College; Accounting.

ISENSEE, Kristin L; Brown HS; Sturgis, SD; 55/208 TrsJrCls; Band; Chr; ChrhWkr; CncrtBnd; DrlTm; HonRl; MrchBnd; NatlFornLg; NHS; PepBnd; PolWkr; SchMus; StuCncl; College; Business.

ISERMAN, Linda; Warren HS; Warren, IL; 6/58 Band; Chrs; CncrtBnd; HonRl; LbryAde; SchMus; TchrAde; EdSchPpr; Freeport Memorial Hosp Sc Of Nursing; Rn.

ISERT, Vivian J; St Paul HS; Highland, IL; 10/52 Band; Chrs; HonRl; LbryAde; SchMus; SecStuCncl; SecRptrYrbk; GAA; S Ill Univ; Communications.

ISGRIG, Tammy L; Mexico HS; Mexico, MO; ALAGirlsSt; Chr; HospAde; SchMus; StuCncl; YthFnd; Yrbk; LatCl; PpCl; AmLegAwd; Williams Woods Coll; Pre Med.

ISHIHARA, Virtue T; Terre Haute North Vigo HS; Terre Haute, IN; 1/600 HonRl; Florida State Univ; Biology.

ISHIKAWA, Hiromi C; Senn HS; Chicago, IL; 5/380 HonRl; NHS; OffAde; TchrAde; KeyCl; SecChrldr; Loyola Univ; Accounting.

ISHMAEL, Debra J; Wheeling Riv HS; Wheeling, MO; SecFrshCls; VPSophCls; TrsJrCls; HonRl; LbryAde; SchPl; Yrbk; SchPpr; LetterBsktbl; LetterTrk; Chillicothe Area Vo Tech Sch.

ISHOL, Larry D; Brookings HS; Brookings, SD; VPFrshCls; VPSrCls; Ftbl; CaptWrstlng; IMSpt; Sd Univ;professional.

ISLEY, Diana; Waldron Jr Sr HS; Shelbyville, IN; 2;65 SecJrCls; VPSrCls; ALAGirlsSt; Band; ChrhWkr; NHS; LatCl; GAA; DARAwd; 4-HAwd; Purdue Univ;animal Science.

ISOM, Timothy J; Pardeeville HS; Pardeeville, WI; ALBoysSt; Band; SctActv; RptrSchPpr; College.

ISRAEL, Donna S; Cardinal Ritter HS; Indianapolis, IN; HonRl; StuCncl; StuGov; CaptBsktbl; IMSpt; PPFtbl; College; Business.

ISTAS, Jon W; Clifton HS; Clifton, KS; ALBoysSt; Band; CncrtBnd; DrmBgl; HonRl; MrchBnd; PepBnd; Bsbl; LetterBsktbl; LetterFtbl; Air Force;.

ITALIANO, Ruth M; Luther HS; Lacrosse, WI; Band; ChrhWkr; CncrtBnd; HonRl; Mdrgl; Orch; PepBnd; YthFlsp; RptrYrbk; Chrldr; Wi Col Conservatory; Elementary Ed.

ITINGER, Tina L; Greenwood Comm HS; Greenwood, IN; ALAGirlsSt; CmntyWkr; HonRl; HospAde; JrNHS; NHS; OffAde; SchPl; StuCncl; StuGov; Indiana Univ; Foreign Language.

ITRICH, Steven J; New Salem HS; New Salem, ND; SecFrshCls; StuCncl; Ftbl; LetterWrstlng; College; Professional.

ITZEN, Debbie K; Osceola Senior HS; Star Prairie, WI; 1/79 Band; CncrtBnd; HonRl; MrchBnd; OffAde; PepBnd; FBLA; FHA; FrCl; College; Secretary.

IVAN, Patricia; New Lothrop HS; New Lothrop, MI; 4/83 TrsSophCls; TrsJrCls; TrsSrCls; SptEdYrbk; FHA; SpnCl; Trk; DARAwd; CitAwd; Clerical Sec In Bank.

IVANCOVICH, John S; Marist HS; Blue Island, IL; 5/393 HonRl; NHS; FrCl; SciCl; College; Physics Research.

IVERS, Susan M; Lincoln Way HS; Frankfort, IL; 63/566 HonRl; RptrSchPpr; FrCl; Univ; Busness.

IVERSON, Aaron C; J M Harlan HS; Chicago, IL; HonRl; NatlMeritCmnd; Bsbl; Ftbl; Univ; Electrical Engineer.

IVERSON, Carrie; Alsen Public HS; Hampden, ND; Chrs; ChrhWkr; CmntyWkr; HonRl; LbryAde; PolWkr; SchPl; StuCncl; SchPpr; St Oalf College; Nursing.

IVERSON, Daniel D; Canton HS; Canton, SD; ALBoysSt; ChrhWkr; PresCmntyWkr; CncrtBnd; HonRl; SchPl; PresYthFlsp; RptrSchPpr; SptEdSchPpr; LetterBsktbl; LetterTrk; Liberal Arts Bible College; Theology.

IVERSON, Glaydon P; Emmons HS; Emmons, MN; TrsFrshCls; PresSrCls; HonRl; SchPl; StuCncl; LetterBsktbl; CaptBsktbl; CaptFtbl; LetterGlf; Coll; Accounting.

IVERSON, Glaydon P; Emmons Public HS; Emmons, MN; 6/30 TrsFrshCls; PresSrCls; HonRl; SchPl; StuCncl; LetterBsbl; CaptBsktbl; CaptFtbl; LetterGlf; College; Cpa Accountant.

IVERSON, Ingrid; East Troy HS; East Troy, WI; ChrhWkr; HonRl; NHS; NatlMeritSF; SchPl; Yrbk; FHA; SecSpnCl; Univ; Art.

IVERSON, Kristi A; Bishop Ryan HS; Minot, ND; 27/85 Chrs; HonRl; JrNHS; NHS; SchMus; Sdlty; Univ; Medical Doctor.

IVERSON, Kristin L; Oak Park HS; Kansas City, MO; 3/602 VPAFS; DrlTm; HonRl; Orch; SchMus; StuCncl; RptrYrbk; Yrbk; PpCl; GAA; IMSpt; University Of Missouri; Child Psychology.

IVERSON, Roger W; Montezuma Comm HS; Malcom, IA; 4-H; VPFFA; Bsktbl; Ftbl; College; Farming.

IVERSON, Sheila R; Lake Park HS; Lake Park, MN; 6/41 Band; Chr; CncrtBnd; HonRl; NHS; SchPl; RptrSchPpr; Sec4-H; PresFHA; VPFTA; Moorhead Vo Tech; Secretary.

IVERSON, Teresa J; Vandercook Lake HS; Jackson, MI; HstSrCls; HonRl; NHS; OffAde; SchPl; SecStuCncl; EdYrBk; PresFHA; DanFAwd; Central Mi Univ; Medicine.

IVES, Christopher; Bancroft HS; Yankton, SD; /32 TrsFrshCls; VPSrCls; HonRl; NHS; SchPl; RptrYrbk; EdSchPpr; SciCl; LetterFtbl; Yankton Coll.

IVESDAL, Georgia L; Starbuck HS; Starbuck, MN; 3/57 Band; HonRl; MrchBnd; NHS; RptrYrbk; RptrSchPpr; EdSchPpr; PpCl; GAA; Univ Of Minnesota; Medical Tech.

IVESON, Sharon R; Ionia HS; Ionia, MI; 24/226 ChrhWkr; HonRl; NatlMeritSchl; Grand Rapids Bapt College; History.

IVICIC, Holly E; St Andrew HS; Detroit, MI; HonRl; SchMus; SchPl; PpCl; IMSpt;.

IVIS, Dan R; Eagle Grove HS; Eagle Grove, IA; 10/130 HonRl; JrNHS; NHS; Ftbl; Wrstlng; RotaryAwd; Ia State Univ; Statistics.

IVY, Stephen C; Chicago Vocational HS; Chicago, IL; 25/1774 HonRl; NHS; NatlMeritSchl; OffAde; Ftbl; Trk; LetterWrstlng; General Motors Inst Of Tech; Mechanics.

IWAND, Marc; Lincoln Northeast Hs; Lincoln, NE; HonRl; Orch; Quill&Scroll; SchMus; RptrSchPpr; Nebraska U;teach German And Spanish.

IWANICKI, Stephen; Albert G Lane Tech HS; Chicago, IL; 1/1209 LbryAde; NHS; NatlMeritFnl; NatlMeritSF; College.

IWANSKI, Joseph G; William J Bogan HS; Chicago, IL; Northern Illinois Univ; Computer Science.

IWEMA, Elaine M; Chicago Christian HS; Evergreen Park, IL; 5/150 Chr; ChrhWkr; HonRl; NHS; OffAde; RptrYrbk; PpCl; Chrldr; Business School; Secretary.

IWEN, Rachel J; Dakota HS; Arthur, ND; TrsSophCls; PresJrCls; SecSrCls; Band; Chr; ChrhWkr; NHS; SecStuCncl; LetterBsktbl; LetterTrk; GAA; IMSpt; Univ; Professional.

IWERSEN, Robert W; Creighton Prep HS; Omaha, NE; HonRl; CaptTennis; IMSpt; College.

IWERT, Doreen M; Hildreth HS; Upland, NE; Chrs; HonRl; NHS; SchPl; Yrbk;.

IZZARD, John; Lake Mills Community HS; Lake Mills, IA; 16/81 Band; CncrtBnd; MrchBnd; PepBnd; SchMus; LetterBsbl; LetterBsktbl; LetterFtbl; IMSpt; Niacc; Engineering.

IZZO, John M; York Community HS; Elmhurst, IL; 5/815 HonRl; Bradley Univ; Law.

J

JABIONSKI, Nancy M; Assumption HS; St Louis, IL; SchPl; StuCncl; RptrYrbk; College.

JABLONSKI, Antoinette; Roseville; Roseville, MI; 130534 HonRl; JrNHS; NHS; EdYrBk; Macomb County Community College; Undecided.

JABLONSKI, Nancy; Center Line Sr HS; Center Line, MI; CmntyWkr; HonRl; LitMag; NHS; NatlMeritCmnd; NatlMeritSF; PolWkr; StuGov; CitAwd; Michigan U; Political Science.

JABLONSKI, Robin A; Saint Marys Academy; New Buffalo, MI; 2/47 CmntyWkr; HonRl; LitMag; NHS; Quill&Scroll; SchPl; SchPpr; FrCl; Northwestern Univ; Medicine.

JABLONSKI, Sharon K; Edsel Ford HS; Dearborn, MI; SecAFS; CmntyWkr; VPNHS; PolWkr; PpCl; SciCl; Chrldr; GAA; IMSpt; BttyCrckrAwd; Univ Of Michigan; Psychology.

JABUSCH, John W; Williamsville HS; Sherman, IL; ChrhWkr; 4-H; 4-HAwd;.

JACHNA, John J; St Laurence HS; Oak Lawn, IL; 21/372 HonRl; GovHonPrgAwd; U Of Ill; Finance Business.

JACKEL, Don P; Irving Crown HS; Carpentersville, IL; Aud/Vis; SctActv; FrCl; College; Forestry.

JACKLIN, Ned W; Geneva Community HS; Geneva, IL; MrchBnd; OffAde; PepBnd; SchAde; SchMus; SchPl; SchPpr; LetterBsbl; LetterFtbl; LetterWrstlng; Jr Coll Transfer To Univ; Tv Studio Technic.

JACKLITCH, Laurie; Campbell Tintah Public HS; Campbell, MN; 4/40 SecFrshCls; StuCncl; Yrbk; EdSchPpr; FBLA; Bsktbl; Trk; GAA; IMSpt; PresAwd; Coll; Phys Educ Or Med.

JACKOBS, Steven C; Superior Sr HS; Superior, WI; 19/549 ALBoysSt; HonRl; PresNHS; NatlMeritSF; StuCncl; StuGov; College; Liberal Arts.

JACKOWSKI, Betty J; Saline HS; Ann Arbor, MI; Band; Chrs; CncrtBnd; HonRl; MrchBnd; SchMus; SchPl; TchrAde; Mi St Univ; Music.

JACKOWSKI, Jayne; Ripon Senior HS; Ripon, WI; Chr; HonRl; NatlThespSoc; SchMus; SchPl; SctActv; RptrYrbk; RptrSchPpr; Univ Wi Madison; Journalism.

JACKS, Chet A; Quigley Prep Seminary S; Chicago, IL; 60/170 Chr; NatlMeritCmnd; SchAde; LetterBsktbl; LetterTrk; Bradley University; Chemist.

JACKS, Tobin E; Iowa City HS; Iowa City, IA; HonRl; NHS; NatlMeritFnl; NatlMeritCmnd; NatlMeritSchl; SecJrCls; GerCl; Bsktbl; Ftbl; Trk; Univ; Doctor.

JACKSON, Ann; Wheaton Central Hs; Wheaton, IL; 29/324 HonRl; StuCncl; YthFlsp; FrCl; U Of Ill; Liberal Arts And Sciences.

JACKSON, Barbara R; Lindblom Tech HS; Chicago, IL; 12/640 ChrhWkr; HonRl; NHS; OffAde; VPStuCncl; TchrAde; RptrYrbk; GerCl; GAA; Bradley Univ; Industrial Engineer.

JACKSON, Bennett J; Winterset HS; Winterset, IA; 15/115 ALBoysSt; ChrhWkr; HonRl; PolWkr; SchMus; TchrAde; SecSciCl; LetterFtbl; LetterTrk; LetterWrstlng; Iowa U; Dentistry.

JACKSON, Brett M; Campion Jesuit HS; Crete, IL; 5/92 SecJrCls; HonRl; StuCncl; StuGov; RptrYrbk; Univ Notre Dame; Elec Engineering.

JACKSON, Cynthia; Laboure HS; St Louis, MO; Chrs; DrlTm; SchMus; SchPl; YthFlsp; FrCl; SpnCl; Trk; College; Commercial Artist.

JACKSON, David; La Crescent HS; La Crescent, MN; Band; CncrtBnd; HonRl; MrchBnd; PepBnd; Ftbl; Glf; Univ Of Wi; Bus Management.

JACKSON, David R; Allen Park HS; Allen Park, MI; Band; CncrtBnd; DrmBgl; MrchBnd; PepBnd; TchrAde; Ferris St Col; Auto Serv.

JACKSON, Don; South Haven Public HS; South Haven, MI; ChrhWkr; CmntyWkr; HonRl; SctActv; TchrAde; YthFlsp; Bsktbl; Ftbl; Univ; Hotel & Restaurant Management.

JACKSON, Donald; Emerson HS; Gary, IN; 80/235 ChrhWkr; HonRl; LbryAde; EdSchPpr; FrCl; SpnCl; CitAwd; In U; Busi Ed.

JACKSON, Don J; Walhalla HS; Walhalla, ND; ALBoysSt; Band; Chr; Chrs; HonRl; MrchBnd; StuCncl; LetterFtbl; LetterTrk; LetterWrstlng; University; Business Admin.

JACKSON, Elizabeth; Jackson Western HS; Parma, MI; ChrhWkr; HonRl; SchPl; TchrAde; College; Elementary Education.

JACKSON, Emma L; Bedford Comm HS; Hopkins, MO; 4/78 AFS; Chrs; ChrhWkr; HonRl; NHS; StuCncl; 4-H; VPFHA; FTA; CaptChrldr; PPFtbl; College; Home Economics.

JACKSON, Frederick E; Divine Heart Seminary; Cazenovia, WI; 2/23 VPJrCls; Chr; CmntyWkr; HonRl; Mdrgl; NHS; SctActv; StuCncl; SpnCl; LetterBsbl; University; Professional.

JACKSON, Frederick; Divine Heart Sem; Cazenovia, WI; VPJrCls; Chr; Chrs; CmntyWkr; OffAde; SctActv; StuCncl; Bsktbl; Socr; Trk; Univ Of Wisconsin; Us Air Force.

JACKSON, Gerilyn S; Avon HS; Avon, IL; Band; CncrtBnd; HonRl; OffAde; SchPl; SctActv; Yrbk; FrCl; Chrldr; College; Medicine.

JACKSON, Gregory; Omaha Creighton Prep; Omaha, NE; NHS; Kansas State U; Pre Med.

JACKSON, Gwendolyn; Spalding HS; Chicago, IL; HonRl; JrNHS; NHS; College.

JACKSON, Janet D; Le Roy HS; Le Roy, IL; Chr; Chrs; ChrhWkr; HonRl; OffAde; SchAde; SctActv; TchrAde; YthFlsp; Yrbk; Ftbl; Socr; LetterTrk; Chrldr; Western Illinois College; Teaching.

JACKSON, Janice L; Granite City South HS; Granite City, IL; 44/630 Chrs; CmntyWkr; HospAde; NHS; StuCncl; Univ Of Il; Physical Therapist.

JACKSON, Javel; Wichita North HS; Wichita, KS; Chr; ChrhWkr; HonRl; NHS; Orch; StuCncl; PpCl; Trk; Wichita St Univ; Pschyologist.

JACKSON, Jeffrey C; Lincoln Park HS; Lincoln Park, MI; 23/126 NHS; LetterGlf; Comm Coll; Acctng.

JACKSON, John A; Centralia HS; Centralia, IL; 11/430 HonRl; NHS; College; Biology.

JACKSON, John E; East HS; Kansas City, MO; 44/170 ALBoysSt; HonRl; SctActv; TchrAde; RptrSchPpr; CaptSwmmng; GodCntryAwd; Nw Missouri State Univ; Business Admin.

JACKSON, June A; Ontonagon Area HS; Ontonagon, MI; PresSophCls; DrmBgl; HonRl; Yrbk; 4-H; Bsktbl; Chrldr; GAA; IMSpt; College; Professional.

JACKSON, Karen K; Logan HS; Logan, KS; 1/25 Band; Chr; ChrhWkr; CncrtBnd; DrlTm; MrchBnd; StuCncl; EdYrBk; PpCl; LetterTrk; Chrldr; BttyCrckrAwd; DanFAwd; Fort Hays Kansas State College; Nursing.

JACKSON, Keith R; Libertyville HS; Libertyville, IL; CmntyWkr; NHS; Orch; RedCrAde; Swmmng; CchngActv; IMSpt; Business U Of Illinois.

JACKSON, Kerry L; Redfield HS; Zell, SD; HonRl; JrNHS; NHS; PepBnd; SchMus; SchPl; YthFlsp; 4-H; Ftbl; LetterWrstlng; Univ; Engineering.

JACKSON, Koblar A; Burlington Comm HS; Burlington, IA; ALBoysSt; NatlFornLg; NHS; StuCncl; Bsbl; LetterFtbl; Trk; IMSpt; DARAwd; University; Astrophysics.

JACKSON, Korey V; Redfield HS; Zell, SD; AFS; Band; Chrs; CncrtBnd; HonRl; MrchBnd; NHS; SchPl; VP4-H; LetterWrstlng; Univ; Engineering.

JACKSON, Larry R; Peru HS; Peru, IN; 17/240 ChrhWkr; HonRl; NHS; SchAde; TchrAde; YthFlsp; FrCl; LetterBsbl; LetterBsktbl; Trk; Taylor Univ; Ministry.

JACKSON, Linda F; North Division HS; Milwaukee, WI; ChrhWkr; HonRl; JA; NHS; OffAde; StuCncl; FSA; FrCl; LatCl; SpnCl; MthCl; SciCl; College; Liberal Arts.

JACKSON, Linda S; Litchfield HS; Litchfield, IL; HonRl; StuCncl; Marry.

JACKSON, Lisa D; Freeburg Comm HS; Freeburg, IL; 19/125 VPFrshCls; PresSophCls; VPJrCls; VPSrCls; CncrtBnd; DrmMjrt; HonRl; MrchBnd; PepBnd; RptrYrbk; St Louis Coll; Pharmacist.

JACKSON, Loretta; Rushville HS; Rushville, NE; SecSophCls; Chrs; ChrhWkr; HonRl; IntrClCncl; YthFlsp; PpCl; Chrldr; GAA; PresAwd; Trade School; Vocation.

JACKSON, Lorraine; Saint Anne HS; Momence, IL; Chr; Chrs; CncrtBnd; HonRl; JA; SchMus; FHA; FNA; AmLegAwd; JAAwd; College; Professional.

JACKSON, Marla; Seneca Township HS; Seneca, IL; Band; Chr; ChrhWkr; HonRl; StuCncl; YthFlsp; 4-H; Chrldr; GAA; 4-HAwd; College; Vocational.

JACKSON, Mary L; Lindblom Tech HS; Chicago, IL; 72/657 HonRl; HospAde; ModUN; NatlMeritCmnd; OffAde; SchAde; StuCncl; TchrAde; SchPpr; FrCl; SciCl; Chrldr; Univ Of Ill; Pharmacist.

JACKSON, Michael; St Ignatius HS; Chicago, IL; 80/210 Band; Chr; ChrhWkr; CmntyWkr; HonRl; RptrYrbk; Yrbk; SchPpr; FDA; FSA; Univ; Professional.

JACKSON, Pamela G; Superior HS; Superior, NE; Band; Chrs; ChrhWkr; HonRl; NHS; Quill&Scroll; SctActv; FshEdYrbk; Chrldr; Ozark Bible College; Music.

JACKSON, Pamela J; Meridian HS; Villa Ridge, IL; 5/117 TrsSrCls; Chrs; HonRl; JA; OffAde; SchMus; SctActv; YthFlsp; GAA; 4-HAwd; William Jewell Clge; Music.

JACKSON, Paul H; Chaffee HS; Leonard, ND; VPJrCls; ALBoysSt; ChrhWkr; HonRl; StuCncl; SptEdSchPpr; PpCl; LetterBsbl; CaptBsktbl; CaptFtbl;.

JACKSON, Phillip D; Marian Catholic HS; Steger, IL; 7/365 ChrhWkr; CncrtBnd; HonRl; MrchBnd; PresNHS; Orch; SchMus; VPLatCl; De Paul University; Music.

JACKSON, Ralph B; Lindblom HS; Chicago, IL; HonRl; IntrClCncl; NHS; StuCncl; TchrAde; YthFlsp; CivCl; SpnCl; Purdue Univ; Engineering.

JACKSON, Rhonda K; Southern Reynolds R2 HS; Ellington, MO; Chr; Chrs; ChrhWkr; CmntyWkr; LbryAde; SchPl; YthFlsp; SchPpr; 4-H; FHA; College; Librarian.

JACKSON, Richard; Bellmont HS; Decatur, IN; 41/251 HonRl; NHS; NatlMeritCmnd; SchPl; LatCl; PpCl; SciCl; Indiana Univ; Doctor.

JACKSON, Ronald; Northeast Nodaway HS; Ravenwood, MO; TrsFrshCls; VPSophCls; Bsbl; College.

JACKSON, Sandra S; Baxter Springs HS; Baxter Springs, KS; SecJrCls; ALAGirlsSt; Band; NatlFornLg; NatlThespSoc; SchMus; SchPl; YthFlsp; RptrYrbk; FHA; College; Medicine.

JACKSON, Shirley S; Hayti HS; Hayti, MO; HonRl; Hannibal Lagrange Jr College; Secretary.

JACKSON, Stephen C; Oakville HS; St Louis, MO; 2/347 HonRl; NHS; NatlMeritFnl; MthCl; Univ; Physics.

JACKSON, Stephen W; South Page HS; Clarinda, IA; HonRl; FFA; Trade School; Diesel Mechanic.

JACKSON, Susan; Warren HS; Warren, MN; 9/61 SecSophCls; Chrs; HonRl; SchPl; StuGov; RptrSchPpr; GerCl; SciCl; GAA; Coll; History.

JACKSON, Teresa L; Heelan HS; Sioux City, IA; 3/250 Chrs; HonRl; JA; NHS; SchMus; SchPl; LetterBsktbl; LetterTrk; St Louis Univ; Social Work.

JACKSON, Terry L; Brownstown Central HS; Brownstown, IN; 9/143 HonRl; NHS; Quill&Scroll; SchPl; TchrAde; EdYrBk; FTA; LatCl; PpCl; Iupui Columbus Center; Elem Education.

JACKSON, Thomas R; Assumption HS; Assumption, IL; PresJrCls; PresSrCls; ChrhWkr; CtyCnl; CmntyWkr; HonRl; NatlThespSoc; SctActv; StuCncl; StuGov; LetterBsbl; LetterBsktbl; LetterFtbl; College; Professional.

JACKSON, Timothy S; Centralia HS; Centralia, IL; HonRl; Bsbl; College; Engineering.

JACKSON, Wallen; Eldora HS; Iowa Falls, IA; Yrbk; ALBoysSt; HonRl; 4-H; SpnCl;.

JACKSON, Walter B; Mchenry West HS; Mchenry, IL; 43/487 ALBoysSt; PresChrs; ChrhWkr; NHS; SchPl; StuCncl; Bsbl; Bsktbl; Ftbl; AmLegAwd; University; Chemistry And Music.

JACOB, Kathleen M; Rochester Community HS; Rochester, IN; 2/152 HonRl; TreasNHS; PepBnd; StuCncl; VPPpCl; U Of Notre Dame; Math.

JACOB, Rick J; Tripoint HS; Kempton, IL; 14/31 Chrs; ChrhWkr; CmntyWkr; HonRl; NatlThespSoc; SchPl; VPFFA; LetterBsbl; CaptBsktbl; LetterFtbl; Kankakee Comm Clg.

JACOB, Rosemary A; Sycamore HS; Sycamore, IL; 43/226 AFS; Chrs; HonRl; LitMag; Yrbk; SpnCl; PpCl; Trk; GAA; PPFtbl; Northern Illinois Univ; Teach Ment Handicap.

JACOB, Thomas N; Sycamore HS; Sycamore, IL; 6/206 HonRl; NHS; Bsktbl; Glf; Trk; U Of Ill; Engineering.

JACOBS, Ben H; Mc Henry HS; Wonder Lake, IL; ChrhWkr; CmntyWkr; 4-H; FFA; Bsbl; Bsktbl; LetterFtbl; LetterTrk; 4-HAwd; Madison Univ; Agriculture.

JACOBS, Beth A; Pius Xi HS; Milwaukee, WI; 9/417 Chrs; HonRl; LbryAde; NatlMeritSF; SchMus; SchPl; TchrAde; SecMthCl; GAA; Marquette Univ; Research Chemist.

JACOBS, Carol A; Serena HS; Sheridan, IL; NHS; OffAde; SchPl; TchrAde; FrCl; AmLegAwd; College; Mathematics.

JACOBS, Christopher L; Hale HS; Hale, MO; 3/19 VPJrCls; ALBoysSt; HonRl; ModUN; NatlFornLg; NatlMeritCmnd; NatlThespSoc; SchPl; StuGov; RptrSchPpr; Coll; Law.

JACOBS, Deborah A; Red Bud Comm Unit HS; Red Bud, IL; 8/100 ALAGirlsSt; Band; Chrs; HonRl; OffAde; SchMus; YthFlsp; FBLA; SpnCl; Belleville Area College; Business.

JACOBS, Debra E; Rockford Sr HS; Rudd, IA; 15/71 TrsJrCls; Band; Chr; NHS; SchPl; PresStuCncl; PresYthFlsp; Pres4-H; Bsktbl; Trk; Chrldr; GAA; IMSpt; Wartburg College; Physical Therapy.

JACOBS, Durrell L; Laker HS; Pigeon, MI; Chr; Chrl; Chrs; HonRl; SchMus; YthFlsp; PpCl; LetterBsktbl; Trk; Univ.

JACOBS, Elizabeth; Dupo Community HS; Dupo, IL; HonRl; LbryAde; NHS; SchAde; FTA; SciCl; Trk; PresAwd;.

JACOBS, Evelyn; Red Bud HS; Red Bud, IL; Band; CncrtBnd; HonRl; MrchBnd; PepBnd; FTA; SpnCl; PpCl; College.

JACOBS, Gordon J; South Decatur HS; Mallhousen, IN; PpCl; SciCl; Ftbl; Trade School.

JACOBS, Gordon M; Gale Ettrick Trempealeau HS; Ettrick, WI; 8/120 PresSophCls; TrsJrCls; Band; HonRl; NHS; SptEdSchPpr; LetterBsbl; Bsktbl; LetterFtbl; Socr; LetterTrk; CchngActv; 4-HAwd; College; Engineering.

JACOBS, Gregory F; Red River HS; Grand Forks, ND; Chr; HonRl; Mdrgl; NHS; NatlMeritSF; NatlThespSoc; SchMus; SchPl; TchrAde; RptrSchPpr; Clg; Physics.

JACOBS, James; Central HS; St Joseph, MO; NHS; SchMus; SchPl; StuCncl; StuGov; TchrAde; YthLg; KeyCl; SciCl; IMSpt; Univ Of California.

JACOBS, Janet L; Green City R 1 HS; Green City, MO; 3cl TrsFrshCls; VPJrCls; HonRl; NHS; OffAde; StuCncl; EdYrBk; RptrSchPpr; FBLA; DanFAwd; Nmsu; Business.

JACOBS, Jean L; Bird Island HS; Olivia, MN; 12/60 SecJrCls; Chr; NatlFornLg; NHS; SchMus; 4-H; Tennis; Trk; PPFtbl; PresAwd; Coll Of St Catherenes; Nursing.

JACOBS, Jeanne F; Thornton Township HS; Riverdale, IL; HonRl; HospAde; StuGov; College; Occupational Therapy Asst.

JACOBS, Jeffrey C; Sullivan HS; Chicago, IL; HonRl; NHS; OffAde; SchAde; Univ; Medical Career.

JACOBS, Joan; Thornton Township HS; Riverdale, IL; 16 HonRl; NHS; Depaul U;accounting.

JACOBS, Joel M; Garber HS; Essexville, MI; ALBoysSt; ChrhWkr; PolWkr; SctActv; StuCncl; YthFlsp; SchPpr; LetterTrk; AmLegAwd; CitAwd; Business.

JACOBS, John; West Fargo HS; West Fargo, ND; 14/142 HonRl; NatlThespSoc; SchPl; Bsbl; Tennis; IMSpt; College; Civil Engineer.

JACOBS, John M; La Salle HS; Cedar Rapids, IA; 1/146 VPBand; Chr; Chrs; VPCncrtBnd; HonRl; Mdrgl; MrchBnd; NHS; SchMus; Yrbk; SchPpr; LetterWrstlng; Notre Dame; Math.

JACOBS, Joseph L; Tri HS; Cambridge City, IN; Aud/Vis; HonRl; NHS; OffAde; SchAde; SciCl;

Ftbl; Trk; Wrstlng; College; Industrial Management.

JACOBS, Joy E; Ainsworth HS; Flint, MI; 17/292 Chr; ChrhWkr; HonRl; TreasNHS; RedCrAde; TchrAde; TreasFTA; Concordia Lutheran Jr College; Special Ed.

JACOBS, Linda M; Quinter HS; Gove, KS; Band; Chrs; CmntyWkr; CncrtBnd; HonRl; MrchBnd; NHS; OffAde; PepBnd; SchAde; SchPl; LetterBsktbl; Chrldr; IMSpt; College; Special Education.

JACOBS, Merlin R; Manistee HS; Manistee, MI; Michigan Tech Univ; Engineer.

JACOBS, Michael S; Walnut HS; Walnut, IL; Band; HonRl; MrchBnd; SptEdYrbk; Carl Sandburg College; Wildlife Management.

JACOBS, Mitchell; Irving Crown HS; Fox River Grove, IL; 35/401 HonRl; JrNHS; NHS; U Of Ill; Metalergical Engineering.

JACOBS, Patricia A; Morrison HS; Morrison, IL; ChrhWkr; NatlThespSoc; SchPl; FHA; College; Medicine.

JACOBS, Patrick C; Springfield Catholic HS; Springfield, MO; PresSrCls; Band; Chrs; HonRl; NatlMeritSchl; StuGov; EdYrBk; EdSchPpr; Bsktbl; EldAwd; Sw Mo St Univ; Commercial Art.

JACOBS, Paul J; Iron Mountain Sr HS; Iron Mountain, MI; KeyCl; LetterBsktbl; LetterFtbl; LetterTrk; LetterWrstlng; IMSpt; KiwanAwd; Marquette Univ; Dentistry.

JACOBS, Rita; Portland HS; Portland, IN; Band; Chr; JrNHS; NatlMeritCmnd; SchPl; YthFlsp; PpCl; Bsktbl; Trk; GAA; Vincennes Univ; Professional.

JACOBS, Roberta; Reavis HS; Burbank, IL; HonRl; LbryAde; SpnCl; College; Recreation Direction.

JACOBS, Robert D; Glenbrook North HS; Northbrook, IL; HonRl; SctActv; Bsbl; Univ Of Ill.

JACOBS, Steven H; Evanston Township HS; Evanston, IL; CtyCnl; HonRl; StuGov; TchrAde; Glf; Nw Univ; Veternarian.

JACOBS, Susan K; Winnebago Lutheran Academy; Fon Du Lac, WI; Chrs; NatlFornLg; SchPl; StuCncl; PpCl; Chrldr; Univ; Medical Tech.

JACOBS, Wade D; University HS; Bloomington, IL; 1/131 PresSophCls; AFS; ALBoysSt; ChrhWkr; HonRl; NatlFornLg; PolWkr; TreasStuCncl; FrCl; MthCl; Trk; Wrstlng; IMSpt; College; Attorney.

JACOBSEN, Barbara A; Fairmont HS; Fairmont, NE; 2/28 Band; Chr; Chrs; ChrhWkr; CncrtBnd; HonRl; MrchBnd; NHS; PolWkr; StuCncl; Univ Of Ne; Music.

JACOBSEN, Bonnie J; Lawton Bronson HS; Lawton, IA; Chr; Chrs; ChmnDrlTm; NatlThespSoc; PpCl; IMSpt; Trade Or Bus Sch; Professional.

JACOBSEN, Don; Audubon HS; Audubon, IA; 17/120 TrsJrCls; AFS; ALBoysSt; Band; HonRl; StuCncl; Bsbl; Bsktbl; Ftbl; Tennis; Trk; Univ Of Ia; Business.

JACOBSEN, Glen M; Central HS; Albert Lea, MN; NatlMeritCmnd; PepBnd; St Olaf College; Environmental Science.

JACOBSEN, Joanna L; New Trier East HS; Winnetka, IL; 68/847 ChrhWkr; HonRl; LbryAde; NatlFornLg; NatlMeritCmnd; OffAde; SchMus; SctActv; StuCncl; College; Foreign Language.

JACOBSEN, Joe D; Humboldt HS; Humboldt, IA; HonRl; Ftbl; Clge; Pro.

JACOBSEN, Joni D; East HS; Sioux City, IA; 12/365 Chrs; ChrhWkr; HonRl; HospAde; NatlMeritSF; OffAde; TchrAde; RptrSchPpr; PpCl; LetterBsktbl; Glf; Swmmng; LetterTrk; Augustana; Nurse.

JACOBSEN, Kathy; Lincoln Sr HS; Bloomington, MN; HospAde; YthFlsp; OptClAwd; Junior College; Nursing.

JACOBSEN, Myra J; Atlantic Comm HS; Atlantic, IA; Chr; Chrl; Chrs; ChrhWkr; CmntyWkr; StuCncl; YthFlsp; Pres4-H; Bsktbl; Trk; 4-HAwd; Des Moines Area Com Col; Exec Secretary.

JACOBSEN, Noel C; Marquette Cons HS; Marquette, NE; HonRl; SchMus; SchPl; YthFlsp; Yrbk; LetterBsbl; Bsktbl; Ftbl; Trk; PresAwd;.

JACOBSEN, Renae L; Wheaton HS; Wheaton, MN; 1/90 Band; Chr; CncrtBnd; Mdrgl; Coustavus Adolphus Coll.

JACOBSEN, Robert J; Assumption HS; Davenport, IA; 10/212 DrmMjrt; NatlFornLg; NHS; NatlMeritFnl; TchrAde; Swmmng; Trk; CchngActv; CaptIMSpt; Univ; Biology.

JACOBSMEIER, Bernadette A; Marquette HS; Hillsboro, IA; Chrs; RptrSchPpr; SchPpr; PpCl; Business School; Secretarial.

JACOBSON, Barbara S; Estherville HS; Estherville, IA; 1/189 Chrs; HonRl; HospAde; NatlFornLg; NatlThespSoc; SchMus; SpnCl; College; Physical Therapy.

JACOBSON, Belinda C; Hatton Public HS; Hatton, ND; 7/27 Band; Chrs; ChrhWkr; LbryAde; SchPl; TchrAde; SchPpr; FHA; Chrldr; Mayville State College; Elementary Educ.

JACOBSON, Cameon L; Rushville HS; Rushville, NE; 7/39 SecJrCls; Band; ChrhWkr; CncrtBnd; HonRl; MrchBnd; NHS; PepBnd; SchPl; PresYthFlsp; PresFTA; SecGerCl; DARAwd; Univ; Psychology.

JACOBSON, Dale E; Almont Public HS; Almont, ND; 1/7 PresFrshCls; PresSrCls; HonRl; SchPl; SctActv; YthFlsp; Yrbk; 4-H; FFA; Bsbl; Bsktbl;.

JACOBSON, Daniel T; Darlington HS; Darlington, WI; Chr; HonRl; NatlMeritSF; SchMus; SchPl; Bsbl; Bsktbl; LetterFtbl; LetterTrk; 4-HAwd; College; Accounting.

JACOBSON, Douglas L; Crocker HS; Richland, MO; 3/63 VPSrCls; ChrhWkr; HonRl; SchPl; SctActv; StuGov; RptrYrbk; RptrSchPpr; SptEdSchPpr; PpCl; LetterBsbl; LetterBsktbl; CaptTrk; College; Professional.

JACOBSON, Dustan J; Almont Public HS; Almont, ND; 1/10 VPSophCls; SecTrsJrCls; ALBoysSt; Chrs; HonRl; SchPl; StuCncl; EdYrBk; Bsktbl; Mary College.

JACOBSON, Elsa M; Evanston Township HS; Evanston, IL; RptrSchPpr; Kansas City Art Inst; Art.

JACOBSON, Eric W; Riverside Brookfield HS; Riverside, IL; 1/489 Chr; HonRl; JrNHS; NHS; SchMus; VPStuCncl; Yrbk; RptrSchPpr; GerCl; CaptSwmmng; Univ; Veterinarian.

JACOBSON, Howard M; Rushford HS; Rushford, MN; Chrs; ChrhWkr; CmntyWkr; HonRl; NHS; SchMus; TchrAde; FTA; LetterBsktbl; LetterFtbl; LetterGlf; AmLegAwd;.

JACOBSON, Jay B; Niles East HS; Morton Grove, IL; 2/653 HstFrshCls; SecTrsSophCls; VPJrCls; VPSrCls; CAP; JrNHS; MrchBnd; Quill&Scroll; YthLg; SptEdYrbk; Bsbl; Bsktbl; Glf; Trade School; Plumber.

JACOBSON, Joann G; Alvarado Public HS; Alvarado, MN; PresSophCls; PresJrCls; Band; Chrs; CncrtBnd; HonRl; Yrbk; FHA; Chrldr; GAA; College; Secretary.

JACOBSON, Kathleen K; Blue Valley HS; Leawood, KS; ChrhWkr; HonRl; JrNHS; NatlFornLg; SchPl; College; Medical Science.

JACOBSON, Kathryn K; Oak Park HS; Kansas City, MO; Band; ChrhWkr; CncrtBnd; HonRl; MrchBnd; TchrAde; FHA; College; Home Economics.

JACOBSON, Le Ann; Halstad Public HS; Lockhart, MN; Band; Chr; Chrs; ChrhWkr; CmntyWkr; CncrtBnd; DrmMjrt; HonRl; LbryAde; Chrldr; Coll; Prof.

JACOBSON, Lynnette M; Ulen Hitterdal HS; Hitterdal, MN; PresFrshCls; Chr; HonRl; JrNHS; NHS; Yrbk; BttyCrckrAwd; Univ; Chemistry.

JACOBSON, Margo E; West HS; Waterloo, IA; 16/481 Chrs; HonRl; NatlMeritCmnd; SchMus; StuGov; SctActv; FrCl; PpCl; RotaryAwd; CitAwd; U Of Ia; Medicine.

JACOBSON, Ralph B; Richmond Burton HS; Ringwood, IL; PresJrCls; Band; DrmBgl; HonRl; NHS; SchPl; YthFlsp; Bsktbl; Ftbl; Trk; Coll; Phys.

JACOBSON, Robert S; New Glarus HS; Mt Horeb, WI; 3/56 TrsFrshCls; PressSrCls; HonRl; JrNHS; NHS; Bsktbl; LetterFtbl; LetterTrk; Univ Of Wisc; Secondary Education.

JACOBSON, Ronald S; Peoria HS; Peoria, IL; 120/480 Band; HonRl; Orch; SctActv; RptrYrbk; RptrSchPpr; Bradley Univ; Medicine.

JACOBSON, Ronald S; Finley Public HS; Finley, ND; 1/30 ALBoysSt; Band; Chr; Chrs; HonRl; LetterBsktbl; AmLegAwd; TIMEAwd; College; Professional.

JACOBSON, Sally B; St Peter HS; St Peter, MN; Band; ChrhWkr; HospAde; TchrAde; GAA; PPFtbl; College; Nursing.

JACOBSON, Scott A; Drake HS; Drake, ND; 1/27 VPFrshCls; Chr; Chrs; HonRl; SchPl; RptrYrbk; SptEdYrbk; PpCl; LetterBsktbl; LetterFtbl; Col; Science.

JACOBUS, Craig H; Amos Alonzo Stagg HS; Hickory Hills, IL; ChrhWkr; HonRl; JrNHS; LitMag; NHS; SchPl; GerCl; SciCl; Tennis; Trinity Christian Coll; Medicine.

JACOBUS, Sindy L; Hillsdale HS; Hillsdale, MI; Band; ChrhWkr; CncrtBnd; MrchBnd; NHS; Orch; PepBnd; 4-H; LatCl; College; Professional.

JACOBY, Renee A; Random Lake HS; Random Lake, WI; VPSophCls; ALAGirlsSt; Band; HonRl; SchPl; EdYrBk; 4-H; PpCl; Chrldr; GAA; College; Professional.

JACOMETTI, Damaris; Gordon HS; Gordon, NE; ;67 Band; CncrtBnd; PepBnd; FNA; FTA; PpCl; Bsktbl; Swmmng; College;vocation.

JACQUES, Henry R; Chillicothe HS; Chillicothe, MO; 18/192 Band; Chr; Chrs; CmntyWkr; CncrtBnd; HonRl; MrchBnd; PepBnd; RedCrAde; StuCncl; LetterFtbl; LetterGlf; IMSpt; Central Methodist; Music.

JACQUES, Jeffrey L; Southern Reynolds R Ii HS; Ellington, MO; VPFrshCls; PresSophCls; PresJrCls; Chrs; HonRl; PpCl; SciCl; Bsbl; College; Medicine.

JACQUES, Saprenia M; Lincoln HS; Warren, MI; HonRl; HospAde; JA; JrNHS; NHS; FrCl; SciCl; LetterSwmmng; Chrldr; CchngActv; GAA; IMSpt; Medical College; Vet.

JA DOUL, Karen L; New Lisbon HS; New Lisbon, WI; 1/57 TrsFrshCls; PresSophCls; Band; HonRl; NHS; SchPl; RptrSchPpr; PpCl; LetterChrldr; GAA; Univ Of Wisconsin; Accounting.

JAECKELS, Susan; Foley HS; Foley, MN; 7/134 Chrs; HonRl; LbryAde; NHS; SchPl; StuCncl; SchPpr; PpCl; Army; Art.

JAECQUES, Tamyra L; Northeast Riv HS; Cairo, MO; SecTrsSophCls; HonRl; SchPl; StuCncl; Yrbk; SchPpr; PpCl; Bsbl; Bsktbl; College.

JAEGER, David M; Towner HS; Towner, ND; TrsSrCls; Band; SchAde; SchPl; StuGov; TchrAde; FFA; LetterFtbl; LetterTrk; Az Inst; Mechanic.

JAEGER, Donna; Guttenberg Comm HS; Sherrill, IA; HonRl; OffAde; SchAde; TchrAde; Area I Dubuque Ia, Nursing.

JAEGER, Roberta L; Cottonwood HS; Cottonwood, MN; 2/40 ALAGirlsSt; Chrs; CncrtBnd; HonRl; Mdrgl; PepBnd; SchPl; 4-H; FHA; Bsktbl; Trk; Gustavas Adolphus College; Biology.

JAEGER, Stephen L; Slater HS; Slater, MO; 11/50 ALBoysSt; ChrhWkr; HonRl; SctActv; EdYrBk; LetterBsktbl; LetterFtbl; LetterWrstlng; College; Chemistry.

JAEGER, William; Chippewa Valley HS; Mt Clemens, MI; Band; ChrhWkr; CmntyWkr; CncrtBnd; HonRl; MrchBnd; ModUN; NHS; PepBnd; GodCntryAwd; Univ; Forestry.

JAEGERS, Donna M; Rosati Kain HS; Richmond Hts, MO; NHS; NatlMeritFnl; NatlMeritSchl; SchPl; SchPpr; SpnCl; Bsktbl; GAA; IMSpt; Univ; Phy Educ.

JAEGLE, Susan K; Wenona HS; Wenona, IL; 19/39 TrsFrshCls; HstJrCls; CncrtBnd; HonRl; MrchBnd; PepBnd; Yrbk; FHA; Chrldr; AmLegAwd; Siu; Physical Thearapy.

JAEHNIG, Joanne E; Hancock Central HS; Hancock, MI; 29/90 TrsJrCls; HonRl; LbryAde; SchPl; Yrbk; 4-H; PPFtbl; Michigan Tecn Univ; Social Services.

JAFFE, Lori B; New Trier West HS; Glencoe, IL; 74/698 HonRl; PolWkr; SchAde; StuGov; TchrAde; SchPpr; Tennis; Vassar Clg; Pre Med.

JAFFE, Robert T; Maine North HS; Niles, IL; HonRl; Orch; StuCncl; RptrSchPpr; SptEdSchPpr; Ftbl; Tennis; Wrstlng; Univ Of Ill; Premedical.

JAGEL, Erik A; Hinsdale Twp Central HS; Hinsdale, IL; 104/596 College; Astrophysicist.

JAGELA, John R; Brother Rice HS; Chicago, IL; 30/416 Ill Inst Of Tech; Mechanical Eng.

JAGER, Donald A; Hanson HS; Fulton, SD; TrsSrCls; Chrs; HonRl; StuCncl; StuGov; PpCl; Bsbl; Bsktbl; CaptFtbl; LetterTrk; Wrstlng; IMSpt; Trade School; Vocation.

JAGER, Marilyn E; St Marys HS; Devils Lake, ND; VPFrshCls; Chrs; HonRl; SchMus; TchrAde; RptrSchPpr; LetterBsktbl; LetterTrk; Chrldr; College.

JAGER, Scott L; Buffalo HS; Buffalo, ND; 3/21 SecTrsJrCls; VPSrCls; ALBoysSt; Band; Chr; HonRl; SptEdYrbk; SptEdSchPpr; Bsktbl; Ftbl; Trk; Univ Of North Dakota; Medical Tech.

JAGGERS, Larry D; Westville HS; Westville, IL; SecFrshCls; ALBoysSt; Band; CmntyWkr; CncrtBnd; MrchBnd; SpnCl; Bsbl; Bsktbl; Trk; College; History.

JAGGI, Franz M; Belleville HS; Belleville, WI; 11/57 PresFrshCls; HstSrCls; VPBand; PresChrs; ModUN; SctActv; PresPpCl; LetterFtbl; Trade School; Masonry.

JAGIELO, Donna J; Hastings HS; Hastings, MI; 31/286 HonRl; NHS; PresNatlThespSoc; SchPl; SpnCl; BttyCrckrAwd; Western Michigan Univ; Engineering.

JAGIELSKI, Michael; Aquinas HS; Woodhaven, MI; 74/249 HonRl; SchMus; Trk; IMSpt; College; Aviation Technology.

JAGIELSKI, Timothy H; Grayslake Comm HS; Lindenhurst, IL; 27/219 ALBoysSt; HonRl; NatlFornLg; NHS; NatlThespSoc; SchPl; StuGov; TchrAde; Ftbl; College; Theatre Teacher.

JAGLAN, Samarjit S; Comstock HS; Kalamazoo, MI; NHS; NatlMeritCmnd; JAAwd; Western Mich Univ; Doctor.

JAGODKA, Paul J; St Patrick HS; Chicago, IL; 143/427 HonRl; JA; SctActv; MthCl; College; Journalism.

JAGODZINSKE, Gail E; Welcome Community HS; Welcome, MN; 1/19 Band; Chrs; ChrhWkr; HonRl; SchPl; YthFlsp; LetterTrk; Chrldr; GAA; BttyCrckrAwd; Rochester Comm College; Anesthesiology.

JAGODZINSKI, Duane; Lincoln HS; Wisconsin Rapids, WI; PresSrCls; ALBoysSt; Band; ChrhWkr; HonRl; NHS; StuCncl; PpCl; Bsbl; Ftbl; Coll Or Military; Business And Marketing.

JAGODZINSKI, Linda L; Tonica HS; Oglesby, IL; Chrs; HonRl; JrNHS; NHS; RptrYrbk; RptrSchPpr; 4-H; FHA;.

JAGODZINSKI, Neil; St Bede Acad; La Salle, IL; HonRl; TchrAde; C; Teaching.

JAGOS, Donald J; Chesaning Union HS; Owosso, MI; 7/211 ALBoysSt; Band; CncrtBnd; HonRl; MrchBnd; PepBnd; LetterTrk; Michigan State Univ; Mechanical Engineering.

JAHN, Alan R; Sheldon Comm HS; Sheldon, IA; Trk; IMSpt; College; Professional.

JAHN, Jeffrey S; Franklin Center HS; Lee Center, IL; 6/40 VPFrshCls; VPSophCls; HonRl; NHS; SptEdSchPpr; Bsbl; Bsktbl; Ftbl; Glf; Trk; University; Computer Analyzing.

JAHN, Linda M; Maine Twshp South HS; Harwoon Hgts, IL; HonRl; GerCl; U Of Il; Biology.

JAHN, Linda S; Dubois HS; Jasper, IN; Band; Chr; Chrs; CaptDrlTm; HospAde; SchMus; SchPpr; FHA; PpCl; Trk; GAA; IMSpt; College; Nurse.

JAHNKE, Diane J; Southwest HS; Green Bay, WI; 125/420 HonRl; LbryAde; Yrbk; 4-H; FBLA; FTA; Trk; St Lukes Hosp Sch; Nursing.

JAHNKE, Janet P; Southwest HS; Green Bay, WI; 62/420 Chr; ChrhWkr; HonRl; TchrAde; YthFlsp; Fox Valley Tech; Conservation Tech.

JAHNKE, Mark S; Appleton West HS; Appleton, WI; ChrhWkr; JA; Ftbl; IMSpt; Central Bible College; Ministry.

JAIME, Margaret; Cathedral HS; Chicago, IL; HonRl; SchAde; RptrYrbk; SpnCl; De Paul Univ; Special Ed.

JAISSLE, Patricia M; Lakeview HS; St Clair Shores, MI; SecSophCls; TrsJrCls; HonRl; NHS; FshEdSchPpr; TchrAde; PpCl;.

JAJOWKA, Anita M; Thornton Fractional So HS; Lansing, IL; 67/596 TrsJrCls; DrlTm; MrchBnd; NHS; EdYrBk; FNA; SecFrCl; GAA; Purdue Univ; Rn.

JAKAB, Susan; William A Wirt HS; Gary, IN; 4/237 ChrhWkr; CncrtBnd; HonRl; HospAde; MrchBnd; NHS; PepBnd; StuGov; SciCl; GAA; Butler Univ; Pharm.

JAKEL, Mark; Oak Lawn HS; Oak Lawn, IL; 25/650 Band; ChrhWkr; HonRl; NHS; SchAde; SctActv; TchrAde; GerCl; Bsbl; Trk; College; Medicine.

JAKOBITZ, Mark A; Buffalo Lake Public HS; Buffalo Lake, MN; 4/35 PresSrCls; Band; CncrtBnd; LetterBsbl; CaptBsktbl; CaptFtbl; CaptTrk; PresAwd; Normandale Comm College.

JAKOBS, Noreen J; Milledgeville HS; Sterling, IL; 6/48 Chr; Chrs; CncrtBnd; HonRl; NHS; SchPl; TchrAde; RptrYrbk; RptrSchPpr; Bsktbl; University; Nursing.

JAKUBEK, Beth A; Immaculate Heart Of Mary HS; Westchester, IL; 16/246 SctActv; TchrAde; SchPpr; Chrldr; CchngActv; GAA; IMSpt; U Of Il Champaigne.

JAKUBIK, Julie A; Millington HS; Millington, MI; 5/200 TrsFrshCls; TrsSophCls; TrsJrCls; TrsSrCls; NHS; RptrSchPpr; PpCl; Bsktbl; VPChrldr; Clg; Dental Lab Tech.

JAKUBOVIE, Jan C; Clark HS; Hammond, IN; 103/260 Chrs; MrchBnd; TchrAde; SpnCl; College; Home Economics.

JAKUBOWICZ, Anne M; St Joseph HS; Chicago, IL; 4/123 Chr; HonRl; NHS; NatlMeritCmnd; Quill&Scroll; RptrSchPpr; SchPpr; 4-H; KeyCl; FrCl; SciCl; 4-HAwd; Ill Inst Of Tech; Food Tech.

JAKUBOWSKI, Steve; West Catholic HS; Grand Rapids, MI; HonRl; JA; NHS; SctActv; StuCncl; IMSpt; Univ.

JAKUBS, Bonnie J; Woodlands Academy; Lake Forest, IL; Chr; ChrhWkr; CmntyWkr; Mdrgl; SchMus; StuCncl; StuGov; FDA; PpCl; Bsbl; CaptFtbl; Tennis; GAA; College; Medicine.

JALKANEN, Karl; Chassell HS; Chassell, MI; TrsFrshCls; PresSophCls; PresJrCls; Band; HonRl; MrchBnd; SchPl;.

JALLAS, Theresa L; North HS; Eau Claire, WI; Band; DrlTm; HonRl; NHS; RptrYrbk; Tennis; DARAwd; JCAwd; SARAwd; CitAwd; U Of Eau Claire; Elementary Education.

JALOWIEC, Donna M; Nazareth Academy; Chicago, IL; 6/160 Chr; ChrhWkr; CmntyWkr; HonRl; NHS; OffAde; SchAde; SchPl; StuCncl; CaptBsbl; Chrldr; GAA;.

JAMES, Andrew D; Larned HS; Larned, KS; ALBoysSt; Band; Chr; Chrs; ChrhWkr; CmntyWkr; CncrtBnd; HonRl; Ftbl; Trk; Kansas Univ; Professional.

JAMES, Constance S; St Mary Cathedral HS; Saginaw, MI; 5/76 HonRl; JrNHS; NHS; PepBnd; SctActv; PresStuCncl; LatCl; PpCl; SciCl; Mercy College; Nurse.

JAMES, Debbie K; Marshall HS; Marshall, WI; TrsSophCls; TrsJrCls; Chr; HonRl; MrchBnd; NHS; Twrl; Yrbk; FFA; FHA; PpCl; LetterBsktbl; Glf; GAA; Coll Of Cosmetology; Cosmetologist.

JAMES, Deborah L; Charlestown HS; Charlestown, IN; VPSophCls; SecSrCls; ALAGirlsSt; HonRl; MrchBnd; SchPl; RptrYrbk; FHA; LatCl; PpCl; Ball St U; Journalist.

JAMES, Edward C; Dwight D Eisenhower HS; Blue Island, IL; 32/692 HonRl; Univ Of Il; Pharmacist.

JAMES, Felicia R; Chicago Vocational HS; Chicago, IL; ChrhWkr; NatlMeritCmnd; OffAde; TchrAde; MthCl; Natl College Of Educ; Elementary Educ.

JAMES, Kim E; Mullen HS; Mullen, NE; 2/27 SecJrCls; Chr; CncrtBnd; HonRl; MrchBnd; PepBnd; SchMus; EdYrBk; College; Accounting.

JAMES, Ladon; Charlestown HS; Charlestown, IN; 8/180 ALAGirlsSt; ChrhWkr; HonRl; NHS; EdSchPpr; SptEdSchPpr; SpnCl; GAA; Indiana University; Physical Education.

JAMES, Lawrence L; William Chrisman HS; Independence, MO; 27/396 Band; CncrtBnd; MrchBnd; NHS; PepBnd; SctActv; Rockhurst Coll; Cpa.

JAMES, Londa; Glenwood City HS; Downing, WI; 1/83 ALAGirlsSt; Band; Chr; ChrhWkr; TchrAde; RptrYrbk; Pillsbury Baptist Bible College Physicas Ed.

JAMES, Maris A; Houston HS; Bucyrus, MO; Band; CncrtBnd; HonRl; MrchBnd; PepBnd; SchPl; TchrAde; PpCl; Trk; IMSpt; College; Clerical.

JAMES, Mark H; Fair Grove HS; Strafford, MO; 1/55 Aud/Vis; HonRl; NatlMeritFnl; NatlMeritSchl; PresMthCl; VPSciCl; Bsktbl; LetterTrk; IMSpt; GovHonPrgAwd; Rice Univ; Physics.

JAMES, Melody G; Armstrong Township HS; Potomac, IL; 1/45 PresJrCls; HonRl; NHS; PepBnd; SchMus; RptrYrbk; 4-H; Chrldr; GAA; 4-HAwd;.

JAMES, Michael K; Pittsburg HS; Pittsburg, KS; 6/230 Band; NatlMeritSF; SctActv; PressStuCncl; FrCl; Ftbl; CchngActv; IMSpt; Univ Of Ks; Chemistry.

JAMES, Myna J; Clay City HS; Center Point, IN; 18/70 Band; Chr; Chrs; ChrhWkr; CncrtBnd; HonRl; MrchBnd; NHS; PepBnd; TchrAde; YthFlsp; Yrbk; Business School; Singer.

JAMES, Patricia; Lindblom Tech HS; Chicago, IL; 229/654 ChrhWkr; JA; LbryAde; NatlMeritCmnd; OffAde; RptrSchPpr; SchPpr; SpnCl; Univ; Army.

JAMES, Paul A; Murray Comm HS; Murray, IA; 2/24 VPJrCls; HonRl; NHS; Yrbk; PpCl; LetterTrk;.

JAMES, Peter L; Stevens HS; Rapid City, SD; College; Professional.

JAMES, Randy J; Henscher HS; Kankakee, IL; 33/160 PresFrshCls; PresSophCls; PresJrCls; PresSrCls; HonRl; NatlMeritFnl; NatlMeritSchl; YthFlsp; RptrSchPpr; PpCl; LetterBsbl; CaptFtbl; LetterWrstlng; AmLegAwd; Illinois State Univ; Dentistry.

JAMES, Randy W; William Chrisman HS; Independence, MO; HonRl; NatlFornLg; NHS; NatlThespSoc; SchPl; StuCncl; LetterGlf; U Of Mo; Arts & Sciences.

JAMES, Roland E; Southern Wells HS; Warren, IN; StuCncl; CaptBsktbl; Trk;.

JAMES, Sandra; Saybrook Arrowsmith HS; Arrowsmith, IL; 1/24 SecSophCls; Chr; ChrhWkr; HonRl; SchMus; YthFlsp; RptrYrbk; EdSchPpr; FHA; PpCl; Secretary.

JAMES, Sandra; East Chicago Roosevelt HS; Gary, IN; 19/217 TrsSrCls; ALAGirlsSt; ChrhWkr; CmntyWkr; HonRl; OffAde; StuGov; YthFnd; FrCl; AmLegAwd; Indiana Univ; Psychology.

JAMES, Steven E; Parkway North HS; Creve Coeur, MO; SecSophCls; AFS; Chr; JA; Orch; SchMus; SchPl; LatCl; Ftbl; Wrstlng; Coll; Vet.

JAMES, Sue E; Warrensburg HS; Warrensburg, MO; 27/150 Band; HonRl; MrchBnd; StuGov; Twrl; GAA; IMSpt; Central Missouri State Univ; Accounting.

JAMES, Suzanne; Carrier Mills HS; Carrier Mills, IL; VPFrshCls; VPSophCls; Chrs; HonRl; SchPl; StuCncl; RptrSchPpr; PresMthCl; PresSciCl; Chrldr; Jr College; General Studies.

JAMES, Teresa K; Central Dallas Comm HS; Polk City, IA; 4/22 DrlTm; HonRl; LbryAde; PresStuCncl; RptrYrbk; RptrSchPpr; LetterBsbl; CaptBsktbl; CchngActv; BttyCrckrAwd;.

JAMES, Thomas D; Lake Central HS; Dyer, IN; 190/450 CmntyWkr; HonRl; StuGov; SptEdSchPpr; LetterBsbl; CaptBsktbl; LetterFtbl; CchngActv; Us Naval Acad; Police Officer.

JAMES, Timothy L; Paxton HS; Paxton, IL; 12/128 Aud/Vis; HonRl; NHS; Bsktbl; Trk; Parkland Jr Col; Farming.

JAMES, Timothy L; Paxton Comm HS; Paxton, IL; 12/125 Aud/Vis; HonRl; NHS; Bsktbl; Trk; College.

JAMESON, Daniel G; Amherst HS; Amherst, NE; Band; Chrl; HonRl; NHS; SchPl; LetterTrk; LetterWrstlng; College.

JAMESON, David B; Amherst HS; Amherst, NE; College.

JAMESON, David L; Serena HS; Earlville, IL; Chr; ChrhWkr; YthFlsp; RptrSchPpr; FFA; LetterBsktbl; LetterSocr; LetterTrk; LetterWrstlng; College; Pro.

JAMESON, Larry D; Amherst HS; Amherst, NE; 2/26 SecJrCls; SecSrCls; Band; Chrs; CncrtBnd; HonRl; NHS; Bsktbl; Ftbl; Trk; College; Professional.

JAMIESON, Ramona M; Lincoln County R 1 HS; Cyrene, MO; Band; Chrs; HonRl; HospAde; PepBnd; SchPl; TchrAde; Yrbk; 4-H; PpCl; Vocational School; Nurse.

JAMISON, Brian C; South Page HS; Braddyville, IA; 1/28 PresSrCls; Band; CncrtBnd; MrchBnd; NHS; SchMus; 4-H; FFA; Bsktbl; Ftbl; University Of Iowa; Business Adm.

JAMISON, Claudia L; Ada HS; Hendrum, MN; Band; Chr; ChrhWkr; HonRl; NatlThespSoc; SchPl; RptrYrbk; FHA; FNA; Chrldr; St Lukes Hosp School; Nursing.

JAMISON, Harry L; Capac Comm HS; Capac, MI; ChrhWkr; CmntyWkr; HonRl; SctActv; VPYthFlsp; VP4-H; FFA; KeyCl; Bsbl; 4-HAwd; St Clair Co Comm Col; Engineering.

JAMISON, Harry N; Forest View HS; Mt Prospect, IL; 13/645 ChrhWkr; CmntyWkr; HonRl; NHS; SchMus; SchPl; SctActv; YthFlsp; Drake University; Acturial Science.

JAMISON, Michael L; Sycamore HS; Sycamore, IL; 40/202 HonRl; LbryAde; SctActv; FFA; SpnCl; Ftbl; LetterWrstlng; Ill State Univ; Medicine.

JAMISON, Pamela S; North Branch HS; North Branch, MI; 18/141 Band; ChrhWkr; CncrtBnd; HonRl; MrchBnd; ModUN; Spring Arbor College; Medical Technology.

JAMISON, Venise; Lindblom Tech HS; Chicago, IL; Chr; Chrs; ChrhWkr; HospAde; LbryAde; Mdrgl; OffAde; SchAde; SchPl; TchrAde; Depaul; Nursing.

JAMMER, Bonnie M; Bay City Western HS; Auburn, MI; 7/448 ChrhWkr; HonRl; LitMag; NHS; 4-H; LatCl; Concordia Lutheran Jr College; Primary Educ.

JANACHOVSKY, Jayne P; Walnut Grove HS; Lucan, MN; 2/41 ALAGirlsSt; Band; Chr; SchMus; LetterTrk; ChmnChrldr; GAA; AmLegAwd; BttyCrckrAwd; 4-HAwd; St Benedict; Elem Ed.

JANACHOWSKI, Stephen R; St Laurence HS; Bridgeview, IL; 10/386 Band; CncrtBnd; MrchBnd; NatlMeritCmnd; OffAde; Orch; SchPl; TchrAde; RptrSchPpr; SciCl; Univ Of Chicago; Medicine.

JANAVS, Anita; Milbank HS; Milbank, SD; VPFrshCls; Chrs; HonRl; HospAde; NHS; SciCl; CitAwd; Augustana Clg; Medicine.

JANDER, Ralph B; Lake Central HS; Dyer, IN; 7/453 ALBoysSt; HonRl; NHS; NatlThespSoc; SchMus; SchPl; SctActv; StuGov; SciCl; LetterBsktbl; Biology.

JANDERA, Beverly A; Jackson HS; Lakefield, MN; 5/108 HonRl; RptrYrbk; FHA; College; Nursing.

JANDERA, Robert; Hanover HS; Hanover, KS; Chrs; HonRl; 4-H; FFA; Bsbl; Trk; 4-HAwd; Trade Sch;professional.

JANDOUREK, Debra A; St Mary Central HS; Menasha, WI; DrlTm; SctActv; Twrl; FrCl; MthCl; LetterBsktbl; LetterTrk; Chrldr; GAA; College.

JANDRAIN, James G; Premontre HS; Green Bay, WI; ChrhWkr; HonRl; OffAde; SctActv; KeyCl; RusCl; IMSpt; EldAwd; College; Professional.

JANDT, Margaret A; The Barstow HS; Prairie Village, KS; SecTrsSophCls; SecTrsJrCls; Chr; Chrl; Chrs; LbryAde; Mdrgl; SchMus; SchPl; StuCncl; StuGov; TchrAde; YthFlsp; University Of Tulsa.

JANDT, Russell M; West Leyden HS; Melrose Park, IL; 7/475 AFS; CAP; CncrtBnd; HonRl; JA; MrchBnd; NHS; GerCl; Tennis; JAAwd; Univ Of Ill; Air Force Pilot.

JANE, Sheryl R; Lakewood HS; Sunfield, MI; 11/203 Band; Chr; ChrhWkr; CncrtBnd; HonRl; MrchBnd; NHS; NatlMeritSF; PepBnd; StuCncl; College.

JANECEK, Sherolyn S; Fort Calhoun HS; Fort Calhoun, NE; TrsJrCls; HonRl; MrchBnd; VPNHS; OffAde; StuCncl; YthFlsp; FBLA; FHA; CaptChrldr; Bus Sch; Interior Decorator.

JANECKE, Mary A; Mount Assisi HS; Palos Park, IL; 22/197 Chrs; HonRl; HospAde; NHS; SchPl; StuCncl; College; Nursing.

JANES, Brian D; Aberdeen Central HS; Aberdeen, SD; 77/423 Chr; Chrs; ChrhWkr; HonRl; Sacrstn; StuGov; YthFlsp; LetterFtbl; IMSpt; Sd Sch Of Mines & Tech; Elec Engr.

JANES, David B; Orangeville HS; Orangeville, IL; 1/58 PresChr; PresNHS; NatlMeritSF; SchMus; StuCncl; University; Engineering.

JANEWAY, Beverly J; Fountain Central HS; Hillsboro, IN; 54/128 Aud/Vis; Band; MrchBnd; PepBnd; SctActv; YthFlsp; Yrbk; 4-H; FHA; Indiana State Univ; Secretary.

JANIAK, James M; Paul Vi HS; Omaha, NE; 3/94 ChrhWkr; HonRl; NHS; SctActv; TchrAde; Creighton Univ; Accounting.

JANIAK, Stephen; Thornton Fractional South Hs; Lansing, IL; 1/600 HonRl; JrNHS; VPNHS; NatlMeritCmnd; SpnCl; Blackburn College; Psychology.

JANICIK, John A; Belleville West HS; Belleville, IL; 1/750 TreasNHS; StuCncl; MthCl; CaptWrstlng; Knox College; Pre Medical.

JANICKE, Marie A; Lincoln Way Comm HS; New Lenox, IL; 2/545 HonRl; NHS; NatlMeritCmnd; MthCl; LetterTrk; CchngActv; GAA; Northwestern Univ; Medicine.

JANICKE, Susan; Winthrop HS; Winthrop, MN; HonRl; NHS; StuGov; RptrSchPpr; FHA; BttyCrckrAwd; College; Teaching.

JANIK, Chester; Glen Lake HS; Cedar, MI; CmntyWkr; HonRl; SctActv; StuCncl; TchrAde; FrCl; PpCl; LetterBsbl; Ftbl; Central Mi; Special Ed.

JANIK, Daniel; Alexander Hamilton HS; Milwaukee, WI; 81/780 Uw Madison.

JANIS, Bruce; Lyons Township Hs; Lagrange Park, IL; 6/1250 ChrhWkr; HonRl; JrNHS; NHS; NatlMeritFnl; NatlThespSoc; SchPl; TchrAde; MthCl; Washington U; Professor Of Microbiology.

JANIS, Paul D; Maine East HS; Nile, IL; ChrhWkr; HonRl; NHS; StuCncl; StuGov; EngCl; MthCl; Northwestern U; Dentist.

JANK, Robert T; St Laurence HS; Burbank, IL; 11/385 HonRl; NHS; NatlMeritSF; StuCncl; StuGov; PpCl; Bsktbl; Tennis; LetterTrk; Augustana College; Law.

JANKE, Cynthia; Glencoe Sr HS; Glencoe, MN; 17/142 VPSophCls; Band; Chr; HonRl; MrchBnd; PepBnd; PPFtbl; Moorhead St; Physical Educ.

JANKE, Myrna J; Gackle Public HS; Fredonia, ND; 1/22 ALAGirlsSt; Band; Chr; HonRl; SchMus; SchPl; SchPpr; Bsktbl; LetterTrk; PPFtbl; Ndsu ;photo.

JANKIEWICZ, Laura M; Mt Assisi Acad; Oak Lawn, IL; 3/144 Chrs; HonRl; NHS; Yrbk; Army; Medical Field.

JANKOUSKY, John; Benton Hs; Benton, IL; 1/168 Band; CncrtBnd; HonRl; NHS; NatlMeritFnl; NatlMeritSF; KeyCl; SpnCl; MthCl; JETSAwd; University; Engineering.

JANKOVICH, Lucia M; St Clement HS; Center Line, MI; 34/98 HonRl; LbryAde; NatlMeritCmnd; StuCncl; PpCl; SciCl; Swmmng; GAA; Trade Sch; Medical Career.

JANKOWSKI, Christine R; Willow Brook HS; Villa Park, IL; 45/822 AFS; Chr; ChrhWkr; CmntyWkr; HonRl; LbryAde; NHS; RedCrAde; SchAde; SchMus; SchPl; TchrAde; KeyCl; Elmhurst College; Special Education.

JANKOWSKI, Ronald J; Marie S Curie HS; Chicago, IL; 9/600 CmntyWkr; HonRl; LbryAde; NHS; SchAde; SchPl; VPStuCncl; TchrAde; SpnCl; MthCl; College Of St Francis; Business Admin.

JANKU, Kathy M; Foley HS; Foley, MN; 3/160 Chrs; HonRl; RedCrAde; SchPl; Yrbk; FHA; FNA; GerCl; PPFtbl; VoiceDemAwd; Scoloud Sco;rn.

JANKY, Bill O; Kewanee HS; Kewanee, IL; 1/220 HonRl; SchMus; SchPl; StuCncl; StuGov; Yrbk; KeyCl; CaptGlf; Tennis; IMSpt; University; Professional Engineering.

JANKY, John G; Central City HS; Chapman, NE; Chrs; HonRl; Bsbl; LetterBsktbl; LetterFtbl; College; Professional.

JANKY, Joseph J; Central City Sr HS; Chapman, NE; OffAde; RptrSchPpr; Bsbl; Bsktbl; LetterFtbl;.

JANNEY, Julia M; York Community HS; Elmhurst, IL; 85/953 Chr; Chrs; HonRl; Mdrgl; NatlFornLg; NHS; NatlThespSoc; SchMus; SchPl; College; Theatre.

JANOFSKI, Phil L; Manchester HS; Manchester, MI; 6/102 Band; ChrhWkr; CncrtBnd; MrchBnd; LetterBsbl; Clge.

JANOSKI, Theresa L; Downers Grove South HS; Downers Grove, IL; 25/830 HonRl; NHS; RptrYrbk; College; Business.

JANOSO, Andrew M; St Laurence HS; Chicago, IL; 30/374 HonRl; JrNHS; College; Science.

JANOV, Lauren L; Rock Island Sr HS; Rock Island, IL; HonRl; JrNHS; PolWkr; SchMus; StuCncl; EdYrBk; RptrSchPpr; PresFrCl; PpCl; IMSpt; College; Law.

JANOVSKY, Molly B; South Newton HS; Kentland, IN; 4/111 ALAGirlsSt; HonRl; SctActv; CivCl; GerCl; PpCl; College; Professional.

JANOWSKI, Barbara; Howell Sr HS; Howell, MI; 55/370 Chr; Chrs; HonRl; JA; JrNHS; NHS; GerCl; College; Rn.

JANOWSKI, Diane L; Wm Howard Taft HS; Chicago, IL; 4/816 Chrs; HonRl; LitMag; NHS; NatlMeritSF; OffAde; SchAde; StuGov; SecFrCl; SpnCl; GAA; BauchLmbAwd; Univ Of Illinois; Math.

JANOWSKI, Susan T; Notre Dame HS; Chicago, IL; 6/282 CmntyWkr; HonRl; NHS; FTA; MthCl; Tennis; GAA; Univ; Math.

JANOWSKY, Susan M; Martin Public HS; Otsego, MI; SecSrCls; HonRl; NHS; SchPl; TchrAde; EdYrBk; RptrSchPpr; 4-H; SpnCl; PpCl; Bsktbl; Chrldr; Michigan State Univ; Special Educ.

JANSA, Lisa D; Prairie Community HS; Gowrie, IA; 2/78 ALAGirlsSt; Chrs; ChrhWkr; HonRl; PresNHS; RedCrAde; TreasFrCl; LetterBsktbl; LetterTrk; GovHonPrgAwd; Augustana Coll; Med Tech.

JANSEN, Bernard J; Highland Park Sr HS; St Paul, MN; SctActv; Socr; Tennis; University; Aero Engineer.

JANSEN, Cindy S; Wahoo HS; Ithaca, NE; Band; HonRl; NHS; StuGov; RptrYrbk; TreasSpnCl; PpCl; LetterBsktbl; LetterTrk; Chrldr; Univ; Nurse.

JANSEN, Geri M; Mater Dei HS; Albers, IL; 5/198 Band; ChrhWkr; CncrtBnd; HonRl; HospAde; MrchBnd; SchMus; FrCl; CchngActv; Eastern Illinois Univ; Psychology.

JANSEN, Jolene K; West HS; Wichita, KS; 98/627 ChrhWkr; CncrtBnd; HonRl; MrchBnd; ModUN; Orch; PepBnd; FrCl; College.

JANSEN, Lu Ann; Hazel Green HS; Hazel Green, WI; 2/83 SecSophCls; HonRl; NHS; SchMus; RptrSchPpr; LetterBsktbl; LetterTrk; Chrldr; GovHonPrgAwd; Platteville; Math.

JANSEN, Roberta P; Leopold R 3 HS; Leopold, MO; HstFrshCls; SecSophCls; TrsJrCls; Chrs; HonRl; SchPl; Yrbk; SchPpr; College; Professional.

JANSEN, Theresa A; St Peter HS; St Peter, MN; Chrs; ChrhWkr; HonRl; NHS; Quill&Scroll; SchPl; RptrYrbk; EdSchPpr; SecFHA; AmLegAwd; College; Professional.

JANSEN, Vicki A; Kimberly Senior HS; Appleton, WI; 41/291 ChrhWkr; CmntyWkr; HonRl; JA; SchMus; Trk; GAA; AmLegAwd; Technical School; Nursing.

JANSMA, Susan J; Walnut Grove Public HS; Walnut Grove, MN; Band; Chr; CncrtBnd; HonRl; MrchBnd; PepBnd; SchMus; SchPl; StuGov; YthFlsp; Pillsbury Baptist Bible Coll; Bible.

JANSON, Dave B; Clarion Community HS; Clarion, IA; YthFlsp; RptrSchPpr; 4-H; FFA; 4-HAwd; Trade School; Farm Power Mechanics.

JANSON, Galen M; Healy HS; Pierz, MN; 4/117 Band; ChrhWkr; CncrtBnd; HonRl; MrchBnd; PepBnd; 4-H; FFA; Bsbl; Trade Schl; Electrician.

JANSSEN, Brent R; Camdenton R Iii HS; Camdenton, MO; TrsSophCls; HonRl; NHS; Bsktbl; Trk; Univ So West Mo State; Pre Law.

JANSSEN, Deana C; Chadwick HS; Chadwick, IL; TrsFrshCls; Band; Chrs; HonRl; PepBnd; SchMus; StuCncl; 4-H; FFA; FHA; University; Business Admin.

JANSSEN, Deborah A; Adams Central HS; Hastings, NE; 7/56 ALAGirlsSt; Band; Chr; ChrhWkr; CncrtBnd; HonRl; HospAde; JrNHS; MrchBnd; NHS; PepBnd; SchPl; YthFlsp; PpCl; LetterTrk; Hastings Col; Elementary Teacher.

JANSSEN, Jana S; Porta HS; Petersburg, IL; 27/122 ALAGirlsSt; Band; CncrtBnd; LbryAde; MrchBnd; NatlThespSoc; PepBnd; GAA; IMSpt; College.

JANSSEN, Janelle L; Nokomis HS; Nokomis, IL; VPJrCls; Chr; Chrs; ChrhWkr; HonRl; LbryAde; StuCncl; Yrbk; Trk; GAA; University; Environmental Fields.

JANSSEN, Joyce I; Zeeland HS; Holland, MI; Chr; HonRl; Floral.

JANSSEN, Karen K; Buckley Loda HS; Buckley, IL; 10/41 ChrhWkr; HonRl; NHS; SchPl; StuCncl; Yrbk; FHA; SpnCl; MthCl; Illinois State Univ; Business.

JANSSEN, Lila M; Lakeview HS; Platte Center, NE; 4/69 SecFrshCls; ALAGirlsSt; Band; Chr; CncrtBnd; MrchBnd; NHS; TchrAde; PpCl; Trk; Platte Coll; Botany.

JANSSEN, Margaret S; Homestead HS; Mequon, WI; 51/415 HonRl; NHS; NatlMeritCmnd; Quill&Scroll; StuCncl; RptrYrbk; Yrbk; PpCl; Swmmng; College; Veterinarian.

JANSSEN, Patricia J; Norway HS; Norway, MI; ChrhWkr; HonRl; OffAde; RptrYrbk; RptrSchPpr; 4-H; FHA; Bay De Noc Community Clge; Accounting.

JANSSEN, R Daniel; Chadwick Dist 399 HS; Chadwick, IL; 11/26 TrsSophCls; Band; HonRl; PepBnd; SchMus; 4-H; FFA; LetterBsbl; Bsktbl; LetterGlf; 4-HAwd; Western Illinois Univ; Business Admin.

JANSSEN, Stanton; Holyrood HS; Lorraine, KS; 2/15 TrsFrshCls; TrsSophCls; TrsJrCls; TrsSrCls; HonRl; RptrSchPpr; Bsbl; LetterBsktbl; LetterFtbl; LetterTrk; Coll; Agri.

JANSSEN, Steven M; Southeastern HS; Augusta, IL; 10/50 Chrs; HonRl; SchMus; SchPl; RptrYrbk; 4-H; FFA; LetterBsbl; LetterBsktbl; IMSpt; Western Illinois Univ; Agriculture.

JANSSENS, Alice L; William H Taft HS; Chicago, IL; 114/816 Band; CAP; CncrtBnd; JA; NHS; Orch; ROTC; SchPl; GAA; JAAwd; Bradley Univ; Mechanical Engineering.

JANSSENS, Mary; St Mary Acad; Monroe, MI; 15/142 PresJrCls; Chr; HonRl; NHS; SchPl; StuCncl; 4-H; KeyCl; FrCl; Eastern Mi Univ; Speech Therapist.

JANSSENS, Mary M; St Mary Academy; Monroe, MI; 15/142 PresJrCls; Chr; Chrl; HonRl; NHS; SchMus; SchPl; StuCncl; Treas4-H; KeyCl; FrCl; PpCl; Bsbl; Monroe Cty Comm College; Speech Therapy.

JANTZEN, James W; Highland HS; Highland, IN; NatlMeritCmnd; SctActv; GerCl; SciCl; AmLegAwd; KiwanAwd; Wabash Coll; Biology Major Pre Med.

JANULEVICIUS, Rima J; Maria HS; Chicago, IL; 22/302 HonRl; LitMag; NHS; Quill&Scroll; RptrSchPpr; EdSchPpr; Northwestern Univ; Journalism.

JANULIS, Eugene P; Argo Community HS; Justice, IL; 1/509 HonRl; NHS; NatlMeritSF; SchAde; Bsbl; Northwestern Univ; Biochemistry.

JANUS, Faith B; Marian Catholic HS; Chicago Heights, IL; 45/375 Chrs; ChrhWkr; DrlTm; HonRl; NHS; SchMus; SchPl; StuCncl; CchngActv; Southern Illinois Univ; Speech Pathologist.

JANUS, J; Notre Dame Hs; Niles, IL; HonRl; PolWkr; U Of Illinois; My Own Business.

JANUS, Rita M; St Louise De Marillac HS; Niles, IL; Chrs; NHS; Social Work.

JANZEN, Mahlon R; Hesston HS; Hesston, KS; 13/55 Band; Chr; CncrtBnd; HonRl; Mdrgl; MrchBnd; PepBnd; SchPl; TchrAde; YthFlsp; College; Ministry.

JANZING, Mary E; O Neill Public HS; O Neill, NE; HonRl; College; Teaching.

JAPINGA, Jeffrey S; Holland HS; Holland, MI; 2/315 HonRl; NHS; NatlMeritCmnd; StuGov; YthFlsp; SptEdYrbk; RptrSchPpr; TreasGerCl; VPSciCl; IMSpt; DanFAwd; Northwestern Univ; Journalism.

JAQUEZ, Steven M; Bremen HS; Posen, IL; 12/457 HonRl; NHS; NatlMeritCmnd; PresSctActv; MthCl; Ftbl; Tennis; Univ Of Ill; Nuclear Eng.

JARBOE, Lori K; Quinter HS; Quinter, KS; SecFrshCls; SecTrsSophCls; PresJrCls; Band; Chr; NHS; StuCncl; Twrl; SecYthFlsp; Chrldr; Optometry.

JARBOE, Paul J; South Shelby HS; Clarence, MO; HonRl; FFA; LetterBsbl; LetterBsktbl; LetterFtbl; LetterWrstlng; Farm.

JARDINA, Patti A; St Mary Academy; Indianapolis, IN; 4/40 PresFrshCls; PresSophCls; Chrl; HonRl; NHS; PresStuCncl; FrCl; Bsktbl; SecIMSpt; College; Medical.

JARDINE, Carol L; Glenbard South HS; Glen Ellyn, IL; 33/292 Band; CncrtBnd; HonRl; Yrbk; College; Math.

JARECKI, Diane M; Holy Family HS; Lindsay, NE; Chrs; HonRl; NHS; SchPl; PpCl; Job.

JARECZEK, Karen A; St Mary Of P H; Chicago, IL; 1/95 PresFrshCls; TrsSophCls; HstJrCls; Chrs; HonRl; MrchBnd; PepBnd; SchPl; SctActv; Sdlty; StuCncl; Loyola U ;doctor.

JARECZEK, Karen A; St Mary Of P H HS; Chicago, IL; 1/95 PresFrshCls; TrsSophCls; HstJrCls; HonRl; MrchBnd; SchPl; Sdlty; StuCncl; FrCl; PpCl; Loyola U Of Chicago; Doctor Of Medicine.

JARES, Floyd L; Motley HS; Motley, MN; PresSophCls; TrsJrCls; HonRl; SchPl; TchrAde; VPFFA; LetterTrk; LetterWrstlng; Trade School; Carpentry.

JARMAN, Timothy K; Excelsior Springs HS; Excelsior Springs, MO; HonRl; JrNHS; LbryAde; StuCncl; RptrSchPpr; SptEdSchPpr; Bsktbl;.

JARMIN, Michael J; Thedford HS; Thedford, NE; 4/19 Band; Chrs; ChrhWkr; HonRl; SchPl; PresStuCncl; Yrbk; Bsktbl; Ftbl; Trk; Brigham Young University; Physics.

JARNECKE, Duane R; Valparaiso HS; Valparaiso, IN; 19/429 Aud/Vis; Band; CncrtBnd; HonRl; LitMag; LbryAde; MrchBnd; NHS; OffAde; SchAde; University; Accounting.

JARNES, Jeff; Lincoln Sr HS; Bloomington, MN; HonRl; JA; JrNHS; NHS; Bsbl; Glf; Socr; College; Professional.

JARNVTOWSKI, Brian F; Gurdon S Hubbard HS; Chicago, IL; 6/500 Chrs; HonRl; NHS; MthCl; LetterTrk; Il U; Archit.

JAROCKI, Karen; Eau Claire Memorial HS; Eau Claire, WI; Chr; ChrhWkr; CmntyWkr; HonRl; HospAde; SchMus; SchPl; TchrAde; SpnCl; PpCl; Swmmng; Coll; Early Chldhd Ed.

JAROS, Cynthia M; Verdigre HS; Verdigre, NE; 8/42 TrsSophCls; TrsJrCls; TrsSrCls; HonRl; NHS; SchPl; TchrAde; Yrbk; PpCl; LetterTrk; Wayne State College; Art.

JAROSCH, George; Elk Grove Hs; Elk Grove Village, IL; 3 Band; CncrtBnd; HonRl; MrchBnd; NHS; SchMus; SctActv; GerCl; LetterBsktbl; Valparaiso U;engineering.

JAROSZ, Deborrah; St Francis Of Assissi HS; Humphrey, NE; SecFrshCls; Chr; Chrs; HonRl; SchMus; StuCncl; StuGov; EngCl; PpCl; Bsbl; Nce Busines College; Vocational.

JAROSZ, Germaine A; Benet Academy; Hinsdale, IL; 21/230 HonRl; NHS; NatlMeritCmnd; Quill&Scroll; RptrYrbk; EdYrBk; SptEdYrbk; PresFrCl; PpCl; LetterTennis; Trk; University; Business Admin.

JAROSZ, Maryann; Lourdes HS; Chicago, IL; 18/281 ChrhWkr; HonRl; HospAde; NHS; SctActv; StuCncl; RptrYrbk; SpnCl; Bsktbl; Marquette Univ; Journalism.

JARRARD, Debra K; Maple Valley HS; Nashville, MI; 2/108 CncrtBnd; HonRl; MrchBnd; PresNHS; PepBnd; SchMus; SchPl; 4-H; 4-HAwd; Mich St Univ; Med Tech.

JARRETT, Debra L; Carroll HS; Flora, IN; Band; HonRl; MrchBnd; NatlFornLg; NHS; NatlThespSoc; SchPl; FrCl; GovHonPrgAwd; Purdue Univ; Home Ec.

JARRETT, Kathryn; Fredericktown Sr HS; Fredericktown, MO; Chr; ChrhWkr; HonRl; HospAde; 4-H; PpCl; Mimeral Area College; Secretary.

JARRETT, Kelly J; Mahomet Seymour HS; Mahomet, IL; 14/130 HonRl; SchAde; SchPl; StuCncl; FrCl; Univ Of Ill; Artist.

JARVI, Cynthia; Negaunee HS; Negaunee, MI; 35/149 Chrs; Orch; College; Data Processing.

JARVI, Mary Lynn J; Baraga HS; Baraga, MI; Band; ChrhWkr; HonRl; LbryAde; NatlFornLg; 4-H; Trk; College; Animal Technician.

JARVI, Steven R; Horace Mann HS; Aurora, MN; ALBoysSt; Band; Chr; CncrtBnd; HonRl; MrchBnd; PepBnd; SctActv; StuCncl; LetterBsbl; College; Professional.

JARVIS, Janet; Litchfield HS; Litchfield, MI; /54 TrsSrCls; AFS; HonRl; JA; Orch; RptrYrbk; RptrSchPpr; CitAwd; Lawrence Ins Of Tech; Arch.

JARVIS, Kelly F; Forest Park HS; Crystal Falls, MI; 5/89 Band; CncrtBnd; HonRl; MrchBnd; PepBnd; Michigan Tech Univ; Nurse.

JARVIS, Russel L; Clarkston HS; Davisburg, MI; 33/451 Aud/Vis; ChrhWkr; HonRl; NHS; SpnCl; LetterGlf; LetterWrstlng; College; Minister.

JARY, Mark L; Whiting Community HS; Whiting, IA; 1/24 ALBoysSt; PresBand; HonRl; MrchBnd; NHS; NatlMeritCmnd; PepBnd; RptrYrbk; PpCl; BauchLmbAwd; Ia State U; Medicine.

JARYSZAK, Rick W; Campion HS; Phelps, WI; Band; ChrhWkr; SchPl; StuGov; LetterBsbl; LetterBsktbl; LetterFtbl; LetterGlf; LetterWrstlng; IMSpt; College.

JARZEMBOWSKI, Celeste M; St Stanislaus Kostka HS; Chicago, IL; 3/79 Band; ChrhWkr; CmntyWkr; HonRl; NHS; Sacrstn; RptrYrbk; SchPpr; FNA; FTA; Mundelein College.

JARZEMSKY, Mary E; Nerinx Hall HS; Webster Groves, MO; TrsSophCls; CmntyWkr; HonRl; SchMus; StuCncl; RptrSchPpr; PpCl; GAA; Clge; Journalism.

JASA, Chris A; Pender Public HS; Thurston, NE; 1/56 SecTrsFrshCls; Aud/Vis; HonRl; LbryAde; SchPl; TchrAde; YthFlsp; RptrYrbk; SptEdSchPpr; FFA; Bsktbl; Glf; CchngActv; Northeast Ne Tech; Diesel Mechanics.

JASA, David W; Pender HS; Thurston, NE; Trk; Trade Sch;.

JASCHEK, Fred; Jennings Sr HS; Jennings, MO; NHS; StuCncl; Bsbl; Ftbl; College.

JASIEN, Paul G; Brother Rice HS; Chicago, IL; 4/416 HonRl; NHS; NatlMeritCmnd; LetterBsbl; IMSpt; De Paul University; Chemistry.

JASINEK, Michael L; Taft HS; Chicago, IL; 254/816 College; Engineering.

JASINEK, Rosie; Thorp HS; Thorp, WI; 26/74 HstSrCls; HonRl; StuCncl; FBLA; FHA; SpnCl; GAA;.

JASINSKI, Rebecca; Buena Vista HS; Saginaw, MI; 30/259 Yrbk; GerCl; Busi Admin.

JASKEY, David G; Fenwick HS; No Riverside, IL; HospAde; NatlFornLg; NHS; SchPl; SctActv; SecStuCncl; RptrYrbk; RptrSchPpr; GerCl; GodCntryAwd; Kalamazoo College; Medicine.

JASKIEWICZ, Roslyn I; East Troy HS; East Troy, WI; Band; HonRl; SecNHS; EdYrBk; 4-H; GAA; IMSpt; College; Pharmacy.

JASKOT, Catherine M; Harrisonville HS; Harrisonville, MO; 8/163 HonRl; SchPl; Yrbk; FrCl; PpCl; PPFtbl; Coll; Prof.

JASKOT, Roger D; Morton West HS; Berwyn, IL; ChrhWkr; HonRl; NHS; ROTC; Illinois Inst Tech; Chemical Engineering.

JASKULSKI, Steven M; St Joseph HS; Bellwood, IL; 3/225 Chrs; NatlMeritCmnd; NatlMeritSF; Univ Of Ill; Astronautical Engineer.

JASPER, Debra L; Holden R Iii HS; Holden, MO; 24/85 TrsFrshCls; HonRl; SpnCl;.

JASPER, Henry A; Carney Nadeau HS; Carney, MI; 3/25 VPFrshCls; VPJrCls; HonRl; SchPl; StuCncl; 4-H; PpCl; Bsktbl; Michigan Tech Univ; Engineering.

JASPERING, Donna J; Normandy HS; St Louis, MO; 16/514 Chr; HonRl; VPNHS; NatlMeritCmnd; Quill&Scroll; SchMus; TchrAde; EdYrBk; PpCl; U Of Mo Col; Science.

JASSAK, Timothy E; Campion Jesuit HS; West Chicago, IL; Band; CncrtBnd; HonRl; MrchBnd; PepBnd; SchMus; StuGov; RptrSchPpr; Tennis; IMSpt; College; Aviation.

JASSEY, Robert; Sibley Comm HS; Sibley, IA; 5/96 ALBoysSt; CncrtBnd; HonRl; JrNHS; NatlMeritSchl; YthFlsp; CchngActv; College; Medicine.

JASTER, Thomas C; West Leyden HS; Northlake, IL; 3/450 CncrtBnd; HonRl; MrchBnd; NHS; Orch; PepBnd; SctActv; GerCl; University; Law.

JASTRZEBSKI, Alexandra M; Marillac HS; Chicago, IL; 22/256 CmntyWkr; Northwestern Univ; Law.

JASZCZAK, Bette J; Paynesville HS; Paynesville, MN; Chr; ChrhWkr; HonRl; SchMus; SchPl; RptrYrbk; EdYrBk; FHA; College; Nursing.

JASZCZYK, Lou; So Milw Senior HS; So Milwaukee, WI; 35/454 AFS; Band; HonRl; SchPl; YthFlsp; 4-H; 4-HAwd; College; Biology.

JAUDEGIS, Ruta R; Bryan HS; Omaha, NE; 16/415 CmntyWkr; CncrtBnd; HonRl; LbryAde; MrchBnd; SctActv; StuGov; University; Field Research.

JAUGILAS, John M; Brother Rice HS; Chicago, IL; 140/460 HonRl; JA; JAAwd; N Ill Univ; Earth Science.

JAURON, Joan M; Harlan Comm HS; Earling, IA; 45/256 HonRl; HospAde; NHS; Quill&Scroll; StuCncl; RptrYrbk; FNA; IMSpt; ChmbCommrsAwd; Bishop Clarkson Sch; Registered Nurse.

JAVINSKY, Edward M; St Louis Park Senior HS; St Louis Park, MN; PolWkr; IMSpt; Univ Of Minnesota; Veterinarian.

JAWOR, Shirley A; St Ann HS; Chicago, IL; SecFrshCls; SecSophCls; SecJrCls; Chr; Chrs; HonRl; LbryAde; NHS; SchAde; StuCncl; Secretary.

JAWORSKI, Judith A; St Clement HS; Warren, MI; 7/126 SecFrshCls; SecJrCls; HonRl; HospAde; RptrYrbk; RptrSchPpr; TreasPpCl; Bsbl; LetterBsktbl; GAA; Coll ; Nursin.

JAWORSKI, Karen E; Marian HS; Osceola, IN; HonRl; SchPl; IMSpt; College; Nurse.

JAWORSKY, Grace M; Hillsboro HS; Hillsboro, KS; Chrs; HonRl; ModUN; OffAde; TchrAde; Teen; LetterBsktbl; LetterTrk; Tabor Coll.

JAYNE, Kathleen I; Thornton Fractional So HS; Lansing, IL; 37/552 HonRl; NHS; OffAde; SchPpr; College; Nursing.

JAYNES, Diane; Edsel Ford HS; Dearborn, MI; Chr; ChrhWkr; HonRl; HospAde; LbryAde; YthFlsp; RptrYrbk; CchngActv; College; Data Processing.

JAYNES, Jeanne K; Bunker Hill HS; Bunker Hill, IL; 1/100 PresJrCls; DrmMjrt; HonRl; NHS; OffAde; SecStuCncl; Twrl; Yrbk; GAA; DARAwd; Southern Ill Univ; Elementary Education.

JAYNES, Lee V; Meadville HS; Meadville, MO; 20/37 PresSophCls; VPJrCls; CncrtBnd; HonRl; NHS; SchPl; StuCncl; CaptBsbl; CaptBsktbl; CaptTrk; Trenton Jr Coll; Agri Bus.

JAZDZYK, Dianne L; Fruitport HS; Muskegon, MI; 6/285 VPJrCls; VPSrCls; HonRl; NHS; SchPl; StuCncl; 4-H; Chrldr; Muskegon Comm College; Medicine.

JEAN, Patty L; Worthing Jefferson HS; Worthington, IN; TrsFrshCls; Band; Chrs; ChrhWkr; HonRl; NHS; PepBnd; 4-H; 4-HAwd; College; Major Study.

JEANBLANC, Ann L; Eagle Grove HS; Vincent, IA; Chrs; HonRl; SchMus; SchPl; StuCncl; RptrYrbk; 4-H; FNA; 4-HAwd; College; Registered Nurse.

JEANES, Michael K; William J Bogan HS; Chicago, IL; 57/704 CaptAud/Vis; HonRl; NHS; TchrAde; LatCl; Loyola Univ; Law.

JEANQUART, Madonna M; Southern Door HS; Sturgeon Bay, WI; HonRl; RptrSchPpr; Vocational Sch; Seamstress Work.

JEANQUART, Sue; St Joseph Academy; Green Bay, WI; 32/156 VPSrCls; Chr; ChrhWkr; CmntyWkr; NHS; StuCncl; TchrAde; GAA; PPFtbl; St Norbert College; Medicine.

JEDELE, Karen S; Grand Blanc Sr HS; Saline, MI; 2/600 SecTrsJrCls; Chr; ChrhWkr; NHS; NatlMeritFnl; SchMus; TchrAde; Concordia Luth Coll; Elem Teacher.

JEDWABNY, Jenifer; St Mary Central HS; Menasha, WI; Band; Chrs; HonRl; SchMus; SpnCl; Univ; Spanish.

JEFFERS, Marsha A; Vandercook Lake HS; Jackson, MI; 11/93 TrsJrCls; PresSrCls; Band; CmntyWkr; HonRl; JA; NHS; PolWkr; SchPl; StuCncl; TchrAde; 4-H; Chrldr;.

JEFFERSON, Diane M; Columbus North Sr HS; Columbus, IN; 53/480 ChrhWkr; CtyCnl; CmntyWkr; ModUN; PolWkr; YthFnd; 4-H; College; Esquestrian Studies.

JEFFERSON, Phyllis; Central HS; St Lois, MO; PresSrCls; Band; Chr; JrNHS; StuCncl; RptrYrbk; FDA; FNA; FTA; GodCntryAwd; Nursing School; Register Nurse.

JEFFERSON, William H; Northwestern HS; Colchester, IL; ChrhWkr; YthFlsp; FFA; MthCl; College; Agriculture.

JEFFERY, Alan K; Center Line HS; Center Line, MI; Aud/Vis; Band; ChrhWkr; HonRl; JrNHS; SchPl; PresSciCl; Clg; Elec Engineer.

JEFFERY, Judith; Usd 277 HS; Guide Rock, NE; SecSophCls; TrsSophCls; SecJrCls; PresJrCls; Band; Chrs; HonRl; MrchBnd; SchPl; PpCl; Friends Univ; Interior Design And Vocal Mus.

JEFFERY, Philip A; St Charles HS; St Charles, MO; Band; CncrtBnd; GerCl; LetterBsktbl; LetterTrk; CchngActv; GodCntryAwd; College Umsl; Business.

JEFFRESS, Bradley J; J D Darnell HS; Geneseo, IL; 12/200 HonRl; Bsktbl; Glf; College; Business Or Engineering.

JEFFREY, John D; Sacred Heart HS; E Grand Forks, MN; Chrs; HonRl; NatlFornLg; SchPl; StuCncl; RptrYrbk; SciCl; LetterWrstlng; CitAwd; Univ; Political Science.

JEFFREYS, David L; Monett HS; Monett, MO; HonRl; NatlMeritFnl; NatlMeritSF; Univ Of Missouri; Elec Engineer.

JEFFREYS, Suzanne; Marian HS; Omaha, NE; HonRl; HospAde; Quill&Scroll; SchPpr; LatCl; Creighton Univ; Nursing.

JEFFRIES, Anne T; West Washington HS; Fredericksburg, IN; Chr; ChrhWkr; CmntyWkr; CncrtBnd; DrlTm; MrchBnd; Orch; 4-H; SpnCl; Indiana Univ; Speech.

JEFFRIES, Deborah L; High School; Hale, MO; TrsJrCls; Band; Chr; Chrs; CncrtBnd; HonRl; Mdrgl; MrchBnd; SchPpr; PpCl; Bsbl; Chrldr; College; Vocation.

JEFFRIES, James; Archie HS; Archie, MO; Band; HonRl; MrchBnd; SctActv; Ftbl; Trade School; Vocation.

JEFFRIES, Sheila; Waukegan East Hs; Waukezan, IL; ALAGirlsSt; Chr; ChrhWkr; HonRl; Mdrgl; NatlFornLg; NHS; NatlThespSoc; StuCncl; College;professional Entertainer.

JEGLUM, Judy A; Pecatonica Area HS; Mt Horeb, WI; HonRl; StuCncl; StuGov; 4-H; FHA; PpCl; College; Ag Dept.

JEHLING, William; St John Vianney HS; Chesterfield, MO; 25/204 HstFrshCls; HstJrCls; HonRl; NHS; StuCncl; Yrbk; SchPpr; SpnCl; IMSpt; VoiceDemAwd; Univ Of Dayton; Mba.

JELASIC, James L; Dearborn HS; Dearborn, MI; TrsSophCls; Chr; HonRl; NatlThespSoc; Orch; SchMus; SchPl; SctActv; StuCncl; StuGov; Mi Univ; Doctorate.

JELIN, Diane M; St Clement HS; Center Line, MI; 5/97 Aud/Vis; HonRl; NHS; Yrbk; FTA; Marygrove College; Special Educ.

JELINEK, Keryl; Wahoo HS; Wahoo, NE; Chrs; CmntyWkr; SchMus; FBLA; FHA; BttyCrckrAwd; TIMEAwd; CitAwd; College; Law Enforcement.

JELINEK, Robin M; Zap HS; Zap, ND; SecTrsJrCls; Chrs; ChrhWkr; HonRl; HospAde; JrNHS; NHS; SchPl; TchrAde; RptrSchPpr;.

JELKEN, Brenda; Wilcox Public HS; Hildreth, NE; 1/26 SecSrCls; Chrs; ChrhWkr; HonRl; NHS; SchMus; SchPl; SpnCl; BttyCrckrAwd; LionAwd; Trade Then College.

JELKS, Sandra M; Principia HS; Chicago, IL; VPFrshCls; Chrs; ChrhWkr; HonRl; NatlMeritSF; SchMus; SchPl; StuCncl; StuGov; RptrYrbk; Bsbl; CaptBsktbl; Socr; Chrldr; Lake Forest College; Social Worker.

JELLEY, Duane J; Austin Catholic Prep; Roseville, MI; 22/115 SecSrCls; HonRl; NatlFornLg; SchMus; StuGov; RptrYrbk; LetterBsktbl; Chrldr; University; Professional.

JELLISON, Susan C; Richmond Senior HS; Richmond, IN; 26/700 SecJrCls; SecSrCls; ChrhWkr; SecDrlTm; NHS; Orch; SchMus; StuGov; PresYthFlsp; 4-H; Purdue; Landscape Architecture.

JELM, Karen S; Serena HS; Serena, IL; 17/96 ALAGirlsSt; SecChrs; ChrhWkr; DrlTm; HospAde; SchMus; SchPl; SecStuCncl; FHA; PresFTA; Il Wesleyan U; Piano Teacher.

JELSMA, Thomas M; Kenowa Hills HS; Grand Rapids, MI; ChrhWkr; HonRl; NHS; SchPl; StuCncl; YthFlsp; EdSchPpr; IMSpt; Grand Rapids Jr Col.

JEMMENS, Patricia M; Lyons Twp HS; Lagrange, IL; HonRl; HospAde; JrNHS; LbryAde; NatlMeritCmnd; OffAde; SchAde; StuCncl; StuGov; MthCl; PpCl; Univ Of Iowa; Nursing.

JENK, Lisa A; Beckman HS; Dyersville, IA; Chrs; HonRl; NHS; SchMus; SchPl; StuCncl; LetterGlf; HstSophCls; GAA; IMSpt; Drake University; Recreation.

JENKIN, Brenda K; Ripon HS; Brandon, WI; SecAFS; ALAGirlsSt; Band; NHS; VPNatlThespSoc; SchMus; SchPl; Yrbk; EdSchPpr; PresGerCl;.

JENKINS, Brian G; Ames Senior HS; Ames, IA; 2/394 ALBoysSt; Chrs; HonRl; PolWkr; SchPl; PresStuCncl; Bsktbl; Trk; DARAwd; PresAwd; College; Broadcast Journalism.

JENKINS, Cheryl L; Thornwood HS; Markham, IL; 25/852 Band; CncrtBnd; HonRl; JrNHS; MrchBnd; NatlFornLg; NHS; NatlThespSoc; SchPl; Univ; Medical Tech.

JENKINS, Christine L; Avon HS; Plainfield, IN; 74/147 TrsSophCls; Chr; DrlTm; HonRl; ModUN; OffAde; SctActv; StuCncl; Chrldr; GAA; Bau St Coll; Phy Educ.

JENKINS, Cynthia; York Community Hs; Elmhurst, IL; 34 HonRl; NHS; NatlMeritCmnd; College;professional.

JENKINS, Dawn R; Oak Park HS; Kansas City, MO; AFS; Chr; HonRl; HospAde; JA; StuCncl; YthLg; 4-H; FBLA; FDA; FNA; Junior College.

JENKINS, Debra K; Liberty HS; Quincy, IL; 6/56 Band; HonRl; NHS; SchPl; Yrbk; FHA; FTA; SpnCl; SciCl; Ne Missouri State Univ; History.

JENKINS, Douglas T; New Trier East HS; Wilmette, IL; 65/847 AFS; CncrtBnd; HonRl; LitMag; StuGov; CivCl; LetterSocr; IMSpt; Middlebury College; Architectural Engineer.

JENKINS, Hersey; Lindblom Tech; Chicago, IL; 333 Chr; ChrhWkr; CmntyWkr; LbryAde; YthFlsp; Yrbk; Electronics Engineer.

JENKINS, Jeffrica J; Auburn Sr HS; Rockford, IL; 16/349 ChrhWkr; HonRl; JA; NHS; NatlMeritCmnd; Univ; Lawyer.

JENKINS, Jennifer L; Garber HS; Essexville, MI; Chr; Chrs; College; Radiologist.

JENKINS, Jim J; Callaway HS; Rr, NE; VPSophCls; SchPl; StuCncl; LetterBsktbl; LetterFtbl; LetterTrk; Coll; Political Sci.

JENKINS, John; Lanphier Hs; Springfield, IL; 19/535 NHS; Ftbl; Swmmng; Ui;agricultural Field.

JENKINS, Joseph T; Dubuque Hempstead HS; Dubuque, IA; 9/509 TrsSrCls; Aud/Vis; HonRl; JrNHS; SchMus; StuCncl; Bsktbl; University; Professional.

JENKINS, Joseph X; Creighton Prep; Omaha, NE; 80/225 CmntyWkr; HonRl; JrNHS; NHS; Bsktbl; LetterFtbl; Socr; IMSpt; RotaryAwd; Creighton Univ; Professional.

JENKINS, Kathleen; Sycamore HS; Sycamore, IL; Chrs; HonRl; StuCncl; FrCl; SpnCl; Tx Christian Univ.

JENKINS, Kathleen A; Warren Township HS; Gurnee, IL; 18/333 NHS; RptrYrbk; EdYrBk; Yrbk; Univ; Home Economics.

JENKINS, Kathryn A; South Newton HS; Kentland, IN; 29/110 Chr; Quill&Scroll; SchPl; Yrbk; SchPpr; FHA; FSA; CaptBsktbl; LetterTrk; PPFtbl; Purdue; Food & Nutrition.

JENKINS, Katrina M; Goreville HS; Goreville, IL; Chrs; HonRl; TchrAde; SchPpr; FHA; PpCl; Undecided;.

JENKINS, Linda E; Kalamazoo Central HS; Kalamazoo, MI; 23/460 HonRl; HospAde; FNA; GerCl; Nursing School; Nurse.

JENKINS, Mary G; Rolling Meadows HS; Arlington Hts, IL; 71/546 Chr; Chrs; HonRl; NHS; NatlThespSoc; Ill Wesleyan Univ; Vocal Music Education.

JENKINS, Mary J; Carbondale Community HS; Murphysboro, IL; 12/223 PresBand; Chr; Chrs; ChrhWkr; PresCncrtBnd; HonRl; PresMrchBnd; NHS; StuGov; 4-H; 4-HAwd; College; Music.

JENKINS, Michelle L; Manchester HS; Manchester, MI; 1/104 SecFrshCls; SecJrCls; SecSrCls; SchPl; TchrAde; RptrSchPpr; 4-H; GerCl; CaptChrldr; Univ Of Michigan; German.

JENKINS, Nancy J; Greensburg HS; Haviland, KS; 3/45 Band; CncrtBnd; HonRl; MrchBnd; PresNHS; PepBnd; SchPl; PresFHA; PpCl; Tennis; Trk; PPFtbl; AmLegAwd; Univ; Home Economics.

JENKINS, Rodney L; Broken Bow HS; Broken Bow, NE; Chr; SchMus; SchPl; StuCncl; YthFlsp; 4-H; PresFFA; Bsktbl; IMSpt; DanFAwd; 4-HAwd; Trade School; Body And Fender.

JENKINS, Sandra B; Wheaton Central HS; Wheaton, IL; Chr; ChrhWkr; HonRl; NatlFornLg; SchMus; SchPl; StuCncl; TchrAde; SecYthFlsp; RptrYrbk; FrCl; College; Education.

JENKINS, Sheila W; Goreville HS; Goreville, IL; 2/31 SecJrCls; Band; Chrs; ChrhWkr; HonRl; PepBnd; EdYrBk; FHA; Chrldr; BttyCrckrAwd; So Illinois Schl Tech; Dental Hygienist.

JENKINS, Timothy J; Polo HS; Polo, IL; Band; CncrtBnd; HonRl; MrchBnd; Bsbl; Bsktbl; Ftbl; Glf; CchngActv;.

JENKOT, George O; Bronson HS; Bronson, MI; HonRl; JA; StuGov; FBLA; FSA; Trk; ChmbCommrsAwd; GovHonPrgAwd; PresAwd; RotaryAwd; Trade School; Plumbing Heating.

JENNE, Deborah L; Civic Memorial HS; Carlyle, IL; 17/221 Band; Chr; ChrhWkr; CncrtBnd; HonRl; MrchBnd; NHS; Treas4-H; GerCl; LetterGAA; 4-HAwd; Millikin Univ; Medical Technology.

JENNEMAN, Tamara A; Bloomer Sr HS; Bloomer, WI; Band; CncrtBnd; MrchBnd; PepBnd; SchMus; 4-H; FHA; GAA; Business Schl; Liberal Arts.

JENNER, Joyce A; Notre Dame HS; Chicago, IL; HonRl; TchrAde; Triton College; Business Mgmt.

JENNESS, Jeanne; West Marshall HS; Saint Anthony, IA; Band; Chrs; CncrtBnd; DrmMjrt; HonRl; MrchBnd; NHS; PepBnd; ModUN; 4-H; Chrldr; 4-HAwd; Marshalltown Community College;nursing.

JENNEY, Wendy; Kalamazoo Central HS; Kalamazoo, MI; HonRl; SchPpr; 4-H; Kalamazoo College; Prof.

JENNIGES, Bruce D; Walnut Grove Public HS; Walnut Grove, MN; 8/41 HonRl; SchMus; SchPl; StuCncl; EdYrBk; LetterWrstlng; Mankato State Clge.

JENNINGS, Barry D; Washburn HS; Washburn, ND; PresJrCls; PresSrCls; Band; CncrtBnd; HonRl; SchPl; SchPpr; FFA; LetterFtbl; LetterTrk; Univ Of Nd; Lawyer.

JENNINGS, Cherry L; Turner HS; Kansas City, KS; 6/300 HonRl; JrNHS; NHS; StuGov; VPSpnCl; LetterPpCl; SecSciCl; U Of Ks.

JENNINGS, Constance A; Washburn HS; Minneapolis, MN; 9/500 Band; HonRl; NatlFornLg; PresNHS; NatlMeritSF; SchMus; YthLg; SchPpr; IMSpt; VoiceDemAwd; Bob Jones Univ; Doctor.

JENNINGS, Crystal; St Anne HS; Papineav, IL; Aud/Vis; Chr; CmntyWkr; HospAde; JCC; LbryAde; OffAde; RedCrAde; StuGov; Kankakee Community College; Child Care Inst.

JENNINGS, Cynthia; Winfield Mi Union HS; Winfield, IA; 1/37 HstSrCls; Chrs; HonRl; NHS; SchPl; EdSchPpr; 4-H; Iowa Wesleyan College; Secondary School Tch.

JENNINGS, Cynthia L; Winfield Mt Union HS; Winfield, IA; 1/37 HonRl; NHS; SchPl; EdSchPpr; 4-H; LetterChrldr; 4-HAwd; Iowa Wesleyan College; Math.

JENNINGS, Debbie K; Stanberry Rii HS; Stanberry, MO; 5/40 PresJrCls; ALAGirlsSt; HonRl; ModUN; EdYrBk; PpCl; Bsktbl; Trk; IMSpt; PresAwd; U Of Mo.

JENNINGS, James S; Pioneer HS; Ann Arbor, MI; Band; CncrtBnd; HonRl; MrchBnd; NatlMeritCmnd; Yrbk; SchPpr; MthCl; Univ Of Calif.

JENNINGS, Judith Ann M; Good Counsel HS; Chicago, IL; 12/248 SecFrshCls; VPSophCls; HonRl; JrNHS; NHS; PresStuCncl; Yrbk; SchPpr; SpnCl; Bsktbl; GAA; Marquette Univ; Journalism.

JENNINGS, Mark S; Prairie City Comm HS; Prairie City, IA; PresFrshCls; HonRl; VPStuCncl; StuGov; Treas4-H; LetterFtbl; LetterTrk; 4-HAwd; Iowa State Univ; Business Administration.

JENNINGS, Mary S; Weaubleau HS; Collins, MO; 1/30 Band; CncrtBnd; DrlTm; HonRl; MrchBnd; PepBnd; FHA; Central Missouri St; History.

JENNINGS, Richard D; Campion HS; Birmingham, MI; 6/74 Aud/Vis; HonRl; StuCncl; StuGov; SchPpr; FSA; Ftbl; Glf; Univ; Physical Science.

JENNINGS, Sharon K; Franklin Public HS; Franklin, NE; 9/54 Chrs; HonRl; LbryAde; TchrAde; FHA; PpCl; Trade; Secretary.

JENNINGS, Steven T; Central HS; Camp Point, IL; 2/75 PresFrshCls; HonRl; VPNHS; StuCncl; LetterTrk; U Of Il; Engineering.

JENNINGS, Thomas; Maroa Forsyth HS; Decatur, IL; 1/70 TrsJrCls; Band; Chr; Chrs; ChrhWkr; CncrtBnd; HonRl; LbryAde; SchPl; StuCncl; College; Engineering.

JENNINGS, Versia C; Englewood HS; Chicago, IL; HonRl; ModUN; NHS; OffAde; TchrAde; University; Pharmicist.

JENNISON, Cynthia A; Salina Central HS; Salina, KS; Chr; Chrs; ChrhWkr; CmntyWkr; LitMag; SchMus; SchPl; StuCncl; TchrAde; 4-H; ChmbCommrsAwd; 4-HAwd; Kansas Wesleyan Univ; English.

JENNY, Ann; Highland Park Sr HS; St Paul, MN; ChrhWkr; HospAde; Orch; PolWkr; SchMus; RptrSchPpr; SchPpr; FrCl; Univ Of Mn; Journalism.

JENSEN, Anne E; Grace HS; St Paul, MN; ChrhWkr; HospAde; TchrAde; College; High School Teacher.

JENSEN, Barbara R; Estherville HS; Estherville, IA; Band; ChrhWkr; CmntyWkr; CncrtBnd; HonRl; OffAde; StuCncl; TchrAde; YthFlsp; Yrbk;.

JENSEN, Becky J; Denver HS; Denver, IA; Chr; ChrhWkr; CmntyWkr; HonRl; JrNHS; NHS; RptrYrbk; EdYrBk; FshEdYrbk; SptEdYrbk; Wartburg Coll; Elem Ed.

JENSEN, Bobbi L; West Central HS; Medaryville, IN; 14/89 DrlTm; HonRl; LbryAde; NHS; RptrYrbk; SchPpr; St Josephs College; Teaching.

JENSEN, Brenda J; Memorial HS; Eau Clair, WI; Chr; HonRl; Orch; SchMus; SchPl; PPFtbl; College Navy.

JENSEN, Bruce D; Tri Center HS; Minden, IA; 4/71 Band; CncrtBnd; HonRl; MrchBnd; TreasNHS; SctActv; PresYthFlsp; Yrbk; LetterBsbl; LetterBsktbl; Ia State U; Accouting.

JENSEN, Carol L; Toluca HS; Toluca, IL; HonRl; 4-H; FHA; SpnCl; PpCl; GAA; Beauty School.

JENSEN, Carol R; Gettysburg HS; Gettysburg, SD; 3/64 PresFrshCls; VPJrCls; PresSrCls; HonRl; NHS; StuCncl; RptrSchPpr; PpCl; Chrldr; Northern State College; Business.

JENSEN, Cheryl L; Northeast Sr HS; Kansas City, MO; 20/347 LetterBand; ChrhWkr; CmntyWkr; CncrtBnd; DrmBgl; HonRl; JA; MrchBnd; OffAde; Orch; Univ Of Mo; Art Teacher.

JENSEN, Christal A; West HS; Iowa City, IA; Band; HonRl; LitMag; NatlMeritCmnd; Quill&Scroll; Yrbk; SchPpr; VPPpCl; LetterTrk; ChmbCommrsAwd; Stanford University; Professional.

JENSEN, Crystal D; North Loup Scotia HS; N Loup, NE; 4/35 SecJrCls; ALAGirlsSt; HonRl; NHS; StuCncl; YthFlsp; 4-H; FHA; PpCl; Bsktbl; Army ; Pro.

JENSEN, Curtis; Sioux Valley HS; Volgo, SD; PresFrshCls; VPSophCls; Band; SchMus; SchPl; SctActv; StuCncl; StuGov; Ftbl; Wrstlng; University Sdsu Or Minn; Pre Law.

JENSEN, Dale R; New Richland Hartland HS; New Richland, MN; 26/69 Band; Chr; ChrhWkr; CmntyWkr; HonRl; SchPl; YthFlsp; Ftbl; North Central Bible College; Evanglism.

JENSEN, David J; Kindred Public HS; Kindred, ND; PresJrCls; Chrs; HonRl; HospAde; LbryAde; StuCncl; Bsbl; LetterBsktbl; LetterFtbl; LetterTennis; LetterTrk; Univ Of North Dakota; Physician.

JENSEN, David K; Rock Island Senior HS; Rock Island, IL; Dartmouth College; Doctor.

JENSEN, David R; Oak Park Sr HS; Gladstone, MO; 4/602 ChrhWkr; HonRl; ROTC; SctActv; TchrAde; Tennis; Univ Of Missouri; Business.

JENSEN, Dean; Clay Center Public HS; Clay Center, NE; 6/28 HonRl; PepBnd; YthFlsp; 4-H; College.

JENSEN, Debra; Courtland HS; Courtland, KS; PresSophCls; PresJrCls; Chrs; DrmMjrt; HonRl; MrchBnd; SchMus; SchPl; StuCncl; PpCl; Trade Sch.

JENSEN, Debra K; Luck Public HS; Luck, WI; Chr; CmntyWkr; JA; 4-H; Bsbl; LetterTrk; GAA; 4-HAwd; JAAwd; PresAwd; Vocational.

JENSEN, Dee A; Roseau HS; Pinecreek, MN; SecTrsSrCls; Band; Chrs; CncrtBnd; HonRl; Mdrgl; SchMus; SchPl; RptrYrbk; LetterTennis; Bemidji State Coll; Bio.

JENSEN, Dennis D; Wenona HS; Wenona, IL; 3/43 VPJrCls; Band; ChrhWkr; HonRl; MrchBnd; TreasNHS; YthFlsp; Yrbk; SchPpr; 4-H; CaptTrk; CchngActv; AmLegAwd; 4-HAwd; Jr College; Medicine.

JENSEN, Diana H; Alpena HS; Alpena, SD; 1/16 PresFrshCls; SecTrsJrCls; SecTrsSrCls; HonRl; NHS; StuCncl; EdSchPpr; Chrldr; BttyCrckrAwd; DARAwd; Coll; Journalism.

JENSEN, Diana L; Powers Lake HS; Powers Lake, ND; PresSrCls; ALAGirlsSt; VPBand; PresChr; HonRl; StuCncl; EdSchPpr; PresPpCl; ChmnBsktbl; LetterTennis; Minot St Colge; Elem Ed.

JENSEN, Diane M; Papillion HS; Papillion, NE; 19/319 HonRl; NHS; SchAde; TchrAde; FBLA; FTA; PpCl; LetterBsktbl; U Of Ne; Medical Technology.

JENSEN, Duane M; Abraham Lincoln HS; Council Bluffs, IA; College; Surgeon.

JENSEN, Emil W; Osborn HS; Detroit, MI; SchPl; EdYrBk; Yrbk; GerCl; Central Mi U; Bus Mgmt.

JENSEN, Gaylis A; Richaland Center HS; Yuba, WI; ALAGirlsSt; Band; CncrtBnd; HonRl; LitMag; MrchBnd; NHS; PepBnd; SchMus; Trk; Univ; Music Therapy.

JENSEN, Glenn T; Fitzgerald HS; Warren, MI; 100/525 HonRl; NatlFornLg; NHS; VoiceDemAwd; Mi State U; Chem Engineering.

JENSEN, James D; Rich Central HS; Olympia Fields, IL; 8/413 HonRl; NHS; YthFlsp; KeyCl; Ftbl; Wrstlng; University; Finance.

JENSEN, Janis M; Spencer HS; Spencer, IA; AFS; ChrhWkr; HonRl; HospAde; NHS; NatlMeritCmnd; NatlThespSoc; SchPl; Oral Roberts Univ.

JENSEN, Jeanne; Elizabeth Seton Hs; Dolton, IL; Chrs; HonRl; Mdrgl; OffAde; SchMus; FrCl; Western Il U; Bus Administration.

JENSEN, Joan M; Ringsted Comm HS; Ringsted, IA; TrsSrCls; Band; HonRl; NHS; SchPl; EdYrBk; EdSchPpr; LetterBsktbl; BttyCrckrAwd; KiwanAwd; Univ.

JENSEN, Jolene M; Jamestown HS; Jamestown, KS; VPSophCls; Chrs; HonRl; SchPl; StuCncl; Chrldr; Col; Speech Therapist.

JENSEN, Jolynne; Osborn HS; Detroit, MI; 46/640 HonRl; JrNHS; NatlFornLg; NHS; NatlMeritFnl; NatlMeritSchl; OffAde; SchAde; SchMus; SchPl; StuCncl; TchrAde; RptrYrbk; Yrbk; Wayne State Univ; Pre Law.

JENSEN, Jonelle; Atlantic HS; Atlantic, IA; 1/148 Chr; HonRl; Mdrgl; NHS; Quill&Scroll; RptrSchPpr; FNA; DARAwd; 4-HAwd; Ia Western Comm College; Lpn.

JENSEN, Julie M; Milbank HS; Milbank, SD; Chrs; ChrhWkr; HonRl; NatlFornLg; NHS; NatlMeritSF; StuCncl; EdYrBk; RptrSchPpr; Coll; Medicine.

JENSEN, Karen; Southeast HS; Lincoln, NE; Band; DrlTm; HonRl; NHS; PpCl; PPFtbl; Univ Ne;legal Sec.

JENSEN, Karen E; Parker HS; Humboldt, SD; 2/44 TrsSrCls; ALAGirlsSt; DrlTm; HonRl; LitMag; NHS; SchPl; SptEdYrbk; EdSchPpr; FHA; Mount Marty Clge; Home Ec.

JENSEN, Karen M; Central Community HS; Montrose, IA; SecFrshCls; PresSophCls; Band; Chr; HonRl; MrchBnd; PepBnd; SpnCl; PpCl; Chrldr; College; Professional.

JENSEN, Katherine K; Deubrook HS; Toronto, SD; 1/35 PresSophCls; SecJrCls; Band; Chrs; ChrhWkr; HonRl; SecStuCncl; PresFHA; TreasPpCl; AmLegAwd; Univ; Nurse.

JENSEN, Kathy; Alveenia HS; Chicago, IL; 18/226 Chrs; ChrhWkr; HonRl; LitMag; LbryAde; NHS; SctActv; RptrYrbk; Yrbk; Coll; Theatre.

JENSEN, Kenny; Oregon Davis HS; Hamlet, IN; TrsFrshCls; PresSophCls; HonRl; Bsktbl; Glf; Trk; IMSpt; 4-HAwd; Trade School; Convention Officer.

JENSEN, Kevin; Beason HS; Kenney, IL; 4/23 PresSophCls; SchMus; SchPl; Yrbk; RptrSchPpr; Bsktbl; Illinois State Univ; Cpa.

JENSEN, Kimberly K; O Neill Public HS; O Neill, NE; Chr; Mdrgl; SchMus; TchrAde; YthFlsp; Sec4-H; PpCl; Chrldr; GAA; PresAwd; College; Liberal Arts.

JENSEN, Kim L; Chamberlain HS; Chamberlain, SD; ALAGirlsSt; Band; CmntyWkr; DrlTm; HonRl; Quill&Scroll; EdYrBk; Pres4-H; PpCl; 4-HAwd; S Dakota St Univ; Animal Science.

JENSEN, Kim R; Brown HS; Sturgis, SD; 2/200 HonRl; NHS; SecStuCncl; RptrSchPpr; SpnCl; SciCl; VoiceDemAwd; Business College; Accounting.

JENSEN, Kurt A; Wasatch Acad; Seward, NE; Band; HonRl; MrchBnd; PepBnd; SctActv; YthFlsp; RptrSchPpr; SchPpr; LetterTennis; IMSpt; College; Computer Prog.

JENSEN, Laurie J; Lasalle HS; Cedar Rapids, IA; 1/136 HonRl; ModUN; NatlFornLg; NHS; SchMus; RptrSchPpr; Univ Of Iowa; Journalism.

JENSEN, Lynette M; Cudahy HS; Cudahy, WI; AFS; HonRl; Coll; Art Teach.

JENSEN, Marcia K; Union HS; Grand Rapids, MI; HospAde; NatlMeritSchl; RedCrAde; Univ Occupational Training.

JENSEN, Marilyn M; Cooperstown HS; Cooperstown, ND; TrsSophCls; TrsJrCls; ALAGirlsSt; Chr; ChrhWkr; HonRl; NHS; 4-H; KeyCl; College; Business.

JENSEN, Mark A; Clarence Lowden HS; Lowden, IA; 2/57 ALBoysSt; Chrs; CncrtBnd; NHS; SchMus; StuCncl; YthFlsp; RptrYrbk; Glf; CchngActv; U Of Ia; Business Administration.

JENSEN, Marlene; Donca HS; Jackson, NE; 3/28 VPJrCls; SecSrCls; HonRl; JrNHS; LbryAde; NHS; SchPpr; Univ Of S Dakota; Elementary Education.

JENSEN, Marlene A; Ponca HS; Jackson, NE; 3/28 VPJrCls; SecSrCls; Chrs; HonRl; NHS; SchPl; SchPpr; Pres4-H; SecPpCl; LetterTrk; Univ Of Sd; Elem Education.

JENSEN, Mary K; Lourde HS; Rochester, MN; Band; CncrtBnd; HonRl; HospAde; MrchBnd; PepBnd; SctActv; 4-H; College; Health Care.

JENSEN, Mary K; Ashby HS; Ashby, MN; SecSophCls; Band; Chr; Chrl; CncrtBnd; DrmMjrt; HonRl; LbryAde; Mdrgl; MrchBnd; NHS; St Cloud Beauty College; Beautician.

JENSEN, Melanie; Exira HS; Exira, IA; 3/46 Band; Chr; ChrhWkr; CmntyWkr; HonRl; HospAde; SchMus; Yrbk; Bsbl; 4-HAwd; Bishop Clarkson Mem Hosp Sch Ofnursing; Rn.

JENSEN, Melodi K; Elk Horn Kimballton HS; Kimballton, IA; SecTrsJrCls; Band; Chrs; ChrhWkr; HonRl; Mdrgl; NHS; SchMus; SchPl; PresFHA; LetterBsbl; IMSpt; College; Professional.

JENSEN, Nancy G; Minden HS; Minden, NE; Band; Chrl; CncrtBnd; MrchBnd; SchMus; SchPl; TchrAde; RptrSchPpr; SchPpr; FTA; Coll; Speech Pathology.

JENSEN, Nels J; Gaylord Comm HS; Gaylord, MI; Band; ChrhWkr; CncrtBnd; HonRl; MrchBnd; NHS; YthFlsp; Ftbl; Tech Univ; Biological Sciences.

JENSEN, Pamela J; Mendota HS; Mendota, IL; 12/187 Chr; DrlTm; Mdrgl; SecNHS; YthFlsp; SecSpnCl; College; Biology.

JENSEN, Patricia S; Detroit Country Day HS; Detroit, MI; SecFrshCls; PresJrCls; Chrs; HonRl; JrNHS; SctActv; TchrAde; FTA; SpnCl; LetterChrldr; College.

JENSEN, Paul A; Montabella HS; Edmore, MI; 13/94 Band; CncrtBnd; MrchBnd; NHS; StuCncl; SptEdSchPpr; SpnCl; LetterBsktbl; LetterFtbl; LetterTrk; CitAwd; Ferris State College; Pharmacy.

JENSEN, Randy D; Dexfield HS; Redfield, IA; Ftbl; Trk; Wrstlng; College; Tool & Die.

JENSEN, Robert M; Arnold HS; Arnold, NE; SecFrshCls; VPSophCls; HstJrCls; Chr; RptrYrbk; EdSchPpr; SptEdSchPpr; Bsktbl; LetterFtbl; LetterGlf; Univ Ne; Journalism.

JENSEN, Roger J; St Laurence HS; Chicago, IL; 40/375 VPSrCls; Aud/Vis; HonRl; StuCncl; RptrSchPpr; Socr; Trk; CchngActv; IMSpt; JETSAwd; Engineering.

JENSEN, Steven D; Chaska HS; Chaska, MN; Aud/Vis; ChrhWkr; CmntyWkr; HonRl; SctActv; StuCncl; TchrAde; YthFlsp; LetterTrk; IMSpt; University; Professional.

JENSEN, Susan G; Alxis HS; Gerlaw, IL; Band; Chr; Chrs; ChrhWkr; CncrtBnd; HonRl; MrchBnd; PepBnd; YthFlsp; FrCl; College; Music.

JENSEN, Suzanne F; Warsaw HS; Warsaw, MO; 6/65 CncrtBnd; HonRl; NHS; SchPl; StuCncl; TchrAde; VPYthFlsp; VPFHA; PpCl; Chrldr; Oral Roberts University.

JENSEN, Vickie K; Ipswich Public HS; Ipswich, SD; 1/50 PresJrCls; ALAGirlsSt; Band; Chrs; HonRl; NHS; StuCncl; YthFlsp; PresFHA; 4-HAwd; College; Math Teacher.

JENSEN, Wendy J; Kennedy HS; Dayton, ND; 6/27 ChrhWkr; CtyCnl; CmntyWkr; PolWkr; SchPl; PresStuCncl; RptrYrbk; Pres4-H; FHA; CaptChrldr; GAA; 4-HAwd; CitAwd; Concordia College; Gen Home Economics.

JENSON, Daniel D; Newman Grove HS; Newman Grove, NE; HonRl; LetterTrk; Navy; Sonar Tech.

JENSWOLD, Janice M; Madison West HS; Madison, WI; HospAde; NatlMeritFnl; NatlMeritSF; GerCl; U Of W; Special Educ.

JENT, Carol S; Plainfield HS; Indianapolis, IN; 35/260 HonRl; SchPpr; FHA; FTA; PresFrCl; PpCl; Purdue Univ; Speech & Hearing Therapy.

JENTLIE, Eric T; North HS; Eau Claire, WI; HonRl; LetterBsktbl; LetterFtbl; CaptTrk;.

JENTZ, Terri L; Lyons Township HS; Western Springs, IL; 14/124 HonRl; NHS; NatlMeritFnl; NatlMeritSF; Quill&Scroll; EdYrBk; Yale Univ; Journalism.

JENUWINE, Gary; Eisenhower HS; Mt Clemens, MI; ChrhWkr; CmntyWkr; HonRl; SchAde; SchPl; TchrAde; 4-H; 4-HAwd; Oakland U; Engineering.

JENUWINE, Laura; Dwight D Eisenhower HS; Washington, MI; 5/535 HonRl; NHS; NatlMeritFnl; NatlMeritSchl; Quill&Scroll; RptrSchPpr; SchPpr; FrCl; MthCl; PpCl; General Motors Inst; Engineering.

JENUWINE, Laura A; Dwight D Eisenhower HS; Washington, MI; 6/543 HonRl; NHS; NatlMeritSF; Quill&Scroll; SctActv; RptrSchPpr; SchPpr; FrCl; MthCl; PpCl; College; Math Major.

JEPPERSON, Craig D; Worthington Senior HS; Worthinton, MN; Aud/Vis; Chr; Chrs; SchPl; StuCncl; LetterBsbl; Bsktbl; Ftbl; Swmmng; IMSpt; St Johns Univ; Professional.

JEPPESEN, Ronald R; Blair HS; Fort Calhoun, NE; Chr; ChrhWkr; HonRl; NHS; PresYthFlsp; 4-H; SecFFA; LetterTrk; Farmer And Mechanic.

JEPPSON, Trudy L; Bancroft Public HS; Bancroft, NE; 12/32 VPJrCls; SecSrCls; Chrs; ChrhWkr; CncrtBnd; HonRl; MrchBnd; NHS; OffAde; PepBnd; Northeast Ne Tech College; Exec Secretary.

JEPSON, Diana; New Hampton Community HS; New Hampton, IA; 1/180 Band; ChrhWkr; HonRl; NHS; PepBnd; StuGov; Glf; GAA; GovHonPrgAwd; PresAwd; Univ Iowa; Pharmacy.

JEPSON, Jac; Ashwaubenon HS; Green Bay, WI; Chr; HonRl; NHS; SctActv; Bsbl; Bsktbl; LetterFtbl; LetterTrk; IMSpt; Ripon Or St Norbert;law.

JEPSON, Paul C; West Monona HS; Little Sioux, IA; 20/81 ALBoysSt; Band; Chr; ChrhWkr; HonRl; MrchBnd; SchMus; SchPl; RptrSchPpr; LetterTrk; Clge; Teach Music.

JERABEK, Joel C; Yorkville HS; Yorkville, IL; 2/156 Band; CncrtBnd; MrchBnd; NHS; Orch; PepBnd; SchMus; SctActv; StuCncl; Trade School; Architecture.

JERBECK, Doreen C; Annawan HS; Sheffield, IL; 1/51 TrsSophCls; JrNHS; LbryAde; SecNHS; StuCncl; TchrAde; PresFHA; TreasGAA; Bus Sch; Acct.

JEREB, Gary W; North Chicago Comm HS; North Chicago, IL; 21/237 HonRl; NHS; SctActv; Bsktbl; Ftbl; LetterGlf; Univ; Mech Engin.

JERGENSEN, Jeff M; Valders HS; Kiel, WI; 7/124 ALBoysSt; Band; CncrtBnd; HonRl; JrNHS; NHS; PepBnd; PresStuCncl; Ftbl; Wrstlng; College; Math.

JERGER, Greg E; Bayard HS; Bayard, NE; 2/43 Chrs; ChrhWkr; CmntyWkr; HonRl; JrNHS; NHS; SchPl; YthFlsp; Bsbl; Bsktbl;.

JERKINS, Mark L; Knoxville Comm HS; Knoxville, IA; Ftbl; Wrstlng;.

JEROME, Kathy R; Humboldt St Vincent HS; Hallock, MN; 6/13 Chrs; HospAde; SchPl; RptrYrbk; SchPpr; FHA; Bsktbl; IMSpt; Vocational School; Surgical Tech.

JEROME, Marlin L; Walhalla Public HS; Walhalla, ND; Band; Chrs; CncrtBnd; MrchBnd; SctActv; Bsktbl; LetterFtbl; LetterTrk; Wrstlng; Trade School; Professional.

JERRY, Eleanor C; Terre Haute South Vigo HS; Terre Haute, IN; 1/586 VPJrCls; ChrhWkr; HonRl; ModUN; NatlFornLg; NatlMeritSF; SchPl; StuCncl; TchrAde; YthFlsp; CaptTrk; AmLegAwd; DARAwd; VoiceDemAwd; Butler University; Speech.

JERSEY, Mary F; Notre Dame For Girls HS; Chicago, IL; 3/262 HonRl; JA; NHS; StuGov; FTA; MthCl; Univ; Zoology Or Engin.

JERSILD, Julie A; Craig Sr HS; Janesville, WI; AFS; Chr; HonRl; LbryAde; PolWkr; StuCncl; RptrYrbk; 4-H; FrCl; Chrldr; College; Journalism.

JERTSON, Paul A; Preston HS; Preston, MN; Band; HonRl; MrchBnd; NHS; SchPl; Yrbk; SchPpr; Bsktbl; LetterWrstlng; VoiceDemAwd; Mn Schl Of Bus; Bus Admin.

JERZAK, James T; Newman HS; Wausau, WI; 4/132 ALBoysSt; Band; HonRl; SchMus; StuCncl; Glf; Trk; IMSpt; EldAwd; GovHonPrgAwd; OptClAwd; Univ Of Wisconsin; Medicine.

JERZAK, Sandra M; Lourdes HS; Chicago, IL; 170/300 ALAGirlsSt; JA; AmLegAwd; St Xavier; Phsical Therapist.

JERZYK, Barbara J; Whiting HS; Whiting, IN; LbryAde; SpnCl; PpCl; ChmnGAA; Secretary.

JESBERG, Christine A; Notre Dame HS; Quincy, IL; Chrs; ChrhWkr; CmntyWkr; HonRl; HospAde; SchMus; SctActv; RptrSchPpr; SpnCl; PpCl; IMSpt; Quincy College; Music.

JESCHKE, Rebecca A; Highland HS; Severance, KS; VPFrshCls; TrsSophCls; Chrs; CncrtBnd; HonRl; StuCncl; PresYthFlsp; RptrSchPpr; CaptChrldr; IMSpt; Graceland College; Occupational Therapist.

JESIOLOWSKI, Maryann; La Salle Peru Township HS; La Salle, IL; 85/519 AFS; HonRl; NHS; PolWkr; FrCl; Trinity College; Political Science.

JESKE, Jill J; Roosevelt HS; Marenisco, MI; 2/19 Chrs; HonRl; LbryAde; NatlThespSoc; SchPl; EdYrBk; SchPpr; 4-H; Bsktbl; 4-HAwd; College.

JESKE, Norbert A; Central HS; Seymour, WI; 3/188 HonRl; Technical School; Agriculture.

JESKEWICH, Sally A; Bedford North Lawrence HS; Bedford, IN; 13/430 SecJrCls; ALAGirlsSt; HonRl; HospAde; NHS; StuCncl; PpCl; Bsktbl; Chrldr; GAA; PPFtbl; University; Pharmacy.

JESOP, Bradley D; Fairfield Community HS; Fairfield, IL; LatCl; Murray St Univ; Accounting.

JESPERSEN, Keryl E; Antler Public HS; Antler, ND; 1/7 SecTrsSophCls; Chr; CmntyWkr; HonRl; SchPl; Yrbk; 4-H; Bsktbl; 4-HAwd; Coll; Pro.

JESS, Jennifer M; Mundelein HS; Mundelein, IL; PresJrCls; PresSrCls; TrsSrCls; HonRl; LitMag; OffAde; SchAde; SchPl; Yrbk; Tennis; Boston Univ; Biomedical Field.

JESSE, Jane; Oak Lawn Community HS; Hometown, IL; HonRl; OffAde; TchrAde;.

JESSE, Janet M; Crandon HS; Argonne, WI; 5/65 Band; CncrtBnd; DrlTm; HonRl; MrchBnd; OffAde; PepBnd; StuCncl; DanFAwd; Nicolet College; Stenographer.

JESSEE, Brent A; South Spencer HS; Richland, IN; 10/131 VPFrshCls; PresSophCls; VPJrCls; NHS; NatlThespSoc; SchMus; StuCncl; EdSchPpr; PpCl; LetterGlf; University; Professional.

JESSEE, Darlene K; Normal Community HS; Normal, IL; 1/500 CncrtBnd; HonRl; MrchBnd; NHS; NatlMeritCmnd; Orch; StuCncl; TchrAde; SpnCl; GAA; Il Univ; Civil Engr.

JESSEN, Jane A; Washington Island HS; Washington Island, WI; TrsFrshCls; TrsSophCls; TrsJrCls; Chr; ChrhWkr; CmntyWkr; HonRl; SchMus; SctActv; RptrYrbk; Univ.

JESSUP, Cynthia R; Oakwood Academy; Deltoit, MI; 1/26 Chr; ChrhWkr; HonRl; HospAde; NatlMeritSF; PresStuCncl; Yrbk; RptrSchPpr; Chrldr; Oakwood College; Nursing.

JESSUP, Garry K; Marion Adams HS; Sheridan, IN; 37/100 Aud/Vis; LbryAde; SchPl; 4-H; FFA; LatCl; SciCl; College; Vocation.

JESSUP, Lynda C; Algonac HS; Harsens Island, MI; CmntyWkr; HonRl; JrNHS; NHS; NatlMeritSchl; BauchLmbAwd; College; Rn Nursing.

JESTER, Jeanne; Center Grove HS; Greenwood, IN; 9/225 Band; MrchBnd; NHS; NatlMeritCmnd; NatlMeritSF; TchrAde; 4-H; PpCl; Trk; Purdue Univ.

JETER, Jerry J; Du Quoin HS; Du Quoin, IL; 7/145 VPSrCls; HonRl; SctActv; VPStuCncl; SciCl; LetterFtbl; LetterTrk; Illinois State Univ; Architecture.

JETT, Marsha E; Washington HS; Elmora, IN; Chr; HonRl; JA; NatlThespSoc; SchPl; TchrAde; RptrSchPpr; FNA; GerCl; PpCl; Vincennes Univ; Respiratory Therapy.

JETTER, Peggy E; Pipestone HS; Pipestone, MN; Band; Chrs; CncrtBnd; HonRl; Mdrgl; MrchBnd; PepBnd; 4-H; SpnCl; IMSpt; Mankato State College; Mathematics.

JETTINGHOFF, Mary K; Plymouth Salem HS; Plymouth, MI; ALAGirlsSt; Chr; HonRl; PresSophCls; SecStuCncl; YthFlsp; 4-H; GAA; PPFtbl; Coll.

JEVITT, Mary E; St Louise De Marillac HS; Chicago, IL; 50/250 NHS; SchPl; StuGov; College; Social Work.

JEWELL, Daniel A; Calumet HS; Gary, IN; 1/330 HonRl; JrNHS; NHS; Trk; College; Psychology.

JEWELL, James M; Pembine HS; Pembine, WI; CmntyWkr; HonRl; NatlThespSoc; SchMus; SchPl; RptrSchPpr; Bsktbl; Ftbl; Glf; College; Electronics Engineer.

JEWELL, Kevin C; Greene Comm HS; Greene, IA; SecSrCls; ChrhWkr; HonRl; SchMus; SchPl; YthFlsp; EdSchPpr; LetterBsbl; LetterBsktbl; LetterFtbl; Iowa State U; Veterinary Med.

JEWELL, Rosemary; Rantoul Township HS; Rantoul, IL; HonRl; SchMus; Calif Inst Of The Arts; Fine Arts.

JEZERC, Joyce A; Appleton HS West; Appleton, WI; ALAGirlsSt; Band; CncrtBnd; MrchBnd; NatlMeritCmnd; Orch; StuCncl; SpnCl; CaptBsktbl; PresGAA; College; Pre Medicine Major.

JEZIER, Michael G; Ridgewood HS; Norridge, IL; 11/369 HonRl; VPNHS; TchrAde; RptrYrbk; SptEdYrbk; Yrbk; LetterTennis; Univ Of Illinois; Business Administration.

JIACIK, Catherine S; Ely Memorial HS; Ely, MN; 12/123 Chr; HonRl; HospAde;.

JICHA, Connie; Oconto Sr HS; Oconto, WI; Aud/Vis; ChrhWkr; CmntyWkr; HonRl; LbryAde; NatlMeritSchl; SchPl; RptrSchPpr; FHA; LetterBsktbl; Uw Oshkosh; Social Work.

JILEK, Dominic; Rush City HS; Rush City, MN; 7/70 Band; Chr; CncrtBnd; HonRl; MrchBnd; NHS; PepBnd; SchPl; RptrYrbk; Bsktbl; St Cloud St Univ.

JILEK, Ed J; Winnebago HS; Seward, IL; 5/107 AFS; Band; ChrhWkr; CmntyWkr; CncrtBnd; HonRl; NHS; Orch; LetterBsktbl; CaptFtbl; Coll; Professional.

JILEK, Elizabeth; Winnebago HS; Seward, IL; 21/115 ChrhWkr; HonRl; StuCncl; 4-H; FHA; GerCl; PpCl; GAA; 4-HAwd; Univ; Medicine.

JILEK, Michael J; Northwestern HS; Mellette, SD; Chrs; ChrhWkr; CncrtBnd; DrmMjrt; HonRl; Mdrgl; MrchBnd; Orch; SchPl; Bsktbl; Moorhead State Col; Music.

JILEK, Sandy J; Dassel Cokato HS; Cokato, MN; 92/138 Chr; DrlTm; HonRl; SchMus; TchrAde; RptrYrbk; SchPpr; FHA; GAA; 4-HAwd; Area Vo Tech.

JILES, Lauren; Kenwood HS; Chicago, IL; 57/413 HonRl; NatlMeritFnl; NatlMeritSF; SctActv; RptrSchPpr; Chrldr; GAA; Northwestern Univ; Tv Anchor Woman.

JILES, Shirley; Robert S Toner HS; Warren, MI; 2/250 SecJrCls; HonRl; NHS; SchAde; SchPl; StuGov; TchrAde; SpnCl; Univ; Math.

JILOT, Theresa M; Sevastopol HS; Sturgeon Bay, WI; VPSophCls; Band; DrmMjrt; MrchBnd; NHS; StuCncl; EdYrBk; SpnCl; Trk; Coll; Professional.

JIMENEZ, Jennifer; Redford HS; Detroit, MI; 27/625 NHS; NatlMeritCmnd; SchAde; RptrSchPpr; SchPpr; SpnCl; VoiceDemAwd; U Of Detroit; Communications.

JIMENEZ, Julio N; Willowbrook HS; Villa Park, IL; Chr; HonRl; NHS; Univ Of Illinois; Physical Therapy.

JIMENEZ, Paula; Sacred Heart Academy; Springfield, IL; 33/143 SecJrCls; PresSrCls; HonRl; StuCncl; PpCl; Illinois State U; Special Education.

JINDRA, Larry; Kiel HS; Kiel, WI; Band; ChrhWkr; NHS; NatlMeritSF; PepBnd; StuGov; SpnCl; Uw; Engineering.

JINKERSON, Darryl L; O Fallon Twp HS; O Fallon, IL; 7/352 Chrs; ChrhWkr; HonRl; SchPpr; MthCl; SciCl; LetterBsbl; LetterBsktbl; CchngActv; AmLegAwd; College; Bible.

JINRIGHT, Bonnie J; B C Central HS; Battle Creek, MI; 95/505 Chr; Chrs; HonRl; Kellogg Comm College; Criminal Justice.

JIPSON, Jeanne A; Nicolet HS; Milwaukee, WI; 2/513 Band; Chr; Chrs; CmntyWkr; CncrtBnd; MrchBnd; NatlMeritSF; SchMus; SchPl; YthFlsp; Coll; Special Ed.

JIROTKA, George M; Lyons Twp HS; Riverside, IL; HonRl; NatlMeritCmnd; Ftbl; LetterSwmmng; College; Corporate Lawyer.

JIROTKA, George M; Lyons Township HS; Riverside, IL; HonRl; NHS; NatlMeritCmnd; LetterSwmmng; Columbia Univ; Lawyer.

JOBB, David W; Lyons Twp HS; Western Springs, IL; PresChrhWkr; CmntyWkr; HonRl; MthCl; Ftbl; Wrstlng; College; Nuclear Physicist.

JOBE, Joann M; Waseca HS; Waseca, MN; Chr; HonRl; Mdrgl; SchMus; SchPl; EdYrBk; GAA; College.

JOBE, Sheila D; Harmony Community HS; Farmington, IA; 3/49 TrsSophCls; TrsJrCls; Band; ChrhWkr; DrmMjrt; HonRl; MrchBnd; Twrl; RptrYrbk; FHA; LetterBsbl; LetterBsktbl; Glf; LetterChrldr; Iowa State University.

JOBST, Roger H; Dexfield HS; Dexter, IA; 13/44 ALBoysSt; HonRl; YthFlsp; 4-H; FFA; Bsbl; Ftbl; Trk; Wrstlng; CitAwd; VoiceDemAwd; Iast Univ; Veterinary Medicine.

JOBST, Roy; Cherry Street HS; Earlham, IA; 44/49 PresFrshCls; HonRl; NHS; StuCncl; YthFlsp; RptrSchPpr; Trk; Ryder.

JOBST, Roy C; Earlham Community HS; Earlham, IA; 4/38 PresFrshCls; HonRl; NHS; StuCncl; PresFFA; LetterBsktbl; LetterFtbl; LetterTrk; Ryder Tech; Mechanics.

JOCHEM, John D; Catholic Boys HS; Quincy, IL; 18/70 HonRl; StuCncl; StuGov; EngCl; Coll; Prof.

JOCHIM, Jo L; Rock Port Rii HS; Rock Port, MO; TrsSophCls; SecSrCls; Chrs; SchPl; StuCncl; FHA; PpCl; Bsbl; DARAwd;.

JOCHIM, Kenneth A; Gibson Southern HS; Owensville, IN; 37/230 ALBoysSt; JrNHS; PresSciCl; OptClAwd; Purdue Univ; Veterinarian.

JOCHIM, Leone E; Malcolm HS; Lincoln, NE; SecFrshCls; VPSophCls; HonRl; NHS; SchPl; RptrYrbk; RptrSchPpr; 4-H; PpCl; LetterBsktbl; Chrldr; 4-HAwd; College; Accountant.

JOCHIM, Nancy J; Flasher HS; Flasher, ND; 1/39 SecSophCls; SecJrCls; SecSrCls; Band; SchPl; 4-H; VPFHA; BttyCrckrAwd; DanFAwd; 4-HAwd; Mary Col; Nursing.

JOCHIMSEN, Gail M; Medford Sr HS; Medford, WI; VPFrshCls; HonRl; NHS; OffAde; SpnCl; Trk; GAA; PresAwd; Medical Institute; Health Field.

JOCKEY, Liana D; Brown County HS; Nashville, IN; 9/206 DrlTm; HonRl; LbryAde; SchMus; TchrAde; SpnCl; PpCl; Principia College; Math.

JOCKISCH, Mary L; Easton HS; Easton, IL; 7/19 HonRl; SchPl; RptrSchPpr; 4-H; FHA; BttyCrckrAwd; Manmouth College; Nurse.

JOE, Larry D; Meridian HS; Alexandria, NE; 5/29 TrsSophCls; ALBoysSt; HonRl; OffAde; EdYrBk; SchPpr; LetterTrk; LetterWrstlng; Kearney St Clg; Phy Ed.

JOEDEMAN, Lucinda A; Stapleton Public HS; Gandy, NE; Chrs; ChrhWkr; HonRl; YthFlsp; 4-H; FHA; Trk; Chrldr; GAA; PPFtbl; College.

JOEKEL, Corey S; Lincoln East HS; Lincoln, NE; Band; ChrhWkr; HonRl; Orch; SchMus; YthFlsp; Bsktbl; LetterTrk; Clge; English & Social Studies.

JOELNER, F Eric; Belleville East HS; Belleville, IL; Band; CncrtBnd; HonRl; LitMag; MrchBnd; NatlMeritCmnd; PepBnd; SchMus; FrCl; College; Medicine.

JOELSON, Andrew J; Rich Twp E Campus HS; Park Forest, IL; 15/355 CncrtBnd; HonRl; NHS; NatlMeritCmnd; SctActv; Univ Of Il; Electrical Engineering.

JOELSON, Peter M S; Rich Twp E Campus HS; Park Forest, IL; HonRl; NHS; NatlMeritCmnd; Univ Of Il; Business Admin.

JOENS, Timothy J; Algona HS; Algona, IA; ALBoysSt; ChrhWkr; SctActv; TchrAde; YthFlsp; MthCl; PpCl; Ftbl; Trk; AmLegAwd; College; Profesional.

JOERGER, Janine; Mendota Township HS; Mendota, IL; Band; HonRl; LbryAde; MrchBnd; RptrSchPpr; SchPpr; FNA; Chrldr; GAA; IMSpt; Southern Ill U; Social Work.

JOERGER, Mark F; Henning Public HS; Vining, MN; VPSophCls; TrsJrCls; Band; HonRl; JrNHS; SchMus; StuCncl; RptrYrbk; FBLA; BauchLmbAwd; College; Business Ed.

JOERN, Brian D; Harlem North HS; Rockford, IL; Chr; Chrl; Chrs; ChrhWkr; HonRl; Mdrgl; SchMus; YthFlsp; Tennis; Trk; College; Professional.

JOERN, Karl; Houston HS; Houston, MO; 18/113 Band; NHS; SctActv; YthFlsp; RptrYrbk; SptEdSchPpr; 4-H; SciCl; Ftbl; Univ Of Mo; Geophysics.

JOESTGEN, Joe W; Mineral Point HS; Mineral Point, WI; 3/92 VPSophCls; ALBoysSt; HonRl; NHS; FFA; KeyCl; SciCl; LetterFtbl; LetterTrk; PresAwd; Univ Of Wisconsin; Elec Engineer.

JOHANN, Micki A; Collinsville HS; Collinsville, IL; 92/670 PresChrhWkr; HonRl; JrNHS; StuCncl; PpCl; Chrldr; PPFtbl; PresAwd; St Johns College; Nursing.

JOHANNES, Carol A; Morrill HS; Morrill, NE; 4/40 Chrs; ChrhWkr; LbryAde; NHS; NatlThespSoc; SchMus; SchPl; StuGov; YthFlsp; 4-H; FHA; PpCl; PPFtbl; Univ Of Nebraska; Human Dvpt.

JOHANNESEN, Debra L; Sentral Community HS; Bancroft, IA; 3/36 Band; Chr; Chrs; ChrhWkr; HonRl; SchMus; SchPl; 4-H; FTA; LetterBsktbl; Trk; 4-HAwd; College.

JOHANNESMAN, Ann K; Duchesne HS; St Charles, MO; Chr; Chrs; HonRl; NHS; SchAde; SchMus; SchPl; RptrYrbk; FrCl; PpCl; College; Math.

JOHANNINGMEIER, Jill A; Riverview Gardens HS; St Louis, MO; 15/800 Chr; HonRl; NHS; NatlMeritSF; OffAde; Orch; TchrAde; YthFlsp; PpCl; Southeast Mo State Univ; Education.

JOHANNINGSMEIER, Belinda G; North Knox HS; Sandborn, IN; 7/150 Band; ChrhWkr; HonRl; HospAde; NHS; PepBnd; YthFlsp; FHA; Vincennes Univ; Secretary.

JOHANNS, Jacquelyne; Platteville HS; Platteville, WI; 13/192 PresJrCls; AFS; CncrtBnd; HonRl; Mdrgl; SchMus; RptrSchPpr; PpCl; KiwanAwd; Univ Of Wi At Platteville; Jour.

JOHANNSEN, Bruce J; Bayard HS; Bayard, NE; PresSophCls; PresJrCls; VPSrCls; HonRl; NHS; SchPl; 4-H; LetterFtbl; LetterTrk; 4-HAwd; College; Agriculture.

JOHANNSEN, Joyce J; Garwin Comm HS; Garwin, IA; 1/32 SecSophCls; TrsJrCls; Band; Chrs; HonRl; MrchBnd; YthFlsp; 4-H; LetterBsktbl; 4-HAwd; College; Vocation.

JOHANNSEN, Kristin L; Pius Xi HS; Milwaukee, WI; LitMag; NatlMeritSF; TchrAde; College.

JOHANNSEN, Robert A; St Johns Military Academy; Downers Grove, IL; 1/39 PresJrCls; DrlTm; HonRl; JA; NHS; Quill&Scroll; ROTC; StuCncl; StuGov; RptrSchPpr; EdSchPpr; Swmmng; AmLegAwd; U S Naval Academy; Civil Engineer.

JOHANNSEN, Wanda L; Lake Central HS; Winfred, SD; 13/159 HonRl; NHS; YthFlsp; 4-H; TreasFHA; PpCl; Trk; GAA; Dakota St College.

JOHANSEN, Brenda; Moose Lake Public HS; Moose Lake, MN; 5/73 Chr; ChrhWkr; HonRl; NHS; OffAde; SchPl; RptrYrbk; 4-H; PpCl; Chrldr; Golden Valley Lutheran Coll; Social Work.

JOHANSEN, Joan T; Lancaster HS; Lancaster, WI; 21/160 ChrhWkr; HonRl; HospAde; SchMus; StuCncl; RptrYrbk; RptrSchPpr; MthCl; PpCl; GAA; Coll; Nursing.

JOHANSEN, Rebecca L; Littlefield Public HS; Brutus, MI; ChrhWkr; CmntyWkr; CncrtBnd; HonRl; MrchBnd; OffAde; PolWkr; StuGov; SchPpr; Bsktbl;.

JOHANSEN, Steven B; Cal Comm HS; Alexander, IA; SecFrshCls; Band; Chrs; HonRl; NHS; YthFlsp; SchPpr; LetterBsbl; LetterBsktbl; LetterTrk; U Of Northern Ia; Accounting.

JOHANSON, Berit E; Geneva Comm HS; Geneva, IL; 28/228 Chr; ChrhWkr; CmntyWkr; HonRl; Mdrgl; SchMus; SchPl; Augustana College.

JOHENGEN, Shirley; Akron Fairgrove HS; Caro, MI; 15/84 HonRl; LbryAde; SchPl; TchrAde; RptrYrbk; RptrSchPpr; Central Michigan Univ.

JOHN, Ann; Dundee Comm HS; Carpentersville, IL; Chrs; NatlFornLg; SecNatlThespSoc; SchPl; StuCncl; GerCl; Loyola Univ; Psychiatrist.

JOHN, Carol D; Ankeny HS; Ankeny, IA; Band; Chrs; HonRl; JrNHS; MrchBnd; NHS; FHA; FrCl; Coll; Curr Of Maj Stu.

JOHN, Ernest; Macomb Sr HS; Macomb, IL; 12/250 CncrtBnd; HonRl; MrchBnd; NatlMeritCmnd; PepBnd; SchMus; RptrSchPpr; IMSpt; Western Ill Univ; Business Major.

JOHN, Ernest K; Macomb Sr HS; Macomb, IL; 12/250 CncrtBnd; HonRl; MrchBnd; NHS; NatlMeritCmnd; PepBnd; SchMus; RptrSchPpr; W Illinois Univ; Business.

JOHN, Lori J; Notre Dame HS; River Forest, IL; 23/261 HonRl; NHS; SchPl; Tennis; IMSpt; College; Medical.

JOHNAS, Julia A; Medford Senior HS; Medford, WI; Chr; HonRl; LbryAde; NHS; NatlMeritSchl; SchMus; JAAwd; College; Professional.

JOHNES, Timothy W; Marquette HS; Godfrey, IL; 6/120 ALBoysSt; HonRl; NHS; Yrbk; LetterBsbl; LetterFtbl; St Benedictine College; Liberal Arts.

JOHNESEE, Patricia A; North Farmington HS; Farmington Hills, MI; 22/450 ALAGirlsSt; HonRl; NHS; OffAde; SchMus; SctActv; LetterSwmmng; Chrldr; CchngActv; GAA; Albion College; Biology.

JOHNMEYER, Tina M; Fayette HS; Fayette, MO; 17/67 HonRl; NHS; OffAde; PresStuCncl; RptrYrbk; SchPpr; VPFTA; OptClAwd; New Mexico St Univ; Conservation.

JOHNS, Alice E; Washington Community HS; Washington, IL; 79/345 RptrYrbk; RptrSchPpr; PpCl; Chrldr; Siu; Design, Phys. Ed..

JOHNS, Carolyn; W G Mather HS; Wetmore, MI; HonRl; NHS; SchPl; PpCl; Bsktbl; PPFtbl;.

JOHNS, Cheryl L; Thornton Township HS; Riverdale, IL; 5/800 HonRl; JA; JrNHS; NHS; NatlMeritFnl; OffAde; PolWkr; StuCncl; AmLegAwd; ChmbCommrsAwd; Busi Sch; Executive Sec.

JOHNS, Deborah J; Tarkio HS; Grandview, MO; 18/65 SecSrCls; Band; Chrs; CncrtBnd; NHS; SchMus; Twrl; YthFlsp; Bsktbl; Swmmng; Trk; Nw Missouri St University.

JOHNS, Harry M; Centralia HS; Centralia, IL; 35/360 TrsJrCls; HonRl; Quill&Scroll; StuCncl; KeyCl; FrCl; Glf; South Ill Univ; Journalism.

JOHNS, Jeff; Reading HS; Reading, KS; Chrs; HonRl; StuCncl; TchrAde; 4-H; EngCl; College.

JOHNS, Margaret A; Charleston HS; Charleston, IL; AFS; Band; Chrs; CncrtBnd; MrchBnd; SchMus; StuCncl; 4-H; GAA; Eastern Ill Univ; Home Economics.

JOHNS, Mary A; Delavan HS; Delavan, IL; 5/55 ALAGirlsSt; Band; HonRl; MrchBnd; OffAde; TchrAde; YthFlsp; RptrSchPpr; SciCl; Mac Murray College; Science.

JOHNS, Ricky R; Dixon HS; Dixon, MO; Band; CncrtBnd; PresFrshCls; LbryAde; MrchBnd; PepBnd; SchPl; StuCncl; Glf; IMSpt; Univ Of Mo.

JOHNSEN, Dave L; East Leyden HS; Franklin Park, IL; HonRl; NHS; RptrYrbk; Northern Ill Univ; Law.

JOHNSEN, Deborah A; Wilcox Public HS; Wilcox, NE; 7/26 PresFrshCls; Band; Chrs; NHS; Orch; PresStuCncl; EdYrBk; RptrSchPpr; PresPpCl; Trk; Col; Pyscology.

JOHNSEN, Debra A; Good Counsel HS; Chicago, IL; 28/286 Chr; ChrhWkr; HonRl; TreasJA; SctActv; SpnCl; SciCl; GAA; IMSpt; JAAwd; College; Pharmacy.

JOHNSEN, Julaine M; Kenowa Hills HS; Grand Rapids, MI; Band; CncrtBnd; HonRl; MrchBnd; NHS; TchrAde; 4-H; CaptGlf; GAA; Ferris State College; Marketing.

JOHNSEN, Scott M; Luther South HS; Chicago, IL; 58/260 Aud/Vis; Band; CncrtBnd; DrlTm; DrmMjrt; MrchBnd; PepBnd; GerCl; Bsktbl; IMSpt; Ill State Univ; Architect.

JOHNSON, Alan; East Monona HS; Moorhead, IA; Band; Chr; Chrs; ChrhWkr; CncrtBnd; HonRl; MrchBnd; PepBnd; Bsbl; Ftbl; Trade School;vocation.

JOHNSON, Alan L; Truman HS; Independence, MO; RedCrAde; SctActv; CaptSwmmng; Kansas U; Architect Engr.

JOHNSON, Amy L; Pioneer HS; Ann Arbor, MI; 54/641 HonRl; NatlMeritCmnd; Orch; SchMus; MthCl; Albion Coll; Medical Field.

JOHNSON, Andrea L; Plaza HS; Plaza, ND; 2/12 Band; Chrs; DrlTm; HonRl; SchPl; EdYrBk; EdSchPpr; 4-H; FHA; 4-HAwd; College.

JOHNSON, Andrew; Grantsburg HS; Grantsburg, WI; VPSophCls; Band; Chr; SchPl; StuCncl; Yrbk; RotaryAwd; College; Advertising Or Drama.

JOHNSON, Ann; Jacksonville HS; Literberry, IL; 64/352 Chr; HonRl; FrCl; PPFtbl; Illinois College; Coach.

JOHNSON, Ann C; Steinmetz HS; Chicago, IL; HonRl; OffAde; ROTC; SchAde; TchrAde; FDA; KeyCl; GAA; IMSpt; Univ Of Illinois; English.

JOHNSON, Anne E; Forest Lake Sr HS; Forest Lake, MN; 3/345 Band; CncrtBnd; HonRl; MrchBnd; NHS; PepBnd; Quill&Scroll; Yrbk; LetterTennis; LetterTrk; College; Dental Hygiene.

JOHNSON, Annie R; Saginaw HS; Saginaw, MI; 6/435 ChrhWkr; PresCmntyWkr; HonRl; LbryAde; TreasNHS; OffAde; SchAde; SecStuCncl; Teen; RptrYrbk; EdSchPpr; Morris Brown College; Business Administrati.

JOHNSON, Arnold A; E St Louis Sr HS; E St Louis, IL; 47/896 HonRl; JA; JrNHS; StuCncl; SptEdYrbk; 4-H; LatCl; MthCl; Ftbl; IMSpt; JAAwd; Illinois St Univ; Medicine.

JOHNSON, Arthur V; New Trier East HS; Glencoe, IL; 189/847 ChrhWkr; HonRl; StuCncl; SciCl; College; Medical Research.

JOHNSON, Autumn E; Balyki HS; Chandlerville, IL; 4/24 VPJrCls; VPSrCls; ChrhWkr; HonRl; JA; LbryAde; NHS; OffAde; SchPl; StuCncl; RptrYrbk; RptrSchPpr; FHA; PpCl;.

JOHNSON, Barbara; Wheaton Warrenville Hs; Wheaton, IL; 100/212 ChrhWkr; CmntyWkr; HonRl; SchMus; StuCncl; TchrAde; Yrbk; GerCl; College Of Dupage;business Management.

JOHNSON, Barbara G; Pelican Rapids HS; Rothsay, MN; ChrhWkr; HonRl; LbryAde; NHS; OffAde; SctActv; TchrAde; FBLA; PpCl; CitAwd; Us Air Force; Social Sci.

JOHNSON, Barbara J; Routt HS; Franklin, IL; 10/62 Chrs; HonRl; SctActv; 4-H; FNA; SpnCl; PpCl; CaptChrldr; Springfield Jr Clg; Dental Technician.

JOHNSON, Barbara L; Sully Buttes HS; Blunt, SD; SecFrshCls; Band; Chr; ChrhWkr; HonRl; StuCncl; Yrbk; RptrSchPpr; Chrldr; Col; Special Education.

JOHNSON, Barbara S; O Fallon Township HS; O Fallon, IL; 4/301 HonRl; ModUN; TreasNHS; PresFHA; SpnCl; Mc Kendree College; Radiology.

JOHNSON, Barry A; Lincoln Sr HS; Bloomington, MN; 45/580 ChrhWkr; CmntyWkr; HonRl; ModUN; NHS; NatlMeritFnl; NatlMeritSF; Quill&Scroll; SchMus; SchPl; LetterSwmmng; College; Professional.

JOHNSON, Barry L; Marshall Sr HS; Marshall, WI; 4/68 Band; HonRl; NHS; RptrSchPpr; SchPpr; Bsbl; Bsktbl; Ftbl; Glf; Uw Madison; Bus Mang.

JOHNSON, Bernadette; St Scholastic HS; Chicago, IL; Aud/Vis; Chr; JA; LbryAde; NatlMeritCmnd; TchrAde; PpCl; Marq U; Psychology.

JOHNSON, Brad; Ottawa HS; Ottawa, IL; LitMag; PolWkr; College;.

JOHNSON, Brad L; Callao C 8 HS; Callao, MO; VPSophCls; Band; ChrhWkr; CmntyWkr; HonRl; MrchBnd; SchAde; StuCncl; CivCl; Bsbl; Tech School; Air Conditioning Technician.

JOHNSON, Bradley A; Dassei Cokato HS; Cokato, MN; HonRl; JrNHS; LbryAde; NHS; Bsktbl; CaptFtbl; Glf; AmLegAwd; College.

JOHNSON, Bradley C; Waverly Shell Rock Sr HS; Waverly, IA; VPSrCls; HonRl; StuCncl; CaptBsktbl; Ftbl; Trk; ChmbCommrsAwd; Univ Of No Iowa; Business.

JOHNSON, Bradley R; Downers Grove South HS; Downers Grove, IL; Band; HonRl; MrchBnd; NHS; SctActv; Univ Of Illinois; Dentistry.

JOHNSON, Brady N; Interlochen Arts Academy; Kalamazoo, MI; Chr; Chrl; HonRl; U Of Mi; Music.

JOHNSON, Brenda A; Jefferson West HS; Meriden, KS; Band; HonRl; PepBnd; YthFlsp; Yrbk; SchPpr; 4-H; FHA; 4-HAwd; Kansas State Univ; Home Economics.

JOHNSON, Brenda L; Forman HS; Manito, IL; ChrhWkr; CmntyWkr; HospAde; NHS; PolWkr; RedCrAde; SchAde; StuCncl; YthFlsp; YthLg; Vocation.

JOHNSON, Brenda L; Millington HS; Millington, MI; 8/167 Band; HonRl; LbryAde; NHS; TchrAde; Chrldr; Mott Coll; Secretary.

JOHNSON, Brenda R; Iowa Falls HS; Iowa Falls, IA; 33/148 HonRl; NatlThespSoc; SchMus; Sdlty; StuCncl; UNYO; YthFlsp; RptrSchPpr; FHA; Business; Professional.

JOHNSON, Brent D; Columbia City Joint HS; Columbia City, IN; YthFlsp; SpnCl; Bsbl; LetterBsktbl; College; Teacher.

JOHNSON, Brian; Parker HS; Chicago, IL; Aud/Vis; Band; CmntyWkr; CncrtBnd; HonRl; JA; MrchBnd; StuCncl; CitAwd; Northwestern Univ; Dentist.

JOHNSON, Brian A; Hamburg Community HS; Hamburg, IA; Band; Chr; Chrl; Chrs; CncrtBnd; MrchBnd; PepBnd; SchMus; SciCl; College; Music.

JOHNSON, Brian K; Memorial HS; Eau Claire, WI; 7/450 PresJrCls; ALBoysSt; NHS; NatlMeritSF; PolWkr; StuCncl; StuGov; SciCl; CaptBsktbl; College; Pre Law.

JOHNSON, Brian K; On HS; Oshkosh, WI; NatlMeritSF; SctActv; StuGov; MthCl; SciCl; U Of Wi; Medicine.

JOHNSON, Brian L; Carpio HS; Carpio, ND; ALBoysSt; CncrtBnd; HonRl; JrNHS; NHS; Bsktbl; Ftbl; AmLegAwd; 4-HAwd; CitAwd; Wabpton Nd; Electrician.

JOHNSON, Bruce; Bowdon Public HS; Bowdon, ND; VPJrCls; SchPl; Bsbl; Bsktbl; Ftbl; Trade School; Vocational.

JOHNSON, Bruce; New Ulm Senior HS; New Ulm, MN; 54/234 PresFrshCls; TrsSophCls; PresJrCls; PresSrCls; StuCncl; Bsbl; Bsktbl; Ftbl; College.

JOHNSON, Bryan J; Almont HS; Almont, ND; 1/7 PresJrCls; Chrs; ChrhWkr; HonRl; JA; JrNHS; SchPl; SctActv; RptrYrbk; 4-H; PpCl; Bsktbl; College.

JOHNSON, Carlton; Oak Park River Forest HS; Oak Park, IL; 348/1072 SecTrsFrshCls; HonRl; ModUN; NatlFornLg; SctActv; StuCncl; FrCl; University; History.

JOHNSON, Carlton W; Penney HS; Hamilton, MO; 36/76 HonRl; RptrSchPpr; SchPpr; FFA; Bsbl; LetterBsktbl; CaptFtbl; LetterGlf; LetterTrk; LetterWrstlng; College; Sports.

JOHNSON, Carol A; East HS; Kansas City, MO; 2/246 ChrhWkr; HonRl; JrNHS; LitMag; ROTC; SchAde; SctActv; PresStuCncl; TchrAde; YthLg; BttyCrckrAwd; College; Doctor.

JOHNSON, Carol A; Fessenden HS; Fessenden, ND; 1/48 ChrhWkr; CncrtBnd; HonRl; MrchBnd; PepBnd; SciCl; Bsbl; CaptBsktbl; Swmmng; IMSpt; N Dakota St Univ; Pharmacy.

JOHNSON, Carol E; St Barbara HS; Chicago, IL; Chr; HonRl; SchPl; StuCncl; RptrYrbk; SchPpr; PpCl; GAA; U Of Illinois; Special Education.

JOHNSON, Carolee E; Langford HS; Langford, SD; SecSrCls; Chr; Chrs; PresHospAde; LbryAde; SchPl; Yrbk; Pres4-H; PresFNA; Bsktbl; Sd St Univ; Modeling.

JOHNSON, Carol L; Gilmore City Bradgate HS; Bradgate, IA; 2/32 TrsFrshCls; SecSrCls; Band; Chrs; ChrhWkr; CncrtBnd; HonRl; MrchBnd; VPNHS; PepBnd; SchMus; SchPl; StuCncl; LetterBsktbl; 4-HAwd; Iowa State Univ; Home Economics.

JOHNSON, Carol L; Mundelein HS; Mundelein, IL; 4/400 HonRl; LitMag; NHS; Quill&Scroll; RptrYrbk; RptrSchPpr; University; Medicine.

JOHNSON, Cathy L; West Sioux Comm HS; Hawarden, IA; Band; Chr; Chrs; ChrhWkr; CncrtBnd; HonRl; MrchBnd; Orch; PepBnd; SchMus; College; Teaching.

JOHNSON, C David; Ottawa Township HS; Ottawa, IL; 12/426 HonRl; NatlFornLg; NHS; NatlMeritCmnd; LetterGlf; Trk; Univ; Physics.

JOHNSON, Charles C; Geneva Community HS; Geneva, IL; 16/220 HonRl; IntrClCncl; NHS; SchPpr; SpnCl; Aurora Clg; Accounting.

JOHNSON, Charles M; Winnetonka HS; Liberty, MO; Aud/Vis; HonRl; LitMag; NatlFornLg; NatlMeritFnl; GerCl; Univ Of Kansas; Medicine.

JOHNSON, Charles R; Huntington North HS; Huntington, IN; 1/587 PresSophCls; ALBoysSt; ChrhWkr; PresStuCncl; Bsktbl; LetterTrk; Purdue Univ; Veterinarian.

JOHNSON, Cheryl; Exira HS; Brayton, IA; HonRl; PolWkr; SchMus; Yrbk; 4-H; FHA; FTA; Tennis; 4-HAwd; CitAwd; Iowa State Univ; Home Ec.

JOHNSON, Cheryl; Hudson Senior Hs; Hudson, WI; Chr; HonRl; SchMus; TchrAde; SchPpr; VP4-H; Chrldr; GAA; 4-HAwd;.

JOHNSON, Cheryl A; Circle HS; Benton, KS; Chr; Chrs; ChrhWkr; CmntyWkr; HonRl; JA; RedCrAde; ROTC; Teen; YthFlsp; SciCl; IMSpt; College; Vocation.

JOHNSON, Cheryl L; New Haven HS; New Baltimore, MI; Chrs; HonRl; OffAde; SchAde; TchrAde; RptrSchPpr; SchPpr; FrCl; PpCl; IMSpt; University; Professional.

JOHNSON, Chris; Wahpeton Senior HS; Wahpeton, ND; ChrhWkr; HonRl; NHS; YthFlsp; FFA; Bsbl; Bsktbl; Ftbl; Trk; CchngActv; Trade School; Preduction Agriculture.

JOHNSON, Chris A; Diamond HS; Diamond, MO; ChrhWkr; CmntyWkr; HonRl; 4-H; Bsktbl; LetterTrk; 4-HAwd;.

JOHNSON, Chris A; Wahpeton Sr HS; Wahpeton, ND; ChrhWkr; CmntyWkr; HonRl; NHS; StuCncl; YthFlsp; FFA; Bsbl; Bsktbl; Ftbl; Trk; Trade School; Agriculture.

JOHNSON, Christopher G; Buhler Rural HS; Hutchinson, KS; TrsJrCls; PresSrCls; HonRl; SchAde; TchrAde; RptrSchPpr; SpnCl; LetterBsktbl; LetterFtbl; LetterTrk; Sw Clge Winfield; Business.

JOHNSON, Cindy A; Dexter HS; Dexter, KS; VPFrshCls; SecTrsJrCls; CncrtBnd; HonRl; MrchBnd; NHS; OffAde; Orch; SchAde; SchMus; Bsktbl; Trk; Chrldr; College; Accounting.

JOHNSON, Claudia F; Elmhurst HS; Ft Wayne, IN; 41/400 SecJrCls; SecTrsSrCls; ALAGirlsSt; Band; Chr; HonRl; HospAde; StuCncl; StuGov; College; Communications.

JOHNSON, Colleen; Nokomis HS; Morrisonville, IL; Chr; PepBnd; ChrhWkr; HonRl; SchMus; FHA; Chrldr; GAA; 4-HAwd; College; Cur Of Major Study.

JOHNSON, Colleen R; Milan HS; Montevideo, MN; 6/31 Band; Chr; Orch; SchPl; RptrYrbk; SchPpr; 4-H; FHA; PpCl; Moorhead State Univ; Medical Technology.

JOHNSON, Connie; Radcliffe Community HS; Radcliffe, IA; 12/34 ALAGirlsSt; Band; Chrs; CncrtBnd; HonRl; MrchBnd; NatlThespSoc; Bsktbl; Trk; Chrldr; Waldorf College; Social Science.

JOHNSON, Constance M; Kinmundy Alma Comm HS; Alma, IL; 3/56 HonRl; NHS; Sec4-H; FHA; SecFrCl; LetterBsktbl; GAA; College; Home Economics.

JOHNSON, Constance; Woodstock Hs; Woodstock, IL; 12/270 AFS; HonRl; NHS; NatlMeritCmnd; StuCncl; Yrbk; Carleton College; Psychology.

JOHNSON, Constance S; Marlette HS; Marlette, MI; SecFrshCls; Chr; HonRl; NHS; RptrYrbk; FBLA; PpCl; LetterChrldr; Western Michigan University; Business.

JOHNSON, Craig; Beaver Dam Senior HS; Beaver Dam, WI; ChrhWkr; RptrSchPpr; CchngActv; IMSpt; College; Broadcasting.

JOHNSON, Curt; Belvidere Hs; Belvidere, IL; HonRl; LetterBsbl; Illinois State U; Math Major.

JOHNSON, Cynthia A; Elkhorn Kimballton Comm HS; Exira, IA; Band; Chrs; CncrtBnd; DrmMjrt; Mdrgl; MrchBnd; PepBnd; SchMus; FHA; LetterBsktbl; GAA; Bishop Clarkson Sch; Nurse.

JOHNSON, Cynthia A; W C HS; Webster City, IA; ChrhWkr; CncrtBnd; HonRl; MrchBnd; PepBnd; RedCrAde; SctActv; TchrAde; Pres4-H; FTA; PpCl; Trk; Chrldr; 4-HAwd; Iowa State Univ; Education.

JOHNSON, Cynthia D; Oklee Public HS; Oklee, MN; PresSophCls; Chrs; ChrhWkr; HonRl; PolWkr; SchPl; RptrSchPpr; 4-H; FHA; 4-HAwd; Business Sch; Secretary.

JOHNSON, Dale H; James H Bowen HS; Chicago, IL; 1/571 Aud/Vis; Band; CncrtBnd; HonRl; NHS; NatlMeritCmnd; NatlSciFnd; Orch; SchAde; FSA; MthCl; SciCl; CaptSwmmng; JETSAwd; California Inst Tech; Engineering.

JOHNSON, Dale K; Montevideo Senior HS; Montevideo, MN; Band; CncrtBnd; HonRl; MrchBnd; StuCncl; CaptBsbl; Ftbl; IMSpt;.

JOHNSON, Dale M; Wahpeton HS; Wahpeton, ND; Band; CncrtBnd; LbryAde; MrchBnd; PepBnd; SchPl; PpCl; Ftbl; Swmmng; IMSpt; Coll; Business Management.

JOHNSON, Daniel C; North Branch HS; Harris, MN; 3/120 HonRl; NHS; NatlMeritCmnd; SchPl; StuCncl; TchrAde; CaptBsbl; CaptBsktbl; BttyCrckrAwd; College; Natural Sci.

JOHNSON, Daniel G; Pittsburg HS; Pittsburg, KS; NatlFornLg; NatlMeritCmnd; PolWkr; SchPl; StuCncl; FrCl; Writing, Teaching.

JOHNSON, Daniel J; Morris Sr HS; Donnelly, MN; HonRl; NHS; SancSoc; CaptBsbl; CaptFtbl; LetterWrstlng; IMSpt; CitAwd; University Of Minnesota; Law.

JOHNSON, Daniel S; Morton HS; Morton, IL; Band; ChrhWkr; CncrtBnd; HonRl; MrchBnd; TchrAde; SciCl; LetterTennis; College; Medicine.

JOHNSON, Darla J; Willow Community HS; Washta, IA; 5/38 SecSophCls; TrsSophCls; HonRl; LbryAde; NHS; SchPl; EdYrBk; SchPpr; Bsktbl; Trk; College; Accounting.

JOHNSON, David; Central HS; Duluth, MN; 29/437 Band; ChrhWkr; CncrtBnd; HonRl; NHS; SchMus; SchPl; StuCncl; RotaryAwd; Umd; Engineering.

JOHNSON, David A; Marion Adams HS; Sheridan, IN; 10/99 Chr; HonRl; JrNHS; NHS; YthFlsp; FSA; LatCl; SciCl; LetterSwmmng; CaptTrk; Ball State Univ; Pharmacist.

JOHNSON, David E; Caledonia HS; Caledonia, MN; Aud/Vis; HonRl; SctActv; Bsbl; LetterBsktbl; LetterFtbl; LetterGlf; College.

JOHNSON, David L; Robinson HS; Robinson, IL; 28/186 ChrhWkr; HonRl; LetterBsbl; Illinois State Univ; Accounting.

JOHNSON, David M; Newton HS; Newton, IL; 18/181 Aud/Vis; Band; Chrs; CncrtBnd; HonRl; MrchBnd; NHS; PepBnd; PolWkr; SchMus; SchPl; College; Law.

JOHNSON, David M; Washington Park HS; Racine, WI; 41/650 AFS; ChrhWkr; CmntyWkr; HonRl; HospAde; JrNHS; NHS; NatlMeritSF; PolWkr; RedCrAde; SchMus; SchPl; Univ Of Wisc; Medicine.

JOHNSON, David P; Hancock Central HS; Hancock, MI; 9/92 VPFrshCls; ChrhWkr; HonRl; SchPl; YthFlsp; Bsbl; Bsktbl; Ftbl; Swmmng; Michigan Tech Univ; Biology.

JOHNSON, David P; Clarkfield HS; Clarkfield, MN; 1/45 Chr; ChrhWkr; HonRl; SchPl; TreasFTA; Sw Minn St Coll; Business Management.

JOHNSON, David R; Red Wing Central HS; Red Wing, MN; HonRl; YthLg; CaptBsbl; Bsktbl; Ftbl; College.

JOHNSON, David W; Thornridge HS; Burnham, IL; 47/649 HonRl; NHS; NatlThespSoc; Illinois Inst Of Tech; Medicine.

JOHNSON, Dawn E; Prairie Farm HS; Prairie Farm, WI; 1/35 Band; Chrs; ChrhWkr; HonRl; NHS; SchPl; Twrl; EdSchPpr; PresFHA; Chrldr; College; Social Work.

JOHNSON, Dean; Sycamore HS; Sycamore, IL; 46/230 Chr; ChrhWkr; CncrtBnd; HonRl; JCC; MrchBnd; PepBnd; FFA; Junior College; Farming.

JOHNSON, Dean A; New Hampton Comm HS; Alta Vista, IA; FFA; Bsktbl; Ftbl; Augustana College.

JOHNSON, Dean H; Sycamore HS; Sycamore, IL; 46/236 Band; VPChrhWkr; CncrtBnd; HonRl; JCC; MrchBnd; PepBnd; PresFFA; Jr College; Farming.

JOHNSON, Deanna R; Concordia HS; Ames, KS; Band; Chr; ChrhWkr; HonRl; StuCncl; Twrl; YthFlsp; FBLA; FTA; 4-HAwd; College.

JOHNSON, Dean W; Greensburg Comm HS; Greensburg, IN; PresSophCls; SchPl; YthFlsp; SchPpr; 4-H; PpCl; Bsbl; Ftbl; LetterTrk; IMSpt; Purdue Univ; Ag Econ Advisor.

JOHNSON, Deatte D; Bowdon HS; Bowdon, ND; 7/18 SecTrsSrCls; Band; HonRl; PepBnd; SchPl; PpCl; CaptBsbl; Bsktbl; IMSpt; 4-HAwd; College; Receptionist.

JOHNSON, Debara; Raymond Public HS; Raymond, MN; SecSrCls; Band; Chr; HonRl; LbryAde; MrchBnd; PepBnd; SchPl; RptrSchPpr;.

JOHNSON, Debbie A; O Fallon Township HS; O Fallon, IL; Clg; Law Enforcement.

JOHNSON, Debbie L; Kearney HS; Kearney, NE; HonRl; Orch; SctActv; TchrAde; College; Interior Design.

JOHNSON, Debbi L; Kapaun Mt Carmel HS; Wichita, KS; Band; CncrtBnd; HonRl; MrchBnd; Orch; PepBnd; StuCncl; Col;.

JOHNSON, Deborah; Mt Pleasant HS; Rosebush, MI; 1/328 VPJrCls; Band; HonRl; NHS; StuCncl; PpCl; DARAwd; Mich Univ; Nursing.

JOHNSON, Deborah J; Faulkner HS; Chicago, IL; PresSophCls; PresJrCls; ChrhWkr; HonRl; JrNHS; NatlThespSoc; VPStuGov; EdYrBk; RptrSchPpr; FrCl; GAA; University; Professional.

JOHNSON, Deborah L; Crown Point HS; Crown Point, IN; 13/450 HonRl; NHS; OffAde; TchrAde; LetterTrk; IMSpt; PPFtbl; AmLegAwd; KiwanAwd; Secretary.

JOHNSON, Deborah R; Beaver Dam Sr HS; Beaver Dam, WI; ALAGirlsSt; Chr; Chrs; ChrhWkr; SchMus; StuCncl; Univ Of Wisconsin; Nursing.

JOHNSON, Debra; Lutheran HS; Detroit, MI; HonRl; NHS; TchrAde; LatCl; PPFtbl; AmLegAwd; Univ; Nursing.

JOHNSON, Debra A; Maine East HS; Des Plaines, IL; Chr; ChrhWkr; HonRl; VPJrNHS; TchrAde; YthFlsp; George Williams College; Recreation Admin.

JOHNSON, Debra D; Tekonsha HS; Tekonsha, MI; 2/41 SecSophCls; Band; CncrtBnd; DrmMjrt; HonRl; MrchBnd; NatlMeritCmnd; PepBnd; SecStuCncl; StuGov; Mi State Univ; Dietetics.

JOHNSON, Debra S; Cambridge HS; Cambridge, IL; 2/59 PresSrCls; Chrs; DrlTm; HonRl; SecNHS; SchPl; StuCncl; RptrYrbk; PpCl; 4-HAwd; Western Ill Univ; Teacher.

JOHNSON, Debra S; Carterville HS; Carterville, IL; CncrtBnd; HonRl; PolWkr; FrCl; PpCl; Business Schl; Secretary.

JOHNSON, Debra S; O Neill Public HS; Page, NE; SchMus; TchrAde; Yrbk; 4-H; PpCl; Trk; Bus Sch; Accounting.

JOHNSON, Denise M; Brainerd HS; Brainerd, MN; Band; CncrtBnd; HonRl; MrchBnd; TchrAde; Tennis; Chrldr; PPFtbl; Community.

JOHNSON, Dennis A; Beresford HS; Beresford, SD; ALBoysSt; HonRl; Bsbl; LetterBsktbl; Ftbl; College; Teacher.

JOHNSON, Dennis W; La Crosse HS; Lc Crosse, KS; 3/35 TrsFrshCls; HonRl; ModUN; Sacrstn; SchPl; SctActv; Sdlty; 4-H; Bsktbl; IMSpt; Kansas St Univ; Chemical Engineering.

JOHNSON, Desiree S; North Boone HS; Capron, IL; 28/101 Chrs; HonRl; SchMus; StuCncl; Twrl; Yrbk; GerCl; PpCl; GAA; College; Teaching.

JOHNSON, Diana L; Cumberland HS; Cumberland, WI; 9/105 HonRl; NHS; StuCncl; RptrYrbk; RptrSchPpr; SpnCl; Bsktbl; Trk; Chrldr; GAA; Marquette Univ; Medicine.

JOHNSON, Diana S; Larkin HS; Elgin, IL; 6/622 PresSrCls; HonRl; StuGov; Bsktbl; LetterTennis; DARAwd; Univ Of Illinois.

JOHNSON, Diane; Washington Twp HS; Valparaiso, IN; 2/29 ALAGirlsSt; HonRl; SchAde; SchPpr; SpnCl; Bsktbl; Trk; Chrldr; 4-HAwd; VoiceDemAwd; Purdue Univ; Nursing Administration.

JOHNSON, Diane M; Mundelein HS; Mundelein, IL; 1/376 PresJrCls; Chrs; HonRl; LitMag; NHS; NatlMeritSF; SchPl; StuGov; RptrSchPpr; EdSchPpr; Marquette U; Medical Technology.

JOHNSON, Donald G; Elk Grove HS; Elk Grove Village, IL; 9/505 HonRl; NatlMeritFnl; PolWkr; CivCl; PresKeyCl; SciCl; Swmmng; Trk; JCAwd; Northeastern Il Univ; Biochemistry.

JOHNSON, Donald L; Roseville Unit HS; Roseville, IL; 10/53 ChrhWkr; CncrtBnd; HonRl; MrchBnd; PepBnd; SctActv; SpnCl; PpCl; LetterBsktbl; LetterFtbl; University; Professional.

JOHNSON, Donald L; Broken Bow HS; Broken Bow, NE; Bsbl; Bsktbl; Ftbl; Trk; Univ Of Nebr; Farming.

JOHNSON, Doris R; Luther HS; Onalaska, WI; Band; Chr; ChrhWkr; CmntyWkr; CncrtBnd; HonRl; MrchBnd; Orch; PepBnd; YthFlsp; College; Elementary Teacher.

JOHNSON, Douglas A; Illiopolis HS; Illiopolis, IL; 2/42 PresFrshCls; PresSophCls; PresJrCls; PresSrCls; HonRl; NHS; NatlMeritSchl; TchrAde; Bsbl; Bsktbl; Trk; College.

JOHNSON, Douglas A; Rockford East HS; Rockford, IL; 69/630 Band; CncrtBnd; HonRl; MrchBnd; NHS; PepBnd; TchrAde; LatCl; Wheaton College; Doctor.

JOHNSON, Douglas B; Russell Community HS; Charitian, IA; Chr; ChrhWkr; LbryAde; Yrbk; Ftbl; PPFtbl; College; Forestry.

JOHNSON, Douglas D; Sacred Heart Public HS; Sacred Heart, MN; VPFrshCls; SecJrCls; Band; Chr; ChrhWkr; CncrtBnd; HonRl; MrchBnd; PepBnd; SctActv; Aflbs Bible School; Farming.

JOHNSON, Douglas D; Atlanta Ciii HS; Atlanta, MO; VPJrCls; PresBand; HonRl; LetterBsbl; LetterBsktbl; College; Dentistry.

JOHNSON, Douglas E; Bushnell Prairie City HS; Bushnell, IL; 9/91 PresSrCls; Band; Chr; Chrs; CncrtBnd; HonRl; MrchBnd; PepBnd; SchMus; SchPl; SctActv; Ftbl; Glf; Western Illinois Univ; Actor.

JOHNSON, Douglas K; Kenwood HS; Chicago, IL; 23/413 Band; CncrtBnd; HonRl; NHS; NatlMeritCmnd; NatlMeritSF; ChmnFtbl; Trk; IMSpt; Harvard; Architecture.

JOHNSON, Dwight S; Park River HS; Park River, ND; 1/62 HonRl; PresStuCncl; TreasFFA; LetterTrk; North Dakota St Univ; Pharmacy.

JOHNSON, Eileen M; Mother Of Sorrows HS; Chicago, IL; HospAde; PolWkr; SchMus; StuCncl; TchrAde; PpCl; PresGAA; IMSpt; VoiceDemAwd; College; Vocation.

JOHNSON, Elizabeth A; Stanton Community HS; Stanton, IA; 1/35 PresSrCls; DrmMjrt; HonRl; NatlMeritSF; StuCncl; EdYrBk; 4-H; Bsktbl; Trk; CaptChrldr; Coll; Teacher.

JOHNSON, Elizabeth E; Lincoln Comm HS; Lincoln, IL; 2/255 Chrs; ChrhWkr; HonRl; NHS; SchMus; PresFrCl; Bsktbl; Trk; Univ Of Illinois; Childhood Development.

JOHNSON, Eric; Jefferson City Sr HS; Jefferson Cy, MO; 21/600 Band; ChrhWkr; CncrtBnd; HonRl; JA; JrNHS; LitMag; MrchBnd; NatlMeritFnl; NatlMeritSF; IMSpt; JAAwd; College; Research Theoretician.

JOHNSON, Eric D; Sandwich Comm HS; Sandwich, IL; PresSophCls; PresSrCls; ALBoysSt; HonRl; NHS; NatlMeritCmnd; Orch; SctActv; LatCl; LetterBsktbl; CaptTrk; College; Engineering.

JOHNSON, Eric D; Eleva Strum Central HS; Eleva, WI; 21/73 SecSophCls; VPJrCls; Aud/Vis; ChrhWkr; CmntyWkr; HonRl; SchAde; SchPl; TchrAde; 4-H; LetterBsbl; CaptBsktbl; Trk; CchngActv; University Of Wisconsin; Art.

JOHNSON, Evonne; Lincoln HS; Demoines, IA; HonRl; StuCncl;.

JOHNSON, Fay E; Allison Bristow Comm HS; Allison, IA; 5/47 TrsJrCls; Chr; Chrs; ChrhWkr; HonRl; HospAde; Mdrgl; SchMus; StuCncl; FNA; Memorial Schl; Nurse.

JOHNSON, Fayrene; Josephinum HS; Chicago, IL; 19/100 VPFrshCls; PresSophCls; ChrhWkr; CmntyWkr; HonRl; LitMag; NatlMeritSF; RedCrAde; SchPl; StuCncl; Lewis Univ; Professional.

JOHNSON, Gail; East Charles Mix HS; Wagner, SD; TrsJrCls; Chrs; ChrhWkr; HonRl; PepBnd; Yrbk; FNA; Dakota Weslyn Univ; Nursing.

JOHNSON, Gail S; Richland HS; Richland, MO; 2/65 PresSrCls; Band; Chrs; HonRl; StuCncl; RptrYrbk; EdYrBk; RptrSchPpr; FHA; FTA; CaptBsbl; CaptBsktbl; IMSpt; Drury Col; Music.

JOHNSON, Gayle R; Forest Lake Sr HS; Forest Lake, MN; 16/363 SecJrCls; SecSrCls; Band; ChrhWkr; CncrtBnd; DrlTm; HonRl; MrchBnd; NHS; Quill&Scroll; SecStuCncl; Yrbk; RptrSchPpr; PpCl; Tennis; College; Nursing.

JOHNSON, Gene H; Wautoma HS; Redgranite, WI; Chr; ChrhWkr; HonRl; SctActv; YthFlsp; FrCl; Bsbl; Bsktbl; Ftbl; Coll; Professnl.

JOHNSON, Geoffrey F; Stevenson HS; Livonia, MI; LetterTennis; IMSpt; Hillsdale Coll.

JOHNSON, Gerald A; Mendel Catholic Prep; Chicago, IL; 40/237 PresJrCls; Chrs; PolWkr; SchAde; VPStuCncl; VPStuGov; TchrAde; 4-H; Bsbl; IMSpt; College; Business Admni.

JOHNSON, Gerald T; Iowa Grant HS; Livingston, WI; 14/120 ALBoysSt; Band; Chr; Chrs; CncrtBnd; HonRl; MrchBnd; NatlThespSoc; SchMus; FFA; Uw Platteville; Ag Mechanics.

JOHNSON, Gerard M; Griffith HS; Griffith, IN; ALBoysSt; ALAGirlsSt; HonRl; NHS; NatlMeritCmnd; NatlMeritSchl; EdYrBk; EdSchPpr; Rose Hulman Inst Of Tech; Eng.

JOHNSON, Glenn A; Sidney HS; Sidney, NE; ChrhWkr; CmntyWkr; HonRl; NatlCathMusEdAsoc; Univ; Law.

JOHNSON, Glenn L; Butte HS; Ruso, ND; AL-

BoysSt; Chr; Chrs; StuCncl; EdSchPpr; LetterBsktbl; LetterTrk; Trade Sch; Auto Mechanics.

JOHNSON, Glenn M; Arlington HS; Arlington Hts, IL; HonRl; SctActv; LetterTrk; Wrstlng; Iowa St Univ; Architecture.

JOHNSON, Greg; South Iron HS; Annapolis, MO; Chr; Chrs; LbryAde; 4-H; PpCl;.

JOHNSON, Gregory; Octavia Hs; Colfax, IL; 4/45 CncrtBnd; HonRl; MrchBnd; NHS; PepBnd; RptrSchPpr; RusCl; MthCl; SciCl; Wrstlng; Concordia College; Dentist.

JOHNSON, Gregory D; Greenview HS; Greenview, IL; 6/49 TrsFrshCls; TrsSophCls; PresJrCls; Chrs; ChrhWkr; NHS; OffAde; SchMus; StuCncl; TchrAde; Yrbk; FSA; FTA; LetterBsktbl; College; Music.

JOHNSON, Gregory T; Northville HS; Northville, MI; Chr; HonRl; Mdrgl; NHS; SchMus; SchPl; TchrAde; RptrSchPpr; SptEdSchPpr; University Of Michigan.

JOHNSON, Gwendolyn F; Towner HS; Towner, ND; Chr; HonRl; SchPl; YthFlsp; Yrbk; SchPpr; 4-H; FHA; PpCl; Hair Styling School.

JOHNSON, Heidi A; Mc Gregor HS; Mc Gregor, MN; 4/66 HonRl; JrNHS; EdYrBk; RptrSchPpr; FHA; PpCl; Bsktbl; LetterTrk; LetterWrstlng; CaptChrldr; GAA; University; Business Administration.

JOHNSON, Hollister; Negaunee HS; Negaunee, MI; Chrs; HonRl; Orch; SctActv; TchrAde; FTA; VoiceDemAwd; Coll; Interpreter.

JOHNSON, Ila R; Williamsville HS; Sherman, IL; Band; ChrhWkr; HonRl; PolWkr; YthFlsp; 4-H; FHA; GAA; Il Central Clge; Accounting.

JOHNSON, James E; Hinckley Big Rock HS; Hinckley, IL; HonRl; NatlFornLg; SctActv; LatCl; Col; Nuclear Physics.

JOHNSON, James J; Mitchell HS; Mitchell, NE; 36/55 LbryAde; SchAde; StuCncl; TchrAde; Yrbk; SchPpr; KeyCl; LetterBsktbl; LetterFtbl; LetterTrk; IMSpt; Washington St Univ; Architecture.

JOHNSON, James P; Menomonee Falls East HS; Menomonee Falls, WI; CncrtBnd; HonRl; University; Professional.

JOHNSON, James R; Ainsworth HS; Ainsworth, NE; HonRl; NatlMeritSF; TchrAde; RptrSchPpr; 4-H; FrCl; Trk; Wrstlng; DanFAwd; EldAwd; Univ Of Nebraska; Math Teacher.

JOHNSON, Jane A; Grayville Comm HS; Grayville, IL; 11/45 Chr; ChrhWkr; HonRl; LbryAde; OffAde; YthFlsp; Bsbl; Tennis; Olney Central College; History.

JOHNSON, Jane E; Berlin HS; Berlin, WI; 1/174 ALAGirlsSt; CncrtBnd; HonRl; Mdrgl; NHS; SchPl; Sec4-H; DanFAwd; 4-HAwd; VFWAwd; College; Medica Doctor.

JOHNSON, Janella L; Evart HS; Hersey, MI; HonRl; LbryAde; NatlFornLg; NHS; OffAde; SchPl; TchrAde; RptrYrbk; Chrldr; CitAwd; College.

JOHNSON, Janell M; Buena Vista HS; Saginaw, MI; 2/274 SecFrshCls; Band; CncrtBnd; HonRl; MrchBnd; PepBnd; Quill&Scroll; EdSchPpr; PpCl; SciCl; Central Michigan Univ; Journalism.

JOHNSON, Jane R; Wauneta HS; Wauneta, NE; SecSophCls; SecJrCls; ALAGirlsSt; ModUN; SchMus; SchPl; StuCncl; PresYthFlsp; YthLg; 4-H; PpCl; LetterTrk; SecGAA; Univ Of Nebraska; Music.

JOHNSON, Jane R; Mandovi HS; Eleva, WI; SecFrshCls; ChrhWkr; CncrtBnd; HonRl; NHS; FshEdSchPpr; FrCl; Trk; College.

JOHNSON, Jane S; Bark River Harris HS; Bark River, MI; TrsSophCls; HonRl; TchrAde; Yrbk; FrCl; College; Lawyer.

JOHNSON, Janet A; Traverse City HS; Traverse City, MI; 42/620 SecJrCls; Band; CncrtBnd; HonRl; NHS; SchMus; StuCncl; RptrSchPpr; PpCl; IMSpt; Central Michigan College; Recreation.

JOHNSON, Janet L; Davis County Comm HS; Bloomfield, IA; Band; ChrhWkr; CmntyWkr; CncrtBnd; HonRl; PepBnd; SchPl; SpnCl; SciCl; LetterTrk; College; Professional.

JOHNSON, Janet S; Washington Comm HS; Washington, IL; 13/345 AFS; Chr; Chrs; HonRl; NHS; Orch; FrCl; College Of St Francis; Medicine.

JOHNSON, Janis R; Paxton Comm HS; Paxton, IL; HonRl; EngCl; LatCl; First National Bank In Paxton.

JOHNSON, Janna L; Galva Community HS; Galva, IA; PresFrshCls; SecTrsJrCls; Band; Chrs; HonRl; StuCncl; CaptBsktbl; LetterTrk; Chrldr; 4-HAwd; Bus Schl; Secretarial.

JOHNSON, Jay K; W Bloomfield HS; W Bloomfield, MI; ChrhWkr; HonRl; YthFlsp;.

JOHNSON, Jeanine M; Louisville Public HS; Louisville, NE; Chr; Chrs; CncrtBnd; MrchBnd; PepBnd; Yrbk; Waye State College; Business.

JOHNSON, Jeffery D; Hutchinson HS; Hutchinson, MN; 3/189 HonRl; LbryAde; PresNHS; FshEdSchPpr; SpnCl; PpCl; Bsbl; IMSpt; St Johns Univ; Economics.

JOHNSON, Jeff R; Richmond Burton HS; Richmond, IL; HonRl; College; Chef.

JOHNSON, Jeffrey; Stephen Decatur Hs; Decator, IL; PolWkr; RptrSchPpr; SchPpr; Eastern Illinois University; English Lit.

JOHNSON, Jeffrey H; Brookville HS; Brookville, IN; 44/170 HonRl; SpnCl; SciCl; Ftbl; LetterTrk; LetterWrstlng; U Of Southern Cal; Telecommunications.

JOHNSON, Jeffrey S; Allendale HS; Allendale, IL; 11/18 HonRl; SchPl; StuCncl; Yrbk; PpCl; LetterBsbl; LetterBsktbl; Wabash Valley Clge; Diesel Hydraulics.

JOHNSON, Jeffrey T; Centennial Sr HS; Circle Pines, MN; HonRl; NHS; Bsbl; LetterTrk; College; Professional.

JOHNSON, Jennifer J; Ash Grove HS; Everton, MO; Band; MrchBnd; Twrl; EdYrBk; Yrbk; SchPpr; FBLA; FHA; PpCl; Trk; College; Business.

JOHNSON, Jennifer J; Coloma HS; Coloma, MI; 11/172 HonRl; NHS; NatlMeritCmnd; SctActv; TchrAde; Yrbk; FNA; FTA; LatCl; Michigan State Univ; Education.

JOHNSON, Jennifer L; Cass Tech HS; Detroit, MI; ChrhWkr; HonRl; HospAde; NatlMeritCmnd; OffAde; PolWkr; FDA; LatCl; Chatham College; Medicine.

JOHNSON, Jeri L; Lockport Twp HS; Lockport, IL; 6/550 ChrhWkr; HonRl; JrNHS; NHS; OffAde; StuCncl; PresStuGov; RptrSchPpr; Tennis; GAA; Lewis Univ; Business Admin.

JOHNSON, Jeri S; Granite City South HS; Granite City, IL; 12/630 Chrs; CncrtBnd; MrchBnd; SecNHS; PepBnd; SchMus; College; Music.

JOHNSON, Jerry M; Hammond Baptist HS; Hammond, IN; VPSophCls; ChrhWkr; HonRl; TchrAde; RptrYrbk; Yrbk; GerCl; CaptSocr; LetterTrk;.

JOHNSON, Jim P; Bangor HS; Bangor, MI; HonRl; SctActv; TchrAde; SchPpr; Univ Of Michigan; Computer Engineering.

JOHNSON, Joann E; St Bernards HS; St Paul, MN; 10/157 HonRl; NHS; OffAde; EdSchPpr; FHA; PresPpCl; LetterBsbl; CaptTrk; U Of Mn; Accounting.

JOHNSON, Joanne; Birch Run HS; Birch Run, MI; /154 CncrtBnd; HonRl; NatlThespSoc; OffAde; PepBnd; StuCncl; YthFlsp; SciCl; Bsbl; Bsktbl; Asbury Coll; Phy Ed.

JOHNSON, Joanne M; Baltic HS; Baltic, SD; 4/19 SecJrCls; Band; Chr; ChrhWkr; CncrtBnd; HonRl; MrchBnd; NHS; PolWkr; SchPl; College; Business.

JOHNSON, Joann S; Marietta Public HS; Morietta, MN; VPSrCls; Band; Chr; ChrhWkr; PepBnd; SchPl; Twrl; EdSchPpr; LetterBsktbl; LetterTrk; Concordia Moorehead Mn; Psychologist.

JOHNSON, Jodi A; Mentor Public HS; Mentor, MN; VPFrshCls; Band; ChrhWkr; HonRl; LbryAde; RptrSchPpr; SptEdSchPpr; FHA; LetterBsktbl; IMSpt; Col; Music Teacher.

JOHNSON, Johanna K; Arlington HS; Indianapolis, IN; 5/500 Chr; CncrtBnd; MrchBnd; NHS; NatlMeritCmnd; PresNatlThespSoc; Orch; SchMus; StuCncl; PPFtbl; NCTE; Purdue Univ; Pharmacy.

JOHNSON, John; Watseka Community HS; Watseka, IL; /150 HonRl; LitMag; Quill&Scroll; RptrYrbk; EdYrBk; RptrSchPpr; SchPpr; SpnCl; Ftbl; Journalism.

JOHNSON, John M; Anderson Senior HS; Anderson, IN; Chr; Chrs; ChrhWkr; HonRl; Mdrgl; SchMus; SctActv; Ftbl; CaptWrstlng; Anderson College; Clergyman.

JOHNSON, John S; Iowa Mennonite HS; Omaha, NE; HstSophCls; Band; HonRl; Orch; CaptBsktbl; Ftbl; Trk; IMSpt; U Of Nebr; Prof Athletics.

JOHNSON, John W; South Iron HS; Arcadia, MO; SciCl; Bsbl; School; Electrician.

JOHNSON, Joseph W; Appleton West HS; Appleton, WI; 13/640 Band; CncrtBnd; MrchBnd; NatlMeritSF; Orch; PepBnd; RptrSchPpr; SchPpr; BauchLmbAwd; Univ Wi; Nuclear Eng.

JOHNSON, Joy Beth; Pine River Area HS; Luther, MI; SecSrCls; Band; ChrhWkr; CmntyWkr; HonRl; NHS; YthFlsp; 4-H; SecFHA; CaptChrldr; College; Elem Teacher.

JOHNSON, Joyce C; Black River Falls HS; Merrillan, WI; 16/140 4-H; FBLA; LatCl; CaptBsbl; LetterBsktbl; LetterGAA; Uw Eau Claire; Med Tech.

JOHNSON, Judith A; S Milwaukee HS; S Milwaukee, WI; 77/435 HonRl; College.

JOHNSON, Judy A; Henry HS; Henry, SD; ALAGirlsSt; Band; Chrs; ChrhWkr; CmntyWkr; HonRl; MrchBnd; PepBnd; SchPl; StuCncl; College; Medical Assistant.

JOHNSON, Judy A; Danville HS; Danville, IL; AFS; Chr; ChrhWkr; HonRl; JA; Mdrgl; SchMus; StuCncl; Yrbk; JAAwd; Univ; Home Economics.

JOHNSON, Judy P; Platte Valley Academy; Max, ND; Chr; ChrhWkr; CmntyWkr; CncrtBnd; HonRl; LbryAde; NatlMeritCmnd; TchrAde; RptrSchPpr; Union Clg.

JOHNSON, Julianne M; Algona HS; Algona, IA; 1/125 ALAGirlsSt; Band; Chrs; CaptDrlTm; HonRl; MrchBnd; SecNHS; PepBnd; 4-H; PresPpCl; Buena Vista College; Education.

JOHNSON, Julie; Alwood Hs; Woodhull, IL; 11/75 Band; Chrs; NHS; NatlMeritCmnd; SchPl; RptrYrbk; 4-H; FTA; Bsktbl; GAA; Coe College; English.

JOHNSON, Julie A; William Chrisman HS; Independence, MO; PresFrshCls; HonRl; NatlThespSoc; OffAde; SchMus; PpCl; Chrldr; PPFtbl; Univ; Pro.

JOHNSON, Julie A; Audubon Public HS; Audubon, MN; 1/36 ALAGirlsSt; Band; Chr; ChrhWkr; HonRl; NHS; SchPl; EdYrBk; FHA; Chrldr; College.

JOHNSON, Julie G; Alma Public HS; Alma, NE; VPJrCls; Chrs; ChrhWkr; HonRl; JrNHS; Mdrgl; NHS; SchAde; StuCncl; 4-HAwd; College; Medical Career.

JOHNSON, Julie K; Warren HS; Gerlaw, IL; Band; CmntyWkr; SchPl; StuCncl; Pres4-H; SecFFA; VPFHA; KeyCl; Bsktbl; GAA; DanFAwd; 4-HAwd; Southeastern La Univ; Agriculture.

JOHNSON, Karen; Waterford Union HS; Waterford, WI; HonRl; NatlFornLg; SchAde; StuCncl; RptrYrbk; PpCl; Chrldr; College; Accounting.

JOHNSON, Karen; Spring Grove Hs; Spring Grove, MN; Band; Chr; RptrYrbk; RptrSchPpr; 4-H; FHA; U Wisconsin Stout; Home Economics.

JOHNSON, Karen A; R Nelson Snider HS; Ft Wayne, IN; 9/508 HonRl; Orch; SchMus; StuCncl; SpnCl; Northwestern Univ; Engineer.

JOHNSON, Karen D; Banner County HS; Potter, NE; 1/14 SecFrshCls; ALAGirlsSt; Band; Chr; CncrtBnd; DrlTm; HonRl; JrNHS; MrchBnd; NHS; PepBnd; Trk; Univ Of Nebr; Education.

JOHNSON, Karen J; Lancaster Public HS; Lake Bronson, MN; Aud/Vis; Chrs; ChrhWkr; HonRl; SchPl; SptEdYrbk; College; Computer Science.

JOHNSON, Karen M; Gothenburg Public HS; Gothenburg, NE; 2/84 Band; Chrs; ChrhWkr; CncrtBnd; DrmMjrt; HonRl; NHS; PepBnd; 4-H; TreasPpCl; College.

JOHNSON, Karen S; Nokomis HS; Nokomis, IL; Chrs; HonRl; OffAde; SchMus; StuCncl; Yrbk; Quill&Scroll; GAA; IMSpt; St Johns School Of Nursing; Reg Nurse.

JOHNSON, Karen S; Stockton R 1 HS; Fair Play, MO; TchrAde; FFA; Bsbl; Bsktbl; Trk; GAA; Univ.

JOHNSON, Karin M; Deerfield HS; Deerfield, IL; 63/500 Chrs; CmntyWkr; HonRl; NatlFornLg; NatlMeritCmnd; RedCrAde; SchPl; StuGov; Univ Of Illinois; Accounting.

JOHNSON, Karin R; Glenburn HS; Lansford, ND; SecTrsJrCls; Band; Chr; HonRl; SchPl; YthFlsp; Yrbk; EdSchPpr; PpCl; Oral Roberts University; Business Admin.

JOHNSON, Karla; Crofton Public HS; Crofton, NE; 1/64 TrsJrCls; Chrs; DrlTm; HonRl; LbryAde; NHS; EdYrBk; PpCl; BttyCrckrAwd; DanFAwd; University Of Nebraska; Journalism.

JOHNSON, Karla; Lakeview Hs; Six Lakes, MI; 12/118 VPFrshCls; CncrtBnd; HonRl; SchMus; SchPl; StuCncl; RptrYrbk; FTA; Chrldr; GAA; Ferris State College;law Enforcement.

JOHNSON, Karlan R; Blackhawk HS; South Wayne, WI; SecFrshCls; ALBoysSt; ChrhWkr; HonRl; NHS; SctActv; Yrbk; LetterBsbl; LetterBsktbl; LetterFtbl; Bus Schl; Vocation.

JOHNSON, Katherine S; Maine South HS; Park Ridge, IL; Chr; ChrhWkr; HonRl; HospAde; NHS; PolWkr; FrCl; Swmmng; Trk; College; French.

JOHNSON, Kathie; Seneca HS; Marseilles, IL; 13/61 SecSrCls; Band; HonRl; LitMag; StuCncl; StuGov; RptrYrbk; FHA; GAA; IMSpt; Jr College; Professional.

JOHNSON, Kathleen; Harding Sr HS; St Paul, MN; 15/724 Chr; HonRl; IntrClCncl; NHS; StuGov; JAAwd; College; Social Work.

JOHNSON, Kathleen S; Tomahawk HS; Tomahawk, WI; 26/158 Chr; Chrs; ChrhWkr; CmntyWkr; HonRl; HospAde; LbryAde; YthFlsp; 4-H; Socr; GAA; IMSpt; PPFtbl; Technical Schl; Nursing.

JOHNSON, Kathy J; Florence HS; Iron Mountain, MI; 12/68 HonRl; LbryAde; OffAde; SchPl; TchrAde; YthFnd; RptrYrbk; Yrbk; FTA; SpnCl; U Of Wisconsin; Teach Art.

JOHNSON, Kathy M; Adlai E Stevenson HS; Buffalo Grove, IL; Band; CncrtBnd; HonRl; MrchBnd; NHS; PepBnd; SchMus; Yrbk; CaptSwmmng; GAA; College; Music.

JOHNSON, Keith; Rantoul Township HS; Rantoul, IL; 17/383 HonRl; NHS; StuCncl; Bsktbl; Ftbl; Agriculture.

JOHNSON, Kenneth E; Thomas Jefferson HS; Council Bluffs, IA; Band; ChrhWkr; CncrtBnd; HonRl; MrchBnd; NHS; Orch; PepBnd; RptrYrbk; RptrSchPpr; SciCl; LetterSwmmng; College; Nuclear Science.

JOHNSON, Kenneth M; Kenowa Hills HS; Grand Rapids, MI; 11/217 CncrtBnd; HonRl; MrchBnd; NHS; PepBnd; SchAde; SctActv; SpnCl; MthCl; IMSpt; Univ Of Mi; Architecture.

JOHNSON, Kent C; Northeast HS; Lincoln, NE; HonRl; StuCncl; TchrAde; Univ Of Nebraska; Science.

JOHNSON, Kent L; United Township HS; East Moline, IL; 8/626 ChrhWkr; HonRl; JrNHS; NHS; SctActv; LetterBsktbl; Coll; Pro.

JOHNSON, Kermit W; Reeder Public HS; Hettinger, ND; 4-H; LetterBsktbl; LetterTrk; Vocationals Sch; Rancher.

JOHNSON, Kevin; East Monona HS; Moorhead, IA; 8/29 ALBoysSt; HonRl; NHS; SchPl; MthCl; Bsbl; Bsktbl; Ftbl; Trk; IMSpt; North Western College.

JOHNSON, Kevin R; North Farmington HS; Farmington Hills, MI; Band; CncrtBnd; HonRl; MrchBnd; NHS; NatlMeritCmnd; PepBnd; SctActv; Bsbl; Tennis; U Of Mi.

JOHNSON, Kevin R; Lanphier HS; Springfield, IL; 10/563 Band; ChrhWkr; CncrtBnd; HonRl; MrchBnd; YthFlsp; KeyCl; Ftbl; LetterWrstlng; Lincolnland Comm Col; Computer Programmer.

JOHNSON, Kimberly; Carroll HS; Bringhurst, IN; 6/132 VPSrCls; Chrs; HonRl; NHS; FHA; FTA; PpCl; College; Ele Education.

JOHNSON, Kimberly J; Coon Rapids HS; Coon Rapids, MN; HonRl; JrNHS; LbryAde; OffAde; TchrAde; EdYrBk; Yrbk; College; Math Teacher.

JOHNSON, Kimberly S; Oelwein Community HS; Oelwein, IA; Chr; ChrhWkr; HonRl; NHS; SchMus; RptrYrbk; PpCl; LetterChrldr; College; Teaching.

JOHNSON, Kirk L; Oskaloosa HS; Oskaloosa, KS; TrsFrshCls; TrsSophCls; TrsJrCls; TrsSrCls; Band; Chr; HonRl; MrchBnd; TreasNHS; PepBnd; Pres4-H; Bsktbl; Ftbl; Trk; Kansas State Univ; Lawyer.

JOHNSON, Krisselle L; Milnor HS; Milnor, ND; Chrs; ChrhWkr; SchPl; YthFlsp; RptrSchPpr; 4-H; FHA; PpCl; CitAwd; Nd State School Of Sci; Business.

JOHNSON, Kristine L; Brainerd HS; Brainerd, MN; 6/467 Band; Chr; ChrhWkr; CncrtBnd; HonRl; NHS; PepBnd; SchPl; YthFlsp; VPGerCl; U Of Mn; Music.

JOHNSON, Kristi S; Alton HS; Alton, MO; CncrtBnd; HonRl; MrchBnd; PepBnd; StuCncl; Yrbk; 4-H; PpCl; Chrldr; EldAwd; Coll.

JOHNSON, Kristy K; Kennedy HS; Bloomington, MN; Band; Chr; Chrs; ChrhWkr; CncrtBnd; HonRl; JrNHS; NHS; SchMus; Swmmng; College; Special Education Music Therapy.

JOHNSON, Larenda R; Wabash HS; Peru, IN; 8/215 HonRl; HospAde; LbryAde; NatlFornLg; NHS; OffAde; PolWkr; YthFlsp; Purdue Univ; Humanities.

JOHNSON, Larry D; Fairbury HS; Fairbury, NE; 45/140 CmntyWkr; HonRl; Pres4-H; FFA; IMSpt; 4-HAwd; PresAwd; College; Professional.

JOHNSON, Larry L; Kennett HS; Kennett, MO; KeyCl; Bsbl; Ftbl; Albany St Coll; Bus.

JOHNSON, Laura J; Butte Public HS; Butte, NE; 3/18 SecTrsFrshCls; SecSophCls; VPJrCls; Band; Chr; EdYrBk; PpCl; LetterBsktbl; LetterTrk; AmLegAwd; U Of Ne.

JOHNSON, Lauren D; Shawnee HS; Jonesboro, IL; 24/61 TrsJrCls; VPStuCncl; Twrl; Yrbk; TreasFHA; PresFTA; Bsktbl; Chrldr; GAA; DanFAwd; Shawnee Junior College; Dietition.

JOHNSON, Lauren R; Parkway Central HS; Creve Coeur, MO; Aud/Vis; Band; CncrtBnd; LitMag; LbryAde; SctActv; YthFlsp; SciCl; IMSpt; Tech; Radiology & Neuclear Med.

JOHNSON, Laurie A; Carl Sandburg HS; Palos Park, IL; SctActv; GAA; Co St U; Social Worker.

JOHNSON, Laurie A; Falls Senior HS; International Fall, MN; 9/285 Band; HonRl; LitMag; MrchBnd; NHS; YthFlsp; Trk; GAA; BttyCrckrAwd; NCTE; College; Journalism.

JOHNSON, Laurie J; Craig Sr HS; Janesville, WI; SecFrshCls; Band; Chrs; HonRl; IntrClCncl; NatlMeritSF; TchrAde; FFA; Swmmng; Trk; GAA; IMSpt; PresAwd; College; Professional.

JOHNSON, Leona J; Plano HS; Plano, IL; Chr; ChrhWkr; HonRl; YthFlsp; 4-H; FNA; College; Vocation.

JOHNSON, Leslie; Mankato East HS; Mankato, MN; 3/227 HonRl; HospAde; LbryAde; NatlMeritFnl; NatlMeritCmnd; RptrYrbk; College.

JOHNSON, Lewis L; Armstrong HS; Armstrong, IA; PresFrshCls; PresJrCls; Band; CncrtBnd; MrchBnd; SchPl; PresStuCncl; Pres4-H; Ftbl; LetterTrk; IMSpt; 4-HAwd; College.

JOHNSON, Linda; Blair HS; Blair, NE; TrsSophCls; ALAGirlsSt; Chr; ChrhWkr; DrlTm; HonRl; NHS; NatlThespSoc; SchPl; Univ Of Ne; Veterinarian.

JOHNSON, Linda; Hanover HS; Hanover, KS; Chrl; Chrs; ChrhWkr; HonRl; HospAde; SchPl; TchrAde; Atchison Convent; Nun.

JOHNSON, Linda J; Morris Sr HS; Morris, MN; 5/162 Band; ChrhWkr; CncrtBnd; HonRl; MrchBnd; NHS; PepBnd; RptrSchPpr; FrCl; Univ Of Mn Morris; Science.

JOHNSON, Linda K; Caledonia HS; Byron Center, MI; Chr; NHS; SchMus; SchPl; VPStuCncl; 4-H; LetterBsktbl; Tennis; Coll.

JOHNSON, Linda L; Tri Valley HS; Lyons, SD; VPSophCls; Band; Chrs; CncrtBnd; VPNHS; PepBnd; VPStuCncl; Yrbk; PpCl; IMSpt; Oral Roberts U; Foreign Missionary.

JOHNSON, Linda L; Merrill HS; Merrill, WI; 43/365 SecSophCls; AFS; Band; Chr; ChrhWkr; HonRl; PepBnd; SchMus; 4-H; GerCl; Uwmc; Medical Tech.

JOHNSON, Linda S; Waverly Senior HS; Waverly, NE; Chr; DrmMjrt; HonRl; HospAde; NHS; Quill&Scroll; TchrAde; Yrbk; TreasFHA; PpCl; Chrldr; Community College; Medicine.

JOHNSON, Linda S; Monmouth HS; Monmouth, IL; 3/142 CncrtBnd; JrNHS; NHS; Orch; StuCncl; StuGov; Yrbk; PresSpnCl; LetterTrk; GAA;.

JOHNSON, Lindell D; Vienna HS; Simpson, IL; CmntyWkr; PepBnd; 4-H; FFA; SciCl; 4-HAwd; College; Professional.

JOHNSON, Lois E; Slater HS; Slater, MO; Chrs; HonRl; OffAde; TchrAde; YthFlsp; RptrYrbk; Sec4-H; VPFHA; FrCl; MthCl; Trade School; Vocation.

JOHNSON, Lonnial D; Murray Wright HS; Detroit, MI; AFS; HonRl; NHS; Yrbk; Wayne St Univ; Dietician.

JOHNSON, Lorene; Ldf Community HS; Legrand, IA; 1/44 Chrs; ChrhWkr; DrlTm; HonRl; NHS; YthFlsp; EdYrBk; PpCl; VoiceDemAwd; Ia State Univ.

JOHNSON, Lori J; Madison HS; Madison, SD; Band; Chrs; CmntyWkr; DrlTm; HonRl; MrchBnd; PolWkr; PpCl; LetterTrk; GAA; U S Army; Optical Specialist.

JOHNSON, Louis A; Pope Co HS; Golconda, IL; PresFrshCls; HstSophCls; HonRl; SchPl; StuCncl; TchrAde; FTA; Tennis; College; Professional.

JOHNSON, Louise E; Brewster Public HS; Brewster, MN; 4/25 SecSrCls; Band; Chrs; HonRl; LbryAde; YthFlsp; EdSchPpr; 4-H; FHA; PpCl; Worthington Comm College; Clerical.

JOHNSON, Luther A; Wauconda HS; Round Lake, IL; 2/240 ALBoysSt; CmntyWkr; NHS; NatlMeritSF; NatlThespSoc; SchPl; StuCncl; RptrSchPpr; LetterFtbl; LetterWrstlng; Univ Of Chgo; Physics.

JOHNSON, Lyle R; Hampton Public HS; Hampton, NE; Chrs; HonRl; StuCncl; TchrAde; FFA; Bsktbl; Ftbl; Trk; IMSpt; College; Law Enforcement.

JOHNSON, Lynette; Timothy Christian HS; Broadview, IL; 26/87 HonRl; LbryAde; IMSpt; Comp Sci.

JOHNSON, Lynette A; Hastings Sr HS; Hastings, MN; Band; ChrhWkr; CncrtBnd; HonRl; MrchBnd; NHS; PepBnd; GAA; College; History.

JOHNSON, Lynette R; Park River HS; Park River, ND; ALAGirlsSt; Band; Chrs; HonRl; HospAde; NHS; SchPl; EdYrBk; 4-H; VPFHA; College.

JOHNSON, Lynett M; Emerson HS; Gary, IN; JrNHS; SchAde; College; Professional.

JOHNSON, Lynn; Edina East HS; Edina, MN; CncrtBnd; MrchBnd; PepBnd; PolWkr; TchrAde; PpCl; College; Law.

JOHNSON, Lynnae J; Hallock HS; Hallock, MN; PresJrCls; Band; Chr; Chrl; Chrs; CncrtBnd; HonRl; Mdrgl; PepBnd; SchPl; RptrYrbk; IMSpt;.

JOHNSON, Lynne L; New Palestine HS; New Palestine, IN; 16/160 Chrl; HonRl; JA; NHS; SctActv; YthFlsp; 4-H; LetterTennis; DARAwd; 4-HAwd; In U Med Cntr; Nursing.

JOHNSON, Lynn R; Crystal Lake HS; Crystal Lake, IL; 17/477 AFS; Chr; ChrhWkr; CmntyWkr; DrmBgl; NHS; SchMus; TchrAde; YthFlsp; College; Medicine.

JOHNSON, Mabel P; Roosevelt HS; Gary, IN; 8/623 SecFrshCls; SecSophCls; ChrhWkr; HonRl; ModUN; NHS; NatlMeritCmnd; OffAde; YthFlsp; FTA; SpnCl; MthCl; PpCl; Purdue Univ; Law.

JOHNSON, Marcia D; Rolla Public HS; Rolla, ND; 4/35 Chrs; ChrhWkr; CncrtBnd; HonRl; MrchBnd; PepBnd; SchPl; SctActv; TchrAde; YthFlsp; Trade Sch; Florist.

JOHNSON, Margaret; Paseo HS; Kansas City, MO; College; Secretary.

JOHNSON, Margaret C; St Mary Acad; Indpls, IN; 1/34 Chrl; HonRl; NHS; SchMus; RptrSchPpr; SecSophCls; Clge; Teaching.

JOHNSON, Marilyn K; Loy Norrix HS; Kalamazoo, MI; 36/521 Chr; HonRl; IntrClCncl; NHS; SchMus; StuGov; YthFlsp; RptrSchPpr; PpCl; Chrldr; Hope College; Bus Admin.

JOHNSON, Marilyn M; Glenbrook North HS; Northbrook, IL; 9/654 HonRl; LitMag; NHS; NatlMeritFnl; NatlMeritSF; GAA; IMSpt; NCTE; U Of Ill; Graphic Arts.

JOHNSON, Marion; Crete Senior HS; Crete, NE; Chrs; SchMus; SchPl; SctActv; TchrAde; Teen; FBLA; FHA; SciCl; IMSpt;.

JOHNSON, Mark; Bay City Central HS; Bay City, MI; 117/630 ChrhWkr; HonRl; SchPl; Mi State Univ; Advertising.

JOHNSON, Mark A; Dodgeville HS; Dodgeville, WI; Chrl; Chrs; ChrhWkr; HonRl; Mdrgl; NatlFornLg; SchMus; PpCl; CaptTrk; Wartburg College.

JOHNSON, Mark A; Crete HS; Crete, NE; Band; Chr; CncrtBnd; HonRl; MrchBnd; PepBnd; StuCncl; FBLA; Univ Of Nebraska.

JOHNSON, Mark L; Sidney HS; Sidney, NE; 1/125 ChrhWkr; HonRl; JrNHS; NHS; Quill&Scroll; RptrYrbk; EdYrBk; RptrSchPpr; PresMthCl; LetterGlf; University; Business Management.

JOHNSON, Mark S; Shawnee HS; Mc Clure, IL; Band; CncrtBnd; HonRl; MrchBnd; PepBnd; PpCl; SciCl; Bsbl; IMSpt; Se Mo Univ; Lawyer.

JOHNSON, Marleen C; Robbinsdale HS; Robbinsdale, MN; 1/808 VPSophCls; VPJrCls; ALAGirlsSt; HonRl; NHS; NatlMeritCmnd; StuCncl; RptrYrbk; PpCl; Clge; Medicine.

JOHNSON, Marshall D; Greenville HS; Greenville, MI; HonRl; LetterTrk; Mi State U; Physics.

JOHNSON, Martin B; Highland HS; Highland, IN; ChrhWkr; CmntyWkr; HonRl; NHS; OffAde; PolWkr; StuCncl; StuGov; TchrAde; KeyCl; ChmnBsktbl; College.

JOHNSON, Mary; Cosmos HS; Cosmos, MN; /42 Band; Chrs; CncrtBnd; HonRl; LbryAde; MrchBnd; OffAde; PepBnd; SchPpr; TreasFHA; Vocational; Med Sec.

JOHNSON, Mary; Humboldt HS; Humboldt, IA; CmntyWkr; HonRl; StuCncl; CivCl; CchngActv; IMSpt; ChmbCommrsAwd; OptClAwd; PresAwd; VoiceDemAwd; College; Vocation.

JOHNSON, Matthew L; West Ottawa HS; Holland, MI; NHS; SchPl; StuGov; TchrAde; VPGerCl; Ftbl; CaptSwmmng; Trk; CchngActv; Msu.

JOHNSON, Maxine; Vienna HS; Belknap, IL; 2/100 Band; ChrhWkr; HonRl; MrchBnd; PepBnd; SchMus; 4-H; FTA; SpnCl; SecMthCl; Shawnee Col; Music.

JOHNSON, Max N; Cooter HS; Steele, MO; 3/20 PresSophCls; TrsSrCls; Band; ChrhWkr; CncrtBnd; HonRl; MrchBnd; Orch; PepBnd; SchPl; StuCncl; StuGov; LetterBsktbl; IMSpt; Univ Of Mo; Architect.

JOHNSON, Melanie L; Sparta HS; Sparta, IL; 14/160 Chrs; CncrtBnd; HonRl; MrchBnd; NHS; PepBnd; SchMus; Yrbk; FrCl; William Woods College; Music.

JOHNSON, Melody A; Cheboygan HS; Cheboygan, MI; 21/217 Band; CncrtBnd; DrmMjrt; HonRl; MrchBnd; StuCncl; StuGov; Twrl; PpCl; Tennis; Eastern Michigan Univ; Court Reporter.

JOHNSON, Meta J; St Pauls College HS; Higginsville, MO; Chr; Chrs; StuGov; YthFlsp; RptrSchPpr; College; Special Education.

JOHNSON, Michael A; Marist HS; Chicago, IL; 32/393 HonRl; SciCl; IMSpt; Coll; Science.

JOHNSON, Michael A; Soutwestern HS; Kane, IL; 5/180 HonRl; NHS; StuCncl; FFA; College; Business.

JOHNSON, Michael C; Lincoln HS; Vincennes, IN; 1/350 ALBoysSt; HonRl; RptrYrbk; Tennis; KiwanAwd; RotaryAwd; Indiana Univ; Pre Med.

JOHNSON, Michael J; Immaculate Conception HS; Berkeley, IL; 23/156 HonRl; Trk; Mc Henery County College; Forestry.

JOHNSON, Michael L; Lake Orion HS; Lake Orion, MI; 15/350 ChrhWkr; HonRl; NHS; NatlMeritCmnd; TchrAde; LetterBsbl; Ftbl; University Of Michigan; Architecture.

JOHNSON, Michael O; Senior HS; Jefferson City, MO; 56/486 ALBoysSt; Chr; ChrhWkr; HonRl; NHS; NatlMeritSF; SctActv; FrCl; SciCl; Bsktbl; Trk; IMSpt; College; Medicine.

JOHNSON, Michael R; Sumner HS; Sumner, NE; PresFrshCls; PresJrCls; Chr; Chrs; ChrhWkr; SchPl; StuCncl; StuGov; YthFlsp; LetterBsbl; LetterBsktbl; LetterFtbl; LetterTrk; University; Law.

JOHNSON, Michael T; Alexandria Monroe HS; Alexandria, IN; 2/198 ALBoysSt; Band; CncrtBnd; MrchBnd; PepBnd; SchPl; PresStuCncl; LetterGlf; U Of In.

JOHNSON, Michele M; Forest Lake HS; Forest Lake, MN; 3/353 HonRl; LitMag; NHS; SchPl; RptrYrbk; SchPpr; LetterTennis; GAA; VoiceDemAwd; U Of Wi River Falls; Law.

JOHNSON, Mike J; Stoughton Sr HS; Stoughton, WI; GerCl; LetterBsbl; LetterFtbl; College; Forestry.

JOHNSON, Minnie L; Chicago Vocational HS; Chicago, IL; 61/778 ChrhWkr; HonRl; SchAde; StuCncl; TchrAde; Northern Ill Univ; Psychology.

JOHNSON, Mitzi L; Ashby Public HS; Ashby, MN; PresJrCls; Chr; HonRl; HospAde; NHS; TchrAde; Yrbk; FHA; LetterBsktbl; LetterTrk; Univ;prof Or Biol.

JOHNSON, Mona L; Maysville Ri HS; Maysville, MO; 9/57 ChrhWkr; HonRl; StuCncl; FHA; SpnCl; PpCl; Secretarial Work.

JOHNSON, Monte S; Central HS; La Crosse, WI; 4 SecFrshCls; TrsSrCls; Chr; Chrs; HonRl; SchAde; SchPl; StuCncl; PresYthFlsp; YthLg; College; Accounting.

JOHNSON, Monte W; Sharon HS; Sharon, ND; PresFrshCls; SecTrsSophCls; SecTrsJrCls; SecFrshCls; HonRl; SchPl; Bsktbl; Col.

JOHNSON, Nancy; Chaska Sr HS; Excelsior, MN; 39/241 HonRl; FrCl; PpCl; GAA; Navy; Communications.

JOHNSON, Nancy; Gary Public HS; Gary, MN; SecTrsFrshCls; PresSophCls; VPJrCls; ALAGirlsSt; Chr; HonRl; StuCncl; RptrSchPpr; SchPpr; FHA; College; Speech Therophy.

JOHNSON, Nancy B; Loomis Public HS; Elm Creek, NE; 2/21 SecJrCls; ALAGirlsSt; Chr; Chrs; ChrhWkr; HonRl; LbryAde; MrchBnd; NHS; PolWkr; SchPl; GAA; AmLegAwd; Univ Of Nebraska; Medical.

JOHNSON, Nancy C; Morris Community HS; Morris, IL; 4/220 TrsFrshCls; HonRl; NHS; PresFrCl; SecPpCl; CaptChrldr; DARAwd; Augustana College.

JOHNSON, Nancy R; Antigo HS; Antigo, WI; ChrhWkr; HonRl; LitMag; FBLA; FHA; GerCl; College; Teaching.

JOHNSON, Nancy S; Kankakee Eastridge HS; Kankakee, IL; 16/269 CncrtBnd; DrmMjrt; HonRl; NHS; Orch; SchMus; StuCncl; YthFlsp; FrCl; 4-HAwd; Univ Of Ill; Animal Science Wildlife.

JOHNSON, Naomi G; Wichita Heights HS; Wichita, KS; 111/413 Chrs; ChrhWkr; HonRl; NatlFornLg; NatlMeritCmnd; OffAde; LatCl; Wichita State Univ; Chemistry.

JOHNSON, Norine S; Hector HS; Hector, MN; 6/48 Band; Chr; ChrhWkr; CncrtBnd; HonRl; MrchBnd; PepBnd; SchPl; StuCncl; SpnCl; Trk; Chrldr; University Of Minnesota; Nursing.

JOHNSON, Norman E; Mather HS; Munising, MI; TrsFrshCls; Band; ChrhWkr; CncrtBnd; HonRl; JA; MrchBnd; PepBnd; PpCl; Ftbl; Construction; Architecture.

JOHNSON, Otis L; Roosevelt HS; St Louis, MO; Band; ChrhWkr; CmntyWkr; CncrtBnd; DrlTm; MrchBnd; Orch; PepBnd; PolWkr; SchMus; TchrAde; YthFlsp; Swmmng; College; Business.

JOHNSON, Pamela; Tescott HS; Culver, KS; Band; CncrtBnd; HonRl; MrchBnd; OffAde; PepBnd; SchPl; Twrl; RptrYrbk; Airline Stewartess.

JOHNSON, Pamela E; Putnam County R 1 HS; Unionville, MO; 6/87 ALAGirlsSt; Band; DrlTm; HonRl; NHS; SchPl; StuCncl; 4-H; PpCl; CaptGlf; Ne Mo State Univ; Accountant.

JOHNSON, Pamela G; Marquand Zion HS; Marquand, MO; Chrs; HonRl; Chrldr; CitAwd; College; Major In Education Elem Teacher.

JOHNSON, Pamela J; Westview HS; Lake City, IA; Band; HonRl; HospAde; Quill&Scroll; YthFlsp; SpnCl; PpCl; Trk; PresAwd; CitAwd; College; Medical Lab Tech.

JOHNSON, Pamela J; Oak Park River Forest HS; Oak Park, IL; 36/1107 HonRl; OffAde; StuGov; Tito Comm College; Art.

JOHNSON, Pamela S; Olympia HS; Minier, IL; 46/236 AFS; Chrs; ChrhWkr; CmntyWkr; HonRl; RptrYrbk; Sec4-H; SecFrCl; PpCl; Bus Coll; Court Reporter.

JOHNSON, Pamella K; Salem HS; Salem, MO; 4/173 SecSrCls; Band; CncrtBnd; HonRl; MrchBnd; OffAde; PepBnd; SchPl; StuCncl; PpCl; U Of Mo;.

JOHNSON, Patricia; Wild Rose Public HS; Wild Rose, WI; Chrs; HonRl; SchMus; SchPl; FHA; PpCl; College; Professional.

JOHNSON, Patricia; Glenbrook South Hs; Glenview, IL; 31/579 AFS; HonRl; HospAde; NHS; Orch; SchMus; StuGov; SchPpr; CchngActv; GAA; Butler U; Doctor Pre Med.

JOHNSON, Patricia A; Plano HS; Plano, IL; 5/97 Band; Chrs; HonRl; JA; NHS; StuCncl; 4-H; Bsbl; Chrldr; GAA; 4-HAwd; College; Legal Secretary.

JOHNSON, Patricia M; Sparta HS; Sparta, WI; Chr; Chrs; HonRl; LbryAde; SchMus; RptrSchPpr; Wwt; Interior Design.

JOHNSON, Patrick C; Moose Lake HS; Moose Lake, MN; 5/71 PresSophCls; PresJrCls; NHS; SchPl; StuCncl; SptEdYrbk; LetterBsktbl; CaptFtbl; CaptTrk; Col;.

JOHNSON, Patti J; Milnor Public HS; Milnor, ND; Band; Chrs; ChrhWkr; PepBnd; SchPl; RptrSchPpr; 4-H; PpCl; Bsktbl; LetterTrk; Nd State U; Journalism.

JOHNSON, Paul A; Benedictine HS; Detroit, MI; 4/148 HonRl; NHS; Case West Reserve Univ; Biomedical Eng.

JOHNSON, Paul A; Black Hawk HS; Gratiot, WI; 14/70 Band; NHS; SctActv; YthFlsp; 4-H; FFA; FHA; LetterBsktbl; Ftbl; Chrldr; Sw Wi Vo Tech School; Agricultural Mechanic.

JOHNSON, Paul C; Sycamore Sr HS; Genoa, IL; ChrhWkr; HonRl; 4-H; FFA; Jr College; Agriculture.

JOHNSON, Paul R; Georgetown HS; Georgetown, IL; 12/100 Band; CncrtBnd; HonRl; MrchBnd; PepBnd; SchPl; Yrbk; SpnCl; Millikin Univ; Law.

JOHNSON, Paul W; Pleasant Valley HS; Bettendorf, IA; Band; ChrhWkr; YthFlsp; Bsktbl; LetterFtbl; Trk; Bethel College; Dentist.

JOHNSON, Peg; St Joseph HS; St Joseph, MI; VPSrCls; HonRl; StuGov; RptrSchPpr; SchPpr; MthCl; Bsktbl; GAA; Butler Univ; Music.

JOHNSON, Peter J; Westview HS; Braham, MN; 3/105 HonRl; JrNHS; NatlMeritCmnd; RptrYrbk; 4-H; LetterBsbl; Bsktbl; Glf; Mankato State College; Computer Science.

JOHNSON, Phil A; Ogden HS; Grand Junction, IA; VPFrshCls; PresSrCls; ALBoysSt; Band; Chr; Chrs; ChrhWkr; CncrtBnd; HonRl; MrchBnd; College.

JOHNSON, Philip E; Lakota HS; Lakota, ND; VPSophCls; Chrl; Chrs; CncrtBnd; HonRl; MrchBnd; SchMus; RptrSchPpr; FFA; LetterBsktbl;.

JOHNSON, Ralph D; Kimberly HS; Menasha, WI; 27/290 HonRl; NHS; SchPl; SctActv; LetterFtbl; LetterWrstlng; IMSpt; Univ Of Wis; Business.

JOHNSON, Randal B; Chase County HS; Imperial, NE; 9/56 Band; ChrhWkr; HonRl; NHS; SctActv; YthFlsp; Swmmng; LetterTrk; Wrstlng; GodCntryAwd; Univ Of Nebraska; Bus Adm.

JOHNSON, Randy H; T H North Vigo HS; Terre Haute, IN; 85/611 Aud/Vis; Band; ChrhWkr; HonRl; JA; Mdrgl; Orch; SchMus; SchPl; RptrSchPpr; Oral Roberts Univ; Music.

JOHNSON, Randy J; West HS; Waterloo, IA; SecALBoysSt; ChrhWkr; HonRl; PolWkr; StuCncl; Tennis; College; Political Science.

JOHNSON, Randy R; Bird City HS; Bird City, KS; ALBoysSt; Chrs; SchMus; SchPl; SctActv; RptrSchPpr; PresFFA; Bsktbl; LetterFtbl; LetterTrk; College.

JOHNSON, Raymond L; Cass Technical HS; Detroit, MI; HonRl; FDA; LatCl; SciCl; AmLegAwd; VFWAwd; CitAwd; University Of Michigan; Medicine.

JOHNSON, R E; Liberty Senior HS; Liberty, MO; AFS; HonRl; LitMag; NatlFornLg; Quill&Scroll; RptrYrbk; SchPpr; Ftbl; Trk; William Jewell Clg; Science Research.

JOHNSON, Rebecca; Moline Senior Hs; Moline, IL; 1/820 HonRl; NHS; NatlThespSoc; SchMus; SchPl; LatCl; SpnCl; GAA; Blackhawk College; Medicine Physician.

JOHNSON, Rebecca S; Waldron HS; Waldron, IN; TreasBand; Chr; HonRl; RptrYrbk; SchPpr; LatCl; PpCl; SecGAA; Nursing.

JOHNSON, Rebecca S; Bradley Bourbonnais HS; Bourbonnais, IL; ChrhWkr; CmntyWkr; HonRl; SchAde; SchMus; SchPl; YthFlsp; RptrYrbk; GerCl; Bsktbl; Trk; College; Journalism.

JOHNSON, Reed G; Tracy HS; Tracy, MN; 10/120 PresJrCls; ALBoysSt; Band; Chr; HonRl; SchPl; StuCncl; LetterBsbl; LetterBsktbl; LetterFtbl; St Olaf Coll; Eduction.

JOHNSON, Renee L; Barnum HS; Barnum, MN; 1/57 HonRl; HospAde; LbryAde; NHS; SchPl; TchrAde; YthFlsp; FrCl; BttyCrckrAwd; Col Of St Teresas; Rn.

JOHNSON, Renee T; J F Kennedy HS; Tower, MN; 8/145 ChrhWkr; HonRl; LitMag; LbryAde; NHS; RptrSchPpr; SchPpr; Pres4-H; GerCl; 4-HAwd; Clge; Med Librarian.

JOHNSON, Rex E; Axtell HS; Beattie, KS; PresFrshCls; ALBoysSt; Band; ChrhWkr; HonRl; SchPl; Yrbk; Bsktbl; LetterFtbl; LetterTrk; College; Vocation.

JOHNSON, Rhonda K; Sheldon HS; Sheldon, IL; 1/25 SecTrsSrCls; CncrtBnd; HonRl; VPStuCncl; EdYrBk; PpCl; Bsktbl; Chrldr; PresGAA; Univ Of Ill; Accounting.

JOHNSON, Richard E; Harlem HS; Loves Park, IL; HonRl; NHS; RptrYrbk; PresMthCl; CaptTennis; CchngActv; College; Coaching.

JOHNSON, Richard J; Rushford Ind HS; Rushford, MN; VPSophCls; AFS; Chrs; HonRl; RptrSchPpr; Bsktbl; LetterFtbl; LetterTrk; VoiceDemAwd; Business School.

JOHNSON, Richard M; Lincoln Sr HS; Thief River Falls, MN; Band; ChrhWkr; HonRl; YthFlsp; LetterBsktbl; LetterTrk; Navy; Nuclear.

JOHNSON, Richard R; Franklin HS; Franklin, IL; 2/45 PresFrshCls; Chr; HonRl; NHS; StuCncl; FFA; SpnCl; AmLegAwd; Coll; Agri.

JOHNSON, Rick D; Lyons Township HS; La Grange Park, IL; 70/1275 HonRl; NHS; CaptFtbl; LetterTrk; Wrstlng; Univ Of Il; Medicine.

JOHNSON, Rick L; Lincoln HS; Park Falls, WI; Band; CncrtBnd; HonRl; MrchBnd; NHS; PepBnd; Ftbl; Wrstlng; Coll; Med.

JOHNSON, Rita M; Nicollet HS; St Peter, MN; 16/42 Band; Chr; ChrhWkr; NHS; SciCl; CaptTrk; CaptChrldr; GAA; 4-HAwd; PresAwd; Nursing School.

JOHNSON, Robert; Luther L Wright HS; Ironwood, MI; Chr; Chrs; CmntyWkr; HonRl; Mdrgl; SchMus; LatCl; College; Law.

JOHNSON, Robert G; West Chicago Comm HS; West Chicago, IL; ALBoysSt; TreasStuCncl; RptrSchPpr; Glf; Trk; Univ; Engineering.

JOHNSON, Robert K; Amos Alonzo Stagg HS; Hickory Hills, IL; 42/480 HonRl; LetterFtbl; LetterTrk; Univ Of Ill; Elec Engineering.

JOHNSON, Robert S; St Laurence HS; Chicag, IL; 2/390 HonRl; NatlMeritCmnd; SctActv; FrCl; MthCl; SciCl; Bsbl; Bsktbl; Wrstlng; IMSpt; Computer Field.

JOHNSON, Robert S; James H Bowen HS; Chicago, IL; 65/595 TchrAde; Yrbk; Chicago Art Inst; Commercial Art.

JOHNSON, Robin A; Mexico HS; Mexico, MO; 72/248 SecSophCls; SecJrCls; HospAde; JA; StuCncl; TchrAde; SchPpr; Sec4-H; LatCl; TreasPpCl; Univ Of Missouri; Business.

JOHNSON, Rockne C; East HS; Duluth, MN; 250/550 CmntyWkr; LetterBsktbl; Trk; Oregon State Col; Business.

JOHNSON, Roger W; Union HS; Union Grove, WI; ALBoysSt; ChrhWkr; CmntyWkr; SchAde; VPStuCncl; YthFlsp; LetterBsbl; LetterBsktbl; White Water Univ; Public Relations.

JOHNSON, Ronald; Menominee HS; Menominee, MI; 30/276 HonRl; NHS; NatlMeritCmnd; Quill&Scroll; SchMus; StuCncl; EdSchPpr; Univ Of Mi; Journalism.

JOHNSON, Ronald B; Cedar Lake Academy; Ithaca, MI; 1/70 TrsJrCls; Band; Chr; HonRl; Mdrgl; NHS; NatlMeritSF; StuCncl; StuGov; Bsktbl; Ftbl; Tennis; Andrews Univ; Physician.

JOHNSON, Ronda L; Plainfield HS; Plainfield, IN; 1/257 ALAGirlsSt; ChrhWkr; CncrtBnd; JrNHS; NHS; NatlMeritCmnd; PepBnd; SecStuCncl; 4-H; SpnCl; DARAwd; Indiana Univ; Medicine.

JOHNSON, Ronnie; Austin HS; Austin, IN; 9/66 ALBoysSt; ChrhWkr; CmntyWkr; HonRl; JrNHS; NHS; SchMus; College; Major Study.

JOHNSON, Roxanne L; Rockwell City Community HS; Jolley, IA; 7/62 TrsSrCls; Band; CncrtBnd; HonRl; MrchBnd; PepBnd; Yrbk; 4-H; 4-HAwd; CitAwd; Ankeny Comm Clge; Criminalistics.

JOHNSON, Roy E; Lincoln Way HS; Frankfort, IL; 165/566 Chr; Chrl; Chrs; ChrhWkr; HonRl; SchAde; SchMus; PpCl; Trk; College; Pharmacy.

JOHNSON, Sandra; Samuel Mumford HS; Detroit, MI; 43/368 HonRl; CitAwd; Detroit Inst Of Tech; Medical Tech.

JOHNSON, Sandy L; Morton West HS; Stickney, IL; Chr; Chrs; ChrhWkr; HonRl; HospAde; JA; LitMag; TchrAde; Robert Morris College; Medical Assistant.

JOHNSON, Sarah; United Township Hs; East Moline, IL; Band; CncrtBnd; HonRl; LbryAde; MrchBnd; NHS; PepBnd; SchMus; SchPl; YthFlsp; Augustana College; Special Education Deaf.

JOHNSON, Sarah E; Watertown Senior HS; Watertown, SD; Band; DrlTm; HonRl; JrNHS; NatlFornLg; PolWkr; StuCncl; Twrl; GerCl; 4-HAwd; Sd State University; Graduate Nurse.

JOHNSON, Scott A; Bowbells HS; Williston, ND; 3/21 PresFrshCls; PresSophCls; PresSrCls; Band; Chrs; ChrhWkr; CncrtBnd; HonRl; MrchBnd; PepBnd; SchPl; Bsbl; LetterBsktbl; LetterFtbl; University; Professional.

JOHNSON, Scott C; Oxford HS; Leonard, MI; TchrAde; UNYO; 4-H; SciCl; Bsbl; LetterFtbl; Wrstlng; 4-HAwd; Lawrence Inst Of Tech; Architect.

JOHNSON, Scott D; Thomas Jefferson HS; Council Bluffs, IA; Band; ChrhWkr; CncrtBnd; MrchBnd; PepBnd; Air Force; Paleontology.

JOHNSON, Scott R; Northwood HS; Northwood, ND; SecFrshCls; TrsSophCls; ALBoysSt; Band; CncrtBnd; HonRl; Bsbl; Bsktbl; Glf; Trk; Univ Of North Dakota; Chemical Engineer.

JOHNSON, Scott R; Northwood Public HS; Northwood, ND; /43 SecFrshCls; TrsSophCls; ALBoysSt; Band; CncrtBnd; HonRl; Bsbl; Bsktbl; Glf; Trk; U Of Nd; Chemical Engineer.

JOHNSON, Shana G; Alton HS; Alton, MO; 2/58 SecFrshCls; SecBand; CncrtBnd; MrchBnd;

PepBnd; VPStuCncl; Twrl; EdYrBk; 4-H; PpCl; SciCl; EldAwd; 4-HAwd; Burge School; Nursing.

JOHNSON, Sharon M; Mora HS; Mora, MN; 19/140 Band; Chr; ChrhWkr; CmntyWkr; CncrtBnd; HonRl; HospAde; MrchBnd; Orch; PepBnd; PolWkr; GAA; College; Psychology.

JOHNSON, Shawn; Central Nable HS; Albion, IN; FHA; Tri State Coll; Business.

JOHNSON, Sheila E; Marietta HS; Marietta, MN; TrsJrCls; PresSrCls; Band; HonRl; PepBnd; SchPl; EdSchPpr; 4-H; FHA; PpCl; LetterBsktbl; LetterTrk; 4-HAwd; University Of Minnesota; El Education.

JOHNSON, Shelia M; Belvidere HS; Belvidere, IL; 130/343 HonRl; JA; SctActv; SchPpr; 4-H; SpnCl; GAA; 4-HAwd;.

JOHNSON, Shelley; Nushwauk Keewatin Sr HS; Pengilly, MN; Band; CncrtBnd; HonRl; MrchBnd; PepBnd; SchPl; Yrbk; Bsktbl; Staples Tec; Commercial Art.

JOHNSON, Shelly D; Irwin Community HS; Kirkman, IA; Chrs; ChrhWkr; College; Nursing.

JOHNSON, Sherrie A; Delton Kellogg HS; Delton, MI; 2/117 HonRl; TchrAde; Michigan St Univ; Veterinary Medicine.

JOHNSON, Sherry C; Our Lady Of Grace HS; Indianapolis, IN; SecJrCls; Chrs; HonRl; PresJA; StuCncl; SchPpr; IMSpt; Herron Sch Of Art; Teach Art.

JOHNSON, Stacey A; Tolley Public HS; Tolley, ND; SecTrsFrshCls; SecTrsSophCls; SecTrsJrCls; SecTrsSrCls; Chrs; SchPl; Yrbk; SchPpr; 4-H; Chrldr; U Of Nd; Social Work.

JOHNSON, Stacy A; De Soto HS; Olathe, KS; 6/90 CmntyWkr; HonRl; HospAde; NatlFornLg; NHS; NatlThespSoc; SchMus; SchPl; Kans St Univ; Pro.

JOHNSON, Stephen D; North Kansas City HS; No Kansas City, MO; VPSrCls; Band; HonRl; StuCncl; LetterBsbl; LetterFtbl; LetterTennis; LetterWrstlng; College.

JOHNSON, Stephen M; Portage Central HS; Portage, MI; HonRl; JA; ModUN; NatlFornLg; NHS; NatlMeritSF; PolWkr; StuCncl; LatCl; Bsbl; LetterBsktbl; LetterFtbl; CchngActv; University Of Michigan; Law.

JOHNSON, Stephen N; Ludington HS; Ludington, MI; Aud/Vis; Band; CncrtBnd; MrchBnd; PepBnd; West Shore Community Clg; Science Field.

JOHNSON, Stephen P; United Township HS; East Moline, IL; 135/600 ChrhWkr; CmntyWkr; HonRl; NatlThespSoc; SchMus; SchPl; SctActv; YthFlsp; Tennis; IMSpt; College.

JOHNSON, Stephen R; Parkhill Sr HS; Kansas City, MO; 7/409 Band; CncrtBnd; HonRl; MrchBnd; ModUN; Bsktbl; University; Lawyer.

JOHNSON, Steven; Roosevelt HS; Minneapolis, MN; 20/600 LbryAde; StuCncl; StuGov; Univ Of Minnesota.

JOHNSON, Steven L; H H Dow HS; Midland, MI; 15/432 CncrtBnd; HonRl; MrchBnd; NatlMeritCmnd; Michigan St Univ; Mathematics.

JOHNSON, Stuart W; West Fargo HS; Harwood, ND; ChrhWkr; CmntyWkr; HonRl; TchrAde; 4-H; LetterFtbl; Trk; IMSpt; 4-HAwd;.

JOHNSON, Susan C; Central Webster HS; Fort Dodge, IA; 1/43 Band; Chrs; HonRl; SchMus; SchPl; Yrbk; RptrSchPpr; 4-H; BttyCrckrAwd; 4-HAwd; U Of Northern Ia.

JOHNSON, Susan C; Resurrection HS; Niles, IL; 9/261 ChrhWkr; HonRl; VPNHS; FrCl; MthCl; GAA; St Norberts College; International Bus.

JOHNSON, Susan E; Belvidere HS; Belvidere, IL; 7/363 Chrs; ChrhWkr; NHS; SchMus; StuCncl; RptrYrbk; FrCl; PpCl; GAA; Bradley University.

JOHNSON, Susan L; Brainerd Sr HS; Brainerd, MN; AFS; Band; College; Medicine.

JOHNSON, Susie I; Stanberry Rii HS; Stanberry, MO; Chr; Chrs; PresChrhWkr; SchPl; Teen; YthFlsp; FHA; Swmmng; PPFtbl;.

JOHNSON, Tamara K; Arlington HS; Indianapolis, IN; Chr; HonRl; Quill&Scroll; RptrSchPpr; SchPpr; GerCl; Ftbl; Indiana Univ; Journalism.

JOHNSON, Tamela R; Cuba HS; Smithfield, IL; 3/68 TrsJrCls; Band; HonRl; NHS; SchMus; SchPl; RptrYrbk; Yrbk; 4-H; FrCl; Ill St; Math.

JOHNSON, Tami R; Mc Pherson Sr HS; Mcpherson, KS; 1/216 HonRl; NHS; TchrAde; RptrYrbk; LetterBsktbl; LetterTrk; Chrldr; University.

JOHNSON, Tami R; Cambridge Public HS; Cambridge, NE; Band; HonRl; SchPl; StuCncl; YthFlsp; Yrbk; FBLA; PpCl; LetterBsktbl; Ne Univ ; Doc.

JOHNSON, Tedra G; Pardeeville HS; Pardeeville, WI; Band; HonRl; PepBnd; SchPpr; GAA; Tech Bus Sch; Acct.

JOHNSON, Teresa A; Pine River HS; Tustin, MI; Chr; CncrtBnd; DrmMjrt; MrchBnd; NHS; NatlMeritSF; StuCncl; LetterTrk; GAA; N Mich Univ; Sociology.

JOHNSON, Teresa K; Schlagle HS; Kansas City, KS; Chr; ChrhWkr; CmntyWkr; HonRl; Mdrgl; NatlFornLg; NHS; SchMus; University; Obstetrics.

JOHNSON, Terri L; Pioneer HS; Ann Arbor, MI; Band; CncrtBnd; HonRl; HospAde; LbryAde; MrchBnd; RedCrAde; CaptBsktbl; GAA; IMSpt; Univ; Physician.

JOHNSON, Terri M; Hoopeston East Lynn HS; E Lynn, IL; 6/133 Chr; CncrtBnd; DrlTm; HonRl; NatlThespSoc; SchMus; SchPl; StuCncl; LetterBsbl; LetterBsktbl; Univ Of Ill; Physical Education.

JOHNSON, Terry; Wheaton HS; Wheaton, MN; PresSrCls; Aud/Vis; ChrhWkr; YthFlsp; SciCl; Us Army; School.

JOHNSON, Terry; Napoleon HS; Kintyre, ND; /61 Chrs; HonRl; SchPpr; 4-H; FFA; Bsbl; Ftbl; CchngActv; 4-HAwd; PresAwd; Trade Sch;farm.

JOHNSON, Terry L; Twin Rivers HS; Bode, IA; 10/40 ChrhWkr; CncrtBnd; HonRl; SchPl; SctActv; Bsbl; Bsktbl; Ftbl; Trk; CchngActv; College; Professnl.

JOHNSON, Thomas; Garber HS; Essexville, MI; 29/200 HonRl; NatlFornLg; NatlMeritFnl; SchPl; Cmu; Chemistry.

JOHNSON, Thomas G; Lakewood HS; Lake Odessa, MI; HonRl; TchrAde; Yrbk; RptrSchPpr; LetterBsbl; LetterBsktbl; Ftbl; College; Business.

JOHNSON, Tim; District 710 HS; Cook, MN; VPFrshCls; Band; HonRl; NHS; SchPl; TchrAde; Yrbk; SchPpr; Tech School; Draftsman.

JOHNSON, Tim A; Northrop HS; Ft Wayne, IN; HonRl; TchrAde; IMSpt; Indiana Univ; Geology.

JOHNSON, Timothy C; Central HS; Red Wing, MN; ChrhWkr; HonRl; SctActv; StuGov; GerCl; Bsktbl; Ftbl; LetterTennis; IMSpt; Inst Of Tec U Of Min; Comp Sciences.

JOHNSON, Timothy P; Milaca HS; Milaca, MN; PresFrshCls; TrsSophCls; PresChrhWkr; CncrtBnd; MrchBnd; PresStuCncl; Pres4-H; Ftbl; Swmmng; DanFAwd; Coll; Social Work.

JOHNSON, Timothy P; La Crosse HS; La Crosse, KS; SchPl; SctActv; Bsktbl; College; Professional.

JOHNSON, Timothy R; Hershey HS; Hershey, NE; 2/39 VPFrshCls; Chr; Chrs; HonRl; NHS; SchMus; SchPl; LetterBsktbl; Trk; IMSpt; U Of Ne; Animal Science.

JOHNSON, Tim R; Shawnee Mission South HS; Overland Park, KS; HonRl; College; Electrical Engineering.

JOHNSON, Todd S; Highland Park Sr HS; St Paul, MN; SctActv; LetterSwmmng; CchngActv; GodCntryAwd; College; Architechure.

JOHNSON, Trudy A; Hanover HS; Hanover, KS; Chrs; ChrhWkr; HonRl; HospAde; NHS; TchrAde; CivCl; Trk; GAA; JAAwd; Coll; Teacher Or Sec.

JOHNSON, Valarie G; Sherrard HS; Aledo, IL; HonRl; LbryAde;.

JOHNSON, Valerie A; Central HS; La Crosse, WI; 46/530 CncrtBnd; HonRl; HospAde; MrchBnd; Orch; PepBnd; Quill&Scroll; StuCncl; RptrSchPpr; FrCl; U Of Wis; Journalism.

JOHNSON, Verlyn M; Wykoff Public HS; Wykoff, MN; 1/32 Band; ChrhWkr; CncrtBnd; HonRl; MrchBnd; NHS; PepBnd; TchrAde; Yrbk; LetterFtbl; IMSpt; AmLegAwd; Luther College; Mathematics.

JOHNSON, Vicki L; Ashby HS; Ashby, MN; 5/26 PresSophCls; HonRl; NHS; TchrAde; YthFlsp; RptrYrbk; FHA; Bsktbl; College; Nursing.

JOHNSON, Vicky L; Roseville HS; Roseville, IL; 3/53 Band; Chr; Chrl; Chrs; ChrhWkr; CmntyWkr; CncrtBnd; Pres4-H; FTA; GAA; DARAwd; 4-HAwd; CitAwd; Iowa Wesleyan College; Nursing.

JOHNSON, Victoria A; Northrop HS; Fort Wayne, IN; Chr; ChrhWkr; HonRl; JA; Mdrgl; SchMus; PpCl; CitAwd; Univ; Law.

JOHNSON, Wallace D; Roosevelt HS; Gary, IN; 17/608 CmntyWkr; HonRl; NHS; SchMus; VPCivCl; VPKeyCl; CaptBsbl; LetterTennis; KiwanAwd; Seton Hall Univ; Accounting.

JOHNSON, Wendy J; Watertown HS; Watertown, SD; AFS; ALBoysSt; HonRl; JrNHS; NatlFornLg; NatlThespSoc; PolWkr; SchPpr; SpnCl; GAA; College; Journalism Law.

JOHNSON, Wendy S; Norris Dist #160 HS; Hickman, NE; 3/76 HonRl; NHS; TchrAde; RptrYrbk; FNA; FrCl; PpCl; AmLegAwd; OptClAwd; Nursing; Rn With Bs Degree.

JOHNSON, William H; Center HS; Kansas City, MO; Band; ChrhWkr; CncrtBnd; MrchBnd; ModUN; Orch; SctActv; YthFlsp; Ftbl; CitAwd;.

JOHNSRUD, Cheryl A; Auburndale HS; Arpin, WI; Band; Chr; ChrhWkr; HonRl; TchrAde; YthFlsp; RptrSchPpr; FBLA; PpCl;.

JOHNSRUD, Judy L; Starbuck HS; Starbuck, MN; 10/57 Band; Chr; HonRl; NHS; SecStuCncl; LetterBsktbl; CaptChrldr; GAA; PPFtbl; VoiceDemAwd; College; Music.

JOHNSRUD, Kevin J; Albert Lea Sr HS; Albert Lea, MN; 15/526 CncrtBnd; HonRl; PepBnd; LetterFtbl; LetterTennis; IMSpt; RotaryAwd; Gustavus Adolphus College; Accounting.

JOHNSTAD, Robyn L; Fertile Beltrami HS; Beltrami, MN; VPSophCls; Band; Chr; CncrtBnd; MrchBnd; NatlThespSoc; OffAde; PepBnd; StuCncl; Chrldr; College; Elementary Education.

JOHNSTON, Annette L; Watervliet HS; Watervliet, MI; PresJrCls; PresSrCls; Band; NHS; SchAde; SchMus; 4-H; LetterTrk; LetterChrldr; 4-HAwd; Business School; Secretary.

JOHNSTON, Brad; Whitewater Senior HS; Whitewater, WI; 58/189 Aud/Vis; Band; HonRl; SctActv; Yrbk; SchPpr; KeyCl; MthCl; SciCl; AmLegAwd; Univ Of Wi; Pre Med.

JOHNSTON, Deborah C; Good Counsel HS; Chicago, IL; Chr; Chrs; HonRl; JA; NatlMeritCmnd; SchMus; SctActv; De Paul Univ; Accountant.

JOHNSTON, Dirk; Romeo HS; Romeo, MI; 30347# HonRl; NHS; NatlMeritFnl; NatlMeritCmnd; NatlMeritSchl; NatlMeritSF; SchPl; TchrAde; IMSpt; PresAwd; Wayne State Univ; Computer Science.

JOHNSTON, Elsie L; Doniphan Ri HS; Fairdeating, MO; Chrs; ChrhWkr; CmntyWkr; HonRl; SchPl; RptrYrbk; RptrSchPpr; PpCl; 4-HAwd; College; Journalism.

JOHNSTON, Glen D; Blue Earth HS; Blue Earth, MN; HonRl; YthFlsp; Yrbk; FFA; Trk; IMSpt; College; Law Enforcement.

JOHNSTON, Jeffrey; Norton Community HS; Norton, KS; ALBoysSt; Band; Chrs; HonRl; NatlThespSoc; SchMus; GodCntryAwd; Ks St Univ; Science.

JOHNSTON, Jill; Rochester Community HS; Rochester, IN; HonRl; HospAde; LbryAde; NHS; OffAde; PolWkr; YthFlsp; LatCl; Purdue Univ; Pre Med.

JOHNSTON, Jill M; Lawrenceburg HS; Lawrenceburg, IN; 5/150 TreasBand; HonRl; MrchBnd; NHS; SchPl; SctActv; StuCncl; LetterBsktbl; CaptSwmmng; GAA; Purdue Univ; Landscape Architecture.

JOHNSTON, John; Weyauwega HS; Fremont, WI; JA; SchPl; FFA; Ftbl; JAAwd; PresAwd;.

JOHNSTON, Johnnie L; Manual HS; Peoria, IL; 44/329 HonRl; Univ; Data Programmer.

JOHNSTON, Judy B; Armstrong Twp HS; Armstrong, IL; 2/38 Chrs; CncrtBnd; HonRl; NHS; SchPl; StuCncl; SpnCl; SciCl; Univ Of Illinois; Lawyer.

JOHNSTON, Kathy M; Effingham HS; Mason, IL; 25/223 Chr; HonRl; LatCl; GAA; Eastern Ill Univ; Mathematics.

JOHNSTON, Kim A; Rolla HS; Rolla, ND; ALAGirlsSt; Band; CncrtBnd; HonRl; MrchBnd; PepBnd; SchPl; RptrSchPpr; FHA; PpCl; University; Accounting.

JOHNSTON, Linda R; Billings HS; Billings, MO; TrsSophCls; HonRl; HospAde; MrchBnd; SchPl; YthFlsp; Yrbk; 4-H; FHA; Chrldr; University; Curriculum Of Major Study.

JOHNSTON, Michael; Geneva Community Hs; Geneva, IL; 17/218 PresSophCls; Band; ChrhWkr; HonRl; IntrClCncl; NHS; NatlMeritCmnd; StuCncl; KeyCl; Trk; Ui;medicine.

JOHNSTON, Monica J; Msgr John R Hackett HS; Kalamazoo, MI; OffAde; LetterBsktbl; LetterIMSpt;.

JOHNSTON, Paula L; Lawrence HS; Lawrence, KS; 5/510 Chr; ChrhWkr; CmntyWkr; CncrtBnd; HonRl; MrchBnd; Orch; PepBnd; TchrAde; 4-H; Kansas University; Elementary Education.

JOHNSTON, Richard L; Norwood HS; Norwood, MO; 7/20 Band; ChrhWkr; HonRl; LbryAde; OffAde; PolWkr; SchPl; RptrYrbk; Bsktbl; Swbc ;coaching.

JOHNSTON, Ron K; Mission Valley HS; Eskridge, KS; LetterBsktbl; LetterFtbl; LetterTrk;.

JOHNSTON, Sharon S; Buhler HS; Burrton, KS; Chrs; HonRl; LetterBsktbl; College; Seamstress.

JOHNSTON, Starla D; Shelbyville HS; Shelbyville, IL; 22/143 DrlTm; HonRl; SchMus; TchrAde; Yrbk; SchPpr; 4-H; PpCl; Trk; Chrldr; 4-HAwd; College; Major Study.

JOHNSTON, Steve L; Garden County HS; Lisco, NE; SctActv; YthFlsp; 4-H; LetterBsktbl; LetterTrk; 4-HAwd; Vocational School; Agriculture.

JOHNSTON, Steven D; Clarkston Senior HS; Clarkston, MI; SctActv; Mi Tenchological Univ; Forestry.

JOHNSTON, Sylvia L; Crete Monee HS; Crete, IL; 18/382 HonRl; LitMag; SecNHS; MthCl; LetterTennis; Purdue Univ; Engineering.

JOHNSTON, Timothy W; Rapid City Central HS; Rapid City, SD; 1/560 TrsFrshCls; TrsSophCls; TrsSrCls; AFS; ALBoysSt; Chr; HonRl; Mdrgl; NatlFornLg; SchMus; SchPl; RptrSchPpr; KeyCl; AmLegAwd; School Of Mines & Tech; Law.

JOHNSTON, Vickie L; Warren HS; Anous, MN; 16/61 Band; ChrhWkr; HonRl; LbryAde; SchMus; SchPl; YthFlsp; 4-H; LetterTrk; 4-HAwd; University; Accounting.

JOHNSTONE, David W; Shorewood HS; Milwaukee, WI; 1/189 Chrs; HonRl; Mdrgl; NHS; NatlMeritSF; SchMus; SchPl; Bsktbl; Swmmng; Trk; Coll; Prof.

JOHNSTONE, Heather A; Maine West Twp HS; Des Plaines, IL; HonRl; JrNHS; GerCl; SpnCl; Univ Of Illinois; Veterinarian.

JOHRING, Craig L; Oneill Public HS; Oneill, NE; Chr; Chrs; ChrhWkr; SchMus; Yrbk; 4-H; LetterFtbl; LetterWrstlng; Nebraska Christian College; Undecided.

JOINER, Cherie L; Catlin HS; Catlin, IL; 2/57 Band; Chr; ChrhWkr; NHS; SchMus; SchPl; TreasStuCncl; StuGov; TchrAde; EdYrBk; GAA; Danville Jr Col; Legal Secretary.

JOINER, Cynthia; Martin Luther HS; West Allis, WI; 11/87 Band; ChrhWkr; HonRl; NHS; PepBnd; RptrSchPpr; IMSpt; Carthage College; Business Admin.

JOINER, Rebecca A; Tiskilwa HS; Tiskilwa, IL; 2/43 SecSophCls; SecJrCls; SecSrCls; HonRl; SctActv; YthFlsp; 4-H; FHA; Trk; GAA; BttyCrckrAwd; Il Valley Comm Coll; Business.

JOINES, David L; United Township HS; East Moline, IL; College; Mathematics.

JOKERST, Robin D; Cahokia Senior HS; Cahokia, IL; 6/559 ALAGirlsSt; Chr; HonRl; NHS; SctActv; Bus Sch; Legal Secretary.

JOLLEY, Susan D; Monroe HS; Monroe, MI; 1/523 Band; CncrtBnd; HonRl; MrchBnd; NHS; SchMus; GerCl; Univ Of Mich; Pre Med.

JOLLY, Connie J; Laurel HS; Laurel, IN; ALAGirlsSt; ChrhWkr; HonRl; LbryAde; NHS; OffAde; RptrSchPpr; EdSchPpr; PpCl; In Univ; Pediatrician.

JOLLY, Lynda S; Arlington HS; Arlington Hts, IL; 46/584 AFS; Band; HonRl; HospAde; VPNatlFornLg; NHS; SchMus; SecYthFlsp; FrCl; GAA; College; Pre Med.

JOLLY, Margaret A; Maplewood Rgts Hts HS; St Louis, MO; HonRl; HospAde; GerCl; PpCl; Trk; Coll; Vet.

JONAS, Karen M; Heelan HS; Sioux City, IA; HonRl; PresJA; NHS; SchAde; SpnCl; JAAwd; College; Law.

JONATHAN, Carla A; Southwest HS; Kansas City, MO; 140/520 CmntyWkr; CncrtBnd; HonRl; HospAde; MrchBnd; SchAde; StuCncl; TchrAde; FrCl; PpCl; Baker Univ; Nursing.

JONES, Amy A; Harrison HS; Harrison, MI; 3/120 PresSrCls; HonRl; NHS; StuCncl; RptrYrbk; LetterBsktbl; DARAwd; CitAwd; N Eastern Sch Of Commerce; Public Relatons.

JONES, Andrea B; Flower Vocational HS; Chicago, IL; HonRl; JA; SchMus; StuCncl; TchrAde; RptrSchPpr; FHA; Bsktbl; Tennis; GAA; Northeastern Ill Univ; Spcial Education.

JONES, Andrew H; Jesup Community HSS; Jesup, IA; 3/108 ALBoysSt; Band; CncrtBnd; HonRl; JA; MrchBnd; PepBnd; SchPl; Economics.

JONES, Anne N; Lake Forest Academy; Lake Forest, IL; College.

JONES, Barbara; Fair Grove HS; Fair Grove, MO; 3/56 Chr; HonRl; LitMag; NatlMeritCmnd; SchPl; StuCncl; SchPpr; FHA; MthCl; SciCl; Attend Southwest Mo State Univ;mjr In Math.

JONES, Becky S; Arlington Public HS; Arlington, NE; 10/62 TrsSophCls; Band; ChrhWkr; CncrtBnd; MrchBnd; PepBnd; Teen; YthFnd; FBLA; Chrldr; Univ Of Ne; Nursing.

JONES, Beth A; Cambria Friesland HS; Randolph, WI; 4/54 VPFrshCls; ALAGirlsSt; HonRl; NHS; SchPl; VPSrCls; Chrldr; GAA; DARAwd; 4-HAwd; Univ Wi; Physician.

JONES, Bob B; Utenbard North HS; Carol Stream, IL; SchAde; LetterBsbl; Bsktbl; LetterAmLegAwd; CitAwd; College; Professional.

JONES, Bradley A; Independence HS; Independence, IA; Band; Chr; HonRl; Mdrgl; MrchBnd; NHS; SchMus; LetterBsbl; LetterBsktbl; LetterTrk; U Of N Ia; Accounting.

JONES, Brenda S; Southwestern HS; Brighton, IL; 8/178 Band; CncrtBnd; CaptDrlTm; HonRl; MrchBnd; NHS; PepBnd; YthFlsp; VPFHA; Hickeys School; Fashion Merchandising.

JONES, Brent S; Osceola HS; Osceola, MO; VPFrshCls; PresSophCls; Chr; Chrs; ChrhWkr; Mdrgl; FFA; SpnCl; PpCl; LetterBsktbl; Agriculture.

JONES, Brian L; Cahokia Sr HS; Cahokia, IL; 28/559 HonRl; JrNHS; NHS; MthCl; Univ Of Il; Engineering.

JONES, Bruce E; Deckerville HS; Deckerville, MI; Band; College; Elec Engineer.

JONES, Catherine C; Crocker HS; Crocker, MO; 4/62 Chrs; HonRl; NHS; Yrbk; FHA; VoiceDemAwd; Southwest Mo U; Languages.

JONES, Cathy S; Murphysboro Twp HS; Murphysboro, IL; SecTrsFrshCls; ChrhWkr; HonRl; SctActv; StuCncl; 4-H; SpnCl; PpCl; SciCl; College; Social Worker.

JONES, Charles A; Colfax Comm HS; Colfax, IA; HonRl; SchMus; SchPl; StuCncl; 4-H; FTA; Bsbl; Bsktbl; CchngActv; College; Professional.

JONES, Charles W; Trinity HS; Hutchinson, KS; VPFrshCls; PresJrCls; HonRl; NHS; StuCncl; FTA; LatCl; LetterBsktbl; LetterFtbl; Trk; U; Engineering.

JONES, Christopher A; Carlson HS; Woodhaven, MI; HonRl; LitMag; SchMus; SchPl; StuCncl; TchrAde; EdYrBk; RptrSchPpr; SchPpr; College; Broadcast.

JONES, Christopher M; Warrensburg HS; Warrensburg, MO; SchPl; RptrSchPpr; SchPpr; Ftbl; Trk; University Of Iowa; Journalism.

JONES, Cindy S; J D Darnall HS; Geneseo, IL; Chr; HonRl; Yrbk; VP4-H; GAA; 4-HAwd;.

JONES, Constance L; Denby HS; Detroit, MI; 33/620 HonRl; JrNHS; LetterBsbl; LetterBsktbl; Central Mi U; Journalism.

JONES, Craig E; Lakeview HS; Battle Creek, MI; ChrhWkr; CmntyWkr; HonRl; JA; YthFlsp; Bsbl; Socr; Trk; Central Michigan Univ; Political Science.

JONES, Cynthia; Civic Memorial HS; Bethalto, IL; 30/250 ChrhWkr; SctActv; GerCl; 4-HAwd; VoiceDemAwd; College; Foreign Interpretor.

JONES, Cynthia D; English HS; English, IN; 1/34 PresSophCls; PresJrCls; PresSrCls; HonRl; LbryAde; NHS; SchPl; StuCncl; EdYrBk; FrCl; Indiana Univ.

JONES, Cynthia F; Golden Plains HS; Gem, KS; Band; HonRl; PepBnd; TreasStuCncl; TchrAde; TreasTeen; PpCl; LetterBsktbl; Trk; LetterGAA; College; Vocation.

JONES, Cynthia G; Naylor HS; Oxly, MO; 3/35 TrsJrCls; Chrs; HonRl; SchPl; EdYrBk; RptrSchPpr; FHA; FTA; Chrldr; Three Rivers Comm Col; Nursing.

JONES, Dana K; Benkelman HS; Benkelman, NE; TrsSrCls; SecTrsSrCls; HonRl; OffAde; SchPl; StuCncl; FHA; PpCl; SciCl; Chrldr; Business School; Professional.

JONES, Daniel; Pope Co HS; Golconda, IL; ChrhWkr; HonRl; SchPl; 4-H; FFA; SpnCl; PpCl; CchngActv; DanFAwd; Univ Of Ill; Aerodynamics.

JONES, David; Catholic Central HS; Livonia, MI; VPJrCls; VPSrCls; HonRl; MrchBnd; StuCncl;

RptrYrbk; RptrSchPpr; FrCl; IMSpt; Us Naval Academy; Engineering.

JONES, David A; Freeman Pulbic HS; Freeman, SD; 6/64 ALBoysSt; ChrhWkr; HonRl; NHS; SchPl; StuCncl; 4-H; SpnCl; Bsktbl; Trk; College.

JONES, David B; Shawnee Mission South HS; Overland Park, KS; CncrtBnd; HonRl; MrchBnd; NHS; PepBnd; Swmmng; U Of Ks; Pre Med.

JONES, David K; Lakin HS; Lakin, KS; 3/45 TrsFrshCls; TrsSophCls; VPJrCls; ALBoysSt; CncrtBnd; HonRl; NHS; RptrSchPpr; LetterFtbl; LetterTrk; Univ; Pre Med.

JONES, David R; Princeton HS; Cainsville, MO; Band; Chr; CmntyWkr; CncrtBnd; HonRl; JA; MrchBnd; NHS; PepBnd; SchMus; Nw Missouri State Univ; Agri Business.

JONES, David V; Richmond Burton HS; Ringwood, IL; HonRl; LbryAde; SctActv;.

JONES, Dawn R; Northridge HS; Meddlebury, IN; 15/109 SecSophCls; DrlTm; HonRl; Mdrgl; NHS; SchMus; SchPl; StuCncl; YthFlsp; PpCl; College; Elementary Ed.

JONES, Deanna L; Holden Senior HS; Kingsville, MO; 4/92 Band; CncrtBnd; HonRl; NHS; SchPl; EdYrBk; 4-H; TreasPpCl; VFWAwd; VoiceDemAwd; Cen Missouri State University; Teaching.

JONES, Debbie; Ponca HS; Ponca, NE; 2/28 VPSophCls; TrsJrCls; VPSrCls; ALAGirlsSt; CmntyWkr; JrNHS; SchPl; RptrSchPpr; MthCl; PpCl; U Of Sd; Math Teacher.

JONES, Debbie S; Earlham Comm HS; Earlham, IA; ALAGirlsSt; Band; Chrs; ChrhWkr; CncrtBnd; DrlTm; MrchBnd; SchMus; 4-H; FHA; Area Xi Community College.

JONES, Debora A; Lillis HS; Kansas City, MO; 39/80 Chr; ChrhWkr; JA; Yrbk; PpCl; IMSpt; College; Professional.

JONES, Deborah M; Porta HS; Petersburg, IL; TrsFrshCls; TrsSophCls; TrsJrCls; Aud/Vis; Band; Chrs; CncrtBnd; HonRl; LbryAde; TreasNHS; VPGAA; IMSpt; 4-HAwd; KiwanAwd; Univ; Accounting.

JONES, Debra A; West Side Sr HS; Gary, IN; HonRl; NHS; NatlMeritCmnd; Orch; PresStuGov; SchPpr; 4-H; DARAwd; Indiana University; Journalist.

JONES, Debra G; S Haven HS; South Haven, MI; Band; Chr; Chrs; ChrhWkr; CncrtBnd; HonRl; JA; MrchBnd; Orch; PepBnd; College; Business Administration.

JONES, Debra M; Bonner Springs HS; Kansas City, KS; SchPl; TchrAde; SptEdSchPpr; FHA;.

JONES, Denise C; Waterford Mott HS; Pontiac, MI; 39/369 CaptChrldr; Michigan St University.

JONES, Dennis R; Lindblom HS; Chicago, IL; NatlMeritSF; TchrAde; College; Medicine.

JONES, Dolores M; Winnebago Lutheran Academy; Fond Du Lac, WI; SecSophCls; Band; Chr; NatlFornLg; SecStuCncl; RptrSchPpr; Bsktbl; Trk; Chrldr; IMSpt; Univ Of Wi.

JONES, Donald E; Calumet HS; Gary, IN; 43/315.

JONES, Douglas; Centreville HS; Centreville, MI; 4/55 ALBoysSt; Chrs; HonRl; SchPl; FrCl; IMSpt; GodCntryAwd; Univ; Pro.

JONES, Duenna L; Canton Sr HS; Canton, IL; 1/280 HstJrCls; CncrtBnd; MrchBnd; NHS; NatlMeritCmnd; NatlThespSoc; SchPl; YthFlsp; Bradley Univ; Hospital Admin.

JONES, Edward C; Mexico HS; Mexico, MO; ALBoysSt; JrNHS; NatlFornLg; StuCncl; KeyCl; Bsktbl; Ftbl; LetterTrk; CchngActv; Univ; Journalism.

JONES, Edward J; Romeoville HS; Romeoville, IL; RptrSchPpr; FrCl; LetterFtbl; IMSpt; Us Air Force; Data Processing.

JONES, Elizabeth M; Springfield HS; Springfield, MI; PresJrCls; ALAGirlsSt; HonRl; PresNHS; NatlMeritSF; NatlSciFnd; Orch; VPStuCncl; ChmnBsktbl; DARAwd; College; Professional.

JONES, Elizabeth A; Shawnee Mission East HS; Shawnee Mission, KS; 6/600 HonRl; NatlFornLg; NatlMeritSF; Univ; Political Science.

JONES, Ellen; Carroll HS; Flora, IN; Chr; Chrs; HonRl; FHA; FrCl; PpCl;.

JONES, Eric L; Grosse Pte South HS; Grosse Pte, MI; 312/612 TchrAde; Bsbl; Ftbl; Trk; College; Phys Ed Coaching.

JONES, Eunita F; Melvern HS; Melvern, KS; 2/24 VPSophCls; SecJrCls; Band; DrlTm; HonRl; NatlFornLg; Bsktbl; Trk; Chrldr; BttyCrckrAwd; Emporia St Coll; Home Ec.

JONES, Evelyn M; Warren Twnsp HS; Wildwood, IL; Band; Chrs; CncrtBnd; HonRl; MrchBnd; GerCl; University; Medicine.

JONES, Gay; St Francis Comm HS; St Francis, KS; Band; Chrl; ChrhWkr; CmntyWkr; DrmMjrt; HonRl; NatlMeritCmnd; SchPl; SctActv; AmLegAwd; Ksu; Biology.

JONES, Gayle L; Council Grove HS; Alta Vista, KS; Chrs; ChrhWkr; HonRl; NHS; SchMus; 4-H; FHA; Trk; 4-HAwd; College; Math.

JONES, Geri L; Reavis HS; Burbank, IL; 18/676 ChrhWkr; HonRl; Mdrgl; NatlFornLg; SecNHS; NatlThespSoc; SchMus; TchrAde; GerCl; MthCl; Millikin Univ; Medical Technologist.

JONES, Glenda C; Rosati Kain HS; St Louis, MO; Aud/Vis; ChrhWkr; CmntyWkr; JA; Swmmng; PPFtbl; Loyola U; Physical Therapy.

JONES, Gwendolyn S; Garden City HS; Garden City, KS; AFS; Chr; ChrhWkr; HonRl; MrchBnd; SchMus; TchrAde; RptrYrbk; FHA; PpCl; Washburn U; Pianist.

JONES, Helen S; Liberty HS; Liberty, MO; SecJrCls; AFS; HonRl; JrNHS; NHS; EdYrBk; PpCl; Chrldr; College; Hospital Admin.

JONES, Holly N; Mitchell HS; Mitchell, NE; Band; Chrl; CncrtBnd; MrchBnd; NatlThespSoc; StuGov; PpCl; Trk; Chrldr; PresAwd; U Of Ne; Professional.

JONES, Jacqueline R; Savannah HS; Savannah, MO; Band; CncrtBnd; HonRl; LbryAde; MrchBnd; NHS; RedCrAde; SchMus; EdYrBk; Yrbk; Clge; Law.

JONES, James; Bellevue Community HS; Bellevue, IA; 4/48 TrsSophCls; TrsJrCls; HonRl; ModUN; NHS; SchPl; RptrYrbk; RptrSchPpr; SpnCl; Ia State; Communications.

JONES, James C; Central HS; Springfield, MO; Chr; Chrs; ChrhWkr; OffAde; SchMus; StuGov; FrCl; Bsktbl; Ftbl; Swmmng; Sw Mo State Univ.

JONES, James J; Brentwood HS; Brentwood, MO; ALBoysSt; Chr; SciCl; Ftbl; Trk; University; Agri Business.

JONES, Jane R; Elk Valley HS; Longton, KS; Chrs; ChrhWkr; HonRl; LbryAde; SchPl; TchrAde; SchPpr; 4-H; SpnCl; PpCl; Business School; Professional.

JONES, Janet; Marinette HS; Marinette, WI; NHS; SpnCl; PpCl; IMSpt; Uw Lacrosse; Physical Therapy.

JONES, Janet S; Downers Grove Comm HS; Downers Grove, IL; Chr; ChrhWkr; HonRl; VPNatlThespSoc; SchMus; SchPl; StuGov; Illinois State Univ; Social Science.

JONES, Janice L; Benzie Central HS; Beulah, MI; SecSrCls; CncrtBnd; HonRl; MrchBnd; NHS; OffAde; PepBnd; StuCncl; TchrAde; Bsktbl; Coll; Medical Records.

JONES, Janice M; Oak Park HS; Kansas City, MO; Chr; Chrl; Chrs; ChrhWkr; HonRl; IMSpt; College; Professional.

JONES, Janice M; St Teresa Academy; Kansas City, MO; Chrs; ChrhWkr; HospAde; JA; LbryAde; Mdrgl; NatlMeritCmnd; TchrAde; Stephens Col; Psychology.

JONES, Janis S; Oak Park HS; Kansas City, MO; Chrl; Chrs; ChrhWkr; CmntyWkr; DrlTm; HonRl; SchMus; TchrAde; SpnCl; PpCl; College.

JONES, Jeffery E; Twin Lakes HS; Monticello, IN; HonRl; JrNHS; NHS; MthCl; Bsktbl; Ftbl; CaptGlf; Auburn Univ; Pharmacy.

JONES, Jennifer L; Phillipsburg HS; Phillipsburg, KS; Chr; Chrs; HonRl; NatlFornLg; NHS; SchPl; EdYrBk; Yrbk; 4-H; FHA; K State U; Journalism.

JONES, Jerry A; Centerville Senior HS; Centerville, IN; HonRl; JA; JCC; TchrAde; SciCl; LetterBsbl; LetterBsktbl; LetterFtbl; LetterTrk; Indiana University; Physical Therapy.

JONES, Jerry J; Sioux Rapids Community HS; Sioux Rapids, IA; SecTrsSophCls; Chr; HonRl; SchPl; StuCncl; YthFlsp; 4-H; LetterBsktbl; LetterFtbl; LetterTrk; Univ ;building Trade.

JONES, Jerry L; Dike Comm HS; Reinbeck, IA; ALBoysSt; Band; CncrtBnd; HonRl; MrchBnd; StuCncl; 4-H; LetterBsktbl; CaptFtbl; CaptTrk; IMSpt; ChmbCommrsAwd;.

JONES, Jill E; Christopher Comm HS; Coello, IL; 4/55 SecJrCls; Band; CncrtBnd; HonRl; MrchBnd; NHS; PepBnd; SchPl; FHA; LetterTrk; Bus School; Secretarial Work.

JONES, Joannie P; Pacific HS; Robertsville, MO; 53/186 HospAde; PresNatlFornLg; NatlThespSoc; SchPl; FNA; SpnCl; Southeast Mo State; Mursing.

JONES, John; Herman Comm HS; Herman, MN; 3/38 Band; HonRl; SchPl; RptrYrbk; Univ Of Minnesota,morris, Recreation Direc.

JONES, John A; Harding County HS; Buffalo, SD; 2/28 VPJrCls; ALBoysSt; HonRl; Bsktbl; BttyCrckrAwd; U Of South Dak; Doctor.

JONES, John A; Carmel Boys HS; Gurnee, IL; 12/164 HonRl; JrNHS; NHS; College; Marine Biology.

JONES, John R; Galatia HS; Galatia, IL; PresFrshCls; ChrhWkr; HonRl; Jr College; Veterinarian.

JONES, Joyce I; Unity HS; Chicago, IL; Chr; ChrhWkr; CmntyWkr; SchAde; SchMus; SchPl; SctActv; Bsbl; CaptChrldr; CitAwd; Loyoly U; Prof.

JONES, Jude; Lake Orion HS; Lake Orion, MI; 70/332 Aud/Vis; HonRl; TchrAde; Oakland Univ; Spanish Communications.

JONES, Karri A; Marysville HS; Marysville, MI; 7/174 VPBand; VPCncrtBnd; HonRl; VPMrchBnd; NHS; NatlMeritCmnd; NatlMeritSF; VPPepBnd; BttyCrckrAwd; College; Nursing.

JONES, Kathleen R; Yale HS; Yale, MI; 4/146 Chr; HonRl; SchPl; TchrAde; 4-H; College; Communication.

JONES, Kathryn; Ss Peter & Paul Area HS; Reese, MI; 2/126 Chrs; CmntyWkr; HonRl; LitMag; NatlFornLg; NHS; SchAde; SchMus; SchPl; RptrYrbk; Central Mich Univ.

JONES, Kathryn L; Lisbon Comm HS; Lisbon, IA; 1/36 Chrs; ChrhWkr; HonRl; LbryAde; NHS; 4-H; FHA; GerCl; Bsktbl; LetterTrk; Military Clg; Vocation.

JONES, Keith R; Pleasant Hill HS; Pleasant Hill, MO; 3/111 HonRl; NHS; SpnCl; SciCl; LetterBsktbl; LetterFtbl; LetterGlf; Univ Of Missouri; Physics.

JONES, Kenneth S; Pratt Sr HS; Pratt, KS; 31/154 ALBoysSt; HonRl; TchrAde; YthFlsp; SpnCl; SciCl; Bsbl; Bsktbl; Ftbl; Kansas St Univ; Aviation.

JONES, Kevin E; Lawrenceville HS; Kansas City, MO; JrNHS; NatlMeritCmnd; SpnCl; Bsbl; Bsktbl; Ftbl; LetterTrk; IMSpt; College; Law Or Political Scien.

JONES, Kevin W; Fremont HS; Fremont, MI; HonRl; SctActv; StuCncl; Bsbl; Ftbl; Trk; IMSpt; Bus Coll; Voc.

JONES, Kim M; Normandy HS; St Louis, MO; ChrhWkr; HonRl; YthFlsp; PpCl; Central Methodist College; English.

JONES, Kim M; Tuscola HS; Tuscola, IL; Chrs; HonRl; Mdrgl; LatCl; Eastern Ill Univ; Accounting.

JONES, Kirk S; Carman HS; Flint, MI; 11/405 HonRl; NatlMeritSF; SchPl; Univ; Professional.

JONES, Laura F; Murray Comm HS; Grand River, IA; TrsSophCls; VPJrCls; CmntyWkr; HonRl; NHS; SchPl; EdYrBk; FHA; FNA; Bsktbl; College.

JONES, Laurie B; Nicolet HS; Milwaukee, WI; 70/485 CmntyWkr; NHS; StuCncl; StuGov; LetterTennis; Williams College; Finance.

JONES, Laurie G; Carroll HS; Carroll, IA; 2/103 VPFrshCls; TrsSophCls; PresJrCls; PresSrCls; NatlFornLg; SctActv; YthFlsp; PpCl; DARAwd; GodCntryAwd; U Of Iowa; Nursing.

JONES, Linda A; Waterford Mott HS; Pontiac, MI; 69/362 Chr; HonRl; Mi St Univ; Bio Chemistry.

JONES, Linnea M; Harvard HS; Harvard, IL; 24/159 AFS; Band; Chrs; TreasChrhWkr; CncrtBnd; HonRl; MrchBnd; PepBnd; SchMus; Sec4-H; PpCl; Glf; GAA; Rockford Memorial Hosp; Nursing.

JONES, Lisa; Hudson Sr HS; Hudson, WI; Band; ChrhWkr; HonRl; MrchBnd; PepBnd; YthFlsp; SchPpr; 4-H; 4-HAwd; Univ; Prof.

JONES, Lisa F; Mahomet Seymour HS; Champaign, IL; Band; HonRl; SpnCl; University; Art.

JONES, Lois; Daleville HS; Daleville, IN; Chrs; DrlTm; NHS; TchrAde; 4-H; LatCl; PpCl;.

JONES, Lorenzo; George Washington HS; Indianapolis, IN; 32/284 JA; NHS; PolWkr; StuCncl; StuGov; YthFlsp; Ftbl; Trk; Wrstlng; IMSpt; College; Art.

JONES, Lori M; Northeastern HS; Richmond, IN; 5/125 Chr; HonRl; JA; NHS; StuCncl; StuGov; TchrAde; Indiana Univ.

JONES, Lynnette; Wahpeton Sr HS; Wahpeton, ND; HonRl; StuGov; FBLA; FHA; GerCl; PpCl; Trk; GAA; Ndsss.

JONES, Mara E; Mc Henry Comm HS; Mc Henry, IL; PresBand; CmntyWkr; CncrtBnd; HonRl; JrNHS; MrchBnd; NHS; OffAde; SchMus; Swmmng; GAA; College; Liberal Arts.

JONES, Margarita C; Kenwood HS; Chicago, IL; 28/420 Chr; HonRl; NatlMeritCmnd; SchMus; StuCncl; TchrAde; Yrbk; Chrldr; CaptGAA; IMSpt; Ma Inst Of Tech; Architect.

JONES, Marilyn J; High School; Rolla, MO; 40/274 Chr; SecChrhWkr; HonRl; VPYthFlsp;.

JONES, Mark; Antigo Sr HS; Antigo, WI; 34/343 Band; ChrhWkr; CncrtBnd; HonRl; MrchBnd; PepBnd; SctActv; Univ Of Wi At Madison; Engineering.

JONES, Mark; Glenwood Comm HS; Mineola, IA; PresFrshCls; ALBoysSt; ChrhWkr; StuCncl; YthFlsp; Bsbl; Bsktbl; Ftbl; IMSpt; AmLegAwd; College; Undecided.

JONES, Mark P; Triopia HS; Arenzville, IL; Chrs; SchPl; StuCncl; CaptCaptLetterTrk; Univ; Coaching Football.

JONES, Marla L; Hammond Baptist HS; Hammond, IN; ChrhWkr; HonRl; HospAde; Purdue Univ; Physical Therapy.

JONES, Martha; Leavenworth HS; Leavenworth, IN; 1/26 ALAGirlsSt; Chr; HonRl; MrchBnd; NHS; SchPl; RptrYrbk; RptrSchPpr; FHA; Trk; Ind Univ.

JONES, Marvin L; North Decatur HS; Greensburg, IN; SecFrshCls; StuCncl; CaptBsbl; LetterFtbl; Univ Cincinnati; Artist.

JONES, Maureen E; Durant Comm HS; Durant, IA; PresFrshCls; Band; CncrtBnd; HonRl; JrNHS; MrchBnd; NHS; PepBnd; StuCncl; SchPpr; LetterBsktbl; LetterTrk; GAA; College; Engineering.

JONES, Maurie E; Jersey Community HS; Jerseyville, IL; 25/275 Band; Chr; CncrtBnd; DrmMjrt; HonRl; MrchBnd; NHS; SchMus; FrCl; MthCl; De Paul University.

JONES, Melinda; Senath Hornersville HS; Hornersville, MO; 3/97 HonRl; MrchBnd; NHS; PepBnd; SchMus; SchPl; FHA; FrCl; SciCl; IMSpt; Univ.

JONES, Michael A; Madison HS; Madison, IN; 3/350 VPJrCls; ALBoysSt; Band; CncrtBnd; NHS; SchMus; PresStuCncl; PresSpnCl; Wrstlng; Purdue U; Pre Vet Med.

JONES, Michael A; Wesclin Jr Sr HS; Trenton, IL; PresAud/Vis; ChrhWkr; HonRl; VPNHS; PresStuCncl; RptrYrbk; LetterBsbl; Bsktbl; LetterGlf; CitAwd;.

JONES, Michael D; Riverton 404 HS; Roverton, KS; Band; Chr; Chrs; ChrhWkr; CncrtBnd; HonRl; Bsbl; LetterBsktbl; Ftbl; CchngActv; College; Vocation.

JONES, Michael D; Providence HS; Lockport, IL; RptrSchPpr; SciCl; Lewis Univ; Aviation.

JONES, Michael E; Kirksville HS; Kirksville, MO; College; Electronics.

JONES, Michael G; Rudyard HS; Rudyard, MI; OffAde; StuCncl; TchrAde; PresFFA; Mich State Univ; Hoticulture.

JONES, Nancy; Anderson HS; Anderson, IN; Chr; HospAde; PolWkr; SchAde; StuCncl; TchrAde; LatCl; PpCl; Chrldr; College;professional.

JONES, Nancy; Sullivan HS; Sullivan, MO; 22/159 Chr; ChrhWkr; CncrtBnd; HonRl; PepBnd; SchMus; SchPl; StuCncl; YthLg; FTA; College; Vocational.

JONES, Nancy K; Woodruff HS; Peoria, IL; 28/281 Chr; Chrs; ChrhWkr; HonRl; SchMus; YthFlsp; KeyCl; College; Economics.

JONES, Pamela S; Lake Park HS; Roselle, IL; 9/536 Band; HonRl; SecStuCncl; StuGov; TchrAde; RptrYrbk; Univ Of Illinois; Mathematics.

JONES, Patricia J; Eastridge HS; Kankakee, IL; 12/286 Chr; HonRl; NHS; SchMus; SchPl; SchPpr; Univ Of Illinois; Engineering.

JONES, Patty; Switzerland Co HS; Canaan, IN; 11/105 Band; CncrtBnd; HonRl; LbryAde; MrchBnd; NHS; PepBnd; PpCl; SciCl; Indiana Voc Tech Col; Accounting.

JONES, Peggy; Redford Union HS; Detroit, MI; Oakland Univ; Political Sci.

JONES, Perry L; East Prairie HS; East Prairie, MO; ALBoysSt; HonRl; StuCncl; YthFlsp; FFA; Bsbl; Ftbl; Trk; PresAwd; CitAwd; College.

JONES, Rachel B; Lindblom Technical HS; Chicago, IL; 23/673 Chr; ChrhWkr; HonRl; JA; NHS; NatlMeritCmnd; SchAde; SchPl; TchrAde; SpnCl; Univ Of Il; Business Admin.

JONES, Randall; Dundee Community Hs; Dundee, IL; 4/362 HonRl; NHS; NatlMeritCmnd; GerCl; SciCl; Ftbl; LetterTennis; Wrstlng; College; Actuarial Science.

JONES, Rebecca; Rock Island HS; Rock Island, IL; JrNHS; LbryAde; Orch; SchMus; EngCl; GerCl; College; Medicine Archaeology.

JONES, Rhys A; Salina Central HS; Salina, KS; AFS; HonRl; LitMag; SptEdYrbk; Swmmng; LetterTrk; Chrldr; GAA; IMSpt; PPFtbl; Kansas St Univ; Art.

JONES, Richard C; O Fallon HS; O Fallon, IL; HonRl; StuCncl; Yrbk; RptrSchPpr; SchPpr; Bsbl; CaptBsktbl; Ftbl; College.

JONES, Richard C; East Troy HS; Elkhorn, WI; ALBoysSt; Band; Chrs; HonRl; 4-H; Bsktbl; Ftbl; Trk; CchngActv; College; Business.

JONES, Richard F; Frederick Jackson HS; Portage, WI; HonRl; NHS; SchAde; StuCncl; TchrAde; GerCl; Ftbl; LetterTennis; IMSpt; Bay De Noc Community College; Water Tech.

JONES, Richard P; Grandin HS; Eardner, ND; 3/15 ALBoysSt; Chr; Chrs; HonRl; SchPl; StuCncl; StuGov; LetterBsktbl; LetterSecJrCls; Trk; College; Farming.

JONES, Ricky D; Kennett HS; Kennett, MO; PresSrCls; KeyCl; LetterBsbl; LetterFtbl; Sw Missouri St Univ; Real Estate.

JONES, Robert A; Lincolnwood HS; Raymond, IL; 5/61 HonRl; LitMag; SctActv; StuCncl; TchrAde; RptrSchPpr; FTA; Bsbl; LetterBsktbl; CchngActv; IMSpt; KiwanAwd; OptClAwd; Millikin Univ; Lawyer.

JONES, Robert D; Alpena HS; Alpena, SD; PresJrCls; ALBoysSt; Chrs; HonRl; SchMus; StuCncl; Bsktbl; Ftbl; CchngActv; Northern State Col; Accounting.

JONES, Robin; Acad Of The Visitation; St Louis, MO; 7/41 Chr; DrlTm; HospAde; JrNHS; NHS; EdYrBk; SpnCl; Chrldr; GAA; IMSpt; Med School; Medicine.

JONES, Robin D; Arcadia Valley HS; Ironton, MO; 16/88 ChrhWkr; CmntyWkr; HonRl; NHS; SchAde; TchrAde; SecFBLA; VPSpnCl; PpCl; IMSpt;.

JONES, Ronald; Harrison HS; Chicago, IL; Chr; ChrhWkr; HonRl; PresJA; NHS; OffAde; SchAde; PresStuCncl; RptrYrbk; JAAwd; University; Computer Programing.

JONES, Ronald; Dundee Community Hs; Dundee, IL; 1/367 HonRl; NHS; StuCncl; GerCl; SciCl; Ftbl; LetterTennis; LetterWrstlng; College; Actuarial Science.

JONES, Ronald; Luckey HS; Manhattan, KS; 2/31 ALBoysSt; HonRl; ModUN; SchPl; SchPpr; FSA; MthCl; SciCl; BauchLmbAwd; BttyCrckrAwd; Univ; Language.

JONES, Sandra G; Southeastern HS; Detroit, MI; 9/220 HonRl; Wayne State Univ; Teacher.

JONES, Sandra L; Potosi HS; Potosi, WI; 13/65 TrsFrshCls; VPSrCls; Chrl; Chrs; CncrtBnd; HonRl; JrNHS; LbryAde; LetterBsktbl; LetterTrk;.

JONES, Shelia K; Zionsville Community HS; Lebanon, IN; 23/150 Band; ChrhWkr; CmntyWkr; HonRl; MrchBnd; NHS; SctActv; YthFlsp; PpCl; Bsktbl; Purdue Univ; Vet.

JONES, Shirley K; Williamsburg Comm HS; Williamsburg, IA; SecTrsSrCls; HonRl; MrchBnd; NHS; SchMus; StuCncl; 4-H; KeyCl; GerCl; Trk; GAA; PPFtbl; Iowa State Univ; Psychology.

JONES, Stephen C; Wheaton Warrenville HS; Wheaton, IL; HonRl; SchPl; SctActv; StuGov; Northern Illinois Univ; Veterinarian.

JONES, Steve; Rock Port R Ii HS; Rock Port, MO; 2/43 ALBoysSt; Band; ChrhWkr; HonRl; NHS; SchPl; FFA; MthCl; DanFAwd; Univ Of Missouri; Veterinarian.

JONES, Steven D; Twin Rivers HS; Ottosen, IA; Band; ChrhWkr; HonRl; SchPl; StuCncl; YthFlsp; 4-H; LetterFtbl; LetterTrk; 4-HAwd; College; Vocation.

JONES, Steven D; Orion HS; Orion, IL; ALBoysSt; HonRl; SpnCl; CaptBsktbl; CaptFtbl; CaptTrk; Trade Sch; Plumbing.

JONES, Stuart A; Benton Central HS; Oxford, IN; 85/270 ALBoysSt; Band; CncrtBnd; HonRl; MrchBnd; SchMus; LetterFtbl; LetterSwmmng; LetterTrk; IMSpt; Univ; Conservation.

JONES, Sue E; Holdrege Sr HS; Holdrege, NE; Band; CncrtBnd; MrchBnd; OffAde; PepBnd; 4-H; FBLA; PpCl; Trk; University; Professional.

JONES, Susan A; North Boone HS; Capron, IL; 1/110 TrsSophCls; Band; HonRl; NHS; RptrYrbk; 4-H; LetterBsbl; LetterBsktbl; KiwanAwd; VoiceDeмAwd; Col; Environmental Science.

JONES, Tanya S; Litchfield HS; Litchfield, MI; 4/51 HonRl; SchPl; TchrAde; Yrbk; 4-H; LetterTrk; Mi State U; Pre Veterianry Medicine.

JONES, Teddie; Emerson HS; Gary, IN; HonRl; JA; OffAde; SchPpr; College; Lawyer.

JONES, Teresa C; Highland HS; Alexandria, IN; 32/245 SecTrsJrCls; HonRl; MrchBnd; NatlThespSoc; Quill&Scroll; SptEdYrbk; Pres4-H; Tennis; GAA; BttyCrckrAwd; 4-HAwd; Anderson College; Nursing.

JONES, Terri M; Shelby Public HS; Shelby, NE; VPBand; Chr; Chrl; Chrs; CncrtBnd; HonRl; MrchBnd; PepBnd; SchMus; SchPl; StuCncl; Yrbk; RptrSchPpr; 4-H; Chrldr; Patricia Stevens College.

JONES, Terry A; Walnut Grovers HS; Walnut Grove, MO; 7/18 Band; CncrtBnd; HonRl; MrchBnd; Draughon Bus College; Accounting.

JONES, Theresa; Nauvoo Colusa HS; Burnside, IL; LbryAde; FHA; GAA; Moser.

JONES, Thomas; Highland HS; Highland, IN; 97/585 HonRl; LetterBsbl; LetterBsktbl; LetterFtbl; IMSpt; Wabash College; Medicine.

JONES, Thomas; Cambria Friesland HS; Randolph, WI; 2/51 Band; CncrtBnd; HonRl; NatlMeritCmnd; SchPl; StuGov; Mass Institute; Engineering.

JONES, Tony L; Edwards Co HS; Ellery, IL; 9/115 ChrhWkr; HonRl; VPNHS; PresYthFlsp; LetterTrk; South Ill Univ; Automotive Tech.

JONES, Tricia S; Jefferson City Sr HS; Jefferson City, MO; 20/500 Band; CmntyWkr; CncrtBnd; HonRl; JrNHS; LitMag; MrchBnd; NatlFornLg; NHS; NatlThespSoc; PepBnd; PolWkr; SchPl; StuCncl; College.

JONES, Valencia M; Kenwood HS; Chicago, IL; TrsSophCls; TrsJrCls; Chrs; StuCncl; Yrbk; Chrldr; Univ Of Il; Criminal Law.

JONES, Valerie J; Monroe Central HS; Ridgeville, IN; 8/74 ALAGirlsSt; Band; NHS; SchPl; SecStuCncl; EdYrBk; EdSchPpr; PresFHA; FTA; BttyCrckrAwd; Ball State Univ; Journalist.

JONES, Valerie S; Benkelman HS; Benkelman, NE; Chr; Chrl; Chrs; ChrhWkr; CmntyWkr; HonRl; YthFlsp; PpCl; SciCl; Trk; Trade School; Cosmetology.

JONES, Vickie; Cumberland HS; Greenup, IL; 2/104 HonRl; NatlMeritCmnd; RptrSchPpr; SpnCl; PpCl; Eastern Ill Univ; Computer Systems Analyst.

JONES, William B; Wheaton Central HS; Wheaton, IL; 50/240 CmntyWkr; HonRl; SchAde; StuCncl; TchrAde; CaptBsbl; CaptSocr; U Of West Il; Busi.

JONES, William J; New Trier West HS; Winnetka, IL; VPFrshCls; Chrs; HonRl; SctActv; StuCncl; StuGov; LetterFtbl; LetterTrk; Univ Of Illinois; Business.

JONES, William R; Minonk Dana Rutland HS; Minonk, IL; 14/60 ChrhWkr; SchPl; FrCl; SciCl; LetterBsbl; LetterBsktbl; Illinois State U; Math.

JONES, Yvonne C; St Thomas Apostle HS; Chicago, IL; 12/44 HonRl; HospAde; SchPl; RptrSchPpr; EngCl; SpnCl; SciCl; GAA; School Of Nursing; Professional.

JONGEKRIJG, Karen S; Holland Christian HS; Leeland, MI; ChrhWkr; HonRl; LbryAde; NHS; OffAde; FBLA; SpnCl; Ferris State Coll; Legal Assist.

JONIETZ, David; Mankato West HS; N Mankato, MN; 80/285 ChrhWkr; HonRl; SctActv; FrCl; Trk; Union College; Chemistry Major.

JONIETZ, David C; High School; N Mankato, MN; ChrhWkr; HonRl; SctActv; FrCl; Trk; Union Clg; Chemistry Major.

JONKER, Lynn M; Holland Christian HS; Holland, MI; 73/260 ChrhWkr; YthFlsp; SpnCl; PpCl; LetterTennis; CaptChrldr; IMSpt; Calvin Col; Physical Education.

JONKOUSKI, Gail; John F Kennedy Hs; Chicago, IL; 2/610 HonRl; JrNHS; NHS; NatlMeritCmnd; SchMus; SpnCl; MthCl; VPPpCl; GAA; U Of Ill; Engineering.

JONKOUSKI, Jill E; John F Kennedy HS; Chicago, IL; HonRl; JrNHS; NHS; Twrl; SpnCl; TreasMthCl; PpCl; CchngActv; GAA; U Of Ill; Marine Science.

JOONAS, Steven R; Lebo HS; Lebo, KS; VPFrshCls; VPSophCls; PresJrCls; ALBoysSt; Band; Chrs; ChrhWkr; CncrtBnd; DrmMjrt; HonRl; MrchBnd; PepBnd; SchPl; Bsbl; LetterBsktbl; College; Coaching.

JOOST, Marvin L; Steeleville Comm HS; Steeleville, IL; 4/55 PresFrshCls; Chrs; HospAde; NHS; RptrYrbk; Yrbk; FBLA; SpnCl; PpCl; St Louis Clge Of Pharm; Pharm.

JOPPA, Chip L; Scranton HS; Gascoyne, ND; CAP; DrlTm; NatlMeritSchl; ROTC; SptEdYrbk; FFA; GerCl; CaptBsktbl; CaptFtbl; LetterTrk; College; Pro Football.

JORDAHL, Clarence W; University School; Milwaukee, WI; TrsSophCls; TrsJrCls; AFS; Chr; Chrl; Chrs; HonRl; NatlMeritSF; StuGov; Yrbk; LetterBsktbl; LetterSocr; Swmmng; Trk; College; History.

JORDAN, Audrey D; Milwaukee Tech HS; Milwaukee, WI; 7/574 Chr; Chrl; HonRl; NHS; NatlMeritCmnd; SchMus; MthCl; ChmnBsktbl; LetterGAA; IMSpt; La Crosse U W; Medical Tech.

JORDAN, Brenda M; Bentley HS; Burton, MI; ChrhWkr; HonRl; LbryAde; SchAde; SchMus; TchrAde; YthFlsp; Yrbk; Trk; College; Special Education.

JORDAN, Carolyn E; Emerson Hubbard HS; Emerson, NE; 2/57 TrsJrCls; Chr; Chrs; NHS; StuGov; Yrbk; 4-H; IMSpt; 4-HAwd; Univ Of Nebraska; Parks & Recreation Manage.

JORDAN, Charles O; Pike HS; Zionsville, IN; 17/234 HonRl; NHS; GerCl; IMSpt; Purdue U; Electrical Engineering.

JORDAN, Colleen M; Lincolnwood HS; Farmersville, IL; Band; HonRl; Yrbk; CivCl; 4-H; SpnCl; PpCl; 4-HAwd; College; Commercial Artist.

JORDAN, Craig E; Alwood Sr HS; Alpha, IL; PresJrCls; ALBoysSt; Band; Chrs; CncrtBnd; MrchBnd; SchMus; SchPl; Southern Ill Univ; Dentistry.

JORDAN, Dorothy A; Fraser HS; Mt Clemens, MI; 24/600 HonRl; JrNHS; NHS; NatlMeritSF; OffAde; StuCncl; YthFlsp; Trk; CchngActv; Wester Mi U; Psych.

JORDAN, James W; Antigo Senior HS; Antigo, WI; 6/420 HonRl; MthCl; Bsktbl; IMSpt; Business School; Vocation.

JORDAN, Janine M; West HS; Davenport, IA; AFS; Chrs; HonRl; NatlMeritSF; Quill&Scroll; StuGov; RptrSchPpr; FrCl; Swmmng; College; Art.

JORDAN, Jeffrey D; Lake Forest HS; Lake Forest, IL; 4/430 Band; NHS; NatlSciFnd; Orch; SchMus; SchPl; RptrSchPpr; SecMthCl; PresSciCl; LetterTrk; University; Applied Physics.

JORDAN, Joann; St Louise De Marillac HS; Chicago, IL; Orch; SchMus; PpCl; Bsbl; Bsktbl; Chrldr; IMSpt; College; Business.

JORDAN, John G; De Smet Jesuit HS; Frontenac, MO; 30/200 HonRl; SchPl; Ftbl; Trk; IMSpt; University; Business Adm.

JORDAN, John T; Mayville HS; Mayville, MI; PresSophCls; PresSrCls; HonRl; LitMag; NHS; SchPl; StuCncl; CaptBsbl; Ftbl; PresAwd; Eastern Mi Univ; Business.

JORDAN, Judy; Moweaqua Hs; Moweaqua, IL; 1/53 TrsSophCls; SecTrsSophCls; Band; Chrs; CncrtBnd; HonRl; JrNHS; Trk; Chrldr; GAA; College; Secretarial.

JORDAN, Karen L; Tri Jr Sr HS; Straughn, IN; SecFrshCls; TrsJrCls; Aud/Vis; Chr; HonRl; SecNHS; NatlMeritSF; TreasNatlThespSoc; StuCncl; Yrbk; RptrSchPpr; FHA; PresSpnCl; PpCl; College.

JORDAN, Kathleen M; Marillac HS; Northbrook, IL; 7/250 Chrs; SchMus; SchPl; StuCncl; StuGov; TchrAde; SpnCl; PpCl; Chrldr; U Of Ill; Business.

JORDAN, Kristine A; Wakefield HS; Wakefield, MI; 9/63 VPJrCls; SecSrCls; HonRl; StuCncl; PpCl; Bsktbl; Gogegie Community Col; Executive Secretary.

JORDAN, Leslie M; Maine Twsp South HS; Park Ridge, IL; HonRl; NHS; NatlThespSoc; PolWkr; SchMus; SchPl; SciCl; Northern Il Univ; Registered Nurse.

JORDAN, Linda C; Northwestern HS; Flint, MI; Chr; ChrhWkr; CmntyWkr; HonRl; University; Dispatcher.

JORDAN, Marvin P; Mott Lincoln HS; Mott, ND; 4-H; FBLA; FFA; Ftbl; DanFAwd; College; Vocation.

JORDAN, Mary; Fraser HS; Mt Clemens, MI; 4/585 Band; HonRl; LitMag; NHS; NatlMeritSF; StuCncl; EdSchPpr; SpnCl; PpCl; Univ Of Mich; Journalism.

JORDAN, Robert M; Duchesne HS; St Charles, MO; Chrs; HonRl; SchMus; SchPl; LetterTrk; University; Accounting.

JORDAN, Sandra L; Paxton HS; Rankin, IL; 20/136 ChrhWkr; HonRl; Mdrgl; NHS; NatlThespSoc; SchPl; Wheaton College; Math.

JORDAN, Steven C; Orangeville HS; Orangeville, IL; Band; Chr; HonRl; SctActv; YthFlsp; FFA; Bsbl; Bsktbl; Ftbl; Trade School; Vocation.

JORDAN, Steve P; Richland HS; Essex, MO; TrsSophCls; PresJrCls; HonRl; College; Liberal Arts.

JORDAN, Syrlilars M; Roosevelt HS; Gary, IN; HonRl; MrchBnd; OffAde; Twrl; SchPpr; FrCl; College; Television Cameraman.

JORDAN, Timothy J; Dekalb HS; Dekalb, IL; 100/350 SecTrsJrCls; ChrhWkr; HonRl; StuCncl; StuGov; YthFlsp; YthLg; Bsbl; Bsktbl; Ftbl; Coll;.

JORDAN, Walter B; Gibson City HS; Gibson City, IL; ALBoysSt; NHS; StuCncl; 4-H; VPFFA; Bsktbl; CaptFtbl; Trk; 4-HAwd; JCAwd; Univ Of Illinois; Forest Science.

JORDAN, William L; Crab Orchard HS; Stonefort, IL; ChrhWkr; CmntyWkr; NHS; NatlMeritSchl; FBLA; FDA; FTA; Bsbl; Bsktbl; JAAwd; JCC; CitAwd; Trade School; Pro.

JORDE, Pam B; Tolna Public HS; Tolna, ND; CncrtBnd; HonRl; NHS; PepBnd; SchPl; Pres4-H; FHA; LetterBsktbl; Trk; JAAwd; Ndsu; Pharmacy.

JORDHEIM, Marsha A; Kindred Public HS; Kindred, ND; 19/46 Band; Chrs; CncrtBnd; HonRl; MrchBnd; NHS; PepBnd; TreasFHA; Tech Sch; Computer Prog.

JORDHEIM, Pamela F; Kindred Public HS; Walcott, ND; ChrhWkr; HonRl; LbryAde; NHS; SchPl; Twrl; Pres4-H; PresFHA; KeyCl; 4-HAwd; College; Vocation.

JORDHEIM, Rhonda J; Kindred HS; Walcott, ND; Chrs; CncrtBnd; MrchBnd; NHS; PepBnd; SchPl; Yrbk; RptrSchPpr; FHA; U Of Northern Colo; Psychology.

JORE, Kathryn; Caledonia Public HS; Caledonia, MN; Band; HonRl; College; Psychology.

JORGENS, Gayle; Elbow Lake Dist 263 HS; Elbow Lake, MN; 1/68 Band; ChrhWkr; CncrtBnd; HonRl; MrchBnd; NHS; PepBnd; TchrAde; YthFlsp; College; Art.

JORGENSEN, Bradley J; Demmark HS; Denmark, WI; 1/145 ALBoysSt; Band; CncrtBnd; DrmMjrt; HonRl; MrchBnd; NHS; PepBnd; StuCncl; RptrSchPpr; College; Medical Profession.

JORGENSEN, Brian K; Lakeview HS; Lakeview, MI; 3/122 PresSophCls; PresJrCls; PresSrCls; Band; HonRl; NHS; StuCncl; RptrYrbk; RptrSchPpr; University Of Michigan; Medicine.

JORGENSEN, Christine; Mt Vernon Public HS; Mt Vernon, SD; Band; Chrs; ChrhWkr; NHS; NatlThespSoc; SchPl; StuCncl; YthFlsp; 4-H; PpCl; Vocational School; Nursing.

JORGENSEN, Connie; Ringsted Community HS; Ringsted, IA; 1/21 SecSrCls; Band; NHS; CivCl; DARAwd; 4-HAwd; KiwanAwd; Ellsworth Comm Collelge; Fashion Merchandis.

JORGENSEN, Danette K; Mitchell Sr HS; Loomis, SD; 8/292 HonRl; South Dakota State Univ; Nursing.

JORGENSEN, Daniel M; Eagle Grove Sr HS; Eagle Grove, IA; Band; Chr; ChrhWkr; CmntyWkr; CncrtBnd; HonRl; MrchBnd; PolWkr; SchMus; SctActv; StuGov; SchPpr; GerCl; Bsktbl; Luther College.

JORGENSEN, David F; St Rita HS; Chicago, IL; 84/424 Univ Of Illinois; Computer Science.

JORGENSEN, Erik; Rochester Senior HS; Rochester, MI; 20/372 Band; CncrtBnd; MrchBnd; NHS; PepBnd; SctActv; Mi Tech Univ; Biological Science.

JORGENSEN, Harold S; Bridgewater Fontanelle HS; Bridgewater, IA; Band; Chrs; HonRl; SchPl; VP4-H; FFA; LetterTrk; 4-HAwd; PresAwd;.

JORGENSEN, James K; Midland Comm HS; Onslow, IA; PresFrshCls; TrsSrCls; Band; Chrs; CncrtBnd; HonRl; MrchBnd; NHS; 4-H; SciCl;.

JORGENSEN, Janice K; Sunshine Bible Academy; Clearfield, SD; 3/29 SecTrsFrshCls; ALAGirlsSt; Chr; HonRl; NatlMeritCmnd; SchPl; EdYrBk; PresPpCl; LetterBsktbl; LetterTrk; Tabor College; Physical Education.

JORGENSEN, Jeffrey A; Minden HS; Minden, NE; 14/106 HonRl; NHS; LetterFtbl; LetterTrk; IMSpt; University Of Nebraska; Business Admin.

JORGENSEN, Lynne M; Manual HS; Peoria, IL; 3/329 HonRl; NHS; OffAde; West Illinois Univ.

JORGENSEN, Marcia A; Manual HS; Peoria, IL; 1/329 HonRl; LbryAde; NHS; OffAde; StuCncl; West Ill Univ; Foreign Languages.

JORGENSEN, Roxann; Parker HS; Parker, SD; 10/45 Chrs; DrlTm; OffAde; PolWkr; RptrYrbk; SchPpr; PpCl; Sdsu Brookings Sd; Sociology.

JORGENSEN, Timothy; Minden HS; Minden, NE; 39/106 Band; PepBnd; SchMus; SchPl; Ftbl; Glf; IMSpt; Sterling College; Ministry.

JORGENSEN, Wanda G; Lake Central HS; Dyer, IN; HonRl; NHS; Quill&Scroll; SctActv; RptrSchPpr; SchPpr; GerCl; Purdue Calumet Univ; Nurse.

JORGENSEN, William P; Medicine Valley HS; Curtis, NE; ChrhWkr; StuCncl; StuGov; YthFlsp; 4-H; Bsbl; LetterBsktbl; LetterFtbl; LetterTrk; 4-HAwd; Kearney St College; Teaching.

JORGENSON, Donald L; Argyle HS; Argyle, MN; 6/31 TrsFrshCls; Band; Chrs; CncrtBnd; LbryAde; MrchBnd; PepBnd; PpCl; University; Commercial Art.

JORGENSON, Karen J; Hempstead HS; Dubuque, IA; Chr; SchMus; FrCl; GAA; College.

JORGENSON, Richard; Hawley HS; Hawley, MN; Band; HonRl; NHS; PepBnd; SchMus; Yrbk; 4-H; FFA; SciCl; College; Vocation.

JORGENSON, Tamera L; Fisher Public HS; Fisher, MN; 3/30 PresFrshCls; Band; Chr; Chrs; ChrhWkr; MrchBnd; PepBnd; SchPl; StuCncl; YthFlsp; University; Professional.

JORGENSON, Tricia L; Hershey HS; Hershey, NE; 1/39 Band; Chrs; HonRl; NHS; SchPl; TchrAde; RptrYrbk; SecPpCl; BttyCrckrAwd; EldAwd; U Of Ne; Accountant.

JORISSEN, Steve M; Chaska HS; Chaska, MN; ChrhWkr; HonRl; Sacrstn; TchrAde; LetterGlf; Socr; Swmmng; College.

JORNS, Ann K; Manhattan HS; Manhattan, KS; 1/400 AFS; ALBoysSt; ChrhWkr; ModUN; Orch; Pres4-H; Tennis; LetterTrk; Kansas State Univ; Pediatrician.

JORNS, Kathleen B; Oconomowoc Senior HS; Oconomowoc, WI; 6/212 HonRl; JrNHS; NHS; FrCl; PpCl; Chrldr; TreasGAA; Univ Of Wisconsin; Business Administration.

JOSE, Joette; Beulah HS; Beulah, ND; 4/54 ChrhWkr; HonRl; GerCl; Coll.

JOSEPH, Betty J; Hampton Public HS; Hampton, NE; 4/20 SecTrsFrshCls; PresSrCls; Band; SecDrlTm; SchPl; StuGov; EdYrBk; VP4-H; TreasWestlyan Univ; Professional.

JOSEPH, Cathy; Our Lady Of Grace Academy; Indianapolis, IN; Chr; Chrs; HonRl; SchMus; RptrSchPpr; SpnCl; Bus Sch; Leg Secty.

JOSEPH, Dana L; Shawnee Mission S HS; Overland Park, KS; ChrhWkr; HonRl; LbryAde; NHS; NatlMeritSF; RptrYrbk; Yrbk; FrCl; LetterSwmmng; Trk; Univ; Professional.

JOSEPH, John; Whitefish Bay HS; Milwaukee, WI; 91/330 ChrhWkr; CmntyWkr; HonRl; SchAde; SchMus; SchPl; IMSpt; Oh Wesleyan Univ; Bus Management And Law.

JOSEPH, Kohli P; Elkhorn HS; Elkhorn, WI; 3/169 ALBoysSt; HonRl; NHS; NatlMeritSF; PolWkr; StuCncl; RptrSchPpr; Trk; IMSpt;.

JOSEPH, Nancy; Acad Of Our Lady; Chicago, IL; 17/160 Chr; HonRl; NHS; SchPl; RptrYrbk; FNA; Ill Institute Of Technology; Biology.

JOSEPH, Simone R; Cowan HS; Muncie, IN; 14/56 ChrhWkr; HonRl; HospAde; LbryAde; YthFlsp; FHA; Univf Accounting.

JOSEPHS, Jeffrey M; Lyons Township HS; Western Springs, IL; 116/1226 HonRl; NHS; LetterTrk; Purdue Univ; Computer Science.

JOSEPHSON, Amy E; St Charles HS; St Charles, MO; 55/600 ChrhWkr; CmntyWkr; HonRl; NHS; SctActv; EdYrBk; MthCl; VPPpCl; ChmnIMSpt; NCTE;.

JOSEPHSON, James K; Edgewood HS; Madison, WI; Aud/Vis; Band; Ftbl; Trade School; Business.

JOSEPHSON, Martha; Central HS; Red Wing, MN; Band; CncrtBnd; HonRl; JrNHS; MrchBnd; NHS; Orch; PepBnd; PPFtbl; Gustavus Adolphus Col; Nursing.

JOSHUA, Alexa; Southeastern HS; Detroit, MI; 3/250 Band; CncrtBnd; HonRl; NHS; SchPl; FDA; Bsktbl; Tennis; Univ; Pre Med.

JOSI, Susan A; Ladysmith HS; Ladysmith, WI; HonRl; LbryAde; NHS; SchMus; RptrSchPpr; SptEdSchPpr; FHA; SpnCl; Univ; Professional.

JOSOFF, Linda M; Bryan HS; Omaha, NE; LbryAde; 4-H; SpnCl; Trk; Coll; Tchr.

JOST, Jane M; Gibson Southern HS; Fort Branch, IN; 51/225 HonRl; FFA; PpCl; Business Sch;.

JOSTEN, Denise M; Sacred Heart Of Mary HS; Palatine, IL; 21/135 Chrs; HonRl; NHS; PolWkr; SchPl; StuGov; TchrAde; RptrSchPpr; St Marys College; Special Ed.

JOSTOCK, Norma J; Lapeer Sr HS; Lapeer, MI; 59/426 HonRl; StuCncl; StuGov; Tennis; Trk; Chrldr; GAA; Lake Superior St College; Accounting.

JOSWIAK, Jill M; Lakeland HS; Woodruff, WI; 3/162 ALAGirlsSt; CncrtBnd; HonRl; NatlFornLg; NHS; SchMus; StuCncl; EdSchPpr; SpnCl; DARAwd;.

JOURNEY, Mark A; Basehor HS; Basehor, KS; CmntyWkr; HonRl; OffAde; TchrAde; RptrYrbk; SchPpr; EngCl; SpnCl; SciCl; Bus Col; Self Employment.

JOWERS, Cynthia O; Soldan HS; St Louis, MO; Band; CncrtBnd; HonRl; JrNHS; MrchBnd; PepBnd; StuCncl; 4-H;.

JOWETT, Micki L; Yale HS; Goodells, MI; SecSrCls; Chr; Chrl; HonRl; SchPl; TchrAde; 4-H; SpnCl; PPFtbl; College; Professional.

JOY, George B; Loup City Public HS; Rockville, NE; ALBoysSt; Aud/Vis; ChrhWkr; HonRl; SchAde; StuGov; TchrAde; FFA; LetterTrk; LetterWrstlng; U Of Nebr; Elec Eng.

JOY, Mark; Peoria Hs; Peoria, IL; 27/450 HonRl; JrNHS; NHS; SctActv; SciCl; Icc; Managarial Accounting.

JOYAL, Joyce M; Naperville Central HS; Naperville, IL; ChrhWkr; NHS; PolWkr; RedCrAde; StuCncl; TchrAde; GerCl; SciCl; Drake University; Pharmacy.

JOYCE, Ann C; Mother Mcauley Lib Arts HS; Chicago, IL; 5/474 Chrs; HonRl; NHS; Orch; SchMus; TchrAde; FTA; SecSpnCl; Bsktbl; LetterSwmmng; Univ Of Notre Dame; Medicine.

JOYCE, Barbara L; Reddick HS; Gardner, IL; 5/42 TrsJrCls; PresSrCls; Band; CncrtBnd; HonRl; MrchBnd; NHS; PepBnd; SchPl; StuCncl; Yrbk; SchPpr; Associated Sch; Airline Service.

JOYCE, David A; Centennial HS; Circle Pines, MN; Aud/Vis; Band; LbryAde; LetterBsktbl; Ftbl; CaptTrk;.

JOYCE, Jeffrey D; Woodruff HS; Peoria, IL; 81/288 ChrhWkr; CmntyWkr; SctActv; KeyCl; GerCl; Bsktbl; Ftbl; LetterTrk; PresAwd; College; X Ray Technician.

JOYCE, John R; St Laurence HS; Burbank, IL; 45/375 HonRl; StuCncl; Bsktbl; LetterFtbl; LetterTrk; College; Accounting.

JOYCE, Maureen B; Reddick HS; Reddick, IL; 1/42 SecTrsFrshCls; Band; Chrs; CncrtBnd; HonRl; MrchBnd; PepBnd; StuCncl; RptrYrbk; SchPpr; 4-H; FHA; GAA; Northern Ill Univ; Nursing.

JOYCE, Patrick H; Carmel HS For Boys; Deerfield, IL; 11/175 SecSrCls; HonRl; NHS; StuCncl; StuGov; Bsbl; LetterGlf; Univ Of Ill; Bio Engr.

JOYCE, Rick; El Dorado HS; El Dorado, KS; JCC; SchMus; SchPl; SctActv; StuGov; IMSpt; RotaryAwd; Butler Co Comm Juco; Cert Opthomic Despinsr.

JOYCE, Sharon; Adams HS; Rochester, MI; TrsFrshCls; NHS; RusCl; Chrldr; BttyCrckrAwd; Univ Of Michigan; Physician.

JOZAITIS, Vytas P; St Rita HS; Chicago, IL; 29/449 HonRl; NHS; SctActv; StuCncl; StuGov; Ill Tech; Engi.

JOZEFIAK, Stanley W; St Rita HS; Chicago, IL; 1/424 LetterChrs; HonRl; NHS; RptrSchPpr; CaptTrk; GovHonPrgAwd; Univ Of Chicago; Lawyer.

JUCIUS, Deborah A; Maria HS; Chicago, IL; HonRl; HospAde; RedCrAde; SctActv; Teen; RptrSchPpr; 4-H; SpnCl; 4-HAwd; Southwest Coll Of Chicago; Nurse.

JUCKETT, Robert S; Maine Twp South HS; Park Ridge, IL; CmntyWkr; HonRl; JrNHS; NHS; NatlMeritCmnd; PolWkr; SctActv; MthCl; SciCl; Colorado State Univ; Biology.

JUDD, Constance J; Troy HS; Troy, MI; NatlFornLg; SchPl; SctActv; TchrAde; FDA; Swmmng; Michigan State Univ; Biological Sciences.

JUDD, Cynthia D; Fairbury HS; Fairbury, NE; 13/148 Band; Chrs; CncrtBnd; HonRl; MrchBnd; PepBnd; SchMus; GerCl; PpCl; Univ Of Nebraska; English.

JUDD, James S; Springfield HS; Springfield, IL; Aud/Vis; ChrhWkr; CmntyWkr; PolWkr; SchMus; SchPl; SchPpr; Parks College; Aviation Management.

JUDD, Lorraine; Adelphian Acad; Holly, MI; Band; CncrtBnd; HonRl; Andrews U; Physical Therapy.

JUDD, Margaret L; Chosen Valley HS; Chatfield, MN; HonRl; SchPl; TchrAde; Yrbk; FTA; College.

JUDD, Thomas R; Glenbard West HS; Glenn Ellyn, IL; 33/515 VPBand; HonRl; Mdrgl; Ftbl; Trk; University Of Illinois; Engineering.

JUDE, Maureen L; Holy Trinity HS; Maple Lake, MN; ChrhWkr; HonRl; HospAde; LbryAde; OffAde; PolWkr; TchrAde; LetterChrldr; IMSpt; PPFtbl; College; Nursing.

JUDGE, Anne M; Shawnee Mission N HS; Shawnee Mission, KS; Chr; Chrs; ChrhWkr; HonRl; HospAde; Mdrgl; SchMus; StuCncl; TchrAde; PpCl; Univ Of Kansas; Modeling.

JUDGE, Joan M; West Holt HS; Atkinson, NE; Chrs; NatlFornLg; SchPl; StuCncl; CivCl; 4-H; PpCl; Chrldr; College.

JUDGE, Marla A; Albia Community HS; Albia, IA; 5/150 Chrs; HonRl; StuCncl; FHA; FNA; Indian Hills Comm College; Nurse.

JUDGE, Rose Ann; West Holt HS; Atkinson, NE; HonRl; Yrbk; FFA; FHA; Bsbl; Trk; Univ Of Nebraska; Veterinarian.

JUDKINS, Elizabeth A; Abraham Lincoln HS; Council Bluffs, IA; AFS; ChrhWkr; HonRl; JA; PolWkr; Teen; FNA; SpnCl; PpCl; IMSpt; College; Nurse.

JUDSON, Daniel; West Catholic HS; Frand Rapids, MI; 24/327 HonRl; NHS; NatlMeritCmnd; NatlMeritSF; SctActv; GerCl; MthCl; SciCl; Mich Tech Univ; Engineering.

JUDY, Julia K; West Richland HS; Noble, IL; ChrhWkr; HospAde; RedCrAde; SchPl; StuCncl; TchrAde; YthFnd; Chrldr; GAA; 4-HAwd; LionAwd; College; Physical Ed.

JUEDES, Laurie M; D C Everest HS; Schofield, WI; CmntyWkr; HonRl; LbryAde; SchPl; Trk; Univ Of Wis; Math.

JUEL, Jacqueline; Elk Horn Kimballton HS; Kimballton, IA; 1/42 Band; Chr; Chrs; CncrtBnd; DrmMjrt; HonRl; Mdrgl; MrchBnd; NHS; PepBnd; Nursing School; Nursing.

JUENEMANN, Catherine; Hill City HS; Hill City, KS; Chrs; HonRl; ModUN; NHS; SchMus; SchPl; FHA; Colby Jr Col; Secretarial.

JUENEMANN, Maureen A; Sanborn HS; Sanborn, MN; 9/29 Chr; ChrhWkr; DrmMjrt; LbryAde; MrchBnd; SchPl; TchrAde; Yrbk; RptrSchPpr; Vo Tech; Comm Tailoring.

JUENEMANN, Rose; Hill City HS; Hill City, KS; 5/55 Chrs; ChrhWkr; CmntyWkr; CncrtBnd; DrlTm; HonRl; LbryAde; SchPl; FHA; PpCl; Jr College; Business.

JUEONG, Lisa L; Maconaquah HS; Peru, IN; HonRl; LbryAde; TchrAde; GerCl; College; Dentist.

JUERGENS, Annette R; Clearfield Comm HS; Clearfield, IA; 1/10 Chrs; ChrhWkr; CmntyWkr; DrmMjrt; HonRl; JA; EdYrBk; 4-H; Bsktbl; CitAwd; Ia St U; Journalism.

JUFFER, Donna; East Charles Mix HS; Wagner, SD; 18/66 ALAGirlsSt; Chr; Chrs; ChrhWkr; CmntyWkr; DrlTm; HonRl; Mdrgl; Bsktbl; Trk; Coll; Science.

JUHL, Jane M; Dike Community HS; Hudson, IA; 1/54 Band; Chrs; CncrtBnd; NHS; SchPl; EdYrBk; Pres4-H; CaptChrldr; ChmbCommrsAwd; 4-HAwd; I St U; Dietetics.

JULIAN, Jean L; Silver Lake HS; Preston, MN; 2/69 Band; Chrs; CncrtBnd; HonRl; NHS; SchPl; FHA; GAA; St Marys Jr Coll; Nurse.

JULIAN, Jennifer; Hobart Sr HS; Hobart, IN; 48/320 ChrhWkr; HonRl; HospAde; Quill&Scroll; SctActv; TchrAde; YthFlsp; SchPpr; SpnCl; Vincennes Ind Univ; Dental Hygiene.

JULIUS, Steve; Northwest Webster HS; Barnum, IA; 2/28 SecSophCls; Aud/Vis; Chr; CncrtBnd; HonRl; NHS; PepBnd; RptrSchPpr; 4-H; 4-HAwd; Iowa State Univ; Agriculture.

JULSON, David J; Osseo Fairchild HS; Osseo, WI; Aud/Vis; HonRl; JrNHS; SchPl; TchrAde; LetterBsktbl; LetterFtbl; LetterTrk; College; Teching Math.

JUMP, Rebecca S; Zionsville Comm HS; Zionsville, IN; DrlTm; HonRl; NHS; Quill&Scroll; TchrAde; EdYrBk; SecLatCl; LetterBsktbl; Chrldr; GAA; Purdue U; Mathematics.

JUNCER, Bartholomew J; Quigley North HS; Waukegan, IL; 12/61 Chrs; ChrhWkr; CmntyWkr; HonRl; HospAde; Sacrstn; SchPl; Teen; RptrSchPpr; Niles College; Priesthood.

JUNCO, William D; Winchester Comm HS; Winchester, IN; Band; CncrtBnd; HonRl; NHS; SctActv; StuCncl; YthFlsp; SpnCl; University; Engineering.

JUNE, Debra K; Turner HS; Kansas City, KS; 19/320 HonRl; NHS; SchPl; StuCncl; RptrSchPpr; PpCl; LetterChrldr; GAA; IMSpt; College; Elementary Or English Teacher.

JUNG, Cheryl D; West Bend East HS; West Bend, WI; HonRl; NatlFornLg; TreasYthFlsp; 4-H; GerCl; PpCl; Technical School; Medical Asst.

JUNG, Dorothy; Wayland Acad; Randolph, WI; 5/75 Chr; HonRl; NatlMeritCmnd; NatlThespSoc; SchPl; StuCncl; Yrbk; FrCl; LetterSwmmng; CaptTennis;.

JUNG, Mary Carol; Immaculata HS; Chicago, IL; 63/200 PresSrCls; CmntyWkr; HospAde; NHS; StuCncl; GAA; Northeastern Coll; Maj Stud.

JUNG, Mary E; West Allis Central HS; West Allis, WI; 10/461 HonRl; NHS; OffAde; PolWkr; StuGov; TchrAde; EdYrBk; SchPpr; MthCl; GAA; Univ Of Wisc; Chemical Engineer.

JUNG, Peter A; Maine West HS; Des Plaines, IL; 95/800 HonRl; JrNHS; NatlMeritCmnd; College; Medicine.

JUNG, Virginia E; Academy Of Our Lady; Chicago, IL; 8/188 HonRl; NHS; SchMus; SchPl; StuGov; TchrAde; RptrYrbk; PpCl; GAA; Univ Of Ill; Theatre.

JUNGBLUTH, Joan M; Arrowhead HS; Hartland, WI; HonRl; NHS; PolWkr; FSA; Trk; Univ; Med.

JUNGELS, Kerry; Rich Central Hs; Park Forest, IL; 1/400 DrlTm; HonRl; NHS; LatCl; MthCl; College; Professional Nursing.

JUNGERMANN, George; Central HS; Aberdeen, SD; PolWkr; Ftbl; Wrstlng; Univ Of Sd; Criminology.

JUNGLES, David G; Aurora Central Catholic HS; Aurora, IL; 3/120 Chrs; ChrhWkr; HonRl; NHS; PresStuCncl; CaptTrk; Waubonsee Jr Coll; Psychology.

JUNION, Lisa M; Algoma HS; Algoma, WI; Chrs; SchMus; SchPl; 4-H; FrCl; PpCl; Bsktbl; Trk; GAA; IMSpt; Green Bay Univ; Primary Education.

JUNIOR, Debra L; Dwight D Eisenhower HS; New Berlin, WI; 9/256 HonRl; JrNHS; NHS; TchrAde; GerCl; Tech Sch;.

JUNIS, Debra; Neponset HS; Neponset, IL; HstSophCls; TrsSrCls; CmntyWkr; HonRl; LbryAde; EdYrBk; FHA; FrCl; Chrldr; Coll; Vocation.

JUNK, Beverly A; Mishicot HS; Manitowoc, WI; ChrhWkr; HonRl; NatlFornLg; SchPpr; 4-H; FBLA; FFA; FHA; LatCl; GAA; Florist.

JUNK, Joseph M; Hudson Comm HS; Waterloo, IA; 5/61 SecTrsFrshCls; SecTrsJrCls; HonRl; JA; 4-H; Ftbl; 4-HAwd;.

JUNKANS, John; Cole R V HS; Jefferson City, MO; Chr; ChrhWkr; HonRl; 4-H; Bsktbl; College; Vetrinarian.

JUNKER, Charlotte R; Mount Lake Public HS; Mountain Lake, MN; Chr; ChrhWkr; HonRl; 4-H; FHA; PpCl; LetterTrk; Chrldr; PresAwd; CitAwd; Col; Elem Teacher.

JUNKER, Debra L; Cass Lake HS; Cass Lake, MN; 4/48 Chrs; HonRl; OffAde; SchPl; Twrl; Yrbk; SchPpr; SecFHA; GerCl; Bsktbl; BttyCrckrAwd; St Paul Bible College; Religion.

JUNKER, Jessie A; Tomahawk HS; Tomahawk, WI; 1/190 PresFrshCls; Band; CncrtBnd; HonRl; MrchBnd; NatlFornLg; NatlSciFnd; PepBnd; GerCl; MthCl; OptClAwd; University; Dr Of Veterinary Medicine.

JUNKER, Lorinda L; Fairbury HS; Fairbury, NE; Chrs; ChrhWkr; HospAde; NHS; SchMus; SctActv; FBLA; GerCl; Wrstlng; College; Professional.

JUNKER, Susan; Illini Bluffs HS; Peoria, IL; 4/78 SecSophCls; ALAGirlsSt; Band; Chr; Chrs; ChrhWkr; HonRl; Illinois Central Coll; Medical Technology.

JUNOKAS, Joyce M; Prospect HS; Mt Prospect, IL; 108/600 HonRl; College; Elementary Education.

JUNTUNEN, Dale A; Baraga HS; Baraga, MI; TrsFrshCls; IMSpt; Kirtland Cc; Aviation Maintenance.

JUNTUNEN, Gwen A; Hamlin HS; Vienna, SD; Band; Chrs; HonRl; MrchBnd; RptrSchPpr; LetterBsktbl; LetterTrk; LetterChrldr; AmLegAwd; 4-HAwd; Sd Univ; Professional.

JUNTUNEN, Jody; Rock Lake HS; Perth, ND; SecTrsJrCls; Band; Chrs; HonRl; NHS; StuCncl; RptrYrbk; 4-H; PpCl; Coll; Professional.

JUNTUNEN, Robert D; Central HS; Grand Forks, ND; HonRl; StuCncl; StuGov; University Of North Dakota; Engineering.

JURANEK, Paul R; John Hersey HS; Mt Prospect, IL; HonRl; NHS; Tennis; Univ; Pre/dentistry.

JURASEK, Stanley; Concord HS; Concord, MI; HonRl; StuGov; RptrSchPpr; Bsktbl; Jackson Comm Coll; Bux Ad.

JURASEK, Stanley B; Concord HS; Concord, MI; HonRl; StuGov; TchrAde; SptEdSchPpr; College; Data Processing.

JURCA, Stephen N; Romeoville HS; Lemont, IL; 125/293 StuCncl; StuGov; CaptCaptIMSpt; Col; Education.

JURCAK, Cynthia L; Denby HS; Detroit, MI; ChrhWkr; CmntyWkr; HonRl; NatlMeritFnl; NatlMeritSchl; OffAde; TchrAde; Wayne St U; Pre Social Work.

JURCAK, Susan M; Regina HS; East Detroit, MI; Chrl; ChrhWkr; CmntyWkr; HonRl; SchAde; SchPl; Trade Or Bus Schl; Professional.

JUREWICZ, Mary Ann; Forest View HS; Mt Prospect, IL; 22/645 HonRl; NHS; Quill&Scroll; College; Exec Secretary.

JUREY, Dwight A; Clifton HS; Clifton, KS; 1/20 TrsFrshCls; PresSophCls; Band; HonRl; NatlMeritSF; YthFlsp; Kansas St Univ; Agricultural Economics.

JURGEMEYER, William M; Rockwell Swaledale HS; Rockwell, IA; HonRl; NHS; FFA; College; Vocation.

JURGENS, Diana L; North Bend Central HS; North Bend, NE; Chr; Chrs; ChrhWkr; HonRl; SchMus; Yrbk; FTA; PpCl; LetterSwmmng; Trk; College; Respiratory Therapy.

JURGENS, Sue; Sheboygan North HS; Sheboygan, WI; Chr; CncrtBnd; HonRl; MrchBnd; PepBnd; StuCncl; College.

JURGENS, Vickie L; Holdrege HS; Holdrege, NE; Chrs; HospAde; SchMus; Sec4-H; SecFBLA; PpCl; 4-HAwd; Lincoln Sch Of Comm; Legal Secty.

JURGENSEN, William W; Creighton Prep; Omaha, NE; 32/250 SecFrshCls; SecSophCls; SecJrCls; ChrhWkr; CmntyWkr; HonRl; NatlMeritSchl; PepBnd; Sdlty; StuCncl; FDA; FSA; Bsbl; Chrldr; Univ; Professional.

JURICEK, Jane; Morton West Hs; Berwyn, IL; 22/760 HonRl; JrNHS; NHS; Yrbk; College Easter Il-;elementary Education.

JURICH, Joseph R; St Francis HS; Glen Ellyn, IL; 3/88 PresJrCls; HonRl; Univ; Dentist.

JURICH, Michele M; Gage Park HS; Chicago, IL; CmntyWkr; HonRl; JrNHS; NHS; NatlMeritCmnd; NatlMeritSchl; PolWkr; RedCrAde; StuCncl; StuGov; College; Psychology.

JURKOWSKI, Robert J; Lasalle Peru Twp HS; Peru, IL; 120/506 Band; ChrhWkr; CncrtBnd; HonRl; MrchBnd; PepBnd; College; Business Administration.

JURMAN, Ronald; Lockport HS; Lockport, IL; HonRl; NatlMeritSF; Univ; Elec Engineering.

JURMU, Dennis R; Wakefield HS; Wakefield, MI; ChrhWkr; LetterFtbl; Us Army; Conservation.

JURRENS, Karen F; Little Rock Community HS; Ellsworth, MN; TrsSrCls; Chr; HonRl; StuCncl; TchrAde; YthFlsp; FTA; PpCl; College; Medicine.

JURSCH, Kris L; Raymore Peculiar HS; Raymore, MO; CncrtBnd; HonRl; PepBnd; RptrSchPpr; FHA; FTA; PpCl; LetterBsktbl; GAA; PPFtbl; College; Police Work.

JURUSOV, Paul M; Austin Prep HS; Grosse Point, MI; Aud/Vis; ChrhWkr; CmntyWkr; SchPl; SciCl; Ftbl; College; Professional.

JURY, Jill; Lowpoint Washburn HS; Washburn, IL; 4/63 SecTrsFrshCls; SecTrsJrCls; Chrs; ChrhWkr; HonRl; NHS; SchPl; EdYrBk; 4-H; GAA; 4-HAwd; Univ Il; Med Tech.

JURY, Mark C; Sparland HS; Sparland, IL; SchPl; SctActv; StuCncl; StuGov; RptrYrbk; PpCl; Trade Sch; Prof.

JURY, Timothy G; Harmony Comm HS; Farmington, IA; 1/60 PresFrshCls; Band; Chr; Chrs; CncrtBnd; HonRl; Mdrgl; MrchBnd; NHS; PepBnd; SchPl; YthFlsp; RptrYrbk; 4-H; University; Architecture.

JUSSEL, Julie K; Wagner HS; Wagner, SD; Chrs; HonRl; PpCl; RotaryAwd; VoiceDemAwd; College; Major Study.

JUST, Larry; Lake Central HS; Schererville, IN; 67/432 TchrAde; SciCl; Nichels Eng School Of Tech; Automotive Eng.

JUSTICE, Blake; Carbondale Comm Hs; Carbondale, IL; HonRl; PolWkr; Yrbk; So Illinois U; Prof Of Pohotography.

JUSTICE, James W; Irwin Community HS; Irwin, IA; 1/38 PresSophCls; ALBoysSt; Band; NHS; YthFlsp; Yrbk; LetterBsbl; CaptBsktbl; LetterFtbl; LetterTrk; IMSpt; College; Vocational.

JUSTICE, Jane; Irwin Comm HS; Irwin, IA; 5/50 SecTrsJrCls; Band; Chr; Chrs; ChrhWkr; MrchBnd; PepBnd; CchngActv; Jennie Edmundson Sch Nursing; Rn.

JUSTICE, Kemberlee; Willow Run HS; Ypsilanti, MI; SecSophCls; SecJrCls; Chr; Chrl; HonRl; NHS; SchPl; StuCncl; RptrYrbk; GerCl; Eastern Mi U; Special Educationfor Blind.

JUSTICE, Michael B; West Chicago Dist 94 HS; Winfield, IL; 20/320 Chrs; CmntyWkr; SctActv; MthCl; SciCl; Univ Of Illinois; Computer Science.

JUSTICE, Sheila L; Clark County R 1 HS; Kahoka, MO; 6/91 HonRl; NHS; PpCl; LetterChrldr; Univ; Comp Sciences.

JUSTICE, Timothy J; Marist HS; Chicago, IL; 25/393 HonRl; SpnCl; College; Law.

JUSTMAN, Bruce C; Stephen Hempstead HS; Dubuque, IA; 2/450 HonRl; ModUN; NHS; SchPpr; TreasGerCl; Tennis; ChmbCommrsAwd; DARAwd; Loras College; Dentistry.

JUSTUS, Cynthia; Okawville HS; Addieville, IL; Band; Chr; HonRl; SchPl; YthFlsp; FHA; PpCl; Trk; Chrldr; GAA; Belleville Area College; Data Procesion.

JUSTUS, Dayna K; Oak Park HS; Kansas City, MO; Chr; Chrs; ChrhWkr; HonRl; SchMus; SctActv; YthFlsp; PpCl; College; Mathematics.

K

KAARDAL, Jean E; Redwood Falls HS; Fedwood Falls, MN; 8/122 AFS; HonRl; NHS; NatlMeritCmnd; StuCncl; Twrl; Yrbk; LetterBsktbl; CaptPPFtbl; GodCntryAwd; U Of Mn Minneapolis; Business Admin.

KAAS, Cindy J; Belvidere HS; Belvidere, IL; Band; ChrhWkr; CncrtBnd; HonRl; JA; MrchBnd; PepBnd; SchMus; StuCncl; RptrSchPpr; SpnCl; MthCl; DARAwd; Southern Illinois Univ; Pre Medicine.

KAAS, Tereasa M; Sauk Centre HS; Sauk Centre, MN; 1/156 ChrhWkr; HospAde; NatlMeritCmnd; RedCrAde; BauchLmbAwd; Hamlin Univ; Chemistry Major.

KABAT, Carol S; Waltonville Comm #1 HS; Waltonville, IL; 3/40 VPSophCls; HonRl; RptrYrbk; FHA; GerCl; PpCl; Rend Lake Jr College.

KABAT, Donald R; Traverse City HS; Traverse City, MI; 58/602 HonRl; NHS; RedCrAde; SchPl; SctActv; RptrSchPpr; EdSchPpr; Nw Michigan College; Nursing.

KABAT, Sharon M; Thornton Township HS; Dolton, IL; HonRl; HospAde; JrNHS; NHS; Thornton Comm Coll; Bus.

KABELE, Jean A; Platteville HS; Platteville, WI; Chr; HonRl; SchMus; SpnCl; KiwanAwd; Uw Platteville; Spanish.

KABES, Debra L; Clarkson Public HS; Clarkson, NE; ALAGirlsSt; Band; Chr; Chrs; ChrhWkr; CmntyWkr; CncrtBnd; HonRl; MrchBnd; PepBnd; Univ Of Nebraska; Home Economics.

KABES, Laurie; Leigh Community HS; Leigh, NE; HonRl; StuCncl; FHA; GerCl; PpCl; PPFtbl; College; Accounting.

KABES, Mike A; Leigh Community HS; Leigh, NE; CmntyWkr; SchPl; Yrbk; FFA; Tech School; Farm.

KABISCH, David E; Walnut Community HS; Walnut, IA; 5/23 Chrs; HonRl; SchPl; MthCl; SciCl; LetterBsbl; LetterBsktbl; Ftbl; LetterTrk; PresAwd; College; Commercial Artist.

KABKE, Joseph P; Lourdes HS; Oshkosh, WI; NatlMeritCmnd; College; Engineering.

KACHEL, David W; Notre Dame HS; Harper Woods, MI; HonRl; NHS; RptrSchPpr; IMSpt; U Of Mi; Architecture.

KACHELEIN, Catherine M; Anderson HS; Anderson, IN; Chr; HonRl; NatlThespSoc; SchMus; SchPl; StuCncl; TchrAde; FTA; LetterTrk; Univ; Elementary Education.

KACHIN, Sharon M; Sacred Heart HS; Dearborn Heights, MI; HonRl; HospAde; NHS; SecFNA; PresFrCl; LetterChrldr; IMSpt; Eastern Mi U; Occupational Therapy.

KACHMARCHIK, Frances L; Bishop Foley HS; Detroit, MI; 13/186 ALAGirlsSt; HonRl; NHS; RptrSchPpr; Bsktbl; Trk; IMSpt; AmLegAwd; Univ Of Mi; Medicine.

KACKLEY, Kevin W; Maryville R Ii HS; Maryville, MO; Chr; ChrhWkr; HonRl; SctActv; YthLg; KeyCl; Bsbl; Bsktbl; LetterFtbl; Trk; GodCntryAwd; College; Engineering.

KACKLEY, Tim; Custer HS; Milwaukee, WI; Chr; Chrs; CmntyWkr; StuCncl; Bsbl; Bsktbl; Trk; CchngActv; PPFtbl; Carroll College; Business Administration.

KACMAR, Lois M; Crown Point HS; Crown Point, IN; 11/493 ALAGirlsSt; HonRl; TreasNHS; StuCncl; TreasLatCl; TreasPpCl; Bsktbl; LetterTrk; CaptChrldr; IMSpt; Purdue Univ; Pharmacy.

KACMAR, Mark A; Andrean HS; Gary, IN; ChrhWkr; StuCncl; MthCl; Ftbl; Trk; College; Engineering.

KACMAR, Rosemarie; Andrean HS; Gary, IN; 61/301 ChrhWkr; HonRl; Quill&Scroll; StuCncl; RptrYrbk; FrCl; MthCl; Saint Marys College; Biology.

KACMARYNSKI, Kathleen S; St Marys HS; Storm Lake, IA; 5/45 Chr; Chrs; HonRl; HospAde; NHS; SchMus; RptrSchPpr; PpCl; Trk; Univ Of Northern Iowa; Med Tech.

KACZINSKI, Mary A; Notre Dame HS; Burlington, IA; 11/74 DrlTm; DrmMjrt; HonRl; HospAde; Yrbk; 4-H; LetterTrk; 4-HAwd; Univ Of Iowa; Physical Therapy.

KACZMAREK, Carol S; Cudahy Senior HS; Cdahy, WI; 16/344 HonRl; NHS; FTA; FrCl; MthCl; U Of Wi Milwaukee; Elementary Ed.

KACZMAREK, Donna M; Gilman HS; Lublin, WI; SecJrCls; HonRl; StuCncl; Yrbk; Bsktbl; GAA; Stewardess.

KACZMAREK, Patricia A; Mother Of Sorrows HS; Blue Island, IL; 4/165 SecFrshCls; Chr; Chrs; ChrhWkr; CtyCnl; CmntyWkr; HonRl; LbryAde; OffAde; PepBnd; SchAde; SchPl; SctActv; Trk; Business College; Accounting.

KACZMAREK, Robert B; Greenfield HS; Greenfield, WI; ALBoysSt; HonRl; ModUN; NatlFornLg; NHS; YthLg; Bsbl; Trk; Wrstlng; AmLegAwd; Univ Of Wi; Medicine.

KACZMAREK, Robert D; Brookfield Central HS; Brookfield, WI; ALBoysSt; Band; CncrtBnd; MrchBnd; NHS; NatlMeritCmnd; PepBnd; CaptTrk; U Of Wi; Optometry.

KACZMAREK, Teri L; Bay View HS; Milwaukee, WI; HonRl; PresJA; NHS; StuGov; SpnCl; Chrldr; College; Psychology.

KACZMARYN, Diane L; Waukegan East HS; Waukegan, IL; SecFrshCls; SecSophCls; VPJrCls; HonRl; OffAde; StuCncl; PpCl; Col; Professional.

KACZOR, Alan B; Neillsville HS; Neillsville, WI; Chrs; ChrhWkr; HonRl; 4-H; FFA; LetterFtbl; LetterTrk; LetterWrstlng; IMSpt; 4-HAwd; Trade School.

KACZOR, Tadeusz; Lake Zurich HS; Lake Zurich, IL; 30/193 HonRl; NHS; LetterBsktbl; LetterFtbl; LetterTrk; Architec.

KACZOROWSKI, Karen; Regina HS; Detroit, MI; Chrl; CmntyWkr; HonRl; JA; SctActv; SchPpr; Coll; Md.

KADAVY, Thomas D; Assumption HS; Davenport, IA; 16/250 ALBoysSt; CmntyWkr; HonRl; JA; JrNHS; NHS; SctActv; CaptBsktbl; LetterFtbl; IMSpt; College; Professional.

KADDATZ, Sheri K; Lincoln HS; Wisconsin Rapids, WI; Chr; Chrs; HonRl; PpCl; SciCl;.

KADEN, Cheryl L; Bogan HS; Chicago, IL; 50/735 HonRl; HospAde; NHS; TchrAde; RptrYrbk; FNA; CaptChrldr; CitAwd; Western College; Special Education.

KADLEC, Debra; Greenhills HS; Ann Arbor, MI; 5/21 SecFrshCls; SecJrCls; Chrs; HonRl; SchMus; SchPl; Yrbk; Univ Of Michigan.

KADLER, Marcia; Mt Pleasant HS; Mt Pleasant, MI; 20/322 Band; CAP; CmntyWkr; CncrtBnd; HonRl; HospAde; MrchBnd; NHS; NatlThespSoc; SchPpr; College; Professional.

KADOLPH, Martha L; Hubbard Comm HS; Hubbard, IA; 5/43 LetterTrk; BttyCrckrAwd; Iowa St U; Food & Nutrition.

KADOUN, Kathy J; Lidgerwood Public HS; Lidgerwood, ND; CncrtBnd; HonRl; NHS; StuCncl; VPFHA; LetterBsktbl; Trk; Chrldr; SecPresAwd; College.

KADOW, Arthur F; Elgin HS; Streamwood, IL; ALBoysSt; PolWkr; SctActv; StuGov; RptrSchPpr; SpnCl; Northern Univ; Politics.

KADRICH, Bryan K; Lincoln HS; Warren, MI; 75/376 Chr; HonRl; PolWkr; SchMus; SctActv; StuCncl; StuGov; FrCl; Ftbl; University Of Michigan; Lawyer.

KADRMAS, Jan; Dickinson HS; Dickinson, ND; Chrl; DrlTm; HonRl; Trade Schl; Cosmetology.

KADY, Nancy J; Jamestown HS; Jamestown, KS; Band; Chrs; CncrtBnd; HonRl; MrchBnd; PepBnd; SchMus; SchPl; Teen; YthFlsp; College.

KAEDING, Christopher C; Eisenhower HS; Decatur, IL; 1/450 PresJrCls; AFS; NHS; NatlThespSoc; SchMus; SchPl; PresStuCncl; RptrYrbk; RptrSchPpr; Trk; College; Medicine.

KAEHLER, Debbie; Milton Senior HS; Milton Jct, WI; 1/175 TrsFrshCls; HonRl; NHS; Quill&Scroll; FBLA; Trk; GAA; 4-HAwd; KiwanAwd; Uw Whitewater; Accounting.

KAELIN, Cindy; St Teresa HS; Decatur, IL; HonRl; SchPl; StuCncl; RptrYrbk; Yrbk; PpCl; Trk; Chrldr; Coll; Med.

KAELIN, George; Northwestern HS; Wentworth, WI; 16/126 PresFrshCls; ChrhWkr; StuGov; 4-H; FFA; Univ; Accounting.

KAEMPF, David A; G C Comm South HS; Granite City, IL; 33/630 Univ Of Illinois; History.

KAESER, Diane R; Marion HS; Marion, IL; 1/273 Band; SecChr; Mdrgl; VPNHS; VPNatlThespSoc; SchMus; SecSpnCl; SecMthCl; IMSpt; PPFtbl; KiwanAwd; LionAwd; Southern Illinois Univ; Dentist.

KAESTER, Joyce; Claflin HS; Hoisington, KS; Chrs; LbryAde; FHA; FNA; PpCl; Fort Hays Kans St Coll; Nursing.

KAESTNER, Susan; Cahokia Sr HS; Cahokia, IL; 5/532 ChrhWkr; HonRl; JA; NHS; RptrSchPpr; MthCl; Univ; Vocation.

KAFKA, Mary J; Slayton Public HS; Slayton, MN; 12/103 PresSrCls; Band; Chr; HonRl; NHS; StuCncl; TchrAde; YthFnd; 4-H; LetterChrldr; Granite Falls Vo Tech; Medical Secretary.

KAGAY, Anita R; John Hersey HS; Arlington Hts, IL; 1/783 AFS; Chr; Chrs; VPChrhWkr; HonRl; NHS; PolWkr; Univ Of Illinois; Business Admin.

KAHL, Sandra K; Clarence Lowden HS; Lowden, IA; TrsFrshCls; TrsSophCls; Band; Chrs; ChrhWkr; CncrtBnd; HonRl; Mdrgl; MrchBnd; PepBnd; SchMus; StuCncl; YthFlsp; RptrSchPpr; Kirkwood Comm College; Secretary.

KAHLE, Claralee A; Owensville HS; Owensville, MO; SecSophCls; Band; HonRl; YthFlsp; RptrYrbk; ChmnPpCl; LetterBsktbl; Chrldr; SecGAA; Sms At Springfield Mo; Physical Ed.

KAHLE, Darla A; Tomahawk HS; Tomahawk, WI; TrsJrCls; Band; ChrhWkr; HonRl; PepBnd; 4-H; SpnCl; MthCl; PpCl; GAA; University.

KAHLE, Donald W; James B Conant HS; Hoffman Estates, IL; 11/600 ChrhWkr; HonRl; NatlFornLg; NHS; NatlThespSoc; SchPl; YthFlsp; RptrSchPpr; Trinity College; Teaching.

KAHLE, John H; Southridge HS; Huntingburg, IN; 1/131 PresSophCls; ChrhWkr; HonRl; StuGov; PresYthFlsp; KeyCl; SpnCl; PpCl; CaptBsbl; LetterTennis; IMSpt; DARAwd; Indiana University; Law.

KAHLE, Karen A; Lexington HS; Lexington, IL; 6/62 TrsFrshCls; VPSophCls; PresJrCls; AFS; Band; HonRl; NHS; NatlMeritCmnd; SchPl; SctActv; StuCncl; TchrAde; RptrYrbk; 4-H; FTA; College; Law.

KAHLE, Keri K; Hoxie HS; Hoxie, KS; 7/78 VPSrCls; ALAGirlsSt; Band; CncrtBnd; HonRl; MrchBnd; NHS; PepBnd; PolWkr; StuCncl; TchrAde; Bsktbl; LetterTrk; Fort Hays State Univ.

KAHLE, Michael M; St Johns Preparatory HS; Gaylord, MN; SecFrshCls; Band; Chr; HonRl; NHS; SchPl; StuCncl; Univ Of Minnesota; Psychology.

KAHLER, Lisa A; Morton HS; Morton, IL; Chrs; PresSophCls; HonRl; HospAde; Mdrgl; MrchBnd; SchMus; SchPl; 4-H; 4-HAwd; St Francis Sch Of Nursing.

KAHLER, Terry D; Garwin Comm HS; Garwin, IA; ALBoysSt; Band; CncrtBnd; HonRl; MrchBnd; SchPl; SctActv; RptrYrbk; RptrSchPpr; Bsktbl; Coll; Biology.

KAHRE, Raymond M; Maconaquah HS; Peru, IN; 2/247 ALBoysSt; HonRl; JrNHS; NHS; SctActv; LatCl; MthCl; Bsbl; Ftbl; Wrstlng; Purdue Univ; Statistician.

KAHRS, Julie A; Franklin HS; Bloomington, NE; Chrs; CncrtBnd; HonRl; MrchBnd; Twrl; YthFlsp; SciCl; College; Professional.

KAI, Shawn J; Pender Public HS; Pender, NE; SchPl; StuCncl; StuGov; TchrAde; FFA; EngCl; LetterFtbl; Coll; Professional.

KAIGLER, Joseph M; Univ Of Detroit HS; Detroit, MI; ChrhWkr; CmntyWkr; NatlMeritCmnd; Col; Law.

KAIRYS, Daiva; Thomas Kelly HS; Chicago, IL; 29/415 TreasNHS; SchAde; SctActv; Univ Of Illinois Cc; Mathematics.

KAISER, Alan D; Chase County HS; Imperial, NE; HonRl; TchrAde; PresYthFlsp; FBLA; FFA; Bsktbl; Trk; Wrstlng; IMSpt; Natl Col Of Bus Rapid City; Computer Prog.

KAISER, Catherine P; Immaculata HS; Leavenworth, KS; Band; CncrtBnd; HonRl; MrchBnd; PepBnd; PolWkr; TchrAde; SpnCl; PpCl; LetterTrk; College; Music.

KAISER, Charles L; Northrop HS; Fort Wayne, IN; 69/647 Chr; HonRl; HospAde; JA; SctActv; StuCncl; TchrAde; Indiana Univ; Law.

KAISER, Debra; Tampico HS; Tampico, IL; 2/36 ChrhWkr; HonRl; LbryAde; SchPl; StuCncl; TchrAde; EdYrBk; Trk; Sauk Valley Jr Coll; Bus.

KAISER, Diane M; Carl Brablec HS; Roseville, MI; Band; Chr; CncrtBnd; HonRl; MrchBnd; SctActv; TchrAde; SciCl; Bsbl; Bsktbl; Lake Superior State Clg; Wildlife Biologist.

KAISER, Douglas R; St Edmond HS; Fort Dodge, IA; TrsFrshCls; Aud/Vis; SchPl; StuGov; FrCl; Bsbl; Bsktbl; Ftbl; LetterGlf; IMSpt; Professional.

KAISER, Jean; William Howard Taft Hs; Chicago, IL; 45/820 Band; ChrhWkr; HonRl; LbryAde; NHS; Orch; YthFlsp; SpnCl; GAA; Mundelein College; Dietetian.

KAISER, Joy A; Tampico HS; Deer Grove, IL; 1/35 Chrs; ChrhWkr; HonRl; SchPl; TchrAde; RptrYrbk; 4-H; GAA; Taylor Univ; Teacher Elementary And Nursing.

KAISER, Kristine; Fenton HS; Bensenville, IL; Band; HonRl; NHS; PepBnd; Yrbk; SchPpr; PresGAA; IMSpt; College; Professional.

KAISER, Lisa K; Immaculate Conception Acad; Batesville, IN; PresSophCls; Chr; ChrhWkr; SchPl; StuCncl; TchrAde; Yrbk; FrCl; LatCl; Bsktbl; Tennis; College; Lawyer.

KAISER, Mark A; Oak Forest HS; Oak Forest, IL; SchPl;.

KAISER, Rodney W; Boone County Rvi HS; Centralia, MO; 4/120 CmntyWkr; HonRl; FFA; Bsbl; LetterBsktbl; LetterFtbl; LetterTrk; College; Engineering.

KAISER, Sheree B; Carrollton HS; Carrollton, MO; 7/100 Band; Chr; ChrhWkr; CncrtBnd; HonRl; MrchBnd; NHS; StuCncl; TchrAde; GerCl; Umc; Journalism.

KAISER, Steven; St Paul Kennedy HS; Chicago, IL; Aud/Vis; Chrs; ChrhWkr; HonRl; IMSpt; College; Pharmacy.

KAISER, Teresa L; Washington HS; Indianapolis, IN; ChrhWkr; HonRl; JrNHS; NHS; Quill&Scroll; StuCncl; RptrSchPpr; SchPpr; Business.

KAISER, Thomas J; Fenwick HS; Bellwood, IL; HonRl; NatlMeritCmnd; SchPl; SecGerCl; LetterTrk; Univ Of Il; Journalism.

KAISER, Tim; Fairmount Public HS; Fairmount, ND; VPFrshCls; ALBoysSt; ChrhWkr; HonRl; SchPl; Trk; CchngActv; College; Professional.

KAISER, Tom C; Sacred Heart HS; E Grand Forks, MN; 15/53 VPFrshCls; Chrs; SchPl; RptrYrbk; SchPpr; Bsktbl; Ftbl; Trk; IMSpt; PresAwd; Northland Comm Col; Bus.

KAKAVECOS, Donald R; Brown County HS; Morgantown, IN; 3/169 TrsSrCls; ChrhWkr; HonRl; NHS; TchrAde; VP4-H; PresLatCl; Tennessee Temple; Psychology.

KAKER, Kyle F; Kohler Public HS; Kohler, WI; PresSrCls; ALBoysSt; CncrtBnd; HonRl; NatlMeritSF; StuGov; LetterBsbl; LetterFtbl; LetterTrk; LetterWrstlng; Us Naval Academy Annapolis; Officer.

KAKIS, Georgia; Amundsen Hs; Chicago, IL; 6 ChrhWkr; CncrtBnd; HonRl; NHS; NatlMeritSchl; OffAde; Orch; Yrbk; MthCl; GAA; College;pharmacy.

KALAL, Patricia A; Forest View HS; Des Plaines, IL; HonRl; Glf; CaptSwmmng; Univ Of Utah; Zoology.

KALANIK, Karen A; Routt HS; Jacksonville, IL; 12/60 HonRl; HospAde; SchPl; SctActv; StuCncl; RptrYrbk; Yrbk; SchPpr; FrCl; Ill State Univ; Veterinarian.

KALER, Kathy J; Rantoul Twp HS; Rantoul, IL; Chr; Chrs; SchMus; SchPl; TchrAde; Bsbl; Bsktbl; LetterTennis; CchngActv; JCAwd; Parkland Colle; Physical Education.

KALETA, David T; Lake Park HS; Itasca, IL; HonRl; NatlMeritCmnd; LetterTennis; GovHonPrgAwd; College; Doctor.

KALETKA, Thomas R; Auburndale HS; Arpin, WI; TrsFrshCls; Band; CncrtBnd; HonRl; MrchBnd; NHS; SecStuCncl; GerCl; Bsktbl; LetterFtbl; College.

KALHAGEN, Orin C; Edmore Public HS; Webster, ND; ALBoysSt; ChrhWkr; HonRl; SchPl; Yrbk; SciCl; FtbslSt; Ftbl; Trk; JETSAwd; CitAwd; Univ; Pro.

KALHAMMER, Scott A; Forman HS; Manito, IL; 20/90 VPFrshCls; PresSophCls; ChrhWkr; HonRl; SchPl; StuGov; Bsbl; Bsktbl; Trk; IMSpt; College; Business Management.

KALHORN, Jim; Dubuque Senior HS; Dubuque, IA; ALBoysSt; HonRl; JrNHS; NHS; YthFlsp; SpnCl; MthCl; JETSAwd; College; Pre Med.

KALIES, Terry; Kimberly HS; Appleton, WI; Band; DrmBgl; HonRl; 4-H; Ftbl; College; Professional.

KALIN, Annette L; Lewiston Consolidated HS; Burchard, NE; Chr; Chrs; ChrhWkr; HonRl; SchMus; SchPl; StuGov; TchrAde; Yrbk; FHA;.

KALINA, Maryann; Immaculate Conception HS; Elmhurst, IL; 11 SecSophCls; HonRl; NHS; RedCrAde; PresStuCncl; StuGov; Yrbk; SecLatCl; PpCl; IMSpt; College; Major In Art.

KALINOWSKI, Kathryn A; St Augustine HS; Chicago, IL; 4/94 TrsSrCls; HonRl; NHS; StuCncl; Yrbk; Chicago Circle; Lab Technician.

KALINOWSKI, Linda L; Wm Howard Taft HS; Chicago, IL; 32/789 HonRl; JrNHS; NHS; EngCl; GAA; Univ Of Ill; Business Adm.

KALINOWSKI, Michael J; West Allis Central HS; West Allis, WI; 8/460 PresSrCls; ALBoysSt; HonRl; NatlMeritCmnd; IMSpt; Univ Of Wisconsin; Law.

KALIS, Rita A; Wells Easton HS; Wells, MN; 28/111 Band; CncrtBnd; HonRl; MrchBnd; PepBnd; 4-H; FHA; St Catherines College; Nursing.

KALIS, Russell; Wells Easton HS; Wells, MN; 1/120 ALBoysSt; ChrhWkr; HonRl; StuCncl; FFA; Ma Inst Tech; Chem Engineering.

KALISEK, Michael W; Howells Public HS; Howells, NE; PresSophCls; HonRl; SchPl; Glf; Tennis; Univ Of Ne Lincoln; Engineering.

KALISH, Ronna S; Niles East HS; Skokie, IL; 50/585 PresCncrtBnd; HonRl; MrchBnd; NHS; Orch; Tennis; Univ Of Illinois.

KALISIAK, Glenn; Proviso West Hs; Westchester, IL; 53/948 Band; CncrtBnd; HonRl; MrchBnd; NHS; Orch; PepBnd; University; Accounting.

KALISZ, Paul J; Oswego Sr HS; Oswego, IL; 14/256 Aud/Vis; HonRl; College; Engineering.

KALIVIANAKIS, Carrie J; United Township HS; Eat Moline, IL; Col.

KALK, Sandra A; Mc Donell Central HS; Chippewa Falls, WI; 5/93 HstSrCls; CmntyWkr; HonRl; ModUN; PepBnd; StuCncl; UNYO; RptrYrbk; RptrSchPpr; LetterBsktbl; Trk; Chrldr; GAA; College; Nursing.

KALKHOFF, Luvern B; Morgan HS; Morgan, MN; Chrs; HonRl; Sacrstn; SchPl; LetterWrstlng; Vocational Sch; Accountant.

KALKOWSKI, Michael J; St Laurence HS; Burbank, IL; 3/379 Band; CncrtBnd; HonRl; MrchBnd; PepBnd; De Paul Univ; Law.

KALKOWSKI, Virginia A; Loup City HS; Rockville, NE; 1/63 ChrhWkr; CncrtBnd; HonRl; MrchBnd; NHS; PepBnd; SchPl; RptrYrbk; RptrSchPpr; 4-H; Kearney State Clge; Elem Teacher Special Ed.

KALKWARF, Michael L; Belmond Community HS; Belmond, IA; Chr; Chrs; ChrhWkr; HonRl; 4-H; FFA;.

KALLEMBACH, Rex H; Monticello HS; Monticello, IL; 9/136 ALBoysSt; HonRl; NHS; SctActv; StuCncl; YthFlsp; RptrSchPpr; PpCl; Bsbl; Ftbl; Trk; Military Academy; Engineering.

KALLEN, Robert S; Von Steuben HS; Chicago, IL; 41/231 Band; CmntyWkr; HonRl; Orch; PolWkr; StuGov; RptrSchPpr; FrCl; LetterTennis; Univ Of Illinois; Lawyer.

KALLENBACH, Cynthia L; Eldorado HS; Eldorado, IL; 14/110 SecBand; HonRl; NatlThespSoc; SchPl; StuCncl; RptrYrbk; GerCl; Murray St Univ; Pharmacy.

KALLENBACH, Sandra A; Niagara HS; Niagara, WI; VPJrCls; Band; Chrs; DrlTm; SctActv; SchPpr; PpCl; Trk; GAA; Technical Sch; Data Processing.

KALLENBERGER, Raydena G; Hardin Central HS; Hardin, MO; HonRl; StuCncl; RptrYrbk; 4-H; FHA; Chrldr; AmLegAwd; OptClAwd; Clge.

KALLHOFF, Bruce A; Dawson Boyd HS; Dawson, MN; Band; Chr; ChrhWkr; CncrtBnd; HonRl; Orch; PepBnd; 4-H; FFA; Glf; Canby Area Voc Tech Inst; Accounting.

KALLIN, Dennis R; Lourdes Academy; Oshkosh, WI; 17/125 HonRl; Univ Of Wisconsin; Accounting.

KALLMEYER, Charles J; Shawnee Mission South HS; Overland Park, KS; HonRl; StuCncl; YthFlsp; SpnCl; LetterBsbl; LetterFtbl; CaptIMSpt; JAAwd; JETSAwd; PresAwd; University; Eng.

KALLOWAY, Kim D; Dubuque Sr HS; Dubuque, IA; 6/469 Chr; JA; NHS; NatlMeritSF; SchMus; RptrSchPpr; GerCl; Clarke Col; Computer Science.

KALMAR, Joyce M; Calumet HS; Gary, IN; 51/330 NHS; SpnCl; College; Math.

KALMER, Beth M; Mater Dei HS; Germantown, IL; Band; Chrs; MrchBnd; SchMus; SchPl; StuCncl; Yrbk; FBLA; FrCl; Patricia Stevens College; Public Relations.

KALMER, Kathleen A; Red Bud Comm Unit HS; Red Bud, IL; 1/130 TrsFrshCls; Band; HonRl; JrNHS; NHS; PepBnd; YthFlsp; FBLA; Belleville Area Coll; Secretary.

KALMES, Jerome D; Evanston Township HS; Evanston, IL; HonRl; NatlMeritCmnd; NatlMeritSF; College.

KALNES, David M; Palmyra HS; Eagle, WI; 10/62 VPSophCls; PresJrCls; ALBoysSt; ChrhWkr; HonRl; PresNHS; SchAde; StuCncl; PresStuGov; CaptTrk; AmLegAwd; 4-HAwd; PresAwd; College; Law.

KALOUS, Karen S; Greenville HS; Pocahontas, IL; 21/183 HonRl; NHS; OffAde; YthLg; 4-H; FTA; LatCl; College.

KALP, K Joanne; Arlington HS; Indianapolis, IN; 19/464 HonRl; JrNHS; NHS; OffAde; Quill&Scroll; SctActv; SchPpr; FrCl; PpCl; Tennis; GAA; College; Business.

KALSKETT, Jeanne M; East Monona Comm HS; Moorhead, IA; SecSrCls; ChrhWkr; CmntyWkr; HonRl; PolWkr; TchrAde; LetterBsbl; Bsktbl; Trk; Chrldr; Northwestern Missouri State Univ; Teacher.

KALSOW, Daniel J; Wis Heights HS; Mazomanie, WI; 11/130 ALBoysSt; Aud/Vis; Chr; HonRl; NHS; SchPl; SctActv; StuGov; TchrAde; Yrbk; EdSchPpr; Bsktbl; LetterTrk; College.

KALTENBACH, Diane C; Rosati Kain HS; Ferguson, MO; 16/111 Chrs; HonRl; NatlMeritCmnd; StuCncl; GodCntryAwd; U; Med.

KALTHOFF, Kenneth R; Niles West HS; Lincolnwood, IL; Band; ChrhWkr; CncrtBnd; HonRl; MrchBnd; PepBnd; SctActv; GerCl; Univ Of Illinois; Architecture.

KALUSHA, Kevin; Pittsburg HS; Pittsburg, KS; Trk; IMSpt; College; Professional.

KALUZA, Diane B; South Lake HS; St Clair Shores, MI; 12/533 HonRl; LbryAde; Lake Superior St College; Technology.

KALWASINSKI, Kathy E; Ewen Trout Creek HS; Troutcreek, MI; Band; HonRl; NatlFornLg; SchPl; Chrldr; College; Professional.

KAMADA, Mika M; St Charles HS; St Charles, MO; 1/600 SecTrsJrCls; ALAGirlsSt; HonRl; TreasNHS; StuCncl; GerCl; Chrldr; IMSpt; CitAwd; VoiceDemAwd; College; Medicine.

KAMBA, Laurene M; Kennedy HS; Chicago, IL; 38/549 Band; CncrtBnd; HonRl; MrchBnd; NHS; SchPl; StuGov; 4-H; GAA; College; Law.

KAMBARA, Eunice A; Amundsen HS; Chicago, IL; 30/344 Chrs; HonRl; NatlMeritCmnd; StuCncl; TchrAde; Yrbk; Chrldr; Univ Of Illinois; Science.

KAMBEITZ, Cynthia; Napoleon Public HS; Napoleon, ND; Chrs; SchPl; Yrbk; PpCl; U N D; Speec Pathology.

KAMENSKI, Michael F; Notre Dame HS; Milwaukee, WI; 4/117 PresFrshCls; PresSophCls; PresJrCls; Band; Chrs; ChrhWkr; HonRl; NHS; SchMus; PresStuCncl; Univ Of Wis Milaukee; Music Teaching Condct.

KAMIDOI, Steve I; Capac HS; Capac, MI; 14/108 PresFrshCls; VPJrCls; HonRl; RptrYrbk; RptrSchPpr; Bsbl; Bsktbl;.

KAMINKY, Scott L; Earlville Comm Unit #9 HS; Earlville, IL; TrsJrCls; ChrhWkr; SctActv; SchPpr; FrCl; LetterBsktbl; LetterFtbl; LetterGlf; Trk; CchngActv; College; Professional.

KAMINSKAS, Robert A; Luther So HS; Chicago, IL; ChrhWkr; CncrtBnd; HonRl; NHS; RptrYrbk; Univ; Science.

KAMINSKI, Elizabeth A; Reeds Spring HS; Kimberling, MO; HonRl; HospAde; OffAde; RptrSchPpr; EdSchPpr; SchPpr; FHA; PpCl; College; Business.

KAMINSKI, Jolaine A; Schuyler Central HS; Schuyler, NE; SecTrsSrCls; ALAGirlsSt; HonRl; JrNHS; LbryAde; NHS; SchMus; TchrAde; MthCl; PpCl; SciCl; College; Dancer.

KAMINSKI, Katharine; William A Wirt HS; Gary, IN; 6/238 ALAGirlsSt; NHS; StuCncl; PpCl; Bsktbl; GAA; LionAwd; Tr State Coll; Business.

KAMINSKI, Laura M; Hinsdale Central HS; Hinsdale, IL; 107/586 ChrhWkr; HonRl; LbryAde; GAA; Moser Business Sch; Legal Secretary.

KAMINSKI, Richard R; Austin Catholic Prep; Detroit, MI; 4/135 HonRl; NHS; RptrSchPpr; LetterBsbl; College.

KAMINSKI, Robert; Homestead HS; Fort Wayne, IN; HonRl; PpCl; Bsbl; Ftbl; CchngActv;.

KAMINSKY, Pamela; George Rogers Clark HS; Hammond, IN; 83/260 ChrhWkr; JA; LbryAde; OffAde; SchAde; StuCncl; RptrYrbk; SchPpr; EngCl; FrCl; PpCl; GAA; IMSpt; Secretary.

KAMKE, Ann; Gillett HS; Gillett, WI; 3/77 Band; ChrhWkr; HonRl; NHS; LatCl; Carroll College; Medical Technology.

KAMKE, Cindy L; North HS; Eau Claire, WI; 37/375 Band; HonRl; JrNHS; NHS; Orch; SchMus; SchPl; FHA; Trk; IMSpt; Coll.

KAMM, Stephen J; Msgr Hackett HS; Kalamazoo, MI; 11/149 HonRl; SchMus; Western Michigan Univ.

KAMMAN, Julie; Urbana HS; Urbana, IL; 1/400 ChrhWkr; HonRl; NHS; SchPl; University; Law.

KAMMANDEL, Richard J; Creighton Prep; Omaha, NE; Band; NatlFornLg; PolWkr; SchPl; Sdlty; SpnCl; CaptTennis; Chrldr; IMSpt; University; Law.

KAMMERAAD, Connie S; Grand Haven Sr HS; Grand Haven, MI; 75/388 Band; CncrtBnd; HonRl; HospAde; MrchBnd; NHS; PepBnd; SchMus; YthFlsp; College; Business Admin.

KAMMERER, Felicia A; De Witt Community HS; Camanche, IA; AFS; Chrs; HonRl; RptrYrbk; Pres4-H; PpCl; SciCl; Bsktbl; Trk; 4-HAwd; Clinton Community; Nurse.

KAMMERER, Kristi K; Alma HS; Republican City, NE; HonRl; Mdrgl; NatlFornLg; NHS; SchPl; SptEdYrbk; 4-H; PpCl; Bsktbl; Trk; DanFAwd; Univ Of Nebr; Liberal Arts.

KAMMERICH, Gary L; Pilot Grove HS; Pilot Grove, MO; 4/36 HstSophCls; PresSrCls; Band; Chr; Chrs; CncrtBnd; HonRl; MrchBnd; PepBnd; SchAde; SchPl; TchrAde; SptEdYrbk; RptrSchPpr; Trade School; Professional.

KAMMERMAN, Tom A; Sherrard HS; Milan, IL; Chr; ChrhWkr; HonRl; YthFlsp; RptrSchPpr;

SptEdSchPpr; SchPpr; PpCl; Ftbl; Wrstlng; Black Hawk Jr College.

KAMMERS, Brian K; Wauwatosa East HS; Wauwatosa, WI; HonRl; SciCl; CaptSwmmng; U Of Wi; Science Field.

KAMMERS, Patricia A; Mona Shores HS; Muskegon, MI; HonRl; LbryAde; NHS; FHA; Muskegon Comm Coll; Elem Ed.

KAMMEYER, Debra; Concordia HS; Concordia, MO; 9/50 HonRl; MrchBnd; NHS; SchMus; SchPl; Twrl; FTA; Trk; Chrldr; PPFtbl; Central Mo State U; Physical Ed.

KAMMEYER, Kathryn L; Warsaw R 9 HS; Warsaw, MO; 1/62 Band; CncrtBnd; HonRl; MrchBnd; NHS; PepBnd; SchPl; Sw Missouri State Univ; Recreation.

KAMMEYER, Ronald F; Woodlan HS; Woodburn, IN; Chrs; ChrhWkr; HonRl; NHS; TchrAde; PresFFA; GerCl; Nw Tech College; Dairy Farmer.

KAMMIN, Cindy J; Roland Story HS; Story City, IA; VPFrshCls; Band; Chrs; CncrtBnd; NHS; PepBnd; StuCncl; FHA; Bsktbl; Trk; Waldorf College; Business.

KAMP, Beth A; Irving Crown HS; Carpentersville, IL; 27/355 VPFrshCls; PresJrCls; PresSrCls; HonRl; NHS; NatlMeritCmnd; University; Law.

KAMPE, Jane C; Rich South HS; Tinley Park, IL; 2/275 ALAGirlsSt; PresChr; ChrhWkr; HonRl; VPNHS; SchPl; Pres4-H; SecGerCl; DanFAwd; 4-HAwd; Illinois State Univ; Education.

KAMPE, Kim R; Quincy Sr HS; Quincy, IL; 26/694 SecAFS; HonRl; NHS; SpnCl; College; Elementary Education.

KAMPFE, Kandace K; Gothenburg Public HS; Gothenburg, NE; 5/84 Band; Chrs; HonRl; Mdrgl; TreasNHS; SchMus; RptrYrbk; EdSchPpr; 4-H; 4-HAwd; Univ Of Nebraska.

KAMPFE, Steven J; Gothenburg HS; Gothenburg, NE; Band; Chrs; ChrhWkr; CmntyWkr; CncrtBnd; HonRl; JrNHS; NHS; NatlThespSoc; PepBnd; Ftbl; University Of Nebraska; Agriculture.

KAMPHAUSEN, Caroline K; Luther North HS; Chicago, IL; 19/200 Chr; ChrhWkr; HonRl; ModUN; SecGerCl; IMSpt; KiwanAwd; Pacific Lutheran Univ; Magazine Journalism.

KAMPHOEFNER, Lois; Washington Hs; Defiance, MO; 2/276 Chrs; ChrhWkr; HonRl; JrNHS; NHS; OffAde; PolWkr; TchrAde; YthFlsp; EldAwd; U; Medical Profession.

KAMPINEN, Deborah A; Republic Michigamme HS; Republic, MI; Yrbk; Northern Michigan Univ; Criminal Justice.

KAMPMAN, Pamela R; Kearney HS; Holt, MO; Band; ChrhWkr; CncrtBnd; HonRl; MrchBnd; FHA; FrCl; PpCl; Bsbl; Bsktbl; College.

KAMPMUELLER, Scott; Tecumseh Senior HS; Tecumseh, MI; VPSophCls; HstSophCls; ALBoysSt; SchMus; SchPl; StuCncl; Ftbl; Trk; Wrstlng; IMSpt; Western Mich Univ; Political Science.

KAMPOVITZ, Janet M; Shelby Public HS; Bellwood, NE; 2/21 Chrs; ChrhWkr; HonRl; NatlMeritCmnd; SchPl; SchMus; StuCncl; RptrYrbk; PpCl; College; Home Ec.

KAMPS, Daniel; Belmont HS; Belmont, WI; HstJrCls; HstSrCls; ChrhWkr; SchPl; UNYO; FFA; PpCl; Bsbl; Bsktbl; 4-HAwd; Uw Platteville; Agric.

KAMPSCHNEIDER, Janet G; Dodge HS; Dodge, NE; TrsFrshCls; Chrs; HonRl; SchMus; SchPpr; 4-H; SpnCl; PpCl; LetterTrk; IMSpt; Lincoln Sch Of Commerce; Executive Sec.

KAMPSCHROEDER, Judith A; Washington HS; Washington, MO; 23/276 Chrs; HonRl; StuCncl; 4-H; FBLA; FHA; SpnCl; MthCl; PpCl; East Central Jr College; Accounting.

KAMPSCHROEDER, Richard F; Owensville HS; Gerald, MO; HonRl; NHS; 4-H; FFA; College; Vo Ag.

KAMPWERTH, Ruth; Carlyle HS; Carlyle, IL; 30/138 ChrhWkr; HonRl; 4-H; FBLA; FrCl; PpCl; Bsbl; 4-HAwd; JAAwd; Eastern Illinois Univ; Business.

KAMROWSKI, Jane M; Arcadia HS; Arcadia, WI; HonRl; OffAde; SchAde; TchrAde; FHA; Winona State Univ; Elem Teacher.

KAMSTRA, Kim E; Brookings HS; Brookings, SD; 100/187 PresSrCls; JA; NHS; NatlMeritSchl; StuCncl; EdYrBk; SpnCl; Bsktbl; Ftbl; Chrldr; Sdsu; Child Devol/spanish.

KANDEL, Edward J; Glenbard North HS; Carol Stream, IL; 52/360 ChrhWkr; HonRl; LbryAde; NatlMeritSF; OffAde; SchAde; Bsktbl; Ftbl; Tennis; Trk; U Of Ill; Civil Eng.

KANDER, Susan J; Sunset Hill HS; Kansas City, MO; 1/30 AFS; Chrs; Mdrgl; NatlMeritSF; SchMus; StuGov; RptrSchPpr; SptEdSchPpr; CaptBsktbl; Tennis; College; Medicine.

KANE, Christine M; Wahlert HS; Dubuque, IA; Chrs; CmntyWkr; SctActv; IMSpt; College; Pro.

KANE, Elizabeth; Smithton HS; Sedalia, MO; SecTrsFrshCls; Band; ChrhWkr; CmntyWkr; HonRl; MrchBnd; NHS; StuCncl; Burge Sch Of Nurs; Rn.

KANE, James E; Tri Point HS; Cullom, IL; 2/32 PresSrCls; ChrhWkr; HonRl; JrNHS; RptrSchPpr; Univ Of Illinois; Political Science.

KANE, James G; Vianney HS; St Louis, MO; HonRl; SctActv; LetterFtbl; LetterTennis; LetterWrstlng; CchngActv; IMSpt; College; Dentristy.

KANE, James P; Wahlert HS; Dubuque, IA; 1/450 PresSrCls; ALBoysSt; NHS; NatlMeritCmnd; PolWkr; SchMus; SchPl; StuCncl; StuGov; MthCl; Washington Univ; Banking.

KANE, Jolene; Raymond Central HS; Valparaiso, NE; ALAGirlsSt; Band; Chrs; CncrtBnd; HonRl; MrchBnd; PepBnd; 4-H; PpCl; U Of Ne; Veterinarians Assist.

KANE, Kelly A; Whitewater HS; Whitewater, WI; AFS; Chr; HonRl; NHS; Quill&Scroll; SchPl; Yrbk; KeyCl; FrCl; Univ Of Wisconsin; Business Admin.

KANE, Rita M; Benet Academy; Naperville, IL; NatlMeritCmnd; I B C College; Doctor Of Medicine.

KANGAS, Alice M; Mc Gregor HS; Mc Gragor, MN; 9/53 JA; 4-H; 4-HAwd; JAAwd; Waseca U; Animal Health Tech.

KANGAS, Jodie; Luther L Wright HS; Ironwood, MI; 20/205 HonRl; HospAde; NatlFornLg; NatlThespSoc; SchMus; SchPl; 4-H; PpCl; GAA; 4-HAwd; Univ Of Mich; Medicine.

KANGAS, Joyce M; Central Cass HS; Harwood, ND; 2/57 Band; Chrs; CncrtBnd; HonRl; MrchBnd; NHS; PepBnd; EdYrBk;.

KANGAS, Matthew; Marshall University; Minneapolis, MN; 30/165 Aud/Vis; HonRl; NatlMeritSchl; SchPl; StuGov; GerCl; Ftbl; Trk; Brown Univ.

KANIA, Donna J; St Joseph HS; Chicago, IL; Chr; Chrl; Chrs; ChrhWkr; LbryAde; SchAde; SchMus; Illinois Circle Campus; Physical Therapy.

KANION, Shaun L; Sunnydale Academy; Kansas City, MO; Band; Chr; Chrl; ChrhWkr; SptEdYrbk; Bsktbl; Ftbl; Trk; IMSpt; Oakwood Clg; Hospital Admin.

KANITZ, Sharon K; Winfield HS; Winfield, KS; Chr; Chrs; ChrhWkr; HonRl; SchMus; SchPl; TchrAde; PpCl; LetterTennis; College.

KANNAPELL, John T; Kirkwood HS; St Louis, MO; Chr; Orch; PolWkr; SchMus; College; Engineering.

KANNAPPAN, Maryann P; New Trier West HS; Winnetka, IL; 51/700 ChrhWkr; HonRl; NatlMeritSF; StuGov; SchPpr; College; Journalism.

KANOST, Loren D; Wauneta HS; Wauneta, NE; 1/29 PresChr; CncrtBnd; HonRl; ModUN; VPNHS; TreasStuCncl; LetterBsbl; LetterBsktbl; LetterTrk; PresAwd; Coll; Food Sci.

KANSANBACK, Cynthia K; Storden Jeffers Cons HS; Sanborn, MN; 6/51 Band; Chr; DrlTm; HonRl; HospAde; PresYthFlsp; 4-H; FHA; LetterBsktbl; GAA; College; Nursing.

KANSIER, Jane A; Hill Murray HS; St Paul, MN; Chr; HonRl; StuCncl; SpnCl; PpCl; Liberal Clge; Sociology Or Math.

KANTERS, Karen M; Dominican HS; Detroit, MI; HospAde; NatlFornLg; SchMus; SchPl; LetterSwmmng; Univ; Pro.

KANTOR, Kathleen A; Evergreen Park HS; Evergreen Park, IL; 12/452 HonRl; NHS; VPNatlThespSoc; SchPl; SpnCl; PpCl; Moser School; Reatil Buyer.

KANTZ, Diane C; Penn HS; South Bend, IN; PresAFS; Band; Chr; MrchBnd; VPNHS; NatlMeritCmnd; SecYthFlsp; 4-H; Chrldr; GAA; DARAwd; 4-HAwd; Memorial Hosp Schl; Nursing.

KAPALA, Lucy T; Frankenmuth HS; Birch Run, MI; HonRl; Sacrstn; TchrAde; RptrYrbk; KeyCl; Saginaw Bus Inst ;secretary.

KAPAUN, Katharine K; Central Cass HS; Casselton, ND; ALAGirlsSt; Chr; Chrs; HonRl; NHS; SchPl; Chrldr; GAA; Univ Of Nd; Education.

KAPERZINSKI, Mary L; Our Lady Of Mercy HS; Royal Oak, MI; Chrl; LbryAde; Orch; SchMus; FrCl; PpCl; SciCl; LetterSwmmng; IMSpt; PPFtbl; Univ Of Michigan; Biology.

KAPLAN, Eliezer Z; Ida Crown Jewish Acad; Lincolnwood, IL; ChrhWkr; NatlMeritFnl; SchPl; RptrYrbk; RptrSchPpr; Chem Engn.

KAPLAN, Eric W; New Trier West HS; Wilmette, IL; 18/698 HonRl; FDA; Ftbl; Stanford Univ; Medicine.

KAPLAN, John E; Ellendale Geneva HS; Ellendale, MN; 6/48 Band; HonRl; MrchBnd; NHS; SchPl; TchrAde; FFA; CaptBsktbl; LetterFtbl; LetterTrk; Winona State University.

KAPLAN, Phyllis E; Maine East Township HS; Morton Grove, IL; HonRl; NHS; PolWkr; SchMus; University Of Arizona; Medical Technology.

KAPLAN, Sharon B; Streator Twp HS; Streator, IL; 13/383 ChrhWkr; CmntyWkr; HonRl; NHS; StuCncl; StuGov; 4-H; FTA; TreasSpnCl; 4-HAwd; St Joseph Hos School Of Nur Reg Nurse.

KAPLAN, Stephen B; Boys Town HS; Boys Town, NE; 6/71 Band; HonRl; JA; PepBnd; SchMus; SchPl; RptrSchPpr; SchPpr; SpnCl; Florida State Univ; Journalism.

KAPOLNEK, Donald S; St Benedicts HS; Chicago, IL; 20/200 Chrs; HonRl; NatlMeritCmnd; SchMus; SchPl; VPStuCncl; PpCl; Loyola Univ; Chemistry.

KAPOLNEK, Ronald; Saint Patrick HS; Chicago, IL; 50/400 SecTrsSophCls; CaptTrk; IMSpt; Coll.

KAPP, Brian C; Riverside Brookfield HS; Brookfield, IL; ChrhWkr; YthFlsp; College.

KAPPER, Lucinda S; Chatsworth HS; Chatsworth, IL; 4/25 VPFrshCls; PresJrCls; AFS; Chrs; HonRl; Mdrgl; NHS; SchPl; VPStuCncl; FHA; SecSpnCl; Chrldr; AmLegAwd; South Ill Univ; Business Teacher.

KAPPERS, Daniel L; Platte HS; Platte, SD; VPSophCls; TrsJrCls; Band; ChrhWkr; HonRl; NHS; NatlMeritSF; StuCncl; YthFlsp; Bsktbl; College; Professional.

KAPPERS, Jo A; Spring Valley HS; Spring Valley, MN; Band; CncrtBnd; HonRl; NHS; Yrbk; Pres4-H; SecFFA; SecFHA; SpnCl; 4-HAwd; U Of Minn Waseca; Ornamental Horticulture.

KAPPES, William H; Holy Angels HS; Minneapolis, MN; VPFrshCls; PresSophCls; StuCncl; Bsbl; Bsktbl; Ftbl; Swmmng; Trk; IMSpt; Navy; Electronics.

KAPPOS, Steven; North Polk Comm HS; Elkhart, IA; 2/34 PresSrCls; HonRl; NHS; SchPl; StuCncl; StuGov; PpCl; KiwanAwd; Drake Univ.

KAPRAUN, Jane L; Roanoke Benson HS; Benson, IL; 4/90 ChrhWkr; CmntyWkr; HonRl; NHS; SchPl; Sec4-H; VPFHA; FNA; PpCl; IMSpt; Col; Legal Secretary.

KAPRELIAN, Mary L; West Allis Central HS; West Allis, WI; 1/465 Band; HonRl; MrchBnd; NHS; OffAde; Orch; PepBnd; SchMus; FrCl; MthCl; Uw Milwaukee; Math.

KAPRICH, Michael J; Centerville HS; Rathbun, IA; HonRl; NHS; Univ; Medicine.

KAPUCIAN, Tim L; Benton Comm HS; Keystone, IA; 25/105 ALBoysSt; DrmMjrt; HonRl; NHS; StuCncl; 4-H; FFA; SciCl; LetterFtbl; Trk; LetterWrstlng; Univ; Medicine.

KARABINUS, Audrey A; Dekalb Sr HS; Dekalb, IL; 1/350 SecTrsFrshCls; Chr; HonRl; Mdrgl; NHS; NatlThespSoc; SctActv; Univ Of Illinois.

KARABIS, Patricia; Evergreen Park Comm HS; Evergreen Park, IL; 17/452 TrsFrshCls; ChrhWkr; HonRl; NHS; SchAde; StuGov; MthCl; Bsktbl; GAA; IMSpt; De Paul U; Acountant.

KARABIS, Patricia; Evergreen Park Community HS; Evergreen Park, IL; 17/452 ChrhWkr; HonRl; NHS; StuCncl; StuGov; TchrAde; MthCl; PpCl; Bsktbl; GAA; De Paul Univ; Accounting.

KARABOYAS, Nick; Riverview Comm HS; Riverview, MI; 15/250 HonRl; JrNHS; TreasNHS; NatlMeritCmnd; LetterBsktbl; LetterTennis; U Of Mi Dearborn; Arts & Sciences.

KARAFF, Nancy L; William Chrisman HS; Sugar Creek, MO; 9/394 DrmBgl; CncrtBnd; JrNHS; MrchBnd; PepBnd; MthCl; U Of Mo; Physical Therapist.

KARAFIAT, Gary G; Benet Academy; Westmont, IL; 28/247 Band; CncrtBnd; HonRl; MrchBnd; NHS; RptrSchPpr; LetterBsbl; LetterBsktbl; LetterTrk; CchngActv; College; Radio Tv Broadcasting.

KARAGIANNAKIS, Evie; Sullivan HS; Chicago, IL; 66/276 ChrhWkr; HonRl; LitMag; LbryAde; SchAde; StuCncl; StuGov; Chr; TchrAde; SchPpr; FrCl; University; Sociology.

KARAM, Therese A; Lakeview HS; St Clair Shores, MI; 67/678 HonRl; NHS; NatlThespSoc; OffAde; RedCrAde; YthLg; SchPpr; SecSpnCl; Bsktbl; Swmmng; VoiceDemAwd; College; Nursing.

KARAPAS, Eleftheria T; H L Richards HS; Oak Lawn, IL; 4/1087 ChrhWkr; CncrtBnd; HonRl; HospAde; LitMag; MrchBnd; NHS; PepBnd; RusCl; VPMthCl; Univ Of Chicago; Medicine.

KARAS, Christopher P; Finney HS; Detroit, MI; 17/400 ChrhWkr; Wayne State University; Professional.

KARAS, Elaine S; Osborn HS; Detroit, MI; 50/650 HonRl; LbryAde; NHS; OffAde; SchAde; SchMus; StuCncl; TchrAde; RptrSchPpr; SpnCl; Wayne St Univ; Fashion Mdsg.

KARAS, Karen L; Pawnee City Public HS; Pawnee City, NE; Band; ChrhWkr; HonRl; YthFlsp; Yrbk; 4-H; FHA; PpCl; Chrldr; Univ Of Nebraska; Home Economics.

KARAS, Suzanne L; Messmer HS; Milwaukee, WI; 11/209 SchPl; StuCncl; EdYrBk; RptrSchPpr; FTA; PpCl; Swmmng; GAA; IMSpt; BttyCrckrAwd; Marquette University; Veterinarian.

KARASEK, Steven F; Roncalli HS; Omaha, NE; Chrs; HonRl; NHS; NatlMeritCmnd; TchrAde; PresMthCl; Wa U; Computer Sci.

KARAZLUA, Julia A; Carl Sandburg HS; Oak Forest, IL; 4/680 CncrtBnd; HonRl; NHS; NatlMeritCmnd; Orch; SchMus; TreasGerCl; MthCl; University Of Illinois; Biomedical Engineer.

KARBOWSKI, Janice M; Pinconning Area HS; Linwood, MI; 2/256 VPSrCls; Band; HonRl; MrchBnd; VPNHS; PepBnd; SchAde; PpCl; CaptPPFtbl; VFWAwd; U Of Michigan; Pharmacy.

KARCH, Kim B; Murphysboro Twp HS; Murphysboro, IL; 20/221 ChrhWkr; HonRl; NHS; SctActv; StuCncl; SpnCl; SciCl; College; Social Worker.

KARCHER, Pamela J; Johnson City HS; Marion, IL; 1/130 HonRl; NHS; SpnCl; MthCl; PpCl; SciCl; CaptChrldr; IMSpt; AmLegAwd; LionAwd; Univ; Teaching.

KARCHER, Sherilyn J; Unity HS; Sadorus, IL; Band; Chr; Chrs; SecChrhWkr; CncrtBnd; MrchBnd; SecNatlThespSoc; PepBnd; SchMus; Chrldr; Business Schl; Vocation.

KARCZ, Valerie A; St Hedwig HS; Detroit, MI; Chr; DrlTm; HonRl; NatlFornLg; NHS; Yrbk; FrCl; Trk; GAA; VoiceDemAwd; College; Nursing.

KARCZEWSKI, Casimir; Rockford East HS; Rockford, IL; 98/655 HonRl; SpnCl; Northwestern Univ; Accounting.

KARCZEWSKI, Emilia; St Joseph HS; South Bend, IN; HonRl; HospAde; SchPl; IMSpt; Nursing School; Nursing.

KARCZEWSKI, Mark T; Lake Central HS; Dyer, IN; 46/456 LetterBsbl; IMSpt; PresAwd; Univ; Architecture.

KARDELL, Janeen; Laurel Public HS; Laurel, NE; 9/62 PresFrshCls; TrsJrCls; TrsSrCls; HonRl; EdYrBk; PpCl; IMSpt; DanFAwd; CitAwd; Univ Of Ne At Lincoln 1 Yr; Registered Nurs.

KARDELL, Karon S; Oak Park HS; Kansas City, MO; Band; ChrhWkr; HonRl; SchMus; PpCl; College; Stewardess.

KARDOKAS, Dana J; Maria HS; Chicago, IL; 45/338 HonRl; SctActv; 4-H; FrCl; 4-HAwd; College; Art.

KARDOS, Nancy K; Joliet West HS; Joliet, IL; 14/520 Chrs; HonRl; NHS; OffAde; RedCrAde; StuCncl; TchrAde; FrCl; PpCl; GAA; Ill State Univ; French.

KAREL, Diane C; Clarkson Public HS; Clarkson, NE; MrchBnd; VPStuCncl; FFA; PpCl; LetterTrk; Midland Luthern Coll; Computer Programmer.

KAREL, Gerald; Hill Murray HS; St Paul, MN; HonRl; NHS; College; Math Major.

KARELS, Sandra K; Milbank HS; Milbank, SD; 13/122 Chr; HonRl; NHS; StuGov; GerCl; College; Vocation.

KARG, Sherry L; Owen Gage HS; Gagetown, MI; Chrs; HonRl; LbryAde; TchrAde; FHA; PpCl; Trade School; Professional.

KARG, Susan M; Litchfield Sr HS; Litchfield, MN; HstSophCls; VPJrCls; HonRl; StuCncl; Yrbk; TreasGerCl; PpCl; LetterBsktbl; Chrldr; GAA; College; Liberal Arts.

KARG, Susan M; North Vermillion HS; Perrysville, IN; Band; Chrs; ChrhWkr; HonRl; NatlThespSoc; SecStuCncl; SpnCl; LetterChrldr; TreasGAA; DARAwd; Indiana Central College; Music.

KARGAS, Eustace A; Beaver Dam Sr HS; Beaver Dam, WI; 5/330 University; Medicine.

KARGAS, George A; Beaver Dam Sr HS; Beaver Dam, WI; 8/330 University; Medicine.

KARGES, Sheila E; High School; Milbank, SD; Chrs; SchPl; StuGov; RptrYrbk; Yrbk; GerCl; PpCl; Trk; College; Professional.

KARI, Shelley L; Jackson HS; Jackson, MN; 1/108 Chr; ChrhWkr; HonRl; TchrAde; SecYthFlsp; EdYrBk; SchPpr; SecFHA; Trk; GAA; Univ Mn; Educ.

KARIAINEN, Emma M; Bergland HS; Bergland, MI; Chr; Chrs; HonRl; LbryAde; 4-H; PpCl; College; Vocation.

KARIS, Mary; Menomonie HS; Menomonie, WI; 6/236 CncrtBnd; NHS; PepBnd; YthFlsp; FrCl; Swmmng; Chrldr; ChmbCommrsAwd; Minn Univ; Education.

KARIS, Terri A; Menomonie HS; Menomonie, WI; ModUN; NHS; Twrl; Yrbk; FrCl; Chrldr; BttyCrckrAwd; Uw Madison.

KARJALAINEN, Joan M; Frederick HS; Frederick, SD; PresJrCls; ChrhWkr; HonRl; SchPl; StuCncl; StuGov; TchrAde; EdYrBk; PpCl; Nc Of Bus ;computer Science.

KARKUT, Helen M; Madonna HS; Chicago, IL; 7/273 PresFrshCls; PresSophCls; TrsJrCls; HonRl; NatlFornLg; NHS; StuCncl; LetterChrldr; GAA; College; Business.

KARL, Brenda L; Blissfield HS; Blissfield, MI; 5/138 SecBand; CncrtBnd; HonRl; MrchBnd; NatlMeritCmnd; PepBnd; SchMus; Jr College; General Liberal Arts.

KARL, Randall J; Loganview HS; Hooper, NE; SchPl; Ftbl; Trk; Wrstlng; Electronics.

KARL, Suellen E; Macarthur HS; Decatur, IL; 39/406 HonRl; SctActv; SchPpr; Southern Illinois Univ; Forestry.

KARLE, Timothy S; Jefferson County No HS; Valley Falls, KS; 6/48 TrsSrCls; Chrs; HonRl; VPNHS; SchMus; StuCncl; TchrAde; FBLA; LetterBsktbl; LetterGlf; Washburn Univ; Math.

KARLEN, Darcy D; Monticello HS; Monticello, WI; SecFrshCls; PresSophCls; Band; Chrs; HonRl; StuCncl; SpnCl; Bsktbl; LetterTrk; 4-HAwd;.

KARLGAARD, Ruth S; Campbell Tintah HS; Doran, MN; Band; Chr; Chrs; CncrtBnd; HonRl; MrchBnd; FBLA; FHA; Trk; GAA; Moorhead Tech; Secretarial.

KARLIN, Brian J; Thomas More Prep School; Hays, KS; HonRl; RptrSchPpr; EdSchPpr; KeyCl; SpnCl; PpCl; Bsbl; Trk; Chrldr; IMSpt; College; Banking.

KARLIN, Marie A; Hays HS; Hays, KS; HonRl; PpCl; Coll; Nursing.

KARLOFF, Cynthia M; Yuton HS; Yuton, NE; 10/25 TrsJrCls; Band; Chrs; NHS; RptrYrbk; RptrSchPpr; PpCl; LetterTrk; LetterChrldr; DanFAwd; College.

KARLOSKE, Diane; Pittsville HS; Vesper, WI; 1/83 Aud/Vis; Band; HonRl; NatlMeritCmnd; Yrbk; EdSchPpr; 4-H; BttyCrckrAwd; 4-HAwd; Univ Wis Eau Claire; Math.

KARLOSKE, Stephen G; Lincoln HS; Arpin, WI; HonRl; University; Professional.

KARLOSKI, Peggy A; Stephen Decatur HS; Decatur, IL; 1/368 Chr; ChrhWkr; CncrtBnd; HonRl; MrchBnd; NHS; PepBnd; SctActv; Ill Wesleyan Univ; Music.

KARLS, David N; Richmond Burton Community HS; Richmond, IL; 20/110 Aud/Vis; CmntyWkr; HonRl; Yrbk; LetterBsktbl; Il St; Accountant.

KARLS, Kristi L; Proviso East HS; Forest Park, IL; Chrs; HonRl; College; Accounting.

KARLS, Teresa; Edgewood HS; Madison, WI; Yrbk; SchPpr; PpCl; Bus Coll; Acc.

KARLSEN, Tom O; Warroad HS; Warroad, MN; PresJrCls; Band; ChrhWkr; SchPl; StuCncl; StuGov; RptrYrbk; EdYrBk; LetterTrk; College; Professional Theatre.

KARLSLYST, Richard J; Stoughton HS; Stoughton, WI; Aud/Vis; TchrAde; SciCl; Marine Corps;.

KARLSON, Lynnelle K; Banner County HS; Potter, NE; 4/14 ALAGirlsSt; ChrhWkr; DrmMjrt; HonRl;

NHS; SchPl; StuCncl; EdYrBk; LetterTrk; Chrldr; 4-HAwd; Univ Of Nebraska; Child Care.

KARLSTAD, Joanne D; Lisbon Public HS; Lisbon, ND; VPFrshCls; PresSophCls; AFS; ALAGirlsSt; HonRl; NHS; Quill&Scroll; RedCrAde; SchPl; StuCncl; YthFlsp; EdYrBk; FHA; PpCl; College; Business.

KARN, Regeana L; Eau Claire HS; Eau Claire, MI; 19/97 Band; Chr; ChrhWkr; CncrtBnd; HonRl; LbryAde; Mdrgl; MrchBnd; PepBnd; SctActv; PpCl; Bsbl; CaptBsktbl; Grand Valley St Col; Special Ed.

KARNATZ, Joanne L; Davenport Comm HS; Davenport, NE; 11/23 VPSrCls; ChrhWkr; SctActv; PresTeen; 4-H; PpCl; Bsbl; LetterTrk; Chrldr; PresAwd; Coll; Interior Design.

KARNES, Janelle S; Hoxie HS; Hoxie, KS; 1/57 SecTrsSophCls; VPBand; CncrtBnd; HonRl; MrchBnd; SchPl; YthFlsp; VPFHA; PpCl; LetterTrk; AmLegAwd; College.

KARNES, William L; Laingsburg HS; Laingsburg, MI; ALBoysSt; ChrhWkr; CmntyWkr; CncrtBnd; SchMus; TreasStuCncl; YthFlsp; LetterBsktbl; LetterFtbl; Trk; College; Elementary Principle.

KARNOSCAK, Bill; St Paul Kennedy HS; Chicago, IL; Aud/Vis; Chrs; HonRl; JrNHS; StuCncl; TchrAde; RptrYrbk; FrCl; MthCl;.

KARNOWSKI, Brian J; Little Falls Comm HS; Little Falls, MN; CAP; HonRl; LbryAde; SctActv; SchPpr; KeyCl; GerCl; IMSpt; Nd St Sch Of Sci; Auto Body.

KARNS, Karen J; Roanoke Benson HS; Roanoke, IL; 13/90 HonRl; HospAde; SecYthFlsp; FHA; TreasFNA; PpCl; GAA; IMSpt; Icc.

KAROLZAK, Kathy; Hamilton HS; Monomonee Falls, WI; 13/276 TrsJrCls; HonRl; HospAde; NHS; PpCl; Swmmng; Chrldr; Univ; Nursing.

KAROW, Gregory L; Columbus HS; Columbus, WI; ALBoysSt; NHS; Yrbk; LetterBsktbl; LetterFtbl; Trk; Wrstlng; IMSpt; Technical School; Horticulture.

KARP, Carol; Dominican Hs; Roseville, MI; Chrl; HonRl; SchMus; SchPl; StuGov; College; English And Science.

KARP, Cynthia; Aurora Central Catholic HS; Avrora, IL; 27/164 HonRl; SchMus; StuCncl; StuGov; RptrYrbk; RptrSchPpr; SchPpr; Univ; Biology.

KARP, Gregory P; White Bear HS; White Bear Lake, MN; LetterTrk; College.

KARPAWICZ, Cheryl A; Nauvoo Colusa HS; Nauvoo, IL; HonRl; MrchBnd; SchAde; FHA; College.

KARPEL, Richard J; Plainfield HS; Plainfield, IL; 6/294 Band; ChrhWkr; CmntyWkr; CncrtBnd; HonRl; MrchBnd; NHS; LetterFtbl; LetterWrstlng; 4-HAwd; Gmi Inst; Electrical Engineer.

KARPEN, Nancy A; Elkhorn HS; Elkhorn, WI; Band; HonRl; PepBnd; 4-H; FFA; KeyCl; Trk; GAA; College; Agriculture.

KARPENSKI, Joseph; Norway HS; Loretto, MI; TrsFrshCls; TrsJrCls; TrsSrCls; HonRl; LbryAde; SchAde; Yrbk; Northern Michigan Univ; History.

KARPIEL, Robert J; St Rita HS; Chicago, IL; 45/447 Band; CncrtBnd; HonRl; MrchBnd; Orch; PepBnd; College; Professional.

KARPINSKI, Sharleen J; Gabriel Richard HS; Wyandotte, MI; HonRl; LbryAde; SchPl; RptrSchPpr; FNA; TreasLatCl; Nazareth College; Nursing.

KARPOWICZ, Michael A; Chaminade College Prep School; St Louis, MO; HonRl; PolWkr; RptrYrbk; EdSchPpr; IMSpt; Kansas State Univ; Landscape Arch.

KARPUS, Thomas J; Batavia HS; Batavia, IL; Bsbl; Bsktbl; LetterFtbl; LetterWrstlng; Southern Illinois Univ; Architect.

KARR, Diane M; Santa Fe Trail HS; Overbrook, KS; 3/85 VPJrCls; TrsSrCls; Chrs; HonRl; SchMus; TchrAde; RptrYrbk; Chrldr; Emporia Kansas State Clg.

KARR, Linda; Bladen Public HS; Bladen, NE; Band; Chrs; HonRl; StuCncl; Twrl; Yrbk; EdSchPpr; PpCl; Kearney State College; Business Administrat.

KARRAS, Christopher G; Huron Senior HS; Huron, SD; 3/300 ALBoysSt; Band; JrNHS; LitMag; NatlFornLg; NHS; NatlMeritSF; StuGov; Yrbk; RptrSchPpr; GerCl; Univ; Law.

KARRE, Marlene K; Hayes County HS; Hayes Center, NE; Chr; CncrtBnd; DrlTm; HonRl; MrchBnd; OffAde; PepBnd; YthFlsp; 4-H; Trk; Wrstlng; EldAwd;.

KARRICK, Melody J; Farmington East HS; Trivoli, IL; 50/150 Chrs; HonRl; PresLbryAde; StuCncl; TchrAde; FTA; FrCl; Trk; LetterGAA; PPFtbl; College; Physical Educ Teacher.

KARRY, Clarice M; Hancock Central HS; Hancock, MI; Bus Schl; Sec Work.

KARSNAK, Robin L; Southside HS; Muncie, IN; 11/323 VPAud/Vis; HonRl; NHS; NatlThespSoc; OffAde; PolWkr; SchPl; VPFHA; PresFTA; PresFrCl; Ball State Univ; Elem Ed.

KARST, Carol E; Angola HS; Angola, IN; 16/179 Chr; Chrl; NHS; Quill&Scroll; StuCncl; RptrYrbk; EdYrBk; Yrbk; PresFTA; Tennis; College; Teacher.

KARTJE, Douglas S; Highland HS; Highland, IN; 143/538 University; Professional.

KARUSHIS, Gina P; Chester HS; Chester, IL; Band; Chrl; Chrs; CncrtBnd; HonRl; MrchBnd; NatlThespSoc; Orch; PepBnd; SchMus; SchPl; Yrbk; South Ill Univ; Journalism.

KARVONEN, John H; New York Mills HS; New York Mills, MN; Band; CncrtBnd; HonRl; MrchBnd; PepBnd; SctActv; Bsbl; Bsktbl; Trk; College; Professional.

KARZ, Lynda G; Notre Dame HS; Chicago, IL; 1/262 HonRl; VPNHS; SchPl; StuCncl; StuGov; TchrAde; FTA; FrCl; MthCl; Tennis; College; Engineer.

KARZEL, Ronald P; J A Craig Senior HS; Janesville, WI; 1/500 ALBoysSt; CmntyWkr; PresNHS; NatlMeritSF; Quill&Scroll; StuCncl; EdYrBk; GerCl; LetterFtbl; LetterTennis; Northwestern Univ; Medicine.

KASEFF, Fred E; North Central HS; Indianapolis, IN; 84/1165 Chr; HonRl; NatlFornLg; NHS; NatlMeritCmnd; NatlThespSoc; SchPl; StuCncl; PresLatCl; Glf; IMSpt; NCTE; Indiana Univ; Accounting.

KASEMAN, Jacqueline M; Wishek Public HS; Wishek, ND; 18/40 Chrs; ChrhWkr; HonRl; MrchBnd; NHS; PolWkr; StuCncl; RptrSchPpr; PpCl; Chrldr; Ndsu; Pro.

KASER, Kenneth; Pender HS; Pender, NE; 4/55 ALBoysSt; Chr; ChrhWkr; HonRl; SchPl; TchrAde; YthFlsp; Yrbk; FFA; Bsktbl; Univ Of Nebraska; Business Ed.

KASER, Phyllis J; Hannibal Senior HS; Hannibal, MO; 8/266 Band; CncrtBnd; HonRl; HospAde; MrchBnd; NHS; SctActv; PpCl; Bsbl; University; Nursing.

KASH, William O; Lyons Twp HS; Lagrange Park, IL; 90/1214 HonRl; JrNHS; NHS; NatlMeritFnl; NatlMeritSF; NatlThespSoc; SchPl; Univ Of Illinois; Medicine.

KASH, William O; Lyons Township HS; La Grange Park, IL; 90/1214 HonRl; JrNHS; NHS; NatlMeritSF; NatlThespSoc; SchMus; SchPl; PpCl; IMSpt; U Of I; Medical Research.

KASHA, Edwin; Mt Vernon HS; Mt Vernon, IN; 7/225 AFS; HonRl; NHS; StuCncl; KeyCl; Glf; IMSpt; Indiana Univ; Dermatolagist.

KASI, Sandra L; Dorchester HS; Dorchester, NE; SecTrsSophCls; VPJrCls; ALAGirlsSt; Band; Chr; Chrs; ChrhWkr; CncrtBnd; DrmMjrt; HonRl; CaptBsktbl; LetterTrk; Chrldr; AmLegAwd; Trade School; Professional.

KASIK, Rebecca A; La Salle Peru HS; Peru, IL; SecJrCls; SecSrCls; Chrs; HonRl; HospAde; LbryAde; SpnCl; PpCl; LetterBsktbl; LetterTennis; LetterTrk; IMSpt; College; Vocation.

KASIMATIS, Mary; Marillac HS; Deerfield, IL; 16/252 ChrhWkr; CmntyWkr; HonRl; HospAde; OffAde; SchMus; Sdlty; TchrAde; Tennis; GovHonPrgAwd; Valparaiso Univ; Bs Degree In Nursing.

KASIN, Susan; Hawley HS; Hawley, MN; HonRl; NHS; FHA; GAA; St Cloud School Of Nursing; Rn.

KASINGER, Susie J; Bloomingdale HS; Pullman, MI; 21/91 HonRl; LbryAde; OffAde; TchrAde; Parsons Bus Schl; Professional.

KASISCHKE, Daniel K; Tawas Area HS; Tawas City, MI; ChrhWkr; CmntyWkr; HonRl; RedCrAde; StuCncl; KeyCl; FrCl; Bsbl; Bsktbl; Glf; Western Michigan Univ; Business Admin.

KASKEY, Mary D; Rockwell City Community HS; Rockwell City, IA; 4/65 TrsFrshCls; Band; Chr; Chrs; CncrtBnd; HonRl; MrchBnd; NHS; NatlMeritCmnd; PepBnd; Buena Vista Coll; Psych.

KASKI, Kathleen J; Escanaba HS; Gladstone, MI; 4/383 Band; Chrl; Chrs; HonRl; JrNHS; MrchBnd; NHS; PepBnd; Northern Mi Univ; Accounting.

KASL, Cecilia; Hillcrest HS; Cuba, KS; 3/16 Band; ChrhWkr; CmntyWkr; HonRl; NHS; Twrl; EdSchPpr; 4-HAwd; Ks State Univ; Home Economics.

KASMARZIK, Thomas P; St Pius X HS; Festus, MO; HonRl; NHS; Ftbl; College; Professional.

KASOWSKI, Collette M; Buffalo HS; Absaraka, ND; 6/21 Band; Chrs; ChrhWkr; CmntyWkr; CncrtBnd; DrmMjrt; Mdrgl; PepBnd; Bsktbl; IMSpt; Ndsu.

KASPAR, Alan J; St Edward Public HS; St Edward, NE; 1/29 VPSophCls; PresJrCls; SptEdYrbk; SciCl; Bsktbl; Ftbl; Trk; Univ Of Nebraska; Engineering.

KASPARI, Daniel K; Lisbon HS; Lisbon, ND; 16/75 AFS; ALBoysSt; Band; CncrtBnd; HonRl; NHS; PresStuCncl; FFA; LetterFtbl; LetterGlf; IMSpt; College; Mechanical Engineering.

KASPARI, Danny K; Lisbon HS; Lisbon, ND; 16/75 AFS; ALBoysSt; Band; HonRl; NHS; PepBnd; PresStuCncl; FFA; LetterFtbl; LetterGlf; Col; Engineering.

KASPER, Danny G; Austin Catholic Prep; St Clair Shores, MI; 35/135 Band; HonRl; SchMus; SchPl; College; Aviation.

KASPER, Diane M; Whiting HS; Whiting, IN; SecJrCls; SecSrCls; Chrs; CmntyWkr; HonRl; RedCrAde; SchAde; StuCncl; TchrAde; IMSpt; College Nursing.

KASPER, Donn; Lake Central HS; St John, IN; 96/463 Chr; Chrs; NatlThespSoc; SchMus; SchPl; Wrstlng; Ftbl; Ue;professional Actor.

KASPER, Donn; Lake Central HS; St John, IN; Chr; Chrs; NatlThespSoc; SchPl; SchPpr; Ftbl; Trk; Wrstlng; New York Neighborhood Playhouse; Actor.

KASPER, Geri Lynn; Downers Grove So HS; Downers Grove, IL; 16/827 HonRl; JrNHS; NHS; SciCl; Northwestern University; Medicine.

KASPER, Joann; Caruthersville HS; Caruthersville, MO; NatlThespSoc; SchPl; FrCl; BttyCrckrAwd; Southeast Mo State.

KASPER, John E; Loyola Academy; Northbrook, IL; 18/442 Chr; PresMthCl; Loyola University; Business.

KASPER, Karen L; Hilbert HS; Hilbert, WI; Band; HonRl; LbryAde; TchrAde; LetterBsktbl; LetterTrk; Vocational School; Child Care.

KASPER, Nina M; Niles West HS; Niles, IL; 65/666 Band; ChrhWkr; VPCncrtBnd; DrmMjrt; HonRl; MrchBnd; NHS; NatlMeritSchl; OffAde; PepBnd; LetterTrk; CchngActv; GAA; Illinois State Univ; Accounting.

KASPER, Sharon K; Barrington Consolidated HS; Barrington, IL; 6/672 CmntyWkr; HonRl; LbryAde; NHS; NatlMeritSF; RedCrAde; YthFlsp; FrCl; AmLegAwd; GovHonPrgAwd; College; Elem Educ.

KASPSZAK, Robert W; Hermantown HS; Duluth, MN; 2/138 CncrtBnd; HonRl; MrchBnd; NHS; NatlMeritFnl; PepBnd; SchPl; FrCl; College; Physician.

KASRICH, Michael A; Edison HS; East Gary, IN; SpnCl; Bsbl; Ftbl; Trk; IMSpt; Indiana Univ; Electronic.

KASS, Edward P; North Central HS; Powers, MI; 3/54 SecFrshCls; PresSophCls; TrsJrCls; TrsSrCls; HonRl; StuCncl; StuGov; Mi Tech Univ; Electrical Engineer.

KASS, Laurie A; Dominican HS; Detroit, MI; ChrhWkr; VPNHS; Trk; Univ Of Detroit; Dental Hygiene.

KASS, Robert J; Wahlert HS; Dubuque, IA; 18/430 PresJA; ModUN; NHS; ChmnStuGov; MthCl; JAAwd; JETSAwd; OptClAwd; VFWAwd; College; Engineering.

KASS, Thomas J; Regis HS; Eau Claire, WI; 3/135 Chr; Chrs; HonRl; JrNHS; NHS; SchMus; FrCl; RotaryAwd; Coll;math.

KASS, Timothy H; Niles Senior HS; Niles, MI; 44/376 HonRl; SctActv; LetterTennis; Trk; IMSpt; Mi State Univ; Medicine.

KASSAB, Anne; Memorial HS; Joplin, MO; VPJrCls; PresSrCls; CmntyWkr; HonRl; NatlFornLg; NatlThespSoc; PolWkr; SchPl; StuCncl; Tennis; Ms Univ; Business, Drama.

KASSEBAUM, Pamela S; Washington HS; New Haven, MO; 11/276 ChrhWkr; CmntyWkr; HonRl; 4-H; FHA; SpnCl; GAA; 4-HAwd; College; Vocation Accounting.

KASSEL, James; Ayrshire Cons; Ayrshire, IA; PresSophCls; ALBoysSt; Band; ChrhWkr; SchMus; SchPl; CchngActv; Ia St Univ; Farm Management.

KASSEL, Stephanie A; Nevada Comm HS; Nevada, JA; Band; ChrhWkr; CncrtBnd; HonRl; MrchBnd; SctActv; UNYO; RptrYrbk; RptrSchPpr; LetterTennis; Iowa State U; Eng.

KASSING, John; Peoria Heights HS; Peoria Heights, IL; 11/100 HonRl; NHS; Quill&Scroll; StuCncl; StuGov; SptEdYrbk; RptrSchPpr; FrCl; GerCl; Univ; Business Law.

KASSING, Stephen W; Central HS; Clayton, IL; 22/72 SecTrsFrshCls; SecTrsSophCls; HospAde; PresStuCncl; PresStuGov; 4-H; GerCl; PpCl; CaptBsbl; CaptFtbl; Trk; IMSpt; College; Professional.

KASSMEIER, Michael L; Dodge Public HS; Dodge, NE; Aud/Vis; Chr; SchPl; LetterFtbl; IMSpt; Clge; Vocation.

KASSNER, Cindy L; Montague HS; Montague, MI; Band; CncrtBnd; HonRl; MrchBnd; NHS; PepBnd; StuCncl; RptrYrbk; GerCl; LetterBsktbl; Muskegon Comm Col; Accounting.

KASSNER, Lori; Pulaski HS; Oneida, WI; 7;194 HonRl; JrNHS; NHS; Quill&Scroll; RptrSchPpr; UNYO; PpCl; Chrldr; GAA; Uw Eauclaire;journalism.

KASSON, Anne L; Galesburg Augusta HS; Galesburg, MI; 1/120 Band; HonRl; JA; NHS; Orch; SctActv; Bsbl; LetterBsktbl; GAA; LionAwd; Olivet Clge; Business Finance/acctng.

KASSON, Robert; Clintonville Senior HS; Clintonville, WI; HonRl; Bsbl; Bsktbl; Trk; IMSpt; U Wi; Bus Adm.

KAST, Debra L; Weston HS; Hill Point, WI; TrsSophCls; TrsSrCls; Chrs; HonRl; NHS; Quill&Scroll; SchPpr;.

KAST, Virginia L; Adrian Sr HS; Drian, MI; 43/390 TrsJrCls; Chr; NHS; SchMus; StuCncl; TchrAde; YthFlsp; FrCl; PpCl; Siena Hts College; Accounting.

KASTBERG, Judith L; Homewood Flossmoor HS; Homewood, IL; 104/942 Chr; ChrhWkr; CmntyWkr; HonRl; SctActv; RptrYrbk; GerCl; Swmmng; Trk; CaptChrldr; Univ Of Il; Science.

KASTE, Carol L; Irving Crown HS; Algonquin, IL; Chr; ChrhWkr; HonRl; SctActv; FrCl; SciCl; Valparaiso U In; Nursing.

KASTELIC, Gia C; Kenwood HS; Chicago, IL; FrCl; Northern; Marine Biology.

KASTELLA, Kurt W; Fergus Falls Sr HS; Fergus Falls, MN; Band; LetterChr; Chrl; Chrs; LetterCncrtBnd; MrchBnd; PepBnd; LetterFtbl; Fergus Falls Comm Col; Meteorology.

KASTEN, Donna K; Spring Valley HS; Spring Valley, MN; Band; NHS; NatlSciFnd; PepBnd; SchMus; FHA; SpnCl; Luther College; Medical Tech.

KASTEN, Edward L; Kirkwood HS; Kirkwood, MO; HonRl; JA; LetterWrstlng; JETSAwd; College; Mechanical Engineer.

KASTEN, Karen J; Caledonia HS; Caledonia, MN; Band; Chr; Chrs; CmntyWkr; HonRl; SchMus; SchPl; SchPpr; LetterBsktbl; IMSpt; College; Psychology.

KASTEN, Russell L; Potter HS; Potter, NE; ALBoysSt; Chrs; HonRl; NHS; SchPl; StuCncl; Bsktbl; CaptFtbl; Trk; PresAwd; Coll; Bus Admin.

KASTENS, Dale D; Monroe HS; St Paul, MN; Band; CncrtBnd; MrchBnd; PepBnd; SchAde; TchrAde; IMSpt; Clge; Pro.

KASTENS, Linette J; Dekalb HS; Rushville, MO; SecFrshCls; Band; CncrtBnd; HonRl; MrchBnd; NHS; StuCncl; PpCl; LetterBsktbl; Chrldr; College.

KASTENS, Randall; Wheeling HS; Wheeling, IL; 1/450 HonRl; NHS; IMSpt; U Of Ill Urbana; Math.

KASTER, Mark A; George Comm HS; Rock Rapids, IA; ALBoysSt; SchPl; FFA; GerCl; LetterBsbl; Nrotc; Navy Or Other Military.

KASTER, Monica; West De Pere HS; De Pere, WI; 183 HonRl; NHS; NatlMeritCmnd; LatCl; University Wis River Falls Dvm.

KASTL, Julie A; Mona Shores HS; Muskegon, MI; Band; CncrtBnd; HonRl; MrchBnd; NHS; TchrAde; SciCl; Muskegon Comm College; Elementary Education.

KASTNER, Roberta L; Schleswig Community HS; Schleswig, IA; 3/51 PresSophCls; Band; CncrtBnd; DrmMjrt; HonRl; MrchBnd; NHS; PepBnd; SchMus; SchPl; Bsktbl; Trk; PPFtbl; University Of South Dakota; Accountant.

KASTNER, Teri L; Pattonville Sr HS; Maryland Hgts, MO; SecFrshCls; DrlTm; HonRl; StuCncl; PpCl; Ftbl; Univ Of Missouri; Special Education.

KASTRUP, Elizabeth A; Wheeling HS; Wheeling, IL; Chrs; DrlTm; HonRl; NHS; SciCl; College; Biology Related Career.

KASUBJAK, Charles H; Clinton HS; Clinton, IN; 10/160 HonRl; NHS; PresLatCl; Bsktbl; Glf; Trk; IMSpt; Purdue Univ; Engineering.

KASZA, Thomas A; St Hedwig HS; Detriot, MI; Band; Chr; ChrhWkr; HonRl; NHS; Sacrstn; SctActv; StuCncl; Yrbk; VoiceDemAwd; Col ; Conservation.

KASZNIA, Connie A; Washington HS; South Bend, IN; 22/332 TrsSophCls; HonRl; JrNHS; NHS; OffAde; Chrldr; School Of Nursing; Rn.

KASZTELAN, Michael J; Cody HS; Detroit, MI; HonRl; MthCl; Wayne State Univ; Medicine.

KASZUBOWSKI, Kenneth E; Buffalo Grove HS; Buffalo Grove, IL; 6/290 VPSrCls; HonRl; NHS; StuCncl; StuGov; KeyCl; Bsbl; Bsktbl; LetterFtbl; LetterTrk; Wrstlng; College; Engineering.

KATAHIRA, Eva J; Lane Technical HS; Chicago, IL; 61/1100 NHS; OffAde; SchMus; SchPl; TchrAde; Oberlin College; Biology.

KATCHER, Kristi A; Divernon HS; Divernon, IL; 5/25 ALAGirlsSt; HonRl; OffAde; EdYrBk; 4-H; FHA; DARAwd; Eastern Illinois University.

KATHKA, David K; Decatur Comm HS; Oberlin, KS; 17/85 ALBoysSt; HonRl; NHS; RptrYrbk; RptrSchPpr; LetterFtbl; Wrstlng; Kansas St Univ; Law.

KATHMAN, Randy J; Doniphan Public HS; Doniphan, NE; ChrhWkr; YthFlsp; Trade School.

KATHOL, Jody; Cedar Catholic Hs; Hartington, NE; PresSophCls; Chrs; ChrhWkr; CmntyWkr; SchMus; SchPl; StuCncl; Bsbl; Bsktbl; Ftbl;.

KATING, Donna C; Fatima HS; Freeburg, MO; Band; CncrtBnd; HonRl; MrchBnd; OffAde; RptrSchPpr; FBLA; FHA; PpCl; TrsFrshCls;.

KATLACK, Thomas P; Litchfield Senior HS; Litchfield, MN; Aud/Vis; HonRl; LbryAde; SchPl; 4-H; LetterBsktbl; LetterTrk; 4-HAwd; College; Wildlife Mgr.

KATO, Karen J; Bay City Central HS; Essexville, MI; 14/518 HonRl; LitMag; NHS; NatlMeritCmnd; NatlMeritSchl; TchrAde; YthFlsp; 4-H; EngCl; IMSpt; Saginaw Valley St Clg; Med Tech.

KATRBA, Frances; Goodridge Public HS; Goodridge, MN; 4/37 TrsJrCls; VPSrCls; HonRl; SchPl; StuCncl; Yrbk; Bsktbl; Trk; GAA; Vocational School.

KATSIAS, Stella; Finney HS; Detroit, MI; 1/507 Chr; ChrhWkr; CmntyWkr; HonRl; NHS; NatlMeritCmnd; NatlMeritSchl; SchAde; TchrAde; PresAwd; College; Cpa.

KATSINAS, Scott A; Champaign Centennial HS; Champaign, IL; ALBoysSt; HonRl; NHS; SchMus; SptEdSchPpr; SchPpr; SpnCl; Bsktbl; Glf; IMSpt; Illinois; Law Political Science.

KATSIS, Peter; Oak Park & River Forest HS; Oak Park, IL; Aud/Vis; HonRl; LitMag; Yrbk; SchPpr; LetterBsktbl; LetterTrk; IMSpt; University; Graphic Design.

KATZ, Caryn T; Mather HS; Chicago, IL; 16/421 Chr; Chrs; HonRl; NHS; SchMus; SchPl; SpnCl; Northwestern Univ.

KATZ, Cindi R; Lakeview HS; Battle Creek, MI; CmntyWkr; HonRl; Western Mich Univ; Sociology/environmental.

KATZ, Judy E; Clayton HS; Clayton, MO; AFS; ModUN; NatlMeritFnl; Washington Univ.

KATZ, Michael E; Berkley HS; Huntington Woods, MI; 1/603 NHS; NatlMeritSF; PolWkr; StuCncl; Yrbk; Univ Of Michigan; Biological Science.

KATZ, Pamela G; East Lansing HS; East Lansing, MI; CmntyWkr; HospAde; NHS; SchPl; TchrAde; Teen; Univ; Nurse.

KATZ, Steven B; Downers Grove South HS; Woodridge, IL; 30/825 HonRl; JrNHS; NHS; Ill Inst Of Tech; Elec Engineering.

KATZENBERG, Jane A; Richmond Burton HS; Richmond, IL; TrsJrCls; HonRl; NHS; FrCl; Chrldr; GAA; College; Professional.

KATZENBERGER, Diane M; Mother Mc Auley HS; Orland Park, IL; 40/480 Chr; HonRl; Mdrgl; SecNHS; PolWkr; TchrAde; FTA; FrCl; MthCl; Univ; International Business.

KATZIORIS, Nancy J; Oak Lawn Comm HS; Oak Lawn, IL; PresJrCls; PresSrCls; VPSrCls; NHS; NatlMeritSF; RptrYrbk; Socr; Chrldr; IMSpt; College; Professional.

KATZNER, Dennis G; Albany Area HS; Albany, MN; 36/129 SciCl; Brainerd Voc Sch; Landscape Tech.

KAUBLE, David W; Wright City HS; Wright City, MO; ChrhWkr; CncrtBnd; HonRl; SctActv; TchrAde; 4-H; FFA; FTA; SecTrsSophCls; LetterTrk; Head Of Own Company.

KAUER, Pamela J; Rudyard HS; Kinross, MI; 49/103 HonRl; TchrAde; RptrSchPpr; FNA; LetterTrk; Lk Superior St College; Physical Therapy.

KAUFFMAN, Eric S; Taylor Center HS; Taylor, MI; ALBoysSt; HonRl; LbryAde; YthFlsp; LetterBsbl; LetterBsktbl; LetterFtbl; LetterSocr; Univ; Pharmacy.

KAUFFMAN, Eunice E; St Josephs Academy; Clayton, MO; HospAde; SchMus; SctActv; StuGov; PpCl; GAA; University Of Missouri; Music Therapy.

KAUFFMAN, Teresa L; Jimtown HS; Elkhart, IN; Chr; HonRl; OffAde; SchPl; TchrAde; FHA; FTA; PpCl; PPFtbl;.

KAUFFMANN, Bruce A; Normal Comm HS; Normal, IL; 25/435 HonRl; NatlMeritCmnd; SpnCl; Socr; IMSpt; Coll; Engr.

KAUFMAN, Alan R; Evanston Township HS; Evanston, IL; HonRl; NatlMeritSF; SctActv; LetterSocr; Tennis; College.

KAUFMAN, Cathy; Westmer HS; New Boston, IL; TrsSophCls; PresJrCls; HonRl; StuGov; FHA; FTA; GAA; PresAwd; Jr College; Dental Asst.

KAUFMAN, Denise L; Northeast HS; Lincoln, NE; Chrs; ChrhWkr; HonRl; HospAde; PpCl; LetterTennis; GAA; Univ Of Nebraska; Dental Hygienist.

KAUFMAN, Dixon B; St Louis Park Senior HS; St Louis Park, MN; Band; MrchBnd; NHS; PepBnd; LetterTennis; Univ Of Mn; Medicine.

KAUFMAN, Eric G; Gridley HS; Gridley, IL; VPFrshCls; Yrbk; LetterBsbl; LetterFtbl; College.

KAUFMAN, Joseph D; Charlevoix HS; Charleviox, MI; 10/450 PresFrshCls; TrsSophCls; PresSrCls; ALBoysSt; Band; HonRl; NHS; Trk; BauchLmbAwd; LionAwd; Central Mi Univ; Attorney At Law.

KAUFMAN, Linda K; Hamilton HS; Waterloo, IN; 10/74 Chr; ChrhWkr; HonRl; NHS; SchAde; SchMus; TchrAde; 4-H; FTA; PpCl; College; Phys Ed Teacher.

KAUFMAN, Michael J; Highland Pk HS; Highland Park, IL; ChrhWkr; CmntyWkr; HonRl; LitMag; ModUN; PolWkr; StuGov; TchrAde; SchPpr; Tennis; University; Law.

KAUFMAN, Peg L; Laville Jr Sr HS; Plymouth, IN; Band; ChrhWkr; CncrtBnd; MrchBnd; TchrAde; YthFlsp; Bsktbl; Glf; GAA; College; Social Work.

KAUFMAN, Robert B; Friend HS; Friend, NE; 1/33 HonRl; LbryAde; RptrYrbk; Univ Of Hawaii; Medicine.

KAUFMAN, Sharon F; Niles North HS; Skokie, IL; 59/632 HonRl; JA; NHS; Indiana Univ; Business.

KAUFMAN, Tamera L; Gering HS; Gering, NE; Band; HonRl; JrNHS; KeyCl; Swmmng; Trk; Nebraska Western College; Physical Educ.

KAUFMAN, Tina M; Ripon Senior HS; Ripon, WI; ChrhWkr; HonRl; LbryAde; OffAde; RptrSchPpr; FHA; PpCl; College; Professional.

KAUFMANN, Lois; Olympia HS; Mc Lean, IL; 41/236 Chr; Chrs; HonRl; HospAde; YthFlsp; 4-H; FNA; GerCl; Bsbl; GAA; Biology.

KAUFMANN, Michael E; Carmel Boys HS; Mundelein, IL; 16/175 HonRl; NHS; NatlMeritCmnd; Univ Of Ill.

KAUFMANN, Stella L; Greenville HS; Greenville, IL; 1/200 CncrtBnd; DrmMjrt; NHS; NatlMeritCmnd; EdYrBk; DARAwd; Greenville College; Medicine.

KAUFMANN, Susan J; Washington Park HS; Racine, WI; AFS; Chr; HonRl; HospAde; NatlMeritSF; Orch; GerCl; Univ; Biochemistry.

KAUFMANN, Thomas C; St Laurence HS; Burbank, IL; 1/385 HonRl; NatlMeritCmnd; StuCncl; LetterSocr; LetterTrk; LetterWrstlng; IMSpt; Univ Of Ill; Pre Med.

KAUFMANN, Timothy J; St Laurence HS; Burbank, IL; 99/390 TrsJrCls; PresSrCls; HonRl; StuCncl; StuGov; Ftbl; Socr; Swmmng; Wrstlng; IMSpt; College.

KAUL, Dorlita J; Mehlville HS; St Louis, MO; Chr; Chrs; ChrhWkr; HonRl; LitMag; LbryAde; Yrbk; TreasGerCl; PpCl; Clge; Curr Of Major Study.

KAUL, Jacki J; Greafton HS; Grafton, WI; HonRl; JrNHS; OffAde; FBLA; LetterTrk; CaptChrldr; PresAwd; College; Professional.

KAUMHEIMER, Amy J; Grafton HS; Grafton, WI; HonRl; MrchBnd; NHS; FBLA; SpnCl; Trk; Chrldr; PresAwd; University.

KAUNE, Michelle M; Hempstead HS; Dubuque, IA; ModUN; PolWkr; StuGov; Us Air Force; Air Traffic Controller.

KAUP, Denise A; Stuart HS; Stuart, NE; 1/32 ALAGirlsSt; Band; Chr; HonRl; Mdrgl; PolWkr; StuCncl; EdYrBk; 4-H; PpCl; College; Medicine.

KAUP, Lajean S; Stuart Public HS; Stuart, NE; HonRl; MrchBnd; PepBnd; SchPl; StuGov; SchPpr; FrCl; PpCl; Chrldr;.

KAUP, Ron E; Bishop Dubourg HS; St Louis, MO; PresSrCls; HonRl; NHS; NatlMeritFnl; NatlMeritSchl; StuCncl; CaptFtbl; LetterSocr; LetterTrk; IMSpt; Southeast Mo; Business Management.

KAUP, Thomas J; Stuart Public HS; Stuart, NE; Band; Chr; CncrtBnd; HonRl; MrchBnd; PepBnd; PolWkr; SchPl; StuCncl; RptrYrbk; EdSchPpr; 4-H; College; Professional.

KAUP, Vencille M; Stuart Public HS; Stuart, NE; 3/32 Band; CncrtBnd; HonRl; MrchBnd; PepBnd; SchPl; PresStuCncl; Yrbk; PpCl; Trk; JAAwd; Business School; Accountant.

KAUPMAN, Michael; Ridgway Community HS; Ridgway, IL; 2/42 VPFrshCls; HonRl; NatlMeritSchl; SpnCl; Univ Of Il; Metallurgical Eng.

KAUS, David L; Browns Valley HS; Brown Valley, MN; 1/40 PresJrCls; Band; CncrtBnd; HonRl; MrchBnd; PolWkr; PepBnd; LetterBsktbl; LetterFtbl; LetterTrk; Coll.

KAUT, Tim E; Center Point Consolidated HS; Center Point, IA; 6/45 Band; Chr; Chrs; CncrtBnd; HonRl; MrchBnd; SchMus; YthFlsp; SpnCl; LetterTrk; Kirkwood Comm Clg; Math.

KAUTH, Monica J; Verdigre HS; Verdigre, NE; Band; Chrs; CncrtBnd; HonRl; MrchBnd; PepBnd; SctActv; TchrAde; Swmmng; Northeast Tech Clg; Nurse.

KAUTZ, Barbara A; Wheaton Christian HS; Wheaton, IL; 1/33 TrsFrshCls; TrsSophCls; TrsJrCls; Chr; HonRl; VPNHS; Yrbk; Wheaton College; Nursing.

KAUTZER, Mary F; Green Lake Public HS; Green Lake, WI; 1/42 VPFrshCls; ALAGirlsSt; Chrs; HonRl; NHS; SchPl; Bsktbl; Chrldr; College.

KAUTZER, Maureen R; Green Lake Public HS; Green Lake, WI; SecJrCls; Chr; Chrs; HonRl; NatlThespSoc; TchrAde; RptrSchPpr; PpCl; GAA; IMSpt; College.

KAVAN, Cindy L; North Bend Central HS; North Bend, NE; 1/55 ALAGirlsSt; SecBand; LetterChrs; CncrtBnd; MrchBnd; NHS; SchMus; FHA; FTA; PresPpCl; Wayne St Coll; Art.

KAVANAGH, Preston B; New Trier East HS; Kenilworth, IL; Chrs; SchPl; StuGov; MthCl; SciCl; Mich Univ.

KAVANAUGH, Michael P; Horton Watkins HS; St Louis, MO; 87/517 JA; NatlMeritSF; StuCncl; Ftbl; Socr; LetterWrstlng; IMSpt; JAAwd; College; Medicine.

KAVER, James; Big Foot HS; Walworth, WI; 18/174 CncrtBnd; HonRl; MrchBnd; PepBnd; IMSpt;.

KAWANO, Susan G; Forest View HS; Des Plaines, IL; CmntyWkr; HonRl; NHS; NatlMeritCmnd; Quill&Scroll; SchPpr; Marquette Univ; Physical Therapy.

KAY, Brad; Lawrence HS; Lawrence, KS; Aud/Vis; PolWkr; IMSpt; Kansas University; Aerospace Engineering.

KAY, Janet A; Medford HS; Medford, MN; PresSophCls; Band; Chr; CncrtBnd; HonRl; PepBnd; StuCncl; RptrYrbk; Yrbk; RptrSchPpr; EdSchPpr; Univ; Journalism.

KAY, Michael; Potosi HS; Potosi, MO; 2/200 Band; HonRl; JrNHS; NHS; NatlThespSoc; SchMus; SchPl; SpnCl; SciCl; U Of Mo Columbia.

KAY, Michael D; Dundee HS; Dundee, MI; 2/124 HonRl; PresNHS; NatlMeritCmnd; SchPl; Yrbk; FTA; LetterFtbl; LetterSwmmng; LetterTrk; OptClAwd; Central Mich U; Computer Sci.

KAY, Sharon; Ladywood HS; Detroit, MI; 7/96 VPSrCls; Chr; HonRl; JrNHS; NHS; NatlMeritSchl; RedCrAde; SchPl; StuCncl; FHA; Henry Fad Hosp Sch Of Nursing; Radiology.

KAY, Tori C; Frankfort HS; Frankfort, IN; 1/300 Band; JrNHS; NHS; SchMus; SchPl; FrCl; PpCl; Swmmng; Chrldr; GAA; College; Law.

KAYE, Thomas H; Carmel HS; Waukegan, IL; 27/153 HonRl; Lake County Col; Law.

KAYFISH, Antonette S; Plainfield HS; Joliet, IL; 10/297 Chr; HonRl; MrchBnd; NHS; Quill&Scroll; RptrYrbk; RptrSchPpr; FrCl; Joliet Jr College; Accounting.

KAYLOR, Kim L; Coldwater HS; Coldwater, MI; HonRl; NatlMeritSchl; W Mi Univ; Business.

KAYLOR, Marcia A; Illiopolis HS; Illiopolis, IL; AFS; ChrhWkr; CmntyWkr; HospAde; NHS; PolWkr; StuGov; UNYO; FSA; Ftbl; Univ; Psychology.

KAYMEN, Stanley P; Homewood Flossmoor HS; Flossmoor, IL; 82/940 AFS; HonRl; LitMag; NatlFornLg; NatlMeritFnl; EdYrBk; Yrbk; MthCl; Tennis; IMSpt; Univ; Medical.

KAYSER, Doris; Caledonia HS; Caledonia, MI; 10/152 HonRl; NatlFornLg; NHS; RedCrAde; SchMus; YthFlsp; Chrldr; Northwestern Mi Coll; Psychology & Music.

KAYSER, Kathleen M; Sanborn Comm HS; Sanborn, IA; Band; Chrs; ChrhWkr; HonRl; NHS; SchPl; LetterGlf; Trk; Coll; Vocation.

KAZECK, Dennis W; Little Falls Comm HS; Little Falls, MN; Band; Chr; CncrtBnd; MrchBnd; PepBnd; SchMus; Bsbl; Bsktbl; LetterFtbl; Clg; Accounting.

KAZIMOUR, Kimberly K; Washington Sr HS; Cedar Rapids, IA; 1/476 TrsFrshCls; Chr; CmntyWkr; HonRl; HospAde; NHS; NatlMeritSF; SchPl; TreasStuCncl; StuGov; Yrbk; RptrSchPpr; SpnCl; DARAwd; Iowa State Univ; Medicine.

KAZMARZICK, Lori; St Marys HS; Essig, MN; /84 Chr; Chrs; TchrAde; SchPpr; 4-H; FFA; FHA; PpCl; GAA; 4-HAwd; Business School; Secretarial Orclerical.

KAZMERZAK, Cathy L; Lake Preston Ind HS; Erwin, SD; 2/37 ALAGirlsSt; Band; CncrtBnd; DrmMjrt; HonRl; Mdrgl; MrchBnd; PepBnd; SchMus; SchPl; LetterBsktbl; Swmmng; LetterTrk; South Dakota State Univ; Engineering.

KAZMIEROWICZ, James; Hinsdale South HS; Darien, IL; 38/445 HonRl; NHS; NatlMeritSchl; Tennis; Univ; Science Geology.

KAZUK, Jane; Maine Twp South HS; Park Ridge, IL; HonRl; HospAde; LitMag; StuGov; PpCl; Tennis; GAA; Univ Of Il.

KEAL, Sandra M; Fargo North HS; Frago, ND; 53/370 AFS; CmntyWkr; NatlFornLg; NHS; StuCncl; StuGov; FrCl; LatCl; EldAwd; KiwanAwd; U Of Nd; Pre Med.

KEALEY, Paula J; Holdrege Sr HS; Holdrege, NE; SecSophCls; Chrs; SchMus; StuCncl; Teen; YthFlsp; FBLA; PpCl; Chrldr; U Of Ne; Elementary Ed.

KEALY, Mark P; Brule HS; Imperial, NE; HonRl; SchAde; SchPl; TchrAde; LetterFtbl; Navy; X Ray Tech.

KEANE, Debbie J; Duchesne HS; St Ann, MO; 40/139 TrsJrCls; HonRl; PpCl; Col; Secondary Teacher.

KEANE, John P; St Laurence HS; Chicago, IL; 28/376 HonRl; St Marys College; Law.

KEANE, Tim; Northeast Hamilton HS; Williams, IA; PresFrshCls; PresSophCls; Chr; Chrs; HonRl; Mdrgl; SchMus; Wrstlng; Iowa Univ; Engineering.

KEAR, Gina M; Golden Plains HS; Menlo, KS; HstFrshCls; HstSophCls; HstJrCls; ALAGirlsSt; Band; Chr; Chrs; HonRl; JrNHS; MrchBnd; Bsktbl; Trk; PPFtbl; Business School; Secretary.

KEARBEY, Kathy K; East HS; Des Moines, IA; 36/488 AFS; ChrhWkr; HonRl; PolWkr; TchrAde; LatCl; PpCl; GAA; IMSpt; Cedarville Clg; Pro.

KEARL, Alan; Wheaton Warrenville HS; Wheaton, IL; 3/250 ChrhWkr; HonRl; NHS; SctActv; StuCncl; FrCl; MthCl; Bsktbl; VoiceDemAwd; Coll-;bank Finance.

KEARN, Matthew T; Muskego HS; Halles Corners, WI; 7/48 HonRl; NHS; NatlSciFnd; SctActv; FSA; SciCl; Glf; BauchLmbAwd; JETSAwd; Marquette Univ; Nuclear Physics.

KEARNEY, Darrell L; St Edmond HS; Fort Dodge, IA; Chrs; ChrhWkr; CmntyWkr; HonRl; NHS; StuCncl; StuGov; FBLA; Bsbl; Bsktbl; Drake Univ; Law Field.

KEARNEY, Jeanne L; Tomah Senior HS; Tomah, WI; CncrtBnd; HonRl; IntrClCncl; JrNHS; MrchBnd; SchPpr; SpnCl; GAA; College; Geography.

KEARNEY, Lawrence J; Austin Catholic Prep; Grosse Pt Farms, MI; 95/115 Chrs; CmntyWkr; NatlFornLg; SchMus; SchPl; College; Business.

KEARNEY, Mary J; Harold L Richards HS; Oak Lawn, IL; 39/1035 HonRl; TchrAde; University; Anthoropology.

KEARNS, Ianne; Salina Central HS; Salina, KS; 1/320 TrsJrCls; ChrhWkr; HonRl; ModUN; NatlFornLg; NatlMeritCmnd; SchMus; SchPl; Univ; Uncertain.

KEARNS, Michelle M; Assumption HS; Davenport, IA; CAP; DrlTm; HospAde; RedCrAde; ROTC; SctActv; Twrl; RptrYrbk; SchPpr; KeyCl; TreasSpnCl; Marycrest College; Nursing.

KEAS, Carolyn J; Pekin Comm HS; Pekin, IL; 23/806 ChrhWkr; CmntyWkr; CncrtBnd; HonRl; MrchBnd; NHS; Orch; PepBnd; SecYthFlsp; FTA; GAA; Il State Univ; Elem Teacher.

KEASLING, Kathleen J; Harvard Public HS; Harvard, NE; 2/30 VPSrCls; Band; ChrhWkr; CncrtBnd; HonRl; HospAde; MrchBnd; NHS; PepBnd; SchPl; StuCncl; YthFlsp; Yrbk; GerCl; Doane College; Sciences.

KEAST, Cynthia H; Cherry Hill HS; Inkster, MI; 1/311 HonRl; NatlFornLg; NHS; NatlMeritCmnd; RptrYrbk; EdYrBk; FrCl; RptrSchPpr; Wayne State Univ.

KEAST, Donald R; Lenox Comm HS; Lenox, IA; 6/45 ALBoysSt; ChrhWkr; HonRl; NHS; SchPl; College; Accounting.

KEASTER, Janet F; Risco HS; Lilbourn, MO; VPJrCls; HonRl; LbryAde; SchPl; Teen; Yrbk; SchPpr; 4-H; FHA; CaptChrldr; Clge; Math Tchr.

KEATH, Steven A; Watseka HS; Watseka, IL; 10/137 HonRl; NHS; Quill&Scroll; SctActv; SptEdSchPpr; SpnCl; MthCl; Bsktbl; Ftbl; Glf; CaptTrk; IMSpt; Illinois St Univ; Accounting.

KEATING, Jeffrey V; Pacelli HS; Austin, MN; ALBoysSt; ChrhWkr; HonRl; SctActv; Yrbk; RptrSchPpr; SchPpr; LetterTennis; College; Law.

KEATING, Mary; Traverse City St Francis HS; Traverse City, MI; 1/82 HonRl; NHS; NatlMeritSF; PpCl; Chrldr; IMSpt; Mich State Univ; Pre Medicine.

KEATING, Moira C; Marian Catholic HS; Flossmoor, IL; 3/336 Band; ChrhWkr; CncrtBnd; HonRl; MrchBnd; NHS; NatlMeritFnl; PepBnd; SchMus; SchPl; StuCncl; Yrbk; University Of Notre Dame; Law.

KEATING, Paula M; Marian Catholic HS; Chicago Heights, IL; ChrhWkr; HonRl; NHS; SchMus; SchPl; StuCncl; University; Professional.

KEAVEY, Philip; Oscoda Area HS; Oscoda, MI; HonRl; FrCl; Trk; IMSpt; Col; Geologist.

KEBE, Frank L; Cathedral HS; Indianapolis, IN; 8/128 HonRl; JrNHS; NHS; EdYrBk; SpnCl; Univ Of Notre Dame; Journalism.

KEBER, Mary L; Spalding Acad; Spalding, NE; VPSophCls; Chrs; HonRl; NHS; SchPl; Sdlty; StuCncl; TchrAde; SchPpr; PpCl; Elem Educ.

KECK, Angela K; Oak Grove Senior HS; Oak Grove, MO; 13/104 HonRl; NatlFornLg; NHS; SchPl; TchrAde; PpCl; IMSpt; PPFtbl; OptClAwd; College; Artist.

KECK, Brenda E; Lone Jack C 6 HS; Lone Jack, MO; 1/16 PresFrshCls; Band; Chr; Chrs; HonRl; JrNHS; NHS; SchMus; Bsktbl; College; Office Admin.

KECK, James; Stevens HS; Rapid City, SD; 70/418 HonRl; Ftbl; Trk; IMSpt; Sd School Tech; Engineering.

KECK, Rick L; Colby HS; Colby, KS; 21/93 ALBoysSt; HonRl; JrNHS; NHS; 4-H; LetterBsktbl; LetterFtbl; Trk; Wrstlng; IMSpt; Ks State U; Computer Science.

KEDLEY, Mary C; Central Community HS; De Witt, IA; 9/166 Chrs; ChrhWkr; HonRl; NHS; OffAde; SchPl; Yrbk; 4-H; SciCl; 4-HAwd; Marycrest Clg; Nursing.

KEDZIOR, Stanley F; Quigley South HS; Chicago, IL; 6/168 ChrhWkr; HonRl; NHS; StuGov; Niles College; Political Science.

KEE, Ramona G; Derby Sr HS; Wichita, KS; 48/371 HonRl; LbryAde; NatlMeritCmnd; StuCncl; SchPpr; FHA; College; Journalist.

KEEBEY, Debbie L; Parkway Central HS; Creve Coeur, MO; 31/450 Band; ChrhWkr; CncrtBnd; JrNHS; NHS; Orch; PpCl; CaptChrldr; PPFtbl; DARAwd; U Of Missouri; Music Therapy.

KEEBLER, Paul; Southwest HS; St Lois, MO; 66/597 Band; ChrhWkr; CncrtBnd; LitMag; MrchBnd; SchMus; Bsktbl; Trk; University; Vocation.

KEEDY, Mary S; Crawfordsville HS; Crawfordsville, IN; 57/233 Chr; DrlTm; MrchBnd; SchMus; SctActv; TchrAde; 4-H; LatCl; PpCl; Ball State Univ; Teacher.

KEEFAUVER, Brad A; Morton HS; Morton, IL; JA; EdSchPpr; College; Journalism.

KEEFE, Kathryn C; Carmel HS; Libertyville, IL; 15/191 VPJrCls; Chrl; Chrs; HonRl; NHS; SchMus; StuCncl; LatCl; Coll.

KEEFE, Steven D; Lane Tech HS; Chicago, IL; 113/1200 ChrhWkr; PresJA; StuCncl; TchrAde; Yrbk; SchPpr; MthCl; Illinois Inst Of Tech; Computer Programmer.

KEEFER, Jane A; Limestone HS; Bartonville, IL; Chr; Chrs; HonRl; SchMus; TchrAde; FNA; University.

KEEFER, Kenneth K; Glenbrook South HS; Northbrook, IL; Aud/Vis; ChrhWkr; HonRl; OffAde; YthFlsp; PpCl; LetterBsbl; Ftbl; College; Science.

KEEFER, Laura; Polo Community Hs; Polo, IL; 1/89 TreasChr; HonRl; NHS; NatlMeritSF; Orch; VPYthFlsp; Pres4-H; FTA; FrCl; GAA; College;computer Science.

KEEFER, Marc G; Elmwood Comm HS; Elmwood, IL; PresBand; Chrs; CncrtBnd; PresMdrgl; MrchBnd; Orch; PepBnd; SchMus; SchPl; StuCncl; CaptBsktbl; LetterTrk; AmLegAwd; Bradley University.

KEEFER, Mary L; Ottawa HS; Ottawa, KS; ALAGirlsSt; Band; Chrl; ChrhWkr; HonRl; NHS; Orch; PepBnd; PolWkr; SchMus; Ozark Bible School; Music.

KEEFNER, Joseph E; Thornridge HS; Harvey, IL; PresChrl; HonRl; Mdrgl; NHS; Bsbl; Bradley Univ; Medicine.

KEEGSTRA, Gary L; Beaver Dam HS; Beaver Dam, WI; Chr; Chrs; ChrhWkr; HospAde; Mdrgl; SchMus; SchPl; Twrl; Tennis; Wu Madison; Occupational Therapist.

KEEGSTRA, Jane E; Benton Harbor HS; Benton Harbor, MI; 18/417 Band; HonRl; MrchBnd; NHS; PepBnd; RptrYrbk; FrCl; LetterKiwanAwd; Msu; Science Math.

KEEHNEN, Sara S; Dakota HS; Dakota, IL; 5/75 SecJrCls; Band; CncrtBnd; HonRl; MrchBnd; OffAde; PepBnd; TchrAde; College; Professional.

KEEL, John W; Shellsburg HS; Shellsburg, IA; Band; ChrhWkr; CmntyWkr; CncrtBnd; HonRl; MrchBnd; PepBnd; SchPl; SctActv; YthFlsp; LetterBsbl; LetterBsktbl; College; Journalist.

KEEL, Mary K; Farmington East HS; Elmwood, IL; 13/131 CmntyWkr; HonRl; VPNHS; StuCncl; 4-H; FFA; FrCl; LetterTrk; LetterChrldr; LetterGAA; Sec4-HAwd; Univ Of Ill; Business.

KEELER, Billie W; Waynesville HS; Ft Leonardwood, MO; 47/255 HonRl; JrNHS; NHS; NatlMeritCmnd; StuGov; SpnCl; LetterBsktbl; Ftbl; LetterTrk; Univ Of Mo; Accounting.

KEELER, Cheryl; Jackson County Western HS; Jackson, MI; Band; ChrhWkr; CncrtBnd; HonRl; MrchBnd; OffAde; PepBnd; Jackson Community College; Secretarial.

KEELER, James A; Sault Area HS; Sault Ste Marie, MI; ChrhWkr; HonRl; NHS; Quill&Scroll; TchrAde; RptrSchPpr; SchPpr; LetterBsbl; LetterBsktbl; Ftbl; Tennis; IMSpt; College; Mech Engineering Technology.

KEELER, Ray J; Thornton HS; Dolton, IL; 60/789 HonRl; NHS; NatlMeritCmnd; NatlMeritSchl; OffAde; SchPl; StuGov; KeyCl; CaptWrstlng; PresAwd; Univ Of Il; Professional.

KEELER, Sharil A; Mt Assisi HS; Chgo Ridge, IL; AFS; ChrhWkr; HonRl; SchMus; SctActv; Sdlty; TchrAde; YthFlsp; GAA; KiwanAwd; Univ; Missionary Teacher.

KEELER, Sharon M; Newlothrop HS; Chesaning, MI; 3/81 HonRl; NHS; SchPl; TchrAde; RptrYrbk; EdSchPpr; 4-H; VPSpnCl; Col; Teaching.

KEELEY, Matthew T; Downers Grove HS; Downers Grove, IL; HonRl; NHS; NatlMeritCmnd; NatlMeritSF; Quill&Scroll; RptrSchPpr; EdSchPpr; Univ Of Il; Engineering.

KEELING, Deborah; New Bloomfield HS; New Bloomfield, MO; ChrhWkr; HonRl; OffAde; SchAde; StuCncl; RptrYrbk; PpCl; CitAwd; Univ Of Mo; Law.

KEELING, Mark A; Oak Creek HS; Oak Creek, WI; 5/323 HonRl; TreasNHS; NatlMeritCmnd; GerCl; IMSpt; BttyCrckrAwd; Uw Madison; Eng.

KEEN, Brenda S; Armstrong HS; Potomac, IL; 1/41 Chrs; HonRl; PresNHS; SchMus; TchrAde; RptrYrbk; VPSpnCl; SciCl; VPGAA; DARAwd; Lakeview Mem Hosp Schl; Nursing.

KEEN, Carol M; Bryant HS; Bryant, IN; 1/36 Chr; ChrhWkr; HonRl; SchPl; EdYrBk; SpnCl; Olivet Nazarene Clg; Home Ec Teaching.

KEEN, Daniel D; Oak Grove HS; Horace, ND; 25/50 HstFrshCls; Aud/Vis; Band; Chr; Chrl; Chrs; ChrhWkr; CmntyWkr; CncrtBnd; Business School; Political Science.

KEEN, Michael R; Armstrong HS; Neenah, WI; Chr; Chrl; ChrhWkr; CmntyWkr; Univ Of Wisconsin; Business Admin.

KEENAN, Alene M; Kee HS; Lansing, IA; Chr; HonRl; StuCncl; TchrAde; Yrbk; FTA; Bsktbl; Trk; BttyCrckrAwd; DanFAwd; College;.

KEENAN, Clarmarie I; Maine Twp South HS; Park Ridge, IL; Chr; HonRl; NHS; VPNatlThespSoc; SchMus; SchPl; StuCncl; SchPpr; GerCl; Bsktbl; CchngActv; Univ Of Michigan; Sociology.

KEENAN, Frank; Athens HS; Athens, WI; HonRl; NHS; FFA; PpCl; Ftbl; Trade.

KEENAN, Kathleen R; Toluca HS; Toluca, IL; 3/40 VPBand; ChrhWkr; HonRl; MrchBnd; NHS; PepBnd; SchPl; FHA; GAA; Delinois Valley Comm Coll; Accting.

KEENAN, Margy A; Sauk Centre HS; Sauk Centre, MN; 3/157 CncrtBnd; HonRl; NHS; NatlMeritSchl; Orch; SchPl; RptrSchPpr; Bsktbl; CaptTrk; Coll; Pht Therapy.

KEENAN, Mary; Waterford Township HS; Union Lake, MI; SecTrsSophCls; ChrhWkr; DrlTm; HonRl; JA; NHS; SchAde; SchMus; Emu; Music Major.

KEENAN, Susan M; Toluca HS; Toluca, IL; 5/26 SecFrshCls; Band; HonRl; JrNHS; MrchBnd; NHS; PepBnd; FHA; SciCl; GAA;.

KEENAN, Tammy E; Victoria HS; Victoria, KS; SecTrsJrCls; CncrtBnd; HonRl; NHS; PepBnd; FHA; SecPpCl; LetterBsktbl; Swmmng; LetterTrk; College; Art Or Med.

KEENE, Andrew J; Libertyville HS; Libertyville, IL; 22/408 HonRl; LetterSwmmng; Univ; Microbiology.

KEENE, Debra K; Potosi HS; Potosi, WI; Band; CncrtBnd; HonRl; LbryAde; MrchBnd; OffAde; PepBnd; TchrAde; PresYthFlsp; Secretarial.

KEENE, Michael E; Triton HS; Tippecanoe, IN; HonRl; NHS; SciCl; Trk; IMSpt; Coll; Engin.

KEENER, Stephen J; Marysville HS; Marysville, MI; ALBoysSt; ChrhWkr; PresFrshCls; NHS; PresSciCl; CaptTrk; Col; Acct.

KEENER, Valerie A; Edwards County Sr HS; Albion, IL; 1/99 SecTrsFrshCls; SecTrsSophCls; ChrhWkr; HonRl; NHS; NatlMeritCmnd; OffAde; EdSchPpr; FTA; FrCl; PpCl; LetterBsbl; LetterChrldr; College; Zoology.

KEENER, Valerie A; Edwards Cty Sr HS; Albion, IL; 1/98 SecFrshCls; SecSophCls; NHS; NatlMeritCmnd; OffAde; EdSchPpr; FrCl; PresPpCl; LetterBsbl; CaptChrldr; College; Life Science.

KEENEY, Kathy K; Red Cloud HS; Blue Hill, NE; SecFrshCls; Band; Chr; Chrs; ChrhWkr; CncrtBnd; DrlTm; HonRl; LbryAde; MrchBnd; OffAde; Bsktbl; Trk; Chrldr; College; Home Economics.

KEENEY, Kimberlee S; Terre Haute Souh Vigo HS; Terre Haute, IN; Chr; HonRl; NatlFornLg; SchMus; 4-H; LatCl; GAA; 4-HAwd;.

KEENEY, Mary C; Good Counsel HS; Chicago, IL; SecJrCls; Chrs; HonRl; NatlFornLg; NHS; SchMus; SchPl; StuCncl; RptrYrbk; De Paul University; Speech.

KEESEY, Mark A; Parkview HS; Brodhead, WI; 8/158 HonRl; NHS; TchrAde; Bsbl; Ftbl; Glf; LetterTrk; Platteville Univ; Engineer.

KEESEY, Michael L; Maine South HS; Park Ridge, IL; HonRl; NHS; RptrYrbk; RptrSchPpr; LetterFtbl; Trk; Univ Of Illinois; Business.

KEESLER, Barbara A; Armstrong HS; Neenah, WI; HonRl; NHS; FBLA; IMSpt; RotaryAwd; Secretarial Work.

KEESLING, Tamra K; Fairfield HS; Sylvia, KS; 7/64 SecSrCls; Band; Chr; HonRl; Mdrgl; SchPl; StuCncl; Twrl; SecPpCl; Bsktbl; Tennis; PPFtbl; BttyCrckrAwd; Oklahoma Christian College; Medical Tech.

KEETON, Anthony D; Elsberry HS; Elsberry, MO; 1/63 HonRl; Northeast Missouri State Univ; Accounting.

KEEVER, Kirk A; Southern HS; Stronghurst, IL; CncrtBnd; HonRl; Bsktbl; Ftbl; College.

KEFFER, Paul N; Osseo Fairchild HS; Osseo, WI; Aud/Vis; HonRl; JrNHS; SctActv; 4-H; GerCl; LetterGlf; LetterWrstlng; College.

KEGLER, Deborah J; Pardeeville Sr HS; Pardeeville, WI; Band; Chrs; CncrtBnd; HonRl; MrchBnd; NatlThespSoc; SchPl; RptrYrbk; Madison Area Tech College; Exec Secretary.

KEGLER, John L; Humboldt HS; St Paul, MN; HonRl; College; Liberal Arts.

KEHE, Renee E; Rolling Meadows HS; Arlington Heights, IL; 4/581 AFS; Chr; Chrs; ChrhWkr; CmntyWkr; HonRl; Mdrgl; NHS; Augustana College; Computer Programer.

KEHL, Stephen R; Almond HS; Almond, WI; ALBoysSt; Aud/Vis; Band; Chrs; CncrtBnd; HonRl; LbryAde; MrchBnd; PresNHS; PepBnd; TchrAde; RptrYrbk; Yrbk; LetterFtbl; Univ Of Wisc; Radio & Tv Broadcasting.

KEHLENBRINK, Joan C; Beaver Dam Sr HS; Beaver Dam, WI; 81/349 Band; Chr; CncrtBnd; MrchBnd; PepBnd; SpnCl; PpCl; GAA; College; Business.

KEHLER, Michael E; Greeley Public HS; Greeley, NE; PresSophCls; ChrhWkr; HonRl; SchPl; StuCncl; StuGov; 4-H; IMSpt; 4-HAwd; Farming.

KEHR, Beverly R; Gaylord Public HS; Winthrop, MN; HonRl; FHA; MasAwd; Golden Valley Luth Coll; Computer Prog.

KEHR, Ralph W; Meadville HS; Meadville, MO; HonRl; NHS; StuCncl; 4-H; LetterBsktbl; LetterTrk; College; Agriculture.

KEHR, Richard R; Sotuheast Nebr Cons HS; Shubert, NE; 8/34 HonRl; FFA; LetterWrstlng; Technical College; Professional.

KEHRER, Pamela A; Wesclin HS; New Memphis, IL; 3/110 HonRl; NHS; RptrYrbk; RptrSchPpr; FHA; GerCl; PpCl; GAA;.

KEHRES, Cheryl A; Stockbridge HS; Webberville, MI; 4/123 HonRl; NHS; Trk; Chrldr; GAA; Michi State Univ; Agriculture.

KEIERLEBER, Jocelyn G; Winner HS; Clearfield, SD; ALAGirlsSt; ChrhWkr; CmntyWkr; NatlFornLg; NatlThespSoc; PolWkr; SchPl; StuGov; 4-H; 4-HAwd; So Dakota State Univ; Speech Therapy.

KEIFER, Michael S; Superior HS; Guide Rock, NE; Chr; HonRl; LitMag; Quill&Scroll; SchPl; SchPpr; LetterFtbl; CaptWrstlng; BttyCrckrAwd; VoiceDemAwd; Kearney St College; Agri Business.

KEIFER, Paul A; Benson HS; Omaha, NE; Band; CncrtBnd; HonRl; MrchBnd; NHS; NatlMeritCmnd; Orch; PepBnd; SchMus; SctActv; Unif; Biochemistry & Math.

KEIGHER, Brian W; Westview HS; Kankakee, IL; 51/254 HonRl; Il Univ; Accntg.

KEIL, David W; Hoisington HS; Russell, KS; Ftbl; Trk; Barton County Comm Jr Clg; Agri Business.

KEIL, Lawrence W; Reitz Memorial HS; Evansville, IN; HonRl; Ftbl; Trk; IMSpt; University.

KEIL, Peggy A; Red Bud HS; Red Bud, IL; Band; Chrl; Chrs; CncrtBnd; DrmMjrt; NHS; SchMus; SchPl; VPStuCncl; PpCl; College; St Louis Col Of Pharmacy.

KEIL, Timothy P; Plattsmouth HS; Plattsmouth, NE; 1/133 VPSophCls; PresJrCls; SecSrCls; ALBoysSt; HonRl; NHS; StuGov; EngCl; VPSpnCl; MthCl; LetterBsbl; LetterBsktbl; LetterTrk; Univ Creighton; Law.

KEILBEY, Lori A; Saint Pius X HS; Kansas City, MO; 11/129 TrsSrCls; SchMus; SctActv; StuCncl; TchrAde; PpCl; LetterChrldr; PresAwd; College; Professional.

KEILHOLTZ, Paula A; Cochrane Fountain City HS; Fountain City, WI; LbryAde; NatlFornLg; SchMus; TchrAde; YthFlsp; EdYrBk; PresFHA; Col; Mass Communications.

KEIM, Debbie S; North Miami HS; Roann, IN; Chr; DrlTm; HonRl; MrchBnd; OffAde; SchMus; SchPl; StuCncl; 4-H; SpnCl; PpCl; GAA; PPFtbl; College; Data Processor.

KEIM, Valerie A; Dekalb HS; Dekalb, IL; 14/370 ChrhWkr; HospAde; NHS; NatlMeritSF; YthFlsp; Vanderbilt Univ; Business.

KEIMIG, Kathy; Clear Lake HS; Clear Lake, SD; 1/5727#3 SecFrshCls; NatlFornLg; PolWkr; SchPl; Trk; BttyCrckrAwd; 4-HAwd; KiwanAwd;.

KEINATH, Elaine E; Millington HS; Millington, MI; Band; ChrhWkr; HonRl; HospAde; MrchBnd; VPNHS; PepBnd; College; Professional.

KEINATH, Howard J; Deerfield HS; Blissfield, MI; Band; CncrtBnd; HonRl; LbryAde; MrchBnd; SchAde; SchPl; StuCncl; StuGov; TchrAde; Bsbl; CaptBsktbl; Ftbl; Trk; College; Vocation.

KEINERT, Paula J; Waterford Mott HS; Pontiac, MI; Chr; Chrl; HonRl; JA; NatlThespSoc; SchMus; SchPl; StuGov; LetterTennis; Univ Of Michigan; Theatre.

KEIRNS, Sara M; Northrop HS; Fort Wayne, IN; 32/643 Chr; ChrhWkr; HonRl; TchrAde; Yrbk; FrCl; PpCl; GAA;.

KEISER, Brian; Gothenburg HS; Gothenburg, NE; LbryAde; NatlThespSoc; TchrAde; 4-H; FFA; IMSpt; ChmbCommrsAwd; 4-HAwd; Univ Of Ne; Agriculture.

KEISER, Gail; Windsor HS; Imperial, MO; 2/60 SecTrsJrCls; VPSrCls; ALAGirlsSt; NHS; StuCncl; Yrbk; FTA; Trk; AmLegAwd; EldAwd; Southeast Mo State Univ; Comm Art.

KEISER, Kenneth R; Pekin HS; Richland, IA; 3/50 PresFrshCls; Band; Chrs; CncrtBnd; HonRl; Mdrgl; NHS; SchMus; StuCncl; EdYrBk; Central College; Music.

KEISER, Laura; Pinckney Hs; Pinckney, MI; TchrAde; SptEdSchPpr; Eastern Mi U; Teaching.

KEISER, Richard L; Wauneta Public HS; Enders, NE; TrsFrshCls; TrsJrCls; HonRl; NHS; YthFlsp; Pres4-H; VPFFA; LetterBsktbl; IMSpt; 4-HAwd; College; Agriculture.

KEISER, Terry L; Griswold Comm HS; Griswold, IA; 2/86 ALBoysSt; NHS; StuCncl; MthCl; LetterBsbl; LetterBsktbl; LetterFtbl; LetterTrk; William Penn Coll; Engr.

KEITH, Barbara J; John Adams HS; South Bend, IN; 6/450 Chr; NatlMeritSF; Quill&Scroll; SchMus; SchPl; Yrbk; SptEdSchPpr; GAA; Indiana Univ; Journalism.

KEITH, Belinda J; Cairo HS; Cairo, IL; 11/67 SecSrCls; Chrs; HonRl; HospAde; NHS; OffAde; StuGov; YthFlsp; EdYrBk; SptEdYrbk; FBLA; PpCl; Bsbl; Patricia Stevens Career College; Secretary.

KEITH, Julie A; Forman HS; Manito, IL; 4/70 SecFrshCls; VPJrCls; VPSrCls; HonRl; NHS; Yrbk; SchPpr; FHA; PpCl; Illinois Central College; Business Admin.

KEITH, Michael E; West Vigo HS; W Terre Haute, IN; 47/194.

KEITH, Peggy; Stephen Decatur HS; Decatur, IL; Band; CncrtBnd; MrchBnd; Orch; SchPl; StuCncl; SpnCl; Chrldr; College; Professional.

KEITH, Regina S; Bruce Public HS; Bruce, WI; PresSophCls; VPJrCls; ALAGirlsSt; Band; HonRl; SchPl; EdYrBk; FNA; PpCl; Chrldr; College; Professional.

KEITH, Shirley; Marion C Early HS; Morrisville, MO; 2/43 SecJrCls; SecSrCls; HonRl; SchPl; EdYrBk; SchPpr; FBLA; FHA; Ozark Bible Coll.

KEITHLEY, Thomas; Luther HS; Oak Lawn, IL; 7/185 Aud/Vis; ChrhWkr; HonRl; NHS; Bsktbl; IMSpt; Concordia Teachers College; H Steacher.

KEKEC, John; North County HS; Bonne Terre, MO; 27/160 SecSrCls; DrmMjrt; HonRl; JCC; JrNHS; NatlFornLg; SctActv; FrCl; IMSpt; College.

KEKICH, John S; Winston Churchill HS; Livonia, MI; Aud/Vis; HonRl; NatlThespSoc; SchMus; SchPl; OptClAwd; U Of Mich; Radio Broadcasting.

KELBEL, Kevin D; Northview HS; Grand Rapids, MI; CncrtBnd; HonRl; MrchBnd; NHS; NatlMeritCmnd; PepBnd; SctActv; GerCl; Bsbl; CchngActv; Univ; Physics.

KELCH, Kevin M; Peoria Heights HS; Peoria Heights, IL; 1/93 HonRl; NHS; LetterFtbl; LetterTrk; KiwanAwd; RotaryAwd; Il Central Coll; Architecture.

KELCH, Raymond E; Fitzgerald HS; Warren, MI; HonRl; LitMag; Quill&Scroll; RptrYrbk; Yrbk; SchPpr; Univ; Forestry.

KELCHEN, Steven L; West Delaware HS; Manchester, IA; 4/198 SecTrsSrCls; HonRl; VPNHS; LetterFtbl; CaptWrstlng; Univ Of Ia; Pro.

KELDER, Peter S; Cary Grove HS; Cary, IL; 31/330 ALBoysSt; HonRl; NHS; Bsktbl; College; Engineering.

KELENYI, Robert; Luther HS; Chicago, IL; 34/213 HonRl; SctActv; Tennis; Wrstlng; IMSpt; Augustana College; Law.

KELL, Sharon M; Aurora East HS; Montgomery, IL; 28/530 DrlTm; HonRl; NHS; Quill&Scroll; SchMus; StuGov; No Illinois Univ; Medicine.

KELLAMS, Martha; Elgin HS; Elgin, IL; CmntyWkr; OffAde; StuCncl; StuGov; GAA; IMSpt; Univ Of Wisc; Biological Sciences.

KELLE, Deborah S; Sterling Public HS; Sterling, NE; TrsSophCls; PresJrCls; SecSrCls; ALAGirlsSt; HonRl; NHS; PepBnd; RptrYrbk; PpCl; Chrldr; Peru St Coll; Medical Secretary.

KELLEHER, Alan R; Ogden Community HS; Perry, IA; ALBoysSt; StuCncl; RptrSchPpr; Bsbl; LetterFtbl; LetterTrk; IMSpt; AmLegAwd; Trade Schl; Mechanics Auto Or Diesel.

KELLEN, Bill D; St Marys HS; Remsen, IA; 13/60 VPFrshCls; Band; Chr; Chrs; CncrtBnd; HonRl; PepBnd; SchMus; SchPl; StuCncl; RptrSchPpr; LetterBsbl; LetterBsktbl; LetterTrk; College; Vocation.

KELLEN, Gary D; Spalding HS; Alton, IA; PresSophCls; VPJrCls; HonRl; Bsbl; Bsktbl; IMSpt; Clge; Pro.

KELLEN, Karen S; Amboy HS; Sublette, IL; Band; CncrtBnd; MrchBnd; FBLA; PpCl; Bsktbl; Trk; PresGAA; Ill Benedictine; Sociology.

KELLEN, Kathy A; Spalding HS; Granville, IA; PresFrshCls; PresJrCls; Chrs; ChrhWkr; HonRl; Trk; Chrldr; College.

KELLEN, Laura J; Marillac HS; Mt Prospect, IL; LitMag; SchMus; SchPl; Univ Of Illinois; Animal Science.

KELLEN, Mary; Adrian Public HS; Rushmore, MN; 11/89 Band; HonRl; MrchBnd; NHS; Trk; Chrldr; GAA; IMSpt; 4-HAwd; PresAwd;.

KELLENBERGER, Vickie L; Sabetha HS; Sabetha, KS; VPSophCls; Band; Chr; CncrtBnd; HonRl; NHS; PepBnd; SctActv; StuCncl; FHA; Univ; Vocal Music Techer.

KELLER, Amy L; Alpena Senior HS; Alpena, MI; Western Michigan Univ; Chemistry.

KELLER, Andrea M; Lincoln HS; Wisconsin Rapids, WI; HonRl; LbryAde; SchAde; TchrAde; 4-H; GerCl; Univ; Teacher.

KELLER, Betty Ann J; Belleville Township W HS; Millstadt, IL; NHS; TchrAde; RptrSchPpr; Belelville Area College; Accountant.

KELLER, Brad M; Frankenmuth HS; Frankenmuth, MI; ALBoysSt; HonRl; NHS; TchrAde; LetterBsbl; LetterBsktbl; LetterFtbl; PresAwd; Michigan State University; Veterinary.

KELLER, Brenda L; Riceville Comm HS; Leroy, MN; 8/80 VPJrCls; ALAGirlsSt; HonRl; NHS; RptrSchPpr; CaptBsktbl; CaptGlf; Trk; IMSpt; PresAwd; Univ; Psychology & Social Work.

KELLER, Bryan I; Shawnee HS; Grand Tower, IL; Band; Chr; Chrl; Chrs; ChrhWkr; CmntyWkr; CncrtBnd; HonRl; MrchBnd; Orch; Bsktbl; IMSpt; Trade Schl; Trade.

KELLER, Cheryl A; Concordia Academy; St Paul, MN; 7/50 SecFrshCls; Chr; HonRl; HospAde; NHS; StuCncl; EdYrBk; RptrSchPpr; GerCl; IMSpt; Lakewood Jr Coll; Secretarial.

KELLER, Christilee A; Fennimore HS; Stitzer, WI; 12/112 Chrs; ChrhWkr; HonRl; NHS; YthFlsp; 4-H; 4-HAwd; College; Interior Design.

KELLER, Cindy; Naper Public HS; Naper, NE; HonRl; MrchBnd; SchPl; StuCncl; Twrl; Yrbk; SchPpr; Chrldr; IMSpt; VoiceDemAwd; Natl Guard; Professional.

KELLER, Craig F; Hamilton HS; Sussex, WI; 51/265 HonRl; NHS; SpnCl; LetterBsktbl; Ftbl; Trk; Univ Of Wisconsin; Secondary Educ.

KELLER, Craig L; Aaustin Catholic Prep; Roseville, MI; 31/115 VPSrCls; HonRl; NatlFornLg; NHS; Quill&Scroll; SchPl; StuCncl; EdYrBk; Yrbk; Univ Of Arizona; Lawyer.

KELLER, Daniel G; St Francis Of Assissi HS; Humphrey, NE; VPFrshCls; Band; CmntyWkr; CncrtBnd; HonRl; Glf; Socr; Trk; IMSpt; Coll; Professional.

KELLER, Dawn K; Isu Labratory; Seelyville, IN; 8/60 TrsSrCls; HonRl; ModUN; PolWkr; StuCncl; TchrAde; GAA; Herron Sch Of Art; Fashion Illustrator.

KELLER, Debbie K; Harvey HS; Selz, ND; 11/83 VPJrCls; TrsSrCls; ALAGirlsSt; HonRl; LbryAde; StuGov; College; Home Economics.

KELLER, Debra L; Joliet East HS; Elwood, IL; 6/425 HonRl; NHS; OffAde; College; Accounting.

KELLER, Deena K; Dongola HS; Dongola, IL; TrsFrshCls; TrsSophCls; PresJrCls; Aud/Vis; Band; Chrs; ChrhWkr; CncrtBnd; HonRl; LbryAde; Business.

KELLER, Dennis A; Washburn HS; Washburn, ND; CmntyWkr; HonRl; SchPl; LetterBsbl; LetterFtbl; Clg; Bus Management.

KELLER, Diane; Elbow Lake HS; Wendell, MN; 4/68 Band; CncrtBnd; HonRl; MrchBnd; NHS; PepBnd; TchrAde; 4-H; Bsktbl; Chrldr; College; Profesional.

KELLER, Donna; Hlv Community HS; Victor, IA; SecTrsFrshCls; Band; HonRl; SchMus; StuCncl; SpnCl; College.

KELLER, Edward E; Murray Community HS; Murray, IA; 6/30 HonRl; SchPl;.

KELLER, Elizabeth H; Woodruff HS; Peoria, IL; Chr; KeyCl; SpnCl; Chrldr; College; Library Science.

KELLER, Gary D; Spalding HS; Alton, IA; PresSophCls; VPJrCls; HonRl; Bsbl; Bsktbl; Coll; Pro.

KELLER, Gerald D; Beulah HS; Beulah, ND; 7/56 HonRl; YthFlsp; SchPpr; 4-H; FFA; Bsktbl; LetterFtbl; Trk; IMSpt; 4-HAwd; No Dakota St Univ; Agriculture.

KELLER, Jo Ann; Nokomis HS; Nokomis, IL; 5/91 PresJrCls; Chrs; ChrhWkr; CmntyWkr; HonRl; OffAde; SchMus; EdYrBk; FHA;.

KELLER, Kathleen M; Newton HS; Willow Hill, IL; Band; Chrs; CncrtBnd; HonRl; TrsFrshCls; MrchBnd; NHS; SchMus; 4-H; IMSpt; Coll; Voc.

KELLER, Kimberly K; Marshall HS; Marshall, MI; 19/255 HonRl; OffAde; SchAde; Univ; Psychology.

KELLER, Larry S; Maine West HS; Des Plaines, IL; Band; Chrs; CncrtBnd; HonRl; MrchBnd; Orch; PepBnd; University; Music.

KELLER, Laura; South Side HS; Fort Wayne, IN; HonRl; OffAde; PolWkr; SchAde; TchrAde; FrCl; IMSpt; Purdue; Pharmacy.

KELLER, Loyd; Dixon HS; Dixon, MO; PresSrCls; HonRl; Bsbl; Univ Mo; Engr.

KELLER, Lynn M; Medford HS; Owatonna, MN; Band; Chr; NHS; SchPl; RptrSchPpr; Pres4-H; TreasFHA; LetterTrk; LetterChrldr; EldAwd; Bemidji State College.

KELLER, Marla; Palco HS; Palco, KS; 1/30 SecJrCls; Band; HonRl; NHS; TchrAde; RptrYrbk; 4-H; FHA; BttyCrckrAwd; 4-HAwd; Colby Comm Jr College; Business.

KELLER, Michael; Jefferson Sr HS; Helenville, WI; 9/164 ALBoysSt; Band; CncrtBnd; HonRl; JrNHS; MrchBnd; NHS; RptrSchPpr; SchPpr; Uwm Milwaukee; Engineer.

KELLER, Michele M; St Scholastica HS; Lincolnwood, IL; 12/233 CmntyWkr; HonRl; HospAde; LitMag; NatlMeritCmnd; Sacrstn; SchMus; RptrSchPpr; CivCl; GerCl; U Of Chicago; Law.

KELLER, Michelle L; Roncalli HS; Omaha, NE; Chr; Chrs; ChrhWkr; SchMus; SchPl; FrCl; PpCl; Chrldr; University Of Nebraska; Elem Education.

KELLER, Nancy; Swartz Creek HS; Flint, MI; ChrhWkr; HonRl; SctActv; YthFlsp; FBLA; EngCl; Michigan Christian College; Social Worker.

KELLER, Pamela; Slayton Public HS; Slayton Public, MN; MrchBnd; NHS; PepBnd; SchPl; StuCncl; 4-H; GerCl; Bsktbl; Chrldr; PPFtbl; University.

KELLER, Rena A; Mt Horeb HS; Mt Horeb, WI; 3/135 ALAGirlsSt; HonRl; JrNHS; NHS; NatlMeritCmnd; Orch; SchMus; FHA; PpCl; College; Home Economics.

KELLER, Ronald L; Dongola HS; Dongola, IL; HonRl; SchPpr; SpnCl; SciCl; Bradley Univ; Psychology.

KELLER, Ross V; Bisbee HS; Bisbee, ND; Band; Chrs; ChrhWkr; HonRl; SchPl; SctActv; SptEdSchPpr; FFA; LetterBsktbl; LetterFtbl; LetterTrk; U Of Mt; Forestry.

KELLER, Sharon K; Campbell Tintah HS; Tenney, MN; Band; Chr; CncrtBnd; HonRl; SchPl; StuCncl; LetterTrk; GAA; PresAwd; Alexandria Tec Sch; Accountant.

KELLER, Sharon S; Palco HS; Zurich, KS; 3/25 SecSrCls; Band; Chr; ChrhWkr; HonRl; NHS; StuCncl; PresFHA; PpCl; LetterBsktbl; Ft Hays St College; Physical Ed.

KELLER, Steve M; Fairfield HS; Fairfield, IA; Aud/Vis; ChrhWkr; CmntyWkr; SctActv; YthFlsp; FFA; LetterFtbl; LetterWrstlng; IMSpt; Trade School; Agriculture.

KELLER, Steven J; Melvin Comm HS; Melvin, IA; PresFrshCls; TrsSophCls; TrsJrCls; Chrs; HonRl; NHS; SchPl; StuCncl; RptrYrbk; RptrSchPpr; Air Force Rotc; Chemistry.

KELLER, Susan K; Colgan HS; Pittsburg, KS; SecSophCls; Chr; NHS; SchMus; SchPl; YthFlsp; Yrbk; PpCl; Chrldr; College; Teaching Children.

KELLER, Thomas; St Mary Central HS; Menasha, WI; Chrs; HonRl; RptrYrbk; SpnCl; Coll; Cmputer Science.

KELLER, Todd R; Kimball HS; Royal Oak, MI; 56/702 Chr; CmntyWkr; HonRl; NHS; NatlThespSoc; SchMus; SctActv; PresSpnCl; LetterTennis; IMSpt; Univ Mi; Business.

KELLER, Vicki J; Edgewood HS; Bloomington, IN; Band; CncrtBnd; HonRl; MrchBnd; PepBnd; TchrAde; FHA; Office Work.

KELLER, William; Proviso West Hs; Westchester, IL; HonRl; OffAde; College; Business.

KELLER, William A; Newell Ind HS; Newell, SD; 3/51 ALBoysSt; Band; Chrs; HonRl; NHS; StuCncl; StuGov; Bsktbl; Ftbl; Trk; IMSpt; Sd Schl Of Mines & Tech; Engineer.

KELLERMAN, Carol A; Bishop Miege HS; Westwood, KS; 46/202 Chr; Chrl; Chrs; HonRl; SchMus; SchPl; SpnCl; PpCl; IMSpt; Benedictine College.

KELLERMAN, Jeffrey F; Kindred Public HS; Davenport, ND; 15/46 HonRl; StuCncl; YthFlsp; FFA; Bsbl; Bsktbl; CaptFtbl; Wrstlng; Bismark Jr Clg; Phy Ed Coach.

KELLERMAN, Kathryn; Kearsley HS; Flint, MI; 4/374 Chr; CmntyWkr; NatlFornLg; NHS; NatlThespSoc; PolWkr; SchMus; SchPl; JAAwd; CitAwd; Mott Comm College; Comm Deve Worker.

KELLETT, Richard M; Horace Mann HS; Fond Du Lac, WI; 13/92 Band; HonRl; NatlMeritCmnd; 4-H; LetterFtbl; LetterWrstlng; IMSpt; EldAwd; 4-HAwd; KiwanAwd; Clge; Industrial Eng.

KELLEY, Allen K; Morton HS; Morton, IL; 39/298 HonRl; NatlMeritSchl; StuCncl; LatCl; SciCl; LetterBsktbl; LetterFtbl; LetterTennis; Trk; PresAwd; Univ Of Il; Dentistry.

KELLEY, Becky A; West Sioux Community HS; Hawarden, IA; 11/79 VPJrCls; SecTrsSrCls; ALAGirlsSt; HonRl; LbryAde; Yrbk; PpCl; Bsbl; Bsktbl; CaptTrk; Sioux Emp Col; History Library Science Coac.

KELLEY, Brian G; Harlan Community HS; Harlan, IA; LetterFtbl; Trk; Wrstlng; University.

KELLEY, Bruce G; Elk Grove HS; Elk Grove Village, IL; 35/507 HonRl; NHS; LetterBsktbl; LetterTennis; Northern Ill Univ; Accounting.

KELLEY, Catherine T; Central Catholic HS; Merna, IL; 6/84 VPSophCls; HonRl; NHS; SchPl; StuCncl; StuGov; TchrAde; 4-H; FrCl; PpCl; Trk; Univ; Professional.

KELLEY, Clark M; Tyndall HS; Tyndall, SD; PresBand; Chrs; HonRl; Mdrgl; MrchBnd; SchPl; PresStuCncl; RptrYrbk; CaptFtbl; LetterTrk; CaptWrstlng; Usd/s College; Professional.

KELLEY, David B; Catholic Central HS; Monroe, MI; SecFrshCls; ALBoysSt; HonRl; NHS; StuCncl; LetterBsktbl; LetterTrk; IMSpt; College; Politics Eng.

KELLEY, Diane E; El Dorado HS; El Dorado, KS; 19/187 Band; CncrtBnd; HonRl; MrchBnd; PpCl; Col; Compurter Programer.

KELLEY, Donald; Hoxie HS; Hoxie, KS; ChrhWkr; 4-H; 4-HAwd;.

KELLEY, Franklin D; Van Buren HS; Brazil, IN; 22/69 HonRl; SchPl; SctActv; TchrAde; 4-H; FTA; KeyCl; LatCl; SciCl; LetterBsbl; LetterBsktbl; IMSpt; Indiana State Univ; Engineering.

KELLEY, Ina E; Tecumseh HS; Adrian, MI; 15/240 Band; LbryAde; NHS; NatlMeritCmnd; EdYrBk; Western Michigan Univ; Librarian.

KELLEY, James H; Walnut Grove HS; Walnut Grove, MO; Band; CncrtBnd; DrlTm; MrchBnd; PepBnd; RptrSchPpr; Bsbl; Bsktbl; Trade School; Vocation.

KELLEY, Janet A; Maroa Forsyth HS; Maroa, IL; ALAGirlsSt; Chrs; ChrhWkr; HonRl; RptrSchPpr; FHA; PpCl; SciCl; AmLegAwd;.

KELLEY, John A; Antioch Community; Lindenhurst, IL; HonRl; NatlMeritCmnd; SctActv; LetterFtbl; LetterTennis; LetterWrstlng; Clge; Law.

KELLEY, John R; St Marys Springs HS; Fond Du Lac, WI; 2/135 PresJrCls; NHS; NatlMeritSF; StuCncl; RptrSchPpr; 4-H; Uw Of Madison; Lawyer Journalist.

KELLEY, Kalen; Danville Community HS; Dandille, IA; 1/35 PresJrCls; Band; HonRl; StuGov; IMSpt; 4-HAwd; College Or U; Agriculture Or Vet Medicine.

KELLEY, Kathy J; Fredericktown Sr HS; Fredericktown, MO; 5/145 SecTrsFrshCls; Band; ChrhWkr; CncrtBnd; HonRl; JrNHS; MrchBnd; NHS; PepBnd; TchrAde; College; Dental Assistant.

KELLEY, Kearn; Gibault HS; Waterloo, IL; HonRl; Army; Gen Const Mach Operator.

KELLEY, Keith D; St Francis HS; Zimmerman, MN; 2/165 VPSrCls; Chrs; HonRl; NatlFornLg; NHS; StuCncl; EdSchPpr; SciCl; LetterBsbl; LetterFtbl; Usma West Point; Engr.

KELLEY, Kim O; Savannah R Iii HS; Savannah, MO; PresFrshCls; VPJrCls; PresSrCls; ALBoysSt; HonRl; NHS; SptEdSchPpr; ChmnBsktbl; ChmnFtbl; Trk; Coll; Mathmatics.

KELLEY, Laura A; Wayland Acad; Buchanan, MI; CncrtBnd; DrlTm; HonRl; MrchBnd; SchMus; SchPl; Yrbk; EdSchPpr; FrCl; SpnCl; Albion Clge; Social Psychology.

KELLEY, Mary M; Central Catholic HS; Normal, IL; 16/94 HonRl; SchPl; StuCncl; TchrAde; RptrSchPpr; 4-H; University; Communications.

KELLEY, Maureen A; Sargent Public HS; Sargent, NE; HonRl; LbryAde; NHS; NatlThespSoc; SchPl; StuGov; TchrAde; SecPpCl; LetterBsktbl; LetterTrk; Trade School; Home Ec.

KELLEY, Nancy S; Westfield Comm HS; Westfield, IA; VPFrshCls; PresSophCls; Chrs; HonRl; NHS; SchPl; StuCncl; EdYrBk; EdSchPpr; BttyCrckrAwd; Univ Of N Iowa; Physical Therapy.

KELLEY, Pamela J; Goreville HS; Goreville, IL; 1/31 SecFrshCls; VPSophCls; SecJrCls; Band; HonRl; StuCncl; EdSchPpr; Southern Illinois Univ; Business.

KELLEY, Patricia A; Carmel Girls HS; Lincolnshire, IL; HonRl; NHS; NatlMeritCmnd; SchMus; SchPl; SecStuCncl; RptrYrbk; VPFrCl; PresPpCl; Tennis; PresAmLegAwd; University; Medicine.

KELLEY, Patrick J; Harper Creek HS; Battle Creek, MI; Band; ChrhWkr; HonRl; ModUN; NHS; PepBnd; PolWkr; SchPl; StuCncl; Clge; Journalism.

KELLEY, Randall E; Omaha South HS; Omaha, NE; 6/611 Chr; HonRl; NHS; NatlMeritCmnd; MthCl; Univ Of Wisconsin; Computer Science.

KELLEY, Robert; Johnson Brock HS; Johnson, NE; Chr; ChrhWkr; SchPl; YthFlsp; 4-H; SciCl; Bsktbl; Ftbl; Trk; 4-HAwd;.

KELLEY, Robin L; Brown County HS; Nashville, IN; 5/206 Band; CncrtBnd; HonRl; MrchBnd; In Univ; Psychologist.

KELLEY, Ruth A; Bridgeport HS; Saginaw, MI; 31/330 CncrtBnd; HonRl; MrchBnd; NHS; Yrbk;.

KELLEY, Sandra L; Carl Sandburg HS; Tinley Park, IL; 10/680 Chr; HonRl; SctActv; YthFlsp; 4-H; Trk; AmLegAwd; College; Psychology.

KELLEY, Sarah; Theodore Roosevelt HS; Des Moines, IA; Chr; ChrhWkr; NatlFornLg; Orch; StuCncl; College; Professional.

KELLNER, Cathy; Sheboygan Falls HS; Sheboygan Falls, WI; 12/185 Band; CncrtBnd; HonRl; MrchBnd; NHS; PepBnd; GerCl; Bsktbl; GAA; College; Music.

KELLOGG, David J; Forest Lake HS; Forest Lake, MN; HonRl; PolWkr; StuCncl; College; Writer.

KELLOGG, Marlyn; Owosso HS; Owosso, MI; 68/80 Band; Chr; CncrtBnd; DrlTm; HonRl; OffAde; College; Medical.

KELLOGG, Mary E; Allegan Sr HS; Allegan, MI; 23/187 ChrhWkr; HonRl; LbryAde; TchrAde; Teen; Yrbk; Trade School; Tour Planner.

KELLOR, Eileen M; Oregon Sr HS; Oregon, WI; 9/200 AFS; Chr; Mdrgl; NHS; NatlMeritSF; SchMus; SchPl; Yrbk; SchPpr; Univ Of Wi; Lawyer.

KELLY, Andrea L; Robbinsdale Sr HS; Robbinsdale, MN; 76/761 ChrhWkr; HonRl; LbryAde; NHS; SctActv; TchrAde; Teen; GerCl; PpCl; College.

KELLY, Anne L; Adlai Stevenson HS; Livonia, MI; HonRl; SchMus; StuCncl; PpCl; CaptChrldr; GAA; College Or Univ; Biology Or Psychology.

KELLY, Annette E; Orleans HS; Orleans, IN; 10/61 HstJrCls; HonRl; NHS; StuCncl; Yrbk; Bsktbl; Trk; Chrldr; GAA; 4-HAwd; Purdue Univ; Physical Ed.

KELLY, Ann F; Mc Donell Central HS; Chippewa Falls, WI; HonRl; HospAde; ModUN; RptrSchPpr; LetterBsktbl; Tennis; Univ Of Wi Eau Claire; Journalism.

KELLY, Ann M; Kirksville HS; Kirksville, MO; Band; ChrhWkr; CmntyWkr; CncrtBnd; DrlTm; MrchBnd; PepBnd; PolWkr; StuCncl; StuGov; YthLg; SchPpr; GAA; DanFAwd; College; Biology.

KELLY, Arthur; Metro HS; St Louis, MO; CmntyWkr; OffAde; PolWkr; StuCncl; Yrbk; Meremac Vmsl; Business Administration.

KELLY, Austin J; Marist HS; Chicago, IL; 16/375 HonRl; NatlMeritSF; PolWkr; College; Economics.

KELLY, Barbara; Sacred Heart HS; Verdon, NE; SecFrshCls; SecSophCls; SecJrCls; SecSrCls; ChrhWkr; CmntyWkr; SchMus; PpCl; Trk; University; Lawyer.

KELLY, Barbara A; Octavia HS; Colfax, IL; 10/47 Band; Chrs; CncrtBnd; HonRl; MrchBnd; PepBnd; Illinois St University.

KELLY, Bobby G; Central HS; St Joseph, MO; ChrhWkr; YthFlsp; LetterFtbl; LetterTrk; LetterWrstlng; CchngActv; Clg# Preacher.

KELLY, Brian V; Marian Catholic HS; Park Forest S, IL; 85/328 ChrhWkr; CAP; HonRl; SchMus; SchPl; Univ Of Chicago; Medicine.

KELLY, Burnie J; St Calhoun HS; Ft Calhoun, NE; PresFrshCls; Aud/Vis; Chr; Chrl; Chrs; CmntyWkr; HonRl; LitMag; OffAde; Bsbl; Dentist Assistant.

KELLY, Catherine; Bethlehem Acad; Faribault, MN; 6/85 PresFrshCls; Chr; HonRl; NHS; SchPl; PresStuCncl; RptrYrbk; LetterBsktbl; GAA; BttyCrckrAwd; Saint Marys College Of Notre Dame;lawyer.

KELLY, Catherine S; Muncie Southside HS; Muncie, IN; 24/323 ChrhWkr; HonRl; NHS; 4-H; PpCl; Olivet Nazarene College; Business Admin.

KELLY, Christopher; Charles City Comm HS; Charles City, IA; CmntyWkr; HonRl; StuGov; RptrSchPpr; SchPpr; MthCl; Ftbl; Tennis; Wrstlng; CchngActv; Iowa State; Engin.

KELLY, Claire; Sacred Heart HS; Verdon, NE; 3/24 CmntyWkr; HonRl; JCC; SchPl; StuGov; SptEdYrbk; 4-H; DARAwd; EldAwd; RotaryAwd; Kearney St Coll; X Ray Tech.

KELLY, Cole D; St Thomas Academy; St Paul, MN; TrsJrCls; Chrs; DrlTm; HonRl; NatlFornLg; ROTC; StuCncl; LetterSocr; LetterTrk; IMSpt; College.

KELLY, Colleen D; Lowell HS; Lowell, MI; Band; ChrhWkr; CncrtBnd; HonRl; MrchBnd; NHS; YthFlsp; 4-H; FTA; IMSpt; Ferris State Col; Court Conference Reporter.

KELLY, Cynthia J; Clinton Comm HS; Clinton, IL; 7/154 ALAGirlsSt; Chrs; ChrhWkr; DrlTm; HonRl; NHS; OffAde; SchPl; SpnCl; PpCl; Lincoln Christian Clg; Christian Educ.

KELLY, Daniel; Springfield Hs; Springfield, IL; Band; NatlMeritCmnd; SchMus; RptrSchPpr; LatCl; Socr;.

KELLY, Dave E; St Edmond HS; Ft Dodge, IA; ChrhWkr; SctActv; SpnCl; Ftbl; Wrstlng; U O Ia; Medicine.

KELLY, Dawn; Mid County HS; Lacon, IL; SecFrshCls; SecSophCls; PresSrCls; Band; Chrs; HonRl; MrchBnd; PepBnd; SchMus; SchPl; StuCncl; StuGov; TchrAde; FHA; College.

KELLY, Deborah; Ralston HS; Omaha, NE; DrlTm; HonRl; NHS; Quill&Scroll; Yrbk; SchPpr; ChmbCommrsAwd; College.

KELLY, Diane E; Belvidere HS; Belvidere, IL; 38/350 Chrs; HonRl; RedCrAde; YthFlsp; FNA; SpnCl; PpCl; LetterGAA; Nursing School; Nursing.

KELLY, Donna; Homer Community HS; Hubbard, NE; CmntyWkr; RptrYrbk; FSA; PpCl; SciCl; College; Professional.

KELLY, Edward G; Thornton Fractional South HS; Lansing, IL; 440/550 CmntyWkr; HonRl; NHS; RptrSchPpr; SptEdSchPpr; Univ Of Ill; Engineer.

KELLY, Georgia A; River Valley HS; Sawyer, MI; 13/130 Aud/Vis; HonRl; SchPl; TchrAde; KeyCl; College; Medical Tech.

KELLY, James P; Holdrege HS; Holdrege, NE; ALBoysSt; Chrs; SchMus; SciCl; Bsbl; Bsktbl; LetterFtbl; Trk; Wrstlng; U Of Neb Lincoln; Law.

KELLY, Jeffrey B; Juda HS; Juda, WI; ChrhWkr; HonRl; SecTrsFrshCls; YthFlsp; FFA; LetterBsktbl; Army ;police Work.

KELLY, Jeffrey P; Loyola Academy; Deerfield, IL; 110/461 PresSophCls; VPSrCls; HonRl; SchMus; Sdlty; TreasStuCncl; VPPpCl; Trk; USJCAwd; University; Law.

KELLY, Jill A; Elmore HS; Elmore, MN; 1/25 VPSophCls; Band; HonRl; NHS; PepBnd; StuCncl; YthFlsp; RptrSchPpr; EdSchPpr; SchPpr; College; Professional.

KELLY, John; Harrison HS; Harrison, MI; ChrhWkr; HonRl; NHS; SctActv; StuCncl; StuGov; TchrAde; Glf; Trk; Coll; Med.

KELLY, John D; Irving Crown HS; Carpentersville, IL; 45/355 Band; CncrtBnd; HonRl; MrchBnd; Ftbl; LetterTennis; LetterWrstlng; Univ Of Illinois; Journalism.

KELLY, Joseph M; Sesser HS; Sesser, IL; 3/50 PresSrCls; ALBoysSt; HonRl; NHS; StuCncl; SptEdYrbk; LetterBsktbl; CaptFtbl; LetterTrk; Rend Lake College; Civil Engineer.

KELLY, Juanita G; Charles City HS; Charles City, IA; 52/225 Band; Chrl; Chrs; MrchBnd; Yrbk; 4-H; SpnCl; LetterBsktbl; College; Foreign Language Major.

KELLY, Julia A; Athens HS; Springfield, IL; 5/52 VPJrCls; SecBand; JrNHS; MrchBnd; NHS; SchPl; SctActv; VPYthFlsp; GAA; IMSpt; Bradley U; Ind Eng.

KELLY, Kathleen A; Brookfield E HS; Brookfield, WI; Chr; Chrs; ChrhWkr; HonRl; HospAde; SchMus; SctActv; Madison Univ; Nursing.

KELLY, Kathy A; St Francis HS; Traverse City, MI; Chr; NHS; PpCl; IMSpt; Col; Creative Writing.

KELLY, Kenneth D; Royal Valley HS; Hoyt, KS; VPSophCls; Yrbk; RptrSchPpr; Bsktbl; Ftbl; Trk; Univ.

KELLY, Kevin L; Sacred Heart HS; E Grand Forks, MN; 14/53 TrsFrshCls; SecTrsSophCls; VPJrCls; HonRl; NatlFornLg; NHS; PepBnd; EdYrBk; Wrstlng; VoiceDemAwd; St Johns; Science.

KELLY, Larry D; Hamilton Sussex HS; Menomonee Falls, WI; HonRl; Ftbl; Trk; IMSpt; College; Business.

KELLY, Laura A; Delta HS; Muncie, IN; PolWkr; SchPl; TchrAde; FrCl; SpnCl; SciCl; LetterBsktbl; CaptTrk; IMSpt; PPFtbl; Indiana Univ; Law.

KELLY, Laurie E; Maine Twp South HS; Park Ridge, IL; ChrhWkr; CmntyWkr; HonRl; JrNHS; NHS; SctActv; SpnCl; PpCl; CchngActv; GAA; College; Pediatrics.

KELLY, Martin J; T F South HS; Lansing, IL; 55/580 NHS; RptrSchPpr; EdSchPpr; LatCl; LetterTrk; College.

KELLY, Mary E; Regina Dominican HS; Evanston, IL; HonRl; HospAde; PolWkr; SchPl; Sdlty; StuCncl; TchrAde; University Of Illinois; Business.

KELLY, Mary K; Resurrection HS; Chicago, IL; Band; Chr; ChrhWkr; CncrtBnd; HonRl; Mdrgl; MrchBnd; RedCrAde; RptrSchPpr; University; Journalism.

KELLY, Maura M; Proviso West HS; Bellwood, IL; HonRl; NHS; TreasOrch; StuCncl; Augustana College.

KELLY, Michael A; Sacred Heart HS; Dearborn, MI; 21/119 HonRl; SptEdSchPpr; LatCl; University; Journalism.

KELLY, Michael J; Loyola Acad; Glenview, IL; 30/442 CmntyWkr; HonRl; NatlMeritSF; StuCncl; Univ Of Il; Medicine.

KELLY, Michael J; Loyola Academy; Glenview, IL; 40/442 ChrhWkr; CmntyWkr; HonRl; NHS; NatlMeritFnl; NatlMeritSF; StuCncl; CivCl; University Of Illinois; Physician.

KELLY, Michael J; Loyola Acad; Glenview, IL; 41/442 CmntyWkr; HonRl; NHS; NatlMeritFnl; NatlMeritSF; StuCncl; U Of Illinois; Medicine.

KELLY, Michael J; Marian Central HS; Woodstock, IL; PresSophCls; PresSrCls; ALBoysSt; Aud/Vis; HonRl; NatlFornLg; NHS; StuCncl; FrCl; Univ Of Illinois; Business Admin.

KELLY, Michael L; Marist HS; Chicago, IL; 9/375 HonRl; NatlMeritCmnd; LetterBsbl; Glf; LetterTennis; IMSpt; CitAwd; Bradley U; Business Administration.

KELLY, Michelle C; St Francis Academy; Joliet, IL; 35/185 Chrs; HonRl; NatlThespSoc; SchMus; SchPl; FrCl; College; Veterinarian.

KELLY, Michelle M; Fonda Community HS; Fonda, IA; CncrtBnd; HonRl; MrchBnd; PepBnd; SchPl; TchrAde; ChrhWkr; Twrl; IMSpt; PPFtbl; Cl; Maycontinue German.

KELLY, Mike W; Lakeview HS; Lake View, IA; Bsktbl; Ftbl; Trk; Trade School.

KELLY, Molly A; St Joseph Academy; Green Bay, WI; 42/170 Chrs; ChrhWkr; OffAde; SchAde; SchPl; TchrAde; Tennis; Chrldr; PPFtbl; TIMEAwd; College; Professional.

KELLY, Nancy A; Mt Assisi Acad; Alsip, IL; 5/144 HonRl; LitMag; NHS; StuCncl; Loyola Univ; Pre Med.

KELLY, Nora J; Allegan HS; Allegan, MI; SecSophCls; Band; CncrtBnd; MrchBnd; OffAde; PepBnd; SchMus; TchrAde; SpnCl; Western Michigan Univ; Speech Pathology.

KELLY, Pamela D; Lindblom Technical HS; Chicago, IL; 42/564 Chr; Chrs; OffAde; College; Journalism.

KELLY, Patrice; Catholic Central HS; Muskegon, MI; 9/191 HonRl; HospAde; LbryAde; NHS; StuCncl; FTA; PpCl;.

KELLY, Paula A; Niles HS; Niles, MI; 52/374 VPSophCls; VPJrCls; SecSrCls; SecChr; NHS; NatlMeritSchl; NatlThespSoc; SchPl; Swmmng; EldAwd; Albion Clge; Special Ed.

KELLY, Robyn L; Dupo HS; E Carondelet, IL; HonRl; NHS; OffAde; StuCncl; YthFlsp; Yrbk; PpCl; SciCl; Chrldr; GAA; College; Interior Design.

KELLY, Ruth; Preston Fountain HS; Fountain, MN; 4/54 VPSrCls; Band; Chr; HonRl; NHS; RptrYrbk; U Of Mn.

KELLY, Sheri L; Pembine HS; Pembine, WI; Chrs; HonRl; StuCncl; RptrYrbk; RptrSchPpr; Trade Schl; Interior Decorating.

KELLY, Stephen A; Marion Institute HS; Portageville, MO; VPFrshCls; SecTrsSophCls; VPJrCls; Band; MrchBnd; ROTC; YthFlsp; CaptBsbl; CaptBsktbl; CaptFtbl; CaptTrk; Univ Of Alabama; Athelete.

KELLY, Stephen J; Chaminade College Prep; St Louis, MO; 9/107 HonRl; JrNHS; NatlFornLg; NHS; StuCncl; RptrYrbk; EdSchPpr; Ftbl; LetterTrk; Stanford Univ; Doctor.

KELLY, Sue A; Derham Hall HS; St Paul, MN; PresFrshCls; PresSrCls; JrNHS; NHS; SchPl; StuCncl; SpnCl; Swmmng; GAA; IMSpt; Coll; Pro.

KELLY, Susan; Mother Mcauley Hs; Chicago, IL; Chrs; HonRl; NHS; NatlMeritCmnd; Quill&Scroll; Yrbk; SchPpr; FTA; FrCl; AmLegAwd; U Of Illinois;business.

KELLY, Terry G; Virden Comm HS; Thayer, IL; HonRl; RptrSchPpr; SchPpr; Bsktbl; Ftbl; LetterTrk; Wrstlng; CchngActv; IMSpt; PresAwd; College; Data Proc.

KELLY, Terry L; Onalaska HS; Onalaska, WI; HonRl; LbryAde; NHS; Yrbk; FrCl; GAA; Univ Of Wi; French.

KELLY, Theresa; J A Craig HS; Janesville, WI; Chr; Chrs; NHS; SchMus; LatCl; Univ; Pro.

KELLY, Thomas; Mount St Benedict HS; Crookston, MN; Chr; Chrs; SchMus; SchPl; Sdlty; StuGov; Ftbl; Coll; Political Science.

KELLY, Timothy E; St Viator HS; Elkgrove, IL; HonRl; NatlMeritCmnd; GerCl; Michigan State Univ; Law Enforcement.

KELLY, Timothy J; Leo HS; Chicago, IL; 9/221 Band; CncrtBnd; HonRl; JA; MrchBnd; NHS; PepBnd; FSA; SciCl; Swmmng; College; Geology & Forestry.

KELLY, Timothy M; Maine Twp So HS; Park Ridge, IL; HonRl; NatlFornLg; NHS; PolWkr; SctActv; StuCncl; Northwestern Univ; Law.

KELM, Louis J; Providence HS; Lockport, IL; 9/125 HonRl; MthCl; SciCl;.

KELNER, Katherine R; Velva Public HS; Velva, ND; Band; Chrs; ChrhWkr; HonRl; NHS; SchPl; SctActv; StuCncl; RptrYrbk; PpCl; College; Broadcasting.

KELNHOFER, Cheryl L; Lincoln HS; Park Falls, WI; CncrtBnd; DrmBgl; HonRl; MrchBnd; PolWkr; TchrAde; Yrbk; FHA; Wi Univ; Home Ec Tchr.

KELPE, Ronald M; Burke HS; Omaha, NE; 7/660 VPSrCls; Band; HonRl; MrchBnd; NHS; StuCncl; StuGov; IMSpt; KiwanAwd; Kansas St Univ; Veterinarian.

KELSAW, Lore; Northrop HS; Ft Wayne, IN; LbryAde; Orch; SchMus; SctActv; TchrAde; SptEdYrbk; Ftbl; Trk; IMSpt; CitAwd; Ball State Univ; Jounalism.

KELSEY, Craig A; Huntington North HS; Roanoke, IN; LetterFtbl; IMSpt; College.

KELSEY, Janet E; Liberal R 2 HS; Mindenmines, MO; 1/46 ChrhWkr; HonRl; NHS; SchPl; Yrbk; SptEdSchPpr; CaptPPFtbl; DanFAwd; Southwest Baptist Col.

KELSEY, Marcia J; Liberal R 2 HS; Mindenmines, MO; 1/46 TrsSophCls; PresJrCls; HonRl; NHS; StuCncl; FHA; PpCl; PPFtbl; CitAwd; Trade School.

KELSHEIMER, Timothy D; Anthon Oto Comm HS; Anthon, IA; Band; CncrtBnd; HonRl; MrchBnd; PepBnd; SctActv; StuCncl; TchrAde; RptrYrbk; LetterBsbl; LetterFtbl; LetterTrk; LetterWrstlng; College; Automotive Mechanic.

KELSICK, Cynthia J; Hallsville Riv HS; Hallsville, MO; Chrs; LbryAde; TchrAde; PpCl; Bsbl; Bsktbl; Trk; IMSpt; PresAwd;.

KELSO, Tom J; Odell Comm HS; Odell, IL; 7/33 Chr; HonRl; OffAde; SpnCl; PpCl; LetterBsbl; LetterBsktbl; LetterGlf; Coll; Pro.

KELTY, Maureen A; Plankinton HS; Plankinton, SD; 2/22 Band; Chrs; HonRl; NHS; SchPl; EdYrBk; RptrSchPpr; 4-H; BttyCrckrAwd; 4-HAwd; Sdsu Brookings; Animal Sci.

KEMBLE, Les L; Shelbyville Sr HS; Shelbyville, IN; Band; Chrs; MrchBnd; SctActv; FTA; Trk; LetterWrstlng; Air Force; Air Traffic Control Operator.

KEMEN, Rose M; Salem Central HS; Bristol, WI; 3/200 ChrhWkr; HonRl; SecNHS; TchrAde; 4-H; VPFHA; FNA; Gateway Tec Inst; Acctg Data Processing.

KEMME, Jilane G; Allendale HS; Allendale, MI; 1/40 Band; ChrhWkr; CmntyWkr; HonRl; MrchBnd; StuCncl; LetterBsktbl; CitAwd; Univ; Vet.

KEMMERER, Philip B; North Clay HS; Louisville, IL; FFA; PpCl; SciCl; CaptTrk; Olney Central College.

KEMMERICK, Sheila; Pacelli HS; Austin, MN; ChrhWkr; HonRl; HospAde; RptrSchPpr; 4-H; PpCl; IMSpt; Coll; Soc Wrk.

KEMMERLING, Patricia A; St Mary Academy; Monroe, MI; VPJrCls; VPSrCls; Chrl; HonRl; NHS; SchMus; SchPl; StuCncl; YthFlsp; FrCl; PpCl; LetterTrk; Concordia Jr College; Special Education.

KEMMET, Marlen J; Napoleon HS; Napoleon, ND; SecTrsFrshCls; ALBoysSt; Chrs; CncrtBnd; DrmBgl; MrchBnd; SctActv; RptrYrbk; RptrSchPpr; Ftbl; U Of Nd; Engr.

KEMNER, Rita F; Manchester HS; Manchester, MI; 21/100 ChrhWkr; CncrtBnd; HonRl; Orch; 4-H; GerCl; PpCl; Bsktbl; GAA; Western Michigan University; Business Admin.

KEMNETZ, Frank J; Chatsworth HS; Strawn, IL; 1/25 PresFrshCls; SecAFS; SecChr; HonRl; NHS; NatlMeritSF; SchPl; PresStuCncl; PresFFA; PresSpnCl; Bsktbl; Univ Of Illinois; Engineering.

KEMNITZ, Linda S; Cavalier Public HS; Cavalier, ND; HstFrshCls; Band; Chr; Chrs; ChrhWkr; CmntyWkr; CncrtBnd; HonRl; HospAde; College; Teacher.

KEMNITZ, Randal S; George S Parker HS; Janesville, WI; 6/517 HonRl; NHS; TchrAde; Bsbl; Bsktbl; LetterFtbl; Trk; AFS; College; Professional.

KEMP, Carol L; Southwestern HS; Brighton, IL; Chrs; LitMag; LbryAde; SchMus; StuCncl; TreasYthFlsp; RptrSchPpr; FTA; IMSpt; PPFtbl;.

KEMP, Charles L; Mid County Sr HS; Lacon, IL; 1/60 VPJrCls; ALBoysSt; Band; ChrhWkr; HonRl; NatlMeritCmnd; SctActv; VPStuCncl; TchrAde; Bsbl; Bsktbl; Trk; AmLegAwd; GodCntryAwd; College; Science.

KEMP, Christine A; Richmond HS; Richmond, IL; Chrs; HonRl; Orch; SchMus; SchPl; LatCl; Swedish Am Nursing Sch; Nursing.

KEMP, Clarence S; Willowbrook HS; Villa Park, IL; 23/800 ChrhWkr; HonRl; NHS; University; Engineer.

KEMP, Cynthia L; North Boone HS; Poplar Grove, IL; ALAGirlsSt; Chrs; ChrhWkr; CmntyWkr; DrlTm; HonRl; HospAde; Bsbl; GAA; CitAwd; College.

KEMP, Jan M; R O V A HS; Oneida, IL; 8/73 Band; HonRl; NHS; StuCncl; 4-H; PpCl; PresSciCl; Chrldr; College; Dental Hygienist.

KEMP, Kathryn D; Belvidere HS; Rockford, IL; 9/336 HonRl; TreasStuCncl; FrCl; PpCl; DARAwd; College; Medical Tech.

KEMP, Kevin L; Southridge HS; Huntingburg, IN; 21/168 ALBoysSt; Chr; HonRl; SchPl; StuGov; YthFlsp; PpCl; CaptFtbl; LetterWrstlng; I S U Terre Haute; Accounting And Law.

KEMPE, Becky; Caston HS; Kokomo, IN; 6/89 Chr; Chrs; HonRl; HospAde; JA; LbryAde; NHS; SchMus; SchPl; DanFAwd; Indiana Central; Registered Nurse.

KEMPER, Donna R; Winnebago HS; Winnebago, IL; AFS; TchrAde; FHA; FTA; PpCl; Nursing School; Reg Nurse.

KEMPER, Philip T; Wahpeton Sr HS; Wahpeton, ND; HonRl; JrNHS; EdSchPpr; LetterFtbl; North Dakota St Schl; Civil Engineer.

KEMPER, Susan J; Washburn Rural HS; Grandview, MO; ChrhWkr; HonRl; ROTC; TchrAde; YthFlsp; FDA; FrCl; PpCl; College.

KEMPER, Susan L; Casey Jr Sr HS; Greenup, IL; 20/94 HonRl;.

KEMPERS, Eunice J; Sioux Center Comm HS; Hull, IA; 13/81 Band; Chr; CncrtBnd; HonRl; MrchBnd; NHS; TreasStuCncl; YthFlsp; 4-H; Chrldr; Iowa State U; Textiles.

KEMPF, Kenneth; Lindbergh HS; St Louis, MO; /980 HonRl; NHS; RptrSchPpr; VPKeyCl; SciCl; Colle; Architect.

KEMPF, Lynn A; Kewaskum HS; Kewaskum, WI; Band; CncrtBnd; HonRl; MrchBnd; PepBnd; SchMus; StuGov; Trk; Chrldr;.

KEMPINGER, Pamela J; Van Horn HS; Kansas City, MO; AFS; CivCl; SpnCl; PpCl; Swmmng; University; Dance.

KEMPLE, Judy L; Culver Community HS; Culver, IN; 6/103 HonRl; NHS; RptrYrbk; EdSchPpr; SpnCl; Trk; Franklin College; Journalism.

KENBEEK, Deborah J; Parchment HS; Parchment, MI; 17/177 Chr; ChrhWkr; CncrtBnd; HonRl; MrchBnd; NHS; TchrAde; YthFlsp; SpnCl; Trk; Hope College; Elementary Education.

KENDALL, David L; Geneva HS; Geneva, IL; ChrhWkr; HonRl; NatlMeritCmnd; Sacrstn; Socr; University Of Michigan.

KENDALL, Debra L; Westwood HS; Hornick, IA; 1/73 Band; CncrtBnd; HonRl; MrchBnd; NHS; PepBnd; RptrSchPpr; LetterGlf; University; Zoology.

KENDALL, Jaye L; Frederick HS; Frederick, SD; PresJrCls; Band; Chr; CncrtBnd; HonRl; MrchBnd; PepBnd; SctActv; PpCl; No Dakota State Univ; Medicine.

KENDALL, Jeffrey M; University Of Detroit HS; Detroit, MI; 79/203 Aud/Vis; ChrhWkr; HonRl; JA; PolWkr; StuGov; SciCl; Trk; IMSpt; JETSAwd; Univ Detroit; Bell Lab.

KENDALL, Laurel; Seaholm HS; Birmingham, MI; 65/709 Band; HonRl; MrchBnd; ModUN; NHS; NatlMeritCmnd; PresSctActv; StuCncl; LetterBsbl; Swmmng; Univ Of Mich; Engin.

KENDALL, Ronald D; Jefferson West HS; N Topeka, KS; VPFrshCls; SecSophCls; HstJrCls; Band; ChrhWkr; CmntyWkr; CncrtBnd; HonRl; JA; MrchBnd; Bsktbl; Trk; AmLegAwd; 4-HAwd; College; Engineering.

KENDALL, Susan L; Reese HS; Reese, MI; 4/130 HonRl; ModUN; NHS; SchPl; TchrAde; YthFlsp; RptrYrbk; EdYrBk; RptrSchPpr; SchPpr; GerCl; Michigan State University; Journalism.

KENDALL, William W; Casey HS; Casey, IL; Chr; HonRl; SchMus; StuCncl; EdSchPpr; FFA; IMSpt; College.

KENDRA, George S; Gordon Tech HS; Chicago, IL; StuCncl; StuGov; KeyCl; PpCl; St Marys College; Socialogy.

KENDRA, Greg D; Highland HS; Highland, IN; 19/543 ChrhWkr; HonRl; TchrAde; LetterFtbl; Trk; Wrstlng; JCAwd; College; Bus Vocation.

KENDRICK, David G; Fort Osage HS; Independence, MO; AFS; Chr; NatlFornLg; NatlThespSoc; Quill&Scroll; SchMus; SchPl; RptrYrbk; SchPpr; SciCl; Univ Of Mo At Kansas Cy; Engineering/med.

KENDRICK, Dennis P; Aurora Central Catholic HS; Aurora, IL; ALBoysSt; HonRl; NHS; SchAde; SctActv; TchrAde; Univ Of Illinois; Social Science.

KENDRICK, Joseph E; Monroe City R 1 HS; Monroe City, MO; 31/95 PresFrshCls; ChrhWkr; CmntyWkr; HonRl; 4-H; FFA; LetterFtbl; LetterTrk; Ne Mo St Univ; Law Enforcement.

KENEALEY, Nancy E; Academy Of The Holy Angels; Richfield, MN; 1/110 LitMag; NHS; NatlMeritSF; SchAde; SchMus; SchPl; RptrYrbk; Michigan State Univ; Interntl Relations.

KENEALY, Lori; Tri Center HS; Neola, IA; Chrs; Yrbk; SchPpr; 4-H; PpCl; Trk; IMSpt; 4-HAwd; Iowa St Univ.

KENEFICK, Patsy A; Highland Park HS; St Paul, MN; SecFrshCls; VPSophCls; VPJrCls; PolWkr; StuCncl; StuGov; TchrAde; PpCl; PresAwd; College; Professional.

KENKEL, Carol A; Missouri Valley HS; Missouri Valley, IA; HonRl; NHS; FHA; PpCl; College; Secretarial Or Accounting.

KENLEY, Anne; Rockville HS; Rockville, IN; HonRl; NHS; SchPl; FHA; LatCl; PpCl; LetterBsktbl; Tennis; GAA; In Univ.

KENLEY, Susan G; West Washington HS; Salem, IN; VPJrCls; SecSrCls; Band; NHS; NatlThespSoc; SchMus; SchPl; StuCncl; EdSchPpr; 4-H; Chrldr; Ball State Univ; Nursing.

KENNEDY, Betty A; Byron Area HS; Byron, MI; 2/71 TrsSrCls; Band; Chrs; HonRl; NHS; NatlMeritSchl; SchPl; Yrbk; Univ Of Michigan; Nursing.

KENNEDY, Christopher L; Bennett HS; Marion, IN; 1/24 PresFrshCls; ChrhWkr; HonRl; NHS; StuCncl; StuGov; SpnCl; Glf; University; Professional.

KENNEDY, David W; Homewood Flossmoor HS; Glenwood, IL; HonRl; Swmmng; IMSpt; Univ; Business Profession.

KENNEDY, Denise K; Broken Bow HS; Broken Bow, NE; ChrhWkr; HonRl; OffAde; Yrbk; FBLA; PpCl; Chrldr; Lincoln Schl Of Commerce; Secretary.

KENNEDY, Jay I; Lafollette HS; Madison, WI; 4/550 PresFrshCls; ALBoysSt; HonRl; NHS; LetterTennis; AmLegAwd; Uw Whitewater; Physics.

KENNEDY, Jo A; Santa Fe Trail HS; Carbondale, KS; Chr; Chrs; HonRl; OffAde; SchMus; SchPl; TchrAde; PpCl; Marriage.

KENNEDY, John G; Chandlerville HS; Chandlerville, IL; 2/16 VPJrCls; PresSrCls; ChrhWkr; HonRl; JrNHS; PresNHS; SctActv; StuCncl; Bsbl; ChmnBsktbl; Trk; Western Il Univ; Agriculture.

KENNEDY, John W; Fairfield HS; Fairfield, IA; Band; CncrtBnd; HonRl; MrchBnd; PepBnd; RptrSchPpr; College; Professional.

KENNEDY, Joseph A; Wawasee HS; Syracuse, IN; Aud/Vis; Band; Chr; CncrtBnd; HonRl; Mdrgl; College; Music.

KENNEDY, Julie M; Swan Valley HS; Saginaw, MI; 14/166 ChrhWkr; CncrtBnd; MrchBnd; VPNHS; RedCrAde; StuCncl; PpCl; Coll; Music.

KENNEDY, Karen A; Manchester HS; Manchester, MI; 5/100 Chr; Chrs; ChrhWkr; HonRl; SchMus; SchPl; StuCncl; YthFlsp; Bsktbl; 4-HAwd; Musical Entertainment & Writing & Business.

KENNEDY, Kathenne; Carmel HS; Carmel, IN; Chrl; DrlTm; Mdrgl; NatlFornLg; NHS; NatlThespSoc; SchMus; SchPl; StuGov; JCAwd; Univ Of Miami; Theatre Actres.

KENNEDY, Kathleen A; Troy HS; Troy, MI; 41/526 Band; CncrtBnd; MrchBnd; Orch; University; Doctor Of Vet Medicine.

KENNEDY, Kathleen J; Our Lady Star Of The Sea HS; Grosse Pointe Wood, MI; ChrhWkr; CmntyWkr; HonRl; PolWkr; SchAde; TchrAde; EdYrBk; Yrbk; EdSchPpr; GAA; University Of Detroit; Montesori Method.

KENNEDY, Kathleen J; Huntington North HS; Huntington, IN; ChrhWkr; CmntyWkr; HonRl; OffAde; StuGov; YthFlsp; FTA; PpCl; Chrldr; Huntington College; Teacher.

KENNEDY, Kevin B; Peoria HS; Peoria, IL; 107/471 HonRl;.

KENNEDY, Kristi K; Girard HS; Girard, KS; SecJrCls; Band; ChrhWkr; CmntyWkr; HonRl; NHS; NatlMeritCmnd; SctActv; RptrYrbk; FHA; College; Professionla.

KENNEDY, Lawrence R; Sts Peter & Paul HS; Saginaw, MI; Chr; Chrs; HonRl; Mdrgl; NHS; OffAde; SchMus; StuCncl; PresStuGov; PpCl; SciCl; IMSpt; University; Electrical Engineering.

KENNEDY, Linda S; Holden HS; Holden, MO; 10/100 ALAGirlsSt; HonRl; NHS; SchPl; PpCl; Trk; Chrldr; University; Vocation.

KENNEDY, Lynn C; Lebanon HS; Lebanon, KS; 4/16 Chr; ChrhWkr; CmntyWkr; HonRl; SctActv; YthFlsp; Trk; Colby Comm College; Asst Veterinarian.

KENNEDY, Mark E; Galesburg Sr HS; Galesburg, IL; 22/567 VPJrCls; CmntyWkr; HonRl; PresIntrClCncl; PresNHS; NatlMeritCmnd; SchPpr; Glf; Swmmng; Wrstlng; Univ Of Il; Engineering.

KENNEDY, Mary E; Heritage Christian HS; Indianapolis, IN; 5/48 Chr; Chrl; HonRl; JA; LbryAde; OffAde; SchMus; TchrAde; CaptChrldr; Grace College; Bs In Nursing.

KENNEDY, Mary P; Arlington HS; Arlington Hts, IL; ChrhWkr; HonRl; NatlMeritCmnd; SpnCl; PpCl; Univ Of Ill; Business Adm.

KENNEDY, Miriam E; Airport Community HS; Belleville, MI; 15/240 ChrhWkr; HonRl; RptrYrbk; Yrbk; FTA; FrCl; VFWAwd; VoiceDemAwd; Eastern College; Medical.

KENNEDY, Pamela J; Delta HS; Muncie, IN; 97/261 LbryAde; PolWkr; TchrAde; 4-H; FHA; PpCl; Ball State University; Special Education.

KENNEDY, Patricia A; St Charles HS; Elburn, IL; CmntyWkr; HonRl; HospAde; Univ; Psychologist.

KENNEDY, Patricia A; Aurora Central Catholic HS; Aurora, IL; 1/120 SecTrsJrCls; Chrs; HonRl; NHS; NatlMeritFnl; StuCncl; RptrSchPpr; Northern Illinois Univ; Accounting.

KENNEDY, Paula J; Carmel HS; Downey, IL; HonRl; HospAde; University; Social Work.

KENNEDY, Peggy; Ward HS; Kansas City, KS; 12/219 ChrhWkr; CmntyWkr; HonRl; ModUN; NHS; PolWkr; PpCl; Ks City Ks Jr College; Business.

KENNEDY, Richard M; Marysville HS; Marysville, MI; Band; ChrhWkr; HonRl; SchAde; StuCncl; SptEdSchPpr; LetterBsbl; Bsktbl; LetterFtbl; Trk; College; Law.

KENNEDY, Roberta A; Josephinum HS; Chicago, IL; 6/90 HonRl; LbryAde; NHS; SchPl; SctActv; StuGov; College; Mathematics.

KENNEDY, Robert W; Western Dubuque HS; Farley, IA; ALBoysSt; HonRl; PolWkr; SctActv; StuCncl; StuGov; LetterBsbl; LetterBsktbl; LetterGlf; JETSAwd; Coll; Elec Engr.

KENNEDY, Ross T; Plymouth Canton HS; Plymouth, MI; HonRl; OffAde; CchngActv; IMSpt; Eastern Michigan U; Accounting.

KENNEDY, Sandra; Santa Fe HS; Waverly, MO; ALAGirlsSt; Chr; ChrhWkr; HospAde; SchPl; StuCncl; RptrYrbk; Univ.

KENNEDY, Scott A; Nevada HS; Deerfield, MO; 1/176 SecFrshCls; ALBoysSt; NHS; PresStuCncl; RptrYrbk; Pres4-H; VPFFA; LetterFtbl; LetterWrstlng; University Of Missouri; Animal Husbandry.

KENNEDY, Sharon L; Seaholm HS; Birmingham, MI; HonRl; HospAde; Oakland Univ; Medical Technology.

KENNEDY, Sheila J; St Scholastica HS; Chicago, IL; 6/220 NHS; University; Biology.

KENNEDY, Shirley A; Mt Vernon HS; Greenfield, IN; 6/149 HonRl; NHS; 4-H; PresPpCl; CaptChrldr; 4-HAwd; Purdue Univ; Home Economics.

KENNEDY, Stanley R; Central HS; Atlanta, KS; PepBnd; SchPl; SptEdSchPpr; 4-H; FFA; LetterBsbl; Bsktbl; LetterFtbl; Trk; 4-HAwd;.

KENNEDY, Vicki J; Wyoming Park HS; Wyoming, MI; ChrhWkr; HonRl; NHS; PolWkr; SchMus; SchPl; StuCncl; PpCl; GAA; PPFtbl; College; Business.

KENNEDY, Virginia L; Frederic Remington HS; Benton, KS; CtyCnl; HospAde; OffAde; RedCrAde; ROTC; StuCncl; TchrAde; FBLA; FTA; Jr College.

KENNEDY, William A; Wisconsin Heights HS; Mazomaine, WI; Yrbk; SchPpr; Bsktbl; IMSpt; Coll; Architecture.

KENNELL, Marilou; Wenona HS; Wenona, IL; 2/45 PresSophCls; HonRl; LbryAde; TchrAde; FHA; FrCl; Trk; AmLegAwd; Moody Bible Inst; Missions.

KENNETT, Cheryl A; Brownstown HS; Vandalia, IL; Chr; HonRl; SchPl; Treas4-H; FHA; FrCl; HstSrCls; 4-HAwd; U; Pro.

KENNEY, Debra J; Downers Grove North HS; Downers Grove, IL; 85/524 Northern Ill Univ; Speech.

KENNEY, Frederic; Bloomfield Hills Andover HS; Bloomfield Hills, MI; Band; HonRl; NHS; CchngActv; IMSpt; College.

KENNEY, Gregory T; Mt Clemens HS; Selfridge Angb, MI; Chr; ChrhWkr; LetterBsbl; CaptFtbl; LetterSocr; Univ; Philosophy Teacher.

KENNEY, Karyn J; Inman HS; Inman, KS; Band; Chrs; ChrhWkr; CmntyWkr; LbryAde; PepBnd; SchPl; TchrAde; 4-H; FHA; PPFtbl; 4-HAwd;.

KENNEY, Kurt J; Y J B HS; Bagley, IA; 1/22 Band; CncrtBnd; HonRl; MrchBnd; NHS; SchPl; StuCncl; 4-H; LetterBsbl; LetterBsktbl; LetterFtbl; LetterTrk; 4-HAwd; Iowa State Univ; Agriculture.

KENNEY, Lynda S; St Pius X HS; Arnold, MO; ChrhWkr; HonRl; SchPl; TchrAde; RptrSchPpr; SchPpr; SciCl; Bsbl; IMSpt; College; History.

KENNEY, Mark F; Creighton Prep; Omaha, NE; Band; Chr; Chrs; CncrtBnd; HonRl; MrchBnd; Orch; PepBnd; SchMus; SchPl; University; Engineering.

KENNEY, Mary E; Elizabeth Seton HS; Chicago, IL; 11/260 ChrhWkr; HonRl; NHS; StuCncl; RptrYrbk; RptrSchPpr; W Illinois University.

KENNEY, Russell W; Sherwood Cass R Viii HS; Holden, MO; ALBoysSt; Chrs; HonRl; Mdrgl; NHS; SchMus; StuCncl; SpnCl; LetterBsbl; LetterBsktbl; College; Teacher.

KENNEY, Sharon A; Glenwood HS; Springfield, IL; 5/143 AFS; HonRl; NHS; SctActv; TchrAde; FHA; FTA; College; Home Economics.

KENNEY, Vicki K; Green Valley HS; Pekin, IL; 2/22 PresSrCls; Chr; HonRl; JrNHS; NHS; PpCl; Chrldr;.

KENNING, Dennis L; Fairbury HS; Endicott, NE; Band; Chrs; ChrhWkr; CncrtBnd; MrchBnd; PepBnd; YthFlsp; 4-H; FFA; SpnCl; Ftbl; Wrstlng; IMSpt; College; Agriculture.

KENNING, Mary K; Spring Valley HS; Spring Valley, MN; Chrs; CncrtBnd; MrchBnd; NatlMeritCmnd; Yrbk; Pres4-H; SpnCl; BttyCrckrAwd; DARAwd; 4-HAwd; St Catherines; Psychiatrist.

KENNINGER, Susan K; Guilford HS; Rockford, IL; 29/658 AFS; HonRl; NHS; FrCl; PpCl; IMSpt; Purdue University; Engineering.

KENNISON, Dora M; Monroe City R 1 HS; Hunnewell, MO; ChrhWkr; HonRl; TchrAde; CivCl; Gem City Business College; Accounting.

KENNY, Eugene R; St Laurence HS; Burbank, IL; 3/400 ChrhWkr; HonRl; SchPl; StuCncl; LetterTrk; IMSpt; Univ Of Notre Dame.

KENNY, Joseph J; Rensselaer Central HS; Rensselaer, IN; HonRl; LitMag; NHS; NatlMeritFnl; PolWkr; Quill&Scroll; StuCncl; EdSchPpr; MthCl; LetterTrk; Earlham Coll; Math.

KENNY, Kathleen A; Shawnee Mission South HS; Overland Park, KS; 1/770 ChrhWkr; ChmnDrlTm; HonRl; NHS; NatlMeritSF; StuCncl; StuGov; LetterTrk; IMSpt; OptClAwd; College; Engineering.

KENNY, Steven J; North Side HS; Ft Wayne, IN; Band; CncrtBnd; MrchBnd; PepBnd; RptrSchPpr; IMSpt; College; Business Admin.

KENSIL, Brian E; Tower Hill HS; Tower Hill, IL; PresJrCls; PresSrCls; HonRl; NHS; SchPl; TchrAde; SptEdYrbk; 4-H; LetterBsbl; LetterBsktbl; LetterTrk; Jr Col; Professional.

KENSOK, Denise; Central Cass HS; Wheatland, ND; ChrhWkr; CmntyWkr; HonRl; SchPl; TchrAde; Yrbk; College; Professional.

KENSOK, Gary P; Fargo North HS; Fargo, ND; CAP; CncrtBnd; DrlTm; HonRl; ROTC; 4-H; AmLegAwd; 4-HAwd; SARAwd; RotaryAwd; Coll; Curr Of Maj Stud.

KENSOK, Richard A; Central Cass HS; Wheatland, ND; TrsSophCls; ALBoysSt; Chrs; ChrhWkr; HonRl; NHS; SchPl; Trade School; Vocation.

KENT, Carol A; Maine Twp West HS; Des Plaines, IL; SecFrshCls; SecJrCls; PresSrCls; HonRl; NatlThespSoc; Quill&Scroll; SchMus; RptrYrbk; RptrSchPpr; Univ Of Texas; Theater.

KENT, Clark S; Chase County HS; Imperial, NE; 1/188 PresSrCls; ALBoysSt; Band; Chr; CmntyWkr; CncrtBnd; HonRl; MrchBnd; SchMus; CaptFtbl; Harvard ;med Res.

KENT, Jill M; Aurora HS; Aurora, IN; 12/136 Band; Chr; CncrtBnd; HonRl; MrchBnd; NHS; SctActv; RptrYrbk; FrCl; VPPpCl; Cl; Pharmacy.

KENT, John; Lakeview HS; St Clair Shores, MI; 22/

650 Band; CncrtBnd; HonRl; MrchBnd; NHS; Orch; PepBnd; SchMus; College; Major Study.

KENT, John G; Marist HS; Oak Lawn, IL; 29/365 HonRl; NatlMeritCmnd; St Xavier College; Accounting.

KENT, Katherine A; Evanston Township HS; Evanston, IL; Chrl; CmntyWkr; HonRl; SchPl; SctActv; TchrAde; YthFlsp; GerCl; MthCl; Knox College; Mathematics.

KENT, Kevin L; Southern HS; Stronghurst, IL; HonRl; SchPl; SchPpr; LetterBsktbl; LetterFtbl; LetterTrk; College; Architecture.

KENT, Patricia G; Oxford HS; Oxford, MI; CmntyWkr; HospAde; NHS; RedCrAde; SchPl; EdYrBk; FDA; FrCl; SciCl; Tennis; Mercy College Of Detroit; Med Technologist.

KENT, Penny; West Delaware HS; Manchester, IA; Chrs; HonRl; StuCncl; EdSchPpr; SchPpr; Trk; Chrldr; GAA; Armes Forces.

KENT, Penny S; Watseka Community HS; Watseka, IL; HonRl; HospAde; TchrAde; GAA; College; Nursing.

KENT, Roger L; N Senior HS; Eau Claire, WI; 1/435 HonRl; HospAde; PolWkr; StuCncl; TchrAde; SecSpnCl; MthCl; Ftbl; LetterTrk; IMSpt; Air Force Academy; Military Career.

KENT, Steven W; Winfield HS; Winfield, KS; HonRl; NatlFornLg; StuCncl; StuGov; TchrAde; SchPpr; SpnCl; Bsbl; OptClAwd; VoiceDemAwd; Univ; Business Major.

KENT, Terri L; Galena HS; Galena, KS; Chr; Chrl; Chrs; ChrhWkr; CmntyWkr; HospAde; OffAde; SchPl; Twrl; SpnCl;.

KENWARD, Barbara; Mankato East HS; Mankato, MN; SecSrCls; Chr; Chrs; ChrhWkr; DrlTm; HonRl; NHS; SchAde; StuCncl; Yrbk; College; Teaching.

KENYON, Colleen M; Mallard Community HS; Mallard, IA; Chrs; ChrhWkr; HonRl; 4-H; FrCl; LetterTrk; LetterChrldr; 4-HAwd; College; Major Study.

KENYON, Timothy R; Creston HS; Creston, IA; ALBoysSt; Band; CncrtBnd; HonRl; MrchBnd; NHS; NatlThespSoc; Orch; PepBnd; SchMus; College; Professional.

KENZY, Julieann M; Gregory HS; Iona, SD; HonRl; Quill&Scroll; Yrbk; RptrSchPpr; SchPpr; Augustana College; Art.

KEOUGH, Colleen M; Monticello HS; Monticello, WI; Band; Chrs; ModUN; OffAde; EdSchPpr; Treas4-H; 4-HAwd; OptClAwd; PresAwd; VoiceDemAwd; University; Broadcasting.

KEOUGH, Gary R; Holy Name Seminary; Monticello, WI; RptrSchPpr; 4-H; Ftbl; Trk; CaptWrstlng; 4-HAwd; Univ Of Wisconsin; Veterinarian.

KEOUGH, Michael J; Almond HS; Bancroft, WI; TrsJrCls; ALBoysSt; 4-H; Ftbl; Trk;.

KEOUGH, William T; St Louis Univ HS; St Louis, MO; HonRl; HospAde; LitMag; NatlMeritSF; CaptSocr; IMSpt; St Louis Univ;.

KEPHART, Robyn E; Holden R Iii HS; Kingsville, MO; 1/90 Chrs; ChrhWkr; DrmMjrt; HonRl; NHS; OffAde; PepBnd; TchrAde; VPSpnCl; University; Elem Teacher.

KEPNER, Daniel E; Griffin HS; Springfield, IL; 11/175 HonRl; NHS; StuCncl; StuGov; PpCl; LetterBsktbl; Ftbl; LetterTennis; LetterTrk; Univ Of Illinois; Law.

KEPNER, Greg G; Centerville HS; Centerville, IA; 3/116 HonRl; ModUN; NHS; NatlMeritSchl; StuCncl; Bsktbl; LetterFtbl; Trk; Univ; Math.

KEPNER, Rodney L; Rochelle Twp HS; Rochelle, IL; 50/212 CncrtBnd; HonRl; MrchBnd; VPKeyCl; LetterFtbl; Glf; Swmmng; LetterTrk; Clge; Dentist.

KEPPEN, Eileen A; Palmyra HS; Palmyra, WI; 7/56 Aud/Vis; CmntyWkr; HonRl; LitMag; LbryAde; NHS; OffAde; SchAde; SctActv; TchrAde; Waukesha Count Tech; Accounting.

KEPPEN, Rose M; Rogers HS; Michigan City, IN; 1/512 AFS; HonRl; JrNHS; NHS; SchMus; SchPl; Yrbk; GerCl; SciCl; KiwanAwd; University; Professional.

KEPPERS, Jane E; Denfeld HS; Duluth, MN; 21/396 ChrhWkr; HonRl; NatlMeritSF; Yrbk; Clge; Elem Ed.

KEPPLINGER, Susan L; Beloit Catholic HS; Beloit, WI; VPSophCls; ALAGirlsSt; NHS; NatlMeritCmnd; SctActv; StuCncl; SchPpr; DARAwd; U Of Wi; Botany Major.

KERANEN, Cheryl A; Ontonagon Area HS; Ontonagon, MI; 15/106 ChrhWkr; HonRl; SchPpr; 4-H; PpCl; Ferris State Col; Medical Secretary.

KERANEN, Debra K; Ontonagon Area HS; Mass, MI; 25/108 PresBand; CncrtBnd; HonRl; HospAde; MrchBnd; PepBnd; Yrbk; SptEdSchPpr; TreasPpCl; GAA; College; Medicine.

KERASOTES, Karen F; Springfield HS; Springfield, IL; 11/585 Chr; Chrs; JrNHS; NHS; SchMus; SchPl; RptrYrbk; Miami Univ; Marketing.

KERBAWY, Gregory A; St Stephen Area HS; Saginaw, MI; HonRl; NHS; Yrbk; Bsbl; Trk; Mich State U; Education.

KERBEL, Laura L; Morrill HS; Morrill, NE; 1/40 Chrs; ChrhWkr; LbryAde; NHS; SchPl; PresYthFlsp; Trk; College; Nursing.

KERBER, Cindy S; Octavia HS; Towanda, IL; 2/45 HstFrshCls; HstSophCls; HstJrCls; HstSrCls; HonRl; NHS; SchMus; SchPl; PresStuCncl; CaptChrldr; GAA; Ill State Univ; Accounting.

KERBER, Mary L; Immaculate Heart Of Mary HS; Westchester, IL; SecJrCls; CmntyWkr; HospAde; NatlMeritCmnd; SchPl; RptrSchPpr; FrCl; Ftbl; Univ; Psyche.

KERCHAL, Kim W; Wauneta Public HS; Wauneta, NE; TrsSrCls; Chr; ChrhWkr; HonRl; NHS; RedCrAde; YthFlsp; FFA; Bsktbl; Trk; IMSpt; College.

KERCHBERGER, John P; Washington Sr HS; Sioux Falls, SD; Band; CncrtBnd; HonRl; MrchBnd; NHS; PepBnd; SchPl; TchrAde; Carleton Clg; Chemistry.

KERESTES, Gloria L; Streator Twp HS; Streator, IL; 9/287 Band; HonRl; LbryAde; VPNHS; StuCncl; GerCl; Illinois St Univ; Social Work.

KERFF, Robert E; R 1 North Callaway HS; Fulton, MO; Chrs; ChrhWkr; CncrtBnd; NHS; NatlThespSoc; SchPl; Yrbk; LetterFtbl; Coll; Pro.

KERKENBUSH, David J; Potosi HS; Potosi, WI; 2/75 HonRl; NHS; TchrAde; RptrSchPpr; MthCl; LetterBsbl; Bsktbl; Ftbl; LetterTrk; College.

KERKER, Krystal; Benton Central HS; W Lafayette, IN; 60/259 Band; DrlTm; MrchBnd; NatlFornLg; SctActv; 4-H; FTA; PPFtbl; 4-HAwd; Purdue Univ; Comuputer Science.

KERKER, Renae C; Alleman HS; Roc Island, IL; Aud/Vis; HonRl; PolWkr; Yrbk; GAA; IMSpt; College; Physical Therapist.

KERKHOFF, Linda A; St Mary HS; Burlington, WI; Chrs; HonRl; LbryAde; SctActv; PpCl; IMSpt; Business School; Business Administration.

KERKMAN, Michelle G; Central HS; Powers Lake, WI; HonRl; RptrYrbk; RptrSchPpr; 4-H; PpCl; Trk; LetterGAA; 4-HAwd; University; Physical Education.

KERKSIEK, Jo Ellen; Oak Park HS; Gladstone, MO; 35/602 HonRl; Nw Missouri St Univ; Accounting.

KERKSTRA, Sherwin; South Christian HS; Byron Center, MI; Band; CncrtBnd; HonRl; MrchBnd; NHS; IMSpt; Calvin College; Dentistry.

KERKVLIET, Tony G; West Lyon Comm HS; Larchwood, IA; 16/81 ChrhWkr; HonRl; NHS; StuCncl; FFA; LetterBsbl; LetterBsktbl; LetterFtbl; LetterGlf; CaptTrk; College Or Trade; Vocation.

KERL, Shari S; Bruning Public HS; Bruning, NE; 2/16 ALAGirlsSt; Band; Chr; Chrs; ChrhWkr; CncrtBnd; HonRl; Mdrgl; MrchBnd; Chrldr; Dana College.

KERLEY, James R; Elverado HS; Elkville, IL; Chr; ChrhWkr; CmntyWkr; SchPpr; 4-H; FFA; Bsbl; Ftbl; IMSpt; John A Logan Jr Coll; Art.

KERLEY, La Donna T; Vienna HS; Vienna, IL; SecTrsSophCls; PresJrCls; FHA; SpnCl; Trade School; Professional.

KERLEY, Ruth E; Brown Cnty HS; Timewell, IL; 8/91 PresJrCls; Chrs; CncrtBnd; HonRl; MrchBnd; NHS; Yrbk; 4-H; Bsbl; Quincy School; Nursing.

KERLIN, Cynthia J; Warsaw Community HS; Warsaw, IN; 4/351 ALAGirlsSt; HonRl; HospAde; VPFHA; Goshen College; Nursing.

KERMICLE, John S; East Richland HS; Dundas, IL; 13/264 ALBoysSt; Band; CncrtBnd; JrNHS; MrchBnd; PepBnd; StuCncl; SchPpr; 4-H; FFA; 4-HAwd; U Of I.

KERN, Bernard J; Beckman HS; Dyersville, IA; ALBoysSt; ChrhWkr; Bus Sch; Electrician.

KERN, Carol R; Weyerhaeuser HS; Weyerhaeuser, WI; HonRl; RptrSchPpr; EdSchPpr; SchPpr; College; Teacher.

KERN, David; Oconomowoc Senior HS; Oconomowoc, WI; 5/237 ALBoysSt; HonRl; NHS; SctActv; YthFlsp; FrCl; IMSpt; Us Naval Acad; Engineering.

KERN, Jill R; East Pike HS; Milton, IL; 4/30 ChrhWkr; HonRl; OffAde; SchPl; FHA; Bsktbl; Tennis; Trk; GAA; 4-HAwd; College.

KERN, Kathleen M; Romeo HS; Romeo, MI; HonRl; LitMag; ModUN; NHS; NatlMeritCmnd; Yrbk; SchPpr; GerCl; 4-HAwd; Eastern Mich Univ; Commercial Art.

KERN, Mark A; East Noble HS; Kendallville, IN; 12/270 JA; SecNatlFornLg; NHS; NatlMeritCmnd; VPYthFlsp; SptEdYrbk; RptrSchPpr; FTA; SciCl; IMSpt; Purdue Univ; Elem Educ.

KERN, Martha L; Willow Run HS; Ypsilanti, MI; 3/225 HonRl; MrchBnd; NHS; Orch; SchMus; SchPl; SctActv; RptrYrbk; Coll; Lawyer.

KERN, Maureen A; Wheaton Central HS; Wheaton, IL; 10/317 Chr; ChrhWkr; DrlTm; HonRl; Mdrgl; NHS; OffAde; StuCncl; PpCl; Ill State Univ; Business.

KERN, Michael P; Hibbing HS; Hibbing, MN; 56/402 HonRl; JrNHS; NHS; SpnCl; PpCl; CaptBsbl; University Of Minnesota; Business.

KERN, Paul H; Frankenmuth HS; Frankenmuth, MI; 41/155 HonRl; Ftbl; Glf; Delta Coll; Electrician.

KERN, Ricky J; La Harpe HS; La Harpe, IL; VPFrshCls; ChrhWkr; HonRl; SptEdSchPpr; 4-H; PresFFA; PpCl; LetterBsbl; CaptBsktbl; CaptFtbl; LetterGlf; LetterTrk; Univ Of Illinois; Veterinarian.

KERN, Robert J; O Fallon Township HS; O Fallon, IL; 7/314 Band; CmntyWkr; CncrtBnd; HonRl; JrNHS; MrchBnd; NHS; PepBnd; SctActv; YthFlsp; RptrSchPpr; FDA; SpnCl; Bsktbl; College; Pre Med.

KERN, Ruth M; Woodlan HS; New Haven, IN; 11/138 HonRl; NHS; FHA; PpCl; LetterBsbl; College; Accounting.

KERN, Teresa; Bethlehem Acad; Faribault, MN; 6/93 CncrtBnd; HonRl; MrchBnd; NHS; PepBnd; SchMus; YthLg; RptrSchPpr; 4-H; 4-HAwd;.

KERNAN, Michael E; Spalding Institute; Peoria, IL; 5/125 SecSophCls; ALBoysSt; HonRl; SctActv; StuCncl; StuGov; Trk; IMSpt; Eng, Architect Or Sci.

KERNEL, Kathy E; St Mary Academy; Indianapolis, IN; 6/34 VPJrCls; PresSrCls; ALAGirlsSt; Chrs; HonRl; NHS; SchPl; StuCncl; VPFrCl; Ball State Univ; Sociology.

KERNER, David C; Northfield HS; Roann, IN; Band; JrNHS; NatlFornLg; NHS; NatlThespSoc; PepBnd; Quill&Scroll; SchMus; Yrbk; SpnCl; Ashand College.

KERNER, George F; Battle Creek Central HS; Battle Creek, MI; ChrhWkr; CmntyWkr; JA; StuCncl; YthFlsp; Swmmng; Trk; Trade School; Carpenter.

KERNER, Laneta S; Concordia HS; Concordia, KS; Band; SchPl; YthFlsp; RptrSchPpr; SchPpr; FTA; SciCl; LetterTrk; IMSpt; PPFtbl; Cloud County Community College; Journalism.

KERNICK, Nicholas J; Sedgwick HS; Sedgwick, KS; 2/30 Chrs; HonRl; Mdrgl; SchMus; SchPl; SctActv; TchrAde; YthFlsp; RptrYrbk; FshEdYrbk; RptrSchPpr; EdSchPpr; Air Force Acad; Elec Tech.

KERNIK, Alan C; Alexander Ramsey HS; St Paul, MN; Orch; SchPl; Tennis; U Of Minn; Md.

KERNS, Patricia R; Wheaton Central HS; Wheaton, IL; 7/317 ChrhWkr; HonRl; JrNHS; NHS; NatlMeritCmnd; Orch; YthFlsp; PpCl; Greenvile College; Elementary Education.

KERO, Charles; Melvindale HS; Melvindale, MI; VPSrCls; ChrhWkr; HonRl; NHS; StuCncl; College; Ministry.

KERR, Barbara; Athens HS; Troy, MI; TrsJrCls; DrlTm; HonRl; NHS; SchPl; StuGov; TchrAde; PpCl; Univ; Biology.

KERR, Becky L; Harmony HS; Farmington, IA; ChrhWkr; CmntyWkr; DrmMjrt; HonRl; Twrl; YthFlsp; Yrbk; LetterBsbl; Chrldr; CchngActv; Gem City Bus Clge; Executive Secretary.

KERR, George D; Hanover Horton HS; Jackson, MI; 2/95 Band; DrlTm; HonRl; MrchBnd; NHS; NatlMeritSF; StuCncl; StuGov; YthFlsp; Michigan State Univ; Advertising Design.

KERR, Jeffery A; Harmony HS; Farmington, IA; ALBoysSt; ChrhWkr; HonRl; SchPl; YthFlsp; Yrbk; PpCl; SciCl; LetterBsktbl; LetterFtbl; Mt Mercy Univ; Med Tech.

KERR, Karen M; Aquinas HS; Southgate, MI; 13/218 CmntyWkr; HonRl; NHS; Trk; IMSpt; PPFtbl; U Of Mi; Medicine.

KERR, Lisa A; Coldwater HS; Coldwater, MI; Band; HonRl; MrchBnd; NHS; PepBnd; SchPpr; 4-H; PpCl; LetterBsktbl; LetterTrk; College; Professional Medicine.

KERR, Marie E; Vienna Twp HS; Buncombe, IL; Yrbk; 4-H; FNA; SpnCl; Univ Of Tennessee; Nursing.

KERR, Mary F; Winfield HS; Winfield, KS; 11/185 Chr; ChrhWkr; HonRl; NatlMeritCmnd; SchMus; SctActv; StuCncl; TchrAde; YthFlsp; Sterling Col Ks; Special Education.

KERR, Mary F; Regina Dominican HS; Mt Prospect, IL; 20/207 TrsSrCls; Chrs; ChrhWkr; HonRl; Mdrgl; OffAde; SchMus; Marquette Univ; Engineering.

KERR, Richard E; Coleman HS; Coleman, WI; 14/83 ALBoysSt; HonRl; TreasFFA; LetterBsktbl; LetterFtbl; Trk; Trade School; Draftsman.

KERR, Robert H; Republican Valley HS; Mccook, NE; TrsFrshCls; TrsJrCls; VPSrCls; StuCncl; Yrbk; CaptBsktbl; CaptFtbl; CaptTrk; LetterWrstlng; Trade School; Professional.

KERR, Susan D; Cimarron HS; Cimarron, KS; Band; ChrhWkr; CmntyWkr; CncrtBnd; MrchBnd; PepBnd; YthFlsp; 4-H; FHA; PpCl; Business School.

KERSCHER, Faye; Southern Door HS; Sturgeon Bay, WI; SecSophCls; HonRl; StuCncl; PpCl; Trk; Nwti.

KERSEY, Linda D; Adel HS; Adel, IA; SecSrCls; Chrs; CncrtBnd; HonRl; Mdrgl; MrchBnd; 4-H; FrCl; Chrldr; School Of Nursing; Missionary.

KERSHAW, Steven; Benson HS; Omaha, NE; DrlTm; HonRl; JA; Orch; ROTC; SchMus; AmLegAwd; JAAwd; CitAwd; University Of Neb; Business.

KERSTEN, Cheryl M; Murdock HS; Ashland, NE; Chrs; CncrtBnd; HonRl; StuCncl; TchrAde; Yrbk; 4-H; PpCl; Blair College; Medical Asst.

KERSTEN, Mark E; Howells HS; Howells, NE; 14/42 PresSrCls; Band; HonRl; StuCncl; LetterBsbl; LetterBsktbl; LetterFtbl; LetterTrk; Lincoln School Of Commerce; Accounting.

KERSULIS, Antonia; Ofallon Township Hs; Belleville, IL; 42/294 U; Nurse.

KERSZYKOWSKI, Shari Lee; Algonac HS; Algonac, MI; Aud/Vis; Chrs; CncrtBnd; HonRl; MrchBnd; NHS; Orch; SchPl; LatCl; Tennis; Oakland U; Pianist.

KERTEZ, Cindy; Riverside Brookfield Hs; North Riverside, IL; Chr; DrlTm; HonRl; JrNHS; NHS; NatlMeritCmnd; NatlThespSoc; SchMus; TreasGerCl; AmLegAwd;.

KERTEZ, Jay; Riverside Brookfield Hs; North Riverside, IL; 4/489 SecBand; CncrtBnd; HonRl; JrNHS; MrchBnd; NHS; PepBnd; TchrAde; GerCl; AmLegAwd;.

KERTH, Robbin; Trego Comm HS; Wa Keeney, KS; PresJrCls; Band; Chr; HonRl; MrchBnd; SctActv; StuCncl; TchrAde; Bsbl; Trk; Ft Hays Stae College; Banking.

KERTZ, Janet M; Valle HS; Ste Genevieve, MO; 10/83 PresHospAde; SecNHS; RptrYrbk; Yrbk; Pres4-H; FHA; PpCl; 4-HAwd; College.

KERWIN, Diana; Cedar Bluffs HS; Cedar Bluffs, NE; SecSophCls; ALAGirlsSt; Band; Chr; HonRl; SchPl; PpCl; Trk; Chrldr; BttyCrckrAwd; Army; Denistry.

KERWIN, Peter; Wheaton North HS; Wheaton, IL; CmntyWkr; HonRl; Univ; Politics.

KESKEL, Charles G; Bremen HS; Midlothian, IL; 42/427 HonRl; IntrClCncl; LbryAde; NHS; RptrSchPpr; PresGerCl; SecMthCl; TreasSciCl; Wrstlng; Southern Illinois Univ; Computer Science.

KESKITALO, Jean E; Batavia HS; Batavia, IL; AFS; ChrhWkr; CmntyWkr; HonRl; SecNHS; OffAde; SchMus; SchPl; SctActv; StuCncl; 4-HAwd; Univ Of Illinois; Home Economics.

KESLER, Jon K; Northwestern HS; Iron River, WI; ALBoysSt; SchPl; Yrbk; VPFTA; College; Professional.

KESLER, Kurt; Rantoul Township Hs; Dewey, IL; 5/389 HonRl; JrNHS; NatlMeritCmnd; PpCl; LetterWrstlng; Ui;agricultural Engineering.

KESLER, Thomas J; Fraser HS; Fraser, MI; 6/565 PresBand; CncrtBnd; HonRl; JrNHS; MrchBnd; NHS; PepBnd; LetterTrk; Mass Of Tech; Architecture.

KESSEL, Patrick J; Detroit Catholic Central HS; Detroit, MI; IMSpt; Univ Of Mich; Medicine.

KESSINGER, Connie J; Girard HS; Girard, IL; TrsFrshCls; Band; ChrhWkr; CncrtBnd; HonRl; MrchBnd; PepBnd; SchMus; SchPl; Yrbk; 4-H; FHA; College; Fashion Design.

KESSINGER, Jackie L; Mendota Twp HS; Compton, IL; Band; ChrhWkr; CmntyWkr; HonRl; YthFlsp; FNA; SpnCl; Trk; GAA; Midstate College; Accounting.

KESSINGER, Roxanna L; Centennial HS; Waco, NE; 16/58 Band; Chrs; NHS; SchPl; RptrSchPpr; 4-H; FTA; PpCl; Chrldr; University Of Nebraska; Music.

KESSLER, Ann A; Rochester HS; Rochester, IL; SecBand; ChrhWkr; CncrtBnd; HonRl; JA; MrchBnd; NHS; SchPl; SecFTA; GAA; Eastern Illinois Univ; Elem Education.

KESSLER, Cheryl M; Dominican HS; Mt Clemens, MI; JA; NHS; TchrAde; 4-H; 4-HAwd; JAAwd; College.

KESSLER, Constance L; Cowan HS; Muncie, IN; DrlTm; HonRl; MrchBnd; NHS; Yrbk; 4-H; FHA; PpCl; Purdue Univ; Fashion Retailing.

KESSLER, Corlynda L; Weeping Water HS; Weeping Water, NE; HonRl; NHS; SchPl; TchrAde; RptrYrbk; SpnCl; Coll; Elem Educ.

KESSLER, Cynthia; Kinmundy Alma Hs; Kinmudy, IL; ChrhWkr; HonRl; NHS; StuCncl; FHA; FrCl; PpCl;.

KESSLER, Jeanne A; Gresham HS; Gresham, NE; 5/13 Band; Chrs; HonRl; SchPl; RptrYrbk; SchPpr; 4-H; VPPpCl; AmLegAwd; BttyCrckrAwd; 4-HAwd; Univ Of Nebraska; Home Economics.

KESSLER, Julie D; Kinmundy Alma HS; Kinmundy, IL; TrsFrshCls; ChrhWkr; HonRl; NHS; SchPl; FHA; PpCl; Univ Of Ill; Special Ed.

KESSLER, Vicki L; Gibson Southern HS; Haubstadt, IN; Chrs; FHA; PpCl; SciCl; Univ; Nursing.

KESTENBAUM, Martha J; E Lansing HS; East Lansing, MI; 30/360 Band; CtyCnl; CncrtBnd; HonRl; MrchBnd; NHS; Orch; PolWkr; TchrAde; RptrSchPpr; Mich State Univ.

KESTER, Terry; Manchester HS; N Manchester, IN; 9/145 HonRl; NatlFornLg; NHS; PolWkr; RptrSchPpr; EldAwd; Manchester College; Doctor Of Medicine.

KESTILA, Larry W; Ishpeming HS; Ishpeming, MI; 40/205 Chr; DrmBgl; HonRl; LetterBsktbl; LetterFtbl; Swmmng; Trk; LetterWrstlng; IMSpt; EldAwd; Mi Tech Univ; Computer Sciences.

KESTLER, Teresa J; Fairfield HS; Arlington, KS; Chr; Chrs; TchrAde; Teen; RptrYrbk; 4-H; PpCl; Bsbl; LetterBsktbl; LetterTrk; Hutchinson Community Jr Clg; Teacher.

KESTNER, Linda L; Central HS; Clayton, IL; Band; ChrhWkr; CmntyWkr; HonRl; NHS; NatlMeritFnl; SctActv; YthFlsp; Sec4-H; Coll; Rn.

KETCHAM, James D; Plattsmouth HS; Plattsmouth, NE; 35/144 Southeast Comm Coll; Draftsman.

KETCHMARK, Janan E; Minonk Dana Rutland HS; Minonk, IL; DrlTm; HonRl; RptrYrbk; SpnCl; PpCl; SciCl; VPGAA; Siu; Law.

KETCHUM, Karen L; Central HS; St Joseph, MO; Chr; ChrhWkr; HospAde; LitMag; LbryAde; University; Journalism.

KETCHUM, Sarah J; Glendale HS; Springfield, MO; AFS; ChrhWkr; HonRl; StuCncl; TchrAde; FBLA; SpnCl; Clg; Business.

KETTELER, Lynne A; Beaver Dam Sr HS; Beaver Dam, WI; 13/289 AFS; Chrs; Mdrgl; SchMus; StuCncl; RptrYrbk; EdYrBk; 4-H; FHA; College.

KETTER, James E; Bishop Miege HS; Shawnee Mission, KS; ALBoysSt; HonRl; College; Veterinary Med.

KETTER, Mary P; Jefferson West HS; Meriden, KS; Band; Chrs; CncrtBnd; DrlTm; HonRl; LbryAde; MrchBnd; NatlMeritSchl; PepBnd; SchMus; SchPl; College; Business.

KETTERER, Molly A; St Elizabeths Academy; Charleston, MO; Chr; Chrs; ChrhWkr; HonRl; OffAde; SchMus; Sdlty; Se Missouri St Univ; Computer Science.

KETTINGER, Linda M; Valle HS; Ste Genevieve, MO; 3/81 SecSophCls; DrlTm; HonRl; HospAde; NHS; SecStuCncl; RptrSchPpr; SchPpr; 4-H; PpCl; College; Nursing.

KETTLER, Cheryl A; Elk Grove HS; Elk Grove Vlg, IL; 1/505 HonRl; LbryAde; NatlFornLg; NHS; NatlMeritCmnd; PolWkr; SctActv; StuCncl; SpnCl; George Washington Univ; Law.

KETTLER, Mark E; Paola HS; Paola, KS; Chr; LbryAde; SchAde; TchrAde; 4-H; FFA; Trade School; Equipment Operator.

KETTNER, Dana M; Charlotte HS; Charlotte, MI; 45/262 Band; CncrtBnd; MrchBnd; NatlThespSoc; PepBnd; SchPl; TchrAde; SchPpr; Lansing Comm Clge Csm; Geologist.

KETTREY, Teresa A; Eastern HS; Pekin, IN; 40/88 Band; CncrtBnd; HonRl; MrchBnd; Orch; PepBnd; TchrAde; TreasSpnCl; PpCl; 4-HAwd; Indiana Univ; Bookkeeper.

KETZNER, Mike; Forest Park Hs; Ferdinand, IN; VPJrCls; Band; CncrtBnd; HonRl; MrchBnd; NHS; PepBnd; GerCl; PpCl;.

KEUER, Dwight; Brillion HS; Brillion, WI; 11/98 HonRl; FFA; IMSpt; Trade; Vocation.

KEUHN, Charles; Owosso HS; Owosso, MI; 60/430 ChrhWkr; NHS; SchAde; Glf; Tennis; Mich Tech Univ; Chem Engineer.

KEUR, Michael H; Fruitport HS; Fruitport, MI; 30/287 Band; Chr; ChrhWkr; CncrtBnd; HonRl; Mdrgl; MrchBnd; NHS; PepBnd; SchAde; SchMus; College; Music.

KEUSCH, John; East Detroit HS; Warren, MI; CmntyWkr; PPFtbl; East Mich Univ;prof Law.

KEWIN, Jennie A; Griswold Comm HS; Griswold, IA; 1/81 PresJrCls; SecSrCls; TrsSrCls; ALAGirlsSt; HonRl; PresNHS; TreasStuCncl; EdYrBk; PresFHA; LetterChrldr; DanFAwd; Drake Univ; Physical Education Teacher.

KEY, Joanna J; Trenton HS; Trenton, MO; 3/132 ALAGirlsSt; SecChrhWkr; VPNHS; StuCncl; PresFFA; VPPpCl; SecSciCl; LetterTennis; GAA; 4-HAwd; Trenton Coll; Horticulture.

KEY, Phyllis A; Cass Technical HS; Detroit, MI; TchrAde; Clge; Pro.

KEY, Susan L; Sauk Prairie HS; Prairie Du Sac, WI; CaptDrlTm; HonRl; HospAde; NHS; SecStuCncl; College; Major Study.

KEYES, John G; Belmont HS; Belmont, WI; 1/53 PresSophCls; PresJrCls; ALBoysSt; Band; HonRl; ModUN; StuCncl; MthCl; Univ; Law.

KEYES, Michael; Beloit Memorial HS; Beloit, WI; HonRl; NHS; SchMus; SchPl; StuCncl; Univ.

KEYES, Richard J; Beloit Memorial HS; Beloit, WI; HonRl; NHS; SchMus; SchPl; StuCncl; University.

KEYLER, Mary; Our Lady Of Grace HS; Beech Grove, IN; 6/60 PresSrCls; Chrs; HonRl; HospAde; NHS; SchMus; SchPl; IMSpt; Indiana Central College; Nursing.

KEYS, Shawn J; Plymouth HS; Plymouth, WI; 3/234 TrsFrshCls; VPJrCls; PresSrCls; AFS; HonRl; LitMag; NHS; StuGov; Yrbk; PresAwd; Beloit College; Medicine.

KEYSER, Cheryl L; Edsel Ford HS; Dearborn, MI; VPAFS; NatlFornLg; NHS; NatlMeritSF; SecNatlThespSoc; SchMus; SchPl; SecStuCncl; FrCl; SciCl; College; Lawyer.

KEZELIS, Robert A; Wheeling HS; Buffalo Grove, IL; SchMus; Northwestern Univ; Law.

KHAN, Jemshed A; Maryville R Ii HS; Maryville, MO; HonRl; NHS; SctActv; StuGov; KeyCl; College; Professional.

KHARASCH, Evan; Niles Township West HS; Lincolnwood, IL; 6/650 CncrtBnd; NHS; NatlMeritCmnd; Orch; SchMus; StuGov; MthCl; SciCl; Socr; BauchLmbAwd; Coll; Medicine.

KHARASCH, Evan D; Niles Twp West HS; Lincolnwood, IL; 5/600 CncrtBnd; NHS; NatlMeritCmnd; Orch; StuGov; TchrAde; PresMthCl; PresSciCl; Socr; BauchLmbAwd; JETSAwd; Brown Univ; Biochemistry.

KHESHGI, Haroon S; Maine North HS; Glenview, IL; 10/350 HonRl; JrNHS; MthCl; Socr; Tennis; Univ Of Ill; Chemical Engineering.

KHOE, Awa P; Downers Grove North HS; Downers Grove, IL; HonRl; NHS; Northern Illinois Univ; Bio Chemistry.

KHOURIE, Tammie A; Hayti HS; Hayti, MO; SecSophCls; Chr; ChrhWkr; HonRl; SecNHS; NatlThespSoc; SchMus; SchPl; StuCncl; TreasYthFlsp; FHA; FTA; Murray State Univ; Accounting.

KHOURY, Holly M; Kingsford HS; Iron Mountain, MI; Band; CncrtBnd; DrmBgl; HonRl; MrchBnd; PepBnd; Michigan Tech Univ; Computer Science.

KHOURY, Michael; Riverside HS; Dearborn Hts, MI; 13/273 ALBoysSt; Band; ChrhWkr; CncrtBnd; HonRl; NHS; NatlThespSoc; SchPl; SctActv; Tennis; Univ Mich; Attorney.

KIBBE, Barbara J; California R 1 HS; California, MO; VPJrCls; Band; Chrs; ChrhWkr; CmntyWkr; CncrtBnd; MrchBnd; Yrbk; FHA; SpnCl; College; Physical Therapist.

KIBLER, Nancy J; West Vigo HS; W Terre Haute, IN; 35/194 ALAGirlsSt; HonRl; NatlFornLg; RptrSchPpr; Indiana State University.

KIBLER, Thomas G; Spring Lake Park HS; Minneapolis, MN; Anoka Ramsey Comm College; Business Mgmt.

KIDD, Carolyn; Cvs HS; Chicago, IL; 49/699 HonRl; JrNHS; ModUN; NHS; NatlMeritCmnd; OffAde; SchAde; TchrAde; Socr; Tennis; College; Professional.

KIDD, Karla M; Prov St Mel HS; Chicago, IL; 5/50 PresSophCls; CmntyWkr; HonRl; LbryAde; NHS; SctActv; RptrYrbk; Trk; Mundelium; Industrial Psychology.

KIDD, Kelly J; Advance HS; Advance, MO; 3/55 ALAGirlsSt; CncrtBnd; HonRl; MrchBnd; StuCncl; PresCollege; Elem Ed.

•KIDD, Lisa M; Washington Catholic HS; Washington, IN; Chrs; ChrhWkr; HonRl; HospAde; TchrAde; PpCl; University; Accountant.

KIDD, Teri D; Morton HS; Morton, IL; HonRl; JA; NHS; 4-H; Il Central Col; Secretary.

KIDDLE, Glenn S; Buffalo Grove HS; Buffalo Grove, IL; 22/280 Chr; HonRl; Mdrgl; NHS; NatlMeritCmnd; SchMus; KeyCl; Simpson College; Music.

KIEBEL, Michael F; New Haven HS; New Haven, IN; 28/250 Chr; ChrhWkr; HonRl; NatlMeritCmnd; TchrAde; PresFrCl; Socr; IMSpt; OptClAwd; Seminary Of Saint Pius; Philosophy.

KIECKER, Pamela L; Mankato East HS; Mankato, MN; HonRl; NatlFornLg; TreasNHS; NatlThespSoc; Orch; StuCncl; PresSciCl; LetterSwmmng; LetterChrldr; RotaryAwd; Carleton College; Medicine.

KIECKHAFER, Donna; Lourdes Acad; Oshkosh, WI; 2/126 Chrs; HonRl; NHS; NatlMeritCmnd; StuCncl; YthLg; Yrbk; SchPpr; KeyCl; IMSpt; Uw Madison; Pharmacy.

KIECKHEFER, Linda M; So Milwaukee Sr HS; So Milwaukee, WI; AFS; CmntyWkr; HonRl; PolWkr; StuCncl; TchrAde; Winona State College; Nursing.

KIECKHOEFER, Jeanne M; Somerset Public HS; New Richmond, WI; 7/59 Chr; EdYrBk; TreasFHA;.

KIEFER, David J; Cheboygan Catholic HS; Cheboygan, MI; LetterBsktbl; LetterFtbl; LetterGlf; Central Mich U; Undecided.

KIEFER, John M; Bremen HS; Bremen, IN; ChrhWkr; SchMus; SchPl; RptrYrbk; RptrSchPpr; SpnCl; Bsktbl; LetterTrk; LetterWrstlng; College; Journalism.

KIEFER, Karen K; Berrien Springs HS; Berrien Springs, MI; Band; Chr; CncrtBnd; HonRl; MrchBnd; NHS; TreasNatlThespSoc; SchMus; SchPl; GerCl; Mi St Univ.

KIEFER, Ray F; Premontre HS; Green Bay, WI; HonRl; NatlSciFnd; SchAde; SctActv; TchrAde; YthFnd; SptEdYrbk; KeyCl; Trk; IMSpt; VFWAwd; Univ Of Mn; Veterinary Medicine.

KIEFER, Robert; Cheboygan Catholic HS; Cheboygan, MI; RptrYrbk; RptrSchPpr; SptEdSchPpr; CchngActv; Central Michigan Univ.

KIEFER, Susan L; Bremen HS; Bremen, IN; 14/104 HonRl; JrNHS; NHS; SpnCl; PpCl; Valparaiso U; Nursing.

KIEFFER, Connie B; Central HS; St Joseph, MO; 25/535 Chr; ChrhWkr; HonRl; HospAde; NHS; SchMus; StuCncl; StuGov; PresYthFlsp; SecGerCl; College; Special Education.

`KIEFFER, Darlene M; Mt Carmel HS; Mt Carmel, IL; NHS; LatCl; SpnCl; GAA; College; Nurse.

KIEFFER, Kim; Galena HS; Galena, IL; SecSrCls; DrlTm; HonRl; SchMus; SctActv; TchrAde; FHA; IMSpt; PresAwd; Coll; Professional.

KIEHL, Marjorie L; Malta Bend R 5HS; Malta Bend, MO; ALAGirlsSt; Band; Chrs; HonRl; NHS; StuCncl; Yrbk; 4-H; FHA; Bsktbl; College; Home Ec.

KIEHLER, William J; Armada HS; Romeo, MI; ChrhWkr; HonRl; SchAde; TchrAde; PpCl; CaptBsktbl; LetterFtbl; LetterTrk; PPFtbl; 4-HAwd; Mi St Univ; Agricultural Engineering.

KIEHNE, G; Campus Hs; Gordonville, MO; 1/36 PresFrshCls; Chr; NHS; StuCncl; RptrSchPpr; EdSchPpr; SpnCl; MthCl; PpCl; AmLegAwd;.

KIEL, Mary A; Iron Mountain HS; Iron Mountain, MI; Chr; ChrhWkr; CmntyWkr; HospAde; NatlThespSoc; SchPl; YthFlsp; RptrSchPpr; FNA; FTA; St Marys Jr Clge Mn; Child Development.

KIELTYKA, Janet T; Lourdes HS; Chicago, IL; 110/300 HonRl; StuCncl; SpnCl; PpCl; IMSpt; College; Nursing.

KIELTYKA, Richard; Marist HS; Chicago, IL; 105/400 CmntyWkr; SctActv; RptrYrbk; Yrbk; LetterFtbl; LetterTennis; Northern Ill Univ.

KIENHOLZ, Roger; Bird Island Lake Lillian HS; Bird Island, MN; 3/60 PresSrCls; Band; HonRl; NHS; SchMus; SchPl; StuCncl; Nd State U; Engineering.

KIENSTRA, Kathleen M; Alton Sr HS; Alton, IL; 10/858 Chrs; HonRl; JrNHS; NHS; NatlThespSoc; SchMus; SchPl; StuCncl; PpCl; Univ Of Illinois.

KIENTZY, Barbara J; Lincoln Co R I HS; Silex, MO; 5/38 TrsSophCls; PresJrCls; ChrhWkr; DrlTm; HonRl; NHS; OffAde; SchPl; Yrbk; 4-H; U Of Mo; Fashion Retailing.

KIES, Debbie R; Crestland HS; Early, IA; Chr; CncrtBnd; HonRl; Mdrgl; NHS; PepBnd; SchPl; Glf; Chrldr; AmLegAwd; Univ; Art.

KIES, Lora L; Nashua HS; Charles City, IA; Band; Chr; ChrhWkr; CncrtBnd; HonRl; MrchBnd; SecNatlThespSoc; PresSchPl; VPStuCncl; FrCl; Wartburg College; Education.

KIESETTER, Dale O; Cornell HS; Pontiac, IL; 1/29 TrsFrshCls; PresSophCls; ALBoysSt; Band; HonRl; SchPl; StuCncl; 4-H; LetterBsbl; LetterBsktbl; DanFAwd; 4-HAwd; Eureka College; Mathematics.

KIESIG, Debbie D; Ottawa Twp HS; Ottawa, IL; 19/420 Chr; HonRl; College; Photojournalism.

KIESLER, Sara J; L P Goodrich HS; Fond Du Lac, WI; Chr; StuCncl; GerCl; College; Psychology.

KIESLING, Douglas; Lincoln HS; Wisconsin Rapids, WI; HonRl; TchrAde; GerCl; Uw Madison; Math & Physics Teach.

KIESOW, Linda M; Waupun Sr HS; Brandon, WI; 16/263 CncrtBnd; HonRl; MrchBnd; NHS; PepBnd; Quill&Scroll; RptrSchPpr; Pres4-H; Bsktbl; Trk; EldAwd; 4-HAwd; College; Animal Science.

KIESOW, Lori K; Waupun HS; Brandon, WI; 13/264 Band; CncrtBnd; HonRl; MrchBnd; NHS; TchrAde; RptrSchPpr; 4-H; Bsktbl; Trk; Chrldr; College.

KIESTER, Katherine J; Bishop Luers HS; Fort Wayne, IN; 5/234 HonRl; FrCl; LetterBsktbl; CchngActv; PPFtbl; ChmbCommrsAwd; In U; Cpa.

KIEWEL, Bradley; Alcester HS; Alcester, SD; 2/37 Band; Chr; HonRl; NHS; SchPl; GerCl; Sd St Univ; Electrical Engr.

KIEWIT, Sue; Brownstone Central HS; Brownstown, IN; 1/143 Chr; HonRl; NHS; Quill&Scroll; SchMus; RptrYrbk; FSA; SciCl; GAA; 4-HAwd; Business School; Acctg.

KIGER, Leanne M; Glenwood Comm HS; Glenwood, IA; 31/120 Chr; ChrhWkr; CmntyWkr; JA; JCC; StuCncl; StuGov; CivCl; FBLA; Bsbl; Business School; Vocational.

KIGER, Mary E; Fulton HS; Fulton, IL; Band; Chr; Chrs; ChrhWkr; CncrtBnd; HonRl; LbryAde; MrchBnd; PepBnd; SctActv; Business School; Vocation.

KIGER, Sharon A; Frontier HS; Brookston, IN; 4/56 HonRl; NHS; TchrAde; PpCl; Chrldr; College; Professional.

KIGGENS, Amber J; Turner Memorial HS; Portage, WI; 9/214 Chr; CmntyWkr; HonRl; HospAde; NHS; PolWkr; TchrAde; EdYrBk; SpnCl; Uw Madison; Md.

KIHLE, Tim L; Bottineau HS; Bottineau, ND; TreasFFA; SciCl; College; Agriculture.

KIHLSTADIUS, Larry A; Albert Leu HS; Albert Lea, MN; 2/526 ALBoysSt; ChrhWkr; CmntyWkr; HonRl; NatlMeritCmnd; YthFlsp; CaptWrstlng; IMSpt; AmLegAwd; RotaryAwd; Coll ; Lawyer.

KIIFNER, Nancy M; St Joseph Ogden HS; St Joseph, IL; HonRl; HospAde; LbryAde; StuCncl; RptrSchPpr; PpCl; U Of Il.

KIISKILA, Gail J; Hancock Central HS; Hancock, MI; Band; Chr; CncrtBnd; HonRl; LbryAde; MrchBnd; PepBnd; SchPl; GAA; Michigan Tech Univ; Engineer.

KIKSTRA, Peggy; Negaunee HS; Negaunee, MI; ChrhWkr; CmntyWkr; HonRl; LbryAde; NHS; OffAde; PolWkr; SchAde; TchrAde; FBLA; Bus Coll.

KIKTA, Tammey A; Downers Grove So HS; Downers Grove, IL; 1/820 Chr; DrmMjrt; Mdrgl; NHS; NatlThespSoc; Orch; SchMus; Saint Louis University; Music.

KILBOURN, Daniel L; Boone Country R Vi HS; Centraliaa, MO; ChrhWkr; HonRl; NHS; SchAde; StuCncl; TchrAde; YthFlsp; FFA; College; Agriculture.

KILBOURN, Sharon K; Sterling HS; Sterling, KS; 4/51 PresFrshCls; TrsSrCls; Band; StuCncl; Twrl; 4-H; Bsbl; LetterTrk; Chrldr; DARAwd; Kansas State Univ; Engineering.

KILBRIDE, Joseph K; Bishop Mcnamara HS; Bradley, IL; 10/173 HonRl; JrNHS; NHS; RptrYrbk; University; Journalism.

KILBRIDE, Madonna L; Wakonda Public HS; Vermillion, SD; 5/20 Chrs; HonRl; OffAde; SchPl;.

KILBURY, Deborah L; Rushford HS; Rushford, MN; SecSrCls; SecSophCls; Chrs; DrlTm; HonRl; NHS; SchPl; RptrSchPpr; PpCl; GAA; Winona State Coll.

KILBY, Robert; Hamburg HS; Hamburg, IA; 1/44 VPFrshCls; Band; HonRl; NHS; SchPl; StuCncl; Univ; Law.

KILCHER, Mary Jo; Dominican HS; Detroit, MI; TrsSrCls; HonRl; Sdlty; StuGov; PpCl; CaptBsbl; CaptBsktbl; Chrldr; GAA; Michigan State Univ; Liberal Arts.

KILCOMMONS, Mark A; St Laurence HS; Chicago, IL; 11/396 HonRl; Wrstlng; Northwestern U; Engineering.

KILCOYNE, Geralyn A; Saint Augustine HS; Chicago, IL; PresSophCls; HonRl; NHS; StuCncl; RptrSchPpr; Bryman School; Medical Assisting.

KILDOW, Candi; Milton Union HS; Milton Jct, WI; AFS; Band; MrchBnd; Quill&Scroll; RptrSchPpr; SchPpr;.

KILE, Amanda C; Brookville HS; Brookville, IN; 4/186 PresFrshCls; TrsSophCls; PresJrCls; PresSrCls; ChrhWkr; CaptDrlTm; NHS; NatlMeritCmnd; StuCncl; DARAwd; Coll;elem Or Spec Ed.

KILE, Christie L; Rushville HS; Rushville, IN; 3/265 Chr; Chrl; NatlFornLg; NHS; SchPl; YthFlsp; Glf; GAA; Butler Univ; Pharmacy.

KILE, Steven A; Washington HS; Red Cloud, NE; HonRl; SchPl; StuCncl; 4-H; FFA; Ftbl; Glf; LetterWrstlng; DanFAwd; 4-HAwd; Univ Of Ne; Farmer.

KILGORE, Dewitt D; St Louis Univ HS; St Louis, MO; Aud/Vis; Band; Chr; ChrhWkr; CncrtBnd; HospAde; NatlMeritSF; SchMus; SchPl; StuCncl; SchPpr; Tennis; Washington Univ; Architecture.

KILGORE, Kaye L; Adelphian Acad; Taylor, MI; SecFrshCls; SecTrsSrCls; HonRl; SchPl; StuGov; TchrAde; RptrYrbk; RptrSchPpr; CaptIMSpt; College Of Tech; Rn.

KILGORE, Kimberly J; Marquette HS; Michigan City, IN; ChrhWkr; HonRl; SpnCl;.

KILGORE, Rebecca J; Lakeland Union HS; Woodruff, WI; HonRl; RptrSchPpr; University Of Wisconsin; Sociology.

KILIAN, Peter W; Washington Sr HS; Sioux Falls, SD; NatlFornLg; GerCl; Ftbl; Trk; IMSpt; Augustana Clg; Artist.

KILKER, Debra R; Forreston HS; Forreston, IL; 13/78 Band; Chrs; ChrhWkr; HonRl; NHS; SchPl; YthFlsp; RptrYrbk; TreasFHA; Trk; CchngActv; GAA; College; Nursing.

KILLEN, Christine D; Leblond HS; St Joseph, MO; 11/110 Chrs; CmntyWkr; HonRl; NatlMeritFnl; Quill&Scroll; SchMus; SchPl; FshEdYrbk; FrCl; LionAwd; Sw Missouri State Univ; Spec Educ Teacher.

KILLIAN, Charles R; Waukegan HS; Waukegan, IL; 26/1004 ALBoysSt; Band; Chr; ChrhWkr; CncrtBnd; DrlTm; HonRl; MrchBnd; NHS; Ftbl; Trk; Wrstlng; IMSpt; Univ Of Ill; Lawyer.

KILLIAN, Dennis M; Lexington Community HS; Lexington, IL; 1/62 SecSophCls; AFS; Band; Chr; HonRl; PresNHS; NatlMeritSF; PresStuCncl; Yrbk; PresSciCl; AmLegAwd; Coll;dr.

KILLIAN, Jane M; Streator Twp HS; Streator, IL; 41/383 Chr; ChrhWkr; CmntyWkr; HonRl; HospAde; LbryAde; NHS; 4-H; SpnCl; St Josephs Hosp; Nursing.

KILLIAN, Kimberly J; Cherry Hill HS; Inkster, MI; Chrs; CmntyWkr; HonRl; HospAde; OffAde; SctActv; Henry Ford Comm College; Accounting.

KILLIAN, Thomas M; West HS; Green Bay, WI; HonRl; NHS; SchMus; StuCncl; RptrYrbk; SptEdYrbk; Yrbk; MthCl; SciCl; ChmnTrk; Marquette Univ; Engineering.

KILLINGSWORTH, Mark M; Beaver Dam Sr HS; Beaver Dam, WI; ALBoysSt; StuCncl; Ftbl; Tennis; CchngActv; College.

KILLION, Katherine B; St Elizabeth Acad; Portageville, MO; 25/120 PresFrshCls; Aud/Vis; HonRl; NHS; OffAde; StuCncl; GAA; PPFtbl; Creighton U.

KILLION, Laurie E; St Elizabeth HS; Portageville, MO; 3/110 HonRl; JrNHS; NHS; SchMus; SchPl; SctActv; StuCncl; 4-H; Tennis; Trk; Notre Dame; Psycologist.

KILPATRICK, Nancy L; Sarcoxie HS; Carthage, MO; 10/65 VPSrCls; Chr; HonRl; Mdrgl; VPNHS; VPFHA; SecFTA; PpCl; Chrldr; DARAwd; College; Floral Designer.

KILZER, Lauretta L; St Marys HS; Bentley, ND; 1/42 SecSrCls; Band; CncrtBnd; HonRl; MrchBnd; PepBnd; PpCl; Trk; Us Army.

KIM, Jae Hu; Lane Tech HS; Chicago, IL; 83/1210 SecTrsSrCls; JA; LbryAde; NatlMeritCmnd; ROTC; Univ; Engineering.

KIMBALL, Diane G; Everly Comm HS; Everly, IA; SecFrshCls; PresSophCls; ChrhWkr; HonRl; NHS; OffAde; 4-H; LetterBsktbl; LetterTrk; 4-HAwd; Coll; Pro.

KIMBALL, James; St Francis Hs; West Chicago, IL; LetterTrk; U Illinois ; Accounting.

KIMBALL, Laurel E; Boone Co R Vi HS; Centralia, MO; ChmnAFS; HonRl; SecJA; SchPl; StuCncl; EdYrBk; RptrSchPpr; VPPpCl; GAA; JAAwd; Columbia Col; Psychology.

KIMBER, Myron E; Paseo HS; Kansas City, MO; 4/290 ChrhWkr; TreasJA; MrchBnd; NHS; Orch; StuCncl; RptrYrbk; SchPpr; SecSciCl; University; Doctor.

KIMBER, Wendy J; Underwood HS; Underwood, MN; ALAGirlsSt; Chr; College; Bookkeeping Or Accounting.

KIMBERLIN, Lisa S; Harrisonville Sr HS; East Lynne, MO; HonRl; YthFlsp; IMSpt; PresAwd;.

KIMBERLIN, Victoria L; Peoria Heights HS; Peoria Heights, IL; 21/93 DrlTm; HonRl; NHS; TchrAde; LetterTrk; College.

KIMBERLING, Denise M; Highland HS; Highland, IN; TrsSrCls; ALAGirlsSt; CmntyWkr; Quill&Scroll; StuCncl; RptrSchPpr; SchPpr; PpCl; Tennis; GAA; PPFtbl; College; Architecture.

KIMBLE, Emma J; Benton Harbor HS; Benton Harbor, MI; ChrhWkr; CmntyWkr; HonRl; NHS; SpnCl; N Mich U; Social Science.

KIMBLER, Deborah L; Franklin Community HS; Franklin, IN; 14/217 TreasAFS; Chr; HonRl; NHS; SchMus; SctActv; EdYrBk; FrCl; PpCl; Campbellsville College; Teaching.

KIMBREL, R K; Ensign HS; Ensign, KS; TrsSrCls; TchrAde; RptrYrbk; FFA; Bsktbl; Trk; Seward Cty Comm Clg; Business Adm.

KIMBRELL, Pamela J; West Richland HS; Noble, IL; 15/33 Band; Chrs; HonRl; SchMus; SchPl; YthFlsp; FHA; FrCl; PpCl; DanFAwd; Buscol ;acct.

KIMBROUGH, Patricia A; Norborne HS; Norborne, MO; 1/25 TrsJrCls; TrsSrCls; Band; ChrhWkr; HonRl; PepBnd; SctActv; StuCncl; FHA; Chrldr; Benedictine College; Chemistry.

KIMBROUGH, Sheila; Norborne Hs; Norbourne, MO; 5/30 VPJrCls; HonRl; NHS; Pres4-H; SecFHA; Bsbl; LetterBsktbl; LetterTrk; LetterChrldr; GAA; Maryville; Home Ec Or Pe.

KIMES, Rita L; South Iron R 1 HS; Des Arc, MO; Chrs; ChrhWkr; CmntyWkr; HonRl; NHS; OffAde; FHA; PpCl; LetterBsktbl; Trk; College; History Teacher.

KIMES, William L; Caledonia Valley HS; Potosi, MO; HonRl; SchPl; College; Science.

KIMLEY, Janet; Lakeshore HS; Baroda, MI; 4/240 HonRl; NHS; Quill&Scroll; TchrAde; SptEdSchPpr; GAA; Lake Michigan College; Journalism.

KIMMELL, Bryan D; Columbus North HS; Columbus, IN; PresChrhWkr; CmntyWkr; HonRl; PolWkr; Tennis; Trk; IMSpt; Purdue Univ; Biology.

KIMMES, Cameron A; L L Wright HS; Ironwood, MI; Chr; SchMus; SchPl; Ftbl; Col; X Ray Tech.

KIMMES, John T; Hastings HS; Hastings, MN; RptrSchPpr; VP4-H; 4-HAwd; Univ; Business.

KIMOVEC, Irene B; Regina Dominican HS; Wilmette, IL; 8/204 Chrs; CmntyWkr; HonRl; NatlMeritCmnd; SchPpr; FDA; GerCl; TreasLatCl; SpnCl; MthCl; SciCl; University; Medicine.

KIMPEL, Mark W; East Noble HS; Kendallville, IN; 4/250 CncrtBnd; HonRl; MrchBnd; NHS; SchMus; YthFlsp; SptEdYrbk; Yrbk; SchPpr; LetterTennis; Univ; Physics.

KIMSEY, Melinda K; Prairie Home HS; Prairie Home, MO; SecFrshCls; TrsSophCls; VPJrCls; Chrs; DrlTm; HonRl; SchPl; SptEdSchPpr; FHA;.

KINAST, John A; Luther HS; Chicago, IL; 5/253 Aud/Vis; ChrhWkr; HonRl; ModUN; NHS; StuCncl; SchPpr; KeyCl; College; Scientist.

KINASZ, Thomas J; Quigley South HS; Chicago, IL; 3/160 Chrs; HonRl; NHS; NatlMeritCmnd; PolWkr; Quill&Scroll; StuGov; RptrYrbk; EdSchPpr; SptEdSchPpr; LetterBsbl; Niles College; Psychology.

KINATE, Greg M; Cathedral HS; Green Bay, WI; 17/93 Aud/Vis; HonRl; SchAde; TchrAde; EdSchPpr; LetterBsktbl; LetterFtbl; LetterGlf; CchngActv; IMSpt; U Of W Green Bay; Accountant.

KINCAID, Brenda J; New Haven HS; New Haven, MI; OffAde; SctActv; TchrAde; SchPpr; PpCl; Bsbl; LetterBsktbl; LetterTrk; Business School; Secretary.

KINCAID, John A; Crandon HS; Crandon, WI; PresSophCls; PresJrCls; ALBoysSt; HonRl; StuCncl; Ftbl; Trk; CaptWrstlng; College; Engineer.

KINCAID, Julie; Shiloh HS; Newman, IL; 2/41 Band; Chrs; HonRl; EdSchPpr; FHA; AmLegAwd; BttyCrckrAwd; DanFAwd; DARAwd;.

KINCAID, Nancy E; Stet HS; Richmond, MO; 1/15 ChrhWkr; HonRl; NHS; PresStuCncl; EdYrBk; Bsbl; Bsktbl; Trk; Chrldr; College.

KINCARE, Karen M; Three Rivers HS; Three Rivers, MI; 7/209 ChrhWkr; HonRl; NHS; Yrbk; SpnCl; PpCl; Bsktbl; Tennis; Trk; Adrian College.

KINCART, Jeffrey E; Davis County Comm HS; Bloomfield, IA; ChrhWkr; HonRl; SctActv; StuGov; FrCl; LetterGlf; Glf; LetterWrstlng; GodCntryAwd; University; Agriculture.

KINCHELOE, Michael J; Magic City Campus HS; Minot, ND; JrNHS; NHS; Bsbl; Ftbl; Swmmng; Coll; Med.

KIND, Larry H; Tomahawk HS; Tomahawk, WI; 9/155 ALBoysSt; Band; ChrhWkr; HonRl; SctActv; VPStuCncl; RptrSchPpr; VPSpnCl; Ftbl; Wrstlng; Univ Of Wisconsin; Wildlife Management.

KINDEL, Keith R; St Clair Senior HS; St Clair, MO; ChrhWkr; CmntyWkr; HonRl; StuCncl; TchrAde; KeyCl; PpCl; LetterBsbl; CaptBsktbl; LetterFtbl; Southeast Missour St; Phsical Ed Teacher.

KINDER, Bruce E; Central HS; Aberdeen, SD; HonRl; NatlFornLg; SchPpr; Col; Pro.

KINDER, Deborah L; Logansport HS; Logansport, IN; ALAGirlsSt; Chr; Chrs; NatlFornLg; NatlThespSoc; PolWkr; Quill&Scroll; SchMus; SchPl; Purdue Univ; Child Development.

KINDER, Jerry; Semco HS; Gilman, IA; ALBoysSt; Band; Chrs; SchMus; TchrAde; RptrYrbk; FTA; Bsbl; Bsktbl; Wartburg Waverly Ia; History.

KINDERKNECHT, Helen; Morland HS; Collyer, KS; 3/21 TrsFrshCls; VPJrCls; SecSrCls; HonRl; LbryAde; SchMus; EdYrBk; Ft Hays Kansas State College; Nursing.

KINDERKNECHT, Lavern F; Grinnell HS; Grinnell, KS; PresSophCls; PresJrCls; Chrs; ChrhWkr; HonRl; StuCncl; Bsktbl; Ftbl; VFWAwd; University.

KINDERNAY, Joseph A; Hillsboro HS; Panama, IL; HonRl; LetterBsbl; CaptFtbl; IMSpt; College.

KINDIG, Randall A; Tippecanoe Valley HS; Mentone, IN; 2/132 ALBoysSt; HonRl; NHS; NatlMeritCmnd; SpnCl; MthCl; SciCl; Bsktbl; Trk; College; Engineering.

KINDL, Karrie L; Willow Brook HS; Villa Park, IL; AFS; Chr; HonRl; NHS; NatlMeritSF; NatlThespSoc; SchMus; SchPl; StuCncl; Oberlin College; Philosophy.

KINDLE, Judy A; Riverside Brookfield Twp HS; Riverside, IL; HonRl; NHS; SchMus; StuCncl; StuGov; PresFrCl; U Of Il; Med Tech.

KINDRED, Dionne S; Bedford North Lawrence HS; Springville, IN; ALAGirlsSt; ChrhWkr; DrlTm; HonRl; NHS; OffAde; StuCncl; TchrAde; FHA;.

KINDRICK, James D; Sault Area HS; Sault Ste Marie, MI; HonRl; TchrAde; LetterWrstlng; IMSpt; Coll.

KINDSCHUH, Kevin K; Wisner Pilger HS; Wisner, NE; HonRl; StuCncl; 4-H; SpnCl; Univ.

KINDT, Christopher R; Wauwatosa West HS; Wauwatosa, WI; ChrhWkr; CmntyWkr; HonRl; SctActv; Swmmng; IMSpt; RotaryAwd; Univ; Law.

KING, Archie T; Glenbrook North HS; Northbrook, IL; 60/650 HonRl; LetterTrk; Univ Of Virginia; Science.

KING, Audrey D; Thornridge HS; Phoenix, IL; 51/794 Chr; Chrs; ChrhWkr; HonRl; NatlFornLg; NHS; College; Nursing.

KING, Barbara J; Estherville HS; Estherville, IA; Band; CncrtBnd; MrchBnd; PepBnd; SchPl; Twrl; College; Medical Technologist.

KING, Brenda J; Kearney HS; Kansas City, MO; 10/86 AFS; Band; Chr; Chrs; ChrhWkr; CncrtBnd; HonRl; LbryAde; MrchBnd; NHS; SchPl; TchrAde; YthFlsp; SpnCl; College; Sociology.

KING, Brenda L; Warren Central HS; Indianapolis, IN; 91/750 Band; CncrtBnd; HonRl; HospAde; JrNHS; OffAde; Orch; PepBnd; SchAde; SchPl; TchrAde; University; Nursing.

KING, Cloveese A; Sts Peter & Paul HS; Saginaw, MI; Chrl; ChrhWkr; CmntyWkr; HospAde; JA; PolWkr; PpCl; CaptBsktbl; GAA; IMSpt; College; Law.

KING, Cynthia; Porta HS; Tallula, IL; 18/128 ChrhWkr; HonRl; HospAde; JA; LbryAde; FHA; IMSpt; 4-HAwd; College; Data Processing.

KING, Daniel F; Saline HS; Saline, MI; PresSrCls; VPSrCls; Band; HonRl; JrNHS; SchMus; StuCncl; StuGov; Bsktbl; IMSpt; Col; Engineering.

KING, Danny; Union HS; Fountain City, IN; HonRl; FFA; IMSpt; Trade Sch; Vocation.

KING, Dave; Maplewood HS; Maplewood, MO; HonRl; TchrAde; College; Forestry.

KING, David; Gladstone HS; Gladstone, MI; 51/179 VPFrshCls; PresSrCls; ALBoysSt; Chrl; ChrhWkr; StuGov; IMSpt; Mich Tech; Sociologist.

KING, David A; Oakville HS; St Louis, MO; 10/357 CmntyWkr; HonRl; YthFlsp; LetterBsktbl; Univ Mo St Louis; Accounting.

KING, David J; Rantoul Township HS; Rantoul, IL; HonRl; NHS; StuCncl; FrCl; LetterFtbl; LetterWrstlng;.

KING, David P; Bethany Christian HS; Goshen, IN; Orch; GerCl; Socr; IMSpt; Clg; Botany.

KING, Deborah A; New Hampton Comm HS; New Hampton, IA; SchMus; SchPl; TchrAde; RptrSchPpr; SpnCl; College; Teach.

KING, Debra; Edwardsburg HS; Edwardsburg, MI; 21/127 CncrtBnd; HonRl; MrchBnd; PepBnd; TchrAde; College; Vocation.

KING, Deidre A; Laboure HS; St Louis, MO; Chr; Chrl; Chrs; CmntyWkr; JA; SchAde; SchMus; SchPl; SctActv; StuCncl; Chrldr; JAAwd; Fontbonne College; Business.

KING, Denise M; Hackett HS; Kalamazoo, MI; 8/143 HonRl; NHS; SchMus; PpCl; CaptChrldr; PPFtbl; DARAwd; College; Dance.

KING, Donald E; Pawnee HS; Divernon, IL; 3/47 PresFrshCls; PresSophCls; HonRl; JrNHS; NHS; PresStuCncl; StuGov; FFA; LetterBsktbl; LetterFtbl; College.

KING, Donna L; St Francis De Sales HS; Chicago, IL; 40/294 HstJrCls; Chrs; CmntyWkr; HonRl; NatlMeritCmnd; SchMus; SchPl; StuCncl; TchrAde; Yrbk; PpCl; Chrldr; Univ Of Chicago; Psychology.

KING, Elizabeth M; Durand HS; Durand, WI; 27/147 AFS; PresChr; Chrs; ChrhWkr; NatlFornLg; Sdlty; SecFrCl; GAA; PresAwd; Trade School; Modeling.

KING, Frances; Mattoon Senior HS; Mattoon, IL; 60/368 Band; ChrhWkr; HonRl; HospAde; NatlFornLg; NHS; NatlThespSoc; SchAde; StuGov; TchrAde; College; Theaatrical Arrs.

KING, Gary A; Shelton HS; Shelton, NE; Chrs; ChrhWkr; LbryAde; SchPl; SctActv; FHA; FrCl; LetterTrk; Ricks College; Law.

KING, Gene R; Superior HS; Superior, NE; 10/97 Band; CmntyWkr; CncrtBnd; HonRl; MrchBnd; Orch; PepBnd; FBLA; Bsktbl; Trk; Univ; Eng.

KING, Gregg; Catholic HS; Joliet, IL; 13 JrNHS; NHS; RptrYrbk; FrCl; GerCl; Bsbl; Tennis; U Of Illinois;accounting.

KING, Heather; Homewood Flossmoor Hs; Homewood, IL; 65 AFS; ChrhWkr; HonRl; TchrAde; YthFlsp; MthCl; Hope College;medical Technology.

KING, James A; Parker HS; Janesville, WI; 1/423 ALBoysSt; HonRl; LitMag; NatlMeritCmnd; Quill&Scroll; StuCncl; TchrAde; SchPpr; LetterTrk; U Of Wi Whitewater; Med Tech.

KING, Jane E; Reddick HS; Reddick, IL; Band; Chrs; ChrhWkr; HonRl; SchPl; StuCncl; Yrbk; 4-H; FrCl; Bsktbl; Trk; Chrldr; GAA; St Marys Notre Dame; Nursing.

KING, Jeffery E; New Trier East HS; Glencoe, IL; Chr; ChrhWkr; SchMus; SchPl; CaptTrk; Univ; Bus Admin.

KING, Jeffrey O; Lincoln Comm HS; Stanwood, IA; 2/64 HonRl; NHS;.

KING, John; Carl Junction Hs; Asbury, MO; Band; HonRl; MrchBnd; SchPl; SctActv; FFA; College;farmer.

KING, John C; Edgewood HS; Bloomington, IN; 55/167 Aud/Vis; Band; Chr; ChrhWkr; CmntyWkr; CncrtBnd; HonRl; Bsbl; Bsktbl; LetterFtbl; LetterGlf; Socr; Swmmng; University; Nuclear Engineer.

KING, John W; Brown County HS; Nashville, IN; HonRl; PolWkr; Ftbl; College.

KING, Joseph B; Connersville HS; Connersville, IN; HonRl; GerCl; Bsbl; Ftbl; College; Engineering.

KING, J Steven; Bishop Mac Namara HS; Kankakee, IL; 28/162 SecTrsJrCls; ChrhWkr; CmntyWkr; HonRl; NHS; SchPl; Yrbk; KeyCl; Bsktbl; Kankakee Comm College; Computer Programer.

KING, Judith D; East Kentwood HS; Grand Rapids, MI; CtyCnl; CAP; CmntyWkr; JCC; PolWkr; RedCrAde; ROTC; StuCncl; StuGov; College; Professional.

KING, Karen D; Mills Prairie HS; Mill Shoals, IL; 1/16 PresSophCls; HonRl; SchPl; StuCncl; RptrYrbk; RptrSchPpr; FHA; Bsktbl; Chrldr; 4-HAwd; Southern Il Univ.

KING, Katherine R; Clarkston Sr HS; Clarkston, MI; 13/434 ChrhWkr; CmntyWkr; HonRl; CaptHospAde; PresNHS; VPYthFlsp; 4-H; GerCl; PPFtbl; JCAwd; Oakland Univ; Chemical Engineering.

KING, Katherine L; Harrison HS; Farmington Hills, MI; Band; CncrtBnd; HonRl; JA; MrchBnd; PepBnd; SchPl; PpCl; LetterTrk; PPFtbl; Univ Of Minnesota; Aeronautical Eng.

KING, Keith R; Dansville HS; Dansville, MI; 8/74 Band; ChrhWkr; CncrtBnd; HonRl; MrchBnd; NHS; PepBnd; TchrAde; Teen; College; Physics.

KING, Kevin D; Riverview Gardens HS; St Louis, MO; Band; CncrtBnd; HonRl; MrchBnd; NHS; Univ Of Missouri; Engineering.

KING, Kyle R; Univer Of Detroit HS; Detroit, MI; ChrhWkr; CmntyWkr; HonRl; JA; PolWkr; StuGov; LetterBsktbl; LetterTrk; CchngActv; IMSpt; University Of Michigan; Pediatrician.

KING, Laura E; Summerfield HS; Petersburg, MI; Chr; Chrs; ChrhWkr; TchrAde; SpnCl; SciCl; Clg; Engr.

KING, Laura J; Taylorville Sr HS; Taylorville, IL; 26/271 Chr; CncrtBnd; HonRl; MrchBnd; NatlThespSoc; Orch; PepBnd; SchMus; RptrSchPpr; FTA; SpnCl; LetterTennis; LetterTrk; College; Education.

KING, Lena L; Nathan Hale HS; West Allis, WI; 1/572 ALAGirlsSt; NatlMeritSF; Orch; StuGov; Yrbk; CivCl; LetterTennis; C; Music.

KING, Mary A; Northern HS; Detroit, MI; Chr; ChrhWkr; HonRl; Trade Sch; Nurse.

KING, Mary J; Pacelli HS; Stevens Point, WI; 9/110 Chrs; ChrhWkr; HonRl; SptEdYrbk; RptrSchPpr; BttyCrckrAwd; Trade; Seamstree.

KING, Mary L; Harper Creek HS; Battle Creek, MI; HonRl; JA; TchrAde; PpCl; JAAwd; Kellogg Comm Coll; W Mi U; Marine Biologist.

KING, Mary T; Harvard HS; Harvard, IL; SecTrsJrCls; Chrs; SchMus; PresSophCls; Yrbk; SpnCl; PpCl; Eastern Ill; Speech.

KING, Maureen F; Walhalla Public HS; Walhalla, ND; 14/58 Chrs; HonRl; LbryAde; TchrAde; 4-H; FBLA; GerCl; SciCl; Trk; University Of No Dakota; Spec Education.

KING, Michael J; St Joseph HS; Westchester, IL; PresFrshCls; PresSophCls; VPJrCls; PresSrCls; CmntyWkr; HonRl; NHS; PepBnd; PolWkr; Quill&Scroll; SchPl; StuCncl; StuGov; EdSchPpr; Socr; College; Real Estate Lawyer.

KING, Nancy L; Ford Central HS; Roberts, IL; 1/62 VPFrshCls; SecTrsSophCls; VPSrCls; Band; Chrs; HonRl; Mdrgl; NHS; SchPl; FHA; Ill St U; Jr High Teacher.

KING, Noma; Sparta Hs; Coulterville, IL; 8 Chrs; HonRl; NHS; SchMus; StuGov; TchrAde; YthFlsp; RptrSchPpr; SchPpr; FHA; College Siu Journalism Psychology.

KING, Nona M; Sparta HS; Coultiville, IL; 8/160 Chr; Chrs; HonRl; NHS; Quill&Scroll; SchMus; RptrSchPpr; SchPpr; FHA; University.

KING, Pamela L; Unity HS; Chicago, IL; SecFrshCls; Chr; SecFHA; University; Law.

KING, Pamela S; Clever HS; Clever, MO; 5/25 SecSophCls; VPSrCls; DrmMjrt; HonRl; PresStuCncl; TreasFBLA; SecFFA; VPFHA; Chrldr; BttyCrckrAwd; DanFAwd; 4-HAwd; Sw Missouri St Univ; Home Economics.

KING, Pam M; Lincoln HS; Wisconsin Rapids, WI; HonRl; SchPl; SctActv; SpnCl; PpCl; Chrldr; Clge; Spanish & English.

KING, Patrica; Nazareth Acad; Berwyn, IL; 8/154 Chrs; HonRl; NHS; NatlMeritCmnd; OffAde; SchMus; TchrAde; FrCl; TreasMthCl; GAA; Ill Inst Of Tech; Mechanical Engineering.

KING, Patricia A; Lamar R 1 HS; Lamar, MO; SecFrshCls; AFS; Chr; Chrs; ChrhWkr; CmntyWkr; DrlTm; NatlFornLg; OffAde; PolWkr; RedCrAde; Bsbl; Bsktbl; Swmmng; Southwest Baptist.

KING, Patrick R; Atkinson HS; Atkinson, IL; CmntyWkr; HonRl; LbryAde; Sdlty; 4-H; FFA; LetterBsktbl; LetterFtbl; LetterTrk; 4-HAwd; Blackhawk Coll.

KING, Peggy; Maconaquah HS; Grissom Afb, IN; 30/200 HonRl; MrchBnd; NHS; OffAde; StuCncl; TchrAde; 4-H; SpnCl; In Busi Col; Private Secretary.

KING, Ray H; Parkside HS; Jackson, MI; 1/410 ALBoysSt; CncrtBnd; HonRl; MrchBnd; PepBnd; SctActv; StuGov; YthFlsp; CivCl; Univ Of Michigan; Medicine.

KING, Rebecca J; Lewis Central Community HS; Council Bluffs, IA; 6/176 Chr; HonRl; NHS; SchMus; 4-H; ChmnBsktbl; Swmmng; LetterTennis; 4-HAwd; JCAwd; Creighton Univ; Pre Med.

KING, Renita; Paoli Jr Sr HS; Paoli, IN; 2/118 HonRl; NHS; SciCl; Purdue Univ; Engineering.

KING, Rhonda L; Pacific HS; Pacific, MO; Chr; HonRl; Mdrgl; NatlFornLg; VPNatlThespSoc; SchMus; SchPl; AmLegAwd; VoiceDemAwd; Univ; Theatre.

KING, Robin L; Sanilac Rd HS; Kingston, MI; ChrhWkr; HonRl; JA; SchPl; SctActv; 4-H; 4-HAwd; JAAwd; Trade Sch; Engineer.

KING, Ron W; Elmore Public HS; Elmore, MN; PresJrCls; Chr; HonRl; IntrClCncl; Mdrgl; StuCncl; YthFlsp; RptrYrbk; Yrbk; RptrSchPpr; SchPpr; Bsktbl; LetterFtbl; LetterTrk; College; Prof.

KING, Russell C; Laville HS; Lakeville, IN; ALBoysSt; Band; ChrhWkr; NHS; SptEdYrbk; Pres4-H; Ftbl; LetterTrk; Wrstlng; 4-HAwd; Indiana State U; Elem Educ.

KING, Sarah J; Galva HS; Kewanee, IL; 2/80 Band; ChrhWkr; DrlTm; HonRl; NHS; PresNatlThespSoc; Yrbk; Pres4-H; Bsktbl; GAA; DanFAwd; 4-HAwd; Univ Of Ill; Interior Design.

KING, Sharon L; Harlem HS; Loves Park, IL; 110/500 Chr; Chrl; Chrs; HonRl; SchMus; GAA; Rock Valley Jr Clge; Dental Assistant.

KING, Stephen; Vianney HS; St Louis, MO; 10/170 Chrs; HonRl; TchrAde; Trk; IMSpt; College; Bus Adm Accounting.

KING, Susan; Mccluer North HS; Florissant, MO; HonRl; JA; LbryAde; JAAwd; Florissant Valley Coll;library Science.

KING, Susan M; Thomas Jefferson Sr HS; Cedar Rapids, IA; 17/500 Band; Chr; Chrs; ChrhWkr; CncrtBnd; HonRl; LitMag; LbryAde; MrchBnd; NHS; NatlMeritSF; Orch; PepBnd; SchMus; SchPl; Univ Of Northern Iowa; Music Educ.

KING, Thomas M; Marian HS; South Bend, IN; HonRl; NHS; SchPl; SctActv; RptrSchPpr; SptEdSchPpr; Purdue Univ; Engineering.

KING, Thomas R; Winner HS; Winner, SD; 1/134 VPJrCls; ALBoysSt; CncrtBnd; NatlFornLg; SchPl; LetterBsktbl; LetterFtbl; LetterGlf; EldAwd; GovHonPrgAwd; Washington Univ; Medicine.

KING, William E; Pekin Community HS; Pekin, IL; NatlFornLg; College; Communications.

KING, William F; Bronson Sr HS; Plymouth, MI; 72/144 Chr; ChrhWkr; NatlThespSoc; SchPl; StuCncl; YthFlsp; Bsbl; Trk; IMSpt; Trade School; Carpenter.

KING, William N; Potosi Riii HS; Flat River, MO; Band; Chr; Chrl; Chrs; ChrhWkr; CncrtBnd; HonRl; LbryAde; Mdrgl; MrchBnd; LetterBsbl; LetterBsktbl; LetterFtbl; College; Professional.

KING, Yvonne; Beaumont HS; Saint Louis, MO; 6/450 HonRl; NHS; BttyCrckrAwd; CitAwd; Barnes Nursing School; Rn.

KINGERY, Cathy; Clay Central HS; Royal, IA; Band; Chr; Chrs; CmntyWkr; HonRl; PepBnd; SchPl; SchPpr; EngCl; Trk; Iowa Lakes Comm Coll; Sec.

KINGERY, Debra; Delphi Community HS; Brookston, IN; 16/132 AFS; HonRl; LbryAde; NHS; NatlMeritCmnd; PolWkr; FTA; GerCl; MthCl; SciCl; Purdue University; Professional Law.

KINGERY, Peter A; Kearney HS; Kearney, MO; ChrhWkr; HonRl; SchPl; Yrbk; RptrSchPpr; LetterBsktbl; LetterTrk; Nw Missouri St Univ; History.

KINGHORN, Bryan; Morrill HS; Morril, NE; 11/44 ALBoysSt; Band; Chrs; ChrhWkr; NHS; NatlThespSoc; SchMus; SchPpr; Univ; Horticulture.

KINGMA, Claudia S; Warsaw HS; Warsaw, MO; 11/62 SecJrCls; TrsJrCls; VPChr; HonRl; NHS; SchMus; YthFlsp; PresFHA; LetterBsbl; Chrldr; Sw Missouri St University.

KINGMA, Melody R; Kalamazoo Christian HS; Middleville, MI; Chr; ChrhWkr; HonRl; JA; NatlMeritSF; GAA; College.

KINGSBURY, Matthew P; Neillsville HS; Neilsville, WI; ChrhWkr; HonRl; NHS; StuGov; TchrAde; LetterTrk; KiwanAwd; Univ Of Wis; Phy Educ/biology.

KINGSLEY, Ann M; Marian HS; Owatonna, MN; 1/55 VPSophCls; ALAGirlsSt; Chr; Chrs; NHS; TchrAde; LatCl; MthCl; Chrldr; DARAwd; St Teresa Clge; Nursing.

KINGSLEY, Gordon A; Liberty Senior HS; Liberty, MO; AFS; ALBoysSt; ChrhWkr; HonRl; NatlFornLg; NHS; Orch; SchMus; SchPl; EdSchPpr; IMSpt; William Jewell College; Journalism.

KINGSLEY, Kathryn A; Nordonia HS; Wheatland, MO; HospAde; TchrAde; 4-H; KeyCl; PpCl; GAA; IMSpt; 4-HAwd; Coll; Stewardess.

KINGSLEY, Kristine D; Harvard HS; Harvard, IL; 21/160 AFS; Chrs; CncrtBnd; HonRl; MrchBnd; StuCncl; Yrbk; FrCl; PpCl; Chrldr; College; Math Major.

KINGSLEY, Lavonne R; Hill City HS; Swatara, MN; 9/28 PresJrCls; SecFrshCls; HonRl; StuCncl; TchrAde; EdYrBk; RptrSchPpr; PpCl; Trk; GAA; Itasca Comm Col; Clerical.

KINGSLEY, Susan C; Richwoods HS; Peoria, IL; 22/449 CmntyWkr; CaptDrlTm; HonRl; NHS; Quill&Scroll; SchMus; SchPl; RptrYrbk; EdYrBk; PpCl; U Of Missouri; Journalism.

KINGSLEY, Toni S; Elk Rapids Sr HS; Kewadin, MI; HonRl; MrchBnd; 4-H; SpnCl; Automation Mach Training Ctr; Computer Oper.

KINGSWOOD, Michael R; Ottawa HS; Ottawa, KS; 13/166 Band; ChrhWkr; CncrtBnd; HonRl; MrchBnd; NHS; PepBnd; SctActv; SpnCl; Univ.

KINKADE, Edward E; Eddyville HS; Eddyville, IA; 13/70 Band; CncrtBnd; HonRl; MrchBnd; PepBnd; SchPl; Central College; Business Admin.

KINKADE, Janet L; Fairbury Cropsey HS; Fairbury, IL; 13/100 Band; Chr; Chrs; ChrhWkr; DrlTm; HonRl; Mdrgl; MrchBnd; NHS; SchMus; SchPl; PresYthFlsp; University; Professional.

KINKADE, Polly; Ada HS; Ada, MN; 13/61 TrsFrshCls; TrsSophCls; TrsJrCls; TrsJrCls; TrsSrCls; Band; HonRl; NHS; NatlThespSoc; StuCncl; EdYrBk; St. Benedict Coll.

KINKEAD, Christina K; Westfield Washington HS; Sheridan, IN; Band; HonRl; Orch; SchMus; SchPl; Yrbk; SchPpr; GAA; IMSpt; PPFtbl; Purdue; Veterinary Med.

KINKELAAR, Michael J; St Anthony HS; Effingham, IL; 3/62 HonRl; NHS; SchPl; StuCncl; StuGov; KeyCl; Bsbl; Bsktbl; LetterGlf; Trk; Univ Of Illinois; Lawyer.

KINKOR, Roger D; S Winneshiek HS; Calmar, IA; 2/110 ALBoysSt; Chrs; ChrhWkr; CmntyWkr; HonRl; Sacrstn; SchPl; TreasStuCncl; PresGerCl; Swmmng; College.

KINLEY, Kevin C; Fairmont Public HS; Fairmont, NE; 1/29 CncrtBnd; HonRl; NHS; SchPl; StuCncl; RptrSchPpr; SciCl; CaptLetterTrk; PresAwd; West Point; Politician.

KINLEY, Margaret; Cardinal Ritter HS; Indianapolis, IN; 1/152 HonRl; NHS; NatlMeritCmnd; Quill&Scroll; SchMus; StuCncl; EdSchPpr; PpCl; Butler Univ; Journalism.

KINLUND, Kurt K; Logan View HS; Hooper, NE; PresFrshCls; VPSrCls; Band; Chrs; CncrtBnd; HonRl; Mdrgl; MrchBnd; PepBnd; PresStuCncl; LetterFtbl; Wrstlng; University Of Nebraska; Biology.

KINNANDER, Arden; Armstrong Comm HS; Armstrong, IA; 6/27 VPFrshCls; PresSrCls; Chr; ChrhWkr; HonRl; StuCncl; TchrAde; 4-H; FFA; IMSpt; Iowa Lakes Community College; Vocational.

KINNARD, Lisa J; Estherville HS; Estherville, IA; SecSrCls; Band; Chrs; DrlTm; HonRl; HospAde; MrchBnd; NHS; SchPl; StuCncl; Teen; RptrYrbk; SpnCl; Sioux Valley Hosp; X Ray.

KINNCY, Jane M; Glenwood HS; Glenwood, MN; 1/150 Band; CncrtBnd; HonRl; NatlFornLg; StuCncl; EdYrBk; RptrSchPpr; FNA; GerCl; PPFtbl; College; Obstetrician.

KINNE, Patrick K; Leland HS; Leland, IL; 7/42 VPJrCls; ALBoysSt; Band; CncrtBnd; HonRl; NHS; SchPl; StuCncl; SpnCl; Bsktbl; CaptGlf; University; Engineering.

KINNETT, Terry R; New Palestine HS; Greenfield, IN; 23/148 HonRl; NHS; Yrbk; EdSchPpr; LatCl; Indiana Central Univ; Medical Technology.

KINNEY, Brenda L; South Shore HS; Port Wing, WI; VPJrCls; Band; Chr; Chrs; HonRl; MrchBnd; SchPpr; 4-H; Trk; Clge; Med.

KINNEY, Cheryl; Millington HS; Millington, MI; 11/180 PresSrCls; ChrhWkr; HonRl; NHS; StuCncl; YthFlsp; FrCl; AmLegAwd; GovHonPrgAwd; Bethel Coll; Bus Management.

KINNEY, David R; La Ville HS; Plymouth, IN; 14/164 Band; CncrtBnd; MrchBnd; NHS; SchMus; RptrYrbk; FrCl; SciCl; LetterGlf; IMSpt; Purude Univ; Pharmacy.

KINNEY, Dick J; Spalding HS; Hospers, IA; 5/49 TrsFrshCls; TrsJrCls; Chrs; ChrhWkr; HonRl; OffAde; SchPl; MthCl; Bsbl; College; Psychology.

KINNEY, Edward V; J E Murphy HS; Hurley, WI; 5/120 ALBoysSt; Band; HonRl; NatlMeritSF; StuCncl; YthFlsp; 4-H; LetterFtbl; LetterTrk; LetterWrstlng; IMSpt; 4-HAwd; College.

KINNEY, Jo E; Riverdale Sr HS; Blue River, WI; 15/80 ALAGirlsSt; Band; Chrs; HonRl; Mdrgl; NHS; RptrYrbk; FHA; LetterBsbl; DARAwd; College; Professional.

KINNEY, Mary C; Elizabeth Seton HS; Chicago, IL; HonRl; Orch; SchPl; StuGov; FrCl; PpCl; Clge.

KINNEY, Michael D; Norfolk Sr HS; Norfolk, NE; Band; LetterBsktbl; LetterFtbl;.

KINNEY, Patrick; St Joseph HS; St Joseph, MI; GerCl; MthCl; Notre Dame; Pre Law.

KINNEY, Richard J; Spalding HS; Hospers, IA; 5/49 TrsFrshCls; TrsJrCls; Chrs; ChrhWkr; HonRl; OffAde; SchPl; MthCl; CaptBsbl; LetterBsktbl; Clge; Psychology.

KINNEY, Richard M; St Joseph Senior HS; Saint Joseph, MI; PresSophCls; PresJrCls; PresIntrClCncl; NHS; PresStuCncl; FrCl; MthCl; SciCl; LetterTennis; IMSpt; College; Law.

KINNEY, Sandra G; Crothersville HS; Crothersville, IN; 8/75 VPFrshCls; SecJrCls; Chr; HonRl; SchPl; FHA; Chrldr; Bus School.

KINNEY, Teresa L; Heelan HS; Sioux City, IA; CmntyWkr; HonRl; StuCncl; PpCl; Chrldr; Clge; Pro.

KINNICK, Ronald C; Neillsville Public HS; Neillsville, WI; Aud/Vis; NHS; TchrAde; RptrSchPpr; EdSchPpr; 4-H; FBLA; FTA; SpnCl; LetterFtbl; Trade School; Auto Mechanics.

KINNISON, Jennifer K; Zalma HS; Arab, MO; TrsFrshCls; HonRl; VPStuCncl; PresFHA; PpCl; Semo State College; Lab Technologist.

KINNUNEN, Daniel R; Grand Rapids HS; Grand Rapids, MN; 7/370 CncrtBnd; MrchBnd; NatlMeritCmnd; PepBnd; SchMus; Univ Of Minnesota; Engineering.

KINOL, Karrie L; Willowbrook HS; Villa Park, IL; 1/800 Chr; HonRl; NatlMeritSF; NatlThespSoc; SchMus; SchPl; Oberlin College; Law.

KINOWSKI, David; Cotter HS; Winona, MN; 2/106 Band; ChrhWkr; HonRl; NHS; StuCncl; EdYrBk; RptrSchPpr; St Marys Col; Natural Science.

KINSCHERFF, Richard P; Griffin HS; Springfield, IL; HonRl; SchPl; StuGov; RptrSchPpr; Ftbl; Univ.

KINSELLA, Jane; Sault Area HS; Sault Ste Marie, MI; 16/356 Chr; DrlTm; HonRl; Mdrgl; NHS; NatlThespSoc; ROTC; SchMus; AmLegAwd; VFWAwd; Norther Mi U; Nurse.

KINSELLA, Jane M; Wahlert HS; Dubuque, IA; 33/450 CmntyWkr; HonRl; JA; NHS; RedCrAde; SchAde; TchrAde; 4-H; FNA; CitAwd; College; Nurse.

KINSELLA, Mary A; Lincoln Way HS; Manhattan, IL; 2/498 HonRl; JrNHS; NHS; OffAde; MthCl; Univ; Med.

KINSER, Michael J; Greenfield HS; Greenfield, IL; 52/75 CmntyWkr; StuCncl; StuGov; 4-H; MthCl; LetterFtbl; IMSpt; DanFAwd; 4-HAwd; College; Agriculture.

KINSER, Stephen; Hugoton HS; Hugoton, KS; Chr; Chrs; SchMus; 4-H; Bsktbl; Ftbl; Trk; Friends Bible College;.

KINSEY, Daniel B; Garrett HS; Garrett, IN; 40/140 HonRl; NatlThespSoc; SchMus; SchPl; YthFlsp; Bsktbl; Glf; Manchester College; Marketing.

KINSEY, Karen; Edison Senior HS; East Gary, IN; 50/179 SecJrCls; ALAGirlsSt; DrlTm; Twrl; RptrYrbk; EdYrBk; FrCl; PpCl; Chrldr; IMSpt; Bryman Careers Inst; Dental Asst Or Hygiens.

KINSLEY, Jodi L; Westside HS; Omaha, NE; Chr; CmntyWkr; Sdlty; GerCl; PpCl; Chrldr; GAA; Col; Social Worker.

KINSLOW, Leona K; Seneca HS; Joplin, MO; AFS; HonRl; FrCl; SpnCl; PpCl; College.

KINTIGH, Robert L; Concord HS; Concord, MI; 3/71 ChrhWkr; CncrtBnd; HonRl; MrchBnd; PresNHS; PresStuCncl; Spring Ardoor Col ;med.

KINTNER, Cathrin L; Oblong HS; Oblong, IL; 14/72 PresBand; SecChrs; HonRl; StuCncl; RptrYrbk; RptrSchPpr; LatCl; GAA; Indiana State Univ; Nurse.

KINTNER, Gail M; Oblong HS; Oblong, IL; 4/72 Chr; HonRl; NHS; StuCncl; YthFlsp; RptrYrbk; RptrSchPpr; LatCl; Indiana State Univ; Music.

KINTZ, Christina M; St Josephs HS; South Bend, IN; Chr; HonRl; Ball State Univ; Architecture.

KINTZELE, Judith; Marquette HS; Michigan City, IN; ChrhWkr; HonRl; HospAde; JA; PolWkr; SchMus; Swmmng; Purdue; Accountant.

KINYOUN, Judith A; Superior HS; Superior, NE; TrsJrCls; ALAGirlsSt; HonRl; StuCncl; FBLA; U Of Nebraska; Nursing.

KINZEL, Cindi L; Rf Senior HS; River Falls, WI; 57/192 Chr; HonRl; StuCncl; EdYrBk; Yrbk; FTA; GerCl; PpCl; Swmmng; Trk; CaptChrldr; GAA; IMSpt; College; Nurse.

KINZEY, Becky S; Sweet Springs HS; Sweet Springs, MO; PresHospAde; SchAde; FHA; PpCl; St Lukes School; Rn.

KINZINGER, Randall D; New Athens Unit Dist #60 HS; New Athens, IL; 12/65 Band; CncrtBnd; HonRl; MrchBnd; NHS; PepBnd; YthFlsp; Parks Air College; Agriculture.

KINZLER, Cynthia M; Williamsburg Community HS; Williamsburg, IA; 12/94 VPFrshCls; Band; Chrs; HonRl; NHS; NatlThespSoc; Quill&Scroll; SchPl; GerCl; KiwanAwd; American Inst Of Bus; Medical Secretary.

KINZLER, Donald J; Lisbon HS; Lisbon, ND; 1/76 ChrhWkr; HonRl; SecCollege; Horticulture.

KIOSKI, Mary; Farwell Area HS; Lake, MI; 2/94 Chr; HonRl; JrNHS; NatlFornLg; NHS; NatlThespSoc; SchMus; RptrYrbk; BttyCrckrAwd; Central Mi Univ; Bfa In Theatre.

KIPER, Kevin J; Bloomington HS; Bloomington, IL; 35/391 NHS; NatlMeritCmnd; NatlThespSoc; SchPl; StuCncl; TchrAde; TreasLatCl; MthCl; PressSciCl; Bsktbl; Ftbl; Univ Of Chicago; Physics.

KIPFER, Scott D; Leo HS; Grabill, IN; Ftbl; Trk; Wrstlng;.

KIPP, Janet; Alma HS; Alma, MI; 100/266 ChrhWkr; OffAde; SchAde; TchrAde; Spring Arbor College; Psychology.

KIPP, Paul; Annawan HS; Annawan, IL; Chrs; HonRl; 4-H; FFA; SpnCl; University; Computer Programmer.

KIPPER, Richard G; Eisenhower HS; Decatur, IL; 1/300 AFS; TreasNHS; NatlMeritCmnd; StuCncl; EdYrBk; LetterFtbl; Glf; Tennis; BauchLmbAwd; College; Law.

KIPPES, Nita D; St Xavier HS; Junction City, KS; 1/30 TrsSrCls; HonRl; RptrYrbk; FHA; Col; Architecture.

KIRALY, Thomas E; Edison Sr Hs HS; East Gary, IN; ALBoysSt; HonRl; PresJrNHS; PresNHS; Bsktbl; LetterTrk; College; Engineering.

KIRBY, Deborah A; Maine Twsp East HS; Niles, IL; TrsSrCls; ChrhWkr; HonRl; StuCncl; IMSpt; Il St U; Mass Communications.

KIRBY, Judy; Jefferson Community HS; Jefferson, IA; 20/115 Band; Chr; Chrs; DrmMjrt; HonRl; NHS; Quill&Scroll; RptrYrbk; RptrSchPpr; 4-HAwd; Northwest Missouri State Univ; Elementary E.

KIRBY, Michael J; Herrin HS; Herrin, IL; 16/218 Band; ChrhWkr; CmntyWkr; CncrtBnd; HonRl; NatlMeritCmnd; SctActv; VPStuCncl; RptrYrbk; 4-H; KeyCl; Bsktbl; Univ Of Ill; Geology.

KIRBY, Nancy E; Zinn County R 4 HS; Linneus, MO; Chrs; ChrhWkr; HonRl; NHS; SchMus; FHA; LionAwd; Univ Of Mo Columbia; Teacher.

KIRBY, Renee E; Greenfield HS; Rockbridge, IL; Band; Chrs; HonRl; Mdrgl; PepBnd; SchMus; RptrYrbk; EdSchPpr; GAA; University.

KIRBY, Sara L; Mac Arthur HS; Decatur, IL; 11/410 Chr; HospAde; NHS; Orch; SctActv; StuCncl; RptrYrbk; RptrSchPpr; SpnCl; Univ Of Ill; Science.

KIRBY, Susan M; Herrin HS; Herrin, IL; Band; Chr; Chrs; ChrhWkr; CmntyWkr; DrlTm; SctActv; RptrSchPpr; 4-H; FHA; Bsbl; College; Home Economics.

KIRBY, Terry F; Fremont HS; Fremont, NE; CmntyWkr; SctActv; Ftbl; IMSpt; PresAwd; Trade; Pro.

KIRBY, Vickie S; Jennings County HS; Butlerville, IN; ChrhWkr; HonRl; NHS; RptrSchPpr; LatCl; College; Journalism.

KIRCHBERG, Patrick A; Wauwatosa East HS; Wauwatosa, WI; NatlMeritSF;.

KIRCHBERL, Pamela S; Madison HS; Madison, MN; TrsSophCls; AFS; HonRl; TchrAde; PpCl; FHA; GAA; IMSpt; PPFtbl; Coll; Teacher.

KIRCHER, Joi; West Sioux Community HS; Hawarden, IA; Band; Chrs; ChrhWkr; CncrtBnd; HonRl; LbryAde; MrchBnd; SchMus; SchPl; Twrl; Nursing Sch; Rn.

KIRCHER, Linda D; Stephen Decatur HS; Decatur, IL; 10/476 AFS; Chr; HonRl; NHS; SchMus; EdYrBk; PresFrCl; PpCl; Univ Of Illinois; Social Welfare.

KIRCHER, Sherry L; Harrisonville Sr HS; Harrisonville, MO; 21/163 Band; CncrtBnd; HonRl; MrchBnd; NatlFornLg; Quill&Scroll; SchPl; Twrl; YthFlsp; Yrbk; RptrSchPpr; 4-H; Chrldr; College; Speech.

KIRCHHOFER, Belinda S; Stewardson Strasburg HS; Shumway, IL; VPJrCls; Chrs; FHA; PpCl; Marriage.

KIRCHHOFF, Connie L; Sumner Community HS; Sumner, IA; 12/81 Band; Chrs; CncrtBnd; HonRl; MrchBnd; NHS; SchMus; SecFHA; U Of Northern Ia; Music Ed.

KIRCHHOFF, David L; Lake Central HS; Dyer, IN; 31/450 HonRl; JrNHS; NHS; OffAde; YthFlsp; Purdue Univ; Computer Tech.

KIRCHHOFF, Gregory F; Gibbon Community HS; Gibbon, MN; PresSophCls; TrsJrCls; TrsSrCls; Band; Chrs; CncrtBnd; Mdrgl; MrchBnd; PepBnd; StuGov; Bsktbl; Wrstlng; College; Business Administration.

KIRCHHOFF, Steve P; Smith Center HS; Cedar, KS; 4/63 ChrhWkr; HonRl; PresNHS; StuCncl; Pres4-H; LetterGlf; Kansas State Univ; Engineering.

KIRCHNER, Ann M; Highland Comm HS; Riverside, IA; 3/54 Band; Chr; Chrs; ChrhWkr; CncrtBnd; HonRl; Mdrgl; MrchBnd; PepBnd; PolWkr; SchMus; SchPl; YthFlsp; SpnCl; College; Accounting.

KIRCHNER, Cynthia M; Coon Rapids HS; Blaine, MN; Chr; HonRl; JrNHS; NHS; College; Accounting.

KIRCHNER, David L; Staunton HS; Brazil, IN; 1/56 PresFrshCls; Band; CncrtBnd; HonRl; MrchBnd; NHS; Bsbl; Bsktbl; CchngActv; Indiana U; Accountant.

KIRCHNER, Lisa A; Chandlerville HS; Virginia, IL; 1/20 SecBand; Chrs; ChrhWkr; HonRl; NHS; Yrbk; SchPpr; PresFHA; Chrldr; CchngActv; 4-HAwd; College; Mathematics.

KIRCHNER, Randal F; St Edmond HS; Fort Dodge, IA; ChrhWkr; HonRl; NHS; SctActv; SpnCl; Ftbl; LetterGlf; University.

KIRCHNER, Renita R; Central Community HS; Donnellson, IA; HonRl; College; Secretary.

KIRCHOFF, Cynthia A; Stewart Public HS; Stewart, MN; Band; HonRl; SchPl; StuCncl; TchrAde; RptrSchPpr; EdSchPpr; FHA; PpCl; GAA; St Cloud State Clg; Mass Communications.

KIRCHOFF, Donna J; Duchesne HS; St Charles, MO; 3/136 PresBand; Chrs; CncrtBnd; HonRl; MrchBnd; NHS; NatlMeritCmnd; PepBnd; PolWkr; SchMus; Northeast Mo; Special Ed.

KIRCHOFF, Pamela S; Monmouth HS; Monmouth, IL; 4/143 HonRl; JrNHS; NHS; StuCncl; SecSpnCl; TreasPpCl; CaptBsktbl; Glf; CaptTrk; PresGAA; EldAwd; Univ Of Iowa; Nurse.

KIRCHOFF, Victoria A; Granite City So HS; Granite City, IL; 21/630 Band; CncrtBnd; LitMag; MrchBnd; NHS; Quill&Scroll; SchPl; Northwestern Univ; Journalism.

KIRICK, George R; Oklee Public HS; Trail, MN; TrsSrCls; ChrhWkr; HonRl; SctActv; GerCl; SciCl; Vocational Tech Inst; Mechanics.

KIRK, Barry S; Galesburg Augusta HS; Galesburg, MI; 11/126 PresJrCls; PresSrCls; HonRl; NHS; StuCncl; TchrAde; SptEdYrbk; Ftbl; Tennis; CaptWrstlng; U Of N Ia; Bus Manager.

KIRK, Franklin R; Sauk Prairie HS; Prairie Du Sac, WI; PresSrCls; ALBoysSt; Aud/Vis; HonRl; NHS; Sacrstn; StuGov; TchrAde; OptClAwd; Loras College; Law.

KIRK, Judy N; Dearborn HS; Dearborn, MI; AFS; HonRl; JA; NHS; NatlMeritFnl; NatlThespSoc; SchMus; SchPl; FrCl; BttyCrckrAwd; Eastern Mich Univ; Home Ed Educ.

KIRK, Linda; Waupaca HS; Waupaca, WI; AFS; Band; ChrhWkr; CncrtBnd; HonRl; MrchBnd; PepBnd; SctActv; FHA; PpCl; Uw Stevens Point; Home Ec.

KIRK, Mary; Sabetha HS; Sabetha, KS; 34/78 CncrtBnd; HonRl; PepBnd; SctActv; StuCncl; SchPpr; FHA; PpCl; Washburn Univ; Comm.

KIRK, Nancy V; Rockford East HS; Rockford, IL; 6/665 HonRl; JA; LbryAde; NHS; NatlMeritCmnd; ChmbCommrsAwd; College; Business.

KIRK, Rose; Mt Pulaski HS; Mt Pulaski, IL; 39/105 HonRl; 4-H; GerCl; GAA; 4-HAwd; Illinois State Univ; Health Education.

KIRK, Teri; Maquoketa Community Hs; Maquoketa, IA; ALAGirlsSt; Band; Chrs; CmntyWkr; 4-H; FBLA; LetterBsbl; CaptBsktbl; Trade School; Secretarial.

KIRK, Timothy R; Riverside Brookfield HS; La Grange Park, IL; De Paul University; Accounting.

KIRKENDALL, Deborah L; Falls City HS; Falls City, NE; Chrs; ChrhWkr; OffAde; SchMus; TchrAde; YthFlsp; GerCl; Trk; GAA; IMSpt; Business School; Secretary.

KIRKES, Bryan B; Green Way HS; Bovey, MN; CmntyWkr; HonRl; PpCl; Bsktbl; IMSpt; Univ Of Minnesota; Law.

KIRKLAND, Eric L; Cass Tech HS; Detroit, MI; TreasChr; HonRl; PresStuCncl; Univ; Architectural Engineer.

KIRKLAND, Robert K; Liberty Sr HS; Liberty, MO; 2/281 PresJrNHS; NatlFornLg; PresNHS; SchMus; SctActv; StuCncl; Yrbk; Bsbl; Bsktbl; LetterTennis; IMSpt; GodCntryAwd; CitAwd; College; Law.

KIRKPATRICK, Donna M; Palco HS; Palco, KS; Chrl; ChrhWkr; HonRl; OffAde; EdYrBk; SchPpr; Tennis; Chrldr; MasAwd; CitAwd; Ft Hays Ks Col; Law Enforcement.

KIRKPATRICK, Dorothy A; Univ Lake HS; Oconomowoc, WI; 4/22 Chrs; EngCl; SpnCl; MthCl; College; Flower Shop Owner.

KIRKPATRICK, Kathryn J; Dundee Com HS; Carpentersville, IL; 17/364 Band; CncrtBnd; HonRl; MrchBnd; NHS; NatlMeritCmnd; PepBnd; 4-H; SpnCl; SciCl; College; Illustration Grafic Design.

KIRKPATRICK, Kathryn J; Jennings HS; Jennings, MO; Chr; HonRl; NHS; FHA; EngCl; PpCl; Tennis; GAA; IMSpt; PresAwd; Col; Special Education.

KIRKPATRICK, Mary E; English Valley HS; North English, IA; 3/60 Chrs; ChrhWkr; DrlTm; HonRl; NHS; SctActv; TchrAde; PresYthFlsp; EdSchPpr; FTA; Vennard Clg; Bible Major.

KIRKPATRICK, Mary L; Fountain Central HS; Wingate, IN; 10/128 ALAGirlsSt; Band; HonRl; NHS; SctActv; TchrAde; RptrYrbk; 4-H; PpCl; Purdue University; Elementary Education.

KIRKTON, Rick L; Gridley Comm HS; Gridley, IL; PresFrshCls; PresSophCls; PresNHS; SchPl; StuCncl; SptEdYrbk; PresFFA; KeyCl; LetterBsbl; LetterBsktbl; College; Business.

KIRKUS, Denise; Mt Vernon HS; Mount Vernon, SD; ALAGirlsSt; Band; Chrs; CncrtBnd; HonRl; MrchBnd; NHS; PepBnd; SchPl; PpCl; Vocational School; Lab Technician.

KIRKWOOD, George R; Lane Tech HS; Chicago, IL; 175/1200 JA; SchAde; LatCl; Socr; Tennis; AmLegAwd; College; Business Law.

KIRKWOOD, John S; De La Salle Institute HS; Chicago, IL; 50/271 ChrhWkr; HonRl; Bsktbl; IMSpt; Western Ill Univ; Accounting.

KIRKWOOD, Sharon L; Marillac HS; Mt Prospect, IL; Band; MrchBnd; Orch; SchMus; SchPl; RptrYrbk; Yrbk; College; Music.

KIRLEY, Tim J; Catholic Memorial HS; Pewaukee, WI; SctActv; RptrYrbk; SptEdYrbk; Bsbl; Bsktbl; Ftbl; Trk; College; Electrical Engr.

KIRN, Dean F; Cape Central 'S; Cape Girardeau, MO; 44/440 ALBoysSt; HonRl; JA; NHS; LetterBsktbl; LetterFtbl; CchngActv; College; Professional.

KIRN, Jonathan; Brookfield East HS; Brookfield, WI; Band; Chrs; HonRl; StuCncl; KeyCl; LatCl; MthCl; LetterTrk; College.

KIRSCH, Cynthia F; Antigo HS; Antigo, WI; 10/363 LatCl; MthCl; St Joseph S School Of Radiology; Radiologis.

KIRSCH, James D; Dickinson HS; Gladstone, ND; 20/189 ChrhWkr; HonRl; YthFlsp; 4-H; FFA; College; Vet.

KIRSCH, Janice A; Fatima HS; Loose Creek, MO; Chr; ChrhWkr; HonRl; NHS; CivCl; FBLA; FHA; SpnCl; College; Secretarial.

KIRSCH, Thomas D; Burke HS; Omaha, NE; HonRl; NatlMeritCmnd; SctActv; EdYrBk; CaptSocr; Creighton University.

KIRSCHLING, Jane M; Assumption HS; Wisc Rapids, WI; Band; Chrs; CncrtBnd; DrmBgl; HonRl; SchMus; SctActv; StuCncl; FrCl; VoiceDemAwd; Coll; Major Study.

KIRSCHMAN, Cindy M; Glenham HS; Glenham, SD; SecTrsJrCls; Chr; Chrs; HonRl; PepBnd; SchPl; RptrSchPpr; College; X Ray Tech.

KIRST, John; Osage Community HS; Osage, IA; 13/154 VPSrCls; ChrhWkr; HonRl; NHS; NatlMeritFnl; NatlMeritCmnd; NatlMeritSF; GerCl; Univ; Farm Operation.

KIRWIN, Wayne C; Walkerville HS; Walkerville, MI; 6/27 PresFrshCls; VPSophCls; PresJrCls; PresSrCls; HonRl; TchrAde; SptEdYrbk; RptrSchPpr; CaptBsbl; CaptBsktbl; Trk; CaptIMSpt; EldAwd; Olivet College; Business Mgmt.

KIS, Sandra; Washington Park HS; Racine, WI; 10/579 HonRl; Quill&Scroll; TchrAde; Yrbk; PpCl; IMSpt; Marquette Univ; Registered Nurse.

KISH, Barbara A; George Rogers Clark HS; Whiting, IN; 48/280 ChrhWkr; TreasJA; MrchBnd; PepBnd; YthFlsp; GerCl; SciCl; College; Vet.

KISH, Bernadette; Schulte HS; Terre Haute, IN; HonRl; SecStuCncl; RptrYrbk; Swmmng; PresGAA; Indiana State Univ; Architecture.

KISH, David; Lakeview HS; St Clair Shores, MI; HonRl; NHS; NatlMeritSchl; PpCl; Wayne St Univ; Busi Adm.

KISH, Mary; Gibault HS; Columbia, IL; PresJrCls; Chrl; Chrs; NatlMeritCmnd; SchMus; SchPl; StuCncl; RptrSchPpr; FrCl; SpnCl; College; Singer.

KISH, Victoria J; Truman HS; Independence, MO; 24/603 HonRl; PresJA; JrNHS; LbryAde; NHS; Orch; SchMus; SpnCl; SciCl; Univ Of Missouri; Marine Biology.

KISNER, John W; Regina HS; Iowa City, IA; 7/47 CmntyWkr; HonRl; NHS; RptrYrbk; SptEdSchPpr; LetterBsbl; Cornell Coll; Journalism.

KISSANE, Barbara E; Barrington HS; Barrington, IL; Band; Chrs; HonRl; HospAde; NHS; NatlMeritFnl; StuGov; Yrbk; RptrSchPpr; FNA; SpnCl; Loyola Univ; Nursing.

KISSANE, Sherry; Ithaca Hs; Ithaca, MI; Chr; ChrhWkr; HonRl; OffAde; SchMus; SchPl; YthFlsp; 4-H; FHA; PpCl; Business School; Business Management.

KISSE, Lauren F; Halliday Public HS; Halliday, ND; Band; VPChrs; CncrtBnd; DrmMjrt; HonRl; MrchBnd; NHS; PepBnd; SchPl; RptrYrbk; Bsktbl; Chrldr; GAA; 4-HAwd; College; Professional.

KISSE, Shereen L; Halliday Public HS; Halliday, ND; 5/31 Band; Chrs; CncrtBnd; HonRl; SchPl; EdYrBk; FHA; LetterBsktbl; Trk; Chrldr; Bismarck Jr Coll; Business.

KISSEE, Kathy S; Logan Rogersville HS; Rogersville, MO; 41/109 Band; Chr; Chrs; ChrhWkr; CncrtBnd; HonRl; MrchBnd; FBLA; FHA; PpCl; Business School; Sec Science.

KISSEE, Tom W; Greenwood HS; Springfield, MO; PresSrCls; Band; Chr; Chrs; HonRl; StuCncl; 4-H; LatCl; LetterBsktbl; LetterFtbl; College.

KISSEL, Debbie; Protection HS; Protection, KS; Chr; Chrs; CmntyWkr; HonRl; SchMus; OffAde; 4-H; PpCl; Coll; Secretary.

KISSEL, Glen J; Protection HS; Protection, KS; 1/22 PresSrCls; Band; HonRl; NatlMeritCmnd; SchMus; Yrbk; 4-H; GerCl; LetterTrk; 4-HAwd; Ok St Univ; Aerospace Engineering.

KISSEL, Kathy A; Gibson Southern HS; Fort Branch, IN; Chrs; ChrhWkr; RptrYrbk; 4-H; LatCl; DanFAwd; Indiana Univ; Library Science.

KISSELL, Brian D; Moberly HS; Moberly, MO; Band; Chr; MrchBnd; OffAde; SchMus; SchPl; SctActv; Bsktbl; Ftbl; Moberly Jr Coll; Law Enforcement.

KISSINGER, Cindy L; Hiawatha HS; Hiawatha, KS; 21/83 ALAGirlsSt; Band; ChrhWkr; CncrtBnd; HonRl; MrchBnd; OffAde; ROTC; SctActv; TchrAde; YthFlsp; PpCl; CaptBsktbl; Trk; University; Airline Stewardess.

KISSINGER, James G; St Pius X HS; Kansas City, MO; 16/138 HonRl; NHS; RptrSchPpr; PpCl; Bsktbl; LetterFtbl; Trk; LetterWrstlng; Univ Of Missouri; Internatl Business.

KISSINGER, Margaret; Regina Dominican HS; Wilmette, IL; 40/210 VPFrshCls; HstJrCls; CmntyWkr; HonRl; PolWkr; Quill&Scroll; SchPl; Sdlty; StuCncl; StuGov; De Pauw Univ; Professional.

KISSIRE, Barbara; Grove HS; Southwest City, MO; Chrs; HonRl; TchrAde; FHA; FrCl; SpnCl; Bsktbl;.

KISSLER, John M; Ralston HS; Omaha, NE; Band; ChrhWkr; CncrtBnd; LbryAde; MrchBnd; PepBnd; SchMus; Coll; Music.

KISSLINGER, Kristi R; Larned Senior HS; Larned, KS; ChrhWkr; HonRl; SchAde; StuCncl; PpCl; LetterGlf; LetterTrk; GAA; PPFtbl; PresAwd; College; Math.

KIST, Larry F; St Pius X HS; Festus, MO; 41/100 ALBoysSt; HonRl; Bsktbl; CaptFtbl; Trk; IMSpt; Coll; Professional.

KISTHARD, James A; Fulton Comm HS; Fulton, IL; Band; Chr; Chrs; CncrtBnd; Mdrgl; MrchBnd; PepBnd; College; Professional.

KISTNER, Cynthia L; Lakeview HS; St Clairs Shores, MI; TrsSophCls; VPSrCls; Chr; HonRl; NHS; PolWkr; StuCncl; StuGov; PpCl; ChmnSwmmng; College; Teacher.

KISZONAS, Anthony; Goodman Armstrong HS; Armstrong Creek, WI; 2/36 PresFrshCls; Band; CncrtBnd; HonRl; MrchBnd; NHS; PepBnd; SpnCl; LetterBsktbl; Ftbl; Univ; Pro.

KITA, Mark S; D C Everest HS; Schofield, WI; 1/340 VPFrshCls; ALBoysSt; Band; Chr; CncrtBnd; HonRl; MrchBnd; NHS; NatlMeritFnl; NatlThespSoc; SchMus; IMSpt; Marquette Univ; Medicine.

KITA, Richard F; Hubbard HS; Chicago, IL; 18/400 Aud/Vis; Band; HonRl; NHS; OffAde; SchPpr; MthCl; Loyola Univ; Medicine.

KITCH, Gayland D; Buhler HS; Hutchinson, KS; Band; CncrtBnd; HonRl; MrchBnd; ModUN; PepBnd; Trk; Hutchison Juco; Architecture.

KITCHEL, Karen E; Holt HS; Holt, MI; 7/270 HonRl; NHS; SchPl; KeyCl; PresSpnCl; PpCl; CaptChrldr; Kalamazoo Coll; Social Science.

KITCHELL, Richard J; Palestine HS; Palestine, IL; 9/47 SecJrCls; Band; Chrl; Chrs; ChrhWkr; CncrtBnd; HonRl; MrchBnd; Orch; PepBnd; Bsbl; CaptBsktbl; IMSpt; College; Business.

KITCHEN, Roger L; Millington HS; Millington, MI; 50/170 Band; CncrtBnd; HonRl; MrchBnd; PepBnd; SchPl; TchrAde; Univ; Gerneral Study.

KITCHEN, Stephen A; Roosevelt HS; Des Moines, IA; ChrhWkr; HonRl; SchMus; SctActv; YthFlsp; LetterSwmmng; GodCntryAwd; CitAwd; Iowa State Univ; Architecture.

KITCHENS, Beatrice K; Paxton HS; Paxton, IL; SecSophCls; SecJrCls; Chr; HonRl; NHS; NatlThespSoc; EdYrBk; Chrldr; GAA; IMSpt; College; Mathematics Or Biology.

KITKOWSKI, Jayne; Wabeno HS; Wabeno, WI; 2/33 SecFrshCls; PresJrCls; Chr; ChrhWkr; HonRl; SecStuCncl; Yrbk; CaptBsktbl; Chrldr; College; Public Accountant.

KITLEY, Lillie B; New Palestine HS; New Palestine, IN; 4/135 Chr; NHS; NatlThespSoc; SchMus; EdYrBk; 4-H; SpnCl; LetterBsktbl; LetterTennis; DARAwd; Taylor Univ; Medical Tech.

KITNER, Melody; La Porte City HS; La Porte City, IA; Chr; Chrs; HonRl; 4-H; PpCl; Chrldr; 4-HAwd; Coll; Occupational Therapy.

KITOWSKI, Mary; Marquette HS; Michigan City, IN; 4/60 ALAGirlsSt; HonRl; LbryAde; NHS; PolWkr; Quill&Scroll; StuCncl; EdSchPpr; BttyCrcKrAwd; Ind Univ; Urban Planning.

KITSON, Mary D; Belleville Township East HS; Fairview Hts, IL; 42/674 HonRl; JrNHS; NHS; OffAde; Orch; TchrAde; FHA; Nursing Sch; Nurse.

KITSON, Michael A; Goshen HS; Goshen, IN; PpCl; VPJrCls; LetterTrk; IMSpt; Coll; Accounting.

KITT, Polly K; Anderson HS; Anderson, IN; 13/615 ChrhWkr; CmntyWkr; HonRl; HospAde; JrNHS; LitMag; LbryAde; NHS; Quill&Scroll; FTA; Ball St Univ; Elementary Ed.

KITTELSON, Cary D; Veiva Public HS; Veiva, ND; PresSophCls; Band; Chr; Chrs; CncrtBnd; HonRl; NHS; Bsbl; Ftbl; College.

KITTELSON, Cynthia K; Watertown HS; Watertown, SD; 8/297 Chrs; HonRl; NHS; PolWkr; Quill&Scroll; SecStuCncl; SchPpr; VPFBLA; LetterTrk; LetterChrldr; PresAwd; College; Secretary.

KITTELSON, Joseph C; Mcintosh HS; Mcintosh, SD; 10/29 ALBoysSt; Band; Chr; Chrs; ChrhWkr; CmntyWkr; CncrtBnd; DrmBgl; MrchBnd; PepBnd; PolWkr; University; Professional.

KITTELSON, Marvin J; Northwestern HS; Wentworth, WI; 15/115 PresFrshCls; PresJrCls; ALBoysSt; Band; StuCncl; LetterFtbl; LetterTrk; College.

KITTELSON, Steven T; Stoughton HS; Stoughton, WI; HonRl; TchrAde; YthFlsp; RptrSchPpr; SpnCl; Bsbl; Bsktbl; Ftbl; IMSpt; Tech Schl & Univ; Law Enforcement.

KITTERMAN, Patricia A; East Carter Co R Ii HS; Grandin, MO; SecTrsSophCls; SecJrCls; CncrtBnd; HonRl; StuCncl; TchrAde; RptrYrbk; EdYrBk; FHA; Chrldr; Three River Jr Coll; Med Asst.

KITTLE, Kathleen M; Dominican HS; Grosse Pte Pk, MI; PresSrCls; SchPl; StuCncl; StuGov; Yrbk; Swmmng; Michigan State University; Nursing.

KITTLESON, David; Maquoketa Valley HS; Earlville, IA; SecTrsJrCls; ALBoysSt; Band; NHS; SchMus; SctActv; StuCncl; College; Professional.

KITTLESON, Edward J; Postville Community HS; Postville, IA; 2/92 VPJrCls; HonRl; NHS; NatlThespSoc; SchPl; LetterBsktbl; LetterFtbl; LetterGlf; LetterTrk; DanFAwd; Coe College; Mathematics.

KITTRICK, Matthew J; Hinckley Big Rock HS; Hinckley, IL; StuCncl; SciCl; CaptSocr; LetterTrk; College; Civil Engineer.

KITZAN, Dwight A; Hebron HS; Richardton, ND; Chr; Chrs; SctActv; StuCncl; YthFlsp; 4-H; FFA; Bsktbl; Ftbl; Trk; North Dakota State Univ; Animal Science.

KITZAN, Rose; Richardton Public HS; Richardton, ND; 41/39 Mary Coll; Accountant.

KITZELMAN, Mark A; Fremont Sr HS; Fremont, NE; SchAde; StuCncl; StuGov; TchrAde; YthFlsp; EdYrBk; SchPpr; LetterFtbl; Trk; CchngActv; Coll; Teach.

KITZINGER, Kathleen; Marinette Senior HS; Marinette, WI; Band; CncrtBnd; JrNHS; MrchBnd; NHS; PepBnd; 4-H; FBLA; 4-HAwd; JAAwd; Coll; Mus Therapy.

KITZMANN, Joleen K; Lutheran HS; Hamburg, MN; 4/65 Chrs; ChrhWkr; HonRl; TchrAde; YthFlsp; EdYrBk; 4-H; FTA; PpCl; SciCl; Trk; Chrldr; College; English.

KITZNER, Catherine M; Schafer HS; Allen Park, MI; 1/290 TrsSophCls; HonRl; NHS; NatlMeritSF; SchMus; StuCncl; FrCl; MthCl; GAA; Mi St U; Veterinary Med.

KIVELA, Richard W; L Anse HS; Covington, MI; 3/87 HonRl; Ftbl; IMSpt; VFWAwd; Univ; Civil Engineering.

KIVISTO, Kevin J; Proctor HS; Duluth, MN; ALBoysSt; PresChrhWkr; HonRl; SctActv; StuCncl; FrCl; College.

KIX, Deborah L; Hubbard Community HS; Hubbard, IA; 10/43 Band; Chrs; HonRl; MrchBnd; TreasYthFlsp; EdYrBk; TreasFBLA; PresFHA; CaptChrldr; CitAwd; American Institute; Medical Receptionist.

KIZER, Georgette V; Hyde Park HS; Chicago, IL; 5/150 HonRl; NHS; De Paul Univ; Physician.

KJELDAHL, Joy K; Cyrus Public HS; Cyrus, MN; 4/20 Band; Chr; HonRl; PepBnd; SchPl; YthFlsp; RptrYrbk; Alexandria Area Tech Univ; Finance.

KJELDGAARD, Karen; Big Springs HS; Big Springs, NE; PresJrCls; ALAGirlsSt; Band; Chr; HonRl; PepBnd; PpCl; Chrldr; Univ; Dental Assistant.

KJELLESVIG, Kip L; Henderson HS; Belle Plaine, MN; 1/36 PresSrCls; Band; Chrs; CncrtBnd; HonRl; LbryAde; MrchBnd; PepBnd; SchMus; SchPl; StuCncl; LetterBsbl; Univ Of Minnesota.

KJELLSEN, Larry D; Arlington HS; Arlington, SD; PresJrCls; ALBoysSt; Band; Chrs; CncrtBnd; HonRl; MrchBnd; StuCncl; Bsktbl; LetterTrk; Coll; Vocation.

KJERGAARD, Leann B; Irene HS; Irene, SD; 2/29 TrsJrCls; Chr; Chrs; ChrhWkr; HonRl; NHS; OffAde; 4-H; FHA; DARAwd; Northern State College; Education.

KJERRUMGAARD, Beth G; New Haven HS; New Haven, MI; CncrtBnd; HonRl; MrchBnd; NHS; PepBnd; StuCncl; College; Professional.

KJOS, Pamela S; Lancaster HS; Lancaster, WI; 5/159 PresFrshCls; SecSophCls; SecJrCls; Band; HonRl; NHS; SchMus; RptrYrbk; FHA; GAA; College; Major Study.

KLAASSEN, Aldon; Ellsworth Public HS; Ellsworth, MN; 2/35 ALBoysSt; Aud/Vis; ChrhWkr; HonRl; Bemidji State; Accounting.

KLABUNDE, David J; Woodstock Comm HS; Woodstock, IL; HonRl; NHS; NatlMeritSchl; SctActv; College; Professional.

KLABUNDE, Holly K; Whiteshield HS; Emmet, ND; SecTrsJrCls; Band; Chrs; CncrtBnd; HonRl; PepBnd; EdSchPpr; LetterBsbl; Bsktbl; IMSpt; Minot State Univ; Occupational Therapy.

KLABUNDE, Jane F; White Shield HS; Emmet, ND; SecTrsFrshCls; Band; Chr; Chrl; Chrs; ChrhWkr; CmntyWkr; CncrtBnd; HonRl; PepBnd; RptrYrbk; PpCl; LetterBsktbl; Chrldr; College; Inhalation Therapy.

KLAESER, Kelly J; Marion HS; Caroline, WI; HonRl; JrNHS; StuCncl; LetterBsbl; LetterWrstlng; Bus Sch; Forestry.

KLAFFER, Johnny L; Brookport HS; Brookport, IL; Chrs; CmntyWkr; LbryAde; StuGov; RptrYrbk; EdYrBk; SptEdYrbk; 4-H; Trk; Paducah Comm; Law.

KLAHN, Roxann J; Durant HS; Wilton, IA; 6/68 Band; VPChrs; ChrhWkr; HonRl; JrNHS; VPNHS; SchMus; Pres4-H; Trk; CaptChrldr; SecGAA; 4-HAwd; Univ; Nurse.

KLAIN, Althea L; Turtle Lake Mercer HS; Turtle Lake, ND; 1/35 Chr; Chrs; ChrhWkr; CmntyWkr; HonRl; SchPl; YthLg; FHA; IMSpt; MasAwd; College.

KLAINSEK, Karen L; North Greene HS; White Hall, IL; 7/116 Band; Chrs; CncrtBnd; HonRl; MrchBnd; NHS; PepBnd; SchMus; Yrbk; MthCl; PpCl; LetterTrk; Chrldr; BttyCrckrAwd; College.

KLAK, Thomas C; St Laurence HS; Chicago, IL; HonRl; StuCncl; LetterTrk; CchngActv; IMSpt; Augustana College; Business.

KLAMER, John M; Kirkwood HS; Frontenac, MO; 5/680 Chr; ChrhWkr; HonRl; NatlMeritSF; NatlThespSoc; SchMus; SchPl; StuCncl; YthFlsp; SchPpr; SpnCl; LetterWrstlng; CitAwd; Univ Of Virginia.

KLAMERUS, Karen J; Montini HS; Lombard, IL; 5/155 HonRl; TreasNHS; EngCl; AmLegAwd; St Louis College; Pharmacy.

KLAMM, Michael; Chester Area HS; Colton, SD; ALBoysSt; HonRl; NatlMeritCmnd; SchPl; RptrYrbk; FFA; Trade School; Power Lineman.

KLANG, John A; Weston HS; Cazenovia, WI; 7/49 PresFrshCls; TrsJrCls; TrsSrCls; ALBoysSt; HonRl; NHS; Quill&Scroll; RptrSchPpr; FFA; Bsbl; Uw Lacrosse; Phy Ed.

KLANN, Kathryn A; Oconomowoc Sr HS; Oconomowoc, WI; 11/223 HonRl; JrNHS; NHS; StuCncl; RptrYrbk; Univ Of Wisconsin; Psychology.

KLAPOTZ, Nancy R; Hutchinson HS; Hutchinson, MN; 1/187 HonRl; Gustavus Adolphus College; Science.

KLAPPER, Sherry L; Park Hill HS; Kansas City, MO; Chr; HonRl; LbryAde; OffAde; SchPpr; FHA; PpCl; Chrldr; PPFtbl; Business School; Professional.

KLAPPERICH, Virginia J; Conde HS; Conde, SD; LetterChrs; HonRl; SchPl; StuCncl; RptrYrbk; EdSchPpr; PpCl; CaptTrk; Chrldr; EldAwd; Nettleton Comm Clg; Acct.

KLAPROTH, Deborah; Jackson Senior HS; Jackson, MO; ChrhWkr; MrchBnd; StuCncl; YthFlsp; RptrYrbk; RptrSchPpr; PpCl; Chrldr; CchngActv; College Or U; Major Study.

KLARICH, Daniel R; Ben Davis HS; Indpls, IN; 10/800 PresStuCncl; YthFlsp; LetterGlf; In U; Law.

KLARICH, Teresa L; Farmington East HS; Trivoli, IL; SecFrshCls; SecSophCls; SecJrCls; Chr; CncrtBnd; Twrl; 4-H; FFA; GAA; 4-HAwd;.

KLARNER, Cimberly A; Lyons Township HS; La Grange Park, IL; 102/1250 HonRl; HospAde; StuCncl; Bsbl; Iowa State Univ; Mathematics.

KLARSCH, James G; Ritenour HS; St Ann, MO; 7/960 ALBoysSt; Chr; Chrs; JrNHS; SchMus; SchPl; SctActv; StuCncl; Tennis; Clge; Dentistry.

KLAS, Paul T; Ozaukee HS; Fredonia, WI; 2/80 PresSrCls; ALBoysSt; Band; HonRl; NHS; SchMus; StuCncl; RptrSchPpr; Bsbl; Bsktbl; Ftbl; Trk; College; Medicine.

KLASEK, Steven C; Carbondale Comm HS; Carbondale, IL; HonRl; JrNHS; NHS; SctActv; YthLg; GerCl; MthCl; Bsbl; Ftbl; Trk; IMSpt; So Illinois Univ; Medicine.

KLASS, John F; Bay City Central HS; Bay Cityu, MI; VPFrshCls; PresJrCls; Band; Chr; MrchBnd; NHS; StuGov; LetterTennis; LetterTrk; Mi Univ; Business Administration.

KLASSEN, Brenda; Hillsboro HS; Hillsboro, KS; Chr; Chrs; ChrhWkr; HonRl; Twrl; YthFlsp; 4-H; FHA; Chrldr; 4-HAwd; Dental Assistant.

KLASSEN, Kathy M; Burke Central HS; Lignite, ND; ALAGirlsSt; Band; Chrs; ChrhWkr; HonRl; SctActv; StuCncl; Bsktbl; Trk; Univ Of No Dakota; Physical Therapy.

KLASSEN, Sandra D; Hillsboro HS; Hillsboro, KS; ChrhWkr; HonRl; OffAde; SchAde; TchrAde; YthFlsp; LetterBsbl; Coll; Child Psy.

KLASSEY, Kenneth A; Monroe HS; Monroe, WI; 5/200 HonRl; SchPl; YthFlsp; PresKeyCl; Whitewater Univ; Cpa.

KLASSY, Debra J; Parkview HS; Orfordville, WI; 5/153 HonRl; VPNHS; TchrAde; PresFHA; MthCl; PpCl; GAA; Bus Sch; Acctng.

KLATT, Bette J; Jamestown C 1 HS; Jamestown, MO; 2/19 VPFrshCls; PresSrCls; Chrs; HonRl; StuCncl; Yrbk; Bsktbl; Trk; Chrldr; BttyCrckrAwd; Central Mo State Univ; Marketing.

KLATT, Diana G; Immanuel Luth HS; Hazel, SD; TrsFrshCls; Chrs; ChrhWkr; Yrbk; 4-H; IMSpt; 4-HAwd; College; Professional Teaching.

KLATT, Reginald V; Lomira HS; Byron, WI; HonRl; NatlMeritSF; StuCncl; FrCl; LetterBsbl; LetterFtbl; LetterTrk; College; Engineering.

KLATT, Ronda K; Clio HS; Clio, MI; HonRl; HospAde; LitMag; NHS; OffAde; SchPl; StuCncl; GerCl; LatCl; College Air Force; Rn.

KLAUCK, Mary L; Kiel HS; Kiel, WI; Band; CmntyWkr; CncrtBnd; HonRl; LbryAde; MrchBnd; NHS; SchMus; SchPl; StuCncl; SchPpr; College; Teacher.

KLAUDA, Paul F; Lourdes HS; Rochester, MN; PresSophCls; SecTrsJrCls; PresSrCls; ALBoysSt; HonRl; JrNHS; StuCncl; EdYrBk; SptEdYrbk; CaptTrk; College; Journalism.

KLAUS, Brenda S; Marian HS; Hays, KS; ChrhWkr; CmntyWkr; DrlTm; SchPl; TchrAde; 4-H; PpCl; Bsbl; Swmmng; Trade Schl; Interior Decorator.

KLAUS, Cindy M; Marian HS; Hays, KS; Band; Chrs; CncrtBnd; MrchBnd; SchPl; StuCncl; Fort Hays State; Music.

KLAUS, Marvelle J; Roosevelt HS; Chicago, IL; TreasBand; ChrhWkr; CncrtBnd; LbryAde; NHS; Orch; StuCncl; TchrAde; FHA; LetterSwmmng; GAA; Northeastern Illinois Univ; Education.

KLAUSEN, Diane L; Loup City HS; Rockville, NE; ChrhWkr; HonRl; SchMus; 4-H; FHA; LetterTrk; 4-HAwd; College.

KLAUSING, Annette T; Webberville HS; Webberville, MI; 1/60 HonRl; NHS; OffAde; Bsktbl; Chrldr; Business School.

KLAUSING, Melissa; Bismarck HS; Bismarck, ND; 26/588 CmntyWkr; HonRl; LitMag; NHS; YthFlsp; SecSophCls; Chrldr; N Dakota State Univ; Zoology Or Vet Tech.

KLAVE, Robert J; Cardinal Muench Seminary; Grand Forks, ND; PresSophCls; PresJrCls; TrsJrCls; ChrhWkr; HonRl; LbryAde; SchPl; SctActv; PresStuCncl; Yrbk; College; Professional.

KLAVER, Kristin J; Stratford Comm HS; Stratford, IA; 8/32 SecJrCls; Band; Chr; Chrs; HonRl; StuCncl; YthFlsp; Bsktbl; Trk; DanFAwd; Iowa Wesleyan Col; Nursing.

KLAVER, Lenny R; Northeast Hamilton HS; Kamrar, IA; 3/42 Band; CncrtBnd; HonRl; MrchBnd; SchPl; StuCncl; YthFlsp; CaptBsbl; CaptBsktbl; LetterFtbl; LetterTrk; College; Physical Educ.

KLAVINS, Sandra; East Kentwood HS; Kentwood, MI; 3/389 ChrhWkr; HonRl; NatlFornLg; NHS; SchAde; TchrAde; PpCl; Chrldr; PPFtbl; Davenport College; Accounting.

KLAWES, Jeffrey N; Rio HS; Rio, WI; NHS; LetterBsktbl; LetterFtbl; KiwanAwd; College; Engineering.

KLEBBA, Brian M; Unionville Sebewaing Area HS; Sebwdvaing, MI; 16/104 PresJrCls; Band; CncrtBnd; HonRl; MrchBnd; StuCncl; RptrYrbk; Yrbk; LatCl; Trk; College; Prfessional.

KLEBBA, John; Maur Hill Prep; Linn, MO; 2/56 PresFrshCls; SecSophCls; VPJrCls; HonRl; Bsbl; IMSpt; Drake Univ; Accounting.

KLEBBA, John P; Holly HS; Holly, MI; Band; Chr; Chrl; Chrs; ChrhWkr; CncrtBnd; Mdrgl; MrchBnd; Orch; Univ Of Michigan; Music.

KLEBE, Kristy J; Beardstown HS; Beardstown, IL; 17/128 Chr; Chrs; ChrhWkr; DrlTm; HonRl; MrchBnd; SchMus; 4-H; Swmmng; College.

KLEBER, Mary Jo; Bishop Dwenger HS; Fort Wayne, IN; SchMus; SchPl; StuCncl; GAA; IMSpt; Trade Schl; Beautician.

KLEBER, Patricia M; Bishop Dwenger HS; Ft Wayne, IN; 8/245 Band; Chrs; CncrtBnd; DrmMjrt; HonRl; MrchBnd; NHS; NatlMeritCmnd; SchMus; ChmbCommrsAwd; University; Agriculture.

KLEBS, Elmer; Mayville HS; Brownsville, WI; 2/122 ALBoysSt; ChrhWkr; HonRl; NatlFornLg; NHS; NatlMeritFnl; EdSchPpr; Ia State Univ; Physics.

KLECAN, Jean M; Thornwood HS; S Holland, IL; 19/842 AFS; HonRl; NHS; Yrbk; SchPpr; PresFrCl; St Josephs College; English.

KLECAN, William J; Odell Public HS; Diller, NE; Aud/Vis; Band; Chrs; CncrtBnd; HonRl; MrchBnd; SchPl; LetterBsktbl; LetterFtbl; PepBnd; College; Professional.

KLECKLER, Curtis D; Mt Morris HS; Mt Morris, IL; 1/76 HonRl; NHS; StuCncl; YthFlsp; EdYrBk; SptEdSchPpr; Bsktbl; CaptGlf; LetterTrk; College; Mathematics.

KLEEB, Carol; Broken Bow HS; Broken Bow, NE; HonRl; StuGov; TchrAde; YthFlsp; RptrYrbk; FHA; PpCl; Coll; Elem Teach.

KLEEKAMP, Jane; St Francis Borgia HS; Washington, MO; 13/98 ALAGirlsSt; HonRl; JrNHS; NHS; OffAde; SchPl; TchrAde; RptrYrbk; MthCl; PpCl; College; Nursing.

KLEEMAN, Diane; Engadine Cons HS; Engadine, MI; HonRl; LbryAde; SchPl; SctActv; SchPpr; FHA; GAA; IMSpt;.

KLEEMAN, Rhonda R; Sarcoxie HS; Sarcoxie, MO; 7/65 Chr; HonRl; NHS; SchPl; SptEdYrbk; SptEdSchPpr; FHA; FTA; MthCl; PpCl; College; Vocational.

KLEEN, Christy J; Franklin Public HS; Franklin, NE; Chrs; ChrhWkr; CmntyWkr; HonRl; SchPl; StuCncl; YthFlsp; YthLg; FHA; PpCl; VFWAwd; Business School.

KLEES, Susan; University City HS; University City, MO; Band; ChrhWkr; HonRl; PolWkr; Drake U; Teacher.

KLEES, Susan; Waukon Senior HS; Monona, IA; Chr; Chrs; ChrhWkr; HonRl; LbryAde; OffAde; Quill&Scroll; SchPl; TchrAde; RptrSchPpr; Vocational.

KLEIBER, Jayne A; Centre HS; Tampa, KS; ALAGirlsSt; Band; CmntyWkr; HonRl; MrchBnd; Twrl; YthFlsp; FHA; Bsbl; LetterGlf; College; Secretary.

KLEIBER, Sandra J; Southern HS; Stronghurst, IL; CmntyWkr; HonRl; HospAde; NHS; RedCrAde; RptrSchPpr; FNA; Bsktbl; Chrldr; GAA; College; Nurse.

KLEIMAN, Lauri; Parkway Central HS; Creve Coeur, MO; 9/450 DrlTm; HonRl; JrNHS; MrchBnd; NHS; FTA; FrCl; PpCl; PPFtbl; Univ Of Ill; Biologist.

KLEIMOLA, Ula M; Concord HS; Jackson, MI; Band; ChrhWkr; CncrtBnd; HonRl; MrchBnd;

Orch; PepBnd; SchMus; TchrAde; VPYthFlsp; College; Nurse.

KLEIN, Barbara A; Freeburg Comm HS; Belleville, IL; 1/124 HonRl; NHS; RptrYrbk; PresFHA; GAA; Belleville Area College; Legal Secretary.

KLEIN, Cindy L; Hoisington HS; Hoisington, KS; Band; Chr; CncrtBnd; HonRl; HospAde; PepBnd; SchPl; YthFlsp; PpCl; Nursing.

KLEIN, Dale J; Arkansaw HS; Arkansaw, WI; CmntyWkr; HonRl; StuCncl; RptrYrbk; SptEdYrbk; SptEdSchPpr; Bsbl; Bsktbl; Trk; 4-HAwd; Trade School; Vocation.

KLEIN, Denise A; Fraser HS; Fraser, MI; CmntyWkr; NatlMeritSF; Northern Mich Univ; Commercial Artist.

KLEIN, Dennis P; Rolla HS; Rolla, ND; VPFrshCls; Band; HonRl; MrchBnd; PepBnd; RptrSchPpr; FFA; Bsbl; Bsktbl; Trade School.

KLEIN, Dennis R; Rich Central HS; Park Forest, IL; 38/364 Band; CmntyWkr; CncrtBnd; HonRl; MrchBnd; PepBnd; Quill&Scroll; TreasStuCncl; StuGov; RptrSchPpr; SchPpr; College; Law.

KLEIN, Diane; Colon HS; Mendon, MI; 6/60 SecSrCls; HonRl; LbryAde; NHS; FrCl; College At Bronson Meth; Registered Nurse.

KLEIN, Evan J; Spalding Institute HS; Peoria, IL; 11/103 NHS; Bsbl; College; Archaeologist.

KLEIN, Glen J; Pewamo Westphalia HS; Pewamo, MI; HonRl; NHS; Mich State Univ; Business Field.

KLEIN, Gwen; Walther Lutheran HS; Glen Ellyn, IL; PresSophCls; VPJrCls; Band; Chr; CncrtBnd; Mdrgl; MrchBnd; StuCncl; YthFlsp; GAA; IMSpt; College; Music.

KLEIN, Holly I; Alma HS; Alma, MI; 44/265 SecSophCls; Band; CncrtBnd; DrmMjrt; MrchBnd; SchPl; StuCncl; TchrAde; Twrl; LetterWrstlng; U Of Mi; Criminal Justice.

KLEIN, Jeffrey C; Burlington Community HS; Burlington, IA; 11/501 HonRl; Ia St U;architecture.

KLEIN, Jeffrey G; Hazen Public HS; Hazen, ND; Band; Chr; ChrhWkr; CncrtBnd; MrchBnd; 4-H; Bsktbl; LetterFtbl; LetterTrk; LetterGAA; 4-HAwd; Mary College; Law.

KLEIN, Jeffrey S; Spalding Inst; Metamora, IL; 2/100 VPFrshCls; PresSophCls; SecJrCls; NatlMeritSF; StuGov; RptrSchPpr; LetterFtbl; LetterTrk; LetterTrk; IMSpt; U Of Dayton; Civil Engineer.

KLEIN, Jelena M; Hazen Public HS; Hazen, ND; Chr; ChrhWkr; CmntyWkr; LbryAde; SchAde; TchrAde; 4-H; CaptBsktbl; LetterTrk; LetterGAA; 4-HAwd; Mary College; Nursing.

KLEIN, Joyce; Saline HS; Saline, MI; SecSophCls; Band; CncrtBnd; HospAde; MrchBnd; NHS; Orch; SchMus; FNA; GerCl; Coll; Nursing.

KLEIN, Julie A; Bentley HS; Livonia, MI; Univ Of Michigan; Business Admin.

KLEIN, Karen C; Tonganoxie HS; Leavenworth, KS; Chr; DrlTm; HonRl; NHS; NatlThespSoc; Yrbk; FHA; PpCl; Bsktbl; LetterTrk; Clge; Rn.

KLEIN, Karen E; Hazelwood East Sr HS; St Louis, MO; 5/490 CncrtBnd; HonRl; TreasNHS; PepBnd; SchMus; SchPl; TchrAde; YthFlsp; PpCl; Chrldr; University; Lawyer.

KLEIN, Kathleen A; Port Huron Northern HS; Port Huron, MI; ChrhWkr; HonRl; HospAde; NHS; OffAde; SchAde; StuCncl; TchrAde; EngCl; OptClAwd; Univ Of Mi; Law.

KLEIN, Kenneth S; Coldwater HS; Coldwater, MI; ALBoysSt; Band; CncrtBnd; MrchBnd; SpnCl; SciCl; LetterFtbl; IMSpt; College; Business.

KLEIN, Kurt D; Wesclin HS; Trenton, IL; 12/105 PresSrCls; HonRl; NHS; YthFlsp; SptEdSchPpr; GerCl; LetterBsbl; LetterBsktbl; LetterTennis; CchngActv; Coll; Voc.

KLEIN, Lisa M; Academy Of Lady Spalding Inst; Metamora, IL; 1/115 CmntyWkr; HonRl; SchPl; RptrSchPpr; GerCl; College; Veterinary Medicine.

KLEIN, Lisa M; Acad Of Our Lady Spalding Ins; Metamora, IL; HonRl; SchPl; EdYrBk; RptrSchPpr; GerCl; College; Veterinarian.

KLEIN, Margaret; Sacred Heart Of Mary Hs; Arlington Hts, IL; 1/135 HonRl; NHS; NatlMeritCmnd; PresStuGov; RptrSchPpr; EdSchPpr; Bsktbl; Northwestern U; Journalism.

KLEIN, Mark A; Spalding HS; Alton, IA; Band; CncrtBnd; HonRl; MrchBnd; PepBnd; SctActv; IMSpt; Trade Sch; Vocation.

KLEIN, Michael J; Lakeshore HS; St Clair Shores, MI; HonRl; Wayne State Univ; Business.

KLEIN, Patricia A; South Knox HS; Wheatland, IN; ALAGirlsSt; Quill&Scroll; TreasStuCncl; EdYrBk; FHA; FNA; LatCl; PpCl; Chrldr; AmLegAwd; College; Dental Hygiene.

KLEIN, Paul H; Spalding HS; Granville, IA; 3/45 Chrs; ChrhWkr; HonRl; SchPl; RptrYrbk; EdYrBk; PresMthCl; Bsbl; Bsktbl; ChmnIMSpt; College.

KLEIN, Paul J; Loyola Academy; Chicago, IL; Loyola Univ; Art.

KLEIN, Perry G; Pella Comm HS; Pella, IA; ALBoysSt; ChrhWkr; StuCncl; VPLetterFtbl; LetterTrk; College; Juv Law.

KLEIN, Rita A; Bishop Ryan HS; Minot, ND; 16/87 Band; Chr; Chrs; ChrhWkr; CmntyWkr; CncrtBnd; HonRl; JrNHS; NHS; SctActv; Sdlty; RptrYrbk; RptrSchPpr; PpCl; Univ; Professional.

KLEIN, Robert J; Riverside Brookfield HS; Brookfield, IL; Band; ChrhWkr; NHS; NatlMeritFnl; PresSctActv; StuCncl; VPYthFlsp; GerCl; LetterFtbl; LetterWrstlng; Univ Of Illinois; Minister.

KLEIN, Robert M; New Trier West HS; Wilmette, IL; HonRl; Univ Of Illinois; Business.

KLEIN, Sharon A; Leo HS; Durango, IA; 1/38 VPFrshCls; Chrs; HonRl; SchMus; StuCncl; TchrAde; Yrbk; RptrSchPpr; PresLatCl; SciCl; Chrldr; IMSpt; Lovas College; Nursing.

KLEIN, Sharon M; Bishop Ryan HS; Minot, ND; 2/90 SecJrCls; PresBand; PresCncrtBnd; PresPresJrNHS; NatlMeritCmnd; SchMus; Sdlty; EdYrBk; Col; Mathematics.

KLEIN, Terry W; Thomas More Prep HS; Ellinwood, KS; Chrs; CncrtBnd; HonRl; MrchBnd; PepBnd; Sacrstn; SchMus; SchPl; EdYrBk; PpCl;.

KLEIN, William J; Wilmington HS; Wilmington, IL; 8/120 HonRl; NHS; SctActv; TchrAde; MthCl; LetterBsbl; CaptBsktbl; Blackburn College; Psychology.

KLEIN, Zane L; Milan C Ii HS; Harris, MO; 25/49 StuCncl; Univ Of Missouri; Agriculture.

KLEINDIENST, Cynthia R; Rockford West HS; Rockford, IL; 4/335 HonRl; NHS; Orch; PresStuCncl; TchrAde; PresGerCl; DARAwd; Rockford College; Math.

KLEINE, Donna R; Aurora HS; Aurora, IN; 12/139 VPSrCls; ALAGirlsSt; Chr; ChrhWkr; HonRl; SecJA; TreasLitMag; LbryAde; NHS; OffAde; Ball State Univ; Business.

KLEINE, Janet; Pierce City HS; Pierce City, MO; 6/60 Band; Chr; Chrs; ChrhWkr; CncrtBnd; HonRl; MrchBnd; NHS; OffAde; PepBnd; StuCncl; TchrAde; RptrYrbk; RptrSchPpr; Univ; Teaching.

KLEINE, Susan G; Delavan Comm HS; Delavan, IL; Band; CncrtBnd; HonRl; MrchBnd; PepBnd; SchMus; FrCl; SciCl; Bsktbl; GAA; Engineering.

KLEINHANS, Karen J; Northwest HS; High Ridge, MO; HonRl; JA; SchPl; TchrAde; RptrYrbk; SchPpr; PpCl; TreasJAAwd; CitAwd; College; Veterinarian.

KLEINHUIZER, David W; Danube HS; Blomkest, MN; ALBoysSt; SchMus; SecYthFlsp; EdSchPpr; Pres4-H; VPFFA; Bsktbl; CaptTrk; 4-HAwd; PresAwd; Univ Of Minnesota; Professional.

KLEINJAN, Kevin E; Edgerton HS; Edgerton, MN; PresSophCls; ALBoysSt; Yrbk; PpCl; Bsbl; Bsktbl; Ftbl; Trk; CchngActv; College; Physical Ed.

KLEINSCHMIDT, Jodi K; Iron Mountain HS; Iron Mountain, MI; Chr; ChrhWkr; HospAde; LbryAde; SchPl; TchrAde; FHA; FNA; FrCl; Mi Tech Univ; Registered Nurse.

KLEINSCHMIDT, Mara; Shawano Hs; Shawano, WI; 14/265 Chrl; ChrhWkr; CmntyWkr; Mdrgl; NHS; 4-H; FrCl; Trk; CaptChrldr; 4-HAwd; University; Law Cultural Arts.

KLEIS, John E; Burlington HS; Burlington, IA; 177/502 Band; HonRl; SchPl; StuCncl; SptEdYrbk; LetterBsbl; LetterBsktbl; LetterGlf; LetterSwmmng; College; Pro Baseball.

KLEIS, Katherine; Holland Christian HS; Holland, MI; Chr; ChrhWkr; HospAde; LitMag; LbryAde; StuGov; Yrbk; 4-H; FNA; SpnCl; Calvin Coll; Nrsng.

KLEIS, Raymond H; Marion Independent HS; Marion, IA; 20/179 HonRl; SctActv; TchrAde; FTA; LetterBsbl; ChmnFtbl; LetterWrstlng; College; Mathematics.

KLEIST, Gary A; Altoona Public HS; Altoona, WI; 13/74 ChrhWkr; CncrtBnd; HonRl; NHS; SchMus; TchrAde; RptrSchPpr; CivCl; Bsktbl; Ftbl; College; Professional.

KLEIST, Janice R; Janesville Craig Sr HS; Janesville, WI; 19/490 Band; Chr; CmntyWkr; CncrtBnd; HonRl; NHS; Orch; VPQuill&Scroll; Yrbk; College; Sociology.

KLEITSCH, Susan I; George Washington HS; Cedar Rapids, IA; NatlFornLg; NHS; TreasNatlThespSoc; Quill&Scroll; RedCrAde; SchMus; SchPl; RptrYrbk; RptrSchPpr; LetterBsktbl; Ia State Univ; Science.

KLEM, Ann L; Dubois HS; Dubois, IN; 20/81 Band; ChrhWkr; HonRl; MrchBnd; PepBnd; SchPl; YthFlsp; 4-H; FHA; PpCl; College.

KLEM, Jackie A; Forest Park HS; Huntingburg, IN; HonRl; NHS; TreasQuill&Scroll; StuCncl; RptrYrbk; EdYrBk; RptrSchPpr; PpCl; GAA; CitAwd;.

KLEM, Stephen; Deerfield Hs; Deerfield, IL; CncrtBnd; HonRl; MrchBnd; NatlMeritCmnd; SchMus; SchPl; TreasYthFlsp; Swmmng; College; Physician Bio Medical Engineering.

KLEMA, Steven D; Russell HS; Russell, KS; /89 Chr; CncrtBnd; HonRl; KeyCl; Bsbl; Bsktbl; LetterFtbl; LetterTrk; IMSpt; College Bethany; Business Administration.

KLEMEK, Buddy C; Mound Westonka HS; Maple Plain, MN; Chr; HonRl; SchAde; TchrAde; Ftbl; Trk; LetterWrstlng; U Of Mn Duluth; Medical.

KLEMENC, Jeri; Thornton Fractional Hs; Calumet City, IL; 48 Chr1; Chrs; HonRl; SchMus;.

KLEMENT, Cynthia D; Ft Atkinson HS; Fort Atkinson, WI; AFS; HonRl; NHS; StuGov; Yrbk; 4-H; PpCl; AmLegAwd; BttyCrckrAwd; 4-HAwd; Univ Wi Madison; Computer Eng.

KLEMETT, Katherine L; Hancock Central HS; Hancock, MI; ALAGirlsSt; Band; CncrtBnd; HonRl; MrchBnd; OffAde; PepBnd; SchPl; RptrYrbk; KeyCl; Trk;.

KLEMKOWSKY, George W; Owen Gage HS; Owendale, MI; VPSophCls; VPJrCls; TrsSrCls; HonRl; JA; NatlFornLg; SchPl; SctActv; RptrYrbk; SchPpr; Business School; Bookkeeping.

KLEMM, Christine P; Kaneland Sr HS; Maple Park, IL; AFS; HonRl; NHS; RptrYrbk; RptrSchPpr; 4-H; FrCl; PpCl; DanFAwd; Nursing Sch; Nursing.

KLEMM, David M; Wessinton Springs HS; Woonsocket, SD; 2/60 TrsJrCls; CncrtBnd; Mdrgl; NHS; NatlThespSoc; SchMus; SchPl; SctActv; StuCncl; RptrYrbk; RptrSchPpr; Univ; Art.

KLEMM, David M; Waterford Mott HS; Pontiac, MI; 4/500 NatlMeritSchl; Wayne State Univ; Law.

KLEMM, Mary A; Maria HS; Chicago, IL; 9/335 SecJrCls; HonRl; NHS; SptEdSchPpr; Bsbl; Bsktbl; GAA; IMSpt; KiwanAwd; College; Law Enforcement.

KLEMM, Steven R; Ludington HS; Ludington, MI; 12/255 Band; HonRl; NHS; StuCncl; LetterBsktbl; Glf; CaptTennis; EldAwd; RotaryAwd; Michigan St University; Chemical Engineer.

KLEMME, Dolores A; Collins Comm HS; Collins, IA; Band; Chr; Chrs; ChrhWkr; SecNHS; YthFlsp; RptrSchPpr; Sec4-H; IMSpt; 4-HAwd; College; Art.

KLEMME, Eileen K; West Marshall HS; State Center, IA; ChrhWkr; HonRl; PresYthFlsp; Pres4-H; TreasFHA; PpCl; DanFAwd; 4-HAwd; University; Vocation.

KLEMME, Kathy A; Stratford HS; Stratford, WI; Band; Chrs; CncrtBnd; HospAde; MrchBnd; PepBnd; FHA; Chrldr; GAA; Training Clg; Med Asst.

KLEMZ, Joyce E; Annandale Public HS; Annandale, MN; Band; CncrtBnd; HonRl; MrchBnd; PepBnd; TchrAde; PpCl; LetterBsktbl; GAA; IMSpt; St Cloud St Univ; Social Work.

KLENDER, Mark A; T L Handy HS; Bay City, MI; VPJrCls; VPSrCls; HonRl; NHS; StuCncl; StuGov; IMSpt; Univ Of Mi; Pre Law.

KLENKLEN, Janet D; Valley Falls HS; Valley Falls, KS; Band; Chr; ChrhWkr; DrlTm; HonRl; LbryAde; OffAde; PresStuCncl; TchrAde; VPFHA; Undecided.

KLEOPFER, Janice K; Mid Prairie HS; Kalona, IA; CncrtBnd; HonRl; MrchBnd; StuCncl; FNA; LetterBsktbl; LetterTrk; Chrldr; Navycrest College; Nursing.

KLEPITSCH, Frank J; Lane Tech HS; Chicago, IL; 42/1100 StuCncl;.

KLEPPEK, Judith A; Howards Grove HS; Howards Grove, WI; 5/57 Band; HonRl; NatlFornLg; SchPl; StuCncl; RptrYrbk; RptrSchPpr; Trk; Chrldr; GAA; College; Medical Technology.

KLEPPER, Janice A; Usd 319 HS; Mc Donald, KS; PresSophCls; TrsJrCls; Chrs; DrmMjrt; MrchBnd; RedCrAde; StuCncl; RptrSchPpr; PpCl; LetterBsktbl; Clge; Nursing.

KLEPSTEEN, Claudia G; Pennfield HS; Battle Creek, MI; 2/176 Band; CncrtBnd; HonRl; JA; JrNHS; NHS; PepBnd; TchrAde; ChmnBsktbl; LetterTrk; U Of Mich; Medicine.

KLESCHEN, Mary Z; Evanston Twnshp HS; Evanston, IL; 25/1100 CmntyWkr; HonRl; NatlMeritCmnd; SchMus; Chrldr; Indiana Univ; Medicine.

KLESSIG, Charles E; Hartford Union HS; Hartford, WI; Band; Chr; Chrs; CncrtBnd; HonRl; JA; Mdrgl; MrchBnd; PepBnd; SchMus; Univ Of Wi; Biology.

KLESZYNSKI, Nancy L; Elizabeth Seton HS; Calumet City, IL; Chrs; SpnCl; College; Nursing.

KLETT, Kim L; Princeton HS; Princeton, IL; 13/198 AFS; Band; HonRl; FrCl; CaptBsktbl; Trk; Univ Of Illinois; French.

KLEVE, Diane; Seward Sr HS; Sewara, NE; 10/134 Chr; HonRl; OffAde; Teen; FHA; PpCl; Work; Insurance.

KLEVE, Kerry L; Turkey Valley Comm HS; Waucoma, IA; ALBoysSt; Chr; Chrs; Mdrgl; NatlFornLg; SchMus; SchPl; 4-H; Bsktbl; LetterFtbl; 4-HAwd; Jr College; Professional.

KLEVER, David M; Freeport Sr HS; Freeport, IL; 4-H; FFA; University; Agriculture.

KLICH, Michele M; Andrean HS; Gary, IN; 5/250 ChrhWkr; HonRl; FrCl; MthCl; Purdue Univ; Psychology.

KLICKSTEIN, Lloyd B; Mt Pleasant HS; Mt Pleasant, MI; 45/348 Aud/Vis; HonRl; NHS; NatlMeritSF; SchPl; SchPpr; SpnCl; LetterFtbl; Univ Of Maine; Fish & Game Warden.

KLIEWER, Carol A; Hillsboro HS; Hillsboro, KS; SecFrshCls; TrsFrshCls; TrsSophCls; HonRl; SchPl; StuCncl; Bsktbl; LetterTrk; IMSpt; AmLegAwd; 4-HAwd; Tabor College.

KLIFF, Steven L; Elk Grove HS; Elk Grove Vlg, IL; 28/500 CmntyWkr; HonRl; JrNHS; NHS; PolWkr; SchAde; TchrAde; YthFnd; KeyCl; FrCl; Bsbl; Bsktbl; Ftbl; Univ Of Michigan; Business.

KLIGERMAN, Daniel; U Of Chicago HS; Chicago, IL; LetterSocr; LetterTrk; College; History Art.

KLIKA, Cynthia A; Wrightstown HS; Greenleaf, WI; CmntyWkr; HonRl; JA; StuCncl; RptrYrbk; SchPpr; 4-H; GAA; 4-HAwd;.

KLIKA, Mark S; Oconto HS; Oconto, WI; 10/141 ChrhWkr; CmntyWkr; CncrtBnd; HonRl; NatlMeritCmnd; SchPl; 4-H; Bsktbl; Ftbl; University; Dentist.

KLIMA, Pamela; L D F Community HS; Marshalltown, IA; 3/44 Chr; HonRl; Mdrgl; NHS; SchMus; SchPl; StuCncl; EdYrBk; Bsktbl; Trk; Wartburg College; Vocal Music Teacher.

KLIMCZAK, Phyllis M; St Marys Academy; West Allis, WI; 5/150 ChrhWkr; CmntyWkr; HonRl; NHS; Orch; SchMus; TchrAde; LatCl; Marquette U; Pre Med.

KLIMEK, John; Muskegon Catholic Central HS; Muskegon Heights, MI; HonRl; Bsktbl; Glf; IMSpt; Muskegon Comm College; Draftingengineer.

KLIMEK, Kristine T; Merrill Sr HS; Merrill, WI; Band; ChrhWkr; CmntyWkr; CncrtBnd; HonRl; MrchBnd; PepBnd; SchPl; Pres4-H; 4-HAwd; University; Elementary Ed.

KLIMEK, Patsy M; Sturgeon Bay HS; Sturgeon Bay, WI; 4/147# PresSophCls; PresSrCls; Chr; HonRl; NHS; RedCrAde; StuCncl; RptrYrbk; CaptSwmmng; Trk; College; Physical Therapy.

KLINDWORTH, Jenelle G; Chester HS; Chester, IL; PresJrCls; ALAGirlsSt; PresBand; Chrs; CncrtBnd; HonRl; MrchBnd; SecNHS; PepBnd; PpCl; Belleville Area College; Accountant.

KLINE, Charles J; Downers Grove No Comm HS; Downers Grove, IL; 13/524 CmntyWkr; HonRl; NHS; LetterFtbl; Trk; IMSpt; Univ Of Illinois; Medical.

KLINE, David H; Seymoor HS; Barry, IL; 15/65 VPSophCls; HonRl; FFA; FrCl; LetterBsbl; LetterBsktbl; University; Vocation.

KLINE, Dennis L; Three Rivers HS; Three Rivers, MI; 10/205 ChrhWkr; HonRl; NatlMeritCmnd; TchrAde; YthFlsp; SpnCl; Bsbl; Bsktbl; CchngActv; Univ; Physics.

KLINE, Elaine A; West Catholic HS; Grand Rapids, MI; 40/310 ChrhWkr; HonRl; NHS; Sdlty; 4-H; Davenport College; Secretary.

KLINE, Kandace S; Gothenburg HS; Gothenburg, NE; ChrhWkr; OffAde; SchPl; College.

KLINE, Katherine W; Apollo HS; St Coud, MN; 1/595 AFS; Band; Chr; CncrtBnd; Mdrgl; NatlMeritSF; Orch; SchMus; SchPl; SctActv; Col ; Musci.

KLINE, Kathleen A; Wilson Campus HS; Mankato, MN; Chr; Chrs; ChrhWkr; SchMus; RptrYrbk; PpCl; BttyCrckrAwd; KiwanAwd; College; Bus Adm.

KLINE, Keith L; Vicksburg HS; Three Rivers, MI; 3/160 PresJrCls; NHS; VPStuCncl; College.

KLINE, Kurt R; Scotus HS; Columbus, NE; ALAGirlsSt; Chrs; HonRl; SchMus; SchPl; Bsbl; CaptBsktbl; Trk; OptClAwd; RotaryAwd; Platte Jr Coll; Broker.

KLINE, Linda; Le Roy HS; Le Roy, IL; TrsFrshCls; HonRl; OffAde; StuCncl; PpCl; Chrldr; GAA; PPFtbl;.

KLINE, Paul J; Kankakee Eastridge HS; Kankakee, IL; 10/257 ChrhWkr; HonRl; NHS; Coll; Psychology.

KLINE, Rex B; Kalkaska HS; Alden, MI; HonRl; NHS; PolWkr; Alma College; Psychology.

KLINE, Richard D; East Union HS; Afton, IA; 4/64 Band; ChrhWkr; CncrtBnd; HonRl; MrchBnd; 4-H; LetterBsktbl; Glf; Trk; 4-HAwd; Iowa State U; Engineering.

KLINE, Suzanne M; Huntington Catholic HS; Huntington, IN; 1/41 PresSrCls; Chrs; HonRl; NHS; RedCrAde; 4-H; GAA; IMSpt; DARAwd; Huntington College; Accounting.

KLINEDINST, Pamela S; Lewistown Community HS; Lewistown, IL; HonRl; MrchBnd; Twrl; Yrbk; RptrSchPpr; FHA; SpnCl; PpCl; GAA; College; Vocation.

KLINEFELTER, Susan E; La Salle Pru Township HS; Peru, IL; 9/500 Chrl; Chrs; HonRl; FrCl; PpCl; Northern Illinois Univ; Physical Thrapy.

KLINER, Gregory J; Boylan Central Catholic HS; Rockford, IL; 26/368 HonRl; RptrYrbk; RptrSchPpr; SciCl; Bsbl; Ftbl; Bradley Univ; Engr.

KLING, Dana L; Meadville R Iv HS; Meadville, MO; 5/39 SecFrshCls; SecSophCls; Band; HonRl; SchPl; StuCncl; LetterBsbl; LetterBsktbl; LetterTrk; GAA;.

KLING, Dan R; Gordon HS; Gordon, NE; 12/70 VPSophCls; PresJrCls; ALBoysSt; TchrAde; 4-H; LetterFtbl; LetterWrstlng; AmLegAwd; 4-HAwd; Univ Of Nebraska; Ag Economics.

KLING, Jane; Eisenhower HS; Decatur, IL; 20/308 VPSophCls; PresJrCls; VPSrCls; HonRl; NHS; NatlThespSoc; SchMus; SchPl; StuCncl; RptrSchPpr; Univ Of Illinois; Pre Medicine.

KLING, John; West Hs; Rockford, IL; Band; CncrtBnd; MrchBnd; ROTC; GerCl;.

KLING, Mark P; Carl Sandburg HS; Palos Heights, IL; 13/700 Band; CncrtBnd; HonRl; JrNHS; MrchBnd; NHS; PepBnd; FrCl; MthCl; Bsbl; Bsktbl; Augustana College; Medicine.

KLING, Peggy A; North Miami HS; Peru, IN; 34/123 Band; DrmMjrt; 4-H; FTA; LetterBsktbl; GAA; Manchester Col; Physical Ed.

KLINGBAIL, Kathleen A; Saint John Cathedral HS; Milwaukee, WI; MrchBnd; SchPl; SctActv; PpCl; Chrldr; University; Medicine.

KLINGBEIL, Timothy; Proviso East HS; Maywood, IL; 4/950 Band; ChrhWkr; HonRl; MrchBnd; NHS; NatlMeritCmnd; Orch; College; Education.

KLINGE, Ronald K; St Louis Park HS; St Louis Park, MN; 172/746 SchMus; Socr; Trk; IMSpt; Univ Of Mn; Chemistry.

KLINGELHUTZ, Michael; Chaska Senior HS; Chanhassen, MN; ChrhWkr; HonRl; SchPl; RptrYrbk; SptEdSchPpr; 4-H; Glf; Socr; College; Natural Sciences.

KLINGENSMITH, Scott L; Monroe HS; Monroe, MI; HonRl; NatlMeritCmnd; StuGov; EdYrBk; Bsbl; Bsktbl; Glf; Central Mi Univ; Business.

KLINGER, Paul C; Fingal Public HS; Oriska, ND; 6/21 PresSophCls; TrsSrCls; ChrhWkr; HonRl; SchPl; SctActv; Sdlty; Yrbk; LetterTrk; Trade Sch; Vo.

KLINGLER, Debbie A; Clay City HS; Noble, IL; SecTrsSophCls; HonRl; 4-H; FHA; PpCl; Chrldr;.

KLINGLER, Kenneth L; West Richland HS; Noble, IL; VPSophCls; Band; StuCncl; 4-H; FrCl; LetterBsbl; LetterBsktbl; Southern Il Univ; Medicine.

KLINGSPON, Mary J; Lakeshore HS; Baroda, MI; ChrhWkr; HonRl; 4-H; LetterTrk; Lk Mi College; Secretary Or Stewardess.

KLINK, Ann M; Hartford Union HS; Rubicon, WI; TrsFrshCls; ChrhWkr; HonRl; NHS; Sdlty; StuCncl; TchrAde; PresLatCl; GAA; IMSpt; College; Rn.

KLINK, Louise; Hartford Union HS; Rubicon, WI; ChrhWkr; HonRl; NHS; Univ Of Wisconsin Whitewater; Accountant.

KLINKEL, Douglas D; Charles City Community HS; Charles City, IA; ALBoysSt; HonRl; Mdrgl; StuCncl; PresYthFlsp; GerCl; PpCl; Bsbl; LetterFtbl; Swmmng; College; Professional.

KLINKENBERG, Grace M; St Louise De Marillac HS; Chicago, IL; PpCl; Bsktbl; GAA; IMSpt; Creighton University; Nursing.

KLINKENBORG, Paul E; Parkersburg Community HS; Parkersburg, IA; VPFrshCls; VPSophCls; PresJrCls; ALBoysSt; PresStuCncl; StuGov; 4-H; LetterFtbl; RotaryAwd; University; Professional.

KLINNER, Roberta L; Antigo Sr HS; Aniwa, WI; 41/373 Band; CncrtBnd; HonRl; MrchBnd; PepBnd; RptrYrbk; 4-H; LatCl; Trk; 4-HAwd; Univ Wis; Rn.

KLIPP, Ronald P; West Chicago Comm HS; Winfield, IL; 4/320 Band; Chr; Chrl; CncrtBnd; HonRl; JrNHS; LitMag; Mdrgl; MrchBnd; NHS; Orch; PepBnd; SchMus; SchPl; Wheaton College; Music.

KLISARES, Steve C; Stephen Decatur HS; Decatur, IL; HonRl; NHS; SctActv; Illinois State University; Accounting.

KLITGAARD, Barbara A; Harlan Community HS; Harlan, IA; 47/252 Band; CncrtBnd; DrmMjrt; HonRl; MrchBnd; NHS; Twrl; YthFlsp; FrCl; PpCl; LetterBsktbl; LetterTrk; GAA; College; Medicine.

KLITZKE, David A; Oakland Craig HS; Oakland, NE; 3/50 PresSrCls; Band; Chr; ChrhWkr; HonRl; NHS; NatlMeritCmnd; SchPl; StuCncl; 4-H; Nebraska Wesleyan Univ; Business Admin.

KLITZKE, Sandra J; Menominee HS; Menominee, MI; Chr; ChrhWkr; HonRl; NHS; TchrAde; YthFlsp; Tennis; Clge; Elem Teaching.

KLITZKE, Tom W; Cambridge Senior HS; Cambridge, MN; SecJrCls; Chr; ChrhWkr; HonRl; JrNHS; NHS; SchPl; StuCncl; YthFlsp; Bsktbl; Ftbl; Trk; IMSpt; College; Teaching & Business Managment.

KLOBE, Deborah A; Southwest HS; St Louis, MO; 28/552 HonRl; OffAde; Yrbk; College; Vocation.

KLOBE, Margaret G; Lester Prairie Public HS; Lester Prairie, MN; LetterCncrtBnd; HonRl; MrchBnd; NHS; PepBnd; TchrAde; FHA; SciCl; LetterTrk; GAA; St Olaf College.

KLOBUCHAR, Louis A; Rich Central HS; Country Club Hills, IL; 28/400 HonRl; NHS; NatlMeritCmnd; PolWkr; GerCl; Northwestern Univ; Lawyer.

KLOCEK, Kimberly J; Winnebago Public HS; Winnebago, MN; 2/39 SecSophCls; Band; Chr; CncrtBnd; HonRl; MrchBnd; PepBnd; Yrbk; FHA; Vocational School; Medical Secretary.

KLOCKE, Arlan; Clay Center Comm HS; Clay Center, KS; ChrhWkr; Kansas State Univ; Landscape Horticulture.

KLOCKE, Craig C; Rockwell City HS; Rockwell City, IA; 3/76 ALBoysSt; HonRl; NHS; 4-H; FFA; Bsbl; Bsktbl; Trk; IMSpt; 4-HAwd; Coll; Agriculture.

KLOCKE, Gregory; Cambridge HS; Cambridge, NE; Band; CncrtBnd; HonRl; MrchBnd; SchPl; StuCncl; Doane Coll; Business Acctg.

KLOCKE, Rae L; Rockwell City HS; Rockwell City, IA; 25/65 Band; CncrtBnd; HonRl; SchMus; Twrl; 4-H; FFA; VPJrCls; LetterTrk; 4-HAwd; Des Moines Area Com Col; Surg Tech.

KLOCKE, Rita K; Rockwell City Community HS; Rockwell City, IA; 1/62 VPSophCls; Band; CncrtBnd; HonRl; LbryAde; MrchBnd; NHS; NatlMeritFnl; PresYthFlsp; Yrbk; Iowa State U; B S In Medical Tech.

KLOECKL, Tim J; Arlington Green Isle HS; Arlington, MN; Chr; ChrhWkr; CmntyWkr; HonRl; RptrYrbk; SpnCl; PpCl; Bsbl; Bsktbl; Ftbl; Trade School.

KLOECKNER, Barry G; Grand Ledge HS; Ealge, MI; ChrhWkr; HonRl; NatlMeritFnl; SctActv; StuCncl; 4-H; SpnCl; Bsbl; Glf; 4-HAwd; Elect Engineer.

KLOEPPEL, Terence L; Malta Bend R 5 HS; Malta Bend, MO; 1/19 ALBoysSt; HonRl; PresNHS; PresStuCncl; SptEdYrbk; RptrSchPpr; PresFFA; LetterBsbl; LetterBsktbl; LetterTrk; AmLegAwd; Univ Of Missouri; Journalist.

KLOEPPER, Gary L; Red Bud HS; Red Bud, IL; Band; Chrs; ChrhWkr; CncrtBnd; HonRl; MrchBnd; PepBnd; SchMus; SchPl; YthFlsp; RptrSchPpr; Bsbl; LetterBsktbl; Jr College; Lab Technician.

KLOEPPER, Janell L; Neligh HS; Tilden, NE; HonRl; LbryAde; TchrAde; 4-H; PpCl; College; Teacher.

KLOEPPER, Rickey J; Red Bud Community HS; Red Bud, IL; Aud/Vis; CmntyWkr; LbryAde; SctActv; SchPpr; SpnCl; SciCl; Trk; University; Professional.

KLOKE, Margaret M; Mendota HS; Mendota, IL; 23/200 HonRl; HospAde; IntrClCncl; YthFlsp; FHA; FNA; Coll; Nurse.

KLOKER, Marsha J; Beardstown Sr HS; Beardstown, IL; 6/130 Chrs; HonRl; SchMus; SctActv; RptrSchPpr; FHA; FTA; SciCl; Trk; IMSpt; U Of Illinois; Chemist.

KLOMSTEN, Debbie A; Gale Ettrick Trempealeau HS; Trempealeau, WI; DrlTm; HonRl; PpCl; GAA; Trade School; Vocation.

KLONT, Jeffrey E; Charlotte HS; Charlotte, MI; 59/265 HonRl; SchAde; TchrAde; Ftbl; RotaryAwd; Ferris Clg; Auto Motive Ser.

KLOOS, Michael R; Canby HS; Canby, MN; Chr; ChrhWkr; HonRl; FFA; LetterBsbl; Wrstlng; Service.

KLOOS, Teresa; Canby HS; Porter, MN; CmntyWkr; Yrbk; College; Law.

KLOOSTERHOUSE, Laurie; Coopersville Sr HS; Coopersville, MI; Chr; HonRl; NHS; SchMus; SchPl; StuCncl; YthFlsp; PpCl; Bsktbl; IMSpt; Hope Coll; Psych.

KLOOSTERHOUSE, Lonnie; Coopersville Senior HS; Coopersville, MI; Chr; ChrhWkr; HonRl; NHS; SchMus; SchPl; StuCncl; PpCl; Chrldr; PPFtbl; Davenport College; Medical Secretary.

KLOOTWYK, Kent W; Knoxville HS; Knoxville, IA; PresFrshCls; VPJrCls; CmntyWkr; HonRl; NatlThespSoc; SchPl; StuCncl; YthFlsp; 4-H; LetterFtbl; Trk; IMSpt; 4-HAwd; PresAwd; University; Professional.

KLOPF, Gary J; Madison HS; Madison, SD; 5/161 ALBoysSt; Chr; Chrs; HonRl; NHS; EdYrBk; FBLA; LetterFtbl; LetterTennis; Augustana College; Bio Chemistry.

KLOPFENSTEIN, Karen S; Huntington North HS; Huntington, IN; Chr; HonRl; NatlThespSoc; SchMus; SchPl; Indiana University; Art.

KLOPPENBORG, Joyce S; O Neill Public HS; O Neill, NE; SecFrshCls; TrsJrCls; NHS; TchrAde; PpCl; Trk; Chrldr; GAA; IMSpt; 4-HAwd; PresAwd; College; Liberal Arts.

KLOPPING, Jeffrey L; Central HS; Omaha, NE; 2/400 HonRl; PresJA; NatlMeritSF; NatlSciFnd; OffAde; SctActv; StuCncl; LatCl; PresMthCl; OptClAwd; College; Physics.

KLOS, Kathryn A; Wausau East HS; Wausau, WI; 17/298 Chr; Chrs; LbryAde; Mdrgl; NHS; SchPl; StuGov; SchPpr; FBLA; GAA; Univ Wisc; Medical Tech.

KLOSE, Carl O; Southwest HS; St Louis, MO; 51/197 Chr; HonRl; ModUN; MthCl; College; Professional.

KLOSS, Brian K; Switzerland County HS; Vevay, IN; ALBoysSt; HonRl; NHS; SchPl; 4-H; FrCl; PpCl; Bsbl; Trk; College; Accountant.

KLOSTERMAN, Anne M; Wyndmere HS; Wyndmere, ND; VPFrshCls; SecSophCls; ALAGirlsSt; Chr; HonRl; NHS; Yrbk; RptrSchPpr; MthCl; Chrldr; College; Pharmacy.

KLOSTERMAN, Craig G; Wahpeton Sr HS; Mooreton, ND; ALBoysSt; Band; HonRl; MrchBnd; Walpeton Trade School; Veterinarian.

KLOSTERMAN, David C; Wyndmere Public HS; Wyndmere, ND; ALBoysSt; Chr; HonRl; SchPl; SctActv; StuCncl; RptrYrbk; SchPpr; MthCl; RotaryAwd; College; Lawyer.

KLOSTERMAN, Debra A; Platte Community HS; Platte, SD; Band; ChrhWkr; HonRl; OffAde; YthFlsp; Yrbk; SchPpr; FHA; PpCl; Chrldr; Univ; Business Ed.

KLOSTERMAN, Susan M; Wyndmere Public HS; Wyndmere, ND; SecSophCls; SecJrCls; ALAGirlsSt; Chr; Chrs; ChrhWkr; HonRl; SchPl; RptrYrbk; EdYrBk; FHA; N Dakota St Univ.

KLOSTERMAN, Victor J; Wahpoton Senior HS; Mooreton, ND; ChrhWkr; HonRl; NHS; Trade School.

KLOTH, Larry W; Cahokia HS; Cahokia, IL; 18/559 Band; ChrhWkr; HonRl; NHS; NatlMeritCmnd; Washington Univ; Political Science.

KLOTTER, Jenine D; Resurrection HS; Chicago, IL; Chr; HonRl; LitMag; Quill&Scroll; RptrSchPpr; Lewis University; Law.

KLOTZ, Steven S; Thomas Jefferson HS; Rockford, IL; 50/335 HonRl; JrNHS; NHS; SctActv; LatCl; LetterBsbl; Bsktbl; LetterFtbl; Augustana College; Medicine.

KLOVSTAD, Stuart; Fergus Falls Senior HS; Fergus Falls, MN; 11/342 ChrhWkr; CmntyWkr; HonRl; PolWkr; LatCl; Bsktbl; Ftbl; CchngActv; DARAwd; College; Lawyer.

KLUCKMAN, Patrick N; Boone HS; Boone, IA; VPJrCls; ALBoysSt; HonRl; StuCncl; LatCl; PpCl; YthFlsp; Bsbl; Bsktbl; Ftbl; Drake; Law.

KLUDJIAN, Michael P; Fordson HS; Dearborn, MI; HonRl; NHS; NatlMeritCmnd; Univ Of Mich.

KLUDT, Beth; Mt Clemens HS; Mt Clemens, MI; 9/400 ChrhWkr; HonRl; NHS; TchrAde; SpnCl; Swmmng; GAA; IMSpt; Michigan St Univ; Business Admin.

KLUEH, Karen S; West Vigo HS; W Terre Haute, IN; 11/200 Chrl; HonRl; SchMus; TchrAde; RptrSchPpr; FTA; GAA; Indiana State Univ; Education.

KLUESNER, Bonnie; Beckman HS; Worthington, IA; GAA; College; Medical Technology.

KLUESNER, Julie K; Beckman HS; New Vienna, IA; Chrs; PpCl; LetterGAA; Voch Tech School.

KLUESNER, Susan E; Jackson HS; Cp Girardeau, MO; 16/211 ChrhWkr; HonRl; NHS; Treas-Quill&Scroll; VPFHA; VPFrCl; PpCl; Se Mo Univ; Nurse.

KLUETER, Ann M; Porta HS; Petersburg, IL; 6/131 Chrs; HonRl; NHS; SchMus; YthFlsp; 4-H; College; Nursing.

KLUETER, Karen; Edwardsville HS; Edwardsville, IL; Chr; Chrs; ChrhWkr; LbryAde; YthFlsp; 4-H; PpCl; GAA; College; Teacher.

KLUEVER, John W; West Bend East HS; West Bend, WI; LetterBsktbl; LetterTrk; College; Professional.

KLUEVER, Linda R; Wausau E Sr HS; Wausau, WI; 15/298 HonRl; NHS; Orch; Teen; YthFlsp; RptrYrbk; MthCl; Trk; U W Madison; Pharmacy.

KLUEVER, Mary; Anita Community HS; Anita, IA; 19/61 SecJrCls; SecSrCls; DrlTm; HonRl; RptrYrbk; SptEdYrbk; 4-H; Bsktbl; Glf; Trk;.

KLUG, Henry J; Roncalli HS; Omaha, NE; HonRl; NHS; SctActv; TchrAde; EdYrBk; Yrbk; SchPpr; SciCl; Coll; Mech Engi.

KLUG, Kathy L; Lakeview HS; Columbus, NE; Band; Chr; CncrtBnd; HonRl; LbryAde; MrchBnd; PepBnd; StuGov; 4-H; PpCl; 4-HAwd; College; Elementary School Teacher.

KLUG, Linda J; Calamus Comm HS; Calamus, IA; ChrhWkr; CncrtBnd; PepBnd; SchMus; SchPl; RptrYrbk; Pres4-H; Glf; Chrldr; 4-HAwd;.

KLUG, Margaret; Lebanon HS; Lebanon, MO; 1/270 SecBand; Chr; CncrtBnd; HonRl; MrchBnd; NHS; VP4-H; VPFTA; Tennis; 4-HAwd; University; Science.

KLUGE, Charles D; Charleston HS; Charleston, IL; Aud/Vis; HonRl; NHS; NatlMeritFnl; NatlMeritCmnd; NatlMeritSF; PolWkr; SchPl; VPStuCncl; University; Mechanical Engineer.

KLUK, Andy S; St Patrick HS; Chicago, IL; 93/427 ChrhWkr; HonRl; StuCncl; Depaul Univ; Sociology.

KLUK, Diane P; Marie S HS; Chicago, IL; NHS; OffAde; StuCncl; Yrbk; RptrSchPpr; Mac Cormac Jr College; Attorney.

KLUMB, David A; Marshfield HS; Marshfield, WI; 26/332 Band; ChrhWkr; HonRl; MrchBnd; NHS; PepBnd; 4-H; PresFFA; EldAwd; LionAwd; Univ Of Wis Madison; Agronomy.

KLUMP, Carol A; Whiteford HS; Ottawa Lake, MI; 2/81 PresBand; ChrhWkr; PresNHS; SchMus; StuCncl; RptrYrbk; RptrSchPpr; SecSpnCl; DARAwd; CitAwd; Spring Arbor College; Youth Counsellor.

KLUMP, Kerstin G; Wheeling HS; Wheeling, IL; 8/450 CncrtBnd; HonRl; HospAde; MrchBnd; NHS; NatlMeritCmnd; Orch; PepBnd; PolWkr; University; Nursing.

KLUMPP, Deann R; Bradford HS; Wyoming, IL; 2/47 Band; Chrs; CncrtBnd; HonRl; LbryAde; NHS; OffAde; RptrSchPpr; FHA; SpnCl; Bsktbl; Methodist Medical Center; Nursing.

KLUNGSETH, Mary A; Hamlin Ind Dist #1 HS; Bryant, SD; Band; Chr; ChrhWkr; HonRl; Yrbk; SchPpr; 4-H; GerCl; PpCl; LetterTrk; College; Nursing.

KLUNK, Linda K; Calhoun HS; Michael, IL; Chrs; HonRl; GAA; Business School; Secretary.

KLUSENDORF, Byran J; Mount Horeb HS; Mount Horeb, WI; Band; ChrhWkr; CncrtBnd; MrchBnd; PepBnd; Bsktbl; LetterFtbl; LetterTrk; IMSpt; RotaryAwd; U Fo Wi Whitewater; Chiropractor.

KLUSKA, Janeen G; Amos Alonzo Stagg HS; Hickory Hills, IL; 10/468 Band; ChrhWkr; LetterCncrtBnd; JrNHS; NHS; NatlMeritSF; TchrAde; YthFlsp; FrCl; SciCl; Bsktbl; GAA; Univ Of Illinois; Professional.

KLUSKA, Maureen; Divine Child HS; Dearborn, MI; HonRl; NatlFornLg; NatlThespSoc; Quill&Scroll; SchMus; SchPl; StuCncl; StuGov; RptrSchPpr; SchPpr; Univ; Business Admid.

KLUTE, Janice E; Lee HS; Wyoming, MI; SecJrCls; Band; HonRl; NHS; SchMus; YthFlsp; EdYrBk; RptrSchPpr; SpnCl; PpCl; Northwestern College; Journalism.

KLUTHE, Dale; North Loop Scotia HS; Scotia, NE; ChrhWkr; CmntyWkr; HonRl; SchPl; FFA; Ftbl; Coll; Pro.

KLUTHE, Donald; Dodge HS; Dodge, NE; HonRl; StuCncl; Bsktbl; IMSpt; Univ.

KLYN, Sharon K; Mt Pleasant HS; Mt Pleasant, IA; 11/160 Chr; Chrl; Chrs; ChrhWkr; HonRl; NHS; 4-H; Bsktbl; Trk; Sioux Falls College; Physician Asst.

KMAK, Ken E; Oak Forest HS; Oak Forest, IL; 31/326 Band; Chr; HonRl; LitMag; Mdrgl; MrchBnd; NHS; PepBnd; SchMus; SchPl; StuCncl; RptrYrbk; RptrSchPpr; College; Conductor.

KMETYK, Tanis; Evanston Twsp HS; Evanston, IL; ModUN; FrCl; University Of Illinois; Social Worker.

KMIATEK, Kim M; Morton Sr HS; Hammond, IN; HonRl; LbryAde; StuCncl; Purdue University; Medical Technology.

KMIEC, Deborah J; Girard HS; Girard, KS; 5/89 ChrhWkr; DrlTm; HonRl; NHS; OffAde; TchrAde; Teen; FHA; PpCl; College; Home Ec.

KMIECIK, Janet C; Lourdes HS; Chicago, IL; 34/277 HonRl; HospAde; NHS; PolWkr; StuCncl; StuGov; FrCl; Univ Of Illinois; Physical Therapist.

KMUCHA, Steven T; Galena HS; Galena, IL; TreasAFS; Band; Chrs; CncrtBnd; HonRl; MrchBnd; SchMus; RptrYrbk; RptrSchPpr; SpnCl; University ;medicine.

KMUCHA, Terri J; Granite City HS; Granite, IL; 21/630 Aud/Vis; Chrs; HonRl; NHS; NatlMeritSchl; OffAde; PpCl; Tennis; Trk; Western Illinois Univ; Accounting.

KNABUSCH, Robert W; Ida HS; Monroe, MI; 4/175 Band; ChrhWkr; CncrtBnd; HonRl; JrNHS; MrchBnd; NHS; PepBnd; 4-H; Bsbl; Glf; Wrstlng; IMSpt; College; Accounting.

KNACK, Connie J; S S Peter & Paul HS; Saginaw, MI; Chrs; CncrtBnd; DrlTm; HonRl; HospAde; Mdrgl; MrchBnd; SchMus; Yrbk; Delta College; Nursing.

KNAGGS, Charles; St Francis De Sales HS; Ottawa Lake, MI; SchPpr; IMSpt; Coll; Pharmacy.

KNAPIK, Patricia; Greenfield HS; Greenfield, WI; Band; CncrtBnd; HonRl; MrchBnd; StuCncl; GAA; Uw Platteville; Engineering.

KNAPP, Cornelia; Charleston HS; Charleston, IL; 11/260 Chrs; NHS; StuCncl; Yrbk; University; Mathematics.

KNAPP, David; Gibson Southern HS; Haubstadt, IN; PresFrshCls; TrsSophCls; ALBoysSt; SctActv; SciCl; Bsbl; Bsktbl; Ftbl; Trk; IMSpt; Purdue Univ; Elec Engineer.

KNAPP, David K; Southgate Aquinas HS; Allen Park, MI; CmntyWkr; HonRl; NHS; StuCncl; StuGov; EdSchPpr; Bsbl; GovHonPrgAwd; JAAwd; VoiceDemAwd; College; Professional.

KNAPP, Debra S; Hamilton Heights HS; Cicero, IN; ChrhWkr; NHS; Quill&Scroll; SchPl; StuGov; EdYrBk; 4-H; PpCl; LetterChrldr; CitAwd; Anderson Coll; Busi.

KNAPP, Gale B; Lancaster Sr HS; Bloomington, WI; PresJrCls; StuCncl; 4-H; FFA; CaptCaptCapt4-HAwd; PresAwd; Col; Vocation.

KNAPP, Lee A; Kingswood HS; Birmingham, MI; ChrhWkr; LitMag; SchMus; SchPl; SctActv; FrCl; Univ Of Cincinnati; Architecture.

KNAPP, Marilyn; Gibson Southern HS; Haubstadt, IN; 14/230 SecSophCls; TrsJrCls; Chr; Chrs; HonRl; StuCncl; RptrSchPpr; KeyCl; SciCl; BauchLmbAwd; Indiana Univ; Health Sci.

KNAPP, Mary; Wanamingo HS; Wanamingo, MN; TrsJrCls; HonRl; NHS; OffAde; TchrAde; EdSchPpr; FHA; Waldorf Coll; Secretary.

KNAPP, Mary K; Newman HS; Mason City, IA; HstSophCls; HstJrCls; HstSrCls; Chr; HonRl; SchMus; StuCncl; Yrbk; CaptTennis; GAA; Clarke College; Music.

KNAPP, Mary M; Newman HS; Wausau, WI; 3/142 Chrs; ChrhWkr; HonRl; LbryAde; ChmnNHS; SchMus; SecSctActv; RptrSchPpr; SpnCl; Trk; Coll.

KNAPP, Patricia A; Galesburg Sr HS; Wataga, IL; 31/588 ChrhWkr; HonRl; IntrClCncl; JrNHS; NHS; TchrAde; RptrYrbk; FrCl; Chrldr; College; Elem Ed.

KNAPP, Russell L; Western Comm HS; Sheffield, IL; 14/54 Band; Chrs; HonRl; MrchBnd; NatlThespSoc; PepBnd; SchPl; SctActv; StuCncl; College; Mechanical Engineer.

KNAPPER, Paul D; Sacred Heart HS; Sacred Heart, MN; PresJrCls; Chrl; HonRl; MrchBnd; PepBnd; SchMus; StuCncl; FFA; CaptBsbl; CaptBsktbl; College.

KNARR, Barbara L; St Mary Acad; Indianapolis, IN; Chr; Chrl; HonRl; VPGerCl; Music.

KNAUER, Carol L; Wauwatosa East HS; Wauwatosa, WI; Band; DrmMjrt; HonRl; MrchBnd; Orch; StuCncl; MthCl; Univ Of Wis; Accounting.

KNAUER, Kim E; Mt Pulaski HS; Mt Pulaski, IL; 6/106 PresJrCls; HonRl; JA; MrchBnd; NHS; StuCncl; EdSchPpr; GerCl; GAA; JAAwd; Ill State Univ; Journalism.

KNAUER, Lorna S; Van Buren HS; Greencastle, IN; 11/73 ALAGirlsSt; NHS; SchPl; SecFTA; PresSpnCl; PpCl; SciCl; GAA; College.

KNAUF, Cathryn M; Bark River Harris HS; Bark River, MI; 1/50 HstSrCls; ChrhWkr; HonRl; NatlMeritFnl; NatlMeritSchl; FNA; MthCl; SciCl; Chrldr; 4-HAwd; College; Nursing.

KNAUS, Kathleen R; John Marshall HS; Milwaukee, WI; CmntyWkr; JA; TchrAde; Bus Sch; Work With Children.

KNAUSS, Richard E; Heritage Christian HS; Indianapolis, IN; PresFrshCls; ChrhWkr; SptEdSchPpr; LetterSocr; Trk; College; Theatrical Writing.

KNECHT, Steven; Brookville HS; Brookville, IN; 1/172 Aud/Vis; NHS; RptrSchPpr; SchPpr; SpnCl; SciCl; Glf; University; Law.

KNECHTGES, Thomas; Holt HS; Holt, MI; 26/252 DrmMjrt; JA; JrNHS; NHS; FTA; SpnCl; Tennis; IMSpt; JAAwd; CitAwd; University Trade; Electrical Engineering.

KNEHANS, Lowell E; Lafayette Co Sch Dist C 1 HS; Higginsville, MO; 5/96 PresJrCls; PresSrCls; PresChrs; HonRl; VPNHS; PresYthFlsp; Pres4-H; SpnCl; BauchLmbAwd; 4-HAwd; U Of Northern Co; Ag Engr.

KNEIFL, Dennis G; West Salem HS; Coon Valley, WI; 4/80 VPSophCls; ChrhWkr; CmntyWkr; HonRl; NHS; StuCncl; SecFFA; LetterFtbl; LetterTrk; IMSpt; W Wisconsin Tech Institute; Agriculture.

KNENCHT, Diane E; Charles City HS; Charles City, IA; 52/227 TchrAde; Clge; Vet.

KNEPP, Larry; New Haven HS; New Haven, IN; 8/240 HonRl; SchPl; SciCl; IMSpt; Anderson College.

KNERL, Molly; Ponca Public HS; Ponca, NE; 1/34 ALAGirlsSt; Band; Chr; Chrs; ChrhWkr; CncrtBnd; HonRl; MrchBnd; NHS; PepBnd; SchPl; SctActv; College.

KNESS, Sheree J; Fairmont HS; Grafton, NE; 3/28 Chrs; ChrhWkr; HonRl; NHS; 4-H; PpCl; Univ Of Nebr; Veterinarian.

KNEZEK, Rhoda M; Hazel Park HS; Ferndale, MI; 15/410 Chr; Chrl; DrlTm; HonRl; NHS; NatlMeritCmnd; GAA; Wayne State; Biologist.

KNEZEVICH, Mike P; Morton Sr HS; Hammond, IN; Indiana University; Cpa.

KNICKERBOCKER, Kevin B; Winfield HS; Winfield, KS; Chr; Chrl; Chrs; Mdrgl; NatlThespSoc; SchAde; SchMus; SchPl; TchrAde; Swmmng; University; Architecture.

KNIEFEL, Terese; Waterville Elysian Public HS; Waterville, MN; 17/72 Band; Chr; Chrs; CncrtBnd; HonRl; MrchBnd; PepBnd; SchMus; GAA; IMSpt; St Cloud State; Special Ed.

KNIEP, Kent; North Boone HS; Poplar Grove, IL; /115 ChrhWkr; HonRl; NHS; LetterBsbl; LetterBsktbl; LetterFtbl; LetterGlf; LetterTrk; AmLegAwd; Coll;pro.

KNIEPKAMP, Wayne M; Belleville Township West HS; Belleville, IL; CncrtBnd; YthFlsp; Bsktbl; Tennis; IMSpt; Illinois State Univ; Cpa.

KNIES, Susan J; Dubois HS; Celestine, IN; 1/76 PresJrCls; VPSrCls; ALAGirlsSt; VPBand; HonRl; VPMrchBnd; PepBnd; SchMus; StuCncl; RptrSchPpr; SchPpr; 4-H; FHA; PpCl;.

KNIESER, Linda M; Kelvyn Park HS; Chicago, IL; NHS; TchrAde; Univ Of Illinois; Social Work.

KNIESLY, Lee Ann; Pioneer HS; Logansport, IN; 14/112 Band; ChrhWkr; CncrtBnd; HonRl; MrchBnd; NHS; YthFlsp; 4-H; SpnCl; College; Professional.

KNIESTEDT, Susan; Pattonville HS; Bridgeton, MO; HonRl; StuCncl; RptrSchPpr; PpCl; Chrldr; Southeast Mo St; Psych.

KNIEVEL, Linda M; Central Catholic HS; West Point, NE; 24/75 HonRl; NHS; SchPl; EngCl; PpCl; LetterTrk; Chrldr; IMSpt; PPFtbl; 4-HAwd; Doane College; Teach Music & Drama.

KNIFFIN, Mary E; Springfield Catholic HS; Springfield, MO; 2/49 Band; Chrs; ChrhWkr; CncrtBnd; HonRl; ModUN; SchMus; SctActv; RptrSchPpr; LetterBsbl; Trk; IMSpt; OptClAwd; College; English.

KNIGGA, Deborah K; Lawrenceburg HS; Lawrenceburg, IN; MrchBnd; NatlThespSoc; Quill&Scroll; SchPl; SctActv; SpnCl; PpCl; LetterTrk; GAA; IMSpt; Coll; Nursing.

KNIGHT, Amerophan; Richland Center HS; Muscoda, WI; HonRl; LetterBsktbl; GAA; PPFtbl; Business Schl; Liberal Arts.

KNIGHT, Dianne M; Monroe HS; Monroe, MI; 4/523 ChrhWkr; CmntyWkr; HonRl; MrchBnd; NHS; PepBnd; StuCncl; YthFlsp; PpCl; Eastern Michigan University; Mathematics.

KNIGHT, Donna L; Jamaica HS; Georgetown, IL; 1/60 PresJrCls; ChrhWkr; CncrtBnd; NHS; StuCncl; EdYrBk; SptEdYrbk; Yrbk; Pres4-H; VoiceDemAwd; Med Tech.

KNIGHT, Herbert T; Genoa Kingston HS; Genoa, IL; 15/94 Band; ChrhWkr; CncrtBnd; HonRl; MrchBnd; NHS; PepBnd; SctActv; College; Engineering.

KNIGHT, Katherine; Edgewood HS; Madison, WI; 5/180 Chrs; HonRl; HospAde; JrNHS; SchMus; StuCncl; Yrbk; PpCl; Univ Wisc; Law.

KNIGHT, Kenneth G; Frankenmuth HS; Frankenmuth, MI; 106/160 Aud/Vis; Band; HonRl; SchAde; SchMus; SchPl; StuGov; TchrAde; GerCl; Ftbl; Central Mi Univ; Pre Law And Bus Admn.

KNIGHT, Kevin; St Johns HS; St Johns, MI; 52/355 ALBoysSt; HonRl; JrNHS; LitMag; NHS; NatlMeritCmnd; StuCncl; StuGov; RptrSchPpr; Central Mi Univ.

KNIGHT, Pamela K; Brazil Sr HS; Brazil, IN; 6/163 HonRl; LbryAde; NHS; Business Schl; Secretary.

KNIGHT, Paul K; Metamora Township HS; East Peoria, IL; 5/175 HonRl; NHS; NatlMeritCmnd; LetterBsbl; CaptBsktbl; AmLegAwd; Bradley U ;med.

KNIGHT, Susan; Fulton HS; Fulton, IL; 14/120 Chr; CncrtBnd; HonRl; MrchBnd; NatlThespSoc; PepBnd; YthFlsp; 4-H; FTA; DARAwd; Work; Sales.

KNIGHT, Susan; Logan Rogersville HS; Rogersville, MO; Band; CncrtBnd; HonRl; LitMag; MrchBnd; NHS; NatlThespSoc; SchPl; SctActv; EdYrBk; College; English Teach.

KNIIVILA, Kim E; George C Bentley HS; Livonia, MI; AFS; Chr; HonRl; StuCncl; TchrAde; SpnCl; PpCl; CaptSwmmng; Chrldr; Western Mi Univ; Music.

KNIPFER, Sherry M; Tomahawk HS; Tomahawk, WI; ALAGirlsSt; Chrs; ChrhWkr; CmntyWkr; HonRl; SchMus; FBLA; SecMthCl; GAA; AmLegAwd; College; Elementary Ed.

KNIPMEYER, Sharon K; Higginsville HS; Higginsville, MO; AFS; Band; Chr; Chrl; ChrhWkr; DrlTm; 4-H; FTA; PpCl; 4-HAwd; Business School; Secretary.

KNIPMEYER, Susan L; Pittsfield HS; Pittsfield, IL; Band; Chrs; ChrhWkr; CmntyWkr; CncrtBnd; MrchBnd; PepBnd; FHA; FTA; LatCl; John Woods Comm Clg; Elem Sch Teacher.

KNIPP, Bradley R; Milton HS; Milton, WI; HonRl; SctActv; TchrAde; YthFlsp; RptrSchPpr; Ftbl; Uw Lacrosse; Pre Professional.

KNIPP, Kenneth G; R 1 North Callaway HS; Auxvasse, MO; PresJrCls; ALBoysSt; HonRl; SchPl; FrCl; Bsktbl; LetterFtbl; Trk; DARAwd; CitAwd; College; Accounting.

KNIPP, Sylvia T; Tipton HS; Tipton, MO; HonRl; NHS; SchPl; RptrYrbk; FHA; SpnCl; Univ Of Mo Columbia; Electrical Engineer.

KNISH, Susan J; Waseca HS; Waseca, MN; 4/205 SecTrsJrCls; Band; Chr; ChrhWkr; HonRl; PepBnd; StuGov; FNA; LetterSwmmng; GAA; College; Professional.

KNISPEL, Nancy M; Marian Catholic HS; Park Forest, IL; 56/302 VPSrCls; HonRl; NHS; StuCncl; Univ Of Illinois; French.

KNITT, Jill C; Flanagan HS; Flanagan, IL; Chr; CncrtBnd; HonRl; PepBnd; YthFlsp; Yrbk; 4-H; EngCl; Trk; 4-HAwd; College; Social Work.

KNOBBE, Patty A; Central Catholic HS; West Point, NE; Chrs; HonRl; NHS; RptrYrbk; Yrbk; RptrSchPpr; SchPpr; 4-H; LatCl; PpCl; College.

KNOBEL, Mark A; Fairbury HS; Fairbury, NE; 5/132 VPJrCls; Band; HonRl; NHS; StuCncl; Pres4-H; PresFBLA; LetterWrstlng; 4-HAwd; OptClAwd; Univ Of Ne; Agronomy.

KNOBEL, Suzan M; New Glarus HS; New Glarus, WI; ALAGirlsSt; Band; ChrhWkr; CncrtBnd; MrchBnd; NHS; PepBnd; YthFlsp; EdYrBk; Chrldr; College; Arts.

KNOBELOCH, Bruce N; Granite City South HS; Granite City, IL; 31/630 ChrhWkr; Southern Ill Univ; Lawyer.

KNOBELOCH, Thomas E; Newark Comm HS; Newark, IL; ChrhWkr; HonRl; NHS; SchPl; StuCncl; Pres4-H; FTA; LetterBsktbl; LetterSocr; LetterTrk; College; Math Sco.

KNOBLAUCH, Roger D; Lowpoint Washburn HS; Lowpoint, IL; 6/60 VPFrshCls; ALBoysSt; Band; Chr; Chrs; ChrhWkr; CmntyWkr; CncrtBnd; HonRl; Mdrgl; College; Special Education Pe.

KNOBLE, Louis J; Shawe Memorial HS; Madison, IN; 1/32 ALBoysSt; HonRl; NHS; NatlMeritSF; SctActv; PresStuCncl; SptEdSchPpr; LetterBsbl; LetterBsktbl; LetterTrk; Notre Dame ; Med.

KNOBLOCK, Glen; Armada HS; Armada, MI; 30/140 ChrhWkr; HonRl; SctActv; SpnCl; PpCl; Bsbl; Bsktbl; Ftbl; IMSpt; AmLegAwd; College.

KNOCHENMUS, Jon P; Roseau HS; Roseau, MN; 15/129 ALBoysSt; Chr; Chrs; CncrtBnd; HonRl; Mdrgl; SchMus; SctActv; RptrYrbk; Univ Of Minnesota; Management.

KNOCK, David D; Williamsburg HS; Williamsburg, IA; ChrhWkr; HonRl; Quill&Scroll; LetterFtbl; LetterGlf; LetterSwmmng; Concordia Seward.

KNODEL, Kerry L; Velva Public HS; Velva, ND; Chrs; HonRl; GerCl; College.

KNOEBEL, Daniel W; Hamilton HS; Menominee Falls, WI; HonRl; NHS; LetterFtbl; LetterTrk; College;.

KNOEBEL, John E; Mendel Catholic Prep HS; Chicago, IL; PresFrshCls; PresSophCls; SecTrsJrCls; TrsSrCls; ChrhWkr; CmntyWkr; HonRl; IntrClCncl; ModUN; NHS; NatlMeritCmnd; NatlMeritSchl; CaptBsbl; CaptFtbl; LetterTrk; College; Doctor.

KNOEBEL, John E; Mendel Catholic HS; Oak Lawn, IL; 21/200 PresFrshCls; PresSophCls; SecTrsJrCls; TrsSrCls; ChrhWkr; HonRl; IntrClCncl; NHS; NatlMeritFnl; CaptBsbl; CaptFtbl; LetterTrk; CaptWrstlng; Harvard Univ; Medicine.

KNOELL, Becky L; Superior HS; Superior, NE; Band; Chr; Chrs; ChrhWkr; CncrtBnd; MrchBnd; PepBnd; YthFlsp; FBLA; Business School; Legal Secretary.

KNOELL, Bunny L; Lewellen Rural HS; Leuellen, NE; PresFrshCls; PresSophCls; Chrs; ChrhWkr; HonRl; SchPl; Twrl; PpCl; Chrldr; 4-HAwd; College; Dietian.

KNOLL, Allen J; Turner HS; Kansas City, KS; 25/330 Band; HonRl; MrchBnd; NHS; PepBnd; SctActv; YthFlsp; PpCl; Trk; Chrldr; College.

KNOLL, Burke L; Adel Community HS; Adel, IA; VPSophCls; HonRl; LetterFtbl; LetterTrk; Wrstlng; Community Col; Farming.

KNOLL, Michael H; Hague Public HS; Hague, ND; 4/13 TrsFrshCls; TrsSophCls; VPJrCls; TrsSrCls; Chrs; HonRl; ModUN; Bsktbl; Trk; IMSpt; Trade School.

KNOLL, Paul; Hamilton HS; Holland, MI; 24/125 Band; Mdrgl; NatlMeritCmnd; StuCncl; GerCl; Ftbl; Trk; College; Technical Vocation.

KNOLLMAN, Brenda J; United Township HS; East Moline, IL; 17/517 Chrs; ChrhWkr; HonRl; LbryAde; NHS; NatlThespSoc; SchMus; SchPl; YthFlsp; Millikin Univ; Sociology.

KNOOP, Shelby J; Neillsville HS; Neillsville, WI; Chr; Chrs; HonRl; LbryAde; Yrbk; Sec4-H; SecFBLA; SpnCl; PpCl; 4-HAwd; Trade School; Medical Assistant.

KNOOT, Marvin R; North Mahaska Comm HS; Rose Hill, IA; 5/63 VPSophCls; VPJrCls; TrsSrCls; HonRl; NHS; StuCncl; PresYthFlsp; PresSciCl; CaptBsktbl; Indian Hill Comm College; Computer Programm.

KNOP, Brent B; Trico HS; Willisville, IL; Band; Chr; Chrs; ChrhWkr; CmntyWkr; CncrtBnd; HonRl; MrchBnd; SchMus; Yrbk;.

KNOP, Nancy L; Clifton Central HS; Clifton, IL; 21/126 TreasBand; Chrs; CncrtBnd; HonRl; Mdrgl; MrchBnd; NatlFornLg; NHS; TreasNatlThespSoc; PepBnd; LetterBsktbl; CaptTrk; VPGAA; Univ Of Illinois; Lawyer.

KNOPER, Carla S; Wheaton North HS; Wheaton, IL; 15/300 AFS; Chr; ChrhWkr; HonRl; LitMag; NHS; NatlMeritCmnd; PolWkr; SchMus; Tennis; Evergreen St Clg; Ecology.

KNOPER, Ronald; Unity Christian HS; Allendale, MI; CncrtBnd; MrchBnd; PepBnd; CaptSocr; College.

KNOPF, Timothy D; Wayne Memorial HS; Westland, MI; Band; ChrhWkr; CmntyWkr; CncrtBnd; HonRl; MrchBnd; NHS; Orch; PepBnd; Trk; Clge; Medicine.

KNOPP, Cindy; Owen Withee Hs; Whithee, WI; 2/98 CmntyWkr; HonRl; NatlSciFnd; SchPl; TchrAde; SchPpr; MthCl; SciCl; 4-HAwd; CitAwd; College; Medical Technology.

KNOPP, Janice E; Girard HS; Girard, KS; SecFrshCls; ALAGirlsSt; Band; HospAde; NHS; StuCncl; Teen; YthFlsp; 4-H; PpCl; Kansas State U; Business Administration.

KNOPP, Steve J; Shelbyville HS; Shelbyville, IN; Band; CncrtBnd; HonRl; MrchBnd; PepBnd; SctActv; YthFlsp; 4-H; Trade Sch; Voc.

KNOPPS, Mary C; Amboy Goodthunder HS; Waseca, MN; 9/44 ChrhWkr; HonRl; HospAde; NatlFornLg; NatlThespSoc; TchrAde; Mankato St College; Elem Teacher.

KNORR, Robert J; Sturgis HS; Sturgis, MI; HonRl; JA; SchAde; SchPl; LatCl; PpCl; LetterFtbl; LetterGlf; LetterSocr; LetterTennis; Lake Superior Clge; Pro Accountant.

KNORR, Scott J; Lanark HS; Lanark, IL; 19/56 TrsFrshCls; Aud/Vis; Chrs; HonRl; StuGov; FrCl; PpCl; Bsktbl; Ftbl; Trk; Univ; Radio Broadcasting.

KNOSP, Betty; Palisade Public HS; Palisade, NE; 1/10 ALAGirlsSt; Band; Chr; ChrhWkr; HonRl; NHS; EdYrBk; EldAwd; 4-HAwd; Mc Cook Community Coll; Secretarial Science.

KNOTEK, Amy L; Aurora Central Catholic HS; Aurora, IL; 10/126 VPJrCls; Chrs; HonRl; JrNHS; NHS; SchMus; StuCncl; RptrYrbk; Chrldr;.

KNOTH, Linda C; Regina HS; Grosse Pointe, MI; ChrhWkr; HonRl; NHS; NatlThespSoc; SchPl; StuCncl; MthCl; Tennis; PPFtbl; Wayne St Univ; Bus Admin.

KNOTT, Brad T; Kuemper HS; Carroll, IA; ALBoysSt; StuCncl;.

KNOTT, Cherlyn M; Holy Trinity HS; Newgermany, MN; Chrs; HonRl; Mdrgl; OffAde; SchMus; 4-H; PpCl; IMSpt; Vocational School; Receptionist.

KNOTT, Doreen P; Holy Trinity HS; New Germany, MN; 2/47 HonRl; OffAde; SchAde; 4-H; St Benedict; Business Admin.

KNOTT, Jonathan E; Muscatine HS; Muscatine, IA; HonRl; University; Professional.

KNOUS, Steven C; Springfield Southeast HS; Springfield, IL; 10/480 JrNHS; NHS; Illinois State University; Accountant.

KNOWLAN, Mary S; Jackson HS; Jackson, MO; 31/212 Band; ChrhWkr; HonRl; MrchBnd; NHS; VPNatlMeritFnl; SchPl; VPStuCncl; SchPpr; FrCl; Univ Of Mo; Speech Drama.

KNOWLES, Bill K; Peru HS; Peru, IN; CncrtBnd; HonRl; MrchBnd; NHS; SchMus; LatCl; Tennis; Trk; Indiana Univ Kokomo; Pre Med.

KNOWLES, James W; Creighton Prep; Omaha, NE; HonRl; NHS; NatlMeritCmnd; Sdlty; Bsbl; Bsktbl; LetterGlf; RotaryAwd; U Of Miami; Law.

KNOWLES, Mark A; Denison HS; Denison, IA; ALBoysSt; HonRl; SchPpr; Bsbl; LetterFtbl; LetterTrk; IMSpt;.

KNOWLES, Martha K; Hillsdale HS; Hillsdale, MI; Band; CncrtBnd; HonRl; MrchBnd; NHS; Orch; SctActv; Teen; 4-H; LetterTennis; University.

KNOX, Barbara A; Catlin HS; Catlin, IL; 2/57 Chr; HonRl; LitMag; NHS; StuCncl; EdYrBk; FrCl; PresSciCl; GAA; BttyCrckrAwd; U Of Dayton; Translator.

KNOX, Barbara S; Sand Creek HS; Sand Creek, MI; SecFrshCls; TrsSophCls; SecJrCls; Band; CncrtBnd; HonRl; NHS; TchrAde; Yrbk; FTA; Coll; Teach%r.

KNOX, Christopher B; Cooley HS; Detroit, MI; ChrhWkr; DrlTm; HonRl; RedCrAde; TchrAde; Lawrence Inst Of Tech; Architectural Tech.

KNOX, Dara L; Ursuline Academy; Springfield, IL; 4/83 Chr; NHS; StuCncl; 4-H; LatCl; Univ Of Illinois; Law.

KNOX, Kathy S; Clifton HS; Clifton, KS; TrsSophCls; PresJrCls; Chrl; Chrs; HonRl; LbryAde; StuCncl; Yrbk; FHA; PpCl; College; Accountant.

KNOX, Kenneth B; Caruthersville HS; Caruthersville, MO; HonRl; PolWkr; SchPl; Bsbl; Bsktbl; University.

KNOX, Linda A; Central HS; Kansas City, MO; 21/350 HonRl; JrNHS; NHS; OffAde; SpnCl; PpCl; SciCl; IMSpt; Creighton Univ; Bus Admin.

KNOX, Nancy L; Parkview HS; Orfordville, WI; 18/163 ChrhWkr; HonRl; TchrAde; FHA; GAA; Freed Hardeman Coll; Accounting.

KNOX, Robert D; Edwardsburg HS; Edwardsburg, MI; 13/146 PresJrCls; HonRl; NHS; StuCncl; Ftbl; Michigan St Univ; Medicine.

KNOX, Teresa K; Woodlawn HS; Woodlawn, IL; SecTrsFrshCls; Band; HonRl; RptrYrbk; RptrSchPpr; SpnCl; PpCl; Chrldr; 4-HAwd; College; Major Study.

KNOX, Twyla J; Monango Public HS; Monango, ND; 4/12 SecSophCls; PresJrCls; Band; Chrs; SchPl; StuCncl; 4-H; LetterBsktbl; LetterTrk; LetterChrldr; 4-HAwd; GodCntryAwd; North Dakota St Univ; Business.

KNOX, William B; Butler HS; Butler, MO; ALBoysSt; Band; CncrtBnd; PepBnd; SchPl; YthFlsp; RptrSchPpr; FrCl; Ftbl; CaptWrstlng; College; Education.

KNUCKEY, Todd A; Rochester Comm HS; Rochester, IL; 7/82 PresJrCls; HonRl; StuCncl; GerCl; Univ; Engineering.

KNUDSEN, Elizabeth A; Watertown Sr HS; Watertown, SD; 24/291 HonRl; NHS; 4-H; GerCl; Northern State College; Business.

KNUDSEN, Karen R; Valentine HS; Valentine, NE; ALAGirlsSt; HonRl; NHS; TchrAde; IMSpt; Clge; Legal Secretary.

KNUDSEN, Kathleen A; Wheaton Christian HS; Wheaton, IL; Chr; Chrs; ChrhWkr; HonRl; YthFlsp; SchPpr; College; Public Relations.

KNUDSEN, Mary A; Durant Comm HS; Durant, IA; 5/68 TrsSophCls; VPJrCls; HonRl; NHS; SchPl; StuCncl; 4-H; LetterBsktbl; LetterTrk; GAA; Univ Of Ia; Pol Sci.

KNUDSON, Greg; Wayne Comm HS; Corydon, IA; 2/76 PresSophCls; HonRl; PresNHS; StuCncl; StuGov; TreasSpnCl; LetterBsbl; LetterBsktbl; LetterFtbl; LetterTrk; University; Professional.

KNUDSON, Gregory J; Bottineau HS; Bottineau, ND; 3/66 PresSrCls; HonRl; SchPl; StuCncl; EdYrBk; SptEdSchPpr; PresSciCl; LetterBsbl; LetterBsktbl; CaptFtbl; College; Professional.

KNUDSON, Jacqueline; Coon Rapids HS; Blaine, MN; Band; Chr; HonRl; MrchBnd; 4-H; AmLegAwd; College; Medical Career.

KNUDSON, Julie A; Rothsay Public HS; Rothsay, MN; Band; Chr; Chrs; CncrtBnd; HonRl; LbryAde; PepBnd; SchMus; PpCl; Bsktbl;.

KNUDSON, Pamela J; Centerville Public HS; Centerville, SD; Band; Chrs; HonRl; LbryAde; MrchBnd; SchPl; EdYrBk; FHA; LetterSwmmng; Chrldr; Sdsu Brookings; Secretary.

KNUDTSON, Elizabeth; Memorial HS; Whitehall, WI; Chrs; HonRl; SctActv; StuCncl; Twrl; RptrSchPpr; Bsktbl; Trk; Chrldr; GAA; College; Professional.

KNUDTSON, Kristin A; Richfield HS; Richfield, MN; 16/800 HonRl; NatlMeritSF; SchAde; TchrAde; PpCl; GAA; IMSpt; St Olaf College; Health Fields.

KNUE, Myra A; Immaculate Conception Academy; Milan, IN; 31/60 ChrhWkr; HonRl; NHS; Sec4-H; SpnCl; Bsktbl; PresGAA; IMSpt; 4-HAwd; College; Agriculture.

KNUETTEL, Kim C; Iola Scandinavia HS; Iola, WI; 4/47 SecSophCls; ALAGirlsSt; Band; Chrs; HonRl; LbryAde; Mdrgl; NHS; SchPl; SctActv; RptrYrbk; RptrSchPpr; Marshfield; Nursing.

KNUETTEL, Marla M; Iola Scandinavia HS; Iola, WI; 4/55 SecSophCls; ALAGirlsSt; Band; Chrs; CncrtBnd; HonRl; JrNHS; LbryAde; MrchBnd; NatlFornLg; NHS; Business School; Vocation.

KNUFFMAN, Janice; Liberty Hs; Liberty, IL; 4/63 Chrs; HonRl; Sdlty; Yrbk; FHA; PpCl; Quincy College; Art.

KNUPP, Linda J; Southern HS; Lomay, IL; Band; Chrs; CncrtBnd; HonRl; HospAde; LbryAde; MrchBnd; PepBnd; StuCncl; Twrl; TreasFHA; Southeastern Comm College; Nursing.

KNURR, Rick A; Omro HS; Omro, WI; 1/112 ALBoysSt; ChrhWkr; HonRl; PresNHS; StuCncl; YthFlsp; SptEdSchPpr; LetterBsktbl; LetterTrk; Lawrence Univ.

KNUST, David J; Forest Park HS; St Anthony, IN; 12/126 PresSrCls; ALBoysSt; PresBand; ChrhWkr; HonRl; VPNHS; OffAde; PresStuCncl; 4-H; PpCl; Purdue Univ; Commercial Airlinepilot.

KNUST, Larry; Petersburg Public HS; Petersburg, NE; 6/25 SecTrsFrshCls; PresSophCls; Chrs; HonRl; RptrYrbk; EdYrBk; Yrbk; Glf;.

KNUTE, Kristina M; Alvarado Public HS; Warren, MN; Band; Chr; HonRl; HospAde; PepBnd; SchPl; PresYthFlsp; 4-H; PpCl; 4-HAwd; Univ Of Minnesota; Special Education.

KNUTH, John R; Beecher HS; Beecher, IL; 18/62 Band; HonRl; SptEdSchPpr; SciCl; LetterBsktbl; Glf; LetterTrk; IMSpt; Eastern Il Univ; Accountant.

KNUTH, Mark W; Portage Central HS; Kalamazoo, MI; Aud/Vis; Band; HonRl; NHS; NatlMeritSF; Orch; SchMus; SchPl; SchPpr; 4-H; K Clg; Biophysics.

KNUTH, Richard H; Elmhurst HS; Ft Wayne, IN; 64/381 HonRl; SctActv; TchrAde; LetterTrk; IMSpt; Purdue Univ; Architecture.

KNUTSEN, Sheree K; Forest Lake HS; Forest Lake, MN; Chr; HonRl; StuCncl; FrCl; GAA; Voc Sch; Child Development.

KNUTSON, Becky S; North HS; West Union, IA; LetterBand; LetterChrs; HonRl; NHS; NatlMeritFnl; PolWkr; SchMus; TreasStuCncl; SciCl; LetterBsbl; Bsktbl; LetterTrk; Univ; Law.

KNUTSON, Blaine A; Auburndale HS; Auburndale, WI; TrsFrshCls; VPJrCls; Band; CncrtBnd; HonRl; MrchBnd; PepBnd; SchAde; TchrAde; SptEdYrbk; College; Professional.

KNUTSON, Carla; Philip HS; Philip, SD; 15/40 VPSophCls; HonRl; StuCncl; StuGov; RptrSchPpr; FHA; PpCl; IMSpt;.

KNUTSON, Deborah; Monona Grove HS; Monona, WI; AFS; ChrhWkr; CncrtBnd; HonRl; JrNHS; NatlMeritCmnd; StuCncl; FrCl; MthCl; OptClAwd; Lawrence Univ; Pre Med.

KNUTSON, Donovan L; Warren HS; Radium, MN; 15/61 ALBoysSt; PresChrhWkr; HonRl; PolWkr; SchMus; SchPl; StuCncl; Pres4-H; AmLegAwd; 4-HAwd; University; Accounting.

KNUTSON, Kathy S; St Martins Academy; Rapid City, SD; CmntyWkr; HospAde; ModUN; NHS; PolWkr; StuCncl; 4-H; FDA; SciCl; CaptBsbl; LetterTrk; GAA; 4-HAwd; College; Medicine.

KNUTSON, Kristina G; Bradford HS; Kenosha, WI; 1/575 Aud/Vis; CAP; HonRl; JA; JrNHS; LbryAde; Mdrgl; NHS; NatlMeritSF; Orch; TchrAde; FTA; GerCl; Carthage College; Prof Biochemist.

KNUTSON, Lanelle J; Clear Lake HS; Clayton, WI; 9/76 CncrtBnd; MrchBnd; NHS; PepBnd; SchPl; 4-H; FHA; LetterTrk; GAA; 4-HAwd; College; Vet Medicine.

KNUTSON, Marice A; Wakonda Public HS; Wakonda, SD; VPJrCls; Band; Chrs; ChrhWkr; DrlTm; HonRl; NHS; SchPl; StuCncl; University; Professional.

KNUTSON, Marijune M; Caledonia Public HS; Caledonia, MN; Chr; HonRl; Yrbk; RptrSchPpr; 4-H; FHA; SpnCl; Trk; 4-HAwd; U Of Wisc; Dietician.

KNUTSON, Nancy S; Durand HS; Durand, WI; 3/150 NatlFornLg; NHS; NatlMeritCmnd; SchPl; PresSctActv; Sdlty; SecStuCncl; EdYrBk; GAA; College; Medicine.

KNUTSON, Patricia A; Sacred Heart HS; Sacred Heart, MN; TrsSophCls; Chr; LbryAde; OffAde; SchAde; SchPl; TchrAde; Yrbk; FHA; PpCl; Anoka Voc Tech; Surgical Tech.

KNUTSON, Paul L; Ashby Public HS; Dalton, MN; 1/25 PresJrCls; Band; Chr; Chrs; PresCncrtBnd; HonRl; SecNHS; PepBnd; SchPl; VP4-H; PresFFA; LetterBsktbl; Ftbl; College; Music Education.

KNUTSON, Perry L; Ashby HS; Ashby, MN; VPFrshCls; PresSophCls; SchPl; PresStuCncl; TchrAde; RptrYrbk; SchPpr; CaptBsktbl; CaptFtbl; CaptTrk; Fergus Falls Comm College; Social Worker.

KNUTSON, Scott M; Ottawa Hills HS; Grand Rapids, MI; HonRl; JrNHS; NHS; PolWkr; TchrAde; Coll; Pre Law.

KNUTSON, Signe A; Joseph A Craig Sr HS; Janesville, WI; Band; ChrhWkr; CncrtBnd; MrchBnd; NatlFornLg; SecNatlThespSoc; Orch; PepBnd; Quill&Scroll; SchMus; SchPl; SchPpr; College; Teacher.

KOBAYASHI, Amy M; Robert A Waller HS; Chicago, IL; 2/214 HonRl; NHS; SchPl; TchrAde; RptrYrbk; RptrSchPpr; KeyCl; PpCl; LetterTennis; IMSpt; Clge; Lib Arts.

KOBE, Anne M; Lake Orion HS; Lake Orion, MI; 41/350 ChrhWkr; CmntyWkr; HonRl; NatlFornLg; NHS; SctActv; TchrAde; GerCl; SciCl; Wrstlng; College; Elementary Teacher.

KOBEL, Jane S; Prairie Home HS; Jamestown, MO; Band; ChrhWkr; HonRl; SecStuCncl; RptrSchPpr; EdSchPpr; FHA; Univ; Social Work.

KOBER, Julie R; Stoughton Senior HS; Southgton, WI; Chrs; Mdrgl; SchMus; SchPl; TchrAde; SchPpr; GAA; Univ Of Wisc; English & Music.

KOBER, Mark; Wakefield HS; Wakefield, NE; 4/38 PresJrCls; HonRl; NatlMeritCmnd; PolWkr; StuGov; EdYrBk; Bsktbl; Trk; Univ; Prof.

KOBERSTINE, Janet; Oak Park River Forest Hs; Oak Park, IL; 87/1100 HonRl; LitMag; SctActv; CivCl; Trk; Uicc; Languages.

KOBIERZYNSKI, Teri; Northville HS; Northville, MI; NHS; NatlMeritFnl; SchMus; Mich St Univ-LAW Enforcement.

KOBIERZYNSKI, Teri A; Northville HS; Northville, MI; NatlMeritSF; SchMus; SchPl; Mi St Univ; Criminal Justice.

KOBILANSKY, Terry L; Glen Ullin HS; Glen Ullin, ND; VPFrshCls; ALBoysSt; Band; Chr; Chrs; HonRl; Mdrgl; SchPl; StuCncl; LetterTrk; Nd State Univ; Veterinarian.

KOBLER, Carole; Willowbrook Hs; Lombard, IL; 63/814 Chr; ChrhWkr; HonRl; YthFlsp; Augustana College; Nursing Major.

KOBLER, Debbie S; Marion Sr HS; Marion, IL; Chr; Chrs; DrlTm; MrchBnd; SchMus; FBLA; PpCl; Southern Illinois Univ; Professional.

KOBUS, William; Daniel J Gross HS; Omaha, NE; 14/169 HonRl; JA; NatlFornLg; NatlMeritCmnd; PpCl; JAAwd; Georgia Tech; Aerospace Engineer.

KOBYLARCZYK, Roger A; Thorp HS; Thorp, WI; CmntyWkr; HonRl; 4-H; FBLA; FFA; Bsktbl; Trk; IMSpt; 4-HAwd; Stout State Univ.

KOBZA, Kimberlee A; Marian HS; Omaha, NE; 25/162 HonRl; LbryAde; NHS; Sdlty; PresFrCl; LetterBsbl; IMSpt; College; Medical Field.

KOCA, Jane; Whitnall HS; Hales Corners, WI; HonRl; NHS; SpnCl; MthCl; GAA; Bryant & Stratton Bus Col; Accountant.

KOCER, Karen M; East Charles Mix HS; Wagner, SD; Chrs; ChrhWkr; HonRl; LbryAde; SctActv; RptrYrbk; RptrSchPpr; FHA; PpCl; RotaryAwd; College; Guideness Counselor.

KOCEVAR, Gail L; Benzie Central HS; Interlochen, MI; 2/123 Chr; DrlTm; HonRl; SecNHS; NatlMeritCmnd; NatlMeritSchl; NatlMeritSF; OffAde; StuCncl; Bsktbl; Trk; Nw Michigan College; Nursing.

KOCH, Annette M; Thornridge HS; So Holland, IL; 30/700 ChrhWkr; HonRl; JA; JrNHS; SecNatlFornLg; NHS; PresNatlThespSoc; OffAde; SchMus; SchPl; Swmmng; CchngActv; GAA; College; Speech.

KOCH, Brenda L; Marathon Cons HS; Marathon, IA; 9/19 PresJrCls; Band; Chr; Chrs; CncrtBnd; HonRl; MrchBnd; SchPl; YthFlsp; Trk; Chrldr; College.

KOCH, Constance; Tremont HS; Tremont, IL; SecFrshCls; Band; HonRl; NHS; Yrbk; FHA; GerCl; PpCl; Univ Of Ill; Business Adm.

KOCH, Dana A; Muskego HS; Muskego, WI; ChrhWkr; HonRl; NatlFornLg; NHS; NatlThespSoc; SchMus; SchPl; SctActv; StuCncl; YthFlsp; College; Professional.

KOCH, Diane; Waterford Mott Hs; Pontiac, MI; 1/384 Band; Chr; ChrhWkr; CmntyWkr; CncrtBnd; HonRl; MrchBnd; PepBnd; SchMus; TchrAde; Michigan State U; Elementary Education.

KOCH, Doyle; Wilber HS; Clatonia, NE; 3/45 HonRl; SchPl; RptrYrbk; RptrSchPpr; FBLA; Trk; CchngActv;.

KOCH, Elizabeth M; Notre Dame HS; Milwaukee, WI; 1/117 HonRl; NHS; OffAde; SchAde; SchMus; Yrbk; SchPpr; TreasFTA; PpCl; SciCl; IMSpt; RotaryAwd; Univ Of Wisconsin; Business Admin.

KOCH, Elizabeth J; Allison Bristow Comm HS; Allison, IA; 1/48 VPFrshCls; SecSophCls; TrsJrCls; Chrs; DrlTm; HonRl; SchPl; TchrAde; Bsktbl; Trk; College; Psychology.

KOCH, James A; Paul Harding HS; Fort Wayne, IN; 125/278 CaptFtbl; LetterTrk; CaptWrstlng; Butler U.

KOCH, James R; Lincoln Comm HS; Stanwood, IA; 11/67 HonRl; SchPl; StuCncl; RptrYrbk; RptrSchPpr; PpCl; SciCl; Ftbl; Trk; Wrstlng; Armed Services; Law Enforcement.

KOCH, John D; Crawford County R Ii HS; Cuba, MO; Band; CncrtBnd; MrchBnd; PepBnd; YthFlsp; 4-H; SpnCl; Bsbl; Bsktbl; Trk; Col; Pro.

KOCH, Katherine J; Kirkwood HS; Kirkwood, MO; 164/633 HonRl; StuCncl; Yrbk; PpCl; Chrldr; College.

KOCH, Kevin J; Br Rice HS; W Bloomfield, MI; 23/206 SecTrsFrshCls; SecTrsSophCls; SecTrsJrCls; HstSrCls; Chrl; Chrs; HonRl; NatlMeritCmnd; OffAde; FDA; Michigan Univ; Doctor.

KOCH, Libby M; Lafayette Co Ci HS; Higginsville, MO; VPChrs; ChmnDrlTm; HonRl; RptrSchPpr; FNA; PpCl; SciCl; IMSpt; College.

KOCH, Mark A; Lake Preston HS; Lake Preston, SD; 5/31 ALBoysSt; Band; ChrhWkr; CncrtBnd; HonRl; MrchBnd; PepBnd; PolWkr; SchMus; SchPl; SctActv; Ftbl; Trk; Air Force Academy; Engineer.

KOCH, Mary A; St Clair HS; St Clair, MI; NatlMeritFnl; NatlMeritCmnd; RptrYrbk; JCAwd; U Of Texas; Social Work.

KOCH, Mary C; Potosi R 3 HS; Cadet, MO; ChrhWkr; HospAde; LbryAde; SecNHS; NatlThespSoc; PolWkr; VP4-H; FNA; PresFTA; DanFAwd; 4-HAwd; College; Profesional.

KOCH, Mary M; Mt Vernon HS; Mt Vernon, SD; Chr; CncrtBnd; HonRl; JrNHS; NatlFornLg; NatlThespSoc; SctActv; SpnCl; Trk; 4-HAwd; Mt Marty Coll; Nursing.

KOCH, Nancy E; Liberty HS; Liberty, IL; 4/56 Band; ChrhWkr; HonRl; NHS; TchrAde; 4-H; FTA; PpCl; SciCl; Illinois Wesleyan Univ; Elem Education.

KOCH, Patricia R; Southwest HS; St Louis, MO; 70/594 Chrs; ChrhWkr; HonRl; SchMus; YthFlsp; FBLA; GerCl; PpCl; Fontbonne College; Early Childhood Educ.

KOCH, Rhonda; Leigh Community HS; Creston, NE; ALAGirlsSt; Chrs; HonRl; SchPl; FFA; GerCl; PpCl; Chrldr; PPFtbl; College; Unknown.

KOCH, Robert A; Forest View HS; Mt Prospect, IL; 95/620 Univ Of So Illinois; Marine Biology.

KOCH, Russell L; Mora HS; Brook Park, MN; 16/140 ALBoysSt; ChrhWkr; HonRl; NHS; Quill&Scroll; RptrSchPpr; FFA; LetterBsbl; CaptFtbl; LetterTrk; LetterWrstlng; PPFtbl; Northwestern College; Missionary.

KOCH, Shirley L; Gothenburg Public HS; Gothenburg, NE; HonRl; LbryAde; StuCncl; PresSophCls; 4-H; PpCl; AmLegAwd; Col; Fashion Merchandising.

KOCH, Terri S; Danville HS; Danville, IL; AFS; DrlTm; HonRl; OffAde; LatCl; SpnCl; LetterTrk; Univ Of Ill; Medicine.

KOCH, Timothy C; Immaclate Conception HS; Elmhurst, IL; Aud/Vis; HonRl; SchPl; RptrYrbk; LatCl; LetterBsktbl; LetterFtbl; LetterTrk; IMSpt; Univ Of Notre Dame; Law.

KOCHALKA, Gary L; Arthur Hill HS; Saginaw, MI; 22/683 NHS; LetterWrstlng; Michigan State Univ; Biologist.

KOCHALKA, Paula A; Maria HS; Chicago, IL; 11/301 SecJrCls; CmntyWkr; HonRl; NHS; PresStuCncl; RptrSchPpr; FrCl; MthCl; Univ Of Ill; Social Work.

KOCHANNY, William F; Hubbard HS; Chicago, IL; 15/400 Chr; Chrs; HonRl; NHS; Quill&Scroll; StuCncl; StuGov; EdSchPpr; MthCl; PresSciCl; Univ Of Ill; Engineering.

KOCHANSKI, Christina U; Addison Trail HS; Addison, IL; 11/510 Aud/Vis; HonRl; ModUN; NHS; SecOrch; PresGerCl; GAA; Univ Of Ill Champaign; Chemical.

KOCHELEK, Matthew J; St Josephs Prep; St Louis, MO; HonRl; NatlSciFnd; SchPl; StuCncl; RptrSchPpr; SchPpr; LetterSocr; CaptTennis; CaptWrstlng; IMSpt; Holy Redeemer Col; Priest.

KOCHENDERFER, Sandra L; George S Dondero HS; Royal Oak, MI; Band; CncrtBnd; MrchBnd; NHS; Yrbk; FrCl; Kalamazoo Col.

KOCHER, Brenda J; Sycamore HS; Sycamore, IL; 91/215 HonRl; HospAde; 4-H; FNA; Bsktbl; Tennis; College; Nursing.

KOCHER, Donna; Hh Bow HS; Midland, MI; 22/440 Chr; ChrhWkr; HonRl; NHS; PolWkr; YthFlsp; SpnCl; KiwanAwd; Hope College; Accounting Business.

KOCHER, Robert J; Roncalli HS; Indianapolis, IN; 10/187 ALBoysSt; HonRl; SctActv; LetterBsbl; LetterFtbl; College; Math.

KOCHIS, Mark P; Fitzgerald HS; Warren, MI; VPJrCls; PresSrCls; HonRl; StuCncl; StuGov; SchPpr; LetterBsbl; CchngActv; IMSpt; College.

KOCHKA, Jane C; Hinsdale Twnshp Central HS; Oak Brook, IL; 162/605 Chr; ChrhWkr; HonRl; NatlMeritCmnd; Orch; SchMus; SchPl; Yrbk; SchPpr; Univ; Medicine.

KOCI, Anita J; Chambers Public HS; Chambers, NE; TrsJrCls; VPSrCls; Chrs; HonRl; LbryAde; NHS; OffAde; SchAde; TchrAde; Yrbk; Col; Pro.

KOCI, Milton L; Wasburn Rural HS; Topeka, KS; VPFBLA; College; Lawyer.

KOCIAN, Stephen T; New Richmond Senior HS; New Richmond, WI; Band; ChrhWkr; CncrtBnd; HonRl; MrchBnd; Orch; PepBnd; SchMus; 4-H; 4-HAwd; Business School; Horticulturist.

KOCIK, Deborah S; Elk Grove HS; Des Plaines, IL; 87/505 ChrhWkr; CncrtBnd; HonRl; MrchBnd; Sweet Briar College; Psychology.

KOCIK, Peter M; Weyerhaeuser Public HS; Weyerhaeuser, WI; 1/30 TrsFrshCls; VPSrCls; CncrtBnd; HonRl; PepBnd; RptrYrbk; EdYrBk; PpCl; LetterBsktbl; CaptFtbl; Tech Sch; Professional.

KOCINSKI, Janice D; Notre Dame Girls HS; Chicago, IL; HonRl; OffAde; SchPl; SchPpr; Univ Of Illinois; Agriculture.

KOCINSKI, Karen S; Good Counsel HS; Chicago, IL; 25/251 HonRl; NatlMeritFnl; GerCl; Loyola Univ; Pre Medicine.

KOCK, Keri; Fremont Senior HS; Fremont, NE; 25/430 Band; ChrhWkr; CncrtBnd; HonRl; MrchBnd; NHS; Glf; GAA; IMSpt; GodCntryAwd; Univ Ne Lincoln; Med Tech.

KOCOLOWSKI, Carol L; Mother Of Sorrows HS; Calumet Park, IL; 3/143 ChrhWkr; HonRl; NHS; FrCl; VFWAwd; VoiceDemAwd; College; Elem Educ.

KOCOUREK, Bruce W; Tyndall HS; Tyndall, SD; 2/55 PresFrshCls; HonRl; StuCncl; FFA; Bsktbl; Ftbl; Glf; Trk; College.

KOCZOT, Ronald S; Marist HS; Chicago, IL; 40/370 CmntyWkr; SpnCl; Bradley Univ; Civil Engineer.

KOCZWARA, Joseph R; Bishop Noll Institute; Hammond, IN; 3/360 HonRl; NHS; IMSpt; NCTE; Purdue Univ; Engineering.

KODA, Kathleen; St Alphonsus HS; Dearborn, MI; 29/109 HonRl; SchMus; StuGov; PpCl; Chrldr; GAA; IMSpt; PPFtbl; Detroit Col Of Business; Certified Accnt.

KODADEK, David R; Proviso West HS; Berkeley, IL; ChrhWkr; CmntyWkr; HonRl; OffAde; SchAde; SctActv; GerCl; Ftbl; University; Business Administration.

KODIS, Anthony G; St Laurence HS; Chicago, IL; 51/386 HonRl; NatlMeritFnl; NatlMeritSF; SctActv; Univ Of Illinois; Chemistry.

KODRON, Beata B; Lourdes HS; Chicago, IL; 69/299 Chr; HonRl; SchMus; Sdlty; Illinois Inst Of Tech; Mathematics.

KOEBBE, Jan; Parkside HS; Jackson, MI; 45/450 TrsJrCls; VPSrCls; Chr; CmntyWkr; HonRl; GerCl; PpCl; Trk; Chrldr; IMSpt; Michigan State Univ; Airline Stewardess.

KOEBEL, Debra K; River Valley HS; Three Oaks, MI; HonRl; SchPpr; 4-H; Art.

KOEBELE, Nancy M; Newton Comm HS; Teutopolis, IL; 24/216 Band; HonRl; MrchBnd; NHS; 4-H; FHA; GAA; IMSpt; 4-HAwd; JAAwd; College; Business Woman.

KOEBER, Randy; Port Washington HS; Saukville, WI; ALBoysSt; ChrhWkr; HonRl; NatlMeritCmnd; MthCl; Bsktbl; KiwanAwd; Geneva Coll; Mechanical Eng.

KOEC, Michael; Frederic HS; Frederic, WI; Chr; HonRl; SchPl; RptrYrbk; Yrbk; IMSpt; Univ Of Minn; Pharmacy.

KOEDAM, Judy; Central Lyon HS; Doon, IA; 4/96 Chr; Chrl; Chrs; HonRl; Mdrgl; NHS; NatlMeritCmnd; SchMus; SchPl; VoiceDemAwd; College; Accountant.

KOEGEBOEHN, Deborah K; Chase County HS; Elmdale, KS; Band; Chrs; CncrtBnd; HonRl; MrchBnd; PepBnd; SchPl; PpCl; College; Accounting.

KOEHL, Jerry L; Forrest Strawn Wing HS; Cropsey, IL; Chr; HonRl; StuCncl; YthFlsp; SchPpr; FFA; LetterBsktbl;.

KOEHL, Joann M; Bishop Owenger HS; Avilla, IN; TchrAde; RptrSchPpr; Iu; Resp Therapy.

KOEHLER, Candy L; Auburn HS; Auburn, IL; 6/60 PresSophCls; TrsJrCls; HonRl; OffAde; SecStuCncl; StuGov; TchrAde; EdYrBk; RptrSchPpr; Tennis; Legal Sec.

KOEHLER, Cindy S; Van Buren HS; Center Point, IN; 7/69 VPSophCls; Band; HonRl; MrchBnd; NHS; Yrbk; Chrldr; GAA; College; Professional.

KOEHLER, Daniel E; South Adams HS; Berne, IN; MrchBnd; StuCncl; YthFlsp; Pres4-H; Bsbl; Bsktbl; LetterFtbl; Glf; CchngActv; 4-HAwd; College; Accounting.

KOEHLER, Debra A; Merrill HS; Merrill, WI; 31/334 Band; HonRl; PepBnd; SchMus; Treas4-H; GerCl; CaptBsktbl; Trk; PresGAA; 4-HAwd; College; Computer Science Major.

KOEHLER, Douglas E; Argonia HS; Argonia, KS; Chr; Chrs; ChrhWkr; SchPpr; LetterBsbl; LetterFtbl; Trk; College; Pro.

KOEHLER, Elizabeth A; Oconomowoc HS; Oconomowoc, WI; AFS; Chr; HonRl; JrNHS; NatlFornLg; NHS; OffAde; SchMus; SchPl; TchrAde; RptrSchPpr; University; Childrens Theater.

KOEHLER, Gerald L; Clay Center HS; Clay Center, NE; TrsSrCls; ChrhWkr; CncrtBnd; HonRl; StuCncl; TchrAde; RptrYrbk; Bsbl; Bsktbl; Ftbl; Midland College; Coaching.

KOEHLER, Kelly J; Wheaton/warrenville HS; Wheaton, IL; 20/300 Chr; Chrs; HonRl; TchrAde; 4-H; IMSpt; KiwanAwd; LionAwd; Univ Of Iowa; Recreation Education.

KOEHLER, Kevin L; Osmond Comm HS; Mc Lean, NE; 11/44 Band; Chr; Chrs; ChrhWkr; CncrtBnd; HonRl; MrchBnd; PepBnd; SchAde; SchMus; LetterBsktbl; LetterFtbl; Trk; Trade School; Vocation.

KOEHLER, Laura J; Roanoke Benson HS; Benson, IL; 11/110 SecSrCls; Chr; HonRl; TrsFrshCls; YthFlsp; FHA; FNA; PpCl; GAA; IMSpt; Coll; Nurse.

KOEHLER, Mindy L; Van Buren HS; Center Point, IN; 2/69 PresJrCls; Band; HonRl; MrchBnd; NHS; RptrYrbk; VPLatCl; Chrldr; GAA; IMSpt; College; Professional.

KOEHLER, Robert F; Mercy HS; Northwoods, MO; HonRl; Col; Forestry.

KOEHLER, Tammy J; Osmond Community HS; Pierce, NE; 14/44 Chr; ChrhWkr; HonRl; SchPl; TchrAde; RptrYrbk; FBLA; Business School; Secretary.

KOEHLER, Timothy A; Lyons Twp HS; Lagrange Park, IL; Univ Of Stevenspoint; Forestry.

KOEHLER, Wayne R; Merril Sr HS; Merrill, WI; 34/380 HonRl; NatlMeritCmnd; GerCl; LetterTrk; Wrstlng; KiwanAwd; VFWAwd; CitAwd; Uw Eau Claire; Nursing.

KOEHN, Danella M; Buhler HS; Buhler, KS; HonRl; StuCncl; TchrAde; Yrbk; FHA; GodCntryAwd; CitAwd; VoiceDemAwd; Coll.

KOEHN, Genette E; Larimore HS; Larimore, ND; Band; Chr; ChrhWkr; CncrtBnd; HonRl; MrchBnd; PepBnd; SchMus; 4-H; Business School; Court Reporter.

KOEHN, Jamie; Harbor Beach Community HS; Harbor Beach, MI; 17/135 ChrhWkr; NHS; St Clair Co Comm Coll;accounting.

KOEHN, Laurie J; Senior HS; Watertown, SD; ChrhWkr; CmntyWkr; HonRl; 4-H; FFA; GerCl; GAA; 4-HAwd; University; Professional.

KOEHN, Perry B; Copeland HS; Copeland, KS; ALBoysSt; ChrhWkr; JCC; RedCrAde; YthFnd; SptEdSchPpr; FDA; Bsktbl; AmLegAwd; CitAwd; Clge; Pro.

KOEHNE, Julianne L; Wayland Academy; Beaver Dam, WI; Chr; Chrs; HonRl; NHS; TreasNatlThespSoc; PolWkr; SchPl; Yrbk; PresFrCl; VPSpnCl; Chrldr; TIMEAwd; College; Foreign Journalism.

KOEHNE, Steven M; Lake Benton Public HS; Lake Benton, MN; Band; Chr; Chrs; CncrtBnd; MrchBnd; PepBnd; SchPl; Vocational School; Carpentry.

KOEL, Dianna L; Lenora HS; Lenora, KS; 12/26 SecTrsSophCls; SecTrsJrCls; Chrs; OffAde; SchAde;.

KOEL, Janet L; Norton Co HS; Norton, KS; Band; CncrtBnd; HonRl; MrchBnd; SchMus; Twrl; PpCl; LetterChrldr; AmLegAwd; College; Science.

KOELE, Lois I; Clinton HS; Clinton, WI; 15/92 ChrhWkr; HonRl; SchMus; VPYthFlsp; RptrYrbk; SchPpr; LetterBsktbl; GAA; IMSpt; KiwanAwd; Secretary.

KOELLIKER, Gregg E; Highland HS; Highland, KS; PresJrCls; ALBoysSt; Band; CncrtBnd; HonRl; MrchBnd; Orch; PepBnd; SchMus; StuCncl; College; Nurse.

KOELLING, Kimberly A; Lincoln Way HS; Manhattan, IL; SecJrCls; SecSrCls; Chrs; HonRl; Mdrgl; SchAde; SchMus; StuCncl; College; Social Work.

KOELSCH, Nancy L A; Wyatt Rd HS; Standish, MI; ChrhWkr; NatlFornLg; SchPl; SctActv; TchrAde; 4-H; 4-HAwd; JAAwd; OptClAwd; Northwood College; Retail Mgmt.

KOENEMAN, Don P; Chester HS; Chester, IL; PresSrCls; ALBoysSt; Band; ChrhWkr; CmntyWkr; CncrtBnd; HonRl; MrchBnd; PepBnd; PolWkr; Yrbk; PpCl; LetterBsktbl; LetterGlf; Univ Of Ind; Attorney.

KOENEMANN, Sue A; Mt Vernon HS; Mt Vernon, MO; 16/97 AFS; VPFrshCls; Chr; HonRl; ModUN; StuCncl; TchrAde; PresYthFlsp; FHA; FTA; Mo Southern State Coll; Legal Secretary.

KOENEN, Julie A; Cal Comm HS; Latimer, IA; VPSrCls; SecChrs; ChrhWkr; HonRl; NHS; SchPl; RptrYrbk; RptrSchPpr; LetterBsktbl; LetterGlf; 4-HAwd; College; Business.

KOENEN, Karen; New Holstein HS; New Holstein, WI; Chr; Chrs; ChrhWkr; HonRl; LitMag; NHS; Yrbk; SpnCl; Trk; Uw Madison; Music Education.

KOENEN, Sherri L; Meservey Thornton HS; Meservey, IA; 2/27 SecJrCls; VPSrCls; HonRl; SchPl; StuCncl; EdYrBk; EdSchPpr; PpCl; CaptBsktbl; LetterTrk; Amer Inst Of Bus; Med Sec.

KOENIG, Alan; Buffalo Lake Public HS; Hector, MN; PresFrshCls; Band; HonRl; SchPl; StuCncl; RptrSchPpr; FFA; U S Army.

KOENIG, Cheryl R; Ewing HS; Ewing, NE; 3/28 Chrs; HonRl; LbryAde; NHS; SecStuCncl; TchrAde; Yrbk; TreasPpCl; Trk; IMSpt; Bus Sch; Prof.

KOENIG, Cheryl R; Ewing Public HS; Ewing, NE; 3/28 Chrs; HonRl; NHS; VPStuCncl; TchrAde; Yrbk; PpCl; IMSpt; Business Schl; Professional.

KOENIG, Glennon G; Bishop Dubourg HS; St Louis, MO; 177/415 Ftbl; Trk; IMSpt; Colleg; Zoology.

KOENIG, Gregory; Hillman Community HS; Hillman, MI; Band; CncrtBnd; HonRl; MrchBnd;

PepBnd; SchMus; SchPl; Bsbl; Ftbl; IMSpt; Coll; Drafting.

KOENIG, Jennie; Odessa R Vii HS; Higginsville, MO; 9/136 Chrs; HonRl; NHS; YthFlsp; 4-H; PpCl; Chrldr; IMSpt; Clerical Work.

KOENIG, Kathy J; Warroad HS; Warroad, MN; 8/63 VPSophCls; SecJrCls; PresSrCls; Band; ChrhWkr; HonRl; MrchBnd; NHS; SchPl; Chrldr; College; Professional.

KOENIG, Kayla J; Prairie HS; Prairie Du Chien, WI; Band; CncrtBnd; MrchBnd; PepBnd; SchPl; TchrAde; Twrl; SpnCl; PpCl; IMSpt; College; Special Ed.

KOENIG, Robert; Gasconade County R 11 HS; Owensville, MO; AFS; ChrhWkr; HonRl; SchPl; YthFlsp; RptrSchPpr; 4-H; MthCl; SciCl; Ftbl; U Of Mo; Law.

KOENIGS, Joe T; Maple Valley HS; Mapleton, IA; TrsSophCls; PresSrCls; Chrs; ChrhWkr; CmntyWkr; StuCncl; Bsbl; Ftbl; Glf; CchngActv; Appliance Sch.

KOENIGSBERG, Joshua M; Yeshiva HS; Oak Park, MI; 4/20 NHS; NatlMeritCmnd; PolWkr; SchPl; StuCncl; RptrSchPpr; MthCl; SciCl; Bsktbl; University; Computer Science.

KOENIGSFELD, Ronald L; Charles City HS; Charles City, IA; 13/250 PresSophCls; PresJrCls; ChrhWkr; HonRl; NHS; SctActv; PresStuCncl; StuGov; GerCl; MthCl; PpCl; LetterBsbl; CaptBsktbl; College.

KOENIGSMAN, Linda M; St Johns HS; Beloit, KS; SecSrCls; ALAGirlsSt; Chrs; HonRl; StuCncl; RptrYrbk; 4-H; PpCl; 4-HAwd; VFWAwd; College; Art.

KOENIGSMAN, Pat A; St Johns HS; Beloit, KS; Chrs; HonRl; PpCl; Trk; Chrldr; PPFtbl; College.

KOENIGSMARK, Joseph J; Elk Grove HS; Elk Grove, IL; 42/505 Chr; Chrs; HonRl; College; Medicine.

KOENITZER, Janet A; Wauwatosa West HS; Wauwatosa, WI; HonRl; NHS; YthFlsp; MthCl; CaptLionAwd; CaptTrk; AmLegAwd; College; Medical Profession.

KOEPKE, Michael J; Kewaskum HS; Kewaskum, WI; 12/178 ALBoysSt; Band; ChrhWkr; HonRl; NHS; Orch; StuGov; LetterBsbl; LetterBsktbl; LetterFtbl; Us Air Force Acad; Economics.

KOEPKE, Susan K; Denver Community HS; Waverly, IA; 15/80 Band; Chrs; CncrtBnd; HonRl; MrchBnd; NHS; PepBnd; SchPl; 4-H; LetterTrk; Univ Of N Iowa; Elementary Music Teacher.

KOEPP, Aaron A; Brownton Public HS; Brownton, MN; 1/32 VPSophCls; Band; HonRl; MrchBnd; StuCncl; GerCl; LetterBsbl; LetterFtbl; LetterTrk; LetterWrstlng; College; Professional.

KOEPPEN, Carrie J; Lytton Comm HS; Jolley, IA; Chr; Chrs; ChrhWkr; HonRl; LbryAde; NHS; YthFlsp; SchPpr; FHA; FTA; Business Sch; Executive Secretary.

KOEPPEN, Gregg R; Valders HS; St Naziane, WI; ChrhWkr; CmntyWkr; HonRl; NHS; SctActv; Ftbl; Swmmng; CchngActv; Trade School; Liberal Arts.

KOEPSELL, Joyce; Cambridge Senior HS; Cambridge, MN; 8/246 ALAGirlsSt; Chr; CncrtBnd; NHS; SchMus; SchPl; StuCncl; Yrbk; IMSpt; College; Engineering.

KOEPSELL, Loren G; Canova Public HS; Canova, SD; VPFrshCls; SecSophCls; HonRl; SchPl; StuCncl; Bsbl; LetterBsktbl; CaptFtbl; LetterTrk; AmLegAwd; Ncb Rapid City, Sd; Computr Programming.

KOERBER, Kathy A; Duquoin HS; Duquoin, IL; 11/141 Chr; Chrs; ChrhWkr; DrlTm; HonRl; MrchBnd; SchMus; 4-H; FHA; College; Child Care.

KOERNER, Scott E; Westview HS; Kankakee, IL; CtyCnl; CmntyWkr; NHS; Quill&Scroll; SchMus; StuCncl; StuGov; Yrbk; University Of Eastern Illinois.

KOESER, Karen K; Howards Grove HS; Sheboygan Falls, WI; 10/75 VPFrshCls; PresSrCls; Chrs; NHS; StuCncl; Yrbk; SchPpr; 4-H; FBLA; DARAwd; Tech Institute; Accounting Marketing.

KOESTER, Lisa M; Ridgway HS; Ridgway, IL; 3/50 SecJrCls; TrsJrCls; SecSrCls; Band; SptEdSchPpr; 4-H; FHA; GAA; AmLegAwd; DARAwd; Univ; Nursing.

KOESTER, Mark; Red Bud HS; Red Bud, IL; 6/109 HonRl; NHS; Univ Of Ill; Engrg.

KOESTER, Rochelle; Red Bud HS; Evansville, IL; 1/115 Chrs; HonRl; NHS; OffAde; RptrYrbk; CivCl; FTA; SpnCl; MthCl; Eastern Ill Univ; Span Ed.

KOESTER, Wayne T; Northwestern Dist #63 HS; Mansfield, SD; Band; Chr; Chrs; ChrhWkr; CncrtBnd; HonRl; SchPl; Bsktbl; Ftbl; Trk; College.

KOESTLER, Catherine A; Stewartville HS; Stewartville, MN; 70/98 HonRl; Yrbk; FHA; GerCl; Trk; College; Professional.

KOETTER, Anna M; Mitchell HS; Bedford, IN; 12/139 Chrs; HonRl; NatlThespSoc; OffAde; SchMus; SchPl; TchrAde; PpCl; Univ; Teach Spanish.

KOETTER, Brenda K; W W Borden Jr Sr HS; Borden, IN; 6/74 HstSophCls; PresJrCls; HonRl; NHS; StuCncl; TchrAde; RptrYrbk; Ind Univ Se; Nursing.

KOETTING, Stephen D; Sacred Heart HS; Salina, KS; PresSophCls; HonRl; StuCncl; FBLA; SpnCl; Bsktbl; Univ; Automotive Engineer.

KOETZ, Natalie; Amos Alonzo Stagg Hs; Worth, IL; 64/488 Band; ChrhWkr; CncrtBnd; HonRl; MrchBnd; NHS; Bsbl; Bsktbl; CchngActv; GAA; College; Nurse.

KOFFMAN, Julie; Albia Comm HS; Albia, IA; 18/145 HospAde; TchrAde; RptrSchPpr; SchPpr; 4-H; FHA; FNA; FTA; SpnCl; 4-HAwd; College; Nursing.

KOFOED, Roberta; Central HS; Salem, WI; ChrhWkr; HonRl; NatlThespSoc; SchPl; RptrSchPpr; GAA; Coll; State Dept.

KOFSTAD, Diane; Grove City HS; Litchfield, MN; CncrtBnd; HonRl; LbryAde; NHS; SchPl; SctActv; EdYrBk; GerCl; GAA; St Benedict Col; Nursing.

KOGER, Sheila; Southside HS; Muncie, IN; 29/323 Band; ChrhWkr; HonRl; HospAde; MrchBnd; NHS; PepBnd; Quill&Scroll; RedCrAde; RptrSchPpr; Ball Stae Univ; Med Tech.

KOGUT, Gregory M; Mount Carmel HS; Chicago, IL; 1/197 HonRl; VPNHS; TchrAde; CaptMthCl; Trk; JETSAwd; College; Engineering.

KOHAKE, Susan D; Nemaha Valley HS; Goff, KS; 3/79 HonRl; NHS; PpCl; LetterBsktbl; LetterTrk; GAA; IMSpt; Washburn Univ; Nursing.

KOHANEK, Mary L; Steinmetz HS; Chicago, IL; 14/619 HonRl; SchAde; Blackburn University; Social Work.

KOHL, Alan; Beaver Dam Sr HS; Beaver Dam, WI; 49/390 CtyCnl; HonRl; SchPl; StuCncl; KeyCl; IMSpt; College; Physician.

KOHL, David A; Central HS; Grand Forks, ND; CmntyWkr; HonRl; NHS; NatlMeritSF; SctActv; College; Civil Engineering.

KOHL, Ellen D; Hardin Central C 2 HS; Hardin, MO; ChrhWkr; HonRl; YthFlsp; 4-H; SecFHA; PpCl; LetterBsktbl; LetterTrk; Univ; Business.

KOHL, Maureen A; Bradley Bourbonnais HS; Bourbonnais, IL; HonRl; NHS; OffAde; SchAde; 4-H; GerCl; GAA; College; Professional.

KOHL, Randall M; Mchenry Comm HS; Mchenry, IL; 8/466 Band; ChrhWkr; CncrtBnd; HonRl; JrNHS; MrchBnd; TreasNHS; PepBnd; LetterGlf; Univ Of Illinois; Computer Science.

KOHL, Samuel L; Lincoln HS; Mechanicsville, IA; 4/63 Band; ChrhWkr; CncrtBnd; HonRl; MrchBnd; NHS; Pres4-H; SecFFA; LetterFtbl; LetterWrstlng; College; Christian Missionary Agricultruali.

KOHL, Samuel L; Lincoln Community HS; Mechanicsville, IA; 3/67 Band; CncrtBnd; HonRl; JrNHS; MrchBnd; NHS; Pres4-H; SecFFA; LetterFtbl; LetterWrstlng; Ag Science; Agriculture.

KOHLBRECHER, Kimberly D; Wesclin Jr Sr HS; Trenton, IL; PresFrshCls; HonRl; JrNHS; NHS; StuCncl; RptrYrbk; VPFHA; FrCl; PpCl; GAA; CitAwd; College; Professional.

KOHLE, Carol M; Stuart Public HS; Stuart, NE; 4/32 Band; CncrtBnd; HonRl; LbryAde; MrchBnd; PepBnd; SchPl; StuCncl; 4-H; TreasPpCl; Chadron State Col; Child Care.

KOHLER, Diane L; Wm Howard Taft HS; Chicago, IL; 37/816 HonRl; NHS; SchAde; StuCncl; Univ Of Illinois; Mathematics.

KOHLER, Jeffrey V; Wheeling HS; Wheeling, IL; 9/449 HonRl; NatlFornLg; NHS; Quill&Scroll; StuGov; EdSchPpr; Univ Of Notre Dame; Business Admin.

KOHLER, Keith A; Remsen Union HS; Remsen, IA; 7/42 Band; HonRl; NHS; RptrYrbk; RptrSchPpr; LetterBsbl; LetterBsktbl; LetterFtbl; LetterTrk; Univ; Tchng.

KOHLER, Mark J; Dekalb Sr HS; Dekalb, IL; 22/350 HonRl; LetterGlf; Coll; Navigator.

KOHLER, Richard J; Bedford HS; Temperance, MI; 1/434 HonRl; NHS; NatlMeritSF; U Of Toledo; Engr.

KOHLER, Suzanne; St Marys Central HS; Biomarck, ND; Band; ChrhWkr; CmntyWkr; CncrtBnd; MrchBnd; PepBnd; Trk; GAA; N Dak St Univ; Professional.

KOHLER, Terry; Cheney HS; Cheney, KS; VPJrCls; VPSrCls; Band; Chr; Mdrgl; StuCncl; RptrYrbk; FFA; Bsktbl; Ftbl; Dodge City Juco College; Agriculture.

KOHLES, Steve J; Sgt Bluff Luton HS; Sergeant Bluff, IA; 1/47 Chrs; HonRl; SctActv; VPStuCncl; LetterBsktbl; LetterTrk; Iowa State College; Computer Science.

KOHLHASE, Mark E; Golden Valley HS; Golden Valley, MN; AFS; CmntyWkr; NatlThespSoc; SchPl; SctActv; TchrAde; GerCl; SciCl; Bsktbl; Ftbl; Hamline U; Medical Practice.

KOHLHASE, Randall K; Richwoods HS; Peoria, IL; 3/449 Band; CncrtBnd; HonRl; MrchBnd; PepBnd; Univ Of Illinois; Medicine.

KOHLHASE, Robert C; Barrington HS; Barrington, IL; Band; ChrhWkr; MrchBnd; PepBnd; SchPl; YthFlsp; Socr; Swmmng; Trk; IMSpt; College.

KOHLMEYER, Thomas L; Central HS; Evansville, IN; ChrhWkr; HonRl; NHS; PolWkr; SctActv; 4-H; GodCntryAwd; Purdue Univ; Nuclear Engineering.

KOHLS, Debra R; Watertown HS; Watertown, WI; HonRl; JA; ModUN; Yrbk; Madison Area Tech Col; Court & Conference R.

KOHLS, Douglas A; Clearwater HS; Clearwater, KS; Band; HonRl; SctActv; Bsktbl; Col; Own A Farm.

KOHLS, Jerome E; Oregon HS; Oregon, WI; HonRl; TchrAde; RptrYrbk; FTA; MthCl; University; Teaching.

KOHLS, William; St Johns HS; St Johns, MI; 42/320 CmntyWkr; CncrtBnd; HonRl; MrchBnd; NHS; YthFlsp; CchngActv;.

KOHLSTEDT, Russell L; Darlington HS; Darlington, WI; 4/122 HstSrCls; AFS; Chrs; CncrtBnd; HonRl; MrchBnd; NatlMeritCmnd; FSA; SpnCl; LetterBsbl; Univ; Chem Eng.

KOHLWEY, Heidi R; Milwaukee Lutheran HS; Grafton, WI; 21/231 AFS; PolWkr; NatlThespSoc; OffAde; SchMus; SchPl; 4-H; GerCl; PpCl; 4-HAwd; College; Veterinarian.

KOHMETSCHER, Catherine R; Lawrence HS; Blue Hill, NE; Band; HonRl; MrchBnd; NHS; SchPl; RptrYrbk; 4-H; VPPpCl; DanFAwd; 4-HAwd; PresAwd; Tech School; Secretary.

KOHMETSCHER, Curt J; Lawrence Public HS; Lawrence, NE; PresSrCls; Band; Chr; CncrtBnd; HonRl; MrchBnd; SchPl; LetterBsktbl; CaptFtbl; Trk; College; Vet.

KOHN, Amy; Tigerton HS; Tigerton, WI; Band; Chrs; ChrhWkr; HonRl; LbryAde; NatlFornLg; NHS; SchPl; SchPpr; AmLegAwd; College; Registered Nurse.

KOHN, Elise C; W E Groves HS; Southfield, MI; 15/689 VPAFS; CmntyWkr; HonRl; JrNHS; NHS; NatlMeritSF; Orch; SctActv; TchrAde; Univ; Med.

KOHN, Gary L; Guide Rock Public HS; Guide Rock, NE; TrsFrshCls; TrsSophCls; PresJrCls; TrsSrCls; Band; StuCncl; EdSchPpr; LetterBsbl; LetterFtbl; College.

KOHN, Jean M; Centerville Public HS; Centerville, SD; Band; Chr; HonRl; MrchBnd; PepBnd; SchPl; YthFlsp; FHA; FNA; Trk; Univ; Pro.

KOHN, Sharon R; University HS; Normal, IL; SecChrs; HonRl; NatlFornLg; NHS; NatlThespSoc; Orch; SchMus; SchPl; SecStuGov; SciCl; U Of Il; Professional Theatre Music.

KOHNE, Kathleen; St Anthony HS; Saint Louis, MO; 7/72 PresJrCls; Chrl; Chrs; HonRl; JA; NHS; SchMus; LatCl; JAAwd; Univ; Professional.

KOHNER, Julie A; Hill Murray HS; St Paul, MN; ChrhWkr; OffAde; TchrAde; CaptChrldr; IMSpt; ALBoysSt; Teach Histroy.

KOHORST, Kevin M; Albany HS; Albany, MN; 1/130 Chrs; HonRl; SchPl; StuCncl; Bsbl; Bsktbl; Ftbl; Coll; Med.

KOHOUT, Michael J; Brother Rice HS; Oak Lawn, IL; 66/416 University Of Ill; Law.

KOHOUTEK, Lani A; Mc Luer North HS; Florissant, MO; HonRl; Coll; Art.

KOHRT, Rick J; Kewaunee HS; Kewaunee, WI; 3/150 AFS; ALBoysSt; HonRl; NHS; NatlThespSoc; PresStuCncl; Ftbl; Glf; CaptChrldr; VoiceDemAwd; College.

KOHUT, Gale M; Alcona HS; Hubbard Lake, MI; 10/120 Band; HonRl; NHS; TchrAde; FTA; SpnCl; SciCl; CaptBsktbl; Trk; PresAwd; Northern Mi Univ; Phy Ed.

KOIF, Valerie J; Buffalo Grove HS; Arlington Hts, IL; 1/400 TrsFrshCls; VPSophCls; VPAFS; CmntyWkr; HonRl; IntrClCncl; NHS; NatlMeritFnl; SchMus; StuCncl; StuGov; Twrl; Georgetown Univ; Interpreter.

KOISTINEN, Gary E; White Pine HS; Ontonagon, MI; PresFrshCls; Band; CncrtBnd; HonRl; MrchBnd; StuGov; Bsbl; Trk; College; Vocation.

KOISTINEN, Sherry L; Hamlin HS; Lake Norden, SD; 10/66 HonRl; LbryAde; FHA; PpCl; Lake Area Vo Tech; Nursing.

KOK, Marie E; Randolph HS; Randolph, WI; 2/58 PresJrCls; ALAGirlsSt; CncrtBnd; MrchBnd; NHS; SchPl; SctActv; LetterBsktbl; LetterTrk; GAA; College; Business.

KOKENGE, Jane L; Nemalta Valley HS; Seneca, KS; Chr; HonRl; ModUN; NHS; SchPl; SpnCl; PpCl; College.

KOKESH, David J; Eas Chas Mix #102 HS; Wagner, SD; Chr; ChrhWkr; HonRl; StuCncl; FFA; Bsktbl; Ftbl; LetterWrstlng; Military Service; Farming.

KOKJOHN, Thomas; Aquinas HS; Ft Madison, IA; ROTC; SchPl; SchPpr; Bsktbl; Trk; Air Force; Union Pilot.

KOKKELER, Susan J; Garrison HS; Garrison, ND; Chr; Chrl; CmntyWkr; HonRl; HospAde; SchMus; RptrYrbk; Bsktbl; Ftbl; Swmmng; Trk; Wrstlng; Univ Of North Dakota; Accounting.

KOKKO, Joanne F; Jeffers HS; South Range, MI; SecSophCls; PresSrCls; Band; SecNHS; PepBnd; SptEdYrbk; FNA; LetterChrldr; IMSpt; Michigan Technological U; Nursing.

KOKONTIS, John M; Regis HS; Cedar Rapids, IA; 1/146 NatlFornLg; NHS; NatlMeritFnl; NatlMeritSF; BauchLmbAwd; Univ Of Chicago; Biology.

KOKORUZ, Susan M; Blair HS; Blair, NE; Trade School; Nursing.

KOKOSA, Edward; Northrop HS; Ft Wayne, IN; 76;-578 ChrhWkr; HonRl; FDA; IMSpt; University;medicine.

KOLAKOWSKI, Anthony S; Fairfield HS; New Paris, IN; 4-H; SpnCl; MthCl; SciCl; Bsbl; Ftbl; IMSpt; 4-HAwd; University; Professional.

KOLANOWSKI, Ronald J; Manistee Catholic HS; Manistee, MI; 15/70 Band; Chr; ChrhWkr; CmntyWkr; CncrtBnd; HonRl; MrchBnd; TreasNHS; PepBnd; StuCncl; RptrYrbk; Yrbk; RptrSchPpr; FrCl; RotaryAwd; Aquinas College; French.

KOLAR, Barry; Walbach Public HS; Wolbach, NE; SecFrshCls; ALBoysSt; ChrhWkr; CmntyWkr; CncrtBnd; SchPl; StuGov; Bsktbl; Ftbl; CchngActv; Univ Of Neb; Journalism.

KOLAR, Mary Anne L; Center Line HS; Warren, MI; Band; CncrtBnd; HonRl; JrNHS; MrchBnd; NHS; SchMus; SctActv; FNA; Michigan State Univ; Medicine.

KOLARIK, Janet M; Saint Francis HS; Traverse City, MI; 6/82 SecJrCls; HonRl; NHS; TchrAde; PpCl; LetterTennis; CaptChrldr; RotaryAwd; Northwestern Mi Clg; Social Worker.

KOLASA, Bernadette M; Madonna HS; Chicago, IL; 7/273 Band; Chr; HonRl; JA; JrNHS; NHS; SctActv; StuGov; RptrYrbk; SciCl; Northern Illinois Univ; Meteorology.

KOLASA, Linda L; St Hedwig; Detroit, MI; VPSrCls; HonRl; NHS; Yrbk; RptrSchPpr; Chrldr; VoiceDemAwd; Coll; Dental Hygienist.

KOLASINSKI, Nanciann M; Good Counsel HS; Chicago, IL; 40/245 HonRl; TreasSciCl; GAA; Loyola University; Biology.

KOLB, Jeanie M; John Glenn HS; Bay City, MI; 29/335 ChrhWkr; HonRl; LitMag; OffAde; RedCrAde; SchAde; TchrAde; OptClAwd; Delta Coll; Spec Ed.

KOLB, Kathy J; Onalaska HS; Onalaska, WI; 3/130 HonRl; NHS; YthFlsp; Yrbk; SchPpr; VPFrCl; College; Nursing.

KOLB, Kenneth E; Dunlap HS; Peoria, IL; Band; HonRl; NatlMeritCmnd; LatCl; VPSciCl; Trk; Bradley Univ; Idustrial Engineering.

KOLB, Mark P; Rich Central HS; Matteson, IL; HonRl; StuCncl; Bsbl; College; Business.

KOLB, Wendy L; Deerfield HS; Deerfield, IL; AFS; ChrhWkr; CmntyWkr; HonRl; LbryAde; RedCrAde; StuCncl; GerCl; Swmmng; Bates College; German.

KOLBACH, Jane F; Port Washington HS; Port Washington, WI; HonRl; JA; LbryAde; SpnCl; JAAwd; Marian College Of Fond Du Lac; Med Tech.

KOLBECK, Cynthia K; Columbus HS; Marshfield, WI; 21/114 Band; HonRl; NHS; Twrl; Yrbk; FrCl; PpCl; LetterBsktbl; LetterTrk; GAA; University; Nurse.

KOLBECK, Kevin; Nevada Community HS; Nevada, IA; 3/129 TrsFrshCls; ALBoysSt; ChrhWkr; HonRl; NHS; SchPl; StuCncl; RptrYrbk; RptrSchPpr; Cornell Coll; Biology.

KOLBECK, Sarah M; St Teresa HS; Decatur, IL; 22/118 Chrs; HonRl; HospAde; NHS; NatlThespSoc; OffAde; SctActv; TchrAde; Illinois State Univ; Mathematics.

KOLBERER, Peggy A; Triopia HS; Chapin, IL; Band; Chrs; ChrhWkr; CmntyWkr; HonRl; HospAde; SchMus; Yrbk; LetterTrk; 4-HAwd; Univ Of Iowa; Pharmacy.

KOLBERG, Leisa K; Gayville Volin HS; Gayville, SD; TrsSophCls; TrsSrCls; ALAGirlsSt; Chrs; HonRl; SchPl; StuCncl; RptrYrbk; LetterBsktbl; LetterTrk; Coll;medicine.

KOLBET, Alan E; New Hampton Comm HS; Alta Vista, IA; 25/178 ChrhWkr; HonRl; N Iowa Area Comm Clg; Automobile Service.

KOLBO, Barbara L; Sparta Senior HS; Sparta, WI; 13/198 Band; HonRl; VPNHS; PepBnd; Western Wis Tech Inst; Accountant.

KOLBUS, James W; Bishop Noll Institute HS; Hammond, IN; HonRl; JrNHS; StuCncl; MthCl; LetterBsbl; LetterFtbl; Wrstlng; IMSpt; University; Theology.

KOLBUSZ, Robert V; Saint Patrick HS; Chicago, IL; 23/456 Band; CmntyWkr; HonRl; NHS; NatlMeritCmnd; NatlMeritSF; PepBnd; SchAde; TchrAde; RptrSchPpr; FDA; SpnCl; Loyola Univ; Doctor.

KOLDEN, Steven; Central HS; Aberdeen, SD; ALBoysSt; HonRl; Wrstlng; Rotc; Us Military.

KOLDERIE, Paul Q; Breck HS; Minneapolis, MN; Band; HonRl; NatlMeritSF; PepBnd; SchPpr; LetterSocr; Tennis; IMSpt; College; Economist.

KOLDYKE, David E; Tippecanoe Valley HS; Warsaw, IN; VPFrshCls; Band; Chrs; HonRl; MrchBnd; StuCncl; YthFlsp; 4-H; SpnCl; MthCl; PpCl; Bsbl; Bsktbl; Ball State University; Accounting.

KOLE, Cheryl A; Holland Christian HS; Holland, MI; 10/260 Band; HonRl; HospAde; MrchBnd; PepBnd; RptrYrbk; RptrSchPpr; FNA; LetterTennis; IMSpt; U Of Mi; Nursing.

KOLEAN, David L; West Ottawa HS; Holland, MI; Band; ChrhWkr; CncrtBnd; HonRl; MrchBnd; Orch; PepBnd; SchMus; SchPl; YthFlsp; Hope College; Natural Resources.

KOLEAN, Warren L; West Ottawa HS; Holland, MI; 33/271 Band; HonRl; MrchBnd; NHS; PepBnd; TchrAde; CaptBsbl; Bsktbl; IMSpt; Muskegon Business College; Accounting.

KOLECKA, Barbara A; Armour HS; Armour, SD; 8/30 SecTrsJrCls; Band; Chr; HonRl; HospAde; OffAde; 4-H; GerCl; ChmbCommrsAwd; VoiceDemAwd; Sd State Univ; Nursing.

KOLEHMAINEN, Kim; Lutheran West HS; Detroit, MI; 24/144 DrlTm; HonRl; JrNHS; NHS; OffAde; GerCl; PpCl; Chrldr; Univ Of Mi Ann Arbor; Special Ed Teacher.

KOLEY, Jerilyn M; Marian HS; Waterloo, NE; Chr; ChrhWkr; DrlTm; HonRl; HospAde; NHS; SchMus; GAA; College Of St Marys; Childhood Educ.

KOLHAGEN, Kelly J; Buena Vista HS; Saginaw, MI; 2/241 HonRl; Quill&Scroll; SchPl; TchrAde; SchPpr; GerCl; PpCl; University; Professional.

KOLICH, Lisa J; St Marys HS; Sugar Creek, MO; Chr; Chrs; DrlTm; HonRl; SchMus; RptrYrbk; PpCl; Swmmng; Chrldr; IMSpt; Clge; Nurse.

KOLINSKI, Patricia G; Our Lady Of Mercy HS; Detroit, MI; Chr; Chrl; Chrs; CmntyWkr; HonRl; NHS; SchMus; SchPl; TchrAde; FrCl; LetterBsbl; Univ Of Michigan; Psychology.

KOLINSKI, Scott F; Oak Lawn Comm HS; Oak Lawn, IL; 93/640 HonRl; NatlMeritSchl; Univ Of Illinois; Law.

KOLKA, Jill L; West Delaware HS; Ryan, IA; Chr; Chrs; ChrhWkr; HonRl; NatlThespSoc; SchMus; StuCncl; RptrYrbk; RptrSchPpr; PpCl; Kirkwood Community College; Dental Asst.

KOLKE, Julie G; Appleton Public HS; Appleton, MN; 12/75 Band; CncrtBnd; HonRl; MrchBnd; RptrYrbk; SptEdYrbk; LetterBsktbl; LetterTrk; Chrldr; PresAwd; Clg; Teacher.

KOLKER, Linda; Le Mars Community HS; Le Mars, IA; 34/214 ChrhWkr; HonRl; NHS; RptrSchPpr; FBLA; Trk; Northern Tech Sch Of Bus; Court Reporting.

KOLL, Nila J; Wimbledon HS; Wimbledon, ND; 8/28 SecSophCls; Band; CncrtBnd; HonRl; MrchBnd; SchPl; EdYrBk; FHA; Chrldr; BttyCrckrAwd; Trade School; Medical Secretary.

KOLL, Theresa M; Pacelli HS; Austin, MN; 5/118 ALAGirlsSt; Chr; Chrs; ChrhWkr; HonRl; HospAde; NHS; SchMus; SchPl; PpCl; Winona State College; Math Teacher.

KOLLAR, Margaret M; Rockridge HS; Reynolds, IL; VPFrshCls; Band; ChrhWkr; HonRl; HospAde; LbryAde; Yrbk; SecFNA; SpnCl; GAA; IMSpt; 4-HAwd; College; Professional.

KOLLASCH, William J; St John HS; Bancroft, IA; 3/44 VPFrshCls; VPJrCls; TrsSrCls; Chrs; HonRl; NatlMeritCmnd; StuGov; Bsbl; Bsktbl; BauchLmbAwd; Ia St Univ; Acct.

KOLLATH, Janet R; Carl Sandburg HS; Orland Park, IL; 17/700 HonRl; NHS; OffAde; MthCl; LetterBsktbl; GAA; Clge.

KOLLAUF, Lynn; Ashland HS; Ashland, WI; ChrhWkr; HonRl; NHS; NatlMeritCmnd; SchPl; SpnCl; Univ Of Wi Superior;pre Med.

KOLLBAUM, Laverne R; Sergeant Bluff Luton HS; Sergeant Bluff, IA; 12/40 LetterFtbl; LetterTrk; IMSpt; College; Architectural Eng.

KOLLER, Craig P; Iron Mountain HS; Iron Mountain, MI; DrmBgl; NatlMeritFnl; NatlMeritCmnd; SchPl; 4-H; KeyCl; SpnCl; Ftbl; Swmmng; Western Michigan University; Pilot.

KOLLER, Jayne A; Lincoln HS; Wis Rapids, WI; 2/540 TreasChr; HonRl; NHS; SchMus; Bsktbl; Trk; GAA; PPFtbl; College; Computer Science.

KOLLIN, Cheryl I; Southfield HS; Southfield, MI; CmntyWkr; HonRl; NatlThespSoc; SchMus; SchPl; RptrYrbk; U Of Mi; Natrual Resouces.

KOLLMANN, Wilbur W; Nashua Community HS; Nashua, IA; HonRl; Air Force.

KOLLMEYER, David; Collinsville Hs; Collsville, IL; Band; ChrhWkr; CncrtBnd; HonRl; MrchBnd; PepBnd; ROTC; Trk; College;physicist.

KOLLROSS, Robert; Auburndale HS; Arpin, WI; PresFrshCls; PresSophCls; PresJrCls; PresSrCls; HonRl; NHS; StuCncl; EdYrBk; BauchLmbAwd; EldAwd; Coll; Engrg.

KOLLSMITH, Richard L; La Salle HS; Cedar Rapids, IA; 17/98 HonRl; NHS; Bsktbl; Iowa State Univ; Agricultural Admin.

KOLMAN, Joseph J; Washington HS; Washington, KS; 2/43 ALBoysSt; ChrhWkr; HonRl; NatlMeritCmnd; Yrbk; SciCl; Bsbl; Bsktbl; LetterFtbl; LetterTrk; Kansas State U; Engr.

KOLODZIEJ, Elizabeth; Franklin HS; Livonia, MI; 39/730 LitMag; OffAde; TchrAde; Michigan State U; Research Chemistry.

KOLODZIEJ, John P; St Bede Academy; La Salle, IL; 30/120 ChrhWkr; CmntyWkr; HonRl; JA; NatlMeritCmnd; SctActv; 4-H; SciCl; Ftbl; IMSpt; Univ Of Illinois; Engineering.

KOLODZIEJ, Ted R; J S Morton West HS; Stickney, IL; 50/800 HonRl; JrNHS; Northwestern Univ; Pilot.

KOLOSIK, Tracy J; English Valleys Community HS; North English, IA; 9/60 Band; Chrs; CncrtBnd; HonRl; MrchBnd; PepBnd; SchMus; RptrYrbk; RptrSchPpr; Bsktbl; LetterTrk; Ia State Univ; Med Tech.

KOLOSOWSKI, Andrew E; Prosser Vocational HS; Chicago, IL; Bsbl; College; Professional.

KOLSCHEFSKY, Debra K; Drake Public HS; Drake, ND; SecFrshCls; TrsFrshCls; Chrs; LbryAde; OffAde; PresStuCncl; Yrbk; FFA; FHA; VPPpCl; Trk; Mayville St Col; Commercial Art.

KOLSTAD, Kimberly S; Gaylord Public HS; Gaylord, MN; 2/67 Chr; CncrtBnd; HonRl; SchMus; TreasFHA; Gustavus Adolphus College; Nursing.

KOLTIS, Mark L; Thorp HS; Thorp, WI; Band; Chrs; CncrtBnd; MrchBnd; PepBnd; SchMus; SctActv; Bsbl; Ftbl; Trade School; Drafting.

KOLTZ, Kay E; Big Foot HS; Walworth, WI; 32/155 AFS; Chr; HonRl; Mdrgl; Orch; SchMus; PpCl; LetterBsktbl; IMSpt; 4-HAwd; PresAwd; College; Social Work.

KOLTZ, Pamela M; Josephinum HS; Chicago, IL; 1/104 VPFrshCls; Chrs; HonRl; LitMag; LbryAde; College; Communications.

KOLTZE, John R; O Gorman HS; Sioux Falls, SD; CmntyWkr; CncrtBnd; HonRl; NatlFornLg; NHS; NatlMeritSchl; NatlThespSoc; Quill&Scroll; StuCncl; College; Teaching Us History.

KOLVE, Diane L; Holmen HS; Onalaska, WI; 17/97 DrlTm; HonRl; Yrbk; FHA; Trade School; Art.

KOLVES, Kimberly A; Balyki Community HS; Bath, IL; 6/26 VPJrCls; Band; ChrhWkr; CmntyWkr; SchPl; 4-H; KeyCl; Chrldr; GAA; DanFAwd; College; Cpa Or Legal Secretary.

KOMAREK, Charles L; Fairmont HS; Fairmont, NE; 7/28 SecSophCls; ALBoysSt; Chrs; HonRl; 4-H; EngCl; GerCl;.

KOMAREK, Cheryl L; Bethlehem Academy; Lonsdale, MN; 1/91 Chr; Chrs; ChrhWkr; HonRl; Mdrgl; NHS; SchMus; SchPl; TchrAde; RptrSchPpr; Coll; Psych.

KOMASA, John S; Stevens Point Area Sr HS; Stevens Point, WI; 9/520 Chr; Chrl; Chrs; ChrhWkr; HonRl; Mdrgl; NHS; Orch; SchMus; SctActv; FrCl; EldAwd; Oberlin College Conservatory Of Music.

KOME, Linda J; Lamphere HS; Madison Heights, MI; 1/430 Band; PresCncrtBnd; HonRl; PresMrchBnd; SecNHS; PepBnd; SchMus; EdYrBk; PPFtbl; EldAwd; Mi State Univ; Teacher.

KOMISTRA, Mark E; St Bonaventure HS; Racine, WI; 8/26 ChrhWkr; PresJA; 4-H; JAAwd; Trade School.

KOMMER, Glenn J; Thornridge HS; Dolton, IL; 46/686 HonRl; JrNHS; NHS; NatlMeritCmnd; NatlMeritSF; FrCl; Glf; College; Dentistry.

KOMMER, Michael W; Metropolis Comm HS; Metropolis, IL; 10/161 NHS; KeyCl; MthCl; SciCl; Bsktbl; Trk; IMSpt; Univ Of Illinois; Chemistry.

KOMP, Thomas R; Joliet Catholic HS; Joliet, IL; 12/170 HonRl; NHS; Ftbl; University; Medicine.

KOMPANOWSKI, Robert D; Holy Cross HS; Norridge, IL; 8/305 ChrhWkr; HonRl; JrNHS; TreasNHS; LatCl; Trk; Loyola Univ; Dentistry.

KOMPELIEN, Kevin M; Lincoln HS; Thief River Falls, MN; 13/254 Band; Chr; Chrl; ChrhWkr; CncrtBnd; HonRl; MrchBnd; PepBnd; LetterTennis; IMSpt; College; Psychology.

KOMPERDA, Joseph J; Maine Township East HS; Park Ridge, IL; PresJrCls; ChrhWkr; HonRl; NatlFornLg; NHS; NatlMeritCmnd; NatlThespSoc; StuCncl; StuGov; LetterBsktbl; LetterFtbl; Tennis; U S Military Academy.

KONCKI, Janet; Greendale HS; Greendale, WI; 45/385 HonRl; NHS; SctActv; Swmmng; GAA; Univ Wi Milwaukee; Computer Sciences.

KONCZAK, Sandra S; Alpena HS; Alpena, MI; LatCl; BttyCrckrAwd; Coll; Med Tech.

KONDAL, Kimberly; Birch Run HS; Birch Run, MI; 1/154 ChrhWkr; CncrtBnd; LitMag; NatlMeritFnl; StuCncl; EdSchPpr; SpnCl; SciCl; RotaryAwd; Concordia Luth Jr Coll; Liturgical Music.

KONDELIS, Nicholas P; New Trier West HS; Wilmette, IL; Aud/Vis; ChrhWkr; HonRl; FDA; FSA; FrCl; SciCl; Univ; Professional.

KONECK, Richard K; Creighton Prep HS; Omaha, NE; HstFrshCls; HstSophCls; HstJrCls; HstSrCls; ChrhWkr; CmntyWkr; HonRl; JA; Sdlty; StuCncl; LatCl; LetterFtbl; Chrldr; JAAwd;.

KONECKI, Mark L; Luke M Powers HS; Flint, MI; 1/306 Chr; Chrs; CmntyWkr; Mdrgl; NHS; NatlMeritCmnd; SchMus; SchPl; RusCl;.

KONEN, Deborah L; Lake Orion HS; Lake Orion, MI; HonRl; SctActv; StuGov; TchrAde; FTA; LetterBsktbl; LetterTennis; LetterTrk; GAA; Michigan State Univ.

KONEN, Jeanne M; Roseland Public HS; Roseland, NE; 2/14 VPFrshCls; PresSophCls; SecJrCls; Chrs; HonRl; StuCncl; PpCl; LetterTrk; Chrldr; Univ Of Ne; Business.

KONEY, Jill; Troy HS; Troy, MI; 41/550 DrlTm; HonRl; NHS; StuGov; EdSchPpr; SpnCl; PpCl; Michigan State Univ; Law.

KONGSHAUG, Phillip; Loyola HS; Mankato, MN; Chrs; HonRl; SchPl; SciCl; Ftbl; College; Chemistry.

KONICEK, Robert R; Beloit Catholic HS; Beloit, WI; ALBoysSt; HonRl; PolWkr; YthLg; EdSchPpr; VoiceDemAwd; College; Law.

KONING, Gerald A; Central Christian HS; Prinsburg, MN; PresFrshCls; PresChr; HonRl; NHS; SchMus; TchrAde; Yrbk; 4-H; LetterBsktbl; LetterBsktbl;.

KONING, Sherri L; Lakeview HS; Battle Creek, MI; CmntyWkr; HonRl; HospAde; ChmnJA; SchMus; StuCncl; FrCl; SciCl; ChmbCommrsAwd; JCAwd; Kellogg Clg; Therapistes.

KONKEN, Robert E; Niobrara HS; Niobrara, NE; TrsFrshCls; PresSophCls; TrsJrCls; ChrhWkr; HonRl; StuCncl; Bsktbl; Ftbl; Trk; PresAwd;.

KONKEN, Robert E; Niobrara Public HS; Niobrava, NE; PresFrshCls; TrsJrCls; ChrhWkr; HonRl; StuCncl; Yrbk; LetterBsktbl; LetterFtbl; LetterTrk; PresAwd; Trade Sch; Vocational.

KONOLD, Cynthia L; Guilford Sr HS; Rockford, IL; 36/700 ChrhWkr; CmntyWkr; HonRl; LitMag; NHS; NatlMeritCmnd; FrCl; PpCl; Drake University; Lawyer.

KONOP, Bonnie M; Kewaunee HS; Kewaunee, WI; AFS; HonRl; HospAde; LbryAde; NatlFornLg; NHS; SchPl; Twrl; RptrYrbk; FHA; SpnCl; SciCl; Technical School; Stenography.

KONOPACKI, Cynthia R; Belleville HS; Brooklyn, WI; 9/61 SecSrCls; ChrhWkr; CmntyWkr; HonRl; NatlFornLg; NHS; 4-H; TreasFHA; 4-HAwd; JAAwd; Uw At Madison; Social Work.

KONRAD, Christine J; Lawrence Central HS; Indianapolis, IN; DrlTm; HonRl; SecJA; SecLbryAde; MrchBnd; TreasSctActv; PpCl; Swmmng; JAAwd; College.

KONRAD, Dieder; Thornton Twp HS; South Holland, IL; HonRl; Illinois State University; Business Admin.

KONRAD, Kerry L; Glenbrook N HS; Northbrook, IL; 1/650 HstSrCls; NatlCathMusEdAsoc; NatlMeritFnl; Sdlty; Teen; FBLA; RusCl; CaptBsktbl; TIMEAwd; VoiceDemAwd; Sw Louisiana St; Dentistry.

KONRAD, Thomas N; Tripp HS; Tripp, SD; U Of Sd;biology.

KONRADY, Linda; Ida Grove Comm HS; Ida Grove, IA; 6/62 HstSrCls; CncrtBnd; HonRl; HospAde; MrchBnd; NatlThespSoc; PepBnd; SchMus; StuCncl; RptrYrbk; Univ Of Iowa College; Rn.

KONSEL, Jack W; Howells HS; Howells, NE; 3/42 VPJrCls; HonRl; SchPl; PresStuCncl; RptrYrbk; TreasFFA; LetterFtbl; LetterWrstlng; Northeast Nebr Tech Comm Coll; Frm Rch Mgnt.

KONSTANT, Steven P; Marist HS; Chicago, IL; 16/365 HonRl; TreasNHS; NatlMeritSF; IMSpt; Notre Dame Univ; Mathematics.

KONYA, Elma S; Laville HS; Bremen, IN; 10/160 NHS; OffAde; PolWkr; TchrAde; FHA; FTA; GerCl; AmLegAwd; In U; German.

KONZ, Colleen G; Saint Albert HS; Neola, IA; ChrhWkr; HonRl; PolWkr; 4-H; SpnCl; PpCl; LetterBsktbl; IMSpt; 4-HAwd;.

KONZ, Geraldine L R; Heelan HS; Salix, IA; Chr; ChrhWkr; HonRl; Sacrstn; SchAde; Sdlty; College; Vocation.

KONZ, Kay; St Albert HS; Neola, IA; 14/93 Chr; ChrhWkr; HonRl; PolWkr; TchrAde; 4-H; PpCl; Bsktbl; IMSpt; 4-HAwd; College; Elem Education.

KONZ, Mary E; St Albert HS; Neola, IA; Chr; ChrhWkr; HonRl; Mdrgl; NHS; PolWkr; SchMus; TchrAde; RptrSchPpr; SptEdSchPpr; Clarke Col; Special Ed.

KONZAK, Anita K; Minnewaukan Public HS; Devils Lake, ND; Band; ChrhWkr; CncrtBnd; HonRl; SchPl; RptrYrbk; 4-H; PpCl; Bsktbl; Trk; College; Science.

KONZEM, Sherry L; St Johns HS; Jewell, KS; 1/20 Band; Chrs; HonRl; MrchBnd; StuCncl; TchrAde; Yrbk; 4-H; LatCl; PpCl; Marymount Coll; Elem Educ.

KOOGLER, Jeff T; Sarcoxie HS; Sarcoxie, MO; ChrhWkr; HonRl; SchPpr; MthCl; Coll; Religion.

KOOI, Sherry A; Woodland HS; Streator, IL; 3/76 HonRl; NHS; TchrAde; FrCl; GAA; Ullinois State U; Math Major.

KOOIMAN, Randall; Eden Prairie HS; Eden Prairie, MN; 6/145 JA; NHS; Bsbl; Tennis; Trk; Wrstlng; ChmbCommrsAwd; JAAwd; Minnesota Univ; Undecided.

KOOISTRA, William J; Sheldon Comm HS; Sheldon, IA; 4/150 Band; Chr; HonRl; NHS; NatlMeritSF; PepBnd; PolWkr; Bsktbl; Glf; Drake Univ; Actuary Science.

KOOLMAN, Sandy; Grass Lake Jr Sr HSF; Grass Lake, MI; 5/91 Band; CncrtBnd; HonRl; NHS; NatlMeritSF; OffAde; StuCncl; Twrl; YthFlsp; BttyCrckrAwd; Jackson Comm Coll; Elementary Education.

KOOMEN, Vicky L; Zeeland HS; Zeeland, MI; Band; ChrhWkr; HonRl; MrchBnd; OffAde; YthFlsp; Secretary Or Medical Recept.

KOONS, Brenda M; Morton HS; Groveland, IL; 7/312 Band; Chrs; ChrhWkr; CncrtBnd; HonRl; MrchBnd; SchMus; SctActv; SpnCl; Bible College; Gospel Music.

KOONS, Pattie; New Hampton HS; New Hampton, IA; Chr; Chrs; ChrhWkr; HonRl; LbryAde; Mdrgl; YthFlsp; RptrYrbk; PpCl; 4-HAwd; Colleg; Art.

KOONTE, Virgil; Rantoul Twp HS; Paxton, IL; HonRl; NHS; SctActv; StuCncl; TchrAde; Trk; Us Air Force; Electronics.

KOONTZ, Jo; Edison Sr HS; East Gary, IN; 16/128 SecSrCls; HonRl; JrNHS; LbryAde; NHS; StuCncl; TchrAde; RptrYrbk; Culver Stockton College; Foriegn Lang Trans.

KOONTZ, Jo L; Edison Sr HS; East Gary, IN; 16/147 SecSrCls; HonRl; JrNHS; LbryAde; NHS; StuCncl; StuGov; TchrAde; RptrYrbk; FrCl; PpCl; Culver Stockton College; Language.

KOOPAL, Steve J; Waverly Shell Rock HS; Waverly, IA; 60/198 VPFrshCls; ChrhWkr; HonRl; StuCncl; GerCl; LetterFtbl; LetterSwmmng; LetterTrk; LetterWrstlng; IMSpt; College; Marine Biology.

KOOPMAN, Barbara J; Unity Christian HS; Hudsonville, MI; 7/197 Band; CncrtBnd; HonRl; MrchBnd; ModUN; CivCl; 4-H; Bsbl; Bsktbl; IMSpt; Butterworth School Of Nursing; Rn.

KOOPMAN, Cheryl M; Martin Public HS; Martin, MI; HonRl; TchrAde; YthFlsp; RptrYrbk; RptrSchPpr; Kalamazoo Valley Comm College; Publications.

KOOPMAN, Douglas L; Hamilton HS; Holland, MI; 4/125 ChrhWkr; HonRl; NHS; NatlMeritFnl; NatlMeritCmnd; NatlMeritSchl; NatlMeritSF; Bsbl; Bsktbl; CaptFtbl; CchngActv; Hope College; Political Science.

KOOPMANS, John S; Cambria Friesland HS; Cambria, WI; Chrs; YthFlsp; SptEdYrbk; FFA; Ftbl; U Of Wi Madison; Agriculture.

KOOSER, Kimberly I; Perry Lecompten HS; Perry, KS; Chr; Chrl; Chrs; CncrtBnd; HonRl; OffAde; SchMus; TchrAde; 4-H; PpCl; College; X Ray Technician.

KOOY, David; Galien Township HS; Galien, MI; 5/52 HonRl; NHS; StuCncl; TchrAde; LetterBsktbl; College.

KOPCHIK, John C; Andrean HS; Merrillville, IN; 2/300 ChrhWkr; HonRl; PresNHS; PolWkr; SchPl; StuCncl; RptrSchPpr; LetterMthCl; LetterTennis; CchngActv; College; Medicine.

KOPERSKI, Barbara J; Central HS; Omaha, NE; Chr; DrlTm; JA; NatlFornLg; NHS; StuGov; FrCl; Swmmng; Tennis; IMSpt; Stephens College ;law.

KOPETSKY, Mark G; Roncalli HS; Maitowoc, WI; 11/140 Aud/Vis; HonRl; NHS; TchrAde; PresKeyCl; MthCl; LetterGlf; IMSpt; University Wisconsin; Pharmacy.

KOPETZ, Kristine L; Mac Arthur HS; Decatur, IL; 21/400 SecSophCls; ChrhWkr; CmntyWkr; HonRl; NHS; NatlMeritCmnd; OffAde; College; Teaching.

KOPFER, Susan L; Jefferson City HS; Jefferson City, MO; 2/349 JrNHS; MrchBnd; NHS; Orch; PepBnd; StuCncl; 4-H; SpnCl; PpCl; GAA; Coll; Teacher.

KOPFF, Matthew J; St Marys HS; St Louis, MO; 2/196 CncrtBnd; HonRl; NHS; StuCncl; RptrYrbk; Bsbl; LetterBsktbl; Ftbl; IMSpt; College; Accounting.

KOPFMAN, Roxanne R; Lakin HS; Lakin, KS; Band; Chr; CncrtBnd; HonRl; OffAde; SchPl; PresStuCncl; Teen; PpCl; Bsktbl; University; Professional.

KOPIETZ, Deborah K; Norfolk Senior HS; Norfolk, NE; Chr; Chrs; HonRl; HospAde; NatlFornLg;.

KOPIETZ, Sandy M; Ryan HS; Omaha, NE; PresNHS; SchMus; PpCl; Bsktbl; Trk; College; Professional.

KOPISH, Penny E; Marinette Sr HS; Marinette, WI; 70/242 Chrs; CmntyWkr; HonRl; YthFlsp; RptrSchPpr; LatCl; Trk; GAA; University; Professional.

KOPKA, Robert J; New Trier West HS; Wilmette, IL; 100/700 HstFrshCls; HstSophCls; HstJrCls; HstSrCls; Aud/Vis; ChrhWkr; CtyCnl; CmntyWkr; DrmBgl; HonRl; LitMag; NatlFornLg; PolWkr; SchPl; StuCncl; University; Politics.

KOPKE, Laura A; Good Counsel HS; Chicago, IL; 59/275 HonRl; HospAde; SchPl; College; Psychology.

KOPLIN, Carol; Lake Mills HS; Lake Mills, WI; Band; CncrtBnd; HonRl; MrchBnd; NatlFornLg; NHS; PepBnd; Tennis; Trk; GAA; Univ; Aviation.

KOPP, Bruce; St Marys Central HS; Bismarck, ND; Bsktbl; Tennis; IMSpt; College; Professional.

KOPP, Carl I; Lexington HS; Lexington, MO; 31/97 Band; CncrtBnd; HonRl; MrchBnd; NatlThespSoc; PepBnd; Central Mo State Univ; Accounting.

KOPP, James O; Anderson Sr HS; Anderson, IN; ALBoysSt; HonRl; NHS; NatlMeritCmnd; Quill&Scroll; Univ Of Notre Dame; Doctor.

KOPP, Jeffrey L; Gale Ettrick Trempealeau HS; Ettrick, WI; HonRl; 4-H; FFA; PpCl; LetterWrstlng; 4-HAwd; Univ Of Wi River Falls; Animal Science.

KOPP, Kristin K; Anita Community HS; Anita, IA; 3/60 Band; CncrtBnd; HonRl; NHS; PepBnd; Quill&Scroll; EdSchPpr; FTA; Trk; Chrldr; Tarkio Coll.

KOPP, Michael; Franklin Central HS; Indls, IN; HonRl; JrNHS; NHS; SchPl; SctActv; Yrbk; 4-H; FFA; LatCl; PpCl; Purdue.

KOPPA, Susan; Wausau East HS; Wausau, WI; 20/297 AFS; NatlFornLg; NHS; Quill&Scroll; StuCncl; SptEdYrbk; SptEdSchPpr; FBLA; SpnCl; Tennis; LetterTrk; GAA; Univ Of Wisconsin; Behavioral Disabilities.

KOPPANG, Miles D; Climax Public No 592 HS; Climax, MN; 6/28 Band; Chr; HonRl; NHS; SchPl; RptrYrbk; FFA; LetterBsbl; LetterBsktbl; LetterFtbl; IMSpt; Concordia College; Teach.

KOPPELMAN, Kevin S; Pekin Comm HS; Pekin, IL; 163/759 ChrhWkr; HonRl; LbryAde; SchPl; Bsbl; Illinois State Univ; Chemistry.

KOPPENAAL, Daniel T; West Ottawa HS; Holland, MI; 16/275 ALBoysSt; CncrtBnd; HonRl; NHS; Orch; SchMus; StuGov; FrCl; LetterTrk; IMSpt; Grand Valley; Bus Admin.

KOPPERUD, Nancy L; Naperville Central HS; Naperville, IL; Band; Chr; Chrs; ChrhWkr; CmntyWkr; SctActv; TchrAde; YthFlsp; College.

KOPPES, Steven; Luckey HS; Manhattan, KS; CmntyWkr; HonRl; SptEdSchPpr; SchPpr; MthCl; SciCl; Glf; Kansas State Univ; Prof In Anthropology.

KOPPINGER, Kathleen A; St Marys HS; New England, ND; Band; Chr; Chrs; CncrtBnd; HonRl; MrchBnd; PepBnd; Coll; Teacher.

KOPPINGER, Lana R; Dickinson HS; Dickinson, ND; ALAGirlsSt; HonRl; HospAde; 4-H; PresFNA; SpnCl; PpCl; PresAwd; College; Medicine.

KOPPMAN, Pamela; Puxico R 8 HS; Puxico, MO; TrsFrshCls; TrsSrCls; HonRl; MrchBnd; FHA; PpCl; IMSpt; College.

KORACH, Elliot; East Maine Township Hs; Morton Grove, IL; 99/900 HonRl; NHS; MthCl; Ui;premedicine.

KORANDA, Debra; Tomah Senior HS; Thomah, WI; 15/283 ALAGirlsSt; HonRl; NHS; RptrSchPpr; PpCl; GAA; College; Professional Math.

KORANDA, Nancy R; Midland Community HS; Wyoming, IA; VPSrCls; CmntyWkr; HonRl; RptrSchPpr; Bsbl; Business School; Legal Secretary.

KORB, Annette J; Georgetown HS; Georgetown, IL; Band; ChrhWkr; CncrtBnd; MrchBnd; PepBnd; RptrYrbk; PpCl; Chrldr; Danville Jr College; Secretary.

KORB, Debra L; Clintonville Senior HS; Clintonville, WI; 20/180 SecFrshCls; HonRl; NHS; TreasSctActv; PpCl; Bsktbl; U Of Wi Eau Claire.

KORB, Heather C; Burr Oak HS; Burr Oak, KS; Band; Chrs; HonRl; SchPl; Teen; Twrl; EdYrBk; SchPpr; 4-H; PpCl; Trk; Chrldr; Kansas St Univ; Liberal Arts.

KORBA, John L; Forest View HS; Des Plaines, IL; 18/465 VPSrCls; Chr; ChrhWkr; HonRl; NHS; SctActv; StuGov; Northwestern Univ; Medicine.

KORBA, Vicki; Cardinal Ritter HS; Indianapolis, IN; 25/165 Chrs; HonRl; MrchBnd; SchMus; StuCncl; Twrl; RptrYrbk; Purdue Univ.

KORBEL, Douglas R; Crete Public HS; Crete, NE; Band; FBLA; LetterWrstlng; Univ Of Nebraska.

KORDAS, Jeffrey J; St Laurence HS; Chicago, IL; 30/385 HonRl; LetterTrk; Univ Of Ill; Accounting.

KORDIK, Steven A; Hononegah HS; Rockton, IL; 8/188 ALBoysSt; HonRl; JA; NatlThespSoc; SchPl; SctActv; Yrbk; SpnCl; Marquette Univ; Dentist.

KORDONOWY, Gerard A; Belfield HS; Belfield, ND; PresSrCls; Band; CncrtBnd; HonRl; MrchBnd; ModUN; NHS; PepBnd; StuCncl; PresSciCl; Bsktbl; BauchLmbAwd; JETSAwd; College; Aerospace Engineer.

KORDUS, Sharon E; Berkley HS; Huntington Woods, MI; Chrl; SchAde; GAA; Clg; Maj Study.

KOREMENOS, Carol M; Lake Central HS; Schererville, IN; 4/453 ChrhWkr; HonRl; NHS; NatlThespSoc; Quill&Scroll; SchAde; SchPl; StuGov; TchrAde; EdSchPpr; Purdue Calumet Campus; Elementary Education.

KOREN, Judy M; Kelly HS; Chicago, IL; HonRl; JrNHS; NHS; OffAde; FrCl; MthCl; University; Mathematics.

KOREN, Michael; John Marshall HS; Milwaukee, WI; Chrs; HonRl; TchrAde; IMSpt; Coll; Teach Us Hist Or Spanish.

KORENIC, Eileen M; Hamilton HS; Milwaukee, WI; 6/900 ALAGirlsSt; Chr; ChrhWkr; HonRl; Mdrgl; NatlMeritCmnd; SchMus; SchPl; TchrAde; RptrYrbk; Mount Mary College; Research Chemistry.

KORESSEL, Lynn A; Reitz Memorial HS; Evansville, IN; HonRl; MrchBnd; SchMus; SchPl; RptrSchPpr; SchPpr; Western Kentucky Univ; Communication.

KORF, Berny H; Bristol HS; Bristol, SD; VPFrshCls; Band; ChrhWkr; CncrtBnd; HonRl; MrchBnd; PepBnd; StuCncl; YthFlsp; IMSpt; Dakota Weslyan U.

KORF, Gina M; Forest Lake HS; Forest Lake, MN; Band; ChrhWkr; CmntyWkr; HonRl; JA; JrNHS; NatlFornLg; NHS; PolWkr; Quill&Scroll; Yrbk; RptrSchPpr; SpnCl; GAA; College; Professional.

KORF, Therese M; Forest Lake Sr HS; Forest Lake, MN; 37/363 HonRl; LitMag; NHS; FFA; SpnCl; Tennis; Trk; College; Nursing.

KORICAN, Donald R; Britton Macon HS; Britton, MI; 16/45 HonRl; SchPl; FFA; Trk; Michigan St Univ; Agriculture.

KORKOSZ, Debbie L; Oak Forest HS; Oak Forest, IL; VPJrCls; CmntyWkr; 4-H; FrCl; PpCl; CaptChrldr; LetterCchngActv; GAA; 4-HAwd; College; Medicine.

KORKOWSKI, Carol J; Brandon HS; Brandon, MN; 1/39 Band; HonRl; OffAde; SchPl; StuCncl; GerCl; Chrldr; GAA; BttyCrckrAwd; DARAwd; Anoka Vo Tech Inst; Legal Secretary.

KORLESKY, Edith A; Roncalli HS; Manitowoc, WI; 8/140 AFS; HospAde; SchPl; MthCl; Trk; GAA; BauchLmbAwd; KiwanAwd; Uw Oshkosh.

KORMAN, David L; Glenbrook North HS; Northbrook, IL; 12/657 HonRl; NHS; NatlMeritCmnd; Miami Univ; Business Admin.

KORN, Daniel W; Cashton HS; Cashton, WI; 15/77 VPJrCls; HonRl; PresFFA; Wrstlng; Trade School; Refrigeration.

KORN, Keith A; Cardinal Ritter HS; Indianapolis, IN; HonRl; SchMus; SchPl; SctActv; Bsktbl; Ftbl; Iupui; Engineering.

KORN, Mike E; Lawrenceburg HS; Lawrenceburg, IN; HstJrCls; NHS; SchPl; ChrhWkr; StuCncl; SptEdYrbk; FSA; KeyCl; PpCl; LetterFtbl; Purdue; Forestry.

KORN, Tim A; Elston Sr HS; Michigan City, IN; 117/378 Bsbl; Bsktbl; Ftbl; KiwanAwd; College.

KORNAUS, Mary Kaye; Pulaski HS; Pulaski, WI; ChrhWkr; HonRl; NHS; Sdlty; MthCl; Bellin Mem Hosp; Reg Nurse.

KORNBLUM, Karen E; Pioneer HS; Ann Arbor, MI; HonRl; LitMag; Orch; SchMus; College.

KORNELIS, Daniel W; Langdon HS; Langdon, ND; HonRl; StuCncl; StuGov; Teen; RptrSchPpr; GerCl; PpCl; Bsbl; CaptBsktbl; Ftbl; Univ Of Nd; Political Science.

KORNELY, Debra J; Mishicot Community HS; Two Rivers, WI; VPJrCls; Chrs; CncrtBnd; MrchBnd; RptrYrbk; Yrbk; RptrSchPpr; SchPpr; LatCl; GAA; Patricia Steven Clg; Professional Model.

KORNOELJE, Kerri L; Jenison Public Sr HS; Granville, MI; 9/265 Chr; ChrhWkr; HonRl; HospAde; Mdrgl; NHS; RedCrAde; SchMus; SecStuCncl; YthFlsp; Calvin Coll; Nursing.

KOROL, Anthony M; Marquette HS; Michigan City, IN; 1/63 HonRl; College; Professional.

KORONKIEWICZ, Frank O; Thornridge HS; Dolton, IL; HonRl; NHS; LetterBsbl; LetterWrstlng; Illinois Inst Of Tech; Architecture.

KORPELA, Michael W; A D Johnston HS; Ramsay, MI; 10/104 Band; HonRl; Bsbl; LetterBsktbl; Trk; College; Lawyer.

KORPI, Wayne I; Ishpeming HS; Ishpeming, MI; HonRl; VPSchAde; IMSpt; Mi Tech Univ; Engineering.

KORSMEYER, Vicky M; Blair Oaks HS; Jefferson, MO; Band; CncrtBnd; HonRl; MrchBnd; PepBnd; SchPl; 4-H; FBLA; KeyCl; PpCl; DanFAwd; College; Business Admin.

KORSMO, Jeffrey O; Lourdes HS; Rochester, MN; HonRl; NHS; PresStuCncl; TchrAde; LetterFtbl; LetterTrk; CchngActv;.

KORSMO, Katherine A; Barrington HS; Barrington, IL; 135/650 HonRl; NHS; Univ; Professional.

KORSON, Philip J; St Mary HS; Lake Leelanau, MI; 4/15 PresFrshCls; TrsSophCls; TrsJrCls; Chrs; HonRl; StuCncl; Yrbk; 4-H; LetterBsktbl; LetterSocr; BauchLmbAwd; 4-HAwd; Michigan State Univ; Agriculture.

KORST, Michael W; High School; Woodstock, IL; CncrtBnd; MrchBnd; GerCl;.

KORST, Michael W; Woodstock Community HS; Woodstock, IL; 90/270 MrchBnd; Orch; StuCncl; LetterBsbl; Ftbl; IMSpt; Illinois St Univ; Chemical Engineer.

KORTE, Bruce E; Leigh Comm HS; Leigh, NE; TrsSophCls; VPJrCls; Chr; HonRl; SchPl; StuCncl; GerCl; Ftbl; LetterWrstlng; College; Accounting.

KORTE, Joseph H; Catholic Central HS; La Salle, MI; Band; CncrtBnd; MrchBnd; NHS; Orch; PepBnd; IMSpt; RotaryAwd; College; Computer Science.

KORTE, Kandi K; Metropolis Community HS; Metropolis, IL; PresBand; HonRl; MrchBnd; RedCrAde; Twrl; EdYrBk; SpnCl; MthCl; SecPpCl; LetterBsktbl; GAA; Univ Of Miss; Nurse.

KORTE, Lorie L; Hillsboro HS; Hillsboro, MO; HonRl; JrNHS; LbryAde; NHS; TchrAde; FTA; SecMthCl; PpCl; Trk; PresAwd; College.

KORTEBEIN, William S; Arlington HS; Arlington Hts, IL; Chr; CncrtBnd; HonRl; MrchBnd; NatlMeritCmnd; Trk; Univ Of Ill; Engineering.

KORTENHOVEN, Donald L; Thornton Fractional S HS; Lansing, IL; Band; CncrtBnd; HonRl; MrchBnd; GerCl; LetterSwmmng; Tennis; Univ Of Illinois; Electrical Engineering.

KORTERING, Randall L; Zeeland HS; Zeeland, MI; Bsktbl; Grand Valley; Engineer.

KORTESOJA, Susan L; Franklin HS; Livonia, MI; College; Computer Programer.

KORTH, Kim M; Humphrey HS; Cornlea, NE; 7/21 HstSrCls; Chr; ChrhWkr; CmntyWkr; RptrYrbk; EdSchPpr; SptEdSchPpr; 4-H; PpCl; IMSpt; Coll; Prof.

KORTH, Peggy; Cathedral HS; Omaha, NE; VPFrshCls; PresSrCls; HonRl; NHS; StuCncl; TchrAde; PpCl; Univ Of Nebr; Undecided.

KORTH, Susan; Manchester HS; Manchester, MI; 1/102 LbryAde; TchrAde; GerCl; LetterTrk;.

KORTH, Tamera M; Randolph Public HS; Randolph, NE; ALAGirlsSt; Band; Chr; Chrs; CncrtBnd; HonRl; Mdrgl; NHS; PepBnd; SchMus; College.

KORTHANKE, Susan K; Hiawatha HS; Robinson, KS; Aud/Vis; Chr; MrchBnd; YthFlsp; PpCl; Chrldr; College.

KORTHAUER, Cathy S; Fenton HS; Bensenville, IL; 25/357 Western Illinois University.

KORTHAUER, Richard; Houston HS; Caledonia, MN; 4/60 Band; HonRl; SchMus; 4-H; FFA; 4-HAwd; Coll.

KORTHAUER, Richard; Hanover Central HS; Cedar Lake, IN; 3/140 PresSophCls; Band; ChrhWkr; CncrtBnd; HonRl; JrNHS; MrchBnd; NHS; PepBnd; StuCncl; Valparaiso U; Civil Engineer.

KORTOKRAX, Michael J; Highland Park HS; Highland Park, IL; CAP; Univ Of Illinois; Pilot.

KORTZ, Audrey J; Litchfield Sr HS; Darwin, MN; Chr; YthFlsp; SchPpr; 4-H; FFA; Swmmng; Chrldr; 4-HAwd; University; Veterinary Medicine.

KORTZ, Dave J; Lourdes HS; Rochester, MN; Band; Chrl; CncrtBnd; DrmMjrt; MrchBnd; SchMus; SchPl; SchPpr; KiwanAwd; College; Music Education.

KORVER, Karen R; Maurice Orangecity Comm HS; Maurice, IA; Chr; Chrl; Chrs; ChrhWkr; CmntyWkr; HonRl; LbryAde; OffAde; SchMus; SchPl; YthFlsp; 4-H; PpCl; LetterTrk; Schl Of Cosmetology; Beautician.

KORZAN, Cheryl L; Kimball Public HS; Kimball, SD; PresFrshCls; Band; CncrtBnd; HonRl; MrchBnd; Yrbk; PpCl; Trk; Chrldr; Sdsu Vermillion; Medical Lab Tech.

KORZENIOWSKI, Matthew C; St Laurence HS; Chicago, IL; 54/385 De Paul Univ; Business Adm.

KOSAK, David W; Webb HS; Reedsburg, WI; 9/227 Band; CncrtBnd; HonRl; MrchBnd; PepBnd; LatCl; LetterTrk; OptClAwd; Uw Green Bay; Envir.

KOSARK, Randy L; Owensville HS; Owensville, MO; ChrhWkr; HonRl; NatlThespSoc; SchPl; PresStuCncl; SpnCl; LetterBsbl; CaptBsktbl; College; Professional.

KOSCHAK, Brad K; Warren HS; Gurnee, IL; 11/361 HonRl; NHS; CaptTrk; College; Agriculture Soil Science.

KOSCHINSKE, Mary E; Lutheran HS; Chaska, MN; 6/62 Band; Chrs; ChrhWkr; HonRl; NHS; SchMus; SchPl; StuCncl; Yrbk; SchPpr; 4-H; SciCl; 4-HAwd; Concordia College; Elem Ed.

KOSCHMEDER, Kent C; Riceville HS; Riceville, IA; Band; CncrtBnd; HonRl; MrchBnd; NHS; FFA; LetterFtbl; Trk; Wrstlng; University; Vocation.

KOSCHOFF, Denise M; Hazelwood West HS; Hazelwood, MO; 8/481 HonRl; LetterNHS; SptEdSchPpr; SchPpr; LetterPpCl; LetterChrldr; Coll; Allied Health Field.

KOSCIELNIAK, Carol J; Foley HS; Hillman, MN; ChrhWkr; HonRl; NHS; OffAde; FNA; College; Nursing.

KOSCO, Mary K; Catholic Memorial HS; Brookfield, WI; JrNHS; NHS; RptrYrbk; U Of Wisconsin Madison; Pharmacy.

KOSENHEIMER, Bruce E; West Bend HS; West Bend, WI; HonRl; NatlMeritCmnd; LetterFtbl; Tennis; Trk; Wrstlng; Univ Of Notre Dame; Business Finance.

KOSER, Kurt; Watertown HS; Watertown, WI; 11/310 AFS; ALBoysSt; ModUN; NHS; NatlThespSoc; StuCncl; RptrSchPpr; SpnCl; Ftbl; RotaryAwd; Carroll College; Theatre Arts.

KOSERRANS, Jo A; Elmwood HS; Elmwood, IL; 1/58 SecBand; NHS; EdYrBk; SpnCl; PpCl; Chrldr; GAA; Univ Of Illinois; Lawyer.

KOSHAK, Alan A; Lincoln HS; Park Falls, WI; 7/107 PresSrCls; ALBoysSt; Band; HonRl; MrchBnd; NHS; SchMus; StuCncl; GerCl; LetterTrk; Air Force Acad; Pilot.

KOSHIOL, Debbie A; Cathedral HS; St Cloud, MN; VPOrch; SchMus; Yrbk; SchPpr; Vocational Sch; Business.

KOSHIOL, Joleen J; Cathedral HS; St Cloud, MN; 17/153 SecTrsSrCls; HonRl; NHS; Yrbk; SchPpr; PpCl; IMSpt; PPFtbl; Voc Tec Inst; Bus Field.

KOSIARA, Robert J; Lincoln Way HS; Mokena, IL; 69/564 Univ Of Illinois; Veterinarian.

KOSIBA, Janet; John F Kennedy HS; Chicago, IL; 20/610 VPNHS; SctActv; Yrbk; FrCl; MthCl; PpCl; SciCl; GAA; Univ Of Chicago; Accountant.

KOSIEK, Janet C; Amos Alonzo Stagg HS; Hickory Hills, IL; 18/468 ChrhWkr; HonRl; NatlMeritCmnd; SpnCl; SciCl; GAA; Lewis Univ; Organic Chemistry.

KOSIFAS, Christopher D; Quigley South HS; Chicago Ridge, IL; Chrs; HonRl; NHS; PolWkr; SchMus; SpnCl; Benedictine Clg; Accounting.

KOSIK, Melodie A; Glenbrook South HS; Northbrook, IL; HstSrCls; AFS; HonRl; NHS; StuGov; SpnCl; College.

KOSINSKI, Thomas M; Bishop Borgess HS; Detroit, MI; SchMus; SchPl; SctActv; RptrSchPpr; SchPpr; Tennis; Trk; IMSpt; U Of Detroit; Elec Engr.

KOSINSKI, Timothy F; St Agatha HS; Southfield, MI; 3/110 ChrhWkr; CmntyWkr; HonRl; NHS; Yrbk; RptrSchPpr; SchPpr; EngCl; LatCl; College; Pre Med.

KOSKA, Catherine; Grandview Sr HS; Grandview, MO; HonRl; JA; MrchBnd; SchMus; SctActv; RptrYrbk; SchPpr; MthCl; JAAwd; Coll; Accountant.

KOSKAMP, Mark A; North Linn HS; Coggon, IA; 1/65 ALBoysSt; Band; Chrs; NHS; SchMus; SecStuCncl; PresYthFlsp; SecSpnCl; Bsktbl; LetterTrk; College; Music.

KOSKI, Anthony J; Lockport Township HS; Lockport, IL; 17/670 Chr; ChrhWkr; HonRl; JrNHS; College; Ornithologist.

KOSKI, Julianne E; John F Kennedy HS; Babbitt, MN; 1/145 ChrhWkr; HospAde; NHS; NatlMeritSchl; BttyCrckrAwd; CitAwd; St Olaf College; Medicine.

KOSKI, Margaret H; Maria HS; Chicago, IL; 13/338 Chr; SchPl; StuCncl; 4-H; SpnCl; Trk; CchngActv; AmLegAwd; 4-HAwd; U Of Ill; Agriculture.

KOSKI, Mitchell R; J E Murphy HS; Upson, WI; HonRl; SchMus; 4-H; LetterFtbl; LetterTrk; IMSpt; College; Vocation.

KOSLOWSKI, Eric A; High School; North Branch, MN; 13/122 TrsJrCls; ALBoysSt; HonRl; NHS; CaptFtbl; CaptTrk; CaptWrstlng; St Johns Univ; Lab Tech.

KOSMAN, Joseph J; Mendel HS; Calumet Park, IL; 28/170 ALBoysSt; ChrhWkr; CmntyWkr; SctActv; StuCncl; KeyCl; PpCl; IMSpt; Univ Of Wisconsin; Veterinarian.

KOSMANOPOULOS, Mary C; Grand Blanc HS; Flint, MI; CmntyWkr; HonRl; TchrAde; PPFtbl; U Of Mi; Psychology.

KOSMATKA, Mark; Oslo HS; West Oslo, MN; ChrhWkr; HonRl; SchPl; Yrbk; SciCl; Trade School; Vocation.

KOSMATKA, Mary E; Minto Public HS; Minto, ND; 4/23 ALAGirlsSt; Band; Chr; Chrs; ChrhWkr; CmntyWkr; CncrtBnd; HonRl; MrchBnd; PepBnd; Bsbl; Bsktbl; Glf; Womens Army Corps; Vocation.

KOSO, Joleen F; Falls City Senior HS; Falls City, NE; ChrhWkr; HonRl; GAA; Beautician School; Secretary.

KOSOGOF, John; Taft HS; Chicago, IL; University; Law.

KOSS, Linda M; East Catholic HS; Detroit, MI; HonRl; ModUN; Wayne State Univ; Journalism.

KOSS, Robert J; Stanley Boyd HS; Stanley, WI; 8/110 HonRl; ROTC; SchPl; SctActv; StuCncl; Bsktbl; Ftbl; Trk; GovHonPrgAwd; Uw Madison; Cpa.

KOSSE, Ronda K; Bladen Public HS; Bladen, NE; 3/11 VPFrshCls; TrsJrCls; VPSrCls; Chrs; HonRl; SchPl; Yrbk; 4-H; PpCl; LetterTrk; Chrldr; 4-HAwd; Mary Lanning School; Nursing.

KOSSEN, Billy R; Platte County R Iii HS; Platte City, MO; PresSophCls; SptEdYrbk; Ftbl; Wrstlng; College; Law Enforcement.

KOSSINA, Lynn M; Warren Co R Iii HS; Warrenton, MO; 8/102 ALAGirlsSt; HonRl; NHS; SctActv; FHA; PpCl; College; Chem.

KOST, Curtis L; Ashley HS; Ashley, ND; 1/41 PresSophCls; Chr; HonRl; Trk; Minot St Col; Bus Management.

KOST, Mary C; Mercy HS; St Louis, MO; 2/180 HonRl; NHS; TchrAde; RptrYrbk; SpnCl; PpCl; Bsktbl; CchngActv; GAA; IMSpt; Coll;prof.

KOST, Vivian J; Lanesville HS; Corydon, IN; Band; ChrhWkr; HonRl; NHS; SchPl; SchPpr; 4-H; Trk; IMSpt; 4-HAwd; Univ; Music.

KOSTAL, Patrick W; Odell Public HS; Wymore, NE; 3/20 PresFrshCls; PresSophCls; VPJrCls; HonRl; PresStuCncl; RptrYrbk; LetterBsktbl; LetterFtbl; LetterTrk; CchngActv; University Of Neb; Computer.

KOSTELLO, Lou C; Lasalle Peru HS; Oglesby, IL; 10/506 AFS; ALAGirlsSt; HonRl; NHS; NatlMeritCmnd; SctActv; SpnCl; College; Biology.

KOSTELNY, Robert J; John Hersey HS; Prospect Hgts, IL; HonRl; NHS; LetterTennis; JETSAwd; Northern Arizona Univ; Environmental Scienc.

KOSTER, Barbara; Dominican Hs; Detroit, MI; ChrhWkr; CmntyWkr; JA; ModUN; NHS; NatlMeritSchl; PolWkr; RptrYrbk; Swmmng; Wayne State U; Journalism.

KOSTERS, Gregory; Sioux Center HS; Sioux Center, IA; 20/81 Band; Chr; Chrs; ChrhWkr; CncrtBnd; HonRl; MrchBnd; PepBnd; SchPl; Ftbl; Iowa State Univ; Pre Medicine Md.

KOSTKA, Ellen M; Gibraltar HS; Sister Bay, WI; Band; CncrtBnd; MrchBnd; PepBnd; GerCl; Trk; IMSpt; College; Vocation.

KOSTOPULOS, Margaret; Oak Park River Forest HS; Oak Park, IL; Aud/Vis; HonRl; Yrbk; Univ Of Mo; Journalism.

KOSTYNIAK, Alan P; Elk Grove HS; Elk Grove Village, IL; 16/505 Northwestern Univ; Professional.

KOSTYO, Nancy J; Morton Sr HS; Hammond, IN; 8/492 Band; CncrtBnd; DrmMjrt; HonRl; NatlFornLg; NHS; PepBnd; StuCncl; StuGov; College.

KOSZCZUK, Georgette; Ridgewood HS; Norridge, IL; 49/369 HonRl; NHS; SchMus; TchrAde; PpCl; Illinois State Univ; Speech Pathology.

KOSZEWSKI, Susan A; Stratford HS; Stratford, WI; 22/90 HonRl; NHS; FHA; Marshfield Tech; Med Stenographer.

KOSZYK, Philip M; Loyola Academy; Chicago, IL; 33/442 HonRl; LetterFtbl; IMSpt; Univ Of Michigan; Medicine.

KOTALIK, Pamela; Tyndall HS; Tabor, SD; CmntyWkr; HonRl; FHA; College And U; Dental Hygienist.

KOTAS, Beth E; Tripp HS; Tripp, SD; ChrhWkr; HonRl; LbryAde; NatlFornLg; SchPl; TchrAde; VPFHA; PpCl; National College Of Business; Secretarial.

KOTECKI, Annette; St Clement HS; Center Line, MI; PresSophCls; PresJrCls; HonRl; JrNHS; StuCncl; SpnCl; SciCl; LetterBsbl; LetterBsktbl; GAA; College; Professional.

KOTECKI, Annette; St Clement HS; Center Ln, MI; PresSophCls; VPJrCls; HonRl; SchPl; StuCncl; SpnCl; PpCl; Bsbl; LetterBsktbl; GAA; College; Professional.

KOTECKI, Judith A; Thorp HS; Thorp, WI; 3/74 HonRl; NHS; StuCncl; VPFHA; SpnCl; LetterBsktbl; GAA; Univ Of Eau Claire; Psychology.

KOTEK, John D; Beaver Dam Sr HS; Beaver Dam, WI; Band; ChrhWkr; CncrtBnd; MrchBnd; PepBnd; Ftbl; Trk; Wrstlng;.

KOTH, Cindy; Pinconning HS; Linwood, MI; 22/255 Band; CncrtBnd; MrchBnd; NHS; RedCrAde; RptrYrbk; FNA; PpCl; PPFtbl; Lake Superior State Coll; Nursing.

KOTH, James R; Ralston HS; Ralston, NE; Band; CncrtBnd; MrchBnd; Univ Of Nebraska; Dentistry.

KOTH, Michelle D; Greendale HS; Greendale, WI; 4/338 Chr; HonRl; LbryAde; ModUN; NHS; PpCl; Chrldr; University; Math.

KOTHBAUER, Kathy; Durano Sr HS; Durano, WI; SecSophCls; Band; PepBnd; HonRl; MrchBnd; SchPl; Yrbk; PpCl; Trk; Voc; Secretarial.

KOTHE, Beverly; Trico HS; Percy, IL; 4/112 Chr; ChrhWkr; HonRl; NHS; RptrYrbk; 4-H; FrCl; PpCl; AmLegAwd; 4-HAwd; Ill St Univ; Physician.

KOTILA, Vicki S; Frederick HS; Frederick, SD; TreasBand; Chrs; ChrhWkr; CncrtBnd; HonRl; LbryAde; MrchBnd; PepBnd; SchPl; StuCncl; Univ; Computer Programming.

KOTINEK, David J; Superior HS; Superior, NE; PresFrshCls; Band; CncrtBnd; HonRl; MrchBnd; StuCncl; StuGov; Bsktbl; LetterTrk; KiwanAwd; College; Music.

KOTLAREK, Deborah L; Solomon Juneau HS; Milwaukee, WI; 5/205 HonRl; NHS; MthCl; Trk; GAA; Marquette Univ;elec Engr.

KOTLARZ, Janice K; South HS; Omaha, NE; SecSrCls; Chr; Chrs; ChrhWkr; HonRl; Swmmng; Chrldr; College; English.

KOTOWSKI, Karen L; La Salle Peru Twp HS; La Salle, IL; 11/490 HonRl; LitMag; SctActv; Sdlty; SpnCl; College; Graphic Design.

KOTOWSKI, Mary A; St Clement HS; Center Line, MI; TrsSrCls; HonRl; JA; JrNHS; PolWkr; FHA; College; Psychology.

KOTRBA, Frances A; Goodridge Public HS; Goodridge, MN; 5/34 TrsJrCls; VPSrCls; SchPl; StuCncl; Yrbk; CaptBsktbl; Trk; GAA; Voc School; Fashion Merchandising.

KOTRBA, Linda K; East Grand Forks Sr HS; Euclid, MN; 11/160 Band; Chrl; SecChrs; HonRl; PresNHS; 4-H; PpCl; Chrldr; GAA; 4-HAwd; College; Nurse.

KOTROUS, Cindy; Verdigre Public HS; Verdigre, NE; Chrs; HonRl; YthFlsp; RptrSchPpr; PpCl; Indefinite; Conservationist.

KOTS, Gary J; West Sioux HS; Ireton, IA; HonRl; FFA; Trade Sch.

KOTT, Mary J; Manistee Public HS; Mainstee, MI; ALAGirlsSt; Band; ChrhWkr; HonRl; NHS; PepBnd; StuCncl; RptrYrbk; GAA; Col; Med Tech.

KOTT, Robert L; St Ladislaus HS; Detroit, MI;

TrsSophCls; HonRl; NatlMeritCmnd; SciCl; Michigan St Univ; Engineering.

KOTTARAS, Demetrios; Oak Lawn Comm Hs; Oak Lawn, IL; 37 Band; ChrhWkr; HonRl; MrchBnd; NHS; PepBnd; SctActv; StuGov; TchrAde; MthCl; Northwestern U;pre Med.

KOTTKE, Jan L; Fredericksburg Community HS; Fredericksburg, IA; Band; Chrs; HonRl; SecStuCncl; SecYthFlsp; Pres4-H; LetterTrk; IMSpt; BttyCrckrAwd; 4-HAwd; Wartburg College; Professional.

KOTTKE, Kandice K; Martin Luther HS; Greendale, WI; 1/87 Band; Chr; HonRl; NHS; PepBnd; SchPl; Yrbk; EdSchPpr; Tennis; AmLegAwd; Nw Univ; Physician.

KOTTLOWSKI, Brian; New Palestine HS; New Palestine, IN; 11/145 HonRl; NatlThespSoc; SchMus; SchPl; FFA; LatCl; Bsktbl; Ftbl; Trk; Military.

KOTTMAN, Gary; West Platte R Ii HS; Weston, MO; Band; CncrtBnd; HonRl; MrchBnd; ModUN; Yrbk; Bsktbl; Missouri Western State College;law Enf.

KOTTWITZ, Melvin E; Bowling Green HS; Bowling Green, MO; 7/128 Band; CncrtBnd; HonRl; MrchBnd; TreasNHS; NatlMeritSF; NatlSciFnd; PepBnd; FBLA; SecMthCl; St Louis College; Pharmacist.

KOTTWITZ, Sandra A; Nokomis HS; Nokomis, IL; 15/98 Band; CncrtBnd; HonRl; HospAde; PepBnd; RedCrAde; Sec4-H; GAA; 4-HAwd; Junior College; Professional.

KOTTWITZ, Terry D; Ritenour HS; St John, MO; 2/850 ChrhWkr; HonRl; JrNHS; NHS; NatlMeritSF; SctActv; 4-H; GerCl; 4-HAwd; Univ Of Mo; Engineering.

KOUBA, Lori A; Clay Center Public HS; Clay Center, NE; 1/25 PresJrCls; ALAGirlsSt; ChrhWkr; CmntyWkr; HonRl; NHS; YthFlsp; Trk; Chrldr; CchngActv; DARAwd; Kearney State Col; Accountant.

KOUBA, Lori A; 200 N Center HS; Clay Center, NE; 1/26 PresJrCls; ALAGirlsSt; ChrhWkr; HonRl; NHS; YthFlsp; Trk; Chrldr; AmLegAwd; DARAwd; Kearney State Col; Accountant.

KOUBA, Paul F; St Joseph HS; Brookfield, IL; 8/176 HonRl; ModUN; SctActv; StuCncl; StuGov; RptrSchPpr; GerCl; PpCl; Socr; IMSpt; University; Accounting.

KOUBEK, Catherine A; Arnold HS; Arnold, NE; 1/33 CmntyWkr; HonRl; FFA; FHA; VPPpCl; Glf; Trk; Univ Of Nebraska; Home Economics.

KOUKOL, Nancy J; Hillcrest HS; Cuba, KS; 2/16 Band; Chrs; HonRl; NHS; StuCncl; PpCl; Bsktbl; Trk; Chrldr; BttyCrckrAwd; Ks State University ;special Ed.

KOUMAS, Michael; Kirksville Senior HS; Kirksville, MO; HonRl; NHS; Orch; SchMus; RptrYrbk; Yrbk; RptrSchPpr; SchPpr; SpnCl; University; Professional.

KOUNS, Cheryl A; Zionsville Comm HS; Zionsville, IN; 4/150 Chr; HonRl; NHS; 4-H; SpnCl; LetterBsktbl; LetterTrk; GAA; 4-HAwd; Purdue University.

KOUNS, Marjorie K; West Leyden HS; Melrose Park, IL; 4/440 AFS; CncrtBnd; DrmMjrt; MrchBnd; VPNHS; SecNatlThespSoc; SchMus; SchPl; SctActv; SecSpnCl; Illinois Wesleyan Univ; Commercial Art.

KOUPMAN, Douglas L; Hamilton HS; Holland, MI; ChrhWkr; HonRl; JrNHS; NHS; NatlMeritSF; Bsbl; Bsktbl; Hope College.

KOURAJIAN, Julia A; Bowbells HS; Bowbells, ND; 2/21 Chrs; HonRl; SchPl; YthFlsp; PpCl; SciCl; Bsbl; LetterBsktbl; LetterChrldr; Und; Biological Research.

KOURI, Stephen A; Spalding HS; East Peoria, IL; 30/100 HonRl; NHS; SchPl; LetterBsbl; LetterFtbl; IMSpt; Creighton; Lawyer.

KOUROS, Joan; Bishop Noll HS; East Chicago, IN; 13/360 ChrhWkr; HonRl; RptrYrbk; FrCl; College; Law.

KOUTEK, Robert J; Riverside Brookfield HS; La Grange Pk, IL; 50/500 HonRl; NHS; TchrAde; LetterBsktbl; Glf; Trk; Northern Il Univ; Design Communications.

KOVACH, Dawn R; Century HS; Karnak, IL; 2/57 Chrs; HonRl; MrchBnd; SchPl; YthFlsp; RptrYrbk; RptrSchPpr; PresFHA; PpCl; IMSpt; Col; Dental Hygienist.

KOVACH, Eugene D; Oakridge Senior HS; Muskegon, MI; 37/119 Band; CncrtBnd; MrchBnd; PepBnd; Trk; Us Army Then College.

KOVACIN, Kenneth L; Thornton Twp HS; Riverdale, IL; Aud/Vis; CmntyWkr; HonRl; NHS; MthCl; Univ Of Il; Engineering.

KOVACK, Michael J; Taylorville Sr HS; Taylorville, IL; 21/251 ChrhWkr; HonRl; NHS; SptEdSchPpr; KeyCl; FrCl; LetterTrk; Univ Of Mo; Chemical Engineer.

KOVACS, Dawn Y; Caro HS; Caro, MI; 1/170 PresJrCls; Band; Chr; ChrhWkr; CncrtBnd; MrchBnd; SchPl; TchrAde; PresYthFlsp; DARAwd; Albion Col; Science.

KOVACS, George P; Joliet Catholic HS; Joliet, IL; 39/170 HonRl; NHS; SchPpr; GerCl; LetterTrk; Bradley Univ; Law.

KOVACS, James; Elgin HS; Hanover Park, IL; Wrstlng; College; Law School.

KOVANDA, Alan E; Exeter Public HS; Milligan, NE; CmntyWkr; HonRl; SctActv; 4-H; FFA; MthCl; LetterTrk; 4-HAwd; Univ Of Nebr; Farming.

KOVAR, Dale E; Silver Lake HS; Silver Lake, MN; ALABoysSt; HonRl; StuCncl; RptrYrbk; SptEdSchPpr; CaptBsbl; LetterBsktbl; CaptFtbl; Trk; CaptAmLegAwd; College; Journalism.

KOVAR, James P; D H Hickman HS; Columbia, MO; NatlMeritSF; Quill&Scroll; StuGov; RptrSchPpr; University Of Missouri; Engineering.

KOVARIK, Janet S; Burwell Jr Sr HS; Burwell, NE; PresJrCls; Band; DrlTm; HonRl; SchPl; MthCl; Bsktbl; Swmmng; LetterTrk; GAA; 4-HAwd; Business School; Secretary.

KOVATS, William D; Ottawa Hills HS; Grand Rapids, MI; JrNHS; NHS; College; Engineering.

KOVELLE, Debbie M; Divine Child HS; Detroit, MI; Chrs; ChrhWkr; CmntyWkr; NHS; NatlThespSoc; SchMus; SchPl; StuCncl; SchPpr;.

KOWAL, Jody A; St Peter HS; St Peter, MN; Chrs; HonRl; NatlThespSoc; SchMus; FHA; U Of Mn Duluth; Elementary Ed.

KOWALCZYK, Alfreda A; Ladywood HS; Garden City, MI; 4/98 HonRl; SecNHS; NatlMeritSF; Quill&Scroll; StuCncl; RptrYrbk; EdSchPpr; SecSciCl; Madonna College; Journalism.

KOWALCZYK, Connie M; Standish Sterling Central HS; Ann Arbor, MI; 4 Chr; NatlMeritCmnd; SchAde; SchPl; TchrAde; YthLg; PPFtbl; VFWAwd; Univ Of Michigan; Lawyer.

KOWALCZYK, Edith A; Gilman HS; Gilman, WI; Band; Chr; TreasChrs; CmntyWkr; MrchBnd; PepBnd; SchPl; StuCncl; RptrSchPpr; Coll; Prof.

KOWALCZYK, Irene; Saint Florian HS; Troy, MI; 3/126 HonRl; LbryAde; NHS; SchMus; SchPl; Yrbk; SchPpr; FrCl; DARAwd; OptClAwd; Michigan State Univ; Medical Technology.

KOWALCZYK, Katherine A; Resurrection HS; Niles, IL; 53/265 SecSrCls; ChrhWkr; CmntyWkr; HonRl; Quill&Scroll; RptrSchPpr; SchPpr; FrCl; College; Journalism.

KOWALCZYK, Michael J; Evergreen Park Comm HS; Evergreen Pk, IL; 38/442 HonRl; JA; NHS; RedCrAde; FDA; FrCl; SciCl; LetterFtbl; LetterWrstlng; Indiana University; Medicine.

KOWALCZYK, Sally B; Rantoul Twp HS; Rantoul, IL; Band; Chrs; CncrtBnd; Mdrgl; MrchBnd; SchMus; StuCncl; AmLegAwd; 4-HAwd; U Of Ill; Professional Singer.

KOWALCZYLE, Denise M; Standish Sterling Central HS; Standish, MI; 30/155 HonRl; NatlMeritSF; RptrSchPpr; EdSchPpr; 4-H; Mid Mi Com Col; Biology/conservation.

KOWALEWSKI, Jean; Divine Savior Holy Angels HS; Milwaukee, WI; 1/121 HonRl; IntrClCncl; SchPl; StuCncl; StuGov; TchrAde; Yrbk; SchPpr; Bsbl; RotaryAwd; Univ; Professional.

KOWALEWSKI, Ron; Loup City HS; Loup City, NE; Band; Chrs; ChrhWkr; CmntyWkr; CncrtBnd; HonRl; MrchBnd; PepBnd; Yrbk; Ftbl; PPFtbl;.

KOWALSKI, Diane M; Imlay City HS; Imlay City, MI; SecFrshCls; ChrhWkr; HonRl; PpCl; LetterBsktbl; IMSpt; Central Michigan Univ; Special Educ.

KOWALSKI, Edward J; Thornton Fractional So HS; Lansing, IL; ALBoysSt; HonRl; NatlFornLg; NHS; Valparaiso Univ; Prelaw.

KOWALSKI, Evett; Tekonsha HS; Tekonsha, MI; 2rd 60 VPFrshCls; Chr; HonRl; LbryAde; OffAde; StuGov; 4-H; Trk; 4-HAwd; CitAwd; College; Psychology.

KOWALSKI, Jody A; St Joseph HS; Chicago, IL; Chrl; HonRl; NHS; Sdlty; FrCl; University Of Illinois; Pharmacy.

KOWALSKI, Robert F; Marian HS; Mishawaka, IN; 31/112 HonRl; SchPl; SctActv; RptrYrbk; SptEdYrbk; RptrSchPpr; CaptSwmmng; LetterTrk; IMSpt; Manchester College; Optometrist.

KOWALSKI, Thomas J; Bedford HS; Temperance, MI; ChrhWkr; CmntyWkr; NatlMeritCmnd; SctActv; GerCl; Trk; Mi St Univ; Tech Writing.

KOWALSKI, Victoria; Waupun HS; Waupun, WI; 6/263 Chr; Chrs; Mdrgl; NHS; Quill&Scroll; SchMus; SchPl; TchrAde; EdSchPpr; Univ Of Wis At Madison; Medicine.

KOWALSKY, David S; New Trier East HS; Glencoe, IL; 151/847 AFS; Chrs; ChrhWkr; HonRl; JA; OffAde; ROTC; University Of Illinois; Architecture.

KOWERT, Daniel; Martin Luther HS; Oak Creek, WI; 4/90 VPSrCls; JrNHS; NHS; NatlMeritCmnd; SchPl; StuCncl; RptrSchPpr; Ftbl; Concordia College; Minister Teacher.

KOWIS, Della M; Reeder Public HS; Reeder, ND; SecTrsJrCls; Chrs; HonRl; SchPpr; LetterBsktbl; GAA; Trade School; Professional.

KOWLES, Douglas R; Winona Sr HS; Winona, MN; Chrs; HonRl; NHS; Bsbl; St Marys College; Mathematics.

KOZACHIK, Jean F; Portland Public HS; Portland, MI; 6/133 Band; ChrhWkr; CncrtBnd; HonRl; MrchBnd; NHS; PepBnd; StuCncl; SecSpnCl; Chrldr; U Of Mi; Medicine.

KOZAK, Trena L; St Teresa HS; Decatur, IL; 25/119 Chrs; ChrhWkr; HonRl; NHS; NatlThespSoc; OffAde; SchMus; SchPl; SctActv; TchrAde; Yrbk; PpCl; College; Medicine.

KOZAKIEWICZ, Richard J; Saint Viator HS; Arlington Heights, IL; 25/252 HonRl; LbryAde; NHS; PolWkr; SctActv; SchPpr; Socr; Univ Of Ill; Business Administration.

KOZANDA, Kenneth J; St Francis De Sales HS; Chicago, IL; 27/294 PresSrCls; VPSrCls; NHS; StuCncl; StuGov; EdYrBk; LetterFtbl; Glf; College; Business Admin.

KOZEL, Donna R; E Grand Forks Sr HS; E Grand Forks, MN; Band; Chrs; ChrhWkr; HonRl; MrchBnd; NHS; PepBnd; 4-H; 4-HAwd; University; Teaching.

KOZEL, Michael; Romeoville Hs; Romeoville, IL; 1/300 HonRl; PresNHS; StuGov; MthCl; CaptBsbl; CaptFtbl; EldAwd; JCAwd; Bradley U; Industrial Engineer.

KOZIEL, Denise L; St Ann HS; Chicago, IL; 1/70 SecJrCls; Chr; HonRl; LbryAde; StuCncl; SpnCl; MthCl; IMSpt; College; Psychology.

KOZIEL, Ruth M; Oak Lawn Comm HS; Oak Lawn, IL; CmntyWkr; HonRl; TchrAde; Jr College; Vocation.

KOZIK, Jack P; St Charles HS; St Charles, IL; HonRl; NHS; College; Computer Science.

KOZINSKI, Robert D; Austin Catholic Prep; Hamtramck, MI; 12/115 HonRl; NHS; SptEdSchPpr; SciCl; CaptBsbl; Bsktbl; Univ Of Michigan; Psychiatry.

KOZIOL, Andy G; Cedar Rapids Public HS; Cedar Rapids, NE; 3/34 Band; ChrhWkr; CncrtBnd; HonRl; NHS; NatlMeritCmnd; SchPl; LetterBsbl; LetterBsktbl; LetterFtbl; College;.

KOZIOL, Christopher J; Lane Tech HS; Chicago, IL; 150/1200 CmntyWkr; LitMag; NatlMeritCmnd; PolWkr; StuCncl; StuGov; RptrSchPpr; SchPpr; Univ Of Chicago; Law.

KOZIOL, Donna M; St Ann HS; Chicago, IL; 2/59 SecSophCls; PresJrCls; PresSrCls; Chrs; HonRl; NHS; StuCncl; StuGov; Roosevelt Univ; Bus Administration.

KOZIOL, Julie A; St Ann HS; Chicago, IL; 9/69 VPFrshCls; ChrhWkr; HonRl; OffAde; StuCncl; StuGov; SpnCl; Bus Sch; Secretary.

KOZIOL, Kristina E; Centerville HS; Centerville, IA; Band; Chrs; NHS;.

KOZIOL, Patrick J; Holy Cross HS; Chicago, IL; 34/314 HonRl; NHS; StuCncl; StuGov; Teen; Univ Of Illinois; Medicine.

KOZISEK, Joan M; David City Public HS; Bruno, NE; ChrhWkr; HonRl; PpCl; PresAwd; Coll; Phy Ed.

KOZLOW, Robert; Catholic Central HS; Detroit, MI; ChrhWkr; HonRl; LitMag; NHS; Sacrstn; SchAde; SchPl; FrCl; OptClAwd; College; Professional.

KOZLOWSKI, James J; Bishop Borgess HS; Detroit, MI; 94/460 CaptFtbl; Bsktbl; LetterTrk; IMSpt; College; Major Study.

KOZLOWSKI, James L; Whiting HS; Whiting, IN; 2/108 TrsJrCls; ALBoysSt; HonRl; NHS; SpnCl; KiwanAwd; Purdue; Professional.

KOZLOWSKI, John L; Gordon Tech HS; Chicago, IL; 25/650 HonRl; GerCl;.

KOZLOWSKI, Linda J; Notre Dame HS; Chicago, IL; PresFrshCls; HonRl; TchrAde; SchPpr; College; English.

KOZLOWSKI, Michael A; St Joseph HS; Brookfield, IL; 2/162 PresJrCls; TrsSrCls; HonRl; ModUN; NHS; NatlMeritCmnd; TreasStuCncl; PresGerCl; Trk; College Of St Thomas; Electrical Engineer.

KOZLOWSKI, Patricia F; Rantoul Twp HS; Rantoul, IL; Band; CAP; CncrtBnd; HonRl; MrchBnd; NatlFornLg; ROTC; StuCncl; SchPpr; SpnCl; Eastern Univ.

KOZLOWSKI, Renata L; Bishop Mcnamara HS; Kankakee, IL; HonRl; LitMag; LbryAde; NHS; NatlThespSoc; PolWkr; SchPl; StuCncl; Yrbk; Univ Of Illinois; Communications.

KOZLOWSKI, Zbigniew A; Lane Tech HS; Chicago, IL; 89/1273 Aud/Vis; Chr; Chrl; Chrs; HonRl; PolWkr; TchrAde; RptrSchPpr; SchPpr; De Paul Univ; Lawyer.

KOZOJED, John F; Quigley South HS; Chicago, IL; Chrs; ChrhWkr; Sacrstn; TchrAde; Niles College; Priesthood.

KOZOJED, Mary E; Maria HS; Chicago, IL; 7/335 CmntyWkr; HonRl; JrNHS; NHS; VPFrCl; GAA; IMSpt; KiwanAwd; College; Special Education.

KOZUBEK, Karen M; Kelvyn Park HS; Chicago, IL; ChrhWkr; NHS; Quill&Scroll; TchrAde; Yrbk; Triton College; Accountant.

KOZUBOWSKI, Laurie E; St Joseph HS; Chicago, IL; HonRl; LbryAde; NHS; Quill&Scroll; RptrYrbk; RptrSchPpr; MthCl; College; Special Ed Teacher.

KOZUK, Cinthia A; Carmel Girls HS; Waukegan, IL; 2/173 HonRl; NHS; FTA; MthCl; PpCl; Univ Of Ill; Chemistry.

KRAAI, Pamela; Zeeland Hs; Zeeland, MI; 4/186 TrsFrshCls; ChrhWkr; HonRl; ModUN; SctActv; 4-H; LetterBsbl; LetterBsktbl; LetterFtbl; 4-HAwd;.

KRAB, Rodney G; Paxton Consolidated HS; Paxton, NE; 1/14 TrsFrshCls; ALBoysSt; HonRl; NHS; SchMus; SchPl; StuCncl; EdYrBk; 4-H; LetterBsktbl; LetterFtbl; Trk; BauchLmbAwd; DanFAwd; Univ Of Nebraska; Agriculture.

KRABER, Gail M; Albia Comm HS; Albia, IA; 5/150 Band; CncrtBnd; HonRl; MrchBnd; NHS; PepBnd; SchPl; SctActv; Yrbk; 4-H; Univ; Chemistry.

KRABIE, Linda M; Oak Park & River Forest HS; Oak Park, IL; 12/1107 TrsFrshCls; HonRl; JrNHS; NHS; NatlMeritSF; PolWkr; StuGov; IMSpt; Univ; Lawyer.

KRABILL, Merrill O; Bethany Christian HS; Goshen, IN; VPJrCls; VPSrCls; HonRl; NatlMeritCmnd; StuCncl; SchPpr; GerCl; LetterSocr; Goshin College; Architect.

KRACHER, Beverly J; Platteview Jr Sr HS; Papillion, NE; VPSophCls; VPJrCls; DrlTm; HonRl; StuCncl; TchrAde; EdYrBk; SpnCl; Univ Of Nebraska.

KRACKE, Pamela S; Johnson Brock HS; Johnson, NE; Band; Chr; CncrtBnd; MrchBnd; PepBnd; Yrbk; PresPpCl; Trk; PPFtbl; 4-HAwd; College; Professional Dental Ass.

KRAEMER, Beverly A; Hutsonville HS; Hutsonville, IL; Band; HonRl; FHA; PpCl; College; Nursing.

KRAEMER, Douglas M; Rochelle HS; Rochelle, IL; ChrhWkr; HonRl; LbryAde; StuCncl; YthFlsp; College; Professional.

KRAEMER, Evelyn M; Paynesville HS; Paynesville, MN; 12/150 Band; Chr; ChrhWkr; CncrtBnd; HonRl; MrchBnd; Yrbk; FHA; GAA; State College; Anesthetist.

KRAEMER, John; Maplewood HS; Richmond Heights, MO; PresSrCls; HonRl; UNYO; CivCl; FBLA; EngCl; GerCl; DanFAwd; JCAwd; USJCAwd; Univ; Law.

KRAEMER, John C; Paris HS; Paris, IL; 59/254 Band; Chr; CncrtBnd; HonRl; MrchBnd; PepBnd; YthFlsp; Tennis; Butler Univ; Pathology.

KRAEMER, Karen; St Johns HS; St Louis, MO; 15/88 Chr; Chrs; HonRl; HospAde; SchMus; SchPl; SctActv; StuCncl; PpCl; IMSpt;.

KRAEMER, Mary C; Columbus HS; Marshfield, WI; Band; Chrs; ChrhWkr; CncrtBnd; HonRl; MrchBnd; OffAde; PepBnd; SchMus; Sdlty; College; Professional.

KRAEMER, Pamela J; Madison Public HS; Madison, MN; AFS; Band; ChrhWkr; HospAde; FHA; PpCl; GAA; PPFtbl;.

KRAENZLE, Dianna L; Valle HS; Ste Genevieve, MO; CmntyWkr; HonRl; HospAde; LbryAde; NHS; SchAde; SchMus; SchPl; StuCncl; IMSpt; Nursing School; Nurse.

KRAENZLER, Erik J; Greendale HS; Greendale, WI; 11/358 ChrhWkr; HonRl; HospAde; NHS; FDA; GerCl; Ftbl; Tennis; IMSpt; Colle; Professional Med.

KRAFFT, Kristi L; West Chicago Community HS; West Chicago, IL; 23/321 Chr; HonRl; JA; PresFrCl; PpCl; Eiu Clge; Study History.

KRAFKA, Martin J; Aquinas HS; Bellwood, NE; 22/100 VPSrCls; ChrhWkr; SchAde; StuCncl; StuGov; TchrAde; SptEdYrbk; EngCl; Bsbl; AmLegAwd; Creighton U; Professional.

KRAFT, Sally A; Huron HS; Ann Arbor, MI; 1/550 ChrhWkr; HonRl; Orch; SchMus; College; Medical Doctor.

KRAFT, Sandy; Canby HS; Canby, MN; Chr; ChrhWkr; CmntyWkr; HonRl; HospAde; SchPl; EdYrBk; 4-H; FHA; PpCl;.

KRAFT, Susan C; Brewster HS; Brewster, MN; Aud/Vis; Band; Chr; Chrs; ChrhWkr; CncrtBnd; LbryAde; MrchBnd; Bsktbl; LetterTrk; Trade Schl; Vocation.

KRAFT, Thomas; Gordon Tech HS; Chicago, IL; HonRl; De Paul Univ; Aviation.

KRAGE, Gerry T; Cotter HS; Dakota, MN; TrsJrCls; Chrs; CmntyWkr; NatlThespSoc; StuGov; RptrSchPpr; LetterFtbl; LetterTrk; IMSpt; Marine Corp; Conservation.

KRAGE, Kellie S; Onaway Area Community HS; Onaway, MI; Band; HonRl; NHS; StuCncl; RptrYrbk; PpCl; LetterBsktbl; LetterChrldr; GAA; Univ; Education.

KRAGENBRING, Kendall A; Atwater Public HS; Atwater, MN; Band; Chr; MrchBnd; 4-H; FFA; Bsbl; CaptFtbl; LetterTrk; CaptWrstlng; 4-HAwd; Vocational School; Agriculture.

KRAGIE, Laura A; Oak Park River Forest HS; Oak Park, IL; 1/1000 HonRl; StuCncl; Univ Of Illinois; Biology.

KRAGNESS, Donna M; Wahpeton Sr HS; Wahpeton, ND; 1/137 ALAGirlsSt; NHS; StuCncl; EdYrBk; PresGerCl; VPSciCl; LetterTennis; BttyCrckrAwd; DanFAwd; EldAwd; Ndsu; Pharmacy.

KRAGON, Steven P; William Howard Taft HS; Chicago, IL; 69/790 HonRl; JrNHS; NHS; TchrAde; U Of I; Literature.

KRAHENBUHL, Mark; William Chrisman HS; Independence, MO; 1/44 HonRl; JrNHS; NHS; KeyCl; Univ Of Missouri; Civil Engineering.

KRAHL, Becky; Sacred Heart HS; Slaina, KS; 6/54 ChrhWkr; CmntyWkr; FBLA; FHA; PpCl; Coll; Compurter Programing.

KRAHNKE, Keith C; Detour HS; Drummond Island, MI; 11/47 ALBoysSt; ChrhWkr; HonRl; NHS; StuCncl; TchrAde; LetterBsktbl; LetterFtbl; CchngActv; Lake Superior St College; Mathematics.

KRAISINGER, Susan K; Pratt HS; Pratt, KS; 5/154 ALAGirlsSt; Band; HonRl; OffAde; RptrYrbk; PpCl; LetterGlf; LetterTennis; IMSpt; PPFtbl; Kansas State Univ; Mathematics.

KRAJESKI, Margaret; George Washington Hs; Chicago, IL; Band; ChrhWkr; CncrtBnd; HonRl; MrchBnd; NHS; SchAde; SctActv; LatCl; GAA; Northwestern U;doctor.

KRAJEWSKI, Carol J; Catholic Central HS; Muskego Heights, MI; 13/215 Chrl; HonRl; LitMag; NHS; PolWkr; StuCncl; EdSchPpr; PpCl; EldAwd; OptClAwd; Marquette U; Theatre.

KRAJNOVICH, Peggy G; Willowbrook HS; Villa Park, IL; ChrhWkr; HonRl; NHS; College; Commercial Art.

KRAKER, Steven; Holland Christian HS; Holland, MI; 38/281 CmntyWkr; HonRl; NHS; NatlMeritSF; FDA; IMSpt; Calvin Col; Med Doctor.

KRAKLOW, David A; Rockridge HS; Illinois City, IL; 74/141 Band; Chr; Chrs; CncrtBnd; MrchBnd; PepBnd; SchMus; FTA; LatCl; LetterWrstlng; College; Music.

KRAKLOW, Michael P; Muscatine HS; Muscatine, IA; ChrhWkr; HonRl; NHS; YthFlsp; VP4-H; FFA; LetterFtbl; 4-HAwd; College; Veterinarian.

KRALIK, Sandra J; Riverside Brookfield HS; N Riverside, IL; 15/488 Chr; HonRl; NHS; NatlMeritSchl; FrCl; GerCl; Trk; GAA; U Of Ill; Math.

KRALIK, Scott D; Marshalltown HS; Marshalltown, IA; Band; CncrtBnd; HonRl; MrchBnd; NatlMeritSF; Ia State Univ; Engineering.

KRALJ, Christine I; Pius Xi HS; Milwaukee, WI; 26/377 University Of Wisconsin; Meteorology.

KRALL, Karen J; Proviso West HS; Hillside, IL; 71/948 HonRl; JA; NHS; PresFrCl; College; Accounting.

KRALL, Mary L; Tekonsha HS; Tekonsha, MI; HonRl; SchPl; PresStuGov; TchrAde; RptrYrbk; EdYrBk; RptrSchPpr; EdSchPpr; University; Phot Journalism.

KRALLMANN, John A; San Jose HS; San Jose, IL; 1/20 Chrs; HonRl; VPNHS; NatlMeritCmnd; SchMus; EdSchPpr; Bsktbl; LetterTrk; Bradley Univ; Elec Engineering.

KRAMB, Michael R; So Lake HS; St Clair Shores, MI; 59/504 CncrtBnd; HonRl; MrchBnd; NHS; PepBnd; SchMus; Swmmng; Mich St U; Attorney.

KRAMBEER, Gary; North HS; West Union, IA; Aud/Vis; ChrhWkr; OffAde; SchAde; SchPl; Ftbl; Trade School; Vocation.

KRAMER, Alan D; Stapleton HS; Gandy, NE; VPJrCls; HonRl; SchPl; StuCncl; StuGov; Ftbl; Trade School; Vocation.

KRAMER, Ann D; Garrigan HS; Bode, IA; 7/104 Chr; Chrs; HonRl; LbryAde; NatlMeritFnl; NatlMeritSF; OffAde; SchMus; 4-H; Bsbl; Bsktbl; College; Nurse.

KRAMER, Bill D; Stuart Public HS; Stuart, NE; 2/32 SecTrsFrshCls; SecTrsSophCls; SecTrsJrCls; TrsSrCls; HonRl; SchPl; StuCncl; StuGov; Ftbl;.

KRAMER, Carla A; Central HS; Aberdeen, SD; Band; Chr; Chrs; HonRl; HospAde; LbryAde; OffAde; Chrldr; Presentation Coll; Nursing.

KRAMER, Carol J; Stuart HS; Stuart, NE; Chrs; HonRl; LbryAde; SchPl; Yrbk; 4-H; PpCl; 4-HAwd; College; Teacher.

KRAMER, Daniel R; Elkhart Central HS; Bristol, IN; ChrhWkr; IMSpt; Indiana Univ; Pre Medicine.

KRAMER, Darlene; Rosary HS; Aurora, IL; 25/67 Chrl; Chrs; HonRl; SchMus; SchPl; StuCncl; TchrAde; LetterTennis; PresTIMEAwd; IMSpt; Univ Of Ill Chicago; Physical Therapy.

KRAMER, Deborah A; Stapleton HS; Gandy, NE; PresJrCls; Band; CncrtBnd; HonRl; NHS; PepBnd; SchPl; Yrbk; FHA; Trade Schl; Professional.

KRAMER, Deborah L; Orchard View HS; Muskegon, MI; ChrhWkr; HonRl; SecNHS; TchrAde; RptrSchPpr; VoiceDemAwd; Grand Rapids Baptist Col.

KRAMER, Douglas R; Drono Sr HS; Wayzata, MN; 1/208 ALBoysSt; Band; CncrtBnd; HonRl; MrchBnd; NHS; NatlMeritFnl; PepBnd; SchPpr; Glf; Yale Univ; Lawyer.

KRAMER, George A; Campion Jesuit HS; Kankakee, IL; 5/91 Band; CncrtBnd; ModUN; PepBnd; SchAde; StuGov; RptrSchPpr; Bsbl; Bsktbl; CaptFtbl; LetterTennis; LetterTrk; Loyola Univ Of Chgo; Doctor.

KRAMER, Gizelle M; Concordia Acad; St Paul, MN; 9/49 PresJrCls; Chr; HonRl; HospAde; JrNHS; NHS; SchMus; StuCncl; LatCl; Trk; Concordia Coll.

KRAMER, James A; Stephen Decatur HS; Decatur, IL; Chr; ChrhWkr; NHS; NatlMeritSF; SchMus; SctActv; GerCl; Trk; CaptWrstlng; College; Medicine.

KRAMER, Jim; Mc Louth HS; Tonganoxie, KS; VPJrCls; ChrhWkr; HonRl; MrchBnd; SchAde; SchPl; TchrAde; YthFlsp; SchPpr; 4-H; College; Curriculum Of Major Study.

KRAMER, John T; Sullivan HS; Chicago, IL; SctActv; TchrAde; RptrSchPpr; College; Writer.

KRAMER, Joy D; Gibson Southern HS; Priceton, IN; Band; ChrhWkr; CncrtBnd; MrchBnd; 4-H; PpCl; Trk; 4-HAwd; College; Secretarial.

KRAMER, Karen J; Coher HS; Winona, MN; 7/108 HonRl; NHS; OffAde; Quill&Scroll; Sdlty; EdSchPpr; SpnCl; IMSpt; Clge Of St Benedicts; Social Welfare.

KRAMER, Kellee R; S F C HS; St Francis, KS; 18/51 ChrhWkr; DrmMjrt; HonRl; RedCrAde; StuCncl; TchrAde; PpCl; LetterBsktbl; GAA; PPFtbl; Jr College; Music Instructor.

KRAMER, Kenneth M; Mather HS; Chicago, IL; 82/442 Chrs; HonRl; SchPpr; University Of Illinois; Professional.

KRAMER, Kerri J; Stapleton HS; Stapleton, NE; HstSophCls; HstJrCls; HstSrCls; Band; Chrs; CncrtBnd; DrmMjrt; HonRl; MrchBnd; PepBnd; StuCncl; Twrl; Trk; College; Vocation.

KRAMER, Lynn; West Dubuque HS; Dyersville, IA; HonRl; MrchBnd; ModUN; NHS; SecTrsFrshCls; PpCl; IMSpt; PPFtbl; Bsktbl; Nursing.

KRAMER, Mardell S; West Holt HS; Atkinson, NE; DrlTm; HonRl; SchPl; RptrYrbk; FHA; PpCl; Trk; Kearney State Clge; Home Ec.

KRAMER, Mark A; Southfield HS; Southfield, MI; 2/678 Chr; Mdrgl; NHS; NatlMeritFnl; NatlSciFnd; NatlThespSoc; SchMus; SchPl; MthCl; SciCl; College; Engineering.

KRAMER, Mary; West Holt HS; Stuart, NE; 12/71 Aud/Vis; HonRl; HospAde; SctActv; TchrAde; Yrbk; FHA; GerCl; PpCl; CitAwd;.

KRAMER, Mary A; Luckey HS; Ogden, KS; 1/31 SecFrshCls; ALAGirlsSt; ChrhWkr; HonRl; ModUN; PresStuCncl; MthCl; SciCl; DARAwd; CitAwd; Kansas St Univ; Architectural Engineer.

KRAMER, Mary G; Marquette HS; Godfrey, IL; 6/150 HonRl; OffAde; SchAde; RptrSchPpr; Bsktbl; GAA; Univ Of Illinois; School Administration.

KRAMER, Nancy C; Garrigan HS; Algona, IA; 1/104 Chr; Chrs; ChrhWkr; CmntyWkr; HonRl; LbryAde; SchMus; College; Rn.

KRAMER, Nancy J; Dickinson Central HS; Dickinson, ND; Band; CncrtBnd; HonRl; MrchBnd; PepBnd; SchMus; GerCl; Tennis; IMSpt; Clge; Elem Educ.

KRAMER, Polly A; Arthur County HS; Hyannis Rr, NE; HonRl; RptrYrbk; 4-H; PpCl; Trk; DARAwd; Chadron State College; Special Education.

KRAMER, Richard F; South Side HS; Ft Wayne, IN; Aud/Vis; HonRl; Ftbl; International Business; Prof Consultant.

KRAMER, Robert L; Norris HS Dist 160; Cortland, NE; Band; ChrhWkr; CncrtBnd; HonRl; MrchBnd; NHS; StuGov; Bsbl; Bsktbl; Ftbl; Univ Of Ne; Scientific Study.

KRAMER, Rodney M; Winnebago HS; Rockford, IL; 4/105 VPJrCls; HonRl; NHS; GerCl; Rockford College; Physics.

KRAMER, Rosalee E; Nemaha Valley HS; Goff, KS; Chrs; ChrhWkr; HonRl; PpCl; College.

KRAMER, Sandra M; Fatima HS; Linn, MO; HonRl; SchPl; TreasStuCncl; Yrbk; RptrSchPpr; TreasFBLA; VPFHA; PpCl; CaptChrldr;.

KRAMER, Sharon L; Metropolitan Studies HS; Chicago, IL; ChrhWkr; CmntyWkr; LitMag; LbryAde; PolWkr; SchAde; StuGov; TchrAde; College.

KRAMER, Susan L; Glenbrook South HS; Glenview, IL; 74/579 Band; HonRl; NHS; TchrAde; LetterSwmmng; LetterTrk; GAA; Il State Univ; Physical Education Teacher.

KRAMER, Teresa; Southwestern HS; Brighton, IL; 13/175 Band; HonRl; NHS; RptrYrbk; PPFtbl; Southern Ill Univ; Television Production.

KRAMER, Thomas M; Argusville HS; Argusville, ND; 1/15 ALBoysSt; HonRl; SchPl; RptrSchPpr; LetterBsktbl; LetterTrk; BauchLmbAwd; College; Physical Science Area.

KRAMKA, James S; Elgin Larkin HS; Elgin, IL; Band; CncrtBnd; HonRl; MrchBnd; NatlFornLg; Orch; PepBnd; SctActv; LatCl; St Olaf College; Physics.

KRAMME, Mark P; Plattsmouth HS; Plattsmouth, NE; HonRl; Bsktbl; Ftbl; CchngActv; University.

KRAMMIN, Jean C; Hastings HS; Hastings, MI; Band; CncrtBnd; HonRl; MrchBnd; PepBnd; SchMus; 4-H; 4-HAwd; Ferris State Clg; Med Tech.

KRAMP, Hermina; Dominican HS; Detroit, MI; HonRl; NHS; PolWkr; SchPl; TchrAde; RptrSchPpr; Trk; GAA; IMSpt; PPFtbl; Mich State Univ; Lawyer.

KRAMSCHUSTER, Brenda L; Bloomer HS; Bloomer, WI; Chrs; DrlTm; MrchBnd; StuCncl; TchrAde; 4-H; FHA; PpCl; Bsktbl; Technical School; Nursing.

KRANCIC, Karen J; La Salle Peru HS; Oglesby, IL; 1/575 AFS; Chrs; HonRl; SchMus; StuCncl; Bradley Univ; Nursing.

KRANE, Margy L; Castlewood HS; Bemis, SD; 16/30 Band; Chrs; ChrhWkr; SchPl; StuCncl; TchrAde; FHA; Trk; Chrldr; IMSpt; University; Elementary Education.

KRANICH, Sylvia L; Bbc HS; Bourbonnais, IL; HonRl; NHS; YthFlsp; GerCl; College; English & German.

KRANT, Douglas; Lester Prairie Public HS; Lester Prairie, MN; Band; HonRl; NHS; 4-H; Bsbl; 4-HAwd;.

KRANTZ, Virginia E; Glenbrook South HS; Glenview, IL; 138/579 HonRl; Univ; Art.

KRANZ, Gary E; Anthon Oto HS; Anthon, IA; HonRl; LetterFtbl; LetterTrk; Farming.

KRANZ, George E; Cahokia Sr HS; Cahokia, IL; 74/550 HonRl; NHS; College; Professional.

KRANZ, Matthew T; Lincoln Park HS; Lincoln Park, MI; HonRl; Tennis; Westminster Mo Clge; Pro Accountant.

KRANZOW, Sherry; Willowbrook Hs; Villa Park, IL; 9 Chr; HonRl; LbryAde; NHS; NatlThespSoc; SchMus; SchPl; StuCncl; KeyCl; SciCl;.

KRAPF, Lynn; Comstock HS; Kalamazoo, MI; 1/252 Band; CmntyWkr; CncrtBnd; HonRl; MrchBnd; NHS; PepBnd; TchrAde; Bsktbl; Michigan Tech Univ; Electrical Engineering.

KRAPIL, Richard J; Carl Sandburg HS; Tinley Park, IL; 67/700 HonRl; NHS; NatlMeritCmnd; Quill&Scroll; StuCncl; SchPpr; GerCl; MthCl; U Of Il; Aeronautical Engineer.

KRAPU, Benita R; East Grand Forks Sr HS; East Grand Forks, MN; 5/191 Chr; ChrhWkr; CmntyWkr; HonRl; HospAde; JA; NHS; TchrAde; FHA; GerCl; GAA; North Dakota State Univ; Computer Science.

KRAS, Timothy E; Marist HS; Worth, IL; 90/350 HonRl; SciCl; Illinois Inst Of Tech; Chemical Engineer.

KRASASKI, John; Romulus HS; Romulus, MI; HonRl; SciCl; Mi State U; Electrician.

KRASIN, Kent; Columbus HS; Marshfield, WI; 4/114 HonRl; NHS; NatlSciFnd; SchPl; RptrYrbk; MthCl; Glf; BauchLmbAwd; EldAwd; RotaryAwd; Lawrence Univ; Research Pgysicist.

KRASIN, Kent A; Columbus HS; Marshfield, WI; 8/117 HonRl; NatlSciFnd; SctActv; TchrAde; RptrYrbk; MthCl; Lawrence U; Chemical Research.

KRASIN, Paul; Columbus HS; Marshfield, WI; 16/105 Chr; HonRl; SchPl; RptrSchPpr; EdSchPpr; FrCl; Bsktbl; IMSpt; Coll; Journ.

KRATCH, Lee P; Cotter HS; Winona, MN; 28/105 Aud/Vis; ChrhWkr; HonRl; Yrbk; RptrSchPpr; SchPpr; IMSpt; Coll; Speech.

KRATCHA, Lynn C; Lidgerwood HS; Cayuga, ND; PresSophCls; VPJrCls; ALBoysSt; Band; HonRl; SchPl; SctActv; StuGov; GerCl; Us Coast Guard Acad; Mathematics.

KRATOCHUIL, Lou A; Madison HS; Madison, NE; Band; Chr; CmntyWkr; CncrtBnd; HonRl; PepBnd; Twrl; 4-H; SpnCl; 4-HAwd; Trade School; Vocation.

KRATOCHVIL, Carol J; Traverse City HS; Traverse City, MI; TrsJrCls; Chr; HonRl; TreasNHS; SchMus; StuCncl; RptrYrbk; PpCl; CchngActv; Comm Coll; Business.

KRATOCHVIL, Mary B; Madison HS; Madison, NE; 2/60 TrsSrCls; Band; Chr; HonRl; LbryAde; NHS; RedCrAde; SchPl; StuCncl; PpCl; VoiceDemAwd;.

KRATZENBERG, Susan; New Glarus HS; Monticello, WI; ALAGirlsSt; Chrs; NHS; YthFlsp; SchPpr; 4-H; FBLA; FTA; PpCl; Univ; Business Ed Teacher.

KRATZENBERG, Susan A; New Glarus HS; Monticello, WI; 8/52 Chrs; NHS; YthFlsp; Pres4-H; FBLA; FTA; PpCl; 4-HAwd; College; Business Ed Teacher.

KRAULIK, Kathleen R; Kennedy Public HS; Donaldson, MN; 1/27 TrsSrCls; Band; Chrs; ChrhWkr; CncrtBnd; HonRl; RptrSchPpr; SpnCl; PpCl; Union College; Music.

KRAUPNER, Patricia; Round Lake Senior HS; Round Lake, IL; HonRl; NHS; StuCncl; GAA; DARAwd; Western Ill Univ;.

KRAUS, Alice M; Helias HS; Jefferson City, MO; 6/180 CmntyWkr; HonRl; HospAde; NHS; PpCl; CitAwd;.

KRAUS, Allan; Homewood Flossmoor HS; Homewood, IL; 53/940 Aud/Vis; CmntyWkr; HonRl; LbryAde; SchAde; StuCncl; StuGov; TchrAde; College; Communications.

KRAUS, Arthur C; Necedah Public HS; Necedah, WI; 1/42 TrsSrCls; HonRl; StuCncl; LetterBsktbl; AmLegAwd; U Of Wi; Meteorology.

KRAUS, Brian W; Trego County HS; Wakeeney, KS; PresFrshCls; TrsJrCls; ALBoysSt; Chrl; HonRl; StuCncl; SciCl; LetterFtbl; LetterTrk; LetterWrstlng; University; Vocation.

KRAUS, Christy M; Wheatland HS; Madrid, NE; 2/22 SecSophCls; VPSrCls; Chr; Chrs; HonRl; OffAde; SchPl; StuCncl; EdYrBk; LetterTrk; Work.

KRAUS, Daniel J; William Howard Taft HS; Chicago, IL; 7/780 Chr; Chrs; ChrhWkr; HonRl; LitMag; LbryAde; NHS; SchMus; SchPl; StuCncl; U Of Il; Biology Major.

KRAUS, Karen; Shullsburg HS; Shullsburg, WI; 10/62 ALAGirlsSt; ChrhWkr; LbryAde; NHS; YthFlsp; Yrbk; RptrSchPpr; 4-H; GAA; 4-HAwd; Cosmetology College; Professional.

KRAVIS, Kathy L; Mission Valley HS; Eskridge, KS; DrlTm; SchPl; 4-H; FHA; PpCl; Trk; Chrldr; Vo Tech Sch; Dental Asst.

KRAUS, Laurie A; Gwinn HS; Little Lake, MI; 1/163 PresSophCls; Chrl; Chrs; ChrhWkr; HospAde; NHS; NatlMeritSF; SchPl; StuCncl; College; Elem Education.

KRAUS, Mark H; Lake Crystal HS; Garden City, MN; Band; CncrtBnd; HonRl; MrchBnd; SchPl; FFA; LetterFtbl; CaptTrk; Univ Of Mn; Farming.

KRAUS, Melissa A; Waukegan East HS; Waukegan, IL; 184/850 ChrhWkr; HonRl; LitMag; NatlThespSoc; SchMus; SchPl; StuCncl; RptrYrbk; VPPpCl; Swmmng; Chrldr; GAA; Northern Ill Univ; Nursing.

KRAUS, Patty M; Kearney HS; Kearney, NE; DrlTm; OffAde; SchAde; SpnCl; PpCl; LetterTennis; GAA; College; Nursing.

KRAUS, Paul R; Evergreen Pk HS; Evergreen Pk, IL; 58/439 HonRl; NHS; LetterSwmmng; Loyola Univ; Medicine.

KRAUS, Paul R; Evergreen Pk HS; Evergreen Park, IL; 58/442 NHS; LetterSwmmng; Loyola Univ; Medical Doctor.

KRAUS, Steven; Blue Mound HS; Decatur, IL; Bsktbl; Trk; Eureka Coll; Math.

KRAUSE, Barbara A; Iron Mountain HS; Iron Mountain, MI; 4/158 HonRl; HospAde; LbryAde; NHS; NatlThespSoc; SchPl; Twrl; Yrbk; FNA; SpnCl; Marian College; Bs Nursing.

KRAUSE, Carmel M; St Stephen Area HS; Saginaw, MI; 15/106 HonRl; HospAde; NHS; RptrYrbk; RptrSchPpr; BttyCrckrAwd; Mich State Univ; Biologicalsci.

KRAUSE, Charles E; Edgar HS; Edgar, WI; 30/84 Chrs; Bsbl; Bsktbl; Ftbl; Trk; Trade School.

KRAUSE, David K; Jefferson HS; Jefferson, IA; ALBoysSt; Aud/Vis; Chr; Chrs; ChrhWkr; HonRl; SchMus; SchPl; StuCncl; StuGov; YthFlsp; College; Law.

KRAUSE, Debra L; Crivitz HS; Crivitz, WI; 17/68 PresJrCls; Band; CncrtBnd; DrmMjrt; HonRl; MrchBnd; PepBnd; StuCncl; Twrl; College; Commercial Art.

KRAUSE, Janelle A; Wessington HS; Wessington, SD; 1/26 SecTrsSophCls; PresSrCls; ALAGirlsSt; Band; Chrs; ChrhWkr; CncrtBnd; DrmMjrt; HonRl; MrchBnd; PepBnd; LetterBsktbl; AmLegAwd; BttyCrckrAwd; S Dakota State Univ; Journalism.

KRAUSE, Kenneth W; Maine South HS; Park Ridge, IL; Band; Chr; ChrhWkr; CncrtBnd; HonRl; MrchBnd; NHS; NatlMeritCmnd; NatlThespSoc; PepBnd; LetterSwmmng; Purdue Univ; Chemical Engineer.

KRAUSE, Lisa A; Mobridge HS; Mobridge, SD; 11/74 Band; Chr; HonRl; NatlThespSoc; SchMus; StuCncl; PpCl;.

KRAUSE, Loren J; Homewood Flossmoor HS; Homewood, IL; 48/940 Chr; Chrl; Chrs; ChrhWkr; HonRl; LitMag; Univ Of Illinois; Foreign Language.

KRAUSE, Paulette; South Clay HS; Marathon, IA; 4/30 HonRl; NHS; SptEdSchPpr; 4-H; IMSpt; DanFAwd; 4-HAwd; CitAwd; College; Curriculum Major Study.

KRAUSE, Ruth A; Amos Alonzo Stagg HS; Palos Hills, IL; 114/535 PresSophCls; Chr; Chrs; DrmMjrt; HonRl; HospAde; Mdrgl; MrchBnd; SchAde; SctActv; Trk; GAA; DanFAwd; College; Nursing.

KRAUSE, Scott D; Ventura Comm HS; Clear Lake, IA; PresFrshCls; TrsSophCls; PresJrCls; NHS; RptrSchPpr; EdSchPpr; FTA; Bsktbl; Ftbl; Glf; Gmi; Pharmacy.

KRAUSE, Shane S; El Dorado HS; El Dorado, KS; SecTrsSophCls; ALBoysSt; HonRl; NatlThespSoc; StuCncl; Bsbl; Bsktbl; CaptFtbl; LetterTrk; CitAwd; College; Vet Medicine.

KRAUSE, Sharon F; Elkhart Memorial HS; Elkhart, IN; 1/441 HonRl; Mdrgl; NatlFornLg; NHS; NatlMeritSF; TreasOrch; SchMus; StuGov; DARAwd; Yale Univ; Computer Systems.

KRAUSE, Stephen; Concordia Acad; Cottage Grove, MN; Chr; NHS; SchMus; StuCncl; College; Professional.

KRAUSE, Stephen P; Roosevelt HS; Minneapolis, MN; HonRl; NatlMeritCmnd; Yrbk; RptrSchPpr; SchPpr; College; Commerical Art.

KRAUSE, Steven D; Tartan HS; St Paul, MN; 12/333 HonRl; NHS; LetterBsktbl; LetterTennis; St Paul Vocational; Carpenter.

KRAUSE, Steven J; Lane Tech HS; Chicago, IL; 167/1400 CmntyWkr; JA; LbryAde; NatlMeritFnl; PolWkr; StuCncl; TchrAde; Yrbk; PresFrCl; JAAwd; Loyola Univ; Medicine.

KRAUSE, Steven W; Alden Community HS; Alden, IA; ALBoysSt; SchPl; FFA; Ftbl; Trk; Wrstlng; AmLegAwd; Univ; Pilot.

KRAUSE, Thomas A; John Marshall HS; Rochester, MN; 4/600 JA; NHS; NatlMeritCmnd; StuCncl; GerCl; RusCl; IMSpt; JAAwd; KiwanAwd; College; Law.

KRAUSERT, Kathryn E; West HS; Green Bay, WI; 9/390 HonRl; JA; TchrAde; RptrSchPpr; College; Accounting.

KRAUSHAAR, Vicki L; North Greene HS; White Hall, IL; HonRl; NHS; FTA; MthCl; GAA; IMSpt; AmLegAwd; Clg; Psych.

KRAUSZ, Dale H; Wesclin HS; New Memphis, IL; 11/100 CncrtBnd; HonRl; IntrClCncl; JrNHS; MrchBnd; NHS; PepBnd; RptrSchPpr; GerCl; LetterBsbl; College; Professional.

KRAVIS, Dean E; Lyons Township HS; La Grange, IL; HonRl; NHS; NatlMeritFnl; PolWkr; College; Doctor.

KRAWCZYK, Albert; Holy Trinity Hs; Chicago, IL; 2/175 HonRl; PresNHS; StuCncl; RptrSchPpr; SptEdSchPpr; MthCl; Tennis; Loyola U Of Chicago;law.

KRAY, James E; Marion HS; Marion, IA; ChrhWkr; CmntyWkr; HonRl; JA; PolWkr; StuCncl; TchrAde; 4-H; LetterFtbl; LetterWrstlng; Computer College;.

KRC, Paul; Luther South HS; Oak Lawn, IL; 15/204 HonRl; NatlMeritFnl; NatlMeritCmnd; NatlSciFnd; YthLg; Tennis; JETSAwd; Univ Of Ill; Engin.

KRC, Paul J; Luther South HS; Oak Lawn, IL; 17/204 Chr; HonRl; NatlMeritFnl; NatlMeritSF; NatlSciFnd; YthLg; Tennis; IMSpt; JETSAwd; Univ Il; Computer Engi.

KRCIL, Debbie A; East Charles Mix HS; Dante, SD; 6/76 Band; Chr; Chrs; ChrhWkr; CmntyWkr; CncrtBnd; DrlTm; HonRl; HospAde; MrchBnd; College; Secretary.

KRCMARIC, Mark C; Andrean Catholic HS; Merrillville, IN; 3/250 TrsSophCls; TrsJrCls; HonRl; NHS; StuCncl; StuGov; MthCl; IMSpt; AmLegAwd; College; Professional.

KRCMARIK, Laurie A; Corunna HS; Corunna, MI; CncrtBnd; HonRl; MrchBnd; TchrAde; Yrbk; 4-H; PpCl; LetterBsktbl; GAA; PresAwd; Michigan St Univ; Law.

KREAGER, David S; West Bloomfield HS; Orchard Lake, MI; 135/444 HonRl; NatlMeritCmnd; Quill&Scroll; StuGov; RptrSchPpr; EdSchPpr; Bsbl; Ftbl; Mi State U; Journalism.

KREBEL, Ann Marie C; Valmeyer HS; Prairie Du Rocher, IL; 6/59 VPFrshCls; ALAGirlsSt; Band; Chr; Chrs; ChrhWkr; HonRl; LbryAde; OffAde; PepBnd; SchAde; SchMus; DanFAwd; Belleville Jr College; Medical Record Tech.

KREBEL, Gary R; Red Bud HS; Prairie Du Rocher, IL; FFA; Bsbl; Trade School; Electrician.

KREBER, Ronald L; Spalding HS; Granville, IA; VPSophCls; Chrs; ChrhWkr; SchPl; Bsbl; Bsktbl; College; Business.

KREBILL, Rhonda B; Central HS; Donnellson, IA; ALAGirlsSt; HonRl; SchPl; VPYthFlsp; PpCl; LetterTennis; Trade School.

KREBS, Amelia J; Charlotte HS; Charlotte, MI; 20/262 NHS; PolWkr; YthFlsp; CitAwd; Calvin College; A Field Of Art.

KREBS, Charles W; Ralston HS; Ralston, NE; 56/254 CivCl; Bsbl; CchngActv; IMSpt; RotaryAwd; U Of Ne; Certified Public Accountant.

KREBS, Gloria; St Marys HS; New England, ND; 10/48 Band; Chr; CncrtBnd; HonRl; MrchBnd; PepBnd; StuCncl; PpCl; Trk; College; Curriculum Of Major Study.

KREBS, Ida; St Marys HS; New England, ND; 14 Band; CncrtBnd; HonRl; MrchBnd; PepBnd; Dickinson St Coll; Secretary.

KREBS, Kathy M; Mater Dei HS; Breese, IL; Band; Chrs; HonRl; JA; NHS; NatlMeritCmnd; SchMus; StuCncl; Trk; Chrldr; Univ.

KREBS, Sharon A; Avon HS; Indianapolis, IN; 28/146 SchAde; PpCl; Marion Co Gen Hosp; Nurse.

KREBS, Wayne; St Marys HS; New England, ND; ALBoysSt; HonRl; Bsbl; Trade School; Mechanico.

KREBSBACH, Laure S; Lomira HS; Brownsville, WI; VPFrshCls; PresSophCls; Band; CncrtBnd; HonRl; MrchBnd; PepBnd; SchPl; RptrYrbk; RptrSchPpr; Univ Of Wi; Occupational Therapy.

KREBSBACH, Robert T; St Johns Preparatory HS; St Joseph, MN; 2/45 SecSophCls; HonRl; JrNHS; NHS; SchPl; StuCncl; StuGov; LetterBsbl; St Johns Univ.

KREBSBACH, Sharon M; Flint Holy Rosary HS; Flint, MI; 10/56 HonRl; HospAde; JA; NHS; RedCrAde; Yrbk; FBLA; Chrldr; CchngActv; Mott Comm College; Legal Secretary.

KRECSMAR, M Christine; Marian HS; Elkhart, IN; ChrhWkr; DrlTm; HonRl; JA; Mdrgl; Iusb; Teaching.

KREEGER, Robert A; Richwoods HS; Peoria, IL; 16/449 ChrhWkr; HonRl; NatlMeritCmnd; SchAde; Univ Of Il; Bioengineering.

KREEGER, Wesley J; Auburndal HS; Arpin, WI; Chrs; HonRl; SchPl; SchPpr; GerCl; PpCl; LetFtbl; Trk; LetterWrstlng; PresAwd; College; Teacher.

KREFFT, Joan B; William Howard Taft HS; Chicago, IL; 17/815 SecHonRl; JrNHS; LbryAde; NHS; Sacrstn; KeyCl; FrCl; SpnCl; MthCl; GAA; Ne Ill Univ; English.

KREFT, Kim; Plaza Public HS; Plaza, ND; 1 12 SecTrsJrCls; Band; ChrhWkr; HonRl; MrchBnd; PepBnd; .SchPl; EdSchPpr; Chrldr; AmLegAwd; Univ Of Nd; Vocation.

KREFT, Marianne L; Maine Township HS; Park Ridge, IL; Chr; HonRl; JrNHS; Mdrgl; NHS; NatlMeritCmnd; NatlThespSoc; SchMus; FrCl; College; Veterinarian.

KREFTMEYER, Linda L; High School; Owensville, MO; Chrs; HonRl; NHS; SchMus; VPYthFlsp; FHA; Columbia Univ; Professional.

KREGEL, Thomas; South HS; Sheboygan, WI; 42/496 HonRl; JA; NatlFornLg; NHS; SctActv; Univ Of Wis; Mecanical Engineer.

KREGER, Michael; Dixon Hs; Franklin Grove, IL; 8/330 PresSophCls; PresSrCls; ALBoysSt; CncrtBnd; HonRl; NHS; StuCncl; EdSchPpr; SARAwd; Ui;civil Engineering.

KREGER, Sheri R; Franklin Center HS; Franklin Grove, IL; 3/50 Chrs; HonRl; TreasNHS; SchMus; TreasFrCl; PpCl; GAA; College.

KREHBIEL, Doris; Central Comm Of Argyle HS; Donnellson, IA; 110 TrsJrCls; AFS; ALAGirlsSt; Band; Chr; HospAde; SchPl; SctActv; FTA; LetterBsbl; College;elementary Teacher.

KREHER, John; Orchard Farm HS; West Alton, MO; HonRl; NHS; KeyCl; College; Art.

KREHER, Marilyn R; Arcadia HS; Fountain City, WI; 50/95 Band; ChrhWkr; CmntyWkr; CncrtBnd; MrchBnd; NHS; PepBnd; SchMus; RptrSchPpr; EdSchPpr; 4-H; FHA; GAA;.

KREIDER, Steven P; Kingsford HS; Kingsford, MI; Chr; ChrhWkr; HonRl; SctActv; StuCncl; SecYthFlsp; Bsbl; Bsktbl; Ftbl; IMSpt; Univ; Pro.

KREIDLKAMP, Karen R; Fingal Public HS; Valley City, ND; SecFrshCls; PresSrCls; Band; Chrs; HonRl; RptrYrbk; Yrbk; RptrSchPpr; Chrldr; BttyCrckrAwd; University.

KREIGHBAUM, Debbie J; Sand Creek HS; Weston, MI; CmntyWkr; HonRl; SchPl; TchrAde; EdYrBk; 4-H; SpnCl; GodCntryAwd; Siena Heights College.

KREIKEMEIER, Cindy J; Central Catholic HS; West Point, NE; 7/78 PresStuCncl; RptrYrbk; RptrSchPpr; 4-H; MthCl; PpCl; Chrldr; IMSpt; PPFtbl; 4-HAwd; Wayne State; Elementary Ed.

KREIKEMEIER, Marcia; Central Catholic HS; West Point, NE; ChrhWkr; HonRl; SchPl; SchPpr; 4-H; MthCl; PpCl; SciCl; Chrldr; St Mary College; Professional Rn.

KREIL, Andrea D; Eisenhower HS; Saginaw, MI; 4/350 CmntyWkr; HonRl; JrNHS; NatlFornLg; NHS; PolWkr; Delta College; Medicine.

KREIL, Katherine M; Reauis HS; Burbank, IL; 130/758 HonRl; NatlMeritCmnd; PpCl; LetterBsbl; LetterBsktbl; GAA; IMSpt; LionAwd; College; Major Study.

KREILEIN, Michael A; Jasper HS; Jasper, IN; 4-H; College; Professional.

KREILING, Kerry; Macomb Senior HS; Macomb, IL; 25/244 Chr; Chrl; CncrtBnd; HonRl; Mdrgl; NHS; Orch; YthFlsp; RptrSchPpr; SchPpr; Univ Of Evansville; Pre Med.

KREILING, Kerry K; Macomb Sr HS; Macomb, IL; 25/244 PresChrhWkr; SecCncrtBnd; DrlTm; HonRl; Mdrgl; MrchBnd; NHS; Orch; PepBnd; Quill&Scroll; SchMus; SchPl; RptrYrbk; RptrSchPpr; SchPpr; Univ Of Evansville; Medicine.

KREINER, Martha; Lee HS; Wyoming, MI; Chr; HonRl; NHS; LetterBsktbl; LetterGAA; IMSpt; University; Surgeon.

KREINER, Rose; Davison HS; Davison, MI; 17/433 HonRl; NHS; Central Michigan Univ; Home Economics.

KREISEL, Kathleen T; Mother Theodore Guerin HS; Chicago, IL; 35/409 ChrhWkr; HonRl; JrNHS; SctActv; RptrYrbk; Yrbk; RptrSchPpr; MthCl; GAA; Loyola Univ; Journalism.

KREISEL, Maureen L; Mother Theodore Guerin HS; Chicago, IL; 21/409 ChrhWkr; CmntyWkr; HonRl; NHS; SctActv; TchrAde; KeyCl; SpnCl; MthCl; Loyola Univ; Pediatrician.

KREISMAN, Bruce S; Niles North HS; Skokie, IL; 60/658 Univ Of Illinois; Lawyer.

KREIZEL, Verna R; Wahoo Public HS; Wahoo, NE; SecFrshCls; SecSophCls; Band; Chrs; ChrhWkr; CmntyWkr; HonRl; SpnCl; PpCl; SciCl; 4-HAwd; Coll; Tch Spec Educ.

KREJCI, Joseph J; Lakeshore HS; Stevensville, MI; 7/260 VPJrCls; HonRl; NHS; Quill&Scroll; SchPl; StuGov; SptEdYrbk; KeyCl; MthCl; Univ Of Mi; Bus Adm.

KREKE, Nancy A; Dieterich HS; Dieterich, IL; 1/37 TrsSrCls; Chrs; HonRl; LbryAde; StuCncl; TchrAde; Yrbk; 4-H; SpnCl; College; Professional.

KREKLOW, Marilyn G; Hibbing HS; Hibbing, MN; 39/400 AFS; ChrhWkr; CmntyWkr; HonRl; HospAde; NatlFornLg; SchPl; TchrAde; RptrSchPpr; 4-H; Central Bible Coll; Psych.

KREKOW, Roger D; Sutherland HS; Sutherland, IA; Band; Chr; Chrl; Chrs; ChrhWkr; CmntyWkr; CncrtBnd; HonRl; Mdrgl; MrchBnd; PepBnd; PolWkr; Bsktbl; Creighton University; Law.

KRELL, Craig; Kenwood HS; Chicago, IL; ChrhWkr; CmntyWkr; HonRl; JrNHS; NHS; GerCl; Socr; College; Vocation Business.

KRELL, Kindra L; Beaver Dam Sr HS; Beaver Dam, WI; 2/290 ALAGirlsSt; Chr; CmntyWkr; LbryAde; Mdrgl; NatlFornLg; SchPl; StuCncl; GAA; University; Architectural Engineer.

KRELL, Sheryl L; Beaver Dam Sr HS; Beaver Dam, WI; 16/300 TchrAde; LetterBsktbl; GAA; IMSpt; College.

KREMER, Cynthia S; New Haven HS; New Haven, IN; HonRl; NatlFornLg; Ball St Univ; Spanish Teacher.

KREMER, John M; St Paul HS; Chicago, IL; 92/544 Bsktbl; Lewis University; Aviation Maintenance.

KREMER, Joy A; Ashley Community HS; Bannister, MI; PresSophCls; TrsSrCls; Band; CncrtBnd; HonRl; MrchBnd; NHS; NatlMeritSF; PepBnd; SchPl; College; Veterinary.

KREMER, Larry R; Fatima HS; Loose Creek, MO; Chr; Chrs; 4-H; FSA; 4-HAwd; College.

KREMER, Linda M; Jennings Sr HS; Jennings, MO; 16/288 ChrhWkr; CmntyWkr; HonRl; HospAde; Yrbk; FHA; FTA; EngCl; PpCl; LetterBsktbl; LetterSwmmng; GAA; IMSpt; College; Conservation.

KREMER, Russell J; Fatima HS; Bonnots Mill, MO; Chrs; HonRl; Pres4-H; PresFFA; Univ Of Mo Columbia; Agriculture.

KREMIN, Denise J; Central HS; Glenwood, MN; 1/135 ChrhWkr; HonRl; LbryAde; ModUN; RptrSchPpr; 4-H; GerCl; LetterBsktbl; LetterTrk; 4-HAwd; Univ Of Mn; Medicine.

KREMITZKI, Janet M; Sacred Heart Academy; Springfield, IL; Chrs; HonRl; SctActv; UNYO; 4-H; FBLA; SpnCl; PpCl; Bsbl; 4-HAwd; Married.

KREMPASKY, Rebecca S; Metropolis Community HS; Metropolis, IL; 49/167 Band; ChrhWkr; PresSophCls; HonRl; MrchBnd; PepBnd; SecSpnCl; VPPpCl; SciCl; Mac Murray Coll; Special Ed.

KRENGER, Teresa A; Abilene HS; Abilene, KS; ALAGirlsSt; Chr; Chrs; DrlTm; HonRl; NatlMeritSF; SchMus; StuCncl; TchrAde; YthFlsp; Yrbk; University; Medicine.

KRENIK, John W; Montgomery HS; Lonsdale, MN; Band; HonRl; SchPl; StuGov; RptrSchPpr; FFA; College.

KRENTZ, Michael L; Ripon Senior HS; Ripon, WI; VPSrCls; HonRl; SctActv; FBLA; Ftbl; IMSpt; Proffessional.

KRENTZ, Terrill; Walther Lutheran HS; Addison, IL; 2/90 TrsSophCls; Chr; ChrhWkr; HonRl; NHS; NatlThespSoc; SchMus; YthLg; RptrYrbk; EdSchPpr; Coll; Undecided.

KRENZ, Jay E; Wheaton HS; Wheaton, MN; Chr; Chrl; Chrs; ChrhWkr; Mdrgl; StuCncl; LetterBsktbl; LetterTrk; Chrldr; Coll; Pro.

KRENZ, Michael R; Central HS; Grand Rapids, MI; CncrtBnd; HonRl; JrNHS; MrchBnd; NHS; NatlMeritCmnd; Orch; PepBnd; SchMus; GerCl; Grand Rapids Jr Col; Criminal Law.

KRENZKE, Patti M; Racine Lutheran HS; Racine, WI; HonRl; NHS; TchrAde; College; Airline Hostess.

KREPPS, Kathy; Breckenridge Jr And Senior Hs; Merrill, MI; 3/94 SecSrCls; HonRl; NHS; StuGov; TchrAde; Sec4-H; SecFFA; PpCl; LetterBsktbl; 4-HAwd; Michigan State U; Veterinary Med.

KREPPS, Kathy S; Breckenridge HS; Merrill, MI; 3/94 HstSophCls; HstJrCls; SecSrCls; HonRl; NHS; StuGov; TchrAde; Sec4-H; SecFFA; LetterBsktbl; Mi St Univ; Pre Veterinary Med.

KREPS, Debra; Southeastern HS; Augusta, IL; 16/49 Band; CncrtBnd; HonRl; MrchBnd; PepBnd; SchPl; Yrbk; FHA; GAA; IMSpt; Accounting.

KREPS, Rita K; Northwestern HS; Blandinsville, IL; PresSophCls; HonRl; NHS; StuCncl; RptrYrbk; FHA; PpCl; Bsbl; Chrldr; GAA; IMSpt; Trade School; Beautician.

KREPS, Ronn B; Central Christian HS; Prinsburg, MN; 3/30 SecTrsSophCls; Band; Chr; PresSophCls; HonRl; PepBnd; SchPl; RptrSchPpr; GerCl; LetterBsktbl; Calvin Col ;law.

KREPS, Timothy J; Cmcs HS; Willmar, MN; 5/29 VPSrCls; Chr; HonRl; SchMus; SchPl; RptrYrbk; GerCl; Bsbl; VFWAwd; VoiceDemAwd; Thief River Falls Voc Sch; Audio Broadcastn.

KRESHA, Andrea; Humphrey HS; Humphrey, NE; 4/22 Chr; Chrl; Chrs; CmntyWkr; HonRl; StuCncl; TchrAde; PpCl; Chrldr; Platte Tech Comm Coll; Executive Secretary.

KRESL, Barbara J; St Francis HS; St Francis, WI; TreasAFS; PresBand; CncrtBnd; HonRl; MrchBnd; NHS; PepBnd; SptEdYrbk; SpnCl; GAA; Wi U; School Psychologist.

KRESS, Alice; Schulte HS; Terre Haute, IN; 7/88 ALAGirlsSt; CmntyWkr; HonRl; StuCncl; YthFlsp; DARAwd; Indiana State Univ; Accountant.

KRESS, Janet; Jac Cen Del HS; Batesville, IN; 12/56 SecSrCls; ALAGirlsSt; HonRl; StuCncl; SchPpr; BttyCrckrAwd; Bell St Univ; Elementary Educ.

KRESS, Kerry A; Beach HS; Beach, ND; CncrtBnd; HonRl; SchPl; RptrSchPpr; FHA; Bismarck Jr Coll; Key Punch Oper.

KRETSCHMAN, Allyson K; Lakeland HS; La Grange, IN; 2/146 AFS; Band; HonRl; NatlFornLg; SchMus; SchPl; StuCncl; YthFlsp; RptrSchPpr; PresSpnCl; PPFtbl; 4-HAwd; Univ; Church Music.

KRETSCHMANN, Debra L; Boscobel HS; Boscobel, WI; Band; Chr; Chrs; CncrtBnd; HonRl; MrchBnd; NatlFornLg; NHS; PepBnd; SchMus; College; Nursing.

KRETTEK, Mary C; St Albert HS; Council Bluffs, IA; 1/93 HonRl; PresNHS; PolWkr; SchMus; SchPl; StuCncl; PpCl; CaptChrldr; IMSpt; BauchLmbAwd; Col Of St Benedict.

KREUTZ, Anna K; John Marshall HS; Milwaukee, WI; 20/711 HonRl; HospAde; NHS; NatlMeritSF; Orch; SctActv; RptrYrbk; SecGerCl; Univ; Physical Therapist.

KREUTZER, Paula M; Derby HS; Derby, KS; ChrhWkr; DrlTm; NHS; RptrYrbk; PpCl; Col; Nursing.

KREUTZFELDT, Michael L; Spencer Independent HS; Spencer, SD; 1/8 SecFrshCls; TrsSophCls; TrsJrCls; VPSrCls; Bsbl; Bsktbl; Ftbl; Glf; Trk; CchngActv; University; Mathematics.

KREVINGHAUS, Janet L; Pinconning HS; Rhodes, MI; 9/253 Chr; HonRl; HospAde; LbryAde; NHS; SctActv; RptrYrbk; EdYrBk; FNA; FTA; Bsktbl; Lansing Com College; Dental Hygienist.

KREYCIK, Ann; Valentine HS; Valentine, NE; 9/92 Chrs; HonRl; NHS; StuCncl; LetterTrk; Chrldr; Lincoln Schl Of Commerce; Secretary.

KREYE, Debra R; Wabasha Kellogg HS; Wabasha, MN; Chrs; HonRl; SchMus; SchPl; SctActv; SpnCl; PpCl; GAA; Trade School; Child Development Asst.

KRIBS, Kathleen B; Corunna HS; Corunna, MI; 25/201 ChrhWkr; TreasJA; Pres4-H; 4-HAwd; JAAwd; Accounting.

KRIBS, Susan M; Edwardsville Senior HS; Edwardsville, IL; Chrs; SchPl; Trk; GAA; IMSpt; College.

KRICH, Karen M; St Charles HS; St Charles, MO; Band; ChrhWkr; CmntyWkr; CncrtBnd; HonRl; MrchBnd; SctActv; VPYthFlsp; IMSpt; AmLegAwd; Southeast Mo; Social Work.

KRICHAU, Cindy L; Bladen Public HS; Bladen, NE; PresSrCls; Band; CncrtBnd; HonRl; PresStuCncl; TchrAde; Twrl; YthFlsp; RptrYrbk; Yrbk; RptrSchPpr; SchPpr; 4-H; PpCl; Chrldr; Business School; Secretary.

KRICK, John R; Reese HS; Reese, MI; 60/130 TrsFrshCls; ChrhWkr; CncrtBnd; PolWkr; PresStuCncl; FFA; LetterBsbl; LetterFtbl; IMSpt; Univ; Farm Management.

KRICK, Sherrie; Triton HS; Bourbon, IN; Chr;.

KRIDER, Candy D; Northridge HS; Middlebury, IN; Band; Chr; DrmMjrt; HonRl; SchMus; StuCncl; YthFlsp; Yrbk; 4-H; PpCl; In Central Univ; Social Work.

KRIDER, Jill K; Pike HS; Indianapolis, IN; 67/267 HonRl; JrNHS; LitMag; Quill&Scroll; SctActv; StuCncl; Bsktbl; Tennis; PPFtbl; JAAwd; Coll; Comm Art.

KRIEBEL, Gary W; Lyons Township HS; Western Springs, IL; CaptSwmmng; De Paul U; Doctor.

KRIEBEL, Lori; Polo Comm HS; Polo, IL; 29#30#41 Mdrgl; MrchBnd; SchPl; Twrl; FrCl; Chrldr; GAA; Private Nurs Sch; Prof.

KRIEG, Carolyn S; Fatima HS; Linn, MO; 6/126 Chr; Chrs; ChrhWkr; HonRl; FBLA; FHA; PpCl; Sw Missouri State; Business.

KRIEG, Jeanie A; Fatima HS; Linn, MO; Chr; ChrhWkr; HonRl; 4-H; FHA; SecSpnCl; PpCl; Chrldr; College; Mathematics.

KRIEG, Wanda K; Kasson Mantorville HS; Kasson, MN; VPBand; SecChr; Chrs; MrchBnd; NHS; FHA; PresFrCl; Bsktbl; CaptChrldr; AmLegAwd; Rochester Vo Tech; Med Sec.

KRIEGER, Elizabeth A; Keya Paha County HS; Springview, NE; 1/23 PresSophCls; TrsJrCls; ALAGirlsSt; Chrs; HonRl; NHS; SchPl; Yrbk; FHA; LetterTrk; College; Chemistry.

KRIEGER, James E; St Patrick HS; Chicago, IL; 40/427 HonRl; NatlMeritSF; OffAde; Air Force Academy; Pilot.

KRIEGER, Karen I; Bemidji HS; Bemidji, MN; Bemidji State College; Accounting.

KRIEHER, Herman F; St Rita HS; Chicago, IL; 30/454 VPSophCls; VPJrCls; VPSrCls; HonRl; NHS; StuCncl; StuGov; TchrAde; LetterBsktbl; CaptFtbl; Univ Of Iowa; Professional.

KRIEHN, Cindy L; Elcho HS; Elcho, WI; Band; Chrs; ChrhWkr; HonRl; NHS; RptrYrbk; SpnCl; SciCl; College; Special Ed.

KRIENKE, Donald H; Lester Prairie Public HS; Lester Prairie, MN; ChrhWkr; YthFlsp; YthFnd; SchPpr; LetterBsktbl; LetterFtbl; LetterTrk; LetterWrstlng; IMSpt; CitAwd; Trade School; Vocation.

KRIEPS, Michele M; Lake Park HS; Roselle, IL; 44/535 HonRl; NatlMeritCmnd; PolWkr; SchPl; StuCncl; RptrYrbk; University; Business Admin.

KRIER, Bonnie M; Pocahontas Community HS; Laurens, IA; Band; CncrtBnd; DrlTm; HonRl; HospAde; MrchBnd; NHS; PepBnd; PpCl; St Josephs Mercy Sch Of Nursing; Rn.

KRIER, Roy P; Columbus HS; Marshfield, WI; PresFrshCls; PresSophCls; VPJrCls; Chrs; ChrhWkr; PolWkr; SchAde; StuCncl; StuGov; RptrYrbk; RptrSchPpr; Bsbl; Bsktbl; Ftbl;.

KRIESCHE, Joyce A; Holmen HS; Holmen, WI; 3/118 ALAGirlsSt; Band; Chr; HonRl; LbryAde; NHS; Orch; PepBnd; RptrSchPpr; Univ Of Wis; Medical Technology.

KRIEWALD, Karen J; North Loup Scotia HS; North Loup, NE; ALAGirlsSt; Chrs; ChrhWkr; HonRl; YthFlsp; 4-H; FFA; FHA; College; Farming.

KRIEWALL, David T; Lisle HS; Lisle, IL; 7/200 Band; DrmMjrt; HonRl; Mdrgl; NHS; NatlMeritCmnd; NatlThespSoc; SchMus; StuCncl; MthCl; Univ; Professional.

KRIHA, Thomas J; New Prague HS; New Prague, MN; VPSrCls; SchPl; StuCncl; CaptFtbl; LetterTrk; Wrstlng; College; Dentist.

KRIISA, Tiina A; Eisenhower HS; Decatur, IL; 9/305 Chr; HonRl; NHS; StuCncl; Chrldr; U Of Il.

KRILCICH, Joseph T; Saint Ignatius Coll Prep; Chicago, IL; 22/155 HonRl; NHS; StuCncl; TchrAde; LetterBsbl; Bsktbl; Univ; Prof.

KRILE, Jeff; Sioux Rapids Comm HS; Sioux Rapids, IA; PresFrshCls; HonRl; SchPl; StuCncl; Bsbl; Bsktbl; Ftbl; Glf; Swmmng; Trk; Univ Of Ia; Prof.

KRIMBILL, Patricia; Midland HS; Midland, MI; 40/422 HonRl; NHS; Tennis; Chrldr; GAA; AmLegAwd; Alma College; Business Accounting.

KRIN, Christine M; So Sioux City HS; So Sioux City, NE; 3/181 ChrhWkr; DrlTm; HonRl; HospAde; JrNHS; NHS; RedCrAde; SctActv; Univ Of Nebraska; Occupational Therapy.

KRING, Kimberly A; Madison Consolidated HS; Madison, IN; 9/285 SecJrCls; HonRl; NHS; StuCncl; GerCl; PpCl; GAA; PPFtbl; University; Math.

KRINGS, Ann G; Notre Dame HS; St Louis, MO; 8/106 TrsSrCls; Chrs; ChrhWkr; HospAde; NHS; OffAde; SchMus; StuCncl; OptClAwd; CitAwd; College; Prof.

KRINGS, Tony F; Lakeview HS; Platte Center, NE; 8/76 ALBoysSt; HonRl; TchrAde; CivCl; FFA; Bsktbl; IMSpt; College.

KRINSKI, Cecile; Nazareth Acad; Chicago, IL; 14/170 SecFrshCls; SecJrCls; NHS; OffAde; SchAde; Bsbl; GAA; Clge.

KRIPOWICZ, John P; Trenton HS; Trenton, MI; PresJrCls; ChrhWkr; NatlMeritSF; PolWkr; Quill&Scroll; RedCrAde; StuGov; SptEdSchPpr; CchngActv; Univ Of Michigan; Journalism.

KRIPPNER, Katherine L; Kimball Area HS; Kimball, MN; HonRl; NHS; TchrAde; Bsktbl; LetterChrldr; IMSpt; PPFtbl; Col; Coaching.

KRIST, Robert J; Creighton Prep; Omaha, NE; PresJrCls; CmntyWkr; HonRl; Sdlty; StuCncl; StuGov; RptrSchPpr; PpCl; Bsbl; Col; Law.

KRISTL, Kevin R; Warsaw Community HS; Warsaw, IN; FrCl; PpCl; LetterSwmmng; College; Md.

KRISTOFITZ, Brian C; Fargo North HS; Fargo, ND; Band; CncrtBnd; Orch; PepBnd; Ftbl; Coast Guard Academy; Engineering.

KRITZMAN, Laurie J; Bridgeport HS; Bridgeport, MI; 5/330 ChrhWkr; HonRl; NHS; SchMus; TchrAde; LetterBsktbl; CchngActv; Delta Coll; Sec Ed.

KRITZMAN, Marilyn S; Deckerville HS; Deckerville, MI; 1/79 ALAGirlsSt; PresNHS; TchrAde; Yrbk; 4-H; FNA; DARAwd; Northern Michigan University; Nursing.

KRIVSKY, Karen J; Argo Comm HS; Bridgeview, IL; 11/432 ChrhWkr; CmntyWkr; HonRl; HospAde; ModUN; NHS; SchAde; StuCncl; TchrAde; YthFlsp; Concordia Teachers College; Teacher.

KRIZAN, Joseph A; Bangor HS; Grand Junction, MI; 10/97 Band; ChrhWkr; CncrtBnd; HonRl; MrchBnd; Orch; PepBnd; SchMus; TchrAde; Western Mi Univ; Med Schl.

KRIZAN, Judy M; Colome HS; Colome, SD; CncrtBnd; HonRl; LbryAde; MrchBnd; SchPl; StuCncl; Yrbk; FHA; 4-HAwd; Marriage.

KRIZAN, Timothy D; Minnehaha Academy; Edina,

MN; PresSophCls; HonRl; StuGov; RptrSchPpr; IMSpt; BauchLmbAwd; Univ Of Minn; Chemistry.

KROCAK, Katherine; New Prague HS; New Prague, MN; 44/195 Chr; HonRl; SchPl; SctActv; SpnCl; PpCl; IMSpt; Mankato State Coll.

KROCZALESKI, Karlia M; Standish Sterling Central HS; Sterling, MI; Band; HonRl; NatlFornLg; PepBnd; YthFlsp; FHA; PpCl; LetterBsktbl; 4-HAwd;.

KROEGER, Craig A; Freeport Sr HS; Freeport, IL; 1/507 Chr; ChrhWkr; CmntyWkr; HonRl; 4-H; SciCl; Univ; Engineering.

KROEGER, Laurie J; Immanuel Lutheran HS; Sleepy Eye, MN; Chr; ChrhWkr; HonRl; Orch; PepBnd; RptrSchPpr; PpCl; Chrldr; IMSpt; College; Teaching.

KROEGER, Susan B; Boone County R Vi HS; Centralia, MO; HonRl; NHS; OffAde; SchPl; Sec4-H; FHA; PpCl; SciCl; Trk; GAA; Blessing Sch Of Nursing; Rn.

KROEMER, Vivian; Bern HS; Seneca, KS; SecSrCls; TrsSrCls; Chrs; HonRl; SchPl; Yrbk; SpnCl; PpCl; IMSpt; Mckavis Beloit Ks; Distributiveeducation.

KROENING, Thomas J; Premontre HS; Green Bay, WI; 1/125 Band; HonRl; NatlCathMusEdAsoc; Orch; ROTC; SchMus; StuCncl; TchrAde; LetterTrk; AmLegAwd; Univ Of Wis; Health Services.

KROENKE, Karol K; Shawano HS; Shawano, WI; Band; MrchBnd; NHS; YthFlsp; 4-H; FBLA; SecFTA; FrCl; MthCl; 4-HAwd; University; Education.

KROENLEIN, Mary M; Lincoln HS; Lincoln, KS; ALAGirlsSt; ChrhWkr; CmntyWkr; NatlFornLg; SecFHA; PpCl; CitAwd; Kansas State Univ; Fashion Merchandising.

KROETER, Clifford A; Quincy Senior HS; Quincy, IL; 77/816 ChrhWkr; HonRl; NHS; VPStuCncl; KeyCl; GerCl; PpCl; Bsbl; Bsktbl; LetterFtbl; Univ Of Ill; Business Lawyer.

KROFT, Janis E; West Central HS; Medaryville, IN; Band; Chr; Chrs; ChrhWkr; CncrtBnd; MrchBnd; PolWkr; RedCrAde; SchPl; 4-H;.

KROFT, Linda S; Kouts HS; Kouts, IN; 2/58 ALAGirlsSt; Band; HonRl; NHS; SchPl; YthFlsp; 4-H; PpCl; GAA; 4-HAwd; Indiana State Univ; Elementary Education.

KROG, Deanna K; Lake Benton Public HS; Lake Benton, MN; 7/48 Chr; HonRl; NHS; RptrSchPpr; 4-H; CaptBsktbl; Trk; BttyCrckrAwd; DARAwd; 4-HAwd; College; Phys Education.

KROGH, Anitra D; Exira Comm HS; Brayton, IA; 14/43 HonRl; RptrSchPpr; EdSchPpr; PresFHA; College; Art Education.

KROGMAN, Terry P; St Marys HS; O Neill, NE; 1/30 Chr; ChrhWkr; SchMus; SctActv; VPStuGov; TchrAde; Bsktbl; IMSpt; Creighton Univ; Pharmacy.

KROGSTAD, Laurie A; Sacred Heart Public HS; Sacred Heart, MN; TrsSrCls; Band; Chr; CncrtBnd; HonRl; MrchBnd; PepBnd; Bsktbl; IMSpt; 4-HAwd; Trade School; Vocation.

KROGSTAD, Ronald O; Baltic Public HS; Baltic, SD; 6/24 ALBoysSt; Band; Chrs; Yrbk; 4-H; FFA; Bsktbl; Ftbl; Trk; 4-HAwd; South Dakota State Univ; Agriculture.

KROH, John S; Wawasee HS; Syracuse, IN; VPJrCls; Band; HonRl; JrNHS; StuCncl; YthFlsp; Bsktbl; Ftbl; LetterTrk; College; Medical.

KROHE, Becky; Cuba HS; Cuba, IL; 5/67 SecFrshCls; Band; Chr; Chrs; ChrhWkr; CncrtBnd; HonRl; Mdrgl; Chrldr; GAA; College; Musical.

KROHN, Carol A; Laker HS; Elkton, MI; ChrhWkr; YthFlsp; 4-H; FFA; KeyCl; GerCl; PpCl; College; Health.

KROHN, Cathy; Harlan Comm HS; Harlan, IA; 35/256 ChrhWkr; HonRl; NHS; StuGov; Tennis; Trk; ChmbCommrsAwd; Univ; Bio.

KROHN, Grant E; Osmond HS; Osmond, NE; 8/45 Band; Chr; Chrs; ChrhWkr; CncrtBnd; HonRl; MrchBnd; NHS; SchPl; FTA; Trade Or Bus Schl; Vocational.

KROHN, Kathryn A; John Edwards HS; Port Edwards, WI; 2/67 PresSophCls; HonRl; NatlMeritFnl; NatlMeritSchl; VPStuCncl; StuGov; RptrYrbk; EdYrBk; LetterTrk; IMSpt; Lawrence Univ; Pediatrics.

KROHN, Kelly D; Harvey HS; Harvey, ND; Band; Chrs; HonRl; Mdrgl; MrchBnd; Orch; PepBnd; SchMus; SchPl; StuCncl; Bsbl; LetterFtbl; LetterTrk; IMSpt; College; Medicine.

KROHN, Kimberly T; Lakeshore HS; Stevensville, MI; SecBand; Chr; CaptDrlTm; HonRl; NHS; NatlThespSoc; SecStuCncl; RptrSchPpr; SecMthCl; DARAwd; Mi State Univ; Dietetics.

KROHN, Larry M; Osmond Community HS; Osmond, NE; 15/44 Band; ChrhWkr; CncrtBnd; HonRl; JrNHS; NHS; PepBnd; SchMus; SchPl; LetterBsktbl; Trade Sch; Vocation.

KROHN, Vickie L; Lancaster Sr HS; Bloomington, WI; 14/159 Chrs; HonRl; Orch; 4-H; FHA; PpCl; Sw Wisc Vocational Tech Inst; Bookkeeper.

KROHSE, Mark A; Luther South HS; Chicago, IL; 23/218 ChrhWkr; CmntyWkr; HonRl; Sacrstn; SctActv; YthFlsp; LetterTrk; CchngActv; IMSpt; LionAwd; Concordia Teachers Coll; Teaching.

KROL, Linda; Thornton Fractional North Hs; Calumet City, IL; 9/433 Chrl; CmntyWkr; HonRl; JrNHS; NHS; Quill&Scroll; RedCrAde; SchMus; SchPpr; Nursing School; Nursing.

KROLAK, Linda M; Riverside Brookfield HS; N Riverside, IL; 10/489 HonRl; LitMag; LbryAde; NHS; RptrYrbk; Univ Of Ill; Accounting.

KROLIKOWSKI, Marie A; Good Counsel HS; Chicago, IL; 21/250 HonRl; StuCncl; FHA; SpnCl; Rosary College; Home Economics.

KROLIKOWSKI, Rhonda M; O L Mt Carmel HS; Wyandotte, MI; 2/61 Chr; HonRl; NHS; SchMus; TchrAde; RptrYrbk; RptrSchPpr; SpnCl; PpCl;.

KROLIKOWSKI, Susan T; Good Counsel HS; Chicago, IL; HonRl; SpnCl; College.

KROLL, Diane M; Brentwood HS; Brentwood, MO; DrlTm; HonRl; ModUN; NHS; StuCncl; FTA; PpCl; LetterBsktbl; Trk; IMSpt; College; Special Education.

KROM, Sarah; Great Bend HS; Great Bend, KS; CmntyWkr; HonRl; HospAde; NatlFornLg; SpnCl; PpCl; Barton Jr Col; Rn.

KROMANAKER, Julie M; Auburndale HS; Marshfield, WI; 3/94 SecSrCls; Chr; Chrs; HonRl; HospAde; NHS; SchPl; RptrSchPpr; FBLA; St Josephs Schl; Nursing.

KROMER, Kim L; Fox Valley Lutheran HS; Kaukauna, WI; 21/109 Chrs; HonRl; HospAde; SchMus; SchPl; RptrYrbk; RptrSchPpr; PpCl; GAA; Fox Valley Tech Ins Appleton; Business.

KROMREY, Wayne A; Ladysmith HS; Ladysmith, WI; 5/150 HonRl; NHS; IMSpt; Uw Eau Claire; Accountant.

KRONE, Cyndi A; Du Quoin HS; Du Quoin, IL; 6/146 Band; Chrs; CncrtBnd; HonRl; MrchBnd; PepBnd; FHA; FTA; University; Music.

KRONE, Daniel F; J E Murphy HS; Hurley, WI; Band; HonRl; NHS; NatlMeritCmnd; RedCrAde; SchMus; SchPl; SpnCl; LetterBsktbl; LetterFtbl; Coll; Dentistry.

KRONE, John J; Fatima HS; Westphalia, MO; ChrhWkr; CmntyWkr; HonRl; SptEdSchPpr; FFA; FSA; SciCl; LetterBsktbl; Trk; Univ Of Missouri; Engineer.

KRONE, Kayla L; Tri City HS; Riverton, IL; Chr; CncrtBnd; HonRl; SchMus; EdSchPpr; Pres4-H; VPFTA; Chrldr; LetterGAA; IMSpt; DARAwd; 4-HAwd; Business College.

KRONEMEYER, Kyle; Jackson County Western HS; Spring Arbor, MI; Band; HonRl; MrchBnd; SchPl; SctActv; TchrAde; Bsktbl; IMSpt; College; Prof.

KRONGARD, Bradley S; Neil A Armstrong HS; Minneapolis, MN; Band; CncrtBnd; HonRl; MrchBnd; NHS; NatlMeritCmnd; PepBnd; PolWkr; StuGov; Yrbk; LetterSwmmng; University Of Minnesota; Chemistry.

KRONING, Victoria L; St Charles HS; St Charles, MN; Chrs; HonRl; TchrAde; Yrbk; FHA; Mankato State Col; Bus Ed Teach.

KRONZ, Elizabeth K; Virden HS; Virden, IL; SecFrshCls; TrsJrCls; Chrs; HonRl; Mdrgl; SctActv; RptrYrbk; RptrSchPpr; FTA; College; Professional.

KROPAUL, John; Luther South HS; Oak Lawn, IL; 1/250 PresSrCls; HonRl; NHS; NatlMeritFnl; EdYrBk; Socr; Swmmng; Tennis; Ball State;gynecology.

KROPP, Jeffrey; Baraboo HS; Baraboo, WI; 70/230 HonRl; KeyCl; Univ Wisc; Business.

KROSKA, Kathryn J; Forest Lake HS; Forest Lk, MN; HonRl; LitMag; NatlFornLg; OffAde; RptrSchPpr; SpnCl; PpCl; Col ; Lang.

KROSZYNSKI, Steven; Hammond Clark HS; Whiting, IN; 1/260 ALBoysSt; HonRl; JrNHS; NatlSciFnd; StuCncl; StuGov; RptrYrbk; GerCl; CaptFtbl; IMSpt; College; Medicine.

KROTZ, Karen L; Highland Community HS; Columbus Jct, IA; 7/49 Band; CncrtBnd; HonRl; MrchBnd; NHS; PepBnd; StuCncl; EdYrBk; SchPpr; College; Social Service.

KROTZ, Kathryn J; Rushville HS; Rushville, NE; 2/40 Band; CncrtBnd; HonRl; MrchBnd; PepBnd; SchPl; RptrYrbk; RptrSchPpr; FTA; GerCl; Trk; College; Special Education.

KROUPA, David L; Kimball HS; Kimball, SD; 3/36 ALBoysSt; Chr; Chrs; HonRl; StuCncl; YthFlsp; 4-H; EngCl; MthCl; SciCl; LetterBsbl; LetterBsktbl; LetterFtbl; College.

KROUSE, Joe R; Crocker HS; Crocker, MO; ALBoysSt; Band; CtyCnl; HonRl; PpCl; CaptBsbl; LetterBsktbl; LetterTrk;.

KROUSE, Patricia; Proctor HS; Duluth, MN; 2/203 HonRl; NHS; FHA; FrCl; PpCl; College.

KRPAN, Thomas J; Taft HS; Chicago, IL; 54/900 Chrl; ChrhWkr; HonRl; JrNHS; NHS; SctActv; TreasYthFlsp; FrCl; SpnCl; MthCl; LetterFtbl; LetterSwmmng; Luther College; Math.

KRUCKEBERG, Kent; North Side HS; Fort Wayne, IN; 25/468 PresFrshCls; Aud/Vis; HonRl; StuCncl; LatCl; IMSpt; Ind Univ; Lawyer.

KRUCKEBERG, Michael G; Edwardsville Sr HS; Worden, IL; 73/437 Chr; Chrl; Chrs; HonRl; YthFlsp; Sec4-H; 4-HAwd; Southern Illinois Univ; Electrical Engineer.

KRUCKENBERG, Diane O; Stanton Public HS; Stanton, ND; 2/17 SecTrsSophCls; Band; Chrs; HonRl; SchPl; RptrYrbk; RptrSchPpr; FFA; PpCl; PresAwd; Humboldt Inst.

KRUCKENBERG, Linda J; Madison HS; Madison, SD; 9/162 ALAGirlsSt; Band; Chrs; ChrhWkr; HonRl; NHS; SctActv; YthFlsp; 4-H; College.

KRUEGER, Brian D; Washington HS; Richfield, WI; 27/210 HonRl; PresNHS; SctActv; YthFlsp; LetterBsbl; CaptBsktbl; LetterFtbl; CaptGlf; AmLegAwd; Univ Of Wisconsin; Business.

KRUEGER, Catherine A; Bunker Hill HS; Bunker Hill, IL; Chr; CmntyWkr; SchPl; SctActv; FHA; GAA; Lewis And Clark College.

KRUEGER, Christine; Crown Point HS; Crown Point, IN; 33/495 ChrhWkr; CncrtBnd; HonRl; MrchBnd; NHS; Orch; Purdue Univ; Psychology.

KRUEGER, Connie; Merrill Senior HS; Merrill, WI; 53/365 ChrhWkr; HonRl; 4-H; FFA; GAA; IMSpt; College; Social Worker.

KRUEGER, David C; Appleton West HS; Appleton, WI; Chr; ChrhWkr; SchMus; Ftbl; Glf; Tennis; Trk; IMSpt; Uw Madison; Chemical Eng.

KRUEGER, Deborah L; Kiel HS; Kiel, WI; Band; Chrs; HonRl; SchMus; StuCncl; 4-H; GerCl; PpCl; Chrldr; GAA; Lakeland Clg; Piano & German.

KRUEGER, Debra K; Winneionne HS; Winneionne, WI; 15/120 Band; CncrtBnd; HonRl; MrchBnd; EdYrBk; RptrSchPpr; SchPpr; FHA; FNA; PpCl; College; Special Ed.

KRUEGER, Dennis A; Riceville Community HS; Saratoga, IA; PresFrshCls; Band; HonRl; StuCncl; YthFlsp; LetterBsbl; LetterFtbl; LetterTrk; LetterWrstlng; CchngActv; College; Education.

KRUEGER, Donald K; Washington Comm HS; Washington, IL; 11/350 HonRl; NHS; NatlMeritFnl; StuCncl; GerCl; Swmmng; LetterTrk; IMSpt; Bradley University; Electrical Engineering.

KRUEGER, Donald K; Washington Community HS; Washington, IL; 12/375 HonRl; NHS; NatlMeritSF; GerCl; ChmnTrk; Math.

KRUEGER, Donald K; Washington Comm HS; Washington, IL; 11/350 HonRl; NHS; NatlMeritFnl; StuCncl; GerCl; Swmmng; LetterTrk; Bradley Univ; Electrical Engineering.

KRUEGER, Dorothy; Cloquet Senior HS; Cloquet, MN; Chr; HonRl; MrchBnd; NHS; Sdlty; RptrSchPpr; PpCl; Chrldr; PPFtbl; Univ Of Minn; Dental Hygiene.

KRUEGER, Gregory W; Jefferson HS; Bloomington, MN; Band; ChrhWkr; CmntyWkr; HonRl; NHS; SctActv; YthFlsp; CaptFtbl; LetterTrk; North Dakota State Univ; Pharmacy.

KRUEGER, Joan; Marquette Hs; Godfrey, IL; 14/115 HonRl; JA; NatlThespSoc; SchPl; RptrYrbk; 4-H; 4-HAwd; JAAwd;.

KRUEGER, John L; Ottawa Township HS; Ottawa, IL; 56/440 CmntyWkr; HonRl; NatlFornLg; NHS; PolWkr; SctActv; StuCncl; TchrAde; SchPpr; LatCl; Bsbl; LetterFtbl; Swmmng; JETSAwd; West Point; Military.

KRUEGER, John M; Clarence Lowden HS; Lowden, IA; ALBoysSt; Band; Chrs; ChrhWkr; CncrtBnd; HonRl; SctActv; YthFlsp; GerCl; Bsktbl; Tennis; College Rotc; Math.

KRUEGER, Julie; Marion HS; Marion, WI; Band; ChrhWkr; CmntyWkr; HospAde; NatlFornLg; StuCncl; FBLA; FDA; FFA; FHA; Bus School.

KRUEGER, Karna K; Larkin HS; Elgin, IL; 46/622 Band; Chr; CncrtBnd; HonRl; MrchBnd; NatlMeritSF; Univ Of Illinois; Nebulous.

KRUEGER, Kathleen A; Thornwood HS; South Holland, IL; 14/875 CncrtBnd; HonRl; MrchBnd; Augustana College.

KRUEGER, Kenneth K; Grover Cleveland HS; St Louis, MO; 40/700 Chr; ChrhWkr; HonRl; PresStuCncl; YthFlsp; LetterBsktbl; IMSpt; KiwanAwd; University; Clinical Psychology.

KRUEGER, Kenneth M; Breckenridge Sr HS; Wheeler, MI; ChrhWkr; HonRl; TreasNHS; VPStuCncl; LetterBsktbl; CaptFtbl; LetterTrk; IMSpt; Univ; Professional.

KRUEGER, Kevin D; Dilworth HS; Dlworth, MN; TchrAde; Bsktbl; LetterFtbl; Trk; Ariz State; Chemical Engr.

KRUEGER, Kristy L; Eisenhower HS; New Berlin, WI; HonRl; PPFtbl;.

KRUEGER, Linda C; Sherrard HS; Milan, IL; HonRl; JA; SchAde; TchrAde; RptrSchPpr; SchPpr; 4-H; Blackhawk College; Zoology.

KRUEGER, Michael; Custer HS; Custer, SD; HstFrshCls; HstSophCls; ChrhWkr; CmntyWkr; OffAde; PolWkr; SchAde; SchPl; Ftbl; Wrstlng; College; Law.

KRUEGER, Michael G; J A Craig HS; Janesville, WI; Band; PepBnd; FBLA; LetterFtbl; LetterTrk; U Of Wi; Accounting.

KRUEGER, Patti A; Gibault HS; Red Bud, IL; Chr; Chrs; HonRl; HospAde; PolWkr; 4-H; PpCl; Swmmng; Univ.

KRUEGER, Randy L; Oconto Falls HS; Oconto Falls, WI; 11/148 HonRl; FBLA; IMSpt; KiwanAwd; Tech Sch; Office Mach Repairman.

KRUEGER, Sharon J; Milton HS; Milton, WI; HonRl; 4-H; FBLA; FHA; Tennis; 4-HAwd; College.

KRUEGER, Sharon R; Luther South HS; Evergreen Park, IL; Chr; ChrhWkr; HonRl; NHS; GerCl; GAA; Coll; Teach Elem.

KRUEGER, Susan; Valders HS; Manitowoc, WI; Band; CncrtBnd; HonRl; PepBnd; EdYrBk; GAA; IMSpt; CitAwd;.

KRUEMPEL, Sue E; Chosen Valley HS; Chatfield, MN; 2/86 ALAGirlsSt; SecChrhWkr; HonRl; NatlMeritCmnd; SctActv; StuCncl; EdSchPpr; FHA; PresFTA; PresSpnCl; Coll; Psychology.

KRUG, Cheryl L; Yorkwood HS; Kirkwood, IL; 2/56 VPSrCls; Band; Chrs; HonRl; NHS; SchPl; EdYrBk; FrCl; Bsktbl; Trk; AmLegAwd; Blackburn College; Music.

KRUG, Debora C; Winnebago Luth Acad; Fond Du Lac, WI; SecFrshCls; SecSophCls; Band; Chr; SchPl; RptrSchPpr; 4-H; PpCl; Bsktbl; Trk; Univ Wi Oshkosh; Music.

KRUG, Patrick M; Hettinger HS; Bucyrus, ND; Band; Chr; Chrs; ChrhWkr; CncrtBnd; SchPl; FFA; LetterFtbl; LetterTrk; IMSpt; College; Vocation.

KRUG, Ralph G; Rochester Adams HS; Rochester, MI; ALBoysSt; CncrtBnd; MrchBnd; NHS; GerCl; Univ Of Mi; Electronic Engineer.

KRUG, Shirley; John Marshall HS; Milwaukee, WI; 53/712 ChrhWkr; HonRl; JA; PolWkr; SchMus; SchPl; SctActv; StuGov; GerCl; PpCl; Univ Milw; Professional Soc Sci.

KRUGEL, Jo Ann V; Carl Schurz HS; Chicago, IL; 7/756 Chr; ChrhWkr; HonRl; JCC; NHS; NatlMeritCmnd; NatlThespSoc; SchPl; StuCncl; GerCl; GAA; AmLegAwd; U C L A; Medical Research.

KRUGER, Calvin J; Sully Buttes HS; Blunt, SD; Band; CncrtBnd; HonRl; MrchBnd; PepBnd; YthFlsp; Trk; Trade School; Vocation.

KRUGER, Cynthia J; Stevens Point Area Senior HS; Stevens Point, WI; 8/525 SecTrsSrCls; ALAGirlsSt; JrNHS; SecNatlFornLg; NHS; NatlMeritCmnd; Quill&Scroll; SctActv; StuCncl; SecYthLg; Univ Of Wi Madison.

KRUGER, Gretchen A; Hallock HS; Hallock, MN; ALAGirlsSt; Chr; HonRl; NHS; SchPl; SctActv; SchPpr; FFA; SciCl; LetterChrldr; College; Professional.

KRUGER, Jeanie K; Randolph Public HS; Randolph, NE; SecJrCls; Chrs; HonRl; NHS; SchPl; SpnCl; PpCl; Trk; Chrldr; Univ.

KRUGER, Kevin L; Campbell Tintah HS; Wheaton, MN; ChrhWkr; HonRl; RptrSchPpr; 4-H; Bsbl; College; Law.

KRUGER, Lisa; Buchanan HS; Jamestown, ND; 1/10 SecFrshCls; SecSophCls; PresJrCls; ALAGirlsSt; Chr; HonRl; SchPl; TchrAde; RptrSchPpr; 4-HAwd; Coll; Music Education.

KRUGER, Robert B; Highland Park HS; Highland Park, IL; PresFrshCls; HonRl; NHS; SchMus; SchPl; StuCncl; StuGov; RptrSchPpr; MthCl; College; Medicine.

KRUGER, Sherilynn E; Pinconning Area HS; Rhodes, MI; Band; CncrtBnd; HospAde; MrchBnd; NHS; PepBnd; SchPl; SptEdYrbk; FNA; Michigan State Univ; Nurse.

KRUGER, Susan; Concordia Acad; St Paul, MN; SecSrCls; ALAGirlsSt; Chr; DrlTm; PresFrshCls; NHS; SchMus; GerCl; Bsktbl; Mounds Midway School; Nursing.

KRUGH, Gary L; Adams Central HS; Decatur, IN; NatlMeritSF; SchPpr; Purdue U; Sociology.

KRUIZE, Kay E; Elbow Lake HS; Wendell, MN; 2/76 Band; CncrtBnd; HonRl; MrchBnd; NHS; NatlMeritCmnd; PepBnd; SchMus; SciCl; GAA; Gustavs Adolphus; Pharmacy.

KRUK, Derek F; St Laurence HS; Chicago, IL; 36/371 HonRl; LetterWrstlng; IMSpt; Ill Institute Of Tech; Engineering.

KRUKOW, Donna L; Dumont Comm HS; Dumont, IA; Band; Chrs; CncrtBnd; HonRl; MrchBnd; NHS; PepBnd; SchPl;.

KRUKOWSKI, Ronald; Weber Hs; Chicago, IL; 17 Band; CncrtBnd; HonRl; MrchBnd; RptrSchPpr; Columbia College;communications Radio Tv.

KRULL, Jeanine M; Thornton Frac South HS; Lansing, IL; HonRl; LbryAde; PolWkr; TchrAde; College; Dental Hygiene.

KRULL, Kalene S; George Community HS; George, IA; 1/55 TrsJrCls; SecTrsSrCls; ChrhWkr; MrchBnd; NHS; RptrYrbk; Pres4-H; FrCl; LetterGlf; 4-HAwd; Rochester Comm Coll; Respiratory Therapy.

KRUMM, Cynthia L; Lake Central HS; St John, IN; 63/433 HonRl; Quill&Scroll; TchrAde; Teen; EdYrBk; Trade Sch; Voc.

KRUMM, Nancy L; Hartley HS; Hartley, IA; SecSrCls; Aud/Vis; HonRl; TreasNHS; RptrYrbk; FHA; PresGerCl; LetterTrk; Chrldr; CitAwd; Northwestern Coll; Marine Bio.

KRUMM, Tim D; So Hamilton HS; Stanhope, IA; 7/83 Band; HonRl; NHS; SchMus; StuCncl; 4-H; FFA; MthCl; Bsktbl; LetterFtbl; 4-HAwd; College; Engineer.

KRUMMEL, Nancy A; Reedsville HS; Cato, WI; 4/99 AFS; HonRl; LbryAde; NHS; RptrYrbk; RptrSchPpr; HstFrshCls; FHA; SpnCl; PpCl; Business; Vocational.

KRUMMEN, Ann; Jefferson Senior HS; Jefferson, WI; AFS; CncrtBnd; HonRl; MrchBnd; SchMus; 4-H; FBLA; Business.

KRUMWIEDE, Donna; Buckley Loda HS; Buckley, IL; Chr; Chrs; HonRl; NHS; YthFlsp; RptrSchPpr; FHA; SecMthCl; PpCl; Bsktbl;.

KRUPA, Steven J; St Gregorys HS; Chicago, IL; HonRl; NHS; NatlMeritSF; PolWkr; EdSchPpr; FBLA; KeyCl; LetterBsbl; Swmmng; College; Law.

KRUPELA, Paul A; Weber HS; Chicago, IL; ChrhWkr; DrlTm; HonRl; ROTC; RptrSchPpr; LatCl; LetterSwmmng; IMSpt; College; Pre Med.

KRUPICKA, Carolyn K; Exeter HS; Exeter, NE; 11/21 Band; HonRl; OffAde; SchPl; RptrYrbk; RptrSchPpr; PpCl; Trk; GAA; CitAwd; School Of Commerce; Executive Secretary.

KRUPICKA, Kristy K; St Alberts HS; Council Bluffs, IA; TrsFrshCls; TrsJrCls; Chr; DrlTm; HonRl; LbryAde; PolWkr; SchMus; StuCncl; PpCl; Iowa State Univ; Fashion Merchandising.

KRUPKA, John F; St Joseph HS; Brookfield, IL; 4/178 Aud/Vis; HonRl; NHS; StuGov; LetterBsktbl; LetterTennis; IMSpt; C; Engineering.

KRUPKA, Thomas; Catholic Memorial HS; New Berun, WI; Na/250 CmntyWkr; PolWkr; SctActv; OptClAwd; Undecided; Physics Engineering.

KRUPOWICZ, James J; Plainfield HS; Plainfield, IL; 5/295 ALBoysSt; TreasBand; JrNHS; VPNHS; NatlMeritCmnd; Quill&Scroll; StuCncl; EdSchPpr; SptEdSchPpr; SecGerCl; Univ Of Ill; Chemical Eng.

KRUPP, Stephen; Connville Sr HS; Connersville, IN; 81/371 CncrtBnd; HonRl; Orch; PepBnd; SctActv; FrCl; SciCl; Ftbl; Trk; Indiana Univ; Pre Med.

KRUPSKI, Carol; Lutheran West HS; Lincoln Park, MI; 2/145 Chr; ChrhWkr; HonRl; NHS; EdYrBk; Coll; Teaching.

KRUSCHEL, Christopher; Northwestern Prep HS; Menomonee Falls, WI; Chrs; HonRl; PepBnd; StuCncl; EdYrBk; EdSchPpr; Ftbl; Wrstlng; IMSpt; Northwestern College; Pastor.

KRUSCHKE, Tracy; Wisconsin Heights HS; Mazomanie, WI; 6/110 Chr; ChrhWkr; MrchBnd; NHS; Orch; StuCncl; YthFlsp; Bsktbl; Tennis;.

KRUSE, Brenda L; Kee HS; New Albin, IA; 11/53 SecSophCls; Band; Chrs; ChrhWkr; HonRl; NHS; StuCncl; FTA; CaptBsktbl; Tennis; Ia St U; Child Dev.

KRUSE, Brett A; St Patricks HS; Sidney, NE; 1/27 PresJrCls; ALBoysSt; ChrhWkr; HonRl; NHS; SchPl; StuCncl; StuGov; LetterBsktbl; AmLegAwd; Clge; Lawyer.

KRUSE, Cary L; Randolph Public HS; Randolph, NE; Band; Chrs; CncrtBnd; MrchBnd; PepBnd; StuCncl; LetterBsktbl; LetterFtbl; Work.

KRUSE, Cinda S; Verdigre Public HS; Winnetoon, NE; Chr; Chrs; HonRl; YthFlsp; PpCl; College; Vocation.

KRUSE, Claudia; Pender Public HS; Pender, NE; PresJrCls; HonRl; PolWkr; SchPl; StuCncl; 4-H; FHA; PpCl; 4-HAwd; VoiceDemAwd; Univ; Cpa.

KRUSE, Debra L; George HS; George, IA; 13/47 PresJrCls; Chr; Chrs; ChrhWkr; CncrtBnd; MrchBnd; PepBnd; SchMus; U Of Utah; Nursing.

KRUSE, Ila M; Bradley Bourbonnais HS; Bourbonnais, IL; 30/365 Aud/Vis; ChrhWkr; NHS; TchrAde; FNA; SpnCl; College; Nursing.

KRUSE, James W; East Central HS; Sunman, IN; ALBoysSt; Aud/Vis; HonRl; IntrClCncl; NHS; StuCncl; SptEdSchPpr; PresFFA; TreasSpnCl; PpCl; Purdue U; Agriculture.

KRUSE, Karen J; Brunswick Rii HS; Brunswick, MO; 1/50 SecJrCls; Band; HonRl; NHS; PepBnd; SchPl; YthFlsp; SchPpr; 4-H; FHA; PpCl; Univ Of Missouri; Art.

KRUSE, Kathy J; Brunswick Rii HS; Brunswick, MO; 2/50 TrsJrCls; Band; Chrs; CncrtBnd; HonRl; LbryAde; MrchBnd; NHS; PepBnd; SchPl; YthFlsp; 4-H; FHA; Univ Of Mo; Art Design.

KRUSE, Laura J; Hanover HS; Hanover, KS; PresSophCls; Band; DrmMjrt; HonRl; NHS; SchPl; StuCncl; YthFlsp; LetterBsktbl; LetterTrk; College.

KRUSE, Linda M; Mt Olive Comm HS; Walshville, IL; 9/60 ChrhWkr; HonRl; LbryAde; MrchBnd; VPStuCncl; VPYthFlsp; Yrbk; TreasFHA; SpnCl; GAA; Belleville Area Col; Physical Therapy.

KRUSE, Linda M; Mt Olive HS; Walshville, IL; 9/60 ChrhWkr; CmntyWkr; HonRl; MrchBnd; VPStuCncl; VPYthFlsp; GAA; IMSpt; VoiceDemAwd; Belleville Area Col; Physical Therapist Ass.

KRUSE, Linus; Sanborn Public HS; Sanborn, MN; VPSophCls; ALBoysSt; Chr; Chrs; LbryAde; PpCl; AmLegAwd; Trade School; Vocation.

KRUSE, Lisa F; Johnson Brock HS; Tecumseh, NE; 8/26 ALAGirlsSt; Chrs; HonRl; RptrYrbk; 4-H; PpCl; Bsktbl; Trk; College; Accounting.

KRUSE, Michael E; Flora HS; Flora, IL; 17/125 ALBoysSt; Band; Chr; Chrs; ChrhWkr; HonRl; Mdrgl; MrchBnd; NHS; PepBnd; SchMus; SchPl; TchrAde; FTA; Olney Central; Anesthetist.

KRUSE, Randall R; Grant Deuel 63 HS; Revillo, SD; Band; Chr; Chrs; ChrhWkr; HonRl; NatlThespSoc; 4-H; Ftbl; IMSpt; 4-HAwd; College; Animal Science.

KRUSE, Roxanne M; Marian HS; Omaha, NE; 4/156 CmntyWkr; CaptDrlTm; HonRl; NHS; Quill&Scroll; SchPl; Sdlty; RptrSchPpr; College; Special Ed.

KRUSE, Susan D; Verdi Public HS; Verdi, MN; 2/12 PresFrshCls; PresSrCls; Band; Chrs; HonRl; SchPl; StuCncl; RptrYrbk; RptrSchPpr; LetterChrldr; College.

KRUSE, Vernamae F; Turkey Valley Comm HS; Waucoma, IA; 2/110 SecFrshCls; Band; Chr; CncrtBnd; HonRl; MrchBnd; NHS; PepBnd; SchMus; Sec4-H; College; Nursing.

KRUSELL, Peggy J; Highland Park Sr HS; St Paul, MN; Chr; HospAde; SchPl; TchrAde; YthFlsp; PpCl; Chrldr; IMSpt; College.

KRUSEMARK, Paula L; Pender Public HS; Thurston, NE; Chr; Chrs; HonRl; HospAde; SchPl; Yrbk; FHA; PpCl; Trk; Chrldr;.

KRUSEMEIER, Melinda S; Thomas Jefferson HS; Rockford, IL; 20/335 AFS; HonRl; Orch; College; Medical Tech.

KRUSENOSKI, Gary R; Marist HS; Calumet Park, IL; 40/365 CmntyWkr; HonRl; JrNHS; SctActv; Bradley Univ; Mech Tech.

KRUSENSTJERNA, Christine A; Spencer HS; Spencer, IA; 66/163 Chr; ChrhWkr; HonRl; HospAde; NatlThespSoc; PolWkr; SchPl; SchPpr; 4-H; PpCl; LetterTrk; IMSpt; Iowa State Univ; Dietetics.

KRUSIEWICZ, Michael R; Ferndale HS; Ferndale, MI; HonRl; NatlMeritSF; SchAde; RptrYrbk; Trk; CchngActv; JAAwd; CitAwd; College; Law.

KRUSKE, Susan C; Lead HS; Lead, SD; Band; Chr; Chrs; CncrtBnd; MrchBnd; Orch; PepBnd; SctActv; TchrAde; PpCl;.

KRUSKOP, Bill P; Lytton Comm HS; Lytton, IA; ALBoysSt; Band; Chrs; NHS; Bsbl; Bsktbl; Ftbl;.

KRUSKOY, William D; Lytton Community HS; Lytton, IA; CAP; LbryAde; FshEdYrbk; FshEdSchPpr; FHA; RusCl; Wrstlng; Chrldr; Notre Dame; Interior Decorating.

KRUSNIAK, Jean M; Catholic Central HS; Manistee, MI; 8/75 ALAGirlsSt; Band; HonRl; MrchBnd; NHS; Orch; PepBnd; TchrAde; AmLegAwd; College; Professional.

KRUSYNA, Susan C; Parchment HS; Parchment, MI; HonRl; NHS; NatlMeritCmnd; TchrAde; SchPpr; SpnCl; Western Mi Univ; Spanish Major.

KRUSZYNSKI, Susan; Holton HS; Holton, MI; 2/55 SecFrshCls; SecJrCls; TrsSrCls; Band; HonRl; NHS; SchPl; YthFlsp; 4-H; Chrldr; Coll; Pub Rel.

KRUTELL, Teresa; Lakeview HS; St Clair Shores, MI; 10/712 CmntyWkr; HonRl; JrNHS; NHS; PolWkr; Wayne State Univ.

KRUTTLIN, John; Alcona HS; Lincoln, MI; HonRl; Cen Mich Univ; Business Major.

KRUTZ, Samuel D; Decatur Central HS; Indpls, IN; 1/360 VPSophCls; ChrhWkr; CmntyWkr; HonRl; JA; JrNHS; NatlMeritCmnd; PolWkr; Quill&Scroll; SchPl; IMSpt; Wabash Col; Pre Med.

KRUZAN, Karla S; Mac Arthur HS; Decatur, IL; Band; Chr; CncrtBnd; HonRl; MrchBnd; Orch; SchMus; YthFlsp; LetterTennis; Ill State Univ; General Curriculum Studies.

KRUZEL, Gregory M; St Patrick HS; Chicago, IL; 7/427 HonRl; VPNHS; SchMus; SchPl; StuGov; EdYrBk; PpCl; Bsktbl; Clg; Professional.

KRYCH, Nancy M; St Alphonsus HS; Detroit, MI; 34/109 TrsJrCls; TrsSrCls; HonRl; NatlMeritSchl; StuCncl; FrCl; PpCl; LetterChrldr; GAA; IMSpt; PPFtbl; Detroit College; Legal Secretary.

KRYDER, Steven P; Freeport HS; Cedarville, IL; 55/507 ChrhWkr; CmntyWkr; HonRl; 4-H; Highland Comm College; Accounting.

KRYGIER, Brad C; Muskego HS; Muskego, WI; Band; CncrtBnd; HonRl; NHS; LetterSwmmng; LetterTrk; College.

KRYMKOWSKI, Daniel H; S Milwaukee Sr HS; S Milwaukee, WI; 67/435 Chr; Chrs; HonRl; IntrClCncl; Mdrgl; SchMus; SchPl; StuCncl; StuGov; Marquette Univ; Biology.

KRYSL, Donald R; West Holt HS; Stuart, NE; Band; CncrtBnd; MrchBnd; PepBnd; SchMus; SchPl; RptrYrbk; EdYrBk; Yrbk; LetterFtbl; Kearney State College.

KRYSL, Mary Jo A; West Holt HS; Stuart, NE; Band; CncrtBnd; DrlTm; HonRl; MrchBnd; NHS; PepBnd; StuCncl; PpCl; Trk; College; Pro.

KRYST, Michael W; Lumen Christi HS; Jackson, MI; 30/233 HonRl; NHS; SctActv; LatCl; LetterFtbl; LetterTrk; IMSpt; Albion Coll; Pro.

KRYSTON, David J; Catholic Central HS; Monroe, MI; 11/106 HonRl; SchPl; StuCncl; SptEdSchPpr; LetterWrstlng; IMSpt; Univ Of Michigan; Engineer.

KRYZER, Avis A; Lewiston HS; Lewiston, MN; 8/87 PresJrCls; HonRl; PresNHS; PresStuCncl; EdSchPpr; Pres4-H; VPFTA; LetterTrk; PresGAA; 4-HAwd; Coll; Med Lab.

KRYZER, Ida J; Lewiston HS; Lewiston, MN; 22/85 AFS; CncrtBnd; HonRl; MrchBnd; NHS; StuCncl; 4-H; CaptChrldr; GAA; 4-HAwd; Rochester Tech; Secretary.

KRYZNOWSKI, Debra S; Bishop Mc Namara HS; Kankakee, IL; 1/161 HonRl; LitMag; NHS; Quill&Scroll; PresSpnCl; CaptChrldr; GAA; Northern Illinois Univ; Nursing.

KRZIZIKE, Betty; Mishicot HS; Mishicot, WI; HonRl; OffAde; SchPl; RptrYrbk; PpCl; College, Medical Secretary.

KRZYEWSKI, Nancy M; Catholic Memorial HS; Hales Corners, WI; Band; Chr; ChrhWkr; CmntyWkr; CncrtBnd; PepBnd; SchAde; SctActv; TchrAde; Univ Of Wisconsin; Physical Therapy.

KRZYSIK, Doreen M; Grosse Pointe N HS; Grosse Point Woods, MI; 9/625 HonRl; NHS; StuCncl; Chrldr; PPFtbl; BttyCrckrAwd; Mich State Univ; Accountant.

KRZYSTON, John J; Chadsey HS; Detroit, MI; 3/308 HonRl; NHS; Quill&Scroll; TchrAde; RptrYrbk; University; Biology.

KRZYWICKI, Debra A; Resurrection HS; Harwood Hts, IL; 21/294 SecFrshCls; SecSophCls; PresJrCls; ChrhWkr; HonRl; HospAde; TreasNHS; StuCncl; GAA; College; Liberal Arts.

KRZYWOSZ, Helene; Morton East HS; Cicero, IL; 22/771 HonRl; JrNHS; NHS; NatlMeritCmnd; SpnCl; University; Professional.

KRZYZEK, Theresa M; Lamoille HS; Arlington, IL; 1/40 Chrs; ChrhWkr; HonRl; NHS; OffAde; SchAde; Yrbk; PresFHA; BauchLmbAwd; DARAwd; Rockford Mem Sch; Reg Nurse.

KSIEZAK, Chris M; Kennedy St Paul HS; Chicago, IL; LbryAde; TchrAde; RptrYrbk; 4-H; GAA; IMSpt; 4-HAwd; College; Teaching.

KUBACKI, James P; Whitko HS; Pierceton, IN; 12/153 TrsFrshCls; SchMus; SchPl; SchPpr; SciCl; CaptFtbl; LetterGlf; LetterTennis; IMSpt; Indiana U; Business.

KUBACKI, Sheri; Onaway Area HS; Onaway, MI; /97 SctActv; TchrAde; 4-H; FHA; PpCl; 4-HAwd; Coll; Rn.

KUBALAK, Sharon M; Green Bay Preble HS; Green Bay, WI; Band; ChrhWkr; CmntyWkr; CncrtBnd; HonRl; MrchBnd; NHS; PepBnd; StuCncl; College; Elementary Educ.

KUBALE, Joseph; Premontre HS; Green Bay, WI; 17/150 Chrs; HonRl; NatlMeritCmnd; NatlMeritSchl; NatlSciFnd; SpnCl; Bsbl; Bsktbl; Ftbl; Trk; Concordia Collegef Science Field.

KUBALL, Lori L; Borup HS; Borup, MN; 5/13 SecTrsSophCls; Band; Chrs; NatlFornLg; PepBnd; SchMus; TchrAde; PpCl; CitAwd; VoiceDemAwd; Trade School; Vocation.

KUBANEK, Geralyn M; Manistee Catholic HS; Manistee, MI; 5/76 VPFrshCls; VPSophCls; Chr; CncrtBnd; DrmMjrt; HonRl; MrchBnd; NHS; Twrl; College; Professional.

KUBASCH, Kent K; Holy Trinity HS; Winsted, MN; Aud/Vis; CmntyWkr; HonRl; StuCncl; StuGov; Bsktbl; LetterFtbl; IMSpt; Trade School; Business.

KUBASTA, Celeste M; Lidgerwood HS; Lidgerwood, ND; 6/50 Band; ChrhWkr; HonRl; OffAde; PepBnd; StuCncl; Yrbk; RptrSchPpr; FHA; SecGerCl; N Dakota State Univ; Pharmacy.

KUBAT, Christopher K; Ryan HS; Omaha, NE; SpnCl; SciCl; Socr; IMSpt; RotaryAwd; University; Professional.

KUBECZKO, David A; St Laurence HS; Chicago, IL; 37/372 HonRl; NatlMeritCmnd; FrCl; SciCl; Bsktbl; Trk; Augustana College.

KUBELA, Brad J; Wahpeton Sr HS; Wahpeton, ND; Band; ChrhWkr; HonRl; MrchBnd; SchMus; SchPpr; FFA; Trade School; Prof Farmer.

KUBERSKI, James R; Tamaroa HS; Tamaroa, IL; VPJrCls; VPSrCls; HonRl; RptrYrbk; RptrSchPpr; 4-H; FFA; LetterBsbl; LetterBsktbl; 4-HAwd; College.

KUBES, Scott K; Niles West HS; Niles, IL; 77/666 Band; ChrhWkr; HonRl; NHS; Bsktbl; Socr; Univ Of Illinois; Engineering.

KUBESH, Vickie L; Bird Island Lake Lillian HS; Bird Island, MN; 15/60 Chr; HonRl; NatlFornLg; NHS; College Of St Catherine; Psychology.

KUBETZ, Deborah L; Marillac HS; Mt Prospect, IL; Chrs; HospAde; NHS; St Francis Hospital School; Nursing.

KUBIAK, Jean M; Comstock Park HS; Comstock Park, MI; 8/147 VPSophCls; PresSrCls; HonRl; LbryAde; PolWkr; StuGov; TchrAde; RptrYrbk; Yrbk; 4-H; PpCl; Bsbl; TreasGAA;.

KUBIAK, Norb; Green Bay Premontre HS; Green Bay, WI; 40/140 Chrs; DrlTm; HonRl; ROTC; IMSpt; Trade Sch; Restaurant Mngmnt.

KUBIC, Kathleen; Marillac HS; Morton Grove, IL; 33/254 NHS; Yrbk; SpnCl; Loyola Univ Of Chicago; Accountant.

KUBICEK, Maxine L; Lincoln Ne HS; Lincoln, NE; 39/555 Band; ChrhWkr; CncrtBnd; HonRl; JA; MrchBnd; PepBnd; SpnCl; PpCl; Trk; GAA; Univ; Sociology.

KUBICKI, Deborah A; St Alphonsus HS; Detroit, MI; 5/145 HonRl; LetterBsbl; IMSpt; PPFtbl; Wayne St Univ ; Sociology.

KUBIK, Darlene Jo; Muskego HS; Hales Corners, WI; 33/324 Band; CncrtBnd; HonRl; MrchBnd; Quill&Scroll; Yrbk; FTA; LetterChrldr; GAA; Univ Wis;.

KUBIK, Keith K; Central Public HS; Valparaiso, NE; 10/63 Band; Chr; Chrs; HonRl; TreasNHS; SchPl; StuCncl; PresFFA; Bsbl; CaptFtbl; LetterTrk; CaptWrstlng; Univ Of Nebraska; Teacher.

KUBIK, Kimberly A; Martansdale St Marys HS; St Marys, IA; 4/35 Chrs; SecNHS; SchPl; EdYrBk; Yrbk; Pres4-H; PpCl; CaptBsktbl; CaptTrk; Grand View; Nursing.

KUBIK, Pamela L; Riverside Brookfield HS; Riverside, IL; Chrs; HonRl; OffAde; FrCl; Chrldr; GAA; Univ; Professional.

KUBINSKI, Kerrinda M; Crocker HS; Crocker, MO; 2/62 ChrhWkr; HonRl; JrNHS; NHS; SchPl; TchrAde; RptrYrbk; RptrSchPpr; DARAwd; VoiceDemAwd; U Of Mo Rolla; Engineer.

KUBISCHTA, Diane M; Dickinson HS; Dickinson, ND; Band; Chr; CmntyWkr; DrlTm; HonRl; OffAde; SchAde; TchrAde; PpCl; Trk; IMSpt; College; Computer Science.

KUBISCHTA, Mary A; Hope Public HS; Hope, ND; 3/13 PresSrCls; Chrs; HonRl; LbryAde; SchPl; Yrbk; Univ; Pro.

KUBISIAK, Donna M; St Mary Acad; Newport, MI; ChrhWkr; HonRl; 4-H; Bsktbl; 4-HAwd; Eastern Mi Univ; Med Tech.

KUBITSCHEK, Sylvia U; Proviso East HS; Maywood, IL; CmntyWkr; HonRl; NatlMeritSF; OffAde; SchAde; StuCncl; GerCl; Ill Inst Of Tech; Medicine.

KUBO, Calvin J; Andrews University Academy; Berrien Springs, MI; PresFrshCls; Chr; Chrs; HonRl; NHS; NatlMeritSF; SchPl; StuCncl; IMSpt; Andrews U; Medicine.

KUC, Terry J; Vianney HS; Crestwood, MO; 45/186 HonRl; Trk; IMSpt; St Louis U; Chemistry.

KUCABA, Jean M; Phillips HS; Catawba, WI; Band; HonRl; SchMus; Yrbk; RptrSchPpr; GAA; Technical College; Commercial Art.

KUCERA, Barbara A; Washington HS; Germantown, WI; 6/215 JA; SecNHS; NatlMeritCmnd; SchPl; RptrSchPpr; EdSchPpr; FrCl; SpnCl; PpCl; LionAwd; Uw Whitewater; Journalsim.

KUCERA, Frank; Reauis Hs; Burbank, IL; 30/760 HonRl; JrNHS; NHS; TchrAde; CaptFtbl; Wrstlng; GovHonPrgAwd; JCAwd; College Pre Medical;ani.

KUCERA, Kathleen A; Lawrence Public HS; Deweese, NE; 5/30 Band; ChrhWkr; CmntyWkr; CncrtBnd; HonRl; MrchBnd; PepBnd; SchPl; SecTrsSophCls; Mary Mount College; Nursing.

KUCERA, Kevin C; Creighton Prep; Omaha, NE; CmntyWkr; Sdlty; PpCl; Glf; Socr; Swmmng; IMSpt; College; Engineering.

KUCERA, Ronald L; Howells HS; Howells, NE; HonRl; SchPl; Yrbk; RptrSchPpr; SchPpr; VPFFA; Bsktbl;.

KUCH, Shirley; St Charles HS; St Charles, MI; CmntyWkr; HonRl; JrNHS; NHS; StuCncl; Bsktbl; Trk; IMSpt; CitAwd; College; Professional.

KUCHAR, Jeannie M; Niobrara Public HS; Niobrara, NE; 2/23 SecSophCls; SecJrCls; TrsSrCls; Aud/Vis; Chrs; DrlTm; HonRl; StuCncl; DanFAwd; VoiceDemAwd; Bus School; Vocation.

KUCHAR, Mike; Lane Tech HS; Chicago, IL; 257/1200 Aud/Vis; HonRl; LbryAde; NatlMeritCmnd; TchrAde; College; Computers.

KUCHAREK, David F; Cody HS; Detroit, MI; 25/625 DrlTm; HonRl; ROTC; Univ Of Detroit; Accounting.

KUCHAREK, Mark T; Gaylord HS; Elmira, MI; Aud/Vis; ChrhWkr; CmntyWkr; HonRl; LbryAde; SctActv; TchrAde; 4-H; Bsktbl; IMSpt; Coll; Data Processing.

KUCHARSKI, James M; St Laurence HS; Burbank, IL; 95/390 ChrhWkr; HonRl; StuCncl; Teen; Bsbl; Ftbl; Wrstlng; Illinois Institute Of Tech; Elec Engineer.

KUCHARZ, Karen A; Lockport Township HS; Lockport, IL; 27/550 Chr; ChrhWkr; HonRl; NHS; SchMus; RptrSchPpr; SchPpr; PpCl; Bsktbl; College; Music.

KUCHARZYK, Donald W; Riverside Brookfield HS; La Grange Park, IL; HonRl; NHS; TchrAde; GerCl; LetterGlf; Loyola Univ; Medicine.

KUCHENBECKER, Kent A; Neillsville HS; Neillsville, WI; HonRl; SchPl; SpnCl; Ftbl; Trk; Uw La Crosse; Major Study.

KUCHENBUCH, Joseph P; Gull Lake HS; Richland, MI; PresSophCls; Band; CncrtBnd; HonRl; MrchBnd; StuCncl; Bsktbl; LetterFtbl; CaptTrk; IMSpt; College; Electronics.

KUCHENMEISTER, Janet; Pontiac Township Hs; Pontiac, IL; 6/189 HonRl; JrNHS; NHS; Quill&Scroll; Yrbk; RptrSchPpr; MthCl; PpCl; GAA;.

KUCHMEK, Marilyn; Hackett HS; Decatur, MI; 21/143 NHS; Msu; Child Development.

KUCHTA, Lauren M; Immaculate Heart Of Mary HS; Westchester, IL; 39/244 HonRl; RedCrAde; SctActv; GAA; St Josephs; Vet.

KUCHTA, Michael G; Kennedy St Paul HS; Chicago, IL; Chrs; RptrYrbk; Yrbk; College; Journalism.

KUCHTA, Michael G; St Paul Kennedy HS; Chicago, IL; Chrs; HonRl; JrNHS; NHS; TreasStuCncl; RptrYrbk; Yrbk; RptrSchPpr; SptEdSchPpr; LetterTrk; Coll; Journalism.

KUCIK, Thomas A; Kennedy St Paul HS; Chicago, IL; Chrs; HonRl; SchAde; SctActv; StuCncl; Yrbk; Bsbl; Bsktbl; Ftbl; LetterTrk; Univ; Chemist.

KUCZYNSKI, Philip J; Manistee Catholic HS; Manistee, MI; 4/68 ALBoysSt; ChrhWkr; CmntyWkr; HonRl; NHS; StuCncl; SptEdYrbk; SptEdSchPpr; CaptBsbl; CaptBsktbl; CaptFtbl; CchngActv; College; Mechanical Engineer.

KUDAN, David B; New Trier East HS; Glencoe, IL; Univ; Judaic Studies.

KUDANOWICZ, Miron; De La Salle HS; Minneapolis, MN; ChrhWkr; JA; Sacrstn; SctActv; Yrbk; SchPpr; Bsbl; Socr; Rutgers University; Philosophy.

KUDEJ, Judy D; Garner Hayfield HS; Britt, IA; 25/63 Band; CncrtBnd; HonRl; MrchBnd; PepBnd; SchPl; FHA; Clg; Speech Therapist.

KUDERA, Donna; Osmond Community HS; Osmond, NE; 5/44 Band; Chr; Chrs; CncrtBnd; HonRl; MrchBnd; OffAde; PepBnd; RptrYrbk; Yrbk; College; Dental Assistant.

KUDLO, Kevin; Lowell Sr HS; Lowell, IN; 34/265 HstSophCls; HstJrCls; HonRl; StuCncl; FFA; Bsbl; Ftbl; Wrstlng; St Joseph Coll; Cpa.

KUDRA, Stanley; Marian Catholic HS; Chicago Heights, IL; 1/335 Chr; Chrs; HonRl; NHS; SchMus; StuGov; RptrSchPpr; LatCl; Wrstlng; Loyola And Medical School; Physcain Medicin.

KUDRNA, Randi; Red Cloud HS; Red Cloud, NE; Band; Chrs; CmntyWkr; CncrtBnd; HonRl; MrchBnd; PepBnd; SchMus; StuCncl; Chrldr; Univ; Medical Technology.

KUDRNA, Randi L; Red Cloud HS; Red Cloud, NE; Band; Chrs; CncrtBnd; DrlTm; HonRl; MrchBnd; PepBnd; SchMus; StuCncl; RptrYrbk; Pres4-H; TreasSpnCl; PpCl; Chrldr; University; Med Tech.

KUEBLER, Janice K; Littlefield Public HS; Alanson, MI; 3/35 CmntyWkr; HonRl; SchPl; TchrAde; YthLg; RptrYrbk; RptrSchPpr; LetterBsktbl; Trk; Chrldr; Coll; Math.

KUEBLER, William R; Fargo North HS; Fargo, ND; 18/362 Band; CncrtBnd; DrlTm; HonRl; MrchBnd; NHS; PepBnd; ROTC; Us Air Force Academy; Officer.

KUEBRICH, Ronald J; Jersey Community HS; Jerseyville, IL; 43/277 Chrs; HonRl; FrCl; MthCl; Bsbl; Ftbl; LetterTrk; University; Engineering.

KUECHLER, Michael G; Lomira HS; Lomira, WI; TrsSophCls; TrsJrCls; Band; CncrtBnd; HonRl; MrchBnd; PepBnd; Sdlty; IMSpt; U Of Wi; Accounting.

KUECK, Rebecca L; Smith Cotton Sr HS; Sedalia, MO; 26/350 Chr; ChrhWkr; HonRl; HospAde; Mdrgl; NHS; Yrbk; RptrSchPpr; LatCl; PpCl; Burge School Of Nursing; Nursing Major.

KUEFFLER, Laurie; Medicine Lake HS; Grenora, ND; /34 ALAGirlsSt; JA; SptEdSchPpr; PpCl; Bsktbl; Trk; 4-HAwd; Coll; Professional.

KUEHBORN, Richard M; Saint Bernard HS; Saint Paul, MN; HonRl; RptrYrbk; GerCl; LetterBsbl; LetterBsktbl; LetterFtbl; LetterTrk; CchngActv; Univ Of Minn; Engineering.

KUEHL, Cynthia L; Canton HS; Canton, SD; 3/95 ALAGirlsSt; Band; Chr; ChrhWkr; HonRl; NHS; SchPl; TchrAde; EdSchPpr; FHA; U Of Sd Vermillion; Music Education.

KUEHL, Daniel J; Harry A Burke HS; Omaha, NE; TchrAde; YthFlsp; MthCl; PpCl; Bsktbl; Sd St; Counseling.

KUEHL, Kathleen; Winnebago Luth Acad; West Bend, WI; Band; Chrs; NatlMeritCmnd; PepBnd; PpCl; Univ Wisc.

KUEHL, Kevin; Tipton HS; Tipton, IA; 19/108 Aud/Vis; Chr; Chrs; HonRl; SchAde; SchPl; TchrAde; YthFlsp; Yrbk; Ftbl; Trade; Professional.

KUEHL, Laurie J; Morrison Comm HS; Morrison, IL; 7/150 Chrs; ChrhWkr; CmntyWkr; HonRl; NHS; FTA; PpCl; Trk; MasAwd; PresAwd; College.

KUEHL, Linda L; Kewaunee HS; Kewaunee, WI; SecSrCls; HonRl; NatlFornLg; NHS; NatlThespSoc; SchMus; Yrbk; RptrSchPpr; FHA; Fox Valley Tech College; Therapist.

KUEHL, Timothy L; York Community HS; Elmhurst, IL; Band; ChrhWkr; CncrtBnd; HonRl; MrchBnd; PepBnd; SchMus; Moody Bible Inst; Christian Work.

KUEHL, William D; Central HS; Davenport, IA; 1/650 ALBoysSt; HonRl; NatlMeritSF; PolWkr; StuCncl; TchrAde; SchPpr; SpnCl; SciCl; IMSpt; U Of Ia; Dr.

KUEHLER, Rita K; Jennings HS; Jennings, MO; 12/240 VPFrshCls; VPSophCls; HonRl; NHS; SchMus; StuCncl; GAA; IMSpt; College; Psychology.

KUEHN, Ann M; Spring Valley HS; Spring Valley, WI; 2/63 TrsFrshCls; SecSophCls; ALAGirlsSt; Band; Chr; ChrhWkr; CncrtBnd; HonRl; Mdrgl; MrchBnd; Augsburg College; Engineering.

KUEHN, Ellen M; New Hampton Comm HS; Iowa City, IA; 4/178 HonRl; NHS; SchPpr; LetterTrk; GAA; College; Commercial Art.

KUEHN, Gary L; Crothersville HS; Crothersville, IN; TrsFrshCls; ModUN; SchPl; StuCncl; FFA; Bsktbl;.

KUEHN, James; Belleville East HS; Belleville, IL; NHS; NatlMeritCmnd; FrCl; LetterLetterBsktbl; LetterFtbl; Wrstlng; CchngActv; IMSpt; OptClAwd; Siu Edgwoodsville Coll; Cpa.

KUEHN, Joyce D; Belview HS; Belview, MN; Chrs; ChrhWkr; HospAde; LbryAde; SchPl; StuGov; YthFlsp; RptrSchPpr; Trk; Canby Voc; Dental Asst.

KUEHN, Julie A; Cathedral HS; New Ulm, MN; 7/90 HonRl; JrNHS; NHS; SchPl; PresSdlty; Pres4-H; PpCl; IMSpt; 4-HAwd; College; Mathematics.

KUEHN, Ronald L; Northeast HS; Lincoln, NE; 20/586 ALBoysSt; Band; ChrhWkr; CncrtBnd; HonRl; JrNHS; MrchBnd; PepBnd; Ftbl; University; Professional.

KUEHN, Stephen J; Franklin HS; Livonia, MI; Band; CncrtBnd; HonRl; MrchBnd; NatlMeritCmnd; PepBnd; SctActv; YthFlsp; GerCl; Western Mi Univ; Business Admn.

KUEHN, Susan C; Sevastopol HS; Egg Harbor, WI; ChrhWkr; JrNHS; NHS; TchrAde; Yrbk; Bsktbl; Trk; Chrldr; GAA; IMSpt; BttyCrckrAwd; Business School.

KUEHNAST, Kathy L; Humboldt HS; Humboldt, IA; Band; ChrhWkr; CncrtBnd; MrchBnd; PepBnd; SchMus; SchPl; StuCncl; Chrldr; IMSpt; College; Vocational.

KUEHNEL, Kathi A; Glenbard South HS; Glen Ellyn, IL; CncrtBnd; HonRl; PresNatlFornLg; NHS; NatlMeritCmnd; VPNatlThespSoc; SchPl; SchPpr; Nw Univ; Biology.

KUEKER, Leisa D; Sweet Springs R 7 HS; Sweet Springs, MO; Chrs; ChrhWkr; SecHonRl; Yrbk; FHA; SecSciCl; College; Accountant.

KUELBS, Meryl L; Sleepy Eye Public HS; Sleepy Eye, MN; 13/73 ChrhWkr; HonRl; NHS; YthFlsp; 4-H; FFA; LetterFtbl; LetterGlf; 4-HAwd; College.

KUELLS, Keith A; Washington HS; Germantown, WI; HonRl; NHS; StuCncl; GerCl; LetterTrk; AmLegAwd; Coll; Pro.

KUEMMEL, Mary; Catholic Memorial HS; Brookfield, WI; ChrhWkr; HospAde; NHS; SchAde; SctActv; TchrAde; FSA; MthCl; GAA; PresAwd; College; Engineering.

KUENEKE, Gerene E; Mater Dei HS; Breese, IL; Chrs; ChrhWkr; HospAde; SchPl; Yrbk; 4-H; 4-HAwd; Southern Ill Univ Carbondale; Comm Writer.

KUENEMAN, Richard R; Highland Comm HS; Ainsworth, IA; Band; Chrs; HonRl; Mdrgl; Quill&Scroll; SchMus; SchPl; SctActv; EdYrBk; Central College; Drama.

KUENKE, Donna S; Hillsboro HS; Hillsboro, MO; 3/200 HonRl; HospAde; VPJrNHS; NHS; 4-H; SpnCl; MthCl; PpCl; SciCl; University.

KUENNEN, Denise; Notre Dame HS; Cresco, IA; 10/26 ChrhWkr; CmntyWkr; HonRl; OffAde; StuGov; Teen; RptrYrbk; SciCl; IMSpt; College; Biology Teacher.

KUENNEN, Lisa W; New Trier West HS; Wilmette, IL; 30/700 AFS; Band; CmntyWkr; CncrtBnd; HonRl; NatlMeritCmnd; OffAde; Orch; PepBnd; PolWkr; SchMus; FrCl; SpnCl; Brown Univ; Archaeology.

KUENNING, Bruce H; Wahoo Public HS; Wahoo, NE; ALBoysSt; Band; Chrs; HonRl; StuCncl; YthFlsp; RptrYrbk; RptrSchPpr; Bsbl; CaptBsktbl; CaptFtbl; Trk; CchngActv; University; Professional.

KUENSTING, Donna M; Jefferson City Sr HS; Jefferson City, MO; 61/473 SecSrCls; AFS; Chr; ChrhWkr; CmntyWkr; HonRl; JrNHS; NHS; SchMus; SecStuCncl; TchrAde; SecFTA; VFWAwd; CitAwd; College; Teacher.

KUENZEL, Betty; St Francis Borgia HS; Washington, MO; 1/95 HonRl; JA; LitMag; NatlSciFnd; SchMus; TchrAde; EdSchPpr; SpnCl; Univ Of Mo; Journ.

KUENZEL, Kristine E; Milwaukee Lutheran HS; Milwaukee, WI; AFS; Chr; Chrs; OffAde; YthFlsp; RptrYrbk; RptrSchPpr; Univ Of Wisconsin; Fashion Merchandising.

KUENZI, Heidi; Wauwatosa East HS; Wauwatosa, WI; Chr; HonRl; NHS; OffAde; SchMus; SctActv; YthFlsp; MthCl; PpCl;.

KUENZLI, Linda A; Alton HS; Alton, IL; 59/803 TrsFrshCls; AFS; Band; Chrs; HonRl; NHS; OffAde; Orch; StuCncl; FrCl; Swmmng; CaptChrldr; Carthage College; Social Worker.

KUEPFER, Christine A; Peshtigo HS; Peshtigo, WI; Band; Chr; CncrtBnd; HonRl; MrchBnd; PepBnd; TchrAde; PPFtbl; College; Nursing.

KUEPPERS, Bettina A; Badger HS; Lake Geneva, WI; 40/248 AFS; ChrhWkr; HonRl; NHS; NatlThespSoc; SchPl; RptrYrbk; SchPpr; FBLA; PresGerCl; College; Major Business.

KUEPPERS, Joseph F; St Thomas Academy; St Paul, MN; Chrs; PolWkr; ROTC; RptrYrbk; LetterSocr; LetterSwmmng; Trk; College; Attorney.

KUESTER, Carla L; California R 1 HS; California, MO; 4/100 Band; Chrs; ChrhWkr; HonRl; NHS; TchrAde; RptrYrbk; 4-H; FBLA; MthCl; College; Accountant.

KUESTER, Debra; Belleville Township Hs West; Millstadt, IL; 16/735 ALAGirlsSt; MrchBnd; NHS; Orch; SchMus; YthFlsp; SecGerCl; Belleville Area College; Accountant.

KUESTER, Kathleen A; Preble HS; Green Bay, WI; 4/480 Chr; HonRl; LitMag; NHS; NatlMeritSF; Orch; PolWkr; Quill&Scroll; SctActv; Univ Of Wisc; Chemical Engineering.

KUESTER, Kerry A; Hutchinson HS; Hutchinson, MN; HonRl; YthFlsp; LetterBsktbl; College St Cloud; Lab Tech.

KUESTERSTEFFEN, Patricia J; Yates Center HS; Yates Center, KS; 4/55 Band; Chrs; NHS; NatlMeritSchl; NatlThespSoc; SchMus; SchPl; SecStuCncl; RptrYrbk; EdSchPpr; Independence Jr Coll; Journalism.

KUETTEL, Janelle L; Derham Hall HS; St Paul, MN; Chr; Chrl; Chrs; ChrhWkr; CmntyWkr; SchMus; SchPl; YthFnd; RptrSchPpr; SpnCl; Univ; Liberal Arts.

KUETTEL, Mike R; St Agnes HS; St Paul, MN; ALBoysSt; ChrhWkr; HonRl; HstFrshCls; NatlFornLg; NHS; SctActv; PresStuGov; PresGerCl; LetterTennis; St Thomas Col; Medicine.

KUFAHL, Jay; Onaga HS; Wheaton, KS; VPFrshCls; VPSophCls; SecJrCls; HonRl; SchPl; YthFlsp; FFA; IMSpt; Tech School; Auto Mechanic Or Farming.

KUFFEL, Ann K; St Joseph HS; Kenosha, WI; ChrhWkr; HonRl; LbryAde; NHS; StuCncl; TchrAde; Yrbk; GerCl; College; Library Science.

KUGEL, Karen D; Glen Bard East HS; Lombard, IL; 6/653 HonRl; JrNHS; NHS; Comm Art School; Commercial Art.

KUGEL, Lynne M; Fairbury HS; Fairbury, NE; Chr; Chrs; ChrhWkr; HonRl; NHS; RedCrAde; SchMus; UNYO; Chrldr; 4-HAwd; Southeast Comm Coll.

KUGLER, Cindy M; Gothenburg Public HS; Gothenburg, NE; Band; Chr; CncrtBnd; HonRl; MrchBnd; PepBnd; SchMus; SchPl; TchrAde; College; Physical Therapy.

KUGLER, Gary R; Stet R Xv HS; Norborne, MO; PresSrCls; ALBoysSt; Chr; CncrtBnd; SchPl; StuCncl; FshEdYrbk; FshEdSchPpr; FFA; Bsbl; Bsktbl; College; Vocation.

KUGLER, Kay L; Underwood HS; Fergus Falls, MN; SecSophCls; FFA; FHA; MthCl; Bsktbl; CaptTrk; GAA; IMSpt; PresAwd; Col; Airline Stewardess.

KUHL, Dennis W; Unionville Sebewaing HS; Sebewaing, MI; Chr; Chrs; ChrhWkr; HonRl; YthFlsp; 4-H; LetterBsbl; LetterBsktbl; LetterFtbl; 4-HAwd; Oh Inst Of Tech; Electronics.

KUHL, Kendall D; Randolph Public HS; Randolph, NE; PresSophCls; ChrhWkr; HonRl; SctActv; LetterFtbl; Trk; LetterWrstlng; PresAwd; College.

KUHL, Lorri M; O Gorman HS; Sioux Falls, SD; Band; CmntyWkr; CncrtBnd; VPDrlTm; PepBnd; SchMus; GerCl; MthCl; SciCl; Swmmng; Trk; IMSpt; KiwanAwd; Univ Of So Dakota; Dental Hygiene.

KUHL, Marsha L; Usa HS; Sebewaing, MI; 3/127 HonRl; PresYthFlsp; SchPpr; 4-H; FHA; LatCl; PpCl; LetterTrk; CaptChrldr; GAA; Western Mich Univ; Art.

KUHL, Patrice E; East Central HS; Miles, IA; PresFrshCls; SecSophCls; ALAGirlsSt; Band; Chr; HonRl; MrchBnd; RptrYrbk; 4-H; LetterGAA; AmLegAwd; College.

KUHL, Richard D; Clay City HS; Newton, IL; 7/47 HonRl; PpCl; LetterBsbl; LetterBsktbl; College; Professional.

KUHLE, Kimberly A; Assumption HS; Assumption, IL; SecJrCls; VPChrs; HonRl; VPYthFlsp; 4-H; LetterTrk; Chrldr; GAA; College; Vocation.

KUHLENSCHMIDT, Virgie; Castle HS; Newburgh, IN; /280 Band; ChrhWkr; CncrtBnd; HonRl; MrchBnd; YthFlsp; FTA; PpCl; Socr; Trk; Wabash Jr Valley Coll;child Care.

KUHLERS, Diane; Belmond Community HS; Meservey, IA; 6/69 SecTrsFrshCls; SecTrsJrCls; ChrhWkr; HonRl; NHS; OffAde; Yrbk; FHA; Chrldr; IMSpt; Spencer School Of Bus; Exec Secretary.

KUHLERS, Douglas D; Clear Lake HS; Clear Lake, IA; CncrtBnd; HonRl; PepBnd; SctActv; LetterBsktbl; VFWAwd; Coll; Bus Admin.

KUHLHORST, Neal W; Dekalb HS; Auburn, IN; 12/287 NHS; StuCncl; YthFlsp; Bsktbl; Ftbl; Trk; IMSpt; Hillsdale Coll; Business Administration.

KUHLMAN, Karen K; Central Lyon HS; Rock Rapids, IA; 20/100 Band; Chr; CncrtBnd; PepBnd; RptrYrbk; RptrSchPpr; Pres4-H; SpnCl; SciCl; LetterTrk; 4-HAwd; Iowa State Univ; Veterinarian.

KUHLMAN, Marsha L; Gothenburg HS; Gothenburg, NE; 7/86 Band; Chrs; HonRl; NHS; NatlThespSoc; SchMus; SchPl; TchrAde; 4-H; PpCl; Univ Of Ne At Lincoln.

KUHLMAN, Rhonda G; Ruthton Public HS; Ruthton, MN; Band; ChrhWkr; CmntyWkr; JA; PresYthFlsp; 4-H; PresFHA; Tennis; Trk; 4-HAwd; JAAwd; Alexandria Voc Inst; Fashion Merch.

KUHLMAN, Susan K; Alden Hebron HS; Hebron, IL; 5/45 Band; Chrs; HonRl; NHS; PepBnd; 4-H; LetterTrk; GAA; DanFAwd; DARAwd; Luthern General Hos School Of Nursing.

KUHLMEIER, Paul D; Washington HS; Sioux Falls, SD; SecSophCls; Band; CncrtBnd; HonRl; NatlFornLg; PepBnd; RptrSchPpr; GerCl; LetterTrk; PresAwd; S Dak State U; Chemical Eng.

KUHN, Deborah L; Hinsdale Central HS; Hinsdale, IL; Chr; Chrs; HonRl; OffAde; SchAde; Business School; Secretary.

KUHN, Eileen L; Seneca HS; Seneca, IL; VPSophCls; SecJrCls; Band; CncrtBnd; HonRl; MrchBnd; StuCncl; Twrl; GerCl; Bsktbl; Socr; Chrldr; GAA;.

KUHN, Frederic G; Elkhart Lake Glenbeulah HS; Elkhart Lake, WI; 5/60 VPJrCls; HonRl; NHS; SchPl; StuCncl; 4-H; FFA; Univ; Ag.

KUHN, Gregg A; Waldron HS; Shelbyville, IN; 6/80 PresFrshCls; HonRl; NHS; TreasStuCncl; Yrbk; 4-H; TreasFFA; KeyCl; PpCl; IMSpt; Purdue Univ; Horticulture.

KUHN, Jacqueline D; Wheeling HS; Wheeling, IL; 19/442 HonRl; NHS; NatlMeritSchl; OffAde; RedCrAde; StuGov; FBLA; GerCl; MthCl; Harper Jr College; Accounting.

KUHN, Jeffery; Lake Benton Public HS; Lake Benton, MN; 1/48 HonRl; NHS; StuCncl; YthFlsp; Bsbl; AmLegAwd; BauchLmbAwd; CitAwd; Univ; Pharmacist.

KUHN, Jerrald W; Palmyra HS; Bennet, NE; 2/38 Band; CncrtBnd; HonRl; MrchBnd; NHS; PepBnd; Col; Engineering.

KUHN, Joletta; Flasher Public HS; Flasher, ND; HonRl; LbryAde; SchPl; Yrbk; GerCl; PpCl; College; Professional.

KUHN, Lori; St Marys HS; Burlington, WI; Chr; HonRl; SctActv; StuCncl; Twrl; PpCl; IMSpt; PPFtbl; Univ; Special Ed Teacher.

KUHN, Mark A; Glenbrook North HS; Northbrook, IL; 108/654 ChrhWkr; HonRl; SchPl; StuGov; TchrAde; YthFlsp; PpCl; LetterFtbl; CchngActv; IMSpt; Colroado St U; Geological Engi.

KUHN, Mary J; Victoria HS; Victoria, KS; HonRl; NHS; OffAde; StuCncl; Yrbk; SchPpr; FHA;.

KUHN, Mary L; Notre Dame HS; Quincy, IL; 19/115 Band; Chr; CncrtBnd; HonRl; MrchBnd; NHS; SchMus; RptrSchPpr; College; Home Economics.

KUHN, Paul M; Mason City HS; Mason City, IA; 40/500 HonRl; Bsktbl; U Of Ia; Pre Med.

KUHN, Rebecca A; Turkey Valley HS; Fort Atkinson, IA; Band; Chr; HonRl; NHS; SchMus; Sdlty; StuCncl; FTA; CaptGlf; CaptChrldr; Univ Of Northern Iowa; Special Education.

KUHN, Robert A; Victoria HS; Victoria, KS; CncrtBnd; HonRl; MrchBnd; NHS; PepBnd; Bsktbl; LetterFtbl; Trk; Trade School; Mechanic.

KUHN, Samuel; Waldron HS; Waldron, IN; 21/75 TrsSophCls; PresJrCls; ChrhWkr; HonRl; MrchBnd; StuCncl; 4-H; Trade School; Vocational.

KUHN, Susan D; Oregon HS; Oregon, IL; 26/136 Band; ChrhWkr; CncrtBnd; DrlTm; HonRl; MrchBnd; PepBnd; Quill&Scroll; SchMus; StuCncl; StuGov; Yrbk; RptrSchPpr; FrCl; Business School; Medical Asst.

KUHN, Susan M; Ashwaubenon HS; Green Bay, WI; Band; HonRl; NHS; StuCncl; Bsktbl; Swmmng; LetterTrk; Chrldr; GAA; College.

KUHN, Teri L; Parkway Central Sr HS; Chesterfield, MO; 25/465 NHS; YthFlsp; College; Physical Therapy.

KUHNLEIN, Claudia M; University Liggett HS; Grosse Pointe, MI; TrsSrCls; CmntyWkr; HonRl; NatlMeritSchl; RedCrAde; SchPl; StuCncl; FrCl; LetterBsbl; Bsktbl; Colgate U;psychology.

KUHNS, Karen M; Sidney HS; Sidney, NE; HonRl; Quill&Scroll; TchrAde; RptrYrbk; RptrSchPpr; 4-H; TreasFHA; PpCl; Chrldr; TreasGAA; PPFtbl; University; Vocation.

KUHNS, Sandra L; Archbishop Wm O Brady HS; South St Paul, MN; 34/145 Chr; Chrs; ChrhWkr; HonRl; NatlThespSoc; Quill&Scroll; SchPl; SchPl; FrCl; MthCl; Coll; Acct Or Computers.

KUHNS, Timothy L; Central Christian HS; Wichita, KS; PresSophCls; Chr; Chrl; ChrhWkr; SchPl; PresStuCncl; SpnCl; Bsktbl; Ftbl; Trk; Tabor Coll; Youth Minister.

KUHNY, Martha; Oak Prk & River Forest HS; Oak Park, IL; 38/1050 HonRl; JrNHS; NHS; NatlMeritCmnd; SchMus; StuGov; RptrSchPpr; Rosary College; Journalism.

KUIPER, Jeanne E; Central Wisc Christian HS; Waupun, WI; SecJrCls; Chr; HonRl; LbryAde; RptrYrbk; RptrSchPpr; Pres4-H; PpCl; Chrldr; 4-HAwd; College; Teacher.

KUIPER, William; Pine River HS; Tustin, MI; ChrhWkr; HonRl; NHS; SpnCl; Bsktbl; College; Missionary.

KUIPERS, Kenneth; Platte HS; Platte, SD; 2 43 VPSophCls; Chrs; HonRl; JA; SchPl; University; Agricailture Lectanology.

KUIPERS, Nick D; Geneva HS; Batavia, IL; 79/228 Band; HonRl; YthFlsp; Bsktbl; Ftbl; Trk; IMSpt; College; Professional.

KUIPERS, Ray N; Dakota Christian HS; Platte, SD; 2/35 VPJrCls; Chr; HonRl; ModUN; SchPl; StuCncl; RptrSchPpr; PpCl; Bsktbl; Trk; College; Veterinary Medicine.

KUIVINEN, Mary K; Preble HS; Green Bay, WI; Chr; JrNHS; Orch; PpCl; Swmmng; Trk; U Of Wi Madison; Psycology.

KUJAK, Betty A; Cochrane Fountain City HS; Fountain City, WI; 5/85 Chr; NHS; SchMus; StuCncl; TchrAde; EdYrBk; FHA; Carroll Col Waukesah; Elem Ed.

KUJATH, Jeffery J; Meridian HS; Daykin, NE; Chrs; SchPl; TchrAde; YthFlsp; 4-H; FFA; Bsktbl; LetterFtbl; LetterTrk; 4-HAwd; Trade School; Agriculture.

KUJAWA, Nancy A; Queen Of Peace HS; Chicago, IL; 29/430 HospAde; SpnCl; University Of Illinois; Physical Therapy.

KUKLA, Karen A; Greenfield HS; Greenfield, WI; HonRl; NHS; SchPl; StuCncl; RptrYrbk; LetterSwmmng; Chrldr; GAA; Univ Of Mn; Veterinarian.

KUKOWSKI, Heide; Lewiston HS; Lewiston, MN; Chrs; HonRl; SchPl; TchrAde; 4-H; FTA; Trk; GAA; 4-HAwd; Vocational Tech Inst; Medical Secretary.

KUKOWSKI, Mary; Beach HS; Beach, ND; 12/43 Band; Chrl; Chrs; ChrhWkr; HonRl; HospAde; LbryAde; PolWkr; SchMus; SchPl; FHA; Univ Of No Dak; Music & Art.

KULA, Gary M; Lane Tech HS; Chicago, IL; ChrhWkr; JA; PolWkr; TchrAde; KeyCl; LetterBsbl; College; English Teacher.

KULA, Judith A; Mercy HS; Omaha, NE; Chrs; SchPl; SchPpr; FrCl; U Of Ne.

KULAS, Bernadette A; Moose Lake HS; Sturgeon Lake, MN; 6/72 Chr; ChrhWkr; HonRl; TreasNHS; OffAde; SchAde; TchrAde; 4-H; FTA; FrCl; Navy; Communications.

KULBABA, Terry J; Farmington HS; Farmington, MI; HonRl; Michigan St Univ; Accounting.

KULDANEK, Gregory A; Gobles Public HS; Gobles, MI; 1/68 TrsSrCls; ALBoysSt; JrNHS; NHS; NatlMeritCmnd; SchPl; StuGov; FrCl; MthCl; CaptWrstlng; Albion College; Medicine.

KULESA, Michaelene C; Bishop Noll Institute HS; East Chicago, IN; 72/342 HonRl; AmLegAwd; Clge; Nursing.

KULHANEK, Leslie D; Broken Bow HS; Berwyn, NE; TrsFrshCls; FFA; LetterFtbl; Trk; LetterWrstlng; Trade School; Civil Engineer.

KULINSKI, Christine A; Divine Savior Holy Angels HS; Milwaukee, WI; 37/119 PresAFS; Chrs; HonRl; PresIntrClCncl; NHS; SchMus; SptEdYrbk; Bsbl; CchngActv; GAA; IMSpt; Ripon College; Archeology.

KULKA, Jeffrey S; Osborn HS; Detroit, MI; 12/110 PresFrshCls; HonRl; KeyCl; LetterBsbl; LetterFtbl; Oakland Univ; Building Trade Shop Owner.

KULL, Deborah L; Queen Of Peace HS; Chicago, IL; HonRl; NHS; TchrAde; Bsktbl; Ftbl; GAA; IMSpt; PPFtbl; U Of N Il; Accounting.

KULL, Grace A; Ashland HS; Ashland, WI; 5/225 ALAGirlsSt; HonRl; NHS; StuCncl; SecGerCl; CaptBsktbl; CaptTennis; GAA; IMSpt; VFWAwd; University; Accounting.

KULL, Kathleen A; Bob Jones Academy; Kewanee, IL; Chrs; SchPl; SptEdSchPpr; Bsbl; Bsktbl; Swmmng; Tennis; Trk; CaptChrldr; PresAwd; Bob Jones U; Phy Fitness.

KULL, Kathleen M; St Mary Academy; Monroe, MI; 10/142 Chrl; HonRl; NHS; Monroe County Comm College; Elem Teacher.

KULL, Lynn; Sacred Heart Public HS; Sacred Heart, MN; ChrhWkr; HonRl; FFA; Wrstlng; College.

KULLMAN, David G; Smithville HS; Smithville, MO; Band; CncrtBnd; HonRl; NHS; PepBnd; SchMus; SchPl; StuCncl; TchrAde; Trk; Univ; Writer.

KULM, Patricia A; Leola Public HS; Leola, SD; 3/50 VPJrCls; ALAGirlsSt; Band; Chrs; ChrhWkr; SchMus; SchPl; PresStuCncl; EdSchPpr; LetterTrk; Augustana; Physical Therapy.

KULM, Patricia A; Leola HS; Leola, SD; 3/50 VPJrCls; ALAGirlsSt; Band; HonRl; SchMus; SchPl; StuCncl; RptrSchPpr; EdSchPpr; LetterTrk; Sd State Univ; Physical Therapy.

KULOSA, Faye M; Resurrection HS; Chicago, IL; 11/294 SecJrCls; HonRl; NHS; VPSpnCl; GAA; IMSpt; University; Business.

KUMLE, Mary E; Marquette HS; Marquette, KS; 1/24 ALAGirlsSt; Band; HonRl; MrchBnd;

PepBnd; SchPl; StuCncl; YthFlsp; PpCl; Trk; Business Sch.

KUMLER, Jane A; Gibson City HS; Gibson City, IL; 10/87 PresJrCls; Chrs; HonRl; Quill&Scroll; SchPl; SchPpr; PpCl; LetterGAA; IMSpt; Parkland Col; Dental.

KUMM, Cathy A; De Soto HS; Stoddard, WI; Chr; ChrhWkr; HonRl; HospAde; MrchBnd; StuCncl; EdYrBk; 4-H; Chrldr; GAA; Trade School; Professional.

KUMM, Kathy M; Pittsville HS; Pittsville, WI; HonRl; NHS; FHA; Trade; Cov.

KUMMER, Carol L; Helias HS; Jefferson City, MO; 35/174 HonRl; SchMus; SchPl; StuCncl; RptrYrbk; RptrSchPpr; SchPpr; PpCl; Chrldr; University Of Missouri; Journalism.

KUMMER, Jean A; Parkston HS; Parkston, SD; 14/97 Chr; HonRl; FHA; Dakota State; Medical.

KUMMER, Kay J; Hastngs Senior HS; Hampton, MN; 25/434 ALAGirlsSt; HonRl; MrchBnd; NHS; StuCncl; FrCl; Inver Hills Jr Clg; Business Management.

KUMMER, Mark; Parkston HS; Parkston, SD; 8/97 HonRl; MthCl; SciCl; Univ Of Sd; Physician.

KUMMERER, Karen L; Fulton HS; Fulton, IL; 21/124 AFS; Chrs; HonRl; NatlThespSoc; SchPl; StuCncl; Yrbk; RptrSchPpr; EdSchPpr; 4-H; FrCl; College.

KUMP, Theresa M; Golden Valley HS; Minneapolis, MN; SecJrCls; NatlThespSoc; SchMus; SchPl; StuCncl; RptrYrbk; RptrSchPpr; EdSchPpr; PpCl; OptClAwd; College; Journalism.

KUNA, Frances B; Roseville HS; Roseville, MI; 132/534 CncrtBnd; MrchBnd; NHS; NatlMeritSF; PepBnd; SchPl; TchrAde; LatCl; Mich St U; Pre Med.

KUNCAITIS, Margarete D; St Johns HS; Independence, IA; 5/27 Chr; Chrs; HonRl; LbryAde; SchMus; Yrbk; FrCl; Upper Ia U.

KUNDERT, Julie; Monroe Sr HS; Monroe, WI; 48/189 HonRl; TchrAde; PpCl; Chrldr; GAA; College; Physical Education.

KUNDINGER, Diana R; Arthur Hill HS; Saginaw, MI; Band; Chr; CncrtBnd; HonRl; MrchBnd; College; Music.

KUNERT, Cynthia M; Centennial HS; Beaver Crossing, NE; 8/60 Band; Chr; Chrs; CncrtBnd; MrchBnd; Yrbk; 4-H; LetterBsktbl; Trade School; Mathematical.

KUNGIE, Matthew; St Edward HS; Elgin, IL; 19/134 HonRl; SctActv; LatCl; MthCl; SciCl; Univ Of Iowa; Medicine.

KUNIEJ, Leynette M; Notre Dame Lebanon Sr HS; Lebanon, IN; CmntyWkr; HonRl; PresNHS; SchPl; SctActv; SpnCl; Loyola Univ; Business Admin.

KUNIN, William E; Washburn HS; Minneapolis, MN; LitMag; NatlFornLg; NHS; NatlMeritFnl; VPStuCncl; PresStuGov; Yrbk; RptrSchPpr; SchPpr; Socr; Col; Psychology.

KUNITZER, Brenda S; Carrollton HS; Saginaw, MI; 9/151 HonRl; NHS; TchrAde; LatCl; PpCl; Coll; Physical Therapist.

KUNKEL, August J; Ottawa Twp HS; Ottawa, IL; HonRl; NHS; PolWkr; 4-H; PpCl; Trk; 4-HAwd; Univ Of Il Champaign; Medicine.

KUNKEL, Kathy; Melvindale HS; Allen Park, MI; Band; CncrtBnd; HonRl; JA; MrchBnd; NatlMeritSF; PepBnd; StuCncl; PPFtbl; JAAwd; College At Mercy Univ; Nursing.

KUNKEL, Paula I; Wellcome Memorial HS; Mankato, MN; Chrs; CmntyWkr; SchPpr; FSA; LetterTrk; JCAwd; PresAwd; CitAwd; College; Music & Biology.

KUNKEL, Susan M; Lakeshore HS; Stevensville, MI; 1/240 VPSrCls; ALAGirlsSt; HonRl; NHS; SchPl; StuCncl; RptrSchPpr; CaptBsktbl; Trk; AmLegAwd; Coll; Doctor.

KUNKLER, William J; Carl Sandburg HS; Orland Park, IL; 10/680 HonRl; NatlMeritCmnd; College; Accounting.

KUNNARI, David J; Negaunee HS; Negaunee, MI; 6/144 HonRl; NHS; Sacrstn; Yrbk; SchPpr; SpnCl; CchngActv; N Mi Univ; Art/advertising.

KUNNEMANN, Duanna D; Chase County HS; Imperial, NE; 5/54 Chr; Chrs; ChrhWkr; HonRl; LbryAde; NHS; SchAde; SchMus; TchrAde; YthFlsp; Yrbk; SchPpr; Trk; Northeastern Jr College; Accounting.

KUNNEMANN, Myron K; Chase County HS; Imperial, NE; 3/60 ChrhWkr; HonRl; NHS; StuCncl; StuGov; TchrAde; 4-H; FFA; Bsktbl; Northeastern Jr College; Agriculture.

KUNTZ, Diann M; Napoleon HS; Napoleon, ND; 14/61 Chrs; CncrtBnd; HonRl; NHS; StuCncl; RptrYrbk; PpCl; Bsktbl; GAA; BttyCrckrAwd; Univ; Professional.

KUNTZ, Joyce A; Belfield HS; Belfield, ND; TrsJrCls; TrsSrCls; HonRl; PresFrshCls; TreasNHS; RptrYrbk; RptrSchPpr; EdSchPpr; PresFHA; TreasPpCl; College; Professional.

KUNTZ, Kathy M; St Mark HS; St Louis, MO; 7/39 HonRl; SptEdSchPpr; IMSpt; Clge; Police Officer.

KUNTZ, Sara J; Gridley HS; Gridley, IL; AFS; Band; Chrs; HospAde; SchMus; SchPl; StuCncl; Yrbk; FHA; PpCl; Bloomington Schl; Nursing.

KUNTZ, Terry E; Dodgeland HS; Juneau, WI; AFS; Band; ChrhWkr; CncrtBnd; MrchBnd; PepBnd; SchPl; 4-H; LetterBsktbl; LetterFtbl; Bus School.

KUNTZ, Thomas S; Brookville HS; Brookville, IN; 15/167 Band; HonRl; NHS; PolWkr; SpnCl; OptClAwd; Clge; Accounting.

KUNTZ, Virgil; Wheatland HS; Park, KS; Band; PepBnd; SchPl; FFA; Farmer.

KUNTZELMAN, Lila J; Leaf River HS; Leaf River, IL; Band; Chrs; CncrtBnd; HonRl; SctActv; 4-H; PpCl; LetterChrldr; LetterGAA; 4-HAwd; Trade School; Cosmetology.

KUNZ, Danita; New Salem Hs; New Salem, ND; Chr; HonRl; LbryAde; OffAde; 4-H; FHA; LetterBsktbl; Trk; 4-HAwd;.

KUNZ, Danny L; Attica HS; Attica, KS; VPJrCls; Chr; Chrs; ChrhWkr; HonRl; RptrYrbk; Bsktbl; Ftbl; Tennis; IMSpt; Auto Sch; Mechanic.

KUNZ, Joan C; St Thomas Aquinas HS; Florissant, MO; 5/300 HonRl; JA; NHS; FrCl; LatCl; GAA; JAAwd; CitAwd; Univ; Medicine.

KUNZ, John P; Larkin HS; Elgin, IL; 14/575 ChrhWkr; HonRl; SchMus; SchPl; StuGov; SchPpr; Univ Of Illinois; Architecture.

KUNZ, Nancy; Lakeview HS; Decatur, IL; VPBand; CncrtBnd; NHS; NatlMeritCmnd; SchMus; SchPl; PresStuCncl; FrCl; Trk; LetterChrldr; Univ Of Ill; Communications.

KUNZA, Mary; Bishop Dubourg HS; St Louis, MO; 12/498 HonRl; HospAde; JrNHS; NHS; PolWkr; TchrAde; RptrYrbk; RptrSchPpr; FTA; PpCl; College; Journalism.

KUNZE, Michele; Orono HS; Long Lake, MN; Band; CncrtBnd; HonRl; MrchBnd; NHS; PPFtbl; Jamestown College; Rn.

KUNZEMAN, Joseph D; Meredosia Chambersburg HS; Meredosia, IL; 1/40 PresFrshCls; PresSophCls; PresJrCls; PresSrCls; HonRl; NHS; PresSciCl; LetterTrk; Univ Of Ill; Chemical Engineer.

KUNZMAN, Carol A; St Agnes Academy; Alliance, NE; 3/22 SecJrCls; HonRl; NHS; SchPl; RptrYrbk; FSA; FrCl; PpCl; SciCl; GAA; College; Elementary Education.

KUNZMAN, Mary K; St Agnes Academy; Alliance, NE; 2/22 ALAGirlsSt; HonRl; LbryAde; StuCncl; EdYrBk; FrCl; PpCl; LetterTrk; GAA; DARAwd; College; Legal Or Political Or Scl Sci.

KUPFER, Thomas P; St Joseph HS; Kenosha, WI; 3/140 PresJrCls; ALBoysSt; HonRl; NHS; SchMus; StuGov; PpCl; Bsktbl; LetterFtbl; CchngActv; College Marquette; Medicine.

KUPIEC, Beverly A; Regina HS; Detroit, MI; Chrl; HonRl; NatlMeritSF; SchMus; SecMthCl; College; Accounting.

KUPPER, John D; Nicolet HS; Milwaukee, WI; NHS; NatlMeritFnl; PolWkr; StuCncl; StuGov; RptrSchPpr; SchPpr; Bsktbl; Socr; Univ; Political Science.

KUPRES, George G; De Lasalle Institute; Chicago, IL; 10/258 CmntyWkr; HonRl; NHS; StuGov; TchrAde; SciCl; LetterBsktbl; LetterTennis; LetterTrk; Univ Of Illinois; Pharmacy.

KUPRIS, Kelly E; Hinsdale South HS; Darien, IL; 39/447 Chr; HonRl; SchMus; SchPl; Yrbk; GerCl; LetterTennis; CchngActv; GAA; IMSpt; Univ Of Il; Bio Med Engineering.

KUPSCO, Marianne T; Morton West HS; Berwyn, IL; 29/756 ChrhWkr; HonRl; HospAde; SecNHS; FNA; GAA; College; Nurse.

KURCZEWSKI, Cheryl A; Hillcrest HS; Hazel Crest, IL; 8/431 SecJrCls; HonRl; SchPl; StuCncl; TchrAde; PpCl; SciCl; LetterChrldr; GAA; OptClAwd; Univ; Major Study.

KURDYS, Gary A; Bedford HS; Lambertville, MI; 38/420 CmntyWkr; HonRl; NHS; SctActv; Bsktbl; LetterFtbl; Swmmng; IMSpt; CitAwd; Univ Of Mi; Engineering.

KURGAN, Mary K; Wells Easton HS; Wells, MN; 8/111 Chrs; HonRl; LbryAde; SchMus; LetterBsktbl; LetterTrk; St Cloud State College; Biology.

KURITZA, Alex P; Taft HS; Chicago, IL; 6/790 Band; HonRl; JrNHS; NHS; StuCncl; StuGov; EdYrBk; FrCl; MthCl; University; Medicine.

KURKLIS, David; Brookhaven HS; Kenosha, WI; 6/475 HonRl; NHS; RusCl; RotaryAwd; Gateway Technical Inst; Horticulture.

KURLE, Yolonda J; Bowdle Public HS; Bowdle, SD; 1/29 TrsJrCls; Band; CmntyWkr; HonRl; SchPl; Yrbk; 4-H; LetterBsktbl; LetterTrk; Chrldr; College; Social Worker.

KURNCZ, Marian; St Johns HS; St Johns, MI; TrsFrshCls; SecSophCls; TrsSrCls; HonRl; StuGov; YthFlsp; RptrYrbk; 4-H; KeyCl; 4-HAwd; Lansing Comm Col; Business.

KUROYE, Kathleen Y; Wheaton Warrenville HS; Wheaton, IL; ChrhWkr; CmntyWkr; HonRl; JA; NHS; SctActv; Illinois Inst Tech; Mathematics.

KURRELMEIER, Kathryn S; Interlochen Arts Academy; Paris, IL; Band; Chr; Chrs; ChrhWkr; CncrtBnd; JA; MrchBnd; Orch; YthFlsp; University; Music.

KURSCHNER, Sharon A; Drummond HS; Grandview, WI; TrsSrCls; CmntyWkr; HonRl; NHS; LetterBsbl; LetterBsktbl; Coll; Professional.

KURSHOFF, Susan; Duluth East HS; Duluth, MN; 168/523 CtyCnl; HonRl; OffAde; Teen; YthFlsp; PpCl; Trk; GAA; IMSpt; PPFtbl; Coll; Respiratory Ther.

KURSINSKY, Randall A; Deckerville HS; Palms, MI; ALBoysSt; HonRl; LbryAde; NHS; PolWkr; TchrAde; Univ;.

KURT, Paul; Monticello Comm HS; Monticello, IA; 5/150 PresJrCls; ALBoysSt; Chr; CncrtBnd; HonRl; NHS; SchMus; SciCl; LetterFtbl; Swmmng; Univ Of Iowa; Medical Technology.

KURTENBACH, Daniel H; Greeley Public HS; Greeley, NE; 1/28 PresJrCls; ChrhWkr; CmntyWkr; HonRl; NatlMeritFnl; NatlMeritSF; SchPl; StuCncl; RptrYrbk; TreasYrbk; EdSchPpr; LetterFtbl; IMSpt; Univ Of Nebraska; Astrophysics.

KURTENBACH, Ralph V; Parkston HS; Dimock, SD; 30/96 Chr; Chrs; NatlFornLg; YthFnd; SchPpr; SciCl; LetterTrk; South Dakota State Univ; Radio Broadcasting.

KURTH, Chuck R; Sgt Bluff Luton Comm HS; Sergeant Bluff, IA; HonRl; StuCncl; StuGov; Bsbl; Bsktbl; Ftbl; University; Accounting.

KURTH, Debra L; Lancaster HS; Lancaster, WI; Band; Chrs; ChrhWkr; CncrtBnd; HonRl; Mdrgl; MrchBnd; SchMus; PpCl; IMSpt; College; English.

KURTH, Rhonda; Mt Horeb HS; Cross Plains, WI; AFS; Band; ChrhWkr; NatlFornLg; SchPl; 4-H; FrCl; PpCl; Bsktbl; IMSpt; M A T C; Occupaional Therapy.

KURTYKA, Jayme; Frankfort HS; Frankfort, MI; 1/65 PresSophCls; HonRl; NHS; SchPl; StuCncl; SptEdYrbk; EdSchPpr; CitAwd; Univ; Performing Arts.

KURTYKA, Kathleen A; Frankfort HS; Frankfort, MI; Chrs; Sdlty; TreasNHS; SchPl; TchrAde; PpCl; Bsktbl; Chrldr; GAA; KiwanAwd; Business Or Phys Ed.

KURTZ, Carol; Osage Community HS; Osage, IA; 6/157 HonRl; HospAde; LitMag; RptrSchPpr; SchPpr; PpCl; 4-HAwd; Allen Memorial Hosp; Registered Nurse.

KURTZ, Charles A; St Bede Academy; Peru, IL; Band; HonRl; MrchBnd; NatlMeritSF; PepBnd; SchMus; StuGov; Tennis; College; Physical Science.

KURTZ, Douglas M; St Mary Of Redford HS; Detroit, MI; 15/160 HonRl; Univ Of Detroit; Accountant.

KURTZ, Gregory K; Carroll HS; Ft Wayne, IN; 11/216 VPSophCls; Chr; HonRl; NHS; StuCncl; 4-H; PresFFA; Bsktbl; Ftbl; LionAwd; Purdue Univ; Pre Vet.

KURTZ, Jane H; Lasalle Peru HS; Peru, IL; 16/505 AFS; HonRl; PpCl; St Francis Hosp; X Ray Tech.

KURTZ, Karen L; Albany HS; Avon, MN; Chr; HonRl; SchPl; Yrbk; U Of Minn; English.

KURTZ, Kathleen M; Clay HS; Granger, IN; 17/379 Chrs; HonRl; NHS; NatlMeritSF; Teen; FrCl; PpCl; De Pauw University; Elem Ed.

KURTZ, Lisa; Raymore Peculiar HS; Peculiar, MO; 12/86 Band; CncrtBnd; HonRl; MrchBnd; NHS; PepBnd; SchMus; GerCl; Univ Of Mo; Business.

KURTZ, Paula; Central Noble HS; Albion, IN; Chr; HospAde; SecStuCncl; RptrYrbk; RptrSchPpr; CaptBsktbl; CaptTrk; Chrldr; GAA; IMSpt; College; Phy Ed.

KURTZ, Phyllis D; Mt Pleasant HS; Mt Pleasant, MI; 55/342 Chr; ChrhWkr; CmntyWkr; HonRl; SchMus; YthFlsp; LetterBsktbl; Trk; GAA; 4-HAwd; Hesston College; Social Work.

KURTZ, Stephenie J; Lees Summit HS; Lees Summit, MO; 80/390 HonRl; NatlFornLg; NHS; TchrAde; RptrYrbk; EdSchPpr; SpnCl; PpCl; IMSpt; Univ; Social Worker.

KURTZ, Wendy L; Pekin HS; Pekin, IL; ChrhWkr; DrlTm; HonRl; HospAde; NHS; SctActv; University Of Illinois; Lawyer.

KURVINK, Mary K; Theodore F Riggs HS; Pierre, SD; 8/254 Band; HonRl; HospAde; NatlFornLg; NHS; NatlMeritSF; PepBnd; VPFNA; SecSciCl; Trk; U Of Sd Vermillion; Pre Med.

KURZ, Kathryn D; Oak Park HS; Gladstone, MO; Chr; Chrs; ChrhWkr; HonRl; SchMus; SctActv; PpCl; College; Teacher.

KURZ, Sue C; Central HS; St Joseph, MO; 32#41#71 TchrAde; EdSchPpr; SciCl; Northwestern Univ; Journalism.

KURZAWA, Mark R; Catholic Central HS; Bloomfield Hills, MI; 11/208 Chr; ChrhWkr; HonRl; NHS; NatlMeritCmnd; TchrAde; SchPpr; VPGerCl; CchngActv; IMSpt; Wayne State; Doctor.

KURZAWSKI, Janet L; Centreville HS; Sturgis, MI; 1/55 TrsFrshCls; TrsSrCls; VPBand; Chr; CncrtBnd; HonRl; LbryAde; MrchBnd; NHS; PepBnd; SchMus; LetterTrk; Chrldr; DARAwd; Central Mich Univ; Music.

KURZDORFER, Richard S; Edison HS; East Gary, IN; Band; HonRl; JrNHS; MrchBnd; PepBnd; CaptBsktbl; Wrstlng; Valparaiso Univ; Science.

KURZEJA, Denise A; Hanover Central HS; Dyer, IN; HonRl; TchrAde; 4-H; LetterBsktbl; GAA; IMSpt; 4-HAwd; PresAwd; Trade Sch; Professnl.

KURZEJA, Robert M; Griffith HS; Griffith, IN; 60/316 Band; CncrtBnd; HonRl; MrchBnd; PepBnd; SchMus; In Northwest U; Medicine.

KURZYNOWSKI, Mary; Lumen Christi HS; Jackson, MI; 27/223 HonRl; JrNHS; NHS; Chrldr; West Mich Univ;public Account.

KUSAY, Denise M; Hillcrest HS; Hazel Crest, IL; 4/474 ChrhWkr; HonRl; NatlFornLg; NHS; SctActv; StuCncl; TchrAde; PpCl; Chrldr; Univ Of Ill; Psychology.

KUSCHEL, Gareth E; Ashwaubenon HS; Green Bay, WI; GerCl; Bsktbl; LetterFtbl; LetterTrk; IMSpt; College; Forestry.

KUSCHEL, Kim E; Lutheran West HS; Detroit, MI; Chr; HonRl; NHS; NatlThespSoc; SchMus; SctActv; StuCncl; SchPpr; Trk; PPFtbl; Physical Therapy.

KUSE, Debra; Wabeno HS; Wabeno, WI; Chr; HonRl; LbryAde; SchPl; TchrAde; Yrbk; 4-H; FBLA; PpCl; 4-HAwd; Prof Artist.

KUSEBUSKI, Sandra; Mason Co Central HS; Ludington, MI; HonRl; StuCncl; Yrbk; W Shore Comm Col; Math.

KUSEK, Elizabeth R; Loup City HS; Loup City, NE; 2/63 ALAGirlsSt; Chr; HonRl; VPNHS; PresStuCncl; Sec4-H; VPPpCl; LetterTrk; EldAwd; 4-HAwd; U Of Ne; Professnl.

KUSEK, Rita A; Loup City HS; Loup City, NE; 3/70 VPSophCls; Band; DrlTm; HonRl; NHS; VPStuCncl; EdYrBk; Trk; Chrldr; 4-HAwd; College.

KUSH, John A; Lawrenceburg HS; Lawrenceburg, IN; 14/140 ALBoysSt; HonRl; JrNHS; MrchBnd; NHS; SchPl; StuCncl; Ftbl; Swmmng; AmLegAwd; College.

KUSH, Michael T; Marmion Military Academy; Chicago, IL; 12/69 Chrl; HonRl; ROTC; SctActv; SpnCl; SciCl; Swmmng; CchngActv; Univ Of St Louis; Meteorology.

KUSHNEREIT, James E; Cousino HS; Warren, MI; ChrhWkr; HonRl; TchrAde; MthCl; Bsbl; CchngActv; IMSpt; Mi State Univ; Psycblogist.

KUSHNIR, Nadia; William Fremd HS; Palatine, IL; Chr; Chrs; HonRl; NHS; SchPl; StuGov; SpnCl; SciCl; BttyCrckrAwd; U Of Il; Physician.

KUSIBAB, Gregory G; Brethren HS; Wellston, MI; CmntyWkr; HonRl; NatlMeritFnl; NatlMeritSchl; NatlMeritSF; SctActv; TchrAde; Teen; SchPpr; LetterBsbl; Clge; Major Study.

KUSINSKI, Daniel; St Patrick Hs; Chicago, IL; 50/427 HonRl; JrNHS; StuCncl; Teen; SchPpr; SecSciCl; LetterWrstlng; U Of Illinois; Pharmacy.

KUSINSKI, Paul E; St Patrick HS; Chicago, IL; 130/377 HonRl; StuCncl; Teen; RptrYrbk; Yrbk; RptrSchPpr; PpCl; LetterWrstlng; IMSpt; University; Law Enforcement.

KUSKE, Craig S; West HS; Green Bay, WI; 31/400 HonRl; SctActv; Michigan Technological Univ; Civil Engineer.

KUSKE, David E; Downers Grove South HS; Downers Grove, IL; 83/830 Chr; HonRl; YthFlsp; Illinois State University; Accountant.

KUSKE, Deborah J; Michigan Lutheran Seminary; Saginaw, MI; Band; Chr; Chrs; HonRl; HospAde; Chrldr; IMSpt; Dr Martin Luther College; Teacher.

KUSLER, Janae E; Central HS; Aberdeen, SD; AFS; Chrs; HonRl; Mdrgl; RptrSchPpr; PpCl; Bsktbl; Tennis; Trk; GAA; Clge; Nursing.

KUSLER, Margaret A; Sherburn Public HS; Sherburn, MN; TrsSophCls; AFS; ALAGirlsSt; Band; ChrhWkr; MrchBnd; SchPpr; BttyCrckrAwd; St Cloud Schl Of Nursing; Nurse Anesthetist.

KUSSMAN, Keith D; Lincoln HS; Wisconsin Rapids, WI; PresChrhWkr; HonRl; Bsbl; Bsktbl; Ftbl; Trk; CchngActv; Milwaukee Schl; Engineering.

KUST, Anne E; West HS; Green Bay, WI; 27/390 Chrs; DrlTm; HonRl; PolWkr; Yrbk; PpCl; GAA; College; Professional.

KUSTNER, Catherine M; Waukesha Memorial HS; Brookfield, WI; .

KUSTRZYK, Kathryn S; St Ladislaus HS; Detroit, MI; Chrl; HonRl; VPMthCl; PPFtbl; Univ; Engineering.

KUSYK, Borys I; Wheeling HS; Prospect Heights, IL; 37/442 ChrhWkr; CmntyWkr; HonRl; NHS; PolWkr; Socr; LetterTrk; Loyola Univ; Medicine.

KUTA, Celeste C; La Porte HS; La Porte, IN; HonRl; NHS; 4-H; FrCl; PpCl; Purdue Univesity; Pre Veterinary Med.

KUTA, Marian J; Immaculate Heart Of Mary HS; Westchester, IL; 11/243 Chrl; ChrhWkr; NHS; NatlMeritCmnd; Univ Of Illinois; Pharmacist.

KUTA, Mary Kay; St Francis HS; Humphrey, NE; 2/35 Chrs; HonRl; NHS; RptrSchPpr; PpCl; SciCl; Trk; AmLegAwd; Coll; Radiologic Tech.

KUTCHER, Richard A; Keokuk HS; Koekuk, IA; 14/202 HonRl; NHS; NatlMeritCmnd; SctActv; SpnCl; LetterBsktbl; LetterTennis; IMSpt; Ia St U; Veterinary Medicine.

KUTTENKULER, Daniel J; Tipton HS; Tipton, MO; 2/84 Chrs; ChrhWkr; HonRl; Mdrgl; NHS; PresStuCncl; CaptFtbl; Trk; Univ Of Missouri; Nuclear Engineering.

KUTTENKULER, Kevin J; Tipton HS; Tipton, MO; 16/85 Chrl; HonRl; NHS; SchPl; StuCncl; Ftbl; Electonic; Electronic.

KUTTENKULER, Russell L; Tipton HS; Tipton, MO; 5/85 ALBoysSt; PresCncrtBnd; PresMrchBnd; NHS; PepBnd; StuCncl; Bsbl; LetterBsktbl; CchngActv; Univ Of Mo Columbia; Chemical Engineering.

KUTTERER, Charles E; Columbia HS; Columbia, IL; SctActv; Pres4-H; PresFFA; FrCl; SciCl; U S Navy.

KUUSISTO, Betty; L Anse HS; Covington, MI; HonRl; 4-H; PpCl; Trk; Chrldr; 4-HAwd; VFWAwd; Mich Tech; Nursing.

KUYKENDALL, Jerri L; Findlay HS; Findlay, IL; 2/38 HonRl; Yrbk; 4-H; FHA; PpCl; Illinois State Univ; Art.

KUYKENDALL, Patricia M; Highland HS; Highland, IN; 72/538 CmntyWkr; CncrtBnd; MrchBnd; SctActv; TreasCivCl; SciCl; Indiana Univ; Medical Tech.

KUYPER, Arend P; Corsica Comm Dist 22 HS; Corsica, SD; VPSophCls; Chr; Chrs; HonRl; Mdrgl; SchMus; StuGov; YthFlsp; RptrYrbk; EdYrBk; Bsbl; Bsktbl; CaptFtbl; Trk;.

KUZANEK, Dwight M; Dwight D Eisenhower HS; Blue Island, IL; 2/700 HonRl; NHS; NatlMeritCmnd; StuCncl; StuGov; YthLg; FrCl; MthCl; SciCl; Bsbl; Ftbl; JETSAwd; University Of Illinois; Cpa.

KUZMA, Robert E; Joliet Catholic HS; Joliet, IL; 16/

176 HonRl; NHS; LatCl; Bsktbl; Trk; Univ Of Illinois; Law.

KUZMIC, Kimberly M; Marian HS; South Bend, IN; 4/119 HonRl; NHS; StuCncl; 4-H; Chrldr; IMSpt; Depaul U;medical Field.

KUZYK, Zenon L; Wisconsin Dells HS; Wisconsin Dells, WI; 21/136 HonRl; KeyCl; SpnCl; Glf; Univ Of Wisconsin; Medicine.

KVALE, Tim J; Lemmon HS; Thunder Hawk, SD; 8/75 HonRl; JA; Pres4-H; PresFFA; 4-HAwd; JAAwd; Trade School; Diesel Mechanic.

KVAM, Richard A; North HS; Sioux City, IA; 1/346 Band; Chr; CncrtBnd; HonRl; NatlMeritFnl; Orch; SchMus; SchPl; StuCncl; StuGov; TchrAde; EdSchPpr; Bsbl; LetterGlf; College; Math.

KVISGAARD, Cynthia B; Mother Guerin HS; Chicago, IL; 26/409 Chrs; ChrhWkr; HonRl; LbryAde; De Paul University; Law.

KWAK, Kathleen A; Mt Assisi Acad; Oak Lawn, IL; Chrs;.

KWASNESKI, Jane A; Durand HS; Swartz Creek, MI; OffAde; TchrAde; 4-H; Bsbl; Bsktbl; 4-HAwd; College; Girls Basketball Coach.

KWATERSKI, Keith M; Premontre HS; Oneida, WI; 9/123 CmntyWkr; HonRl; PepBnd; TchrAde; CchngActv; IMSpt; College; Business Law.

KWIECIEN, Mary L; Mona Shores HS; Muskegon, MI; Band; HonRl; MrchBnd; NHS; NatlMeritCmnd; Michigan State; Engineering.

KWIECINSKI, Patrick J; St Patrick HS; Chicago, IL; HonRl; PolWkr; LetterTrk; Univ Of Ill; Business Admin.

KWIRANT, Cynthia E; Big Springs HS; Big Srpings, NE; ALAGirlsSt; Band; ChrhWkr; HonRl; MrchBnd; PepBnd; StuCncl; YthFlsp; FHA; PpCl; Business School; Secretarial Field.

KYES, Kristi M; Farmington East HS; Farmington, IL; 8/140 Chrs; HonRl; LbryAde; PolWkr; SchMus; SchPl; FrCl; Bradley Univ; French.

KYGER, Ronald K; Southmont HS; Crawfordsville, IN; 53/159 HonRl; JrNHS; Trade School; Computer Programming.

KYKER, Wynell M; Polo Comm HS; Polo, IL; 5/104 CmntyWkr; HonRl; NHS; StuCncl; EdSchPpr; LetterTrk; Chrldr; CchngActv; GAA; IMSpt; University; Chiropractics.

KYKO, Mary B; Huron HS; New Boston, MI; 10/170 Band; CncrtBnd; HonRl; HospAde; MrchBnd; PepBnd; Twrl; SpnCl; PpCl; Univ Of Michigan; Medicine.

KYLANDER, Carol B; Tuscola HS; Tuscola, IL; ALAGirlsSt; Chrs; HonRl; 4-H; FTA; LatCl; PpCl; 4-HAwd; Univ Of Il; Special Education.

KYLE, Dallas; Wyandotte HS; Kansas City, KS; 2/428 HonRl; NHS; Bsbl; Technical Training.

KYLE, Lois J; Ballard HS; Kelley, IA; 3/74 Band; HonRl; NHS; NatlThespSoc; SchMus; SchPl; StuCncl; FTA; Swmmng; LetterTrk; Iowa St U; Drafting.

KYLE, Ronna S; Woodruff HS; Peoria, IL; 19/268 Chr; ChrhWkr; HonRl; OffAde; SchMus; FrCl; Il Cent Coll; Secretarial.

KYLE, Shirley A; Beaumont HS; St Louis, MO; Chr; HonRl; JrNHS; NHS; RptrYrbk; FshEdSchPpr; FNA; FTA; GAA; CitAwd; College; Therapist.

KYLER, Diane S; Columbia City Joint HS; Columbia City, IN; 25/290 ChrhWkr; CmntyWkr; OffAde; TchrAde; YthFlsp; Sec4-H; FHA; KeyCl; SpnCl; GAA; DanFAwd; 4-HAwd; Purdue Univ; Home Economics.

KYLLO, Paul E; Goodhue HS; Goodhue, MN; Chr; ChrhWkr; HonRl; MrchBnd; SchPl; YthFlsp; Yrbk; FFA; LetterBsktbl; LetterFtbl;.

L

LAABS, Bruce H; Milwaukee Lutheran HS; West Bend, WI; 22/220 ALBoysSt; Chr; NHS; College; Ministry.

LAABS, Douglas W; West Bend East HS; West Bend, WI; 70/310 Band; ChrhWkr; MrchBnd; Orch; PepBnd; YthFlsp; YthFnd; Ftbl; Glf; U Of Wis Madison; Pharmacy.

LAABS, Janet S; Sentral HS; Lone Rock, IA; Chrs; CncrtBnd; HonRl; MrchBnd; PepBnd; SchMus; TchrAde; RptrYrbk; 4-H; College; Music Education.

LAACKMANN, Kristi L; Jasper HS; Sherman, SD; HonRl; HospAde; SchMus; SchPl; StuCncl; 4-H; FHA; PPFtbl; 4-HAwd; Granite Falls Area Tech; Legal Secretary.

LAAKER, Debra A; Dillsboro Public HS; Dillsboro, IN; 3/31 TrsFrshCls; HstSophCls; TrsJrCls; TrsSrCls; HonRl; NatlMeritCmnd; MrchBnd; RptrYrbk; EdYrBk; RptrSchPpr; Indiana Univ; Dental Assistant.

LAAKER, Julia A; Springfield HS; Springfield, IL; 3/585 AFS; ChrhWkr; HonRl; JrNHS; LbryAde; NHS; YthFlsp; MthCl; Illinois State Univ; Special Educ Teacher.

LAAKER, Susan K; Starmont HS; Masonville, IA; Band; CncrtBnd; HonRl; MrchBnd; NHS; PepBnd; SchPl; YthFlsp; 4-H; FTA; Univ Of Northern Iowa; Art Major.

LAAKMAN, Tamara; Rivet HS; Vincennes, IN; 4/50 ALAGirlsSt; Chrl; HonRl; ModUN; StuCncl; RptrYrbk; FHA; PpCl; College; Psychology.

LAATSCH, Therese M; Everett HS; Lansing, MI; 14/520 ChrhWkr; CmntyWkr; HonRl; JrNHS; NHS; Yrbk; PpCl; PPFtbl; Mi State Univ; Graphic Designer.

LA BARGE, Jane A; Concordia HS; Concordia, KS; Chrs; DrlTm; HonRl; SchPl; StuCncl; Twrl; FTA; Univ Of S California; Physical Education.

LABAT, Maria M; St Louise De Marillac HS; Northbrook, IL; OffAde; Northwestern Univ; Engineering.

LABEDZ, Carol J; Bryan Sr HS; Omaha, NE; HonRl; SctActv; PpCl; Univ Of Nebraska; Interior Design.

LABELLA, Peter M; Ann Arbor Pioneer HS; Ann Arbor, MI; CmntyWkr; HonRl; NatlMeritSF; PolWkr; SchPl; RptrSchPpr; LatCl; Univ Of Michigan; Journalism.

LABELLE, Jeff B; Athens HS; Athens, WI; Aud/Vis; Chr; CncrtBnd; MrchBnd; PepBnd; SchPl; Yrbk; FBLA; Bsbl; Ftbl; Clge; Musical Sound Eng.

LA BELLE, Lenard W; Zion Benton Township HS; Zion, IL; 1/405 VPSrCls; HonRl; NHS; GerCl; Ftbl; Glf; Trk; Univ Of Ill; Doctor.

LABER, Jennifer K; Sykeston Public HS; Sykeston, ND; 7/18 Chr; Chrs; SchPl; RptrSchPpr; 4-H; PpCl; LetterBsktbl; LetterTrk; Chrldr; 4-HAwd; Nd State U; Home Economics.

LABER, Ricky; Port Huron Central HS; Port Huron, MI; 3/220 Band; ChrhWkr; CncrtBnd; HonRl; MrchBnd; NHS; PepBnd; StuCncl; CaptTennis; Trk; Mi Univ; Cpa.

LA BERGE, Rachelle L; South Division HS; Milwaukee, WI; VPSrCls; Chr; Chrs; HonRl; LbryAde; Mdrgl; SchAde; SchPl; StuGov; PpCl; College.

LA BINE, Bonnie B; Ontonagon Area HS; Ontonagon, MI; DrmBgl; HonRl; SecNHS; Teen; VPPpCl; Bsktbl; Trk; TreasGAA; CaptIMSpt; Gagebic Comm Coll; Cosmetology.

LABORDE, Mark S; Maconaquah HS; Grissom Afb, IN; Band; CncrtBnd; HonRl; MrchBnd; PepBnd; College; Professional.

LA BOV, Allen D; Snider HS; Ft Wayne, IN; CmntyWkr; HonRl; CitAwd; In U; Music Composer Or Performer.

LABOY, Socorro; Emerson HS; Gary, IN; 4/223 ALAGirlsSt; HonRl; NHS; OffAde; SchPl; SpnCl; AmLegAwd; LionAwd; Indiana U; Business.

LABOYTEAUX, Kimberly A; Hagerstown Jr Sr HS; Queens Fork, IN; Chr; HonRl; NHS; RptrSchPpr; 4-H; FrCl; SciCl; Univ; Professional.

LABOZZETTA, Lucian M; Creston HS; Grand Rapids, MI; Chr; SctActv; TchrAde; PpCl; LetterFtbl; LetterTrk; LetterWrstlng; LetterCchngActv; IMSpt; Olivet Clg; Teacher.

LABRUYERE, Pamela; Northwest HS; House Springs, MO; ChrhWkr; CmntyWkr; CncrtBnd; HonRl; JA; MrchBnd; SctActv; TchrAde; PpCl; Coll; Physical Ed.

LA BRUZZO, Thomas K; Truman HS; Independence, MO; HonRl; IntrClCncl; SctActv; Ftbl; IMSpt; Univ Of Mo At Columbia; Vet Medicine.

LA BUDA, Denise M; Warren Woods HS; Warren, MI; 6/290 PresSrCls; HonRl; NHS; NatlMeritCmnd; NatlMeritSF; SctActv; TchrAde; Bsbl; CaptBsktbl; LetterTrk; University; Proffesional.

LA BUDA, Gerald; Lincoln Park HS; Lincoln Park, MI; ALBoysSt; Band; CncrtBnd; HonRl; JA; MrchBnd; NHS; Orch; AmLegAwd; JAAwd; College; Pilot.

LABUTTE, Jayne L; Pinckney HS; Lakelan, MI; HonRl; NHS; OffAde; StuCncl; PresAwd; CitAwd; Bus ; Sect.

LABUZ, Joseph; Lane Technical Hs; Chicago, IL; 63/1215 ChrhWkr; HonRl; TchrAde; GerCl; Illinois Inst Of Tech; Civil Eng.

LA CASSE, Deborah A; Garden City Sr HS; Garden Cy, MI; 16/488 ChrhWkr; HonRl; JA; LitMag; NHS; EdYrBk; FrCl; GAA; Kalamazoo College; Chemistry.

LACEY, Kevin P; Heelan HS; Sioux City, IA; 30/245 HonRl; NHS; Ftbl; IMSpt; U Of Sd; Accountant.

LACEY, Terry L; Holton HS; Holton, KS; Chr; Chrl; Chrs; CmntyWkr; HonRl; HospAde; LbryAde; OffAde; RedCrAde; SchAde; SchMus; TchrAde; Yrbk; Chrldr; University; Nurse.

LA CHANCE, Charles P; Saint Laurence HS; Chicago Ridge, IL; 10/426 HonRl; PolWkr; SchPl; StuCncl; LetterTennis; IMSpt; LionAwd; CitAwd; College; Sociology.

LA CHANCE, Roy P; Potosi HS; Potosi, MO; ChrhWkr; HonRl; Ftbl; College.

LA CHAPELLE, Suzanne M; Gabriel Richard HS; Flat Rock, MI; 1/157 HonRl; HospAde; NatlMeritCmnd; SchMus; StuGov; YthFlsp; FNA; VPLatCl; CaptChrldr; Col; Nursing.

LACHER, Joan; Lourdes HS; Rochester, MN; Band; Chr; Chrl; CmntyWkr; CncrtBnd; MrchBnd; PepBnd; SchMus; TchrAde; College; Medical Laboratory Worker.

LACHER, Julie M; St Martys Central HS; Bismarck, ND; Band; CncrtBnd; MrchBnd; PepBnd; SchAde; SctActv; TchrAde; FrCl; PpCl; GAA; Trade School; Cosmatition.

LACHOWICZ, James; Gordon Tech Hs; Chicago, IL; 19/650 HonRl; U; Mathematics.

LACINE, Stephen G; York Comm HS; Elmhurst, IL; 120/961 ChrhWkr; HonRl; NHS; NatlMeritFnl; YthFlsp; LetterBsktbl; Glf; LetterSocr; Eastern Illinois Univ; Computer Science.

LACKAS, Barbara R; Lomira HS; Theresa, WI; SecSophCls; AFS; ALAGirlsSt; HonRl; NHS; FrCl; PpCl; Voc School; Vocation.

LACKAS, Karla; Randolph Public HS; Mclean, NE; Chr; Chrs; DrlTm; HonRl; SchAde; StuCncl; Yrbk; PpCl; Bsbl; Trk; Trade School; Secretary.

LACKENS, Gregory D; Academy Of Holy Angels; Minneapolis, MN; University; Law.

LACKEY, Brian C; Lapel HS; Lapel, IN; Band; Chr; CncrtBnd; HonRl; MrchBnd; NHS; PepBnd; SchMus; Ball St University; Music.

LACKEY, Keith W; St Charles Senior HS; St Charles, MO; ChrhWkr; CmntyWkr; HonRl; SctActv; Ftbl; LetterTrk; IMSpt; OptClAwd; PresAwd; College; Chemist.

LACKOVIC, Patricia A; Ryan HS; Omaha, NE; VPJrCls; NHS; SchPl; TchrAde; RptrYrbk; PpCl; Glf; Tennis; Chrldr; Univ; Physical Therapist.

LACKOWSKI, Joan M; Resurrection HS; Chicago, IL; 3/260 HonRl; NHS; NatlMeritCmnd; FrCl; College; Communictions.

LA COMBE, Lawrence B; Mackinaw City HS; Mackinaw City, MI; 1/22 ALBoysSt; CmntyWkr; HonRl; NHS; TchrAde; PpCl; Bsktbl; Ftbl; Trk; College; Computer Tech.

LA COUNT, Suzanne K; Cedar Lake Academy; Berrien Springs, MI; 3/73 ChrhWkr; CmntyWkr; HonRl; LitMag; NHS; OffAde; TchrAde; EngCl; Andrews Univ; Teacher.

LACOVIC, Laurie A; Lyons Township HS; Brookfield, IL; HonRl; University Of Illinois; Spanish.

LA CROIX, Cheryl A; Valders HS; Newton, WI; AFS; Chrs; HonRl; LbryAde; RptrYrbk; 4-H; SecFHA; PpCl; Trk; GAA; IMSpt; PPFtbl; Northeastern Wisconsin Univ; Dental Hygiene.

LA CROIX, Cheryl A; Bethlehem Academy; Faribault, MN; 55/84 ALBoysSt; ALAGirlsSt; CmntyWkr; HonRl; NHS; OffAde; StuCncl; TchrAde; YthLg; RptrYrbk; Winona State College; History.

LA CROIX, Douglas; Midland HS; Midland, MI; HonRl; SctActv; GerCl; IMSpt; College; Professional.

LACY, Brian W; Lyons Twp HS; Brookfield, IL; Green Tech Inst; Auto Tech Engineer.

LACY, Nathan; Southern Boone County Ri HS; Ashland, MO; VPJrCls; Band; HonRl; MrchBnd; PepBnd; Business School.

LACY, Pamela M; Bishop Ward HS; Kanss City, KS; 45/234 CmntyWkr; HonRl; PolWkr; StuGov; SpnCl; LetterBsktbl; Chrldr; BauchLmbAwd; JCAwd; USJCAwd; University; Professional.

LACY, Susan; Bishop Miege HS; Shawnee Mission, KS; 10/201 Chr; Chrl; Chrs; DrlTm; HonRl; ModUN; RedCrAde; SchMus; TchrAde; PpCl; Kansas State U; Chemical Engineering.

LADAGE, Brent A; Auburn HS; Auburn, IL; 5/59 ChrhWkr; CmntyWkr; HonRl; NHS; StuCncl; YthFlsp; 4-H; FFA; KeyCl; PpCl; LetterBsktbl; DanFAwd; 4-HAwd; College; Carpenter.

LADD, Joanne; Acad Of The Visitation; St Louis, MO; 4/47 SecJrCls; CmntyWkr; NHS; SchPl; GAA; IMSpt;.

LADD, Merry M; Hanover Horton HS; Harton, MI; Band; CncrtBnd; HonRl; LbryAde; MrchBnd; PepBnd; TchrAde; PresFTA; Hillsdale College; Social Work.

LADD, Merry M; Hanover Horton HS; Horton, MI; Band; NHS; PresFTA; Coll; Social Work.

LADE, Darcie; Tarkio HS; Tarkio, MO; SecJrCls; Band; ChrhWkr; HonRl; NHS; RedCrAde; RptrYrbk; FHA; Bsktbl; LetterTrk;.

LADEN, Kathy L; South Pemiscot HS; Steele, MO; 10/67 PresSrCls; Band; ChrhWkr; CncrtBnd; MrchBnd; NHS; OffAde; PepBnd; SctActv; StuCncl; YthFlsp; RptrYrbk; Chrldr; College; Teacher.

LADENBURGER, Jay T; Wheatland HS; Grainfield, KS; VPSrCls; ALBoysSt; Chrs; HonRl; SctActv; StuCncl; LetterBsktbl; LetterFtbl; LetterTrk; Coll; Voc.

LADENBURGER, Mary C; Wheatland HS; Grainfield, KS; SecFrshCls; VPJrCls; HstSrCls; ChrhWkr; HonRl; PolWkr; SchPl; SctActv; StuCncl; Yrbk; FHA; KeyCl; PpCl; Bsktbl; Kansas Univ; Physical Educ.

LADING, Karen S; Stewardson Strasburg HS; Strasburg, IL; 1/50 VPSophCls; TrsJrCls; PresSrCls; Band; Chrs; ChrhWkr; NHS; 4-H; FHA; 4-HAwd; Lake Land Jr College; Accounting.

LADMAN, Brenda J; Crete Sr HS; Crete, NE; 18/98 Chrs; HonRl; NHS; SctActv; PresFTA; PpCl; Bsktbl; CaptGlf; LetterTrk; Chrldr; IMSpt; AmLegAwd; College; Teaching.

LADOMERSKY, Janet; Cabrini HS; Allen Park, MI; 15/167 HonRl; NHS; Trk; GAA; Univ Of Mi; Nursing.

LADOUCEUR, Tom A; Proviso East HS; Forest Park, IL; 49/984 Band; HonRl; Mdrgl; MrchBnd; Orch; PepBnd; SchMus; Swmmng; Tennis; College; Music Education.

LAFAVE, Corinne; Owen Gage HS; Gagetown, MI; Chr; ChrhWkr; HonRl; HospAde; LbryAde; OffAde; SchPl; Yrbk; PpCl; Central Mich Or Ferris State; Health Or Nur.

LA FAVE, Roberta K; Oseoda HS; Oseoda, MI; 51/222 Band; Chr; ChrhWkr; HonRl; NatlThespSoc; SchPl; TchrAde; Chrldr; GAA; IMSpt; College; Secretary.

LAFAYETTE, Jack N; Southern HS; Stronghurst, IL; Band; CncrtBnd; HonRl; StuCncl; FFA; LetterBsktbl; LetterFtbl; LetterGlf; Augustana College.

LAFEVER, Joni L; Burlington Comm HS; Burlington, IA; 32/501 HonRl; NHS; StuCncl; PpCl; LetterTrk; Chrldr; IMSpt; PPFtbl; Ia State Univ; Liberal Arts.

LA FEVRE, Lauryl K; Northville HS; Northville, MI; CmntyWkr; HonRl; NHS; StuGov; TchrAde; SchPpr; 4-H; LetterTrk; GAA; IMSpt; Mi St Univ; Busi Adman.

LAFEW, Valerie S; Jefferson HS; Rockford, IL; College; Secretarial.

LAFFERTY, Carol L; Wheeler HS; Wheeler, IN; Chr; ChrhWkr; CmntyWkr; DrlTm; DrmMjrt; HonRl; TchrAde; Bsktbl; GAA; CitAwd; Work.

LAFFERTY, Mark E; Crestwood HS; Dearborn Heights, MI; JA; SciCl; LetterTennis; IMSpt; Wayne St Univ; Biology.

LAFFEY, Holly F; Bloomington HS; Bloomington, IL; 24/391 ChrhWkr; HonRl; HospAde; LbryAde; StuCncl; TchrAde; YthFlsp; SpnCl; MthCl; PpCl; College; Urban Studies.

LAFFIN, Roberta L; Newman HS; Wausau, WI; 50/130 ChrhWkr; HonRl; SctActv; Yrbk; FHA; SpnCl; CaptBsktbl; LetterTennis; LetterTrk; GAA; Univ Of Wi Lacrosse; Phy Ed.

LAFFOON, Renee; Chicago Vocational HS; Chicago, IL; 50/785 Chr; Chrs; HonRl; Orch; ROTC; SchMus; SchPl; College; Professional.

LAFKY, Karyn J; Logan HS; La Crosse, WI; 26/228 Band; ChrhWkr; HonRl; NHS; SchPl; StuCncl; EdSchPpr; SpnCl; PpCl; KiwanAwd; Univ Wis Lacrosse; Mass Comm.

LA FLEUR, Jill; Madison HS; Madison, NE; 7/60 ChrhWkr; LbryAde; NHS; SchPl; 4-H; SpnCl; PpCl; SciCl; Trk; PresAwd; Univ Of Nebraska; Hist Or Journ.

LA FLEUR, Scott; Menominee Senior HS; Menominee, MI; 15/270 HonRl; NHS; Quill&Scroll; RptrSchPpr; Bsktbl; Tennis; College.

LA FOE, Bruce A; Zionsville Comm HS; Zionsville, IN; 4-H; LetterBsbl; LetterBsktbl; LetterFtbl; College; Coaching.

LA FOLLETTE, Denise M; Onsted Community HS; Onsted, MI; 3/121 ALAGirlsSt; Band; CncrtBnd; HonRl; MrchBnd; NHS; PepBnd; SchPl; FFA; Univ Of Mi; Pre Veteninary.

LA FOND, Nicholas P; St Johns Prep HS; St Joseph, MN; ALBoysSt; HonRl; NHS; RptrYrbk; SchPpr; IMSpt; College; Medicine.

LAFOND, Norman S; Spalding Inst; Pekin, IL; ChrhWkr; HonRl; NHS; NatlMeritCmnd; SctActv; EdSchPpr; LatCl; VoiceDemAwd; Loyola; Physics.

LA FORCE, Annette G; Harper Creek HS; Battle Creek, MI; HonRl; StuGov; YthFlsp; 4-H; PpCl; LetterBsbl; CaptBsktbl; LetterTennis; 4-HAwd; PresAwd; Univ; Professional.

LA FORTUNE, Rosann M; St Benedict HS; Chicago, IL; 3/183 Chrs; SecNHS; FshEdSchPpr; GAA; Univ; Journalism.

LA FRANCE, Sharon; Montgomery HS; Montgomery, MN; 3/94 Chr; HonRl; LbryAde; NatlFornLg; NHS; OffAde; SchPl; Yrbk; RptrSchPpr; PpCl; St Catherines Coll; Law.

LAFUSE, Brad A; Union County HS; Liberty, IN; Aud/Vis; 4-H; Bsbl; LetterTennis; College; Electrical Tech.

LAGACY, Theresa A; Grant Park HS; Momence, IL; 7/57 ChrhWkr; HonRl; NHS; VPStuCncl; StuGov; TreasFHA; SpnCl; PpCl; Bsktbl; Glf; College; X Ray Tech.

LAGEMANN, David P; Elsberry HS; Elsberry, MO; Aud/Vis; Band; Chr; ChrhWkr; CncrtBnd; HonRl; MrchBnd; NHS; PepBnd; FFA; Navy; Nuclear Technician.

LAGEMANN, Debbie K; Alton Sr HS; Godfrey, IL; 87/868 Chrs; HonRl; NHS; OffAde; StuCncl; Yrbk; College; Medicine.

LAGEMANN, John D; Concordia HS; Concordia, KS; HonRl; PolWkr; SctActv; EdSchPpr; SptEdSchPpr; SciCl; Glf; Trk; ChmbCommrsAwd; GodCntryAwd;.

LAGER, Benadict W; Scottsbluff HS; Scottsbluff, NE; HonRl; StuGov; 4-H; PresFFA; LetterFtbl;.

LAGER, Donna J; Caledonia HS; Caledonia, MN; 3/148 TrsJrCls; HonRl; SchPl; StuGov; RptrYrbk; RptrSchPpr; Trk; Luther Col; Biochemistry.

LAGERHAUSEN, Thomas L; Woodstock HS; Woodstock, IL; 25/265 TrsSrCls; ALBoysSt; PresBand; ChrhWkr; CncrtBnd; HonRl; MrchBnd; NHS; Orch; PepBnd; SchMus; LetterBsbl; LetterAugustana College; Accounting.

LAGESON, Allen M; Medford HS; Medford, MN; 6/43 VPSophCls; HonRl; SchPl; LetterFtbl; LetterTrk; LetterWrstlng; Trade School; Auto Mechanics.

LAGESON, Wendy L; Maddock Public HS; Maddock, ND; SecSophCls; PresJrCls; Band; Chrs; HonRl; PepBnd; StuCncl; TchrAde; RptrSchPpr; SchPpr; FHA; PpCl; LetterChrldr; Business Schl; Professional.

LAGORIN, Kathy A; Kenmare Public HS; Kenmare, ND; TrsJrCls; Band; Chrs; ChrhWkr; CncrtBnd; MrchBnd; PepBnd; Souix Falls College.

LA GOW, Kim M; Oswego HS; Oswego, IL; 37/225 Chr; HonRl; NHS; NatlThespSoc; SchMus; StuCncl; PpCl; Chrldr; Jr Coll; Exec Secretary.

LA GRANGE, Rose; Norway HS; Amana, IA; 3/33 Chrs; HonRl; LbryAde; NHS; SchPl; RptrYrbk; Univ Of Northern Ia; Photography.

LA GRECA, Celia A; Marian HS; Omaha, NE; 17/155 Chr; Chrs; DrlTm; HonRl; JA; Mdrgl; NHS; Quill&Scroll; Sdlty; RptrSchPpr; SpnCl; Chrldr; Kearney State College; Public Relations.

LA HAIE, Kathryn L; Alpena HS; Alpena, MI; 95/750 Chr; Chrl; ChrhWkr; Orch; SchMus; YthFlsp; Alpena Comm Clg; Med Tech.

LA HAIE, Linda S; Cheboygan Area Public HS; Cheboygan, MI; HonRl; HospAde; LbryAde; 4-H; FHA; FrCl; PpCl; 4-HAwd; Lake Superior State Clg; Elementary Teachng.

LAHMAN, Barbara A; Franklin Center HS; Franklin Grove, IL; 8/32 Band; Chrs; CncrtBnd; HonRl; NHS; SchMus; PresStuCncl; EdYrBk; 4-H; VPGAA; 4-HAwd; College; Professional.

LAHMAN, Lisa; Broad Ripple HS; Indianapolis, IN; HonRl; LitMag; NHS; NatlMeritCmnd; NatlThespSoc; Quill&Scroll; SchPl; SctActv; TchrAde; Teen; Purdue Univ; Neurosurgeon.

LAHNER, Larry; Harvard Community HS; Harvard, IL; 11/161 ALBoysSt; HonRl; SchPl; Bsktbl; Ftbl; CaptGlf; Trk; Eastern Ill Univ; Business Administration.

LAHR, Cynthia A; Arlington HS; Indianapolis, IN; 2/390 Chr; Mdrgl; NHS; NatlMeritSF; NatlThespSoc; Orch; SchMus; SctActv; Twrl; 4-H; FrCl; Univ; Professional.

LAHR, Patricia D; Monrovia HS; Martinsville, IN; 3/104 HonRl; OffAde; StuCncl; FrCl; LetterFtbl; Indiana Univ; Medicine.

LAHR, Terry L; Gibson City HS; Foosland, IL; 25/89 Band; Chrs; HonRl; Quill&Scroll; StuCncl; EdYrBk; VPFHA; Eastern Ill Univ; Journalism.

LAHTI, Cathy L; Marquette Sr HS; Marquette, MI; 11/388 ChrhWkr; HonRl; HospAde; LbryAde; Northern Michigan University; Elem Educ.

LAHTI, Christine; Calumet HS; Mohawk, MI; 19/161 ChrhWkr; HonRl; HospAde; NHS; Yrbk; FNA; Suomi College; General Business.

LAHTI, David A; Lincoln Way HS; Frankfort, IL; Band; ChrhWkr; HonRl; MrchBnd; University Of Illinois; Engineering.

LAHTI, Kai J; N A Armstrong HS; New Hope, MN; CtyCnl; HonRl; RedCrAde; RptrYrbk; RptrSchPpr; FSA; MthCl; SciCl; LetterTrk; VoiceDemAwd; U Of Mn; Math.

LAHTI, Sandra G; South Shore HS; Herbster, WI; Band; Chr; HonRl; PepBnd; PresStuCncl; RptrYrbk; RptrSchPpr; 4-H; FHA; Bsktbl; Trk; 4-HAwd; Vocational.

LAIB, Dale; Turtle Lake Mercer HS; Mercer, ND; 1/43 ChrhWkr; HonRl; 4-H; FFA; 4-HAwd; MasAwd; Univ Of North Dakota; Accounting.

LAIBLE, Alan J; Lowpoint Washburn HS; Washburn, IL; 9/67 VPJrCls; Band; HonRl; MrchBnd; PepBnd; Yrbk; 4-H; FFA; LetterTrk; CchngActv; Ill Central Clg; Diesel Mech.

LAIBLE, Rick E; St Marys HS; O Neill, NE; 7/30 ALBoysSt; Chr; Chrs; CmntyWkr; SchMus; SchPl; Bsbl; Bsktbl; Ftbl; Trk; Chadron State College; Criminal Justice.

LAIN, Valerie; Hopkins HS; Dorr, MI; 5/80 HonRl; JrNHS; NHS; StuGov; TchrAde; Yrbk; FrCl; Bsktbl; GAA; IMSpt; W Mich Univ; Elementary Educa.

LAINDENBERGER, Debra K; Underwood Public HS; Underwood, ND; 1/23 ALAGirlsSt; Chr; ChrhWkr; HonRl; EdYrBk; RptrSchPpr; PpCl; BttyCrckrAwd; Trinity School Of Nursing; Nursing.

LAING, Lynda L; Harper Creek HS; Battle Creek, MI; Chr; Chrs; ChrhWkr; CmntyWkr; HonRl; LbryAde; NHS; OffAde; Orch; PolWkr; TIMEAwd; 4-HAwd; CitAwd; Univ; Pre Law.

LAING, Robert R; Bonner Springs HS; Bonner Springs, KS; Chr; ChrhWkr; HonRl; OffAde; Bsktbl; LetterFtbl; LetterGlf; Trk; LetterWrstlng; University; Medicine.

LAIR, Russel R; Estherville HS; Estherville, IA; 20/190.

LAIRD, David L; Civic Memorial HS; Cottage Hills, IL; 67/203 CncrtBnd; HonRl; MrchBnd; PepBnd; SchPl; StuCncl; SptEdSchPpr; PpCl; Bsbl; LetterTrk; Southern Il U; Teach Music.

LAIRD, Ginger E; Mitchell HS; Fulton, SD; 1/289 CncrtBnd; HonRl; JrNHS; MrchBnd; NHS; SchMus; 4-H; KeyCl; SpnCl; Trk; Univ; Chemistry.

LAIRD, Mickal E; Du Quoin HS; Du Quoin, IL; 12/150 Chr; Chrs; HonRl; SchMus; SchPl; Univ Of Ill; Law.

LAIRD, Roger D; Waldron HS; Waldron, IN; 29/69 TrsJrCls; Chr; Chrl; Chrs; ChrhWkr; SchMus; SchPl; YthFlsp; KeyCl; Bsbl; Bsktbl; CchngActv; Banking; Vocation.

LAISURE, Mary C; Garber HS; Essexville, MI; 12/183 ChrhWkr; HonRl; RptrYrbk; PpCl; Bsbl; Trk; PPFtbl; Clge; Pro.

LAITI, John R; Hancock Central HS; Hancock, MI; PresJrCls; HonRl; SchPl; TreasStuCncl; LetterBsktbl; LetterFtbl; LetterTrk; Michigan Techn Univ; Engineering.

LAITY, Cathy R; Lakeview HS; St Clair Shores, MI; ChrhWkr; HonRl; LitMag; NHS; FTA; Wayne U; Liberal Arts.

LAKE, James R; Pender Public HS; Pender, NE; 16/53 ALBoysSt; Chr; Chrs; ChrhWkr; PresFrshCls; Mdrgl; Yrbk; LetterBsktbl; LetterFtbl; LetterTrk; Wayne St Coll; Busi.

LAKE, Julie; Pioneer HS; Ann Arbor, MI; 26/646 Band; HonRl; MrchBnd; SchMus; SchPl; YthFlsp; GerCl; Swmmng; GAA; College.

LAKE, Katherine A; Solomon Juneau HS; Milwaukee, WI; 21/218 ChrhWkr; CmntyWkr; HonRl; HospAde; LbryAde; OffAde; SchAde; TchrAde; RptrYrbk; SchPpr; Matc; Professional.

LAKEBRINK, Kathy L; Union HS; Union, MO; 33/172 ChrhWkr; HonRl; SecStuCncl; RptrYrbk; 4-H; SpnCl; PpCl; PPFtbl; 4-HAwd; College; Professional.

LAKEMACHER, Laura L; Mound Westonka HS; Excelsior, MN; AFS; ChrhWkr; HonRl; LitMag; Quill&Scroll; SchPl; StuCncl; SchPpr; GerCl; LetterBsktbl;.

LAKEMAN, Michael C; Beckman HS; Dyersville, IA; SecTrsFrshCls; ALBoysSt; Chr; Chrl; ChrhWkr; SchMus; SchPl; StuCncl; StuGov; EngCl; LetterBsktbl; LetterFtbl; Glf; IMSpt; University; Professional.

LAKEMPER, Daniel A; E Peoria Community HS; E Peoria, IL; 30/446 Orch; StuGov; GerCl; Bradley Univ; Law.

LAKEN, Michael R; Gwinn Area Community HS; Gwinn, MI; Band; CncrtBnd; HonRl; NHS; NatlMeritFnl; NatlMeritSchl; NatlMeritSF; StuCncl; Bsbl; LetterBsktbl; LetterFtbl; LetterTennis; Univ Of Mich; Nuclear Engineer.

LAKER, David; Oakwood Twnship HS; Danville, IL; 30/95 Chr; Chrl; Chrs; HonRl; NatlThespSoc; SchMus; SchPl; SctActv; RptrSchPpr; SchPpr; College;acting.

LAKES, Marsha K; P A Allen HS; Bluffton, IN; 2/129 Chr; HonRl; NHS; NatlThespSoc; Quill&Scroll; SchPl; FshEdYrbk; EdSchPpr; LatCl; PpCl; Purdue Univ; Pre Medicine.

LAKEY, Connie S; Viburnum C 4 HS; Boss, MO; HonRl; SecStuCncl; RptrSchPpr; FHA; SpnCl; Missouri Univ At Rolla; Chemistry.

LAKIAN, Susan E; W Bloomfield HS; W Bloomfield, MI; HonRl; NHS; Tennis; Univ; Design.

LAKNER, Greg A; Bremen HS; Bremen, IN; 11/125 ALBoysSt; ChrhWkr; CmntyWkr; HonRl; NHS; Bsktbl; LetterTrk; University; Professional.

LAKOWSKI, David E; Gordon Tech HS; Chicago, IL; 47/618 HonRl; NHS; PolWkr; StuCncl; LetterFtbl; IMSpt; Loyola Univ; Law.

LAKOWSKI, Judith A; St Scholastica HS; Chicago, IL; Chr; Chrs; JA; PpCl; College; Speech.

LAKSO, Jeanne R; Gilbert HS; Gilbert, MN; 2/80 ALAGirlsSt; Band; Chr; HonRl; NatlMeritFnl; NatlThespSoc; Orch; FHA; BttyCrckrAwd; CitAwd; Univ Of Minnesota; English Major.

LAKSONEN, Ruth L; Ishpeming HS; Ishpeming, MI; Chrs; HonRl; HospAde; NHS; LatCl; AmLegAwd; Nursing Sch; Nursing.

LALEMAN, Helen L; Minneota Public HS; Minneota, MN; Band; CncrtBnd; HonRl; MrchBnd; PepBnd; GerCl; PpCl; Bsktbl; College.

LALL, Al V; Duchesne HS; St Charles, MO; 45/182 Chrs; HonRl; SchMus; University; Professional.

LALLENSACK, Margaret J; Kiel HS; Newton, WI; HonRl; RptrSchPpr; EdSchPpr; SpnCl; Journalism.

LALLIER, Michelle M; Forest Lake HS; Hugo, MN; HonRl; PolWkr; 4-H; FrCl; 4-HAwd; Coll.

LA LONDE, David A; Sault Area HS; Sault Ste Marie, MI; Band; CncrtBnd; DrlTm; HonRl; MrchBnd; Orch; PepBnd; ROTC; SctActv; IMSpt; College; Auto Mech.

LA LONDE, Pamela J; Adelphian Acad; Saginaw, MI; ChrhWkr; CmntyWkr; OffAde; RptrSchPpr; SchPpr; Bsbl; Bsktbl; Ftbl; Coll; Rn.

LAM, Jeanine; Norborne Hs; Norborne, MO; SecSophCls; Band; HonRl; NHS; RptrSchPpr; FHA; Bsbl; Bsktbl; Trk; GAA;.

LAM, Mee Lon; Lindblom Tech; Chicago, IL; 45/722 CmntyWkr; HonRl; NHS; NatlMeritFnl; NatlMeritSchl; NatlMeritSF; RedCrAde; StuCncl; RptrSchPpr; FDA; Coll; Library Sci.

LAMAL, William J; Ashland Sr HS; Ashland, WI; 80/221 CmntyWkr; HonRl; ModUN; GerCl; CaptBsbl; U Of Wyoming; Lawyer.

LAMAN, Patricia E; Maine East HS; Morton Grove, IL; VPFrshCls; TrsSophCls; VPSrCls; Chr; HonRl; JrNHS; Mdrgl; SchMus; Swmmng; Chrldr; Univ Of Il; Nurse.

LA MANTIA, Gary M; William Howard Taft HS; Chicago, IL; 4/859 HonRl; NHS; College; Math.

LAMANTIA, Victor A; St Viator HS; Arlington Heights, IL; 6/314 VPJrCls; VPSrCls; CtyCnl; HonRl; NHS; PolWkr; StuCncl; RptrSchPpr; SpnCl; Northwestern Univ; Journalism.

LA MAR, Brenda; Gideon HS; Gideon, MO; ALAGirlsSt; HonRl; NHS; PepBnd; SchPpr; Chrldr; AmLegAwd; DanFAwd; Freed Hardeman College; Buss Adminstration.

LA MAR, James N; Centerville HS; Richmond, IN; 1/140 ALBoysSt; CncrtBnd; HonRl; MrchBnd; NHS; PepBnd; SctActv; YthFlsp; RptrYrbk; University; Business Admin.

LAMAR, Paul W; Rosiclare HS; Rosiclare, IL; PresFrshCls; PresSophCls; Band; CncrtBnd; HonRl; MrchBnd; StuCncl; Bsbl; Bsktbl; E Illinois University.

LA MARCHE, Patricia A; Van Buren HS; Brazil, IN; 7/71 ALAGirlsSt; DrlTm; HonRl; NHS; FBLA; In State U; Business College.

LA MARR, Margaret K; Cairo HS; Cairo, IL; 3/76 ALAGirlsSt; NHS; OffAde; SctActv; EdSchPpr; PpCl; Bsktbl; Chrldr; GAA; EldAwd; College; Physical Education.

LA MARTINA, Salvatore P; Westport HS; Kansas City, MO; 19/170 AFS; Aud/Vis; ChrhWkr; CmntyWkr; HonRl; NatlFornLg; SchAde; SchPl; TchrAde; Tennis; Univ Of Missouri; Radio Tv Film.

LA MASTERS, Karen K; Eisenhower HS; Decatur, IL; 10/301 ChrhWkr; NHS; SchMus; YthFlsp; FSA; FrCl; IMSpt; Wheaton Christian College.

LAMB, Amalie S; Excelsior Springs West HS; Excelsior Springs, MO; 10/230 ALAGirlsSt; ChrhWkr; HonRl; NHS; YthFlsp; Tennis; Chrldr; GAA; IMSpt; OptClAwd; College.

LAMB, Beverley J; Charlestown HS; Charlestown, IN; Chr; HonRl; Business College; Professional.

LAMB, Dave J; Gillett HS; Pulcifer, WI; PresFrshCls; TchrAde; Bsktbl; Ftbl; Master Plumber.

LAMB, Duane; Southeast HS; Kansas City, MO; JrNHS; RptrYrbk; IMSpt; JAAwd; Col; Computer Tech.

LAMB, Janice E; Elsberry HS; Elsberry, MO; 8/63 Chr; HonRl; LbryAde; NHS; FHA; Chrldr;.

LAMB, Janine E; Brookwood HS; Ontario, WI; VPSophCls; VPJrCls; Chr; Chrs; HonRl; NHS; StuCncl; RptrSchPpr; SpnCl; Trk; Tech Sch; Nurse.

LAMB, Joyce D; Zionsville Comm HS; Zionsville, IN; 3/123 TrsJrCls; ALAGirlsSt; Chr; Chrs; NHS; NatlMeritSF; 4-H; LatCl; LetterTrk; GAA; Purdue; Engr.

LAMB, Kathleen C; Terre Haute North Vigo HS; Terre Haute, IN; 21/642 HonRl; NHS; SctActv; Teen; FrCl; Ind Univ; Business Administration.

LAMB, Kirk D; Red Oak Community HS; Red Oak, IA; 10/122 PresSrCls; HonRl; StuCncl; RptrSchPpr; LetterBsbl; LetterGlf; IMSpt; Univ; Law.

LAMB, L L; Oak Park Academy; Murray, IA; 8/30 Chrl; ChrhWkr; CmntyWkr; HonRl; StuCncl; EdYrBk; Nurses Aide ;nurse.

LAMB, Lowell; Tuscola Hs; Tuscola, IL; 7/147 ChrhWkr; HonRl; SctActv; StuGov; UNYO; YthFlsp; SchPpr; FFA; LetterFtbl; Trk; U Of Illinois; Engineering.

LAMB, Mark B; Pecatonica HS; Winnebago, IL; 9/80 Band; CncrtBnd; HonRl; JrNHS; MrchBnd; NHS; PepBnd; SchMus; YthFlsp; 4-H; FrCl; LetterFtbl; 4-HAwd; Univ Of Ill; Veterinary Medicine.

LAMB, Mark E; Franklin Public HS; Franklin, NE; Band; Chrs; CncrtBnd; HonRl; SchAde; SchPl; TchrAde; 4-H; Bsktbl; Trk; Univ; Pro Engineer.

LAMB, Mary E; St Pius X HS; Kansas City, MO; Band; HonRl; HospAde; JrNHS; NHS; OffAde; SchMus; SchPl; SctActv; St Marys At Leavenworth; Mathematics.

LAMB, Mel G; Wapahani HS; Selma, IN; VPSrCls; HonRl; NHS; PolWkr; Pres4-H; 4-HAwd; Ball State U; Funeral Director.

LAMB, Sandra K; Oak Park Academy; Murray, IA; TrsSophCls; Chrs; HonRl; College; Nursing.

LAMB, Shirley; Murray Community HS; Murray, IA; 5/30 SecSophCls; Band; ChrhWkr; HonRl; HospAde; MrchBnd; SchPl; FHA; FNA; PpCl; College; Psychelogy.

LAMBDIN, Diana L; Shawnee HS; Wolf Lake, IL; HstFrshCls; Band; HonRl; YthFlsp; PresFBLA; PresFHA; PresFrCl; PpCl; Chrldr; PresGAA; College.

LAMBERS, Beth D; Holland Christian HS; Holland, MI; 51/261 Band; ChrhWkr; CncrtBnd; MrchBnd; NatlMeritSchl; PepBnd; Hope College; Elementary Educ.

LAMBERSON, Brent A; Oakland Christian HS; Pontiac, MI; Aud/Vis; Chr; ChrhWkr; LbryAde; SctActv; StuCncl; Teen; YthFlsp; John Wesley College; Law Enforcement.

LAMBERSON, Kimberly S; Ladywood St Agnes HS; Indianapolis, IN; VPSophCls; Chr; ChrhWkr; HospAde; JA; Mdrgl; SchMus; StuCncl; Chrldr; Indiana Univ; Pre Med.

LAMBERSON, Linda D; Kimball County HS; Kimball, NE; Band; Chr; CncrtBnd; HonRl; MrchBnd; PepBnd; SchAde; SchMus; TchrAde; SpnCl; PpCl; University Of Nebraska; Nursing.

LAMBERT, Ada A; Franklin Public HS; Riverton, NE; 5/32 VPSophCls; SecBand; Chr; Chrs; ChrhWkr; SecCncrtBnd; HonRl; SecMrchBnd; SecPepBnd; AmLegAwd; DARAwd; 4-HAwd; LionAwd; Kearney State College.

LAMBERT, Alan E; Artesian HS; Fulton, SD; 13/25 Band; Chrs; HonRl; MrchBnd; SchPl; RptrYrbk; 4-H; LetterFtbl; LetterTrk; 4-HAwd; College; Animal Science.

LAMBERT, Cynthia A; Northrop HS; Fort Wayne, IN; 2/564 HonRl; NatlFornLg; NatlMeritFnl; SchAde; SchPpr; PpCl; Ft Wayne Univ; Political Science.

LAMBERT, Debbie L; Pleasant Ridge HS; Leavenworth, KS; TrsFrshCls; Chrs; ChrhWkr; NatlThespSoc; PolWkr; SchPl; StuCncl; 4-H; KeyCl; SpnCl; Univ; Professional.

LAMBERT, James J; Baraga HS; Baraga, MI; HonRl; NHS; Bsktbl; Ftbl; Trk; College; Veterinarian.

LAMBERT, Jayne M; Brookfield HS; Brookfield, MO; 1/130 PresJrCls; CncrtBnd; HonRl; MrchBnd; NHS; StuCncl; LetterBsktbl; LetterTennis; LetterTrk; IMSpt; Ne Mo St Univ; Law Enforcement.

LAMBERT, Kimberly E; George Washington HS; Chicago, IL; 25/528 HonRl; JrNHS; NatlMeritCmnd; SchAde; StuCncl; TchrAde; VPSpnCl; Western Ill Univ; Writing.

LAMBERT, Ronda S; U D #237 HS; Smith Center, KS; HonRl; SchPl; TchrAde; YthFlsp; 4-H; FHA; College; Home Ec.

LAMBERT, Stephen G; Marian HS; Mishawaka, IN; 8/118 HonRl; NHS; Bsbl; Univ; Engineering.

LAMBERT, Susan K; Alwood HS; Woodhull, IL; 2/75 PresSrCls; Band; Chrs; CncrtBnd; HonRl; LbryAde; MrchBnd; NHS; SchMus; SchPl; GAA; Univ Of Ill; Business Admin.

LAMBERT, Susan L; Lyons Township HS; La Grange, IL; HonRl; SctActv; Bsktbl; Trk; Ripon College; Professional.

LAMBERT, Susan M; Saunemin Community HS; Odell, IL; 4/21 PresJrCls; Band; NHS; StuCncl; TchrAde; Yrbk; SchPpr; 4-H; FFA; 4-HAwd; Ill St U; Elem Education.

LAMBERT, Ted C; Sterling Heights HS; Troy, MI; ChrhWkr; HonRl; NatlMeritSF; Univ; English.

LAMBERT, Vinita; Pattonsburg R 2 HS; Pattonsburg, MO; SecSrCls; Band; Chrs; ChrhWkr; HonRl; SchPl; Yrbk; PpCl; BttyCrckrAwd; College; Nursing.

LAMBERTY, Thomas P; Willowbrook HS; Villa Park, IL; 105/814 Chr; HonRl; ModUN; NHS; SctActv; TchrAde; YthFlsp; College Of Dupage; Physical Or-political Sci.

LAMBETH, Nancy; Jasper R 5 HS; Jasper, MO; Band; ChrhWkr; CncrtBnd; HonRl; MrchBnd; SchPl; YthFlsp; FTA; GAA; College; Music.

LAMBORNE, Brett A; Highland HS; Alexandria, IN; 93/243 JA; TchrAde; Ftbl; College; Jet Engine Mechanic.

LAMBRECHT, Rose M; Perry Lecompton HS; Grantville, KS; VPFrshCls; HonRl; NHS; NatlThespSoc; SchPl; Yrbk; SchPpr; LetterBsktbl; LetterTrk; CchngActv;.

LAMBRIGHT, Richard W; Litchfield HS; Litchfield, MI; 1/51 ChrhWkr; HonRl; SchMus; TchrAde; Albion College; Medicine.

LAMER, Cheryl A; Elk Horn Kimballton HS; Walnut, IA; Chrs; Mdrgl; SchMus; SchPl; EdYrBk; 4-H; Patricia Stevens College; Secretary.

LAMERMAYER, Elizabeth M; Regina Dominican HS; Morton Grove, IL; 15/208 Chr; HonRl; LitMag; Mdrgl; Orch; SchMus; SchPl; SchPpr; Marquette University; Physical Therapy.

LAMERS, Sharon A; Appleton West HS; Appleton, WI; HonRl; HospAde; Yrbk; FNA; MthCl; PpCl; SciCl; CitAwd; College; Professional.

LAMEY, Nancy J; Gibson Southern HS; Haubstadt, IN; TrsFrshCls; PresSophCls; SecJrCls; 4-H; FHA; PpCl; SciCl; Trk; IMSpt; PPFtbl; Coll; Elem Ed.

LAMKIN, Angi C; Lincoln HS; Willis, MI; 12/185 Chr; HonRl; HospAde; MrchBnd; NatlFornLg; NHS; NatlThespSoc; SchAde; SchMus; Twrl; Swmmng; Chrldr; 4-HAwd; Univ Of Florida; Music Therapy.

LAMKIN, Edward; Petoskey HS; Petoskey, MI; StuCncl; 4-H; Ftbl; Wrstlng; 4-HAwd; Mi Tech Univ; Civil Engineer.

LAMM, Darla J; Mt Pleasant HS; Mt Pleasant, IA; Chr; ChrhWkr; CmntyWkr; HonRl; HospAde; TchrAde; RptrSchPpr; SchPpr; CivCl; MasAwd; North Central Bible Coll; Missions.

LAMM, Kathleen A; Ogallala HS; Ogallala, NE; Band; HonRl; NHS; OffAde; TchrAde; YthFlsp; PpCl; Chrldr; Univ Of Nebraska; Medicine.

LAMM, Pamela J; Norris HS; Hickman, NE; StuGov; TchrAde; RptrYrbk; Pres4-H; SecTrk; Univ; Journalism.

LAMMERS, Daniel R; Notre Dame HS; Burlington, IA; 12/69 ALBoysSt; SchMus; ModUN; RptrSchPpr; EdSchPpr; LetterBsbl; LetterBsktbl; LetterFtbl; LetterGlf; LetterTrk; Ia State Univ Ames.

LAMMERS, Germaine M; Chatard HS; Indianapolis, IN; 3/192 HonRl; NHS; Indiana U.

LAMMERS, Tracy L; Everly Community HS; Everly, IA; 4/34 ChrhWkr; CmntyWkr; HonRl; StuCncl; YthFlsp; College.

LAMMERS, Vivian L; Sandoval Community HS; Sandoval, IL; Band; ChrhWkr; HonRl; MrchBnd; StuCncl; TchrAde; YthFlsp; EdSchPpr; Pres4-H; SecFTA; Kaskaskia College; School Teacher.

LAMMERT, Gregory J; Duchesne HS; St Charles, MO; Chrs; HonRl; PresNHS; PolWkr; SchMus; StuCncl; KeyCl; IMSpt; U Of Missouri; Engineer.

LAMMERT, Paul; Duchesne HS; St Charles, MO; HonRl; NHS; SchMus; StuCncl; LatCl; Univ; Engineering.

LAMON, Margaret J; Floyd Central HS; Lanesville, IN; 91/300 Chr; ChrhWkr; CmntyWkr; HonRl; SctActv; TchrAde; PPFtbl; GodCntryAwd; OptClAwd; Univ Of Evansville; Medical Doctor.

LA MONTAGNE, Rochelle A; Marian HS; Southfield, MI; TrsFrshCls; CmntyWkr; HonRl; PolWkr; StuCncl; StuGov; University; Professional.

LAMORE, Karen A; River Valley HS; New Buffalo, MI; 13/160 HonRl; NHS; SctActv; TchrAde; Twrl; RptrYrbk; Yrbk; Univ Of Notre Dame; Architecture.

LAMOTT, Donna K; Blackford HS; Upland, IN; HstSophCls; HonRl; YthFlsp; FHA; SpnCl; PpCl; GAA; College.

LA MOTTE, Dorothy J; Houghton HS; Houghton, MI; SecJrCls; Band; Chrs; ChrhWkr; CncrtBnd; HonRl; MrchBnd; NatlFornLg; Orch; Yrbk; Michigan Tech Univ; Elem Education.

LAMOUR, Anita M; St Mary Academy; Monroe, MI; 5/144 Chrl; ChrhWkr; CmntyWkr; HonRl; Monroe County Comm College; Lawyer.

LAMP, Lisa A; Monett HS; Monett, MO; Band; CncrtBnd; MrchBnd; PepBnd; SctActv; FHA; FTA; SpnCl; GAA; Clg; Entertainment Field.

LAMPE, Cindy; St Anthonys HS; St Louis, MO; 4/72 Chrs; HonRl; NHS; SchMus; StuCncl; LatCl; PresAwd; College; Professional Architecture.

LAMPE, Donna M; Bishop Du Bourg HS; Saint Louis, MO; HonRl; LbryAde; LatCl; AmLegAwd; Col; Pro.

LAMPE, Mary M; Campbell HS; Campbell, MO; 2/66 ChrhWkr; HonRl; NHS; SchPl; 4-H; FHA; Bsbl; Bsktbl; College; Journalism.

LAMPE, Roger L; Falls City HS; Falls City, NE; ChrhWkr; CmntyWkr; SctActv; StuGov; LetterFtbl; LetterTrk; Trade School.

LAMPEN, Mary C; Mater Dei HS; Carlyle, IL; 3/198 SecJrCls; TrsSrCls; ChrhWkr; HonRl; LbryAde; NHS; GerCl; Univ Of Illinois; Medicine.

LAMPHIEAR, Julie; Central City Sr HS; Central City, NE; Band; Chrs; CncrtBnd; HonRl; MrchBnd; PepBnd; Univ.

LAMPHIER, Mark A; Rochester HS; Rochester, MI; Band; ChrhWkr; HonRl; MrchBnd; NHS; PepBnd; StuGov; MthCl; CaptBsktbl; CaptTennis; Mich State U; Mech Eng.

LAMPINEN, Karen L; Chassell HS; Chassell, MI; 6/24 SecJrCls; TrsSrCls; HonRl; HospAde; LbryAde; SchPl; TchrAde; Yrbk; 4-H; Suomi College; Computer Operator.

LAMPING, Laura A; Lumen Christi HS; Jackson, MI; 6/222 TrsSrCls; HonRl; LitMag; NHS; SctActv; StuCncl; RptrSchPpr; LatCl; PpCl; IMSpt; Gen Mtrs Inst; Indus Engr.

LAMPING, William P; Wilmington HS; Wilmington, IL; 2/129 HonRl; NHS; TchrAde; Purdue Univ; Pharmacy.

LAMPKE, David N; Northrop HS; Fort Wayne, IN; 40/643 Aud/Vis; HonRl; SciCl; Indiana Univ; Medicine.

LAMPRECHT, Janis L; Gretna HS; Gretna, NE; 10/79 SecFrshCls; SecSophCls; SecJrCls; SecSrCls; Chrs; HonRl; LbryAde; Mdrgl; NHS; SchMus; Midland Lutheran Clge; Elem Teacher.

LAMPRECHT, Kathy; Bloomfield HS; Wausa, NE; 9/43 SecSophCls; ALAGirlsSt; Band; ChrhWkr; OffAde; StuCncl; PpCl; PresAwd; CitAwd; Northeast Ne Tech College; Secretarial.

LAMPROS, George L; Hinsdale Central HS; Oak Brook, IL; ALBoysSt; HonRl; IntrClCncl; JrNHS; NHS; StuCncl; KeyCl; LetterSocr; Univ Of Illinois; Lawyer.

LAMPSON, Debora S; Nashua HS; Nashua, IA; 8/86 Chr; Chrl; Chrs; HonRl; Mdrgl; FHA; College; Business Education.

LAMPTON, Brent M; Hardin Central HS; Hardin, MO; TrsSophCls; HonRl; StuCncl; Yrbk; Washington Univ; Lawyer.

LANAHAN, Donald J; Triad HS; Troy, IL; 8/185 HonRl; ModUN; NHS; StuGov; FTA; CaptFtbl; CaptTennis; CchngActv; IMSpt; Augustana Coll; Medicine.

LANCASTER, David E; Nevada HS; Nevada, MO; 20/178 Chrs; ChrhWkr; NatlThespSoc; SchMus; SchPl; SctActv; LatCl; SpnCl; SciCl; LetterFtbl; Coll; Natural Sciences.

LANCASTER, Janice C; Comstock Park HS; Comstock Park, MI; Aud/Vis; ChrhWkr; HonRl; HospAde; LbryAde; NHS; YthFlsp; RptrSchPpr; OptClAwd; College; Library Science.

LANCE, Dennis W; Manchester HS; N Manchester, IN; HonRl; SpnCl; MthCl; SciCl; IMSpt; Indiana Univ; Mathematics.

LANCE, Melody A; Waltonville Comm Unit #1 HS; Waltonville, IL; VPFrshCls; SecSophCls; TrsJrCls; ChrhWkr; CmntyWkr; HonRl; FHA; PpCl; GAA; Business School; Vocation.

LANCELLE, Paul; Denmark HS; Green Bay, WI; TrsSophCls; Band; HonRl; PepBnd; StuCncl; FFA; PpCl; Bsbl; Bsktbl; Ftbl; College; Professional Agriculture.

LANCTOT, Chet D; Wylie E Groves HS; Southfield, MI; Aud/Vis; CmntyWkr; HonRl; JrNHS; NHS; NatlMeritCmnd; NatlMeritSF; NatlThespSoc; SchAde; SchMus; SchPl; University; Medicine.

LANCTOT, Jay J; Hancock Central HS; Hancock, MI; 15/92 SecFrshCls; PresSrCls; HonRl; NatlMeritCmnd; StuCncl; StuGov; Ftbl; Mi State Univ; Business Administration.

LAND, Julie M; Litchfield Sr HS; Litchfield, IL; 39/149 ChrhWkr; DrlTm; HonRl; OffAde; YthFlsp; Yrbk; 4-H; FrCl; GAA;.

LAND, Ramona K; Valley Of Caledonia HS; Caledonia, MO; SecJrCls; Band; Chrs; ChrhWkr; HonRl; SchPl; RptrSchPpr; FHA; SpnCl;.

LANDBECK, Kathleen; Lyons Township Hs; Western Springs, IL; Marquette U;physical Therapy.

LANDEM, Carol M; Taft HS; Chicago, IL; 29/816 Band; CncrtBnd; NHS; NatlMeritCmnd; Univ Of Ill; Pharmacologist.

LANDERS, Craig C; Scottsbluff Sr HS; Scottsbluff, NE; 32/275 VPFrshCls; HonRl; NHS; StuGov; KeyCl; Bsktbl; LetterFtbl; LetterTrk; GodCntryAwd; Hasting College; Business Admin.

LANDERS, Karen A; Mendota HS; Earlville, IL; Chr; HonRl; OffAde; TchrAde; 4-H; College; Business.

LANDERS, Marcia; Hartville HS; Hartville, MO; HonRl; SchPl; FFA; FHA; MthCl; PpCl; SciCl; Southwest Missouri St Univ; Psychology.

LANDERS, Sharlene K; Tri County Comm HS; What Cheer, IA; 5/29 Chrs; CncrtBnd; HonRl; Mdrgl; PepBnd; SchMus; SchPl; StuCncl; Twrl; Yrbk; Pres4-H; Trade School; Business.

LANDERS, Steven W; Risco HS; Lilbourn, MO; SchMus; 4-H; FFA; LetterBsktbl; LetterTrk; 4-HAwd; Trade School; Agriculture.

LANDES, Richard; Maple Valley HS; Vermontville, MI; HonRl; SchPl; RptrSchPpr; SchPpr; Bus School; Professional.

LANDESS, Cynthia M; Wenona HS; Wenona, IL; Band; Chrs; HonRl; SchMus; TchrAde; Yrbk; Pres4-H; TreasFTA; FrCl; GerCl; Univ; Law.

LANDGRAF, Anne M; St Marys HS; Early, IA; Chrs; CmntyWkr; HonRl; HospAde; RedCrAde; SchMus; Twrl; SchPpr; 4-H; 4-HAwd; Mt Mercy Col; Nursing.

LANDGRAF, Nancy A; Althoff Cath HS; Fairview Hts, IL; 17/334 Chrs; ChrhWkr; HonRl; NHS; SchMus; SchPl; StuCncl; SchPpr; LatCl; Univ Of Ill; Nurse.

LANDGRAF, Victoria M; Boylan Central Catholic HS; Rockford, IL; 14/360 HonRl; HospAde; JA; LitMag; St Anthony Hospital; Medicine.

LANDGREN, David G; Evanston Twp HS; Evanston, IL; Chr; Chrs; ChrhWkr; CncrtBnd; HonRl; SchMus; YthFlsp; Glf; LetterSocr; IMSpt; Michigan St Univ; Physics.

LANDIS, Diane R; William Henry Harrison HS; West Lafayette, IN; 1/273 ALAGirlsSt; Band; CncrtBnd; HonRl; MrchBnd; NatlFornLg; SecNHS; Twrl; MthCl; SciCl; AmLegAwd; OptClAwd; CitAwd; De Pauw Univ; Psychology.

LANDIS, James H; Byron HS; Oregon, IL; Band; HonRl; NHS; StuCncl; LetterBsbl; LetterBsktbl; LetterFtbl; LetterTrk; AmLegAwd; Ripon College; Business.

LANDIS, Pamela J; Goshen HS; Goshen, IN; 11/252 Band; Chr; NHS; NatlThespSoc; SchMus; StuCncl; RptrYrbk; SpnCl; PpCl; Trk; Purdue University; Business Administration.

LANDIS, Tina F; Bullock Creek HS; Midland, MI; CncrtBnd; HonRl; MrchBnd; NHS; SecStuCncl; Treas4-H; Mi State U; Criminology.

LANDMAN, Kathy J; Larimore Public HS; Northwood, ND; 3/70 ALAGirlsSt; Band; Chr; CncrtBnd; HonRl; MrchBnd; PepBnd; SchPl; RptrYrbk; FBLA; Univ Of N Dakota; Business.

LANDOLL, Joyce M; Pierce City HS; Pierce City, MO; ChrhWkr; HonRl; HospAde; OffAde; FHA; PpCl; LetterBsktbl; Trk; Chrldr; GAA; College; Liberal Arts.

LANDON, Barry R; Beresford HS; Beresford, SD; 23/67 TrsJrCls; Band; HonRl; MrchBnd; PepBnd; SchMus; StuGov; 4-H; Bsktbl; LetterTrk; Augustano Coll; Pre Med.

LANDON, Diane M; Lancaster HS; Lancaster, WI; AFS; Chrs; ChrhWkr; CncrtBnd; HonRl; MrchBnd; NHS; PepBnd; YthFlsp; PpCl; Coll.

LANDON, John A; Carrington Sr HS; Carrington, ND; PresJrCls; PresSrCls; ALBoysSt; Band; Chr; HonRl; MrchBnd; PepBnd; 4-H; Ftbl; Wrstlng; 4-HAwd; College.

LANDRETH, Linda L; Anna Jonesboro Comm HS; Jonesboro, IL; Band; ChrhWkr; CncrtBnd; HonRl; MrchBnd; PepBnd; SctActv; StuCncl; RptrYrbk; 4-H; FTA; Eastern Ill Univ; Music Teacher.

LANDRUM, Debra; Chicago Vocational HS; Chicago, IL; 20/977 Chr; Chrl; Chrs; ChrhWkr; HonRl; SchMus; TchrAde; Yrbk; SchPpr; FTA; College; Teach Music.

LANDRUM, Jane E; Huntington North HS; Warren, IN; TchrAde; Bsktbl; Trk; GAA; 4-HAwd; Bus Sch; Vocation.

LANDRY, Donald A; East HS; Kansas City, MO; HonRl; ROTC; SctActv; TchrAde; Mo Western State; Biology.

LANDRY, Margaret E; Florence HS; Florence, WI; VPSophCls; Band; CmntyWkr; HonRl; NHS; RedCrAde; RptrSchPpr; 4-H; PpCl; Chrldr; GAA; College; Medical Field.

LANDRY, Timothy W; H L Richards HS; Chicago Ridge, IL; ChrhWkr; HonRl; OffAde; Orch; Sacrstn; Tennis; Northern Ill Univ; Medicine.

LANDSKRON, Donald J; Menasha HS; Menasha, WI; HonRl; NHS; OffAde; Trades School; Vocation.

LANDSTROM, David E; Mitchell HS; Mitchell, NE; Band; MrchBnd; PepBnd; LetterFtbl; College; Engr & Auto Mechanics.

LANDSTRUM, Mike J; No Mahaska HS; Barnes City, IA; 17/46 TrsSophCls; Band; CncrtBnd; HonRl; MrchBnd; PepBnd; StuCncl; 4-H; LetterBsbl; LetterBsktbl; LetterFtbl; Trk; 4-HAwd; College; Accounting.

LANDUYT, Gail M; Walnut Grove Public HS; Walnut Grove, MN; Chrs; HonRl; OffAde; SchPl; StuGov; RptrSchPpr; SchPpr; EngCl; Tennis; IMSpt; Bus Coll; Accounting.

LANDVIK, Erik J; Nashwauk Keewatin HS; Nashwauk, MN; PresJrCls; PresSrCls; Chr; HonRl; SchPl; StuCncl; StuGov; FrCl; LetterFtbl; LetterSwmmng; St Olaf College; Lawyer.

LANE, Bonnie M; Lincolnway HS; Manhattan, IL; 39/498 PresJrCls; Chrs; HonRl; NHS; StuCncl; StuGov; TchrAde; Trk; Illinois St Univ; Physical Therapy.

LANE, Burel H; St Thomas Public HS; St Thomas, ND; 6/23 PresFrshCls; PresSophCls; Band; Chrs; ChrhWkr; StuCncl; SchPpr; 4-H; FFA; LetterBsktbl; College; Market Management.

LANE, David A; Rensselaer Central HS; Rensselaer, IN; ChrhWkr; HonRl; JrNHS; NHS; StuCncl; FrCl; PpCl; Bsktbl; CaptTrk; IMSpt; KiwanAwd; In State U; State Police.

LANE, Donna S; Wainwright HS; Lafayette, IN; 9/105 SecNatlFornLg; SecNHS; TreasStuCncl; Pres4-H; PresFHA; BttyCrckrAwd; DARAwd; 4-HAwd; Purdue Univ; Pub Relaions In Foods & Nutrit.

LANE, Dwight D; South Page HS; Blanchard, IA; Band; CmntyWkr; CncrtBnd; HonRl; MrchBnd; SchMus; StuCncl; LetterBsktbl; LetterFtbl; LetterTrk; College At Nwmsu; Disc Jockey Program Drctr.

LANE, Ellen R; Arkansas City HS; Arkansas City, KS; PresAFS; Band; HonRl; NatlMeritCmnd; SchMus; SchPl; FrCl; PpCl; SciCl; DARAwd; Texas Christian Univ; Pre Med.

LANE, Gary G; Bon Homme 96# HS; Tabor, SD; ALBoysSt; HonRl; SchMus; SchPl; Coll; Prof.

LANE, Gregory L; Wm Chrisman HS; Independence, MO; PresChr; HonRl; Mdrgl; SchMus; SctActv; StuCncl; LetterFtbl; LetterWrstlng; College.

LANE, Laura L; Wheaton North HS; Wheaton, IL; 4/320 Band; NatlMeritCmnd; NatlMeritSF; Orch; SchMus; StuCncl; StuGov; YthFlsp; FrCl; LetterTrk; Carleton College; Music.

LANE, Laurie E; Williamston HS; Williamston, MI; 11/147 SecSophCls; HstJrCls; Band; HonRl; JrNHS; NatlMeritSF; PresStuCncl; RptrYrbk; Trk; Chrldr; Michigan State Univ; Fashion Designer.

LANE, Madalyn A; William Howard Taft HS; Chicago, IL; 21/790 HonRl; JrNHS; NHS; GAA; Roosevelt Univ; Interior Design.

LANE, Mari K; Kimball County HS; Kimball, NE; 3/100 ALAGirlsSt; HonRl; PresNHS; SchAde; Yrbk; SchPpr; FHA; PpCl; Glf; VoiceDemAwd; U ;law.

LANE, Mary E; Waukesha North HS; Waukesha, WI; 1/325 Band; HonRl; MrchBnd; NHS; NatlMeritSF; PepBnd; RptrSchPpr; EdSchPpr; VPFrCl; PresMthCl; Purdue Univ; Mathematics.

LANE, Michael S; Valley Community HS; Wadena, IA; 15/50 PresSophCls; Band; Chrs; CncrtBnd; MrchBnd; PepBnd; SctActv; Area 1 Vocational Tech Schl; Carpentry.

LANE, Pamela A; Stanley Boyd HS; Stanley, WI; 11/113 Band; CncrtBnd; MrchBnd; NatlMeritCmnd; PepBnd; SchPl; FHA; SciCl; U W Eau Claire; Music Teacher.

LANE, Pamela J; Manson Community HS; Manson, IA; 9/86 Band; CncrtBnd; HonRl; PresLbryAde; MrchBnd; SecNHS; Orch; Yrbk; RptrSchPpr; LetterBsktbl; U Of Northern Ia; Library Sce.

LANE, Pamela M; Glenwood HS; Springfield, IL; TrsFrshCls; Chr; HonRl; HospAde; SchMus; SctActv; FHA; FNA; FTA; FrCl; Univ Southern Il; Architecture.

LANE, Sandra E; Evanston Township HS; Evanston, IL; 36/1500 HonRl; NHS; NatlMeritFnl; NatlMeritCmnd; NatlMeritSF; Quill&Scroll; SctActv; TchrAde; LetterBsktbl; College; Biology.

LANE, Sherry M; Marian Catholic HS; Chicago Heights, IL; HospAde; NHS; Univ Of Illinois; Veterinarian.

LANE, Tony L; Westmer HS; New Boston, IL; 16/78 Chrs; HonRl; FTA; SpnCl; SciCl; Bsbl; LetterBsktbl; LetterFtbl; LetterTrk; College.

LANFEAR, Janine M; St Ladislaus HS; Detroit, MI; 2/112 PresSrCls; HonRl; StuCncl; MthCl; CitAwd; U Of Mich; Pre Med.

LANG, Anton J; Brother Rice HS; Oak Lawn, IL; 1/431 Aud/Vis; HonRl; LbryAde; NHS; NatlMeritSF; Quill&Scroll; SptEdSchPpr; Univ Of Illinois; Biology.

LANG, Barbara L; Newman HS; Wausau, WI; 1/145 Band; ChrhWkr; CncrtBnd; HonRl; LbryAde; SchMus; RptrYrbk; EdSchPpr; FBLA; FHA; University; Music.

LANG, Brenda K; Sandy Creek HS; Edgar, NE; 1/52 Band; HonRl; NHS; SchMus; SchPl; LetterTrk; IMSpt; BauchLmbAwd; DanFAwd; PresAwd; U Of Ne Med Cntr; Nursing.

LANG, Christine M; Lake Central HS; Madison, SD; 7/161 ALAGirlsSt; Band; Chr; Chrs; CncrtBnd; DrlTm; HonRl; MrchBnd; NHS; PepBnd; SchPl; LetterBsktbl; Tennis; Trk; Mt Marty College; Nursing.

LANG, Dennis; Crown Point HS; Crown Point, IN; Purdue Univ; Material Engineering.

LANG, Diane M; Naperville Central HS; Naperville, IL; 8/889 AFS; HonRl; JrNHS; NHS; YthFlsp; FrCl; GerCl; SpnCl; Ill Benedictine College; Interpreter.

LANG, Donna M; South Lake HS; St Clair Shores, MI; HonRl; NHS; NatlMeritSchl; SchMus; Swmmng; Chrldr; Center For Creative Studies; Art.

LANG, Kathryn M; Rocori HS; Richmond, MN; 10/175 CmntyWkr; HonRl; NHS; SchMus; SchPl; Bsbl; Col; Grade Teache.

LANG, Kent; Rockwell City Comm HS; Rockwell City, IA; 11/70 HonRl; NHS; StuCncl; 4-H; FFA; Univ Of Nebr; Ag Business.

LANG, Lana K; Franklin HS; Franklin, NE; 3/32 TrsSrCls; Chrs; CmntyWkr; HonRl; NHS; SchAde; StuCncl; TchrAde; Yrbk; SchPpr; Col; Professional Nursing.

LANG, Laurie J; Stoughton HS; Stoughton, WI; AFS; Band; CncrtBnd; MrchBnd; PepBnd; TchrAde; GerCl; PpCl; Bsktbl; PPFtbl; Suomi Clge.

LANG, Lori; Johannesburg Lewiston HS; Lewiston, MI; ChrhWkr; HonRl; OffAde; SchPl; TchrAde; RptrYrbk; SchPpr; GAA; Mi St Univ; Journalism.

LANG, Mary; Brookville HS; Brookville, IN; VPSophCls; ChrhWkr; HonRl; OffAde; RptrYrbk; GAA; Business; Vocation.

LANG, Michelle A; Worthington Sr HS; Worthington, MN; Band; Chr; Chrl; Chrs; ChrhWkr; CncrtBnd; HonRl; MrchBnd; Orch; PepBnd; Bsktbl; Tennis; IMSpt; Worthington Jr College; Law.

LANG, Nancy; Elgin HS; Elgin, IL; Chr; Orch; StuGov; PpCl; GAA; IMSpt; Elgin Comm Coll; Secretarial Work.

LANG, Renee S; Stratford HS; Stratford, WI; HonRl; Yrbk; FHA; Trk; GAA; PPFtbl; Hospital; Unit Clerk.

LANG, Rodney A; Custer HS; Custer, SD; 27/58 VPFrshCls; Chr; Chrs; ChrhWkr; Mdrgl; SchPl; StuCncl; YthFlsp; 4-H; GerCl; CaptFtbl; CaptWrstlng; 4-HAwd; CitAwd; College; Social Work.

LANG, Susan F; New Ulm Sr HS; Lafayette, MN; 1/250 TrsJrCls; TrsSrCls; HonRl; SchPl; TchrAde; RptrYrbk; RptrSchPpr; EdSchPpr; Tennis; Mankato State College.

LANG, Timothy D; Thomas More Prep HS; Hays, KS; HonRl; LetterTrk; College; Engineering.

LANG, Virginia M; Grundy Center Comm HS; Grundy Center, IA; 27/81 Band; CncrtBnd; HonRl; MrchBnd; PepBnd; 4-H; FBLA; SpnCl; PpCl; PPFtbl; College; Nursing.

LANGAN, Ann L; West Holt HS; Atkinson, NE; Chrs; DrlTm; SchPl; StuGov; RptrYrbk; VP4-H; SecFHA; PpCl; LetterKearney College.

LANGAN, Barbara; Quincy Notre Dame HS; Quincy, IL; HonRl; Nursing School.

LANGDALEN, Elvina E; Wildrose Public HS; Wildrose, ND; 1/14 SecTrsSophCls; ALAGirlsSt; Band; Chrs; ChrhWkr; CncrtBnd; HonRl; PepBnd; SchPl; Yrbk; SchPpr; PpCl; St Paul Bible College.

LANGE, David A; Seward HS; Seward, NE; Chr; HonRl; Mdrgl; SchMus; SchPl; PresStuCncl; Yrbk; IMSpt; Coll; Engin.

LANGE, Denise K; Regina HS; Detroit, MI; HonRl; SctActv; LetterBsbl; LetterBsktbl; LetterTrk; GAA; Vocation.

LANGE, Kurt R; Cordon Tech HS; Chicago, IL; SctActv; RptrYrbk; RptrSchPpr; SptEdSchPpr; GerCl; Bsbl; VFWAwd; Marquette U; Journilism.

LANGE, Larry W; Benton HS; Benton, WI; 9/34 ChrhWkr; HonRl; SchPl; RptrYrbk; SptEdYrbk; RptrSchPpr; SptEdSchPpr; LetterBsbl; LetterBsktbl; LetterFtbl; Trk; University; Business.

LANGE, Linda L; Notre Dame HS; Cudahy, WI; VPSophCls; VPJrCls; VPSrCls; HonRl; HospAde; SchMus; SchPl; VPStuCncl; VPPpCl; Tennis; Chrldr; Univ Of Wisconsin; Occup Therapy.

LANGE, Mary E; Lasalle Peru Twp HS; Lasalle, IL; 179/575 CmntyWkr; HonRl; HospAde; LitMag; OffAde; PolWkr; 4-H; SpnCl; VoiceDemAwd; Ill Valley Comm Coll; Nurse.

LANGE, Melody J; Auburndale HS; Auburndale, WI; SecSophCls; PresJrCls; Band; CncrtBnd; HonRl; MrchBnd; PepBnd; EdYrBk; Coll; Professional.

LANGE, Paula; Huntington North HS; Huntington, IN; Chr; ChrhWkr; HonRl; Quill&Scroll; SchPl; RptrSchPpr; EdSchPpr; SchPpr; Univ; Journalism.

LANGE, Richard R; Forest Park HS; Ferdinand, IN; Band; ChrhWkr; CncrtBnd; HonRl; MrchBnd; PepBnd; Pres4-H; LetterTrk; 4-HAwd; Coll; Agricultural Work.

LANGE, Roberta A; St Marys Acad; So Milwaukee, WI; 25/150 AFS; HonRl; HospAde; NHS; PolWkr; TchrAde; SchPpr; LatCl; CchngActv; VFWAwd; Uw Milwaukee; Rn.

LANGE, Susan; Winnebago HS; Rockford, IL; Band; CncrtBnd; DrmBgl; JA; MrchBnd; RptrSchPpr; GerCl; GAA;.

LANGE, Thomas W; Peoria HS; Peoria, IL; Tennis; LetterTrk; IMSpt; Western Illinois Univ; Business.

LANGE, Vernon J; Seymour HS; Black Creek, WI; 29/182 HonRl; Trk; CaptIMSpt; University; Science.

LANGEHAUG, Gregory; Crookston Central HS; Crookston, MN; RptrSchPpr; LetterBsbl; CaptBsktbl; LetterFtbl; LetterTrk; Univ Of North Dakota; Police Administration.

LANGEL, Janet M; West Delaware HS; Manchester, IA; 38/204 LetterBand; CncrtBnd; DrmMjrt; HonRl; MrchBnd; PepBnd; SchPl; SecPpCl; Bsktbl; PPFtbl;.

LANGEL, John M; Grosse Pointe South HS; Grosse Pointe Park, MI; ChrhWkr; CmntyWkr; PolWkr; StuCncl; YthFlsp; Bsbl; Ftbl; CaptIMSpt; EldAwd; College; Lawyer.

LANGEL, Scott P; Gehlen HS; Le Mars, IA; TrsFrshCls; TrsSophCls; ChrhWkr; HonRl; StuCncl; 4-H; Bsktbl; Ftbl; College.

LANGEN, Beth A; Marquette HS; Alton, IL; 21/110 SecSrCls; Chrs; HonRl; SchPl; StuCncl; RptrSchPpr; IMSpt;.

LANGEN, David W; Kennedy Public HS; Kennedy, MN; 7/27 VPSophCls; HonRl; LetterBsbl; LetterBsktbl; LetterFtbl; North Dakota State; Professional.

LANGENBAHN, Mary L; Culver Community HS; Monterey, IN; 10/102 Chr; ChrhWkr; HonRl; NHS; Sacrstn; FTA; FrCl; Valparaiso U.

LANGENBERG, Keith A; Platt Valley Academy; Hoskins, NE; Band; Chr; HonRl; JrNHS; NHS; TchrAde; Yrbk; CaptBsktbl; College; Optometrist.

LANGENDONK, David P; Niles Sr HS; Niles, MI; 56/384 Band; CncrtBnd; HonRl; MrchBnd; PepBnd; RptrSchPpr; Western Michigan Univ; Electrical Engineer.

LANGENECKER, Walter F; Slinger Community HS; Allenton, WI; HonRl; PresFFA; U W Madison; Vocation.

LANGENFELD, Cheryl; Dunlap Community HS; Dunlap, IA; 2/56 Chr; Chrs; ChrhWkr; HonRl; NHS; FHA; FTA; PpCl; Iowa Cetr Com Col; Fashion Merch.

LANGENFELD, Forrest A; Centralia HS; Irvington, IL; HonRl; RptrYrbk; SchPpr; Bsktbl; College; Communications.

LANGENFELD, Jeanne; Harlan Community HS; Earling, IA; 4/260 ChrhWkr; HonRl; NHS; IMSpt; ChmbCommrsAwd; DanFAwd; College; Art Major.

LANGENFELD, Marita A; Marian Catholic HS; Chicago Hts, IL; 99/335 Chr; Chrs; ChrhWkr; CmntyWkr; DrlTm; HonRl; SchMus; SchPl; Sdlty; College; Music.

LANGENFELD, Phillip M; Harlan Community HS; Harlan, IA; ALBoysSt; ChrhWkr; HonRl; SctActv; LetterFtbl; LetterTrk; LetterWrstlng; AmLegAwd; GodCntryAwd; JAAwd; Univ; Major Acctg.

LANGENWALTER, Brian; Manson Community HS; Manson, IA; Chr; Chrs; StuCncl; Yrbk; SpnCl; Ft Dodge Comm Coll; Construction.

LANGENWALTER, Mary J; Wahpeton HS; Fairmount, ND; 2/137 PresAFS; HonRl; JrNHS; NHS; RptrYrbk; RptrSchPpr; 4-H; GerCl; Chrl; CAP; Nd State Sch Of Sci; Med Technology.

LANGER, Joan P; Guide Rock HS; Guide Rock, NE; 6/12 ALAGirlsSt; LetterBand; LetterChrs; ChrhWkr; DrmMjrt; TchrAde; Pres4-H; LetterPpCl; Bsktbl; LetterTrk; LetterChrldr; Josephs College Of Beauty; Beautician.

LANGER, John B; Northfield Mt Hermon HS; Aberdeen, SD; Band; CncrtBnd; HonRl; NatlMeritFnl; YthLg; SchPpr; LetterBsbl; LetterFtbl; Coll; Philosophy.

LANGER, Kathy A; Ness City HS; Ness City, KS; 10/57 ALAGirlsSt; Band; HonRl; NHS; FHA; PpCl; LetterBsktbl; LetterTrk; AmLegAwd; PresAwd; College.

LANGER, Lawrence P; Northfield Sr HS; Northfield, MN; 58/255 Aud/Vis; LitMag; SptEdYrbk; SptEdSchPpr; LetterFtbl; LetterTrk; LetterWrstlng; CchngActv; IMSpt; 4-HAwd; College; Teacher Farmer Writer.

LANGER, Murray J; Owatonna HS; Owatonna, MN; ChrhWkr; HonRl; JA; SctActv; LetterTrk; Wrstlng; Trade; Pof Draftman.

LANGERUD, Gary H; Ulen Hitterdal HS; Minnesota, MN; 6/43 NHS; StuCncl; LetterBsktbl; CaptUniv; Farm.

LANGFORD, James B; Lanphier HS; Springfield, IL; Chr; StuCncl; TchrAde; KeyCl; PresSpnCl;.

LANGFORD, Jon A; Beaumont HS; St Louis, MO; PresSrCls; Aud/Vis; ChrhWkr; CncrtBnd; NHS; StuCncl; EdYrBk; EdSchPpr; Ftbl; Wrstlng; Univ; Medicine.

LANGFORD, Mark; Fairmont Sr HS; Fairmont, MN; Chr; Orch; SchMus; YthFlsp; RptrYrbk; Ftbl; Wrstlng; CchngActv; IMSpt; Mankato State College; Major In Sociology.

LANGHAM, Rex W; Greenville HS; Keyesport, IL; 14/183 ChrhWkr; NHS; NatlMeritCmnd; 4-H; FrCl; PpCl; LetterFtbl; LetterTrk; Greenville College.

LANGHEIM, Teresa M; Alleman HS; Rock Island, IL; 65/225 Chr; HonRl; HospAde; FrCl; PpCl; Us Navy; Nursing.

LANGHENRY, Barbara A; Sacred Heart Of Mary HS; Arlington Hgts, IL; 4/134 CmntyWkr; HonRl; NHS; SchMus; SchPl; SecStuGov; EdSchPpr; Bsktbl; GAA; Coll; Law.

LANGHOLZ, Mary J; Primghar Community HS; Primghar, IA; Band; Chr; ChrhWkr; CmntyWkr; HonRl; NHS; StuCncl; RptrSchPpr; Ftbl; LetterTrk; College; Professional.

LANGLAIS, Jean M; Hastings HS; Hastings, MN; HonRl; IMSpt; Coll; Peace Corps.

LANGLAND, Joanne M; Harold L Richards HS; Oak Lawn, IL; 126/977 Band; CncrtBnd; HonRl; OffAde; Eastern Illinois Univ; Music.

LANGLAND, Rebecca A; North Senior HS; Eau Claire, WI; 28/350 Chr; Chrs; ChrhWkr; HonRl; NatlFornLg; Orch; SchPl; PresFHA; PpCl; Voc Sch; Accounting.

LANGLE, Lee Ann M; Emery HS; Emery, SD; Chrs; ChrhWkr; DrlTm; SchMus; SchPl; YthFlsp; 4-H; FHA; Trk; PresAwd; Working.

LANGLEE, Susan A; Crystal Lake Comm HS; Crystal Lake, IL; 30/490 HonRl; NHS; StuCncl; StuGov; SpnCl; Univ Of Ill; Architecture.

LANGLEY, Jean; Sheyenne Public HS; Sheyenne, ND; Band; Chrs; CncrtBnd; HonRl; MrchBnd; SchPl; RptrSchPpr; FHA; PpCl; Bsktbl; College.

LANGLEY, Ronald E; Redford HS; Detroit, MI; Band; CncrtBnd; MrchBnd; Orch; PepBnd; Michigan St; Math.

LANGLIE, Shelly; Lincoln Sr HS; Thief River Falls, MN; 16/239 PresSrCls; Band; Chr; HonRl; SchMus; StuCncl; Trk; GAA; College; Science.

LANGLOIS, Sandra J; Grant Park HS; Grant Park, IL; TrsJrCls; HonRl; NHS; SchPpr; SpnCl; PpCl; Trk; CaptChrldr; GAA; College; Airlines.

LANGNESS, Terry L; Minot Magic City Campus HS; Minot, ND; College; Elec Engineer.

LANGOWSKI, Patricia; Mt Iron HS; Mt. Iron, MN; PresSophCls; HonRl; StuCncl; RptrYrbk; RptrSchPpr; FHA; FNA; PpCl; Trk; Chrldr; Jr. College; Accounting.

LANGRECK, Donna M; Notre Dame HS; Cresco, IA; 2/26 TrsJrCls; Chrs; HonRl; NHS; SchMus; StuCncl; Yrbk; 4-H; SpnCl; Chrldr; Iowa State U; Industrial Admin.

LANGREHR, Stuart J; Red Bud HS; Evansville, IL; Chr; ChrhWkr; HonRl; StuCncl; RptrSchPpr; SptEdSchPpr; FFA; Bsbl; Bsktbl; IMSpt; College; Professional.

LANGSTON, Ava R; Maplewood HS; Richmond Hgts, MO; 21/250 HonRl; SchPl; SchPpr; FrCl; SpnCl; ChmnChrldr; GAA; IMSpt; Univ; Medicine.

LANGSTON, Brenda A; Watervliet HS; Watervliet, MI; HonRl; JCC; NatlMeritSchl; NatlMeritSF; PolWkr; StuGov; CivCl; AmLegAwd; GovHonPrgAwd; PresAwd; Coll; Secretary.

LANGTON, Cathleen J; Perry Lecompton HS; Perry, KS; 5/65 DrlTm; HonRl; SecNHS; OffAde; SchAde; SchPl; TchrAde; Pres4-H; VPPpCl; 4-HAwd; Ks State Univ; Animal Science.

LANHAM, Connie J; Dundee Comm HS; East Dundee, IL; 7/360 Band; ChrhWkr; CncrtBnd; HonRl; JrNHS; MrchBnd; NHS; NatlMeritCmnd; Orch; FTA; VPGerCl; GAA; College; Guidance Counselor.

LANHAM, Mary K; Monroe City R 1 HS; Monroe City, MO; 6/100 Chr; Chrs; ChrhWkr; CmntyWkr; HonRl; NHS; NatlThespSoc; SchAde; StuCncl; TchrAde; RptrSchPpr; FHA; PpCl; LetterBsktbl; College.

LANIGAN, David C; Midland HS; Midland, MI; HonRl; NHS; NatlMeritSF; LetterFtbl; LetterTrk; Ctrl Mi Coll; Geology.

LANIGAN, Nancy M; Philippine Duchesne HS; St Charles, MO; 3/184 Chr; Chrs; ChrhWkr; HonRl; VPNHS; SchPl; SctActv; StuCncl; Twrl; FrCl; PpCl; Chrldr; IMSpt; VoiceDemAwd; College; Art.

LANIK, Glenda J; Mead Public HS; Mead, NE; Band; Chr; Chrs; ChrhWkr; CncrtBnd; DrmMjrt; HonRl; LbryAde; MrchBnd; College; Professional.

LANK, Brent C; South Western HS; Lafayette, IN; Aud/Vis; Chr; ChrhWkr; CmntyWkr; SctActv; YthFlsp; Bsbl; Ftbl; Swmmng; IMSpt; College; Professional.

LANKFORD, Ann C; Mexico HS; Mexico, MO; PresSophCls; Band; MrchBnd; PepBnd; SctActv; StuCncl; FrCl; LatCl; PpCl; Bsktbl; Univ; Foreign Languages.

LANKFORD, Rhonda; Seneca HS; Seneca, MO; Band; DrmMjrt; LbryAde; NHS; Twrl; 4-H; FHA; IMSpt; PPFtbl; 4-HAwd; College.

LANKHAAR, Cheryl L; Sullivan HS; Merom, IN; 15/139 HonRl; NHS; 4-H; PresSpnCl; GAA; In U; Nursng.

LANKSTON, John L; Mccluer North HS; Florissant, MO; Band; CncrtBnd; MrchBnd; NatlMeritSF; Orch; U Of Mo; Composer.

LANNEN, Julie G; Polo Comm HS; Polo, IL; 5/88 Chr; ChrhWkr; HonRl; NHS; StuCncl; PresYthFlsp; 4-H; VPFTA; GAA; 4-HAwd; College; Special Education.

LANNIGAN, Barbara J; Lincoln HS; Park Falls, WI; 1/114 Band; CncrtBnd; DrmBgl; HonRl; MrchBnd; NHS; PepBnd; StuGov; SpnCl; GAA; University; Medical.

LANNIN, Cindy L; Benzie Central HS; Benzonia, MI; 6/120 TrsSophCls; HonRl; VPNHS; StuCncl; VPYthFlsp; 4-H; CaptBsktbl; 4-HAwd; KiwanAwd; MasAwd; Ferris State Col Mi; Optometry.

LANNING, Alan D; Elk Point HS; Elk Point, SD; 4/54 PresJrCls; ALBoysSt; HonRl; SchPl; StuCncl; Bsbl; Bsktbl; Ftbl; Glf; Trk; Clge; Pro.

LANNING, Linda D; Paul Harding HS; New Haven, IN; 21/276 Band; CncrtBnd; HonRl; MrchBnd; NHS; PepBnd; RedCrAde; SchMus; Purdue Univ; Pre Med.

LANNON, Cheryl; Bishop Noll Inst; Hammond, IN; 67/360 HonRl; MthCl; PpCl; GAA; College Or Business School.

LANNON, Kathryn A; Elizebeth Seton HS; Dolton, IL; Chrs; ChrhWkr; HospAde; Mdrgl; RedCrAde; FNA; Evangelical Schl Of Nursing; Nurse.

LANNOO, Michael J; Moline HS; Moline, IL; 24/822 Chr; HonRl; NHS; Yrbk; 4-H; LatCl; SciCl; Iowa State Univ; Veterinarian.

LANNOYE, Gregory S; Premontre HS; Green Bay, WI; Band; DrlTm; JA; ROTC; SchMus; SptEdYrbk; LetterTrk; Marquette Univ; Medicine.

LANOUETTE, Mary; Pius Xi HS; Wauwatosa, WI; Chrs; NatlMeritCmnd; TchrAde; FTA; MthCl; Univ Of Wi Whitewater; Special Education.

LANSER, Cindy; Port Washington HS; Port Washington, WI; 23/255 TrsJrCls; HonRl; NHS; StuCncl; Yrbk; SchPpr; FBLA;.

LANSER, Richard L; Benet Academy; Lisle, IL; Aud/Vis; Chrl; HonRl; LitMag; LbryAde; NatlMeritCmnd; PolWkr; StuGov; Marquette Univ; Lawyer.

LANSING, Lorrie M; Grafton Central HS; Grafton, ND; 5/125 CncrtBnd; HonRl; StuCncl; EdSchPpr; FBLA; FHA; PpCl; U Of North Dakota; Accounting.

LANSMAN, Diane L; Walnut Community HS; Walnut, IA; PresSophCls; Band; Chrs; NHS; StuCncl; YthFlsp; EdSchPpr; 4-H; Bsktbl; 4-HAwd; U Of N Ia; Special Ed.

LANTEIGNE, David J; Duchesne HS; St Charles, MO; 1/187 HonRl; NHS; RptrSchPpr; Univ ;physics.

LANTER, Randolph L; Maroa Forsyth HS; Maroa, IL; SecJrCls; HonRl; LbryAde; StuCncl; SciCl; Bsktbl; Univ Ill State; Major Study.

LANTERMAN, Lynn A; Athens HS; Cantrall, IL; Band; Chrs; HonRl; NHS; StuCncl; FHA; Chrldr; College; Law.

LANTSBERGER, Elizabeth H; Watertown Senior HS; Watertown, SD; 7/326 Chrs; HonRl; GerCl; Watertown Business U; Accounting.

LANTZ, Jerry R; Avon HS; Indianapolis, IN; ModUN; LetterBsktbl; CaptFtbl; Cedarville College; History Teacher.

LANTZ, Mary J; Richardton HS; Richardton, ND; 9/40 HstFrshCls; SecSrCls; Chrs; DrlTm; HonRl; SchAde; Yrbk; SchPpr; 4-H; LetterTrk; Dickinson State Clge; Med Sec.

LANTZER, Marty R; Kimball County HS; Kimball, NE; 39/90 HonRl; LetterBsktbl; LetterFtbl; LetterTrk; Nebraska Western Tech; Auto Mechamic.

LANZ, Kathy S; Wapello HS; Oakville, IA; Band; CncrtBnd; HonRl; MrchBnd; FHA;.

LANZ, Michael R; Pender HS; Pender, NE; ChrhWkr; HonRl; SchPl; TchrAde; Bsktbl;.

LA ORANGE, Desiree L; Pope County HS; Golconda, IL; 2/70 HonRl; NHS; FrCl; SpnCl; PpCl; LetterBsktbl; Trk; College.

LAPAK, Cheryl L; Birch Run HS; Birch Run, MI; 18/154 Band; CncrtBnd; HonRl; MrchBnd; PepBnd; Univ Of Michigan; Medical Technology.

LA PARCHE, Marla S; Westwood HS; Champion, MI; CmntyWkr; HonRl; 4-H; FHA; Bsbl; Bsktbl; Chrldr;.

LA PARL, Danny R; Algonac Community HS; Algonac, MI; CncrtBnd; MrchBnd; Central Michigan Univ; Law.

LAPCEWICH, Michael J; Prospect HS; Mt Prospect, IL; ChrhWkr; HonRl; NHS; NatlMeritCmnd; SctActv; Bsbl; Univ Of Illinois; Medicine.

LAPE, Debra L; Falls City HS; Falls City, NE; Band; ChrhWkr; CmntyWkr; CncrtBnd; DrlTm; HonRl; MrchBnd; PepBnd; StuGov; Twrl; Trk; GAA; Nebraska University; Teaching.

LAPE, Ken B; Matthews HS; Sikeston, MO; 6/34 PresFrshCls; PresJrCls; Band; Chr; HonRl; SchPl; StuCncl; FFA; LetterBsbl; LetterBsktbl; University Of Missouri; Ag Engineering.

LA PEER, Randy L; Cass City HS; Cass City, MI; 14/130 PresBand; CncrtBnd; HonRl; MrchBnd; NHS; PepBnd; Pres4-H; SecGerCl; 4-HAwd; College; Chemical Engineering.

LAPEIKIS, Edward G; Austin Catholic Prep; Grosse Pt Woods, MI; 21/135 College; Medicine.

LAPENSKY, Michael M; Acad Of The Holy Angels; Richfield, MN; MthCl; LetterTennis; IMSpt; College; Science Or Math.

LAPHAM, Deborah L; Harbor Beach HS; Harbor Beach, MI; 9/135 Chr; Chrl; ChrhWkr; HospAde; NHS; SchMus; StuGov; TchrAde; PresYthFlsp; FHA; LatCl; Trk; 4-HAwd; St Clair Comm College; Secretary.

LA PIANA, Janet G; Thornton Fractional North HS; Burnham, IL; 14/447 Chrs; CaptDrlTm; HonRl; JrNHS; NHS; StuCncl; SpnCl; PpCl; AmLegAwd; College; Computer Science.

LAPINE, David; Crocker HS; Crocker, MO; Band; CncrtBnd; HonRl; EngCl; SpnCl; Bsbl; Bsktbl; CchngActv; College; Vocation.

LA PINE, Mary M; Gladstone HS; Gladstone, MI; 24/180 Chrs; HonRl; NHS; StuCncl; StuGov; RptrYrbk; RptrSchPpr; FHA; GAA; Bay De Noc Comm College; Mathematics.

LA PINTA, Joel K; Belvidere HS; Belvidere, IL; Band; ChrhWkr; MrchBnd; NatlThespSoc; PepBnd; SchPl; RptrYrbk; SchPpr; Tennis; University; Professional.

LAPISH, Martha J; Port Huron Northern HS; Port Huron, MI; 40/436 HonRl; PolWkr; SchAde; SpnCl; Tennis; Central Michigan; Special Education.

LAPKA, Pamela; Otis Bison Sr HS; Timken, KS; SecJrCls; Band; CncrtBnd; HonRl; MrchBnd; NatlFornLg; PepBnd; SchPl; Chrldr; College; Special Education Teacher.

LA POINTE, Barbara A; Roanoke Benson HS; Benson, IL; 7/93 ALAGirlsSt; CncrtBnd; HonRl; MrchBnd; NHS; SctActv; FHA; SpnCl; Chrldr; DARAwd; Ill Central College; Accounting.

LA POINTE, David; Franklin HS; Livonia, MI; VPSrCls; Chr; CmntyWkr; HonRl; StuCncl; 4-H; Bsbl; Bsktbl; CchngActv; IMSpt; Usafa; Air Force.

LA POINTE, Debra L; Lyons Township HS; Lagrange Park, IL; HonRl; HospAde; NHS; StuGov; TchrAde; Winona State College; Medical Technology.

LA POINTE, Loretta E; Portage Central HS; Portage, MI; 4-H; Bsktbl; GAA; Mi St Univ; Physical Educ.

LA POINTE, Mark H; Premontre HS; Green Bay, WI; 20/125 Chr; Chrs; ChrhWkr; HonRl; SchMus; LetterFtbl; LetterTrk;.

LA PONSIE, Grace; Cass City HS; Cass City, MI; 2/157 Chr; HonRl; JrNHS; NHS; TchrAde; FTA; SpnCl; Coll; Nursing.

LA PORTE, Jacqueline B; Saginaw HS; Saginaw, MI; Chr; ChrhWkr; HonRl; JCC; CaptSwmmng; Tennis; College.

LAPP, Faye E; Central HS; Fline, MI; CmntyWkr; HonRl; JA; LbryAde; NHS; NatlMeritSchl; NatlMeritSF; SchPl; YthFlsp; SciCl; College; Physician.

LAPPE, Sharon A; Harrisonville HS; Harrisonville, MO; 14/157 ChrhWkr; HonRl; LbryAde; SchAde; TchrAde; 4-H; FHA; Bsbl; Trk; 4-HAwd;.

LAPPIN, John A; Clinton Comm HS; Clinton, IL; 19/180 Band; ChrhWkr; CmntyWkr; CncrtBnd; HonRl; MrchBnd; StuCncl; YthFlsp; Pres4-H; VPFFA; Bsktbl; LetterTrk; DanFAwd; College; Conservation.

LAPPING, Shale S; New Trier West HS; Wilmette, IL; 3/694 TrsFrshCls; PresSrCls; CncrtBnd; HonRl; NatlMeritFnl; NatlSciFnd; ROTC; EdSchPpr; FDA; CaptFtbl; LetterSwmmng; GodCntryAwd; VoiceDemAwd; Harvard; Doctor.

LAPSANSKY, Gregory; Quigley South Hs; Chicago, IL; 28 Band; HonRl; SchMus; SctActv; Tennis;.

LARAMEE, Robert M; Clinton Community HS; Clinton, IL; 22/154 CncrtBnd; Yrbk; 4-H; FFA; FrCl; Bsktbl; Ftbl; University.

LARDINOIS, Cindy L; Seymour Comm HS; Bonduel, WI; ChrhWkr; SchPpr; FrCl;.

LARDINOIS, Kay A; Southern Door HS; Sturgeon Bay, WI; TrsSophCls; Chrs; HonRl; SchMus; 4-H; PpCl; Chrldr; IMSpt; 4-HAwd;.

LARESE, Albert R; Cody HS; Detroit, MI; 36/668 HonRl; NHS; NatlMeritSchl; OffAde; Quill&Scroll; StuGov; TchrAde; SptEdSchPpr; PresSpnCl; Wayne St Univ; Medical Field.

LAREY, Erin J; Galena HS; Galena, IL; Chrs; CncrtBnd; HonRl; Mdrgl; MrchBnd; PepBnd; SchMus; YthFlsp; PresPpCl; Glf; Blackhawk Jr College; Lpn.

LARGE, Constance; West Chicago Comm Hs; West Chicago, IL; 8 HonRl; NHS; Orch; SchMus; YthFlsp; SpnCl; GAA;.

LARGE, Kevin E; Chase County HS; Wauneta, NE; PresSophCls; Chrs; SchPl; YthFlsp; 4-H; FFA; Bsbl; LetterBsktbl; LetterFtbl; LetterTrk; Univ Of Nebr; Farmer.

LARGE, Kevin M; Comstock HS; Kalamazoo, MI; HonRl; NHS; SchPl; SctActv; GerCl; College; Biology.

LARGE, Leslie A; Beardstown Senior HS; Beardstown, IL; Chr; Chrs; ChrhWkr; HonRl; LbryAde; OffAde; SchMus; TchrAde; YthFlsp; Yrbk; Lincolnland Junior College; Art.

LARGE, Mary E; Calhoun HS; Fieldon, IL; Band; Chr; CmntyWkr; CncrtBnd; HonRl; MrchBnd; NHS; PepBnd; FHA; Trade School; Professional.

LARGE, Robin S; Sullivan HS; Sullivan, MO; 50/206 ChrhWkr; HospAde; YthFlsp; RptrSchPpr; FTA; College; Anthropology.

LARGENT, Kyle D; East HS; Elizabethtown, IN; 93/363 HonRl; SpnCl; Bsktbl; Ftbl; LetterGlf; IMSpt; Univ; Business Or Industrial Management.

LARGENT, Pennisue; Hot Springs HS; Hot Springs, SD; DrlTm; HonRl; RptrSchPpr; FrCl; PpCl; Chrldr; GAA; PresAwd; College; Criminology.

LARICCIA, Valery J; Thornwood HS; Calumet City, IL; AFS; HonRl; SchAde; SctActv; RptrSchPpr; PpCl; Thornton Comm Clg; Go Into Radio Or Tv.

LARIMORE, Carmen B; Tipton HS; Tipton, MO; 7/84 HstSrCls; Band; Chrs; ChrhWkr; CmntyWkr; HonRl; NHS; SchMus; SchPl; Sw Baptist College; English.

LARIMORE, Lori L; Seymour HS; Plainville, IL; 3/65 Band; Chrs; CncrtBnd; HonRl; MrchBnd; PepBnd; StuCncl; YthFlsp; 4-H; GAA; College; Nurse.

LARIMORE, Teresa A; Milford Township HS; Milford, IL; Band; ChrhWkr; HonRl; NHS; Quill&Scroll; SchPpr; Pres4-H; TreasGerCl; SecSciCl; Trk; Lincoln Christian Coll; Chrsitian Educa.

LARISON, Janet; Westplatte HS; Weston, MO; 6/45 PresSrCls; NHS; TchrAde; EdYrBk; SpnCl; SciCl; Chrldr; PPFtbl; William Jewell Coll; Physc.

LARK, Jeanne M; Larkin HS; Elgin, IL; Chrs; HonRl; LitMag; LbryAde; PolWkr; 4-H; FrCl; Florida Ins Of Tech; Space Science.

LARKIN, Ann B; Benilde St Margarets HS; Excelsior, MN; Chrs; JrNHS; NHS; StuGov; RptrSchPpr; FrCl; Trk; University; Rotc Or Journalism.

LARKIN, John P; Normal Community HS; Normal, IL; HonRl; StuGov; 4-H; FFA; KeyCl; LetterFtbl; Trk; Wrstlng; DanFAwd; 4-HAwd; Univ Of Illinois; Agriculture.

LARKIN, Nancy A; Winamac Community HS; Winamac, IN; HonRl; NHS; OffAde; SchPl; SpnCl; PpCl; Chrldr; Valparaiso U; Accounting.

LARKIN, Veronica A; Lexington HS; Towanda, IL; 9/64 SecFrshCls; VPSrCls; AFS; HonRl; StuCncl; RptrYrbk; EngCl; SciCl; GAA; IMSpt; Clarke Clge; Cpa.

LAROCCA, Beth A; Homewood Flossmoor HS; Homewood, IL; 19/932 HonRl; NHS; LetterBsbl; Bsktbl; IMSpt; Teaching.

LA ROCQUE, Anthony F; Eastridge HS; Kankakee, IL; HonRl; Eastern Illinois Univ; Biology.

LA ROSH, James; Sully Buttes HS; Onida, SD; 3 VPSophCls; VPJrCls; HonRl; SchPl; StuGov; Trade Or Business; Vocation.

LA ROSH, Kathy M; Osborne HS; Natoma, KS; SecJrCls; ChrhWkr; CmntyWkr; HonRl; YthFlsp; Pres4-H; FFA; FHA; SecPpCl; LetterBsktbl; LetterTrk; PPFtbl; 4-HAwd; Colby Comm College; Animal Health Technicia.

LA ROUERE, Michael J; University Of Detroit HS; Detroit, MI; 10/203 CmntyWkr; HonRl; HospAde; NHS; PpCl; SciCl; LetterGlf; IMSpt; AmLegAwd; JETSAwd; U Of Mich; Md.

LA ROWE, Karen L; Lutheran HS; Taylor, MI; 6/144 Aud/Vis; Chr; HonRl; LbryAde; NHS; VPNatlThespSoc; SchMus; SchPl; RptrSchPpr; GerCl; College; Computer Science.

LA ROWE, Marjorie G; Laingsburg HS; Laingsburg, MI; Chr; ChrhWkr; HonRl; NatlFornLg; SchPl; 4-H; Bsbl; Ftbl; PPFtbl; AmLegAwd; Clge; Theatre & Fine Arts.

LARR, Walt; Huntington North HS; Huntington, IN; Band; CncrtBnd; JrNHS; MrchBnd; 4-H; IMSpt; 4-HAwd; Purdue Univ.

LARSEN, Arnold P; Norway HS; Vulcan, MI; 9/109 ChrhWkr; HonRl; NHS; Teen; YthFlsp; EdSchPpr; LetterBsktbl; LetterTennis; IMSpt; Michigan Tech Univ; Forestry.

LARSEN, Barbara A; Wolsey Public HS; Wolsey, SD; ChrhWkr; HonRl; SchPl; YthFlsp; Yrbk; EdSchPpr; FHA; SciCl; DARAwd; College; Math Teacher.

LARSEN, Brent R; Gladbrook Comm HS; Gladbrook, IA; PresFrshCls; PresJrCls; Chrs; HonRl; ModUN; StuCncl; 4-H; LetterBsbl; LetterBsktbl; LetterFtbl; Ia St Univ; Agriculture.

LARSEN, Cindi M; Broken Bow HS; Broken Bow, NE; HonRl; NHS; 4-H; FHA; PpCl; LetterTrk; Chrldr; IMSpt; 4-HAwd; College; Art.

LARSEN, Deborah M; Marian Catholic HS; Homewood, IL; 8/365 Band; ChrhWkr; CmntyWkr; CncrtBnd; HonRl; MrchBnd; NHS; NatlMeritCmnd; PepBnd; SchMus; U Of Mich; Attorney.

LARSEN, Don; Marquette Sr HS; Marquette, MI; 6/387 HonRl; SciCl; IMSpt; Mich Tech Univ; Metallurgical Engineering.

LARSEN, Jeanette M; Pontiac Township HS; Pontiac, IL; Band; Chr; CncrtBnd; HonRl; MrchBnd; PepBnd; SchMus; Yrbk; 4-H; GAA; Bradley U; Registered Nurse.

LARSEN, Jenean; Springfield Hs; Springfield, IL; 4/540 CncrtBnd; MrchBnd; NHS; RedCrAde; TreasStuCncl; PresYthFlsp; EdYrBk; TreasMthCl; LetterTrk; TreasGAA; Iowa State U; Biomedical Engineering.

LARSEN, Jennifer A; Gross HS; Bellevue, NE; HonRl; VPJrCls; Chrldr; College; Nurse.

LARSEN, Judi L; Broken Bow HS; Broken Bow, NE; ChrhWkr; HonRl; PresStuCncl; YthFlsp; Pres4-H; FHA; LetterTrk; Chrldr; GAA; 4-HAwd; College.

LARSEN, Kris A; Niobrara Public HS; Verdigro, NE; 3/31 PresJrCls; Band; Chr; Chrs; ChrhWkr; CncrtBnd; HonRl; MrchBnd; PepBnd; SchMus; Chrldr; IMSpt; VFWAwd; College; Music.

LARSEN, Lauri L; Niobrara Public HS; Verdigre, NE; Band; Chr; Chrs; HonRl; MrchBnd; PepBnd; SchMus; YthFlsp; PpCl; Chrldr; College; Special Education Teacher.

LARSEN, Leslie J; Keya Paha County HS; Springview, NE; 5/23 ALBoysSt; HonRl; JrNHS; TreasNHS; NatlSciFnd; SchPl; SctActv; 4-H; LetterFtbl; AmLegAwd; 4-HAwd; Wesleyan Univ; Ecologist.

LARSEN, Leslie J; Keya Paha Co HS; Springview, NE; 5/23 ALBoysSt; HonRl; NHS; NatlSciFnd; SchPl; SctActv; 4-H; LetterFtbl; AmLegAwd; DanFAwd; EldAwd; 4-HAwd; Nebraska Wesleyan Univ; Biology.

LARSEN, Linda J; Cal Comm HS; Hampton, IA; Chrs; ChrhWkr; HonRl; HospAde; MrchBnd; SchMus; SchPl; PresYthFlsp; Bsktbl; LetterTrk; Trade Sch; Acct.

LARSEN, Marguerite E; Batavia Sr HS; Batavia, IL; 6/219 Chr; HonRl; OffAde; SchMus; SchPl; StuCncl; StuGov; Univ Of Ill; Math.

LARSEN, Theodore L; Broken Bow HS; Broken Bow, NE; Aud/Vis; HonRl; NHS; PresStuCncl; 4-H; Bsbl; LetterBsktbl; LetterFtbl; LetterTrk; IMSpt; 4-HAwd; VoiceDemAwd; Technical School; Radio Announcer.

LARSEN, Thomas; Burt Comm HS; Burt, IA; PresSophCls; SecJrCls; Band; CncrtBnd; HonRl; MrchBnd; NHS; PepBnd; Bsktbl; CitAwd; Iowa State Univ; Veterinary.

LARSEN, Victoria C; Hancock HS; Hancock, MN; Chr; Chrs; HonRl; SchPl; YthFlsp; SchPpr; FHA; BttyCrckrAwd; Willmar Are Vo Tech Inst; Tech Art & Ill.

LARSH, Scott D; Pennville HS; Pennville, IN; 3/40 Band; Chr; CncrtBnd; HonRl; MrchBnd; NHS; PepBnd; In U; Music.

LARSON, Anita M; Salem Public HS; Montrose, SD; 8/54 Chrs; ChrhWkr; CncrtBnd; HonRl; MrchBnd; PepBnd; TchrAde; RptrYrbk; 4-H; 4-HAwd; College; Christian Education.

LARSON, Bonnie; Decatur Community HS; Obwerlin, KS; CmntyWkr; CncrtBnd; HonRl; SchPl; YthFlsp; SchPpr; FTA; Swmmng; Tennis; IMSpt; Jr College; Theology.

LARSON, Brian; Blackhawk Hs; South Wayne, WI; 20/78 Chrs; HonRl; SptEdSchPpr; 4-H; FFA; LetterBsbl; LetterBsktbl; CaptFtbl; 4-HAwd; U Of Wi; Agri Business Career.

LARSON, Bruce E; Spring Valley HS; Spring Valley, MN; 13/80 Chrs; HonRl; StuCncl; StuGov; Winona Vo Tech; Electronics.

LARSON, Bruce W; Potter HS; Potter, NE; 10/20 Band; Chr; Chrs; CncrtBnd; HonRl; MrchBnd; PepBnd; SchPl; Bsktbl; Ftbl; College; Journalism.

LARSON, Candyce J; Jamestown HS; Jamestown, KS; 1/6 HonRl; PresStuCncl; EdYrBk; EdSchPpr; 4-H; PpCl; LetterBsktbl; LetterTrk; Chrldr; 4-HAwd; Stephens College; Fashion Merchandising.

LARSON, Carol M; Mt Horeb HS; Mt Horeb, WI; 23/135 TrsFrshCls; Band; ChrhWkr; HonRl; NHS; NatlThespSoc; SchPl; EdYrBk; Swmmng; Trk; GAA; Univ Of Wisconsin; Engineering.

LARSON, Charlene R; Cass Lake HS; Cass Lake, MN; 2/48 Band; CncrtBnd; HonRl; PresLbryAde; SchPl; Yrbk; EdSchPpr; PresGerCl; DARAwd; LionAwd; St Cloud St Coll; Math.

LARSON, Christy; Wheeling Hs; Arlington Hts, IL; 35 Chr; Chrs; ChrhWkr; HonRl; NHS; YthFlsp; College;professional.

LARSON, Christy A; Pepin HS; Stockholm, WI; TrsSophCls; TrsJrCls; ChrhWkr; HonRl; LbryAde; NHS; StuCncl; FHA; LatCl; Business Schl; Vocation.

LARSON, Cindy K; Bisbee HS; Bisbee, ND; 8/16 ALAGirlsSt; ChrhWkr; CmntyWkr; RedCrAde; SchMus; SchPl; TchrAde; EdYrBk; FBLA; Trade School; Dental Hygiene.

LARSON, David L; Milbank HS; Labolt, SD; ChrhWkr; HonRl; JrNHS; NHS; StuCncl; YthFlsp; KeyCl; PpCl; Bsbl; Wrstlng; College; Major Study.

LARSON, David R; Velva Public HS; Velva, ND; ALBoysSt; CncrtBnd; NHS; NatlThespSoc; SctActv; EdYrBk; SciCl; LetterBsbl; LetterBsktbl; GodCntryAwd; College; Physics.

LARSON, Dean A; Clay Center Comm HS; Green, KS; 1/3/130 HonRl; JrNHS; StuCncl; YthFlsp; 4-H; FFA; 4-HAwd; Univ; Agriculture.

LARSON, Deanna L; Warren HS; Warren, MN; Chrs; ChrhWkr; CmntyWkr; CncrtBnd; HonRl; HospAde; MrchBnd; PepBnd; GerCl; SciCl; Tennis; GAA; Moorehead St College; Nursing.

LARSON, Deborah L; Cahokia HS; Cahokia, IL; 10/559 HonRl; JA; NHS; OffAde; Quill&Scroll; RptrSchPpr; SchPpr; College; Journalism.

LARSON, Dessalee; Negaunee HS; Negaunee, MI; Chrs; HonRl; Yrbk; PpCl; Northern Michaigan U; Veterinarian.

LARSON, Diana K; Marian HS; Omaha, NE; DrlTm; Col; Child Physical Therapy.

LARSON, Diane D; Pecatonica HS; Blanchardville, WI; HonRl; SchMus; College; Law.

LARSON, Dianne M; Stromsburg HS; Stromsburg, NE; SecJrCls; ChrhWkr; HonRl; LbryAde; ModUN; NHS; OffAde; TchrAde; LetterTrk; Kearney St Coll; Social Science.

LARSON, Donna S; Dekalb HS; Dekalb, IL; HonRl; Rock Valley College; Nursing.

LARSON, Doris A; Chamberlain HS; Pukwana, SD; 18/97 Chrs; ChrhWkr; HonRl; SchPl; FHA; PpCl; Black Hills State College; Medical Tech.

LARSON, Douglas C; Lake Central HS; Madison, SD; ALBoysSt; Chrs; ChrhWkr; HonRl; NatlMeritCmnd; SchPl; Yrbk; SchPpr; IMSpt; 4-HAwd; Concordia Teachers Col;.

LARSON, Douglas W; New Rockford Central HS; New Rockford, ND; 11/67 VPJrCls; Chrs; HonRl; SchMus; SchPl; CivCl; LetterBsbl; LetterBsktbl; LetterFtbl; EldAwd; North Dakota St Univ; Architecture.

LARSON, Edmund M; Union HS; Grand Rapids, MI; HonRl; ModUN; NHS; Orch; SctActv; LetterTennis; JETSAwd; University; Astrophysics.

LARSON, Eric D; Evanston Twp HS; Evanston, IL; 33/1100 Chrl; HonRl; Mdrgl; NatlMeritCmnd; SchMus; RptrSchPpr; SptEdSchPpr; LetterBsbl; Socr; CchngActv; Univ; Engineer Or Teacher.

LARSON, Gail D; Fargo North HS; Fargo, ND; ChrhWkr; HonRl; HospAde; NHS; College.

LARSON, Galen L; Banner County HS; Potter, NE; Band; CncrtBnd; HonRl; MrchBnd; PepBnd; StuCncl; RptrSchPpr; 4-H; LetterBsktbl; LetterFtbl; U Of Nebraska.

LARSON, Gregory L; Grand Rapids Sr HS; Grand Rapids, MN; 17/377 NatlMeritCmnd; LetterFtbl; CaptTrk; IMSpt; Hamline U; Reseach Biology.

LARSON, James; Rossville HS; Rossville, KS; 7/48 ChrhWkr; TchrAde; Bsktbl; Ftbl; Glf; Trk; IMSpt; Coll; Business Administration.

LARSON, James A; Oklee Public HS; Oklee, MN; PresSrCls; Chrs; ChrhWkr; CncrtBnd; PepBnd; PolWkr; SchPl; StuCncl; RptrYrbk; Moorhead State College; Agriculture.

LARSON, Janet L; Fargo South HS; Fargo, ND; ALAGirlsSt; Band; CncrtBnd; HonRl; NHS; Orch; StuCncl; PresSpnCl; Chrldr; Univ Of North Dakota; Occupational Therapy.

LARSON, Jay S; Appleton West HS; Appleton, WI; Band; MrchBnd; Bsbl; Ftbl; IMSpt; Uw Madison; Elec Engr.

LARSON, Jerald; Marshall County Central HS; Newfolden, MN; Band; CncrtBnd; MrchBnd; NatlThespSoc; FFA; Ftbl; Univ; Professional.

LARSON, Joanne E; Ludington HS; Ludington, MI; Band; ChrhWkr; HonRl; HospAde; YthFlsp; FNA; SpnCl; Trinity College; Medical Technologist.

LARSON, Joel S; Waseca HS; Waseca, MN; 9/210 Band; Chr; HonRl; MrchBnd; PepBnd; StuCncl; YthFlsp; LetterBsbl; LetterBsktbl; LetterFtbl; Drake Univ; Biology.

LARSON, John; Littlefork Big Falls HS; Littlefork, MN; 5/44 CncrtBnd; HonRl; NHS; SchPl; StuCncl; Yrbk; Bsktbl; Ftbl; Glf; Trk; College; Professionall.

LARSON, Jon D; North HS; N St Paul, MN; ChrhWkr; CmntyWkr; CncrtBnd; HonRl; NHS; SctActv; LetterBsbl; LetterBsktbl; LetterFtbl; College; Education.

LARSON, Judy M; Clear Lake HS; Clear Lake, IA; AFS; Chrs; HonRl; Yrbk; RptrSchPpr; SecFHA; LatCl; VPPpCl; North Ia Area Comm Clg; Physical Therapist.

LARSON, Karen L; East Grand Forks Senior HS; E Grand Forks, MN; Band; HonRl; LbryAde; NHS; PepBnd; RptrYrbk; Yrbk; SchPpr; SecFHA; University; Business Ed Teacher.

LARSON, Kathleen E; Durand HS; Durand, WI; 34/147 Band; ChrhWkr; CncrtBnd; HonRl; MrchBnd; PepBnd; GerCl; PpCl; LetterBsktbl; GAA; Univ; Nursing.

LARSON, Kay A; Potter Public HS; Potter, NE; 3/16 PresJrCls; ALAGirlsSt; Band; Chr; Chrs; CncrtBnd; HonRl; MrchBnd; NHS; EdYrBk; Midland Lutheran Coll; Accountant.

LARSON, Keith R; Hinsdale Central HS; Hinsdale, IL; ChrhWkr; CmntyWkr; HonRl; YthFlsp; Ftbl; LetterSocr; Univ Of Illinois; Architect.

LARSON, Kenneth J; Glaesburg Sr HS; Galesburg, IL; 42/650 PresChrhWkr; HonRl; LbryAde; NHS; SchPl; SpnCl; Maranatha Baptist Bible; Missionary.

LARSON, Kevin C; East HS; Rockford, IL; Chr; HonRl; Orch; College; Architecture.

LARSON, Landis; Carpio HS; Foxholm, ND; Chrs; HonRl; SchPl; YthFlsp; Bsktbl; Ftbl; Trk; IMSpt; College; Engineering.

LARSON, Laurie A; Florence HS; Iron Mtn, MI; 13/69 Chr; ChrhWkr; HonRl; NHS; SchPl; 4-H; GAA;.

LARSON, Laurie J; Gibbon Public HS; Winthrop, MN; Band; Chr; HonRl; MrchBnd; PepBnd; SchPl; 4-H; FFA; FHA; 4-HAwd; Sw State U; Elem Education.

LARSON, Laurn R; Anamoose Public HS; Anamoose, ND; SecTrsFrshCls; HonRl; LbryAde; SchPl; SchPpr; Bsktbl; LetterFtbl; Trk; Univ; Pro.

LARSON, Leanne M; North Platte Sr HS; North Platte, NE; Chr; Chrs; CmntyWkr; DrlTm; HonRl; RedCrAde; SchMus; FrCl; PpCl; Chrldr;.

LARSON, Linda; John F Kennedy HS; Bloomington, MN; AFS; HonRl; LitMag; NatlMeritSchl; SchAde; TchrAde; University.

LARSON, Lori A; Borup HS; Borup, MN; Band; Chrs; HonRl; NatlThespSoc; SchMus; SchPl; 4-H; Bsktbl; Trk; GAA; Ndsu; Social Worker.

LARSON, Lori A; Watertown HS; Watertown, SD; 23/340 AFS; Band; ChrhWkr; HonRl; MrchBnd; NatlFornLg; PepBnd; StuCncl; GerCl; Augustana College; Biology.

LARSON, Lorie; Anderson Sr HS; Anderson, IN; 5/597 Chr; HonRl; NHS; NatlMeritSF; NatlThespSoc; SpnCl; Trk; GAA; AmLegAwd; Purdue University; Engineering.

LARSON, Lori L; Trego Community HS; Wakeeney, KS; LbryAde; FHA; College; Nursing.

LARSON, Lori L; Armstrong Sr HS; Neenah, WI; Band; CncrtBnd; HonRl; MrchBnd; Orch; SchMus; LetterBsktbl; Voc Sch; Acctng.

LARSON, Lorraine B; Curie HS; Chicago, IL; 13/600 Chrs; HonRl; VPNHS; SchAde; SchPl; StuGov; Yrbk; PpCl; LetterChrldr; GovHonPrgAwd; Mccormac Jr Clg; Court Reporting.

LARSON, Lorrie; Oak Park Acad; Des Moines, IA; SecTrsFrshCls; Chr; ChrhWkr; JA; OffAde; SchAde; SecTrsFrshCls; TchrAde; RptrYrbk; Bsktbl; College; Elementary Education.

LARSON, Lowell W; Worthington Sr HS; Worthington, MN; Band; Chr; ChrhWkr; CncrtBnd; JrNHS; MrchBnd; NHS; PepBnd; SchMus; LetterTrk; College; Education.

LARSON, Luan K; Mondovi HS; Mondovi, WI; SecJrCls; Band; ChrhWkr; CncrtBnd; HonRl; HospAde; MrchBnd; NHS; RptrSchPpr; SchPpr;.

LARSON, Lynn M; Kaneland Sr HS; Maple Park, IL; ChrhWkr; DrlTm; HonRl; SchPl; 4-H; PpCl; Bsbl; CaptBsktbl; Trk; GAA; 4-HAwd; Univ Of Wisconsin; Agriculture.

LARSON, Mark H; Immaculate Conception HS; Elmhurst, IL; Aud/Vis; HonRl; JrNHS; NHS; NatlMeritCmnd; NatlMeritSF; SctActv; LatCl; LetterFtbl; LetterTrk; Northwestern Univ; Teacher.

LARSON, Mary; East Leyden HS; Franklin Pk, IL; 184/614 SecFrshCls; SecSophCls; StuCncl; PpCl; Swmmng; Chrldr; IMSpt; PresAwd; College; Pro.

LARSON, Mary Jo; North Farmington HS; Farmington Hills, MI; Chrl; CncrtBnd; HonRl; Mdrgl; MrchBnd; NHS; NatlMeritFnl; SchMus; PresYthFlsp; FrCl; Kalamazoo Clg; Lawyer.

LARSON, Nancy J; Pioneer HS; Ann Arbor, MI; 68/690 Chr; HonRl; LitMag; RptrYrbk; SchPpr; St Olaf Clge; Natural Resources.

LARSON, Nancy L; Ashby Public HS; Dalton, MN; HonRl; NHS; TchrAde; Yrbk; Fergus Falls Comm College; Med Technician.

LARSON, Nels A; Vassar HS; Tuscola, MI; 84/148 Chr; SchMus; SchPl; TchrAde; FHA; SpnCl;.

LARSON, Pamela R; Montevideo HS; Montevideo, MN; 12/149 Band; ChrhWkr; CncrtBnd; HonRl; Orch; TchrAde; FHA; SpnCl; KiwanAwd; VoiceDeMAwd; Univ Of Minnesota; Law.

LARSON, Pamela S; Kewanee HS; Kewanee, IL; HonRl; OffAde; FrCl; Swmmng; Business School; Accountant.

LARSON, Paul K; Elgin HS; Streamwood, IL; 8/734 Chrs; ChrhWkr; HonRl; VPSophCls; College; Electrical Engineer.

LARSON, Randal R; Auburndale HS; Auburndale, WI; 10/127 Chrs; ChrhWkr; HonRl; JrNHS; NHS; SchPl; StuCncl; YthFlsp; SptEdSchPpr; 4-H; FBLA; Bsktbl; Ftbl; Eau Claire Univ; Chemistry.

LARSON, Robert D; Hillcrest HS; Country Club Hills, IL; 13/474 VPSrCls; HonRl; LitMag; VPNHS; SecNatlThespSoc; SchPl; StuCncl; MthCl; Swmmng; GodCntryAwd; Univ Of Ill; Nuclear Physics.

LARSON, Robert S; Rockford West HS; Rockford, IL; 84/356 ChrhWkr; HonRl; PresSctActv; VPYthFlsp; Tennis; GodCntryAwd; Eastern Illinois; Environmental Bio.

LARSON, Robert W; Bertha Hewitt HS; Bertha, MN; 11/53 ALBoysSt; Aud/Vis; Band; ChrhWkr; HonRl; SchPl; StuGov; EdYrBk; FFA; Bsktbl; Ftbl; Wrstlng; AmLegAwd; Univ Of Minnesota; Business Admin.

LARSON, Ross R; Schleswig Comm HS; Deloit, IA; 1/50 SecJrCls; Band; Chrs; CncrtBnd; HonRl; MrchBnd; NHS; Orch; PepBnd; SchPl; College.

LARSON, Russell M; West Sioux Comm HS; Howarden, IA; 16/78 HonRl; CaptBsktbl; CaptFtbl; Air Force.

LARSON, Russell M; Mead Public HS; Mead, NE; TrsFrshCls; TrsSophCls; Band; CncrtBnd; YthFlsp; FFA; LetterBsktbl; CaptFtbl; LetterTrk; Univ Of Nebraska; Forestry.

LARSON, Sandra K; Summit Independent HS; Summit, SD; 4/21 VPSophCls; VPJrCls; Band; Chrs; HonRl; StuCncl; Yrbk; FNA; LetterBsktbl; Trk; Northern State College; Teacher Math.

LARSON, Scott D; River Falls Sr HS; River Falls,

LARSON, Sharon R; Stanton HS; Stanton, NE; 2/40 SecFrshCls; TrsSophCls; PresBand; Chrs; HonRl; MrchBnd; NHS; EdYrBk; 4-H; GAA; U Of Neb; Lawyer.

LARSON, Shelly J; Glenburn Public HS; Glenburn, ND; CncrtBnd; HonRl; MrchBnd; SchPl; PresStuCncl; YthFlsp; RptrSchPpr; Bsktbl; Chrldr; GAA; Minot St Clg; Spe Educ Mentally Retarded.

LARSON, Shirley J; Prairie HS; Swisher, IA; Chrs; HonRl; JrNHS; LbryAde; Yrbk; SchPpr;.

LARSON, Stephen P; Parkway West HS; Ballwin, MO; 122/722 NHS; NatlMeritCmnd; TchrAde; GerCl; Bsbl; LetterBsktbl; Ftbl; College; Business.

LARSON, Susan; Dwight D Eisenhower HS; Saginaw, MI; PresSrCls; Band; HonRl; PepBnd; PolWkr; StuCncl; StuGov; SchPpr; FrCl; SpnCl; Albion College; Lawyer.

LARSON, Susan K; Iron Mountain HS; Iron Mountain, MI; 19/159 Band; Chr; Chrs; ChrhWkr; CncrtBnd; MrchBnd; NatlMeritFnl; Northern Michigan Univ; Accounting.

LARSON, Terry H; Winnebago HS; Winnebago, MN; 3/45 PresJrCls; ALBoysSt; HonRl; Mdrgl; NHS; SchPl; StuCncl; CaptBsbl; CaptBsktbl; CaptFtbl; IMSpt; Hamline Univ; Business.

LARSON, William C; Orion HS; Andover, IL; Chr; CncrtBnd; HonRl; MrchBnd; PepBnd; LetterTrk; CchngActv; College; Civil Engineer.

LARTZ, John A; Niles Township HS; Lincolnwood, IL; HonRl; PresOrch; PolWkr; PresYthFlsp; KeyCl; Glf; Purdue Univ; Political Science.

LARTZ, Raymond; University Hs; Normal, IL; 1/125 PresSrCls; ALBoysSt; HonRl; NHS; PpCl; LetterFtbl; CaptSwmmng; Tennis; GodCntryAwd; SARAwd; Ui;accounting.

LARTZ, Raymond C; University HS; Normal, IL; 1/125 PresSrCls; ALBoysSt; Band; ChrhWkr; NHS; LetterFtbl; CaptSwmmng; SARAwd; RotaryAwd; University Of Illinois; Business.

LA RUE, Cheryl A; Whitko Comm HS; Pierceton, IN; HonRl; Quill&Scroll; Yrbk; SchPpr; Ball State University; History.

LA RUE, Deletta L; Lincoln Park HS; Lincoln Park, MI; 25/552 PresSrCls; ChrhWkr; HonRl; NHS; NatlMeritSchl; SchMus; SchPl; StuGov; 4-H; GAA; Bookkeeping Or Accounting.

LA RUE, Donald L; Churubusco HS; Churubusco, IN; HonRl; LbryAde; CaptBsktbl; LetterFtbl; LetterTrk; AmLegAwd; Design School; Kitchen Designer.

LA RUE, Gary W; Northwest HS; Cedar Hill, MO; 15/376 HonRl; RptrSchPpr; Coll; Professional.

LARUE, Leslie; Lyons Township Hs; Lagrange, IL; 42/1262 ALAGirlsSt; HonRl; JrNHS; NHS; SchPl; YthFlsp; MthCl; PpCl; Trk; AmLegAwd; Illinois State; Cpa In Accounting.

LARZELERE, Mark; Howell HS; Howell, MI; 14/374 Band; HonRl; MrchBnd; StuGov; Univ Of Mich; Engineering.

LASACK, Barbara A; Oxford Junction Cons HS; Oxford Junction, IA; 3/27 Band; Chrs; HonRl; NHS; SchPl; 4-H; LetterBsbl; LetterBsktbl; LetterTrk; 4-HAwd; College; Professional.

LASATER, Tom J; Dodge City HS; Dodge City, KS; 52/265 ALBoysSt; HonRl; NHS; SctActv; StuGov; Yrbk; EdSchPpr; LetterFtbl; LetterTrk; IMSpt; GodCntryAwd; Univ; Law.

LA SCHUM, Paul H; Monona Grove HS; Wild Rose, WI; 19/46 Aud/Vis; Band; CncrtBnd; HonRl; MrchBnd; PepBnd; SchMus; SchPl; SctActv; Yrbk; PpCl; Univ Of Wisconsin; Physician.

LASCU, David M; Lincoln Sr HS; Warren, MI; Band; HonRl; JrNHS; NHS; PolWkr; SchPl; StuCncl; StuGov; TchrAde; EdYrBk; LetterSwmmng; College.

LASECKI, Ann; Wheaton North Hs; Wheaton, IL; 36/308 SecSrCls; HonRl; TchrAde; College; Teacher.

LASEE, Mark E; Southern Door HS; Sturgeon Bay, WI; 14/131 HonRl; NHS; RptrYrbk; Trk; U Of Wi Green Bay; Law.

LASER, Bradly J; Waldron Area HS; Waldron, MI; PresFrshCls; PresSophCls; ALBoysSt; Band; CncrtBnd; MrchBnd; NatlCathMusEdAsoc; PepBnd; SchPl; StuCncl; TchrAde; Bsbl; Bsktbl; Ftbl; Ferris State University; Teacher Coach.

LASH, Edward G; Mattoon Sr HS; Mattoon, IL; 5/435 Chrs; ChrhWkr; CmntyWkr; HonRl; NHS; SchMus; SchPl; StuGov; PpCl; SciCl; CaptBsbl; Bsktbl; Ftbl; University; Medicine.

LASH, John P; Tippecanoe Valley HS; Mentone, IN; HonRl; NHS; 4-H; FFA; LatCl; MthCl; SciCl; Bsktbl; Trk; University; Agri Business.

LASH, Stephen; Berkley HS; Brooksville, MI; ChrhWkr; HonRl; OffAde; TchrAde; YthFlsp; Bsbl; Ftbl; Col; Prof.

LASHLEY, Gilda A; Mckinley HS; St Louis, MO; 20/165 HonRl; SchPpr;.

LASINE, Jaye D; Amundsen HS; Chicago, IL; 6/344 HonRl; LitMag; NHS; RptrYrbk; EdSchPpr; Univ Of Illinois.

LASK, Linda; Merrill Sr HS; Merrill, WI; Aud/Vis; Band; Chr; ChrhWkr; HonRl; NatlFornLg; SchMus; SchPl; YthFlsp; GerCl; Medical Institute Of Mn; Med Technology.

LASKER, Edward M; W E Groves HS; Birmingham, MI; 1/700 HonRl; JrNHS; NHS; NatlMeritSF; Orch; NCTE; Univ.

LASKO, Keith A; Oak Park River Forest HS; Willow Springs, IL; 100/1210 HonRl; TchrAde; RptrSchPpr; Bsktbl; Glf; University; Architecture.

LASKOWSKI, Ginny; Niles HS; Niles, MI; ChrhWkr; CmntyWkr; HonRl; SctActv; Yrbk; OptClAwd; Mi St Univ; Child Psychiatrist.

LASKOWSKI, Thomas M; Pacific HS; Villa Ridge, MO; HonRl; TchrAde; SciCl; LetterTrk; Univ Of Missouri; Mechanical Engineer.

LASKY, Phillip L; Notre Dame Boys HS; Chicago, IL; 11/266 HonRl; NHS; SchAde; TchrAde; Univ Of Illinois; Biology.

LASKY, Robin L; Stephen Tyng Mather HS; Chicago, IL; 91/421 HonRl; LitMag; Orch; SchPl; TchrAde; Univ; Dental Hygiene.

LASNIER, Charles J; Hayden HS; Topeka, KS; 4/200 Aud/Vis; HonRl; NHS; NatlMeritSF; SchMus; StuCncl; Coll; Physics.

LASOWSKI, Carol; Grass Lake HS; Grass Lake, MI; HonRl; OffAde; SctActv; TchrAde; YthFlsp; PpCl; Bsktbl; Chrldr; 4-HAwd; JAAwd; Jackson Com Coll Mi State; Bus.

LASSALINE, William J; Catholic Central HS; Livonia, MI; HonRl; NHS; Trk; IMSpt; Univ Of Mi; Engineering.

LASSEN, Karen; St Scholastica HS; Chicago, IL; 29/220 Chr; Chrs; HospAde; OffAde; Sacrstn; SchAde; SchMus; RptrYrbk; Bsktbl; Chrldr; Loyola Univ; Law.

LASSETER, Gwenda M; Blue Eye HS; Blue Eye, MO; VPFrshCls; Band; Chr; Chrs; ChrhWkr; HonRl; SchMus; SchPpr; FHA; College; Music.

LASSILA, Kathy S; Stratford Public HS; Edgar, WI; 2/90 HonRl; HospAde; NHS; SchPl; FshEdYrbk; Yrbk; FHA; Trk; EldAwd; VoiceDemAwd; Uw Eau Claire; Public Relations.

LASSITER, Barbara M; Okemos HS; Okemos, MI; 20/277 Chr; Chrs; ChrhWkr; HonRl; LitMag; NHS; SchMus; StuCncl; StuGov; YthFlsp; SchPpr; GerCl; CaptBsktbl; Tennis; Univ; Professional.

LASSLETT, Brenda K; Dryden Comm HS; Dryden, MI; SecSrCls; ChrhWkr; HonRl; NHS; SctActv; StuCncl; TchrAde; FrCl; Trk; CaptChrldr; College; Professional.

LASSMANN, Anne M; Notre Dame HS; Chicago, IL; 13/303 Chrs; HospAde; NHS; RedCrAde; SchMus; SctActv; TchrAde; Yrbk; Loyola Univ; Science.

LASSNANN, Anne M; Notre Dame Foratris HS; Chicago, IL; 13/303 Chrs; HonRl; HospAde; NHS; RedCrAde; SchMus; SctActv; TchrAde; Yrbk; Tennis; Loyola Univ; Biology.

LASSWELL, Robert A; Lakeland R 3 HS; Deepwater, MO; College;.

LASZEWSKI, Ronald; Malden HS; Malden, MO; HonRl; IMSpt; TIMEAwd; Building Industries.

LATCH, Doris I; Stewardson Strasburg HS; Stewardson, IL; HonRl; SchPl; YthFlsp; Chmn4-H; SecF-HA; TreasPpCl;.

LATENSER, Barbara; Bishop Hogan HS; Kansas City, MO; Chrs; HonRl; LbryAde; SchMus; TreasStuCncl; SpnCl; PpCl; OptClAwd; Bus Sch; Sec.

LATHAM, Edgar A; Southwestern HS; Flint, MI; Band; HonRl; SctActv; Univ; Mech Tech.

LATHAM, Jan P; Savannah HS; Savannah, MO; SecFrshCls; TrsSophCls; Chr; HonRl; NHS; StuCncl; YthFlsp; RptrSchPpr; CaptChrldr; CitAwd; College; Special Education.

LATHAM, Judy L; Savannah HS; Savannah, MO; ALAGirlsSt; HonRl; SctActv; Yrbk; FHA; LatCl; PpCl; Swmmng; GAA; PresAwd; College; History.

LATHAM, Pam; Triplains HS; Winona, KS; TrsSophCls; Chr; CmntyWkr; CncrtBnd; HonRl; LbryAde; PepBnd; StuCncl; Yrbk; Univ; Professional.

LATHEN, Margaret L; Simley HS; Inver Grove Hts, MN; 7/228 AFS; HonRl; NHS; Winona St Col; Accounting.

LATHROP, Stephen W; Granite South HS; Granite City, IL; Chrs; ChrhWkr; Mdrgl; SchMus; SchPl; YthFlsp; VPSciCl; South Ill Univ; Psychology.

LATINO, Dennis J; Streator Twp HS; Streator, IL; HonRl; Yrbk; Univ Of Illinois; Pharmacy.

LA TOURELLE, Brian G; Lincoln HS; Wisconsin Rapids, WI; 40/570 ALBoysSt; HonRl; NHS; U Of Wi Madison; Chemical Engineering.

LATSHAW, Ralph A; Shawnee Mission East HS; Leawood, KS; ChrhWkr; CncrtBnd; HonRl; MrchBnd; SctActv; YthFlsp; PpCl; University; Business.

LATSHAW, Rick J; Purdy HS; Purdy, MO; 4/40 VPFrshCls; PresSophCls; Chr; ChrhWkr; HonRl; NHS; Yrbk; FFA; MthCl; Bsktbl; Col; Professional.

LATTA, Todd E; Stratton HS; Stratton, NE; PresFrshCls; PresSophCls; VPJrCls; VPSrCls; Band; CncrtBnd; HonRl; MrchBnd; StuCncl; EdYrBk; RptrSchPpr; EdSchPpr; SptEdSchPpr; LetterLionAwd; LetterMasAwd; Voc Tech Sch; Vocation.

LATTERELL, Dan; Sheldon Senior HS; Sheldon, IA; 50/150 HonRl; Quill&Scroll; EdSchPpr; FSA; SciCl; Tech Voc School; Watchmaking.

LATTERELL, Lori D; Atwater HS; Kandiyohi, MN; VPFrshCls; Band; Chr; Chrs; ChrhWkr; HonRl; TchrAde; LetterChrldr; GAA; 4-HAwd; Med Office Assitant.

LATTIN, Lisa J; Smith Center HS; Smith Center, KS; ALAGirlsSt; Chrs; ChrhWkr; CncrtBnd; HonRl; MrchBnd; NHS; SchPl; RptrSchPpr; 4-H; Trk; College; Professional.

LATVIS, James J; Ontonagon Area HS; Mass, MI; HonRl; JA; LetterBsktbl; JAAwd; College.

LATWAITIS, Diane M; Blair HS; Ford Calhoun, NE; ALAGirlsSt; Chr; CncrtBnd; HonRl; NHS; NatlMeritCmnd; StuCncl; RptrYrbk; FSA; PpCl; Univ Of Nebraska; Zoology Major.

LATWAITIS, Donna L; Blair HS; Ft Calhoun, NE; Band; Chr; Chrs; CncrtBnd; HonRl; MrchBnd; NatlThespSoc; PepBnd; SchMus; SchPl; University; Professional.

LAU, Clayton E; Hale HS; Hale, MI; College; Mahtematics.

LAUBE, Diane M; Carmel HS; Waukegan, IL; 36/173 Aud/Vis; ChrhWkr; HonRl; NHS; SctActv; Sdlty; TchrAde; Coll Of Lake Co; Horticulturist.

LAUBE, Jeffrey A; Owen Withee HS; Owen, WI; TrsJrCls; TrsSrCls; Band; HonRl; NHS; StuCncl; LetterBsbl; CaptFtbl; LetterTrk; CaptWrstlng; Univ; Professional.

LAUBER, Jeffrey M; South Ripley HS; Holton, IN; 1/99 PresFrshCls; PresSrCls; ALBoysSt; HonRl; NHS; Trk; CaptIMSpt; College; Mechanical Engineer.

LAUBER, Ron L; West Holt HS; Atkinson, NE; Chr; Chrl; Chrs; ChrhWkr; CmntyWkr; Mdrgl; MrchBnd; SctActv; YthFlsp; College; Elementary Education.

LAUBNER, Randal L; Hershey HS; Hershey, NE; PresFrshCls; SecTrsSophCls; HonRl; TchrAde; LetterBsktbl; LetterFtbl; LetterTrk; PresAwd; Trade School.

LAUBY, Elizabeth; St Ann HS; Lexington, NE; Band; Chrs; HonRl; PepBnd; SchPl; PpCl; Tennis; Business School; Vocation.

LAUBY, Mark G; Wausau East HS; Wausau, WI; 33/387 Chr; HonRl; NHS; Orch; SctActv; StuCncl; Trk; CchngActv; IMSpt; RotaryAwd; Uwmc; Eng Or Archelogist.

LAUDANI, Debra; Roosevelt HS; Chicago, IL; 30/300 HonRl; JrNHS; NHS; OffAde; StuCncl; TchrAde; RptrYrbk; Yrbk; RptrSchPpr; SchPpr; SpnCl; Western Ill Univ; Psychologist.

LAUDE, Mary A; Homewood Flossmoor HS; Homewood, IL; 111/910 Chr; ChrhWkr; HonRl; NatlThespSoc; SchMus; University Of Illinois; Retailing.

LAUDENBACH, Charles W; Sartell HS; St Cloud, MN; 4/75 HonRl; NatlFornLg; NHS; NatlMeritCmnd; SchAde; TchrAde; LetterTrk; Univ; Professional.

LAUDERDALE, Allison L; Junction City Senior HS; Junction City, KS; AFS; Band; Chr; ChrhWkr; CmntyWkr; HonRl; MrchBnd; SctActv; StuGov; YthFlsp; College; Medical Tech.

LAUE, Dale A; Wethersfield HS; Kewanee, IL; 14/64 HonRl; SciCl; LetterBsktbl; LetterTrk; Illinois State Univ; Retail Mgmt.

LAUE, Lonnie R; Washington HS; Greenleaf, KS; ALBoysSt; ChrhWkr; HonRl; VPStuCncl; RptrSchPpr; SptEdSchPpr; SchPpr; Bsbl; Bsktbl; LetterTrk;.

LAUE, Rolanda J; Washington HS; Greenleaf, KS; 9/45 ALAGirlsSt; ChrhWkr; HonRl; HospAde; JrNHS; SctActv; Yrbk; FHA; PpCl; SciCl; Bsktbl; College; Nursing.

LAUE, Sharon F; Washburn Rural HS; Topeka, KS; Chr; ChrhWkr; CmntyWkr; DrlTm; HonRl; OffAde; PolWkr; SchAde; SchMus; Bsbl; Univ; Curr Of Major Study.

LAUER, Debra L; Lincoln Community HS; Lincoln, IL; 27/252 Band; HospAde; MrchBnd; NHS; SchMus; LatCl; Illinois State University; Accounting.

LAUER, Elizabeth A; Collinsville HS; Collinsville, IL; 40/625 Chr; Chrs; HonRl; TrsFrshCls; SchMus; SchPl; FrCl; Southern Ill; Communications.

LAUER, Irene M; Madonna HS; Chicago, IL; 33/273 Chrs; HonRl; NHS; SchMus; SchPl; StuGov; EdYrBk; RptrSchPpr; PresGerCl; SciCl; Bsktbl; GAA; Illinois Inst Of Tech; Envrnmentl Engineer.

LAUER, Julie; Albany Senior HS; Richmond, MN; 3/129 Chrs; HonRl; OffAde; SchPl; FHA; College Of St Teresa.

LAUER, Wayne F; Barrett Public HS; Barrett, MN; 1/19 VPJrCls; Band; ChrhWkr; CmntyWkr; CncrtBnd; HonRl; JrNHS; StuCncl; RptrYrbk; 4-H;.

LAUERDIERE, Janet M; Macomb Sr HS; Macomb, IL; PresJrCls; Chr; ChrhWkr; HonRl; SchMus; StuCncl; SpnCl; Chrldr; Western Ill Univ; Psychology.

LAUERMAN, Maureen K; Menominee HS; Menominee, MI; AFS; HonRl; HospAde; JrNHS; Quill&Scroll; RptrYrbk; SpnCl; Glf; Chrldr; VoiceDemAwd; Col ;pro.

LAUFENBERG, Donna; Mt Horeb HS; Mount Horeb, WI; Chr; ChrhWkr; SchPl; FHA; FrCl; PpCl; GAA; Vocational; Professional Broadcasting.

LAUFENBERG, Sheryl; Brookwood HS; Cashton, WI; 2/56 SecJrCls; HonRl; LbryAde; NHS; RptrYrbk; RptrSchPpr; PpCl; Wwti Lacrosse; Administrative Secretary.

LAUFER, William P; Christian Brothers HS; St Louis, MO; 7/170 HonRl; NHS; Quill&Scroll; ROTC; Sdlty; SchPpr; University; Business Admin.

LAUFFER, Kim; Perry Lecompton HS; Perry, KS; Chr; DrlTm; HonRl; NHS; RptrYrbk; RptrSchPpr; FHA; PpCl; Bsktbl; Chrldr; Coll; Teach.

LAUFMAN, James D; New Trier West HS; Glencoe, IL; 129/698 Aud/Vis; HonRl; NatlMeritFnl; SchPl; Bsktbl; Colgate Univ; Doctor.

LAUGAL, James A; Lostant HS; Lostant, IL; 1/16 TrsFrshCls; PresSophCls; PresJrCls; PresSrCls; PresBand; HonRl; NHS; SchMus; SchPl; StuCncl; EdSchPpr; LetterBsktbl; LetterGlf; College; Engineering.

LAUGHERY, Kevin M; St Teresa HS; Oreana, IL; 5/117 ChrhWkr; CmntyWkr; HonRl; NHS; NatlMeritCmnd; SecNatlThespSoc; PolWkr; SchMus; SchPl; SptEdYrbk; Yrbk; Trk; College; Religion.

LAUGHLIN, Donald A; South Nodaway R Iv HS; Guilford, MO; 4/17 VPFrshCls; Band; HonRl; LbryAde; NHS; VPStuCncl; RptrSchPpr; Trk; DanFAwd; 4-HAwd; Nw Mo State & Kan State; Animal Husbandry.

LAUGHLIN, Kathleen J; Wm Chrisman Sr HS; Independence, MO; 21/396 Band; ChrhWkr; CncrtBnd; HonRl; MrchBnd; Orch; SchMus; GerCl; SciCl; Trk; College; Professional.

LAUGHLIN, Kelley L; East Alton Wood River HS; Wood River, IL; 49/312 Chr; DrlTm; HonRl; HospAde; NHS; OffAde; StuCncl; RptrSchPpr; FNA; St Johns School; Nursing.

LAUGHNER, Danny D; Clinton Central HS; Frankfort, IN; 14/105 Band; CncrtBnd; MrchBnd; RptrYrbk; 4-H; PresFFA; MthCl; SciCl; Glf; 4-HAwd; Purdue Univ; Agriculture.

LAUGHTER, David F; Parkway North Sr HS; Creve Coeur, MO; Chr; Chrs; ChrhWkr; SctActv; StuGov; YthFlsp; Ftbl; Trk; Wrstlng; CchngActv; University; Professional.

LAUGLE, Theresa; Scecina Memorial HS; Indianapolis, IN; 13/188 Band; CncrtBnd; HonRl; MrchBnd; PepBnd; RedCrAde; SctActv; Ball State Univ; Accountat.

LAUKE, Theodore M; Adlai E Stevenson HS; Lincolnshire, IL; 19/239 HonRl; NHS; GerCl; College.

LAUNDERVILLE, Dorothy R; Holdrege HS; Holdrege, NE; Chrs; HonRl; SchPl; RptrSchPpr; FHA; Army; Teletype Operator.

LAUNDERVILLE, Gary; St Marys Hs; Storm Lake, IA; HstFrshCls; PresSophCls; PresJrCls; ChrhWkr; HonRl; NatlThespSoc; Bsbl; Bsktbl; Trk; KiwanAwd;.

LAUNER, Jeannine K; Virginia HS; Virginia, IL; CncrtBnd; DrmMjrt; HonRl; SchPpr; 4-H; Trk; Chrldr; GAA; DanFAwd; 4-HAwd;.

LAUNER, Sheila F; Warsaw HS; Warsaw, IL; HstJrCls; HonRl; OffAde; Trade School; Professional.

LAURENTIUS, Debra S; Oak Ridge R 6 HS; Perryville, MO; 6/18 TrsFrshCls; SecSophCls; PresJrCls; HonRl; SchPl; StuCncl; FHA; Chrldr; Univ; Professional.

LAURENZ, Steven L; Ithaca HS; Ithaca, MI; 3/180 ChrhWkr; CncrtBnd; HonRl; MrchBnd; NHS; 4-H; 4-HAwd; RotaryAwd;.

LAURITZEN, Wendy; Arkansas City HS; Arkansas City, KS; 10/200 AFS; ALAGirlsSt; HonRl; OffAde; TchrAde; FFA; PpCl; Trk; PPFtbl; CitAwd; Ks St Univ; Wildlife Conservation.

LAURSEN, Mark; Milford Comm HS; Milford, IA; 4/78 ALBoysSt; NatlMeritFnl; BauchLmbAwd; Iowa State Univ; Veterinarian Medicin.

LAUSCHKE, Catherine A; Alton Sr HS; Alton, IL; 30/830 Chr; ChrhWkr; CmntyWkr; LetterCncrtBnd; HonRl; NHS; SctActv; TchrAde; LetterTennis; LetterChrldr; GAA; Colorado State Univ; Wildlife Biology.

LAUTENBACH, Arthur F; Sevastopol HS; Egg Harbor, WI; TrsJrCls; TrsSrCls; NHS; SecFFA; IMSpt; University; Animal Science.

LAUTENBACH, Deborah; Weston HS; Hillpoint, WI; SecSophCls; Band; Chrs; CncrtBnd; HonRl; MrchBnd; PepBnd; FHA; Bsktbl; Chrldr; Trade.

LAUTENSCHLAGER, Heidi M; Milford Twp HS; Milford, IL; VPSophCls; RptrYrbk; SpnCl; MthCl; SciCl; LetterBsktbl; Swmmng; LetterTrk; Chrldr; GAA; College; Professional.

LAUTERI, Theresa L; Marian Catholic HS; Chicago Hgts, IL; 10/328 ChrhWkr; HonRl; NHS; SchAde; TchrAde; Yrbk; College; Professional.

LAUTERS, Debbie S; Marcus Comm HS; Marcus, IA; 7/73 ChrhWkr; HonRl; LbryAde; 4-H; LetterTrk; DARAwd; 4-HAwd; PresAwd; Iowa State U; Home Econ.

LAUTH, Jean L; Wheaton North HS; Wheaton, IL; 12/302 Chr; HonRl; NHS; NatlThespSoc; SchMus; StuCncl; TchrAde; CaptYthFlsp; Chrldr; GAA; KiwanAwd; CitAwd; College; Education.

LAUTH, Tom; Beaver Dam Senior Hs; Beaver Dam, WI; 156/349 Chrs; DrlTm; Mdrgl; Orch; SchMus; SchPl; StuCncl; Bsktbl; Trk; 4-HAwd; College; Policeman.

LAUTZENHEISER, Douglas A; Charlotte HS; Charlotte, MI; 65/263 CncrtBnd; MrchBnd; TchrAde; CaptTrk; IMSpt; KiwanAwd; CitAwd; Hillsdale; Acct.

LAUVER, Ann L; Lakeland HS; Howe, IN; 1/146 Band; Chr; ChrhWkr; HonRl; HospAde; NHS; StuCncl; YthFlsp; FNA; MthCl; Bible School; Christian Service.

LAUX, Debra A; Appleton West HS; Appleton, WI; 7/640 AFS; Band; ChrhWkr; CncrtBnd; NatlFornLg; NHS; Orch; PolWkr; SchMus; SchPpr; University; Speech Pathology.

LAUX, Lori A; Pius X HS; Lincoln, NE; DrlTm; HonRl; ModUN; EdYrBk; PpCl; Univ Of Ne; Fasion.

LAUZON, Gerald J; L L Wright HS; Ironwood, MI; Aud/Vis; ChrhWkr; CmntyWkr; VPNatlThespSoc; ROTC; SchPl; SctActv; 4-H; 4-HAwd; Trade School; Chef.

LAVALEY, Sherry L; Sutherland HS; Sutherland, NE; Band; HonRl; SchPl; StuCncl; YthFlsp; RptrYrbk; 4-H; PpCl; Trk; GAA;.

LA VALLA, Christie L; Indus HS; Littlefork, MN; 3/14 PresFrshCls; Chrs; SchPl; SctActv; StuCncl; EdYrBk; 4-H; LetterTrk; Chrldr; GAA; College; Medical Technology.

LA VALLA, Christi L; Indus HS; Littlefork, MN; 3/14 PresFrshCls; Chr; Chrs; ChrhWkr; SchPl; SctActv; StuCncl; EdYrBk; 4-H; LetterTrk; Chrldr; GAA; 4-HAwd; College; Medical Technology.

LA VALLEY, Kari L; Dallas Community HS; Dallas Center, IA; Band; PresSophCls; HonRl; MrchBnd; PepBnd; SchMus; EdYrBk; Bsktbl; Wrstlng; Chrldr; Area Xi Comm Coll; Home Ec.

LAVASTIDA, Lisa; Whitmore Lake HS; South Lyon, MI; VPJrCls; Band; CncrtBnd; HonRl; JrNHS; MrchBnd; NHS; PepBnd; StuCncl; 4-H; FrCl; CaptBsktbl; Tennis; GAA; Univ; Professional.

LAVELL, Kym A; Hamady HS; Flint, MI; 10/200 PresSrCls; Band; CncrtBnd; HonRl; MrchBnd; NHS; NatlMeritCmnd; Orch; PepBnd; StuCncl; University; Professional.

LAVELLE, Elizabeth; Mercy HS; Omaha, NE; 35/75 SchMus; SchPl; StuCncl; StuGov; RptrYrbk; EdYrBk; FrCl; LatCl; Bsbl; GAA; College; Respiratory Therapist.

LAVELLE, Janet L; Mercy HS; Omaha, NE; VPSrCls; Chrs; ChrhWkr; HonRl; NatlCathMusEdAsoc; NatlFornLg; NHS; Quill&Scroll; SchMus; SchPl; Sdlty; LetterBsktbl; Tennis; CchngActv; Creighton University; Theater.

LAVELLE, Larry W; Hordville Public HS; Clarks, NE; VPFrshCls; TrsSophCls; PresJrCls; PresSrCls; ALBoysSt; Chr; ChrhWkr; HonRl; SchMus; SchPl; SctActv; StuCncl; Yrbk; RptrSchPpr; CaptFtbl; Rockmont College.

LAVELOCK, Tammie L; Carrollton HS; Carrollton, MO; 6/100 Chrs; HonRl; NHS; TchrAde; 4-H; SpnCl; Chrldr; IMSpt; DARAwd; University; Secretary.

LAVEN, Kent P; Homewood Flossmoor HS; Flossmoor, IL; 119/940 ChrhWkr; NHS; FrCl; LetterSwmmng; Southern Ill Univ; Forestry.

LAVENAU, David B; Proviso West HS; Westchester, IL; 227/948 Band; ChrhWkr; CncrtBnd; HonRl; MrchBnd; Orch; PepBnd; Wheaton Coll; Law/econ.

LA VERE, Mary S; Big Rapids HS; Big Rapids, MI; Chr; Chrs; HonRl; NatlMeritSF; SchMus; SchPl; Ferris State Col; Physician Asst.

LA VERGNE, Debra K; Lake Linden Hubbell HS; Laurium, MI; 3/59 Band; CncrtBnd; HonRl; JA; MrchBnd; Orch; PepBnd; SchPl; TchrAde; EdSchPpr; Northern Mi Univ; Social Worker.

LA VERRE, Mary; Big Rapids HS; Big Rapids, MI; Chr; HonRl; NatlMeritFnl; NatlMeritSF; SchMus; RptrSchPpr; LatCl; Ferris State College; Physicians Assistant.

LAVERS, Marsha R; Sheboygan N HS; Sheboygan, WI; ChrhWkr; HonRl; RedCrAde; Trk; IMSpt; University; Professional.

LAVERY, Donald L; Tri County Area HS; Sand Lake, MI; 13/90 Band; ChrhWkr; HonRl; NHS; StuCncl; Trk; Gods Bible School; Minister.

LA VESSER, Donna M; John Marshall 'S; Milwaukee, WI; HonRl; HospAde; OffAde; Quill&Scroll; SchAde; StuCncl; SchPpr; PpCl; Chrldr; College; Business.

LAVEY, Martha A; Immaculata HS; Detroit, MI; VPSophCls; VPJrCls; VPSrCls; CmntyWkr; HonRl; JrNHS; NHS; NatlMeritFnl; NatlMeritSF; SchPl; StuCncl; StuGov; Northwestern Univ; Theatre.

LA VIGNE, Frank J; Big Bay De Noc HS; Nahma, MI; 4/53 Band; CncrtBnd; HonRl; NHS; SchPl; SchPpr; FrCl; LatCl; LetterBsktbl; CaptTrk; Coll; Study.

LAVOIE, Thomas W; Alpena HS; Alpena, MI; LetterBsktbl; LetterTrk; Central Mi Univ; Pro Bus Ed.

LA VOY, Lori L; Lincoln HS; Lake City, MN; AFS; Chr; Chrs; HonRl; SchPl; SctActv; Yrbk; GAA; PPFtbl; KiwanAwd; Gustavus Adolphus College; Pediatrician Med.

LAVRA, Albert C; St Johns HS; St Johns, MI; 36/333 HonRl; JrNHS; LitMag; NHS; NatlMeritCmnd; Bsbl; IMSpt; Mich Tech Univ; Chem Engr.

LAVRINOVICH, Lee A; Crown Point HS; Crown Point, IN; 30/500 Chr; HonRl; NHS; NatlMeritCmnd; Indiana Univ; Medicine.

LAW, Deborah; Litchfield HS; Walshville, IL; ChrhWkr; HonRl; HospAde; TchrAde; FrCl; Siu E; Math Major.

LAW, Martha D; Central HS; St Joseph, MO; 8/560 Chrl; ChrhWkr; CtyCnl; CmntyWkr; HonRl; NHS; SchPl; StuGov; FrCl; University.

LAW, Nancy E; Hill City HS; Hill City, KS; 21/55 Band; Chr; Chrs; ChrhWkr; HonRl; PepBnd; 4-H; FHA; PpCl; 4-HAwd; Fort Hays State Coll; Music.

LAW, Richard; Oxford Jct Cons HS; Oxford Jct, IA; 2/28 SecFrshCls; ALBoysSt; HonRl; NHS; PepBnd; SchMus; SctActv; Bsbl; Bsktbl; Trk; Univ; Engineering.

LAW, Tom S; Kingsley Pierson Comm HS; Pierson, IA; 10/59 ALBoysSt; Chr; ChrhWkr; HonRl; SchMus; 4-H; FFA; Glf; 4-HAwd; College; Farming.

LAWANZ, Steven; Midland HS; Midland, MI; Band; CncrtBnd; MrchBnd; GerCl; College; Medicine.

LAWHEAD, Nanci J; Minden HS; Kearney, NE; Chrs; ChrhWkr; OffAde; TchrAde; Yrbk; RptrSchPpr; SchPpr; 4-H; FHA; Lincoln School Of Commerce; Secretary.

LAWHORN, Cindi L; Central HS; La Crosse, WI; Chrs; HonRl; Uw La Crosse; Commercial Artist.

LAWLER, Barbara A; Washington HS; Two Rivers, WI; Band; ChrhWkr; CncrtBnd; DrmBgl; JA; MrchBnd; OffAde; PepBnd; TchrAde; College; Elementary Education.

LAWLER, Daniel T; Marquette Univ HS; Wauwatosa, WI; 17/270 VPSophCls; VPJrCls; SecSrCls; CmntyWkr; HonRl; NatlMeritCmnd; SchPl; SecStuCncl; StuGov; LetterChrldr; Univ Of Wisconsin.

LAWLER, Kirk S; Glenbard East HS; Lombard, IL; HonRl; NatlMeritCmnd; PolWkr; StuCncl; StuGov; University Of Wisconsin; Social Work.

LAWLER, Margaret A; Rock Lake Public HS; Hansboro, ND; 4/26 Band; Chrs; CncrtBnd; HonRl; MrchBnd; PepBnd; SchPl; StuCncl; Twrl; FHA; U Of North Dakota; Professional.

LAWLER, Margie C; Anna Jonesboro HS; Anna, IL; 14/137 HonRl; HospAde; SctActv; FTA; SpnCl; Southern Ill; Elementary Education.

LAWLESS, Gayle J; North Farmington HS; Farmington Hills, MI; 18/461 Michigan State Univ; Elementary Educ.

LAWLESS, Linda; Belle Plaine HS; Belle Plaine, KS; 5/44 Band; ChrhWkr; CmntyWkr; HonRl; StuCncl; TchrAde; Yrbk; 4-H; PpCl; 4-HAwd; Cowley Cnty Cmm; Accounting Tech.

LAWLESS, Timothy; Spalding Hs; Peoria, IL; Bsktbl; Ftbl; Tennis;.

LAWLESS, Timothy J; Spalding HS; Peoria, IL; LetterBsktbl; LetterFtbl; LetterTennis; College.

LAWNICHAK, Robin R; Gaylord HS; Gaylord, MI; 18/210 HonRl; NHS; OffAde; 4-H; KeyCl; CaptBsktbl; Central Mi Clge; Accounting.

LAWRENCE, Evelyn; Bradleyville HS; Oldfield, MO; HonRl; Army; Phys Ther.

LAWRENCE, Gerald T; Buffalo Grove HS; Arlington Hts, IL; 47/300 HonRl; Univ Il; Eng.

LAWRENCE, Janet; Ames Senior HS; Ames, IA; HonRl; OffAde; Orch; PepBnd; SchMus; SchPl; TchrAde; YthFlsp; 4-H; Trk; College; Piano Teacher.

LAWRENCE, Jeffery C; Jonesville HS; Jonesville, MI; 12/86 PresSophCls; ALBoysSt; HonRl; LetterBsbl; LetterFtbl; LetterWrstlng; College; Business.

LAWRENCE, John M; Dwight David Eisenhower HS; Saginaw, MI; 12/365 HonRl; NHS; SctActv; Delta College.

LAWRENCE, Joni M; Gull Lake HS; Richland, MI; HonRl; HospAde; SchPl; VPStuCncl; VPStuGov; 4-H; FrCl; PpCl; Chrldr; GAA; PPFtbl; 4-HAwd; Univ; Rn.

LAWRENCE, Julia K; A Jchs HS; Anna, IL; Band; Chrs; ChrhWkr; HonRl; NatlFornLg; NatlMeritCmnd; NatlMeritSF; SchPl; SecStuCncl; SchPpr; FTA; TreasLatCl; Southeast Mo Univ; Medicine.

LAWRENCE, Julie A; Lapeer HS; Lapeer, MI; 5/426 HospAde; NHS; SctActv; Yrbk; SpnCl; U Of Mi ;dr.

LAWRENCE, Kathleen M; Larkin HS; Elgin, IL; 143/573 Aud/Vis; CncrtBnd; HonRl; MrchBnd; PepBnd; College; Veterinarian.

LAWRENCE, Kenneth J; Wayland Academy; Horicon, WI; 4/70 HonRl; LetterBsktbl; LetterFtbl; LetterTennis; College.

LAWRENCE, Kurt A; Proviso West HS; Hillside, IL; 89/1256 HonRl; NHS; NatlMeritSchl; SctActv; LetterTrk;.

LAWRENCE, Leann R; Sturgis HS; Sturgis, MI; ALAGirlsSt; HonRl; NHS; RedCrAde; StuCncl; FrCl; PpCl; Tennis; Chrldr; PPFtbl; W Mi Univ; Occupational Therapy.

LAWRENCE, Lynette T; Owosso HS; Owosso, MI; 124/452 ChrhWkr; LbryAde; OffAde; YthFlsp; LatCl; College; Medical Secretary.

LAWRENCE, Nyla L; Harper Creek HS; Battle Creek, MI; Band; HonRl; LitMag; SchMus; SctActv; RptrSchPpr; SpnCl; Trk; 4-HAwd; OptClAwd; College; Nursing.

LAWRENCE, Perry D; Kennedy Sr HS; Cedar Rapids, IA; ModUN; Trk; Wrstlng; College; Law.

LAWRENCE, Sharon B; Wisconsin Academy; Westchester, IL; Band; Chr; ChrhWkr; HonRl; NHS; OffAde; University; Social Work.

LAWRENCE, Stephen A; Saline HS; Saline, MI; VPJA; NHS; SctActv; Bsbl; Trk; IMSpt; Univ; Professional.

LAWRENCE, Susan C; Litchfield Sr HS; Litchfield, MN; 4-H; SpnCl; College.

LAWRENCE, Teresa G; Raytown HS; Independence, MO; AFS; ChrhWkr; DrlTm; HonRl; Univ Of Mo; Art.

LAWRENCE, Tony D; Faifax R 3 HS; Craig, MO; 1/27 Band; Chr; CncrtBnd; DrlTm; HonRl; MrchBnd; PepBnd; SchPl; Yrbk; FHA; PpCl; Chrldr; College; Professional.

LAWRENCE, Tracy K; Evanston Township HS; Evanston, IL; CmntyWkr; HonRl; PolWkr; SchMus; SchPl; Emerson College; Theatre.

LAWRENZ, Robert W; Baldwin HS; Baldwin City, KS; VPJrCls; ALBoysSt; Band; Chr; CncrtBnd; HonRl; MrchBnd; NHS; PepBnd; SchPl; SctActv; Bsktbl; Ftbl; College; Professional.

LAWS, Brenda K; Avon HS; Indianapolis, IN; 7/173 CncrtBnd; DrmMjrt; HonRl; ModUN; NHS; YthFnd; FrCl; PpCl; Bsktbl; GAA; Col; Social Worker.

LAWS, Suzanne D; Quincy Sr HS; Quincy, IL; 9/815 Band; JrNHS; MrchBnd; NHS; NatlMeritCmnd; SpnCl; Swmmng; Univ.

LAWSHE, Jan M; Bishop Noll Institute; Gary, IN; 23/360 ChrhWkr; CncrtBnd; HonRl; HospAde; JrNHS; MrchBnd; NHS; StuCncl; University; Professional.

LAWSON, Beverly A; Benton Consolidated HS; Benton, IL; 3/170 VPSrCls; Aud/Vis; Band; Chr; Chrs; ChrhWkr; CncrtBnd; DrmMjrt; HonRl; JrNHS; Trk; GAA; Rend Lake Jr Coll; Air Traffic Controller.

LAWSON, Catherine A; Lyons Twp HS; La Grange, IL; Chr; Chrs; ChrhWkr; HonRl; NHS; OffAde; SchMus; SchPl; StuGov; College; Business.

LAWSON, Cynthia; Ishpeming HS; Ishpeming, MI; 11/200 Chrs; HonRl; NHS; IMSpt; Central Michigan Univ; Office Administratio.

LAWSON, David G; Armstrong HS; Crystal, MN; 14/603 Aud/Vis; Band; CmntyWkr; HonRl; LbryAde; NHS; Socr; College; Professional.

LAWSON, Debra E; Pius X HS; Lincoln, NE; HonRl; NHS; PpCl; Chrldr; Univ Of Nebr; Social Worker.

LAWSON, John C; Crestland Community HS; Early, IA; 6/30 ALBoysSt; HonRl; StuCncl; YthFlsp; SptEdSchPpr; LetterBsbl; LetterBsktbl; LetterFtbl; LetterTrk; College; Accounting.

LAWSON, Kathryn A; Highland HS; Labelle, MO; TrsSophCls; TrsJrCls; ALAGirlsSt; ChrhWkr; HonRl; JrNHS; NHS; FrCl; Bsktbl; 4-HAwd; College; Medical Assistant.

LAWSON, Kathryn L; Central Noble HS; Albion, IN; Band; Chr; CmntyWkr; MrchBnd; SchPl; TchrAde; YthFlsp; 4-H; PpCl; Bsktbl; Trk; College; Law.

LAWSON, Lonnie L; Hayes County HS; Hayes Center, NE; Band; Chrs; ChrhWkr; PepBnd; 4-H; FFA; Bsktbl; Nw Kansas Area Voc Tech; Auto Mechanic.

LAWSON, Mary M; Hayes County HS; Hayes Center, NE; 18/24 SecTrsJrCls; VPSrCls; Chr; SctActv; Sdlty; Yrbk; SchPpr; 4-H; Mc Cook Community.

LAWSON, Nancy; Stewartville HS; Racine, MN; Chr; HonRl; YthFlsp; FHA; College; Liberal Arts.

LAWSON, Patricia S; Huron HS; Ann Arbor, MI; 72/565 Band; ChrhWkr; CncrtBnd; MrchBnd; PepBnd; SpnCl; CaptBsktbl; Trk; PresGAA; Mi St Univ; Physical Education.

LAWSON, Ray A; West Side HS; Gary, IN; CncrtBnd; HonRl; JrNHS; NHS; LetterBsbl; LetterFtbl; University; Engineering.

LAWSON, Theresa L; Mattoon HS; Mattoon, IL; 60/400 VPSophCls; Chr; CmntyWkr; HonRl; NHS; NatlThespSoc; StuCncl; Yrbk; 4-H; DanFAwd; Clge; Music.

LAWTON, Kathleen M; Our Lady Of Mercy HS; Livonia, MI; 2/253 LbryAde; NHS; TchrAde; Univ Of Michigan; Law.

LAWTON, Kent C; Richland Center HS; Richland Center, WI; 17/186 ChrhWkr; HonRl; NHS; KeyCl; Bsktbl; LetterTrk; University; Business Admin.

LAWTON, Linda J; Heritage Christian HS; Indianapolis, IN; 2/24 VPFrshCls; VPSophCls; ChrhWkr; HonRl; Quill&Scroll; SchPl; TchrAde; YthFlsp; EdYrBk; CaptBsktbl; LetterTrk; CchngActv; Stetson Univ; Secondary Ed.

LAWTON, Mark A; South Central HS; Elizabeth, IN; SecFFA; Trade Schl; Horse Trainer.

LAWYER, Jan M; Yankton Sr HS; Yankton, SD; TrsFrshCls; SecSophCls; VPJrCls; VPSrCls; HonRl; NHS; SchPl; StuGov; VoiceDemAwd; Sdsu; Pharmacy.

LAY, Thomas; Richmond Burton HS; Spring Grove, IL; 15/90 ALBoysSt; CmntyWkr; HonRl; RptrSchPpr; SptEdSchPpr; Bsbl; Bsktbl; Ftbl; AmLegAwd; Northern Il Univ; Accounting.

LAY, Tonya N; Houston HS; Houston, MO; Chrs; ChrhWkr; HonRl; NHS; OffAde; 4-H; FHA; Business School.

LAYBOURN, Paul J; North HS; Fargo, ND; ALBoysSt; Band; Chr; Chrs; ChrhWkr; CncrtBnd; NatlThespSoc; PepBnd; FBLA; Ftbl; Military Acad; Scuba Diver.

LAYDON, James R; Iron Mountain HS; Iron Mountain, MI; Chrs; PresIntrClCncl; NatlMeritCmnd; NatlMeritSF; TchrAde; YthLg; Bsktbl; Ftbl; LetterTennis; IMSpt; Lake Superior St College; Mech Engineer.

LAYHER, Patricia; Saline HS; Saline, MI; Band; Chrs; HonRl; MrchBnd; SchMus; YthFlsp; Eastern Mi Univ; Acc.

LAYHER, Susan K; Vandercook Lake HS; Jackson, MI; 4/101 PresJrCls; Band; DrmMjrt; JrNHS; MrchBnd; EngCl; PpCl; GAA; 4-HAwd; CitAwd; Univ Of Mi ; Med.

LAYMAN, Cynthia E; Mt Carmel HS; Downers Grove, IL; 2/21 Chrs; ChrhWkr; HonRl; SchPl; EdYrBk; Bible Sch; Missionary Teacher.

LAYMAN, Lisa M; Lawrence Central HS; Indianapolis, IN; 244/734 ChrhWkr; HonRl; OffAde; TchrAde; YthFlsp; Yrbk; FTA; Purdue Univ; Dental Assistant.

LAYNE, Jennifer T; Visitation HS; Chicago, IL; Chrs; SchPl; SctActv; Chicago State University; Accounting.

LAYNE, Kathy S; R Iii Central HS; Elvins, MO; 1/163 Band; CncrtBnd; HonRl; MrchBnd; NHS; PepBnd; College.

LAYNE, Michael L; Santa Fe Trail HS; Carbondale, KS; PresFrshCls; ALBoysSt; HonRl; SchPl; Trk; Wrstlng; IMSpt; Col; Bus Management.

LAYTON, Laura L; Wellsville HS; Wellsville, KS; 7/67 TrsJrCls; Band; Chrs; NHS; SchMus; EdYrBk; LetterTrk; Chrldr; CitAwd; Univ Of Arkansas; Social Work.

LAZAR, Deborah R; Argo Comm HS; Bridgeview, IL; 2/508 HonRl; LitMag; LbryAde; ModUN; NHS; George Williams College; Natural Science.

LAZAR, Robert A; Port Washington HS; Port Washington, WI; 15/235 ALBoysSt; HonRl; SpnCl; MthCl; KiwanAwd; Col; City Planning.

LAZAR, Vickie R; Ladysmith Hawkins HS; Hawkins, WI; HonRl; SecLbryAde; RptrYrbk; SecFBLA; FHA; FTA; VPSpnCl; Business School; Secretary.

LAZARCHEFF, Georgann; Pattonville HS; Creve Coeur, MO; HonRl; NHS; SchAde; StuCncl; LatCl; PpCl; Chrldr; PPFtbl;.

LAZAROFF, Pete L; Pennfield HS; Battle Creek, MI; Band; CncrtBnd; HonRl; JA; MrchBnd; PepBnd; TchrAde; Olivet College; Music.

LAZETTE, Rhonda E; St Mary Academy; Monroe, MI; 1/142 Chrl; HonRl; NHS; SchPl; EdSchPpr; 4-H; College; Accountant.

LAZO, Joy; Immaculata HS; Chicago, IL; 10/201 Chrs; HonRl; JA; NHS; SchPl; StuCncl; SchPpr; Chrldr; AmLegAwd; Northwestern Univ; Journalist.

LAZZARA, Alan A; Marist HS; Chicago, IL; 19/393 HonRl; Ftbl; Trk; IMSpt; Univ; Economics.

LEACH, Gail A; Lincolnwood HS; Atwater, IL; 15/53 HonRl; LbryAde; OffAde; EdYrBk; SchPpr;.

LEACH, Kenneth J; Fox Of Arnold HS; House Springs, MO; HonRl; Yrbk; SchPpr; LetterBsbl; LetterBsktbl;.

LEACH, La Donna F; Mc Cluer HS; Florissant, MO; 100/798 ChrhWkr; CmntyWkr; CncrtBnd; HonRl; MrchBnd; NHS; Orch; PresSchMus; CaptBsktbl; IMSpt; GodCntryAwd; MasAwd; Washington Univ; Physical Therapy.

LEACH, Linda L; Onaway HS; Onaway, MI; 8/99 HonRl; SchPl; Yrbk; SciCl; MasAwd; Suomi Coll; Law Enforcement.

LEACH, Mark A; Waukesha North HS; Waukesha, WI; HonRl; NHS; University; Medicine.

LEACH, Michele R; Immaculata HS; Detroit, MI; 10/110 Chr; HonRl; JA; StuGov; TchrAde; Univ Of Michigan; Physician.

LEACH, Roger; Joliet Central Hs; Joliet, IL; 48/495 TreasBand; ChrhWkr; CncrtBnd; HonRl; MrchBnd; NHS; SchMus; GerCl; LetterGlf; Augustana Col; Chemistry Major.

LEACH, Susan A; Orchard Farm HS; St Charles, MO; 25/109 VPFrshCls; PresSophCls; TrsJrCls; CaptDrlTm; HonRl; VPJA; VPStuCncl; StuGov; Yrbk; College; Oceanography.

LEACH, Theresa L; Waconia HS; Waconia, MN; HonRl; TreasJA; NatlThespSoc; FHA; LetterTrk; LetterChrldr; TreasGAA; IMSpt; JAAwd; College; Accounting.

LEACH, Wanda M; Lead Deadwood HS; Lead, SD; 9/168 Band; CncrtBnd; HonRl; MrchBnd; NatlMeritCmnd; PepBnd; Quill&Scroll; SctActv; GerCl; College.

LEACH, Wilbur I; Valley HS; Middlebrook, MO; VPSophCls; ALBoysSt; Band; ChrhWkr; CncrtBnd; HonRl; NHS; PepBnd; SchMus; RptrSchPpr;.

LEACH, Willie A; Beaumont HS; St Louis, MO; PresFrshCls; PresSophCls; PresJrCls; Aud/Vis; Band; ChrhWkr; CmntyWkr; CncrtBnd; HonRl; JA; Clg Or Univ; Politics Or Medicine.

LEACHMAN, Robert E; Platte County HS; Platte City, MO; 1/78 PresFrshCls; NHS; StuCncl; LetterFtbl; LetterTrk; CchngActv; DARAwd; CitAwd; Nw Missouri St Univ; Secondary Education.

LEADERS, Gary D; Underwood HS; Minden, IA; VPFrshCls; Chrs; HonRl; NHS; OffAde; SchMus; StuCncl; YthFlsp; LetterBsktbl; College; Mathematics.

LEADLOVE, Mark B; Mehlville Sr HS; Kirkwood, MO; 3/540 ALBoysSt; HonRl; NHS; Ftbl; LetterGlf; Wrstlng; College; Law.

LEAF, Curtis D; Ogden Comm HS; Boone, IA; Band; ChrhWkr; CmntyWkr; CncrtBnd; HonRl; MrchBnd; NHS; NatlMeritFnl; NatlMeritSF; PepBnd; TchrAde; College; Architecture.

LEAF, John P; Moline Sr HS; Moline, IL; SptEdSchPpr; KeyCl; SpnCl; SciCl; Glf; College.

LEAFGREEN, Ronald L; Fairfield HS; Fairfield, IA; 28/183 ChrhWkr; HonRl; NHS; RptrSchPpr; LetterTrk; LetterIMSpt; College; Professional.

LEAHY, Catherine S; St Paul Kennedy HS; Chicago, IL; Chrs; ChrhWkr; HonRl; OffAde; StuCncl; Yrbk; 4-H; VPFNA; PpCl; CaptChrldr; GAA; 4-HAwd; CitAwd; College; Nursing.

LEAHY, Mary K; Adrian HS; Adrian, MI; 53/389 PresJrCls; DrmMjrt; HonRl; NatlMeritCmnd; SchAde; TreasStuCncl; Twrl; RptrYrbk; FrCl; LatCl; Comm Clg; Special Ed.

LEAHY, Michael; Christian Bros College HS; St Charles, MO; 15/165 HonRl; ROTC; Bsbl; IMSpt; St Marys Coll; Dentist.

LEAHY, Patricia L; Carl Sandburg HS; Orland Park, IL; 50/680 HonRl; HospAde; TchrAde; SpnCl; MthCl; College; Nursing.

LEAL, David; Fremont HS; Fremont, NE; LetterFtbl; LetterWrstlng; Trade Sch.

LEAL, Rosa M; Holland HS; Holland, MI; TchrAde; VPFHA; FTA; FrCl; LatCl; SpnCl; College; Professional.

LEAMY, Martin J; St Rita HS; Chicago, IL; 30/424 SecSrCls; NHS; StuCncl; LetterFtbl; LetterTrk; Bradley U; Computer Science.

LEANNAH, James M; Lincoln HS; Manitowoc, WI; 28/604 Chrs; HonRl; JrNHS; NHS; SchMus; SchPl; SctActv; Ftbl; Trk; Univ Of Wisconsin; Accountant.

LEANNAH, Michael F; Marinette Catholic Centrl HS; Marinette, WI; 4 PresJrCls; HonRl; SchPl; SctActv; StuCncl; TchrAde; RptrSchPpr; MthCl; PpCl; SciCl; Ftbl; Trk; Univ Of Wisconsin; Psychology.

LEAR, Bruce E; Shellsburg Comm HS; Shellsburg, IA; 4/16 PresFrshCls; PresJrCls; HonRl; MrchBnd; SchMus; SctActv; StuCncl; RptrYrbk; RptrSchPpr; LetterBsktbl; Central Coll; Educ.

LEAR, Mark D; Rockville HS; Rockville, IN; ChrhWkr; CmntyWkr; 4-H; FFA; LetterBsbl; Bsktbl; Wrstlng; IMSpt; 4-HAwd; College; Agriculture.

LEARN, Leo D; Lyle Public HS; Lyle, MN; Band; CncrtBnd; HonRl; MrchBnd; PepBnd; 4-H; FFA; 4-HAwd; Vocational; Food Preparation.

LEARNARD, Anne; Warrensburg Latham Hs; Warrensburg, IL; 1/73 HonRl; JrNHS; TchrAde; Sec4-H; PresFHA; BttyCrckrAwd; DARAwd; Illinois State University; Chemistry.

LEARY, Christopher C; Homewood Flossmoor HS; Homewood, IL; 3/720 Band; Chrs; ChrhWkr; CncrtBnd; HonRl; MrchBnd; NatlMeritFnl; NatlMeritSF; PepBnd; StuGov; MthCl; Coll.

LEASE, Michael W; Litchfield HS; Litchfield, MN; ALBoysSt; Chr; HonRl; SchPl; GerCl; Ftbl; Swmmng; Trk; IMSpt; JCAwd; Bus Sch.

LEASON, Stephen; Thornridge HS; Dolton, IL; 67/680 ChrhWkr; HonRl; LitMag; NHS; Univ Of Ill Urbana; Medical Ill.

LEASURE, Janice K; Cambridge Sr HS; Cambridge, MN; SecSrCls; StuCncl; St Cloud State Univ; Psychologist.

LEATH, James L; Warren HS; Cameron, IL; 3/39 Band; HonRl; SchPl; SctActv; YthFlsp; LetterBsktbl; Ftbl; LetterTrk; College; Mathematics.

LEATHERMAN, Cynthia L; Pardeeville HS; Pardeeville, WI; Band; Chrs; CncrtBnd; HonRl; HospAde; MrchBnd; NatlThespSoc; PepBnd; EdYrBk; GAA; Uw Stout; Home Economics.

LEATHERMAN, Daniel T; Central Noble HS; Albion, IN; Band; CncrtBnd; Mdrgl; MrchBnd; PepBnd; SchMus; SctActv; Trk; IMSpt; Trade School.

LEATHERMAN, Phillip R; Eureka HS; Eureka, IL; 20/120 Band; Chrs; ChrhWkr; CmntyWkr; HonRl; JrNHS; NHS; SchMus; Bsktbl; College; Data Processing.

LEATHERS, Patricia L; Battle Creek HS; Norfolk, NE; 2/37 PresJrCls; ALAGirlsSt; HonRl; LbryAde; OffAde; SchPl; StuCncl; 4-H; PpCl; PPFtbl; Housewife.

LEAVELL, Mary S; Mt Vernon HS; Indianapolis, IN; 27/146 Band; ChrhWkr; CncrtBnd; HonRl; JrNHS; MrchBnd; NHS; PepBnd; YthFlsp; 4-H; Trk; GAA; DARAwd; Purdue Univ; Veterinarian.

LEAVER, Thomas A; Juda HS; Juda, WI; 4/30 TrsJrCls; Band; CncrtBnd; HonRl; MrchBnd; PepBnd; StuGov; SptEdYrbk; SptEdSchPpr; 4-H; FFA; FHA; LetterBsktbl; LetterFtbl; College; Liberal Arts.

LEAVITT, Andrew D; Carman HS; Flint, MI; 2/374 HonRl; NHS; Ftbl; LetterGlf; AmLegAwd; U Of Mich; Health Care.

LEAVITT, James W; Marcus Com HS; Marcus, IA; 3/76 PresSophCls; Band; PresSophCls; HonRl; StuCncl; YthFlsp; SpnCl; LetterFtbl; LetterWrstlng; PresAwd;.

LEAVITT, James W; Marcus Community HS; Marcus, IA; 3/76 PresSophCls; Band; CncrtBnd; HonRl; MrchBnd; LetterFtbl; Trk; LetterWrstlng; CchngActv; PresAwd; Coll.

LEAVITT, Lauren A; New Trier West HS; Glencoe, IL; CmntyWkr; HonRl; HospAde; SchPpr; College; Psychology.

LEAZENBY, Keith E; Eastern Pulaski HS; Star City, IN; HonRl; NHS; NatlMeritFnl; NatlMeritCmnd; NatlMeritSchl; NatlMeritSF; YthFlsp; FBLA; GovHonPrgAwd; College; Accounting.

LEBBIN, William; Lane Tech; Chicago, IL; 58/1213 CmntyWkr; DrlTm; HonRl; LbryAde; NHS; ROTC; VPSctActv; KeyCl; FrCl; LetterFtbl; Loyola U;professional Biology.

LEBED, Kathleen; West Central Jr Sr HS; Medaryville, IN; 1/89 HonRl; LbryAde; NHS; NatlMeritCmnd; RptrYrbk; FTA;.

LEBEN, Gail D; Pope Co Comm HS; Galconda, IL; 6/52 Band; Chrl; ChrhWkr; HonRl; OffAde; SchMus; StuCncl; RptrYrbk; PpCl; Trk; Southern Illinois University.

LEBENS, John; De La Salle HS; Minneapolis, MN; Chrs; CmntyWkr; HonRl; LbryAde; NHS; NatlMeritFnl; SctActv; Tennis; Univ Of Minnesota.

LE BLANC, Brian J; Luke M Powers HS; Flint, MI; 31/306 CmntyWkr; HonRl; JA; Univ Of Michigan; Computer Science.

LEBNER, Matthew E; Quincy HS; Quincy, IL; SchPl; LetterFtbl; LetterTrk; Monmouth College; Civil Engineering.

LEBRON, Maria S; St Andrew HS; Detriot, MI; HonRl; Yrbk; IMSpt; Col ; Home Ec.

LEBUS, Joan; Central Cass HS; Davenport, ND; 11/57 PresFrshCls; Chrs; HonRl; NHS; SchPl; StuCncl; YthFlsp; 4-H; 4-HAwd; Nd St Univ; Chd Devel/fam Relat.

LECHELER, Bruce A; Elmwood Area HS; Elmwood, WI; TrsFrshCls; PresSophCls; ALBoysSt; Aud/Vis; HonRl; NHS; Bsbl; Bsktbl; Ftbl;.

LECHOWICZ, Alan E; Notre Dame HS; Chicago, IL; 47/266 HonRl; Univ Of Illinois; Accountant.

LECHTENBERG, Roger E; Butte HS; Butte, NE; PresSrCls; Band; Chr; Chrs; ChrhWkr; CncrtBnd; HonRl; Mdrgl; MrchBnd; PepBnd; LetterBsbl; LetterBsktbl; CaptFtbl; University; Vocational.

LECHTERMAN, Marcella; Bowler Hs; Bowler, WI; 2/37 VPSophCls; SecJrCls; HonRl; RptrYrbk; RptrSchPpr; FHA; SciCl; Chrldr; GAA;.

LECKBAND, Stephanie; Brewster Public HS; Brewster, MN; 1/32 Band; CncrtBnd; MrchBnd; FFA; PpCl; Bsktbl; Trk;.

LECKIE, Frederick J; Buffalo Grove HS; Buffalo Grove, IL; 32/300 HonRl; NHS; LetterBsbl; Univ Of Illinois; Business Admin.

LECKMAN, Linda; Washington HS; Chicago, IL; 73/491 Band; HonRl; MrchBnd; NHS; OffAde; TchrAde; FNA; LatCl; Indiana Univ N W; Radiology Tech.

LE CLAIR, Cora; Clay Central Comm HS; Royal, IA; 10/40 Band; Chr; Chrl; HonRl; HospAde; Mdrgl; MrchBnd; Orch; PepBnd; SchMus; College; Nurse.

LECLAIR, Francis J; Clay Central Comm HS; Royal, IA; Chr; Chrs; ChrhWkr; HonRl; StuCncl; Yrbk; IMSpt; CitAwd; Loras Clg; Hwy Patrol.

LE CLAIR, Roger E; Belleville Township E HS; Belleville, IL; 55/670 Band; CncrtBnd; MrchBnd; TchrAde; U Of Il; Electrical Eng.

LECLERE, Jane A; Perry Central HS; Tell City, IN; 11/85 PresSrCls; LbryAde; VPNatlThespSoc; SchPl; StuCncl; FrCl; PpCl; DARAwd; Indiana U; Medical Technology.

LECLERE, William E; Pinckney HS; Brighton, MI; RptrSchPpr; Glf;.

LEDBETTER, Calvin D; Jefferson Co North HS; Winchester, KS; HonRl; TreasNHS; SctActv; YthFlsp; Treas4-H; LetterBsktbl; LetterFtbl; LetterTrk; 4-HAwd; Jr Clg; Industrial Arts.

LEDBETTER, Pamela J; Hayti HS; Hayti, MO; 10/87 Chr; HonRl; NHS; NatlThespSoc; SchPl; RptrYrbk; RptrSchPpr; FTA; SpnCl; PpCl; Se Missouri State Univ; Accounting.

LEDERER, Dean; Valley Falls HS; Valley Falls, KS; PresFrshCls; VPSophCls; HonRl; SchPl; StuCncl; LetterBsktbl; LetterFtbl; College; Business.

LEDERLEITNER, Robert J; Saint Viator HS; Mount Prospect, IL; 9/244 HonRl; Northwestern Univ; Medicine.

LEDFORD, Darlene; East Peoria Comm HS; East Peoria, IL; 9/446 DrlTm; HonRl; NHS; TchrAde; TreasYthFlsp; FTA; FrCl; MthCl; PpCl; GAA; Ill State Univ; Foreign Language.

LEDGER, Randall G; Pekin Comm HS; Fairfield, IA; 8/50 Aud/Vis; Band; Chrs; CncrtBnd; HonRl; MrchBnd; NHS; PepBnd; SchMus; SchPl; U Of Iowa; Civil Engr.

LEDGERWOOD, Brenda M; Alton HS; Alton, MO; 6/89 HstFrshCls; LetterBand; HonRl; RptrYrbk; Yrbk; 4-H; PpCl; SciCl; LetterChrldr;.

LEDMAN, Penny A; North Chicago HS; Great Lakes, IL; Chr; ChrhWkr; HonRl; ROTC; TchrAde; Yrbk; IMSpt;.

LEDOUX, Judy N; Bishop Lillis HS; Kansas, MO; PresFrshCls; HonRl; JA; LbryAde; SchPl; StuCncl; SpnCl; PpCl; College; Psychology.

LE DUC, Deborah M; Clyde HS; Clyde, KS; 6/34 Band; Chrs; CncrtBnd; HonRl; MrchBnd; OffAde; PepBnd; PpCl; Trk; GAA; College; Teaching.

LE DUC, Katherine A; Escanaba Area Public HS; Escanaba, MI; 25/383 Chrs; HonRl; JA; NHS; NatlMeritSF; Orch; SchMus; TchrAde; Northern Michigan University; Music.

LEDVINA, Richard J; Rock HS; Rock, MI; 4/26 SctActv; StuCncl; Ftbl; Trk; Trade; Electronics.

LEE, Alan L; Bishop Noll HS; Gary, IN; Aud/Vis; RptrYrbk; RptrSchPpr; EdSchPpr; SptEdSchPpr; EngCl; FrCl; LetterBsbl; LetterBsktbl; LetterFtbl; CchngActv; IMSpt; Univ Of Wisconsin; Journalism.

LEE, Angela J; Charleston Sr HS; Charleston, IL; 16/280 VPAFS; ChrhWkr; HonRl; NHS; LetterTrk; GAA; Jr College; Child Care.

LEE, Barbara J; Glenbard West HS; Glen Ellyn, IL; 8/522 Band; CncrtBnd; HonRl; MrchBnd; NatlMeritCmnd; PepBnd; 4-H; College; Lawyer.

LEE, Bonita M; Gregory HS; Dallas, SD; 4/58 ALAGirlsSt; Chrs; ChrhWkr; HonRl; NatlFornLg; NHS; NatlThespSoc; YthFlsp; SchPpr; FBLA; U Of Sd; Speech Communication.

LEE, Bonnie M; Lucy Flower HS; Chicago, IL; TrsFrshCls; VPSophCls; PresJrCls; SecSrCls; Band; CncrtBnd; DrmBgl; MrchBnd; PepBnd; StuCncl; Bsbl; Bsktbl; College; Professional.

LEE, Brian E; Mentor Public HS; Mentor, MN; Univ; Profesional.

LEE, Carin; Manitowoc Lutheran HS; Kiel, WI; 8/81 TrsFrshCls; SecSrCls; Band; Chr; HonRl; PolWkr; SchPl; RptrSchPpr; Chrldr; IMSpt; College; Eng His Secondary Ed.

LEE, Cheryl L; New Trier East HS; Wilmette, IL; 13/847 HonRl; NatlMeritFnl; Orch; RedCrAde; SctActv; LetterSwmmng; University Of Illinois.

LEE, Chris E; St Edmond HS; Fort Dodge, IA; ChrhWkr; HospAde; PolWkr; StuCncl; YthFlsp; SpnCl; PpCl; Bsktbl; Glf; Trk; Nurse.

LEE, Christy E; Scottsbluff Sr HS; Scottsbluff, NE; Band; HonRl; HospAde; SctActv; StuCncl; LetterTrk; GAA; IMSpt; PresAwd; College; Teacher.

LEE, Clayton R; Lafayette HS; Red Lake Falls, MN; ChrhWkr; HonRl; RptrSchPpr; Trk; North Dakota Univ; Mechanical Engr.

LEE, Daneen R; East Monona HS; Soldier, IA; SecTrsSophCls; PresJrCls; Band; SecChr; ChrhWkr; HonRl; SchPl; SptEdYrbk; Yrbk; RptrSchPpr; Bsktbl; LetterTrk; 4-HAwd; College; Professional Singing.

LEE, Danette J; Saline HS; Britton, MI; NHS; StuCncl; FTA; SpnCl; LetterBsktbl; College; Theology.

LEE, Daniel; Mendel Cath Prep HS; Chicago, IL; 2/170 HonRl; JrNHS; PresNHS; OffAde; StuCncl; RptrYrbk; RptrSchPpr; MthCl; SciCl; Northwestern Univ; Engineering.

LEE, Daniel; Mendel Catholic Prep HS; Chicago, IL; 2/170 CmntyWkr; HonRl; PresNHS; OffAde; StuGov; RptrYrbk; RptrSchPpr; MthCl; IMSpt; Northwestern Univ; Bio Med Engineer.

LEE, David R; Kirksville HS; Kirksville, MO; 4/175 HonRl; SctActv; YthFlsp; SpnCl; SciCl; Univ Of Missouri; Medicine.

LEE, David W; Central HS; Aberdeen, SD; 41/420 ALBoysSt; HonRl; JrNHS; NHS; StuCncl; StuGov; Bsbl; Bsktbl; Glf; IMSpt; So Dakota Schl Of Mines & Tech; Engineer.

LEE, Deborah M; New Haven HS; New Haven, MI; CmntyWkr; HonRl; LbryAde; NHS; PolWkr; TchrAde; SchPpr; FBLA; FHA; Univ Of Mi; Physical Therapy.

LEE, Debra; Mt Pulaski Township HS; Mt Pulaski, IL; 8/103 Chrs; CncrtBnd; HonRl; MrchBnd; Orch; PepBnd; EdYrBk; Tennis; GAA; College; Fashion Illiustrating.

LEE, Debra A; Carpio HS; Donnybrook, ND; Band; Chrs; HonRl; SchPl; YthFlsp; SchPpr; 4-H; PpCl; Bsktbl; 4-HAwd; College; Medicine.

LEE, Dema K; Westfield HS; Westfield, IL; 2/18 VPSophCls; TrsJrCls; HonRl; NHS; StuCncl; YthFlsp; Yrbk; SchPpr; 4-H; MthCl; GAA; Lake Land Jr Col; Accounting.

LEE, Dinah F; Westhope Public HS; Westhope, ND; VPJrCls; PresSrCls; Band; Chr; CncrtBnd; HonRl; MrchBnd; PepBnd; SchPl; StuCncl; TchrAde; RptrYrbk; EdSchPpr; Univ; Secretary.

LEE, Eric M; Cc HS; Carbondale, IL; Band; HonRl; RptrYrbk; SciCl; Univ; Engineer.

LEE, Gary R; Gull Lake Community HS; Richland, MI; 2/280 Band; CncrtBnd; HonRl; MrchBnd; TchrAde; 4-H; Trk; Western Michigan Univ; Biochemistry.

LEE, Gloria E; Bloom Township HS; Glenwood, IL; 33/1018 Chr; ChrhWkr; HonRl; NHS; SchPl; YthFlsp; Concordia College; Music.

LEE, Gregory; Superior Sr HS; Superior, WI; 42/540 Chr; HonRl; StuGov; GerCl; Univ Of Wisc; Comp Engineer.

LEE, Greg R; St Charles HS; St Charles, IL; 3/473 Chr; HonRl; NHS; PolWkr; SchMus; SchPl; StuCncl; StuGov; TchrAde; SchPpr; KeyCl; FrCl; LetterTennis; LetterWrstlng; Univ; Lawyer.

LEE, Haeok; Lane Technical HS; Chicago, IL; Chr; ChrhWkr; JA; NatlMeritCmnd; OffAde; TchrAde; Yrbk; RptrSchPpr; GerCl; Univ Of Ill; Mechanical Engineering.

LEE, Henry; Mendel Catholic Prep HS; Chicago, IL; 3/165 HonRl; OffAde; SchAde; TchrAde; MthCl; Trk;.

LEE, Jacqueline A; St Francis HS; Wyoming, MN; Chr; ChrhWkr; SchMus; SchPl; 4-H; GerCl; College.

LEE, Jacqueline F; St Thomas Public HS; St Thomas, ND; 6/20 Chrs; ChrhWkr; HonRl; SchPl; SctActv; RptrSchPpr; SchPpr; SecTrsSophCls; GAA; PPFtbl; Univ; Professional.

LEE, Jacqueline S; Prairie Heights HS; Angola, IN; 18/113 TchrAde; FTA; IMSpt; College; Art.

LEE, James E; Pillager HS; Cushing, MN; PresSrCls; HonRl; NHS; SchPl; StuCncl; EdYrBk; FBLA; LetterBsktbl; CchngActv; GovHonPrgAwd; Col; Electronics.

LEE, Jana L; Calamus HS; Calamus, IA; 3/26 SecSrCls; Chrs; HonRl; LbryAde; SchMus; SchPl; TchrAde; GerCl; Glf; College; Professional.

LEE, Janet S; Bloomfield Hills Lanser HS; Bloomfield Hills, MI; 15/465 Chrl; ChrhWkr; CncrtBnd; MrchBnd; NHS; Orch; PepBnd; SchMus; YthFlsp; GerCl; Adrian Coll; Music.

LEE, Jeffrey D; Sturgis HS; Sturgis, MI; Chrs; HonRl; NHS; NatlMeritCmnd; Orch; SchMus; Yrbk; LatCl; University Of Mi; Music.

LEE, Jeffrey W; Rockville HS; Rockville, IN; FFA; Bsktbl; Ftbl; Trk; Itt In Indianapolis; Electronics.

LEE, John; Duluth Cathedral HS; Duluth, MN; 10/150 HonRl; NatlMeritCmnd; SchPpr; Lake Forest Coll; Attorney.

LEE, Jovita D; Chicago Vocational HS; Chicago, IL; 94/778 HstSrCls; HonRl; FHA;.

LEE, Judith A; Shelbyville HS; Shelbyville, IL; 1/133 Band; CncrtBnd; HonRl; MrchBnd; NHS; TchrAde; PresFrCl; GAA; Eastern Ill Univ; Elem Teacher.

LEE, Julie A; Mound Westonka HS; Wayzata, MN; 5/293 Chr; ChrhWkr; HonRl; NHS; YthFlsp; GerCl; MthCl; PpCl; College; Med.

LEE, Karen S; North White HS; Monticello, IN; Band; CncrtBnd; MrchBnd; Yrbk; 4-H; FTA; GerCl; PpCl; Trk; 4-HAwd; College.

LEE, Karla R; Parkview HS; Brodhead, WI; Chr; Chrl; Chrs; HonRl; SchMus; SchPl; StuCncl; CivCl; PpCl; Chrldr; College.

LEE, Kathleen D; Williamsville HS; Springfield, IL; TrsSrCls; Chr; ChrhWkr; HonRl; LbryAde; OffAde; SchPl; StuCncl; TchrAde; EdYrBk; Business College; Accounting.

LEE, Kathryn E; Marian HS; Birmingham, MI; HonRl; ModUN; NHS; Quill&Scroll; SctActv; RptrSchPpr; EdSchPpr; LetterSwmmng; Coll; Marine Biology.

LEE, Kathryn J; Lourdes HS; Rochester, MN; HonRl; JrNHS; SchPl; Yrbk; FrCl; LetterBsktbl; LetterTennis; CaptTrk; College; Medicine.

LEE, Kim; Northwestern HS; Flint, MI; OffAde; TchrAde; Bsktbl; Swmmng; Airlines Stewardess Coll; Airline Stewardes.

LEE, Kristy R; Lamar R 1 HS; Lamar, MO; 33/91 SecSophCls; AFS; Band; Chr; CncrtBnd; HonRl; MrchBnd; YthFlsp; PpCl; Chrldr;.

LEE, Larry D; Doniphan HS; Doniphan, MO; 5/160 ChrhWkr; HonRl; LetterPpCl; VoiceDemAwd; College; Government.

LEE, Laura J; St Edmond HS; Fort Dodge, IA; 3/119 HonRl; StuCncl; PpCl; LetterGlf; IMSpt; Univ; Optometry.

LEE, Michael; Cass Tech HS; Detroit, MI; College; Electronics Engr.

LEE, Michael F; Marion HS; Marion, MI; 10/57 CncrtBnd; DrmMjrt; HonRl; MrchBnd; NHS; OffAde; StuCncl; YthFlsp; EdSchPpr; 4-H; Mi St Univ; Dairy Science.

LEE, Patricia; Dundee Community Hs; Carpentersville, IL; Chr; TreasChrs; HonRl; Mdrgl; NHS; SchMus; TchrAde; FrCl; SciCl; De Paul U; Music Education.

LEE, Patrick J; Wheatland HS; Elsie, NE; 2/20 PresFrshCls; VPSophCls; VPJrCls; HonRl; SchPl; 4-H; Bsktbl; Ftbl; Trk; 4-HAwd; U Of Ne; Computer.

LEE, Paula R; Parkview HS; Broadhead, WI; PresFrshCls; VPJrCls; ALAGirlsSt; Band; Chrs; HonRl; NHS; NatlThespSoc; PresStuCncl; ChmnChrldr; College; Guidance.

LEE, Priscilla G; Charleston HS; Charleston Il, IL; Chr; ChrhWkr; CncrtBnd; HonRl; HospAde; MrchBnd; StuCncl; PresYthFlsp; Sec4-H; TreasFNA; Univ.

LEE, Puwen; Huron HS; Ann Arbor, MI; 23/576 TrsJrCls; SecSrCls; HonRl; LitMag; Orch; SchMus; StuGov; FrCl; College; History.

LEE, Randy; Marion HS; Marion, MI; 5/58 Aud/Vis; Band; ChrhWkr; CncrtBnd; HonRl; MrchBnd; PepBnd; StuCncl; Bsbl; Ftbl; Ferris State College; Heavy Equip Service.

LEE, Regina S; Highland Park HS; Highland Park, IL; 54/605 Aud/Vis; ChrhWkr; NHS; RedCrAde; SchMus; SchPl; TchrAde; Yrbk; LetterBsktbl; Univ Of California; Medicine.

LEE, Robert E; Maine South HS; Park Ridge, IL; 51/849 HonRl; LitMag; NatlFornLg; NHS; PolWkr; Quill&Scroll; StuCncl; SpnCl; Bsktbl; CaptTennis; Univ; Business.

LEE, Robert S; Bosworth HS; Tima, MO; 3/18 PresSophCls; Band; HonRl; PepBnd; SchPl; EdYrBk; EdSchPpr; Trk; Clg At Rolla Mo; Petroleum Eng.

LEE, Robert S; Malcolm HS; Lincoln, NE; PresFrshCls; Chrs; HonRl; NHS; StuCncl; SchPpr; Ftbl; Coll; Attnt.

LEE, Sandra A; Puxico R 8 HS; Puxico, MO; Chrs; ChrhWkr; HonRl; MrchBnd; PepBnd; FHA; SciCl; Bsktbl; Ftbl; Socr; Tennis; Trade Sch; Vocation.

LEE, Sharon K; Cambridge HS; Cambridge, WI; Chrs; SchPl; SchPpr; SpnCl; Uw Eau Claire; Nursing.

LEE, Sheree T; St Charles HS; St Charles, IL; ALAGirlsSt; Chr; CmntyWkr; HonRl; JrNHS; NHS; Orch; PolWkr; StuCncl; StuGov; CaptChrldr; College; Child Psychology.

LEE, Shirley J; Southeast HS; Kansas City, MO; 16/300 Band; Chr; ChrhWkr; CncrtBnd; HonRl; MrchBnd; NHS; SchPl; Univ Of Denver; Psychiatry.

LEE, Stephanie; Roncalli HS; Indianapolis, IN; 32/139 SecSrCls; Band; CncrtBnd; HonRl; MrchBnd; OffAde; SchMus; StuCncl; FrCl; PPFtbl; Ball St Univ; Nrsng.

LEE, Steven A; Rich South HS; Park Forest, IL; HonRl; NatlFornLg; PolWkr; SchPl; StuCncl; StuGov; RptrSchPpr; SchPpr; KeyCl; Univ Of Illinois; Doctor.

LEE, Susan; Carbondale Community Hs; Carbondale, IL; Band; HonRl; YthLg; Yrbk; SciCl; Tennis; Chrldr; U Of Illinois; Medicine.

LEE, Susan E; Carthage HS; Webb City, MO; 1/234 AFS; Chr; ChrhWkr; HonRl; ModUN; NHS; NatlMeritSF; MthCl; DARAwd; Univ Of Mo; Medical Doctor.

LEE, Susanne L; Lansford Public HS; Lansford, ND; 3/14 Band; CncrtBnd; HonRl; StuCncl; RptrYrbk; CaptBsktbl; LetterChrldr; AmLegAwd; BttyCrckrAwd; Capital Commercial Col; Fashion Merchandisi.

LEE, Tak K; Cass Technical HS; Detroit, MI; HonRl; NHS; NatlSciFnd; TchrAde; Univ Of Michigan; Medicine.

LEE, Tamara D; Rockford Lutheran HS; Rockford, IL; VPSophCls; SecJrCls; Chr; HonRl; HospAde; RptrYrbk; PpCl; Trk; GAA; IMSpt; Rockford College; Social Work.

LEE, Terri A; Holmen HS; Holmen, WI; 1/116 SecSophCls; TrsSrCls; ALAGirlsSt; HonRl; NHS; YthFnd; RptrYrbk; Chrldr; AmLegAwd; BttyCrckrAwd; Univ; Teaching.

LEE, Terri R; Pochontas Comm HS; Pocahontas, IA; 8/70 VPJrCls; ALAGirlsSt; Band; Chr; CncrtBnd; HonRl; MrchBnd; SecNHS; SchMus; SecPpCl; Univ; Education.

LEE, Thomas J; Roncalli HS; Omaha, NE; HonRl; JA; NHS; Tennis; Univ; Law.

LEE, Thomas J; La Crescent HS; La Crescent, MN; Band; Chr; HonRl; MrchBnd; SchPl; SchPl; SptEdSchPpr; FrCl; LetterFtbl; LetterWrstlng; U Of Wi Lacrosse; Medical.

LEE, Thomas L; Veblen Ind HS; Veblen, SD; Band; Chr; Chrs; ChrhWkr; MrchBnd; RptrYrbk; Bsbl; LetterBsktbl; CaptFtbl; LetterTrk; College; Agri Business.

LEE, Timothy; Garber HS; Essexville, MI; PresJrCls; VPSrCls; Chrs; ChrhWkr; CmntyWkr; HonRl; StuCncl; StuGov; RptrYrbk; PpCl; Central Michigan U; Political Science.

LEE, Tracie A; Wesclin HS; Trenton, IL; 8/100 HonRl; IntrClCncl; JrNHS; NHS; StuCncl; FBLA; FHA; FrCl; PpCl; ChmnChrldr; U Of Il; Home Ec.

LEE, Wanda J; Grantsburg HS; Grantsburg, WI; Chr; ChrhWkr; LbryAde; StuCncl; SpnCl; SecTrsSophCls; IMSpt;.

LEE, William J; De Andreis HS; St Louis, MO; 9/83 ChrhWkr; HonRl; JA; NatlMeritCmnd; SchPl; Yrbk; SchPpr; LetterFtbl; HstSophCls; Univ Of Missouri; Actuary.

LEEK, Pamela; Rochester HS; Rochester, IL; Chr; HospAde; JA; SchPl; RptrSchPpr; SpnCl; GAA; Lincoln Land Comm Coll; Nurse.

LEEMAN, Sandra K; Ritenour HS; Overland, MO; DrlTm; College; Business.

LEEMIS, Lawrence M; York HS; Elmhurst, IL; 35/880 ChrhWkr; CmntyWkr; HonRl; Quill&Scroll; SptEdSchPpr; Purdue Univ.

LEENERTS, Rebecca J; Unity HS; Fowler, IL; HstFrshCls; TrsSrCls; PresBand; HonRl; MrchBnd; PepBnd; StuCncl; Yrbk; 4-H; 4-HAwd; Western Ill State Univ; Veternarian.

LEEPER, Gary D; Bremen HS; Bremen, IN; Chr; HonRl; StuCncl; SptEdYrbk; SptEdSchPpr; FrCl; LetterBsktbl; LetterFtbl; LetterGlf; IMSpt; Arizona Univ; Health.

LEEPER, Jayne A; Earlham Community HS; Earlham, IA; 4/38 SecFrshCls; Band; HonRl; RedCrAde; EdYrBk; Pres4-H; PresFHA; CaptChrldr; 4-HAwd; Jr College; Vocation.

LEEPER, Jayne A; Earlham Comm HS; Earlham, IA; 4/40 Band; DrlTm; HonRl; NHS; RedCrAde; EdYrBk; PresFHA; Chrldr; 4-HAwd; Coll; Vocation.

LEEPER, Michael; Westport HS; Kansas City, MO; NHS; Orch; Quill&Scroll; StuCncl; SptEdYrbk; SptEdSchPpr; FTA; GerCl; Bsktbl; Ftbl; Coll.

LEER, Douglas A; Sturgis HS; Sturgis, MI; HonRl; NHS; NatlMeritSF; SctActv; KeyCl; Glf; IMSpt; U S A F Academy; Computer Sci.

LEER, Mark D; Stanton HS; Stanton, ND; 2/14 VPFrshCls; VPSophCls; Band; CncrtBnd; HonRl; NHS; NatlMeritSchl; PepBnd; SchPl; LetterBsktbl; Univ Nd; Electrician.

LEERHOFF, Diana; Leaf River Hs; Leaf River, IL; 2/33 Chrs; HonRl; SchPl; YthFlsp; RptrYrbk; PpCl; GAA; Augustana College; Science.

LEESEBERG, Linda M; West Chicago Comm HS; West Chicago, IL; 16/311 HonRl;.

LEESEBERG, Rodney W; Nevis HS; Nevis, MN; PresSophCls; PresJrCls; ALBoysSt; Chr; HonRl; EdYrBk; Yrbk; EdSchPpr; SchPpr; College; Elementary Education.

LEET, Gregory S; Riii Central HS; Flat River, MO; 5/150 ALBoysSt; HonRl; NHS; Quill&Scroll; RptrSchPpr; FTA; SciCl; CaptBsktbl; LetterGlf; IMSpt; University; Optometry.

LEET, Sandra S; North HS; Eau Claire, WI; DrmBgl; NatlFornLg; NHS; Orch; SchPl; 4-H; FrCl; SciCl; LetterSwmmng; 4-HAwd; Oceanography.

LEETH, Paul W; White Pigeon Community HS; Sturgis, MI; Band; Chr; ChrhWkr; SctActv; YthFlsp; Pres4-H; LetterFtbl; LetterTrk; SecSrCls; 4-HAwd; Collge; Vocational.

LEEUW, Kathryn M; Lake City Area HS; Lake City, MI; 6/62 Band; CncrtBnd; HonRl; JrNHS; MrchBnd; NHS; DanFAwd; N Mich U; Med Tech.

LEEUW, Thomas; Bishop Dwenger HS; Fort Wayne, IN; ChrhWkr; HonRl; SctActv; StuCncl; FrCl; PpCl; Bsbl; IMSpt; Trade Sch; Contractor.

LEEVER, Steven P; Bayard HS; Bayard, NE; HonRl; FFA; CaptFtbl; LetterWrstlng; Trade School; Mechanics.

LE FAIVE, Jane A; Michigan Center HS; Jackson, MI; Chr; Chrs; ChrhWkr; CmntyWkr; RedCrAde; SchMus; SctActv; FHA; CaptGlf; GAA; Nazareth College; Physical Educ.

LE FEVERS, Margaret J; Joliet East HS; Joliet, IL; HonRl; ROTC; CitAwd; Vet Or Government Work.

LE FEVRE, Carol E; Carl Schurz HS; Chicago, IL; 31/756 ChrhWkr; HonRl; LbryAde; NHS; RptrYrbk; North Park College; Nurse.

LE FEVRE, Ronona R; West HS; Green Bay, WI; 50/390 Chr; Chrs; HonRl; NHS; OffAde; TchrAde; SpnCl; PpCl; GAA; IMSpt; Clge; Social Sciences.

LEFEVRE, Victoria L; St Stephen Area HS; Saginaw, MI; HonRl; NHS; StuCncl; StuGov; PpCl; CaptSwmmng; Tennis; Univ; Business Adm.

LEFF, Gwendolyn J; Hector HS; Hector, MN; 4/49 Band; Chr; CncrtBnd; HonRl; MrchBnd; NHS; PepBnd; Sec4-H; FHA; SpnCl; SciCl; Concordia College; Secondary Education.

LEFFEL, Suzan G; East De Pere HS; De Pere, WI; NHS; PolWkr; SchPpr; Bsbl; GAA; U Of Wi; International Relations.

LEFFLER, Marlene M; Kadoka HS; Kadoka, SD; Band; Chrs; HonRl; PepBnd; SchAde; YthFlsp; Yrbk; LetterBsktbl; LetterTrk; GAA; College; Business.

LEFKO, James B; Shawnee Mission South HS; Shawnee Mission, KS; HonRl; StuCncl; IMSpt; Clge; Pro.

LEFOR, Gregory A; Trinity HS; Dickinson, ND; HonRl; SctActv; Bsbl; Trk; College.

LE FORT, Peggy J; Sunnydale Academy; Overland, MO; Chr; Chrl; ChrhWkr; SchMus; SchPl; SctActv; RptrSchPpr; SpnCl; PpCl; College; Nurse.

LEFSTEIN, Lori R; Rock Island HS; Rock Island, IL; ChrhWkr; HonRl; JrNHS; SchMus; SpnCl; PpCl; Tennis; Univ; Law.

LEGAT, Diane; Custer HS; Custer, SD; 21/55 Band; CmntyWkr; HonRl; NatlThespSoc; OffAde; PolWkr; Bsktbl; Ftbl; GAA; 4-HAwd; Sd State Univ; Plant Pathologist.

LE GAULT, Mary B; Gladstone Area HS; Gladstone, MI; 4/177 SecFrshCls; PresJrCls; Chrl; Chrs; NHS; StuCncl; StuGov; EdSchPpr; Chrldr; GAA; PPFtbl; Central Michigan Univ; Special Educ.

LEGERE, Donella A; Morland HS; Penokee, KS; 4/21 PresSophCls; SecJrCls; HonRl; MrchBnd; PepBnd; SchPl; VPSophCls; 4-H; BttyCrckrAwd; 4-HAwd; Colby Community Coll.

LEGG, Billy G; Hammond Tech Voc HS; Hammond, IN; 8/300 NHS; NatlThespSoc; SchPl; StuCncl; LetterTrk; College; Law Enforcement.

LEGGETT, Crystal A; Freeport HS; Freeport, IL; 9/507 HonRl; StuCncl; SpnCl; PpCl; Clge; Secretarial.

LEGGITT, Danny L; Palestine HS; Palestine, IL; ALBoysSt; Chrs; ChrhWkr; HonRl; OffAde; SchMus; YthFlsp; Yrbk; RptrSchPpr; IMSpt; Clg; Voc.

LEGGITT, Deborah; Arthur Hill HS; Saginaw, MI; HonRl; HospAde; NHS; SchAde; College; Business.

LEGGOTT, Rick D; Elwood HS; Elwood, NE; 3/25 ALBoysSt; ChrhWkr; HonRl; NHS; StuCncl; CaptBsktbl; CaptFtbl; LetterTrk; GodCntryAwd; PresAwd; University; Professional.

LEGLEITER, Mary R; Lacrosse HS; Liebenthal, KS; Band; HonRl; LbryAde; MrchBnd; PepBnd; SchPl; StuCncl; 4-H; FHA; PpCl; College; Vocation.

LEGLER, Corrine K; Tower City HS; Tower City, ND; 1/13 SecTrsFrshCls; PresJrCls; ALAGirlsSt; HonRl; NHS; StuCncl; FHA; Trk; Chrldr; DanFAwd; Univ Of Nd; Bus Accounting.

LE GRAND, Joseph N; Mt Vernon Twp HS; Mt Vernon, IL; 94/435 ChrhWkr; HonRl; TchrAde; 4-H; Bsktbl; Ftbl; Trk; CchngActv; IMSpt; College; Electronic Engineer.

LE GRAND, Sharon K; Carlyle HS; Carlyle, IL; 6/150 NHS; SchPl; FBLA; PpCl; Jr College; Exec Secretary.

LEGUEY FEILLEUX, Michele; Incarnate Word Academy; St Louis, MO; Chr; Chrs; SchMus; University; French Major.

LEH, Kathryn; Pontiac Catholic HS; Pontiac, MI; HonRl; NatlMeritSchl; NatlMeritSF; StuCncl; Chrldr; GAA; PPFtbl; Ferris State Col; Radiologic Technology.

LEHENBAUER, Kathy S; Monroe City R 1 HS; Monroe City, MO; Band; Chr; ChrhWkr; CncrtBnd; HonRl; MrchBnd; PepBnd; TchrAde; YthFlsp; Ne Missouri St Univ; Medical Secretary.

LE HEW, Laura J; Ritenour Sr HS; Overland, MO; CmntyWkr; HospAde; NatlMeritCmnd; NatlMeritSchl; PolWkr; RedCrAde; SctActv; StuCncl; SchPpr; College; Writer.

LEHMAN, Debra; South Adams HS; Berne, IN; Chr; ChrhWkr; CncrtBnd; Mdrgl; MrchBnd; SchMus; YthFlsp; 4-H; FrCl; Coll; Music.

LEHMAN, Dexter K; Westview HS; Topeka, IN; 10/69 HonRl; VPNHS; EdSchPpr; LetterTrk; IMSpt; College.

LEHMAN, Jeffery J; Wheaton Warrenville HS; Wheaton, IL; 14/312 HonRl; SchMus; SchPl; StuCncl; StuGov; SpnCl; Purdue Univ; Engineer.

LEHMAN, Jeffrey C; Hampshire HS; Hampshire, IL; 1/75 CmntyWkr; HonRl; VPNHS; StuCncl; TchrAde; SptEdYrbk; Trk; College; Mathematics.

LEHMAN, Jill M; Adams Central HS; Berne, IN; 7/125 Band; ChrhWkr; CncrtBnd; HonRl; SecNHS; VPYthFlsp; Pres4-H; GAA; IMSpt; BttyCrckrAwd; Univ.

LEHMAN, Joanne L; Mt Vernon HS; Mt Vernon, SD; SecSrCls; ALAGirlsSt; HonRl; NHS; SchPl; SchPpr; SpnCl; PpCl; Trk; DARAwd; Voc Sch; Practical Nursing.

LEHMAN, John J; Versailles HS; Versailles, MO; 15/78 TrsFrshCls; SecJrCls; ALBoysSt; SecChrhWkr; HonRl; SchPl; PresYthFlsp; Yrbk; IMSpt; VFWAwd; VoiceDemAwd; College; Physical Educ.

LEHMAN, Laura S; Deerfield HS; Deerfield, IL; 41/561 Chr; Chrs; ChrhWkr; HonRl; NHS; Bsbl; Ftbl; Swmmng; Trk; GAA; Bucknell Univ; Medicine.

LEHMAN, Laurinda; Westview Jr Sr HS; Topeka, IN; Band; Chr; ChrhWkr; HonRl; SchPl; RptrYrbk; RptrSchPpr; FHA; FNA; FTA; Anderson College; Elementary Educ.

LEHMAN, Martha L; Oak Park River Forest HS; Oak Park, IL; 64/1107 SecSophCls; Chr; Chrl; ChrhWkr; CmntyWkr; HonRl; SchMus; StuGov; Med Sch ;phy.

LEHMAN, Roni M; Saint Patrick HS; Portland, MI; 6/38 Chr; HonRl; NHS; StuCncl; TchrAde; Yrbk; CitAwd;.

LEHMAN, Terese S; Grand Ledge HS; Lansing, MI; SecSophCls; VPSrCls; HonRl; StuCncl; TchrAde; LatCl; PpCl; Swmmng; Tennis; Chrldr; Mi State U; Biological Science.

LEHMANN, Catherine; Bishop Du Bourg HS; St Louis, MO; Chrs; HonRl; Mdrgl; SchAde; SchMus; SchPl; IMSpt; Benedictine Coll; Drama Music.

LEHMANN, Debra L; Davenport West HS; Davenport, IA; HonRl; NatlMeritSF; PolWkr; Quill&Scroll; StuGov; EdYrBk; RptrSchPpr; FrCl; PresSpnCl; College; Pre Law.

LEHMANN, Jeffrey; Beaver Dam Senior HS; Beaver Dam, WI; IMSpt; Tech School; Drafting.

LEHMANN, Thomas R; Falls Sr HS; Intl Falls, MN; 4-H; IMSpt; Air Force; Auto Mech.

LEHMANN, Timothy L; Leo HS; Durango, IA; Chrs; CmntyWkr; 4-H; Bsbl; Bsktbl; 4-HAwd;.

LEHMOINE, Rachelle; Allegan Sr HS; Allegan, MI; HospAde; RptrSchPpr; Ferris State College; Medical Technologist.

LEHNER, Maureen A; Mother Mc Auley HS; Chicago, IL; 114/475 Chr; HonRl; OffAde; College; Education.

LEHOLM, Mary J; Columbus Public HS; Columbus, ND; SecTrsJrCls; PresSrCls; ALAGirlsSt; Band; Chrs; HonRl; SchPl; EdYrBk; RptrSchPpr; Chrldr; Univ; Medicine.

LEHRER, Mike; Menasha Public HS; Menasha, WI; 98/365 VPJrCls; JA; LitMag; StuCncl; SchPpr; Ftbl; Socr; Trk; Wrstlng; IMSpt; College; Business Management.

LEHST, Elaine J; Holy Family Acad; Chicago, IL; Chrs; HonRl; Twrl; Bsktbl; Coll; Pro.

LEIB, Mari E; Guthrie Center Community HS; Guthrie Center, IA; ChrhWkr; CncrtBnd; HonRl; MrchBnd; NHS; PepBnd; RptrSchPpr; Glf; DARAwd; 4-HAwd; Univ; Math.

LEIB, Mary R; Lourdes HS; Chicago, IL; 32/299 HonRl; HospAde; NHS; TchrAde; College; Nursing.

LEIBACH, Richard W; Central Catholic HS; Bloomington, IL; HonRl; StuCncl; LetterBsbl; Bsktbl; Ftbl; LetterTrk; IMSpt;.

LEIBBRANDT, Gary; Wilsonville HS; Wilsonville, NE; HstFrshCls; SecTrsSophCls; Band; CncrtBnd; HonRl; SchPl; StuCncl; YthFlsp;.

LEIBFRIED, Allen D; Spring Valley HS; Spring Valley, MN; HonRl; PresFFA; Bsktbl; IMSpt; Trade School; Carpentry.

LEIBFRIED, Robert T; Chisholm Sr HS; Chisholm, MN; 23/126 PresSrCls; ChrhWkr; HonRl; KeyCl; FrCl; LetterBsktbl; Vermilion Comm College; Computer Science.

LEIBHART, Larry K; Anselmo Merna Public HS; Merna, NE; 1/26 PresJrCls; HonRl; NHS; SchPl; StuCncl; YthFlsp; 4-H; LetterFtbl; AmLegAwd; 4-HAwd; Univ; Agricultural Research.

LEIBLE, James E; Oshkosh West HS; Oshkosh, WI; NHS; NatlMeritSF; Quill&Scroll; EdSchPpr; KeyCl; TreasLatCl; Swmmng; IMSpt; Univ; Nuclear Engineering.

LEIBLE, Michael R; Charleston R 1 HS; Charleston, MO; Band; ChrhWkr; SctActv; SptEdSchPpr; SchPpr; LetterFtbl; College; Business.

LEIBRAND, Larry A; Park Hill Sr HS; Kansas City, MO; Band; HonRl; MrchBnd; PepBnd; SctActv; Bsbl; Bsktbl; LetterFtbl; Tennis; Trk; Sterling College; Business.

LEIBRANDT, Barbara J; Mc Cook HS; Mc Cook, NE; 32/165 SecTrsSophCls; AFS; HonRl; NHS; Quill&Scroll; YthFlsp; EdYrBk; PpCl; GAA; 4-HAwd; Mc Cook Comm Clge; Political Science.

LEICHSENRING, Kay L; Amana Comm HS; Amana, IA; VPJrCls; ChrhWkr; CncrtBnd; ModUN; NHS; PresTeen; EdYrBk; RptrSchPpr; 4-H; 4-HAwd; Univ Of Iowa; Social Work.

LEICHTMAN, Gayle A; St Joseph HS; South Bend, IN; 7/232 Chrs; CmntyWkr; HonRl; HospAde; NHS; NatlMeritSF; SctActv; StuGov; 4-H; IMSpt; Notre Dame; Med Tech.

LEICK, Greg J; Stratford Public HS; Stratford, WI; VPSrCls; ALBoysSt; HonRl; StuGov; FHA; CaptBsbl; CaptBsktbl; CaptFtbl; Univ; Pro.

LEICK, Jon; St Francis HS; Humphrey, NE; 7/32 HonRl; JrNHS; LitMag; NHS; SchPl; StuCncl; RptrSchPpr; Ftbl; Trk; IMSpt; Kearney St Univ; Education.

LEICK, Lori; Watertown Senior HS; Watertown, WI; 52/301 HonRl; PpCl; Univ Of Wi Stevens Pt.

LEIDIG, Kristen M; Plano HS; Plano, IL; SecBand; HonRl; Mdrgl; NHS; NatlThespSoc; SchMus; SchPl; SecStuCncl; RptrYrbk; GAA; College; Teacher.

LEIER, Debra; Esmond HS; Esmond, ND; PresSophCls; PresJrCls; HonRl; LbryAde; SchPl; StuCncl; TchrAde; Yrbk; SchPpr; PpCl;.

LEIER, Glenn A; Linton Public HS; Linton, ND; ALBoysSt; HonRl; PresNHS; TreasStuCncl; RptrYrbk; SptEdSchPpr; Pres4-H; LetterBsktbl; 4-HAwd; College.

LEIF, Betty J; Chadwick HS; Chadwick, IL; 3/24 Band; Chrs; HonRl; SchPl; TchrAde; YthFlsp; FHA; FTA; PpCl; GAA; Sauk Valley Clge; Elem Ed.

LEIF, James E; Chadwick HS; Chadwick, IL; 18/32 HonRl; LbryAde; SchPl; TchrAde; FFA; FTA; PpCl; IMSpt; ; Auto Mech.

LEIFELD, Jean M; Petersburg Public HS; Petersburg, NE; 3/15 SecFrshCls; VPJrCls; TrsSrCls; ALAGirlsSt; Chr; SchPl; Columbus Bty Schl; Beautician.

LEIGH, Jeffrey T; Maine South HS; Park Ridge, IL; HonRl; FrCl; PpCl; LetterSwmmng; Northwestern Univ; Law.

LEIGH, Tami J; Callaway Public HS; Oconto, NE; 8/24 VPFrshCls; TrsSophCls; Band; HonRl; MrchBnd; StuCncl; YthFlsp; 4-H; Bsktbl; LetterTrk; College; Secretarial.

LEIGHTON, Linda K; Hancock HS; Hancock, MN; PresFrshCls; RptrYrbk; RptrSchPpr; SchPpr; FFA; FHA; FNA; FSA; FTA; LetterTrk; Coll; Lab.

LEIGHTY, Wade M; Lawrenceville HS; Lawrenceville, IL; 25/176 VPSrCls; ALBoysSt; Band; ChrhWkr; HonRl; MrchBnd; SchMus; StuCncl; LatCl; SciCl; Ftbl; Indiana University; Finance.

LEIKER, Diane M; Mc Pherson HS; Mc Pherson, KS; Wichita State Univ; Accounting.

LEINBERGER, Kathryn K; Freeland HS; Freeland, MI; 2/115 HonRl; NatlFornLg; NHS; NatlMeritCmnd; SchAde; TchrAde; Yrbk; 4-H; GerCl; LetterBsktbl; U Of Mich; Nursing.

LEINENKUGEL, Therese M; Osage Comm HS; Osage, IA; SchPl; StuGov; YthFlsp; 4-H; PpCl; LetterTrk; Coll; Pro.

LEININGER, Kathy L; O Fallon Township HS; Belleville, IL; 6/310 Chrs; ChrhWkr; CmntyWkr; HonRl; JrNHS; LbryAde; Mdrgl; NHS; RedCrAde; SctActv; RptrSchPpr; SpnCl;.

LEINIUS, Randy M; Stanton HS; Stanton, ND; 1/14 HonRl; SchPl; LetterBsktbl; LetterFtbl; CchngActv; College; Vocation.

LEINS, Sheila M; Lockport Central HS; Lockport, IL; 2/550 ChrhWkr; PresNHS; NatlThespSoc; SchMus; SchPl; TchrAde; MthCl; LetterTrk; CaptChrldr; GAA; Univ Of Michigan; Psychiatry.

LEIPZIG, Laura L; Taft HS; Chicago, IL; Chr; Chrl; Chrs; ChrhWkr; CmntyWkr; HonRl; HospAde; JA; LitMag; Mdrgl; Illinois State Univ; Music Education.

LEIS, Charlotte; Rose Hill HS; Augusta, KS; Chr; CmntyWkr; HonRl; LbryAde; SchMus; SchPl; StuCncl; FHA; SpnCl; PpCl; College; High Sch English Teacher.

LEIS, Wayne L; Cashton HS; Caston, WI; PresSrCls; ALBoysSt; CmntyWkr; HonRl; NHS; PolWkr; RedCrAde; StuCncl; Ftbl; Farmer.

LEISCHNER, Marlon W; New Leipzig HS; New Leipzig, ND; ALBoysSt; LbryAde; SchPl; YthFnd; EdYrBk; Bsktbl; Ftbl; U Of Nd; Accountant.

LEISE, Karen A; Cedar Catholic HS; Hartington, NE; 11/67 TrsSophCls; VPJrCls; Band; Chr; HonRl; JCC; NHS; FrCl; Chrldr; GAA; U Of N; Business.

LEISEROWITZ, Bruce H; Theodore Roosevelt HS; Des Moines, IA; 5/441 LbryAde; NatlFornLg; NatlMeritSF; StuCncl; StuGov; College; Political Science.

LEISINGER, Julie A; New Bloomfield Riii HS; Holt Summit, MO; Band; Chrs; HonRl; NHS; StuCncl; TchrAde; RptrSchPpr; FrCl; LetterBsktbl; Chrldr; College; Musician.

LEISSON, Tim; Leaf River Hs; Leaf River, IL; PresFrshCls; PresJrCls; Band; Chrs; HonRl; PresStuCncl; CaptBsbl; CaptBsktbl; CaptFtbl; CchngActv; Illinois State U; Accounting.

LEISZLER, Phyllis J; Clifton Rural HS; Clifton, KS; SecFrshCls; SecJrCls; Band; Chrl; ChrhWkr; CncrtBnd; HonRl; MrchBnd; PepBnd; SchPl; Twrl; Yrbk; FHA; PpCl; University; Professional.

LEITCH, Jeff P; Fergus Falls HS; Fergus Falls, MN; FFA; LetterFtbl; IMSpt; Trade; Vocation.

LEITER, Anne; Barstow HS; Shawnee Mission, KS; SecJrCls; Aud/Vis; LitMag; SchMus; SchPl; RptrYrbk; RptrSchPpr; SchPpr; College; Artist Or Pilot.

LEITER, Jo L; Homestead HS; Ft Wayne, IN; ChrhWkr; HonRl; MrchBnd; PepBnd; RedCrAde; StuCncl; PpCl; Purdue University; Nursing.

LEITER, Mark D; Indiana School For The Deaf; Martinsville, IN; 3/40 SchAde; RptrYrbk; LetterBsbl; LetterTrk; LetterWrstlng; Ntl Tech Inst For Deaf; Cptr Progmng Eng.

LEITERMANN, Eugene C; Kimberly Senior HS; Kimberly, WI; Aud/Vis; ChrhWkr; HonRl; NHS; NatlMeritSF; SchPl; College; Math.

LEITERMANN, Richard; Wauwatosa East HS; Mawwatosa, WI; 10/425 HonRl; JA; JrNHS; NatlFornLg; NHS; NatlMeritCmnd; RptrSchPpr; MthCl; SciCl; JAAwd; Ins Tech.

LEITHLITER, James N; Carmi Community HS; Carmi, IL; 38/139 Aud/Vis; HonRl; NHS; SciCl; Bsbl; Trk; IMSpt; VoiceDemAwd; So Ill U; Medicine.

LEITNAKER, Craig A; Ottawa HS; Ottawa, KS; 27/185 VPSophCls; Band; Chrs; HonRl; MrchBnd; SchPl; PresStuCncl; RptrSchPpr; LetterFtbl; LetterTennis; Baker U; Business.

LEITNER, Wayne H; Cathay HS; Cathay, ND; 1/11 PresSophCls; PresJrCls; PresSrCls; Band; Chrs; NHS; SchPl; RptrSchPpr; Bsbl; Bsktbl; CaptTrk; College; Forestry.

LEITZ, Carol; Ripon Senior HS; Ripon, WI; /170 Chr; Chrs; ChrhWkr; HonRl; NatlFornLg; Bsktbl; Trk; GAA; IMSpt; PPFtbl; Coll; Vocation.

LEITZ, Frederick W; Eau Claire HS; Sodus, MI; HonRl; PresNHS; StuCncl; MthCl; LetterFtbl; LetterWrstlng; LionAwd; Michigan State Univ; Agriculture.

LEITZINGER, Jean M; Monroe HS; Monroe, WI; HonRl; NatlMeritCmnd; College.

LEIX, Patricia; Iowa Grant HS; Montfort, WI; 2/118 TrsFrshCls; TrsSophCls; SecJrCls; ALAGirlsSt; SecSophCls; Chrs; DrmMjrt; NHS; SchMus; EdSchPpr; Uw; Nuclear Medical Technology.

LEJA, David P; Stanley Boyd HS; Stanley, WI; 20/115 Aud/Vis; ChrhWkr; HonRl; NatlFornLg; SchPl; SpnCl; CaptBsktbl; Ftbl; LetterTrk; CchngActv; U W Stout; Inustrial Tech.

LEKSEN, Laurel E; Greenway HS; Coleraine, MN; Band; Chr; HonRl; RptrYrbk; RptrSchPpr; SchPpr; GerCl; Bsktbl; CchngActv; GAA; IMSpt; College; Journalism.

LELAND, Peter S; Nashville Zenda HS; Spivey, KS; HonRl; SchPl; Yrbk; LatCl; LetterTrk; Clg; Prof Artist.

LELENIEWSKI, Frances B; St Stanislaus Kostka HS; Chicago, IL; 6/64 Chrs; HonRl; HospAde; NHS; TchrAde; RptrSchPpr; Blackburn College; Teacher.

LELONEK, Lisa H; Pinckney HS; Pinckney, MI; Chr; HonRl; SchPl; StuCncl; TchrAde; RptrSchPpr; SchPpr; Trk; PresAwd; CitAwd; Journalism School; Writer.

LEMAN, Benjamin; Roanoke Benson HS; Roanoke, IL; Chrs; CncrtBnd; HonRl; Mdrgl; ModUN; NHS; PolWkr; StuCncl; RptrSchPpr; MthCl; College; Business.

LEMAN, Delores K; Roanoke Benson HS; Roanoke, IL; 33/98 PresSophCls; Chr; SchMus; PresFHA; FNA; Bsbl; IMSpt; Il Central Col; Physical Ed.

LEMAN, Kathleen J; Roanoke Benson HS; Roanoke, IL; Band; Chr; HonRl; Mdrgl; ModUN; NHS; PresStuCncl; RptrSchPpr; Pres4-H; FNA; Methodist Sch Of Nursing; Nurse.

LEMAN, Scott A; Eureka HS; Eureka, IL; 5/105 Chr; Chrl; Chrs; HonRl; Mdrgl; NatlMeritCmnd; SchMus; SchPl; StuGov; LetterBsktbl; LetterGlf; Tennis; College; Mechanical Engineer.

LEMANSKI, Lynn M; Verona HS; Verona, WI; 3/122 TrsSophCls; ALAGirlsSt; Band; CncrtBnd; LbryAde; MrchBnd; NHS; PepBnd; SchMus; SchPl; Uw Madison; Medicine.

LEMAR, Dora F; Drake Public HS; Drake, ND; CmntyWkr; HonRl; SchMus; SchPl; TchrAde; FHA; PpCl; College; Accounting.

LEMAR, Lora K; Drake Public HS; Drake, ND; 2/27 CmntyWkr; HonRl; SchMus; SchPl; TchrAde; FHA; PpCl; Trk; JAAwd; College At Grand Forks.

LE MASTERS, Pat J; Verdigre Public HS; Orchard, NE; CmntyWkr; SchPl; TchrAde; RptrSchPpr; 4-H; FHA; SpnCl; CchngActv; GAA; IMSpt; 4-HAwd; Norfolk Tech College; Vocational.

LEMASTERS, Sharon K; Marion HS; Marion, IL; 14/273 Chr; ChrhWkr; DrlTm; HonRl; CivCl; SpnCl; Univ Of Evansville; Med Tech.

LEMBEKE, David A; Morris HS; Morris, MN; TchrAde; KeyCl; CaptBsbl; CaptBsktbl; LetterFtbl; U Of Mn; Phy Ed Or Economics.

LEMBERGER, Lynn K; Valders HS; Whitelaw, WI; 8/110 Chrs; DrlTm; HonRl; Mdrgl; NHS; PresStuCncl; FHA; IMSpt; PPFtbl; Silver Lake College; Music.

LEMBKE, Dale; Watervliet HS; Wateruliet, MI; HonRl; SctActv; RptrYrbk; IMSpt; Western Mi College; Engineering.

LEMBURG, Timothy; Centura Public HS; Dannebrog, NE; Aud/Vis; ChrhWkr; NHS; ROTC; GerCl; Trk; Trade School; Draftsman.

LEMCKE, Ranae L; Oak Park Academy; Sioux Falls, SD; 1/35 SecJrCls; VPSrCls; ChrhWkr; CncrtBnd; HonRl; NatlMeritSF; OffAde; StuCncl; EdYrBk; RptrSchPpr; Union Coll; Med.

LEMENAGER, Jann E; Central HS; Clifton, IL; Chrs; HospAde; Mdrgl; VPNatlFornLg; NatlThespSoc; SchMus; Twrl; Yrbk; Pres4-H; GAA; AmLegAwd; 4-HAwd; Depaul Univ; Nursing.

LEMENSE, Melissa R; Southern Door HS; Brussels, WI; Chrs; HonRl; SchMus; StuCncl; SchPpr; PpCl; Chrldr; GAA; LionAwd; College; Inhalation Therapist.

LE MER, Julie; Balfour Public HS; Balfour, ND; 2/12 Chrs; HonRl; SchPl; SctActv; StuCncl; RptrYrbk; EdSchPpr; PpCl; Chrldr; Univ; Professional.

LEMER, Kevin L; Drake Public HS; Drake, ND; 5/23 HonRl; FFA; PpCl; LetterBsbl; LetterFtbl; College; Vocational.

LEMIESZ, Kathleen M; St Stephens HS; Saginaw, MI; Chr; Chrs; ChrhWkr; SchAde; SchMus; SchPl; TchrAde; PpCl; College; Journalism.

LE MIEUR, Steven T; L F Community HS; Little Falls, MN; Aud/Vis; CmntyWkr; PolWkr; SctActv; TchrAde; Ftbl; College; Vocation.

LE MIEUX, Jerome A; Sheboygan South HS; Sheboygan, WI; 17/495 HonRl; JA; NatlFornLg; NHS; SctActv; StuCncl; Ftbl; Glf; Wrstlng; University Madison; Electronics.

LEMKAU, Terri L; Clay Center HS; Clay Center, NE; SecFrshCls; SecSophCls; ALAGirlsSt; Chrs; ChrhWkr; HonRl; SchPl; TchrAde; Chrldr; Univ.

LEMKE, Beth E; Lester Prairie Public HS; Lester Prairie, MN; 5/43 PresJrCls; ALAGirlsSt; Band; Chr; ChrhWkr; PresNHS; 4-H; CaptBsktbl; PresGAA; 4-HAwd; Lakeland Clg; Math.

LEMKE, David M; North HS; Eau Claire, WI; VPBand; CncrtBnd; MrchBnd; Orch; PepBnd; SctActv; Univ; Civil Engr.

LEMKE, Gary A; Lawrence Public HS; Lawrence, NE; LetterFtbl;.

LEMKE, Janell E; Bayard Community HS; Bayard, IA; 1/31 SecSophCls; Chrs; HonRl; NHS; SchMus; SchPl; 4-H; SciCl; VoiceDemAwd; College; Nursing.

LEMKE, Judy; Wisner Pilger HS; Wisner, NE; 5/74 HonRl; LbryAde; NHS; Yrbk; FBLA; PpCl; Northeast Nebr Tech Com Coll; Secretarial.

LEMKE, Scott W; Jesup Community HS; Waterloo, IA; 3/89 Band; Chr; CncrtBnd; HonRl; NHS; NatlMeritSF; PepBnd; 4-H; FrCl; SciCl; Bsktbl; Ftbl; Wrstlng; College; Law.

LEMKE, Steven R; Ashwaubenon HS; Green Bay, WI; 73/214 KeyCl; Uw Green Bay; Pre Medical.

LEMME, Karen A; Bluffs HS; Bluffs, IL; 5/32 CmntyWkr; HonRl; NHS; SchAde; PresStuCncl; Twrl; SptEdYrbk; FHA; Chrldr; GAA; Business School.

LEMMEN, Karen J; Hamilton HS; Hamilton, MI; 13/125 TrsSrCls; Band; CncrtBnd; HonRl;

MrchBnd; VP4-H; FBLA; VPFTA; GerCl; PpCl; Davenport Coll Of Bus; Secretarial.

LEMMEN, Susan K; Holland HS; Holland, MI; Chr; ChrhWkr; RedCrAde; YthFlsp; YthLg; FDA; FHA; FNA; Coll; Psychology.

LEMMER, James C; Glenbard West HS; Glen Ellyn, IL; 42/522 HonRl; LbryAde; PolWkr; SchPl; SctActv; Purdue Univ; Engineering.

LEMMER, Joel K; Kalamazoo Christian HS; Kalamazoo, MI; Chr; NatlMeritSF; SchMus; PpCl; Ftbl; IMSpt; Mich State; Lawyer.

LEMMER, Marilyn A; Oconto Falls HS; Oconto Falls, WI; 14/153 Chr; Chrs; DrlTm; HonRl; NatlFornLg; NatlThespSoc; SchPl; FHA; SpnCl; GAA; Uw Stevens Point; Home Economics.

LEMMER, Mary; Redfield HS; Redfield, SD; 5/91 AFS; Band; Chrs; HonRl; NHS; SchMus; SchPl; 4-H; FHA; 4-HAwd; Coll; Radiological Tech.

LEMMER, Mary L; Merrill HS; Merrill, WI; 111/334 Chr; HonRl; NatlMeritCmnd; RptrYrbk; GerCl; 4-HAwd; St Jos Sch Of Nursing.

LEMMERMAN, Greg A; Campbell Public HS; Campbell, NE; PresFrshCls; Band; Chr; Chrs; ChrhWkr; HonRl; MrchBnd; PepBnd; SchPl; Bsbl; LetterBsktbl; LetterFtbl; Trk; 4-HAwd; College.

LEMMERT, Rocky E; Pontiac Northern HS; Pontiac, MI; Band; ChrhWkr; CncrtBnd; HonRl; MrchBnd; Orch; PepBnd; SchMus; YthFlsp; Bsbl; Lee College; Music.

LEMMON, Patricia; Caston Educational Center; Lucerne, IN; 4/85 Chrs; ChrhWkr; HonRl; NHS; TchrAde; RptrSchPpr; EdSchPpr; FTA; GerCl; Olivet Nazarene College.

LEMMONS, Keith M; Pittsburg Senior HS; Pittsburg, KS; AFS; CncrtBnd; HonRl; MrchBnd; Orch; PepBnd; SctActv; College; Music.

LEMNUS, Martin M; Enderlin Public HS; Enderlin, ND; 22/44 Band; PresChr; Chrs; ChrhWkr; CncrtBnd; Mdrgl; SchMus; LetterBsktbl; LetterFtbl; 4-HAwd; Nd State Univ; Ag Bus.

LEMON, Alan C; Gull Lake HS; Delton, MI; 30/210 HonRl; PresJA; SchPpr; LetterTennis; Wrstlng; JAAwd; College; Accounting.

LEMON, Margie D; Hayes County HS; Palisade, NE; Chr; CncrtBnd; DrlTm; PepBnd; 4-H; FFA; PpCl; LetterTrk; AmLegAwd; 4-HAwd; Trade School.

LEMON, Steven B; Grant Park HS; Grant Park, IL; PresFrshCls; ChrhWkr; CncrtBnd; HonRl; TchrAde; SptEdSchPpr; VPMthCl; LetterBsktbl; LetterGlf; Trk; PPFtbl; College; Mathematics.

LEMONDS, Susan C; Plainfield HS; Palinfield, IN; 45/259 Chr; Chrs; ChrhWkr; HonRl; NatlThespSoc; SchMus; SchPl; TchrAde; RptrYrbk; AmLegAwd; In U; Ed.

LEMONS, Jay D; Dexter HS; Dexter, MO; 4/140 PresSrCls; Band; HonRl; JrNHS; NHS; SptEdYrbk; Yrbk; SchPpr; CaptFtbl; CaptTrk; Clge; Pro Medicine.

LEMONS, Terry L; Hartville HS; Hartville, MO; LetterBsbl; Trade School.

LEMORIE, Robert E; Shepherd HS; Shepherd, MI; 12/128 VPSrCls; Chr; HonRl; NHS; SctActv; StuCncl; LatCl; PpCl; LetterBsbl; LetterBsktbl; LetterFtbl; CchngActv; Michigan Tech University; Forestry.

LEMP, Gail M; Nerinx Hall HS; St Louis, MO; TrsFrshCls; HonRl; StuCncl; PpCl; Bsktbl; Swmmng; Tennis; Univ Of Mo; Accounting.

LEMP, Susanne M; Osceola HS; Columbus, NE; 2/50 Chr; Chrs; CncrtBnd; HonRl; MrchBnd; SchPl; YthFlsp; SpnCl; Trk; 4-HAwd; Univ; Child Developement.

LEMPA, Luanne; Maria HS; Chicago, IL; 56/335 TrsFrshCls; Aud/Vis; HonRl; LitMag; NHS; SecNatlThespSoc; SchMus; SchPl; StuCncl; GAA; Univ; Performing Arts.

LEMPKA, Dianne M; Sterling HS; St Mary, NE; Chrs; ChrhWkr; CmntyWkr; SchPl; TchrAde; Twrl; Bsktbl; Tennis; LetterTrk; Chrldr; Business School; Prof Sectary.

LEMPKE, Gregory J; Twin Rivers HS; Livermore, IA; TrsFrshCls; PresSrCls; ChrhWkr; HonRl; NHS; StuCncl; LetterBsbl; LetterBsktbl; LetterFtbl; LetterTrk; Coll; Journalism.

LEMS, Susan K; Canton HS; Canton, SD; HonRl; NHS; VPStuCncl; Yrbk; FHA; LetterTrk; LetterChrldr; IMSpt;.

LENAGHAN, Karen M; Earlham HS; Earlham, IA; PresSophCls; Chrs; ChrhWkr; HonRl; StuCncl; TchrAde; Teen; RptrYrbk; EdYrBk; 4-H; SpnCl; Beauty Academy; Beautician.

LENARDSON, Carol L; Bullock Creek HS; Midland, MI; HonRl; NHS; OffAde; RptrYrbk; 4-H; PresFrCl; LetterTrk; GAA; DanFAwd; 4-HAwd; Univ; Civil Engr.

LENART, Barbara; St Alphonsus HS; Dearborn, MI; 10/115 HonRl; College; Secretary.

LENAU, Katherine M; Union HS; Beaufort, MO; 21/165 Band; CncrtBnd; HonRl; JA; LbryAde; MrchBnd; PepBnd; SchMus; Yrbk; Trade School; Beautician.

LENAU, Mary; Union HS; Beaufort, MO; Chrs; HonRl; JA; 4-H; Coll; Nurse.

LENCIONI, Catherine M; Wheaton Central HS; Wheaton, IL; 5/324 SecSophCls; VPJrCls; HonRl; LitMag; NHS; StuCncl; SecStuGov; SchPpr; FrCl; PpCl; Univ Of Illinois; Journalism.

LENDEL, Dorothy J; Our Lady Of Mount Carmel HS; Ecorse, MI; 6/61 SecSophCls; Chrs; HonRl; HospAde; NHS; SchMus; RptrYrbk; RptrSchPpr; SpnCl; IMSpt; Univ; Nursing, Med.

LENDING, Carol E; University City HS; University City, MO; 30/433 Chr; HonRl; HospAde; Orch; FrCl; College; Professional.

LENDMAN, Louis A; Cathedral HS; Chicago, IL; 1/103 PresJrCls; PresSrCls; HonRl; NHS; StuCncl; Univ Of Illinois; Lawyer.

LENERTZ, Sandra M; Mt St Benedict HS; Balfour, ND; SecFrshCls; CmntyWkr; HonRl; StuCncl; StuGov; Yrbk; 4-H; PpCl; Trk; Chrldr; University.

LENFESTEY, Jeffery D; Marion HS; Marion, IN; VPSrCls; ChrhWkr; HonRl; NHS; Bsbl; Bsktbl; Ftbl; Trk; CaptWrstlng; Purdue Univ; Industrial Mgmt.

LENGERICH, David; Bellmont HS; Decatur, IN; 57/251 HonRl; 4-H; PpCl; 4-HAwd;.

LENGES, Linda M; West Vigo HS; West Terre Haute, IN; ChrhWkr; CmntyWkr; HonRl; NatlFornLg; SchPl; TchrAde; Teen; RptrSchPpr; 4-H; SpnCl; LetterTrk; LetterWrstlng; LetterGAA; Indiana St Univ; Law.

LENHART, Ned; Fairfield Comm HS; Fairfield, IA; Band; CncrtBnd; SctActv; YthLg; PresSrCls; CchngActv; GodCntryAwd; College; Criminal Justice Major.

LENHART, Pamela R; Watseka Comm HS; Watseka, IL; 17/147 SecAFS; ChrhWkr; HonRl; TchrAde; Pres4-H; VPFTA; SpnCl; GAA; 4-HAwd; Illinois St Univ; Special Ed.

LENICH, Ann C; Maconaquah HS; Peru, IN; 1/400 HonRl; HospAde; NHS; OffAde; RedCrAde; TchrAde; LatCl; Trk; 4-HAwd; PresAwd; Collegef Vet Medicine.

LENKEY, James J; Perry Meridian HS; Indianapolis, IN; Band; HonRl; NHS; NatlMeritCmnd; Orch; SctActv; StuCncl; LetterBsktbl; LetterFtbl; LetterTrk; Purdue Univ; Aeronautical Engineer.

LENNEMANN, Jolene A; Elkhorn Valley HS; Tilden, NE; Band; CncrtBnd; HonRl; MrchBnd; Orch; PepBnd; RptrYrbk; Yrbk; FHA; PpCl; AmLegAwd; Ne Tech Comm College; Lpn.

LENNERT, Julie A; Libertyville HS; Libertyville, IL; 31/483 Chr; ChrhWkr; HonRl; NHS; FrCl; Univ Of Illinois; Medicine.

LENNON, Colleen E; St Francis HS; Winfield, IL; 6/129 Chrs; ChrhWkr; HonRl; LbryAde; NHS; SchMus; StuCncl; PpCl; Wrstlng; Creighton Univ; Medical.

LENNOX, Roger; North Linn HS; Coggon, IA; FDA; Farming.

LENOX, Guy R; Pleasant Hill HS; Pleasant Hill, MO; 2/111 ALBoysSt; HonRl; NHS; StuCncl; StuGov; SciCl; Bsktbl; LetterFtbl; LetterGlf; LetterWrstlng; University; Nuclear Science.

LENT, David S; Churchill HS; Livonia, MI; 26/853 Chr; Chrl; HonRl; Schoolcraft College; Bus Admin.

LENT, Penny L; Van Far R I HS; Vandalia, MO; 11/90 ChrhWkr; CncrtBnd; MrchBnd; SecNHS; PepBnd; Quill&Scroll; SchMus; SchPl; Yrbk; VPFTA; VPFrCl; SpnCl; Univ; Music.

LENTH, Gary J; Garnavillo Community HS; Garnavillo, IA; 1/45 Band; Chr; HonRl; MrchBnd; NHS; NatlMeritSF; PepBnd; LetterBsktbl; LetterGlf; College; Biology.

LENTI, Mary Jo; Morgan Park HS; Chicago, IL; 3/559 Chrs; HonRl; JrNHS; LbryAde; NHS; SchMus; PresFTA; SecSpnCl; SecMthCl; GAA; Eastern Illinois Univ; Special Education.

LENTS, Terry A; Rolling Meadows HS; Arlington Hts, IL; 97/549 Band; CncrtBnd; HonRl; MrchBnd; NHS; Orch; PepBnd; SchMus; SchPl; Arizona State Univ; Business.

LENTSCH, Donna M; Garrigan HS; Algona, IA; 5/100 Chrs; HonRl; LbryAde; NHS; SchPl; LatCl; MthCl; LetterTennis; IMSpt; St Joseph Merch Sch Of Nursing; Rn.

LENTZ, Amy M; South HS; Westport, IN; Band; CncrtBnd; HonRl; MrchBnd; PepBnd; SpnCl; PpCl; Iupui; Medical.

LENTZ, Charles W; Standish Sterling Central HS; Standish, MI; 12/155 CncrtBnd; HonRl; MrchBnd; PepBnd; SchPl; SctActv; FrCl; LetterBsktbl; LetterFtbl; LetterTrk; Clg; Engineer.

LENTZ, Danieta J; Jefferson Cnty North HS; Winchester, KS; 14/48 Band; Chrs; ChrhWkr; CncrtBnd; HospAde; MrchBnd; PepBnd; SchMus; RptrYrbk; Kansas State Univ; Nurse.

LENTZ, Gregory H; John Glenn HS; Bay City, MI; 59/335 Aud/Vis; ChrhWkr; CmntyWkr; HonRl; LbryAde; YthFlsp; Alma College; Business Admin.

LENTZ, Jeff D; New England Public HS; New England, ND; Chr; HonRl; ModUN; NHS; LetterBsktbl; LetterFtbl; Glf; LetterTrk; University; Professional.

LENTZ, Jo; La Monte R Iv HS; La Monte, MO; 1/25 SecFrshCls; PresSophCls; VPSrCls; HonRl; MrchBnd; StuCncl; EdYrBk; 4-H; FFA; Chrldr; Univ Of Mo Columbia; Agricultural Journalis.

LENTZ, Linford L; Neosho Sr HS; Neosho, MO; 43/243 Chr; HonRl; NatlFornLg; NHS; NatlThespSoc; SchMus; SchPl; SciCl; KeyCl; MthCl; LetterGlf; University; Business Mgmt.

LENTZ, Nicolette R; Manchester HS; Manchester, MI; 7/100 PresSophCls; TrsSophCls; PresJrCls; ALAGirlsSt; ChrhWkr; StuCncl; YthFlsp; 4-H; GerCl; PpCl; CaptBsktbl; CaptTrk; CaptChrldr; Michigan State Univ; Physical Educ.

LENTZ, Paul; Valley City HS; Valley City, ND; 21/161 ALBoysSt; HonRl; NHS; StuCncl; Bsbl; Trk; CitAwd; North Dakota State Univ; Achitecture.

LENTZ, Rickie D; Ainsworth HS; Ainsworth, NE; HonRl; NatlThespSoc; SchPl; SctActv; TchrAde; SchPpr; Ftbl; IMSpt; College; Prog.

LENTZ, Valerie A; Avon HS; Indianapolis, IN; 5/165 ChrhWkr; HonRl; LbryAde; NHS; NatlMeritCmnd; SchPl; TchrAde; FrCl; GerCl; JAAwd; Milligan Clg; Linguistics Mjr.

LENZ, Annette M; Manson Comm HS; Manson, IA; Chrs; HonRl; LbryAde; OffAde; SchMus; SchPpr; 4-H; Bsktbl; Trk; College; Vocation.

LENZ, Daniel M; St Michael Albertville HS; St Michael, MN; 2/76 VPJrCls; HonRl; SchPl; StuGov; SchPpr; 4-H; SpnCl; CaptBsbl; CaptFtbl; CchngActv; Univ Of Minnesota; Communications.

LENZ, Dawn; Wapello HS; Wapello, IA; Chrs; HonRl; PepBnd; SchPl; TchrAde; Yrbk; 4-H; FTA; Coll; Nurse.

LENZ, Douglas M; Burr Oak HS; Burr Oak, KS; 1/17 Chrs; ChrhWkr; HonRl; SchPl; YthFlsp; LetterBsktbl; LetterTrk; Ks Wesleyan; Med.

LENZ, Judy A; Ricevill Comm HS; Riceville, IA; Chrs; CncrtBnd; DrlTm; HonRl; MrchBnd; NHS; PepBnd; YthFlsp; FNA; Glf; Nursing Schl; Pro.

LENZ, Kim; West Delaware HS; Manchester, IA; HonRl; HospAde; NHS; SchAde; FshEdYrbk; Yrbk; RptrSchPpr; Business School.

LENZ, Martina E; Waterford Mott HS; Pontiac, MI; SecJrCls; JA; StuCncl; TchrAde; PpCl; Bsbl; Bsktbl; Central Michigan Univ; Medical Tech.

LENZ, Patricia A; Ellsworth HS; Adrian, MN; TrsFrshCls; SecSophCls; VPJrCls; PresSrCls; Band; Chr; HonRl; SchPl; StuCncl; TchrAde; Yrbk; Trade School; Beautician.

LENZ, Richard; Glenbard North Hs; Wheaton, IL; 112/483 Band; CncrtBnd; HonRl; MrchBnd; PepBnd; SchPpr; 4-H; GerCl; DanFAwd; College; Art.

LENZ, Stephen D; Pendleton Heights HS; Middletown, IN; 4/290 HonRl; VPNHS; NatlMeritCmnd; OffAde; Pres4-H; TreasFFA; GerCl; SciCl; LetterFtbl; LetterTrk; LionAwd; Purdue University; Vet.

LENZ, William P; Ellworth Public HS; Ellsworth, MN; 2/36 ALBoysSt; Chr; ChrhWkr; HonRl; JrNHS; SchAde; SchMus; SchPl; StuCncl; CaptBsktbl; U Of Minnesota; Vet.

LENZINI, Cindy S; Du Quoin HS; Du Quoin, IL; 3/122 SecFrshCls; Chrs; HonRl; SchAde; StuCncl; TchrAde; RptrSchPpr; FHA; FTA; KeyCl; SpnCl; PpCl; LetterBsbl; Chrldr; Univ Of Illinois; Physical Education.

LENZINI, Robert W; Libertyville HS; Libertyville, IL; 16/458 ALBoysSt; HonRl; NHS; PresYthFlsp; Bsktbl; LetterFtbl; LetterTrk; Univ Of Illinois; Civil Engineer.

LEON, Mel; Horace Mann HS; Gary, IN; 10/262 HonRl; JrNHS; NHS; MthCl; SciCl; Ftbl; Valparaiso Univ; Engineering.

LEONARD, Alfred L; Tri Center HS; Portsmouth, IA; Band; CncrtBnd; HonRl; MrchBnd; PepBnd; Vocation.

LEONARD, Brenda K; White City HS; White City, KS; 2/15 Band; Chr; ChrhWkr; HonRl; StuCncl; Twrl; Yrbk; Bsbl; Bsktbl; Chrldr; Ks State U; Bus Adm.

LEONARD, Brian K; Peotone HS; Peotone, IL; CAP; HonRl; JA; NatlMeritCmnd; Quill&Scroll; SctActv; RptrYrbk; SchPpr; GerCl; MthCl; College; Aerospace Engineering.

LEONARD, Carol E; St Mary Academy; Indianapolis, IN; Chr; ChrhWkr; HonRl; JrNHS; NHS; SchMus; SchPl; StuCncl; FrCl; GAA; University; Art.

LEONARD, Charles H; Wakefield HS; Wakefield, NE; 4/45 PresSophCls; ALBoysSt; HonRl; SchPl; StuCncl; StuGov; CaptFtbl; LetterTrk; LetterWrstlng; Univ Of Nebr; Agriculture.

LEONARD, Derek; Rc Stevens HS; Rapid City, SD; 45/430 ALBoysSt; HonRl; NatlFornLg; PolWkr; SctActv; StuCncl; Col; Law.

LEONARD, Emily L; Jefferson City Sr HS; Jefferson City, MO; 4/502 CncrtBnd; HonRl; JrNHS; MrchBnd; NHS; Orch; SchMus; VPFrCl; PpCl;.

LEONARD, Frederick G; Premontre HS; Green Bay, WI; 8/157 Chrs; HonRl; JA; NHS; SchMus; SchPl; TchrAde; Ftbl; Trk; Nw Univ; Professional.

LEONARD, Gillis C; Harrisonville Cass R9 HS; Harrisonville, MO; 14/161 Band; Chrs; HonRl; NHS; StuCncl; UNYO; RptrSchPpr; SptEdSchPpr; FTA; LetterBsbl; LetterBsktbl; LetterFtbl; LetterTrk; Univ Of Mo; Law.

LEONARD, Helen K; Pioneer HS; Ann Arbor, MI; HonRl; HospAde; RptrYrbk; Yrbk; SpnCl; Tennis; University; Art History.

LEONARD, Janice; Wahlert HS; Dubuque, IA; 30/500 Chr; ChrhWkr; HonRl; ModUN; NHS; StuGov; MthCl; EldAwd; Loras Coll; Law.

LEONARD, Joan; Pecatonica HS; Hollandale, WI; VPJrCls; ChrhWkr; HonRl; EdYrBk; Business School.

LEONARD, John; Brookfield Central HS; Brookfield, WI; 4/474 AFS; ALBoysSt; JrNHS; NHS; NatlMeritCmnd; Quill&Scroll; RptrYrbk; SptEdYrbk; IMSpt; Univ Of Wisconsin; Medicine.

LEONARD, Kolin; New Trier East HS; Kenilworth, IL; Chr; Chrs; ChrhWkr; CmntyWkr; PolWkr; SchMus; SchPl; StuGov; Ftbl; Socr; Geo Washington U; Government.

LEONARD, Laura J; Pecatonica HS; Hollandale, WI; ALAGirlsSt; ChrhWkr; HonRl; OffAde; EdYrBk; SchPpr; PpCl; Tech Sch; Stenography.

LEONARD, Laura L; Farmington Grosse Ile HS; Grosse Ile, MI; Band; CmntyWkr; CncrtBnd; HonRl; HospAde; MrchBnd; NHS; NatlMeritCmnd; Orch; RedCrAde; College; Medical Tech.

LEONARD, Lori J; Dekalb Sr HS; Dekalb, IL; ChrhWkr; CmntyWkr; CncrtBnd; HonRl; MrchBnd; StuCncl; YthFlsp; 4-H; GAA; College; Professional.

LEONARD, Lynn A; Dekalb Sr HS; Dekalb, IL; Band; Chr; ChrhWkr; CncrtBnd; HonRl; MrchBnd; NHS; Orch; PepBnd; SchMus; StuCncl; 4-H; College; Professional.

LEONARD, Mark L; Logan Magnolia HS; Logan, IA; 4/52 PresFrshCls; PresJrCls; ALBoysSt; HonRl; NHS; SptEdYrbk; LetterBsbl; LetterFtbl; LetterTrk; MasAwd; PresAwd; Commercial Extension; Accounting.

LEONARD, Nancy; Nauvoo Colusa Hs; Niota, IL; 1/50 Band; ChrhWkr; HonRl; MrchBnd; StuCncl; YthFlsp; FHA; PpCl; LetterChrldr; 4-HAwd;.

LEONARD, Peg; O Neill HS; O Neill, NE; Band; Chrs; HonRl; Mdrgl; NHS; PepBnd; SchMus; Chrldr; IMSpt;.

LEONARD, Wendy L; Kiel HS; Kiel, WI; 34/164 ChrhWkr; HonRl; LbryAde; GerCl; PpCl; GAA; College; Architectural Design.

LEONARDO, Dawn M; Roncalli HS; Omaha, NE; VPSophCls; HonRl; HospAde; NHS; SchPl; StuCncl; 4-H; LetterBsktbl; LetterSciCl; 4-HAwd; Nurse Sch; Rn.

LEONARDSON, Scott; Memorial HS; Eau Claire, WI; 48/334 Chr; Chrs; ChrhWkr; HonRl; SchPl; Ftbl; Wrstlng; IMSpt; Technical School.

LEONE, Mark S; Maine South HS; Park Ridge, IL; Southern Ill Univ; Law Enforcement.

LEONETTI, John P; Wheeling HS; Buffalo Grove, IL; 5/450 HonRl; VPNHS; MthCl; SciCl; CaptGlf; CaptIMSpt; Augustana College; Psychiatry.

LEONG, James; Thomas Kelly HS; Chicago, IL; 3/503 PresJrCls; Aud/Vis; Chr; Chrs; ChrhWkr; HonRl; IntrClCncl; LbryAde; NHS;.

LEONG, Mildred K; Carter H Harrison HS; Chicago, IL; 4/408 CtyCnl; CmntyWkr; HonRl; JA; JrNHS; VPNHS; NatlMeritSchl; OffAde; CitAwd; Univ Of Illinois; Dietitian.

LEONG, Yim F; Kickapoo HS; Springfield, MO; HonRl; SchMus; StuCncl; CivCl; FHA; FSA; EngCl; VPFrCl; PpCl; GAA; IMSpt; College; Fashion.

LEONHARD, Don J; Flambeau HS; Tony, WI; 21/68 CmntyWkr; HonRl; 4-H; FFA; Bsbl; Bsktbl; Ftbl; Trk; IMSpt; 4-HAwd; College; Professional.

LEONHARD, Terese M; Kiel HS; Kiel, WI; AFS; Band; Chrs; HonRl; LbryAde; SchMus; SchPl; SecYthFlsp; Sec4-H; SpnCl; College; Law.

LEOSCHKE, Mark J; Glenbrook South HS; Glenview, IL; 14/579 ChrhWkr; CmntyWkr; HonRl; Valparaiso Univ; Biology.

LEPANT, Dora F; Central Catholic HS; Grand Island, NE; HonRl; NHS; OffAde; Quill&Scroll; StuCncl; RptrSchPpr; EdSchPpr; SchPpr; 4-H; 4-HAwd; College; Journalism.

LEPERT, Joyce E; Plattsmouth Senior HS; Plattsmouth, NE; Chr; Chrs; HonRl; LbryAde; Mdrgl; SchMus; TchrAde; FrCl; PpCl; 4-HAwd; Univ Of Nebr; Music Or Special Ed.

LEPIRD, Sharon J; Estherville Sr HS; Estherville, IA; Band; Chr; Chrs; ChrhWkr; HonRl; Mdrgl; NHS; 4-H; FFA; GAA; IMSpt; 4-HAwd; College; Nursing.

LEPISTO, Mary A; Rock Public HS; Roc, MI; 6/26 TrsSrCls; Band; ChrhWkr; CmntyWkr; HonRl; SchPl; EdSchPpr; PpCl; Bsktbl; Chrldr; Dunwoody Ind Inst; Commercial Art.

LEPPEK, Linda; Traverse City Senior HS; Traverse City, MI; HonRl; YthLg; 4-H; PpCl; PresAwd; Collge; Consevation.

LEPPER, Curtis A; Cole R Y HS; Eugene, MO; TrsJrCls; ChrhWkr; CmntyWkr; HonRl; LbryAde; SchAde; StuCncl; FFA; Bsbl; College; Professional Accounting.

LEPPER, Kevin M; Houghton Lake HS; Houghton Lake, MI; HonRl; NHS; SctActv; Bsbl; Bsktbl; Ftbl; IMSpt; KiwanAwd; LionAwd; Hardware Management.

LEPPERT, Hollace D; Columbia Central HS; Brooklyn, MI; 2/154 SecFrshCls; Band; CncrtBnd; HonRl; MrchBnd; NHS; Orch; PepBnd; SchMus; SchPl; StuCncl; SptEdYrbk; Yrbk; Bsktbl; Jackson Comm College; Mathematics.

LEPPERT, Jeff; Kee HS; Lansing, IA; TrsFrshCls; HonRl; 4-H; IMSpt; 4-HAwd; Trade School;.

LEPPERT, Josey R; Kee HS; Lansing, IA; 8/67 CncrtBnd; HonRl; MrchBnd; NHS; Quill&Scroll; RptrSchPpr; PpCl; LetterBsktbl; LetterTrk; IMSpt; College; Education.

LEPPERT, Melissa; Wheaton North HS; Wheaton, IL; 52/312 Band; CmntyWkr; HonRl; MrchBnd; Cornell College; Biology.

LEPPINK, Craig K; Lakeview HS; Lakeview, MI; ChrhWkr; HonRl; SctActv; StuCncl; TchrAde; YthFlsp; Ftbl; Trk; Wrstlng; IMSpt; Military Acad; Marine Biology.

LERCH, Brenda; La Crosse HS; Wanatah, IN; Chrs; HonRl; FHA; College; Prof.

LERCH, Debra L; Alleman HS; Rock Island, IL; PresHospAde; JrNHS; NHS; RptrYrbk; SptEdYrbk; FrCl; GAA; U Of Ia; Pharmacy.

LERCH, Sue E; Northwest HS; Cecar Hill, MO; DrlTm; HonRl; RptrYrbk; EdYrBk; FHA; PpCl; PresAwd; VoiceDemAwd; College; History Teacher.

LERCH, Timothy H; Valmeyer HS; Valmeyer, IL; 12/59 Band; CncrtBnd; HonRl; MrchBnd; Orch;

PepBnd; SchMus; FFA; MthCl; Bsbl; Univ; Accountant.

LERDAL, Susan L; Humboldt Community HS; Humboldt, IA; 16/140 Band; ChrhWkr; CncrtBnd; HonRl; NHS; PepBnd; StuCncl; 4-H; PpCl; 4-HAwd; Iowa State U; Biology.

LERMA, Sylvia; Bishop Noll HS; Gary, IN; 107/360 HonRl; College; Accounting.

LERNER, Marla S; Maria HS; Chicago, IL; 35/301 HonRl; NHS; SchMus; StuCncl; LatCl; MthCl; SciCl; Ill Wesleyan Univ; Nursing.

LE ROSE, Leonard J; Morgan Park Academy; Olympia Fields, IL; VPFrshCls; TrsJrCls; HonRl; NHS; RptrYrbk; SptEdSchPpr; KeyCl; SpnCl; LetterBsbl; Bsktbl; Notre Dame; Accounting.

LEROY, Cynthia L; Southern Door HS; Brussels, WI; Band; CncrtBnd; HonRl; JrNHS; MrchBnd; PepBnd; SchMus; College.

LEROY, Steven L; Dundee Commuinty HS; Barrington, IL; PresFrshCls; HonRl; NatlThespSoc; StuCncl; StuGov; 4-H; KeyCl; Wrstlng; DanFAwd; 4-HAwd; College; Veterinarian.

LE SAC, Nancy C; Oconomowoc Sr HS; Oconomowoc, WI; AFS; NHS; Orch; SchMus; Vanderbilt Univ; Medicine.

LESAN, Harvey C; Joliet Catholic HS; Joliet, IL; 10/140 HonRl; LitMag; TchrAde; RptrSchPpr; LatCl; RusCl; University Of Miami; Biology.

LESER, Catherine C; Regis HS; Eau Claire, WI; 1/132 ChrhWkr; HonRl; NHS; Orch; GerCl; SpnCl; MthCl; SciCl; LetterBsktbl; LetterTennis; U Of W Madison; Medicine.

LESER, Dennis; Grand Blanc HS; Grand Blanc, MI; 50/618 HonRl; JrNHS; NHS; SchPl; GerCl; Mott Community College;sociology.

LESHER, Linda S; Clarion HS; Clarion, IA; 13/93 Band; Chr; CncrtBnd; DrmMjrt; HonRl; MrchBnd; NHS; NatlThespSoc; SchPl; StuCncl; Glf; Chrldr; Univ Of N Iowa; Elementary Ed.

LESHLEY, Greg S; Newton HS; Newton, IL; Chrs; HonRl; Mdrgl; NHS; SchMus; Bsktbl; Ftbl; Macmurray College; Elem Teacher.

LESKA, Catherine E; Carmel Girls HS; Grayslake, IL; HonRl; LbryAde; OffAde; SchMus; SchPl; SctActv; 4-H; SpnCl; Loyola Univ; Nursing.

LESKE, Renee L; Hutchinson HS; Hutchinson, MN; HonRl; LbryAde; Treas4-H; Col; Biology.

LESKO, Mark L; St Laurence HS; Chicago, IL; 39/372 CmntyWkr; NHS; NatlMeritFnl; StuCncl; SptEdYrbk; SpnCl; MthCl; Bsktbl; Ftbl; BauchLmbAwd; U Of Ill; Bio Sciences.

LESLE, Linda D; Wall Lake Comm HS; Wall Lake, IA; VPSophCls; HonRl; JrNHS; MrchBnd; Yrbk; RptrSchPpr; FrCl; Bsktbl; LetterTrk; AmLegAwd; Nursing Clge; Rn.

LESLEY, Kim R; University City Senior HS; University City, MO; 46/401 Chr; ChrhWkr; HonRl; SpnCl;.

LESLIE, Barry; Lake Park HS; Audubon, MN; 7/40 ChrhWkr; HonRl; NHS; OffAde; Wrstlng; VFWAwd; College; Christian Radio.

LESLIE, Ben B; Jimtown HS; Elkhart, IN; HonRl; RptrSchPpr; FrCl; SciCl; Indiana Inst; Computer Engineering.

LESLIE, Colleen M; Cass City HS; Decker, MI; 8/150 ChrhWkr; CmntyWkr; HonRl; JrNHS; NHS; YthFlsp; 4-H; FTA; SpnCl; PpCl; College; Elementary Teaching.

LESLIE, D Ann C; Kingsville HS; Kingsville, MO; 2/22 HonRl; JrNHS; NHS; SchPl; StuCncl; 4-H; PpCl; SciCl; Bsbl; CaptBsktbl; Central Missouri St University.

LESLIE, Dann C; Kingsville HS; Kingsville, MO; 2/22 Chrs; HonRl; NHS; SchPl; StuCncl; RptrYrbk; 4-H; HstSophCls; LetterBsbl; LetterBsktbl; Cen Mo St Univ.

LESLIE, David L; York Community HS; Elmhurst, IL; 14/950 Band; CncrtBnd; HonRl; NHS; NatlMeritCmnd; University Of Illinois.

LESLIE, Deanna S; South Clay HS; Gillett Grove, IA; 2/30 HonRl; LbryAde; NHS; SchPl; SctActv; RptrSchPpr; PpCl; LetterTrk; PPFtbl; Iowa St University.

LESLIE, Kenneth E; Shrine HS; Royal Oak, MI; 15/163 HonRl; JA; NHS; NatlMeritSF; Bsbl; LetterFtbl; IMSpt; Western Mich Univ; Accounting.

LESLIE, Mary; Larned Sr HS; Larned, KS; Chrs; HonRl; HospAde; SchMus; SchPl; SctActv; StuCncl; StuGov; PpCl; Chrldr; College; Interior Design.

LESLIE, Sue A; Fenton HS; Fenton, MI; Chr; Chrl; HonRl; TreasNHS; GerCl;.

LESMEISTER, Jerome P; New Rockford Central HS; New Rockford, ND; 10/67 Band; ChrhWkr; CmntyWkr; CncrtBnd; HonRl; MrchBnd; PepBnd; MthCl; SciCl; IMSpt; College; Construction Engineering.

LESMEISTER, Lynne A; Plymouth Canton HS; Plymouth, MI; CncrtBnd; HonRl; MrchBnd; NHS; SchPl; Twrl; RptrSchPpr; FrCl; GovHonPrgAwd; Michigan St Univ; Dentist.

LESNIAK, John J; Bloom Township HS; Steger, IL; 60/903 Band; CncrtBnd; HonRl; MrchBnd; NHS; Orch; PepBnd; StuGov; Junior College; Business Accounting.

LESNIEWSKI, Diane; St Francis De Salles Hs; So Holland, IL; 30/294 Chrs; DrlTm; NHS; SchPl; StuCncl; EdSchPpr; Chrldr; GAA; Illinois State U; Dance Education.

LESNIEWSKI, Robert F; St Laurence HS; Chicago, IL; 1/396 HonRl; StuCncl; RptrYrbk; Univ Of Notre Dame; Physical Science.

LESPERANCE, Michele L; St Joseph Acad; Green Bay, WI; PresFrshCls; ChrhWkr; CmntyWkr; DrlTm; HospAde; StuCncl; FNA; PPFtbl; College; Occupational Therapist.

LESS, Michael; Maine Twp Hs East; Morton Grove, IL; 91/900 Aud/Vis; HonRl; NHS; SchPl; Swmmng; U Of Ill; Medical Doctor.

LESSARD, James; Hot Springs HS; Hot Springs, SD; SctActv; RptrSchPpr; KeyCl; Bsktbl; Ftbl; Trk; College.

LESSENS, George D; Lowell HS; Lowell, MI; 6/214 TrsJrCls; TrsSrCls; Chr; CncrtBnd; MrchBnd; NHS; SctActv; TreasStuCncl; SptEdSchPpr; LetterBsktbl; Grand Rapids Jc; Meteorologist.

LESSMAN, Randall M; Tracy HS; Tracy, MN; Band; Chr; CncrtBnd; MrchBnd; PepBnd; SchMus; 4-H; FFA; LetterBsktbl; Ftbl; Agriculture College.

LESSNER, Joyce E; Thornton Fractional North HS; Calumet City, IL; 16/433 Chrs; HonRl; NHS; Thornton Comm Col; Med Records Tech.

LESTER, Brenda; Benton Central HS; Otterbein, IN; 51/267 Band; CmntyWkr; CncrtBnd; HonRl; SchPl; PpCl; Swmmng; IMSpt; PPFtbl; Ivy Tech; Dental Asst.

LESTER, David D; Crystal Lake Comm HS; Crystal Lake, IL; HonRl; NHS; SctActv; StuCncl; Ftbl; Swmmng; Illinois St Univ; Oceanographer.

LESTER, Donald L; Colfax HS; Colfax, IA; ALBoysSt; ChrhWkr; HonRl; SchPl; SctActv; YthFlsp; Yrbk; SpnCl; LetterBsktbl; Forestery.

LESTER, Jannette E; Kingston Comm HS; Mayville, MI; 3/49 Band; Chr; DrmMjrt; HonRl; NHS; SchPl; StuCncl; RptrSchPpr; FrCl; Chrldr; Bus Sch

LESTER, Kimberley S; Moline Sr HS; Moline, IL; HonRl; LbryAde; NHS; OffAde; Quill&Scroll; SchPpr; SpnCl; Northern Illinois Univ; Accountant.

LESTER, Pamela S; Malden HS; La Moille, IL; 1/13 HstFrshCls; SecSrCls; Chr; Chrs; ChrhWkr; HonRl; SchPl; TreasStuCncl; PresFrCl; PresPpCl; CaptChrldr; Business School; Legal Secretary.

LESTER, Polly J; Sullivan HS; Sullivan, IN; Band; ChrhWkr; DrlTm; HonRl; JrNHS; NHS; YthFlsp; 4-H; Tennis; Trk; GAA; In State Univ; Law.

LESTER, Rhonda; Goldfield Comm HS; Goldfield, IA; SecSophCls; SecJrCls; Band; CncrtBnd; HonRl; MrchBnd; YthFlsp; 4-H; Chrldr; Ia St Univ; Interior Design.

LESTER, Sharon K; St Charles HS; Brant, MI; Band; CncrtBnd; HonRl; HospAde; MrchBnd; StuCncl; 4-H; Bsktbl; Trk; Chrldr; College; Vocation.

LESTER, Teri A; Raymore Peculiar HS; Raymore, MO; HonRl; NHS; NatlThespSoc; SchMus; TchrAde; SchPl; YthFlsp; FTA; Bsbl; Chrldr; College; Professional.

LESTON, Gregory W; Glenbard East HS; Lombard, IL; Band; CAP; CncrtBnd; HonRl; Univ Of Illinois; Biology.

LE SUEUR, Joan M; Rochester HS; Rochester, IN; HonRl; NHS; OffAde; SchPl; FrCl; Coll; Nursing.

LESZCZYNSKI, Susan M; La Salle Peru Twp HS; Lasalle, IL; CmntyWkr; HonRl; SpnCl; PpCl; I V C C; Journalist.

LETE, Cathy M; Westville HS; Westville, IL; HonRl; NHS; RptrYrbk; SpnCl; SciCl; IMSpt;.

LETH, Kristine K; St Paul Public HS; St Paul, NE; Band; Chr; ChrhWkr; CncrtBnd; HonRl; MrchBnd; NHS; PepBnd; SchMus; TchrAde; Coll; Neurologist.

LETIZIA, Michelle E; Homestead Jr Sr HS; Fort Wayne, IN; Chr; HonRl; JA; Mdrgl; SchMus; StuCncl; TchrAde; FrCl; PpCl; De Paul Univ; Attorney.

LETNER, Paula J; Eisenhower HS; Decatur, IL; 1/301 VPSrCls; CncrtBnd; MrchBnd; NHS; NatlMeritCmnd; Orch; SchMus; SchPl; StuGov; Washington Univ; Sociology.

LETO, Kathleen G; East HS; Des Moines, IA; 1/496 Chr; PresChrs; HonRl; Mdrgl; SchMus; SciCl; ChmbCommrsAwd; Univ Of Northern Iowa; Math.

LE TOURNEAU, David; Batavia HS; Batavia, IL; 18/225 HonRl; NHS; Quill&Scroll; SptEdYrbk; SptEdSchPpr; MthCl; Bsbl; Bsktbl; College; Lawyer.

LE TOURNEAU, David J; Iron Mountain HS; Iron Mountain, MI; PresFrshCls; StuCncl; Ftbl; CchngActv; IMSpt; Trade Sch; Armed Forces.

LETSON, Larry D; Mauston Area HS; Mauston, WI; AFS; HonRl; SchMus; SchPl; SctActv; RptrYrbk; SchPpr; LetterFtbl; Trk; Wrstlng; U Of Wis.

LETSOS, Lorraine; Marian Catholic Hs; E Hazel Crest, IL; 6/328 NHS; NatlMeritCmnd; Yrbk; GAA; Secretarial School; Secretarial Field.

LETT, Ann E; New Berlin HS; New Berlin, IL; 2/63 Band; Chr; ChrhWkr; NHS; NatlMeritCmnd; PepBnd; StuCncl; 4-H; PresFHA; PresGerCl; GAA; 4-HAwd; Univ; Dietetics.

LETTENMAIER, Maribeth; North Central Of Barnes HS; Sanborn, ND; 1/30 PresJrCls; PresSrCls; HonRl; PepBnd; StuCncl; Yrbk; RptrSchPpr; Chrldr; 4-HAwd; Mary College; Rn.

LETTIERE, John T; Hubbard HS; Chicago, IL; 14/401 Aud/Vis; CmntyWkr; HonRl; NHS; OffAde; TchrAde; De Paul Univ; Accounting.

LETTMAN, Gail A; Lindblom HS; Chicago, IL; 60/750 HonRl; NHS; OffAde; SchAde; TchrAde; SpnCl; Univ Of Illinois; Mechanical Engineer.

LETTS, Penny L; Battle Creek Central HS; Battle Creek, MI; PresSrCls; VPSrCls; CmntyWkr; HonRl; SchMus; SchPl; Swmmng; CchngActv; GAA; University; Professional.

LETURNO, Betty; Irving Crown Hs; Capentersville, IL; 4/350 Band; Chrs; CncrtBnd; HonRl; MrchBnd; NHS; SchMus; SctActv; LetterBsktbl; LetterTennis; College; Teacher.

LETVIN, Craig A; Butte Public HS; Kief, ND; 3/17 PresFrshCls; TrsJrCls; SecSrCls; Chr; Chrs; HonRl; SptEdYrbk; EdSchPpr; LetterBsktbl; LetterTrk; No Dakota State Univ; Computer Science.

LETZE, Cindy G; Summit HS; Summit, SD; 3/21 Chrs; HonRl; SchPl; EdYrBk; SchPpr; 4-H; Bsktbl; Trk;.

LEUKER, Janet K; William Horlick HS; Racine, WI; HonRl; OffAde; TchrAde; RptrSchPpr; Univ Of Wisc Parkside; Forestry.

LEUM, Georgina L; Cashton HS; Cashton, WI; 8/66 SecJrCls; PresSrCls; ChrhWkr; HonRl; NHS; SptEdYrbk; PresSpnCl; PresPpCl; DARAwd; U Of Wi La Crosse; Clinical Psychology.

LEUM, Martin D; Cashton HS; Cashton, WI; VPFrshCls; Chrs; HonRl; LetterFtbl; Wrstlng; Air Force.

LEUPOLD, Linda J; Wauwatosa East HS; Wauwatosa, WI; AFS; HonRl; NHS; PolWkr; RptrSchPpr; MthCl; PpCl; Tennis; IMSpt; University.

LEUTHEUSER, Karen S; Hillsdale HS; Hillsdale, MI; VPFrshCls; SecSophCls; Chr; HonRl; NHS; StuCncl; StuGov; PresFrCl; LetterTrk; SecChrldr; Coll; Pro.

LEUTHNER, Beth; Winsted Holy Trinity HS; Victoria, MN; Chrs; HonRl; SchAde; SchMus; TchrAde; Yrbk; 4-HAwd; Voc School; Comm Art.

LEUWERKE, Kathlene L; Ventura Comm HS; Ventura, IA; Chrs; ChrhWkr; HonRl; NatlThespSoc; SchPl; LetterTrk; College; Vocation.

LE VALLEY, Mary S; Luckey HS; Manhattan, KS; HstFrshCls; HstSophCls; HonRl; JrNHS; StuCncl; Bsbl; CaptBsktbl; Swmmng; IMSpt; CitAwd; Ks State U; Teacher Elementary.

LEVANDOSKI, Linda A; D C Everest Senior HS; Hatley, WI; 20/337 ChrhWkr; CmntyWkr; RptrSchPpr; 4-H; FHA; PpCl; LionAwd; North Central Technical Inst; Data Proc.

LE VASSEUR, Mary Ann; All Saints Central HS; Bay City, MI; Chr; HonRl; NHS; PolWkr; TchrAde; College; Professional.

LEVELSTON, Derrick; Saginaw Hs; Saginaw, MI; Band; DrlTm; HonRl; MrchBnd; PepBnd; SchMus; Ftbl; Tennis;.

LEVENDUSKY, Diane M; Appleton West HS; Appleton, WI; AFS; Band; CmntyWkr; CncrtBnd; JA; MrchBnd; Orch; StuGov; YthLg; College; Law.

LEVENFELD, David M; Highland Park HS; Highland Park, IL; StuGov; LetterBsbl; Trk; Tufts University.

LEVERENCE, Kathy M; Burr Oak HS; Burr Oak, MI; 1/34 SecFrshCls; TrsSophCls; Band; Chr; HonRl; LbryAde; NHS; SchMus; SchPl; TchrAde; Huntington College; Mathematics.

LEVERENZ, Linda L; York Comm HS; Elmhurst, IL; Band; CncrtBnd; HonRl; MrchBnd; PepBnd; SchMus; Univ Of Illinois; Business Admin.

LEVERETTE, Wanda Y; Cass Tech HS; Detroit, MI; 242/1004 PresSrCls; VPSrCls; TrsSrCls; ChrhWkr; HonRl; NHS; FDA; Univ Of Michigan; Medicine.

LEVERTON, Beverly A; Lena Winslow HS; Lena, IL; SecFrshCls; SecSrCls; HonRl; HospAde; LbryAde; NHS; Yrbk; FHA; Freeport Mem Hosp; Nursing.

LEVEY, George; Max Public HS; Benedict, ND; 1/15 TrsJrCls; ALBoysSt; Chrs; HonRl; StuCncl; PpCl; Wrstlng; College;.

LEVEY, Michael; The Valley HS; Flint, MI; ChrhWkr; CmntyWkr; PolWkr; SchAde; SchPl; StuCncl; StuGov; SchPpr; Bsktbl; Univ Of Mich; Am History Pre Law.

LEVI, Betty; Berkley HS; Oak Park, MI; 41/576 CmntyWkr; JrNHS; NHS; OffAde; SchAde; TchrAde; SciCl; College; Professional.

LEVI, Linda S; Roger C Sullivan HS; Chicago, IL; 25/276 HonRl; JA; NHS; SecStuCncl; RptrYrbk; SchPpr; VPKeyCl; Swmmng; DARAwd; JAAwd; Univ Of Iowa; Science.

LEVICKI, Steven W; Dundee HS; Dundee, MI; 2/128 Chr; HonRl; PresNHS; SchMus; TchrAde; FTA; GerCl; Tennis; Univ Of Michigan; Dentistry.

LEVIN, Elaine R; Elmwood Park HS; Elmwood Park, IL; 3/306 HonRl; SchMus; SchPl; RptrSchPpr; CaptBsktbl; Tennis; Trk; College; Communications.

LEVIN, Jeffrey H; Evanston Twp HS; Skokie, IL; 133/1100 Univ Of Il; Accounting.

LEVIN, Leonard A; Ernest W Seaholm HS; Birmingham, MI; CmntyWkr; CncrtBnd; JA; NatlFornLg; NHS; NatlMeritSF; JAAwd; College; Medicine.

LEVIN, Marci L; Smith Center HS; Smith Center, KS; TrsSophCls; Chrs; DrlTm; HonRl; NHS; TchrAde;.

LEVIN, Rebekah A; Oak Park Riverforest HS; Oak Park, IL; Band; Chr; ChrhWkr; CncrtBnd; MrchBnd; NHS; Orch; PepBnd; PolWkr; Oberlin College; Human Services.

LEVIN, Robert A; St Paul Acad; St Paul, MN; CmntyWkr; HonRl; LitMag; NatlMeritSF; PolWkr; StuGov; SchPpr; PresCivCl; Tennis; CitAwd; Coll;law.

LEVIN, Sharon R; Sidney HS; Sidney, NE; Band; Chrs; ChrhWkr; HonRl; HospAde; NHS; Quill&Scroll; MthCl; SciCl; PresSciCl; Univ; Medicine.

LEVINE, Linda S; Robbinsdale HS; Minneapolis, MN; 47/761 Chr; CmntyWkr; HonRl; HospAde; NatlMeritCmnd; SchPl; SctActv; TchrAde; SchPpr; Trk; College; Physician.

LEVINE, Shauna; Niles Township West Hs; Lincolnwood, IL; 56/626 CmntyWkr; HonRl; PolWkr; Macalester College; Anthropology And Sociol.

LE VINE, Trudy J; Isaac C Elston HS; Michigan City, IN; Chr; Chrs; HonRl; SchPl; RptrSchPpr; Bsbl; LetterBsktbl; Purdue Univ; Journalism.

LEVINGER, Jeff S; Yankton HS; Yankton, SD; 1/250 ALBoysSt; Band; Chrs; HonRl; NatlMeritSF; SctActv; VPStuCncl; EdSchPpr; LetterTennis; LetterTrk; IMSpt; AmLegAwd; College; Law.

LEVINGER, Michael; North HS; Sioux City, IA; 7/320 Chr; ChrhWkr; NatlFornLg; NatlMeritFnl; SchMus; StuCncl; SchPpr; Swmmng; Tennis; BauchLmbAwd; University.

LEVINGER, Michael J; North HS; Sioux City, IA; 8/320 Chr; ChrhWkr; CmntyWkr; NatlMeritSF; NatlThespSoc; SchMus; StuCncl; SchPpr; LetterSwmmng; Univ.

LEVINSKY, Cheryl A; Plainfield HS; Plainfield, IL; 10/279 HonRl; Ill State Univ; Math Teacher.

LEVITAN, Mina; Highland Park HS; Highland Park, IL; Chr; CmntyWkr; NatlFornLg; NHS; NatlMeritCmnd; SchPl; College.

LE VON, Steven N; Evanston Township HS; Evanston, IL; Band; NatlMeritSchl; Orch; SctActv; N Ill Univ.

LEVSCH, Robert A; Red Wing Central HS; Red Wing, MN; HonRl; NatlFornLg; Univ Of Chicago; Biology.

LEVTZINGER, Randall D; St Pius X HS; Festus, MO; ALBoysSt; HonRl; NHS; RptrYrbk; Yrbk; Bsbl; College; Wildlife Management & Biology.

LEVY, Bradford K; Shawnee Mission East HS; Prairie Village, KS; Aud/Vis; NatlMeritSF; SctActv; StuGov; TchrAde; GerCl; MthCl; U Of Kansas; Comp Engineering.

LEVY, Diane R; J B Conant HS; Hoffman Estates, IL; HonRl; LitMag; NatlFornLg; NHS; SchPl; RptrYrbk; Yrbk; RptrSchPpr; SpnCl; NCTE; Northern Iu; Speech Drama Teach.

LEVY, Jeffrey S; Parkway North HS; St Louis, MO; 7/513 JrNHS; NHS; StuCncl; StuGov; LetterBsbl; LetterBsktbl; CaptFtbl; LetterTennis; CchngActv; Coll; Medicine.

LEVY, Lisa A; Avon Jr Sr HS; Plainfield, IN; CncrtBnd; MrchBnd; NHS; PepBnd; SchMus; SctActv; TchrAde; VPFrCl; SciCl; CaptSwmmng; Purdue University; Biology.

LEVY, Michael F; Highland Park HS; Highland Park, IL; NHS; NatlMeritSF; Co Sch Mines; Geo Engr.

LEVY, Steven M; Niles Township East HS; Skokie, IL; 57/564 NatlMeritCmnd; University; Law.

LEW, Branch R; R Nelson Snider HS; Forty Wayne, IN; 27/506 HonRl; LetterBsbl; LetterBsktbl; LetterTennis; Indiana Univ; Law.

LEW, Janet M; Thornridge HS; Dolton, IL; 67/684 AFS; Chr; HonRl; NHS; NatlThespSoc; MthCl; University; Nursing.

LEWALLEN, George M; Southridge HS; Huntingburg, IN; ChrhWkr; Swmmng; LetterTrk; College;.

LEWALLEN, Jeffery M; Wild Rose Public HS; Wautoma, WI; Band; Chrs; MrchBnd; PepBnd; SchMus; SchPl; TchrAde; LetterBsbl; LetterBsktbl; CaptFtbl; College; Teacher.

LE WAN, James; Mount Carmel Hs; Chicago, IL; 19/205 ChrhWkr; HonRl; JrNHS; NHS; SctActv; RusCl; LetterBsktbl; LetterTrk;.

LEWANDOWSKI, Barbara; Lamphere HS; Madison Heights, MI; 24/433 HonRl; NHS; NatlMeritSF; OffAde; RedCrAde; SchAde; TchrAde; SpnCl; IMSpt; PPFtbl; Western Mi Univ; Medical Technology.

LEWANDOWSKI, Daniel J; St Pius X HS; Arnold, MO; ChrhWkr; HonRl; NHS; SctActv; College; Banking.

LEWANDOWSKI, Karen; Loup City HS; Ashton, NE; Chr; HonRl; LbryAde; TchrAde; Yrbk; FHA; Bus School; Bookkeeper.

LEWANDOWSKI, Kathleen J; St Anthony HS; St Louis, MO; 1/72 SecTrsFrshCls; ALAGirlsSt; Chrs; HonRl; NHS; RptrSchPpr; LatCl; University.

LEWANDOWSKI, Patricia L; Prospect HS; Mt Prospect, IL; 54/610 Chrs; ChrhWkr; HonRl; NHS; NatlThespSoc; SchMus; SchPl; PpCl; U Of Il; Home Ec Major.

LEWANDOWSKI, Steven J; Thorp HS; Thorp, WI; HonRl; Ftbl; Wrstlng; Vocation.

LEWANDOWSKI, Vincent; West Washington HS; Campbellsburg, IN; 9/81 Band; Chrs; CncrtBnd; HonRl; MrchBnd; NHS; NatlMeritSchl; PepBnd; SchMus; SciCl; Us Navy; Electronics.

LEWANSKI, Judith A; Queen Of Peace HS; Chicago, IL; Chrs; ChrhWkr; HonRl; SchMus; TchrAde; Univ Of Illinois; Special Education.

LEWELLEN, Sharon A; Sycamore HS; Sycamore, IL; 85/220 Chrs; ChrhWkr; DrlTm; HonRl; OffAde; SctActv; YthFlsp; FrCl; PpCl; College; Sociology.

LEWELLYN, Janet R; Clarion Comm GS; Gale, IA; 2/93 Chr; Chrs; DrlTm; HonRl; Mdrgl; NHS; SchMus; YthFlsp; Yrbk; Pres4-H; Univ; Social Work.

LEWELLYN, Kenneth; Center Grove HS; Greenwood, IN; 68/215 NHS; PolWkr; Quill&Scroll; StuCncl; EdYrBk; RptrSchPpr; 4-H; IMSpt; Ball State Univ; Architecture.

LEWIN, Felice H; Niles East HS; Skokie, IL; 36/581 HonRl; SchPl; TchrAde; Univ Of Illinois; Special Education.

LEWINSKI, Julee A; St Thomas HS; Ann Arbor, MI; 17/78 HonRl; NHS; NatlMeritSchl; SchPpr; SpnCl; PpCl; Mi St Univ; Accounting.

LEWIS, Alan J; B C HS; Burlington, IA; 50/440 Band; CncrtBnd; HonRl; MrchBnd; Orch; PepBnd; SchMus; LetterGlf; KiwanAwd; Jr College.

LEWIS, Andrea E; Henry Ford HS; Detroit, MI; Chr; Chrl; Chrs; HonRl; Mdrgl; NatlMeritCmnd; SchMus; StuGov; SchPpr; Eastern Michigan Univ; Psychology.

LEWIS, Anthony; Edison Sr HS; East Gary, IN; 5/187 ALBoysSt; ChrhWkr; HonRl; JrNHS; NHS; Bsbl; Trk; Wrstlng; IMSpt; Univ; Pro.

LEWIS, Anthony W; Edison Sr HS; East Gary, IN; ChrhWkr; HonRl; JrNHS; NHS; YthFlsp; Trk; LetterWrstlng; IMSpt; Univ; Professional.

LEWIS, Audrey; John Marshall Harlan HS; Chicago, IL; 17/707 HonRl; JA; NHS; StuCncl; TchrAde; RptrSchPpr; FTA; MthCl; Univ Of Ill; Pediatrics.

LEWIS, Bradley; Dodge Center HS; Dodge Center, MN; 1/54 VPSrCls; Chrs; HonRl; NHS; PepBnd; SctActv; StuCncl; Bsbl; Ftbl; Trk; St Cloud Coll; Physical Therapy.

LEWIS, Brenda S; Salem Sr HS; Salem, MO; 13/173 HonRl; SchPl; TchrAde;.

LEWIS, Candace; Savannah HS; Savannah, MO; Chr; HonRl; SchMus; SpnCl; PpCl; Trk; GAA; Coll.

LEWIS, Cheryl A; Elk Grove HS; Elk Grove, IL; 14/540 Chr; Chrs; HonRl; Mdrgl; Eastern Ill Univ; English Major.

LEWIS, Christine A; Aurora Sr HS; Aurora, IN; Chr; ChrhWkr; HonRl; NHS; YthFlsp; EdSchPpr; FrCl; PpCl; MasAwd; Indiana Univ; Journalism.

LEWIS, Daronda J; Bell City HS; Bell City, MO; HstJrCls; Chrs; HonRl; SchPl; Yrbk; RptrSchPpr; FHA; PpCl; SciCl; IMSpt; Vocation.

LEWIS, Deborah A; Taylor Center HS; Inkster, MI; Band; HonRl; MrchBnd; ROTC; Trk; GAA; CitAwd; Coll.

LEWIS, Denise; Silver Lake HS; Topeka, KS; ALAGirlsSt; CmntyWkr; HonRl; RptrYrbk; Yrbk; 4-H; FFA; Bsktbl; IMSpt; 4-HAwd; College; Vet Assistant.

LEWIS, Dennis R; Kearney HS; Kearney, NE; HonRl; Bsbl; LetterBsktbl; LetterFtbl; LetterTrk; College; Curriculum.

LEWIS, Diane M; Thomas Jefferson HS; Rockford, IL; HonRl; No Ill Univ; Special Education.

LEWIS, Donald; Griffith Senior HS; Griffith, IN; 14/312 CmntyWkr; DrmBgl; ChrhWkr; HonRl; MrchBnd; NHS; Quill&Scroll; StuCncl; SptEdSchPpr; SchPpr; Cedarville College.

LEWIS, Duane C; Concordia HS; Ames, KS; HonRl; YthFlsp; 4-H; FFA; SciCl; 4-HAwd; Vo Tech; Drafting.

LEWIS, Edward W; South Clay HS; Dickens, IA; Chrs; Iowa Lakes Comm College; Law Enforcement.

LEWIS, Evonne H; North Central HS; Hansboro, ND; 6/26 Band; Chr; Chrs; HonRl; SchPl; EdYrBk; SchPpr; FHA; Chrldr; VoiceDemAwd; Trade Sch; Vocational.

LEWIS, Florence E; Lindblom Technical HS; Chicago, IL; HonRl; SctActv; StuCncl; TchrAde; University; Engineering.

LEWIS, George R; Colchester HS; Colchester, IL; 10/36 HonRl; NHS; StuCncl; Yrbk; SpnCl; MthCl; Bsktbl; University; Computer Programming.

LEWIS, Harlan E; Webster Groves HS; Webster Groves, MO; CmntyWkr; StuGov; Bsbl; Southwest Mo St Univ.

LEWIS, Jacqueline J; Morgan Park HS; Chicago, IL; 7/680 Band; Chr; ChrhWkr; CmntyWkr; CncrtBnd; HonRl; JrNHS; MrchBnd; NHS; PepBnd; StuCncl; StuGov; TchrAde; GAA; Purdue Univ; Chemical Engineering.

LEWIS, James A; Emmerich Manual HS; Indianapolis, IN; 51/473 VPChr; CaptCncrtBnd; HonRl; Mdrgl; CaptMrchBnd; NatlThespSoc; SecKeyCl; Trk; KiwanAwd; Butler Univ; Music.

LEWIS, James B; Avon HS; Danville, IN; 21/159 PresSrCls; Band; HonRl; ModUN; NHS; SchPl; StuCncl; StuGov; YthFlsp; SciCl; Bsktbl; Ftbl; Trk; Franklin College; Business.

LEWIS, James P; Salem HS; Salem, IN; 5/171 ALBoysSt; HonRl; VPNHS; NatlMeritSchl; TchrAde; LetterBsktbl; Glf; Trk; Ball State Univ; Teaching.

LEWIS, Janet L; Orchard Farm HS; St Charles, MO; HonRl; PpCl; College.

LEWIS, Julia M; Triad HS; Troy, IL; 13/185 ChrhWkr; HonRl; NHS; SchPpr; 4-H; FTA; PpCl; GAA; IMSpt; PresAwd; Eastern Il Univ; Medical Technologist.

LEWIS, Katherine; Southwestern HS; Brighton, IL; Chrs; ChrhWkr; CmntyWkr; HonRl; NHS; SchMus; TchrAde; RptrYrbk; RptrSchPpr; FTA; College; Teacher.

LEWIS, Kathleen W; St Charles HS; St Charles, MO; HonRl; SchPl; PpCl; LetterCchngActv; Univ; Vet.

LEWIS, Kenneth V; Truman Public HS; Lewisville, MN; 1/52 PresSophCls; TrsJrCls; ALBoysSt; HonRl; NHS; SchPl; StuCncl; 4-H; FFA; LetterFtbl; LetterTrk; LetterWrstlng; 4-HAwd; Vo Tech School; Ag Production.

LEWIS, Kevin; Quenemo HS; Quenemo, KS; 4/13 PresSophCls; Band; HonRl; SchPl; TchrAde; RptrSchPpr; Bsktbl; Ftbl; Tennis; Trk; Emporia Kansas State College; Elementary Ed.

LEWIS, Kimberly D; Elkhart Central HS; Bristol, IN; 182/483 JA; Quill&Scroll; TchrAde; RptrYrbk; Yrbk; RptrSchPpr; SchPpr; Indiana State University; Journalism.

LEWIS, Laura J; Arlington HS; Indianapolis, IN; 27/500 Chr; Chrs; HonRl; NHS; Quill&Scroll; StuCncl; Yrbk; FrCl; PpCl; PPFtbl; Univ; Journalism.

LEWIS, Laurine A; Murdock Public HS; Murdock, MN; 1/22 PresSrCls; Band; Chr; HonRl; NatlMeritSF; SchPl; EdYrBk; VP4-H; LetterBsktbl; LetterTrk; Univ Of Mn; Home Economics.

LEWIS, Lori A; Genoa Public HS; Monroe, NE; TrsJrCls; Band; CmntyWkr; CncrtBnd; HonRl; StuCncl; YthFlsp; 4-H; Chrldr; 4-HAwd;.

LEWIS, Mark A; Ballard HS; Cambridge, IA; ChrhWkr; HonRl; NHS; SchAde; LetterBsbl; LetterBsktbl; University; Farming.

LEWIS, Marlene; Coleman HS; Coleman, MI; 13/85 Band; ChrhWkr; CncrtBnd; HonRl; MrchBnd; NHS; TchrAde; YthFlsp; 4-H; FTA; Delta College; Legal Secretary.

LEWIS, Martha G; Hudson HS; Hudson, WI; ChrhWkr; CmntyWkr; HonRl; SctActv; YthFlsp; GerCl; University; Dietetics.

LEWIS, Mary L; North Clay HS; Louisville, IL; Band; Chrs; ChrhWkr; HonRl; NHS; SchPl; StuCncl; RptrYrbk; EdYrBk; College; Med Secretary.

LEWIS, Melanie G; Mendota Twp HS; Mendota, IL; 6/190 SecTrsFrshCls; Band; SecChr; NHS; SchPl; StuCncl; YthFlsp; EdYrBk; FrCl; Chrldr; Northwestern Univ; Acting.

LEWIS, Michael S; Brown County HS; Nashville, IN; 3/207 PresFrshCls; PresSophCls; HonRl; Quill&Scroll; PresStuCncl; RptrSchPpr; LatCl; CaptFtbl; LetterTrk; OptClAwd; College; Law Or Journalism.

LEWIS, Norma M; Red Bud HS; Red Bud, IL; Band; HonRl; HospAde; TchrAde; Yrbk; RptrSchPpr; FTA; SpnCl; PpCl; College; Professional.

LEWIS, Norman P; Princeton HS; Princeton, IL; ChrhWkr; HonRl; RptrSchPpr; SchPpr; Bsktbl; Glf; LetterTrk; Eastern Illinois Univ; Computer Science.

LEWIS, Pamela S; Hancock Central HS; Hancock, MI; 1/90 Band; CncrtBnd; MrchBnd; PepBnd; SchPl; Twrl; TreasKeyCl; VPGAA; Michigan Tech Univ; Med Tech.

LEWIS, Pamela S; Pomeroy Comm HS; Pomeroy, IA; VPJrCls; PresBand; Chrs; ChrhWkr; CncrtBnd; HonRl; MrchBnd; NHS; OffAde; PepBnd; College.

LEWIS, Patricia E; Delavan HS; Delavan, IL; TrsSrCls; Band; ChrhWkr; CmntyWkr; CncrtBnd; HonRl; MrchBnd; NHS; SctActv; YthFlsp; U Of Il; Teach High School Home Ec.

LEWIS, Paul; Central HS; St Joseph, MO; 9/504 ChrhWkr; HonRl; NHS; Quill&Scroll; TchrAde; RptrSchPpr; SchPpr; GerCl; SciCl; IMSpt; Coll; Miniserial.

LEWIS, Rex D; Genoa Public HS; Monroe, NE; TrsFrshCls; TrsSophCls; Band; ChrhWkr; CmntyWkr; CncrtBnd; MrchBnd; PepBnd; StuCncl; YthFlsp; 4-H; 4-H; FFA; Bsktbl; LetterFtbl; Trade School; Mechanic.

LEWIS, Robin; Niles Twp North Division Hs; Skokie, IL; 1 HonRl; NHS; PolWkr; StuGov; Bsbl; Ftbl; LetterSocr; LetterTennis; CchngActv; GAA; College;pre Medicine.

LEWIS, Sara J; Lourdes 's; Rochester, MN; Chr; HospAde; SctActv; SciCl; College; Law Enforcement.

LEWIS, Shari; Zionsville HS; Zionsville, IN; Chr; Chrl; Chrs; HonRl; SchMus; SctActv; YthFlsp; LatCl; IMSpt; PresAwd; John Herron Art School; Commercial Artist.

LEWIS, Sharon L; Southeast HS; Springfield, IL; 23/503 Band; Chr; ChrhWkr; RedCrAde; SchPl; SctActv; VPStuCncl; SecMthCl; DARAwd; Illinois State Univ; Law.

LEWIS, Sharon T; St Thomas HS; Ann Arbor, MI; HonRl; NHS; NatlMeritCmnd; NatlMeritSF; OffAde; SctActv; SpnCl; PpCl; Bsbl; Bsktbl; Michigan St Univ; Accounting.

LEWIS, Steven D; Mendel Prep HS; Chicago, IL; CmntyWkr; JrNHS; NHS; SchPl; StuGov; TchrAde; Bsbl; LetterFtbl; IMSpt; PresAwd; College; Stock Broker.

LEWIS, Susan E; Marshall HS; Marshall, MO; Chrs; DrlTm; HonRl; Orch; PpCl; Bsktbl; Tennis; University Of Missouri; English.

LEWIS, Teresa A; Chelsea HS; Grass Lake, MI; 10/210 CaptDrlTm; HonRl; HospAde; NHS; Pres4-H; 4-HAwd; Michigan St Univ; Biology.

LEWIS, Thomas L; Mendel Prep; Chicago, IL; 67/177 CmntyWkr; JA; PolWkr; PpCl; LetterTrk; LetterWrstlng; IMSpt; JAAwd; College; Accounting.

LEWIS, Timothy; Monroe Catholic Central; Erie, MI; Band; CncrtBnd; HonRl; MrchBnd; PepBnd; SchMus; SchPl; Olivet College; Music Teacher.

LEWIS, Tina M; Hoxie HS; Studley, KS; 4/57 SecFrshCls; TrsSophCls; PresJrCls; Band; HonRl; HospAde; SchPl; StuCncl; FHA;.

LEWIS, Valerie D; Northern HS; Flint, MI; TrsJrCls; PresSrCls; CmntyWkr; HonRl; LitMag; NatlFornLg; NHS; NatlMeritSF; Chrldr; Univ; Physician.

LEWIS, Vonda; Fordville Public HS; Fordville, ND; Chrs; HonRl; NHS; RptrSchPpr; 4-H; PpCl; Mayville State Coll; Teach.

LEWIS, William D; South Iron HS; Annapolis, MO; Band; CncrtBnd; HonRl; MrchBnd; SciCl; Univ Of Mo; Chemical Engineer.

LEWITZ, Alan H; Highland Park HS; Highland Park, IL; Aud/Vis; SchPl; SctActv; StuCncl; Trk; Univ; Communications.

LEWITZKE, Timothy L; Wausau East HS; Wausau, WI; Aud/Vis; ChrhWkr; StuCncl; YthFlsp; KeyCl; MthCl; LetterBsbl; LetterFtbl; IMSpt; AmLegAwd; University Of Wisconsin; Accounting.

LEWTON, Mary L; Barry HS; Barry, IL; HonRl; HospAde; MrchBnd; NHS; SchPl; StuCncl; FHA; FrCl; SciCl; Chrldr; Univ; Nursing.

LEY, Barbara; Allen HS; Bluffton, IN; 4/139 Chrs; ChrhWkr; HonRl; LitMag; NHS; YthFlsp; RptrYrbk; RptrSchPpr; SpnCl; GAA; Ball Univ; Nursing Rn.

LEY, Diane M; Mineral Point HS; Mineral Point, WI; 37/94 Band; Chrs; ChrhWkr; HonRl; Mdrgl; SchMus; Sec4-H; SecFHA; SpnCl; GAA; Viterbo College; Nursing.

LEY, Gretchen W; Columbus HS; Marshfield, WI; Chrs; HonRl; SctActv; SecStuCncl; TchrAde; FrCl; SpnCl; PpCl; GAA; JAAwd; College; Psychology.

LEY, Patricia M; Notre Dame HS; Quincy, IL; 7/109 PpCl; Quincy College; Accounting.

LEYDON, Mary L; St Bede Academy; Peru, IL; 9/120 Chrs; ChrhWkr; HonRl; RedCrAde; SchMus; SchPl; StuGov; LetterTrk; PresGAA; University.

LEYVA, Yolanba; Gage Park HS; Chicago, IL; 33/286 HonRl; ROTC; TchrAde; Northeastern Cir Campus; Rn.

LEZOVICH, Annemarie; Corunna HS; Vernon, MI; 30/212 ChrhWkr; CmntyWkr; HonRl; JA; PolWkr; SchMus; SchPl; StuGov; TchrAde; RptrYrbk; Univ Of Michigan; Physical Therapy.

LI, Abby; Kenwood HS; Chicago, IL; 2/460 HonRl; NHS; GerCl; Swmmng; Univ Of Chicago; Chemistry.

LI, Laurence H; Bentley HS; Livonia, MI; HonRl; NatlMeritSF; StuCncl; U Of Mi; Engineering.

LI, Lorinda M; New Haven HS; New Haven, IN; 18/248 DrlTm; HonRl; HospAde; NatlMeritSF; ROTC; SciCl; AmLegAwd; Col; Scientist.

LIAKOS, Georgia; Alliance HS; Alliance, NE; 38/154 HonRl; NHS; Quill&Scroll; SchPl; RptrYrbk; SchPpr; Chadron State College; Business.

LIAKOS, Peggy A; Bayard HS; Bayard, NE; 10/44 Chrs; ChrhWkr; HonRl; SchPl; StuGov; YthFlsp; 4-H; FHA; PpCl; LetterTrk; 4-HAwd; PresAwd; Business School; Secretary.

LIALIOS, Connie; Amundsen HS; Chicago, IL; HonRl; NHS; OffAde; SchAde; StuCncl; TchrAde; Yrbk; FTA; SpnCl; GAA; Univ; Anthropology.

LIANG, Jean N; Rich Central HS; Olympia Fields, IL; 35/364 DrlTm; HonRl; TchrAde; MthCl; PpCl; St Marys College.

LIBBERT, Loyd; St Elizabeth HS; Meta, MO; TrsJrCls; SchPl; PpCl; Bsbl; College; Chemical Engineer.

LIBBERTON, Larry D; Mt Carroll HS; Mt Carroll, IL; 4/70 VPSrCls; HonRl; NHS; SchMus; SchPl; Yrbk; SchPpr; University; Orthodontistry.

LIBERATO, Leilani M; Harding Sr HS; St Paul, MN; ChrhWkr; StuCncl; TchrAde; PpCl; Trk; Chrldr; GAA; IMSpt; College; Elementary Educ.

LIBERTY, Lynn M; Wayne Memorial HS; Westland, MI; 69/649 Chrs; CncrtBnd; HonRl; MrchBnd; NHS; NatlMeritSF; Orch; PepBnd; SchMus; MthCl; U Of Detroit; Dental Hygiene.

LIBERTY, Phyllis E; West Platte HS; Weston, MO; AFS; Band; Chr; CncrtBnd; HonRl; ModUN; TchrAde; FBLA; PpCl; SciCl; Chrldr; PPFtbl; Business School; Secretary.

LIBES, Valerie A; Delta HS; Muncie, IN; PresChrhWkr; HonRl; NHS; FHA; LatCl; University; Science.

LIBOLT, Kristy K; Keya Baha County HS; Springview, NE; 4/23 TrsSophCls; HonRl; NHS; NatlSciFnd; PepBnd; StuCncl; TreasPpCl; LetterTrk; Chrldr; GAA; College; Medical Technology.

LIBOLT, Kristy K; Keya Raha Co HS; Springview, NE; 4/23 TrsSophCls; Band; Chrs; HonRl; NatlSciFnd; SchPl; TreasPpCl; LetterTrk; Chrldr; SecGAA; College; Medical Technology.

LIBSACK, Jamy B; Lyman HS; Lyman, NE; 4/19 HstFrshCls; TrsSophCls; PresJrCls; HonRl; JrNHS; NHS; SchMus; SchPl; StuCncl; EdSchPpr; CaptFtbl; Trk; 4-HAwd; Col; Vocation.

LIBSACK, Sandy K; Lyman HS; Lyman, NE; ChrhWkr; HonRl; NHS; PepBnd; YthFlsp; 4-H; FHA; PpCl; LetterTrk; Chrldr; 4-HAwd; MasAwd; College; Music.

LICHAMER, Joseph C; Luther South HS; Chicago, IL; 18/215 Aud/Vis; HonRl; NHS; SctActv; Illinois Inst Of Technology; Computer Prog.

LICHT, Curtis R; Ft Dodge HS; Ft Dodge, IA; NatlMeritCmnd; GerCl; LetterFtbl; Swmmng; LetterTrk; College.

LICHT, Dawn D; Northwest Webster HS; Clare, IA; 9/28 SecJrCls; Band; TreasChrs; HonRl; PepBnd; SchPl; TchrAde; RptrSchPpr; PpCl; CaptCchngActv; Ia Central Com Col; Dental Assistant.

LICHTE, Susan K; Webb HS; Reedsburg, WI; 29/210 ChrhWkr; CncrtBnd; HonRl; MrchBnd; NatlThespSoc; Orch; SchMus; YthFlsp; FrCl; University; Professional.

LICHTENBERG, Darcy; Norfolk Sr HS; Norfolk, NE; Chr; Chrs; DrlTm; HonRl; NHS; OffAde; SchMus; SchPl; TchrAde; 4-H; Univ Ne; Teacher.

LICHTENBERG, Donna K; Galva Community HS; Aurelia, IA; SecSophCls; Band; Chrs; HonRl; MrchBnd; SchPl; YthFlsp; Yrbk; 4-H; Trk; College; Vocational.

LICHTENBERG, James; Clintonville Sr HS; Embarrass, WI; Band; CncrtBnd; HonRl; MrchBnd; NHS; PepBnd; Univ Of Wi At Eau Claire; Bus Adminis.

LICHTENBERGER, M Ann; Richwoods HS; Peoria, IL; 30/474 Chr; HonRl; NHS; Quill&Scroll; SchMus; StuCncl; TchrAde; EdYrBk; No Illinois Univ; Journalism.

LICHTENBERGER, Robert B; Fairfield Community HS; Fairfield, IL; VPFrshCls; PresSophCls; ALBoysSt; HonRl; PolWkr; LatCl; SciCl; LetterFtbl; CaptWrstlng; College; Medical Technology.

LICHTENSTEIN, Carol A; Blue Valley HS; Stilwell, KS; Band; CmntyWkr; HonRl; NHS; OffAde; RptrYrbk; RptrSchPpr; 4-H; PpCl; LetterBsktbl; College; Professional.

LICHTER, Elizabeth; Macomb Senior HS; Macomb, IL; Chr; HonRl; SchMus; Yrbk; FHA; IMSpt; Western Ill Univ; Medical Technologist.

LICHTER, Timothy J; Mitchell HS; Mitchell, SD; 19/304 ALBoysSt; HonRl; NHS; LetterFtbl; Trk; Wrstlng; IMSpt; AmLegAwd; EldAwd; JCAwd; College; Biomedical Engineering.

LICHTI, Timothy C; Shickley Public HS; Shickley, NE; 2/29 PresSrCls; Band; HonRl; SchPl; YthFlsp; Yrbk; Pres4-H; Bsktbl; Ftbl; Trk; Doane Clg; Business Administration.

LICHTSCHEIDL, Susan M; Dist #140 HS; Taylors Falls, MN; Band; CncrtBnd; HonRl; NatlMeritCmnd; PepBnd; SchPl; StuGov; TchrAde; FHA; PpCl; College; Art Teaching.

LICKEY, Kaiya L; Hamilton Se HS; Noblesville, IN; 26/133 HonRl; Quill&Scroll; SchMus; EdYrBk; Yrbk; SchPpr; VP4-H; SpnCl; PpCl; GAA; 4-HAwd; College; Art.

LICKTEIG, Donald; Central Heights HS; Richmond, KS; VPSophCls; CmntyWkr; HonRl; NHS; SchPl; StuCncl; TchrAde; RptrYrbk; SciCl; Coll; Teacher.

LICKTEIG, Linda M; Central Heights HS; Greeley, KS; 1/40 TreasChr; HonRl; PresNHS; SchPl; StuCncl; TchrAde; TreasFHA; PpCl; CchngActv; College; Medical Field.

LIDDELL, Cynthia M; Griswold Comm HS; Villisca, IA; 10/84 VPJrCls; CmntyWkr; HonRl; HospAde; NHS; RedCrAde; SchAde; FDA; FFA; FHA; LetterBsktbl; LetterTrk; LetterWrstlng; College; Nursing.

LIDDICOATT, Cathryn A; Lake Orion HS; Lk Orion, MI; 5/364 HonRl; NHS; NatlMeritCmnd; RptrYrbk; Yrbk; RptrSchPpr; LetterTennis; M S U; Commercial Art.

LIDDLE, Cheryl A; Park River HS; Park River, ND; 16/66 SecJrCls; VPSrCls; Chrs; ChrhWkr; LbryAde; RptrYrbk; EdSchPpr; VPFHA; DanFAwd; College; Nursing.

LIDDLE, Lynne D; Lawrenceburg HS; Lawrenceburg, IN; Band; DrlTm; MrchBnd; NHS; NatlThespSoc; PepBnd; SchPl; PpCl; GAA;.

LIDTKE, Roberta K; Riceville Comm HS; Lime Springs, IA; 12/79 Band; Chrs; CmntyWkr; HonRl; NHS; SchPl; 4-H; FTA; Bsktbl; Glf; Univ Of Northern Ia; Elem Teacher.

LIEB, Nancy S; Joliet Twsp HS; Joliet, IL; 1/520 Chr; ChrhWkr; HonRl; NHS; NatlMeritSF; SctActv; PresMthCl; KiwanAwd; Wa Univ; Medicine.

LIEB, Rose Marie; Elizabeth HS; Elizabeth, IL; 3/28 SecJrCls; ALBoysSt; Chr; Chrs; CncrtBnd; HonRl; Mdrgl; MrchBnd; PepBnd; SchPl; Coll; Med Lab Tech.

LIEBENSTEIN, Brian C; Port Washington HS; Port Washington, WI; HonRl; YthFlsp; College; Flight Training.

LIEBERG, Nathan W; Dassel Cokato HS; Dassel, MN; 4/122 CmntyWkr; HonRl; NHS; FFA; Junior Coll; Farm Management.

LIEBERMAN, Joshua M; Homestead HS; Mequon, WI; 12/407 AFS; Chr; JrNHS; NatlMeritCmnd; SctActv; Socr; Univ Of Wisc; Medicine.

LIEBHART, Cynthia L; Lasalle Peru Twp HS; Oglesby, IL; 23/485 AFS; ALAGirlsSt; Chrs; ChrhWkr; HonRl; LitMag; SchMus; SctActv; RptrSchPpr; FrCl; College; English & Speech.

LIEBHART, Jan L; Bucklin R 2 HS; New Boston, MO; SecSophCls; Band; HonRl; NHS; SchPl; Twrl; FHA; SciCl; Trk; College; Doctor Or Prof Musician.

LIEBL, Jana M; Hamilton HS; Menomoniee Falls, WI; VPJrCls; HonRl; NHS; StuCncl; PpCl; Swmmng; Chrldr; IMSpt; Univ Of Wis Madison; Letters & Science.

LIECHTI, Stan M; Faulkton HS; Seneca, SD; VPFrshCls; ALBoysSt; Band; Chrs; CmntyWkr; HonRl; SchMus; LetterBsbl; Bsktbl; Ftbl; Trade Sch; Pro.

LIECHTY, Tab A; South Adams HS; Berne, IN; Aud/Vis; ChrhWkr; CncrtBnd; RptrSchPpr; SpnCl; Bsbl; Ftbl; Swmmng; Wrstlng; RotaryAwd; College; Professional.

LIEDER, Carol R; Minnehaha Academy; Minneapolis, MN; Chr; ChrhWkr; CncrtBnd; HonRl; HospAde; PepBnd; SctActv; TchrAde; GerCl; GAA; College; Business.

LIEFER, Kimberly; Red Bud Hs; Red Bud, IL; 14/131 HonRl; NatlMeritCmnd; Yrbk; Sec4-H; SpnCl; PpCl; GAA; DanFAwd; 4-HAwd; University Of Illinois; Pharmacy.

LIEFER, Marla; Trico HS; Campbell Hill, IL; HonRl; Yrbk; 4-H; PpCl;.

LIEGL, Joseph G; Medford Sr HS; Stetsonville, WI; 1/254 HonRl; NHS; VPFFA; Trk; Wrstlng; College; Agriculture.

LIEN, James A; William Jennings Bryan HS; Omaha, NE; 14/344 ALBoysSt; CaptBand; HonRl; CaptMrchBnd; PresNHS; ROTC; TchrAde; Ftbl; CaptWrstlng; AmLegAwd; RotaryAwd; VFWAwd; Wichita State Univ; Professional.

LIEN, Karen K; Columbia Heights Sr HS; Minneapolis, MN; 16/565 Chr; HonRl; Mdrgl; MrchBnd; NHS; SpnCl; Augsburg Col; Mus Ed Child Pshych.

LIEN, Kevin R; Milbank HS; Milbank, SD; ALBoysSt; Chrs; HonRl; SchMus; College; Professional.

LIEN, Kristi J; Border Central HS; Sarles, ND; 2/9 SecTrsSophCls; VPJrCls; Band; Chrs; ChrhWkr; HonRl; SchPl; RptrSchPpr; SchPpr; College; Dental Hygiene.

LIENEMANN, David L; Randolph HS; Mclean, NE; 14/57 Band; ChrhWkr; HonRl; MrchBnd; SctActv; StuCncl; FFA; Bsktbl; Ftbl; Trk;.

LIENEMANN, Johnny H; Hildreth HS; Hildreth, NE; 3/22 TrsFrshCls; TrsSophCls; Band; HonRl; NHS; SchPl; RptrYrbk; 4-H; Ftbl; LetterTrk; Kearney State College; Major Inbiology.

LIENHART, Leslie A; Elkhart Memorial HS; Elkhart, IN; Band; HonRl; NHS; NatlMeritSF; SchMus; SchPl; EdSchPpr; LetterBsktbl; LetterTrk; IMSpt; College.

LIENKE, Kris L; Columbus HS; Columbus, WI; AFS; Band; Chrs; ChrhWkr; CmntyWkr; HospAde; PolWkr; SctActv; StuCncl; RptrYrbk; University; Social Work.

LIERLE, Ava; Liberty Comm Unit 2 Hs; Liberty, IL; 10/56 SecSrCls; Chrs; HonRl; NHS; SchPl; StuCncl; Yrbk; RptrSchPpr; PpCl; Chrldr; Quincy College;medical Technology.

LIES, John E; Yorkville HS; Yorkville, IL; 56/156 Band; Orch; SchPl; TchrAde; Pres4-H; PresFFA; Bsbl; Bsktbl; LetterFtbl; 4-HAwd; College; Professional.

LIESEMEYER, Brent R; Mc Cook HS; Mc Cook, NE; AFS; Band; HonRl; MrchBnd; PepBnd; Swmmng; Trk; IMSpt; College; Science.

LIETER, Kimberly R; Red Bud HS; Baldwin, IL; 1/100 ChrhWkr; HonRl; JrNHS; NHS; PresFTA; VPSpnCl; TreasPpCl; Trk; Univf Elementary Teaching.

LIETO, Constance A; St Mary Acad; Monroe, MI; HonRl; HospAde; JrNHS; NHS; SchPl; 4-H; FNA; FrCl; SciCl; 4-HAwd; Mercy School Of Nursing; Rn.

LIETZ, Charles M; Tomahawk HS; Tomahawk, WI; ChrhWkr; CmntyWkr; 4-H; FrCl; Bsbl; Bsktbl; LetterFtbl; CaptSocr; Trk; LetterWrstlng; CchngActv; IMSpt; University; Professional.

LIETZ, Thomas R; Thomas More Prep; Hays, KS; 1/86 PresFrshCls; SecTrsSophCls; ChrhWkr; CtyCnl; JCC; NatlFornLg; StuCncl; Yrbk; SchPpr; PpCl; IMSpt; AmLegAwd; ChmbCommrsAwd; Harvard; Lawyer.

LIETZAU, Laura A; Wheaton Warrenville HS; Wheaton, IL; HonRl; NHS; SchPl; StuCncl; VPFrCl; PpCl; Chrldr; Univ Of Illinois; Business.

LIEVERS, Elizabeth A; Pope County Community HS; Golconda, IL; 1/60 PresSophCls; ChrhWkr; CncrtBnd; HonRl; MrchBnd; EdSchPpr; PresFHA; KeyCl; GAA; DanFAwd; 4-HAwd; College; Business.

LIEVOIS, Elise A; Goodrich HS; Goodrich, MI; SecSophCls; TrsJrCls; SecSrCls; HonRl; OffAde; SchMus; StuCncl; EdYrBk; Chrldr; 4-HAwd; Central Mi Univ; Dramatic Arts.

LIEVOIS, James E; Brother Rice HS; Birmingham, MI; VPSophCls; PresSrCls; LetterFtbl; LetterTrk; IMSpt; Michigan State University.

LIFFICK, Kathy A; Willow Springs HS; Willow Springs, MO; HonRl; SchPl; TchrAde; RptrYrbk; RptrSchPpr; FHA; FTA; PpCl; Sch Of The Ozarks; Comm At.

LIGGETT, George R; Northrop HS; Fort Wayne, IN; HonRl; LetterFtbl; LetterTrk; Coll; Accounting.

LIGGETT, Jeffrey K; Catlin HS; Catlin, IL; 6/63 ALBoysSt; PresChr; HonRl; PresNHS; StuCncl; LetterBsbl; Ftbl; LetterWrstlng; Univ Of Illinois; Architect.

LIGGETT, Kenneth L; Churubusco HS; Churubusco, IN; VPSophCls; VPJrCls; PresSrCls; PresStuCncl; 4-H; FFA; Bsbl; Bsktbl; Ftbl; Trk;.

LIGGETT, Nancy J; Centennial HS; Utica, NE; 2/68 PresJrCls; ALAGirlsSt; CncrtBnd; HonRl; NHS; SchPl; YthFlsp; PresMthCl; LetterTrk; College; Physical Therapy.

LIGHT, Gail L; Anamoose Public HS; Anamoose, ND; Band; Chrs; SecChrhWkr; CncrtBnd; HonRl; MrchBnd; NatlThespSoc; PepBnd; ROTC; SchMus; Bsktbl; Chrldr; 4-HAwd; VFWAwd; Valley City State College; Science.

LIGHT, Joan M; Yankton HS; Yankton, SD; ALAGirlsSt; Chrs; HonRl; StuCncl; Glf; Swmmng; Trk; College.

LIGHTBODY, Jody G; Meservey Thornton HS; Thornton, IA; SecFrshCls; Band; ChrhWkr; CmntyWkr; CncrtBnd; HonRl; Bsktbl; LetterTrk; Chrldr; Business Sch; Secretary.

LIGHTFOOT, Kip K; Huron HS; Ann Arbor, MI; Band; Chr; CncrtBnd; MrchBnd; PolWkr; SchMus; SctActv; YthFlsp; Ftbl; Univ; Communications.

LIGHTFOOT, Lori R; John M Harlan HS; Chicago, IL; CmntyWkr; HonRl; HospAde; JrNHS; ModUN; NHS; SchPl; VPStuCncl; TchrAde; UNYO; RptrSchPpr; GerCl; LatCl; Carlton College; Veterinarian.

LIGHTFOOT, Nancy S; Clay City HS; Bowling Green, IN; 13/65 TrsSophCls; Band; CncrtBnd; DrlTm; HonRl; NHS; StuCncl; 4-H; MthCl; GAA; Indiana St Univ; Nursing.

LIGHTNER, Carroll J; Solomon HS; Solomon, KS; ChrhWkr; HonRl; SctActv; YthFlsp; Bsbl; Bsktbl; LetterFtbl; Trk; GodCntryAwd;.

LIGHTNER, Monte J; Huntington North HS; Huntington, IN; ALBoysSt; HonRl; NatlMeritFnl; RedCrAde; StuCncl; TchrAde; SchPpr; Bsbl; Bsktbl; IMSpt; University; Accounting.

LIHS, David J; Bon Homme #96 HS; Tyndall, SD; TrsFrshCls; SecJrCls; ALBoysSt; Chr; Chrs; ChrhWkr; Bsktbl; Ftbl; Glf; Trk; College.

LIIBBE, Janet M; West Point Jr/sr HS; West Point, NE; 5/59 Band; HonRl; MrchBnd; PepBnd; RedCrAde; SchPl; RptrYrbk; SecFHA; VPPpCl; LetterTrk; Yankton Coll.

LIIKE, Mary E; Avondale HS; Troy, MI; 9/243 ALAGirlsSt; NHS; PolWkr; SchMus; SchPl; EdSchPpr; FSA; Alma College.

LIKENS, Tony L; Fairbury HS; Steele City, NE; PresJrCls; Band; NHS; SchMus; StuCncl; 4-H; FFA; LetterFtbl; LetterTrk; LetterWrstlng; 4-HAwd; Univ Of Ne; Teaching.

LIKES, Kevin L; Eastside HS; Butler, IN; 5/120 VPFrshCls; HonRl; NHS; SctActv; StuCncl; FrCl; SciCl; Bsbl; LetterFtbl; Glf; University; Aviation.

LIKES, Rhonda L; Bunker Hill HS; Bunker Hill, IL; 11/82 SecJrCls; TrsSrCls; HonRl; NHS; Yrbk; Socr; GAA; IMSpt; AmLegAwd; Lewis & Clark Jr Clg; Med Lab Tech.

LILE, Lawrence O; Rock Bridge HS; Columbia, MO; HonRl; LitMag; NatlMeritSF; SctActv; College; Engineering.

LILES, Anita M; Metz R 2 HS; Horton, MO; SecSrCls; Band; ChrhWkr; HonRl; EdYrBk; Pres4-H; PresPpCl; LetterBsktbl; DARAwd; 4-HAwd; Sw Baptist College; Teacher.

LILIANSTROM, Margaret S; Elgin HS; Hanover Park, IL; 37/719 ChrhWkr; HonRl; SchPl; YthFlsp; Northern Il U; Biology.

LILIENKAMP, Joel E; Normand Senior HS; St Louis, MO; 2/525 Band; MrchBnd; NHS; Orch; SchMus; SctActv; SchPpr; SciCl; IMSpt; GodCntryAwd; College; Engineering.

LILIENTHAL, Kim S; Glencoe Sr HS; Plato, MN; SecYthFlsp; PresFFA; CaptBsktbl; LetterTrk; GAA; Univ Of Minn; Food Science.

LILJENBERG, Laurie S; Forest Lake Sr HS; Forest Lake, MN; 12/353 HonRl; HospAde; JrNHS; LitMag; NHS; RptrYrbk; RptrSchPpr; FrCl; College; Physical Therapist.

LILL, Michael A; St Mary Of Perpetual Help HS; Chicago, IL; 6/100 Band; ChrhWkr; CmntyWkr; CncrtBnd; DrmBgl; HonRl; OffAde; SchAde; SctActv; Yrbk; CivCl; LetterBsktbl; Trk; College; Professional.

LILLARD, Steven V; Collins Community HS; Collins, IA; VPJrCls; ALBoysSt; CncrtBnd; HonRl; PepBnd; SctActv; StuCncl; Yrbk; LetterBsbl; LetterBsktbl; LetterTrk; College; Secret Service.

LILLARD, Yvonne; Soldan HS; St Louis, MO; Chrs; ChrhWkr; CmntyWkr; DrlTm; HonRl; ModUN; PolWkr; StuCncl; TchrAde; PpCl; CaptChrldr; CitAwd; College; Doctor.

LILLEHAUG, Steven L; Washington HS; Sioux Falls, SD; ALBoysSt; Chr; CncrtBnd; HonRl; MrchBnd; NatlFornLg; NatlMeritSF; Orch; StuGov; RptrSchPpr; College; Physician.

LILLEMOE, Kent O; Northwestern HS; Mellette, SD; 2/50 ALBoysSt; Band; Chrs; HonRl; NHS; SchPl; StuCncl; SptEdSchPpr; LetterBsktbl; LetterFtbl; U Of Sd; Medicine.

LILLEVOLD, Joan E; Fergus Falls HS; Fargus Falls, MN; 14/310 HonRl; NHS; Orch; Moorhead State Clge.

LILLEY, Gail A; Ottawa HS; Ottawa, IL; 19/420 Chr; Chrs; ChrhWkr; HonRl; NHS; 4-H; College; Nursing.

LILLIBRIDGE, Gregory; Guilford Hs; Rockford, IL; 29 Chrl; HonRl; JrNHS; Mdrgl; SchMus; YthFlsp; LetterTrk; College;administration Or Math.

LILLIE, Ross J; West Senior HS; Rockford, IL; 30/335 Univ Of Ill; Mechanical.

LILLIG, Jeanne M; Bishop Hogan HS; Kansas City, MO; ChrhWkr; HonRl; SchMus; SchPl; StuGov; RptrYrbk; FBLA; Chrldr; CchngActv; GAA; College; Professional.

LILLIS, Anthony C; Apollo HS; Saint Cloud, MN; 25/550 Band; Chr; Mdrgl; SctActv; College; Vocation Broadcasting.

LILLY, Carol A; Blair HS; Blair, NE; CncrtBnd; HonRl; HospAde; MrchBnd; PepBnd; StuCncl; 4-H; PpCl; LetterBsktbl; LetterTrk; Col; Pharmacy.

LILLY, Catherine C; H S Truman HS; Taylor, MI; HonRl; NHS; NatlMeritSchl; StuGov; LetterSwmmng; LetterChrldr; GAA; JCAwd; Mich St U; Med Tech.

LILLY, Denise J; Lakeview HS; Decatur, IL; 1/184 VPSophCls; HonRl; HospAde; VPSophCls; HonRl; VPHospAde; VPNHS; EdYrBk; PresFNA; SciCl; LetterTennis; Trk; BauchLmbAwd; Illinois Wesleyan; Nurse.

LILLY, Douglas P; Monticello HS; Monticello, IL; TrsJrCls; Chrs; ChrhWkr; Mdrgl; StuCncl; StuGov; YthFlsp; LetterBsktbl; LetterFtbl; LetterTrk; Eastern Il U; Computer Tech.

LILLY, Gregory A; Tower Hill HS; Tower Hill, IL; Chrs; HonRl; NHS; SchMus; SchPl; StuCncl; EdYrBk; 4-H; Bsbl; Bsktbl; Southern Il U; Conservation.

LIMBERG, Debra S; Streator Twp HS; Streator, IL; 26/383 HonRl; 4-H; FFA; GerCl; CaptBsktbl; LetterTennis; 4-HAwd; College; Recreation.

LIMBERG, Hollis; Glenwood City HS; Glenwood City, WI; 2/81 Band; HonRl; NHS; PepBnd; SctActv; FBLA; AmLegAwd; Univ Of Wis; Accounting.

LIMBURG, Ronald L; Richmond HS; Richmond, IN; SpnCl; IMSpt; Ball State U; Cpa.

LIME, Rita; Our Lady Of Grace Acad; Beech Grove, IN; Chrs; JA; RptrYrbk; SpnCl; IMSpt; College Iupui; Prof.

LIMERICK, Kenneth; Laville HS; Lakeview, IN; 22/164 ALBoysSt; MrchBnd; NatlFornLg; NHS; NatlThespSoc; PepBnd; SchMus; SchPl; Tennis; IMSpt; Ball State Univ; Music Teacher.

LIMKE, Mark A; Dowling HS; Urbandale, IA; 23/273 Band; CncrtBnd; HonRl; MrchBnd; NatlMeritSF; PepBnd; PolWkr; SctActv; Iowa State Univ; Economics.

LIMKEMAN, Daniel; United Township HS; Silvis, IL; 24/687 Band; Chr; ChrhWkr; CncrtBnd; HonRl; MrchBnd; NHS; PepBnd; YthFlsp; GerCl; Christian Coll; Music.

LIMKEMAN, Marcia A; United Twp HS; Silvis, IL; Band; ChrhWkr; HonRl; MrchBnd; NHS; Wheaton College; Medicine.

LIMPERT, John W; Winona Sr HS; Winona, MN; HonRl; NHS; GerCl; University; Mathematics.

LIN, Albert N; Central HS; St Joseph, MO; 3/550 ALBoysSt; HonRl; ModUN; NHS; NatlMeritSF; TchrAde; EdSchPpr; MthCl; PresSciCl; Trk; IMSpt; Univ Of Missouri; Engineering.

LIN, Della M; University HS; Champaign, IL; LitMag; NatlMeritCmnd; SchMus; SchPl; EdYrBk; RptrSchPpr; GerCl; Univ Of Illinois; Physiology.

LINCE, Martha A; Crispus Attucks HS; Indianapolis, IN; VPFrshCls; PresSophCls; VPJrCls; CmntyWkr; HonRl; JA; NHS; SctActv; StuCncl; CaptChrldr; In State Univ; Special Ed.

LINCICUM, Gregory L; Black Hawk HS; South Wayne, WI; SecSophCls; HonRl; NHS; RptrSchPpr; VPFFA; FrCl; U Of Wi Oshkosh; Mathematics Teacher.

LINCOLN, Gerald; Woodland HS; Millersville, MO; 5/82 ALBoysSt; Band; CncrtBnd; HonRl; MrchBnd; PepBnd; Bsbl; Mo Univ; History.

LINCOLN, John A; Okemos HS; Okemos, MI; NHS; NatlMeritFnl; SctActv; StuCncl; YthFlsp; GerCl; LetterBsbl; Bsktbl; LetterFtbl; DARAwd; U Of Mich; Engineering.

LINCOLN, Mary E; Granite South HS; Granite City, IL; 5/550 PresSophCls; Chrs; ChrhWkr; NHS; OffAde; Quill&Scroll; Yrbk; GAA; College; Christian Educ.

LINCOLN, Robert; Osage Comm HS; Osage, IA; ALBoysSt; ChrhWkr; CmntyWkr; NHS; SchPl; SctActv; RptrYrbk; RptrSchPpr; GodCntryAwd; College.

LINCOLN, Robin L; Madrid Community HS; Madrid, IA; 20/65 Chrs; ChrhWkr; DrlTm; HonRl; ModUN; NHS; SchMus; SchPl; YthFlsp; RptrYrbk; Yrbk; FrCl; LetterTrk; Chrldr; Taylor Univ; Elementary Ed.

LINCOLN, Timothy T; Newton Community HS; Newton, IA; HonRl; Yrbk; FrCl; Bsbl; Bsktbl; Ftbl; University; Professional.

LIND, Diana K; Colfax Comm HS; Colfax, IA; Band; HonRl; NHS; SchPl; Twrl; FTA; SpnCl; PpCl; Trk; Trade Schl; Accounting.

LIND, Donna L; Huron Sr HS; Huron, SD; 27/301 ALAGirlsSt; Band; Chr; ChrhWkr; PepBnd; SchMus; YthFlsp; GerCl; PpCl; Chrldr; Foreign Languages & Music.

LIND, Jane K; Franklin Township HS; Corydon, IN; 2/44 Band; Chrs; ChrhWkr; HonRl; NHS; NatlMeritSF; SptEdYrbk; 4-H; FHA; GAA; Purdue U; Veterinarian.

LIND, Jennifer L; Kalamazoo Central HS; Kalamazoo, MI; 85/458 ChrhWkr; HospAde; NatlMeritCmnd; OffAde; YthFlsp; FNA; FrCl; PPFtbl; Nazareth College; Registered Nurse.

LIND, Kimberly K; Bertha Hewitt HS; Bertha, MN; 6/53 VPSrCls; ALAGirlsSt; ChrhWkr; HonRl; PolWkr; StuCncl; TchrAde; PresYthFlsp; 4-H; SecFFA; Moorhead St College; Mass Communications.

LIND, Susan L; Cedar Falls HS; Cedar Falls, IA; Band; CncrtBnd; HonRl; Mdrgl; MrchBnd; Orch; U Of Northwestern Ia; English.

LINDAHL, Kimberly S; Elgin HS; Streamwood, IL; 198/868 ChrhWkr; LbryAde; Orch; SctActv; PresYthFlsp; SpnCl; Moody Bible Institute; Music.

LINDAHL, Paul A; Von Stenben HS; Chicago, IL; 7/231 ChrhWkr; HonRl; TchrAde; MthCl; SciCl; Glf; North Park Col; Bio Chemist.

LINDAUER, Martha; Gibson Southern HS; Fort Branch, IN; 19/229 Band; Chr; Chrs; CncrtBnd; HonRl; LbryAde; MrchBnd; RedCrAde; SchPpr; FHA; Univ Of Evansville; Nursing.

LINDAUER, Pamela L; Iowa Grant HS; Cobb, WI; 12/120 SecFrshCls; VPSophCls; Band; CncrtBnd; HonRl; JrNHS; NHS; StuCncl; EdYrBk; Vocational School; Data Processing.

LINDAUER, Randy; Gibson Southern HS; Fort Branch, IN; RptrYrbk; Yrbk; RptrSchPpr; SchPpr; LetterBsbl; LetterBsktbl; Ftbl; Trk; Wrstlng; Trade School;professionalarchitect.

LINDAUER, Terry; Springfield HS; Battle Creek, MI; PresJrCls; HonRl; NHS; StuCncl; Ftbl; Trk; Wrstlng; College; Data Processing.

LINDBECK, Mark A; Hastings HS; Hastings, MN; Band; CncrtBnd; HonRl; MrchBnd; Yrbk; SchPpr; College; Photographer & Naturalist.

LINDBERG, Brian H; Albia HS; Albia, IA; PresSophCls; ALBoysSt; ChrhWkr; HonRl; YthFlsp; 4-H; LetterFtbl; LetterTrk; LetterWrstlng;.

LINDBERG, Daniel; Grace HS; Minneapolis, MN; 28/208 College Of St Thomas; Biologist.

LINDBERG, Frederick S; South Shore HS; Chicago, IL; 1/500 Band; HonRl; NHS; NatlMeritFnl; NatlMeritSF; PolWkr; StuGov; TchrAde; Dartmouth Col; Medicine.

LINDBERG, Jeff R; Galesburg Sr HS; Galesburg, IL; ChrhWkr; HonRl; NHS; SctActv; TchrAde; YthFlsp; 4-H; IMSpt; Univ Of Illinois; Engineering.

LINDBERG, Jolette; Albia Comm HS; Albia, IA; 11/155 Chrs; ChrhWkr; CncrtBnd; HonRl; MrchBnd; PepBnd; FHA; FTA; 4-HAwd; Trade; Child Care.

LINDBERG, Mark W; Intl Falls Sr HS; Ravier, MN; HonRl; Ftbl; IMSpt; College; Proffesional.

LINDBERG, Sandra A; Homewood Flossmoor HS; Homewood, IL; 203/932 HonRl; NatlThespSoc; Orch; SchMus; FTA; FrCl; Clge; Drama.

LINDBERG, Theresa L; Holy Angels HS; Minneapolis, MN; Aud/Vis; Chrs; PolWkr; SchAde; StuCncl; TchrAde; IMSpt; Coll; Phy Therapist.

LINDBLOOM, Leslie M; Lake Shore HS; St Clair Shores, MI; CmntyWkr; HonRl; NHS; NatlMeritFnl; NatlMeritSchl; NatlSciFnd; SchPl; StuCncl; StuGov; Yrbk; Western Mich Univ; Geogolgy.

LINDBORG, Mark R; Twin Lakes HS; Monticello, IN; 12/206 PresSrCls; Chr; HonRl; NHS; StuCncl; StuGov; YthFlsp; SpnCl; LetterFtbl; LetterSwmmng; U Of In; Md Veternarian.

LINDE, Diane M; Beaver Dam Sr HS; Beaver Dam, WI; ALAGirlsSt; SpnCl; Bsktbl; Trk; GAA; College; Physical Therapy.

LINDE, Janet L; Beaver Dam Sr HS; Beaver Dam, WI; 23/349 VPAFS; StuCncl; RptrYrbk; PpCl; LetterTennis; GAA; IMSpt; College; English.

LINDE, Thomas G; Beaver Dam Sr HS; Beaver Dam, WI; 102/302 PpCl; Bsbl; LetterBsktbl; IMSpt;.

LINDELL, Kirk A; New Richmond Senior HS; New Richmond, WI; Band; Chr; CncrtBnd; HonRl; MrchBnd; KeyCl; LetterBsktbl; LetterFtbl; LetterTrk; PresAwd; Gustavus Adolphus; Law.

LINDEMAN, Blayne; Ripon Sr Hs; Brandon, WI; 4-H; FFA; 4-HAwd; Um Short Course;farmer.

LINDEMAN, Jeffrey M; Albert City Truesdale Cm HS; Albert City, IA; VPSophCls; Chrs; CncrtBnd; HonRl; PepBnd; SctActv; Bsbl; Bsktbl; Ftbl; DanFAwd; Wayne State; Communication Arts.

LINDEMAN, Lori; Rosemount HS; Apple Valley, MN; TrsSophCls; PresJrCls; Band; HonRl; NHS; StuCncl; StuGov; Chrldr; PPFtbl; Business School; Secretary.

LINDEMANN, Betsy L; Dundee Community HS; West Dundee, IL; 47/377 SecFrshCls; SecSophCls; Chr; Chrl; Chrs; HonRl; Mdrgl; SchMus; StuCncl; FrCl; Univ; Dietetics.

LINDEMANN, Gene; Trinity HS; Dickinson, ND; 10/137 Band; Chrs; ChrhWkr; CncrtBnd; MrchBnd; PepBnd; Sacrstn; SchMus; StuCncl; St Thomas Seminary Denver; Priesthood.

LINDEMANN, Lori A; Lake Benton HS; Lake Benton, MN; ALAGirlsSt; HonRl; LbryAde; NHS; SchPl; RptrYrbk; RptrSchPpr; AmLegAwd; Vo Tech School; Cosmetology.

LINDEMUTH, Donna L; Rosemount HS; Rosemount, MN; 74/347 Chr; HonRl; GerCl; Junior College; Commercial Art.

LINDEN, David J; Heelan HS; Sioux City, IA; HonRl; FrCl; LetterFtbl; Trk; Wrstlng; IMSpt; Univ; Dentist.

LINDEN, Jane E; William Horlick HS; Racine, WI; 18/544 Band; ChrhWkr; CncrtBnd; DrmBgl; HonRl; PepBnd; SchMus; TchrAde; GerCl; Univ Of Wisconsin; Physical Therapy.

LINDEN, Ralph A; Holdrege Sr HS; Holdrege, NE; HonRl; U Of Neb; Law.

LINDENMEYER, Jill A; Willowbrook HS; Lombard, IL; Chr; HonRl; JrNHS; LitMag; NHS; Quill&Scroll; RptrYrbk; SptEdYrbk; Millikin Univ; Physical Therapist.

LINDER, Becky A; Wells Easton HS; Easton, MN; 26/114 Chr; Chrs; ChrhWkr; CmntyWkr; HonRl; OffAde; SchPl; StuCncl; 4-H; LetterBsktbl; Winona State; Physical Education.

LINDER, Duane A; Tivola Meadowlands HS; Meadowlands, MN; Aud/Vis; HonRl; SchPl; Yrbk; FFA; Bsbl; Ftbl; IMSpt; U Of Mn; Chemistry.

LINDER, John M; East Richland HS; Olney, IL; 2/260 ChrhWkr; NHS; NatlMeritCmnd; CaptFtbl; Trk; Coast Guard Academy; Elec Communications.

LINDER, Joseph W; North Side HS; Fort Wayne, IN; 40/438 HonRl; JA; NHS; SptEdYrbk; SptEdSchPpr; LatCl; PpCl; LetterFtbl; LetterGlf; LetterTrk; U Of Notre Dame; Bus Adm.

LINDER, Teresa G; Carl Junction HS; Joplin, MO; 5/99 ChrhWkr; DrmBgl; HonRl; NHS; TchrAde; FrCl; MthCl; LetterTennis; DARAwd; OptClAwd; Col; Professional.

LINDERMAN, De Wayne M; Hartford HS; Hartford, MI; HonRl; OffAde; PolWkr; TchrAde; College; Business Admin.

LINDERMAN, John T; Danville HS; Danville, IL; 1/545 ChrhWkr; HonRl; SctActv; StuCncl; YthLg; LetterTrk; RotaryAwd; University; Engineering.

LINDFIELD, Denise R; Missouri Valley HS; Honey Creek, IA; Chrs; HonRl; ModUN; NHS; NatlThespSoc; PolWkr; SchMus; TchrAde; Yrbk; Drake University; Journalism.

LINDFORS, Connie G; Eben HS; Chatham, MI; 1/35 TrsSrCls; Band; CmntyWkr; HonRl; NatlMeritSF; OffAde; StuCncl; EdYrBk; SchPpr; Michigan State Univ; Business.

LINDGREN, Barbara J; Wahoo HS; Wahoo, NE; SecJrCls; Band; Chrs; ChrhWkr; CncrtBnd; HonRl; MrchBnd; PepBnd; StuGov; RptrYrbk; Tech School; Vocation.

LINDGREN, Brian D; Baraboo HS; Baraboo, WI; Chr; HonRl; Bsktbl; Ftbl; LetterTennis; IMSpt; JCAwd; U Of Wi; Business Administration.

LINDGREN, Del A; Wahoo HS; Malmo, NE; ALBoysSt; Band; CncrtBnd; HonRl; MrchBnd; PepBnd; 4-H; SpnCl; College; Education.

LINDHOLM, Andrew C; Isle HS; Isle, MN; HonRl; LbryAde; SchPl; StuGov; YthFlsp; RptrYrbk; RptrSchPpr; SptEdSchPpr; Bsktbl; Ftbl; Musician; Prof.

LINDHOUT, Cindy L; Comstock Park HS; Comstock Park, MI; 4/147 VPJrCls; HonRl; SecNHS; TchrAde; RptrYrbk; PpCl; GAA; College; Vocational.

LINDKE, Loraine; Imlay City HS; Imlay City, MI; 2/134 Chr; Chrl; HonRl; NHS; StuCncl; StuGov; YthFlsp; GAA; Faithway Baptist College; English Teacher.

LINDLEY, Hank; Diamond HS; Diamond, MO; 3/65 HonRl; NHS; SchMus; SchPl; 4-H; FFA; MthCl; LetterBsbl; Bsktbl; 4-HAwd; Crowder College; Agriculture.

LINDLEY, Kim D; Neoga HS; Neoga, IL; 3/80 SecSrCls; ALAGirlsSt; Band; Chr; HonRl; NatlMeritCmnd; OffAde; PepBnd; SchPl; VPSdlty; Ill State; Special Ed Teacher.

LINDLEY, Robert L; Belton HS; Belton, MO; 4/295 CncrtBnd; HonRl; MrchBnd; NHS; NatlMeritSF; PepBnd; SchMus; SctActv; YthFlsp; FrCl; College; Eltrical Engineering.

LINDNER, Dirk F; Stanton Community HS; Stanton, IA; 4/35 Chr; Chrs; ChrhWkr; HonRl; SchMus; FrCl; Northwestern Col; Music.

LINDON, Donna S; Crossville Comm HS; Crossville, IL; 1/25 TrsFrshCls; HonRl; NHS; SchPl; StuCncl; Yrbk; FHA; MthCl; PpCl; Chrldr; Deaconess Sch Of Nursing; Rn.

LINDOW, Edgar J; Marengo Community HS; Marengo, IL; ChrhWkr; CmntyWkr; HonRl; SctActv; SciCl; Northern Ill Univ; Engineering.

LINDOW, Kelly G; Ripon Senior HS; Ripon, WI; HonRl; Trk; Univ Of Wis Stevens Point; General Science.

LINDQUIST, Daniel P; Pine River HS; Leroy, MI; TrsSophCls; CncrtBnd; HonRl; MrchBnd; NHS; PepBnd; SctActv; SpnCl; Ftbl; GodCntryAwd; College; Professional.

LINDQUIST, David; W G Mather HS; Munising, MI; 10/125 CmntyWkr; HonRl; NHS; SchPl; SctActv; StuGov; SptEdSchPpr; Michigan Tech; Electrical Engineer.

LINDQUIST, Deedee K; Mundelein HS; Mundelein, IL; 4/360 SecJrCls; SecSrCls; HonRl; NHS; NatlMeritCmnd; SchAde; StuCncl; StuGov; TchrAde; RptrYrbk; RptrSchPpr; PpCl; University; Business.

LINDQUIST, Matthew P; William Freind HS; Rolling Mdws, IL; Band; ChrhWkr; CncrtBnd; HonRl; MrchBnd; NatlThespSoc; PepBnd; SchMus; SchPl; Bsktbl; Augustana College; Science.

LINDQUIST, Nancy L; De Pue Public HS; De Pue, IL; Band; Chrs; CncrtBnd; HonRl; MrchBnd; PepBnd; SchMus; SchPl; GAA; College; Biological Science.

LINDQUIST, Nancy R; Chisago Lakes Sr HS; Lindstrom, MN; Band; Chr; HonRl; HospAde; MrchBnd; PepBnd; YthFlsp; Yrbk; PpCl; LetterBsktbl; College; Health.

LINDQUIST, Paul J; Chisago Lakes HS; Lindstrom, MN; 4/140 ALBoysSt; Band; SecFrshCls; TrsFrshCls; SecJrCls; StuCncl; EdSchPpr; LetterTrk; LionAwd; Concordia Coll.

LINDQUIST, Sherilie G; Kenmare Public HS; Kenmare, ND; ALAGirlsSt; SchAde; SchPl; SctActv; YthFnd; RptrSchPpr; FBLA; FHA; Bsktbl; Trk; GAA; Univ Of No Dakota; Law.

LINDQUIST, Sheryl; East Hs; Rockford, IL; 20/760 Band; ChrhWkr; HonRl; SchMus; FrCl; Wheaton College; Biological Sciences.

LINDSAY, Carol A; Mankato West HS; Mankato, MN; 3/295 DrlTm; HonRl; HospAde; NatlFornLg; NHS; NatlMeritSF; NatlThespSoc; Orch; StuCncl; YthFlsp; Univ; Humaities.

LINDSAY, Lisa; Belleville Twp Hs East; Fairview Hghts, IL; CmntyWkr; HonRl; NHS; TchrAde; SpnCl; College Mckendree; Law.

LINDSEY, Diana; Chilhowee HS; Warrensburg, MO; Chrs; HonRl; RptrYrbk; RptrSchPpr; FHA; PpCl; Chrldr; Vocational Tech; Secretary.

LINDSEY, Eva K; Springs Valley HS; French Lick, IN; 6/85 HonRl; NHS; OffAde; StuCncl; Yrbk; PpCl; Bsktbl; IMSpt; Univ;.

LINDSEY, Jo A; Astoria HS; Astoria, IL; 6/45 PresBand; Chrs; CncrtBnd; HonRl; MrchBnd; NHS; PresStuCncl; FrCl; PresGAA; DARAwd; Western Ill U; Music Education.

LINDSEY, Kathy D; Chicago Vocational HS; Chicago, IL; 51/789 HonRl; MrchBnd; SchPl; TchrAde; Trk; GAA; Howard Univ; Lawyer.

LINDSEY, Michael D; Rantoul Township HS; Rantoul, IL; 50/400 TrsSophCls; HonRl; NHS; StuCncl; TchrAde; RptrSchPpr; LetterBsktbl; LetterFtbl; CaptTrk; U S Air Force Academy; Pilot.

LINDSEY, Myra; Lindblom Tech HS; Chicago, IL; 80/640 TrsSrCls; Chrs; HonRl; VPLbryAde; StuGov; Yrbk; GerCl; Chrldr; GAA; SecJETSAwd; Purdue Univ; Civil Engineering.

LINDSEY, Robert L; Beaumont HS; St Louis, MO; Bsbl; Ftbl; Trk; College.

LINDSTEDT, Michael J; Chesterton HS; Chesterton, IN; 18/321 Band; MrchBnd; NHS; Bsbl; Purdue Univ; Science.

LINDSTROM, Brenda S; Newton HS; Newton, IA; Band; CncrtBnd; HonRl; MrchBnd; PepBnd; PresFHA; Des Moines Area Comm Coll; Secretarial.

LINDSTROM, Brent A; Kingsford HS; Kingsford, MI; ChrhWkr; HonRl; LbryAde; RedCrAde; SptEdSchPpr; LetterBsbl; LetterBsktbl; LetterFtbl; LetterTrk; IMSpt; PresAwd; Coll; Engr.

LINDSTROM, Bruce R; Southside HS; Muncie, IN; 30/458 Band; CncrtBnd; HonRl; JA; MrchBnd; Orch; Bsktbl; Ftbl; Glf; JAAwd; College; Teacher.

LINDSTROM, Dean; Chicago Christian Hs; Blue Island, IL; 1/165 PresHonRl; NHS; Bsbl; Purdue U;electrical Engineering.

LINDSTROM, Heather A; Harry A Burke HS; Omaha, NE; AFS; ALAGirlsSt; HonRl; JrNHS; NHS; NatlMeritSF; SctActv; StuGov; YthFlsp; PresFrCl; Wellesley Col; Business.

LINDSTROM, Paul D; Sycamore HS; Sycamore, IL; HonRl; 4-H; FFA;.

LINDSTROM, Paul R; Merrill HS; Merrill, WI; 50/376 Band; CncrtBnd; NatlMeritFnl; PepBnd; GerCl; MthCl; Ftbl; Trk; Wrstlng; AmLegAwd; U Of Wi Madison; Computer Sci.

LINDSTROM, Peter; Wichita HS; Wichita, KS; Aud/Vis; JA; NatlMeritSchl; Swmmng; CchngActv; North Park College; Lawyer.

LINDSTROM, Peter W; Central Cass HS; Amenia, ND; 9/57 ALBoysSt; Chrs; CncrtBnd; HonRl; NHS; PepBnd; SchPl; 4-H;.

LINDSTROM, Rebekka K; Manson HS; Manson, IA; 7/82 VPJrCls; VPChr; HonRl; NHS; SchMus; SchPl; StuCncl; RptrYrbk; EdYrBk; RptrSchPpr; Univ; Art.

LINDSTROM, Roberta; Rockford East HS; Rockford, IL; 68/645 VPSrCls; Chr; Chrs; HonRl; StuGov; YthFlsp; RptrSchPpr; PpCl; Coll;pro.

LINDSTROM, Steve; Holdrege HS; Funk, NE; Chr; Chrl; Chrs; SchMus; SctActv; IMSpt; University; Astronomy.

LINDTEIGEN, Claire; Turtle Lake Public HS; Turtle Lake, ND; 4/44 Band; ChrhWkr; HonRl; TchrAde; FHA; Trk; Chrldr; DanFAwd; 4-HAwd; CitAwd; North Dakota State Univ.

LINDVIG, Peggy A; Westby HS; Viroqua, WI; 5/116 HonRl; NHS; TreasSpnCl; Uw Eau Claire; Accounting.

LINDWURM, Linda A; Madonna HS; Chicago, IL; 21/273 Chr; ChrhWkr; LbryAde; NatlFornLg; NHS; GerCl; MthCl; SciCl; Univ Of Illinois; Medicine.

LINEBACK, Laura J; Huntington North HS; Huntington, IN; Band; CncrtBnd; MrchBnd; PepBnd; SchMus; College Iu Or Isu; Social Work Sociology.

LINEBERRY, Catherine; Pershing HS; Plummer, MN; 1/15 Band; CncrtBnd; HonRl; SchPl; EdYrBk; RptrSchPpr; AmLegAwd; BttyCrckrAwd; CitAwd; Univ Of Minn Tech Coll; Court Reporting.

LINEWEAVER, Joy; Calumet HS; Laurum, MI; Band; Chr; CncrtBnd; HonRl; MrchBnd; NatlFornLg; NHS; PepBnd; Yrbk; Michigan Tech Univ; Accounting.

LING, Mary; Jackson HS; Jackson, MN; Band; Chr; CncrtBnd; MrchBnd; PepBnd; TchrAde; Yrbk; FrCl; Trk; VFWAwd; College; Medicine.

LINGAFELTER, Sherryl A; Mt Zion HS; Decatur, IL; 18/200 Band; CncrtBnd; HonRl; MrchBnd; NHS; Orch; PepBnd; Bsktbl; Richland Comm Coll; Accounting.

LINGEN, Ruth H; Lyman HS; Presho, SD; Band; Chrs; HonRl; IntrClCncl; NHS; StuCncl; SchPpr; FFA; Bsktbl; Trk; Univ; Commercial Art.

LINGENFELTER, Mary J; Hartford HS; Emporia, KS; Chr; Chrl; Chrs; ChrhWkr; HonRl; HospAde; SchMus; FrCl; College; Biologist.

LINGLE, Lynn R; Lakeshore HS; St Joseph, MI; Chr; HospAde; Yrbk; FrCl; PpCl; Tennis; LetterTrk; DARAwd; Coll; Social Ser.

LINGLE, Steven; Bismarck Senior HS; Bismarck, ND; 12/591 NHS; Swmmng; BauchLmbAwd; Univ Of Nd; Pre Med.

LINGLEY, Dean R; Wellington HS; Hoopeston, IL; 6/20 VPSophCls;.

LINHARD, Thomas L; Harvard HS; Harvard, IL; 4-H; FFA; GerCl; LetterFtbl; LetterTrk; LetterWrstlng; 4-HAwd; College; Pilot.

LININGER, Bruce D; Wethersfield HS; Kewanee, IL; 3/64 PresFrshCls; AFS; Band; CncrtBnd; HonRl; MrchBnd; NHS; PolWkr; SchMus; SchPl; PresStuCncl; SptEdYrbk; SptEdSchPpr; Trk; Illinois Wesleyan Univ; Math.

LINK, Angelo; Chase Rural HS; Chase, KS; 3/31 VPSophCls; HonRl; SchPl; StuCncl; SpnCl; Bsktbl; Trk; CitAwd; VoiceDemAwd; Marymount College; Nursing.

LINK, Linda K; Central HS; Aberdeen, SD; HonRl; YthFlsp; Northern St Coll.

LINK, Patricia A; Brimley HS; Brimley, MI; 6/34 Band; ChrhWkr; HonRl; OffAde; PepBnd; 4-H; PpCl; LetterBsktbl; GAA; IMSpt; CitAwd;.

LINK, Peggy A; Madonna HS; Chicago, IL; 25/273 HonRl; NHS; SchMus; StuGov; RptrYrbk; LetterBsbl; GAA; Northeastern Ill; Speech.

LINK, Scott W; Marshall University HS; Minneapolis, MN; 4/165 HonRl; SctActv; LetterBsbl; LetterTennis; IMSpt; PresAwd; University; Mathematics.

LINK, Timothy G; Kapaun Mt Carmel HS; Wichita, KS; Chrs; HonRl; NHS; NatlThespSoc; SchMus; SchPl; StuCncl; StuGov; Coll; Prof.

LINK, William H; Maine West HS; Des Plaines, IL; ChrhWkr; HonRl; NHS; NatlThespSoc; Orch; SchMus; StuCncl; YthFlsp; PresKeyCl; Univ Of Ill; Med Lab Technician.

LINKUGEL, Carolyn R; Marysville HS; Bremen, KS; VP4-H; SpnCl; PpCl; 4-HAwd; KiwanAwd; College.

LINN, Cheryl; East HS; Wichita, KS; 17/623 Chr; ChrhWkr; CncrtBnd; HonRl; MrchBnd; Orch; PepBnd; SctActv; FrCl; Bethel Coll; Hist.

LINN, Kenny J; So Haven HS; South Haven, MI; Band; CncrtBnd; HonRl; MrchBnd; PepBnd; TchrAde; Ftbl; U S Navy; Aviation Electronics.

LINN, Sharon; Warsaw Community HS; Warsaw, IN; 5/380 VPSrCls; ALAGirlsSt; Band; ChrhWkr; CncrtBnd; HonRl; HospAde; PepBnd; PolWkr; SchPl; College; Mathematics.

LINNAN, Brian D; Saint Marys HS; Storm Lake, IA; VPSophCls; ALBoysSt; Chrs; ChrhWkr; HonRl; Sacrstn; Yrbk; Bsbl; Bsktbl; Glf; Clge; Pro.

LINNELL, Donald A; Bluestem HS; Leon, KS; 3/45 ChrhWkr; HonRl; JrNHS; SchPl; StuCncl; StuGov; YthFlsp; LetterBsktbl; LetterFtbl; Trk; Coll; Usaf.

LINNEMAN, Larry W; Moberly Sr HS; Moberly, MO; 6/200 HstFrshCls; Band; ChrhWkr; CncrtBnd; HonRl; MrchBnd; NHS; PepBnd; PolWkr; StuGov; KeyCl; MthCl; LetterFtbl; KiwanAwd; College; Computer Tech.

LINNENBRINK, Michael G; Marquette Inc HS; West Point, IA; ALBoysSt; Chrs; HonRl; MrchBnd; Orch; PepBnd; SancSoc; 4-H; FFA; 4-HAwd; College; Agricultural Education.

LINNENBURGER, Cynthia; Hamilton HS; Hamilton, IL; PresFrshCls; HstSophCls; PresJrCls; AFS; HonRl; StuCncl; StuGov; FTA; PresAwd; College.

LINOSKI, Allen R; St Clement HS; Center Line, MI; VPFrshCls; HonRl; PolWkr; SchPl; StuCncl; StuGov; SpnCl; SciCl; IMSpt; University; Natural Resources.

LINSCHEID, Jeffrey A; Milledgeville HS; Sterling, IL; 8/40 Chr; ChrhWkr; HonRl; SchPl; TchrAde; RptrYrbk; Yrbk; 4-H; FFA; 4-HAwd; College; Agriculture Major.

LINSE, Jan L; Memorial HS; Eau Claire, WI; VPAFS; ChrhWkr; NatlMeritSF; Orch; SctActv; StuCncl; Pres4-H; IMSpt; 4-HAwd; CitAwd; University; Physician.

LINSMEYER, Patricia J; Pembine HS; Pembine, WI; 12/32 ChrhWkr; DrmMjrt; HonRl; NatlFornLg; NatlThespSoc; SchMus; SchPl; RptrSchPpr; Bsktbl; Trk; Nwti Green Bay; Child Care Assistant.

LINSSEN, Theresa A; White Lake HS; Lakewood, WI; 2/40 TrsSrCls; Chrs; HonRl; SchPl; TchrAde; PresSpnCl; CaptBsktbl; DARAwd; CitAwd; Coll; Phy Ed.

LINTECUM, Robert E; Buhler HS; Buhler, KS; /100 HonRl; Jr College; History And Science Professor.

LINTNER, Morris R; Madison HS; Madison, NE; Band; Chr; CncrtBnd; HonRl; MrchBnd; PepBnd; College; Accounting.

LINTON, Alan C; Marseilles HS; Marseilles, IL; VPSrCls; Band; Chr; Chrs; ChrhWkr; Mdrgl; NatlThespSoc; SchMus; SchPl; LetterFtbl; Glf; Wrstlng; College; Music.

LINTON, Darrick O; Chicago Vocational HS; Chicago, IL; HonRl; Bsbl; CaptSwmmng; KiwanAwd; College.

LINTON, Hans M; Harlan Comm HS; Harlan, IA; 14/257 VPJrCls; PresSrCls; HonRl; NHS; SchPl; Bsktbl; CaptFtbl; Univ Of Ia; Bio Med Engineer.

LINTON, Marsha L; Mulberry Grove HS; Smithboro, IL; CncrtBnd; PepBnd; YthFlsp; Yrbk; SchPpr; FHA; PpCl; GAA; Nursing Sch; Nursing.

LINZ, Bruce W; Forest Lake HS; Forest Lake, MN; 50/363 Aud/Vis; ChrhWkr; HonRl; MrchBnd; SchMus; SchPl; SctActv; StuCncl; RptrYrbk; Yrbk; FFA; Ftbl; Swmmng; College; Meteorologist.

LINZ, Curt; Albany Sr HS; Richmond, MN; Chrs; HonRl; 4-H; FFA; Ftbl; Trk; IMSpt; 4-HAwd; PresAwd; Trade School; Vocational.

LINZMEIER, Robert J; John F Kennedy HS; Chicago, IL; 20/610 HonRl; StuGov; PepBnd; CaptTrk; De Paul U; Law.

LIONBERGER, Martha R; North Chicago HS; Great Lakes, IL; Chr; ChrhWkr; CncrtBnd; HonRl; HospAde; NHS; NatlMeritCmnd; SchMus; SchPl; CaptTennis; College; Literature.

LIPARI, Louis; St Pius X HS; Kansas City, MO; 4/137 Chrs; HonRl; NHS; LetterBsktbl; LetterFtbl; LetterTrk.

LIPAROTO, Mark W; Monroe HS; Monroe, MI; HonRl; Usaf; Professional.

LIPCAMAN, Lisa M; Huron HS; Ann Arbor, MI; HonRl; StuCncl; StuGov; Yrbk; SchPpr; GerCl; LatCl; IMSpt; University Of Michigan.

LIPE, Glenda F; Egyptian HS; Olive Branch, IL; 7/67 ChrhWkr; CmntyWkr; HonRl; JA; NHS; RedCrAde; YthFlsp; YthFnd; 4-H; FHA; Shawnee College; Retailing.

LIPETZKY, Roger J; Kensal HS; Kensal, ND; 5/17 SecTrsFrshCls; VPSophCls; VPJrCls; ALBoysSt; Band; CncrtBnd; HonRl; MrchBnd; SchPl; PresStuCncl; Valley City State Clg; Teacher.

LIPINSKI, Vickey L; Triad HS; Troy, IL; HonRl; NHS; 4-H; Data Processing.

LIPKA, Bertha E; Bishop Noll Institute HS; East Chicago, IN; HonRl; StuCncl; StuGov; College; Teacher.

LIPKA, Dom L; La Salle Peru Twp HS; Peru, IL; 31/516 HonRl; GerCl; Bsktbl; Illinois Valley Comm College; Political Sci.

LIPMAN, Ross S; Connersville HS; Connersville, IN; 6/385 HonRl; PresNHS; NatlMeritCmnd; NatlThespSoc; GerCl; SciCl; Glf; RotaryAwd; College; Law.

LIPPERT, Daniel J; Danube Public HS; Blomkest, MN; PresJrCls; PresSrCls; VPStuCncl; Pres4-H; PresFFA; LetterFtbl; LetterWrstlng; Univ Of Mn; Agricultural Production.

LIPPERT, Don M; St Josephs HS; Kenosha, WI; 5/160 Chr; Chrs; HonRl; LbryAde; RedCrAde; SchMus; SchPl; StuCncl; YthFnd; PpCl; Glf; LetterTrk; IMSpt; Univ Of Mn; Medicine.

LIPPERT, Donna M; Union HS; Union, MO; 3/174 ALAGirlsSt; Band; DrmMjrt; HonRl; HospAde; NHS; SchMus; SctActv; StuCncl; 4-H; PpCl; PPFtbl; University; Professional.

LIPPERT, Nila; Kouts HS; Kouts, IN; 1/54 Band; DrmMjrt; HonRl; MrchBnd; NHS; Univ; Medical Doctor.

LIPPERT, Patrick R; St Thomas Academy; St Paul, MN; 5/108 HonRl; JA; PolWkr; ROTC; RptrYrbk; RptrSchPpr; LatCl; Wrstlng; St Thomas College; Political Science.

LIPPOLD, Terry L; Escanaba Area HS; Escanaba, MI; 41/383 Chr; Chrs; NHS; NatlMeritCmnd; StuGov; YthLg; RptrYrbk; PpCl; LetterGlf; Central Mi Univ; Computer Science.

LIPSCHULTZ, Traci J; Portage Central HS; Portage, MI; HonRl; TchrAde; FrCl; PpCl; LetterChrldr; Central Mi Univ; Secondary Ed.

LIPSETT, James S; Lakeview HS; St Clair Shores, MI; HonRl; NHS; RptrSchPpr; IMSpt; College; Engineering.

LIPSHAW, Michael R; Berkley HS; Huntington Wds, MI; 69/578 PresSrCls; CtyCnl; CmntyWkr; LbryAde; NHS; OffAde; StuCncl; StuGov; TchrAde; SpnCl; Oakland U; Psychologist.

LIPSHITZ, Hiram W; Fulton Tech HS; Fulton, MI; 43/47 HstFrshCls; CAP; NatlThespSoc; Sacrstn; Sdlty; FFA; LatCl; PPFtbl; DanFAwd; GodCntryAwd; Marines; Farmer.

LIPSITZ, Dean L; Rich East HS; Park Forest, IL; AFS; HonRl; NatlFornLg; NatlMeritCmnd; NatlThespSoc; SchPl; RptrSchPpr; LatCl; Tennis; University Of Arizona; Liberal Arts.

LIPSKI, Wayne E; St Laurence HS; Chicago, IL; 17/385 HonRl; SciCl; Loyola Univ; Accounting.

LIRONES, Margaret E; Saline HS; Saline, MI; Band; HonRl; FrCl; Michigan St Univ; Veterinarian.

LIS, Edward J; Fitzgerald HS; Warren, MI; 43/400 Band; ChrhWkr; CncrtBnd; HonRl; MrchBnd; NHS; Orch; PepBnd; SchMus; SchPl; RptrSchPpr; SchPpr; Wayne State University; Pharmacy.

LIS, Scott M; Forest Hills Central HS; Grand Rapids, MI; 96/180 Band; CncrtBnd; JA; MrchBnd; NatlMeritSF; PepBnd; JAAwd; Univ; Music.

LISIECKI, John A; St Andrew HS; Detroit, MI; 15/110 TrsSrCls; SctActv; StuGov; RptrYrbk; PpCl; Bsbl; Trk; General Motors Inst; Electrical Engineering.

LISKA, Karen J; Northwestern HS; Maple, WI; ChrhWkr; CncrtBnd; HonRl; LbryAde; MrchBnd; OffAde; PepBnd; PresFHA; Indianhead Tech Inst; Seamstress.

LISKA, Raymond B; Hillsboro HS; Hillsboro, WI; 4/74 Band; CncrtBnd; HonRl; MrchBnd; VPNHS; PepBnd; SchPl; Pres4-H; FFA; Bsbl; Bsktbl; Ftbl; IMSpt; 4-HAwd; Univ Of Wis; Agriculture.

LISKE, Jolee G; Medford Sr HS; Medford, WI; 60/254 Band; ChrhWkr; HonRl; TchrAde; FDA; SciCl; Swmmng; Trk; LetterGAA; JCAwd; College; Med Field.

LISKOW, Cady L; Ypsilanti HS; Ypsilanti, MI; ChrhWkr; HonRl; NHS; SctActv; YthFlsp; SpnCl; LetterTennis; Univ Mich; Math Computer Science.

LISS, Timothy; La Salle Peru Township HS; La Salle, IL; HonRl; NHS; GerCl; Coll; Acc.

LISSAK, Mark C; Homewood Flossmoor HS; Homewood, IL; 87/910 HonRl; NHS; CaptBsktbl; Ftbl; University Of Kansas; Business Admin.

LIST, Laurie A; Frankenmuth HS; Birch Run, MI; 8/176 Band; ChrhWkr; CncrtBnd; HonRl; MrchBnd; NHS; College; Nursing.

LIST, Lorna E; Edina East HS; Edina, MN; Band; ChrhWkr; HonRl; MrchBnd; Twrl; FrCl; Washington Univ; Med.

LISTER, Jane M; Ottawa HS; Williamsburg, KS; 45/183 Chr; Chrs; ChrhWkr; CmntyWkr; DrlTm; HonRl; SchAde; SctActv; TchrAde; SchPpr; 4-H; SpnCl; PpCl; University; Art.

LISTER, Rosalynn; St Charles HS; St Charles, MI; CmntyWkr; CncrtBnd; MrchBnd; NHS; PepBnd; CivCl; GAA; PPFtbl; Clge; Curr Of Major Study.

LISTON, Patty; St Albert HS; Council Bluffs, IA; Chr; ChrhWkr; CmntyWkr; HonRl; HospAde; NHS; SchMus; PpCl; Clarke College; Music Therapy.

LISTRO, Anita K; Morton Sr HS; Hammond, IN; 14/492 HonRl; NatlFornLg; NHS; StuGov; TchrAde; FTA; College; Professional.

LISY, Beverlee F; St Francis Academy; Joliet, IL; HonRl; NHS; NatlMeritCmnd; SpnCl; LetterTrk; VPGAA; Lewis Univ; C P A.

LISZEWSKI, Rita; Gilman Public HS; Lublin, WI; 1/80 ALAGirlsSt; Band; Chrs; NHS; NatlMeritCmnd; SchPl; StuCncl; EdSchPpr; 4-H; 4-HAwd; Univ; Professional.

LITAK, Theodore R; Dwight D Eisenhower HS; Chicago, IL; 8/565 CncrtBnd; HonRl; JrNHS; LitMag; MrchBnd; NHS; NatlMeritCmnd; Moraine Valley Comm College.

LITCHIN, Kent; Homestead HS; Fort Wayne, IN; TrsJrCls; ChrhWkr; StuCncl; SptEdYrbk; Bsktbl; LetterFtbl; LetterTrk; IMSpt; Bus.

LITHGOW, Sharon L; Richwoods HS; Peoria, IL; 11/449 Chr; Chrs; ChrhWkr; HonRl; SchPl; SchPpr; SpnCl; John Brown Univ; Business.

LITHIO, Tom A; Downers Grove South HS; Downers Grove, IL; 25/820 HonRl; NatlMeritCmnd; Univ Of Illinois; Engineering.

LITKE, Douglas W; Clay County Comm HS; Clay Center, KS; 18/130 Band; CncrtBnd; HonRl; MrchBnd; NHS; Orch; PepBnd; StuCncl; FBLA; SciCl; Air Force; Electronic.

LITKE, Thomas M; Healy HS; Pierz, MN; 20/120 ALBoysSt; Chr; ChrhWkr; CmntyWkr; HonRl; LbryAde; PolWkr; TchrAde; CaptTrk; Trade Sch; Sales Mgmt.

LITRENTI, Gail A; Maine Township South HS; Park Ridge, IL; HonRl; JrNHS; NHS; FrCl; PpCl; U Of I; Interpreter.

LITTEKER, Debra A; Mater Dei HS; Trenton, IL; 21/197 Chrs; ChrhWkr; CmntyWkr; HonRl; HospAde; NatlMeritCmnd; NatlMeritSchl; SchMus; SchPl; FBLA; Eastern Illinois University; Special Educ.

LITTEL, Laura J; St Louise De Marillac HS; Glenview, IL; 32/254 Chrs; NHS; SchMus; SctActv; VPTeen; Yrbk; SpnCl; College; Mass Communications.

LITTEL, Robert L; Evanston Township HS; Evanston, IL; HonRl; Bsbl; Ftbl; IMSpt; Col; Engineering.

LITTELL, Larry F; Mahomet Seymour HS; Mahomet, IL; 28/132 HonRl; SchPl; FrCl; Glf; LionAwd; U Of Il; Engineer.

LITTELL, Leslie L; Heyworth HS; Heyworth, IL; Chrs; HospAde; PepBnd; RptrYrbk; SpnCl; PpCl; SciCl; Tennis; Chrldr; GAA; College; Professional.

LITTERER, Tammy; Clarksville Comm HS; Clarksville, IA; TrsSophCls; ChrhWkr; HonRl; NHS; YthFlsp; Ellsworth Comm College; Social Work.

LITTIG, Christine E; Bluffs HS; Bluffs, IL; Chrs; ChrhWkr; HonRl; LbryAde; SecNHS; SchMus; SctActv; StuCncl; TchrAde; TreasYthFlsp; Yrbk; 4-H; CchngActv; GAA; College; Cosmotologist.

LITTLE, Carol; Cass City HS; Cass City, MI; 2/132 Band; ChrhWkr; CncrtBnd; HonRl; JrNHS; MrchBnd; NHS; NatlMeritSF; FBLA; TchrAde; Great Lakes Bible College; Chemical Energin.

LITTLE, David; Garner Hayfield HS; Garner, IA; 14/70 Band; Chr; Chrs; ChrhWkr; CncrtBnd; HonRl; MrchBnd; PepBnd; YthFlsp; Glf; Univ; Engineering.

LITTLE, Gwendolyn; Normandy HS; St Louis, MO; Chr; Chrs; CmntyWkr; HonRl; JrNHS; MrchBnd; SchMus; TchrAde; Coll; Voc.

LITTLE, Janet L; Mitchell HS; Mitchell, IN; 9/120 HonRl; TreasNHS; OffAde; TreasQuill&Scroll; TchrAde; Yrbk; FHA; RotaryAwd; Homemaker.

LITTLE, Karla W; Lincoln Way HS; Mokena, IL; 13/566 Chrs; ChrhWkr; HonRl; OffAde; MthCl;.

LITTLE, Leann J; Northwestern HS; Mellette, SD; 1/35 ALAGirlsSt; HonRl; LbryAde; NHS; NatlThespSoc; SchPl; RptrYrbk; PpCl; IMSpt; DARAwd; Ia State U; Vet.

LITTLE, Linda L; Riggs HS; Pierre, SD; 13/250 Chr; Chrs; ChrhWkr; HonRl; Mdrgl; NatlMeritSF; SchPl; RptrYrbk; PpCl; IMSpt; S D School Of Mines; Chemical Engineering.

LITTLE, Paul A; Lindblom HS; Chicago, IL; 32/599 ChrhWkr; HonRl; ROTC; SctActv; StuCncl; TchrAde; GerCl; Northwestern Univ; Medicine.

LITTLE, Richard L; Santa Fe Trail HS; Carbondale, KS; ALBoysSt; HonRl; LbryAde; NatlFornLg; Kansas State University; Business Admin.

LITTLE, Richard S; Watertown Sr HS; Watertown, SD; ALBoysSt; Chr; NatlFornLg; NatlMeritSF; SchMus; 4-H; FFA; Wrstlng; South Dakota State Univ; Agriculture.

LITTLE, Roger L; Tri County Community HS; What Cheer, IA; Band; LetterChr; LetterChrs; HonRl; LetterMdrgl; SchMus; SchPl; StuCncl; 4-H; FFA; College.

LITTLE, Shirley A; St Paul HS; Walnut, KS; Chr; Chrs; ChrhWkr; CmntyWkr; DrlTm; HonRl; LbryAde; RptrYrbk; PpCl; IMSpt; College; Major Study.

LITTLE, Susanne M; St Francis HS; St Francis, KS; PresFrshCls; Band; Chr; Chrl; HonRl; PepBnd; SchPl; PresTeen; 4-H; Bsktbl; College; P E Major.

LITTLE, Tammara J; Lincoln HS; Beverly, KS; 2/60 TrsJrCls; TrsSrCls; CncrtBnd; HonRl; MrchBnd; OffAde; PepBnd; SchMus; TchrAde; PpCl; Brown Mackie Sch Of Bus; Secretarial.

LITTLEJOHN, Doris E; Oskaloosa HS; Oskaloosa, IA; 16/198 Chr; ChrhWkr; CncrtBnd; HonRl; MrchBnd; YthFlsp; DARAwd; U Of Northern Ia; Home Economics.

LITTLEJOHN, Liza J; St Thomas HS; St Thomas, ND; ALAGirlsSt; Band; Chrs; HonRl; JA; LbryAde; SptEdSchPpr; Chrldr; GAA; U Of Nd; Psychology.

LITTLER, Cheryl A; John F Kennedy HS; Babbitt, MN; Chr; HonRl; OffAde; SchMus; StuCncl; TchrAde; 4-H; LetterSwmmng; 4-HAwd; College; Physical Education.

LITTLES, Leo; Harlan HS; Chicago, IL; Band; Chr; Bsktbl; IMSpt; Univ; Architecture.

LITTLE WOUNDED, Karen; Cheyenne Eagle Butte HS; Eaglebutte, SD; /57 StuCncl; YthFlsp; RptrYrbk; PpCl; College In Sd; Executive Secretary.

LITTREL, Patty J; English Valleys HS; N English, IA; 1/60 CncrtBnd; HonRl; SecNHS; StuCncl; TchrAde; Twrl; FTA; PpCl; Bsktbl; LetterChrldr; Univ Of Iowa.

LITTRELL, Curtis W; Sedan HS; Sedan, KS; PresSophCls; HonRl; StuCncl; TchrAde; 4-H; FSA; SciCl; Bsktbl; LetterFtbl; Trk; Kansas St; Voc.

LITTRELL, Donald R; Jennings County HS; Commiskey, IN; CmntyWkr; CncrtBnd; HonRl; PepBnd; FFA; LetterBsbl; LetterBsktbl; LetterFtbl; CchngActv; Trade School; Radio & Tv Repair.

LITTRELL, Pamela; Wheeling R Iv HS; Wheeling, MO; CmntyWkr; HonRl; SchPl; StuCncl; Yrbk; 4-H; PpCl; Chrldr; Business School; Sec.

LITVIAK, Michael E; Bogan HS; Chicago, IL; 88/700 HonRl; NHS; SchMus; SchPl; StuCncl; KeyCl; Northern Ill Univ; Broadcasting.

LITWILLER, Christina M; Olympia HS; Delavan, IL; 4/192 AFS; Band; Chr; ChrhWkr; MrchBnd; NHS; NatlMeritFnl; PepBnd; PresFHA; SpnCl; Goshen College.

LITWILLER, Gary D; South Adams HS; Berne, IN; 20/125 Band; Chr; ChrhWkr; CncrtBnd; Mdrgl; MrchBnd; Orch; PepBnd; SchMus; SchPl; Fort Wayne Bible College; Christian Educatn.

LITWIN, Leonard D; Evanston Twp HS; Skokie, IL; 101/1100 CmntyWkr; HonRl; SpnCl; LetterBsbl; IMSpt; DARAwd; University Of Illinois; Law.

LITZ, Melody B; Mt Zion HS; Mt Zion, IL; 9/195 VPJrCls; HonRl; NHS; StuCncl; StuGov; RptrYrbk; EdYrBk; 4-H; Bsbl; Wrstlng; Illinois State Univ; Sociology.

LITZENBERG, Paul H; Taylorville HS; Taylorville, IL; 8/271 ChrhWkr; HonRl; NHS; NatlMeritCmnd; PresYthFlsp; College; Elec Engineer.

LIVELY, Cinda M; Shawneetown HS; Junction, IL; 4/30 Band; HonRl; LbryAde; MrchBnd; StuCncl; FHA; MthCl; Bsktbl; GAA; Siu; Teacher.

LIVERMORE, Jean A; Southern HS; Raritan, IL; 7/57 SecJrCls; ChrhWkr; CmntyWkr; HonRl; NHS; EdYrBk; 4-H; FTA; DanFAwd; 4-HAwd; Business Sch; Secretary.

LIVERNASH, Darlene C; Lincoln HS; Wisconsin Rapids, WI; Band; Chrs; CncrtBnd; HonRl; MrchBnd; PepBnd; FrCl; PpCl; SciCl; College.

LIVERS, Don; Crispus Attucks Hs; Indianapolis, IN; 38/325 HstJrCls; ChrhWkr; HonRl; JA; ModUN; StuCncl; YthFlsp; Bsktbl; LetterFtbl; Trk; Air Force Acad; Professional Law.

LIVERTON, Audrey E; Addison Trail HS; Addison, IL; 12/563 HonRl; NHS; NatlMeritSF; NatlThespSoc; Quill&Scroll; SchPl; StuCncl; Yrbk; U Of I; Drama Speech.

LIVESAY, Deborah J; Holly Hill HS; Holly Hill, IL; 6/99 Chrs; StuCncl; TchrAde; 4-H; FTA; FrCl; PpCl; Bsktbl; College; Biology.

LIVESAY, Janice; Jackson County Western HS; Parma, MI; 4/157 TrsSrCls; ModUN; DARAwd; Auto Mach Train Cntr; Computer Progammer.

LIVESAY, Sherry R; Shawnee HS; Wolf Lake, IL; HonRl; FBLA; FHA; PpCl; GAA; Shawnee Jr Coll; Computer Programming.

LIVESAY, Tracy D; Anna Jonesboro Comm HS; Anna, IL; VPFrshCls; PresSophCls; VPBand; CncrtBnd; HonRl; MrchBnd; PepBnd; KeyCl; PresLatCl; Bsbl; Bsktbl; Ftbl; Univ Of Ill; Political Science.

LIVGREN, Judy M; Clay Center Public HS; Harvard, NE; TrsJrCls; Band; HonRl; SchMus; TchrAde; YthFlsp; RptrSchPpr; 4-H; PpCl; Trk; U Of Nb Lincoln; Human Dev & Family.

LIVINGSTON, Carol A; Cumberland HS; Toledo, IL; 3/108 ChrhWkr; HonRl; SecNHS; SecStuCncl; VP4-H; SpnCl; PpCl; TreasSciCl; GAA; AmLegAwd; DanFAwd; Eastern Illinois Univ; Accounting.

LIVINGSTON, Crystal J; Hayes Center Public Schools; Wauneta, NE; SecTrsSrCls; Band; Chrs; ChrhWkr; CncrtBnd; HonRl; MrchBnd; OffAde; PpCl; 4-HAwd; Bartlesville Weslyan College; Secretary.

LIVINGSTON, Doyle L; Tri County HS; Emery, SD; SchPl; Bsktbl; LetterFtbl; CaptTrk; LetterWrstlng; Trade School; Welding.

LIVINGSTON, Eric T; Boys Town HS; Minneapolis, MN; 15/42 JA; RedCrAde; SctActv; IMSpt; CitAwd; Okla St U; Fire Protection.

LIVINGSTON, Kristie R; Lawrence Central HS; Indianapolis, IN; 5/749 Band; CncrtBnd; HonRl; MrchBnd; OffAde; PepBnd; StuCncl; TchrAde; PpCl; Bsbl; College; English.

LIVINGSTON, Richard B; Chatsworth HS; Chatsworth, IL; 7/44 Band; Chrs; CncrtBnd; HonRl; MrchBnd; PepBnd; SchMus; SchPl; 4-H; Illinois Weslyan; Pharmacy.

LIVINGSTONE, Margery A; Homewood Flossmoor HS; Homewood, IL; 175/940 HonRl; LitMag; NatlFornLg; Quill&Scroll; SchMus; SchPl; RptrSchPpr; EdSchPpr; University; Journalism.

LIZAROWSKI, Noel M; Drayton HS; Drayton, ND; 9/35 TrsSrCls; Chrs; ChrhWkr; HonRl; SchMus; SchPl; Trk; Univ Of North Dakota; X Ray Technichian.

LLOYD, Bruce D; Lincoln Northeast HS; Lincoln, NE; HonRl; Ftbl; IMSpt; Univ; Business Ad.

LLOYD, Donald F; Plymouth Canton HS; Plymouth, MI; HstFrshCls; Chr; HonRl; TchrAde; PpCl; LetterBsbl; LetterBsktbl; LetterFtbl; CchngActv; IMSpt; Cleary Business College; Business.

LLOYD, Karen A; Ladywood St Agnes HS; Indianapolis, IN; CmntyWkr; JA; PolWkr; TchrAde; Yrbk; GAA; De Pauw Univ; Law.

LLOYD, Linda J; Eastridge HS; Kankakee, IL; Chr; ChrhWkr; NHS; Orch; Illinois State Univ; Music.

LLOYD, Margaret A; Humphrey HS; Lindsay, NE; SecSrCls; ALAGirlsSt; HonRl; SchMus; StuCncl; EdYrBk; 4-H; EldAwd; 4-HAwd; LionAwd; Wesleyan Univ; Med.

LLOYD, Michelle M; St Marys Springs; Fond Du Lac, WI; SecTrsSophCls; SciCl; Chrldr; GAA; Marquette Univ.

LLOYD, Randy C; Evart HS; Evart, MI; 18/90 HonRl; NHS; Bsbl; Bsktbl; LetterFtbl; LetterTrk; Collge; Biology.

LLOYD, Robert F; Muskego HS; Hales Corners, WI; 2/330 ALBoysSt; Band; CncrtBnd; HonRl; MrchBnd; ModUN; NatlFornLg; NHS; NatlMeritSF; NatlThespSoc; PepBnd; SchPl; SciCl; Univ Of Wisconsin; Physics.

LOBACZ, Donald D; Bishop Dwenger HS; Ft Wayne, IN; HonRl; NatlMeritCmnd; LetterWrstlng; IMSpt; Col; Engineering.

LOBBES, Henry C; Curie HS; Chicago, IL; 74/620 ChrhWkr; CncrtBnd; NHS; MthCl; CaptTrk; Ill Inst Of Tech; Mech Eng.

LOBENSTEIN, Judith A; Mauston Area HS; Mauston, WI; HonRl; RptrYrbk; LatCl; Univ Of Milwaukee; Nursing.

LOBOSCHEFSKI, Nancy L; Sand Creek HS; Jasper, MI; Chr; ChrhWkr; HonRl; NHS; NatlThespSoc; SchMus; SchPl; EdSchPpr; SchPpr; FHA; PpCl; LetterBsktbl; Univ Of Michigan; Lawyer.

LOCASCIO, Clare A; St Charles HS; St Charles, IL; 18/431 Chr; Chrl; HonRl; NHS; Bradley University; Pediatrics.

LOCASCIO, Lawrence J; Brother Rice HS; Chicago, IL; 16/416 PresSophCls; HonRl; NHS; NatlMeritCmnd; StuCncl; SptEdYrbk; SchPpr; KeyCl; PpCl; LetterSwmmng; Univ Of Notre Dame; Law.

LOCH, Pamela S; Fairbury HS; Fairbury, NE; Chrs; HonRl; PpCl; Business School; Legal Secretary.

LOCHBIHLER, David A; Bishop Dwenger HS; Fort Wayne, IN; HonRl; NHS; RptrSchPpr; IMSpt; U Of Notre Dame; Lawyer.

LOCHER, Mark A; St Charles HS; St Charles, IL; 29/457 HonRl; NHS; NatlMeritSF; SctActv; RptrSchPpr; LetterTrk; College; Military.

LOCHMANN, Stephanie M; Jetmore HS; Jetmore, KS; Band; ChrhWkr; MrchBnd; SchPl; Twrl; YthFlsp; Yrbk; SchPpr; FHA; PpCl; Emporia St College; Broadcasting.

LOCK, Beverly J; Carrollton HS; Carrollton, MO; VPJrCls; Band; Chr; Chrs; ChrhWkr; CmntyWkr; HonRl; MrchBnd; SchMus; SctActv; 4-H; GerCl; DARAwd; Univ Of Missouri; Special Ed.

LOCK, Eugene M; Belgrade Public HS; Belgrade, MN; 8/59 HonRl; NHS; SchPl; Bsktbl; Ftbl; Trk; JCAwd; Vo Teeh; Accounting.

LOCK, Jane A; Carrollton HS; Carrollton, MO; Band; Chr; Chrs; CncrtBnd; NHS; NatlThespSoc; PepBnd; SchMus; SchPl; SctActv; Swmmng; Conservatory Of Music; Music Therapy.

LOCK, M J; Central HS; Glewood, MN; 13/142 HonRl; PepBnd; StuCncl; EdSchPpr; GerCl; Bsktbl; Trk; Chrldr; GAA; PPFtbl; Tech Inst ;floristry.

LOCK, Richard D; Avon HS; Avon, IL; ChrhWkr; SctActv; YthFlsp; 4-H; FFA; Ftbl;.

LOCKAMY, Sheila D; Excelsior Springs West HS; Excelsior Springs, MO; HonRl; JrNHS; NHS; FBLA; FTA; PpCl; SciCl; Chrldr; GAA; Secretarial.

LOCKARD, Catherine E; Herbert Hoover HS; Des Moines, IA; 9/355 Band; ChrhWkr; CncrtBnd; HonRl; MrchBnd; PepBnd; Univ Of Northern Iowa; Accounting.

LOCKARD, Kim M; Clarkston HS; Clarkston, MI; 6/430 Aud/Vis; HonRl; NHS; TchrAde; 4-H; Art School; Art.

LOCKARD, Mark W; West HS; Excelsior Springs, MO; ChrhWkr; HonRl; JrNHS; NHS; OffAde; StuCncl; SecSciCl; Bsbl; Bsktbl; Trk; OptClAwd; Univ Of Mo; Veterinarian.

LOCKE, Hugh W; Noblesville HS; Noblesville, IN; 22/250 ALBoysSt; HonRl; LbryAde; NHS; 4-H; LatCl; MthCl; Glf; Wrstlng; AmLegAwd; Ball State Univ; Computer Sci.

LOCKEN, Colleen K; Aberdeen Central HS; Bath, SD; AFS; ChrhWkr; CncrtBnd; DrlTm; HonRl; NHS; NatlMeritCmnd; Orch; 4-H; Univ Of So Dakota.

LOCKETT, Dean E; Sidney Comm HS; Sidney, IA; 3/32 SecFrshCls; ALBoysSt; Band; HonRl; NHS; SctActv; YthFlsp; MthCl; LetterFtbl; LetterWrstlng; Univ; Math.

LOCKHART, Scott M; Wellington HS; Wellington, IL; 5/21 PresFrshCls; Chrs; HonRl; StuCncl; YthFlsp; PpCl; Bsbl; Bsktbl; Trk; College; Major Study.

LOCKHART, Tom D; Humboldt HS; St Paul, MN; Aud/Vis; Band; CncrtBnd; HonRl; LbryAde; MrchBnd; Orch; PepBnd; SchPl; SctActv; StuCncl; Ftbl; Trade Schl; Accounting.

LOCKHORST, Melodee; West Sioux Community HS; Ireton, IA; 12/82 Chr; Chrs; Chrl; OffAde; SchMus; SchPl; FTA; Northwestern Coll; Business.

LOCKMAN, Donald; Winona R Iii HS; Winona, MO; 2/36 HonRl; PolWkr; SchPl; StuCncl; EdYrBk; FBLA; PpCl; Smsu; Business.

LOCKMAN, Donald H; Winona R Iii HS; Winona, MO; 2/33 ALBoysSt; PresBand; ChrhWkr; HonRl; PresMrchBnd; PresNHS; StuCncl; EdYrBk; FBLA; LetterBsbl; LetterBsktbl; IMSpt; Univ Of Missouri; Business.

LOCKNER, Lori; Polo Community HS; Polo, IL; 22/96 HonRl; JrNHS; NHS; SchAde; FHA; PpCl; Chrldr; GAA; Coll;.

LOCKRIDGE, Judith A; Tri County HS; Jamesport, MO; Chrs; HonRl; SchMus; SchPl; StuCncl; 4-H; FHA; PpCl; LetterChrldr; 4-HAwd; Univ; Liberal Arts.

LOCKWITZ, Todd A; St Joseph HS; St Joseph, MI; Band; CncrtBnd; HonRl; HospAde; MrchBnd; NHS; NatlMeritFnl; NatlMeritCmnd; Orch; PepBnd; SchMus; FDA; MthCl; Michigan State Univ; Medicine.

LOCKWOOD, David M; Manistee HS; Manistee, MI; ALBoysSt; NHS; NatlMeritSF; RptrYrbk; Mi State Univ; Veterinary Medicine.

LOCKWOOD, Denise D; Galien HS; Galien, MI; 9/52 SecSophCls; Band; ChrhWkr; CncrtBnd; DrlTm; HonRl; MrchBnd; NHS; OffAde; SchPl; StuCncl; RptrYrbk; RptrSchPpr; PpCl; Ferris State College; Court Reporter.

LOCKWOOD, Gail J; South Sioux HS; South Sioux City, NE; Chr; HospAde; 4-H; FHA; PpCl; Chrldr; 4-HAwd; Univ; Nurse.

LOCKWOOD, Jolene K; Akron Comm HS; Akron, IA; 10/60 HonRl; StuCncl; EdYrBk; PpCl; LetterBsbl; LetterBsktbl; LetterTrk; Chrldr; GAA; Wit Ia; Secretarial.

LOCKWOOD, Scott A; Elmhurst HS; Fort Wayne, IN; HonRl; SctActv; LetterSocr; Trk; College; Mathematics Or Engineering.

LOCKYEAR, Lisa A; Central HS; Evansville, IN; 47/630 HonRl; NHS; StuCncl; StuGov; PPFtbl; Purdue; Pharmacy.

LODER, John M; Minot HS; Minot, ND; CncrtBnd; HonRl; MrchBnd; NatlFornLg; Orch; PepBnd; StuCncl; JETSAwd; College; Law.

LODGE, Debra K; Trico HS; Willisville, IL; SecJrCls; Band; Chrs; HonRl; PepBnd; SchMus; Twrl; SecFBLA; PresPpCl; Chrldr; 4-HAwd; Univ Of Illinois; Nursing.

LODHOLZ, Leo C; Ankeny Senior HS; Ankeny, IA; Aud/Vis; Chrs; ChrhWkr; CmntyWkr; HonRl; JrNHS; LbryAde; PolWkr; Sacrstn; SchPl; University; Law.

LODINE, James P; Evanston Township HS; Evanston, IL; Chr; Chrl; Chrs; HonRl; NatlMeritFnl; SchMus; Haverford College; Teaching.

LODMELL, Ricki L; Dell Rapids Public HS; Dell Rapids, SD; 4/50 ALBoysSt; Band; HonRl; NHS; PresStuCncl; StuGov; GerCl; LetterFtbl; Univ; Law, Politics.

LODS, Dennis D; Connerville HS; Connersville, IN; HonRl; NHS; GerCl; LetterBsbl; LetterFtbl; IMSpt; College; Engineer.

LOE, Janette C; Welcome Comm HS; Welcome, MN; 2/19 TrsSophCls; Band; Chr; ChrhWkr; HonRl; NHS; Mankato Comm College; Medical Secretary.

LOEB, Geralyn M; St Gertrudes HS; Raleigh, ND; 2/20 Chrs; HonRl; LbryAde; SchPl; SchPpr; College; Social Work.

LOEBEL, John B; St Johns Mil Academy; Wauwatosa, WI; 2/40 PresFrshCls; VPJrCls; VPSrCls; DrlTm; HonRl; NHS; ROTC; StuCncl; LetterBsktbl; LetterFtbl; LetterGlf;.

LOECHEL, Steven C; Topeka West HS; Topeka, KS; NatlMeritSF; KeyCl; GerCl; LatCl; SpnCl; Univ; Medicine.

LOECHELT, Cheryl S; Laconia HS; Fairwater, WI; 8/75 Band; Chr; HonRl; NHS; Vocational School; Radio Broadcaster.

LOEDTKE, Ralph; Mosinee HS; Mosinee, WI; 31/153 Chrs; ChrhWkr; HonRl; NHS; PepBnd; SchMus; SctActv; StuCncl; TchrAde; MthCl; Univ Of Wi; Nurse.

LOEFFLER, Barbara E; Burwell HS; Burwell, NE; 4/37 PresJrCls; ChrhWkr; HonRl; NHS; SchMus; SchPl; StuCncl; TchrAde; Yrbk; FHA; U Of Ne Lincoln; Anthropology.

LOEFFLER, Cheryl L; Owendale Gagetown Area HS; Gagetown, MI; 18/48 Chr; HonRl; HospAde; LbryAde; OffAde; SchPl; PpCl; Lpn Sch; Nursing.

LOEFFLER, Cindy; Washington HS; Brighton, IA; Chrs; HonRl; TchrAde; YthFlsp; FBLA; FTA; SciCl; Bsktbl; Trade Or Bus School; Receptionist.

LOEFFLER, Marnee M; Central HS; La Crosse, WI; 1/536 HonRl; NHS; TchrAde; RptrSchPpr; SpnCl; MthCl; LetterBsktbl; LetterTennis; ChmbCommrsAwd; GovHonPrgAwd; College; Mathematics.

LOEFFLER, Michael T; Mauston Area HS; Mauston, WI; 2/85 Band; CncrtBnd; JrNHS; MrchBnd; NHS; NatlMeritSF; StuCncl; Yrbk; LatCl; LetterTrk; General Motors Inst; Engineering.

LOEFFLER, Michael T; Creighton Prep; Omaha, NE; ChrhWkr; CmntyWkr; NatlFornLg; NHS; SctActv; StuCncl; EdSchPpr; Benedictine College; Law.

LOEFFLER, Richard A; Green Lake HS; Green Lake, WI; 5/42 HonRl; NHS; SchPl; RptrSchPpr; FrCl; LetterWrstlng; College; Electrical Engineer.

LOEFFLER, Susan; Barrington Hs; Barrington Hills, IL; Chr; HonRl; U; Earth Sciences.

LOEHMER, Christine; Beaver Dam HS; Beaver Dam, WI; 25/300 HonRl; PpCl; IMSpt; Coll; Med Tech.

LOEHNIS, Jeffrey R; Northfield HS; Wabash, IN; ALBoysSt; Band; CncrtBnd; HonRl; MrchBnd; NHS; SchMus; RptrSchPpr; SpnCl; MthCl; College.

LOEHRLEIN, Marietta M; Reitz Memorial HS; Evansville, IN; Chrs; HonRl; SctActv; GerCl; SpnCl; Ball State U; Special Education.

LOEPKER, Sandy K; Mater Del HS; Bartelso, IL; 14/200 Band; CncrtBnd; HonRl; MrchBnd; PepBnd; SchPl; College; Accounting.

LOEPKER, Sandy K; Mater Dei HS; Bartelso, IL; 12/189 Band; CncrtBnd; HonRl; MrchBnd; PepBnd; SchMus; Kaskaskia College; Accounting.

LOESCH, Donald John; Illinois Valley Central Hs; Dunlap, IL; Band; ChrhWkr; CncrtBnd; HonRl; MrchBnd; PepBnd; PolWkr; SchPl; SctActv; I S U; Preveterinarian.

LOESCHEN, Jeff L; Titonka Consolidated HS; Woden, IA; FFA; Bsbl; LetterBsktbl; LetterFtbl;.

LOESING, Patti; Rolla HS; Rolla, MO; HonRl; Swmmng; Tennis; Trk; GAA; IMSpt; Nursing School.

LOEWE, Llewellyn E; Freeport Sr HS; Freeport, IL; ALBoysSt; HonRl; NatlFornLg; Orch; StuCncl; PresLatCl; PresMthCl; SciCl; Glf; LetterTennis; Rockford College; Law.

LOEWE, Lorie J; Spalding Public HS; Spalding, NE; 3/15 SecSrCls; Band; Chrs; NHS; SchPl; RptrSchPpr; LetterBsktbl; LetterTrk; LetterChrldr; 4-HAwd; U Of Neb; Home Ec.

LOEWEN, Virgil R; Meade HS; Meade, KS; 1/50 Band; Chr; Chrs; ChrhWkr; CncrtBnd; HonRl; Mdrgl; MrchBnd; PepBnd; College; Professional.

LOFDAHL, Dana A; Les Cheneaux HS; Cedarville, MI; Band; HonRl; VPStuCncl; TchrAde; SptEdSchPpr; LetterBsbl; LetterBsktbl; LetterFtbl; LetterTrk;.

LOFF, Lori J; Richland #44 HS; Wahpeton, ND; 6/27 TrsJrCls; HonRl; StuCncl; RptrYrbk; EdYrBk; RptrSchPpr; FHA; PpCl; LetterTrk; Chrldr; Univ; Home Ec.

LOFGREN, Daniel K; Princeton HS; Princeton, MN; 22/156 Band; Chr; CncrtBnd; HonRl; JrNHS; MrchBnd; NHS; PepBnd; StuCncl; SpnCl; PpCl; Bsbl; Bsktbl; College; Professional.

LOFQUEST, Mary J; Ewing Public HS; Ewing, NE; 2/28 Chrs; ChrhWkr; HonRl; NHS; StuCncl; FFA; LetterBsktbl; LetterTrk; IMSpt; BttyCrckrAwd; Kearney State College.

LOFTIS, Charles G; Carterville Community HS; Carterville, IL; Band; CncrtBnd; HonRl; MrchBnd; SchMus; FrCl; SciCl; Bsktbl; LetterFtbl; LetterTrk; S Illinois Univ; Dentist.

LOFTIS, Nancy L; Seward HS; Seward, NE; Chr; HonRl; ModUN; NatlMeritFnl; NatlMeritSF; SchMus; YthFlsp; RptrYrbk; 4-H; PresPpCl; Swmmng; Trk; Univ; Professional.

LOFTIS, Stephanie; Emil G Hirsch HS; Chicago, IL; 6/250 CmntyWkr; HonRl; JrNHS; LitMag; NHS; SchAde; Northwestern Univ; Journalism.

LOFTNESS, Theodore J; Gibbon Public HS; Gibbon, MN; 3/42 TrsFrshCls; PresSophCls; VPJrCls; VPSrCls; Chr; NHS; RptrYrbk; GerCl; LetterBsbl; LetterFtbl; Letter Trk; St Olaf Coll; Pre Med.

LOFTON, Lamont G; Clayton HS; Claytn, MO; PresJrCls; CmntyWkr; CncrtBnd; NatlMeritSF; Orch; StuCncl; StuGov; LetterBsbl; LetterBsktbl; LetterFtbl;.

LOFTSGARD, Debora D; Park River HS; Park River, ND; Chr; Chrl; Chrs; ChrhWkr; DrlTm; HonRl; 4-H; FHA; Trk; 4-HAwd; Northwestern Col; Medical Work.

LOFTSGARD, Julie K; Park River HS; Park River, ND; 5/63 PresSrCls; Chrs; ChrhWkr; HonRl; NHS; EdYrBk; FHA; FrCl; Concordia College;.

LOGAN, Dennie B; Lindblom Tech HS; Chicago, IL; 26/637 ChrhWkr; HonRl; LbryAde; TchrAde; SpnCl; Business School; Computer Programming.

LOGAN, Linda K; St Francis Borgia HS; Washington, MO; DrlTm; HonRl; NHS; SchPl; RptrYrbk; RptrSchPpr; PpCl; Coll; Nurse.

LOGAN, Lori A; Leola HS; Leola, SD; PresFrshCls; Band; Chrs; HonRl; RptrYrbk; Yrbk; RptrSchPpr; FHA; PpCl; Chrldr; Univ; Law.

LOGAN, Margaret A; Washington HS; Washington, IA; 39/157 HonRl; Iowa St Univ; Vet Med.

LOGAN, Scott; East Alton Wood River Hs; Wood River, IL; HonRl; NHS; StuCncl; LatCl; BauchLmbAwd; U Of Illinois; Medicine.

LOGAN, Steve; Pine River HS; Tustin, MI; Chr; RptrYrbk; RptrSchPpr; IMSpt; Central Michigan Univ; Radio Broadcasting.

LOGAN, William T; Keokuk Sr HS; Keokuk, IA; 1/186 ChrhWkr; HonRl; NatlFornLg; NHS; MthCl; Glf; Swmmng; KiwanAwd; CitAwd; Stanford University.

LOGEMAN, Connie; Metropolis Comm HS; Metropolis, IL; 2/161 ChrhWkr; HonRl; NHS; YthFlsp; 4-H; GerCl; MthCl; PpCl; SciCl; Washington Univ; X Ray Technology.

LOGEMAN, Connie S; Metropolis Comm HS; Metropolis, IL; 2/161 ChrhWkr; HonRl; NHS; YthFlsp; 4-H; GerCl; PpCl; Belleville Area College; Radiologic Tech.

LOGEMAN, Rebecca E; Lincoln Comm HS; Lincoln, IL; Chr; Chrs; ChrhWkr; HonRl; HospAde; NHS; Orch; SchMus; StuCncl; StuGov; Siu; Medical Technologist.

LOGRASSO, Steven J; Oakville Sr HS; St Louis, MO; 48/336 HonRl; College; Medical Doctor.

LOGSDON, Becky S; North Nodaway Rvi; Maryville, MO; 8/35 SecJrCls; SecSrCls; Chrs; CncrtBnd; RptrSchPpr; FHA; LetterBsktbl; LetterTrk; IMSpt; 4-HAwd; Tarkio Clg; Phy Ed.

LOGSDON, Thomas R; Galesburg Sr HS; Galesburg, IL; ChrhWkr; HonRl; RedCrAde; SctActv; FFA; SpnCl; SciCl; Illinois Wesleyan Univ; Minister.

LOGUE, Debbie Jo A; St Elmo HS; St Elmo, IL; 1/56 Band; Chr; ChrhWkr; CmntyWkr; CncrtBnd; HonRl; MrchBnd; YthFlsp; FHA; SpnCl;.

LOGUE, Terri; Blue Mound Hs; Decatur, IL; 1/40 VPSophCls; SecJrCls; ALAGirlsSt; HospAde; PresNHS; SchPl; SecStuCncl; RptrSchPpr; CaptChrldr; EldAwd; Millikin U.

LOH, Gary; Andrean HS; Gary, IN; 3/300 Band; NHS; NatlMeritFnl;.

LOH, Perry; Valley City HS; Valley City, ND; 13/161 PresFrshCls; ALBoysSt; Aud/Vis; Band; CncrtBnd; HonRl; JrNHS; Ftbl; Univ; Engineer.

LOHMAN, Mary E; Marquette Inc HS; West Point, IA; CncrtBnd; LbryAde; MrchBnd; PepBnd; 4-H; PpCl; Trk; College; Nursing.

LOHMAR, Ellen E; Marceline R V HS; Marceline, MO; PresSrCls; ALBoysSt; ALAGirlsSt; ChrhWkr; CmntyWkr; NHS; RptrYrbk; FBLA; DanFAwd; University; Fashion Mdse.

LOHMEYER, Jill R; Melvin Sibley HS; Strawn, IL; SecJrCls; SecSrCls; Band; Chr; HonRl; Quill&Scroll; StuCncl; LetterBsktbl; LetterTrk; GAA; Parkland Clge; Major In Drama.

LOHMEYER, Luke C; Woodstock HS; Woodstock, IL; 7/270 NHS; Ftbl; Trk; University; Veterinarian.

LOHNES, Daniel J; Pekin Community HS; Pekin, IL; 170/800 ChrhWkr; CmntyWkr; HonRl; YthFlsp; University Of Illinois; Veterinarian.

LOHR, Barbara C; Marian HS; Omaha, NE; 7/159 Chrs; HonRl; LitMag; NHS; Quill&Scroll; SchMus; SchPl; Sdlty; EdSchPpr; FrCl; MthCl; Creighton Univ; Journalism.

LOHR, Ed O; Lohrville HS; Lohrville, IA; 5/25 Band; Chr; Chrs; ChrhWkr; CmntyWkr; CncrtBnd; Mdrgl; StuCncl; PresYthFlsp; SptEdSchPpr; Air Force.

LOHRBACH, Jan E; Cal Community HS; Latimer, IA; LetterBand; Chrl; Chrs; CncrtBnd; HonRl; Mdrgl; SchMus; Bsbl; Bsktbl; LetterTrk; LetterChrldr; GAA; IMSpt; College; Music.

LOHRUM, Rick A; Milan Jr Sr HS; Milan, IN; ChrhWkr; CmntyWkr; PresYthFlsp; 4-H; LetterBsbl; LetterFtbl; CchngActv; Indiana Central; Physical Education.

LOHSE, Lori A; Marysville HS; Marysville, KS; Chrs; ChrhWkr; HonRl; FHA; College; Business.

LOHUIS, Beth; Maine South Hs; Park Ridge, IL; Chr; Chrs; ChrhWkr; HonRl; HospAde; NHS; SchMus; StuGov; YthFlsp; Swmmng; U Of Illinois;special Education.

LOIACONO, Christina R; Du Quoin HS; Du Quoin, IL; 2/143 ChrhWkr; DrlTm; HonRl; SchPl; SecStuCncl; RptrSchPpr; EdSchPpr; SchPpr; SecLatCl; PpCl; GAA; DARAwd; Univ Of Ill; Medical Tech.

LOIDA, Russell H; Valle HS; Ste Genevieve, MO; 6/80 TrsFrshCls; ALBoysSt; HonRl; NHS; SchPl; StuCncl; MthCl; PpCl; LetterBsktbl; LetterFtbl; Univ Of Mo; Engi.

LOILAND, Vicki L; Thompson Public HS; Thompson, ND; VPSophCls; Chrs; CmntyWkr; HonRl; SchMus; SchPl; RptrYrbk; 4-H; PpCl; 4-HAwd; E Grand Forks Avti ;moa.

LOISEL, Catherine L; Brussels Community HS; Golden Eagle, IL; PresSrCls; HonRl; HospAde; StuCncl; Yrbk; RptrSchPpr; FHA; Chrldr; College; Dental.

LOJEK, Leslie M; St Alphonsus HS; Detroit, MI; 7/145 HonRl; SchMus; IMSpt; Wayne State Uni; Occupational Therapy.

LOJKUTZ, Debbie A; Madonna HS; Chicago, IL; 13/300 Chr; Chrs; ChrhWkr; HonRl; JA; NHS; SchMus; SchPl; StuCncl; StuGov; Trk; Chrldr; GAA; No Illinois Univ; Dietician.

LOKANC, Mark A; Marist HS; Alsip, IL; CmntyWkr; HonRl; CaptFtbl; IMSpt; Univ; Law.

LOKAY, Mary; Carmel Hs For Girls; Zion, IL; 8 HonRl; NHS; U;science.

LOKEN, Richard B; Velva Public HS; Velva, ND; ALBoysSt; Band; HonRl; NHS; SctActv; RptrYrbk; LetterBsbl; LetterBsktbl; Trk;.

LOKER, Louise A; Highland HS; Highland, IN; HospAde; FrCl; Swmmng; GAA; University; Professional.

LOKKEN, Sylvia D; Pelican Rapids HS; Pelican Rapids, MN; Chr; ChrhWkr; CncrtBnd; HonRl; Mdrgl; PepBnd; SchMus; SchPl; RptrYrbk; FHA; College.

LOKKER, Mary L; Holland Christian HS; Holland, MI; Band; ChrhWkr; CmntyWkr; CncrtBnd; MrchBnd; SpnCl; CaptSwmmng; LetterChrldr; IMSpt; Calvin Col; Special Ed.

LOKOS, Sylvia A; Evergreen Park HS; Evergreen Park, IL; 1/439 Chrs; CmntyWkr; LbryAde; NHS; SctActv; TchrAde; FrCl; MthCl; St Xavier College; Medical.

LOLICH, Karen L; Parkside HS; Jackson, MI; Band; HonRl; IntrClCncl; MrchBnd; Quill&Scroll; StuGov; YthFlsp; RptrSchPpr; SchPpr; PpCl; Mi St Univ; Engineering.

LOMAN, Barbara; Oak Lawn Community Hs; Oak Lawn, IL; 66/686 ChrhWkr; CmntyWkr; HonRl; LbryAde; NatlMeritCmnd; TchrAde; Trade School;cosmetologist.

LOMAS, Elizabeth; Douglas Macarthur HS; Saginaw, MI; 2/289 ChrhWkr; CmntyWkr; HonRl; JrNHS; NHS; RedCrAde; TchrAde; FBLA; FrCl; PpCl; Coll;med.

LOMAS, John L; Mt Vernon HS; Mt Vernon, MO; ChrhWkr; CmntyWkr; HonRl; Pres4-H; SecFFA; ChmbCommrsAwd; 4-HAwd; Univ Of Mo Rolla; Computer Science.

LOMAX, Michael J; Jos A Craig HS; Janesville, WI; 3/472 HonRl; LbryAde; NHS; PolWkr; Quill&Scroll; RptrSchPpr; EdSchPpr; Univ Of Wisconsin; Business Admin.

LOMBARD, Laura D; Northside HS; Ft Wayne, IN; 30/493 VPJrCls; HonRl; JrNHS; NHS; StuCncl; EngCl; VPLatCl; LetterBsktbl; LetterTennis; Chrldr; College.

LOMBARD, Rebecca J; Rushford HS; Rushford, MN; Band; CncrtBnd; HonRl; LbryAde; MrchBnd; Sacrstn; SchPl; SecYthFlsp; FHA;.

LOMBARDO, Michael; St Pius X HS; Kansas City, MO; 52/132 PresFrshCls; Chrs; HonRl; StuCncl; Bsktbl; Ftbl; Glf; Wrstlng; Imkc; Business.

LOMBARDO, Vicki J; St Pius X HS; Kansas City, MO; Chr; HonRl; PolWkr; Twrl; College; Teacher.

LOMELIND, Renee; Deer Creek Mackinaw HS; Mackinaw, IL; 9/56 Chrs; DrlTm; HonRl; Mdrgl; NHS; SchPl; RptrSchPpr;.

LOMEN, Allyn F; Bemidji HS; Solway, MN; 7/343 HonRl; NHS; Bemidji State College; Accounting.

LOMHEIM, Kathy M; Sully Buttes HS; Onida, SD; 1/51 Chr; Chrs; HonRl; NHS; Quill&Scroll; TchrAde; EdYrBk; RptrSchPpr; PpCl; Bsktbl; LetterTrk; AmLegAwd;.

LOMNES, Roxane L; Hudson HS; Hudson, WI; AFS; Band; ChrhWkr; CmntyWkr; CncrtBnd; HonRl; MrchBnd; PepBnd; SchPl; YthFlsp; Business School; Secretarial.

LONAHAN, Robert M; Univ Of Detroit HS; Royal Oak, MI; Aud/Vis; ChrhWkr; HonRl; JrNHS; ModUN; NHS; PolWkr; TchrAde; Yrbk; PpCl; U Of Detroit; Professional.

LONDO, Catherine M; Southwest HS; Green Bay, WI; TrsJrCls; VPSrCls; HonRl; StuCncl; StuGov; SpnCl; PpCl; College; Elem Educ.

LONDO, Donald; Sevastpol HS; Sturgeon Bay, WI; Ftbl; CchngActv; IMSpt; Trade School.

LONDO, Larry J; Ontonagon Area HS; Ontonagon, MI; 3/108 HstSrCls; HonRl; VPNHS; PresTeen; LetterBsktbl; LetterFtbl; LetterTrk; Univ; Professional.

LONDO, Linda; Big Bay De Noc HS; Cooks, MI; NatlFornLg; SchAde; SchPl; StuCncl; TchrAde; FHA; FNA; GerCl; PpCl; GodCntryAwd; College.

LONDON, Julie; De Kalb HS; Dekalb, IL; Chr; Chrs; HonRl; HospAde; StuCncl; FNA; SciCl; Waubonsee Com College; Registered Nurse.

LONDON, Regina A; Madison Sr HS; Madison, IL; 17/117 SecSophCls; TrsJrCls; Chrs; ChrhWkr; CmntyWkr; HonRl; JrNHS; NHS; SctActv; Business School; Stenographer.

LONDON, Shannon; Jeffersonville HS; Jeffersonville, IN; Band; Chr; Chrl; Chrs; SchMus; RptrSchPpr; SchPpr; FHA; PPFtbl;.

LONDRIGAN, William M; Griffin HS; Springfield, IL; 4/180 ChrhWkr; HonRl; TreasNHS; StuCncl; Yrbk; PresKeyCl; DARAwd; Southern Illinois Univ; Medicine.

LONE, Patricia; Charleston HS; Charleston, MO; 20/170 TrsJrCls; Band; Chr; CncrtBnd; HonRl; LbryAde; NHS; VPSrCls; SchPl; StuCncl; StuGov; Southeast Mo State Univ.

LONERGAN, Kevin; Plainfield Hs; Planfield, IL; 40/301 ALBoysSt; PolWkr; SchMus; YthLg; 4-H; KeyCl; LatCl; Bsktbl; Ftbl; LetterTrk; Us Air Force Acad; Lawyer.

LONERGAN, Susan D; Tremont HS; Tremont, IL; 25/78 Chrs; DrlTm; HonRl; LbryAde; 4-H; PpCl; CaptBsktbl; LetterTrk; GAA; PresAwd; Illinois State University; English.

LONESOME, Sheila K; Rosati Kain HS; Northwoods, MO; Chrs; ChrhWkr; HospAde; JA; NatlMeritCmnd; SchMus; SchPl; YthFnd; RptrYrbk; Univ; Psychology.

LONEY, Joyce D; Derham Hall HS; St Paul, MN; 5/127 Univ Of Mn; Business.

LONEY, Virginia L; Traverse City HS; Grawn, MI; Band; 4-H; Ferris St College; Accounting.

LONG, Angela; Waldron HS; Shelbyville, IN; 5/67 Band; Chr; HonRl; LbryAde; MrchBnd; NHS; NatlMeritSch; SchPl; Yrbk; 4-H; Purdue Univ; Fashion Merchandise.

LONG, Ann R; Newman Catholic HS; Dixon, IL; 3/75 TrsJrCls; VPSrCls; Chr; HonRl; NHS; LetterTrk; GAA; AmLegAwd; College; Business.

LONG, Barbara A; Holdrege HS; Holdrege, NE; Chrs; HospAde; PresNatlThespSoc; SchPl; StuCncl; Yrbk; SchPpr; PpCl; Chrldr; St Mary Of The Woods; Communications.

LONG, Brian; Glenwood HS; Glenwood, MN; HonRl; SchPl; StuCncl; TchrAde; RptrSchPpr; Bsktbl; CchngActv; Saint Olaf College; Economics.

LONG, Buddy R; Dadeville HS; Aldrich, MO; Band; Chrs; ChrhWkr; CmntyWkr; HonRl; SchPl; SctActv; Yrbk; SchPpr; FBLA; FFA; LetterBsbl; LetterBsktbl; LetterTrk; Trade School.

LONG, Carol A; Monroe HS; Palmyra, MO; ChrhWkr; CmntyWkr; HospAde; NHS; FHA; College; Nursing.

LONG, Cindy L; West Holt HS; Atkinson, NE; VPJrCls; Chrs; DrlTm; HonRl; SchPl; YthFlsp; Yrbk; LetterBsktbl; LetterTrk; GAA; Coll; Prof.

LONG, Cyril S; Dixon HS; Dixon, IL; 54/333 Band; Chr; Chrs; ChrhWkr; CmntyWkr; CncrtBnd; DrmBgl; HonRl; MrchBnd; NHS; CchngActv; St Olaf College; Tech Eng.

LONG, Daniel J; Bedford HS; Bedford, IN; HonRl; Bsktbl; Trk; College; Forestry.

LONG, Danna K; Oak Park HS; Kansas City, MO; Chr; Chrs; HonRl; Orch; SchMus; SctActv; StuCncl; RptrSchPpr; PpCl; College.

LONG, Darla J; Centerville HS; Centerville, IA; Band; Chr; ChrhWkr; CncrtBnd; HonRl; MrchBnd; RptrYrbk; SchPpr; 4-H; Baptist Bible Clg.

LONG, Darryl R; New Berlin HS; Loami, IL; ALBoysSt; Chr; ChrhWkr; HonRl; NatlMeritCmnd; VPYthFlsp; FFA; LetterBsbl; LetterBsktbl; College; Business.

LONG, Debra; Colfax Comm HS; Colfax, IA; Chr; Chrl; ChrhWkr; HonRl; HospAde; SchAde; SchMus; TchrAde; YthFlsp; Trk; College; Social Work.

LONG, Douglas J; Alma Public HS; Alma, NE; PresFrshCls; TrsSophCls; Band; HonRl; NHS; Bsbl; Bsktbl; CaptFtbl; Trk; AmLegAwd; U Of Ne ;wildlife.

LONG, Eva L; Mt Vernon HS; Mc Cordsville, IN; ChrhWkr; University; Occup Therapist.

LONG, Gayle A; Medford HS; Medford, WI; 25/256 Chr; Chrl; Chrs; HonRl; NHS; SchMus; StuCncl; 4-H; Trk; PresAwd; Uc Denver; Conservation.

LONG, Holly A; Tippecanoe Valley HS; Rochester, IN; 15/145 Chr; HonRl; SchMus; StuCncl; Pres4-H; SpnCl; PpCl; LetterGAA; College; Vocation.

LONG, James H; North County R 1 HS; Desloge, MO; 7/180 HonRl; Mdrgl; NHS; NatlMeritCmnd; StuCncl; Bsktbl; Ftbl; Tennis; CaptTrk; PresAwd; Clge; Medicine.

LONG, James W; Edwardsville HS; Edwardsville, IL; 6/451 Band; HonRl; NHS; PepBnd; Tennis; Clg At Siue;.

LONG, Janice A; Cassville R 4 HS; Cassville, MO; 16/99 ALAGirlsSt; Band; CmntyWkr; CncrtBnd; MrchBnd; NHS; 4-H; FBLA; FHA; FTA; PpCl; Chrldr; Univ Of Missouri; Interior Design.

LONG, Joann F; Ash Grove R 4 HS; Bois D Are, MO; 7/56 HonRl; SchPl; YthFlsp; FBLA; MthCl; PpCl; SciCl; Bsbl; Bus Schl; Clerk.

LONG, John M; Goshen HS; Goshen, IN; 72/284 Chr; ChrhWkr; NatlFornLg; NHS; NatlThespSoc; SchMus; SchPl; StuCncl; YthFlsp; LatCl; Swmmng; Indiana University; Business.

LONG, Keith L; Topeka West HS; Topeka, KS; 24/446 HonRl; LbryAde; StuGov; LatCl; LetterTrk; IMSpt; U Of Tulsa; Eye Surgeon.

LONG, Lori A; Kimball HS; Royal Oak, MI; 124/702 ChrhWkr; CmntyWkr; HonRl; JA; NatlMeritSchl; StuGov; YthFlsp; GerCl; LetterSwmmng; CaptChrldr; Western Mi Univ; Medical Technology.

LONG, Lynette A; Farmington East HS; Farmington, IL; HonRl; LitMag; SchPl; StuGov; TchrAde; RptrSchPpr; FTA; SpnCl; SciCl; Chrldr; Bradley U; Eng.

LONG, Mary J; Manteno HS; Manteno, IL; 5/71 Band; HonRl; NHS; SchPl; StuCncl; FTA; FrCl; SciCl; CaptChrldr; GAA; Coll; Sec Educ.

LONG, Melissa C; United Township HS; E Moline, IL; 31/517 Chr; HonRl; NatlFornLg; NHS; NatlThespSoc; OffAde; SchMus; SchPl; Univ Of Wisc; Social Work.

LONG, Michael A; Cardinal Muench Seminary; Berlin, ND; Band; Chr; Chrs; HonRl; SchPl; SctActv; 4-H; Bsktbl; IMSpt; 4-HAwd; Univ; Secondary Ed.

LONG, Nancy L; Estherville Sr HS; Estherville, IA; 4/166 Band; Chr; Chrs; HonRl; MrchBnd; NatlFornLg; NHS; SchMus; StuCncl; TchrAde; LetterBsktbl; LetterTrk; CchngActv; GAA; College; Teaching.

LONG, Phillip J; Washington Senior HS; Washington, IA; CmntyWkr; HonRl; YthFlsp; FFA; SciCl; LetterBsbl; Bsktbl; LetterFtbl; PresAwd; College; Farming.

LONG, Randy A; Bell City HS; Bloomfield, MO; 2/27 HonRl; PpCl;.

LONG, Richard B; L R HS; Lewellen, NE; SecFrshCls; TrsFrshCls; SptEdYrbk; Bsktbl; Ftbl; Trk; Western Nebraska Tech College; Electronics.

LONG, Roger A; Wichita Hts HS; Wichita, KS; ALBoysSt; Band; CncrtBnd; HonRl; MrchBnd; NatlFornLg; NHS; Orch; SctActv; Friends Univ; Business Adm.

LONG, Ron R; Amherst Public HS; Amherst, NE; 3/26 VPFrshCls; VPSophCls; HonRl; NHS; SchPl; StuCncl; RptrYrbk; RptrSchPpr; SchPpr; LetterBsktbl; LetterFtbl; LetterTrk; College; Liberal Arts.

LONG, Sherryn J; Garden County HS; Oshkosh, NE; 8/42 Chr; ChrhWkr; CmntyWkr; HonRl; NatlMeritSchl; SctActv; YthFlsp; 4-H; Bartlesville Wesleyan; Nursing.

LONG, Stephen D; Warsaw Comm HS; Winona Lake, IN; 2/351 ALBoysSt; HonRl; NatlFornLg; NatlMeritCmnd; YthFlsp; Ftbl; Glf; AmLegAwd; RotaryAwd; Taylor Univ.

LONG, Stephen M; Beardstown HS; Beardstown, IL; HonRl; College; Professional.

LONG, Steve E; Leeds Public HS; Leeds, ND; TrsSophCls; HonRl; SchPl; RptrYrbk; SptEdSchPpr; SciCl; Bsktbl; Ftbl; Trk; College; Professional.

LONG, Sue; Manning Comm HS; Manning, IA; 6/66 CmntyWkr; HonRl; HospAde; MrchBnd; Quill&Scroll; SchMus; Twrl; Yrbk; PpCl; Coll; Professional.

LONG, Susan K; Saline HS; Saline, MI; HonRl; NHS; TchrAde; FHA; SpnCl; PpCl; Chrldr; Clge; Lawyer Or Social Work.

LONG, Susan M; Edwardsville HS; Edwardsville, IL; 4/439 PresBand; Chr; CncrtBnd; HonRl; MrchBnd; NHS; PepBnd; TchrAde; GerCl; College; Professional.

LONG, Teresa L; Milan Cii HS; Milan, MO; HonRl; JrNHS; NHS; SchPl; StuCncl; RptrSchPpr; FHA; LetterBsktbl; LetterTrk; Business School; Secretary.

LONG, Teri L; Mt Pleasant Comm HS; Mt Pleasant, IA; 42/154 Chr; ChrhWkr; CncrtBnd; HonRl; MrchBnd; NHS; PepBnd; YthFlsp; PpCl; Se Comm College; Nurse.

LONG, Walter A; Richland HS; Richland, MO; ALBoysSt; Bsbl; Bsktbl; Trk;.

LONG, Wanda D; St Francis Academy; Joliet, IL; 40/178 Chrs; HonRl; NatlMeritCmnd; St Joseph Hosp; Nursing.

LONG, William; Girard Hs; Girard, IL; 4/65 HonRl; FrCl; PresSciCl; LetterBsktbl; LetterFtbl; LetterGlf; Augustana College; Math.

LONG, William E; Elwood HS; Elwood, KS; VPJrCls; ALBoysSt; Chrs; HonRl; SchPl; StuCncl; SptEdYrbk; LetterFtbl; GodCntryAwd; USJCAwd; College; Cpa.

LONG, William P; Girard HS; Girard, IL; 6/59 HonRl; PresSciCl; LetterFtbl; LetterGlf; Augustane College; Math.

LONG, William S; Central HS; St Joseph, MO; VPFrshCls; CmntyWkr; HonRl; StuCncl; StuGov; MthCl; SciCl; LetterBsktbl; LetterFtbl; LetterTrk; University.

LONGANBACH, Terry A; Portland Public HS; Portland, MI; 1/118 SecTrsJrCls; SecTrsSrCls; Band; HonRl; NHS; PepBnd; PresStuCncl; FrCl; Chrldr; DARAwd; Mi St Univ; Pre Med.

LONGAR, James K; Wentzville HS; Wentzville, MO; Band; ChrhWkr; CmntyWkr; HonRl; JA; Mdrgl; NHS; PepBnd; LetterTrk; LetterWrstlng; Service Academy; Electrical Engineer.

LONGAWA, John; Morton Hs; Hammond, IN; 18/492 Band; CncrtBnd; HonRl; MrchBnd; NHS; Orch; PepBnd; SciCl;.

LONGBONS, Robert; Edwards County Hs; Albion, IL; 17/102 NHS; SchPl; StuCncl; FFA; CaptFtbl; Trk; Southern Illinois U; Forestry.

LONGBOTHAM, Steven M; Cretin HS; St Paul, MN; 2/214 HonRl; NHS; NatlMeritCmnd; ROTC; LetterBsktbl; Socr; LetterTrk; IMSpt; BauchLmbAwd; College Of St Thomas; Law.

LONGDON, Linda; Malden HS; Malden, MO; Band; ChrhWkr; CmntyWkr; JrNHS; NatlMeritFnl; PolWkr; RedCrAde; SancSoc; SctActv; College; Law.

LONGEJANS, Thomas J; Holland Christian HS; Holland, MI; Band; Chr; CncrtBnd; MrchBnd; Orch; PepBnd; SpnCl; Hope College; Fine Arts.

LONGENECKER, Jennifer C; Wawasee HS; N Webster, IN; 29/218 ALAGirlsSt; Chr; ChrhWkr; HonRl; NHS; StuCncl; StuGov; TchrAde; LetterSwmmng; LetterTrk; GAA; Purdue Univ; Teacher.

LONGEST, Kim D; Argenta Oreana HS; Oreana, IL; TrsSrCls; ALAGirlsSt; Band; HonRl; HospAde; NHS; StuCncl; EdYrBk; LetterWrstlng; GAA; DARAwd; College; Professional.

LONGHORST, Gail; Howells Public HS; Howells, NE; ChrhWkr; CmntyWkr; HonRl; NHS; NatlMeritSchl; DanFAwd; GovHonPrgAwd; PresAwd; CitAwd; VoiceDemAwd; College; Professional.

LONGLEY, Ted W; Forest Lake HS; Forest Lake, MN; 11/337 Band; CncrtBnd; HonRl; JrNHS; MrchBnd; NHS; PepBnd; SchMus; U Of Mn; Music.

LONGO, Walter; Jacksonville HS; Jacksonville, IL; 139/363 PresSrCls; StuGov; KiwanAwd; Siv Carbondale ;conservation.

LONGORIA, Mario R; Clark HS; Hammond, IN; 57/260 ALBoysSt; Band; JrNHS; MrchBnd; PepBnd; StuCncl; SpnCl; CaptFtbl; College; Engineering.

LONGSDORF, Larry D; H H Dow HS; Midland, MI; ChrhWkr; CncrtBnd; HonRl; TchrAde; PresYthFlsp; LetterFtbl; LetterTrk; LetterWrstlng; College; Mechanic.

LONGSDORF, Randy J; Plum City HS; Arkansaw, WI; ALBoysSt; ChrhWkr; HonRl; StuCncl; SptEdYrbk; FDA; LetterBsbl; Ftbl; AmLegAwd; VoiceDemAwd; Clge; Journ.

LONGSHORE, Karl; Grayslake Hs; Grayslake, IL; 4/238 VPSrCls; HonRl; NHS; NatlMeritFnl; PresSpnCl; SecPpCl; LetterBsktbl;.

LONGTINE, Terry W; Audubon Public HS; Audubon, MN; Band; Chr; Chrs; CncrtBnd; HonRl; Mdrgl; LetterBsbl; LetterBsktbl; LetterFtbl; LetterTrk; Clge; Elec Tech.

LONIE, Gwendolyn V; Englewood HS; Chicago, IL; Chr; ChrhWkr; CmntyWkr; HonRl; JrNHS; ModUN; TchrAde; YthFlsp; FTA; Trk; Univ Of Northern Illinois.

LONN, Jeffrey; Palatine Hs; Palatine, IL; HonRl; NHS; NatlMeritFnl; U Of Denver; Pre Med.

LONN, Jeffrey D; Palatine HS; Palatine, IL; HonRl; NatlMeritSF; Colorado Coll; Medicine.

LONOWSKI, Diane K; Marian HS; Omaha, NE; HonRl; NatlFornLg; NHS; PolWkr; Quill&Scroll; SchPl; RptrSchPpr; SchPpr; PresLatCl; Univ Of Nebraska; Journalism.

LOOCK, Douglas R; Fremont Sr HS; Fremont, NE; 160/425 LetterBand; Chr; Chrs; CncrtBnd; MrchBnd; PepBnd; SchMus; GerCl; IMSpt; OptClAwd; Univ Of Nebraska; Professional.

LOOKER, Gayle L; Milford HS; Milford, IL; Chrs; ChrhWkr; CncrtBnd; HonRl; HospAde; MrchBnd; PepBnd; YthFlsp; MthCl; Chrldr;.

LOOMIS, Deborah J; Rosedale HS; Bridgeton, IN; 6/60 TreasBand; MrchBnd; ModUN; SchAde; TchrAde; CaptBsktbl; Chrldr; CchngActv; PresGAA; IMSpt; In State Univ; Accountant.

LOOMIS, Donald E; Millington HS; Millington, MI; 4/178 ALBoysSt; Band; HonRl; NHS; NatlMeritSchl; PepBnd; Glf; AmLegAwd; College; Greens Superintendent.

LOOMIS, Donna J; Earlham Community HS; Earlham, IA; Band; Chr; Chrs; ChrhWkr; CmntyWkr; CncrtBnd; DrlTm; MrchBnd; OffAde; PepBnd; Bsktbl; Trk; PPFtbl; Hawkeye Tech; Interior Decorator.

LOOMIS, Frederick S; Pratt HS; Pratt, KS; ALBoysSt; HonRl; SctActv; SpnCl; SciCl; Ftbl; Tennis; IMSpt; Baker University; Architecture.

LOOMIS, Gale M; Ayrshire Consolidated HS; Ayrshire, IA; 3/16 SecTrsJrCls; Band; HonRl; StuCncl; EdYrBk; 4-H; SpnCl; CaptBsktbl; AmLegAwd; PresAwd; Spencer Sch Of Bus; Fashion Advertising.

LOOMIS, John G; St Thomas Aquinas HS; Florissant, MO; ChrhWkr; CtyCnl; Bsktbl; LetterGlf; IMSpt; Univ Of Minnesota; Wildlife Mgmt.

LOOMIS, Lynda A; Stevenson HS; Livonia, MI; ALAGirlsSt; Chr; HospAde; OffAde; SchMus; SchPl; MasAwd; University; Business.

LOOMIS, Malinda; Elmhurst HS; Fort Wayne, IN; AFS; College; Teach Speech & Therapy.

LOOMIS, Rebecca J; Anna Jonesboro C HS; Anna, IL; 1/143 Chrs; ChrhWkr; HonRl; HospAde; LbryAde; NatlFornLg; StuCncl; Yrbk; 4-H; VPFNA; PresSpnCl; Trk; TreasGAA; Univ; Medicine.

LOON, Deanna R; Hanson Ind #40 HS; Alexandria, SD; Band; Chr; Chrs; ChrhWkr; CncrtBnd; HonRl; LbryAde; Mdrgl; MrchBnd; PepBnd; College; Religion.

LOONEY, Darlene M; North Scott Community HS; Long Grove, IA; 15/200 Band; ChrhWkr; HonRl; NHS; FHA; FTA; SpnCl; LetterTrk; GovHonPrgAwd; JAAwd; Trade Schl; Certified Laboratory Assistant.

LOOP, Lee W; Diamond R 4 HS; Carthage, MO; 4/62 ChrhWkr; HonRl; JrNHS; NHS; NatlMeritCmnd; Quill&Scroll; SchAde; SchMus; SchPl; SctActv; LetterBsbl; LetterBsktbl; LetterTrk; College; Computer Science.

LOOPER, Veronica L; Calhoun HS; Kampsville, IL; ChrhWkr; CmntyWkr; HonRl; 4-H; PpCl; Chrldr; LetterGAA; LetterIMSpt; 4-HAwd; Bus Sch.

LOOS, Keith A; Unit Dist 312 HS; Milledgeville, IL; CmntyWkr; HonRl; MrchBnd; SctActv; Pres4-H; FFA; LetterBsbl; LetterBsktbl; LetterFtbl; 4-HAwd; University; Wildlife Biologist.

LOOS, Keith E; Seymour HS; Payson, IL; 1/68 HonRl; FrCl; PpCl; LetterBsbl; LetterBsktbl; LetterTrk; IMSpt; College; Law.

LOOS, Mary E; Chillicothe HS; Chillicothe, MO; 20/179 CmntyWkr; HonRl; HospAde; LbryAde; NHS; NatlMeritCmnd; Quill&Scroll; SchPl; StuCncl; Univ Of Missouri; Medicine.

LOOS, Stephen R; Unity HS; Mendon, IL; 2/79 ChrhWkr; HonRl; Quill&Scroll; SptEdSchPpr; Pres4-H; MthCl; SciCl; KiwanAwd; College; Law.

LOPEMAN, Linda L; Yates City HS; Elmwood, IL; VPSrCls; Band; LbryAde; PepBnd; SchPl; TchrAde; RptrSchPpr; SchPpr; 4-H; SecFHA; FTA; SpnCl; GAA; 4-HAwd; Illinois State University; Home Economics.

LOPEMAN, Nancy; Alden Hebron Hs; Hebron, IL; 4/45 ALAGirlsSt; Band; NHS; SchPl; SctActv; YthFlsp; EdYrBk; LetterTrk; CaptChrldr; PresGAA; College; Communications Theatre.

LOPER, Lynn M; Kingsford HS; Kingsford, MI; 5/168 HonRl; HospAde; JrNHS; NatlFornLg; NHS; TchrAde; RptrYrbk; PresFNA; PpCl; Northern Michigan U; Special Ecucation Teac.

LOPER, Sally A; Wauwatosa East HS; Wauwatosa, WI; Chrs; HonRl; RptrSchPpr; SchPpr; PpCl; College; Veterinarian.

LOPEZ, Allan R; St Marys Of Perpetual HS; Chicago, IL; TrsSrCls; HonRl; StuCncl; SptEdYrbk; SptEdSchPpr; Bsktbl; College; Lawyer.

LOPEZ, Amada M; St Joseph HS; Chicago, IL; 27/103 SecFrshCls; SpnCl; IMSpt; Southwest College.

LOPEZ, Eugene T; St Mary Of Perpetual Help HS; Chicago, IL; Band; CncrtBnd; Yrbk; LetterTrk; Engineering.

LOPEZ, Gloria M; St Procopius HS; Chicago, IL; CtyCnl; HospAde; JrNHS; NHS; RedCrAde; YthFnd; FBLA; FDA; GAA; BttyCrckrAwd; College; Professional.

LOPEZ, Kent V; Valentine HS; Valentine, NE; PresFrshCls; PresSophCls; PresJrCls; HonRl; TchrAde; 4-H; Bsbl; Ftbl; Trk; Wrstlng; College.

LOPEZ, Marguerite M; Morgan Park Academy; Chicago, IL; Chrs; ChrhWkr; ModUN; NHS; SchPl; YthLg; PresSpnCl; CaptChrldr; GAA; DARAwd; Northwestern University.

LOPEZ, Mark; Greenfield Central HS; Greenfield, IN; 38/252 Chr; Chrs; JA; SchMus; SchPl; StuCncl; SpnCl; IMSpt; Iupui; Computer Engineering.

LOPEZ, Rosemarie; Andrean HS; Crown Point, IN; 36/250 HonRl; SecNHS; RptrYrbk; Yrbk; GAA; PPFtbl; St Marys Of Notre Dame; Science.

LOPRESTI, Philip J; Elmwood Park HS; Elmwood Park, IL; 41/280 Band; CncrtBnd; HonRl; Triton College; Journalism.

LOPUS, Paul V; St Mary Of Redford HS; Detroit, MI; 9/165 TrsSrCls; HonRl; JrNHS; NHS; SchPl; StuCncl; StuGov; SptEdYrbk; PpCl; Ftbl; College; Business Education.

LORANCE, Loretta J; Robinson HS; Robinson, IL; 19/180 HonRl; ModUN; SchPl; StuCncl; SchPpr; FHA; FrCl; PpCl; Univ Of Illinois; Psychiatry.

LORANG, Kathleen; Carmel HS; Lake Villa, IL; 107/170 Chr; Chrs; HonRl; SchMus; SchPl; StuCncl; Tennis; Coll; Nrsng.

LORBEER, Lynnette; Hays HS; Hays, KS; 24/188 CmntyWkr; CncrtBnd; HonRl; LbryAde; MrchBnd; PepBnd; SchMus; Twrl; LetterTennis; IMSpt; Tx Christian Univ;med Tech.

LORBETSKE, Laura J; Three Lakes HS; Rhinelander, WI; Band; Chr; CncrtBnd; HonRl; MrchBnd; PepBnd; StuCncl; TchrAde; FTA; SpnCl; College.

LORD, Cindy; Watervliet HS; Watervliet, MI; 10/96 Chr; Chrl; ChrhWkr; HonRl; HospAde; NHS; SpnCl; Andrews Univ;rn.

LORD, David; Perry Community HS; Perry, IA; 4/145 ALBoysSt; Band; ChrhWkr; HonRl; ModUN; Quill&Scroll; Yrbk; RptrSchPpr; FrCl; KiwanAwd; Ia St Univ; Nuclear Pys.

LORD, Howard M; Onalaska HS; Onalaka, WI; CmntyWkr; HonRl; SchAde; Swmmng; Western Wis Tech; Com Prog.

LORD, Melinda M; Washington HS; Washington, IA; Aud/Vis; HonRl; 4-H; FBLA; SpnCl; SciCl; BttyCrckrAwd; 4-HAwd;.

LORD, Patrick K; Waynesville HS; Fort Wood, MO; ChrhWkr; HonRl; LetterFtbl; Sw Mo St Univ; Psych.

LORD, Robert J; Menominee HS; Menominee, MI; HonRl; RptrSchPpr; Ftbl; LetterTennis; LetterWrstlng; CchngActv; IMSpt; College; Communications.

LORDEN, Colette; Qn Of Peace Hs; Chicago, IL; 22/432 HonRl; NHS; Yrbk; FrCl; SpnCl; PpCl; Rosary College;international Finance.

LORE, Mary J; Dearborn HS; Dearborn, MI; 1/547 SecFrshCls; SecJrCls; CmntyWkr; CncrtBnd; DrmMjrt; HonRl; LitMag; NHS; NatlMeritCmnd; Orch; IMSpt; BauchLmbAwd; EldAwd; University Of Michigan; Accounting Law.

LORE, Randall J; Charles City Community HS; Charles City, IA; 10/250 Band; CncrtBnd; HonRl; MrchBnd; Orch; StuCncl; MthCl; LetterBsktbl; LetterFtbl; College; Architect.

LORENAT, Michael J; J S Morton East HS; Cicero, IL; HonRl; NHS; NatlMeritSF; RptrSchPpr; RusCl; BauchLmbAwd; Nw Univ; Md.

LORENC, Barbara A; Joliet Twp West HS; Joliet, IL; 80/487 Chr; Chrs; ChrhWkr; HonRl; HospAde; IntrClCncl; NHS; StuCncl; FrCl; Univ Of Illinois; Liberal Arts.

LORENGER, Bradley P; East HS; Sioux City, IA; VPFrshCls; ChrhWkr; HonRl; StuGov; LetterBsktbl; Ftbl; LetterTrk; IMSpt; University; Professional.

LORENGER, Jeannine M; Immaculata HS; Detroit, MI; 11/106 Chr; HonRl; ModUN; RptrYrbk; SchPpr; Univ Of Detroit; Music.

LORENTZ, Trudy L; Howard Lake Waverly HS; Howard Lake, MN; 5/87 AFS; ChrhWkr; CncrtBnd; HonRl; NatlFornLg; SchPl; TchrAde; RptrSchPpr; LetterVoiceDemAwd; Univ; Professional.

LORENZ, Cheryl; Luther North Hs; Chicago, IL; 4/250 HonRl; NHS; SchPpr; LatCl; Loyal U; Accounting.

LORENZ, Debbie D; Treynor Comm; Treynor, IA; Band; Chr; Chrs; DrlTm; HonRl; SchMus; FHA; Glf; Trk; PPFtbl; Sec.

LORENZ, Rose M; Grant Park HS; Grant Park, IL; 8/87 ChrhWkr; CmntyWkr; HonRl; NHS; StuCncl; TreasYthFlsp; Pres4-H; VPFHA; AmLegAwd; 4-HAwd; College; Nursing.

LORENZ, Sandra L; Chesterton HS; Chesterton, IN; AFS; HonRl; NHS; OffAde; StuGov; 4-H; FBLA; SpnCl; PpCl; GAA; Coll; Medical.

LORENZEN, Cynthia; Chrisman HS; Chrisman, IL; Chr; HonRl; LbryAde; SchPl; SchPpr; 4-H; PpCl; 4-HAwd;.

LORENZEN, Kim M; Denison Community HS; Denison, IA; 2/140 ALBoysSt; Chr; Chrs; ChrhWkr; HonRl; NHS; SchPl; Bsbl; Bsktbl; AmLegAwd; Unif Of Sd ;medical Tech.

LORENZEN, Lowell L; Jasper HS; Sherman, SD; 9/52 PresSrCls; Chr; Chrs; ChrhWkr; HonRl; SchPl; StuCncl; StuGov; PresYthFlsp; 4-H; VPFFA; Bsbl; LetterBsktbl; College; Agriculture.

LORESCH, John D; Sturgeon Bay Sr HS; Sturgeon Bay, WI; 33/150 Chr; HonRl; NHS; SchMus;.

LORET DE MOLA, Karen; Bishop Mc Namara HS; Kankakee, IL; 9/162 ChrhWkr; HonRl; NHS; SchPl; Yrbk; SpnCl; GAA; Ill State; Elementary Education.

LORIMER, Tena M; Wauneta Public HS; Wauneta, NE; CncrtBnd; MrchBnd; PepBnd; SchPl; SctActv; College; Nursing.

LORIMOR, Matthew K; Fremont Mill HS; Thurman, IA; 4/57 Band; CncrtBnd; HonRl; MrchBnd; NHS; NatlThespSoc; OffAde; SchPl; StuCncl; Bsktbl; College; Math.

LORINE, Thomas M; Parkers Prairie HS; Parkers Prairie, MN; Band; Chr; CncrtBnd; HonRl; Yrbk; GerCl; PpCl; CaptBsbl; LetterBsktbl; Ftbl; Devry Inst Of Tech; Electronics.

LORSBACH, Charles W; Calhoun HS; Batchtown, IL; PresSrCls; Chrs; HonRl; RptrYrbk; Yrbk; Southern Illinois University; Accounting.

LORSBACH, Terese E; Calhoun HS; Hardin, IL; HonRl; HospAde; NHS; PolWkr; Chrldr; Trade School; Retailing Merchandising.

LORTON, Cindy J; Calhoun HS; Hardin, IL; ALAGirlsSt; CmntyWkr; HonRl; FHA; FrCl; PpCl; Bsktbl; GAA; School Of Cosmetology; Vocation.

LOS, Jill M; Western Mich Chr HS; Grand Haven, MI; 5/140 Band; Chr; HonRl; NHS; PepBnd; SchPl; StuCncl; SpnCl; MthCl; CitAwd; Calvin Coll; Speec Pathologist.

LOSCH, Ellen K; Belton HS; Richards Gebaur, MO; 10/288 Chr; ChrhWkr; CAP; HonRl; NHS; SchPl; StuCncl; MthCl; PpCl; EldAwd; Central Mo State Univ; Nursing.

LOSE, John C; St Edmond HS; Fort Dodge, IA; 10/117 VPSrCls; HonRl; NHS; PolWkr; StuCncl; StuGov; SpnCl; LetterBsktbl; CaptGlf; LetterTrk; College Of St Thomas; Accounting.

LOSE, Michael; St Edmond HS; Fort Dodge, IA; 5/135 PresSophCls; TrsJrCls; ALBoysSt; CmntyWkr; JrNHS; NHS; StuCncl; SpnCl; Bsktbl; Glf; College Or U.

LOSEFF, Steven M; York Comm HS; Elmhurst, IL; 48/912 HonRl; NHS; NatlThespSoc; SctActv; MthCl; LetterGlf; Univ Of Illinois; Engineering.

LOSEKE, Diane B; Lakeview HS; Columbus, NE; 3/68 PresJrCls; HospAde; Mdrgl; NHS; RptrYrbk; PpCl; Bsktbl; LetterTrk; CaptChrldr; VPGAA; Platte College; Optometrist.

LOSENSKY, Paul E; Niles HS; Niles, MI; Band; ChrhWkr; HonRl; LitMag; NatlMeritFnl; Orch; StuCncl; TchrAde; Yrbk; GodCntryAwd; U Of Chgo; Education Writing.

LOSEY, Debra A; Saline HS; Saline, MI; ALAGirlsSt; Band; CncrtBnd; HonRl; JrNHS; MrchBnd; NHS; NatlMeritCmnd; Orch; StuGov; College; Health Occupations.

LOSEY, Jane L; Jennings Co HS; Scipio, IN; 83/270 Nursing Sch; Rn.

LOSHAW, Kim L; Vanderbilt Area HS; Vanderbilt, MI; 2/21 SecTrsFrshCls; VPSophCls; PresSrCls; HonRl; PresStuCncl; EdYrBk; CaptBsktbl; Trk; Chrldr; IMSpt; College; Veterinarian.

LOSIN, Eric R; Greencatle HS; Greencastle, IN; 79/158 LatCl; SciCl; LetterBsbl; LetterBsktbl; OptClAwd; Ball State Univ; Teaching Phy Ed.

LOSINSKI, Cynthia J; Alpena HS; Alpena, MI; Chr; ChrhWkr; LbryAde; OffAde; LatCl; LetterBsbl; PPFtbl; Western Mi University.

LOSINSKI, Nancy K; St Joseph Academy; Green Bay, WI; 2/150 Chr; Chrs; CmntyWkr; HospAde; NHS; TchrAde; RptrSchPpr; FNA; LatCl; PresAwd; St Norbert College; Pharmacist.

LOSOLE, Jessica A; Lourdes HS; Chicago, IL; 19/304 HonRl; SchMus; SchPl; PresSpnCl; Bus Sch; Secretary.

LOSOLE, Nicholas J; St Rita HS; Chicago, IL; 13/421 NHS; LetterBsbl; LetterFtbl; Trk; Northwestern Univ; Engineer.

LOSSMAN, Pamela J; Maine South HS; Park Ridge, IL; Chr; Chrs; ChrhWkr; CmntyWkr; HonRl; JrNHS; NHS; NatlMeritCmnd; PolWkr; Ill State Univ; Special Education.

LOTH, Karen P; John Marshall HS; Milwaukee, WI; 74/711 ChrhWkr; DrlTm; HonRl; NHS; Orch; SchMus; StuCncl; YthFnd; FBLA; GAA; Univ Of Wi; Business Admn.

LOTHERT, Nancy M; Morton Public HS; Morton, MN; VPJrCls; Chrs; HonRl; SchMus; StuCncl; Yrbk; RptrSchPpr; SchPpr; LetterTrk; LetterChrldr; Worthington Comm College; Teacher.

LOTHROP, Gary F; Crete HS; Crete, NE; Band; HonRl; NHS; SchAde; SctActv; 4-H; FBLA; Bsbl; LetterBsktbl; LetterFtbl; Univ Of Nebraska; Veterinarian.

LOTHSON, Patricia; Dekalb Senior Hs; Dekalb, IL; 71/350 Band; ChrhWkr; CmntyWkr; CncrtBnd; HonRl; MrchBnd; Orch; YthFlsp; FrCl; GAA; University; Education.

LOTHSON, Sandra; Dekalb Senior Hs; Dekalb, IL; Aud/Vis; ChrhWkr; HonRl; SchPpr; 4-H; 4-HAwd; University; Commercial Art.

LOTHSPEICH, Linda M; Shanley HS; Fargo, ND; Chrs; CmntyWkr; HospAde; LitMag; StuCncl; PresFBLA; PpCl; GAA; 4-HAwd; KiwanAwd; Inter Bus Coll; Sec.

LOTSOF, Ruth A; Dekalb HS; Dekalb, IL; VPJrCls; StuCncl; FrCl; Chrldr; IMSpt; PPFtbl; University; Social Work.

LOTSPEICH, Ross A; Hyannis HS; Bingham, NE; CmntyWkr; StuCncl; StuGov; FFA; CaptBsktbl; CaptFtbl; LetterTrk; PresAwd; Vo Tech School; Rancher.

LOTT, David B; Sioux Valley Community HS; Peterson, IA; 6/42 Band; Chr; Chrs; CncrtBnd; Mdrgl; MrchBnd; PepBnd; SchMus; SchPl; RptrYrbk; Wartburg Col; Pro Musician.

LOTT, Monica L; Webberville HS; Webberville, MI; 4/50 CmntyWkr; HonRl; OffAde; SptEdSchPpr; 4-H; PpCl; LetterBsktbl; PresGAA; 4-HAwd; KiwanAwd;.

LOTT, Nancy R; Adrian HS; Adrian, MI; CmntyWkr; HospAde; OffAde; SchMus; StuCncl; PpCl; Trk; GAA; IMSpt; AmLegAwd; Univ;.

LOTTERER, James B; Warsaw HS; Warsaw, MO; Band; Chr; Chrs; NatlThespSoc; SchMus; SchPl; YthFlsp; PpCl; SciCl; Missouri State Univ; Lawyer.

LOTTES, Ann L; Incarnate Word HS; St Louis, MO; Chr; HonRl; NHS; SchMus; SchPl; SpnCl; MthCl; Coll; Pro.

LOTTES, Paul W; Naperville Central HS; Naperville, IL; 56/844 HonRl; NHS; NatlMeritCmnd; Univ Of Illinois; Medicine.

LOTZ, Donald S; Downers Grove North HS; Downers Grove, IL; 24/509 Band; ChrhWkr; CncrtBnd; HonRl; MrchBnd; NHS; Univ Of Illinois; Engineer.

LOTZ, Kathy S; La Grove Comm HS; St Peter, IL; 2/34 Chr; Chrs; HonRl; NHS; SchMus; YthFlsp; FrCl; PpCl; SciCl;.

LOTZ, Morene A; Streator Twp HS; Streator, IL; Chr; Chrs; ChrhWkr; CmntyWkr; HonRl; SchMus;

StuGov; YthFlsp; 4-H; Trk; University; Special Education.

LOUDEN, Janice E; Lisbon HS; Lisbon, ND; Band; Chr; Chrl; Chrs; CncrtBnd; HonRl; MrchBnd; PepBnd; SchPl; StuCncl; PresGerCl; PpCl; College; Liberal Arts.

LOUDEN, Raymond S; Harlem HS; Rockford, IL; HonRl; HospAde; StuCncl; SptEdSchPpr; Bsktbl; Ftbl; Wrstlng; Univ Of Iowa; Medicine.

LOUDEN, Susan; Avon HS; Danville, IN; Chrs; ModUN; NHS; OffAde; SchMus; StuCncl; In Univ; Social Work.

LOUDENBURG, Hollis A; Woodruff HS; Peoria, IL; 47/268 Chr; Chrs; ChrhWkr; CmntyWkr; SchMus; SctActv; TchrAde; YthFlsp; KeyCl; Tennis; I Central Coll.

LOUDENSLAGER, Karen S; Colon HS; Burr Oak, MI; 12/75 VPJrCls; ALAGirlsSt; HonRl; NHS; StuCncl; Pres4-H; KeyCl; Chrldr; BttyCrckrAwd; 4-HAwd; Us Army Med Sch; Rn.

LOUDON, Kelly A; Maria HS; Chicago, IL; CmntyWkr; HospAde; NHS; NatlThespSoc; SchMus; SchPl; SctActv; StuCncl; Chrldr; CchngActv; PresAwd; College; Special Education.

LOUGH, Jane M; Lakeshore HS; Saint Joseph, MI; Chr; ChrhWkr; CmntyWkr; HonRl; PpCl; Bsktbl; GAA; College; Psychology.

LOUGH, Mark V; Salem Sr HS; Salem, MO; HonRl; SptEdYrbk; SptEdSchPpr; PpCl; SciCl; Bsktbl; LetterFtbl; LetterGlf; Southwest Mo St Univ; Math.

LOUGHARY, Sandra A; Valley R 6 HS; Caledonia, MO; HonRl; NHS; SctActv; PresStuCncl; PresYthFlsp; SchPpr; FHA; PpCl; C Of Mineral Area; Nurse.

LOUGHRAN, Luther N; Eastern HS; Pekin, IN; VPJrCls; PresSrCls; Band; HonRl; LitMag; RptrYrbk; SptEdYrbk; GovHonPrgAwd; Western Ky Univ; Journalism Teaching.

LOUIE, Kenneth T; Lane Tech HS; Chicago, IL; 21/1200 ALBoysSt; LbryAde; NHS; ROTC; StuCncl; StuGov; TchrAde; SecKeyCl; AmLegAwd; DARAwd; Northwestern Univ; Medicine.

LOUIS, Roberta L; New Trier East HS; Glencoe, IL; 23/847 HonRl; NatlFornLg; LetterTennis; University; Lawyer.

LOUND, Diane O; Holland HS; Holland, MI; ChrhWkr; CtyCnl; CmntyWkr; HonRl; JrNHS; NHS; NatlMeritSF; YthFlsp; FrCl; PpCl; College; Professional Education.

LOUNSBURY, Lola J; Huron HS; Huron, SD; Chr; Chrs; ChrhWkr; CmntyWkr; OffAde; SchMus; RptrSchPpr; SchPpr; Trk; LetterGAA; Clge; Elem Educ.

LOUPEE, Burton J; Culver Military Acad; Augusta, KS; LitMag; NatlMeritCmnd; ROTC; SchPpr; LetterSocr;.

LOUPEE, Rhonda L; Williamsburg HS; Williamsburg, IA; Band; CncrtBnd; LbryAde; MrchBnd; Orch; PepBnd; Quill&Scroll; SchPl; SctActv; YthFlsp; RptrSchPpr; 4-H; FHA; Glf; Kirkwood Comm College; Accounting.

LOUSHIN, Gerald P; Memorial HS; Ely, MN; 27/125 HonRl; Vermillion Jr College; Electronics.

LOUTSCH, Julie; St Marys HS; Remsen, IA; Chrs; HonRl; SchMus; SchPl; 4-H; SecTrsSophCls; Col.

LOUX, James R; Clarion Community HS; Clarion, IA; 8/93 HonRl; NatlMeritCmnd; SchPl; RptrSchPpr; SchPpr; FTA; Luther College Decorah; Psychology.

LOVALD, Frederick G; Cottonwood HS; Marshall, MN; HonRl; Yrbk; SchPpr; Bsktbl; IMSpt; Vo Tech; Accountant.

LOVE, Barbara A; Dixon HS; Dixon, IL; 52/333 PresFrshCls; SecChr; HonRl; JrNHS; NHS; NatlThespSoc; SchMus; StuCncl; RptrSchPpr; Bsbl; Chrldr; GAA; College; Medicine.

LOVE, Brett M; Winfield HS; Winfield, KS; ChrhWkr; StuCncl; TchrAde; Ftbl; Kansas St Univ; Wildlife Biology.

LOVE, David R; Memorial HS; Joplin, MO; HonRl; ModUN; NatlFornLg; NatlThespSoc; SchPl; StuCncl; YthFlsp; Ftbl; Kansas State Univ; Milling Science.

LOVE, Debra K; Goshen HS; Goshen, IN; HonRl; HospAde; OffAde; PresFNA; SpnCl; College; Registered Nurse.

LOVE, Floresia; Dunbar Voc HS; Chicago, IL; 10/468 Band; HonRl; TreasNHS; StuCncl; TchrAde; RptrSchPpr; FBLA; SpnCl; MthCl; SecSciCl; GAA; Bradley Univ; Industrial Eng.

LOVE, James; East HS; Des Moines, IA; HonRl; Bsktbl; Ftbl; Trk; Iowa St Univ; Vet.

LOVE, Jonathan M; Lake Forest Academy; Glencoe, IL; HonRl; PolWkr; SchAde; StuGov; Ftbl; College; History.

LOVE, Linda; Laplata R Ii Hs; Laplata, MO; 3/41 Band; ChrhWkr; HonRl; NHS; SchPl; Yrbk; SchPpr; FHA; PpCl; Bsktbl;.

LOVE, Michael R; North Callaway HS; Auxvasse, MO; 7/77 VPSophCls; ALBoysSt; ChrhWkr; HonRl; StuCncl; RptrYrbk; Yrbk; FrCl; SpnCl; CaptBsktbl; Trk; LionAwd; CitAwd; College.

LOVE, Paul R; Wylie E Groves HS; Birmingham, MI; 6/675 Aud/Vis; Band; CmntyWkr; HonRl; JrNHS; NHS; NatlMeritSF; TchrAde; FrCl; IMSpt; U Of Mi; Medicine.

LOVE, Scott A; Fisher Public HS; Euclid, MN; VPFrshCls; VPJrCls; Band; ChrhWkr; CncrtBnd; YthFlsp; 4-H; LetterFtbl; 4-HAwd; PresAwd; College; Agriculture.

LOVE, Steven M; Adrian HS; Adrian, MI; NHS; StuCncl; Ferris State College; Pharmacy.

LOVEALL, Julie E; Oak Park HS; Gladstone, MO; ALAGirlsSt; HonRl; NHS; SctActv; TchrAde; GAA; College; Technology.

LOVEALL, Marian L; Monrovia HS; Monrovia, IN; 2/104 TrsFrshCls; TrsSophCls; TrsJrCls; TrsSrCls; ALAGirlsSt; ChrhWkr; CncrtBnd; HonRl; MrchBnd; NHS; Indiana Coll; Medical.

LOVEALL, Rick D; Lone Jack HS; Lone Jack, MO; 7/50 HonRl; JrNHS; NHS; StuCncl; PpCl; LetterBsbl; LetterBsktbl; LetterFtbl; LetterTrk; LetterWrstlng; Ar U; Electrician.

LOVEGROVE, Sandra; Frankfort HS; Elherta, MI; 3/62 Band; Chrs; HonRl; SchPl; TchrAde; YthFlsp; 4-H; KiwanAwd;.

LOVEJOY, Earlene J; Bladen Public HS; Inavale, NE; Band; Chrs; HonRl; SchPl; PpCl; Bsbl; LetterTrk; Chrldr; 4-HAwd; College.

LOVEJOY, Gayle M; Greenway HS; Coleraine, MN; Chr; HonRl; SchPl; FrCl; PpCl; Law School; Lawyer.

LOVEKAMP, Scott A; Triopia Jr Sr HS; Arenzville, IL; 3/50 ChrhWkr; HonRl; NHS; StuCncl; 4-H; LetterBsktbl; LetterFtbl; LetterTrk; CchngActv; Southern Il Univ; Teacher.

LOVEKAMP, Susan D; Triopia HS; Arenzville, IL; HonRl; HospAde; SecYthFlsp; 4-H; LetterTrk; Chrldr; IMSpt; AmLegAwd; 4-HAwd; JAAwd; College; Nursing.

LOVELACE, Robert S; Adrian R 3 HS; Adrian, MO; 22/55 StuCncl; Bsktbl; Ftbl; Trk; IMSpt;.

LOVELACE, Sarah E; Maine Twp South HS; Park Ridge, IL; HonRl; NatlThespSoc; Orch; PolWkr; SchMus; FrCl; AmLegAwd; Lawrence U; Pro Musician.

LOVELACE, Vera L; Dekalb R Iv; De Kalb, MO; PresJrCls; ChrhWkr; HonRl; JrNHS; SecStuCncl; PpCl; CaptChrldr; Bible Coll; Vocational.

LOVELAND, Jane A; Canton HS; Canton, SD; 10/95 Band; Chr; CncrtBnd; HonRl; MrchBnd; PepBnd; RptrYrbk; PresRptrSchPpr; LetterTrk; IMSpt; Creighton Univ; Law.

LOVELAND, Richard B; Loveland Hurst HS; Ann Arbor, MI; 26/206 Band; YthFlsp; KeyCl; SpnCl; LetterFtbl; LetterTrk; Wrstlng; Adrian College; Family Business.

LOVELASS, Patricia L; Watseka Comm HS; Watseka, IL; Band; CncrtBnd; MrchBnd; PepBnd; SchMus; SpnCl; Trk; VPGAA; JCAwd; Coll; Accounting.

LOVELL, David L; Southern Wells HS; Marion, IN; 22/97 PresSrCls; ALBoysSt; Chr; ChrhWkr; HonRl; StuCncl; Bsktbl; LetterTrk; PresAwd; Trade School; Professional.

LOVELL, James P; Clear Lake HS; Clear Lake, IA; 2/141 AFS; ALBoysSt; Chr; Chrs; CncrtBnd; HonRl; NHS; PepBnd; StuCncl; Bsktbl; Luther College; Pre Med.

LOVELL, Kimberli; United Township HS; Suluis, IL; 53/686 Aud/Vis; Chr; HonRl; HospAde; Mdrgl; Nursing School; Rn.

LOVELL, Nancy E; Forman HS; Manito, IL; 16/46 PresSophCls; Chrl; Chrs; HonRl; SchMus; StuCncl; RptrYrbk; EdSchPpr; Bsktbl; Trk; Chrldr; College; Journalism.

LOVELLETTE, Greg D; West HS; N Aurora, IL; 147/625 SctActv; Community College; Science.

LOVELY, Kirk J; Mendel Catholic Prep; Chicago, IL; 19/191 Aud/Vis; ChrhWkr; CmntyWkr; HonRl; IntrClCncl; LbryAde; OffAde; SchAde; SctActv; Teen; LetterFtbl; Trk; IMSpt; CitAwd; Southern Ill Univ; Aviation.

LOVEN, Keith H; Valley City HS; Valley City, ND; 1/160 TrsJrCls; PresSrCls; HonRl; PresNHS; StuCncl; SciCl; LetterFtbl; LetterTrk; IMSpt; KiwanAwd; University Of North Dakota; Medicine.

LOVESTRAND, Daniel J; Spencer HS; Spencer, IA; Chr; HonRl; Mdrgl; NHS; NatlMeritSF; SchMus; Wrstlng; College.

LOVETT, Richard L; Redfield HS; Redfield, SD; AFS; StuCncl; Bsktbl; Ftbl; LetterTrk; College; Liberal Arts.

LOVETT, Stephanie B; H H Dowtts HS; Midland, MI; HonRl; NHS; StuGov; Mich St U; Envir Design.

LOVEWELL, Rhonda S; Courtland HS; Courtland, KS; 6/22 Band; CncrtBnd; HonRl; MrchBnd; SchPl; YthFlsp; Yrbk; PpCl; LetterBsktbl; LetterTrk; Junior College; Physical Education.

LOVGREN, Burton K; River Valley HS; Lakeside, MI; HonRl; RedCrAde; SctActv; Bsktbl; Ftbl; College; Business.

LOVGREN, Janet; Crivitz HS; Crivitz, WI; SecTrsSophCls; PresJrCls; Chrs; ChrhWkr; HonRl; NatlFornLg; NHS; SchMus; SchPl; Univ Of Wis Milwaukee; Theatre.

LOVGREN, Karin; Crivitz HS; Crivitz, WI; Band; ChrhWkr; CncrtBnd; HonRl; MrchBnd; PepBnd; Vocational School; Vocation.

LOVIK, Mark; Kennedy HS; Cedar Rapids, IA; Band; ChrhWkr; CncrtBnd; HospAde; MrchBnd; Orch; PepBnd; SchMus; SctActv; Coll; Music Or Physics.

LOVITT, Cindy L; Concord HS; Concord, MI; 7/69 HonRl; NHS; TchrAde; RptrYrbk; RptrSchPpr; CaptBsktbl; Jackson Comm College; Child Services.

LOVITT, Max A; Stapleton Public HS; Stapleton, NE; 7/30 ALBoysSt; Chr; HonRl; NHS; VPStuCncl; 4-H; Bsbl; LetterBsktbl; CaptFtbl; LetterTrk; AmLegAwd; 4-HAwd; National College; Agriculture.

LOVITT, Sue J; Ida HS; Temperance, MI; Chr; ChrhWkr; CmntyWkr; HonRl; HospAde; LbryAde; NatlThespSoc; PolWkr; SchAde; SchMus;.

LOVRIEN, Keith; Clarksville Comm HS; Clarksville, IA; VPJrCls; HonRl; RptrYrbk; RptrSchPpr; PpCl; Ia State Univ.

LOVRINIC, Joseph; George Rogers Clark HS; Hammond, IN; 44 ALBoysSt; Band; CncrtBnd; MrchBnd; NHS; Quill&Scroll; RptrSchPpr; EdSchPpr; GerCl; College; Journalism.

LOW, Tammy D; Jefferson County North HS; Nortonville, KS; CaptDrlTm; HonRl; MrchBnd; SchMus; SchPl; TchrAde; EdYrBk; EdSchPpr; SecFHA; SecPpCl; Job.

LOWDER, Mark W; Scottsbluff HS; Scottsbluff, NE; Bsbl; Ftbl; Trk; IMSpt; U Of Neb; Architect.

LOWE, Andy M; Crocker HS; Crocker, MO; 5/62 NHS; CaptBsbl; CaptBsktbl; Glf; Swmmng; Tennis; VoiceDemAwd; College; Business.

LOWE, David J; Bonner Springs HS; Bonner Springs, KS; TchrAde; SciCl; Bsktbl; Trk; Junior College; Data Processing.

LOWE, David W; Sacred Heart HS; Detroit, MI; HonRl; SctActv; RptrSchPpr; Wayne State; Law.

LOWE, Greg W; T L Handy HS; Bay City, MI; 20/361 Band; CtyCnl; HonRl; LitMag; MrchBnd; NHS; PepBnd; SchMus; GerCl; Univ; Bs In Science For Dentistry.

LOWE, Kathleen M; Jefferson HS; Rockford, IL; 35/360 Band; CncrtBnd; HonRl; MrchBnd; OffAde; PepBnd; SctActv; TchrAde; Nursing School; Nursing.

LOWE, Kimberlyn J; Normandy HS; St Louis, MO; Band; Chrs; CncrtBnd; HonRl; MrchBnd; TchrAde; FrCl; IMSpt; Clg; Elem/special Educ.

LOWE, Lawrence; Ft Scott HS; Fort Scott, KS; 48/167 PresFrshCls; ALBoysSt; HonRl; YthFlsp; PpCl; Bsbl; Univ Of Ia; Coaching.

LOWE, Melinda; Liberty Senior HS; Liberty, MO; 22/297 AFS; HonRl; HospAde; JrNHS; NHS; OffAde; Southwest Mo State Univ; Landscape Architec.

LOWE, Peggy A; Lincoln Northeast HS; Lincoln, NE; 17/556 Chr; HonRl; Orch; SchMus; 4-H; PpCl; LetterTrk; Chrldr; GAA; College; Nursing.

LOWE, Ricky R; Pierce City R 6 HS; Wentworth, MO; 16/60 HonRl; NHS; TchrAde; FFA; SciCl; Bsktbl; Ftbl; Trk; CchngActv; USJCAwd; Coll.

LOWE, Russell E; Waupaca HS; Waupaca, WI; 14/180 PresFrshCls; PresSophCls; PresSrCls; Chr; HonRl; Mdrgl; SchMus; StuCncl; StuGov; PresKeyCl; Law.

LOWE, Sally A; Witt Public HS; Witt, IL; VPJrCls; Chrs; HonRl; OffAde; SchMus; SchPl; StuCncl; Yrbk; SchPpr; 4-H; FHA; Chrldr; College.

LOWE, Susan; New Palestine HS; New Palestine, IN; 25/165 Band; CncrtBnd; HonRl; MrchBnd; OffAde; StuCncl; RptrYrbk; Yrbk; IMSpt; PPFtbl; Professional.

LOWE, Teresa A; Senath H'ville HS; Kennett, MO; Chrs; HonRl; LbryAde; NHS; SchPl; FHA; PpCl; SciCl; Chrldr; Nursing Sch; Nurse.

LOWE, Teresa A; Senath Hornersville HS; Kennett, MO; Chrs; HonRl; LbryAde; NHS; SchMus; SchPpr; FHA; PpCl; Chrldr; BttyCrckrAwd; Army; College.

LOWELL, Debbie A; Watseka Community HS; Watseka, IL; HonRl; HospAde; GAA; Kcc; Registered Nurse.

LOWELL, Gregory E; Northridge HS; Bristol, IN; Chr; HonRl; 4-H; 4-HAwd; CitAwd; College.

LOWELL, Kirk G; Concordia HS; Concordia, KS; VPSrCls; ALBoysSt; Aud/Vis; CmntyWkr; HonRl; LbryAde; SchPl; StuCncl; SciCl; Ftbl; Trk; Wrstlng; Colege Or Trade; Professional.

LOWENTHAL, Mark S; Oak Park HS; Oak Park, MI; 9/480 HonRl; EdYrBk; EdSchPpr; RotaryAwd; Univ Of Mich; Social Sci.

LOWER, Barbara C; Ladywood St Agnes HS; Indianapolis, IN; 7/92 Chr; Chrs; ChrhWkr; HonRl; Mdrgl; NatlFornLg; SchMus; StuCncl; StuGov; LatCl; University; Law.

LOWER, Debra L; Rich Central HS; C C Hills, IL; 78/400 VPBand; DrlTm; HonRl; NatlThespSoc; SchAde; SchPl; SctActv; TchrAde; Bsktbl; GAA; College; Doctor.

LOWER, Rayann; Guthrie Center HS; Guthrie Center, IA; Band; Chr; CncrtBnd; HonRl; LbryAde; MrchBnd; SchPl; YthFlsp; RptrSchPpr; EdSchPpr; Glf; College; Vocational.

LOWERY, Carol S; M V K Comm HS; Mazon, IL; 7/43 ChrhWkr; CncrtBnd; NHS; Yrbk; 4-H; FFA; SecChrldr; AmLegAwd; 4-HAwd; Jr College; Ag Business.

LOWERY, Connie F; Davenport HS; Oak, NE; TreasBand; Chr; ChrhWkr; CmntyWkr; CncrtBnd; MrchBnd; PepBnd; SchMus; LetterTrk; 4-HAwd; Vocational School; Data Processing.

LOWERY, Debra L; Morton HS; Morton, IL; 11/287 HonRl; NHS; RptrSchPpr; PpCl; Illinois Central College; Nursing.

LOWERY, Kathy I; Olympia HS; Waynesville, IL; PresChrhWkr; HospAde; SchMus; 4-H; FNA; Trk; Chrldr; GAA; 4-HAwd; PresAwd; College; Ba In Nursing.

LOWERY, Marc H; Plainfield HS; Plainfield, IL; 25/297 Band; CncrtBnd; HonRl; MrchBnd; Orch; PepBnd; SchMus; MthCl; PpCl; U Of I; Music.

LOWING, Bruce A; Jenison Public HS; Jenison, MI; 51/262 ALAGirlsSt; NatlMeritFnl; SchPl; SctActv; SecJrCls; LetterTennis; IMSpt; AmLegAwd; Mich Tech U; Civil Eng.

LOWING, Thomas B; Coopersville HS; Coopersville, MI; 1/163 PresSrCls; NHS; NatlMeritCmnd; GerCl; LetterFtbl; LetterTrk; CaptWrstlng; Univ Of Michigan; Architect.

LOWNEY, Robert J; Houghton HS; Houghton, MI; PresFrshCls; ALBoysSt; Band; Chrs; CncrtBnd; HonRl; MrchBnd; NatlMeritSF; PepBnd; CivCl; Central Mich Univ; Music Ed.

LOWRANCE, June L; Assumption Jr Sr HS; Assumption, IL; 10/35 Chrs; ChrhWkr; HonRl; LbryAde; SchPl; Yrbk; SchPpr; 4-H; FHA; FrCl; GAA; Lakeland Jr College; Liberal Arts.

LOWRY, Brian R; Marquette HS; Milwaukee, WI; 5/238 Chrs; CmntyWkr; HonRl; LbryAde; OffAde; SchMus; SchPl; StuCncl; StuGov; HstSophCls; Univ Of Dayton; Special Education.

LOWRY, Karen; Brighton HS; Brighton, MI; HonRl; NHS; Quill&Scroll; SchPl; StuCncl; RptrSchPpr; SchPpr; GAA; College; General Practioner.

LOWRY, Ladona L; Maysville HS; Maysville, MO; 18/57 Chrs; HonRl; HospAde; NatlMeritSchl; TchrAde; Yrbk; FHA; SpnCl; College; Nursing.

LOWRY, Michael; Cleveland HS; St Louis, MO; 30/546 ALBoysSt; Aud/Vis; CmntyWkr; HonRl; TchrAde; SchPpr; AmLegAwd; Univ Of Ks; Architectural Engineering.

LOWRY, Patricia; Culver Community HS; Culver, IN; 1/120 ALAGirlsSt; ChrhWkr; HonRl; NHS; FrCl; PpCl; Ind Univ; Business Education.

LOWRY, Peggy; Memorial HS; Eau Claire, WI; CmntyWkr; OffAde; YthFlsp; RptrYrbk; PpCl; Bsktbl; Chrldr; IMSpt;.

LOY, Debra A; Heritage Christian HS; Indianapolis, IN; 10/23 VPSrCls; ChrhWkr; HonRl; SchMus; SchPl; TchrAde; SchPpr; PpCl; Chrldr; ChmbCommrsAwd; College;professional.

LOY, Erik R; Parker HS; Janesville, WI; 11/598 Chr; Chrs; HonRl; Mdrgl; Orch; Quill&Scroll; SchMus; RptrSchPpr; DARAwd; VoiceDemAwd; College; Law Journalism.

LOY, Jan M; Valley Falls HS; Valley Falls, KS; Band; Chrs; ChrhWkr; DrlTm; HonRl; MrchBnd; PepBnd; TchrAde; 4-H; PpCl; College; Sociology.

LOY, Kelly; Northwestern HS; Good Hope, IL; HonRl; SpnCl; Bsktbl; Ftbl; Glf; College; Pe Major.

LOY, Steven E; Bloomington HS; Bloomington, IL; 8/391 ALBoysSt; Chr; CncrtBnd; HonRl; NHS; MthCl; LetterSwmmng; Ill State Univ; Accounting.

LOY, Timothy S; Kinmundy Alma HS; Kinmundy, IL; PresFrshCls; ChrhWkr; HonRl; NHS; SctActv; StuCncl; YthFlsp; Bsbl; Bsktbl; College; Physical Education.

LOYD, Jacqueline; N Division HS; Milwaukee, WI; VPSrCls; ChrhWkr; CmntyWkr; DrlTm; HonRl; SctActv; StuCncl; Yrbk; FNA; MthCl; Marquette Univ; Engineering.

LOYD, Karen L; Southern Boone R 1 HS; Ashland, MO; HonRl; IntrClCncl; LbryAde; Chrs; SchPl; StuCncl; YthFlsp; 4-H; FHA; Chrldr; Central Mo St Univ; Home Ec.

LOYD, Rebecca J; Brazil HS; Brazil, IN; ChrhWkr; HospAde; SchMus; StuCncl; PresYthFlsp; FHA; PpCl;.

LOZA, Christopher L; Northwestern Military Academy; Chicago, IL; DrlTm; DrmBgl; HonRl; MrchBnd; ROTC; SctActv; StuGov; LetterTennis; Trk; LetterWrstlng; Wentworth Military Academy; Military Pilot.

LOZANO, Mary M; Bowen HS; Chicago, IL; 4/590 HonRl; StuCncl; RptrYrbk; FDA; SpnCl; MthCl; Bsktbl; CaptSwmmng; Tennis; ChmnGAA; Ill Inst Of Tech; Chem Entr.

LOZANO, Nancy; George Rogers Clark HS; Whiting, IN; 13/260 Chr; NHS; StuCncl; Yrbk; SpnCl; Indiana Univ; Psychiatry Eng.

LOZIER, Cheryl A; Farmington East HS; Farmington, IL; SecSrCls; Chrs; CncrtBnd; HonRl; HospAde; MrchBnd; SchMus; YthFlsp; RptrYrbk; GAA; IMSpt; St Francis Schl; Nursing.

LOZIER, James R; Maconaquah HS; Peru, IN; CncrtBnd; HonRl; MrchBnd; Bsbl; Bsktbl; Trk; IMSpt; Erade Sch; Vocation.

LOZIER, Jay N; North Central HS; Indianapolis, IN; ChrhWkr; CncrtBnd; HonRl; MrchBnd; In Univ; Medicine.

LUALLEN, Louann; Ladywood HS; Livonia, MI; Chr; CmntyWkr; HonRl; JA; LitMag; PolWkr; SctActv; StuCncl; PresFNA; IMSpt; Henry Ford Hosp Sch Of Nurse; Nursing.

LUBBEN, Gregg W; Holland Chr HS; Holland, MI; Aud/Vis; FBLA; SpnCl; SciCl; LetterTrk; IMSpt; Davenport Business Sch; Accountant.

LUBBERS, Patricia J; Hamilton HS; Hamilton, MI; 1/125 ChrhWkr; HonRl; Mdrgl; NHS; NatlMeritSF; TchrAde; RptrSchPpr; GerCl; Chrldr; Hope College; Elem Teaching.

LUBBERS, Patricia L; Grinnell HS; Grinnell, KS; VPJrCls; HonRl; MrchBnd; OffAde; PepBnd; StuCncl; RptrYrbk; 4-H; PpCl; Bsktbl; Garden City Comm Jr Col; Business.

LUBBERSTEDT, Leann; Allen HS; Dixon, NE; 10/36 SecFrshCls; SecJrCls; Chr; ChrhWkr; HonRl; StuCncl; StuGov; RptrYrbk; RptrSchPpr; Chrldr; Florist And Techhology School.

LUBBERT, Richard G; Port Huron HS; Port Huron, MI; 83/390 TreasYthFlsp; LetterFtbl; Dana College; Broadcasting.

LUBECK, Joy B; Weyauwega HS; Pine River, WI; 9/85 TrsFrshCls; SecSophCls; TrsJrCls; PresSrCls; Chr; ChrhWkr; HonRl; NHS; SecTrsFrshCls; SpnCl; University Wisconsin; Nurse.

LUBENOW, Gary H; Wayne Memorial HS; Wayne, MI; ChrhWkr; CncrtBnd; HonRl; JrNHS; MrchBnd; NHS; NatlMeritSchl; PepBnd; FrCl; Tennis; College; Pastor.

LUBIENSKI, Mark B; Catholic Central HS; Dearborn Hgts, MI; PresFrshCls; ChrhWkr; HonRl; NHS; StuGov; LetterFtbl; CaptTennis; Wrstlng; IMSpt; College; Law.

LUBINSKI, James M; Palatine HS; Palatine, IL; 76/440 HonRl; NHS; LetterBsbl; LetterFtbl; GovHonPrgAwd; College; Accountant.

LUBISCHER, Carol F; Ryan HS; Omaha, NE; Chrs; NHS; SchMus; StuCncl; TchrAde; Yrbk; PpCl; Chrldr; College; Law.

LUBKEMAN, David L; Chewoa HS; Chewoa, IL; 1/57 Chrs; NHS; NatlMeritCmnd; SchMus; SchPl; StuCncl; Purdue Univ; Engineering.

LUBY, James J; Edgewood HS; Madison, WI; Chrl; CmntyWkr; HonRl; JrNHS; LitMag; NHS; NatlMeritSF; PolWkr; StuGov; TchrAde; Trk; Univ; Agricultural Research.

LUBY, Janet; St Scholastica Hs; Skokie, IL; 50/230 HospAde; NatlMeritCmnd; SchPl; StuCncl; StuGov; TchrAde; RptrSchPpr; PpCl; College; Mathematics Major.

LUBY, Julie M; Edgewood HS; Madison, WI; 1/138 SecSophCls; SecJrCls; Chrs; HonRl; NHS; SecStuCncl; PpCl; LetterBsktbl; GAA; College; Study Home Econ.

LUCANDER, Christer D; Grosse Pointe South HS; Grosse Pointe, MI; 37/637 ChrhWkr; CmntyWkr; HonRl; NHS; RedCrAde; SctActv; PpCl; Swmmng; Tufts Univ; Md.

LUCARI, Kathy A; Deerfield HS; Deerfield, IL; Univ Of Iowa; Health Science.

LUCAS, Bernice C; Covert HS; Covert, MI; 3/52 Band; HonRl; MrchBnd; NHS; PepBnd; EdYrBk; FHA; Trk; Engineering College; Civil Engineer.

LUCAS, Caryn E; Rich Central HS; Matteson, IL; 36/364 Chr; ChrhWkr; HonRl; OffAde; SctActv; YthFlsp; SpnCl; Univ; Marketing Research.

LUCAS, Crystal L; Tiskilwa HS; Tiskilwa, IL; Band; Chrs; CncrtBnd; HonRl; MrchBnd; PepBnd; SchPl; StuCncl; SchPpr; 4-H; Trade School; Beauty Culture.

LUCAS, Jeffrey L; Jennings County HS; Seymour, IN; 5/300 HonRl; NHS; SctActv; SpnCl; PpCl; LetterBsbl; University; Liberal Arts.

LUCAS, Jonathan P; De La Salle Institute; Chicago, IL; 47/258 VPSrCls; HstSrCls; Band; CncrtBnd; HonRl; MrchBnd; SchPl; StuCncl; StuGov; IMSpt; Depaul U; Cpa.

LUCAS, Karen; St Barbara HS; Chicago, IL; 1/83 TrsSophCls; HonRl; HospAde; OffAde; StuCncl; RptrSchPpr; SchPpr; College; Physician.

LUCAS, Karen L; Festus HS; Festus, MO; 6/160 VPSrCls; Chr; CncrtBnd; NHS; Yrbk; Chrldr; RotaryAwd; Univ; Electrical Engineer.

LUCAS, Kathryn M; East Peoria Community HS; East Peoria, IL; 18/446 NHS; StuGov; Yrbk; FrCl; GAA; Augustana Coll; Foreign Lang.

LUCAS, Kenneth R; Hobart Senior HS; Hobart, IN; AFS; Chrs; HonRl; NHS; NatlThespSoc; SchMus; StuCncl; TchrAde; GerCl; CitAwd; Indiana University; Professional.

LUCAS, Lori L; Plano HS; Plano, IL; Band; HonRl; JrNHS; NHS; RptrYrbk; Socr; GAA; IMSpt; Coll; Journalism,acct.

LUCAS, Luanne L; La Moille Comm HS; Arlington, IL; TrsFrshCls; Chrs; HonRl; SchMus; StuCncl; RptrSchPpr; PpCl; LetterTrk; CaptChrldr; LetterGAA; Jr Coll; Elem Ed.

LUCAS, Madeline; Brown County HS; Nashville, IN; Band; DrmMjrt; HonRl; MrchBnd; OffAde; StuCncl; YthFlsp; 4-H; PpCl; 4-HAwd; Marion Hosp; Nurse.

LUCAS, Marijane A; Wanwatosa West HS; Wanwatosa, WI; AFS; HonRl; NatlFornLg; NHS; NatlThespSoc; SchPl; SctActv; StuCncl; StuGov; 4-H; MthCl; AmLegAwd;.

LUCAS, Mark E; Plainfield HS; Joliet, IL; 23/297 HonRl; SpnCl; LetterBsbl; Bsktbl; Ftbl; College; Business Administration.

LUCAS, Mark W; Morton HS; Morton, IL; 87/287 Aud/Vis; Chr; College; Electronics Tech.

LUCAS, Martin L; Sigourney HS; Sigourney, IA; 8/80 ALBoysSt; HonRl; NatlThespSoc; SchPl; StuGov; RptrYrbk; SchPpr; FFA; FrCl; SciCl; Rotc; Farmer.

LUCAS, Mary L; Leo HS; New Vienna, IA; PresFrshCls; PresJrCls; VPSrCls; CmntyWkr; HonRl; SchMus; SchPl; RptrYrbk; EdSchPpr; SciCl; Loras College; Psychology.

LUCAS, Michael A; Bismarck HS; Bismarck, ND; ChrhWkr; CmntyWkr; SchPl; IMSpt; Coll; Prof.

LUCAS, Michael D; Macomb HS; Macomb, IL; ALBoysSt; ChrhWkr; HonRl; YthFlsp; SpnCl; Bsbl; Bsktbl; Ftbl; CchngActv; IMSpt; Wiu; Engueering.

LUCAS, Patricia; Custer HS; Milwaukee, WI; CmntyWkr; HonRl; JA; NHS; StuGov; YthFlsp; GerCl; CchngActv; College; Professional.

LUCAS, Robert A; Lawrence Central HS; Indianapolis, IN; HonRl; SctActv; Tennis; Wrstlng; IMSpt; College; Professional.

LUCAS, Stephen G; Roosevelt HS; Gary, IN; 90/623 Band; MrchBnd; SchPl; 4-H; FTA; KeyCl; MthCl; LetterGlf; Tennis; 4-HAwd; Indiana Univ; Communications.

LUCAS, Thomas F; St Bede Acad; Oglesby, IL; 1/90 HonRl; NatlMeritCmnd; StuCncl; Bsbl; Bsktbl; ChmnFtbl; Iowa City College; Psychiatrist.

LUCAS, Valerie J; Madison Consolidated HS; Madison, IN; HonRl; NHS; Quill&Scroll; SchMus; YthFlsp; Yrbk; SpnCl; PpCl; Nursing School; Nurse.

LUCAS, Vickie A; Fairfield HS; Fairfield, IA; HonRl; SctActv; College; Spanish.

LUCCA, Mark L; Belle Fourche HS; Belle Fourche, SD; 5/119 NHS; SecNatlThespSoc; SchMus; VPSctActv; Yrbk; SchPpr; Bsktbl; LetterFtbl; LetterTrk; IMSpt; Univ Of Mt; Biological Sciences.

LUCE, Daniel L; Highland HS; Highland, IN; 250/532 Aud/Vis; CmntyWkr; HonRl; TchrAde; LetterWrstlng; CchngActv; IMSpt; Trade Schl; Vocation.

LUCE, Dixie A; Lockwood HS; Jerico Springs, MO; Chrs; HonRl; OffAde; SchPl; StuCncl; FHA; PpCl; PPFtbl; College; Vocation.

LUCE, Jeff; Wapahani HS; Muncie, IN; HonRl; NHS; RptrSchPpr; LetterBsbl; LetterBsktbl; LetterTrk; Purdue Univ; Pre Pharmacy.

LUCE, Jeffrey L; Trego Unified Sd #208 HS; Collyer, KS; HonRl; FFA; LetterTrk; LetterWrstlng; CchngActv; Coll.

LUCE, Kimberly; Warren T HS; Gurnee, IL; Band; CncrtBnd; HonRl; MrchBnd; NHS; PepBnd; RptrSchPpr; GAA; IMSpt; College; Music.

LUCERTO, Laura J; Oak Lawn Comm HS; Hometown, IL; 6/686 HonRl; NatlFornLg; SecNHS; SchAde; FrCl; MthCl; GAA; Univ Of Illinois; Medicine.

LUCEY, Anne C; Beloit Memorial HS; Beloit, WI; VPAFS; HonRl; NHS; SchPl; StuGov; SchPpr; LetterSwmmng; LetterTrk; CchngActv; College; Law.

LUCHETTA, Tracy L; York Comm HS; Elmhurst, IL; HonRl; NHS; NatlMeritCmnd; FHA; Illinois St Univ; Psychology.

LUCHRING, Lesley A; Dekalb HS; Dekalb, IL; 27/370 DrlTm; HonRl; NHS; StuCncl; RptrYrbk; SptEdSchPpr; PpCl; Bsktbl; Trk; GAA; Junior College; Bus, Secretarial.

LUCHSINGER, Diane L; Edgerton HS; Edgerton, WI; 10/160 AFS; ChrhWkr; CncrtBnd; MrchBnd; PepBnd; Yrbk; 4-H; SpnCl; Trk; 4-HAwd; Univ Of Wi Madison.

LUCHSINGER, Lori J; New Glarus HS; New Glarus, WI; Band; Chrs; ChrhWkr; CmntyWkr; HospAde; PepBnd; YthFlsp; 4-H; FTA; 4-HAwd; College.

LUCHT, Janet K; Lake View Auburn Comm HS; Lake View, IA; 3/44 Band; Chr; Chrs; HonRl; NHS; TchrAde; LetterBsktbl; LetterTrk; CchngActv; PresAwd; Ia St Univ; Elem Ed.

LUCHTEFELD, Mary T; Edwardsville HS; Edwardsville, IL; 8/461 HonRl; LitMag; NHS; NatlMeritCmnd; StuCncl; 4-H; FHA; GerCl; Bsktbl; Univ Of Illinois; Computer Engineer.

LUCIDO, Ann Marie; Regina HS; Detroit, MI; HonRl; JA; StuCncl; College; Proessional.

LUCIE, Teresa J; Warsaw HS; Basco, IL; 10/70 AFS; HonRl; LbryAde; NHS; StuCncl; Yrbk; 4-H; GerCl; SpnCl; Illinois State Univ; Psychology.

LUCK, Julie D; Hill City HS; Hill City, KS; Band; Chr; Chrs; CncrtBnd; HonRl; MrchBnd; PepBnd; SchMus; FHA; PpCl; College; Teacher.

LUCK, Paula J; Muskego HS; Muskego, WI; DrlTm; EdYrBk; 4-H; FrCl; PpCl; GodCntryAwd; Whitewater; Spec Education Teacher.

LUCKER, Robin A; West Aurora HS; Aurora, IL; Band; CmntyWkr; HonRl; NHS; NatlThespSoc; SchMus; SchPl; PpCl; Chrldr; College; Business.

LUCKETT, Dirk R; Marion Sr HS; Marion, IL; 4/277 HonRl; NHS; NatlThespSoc; SchMus; SchPl; TreasFrCl; MthCl; College; Chemistry.

LUCKEW, Catherine A; Taft HS; Chicago, IL; 72/816 ChrhWkr; CmntyWkr; HonRl; SchPpr; KeyCl; Univ Of Illinois; Advertising.

LUCKEY, Linda R; Western Mich Chr HS; Muskegon, MI; 6/133 NHS; SchPl; Yrbk; 4-H; PpCl; LetterBsbl; CaptBsktbl; GAA; Calvin Clg; Medicine.

LUCKEY, Patricia A; Univercity HS; St Louis, MO; 84/580 CaptBsktbl; LetterTrk; GAA; IMSpt; College; Field Of Education.

LUCKHARDT, William W; Manchester HS; N Manchester, IN; Aud/Vis; HonRl; LitMag; NatlFornLg; NHS; StuGov; Bsbl; LetterFtbl; Trk; Wrstlng; Marietta College; Radio Tv.

LUCUS, Beverly J; Dwight Twp HS; Dwight, IL; NatlMeritCmnd; 4-H; FHA; SpnCl; College; Art Design.

LUCY, Jackie M; Powers Lake HS; Powers Lake, ND; VPFrshCls; SecSophCls; SecTrsJrCls; Band; ChrhWkr; HonRl; PepBnd; SchPl; RptrYrbk; FshEdSchPpr; Univ; Professional.

LUCY, Maria B; Powers Lake HS; Powers Lake, ND; SecSrCls; ALAGirlsSt; Band; Chr; Chrs; CncrtBnd; HonRl; Mdrgl; MrchBnd; PepBnd; Monot St Coll; Law.

LUCY, Renita L; Powers Lake HS; Powers Lake, ND; Band; CncrtBnd; HonRl; MrchBnd; PepBnd; SchPl; YthFlsp; VP4-H; FHA; PpCl; College; Medicine.

LUCZYNSKI, Michael; South HS; Omaha, NE; Chr; HonRl; NHS; PolWkr; SchPl; StuCncl; SchPpr; GerCl; Glf; CitAwd; Univ Of Ne; Medicine.

LUDEK, Kathryn A; Auburn HS; Auburn, IL; SecTrsFrshCls; SecTrsSophCls; PresSrCls; ALAGirlsSt; Band; Chrs; HonRl; NHS; SchMus; GAA; College; Psychology.

LUDEKE, Jeanne M; Auburn HS; Rockford, IL; 4/300 HonRl; HospAde; JA; TreasNHS; NatlMeritCmnd; StuCncl; GAA; Rockford College; Accountant.

LUDEMA, Gary; Battle Creek Central HS; Battle Creek, MI; 7/506 HonRl; NHS; YthFlsp; Trk; Wrstlng; Calvin College; Pre Engineering.

LUDEMAN, Kary D; Washington HS; Sioux Falls, SD; 65/735 ALBoysSt; ChrhWkr; HonRl; NHS; SchPpr; GerCl; LetterFtbl; Trk; Wrstlng; PresAwd; Sd Sch Of Mines & Tech; Engineering.

LUDEMANN, Susan F; St Paul HS; St Paul, NE; Band; Chr; DrmMjrt; HonRl; MrchBnd; OffAde; PepBnd; SecFHA; PpCl; LetterBsktbl; School; Secretary.

LUDER, Kay E; Ulysses HS; Ulysses, KS; SecFrshCls; TrsFrshCls; Chrs; ChrhWkr; HonRl; LbryAde; NHS; NatlMeritSF; SchPl; SchPpr; Trk; College.

LUDKE, Lynn; Pulaski HS; Green Bay, WI; SecJrCls; PresSrCls; HonRl; JrNHS; NHS; SpnCl; PpCl; Bsbl; Marian College.

LUDLOW, Kurt A; Hillsdale HS; Hillsdale, MI; HonRl; NHS; SpnCl; LetterFtbl; CaptTennis; CchngActv; University; Computer Prog.

LUDLUM, Michael T; Eisenhower HS; Saginaw, MI; 73/316 College; Fish & Game Wildlife Management.

LUDOWESE, Ann C; Stewart Public HS; Stewart, MN; VPJrCls; Band; Chrs; MrchBnd; PepBnd; StuCncl; TchrAde; FHA; PpCl; Chrldr; College;.

LUDOWESE, Kevin G; St Johns Prep HS; Stewart, MN; Band; CncrtBnd; HonRl; NHS; OffAde; PepBnd; SchPl; TchrAde; RptrYrbk; Yrbk; GerCl;.

LUDVIK, Elizabeth A; Mead HS; Ithaca, NE; Band; Chr; Chrs; ChrhWkr; CncrtBnd; HonRl; MrchBnd; NHS; NatlThespSoc; PepBnd; Univ Of Ne; Music.

LUDWIG, Betty E; Culver Community HS; Monterey, IN; 21/100 Chr; HonRl; University; Professional.

LUDWIG, Carol A; Sioux Rapids Comm HS; Sioux Rapids, IA; HstSophCls; Chr; HonRl; Chrldr;.

LUDWIG, Carol I; Adair Casey Comm HS; Casey, IA; 4/48 Chr; HonRl; U Of Iowa; Medical Technologist.

LUDWIG, Daniel L; Keokuk HS; Keokuk, IA; Band; HonRl; NHS; Bsktbl; IMSpt; AmLegAwd; PresAwd; CitAwd;.

LUDWIG, Jennifer A; Bishop Mc Namara HS; Kankakee, IL; 14/161 SecTrsJrCls; PresSrCls; HonRl; NHS; StuCncl; Univ Of Illinois; Social Work.

LUDWIG, Joan; Polo Community HS; Forreston, IL; 32/85 Band; ChrhWkr; CncrtBnd; MrchBnd; YthFlsp; FHA; FNA; Nursing Sch; Nursing.

LUDWIG, Niklas R; Rogers HS; Michigan City, IN; Chr; HonRl; LitMag; NHS; Quill&Scroll; SchMus; SctActv; StuGov; SchPpr; GerCl; Indiana Univ; Law.

LUDWIG, Patricia; Chilton HS; Chilton, WI; 20/141 Band; CncrtBnd; HonRl; NHS; PepBnd; SchMus; GAA; IMSpt; BttyCrckrAwd; Fox Valley Technical Inst; Practical Nurse.

LUDWIG, Ronald D; Southwest HS; St Louis, MO; LetterFtbl;.

LUDWIG, Stephen; Adair Casey Community HS; Casey, IA; 1/48 HonRl; NHS; SctActv; RptrSchPpr; PpCl; Bsbl; Univ Of Northern Iowa; Accounting.

LUDWIGS, Brian; Hinton Comm HS; Hinton, IA; 16/45 ALBoysSt; Band; HonRl; SctActv; StuCncl; Ftbl; GodCntryAwd; Trade School; Vocation.

LUDWIGSON, Randy L; Cornell HS; Cornell, WI; TrsFrshCls; TrsSophCls; PresJrCls; TrsSrCls; ALBoysSt; ChrhWkr; HonRl; StuCncl; StuGov; YthFlsp; Bsktbl; CaptFtbl; LetterGlf; IMSpt; Univ Of Wisconsin; Zoology.

LUEBBERING, Teresa L; Menomonee Falls East HS; Menomonee Falls, WI; 14/347 CncrtBnd; JrNHS; LitMag; MrchBnd; NHS; NatlMeritSF; SpnCl; MthCl; LetterTrk; Univ Wi; Prof.

LUEBBERT, John A; St Elizabeth R Iv HS; St Elizabeth, MO; 14/38 PresSophCls; StuCncl; Bsbl; Bsktbl; Techinical School; Draftsman.

LUEBKE, Thomas W; Lutheran HS; Mayer, MN; ALBoysSt; Aud/Vis; Band; Chr; Chrs; ChrhWkr; CmntyWkr; CncrtBnd; PolWkr; SchMus; SchPl; Bsbl; Bsktbl; Trade School; Agriculture.

LUECK, Lori M; Okabena Public HS; Okabena, MN; 10/24 Band; Chr; Chrs; ChrhWkr; HonRl; HospAde; GAA; Mankato Vocational School; Lpn.

LUECKE, Brenda L; Milford Twp HS; Milford, IL; 6/68 ALAGirlsSt; Band; Chr; ChrhWkr; HonRl; SchPl; RptrYrbk; RptrSchPpr; MthCl; SciCl; GAA; AmLegAwd; Illinois State Univ; Accounting.

LUECKE, Paul R; Hays HS; Hays, KS; Band; Chr; Chrs; ChrhWkr; CncrtBnd; HonRl; Orch; PepBnd; SchMus; SchPl; College; Electronics.

LUECKE, Teresa A; Buckley Loda Comm HS; Buckley, IL; 1/42 SecFrshCls; SecSrCls; ALAGirlsSt; Band; Chr; Chrs; NHS; PepBnd; SchPl; SctActv; Chrldr; GAA; Illinois State Univ; Accounting.

LUECKENHOFF, Edith A; Blair Oaks HS; Jefferson City, MO; 6/55 Band; Chrs; ChrhWkr; CncrtBnd; HonRl; MrchBnd; NHS; SchPl; StuCncl; SptEdYrbk; Bookkeeper.

LUECKER, Elizabeth B; Evanston Township HS; Evanston, IL; Band; Chr; ChrhWkr; CmntyWkr; HonRl; Mdrgl; NatlMeritCmnd; SchPl; YthFlsp; CivCl; Duke University; Biomedical Engineering.

LUECKING, Betty A; Gibault HS; Waterloo, IL; HonRl; NHS; SchMus; SchPl; RptrYrbk; SchPpr; College; Psychology.

LUEDDERS, Sandy G; Marysville HS; Odell, NE; Chrl; Chrs; HonRl; StuGov; 4-H; VPFHA; PpCl; LetterTrk; 4-HAwd; Trade; Vocation.

LUEDER, Connie S; Campus HS; Cape Girardeau, MO; 3/32 Chr; ChrhWkr; CmntyWkr; NHS; OffAde; StuCncl; EdYrBk; PpCl; DARAwd; Univ; Tchr.

LUEDTKE, Cindy S; Winnebago Luthern Academy; Fond Du Lac, WI; Band; 4-H; PpCl; IMSpt; 4-HAwd; Univ Of Wisc; Interpretor.

LUEDTKE, Diane M; W Liberty HS; W Liberty, IA; 1/95 PresFrshCls; Chrs; MrchBnd; NHS; PresStuCncl; RptrYrbk; RptrSchPpr; Pres4-H; LetterBsbl; LetterBsktbl; GAA; 4-HAwd; Iowa State University.

LUEDTKE, Marilyn K; Wausau West HS; Wausau, WI; 14/410 Band; NHS; Orch; PepBnd; Twrl; FrCl; PpCl; LetterChrldr; LetterGAA; Univ Of Wisc; Office Management.

LUEGERING, Mary S; Aquinas HS; Fort Madison, IA; 7/46 SecSophCls; Yrbk; FHA; FrCl; PpCl; Chrldr; Coll; Medical Tech.

LUEHR, Dennis R; Trico HS; Campbell Hill, IL; Aud/Vis; ChrhWkr; HonRl; LbryAde; Southern Il U ;doctor.

LUEHRING, Cynthia A; Hanover Public HS; Hollenberg, KS; SecTrsFrshCls; Aud/Vis; ChrhWkr; TchrAde; YthFlsp; FHA; Bsktbl; Chrldr; Bethany; P E Major.

LUEHRING, Joan E; Gibbon Public HS; Gibbon, MN; 10/41 Band; Chr; ChrhWkr; HonRl; MrchBnd; OffAde; 4-H; LetterTrk; GAA; IMSpt; St Cloud State College.

LUEHRMAN, Lois; Lafayette Co HS; Higginsville, MO; 9/100 AFS; CncrtBnd; HonRl; MrchBnd; NHS; PepBnd; YthFlsp; 4-H; SpnCl; PpCl; Univ Of Mo; Math And Engineering.

LUEKEN, Nancy; Marshall HS; Marshall, IL; 1/115 Band; CncrtBnd; HonRl; NHS; TchrAde; Twrl; SchPpr; FHA; SpnCl; SciCl; Eastern Il; Elementary Education.

LUELLMAN, Steven L; Norfolk Senior HS; Norfolk, NE; Band; CncrtBnd; Orch; PepBnd; MthCl; SciCl; LetterFtbl; College; Data Processing.

LUEMPERT, Arthur F; Columbia Central HS; Clark Lake, MI; 13/153 HonRl; JrNHS; NHS; SctActv; StuCncl; StuGov; TchrAde; Bsbl; Bsktbl; LetterFtbl; College; Pre Med.

LUENSMANN, Michael; West Dubuque HS; New Vienna, IA; 8/243 HonRl; NHS; IMSpt;.

LUEPKE, Kathy J; Sheldon Comm HS; Sheldon, IA; Chr; ChrhWkr; HonRl; RptrYrbk; PpCl; IMSpt;.

LUEPKE, Mark S; Sheldon Comm HS; Sheldon, IA; 8/146 PresJrCls; Chr; ChrhWkr; HonRl; VPNHS; SchMus; SchPl; TreasStuCncl; CaptFtbl; CitAwd; U Of Northern Ia.

LUEPTOW, Kris J; Pardeeville HS; Pardeeville, WI; Aud/Vis; Band; Chr; Chrs; ChrhWkr; HonRl; LbryAde; MrchBnd; PepBnd; SchMus; College.

LUERDING, Jeffrey; St Charles HS; St Charles, MO; 7/547 ALBoysSt; CncrtBnd; HospAde; NHS; Orch; StuCncl; KeyCl; Ftbl; Wrstlng; William Jewell College; Medicine.

LUERS, Kevin R; Keota Comm HS; Keota, IA; ALBoysSt; PresBand; Chr; Chrl; Chrs; ChrhWkr; CncrtBnd; Mdrgl; MrchBnd; PepBnd; Trade School; Farm Management.

LUESSMAN, Cathy R; Poynette HS; Poynette, WI; 6/102 SecSophCls; ALAGirlsSt; Band; Chrs; HonRl; NHS; StuCncl; RptrYrbk; VPPpCl; LetterChrldr; Univ Wi; Nursing.

LUETKENHAUS, Susan M; Duchesne HS; St Charles, MO; Chrs; HonRl; NHS; SchMus; SctActv; RptrYrbk; SpnCl; PpCl; IMSpt; College.

LUETTEL, Kenneth F; Pope John Xxiii Central HS; Petersburgh, NE; PresSophCls; CmntyWkr; IntrClCncl; ModUN; PolWkr; StuCncl; StuGov; Bsktbl; CchngActv; TIMEAwd; Rockhurst Coll; Bus Admin.

LUETZOW, Lynn E; Bay View HS; Milwaukee, WI; Orch; Quill&Scroll; SchMus; SchPpr; Univ Wi; Chemistry.

LUFT, Sherry L; Alpena HS; Alpena, MI; ChrhWkr; Orch; SchMus; SchPl; SctActv; TchrAde; Oakland Univ; Registered Nurse.

LUGIBILL, Glenn; Williamsville HS; Williamsville, IL; ChrhWkr; CmntyWkr; HonRl; NHS; SchPl; Bsbl; Bsktbl; Vocation.

LUGINBILL, Mark D; Bluffton HS; Bluffton, IN; ALBoysSt; ChrhWkr; HonRl; SchPl; YthFlsp; RptrSchPpr; Bsbl; University; Professional.

LUGINBILL, Penny S; Nemaha Valley HS; Seneca, KS; Band; Chrs; HonRl; NHS; SchPl; Twrl; PpCl; SciCl; Trk; Chrldr; College; Nursing.

LUHMAN, Gary; Milford HS; Milford, IL; 2/70 Band; HonRl; NHS; NatlMeritCmnd; SchPpr; KeyCl; LatCl; Trk; DanFAwd; Coll; Lawyer.

LUHMAN, Gary L; Milford Township HS; Milford, IL; 2/68 Band; Chr; Chrs; CncrtBnd; HonRl; MrchBnd; NHS; NatlMeritCmnd; PepBnd; SchPl; RptrSchPpr; 4-H; CaptFtbl; Trk; College; Law.

LUHRING, Cynthia S; Sterling HS; Sterling, IL; 54/435 Chr; HonRl; SchPpr; 4-H; GerCl; PpCl; College; Medical Technology.

LUHRING, Pamela S; Dike Community HS; Parkersburg, IA; 1/39 VPJrCls; Chrs; ChrhWkr; CncrtBnd; HonRl; MrchBnd; NHS; PepBnd; SchPl; SctActv; PresYthFlsp; RptrYrbk; Trk; Iowa State University.

LUHRSEN, Leslie E; Buckley Loda HS; Buckley, IL; VPFrshCls; ChrhWkr; HonRl; LbryAde; NHS; SctActv; StuCncl; SptEdSchPpr; SchPpr; PpCl; LetterBsbl; Bsktbl; LetterGlf; Concordia College; Religion.

LUIKEN, Marc; Ballard HS; Huxley, IA; 8/100 Chrs; ChrhWkr; HonRl; NHS; NatlThespSoc; SchPl; SptEdSchPpr; Bsbl; College.

LUING, Philip; Barnum HS; Mahtowa, MN; 2/59 PresJrCls; PresSrCls; ALBoysSt; NatlFornLg; NHS; SchPl; EdYrBk; EdSchPpr; CitAwd; Cornell College; Lawyer.

LUITEN, Linda M; Proctor HS; Duluth, MN; 30/207 Band; CncrtBnd; HonRl; NHS; Orch; PepBnd; Twrl; RptrYrbk; FTA; GerCl; U Of Mn Duluth; Social Worker.

LUKACEK, Richard A; George Washington HS; Chicago, IL; Band; ChrhWkr; CncrtBnd; DrmBgl; MrchBnd; NHS; Orch; SchPl; De Paul University.

LUKACH, Ann M; Bishop Ryan HS; Minot, ND; 3/89 SecJrCls; HonRl; NHS; Sdlty; StuCncl; Nd U; Medicine.

LUKASIK, Kathleen M; Notre Dame HS; Chicago, IL; 26/302 Chrs; HonRl; HospAde; NHS; Univ; Medicine.

LUKE, Deborah D; Alma HS; Alma, MI; 6/266 TrsJrCls; CncrtBnd; HonRl; MrchBnd; NatlFornLg; NHS; NatlMeritFnl; StuGov; Swmmng; Alma College; Psychology.

LUKE, Denise J; Hutchinson Jr Sr HS; Hutchinson, MN; 6/200 AFS; Aud/Vis; Band; Chr; Chrs; ChrhWkr; HonRl; NHS; OffAde; SchPl; College.

LUKE, Jeffrey W; Cardinal HS; Eldon, IA; VPSrCls; Band; Chrs; CncrtBnd; MrchBnd; PepBnd; Bsbl; Bsktbl; Ftbl; Trk; Ryder Tech Des Moines.

LUKE, Jo B; Moweaqua HS; Moweaqua, IL; 8/51 Chrs; ChrhWkr; CmntyWkr; HonRl; LbryAde; NHS; SchMus; EdYrBk; FHA; Chrldr; College; Professional.

LUKE, Keith W; Malden HS; Malden, MO; 11/110 VPFrshCls; VPSophCls; PresJrCls; Band; ChrhWkr; CncrtBnd; HonRl; OffAde; LetterFtbl; LetterTrk; College; Farming.

LUKE, Larry M; Coldwater HS; Coldwater, MI; PresChr; HonRl; Mdrgl; NHS; SchMus; SchPl; SctActv; Ftbl; CaptTrk; Michigan St Univ; History.

LUKE, Linda A; Northeast Nodaway HS; Maryville, MO; 1/28 HonRl; PresNHS; SecStuCncl; RptrYrbk; PpCl; Bsbl; LetterBsktbl; LetterTrk; Nw Mo St Univ.

LUKE, Lonny D; Sherwood Public HS; Sherwood, ND; 9#41#54# SchPl; StuCncl; YthFnd; Bsktbl; Ftbl; CchngActv; 4-HAwd; U Or Nd; Missionary Bush Pilot.

LUKE, Margaret C; Kirkwood HS; Glendale, MO; 10/660 Chr; NatlMeritCmnd; StuCncl; YthLg; University Of Kansas; Mathematics.

LUKE, Paul J; Northeast Nodaway Rv HS; Maryville, MO; 3/24 PresJrCls; SecSrCls; Chrs; HonRl; NHS; SchMus; SchPl; PresStuCncl; RptrYrbk; Nw Mo U; Business.

LUKE, Sheena M; Eagle Grove HS; Eagle Grove, IA; 31/126 Chrs; HonRl; RptrYrbk; FNA; Univ Of Iowa; X Ray Tech.

LUKEHART, Rickey L; Peoria Heights HS; Peoria Heights, IL; Band; CncrtBnd; PepBnd; SctActv; KeyCl; PpCl; LetterBsktbl; LetterFtbl; IMSpt; PresAwd; Music.

LUKEN, Denise; Hamlin HS; Hzael, SD; 4/66 SecSrCls; ChrhWkr; HonRl; PolWkr; SchPl; RptrYrbk; Yrbk; EdSchPpr; Bsktbl; South Dakota State U; Biology.

LUKENS, Jeffrey D; O Gorman HS; Sioux Falls, SD; HonRl; TchrAde; Bsktbl; Ftbl; Colorado State Univ; Biology.

LUKER, Brent D; Uniontown HS; Uniontown, KS; ChrhWkr; 4-H; FFA; Ftbl; Trk; College; Psychology.

LUKER, Joyce E; Southridge HS; Huntingburg, IN; Band; Chr; Chrl; Chrs; ChrhWkr; CncrtBnd; DrlTm; DrmMjrt; HonRl; MrchBnd; LetterSwmmng; Trk; CaptChrldr; GAA; Purdue University; Pharmacy.

LUKING, Laura C; Connersville HS; Connersville, IN; 46/371 SecSrCls; ChrhWkr; HonRl; StuCncl; Pres4-H; PresFHA; FTA; SpnCl; IMSpt; 4-HAwd; Purdue Univ; Home Ec.

LUKKONEN, Gordon R; Two Harbors HS; Duluth, MN; 12/180 ChrhWkr; HonRl; NHS; LetterBsbl; LetterBsktbl; LetterFtbl; Tennis; College; Law.

LUKOWSKI, Diane L; Nehawka HS; Nehawka, NE; TrsJrCls; Chrs; HonRl; SchPl; GerCl; Business School.

LUKSAN, Linda M; Armstrong HS; Golden Valley, MN; 7/599 PresAFS; Chr; ChrhWkr; HospAde; LitMag; NHS; NatlMeritSF; PolWkr; SchMus; SchPpr; GAA; Univ; Business Admin.

LUKSUS, Kevin; Andrean Hs; Gary, IN; 5/306 NHS; NatlMeritCmnd; MthCl; PresSciCl; Rose Hulman Inst; Environmental.

LULEY, Ann; Bishop Dwenger HS; Fort Wayne, IN; Chrs; HonRl; HospAde; FrCl; GAA; Coll; Special Education.

LULLO, Geraldine J; Oak Lawn Comm HS; Oak Lawn, IL; SecChrs; OffAde; StuCncl; TchrAde; SpnCl; De Paul; Teacher.

LULOFF, James R; Waverly Shell Rock HS; Waverly, IA; ChrhWkr; HonRl; SchMus; SchPl; StuCncl; TreasGerCl; LetterBsbl; CchngActv; IMSpt; College; Coaching.

LUMBARD, Michael L; East HS; Des Moines, IA; ChrhWkr; HonRl; LitMag; StuCncl; StuGov; RptrSchPpr; FrCl; LetterBsktbl; Ftbl; Trk; Oral Roberts University; Theology.

LUMMER, Scott L; Proviso East HS; Melrose Park, IL; 27/990 TrsFrshCls; HonRl; IntrClCncl; NHS; PolWkr; SchPl; StuGov; YthLg; Tennis; Purdue University; Professional.

LUMSDEN, Veronica A; Vassar HS; Vassar, MI; Chr; HonRl; NatlThespSoc; SchPl; TchrAde; Yrbk; FHA; GerCl; SpnCl; College; Law Enforcement.

LUNA, Gregory M; Ritenour HS; St Louis, MO; 25/867 PresFrshCls; HonRl; NHS; StuCncl; YthFlsp; ChmnBsbl; LetterBsktbl; LetterFtbl; Coll; Bus Admin.

LUNARDINI, Karen; St Mary Acad; Monroe, MI; Chr; ChrhWkr; HonRl; NHS; NatlMeritFnl; NatlMeritSchl; PolWkr; SchPl; Aquinas Grand Rapids Mi; Education.

LUND, Alicia A; Greenville Sr HS; Greenville, MI; VPChr; HonRl; NatlFornLg; NatlMeritCmnd; SchMus; StuCncl; 4-H; TreasFrCl; PpCl; GAA; Kellogg Comm Col; Physical Therapy Asst.

LUND, Bruce A; Lyons Township HS; Western Springs, IL; College; Engineering.

LUND, Craig R; Pecatonica HS; Pecatonica, IL; 5/78 SecSophCls; HonRl; JrNHS; NHS; Quill&Scroll; SctActv; RptrSchPpr; 4-H; FrCl; LetterBsktbl; LetterFtbl; DanFAwd; 4-HAwd; College.

LUND, Doloris B; Lisbon Public HS; Lisbon, ND; 21/74 AFS; Band; HonRl; StuCncl; 4-H; VPFBLA; FHA; BttyCrckrAwd; 4-HAwd; N Dakota State Univ; Home Economics.

LUND, Donna E; St Clair HS; Janesville, MN; 2/42 PresSophCls; PresJrCls; HonRl; NHS; SchAde; SchPl; PresStuCncl; TchrAde; EdYrBk; RptrSchPpr; FHA; PresFTA; GerCl; College; Interpreter.

LUND, John A; Pelican Rapids HS; Pelican Rapids, MN; HonRl; SctActv; SpnCl; LetterBsbl; LetterBsktbl; CaptFtbl; LetterGlf; CchngActv; IMSpt; LionAwd; Univ; Pro.

LUND, Karen K; La Porte City HS; Brandon, IA; 3/68 PresSophCls; PresJrCls; Band; ChrhWkr; CmntyWkr; CncrtBnd; HonRl; MrchBnd; NHS; SchPl; VPStuCncl; CaptBsktbl; Tennis; CchngActv; Allen Sch; Radiological Tech.

LUND, Kathleen C; Cathedral HS; St Cloud, MN; 15/163 Chrs; Mdrgl; SchPl; StuCncl; Yrbk; SchPpr; PpCl; Chrldr; IMSpt; PPFtbl; U Of Minn; Liberal Arts.

LUND, Mary; West HS; Green Bay, WI; 90/390 Chrs; HonRl; NHS; SchMus; SchPl; StuCncl; FNA; PpCl; Bellin School Of Nursing; Rn.

LUND, Melody A; Hastings HS; Hastings, MN; 40/428 Chr; HonRl; JrNHS; NHS; NatlThespSoc; SchMus; SchPl; RptrSchPpr; Winona State Univ; English Lit.

LUND, Victoria A; Mundelein HS; Mundelein, IL; SctActv; College; Horticulture.

LUNDAY, Marga C; Sheyenne River Academy; Bismarck, ND; SecSrCls; Band; HospAde; LbryAde; Orch; TchrAde; College.

LUNDBERG, Caroyl; Rush City HS; Rush City, MN; HonRl; NHS; SchPl; RptrYrbk; FHA; PpCl; BttyCrckrAwd; VoiceDemAwd; St Cloud St Coll; Photojournalism.

LUNDBERG, Karen; North HS; Fargo, ND; 15/366 NHS; College; Major In Horticulture.

LUNDBERG, Karen; Northwest HS; House Springs, MO; 3/370 VPSrCls; Band; CncrtBnd; HonRl; MrchBnd; NHS; PpCl; Chrldr; Washington Univ St Louis; Major In Music.

LUNDBERG, Robin G; Hillcrest HS; Oak Forest, IL; 4/474 Chr; Chrs; HonRl; Mdrgl; NHS; NatlThespSoc; SchMus; StuCncl; SpnCl; MthCl; College.

LUNDBERG, Steve P; Southeast Warren HS; Milo, IA; PresFrshCls; PresSophCls; PresJrCls; PresSrCls; ChrhWkr; CmntyWkr; JCC; NHS; StuCncl; StuGov; YthFlsp; YthLg; LetterBsbl; LetterBsktbl; College; Forestry.

LUNDBERG, Sue K; Grant Deuel HS; Strandburg, SD; 5/46 Band; Chrs; NHS; NatlThespSoc; StuCncl; 4-H; FHA; CaptChrldr; DARAwd; 4-HAwd; College; Nursing.

LUNDE, John; Beaver Dam HS; Beaver Dam, WI; Bsktbl; Ftbl; Glf; Madison Area Tech College; Surveyor.

LUNDE, Kristi J; Bottineau HS; Bottineau, ND; 9/67 ALAGirlsSt; Chr; CncrtBnd; HospAde; SchMus; StuCncl; RptrYrbk; PpCl; FFA; Chrldr; Ndsu Bbif; Secretarial.

LUNDEEN, Kathy A; Elkhorn HS; Elkhorn, WI; 16/167 Chr; CncrtBnd; HonRl; MrchBnd; SchMus; SchPl; Sec4-H; PresFHA; 4-HAwd; Wartburg College; Internationalbusiness.

LUNDEEN, Sandra K; Arlington HS; Arlington Heights, IL; 22/585 ChrhWkr; HonRl; LitMag; NHS; SchPl; SctActv; StuCncl; Ripon College; Special Education.

LUNDELL, Janelle M; Kennedy Public HS; Kennedy, MN; Band; Chrs; ChrhWkr; HonRl; PepBnd; Yrbk; VPFHA; PpCl; Chrldr; GAA; 4-HAwd;.

LUNDELL, Julie A; W Michigan Christian HS; Muskegon, MI; ChrhWkr; CmntyWkr; HonRl; NHS; NatlMeritCmnd; SchPl; TchrAde; Yrbk; FTA; CitAwd; Calvin College Grand Rapids Mi; Art Ed.

LUNDER, Jeff A; Monona Grove HS; Monona, WI; 31/270 Band; CncrtBnd; HonRl; MrchBnd; NHS; PepBnd; LetterBsktbl; LetterFtbl; Tennis; IMSpt; U W Mdison; Engr.

LUNDEWALL, Ralph H; Morton Sr HS; Gary, IN; 61/545 HonRl; Glf; University.

LUNDGREN, Debbie; Allen Consolidated HS; Dixon, NE; 3/36 TrsSophCls; VPJrCls; PresSrCls; Chr; HonRl; SchPl; StuGov; EdYrBk; RptrSchPpr; Chrldr; College; Secretarial.

LUNDIE, Gregory P; Holland HS; Holland, MI; 16/316 HonRl; NHS; SctActv; SciCl; BauchLmbAwd; Hope College.

LUNDIN, Judy M; Litchfield HS; Litchfield, MN; Band; CncrtBnd; HonRl; JrNHS; EdYrBk; 4-H; Ftbl; LetterTrk; GAA; 4-HAwd; College; Vocation.

LUNDQUIST, Diane M; Brookfield East HS; Brookfield, WI; 14/520 HonRl; NHS; SctActv; MthCl; Univ; Med Tech.

LUNDQUIST, Janice; Clifton Rural HS; Clifton, KS; ALAGirlsSt; ChrhWkr; CncrtBnd; HonRl; PepBnd; StuCncl; YthFlsp; Yrbk; Chrldr; PPFtbl; College; Professional.

LUNDQUIST, Wayne L; Beresford HS; Beresford, SD; ALBoysSt; Band; Chr; ChrhWkr; CmntyWkr; CncrtBnd; DrmMjrt; HonRl; MrchBnd; Univ Of Sd; Professional.

LUNDSTROM, Carol A; Elizabeth Seton HS; Calumet Park, IL; ChrhWkr; HonRl; RptrYrbk; RptrSchPpr; Univ; Accountant.

LUNDT, Holmes T; Rockwell Swaledale Comm HS; Dougherty, IA; 1/45 TrsSophCls; VPSrCls; HonRl; JrNHS; PresNHS; NatlMeritFnl; RptrYrbk; PresFFA; PpCl; LetterBsktbl; JETSAwd; Upper Iowa Univ; Mathematics.

LUNDT, Judy L; Sioux Valley Community HS; Linn Grove, IA; 9/42 SecJrCls; HonRl; NHS; SchMus; SchPl; 4-H; CaptBsktbl; CaptTrk; Chrldr; Northwestern College; Phys Ed.

LUNDT, Kenneth; Green Lake HS; Green Lake, WI; VPSophCls; VPSrCls; SchPl; EdSchPpr; SchPpr; Bsbl; Bsktbl; Ftbl; Wrstlng; Tech School.

LUNDWALL, Janelle K; Chisago Lakes Area HS; Chisago City, MN; ALAGirlsSt; ChrhWkr; HonRl; Yrbk; College; Occupational Therapist.

LUNGER, Laura B; Sparta HS; Sparta, MI; 1/256 Chr; ChrhWkr; HonRl; PresNHS; NatlMeritFnl; SchPl; StuCncl; RptrYrbk; VPSpnCl; VPSciCl; DARAwd; OptClAwd; RotaryAwd; College; English.

LUNGREN, Kevin B; Frankfort Sr HS; Frankfort, IN; 21/241 Band; CncrtBnd; MrchBnd; NHS; Orch; PepBnd; SchMus; SchPl; KeyCl; SpnCl; MthCl; Tennis; Wabash College; Lawyer.

LUNIK, Maurice C; Springfield Southeast HS; Springfield, IL; 23/464 NHS; Springfield College.

LUNING, Karen A; Rosati Kain HS; St Louis, MO; TrsSrCls; Aud/Vis; HospAde; PepBnd; SchPl; StuCncl; StuGov; Yrbk; FrCl; PpCl; GAA; Macalester College.

LUNKENHEIMER, Julie K; Mc Henry Comm HS; Mc Henry, IL; 12/475 Chrs; ChrhWkr; HonRl; JrNHS; NHS; GAA; Rosary College; Medical Research.

LUNN, Rose M; Lillis HS; Kansas City, MO; 1/84 Chrs; HonRl; NHS; SchMus; College; Engineer.

LUNOE, Joan E; Homewood Flossmoor HS; Homewood, IL; Aud/Vis; Chrs; LbryAde; NHS; NatlThespSoc; SchMus; SchPl; TchrAde; Stephens College; Communications.

LUNSFORD, Sherry A; Richmond Sr HS; Richmond, IN; 25/600 ChrhWkr; CmntyWkr; HonRl; NHS; Orch; PolWkr; StuGov; Teen; College; Teaching.

LUNSTRUM, Paul O; Lexington HS; Lexington, IL; 3/62 Chr; CncrtBnd; MrchBnd; NHS; PepBnd; SchPl; SciCl; Valparaiso Univ; Elec Engineering.

LUNT, Jerry; Southeastern HS; Bowen, IL; /49 HonRl; SchMus; SchPl; TchrAde; PpCl; Bsktbl; Glf; Trk; IMSpt; Univ;agric.

LUNZ, Pamela J; Newcastle Public HS; Newcastle, NE; DrlTm; HonRl; SchPl; StuGov; RptrYrbk; 4-H; PpCl; Trk; Ia Tech Col; Secretary.

LUOMA, Janice M; Annandale HS; Annandale, MN; Minnesota Schl Of Business; Accounting.

LUPER, Craig D; Augusta HS; Augusta, KS; 20/160 PresJrCls; Band; ChrhWkr; CncrtBnd; HonRl; SchPl; StuCncl; Bsktbl; Ftbl; Ozark Bible College; Preacher.

LUPKE, Diane C; Elmhurst HS; Ft Wayne, IN; CncrtBnd; HonRl; MrchBnd; NatlFornLg; Orch; PolWkr; SctActv; Yrbk; SchPpr; TreasJAAwd; College; Law.

LUPTON, Christine Y; Northwestern HS; Blandinsville, IL; 2/55 AFS; Band; ChrhWkr; CmntyWkr; CncrtBnd; HonRl; HospAde; MrchBnd; PresNHS; VPStuCncl; Bsktbl; Trk; GAA; IMSpt; College; Special Educ.

LURA, James C; Owatonna HS; Owatonna, MN; 40/320 HonRl; Pres4-H; PresFFA; Trk; Wrstlng; 4-HAwd; U Of Mn; Animal Science.

LURQUIN, Jerome T; Harold L Richards HS; Oak Lawn, IL; 311/1035 Chr; Chrs; ChrhWkr; HonRl; SchMus; TchrAde; 4-H; Wrstlng;.

LUSA, Deborah M; Thornwood HS; Calumet City, IL; Chr; Chrs; HonRl; Mdrgl; NatlFornLg; NHS; NatlThespSoc; Univ; English.

LUSCOMB, Steve L; Belleville Township East HS; Fairview Heights, IL; Chr; Southern Ill Univ; Music.

LUSHER, Douglas H; Concord HS; Concord, MI; ChrhWkr; HonRl; StuCncl; YthFlsp; RptrSchPpr; College; Agriculture.

LUSHER, Douglas H; Concord Comm HS; Concord, MI; 1/80 ChrhWkr; HonRl; StuCncl; RptrSchPpr; SchPpr; Col; Bible.

LUSSKY, Glenn R; Minneapolis Lutheran HS; Bloomington, MN; Band; Chr; CncrtBnd; HonRl; YthFlsp; Bsbl; Bsktbl; Glf; Wrstlng; IMSpt; Col; Fish And Game.

LUSSKY, Steven J; Minneapolis Lutheran HS; Bloomington, MN; Band; ChrhWkr; CncrtBnd; PepBnd; YthFlsp; LetterBsktbl; LetterTrk; College; Mathematics.

LUSTER, Freddie J; Mendel HS; Chicago, IL; 41/173 HonRl; SchAde; SchPl; LetterBsktbl; LetterFtbl; IMSpt; Bradley Univ.

LUSTFELDT, Sandra K; Onarga HS; Onarga, IL; VPSrCls; Band; Chrs; HonRl; MrchBnd; NHS; AmLegAwd; DARAwd; 4-HAwd; CitAwd;.

LUSTGRAAF, Cheryl A; Underwood HS; Council Bluffs, IA; Band; Chr; HonRl; NHS; SchMus; SchPl; 4-H; FHA; LetterBsbl; Bsktbl; IMSpt; College; Teacher.

LUSTGRAAF, Jan J; Wahoo Public HS; Colon, NE; 2/75 ALAGirlsSt; Chr; Chrs; HonRl; SctActv; PpCl; Trk; Univ Of Nebraska; Nursing.

LUSTIG, Keith C; Sterling Hts HS; Sterling Hts, MI; 35/520 HonRl; NatlMeritFnl; NatlMeritCmnd; NatlMeritSchl; PolWkr; StuCncl; LetterBsktbl; Ftbl; PresAwd; University; Proffessional.

LUSUARDI, Anthony A; St Bede Academy; Oglesby, IL; HonRl; College; Lawyer.

LUTER, Pamela J; Thomas Jefferson HS; Rockford, IL; 26/361 Chr; ChrhWkr; HonRl; HospAde; Mdrgl; College; Special Ed Teacher.

LUTGEN, Barbara; St Johns HS; Beloit, KS; 3/21 ALAGirlsSt; ChrhWkr; HospAde; NHS; SchAde; Trk; Chrldr; PPFtbl; CitAwd; VoiceDemAwd; Barton Co Comm Jr College; Rn.

LUTH, Mary E; Harvard HS; Harvard, IL; HonRl; Treas4-H; LetterTrk; 4-HAwd; PresAwd; Mchenry Co Jr College; Art.

LUTH, Rhonda; Kearney Senior HS; Kearney, NE; 30/248 Chrs; OffAde; TchrAde; Yrbk; SchPpr; PpCl; SciCl; NCTE; Coll; Professional.

LUTHER, Glen D; Greenfield HS; Greenfield, WI; 88/378 HonRl; NHS; CaptFtbl; CaptTrk; IMSpt; Coll; Social Sci.

LUTHER, Hildi C; St Bede Academy; Spring Valley, IL; Chrs; HonRl; SchMus; Trk; Univ Of Illinois; Accounting.

LUTHER, Julie A; Prescott Comm HS; Prescott, IA; 4/11 VPSophCls; SecSrCls; Band; Chrs; ChrhWkr; CncrtBnd; HonRl; MrchBnd; OffAde; PepBnd; SchAde; Bsbl; Bsktbl; College; Physical Education.

LUTHER, Sherrye L; Unionville Sebewaing Area HS; Unionville, MI; 3/125 ChrhWkr; CncrtBnd; HonRl; VPNHS; EdYrBk; Bsktbl; LetterTrk; GAA; 4-HAwd; CitAwd; Central Mi U; Bio.

LUTKE, Kenneth D; Mc Bain Northern ChristianHS; Marion, MI; 10/40 HonRl; NatlMeritCmnd; NatlMeritSF; YthFlsp; IMSpt; Mi State Univ; Farm Sales & Management.

LUTMAN, Micheal N; W C Community HS; West Chicago, IL; CAP; HonRl; SctActv; LatCl; Bsbl; Ftbl; Trk; Us Air Force Academy; Aeronautical Eng.

LUTON, Linda M; Labette County HS; Parsons, KS; 13/150 ChrhWkr; HonRl; PresHospAde; SchAde; TchrAde; YthFlsp; FBLA; VPSpnCl; PpCl; SciCl; Coll; Nurse.

LUTRINGER, Janell; Seward HS; Seward, NE; Band; Chrs; DrlTm; MrchBnd; 4-H; SecFFA; PpCl; IMSpt;.

LUTTENTON, Rebecca; Concord HS; Concord, MI; 16/69 HstSrCls; Band; DrlTm; NHS; OffAde; YthFlsp; RptrSchPpr; PpCl; Bsktbl; Trk; Patricia Stevens Career College; Fash Merch.

LUTTERMOSER, Donald G; John F Kennedy HS; Taylor, MI; 41/430 HonRl; NHS; SchMus; SchPl; MthCl; SciCl; U Of Mich; Astronomy.

LUTTERS, Marie J; Ransom HS; Ransom, KS; Band; Chr; ChrhWkr; CmntyWkr; HonRl; StuGov; PresPpCl; LetterBsktbl; VFWAwd; VoiceDemAwd; University; Professional.

LUTTERS, Timothy; Ransom HS; Ransom, KS; 3 Chr; ChrhWkr; CmntyWkr; HonRl; NatlMeritSchl; SchMus; FrCl; MthCl; LetterFtbl; LetterTrk; Trade School; Vocation.

LUTTICH, Mary; Geneva HS; Ohiowa, NE; Band; Chrs; ChrhWkr; CncrtBnd; HonRl; MrchBnd; NHS; PepBnd; SchPpr; LionAwd; Univ Of Nebraska; Business Education.

LUTTIG, Kathleen; Fowler HS; Fowler, MI; 4/68 TrsSrCls; HonRl; NHS; TchrAde; Yrbk; 4-H; SpnCl; Trk; 4-HAwd; Ferris State College; Accountant.

LUTTMAN, Mark E; Red Bud HS; Red Bud, IL; HonRl; Bsbl; Bsktbl;.

LUTTRELL, Debra F; Milford Township HS; Milford, IL; SecJrCls; Chr; HonRl; Quill&Scroll; SchPl; Yrbk; SchPpr; LatCl; PpCl; College; Vocational.

LUTZ, Dennis C; East Kentwood HS; Grand Rapids, MI; Chr; HonRl; YthFlsp; Grnd Rpds Baptst Coll; Christian Ed Drctor.

LUTZ, Emily E; Benkelman HS; Benkelman, NE; 5/31 Band; Chrs; CncrtBnd; DrmMjrt; HonRl; MrchBnd; NHS; PepBnd; FHA; Cottey College; Medicine.

LUTZ, Janice; Bishop Leblond HS; St Joseph, MO; 7/115 Chrs; HonRl; NatlFornLg; NHS; Quill&Scroll; RptrYrbk; PpCl; W Mo St Coll; Teach.

LUTZ, John J; Wenona HS; Wenona, IL; 4/38 ChrhWkr; CmntyWkr; HonRl; NHS; SchMus; SchPl; RptrYrbk; EdYrBk; FTA; University; Political Science.

LUTZ, Lon; Reeder HS; Reeder, ND; 3/17 Chrs; HonRl; SctActv; RptrYrbk; N D State Univ; Pharmacy.

LUTZ, Mary; Sandoval Community HS; Sandoval, IL; 3/47 PresJrCls; SecSrCls; SecBand; ChrhWkr; CncrtBnd; HonRl; SchPl; Yrbk; FTA; LionAwd; Jr Coll Univ; Pro.

LUTZ, Michael E; Bronson HS; Bronson, MI; PresSrCls; ALBoysSt; SchMus; SchPl; StuCncl; Bsbl; LetterBsktbl; Ftbl; Tennis; College; Armed Service.

LUTZ, Pamela; Capac HS; Emmett, MI; 16/108 Band; CmntyWkr; HonRl; NHS; OffAde; SchAde; TchrAde; PpCl; Trk; CchngActv; Michigan State U; Zoology.

LUTZ, Scott A; Benkelman HS; Parks, NE; VPFrshCls; PresSophCls; ALBoysSt; HonRl; NHS; 4-H; SciCl; Ftbl; AmLegAwd; Univ Of Nebraska; Physics.

LUTZ, Susan M; Carmel Girls HS; Northbrook, IL; 10/195 Chr; VPChrs; ChrhWkr; HonRl; JrNHS; SchMus; College; Music.

LUTZ, Tony E; Benkelman HS; Parks, NE; 7/42 Band; Chrs; CncrtBnd; MrchBnd; NHS; PepBnd; SchPpr; SciCl; LetterTrk; Business School; Accounting.

LUTZE, Amy D; Lake Ville Memorial HS; Otisville, MI; 1/183 NHS; SchPl; CaptBsktbl; Trk; VPGAA; In Inst; Recreation.

LUTZE, Kary K; Manitowoc Lutheran HS; Manitowoc, WI; 4/81 Chr; LbryAde; Yrbk; PpCl; Uw Milwaukee; Early Childhood Educ.

LUTZKE, Thomas E; Merrill Sr HS; Irma, WI; 16/385 Band; HonRl; LetterBsbl; LetterFtbl; Wrstlng; College; Military Air Science.

LUTZOW, James H; Rockford East Sr HS; Rockford, IL; 2/660 Band; CncrtBnd; MrchBnd; NHS; NatlMeritCmnd; PepBnd; SchMus; SchPl; Western Ill Univ; Math.

LUX, Brian P; Aberdeen Central HS; Aberdeen, SD; Band; CncrtBnd; HonRl; Bsbl; LetterBsktbl; LetterFtbl; LetterTrk; CchngActv; University; Wild Life Conservation.

LUX, Mark J; Vianney HS; St Louis, MO; 16/170 HonRl; SecNHS; StuCncl; RptrYrbk; Bsktbl; Trk; IMSpt; Southwest Missouri State Univ; Veterinarian.

LUX, Robert G; Charles City Comm Sr HS; Charles City, IA; 30/227 Band; HonRl; NHS; MthCl; LetterBsbl; LetterTrk; Univ Of Ia; Bus Admn.

LUX, Sharon K; Central Catholic HS; West Point, NE; Band; Chr; HonRl; OffAde; 4-H; SpnCl; Business Sch;.

LUX, Susan K; John Marshall HS; Milwaukee, WI; HospAde; RptrYrbk; College; Professional.

LUZECKY, Mark A; Bishop Dubourg HS; St Louis, MO; 5/450 ChrhWkr; HonRl; NHS; OffAde; TreasSdlty; StuCncl; RptrSchPpr; LatCl; LetterSocr; Trk; College; Professional.

LYBACK, Susan M; Isle HS; Wahkon, MN; 1/57 ALAGirlsSt; Band; Chr; ChrhWkr; HonRl; NHS; SchPl; FHA; SciCl; AmLegAwd; Augsburg College; Science.

LYBARGER, Louise A; Clay City HS; Noble, IL; 2/45 HonRl; StuCncl; RptrYrbk; EdSchPpr; TreasPpCl; VPGAA; DARAwd; Olney Central College; Secretarial.

LYBARGER, Ronald L; William Chrisman HS; Independence, MO; Quill&Scroll; EdYrBk; SchPpr; KeyCl; Ftbl; Swmmng; Trk;.

LYCAN, Connie M; Niosho HS; Joplin, MO; ALAGirlsSt; Band; ChrhWkr; CncrtBnd; HonRl; LbryAde; MrchBnd; PepBnd; TchrAde; 4-H; EngCl; PpCl; DanFAwd; College; Secretarial Position.

LYCHUK, Paul S; Lake Orion HS; Lake Orion, MI; 22/350 ALBoysSt; HonRl; NHS; LetterBsktbl; LetterTrk; Central Mi; Law.

LYCHYK, Victor G; Oak Park River Forest HS; River Forest, IL; 70/1107 HonRl;.

LYDY, Kathryn H; Hastings HS; Hastings, MI; HonRl; ModUN; TchrAde; Trk; Kellogg Comm; Spec Ed.

LYERLA, Robin L; Columbia HS; Columbia, IL; 14/126 Chrs; CncrtBnd; HonRl; MrchBnd; NHS; SchPl; StuCncl; EdYrBk; FTA; OptClAwd; Se Mo Univ; Medicine.

LYKINS, Christine L; Maple Valley HS; Nashville, MI; Band; CncrtBnd; HonRl; MrchBnd; PepBnd; PresFrshCls; 4-H; Bsktbl; IMSpt; CAP;.

LYKKEN, Joseph D; Phillips Exeter Acad; Minneapolis, MN; CAP; HonRl; LitMag; MrchBnd; NatlMeritSF; EdSchPpr; SciCl; U Of Mn; Mortuary Science.

LYLE, Donna L; Edgewood HS; Bloomington, IN; PresBand; Chrs; CncrtBnd; DrmMjrt; MrchBnd; PepBnd; StuCncl; 4-H; GerCl; 4-HAwd; College.

LYLE, Gregg P; Beresford HS; Beresford, SD; CaptFtbl; LetterTrk; CaptWrstlng; College; Physical Therapist.

LYLES, Fragelia D; Roosevelt HS; Gary, IN; Chr; ChrhWkr; CmntyWkr; CncrtBnd; HonRl; HospAde; MrchBnd; OffAde; PpCl; Trk; College; Professional.

LYLES, Frederick D; Crispus Attucks HS; Indianapolis, IN; 49/249 MrchBnd; Bsbl; ChmnFtbl; Swmmng; LetterTrk; ChmnWrstlng; Oh St; Archit.

LYMAN, Luba D; Elwood Community HS; Elwood, IN; Band; Chr; ChrhWkr; CncrtBnd; VPJA; MrchBnd; PresYthFlsp; FTA; LatCl; Vincennes University; Physical Therapy.

LYMBEROPOULOS, Gregory A; Princeton HS; Princeton, IL; HonRl; FrCl; Bsbl; Bsktbl; Ftbl; Glf; College; Baseball.

LYNAM, Anne E; Atlantic Sr HS; Atlantic, IA; 31/165 Chrs; HonRl; LbryAde; RedCrAde; StuCncl; YthFlsp; RptrYrbk; 4-H; Swmmng; 4-HAwd; College; Biology.

LYNAM, Carolyn D; Stanton Community HS; Stanton, IA; VPJrCls; TrsSrCls; Band; Chr; CncrtBnd; MrchBnd; Pres4-H; PpCl; LetterBsktbl; LetterTrk; Clarinda Comm Col; Secretarial.

LYNCH, Delyn L; Watervliet HS; Watervliet, MI; ChrhWkr; CmntyWkr; CncrtBnd; HonRl; MrchBnd; SchAde; StuCncl; RptrYrbk; RptrSchPpr; CitAwd; College; Professional.

LYNCH, Diane; Turkey Valley HS; Lawler, IA; HonRl; RptrYrbk; Coll; Professional.

LYNCH, Gayle S; Calumet HS; Gary, IN; 32/315 ALAGirlsSt; HonRl; Quill&Scroll; PresSchPl; Yrbk; RptrSchPpr; GAA; PPFtbl; Indiana University; Medical Technology.

LYNCH, James L; Le Sueur HS; Le Sueur, MN; TrsFrshCls; Chr; HonRl; JA; JrNHS; NHS; StuCncl; Bsktbl; Glf; IMSpt; College; Science Field.

LYNCH, James L; E Richland HS; Claremont, IL; 8/264 ALBoysSt; JrNHS; NHS; StuCncl; Bsbl; Eastern Il Univ; Accounting.

LYNCH, Janet K; Edwardsville HS; Edwardsville, IL; Chrl; Chrs; ChrhWkr; Mdrgl; FrCl; Trk; Western Ill Univ; Science.

LYNCH, Lenard L; Lake Central HS; Crown Point, IN; CncrtBnd; MrchBnd; NatlThespSoc; Orch; PepBnd; SchMus; SchPl; Purdue University; Science.

LYNCH, Lindley J; West Noble HS; Kimmell, IN; 6/123 ALBoysSt; ChrhWkr; HonRl; PresNHS; SctActv; PresYthFlsp; PresSciCl; LetterFtbl; CaptTrk; EldAwd; Purdue U; Aerospace Engr.

LYNCH, Marian P; Good Counsel HS; Chicago, IL; Chrl; ChrhWkr; CmntyWkr; HonRl; JA; NatlFornLg; FBLA; FNA; GAA; IMSpt; Moser Clg; Business.

LYNCH, Mary A; St Andrew HS; Detroit, MI; 2/110 ChrhWkr; HonRl; LbryAde; NHS; RptrYrbk; PpCl; LetterBsbl; LetterBsktbl; IMSpt; PresAwd; Wayne State U; Medical.

LYNCH, Michael P; New Haven HS; Fort Wayne, IN; 9/250 VPSophCls; PresJrCls; Aud/Vis; HonRl; IntrClCncl; LbryAde; NatlFornLg; SchPl; PresFSA; PresSciCl; Northwestern Univ; Urban Planning.

LYNCH, Nancy L; Hillsboro HS; Hillsboro, IL; 24/190 DrlTm; HonRl; OffAde; GAA; Beauty School; Beautician.

LYNCH, Patricia; Kalamazoo Central HS; Kalamazoo, MI; 74/536 ChrhWkr; CmntyWkr; Quill&Scroll; SchMus; SchPpr; GerCl; IMSpt; Michigan State Univ; Agriculture.

LYNCH, Randall G; Lutheran West HS; Detroit, MI; Band; CncrtBnd; HonRl; JrNHS; MrchBnd; NHS; NatlMeritSchl; NatlMeritSF; PepBnd; StuCncl; StuGov;.

LYNCH, Rhonda S; Trenton HS; Trenton, MO; 12/128 AFS; ChrhWkr; HonRl; StuCncl; YthFlsp; 4-H; FFA; PpCl; SciCl; LetterBsktbl; Trenton Jr Coll; Secondary Edu.

LYNCH, Robert L; Pleasant Plains HS; Springfield, IL; HonRl; JA; SctActv; Trk; LetterWrstlng; Western Illinois Univ; Business Adm.

LYNCH, Sandra A; Brainerd Senior HS; Brainerd, MN; 39/475 HonRl; NatlFornLg; NHS; Quill&Scroll; StuCncl; StuGov; Yrbk; RptrSchPpr; EngCl; Hamline Univ St Paul Mn.

LYNCH, Terry F; Fonda Comm HS; Varina, IA; TrsFrshCls; ALBoysSt; CmntyWkr; HonRl; SchPl; CivCl; LetterBsbl; LetterBsktbl; LetterFtbl; IMSpt; AmLegAwd; University; Liberal Arts.

LYND, Lee H; Harvard St George HS; Chicago, IL; StuCncl; StuGov; RptrYrbk; LetterBsbl; LetterBsktbl; JCAwd; Bates Coll; Law.

LYNEMA, Clifford L; Northridge HS; Goshen, IN; 34/140 TrsJrCls; HonRl; SchPl; Yrbk; KeyCl; Purdue Univ; Accounting.

LYNG, Kent A; Central Valley HS; Cummings, ND; 9/24 Band; Chrs; CncrtBnd; HonRl; PepBnd; 4-H; PresFFA; 4-HAwd; No Dakota Schl Of Science; Elec Technology.

LYNGE, Elaine A; Mother Theodore Guerin HS; Chicago, IL; 6/410 ChrhWkr; HonRl; NHS; SctActv; StuCncl; EdYrBk; Purdue Univ; Pharmacist.

LYNN, Andrew W; Taylor HS; Kokomo, IN; 62/179 Aud/Vis; SchPl; PpCl; Ftbl; Wrstlng; IMSpt; Purdue University; Podiatry.

LYNN, Catherine S; Truman HS; Independence, MO; PresAFS; ChrhWkr; CmntyWkr; SctActv; PresStuCncl; FrCl; Nursing School; Registered Nurse.

LYNN, Cheryl J; Woodland HS; Marble Hill, MO; HonRl; HospAde; StuCncl; RptrYrbk; SpnCl; PpCl; SciCl; Trk; Chrldr; PresAwd; Coll; Vet.

LYNN, Diane K; Lake Benton Public HS; Verdi, MN; Band; Chrs; CncrtBnd; HonRl; NHS; SchPl; YthFlsp; FHA; EngCl; Chrldr;.

LYNN, Gary S; Arlington HS; Indianapolis, IN; 9/404 VPSrCls; ALBoysSt; HonRl; IntrClCncl; ModUN; NatlMeritSF; SchPl; StuCncl; SecIMSpt; Northwestern Univ; Medicine.

LYNN, Lauren J; Wayne HS; Ft Wayne, IN; Chr; Chrl; PolWkr; SchMus; FrCl; PpCl; Airline Company.

LYNN, Marie M; Benet Academy; Glen Ellyn, IL; 85/247 Band; CncrtBnd; HonRl; MrchBnd; Western Illinois Univ; Accounting.

LYNN, Michael A; Orchard View HS; Muskegon, MI; Chr; HonRl; LbryAde; Mdrgl; NatlMeritCmnd; NatlMeritSchl; SchMus; SchPl; FrCl; PpCl; American Acad/performing Arts; Acting.

LYNN, Michael R; Maine Twp East HS; Park Ridge, IL; CmntyWkr; Univ Of Illinois; Veterinarian.

LYNN, Robert S; Morton HS; Morton, IL; 23/292 HonRl; NatlMeritCmnd; LatCl; LetterWrstlng; Univ Of Ill; Dentistry.

LYNN, Robert T; Farragut HS; Shenandoah, IA; 9/35 Band; CncrtBnd; HonRl; MrchBnd; PepBnd; PresFBLA; SecFFA; 4-HAwd;.

LYNNE, Kim G; Plaza HS; Plaza, ND; PresSophCls; VPJrCls; HonRl; MrchBnd; RptrSchPpr; 4-H; CaptBsbl; CaptBsktbl; CaptTrk; 4-HAwd; U Of Nd Williston; Athletic Trainer.

LYON, Agatha C; Bishop Lillis HS; Kansas City, MO; 17/86 Chr; ChrhWkr; CmntyWkr; HonRl; SchMus; StuCncl; YthLg; LatCl; SpnCl; PpCl; College; Special Ed.

LYON, David L; Elmore HS; Elmore, MN; Chr; Chrl; Chrs; SchPl; SctActv; Ftbl; Marine Corps; Science.

LYON, Delilah M; Calhoun HS; Windsor, MO; 1/10 SecFrshCls; PresSophCls; Chrs; HonRl; StuCncl; EdYrBk; EdSchPpr; 4-H; PpCl; LetterBsktbl; Chrldr; CitAwd; Univ Of Mo; Pediatrics.

LYON, Denice M; Coldwater HS; Coldwater, MI; 26/277 CmntyWkr; HospAde; NHS; PresCivCl; 4-H; VPGerCl; PpCl; SciCl; LetterTrk; Chrldr; 4-HAwd; Kellogg Comm College; Nursing.

LYON, Diane C; Portland Public HS; Portland, MI; 11/120 Band; CncrtBnd; HonRl; LbryAde; MrchBnd; NHS; PepBnd; FTA; Central Mi Univ; Teacher Of Elementary Ed.

LYON, Gary R; Homer Community HS; Homer, NE; 1/22 PresSophCls; ALBoysSt; HonRl; JrNHS; NHS; SchPl; StuCncl; RptrYrbk; SciCl; LetterFtbl; Us Air Force Academy; Computer Sciences.

LYON, Lili R; Estherville Sr HS; Estherville, IA; Band; Chr; Chrs; ChrhWkr; HonRl; Mdrgl; MrchBnd; NatlFornLg; NHS; SchMus; SchPl; Univ Of Iowa; Library Science.

LYON, Sara E; Bogard R4 HS; Bogard, MO; 3/10 TrsFrshCls; SecSophCls; SecSrCls; Chr; Chrs; ChrhWkr; HonRl; SchPl; TchrAde; RptrYrbk; LetterBsbl; CaptBsktbl; CaptTrk; LetterChrldr; N W Missouri State Univ; Accountant.

LYON, Twyla P; Calhoun HS; Windsor, MO; 1/8 PresFrshCls; PresSophCls; PresJrCls; Chrs; HonRl; StuCncl; 4-H; PpCl; LetterBsktbl; College.

LYONS, Barbara; Sunset Hill HS; Kansas City, MO; PresSophCls; AFS; Chrl; Orch; RedCrAde; SchMus; StuGov; RptrYrbk; Univ; Biology.

LYONS, Connie L; Oak Park Sr HS; Kansas City, MO; 86/545 Chr; ChrhWkr; HonRl; Ozark Bible College; Special Educ Teacher.

LYONS, Deborah S; Mather HS; Chicago, IL; 12/442 CmntyWkr; HonRl; HospAde; NHS; NatlSciFnd; Orch; SchMus; SchPl; StuCncl; StuGov; FTA; SpnCl; Univ Of Illinois; Medicine.

LYONS, Eric W; Cherry Hill HS; Inkster, MI; HonRl; NHS; LetterBsbl; LetterBsktbl; Mi State U; Landscape Architect.

LYONS, Jack L; Central City HS; Central City, NE; 36/92 Band; HonRl; MrchBnd; PepBnd; Bsktbl; Ftbl; Trk; College.

LYONS, Kimberly A; Hubbard HS; Chicago, IL; Chrs; HonRl; OffAde; Quill&Scroll; StuCncl; TreasStuGov; SchPpr; FTA; MthCl; PpCl; GAA; PPFtbl; College; Art.

LYONS, Laura L; Mt Pulaski HS; Elkhart, IL; 2/98 VPSophCls; PresJrCls; HonRl; NHS; NatlMeritCmnd; Orch; RptrYrbk; RptrSchPpr; 4-H; FrCl; U Of Il; Psychology.

LYONS, Mary T; Cathedral HS; Omaha, NE; CmntyWkr; HonRl; LbryAde; NHS; PolWkr; Univ Of Nebraska; Politics.

LYONS, Matthew R; Brother Rice HS; Lathrup Vlg, MI; 10/225 ALBoysSt; HonRl; StuCncl; StuGov; EdSchPpr; LetterFtbl; IMSpt; Col; Economics.

LYONS, Michael T; Marist HS; Chicago, IL; HstSrCls; CmntyWkr; HonRl; NHS; StuCncl; StuGov; CivCl; LatCl; LetterTrk; Northern Ill; Business.

LYONS, Steven L; Jamaica HS; Sidell, IL; TrsJrCls; PresSrCls; Chr; HonRl; MrchBnd; PepBnd; SchPl; StuCncl; Glf; 4-HAwd; School; Conservation.

LYONS, Terry L; Virginia Comm Unit #64 HS; Virginia, IL; HonRl; FFA; Bsktbl; Ftbl;.

LYONS, Theresa S; Cornell HS; Odell, IL; 5/29 ALAGirlsSt; DrmMjrt; HonRl; SchPl; StuCncl; Yrbk; SchPpr; 4-H; Chrldr; Wesleyan Univ; Physics.

LYSAKER, Susan K; Logan Senior HS; La Crosse, WI; 1/226 ALAGirlsSt; ChrhWkr; HonRl; NHS; OffAde; StuCncl; TchrAde; PresYthFlsp; SpnCl; PpCl; U Of Wis; Chemistry.

LYSTE, Maribeth L; Sharon Public HS; Sharon, ND; VPJrCls; Chr; HonRl; SchPl; TchrAde; YthFlsp; RptrSchPpr; PpCl; LetterBsktbl; LetterTrk; AmLegAwd; Univ Of North Dakota; Accounting.

LYTER, Edward A; Valley City HS; Sanborn, ND; 48/158 Band; HonRl; NHS; FFA; Ftbl; IMSpt; Valley City St College; Accountant.

LYTHJOHAN, Connie; Oregon Senior HS; Oregon, WI; Chrs; ChrhWkr; CncrtBnd; LbryAde; MrchBnd; NHS; TchrAde; RptrYrbk; College; Elementary Educ.

LYTLE, Alan D; Ottawa HS; Ottawa, KS; Band; ChrhWkr; HonRl; MrchBnd; SctActv; TchrAde; YthFlsp; Bsbl; LetterTrk; IMSpt; College; Electronics.

LYTLE, Pamela J; English HS; Eckerty, IN; TrsFrshCls; TrsJrCls; Band; HonRl; MrchBnd; NHS; PepBnd; 4-H; FHA; CaptChrldr; Bus School; Secretary.

LYTTLE, Dani; Lejeune HS; Austin, IN; 3/120 Chrs; HonRl; JrNHS; LitMag; LbryAde; NHS; NatlMeritCmnd; StuGov; RptrYrbk; FrCl; College; Law.

LYTTLE, Daniel W; Aurora HS; Aurora, IN; 6/150 Band; Chr; CncrtBnd; HonRl; NHS; NatlMeritCmnd; SchPl; SctActv; 4-H; PpCl; SciCl; Rose Hulman Inst Of Tech; Electrical Engr.

LYTTLE, Heather J; Fort Zumwalt HS; Ofallon, MO; SecSrCls; Chr; HonRl; OffAde; PpCl; Chrldr; GAA; PPFtbl; PresAwd; College; Professional.

LYTTON, Lisa M; Washington Catholic HS; Washington, IN; TrsSophCls; PresJrCls; Chrs; HonRl; NHS; PpCl;.

Mc

MC ADAMS, Steven J; Walter B Hammer HS; Estherville, IA; PresJrCls; Chrs; HonRl; Mdrgl; NatlFornLg; SchMus; SchPl; StuCncl; RptrYrbk; College; History.

MC AFEE, Barbara; Union County HS; Liberty, IN; HonRl; NHS; OffAde; SchPl; SpnCl; PpCl; Tennis; Univ; Nursing.

MC AFEE, Kimberly S; Mason City HS; Mason City, IL; 1/46 PresSrCls; Chr; Chrs; ChrhWkr; HonRl; NHS; StuCncl; PresYthFlsp; FTA; PpCl; Junior College; Accounting.

MC AFEE, Louise R; Soldan HS; St Louis, MO; 8/625 CmntyWkr; HonRl; NHS; StuGov; PpCl; College; Medicine.

MC AFEE, Paul G; Fullerton HS; Fullerton, NE; 17/59 ChrhWkr; HonRl; YthFlsp; 4-H; FFA; LetterFtbl; Trade Schl; Vocation.

MC AKAR, Gary; Catholic Memorial HS; New Berlin, WI; 29/148 ChrhWkr; HonRl; NHS; Trk; IMSpt; Marquette Univ; Engrg.

MC ALEXANDER, Earl D; Mt Ayr Comm HS; Beaconsfield, IA; Band; HonRl; SchPl; TreasStuCncl; PresFFA; LetterBsbl; LetterBsktbl; LetterFtbl; LetterTrk; 4-HAwd; Iowa State Univ; Forestry.

MC ALEXANDER, Gregory; Mormon Trail HS; Humeston, IA; 15/40 SecSrCls; ALBoysSt; Band; CncrtBnd; HonRl; MrchBnd; SchMus; Iowa State Univ.

MC ALISTER, David L; Sedan HS; Sedan, KS; SchPl; SctActv; StuCncl; TchrAde; SptEdYrbk; RptrSchPpr; FSA; LetterBsktbl; Ftbl; Ks St Univ; Forest Ranger.

MC ALISTER, Teresa D; Lafayette HS; St Joseph, MO; Chr; Chrs; HonRl; HospAde; SctActv; FHA; College; Professional.

MC ALISTER, Terri D; Central HS; Omaha, NE; Chr; Chrs; ChrhWkr; HonRl; LbryAde; NatlMeritCmnd; SchAde; SchPl; SctActv; YthFlsp; Yrbk; Creighton Univ; Broadcast Journalist.

MC ALLASTER, Darlene; Lyons HS; Lyons, KS; 1/97 HonRl; ModUN; NatlMeritFnl; OffAde; PolWkr; Quill&Scroll; SchPl; TchrAde; RptrYrbk; Trk; Univ; Professional.

MC ALLASTER, Darlene M; Lyons HS; Lyons, KS; 2/92 HonRl; ModUN; NatlMeritSF; OffAde; PolWkr; SchPl; TchrAde; RptrYrbk; EdSchPpr; University.

MC ALLASTER, Robert C; Powhattan HS; Powhattan, KS; SecTrsFrshCls; TrsSophCls; HonRl; SchMus; Yrbk; SptEdSchPpr; FFA; Bsktbl; Ftbl; Trk; Hutchison Jr Clge.

MC ALLISTER, Amazair; Rockhurst HS; Kansas City, MO; HstSophCls; NatlMeritCmnd; SchMus; StuGov; Bsktbl; Ftbl; Univ; Medical Doctor.

MC ALLISTER, Barry; Plainfield HS; Joliet, IL; HonRl; LitMag; NHS; SchPpr; Private Univ.

MC ALLISTER, Christopher P; Mac Arthur HS; Decatur, IL; Band; ChrhWkr; CncrtBnd; HonRl; MrchBnd; SctActv; Univ Of Colorado; Architect.

MC ALLISTER, Connie M; Oriska Public HS; Oriska, ND; TrsJrCls; Chr; CncrtBnd; HonRl; PepBnd; SchPl; StuCncl; LetterBsktbl; LetterTrk; Chrldr; Trade; Vocation.

MC ALLISTER, John W; Parkwood HS; Joplin, MO; ALBoysSt; Band; CncrtBnd; HonRl; PepBnd; SctActv; StuCncl; RptrYrbk; SchPpr; MthCl; LetterTennis; Univ; Dentistry.

MC ALLISTER, Peggy; Lebanon HS; Lebanon, IL; SecJrCls; Band; Chr; Chrs; OffAde; StuCncl; PpCl; Bsktbl; Swmmng; Business School.

MC ALLISTER, Peggy L; Paul Harding HS; Ft Wayne, IN; Chr; ChrhWkr; HospAde; OffAde; SchPl; TchrAde; RptrYrbk; PpCl; Swmmng; Chrldr; Ind Univ.

MC ALLISTER, Sidney G; Union HS; Grand Rapids, MI; HonRl; NatlFornLg; NHS; SchMus; ChmnSwmmng; Trk; IMSpt; Grand Rapids Jr Clge; Phy Educ.

MC ALLISTER, Teresa L; Mexico HS; Mexico, MO; Chr; Chrs; HospAde; JA; StuCncl; TchrAde; EdYrBk; FBLA; LatCl; PpCl; Nmsu Kirksville Mo; Medical Secretary.

MC ALOON, Greg A; Carmel HS; Carmel, IN; LetterBsktbl; IMSpt; College; Business Administration.

MC ALVEY, Jane E; Benton Harbor HS; Benton Harbor, MI; 25/413 NHS; YthFlsp; MthCl; Michigan State Univ; Veterinary.

MC ANARY, Kim H; Merrill HS; Merrill, MI; 14/106 SecFrshCls; Band; ChrhWkr; HonRl; NHS; StuCncl; TchrAde; YthFlsp; FHA; CaptBsktbl; Central Michigan University; Special Educat.

MC ANDREW, Paul J; Mid Prairie HS; Kalona, IA; 1/75 PresFrshCls; PresSrCls; Aud/Vis; Band; CncrtBnd; HonRl; MrchBnd; NatlMeritCmnd; NatlMeritSchl; StuCncl; StuGov; FSA; LetterBsbl; LetterBsktbl; Univ Of Iowa; Law.

MC ANELLY, Deborah; Blue Valley HS; Shawnee Mission, KS; Chr; Chrl; DrlTm; HonRl; NHS; SchPl; Yrbk; SchPpr; FTA; PpCl; Coe College; Botany.

MC ANINCH, David H; West Sioux HS; Hawarden, IA; HonRl; Trade Schl; Vocation.

MC ARDLE, David L; St Anns HS; Lexington, NE; VPSophCls; ALBoysSt; SchPl; SctActv; StuCncl; Yrbk; Bsktbl; Ftbl; U Of Ne; Engineering.

MC ARDLE, Gregory; Gordon Technical; Chicago, IL; 71/584 CmntyWkr; PolWkr; YthFlsp; IMSpt; Coll; Electronics.

MC ARTON, Paula J; Irene Public HS; Irene, SD; VPFrshCls; Band; Chrs; CncrtBnd; HospAde; MrchBnd; SchPl; SecStuCncl; VPFHA; LetterBsktbl; Sd State Univ; Pharmacy.

MC ARTON, Paula J; Irene HS; Irene, SD; 4/36 VPSophCls; HstJrCls; Chrs; CncrtBnd; HonRl; HospAde; NHS; PepBnd; SchPl; SecStuCncl; VPFHA; LetterBsktbl; University; Pharmacy.

MC ATEE, Charles; J H Bowen HS; Chicago, IL; 4/613 Band; CncrtBnd; HonRl; MrchBnd; NHS; SchAde; EdYrBk; FSA; LatCl; Us Navy, Nuclear Power.

MC AULEY, Joan; Palatine Hs; Palatine, IL; HonRl; RptrYrbk; Bsktbl; Augustana College; Speech Therapist.

MC AULIFFE, Kathleen A; Sterling Public HS; St Mary, NE; PresFrshCls; TrsJrCls; PresSrCls; ALAGirlsSt; HonRl; NHS; SchPl; EdYrBk; PpCl; Chrldr;.

MC AULIFFE, Kevin P; Forest View HS; Des Plaines, IL; 115/650 Band; CncrtBnd; MrchBnd; NHS; Orch; PepBnd; PolWkr; College; Law.

MC AULIFFE, Meg; Adrian HS; Adrian, MI; ChrhWkr; HonRl; StuCncl; RptrYrbk; SptEdYrbk; Tennis; Trk; College; High School Counslor.

MC AVOY, Brian R; Owosso HS; Owosso, MI; NHS; NatlMeritCmnd; SchAde; StuCncl; LatCl; LetterBsbl; LetterFtbl; Univ Of Michigan; Medicine.

MC AVOY, Jane E; Burlington Comm HS; Burlington, IA; 3/501 Band; Chr; ChrhWkr; CncrtBnd; HonRl; Mdrgl; MrchBnd; NHS; Orch; PepBnd; SchMus; College; Music Ed.

MC BAIN, Douglas S; Omaha Benson HS; Omaha, NE; ChrhWkr; HonRl; NHS; Orch; SctActv; AmLegAwd; Doane Col; Medicine.

MC BEE, Lisa; Blue Valley HS; Stilwell, KS; Band; CncrtBnd; HonRl; HospAde; MrchBnd; NHS; PepBnd; TchrAde; FTA; PpCl; Kansas St Univ.

MC BRAYER, Charles W; Unionville Sebewaing Area HS; Sebewaing, MI; ALBoysSt; Chrs; HonRl; NatlMeritFnl; NatlMeritCmnd; NatlMeritSF; YthFlsp; Bsbl; Bsktbl; Saginaw Valley State Coll; Accounting.

MC BRIDE, Anthony C; Haless Franciscan HS; Chicago, IL; 3/80 TrsJrCls; TrsSrCls; HonRl; LbryAde; NatlMeritCmnd; NatlMeritSchl; StuGov; FshEdYrbk; PpCl; Bradley Univ; Bus Admin.

MC BRIDE, Dave A; West Ottawa HS; Holland, MI; CmntyWkr; HonRl; Grand Valley Central Univ; Medicine.

MC BRIDE, Erin N; East Charles Mix #102 HS; Wagner, SD; PresFrshCls; PresJrCls; Band; Chrs; CncrtBnd; HonRl; NHS; NatlMeritSF; SchPl; RotaryAwd; College.

MC BRIDE, Garry L; Coldwater HS; Coldwater, MI; VPFrshCls; Band; ChrhWkr; CmntyWkr; CncrtBnd; HonRl; MrchBnd; PepBnd; PolWkr; SctActv; StuCncl; TchrAde; IMSpt; ChmbCommrsAwd; Michigan State University; Agriculture.

MC BRIDE, George E; Waupun HS; Waupun, WI; 10/243 ALBoysSt; TreasNHS; StuCncl; LetterFtbl; CaptGlf; GovHonPrgAwd; RotaryAwd; U S Air Force; Engineer.

MC BRIDE, Julia K; Providence HS; Clarksville, IN; Aud/Vis; Chr; ChrhWkr; CmntyWkr; SchMus; PpCl; Chrldr; PPFtbl; OptClAwd; College; Professional.

MC BRIDE, Kalvin R; Nickerson HS; S Hutchinson, KS; Aud/Vis; Band; CncrtBnd; MrchBnd; NHS; Kansas State College Univ; Electronic Eng.

MC BRIDE, Kenneth W; Northrop HS; Ft Wayne, IN; Aud/Vis; HonRl; RptrSchPpr; Bsktbl; Ftbl; IMSpt; College; Environmental Science.

MC BRIDE, Kris; Blue Valley HS; Leawood, KS; CncrtBnd; HospAde; MrchBnd; NHS; Orch; PepBnd; SchMus; 4-H; College; Medicine.

MC BRIDE, Linda K; Berkeley HS; Hazelwood, MO; Band; Chr; ChrhWkr; CncrtBnd; HonRl; MrchBnd; Orch; StuCncl; SchPpr; Coll; Law.

MC BRIDE, Lois F; Burwell Jr Sr HS; Burwell, NE; Chrs; DrlTm; HonRl; LbryAde; Mdrgl; RptrSchPpr; SchPpr; 4-H; College; Accounting.

MC BRIDE, Mark A; Centennial HS; Champaign, IL; 17/355 NHS; NatlMeritSF; SchMus; SchPl; PresStuCncl; SchPpr; Clge; Lib Arts.

MC BRIDE, Mary L; Walled Lake Central HS; Traverse City, MI; Chr; HonRl; HospAde; NHS; SchMus; TchrAde; LetterSwmmng; Michigan Technological Univ; Nursing.

MC BRIDE, Michael; Beckman HS; Dyersville, IA; SecSrCls; ALBoysSt; Band; Chr; Chrs; ChrhWkr; CncrtBnd; MrchBnd; PepBnd; N Ia Univ.

MC BRIDE, Robert M; Rosemount HS; Inver Grove Hts, MN; 27/423 Chr; HonRl; NatlFornLg; SchPl; StuGov; RptrSchPpr; 4-H; GerCl; 4-HAwd; College; English.

MC BRIDE, Shelly K; Joppa Community HS; Metropolis, IL; 4/26 PresFrshCls; SecJrCls; HonRl; OffAde; StuCncl; TchrAde; PpCl; Chrldr; IMSpt; DARAwd;.

MC BRIDE, Sherry L; Fulton HS; Fulton, MO; ChrhWkr; CmntyWkr; HospAde; JA; JCC; YthFlsp; CivCl; FBLA; FNA; SpnCl; Columbia College; Business Admin.

MC BRIDE, Susan E; Aurora HS; Aurora, NE; Band; CmntyWkr; HonRl; TchrAde; PresTeen; Yrbk; SchPpr; FBLA; PpCl; Bendictine Clge; Professional.

MC BRIDE, Vicki; Metropolis Community Hs; Belknop, IL; 26/177 ChrhWkr; CmntyWkr; HonRl; HospAde; TrsFrshCls; 4-H; DanFAwd; 4-HAwd; Business School; Business Dministrator.

MC BRIEN, Carol C; Pekin HS; Pekin, IL; Band; Chr; ChrhWkr; CncrtBnd; HonRl; MrchBnd; PepBnd; College; Religion.

MC BROOM, Elizabeth D; Clarke Community HS; Osceola, IA; 5/104 TrsSrCls; AFS; Chr; Chrs; HonRl; NHS; SchPl; YthFlsp; 4-H; Bsktbl; Iowa State; Veterinary.

MC BROOM, Kathryn J; Hillsboro HS; Butler, IL; Chrs; ChrhWkr; DrlTm; HonRl; OffAde; SchPl; RptrSchPpr; Pres4-H; SpnCl; 4-HAwd; Lincoln Land Comm College; Computer Prog.

MC BURNEY, Brian A; Clawson HS; Clawson, MI; ChrhWkr; PolWkr; LetterGlf; Oakland Univ; Engr.

MC BURNEY, David M; Caro HS; Caro, MI; Band; CncrtBnd; MrchBnd; PepBnd; SchPl; TchrAde; SpnCl; Western Michigan Univ; Teacher.

MC BURNEY, Vinona M; Humboldt HS; Humboldt, IA; 10/140 Chr; CmntyWkr; HonRl; LbryAde; SchMus; SchPl; Iowa State University; Computer Science.

MC CABE, Carol J; Marillac HS; Niles, IL; College; Business Admin.

MC CABE, Colleen M; Beloit Catholic HS; Beloit, WI; 7/87 HonRl; EdSchPpr; PresSpnCl; Uw Whitewater; Spanish.

MC CABE, Henry D; Mascoutah HS; Safb, IL; ALBoysSt; ChrhWkr; HonRl; JA; LbryAde; Bsktbl; Ftbl; Glf; CchngActv; IMSpt; College; Air Force.

MC CABE, Joan E; Northwest Webster HS; Clare, IA; TrsJrCls; Chrs; HonRl; SchPl; TchrAde; SchPpr; PpCl; LetterTrk; CaptChrldr; Mo St Univ ;elem Educ.

MC CABE, Kathleen; Kirksville HS; Kirksville, MO; Band; ChrhWkr; HonRl; HospAde; MrchBnd; PepBnd; SctActv; FrCl; SecTrsSophCls; SciCl; College; Nursing.

MC CABE, Larry G; Clinton Prairie HS; Frankfort, IN; Pres4-H; PresFFA; 4-HAwd; Purdue Univ; Farming.

MC CABE, Mary A; Newcastle Public HS; Newcastle, NE; 5/24 PresFrshCls; SecSrCls; Band; CncrtBnd; DrlTm; HonRl; MrchBnd; PepBnd; SchPl; TchrAde; RptrSchPpr; Bsktbl; Trk; Chrldr; Trade Schl; Nursing.

MC CABE, Mary Beth; Sacred Heart Of Mary HS; Arlington Hts, IL; 5/134 ChrhWkr; NatlFornLg; NHS; SchMus; SchPl; StuGov; TchrAde; RptrSchPpr; SchPpr; Bsbl; LetterBsktbl; Ftbl; Swmmng; Trk; Univ Of Dayton; Communication Arts.

MC CABE, Patrick; Newman HS; Mason City, IA; 7/103 VPFrshCls; PresSophCls; PresJrCls; ALBoysSt; Band; HonRl; OffAde; Tennis; BauchLmbAwd; OptClAwd; Niacc Univ; Professional.

MC CABE, Patrick G; Consolidated HS; Elcho, WI; VPFrshCls; HonRl; NatlFornLg; TchrAde; MthCl; SciCl; Coll; Botony.

MC CABE, Sheila; Northwest Webster HS; Clare, IA; PresSrCls; Band; Chrs; HonRl; LbryAde; OffAde; SchMus; Glf; Mankato State College.

MC CABE, Toni A; Aurelia Comm HS; Alta, IA; TrsSrCls; CncrtBnd; StuCncl; Twrl; Yrbk; RptrSchPpr; 4-H; FHA; PpCl; LetterGlf; National Col Of Bus; Business Accounting.

MC CAFFERTY, Kathleen A; Rochester HS; Rochester, IL; 3/74 Band; Chr; ChrhWkr; CmntyWkr; HonRl; NHS; NatlMeritCmnd; NatlMeritSF; SchMus; YthFlsp; Oral Roberts Univ; Ministry.

MC CAFFREY, Eileen M; Amboy HS; Dixon, IL; Chrl; HonRl; SchMus; TchrAde; Coll; Speech.

MC CAIN, Caren J; Bedford HS; Bedford, IA; Aud/Vis; Chr; Chrl; Chrs; CmntyWkr; HonRl; Mdrgl; YthFlsp; SpnCl; College; Sociology.

MC CAIN, Carol J; Bedford HS; Bedford, IA; Aud/Vis; Chr; Chrl; Chrs; ChrhWkr; CmntyWkr; HonRl; Mdrgl; OffAde; Quill&Scroll; SchMus; YthFlsp; RptrYrbk; Yrbk; Buena Vista College.

MC CAIRNS, Sharon E; Elkton Pigeon Bay Port HS; Caseville, MI; 21/146 Chrs; NHS; TchrAde; PresFHA; PpCl; Bsktbl; GAA; PPFtbl; CitAwd; Michigan St Univ; Biology.

MC CALL, Allen D; East Richland HS; Olney, IL; NHS; Ftbl; Loyola Univ; Dentistry.

MC CALL, Doris M; Woodland HS; Glen Allen, MO; ChrhWkr; CtyCnl; HonRl; HospAde; JrNHS; FFA; FHA; PpCl; Bsktbl; Chrldr; Trade School; Professional.

MC CALL, Jon K; Mediapolis Community HS; Mediapolis, IA; 14/85 HonRl; SctActv; YthFlsp; PpCl; LetterFtbl; Trk; CaptWrstlng; CchngActv; IMSpt; Kirkwood Comm College; Computer Science.

MC CALL, Timothy J; Meredosia Chambersburg HS; Meridosia, IL; 12/43 ChrhWkr; CmntyWkr; DrmMjrt; HonRl; NHS; SchMus; SchPl; StuCncl; RptrYrbk; Millikin University; Art.

MC CALLEY, Mark A; Jefferson HS; Cedar Rapids, IA; TchrAde; YthFlsp; Ftbl; College; Coach.

MC CALLIE, Machelle; Kimball Consolidated HS; Kimball, SD; PressSophCls; Chrl; Chrs; ChrhWkr; HonRl; SchMus; StuCncl; PresPpCl; CaptBsktbl; CchngActv; College; Education.

MC CALLISTER, Karen L; Joliet West HS; Joliet, IL; 51/521 HonRl; NHS; Univ Of Ill; Business.

MC CALLISTER, Kathryn; Houston R I HS; Houston, MO; Band; ChrhWkr; CncrtBnd; HonRl; MrchBnd; NHS; PepBnd; SchPl; StuCncl; CivCl; Business School; Secretary.

MC CALLUM, George R; Carl Junction HS; Joplin, MO; HonRl; OffAde; TchrAde; UNYO; Pres4-H; VPFFA; LetterBsbl; LetterBsktbl; LetterFtbl; 4-HAwd; Kansas State Univ; Ranch Manager.

MC CALLUM, Lisa M; Lasalle Peru Twp HS; Peru, IL; AFS; Chrs; CmntyWkr; DrlTm; HonRl; SchMus; SpnCl; PpCl; University; Library Science.

MC CALLUM, Mary T; Dominican HS; St Clair, MI; CmntyWkr; NatlMeritSF; SctActv; TchrAde; Univ Of Mich.

MC CALLUM, Vicky; Horicon HS; Horicon, WI; Band; HonRl; JrNHS; MrchBnd; NHS; PepBnd; Wi Univ Oshkosh; Music.

MC CALPIN, William F; St Louis HS; Glendale, MO; 2/210 VPSrCls; HonRl; NHS; SchPl; StuCncl; Bsktbl; LetterFtbl; Glf; IMSpt; Williams College; Law.

MC CAMMON, John M; Whitko HS; S Whitley, IN; 1/160 TrsJrCls; ALBoysSt; Band; ChrhWkr; CncrtBnd; HonRl; MrchBnd; Bsbl; Ftbl; IMSpt; Medical Field.

MC CAMMON, John M; Whitko HS; So Whitley, IN; 1/153 CncrtBnd; NHS; NatlMeritSchl; NatlThespSoc; SchMus; SchPl; EdSchPpr; SciCl; Bsbl; LetterFtbl; AmLegAwd; 4-HAwd; Wabash College; Physics.

MC CAMMON, Pamela; Hutsonville HS; Annapolis, IL; Chr; HonRl; SchPl; FHA; PpCl; Lincoln Trail Jr Coll; Public Relation Bus.

MC CAMMON, Patricia L; Hutsonville HS; Annapolis, IL; Chr; VPChrs; SecChrhWkr; HonRl; PepBnd; SchPl; FHA; PpCl; Lincoln Trail Jr College; Business.

MC CAMPBELL, Cheryl A; Northwestern HS; Mendon, MO; Chrs; HonRl; NHS; FHA; GerCl; SciCl; LetterBsbl; Univ; Med Tech.

MC CANCE, Steve S; Gregory HS; Dallas, SD; VPSrCls; ALBoysSt; Chr; HonRl; SchPl; Bsbl; Ftbl;.

MC CANDLESS, Lillian I; Highland HS; Highland, IN; 117/534 Band; CncrtBnd; MrchBnd; PresFrCl; Purdue University; Home Ec.

MC CANLESS, Suzette; Oak Ridge HS; Oak Ridge, MO; Chrs; ChrhWkr; HonRl; PpCl; Sch Of The Ozarks; Commercial Art.

MC CANN, David J; St Alberts HS; Council Bluffs, IA; HonRl; PolWkr; SchPpr; Ftbl; Trk; Wrstlng; Creighton U; Attorney.

MC CANN, Janet M; Mother Of Sorrows HS; Chicago, IL; HonRl; StuCncl; RptrSchPpr; FrCl; Col; Business Admini.

MC CANN, Kevin D; Mount Carmel HS; Chicago, IL; 1 203 ChrhWkr; HonRl; JrNHS; ModUN; NatlFornLg; FshEdYrbk; RptrSchPpr; GerCl; LetterTennis; VoiceDemAwd; Clg; Communications.

MC CANN, Kristine B; Tyndall HS; Springfield, SD; PresSophCls; HstJrCls; Band; HonRl; SchPl; StuCncl; Bsktbl; Trk; Chrldr; AmLegAwd; U Of Sd, Vermillion.

MC CANN, Laurie F; Buffalo HS; Buffalo, ND; TrsSrCls; Band; HonRl; SchPl; StuCncl; YthFlsp; FHA; PpCl; Bsktbl; Chrldr; N D S U At Fargo; Fashion Merchandising.

MC CANN, Mary J; St Mary Perpetual Help HS; Chicago, IL; HonRl; Sdlty; SpnCl; De Paul Univ; Accounting.

MC CANN, Michael G; Minto HS; Grafton, ND; VPSrCls; Band; Chr; CncrtBnd; HonRl; MrchBnd; PepBnd; SchMus; SchPl; SctActv; StuCncl; Bsktbl; Ftbl; Univ Of N Dakota; Farming.

MC CANN, Robert A; East Pike HS; Milton, IL; 10/29 PresSrCls; HonRl; SchPl; Yrbk; 4-H; FFA; LetterBsbl; Lewis And Clark Comm College; Vocation.

MC CANN, Sandy R; Buffalo HS; Buffalo, ND; Band; Chr; Chrs; CncrtBnd; HonRl; Mdrgl; PepBnd; YthFlsp; RptrSchPpr; SchPpr; Ndsu; Science Math.

MC CARRELL, Clark G; Hales Franciscan HS; Chicago, IL; 18/80 Band; HonRl; RptrYrbk; RptrSchPpr; SpnCl; SciCl; Tennis; Trk; IMSpt; JETSAwd; Chicago State Univ; Nuclear Power Research.

MC CARROLL, Leigh A; Excelsior Springs HS; Excelsior Springs, MO; Chr; NHS; SchMus; SptEdYrbk; FTA; LetterBsktbl; Chrldr; College; Teacher.

MC CART, Brenda K; Wayne Community HS; Corydon, IA; CmntyWkr; DrlTm; HonRl; NHS; RptrYrbk; FshEdYrbk; SptEdYrbk; Yrbk; FHA; Trk; Univ Of Ia; Pjysical Therapy.

MC CARTER, James L; Oskaloosa HS; Oskaloosa, KS; HonRl; SchPl; FBLA; Bsbl; Bsktbl; Professional.

MC CARTER, Kirk R; Shawnee Heights HS; Topeka, KS; SchPl; College; Medicine Or Law.

MC CARTER, Maureen R; Grosse Pointe South HS; Grosse Pointe, MI; CmntyWkr; HonRl; HospAde; OffAde; StuCncl; Bsktbl; Albion Col; Bus.

MC CARTER, Michael A; Campus HS; Blue Springs, MO; RptrYrbk; RptrSchPpr; LetterWrstlng; Nw Mo State; Vet.

MC CARTHY, Aileen C; Hayden HS; Topeka, KS; HonRl; JrNHS; NHS; NatlMeritSF; StuCncl; FrCl; PpCl; GAA; Ks University; Physician.

MC CARTHY, Anne B; Divine Child HS; Dearborn Hgts, MI; ChrhWkr; HonRl; SchPl; StuCncl; StuGov; RptrSchPpr; Bsktbl; CchngActv; Col; Law.

MC CARTHY, Brian; Marist HS; Chicago, IL; 002/364 Band; CncrtBnd; HonRl; MrchBnd; NatlMeritCmnd; PepBnd; Northern Illinois University.

MC CARTHY, Brian V; Marist HS; Chicago, IL; 4/364 Band; CncrtBnd; HonRl; MrchBnd; NatlMeritCmnd; PepBnd; Northern Illinois Univ; Business.

MC CARTHY, Cheryl M; Galena HS; Galena, IL; 20/115 AFS; ALBoysSt; 4-H; PresPpCl; LetterTennis; AmLegAwd; 4-HAwd; Trade Sch.

MC CARTHY, Dianne; West Catholic HS; Grand Rappids, MI; 23 310 Chr; JA; NHS; StuCncl; StuGov; GerCl; LetterTrk; IMSpt; PPFtbl; Mi Univ; Physical Educ.

MC CARTHY, Garry P; Manhattan HS; Manhattan, KS; VPFrshCls; Chr; Chrs; ChrhWkr; HonRl; YthFlsp; YthFnd; SchPpr; Bsktbl; CaptFtbl; College.

MC CARTHY, John D; Nashua HS; Nashua, IA; PresJrCls; HonRl; LbryAde; NHS; StuCncl; EdSchPpr; FrCl; LetterBsbl; LetterFtbl;.

MC CARTHY, John F; East Lansing HS; E Lansing, MI; NHS; TchrAde; Bsbl; Swmmng; Univ Of Mich; Engineer.

MC CARTHY, Joyce M; Riceville Community HS; Mc Intire, IA; 12/79 Chrs; HonRl; OffAde; Sdlty; RptrSchPpr; FNA; GAA; Rochester Jr Coll; Nursing.

MC CARTHY, Karen A; Lakeview HS; St Clair Shores, MI; ChrhWkr; HonRl; HospAde; JrNHS; RptrSchPpr; LetterBsbl; LetterBsktbl; Trk; College; Medicine.

MC CARTHY, Kathleen; West Ottawa HS; Holland, MI; 13/271 Band; CncrtBnd; HonRl; MrchBnd; NHS; Orch; FrCl; Tennis; Hope College; Music Major.

MC CARTHY, Kerry K; Mt St Scholastica Academy; Atchison, KS; Chr; Chrs; DrlTm; HonRl; SchMus; SchPl; Sdlty; SpnCl; PpCl; Chrldr; GAA; College; Professional.

MC CARTHY, Kevin M; George Washington HS; Chicago, IL; SchMus; SchPl; StuCncl; TchrAde; RptrSchPpr; College.

MC CARTHY, Linda L; Wauzeka Public HS; Wauzeka, WI; Band; ChrhWkr; DrmMjrt; HonRl; StuCncl; EdYrBk; Pres4-H; LetterBsktbl; LetterTrk; Chrldr;.

MC CARTHY, Mary; Catholic Memorial HS; Brookfield, WI; 2/150 HonRl; JrNHS; NHS; PpCl; Wu Madison; Business.

MC CARTHY, Michael R; West Catholic HS; Grand Rapids, MI; HonRl; SchMus; SpnCl; Wrstlng; IMSpt; Grand Rapids Jr Coll; Business Admin.

MC CARTHY, Nancy; East Dubuque HS; East Dubuque, IL; ChrhWkr; HonRl; JrNHS; NHS; SchPl; TchrAde; RptrYrbk; FHA; Bsbl; IMSpt; College.

MC CARTHY, Roger; Wauzeka Public HS; Wauzeka, WI; 8/30 PresFrshCls; HonRl; LbryAde; SchPl; StuCncl; RptrYrbk; 4-H; Bsktbl; Ftbl; AmLegAwd; College; Vocation.

MC CARTHY, Timothy D; St Viator HS; Arlington Hts, IL; 30/250 Band; CncrtBnd; HonRl; MrchBnd; SchMus; EdSchPpr; Univ Of Illinois; Electrical Engineer.

MC CARTIN, Joseph G; Marist HS; Palos Heights, IL; 100/400 PolWkr; College; Medicine.

MC CARTNEY, Dawn M; Kelvyn Park HS; Chicago, IL; 5/299 NHS; FNA; SpnCl; PpCl; Northern Ill Univ; Pediatrician.

MC CARTNEY, James E; Toman Sr HS; Toman, WI; 33/284 HonRl; NHS; TchrAde; SptEdYrbk; SptEdSchPpr; SpnCl; Bsktbl; Ftbl; Glf; PresRotaryAwd; University; Law.

MC CARTNEY, Michael L; Lebanon HS; Lebanon, KS; VPSophCls; VPJrCls; SchPl; StuCncl; 4-H; FFA; LetterFtbl; LetterTrk; Trade School; Vocation.

MC CARTNEY, Reta R; Fairfax R Iii HS; Tarkio, MO; 3/27 Band; Chr; PresStuCncl; PresYthFlsp; Yrbk; TreasFHA; VPPpCl; LetterBsktbl; PPFtbl; DanFAwd; Central Missouri St Univ; Teacher.

MC CARTNEY, Wm C; Decatur Central HS; Indianapolis, IN; HonRl; NHS; Quill&Scroll; Yrbk; LionAwd; Marian College; Biology Major.

MC CARTY, Branna L; Noblesville HS; Noblesville, IN; 53/320 Chr; Chrs; CmntyWkr; HonRl; Mdrgl; SchMus; 4-H; FHA; EngCl; LatCl; PpCl; Univ; Vocational.

MC CARTY, Brenda L; Medina Public HS; Medina, ND; 4/20 Band; Chrs; DrlTm; HonRl; MrchBnd; RptrYrbk; Pres4-H; FHA; PpCl; LetterChrldr; Criminal Law Lawyer.

MC CARTY, Carolyn; South Spencer; Rockport, IN; ALAGirlsSt; Band; Chr; CncrtBnd; HonRl; MrchBnd; Orch; SchMus; 4-H; Owensboro Business College; Secretarial.

MC CARTY, Daniel P; Gehlen HS; Le Mars, IA; Band; Chrs; ChrhWkr; CncrtBnd; HonRl; MrchBnd; PepBnd; LetterBsktbl; CaptFtbl; LetterTrk; Trade School; Architecture.

MC CARTY, Danny J; Hastings HS; Hastings, NE; HonRl; EdYrBk; Swmmng; ChmbCommrsAwd; Columbus University; Law.

MC CARTY, Debra L; Shawnee HS; Shawneetown, IL; 3/40 Band; CncrtBnd; HonRl; MrchBnd; StuCncl; Bsbl; Bsktbl; IMSpt; Southern Illinois U; Medical Profession.

MC CARTY, Kendra S; Lincoln Way HS; Mokena, IL; 93/566 HonRl; College; Veterinarian.

MC CARTY, Kevin M; Pennfield HS; Battle Creek, MI; Chr; ChrhWkr; HonRl; NHS; NatlMeritCmnd; SchMus; SchPl; FBLA; SpnCl; College; Secretary.

MC CARTY, Linda J; Bucklin Rii HS; Bucklin, MO; Band; Chrs; HonRl; NHS; PepBnd; Yrbk; EdSchPpr; Ne Mo State Univ; Political Science.

MC CARTY, Michael K; Anderson HS; Anderson, IN; 39/576 Band; Chr; DrmBgl; HonRl; JrNHS; NHS; SchMus; SpnCl; ChmbCommrsAwd; CitAwd; Indiana State U; Prof.

MC CARTY, Patrick K; Southwestern HS; Lafayette, IN; 18/120 VPSrCls; Band; CncrtBnd; MrchBnd; NHS; 4-H; Ftbl; Trk; IMSpt; Purdue University; Construction.

MC CARTY, Peggy; Clinton HS; Clinton, IL; HonRl; HospAde; OffAde; RptrSchPpr; 4-H; FNA; FrCl; PpCl; Trk; IMSpt; College; Professional.

MC CARTY, Renee; Fairfield HS; Fairfield, IA; CmntyWkr; HonRl; CchngActv; PPFtbl; College; Business.

MC CARTY, Sandra E; South Newton HS; Kentland, IN; 10/98 Band; CncrtBnd; HonRl; HospAde; MrchBnd; 4-H; GAA; PPFtbl; Purdue Univ; Nursing.

MC CARTY, Susan M; Heelan HS; Sioux City, IA; Chr; Chrs; DrlTm; SchMus; JrNHS; NHS; RedCrAde; StuCncl; TchrAde; SpnCl; College; Elem Teacher.

MC CARTY, Timothy J; Farmer City Mansfield HS; Farmer City, IL; 8/78 AFS; Band; ChrhWkr; HonRl; NatlMeritFnl; SchPl; 4-H; SciCl; LetterBsbl; Ftbl; LetterTrk; 4-HAwd; College; Elec Engineer.

MC CARTY, William; Tuscola HS; Tuscola, IL; 11/124 VPSrCls; ALBoysSt; HonRl; NHS; SchPl; SciCl; Bsbl; Bsktbl; Ftbl; Trk; Univ Il; Banking.

MC CARTY, William S; Rushville Memorial HS; Rushville, IN; 11/356 HonRl; NHS; StuCncl; RptrYrbk; RptrSchPpr; SpnCl; MthCl; SciCl; Iu; Radiologist.

MC CARVER, Michael J; Central HS; Flat River, MO; 11/150 SecTrsJrCls; Band; Chrs; HonRl; NHS; SecStuCncl; LetterBsktbl; CaptBsktbl; CaptFtbl; LetterTrk; CchngActv; College; Pharmacist.

MC CARVER, Michelle K; Pekin Community HS; Pekin, IL; Band; Chr; ChrhWkr; HonRl; NHS; RedCrAde; StuCncl; StuGov; YthFlsp; JAAwd; College.

MC CASLIN, Howard S; Hillsboro HS; Hillsboro, IL; 63/185 HonRl; SchPl; StuCncl; StuGov; GerCl; IMSpt; University.

MC CASLIN, Susan C; Roncalli HS; Omaha, NE; HonRl; NHS; SchMus; SchPl; StuGov; RptrYrbk; Yrbk; RptrSchPpr; EdSchPpr; SchPpr; Coll; English.

MC CAULEY, Chris M; Clay Center Public HS; Edgar, NE; 9/30 Band; CncrtBnd; HonRl; MrchBnd; PepBnd; SchAde; SchMus; SchPl; TchrAde; Teen; PpCl; LetterTrk; Univ Of Nebraska; Physical Ed.

MC CAULEY, Daniel K; Madison Consolidated HS; Madison, IN; HonRl; NHS; StuCncl; GerCl; LetterBsktbl; CchngActv; College; Professional.

MC CAULEY, Diana; Triad HS; Troy, IL; Chrs; ChrhWkr; HonRl; LbryAde; SchMus; 4-H; FTA; PpCl; 4-HAwd; PresAwd; College; Special Ed Teacher.

MC CAULEY, Karen L; Princeton HS; Ohio, IL; 16/164 HonRl; Yrbk; College.

MC CAULEY, Kathleen A; Maconaquah HS; Grissom Afb, IN; CmntyWkr; DrlTm; HonRl; JrNHS; MrchBnd; OffAde; ROTC; TchrAde; Trade School; Travel.

MC CAULEY, Michael J; St Ignatius Prep; Chicago, IL; 100/210 ChrhWkr; CmntyWkr; HonRl; RptrSchPpr; Bsbl; IMSpt; College; Professional.

MC CAULLEY, Jeanne M; Pecatonica HS; Hollandale, WI; Chrs; HonRl; StuCncl; RptrSchPpr; FHA; Bsktbl; Chrldr; GAA; Univ; Nursing.

MC CAUSLAND, Jonathan D; Beardstown HS; Beardstown, IL; Chr; Chrs; HonRl; Mdrgl; NHS; SchMus; SchPl; SctActv; SptEdYrbk; RptrSchPpr; SptEdSchPpr; SciCl; Western Illinois Univ; Army.

MC CAUSLIN, Kimberly G; Cheboygan Public HS; Cheboygan, MI; HonRl; SctActv; TchrAde; Yrbk; 4-H; FHA; FrCl; College; Day Care.

MC CHANE, Richard H; Roncalli HS; Omaha, NE; HonRl; NHS; NatlMeritSF; Sdlty; StuCncl; MthCl; Socr; Chrldr; College; Medicine.

MC CLAFLIN, Darryln; Litchville Public HS; Litchville, ND; PresSophCls; Chrs; ChrhWkr; CmntyWkr; HonRl; SchMus; RptrYrbk; RptrSchPpr; PpCl; Chrldr;.

MC CLAIN, Carol A; Anna Jonesboro Comm HS; Anna, IL; 5/144 HonRl; Yrbk; FTA; PresFrCl; PpCl; SciCl; Bsktbl; GAA; IMSpt; College; Biology.

MC CLAIN, Carol A; Anna Jonesboro HS; Anna, IL; 5/144 HonRl; NHS; RptrYrbk; RptrSchPpr; FTA; FrCl; PpCl; SciCl; Bsktbl; GAA; Univ.

MC CLAIN, Diana; Franklin Central HS; Indianapolis, IN; ALAGirlsSt; HonRl; NHS; SctActv; YthFlsp; 4-H; FrCl; 4-HAwd; Univ; Home Economics.

MC CLAIN, Karen; Kelloggsville HS; Kentwood, MI; TchrAde; YthFlsp; PPFtbl;.

MC CLAIN, Karen D; Southeastern HS; Detroit, MI; 85/169 PresFrshCls; PresSophCls; SecSrCls; Chrs; ChrhWkr; HonRl; Orch; SchPl; StuCncl; PpCl; Tennis; Michigan St Univ; Physical Therapy.

MC CLAIN, Mary J; Holden R 111 HS; Holden, MO; 3/82 Chrs; CncrtBnd; HonRl; MrchBnd; NHS; PepBnd; SpnCl; University; Elem Ed.

MC CLAIN, Robert W; Stevenson HS; Livonia, MI; Aud/Vis; JA; SchPl; SctActv; YthFlsp; Cmu; Broacsting Or Cinema.

MC CLANNAHAN, Michael A; West Harrison HS; Mondamin, IA; ALBoysSt; HonRl; NHS; Ia St Univ; Mech Engin.

MC CLAREY, Donald R; Paris HS; Paris, IL; 19/256 HonRl; NHS; NatlMeritCmnd; VPStuCncl; SecSpnCl; Univ Of Ill; Army Officer.

MC CLASKEY, Carolyn K; Girard HS; Girard, KS; 15/98 HonRl; NHS; 4-H; FHA; College; Professional.

MC CLASKY, Gregory J; Grayslake Comm HS; Grayslake, IL; 2/219 PresSrCls; AFS; ALBoysSt; HonRl; NHS; ROTC; SchPl; TreasStuCncl; StuGov; RptrSchPpr; PresPpCl; Ftbl; College; Accounting.

MC CLASKY, Lila J; Smithville HS; Smithville, MO; 9/75 HonRl; JrNHS; NHS; TchrAde; Yrbk; FBLA; FHA; Undecided; Legal Secretary.

MC CLATCHEY, Anita A; Watseka Community HS; Watseka, IL; Band; DrmMjrt; HonRl; HospAde; NHS; RptrYrbk; FHA; SpnCl; Tennis; GAA; College; Elementary Ed.

MC CLATCHEY, Brian; Knoxville Senior HS; Knoxville, IA; TrsFrshCls; TrsSophCls; ALBoysSt; HonRl; NHS; NatlThespSoc; SchPl; StuCncl; RptrSchPpr; Univ Of Ia.

MC CLEAN, Alicia J; Valparaiso HS; Valparaiso, IN; 90/438 HonRl; NatlMeritSF; OffAde; Teen; Twrl; PpCl; Law School; Attorney.

MC CLEAN, Cheryl D; La Salle HS; Cedar Rapids, IA; 28/149 Chr; HonRl; NatlFornLg; NHS; PolWkr; SchMus; SchPl; StuCncl; College; Teacher.

MC CLEAR, Kathleen A; Jackson HS; Jackson, MI; 2/375 Chr; HonRl; NHS; NatlMeritCmnd; PolWkr; SchMus; Michigan Tech Univ; Engineer.

MC CLEARY, Kevin H; Bradley Bourbonnais HS; Bradley, IL; ChrhWkr; HonRl; NHS; SchPl; TreasYthFlsp; SpnCl; Eastern Illinois Univ; Mathematics.

MC CLEERY, James; Glasgow HS; Glasgow, MO; 10/65 HonRl; NHS; FFA; Trk; Trade; Pro.

MC CLEISH, Roberta A; East Alton Wood River HS; Woodriver, IL; 5/331 Chr; CmntyWkr; DrlTm; HonRl; NHS; College; Physical Therapy.

MC CLELLAN, David B; Deerfield HS; Deerfield, IL; PresChrhWkr; HonRl; NatlMeritFnl; NatlMeritSchl; NatlMeritSF; Grinnell College; Law.

MC CLELLAN, Debra L; Lindblom Tech HS; Chicago, IL; 14/750 Chrs; HonRl; TchrAde; FrCl; Northwestern Univ; Science.

MC CLELLAN, Karen R; Platte County R Iii HS; Ferrelview, MO; AFS; HonRl; NHS; OffAde; YthFlsp; SchPpr; FHA; FrCl; PpCl; CaptChrldr; Bus Clge; Secretarial.

MC CLELLAN, Manulita G; Mother Mcauley Lib Arts HS; Chicago, IL; Chr; Chrs; ChrhWkr; CmntyWkr; OffAde; PolWkr; SchMus; SchPl; TchrAde; Teen; Bsbl; Loyola Univ; Biological Science.

MC CLELLAND, Connie J; Troy HS; Troy, KS; 3/51 TrsSrCls; CncrtBnd; HonRl; ModUN; PresNHS; PepBnd; SecPpCl; College.

MC CLELLAND, Phyllis G; Harvard HS; Harvard, IL; 8/160 Band; Chr; Chrl; Chrs; CncrtBnd; HonRl; MrchBnd; Western Ill Univ; Business Adm.

MC CLENDON, Debbie A; Carthage Sr HS; Carthage, MO; AFS; Chrs; DrlTm; HonRl; NatlThespSoc; SchPl; FrCl; PpCl; Bsktbl; Swmmng; Chrldr; CchngActv; College; Gymnastics.

MC CLENDON, Terri D; John Marshall HS; Chicago, IL; 6/950 HonRl; NHS; TchrAde; EdSchPpr; FTA; PresSpnCl; Chrldr; GAA; CitAwd; Memphis St Univ; Elementary Educ.

MC CLENDON, Toni; Lutheran North HS; St Louis, MO; Band; ChrhWkr; CmntyWkr; DrmMjrt; HospAde; JA; SchPl; SctActv; YthFlsp; Trk; University; Professional.

MC CLERNON, Timothy R; St Johns Prepatory HS; Tenney, MN; PresSophCls; Band; Chrs; CncrtBnd; HonRl; NHS; PepBnd; SchPl; StuCncl; 4-H; St Johns Univ; Humanities.

MC CLERREN, Robert L; Thompsonville HS; Thompsonville, IL; 2/27 VPJrCls; PresSrCls; HonRl; ModUN; NHS; SchPl; StuCncl; RptrYrbk; 4-H; FFA; LetterBsktbl; Trk; AmLegAwd; BttyCrckrAwd; College; Law.

MC CLEW, Michael D; Southwestern HS; Hanover, IN; Chr; Chrs; ChrhWkr; HonRl; NatlThespSoc; SchMus; SchPl; Trk; IMSpt; Valparaiso Univ; Economics.

MC CLINTICK, Donna L; Hammond Baptist HS; Griffith, IN; 26/88 Chr; Chrs; ChrhWkr; HonRl; JrNHS; SchMus; SchPpr; GerCl; PpCl; College; Nursing.

MC CLINTOCK, Carol E; Council Grove HS; Council Grove, KS; ChrhWkr; HonRl; SctActv; StuCncl; FBLA; PpCl; PPFtbl; Butler County Comm Jr College; Nursing.

MC CLINTOCK, Daniel L; Joliet Central HS; Joliet, IL; VPJrCls; PresSrCls; HonRl; JA; NHS; OffAde; SctActv; Western Ill Univ; Business Administration.

MC CLINTOCK, Jo E; Jasper R#5 HS; Jasper, MO; PresBand; CncrtBnd; DrmMjrt; HonRl; NHS; PresFHA; FTA; CaptChrldr; GAA; PPFtbl; College; Vocation.

MC CLINTOCK, Mark B; Walled Lake Central HS; Dearborn, MI; HonRl; Bsbl; Eastern Mi Univ; Criminal Justice.

MC CLISH, Leeann K; Cooper HS; Crystal, MN; 190/600 Band; ChrhWkr; CncrtBnd; DrlTm; HonRl; MrchBnd; OffAde; PepBnd; SchPpr; PresPpCl; Trk; GAA; College.

MC CLOUD, Cathy; Cloverdale HS; Spencer, IN; ChrhWkr; HonRl; NHS; Trk; GAA; OptClAwd; RotaryAwd; CitAwd;.

MC CLOUD, Natalie Y; Kingsville HS; Kingsville, MO; 2/25 SecFrshCls; VPJrCls; ChrhWkr; CmntyWkr; HonRl; JrNHS; NHS; StuCncl; LetterBsktbl; Chrldr; Univ; Professional.

MC CLUN, Barbara A; Louisville Public HS; Louisville, NE; 9/40 ALAGirlsSt; Chrs; LbryAde; Yrbk; FHA; LetterBsktbl; LetterTrk; GAA; Trade School; Beautician.

MC CLURE, Douglas J; Mason County Central HS; Scottville, MI; SchMus; SchPl; SctActv; 4-H; Bsktbl; LetterFtbl; Trk; Wrstlng; Mi State U; Veterinary Medicine.

MC CLURE, Georgene E; Streator Twp HS; Streator, IL; Chr; ChrhWkr; CmntyWkr; HonRl; HospAde; SctActv; StuGov; VPYthFlsp; SecGerCl; LetterBsktbl; Univ; Nurse.

MC CLURE, Jane E; Klemme Community HS; Klemme, IA; 7/34 Band; PolWkr; SchPl; SptEdYrbk; EdSchPpr; Pres4-H; VPFTA; PresSciCl; Bsktbl; Glf; Trk; 4-HAwd; Univ Of Iowa; Journalism.

MC CLURE, Lareita F; South Harrison R Ii HS; Bethany, MO; Band; CncrtBnd; HonRl; MrchBnd; 4-H; PpCl; Chrldr; 4-HAwd; College; Secretary.

MC CLURE, Lori S; Huntington North HS; Roanoke, IN; SecFrshCls; ChrhWkr; JrNHS; RedCrAde; StuCncl; RptrSchPpr; SchPpr; 4-H; GAA; 4-HAwd; College; Business.

MC CLURE, Martin R; Marion HS; Marion, IA; 19/180 Aud/Vis; NatlMeritSF; Quill&Scroll; SchMus; SchPl; SctActv; TchrAde; RptrYrbk; Yrbk; RptrSchPpr; U Of Iowa; Computer Science.

MC CLURE, Michael M; Effingham HS; Effingham, IL; 35/219 VPJrCls; Chr; Chrs; HonRl; NatlMeritCmnd; SchMus; SchPl; Yrbk; KeyCl; VPSrCls; Coll; Psychiatrist.

MC CLURE, Steven D; United Township HS; East Moline, IL; TrsFrshCls; Band; CmntyWkr; CncrtBnd; NatlThespSoc; PepBnd; SchMus; PresStuCncl; KeyCl; PpCl; Knox College; Public Relations.

MC CLURE, William D; O Fallon Twp HS; O Fallon, IL; ALBoysSt; CncrtBnd; MrchBnd; PepBnd; SctActv; LetterBsktbl; LetterTrk; College; Law.

MC CLURG, Nancy J; Maryville R2 HS; Maryville, MO; 12/121 Band; ChrhWkr; CmntyWkr; CncrtBnd; HonRl; LbryAde; MrchBnd; Orch; 4-H; FHA; SpnCl; Tennis; IMSpt; College; Assistant Veterinary.

MC CLURG, Nancy J; Maryville Rii HS; Maryville, MO; 12/121 Band; CncrtBnd; HonRl; MrchBnd; 4-H; FHA; SpnCl; PpCl; Tennis; Nw Missouri St Univ; Asst Veterinarian.

MC CLUSKEY, Larry W; Virden HS; Virden, IL; PresFrshCls; PresSophCls; Chrs; ChrhWkr; SchMus; YthFlsp; PpCl; Bsbl; CaptBsktbl; Trk; IMSpt;.

MC CLUSKEY, Laura A; Downers Grove North HS; Downers Grove, IL; 55/524 Chrs; HonRl; Northern Illinois Univ; Physical Therapy.

MC CLUSKEY, Phyllis A; Naperville Central HS; Naperville, IL; 206/864 Band; Chrs; HonRl; JrNHS; MrchBnd; SchMus; StuCncl; Western Illinois Univ; Pharmacist.

MC CLUSKEY, Thomas A; Hillsdale HS; Hillsdale, MI; VPJrCls; HonRl; LitMag; SchPl; StuGov; EdYrBk; RptrSchPpr; KeyCl; Bsktbl; RotaryAwd; College; Financial Management.

MC CLUSKEY, Todd; Arlington Public HS; Arlington, SD; /48 VPSophCls; TrsJrCls; ALBoysSt; Ftbl; Wrstlng; KiwanAwd; ;professional.

MC COACH, Angela C; Glenwood HS; Chatham, IL; Band; ChrhWkr; CncrtBnd; HospAde; LbryAde; TchrAde; RptrYrbk; RptrSchPpr; FNA; College; Nursing.

MC COID, Kimberly K; Mason City Senior HS; Mason City, IA; HonRl; NHS; Orch; University; Medicine.

MC COLL, Fiona E; Fenton HS; Bensenville, IL; 6/407 Chr; ChrhWkr; HonRl; NatlMeritSF; SchMus; LionAwd; CitAwd; Coll; Dr.

MC COLLOUGH, Alan; Eagle Grove Community Hs; Eagle Grove, IA; Band; YthFlsp; 4-H; FFA; Ftbl; 4-HAwd; College; Agriculture.

MC COLLOUGH, David D; La Ville HS; Lapaz, IN; 6/165 ALBoysSt; Band; MrchBnd; NHS; 4-H; LetterBsbl; LetterFtbl; AmLegAwd; 4-HAwd; Manchester Clg; Secondary Educ.

MC COLLUM, James W; St Francis De Sales HS; Lansing, IL; HonRl; JrNHS; NHS; NatlMeritCmnd; PolWkr; SptEdSchPpr; Bsbl; Bsktbl; Ftbl; GovHonPrgAwd; Univ; Doctor.

MC COLLUM, Judy K; Northwestern HS; Mendon, MO; VPSophCls; Chrs; HonRl; StuCncl; TreasGerCl; LetterTrk; Trade School; Home Decorator.

MC COLLUM, Madeline M; Clinton HS; Tipton, MI; 4/93 TrsSrCls; PresBand; TreasChr; HonRl; NHS; SchPl; TreasStuGov; TchrAde; YthFlsp; Chrldr; GAA; IMSpt; Central Michigan Univ; Music.

MC COLLUM, Marcia K; North Clay Comm HS; Louisville, IL; Chrs; CncrtBnd; HonRl; MrchBnd; PepBnd; RedCrAde; SchMus; SchPl; RptrSchPpr; S Illinois Univ; Theater.

MC COLLUM, Mike L; Vandalia HS; Vandalia, IL; 25/117 Band; HonRl; MrchBnd; NHS; NatlThespSoc; SchPl; Bsbl; CaptBsktbl; Greenville College; Medicine.

MC COLLUM, Pamela A; Mather HS; Autrain, MI; 30/124 VPSophCls; VPJrCls; Band; ChrhWkr; CmntyWkr; CncrtBnd; HonRl; MrchBnd; PepBnd; SchPl; SctActv; PpCl; Swmmng; University; Professional.

MC COLLUM, Pamela S; Palisade HS; Palisade, NE; Chr; Chrs; ChrhWkr; HonRl; SchPl; 4-H; PpCl; GAA; College.

MC COLLUM, T; Stevenson HS; Livonia, MI; VPFrshCls; SctActv; StuCncl; Michigan St Univ.

MC COLLUM, Terry R; Trenton HS; Trenton, MO; HonRl; NHS; SpnCl; Trk; University; Mass Communications.

MC COMAS, Claire E; Novi HS; Novi, MI; Chrs; CmntyWkr; HonRl; NatlFornLg; NHS; SchPl; RptrYrbk; PresFrCl; SciCl; Univ Of Michigan; Political Science.

MC COMB, Kathie L; Harvard HS; Harvard, IL; SecAFS; Chrs; ChrhWkr; CncrtBnd; HonRl; Mdrgl; NHS; PepBnd; SecFrCl; College; Computer Science.

MC COMBS, Darrell; L Community HS; Lewistown, IL; PresFrshCls; Chrs; SchMus; StuGov; PpCl; Bsbl; Bsktbl; Ftbl; Trk; College; Vocation.

MC CONKEY, Elizabeth A; Collinsville HS; Collinsville, IL; 60/651 HonRl; NHS; YthFlsp; Yrbk; TreasSpnCl; PpCl; SecSciCl; S Illinois Univ; Music.

MC CONKEY, John A; Richmond Sr HS; Richmond, IN; VPFrshCls; Band; CncrtBnd; DrmBgl; HonRl; MrchBnd; Trk; Univ In Purdue; Vet Medical Field.

MC CONNELL, Andrew S; Darlington Comm HS; Darlington, WI; 14/126 PresJrCls; Chrs; CncrtBnd; SchMus; StuGov; 4-H; LetterBsbl; LetterBsktbl; LetterFtbl; LetterTrk; Univ Wi; Engr.

MC CONNELL, Bradley L; Vestaburg HS; Edmore, MI; Band; HonRl; SchPl; TchrAde; PpCl; Bsbl; Bsktbl; Ftbl;.

MC CONNELL, Cathleen A; Elston HS; Michigan City, IN; Chr; ChrhWkr; CmntyWkr; HonRl; JrNHS; NHS; OffAde; RptrYrbk; SpnCl; IMSpt; Coll; Radiologic Tech.

MC CONNELL, Charlene J; Sidney Public HS; Sidney, NE; 33/119 Band; Chr; Chrs; CncrtBnd; HonRl; JrNHS; SctActv; SctActv; PpCl; Trk; Trade School; Vocational.

MC CONNELL, Cheryl A; West HS; Davenport, IA; 70/800 Chrs; HonRl; GAA; College; Professional.

MC CONNELL, Danny R; Kingsley Pierson HS; Kingsley, IA; Bsbl; Bsktbl; Ftbl; Glf; Trk;.

MC CONNELL, Geraldine E; North Scott HS; Davenport, IA; 10/197 HonRl; NHS; TchrAde; SecFTA; VPSciCl; U Of Northern Ia; Home Ec.

MC CONNELL, Janet; Benton Central HS; Fowler, IN; ChrhWkr; HonRl; OffAde; StuCncl; YthFlsp;.

MC CONNELL, John B; Malden HS; Malden, MO; 1/135 HonRl; NatlThespSoc; SchPl; College; Marine Biology.

MC CONNELL, Katherine M; Superior Senior HS; Superior, WI; HonRl; NHS; StuCncl; StuGov; YthLg; FrCl; Chrldr; GAA; AmLegAwd; PresAwd; University; Pharmacist.

MC CONNELL, Lee A; Central HS; Davenport, IA; 1/600 ALBoysSt; LetterTennis; College; Lawyer.

MC CONNELL, Lynn E; Davis County HS; Bloomfield, IA; Band; Chr; Chrs; ChrhWkr; CmntyWkr; CncrtBnd; HonRl; MrchBnd; PepBnd; PresFBLA; Interior Decorator.

MC CONNELL, Mary M; Harvard HS; Harvard, IL; Band; Chrs; ChrhWkr; CncrtBnd; HonRl; SchMus; 4-H; Bsbl; Univ Of Wi; Business Admin.

MC CONNELL, Mary R; Clinton Comm HS; Clinton, IL; 2/155 VPSrCls; Band; CncrtBnd; HonRl; MrchBnd; NHS; PpCl; Bsktbl; VPGAA; Eastern Ill Univ; Mathematics.

MC CONNELL, Nancy E; Delavan HS; Delavan, IL; 27/55 Chr; Chrs; HonRl; Mdrgl; SchMus; SchPl; TchrAde; YthFlsp; GAA; College; Music Teacher.

MC CONNELL, Patricia E; Clinton HS; Clinton, MI; Band; HonRl; MrchBnd; NHS; PepBnd; SchMus; TchrAde; IMSpt; York Univ;.

MC CONVILLE, Debra E; Kingsville HS; Holden, MO; VPFrshCls; Chrs; HonRl; NHS; 4-H; FNA; CaptBsktbl; Chrldr; IMSpt; 4-HAwd; Trade Sch; Prof.

MC CONVILLE, Rita J; H L Richards HS; Oak Lawn, IL; Chrs; HonRl; NHS; NatlMeritSF; FrCl; MthCl; Northwestern Univ; Physical Therapy.

MC CORD, Mitzi D; Northeast Nodaway R V HS; Ravenwood, MO; SecJrCls; ALAGirlsSt; HonRl; NHS; SchMus; SchPl; EdYrBk; Bsbl; Bsktbl; Chrldr; Nw Mo St U;vocal Music.

MC CORD, Rebecca L; Harrisonville Sr HS; Harrisonville, MO; ChrhWkr; HonRl; VPFHA; PpCl; CaptChrldr; Graceland Clg; Nursing.

MC CORD, Richard L; Verona R 7 HS; Verona, MO; 2/32 Chr; ChrhWkr; HonRl; NHS; StuCncl; Yrbk; FBLA; MthCl; Bsbl; Bsktbl; University.

MC CORKLE, Karla; Clinton Prairie Hs; Frankfort, IN; TrsFrshCls; Band; HonRl; OffAde; SchMus; SpnCl; PpCl; Trk; Chrldr; College; Teacher.

MC CORMACK, Anne M; Nazareth Academy; Lyons, IL; 14/154 Chrs; ChrhWkr; HonRl; LbryAde; NHS; OffAde; SchMus; TchrAde; SchPpr;.

MC CORMACK, Brian J; Yankton HS; Yankton, SD; ALBoysSt; Chrs; HonRl; NatlFornLg; SchMus; YthLg; RptrSchPpr; PresSciCl; LetterTennis; EldAwd; College; Professional.

MC CORMACK, James K; Central HS; Salem, WI; CncrtBnd; HonRl; NHS; Pres4-H; SciCl; Ftbl; Glf; LetterWrstlng; 4-HAwd; Univ Of Mn; Vet Med.

MC CORMACK, Karen A; St Francis Academy; Joliet, IL; 5/172 HonRl; NHS; RptrYrbk; RptrSchPpr; FrCl; LetterTennis; VoiceDemAwd; Journalism.

MC CORMACK, Mark A; Joliet West HS; Joliet, IL; 81/495 College; Accounting.

MC CORMICK, Bobby G; Centennial HS; Champaign, IL; 1/355 NHS; FrCl; IMSpt; Clg; Engr.

MC CORMICK, Cindy L; Allegan HS; Allegan, MI; 2/196 HonRl; IntrClCncl; JrNHS; NHS; NatlMeritFnl; NatlMeritCmnd; OffAde; StuCncl; Central Michigan Univ; Business Admin.

MC CORMICK, Colleen M; Mound Westonka HS; Mound, MN; Chr; HonRl; HospAde; LetterTennis; Trk; College; Law.

MC CORMICK, Daniel A; Flora HS; Flora, IL; ALBoysSt; HonRl; RptrSchPpr; SchPpr; FHA; College; Business.

MC CORMICK, David L; Independent Dist 76 HS; Gary, SD; 8/57 PresSophCls; PresJrCls; ALBoysSt; Band; CncrtBnd; HonRl; NHS; StuGov; CaptFtbl; AmLegAwd; Univ; Music Education.

MC CORMICK, David R; U I T Jr Sr HS; Vermont, IL; 2/698 PresSrCls; HonRl; NHS; SchPl; TchrAde; FFA; SciCl; LetterTrk; Western Ill Univ.

MC CORMICK, Debbie; Louisburg HS; Louisburg, KS; 3/63 Band; CaptDrlTm; HonRl; SchPl; StuCncl; TchrAde; PpCl; Chrldr; Coll; Child Develop.

MC CORMICK, Edward T; Montini HS; Lombard, IL; 19/159 PresSophCls; HonRl; NHS; StuCncl; TchrAde; FrCl; LetterBsbl; LetterFtbl; LetterGlf; Illinois State Univ; Accounting.

MC CORMICK, James P; West HS; Green Bay, WI; 34/366 Chr; Chrl; Chrs; HonRl; Mdrgl; SchMus; SchPl; StuCncl; StuGov; Marquette Univ; Humanities.

MC CORMICK, James P; St Louis HS; St Louis, MO; ChrhWkr; CtyCnl; CmntyWkr; HospAde; NatlMeritFnl; NatlMeritSF; StuCncl; StuGov; RptrYrbk; SptEdYrbk; St Louis Univ; Dentistry.

MC CORMICK, Jana L; Blue Springs Campus HS; Blue Springs, MO; 29/293 Band; Chr; Chrl; Chrs; HonRl; Mdrgl; MrchBnd; ModUN; NHS; PpCl; SciCl; Burge School Of Nursing; Rn.

MC CORMICK, Julie A; Cal Comm HS; Latimer, IA; Chrs; CncrtBnd; HonRl; NHS; SchMus; SchPl; StuCncl; YthFlsp; RptrYrbk; College; Theatre.

MC CORMICK, Karen G; Crystal Lake Comm HS; Crystal Lake, IL; 1/473 HonRl; NHS; Orch; Univ Of Illinois; Mathematics.

MC CORMICK, Keith C; Creighton Prep; Omaha, NE; Bsbl; Bsktbl; ChmnFtbl; IMSpt; Clge; Government Or Agri Business.

MC CORMICK, Mark A; Mt Pulaski HS; Mt Pulaski, IL; 14/101 Band; Chrs; ChrhWkr; CncrtBnd; HonRl; JA; MrchBnd; NHS; Orch; PepBnd; SchMus; 4-H; Univ Of Ill; Agriculture.

MC CORMICK, Michael J; Caledonia HS; Caledonia, MN; PresSrCls; HonRl; StuCncl; RptrSchPpr; 4-H; SpnCl; College; Health.

MC CORMICK, Philip A; Airport HS; Carleton, MI; ChrhWkr; CmntyWkr; HonRl; 4-H; Bsbl; LetterBsktbl; Ftbl; LetterGlf; VPTennis; 4-HAwd; College; Teaching.

MC CORMICK, Randal J; Belding HS; Belding, MI; 32/160 ALBoysSt; HonRl; NHS; CaptBsbl; Bsktbl; Ftbl; AmLegAwd; Hope College; Pysics.

MC CORMICK, Rhonda S; Urbana Sr HS; Urbana, IL; 44/525 TrsJrCls; TrsSrCls; ChrhWkr; CtyCnl; HonRl; NHS; StuCncl; StuGov; 4-H; Univ Of Ill; Forest Science.

MC CORMICK, Russell W; Winner HS; Winner, SD; ChrhWkr; CmntyWkr; SchPl; LetterBsbl; CaptBsktbl; CaptFtbl; CaptTrk; College; Zoology.

MC CORMICK, Susan A; Oscoda Area HS; Wurtsmith Afb, MI; Chrs; LbryAde; SctActv; SchPpr; College; Cpa.

MC CORMICK, Susan A; Garden County HS; Oshkosh, NE; VPBand; Chrs; ChrhWkr; HonRl; PepBnd; SchMus; RptrYrbk; Pres4-H; PpCl; LetterTrk; 4-HAwd; College; Business Admin.

MC CORMICK, W Craig; Keya Paha Co HS; Valentine, NE; 5/26 Chrs; HonRl; MrchBnd; SchMus; SchPl; StuCncl; StuGov; YthFlsp; EdYrBk; LetterBsktbl; LetterFtbl; LetterGlf; University; Optometry.

MC CORNACK, Robert P; Henry Ford HS; Detroit, MI; ChrhWkr; HonRl; NHS; OffAde; TchrAde; Yrbk; Ftbl; IMSpt; Coll; Prof.

MC COSH, Karen L; Hillsdale HS; Hillsdale, MI; 28/190 HonRl; NHS; SchPpr; LetterTrk; GAA; Central Mi Univ; Writer.

MC COWAN, Elizabeth A; Kokomo HS; Kokomo, IN; 14/363 HonRl; JrNHS; UNYO; SchPpr; FNA; FrCl; PpCl; Indiana U; Nurse.

MC COY, Anne T; Pekin Community HS; Pekin, IL; Chr; Chrs; ChrhWkr; HonRl; StuCncl; College; Professional.

MC COY, Bruce; Chillicothe HS; Chillicothe, MO; Band; CncrtBnd; HonRl; Orch; PepBnd; SctActv; Bsktbl; Ftbl; Trk; Univ Missouri Rolla; Elect Eng.

MC COY, Carmita L; Lindblom Tech HS; Chicago, IL; 100/657 TrsJrCls; VPSrCls; HonRl; NatlMeritCmnd; NatlMeritSchl; OffAde; StuCncl; StuGov; TchrAde; Ill State Univ; Psychologist.

MC COY, Catherine M; Jersey Comm HS; Jerseyville, IL; 8/275 ALAGirlsSt; Chrs; ChrhWkr; HonRl; NHS; PolWkr; SchPl; RptrYrbk; SpnCl; Lewis & Clark Comm College; Economics.

MC COY, Cynthia; Jones Commercial HS; Chicago, IL; 6/437 PresFrshCls; HonRl; JrNHS; NHS; StuGov; RptrSchPpr; FrCl; HstSophCls; Glf; PPFtbl; Coll; Cpa.

MC COY, David L; Sts Peter & Paul HS; Saginaw, MI; Chrs; HonRl; NHS; SchPpr; MthCl; PpCl; Bsbl; Bsktbl; Ftbl; Trk; College; Business.

MC COY, David R; Mehlville Sr HS; St Louis, MO; ChrhWkr; CncrtBnd; JA; MrchBnd; NHS; PepBnd; SchMus; YthFlsp; EdSchPpr; University; Music.

MC COY, Dennis E; Larimore HS; Northwood, ND; VPSophCls; SecJrCls; ChrhWkr; HonRl; SecFFA; SecSciCl; Nd State U; Agriculture.

MC COY, James; Monona Grove HS; Monona, WI; 27/273 ALBoysSt; CmntyWkr; HonRl; NHS; TchrAde; YthFlsp; AmLegAwd; Univ Wisc; Chemical Eng.

MC COY, Jana L; Ozark HS; Ozark, MO; 2/93 Band; CncrtBnd; HonRl; MrchBnd; StuCncl; Twrl; RptrYrbk; RptrSchPpr; EdSchPpr; PpCl; Smsu; Eng.

MC COY, Louis J; Brady HS; W St Paul, MN; Band; Chrs; HonRl; NatlMeritSF; NatlThespSoc; SchMus; SchPl; St Marys College; Lawyer.

MC COY, Margaret T; Bloomington HS; Bloomington, IL; 26/391 ChrhWkr; CmntyWkr; HonRl; JrNHS; OffAde; PolWkr; YthFlsp; SpnCl; PpCl; Bsktbl; Auburn Univ; Special Education.

MC COY, Mary Beth; St Charles Sr HS; St Charles, MO; 6/600 ChrhWkr; HonRl; NHS; SctActv; IMSpt; Univ Of Mo; Medicine.

MC COY, Michael; Frederic Remington HS; Whitewater, KS; ALBoysSt; Band; HonRl; SchAde; SctActv; StuCncl; TchrAde; Ftbl; Wichita State U; Law.

MC COY, Monty J; Erie HS; Chanute, KS; 1/63 VPFrshCls; PresSophCls; VPJrCls; ALBoysSt; HonRl; NHS; NatlMeritSF; VPStuCncl; Pres4-H; PresSciCl; Ks St Univ; Chemical Engr.

MC COY, Ramona T; Brown County HS; Mt Sterling, IL; Chr; ChrhWkr; HonRl; LbryAde; Western Illinois Univ; Medicine.

MC COY, Valerie D; Leadwood HS; Leadwood, MO; 7/47 HonRl; LitMag; Mdrgl; NHS; SchPl; StuCncl; Twrl; RptrYrbk; EdSchPpr; PresFHA; College; Dentistry.

MC CRACKEN, Ross W; Bettendorf HS; Bettendorf, IA; 34/425 NHS; Ftbl; Wrstlng; Univ Of Iowa.

MC CRANE, Marie; New Hampton Comm HS; Ionia, IA; 23/181 PresJrCls; Band; Chrs; CncrtBnd; HonRl; MrchBnd; Mdrgl; SpnCl; Trk; Trade School.

MC CRANEY, John J; Moline HS; Moline, IL; 89/890 HonRl; NHS; LetterBsbl; LetterGlf; College; Professional.

MC CRARY, Carolyn; Notre Dame De Siou HS; Kansas City, MO; 2/32 ChrhWkr; CmntyWkr; LbryAde; NatlMeritFnl; PolWkr; Yrbk; GerCl; Bryn Mawr Coll; Translator.

MC CRARY, Carolyn B; Notre Dame De Sion HS; Kansas City, MO; 2/32 ChrhWkr; HonRl; LbryAde; NatlMeritSF; PolWkr; Yrbk; College; Professional.

MC CRARY, William T; Greenwood HS; Springfield, MO; Aud/Vis; Chr; Chrs; ChrhWkr; SctActv; FSA; LatCl; SciCl; LetterFtbl; College; Science.

MC CRAY, Cindy L; St Charles HS; St Charles, MO; CmntyWkr; HonRl; NHS; TchrAde; RptrYrbk; RptrSchPpr; PpCl; CaptChrldr; IMSpt; PresAwd; Lindenwood College; Accountant.

MC CRAY, Diane; Nerinx Hall HS; St Louis, MO; Chrl; CmntyWkr; DrmBgl; JA; SchMus; StuGov; Univ Of Il; Professional Nurse.

MC CREA, Dee A; King City Ri HS; King City, MO; TrsJrCls; ChrhWkr; CmntyWkr; HonRl; SchPl; StuCncl; TchrAde; Twrl; FHA; College; Professional.

MC CREA, Douglas G; Maysville HS; Maysville, MO; VPSophCls; PresJrCls; ALBoysSt; Chr; HonRl; SctActv; StuCncl; FFA; LetterBsbl; LetterBsktbl; LetterFtbl; Swmmng; AmLegAwd; Trade School; General Farming.

MC CREE, Frank K; Crab Orchard HS; Marion, IL; PresFrshCls; HospAde; SctActv; PpCl; Bsbl; Bsktbl; Trk; CchngActv; College; Science.

MC CREREY, Jim; Powhattan HS; Hiawatha, KS; SecSophCls; VPSrCls; Band; CncrtBnd; HonRl; MrchBnd; NHS; PepBnd; SchPpr; FFA; Trade School; Vocation.

MC CROSSEN, Melanie; Chippewa Falls HS; Chippewa Falls, WI; 12/365 HonRl; JrNHS; ModUN; NHS; NatlMeritSF; FrCl; TreasSpnCl; PpCl; College; Languages.

MC CROTTY, Stephen E; Springfield Se HS; Springfield, IL; 60/500 ChrhWkr; CmntyWkr; NHS; Illinois State Univ; Biology.

MC CRUDDEN, Vicki L; Little Falls Community HS; Little Falls, MN; Band; Chr; ChrhWkr; CncrtBnd; HonRl; PepBnd; SchMus; StuCncl; 4-H; GerCl; Nurses Training.

MC CRUMB, Linda; Portland HS; Eagle, MI; 4/120 VPJrCls; HonRl; NHS; NatlMeritCmnd; NatlMeritSchl; 4-H; SpnCl; GAA; PPFtbl; Ferris State College; Nursing.

MC CUDDEN, Gerard; Reavis Hs; Burbank, IL; 47/676 Band; CncrtBnd; HonRl; MrchBnd; PepBnd; LetterBsbl; LetterFtbl; LetterTrk; Lewis U; Business Administration.

MC CUE, Michael E; Alma HS; Alma, NE; 2/27 PresFrshCls; PresJrCls; Band; Chr; CncrtBnd; HonRl; MrchBnd; NHS; LetterBsktbl; CaptFtbl; LetterTrk; Univ Of Nebraska; Law.

MC CUEN, Joan L; York Comm HS; Elmhurst, IL; 75/1000 CmntyWkr; HonRl; NHS; Quill&Scroll; RptrYrbk; RptrSchPpr; Univ Of Illinois; Communications.

MC CUEN, Mary L; Mt Pleasant Community HS; Mt Pleasant, IA; 15/150 PresFrshCls; SecJrCls; CncrtBnd; HonRl; HospAde; MrchBnd; ModUN; NHS; StuCncl; Coe College; Political Science.

MC CUISTON, Debbie J; Castle HS; Chandler, IN; Chr; CAP; HonRl; StuCncl; 4-H; FTA; LatCl; PpCl; 4-HAwd; College; Training Of The Handicapped.

MC CULLAGH, James P; Cowan HS; Muncie, IN; 3/57 VPJrCls; PresSrCls; ALBoysSt; HonRl; VPNHS; StuCncl; PresYthFlsp; Yrbk; LetterTrk; Purdue Univ; Architecture.

MC CULLEY, Rhea; Jacksonville Hs; Jacksonville, IL; 14/363 CncrtBnd; HonRl; MrchBnd; NHS; NatlMeritCmnd; TreasStuGov; Twrl; LetterTennis; Trk; U Of Iowa; Pharmacy.

MC CULLEY, Thomas O; Harlem HS; Loves Park, IL; 30/530 Chr; HonRl; Mdrgl; NHS; Quill&Scroll; SchMus; SchPl; StuCncl; RptrYrbk; LetterFtbl; GodCntryAwd; Mac Murray College; Teacher.

MC CULLOCH, Betsy A; Milton Sr HS; Milton, WI; 3/186 AFS; CncrtBnd; HonRl; MrchBnd; StuCncl; YthFlsp; EdYrBk; SpnCl; PpCl; Bsktbl; Univ Wis; Psychology.

MC CULLOCH, Gregory S; Frederick HS; Westport, SD; VPSrCls; HonRl; YthFlsp; 4-H; 4-HAwd; College; Veterinarian.

MC CULLOUGH, Shawn M; Lincoln Community HS; Lincoln, IL; 15/255 NHS; NatlThespSoc; PolWkr; SchMus; VPStuGov; PresPpCl; Bsktbl; Glf; DARAwd; Stephens College; Computer Science.

MC CULLOUGH, Sheryl K; Grinnell HS; Grinnell, KS; Band; Chrs; ChrhWkr; CncrtBnd; HonRl; MrchBnd; PepBnd; PpCl; LetterBsktbl; VoiceDemAwd; Kansas State Univ; Special Education.

MC CULLY, David C; Toluca HS; Toluca, IL; 19/40 TrsFrshCls; SecJrCls; Band; Chr; ChrhWkr; CmntyWkr; HonRl; MrchBnd; PepBnd; SchPl; StuCncl; PpCl; Bsbl; CaptBsktbl; College; Business.

MC CULLY, Marjorie A; Mid County Sr HS; Varna, IL; 4/60 Band; Chr; Chrs; HonRl; Mdrgl; SchPl; PresStuCncl; StuGov; PresFHA; Western Illinois Univ; Business Administ.

MC CUMBER, Timothy; West Holt HS; Atkinson, NE; HonRl; StuCncl; RptrYrbk; RptrSchPpr; 4-H; FrCl; Bsktbl; 4-HAwd; PresAwd; College.

MC CUMBERS, Allen E; Loomis Public HS; Atlanta, NE; HonRl; SchPl; StuCncl; TchrAde; LetterWrstlng;.

MC CUNE, M S; Dubois HS; French Lick, IN; VPJrCls; PresSrCls; HonRl; PepBnd; RptrYrbk; RptrSchPpr; EdSchPpr; SchPpr; PpCl; TIMEAwd; Musican.

MC CUNE, Roy A; David H Hickman HS; Columbia, MO; HonRl; LbryAde; NHS; NatlMeritSF; SctActv; SchPpr; FrCl; SciCl; College; Vet.

MC CURDY, Brian J; Springfield Southeast HS; Springfield, IL; 18/450 PresSrCls; NHS; StuCncl; TreasKeyCl; TreasMthCl; JETSAwd; Univ Of Notre Dame; Mechanical Engineer.

MC CURDY, Donald R; Centerville HS; Richmond, IN; 3/160 ChrhWkr; HonRl; NHS; SctActv; StuCncl; FFA; Trk; University; Science.

MC CURDY, Mary K; Woodlands Acad Of Sacred Hear; Winnetka, IL; 4/75 HonRl; HospAde; College; Political Science.

MC CURDY, Timothy M; Onalaska HS; Onalaska, WI; 7/144 HonRl; NHS; NatlMeritCmnd; PresSrCls; Usaf;.

MC CUTCHAN, Stephen R; Plymouth HS; Plymouth, IL; 1/26 SecSophCls; ALBoysSt; Band; HonRl; SctActv; YthFlsp; FFA; SpnCl; PpCl; Bsbl; Bsktbl; Millikin Univ; Accountant.

MC CUTCHAN, Valerie J; Plymouth HS; Plymouth, IL; 2/22 Band; CncrtBnd; HonRl; MrchBnd; PepBnd; SchPl; SctActv; StuCncl; RptrYrbk; RptrSchPpr; FHA; SpnCl; PpCl; LetterBsbl; College; Professional.

MC CUTCHEON, Aubrey V; Cass Technical HS; Detroit, MI; Band; HonRl; NHS; NatlMeritCmnd; PolWkr; RedCrAde; SctActv; CivCl; TreasSpnCl; LetterSwmmng; College; Professional.

MC CUTCHEON, Brian J; Arthur Hill HS; Saginaw, MI; CncrtBnd; HonRl; NHS; SchMus; GerCl; SciCl; Ftbl; Swmmng; LetterTrk; Michigan State University; Law.

MC CUTCHEON, Patrick C; Arthur Hill HS; Sagniaw, MI; HonRl; NHS; GerCl; SciCl; LetterFtbl; Swmmng; U Of Mich; Chem Eng.

MC CUTCHEON, Peggy R; Diamond R4 HS; Joplin, MO; 9/62 Band; Chrs; CncrtBnd; HonRl; Mdrgl; MrchBnd; NHS; PepBnd; SchAde; SchMus; 4-H; FHA; College; Professional.

MC DADE, Joseph E; Burlington HS; Burlington, IA; Band; Chr; Mdrgl; SchMus; StuCncl; LetterBsbl; Bsktbl; LetterFtbl; Univ.

MC DANEL, Jeffery C; Moravia Community HS; Centerville, IA; Chr; Chrs; HonRl; SchMus; SchPl; StuCncl; 4-H; LetterBsbl; LetterBsktbl; VP4-HAwd; Trade Sch; Carpentry.

MC DANIEL, Anita J; Bloomington HS; Bloomington, IL; 16/391 ALAGirlsSt; HonRl; NHS; NatlMeritCmnd; Orch; SecSpnCl; TreasMthCl; PpCl; SciCl; GAA; Univ Of Il; Electrical Engineering.

MC DANIEL, Brian K; Wateruliet HS; Wateruliet, MI; HonRl; NHS; TchrAde; Mi State U; Engineering.

MC DANIEL, Charles P; Abl HS; Broadlands, IL; 4/24 ALBoysSt; ChrhWkr; CmntyWkr; HonRl; PresStuCncl; PresStuGov; PresTeen; TreasFSA; TreasSciCl; LetterBsbl; College; Medical Doctor.

MC DANIEL, Cynthia E; Dupree HS; Dupree, SD; 1/17 PresJrCls; VPSrCls; ALAGirlsSt; Chrs; HonRl; LbryAde; PolWkr; SchPl; StuCncl; CitAwd; Sd St Univ.

MC DANIEL, Larry L; Shiloh HS; Redmon, IL; 4/46 HonRl; SctActv; Bsktbl; Trk; College; Doctor.

MC DANIEL, Laveta; Spokane Hs; Highlandville, MO; Band; Chrs; HonRl; PepBnd; SchPl; StuCncl; Yrbk; 4-H; FHA; School Of The Ozarks; Business.

MC DANIEL, Lesa G; South Knox HS; Wheatland, IN; Chrs; ChrhWkr; HonRl; NHS; Quill&Scroll; EdSchPpr; FHA; FNA; MthCl; Vincennes Univ; Nursing.

MC DANIEL, Marilyn L; Belle HS; Belle, MO; 10/58 HonRl; SecMrchBnd; SecNHS; StuCncl; RptrSchPpr; FHA; PresPpCl; CaptBsbl; CaptBsktbl; Trk; CchngActv; Cntrl Missouri St Univ; Physical Therapy.

MC DANIEL, Mary K; Hudson Sr HS; Hudson, WI; 88/270 SchPl; TchrAde; RptrSchPpr;.

MC DAVID, Daniel T; Terre Haute South HS; Terre Haute, IN; 144/564 HonRl; SctActv; GerCl; LetterBsktbl; Ftbl; Trk; ChmbCommrsAwd; CitAwd; Univ Of Nc; Language.

MC DAVID, Valerie G; Romeoville HS; Lockport, IL; PresSophCls; PresSrCls; ChrhWkr; CncrtBnd; DrlTm; HonRl; LitMag; MrchBnd; SecNHS; StuGov; U Of Il; Pre Medicine.

MC DAVITT, Douglas G; Monticello HS; Monticello, IL; 29/168 Band; Chr; Chrs; PresCncrtBnd; HonRl; MrchBnd; PresNatlThespSoc; PepBnd; SchMus; SchPl; Bsbl; Ftbl; Trk; Wrstlng; College; Advertising.

MC DERMIT, Michael; Auxvasse HS; Auxuasse, MO; HonRl; NHS; SchPl; 4-H; Bsbl; Bsktbl; Ftbl; Trk; PresAwd; CitAwd; Trade Sch.

MC DERMOTT, Dallas R; Elk Horn Kimbalton HS; Harlan, IA; 4/37 NHS; SchPl; SctActv; 4-H; FFA; CaptFtbl; LetterTrk; LetterWrstlng; IMSpt; 4-HAwd; Iowa State Univ; Agriculture Business.

MC DERMOTT, Dallas R; Elkhorn Kimballton HS; Harlon, IA; 4/37 NHS; 4-H; FFA; CaptFtbl; LetterTrk; CaptWrstlng; IMSpt; 4-HAwd; CitAwd; Ia St Univ; Agri Business.

MC DERMOTT, Deborah; Illiopolis HS; Illiopolis, IL; TrsJrCls; Chrs; HonRl; NHS; NatlThespSoc; SchPl; TchrAde; EdYrBk; FHA; GAA; College; Teacher.

MC DERMOTT, Dennis J; Elkhorn Kimballton HS; Harlan, IA; 10/37 SchPl; 4-H; CaptFtbl; CaptWrstlng; 4-HAwd; Ia St Univ; Agriculture Business.

MC DERMOTT, Jacqueline; Newton Sr HS; Newton, IA; Chr; Chrl; Chrs; ChrhWkr; HonRl; NatlThespSoc; SchMus; SchPl; StuCncl; YthFlsp; University.

MC DERMOTT, Molly M; Aquin HS; Epworth, IA; 1/66 SecFrshCls; HonRl; StuCncl; SchPpr; PpCl; IMSpt; Nursing Sch; Nursing.

MC DERMOTT, Nancy; Sacred Heart HS; Salina, KS; ALAGirlsSt; Band; Chrs; CncrtBnd; DrlTm; Mdrgl; NHS; PepBnd; FHA; College.

MC DERMOTT, Pamela A; Chassell HS; Chassell, MI; HonRl; SchPl; LetterBsktbl; Us Navy; Data Processing.

MC DERMOTT, Patrick E; Pacelli HS; Austin, MN; 1/118 Chrs; HonRl; NHS; SchMus; MthCl; CaptTrk; CaptWrstlng; EldAwd; College Of St Thomas; Chemist.

MC DERMOTT, Sharon; St Marys Acad; Chicago, IL; PresFrshCls; PresSophCls; ChrhWkr; PolWkr; StuCncl; TchrAde; Teen; SchPpr; LatCl; Bsbl; Wesley Pass Sch Of N; Nursing.

MC DEVITT, Catherine L; Robinson HS; Robinson, IL; 1/180 ChrhWkr; NatlMeritCmnd; NatlThespSoc; SptEdYrbk; FrCl; SciCl; LetterBsktbl; Tennis; BauchLmbAwd; DARAwd; Knox Coll; Pre Law.

MC DEVITT, David D; Dwight HS; Dwight, IL; 12/111 AFS; ChrhWkr; HonRl; NHS; SchAde; LatCl; LetterGlf; CaptTrk; Wrstlng; RotaryAwd; U Of Il; Engineering.

MC DEVITT, Kathleen; Grant Community HS; Fox Lake, IL; 51/201 Band; Orch; SchMus; FNA; Bsbl; Bsktbl; PresAwd; Barat Col; Art.

MC DIFFETT, Shelley L; Council Grove HS; Alta Vista, KS; 12/118 Chrs; ChrhWkr; HonRl; LbryAde; NHS; SchMus; TchrAde; RptrYrbk; RptrSchPpr; PpCl; Ks State U; Horticulture.

MC DOLE, Rhonda; Madison Cons HS; Madison, IN; Band; Quill&Scroll; SchPpr; GerCl; PpCl; GAA; IMSpt; PPFtbl; Ball State Univ; Retailoring.

MC DONAGH, Anne M; Good Counsel HS; Chicago, IL; Chrs; CmntyWkr; HonRl; JA; PolWkr; StuCncl; SpnCl; GAA; AmLegAwd; JAAwd; Northeastern Ill Univ; Law.

MC DONAGH, Mary B; Queen Of Peace HS; Oak Lawn, IL; Chrs; SpnCl; St Xavier College; Nursing.

MC DONALD, Angela M; Chicago Vocational HS; Chicago, IL; Band; Chr; Chrs; ChrhWkr; CncrtBnd; DrlTm; HonRl; LbryAde; MrchBnd; Orch; SchPl; StuCncl; TchrAde; Tennis; Iowa State Univ; Music.

MC DONALD, Ann D; Barr Reeve HS; Montgomery, IN; HstJrCls; HonRl; OffAde; FHA; PpCl; Chrldr; Beauty College.

MC DONALD, Ann M; Sacred Heart Acad; Mt Pleasant, MI; 11/54 Chr; HonRl; Mdrgl; NHS; StuCncl; PpCl; DARAwd; Western Mi Univ Kalamazoo; Elem Ed.

MC DONALD, Beth A; Ada HS; Lockhart, MN; Band; Chr; ChrhWkr; CncrtBnd; HonRl; HospAde; MrchBnd; NatlFornLg; NHS; NatlThespSoc; PepBnd; GAA; Univ Of North Dakota; Medicine.

MC DONALD, Bradley T; Manhattan HS; Manhattan, KS; 8/350 ALBoysSt; ChrhWkr; CncrtBnd; HonRl; ModUN; NatlFornLg; SctActv; StuGov; Glf; OptClAwd; College; Law.

MC DONALD, Brian; Charleston HS; Charleston, IL; 47/237 Band; CncrtBnd; HonRl; MrchBnd; PepBnd; Bsktbl; IMSpt; Eastern Illinois Univ; Computerscience.

MC DONALD, Bruce A; New Trier East HS; Glencoe, IL; NatlMeritCmnd; SchPl; YthFlsp; Colgate University.

MC DONALD, Charles J; Taylorville HS; Taylorville, IL; 1/251 Chr; ChrhWkr; HonRl; NHS; Yrbk; Bsktbl; University; Industrial Tech.

MC DONALD, Colleen A; Hawley HS; Hawley, MN; SecSophCls; Band; HonRl; SchMus; SchPl; RptrSchPpr; FHA; FTA; SciCl; Trk; Trade School CHEF.

MC DONALD, Colleen R; Perkins County HS; Grant, NE; 4/41 Band; CncrtBnd; HonRl; MrchBnd; NHS; StuCncl; 4-H; FHA; Chrldr; Univ Of Ne; Computer Science.

MC DONALD, Elizabeth A; Schlarman HS; Sidell, IL; 5/76 Band; CncrtBnd; HonRl; HospAde; NHS; PepBnd; SchMus; SctActv; 4-H; DanFAwd; St Johns; Nursing.

MC DONALD, Erin M; Argyle HS; Argyle, WI; Band; Chr; HonRl; Mdrgl; ModUN; PepBnd; PolWkr; Yrbk; RptrSchPpr; Trk; College.

MC DONALD, Gail; Cavalier Public; Cavalier, ND; ALAGirlsSt; Chrs; HonRl; RptrSchPpr; PpCl; Bsktbl; IMSpt; Uneversity; Registered Nurse.

MC DONALD, Gary A; Holmen HS; Holmen, WI; ChrhWkr; CmntyWkr; HonRl; NHS; LetterFtbl; LetterTrk; IMSpt; Univ; Professional.

MC DONALD, Gayle; Midland HS; Midland, MI; Chr; HonRl; LbryAde; RptrYrbk; RptrSchPpr; EdSchPpr; PpCl; Michigan Tech U; Biological Scientist.

MC DONALD, James L; North HS; Fargo, ND; ALBoysSt; ChrhWkr; CmntyWkr; HonRl; NHS; OffAde; Orch; SctActv; YthFlsp; FrCl; Bsktbl; Trk; University; Dentist.

MC DONALD, Jane; West Bloomfield HS; West Bloomfield, MI; TrsSrCls; HonRl; SctActv; Central Mich Univ; Education.

MC DONALD, Janet L; Midland HS; Midland, MI; ChrhWkr; HonRl; LbryAde; NHS; NatlMeritFnl; Michigan State Univ.

MC DONALD, Jean; New Providence HS; New Providence, IA; 2/7 Chr; Chrs; DrmMjrt; HonRl; SchMus; SchPl; DanFAwd; William Penn College; Elem Education.

MC DONALD, Jenny L; Brown County HS; Nashville, IN; ChrhWkr; HonRl; NHS; StuCncl; TchrAde; Yrbk; PpCl; Chrldr; IMSpt;.

MC DONALD, John C; Quigley Prep North; Chicago, IL; 8/72 PresSrCls; HonRl; Sacrstn; SchPl; EdYrBk; FBA; LatCl; MthCl; PresAwd; CitAwd; Lake Forest Clg; Medicine.

MC DONALD, Johnia J; Golden City HS; Lamar, MO; 1/18 ALAGirlsSt; HonRl; OffAde; SchPl; StuCncl; EdYrBk; RptrSchPpr; FHA; MthCl; PPFtbl; Missouri Southern College; Accounting.

MC DONALD, Julie M; Marillac HS; Glenview, IL; NHS; SecStuCncl; StuGov; College; Pre Law.

MC DONALD, Kathryn I; Pinckney HS; Pinckney, MI; HonRl; TchrAde; College; Photography.

MC DONALD, Kathy L; Shakamak HS; Jasonville, IN; 5/79 SecFrshCls; SecSophCls; ChrhWkr; DrlTm; HonRl; LbryAde; NHS; TchrAde; FHA; PpCl;.

MC DONALD, Kevin; Southeast Fountain HS; Hillsboro, IN; 13/130 Band; CncrtBnd; HonRl; MrchBnd; PepBnd; SchMus; SchPl; Yrbk; 4-H;.

MC DONALD, Lindy L; Princeton HS; Princeton, IL; Band; ChrhWkr; HospAde; SctActv; YthFlsp; 4-H; GAA; DanFAwd; Ill State Univ; Medical Technology.

MC DONALD, Mary E; St Marys HS; Independence, MO; 20/115 ALAGirlsSt; Chr; DrlTm; HonRl; NHS; SchPl; SchPl; EdYrBk; GerCl; PpCl; College; Journalism.

MC DONALD, Mary K; Minooka Comm HS; Minooka, IL; 26/109 HonRl; FTA; IMSpt; PresAwd; College; Guidance Counseling.

MC DONALD, Michael A; Premontre HS; Green Bay, WI; ROTC; CivCl; CaptFtbl; Trk; AmLegAwd; KiwanAwd; OptClAwd; VFWAwd; Col; Optimalogist.

MC DONALD, Michael P; Chisholm Senior HS; Chisholm, MN; 3/131 ALBoysSt; HonRl; NHS; KeyCl; Bsktbl; Ftbl; St Olaf Clg; Law.

MC DONALD, Phil; Underwood Comm HS; Underwood, IA; HonRl; Trk; 4-HAwd; Iowa State Univ; Civil Engineering.

MC DONALD, Richard S; Mitchell HS; Mitchell, NE; 11/57 Chrs; CmntyWkr; HonRl; StuGov; YthFlsp; VPKeyCl; LetterBsktbl; Swmmng; LetterTrk; MasAwd; Coll; Agri,cpa,lawyer.

MC DONALD, Robert D; Union HS; Union, MO; 3/165 VPSophCls; ALBoysSt; Band; ChrhWkr; CncrtBnd; HonRl; MrchBnd; Orch; PepBnd; PolWkr; SchMus; LetterBsbl; LetterBsktbl; LetterFtbl; William Jewell College; Law.

MC DONALD, Robert S; Satanta HS; Satanta, KS; 5/44 Band; CncrtBnd; MrchBnd; NHS; Orch; PepBnd; SchPl; StuCncl; Bsktbl; College; Business.

MC DONALD, Steven; Danville Hs; Danville, IL; 27/629 HonRl; PresJA; NatlMeritCmnd; Quill&Scroll; StuCncl; YthFlsp; SchPpr; LetterBsbl; Bsktbl; Ftbl; Illinois Wesleyan; Psychology.

MC DONALD, Susan; Black Hawk HS; Gratiot, WI; VPFrshCls; VPSrCls; ALAGirlsSt; ChrhWkr; HonRl; EdYrBk; Univ Of Wi At Platteville, Education.

MC DONALD, Terry L; West Liberty HS; W Liberty, IA; 35/90 PresSophCls; Chrs; Teen; 4-H; FFA; LetterBsbl; LetterBsktbl; LetterFtbl; LetterTrk; CchngActv; College; Vocational.

MC DONALD, Thomas L; Tustin HS; Mequon, WI; 138/480 SchPl; YthFlsp; CaptFtbl; IMSpt; Us Naval Acad; Eng.

MC DONALD, Timothy B; Cathedral HS; Indianapolis, IN; HonRl; JA; NHS; NatlMeritCmnd; SchPl; StuCncl; StuGov; SchPpr; LetterTrk; IMSpt; OptClAwd; College Of Liberal Arts; Medicine.

MC DONALD, Valarie R; Diagonal HS; Diagonal, IA; 4/17 SecJrCls; Band; ChrhWkr; HonRl; NatlMeritCmnd; SchMus; Yrbk; Bsbl; Bsktbl; CitAwd; Des Moines Are Clg; Medical Secretary.

MC DONNELL, Bridget A; Nazareth Academy; La Grange, IL; SecFrshCls; CmntyWkr; HospAde; SchAde; SchPl; StuCncl; Trk; CchngActv; GAA; Mt Mary College; Occupational Therapy.

MC DONNOUGH, Cynthia B; Carlinville HS; Carlinville, IL; Chr; Chrs; ChrhWkr; HonRl; JrNHS; NHS; SchPl; VPSpnCl; Ouachita Baptist Univ; Music.

MC DONNOUGH, Sylvia D; Carlinville HS; Carlinville, IL; 20/163 Chrs; ChrhWkr; HonRl; JrNHS; University; Professional.

MC DONOFF, Thomas G; Pellston HS; Levering, MI; NatlMeritCmnd; SchPl; StuCncl; EdYrBk; Bsktbl; Ftbl; Trk; BttyCrckrAwd; Northern Mi Univ; Business Management.

MC DONOUGH, Mary E; Marillac HS; Northbrook, IL; 14/252 Chrl; Chrs; ChrhWkr; CmntyWkr; NHS; StuCncl; Univ Of Illinois; Medicine.

MC DONOUGH, Maureen; St Clement HS; Centerline, MI; 7/98 VPSophCls; HonRl; NHS; SchPl; StuCncl; Bsbl; Bsktbl; Chrldr; GAA; IMSpt; Eastern Mi; Drama Dance.

MC DOUGALL, Kenneth G; Redford Union HS; Redford Twp, MI; ChrhWkr; NHS; Trk; Wrstlng; Community College; Automotive Technician.

MC DOUGAN, Charles M; Marceline HS; Marceline, MO; ALBoysSt; Chr; Chrs; ChrhWkr; HonRl; EdYrBk; SciCl; Bsktbl; Ftbl; Trk; Wrstlng; Hannibal La Grange College; Ministry.

MC DOWELL, Ann; Horton Watkins HS; Creve Coent, MO; HonRl; JCC; NatlMeritCmnd; Purdue Univ; Veterinary.

MC DOWELL, Carla A; Westport HS; Kansas City, MO; CmntyWkr; NatlMeritSF; SpnCl; PpCl; Penn Valley Jr College; Nursng.

MC DOWELL, Frederick W; Morgan Park HS; Chicago, IL; 99/498 Chr; Chrs; ChrhWkr; CmntyWkr; SctActv; TchrAde; YthFlsp; KeyCl; LetterSwmmng; U Of Ill; Food Science.

MC DOWELL, John R; Glenbrook North HS; Northbrook, IL; 160/700 HonRl; NatlMeritFnl; NatlMeritSF; OffAde; PolWkr; SchPl; StuGov; RptrSchPpr; SchPpr; University; Communications.

MC DOWELL, Marcia K; Eddyville Comm HS; Ottumwa, IA; 3/70 Band; Chr; Chrs; ChrhWkr; CncrtBnd; HonRl; MrchBnd; PepBnd; SchPl; TchrAde; 4-H; SpnCl; Bsktbl; University; Optometry.

MC DOWELL, Rex A; Wm Henry Harrison HS; Lafayette, IN; 4/280 Band; ChrhWkr; HonRl; JrNHS; Mdrgl; MrchBnd; NHS; NatlMeritSF; Trk; CitAwd; Bible Sch; Minister.

MC DOWELL, Roberta J; Winner HS; Winner, SD; 7/135 ALAGirlsSt; Chrs; DrlTm; HonRl; NatlFornLg; NatlThespSoc; SchMus; SchPl; StuCncl; So Dakota St College; Biology.

MC DOWELL, Stephanie; Huntington North HS; Huntington, IN; Chr; ChrhWkr; HonRl; Mdrgl; SchMus; YthFlsp; Univ; Language Major.

MC DUFFIE, Mark E; West Side HS; Gary, IN; ALBoysSt; Band; ChrhWkr; JrNHS; NHS; NatlMeritSF; Orch; SchPl; StuCncl; Purdue Univ; Electrical Engineering.

MC EACHEN, Joan; Walled Lake Central HS; Union Lake, MI; HonRl; JA; NatlMeritFnl; NatlMeritCmnd; NatlMeritSchl; NatlMeritSF; FshEdSchPpr; TchrAde; PpCl; Coll; Law.

MC EACHERN, Anne G; Hannibal HS; Hannibal, MO; Band; ChrhWkr; HonRl; NHS; SchPl; VPFTA; SecFrCl; PpCl; University Of Missouri; French.

MC ELDERRY, Dennis R; Davis County Comm HS; Bloomfield, IA; HonRl; SctActv; LetterTrk; Trade School ;farm.

MC ELDOWNEY, Janet L; Rich South HS; Park Forest, IL; 18/279 Band; CmntyWkr; HonRl; HospAde; LbryAde; MrchBnd; NatlMeritFnl; NatlMeritSF; PolWkr; College; Liberal Arts.

MC ELDOWNEY, Patrick J; Rhinelander HS; Rhinelander, WI; HonRl; NHS; RptrSchPpr; Bsktbl; Glf; Trk; Un Wis Stevens Point; Biology Major.

MC ELFRESH, Scott D; Osceola HS; Osceola, WI; Chr; ChrhWkr; SchPl; StuCncl; TchrAde; LetterBsbl; LetterBsktbl; LetterFtbl; LetterTrk; College.

MC ELHINEY, Timothy K; Avon HS; Avon, IL; 14/39 CmntyWkr; JA; NHS; NatlMeritCmnd; RedCrAde; ROTC; StuCncl; YthLg; 4-H; FHA; Trade Sch; Construction.

MC ELHINNEY, Bruce H; Earnest W Seaholm HS; Birmingham, MI; HonRl; JrNHS; NatlMeritSF; RptrYrbk; EdSchPpr; LetterBsbl; Bsktbl; Ftbl; LetterSocr; OptClAwd; Univ; Journalism.

MC ELLIGOTT, Timothy R; Wauwatosa East HS; Wauwatosa, WI; VPJrCls; HonRl; SctActv; SpnCl; MthCl; LetterSwmmng; IMSpt; Wisconsin St Schl; Sociology.

MC ELROY, Keith T; Rockford Sr HS; Rockford, IA; ALBoysSt; HonRl; RptrSchPpr; Ftbl; Wrstlng; Trade; Electronics.

MC ELYEA, Charles S; Southwestern HS; Flint, MI; 1/577 NHS; Quill&Scroll; Yrbk; SchPpr;.

MC EWAN, Dorothy M; Melvindale HS; Melvindale, MI; Band; CncrtBnd; HonRl; MrchBnd; Eastern Michigan Univ; Special Education.

MC EWAN, Laura A; Sts Peter & Paul Area HS; Saginaw, MI; SecTrsSophCls; PresJrCls; VPSrCls; Chrs; DrlTm; HonRl; Mdrgl; NHS; Chrldr; GAA; College.

MC EWEN, Diana J; Carlinville HS; Carlinville, IL; 17/161 TrsSophCls; CncrtBnd; HonRl; HospAde; JrNHS; MrchBnd; SchPl; TchrAde; FrCl; Western Illinois Univ; Special Educ.

MC FADDEN, Barb; Blair Oaks HS; Jefferson City, MO; VPJrCls; ChrhWkr; CncrtBnd; HonRl; MrchBnd; NHS; PepBnd; SchPl; StuCncl; Chrldr; Univ Ks.

MC FADDEN, Beth I; Mullinville HS; Mullinville, KS; 1/13 TrsFrshCls; Aud/Vis; Chrs; SchPl; StuCncl; RptrSchPpr; FHA; Sw Kansas Area Vo Tech; Cosmetology.

MC FADDEN, James; Tippecanoe Valley HS; Claypool, IN; HonRl; NHS; Bsktbl; IMSpt; College; Accounting.

MC FADDEN, James F; Parkway North Sr HS; St Louis, MO; CncrtBnd; LbryAde; SctActv; St Louis College; Professional.

MC FADDEN, Mary A; Whiting HS; Whiting, IN; 6/102 ALAGirlsSt; HonRl; JA; NHS; PolWkr; SctActv; TchrAde; Yrbk; SecFTA; SpnCl; St Marys Coll; Elementary Ed.

MC FADDEN, Shauna M; Oak Park HS; Gladstone, MO; Chr; Chrs; ChrhWkr; HonRl; NHS; SchMus; StuCncl; YthFlsp; RptrYrbk; University Of Missouri; Education.

MC FALL, Brian K; Fort Scott HS; Fort Scott, KS; ALBoysSt; ChrhWkr; HonRl; NatlFornLg; StuCncl; LetterBsktbl; LetterFtbl; LetterTrk; College; Professional.

MC FALL, Debra K; City HS; Iowa City, IA; 4/278 HonRl; NHS; NatlMeritCmnd; Quill&Scroll; SchPl; StuCncl; RptrSchPpr; SchPpr; PpCl; ChmbCommrsAwd; Univ; Business.

MC FALL, Jerry D; Crothersville HS; Crothersville, IN; ALBoysSt; Band; ChrhWkr; CncrtBnd; HonRl; MrchBnd; NHS; PepBnd; SchPl; PpCl; Ball State Univ; Pro Architect.

MC FALL, Kathryn R; Central Of Argyle HS; Donnellson, IA; AFS; HonRl; LbryAde; SchPl; YthFlsp; FTA; Bsbl; MasAwd; College; Professional.

MC FALL, Treveda K; Heights HS; Wichita, KS; Chr; DrlTm; HonRl; LbryAde; Mdrgl; NatlMeritCmnd; NatlMeritSF; OffAde; SchPpr; FrCl; Kansas State Univ; Mathematics.

MC FANN, Tanya R; Wellington HS; Milford, IL; 1/20 Chrs; HonRl; StuCncl; StuGov; RptrSchPpr; SchPpr; Pres4-H; PresFHA; Chrldr; GAA; Coll; Vocation.

MC FARLAND, Arthur M; Louisiana HS; Louisiana, MO; PresFrshCls; Band; Chr; Chrs; ChrhWkr; CncrtBnd; HonRl; JrNHS; Mdrgl; SpnCl; Univ; Pro.

MC FARLAND, Barbara J; Hartford HS; Hartford, MI; VPSophCls; ChrhWkr; HonRl; SchPl; StuCncl; College; Psychology.

MC FARLAND, Debra E; Mc Cluer North HS; Florissant, MO; 72/750 Band; HonRl; SctActv; GodCntryAwd; Univ Of Missouri; Nursing.

MC FARLAND, Gary L; Mexico HS; Mexico, MO; ALBoysSt; Chr; SchPl; StuCncl; TchrAde; RptrSchPpr; LatCl; LetterBsbl; LetterBsktbl; LetterFtbl; College Or Univ; Professional.

MC FARLAND, Gem E; Platte Co HS; Kansas City, MO; 4/85 Chr; HonRl; NHS; OffAde; TchrAde; YthFlsp; FrCl; SpnCl; SciCl; Trk; Manhattan Christian Col; Sociology.

MC FARLAND, Leslie L; Wayne HS; Fort Wayne, IN; Chr; Chrs; ChrhWkr; SchPl; Business School; Secretary.

MC FARLAND, Lois; Academy Of Mount Saint Schi; Atchinson, KS; /42 Chr; Chrs; OffAde; Sdlty; RptrYrbk; RptrSchPpr; SchPpr; SpnCl; PpCl; GAA; Benedictine College.

MC FARLAND, Mary A; Eisenhower HS; Decatur, IL; 25/308 Band; CncrtBnd; HospAde; MrchBnd; NHS; NatlMeritCmnd; SctActv; Yrbk; FrCl; Illinois State Univ; Medicine.

MC FARLAND, Paul D; Plainfield HS; Joliet, IL; 45/293 YthFlsp; Junior College; Professional.

MC FARLAND, Randall C; Bronaugh R 7 HS; Moundville, MO; PresFrshCls; Band; CncrtBnd; HonRl; MrchBnd; NHS; NatlThespSoc; SchPl; StuCncl; SptEdYrbk; Trade School; Professional.

MC FARLAND, Vicki G; Rolla HS; Rolla, MO; 135/309 Chr; OffAde; StuGov; FHA; PpCl; Chrldr; IMSpt; Univ; Busi.

MC FARLANE, Jeri; Southwest HS; Green Bay, WI; 166/427 Chrs; ChrhWkr; DrmBgl; HonRl; LbryAde; SchPl; SpnCl; Trk; IMSpt; Univ Wisconsin Green Bay; Professional.

MC FARLANE, Leann M; Roseau HS; Wannaska, MN; HonRl; SchPl; RptrSchPpr; 4-H; FHA; Bsktbl; Trk; GAA; IMSpt; 4-HAwd; College; Curriculum Of Major Study.

MC FARLIN, Linda J; Brainerd HS; Brainerd, MN; Chr; ChrhWkr; TchrAde; Yrbk; FTA; Swmmng; College; Professional.

MC FARREN, Peggy A; Chatard HS; Indianapolis, IN; 41/192 HonRl; PresNHS; Quill&Scroll; SptEdYrbk; CchngActv; IMSpt; Purdue; Veterinary Medicine.

MC FEETERS, Debra J; Clinton Comm HS; Clinton, IL; 14/154 TrsFrshCls; HonRl; SecNHS; SchMus; StuCncl; TreasStuGov; RptrSchPpr; CaptBsbl; LetterBsktbl; GAA; University; Nursing.

MC FERRON, Kenneth F; Advance HS; Advance, MO; 3/40 HonRl; PresStuCncl; VPFFA; PresSciCl; Se Missouri Univ; Agriculture.

MC FETERS, Mary A; Concord HS; Concord, MI; 4/65 ChrhWkr; HonRl; NHS; SchAde; TchrAde; YthFlsp; RptrYrbk; RptrSchPpr; PpCl; Swmmng; Tennis; Adrian College; Engineering.

MC GAHEY, Charlie A; Evanston Township HS; Evanston, IL; HonRl; Bsbl; Ftbl; IMSpt; College; Professional.

MC GANN, William F; Spalding Inst; Peoria, IL; 10/210 HonRl; NHS; EdYrBk; KeyCl; Bsbl; St Louis U; Pre Med.

MC GANNON, Patrick J; Hinsdale Central Township HS; Hinsdale, IL; 4 ChrhWkr; CmntyWkr; HonRl; GerCl; Ftbl; Univ Of Dayton; Engineering.

MC GARRY, Bridget; Thomas Kelly HS; Chicago, IL; 19/503 StuCncl; TreasFTA; LetterGAA; College.

MC GARRY, Cathy J; H L U Community HS; Victor, IA; Band; Chrs; CncrtBnd; HonRl; MrchBnd; PepBnd; SchMus; SchPl; SpnCl; PpCl; Work.

MC GAUGH, Annamaria P; Central HS; St Joseph, MO; 51/532 HonRl; 4-H; LatCl; MthCl; PpCl; College; Legal Secretary.

MC GAUGHEY, Ann E; Stephen Decatur HS; Decatur, IL; 37/368 AFS; Band; ChrhWkr; HonRl; StuCncl; Lindenwood College; Journalism.

MC GAUGHEY, Bob; Beloit HS; Beloit, KS; 14/62 HonRl; SchPl; SciCl; Bsktbl; Ftbl; Trk; PPFtbl; DARAwd; Coll; Soc.

MC GAUGHY, Roger L; Elwood HS; Elwood, KS; 11/20 HstFrshCls; SchPl; StuCncl; StuGov; SptEdYrbk; Bsbl; Bsktbl; Ftbl; Trk; PresAwd; Coll;.

MC GEE, Barbara A; Sacred Heart Academy; Springfield, IL; 22/149 HonRl; NHS; SchMus; SchPl; RptrSchPpr; FrCl; PpCl; Springfield College; Education.

MC GEE, David P; Fordson HS; Dearborn Hgts, MI; Band; CncrtBnd; HonRl; JA; MrchBnd; SctActv; GerCl; Trk; U Of Mich Dearborn; Engineering.

MC GEE, Dianna L; St Anthony HS; St Louis, MO; 1/70 Chrs; HonRl; LbryAde; NHS; SchMus; SchPl; RptrSchPpr; SchPpr; LatCl; St Louis Univ; Physical Therapy.

MC GEE, Jeri A; Albia Community HS; Melrose, IA; 5/160 VPSrCls; HonRl; NHS; SpnCl; BttyCrckrAwd; Univ Of Iowa; Science.

MC GEE, Joanna M; Sumner HS; Kansas City, KS; 1/225 SecSrCls; HonRl; NHS; NatlMeritCmnd; StuCncl; Univ Of Houston.

MC GEE, Kevin J; St Francis HS; Traverse City, MI; PresSrCls; HonRl; NHS; TchrAde; IMSpt; RotaryAwd; Mi Tech Univ; Elec Eng.

MC GEE, Lowell I; Riverdale HS; Riverdale, ND; 1/15 PresSophCls; ALBoysSt; Band; NatlFornLg; SchPl; StuCncl; Yrbk; EdSchPpr; SpnCl; LetterTrk; Ndsu; Veterinary Medicine.

MC GEE, Patricia; Lawrence Central HS; Lawrence, IN; Chr; CmntyWkr; HonRl; SctActv; Interior Decoration.

MC GEE, Patricia A; Quincy Notre Dame HS; Quincy, IL; TrsFrshCls; Chr; Chrl; HonRl; SchMus; FrCl; Chrldr; IMSpt; College; Teaching.

MC GEE, Phyllis; Simpson HS; Chicago, IL; Chrs; DrlTm; HonRl; JA; Orch; SchPl; StuCncl; Bsktbl; JAAwd; CitAwd; College; Teaching.

MC GEE, Sandra J; New Palestine HS; New Palestine, IN; 12/179 ALAGirlsSt; Chrs; ChrhWkr; SecCncrtBnd; SecMrchBnd; NHS; PepBnd; TchrAde; YthFlsp; SecLatCl; College; Professional.

MC GEEHAN, Marie L; Parkway West Sr HS; Manchester, MO; 1/740 Chr; JrNHS; VPNHS; StuCncl; GAA; Drake Univ.

MC GEHEE, Rex; United Township HS; Silvis, IL; 11/580 Chr; ChrhWkr; HonRl; Mdrgl; NHS; SchMus; FrCl; Northwestern Univ; Medicine.

MC GEHEE, Sharon L; Fair Grove HS; Fair Grove, MO; 10/50 ChrhWkr; HonRl; MrchBnd; PolWkr; StuCncl; StuGov; FHA; PpCl; College; Med Technology.

MC GHEE, James W; Stillman Valley HS; Stillman Valley, IL; HonRl; TchrAde; YthFlsp; FTA; Bsbl; Ftbl; College; Professional.

MC GHEE, Laura J; Dexter Sr HS; Dexter, MO; Band; CtyCnl; HonRl; JrNHS; NHS; NatlMeritSchl; SchPl; EdYrBk; EdSchPpr; University; Psychology.

MC GILL, Terri; Central HS; Kenosha, WI; HonRl; SctActv; StuCncl; SptEdYrbk; 4-H; FHA; PpCl; Chrldr; GAA; 4-HAwd; Gate Way Tech Inst; Florist.

MC GILLEM, Kenton; Washington HS; Washington, IN; 70/240 HonRl; GerCl; Bsktbl; IMSpt; In Univ; Retailing.

MC GILLEM, Randall; Lincoln HS; Pershing, IN; Band; CncrtBnd; HonRl; MrchBnd; Bsktbl; College; Journalism.

MC GILLEN, Edward; St Willibrord Hs; Chicago, IL; 3/80 NHS; NatlMeritCmnd; PresStuCncl; RptrYrbk; SptEdSchPpr; LatCl; MthCl; TreasSciCl; LetterBsktbl; CaptSocr; Marquette U; Lawyer Journalist.

MC GILLICUDDY, John K; Jacksonville HS; Jacksonville, IL; University; Engineering.

MC GILLIN, Thomas S; St Pius X HS; Kansas City, MO; 8/136 Band; ChrhWkr; CncrtBnd; HonRl; NHS; PepBnd; SchMus; SchPl; College; Business.

MC GILURY, Pamela J; Ash Grove HS; Willard, MO; HonRl; TreasJrNHS; SecNHS; 4-H; FHA; PpCl; Trk; Chrldr; PPFtbl; Sw Ms State; Business.

MC GINLEY, Charlotte A; A Lincoln HS; Bloomington, MN; Chr; DrlTm; HonRl; MrchBnd; NHS; College; Professional.

MC GINN, Mary G; Delwood HS; Delmar, IA; 1/30 TrsSophCls; Band; Chr; HonRl; LbryAde; NHS; SchPl; RptrYrbk; EdSchPpr; FrCl; LetterBsktbl; Creighton Univ; Law.

MC GINNESS, Daniel L; Shiloh HS; Brocton, IL; HonRl; Univ Of Ill; Medicine.

MC GINNESS, David S; Lake Crystal HS; Lake Crystal, MN; 6/62 CncrtBnd; HonRl; MrchBnd; NatlMeritCmnd; SchPl; Ftbl; Drake U; Physics Math Major.

MC GINNESS, Rose M; Geneva HS; Geneva, NE; PresSophCls; Band; Orch; SctActv; StuCncl; TchrAde; Twrl; RptrSchPpr; FDA; Swmmng; Augustana; Psychologist.

MC GINNIS, Catherine C; Morris HS; Morris, MN; ALAGirlsSt; HonRl; HospAde; ModUN; NHS; NatlMeritSF; SchPl; SpnCl; Swmmng; LetterTrk; Univ; Med.

MC GINNIS, Cindy M; Faith HS; Faith, SD; Band; Chr; DrlTm; HonRl; MrchBnd; SchPl; TchrAde; PpCl; Trk; Chrldr; Housewife.

MC GINNIS, Michael R; Algona Comm HS; Algona, IA; 4/130 PresSrCls; AFS; Aud/Vis; CtyCnl; HonRl; HospAde; NHS; PolWkr; StuCncl; StuGov; Bsbl; Ftbl; LetterTrk; GovHonPrgAwd; Univ Of Iowa; Law.

MC GINTY, Douglas; Dunlap HS; Dunlap, IL; 22/94 HonRl; PolWkr; LatCl; PpCl; SciCl; Southern Ill; Law.

MC GINTY, Katheryn M; Proviso East HS; Maywood, IL; Triton Jr College; Accountant.

MC GINTY, Robert J; Macksville HS; Seward, KS; Band; Chr; Chrs; MrchBnd; PepBnd; SchPl; Computer Programmer.

MC GIRR, Craig L; Hinckley Big Rock HS; Hinckley, IL; 2/77 Band; Chrs; ChrhWkr; PresNHS; SchMus; SchPl; SciCl; AmLegAwd; EldAwd; Bradley Univ; Mech Engineering.

MC GIVERN, Eugene J; Assumption HS; Davenport, IA; 40/230 ALBoysSt; ChrhWkr; PolWkr; StuCncl; CaptTrk; IMSpt; College.

MC GLINCHEY, Mark M; Southwestern HS; Flint, MI; VPJA; NHS; SctActv; University; Electrical Engineering.

MC GLINN, Thomas C; St Joseph HS; South Beno, IN; 9/230 HonRl; IMSpt; Univ; Sci.

MC GLYNN, Kathleen J; Immaculata HS; Detroit, MI; CmntyWkr; HonRl; JA; SctActv; Mich St U; Vet Med.

MC GOFF, Christine M; Msgr John R Hackett HS; Kalamazoo, MI; 30/150 HonRl; SctActv; SpnCl; LetterBsktbl; IMSpt; PPFtbl; Parsons Business School; Business Admin.

MC GONAGLE, Mary C; Mother Guerin HS; Chicago, IL; HonRl; NatlMeritCmnd; StuGov; SchPpr; De Paul Univ; Law.

MC GOREY, Margaret M; Immaculate Conception HS; Bellwood, IL; HonRl; NHS; OffAde; SctActv; SchPpr; SpnCl; PresPpCl; LetterTrk; Chrldr; Ill St U; Acct.

MC GOUGH, Timothy J; St Thomas Acad; St Paul, MN; HonRl; ROTC; LetterBsktbl; Coll;eng.

MC GOVERN, Celeste M; Mother Mcauley HS; Chicago, IL; 77/474 HonRl; NatlMeritCmnd; Quill&Scroll; TchrAde; EdSchPpr; FTA; FrCl; MthCl; College; Law.

MC GOVERN, Donald T; Weber HS; Chicago, IL; 26/193 VPSrCls; HonRl; NHS; SctActv; StuGov; Ftbl; Uicc; Occupational Therapist.

MC GOVERN, Kelle K; Hempstead HS; Dubuque, IA; 15/455 HonRl; JA; NHS; PolWkr; RedCrAde; StuGov; SchPpr; SpnCl; LetterGlf; ChmbCommrsAwd; College; Interior Design.

MC GOVERN, Melinda K; Prairie Community HS; Gowrie, IA; Band; Chrs; ChrhWkr; CmntyWkr; MrchBnd; SchMus; YthFlsp; RptrYrbk; RptrSchPpr; FHA; Trade School.

MC GOWAN, Bridget A; Mauston HS; Lyndon Sta, WI; HonRl; NHS; 4-H; FHA; FrCl; LatCl;.

MC GOWAN, James K; Leo HS; Chicago, IL; 16/199 HonRl; College; Audio Visual.

MC GOWAN, Joanne L; Pecatonica Area HS; Blanchardville, WI; SecJrCls; Band; ChrhWkr; CncrtBnd; HonRl; MrchBnd; PepBnd; SchMus; FHA; Bsktbl; Mad Acad Of Bty Cul; Beautician.

MC GOWAN, Kathleen A; Academy Of Our Lady; Peoria, IL; 16/99 Chr; HonRl; HospAde; NHS; SchMus; SchPl; SctActv; Yrbk; SchPpr; Trinity College; Pediatrician.

MC GOWAN, Kendall; Beaumont HS; Saint Louis, MO; NatlMeritFnl; OffAde; SchAde; StuCncl; SpnCl; College; Teacher.

MC GOWAN, Kevin; Arlington Hs; Arlington Heights, IL; 107/598 HonRl; NHS; Bsktbl; College; Professional.

MC GOWAN, Mary B; Midland HS; Midland, MI; 41/433.

MC GOWAN, Michael J; Marist HS; Chicago, IL; CtyCnl; PolWkr; StuCncl; StuGov; PpCl; College; Professional.

MC GOWAN, Roland M; Norwich HS; Kingman, KS; 3/30 SchPl; StuCncl; Yrbk; College.

MC GOWAN, Susan; Rockford East Hs; Rockford, IL; 44/665 HonRl; SchPl; StuGov; Yrbk; PpCl; Swmmng; Rock Valley College; Inhalation Therapist.

MC GOWAN, William; Sts Peter And Paul Area HS; Saginaw, MI; Chrs; LbryAde; SchPl; College; Vocation.

MC GOWEN, Mary K; Emerson Hubbard HS; Hubbard, NE; 12/58 ALAGirlsSt; Chrs; CncrtBnd; HonRl; PepBnd; Twrl; 4-H; PpCl; GAA; PresAwd; Coll; History.

MC GOWEN, Robin; Puxico R 8 HS; Puxico, MO; TreasBand; HonRl; JA; ModUN; OffAde; SchPl; SecStuCncl; PpCl; SciCl; IMSpt; Bus Sch; Voc.

MC GRAIL, Timothy; St Thomas Sem; Jefferson City, MO; 6/11 PresSophCls; Chr; CmntyWkr; HonRl; SchPl; SctActv; StuGov; RptrYrbk; Yrbk; Quincy Coll, Chemistry.

MC GRATH, Daniel W; Maine South HS; Park Ridge, IL; TrsFrshCls; Chrs; ChrhWkr; CmntyWkr; HonRl; NHS; Quill&Scroll; PresStuCncl; SptEdSchPpr; Ftbl; Loyola Univ; Law.

MC GRATH, Eileen M; Mother Mcauley HS; Oak Lawn, IL; 11/483 Chr; Chrs; CmntyWkr; HonRl; Bsbl; Bsktbl; Ftbl; Trk; Univ Of Ill; Physical Therapist.

MC GRATH, Jane A; Gibson City HS; Gibson City, IL; 8/90 TrsSophCls; Band; HonRl; NHS; SchPl; StuCncl; Yrbk; SecSpnCl; Chrldr; GAA; Univ Of Ill.

MC GRATH, Janice L; South Newton HS; Goodland, IN; 12/94 Band; CncrtBnd; HonRl; LbryAde; MrchBnd; NHS; Orch; PepBnd; SchMus; SchPl; Bsbl; LetterBsktbl; GAA; PPFtbl; Illinois State Univ; Professional.

MC GRATH, Joan M; Hubbard HS; Chicago, IL; PresChr; PresChrs; HonRl; NHS; PresSpnCl; PPFtbl; CitAwd; Business Schl; Secretarial.

MC GRATH, Kim; Wauwatosa East HS; Wauwatosa, WI; HonRl; PpCl; Swmmng; GAA; IMSpt; College; Mass Communications.

MC GRATH, Raymond G; Marmion Mlt Academy; Palatine, IL; Band; CncrtBnd; HonRl; MrchBnd; NHS; NatlMeritCmnd; ROTC; Sacrstn; RptrYrbk; Ftbl; Trk; IMSpt; Univ Of Notre Dame; Law.

MC GRATH, Robert A; Sparta Senior HS; Sparta, WI; HonRl; FFA; Undecided; Undecided.

MC GRATH, Vicki A; Edinburg HS; Edinburg, IL; VPSophCls; CncrtBnd; HonRl; LbryAde; SchPl; RptrYrbk; VPFHA; PresFrCl; Univ Of Ill; Law.

MC GRAW, Kathleen M; Sts Peter & Paul HS; Saginaw, MI; Chrs; DrlTm; HonRl; Mdrgl; College; Radiology.

MC GRAW, Timothy J; Milaca Sr HS; Foreston, MN; 63/145 Chr; HonRl; Mdrgl; SchMus; Pres4-H; FFA; Wrstlng; 4-HAwd; Trade School; Vocation Auto Mechanic.

MC GREGOR, Joseph A; Duchesne HS; St Peters, MO; Band; Chrs; CmntyWkr; HonRl; NatlSciFnd; SchMus; StuCncl; MthCl; SciCl; College; Professional.

MC GREGOR, Kevin; Gibbon HS; Gibbon, NE; 1/59 VPJrCls; Band; HonRl; NatlMeritFnl; NatlMeritSF; SctActv; StuCncl; RptrYrbk; Univ Of Ne; Engineering.

MC GREGOR, Kevin B; Gibbon HS; Gibbon, NE; 1/60 VPJrCls; Band; Chr; HonRl; NatlMeritSF; SctActv; StuGov; EdYrBk; LetterBsktbl; LetterTrk; U Of Ne; Electrical Engineer.

MC GREGOR, Steven; Nashua Community HS; Nashua, IA; Aud/Vis; Band; MrchBnd; PepBnd; PolWkr; YthFlsp; 4-H; FFA; SciCl; Wrstlng; Iowa State Univ; Agricultural.

MC GREGOR, Susan K; Kimball Public HS; Kimball, SD; ALAGirlsSt; Chr; Chrs; ChrhWkr; HonRl; Mdrgl; TchrAde; FHA; College; Elementary Education.

MC GREGORR, Monica J; Two Harbors HS; Two Harbors, MN; 20/180 Chr; Mdrgl; NHS; NatlMeritSF; Twrl; Yrbk; College; Social Work.

MC GREW, Gordon N; Richwoods HS; Peoria, IL; NatlMeritCmnd; Knox College; Engineering.

MC GREW, Lynne A; Bryan Sr HS; Omaha, NE; 101/390 HonRl; JA; JrNHS; NatlFornLg; SecStuCncl; UNYO; IMSpt; College; Stewardess.

MC GROARTY, Susan M; St Josephs Academy; Crestwood, MO; 45/129 Chr; Chrs; CmntyWkr; IntrClCncl; LitMag; SchMus; SchPl; FrCl; PpCl; IMSpt; Drury College; Business.

MC GUCKIN, Patrick J; Griffin HS; Springfield, IL; 69/173 PresFrshCls; VPSophCls; LitMag; StuCncl; EdYrBk; College; Pre Journalism.

MC GUIGAN, Jane P; Albion Sr HS; Albion, MI; HonRl; SchAde; StuGov; TchrAde; PpCl; LetterGlf; Chrldr; East Mich Univ; Special Educ.

MC GUIGAN, Susan M; Kearney Catholic HS; Kearney, NE; Chrs; SchMus; SptEdYrbk; SpnCl; PpCl; LetterBsktbl; LetterTrk; Kearney State Coll; Phy Ed.

MC GUINNESS, James P; Bishop Foley HS; Clawson, MI; PresFrshCls; PresSophCls; PresJrCls; PresSrCls; ALBoysSt; HonRl; PresJA; JrNHS; NHS; SctActv; StuCncl; CaptBsktbl; CaptFtbl; Trk; Michigan State University; Business Mgmt.

MC GUINNESS, Kathleen; Lake Fenton; Fenton, MI; 2/147 VPSrCls; ChrhWkr; HonRl; NHS; SchAde; StuCncl; TchrAde; Yrbk; RptrSchPpr; EdSchPpr; College; Med Tech.

MC GUIRE, Brian; Black Hawk HS; Browntown, WI; 2/75 TrsSrCls; Band; CncrtBnd; HonRl; MrchBnd; NHS; PepBnd; Univ Of Wi At La Crosse, Med Tech.

MC GUIRE, Cathleen J; Ovid Elsie HS; Elsie, MI; Chr; HonRl; Mdrgl; SchMus; YthFlsp; 4-H; LetterTrk; Grand Rapids Sch; Church Secretary.

MC GUIRE, Corinne D; Perham Public HS; Perham, MN; 16/139 NHS; 4-H; CaptBsktbl; CaptTrk; GAA; PPFtbl; 4-HAwd; PresAwd; North Dakota St Univ; Physical Educ.

MC GUIRE, Daniel J; Holstein HS; Holstein, IA; 6/56 PresFrshCls; PresSrCls; HonRl; NHS; SchPl; StuCncl; SptEdSchPpr; Bsktbl; Ftbl; Trk; Creighton Univ; Pre Med.

MC GUIRE, Gregory R; Springfield HS; Springfield, IL; ChrhWkr; HonRl; JrNHS; NHS; NatlMeritCmnd; StuCncl; FrCl; LetterTennis; University; Social Work.

MC GUIRE, James; St Laurence HS; Bridgeview, IL; 159/380 HonRl; SctActv; Ftbl; Trk; Wrstlng; College; Architecture.

MC GUIRE, John D; Griffin HS; Springfield, IL; HonRl; LitMag; Lincolnland Comm College; Mathematics.

MC GUIRE, Judy L; Eastern Heights HS; Phillipsburg, KS; Band; HonRl; FHA;.

MC GUIRE, Karen M; Highland HS; Highland, WI; 5/52 Band; Chr; ChrhWkr; CncrtBnd; HonRl; SchMus; StuGov; FHA; Trk; GAA; College.

MC GUIRE, Kathleen M; St Joseph Academy; De Pere, WI; 1/160 HospAde; JrNHS; NHS; NatlMeritCmnd; 4-H; SpnCl; University.

MC GUIRE, Mark J; O Gorman HS; Sioux Falls, SD; SctActv; Bsbl; LetterTrk; IMSpt; BauchLmbAwd; Ndsu; Forestry.

MC GUIRE, Marla J; Watseka Comm HS; Watseka, IL; SecJrCls; Band; HonRl; Chrldr; College; Nursing.

MC GUIRE, Mary C; Nerinx Hall HS; Webster Groves, MO; TrsSophCls; Chr; HonRl; HospAde; LbryAde; OffAde; SchAde; SchMus; SchPl; TchrAde; St Louis Univ; Acting.

MC GUIRE, Monica T; Crystal Lake HS; Crystal Lake, IL; TrsJrCls; SecSrCls; Chrs; HonRl; PolWkr; Mac Murray College; Nursing.

MC GUIRE, Nancy C; Burt Comm HS; Burt, IA; Chrs; HonRl; Mdrgl; TchrAde; RptrSchPpr; EdSchPpr; 4-H; FTA; LetterBsbl; LetterBsktbl; Trk; 4-HAwd; Business School; Vocation.

MC GUIRE, Stephen J; Wisner Pilger HS; Wisner, NE; 17/70 ALBoysSt; HonRl; NHS; 4-H; SecFFA; SpnCl; Bsktbl; IMSpt; 4-HAwd; Univ Of Ne; Ag.

MC GUIRE, Stephen T; Garrigan HS; West Bend, IA; Chr; Chrs; SchMus; Yrbk; SchPpr; 4-H; College; Photography.

MC GUIRE, Susan E; Morton HS; Morton, IL; 42/296 Band; Chrs; CncrtBnd; HonRl; HospAde; MrchBnd; PepBnd; YthFlsp; PpCl; GAA; Il Central College; Registered Nurse.

MC GUIRE, Susan R; Fort Zumwalt HS; Ofallon, MO; VPSophCls; VPJrCls; VPSrCls; SctActv; SptEdYrbk; Chrldr; PPFtbl; Southeast Missouri; Teaching.

MC GUIRE, Therese A; Notre Dame HS; Chicago, IL; TrsJrCls; HonRl; StuGov; Bsktbl; IMSpt; Univ; Medicine.

MC GUIRE, Tom H; Highland HS; Highland, WI; 3/50 PresSrCls; HonRl; LetterBsbl; LetterBsktbl; LetterTrk; Clge; Bus.

MC GUIRE, Walter J; Wichita West HS; Wichita, KS; Band; HonRl; MrchBnd; NHS; SchPl; StuCncl; GerCl; Bsbl; Univ Of Mi; Science.

MC GUIRE, Wendy A; Ft Madison Sr HS; Fort Madison, IA; 3/250 NHS; NatlMeritCmnd; Yrbk; SchPpr; LionAwd; College; Art.

MC GURN, Anita M; Bishop Ward HS; Kansas, KS; 4/225 Band; ChrhWkr; HonRl; LitMag; ModUN; NHS; NatlMeritCmnd; PolWkr; SchAde; TchrAde; SchPpr; 4-H; KiwanAwd; NCTE; Benedictine College; History.

MC GURRAN, Ann M; Hoople HS; Hoople, ND; HonRl; NHS; RptrYrbk; University Of North Dakota; Sociology.

MC GUSHIN, Maureen M; Marian Catholic HS; Homewood, IL; 49/335 Chrs; HonRl; StuCncl; Yrbk; 4-H; FrCl; 4-HAwd; Collegef Dietician.

MC HENRY, Brenda L; Hays HS; Hays, KS; Chr; ChrhWkr; DrlTm; HonRl; TchrAde; College; Vocation.

MC HENRY, Jeffrey R; Harrisonville Sr HS; Harrisonville, MO; 3/140 ChrhWkr; DrmBgl; HonRl; Quill&Scroll; SctActv; StuCncl; Yrbk; SpnCl; Ftbl; LetterGlf; GodCntryAwd; CitAwd; Mo Univ; Accounting.

MC HENRY, William K; Rich Central HS; Park Forest, IL; 2/400 VPBand; CncrtBnd; HonRl; JrNHS; MrchBnd; NatlFornLg; NatlMeritSF; Orch; PepBnd; SchPpr; RusCl; MthCl; SciCl; Tennis; College; Economics.

MC HONE, Steven J; Clarion HS; Clarion, IA; Band; CncrtBnd; HonRl; MrchBnd; PepBnd; SchMus; SchPl; RptrSchPpr; Central College; Business.

MC HUGH, Debra S; Carthage HS; Carthage, IL; 10/88 HonRl; SchMus; SctActv; SecYthFlsp; FrCl; GAA; Univ Of Iowa; Surgeon.

MC HUGH, James F; Proviso West HS; Northlake, IL; 78/1141 HonRl; RptrSchPpr; LetterTrk; University; Engineering.

MC HUGH, Paula M; Lake Forest HS; Lake Forest, IL; Chrs; CmntyWkr; HonRl; PolWkr; SctActv; RptrSchPpr; Northwestern Univ; Medicine.

MC HUGH, Peter J; St Thomas Academy; St Paul, MN; HonRl; NatlMeritCmnd; RedCrAde; SchPl; RptrYrbk; RptrSchPpr; GerCl; Colorado College; Architecture.

MC HUGH, Susan; St Mary Acad; Indianapolis, IN; Chrs; ChrhWkr; CmntyWkr; HonRl; JA; StuCncl; SpnCl; PpCl; IMSpt; PPFtbl; College; Professional.

MC ILHARGIE, Gloria J; Laker HS; Kinde, MI; 7/146 HonRl; NHS; SchAde; 4-H; FHA; VPPpCl; Northwood Inst; Secretary.

MC ILRATH, Kevin H; Huntington North HS; Huntington, IN; SchPl; TchrAde; Swmmng; LetterTennis; IMSpt; Indiana Univ; Archeology.

MC ILRATH, Paul K; Stockton HS; Stockton, IL; Band; Chrs; HonRl; Mdrgl; NatlMeritCmnd;.

MC ILVAIN, Gerald F; Marian Catholic HS; Country Club Hills, IL; 77/365 Chr; ChrhWkr; HonRl; Mdrgl; SchMus; SchPl; Bsbl; LetterFtbl; LetterTrk; College; Social Science.

MC ILVENNA, Mary J; Ogorman HS; Sioux Falls, SD; Chrs; LitMag; LbryAde; Quill&Scroll; SchPl; Business; Vocation.

MC INERNEY, John V; Brother Rice HS; Chicago, IL; 46/416 ChrhWkr; HonRl; HospAde; NHS; RedCrAde; SctActv; StuCncl; KeyCl; Trk; LetterWrstlng; Loyola U Of Chgo; Medical.

MC INERNEY, Kevin P; St Laurence HS; Burbank, IL; 16/400 HonRl; Ftbl; Trk; Univ Of Wisconsin; Math.

MC INERNEY, Patrick J; Holy Cross HS; Elmwood Park, IL; Loyola Univ; Business Admin.

MC INERNEY, Sally J; All Saints Central HS; Bay City, MI; Chrl; HonRl; Mdrgl; NatlCathMusEdAsoc; NHS; RedCrAde; SchMus; College; Nursing.

MC INNES, Kim K; Marion HS; Marion, ND; Band; CncrtBnd; MrchBnd; PepBnd; SchPl; SctActv; TchrAde; YthFlsp; LetterBsbl; LetterBsktbl; Univ; Business Accounting.

MC INNIS, Deborah L; Tri County HS; Howard City, MI; 23/94 Band; CncrtBnd; HonRl; MrchBnd; NHS; StuCncl; EdYrBk; EdSchPpr; FrCl; IMSpt; Grand Rapids Jr Clg; Elem Ed.

MC INNIS, Martha J; Golden Valley HS; Goldenvalley, MN; 9/160 CmntyWkr; NatlFornLg; NatlMeritCmnd; SchPl; RptrYrbk; FrCl; Bsktbl; College; Psychology.

MC INTEE, John D; Bettendorf HS; Bettendorf, IA; 36/425 ChrhWkr; HonRl; NHS; TchrAde; PresSpnCl; Ftbl; LetterSwmmng; IMSpt; EldAwd; JAAwd; U Of Notre Dame; Business Admin.

MC INTEE, Rae A; Williston Sr HS; Williston, ND; SecSrCls; Band; Chr; PolWkr; Yrbk; EdSchPpr; FDA; SciCl; Bsktbl; Ftbl; Swmmng; Tennis; Univ Of North Dakota; Medicine.

MC INTEER, Jan; South Central HS; Elizabeth, IN; 8/60 ALAGirlsSt; Chr; HonRl; NHS; OffAde; StuCncl; YthFlsp; Yrbk; 4-H; Trk; IMSpt; College; Denistry.

MC INTIRE, Cheryl A; East Union Community HS; Afton, IA; 1/51 TrsSrCls; Band; CncrtBnd; HonRl; MrchBnd; SchPl; LetterBsktbl; LetterTrk; Graceland Clg; Nursing.

MC INTIRE, Evelyn R; Nevada HS; Milo, MO; 10/174 PresFrshCls; ChrhWkr; HonRl; LitMag; NatlFornLg; NHS; PresNatlThespSoc; SchPl; SecStuCncl; RptrYrbk; 4-H; VPLatCl; Univ Of Missouri; Law.

MC INTOSH, Angela K; Irwin Comm HS; Defiance, IA; PresFrshCls; VPJrCls; Band; Chr; CncrtBnd; DrmMjrt; MrchBnd; NHS; Bsktbl; Trk; GAA; College.

MC INTOSH, Connie K; Broken Bow Senior HS; Broken Bow, NE; ChrhWkr; HonRl; NHS; TchrAde; LetterTrk; CaptIMSpt; College; Professional.

MC INTOSH, Deborah K; Ridgeway HS; Ridgeway, MO; 4/18 TrsSophCls; TrsJrCls; Band; Chrs; ChrhWkr; CmntyWkr; HonRl; LbryAde; OffAde; PepBnd; Bsktbl; Trk; Univ; Nurse.

MC INTOSH, Julia A; Bedford HS; Temperance, MI; 16/324 VPSrCls; CmntyWkr; HonRl; HospAde; NHS; PolWkr; StuCncl; StuGov; FrCl; DARAwd; Randolph Macon Womans Coll; Biological Sci.

MC INTOSH, Kathryn J; Raymond Central HS; Ceresco, NE; 2/60 SecJrCls; Band; Chrs; CncrtBnd; HonRl; NHS; SchPl; StuCncl; Yrbk; University; Liberal Arts.

MC INTOSH, Kimberly A; Tarkio HS; Tarkio, MO; 7/65 Band; ChrhWkr; DrmMjrt; HonRl; NHS; PpCl; CaptBsktbl; Chrldr; GAA; IMSpt; Tarkio College; Physical Therapist.

MC INTOSH, Pamela; Eureka HS; Eureka, SD; Band; CncrtBnd; HonRl; MrchBnd; SchPl; StuCncl; RptrYrbk; RptrSchPpr; PpCl; GAA; Univ Of Sd; Med Tech.

MC INTOSH, Terry W; Woodruff HS; Peoria, IL; 19/232 ChrhWkr; HonRl; NHS; Orch; SchPl; YthFlsp; KeyCl; SpnCl; LetterFtbl; GodCntryAwd; Western Illinois Univ; Chemistry.

MC INTYRE, Carol A; Sparta HS; Sparta, IL; ChrhWkr; HonRl; Covenant College.

MC INTYRE, Colleen L; Jefferson HS; Rockford, IL; 13/335 Chr; Chrs; ChrhWkr; CmntyWkr; HonRl; SchAde; SctActv; TchrAde; 4-H; 4-HAwd; Univ Of Il; Medicine.

MC INTYRE, Diane K; Dowling HS; Grimes, IA; 6/455 Chrs; HonRl; Yrbk; 4-H; FrCl; Bsktbl; Trk; Univ; Agriculture.

MC INTYRE, Glen A; Bridgeport HS; Bridgeport, MI; 5/330 Chr; ChrhWkr; HonRl; NHS; SchMus; SchPl; YthFlsp; LetterBsktbl; LetterTrk; CchngActv; Saginaw Valley State Clg; Methodist Ministr.

MC INTYRE, James R; Holden HS; Holden, MO; VPSophCls; CmntyWkr; YthFlsp; RptrSchPpr; SptEdSchPpr; Bsktbl; Ftbl; Trk; Wrstlng;.

MC INTYRE, Kathy S; Rogers HS; Michigan City, IN; AFS; HonRl; College; Math.

MC INTYRE, Kimberly A; Mound Westonka HS; Mound, MN; Band; Chr; DrmMjrt; HonRl; MrchBnd; NHS; PepBnd; StuCncl; YthFlsp; RptrYrbk; College; Nursing.

MC INTYRE, Lorraine R; Fullerton HS; Decar Rapids, NE; 13/60 Chrs; ChrhWkr; HonRl; HospAde; StuCncl; Yrbk; 4-H; FHA; PpCl; AmLegAwd; Methodist School Of Nursing; Nursing.

MC INTYRE, Lorri S; Triton HS; Tippecanoe, IN; SecJrCls; ChrhWkr; HonRl; NHS; SchPl; 4-H; FHA; PpCl; 4-HAwd; College.

MC INTYRE, Mark D; Loyola Academy; Wilmette, IL; TrsJrCls; HonRl; OffAde; PolWkr; SchMus; SchPl; TchrAde; EdSchPpr; SpnCl; IMSpt; Stanford U; Justice Of Supreme Court.

MC INTYRE, Sharon J; Clearwater HS; Clearwater, KS; Chrs; HonRl; LbryAde; NHS; OffAde; SchMus; SchPl; TchrAde; Yrbk; PpCl; Southwestern College; Nursing.

MC INTYRE, Walter W; East Alton Wood River HS; Wood River, IL; 48/312 ChrhWkr; HonRl; SctActv; TchrAde; YthFlsp; LatCl; LetterTrk; U S Naval Academy; Professional.

MC KANNA, Debra A; Luray HS; Luray, KS; 1/19 HstSophCls; TrsSrCls; Band; HonRl; SchPl; Yrbk; EdSchPpr; PpCl; LetterBsktbl; LetterTrk; Chrldr; Fort Hays Kansas State; Medicine.

MC KARNER, Karen R; Girard HS; Palmyra, IL; 5/69 SecSophCls; HonRl; NHS; 4-H; FHA; SciCl; GAA; 4-HAwd; College.

MC KAY, Cathleen M; Portage Central HS; Kalamazoo, MI; HonRl; NatlMeritCmnd; TchrAde; PresSpnCl; University Of Michigan; Law.

MC KAY, Charles D; Lincoln Co R Ii HS; Troy, MO; 21/63 Band; Chr; Chrs; ChrhWkr; CncrtBnd; HonRl; MrchBnd; PepBnd; TchrAde; College; Music.

MC KAY, Jay; Liberal HS; Mulberry, KS; 5/60 PresFrshCls; VPSophCls; ALBoysSt; NHS; Univ;professional.

MC KAY, Jerry A; South Pemiscot HS; Steele, MO; VPFrshCls; PresSophCls; ChrhWkr; JrNHS; NHS; SchAde; SchPl; StuCncl; FFA; KeyCl; SpnCl; Bsbl; Bsktbl; College.

MC KAY, Kevin J; Catholic Central HS; Detroit, MI; 26/151 VPJrCls; PresSrCls; Chrs; HonRl; NHS; StuCncl; RptrYrbk; LetterWrstlng; IMSpt; OptClAwd; Univ Of Mi; Dentistry Or Psychology.

MC KAY, Kimberly A; Joliet East HS; Joliet, IL; 83/481 Chr; Chrl; Chrs; HonRl; OffAde; SchMus; GAA;.

MC KAY, William D; Grand Blanc HS; Grand Blanc, MI; CchngActv; KiwanAwd; Univ; Professional.

MC KEAG, James W; Shelby Public HS; Shelby, NE; TrsFrshCls; TrsSophCls; TrsJrCls; PresSrCls; ALBoysSt; Chrs; HonRl; SchPl; SptEdYrbk; Bsbl; Bsktbl; LetterFtbl; LetterTrk; CchngActv; Platte Comm Tech College; Business.

MC KEAGUE, Michael J; Alexis HS; Alexis, IL; 3/48 VPSophCls; TrsSrCls; Chrs; HonRl; NHS; SchPl; YthFlsp; Yrbk; RptrSchPpr; Bsbl; LetterBsktbl; LetterFtbl; LetterTrk; College; Pharmacy.

MC KEAN, Helen; Goldfield Community HS; Goldfield, IA; 10/32 ALAGirlsSt; Band; Chr; CncrtBnd; HonRl; MrchBnd; PepBnd; SchMus; SchPl; Ia Lks Comm Coll; Registered Nurse.

MC KEAN, Lise D; Immaculate Conception HS; Elmhurst, IL; 8/145 PresFrshCls; VPSophCls; PresJrCls; HospAde; NHS; NatlMeritCmnd; StuCncl; PresLatCl; CaptTennis; LetterTrk; Chrldr; AmLegAwd; BttyCrckrAwd; Northwestern Univ; Geology.

MC KEAN, Martha M; Bradford HS; Bradford, IL; Aud/Vis; Band; OffAde; PepBnd; SchPl; StuCncl; 4-H; FHA; PpCl; LetterBsktbl; Coll; Art.

MC KEAN, Mary; Bradford HS; Bradford, IL; TrsSophCls; Chrs; ChrhWkr; HonRl; OffAde; SchPl; 4-H; FHA; PpCl; GAA; Coll.

MC KEAN, Patty A; Clay City HS; Centerpoint, IN; Chr; HonRl; LbryAde; SchMus; TchrAde; RptrYrbk; RptrSchPpr; FBLA; SpnCl; PpCl; Bus Sch; Pro.

MC KEE, Cathy M; Maquoketa Valley HS; Earlville, IA; Chr; Chrs; HonRl; RptrSchPpr; 4-H; FHA; PpCl; College; Elementary Teaching.

MC KEE, Charles D; Salina South HS; Salina, KS; 18/350 HonRl; TchrAde; GerCl; PpCl; LetterBsktbl; LetterFtbl; LetterTennis; PPFtbl; Kansas State; Civil Engineering.

MC KEE, Deborah; South Shore HS; Chicago, IL; 16/578 SecSrCls; PresFrshCls; NHS; NatlMeritSF; StuCncl; StuGov; RptrSchPpr; College; Law.

MC KEE, Janet; Lowpoint Washburn HS; Washburn, IL; 3/60 SecSophCls; PresJrCls; AFS; ALAGirlsSt; HonRl; SchPl; RptrSchPpr; FFA; GAA; Coll; Communications.

MC KEE, Jeanette M; Rich South HS; Richton Park, IL; TrsFrshCls; HonRl; StuCncl; FrCl; PpCl; Bsbl; Trk; Chrldr; College; Professional.

MC KEE, Jim E; South Side HS; Fort Wayne, IN; ChrhWkr; College; Lawyer.

MC KEE, Kathleen; Wabash HS; Wabash, IN; 2/216 Band; CncrtBnd; HonRl; NatlFornLg; NatlMeritCmnd; PepBnd; SchMus; StuCncl; YthFlsp; Purdue Univ; Pharmacy.

MC KEE, Kathleen M; Mt Clemens HS; Mt Clemens, MI; Chr; Chrs; HonRl; JA; NHS; NatlMeritFnl; OffAde; SchMus; KeyCl; FrCl; Mi St Univ; Vet.

MC KEE, Mark S; Park Hill Sr HS; Kansas City, MO; 51/409 Band; CncrtBnd; HonRl; MrchBnd; PepBnd; SctActv; Bsbl; LetterFtbl; LetterGlf; Umkc; Vet Med.

MC KEE, Mark W; Monrovia Jr Sr HS; Hall, IN; 2/112 ChrhWkr; HonRl; NHS; StuCncl; TchrAde; SptEdYrbk; SpnCl; SciCl; LetterFtbl; CchngActv; Univ; Prof.

MC KEE, Mary A; Allen HS; Bluffton, IN; Chr; DrlTm; HonRl; NatlThespSoc; SchPl; Teen; RptrYrbk; Yrbk; EdSchPpr; SchPpr; PpCl; Bsbl; GAA; Purdue Univ; Veterinarian.

MC KEE, Mary J; St Josephs Academy; St Louis, MO; SecJrCls; PresChr; HonRl; HospAde; NHS; SchMus; SchPl; StuGov; FrCl; MthCl; Bsbl; Bsktbl; GAA; Univ Of Missouri; Nursing.

MC KEE, Randy; Greenview HS; Greenview, IL; VPJrCls; PresSrCls; Band; Chr; CncrtBnd; HonRl; SchMus; Sdlty; StuCncl; 4-H; Bsbl; Western Illinois; Journalism.

MC KEE, Richard A; Manhattan HS; Manhattan, KS; Pres4-H; SecFFA; Bsbl; CchngActv; 4-HAwd; College.

MC KEE, Sally J; Lowpoint Washburn HS; Washburn, IL; 1/68 HonRl; LbryAde; SchMus; Yrbk; SchPpr; 4-H; FFA; GAA; Univ Of Illinois; Agriculture.

MC KEE, Scott D; Adel HS; Adel, IA; 1/80 Band; Chrs; HonRl; NHS; NatlMeritFnl; SchMus; SchPl; StuCncl; FTA; Bsktbl; Trk; Iowa State Univ; Math.

MC KEE, Susan L; Riverside Brookfield HS; Brookfield, IL; 295/489 Band; Chr; Chrl; Chrs; ChrhWkr; CncrtBnd; MrchBnd; Orch; PepBnd; SchMus; SchPl; SctActv; College; Liberal Arts.

MC KEEVER, Janice A; Odell Public HS; Wymore, NE; ALAGirlsSt; Band; Chrs; MrchBnd; YthFlsp; Yrbk; LetterTrk; Chrldr; Bus Sch; Gen Off Wrk.

MC KELVEY, Patrick M; Hastings HS; Hastings, MI; 16/286 Band; CncrtBnd; HonRl; MrchBnd; NHS; PepBnd; SchPl; SctActv; LetterTrk; IMSpt; Univ Of Michigan; Architecture.

MC KELVY, Kerry; Mount St Scholastica Acad; Atchison, KS; Chrs; CmntyWkr; HonRl; Bsbl; Swmmng; Tennis; Trk; Chrldr; GAA; PPFtbl; College.

MC KELVY, Mary; Morgan Park HS; Chicago, IL; 13/459 CmntyWkr; HonRl; LitMag; NHS; Yrbk; CivCl; EngCl; LatCl; MthCl; CitAwd; Pennsylvania State Univ; Advertising.

MC KENNA, Donna M; Gladwin HS; Harrison, MI; PresSophCls; VPJrCls; HonRl; StuCncl; EdYrBk; RptrSchPpr; Bsktbl; Central Michigan Univ; Journalism.

MC KENNA, Kathy L; Carson City Crystal Area HS; Carson City, MI; 1/114 Band; CncrtBnd; HonRl; MrchBnd; SecNHS; OffAde; PepBnd; PolWkr; LetterBsktbl; SecGAA; Ferris St Coll; Allied Health.

MC KENNA, Maureen C; Daniel J Gross HS; Bellevue, NE; SchPl; Chrldr; College.

MC KENNA, Timothy J; Red River HS; Grand Forks, ND; 7/385 ALBoysSt; Band; Chr; Mdrgl; NHS; NatlMeritSF; PepBnd; SchMus; SctActv; LetterTrk; Univ; Music.

MC KENRICK, Gary D; Central Comm HS; Low Moor, IA; Chrs; ChrhWkr; HonRl; NHS; PolWkr; SchMus; YthFlsp; LetterFtbl; Cornell College; Political Science.

MC KENZIE, Cathy; Kingsford HS; Kingsford, MI; /164 SecSrCls; Band; CncrtBnd; HonRl; HospAde; MrchBnd; NHS; StuCncl; RptrSchPpr; Chrldr; Bellin Mem Sch Nurs;rn.

MC KENZIE, Crystal; Norris City Omaha Hs; Norris City, IL; Chrs; HonRl; SchPl; TreasYrbk; FHA; So Eastern Illinois College;social Sciences.

MC KENZIE, Dawn M; Rosemount Sr HS; Rosemount, MN; SecSrCls; Aud/Vis; ChrhWkr; CncrtBnd; HonRl; NHS; SchPl; Yrbk; Chrldr; VoiceDemAwd; College; Spec Educ.

MC KENZIE, Frances; Pecatonica HS; Hollandale, WI; PresJrCls; ALAGirlsSt; HonRl; 4-H; FHA; 4-HAwd; Univ.

MC KENZIE, Joanne M; Derham Hall HS; St Paul, MN; Chrs; CmntyWkr; LitMag; NHS; StuCncl; PresFrCl; St Catherines Col; Writer.

MC KENZIE, Kay A; Park River HS; Park River, ND; HonRl; NHS; NatlMeritFnl; NatlMeritCmnd; NatlMeritSchl; StuCncl; StuGov; GovHonPrgAwd; PresAwd; Univ Of Nd; Business.

MC KENZIE, Mary J; Bradford HS; Bradford, IL; 1/44 PresSophCls; PresSrCls; Band; CncrtBnd; HonRl; PresNHS; PepBnd; StuCncl; Treas4-H; VPFHA; Bsktbl; GAA; 4-HAwd; Marian College; Special Education.

MC KENZIE, Steven; Argo Comm HS; Bridgeview, IL; 26/432 ChrhWkr; NHS; St Josephs College; Computer Programmer.

MC KENZIE, Susan E; Meadville Riv HS; Meadville, MO; Band; CncrtBnd; HonRl; HospAde; NHS; SchPl; StuCncl; Twrl; Bsktbl; Trk; Chrldr; Missouri W St College.

MC KENZIE, Suzanne; Mason HS; Mason, MI; 12/238 Band; CncrtBnd; NHS; PepBnd; SchMus; FrCl; PpCl; IMSpt; PPFtbl; Olivet Col; Music.

MC KENZIE, Teresa S; Immaculate Heart Of Mary HS; Forest Park, IL; 34/244 ChrhWkr; Loyola University; Psychology.

MC KEON, Kimberley M; Lincoln Sr HS; Sioux Falls, SD; ALAGirlsSt; HonRl; HospAde; RedCrAde; FDA; PpCl; CaptTrk; IMSpt; College; Medicine.

MC KEOUGH, Eugene M; Menasha HS; Menasha, WI; 10/330 PresJA; PresNHS; NatlMeritSF; JAAwd; RotaryAwd;.

MC KEOUGH, Margaret A; St Agatha HS; Detroit, MI; TrsFrshCls; HonRl; NHS; SecFrshCls; PpCl; Chrldr; U Of Mi;medical Prof.

MC KEOWN, James T; Columbus HS; Marshfield, WI; 2/108 HonRl; SchPl; VPStuCncl; RptrSchPpr; FrCl; Bsktbl; LetterFtbl; College.

MC KEOWN, Joseph W; Brother Rice HS; Chicago, IL; 106/419 HonRl; Marquette Univ; Business Admin.

MC KERNAN, Michael F; Milbank HS; Twin Brooks, SD; Aud/Vis; Chr; Chrs; HonRl; Mdrgl; SchMus; StuCncl; RptrYrbk; 4-H; FFA; College; Farming.

MC KIBBEN, Debra J; Phillips HS; Phillips, WI; 6/107 HonRl; RptrSchPpr; SptEdSchPpr; FHA; SpnCl; PpCl; Eau Claire Tech Inst; Med Lab Tech.

MC KIBBEN, Ruth A; Milaca HS; Foley, MN; 4/150 Chr; Chrs; HonRl; Mdrgl; SchMus; SchPl; 4-H; FHA; IMSpt; Business School; Secretary.

MC KIBBIN, Karen L; Camden Frontier HS; Camden, MI; 2/43 HonRl; FrCl; College; Accounting.

MC KIERNAN, Jane L; La Salle HS; Cedar Rapids, IA; 4/91 HstSophCls; HstJrCls; Chr; Chrl; Chrs; HonRl; Mdrgl; ModUN; NHS; TchrAde; PpCl; College; Government Work.

MC KILLEN, Elizabeth A; Holy Child HS; Waukegan, IL; 5/50 LbryAde; SchPl; StuCncl; RptrSchPpr; Bsktbl; College; Political Science.

MC KILLIP, D Tim; Hayes County HS; Hayes Center, NE; Band; 4-H; FFA; LetterBsktbl; LetterTrk; 4-HAwd; Univ School Tech; Agriculture.

MC KIM, Debra A; New Bloomfield HS; New Bloomfield, MO; 1/46 SecJrCls; HonRl; JrNHS; NHS; TchrAde; RptrYrbk; RptrSchPpr; PresFrCl; KiwanAwd; College; Law.

MC KIM, Larry J; North Platte Sr HS; North Platte, NE; 21/504 College; Professional.

MC KIM, Ronna F; Kirksville HS; Kirksville, MO; CmntyWkr; HonRl; TchrAde; FshEdYrbk; GAA; IMSpt; PresAwd; Univ; English Teacher.

MC KIM, Sandra K; Daniel J Gross HS; Omaha, NE; 5/170 Band; HonRl; SecNHS; NatlSciFnd; Quill&Scroll; SptEdYrbk; SchPpr; PpCl; BttyCrckrAwd; Univ Of Southern Ca; Biochemistry.

MC KIM, Wanda K; Kirksville Senior HS; Kirksville, MO; ChrhWkr; HonRl; Northeast Mo State Univ; Legal Secretary.

MC KINLEY, Chere L; Culver Comm HS; Monterey, IN; Chr; HonRl; NHS; SchMus; StuCncl; Treas4-H; FTA; SpnCl; AmLegAwd; 4-HAwd; Indiana Voca Tech School; Accounting.

MC KINLEY, Jeanette; Belton Hs; Belton, MO; 57/282 Chr; HonRl; NHS; PpCl; Trk;.

MC KINLEY, Richard; South Lyon HS; South Lyon, MI; 14/237 PresSophCls; CncrtBnd; JrNHS; NHS; NatlMeritCmnd; SchPl; YthFlsp; Ftbl; Wrstlng; Michigan State Univ; Political Science.

MC KINNEY, Betsy; Wilmot HS; Antioch, IL; 25/215 HonRl; NHS; SpnCl; MthCl; Married.

MC KINNEY, Charles R; Eastalton Wood River HS; Wood River, IL; 31/316 Chrs; HonRl; JA; JrNHS; NHS; SchPl; RptrYrbk; GerCl; JAAwd; So Illinois Univ; Banking.

MC KINNEY, Darlene D; Potter Public HS; Potter, NE; Chrs; ChrhWkr; HonRl; OffAde; SchPl; YthFlsp; 4-H; PpCl; 4-HAwd; Nebraska Western Clg; Special Ed Teacher.

MC KINNEY, Elizabeth; Lockwood HS; Golden City, MO; 18/48 SecJrCls; HonRl; SchPl; RptrYrbk; SchPpr; FHA; FTA; College.

MC KINNEY, Janet G; Field Kindley HS; Coffeyville, KS; 10/244 ChrhWkr; HonRl; NHS; TchrAde; Yrbk; Coffeyville Jr College; Journalism.

MC KINNEY, Joanne M; Luther S HS; Chicago, IL; 1/194 ChrhWkr; CncrtBnd; HonRl; NHS; NatlMeritCmnd; RptrYrbk; GerCl; LetterTrk; GAA; IMSpt; Bradley Univ; Engineering.

MC KINNEY, John D; Yorkville HS; Yorkville, IL; 29/120 ChrhWkr; SchPl; SctActv; SecTrsFrshCls; StuGov; PresYthFlsp; SptEdYrbk; CaptBsbl; LetterBsktbl; LetterFtbl; Trk; College; Professional.

MC KINNEY, Marcia R; Belton HS; Belton, MO; HonRl; LbryAde; NatlFornLg; NHS; SchMus; StuCncl; SchPpr; FHA; PpCl; University Of Arkansas; Zoology.

MC KINNEY, Michael C; Tipton HS; Kempton, IN; 9/172 Chr; Chrs; HonRl; NHS; StuCncl; VP4-H; SciCl; Bsbl; LetterBsktbl; 4-HAwd; Purdue Univ; Mech Engineer.

MC KINNEY, Myra J; Lytton Comm HS; Lytton, IA; TrsSophCls; PresSrCls; Chr; Chrs; HonRl; NHS; YthFlsp; SchPpr; FHA; American Institute Of Business; Accountant.

MC KINNEY, Rebecca A; Pacific HS; Pacific, MO; Band; MrchBnd; NatlFornLg; NatlThespSoc; SchMus; SchPl; StuGov; RptrYrbk; OptClAwd; VoiceDemAwd; Jr/clge; History.

MC KINSTRY, Ann M; East HS; Waterloo, IA; SecSrCls; SecBand; CncrtBnd; HonRl; IntrClCncl; MrchBnd; Twrl; CaptSwmmng; CaptTennis; CitAwd; Ia St U;vet.

MC KINZIE, Pamela L; Okawville HS; Venedy, IL; 7/5 TrsJrCls; HonRl; NHS; NatlThespSoc; YthFlsp; Yrbk; 4-H; Bsktbl; Chrldr; IMSpt; Jr Col; Elem Ed.

MC KINZIE, Rikki R; Huntington North HS; Huntington, IN; ChrhWkr; CtyCnl; HonRl; StuCncl; EdYrBk; SptEdYrbk; EdSchPpr; SptEdSchPpr; LetterFtbl; LetterTrk; College; Business Accounting.

MC KIRGAN, Ginger; Plano HS; Plano, IL; Chr; Chrs; ChrhWkr; HonRl; Mdrgl; NHS; SchPl; VFWAwd; College; Music Major.

MC KISSICK, Karen M; Naperville Central HS; Naperville, IL; Chrs; ChrhWkr; CmntyWkr; HonRl; HospAde; YthFlsp; PpCl; Univ; Special Ed.

MC KITTRICK, Dawna E; Mayer Lutheran HS; Watertown, MN; Band; Chrs; ChrhWkr; CmntyWkr; HonRl; HospAde; YthFlsp; EngCl; GerCl; SciCl; Augburg College; Medical Technology.

MC KITTRICK, Julie L; Georges Parker HS; Janesville, WI; 26/598 CncrtBnd; HonRl; HospAde; MrchBnd; Tennis; University.

MC KITTRICK, Robin A; Wauwatosa West HS; Wauwatosa, WI; 10/426 ChrhWkr; CmntyWkr; HonRl; NHS; SchAde; TchrAde; YthFlsp; FTA; MthCl; Calvin College; Mathematics.

MC KNIGHT, Jane A; Rockford Lutheran HS; Belvidere, IL; TrsSophCls; PresBand; SecChr; Chrs; ChrhWkr; PresCncrtBnd; HonRl; LbryAde; CaptChrldr; GAA; IMSpt; VoiceDemAwd; Rock Valley College; Secretary.

MC KNIGHT, Michael G; Fenton HS; Bensenville, IL; 43/427 Band; CncrtBnd; HonRl; MrchBnd; NatlMeritCmnd; PepBnd; Pre Law.

MC KNIGHT, Paul W; Cleveland HS; St Louis, MO; 13/546 Chr; HonRl; NHS; NatlThespSoc; SchMus; SchPl; LetterBsbl; LetterFtbl; BttyCrckrAwd; KiwanAwd; U Of Wa; Business.

MC KNIGHT, Scott J; Plattsmouth HS; Plattsmouth, NE; 11/133 Band; HonRl; PresNHS; PresStuCncl; VPMthCl; LetterBsbl; ChmnBsktbl; Trk; RotaryAwd; VoiceDemAwd; Pre Med.

MC KNIGHT, Susan K; Erie HS; Erie, IL; 6/80 SecFrshCls; TreasAFS; HonRl; YthFlsp; RptrYrbk; RptrSchPpr; FTA; Trk; GAA; Blackburn College; Education.

MC KNIGHT, Tacoma A; Lindblom Tech HS; Chicago, IL; 1/600 Chr; ChrhWkr; HonRl; JA; TchrAde; FrCl; MthCl; PpCl; Northwestern Univ; Pediatrician.

MC KNIGHT, Thomas M; Bedford N Lawrence HS; Bedford, IN; 23/376 TrsSophCls; Band; Chr; NHS; VPSpnCl; MthCl; Indiana Univ; Music.

MC KNIGHT, William P; Gladstone HS; Gladstone, MI; PresSophCls; Chr; Chrl; Chrs; CtyCnl; Mdrgl; SchMus; StuCncl; StuGov; YthFlsp; SchPpr; LetterBsktbl; CaptFtbl; LetterTrk; College; Professional.

MC KONE, Timothy K; Kuemper HS; Carroll, IA; 8/289 PresSophCls; Chrs; HonRl; Mdrgl; StuCncl; SciCl; Univ Of Ia; Pre Med.

MC KOWEN, Jane D; Highland HS; Alexandria, IN; 3/245 Chr; ChrhWkr; HonRl; NHS; SchAde; YthFlsp; RptrSchPpr; Pres4-H; GAA; ChmbCommrsAwd; 4-HAwd; College; Christian Education.

MC LACHLAN, Donald H; Serena Community HS; Earlville, IL; VPFrshCls; HonRl; StuCncl; 4-H; FFA; PpCl; LetterBsbl; LetterBsktbl; LetterSocr; Purdue University; Agriculture.

MC LACHLAN, James; New Haven HS; New Haven, IN; 75/234 Band; ChrhWkr; CmntyWkr; CncrtBnd; HonRl; MrchBnd; Orch; SctActv; YthFlsp; Wrstlng; Indiana State U/psychology.

MC LAIN, Carol A; St Charles HS; St Charles, MO; Band; Chr; CncrtBnd; DrmMjrt; HonRl; MrchBnd; NHS; PepBnd; IMSpt; College; Music.

MC LAIN, Kelly V; Portage Northern HS; Portage, MI; ChrhWkr; HonRl; NatlMeritCmnd; SchAde; TchrAde; YthFlsp; 4-H; GerCl; Trk; 4-HAwd; Hope College; German.

MC LAIN, Randel; Portage Central HS; Portage, MI; Band; CncrtBnd; DrmMjrt; HonRl; MrchBnd; Orch; PepBnd; SchMus; KeyCl; SciCl; Montana Col Of Mining; Petroleum Engineer.

MC LAIN, Timothy P; Niles HS; Niles, MI; Band; CncrtBnd; HonRl; MrchBnd; OffAde; PepBnd; RptrSchPpr; U Of Mi; Acct.

MC LAREN, Debra M; Farragut Community HS; Farragut, IA; TrsJrCls; Band; Chr; Chrs; CncrtBnd; HonRl; MrchBnd; PepBnd; SchMus; SchPl; Iowa State Univ; Accounting.

MC LAREN, Kathy R; Corunna HS; Owosso, MI; 40/225 HonRl; JA; StuCncl; RptrYrbk; EdYrBk; Yrbk; PpCl; LetterSwmmng; Chrldr; GAA; Business School; Vocational.

MC LARIO, Lori L; Menomonee Falls East HS; Menomonee Falls, WI; Band; ChrhWkr; CmntyWkr; HonRl; MrchBnd; NatlFornLg; NHS; Orch; PepBnd; Bob Jones Univ; Nursing.

MC LAUGHLAN, Bruce L; Howell HS; Howell, MI; 4/250 Aud/Vis; ChrhWkr; HonRl; NHS; SctActv; YthFlsp; SpnCl; LetterTrk; Coll; Engi.

MC LAUGHLIN, Carol A; Mendota Twp HS; Troy Grove, IL; 18/187 Band; CncrtBnd; HonRl; HospAde; MrchBnd; FNA; Northern Illinois Univ; Nursing.

MC LAUGHLIN, Cynthia L; Mt Vernon Community HS; Greenfield, IN; 37/150 HonRl; JA; ROTC; TchrAde; SpnCl; Indiana Central Univ; Nurse.

MC LAUGHLIN, Dave W; Leo HS; Palos Heights, IL; 1/211 Aud/Vis; ChrhWkr; HonRl; ModUN; PresNHS; Quill&Scroll; TchrAde; SchPpr; PresPpCl; Bsbl; CaptTrk; JCAwd; College; Communications.

MC LAUGHLIN, Debra K; Bloomington HS; Bloomington, IL; 8/391 Chr; NHS; FrCl; SecMthCl; PpCl; SciCl; Illinois State Univ; Math.

MC LAUGHLIN, Dianne M; Mother Mc Auley HS; Evergreen Park, IL; 21/480 Chrs; HonRl; HospAde; NHS; Orch; SchMus; SpnCl; IMSpt; Wesley Bassavant Sch Of Nursing; Nurse.

MC LAUGHLIN, Jamie P; Eau Claire Memorial HS; Eau Cliare, WI; SecSophCls; Chr; HonRl; HospAde; LitMag; Mdrgl; SchMus; TchrAde; SpnCl; Swmmng; U Of Wi; English.

MC LAUGHLIN, John J; Joliet Catholic HS; Joliet, IL; 7/175 TrsFrshCls; TrsSophCls; Chr; HonRl; NHS; NatlMeritCmnd; SchMus; StuCncl; YthLg; CaptBsktbl; Miami Univ; Law.

MC LAUGHLIN, Larry; Denison Comm HS; Denison, IA; ALBoysSt; HonRl; NHS; SchAde; Bsbl; Bsktbl; Ftbl; Tennis; Trk; CchngActv; College; Professional.

MC LAUGHLIN, Patricia A; St Louise De Marillac HS; Park Ridge, IL; NatlMeritCmnd; SchMus; University.

MC LAUGHLIN, Shannon M; Normandy HS; St Louis, MO; Chr; CmntyWkr; DrlTm; HonRl; MrchBnd; NatlThespSoc; SchMus; SchPl; StuCncl; Yrbk; College; Architect.

MC LAURY, Pamela R; Sheldon Community HS; Sheldon, IA; 54/112 Band; ChrhWkr; CncrtBnd; HospAde; MrchBnd; PepBnd; PpCl; IMSpt; College; Professional.

MC LAWHON, Ronald W; Amos Alonzo Stagg HS; Palos Hills, IL; 34/468 HonRl; JrNHS; SctActv; MthCl; College; Medicine.

MC LEAN, Elizabeth; Eldora HS; Eldora, IA; 16 VPJrCls; Aud/Vis; HonRl; SchPl; StuCncl; RptrYrbk; LetterBsktbl; Trk; PPFtbl; Vocational Sch; X Ray Tech.

MC LEAN, John L; Sandwich HS; Sandwich, IL; 22/130 Chrs; HonRl; NatlThespSoc; SchPl; FTA; College; Business Admin.

MC LEAN, Mark P; De Kalb HS; De Kalb, IL; 44/350 CmntyWkr; CncrtBnd; HonRl; NHS; NatlThespSoc; Orch; StuCncl; FSA; FrCl; LetterTennis; Southern Illinois Univ; Pre Medicine.

MC LEAN, Pamela; Circle HS; Towanda, KS; Chr; ChrhWkr; CmntyWkr; HonRl; LbryAde; SchMus; PpCl; SciCl; IMSpt; Coll; Legal Sec.

MC LEES, Harry F; Seneca HS; Joplin, MO; ChrhWkr; HonRl; NHS; MthCl; LetterFtbl; College; Pilot.

MC LEESE, Mary E; New Trier East HS; Wilmette, IL; College; Psychology.

MC LEMORE, Joyce L; Osceola Public HS; Osceola, MO; 4/45 SecSrCls; Chrs; HonRl; HospAde; NHS; SchPl; StuCncl; Yrbk; FNA; University Of Missouri; Nursing.

MC LEMORE, Theresa; Clearwater HS; Piedmont, MO; 17/95 Band; Chr; CmntyWkr; CncrtBnd; HonRl; MrchBnd; SchAde; YthFlsp; FHA; SciCl; College; Home Economics Tchr.

MC LEOD, Michael J; Wellington HS; Wellington, KS; 16/160 ALBoysSt; Band; CncrtBnd; HonRl; MrchBnd; PepBnd; SctActv; Wichita Tech Inst; Electronics Technician.

MC LEOD, Robert J; Bentley Sr HS; Burton, MI; Chr; CncrtBnd; MrchBnd; SchMus; Eastern Mi U; Concert Pianist.

MC LIN, Joann; Princeton HS; Princeton, MO; HonRl; LbryAde; TchrAde; 4-H; FHA; PpCl; Chrldr; 4-HAwd; College; Secretarial.

MC LINDEN, Mark O; Westport HS; Kansas City, MO; 2/175 HonRl; NHS; NatlMeritCmnd; Univ Of Missouri; Chemical Engineering.

MC MAHAN, Debbie J; Missouri Valley HS; Missouri Valley, IA; Chr; StuCncl; FHA; FSA; PpCl; SciCl; Chrldr; College.

MC MAHAN, Starlet; Alton HS; Alton, MO; Chrs; ChrhWkr; HonRl; SchPl; TchrAde; FFA; PpCl; SciCl; CchngActv; GAA; College; Vocaion Career.

MC MAHEL, Jon K; Rushville Consolidated HS; Rushville, IN; 37/267 ALBoysSt; Band; MrchBnd; NHS; PolWkr; SctActv; Yrbk; SpnCl; Indiana Univ; Doctor.

MC MAHON, Anne E; St Joseph HS; Racine, WI; SecSrCls; Chrs; HospAde; StuCncl; RptrSchPpr; Tennis; College; Nursing.

MC MAHON, Anne L; Hudson HS; Hudson, WI; 11/220 Band; CncrtBnd; HonRl; MrchBnd; PepBnd; SchMus; RptrSchPpr; SchPpr; GerCl; Univ Of Minnesota; Law.

MC MAHON, Cynthia R; Scranton Consolidated HS; Scranton, IA; 9/18 PresSophCls; Band; Chrs; HonRl; HospAde; Mdrgl; NHS; SchMus; Twrl; LetterBsktbl; Methodist Sch; Nurse.

MC MAHON, Denice A; Desoto HS; Shawnee, KS; HonRl; NHS; FFA; PpCl; Bsktbl; Baker Univ; Medical Field.

MC MAHON, Janet M; Lincoln HS; Wis Rapids, WI; Band; Chrs; HonRl; LbryAde; MrchBnd; NHS; NatlMeritSF; PepBnd; Univ.

MC MAHON, Jerry L; Brownstown Central HS; Brownstown, IN; 50/142 4-H; Ftbl; LetterTrk; CaptIMSpt; College; Professional.

MC MAHON, Mary T; Manlius HS; Sheffield, IL; 6/27 SecJrCls; Band; Chr; ChrhWkr; CncrtBnd; HonRl; MrchBnd; RptrSchPpr; 4-H; FHA; Augustana Clge; Social Worker.

MC MAHON, Patricia L; Fort Zumwalt HS; O Fallon, MO; ChrhWkr; HonRl; IntrClCncl; StuCncl; RptrYrbk; RptrSchPpr; PpCl; Chrldr; GAA; College; Business.

MC MAHON, Patricia L; Joliet Twp HS; Joliet, IL; 1/509 Chr; HonRl; NatlMeritSF; SchMus; YthFlsp; RptrYrbk; FrCl; Tennis; GAA; University; Engineering.

MC MAHON, Patsy A; Our Lady Of Grace Academy; Indianapolis, IN; 4/54 PresFrshCls; PresSrCls; HonRl; HospAde; NHS; SchMus; StuGov; College; Political Science.

MC MAHON, Robert J; Mendota HS; Mendota, IL; 1/215 Band; CncrtBnd; DrmMjrt; HonRl; MrchBnd; NHS; PepBnd; FrCl; LionAwd; Univ Of Illinois; Chemistry.

MC MAHON, Teresa K; Rio Public HS; Rio, WI; 3/58 TrsSophCls; TrsJrCls; ALAGirlsSt; HonRl; NHS; SchPl; StuCncl; PpCl; Chrldr;.

MC MAINS, Michael B; North White HS; Monon, IN; Chr; ChrhWkr; HonRl; OffAde; SctActv; StuCncl; 4-H; KeyCl; GerCl; SciCl; LetterBsktbl; LetterFtbl; LetterGlf; Purdue Univ; Medicine.

MC MANAMA, Cynthia; Haworth HS; Kokomo, IN; 114/453 IntrClCncl; JA; StuCncl; PpCl; ChmnChrldr; PPFtbl; Ball State; Secretary.

MC MANAMON, Mary B; Alvernia HS; Chicago, IL; 10/252 NHS; PolWkr; TchrAde; RptrSchPpr; Univ Of Illinois; Medicine.

MC MANIMON, Thomas; Rushford Public HS; Rushford, MN; PresFrshCls; TrsJrCls; ChrhWkr; HonRl; SchPl; StuGov; SptEdSchPpr; 4-H; FHA; Ftbl; College; Business Admin.

MC MANIS, Cyndi A; Keokuk HS; Keokuk, IA; 14/192 AFS; Band; Chr; HonRl; NHS; SchMus; YthFlsp; FrCl; Bsktbl; KiwanAwd; Univ Of Ia; Nursing.

MC MANUS, Carolyn M; Lahser HS; Bloomfield Hills, MI; 24/464 ChrhWkr; LbryAde; PolWkr; SpnCl; PPFtbl; Univ Of Michigan; Accounting.

MC MANUS, Connie M; Savannah HS; Clarksdale, MO; VPSophCls; SecJrCls; TrsSrCls; Chr; NHS; StuCncl; EdSchPpr; PresLatCl; CaptBsktbl; LetterTrk; LetterGAA; 4-HAwd; PresAwd; Nw Missouri St Univ; Physical Educ.

MC MANUS, Daniel M; Sherrard HS; Aledo, IL; 1/98 ChrhWkr; HonRl; NHS; 4-H; FFA; FrCl; PpCl; SciCl; Bsbl; LetterBsktbl; Ftbl; 4-HAwd; Univ Of Illinois; Veterinarian.

MC MANUS, Kathleen; Sherrard HS; Aledo, IL; 7/120 SecJrCls; HonRl; NHS; StuCncl; StuGov; Yrbk; 4-H; FrCl; SciCl; Chrldr; Nurses Training.

MC MANUS, Kathleen; Hartland HS; Fenton, MI; 4/155 ALAGirlsSt; Band; CncrtBnd; HonRl; MrchBnd; NHS; Trk; Wrstlng; IMSpt; Michigan State U; Engineering.

MC MANUS, Kathryn A; Huron HS; Huron, SD; 10/300 Band; Chr; CncrtBnd; JrNHS; Mdrgl; MrchBnd; NHS; SchMus; RptrSchPpr; FBLA; GerCl; PpCl; College; Secretarial Science And English.

MC MANUS, Michael L; Carmel Boys HS; Lake Bluff, IL; 3/166 HonRl; LitMag; NHS; SpnCl; Glf; University; Physician.

MC MANUS, Teresa A; Regis HS; Eau Claire, WI; 6/150 Band; ChrhWkr; CncrtBnd; DrmBgl; HonRl; HospAde; NHS; Orch; RptrYrbk; FrCl; U Of Wi; Nurse.

MC MARTIN, Dean J; West Lyon Comm HS; Larchwood, IA; 4-H; LetterBsktbl; Ftbl; 4-HAwd; Browns Inst; Sportcaster.

MC MASTER, Jeffry S; Southwestern HS; Romney, IN; ChrhWkr; HonRl; NHS; SctActv; StuCncl; 4-H; FTA; SpnCl; Ftbl; LetterGlf; LetterWrstlng;.

MC MASTER, Joan E; South Sioux City HS; Suth Sioux City, NE; 15/170 AFS; PresChrs; HonRl; Teen; SpnCl; PpCl; Chrldr; CchngActv; Univ Nebraska; Art & Science.

MC MICHAEL, John G; Dowling HS; Des Moines, IA; 5/455 CmntyWkr; HonRl; StuCncl; LetterTrk; College.

MC MICHAEL, Kevin; Swan Valley HS; Saginaw, MI; 1/166 Aud/Vis; HonRl; JrNHS; NHS; SctActv; RptrYrbk; RptrSchPpr; SchPpr; SciCl; JCAwd; U Of Michigan; Pre Law.

MC MILLAN, Danny J; Ida HS; Temperance, MI; 4-H; Ftbl; Wrstlng; IMSpt; 4-HAwd; Coll; Coaching.

MC MILLAN, Lori K; Grundy R V HS; Galt, MO; PresSophCls; Band; Chrs; ChrhWkr; CncrtBnd; HonRl; MrchBnd; NHS; PepBnd; SchPl; Chrldr; 4-HAwd; College; English Lit.

MC MILLAN, Lorraine; Winona Sr HS; Winona, MN; 40/460 Chr; CmntyWkr; HonRl; JrNHS; NatlFornLg; NatlThespSoc; SchPl; StuGov; RptrSchPpr; Carroll College.

MC MILLAN, Mary A; Escanaba Area HS; Escanaba, MI; 43/382 ChrhWkr; HonRl; NHS; EdSchPpr; Mich Technological U; Nursing.

MC MILLAN, Scott; Ripon HS; Ripon, WI; HonRl; TchrAde; SptEdYrbk; SchPpr; U W Stout; Teacher Of Industrial Arts.

MC MILLEN, Barbara; Good Counsel HS; Chicago, IL; Aud/Vis; Chrs; HonRl; NatlMeritCmnd; SchMus; SchPl; Yrbk; GerCl; SciCl; GAA; Coll; Law.

MC MILLEN, Johnny W; King City R I HS; King City, MO; 16/39 Band; CncrtBnd; HonRl; MrchBnd; NHS; PepBnd; SchMus; SchPl; StuCncl; Bus Sch; Cpa.

MC MILLEN, Mary A; Southeastern HS; West Point, IL; 27/49 VPSrCls; Band; Chrs; ChrhWkr; CncrtBnd; HonRl; MrchBnd; PepBnd; SchMus; Junior College; Professional.

MC MILLIN, Phillip C; Lincoln County R Ii HS; Elsberry, MO; Band; ChrhWkr; CncrtBnd; HonRl; MrchBnd; PepBnd; SchAde; StuCncl; LetterBsbl; LetterBsktbl; LetterGlf; LetterTrk; College; Professional.

MC MORROW, Debbie L; Beech Grove HS; Beech Grove, IN; HonRl; NHS; PpCl; Tennis; Chrldr; HstSrCls; DanFAwd; In U; Doctor.

MC MULLAN, Carlette C; Woodlands Acad; Lake Forest, IL; 2/65 Chrs; ChrhWkr; CmntyWkr; LitMag; SchAde; StuGov; TchrAde; RptrSchPpr; DARAwd; College; Journalist.

MC MULLEN, David J; Vianney HS; Kirkwood, MO; 40/185 HonRl; SctActv; Ftbl; PresAwd; Univ; Business Career.

MC MULLEN, Diane M; Greenway HS; Bovey, MN; 16/155 CmntyWkr; HonRl; HospAde; NHS; StuGov; TchrAde; RptrSchPpr; Pres4-H; VPPpCl; LetterGAA; 4-HAwd; Hibbing Comm College; Nursing.

MC MULLEN, Ginny L; Sterling HS; Sterling, IL; 20/374 Chrs; HospAde; NHS; NatlMeritCmnd; Quill&Scroll; StuCncl; Tennis; Trk; GAA; Drake Univ; Business.

MC MULLEN, Jerrilyn K; Rockville HS; Rockville, IN; 1/87 PresJrCls; PresNHS; NatlMeritCmnd; YthFlsp; EdYrBk; Bsktbl; Tennis; LetterTrk; GAA; DARAwd; Purdue Univ; Agricultural Communications.

MC MULLEN, Sharon; Our Lady Of Mercy HS; Huntington Woods, MI; NHS; Univ Of Detroit.

MC MULLEN, Sharon K; Geneva HS; Geneva, NE; 5/63 Chrs; CncrtBnd; HonRl; MrchBnd; NHS; PepBnd; SchPl; StuGov; FBLA; TreasPpCl; Secretarial Work; Professional.

MC MULLIN, Craig; Prairie City Comm HS; Mitchellville, IA; 8/50 TrsSrCls; StuCncl; StuGov; 4-H; SpnCl; Ftbl; 4-HAwd; Iowa State Univ; Business.

MC MULLIN, Cynthia M; St Charles HS; St Charles, IL; 17/450 Chr; ChrhWkr; DrlTm; HonRl; NHS; OffAde; LetterBsktbl; Northern Il Univ; Medical Tech.

MC MUNIGAL, Mary J; Wakonda Independent HS; Wakonda, SD; SecJrCls; ALAGirlsSt; Band; Chrs; CncrtBnd; HonRl; MrchBnd; NHS; Trk; CaptChrldr; U Of South Dakota; English Literature.

MC MURDIE, Judith A; Macomb HS; Macomb, IL; 1/241 Chr; Mdrgl; NHS; NatlMeritCmnd; SecNatlThespSoc; PresOrch; SchMus; Yrbk; PpCl; EldAwd; Univ Of Ill; Music.

MC MURRAY, Dru A; Alton HS; Alton, IL; Aud/Vis; ChrhWkr; OffAde; LetterFtbl; LetterTrk; IMSpt; Western Il Univ; Pre Dental.

MC MURRAY, Janes F; Brebeuf Prep; Indianapols, IN; 27/117 NHS; TchrAde; LetterFtbl; Glf; IMSpt; Indiana U; Bus.

MC MURRAY, John R; James H Bowen HS; Chicago, IL; 2/650 Aud/Vis; HonRl; NHS; NatlMeritCmnd; StuCncl; TchrAde; Yrbk; PresFSA; CaptTennis; BauchLmbAwd; Univ Of Illinois; Elec Engineering.

MC MURRAY, Kristin M; Belton HS; Richard Gebaur Afb, MO; Chr; HonRl; JrNHS; NHS; NatlThespSoc; SchMus; SchPl; StuCncl; FHA; SpnCl; PpCl; College; Zoology.

MC MURTRY, Cynthia E; Rich East HS; Park Forest, IL; 73/329 HonRl; HospAde; NHS; RedCrAde; SctActv; SpnCl; PpCl; Bsktbl; Tennis; IMSpt; Univ; Pre Med Education.

MC NABB, Jean S; Calhoun HS; Hardin, IL; SecSrCls; ALAGirlsSt; Band; CncrtBnd; HonRl; NHS; PepBnd; FrCl; PpCl; Bsktbl; GAA; IMSpt; University; Nursing.

MC NABNEY, Charles M; High School; Grandview, MO; Band; ChrhWkr; CncrtBnd; HonRl; MrchBnd; SchAde; Clg; Architectural Engineer.

MC NAIL, Carol L; Southern R 2 HS; Centerville, MO; SecTrsFrshCls; SecTrsSophCls; SecTrsJrCls; HonRl; Twrl; PpCl; Chrldr; Trade School.

MC NAIR, Kathleen; Scotus Central HS; Clumbus, NE; HonRl; HospAde; NHS; NatlMeritCmnd; PpCl; IMSpt; Kearney State College.

MC NALLY, Robert R; Lasalle Peru Twp HS; Peru, IL; 69/516 HonRl; SctActv; RptrYrbk; SchPpr; SpnCl; CaptSwmmng; Bradley Univ; Chemistry.

MC NAMAR, Brian; Van Buren Commu HS; Keosauqua, IA; 11/87 HonRl; Mdrgl; MrchBnd; NHS; Orch; PepBnd; YthFlsp; SpnCl; Bsbl; Central College; Business.

MC NAMARA, Bruce D; Hastings HS; Hastings, MN; HonRl; ROTC; MthCl; SciCl; Coll.

MC NAMARA, Carol S; Oakwood HS; Fithian, IL; PresJrCls; Band; StuCncl; SpnCl; Univ Of Illinois; Veterinarian.

MC NAMARA, Cathy A; Dwight HS; Dwight, IL; SecSrCls; HonRl; LbryAde; NHS; SchAde; TchrAde; VPSpnCl; Tennis; CaptChrldr; GAA; College; Physical Education Teacher.

MC NAMARA, Jean M; Goodhue Public HS; Goodhue, MN; 4/76 Chr; HonRl; NHS; TchrAde; RptrSchPpr; SchPpr; FFA; FHA; Winona St; Elem Educ.

MC NAMARA, Kathleen M; Our Lady Of Mercy HS; Detroit, MI; Chrl; ChrhWkr; CmntyWkr; NHS; PolWkr; RedCrAde; StuGov; TchrAde; Swmmng; PPFtbl; Wayne State Univ.

MC NAMARA, Michelle M; Pecatonica HS; Pecatonica, IL; 2/60 Chrs; HonRl; JrNHS; LbryAde; NHS; SchPl; TchrAde; RptrSchPpr; 4-H; LetterBsktbl; LetterTrk; GAA; IMSpt; Army; Biology.

MC NAMARA, Monica; Bishop Ward HS; Kansas, KS; 2/195 ChrhWkr; CmntyWkr; HonRl; JrNHS; FrCl; MthCl; College; Medicine.

MC NAMARA, William; Brother Rice Hs; Chicago, IL; 39/414 HonRl; JrNHS; NHS; Bsktbl; Glf; Northwestern U; Social Sciences.

MC NAMARA, William J; Brother Rice HS; Chicago, IL; 33/438 HonRl; JrNHS; NHS; StuGov; Bsktbl; Glf; Northwestern University; Social Science.

MC NAMEE, Lucy; Bloomington Hs; Bloomington, IL; 102/391 HonRl; HospAde; SchPl; FrCl; MthCl; PpCl; GAA; Illinois State U; Business Administration.

MC NAMEE, Penny R; Leaf River Community HS; Leaf River, IL; 5/39 Chrs; CncrtBnd; HonRl; MrchBnd; PepBnd; SchPl; Bsbl; Bsktbl; Chrldr; AmLegAwd; Vocation.

MC NANARA, Steven T; Huntington Catholic HS; Huntington, IN; PresFrshCls; VPSophCls; PresJrCls; ALBoysSt; LetterBsktbl; LetterGlf; LetterTrk; OptClAwd;.

MC NARY, Paul E; Penney HS; Hamilton, MO; Band; ChrhWkr; CncrtBnd; MrchBnd; PepBnd; SctActv; RptrSchPpr; FFA; LetterFtbl; LetterWrstlng; Univ Of Mo; Farming.

MC NARY, Sheila G; Lourdes HS; Rochester, MN; Band; CncrtBnd; HonRl; MrchBnd; NHS; SchMus; RptrSchPpr; FrCl; Trk; Coll.

MC NATT, Gwen E; Wheaton Warrenville HS; Wheaton, IL; Band; ChrhWkr; DrlTm; HonRl; NatlFornLg; StuCncl; StuGov; EdSchPpr; Univ Of Iowa; Nursing.

MC NATT, Joel H; Carroll HS; Wichita, KS; 9/270 PresFrshCls; ALBoysSt; Chr; HonRl; Mdrgl; NatlFornLg; NHS; NatlMeritCmnd; SchMus; StuCncl; TchrAde; EdYrBk; EdSchPpr; Bsktbl; University; Professional.

MC NAUGHTON, Barbara C; Sault Area HS; Sault Ste Marie, MI; HonRl; Quill&Scroll; RptrYrbk; EdYrBk; PpCl; Trk; GAA; Central Mi Univ; Phy Educ.

MC NAUGHTON, Stephen M; Webberville HS; Webberville, MI; 2/65 ChrhWkr; HonRl; NHS; NatlMeritSchl; TchrAde; YthFlsp; FrCl; University; Mathematics.

MC NAUGHTON, Steven C; Durand Unified HS; Eau Galle, WI; PresSophCls; HonRl; JA; StuCncl; YthFlsp; CaptFtbl; LetterTrk; LetterWrstlng; 4-HAwd; JAAwd; Clge; Math & Science.

MC NEA, Debra L; Bottineau HS; Bottineau, ND; 12/85 ALAGirlsSt; Chr; CncrtBnd; HonRl; SchPl; 4-H; FHA; PpCl; Trk; College; Science.

MC NEAL, Cathy; Missouri Valley HS; Home Creek, IA; HonRl; 4-H; FHA; 4-HAwd; Secretarial.

MC NEAL, Marice; Washington Park HS; Racine, WI; 40/550 CmntyWkr; HonRl; TchrAde; IMSpt; College; Business Management.

MC NEAL, Nancy L; Arlington HS; Arlington Hts, IL; 37/581 Chr; Chrs; HonRl; JrNHS; Mdrgl; NHS; NatlMeritCmnd; NatlThespSoc; SchMus; Univ Of Illinois; Horticulture.

MC NEAL, Suzanne; Holland HS; Holland, MI; 25/317 ChrhWkr; HonRl; LitMag; Orch; RedCrAde; SchPl; RptrSchPpr; FDA; LatCl; College; Medical Doctor.

MC NEEL, Mary L; Burlington HS; Burlington, WI; 7/281 Band; Chr; NHS; PepBnd; SpnCl; Univ; English.

MC NEELEY, Patricia D; Dexter HS; Dexter, MO; Chr; ChrhWkr; HonRl; SpnCl; College; Professional.

MC NEELY, Barbara J; Risco HS; Risco, MO; PresJrCls; TrsSrCls; ChrhWkr; HonRl; SchPl; Yrbk; FHA; Bsktbl; Chrldr; College; Physical Educ.

MC NEELY, Jayne; Franklin Central HS; Greenwood, IN; 21/249 HonRl; NHS; OffAde; SchPl; TchrAde; FHA; SpnCl; IMSpt; Indiana Univ; Elementary Teacher.

MC NEELY, Jeffrey K; Anna Jonesboro Chs; Anna, IL; 8/137 Band; CncrtBnd; HonRl; MrchBnd; NHS; PepBnd; SctActv; SchPpr; 4-H; LatCl; PresSciCl; Univ Of Illinois; Aerospace Engineering.

MC NEELY, Kathy A; Cary Grove HS; Cary, IL; 56/280 CncrtBnd; HonRl; MrchBnd; PepBnd; SchPl; YthFlsp; EdYrBk; RptrSchPpr; FHA; Bradley University; Law.

MC NEELY, Peggy A; Lexington HS; Lexington, IL; 12/64 AFS; Band; CncrtBnd; HonRl; MrchBnd; SchPl; YthFlsp; FTA; Tennis; GAA; Millikin Univ.

MC NEELY, Steven M; Marion HS; Marion, IN; ALBoysSt; Chr; ChrhWkr; HonRl; Mdrgl; NHS; SchMus; YthFlsp; Bsktbl; LetterFtbl; Wheaton College; Christian Service.

MC NEIL, John J; Richland HS; Richland, MO; 9/66 Band; Chrs; ChrhWkr; CmntyWkr; CncrtBnd; HonRl; MrchBnd; NatlCathMusEdAsoc; FTA; Swmmng; Trk; Central Methodist College; Music.

MC NEIL, Leesa A; Aberdeen Central HS; Warnes, SD; 9/440 ALAGirlsSt; ChrhWkr; HonRl; NatlFornLg; NHS; SchAde; SchPpr; FHA; BttyCrckrAwd; Private School; Lawyer.

MC NEIL, Peggy; Clay County Community HS; Wakefield, KS; Band; CncrtBnd; HonRl; MrchBnd; NHS; Orch; PepBnd; SchPl; Washburn Univ; Nursing.

MC NEIL, Scott W; Ithaca HS; Ithaca, MI; 20/150 Aud/Vis; ChrhWkr; CmntyWkr; HonRl; IntrClCncl; YthFlsp; Bsbl; Glf; Trk; LetterWrstlng; Elec Engr U Of Mi; Elec Engr.

MC NEIL, Tamara K; Clay Center Comm HS; Idana, KS; 16/127 Band; CncrtBnd; MrchBnd; PepBnd; SchPl; PpCl; Trk; Kansas State Univ ;nursing.

MC NEIL, Teresa A; Richland HS; Richland, MO; SecSophCls; Band; ChrhWkr; CmntyWkr; CncrtBnd; DrmBgl; DrmMjrt; HonRl; MrchBnd;

PepBnd; StuCncl; Bsbl; Bsktbl; Trk; Business Schl; Professional.

MC NEILL, Laurie B; Mineral Point HS; Mineral Point, WI; Band; Chr; CncrtBnd; HonRl; MrchBnd; NHS; PepBnd; SchMus; YthFlsp; 4-H; 4-HAwd; University Of Wisconsin; Music.

MC NEILL, Lisa L; Fairfield Comm HS; Fairfield, IL; VPSrCls; Band; Chrs; CmntyWkr; HonRl; HospAde; MrchBnd; StuCncl; SchPpr; SptEdYrbk; Yrbk; FHA; FrCl; SpnCl; LetterTennis; College; Law.

MC NEILLY, Catherene; Mt Pleasant HS; Mount Pleasant, MI; 3/342 HonRl; NHS; NatlMeritCmnd; Orch; TchrAde; SchPpr; SpnCl; Bsktbl; Central Michigan Univ; Secondary Mathematic.

MC NEIVE, Julie A; St Marys HS; Emmett, KS; ALAGirlsSt; Band; Chrs; HonRl; NHS; RptrYrbk; RptrSchPpr; 4-H; Trk; Chrldr; College; Social Work.

MC NELLIS, Lucille J; Somerset HS; Hudson, WI; Band; Chr; CncrtBnd; HonRl; MrchBnd; NatlFornLg; PepBnd; StuCncl; 4-H; University.

MC NELLY, Debra L; Egyptian HS; Thebes, IL; 2/67 VPJrCls; Band; ChrhWkr; CncrtBnd; HonRl; LbryAde; SecNHS; OffAde; SchPl; TchrAde; TreasCivCl; FHA; PpCl; LetterChrldr; Mckendree College; Elem Ed.

MC NERNEY, William E; Oak Park River Forest HS; Oak Park, IL; 144/1012 NatlMeritCmnd; MthCl; LetterGlf; Univ Of Illinois; Opthalmologist.

MC NESS, Tami R; Hartford HS; Hartford, MI; TrsFrshCls; Chr; ChrhWkr; HonRl; SchAde; SchPl; TchrAde; 4-H; SpnCl; PpCl; Western Mi Univ; Legal Secretary.

MC NETT, Jo Dee A; Vicksburg HS; Vicksburg, MI; Band; YthFlsp; JAAwd; Kelloge Comm Coll; Phy Therapist.

MC NICHOLAS, Jean M; Mother Mc Auley HS; Oak Lawn, IL; PresFrshCls; PresSophCls; PresJrCls; HonRl; NHS; SchMus; Yrbk; FrCl; Tennis; Marquette Univ; Accounting.

MC NICOLL, Steven; Ashwaubenon HS; Green Bay, WI; 108/228 HonRl; College; Aeronautical.

MC NULTY, Carol; Garden City East HS; Garden City, MI; 76/350 HonRl; SpnCl; PpCl; GAA; College; Biological Science.

MC NULTY, Lauren K; Benet Acad; Downers Grove, IL; 3/240 Band; Chrs; CncrtBnd; HonRl; MrchBnd; NatlMeritSF; RptrYrbk; PPFtbl; AmLegAwd; Notre Dame; Math.

MC NULTY, Mickie L; Hill City HS; Keystone, SD; 4/30 ALAGirlsSt; DrlTm; HonRl; OffAde; PresStuCncl; StuGov; RptrYrbk; Yrbk; Chrldr; GAA; IMSpt; AmLegAwd; 4-HAwd; College; Guidance Counselor.

MC NULTY, Owen K; Whiteford Agricultural HS; Ottawa Lake, MI; 11/83 Band; HonRl; MrchBnd; NHS; StuCncl; RptrYrbk; RptrSchPpr; SchPpr; LetterBsktbl; Univ Of Mich.

MC NURLIN, Joe; Gurley HS; Gurley, NE; Chrs; 4-H; Bsbl; Bsktbl; Ftbl; Trk; CchngActv; 4-HAwd; College; Agribusiness.

MC NUTT, Lori J; Larkin HS; Elgin, IL; 11/600 SecJrCls; SecSrCls; HonRl; StuCncl; Elgin Comm College.

MC OSKER, Richard D; Turner HS; Kansas City, KS; HonRl; JrNHS; NHS; SctActv; TchrAde; SpnCl; Ftbl; Ks City College; Mechanical Eng.

MC PEAK, Mark; Catholic Central HS; Farmington Hills, MI; Ftbl; IMSpt; Mich Tech Univ.

MC PEAK, Maureen M; Our Lady Of Mercy HS; Farmington Hills, MI; Geo Washington Univ; Archeologist.

MC PECK, Cindy M; Deforest HS; Deforest, WI; Band; ChrhWkr; CncrtBnd; HonRl; NHS; PepBnd; SctActv; StuCncl; YthFlsp; SecGAA; College; Teacher.

MC PEEK, Jennifer R; Lake City HS; Lake City, MI; 3/62 PresSrCls; Band; Chr; CncrtBnd; DrmMjrt; HonRl; MrchBnd; NHS; RptrYrbk; Bsktbl; Univ; Psychology.

MC PHEE, Carol; Sts Peter And Paul Area HS; Saginaw, MI; TrsSrCls; CmntyWkr; Mdrgl; NHS; SchMus; StuGov; RptrYrbk; Bsbl; Bsktbl; GAA; Delta Comm College; Accounting.

MC PHEETERS, Kay L; Gothenburg HS; Gothenburg, NE; 2/8 PresJrCls; Chrs; ChrhWkr; CncrtBnd; HonRl; VPNHS; PresStuCncl; YthFlsp; PpCl; 4-HAwd; University Of Neb; Teaching.

MC PHERRON, Caroline J; Southridge HS; Holland, IN; 1/160 SecBand; CncrtBnd; HonRl; MrchBnd; PepBnd; SchMus; SctActv; PpCl; Trk; Purdue Univ; Engineering.

MC PHERRON, Michael J; Southridge HS; Holland, IN; 1/135 PresBand; CncrtBnd; HonRl; MrchBnd; SchMus; SchPl; StuCncl; Yrbk; Bsktbl; LetterTrk; Rose Hulman Inst; Chemical Engineer.

MC PHERRON, Randy; Bremen HS; Bremen, IN; HstSrCls; ChrhWkr; HonRl; SchPl; YthFlsp; IMSpt; Indiana Univ.

MC PHERSON, Dean O; Adams Public HS; Adams, NE; 6/26 Chrs; ChrhWkr; HonRl; SctActv; PresStuCncl; PresYthFlsp; LetterFtbl; LetterWrstlng; CchngActv; U Of Ne; Ministry.

MC PHERSON, Jerald J; West Sioux HS; Hawarden, IA; 13/79 VPSophCls; ALBoysSt; Chrs; HonRl; SchMus; SchPl; SctActv; StuCncl; YthFlsp; CaptFtbl; Military; Us Air Force.

MC PHERSON, Maureen A; St Louis HS; St Louis, MI; 40/114 HstSophCls; HonRl; OffAde; SchPl; StuCncl; RptrYrbk; Yrbk; EdSchPpr; SpnCl; PpCl; Central Mich Univ; Industrial Relations.

MC PHERSON, Shirley; Sumner HS; St Louis, MO; Aud/Vis; HonRl; JA; 4-H; FBLA; LatCl; MthCl; Bsbl; College.

MC PHERSON, Timothy W; Willow Springs HS; Willow Springs, MO; 15/98 VPSophCls; Chrs; HonRl; SchPl; StuCncl; LetterBsbl; CaptFtbl; LetterSwmmng; LetterTrk; CaptWrstlng; CchngActv; Central Methodist College; Medicine.

MC PHILLIPS, Ronald P; Holy Family HS; Lindsay, NE; Chrs; ChrhWkr; CmntyWkr; Sacrstn; SchMus; SchPl; TchrAde; LetterBsktbl; LetterTrk; IMSpt;.

MC QUADE, James; Plymouth HS; Plymouth, MI; HonRl; NatlMeritSF; Artist.

MC QUADE, Thomas J; Buena Vista HS; Saginaw, MI; 16/259 Aud/Vis; Band; HonRl; OffAde; SchPl; MthCl; Delta Coll; Secondary Ed.

MC QUEEN, Barbara J; South Side HS; Fort Wayne, IN; 117/427 SecTrsSophCls; AFS; HonRl; JA; OffAde; StuCncl; TchrAde; Yrbk; SpnCl; College; Law.

MC QUEEN, Jeffrey D; South Side HS; Fort Wayne, IN; 110/427 HonRl; Bsbl; Ftbl; LetterWrstlng; IMSpt; College; Accounting Cpa.

MC QUEEN, Penny J; Eastern HS; Solsberry, IN; 3/63 PresJrCls; ChrhWkr; NHS; Quill&Scroll; SchMus; RptrYrbk; EdSchPpr; SciCl; Chrldr; DARAwd; Ky Christian Col; Christian Service.

MC QUISTAN, Janelle L; Pender Public HS; Pender, NE; SecTrsJrCls; Band; Chr; HonRl; SchPl; StuCncl; RptrYrbk; FHA; Swmmng; Chrldr; Univ; Professional.

MC QUISTON, Clifford J; Ashley HS; Brant, MI; HonRl; NHS; SchPl; TchrAde; Teen; YthFlsp; 4-H; FTA; LetterBsbl; LetterBsktbl; Ftbl; Trk; IMSpt; Michigan Tech University; Civil Engineering.

MC QUISTON, James H; Ecorse HS; Ecorse, MI; 1/207 Chrs; HonRl; NHS; NatlMeritSF; SchAde; StuCncl; TchrAde; YthFlsp; CaptSwmmng; AmLegAwd; Kalamazoo Coll; Medicine.

MC RAE, Mary; Grace HS; St Paul, MN; ChrhWkr; SchPl; SctActv; StuCncl; Yrbk; SchPpr; 4-H; PpCl; Trk; CchngActv; College; Psycology.

MC RAY, David W; O Fallon Twp HS; O Fallon, IL; Band; CmntyWkr; CncrtBnd; HonRl; SctActv; YthFlsp; SpnCl; LetterBsbl; LetterBsktbl; LetterFtbl; College; Business Admin.

MC REYNOLDS, Curtis N; Gibson Southern HS; Owensville, IN; 23/229 ChrhWkr; StuCncl; SciCl; LetterFtbl; Wrstlng; Purdue Univ; Sci.

MC REYNOLDS, Lori L; Central Comm HS; De Witt, IA; Chrs; CmntyWkr; CncrtBnd; HonRl; JrNHS; NatlFornLg; NHS; SchMus; StuCncl; SciCl; Chrldr; GAA; College; Music.

MC REYNOLDS, Myron C; Bremen HS; Markham, IL; Band; ChrhWkr; CncrtBnd; HonRl; MrchBnd; NatlMeritCmnd; PepBnd; SchMus; Bsbl; College; Music.

MC RIPLEY, Gil W; Ferndale HS; Ferdale, MI; ChrhWkr; HonRl; Ftbl; Trk; U Of Detroit; Law.

MC ROBERTS, Lauralee; Bullock Creek HS; Midland, MI; 11/170 Chr; ChrhWkr; HonRl; IntrClCncl; NHS; 4-H; PpCl; Bsktbl; Trk; LetterGAA; Central Mich Univ; Sec Educ.

MC SHEA, John J; St Viator HS; Palatine, IL; 31/245 HstFrshCls; Chrs; HonRl; SchPl; SctActv; StuCncl; Teen; SpnCl; Bsbl; LetterFtbl; LetterTrk; CchngActv; College; Political Science.

MC SHERRY, James T; Belleville W HS; Millstadt, IL; HonRl; StuCncl; RptrSchPpr; LatCl; Bsktbl; Trk; Air Force Acad; Engineering.

MC SORLEY, Brian P; Nathan Hale HS; West Allis, WI; 14/540 ChrhWkr; HonRl; Marquette College; Medicine.

MC SWEENEY, John T; Fenwick HS; Berwyn, IL; PresFrshCls; HonRl; NatlFornLg; NHS; NatlMeritCmnd; PolWkr; SchMus; SchPl; StuCncl; Northwestern Univ; Law.

MC TAGGART, Janice M; Laker HS; Bad Axe, MI; PresJrCls; HonRl; NHS; EdYrBk; Treas4-H; FHA; PpCl; Trk; Chrldr; 4-HAwd; M S U; Architecture.

MC TAGGART, Janice M; Elkton Pigeon Bay Port HS; Bad Axe, MI; TrsSophCls; HonRl; NHS; EdYrBk; 4-H; FHA; VPPpCl; Trk; Chrldr; 4-HAwd; College; Art.

MC TAGGART, Richard E; Watseka Comm HS; Watseka, IL; Aud/Vis; HonRl; PresFFA;.

MC TAVISH, Daniel P; D C Everest HS; Rothschild, WI; 34/347 LetterFtbl; Trk; Wrstlng; N Central Tech Inst; Electronics.

MC TRUSTY, Jodi L; Florence HS; Florence, WI; Band; Chrs; NatlFornLg; NHS; PolWkr; Yrbk; FTA; SpnCl; PpCl; College; Accounting.

MC VANE, Randy; St Ignatius College Prep; Chicago, IL; 49/200 ChrhWkr; CmntyWkr; HonRl; OffAde; StuCncl; StuGov; Teen; FDA; Bsktbl; LetterTrk; IMSpt; College; Medicine.

MC VARY, Kevin T; Campion HS; Springfield, IL; 2/100 ModUN; SchPl; StuCncl; StuGov; TchrAde; RptrYrbk; RptrSchPpr; CaptFtbl; CaptSwmmng; PresAwd; Northwestern Univ; Medicine.

MC VAY, Amy L; Whitko HS; South Whitley, IN; 31/153 HonRl; LbryAde; NatlFornLg; NatlThespSoc; Quill&Scroll; SchPl; YthFlsp; RptrYrbk; RptrSchPpr; PpCl; Ball State Univ; Publications.

MC VAY, Marie L; Morenci HS; Morenci, MI; HonRl; NHS; NatlMeritFnl; NatlMeritCmnd; NatlMeritSchl; NatlMeritSF; TchrAde; FTA; PpCl; Cap Bsktbl; Siena Heights Coll; Math.

MC VEIGH, Crystal R; Elk Grove HS; Elk Grove Vlg, IL; 26/505 HonRl; LbryAde; NHS; Quill&Scroll; RptrSchPpr; PpCl; University; Computer Engineering.

MC VEY, Mary C; Cor Jesu Acad; St Louis, MO; PresSophCls; Chr; HonRl; HospAde; NatlCathMusEdAsoc; PolWkr; SchMus; SchPl; StuCncl; RptrYrbk; Maryville Clge; Music Therapist.

MC VEY, Sharon A; Waldron HS; Waldron, IN; 6/71 Band; CncrtBnd; HonRl; VPYthFlsp; Yrbk; Pres4-H; TreasFHA; GAA; MasAwd; College; Computer Business.

MC VICKER, Barbara; Liberty HS; Mountain View, MO; ChrhWkr; DrlTm; Mdrgl; NHS; SchMus; StuCncl; FHA; SpnCl; VoiceDemAwd; Sw Baptist College; Home Ec.

MC VICKER, Karen L; Wabash HS; Wabash, IN; Chr; DrmBgl; HonRl; HospAde; LbryAde; MrchBnd; SecNHS; YthFlsp; EdYrBk; PresSciCl; Purdue Univ; Nursing.

MC WALTERS, Susan E; William J Bogan HS; Chicago, IL; 50/704 HonRl; HospAde; NHS; OffAde; SpnCl; Univ Of Illinois.

MC WATT, Kevin A; East Detroit HS; East Detroit, MI; Aud/Vis; ChrhWkr; OffAde; PolWkr; SctActv; KeyCl; MthCl; LetterTennis; Central Michigan University.

MC WETHY, Mark E; Milford Sr HS; Highland, MI; Aud/Vis; HonRl; NHS; SchAde; Trade Schl; Mechanic.

MC WHIRT, Melaney; Jetmore HS; Jetmore, KS; 3/37 PresSrCls; CncrtBnd; HonRl; SchMus; StuCncl; Tennis; Trk; Chrldr; GAA; Univ; Medical Tech.

MC WILLIAM, Elizabeth A; West Marshall HS; Melbourne, IA; 8/88 Band; CncrtBnd; HonRl; MrchBnd; NHS; PepBnd; YthFlsp; Bsktbl; Ia State U; Food And Nutrition.

MC WILLIAMS, Deborah A; William Fremd HS; Palatine, IL; HonRl; JA; NHS; NatlMeritCmnd; PPFtbl; U Of Il; Chem Eng Or Biochem.

MC WILLIAMS, Jean A; Gallatin HS; Gallatin, MO; Band; Chr; CncrtBnd; HonRl; LbryAde; MrchBnd; NHS; PepBnd; SchMus; RptrYrbk; SchPpr; LetterBsktbl; LetterGlf; Trk; Correspondence Schl; Commercial Art.

MC WILLIAMS, Karen M; Oakhawn Comm HS; Oakhawn, IL; 150/610 Chr; Chrs; ChrhWkr; HonRl; SchPl; YthFlsp; College; Pro.

MC WILLIAMS, Laurie V; Hilbert HS; Hilbert, WI; 15/65 HonRl; Yrbk; GAA; IMSpt; Technical Sch; Pediatric Therapy.

MC WILLIAMS, Marsha A; Girard HS; Girord, KS; TrsSophCls; Band; CncrtBnd; HonRl; NHS; SctActv; Twrl; FHA; LetterBsktbl; LetterTrk; Kansas St U; Business.

MC WILLIAMS, Marsha A; Girard HS; Girard, KS; 1/83 TrsSophCls; Band; HonRl; NHS; OffAde; SctActv; Twrl; FHA; PpCl; LetterBsktbl; Kansas St Col; Home Ec.

MC WILLIAMS, Terrence P; W J Bryan HS; Omaha, NE; LetterBsbl; LetterBsktbl; LetterFtbl; Math.

MC YARY, Kevin T; Campion Jesuit HS; Springfield, IL; 2/100 ChrhWkr; CmntyWkr; HonRl; JrNHS; ModUN; NHS; PolWkr; StuCncl; StuGov; TchrAde; UNYO; CaptFtbl; CaptSwmmng; College; Medicine.

M

MAAG, Cynthia; Hermitage HS; Pittsburg, MO; 1/23 PresJrCls; TrsSrCls; HonRl; NHS; StuCncl; SpnCl; PpCl; Bsktbl; Chrldr; IMSpt; Coll; Account.

MAAG, Cynthia A; Hermitage HS; Pittsburg, MO; 1/23 PresJrCls; TrsSrCls; HonRl; NHS; SpnCl; PpCl; Bsbl; Chrldr; College; Secretary.

MAAG, Gregory J; Edwardsville Sr HS; Edwardsville, IL; 47/461 VPChr; HonRl; Mdrgl; NHS; TchrAde; Bsktbl; LetterTrk; Univ; Professional.

MAAG, Mary L; Savannah Riii HS; Cosby, MO; VPJrCls; Chr; ChrhWkr; Mdrgl; SchMus; StuCncl; YthFlsp; SchPpr; LatCl; PpCl; College; Professional.

MAAKESTAD, James M; Glenbrook South HS; Northbrook, IL; 75/579 HonRl; SctActv; TchrAde; Socr; Coll; Prof.

MAAS, Allan C; Dubuque HS; Dubuque, IA; 43/445 ChrhWkr; HonRl; JA; NHS; YthFlsp; KeyCl; GerCl; Bsktbl; LetterGlf; IMSpt; Univ; Eng.

MAAS, Amy; Hebron HS; Hebron, ND; 11/36 ALAGirlsSt; ChrhWkr; HonRl; LbryAde; SchPl; YthFlsp; RptrYrbk; SchPpr; Chrldr; GAA; N D St Univ; Home Econ.

MAAS, Gregory W; Westview HS; Kankakee, IL; Chr; HonRl; Mdrgl; NHS; PresNatlThespSoc; Quill&Scroll; SchMus; SchPl; RptrYrbk; Wheaton College; Music.

MAAS, Karma K; Chambers Public HS; Chambers, NE; Band; Chrs; CncrtBnd; MrchBnd; PepBnd; 4-H; FHA; PpCl; Trk; Chrldr;.

MAAS, Linda S; Pierce HS; Pierce, NE; ChrhWkr; HonRl; HospAde; SchAde; SchPl; TchrAde; RptrYrbk; RptrSchPpr; FHA; PpCl; Trk; IMSpt;.

MAAS, Marikay; Custer HS; Milwaukee, WI; Chrs; HonRl; LbryAde; MrchBnd; PolWkr; TchrAde; SchPpr; GerCl; College; Psychology.

MAAS, Marilyn K; Williamsburg Comm HS; Marengo, IA; 20/94 HonRl; NHS; Quill&Scroll; SchPpr; FFA;.

MAAS, Susan M; Huron HS; Huron, SD; ALAGirlsSt; ChrhWkr; CmntyWkr; HonRl; NHS; NatlMeritCmnd; StuCncl; StuGov; Yrbk; PresAwd; Univ; Business Career.

MAASKE, Leslie L; Cozad HS; Cozad, NE; VPJrCls; Band; Ftbl; Trk; Wrstlng; Trade School.

MAASSEN, Denise; Mercy HS; St Louis, MO; 34/166 NHS; RptrYrbk; PpCl; IMSpt; VoiceDemAwd; Depaul School Of Nursing.

MAASSEN, Ilyeen K; Avoha Community HS; Avoca, IA; 1/45 CncrtBnd; HonRl; MrchBnd; NHS; PepBnd; YthFlsp; Yrbk; 4-H; Trk; 4-HAwd; Drake; Pharmacy.

MAAT, Beverly A; Zeeland HS; Zeeland, MI; Band; HonRl; HospAde; JrNHS; ModUN; NHS; PepBnd; PpCl; Bsbl; Chrldr; Bronson Methodist Nursing Sch; Nursng.

MAAT, Janice E; Kenowa Hills HS; Grand Rapids, MI; /200 Band; Chr; HonRl; NHS; SchMus; SchPl; RptrYrbk; RptrSchPpr; PpCl; PPFtbl; Grand Valley State College; Counselor.

MABBITT, Kathryn; West Harrison Hs; Mondamin, IA; Band; Chr; Chrs; CncrtBnd; HonRl; Mdrgl; MrchBnd; SchPl; Bsktbl; College ; Dentist Or Law.

MABBITT, Ronald D; West Harrison HS; Mondamin, IA; 1/51 Band; Chr; Chrs; CncrtBnd; HonRl; MrchBnd; NHS; M I T; Physics.

MABBS, Kathryn L; Batavia HS; Batavia, IL; 35/219 AFS; HonRl; OffAde; SchMus; SchPl; SctActv; PpCl; Bsbl; GAA; IMSpt; Northern Il Univ; Art.

MABERRY, Steven G; Tina Avalon HS; Dawn, MO; 3/13 ALBoysSt; Band; HonRl; FFA; LetterBsbl; LetterBsktbl; 4-HAwd; College; Agriculture.

MABIE, Jamie F; Quincy HS; Quincy, IL; SctActv; SpnCl; Ftbl; Univ Of Illinois; Aviation.

MABRY, Anita L; O Fallon Twnsp HS; O Fallon, IL; 13/316 DrlTm; HonRl; NHS; RedCrAde; SchPl; SctActv; StuCncl; SpnCl; Belleville Area Jr Clg; Lab Tech.

MAC AINSH, Teresa G; Pinckney HS; Pinckney, MI; HonRl; TchrAde; Trk;.

MACAK, Phillip; Jesse Spalding HS; Chicago, IL; 2/47 HonRl; LbryAde; NHS; RptrYrbk; MthCl; Univ Of Illinois; Chemistry.

MACAS, George; Hubbard HS; Chicago, IL; 68/492 Chrl; Chrs; HonRl; Mdrgl; NHS; NatlMeritCmnd; Quill&Scroll; SchMus; StuCncl; TchrAde; RptrSchPpr; SchPpr; FTA; Northern Illinois Univ; Broadcasting.

MAC ASKILL, Douglas J; Hillcrest HS; Hazel Crest, IL; 15/474 HonRl; NHS; SctActv; StuCncl; SciCl; CaptSwmmng; Tennis; CchngActv; AmLegAwd; University; Biology.

MACAULAY, Lorna A; Maria HS; Chicago, IL; Chr; Chrl; Chrs; DrlTm; HospAde; JA; MrchBnd; SchMus; Twrl; GAA; College; Vocation.

MACAULAY, Timothy; Hale Area HS; Hale, MI; 3 Chr; HonRl; LbryAde; StuCncl; RptrSchPpr; StuCncl; Bsbl; Bsktbl; Ftbl; IMSpt; 4-HAwd; College; Prof.

MACAULAY, Timothy R; Hale Area HS; Hale, MI; VPSophCls; Chr; HonRl; LbryAde; NHS; StuCncl; RptrSchPpr; 4-H; Bsbl; Ftbl; College; Prof.

MACCO, Barbara A; St Joseph Acad; De Pere, WI; 4/160 Chrs; HonRl; SchMus; TchrAde; PresSpnCl; PpCl; Chrldr; GAA; IMSpt; RotaryAwd; U Of Wi Madison; Pre School Ed.

MACDERMOTT, Alice M; Bishop Borgess HS; Detroit, MI; CmntyWkr; NHS; PolWkr; TchrAde; GerCl; CchngActv; College; Ba In Police Science Occ Park Rngr.

MAC DONALD, Anne M; Wayne Memorial HS; Wayne, MI; ChrhWkr; HonRl; NHS; SpnCl; E Mi U; Special Ed & Art.

MAC DONALD, Gregory G; John Glenn HS; Westland, MI; ChrhWkr; CncrtBnd; HonRl; MrchBnd; NHS; Orch; Eastern Michigan Univ; Physics.

MAC DONALD, James S; Marshall Sr HS; Marshall, MN; 6/220 PresFrshCls; Band; Chr; CncrtBnd; MrchBnd; Bsktbl; CaptFtbl; Trk; U Of Mn Twin Cities; Psychology.

MAC DONALD, Jeffery J; Byron HS; Byron, MI; 7/71 Aud/Vis; HonRl; NHS; Swmmng; Trk; Wrstlng; CchngActv; Michigan State Univ; Accounting.

MAC DONALD, Karen R; Holy Redeemer HS; Detroit, MI; 32/184 CmntyWkr; HonRl; NHS; Business School; Professional.

MAC DONALD, Laurie E; Lake Orion HS; Lake Orion, MI; Chrs; HonRl; JrNHS; LbryAde; NHS; SchPl; TchrAde; Oakland Univ; Social Studies.

MACDONALD, Lori M; North HS; Sheboygan, WI; AFS; Band; CncrtBnd; HonRl; PepBnd; SchPl; StuCncl; YthFlsp; RptrSchPpr; SpnCl;.

MAC DONALD, Michael A; St Catherine HS; Sturtevant, WI; HonRl; NatlMeritSF; SpnCl; LetterBsbl; Bsktbl; LetterFtbl; CaptWrstlng; Chrldr; College; Electrical Eng.

MACE, Barbara A; Clarks Public HS; Clarks, NE; 2/25 SecSrCls; Band; Chrs; CncrtBnd; HonRl; MrchBnd; PepBnd; SchPl; StuCncl; TchrAde;.

MACE, Cynthia A; Greenwood HS; Springfield, MO; TrsJrCls; VPSrCls; ChmnDrmBgl; HonRl; StuCncl; SecFrCl; SecLatCl; SecSpnCl; LetterTennis; LetterChrldr;.

MACE, Jean M; University City HS; University City, MO; StuCncl; GAA; IMSpt; Special Ed Teacher.

MACEK, Kenneth R; St Andrew HS; Detroit, MI; 7/111 HonRl; IntrClCncl; JA; VPNHS; TreasStuCncl; StuGov; RptrYrbk; Bsbl; Bsktbl; Ftbl; Accounting Computer Programming.

MAC FARLANE, David S; Rich Central HS; Country Club Hills, IL; 5/409 AFS; Chr; ChrhWkr; HonRl; Mdrgl; NHS; NatlMeritSF; SctActv; StuCncl; VPGerCl; MthCl; SciCl; AmLegAwd; College; Biology.

MAC GIRR, Scott K; Spring Lake Jr Sr HS; Spring Lake, MI; Muskegor Bus Clg; Architecutral Drafting.

MACH, Linda M; Manitowoc Lutheran HS; Kewaunee, WI; 46/81 Chr; PpCl; Northeast Wis Tech; Retail Sales.

MACH, Tony W; East Charles Mix #102 HS; Wagner, SD; 28/66 ChrhWkr; CmntyWkr; HonRl; LbryAde; Bsktbl; Ftbl; College; Draftsman.

MACHA, Richard M; Washburn Rural HS; Topeka, KS; 22/199 Band; ChrhWkr; CncrtBnd; HonRl; MrchBnd; StuCncl; EdYrBk; FBLA; FrCl; Ftbl; College; Accounting.

MACHAL, Diane E; Fairmont Public HS; Fairmont, NE; 1/27 Band; ChrhWkr; CmntyWkr; HonRl; SchPl; StuCncl; RptrYrbk; RptrSchPpr; Trk; Chrldr; Univ Of Ne ; Home Ec Teach.

MACHAL, Godfrey P; Fairmont Public HS; Fairmont, NE; 6/28 Band; Chr; Chrs; ChrhWkr; CncrtBnd; HonRl; MrchBnd; NHS; PepBnd; PolWkr; Bsktbl; LetterFtbl; LetterTrk; Univ Of Nebraska; Computer Science.

MACHALA, Christine M; Taft HS; Chicago, IL; 145/790 HonRl; NatlMeritSchl; SchAde; StuCncl; SpnCl; PpCl; Univ Of Illinois; Sociology.

MACHAMER, Joan E; Grosse Pte South HS; Grosse Pte, MI; ChrhWkr; CmntyWkr; HonRl; NHS; RptrYrbk; College.

MACHART, Laurel G; Lankin Public HS; Lankin, ND; PresSophCls; ALAGirlsSt; HonRl; SchPl; StuCncl; RptrYrbk; EdSchPpr; Pres4-H; LetterChrldr; 4-HAwd; Und.

MACHATKA, Diane E; Downers Grove South HS; Downers Grove, IL; 43/830 Chr; Chrs; Mdrgl; NatlMeritCmnd; Augustana College.

MACHKOVITZ, Cheryl L; Beaver Dam Sr HS; Beaver Dam, WI; Chrl; Chrs; OffAde; PpCl; Trk; Chrldr; GAA; University; Marine Biology.

MACHOLAN, Daniel; Blair HS; Blair, NE; 5/133 VPJrCls; ALBoysSt; HonRl; NHS; NatlThespSoc; SchMus; FSA; Bsktbl; Univ Neb; Mechanical Engineer.

MACHONGA, John; Holy Cross; Chicago, IL; FrCl; Trk; CaptCchngActv;.

MACIAS, Mary P; Mound Westonka HS; Mound, MN; Chr; Chrs; ChrhWkr; HonRl; JA; YthFlsp; SpnCl; College; Veterinary Medicine.

MACIAS, Rebecca; St Joseph HS; Chicago, IL; Chr; HonRl; NHS; OffAde; SchMus; Loyola; Doctor.

MACIAS, William L; Marian HS; South Bend, IN; 13/120 HonRl; CaptWrstlng; Marquette Univ; Medicine.

MACIASZKIEWICZ, John F; Gordon Tech HS; Chicago, IL; 63/618 ChrhWkr; JA; SchAde; FrCl; MthCl; PpCl; LetterFtbl; De Paul Univ; Accounting.

MACIEJAUSKAS, Ramune R; Maria HS; Chicago, IL; Chrs; HonRl; HospAde; NHS; SctActv; Loyola Univ; Physician.

MACIEJEWSKI, Anne L; Maria HS; Chicago, IL; 31/301 HonRl; NHS; SctActv; StuCncl; PresLatCl; MthCl; Loyola Univ; B.s. In Nursing.

MACIEJEWSKI, Christine M; S Milwaukee Sr HS; South Milwaukee, WI; 11/432 Chr; HonRl; NHS; SchMus; StuCncl; TchrAde; RptrYrbk; FBLA; PpCl; Business School; Business Administration.

MACIEJEWSKI, Cynthia A; Loup City HS; Loup City, NE; 10/64 Chr; Chrs; ChrhWkr; HonRl; NHS; SchMus; FHA; College; Nursing.

MACIEJEWSKI, John T; Mendota Twp HS; Mendota, IL; 19/200 Band; CncrtBnd; HonRl; MrchBnd; PepBnd; SciCl; LetterTennis; Trk; Illinois Wesleyan Univ; Medicine.

MACIEJEWSKI, Linda M; Nazareth Academy; Cicero, IL; Chrs; HonRl; JrNHS; NHS; SchMus; StuGov; TchrAde; RptrYrbk; FrCl; Purdue University; Engineering.

MACIK, Dale D; Cosmos HS; Lake Lillian, MN; VPFrshCls; HonRl; 4-H; FFA; LetterBsbl; CaptBsktbl; LetterFtbl; Trk; 4-HAwd; Hutch Vocational; Farming & Mechanics.

MACIOLEK, Ardis A; Saint Mary Academy; New Boston, MI; 11/142 ChrhWkr; CmntyWkr; NHS; Yrbk; EdSchPpr; FrCl; SciCl; University Of Michigan; Astronomy.

MACIOLEK, Ardis A; Saint Mary Acad; New Boston, MI; ChrhWkr; HonRl; NHS; RptrYrbk; Yrbk; EdSchPpr; FrCl; PresSciCl; Bsbl; CchngActv; U Of Mi; Stronomy.

MACIOLEK, Cynthia; Frank Cody HS; Detroit, MI; 9/666 HonRl; NHS; Quill&Scroll; SchAde; RptrSchPpr; Mich Univ; Fashion Designer.

MACISAAC, Douglas; Waukegan Hs East; Waukegan, IL; 109/1004 HonRl; Bsbl; Bsktbl;.

MACK, Bobbi; Hastings HS; Hastings, NE; HonRl; LbryAde; Coll; Phy Ed.

MACK, Brenda K; Mounds View HS; New Brighton, MN; 141/640 ChrhWkr; JA; JrNHS; TchrAde; FrCl; PpCl; VPJAAwd; Bemidji State Univ; Business Admin.

MACK, Carol M; Irondale Sr HS; New Brighton, MN; Band; ChrhWkr; JA; JrNHS; MrchBnd; PepBnd; SpnCl; PpCl; IMSpt; College; Medicine.

MACK, Christie M; Forest View HS; Mt Prospect, IL; 17/635 HonRl; HospAde; NHS; StuCncl; SecStuGov; SecFrCl; Trk; GAA; Univ Of Iowa; Accountant.

MACK, Connie; Balta HS; Balta, ND; 1/10 TrsJrCls; Chr; Chrs; ChrhWkr; HonRl; LbryAde; SchMus; Chrldr; CchngActv; IMSpt; Minot State College; Medical.

MACK, Franklin; Union City HS; Union City, MI; HonRl; Bsktbl; College; Professional.

MACK, Gary; Sussex Hamilton HS; Men Falls, WI; HonRl; RptrYrbk; RptrSchPpr; IMSpt;.

MACK, James; Alleman Hs; Rock Island, IL; 10/250 CmntyWkr; HonRl; NHS; NatlMeritSF; FrCl; LetterBsbl; U Of Illinois; General Engineering.

MACK, James W; John M Harlan HS; Chicago, IL; 1/450 Band; HonRl; JrNHS; NHS; NatlMeritCmnd; RptrSchPpr; SptEdSchPpr; FrCl; MthCl; SciCl; Carleton; Chemistry.

MACK, John E; Beatrice Sr HS; Beatrice, NE; 66/219 ALBoysSt; IntrClCncl; LetterBsktbl; LetterFtbl; College; Professional.

MACK, Julie M; Harvey HS; Harvey, ND; SecFrshCls; ALAGirlsSt; Chr; Chrs; ChrhWkr; CmntyWkr; HonRl; LbryAde; SchMus; SchPl; StuGov; GAA; College; Nurse.

MACK, Kiernan A; Arlington HS; Arlington Hts, IL; HonRl; VPNHS; TchrAde; CaptSwmmng;.

MACK, Larry G; Washington HS; South Bend, IN; 20/340 HonRl; NHS; Trk; KiwanAwd; Univ Of In; Electronics.

MACK, Mark A; Libertyville HS; Lake Forest, IL; 8/431 ALBoysSt; HonRl; NHS; Univ Of Ill; Electrical Engineering.

MACK, Michael G; Herculaneum HS; Pevely, MO; 8/99 PresSrCls; ALBoysSt; HonRl; JA; StuCncl; LetterBsktbl; LetterFtbl; Jefferson Coll; Engr Or Acct.

MACK, Shirley A; Karlsruhe Public HS; Karsruhe, ND; SecJrCls; Band; HonRl; SchPl; StuCncl; Yrbk; 4-H; LetterBsktbl; LetterTrk; LetterChrldr; Trade Sch; Vocation.

MACKAY, James R; Lincolnwood HS; Raymond, IL; VPSophCls; ChrhWkr; StuCncl; FFA; LetterBsktbl; College; Agriculture.

MACKE, Jerri L; Hagerstown Jr Sr HS; Hagerstown, IN; 17/146 HstSrCls; HonRl; LbryAde; NHS; 4-H; FHA; FrCl; PpCl; LetterGlf; Business School.

MACKE, Joseph E; Mater Dei HS; Evansville, IN; 8/172 HonRl; JrNHS; NHS; NatlMeritCmnd; StuCncl; StuGov; SciCl; Bsbl; Bsktbl; College; Engineer.

MACKEL, Cynthia E; Alton Sr HS; Godfrey, IL; 93/856 Band; HonRl; MrchBnd; NHS; Orch; Yrbk; Southern Illinois U; Photography.

MACKENBURG, Mary D; Hill Murray HS; St Paul, MN; Chr; Chrl; Chrs; HonRl; OffAde; SchMus; SchPl; SctActv; FrCl; Col; Nursing.

MACKENTHUN, Cynthia L; Glencoe HS; Glencoe, MN; 4/141 SecSophCls; HonRl; StuCncl; RptrYrbk; RptrSchPpr; FHA; SciCl; Chrldr; GAA; St Cloud St Col; History.

MACKENZIE, Gerald; Onekama HS; Kaleva, MI; Band; HonRl; SctActv; Bsktbl; LetterFtbl; IMSpt; Univ; Bus Admin.

MACKENZIE, Mark L; Orangeville HS; Dakota, IL; ChrhWkr; PpCl; LetterBsbl; LetterBsktbl; LetterFtbl; LetterTrk; College; Curriculum.

MACKEVICH, Jeffrey B; New Trier East HS; Winnetka, IL; Band; CncrtBnd; HonRl; Orch; SchMus; LetterTennis; College; Business.

MACKEY, Barbara A; Memorial HS; Elkhart, IN; 39/441 HonRl; NHS; Univ Of Notre Dame; Engineering.

MACKEY, Chris A; Central Usd462 HS; Burden, KS; PresFrshCls; PresSophCls; TrsJrCls; ChrhWkr; HonRl; SchPl; 4-H; FFA; Bsbl; Ftbl;.

MACKEY, Coleen; Capac HS; Capac, MI; 2/108 CncrtBnd; HonRl; NHS; StuCncl; FrCl; Chrldr; GAA; 4-HAwd; Coll; Professional.

MAC KEY, Deborah A; Marshfield HS; Marshfield, MO; HstFrshCls; ChrhWkr; HonRl; SchAde; SchPl; StuCncl; TchrAde; FDA; FNA; GAA; Asbury Clg; Medicine.

MACKEY, Jeffrey L; Middleton HS; Middleton, WI; Band; CncrtBnd; HonRl; MrchBnd; 4-H; 4-HAwd; Univ Of Wi; Eng.

MACKEY, Milon L; Bancroft HS; Bancroft, NE; 5/32 HonRl; NatlMeritSF; PresSciCl; College; Mathematics.

MACKEY, Valerie; United Community HS; Boone, IA; 1/40 Band; HonRl; NHS; PepBnd; SchPl; StuCncl; EdSchPpr; 4-H; Bsbl; Univ Of Northern Iowa; Math.

MACKEY, William C; Seymour HS; Seymour, IN; 16/245 HonRl; NatlMeritCmnd; YthFlsp; SpnCl; PpCl; LetterBsbl; LetterSwmmng; IMSpt; Indiana Univ; Business.

MACKH, Eugenia; Larkin Hs; Elgin, IL; 28#48#56 Orch; SctActv; EdSchPpr; University; Professional.

MACKIE, Charles E; New Trier East HS; Wilmette, IL; Chrs; Quill&Scroll; SchMus; SchPpr; Socr;.

MACKIN, Mary B; St Josephs HS; South Bend, IN; Band; CncrtBnd; HonRl; MrchBnd; PepBnd; SchMus; RptrYrbk; Yrbk; Trk; IMSpt; College; Psychology.

MACKINTOSH, David; Hyannis HS; Whitman, NE; CncrtBnd; HonRl; MrchBnd; NHS; PepBnd; 4-H; 4-HAwd; College; Agriculture.

MACKINTOSH, Rebecca S; Hyannis HS; Whitman, NE; ChrhWkr; LbryAde; Yrbk; Sec4-H; FHA; PpCl; LetterBsktbl; LetterTrk; 4-HAwd; Lincoln School; Legal Secretary.

MAC KINTOSH, Rebecca S; Hyannis HS; Whitman, NE; ChrhWkr; LbryAde; RptrYrbk; 4-H; FBLA; FHA; PpCl; LetterBsktbl; LetterTrk; 4-HAwd; Lincoln School Of Comm; Legal Secretary.

MACKIW, Patti A; Maria HS; Chicago, IL; 31/335 Chrl; HonRl; HospAde; NHS; StuCncl; RptrSchPpr; EdSchPpr; GAA; College; Journalism.

MACKLAND, Thomas W; Thomas Jefferson HS; Crescent, IA; ALBoysSt; ChrhWkr; HonRl; NHS; EdSchPpr; 4-H; Bsktbl; LetterFtbl; LetterTrk; Col; Mathematics Major.

MACKLEY, Marie A; South Iron HS; Annapolis, MO; TrsJrCls; Chrs; HonRl; Yrbk; 4-H; FHA; PpCl; Clge; Vocation.

MACKMILLER, David; Hudson HS; Hudson, WI; Trk;.

MACKOWIAK, Gail A; Schlarman HS; Westville, IL; 11/79 CncrtBnd; HonRl; PepBnd; RptrYrbk; RptrSchPpr; FrCl; Trk; Chrldr;.

MAC LAREN, Roger A; Belding HS; Belding, MI; 13/150 ChrhWkr; HonRl; Ftbl; Coll; Voc.

MAC LENNAN, Mark A; Muscatine HS; Muscatine, IA; PresSrCls; ALBoysSt; StuCncl; RptrSchPpr; Univ Of Iowa; Optometrist.

MAC MILLAN, Carrie J; Grosse Pointe North HS; Grosse Pt Woods, MI; ChrhWkr; HonRl; NHS; FrCl; College; Environmental Science.

MAC MILLAN, Nicholas J; Memorial HS; Evansville, IN; VPSrCls; HonRl; HospAde; PolWkr; StuCncl; TchrAde; Ftbl; Trk; Univ; Doctor.

MAC MURRAY, Margery P; Tawas Area HS; East Tawas, MI; Band; CAP; HonRl; HospAde; LitMag; NHS; NatlMeritSF; RedCrAde; SchPl; Yrbk; Coll; Med Tech.

MAC NAIR, Rachel M; Paseo HS; Kansas City, MO; 1/295 ChrhWkr; CmntyWkr; HonRl; LbryAde; NatlMeritCmnd; PolWkr; SchPl; SpnCl; SciCl; Univ Of Mo; Doctor.

MACOMBER, Scott A; Troy HS; Troy, MI; 4/560 JrNHS; NatlMeritCmnd; CaptSwmmng; Univ Of Michigan; Engineering.

MACON, Gwendolyn S; Junction City Sr HS; Junction City, KS; 53/335 DrlTm; HonRl; LbryAde; TchrAde; Twrl; SpnCl; PpCl; Bsktbl; Tennis; LetterTrk; IMSpt; PPFtbl; PresAwd; Wichita State Univ; Secretarial Field.

MAC QUEEN, Brian W; West HS; Iowa City, IA; PresFrshCls; VPJrCls; ALBoysSt; HonRl; PresNatlThespSoc; PolWkr; SchMus; SchPl; LetterFtbl; LetterTrk; Univ; Soc Sci.

MACUGA, Mary A; Our Lady Of The Lakes HS; Prayton Plains, MI; HonRl; HospAde; LbryAde; NHS; SchAde; TchrAde; LetterBsbl; Patricia Stevens College; Airline Stew.

MACUR, Mark J; Notre Dame Boys HS; Niles, IL; 21/266 HonRl; RptrSchPpr; SchPpr; SpnCl; De Paul Univ; Legal.

MACY, Marla; Winchester Community HS; Winchester, IN; 8/153 HonRl; NHS; TchrAde; RptrYrbk; 4-H; FBLA; FHA; FTA; FrCl; Chrldr; Ind St East; Business.

MADAJ, Mary M; Mount Assisi Acad; Hickory Hills, IL; PresFrshCls; ChrhWkr; HonRl; NHS; StuCncl; RptrYrbk; Loyola U Of Chicago; Chemistry.

MADALINSKI, Sheila; Allegan Senior HS; Pullman, MI; Chr; ChrhWkr; HonRl; OffAde; SpnCl; Univ; Social Work.

MADAY, David R; Standish Sterling Central HS; Sterling, MI; 13/156 HonRl; NatlFornLg; SchPl; TchrAde; 4-H; 4-HAwd; Mi State Univ; Fashion Design.

MADAY, Kathy; Elizabeth Seton Hs; Dolton, IL; Chrl; HonRl; NHS; NatlMeritCmnd; StuCncl; FSA; LatCl; MthCl; Purdue U; Physics.

MADDALENA, Laura; Lumen Christi HS; Jackson, MI; 10/222 Chrs; CmntyWkr; HonRl; LitMag; NHS; SchAde; LatCl; PpCl; IMSpt; OptClAwd; Univ Of Detroit; Accounting.

MADDAUS, David E; St Thomas Academy; Minneapolis, MN; PresFrshCls; PresJrCls; PresSrCls; DrlTm; ROTC; SchPl; StuCncl; Yrbk; RptrSchPpr; LetterFtbl; LetterTrk; IMSpt; Univ Of Minnesota; Math.

MADDEN, Brenda S; Manistee Catholic Central HS; Manister, MI; 13/76 SecSrCls; Band; CncrtBnd; HonRl; MrchBnd; PepBnd; GAA; IMSpt; Busi School; Accounting.

MADDEN, Elizabeth J; Junior Sentral HS; Armstrong, IA; Band; Chr; Chrs; ChrhWkr; CncrtBnd; HonRl; MrchBnd; PepBnd; SchMus; SchPl; StuCncl; YthFlsp; SptEdYrbk; College; Nursing.

MADDEN, James J; Benet Academy; Naperville, IL; NatlMeritCmnd; LetterFtbl; LetterTrk; U Of I; Engineering.

MADDEN, Jeanne; Our Lady Of Grace HS; Indianapolis, IN; 16/54 VPJrCls; Chrs; ChrhWkr; CmntyWkr; HonRl; HospAde; SchMus; RptrYrbk; Swmmng; Coll; Rn Nurse.

MADDEN, Katherine T; Freeport Sr HS; Freeport, IL; 19/503 HonRl; MrchBnd; Orch; SchMus; SchPl; TchrAde; SpnCl; MthCl; PpCl; College; Science.

MADDEN, Margaret; Western HS; Kokomo, IN; 6/153 Band; Chr; HonRl; MrchBnd; NHS; NatlMeritSF; SpnCl; Swmmng; Trk; Pordue Univ; Special Education.

MADDEN, Mark A; Hemlock HS; Hemlock, MI; 3/170 HonRl; JrNHS; LbryAde; NHS; SchPl; 4-H; FrCl; LetterBsbl; LetterBsktbl; LetterFtbl; Coll; Cpa.

MADDEN, Maureen T; Thornwood HS; South Holland, IL; HonRl; NHS; StuCncl; FrCl; MthCl; SciCl; Univ Of Il; Deaf Ed.

MADDEN, Trina J; Airport HS; S Rockwood, MI; ALAGirlsSt; HonRl; NHS; StuCncl; RptrYrbk; EdYrBk; RptrSchPpr; SchPpr; SpnCl; Trk; E Michigan Univ; Journalism.

MADDIGAN, Mary; Oelwein Community HS; Oelwein, IA; 80/183 AFS; CmntyWkr; HonRl; PolWkr; StuGov; UNYO; RptrSchPpr; PpCl; College; Law.

MADDOCK, Kurt A; North Knox HS; Bickwell, IN; LetterFtbl; LetterTrk; Purdue Univ; Engineering.

MADDOCK, Linda J; Grant Community HS; Ingleside, IL; 9/200 Band; ChrhWkr; CncrtBnd; HonRl; LbryAde; MrchBnd; NHS; SchMus; FNA; GAA; N Illinois Univ; Nursing.

MADDOCK, Rick J; Ogeman Heights HS; W Branch, MI; 3/150 HonRl; NHS; NatlMeritCmnd; TchrAde; EdSchPpr; SptEdSchPpr; LetterBsbl; Bsktbl; Glf; AmLegAwd; U Of Mi; Journalism.

MADDOCK, Rick J; Ogeman Hts HS; West Branch, MI; HonRl; NHS; TchrAde; RptrSchPpr; EdSchPpr; SptEdSchPpr; LetterBsbl; LetterBsktbl; CchngActv; Univ Of Michigan; Journalism.

MADDOX, Dee E; Washington Comm HS; Washington, IL; 82/345 AFS; TreasChr; Chrs; CaptDrlTm; SchMus; FrCl; PpCl; Col; Art.

MADDOX, Gregory R; Pontiac Northern HS; Pontiac, MI; 165/409 ChrhWkr; HonRl; TchrAde; YthFlsp; SptEdSchPpr; Ftbl; Trk; Wrstlng; Carthage College; Reverend.

MADDOX, Marilee S; Isle HS; Isle, MN; VPSrCls; Band; Chr; PepBnd; SchPl; RptrYrbk; Yrbk; PpCl; SciCl; Chrldr; College; Music.

MADDOX, Michael; South Shelby HS; Shelbina, MO; NatlMeritCmnd; SchPl; StuCncl; SciCl; Wrstlng; IMSpt; EldAwd; College; Pre Med.

MADDOX, Rebecca J; Palestine HS; Palestine, IL; 6/40 Band; Chrs; CncrtBnd; HonRl; MrchBnd; PepBnd; SchMus; StuCncl; 4-H; VPGAA; Jr College.

MADEJ, Darlene L; Maria HS; Chicago, IL; 26/302 HonRl; HospAde; NHS; SctActv; TreasStuCncl; SpnCl; Western Illinois Univ; Accounting.

MADEJA, David E; Oak Lawn Comm HS; Oak Lawn, IL; 77/856 HonRl; TchrAde; SptEdSchPpr; KeyCl; Bsktbl; Tennis; College; Professional.

MADEJA, Diane M; Lemont Twsp HS; Lemont, IL; 1/148 Band; CncrtBnd; DrmMjrt; MrchBnd; NatlFornLg; TreasNHS; PresStuCncl; SptEdSchPpr; SecFTA; PresSpnCl; U Of Il; Mathematics.

MADEMANN, Paul H; Maine West HS; Des Plaines, IL; NHS; Trk; Purdue; Eng.

MADER, Bonnie J; Forest Lake HS; Wyoming, MN; Chr; HonRl; StuCncl; RptrYrbk; RptrSchPpr; Tennis; Coll ; Med.

MADER, David J; Appleton West HS; Appleton, WI; VPFrshCls; Band; CmntyWkr; StuGov; RptrSchPpr; KeyCl; Bsbl; LetterFtbl; LetterSwmmng; IMSpt; College; Mathematics.

MADER, Gregory G; Holy Trinity HS; Mound, MN; 1/49 PresFrshCls; PresSophCls; ChrhWkr; CmntyWkr; HonRl; ModUN; PolWkr; StuCncl; RptrYrbk; Glf; Univ Of Min ;broadcastin.

MADETZKE, Julie; Elmore Public HS; Elmore, MN; Band; ChrhWkr; CncrtBnd; HonRl; LbryAde; Mdrgl; SchPl; Yrbk; FHA; GerCl; Vocation.

MADICK, Mary A; St Pius X HS; Kansas City, MO; 10/136 ALAGirlsSt; Chrs; HonRl; NHS; OffAde; PolWkr; SchMus; SchPl; Creighton Univ; Journalism.

MADIGAN, Denise R; Wausau West HS; Wausau, WI; 1/450 SecTrsSrCls; ALAGirlsSt; Band; Chr; NatlMeritCmnd; Orch; AmLegAwd; DARAwd; EldAwd; Northwestern Univ; Law.

MADIGAN, Scott H; Mankato West HS; Mankato, MN; PresFrshCls; TrsJrCls; HonRl; StuCncl; StuGov; Ftbl; Trk; Wrstlng; CchngActv; IMSpt; Clge; Pro.

MADILL, Karen R; Delta HS; Muncie, IN; 36/240 Band; Chr; Chrs; ChrhWkr; CncrtBnd; HonRl; HospAde; MrchBnd; PepBnd; SchMus; StuCncl; YthFlsp; 4-H; FHA; Purdue Univ; Retail Mdse.

MADISON, Gary M; Pine City HS; Minneapolis, MN; PresAFS; Band; Chr; Chrl; Chrs; ChrhWkr; CncrtBnd; HonRl; MrchBnd; Tennis; Cincinnati Consrvatory Of Music; Actor.

MADISON, Michael J; Austin Catholic Prep; Grosse Pt Park, MI; 46/115 Wayne State Univ; Business.

MADISON, Pamela S; Carthage Public HS; Carthage, SD; ALAGirlsSt; Band; Chrs; ChrhWkr; HonRl; PepBnd; RptrYrbk; Yrbk; PpCl; GAA; Univ Of Sd; Psychology.

MADISON, Warren L; So Harrison HS; Bethany, MO; Chr; ChrhWkr; CmntyWkr; PolWkr; 4-H; FFA; Bsbl; Bsktbl; Ftbl; IMSpt; College; Agriculture.

MADISON, William H; John Adams HS; S Bend, IN; 126/449 LetterBsbl; In Univ Of S Bend; Denistry Or Accounting.

MADRID, Joseph P; St Marys HS; Independence, MO; ChrhWkr; HonRl; ModUN; SchMus; RptrYrbk; EdYrBk; LatCl; LetterFtbl; LetterTrk; RotaryAwd; Cmsu; Business & Industrial Relations.

MADRID, Louis A; St Marys HS; Independence, MO; 41/120 TrsJrCls; ALBoysSt; HonRl; SchMus; Sdlty; StuCncl; FrCl; Bsktbl; LetterFtbl; Trk; Coll; Bus Admin.

MADSEN, Cindy J; Graceville Public HS; Graceville, MN; ALBoysSt; Chrs; HonRl; SchPl; Yrbk; SchPpr; SecFHA; Chrldr; PPFtbl; AmLegAwd; Vo Tech Sch; Voc.

MADSEN, Daven L; Lincoln Northeast HS; Lincoln, NE; ALBoysSt; Chr; HonRl; Mdrgl; SchMus; SctActv; FFA; LetterFtbl; Swmmng; LetterTrk; College; Music.

MADSEN, Kevin D; Superior HS; Superior, NE; 5/80 PresSophCls; HonRl; NHS; Quill&Scroll; StuCncl; EdSchPpr; PresKeyCl; LetterBsktbl; LetterFtbl; LetterTrk; Kearney St Col Neb; Dentistry.

MADSEN, Lana J; Kaneland HS; Elburn, IL; 8/155 HonRl; JrNHS; NHS; StuCncl; FrCl; PpCl; Trk; Northern Illinois Univ; Biology.

MADSEN, Laurie A; Thornton Fractional North HS; Calumet City, IL; Chrl; Chrs; ChrhWkr; HonRl; JrNHS; NatlFornLg; NHS; SchMus; SchPl; Little Co Of Mary Sch; Nurse.

MADSEN, Linda M; L C Mohr HS; South Haven, MI; HonRl; TchrAde; 4-H; PpCl; Tennis; Trk; 4-HAwd; College; Professional.

MADSEN, Melvin O; Nevis HS; Nevis, MN; Band; Chr; CncrtBnd; HonRl; MrchBnd; PepBnd; StuCncl; Yrbk; SchPpr; Bsbl;.

MADSEN, Robert B; Charles City Sr HS; Charles City, IA; 51/250 Band; CncrtBnd; HonRl; MrchBnd; Orch; PepBnd; LetterFtbl; Univ Of Iowa; Computer Science.

MADSON, Arthur L; Lk Orion HS; Lk Orion, MI; 25/300 ALBoysSt; HonRl; NHS; PolWkr; StuGov; TchrAde; 4-H; LetterBsktbl; LetterTennis; AmLegAwd; 4-HAwd; Lawrence Inst; Architecture.

MADSON, George M; Hudson Sr HS; Hudson, WI; 42/226 PresJrCls; HonRl; SchPl; SctActv; StuGov; RptrSchPpr; SptEdSchPpr; CaptBsbl; CaptBsktbl; Ftbl; U S Air Force Academy; Engineering.

MADZIARCZYK, Michele; Sacred Heart Of Mary HS; Mt Prospect, IL; 14/139 Chrs; CmntyWkr; HonRl; NHS; SchPl; TchrAde; RptrSchPpr; Miami U; Bus Admin.

MAEDA, Joan M; Frank B Kellogg HS; St Paul, MN; 5/559 PresBand; ChrhWkr; MrchBnd; NatlFornLg; NHS; NatlMeritSF; Orch; PepBnd; SctActv; StuCncl; SchPpr; Bethel College; Sociology.

MAEDKE, Anne K; Algoma HS; Algoma, WI; SecFrshCls; VPJrCls; Band; Chr; CncrtBnd; HonRl; JrNHS; MrchBnd; PepBnd; SchMus; SchPl; Bsktbl; LetterTrk; GAA; College; Nurse.

MAEDKE, Daniel J; Coleman HS; Coleman, WI; PresSophCls; HonRl; FFA; LetterBsktbl; LetterFtbl; LetterTrk; Business; Vocation.

MAEL, Paula A; Almond HS; Almond, WI; 1/33 TrsSrCls; Band; Chrs; HonRl; NHS; EdYrBk; EdSchPpr; Chrldr; DARAwd; EldAwd; Coll; Med Tech.

MAENZA, Joseph; St Joseph HS; Hillside, IL; HonRl; ModUN; NHS; PolWkr; StuCncl; StuGov; EdYrBk; GerCl; MthCl; Univ Of Illinois; Law.

MAERTENS, Theresa A; Cooperstown HS; Cooperstown, ND; 10/36 HonRl; SchPl; 4-H; IMSpt; 4-HAwd; PresAwd; University; Entomologist.

MAERZ, Brenda L; Stoughton HS; Stoughton, WI; 2/243 Band; CncrtBnd; JrNHS; NHS; StuCncl; TchrAde; 4-H; GerCl; MthCl; GAA; Coll; Fashion.

MAESCHEN, David M; Mitchell HS; Mitchell, SD; 7/304 JrNHS; NatlMeritSF; FrCl; SciCl; KiwanAwd; Univ; Astro Physics.

MAESTRANZI, Loretta; Notre Dame HS; Niles, IL; 21/296 Chrl; HonRl; NHS; SchMus; StuCncl; Univ; Biology Pharmacy.

MAETZOLD, Jane C; Mayer Lutheran HS; Mayer, MN; Band; Chr; ChrhWkr; HonRl; NHS; YthFlsp; PpCl; Trk; College; Education.

MAEVERS, Curtis W; Campus HS; Cape Gir, MO; VPFrshCls; VPJrCls; PpCl; IMSpt; Se Mo St.

MAGALSKY, Teresa L; West HS; Waterloo, IA; Band; Chrs; CncrtBnd; HonRl; MrchBnd; RedCrAde; StuCncl; FTA; FrCl; Swmmng; Iowa St Univ; Teacher.

MAGANDY, Barbara E; North Shore HS; Ryder, ND; 2/27 ALAGirlsSt; CmntyWkr; HonRl; StuGov; RptrYrbk; RptrSchPpr; 4-H; BauchLmbAwd; TIMEAwd; VoiceDemAwd; Clge; Pro.

MAGBY, Carol L; Skyline HS; Urbana, MO; 11/50 HonRl; StuCncl; 4-H; FTA; LetterBsbl; LetterBsktbl; CchngActv; Southwest Baptist College; Physical Educ.

MAGDEN, Donna L; So Soo City Comm HS; South Sioux City, NE; AFS; Chr; ChrhWkr; HonRl; JrNHS; FHA; PpCl; Community Col; Med Lab Tech.

MAGDZIARZ, Rosalie M; Willow River HS; Sutrgeon Lake, MN; 3/40 SecFrshCls; SecSophCls; SecJrCls; HonRl; NHS; SchPl; TreasPpCl; LetterTrk; LetterChrldr; GAA; College; Professional.

MAGEDANZ, Gary L; Grant Deuel HS; Revillo, SD; TrsFrshCls; TrsSophCls; TrsJrCls; Chrs; HonRl; 4-H; FFA; LetterBsktbl; LetterTrk; Col; Major Study.

MAGEE, Beverly M; Porta HS; Petersburg, IL; 1/100 TrsSrCls; Chr; HonRl; NHS; NatlMeritCmnd; YthFlsp; EdYrBk; RptrSchPpr; GAA; IMSpt; Univ Wi; Mat.

MAGEE, John A; Round Lake HS; Round Lake, IL; 34/184 PresJrCls; CmntyWkr; JCC; PolWkr; ROTC; SctActv; StuGov; Bsbl; Bsktbl; Ftbl; U Of Il; Accountant.

MAGEE, Mark J; Marist HS; South Holland, IL; 47/393 HonRl; SpnCl; Glf; IMSpt; Univ; Business.

MAGEE, Nancy G; Mc Cook Sr HS; Mc Cook, NE; 8/160 Chr; Chrs; HonRl; NHS; SchMus; SchPl; 4-H; MthCl; College; Commercial Or Indsutral Art.

MAGEE, Wanda; Stanley County HS; Ft Pierce, SD; Chrs; HonRl; JrNHS; LbryAde; Chrldr;.

MAGENNIS, Mark P; Saint Edmond HS; Fort Dodge, IA; PresJrCls; StuCncl; RptrYrbk; Yrbk; SchPpr; FrCl; LetterBsktbl; CaptTrk; CaptWrstlng; Loras U; Psychology.

MAGGARD, Jennifer L; Benton HS; Benton, IL; ChrhWkr; CmntyWkr; NatlMeritSchl; PolWkr; Quill&Scroll; SchMus; StuCncl; RptrSchPpr; EdSchPpr; CivCl; Glf; East Il Univ; Journalism.

MAGGARD, Marshal G; United Township HS; Silvis, IL; 171/625 HonRl; Ftbl; Wrstlng; College; Medicine.

MAGGARD, Patrick J; Southwest HS; Kansas City, MO; 130/500 Bsktbl; Ftbl; Univ Of Mo; Engineering.

MAGILL, Daniel L; Blair HS; Blair, NE; HonRl; StuGov; 4-H; FFA; 4-HAwd; Farming.

MAGILL, Robert; Prospect Hs; Mt Prospect, IL; 62/611 Chr; ChrhWkr; HonRl; NHS; SchMus; SctActv; Tennis; College; Music.

MAGILL, Robert M; Holdrege HS; Holdrege, NE; SecJrCls; Band; Chrs; ChrhWkr; CncrtBnd; HonRl; MrchBnd; PepBnd; SchMus; StuCncl; College; Professional.

MAGINNIS, Steven G; Sault Area HS; Sault Ste Marie, MI; 4/412 ChrhWkr; HonRl; LitMag; PolWkr; TchrAde; College; Medicine.

MAGINOT, Thomas J; Munster HS; Munster, IN; 82/435 HonRl; LetterBsbl; St Louis University; Medicine.

MAGNAN, John A; Pontiac Catholic HS; Pontiac, MI; TrsSophCls; TrsJrCls; Chrs; HonRl; StuCncl; SptEdSchPpr; Eastern Mi Univ; Acctg.

MAGNER, Paula J; Taylors Falls HS; Shafer, MN; 2/27 TrsJrCls; TrsSrCls; Band; HonRl; NatlMeritSchl; SchPl; RptrYrbk; Yrbk; FHA; GAA; Coll; Teacher.

MAGNER, Richard D; Jennings County HS; North Vernon, IN; Band; ChrhWkr; CncrtBnd; MrchBnd; PepBnd; YthFlsp; SecFTA; SpnCl; Business School; Professional.

MAGNUSON, Douglas K; Mounds View HS; New Brighton, MN; 7/673 Chr; Chrs; ChrhWkr; HonRl; JrNHS; Mdrgl; NatlFornLg; NHS; NatlMeritSF; Bsbl; Tennis; Bethel College.

MAGNUSON, Gae; Niagara HS; Niagara, WI; DrlTm; DrmMjrt; OffAde; TchrAde; Twrl; SchPpr; PpCl; IMSpt; Nwti Green Bay Wi; Data Proc.

MAGNUSON, Janet M; Hill Murray HS; St Paul, MN; HonRl; NHS; RptrSchPpr; Socr; Chrldr; St Cloud St Col; Psychology.

MAGNUSON, Scott W; Luther HS; Chicago, IL; 32/265 HonRl; NHS; SchAde; TchrAde; Yrbk; SchPpr; LetterWrstlng; IMSpt; Southern Ill U; Photography.

MAGNUSON, Steve L; La Ville HS; Plymouth, IN; ALBoysSt; CmntyWkr; LbryAde; ROTC; TchrAde; FrCl; Bsbl; Bsktbl; Tennis; IMSpt; Policeman.

MAGNUSSON, Carol I; Luther South HS; Chicago, IL; 18/212 ChrhWkr; CmntyWkr; HonRl; SchMus; SchPl; GAA; Med Sch; Reg Nurse.

MAGNUSSON, Marilyn S; Udall HS; Udall, KS; 1/22 HonRl; PresStuCncl; YthFlsp; LetterBsktbl; Trk; Chrldr; BttyCrckrAwd; DanFAwd; 4-HAwd; College; Social Work.

MAGNUSSON, Mary C; David H Hickman HS; Columbia, MO; 16/569 CmntyWkr; HonRl; LbryAde; NHS; SecQuill&Scroll; StuGov; TchrAde; SptEdSchPpr; SpnCl; Bsbl; Bsktbl; Swmmng; Tennis; Univ Of Missouri; Physical Educ.

MAGNUSSON, Ronald M; Argyle HS; Argyle, MN; 2/31 PresFrshCls; PresSophCls; PresSrCls; ALBoysSt; SchPl; PresStuCncl; Yrbk; Bsbl; LetterBsktbl; College; Accounting.

MAGOUIRK, Sheila; Holcomb HS; Holcomb, MO; 8/36 SecTrsSophCls; PresJrCls; VPSrCls; ChrhWkr; HonRl; SchPl; TchrAde; FHA; PpCl; IMSpt; College; Medical Secretary.

MAGRUDER, Robert D; Waynesville Senior HS; Waynesville, MO; Band; CncrtBnd; HonRl; JrNHS; MrchBnd; NHS; PepBnd; RptrYrbk; KeyCl; College; Research.

MAGSTADT, Tod; Rapid City Stevens HS; Rapid City, SD; ALBoysSt; HonRl; NatlFornLg; StuGov; Yrbk; Bsbl; Sd School Of Mines; Engineering.

MAGUIRE, Colleen A; Carmel Girls HS; Mundelein, IL; 21/183 PresFrshCls; Chrs; CmntyWkr; HonRl; NHS; PolWkr; SchMus; VPFrshCls; StuCncl; GAA; Political Science.

MAGUIRE, Sheilah C; Downers Grove South HS; Downers Grove, IL; Chr; Chrs; ChrhWkr; HonRl; SctActv; University; Political Science.

MAGYARI, Patricia A; Howell HS; Howell, MI; 3/372 Chr; HonRl; MrchBnd; SchMus; VP4-H; Chrldr; Albion College; Journalism.

MAHAFFEY, Gaila A; University HS; Warrensburg, MO; PresJrCls; Chrs; HonRl; SchMus; StuCncl; Yrbk; SchPpr; SpnCl; Central Mo State Univ; Special Ed.

MAHALAK, Catherine M; O L Of Mt Carmel HS; Wyandotte, MI; 5/55 PresJrCls; Chr; HonRl; NHS; SchMus; SchPl; PresStuCncl; Yrbk; RptrSchPpr; PpCl; Michigan St U; Accounting.

MAHALKO, William J; Riverside Brookfield HS; N Riverside, IL; PresRusCl; U Of Ill; Architecture.

MAHAN, Charlotte E; Ofallon HS; Ofallon, IL; Band; Chr; Chrl; Chrs; CmntyWkr; HonRl; Mdrgl; OffAde; SchMus; SpnCl; Univ; Music.

MAHAN, Michael M; Heelan HS; Sioux City, IA; 29/260 HonRl; NHS; Ftbl; Trk; Univ Of South Dakota; Professional.

MAHANNAH, William R; Cuba HS; Cuba, IL; ChrhWkr; HonRl; NHS; YthFlsp; LatCl; LetterBsbl; LetterFtbl; U Of Ia; Pre Medicine.

MAHANY, Barbara A; Deerfield HS; Deerfield, IL; ChrhWkr; CmntyWkr; HonRl; HospAde; StuCncl; StuGov; RptrSchPpr; PpCl; Marquette Univ; Nursing.

MAHAR, Dawn S; Cavalier Public HS; Cavalier, ND; Chr; Chrs; ChrhWkr; CmntyWkr; DrlTm; HonRl; OffAde; SchPl; 4-H; Ftbl; 4-HAwd; GodCntryAwd; College.

MAHAR, Lisa M; Oscoda Area HS; Oscoda, MI; 17/222 HonRl; NHS; NatlMeritSF; StuCncl; TchrAde; YthFlsp; PresSwmmng; Chrldr; GAA; Olivet Coll; Bus.

MAHER, Brian B; Howell Sr HS; Howell, MI; 112/500 HonRl; LetterWrstlng; College; Natual Science.

MAHER, Daniel L; Griffin HS; Springfield, IL; HonRl; StuCncl; RptrSchPpr; LetterBsktbl; LetterFtbl; Trk;.

MAHER, Debra M; Forest View HS; Mt Prospect, IL; 36/645 HonRl; HospAde; NHS; FNA; GAA; University Of Illinois; Medicine.

MAHER, Douglas E; Stanton Comm HS; Stanton, IA; VPSophCls; PresJrCls; Chr; HonRl; MrchBnd; StuCncl; FFA; LetterBsbl; CaptBsktbl; CaptFtbl; LetterTrk; 4-HAwd;.

MAHER, Jeffrey A; West Vigo HS; W Terre Haute, IN; ChrhWkr; HonRl; TchrAde; 4-H; TreasFTA; KeyCl; Ftbl; LetterSwmmng; Tennis; 4-HAwd; Indiana State; Cpa.

MAHER, Joseph M; Holy Redeemer HS; Detroit, MI; 8/189 PresSrCls; ChrhWkr; CmntyWkr; HonRl; JA; NHS; PolWkr; Teen; RptrYrbk; SpnCl; Harvard Univ; Lawyer/politician.

MAHER, Judy; Merrill HS; Brant, MI; HonRl; LbryAde; IMSpt; Business School; Vocational.

MAHER, Mary E; Brimfield HS; Brimfield, IL; ChrhWkr; HonRl; 4-H; FHA; SpnCl; PpCl; 4-HAwd; Nursin School; Rn Nurse.

MAHER, Mary K; Southeast HS; Springfield, IL; 15/463 SecSrCls; ChrhWkr; College; Law.

MAHER, Mary L; Ladywood HS; Livonia, MI; Chr; HonRl; NHS; Orch; PolWkr; SchMus; SecStuCncl; TchrAde; FBLA; Tennis; Ferris State Col; Court Reporter.

MAHER, Michael J; Marquette HS; Alton, IL; 48/120 SchPl; SptEdYrbk; LatCl; CaptBsbl; LetterFtbl; LetterFtbl; IMSpt; College; Professional.

MAHER, William M; St Pius X HS; Imperial, MO; 16/101 Chrl; HonRl; StuCncl; Yrbk; LetterBsktbl; LetterFtbl; U S Air Force Academy; Air Force Commission.

MAHLANDT, Louise A; Union Star Rii HS; Helena, MO; 3/20 ALAGirlsSt; ChrhWkr; HonRl; LbryAde; SchPl; TchrAde; Twrl; PpCl; Bsktbl; Trk; College; Teaching.

MAHLER, Debra A; Emerson Hubbard HS; Emerson, NE; 8/56 ChrhWkr; HonRl; TchrAde; RptrYrbk; 4-H; PpCl; Bsktbl; LetterTrk; CaptChrldr; PresAwd; College; Physical Education.

MAHLER, Karen J; Fairmount HS; Fairmount, ND; TrsSophCls; Band; Chrs; CncrtBnd; HonRl; NHS; PepBnd; EdSchPpr; PresPpCl; Bsktbl; Nd St U; Educ.

MAHLER, Kathy J; Fairmount HS; Fairmount, ND; PresSophCls; Band; Chrs; HonRl; MrchBnd; YthFlsp; Yrbk; RptrSchPpr; PpCl; LetterBsktbl; LetterTrk; Chrldr; N Dakota State Univ; Teaching.

MAHLER, Mary K; Whitefish Bay HS; Milwaukee, WI; 19/330 ChmnCmntyWkr; HonRl; NHS; NatlMeritCmnd; NatlThespSoc; PresOrch; PolWkr; SchMus; SchPl; GerCl; Univ; International Relationships.

MAHLER, Norma; Fairmount HS; Fairmount, ND; SecFrshCls; SecJrCls; TrsJrCls; Band; Chrs; ChrhWkr; HonRl; PepBnd; SchPl; RptrSchPpr;.

MAHLER, Ricky L; St Charles HS; St Charles, MI; NHS; RptrYrbk; LetterFtbl; LetterTrk; LetterWrstlng; Doctor.

MAHLOCH, Jane M; Northwest HS; Grand Island, NE; 14/142 Band; ChrhWkr; CncrtBnd; HonRl; MrchBnd; NatlThespSoc; PepBnd; SchPl; FHA; Marymount College; Math & Music Teacher.

MAHLUM, Alta M; Sacred Heart Public HS; Sacred Heart, MN; HonRl; 4-H; 4-HAwd; Technical School; Dietic Assistant.

MAHN, Michelle L; Oak Creek Sr HS; Oak Creek, WI; 9/370 Chr; Chrs; HonRl; JrNHS; Mdrgl; NHS; SchPl; 4-H; Bsbl; LetterGAA; College; Music.

MAHNKEN, Garold W; Perkins County HS; Ogallala, NE; 10/33 Chrs; HonRl; SchPl; StuCncl; TreasFFA; Trk; College.

MAHON, Daniel L; Aledo HS; Aledo, IL; 2/101 SchPpr; Univ Of Illinois; Chemical Engineer.

MAHONEY, Colleen M; Lourdes HS; Rochester, MN; Band; CncrtBnd; MrchBnd; PepBnd; Sacrstn; SchMus; SpnCl; College; Special Educ.

MAHONEY, Dan R; St Mary Central HS; Manasha, WI; Band; Chrs; CncrtBnd; HonRl; MrchBnd; NatlFornLg; SchMus; SchPl; RptrYrbk; IMSpt; Wittenburg Univ; Biology.

MAHONEY, Donald; St Viator Hs; Elf Grove Vlg, IL; 65/250 Chrs; SctActv; Glf; University; Professional.

MAHONEY, Frederick W; Perry HS; Perry, MI; HonRl; NHS; StuCncl; SchPpr; 4-H; Bsktbl; Ftbl; 4-HAwd; Univ Of Mi; Architectre.

MAHONEY, Kathy A; New Lothrop HS; New Lothrop, MI; HonRl; Yrbk; RptrSchPpr; 4-H; SpnCl; Western Mi Col; Medical Tech.

MAHONEY, Maria J; Muskegon Catholic Central HS; Muskegon, MI; ChrhWkr; CmntyWkr; HonRl; JA; SchMus; SchPl; StuCncl; StuGov; FrCl; Mi St U; Surgical Nurse.

MAHONEY, Meg M; Minot HS; Minot, ND; ALAGirlsSt; Chr; ChrhWkr; HonRl; JrNHS; NatlThespSoc; SchMus; FrCl; PpCl; Chrldr; Clge; Theatre.

MAHONEY, Michael P; Northwest HS; High Ridge, MO; 10/374 PresFrshCls; ALBoysSt; HonRl; StuCncl; Bsktbl; Ftbl; OptClAwd; University.

MAHONEY, Patricia; Maine Twp South Hs; Park Ridge, IL; HonRl; LbryAde; NHS; Orch; SchMus; SchPl; SctActv;.

MAHONEY, Patrick J; Niles HS; Niles, MI; Chr; HonRl; JA; PolWkr; SchMus; College.

MAHONEY, Rebecca; Lees Summit Sr HS; Lees Summit, MO; Chr; DrlTm; HonRl; StuGov; PpCl; Chrldr; CitAwd; Jr Coll.

MAHONEY, Susan K; Chesaning Union HS; St Charles, MI; HospAde; StuCncl; Teen; Trk; TreasChrldr; GAA; 4-HAwd; Michigan State Univ; Medicine.

MAHONEY, Terence J; Downers Grove HS; Oakbrook, IL; HonRl; NHS; NatlMeritSF; NatlSciFnd; MthCl; Graduate Schl; Medicine.

MAHONEY, Timothy P; Midland HS; Midland, MI; 138/416 SctActv; SecFrCl; Tech Univ; Biology.

MAHONY, Debbie G; Whiting HS; Whiting, IN; 15/100 Band; CmntyWkr; RedCrAde; YthFlsp; Bsktbl; Swmmng; Trk; Chrldr; GAA; IMSpt; College; Nursing.

MAHR, Gregory C; Detroit Catholic Central HS; Dearborn, MI; 7/180 HonRl; NHS; NatlMeritSF; RptrSchPpr; College; Biology.

MAHR, Jon R; Spoon River Valley HS; Ellisville, IL; PresFrshCls; HonRl; 4-H; FFA; LetterBsktbl; LetterTrk; 4-HAwd; Spoon River Jr College; Farm Mechanics.

MAHYNSKI, Theresa M; Fruitport HS; Nunica, MI; 11/300 Band; ChrhWkr; CncrtBnd; HonRl; MrchBnd; NHS; Grand Valley State Coll; Chemistry Major.

MAI, Cara J; West Smith County HS; Kensington, KS; TrsSophCls; Chr; DrlTm; MrchBnd; StuCncl; RptrYrbk; RptrSchPpr; 4-H; PpCl; College; Librarian.

MAI, Carolyn M; Troge Community HS; Wakeeney, KS; Band; Chr; Chrl; HonRl; RedCrAde; SchPl; YthFlsp; FHA; SciCl; College; Professional.

MAIBENCO, Douglas C; Wheaton Christian HS; Wheaton, IL; 1/31 VPSrCls; CmntyWkr; HonRl; JrNHS; SctActv; StuGov; University; Professional.

MAICHEL, Laura; Southwest HS; St Louis, MO; HospAde; Quill&Scroll; StuCncl; RptrYrbk; Chrldr; IMSpt; Coll; Psych.

MAIDENBERG, Jill H; Marion HS; Marion, IN; 2/750 Chr; HonRl; Mdrgl; NHS; NatlThespSoc; OffAde; PolWkr; SchMus; StuGov; Indiana Univ; French.

MAIER, Diane L; Columbus HS; Columbus, WI; 15/140 AFS; Band; CmntyWkr; CncrtBnd; MrchBnd; PepBnd; Sec4-H; FHA; Bsktbl; LetterTrk; Business School; Accountant.

MAIER, Laurie L; Joliet Central HS; Joliet, IL; 103/481 CmntyWkr; HospAde; StuCncl; RptrYrbk; FNA; Chrldr; GAA; DanFAwd; 4-HAwd; CitAwd; Robert Morris Schl; Pro Nursing.

MAIER, Sherry A; Ellendale HS; Monango, ND; Band; Chr; Chrs; PepBnd; SchPl; RptrSchPpr; SchPpr; LetterBsktbl; Ndsu; Med Tech.

MAIER, Sue Ann D; Glidden Public HS; Glidden, WI; Band; SecChr; ChrhWkr; HonRl; RptrYrbk; RptrSchPpr; PpCl; Bsbl;.

MAIER, Susan L; Gibson Southern HS; Fort Branch, IN; ChrhWkr; NHS; Yrbk; FHA; LatCl; PpCl; Indiana Univ; Computer Science.

MAIER, Thomas M; Forest Lake Sr HS; Hugo, MN; HonRl; College; Journalism.

MAIERS, Jo Ann; Leo HS; Holy Cross, IA; 4/44 HonRl; LbryAde; StuCncl; RptrYrbk; RptrSchPpr; SpnCl; SciCl; Glf; Chrldr; IMSpt; Coll; Sci.

MAIERS, Ted M; Leo HS; Holy Cross, IA; ALBoysSt; HonRl; SchMus; SctActv; LetterBsbl; Bsktbl; Ftbl; IMSpt; AmLegAwd; CitAwd;.

MAIJALA, Vivian A; Mascoutah Comm HS; Mascoutah, IL; 8/251 DrlTm; HonRl; NHS; SchMus; SecStuCncl; SpnCl; GAA; Eastern Illinois Univ; Education.

MAILE, Laura; Newaygo HS; Newaygo, MI; SecFrshCls; PresSophCls; ChrhWkr; HonRl; NHS; SchPl; StuCncl; YthFlsp; LatCl; College; Bible Major.

MAILHOT, Charles J; Union HS; Grand Rapids, MI; 11/400 ALBoysSt; HonRl; ModUN; NHS; NatlMeritSchl; SpnCl; CaptBsbl; IMSpt; University Of Michigan; Engineering.

MAIN, Brenda L; South Hamilton HS; Ellsworth, IA; 12/91 HonRl; Yrbk; FHA; MthCl; BttyCrckrAwd; Ia State U; Industrial Administration.

MAIN, Kim A; Freeburg Comm HS; Freeburg, IL; Band; ChrhWkr; CncrtBnd; DrlTm; HonRl; MrchBnd; NHS; NatlMeritCmnd; NatlThespSoc; SchMus; SchPl; Swmmng; Chrldr; College.

MAIN, Kristy K; Springfield HS; Springfield, IL; 85/600 VPChr; NHS;.

MAIN, Roxanna J; Turner HS; Kansas City, KS; Chr; HonRl; PresJrNHS; NHS; StuCncl; PresStuCncl; EdYrBk; FrCl; PpCl; College; Doctor.

MAINE, Joseph E; Dixon HS; Dixon, IL; 111/333 Band; ChrhWkr; CncrtBnd; HonRl; MrchBnd; SchMus; SchPl; SctActv; YthFlsp; SecIMSpt; N Illinois Univ; Dentist.

MAINES, Traci L; Randolph Southern HS; Lynn, IN; 4/55 SecFrshCls; SecSophCls; Chrs; DrmMjrt;

HonRl; NHS; TchrAde; Chrldr; GAA; In Univ; Accountant.

MAINO, Jeanne; Negaunee HS; Negaunee, MI; ChrhWkr; CmntyWkr; HonRl; IntrClCncl; StuCncl; StuGov; CivCl; Bsbl; IMSpt; PPFtbl; Michigan State Univ; Veterinary Med.

MAINORD, Martha; East Prairie HS; East Prairie, MO; Band; Chr; Chrl; Chrs; ChrhWkr; CncrtBnd; MrchBnd; SchPl; YthFlsp; College; Professional.

MAINPRIZE, Susan L; Houghton Lake HS; Houghton Lk, MI; SecFrshCls; TrsSophCls; VPSrCls; Band; HonRl; NHS; EdSchPpr; SchPpr; FTA; Univ Of Michigan; Physical Therapy.

MAINZER, Tod D; John Hersey HS; Mt Prospect, IL; Band; CncrtBnd; PepBnd; SchMus; VPFrshCls; SctActv;.

MAIORANO, Vito M; St Joseph HS; Cicero, IL; 3/170 NHS; NatlMeritSF; Quill&Scroll; StuGov; RptrYrbk; Tennis; Trk; IMSpt; Univ; Professional.

MAIROSE, Steven C; Kimball HS; Kimball, SD; Chrs; ChrhWkr; HonRl; SchPl; SchPl; RptrYrbk; SptEdYrbk; 4-H; LetterBsktbl; LetterFtbl; Us Air Force Academy.

MAIRS, Danny D; Lisbon HS; Lisbon, ND; 10/80 PresJrCls; ChrhWkr; HonRl; StuCncl; 4-H; FFA; Ftbl; Wrstlng; IMSpt; 4-HAwd; Trade School; Electrician.

MAIRS, Loren K; Lisbon HS; Lisbon, ND; ChrhWkr; HonRl; LbryAde; NHS; NatlThespSoc; SchPl; StuCncl; 4-H; FBLA; IMSpt; Ndsu; Ag Engineering.

MAISZEWSKI, Edmond T; Mount Carmel HS; Chicago, IL; 2/197 PresNHS; TreasSciCl; Purdue Univ; Chemical Engineer.

MAITLEN, Connie S; Southwester HS; Lafayette, IN; 24/131 Band; ChrhWkr; CtyCnl; CmntyWkr; DrlTm; HonRl; HospAde; MrchBnd; NatlFornLg; OffAde; Purdue U; Nursing.

MAJCINA, Dale G; Marseilles HS; Marseilles, IL; 9/78 VPFrshCls; HonRl; NatlThespSoc; SchMus; StuGov; RptrSchPpr; SptEdSchPpr; Bsktbl; Ftbl; Trk; College; Cpa.

MAJERUS, Helen B; Petersburg Public HS; Albion, NE; 1/15 TrsSophCls; PresSrCls; Chrs; HonRl; NHS; SchPl; Yrbk; SchPpr; PpCl; AmLegAwd; College; Secretarial.

MAJERUS, Kenneth W; Goodhue HS; Bellechester, MN; VPSrCls; Band; Chr; ChrhWkr; HonRl; MrchBnd; NHS; PresStuCncl; SptEdSchPpr; GerCl; Ftbl; Wrstlng; U Of Mn; Veterinarian.

MAJERUS, Ruth A; Petersburg HS; Albion, NE; 3/25 TrsJrCls; Band; Chr; Chrs; CncrtBnd; Orch; PepBnd; SchPl; Yrbk; SchPpr; College; Medicine.

MAJEWSKI, Anne L; Irving Crown HS; Algonquin, IL; 1/360 HonRl; NHS; LetterBsktbl; Tennis; CchngActv; DARAwd; Univ Of Notre Dame; Engineer.

MAJEWSKI, Chris; Sacred Heart Acad; Springfield, IL; /143 HonRl; NHS; LatCl; MthCl; MthCl; Lincoln Land Comm Coll;cpa.

MAJEWSKI, Gail; Mt Assisi Acad; Worth, IL; 39/189 CmntyWkr; HonRl; HospAde; NatlSciFnd; SchPl; StuGov; SchPpr; FrCl; Bsktbl; GAA; Coll; Nursing Med Field.

MAJKOWICZ, Kenneth S; Gordon Technical HS; Chicago, IL; 1/680 ChrhWkr; HonRl; NHS; StuCncl; StuGov; PpCl; Roosevelt Univ; Business.

MAJOR, Glenda; Camdonton HS; Camdenton, MO; HonRl; ModUN; NHS; Yrbk; SchPpr; IMSpt;.

MAJOR, Lisa M; Ankeny Comm HS; Ankeny, IA; Chrs; ChrhWkr; HonRl; JA; Orch; SchMus; TchrAde; PpCl; Univ Of No Iowa; Education.

MAJOR, Norman D; Albia Comm HS; Lovilia, IA; ChrhWkr; CmntyWkr; SctActv; YthFlsp; LetterBsktbl; Ftbl; Coll; Counselor.

MAJOR, Terry D; West Nodaway HS; Burlington Jct, MO; VPSophCls; PresJrCls; ALBoysSt; CncrtBnd; MrchBnd; StuCncl; Ftbl; Trade School; Refrigeration.

MAJOR, Thomas I; Prospect HS; Mt Prospect, IL; CAP; CmntyWkr; HonRl; SctActv; Purdue Univ; Astronautical Engineer.

MAJOREK, Stephanie E; Marian HS; Omaha, NE; HonRl; FNA; SpnCl; Trade Sch; Med Asst.

MAJOROWICZ, Therese R; Rolfe Community HS; Rolfe, IA; Chrs; ChrhWkr; CncrtBnd; HonRl; MrchBnd; NHS; PepBnd; TchrAde; College; Music.

MAJORS, Carol; Spring Valley HS; Spring Valley, MN; 17/78 Chr; ChrhWkr; CmntyWkr; HonRl; NHS; SchMus; TchrAde; RptrSchPpr; FHA; GerCl; St Cloud State College.

MAJORS, Sandi; Ill Valley Central Hs; Peoria, IL; 24/257 Chrs; HonRl; NHS; LatCl; GAA; Bradley U; Nuclear Phycicist.

MAJORS, Terri L; Auburn HS; Auburn, NE; Band; Chr; ChrhWkr; DrlTm; HonRl; SchMus; SecYthFlsp; EngCl; SpnCl; Chrldr; Univ Of Nebraska; Business Admin.

MAJUSIAK, Jerome E; Wtn HS; Watertown, SD; ALBoysSt; Chr; Chrs; HonRl; NatlFornLg; NHS; SchMus; StuGov; Sd Sch Of Mines; Engineering.

MAKA, Andrea; Maria Hs; Chicago, IL; 5/300 HonRl; SecLatCl; MthCl; U Loyola; Medical Technologist.

MAKELA, Jacqueline L; Richmond HS; Richmond, IN; HonRl; TreasJA; ModUN; NHS; Orch; SchMus; Trk; Ball State Univ; Medical Technonology.

MAKI, Ann M; Milan HS; Milan, IN; 12/66 CncrtBnd; HonRl; MrchBnd; NHS; SecStuCncl; TchrAde; PresFTA; LatCl; SecPpCl; Bsktbl; College; Special Education.

MAKI, Crystal R; Horace Mann HS; Gilbert, MN; HonRl; SctActv; RptrSchPpr; PpCl; Trk; GAA; Univ Minnesota; Medical Technology.

MAKI, Hope S; Aurora Hoyt Lakes HS; Hoyt Lakes, MN; PresSrCls; HonRl; NatlMeritCmnd; StuCncl; Yrbk; PpCl; Bsktbl; Trk; Chrldr; Univ; Med.

MAKI, Jay H; Forest Park HS; Crystal Falls, MI; 20/89 Aud/Vis; ChrhWkr; CmntyWkr; HonRl; RedCrAde; LetterSchPl; SctActv; TchrAde; Yrbk; SchPpr; Bsktbl; BauchLmbAwd; Michigan St Univ; Veterinarian.

MAKI, Kerry E; South Shore HS; Iron River, WI; 4/37 PresFrshCls; PresSophCls; PresJrCls; PresSrCls; StuGov; Ftbl; Trk; AmLegAwd; GovHonPrgAwd; U W Platteville; Radio Tv Broadcasting.

MAKI, Lee D; Wakefield HS; Wakefield, MI; 13/63 VPFrshCls; VPSophCls; Band; ChrhWkr; CncrtBnd; HonRl; MrchBnd; PepBnd; RptrYrbk; RptrSchPpr; Northern Michigan Univ; Social Work.

MAKOLA, Mary; Cameron HS; Cameron, WI; 5/50 ChrhWkr; CncrtBnd; DrmMjrt; MrchBnd; NHS; EdYrBk; GerCl; DanFAwd; Univ Of Wi.

MAKOVICKA, Ron T; York HS; York, NE; 13/130 HonRl; NHS; SecFFA; AmLegAwd; Univ Of Nebraska; Veterinarian.

MAKOWSKI, Cheryl A; Sacred Heart HS; Dearborn, MI; Chr; HonRl; StuCncl; SchPpr; SpnCl; Univ; Speech Communications.

MAKOWSKI, Mark J; Lane Technical HS; Chicago, IL; 58/1200 HonRl; TchrAde; RusCl; Ftbl; Trade School.

MAKOWSKI, Robert J; Thomas More HS; Milwaukee, WI; 1/155 Band; CncrtBnd; HonRl; MrchBnd; NHS; PepBnd; SctActv; StuCncl; IMSpt; RotaryAwd; Marquette Univ; Math.

MAKREAS, Antonia; South Side HS; Fort Wayne, IN; VPJrCls; Band; CncrtBnd; HonRl; MrchBnd; OffAde; Orch; PepBnd; SchMus; University.

MAKULA, Dennis E; Waldron HS; Waldron, MI; VPFrshCls; PresSophCls; VPJrCls; ChrhWkr; HonRl; NatlMeritSF; SchPl; StuCncl; RptrSchPpr; Ftbl; Mi State.

MALANE, Marsha L; Port Huron HS; Port Huron, MI; 4/390 HonRl; SecNHS; NatlMeritCmnd; StuCncl; PresMthCl; VoiceDemAwd; Community College; Business Admin.

MALAVOLTI, Timothy N; Blue Mound HS; Boody, IL; 4/53 PresSrCls; AFS; Chrs; HonRl; LbryAde; NHS; SchMus; SchPl; RptrSchPpr; EdSchPpr; FTA; SciCl; University; Professional.

MALCHEFF, Susan A; Homewood Flossmoor HS; Homewood, IL; 6/940 AFS; HonRl; NHS; Yrbk; MthCl; Swmmng; College; Veterinarian.

MALCOLM, Kathryn M; Whiteland Community HS; New Whiteland, IN; 4/183 HonRl; HospAde; VPNHS; NatlThespSoc; SchMus; SchPl; TchrAde; 4-H; SecSpnCl; PpCl; Ball State Univ; Accounting.

MALCOLM, Marla K; Kouts HS; Kouts, IN; Band; Chr; ChrhWkr; MrchBnd; SchPl; FHA; SciCl; College; English Major.

MALCOLM, Rick D; Chase County HS; Imperial, NE; Band; CncrtBnd; MrchBnd; TchrAde; Bsbl; CaptFtbl; CaptWrstlng; College; Football.

MALCOM, Debra R; Dekalb HS; Dekalb, IL; 15/370 Chr; ChrhWkr; HonRl; NatlMeritCmnd; NatlThespSoc; TchrAde; 4-H; GAA; BttyCrckrAwd; 4-HAwd; Il St U; Home Ec.

MALCOM, Kathy A; Griswold Community HS; Griswold, IA; 28/86 Chrs; ChrhWkr; CmntyWkr; HonRl; PolWkr; NatlMeritSchl; RedCrAde; SchMus; SchPl; StuGov; College; Professional.

MALE, Kathryn A; Arthur HS; Arthur, IL; PresJrCls; VPJrCls; HonRl; HospAde; LbryAde; NHS; StuCncl; 4-H; FHA; FNA; GAA; College; Nursing.

MALEC, Janet C; Belleville Township HS; Belleville, IL; StuCncl; Southern Ill Univ; Biology.

MALEC, Raymond A; Luthern HS; Birmingham, MI; 1/16 PresSophCls; PresJrCls; PresFrshCls; ChrhWkr; HonRl; NHS; PresStuCncl; PresStuGov; EdYrBk; LetterTrk; College.

MALECKI, Elizabeth A; John Hersey HS; Arlington Hts, IL; 48/783 SecSrCls; Band; CncrtBnd; HonRl; MrchBnd; NHS; Orch; SchMus; StuCncl; Univ Of Ill; Dancer.

MALES, Eric; Glenbard West HS; Glen Ellyn, IL; Chr; ChrhWkr; NHS; SctActv; RptrYrbk; MthCl; Tennis; Texas Christian Univ; Biology.

MALIKOWSKI, Carolyn R; Harper Creek HS; Battle Creek, MI; 11/261 ChrhWkr; HonRl; HospAde; LbryAde; NHS; OffAde; RedCrAde; SchMus; SctActv; EdYrBk; 4-HAwd; Ferris State College; Pharmacy.

MALIN, David; Lincoln HS; Wisconsin Rapids, WI; 13/600 HonRl; NatlFornLg; NHS; NatlMeritCmnd; PolWkr; SciCl; Univ Of Wis; Statistics.

MALINA, Helen A; Walther Lutheran HS; Melrose Park, IL; 27/90 Chr; Chrs; HonRl; NatlMeritSF; SchMus; StuGov; Bsktbl; LetterTennis; Trk; GAA; University; Music.

MALINGER, Michael; West Milwaukee HS; West Allis, WI; 3/200 HonRl; NHS; StuCncl; SptEdSchPpr; Trk; LionAwd; De Vry Inst Of Technology; Engineer.

MALINOFF, Deborah S; Edison Sr HS; East Gary, IN; ALAGirlsSt; HonRl; SecNHS; FrCl; SciCl; Purdue University.

MALINOWSKI, Donna M; St Ladislaus HS; Hamtramck, MI; HonRl; SchPl; SecStuCncl; StuGov; FBLA; FSA; PpCl; SciCl; CaptBsbl; Bsktbl; Macomb County Comm College; Social Science.

MALINOWSKI, Kathy J; Resurrection HS; Chicago, IL; CncrtBnd; HonRl; SchMus; SctActv; PresSpnCl; GAA; IMSpt; College; Nursing.

MALINOWSKI, Mark; Loyal Public HS; Loyal, WI; Band; CncrtBnd; MrchBnd; SchPl; Yrbk; FFA; EldAwd; College; Mechanical Engineering.

MALINOWSKI, Stephanie L; Yorkville HS; Yorkville, IL; 4/130 VPChrs; CmntyWkr; HospAde; NHS; SchMus; SptEdYrbk; Yrbk; FHA; PresSpnCl; GAA; Waubonsee Jr Col; Social Work.

MALINOWSKI, Thomas A; Elkgrove HS; Elkgrove, IL; 35/505 Band; CncrtBnd; HonRl; JrNHS; MrchBnd; NHS; Bsbl; CaptFtbl; LetterWrstlng; Marquette University; Biology.

MALKIEWICZ, Robert S; St Alphonsus HS; Detroit, MI; Chrs; HonRl; NHS; StuCncl; TchrAde; LetterTrk; IMSpt; Detroit College; Accountant.

MALLAK, Kenneth G; Rantoul Township HS; Rantoul, IL; Chr; HonRl; LatCl; SpnCl; College; Music.

MALLAS, Rebecca J; Perry Community HS; Perry, IA; HonRl; MrchBnd; Twrl; 4-H; SpnCl; LetterTrk; 4-HAwd; College; Professional.

MALLEN, Martin J; St Patrick HS; Chicago, IL; 150/377 CmntyWkr; HonRl; PolWkr; SctActv; StuCncl; StuGov; SchPpr; PpCl; LetterFtbl; LetterTrk; IMSpt; College; Law.

MALLERS, Elaine M; Paul Harding HS; Fort Wayne, IN; ChrhWkr; DrlTm; HonRl; JrNHS; SchMus; PpCl; LetterChrldr; College; Dance.

MALLET, Sharon A; Dominican HS; Detroit, MI; Chr; HonRl; Mdrgl; NHS; PolWkr; StuGov; TchrAde; Trk; LetterChrldr; CaptCchngActv; Coll; Speech.

MALLETT, Dianna M; So Sioux City HS; So Sioux City, NE; 5/140 Band; CncrtBnd; HonRl; MrchBnd; PepBnd; SchMus; SpnCl; Trade School; Accounting.

MALLETT, Karen M; Sioux Valley HS; Bruce, SD; 23/68 TrsJrCls; Chrs; CmntyWkr; CncrtBnd; HonRl; SchPl; StuCncl; YthFlsp; Yrbk; PresFHA; PpCl; Trk; Vocational School; Cosmetology.

MALLETTE, Gary J; West View HS; Topeka, IN; ChrhWkr; CmntyWkr; HonRl; NHS; SchPl; TchrAde; YthFlsp; RptrSchPpr; FTA; In U; Md.

MALLETTE, Stanley L; Bloomfield Community HS; Bloomfield, NE; 2/66 Band; Chr; ChrhWkr; HonRl; MrchBnd; NHS; PepBnd; SctActv; Yrbk; GerCl; Bsbl; Bsktbl; LetterGlf; IMSpt; Augustana College; Mathematics.

MALLEY, Sharon R; Marian HS; Southfield, MI; Chrl; HonRl; LbryAde; ModUN; NHS; Bsktbl; Oakland U; Nursing.

MALLICOAT, Carolyn M; Ashland HS; Ashland, IL; 2/29 Band; HonRl; VPNHS; PolWkr; SchMus; SchPl; StuCncl; YthFlsp; EdSchPpr; GAA; 4-HAwd; Gem City Business College; Legal Secretary.

MALLIET, Randal V; Greendale HS; Greendale, WI; 25/332 HonRl; NHS; OffAde; Sacrstn; SctActv; Bsbl; Bsktbl; College; Engineer.

MALLOCK, Kerry A; Laura F Osborn HS; Detroit, MI; 5/632 HonRl; NHS; TchrAde; SpnCl; CaptTennis; IMSpt; CitAwd; University Of Detroit; Dentist.

MALLON, Dorothy A; Luckey HS; Manhattan, KS; ALAGirlsSt; HonRl; ModUN; PolWkr; StuCncl; UNYO; SchPpr; FBLA; CaptBsktbl; CchngActv; U Of Ks; Political Science.

MALLON, Stephen A; Oak Park River Forest HS; Oak Park, IL; 111/1012 Univ Of Illinois; Biology.

MALLORY, Kenneth A; Owosso HS; Owosso, MI; 40/452 HonRl; JrNHS; NHS; OffAde; LetterTrk; Ferris St Col; Acct.

MALLORY, Kimberly A; Mt Vernon Sr HS; Mt Vernon, IN; 18/220 AFS; HonRl; NHS; StuCncl; 4-H; GAA; PPFtbl; 4-HAwd; Univ; Pharmacist.

MALLOY, Donna J; Elk Point Public HS; Elk Point, SD; 29#32#37 MrchBnd; PepBnd; SchPl; RptrYrbk; RptrSchPpr; PpCl; Chrldr; College.

MALLOY, Erin L; Sullivan HS; Sullivan, IL; Band; CncrtBnd; HonRl; MrchBnd; RedCrAde; SchPpr; 4-H; FTA; FrCl; GAA; College.

MALLOY, Mary; Williamsburg Community HS; Williamsburg, IA; 9/95 Chrs; HonRl; SchPl; StuCncl; GerCl; GAA; IMSpt; PPFtbl; KiwanAwd; Iowa State U; Biology.

MALLOY, Thomas G; Marquette Univ HS; Elm Grove, WI; ChrhWkr; CmntyWkr; HonRl; Glf; Marquette Univ; Doctor.

MALLY, Barbara G; Carl Sandburg HS; Palos Park, IL; 48/700 SecChr; Chrl; TreasNHS; GerCl; GAA; Mich St Univ; Engineering.

MALM, Jonathan C; Merrill HS; Merrill, WI; PresJrCls; ALBoysSt; ChrhWkr; HonRl; StuCncl; StuGov; Bsktbl; Ftbl; Glf; CchngActv; Univ; Professnl.

MALNOR, Kirk A; West HS; Green Bay, WI; PresSophCls; PresJrCls; Band; CncrtBnd; HonRl; MrchBnd; PepBnd; StuCncl; College; Engineer.

MALNORY, Robert W; Waupun Sr HS; Waupun, WI; CncrtBnd; HonRl; NHS; Quill&Scroll; SchPl; SptEdSchPpr; LetterBsbl; LetterFtbl; RotaryAwd; Univ Of Wisc; Pharmacy.

MALONE, Jean M; Wyoming Park HS; Wyoming, MI; VPJrCls; NHS; RedCrAde; LetterTennis;.

MALONE, Kathryn D; Onaga HS; Onaga, KS; Band; Chrs; CncrtBnd; MrchBnd; PepBnd; SchPl; TchrAde; YthFlsp; RptrSchPpr; EdSchPpr; Emporia State Clg; Medical Tech.

MALONE, Kevin M; Clarinda Comm HS; Clarinda, IA; ChrhWkr; HonRl; StuCncl; StuGov; LetterBsbl; Bsktbl; LetterFtbl; LetterGlf; Swmmng; Wrstlng; Wayne State University; Psychology.

MALONE, Leann; Henry Senachwine HS; Henry, IL; 3/73 Band; HonRl; ModUN; VPNHS; NatlMeritSF; OffAde; SchPl; SctActv; SecStuCncl; PpCl; GodCntryAwd; Univ Of Illinois.

MALONE, Michael T; Heelan HS; Sioux City, IA; 41/249 HonRl; NHS; StuGov; TchrAde; SpnCl; LetterBsktbl; LetterTrk; IMSpt; College.

MALONE, Robert A; Airport HS; Carleton, MI; Bsktbl; CaptTrk; IMSpt; College.

MALONE, Rogers W; Kirkwood HS; St Louis, MO; ALBoysSt; HonRl; SctActv; YthFlsp; EdYrBk; LetterTrk; Col; Artech.

MALONEY, Ann M; Sunnydale Academy; Lees Summit, MO; VPJrCls; Band; Chr; ChrhWkr; HonRl; SchPl; TchrAde; RptrYrbk; EdYrBk; IMSpt; College; Professional.

MALONEY, Janice L; Mc Leansboro HS; Dahlgren, IL; 3/160 HonRl; NHS; SchPpr; FHA; SecMthCl; College; Elem Education.

MALONEY, Kathleen A; Bay City Central HS; Bay City, MI; 4/536 TrsJrCls; HonRl; LbryAde; NHS; StuCncl; EngCl; GAA; PPFtbl; Delta Coll; Forestry.

MALONEY, Kathleen M; Marian Cath HS; Dolton, IL; 126/335 SecJrCls; SecSrCls; ChrhWkr; CmntyWkr; HonRl; HospAde; StuCncl; StuGov; 4-H; College; Nursing.

MALONEY, Kevin A; Ridgway HS; Ridgway, IL; 10/42 PresFrshCls; PresSophCls; PresJrCls; HonRl; NatlMeritFnl; StuCncl; RptrYrbk; RptrSchPpr; FFA; Univ Of Illinois; Agriculture.

MALONEY, Margaret A; Hibbing HS; Hibbing, MN; Chr; HonRl; HospAde; JA; NHS; SchMus; VPFTA; PpCl; Chrldr; JAAwd; U Of Mn; Dental Hygiene.

MALONEY, Mark D; St Ignatius HS; Chicago, IL; 35/155 HonRl; PolWkr; TchrAde; Socr; Trk; Loyola University; Doctor.

MALONEY, Mark T; Thornton Twp HS; Dolton, IL; 17/750 HonRl; NHS; NatlMeritCmnd; MthCl; LetterTennis; Univ Of Ill; Chemist.

MALONEY, Philip A; York Comm HS; Elmhurst, IL; 40/950 ChrhWkr; CmntyWkr; HonRl; NHS; FrCl; St Joseph College; Mathematics.

MALOTKY, Elaine; Centennial HS; Waco, NE; 2/60 PresJrCls; Band; Chrs; HonRl; NHS; PepBnd; SchPl; EdYrBk; PpCl; JCAwd; Concordia; Teacher.

MALOTKY, Elaine M; Centennial HS; Waco, NE; 2/65 PresJrCls; Band; Chrs; CncrtBnd; HonRl; MrchBnd; NHS; PepBnd; SchPl; YthFlsp; RptrYrbk; RptrSchPpr; Concordia College; Teaching.

MALOY, Annette E; La Moille Comm HS; La Moille, IL; 2/45 Band; CncrtBnd; MrchBnd; NHS; PepBnd; YthFlsp; Yrbk; FHA; FrCl; Judson College; Special Education.

MALOY, Teresa L; Charleston HS; Charleston, IL; 7/266 Chrs; ChrhWkr; HonRl; NHS; Orch; SchMus; StuCncl; FTA; Eastern Ill Univ; Music.

MALTBY, Gregory C; Wetmore HS; Wetmore, KS; 2/25 PresJrCls; ALBoysSt; Chrs; CncrtBnd; HonRl; NHS; SchMus; EdYrBk; CaptFtbl; CaptTrk; U Of Ks; Md.

MALTBY, John A; Pinckney Comm HS; Pinckney, MI; 10/238 Aud/Vis; Band; HonRl; LbryAde; MrchBnd; Orch; SctActv; StuCncl; 4-H; Univ; Professional.

MALUEG, Annette J; Marion HS; Marion, WI; HstFrshCls; VPSophCls; PresJrCls; VPSrCls; Band; HonRl; StuCncl; TchrAde; EdYrBk; FTA;.

MALUEG, Nancy; Marion HS; Marion, WI; 9/83 Band; HonRl; NatlFornLg; NHS; StuCncl; FHA; FTA; Chrldr; BttyCrckrAwd; 4-HAwd; College Stevens Point; Home Ec Teacher.

MALWITZ, Wade L; Blue Earth HS; Blue Earth, MN; HonRl; NHS; Orch; SchMus; StuCncl; MasAwd; Mankato State U.

MALY, Jane; Verdigre HS; Verdigre, NE; 1/43 SecSophCls; HospAde; PepBnd; SchMus; SchPl; SchPpr; SpnCl; Chrldr; Univ Of Nebr At Omaha; Medicine.

MALY, Joyce C; Marshall Public HS; Marshall, WI; 12/68 HonRl; SchPpr; FHA; CaptTrk; LetterChrldr; LetterGAA; PPFtbl; Menomonie University; Home Economics.

MALY, Mary F; Marshall HS; Marshall, WI; 11/68 HonRl; NHS; FHA; CaptTrk; PPFtbl; Univ Of Wisconsin; Physical Ed.

MAMMEL, James B; Wylie E Groves HS; Birmingham, MI; 54/683 PresAFS; CncrtBnd; MrchBnd; NHS; Orch; SchMus; SctActv; PresStuCncl; Tennis; OptClAwd; Univ Of Michigan; Medicine.

MAMMEN, David L; Limestone Comm HS; Bartonville, IL; 5/390 ChrhWkr; HonRl; NHS; NatlMeritSF; TreasYthFlsp; KeyCl; TreasSpnCl; Univ Of Ill; Computer Programming.

MAMROTH, Merritt D; Parkway Central HS; Creve Coeur, MO; CmntyWkr; PolWkr; LetterBsbl; LetterFtbl; LetterTrk; LetterWrstlng; CchngActv; IMSpt; Missouri Univ; Accounting.

MANARD, Mary E; Moberly Sr HS; Moberly, MO; VPSophCls; VPJrCls; AFS; ALAGirlsSt; Chr; ChrhWkr; HonRl; JrNHS; NHS; StuCncl; Missouri U; Pharmacy.

MANARD, Timothy J; New London Community HS; New London, IA; ALBoysSt; Chr; Chrl; Chrs; ChrhWkr; Mdrgl; SchMus; SchPl; SctActv; EdYrBk; EdSchPpr; College; Journalism.

MANCE, Donna M; Lansing HS; Leavenworth, KS; Chr; HonRl; NatlFornLg; NatlThespSoc; OffAde; SchAde; SchPl; TchrAde; VFWAwd; CitAwd; Clge; Curr Of Major Study.

MANCE, Stuart M; Broad Ripple HS; Indianapolis, IN; HonRl; NatlMeritSF; PolWkr; StuCncl; StuGov; College; Lawyer.

MANCHA, Regina A; Thornridge HS; Harvey, IL; 198/670 Chr; Chrl; HonRl; Swmmng; Bradley Univ; Rn.

MANCHESTER, Bret E; Central Heights HS; Lane, KS; Trade School; Auto Mechanic.

MANCHESTER, John K; Deerfield HS; Riverwoods, IL; PresChr; CncrtBnd; Mdrgl; MrchBnd; NHS; NatlMeritCmnd; Orch; PepBnd; SchMus; SctActv; College Of Wooster; Lawyer.

MANCINI, Brian M; Romeoville HS; Bolingbrook, IL; HonRl; University Of Illinois; Engineering.

MANCUSO, Roseanne L; South Lake HS; St Clair Shores, MI; SecJrCls; Chrs; Dog Handler.

MANDERFIELD, Dennis; Turkey Valley HS; Waucoma, IA; 1/115 Chr; ChrhWkr; HonRl; Mdrgl; NHS; SchMus; SchPl; 4-H; Bsktbl; College; Major Study.

MANDERNACK, Barbara J; Yorkville HS; Newark, IL; Chrs; DrlTm; MrchBnd; SpnCl; PpCl; Tennis; IMSpt; PPFtbl; 4-HAwd; College; Nursing.

MANDERS, Judy; Summerfield HS; Petersburg, MI; 14/69 HonRl; NHS; TchrAde; SpnCl; College; Professional Secretary.

MANDERSCHEID, Cheryl A; Andrew HS; Maquoketa, IA; SecJrCls; NHS; PresNatlThespSoc; SchPl; StuCncl; VPGerCl; LetterBsktbl; Trk; Vocational School; Secretary.

MANDLE, Diane M; Jennings Senior HS; Jennings, MO; 7/250 HonRl; NHS; SchMus; SchPl; TreasStuCncl; Yrbk; EngCl; PpCl; LetterBsktbl; LetterSwmmng; Quincy College; Medical Technologist.

MANDLE, Donna; Jennings Sr HS; Jennings, MO; 28/288 HonRl; NHS; NatlThespSoc; StuCncl; Yrbk; PpCl; GAA; IMSpt; PPFtbl; Coll; Child Care.

MANDLI, Mary; Washington Park HS; Racine, WI; /550 CmntyWkr; DrmBgl; HonRl; ModUN; StuGov; UNYO; EdYrBk; 4-H; FDA; KeyCl; Univ Parksidemadison;phys Ther.

MANDRELL, Sherry L; Mt Vernon HS; Waltonville, IL; Chr; HonRl; CivCl; 4-H; SpnCl; Eastern Univ; Elem Educ.

MANER, Emily; Shermer Hs; Northbrook, IL; 82 LitMag; StuGov; TchrAde; LetterTennis;.

MANES, Sharon A; Jefferson City Sr HS; Jefferson City, MO; 25/502 AFS; Chr; HonRl; NHS; StuCncl; SpnCl; PpCl; Chrldr; Univ; Teaching.

MANETH, Marla A; Otis Bison HS; Albert, KS; Band; Chrs; DrmBgl; HonRl; NHS; PepBnd; SchPl; Twrl; LetterPpCl; LetterTrk; College.

MANEY, Maureen; Proviso West HS; Hillside, IL; 46/1141 Chr; HonRl; Mdrgl; StuCncl; PpCl; AmLegAwd; Coll; Dentistry.

MANFORD, Maryann L; Holden HS; Holden, MO; 8/90 ChrhWkr; CmntyWkr; HonRl; LbryAde; NHS; TchrAde; 4-H; FBLA; LetterPpCl; BttyCrckrAwd; VFWAwd; University; Elementary Education.

MANG, Judith K; Frankfort HS; Frankfort, IN; Band; CmntyWkr; CncrtBnd; MrchBnd; PepBnd; VPFTA; PpCl; Ball State Univ; English.

MANG, William R; Triton Central HS; Fairland, IN; 20/158 Chr; HonRl; NHS; SchPl; SptEdYrbk; KeyCl; Bsbl; Bsktbl; LetterFtbl; LetterTrk; Indiana U; Bus Admin.

MANGAN, Jane; Melvin Sidley HS; Strawn, IL; Chr; Chrs; ChrhWkr; HonRl; PepBnd; SchPl; Bsktbl; Trk; GAA; 4-HAwd; Parkland Jr College; Legal Secretary.

MANGE, Joyce E; Horton Watkins HS; St Louis, MO; 36/515 PresFrshCls; PresSophCls; PresJrCls; PresSrCls; HonRl; NHS; NatlMeritSchl; StuCncl; FrCl; JAAwd; Syracuse U; Special Education Teacher.

MANGELS, John T; Winside Public HS; Winside, NE; 3/28 PresSophCls; HonRl; SchPl; EdSchPpr; SchPpr; LetterFtbl; LetterTrk; Ne Ne Tech Community College; Farming.

MANGERS, Janet M; Roseland Public HS; Roseland, NE; TrsJrCls; HonRl; SchPl; Yrbk; PpCl; Chrldr; College.

MANGES, Kathy J; Bremen HS; Bremen, IN; 1/122 ALAGirlsSt; Band; Chr; ChrhWkr; DrmMjrt; NHS; SchMus; PresYthFlsp; VPFTA; TreasFrCl; College.

MANGIN, Kevin A; Ellendale HS; Ellendale, ND; 4/45 PresFrshCls; Bsktbl; Ftbl; Trk; U Of Nd; Mathematics.

MANGINI, Danna M; Morton West HS; Berwyn, IL; Chrl; Chrs; SchMus; CaptChrldr; Coll; Physical Therapy.

MANGOLD, Gregory; University Of Detroit HS; Southfiled, MI; HonRl; NatlMeritFnl; NatlSciFnd; RptrSchPpr; CivCl; IMSpt; Univ Of Ntre Dame; Computer Science.

MANGOLD, Jackie; West Delaware HS; Ryan, IA; ChrhWkr; HonRl; NatlThespSoc; PolWkr; SchMus; SchPl; 4-H; PpCl; Bsktbl; 4-HAwd; University; Curr Of Major Study.

MANGOLD, N Michael; Barrington HS; Barrington, IL; 11/652 ChrhWkr; HonRl; NHS; RptrSchPpr; PresLatCl; Ftbl; Wrstlng; IMSpt; College; Biologist.

MANHART, Jean L; Wheatland HS; Grainfield, KS; Chr; Chrl; HonRl; SchMus; SchPl; FHA; MthCl; Trk; Chrldr; AmLegAwd;.

MANI, Kathy L; Mt Horeb HS; Mt Horeb, WI; AFS; Chr; Chrl; ChrhWkr; Mdrgl; OffAde; SchMus; SchPl; PresYthFlsp; VPFHA; Madison Area Tech Col; Legal Secretary.

MANICAL, Cynthia L; Pontiac Twp HS; Pontiac, IL; Chr; HonRl; Quill&Scroll; SchPl; SchPpr; Trk; Chrldr; Univ Of Illinois; Accounting.

MANINA, Michelle A; Auburndale Sr HS; Arpin, WI; Chrs; HonRl; LbryAde; SchPl; PpCl; College; Graphic Arts.

MANION, Julie; Rushford Public HS; Rushford, MN; ChrhWkr; DrlTm; LbryAde; TchrAde; FHA; FTA; PpCl; GAA; Tech Sch; Med Or Leg Sec.

MANIS, Beverly D; Cowan HS; Muncie, IN; 13/57 VPSrCls; ChrhWkr; NHS; EdYrBk;.

MANIS, Elizabeth A; Hoopeston HS; Hoopeston, IL; 5/135 VPSophCls; Band; Chr; ChrhWkr; NHS; 4-H; LetterBsbl; LetterBsktbl; GAA; BttyCrckrAwd; 4-HAwd; Jr College; Accounting.

MANIS, Rick L; Cowan HS; Muncie, IN; ChrhWkr; HonRl; StuCncl; StuGov; YthFlsp; LetterBsbl; LetterBsktbl; CchngActv; Ball State College.

MANKE, Leslie A; Poynette Sr HS; Arlington, WI; AFS; Chrs; HonRl; RptrYrbk; PpCl; Univ Of Wisconsin; Microbiology.

MANKE, Robert P; Mundelein HS; Mundelein, IL; 24/411 HonRl; LitMag; TchrAde; College; Architecture.

MANKE, Susan; Poynette HS; Arlington, WI; 14/101 Chrs; ChrhWkr; HonRl; SchPl; Yrbk; 4-H; 4-HAwd; Uw Oshkosh; Nursing.

MANKER, Cathy J; Eastridge HS; Kankakee, IL; 23/306 HonRl; HospAde; NatlMeritSchl; PresNatlThespSoc; PolWkr; RedCrAde; ROTC; SchPl; StuGov; YthFlsp; Univ; Dietition.

MANKER, James B; New Trier East HS; Wilmette, IL; SctActv; Yrbk; LatCl; Baylor Univ ;pre Denist.

MANKER, Melinda; Pittsfield HS; Pittsfield, IL; CmntyWkr; HonRl; NHS; OffAde; FHA; PpCl; GAA; IMSpt; VoiceDemAwd; Gem City College; Secretarial Work.

MANKOSKI, Rita M; United Twp HS; East Moline, IL; 3/651 Chr; HonRl; JA; NHS; SchPl; Teen; YthFlsp; RptrSchPpr; GAA; ChmbCommrsAwd; JAAwd; OptClAwd; No Illinois Univ; Accounting.

MANKOWSKI, Mariann R; Dominican HS; Hamtramck, MI; Band; CncrtBnd; Orch; TchrAde; CaptBsktbl; PresGAA; Mich St U; Wildlife Conservation.

MANLEY, Marlan M; Gaylord HS; Gaylord, MI; HonRl; MrchBnd; NHS; SctActv; StuCncl; TchrAde; Bsbl; Bsktbl; Ftbl; College; Professional.

MANLICK, Kathy J; Columbus HS; Marshfield, WI; Chr; HonRl; NatlCathMusEdAsoc; RedCrAde; StuCncl; RptrYrbk; FrCl; PpCl; Chrldr; University; Vocation.

MANLICK, Mike L; Auburndale HS; Auburndale, WI; CmntyWkr; HonRl; NHS; Sacrstn; StuCncl; FFA; Trade School.

MANN, Cheryl L; Turner HS; Kansas City, KS; DrlTm; HonRl; JrNHS; SchPl; StuCncl; TchrAde; Yrbk; SpnCl; PpCl; GAA; Trade School; Professional.

MANN, Diana K; Glenwood HS; Chatham, IL; 11/143 Chr; Chrs; HonRl; NHS; SchMus; GerCl; Univ; Lawyer.

MANN, Francie A; Warsaw Comm HS; Warsaw, IN; ChrhWkr; CtyCnl; CmntyWkr; JA; JCC; SchAde; SctActv; StuGov; YthFlsp; College; Fashion Merchandising.

MANN, George R; Pittsburg HS; Pittsburg, KS; LetterFtbl; IMSpt; College; Major Study.

MANN, Harper E; Quincy Senior HS; Quincy, IL; Aud/Vis; ChrhWkr; CmntyWkr; HonRl; PolWkr; RedCrAde; SchPl; SctActv; StuGov;.

MANN, James E; Robinson HS; Robinson, IL; 8/180 Band; Chr; ChrhWkr; HonRl; ModUN; SchPl; YthFlsp; SchPpr; PresSciCl; Glf; Rose Hulman Inst Of Tech; Physicist.

MANN, John F; Nebr City Sr HS; Nebraska City, NE; Aud/Vis; ChrhWkr; CAP; CmntyWkr; PolWkr; SchMus; SctActv; YthFlsp; RptrYrbk; CivCl; Univ Nebr; Medicine.

MANN, Kendra F; Haigler Public HS; Haigler, NE; 2/8 SecTrsFrshCls; PresSophCls; HonRl; SchPl; 4-H; PpCl; Bsbl; LetterTrk; LetterIMSpt; 4-HAwd; College; Secretarial.

MANN, Kent; Herrin Hs; Herrin, IL; 17/209 PpCl; Bsktbl; Souther Illinois U; Pre Law.

MANN, Kevin; Elkhart Central HS; Bristol, IN; HonRl; Engineering.

MANN, Kimberly C; Reitz Memorial HS; Evansville, IN; CncrtBnd; HonRl; MrchBnd; PepBnd; SchMus; GerCl; IMSpt; KiwanAwd; Univ; Engineer.

MANN, Kirk D; Gibson Southern HS; Haubstadt, IN; Band; ChrhWkr; CncrtBnd; MrchBnd; PepBnd; PolWkr; YthFlsp; LatCl; PpCl; Univ; Professional.

MANN, Larry C; Hannibal HS; Hannibal, MO; Band; CncrtBnd; MrchBnd; PepBnd; PolWkr; SctActv; LetterTrk; IMSpt; Us Army; Military.

MANN, Mary T; Bishop Le Blond HS; St Joseph, MO; NatlFornLg; NHS; Quill&Scroll; RedCrAde; EdSchPpr; SciCl; Missouri Western State; Medical Doctor.

MANN, Michael D; Alsen Public HS; Alsen, ND; 1/6 PresSrCls; Chr; HonRl; LbryAde; SchPl; StuCncl; RptrSchPpr; MthCl; LetterBsbl; Bsktbl; 4-HAwd; PresAwd; College; Mathematics.

MANN, Michael J; Bayless HS; St Louis, MO; CaptBsbl; CaptBsktbl; College; Business.

MANN, Nancy R; Montezuma Comm HS; Malcom, IA; AFS; ALAGirlsSt; Band; Chr; ChrhWkr; HonRl; MrchBnd; NHS; NatlThespSoc; Quill&Scroll; SchPl; StuCncl; Trk; CaptChrldr; College; Elementary Education.

MANN, Roger E; R Iii HS; Savannah, MO; CncrtBnd; MrchBnd; LetterBsktbl; LetterFtbl; LetterTrk; CchngActv; College.

MANN, Roy V; Northern Heights HS; Allen, KS; 4/40 ALBoysSt; Band; Chrs; HonRl; ModUN; NHS; SchMus; YthFlsp; FBLA; LetterBsbl; CaptFtbl; LetterTrk; AmLegAwd; Emporia Kansas St College; Music.

MANN, Stephen G; Griffin HS; Springfield, IL; College; Biology.

MANN, Tracy J; Glenbrook North HS; Northbrook, IL; 10/610 HonRl; NHS; TchrAde; Bsbl; CchngActv; College; Physical Ed.

MANNING, Arthur; Festus Senior HS; Festus, MO; 102/156 HonRl; SctActv; PpCl; IMSpt; Univ Mo; Basketball Bus Adm.

MANNING, Cheryl J; Yorkville HS; Minooka, IL; TrsSophCls; DrlTm; MrchBnd; YthFlsp; 4-H; Chrldr; GAA; 4-HAwd; PresAwd; VFWAwd; Joliet Jr Clge; Secretarial.

MANNING, Christine D; Sullivan HS; Sullivan, MO; 13/159 Chr; ChrhWkr; DrlTm; HonRl; NHS; FTA; SpnCl; RotaryAwd; College; Teacher.

MANNING, Cynthia L; Cloverdale HS; Poland, IN; ALAGirlsSt; HonRl; SpnCl; Indiana State University; Law.

MANNING, David M; North Central HS; Indianapolis, IN; 175/1165 ALBoysSt; PresChr; HonRl; ModUN; NHS; SchMus; SctActv; StuCncl; TreasKeyCl; U S Air Force Acad; Pilot.

MANNING, Duane R; Heritage Christian HS; Anderson, IN; PresJrCls; PresSrCls; Chr; LbryAde; SchMus; SchPl; Yrbk; 4-H; LetterBsktbl; LetterSocr; 4-HAwd; College; Mission Work.

MANNING, Edward B; Chadwick HS; Chadwick, IL; Band; Chrs; ChrhWkr; HonRl; LbryAde; PepBnd; SchMus; SchPl; StuCncl; University Of Dubuque; Business Admin.

MANNING, Maria V; Bergan HS; Peoria, IL; 17/208 DrlTm; HonRl; StuGov; RptrSchPpr; EdSchPpr; Univ Il.

MANNING, Mark; Exeter Public HS; Fairmont, NE; PresJrCls; Band; Chr; CncrtBnd; HonRl; NHS; College; Professional.

MANNING, Paula G; Pipestone HS; Pipestone, MN; 8/135 Chrs; HonRl; NHS; SchMus; LetterTrk; Chrldr; CchngActv; GAA; IMSpt; PresAwd; VFWAwd; College; Physical Educ.

MANNING, Scott; Exeter Hs; Fairmont, NE; Band; CncrtBnd; HonRl; SchPl; SptEdYrbk; Pres4-H; SecFFA; MthCl; LetterFtbl; LetterGlf; U Of Nebraska; Math.

MANNING, William R; Kapaun Mt Carmel HS; Wichita, KS; 6/175 CmntyWkr; HonRl; ModUN; NHS; StuCncl; StuGov; SptEdSchPpr; Bsktbl; Swmmng; Trk; Univ Of Kansas; Attorney.

MANNION, William; Montini Hs; Lombard, IL; 18/155 HonRl; TchrAde; Yrbk; EngCl;.

MANNIX, Teri L; Mitchell Jr Sr HS; Mitchell, IN; 10/150 SecTrsJrCls; Band; Chr; DrmMjrt; HonRl; MrchBnd; NatlThespSoc; SchMus; SchPl; PpCl; College; Pianist.

MANNS, Davis; Bentley HS; Livonia, MI; Band; Chr; Chrl; Chrs; HonRl; IntrClCncl; StuCncl; StuGov; TchrAde; PpCl; College; Professional.

MANNS, Susan; Marquette HS; Godfrey, IL; 1/130 Chrs; HonRl; NatlThespSoc; SchMus; SchPl; EdSchPpr; LatCl; MthCl; Univ; Medicine.

MANOR, Diane M; Gabriel Richard HS; Wyandotte, MI; CtyCnl; CmntyWkr; HonRl; NHS; NatlMeritFnl; PolWkr; SchPl; StuCncl; YthLg; RptrSchPpr; Marquette Univ; Accounting.

MANS, Lavonne B; Harrisburg HS; Sioux Falls, SD; Chrs; HonRl; SchMus; YthFlsp; RptrYrbk; EdYrBk; RptrSchPpr; SchPpr; FHA; PpCl;.

MANSELL, Patricia; Midland HS; Midland, MI; 24/419 ChrhWkr; HonRl; Mich Christian College; Science.

MANSFIELD, Caren S; Pana Sr HS; Pana, IL; ChrhWkr; HonRl; OffAde; RptrYrbk; RptrSchPpr; SchPpr; 4-H; FTA; GAA; College; Horticulture.

MANSFIELD, Donn; Jackson Parkside HS; Jackson, MI; 7/415 ChrhWkr; CncrtBnd; HonRl; MrchBnd; NatlMeritCmnd; PepBnd; IMSpt; Univ Of Michigan; Business Admin.

MANSFIELD, Eileen M; Our Lady Star Of The Sea HS; Grosse Pte Wds, MI; HospAde; OffAde; SchPl; TchrAde; PpCl; Bsbl; ChmnSwmmng; Tennis; GAA; IMSpt; College; Nursing.

MANSFIELD, Emilei M; Morenci Area HS; Morenci, MI; 4/81 Band; Chrs; ChrhWkr; RptrSchPpr; FHA; PpCl; CaptBsktbl; PresGAA; Kellogg Comm Col ;rn.

MANSFIELD, John J; Sault Area HS; Sault Ste Marie, MI; HonRl; ROTC; TchrAde; Armed Forces.

MANSFIELD, Laura J; John Hersey HS; Mt Prospect, IL; 65/786 HonRl; JA; JrNHS; NHS; GAA; Univ Of Illinois; Law.

MANSKE, Scott B; Oconomowoc HS; Oconomowoc, WI; 6/256 ALBoysSt; Band; Chr; HonRl; JrNHS; MrchBnd; NatlFornLg; NHS; SchMus; SchPl; University,madison; Law.

MANSKER, Gregory E; Hazel Park HS; Hazel Park, MI; 51/410 HonRl; Coll; Lawyer.

MANSON, David J; Aquin Central Catholic HS; Freeport, IL; 7/40 Chrs; HonRl; NHS; SchMus; MthCl; Bsktbl; Glf; Col; Curriculum Of Major Study.

MANSON, Karin C; Jefferson HS; Independence, IA; 28/130 Univ; Dentist.

MANSON, Kathy M; Aquin Central HS; Freeport, IL; PresSrCls; Chrs; CmntyWkr; HospAde; LbryAde; RedCrAde; EdYrBk; RptrSchPpr; GAA; College; Special Ed.

MANSOUR, Christopher J; Bentley HS; Davison, MI; ChrhWkr; HonRl; NHS; PolWkr; LetterFtbl; U Of Mi; Engineer.

MANSSEN, Keith R; Gilman HS; Danforth, IL; 3/50 SecJrCls; TrsJrCls; PresSrCls; Band; CncrtBnd; HonRl; MrchBnd; NHS; PepBnd; EdYrBk; Univ Of Illinois; Elec Engineering.

MANTEL, Jayne A; Hanover Central HS; Cedar Lake, IN; HonRl; JrNHS; NHS; StuCncl; RptrYrbk; FrCl; PpCl; Chrldr; GAA; PresAwd; Coll; Nursing.

MANTERNACH, Michael L; West Delaware HS; Manchester, IA; HonRl; Junior College; Agri Business.

MANTESE, Vito A; Oakville HS; St Louis, MO; 40/350 NHS; SchPl; MthCl; LetterWrstlng; JAAwd; U Of Mo St Louis; Medicine.

MANTEY, Robert J; Akron Fairgorve; Fairgrove, MI; 6/80 HonRl; NHS; StuCncl; TchrAde; Bsktbl; Ftbl; Trk; Mi State Univ; Vet Medicine.

MANTHEY, Candace R; Colome HS; Colome, SD; 1/34 VPJrCls; ALAGirlsSt; Band; HonRl; SchPl; StuCncl; EdYrBk; Yrbk; PpCl; AmLegAwd; College; Park Service.

MANTZ, Steve L; Slinger HS; Richfield, WI; Chr; ChrhWkr; YthFlsp; 4-H; FFA; SpnCl; LetterBsktbl; LetterFtbl; Trk; IMSpt; Trade School; Salesman Or Construction.

MANUEL, Jeffrey K; Argenta Oreana HS; Oreana, IL; 5/102 PresFrshCls; HonRl; NHS; SctActv; FrCl; Bsbl; Bsktbl; Ftbl; Adrian Col; Medicine.

MANUEL, Michael; Vianney HS; St Louis, MO; 57/186 PresSrCls; HonRl; StuCncl; EdYrBk; EdSchPpr; FDA; Ftbl; Tennis; IMSpt; U; Prof.

MANULIK, Paul E; Mary D Bradford HS; Kenosha, WI; 38/550 HonRl; Orch; Uw Parkside; Music.

MANUS, Brandon E; Delavan Community HS; Delavan, IL; ChrhWkr; HonRl; SchMus; SchPl; YthFlsp; RptrSchPpr; SchPpr; W Illinois Univ; Political Science.

MANUS, Cheryl A; Providence HS; New Albany, IN; PresSrCls; Chr; ChrhWkr; HonRl; NatlMeritSchl; SchPl; StuCncl; RptrYrbk; CchngActv; PresAwd; Ind Univ; Business.

MANVILLE, Toni; Webb HS; Ironton, WI; HonRl; PpCl; IMSpt; Madison Area Tech College; Med Secretary.

MANZER, Cindy A; Pierce Public HS; Pierce, NE; VPSrCls; Chr; HonRl; NatlThespSoc; TchrAde; PpCl; College; Nursing.

MANZER, Susan K; Pierce Public HS; Pierce, NE; Chr; HonRl; StuGov; 4-H; PpCl; Chrldr; 4-HAwd; PresAwd; College.

MAPES, Daniel P; Muskegon Catholic Central HS; Muskegon, MI; 73/215 ChrhWkr; HonRl; PolWkr; SchMus; Col; Pharmacy.

MAPES, Mary R; West Sioux Community HS; Hawarden, IA; 8/79 PresSophCls; HonRl; PresLbryAde; NHS; SchPl; RptrSchPpr; Buena Vista; English Teacher.

MAPES, Terry D; Nauvoo Colusa HS; Nauvoo, IL; SecJrCls; SchPl; YthFlsp; EdYrBk; FFA; Western Ill U; Lawyer.

MAPILI, Nina E; Owatonna HS; Owatonna, MN; VPJrCls; SecTrsSrCls; AFS; Chr; NatlMeritFnl; SecStuCncl; Yrbk; RptrSchPpr; SchPpr; SecSpnCl; LetterChrldr; GAA; IMSpt; Arizona St Univ; Architect.

MAR, Doreen H; Crispus Attucks HS; Indianapolis, IN; 1/205 CmntyWkr; HonRl; NHS; NatlMeritCmnd; PresStuCncl; SciCl; Univ; Medicine.

MARAN, Edward E; St Charles HS; St Charles, MO; 51/600 HonRl; PolWkr; Swmmng; Tennis; Trk; Military Academy; Lawyer.

MARAS, Jerald; Windom Area HS; Windom, MN; 19/138 ALBoysSt; Band; CncrtBnd; HonRl; MrchBnd; NHS; PepBnd; FFA; Bsbl; Ftbl;.

MARAZITA, Dominic; Waverly HS; Lansing, MI; NHS; TchrAde; Bsbl; Bsktbl; Ftbl; Glf; Trk; U Of Mi; Business Admin.

MARBLE, Sheryl L; La Grove Com HS; Farina, IL; 2/33 Band; Chrs; HonRl; SchPl; RptrYrbk; 4-H; FHA; FrCl; PpCl; Chrldr; GAA;.

MARBURGER, Edward J; Mt Olive HS; Mt Olive, IL; 5/60 PresJrCls; PresSrCls; Band; CncrtBnd; HonRl; PepBnd; PresStuCncl; Yrbk; PpCl; LetterWrstlng; U Of Il; Agriculture.

MARBURY, Cheryl P; Immaculata HS; Detroit, MI; ChrhWkr; CmntyWkr; HospAde; SchAde; SctActv; University; Nursing.

MARCACCIO, David A; Lakeshore HS; St Clair Shores, MI; Band; CncrtBnd; MrchBnd; SchMus; W Mi U; Music Minor.

MARCADIS, David B; Terre Haute So Vigo HS; Terre Haute, IN; 1/600 PresJrCls; PresSrCls; ALBoysSt; HonRl; SecKeyCl; VPSciCl; Ftbl; Wrstlng; University; Oceanography.

MARCANGELO, Margaret; Taft Hs; Chicago, IL; HonRl; NHS; SchPl; SctActv; GAA; U Of Ill; Business.

MARCEAU, Daniel J; Walled Lake Western HS; Walled Lake, MI; 52/397 HonRl; NHS; NatlMeritSF; RptrYrbk; EdYrBk; Yrbk; LetterTrk; Eastern Michigan University; Chemistry.

MARCELLETTI, Nicholas L; Paw Paw HS; Paw Paw, MI; ChrhWkr; Pres4-H; LetterTrk; 4-HAwd; College; Geology.

MARCH, Charles J; J F Kennedy HS; Chicago, IL; 14/610 Chrs; ChrhWkr; CmntyWkr; HonRl; JA; NHS; Orch; RedCrAde; Sacrstn; SctActv; Bsktbl; IMSpt; JCAwd; Illinois Institute; Engineer.

MARCH, Gary A; United Township HS; East Moline, IL; 97/600 HonRl; NHS; SpnCl; Bsktbl; Ftbl; Trk;.

MARCHAND, Patricia D; Woden Crystal Lake HS; Woden, IA; Band; CncrtBnd; HonRl; LbryAde; MrchBnd; SctActv; FBLA; FNA; College; Biology.

MARCHAND, Vicky L; Limestone HS; Peoria, IL; 67/403 VPSophCls; HonRl; StuCncl; TchrAde; RptrSchPpr; PpCl; Trk; Chrldr; Coll; Writing,social Work, Child Develop.

MARCHEK, Kevin F; Grand Ledge HS; Lansing, MI; 75/400 HonRl; LetterFtbl; LetterSwmmng; RotaryAwd; Coll; Eng.

MARCHEL, Sarah L; St Joan Antida HS; Milwaukee, WI; 11/105 Chr; ChrhWkr; HonRl; NHS; RedCrAde; StuCncl; TchrAde; FTA; VoiceDemAwd; College;psychologist.

MARCHELLO, Sandra M; Amos Alonzo Stagg HS; Hickory Hills, IL; 23/468 HonRl; TreasNHS; StuCncl; TchrAde; Twrl; SpnCl; SciCl; Trk; CaptChrldr; GovHonPrgAwd; Purdue Univ; Chemical Engineering.

MARCHETTI, Kathleen; Southwest HS; Green Bay, WI; 15/427 ALAGirlsSt; HonRl; NHS; StuCncl; PpCl; Tennis; GAA; DARAwd; JCAwd; Univ Of Wi; Accounting.

MARCHI, Susan C; Mother Of Sorrows HS; Chicago, IL; 31/143 HonRl; Yrbk; SpnCl; MthCl; College.

MARCHINO, Linda M; South Knox HS; Vincennes, IN; 2/130 SecSophCls; TrsJrCls; HonRl; NHS; FHA; MthCl; Vincennes Univ; Accounting.

MARCHINO, Rex A; South Knox HS; Wheatland, IN; 23/130 HonRl; Quill&Scroll; YthFlsp; Yrbk; SchPpr; Sec4-H; FFA; MthCl; Bsbl; Bsktbl; IMSpt; 4-HAwd;.

MARCHIORI, David A; Loyola Academy; Norridge, IL; 48/442 HonRl; NatlMeritCmnd; SpnCl; MthCl; Swmmng; University Of Notre Dame; Engineering.

MARCIN, Robert J; O Fallon Twp HS; O Fallon, IL; 35/315 HonRl; Comm Coll; Computer Science.

MARCINIAK, Francesca L; St Scholastica HS; Chicago, IL; NatlMeritCmnd;.

MARCK, Lori L; Beaver Dam Sr HS; Beaver Dam, WI; Bsktbl; LetterTrk; CaptChrldr; GAA; IMSpt; College.

MARCKS, Susan K; Pepin HS; Pepin, WI; TrsFrshCls; Chrs; HonRl; LbryAde; SchPl; TchrAde; EdSchPpr; FHA; PpCl; Chrldr; Business School.

MARCO, Philip L; St Joseph HS; Westchester, IL; 25/175 PresChrs; HonRl; NHS; Yrbk; PpCl; LetterBsbl; LetterBsktbl; CaptFtbl; IMSpt; AmLegAwd; College; Physical Education.

MARCOE, Elyse A; St Marys Springs HS; Fond Du Lac, WI; Band; HospAde; SchPpr; FHA; LatCl; Trk; Fond Du Lac Branch; Comm Art.

MARCOE, Kathleen; Horace Mann HS; Fond Du Lac, WI; 8/98 TrsFrshCls; Chr; Chrs; HonRl; NHS; SchPl; GAA; IMSpt; EldAwd; Vocational School; Medical Records Tech.

MARCOOT, Mary L; Mulberry Grove HS; Smithboro, IL; HonRl; NHS; OffAde; EdYrBk; FTA; Chrldr; GAA; DanFAwd; 4-HAwd; PresAwd; College; Teacher.

MARCOTT, Terry L; Medora HS; Medora, IN; 3/34 HstSophCls; Chr; ChrhWkr; CmntyWkr; HonRl; LbryAde; NHS; StuCncl; StuGov; RptrYrbk; LetterBsbl; CaptTrk; Franklin Col; Accounting.

MARCOTTE, Janet L; Westwood HS; Ishpeming, MI; PresBand; CncrtBnd; HonRl; MrchBnd; PepBnd; RptrYrbk; SptEdYrbk; SchPpr; Swmmng; LetterTrk; IMSpt; Hibbing Area Voc Tech Inst; General Office.

MARCOTTE, Susan M; Westhope Public HS; Westhope, ND; PresFrshCls; PresJrCls; Chr; CncrtBnd; HonRl; PepBnd; SchPl; StuCncl; PpCl; CaptBsktbl; IMSpt; Minot St Col; Psychology.

MARCOTTE, Theresa M; Bishop Mc Namara HS; Kankakee, IL; 25/161 HonRl; LitMag; LbryAde; StuCncl; GAA; Eastern Ill Univ; Special Education.

MARCOUILLER, Joan E; Hinsdale Twp HS; Hinsdale, IL; CmntyWkr; HonRl; HospAde; PpCl; College; Economics.

MARCQUENSKI, Susan V; Marillac HS; Glenview, IL; 41/250 Chrs; ChrhWkr; HospAde; LitMag; NHS; NatlMeritCmnd; SchMus; TchrAde; Univ Of Illinois; Veterinarian.

MARCUM, Jean M; Bishop Dubourg HS; St Louis, MO; HonRl; JrNHS; NHS; OffAde; SchAde; StuGov; TchrAde; IMSpt; Univ Of Mo; Chemical Engineer.

MARCUM, Pamela S; Union County HS; Liberty, IN; CmntyWkr; HonRl; JA; NHS; TchrAde; RptrYrbk; Yrbk; RptrSchPpr; FHA; PpCl; Purdue; Journalism.

MARCUSSE, Darlene K; Northern Mich Chr HS; Falmouth, MI; 7/41 HonRl; TchrAde; 4-H; PpCl; LetterBsktbl; Trk; IMSpt; 4-HAwd; Vocation.

MARDEN, Collyer L; Iowa City HS; Iowa City, IA; 1/279 HonRl; NHS; NatlMeritFnl; NatlMeritCmnd; Mit; Biochemistry.

MARDI, Alan M; Benson HS; Omaha, NE; Band; ChrhWkr; HonRl; MrchBnd; PepBnd; SctActv; LetterTrk; College; Teacher.

MARECEK, Michael W; Southwest HS; St Louis, MO; 150597 ChrhWkr; HonRl; TchrAde; CaptTennis; College.

MAREK, Margaret A; Willowbrook HS; Villa Park, IL; Chr; ChrhWkr; HonRl; JrNHS; Orch; SchAde; SchMus; TchrAde; Illinois Benedictine College; Theology.

MAREK, Mary P; Elizabeth Seton HS; Riverdale, IL; 46/252 HonRl; NHS; SchMus; Univ Of Illinois; Fine Arts.

MARES, Paula; Schuyler Central HS; Schuyler, NE; Chr; Chrs; HonRl; NHS; 4-H; FHA; GerCl; 4-HAwd; RotaryAwd; Universityofnebraska;zoology-or Psychology.

MARESCALCO, Regina L; South HS; Omaha, NE; 34/703 HonRl; NHS; OffAde; SchAde; SchPl; Coll; Nurse.

MARESH, Mary M; Brady HS; West St Paul, MN; Band; CmntyWkr; SchMus; College.

MARESKAS, Denise E; Warren Township HS; Waukegan, IL; 6/330 Band; CncrtBnd; HonRl; JrNHS; MrchBnd; NHS; PepBnd; FrCl; Siu; Dental Hygienist.

MARESKI, Ken D; Marysville HS; Marysville, MI; HonRl; Quill&Scroll; SchPl; PresStuCncl; RptrSchPpr; Ftbl; Trk; College.

MARG, Kathleen J; Neillsville HS; Neillsville, WI; 7/114 HonRl; NHS; Yrbk; SchPpr; FHA; EldAwd; Technical School; Fashion Merchandising.

MARGARIAN, Melanie A; Collinsville HS; Collinsville, IL; Chr; ChrhWkr; CmntyWkr; HonRl; TchrAde; SpnCl; SciCl; Southern Ill Univ; Nursing.

MARGESON, Lindy E; Huron HS; Ann Arbor, MI; 42/570 Band; HonRl; MrchBnd; PepBnd; StuGov; Yrbk; FrCl; LetterBsktbl; Trk; GAA; University Of Michigan.

MARGET, Don A; Fairmont Public HS; Fairmont, NE; 10/30 Chrs; HonRl; StuGov; RptrYrbk; Yrbk; SchPpr; Bsktbl; Ftbl; Trk; College; Vocation.

MARGHEIM, Ronald; Kearney Sr HS; Kearney, NE; Chr; Chrs; SchMus; SctActv; RptrYrbk; Yrbk; RptrSchPpr; SchPpr; Bsktbl; IMSpt; Business School; Accountant.

MARGOLIS, Merle I; Community HS; West Chicago, IL; 10/320 HonRl; VPJA; NatlMeritCmnd; NatlThespSoc; SctActv; RptrSchPpr; VPSpnCl; GAA; Univ Of Ill; Pharmacy.

MARGUART, Leann; Portland HS; Portland, MI; 16/150 VPSophCls; ChrhWkr; HonRl; NHS; SchPl; StuCncl; YthFlsp; RptrSchPpr; 4-H; FrCl; Chrldr; Sterling College; Church Youth Coordinator.

MARGULES, Mai Mai; Murphysboro Township Hs; Murphysboro, IL; NHS; NatlMeritSF; NatlSciFnd; PolWkr; SchPl; SchPpr; SciCl;.

MARI, Jeff L; Bottineau HS; Bottineau, ND; TrsJrCls; HonRl; SctActv; FFA; PpCl; College; Medicine.

MARIANI, Randy R; Toluca HS; Toluca, IL; 1/41 VPJrCls; VPSrCls; ChrhWkr; HonRl; NHS; NatlMeritCmnd; NatlMeritSF; StuCncl; Bsbl; Bsktbl; Il Valley Comm Col; Law.

MARIENAU, Kenneth; Kearney Senior HS; Kearney, NE; 9/248 HonRl; NatlMeritFnl; Quill&Scroll; SctActv; IMSpt; AmLegAwd; EldAwd; Univ Of Ne; Chemical Engineering.

MARIENAU, Kenneth H; Kearney HS; Kearney, NE; 9/258 HonRl; VPNatlFornLg; NatlMeritSF; Quill&Scroll; SctActv; VPStuCncl; Yrbk; SchPpr; SecKeyCl; IMSpt; U Of Ne; Business Administration.

MARIENAU, Valerie; West Sioux Community HS; Hawarden, IA; 1/79 Band; Chrs; CncrtBnd; HonRl; MrchBnd; NHS; NatlMeritCmnd; SchMus; Bsktbl; Glf; Southwestern Ok State Univ; Med Rec Admin.

MARIETTA, Janis E; Paris HS; Paris, IL; 1/265 CncrtBnd; HonRl; MrchBnd; SecSpnCl; Purdue Univ; Language Major.

MARIETTA, Tamara L; Marathon Cons HS; Marathon, IA; 6/19 VPFrshCls; VPSophCls; PresSrCls; Chr; HonRl; StuCncl; RptrYrbk; RptrSchPpr; Bsktbl;.

MARIHUGH, Mary J; Harbor Springs HS; Harbor Springs, MI; HonRl; TchrAde; RptrYrbk; FshEdSchPpr; PpCl;.

MARIKOS, Mark R; Rantoul Twp HS; Gifford, IL; ALBoysSt; NHS; Bsktbl; Ftbl; Univ; Professional.

MARINANGEL, Jeffrey A; Fenton HS; Bensenville, IL; HonRl; LetterBsbl; LetterBsktbl; LetterFtbl; GovHonPrgAwd; Univ Of Illinois; Agriculture.

MARINELLO, Michele A; Douglas Mac Arthur HS; Saginaw, MI; 59/302 HonRl; NHS; PolWkr; SchPl; StuCncl; StuGov; TchrAde; SpnCl; PpCl; Michigan State Univ; Psychology.

MARINER, William G; Fenwick HS; Oak Park, IL; 22/223 Band; HonRl; NHS; StuCncl; RptrSchPpr; GerCl; Providence College; Medicine.

MARINO, Alfonso E; Warren Woods HS; Warren, MI; 30/300 Band; CncrtBnd; HonRl; MrchBnd; TreasNHS; NatlMeritCmnd; NatlMeritSchl; NatlMeritSF; CaptTrk; Mich State Univ; Eng.

MARINO, Josephine; St Clement HS; Center Line, MI; 41#44#46 NHS; FHA; PpCl; Busi.

MARION, James N; Southwest HS; St Louis, MO; Chrs; ChrhWkr; SctActv; Wrstlng; IMSpt; GodCntryAwd; PresAwd; University; Vocation.

MARION, Scott R; Brentwood HS; Brentwood, MO; SpnCl; College; Science.

MARIS, Roxy L; Wauneta HS; Hamlet, NE; SecSrCls; ChrhWkr; HonRl; RedCrAde; StuCncl; YthFlsp; Swmmng; Trk; College; Medical Technician.

MARISCH, Cindy; Maple Valley HS; Nashville, MI; 1/108 Band; CncrtBnd; HonRl; MrchBnd; NHS; Orch; PepBnd; StuGov; 4-H; SpnCl; Univ; Major Study.

MARISCH, Diane; Spalding Public HS; Spalding, NE; 2/15 SecFrshCls; TrsSophCls; Chrs; HonRl; NHS; OffAde; SchPl; FHA; PpCl; Lincoln School Of Commerce; Ex Sec Course.

MARJASON, Ruth E; Elkhart Central HS; Elkhart, IN; 60/500 Chr; HonRl; OffAde; TchrAde; Teen; FrCl; Purdue; Veterinary Medicine.

MARK, Brian J; Dearborn HS; Dearborn, MI; Band; Chr; HonRl; NatlMeritSF; NatlThespSoc; Orch; SchPl; U Of Michigan; Music.

MARK, Debra; Fowlerville HS; Fowkrville, MI; DrlTm; JA; NHS; SchPl; PpCl; GAA; PPFtbl; BttyCrckrAwd; Cllege; Corporate Lawyer.

MARK, Gregory A; Truman HS; Independence, MO; ALBoysSt; Band; Chr; ChrhWkr; VPCncrtBnd; HonRl; MrchBnd; NHS; Orch; PepBnd; SchMus; LetterBsktbl; LetterGlf; Trk; Graceland College; Medicine.

MARK, Marie; Rochester HS; Rochester, IN; 3/163 HonRl; NHS; OffAde; YthFlsp; 4-H; GerCl; Rn.

MARK, Stephen F; Hubbard HS; Chicago, IL; 5/512 Aud/Vis; CncrtBnd; HonRl; NHS; OffAde; TchrAde; TreasMthCl; CaptBsktbl; Ftbl;.

MARKEE, Mary K; Columbus HS; Marshfield, WI; 27/105 HonRl; MrchBnd; Business Schl; Secretary.

MARKEE, Wendy L; O Fallon Twp HS; O Fallon, IL; HonRl; JrNHS; ModUN; NatlFornLg; NHS; SchPl; SctActv; FSA; SciCl; Univ; Law Or Chem.

MARKEL, Karen E; Evanston Twp HS; Evanston, IL; Chrl; ChrhWkr; HonRl; NatlMeritCmnd; SchMus; St Olaf College; English.

MARKEL, Richard L; Mc Ward Cottrell HS; Marine City, MI; 18/162 HonRl; NHS; SchPl; StuCncl; Trk; Wrstlng; CitAwd; Central Mi Univ; Architecture.

MARKEL, Robert F; Marine City HS; Marine City, MI; 19/162 CmntyWkr; HonRl; SchAde; StuGov; TchrAde; 4-H; KeyCl; St Clair Comm Coll; Electonics Tech.

MARKELIS, Daiva M; Morton East HS; Cicero, IL; HonRl; NatlFornLg; NatlThespSoc; OffAde; SchMus; SchPl; College.

MARKER, Lorri L; Unionville Sebewaing HS; Unionville, MI; Aud/Vis; HonRl; YthFlsp; PpCl;.

MARKERT, Carol; Winneconne HS; Winneconne, WI; 6/130 AFS; CmntyWkr; HonRl; NHS; NatlMeritCmnd; SchPl; RptrYrbk; 4-H; Univ Of Wis; Occupational Therapy.

MARKEY, Deana R; Athens HS; Cantrall, IL; 1/59 ChrhWkr; HonRl; NHS; FHA; CaptBsktbl; Chrldr; Secretarial Work.

MARKGRAF, Brenda D; Stewart Public HS; Willman, MN; 24/37 Chrs; HonRl; LbryAde; SchPl; EdYrBk; RptrSchPpr; FHA; Willmar Vo Tech; Med Office Assistant.

MARKGRAF, Cheryl L; Concordia Academy; St Paul, MN; Chr; Chrl; Chrs; ChrhWkr; HonRl; OffAde; Orch; SchMus; SchPl; TchrAde; Concordia Col; Music Educ.

MARKGRAF, Janet L; Joliet East HS; Joliet, IL; 20/407 Chr; HonRl; NHS; OffAde; Quill&Scroll; SchPl; TchrAde; FshEdYrbk; FrCl; Chrldr; Northern Ill Univ; Education.

MARKGRAF, Steven R; St Louis Park HS; St Louis Park, MN; Bsbl; CaptIMSpt; College; Professnl.

MARKHAM, Beth A; Lake Forest HS; Lake Forest, IL; 60/445 ChrhWkr; HonRl; LitMag; SchMus; SchPl; RptrYrbk; Swmmng; GAA; Purdue Univ; Lawyer Political Science.

MARKHAM, Kristine M; Galesburg Sr HS; Galesburg, IL; 88/588 SecSrCls; Chr; HonRl; StuCncl; PpCl; University Of Iowa; Physical Therapy.

MARKIEWICZ, Janice M; Marian HS; South Bend, IN; 2/120 ALAGirlsSt; HonRl; NHS; NatlMeritCmnd; Purdue Univ; Computer Science.

MARKIEWICZ, John J; St Laurence HS; Chicago, IL; 68/386 HonRl; NatlMeritCmnd; NatlMeritSF; StuCncl; StuGov; Bsktbl; Northern Ill Univ; Business Admin.

MARKL, Cynthia A; Barstow HS; Overland Park, KS; Chr; Chrs; OffAde; SchMus; SchPl; TchrAde; LetterGlf; LetterChrldr; CchngActv; College; Business & Law.

MARKLEIN, Robert A; Janesville Craig Sr HS; Janesville, WI; 19/478 ChrhWkr; CmntyWkr; HonRl; LbryAde; NHS; Orch; TchrAde; 4-H; MthCl; Univ Of Wisconsin; Science.

MARKLEY, Bernard A; Donovan HS; Iroquois, IL; 2/51 Chrs; CncrtBnd; HonRl; Mdrgl; VPNHS; SchMus; LetterBsktbl; Glf; University; Music.

MARKLEY, Dagmar M; West Noble HS; Cromwell, IN; DrlTm; SchPl; RptrYrbk; RptrSchPpr; VPSpnCl;.

MARKLEY, Greg A; Aberdeen Central HS; Aberdeen, SD; AFS; Band; ChrhWkr; CncrtBnd; HonRl; MrchBnd; PepBnd; SchMus; SctActv; Ftbl; College; Veterinary.

MARKLEY, Lance J; West Elk HS; Howard, KS; ALBoysSt; Band; Chrs; ChrhWkr; CncrtBnd; HonRl; MrchBnd; PepBnd; 4-H; FFA; College.

MARKLEY, Mary J; Centerville HS; Richmond, IN; ALAGirlsSt; ChrhWkr; NHS; TchrAde; PresTeen; EdYrBk; VPFrCl; CaptTennis; GAA; Univ; Phy Educ.

MARKLEY, Merl A; Spoon River Valley HS; Ellisville, IL; VPSophCls; Chrs; HonRl; SchAde; SchPl; TchrAde; FFA;.

MARKMAN, Thomas I; Highland Pk HS; Highland Park, IL; SecTrsJrCls; PresSrCls; Aud/Vis; HonRl; NHS; SchMus; SchPl; StuGov; LetterSocr; Univ Of Ill; Business.

MARKO, Kathy; Whiting HS; Whiting, IN; 8/101 Chr; Chrs; CmntyWkr; HonRl; TchrAde; YthFlsp; Yrbk; FTA; PpCl; KiwanAwd; College; Prof Interior Decorator.

MARKOW, Nancy A; Dundee Community HS; Dundee, IL; 12/368 Band; DrlTm; HonRl; JrNHS; MrchBnd; NHS; NatlMeritSchl; E C C; Forestry.

MARKOWITZ, David L; Mayo HS; Rochester, MN; 72/423 Band; Chr; CncrtBnd; NHS; SchMus; SchPl; RusCl; SciCl; Bsbl; Ftbl; U Of Mn.

MARKS, Barry S; Glenbrook North HS; Northbrook, IL; 27/610 VPSrCls; HonRl; JrNHS; NHS; LetterBsbl; LetterFtbl; University; Business.

MARKS, Dean W; Jefferson Community HS; Jefferson, IA; ALBoysSt; Aud/Vis; Chr; HonRl; StuCncl; Yrbk; SchPpr; AmLegAwd; College; Accounting.

MARKS, Dorothea; Crispus Attuck HS; Indianapolis, IN; 14/264 TrsJrCls; TrsSrCls; HonRl; NHS; StuCncl; PpCl; Tennis; Chrldr; Vincennes U; Data Proc.

MARKS, Gayle M; Clarence M Kimball HS; Royal Oak, MI; 67/703 Band; ChrhWkr; HonRl; MrchBnd; NHS; NatlMeritCmnd; PresFNA; U Of Mi; Bus Admn.

MARKS, Gregory L; Chilton Public HS; Chilton, WI; AFS; HonRl; NHS; NatlMeritCmnd; 4-H; FrCl; Bsktbl; Tennis; IMSpt; College; Med Profession.

MARKS, Jimmie O; Southeast HS; Wichita, KS; Band; CncrtBnd; HonRl; MthCl; LetterFtbl; CaptWrstlng; Naval Acad; Major Study.

MARKS, Kim M; Hamilton Southeastern HS; Fishers, IN; 8/141 TrsFrshCls; VPSophCls; VPJrCls; Band; HospAde; NHS; GerCl; College; Nursing.

MARKS, Kim R; Arlington HS; Indianapolis, IN; 30/465 HonRl; MrchBnd; NHS; FrCl; LetterTennis; GAA; College; Professional.

MARKS, Linda M; Corwith Wesley HS; Corwith, IA; PresJrCls; Chr; ChrhWkr; HonRl; Mdrgl; NHS; SchMus; PresYthFlsp; FshEdSchPpr; LetterTrk; Mount Mercy College; Registered Nurse.

MARKS, Mari L; Waupun HS; Oakfield, WI; Chr; ChrhWkr; CncrtBnd; MrchBnd; PepBnd; SchPl; YthFlsp; 4-H; CaptBsktbl; Trk; CaptChrldr; GAA; 4-HAwd; College; Vet Aide.

MARKS, Marvin E; L L Wright HS; Ironwood, MI; Aud/Vis; ChrhWkr; CncrtBnd; HonRl; LbryAde; NatlFornLg; PresStuCncl; SchPpr; PresKeyCl; GerCl; Col; Professional.

MARKS, Michael D; Evanston Township HS; Evanston, IL; NatlMeritFnl; NatlMeritSF; PolWkr; SctActv; SciCl; IMSpt; Univ;engineering.

MARKS, Michael R; Winnebago HS; Winnebago, MN; CmntyWkr; HonRl; JA; JrNHS; NHS; NatlSciFnd; LetterTrk; IMSpt; JAAwd; PresAwd; Trade School.

MARKS, Sally; Cedarburg HS; Cedarburg, WI; AFS; ChrhWkr; HonRl; SctActv; TchrAde; Bsktbl; GAA; PPFtbl; Univ Wis Whitewater; Special Education.

MARKS, Steven R; Pine River Area HS; Leroy, MI; Aud/Vis; Chr; ChrhWkr; HonRl; YthFlsp; EdYrBk; Bsbl; Bsktbl; LetterFtbl; Bus Sch; Accountant.

MARKS, Terry L; Collinsville HS; Collinsville, IL; ChrhWkr; SctActv; LetterFtbl; Trk; GodCntryAwd; College.

MARKWALD, Christine; Luther Hs North; Chicago, IL; 6/236 HonRl; LbryAde; ModUN; GerCl; Wartburg College; International Business.

MARKWARD, Lisa K; Indian Creek HS; Franklin, IN; 9/112 TrsJrCls; ALAGirlsSt; SecBand; VPNHS; StuCncl; PresYthFlsp; EdSchPpr; Pres4-H; SecPpCl; GAA; Ball State U; Journalism.

MARKWARDT, John E; Verona HS; Oregon, WI; SctActv; FFA; LetterTrk; Wrstlng; IMSpt; Uw Madison; Agriculture.

MARKWAY, Theresa L; Pattonville Sr HS; St Ann, MO; Chr; ChrhWkr; DrlTm; DrmBgl; HonRl; JA; PpCl; IMSpt; PPFtbl; Jr College; Art Teacher.

MARKWELL, Dennis L; Cumberland HS; Greenup, IL; 1/103 Band; HonRl; PresNHS; TreasStuCncl; AmLegAwd; Eastern Illinois Univ; Medicine.

MARLATT, Julia L; Sarcovie HS; Sarcovie, MO; 2/64 SecSrCls; Band; Chr; CncrtBnd; HonRl; MrchBnd; PolWkr; StuCncl; FTA; PpCl; College.

MARLATT, Nancy J; Alliance HS; Alliance, NE; 13/153 TrsSophCls; TrsJrCls; HonRl; NHS; PpCl; DARAwd; CitAwd; Nursing Sch; Professional.

MARLETT, Bonita L; Keokuk Senior HS; Keokuk, IA; AFS; CncrtBnd; DrlTm; HonRl; MrchBnd; NHS; NatlThespSoc; SchMus; HospAde; PpCl; Univ Of Northern Iowa; Mathematics.

MARLETTE, Ann E; Northwestern HS; Melette, SD; Band; Chrs; CncrtBnd; HonRl; PepBnd; College; Foreign Languages.

MARLETTE, Bill D; Redfield HS; Redfield, SD; AFS; ALBoysSt; Chrs; HonRl; NHS; SchMus; SctActv; Ftbl; Trk; Wrstlng;.

MARLETTE, Janel; Redfield Public School; Redfield, SD; PresSophCls; CncrtBnd; HonRl; MrchBnd; SchMus; SchPl; StuCncl; PpCl; LetterBsktbl; Chrldr;.

MARLEY, Daniel S; Bloomington HS; Bloomington, IL; 4/393 HonRl; NHS; NatlMeritFnl; NatlMeritCmnd; NatlMeritSF; Illinois St Univ; Forestry.

MARLIN, Owen M; Derby HS; Derby, KS; 60/355 HonRl; JrNHS; NHS; LetterBsbl; CaptBsktbl; IMSpt; College; Liberal Arts.

MARLOW, Annetta K; North Platte Senior HS; North Platte, NE; HonRl; RedCrAde; PresSctActv; YthFlsp; FNA; PpCl; Tennis; GAA; IMSpt; Univ Of Ne; Medicine.

MARLOW, Catherine J; Tamaroa HS; Tamaroa, IL; Chrs; HonRl; HospAde; SchMus; TchrAde; EdYrBk; EdSchPpr; 4-H; FHA; PpCl; Coll; Teaching Or Secretarial.

MARLOW, Julie K; Morton Sr HS; Hammond, IN; 1/529 ALAGirlsSt; ChrhWkr; HonRl; VPNHS; SciCl; College; Law.

MARLOW, Susan J; Northwest HS; High Ridge, MO; TrsJrCls; HonRl; LitMag; NHS; OffAde; RptrSchPpr; SecFBLA; College; Journalism.

MARMET, Brenda K; Sabetha HS; Sabetha, KS; 2/67 ChrhWkr; HonRl; NHS; NatlMeritCmnd; StuCncl; PpCl; Bsbl; CaptBskbtl; CchngActv; GAA; Kansas State U; Mathematics.

MARMION, Marleen W; Granite City South HS; Granite City, IL; 36/630 Chrs; NHS; NatlMeritCmnd; SchPl; StuCncl; Southern Ill Univ; Accounting.

MARMUL, Lawrence J; St Andrew HS; Detroit, MI; TrsSophCls; Chrl; SchAde; CaptBskbtl; IMSpt; College; Conservation.

MARNER, Linda K; Iowa Mennonite HS; Marengo, IA; SecSophCls; Chr; JrNHS; RptrYrbk; IMSpt; Kirkwood; Bookkeeping.

MARNEY, Tim J; Exeter HS; Cassville, MO; Chr; Chrs; HonRl; StuCncl; TchrAde; 4-H; Bsbl; Bskbtl; Trk; CchngActv;.

MARO, Michael P; Kewanee HS; Kewanee, IL; HonRl; StuGov; KeyCl; VPLatCl; SciCl; CchngActv; Black Hawk East College; Mech Engineering.

MAROHL, Merrie K; Shawano HS; Shawano, WI; TrsSophCls; TrsJrCls; StuCncl; LetterTrk; LetterChrldr; GAA; College.

MAROLT, Ray A; Notre Dame HS; W Milwaukee, WI; 51/117 ChrhWkr; CmntyWkr; HonRl; JCC; PolWkr; StuCncl; PpCl; LetterBsbl; LetterBskbtl; Univ Of Wisconsin; Education.

MARONDE, Mark E; Columbia Hts Sr HS; Columbia Hts, MN; 15/565 Band; Chr; ChrhWkr; CncrtBnd; HonRl; MrchBnd; NHS; NatlMeritCmnd; College; Liberal Arts.

MARONE, Sally A; Highland Pk HS; Highland Park, MI; 2/250 Band; CncrtBnd; HonRl; LbryAde; MrchBnd; NHS; LetterSwmmng; LetterTennis; BauchLmbAwd; U Of Mi ;med.

MARONEY, Ann E; Tiskilua HS; Tiskilwa, IL; 9/35 Band; Chrs; CncrtBnd; HonRl; MrchBnd; PepBnd; FHA; Chrldr; GAA; AmLegAwd; College; Professional.

MAROTHY, Beth A; Harper Creek HS; Battle Creek, MI; Band; Chrl; ChrhWkr; CncrtBnd; HonRl; MrchBnd; NHS; PepBnd; StuCncl; RptrYrbk; EdYrBk; College; Elem Ed.

MAROTTE, Joan; Wauwatosa East HS; Wauwatosa, WI; TrsJrCls; Chr; Chrs; CmntyWkr; StuCncl; Bsbl; College.

MAROTZKE, Gail A; Fulda HS; Fulda, MN; 21/84 Chr; ChrhWkr; CncrtBnd; MrchBnd; PepBnd; LetterBskbtl; Augsburg College; Math.

MAROZAS, Dianne C; St Francis Academy; Joliet, IL; 25/178 Band; HonRl; NatlMeritCmnd; StuCncl; RptrYrbk; SchPpr; LatCl; SciCl; IMSpt; Northwestern Univ; Science.

MARQUARDT, Cheryl; Lebanon HS; Lebanon, IL; 17/95 HonRl; OffAde; StuCncl; TchrAde; YthFlsp; PpCl; IMSpt; Univ; Business Educ.

MARQUARDT, Daniel W; Bottineau HS; Bottineau, ND; 8/68 HonRl; PresFFA; CaptBskbtl; Ftbl; Trk; College; Agriculture.

MARQUARDT, Deborah A; Kingston HS; Kingston, MI; Band; HonRl; LbryAde; MrchBnd; TchrAde; Yrbk; College; Nurse.

MARQUARDT, Glenna J; Lacrosse HS; Wanatah, IN; 6/48 VPSophCls; ALAGirlsSt; Chr; Chrs; ChrhWkr; HonRl; LitMag; StuCncl; TchrAde; YthFlsp; Beauty School; Beautician.

MARQUARDT, Joyce L; Schleswig Comm HS; Schleswig, IA; 10/50 SecJrCls; SecTrsSrCls; Chrs; ChrhWkr; NHS; FHA; LetterBskbtl; Buena Vista College; Special Education.

MARQUARDT, Marcia K; Osage Comm HS; Osage, IA; Band; ChrhWkr; CncrtBnd; MrchBnd; PepBnd; SctActv; TchrAde; YthFlsp; FTA; Bsbl; Ellsworth Jr Clg; Human Services.

MARQUARDT, Rita F; Van Meter Community HS; Booneville, IA; 6/36 VPFrshCls; SecJrCls; SecSophCls; VPFrshCls; ChrhWkr; NHS; RptrYrbk; LetterBskbtl; ChmnTrk; 4-HAwd; School Of Nursng.

MARQUARDT, Rock D; Bryant HS; Rich Hill, MO; VPFrshCls; HonRl; SchPl; SctActv; YthFlsp; SptEdYrbk; FFA; Bsbl; Bskbtl; Ftbl; Trk; Univ Of Mo.

MARQUARDT, Sharon; Bloomer HS; Bloomer, WI; Band; ChrhWkr; HonRl; MrchBnd; NatlSciFnd; SciCl; GAA; IMSpt; 4-HAwd; College; Professional.

MARQUART, Barbara J; Lakota HS; Lakota, ND; ChrhWkr; CmntyWkr; HonRl; NHS; SchPl; 4-H; FHA; PpCl; Bskbtl; Univ Of North Dakota; X Ray Tech.

MARQUART, Melody J; Rolla Public HS; Rolla, ND; 6/35 Band; CncrtBnd; HonRl; MrchBnd; PepBnd; SchPl; Mary Col; Med Technician.

MARQUART, Nancy J; Arlington HS; Indianapolis, IN; 5/350 Band; CncrtBnd; HonRl; HospAde; JrNHS; MrchBnd; NHS; Orch; PepBnd; Purdue Univ; Veterinary Medicine.

MARQUART, Patti L; Lakota Public HS; Lakota, ND; PresFrshCls; Band; Chr; ChrhWkr; HonRl; NHS; SecStuCncl; LetterBskbtl; Chrldr; 4-HAwd; U Of North Dakota; Professional.

MARQUART, Scott E; Whitewater HS; Delavan, WI; Band; ChrhWkr; CncrtBnd; MrchBnd; SchMus; SchPl; 4-H; SecFFA; Ftbl; Trk; Wrstlng; Univ Of Wisconsin; Farm Owner.

MARQUES, Robert; St Patrick HS; Chicago, IL; HonRl; U S Marine Corp; Tele Comm Electronics.

MARQUETTE, Kristy L; Sterling Public HS; Sterling, NE; TrsFrshCls; PresSophCls; Chrs; HonRl; NHS; SchPl; TchrAde; PpCl; CaptBskbtl; Chrldr; Univ Of Nebraska; Child Educ.

MARQUIS, Elizabeth A; Sunset Hill HS; Kansas City, MO; PresFrshCls; PresJrCls; AFS; Chrs; Mdrgl; Quill&Scroll; SchMus; SchPl; SchPpr; FrCl; College; Chemistry.

MARQUIS, Janice K; David City HS; Rising City, NE; 10/51 SecSrCls; PresBand; Chr; CncrtBnd; DrmMjrt; HonRl; MrchBnd; NatlThespSoc; PepBnd; SchMus; Twrl; SecPpCl; Glf; Trk; College; Vocation.

MARQUIS, Jocelyn; Randolph Southern HS; Lynn, IN; 13/61 Band; Chrs; HonRl; MrchBnd; PepBnd; SchMus; TchrAde; YthFlsp; 4-H; Bsbl; College; Vocation.

MARQUIS, Patrick; St Marys HS; Independence, MO; PresJrCls; TrsSrCls; ALBoysSt; HonRl; SchMus; SctActv; StuCncl; GerCl; Trk; Wrstlng; College; Politics.

MARQUISOS, George N; Lane Technical HS; Chicago, IL; 80/1213 ChrhWkr; HonRl; LbryAde; NHS; SctActv; StuGov; TchrAde; MthCl; Bskbtl; Northwestern Univ; Medical Doctor.

MARR, Colleen K; Rosalie Public HS; Rosalie, NE; VPSophCls; Chrs; HonRl; SchMus; SchPl; PpCl; Chrldr; Business School; Fashion Merchandising.

MARR, Joe K; Superior HS; Superior, NE; CmntyWkr; StuGov; RptrSchPpr; College; Game Management.

MARR, Nils K; Papillion HS; Papillion, NE; YthFlsp; RptrYrbk; Yrbk; RptrSchPpr; SchPpr; Bskbtl; Ftbl; Univ Of Nebraska; Marine Biology.

MARR, Vera L; Portageville HS; Portageville, MO; 29/74 Chrs; ChrhWkr; HonRl; StuCncl; FBLA; FSA; FTA; FrCl; PpCl; DanFAwd; Col; Pro.

MARRAN, Jay F; New Trier East HS; Wilmette, IL; PresSophCls; ChrhWkr; PolWkr; Dickinson College; Pre Law.

MARREN, Daniel G; Griffith HS; Griffith, IN; 1/310 JrNHS; NHS; NatlMeritSF; PresQuill&Scroll; EdYrBk; AmLegAwd; Univ Of Notre Dame; Accounting.

MARRIES, Christine E; Rochester Sr HS; Rochester, MI; HospAde; JA; NHS; SpnCl; LetterBskbtl; CchngActv; GAA; AmLegAwd; Oakland U; Med Tech.

MARRIOTT, Melinda K; Clinton HS; Clinton, MO; 20/161 Chr; Chrl; Chrs; ChrhWkr; HonRl; Mdrgl; YthFlsp; College.

MARRISON, Randy L; Mason County Central HS; Scottville, MI; Chr; HonRl; YthFlsp; 4-H; West Shore Comm Clge; Physicist.

MARRS, Richard L; Reed Custer HS; Braceville, IL; 1/65 Band; ChrhWkr; CncrtBnd; HonRl; NHS; PepBnd; SchMus; SchPl; SctActv; StuCncl; Trk; Wrstlng; Us Naval Academy; Officer.

MARSAGLIA, Kathleen M; Sacred Heart Academy; Springfield, IL; 8/150 HonRl; NatlMeritCmnd; SchPl; StuGov; Yrbk; MthCl; Univ Of Illinois; Engineer.

MARSALLI, Michael; St Ignatius HS; Park Ridge, IL; 5/156 HonRl; NHS; NatlMeritSF; RptrSchPpr; LetterSocr; Harvard Univ; Law.

MARSCHMAN, Monte K; Meridian HS; Alexandria, NE; Chrs; HonRl; StuCncl; Bskbtl; Wrstlng;.

MARSDEN, Dana S; Bottineau HS; Bottineau, ND; 2/70 PresJrCls; TrsSrCls; ALBoysSt; Chr; HonRl; SchMus; TreasStuCncl; Bsbl; LetterBskbtl; LetterFtbl; Glf; LetterTrk; University; Accounting.

MARSDEN, James F; St Patrick HS; Chicago, IL; CtyCnl; JA; JrNHS; NatlMeritSchl; RedCrAde; SchAde; SctActv; StuCncl; StuGov; YthFlsp; College; Professional.

MARSEILLE, Robert G; Hinsdale Central HS; Hinsdale, IL; 11/608 HonRl; LitMag; NHS; SchAde; Yrbk; SchPpr; Ftbl; LetterSocr; LetterTrk; College; Law.

MARSH, Anthony E; Lakeland Union HS; Boulder Jct, WI; Band; CncrtBnd; HospAde; PepBnd; StuCncl; RptrSchPpr; LetterFtbl; LetterWrstlng; College.

MARSH, Cindy S; Southeast Warren HS; Milo, IA; Chrs; CncrtBnd; HonRl; SchPl; RptrSchPpr; 4-H; SpnCl; Bskbtl; Trk; Trade School; Legal Secretary.

MARSH, Clare; Sycamore HS; Sycamore, IL; ChrhWkr; CncrtBnd; HonRl; MrchBnd; PepBnd; Univ; Professional.

MARSH, Dean A; Frederick HS; Westpoint, SD; 7/34 VPSophCls; SecTrsSrCls; Chrs; HonRl; SptEdYrbk; 4-H; PpCl; Bskbtl; Ftbl; Trk; Clge; Archit.

MARSH, Henry E; Prosser Voc HS; Chicago, IL; Chr; ChrhWkr; HonRl; PresTeen; LetterFtbl; LetterWrstlng; Lee Col; Preacher.

MARSH, Jacque; Neligh Public HS; Neligh, NE; PresSrCls; VPSrCls; Chr; DrlTm; HonRl; StuCncl; YthFlsp; 4-H; Business Sch; Law.

MARSH, James E; Reading HS; Reading, MI; 12/66 PresSophCls; Band; CncrtBnd; HonRl; JrNHS; MrchBnd; StuCncl; LetterBsktbl; LetterTrk; CaptIMSpt; Grand Vly St College; Sec Schl Admin.

MARSH, James I; Lakeland Union HS; Boulder Junction, WI; ALBoysSt; Band; CncrtBnd; StuCncl; SpnCl; LetterFtbl; Wrstlng; College.

MARSH, Joy L; St Louis HS; St Louis, MI; Band; Chr; Chrl; Chrs; ChrhWkr; CncrtBnd; HonRl; Mdrgl; MrchBnd; PepBnd; SchAde; SchMus; SchPl; TchrAde; College; Music Teacher.

MARSH, Mark A; Pontiac Northern HS; Pontiac, MI; ALBoysSt; Band; ChrhWkr; CncrtBnd; HonRl; MrchBnd; PepBnd; StuGov; RptrSchPpr; Swmmng; Mi St Univ; Veterinary Medicine.

MARSH, Michael L; Union City HS; Union City, MI; 8/92 VPFrshCls; HonRl; SchPl; StuCncl; LetterFtbl; CaptWrstlng; Tri State Clge; Eng.

MARSH, Richard J; Atlanta HS; La Plata, MO; TrsSophCls; ChrhWkr; CmntyWkr; HonRl; LbryAde; VPNHS; TreasStuCncl; TreasYthFlsp; Pres4-H; FFA; SciCl; LetterBsktbl; DanFAwd; Univ Of Missouri; Agriculture.

MARSH, Roger W; Kingsville HS; Kingsville, MO; 3/22 PresFrshCls; VPSrCls; HonRl; JrNHS; VPNHS; SchPl; SptEdSchPpr; LetterBsbl; LetterBskbtl; CitAwd; Central Mo State.

MARSH, Sandra; South Heart HS; Dickinson, ND; 15/25 Chrs; HonRl; LitMag; SchPl; Sdlty; StuCncl; TchrAde; EdSchPpr; FHA; PpCl; College; Secretarial.

MARSH, Shane L; Marion Adams HS; Whitestown, IN; 10/105 PresSrCls; Chr; HonRl; JrNHS; LbryAde; OffAde; StuCncl; TchrAde; FTA; SpnCl; Indiana U; Teacher.

MARSH, Stephen M; Hartington Public HS; Hartington, NE; 5/32 ALBoysSt; Band; Chrs; ChrhWkr; CncrtBnd; HonRl; MrchBnd; SchMus; StuCncl; 4-H; Univ Of Nebraska; Agriculture.

MARSH, Thomas R; Webster City HS; Webster City, IA; 18/185 ALBoysSt; Band; Chr; Chrl; Chrs; ChrhWkr; CmntyWkr; CncrtBnd; HonRl; Mdrgl; Bsbl; Bsktbl; LetterGlf; LetterTrk; Iowa St College; Engineering.

MARSHALL, Brenda J; Newton HS; Newton, IL; TrsFrshCls; SecSophCls; HonRl; SchPpr; FBLA; College; Business.

MARSHALL, Chrystal K; Kenwood HS; Chicago, IL; ChrhWkr; CmntyWkr; LitMag; NatlMeritCmnd; StuCncl; SchPpr; SpnCl; SciCl; College; Medicine.

MARSHALL, Deatrice L; St Marys HS; Chicago, IL; TrsJrCls; Chr; Chrs; CmntyWkr; HonRl; OffAde; SchAde; SchPl; TchrAde; MthCl; PpCl; Trk; CchngActv; College; Computer Programming.

MARSHALL, Debbie; Hancock HS; Hancock, MI; Chr; HonRl; SchPl; Dental.

MARSHALL, Diane M; Calamus Comm HS; Calamus, IA; 1/26 SecJrCls; Band; NHS; SchMus; SchPl; StuCncl; VP4-H; LetterBsbl; Bsktbl; LetterGlf; Chrldr; AmLegAwd; College; Music.

MARSHALL, Donna J; Mullen HS; Mullen, NE; TrsSophCls; VPJrCls; Chr; Chrs; JA; SchPl; StuCncl; StuGov; 4-H; FHA;.

MARSHALL, Elizabeth L; Culver Academy For Girls; Culver, IN; 3/169 PresFrshCls; HonRl; JrNHS; NHS; SchPl; StuGov; LetterBsktbl; IMSpt; I U At Bloomington; Foreign Languages.

MARSHALL, Gwendolyn; Southwestern HS; Detroit, MI; 19/240 Chr; ChrhWkr; CmntyWkr; HonRl; HospAde; NHS; ROTC; SchAde; TchrAde; FHA; Univ Of Detroit; Dentist.

MARSHALL, James; Clarion Community Hs; Clarion, IA; PresFrshCls; ChrhWkr; HonRl; StuCncl; 4-H; FFA; Ftbl; Trk; LetterWrstlng; 4-HAwd; College; Vocational.

MARSHALL, James E; Washington HS; Washington, IL; VPSophCls; Band; CncrtBnd; HonRl; MrchBnd; PepBnd; University; Engineering.

MARSHALL, John S; Serena HS; Ottawa, IL; 1/80 VPSophCls; HonRl; PresNHS; OffAde; SchPl; Yrbk; TreasFFA; FrCl; Socr; 4-HAwd; University Of Illinois; Medicine.

MARSHALL, Judy A; Southern Boone Co HS; Hartsburg, MO; HonRl; Quill&Scroll; TchrAde; RptrYrbk; Yrbk; RptrSchPpr; SchPpr; FBLA; FHA; College; Journalist.

MARSHALL, Margaret A; Fountain Central HS; Veedersburg, IN; Band; CncrtBnd; HonRl; MrchBnd; YthFlsp; Yrbk; 4-H; FHA; Indiana Univ; Nursing.

MARSHALL, Mark H; St John Vianney HS; St Louis, MO; HonRl; SchPl; SctActv; StuCncl; CaptWrstlng; St Louis Univ; Law.

MARSHALL, Marsha R; West Washington HS; Campbellsburg, IN; TrsSophCls; Band; ChrhWkr; CmntyWkr; CncrtBnd; HonRl; MrchBnd; PepBnd; SchPl; StuCncl; TchrAde; Twrl; Dental School.

MARSHALL, Mary C; Sully Buttes HS; Blunt, SD; 12/55 Chr; Chrs; HonRl; LbryAde; Quill&Scroll; SchPl; Yrbk; RptrSchPpr; EdSchPpr; Chrldr; Univ; General.

MARSHALL, Mary J; Pillager HS; Pillager, MN; 6/35 Band; Chr; ChrhWkr; HonRl; LbryAde; SchPl; RptrSchPpr; 4-H; FHA; 4-HAwd; College Hibbing; Nursing.

MARSHALL, Michael L; Mt Morris HS; Mt Morris, IL; 12/76 VPSrCls; HonRl; NHS; PresStuCncl; PresYthFlsp; SARAwd; PresAwd; VoiceDemAwd; Centenary College; Teacher.

MARSHALL, Michael W; Marquette HS; Godfrey, IL; 46/117 HonRl; NHS; SctActv; RptrYrbk; Univ Of Missouri; Physical Therapy.

MARSHALL, Pamela M; Superior HS; Superior, NE; Band; CncrtBnd; DrlTm; MrchBnd; PepBnd; Quill&Scroll; Yrbk; RptrSchPpr; PpCl; Cntcc; Dental Assisting.

MARSHALL, Paul L; Chelsea HS; Chelsea, MI; 6/216 Band; HonRl; MrchBnd; NHS; College; Engineering.

MARSHALL, Peter C; Maine Twp East HS; Park Ridge, IL; ChrhWkr; CmntyWkr; HonRl; NHS; PolWkr; YthFlsp; YthFnd; MthCl; Ftbl; Texas Christian Univ; Medicine.

MARSHALL, Richard D; Tonica HS; Tonica, IL; ChrhWkr; HonRl; NHS; FrCl; Glf;.

MARSHALL, Richard S; Zionsville Comm HS; Zionsville, IN; Chr; Chrs; StuCncl; YthFnd; PresFrCl; SpnCl; LetterFtbl; Trk; IMSpt; College.

MARSHALL, Rod; Vestaburg HS; Vestaburg, MI; 11/62 VPJrCls; ALBoysSt; HonRl; StuCncl; TchrAde; SchPpr; Bsbl; Bsktbl; Ftbl; Trk; College.

MARSHALL, Rose; Neligh HS; Neligh, NE; 5/60 HonRl; LbryAde; NHS; TchrAde; 4-H; FHA; PpCl; DanFAwd; 4-HAwd; Community College; Secretarial.

MARSHALL, Sheila J; Westwood HS; Ishpeming, MI; TrsFrshCls; Band; HonRl; SchPl; StuCncl; RptrYrbk; RptrSchPpr; FrCl; PpCl; PresAwd; Data Processing.

MARSHALL, Susan C; Auburn HS; Auburn, IL; 3/60 NHS; 4-H; Glf; Swmmng; LetterTrk; LetterChrldr; LetterGAA; DanFAwd; VoiceDemAwd; Univ; Md.

MARSHALL, Suzanne M; Sumner HS; Eddyville, NE; Band; Chr; Mdrgl; SchPl; SecStuCncl; PresYthFlsp; Yrbk; Pres4-H; FHA; PresPpCl; Lincoln School; Business.

MARSHALL, Tim J; La Porte City HS; La Porte City, IA; 10/80 HonRl; PresNHS; SchMus; LetterBsbl; LetterBsktbl; LetterFtbl; LetterGlf; PresAwd; College; Math.

MARSHALL, Tracy L; Decatur Comm HS; Oberlin, KS; VPSrCls; Chr; ChrhWkr; HonRl; NHS; SchMus; SchPl; StuGov; 4-H; SpnCl; Navy.

MARSHALL, Wendy; Lanse Crause HS; Mt Clemons, MI; 29/564 ChrhWkr; HonRl; JrNHS; NHS; PpCl; Michigan State Univ; Med Tech.

MARSKE, Julie; Frederick HS; Westport, SD; 3/46 PresSrCls; HonRl; MrchBnd; NatlMeritCmnd; PepBnd; SchAde; RptrYrbk; SptEdYrbk; Bsktbl; Trk; South Dakota Stae Univ; Teach.

MARSLAND, Gerald P; Windsor HS; Windsor, IL; Band; HonRl; SchPl; SpnCl; PpCl; Trk; College; Forestry.

MARSNIK, Colleen M; Horace Mann HS; Biwabik, MN; SecFrshCls; SecSophCls; Band; CmntyWkr; CncrtBnd; HonRl; MrchBnd; PolWkr; SchPl; RptrYrbk; College; Special Education.

MARSTON, Sarah; Central HS; St Joseph, MO; ChrhWkr; CmntyWkr; HonRl; JrNHS; OffAde; SchPl; StuGov; GerCl; SciCl; Glf; University; Social Worker.

MARSYLA, Nancy J; John F Kennedy HS; Babbitt, MN; 24/145 Band; SecChr; PresDrmBgl; HonRl; JrNHS; PepBnd; SchMus; LetterSwmmng; LetterTrk; GAA; Clg; Med Lab Tech.

MARSZALEC, Steve; Harbor Springs HS; Harbor Springs, MI; HonRl; LbryAde; SchPl; SctActv; StuCncl; TchrAde; Bsbl; IMSpt; Central Mich Univ; Accountant.

MARTA, Terri; Negaunee HS; Negaunee, MI; Chrs; DrmBgl; HonRl; NatlFornLg; FrCl; SciCl; IMSpt; JCAwd; USJCAwd; N Mi U; Psychology.

MARTALOCK, Jeff; Royall HS; Ontario, WI; 24/114 VPFrshCls; PresJrCls; VPSrCls; ALBoysSt; HonRl; Uw River Falls; Business.

MARTCHINSKE, Jan M; Faulkton HS; Miranda, SD; ChrhWkr; HonRl; HospAde; SchPl; YthFlsp; 4-H; FHA; PpCl; LetterTrk; 4-HAwd; Presentation College; Diatician.

MARTEL, John; Holy Rosary HS; Funt, MI; HonRl; NatlFornLg; NatlMeritFnl; NatlMeritCmnd; SctActv; StuCncl; StuGov; Michigan Tech; Elctrcl Engrg.

MARTEL, Vicki L; Wishek Public HS; Wishek, ND; 8/40 SecSophCls; SecSrCls; Chr; Chrl; Chrs; ChrhWkr; HonRl; HospAde; LbryAde; OffAde; SchMus; FHA; PpCl; Bismarck Hospital; Nurse.

MARTELL, Angelo J; St Patrick HS; Chicago, IL; PresChrs; JA; Trk; Wrstlng; IMSpt; Lewis College; Business Admin.

MARTELL, Virginia L; L L Wright HS; Rionwood, MI; 14/201 TrsSophCls; TrsJrCls; Band; Chr; JrNHS; NHS; NatlMeritSchl; NatlMeritSF; LetterBsktbl; LetterChrldr; Gustavus Adolphus; Ele Education.

MARTEN, Julie K; Weyauwega HS; Fremont, WI; Band; Chrs; CncrtBnd; HonRl; SchPl; StuGov; UNYO; FBLA; PpCl; GAA; Vocational School; Medical.

MARTEN, Vicky L; Hendricks Public HS; Hendricks, MN; TrsFrshCls; HonRl; StuCncl; Yrbk; PpCl; Chrldr; Vo Tech Schl; Med Secretary.

MARTENS, James; East Leyden HS; River Grove, IL; ALBoysSt; ChrhWkr; CncrtBnd; HonRl; NHS; Orch; SchMus; SciCl; Ill Inst Of Tech; Aeronaut Eng.

MARTENS, Janet L; Earlham Comm HS; Winterset, IA; 5/38 Band; Chrs; CncrtBnd; DrlTm; HonRl; MrchBnd; NHS; PepBnd; SchAde; StuCncl; TchrAde; EdYrBk; 4-H; LetterBsbl; Area Xi; Fashion Merchandising.

MARTENS, Sara A; Fremont Sr HS; Fremont, NE; 42/412 Chr; ChrhWkr; CncrtBnd; HospAde; MrchBnd; Quill&Scroll; SchMus; SchPpr; Treas4-H; PpCl; College; Medicine.

MARTENS, Wayne G; Martensdale St Marys HS; Martensdale, IA; Band; Chrs; CncrtBnd; HonRl;

MrchBnd; PepBnd; SchPl; 4-H; PpCl; Bsbl; Bsktbl; Trk; College; Agriculture.

MARTENSON, Karla A; Shabbona HS; Shabbona, IL; 7/44 CncrtBnd; HonRl; SchPl; PresStuCncl; Twrl; Yrbk; 4-H; Glf; CaptSocr; GAA; 4-HAwd; Il State Univ; Stewardess.

MARTH, Vickie L; Plymouth HS; Plymouth, WI; Chr; HonRl; NHS; PpCl; Bsbl; LetterBsktbl; LetterTrk; LetterChrldr; IMSpt; PresAwd;.

MARTI, Edwin A; Adams Friendship HS; Friendship, WI; 1/152 PresFrshCls; HonRl; NHS; StuCncl; 4-H; LetterBsktbl; LetterFtbl; LetterTrk; 4-HAwd; Clg; Med Tech.

MARTI, Marla L; Waukon HS; Lansing, IA; 30/155 HstSophCls; Chr; DrlTm; HonRl; YthFlsp; 4-H; TrsSophCls; TrsSophCls; PpCl; IMSpt; Coll; Spec Educ Teacher.

MARTI, Michele; Regina HS; St Clair Shores, MI; HonRl; HospAde; JA; NatlThespSoc; SchPl; PPFtbl; Wayne State Col; Registered Nurse.

MARTI, Patricia A; St Paul HS; Highland, IL; 2/55 Aud/Vis; Chr; HonRl; PepBnd; SchMus; StuCncl; Yrbk; Trk; SecGAA; 4-HAwd; Southern Il U; Commercial Art.

MARTICKE, Donna; Stanberry R Ii HS; Stanberry, MO; HonRl; ModUN; SchPl; Twrl; Yrbk; PpCl; College.

MARTIGNACCO, Peter M; Robbinsdale HS; Minneapolis, MN; HonRl; JA; NatlMeritSF; StuCncl; IMSpt; Int Of Tech; Physics.

MARTIN, Allen A; Bayard HS; Bayard, NE; 1/45 HonRl; CitAwd; Clge.

MARTIN, Angela; Havana HS; Peoria, IL; 11/94 VPSrCls; Band; Chrs; CncrtBnd; HonRl; Mdrgl; StuCncl; Trk; GAA; Western Ill Univ, Microbiologist.

MARTIN, Anne; Washington HS; Cedar Rapids, IA; Chr; HonRl; MrchBnd; StuGov; Bsktbl; Coll; Professional.

MARTIN, Annette E; Logansport HS; Logansport, IN; 23/421 Band; Chr; JrNHS; MrchBnd; NatlFornLg; PepBnd; SchPl; PresYthFlsp; VP4-H; MthCl; 4-HAwd; Univ; Professional Mathematics.

MARTIN, Anthony J; Mosinee HS; Edgar, WI; 8/164 HonRl; NHS; PresFFA; Bulk Milk Hauler.

MARTIN, Barbara L; St Thomas Aquinas HS; Florissant, MO; 10/350 ChrhWkr; HonRl; NHS; SchMus; SchPl; Yrbk; SpnCl; GAA; CitAwd; U Of Mo Columbia; Interior Design.

MARTIN, Benjamin J; Pender Public HS; Pender, NE; SecFrshCls; VPJrCls; Chr; Chrs; HonRl; Mdrgl; SchPl; Bsktbl; Ftbl; Swmmng; College; Medicine.

MARTIN, Betsy F; Edgewood HS; Madison, WI; 39/176 PresBand; Chrs; HonRl; NHS; PepBnd; SchMus; StuCncl; SciCl; KiwanAwd; College; Music.

MARTIN, Bonita K; Deland Weldon HS; Clinton, IL; AFS; ChrhWkr; JA; SchAde; SchPl; TchrAde; YthFlsp; Yrbk; 4-H; Trade School; Teachers Aid.

MARTIN, Brenda J; Joliet Central HS; Joliet, IL; Chr; ChrhWkr; HonRl; VPJA; NHS; ROTC; SchMus; YthFlsp; Pres4-H; GerCl; Univ Of Ill; Nursing.

MARTIN, Brenda J; Forbes Public HS; Forbes, ND; 1/12 ChrhWkr; HonRl; SchPl; StuCncl; EdYrBk; RptrSchPpr; 4-H; CaptBsktbl; LetterTrk; CaptChrldr; U Of Nd; Journalism.

MARTIN, Brenda L; Oregon Davis HS; Walkerton, IN; Chr; IntrClCncl; LbryAde; FHA; Business College.

MARTIN, Byron L; Ritenour Sr HS; St Ann, MO; LetterBsktbl; LetterFtbl; LetterTrk; IMSpt; U Of Mo; Animal Husbandry.

MARTIN, Carrie L; Hamilton HS; Warsaw, IL; PresJrCls; Band; Chrs; ChrhWkr; DrmMjrt; HonRl; MrchBnd; StuCncl; Chrldr; GAA; Univ; Maj Study.

MARTIN, Catherine M; Ames Senior HS; Ames, IA; ChrhWkr; HospAde; RptrSchPpr; PpCl; College; Nursing.

MARTIN, Cathy; Riceville Comm HS; Riceville, IA; 16/65 HonRl; RedCrAde; SchAde; SchPl; StuCncl; RptrSchPpr; SchPpr; 4-H; GAA; 4-HAwd; VoiceDemAwd; Iowa State Univ; Journalism.

MARTIN, Cheryl L; Richland Center HS; Richland Center, WI; 73/183 Band; SchPl; 4-H; LetterBsbl; 4-HAwd; University Of Minnesota; Veterinarian.

MARTIN, Cynthia S; Thomas W Kelly HS; Blodgett, MO; 8/66 Band; ChrhWkr; HonRl; MrchBnd; PepBnd; StuCncl; FHA; SpnCl; SecTrsSophCls; Chrldr; Freed Hardeman College; Business Educ.

MARTIN, Daniel L; Danville Sr HS; Danville, IL; 18/629 Band; CncrtBnd; HonRl; MrchBnd; SchMus; SctActv; YthLg; RptrSchPpr; IMSpt; Purdue Univ; Engineering.

MARTIN, Daniel R; Chesaning Union HS; Chesaning, MI; HonRl; LetterBsktbl; LetterGlf; IMSpt; College; Mortician.

MARTIN, David A; Westview HS; Shipshewana, IN; 7/70 Band; CncrtBnd; HonRl; MrchBnd; NHS; PepBnd; SchPl; LetterBsbl; LetterBsktbl; LetterTrk; College; Comm Pilot Or Computer Work.

MARTIN, David N; Chenoa HS; Chenoa, IL; 6/65 ALBoysSt; HonRl; NHS; SchMus; YthFlsp; SptEdYrbk; LetterBsbl; Bsktbl; LetterFtbl; Purdue Univ; Engineering.

MARTIN, David P; Essex Community HS; Essex, IA; SecTrsFrshCls; Band; Chr; CmntyWkr; Bsktbl; Ftbl; Glf; Swmmng; Tennis; Trk; Peru St Col; Musci.

MARTIN, David W; Waukegan East HS; Waukegan, IL; 24/856 HonRl; JrNHS; NHS; NatlMeritCmnd; GerCl; LetterSocr; LetterSwmmng; LetterTennis; De Pauw Univ; Economics.

MARTIN, Debbie L; Johnston City HS; Johnston City, IL; 5/82 SecTrsFrshCls; PresSophCls; CmntyWkr; HonRl; HospAde; NHS; OffAde; StuCncl; FHA; LionAwd; Univ; Acct.

MARTIN, Debora F; Puxico HS; Dudley, MO; Band; Chr; ChrhWkr; CmntyWkr; HonRl; Yrbk; FHA; PpCl; SciCl; Chrldr; College; Nurse.

MARTIN, Deborah; Southeast HS; Weir, KS; PresJrCls; ALAGirlsSt; Band; HonRl; NHS; RptrSchPpr; CchngActv; BttyCrckrAwd; College; Ele Education.

MARTIN, Deborah A; Spring Hill HS; Spring Hill, KS; 7/59 Chr; Chrs; HonRl; LbryAde; NHS; TchrAde; SptEdYrbk; FHA; PpCl; Bsktbl; Chrldr; College; Vocation.

MARTIN, Debra J; Fayette Community HS; Fayette, IA; 1/39 Band; ChrhWkr; CmntyWkr; DrmMjrt; HonRl; EdYrBk; 4-H; SpnCl; LetterBsbl; CaptBsktbl; LetterTrk; Univ Of N Ia; Physical Therapist.

MARTIN, Denise; Northwest Webster HS; Clare, IA; 5/20 Chrs; HonRl; RptrSchPpr; 4-H; Bsktbl; Trk; Horse Husbandry.

MARTIN, Dennis E; Boone Valley HS; Renwick, IA; LetterBand; LetterChrs; HonRl; Mdrgl; PepBnd; SchPl; YthFlsp; LetterFtbl; LetterGlf; 4-HAwd; Iowa St Univ; Aerospace Engineering.

MARTIN, Diane A; Dupree Public HS; Dupree, SD; SecFrshCls; VPJrCls; DrlTm; HonRl; RptrYrbk; RptrSchPpr; PpCl; Bsktbl; AmLegAwd; CitAwd; Sturgis Vocational Sch; Secretarial Busines.

MARTIN, Diane G; Moscow HS; Moscow, KS; 2/7 PresChrs; HonRl; PresStuCncl; Twrl; LetterBsktbl; LetterTrk; College Or Bus Schl; Business Job.

MARTIN, Donna; Eastern HS; Solosberry, IN; ChrhWkr; HospAde; TchrAde; PpCl;.

MARTIN, Donna K; Streator Twp HS; Streator, IL; 20/379 CncrtBnd; HonRl; MrchBnd; NHS; OffAde; PepBnd; SchMus; StuCncl; Yrbk; Isu; Psychology.

MARTIN, Elizabeth J; Mac Arthur Jr Sr HS; Decatur, IL; 51/400 VPAFS; Chr; HonRl; LitMag; OffAde; SchMus; KeyCl; FrCl; LetterTennis; LetterChrldr; Isu; Elementary Teacher.

MARTIN, Elizabeth J; Greenfield Central HS; Greenfield, IN; Univ Of Evansville; Nursing.

MARTIN, Elizabeth A; Lyons Twp HS; La Grange Park, IL; HonRl; OffAde; MthCl; Bsbl; Bsktbl; GAA; IMSpt; PPFtbl; Illinois St Univ; Business Admin.

MARTIN, Faye M; Mt Clemens HS; Mt Clemens, MI; 17/450 ALAGirlsSt; PresChr; HonRl; NHS; NatlMeritSF; Swmmng; DARAwd; Howard Univ; Criminal Law.

MARTIN, Florence P; St Marys Cntr For Learning; Chicago, IL; SecJrCls; SecSrCls; Chrs; OffAde; SchAde; SchMus; SchPl; TchrAde; Yrbk; College; Music.

MARTIN, Galen R; Magic City Campus Minot HS; Minot, ND; 1/650 TrsSrCls; AFS; Band; Chr; NHS; PepBnd; SchMus; StuCncl; SptEdSchPpr; LetterTrk; CitAwd; College; Education.

MARTIN, Gary L; Greenfield Central HS; Greenfield, IN; 49/275 StuCncl; FTA; GerCl; SpnCl; MthCl; LetterBsktbl; LetterFtbl; LetterTrk; College; Accounting.

MARTIN, Glenda M; Lakeview HS; Gowen, MI; 34/121 HonRl; HospAde; 4-H; FNA; SpnCl; DanFAwd; 4-HAwd; Butterworth School; Nurse.

MARTIN, Gregory L; Memorial HS; Evansville, IN; Band; CncrtBnd; HonRl; MrchBnd; PepBnd; SchPl; VPFrCl; IMSpt; Indiana Univ; Music.

MARTIN, Gregory P; Douglas Macarthur HS; Decatur, IL; Band; CncrtBnd; HonRl; MrchBnd; PepBnd; Millikin Univ; Business Admin.

MARTIN, Harvey; Hesperia Comm HS; Hesperia, MI; 12/98 HonRl; NHS; 4-H; Bsbl; Ftbl; Trk; IMSpt; Muskegon Bus Coll;data Proc.

MARTIN, Homer L; Edinburg HS; Edinburg, IN; 1/100 HonRl; FrCl; College; Teaching.

MARTIN, Jackie A; Southeast Of Saline HS; Assaria, KS; Chrs; ChrhWkr; DrlTm; NatlFornLg; Orch; SchMus; SchPl; VPStuCncl; SchPpr; PpCl; Kansas State University; Child Development.

MARTIN, James A; Sacred Heart HS; Solomon, KS; 2/56 PresFrshCls; VPSophCls; HonRl; NHS; PresStuCncl; Yrbk; FBLA; LetterBsktbl; LetterFtbl; OptClAwd; College; Accounting.

MARTIN, James L; Sigourney Community HS; Sigourney, IA; 5/78 Chrs; NHS; NatlThespSoc; StuCncl; LetterWrstlng; GovHonPrgAwd; Drake Univ; Attorney At Law.

MARTIN, Jane; Benton Harbor HS; Benton Harbor, MI; Band; CncrtBnd; MrchBnd; NHS; PepBnd; Northern Mich Univ; Agriculture.

MARTIN, Jan L; North Decatur HS; Greensburg, IN; 5/108 Band; DrlTm; HonRl; NHS; SchPl; YthFlsp; 4-H; FrCl; PpCl; Trk; GAA; 4-HAwd; Undecided; Science.

MARTIN, Joan; Petersburg HS; Concordia, KS; HonRl; NHS; SchMus; FHA; PpCl; SciCl; Trk; IMSpt;.

MARTIN, Joan; Morton HS; Morton, IL; Chr; ChrhWkr; CncrtBnd; HonRl; Mdrgl; RedCrAde; StuCncl; SchPpr; 4-H; College.

MARTIN, Joan; Rogers City HS; Rogers City, MI; 5/156 Chr; CmntyWkr; HonRl; Mdrgl; NHS; NatlThespSoc; SchPl; SctActv; TchrAde; 4-H; 4-HAwd; Univ Of Mi; Physical Therapy.

MARTIN, Joanne D; Parkway Central HS; Chesterfield, MO; 10450 VPSophCls; ALAGirlsSt; DrlTm; ModUN; VPNatlFornLg; PresNHS; NatlMeritSF; StuCncl; Twrl; NCTE; University; Law.

MARTIN, Jodi L; Jefferson City HS; Jefferson City, MO; 29/520 Chr; Chrl; Chrs; ChrhWkr; HonRl; HospAde; NHS; SchMus; PresYthFlsp; SpnCl; Baylor U; Voice Major.

MARTIN, Joe W; South Pemiscot HS; Steele, MO; Band; ChrhWkr; CncrtBnd; DrlTm; HonRl; JrNHS; MrchBnd; NHS; PepBnd; SchMus; FFA; Bsbl; Bsktbl; College.

MARTIN, John K; Southwest HS; Kansas City, MO; Band; CmntyWkr; CncrtBnd; HonRl; MrchBnd; Orch; SchPl; SctActv; TreasStuCncl; FFA; University; Journalism.

MARTIN, Joseph B; Carmel HS; Carmel, IN; 100/528 ALBoysSt; NHS; Quill&Scroll; StuGov; Yrbk; PpCl; LetterBsbl; LetterLetterTrk; IMSpt; Purdue U; Industrial Management.

MARTIN, Joyce A; Bloomington HS; Bagley, WI; 4/58 TrsSophCls; Band; Chrs; CncrtBnd; HonRl; Mdrgl; MrchBnd; NHS; PepBnd; SchMus; College; Speech Therapist.

MARTIN, Julia A; Palatine HS; Palatine, IL; 1/440 HonRl; LitMag; NHS; NatlMeritSF; PolWkr; RptrSchPpr; SchPpr; FrCl; Univ Of Il; Journalism.

MARTIN, Karen; Henderson HS; Henderson, MN; 1/36 SecTrsSrCls; Band; Chr; BttyCrckrAwd; Medicine.

MARTIN, Karen A; Western HS; Kokomo, IN; 12/160 Band; Chr; DrmMjrt; HonRl; Mdrgl; MrchBnd; NHS; TchrAde; SpnCl; College; Music Educ.

MARTIN, Kelly J; Buckley Loda HS; Buckley, IL; TrsSophCls; ChrhWkr; CncrtBnd; NHS; StuCncl; Yrbk; RptrSchPpr; FHA; FSA; MthCl; College; Medicine.

MARTIN, Kevin R; Schafer HS; Allen Park, MI; HonRl; NHS; SctActv; StuCncl; TchrAde; MthCl; CaptSwmmng; CaptTrk; CitAwd; Lawrence Inst Technology; Architecture.

MARTIN, Laurie J; Lefor HS; Lefor, ND; SecTrsFrshCls; PresSophCls; VPJrCls; HospAde; PepBnd; SchPl; StuCncl; EdSchPpr; LetterBsktbl; LetterChrldr; Col; Pro.

MARTIN, Linda F; Aurora Senior HS; Aurora, IN; 1/140 Chr; ChrhWkr; CncrtBnd; HonRl; NHS; EdYrBk; FrCl; PpCl; BauchLmbAwd; Indiana State University; Medicine.

MARTIN, Linda J; Salem HS; Salem, IN; Chr; ChrhWkr; HonRl; NHS; SchMus; RptrYrbk; FHA; Vincennes Univ; Nursing.

MARTIN, Lora L; Van Buren HS; Brazil, IN; 1/67 Band; NHS; TchrAde; RptrSchPpr; FTA; CaptBsktbl; PresGAA; DARAwd; College; Professional.

MARTIN, Louisa M; Solomon HS; Salina, KS; Chrs; HonRl; LbryAde; SchPl; FHA; PPFtbl; College; Art Teacher.

MARTIN, Marg A; David City HS; David City, NE; Band; HonRl; Quill&Scroll; TchrAde; EdYrBk; PpCl; LetterTrk; LetterGAA; PresAwd; VoiceDemAwd; Coll; Prof.

MARTIN, Mark E; Slater HS; Slater, MO; VPSophCls; Band; CncrtBnd; HonRl; MrchBnd; Missouri Univ; Science.

MARTIN, Mary; Mercy HS; Omaha, NE; /76 PresFrshCls; IntrClCncl; SchPl; StuCncl; SchPpr; LatCl; Bsbl; Bsktbl; Trk; IMSpt; Univ; Prof.

MARTIN, Mary E; Dubuque HS; Dubuque, IA; 13/450 Chr; Chrs; ChrhWkr; HonRl; HospAde; LbryAde; NHS; NatlMeritSF; SchMus; GerCl; Coll; Med.

MARTIN, Mary J; Duquoin HS; Du Quoin, IL; VPJrCls; ChrhWkr; CmntyWkr; HonRl; SctActv; SptEdYrbk; PresPpCl; LetterGAA; IMSpt; AmLegAwd; John A Logan Jr College.

MARTIN, Melissa I; North Greene HS; White Hall, IL; Band; CncrtBnd; HonRl; MrchBnd; SecNHS; PepBnd; Yrbk; PpCl; LetterTrk; Shawnee College; Wildlife Tech.

MARTIN, Michael; Grosse Pointe South HS; Grosse Pointe Park, MI; CmntyWkr; HonRl; NHS; NatlThespSoc; Quill&Scroll; SchMus; RptrYrbk; EdSchPpr; SptEdSchPpr; SchPpr; Mi St Univ; Writer.

MARTIN, Monty K; Perry HS; Baylis, IL; 2/16 VPFrshCls; PresSophCls; PresJrCls; PresSrCls; VPBand; SchPl; PresStuCncl; SptEdYrbk; Sec4-H; PresFFA; Ne Missouri St Univ; Agriculture.

MARTIN, Oscar M; Marquette HS; Marquette, MI; Chr; HonRl; PpCl; Trk; Trade School; Meat Production.

MARTIN, Pamela A; Lake Fenton HS; Fenton, MI; 29/147 HonRl; NatlFornLg; NHS; RedCrAde; SctActv; Yrbk; FrCl; PpCl; SciCl; IMSpt; Western Michigan Univ; Physical Therapist.

MARTIN, Pamela R; Immaculata HS; Detroit, MI; PresSrCls; ChrhWkr; HonRl; NatlFornLg; NatlMeritSF; TchrAde; FrCl; PpCl; College; Law.

MARTIN, Patricia; Corydon Central HS; Corydon, IN; 2/139 HonRl; FrCl; MthCl; PpCl; GAA; DARAwd; College; Professional.

MARTIN, Patricia A; Taft HS; Chicago, IL; 64/800 HstFrshCls; HonRl; JrNHS; NHS; OffAde; StuCncl; TchrAde; KeyCl; LetterGAA; Loyola Univ; Social Work.

MARTIN, Patricia A; North HS; West Union, IA; 6/103 Band; HonRl; MrchBnd; NatlMeritSF; PepBnd; StuCncl; SciCl; LetterTrk; DARAwd; U North Ia; Dietitian.

MARTIN, Peggy J; Pekin Comm HS; Pekin, IL; 48/803 SecJrCls; SecSrCls; ChrhWkr; HonRl; LbryAde; NatlFornLg; NHS; StuGov; Univ Of Illinois; Occuptl Therapy.

MARTIN, Perry J; Perry Comm HS; Perry, IA; 3/153 HonRl; NHS; NatlThespSoc; Quill&Scroll; SchMus; SchPl; RptrYrbk; RptrSchPpr; FrCl; Bible College; Math.

MARTIN, Phillip D; St Louis Country Day HS; St Louis, MO; HonRl; ModUN; NatlMeritFnl; NatlMeritSF; SchPl; Yrbk; SchPpr; College; Law.

MARTIN, Phyllis; De Soto Sr HS; De Soto, MO; HonRl; JrNHS; NHS; TchrAde; FHA; PpCl; DARAwd; EldAwd; 4-HAwd; Se State Univ; Math.

MARTIN, Randall L; Rolfe Comm HS; Pocahontas, IA; 1/29 PresFrshCls; PresSophCls; ALBoysSt; NHS; StuCncl; LetterBsktbl; LetterFtbl; LetterTrk; BauchLmbAwd; 4-HAwd; Ia State U; Architectural Eng.

MARTIN, Randy G; Dexfield HS; Redfield, IA; HonRl; YthFlsp; Bsktbl; Ftbl; Trk; Coll; Prof.

MARTIN, Rebecca; Andale Rural HS; Colwich, KS; 4/90 Band; Chr; Chrs; CmntyWkr; CncrtBnd; IntrClCncl; LbryAde; MrchBnd; PepBnd; SchMus; College; Communications.

MARTIN, Rebecca A; Southeast HS; Cherokee, KS; 1/60 TreasBand; CtyCnl; HonRl; MrchBnd; NHS; StuCncl; Pres4-H; PresSciCl; LetterBsktbl; LetterTrk; Kansas State College; Accounting.

MARTIN, Reginald K; Lindblom HS; Chicago, IL; 67/612 HonRl; TchrAde; College; Electrical Engineer.

MARTIN, Rhonda M; Gibson Southern HS; Ft Branch, IN; ChrhWkr; CmntyWkr; PolWkr; SchMus; StuCncl; FHA; FSA; Bsktbl; GovHonPrgAwd; PresAwd; College.

MARTIN, Richard E; Westhope HS; Westhope, ND; 1/17 ALBoysSt; Band; Chrs; HonRl; SchPl; SptEdSchPpr; FFA; CaptBsktbl; CaptFtbl; LetterTrk; Nd State Univ; Bio Chemistry.

MARTIN, Richard K; Falls City HS; Falls City, NE; Chrl; Chrs; CmntyWkr; NatlThespSoc; PolWkr; SchMus; SchPl; YthFlsp; University; Professional.

MARTIN, Richard S; Blue Mound HS; Blue Mound, IL; 7/40 CmntyWkr; HonRl; SchPl; SecTrsSophCls; Bsktbl; Trk; IMSpt; Millikin Univ; Bus Mangmt.

MARTIN, Roberta; Plainview HS; Plainview, MN; 11/93 ALAGirlsSt; Band; Chr; DrlTm; SchPl; StuCncl; RptrYrbk; SptEdSchPpr; GerCl; College Of St Catherine; Economics.

MARTIN, Robin M; Proviso West HS; Westchester, IL; HonRl; Illinois State Univ; Special Education.

MARTIN, Roger P; Johnson Creek HS; Watertown, WI; 2/50 SecSophCls; PresJrCls; HonRl; StuCncl; Ftbl; Trk; IMSpt; College; Math Major.

MARTIN, Roy C; Austin Catholic Prep; St Clair Shores, MI; 4/128 TrsSrCls; HonRl; NHS; NatlMeritFnl; NatlMeritSF; RedCrAde; SchMus; SchPl; LetterBsbl; IMSpt; Univ Of Mi; Pre Med.

MARTIN, Sandy A; Pulaski HS; Pulaski, WI; 17/190 PresSophCls; VPSrCls; Quill&Scroll; Sdlty; RptrSchPpr; SchPpr; Bsktbl; Trk; GAA; DARAwd; Marguette University.

MARTIN, Scott; Gibbon HS; Gibbon, MN; 23/42 Chr; CmntyWkr; Mdrgl; SctActv; StuGov; Ftbl; Trk; PresAwd; College; Airline Administration.

MARTIN, Scott A; Hersey HS; Arlington Hts, IL; 32/783 Band; CncrtBnd; HonRl; MrchBnd; NHS; NatlMeritSF; PepBnd; SchMus;.

MARTIN, Scott D; Marinette Sr HS; Marinette, WI; 17/232 ALBoysSt; Band; NHS; NatlMeritCmnd; PepBnd; SchMus; SchPl; SctActv; LetterWrstlng; Univ Of Wisconsin; Medicine.

MARTIN, Shirley A; Benton Harbor HS; Benton Harbor, MI; SecJrCls; Chr; ChrhWkr; HonRl; NatlMeritSchl; NatlMeritSF; NatlThespSoc; OffAde; SchPl; StuCncl; Trk; VFWAwd; Howard Univ; Law.

MARTIN, Stan W; Bethany Christian HS; Warsaw, IN; VPFrshCls; VPSophCls; VPJrCls; Chr; Chrl; ChrhWkr; HonRl; GerCl; LetterBsktbl; LetterTrk; College.

MARTIN, Stephen P; Springville Comm HS; Springville, IA; 5/60 HonRl; VPNHS; PresYthFlsp; FSA; Iowa State University; Business.

MARTIN, Sue; Parkwood HS; Joplin, MO; HonRl; LitMag; Quill&Scroll; EdSchPpr; College; Journalism.

MARTIN, Susan; North Harrison HS; New Salisbury, IN; 1/125 ALAGirlsSt; Band; Chr; NHS; SchMus; Chrldr; GAA; DARAwd; College Indiana; Physical Therapy.

MARTIN, Susan E; Ashland HS; Alexander, IL; 6/35 SecSophCls; SecSrCls; Band; HonRl; MrchBnd; NHS; SchPl; RptrSchPpr; SciCl; GAA; IMSpt; Western Illinois Univ; Medical Technology.

MARTIN, Susan L; Rural Route HS; Nauvoo, IL; 20/55 TrsSophCls; PresSrCls; Band; PepBnd; RedCrAde; YthFlsp; Yrbk; TreasFBLA; Glf; LetterChrldr; Univ; Medical Tech.

MARTIN, Terrilyn E; Lakeland HS; Wolcottville, IN; AFS; CncrtBnd; MrchBnd; StuCncl; 4-H; PpCl; Trk; Chrldr; GAA; PPFtbl; Trade School; Vocation.

MARTIN, Terry E; Roseville HS; Roseville, IL; 3/50 VPSrCls; HonRl; NHS; RptrSchPpr; Bsktbl; LetterFtbl; DanFAwd; DARAwd; SARAwd; Junior College; Automotive Mechanics.

MARTIN, Thomas A; Boone Valley HS; Renwick, IA; ChrhWkr; CncrtBnd; HonRl; Mdrgl; SchPl; YthFlsp; SptEdYrbk; Bsbl; Bsktbl; Ftbl; Trk; CchngActv; College; Coaching.

MARTIN, Vanita D; Gods Bible HS; Leavenworth, IN; 3/18 HonRl; Gods Bible College.

MARTIN, Vicki L; Lake Fenton HS; Fenton, MI; 6/179 Chr; HonRl; NHS; TchrAde; RptrYrbk; Bsktbl; LetterTrk; LetterChrldr; IMSpt; PPFtbl; College.

MARTIN, Victoria L; Leaf River HS; Leaf River, IL; 2/40 ALAGirlsSt; Band; Chrs; HonRl; NHS; SecFHA; FTA; SecPpCl; Chrldr; TreasGAA; Business School; Liberal Arts.

MARTIN, Victoria Y; Lindblom Tech HS; Chicago, IL; 330669 ChrhWkr; HonRl; LbryAde; NatlMeritCmnd; OffAde; StuCncl; StuGov; FrCl; MthCl; Loyola Univ; Law Field.

MARTIN, William J; Lawrence Central HS; Lawrence, IN; Band; Chr; ChrhWkr; MrchBnd; NHS; PepBnd; SchMus; Col; Music.

MARTIN, William T; Our Lady Of Providence HS; Jeffersonville, IN; 5/130 HonRl; StuCncl; MthCl; Trk; Wrstlng; Purdue Univ; Engineer.

MARTIN, Wyman E; Danville HS; Danville, IA; VPFrshCls; PresBand; ChrhWkr; HonRl; SchMus; SchPl; LetterBsktbl; LetterFtbl; LetterTrk; CchngActv; College; Vocational.

MARTINDELL, Stan A; Hutchinson HS; Hutchinson, KS; SecFrshCls; TrsFrshCls; HonRl; NatlFornLg; StuCncl; StuGov; TchrAde; SciCl; GodCntryAwd; Univ Ks; Law.

MARTINE, John J; St Thomas Aquinas HS; Florissant, MO; 71/352 HonRl; ROTC; StuGov; Trk; Univ Of Mo At Rolla; Professional.

MARTINEK, Joanne H; New Effington HS; New Effington, SD; 5/17 Band; Chr; Chrs; CncrtBnd; HonRl; MrchBnd; PepBnd; StuCncl; EdYrBk; Univ Of So Dakota; Teaching.

MARTINEK, Virginia; Holy Trinity HS; Waverly, MN; Chr; Chrs; ChrhWkr; HonRl; SchMus; SchPl; TchrAde; JCAwd; OptClAwd; College; Special Teaching Music.

MARTINEZ, Alice; Saginaw HS; Saginaw, MI; 4/435 ChrhWkr; HonRl; Cntrl Mich Univ; Revenue Agent.

MARTINEZ, Dolores P; St Francis De Sales HS; Chicago, IL; 13/296 Chrs; HonRl; NHS; NatlMeritCmnd; SchMus; SchPl; StuCncl; Univ Of Chicago; Anthropology.

MARTINEZ, Eloy; Elgin HS; Streamwood, IL; 149/1000 SchPl; LetterGlf; LetterWrstlng; College; Architect.

MARTINEZ, Judith A; Osseo HS; Osseo, MN; Chr; ChrhWkr; HonRl; NatlMeritCmnd; SchMus; SchPl; StuCncl; RptrSchPpr; SpnCl; CaptChrldr; Univ Of Mn Morris.

MARTINEZ, Julio; Prosser Voc HS; Chicago, IL; 2/300 SecJrCls; DrlTm; HonRl; JrNHS; NHS; SchPpr; Wrstlng; IMSpt; Univ Of Il Urbana; Aerospace Engineer.

MARTINEZ, Marie C; Academy Of Sacred Heart; Chicago, IL; Chr; ChrhWkr; HonRl; HospAde; LitMag; SchPl; StuCncl; StuGov; RptrSchPpr; Tennis; Univ; Law.

MARTINEZ, Mary G; Torrington HS; Morrill, NE; 13/128 ALAGirlsSt; HonRl; NHS; SchMus; SchPl; StuCncl; TchrAde; 4-H; FTA; SpnCl; Carroll College; Education Adm.

MARTINEZ, Paul T; Romeoville HS; Romeoville, IL; 7/293 HonRl; University; Elec Engineering.

MARTINEZ, Veronica L; George Rogers Clark HS; Hammond, IN; TchrAde; FBLA; SpnCl; Office Work.

MARTINIE, Connie; Morton HS; Morton, IL; 39/325 PresJrCls; HonRl; StuCncl; StuGov; YthFlsp; Yrbk; PpCl; Chrldr; GAA; PPFtbl; College.

MARTINSON, Douglas; Mundelein Hs; Mundelein, IL; HonRl; LetterBsbl; Bsktbl;.

MARTINSON, Mark A; Emmons HS; Emmons, MN; VPJrCls; HonRl; NHS; SchPl; LetterBsbl; LetterBsktbl; LetterFtbl; College; Business Admin.

MARTINSON, Mary E; Ogemaw Heights HS; West Branch, MI; VPFrshCls; HonRl; JrNHS; NHS; SchAde; SctActv; SchPpr; Bsbl; Bsktbl; Trk; Chrldr; GAA; IMSpt; University; Medicine.

MARTINSON, Nancy E; Ashby Public HS; Ashby, MN; TrsFrshCls; HonRl; TchrAde; RptrYrbk; FFA; PpCl; CaptBsktbl; GAA; Trade School; Horticulture.

MARTINSON, Peggy A; Cloquet Sr HS; Cloquet, MN; 21/245 HonRl; HospAde; ModUN; NHS; RptrYrbk; Yrbk; RptrSchPpr; PpCl; PPFtbl; Hibbing Comm Clge; Nursing.

MARTONSON, John K; Macomb Sr HS; Macomb, IL; 51/241 Chrl; ChrhWkr; CncrtBnd; HonRl; Mdrgl; MrchBnd; NHS; NatlThespSoc; PepBnd; SchMus; Swmmng; Univ Of Illinois; Electrical Engineer.

MARTSCHING, Gregory A; Cardinal HS; Agency, IA; 9/70 HonRl; NHS; CaptBsbl; LetterBsktbl; College; Engineering.

MARTTILA, Debra K; Ellendale HS; Ellendale, ND; 5/45 PresFrshCls; SecSrCls; Chrs; HospAde; SchPl; Yrbk; 4-H; FHA; PpCl; Chrldr; College; Art.

MARTURANO, Dominic E; Grant Community HS; Spring Grove, IL; 25/200 HonRl; NHS; LetterBsbl; LetterBsktbl; IMSpt; College; Data Processing.

MARTUS, Ronald F; Avondale Sr HS; Auburn Hts, MI; ALBoysSt; CmntyWkr; HonRl; PolWkr; RedCrAde; SchPl; SctActv; RptrYrbk; Ferris St College; Pharmacy.

MARTUSCIELLO, Anna Marie A; Steinmetz HS; Chicago, IL; 48/630 Chrs; HonRl; NHS; RptrYrbk; FDA; KeyCl; MthCl; SciCl; LetterCchngActv; LetterGAA; Univ Of Il; Professional.

MARTYN, Rebecca L; Lasalle Peru HS; Peru, IL; 28/520 Chrs; HonRl; SpnCl; PpCl; Il Valley Comm College; Dental Technition.

MARTYNENKO, Alexander V; Marshall Univ HS; Minneapolis, MN; 19/180 Band; CncrtBnd; HonRl; JrNHS; NHS; Orch; SchAde; LetterFtbl; U S Naval Acad; Nuclear Matine Engineer.

MARTZ, Anita M; Marion Adams HS; Sheridan, IN; 10/103 HonRl; JrNHS; LbryAde; NHS; SchMus; SchPl; TchrAde; RptrYrbk; RptrSchPpr; 4-H; DARAwd; Col; Elem Teaching.

MARUNCZAK, Elizabeth R; New Haven HS; Mt Clemens, MI; TrsFrshCls; TrsSophCls; PresJrCls; Chrs; DrmMjrt; HonRl; JA; MrchBnd; OffAde; SchAde; Macomb Comm Col; Executive Secretary.

MARUSCHAK, Ruth J; Glenbard East HS; Lombard, IL; 10/653 SecAFS; Chr; JrNHS; Mdrgl; NatlFornLg; NHS; NatlThespSoc; SchPl; StuCncl; Pres4-H; College; Commercial Art.

MARUSKA, Barbara J; New Prague HS; New Prague, MN; 37/204 HospAde; LbryAde; OffAde; RptrSchPpr; SecFHA; FTA; TreasSpnCl; PpCl; St Marys Jr Clg; Nursing.

MARVEL, Deborah C; Carmel HS; Carmel, IN; 24/596 ChrhWkr; CncrtBnd; HonRl; LitMag; MrchBnd; NHS; YthFlsp; 4-H; GAA; 4-HAwd; Purdue Univ; Engineer.

MARVEL, Kathy Jean; Wisconsin Heights HS; Black Earth, WI; 15/109 Chr; HonRl; NHS; SchMus; SchPl; SecStuCncl; FHA; GerCl; LetterTrk; GAA; Army; Policeperson.

MARVIN, Jeri L; Hartford Union HS; Hubertus, WI; AFS; HonRl; RptrSchPpr; EdSchPpr; SptEdSchPpr; SchPpr; SpnCl; Bsktbl; GAA; U Of Wi Whitewater; Journalism.

MARVIN, Michael A; Chrisman HS; Chrisman, IL; 10/43 ChrhWkr; HonRl; SchPl; SctActv; FFA; SpnCl; LetterBsbl; LetterBsktbl; LetterTrk; BttyCrckrAwd; College; Engineering.

MARVIN, Sally S; Tri City HS; Mechanicsburg, IL; 11/55 Chr; ChrhWkr; HonRl; SchMus; SchPl; TchrAde; 4-H; FTA; GAA; Business School; Legal Secretary.

MARVNA, Marie A; J F Kennedy HS; Chicago, IL; Chrs; ChrhWkr; HonRl; NHS; SchMus; SctActv; FBLA; SpnCl; GAA; KiwanAwd; Business Clg; Bus Managing.

MARX, Arlie J; Woodstock HS; Woodstock, IL; Band; Chrs; HonRl; Mdrgl; NatlFornLg; NatlMeritCmnd; NatlThespSoc; SchMus; SchPl; Univ Of Illinois; Engineering.

MARX, Jeanne; Kewaskum HS; Kewaskum, WI; 21/180 AFS; HonRl; NHS; SchMus; SchPl; RptrYrbk; FTA; SpnCl; BttyCrckrAwd; University Of Wi Oshkosh; Undecided.

MARX, Kathryn; Shakamak HS; Jasonville, IN; /73 Chrs; HonRl; NHS; TchrAde; LatCl; PpCl; Trade School; Interior Decor.

MARX, Laura M; Fulton HS; Fulton, IL; ALAGirlsSt; Band; Chrs; CncrtBnd; HonRl; MrchBnd; NatlThespSoc; PepBnd; SchMus; SchPl; SctActv; FHA; FTA; Bsktbl; College; Elem Education.

MARX, Steven L; Sparta HS; Sparta, WI; Band; ChrhWkr; CncrtBnd; HonRl; MrchBnd; LetterFtbl; IMSpt; Wwti; Build Contractor.

MARXHAUSEN, Mary B; Concordia Acad; White Bear Lake, MN; 1/50 Chr; ChrhWkr; CmntyWkr; HonRl; NHS; StuCncl; StuGov; LetterBsktbl; PPFtbl; KiwanAwd; Concordia Coll; Elem Teacher.

MARZAHL, Steve W; Richmond Burton HS; Mchenry, IL; SecJrCls; HonRl; LetterBsktbl; LetterFtbl; CchngActv;.

MASBRUCH, Mark D; Belmont HS; Belmont, WI; 4-H; FFA; LetterWrstlng; IMSpt; Milwaukee Area Tech Coll; Masonry.

MASCARI, Richard M; Schulte HS; Terre Haute, IN; HonRl; KeyCl; Bsktbl; Trk; Univ Of Indiana.

MASCARO, Anita; Simley HS; Inver Grove Hgts, MN; PresFrshCls; HstJrCls; HstSrCls; Chr; HonRl; LbryAde; NHS; SchMus; PpCl; Trk; Vocational School; Interior Ecoratior.

MASCHAL, Kathy S; Mascoutah Comm HS; Mascoutah, IL; 25/251 Chr; Chrs; HonRl; NHS; OffAde; YthFlsp; Yrbk; FHA; FTA; LetterTennis; Belleville Area College; Education.

MASCHER, Helen K; Marshall HS; Marshall, IL; 8/115 Band; Chr; Chrs; ChrhWkr; CncrtBnd; DrlTm; MrchBnd; PepBnd; SchAde; SchMus; Butler University; Pharmacist.

MASCHER, Jane E; Eastridge HS; Kankakee, IL; 49/255 HonRl; LbryAde; SchMus; SchPl; 4-H; SpnCl; Illinois State Univ; Librarian.

MASCHER, Rebecca J; Marshall HS; Marshall, IL; 17/128 Band; Chr; ChrhWkr; CncrtBnd; MrchBnd; PepBnd; YthFlsp; 4-H; SciCl; GAA; Univ Of Ill; Computer Science.

MASCHING, John M; Saunemin HS; Saunemin, IL; TrsJrCls; HonRl; NHS; SchPl;.

MASCHMAN, Lisa L; Meridian HS; Daykin, NE; 5/36 TrsFrshCls; TrsJrCls; Band; Chrs; CncrtBnd; HonRl; NHS; SchPl; PpCl; Chrldr; Coll; Major Study.

MASCHMANN, Kim M; Deshler HS; Deshler, NE; 8/27 Band; Chrs; HonRl; SchPl; Yrbk; 4-H; SecPpCl; Trk; DanFAwd; 4-HAwd; U Of Neb; Fashin Design.

MASDEN, Kirk S; Boscobel HS; Boscobel, WI; Band; Chrs; CncrtBnd; HonRl; MrchBnd; Orch; PepBnd; SchMus; Trk; College; Musician.

MASEBERG, Dwight E; Thedford HS; Thedford, NE; 1/19 PresFrshCls; VPJrCls; PresSrCls; HonRl; RptrYrbk; EdSchPpr; LetterBsktbl; LetterFtbl; LetterTrk; AmLegAwd; Univ; Veterinary Science.

MASEK, Holly K; Hastings HS; Hastings, NE; HonRl; HospAde; SctActv; StuCncl; TchrAde; Teen; 4-H; PpCl; PresAwd; Tech Col; Dental Lab Technitian.

MASEK, Mark A; Odell Public HS; O Dell, NE; 4/20 SecSophCls; VPJrCls; PresSrCls; PresBand; CncrtBnd; HonRl; MrchBnd; PepBnd; SchPl; RptrYrbk; EdSchPpr; LetterBsktbl; LetterFtbl; LetterTrk; University Of Nebraska; Lawyer.

MASEK, Mark J; Joliet West HS; Joliet, IL; 45/492 HonRl; NHS; VPKeyCl; TreasLatCl; Univ Of Illinois; Pharmacy.

MASEK, Tina C; Elcho HS; Deerbrook, WI; 12/55 PresJrCls; Chrs; HonRl; NHS; SchPl; RptrYrbk; SpnCl;.

MASER, Debra K; Limestone Comm HS; Bartonville, IL; 51/396 Band; ChrhWkr; CncrtBnd; MrchBnd; NHS; PepBnd; Jr College; Accounting.

MASER, Robin L; Oak Park HS; Kansas City, MO; HonRl; SchPl; Trk; GAA; College; Biology.

MASER, Sandra G; Oak Park HS; Gladstone, MO; Chr; Chrs; HonRl; NHS; SchMus; StuCncl; TchrAde;.

MASHNI, Elizabeth J; Whitmore Lake HS; Ann Harbor, MI; 1/77 HonRl; JrNHS; NHS; StuCncl; TchrAde; FrCl; U Of Michigan; Medicine.

MASILIONIS, Kathleen D; Washburn Rural HS; Topeka, KS; Chrs; HonRl; LbryAde; SchMus; Yrbk; PpCl; Washburn Univ.

MASINI, Linda M; Morton West HS; Berwyn, IL; HonRl; JrNHS; NHS; SchPl; GAA; College; English.

MASINI, Lita H; Lake Michigan Catholic HS; St Joseph, MI; 5/90 PresFrshCls; HonRl; NatlThespSoc; SchPl; StuCncl; Chrldr; College; Law.

MASINI, Raymond A; St Patrick HS; Chicago, IL; 84/427 Band; Chrs; De Paul Univ; Accounting.

MASINICK, Betsy A; East Detroit HS; Warren, MI; Chr; HonRl; NatlFornLg; NHS; RptrYrbk; EdYrBk; Univ Of Michigan; Business Admin.

MASKE, David; North HS; Eau Claire, WI; ChrhWkr; HonRl; NHS; CaptBsbl; Bsktbl; CaptFtbl; Uw Eau Claire.

MASKE, Debbie M; Our Lady Of Mount Carmel HS; Wyandotte, MI; 6/61 Chrs; HonRl; NHS; SchMus; RptrYrbk; RptrSchPpr; PpCl; Chrldr; Coll;nurse.

MASKO, Mitchell J; Grand Haven Sr HS; Grand Haven, MI; TrsSophCls; ALBoysSt; ChrhWkr; HonRl; NHS; NatlMeritCmnd; StuCncl; KeyCl; SpnCl; Univ Of Mich; Political Science.

MASLIKOSA, Marianne M; Geo Washington HS; Chicago, IL; 1/480 Chr; HonRl; JrNHS; NHS; NatlMeritCmnd; Quill&Scroll; TchrAde; RptrSchPpr; PresLatCl; GAA; Univ Of Il; Pre Pharmacy.

MASLOWSKI, Michael G; So Milwaukee Senior HS; South Milwaukee, WI; 17/442 VPJrCls; HonRl; SctActv; StuCncl; Colorado School Of Mines; Geology.

MASLOWSKI, Michelle A; Mankato West HS; Mankato, MN; Chr; HonRl; NatlThespSoc; SchMus; College.

MASON, Barbara M; Douglas Mac Arthur HS; Decatur, IL; 1/400 HstJrCls; HstSrCls; HonRl; JrNHS; LitMag; NHS; OffAde; SptEdSchPpr; PresFrCl; Vanderbilt; Nursing.

MASON, Brian K; White Bear Mariner HS; White Bear Lake, MN; 68/442 ChrhWkr; NHS; StuCncl; YthFlsp; Bsbl; Bsktbl; Ftbl; St Olaf Coll; Math Sci.

MASON, Craig; Elkhart Central HS; Elkhart, IN; 6/450 HonRl; YthFlsp; Univ; Architect.

MASON, Crystal; M Boro Twp HS; Murphysboro, IL; HonRl; College; Professional.

MASON, Dave L; Sullivan HS; Sullivan, MO; StuCncl; StuGov; College; Law.

MASON, David L; Washburn HS; Minneapolis, MN; TrsSophCls; HonRl; NatlMeritFnl; NatlMeritSF; Vocational School; Surveying.

MASON, Deborah J; Prospect HS; Mt Prospect, IL; 158/614 CmntyWkr; HospAde; NatlMeritCmnd; YthFlsp; Univ Of Illinois; Ecologist.

MASON, Deval M; Elwood HS; Elwood, KS; 1/19 VPSophCls; TrsJrCls; ALBoysSt; Band; ChrhWkr; HonRl; PepBnd; StuCncl; RptrYrbk; EdYrBk; Bsktbl; Ftbl; AmLegAwd;.

MASON, Dwayne L; Tech HS; Indianapolis, IN; 75/1000 PresJrCls; ChrhWkr; HonRl; PresJA; SchAde; StuCncl; PresKeyCl; LetterFtbl; LetterTrk; JAAwd; Purdue Univ; Chemical Engineering.

MASON, Elaine A; Van Buren HS; Brazil, IN; 5/70 HonRl; NHS; PpCl; LetterTrk;.

MASON, Helen; Marysville HS; Beattie, KS; Chrs; HonRl; 4-H; FHA; PpCl; Trk; Chrldr; Business College; Vocation.

MASON, Joanne L; Stet HS; Norborne, MO; Band; Chrs; ChrhWkr; CmntyWkr; HonRl; SchPl; Yrbk; SchPpr; Chrldr; CitAwd; College; Business.

MASON, John H; Pekin Comm HS; Pekin, IL; Band; Chr; ChrhWkr; CncrtBnd; HonRl; MrchBnd; NHS; Orch; PepBnd; SchMus; SctActv; VPYthFlsp; Univ Of Ill; Medicine.

MASON, Joyce L; Glendale HS; Springfield, MO; ChrhWkr; CmntyWkr; HonRl; SchPl; Bsktbl; LetterTrk; PresAwd; Sw Mo State Univ; Physical Ed.

MASON, Judy A; Eastern HS; Greentown, IN; Chr; Chrs; HonRl; HospAde; NHS; SchMus; StuCncl; TchrAde; Pres4-H; PpCl; University.

MASON, Kathy A; Marian Catholic HS; Riverdale, IL; 54/328 Chrs; HonRl; SecGAA; St Francis College; Teacher.

MASON, Keith C; Soldan HS; St Louis, MO; 2/608 HonRl; ModUN; NHS; PolWkr; StuCncl; American Univ; Philosophy.

MASON, Keith D; Beloit Memorial HS; Beloit, WI; HonRl; NHS; SchAde; StuCncl; CaptSwmmng; IMSpt; ChmbCommrsAwd; LionAwd; RotaryAwd; College.

MASON, Kenneth A; Wayne Community HS; Russell, IA; 1/77 HstFrshCls; HstJrCls; VPSrCls; Band; ChrhWkr; CmntyWkr; CncrtBnd; HonRl; MrchBnd; ModUN; Bsktbl; CchngActv; Iowa St Univ; Science.

MASON, Martin D; Sullivan HS; Sullivan, IN; 16/133 Chrs; HonRl; SchPl; YthFlsp; Rose Hulman Inst; Engineering.

MASON, Mary J; Moulton Udell HS; Udell, IA; 1/40 PresSophCls; Chrs; CncrtBnd; HonRl; MrchBnd; PepBnd; YthFlsp; 4-H; FFA; College; Doctor.

MASON, Patty S; Cashton HS; Cashton, WI; 6/65 Chr; HonRl; Mdrgl; SchPl; YthFlsp; FHA; SpnCl; PpCl; GovHonPrgAwd; Wis Inst; Mech Design.

MASON, Phyllis S; North Chicago Community HS; Great Lakes, IL; ChrhWkr; HonRl; Glf; Swmmng; Trk; CchngActv; IMSpt; Business School; Accounting.

MASON, Rita U; Hall HS; Spring Valley, IL; 7/125 Chrs; ChrhWkr; CmntyWkr; HonRl; LbryAde; SctActv; StuCncl; RptrSchPpr; EdSchPpr; PpCl; GAA; College; Art.

MASON, Sharon L; Usa HS; Sebewaing, MI; Band; Chr; ChrhWkr; CncrtBnd; HonRl; MrchBnd; NatlMeritCmnd; SchMus; YthFlsp; FHA; Concordia Rf; Dir Of Parish Music Ed.

MASON, Shelby J; Noble Community HS; Noble, IL; ALAGirlsSt; ChrhWkr; CmntyWkr; HonRl; PresStuCncl; StuGov; Yrbk; FDA; FSA; 4-HAwd; College; Psychology.

MASON, Stanley W; Edwards HS; Albion, IL; HonRl; NHS; PpCl; LetterBsktbl; CaptFtbl; Trade School; Mechanic.

MASON, Steven D; Community HS; Little Falls, MN; 56/329 Band; Chr; ChrhWkr; CncrtBnd; MrchBnd; PepBnd; Bsktbl; Glf; College; Accounting.

MASON, Teri L; Tri Center HS; Minden, IA; Band; CncrtBnd; DrlTm; HonRl; MrchBnd; NHS; PepBnd; Bsktbl; College; Vocation.

MASSA, Heidi J; York Community HS; Elmhurst, IL; 2/912 HonRl; NHS; NatlMeritFnl; NatlMeritSF; Orch; PolWkr; TchrAde; MthCl; Univ; Corporate Law.

MASSANISSO, Josephine; Notre Dame Hs; Chicago, IL; HonRl; HospAde; NHS; FNA; Bsktbl; U; Professional.

MASSARO, Adrea L; Maria HS; Chicago, IL; HospAde; JA; StuCncl; Lewis Univ; Accounting.

MASSAT, Laura J; Luther South HS; Posen, IL; 5/204 Chr; HonRl; NHS; OffAde; SchMus; SchPl; GerCl; College; Secondary Education.

MASSEE, Karen R; Sioux Rapids Comm HS; Sioux Rapids, IA; Chr; ChrhWkr; CncrtBnd; HonRl; LbryAde; MrchBnd; SchPl; YthFlsp; Yrbk; Iowa Lakes Comm College; Horticulture.

MASSELINK, Jane I; Holland Christian HS; Zeeland, MI; Band; ChrhWkr; YthFlsp; 4-H; LetterBsktbl; IMSpt; Calvin Clge; Special Ed Teacher.

MASSENGALE, Roger; Blue River Valley HS; New Castle, IN; SecFrshCls; TchrAde; 4-H; SpnCl;.

MASSEY, Dorothy M; Arlington HS; Arlington Hts, IL; Chr; Chrs; ChrhWkr; HonRl; NatlMeritCmnd; PolWkr; TchrAde; FrCl; PpCl; LetterTennis; GAA; Illinois State Univ; Animal Science.

MASSEY, Edward H; Sycamore HS; Sycamore, IL; PresFHA; Bsktbl; Ftbl; Trade; Chef.

MASSEY, Julianne; Tipton HS; Tipton, IN; PresChr; HonRl; RedCrAde; SecStuCncl; FTA; SecGAA; DARAwd; Ball State Univ; Special Ed.

MASSEY, Linda M; Bayard HS; Bayard, NE; 4/46 TrsSrCls; Chrs; ChrhWkr; HonRl; NHS; OffAde; StuGov; FHA; PpCl; CitAwd; Kearney State Clge; Nursing.

MASSEY, Timothy; Carmel HS; Carmel, IN; CmntyWkr; HonRl; IMSpt; Univ; Bus.

MASSIALA, Christina A; Ann Arbor Huron HS; Ann Arbor, MI; 160/570 Band; LbryAde; SchPl; RptrYrbk; Yrbk; EngCl; FrCl; RusCl; SpnCl; Swmmng; Tennis; University; International Relations.

MASSIE, Anita G; Southern R Ii HS; Ellington, MO; CAP; CmntyWkr; HospAde; RedCrAde; ROTC; YthFlsp; FDA; FHA; FNA; FTA; Coll; Teacher.

MASSIE, Delia Y; Washburn HS; Topeka, KS; HonRl; JrNHS; LbryAde; NatlFornLg; NatlMeritCmnd; Howard Univ; Political Science.

MASSIE, Michael K; Palestine HS; Palestine, IL; HstSophCls; PresJrCls; HstJrCls; HonRl; StuCncl; FFA; LetterBsbl; LetterBsktbl; LetterFtbl; Indiana University; Physical Therapy.

MASSIGNAN, Dale T; Kingsford HS; Kingsford, MI; 4/163 PresFrshCls; ALBoysSt; HonRl; Ferris State College; Optometry.

MASSINGALE, Bryan N; Pius Xi HS; Milwaukee, WI; 9/375 ALBoysSt; Chr; ChrhWkr; NatlMeritCmnd; StuCncl; FTA; Marquette U; Psych.

MASSINGILL, Melody L; Galesburg HS; Galesburg, IL; Chr; HonRl; NHS; NatlMeritCmnd; SchMus; Yrbk; Illinois State Univ; Special Ed.

MASSMAN, Brant L; Centerville HS; Centerville, IA; HonRl; SchPl; Pres4-H; VPFFA; 4-HAwd; College; Law.

MASSURA, Mary J; Lourdes HS; Chicago, IL; 8/277 HonRl; NatlMeritCmnd; NatlMeritSF; 4-H; Nursing School; Nursing.

MAST, Alan L; Hart HS; Hart, MI; Band; CncrtBnd; HonRl; MrchBnd; PepBnd; LetterBsbl; LetterBsktbl; Ferris State College; Pharmacy.

MAST, Andrea C; Comstock Park HS; Comstock Park, MI; Chr; Chrs; HonRl; SchMus; RptrYrbk; Trk; GAA; IMSpt; Hope College; Psychology.

MAST, David J; Chisholm HS; Chisholm, MN; HonRl; SchMus; SchPl; FDA; FrCl; CaptSwmmng; College; Medicine.

MAST, Jonathan W; Delwood HS; Elwood, IA; 2/29 PresJrCls; ALBoysSt; CncrtBnd; HonRl; NHS; PepBnd; SctActv; LetterBsktbl; LetterTrk; U Of Ia; Engineer.

MAST, Nicholas C; Glenbrook South HS; Glenview, IL; 79/594 CmntyWkr; HonRl; NHS; LetterBsbl; LetterBsktbl; LetterFtbl; Trk; Cornell Univ; Law.

MAST, Timothy; Bergan Hs; Peoria, IL; 34/200 ChrhWkr; CmntyWkr; HonRl; SctActv; StuCncl; LetterWrstlng; Ill Central College; Accounting.

MAST, Vicki; Arthur HS; Arthur, IL; Band; Chrs; HonRl; MrchBnd; YthFlsp; Yrbk; 4-H; FHA; FTA; GAA; Manatee Jr Coll; Secretarial Studies.

MASTA, Janice A; Saint Agatha HS; Detroit, MI; Chr; HonRl; JA; Bsbl; Swmmng; ALBoysSt; JAAwd; College; Professional.

MASTALIR, Mary C; Kewaunee HS; Kewaunee, WI; AFS; Chr; Chrs; Mdrgl; NHS; NatlThespSoc; SchMus; SchPl; RptrYrbk; Yrbk; Tech Schl; Operating Room Assistant.

MASTANTUONO, Laura L; Elizabeth Seton HS; Blue Island, IL; 76/238 Chr; CmntyWkr; HonRl; HospAde; Orch; SpnCl; MthCl; College; Music.

MASTBERGEN, Brian K; George Comm HS; George, IA; Chrs; HonRl; NHS; SchMus; Bsktbl; LetterFtbl;.

MASTELLER, Susan R; Mishawaka HS; Mishawaka, IN; 8/425 Chr; HonRl; LitMag; NHS; NatlMeritSchl; Quill&Scroll; TreasYthFlsp; RptrYrbk; GerCl; BttyCrckrAwd; Univ; Engineering.

MASTERS, Deborah A; Chillicothe HS; Chillicothe, MO; 2/200 AFS; HonRl; SchPl; StuCncl; FBLA; FTA; PresSpnCl; PpCl; GAA; OptClAwd; PresAwd; Univ Of Missouri; Interior Design.

MASTERS, Gayla J; Oak Park HS; Gladstone, MO; Chrs; ChrhWkr; HonRl; NHS; SchAde; SctActv; TchrAde; RptrSchPpr; SpnCl; PpCl; Trk; IMSpt; CaptPPFtbl; Univ Of Mo; Journalism.

MASTERS, Michael W; Pekin Community HS; Pekin, IL; 49/744 Chr; JrNHS; LitMag; NHS; Quill&Scroll; SchPl; StuCncl; RptrYrbk; University; History.

MASTERS, Sally M; Excelsior Springs HS; Excelsior Springs, MO; 4/226 PresSophCls; CmntyWkr; HonRl; NHS; StuCncl; SptEdYrbk; Yrbk; FTA; PpCl; Bsbl; Bsktbl; CaptTennis; GAA; William Jewell Col; Physical Ed.

MASTERSON, Marcia E; Fairfield Comm HS; Fairfield, IL; ChrhWkr; CmntyWkr; HonRl; LbryAde; NHS; OffAde; Quill&Scroll; College; Journalism.

MASTIO, Dave M; East Richland HS; Olney, IL; 24/264 Band; CncrtBnd; MrchBnd; NHS; SchMus; YthFlsp; Tennis; Univ Of Illinois; Pre Medicine.

MASTNY, Brian J; Howells Public HS; Clarkson, NE; VPSophCls; ChrhWkr; CmntyWkr; SchPl; StuCncl; 4-H; FFA; Bsbl; Bsktbl; College.

MASTNY, Denise K; Howells Public HS; Clarkson, NE; Chrs; ChrhWkr; HonRl; MrchBnd; Twrl; 4-H; FHA; PpCl; Chrldr; 4-HAwd; University.

MASYGA, Patricia A; Cumberland HS; Cumberland, WI; 3/126 SecFrshCls; SecJrCls; Band; CncrtBnd; HonRl; MrchBnd; PepBnd; SchPl; SctActv; StuCncl; FHA; PpCl; Univ; Business.

MATASOVSKY, Harlan W; Lakefield HS; Jackson, MN; 25/76 Chr; Chrs; HonRl; StuCncl; PresYthFlsp; Pres4-H; PresFFA; Bsbl; 4-HAwd; College; Plant Science.

MATCHEN, Henry J; Macon County R 1 HS; Macon, MO; 8/118 ALBoysSt; HonRl; FrCl; SpnCl; LetterFtbl; DARAwd; College; Military.

MATCHEY, Nancy; Whitehall Memorial HS; Whitehall, WI; 8/73 Band; HonRl; NHS; Yrbk; SchPpr; Bsktbl; GAA; Univ Of Wisc Stout; Graphic Arts.

MATEER, David A; Dunlap HS; Peoria, IL; 1/93 AFS; ChrhWkr; HonRl; PresNHS; SpnCl; SciCl; Bsktbl; DARAwd; Bradley U; Industrial Engi.

MATEER, Pamella; Forest Lake Sr Hs; Forest Lake, MN; Band; ChrhWkr; CncrtBnd; HonRl; MrchBnd; Yrbk; College;certified Public Accountant.

MATEJCAK, Robert; Joliet Catholic HS; Joliet, IL; 38/169 Aud/Vis; SchMus; SchPpr; GerCl; LatCl; PpCl; LetterFtbl; CaptTrk; IMSpt; Joliet Jr College; Pilot.

MATEK, Michael; Evanston Township Hs; Evanston, IL; CmntyWkr; HonRl; PolWkr; College;politics.

MATERI, Wayne B; Emmons Central HS; Strasburg, ND; Aud/Vis; Chrs; NatlMeritCmnd; NatlMeritSchl; PolWkr; SchMus; SchPl; RptrYrbk; SptEdSchPpr; FFA; Trade School; Professional.

MATERKA, Kathryn A; Regina HS; Detroit, MI; HonRl; HospAde; StuCncl; LetterChrldr; GAA; IMSpt; College; Medical.

MATEVICH, William; Saint Laurence Hs; Chicago, IL; 12/374 CmntyWkr; HonRl; StuCncl; StuGov; FrCl; SciCl; CaptGlf; LetterTrk; U Of Miami; Corporate Lawyer.

MATEYKO, Barbara H; Marillac HS; Glenview, IL; Chrs; ChrhWkr; CmntyWkr; HospAde; NatlMeritCmnd; SctActv; TchrAde; RptrYrbk; Northern Ill Univ; Doctor.

MATHENY, John R; East Alton Wood River Com HS; East Alton, IL; 14/276 Aud/Vis; Band; ChrhWkr; HonRl; MrchBnd; NHS; VPNatlThespSoc; OffAde; SchPl; StuCncl; U Of Il; Electrical Engineering.

MATHENY, Leonard; Woodruff Hish HS; Peoria, IL; 59/232 PresSrCls; Band; ChrhWkr; CmntyWkr; StuCncl; Swmmng; Trk; Wrstlng; JETSAwd; Isu; Tech Eng.

MATHENY, Ronda J; Bedford Comm HS; Bedford, IA; SecSophCls; ALAGirlsSt; HonRl; NHS; SchPl; StuCncl; EdYrBk; PpCl; Chrldr; MasAwd; College; Elem Ed.

MATHER, Kathleen; Laurens Community HS; Laurens, IA; 1/48 ChrhWkr; CncrtBnd; HonRl; MrchBnd; NHS; Bsbl; Bsktbl; Trk; GovHonPrgAwd; CitAwd; Iowa State University; Physical Therapy.

MATHER, Susan G; Mitchell HS; Mitchell, IN; 15/120 ALAGirlsSt; NHS; SecQuill&Scroll; EdSchPpr; PpCl; GAA; Indiana Univ.

MATHES, Jeffrey G; Unionville HS; Livonia, MO; 4/75 ALBoysSt; Band; CncrtBnd; HonRl; MrchBnd; NHS; SchPl; Bsbl; 4-HAwd; Navy.

MATHEWS, Alan M; Lake Central HS; St John, IN; HonRl; NHS; FrCl; AmLegAwd; Purdue U; Electrical Eng.

MATHEWS, Dawn L; Highland HS; Chesterfield, IN; 17/236 ALAGirlsSt; Chr; Chrs; HonRl; NatlThespSoc; SchPl; TchrAde; FHA; SciCl; Anderson Clg; Medical Tech.

MATHEWS, Elaine M; Yorktown HS; Muncie, IN; 4/188 HonRl; JA; NHS; NatlMeritSF; Orch; SchPl; FrCl; GerCl; SpnCl; SciCl; Ballstate U; Foreign Language.

MATHEWS, Glenn T; Lacrosse HS; Lacrosse, IN; 2/50 VPJrCls; ALBoysSt; Band; CncrtBnd; HonRl; LitMag; NHS; RptrYrbk; Trk; IMSpt; Purdue Univ; Medicine.

MATHEWS, Joanna M; Centerville HS; Richmond, IN; Band; Chr; ChrhWkr; NHS; PolWkr; StuGov; YthFlsp; Chrldr; CchngActv; IMSpt; Purdue Univ; Elementary Education.

MATHEWS, John F; Spirit Lake HS; Spirit Lake, IA; ALBoysSt; Band; Chrs; CncrtBnd; SchMus; SchPl; SctActv; StuCncl; LetterFtbl; LetterTrk; College; Music.

MATHEWS, John H; Fairfield Comm HS; Fairfield, IL; Band; CncrtBnd; HonRl; MrchBnd; PepBnd; SpnCl; SciCl; S Illinois Univ; Medicine.

MATHEWS, Kathleen A; Riverdale HS; Muscoda, WI; AFS; Aud/Vis; Chr; Chrs; HonRl; SctActv; StuCncl; 4-H; SciCl; GAA; Armed Services.

MATHEWS, Kimberly J; Thomas Jefferson HS; Council Bluffs, IA; 15/460 HonRl; MrchBnd; NHS; Orch; Twrl; AmLegAwd; Clg; History Psychcology.

MATHEWS, Kirby A; Richmond Sr HS; Richmond, IN; PresChr; JA; Mdrgl; ModUN; SchMus; RptrSchPpr; LetterTrk; LetterWrstlng; CchngActv; PresAwd; Earlham U; Medicine.

MATHEWS, Marcia K; Union County HS; Liberty, IN; SecTrsFrshCls; TrsSophCls; TrsJrCls; Chrs; CmntyWkr; HonRl; SchPl; RptrSchPpr; SecFHA; PpCl; Col; Bus Major.

MATHEWS, Michael R; Brown HS; Sturgis, SD; 38/206 HonRl; TchrAde; Univ Of So California; Medicine.

MATHEWS, Randall G; Columbia HS; Columbia, IL; 4/120 PresFrshCls; PresSophCls; PresJrCls; PresSrCls; HonRl; PresNHS; PresGerCl; PresMthCl; LetterBsbl; LetterBsktbl; College; Accounting.

MATHEWS, Richard D; O Fallon Township HS; O Fallon, IL; ALBoysSt; HonRl; NHS; NatlThespSoc; SchPl; PresStuCncl; SpnCl; CaptTrk; Eastern Ill Univ; Psychology.

MATHEWS, Tamara L; Marian HS; Birmingham, MI; HonRl; LbryAde; Chrl; NHS; PolWkr; StuGov; Engineering.

MATHEWSON, Joseph K; New Trier East HS; Winnetka, IL; VPJrCls; VPSrCls; HonRl; NatlMeritCmnd; StuGov; LetterSocr; Tennis; Dartmouth College.

MATHIAS, Christine; Waukegan East HS; Waukegan, IL; 19/1000 HonRl; JrNHS; NHS; FBLA; Northern Il Univ; Accounting.

MATHIAS, Elizabeth A; North Huron HS; Port Austin, MI; 9/43 SecFrshCls; Band; CncrtBnd; HonRl; MrchBnd; NHS; LetterBsktbl; Trk; IMSpt; 4-HAwd; Lansing Community Clge; Radiologic Tech.

MATHIAS, Margaret; Northrop HS; Fort Wayne, IN; 18/650 Chr; HonRl; StuCncl; PpCl; College; Mathematics.

MATHIASON, Diane K; Edmore Public HS; Fairdale, ND; 6/24 PresFrshCls; SecJrCls; TrsJrCls; ALAGirlsSt; Chr; Chrs; ChrhWkr; Chrldr; GAA; 4-HAwd; University.

MATHIESON, Melanie; Walnut Grove Public HS; Walnut Grove, MN; 4/41 Chr; HonRl; MrchBnd; NatlMeritSF; SchMus; StuCncl; RptrSchPpr; GAA; Univ Minn; Accounting.

MATHIEU, Mark A; Houghton HS; Chassell, MI; PresJrCls; PresSrCls; ALBoysSt; HonRl; LetterBsktbl; LetterTrk; Mich Tech Univ.

MATHIS, Crystal L; Pittsburg HS; Pittsburg, KS; ChrhWkr; HonRl; OffAde; StuCncl; VPStuGov; YthFlsp; FTA; PresPpCl; LetterTrk; GAA; College; Professional.

MATHIS, Dana; Lafayette Co Cl HS; Higginsville, MO; SecSophCls; SecJrCls; Band; HonRl; MrchBnd; StuCncl; RptrSchPpr; SchPpr;.

MATHIS, Daniel M; De La Salle HS; Minneapolis, MN; 14/127 JrNHS; NHS; StuGov; RptrSchPpr; PpCl; LetterBsktbl; LetterFtbl; LetterTrk; IMSpt; Moorhead State College; Engineering.

MATHIS, Deena G; Walker R Iv HS; Walker, MO; SecJrCls; HonRl; SchPl; TreasStuCncl; Yrbk; PpCl; LetterBsktbl; Chrldr; CitAwd;.

MATHIS, Elizabeth J; Brown County HS; Nashville, IN; 13/169 HonRl; SctActv; VPStuCncl; TchrAde; LatCl; SpnCl; PpCl; Chrldr; GAA; In Central Col; Nurse.

MATHIS, Julia L; Brown County HS; Nashville, IN; ChrhWkr; HospAde; TchrAde; FHA; PresLatCl; GAA; College; Nursing.

MATHIS, Kathryn A; Streator Twp HS; Streator, IL; ChrhWkr; NatlMeritCmnd; NatlMeritSchl; TchrAde; RptrYrbk; EdYrBk; 4-H; VPFTA; GerCl; Illinois State Univ; Mathematics.

MATHIS, Larry A; Pennfield HS; Battle Creek, MI; HonRl; NHS; TchrAde; RptrSchPpr; SciCl; LetterBsktbl; CaptFtbl; LetterTrk; CchngActv; AmLegAwd; Kalamazoo College; Medicine.

MATHIS, Luella; Brown County HS; Columbus, IN; 2/206 HonRl; LatCl; College; Elem Education.

MATHIS, Pamela S; Wesclin HS; Trenton, IL; VPSrCls; Band; CncrtBnd; LbryAde; SchPl; RptrSchPpr; PresFBLA; SecPpCl; Trk; GAA; Hickey Sch; Secretary.

MATHIS, Patricia A; Mount Vernon HS; Letcher, SD; 11/29 Chrs; ChrhWkr; DrlTm; SpnCl; PpCl;.

MATHIS, Robert E; Mt Vernon Public HS; Mt Vernon, SD; ALBoysSt; HonRl; NHS; SchPl; Treas4-H; Bsbl; LetterBsktbl; CaptFtbl; LetterTrk; CchngActv; West Point; Army.

MATHIS, Sherry; Vienna HS; Belknap, IL; 8/94 Band; ChrhWkr; CncrtBnd; HonRl; MrchBnd; NHS; 4-H; SpnCl; MthCl; CitAwd; Coll; Ed.

MATHIS, Steven E; Samuel C Mumford HS; Detroit, MI; 15/382 HonRl; NHS; NatlMeritCmnd; Univ; Professional.

MATHIS, Tammy A; Wesclin Senior HS; Trenton, IL; SecFrshCls; SecJrCls; HonRl; NHS; TchrAde; SptEdSchPpr; PpCl; Trk; Chrldr; GAA; College; Physical Educ Teacher.

MATHIS, Twila S; Stewardson Strasburg HS; Strasburg, IL; ALAGirlsSt; Band; CncrtBnd; LbryAde; SchPl; RptrYrbk; RptrSchPpr; EdSchPpr; SchPpr; FHA; Lake Land Jr College; Journalism.

MATHISON, Debra; Hector Community HS; Hector, MN; Band; Chr; CncrtBnd; HonRl; MrchBnd; PepBnd; SchPl; FHA; Faibault Vti; Lpn.

MATHISON, Diane M; Stanley Boyd HS; Thorp, WI; 6/113 ChrhWkr; TreasStuCncl; VPYthFlsp; SecFHA; GerCl; CaptChrldr; VPGAA; DARAwd; EldAwd; Univ Of Wisconsin; Fashion Merchandising.

MATIAS, Dawn C; Tri HS; New Castle, IN; 15/92 HonRl; OffAde; RptrYrbk; RptrSchPpr; SchPpr; FFA; FHA; PpCl; GAA; 4-HAwd; College; Vet Science.

MATKIN, Lori; Liberal HS; Liberal, KS; ChrhWkr; CmntyWkr; TchrAde; YthFlsp; FTA; FrCl; College; Teaching.

MATLACK, Rex W; Clearwater HS; Clearwater, KS; ALBoysSt; Band; Chr; ChrhWkr; SchMus; StuCncl; 4-H; Wrstlng; 4-HAwd; MasAwd; College; Business Admin.

MATLICK, Kyle E; Rockridge HS; Reynolds, IL; SchMus; StuCncl; LatCl; Bsbl; Bsktbl; Ftbl; Trk; IMSpt; College; Liberal Arts.

MATLOCK, Dianna L; Sullivan HS; Sullivan, MO; 27/150 Band; ChrhWkr; CncrtBnd; HonRl; StuCncl; TchrAde; RptrYrbk; RptrSchPpr; SchPpr; East Central Jr College; Professional.

MATNEY, Clarence R; Oak Park HS; Kansas City, MO; SecTrsFrshCls; ChrhWkr; HonRl; RptrSchPpr; Bsktbl; Ftbl; Trk; Missouri Univ; Veterinarian.

MATNEY, Constance M; Turner HS; Kansas City, KS; 27/330 Band; Chr; TreasChrhWkr; HonRl; HospAde; NHS; SchMus; TchrAde; FrCl; SciCl; Univ; Med Tech.

MATOUSEK, John M; Solomon Juneau HS; Wood, WI; CtyCnl; HonRl; Orch; RptrYrbk; MthCl; SciCl; Tennis; Trk; University; Medicine.

MATOVINA, Mark T; Andrean HS; Mrrillville, IN; 6/305 NHS; Yrbk; Glf; Indiana Univ; Law Schl.

MATRY, Kimberly K; Bismarck Henning HS; Danville, IL; 7/76 SecSrCls; Chrl; Chrs; ChrhWkr; HonRl; TchrAde; Bsktbl; CaptFtbl; Trk; Danville Jr Coll; Market.

MATSEY, Madeline M; Hobart Sr HS; Hobart, IN; AFS; Chrs; HonRl; PolWkr; Quill&Scroll; TchrAde; RptrSchPpr; FHA; SpnCl; Valparaiso Univ; Medicine.

MATSON, Diane; Yankton HS; Yankton, SD; 4/233 Chrs; ChrhWkr; CncrtBnd; DrmMjrt; HonRl; NHS; SchMus; Bsktbl; Trk; BttyCrckrAwd; Gustavus Adolphus Coll;soc Sci.

MATSUMURA, Alan A; Joliet Catholic HS; Joliet, IL; 6/170 CmntyWkr; HonRl; NHS; NatlMeritCmnd; TchrAde; LatCl; RusCl; University; Biology.

MATSUTANI, Carolyn M; Hershey Public HS; North Platte, NE; 12/39 SchPl; TreasStuCncl; RptrYrbk; Pres4-H; PresPpCl; 4-HAwd; U Of Ne; Home Ec.

MATSUURA, Rhonda; Abraham Lincoln Sr HS; Bloomington, MN; AFS; CmntyWkr; HonRl; HospAde; Teen; ModUN; RptrYrbk; PpCl; OptClAwd; College; Rh.

MATT, Diana L; Rushville HS; Pine Ridge, SD; Band; CncrtBnd; HospAde; LbryAde; MrchBnd; NatlFornLg; PepBnd; Dakota St College; Psychology.

MATT, Marshall W; Marshalltown HS; Marshalltown, IA; PresFrshCls; ALBoysSt; StuCncl; LetterBsktbl; CaptFtbl; LetterTrk; College; Business Administration.

MATTAS, Kathleen A; Wilson HS; Wilson, KS; 1/26 TrsJrCls; Chrs; HonRl; LbryAde; Mdrgl; SchPl; RptrYrbk; RptrSchPpr; EdSchPpr; BttyCrckrAwd; Marymount College; Med Tech.

MATTEI, Leeann T; Lasalle Peru Twp HS; Peru, IL; Chrs; HonRl; SchMus; SchPl; SpnCl; Illinois Valley Comm College; Mathematics.

MATTEK, Judi M; Antigo Senior HS; Deerbrook, WI; Chr; CncrtBnd; NatlFornLg; SchPl; VP4-H; IMSpt; PresAwd; Busines Schf Vocation.

MATTER, Daniel; Custer HS; Milwaukee, WI; NHS; TchrAde; MthCl; SciCl; Iit; Majoe In Phsics.

MATTERN, Myron D; Lakota HS; Lakota, ND; Chrs; HonRl; JrNHS; StuCncl; RptrSchPpr; Bsbl; LetterFtbl; LetterTrk; Coll Or Military; Professional.

MATTES, Kim M; Marion HS; Marion, WI; 22/84 SecTrsFrshCls; SecTrsSophCls; SecTrsJrCls; Chrs; NatlFornLg; StuCncl; TchrAde; Yrbk; FHA; Chrldr; Tech; Teacher.

MATTESON, Elizabeth A; Lincoln Way HS; Manhattan, IL; Band; Chrs; ChrhWkr; CncrtBnd; HonRl; MrchBnd; PepBnd; YthFlsp; 4-H; FTA; GerCl; MthCl; PpCl; College.

MATTESON, Kathleen A; Orono Sr HS; Long Lake, MN; 2/225 HonRl; HospAde; NHS; StuCncl; StuGov; SchPpr; BttyCrckrAwd; OptClAwd; VFWAwd; Oxford Univ; Medicine.

MATTESON, Lyle E; Central Community HS; Argyle, IA; AFS; Band; Chr; ChrhWkr; HonRl; NHS; SchPl; YthFlsp; FTA; LetterTrk; Study Math.

MATTESON, Nan E; Culver Girls Academy; Brookston, IN; HonRl; SchPl; StuGov; LetterTrk; GAA; Allegheny College; Drama.

MATTESON, Shirley M; Durand HS; Durand, IL; 1/62 PresBand; ChrhWkr; CncrtBnd; HonRl; MrchBnd; NHS; PepBnd; SchMus; SchPl; EdYrBk; 4-H; GerCl; GAA; College; Music.

MATTHEIS, Jill A; Hagerstown HS; Hagerstown, IN; 3/125 ALAGirlsSt; HonRl; NHS; PolWkr; SctActv; TchrAde; 4-H; PpCl; GAA; 4-HAwd; Coll.

MATTHEWS, Colette A; Carl Sandburg HS; Oak Forest, IL; 63/680 MrchBnd; NHS; SchPl; YthFlsp; SchPpr; FTA; PpCl; Trk; Chrldr; GAA; AmLegAwd; Drake University; English.

MATTHEWS, Deborah J; Junction City Sr HS; Fort Riley, KS; HonRl; NHS; NatlMeritCmnd; NatlSciFnd; RedCrAde; StuCncl; TchrAde; FrCl; Georgia Inst Of Tech; Chemical Engineer.

MATTHEWS, Diane; Negaunee HS; Negaunee, MI; Chrs; HonRl; Yrbk; Univ; Major Study.

MATTHEWS, Jackie L; Miller R 2 HS; Miller, MO; Chr; ChrhWkr; CmntyWkr; HonRl; NHS; TchrAde; RptrSchPpr; FHA; FTA; TreasSciCl; Coll; Home Economics.

MATTHEWS, Kirk C; Parkway West Senior HS; Ballwin, MO; 99/742 Chrs; ChrhWkr; NatlMeritCmnd; StuCncl; StuGov; YthFlsp; SciCl; Glf; Swmmng; LetterWrstlng; Univ Of Mo Columbia; Veterinary Medicine.

MATTHEWS, Lori L; Oak Park HS; Kansas City, MO; Band; CncrtBnd; HonRl; JrNHS; MrchBnd; NHS; OffAde; TchrAde; PresFrCl; MthCl; College; Professional.

MATTHEWS, Martin A; Pekin Community HS; Pekin, IL; 124/780 HonRl; College; Computer Programmer.

MATTHEWS, Mary A; Boyne City HS; Boyne City, MI; 6/137 Chr; ChrhWkr; CmntyWkr; HonRl; OffAde; TchrAde; FHA; FNA; FrCl; Trade School; Professional.

MATTHEWS, Mary E; Liberty Sr HS; Birch Tree, MO; LetterChr; Chrs; HonRl; Mdrgl; PpCl; LetterTrk; PPFtbl; University.

MATTHEWS, Pauline R; St Benedict HS; Chicago, IL; 9/180 HonRl; JA; NHS; Northeastern Univ; Art.

MATTHEWS, Robin; Walnut Comm HS; Walnut, IL; Chrs; HonRl; JrNHS; VPNHS; SchPl; VPStuCncl; RptrYrbk; RptrSchPpr; LetterTrk; Chrldr;.

MATTHEWS, Robin J; Fairview HS; Fairview, MI; SecSophCls; SecJrCls; HonRl; GAA; University; Medicine.

MATTHEWS, Rob J; Lawrence HS; Lawrence, KS; ChrhWkr; ModUN; NatlFornLg; PolWkr; StuCncl; SchPpr; Tennis; Kansas Univ; Psychologost.

MATTHEWS, Sandra G; Potosi HS; Potosi, MO; Chr; Chrs; HonRl; NatlMeritCmnd; OffAde; YthFlsp; FNA; PpCl; Mineral Area Jr Clg; Business Management.

MATTHEWS, Timothy J; Arlington HS; Arlington, NE; 16/57 HonRl; NHS;.

MATTHIAS, Mark S; Technical HS; St Cloud, MN; 5/465 Band; ChrhWkr; CncrtBnd; MrchBnd; NHS; SchPl; YthFlsp; LetterTennis; Wrstlng; College; Mortuary Sci.

MATTHIES, Bonnie; Clarkson Public HS; Clarkson, NE; 1/38 Chrs; CncrtBnd; HonRl; MrchBnd; NHS; PepBnd; SchPl; Wayne State College;.

MATTHIES, Bonnie S; Clarkson HS; Clarkson, NE; Chrs; CncrtBnd; HonRl; MrchBnd; NHS; PepBnd; SchPl; PresFBLA; PresFHA; PpCl; Wayne State College.

MATTHIES, Charles R; Prosser Vocational HS; Chicago, IL; HonRl; College; Computer Science.

MATTHIES, Timothy J; Gothenburg HS; Gothenburg, NE; 32/85 NatlThespSoc; OffAde; SchPl; StuCncl; TchrAde; 4-H; FFA; Ftbl; LetterWrstlng; IMSpt; College; Major Study.

MATTHIESSEN, Randy M; Anamosa HS; Anamosa, IA; Band; CncrtBnd; MrchBnd; PepBnd; SctActv; PresYthFlsp; LetterBsbl; LetterFtbl; LetterTrk; University; Study Business.

MATTHYS, Don A; Barron Sr HS; Almena, WI; Band; Chr; HonRl; MrchBnd; SctActv; SchPpr; 4-H; FFA; LetterFtbl; LetterTrk; 4-HAwd; College; Agriculture.

MATTICE, Thomas H; Xavier HS; Appleton, WI; 5/106 Chrs; HonRl; NHS; SpnCl; BauchLmbAwd; Univ Of Wi; Physician.

MATTILA, Rebecca A; Jeffers HS; Toivola, MI; PresJrCls; HonRl; HospAde; NHS; TchrAde; Yrbk; PpCl; IMSpt; College; Social Work.

MATTINGLY, Daniel L; Freeport Sr HS; Freeport, IL; 1/507 HonRl; VPSpnCl; MthCl; SciCl; Rockford College; Pharmacy.

MATTINGLY, Linda; Franklin HS; Westland, MI; Chrs; HonRl; LitMag; RptrYrbk; EdYrBk; Yrbk; College; Bio/chem Research / Writing.

MATTINGLY, Linda J; Jefferson HS; Lafayette, IN; 52/609 ALAGirlsSt; HonRl; VPJA; JrNHS; NatlFornLg; SchMus; TreasStuCncl; 4-H; 4-HAwd; JAAwd; Purdue Univ; Teaching.

MATTINGLY, Patricia A; Washington Catholic HS; Washington, IN; 5/34 TrsFrshCls; SecSophCls; Chrs; HonRl; StuCncl; Univ Of Evansville; X Ray Technician.

MATTINGLY, Rebecca S; Mt Vernon Twp HS; Mt Vernon, IL; 25/400 Band; Chr; ChrhWkr; CmntyWkr; CncrtBnd; HonRl; HospAde; JrNHS; Mdrgl; MrchBnd; College; Medicine.

MATTISON, Julie; Jackson HS; Jackson, MN; 6/108 Chr; OffAde; RptrYrbk; FrCl; Business College; Medical Assisatant.

MATTKE, Candie S; Delwood Community HS; Maquoketa, IA; Band; HonRl; MrchBnd; NHS; SchPl; StuCncl; FrCl; Trk; CaptChrldr; Clge; Art.

MATTKE, Jill A; Plymouth HS; Plymouth, IN; 47/215 Chr; HonRl; SchMus; SchPl; EngCl; SpnCl; Ivy Tech; Computer Programming.

MATTLER, Steven J; Midland HS; Midland, MI; 28/454 Chr; ChrhWkr; HonRl; NHS; Mi Tec U; Chemical Engineering.

MATTLEY, Phyllis J; Burwell Jr Sr HS; Burwell, NE; Band; ChrhWkr; HonRl; HospAde; SchPl; SctActv; YthFlsp; Yrbk; 4-H; 4-HAwd; Mary Lanning Schl Of Nursing; Nurse.

MATTMILLER, Rick W; Antigo HS; Mattoon, WI; Band; ChrhWkr; CncrtBnd; HonRl; MrchBnd; PepBnd; GerCl; Bsbl; LetterFtbl; IMSpt; Vocational School; Vocation.

MATTOX, Debra A; Staunton HS; Braxil, IN; Band; CncrtBnd; HonRl; LbryAde; MrchBnd; PepBnd; StuGov; EdSchPpr; 4-H; FHA; LatCl; Indiana St Univ; Special Education.

MATTOX, Sherry A; Archie HS; Archie, MO; Chr; Chrs; HonRl; HospAde; SchPl; YthFlsp; SchPpr; FHA; PpCl; Trk; Business School; Secretary.

MATTSFIELD, Deirdre A; Litchfield HS; Darwin, MN; Band; Chr; CmntyWkr; SchPpr; FHA; GerCl; Wrstlng; 4-HAwd; LionAwd; PresAwd; College; Professional.

MATTSON, Gayle L; Luther L Wright HS; Ironwood, MI; 13/210 Chr; HonRl; NHS; NatlMeritCmnd; NatlMeritSF; NatlThespSoc; SchMus; SchPl; FrCl; Gogebic Comm College; Med Secretary.

MATTSON, Kay; Kennedy Public HS; Kennedy, MN; ChrhWkr; CmntyWkr; HospAde; SchAde; StuGov; FFA; FHA; FSA; Ftbl; Trade School; Vocation.

MATTSON, Kenneth F; Batavia Sr HS; Batavia, IL; 13/219 HonRl; NHS; TchrAde; MthCl; Bsbl; Eastern Ill Univ; Accounting.

MATTSON, Lila J; Glenwood HS; Glenwood, MN; 35/130 Chr; HonRl; OffAde; SchMus; FHA; College; Elementary Teacher.

MATTSON, Mark R; Milaca Sr HS; Milaca, MN; Chrs; CncrtBnd; HonRl; MrchBnd; PepBnd; SchMus; RptrSchPpr; 4-H; DanFAwd; Trade School; Vocation.

MATTSON, Nathan C; Muskegon HS; Muskegon, MI; Chr; ChrhWkr; CncrtBnd; HonRl; MrchBnd; NHS; Orch;.

MATTSON, Pamela A; Glenbrook South HS; Glenview, IL; 11/579 AFS; Chr; ChrhWkr; HonRl; NHS; StuCncl; PresSwmmng; GAA;.

MATTSON, Pamela K; Jefferson C 123 HS; Conception Jct, MO; 9/27 VPSophCls; VPJrCls; VPSrCls; HonRl; StuCncl; FHA; PpCl; Bsbl; LetterBsktbl; LetterTrk; College; Professional.

MATTSON, Raymond C; Republic Michigamme HS; Republic, MI; 16/54 HonRl; Michigan Univ; Civil Engineer.

MATTSON, Richard A; Albrook HS; Saginaw, MN; 7/56 Band; Chr; ChrhWkr; HonRl; Yrbk; SchPpr; LetterFtbl; Trk; College; Accounting.

MATTUCCI, Teresa C; Notre Dame HS; Chicago, IL; 4/302 HonRl; NHS; SpnCl; CaptChrldr; U Of Ill; Med Tech.

MATULA, Barbara B; Gwinn HS; Carlshend, MI; NatlMeritCmnd; 4-H; University; Business Educ.

MATULA, Timothy J; Glenwood Com HS; Pacific Junction, IA; PresSrCls; CtyCnl; HonRl; NHS; SchPl; SctActv; StuCncl; StuGov; LetterWrstlng; JAAwd; PresAwd; RotaryAwd;.

MATULIS, Michael P; Limestone HS; Peoria, IL; HonRl; StuCncl; EdSchPpr; KeyCl; LetterTennis; Il State Univ; History Teacher Journalist.

MATULKA, Joe F; Aquinas HS; David City, NE; Band; CmntyWkr; NatlMeritSchl; YthFnd; FBLA; FFA; MthCl; Ftbl; Wrstlng; GAA; Trade School; Electronics.

MATULKA, Laura S; Raymond Central HS; Valparaiso, NE; Chr; Chrs; ChrhWkr; CmntyWkr; HonRl; NHS; StuCncl; 4-H; SpnCl; PpCl; College; Work With Children.

MATULKA, Mary J; Raymond Central HS; Valparaiso, NE; 3/57 SecJrCls; VPSrCls; ALAGirlsSt; MrchBnd; PresNHS; Pres4-H; PresPpCl; GAA; DARAwd; 4-HAwd; JCAwd; PresAwd; Univ Of Ne; Speech Therapy.

MATUREN, Daniel J; Mahtomedi HS; Mahtomedi, MN; 1/144 HonRl; JA; JrNHS; NHS; GerCl; Bsbl; Bsktbl; Ftbl; Carleton College; Electrical Engineering.

MATUREN, Debra L; Battle Creek Central HS; Battle Creek, MI; 22/480 Chr; ChrhWkr; HonRl; NHS; SchMus; SchPl; YthFlsp; AmLegAwd; Coll; Legal Sect.

MATUSHEK, Kurt J; Marist HS; Harvey, IL; 9/375 HonRl; NatlMeritSF; SchPpr; LatCl; IMSpt; Chicago U; Medicine.

MATUSIAK, Cynthia M; Oregon Davis HS; Grovertown, IN; TrsFrshCls; Chr; HonRl; SchMus; SchPl; 4-H; SpnCl; PpCl; LetterTrk; LetterChrldr; GAA; 4-HAwd; PresAwd; Nursing Schl; Nursing.

MATUSZEWSKI, Annette C; Maria HS; Chicago, IL; 150/300 Chrl; HonRl; StuCncl; SpnCl; De Paul Univ; Accounting.

MATUSZEWSKI, Karl A; Lane Tech HS; Chicago, IL; 75/1300 TchrAde; Univ Of Illinois; Architecture.

MATYE, Scott A; Osseo Fairchild HS; Osseo, WI; 8/90 TrsJrCls; Aud/Vis; HonRl; JrNHS; SctActv; TchrAde; LetterBsbl; LetterBsktbl; LetterFtbl; LetterTrk; Clge.

MATZ, Diane; Johnson Creek HS; Helenville, WI; PresFrshCls; HonRl; StuCncl; GerCl; Univ; Professional.

MATZ, Jennifer A; Highland Park HS; Highland Park, IL; Aud/Vis; PolWkr; SchPl; StuGov; TchrAde; University; Communications.

MATZ, Paul L; Prospect HS; Arlington Hts, IL; 110/625 HonRl; NatlFornLg; NatlMeritCmnd; SctActv; Harper Jr College; Marketing.

MATZEK, Robert W; Plum City HS; Maiden Rock, WI; PresFrshCls; ALBoysSt; Band; CncrtBnd; HonRl; PepBnd; SctActv; StuCncl; StuGov; TchrAde; 4-H; LetterBsktbl; IMSpt; AmLegAwd; Col; Farming.

MATZKE, Lisa M; High School; Minneapolis, MN; VPJrCls; Chr; SpnCl; Bsktbl; Trk; Wrstlng; College; Professional.

MATZKE, Tim J; El Paso HS; El Paso, IL; ChrhWkr; CmntyWkr; HonRl; Technical Schl; Auto Mechanic.

MATZO, Marianne; Aquinas HS; Lincoln Park, MI; 24/205 Chr; ChrhWkr; HonRl; NHS; SchMus; SchPl; Teen; RptrSchPpr; Tennis; School Nurse; Nurse.

MAU, Gary; Sherburn Jr Sr HS; Sherburn, MN; 2/64 VPFrshCls; VPSrCls; ALBoysSt; Band; Chr; HonRl; NHS; SchPl; Ftbl; Trk; St Cloud St College; Professional.

MAUBACH, Theresa; Odell Community HS; Odell, IL; 4/33 Chrs; HonRl; FHA; PpCl; Trade School; X Ray Technician.

MAUBACH, Theresa M; Odell Community HS; Odell, IL; 4/33 Chrs; HonRl; FHA; College; Executive Secretary.

MAUCH, Mavis M; Goodrich HS; Goodrich, ND; Chr; CncrtBnd; HonRl; MrchBnd; PepBnd; SchPl; StuCncl; Yrbk; PpCl; GAA; College; Professional.

MAUCH, Rosie; Adrian Public HS; Adrian, MN; Band; CncrtBnd; DrmMjrt; MrchBnd; NHS; StuCncl; Twrl; RptrSchPpr; EdSchPpr; PresAwd; Uw Madison; Commercial Art.

MAUCH, Scott D; Lake Central HS; St John, IN; 40/450 ChrhWkr; CmntyWkr; HonRl; GerCl; PpCl; Bsbl; Ftbl; College; Electrical Engineering.

MAUCK, Tammy W; Stockton HS; Stockton, KS; Band; ChrhWkr; CmntyWkr; HonRl; NHS; YthFlsp; 4-H; PpCl; LetterTrk; Chrldr; PPFtbl; Kansas Univ; Medicine.

MAUDAL, Ann L; Wheaton HS; Wheaton, MN; 4/87 VPSrCls; Band; Chr; CncrtBnd; Mdrgl; PepBnd; DARAwd; Jackson Area Voc; Court Reporting.

MAUDLIN, Phylis J; Worth County R 1 HS; Grant City, MO; 17/40 ChrhWkr; CmntyWkr; HonRl; SchMus; SchPl; Pres4-H; PresPpCl; Swmmng; DanFAwd; 4-HAwd; Business Sch; Secretary.

MAUEL, Linda; Owen Whithee HS; Owen, WI; 5/75 Band; HonRl; HospAde; NHS; TchrAde; Yrbk; 4-H; FHA; Uw Eau Claire; Special Ed Teacher.

MAUEL, Linda A; Owen Withee HS; Owen, WI; 5/75 Band; NHS; TchrAde; Yrbk; FHA; PpCl; LetterBsktbl; LetterGlf; BttyCrckrAwd; College; Special Education.

MAUER, Denise K; Tri Center Comm HS; Minden, IA; 1/72 Chrs; ChrhWkr; MrchBnd; NHS; Yrbk; PpCl; Bsbl; Bsktbl; DARAwd; PresAwd; Ia St U; Elem Teacher.

MAUER, Paul; Oregon HS; Oregon, WI; Bsbl; Armed Forces, Work For Dept Of Nat Resource.

MAUERMAN, Linda K; Monroe Senior HS; Monroe, WI; 11/245 Chr; ChrhWkr; HonRl; YthFlsp; RptrYrbk; FrCl; PpCl; Tennis; Stout State Univ; Vocational Home Ec.

MAUGHAN, Steven H; Rochester Community HS; Rochester, IN; 33/150 PresSrCls; ALBoysSt; HonRl; ModUN; NHS; PolWkr; Colleg.

MAUK, Michelle M; Appleton West HS; Appleton, WI; ChrhWkr; CmntyWkr; RptrSchPpr; FrCl; Univ Of Wis Madison; Pharmacy.

MAUL, Terry L; St Johns Military HS; Hastings, NE; Aud/Vis; Band; Chr; CncrtBnd; DrlTm; HonRl; IntrClCncl; LbryAde; ROTC; KeyCl; SpnCl; MthCl; Bsktbl; College; Professional.

MAULE, Dave A; Shawnee Mission South HS; Libertyville, IL; HonRl; SctActv; Ftbl; LetterSocr; CchngActv; IMSpt; PresAwd; University; Forestry.

MAULE, Michael; Leola Ind HS; Leola, SD; ALBoysSt; Band; Chrs; HonRl; Mdrgl; SchMus; SchPl; LetterBsktbl; LetterFtbl; LetterTrk; College; Business.

MAULE, Michael R; Leola Ind Dist 2 HS; Leola, SD; 12/47 Chrs; ChrhWkr; CncrtBnd; HonRl; Mdrgl; SchMus; SchPl; LetterBsktbl; LetterFtbl; LetterTrk; College.

MAUNE, Laurie A; William Christian HS; Independence, MO; 30/430 ChrhWkr; HonRl; NHS; PpCl; Bus Sch; Professional.

MAUNEZ, Maria E; Springfield HS; Springfield, IL; 82/535 SchPpr; GerCl; Springfield Coll Il; Medical Technology.

MAUPIN, Jane A; Princeton HS; Princeton, IL; 12/178 Chrs; HonRl; Mdrgl; Univ Of Iowa; Nurse.

MAUPIN, Marilyn K; Mexico HS; Mexico, MO; ALAGirlsSt; NHS; StuCncl; LatCl; PpCl; Bsktbl; LetterTrk; Univ Of Mo; Biology.

MAUPIN, Michael L; South Shelby HS; Clarence, MO; 40/110 HonRl; NHS; SciCl; LetterFtbl; LetterTrk; Univ Of Missouri Rolla; Computer Science.

MAUPIN, Timothy D; Natoma HS; Paradise, KS; 8/29 VPSophCls; PresJrCls; ALBoysSt; HonRl; SchPl; StuGov; SptEdSchPpr; Bsktbl; Ftbl; Trk; College; Vocation.

MAURER, Cheryl K; Waconia HS; Wconia, MN; 6/140 Chrs; HonRl; Mdrgl; NHS; SchMus; PresStuCncl; PresFHA; GAA; Mankato State Col; Medical Thechnology.

MAURER, David J; Manitowoc Lutheran HS; Manitowoc, WI; Band; Chr; Chrl; NatlMeritCmnd; PepBnd; SchPl; StuCncl; MthCl; Ftbl; LetterGlf; Law.

MAURER, Dennis R; Medford HS; Medford, WI; 33/254 Chr; ChrhWkr; CmntyWkr; HonRl; Mdrgl; TchrAde; Pres4-H; FFA; 4-HAwd; Col; Music.

MAURER, Julie A; Silver Creek Public HS; Silver Creek, NE; HstJrCls; Chr; Chrl; Chrs; ChrhWkr; HonRl; SchPl; YthFlsp; 4-H; 4-HAwd; Coll; Med Records Tech.

MAURER, Mary J; Parsons Sr HS; Parsons, KS; Chrs; CmntyWkr; HonRl; HospAde; PolWkr; College; Sociology.

MAURER, Patty D; Jacksonville HS; Jacksonville, IL; Chr; CncrtBnd; HonRl; MrchBnd; NHS; CaptTwrl; 4-H; FrCl; LetterTennis; LetterChrldr; Eastern Illinois University.

MAURER, Sara L; Columbus HS; Marshfield, WI; 42/117 Chrs; CmntyWkr; HonRl; HospAde; OffAde; RedCrAde; SchMus; SchPl; Bsktbl; LetterSwmmng; LetterTrk; Chrldr; IMSpt; St Col Of Beauty Culture.

MAURIZI, Laura B; Morton West HS; Berwyn, IL; CmntyWkr; HonRl; LitMag; ModUN; PolWkr; Quill&Scroll; StuGov; RptrSchPpr; SchPpr; VFWAwd; Southern Ill U; Journalist Or Lawyer.

MAURO, Laura E; Our Lady Of The Lakes HS; Waterford, MI; 6/53 VPSrCls; Chr; HonRl; HospAde; NHS; TchrAde; SpnCl; PpCl; LetterBsktbl; Chrldr; Oakland Comm Clg; Mental Health.

MAURSTAD, Jacqueline D; Beatrice HS; Beatrice, NE; HonRl; Orch; PpCl; LetterGlf; Bsktbl; LetterTennis; Univ.

MAUS, Christopher P; Sacred Heart HS; Dearborn Hts, MI; HonRl; LatCl; College; Journalism.

MAUS, David E; Alburnett HS; Alburnett, IA; Band; Chrs; CncrtBnd; HonRl; MrchBnd; PepBnd; SchMus; SciCl; Bsbl; CaptFtbl; College; Prof.

MAUS, Margaret J; Sacred Heart HS; Grand Forks, ND; 1/53 VPSophCls; PresJrCls; ChrhWkr; CmntyWkr; CncrtBnd; CaptTrk; GAA; IMSpt; SecJrCls; Univ; Nurse.

MAUS, William A; Andale HS; Colwich, KS; NatlMeritCmnd; RptrSchPpr; SptEdSchPpr; SpnCl; LetterFtbl; LetterTrk; LetterWrstlng; IMSpt; College; Professional.

MAUSEY, Vickie; Crab Orchard HS; Creal Springs, IL; SecFrshCls; HonRl; SchPl; RptrSchPpr; FHA; PpCl; College; Professional.

MAUSKAPF, Ilese; Homewood Flossmoor Hs; Homewood, IL; 61/941 CmntyWkr; HonRl; IntrClCncl; NatlMeritCmnd; PolWkr; StuCncl; StuGov; Knox College; Law.

MAUTE, Teresa; Grass Lake HS; Grass Lake, MI; 9/92 Band; CncrtBnd; HonRl; NHS; RedCrAde; RptrYrbk; 4-H; Bsktbl; DARAwd; 4-HAwd; Coll; Pharmacy.

MAUZY, David; Carroll HS; Ft Wayne, IN; NHS; SchMus; YthFlsp; PpCl; Ftbl; Indiana Univ; Business.

MAVEL, Yolanda; Lawson HS; Lawson, MO; Band; Chrs; HonRl; NHS; PepBnd; EdYrBk; Bsktbl; Chrldr; DanFAwd; Mo Western St Univ; Elem Ed.

MAVES, Kathleen R; Lyman HS; Presho, SD; Chr; ChrhWkr; CmntyWkr; CncrtBnd; HonRl; MrchBnd; PepBnd; PolWkr; 4-H; Trk; South Dakota State Univ; Social Work.

MAVIS, Janet K; Shawnee Mission South HS; Leawood, KS; Chr; Chrl; HonRl; SpnCl; PpCl; University; Law.

MAVIS, Sharon L; Pleasant Plains HS; Springfield, IL; 7/57 SecJrCls; Band; Chrs; Mdrgl; SecNHS; SchMus; StuCncl; YthFlsp; EdYrBk; Pres4-H; SecGAA; 4-HAwd; Millikin University; Physical Therapist.

MAWER, Mark R; Deforest HS; Deforest, WI; HonRl; NatlFornLg; SchPl; StuCncl; Yrbk; Glf; Swmmng; CitAwd; U Of Wis; Journalism.

MAXA, Lorri A; Bethlehem Academy; Lakeville, MN; Chr; Chrl; Chrs; ChrhWkr; HonRl; Mdrgl; SchMus; SchPl; TchrAde; Business School; Secretary.

MAXEDON, Terry S; St Charles HS; St Charles, MO; 33/556 HonRl; Orch; SchMus; LetterTrk; IMSpt; Kansas City Art Inst; Commercial Artist.

MAXIMIUK, Alan D; Farmington HS; Farmington, MI; HonRl; RptrYrbk; IMSpt; College; Accountant.

MAXIMOVICH, Stanley P; St Patrick HS; Chicago, IL; 11/441 HonRl; OffAde; FDA; Ftbl; Brown University; Medicine.

MAXSON, David S; Cedar Springs HS; Cedar Springs, MI; PresSophCls; HonRl; NatlMeritSF; StuCncl; StuGov; LetterFtbl; LetterTennis; College.

MAXSON, Julie; Pontiac Township Hs; Pontiac, IL; 33/203 Chrs; HonRl; NatlMeritFnl; NatlMeritCmnd; NatlMeritSF; SctActv; SpnCl; PpCl; GAA; Parkland Jr College;pyschology.

MAXSON, Mark; Western HS; Bay City, MI; 17/448 Band; Chr; MrchBnd; NHS; NatlMeritCmnd; SchMus; SchPl; SctActv; GerCl; Western Mich Univ; Chemical Engineer.

MAXSON, Sharon; Pontiac Township Hs; Pontiac, IL; 7/200 Chrs; HonRl; NHS; SpnCl; PpCl; GAA; Jr College; Data Processing.

MAXWELL, Barbara L; Mingo Comm HS; Collins, IA; 2/25 PresSrCls; Band; Chrs; HonRl; SchPl; PresStuCncl; EdYrBk; PresFHA; Chrldr; CitAwd; J Edmundson Mem Hosp; Radiology Tech.

MAXWELL, Deborah A; Meridian HS; Hope, MI; Chr; ChrhWkr; SchMus; YthFlsp; RptrYrbk; RptrSchPpr; 4-H; Bsktbl; Trk; College.

MAXWELL, Jeffrey W; Marion Adams HS; Lebanon, IN; ChrhWkr; HonRl; JrNHS; NHS; SpnCl; LetterFtbl; Swmmng; Trk; University; Elec Engineering.

MAXWELL, Jon R; Milan HS; Milan, IN; Band; CncrtBnd; MrchBnd; SchPl; 4-H; LatCl; Bsbl; Bsktbl; LetterFtbl; 4-HAwd; Clg; Phy Ed.

MAXWELL, Julie A; Platte Co R Iii HS; Platte City, MO; 2/87 AFS; Band; NHS; NatlThespSoc; Chrldr; PPFtbl; University Of Missouri; Elementary Educ.

MAXWELL, Karen S; Peoria HS; Peoria, IL; 32/450 Chrs; HonRl; HospAde; JrNHS; NHS; Yrbk; FNA; SpnCl; Moline Public School; Nurse.

MAXWELL, Kevin M; Lisle Sr HS; Lisle, IL; 24/200 HonRl; NHS; NatlMeritSchl; SchPl; SctActv; StuCncl; SptEdYrbk; LetterFtbl; LetterWrstlng; IMSpt; Iowa State University; Engineering.

MAXWELL, Michael D; United Township HS; East Moline, IL; 27/687 HonRl; NHS; SctActv; Service Academy; Us Marine Corp.

MAY, Anita J; Circle HS; Towanda, KS; Band; CncrtBnd; HonRl; MrchBnd; PepBnd; TreasPpCl; Bsktbl; IMSpt; Clge; Pro.

MAY, Annette J; Norris HS; Hickman, NE; 17/96 Band; CncrtBnd; MrchBnd; NatlThespSoc; SctActv; TchrAde; RptrYrbk; PpCl; Chrldr; Wesleyan; Child Psychology.

MAY, Carla S; Lawrenceville HS; Lawrenceville, IL; HonRl; NHS; StuCncl; Yrbk; FHA; LatCl; Lincoln Trail College.

MAY, Carolyn J; Nashville Community HS; Nashville, IL; Band; Chr; Chrl; Chrs; CmntyWkr; CncrtBnd; HonRl; HospAde; MrchBnd; PepBnd; U Of Il Carbondale; Executive Secretary.

MAY, Crystal; Tipton HS; Hunter, KS; 4/22 PresJrCls; HonRl; StuCncl; EdYrBk; Chrldr; GAA; IMSpt; PPFtbl; Marymount College.

MAY, Daniel G; Heritage HS; New Haven, IN; Chr; NatlFornLg; NHS; SchMus; SchPl; RotaryAwd; Purdue Univ; Pro Theatre.

MAY, Debbie A; Adrian HS; Adrian, MI; SecSrCls; SecBand; CncrtBnd; HonRl; MrchBnd; NHS; PepBnd; SchMus; Yrbk; Bsktbl; IMSpt; Michigan St Univ; Veterinarian.

MAY, Debra K; Riverton HS; Baxter Springs, KS; ALAGirlsSt; HonRl; NHS; RedCrAde; SchPl; StuCncl; Yrbk; VPPpCl; Bsktbl; CaptChrldr; Trade School; Business Admin.

MAY, James R; Milan C Ii HS; Milan, MO; 2/58 TrsFrshCls; TrsJrCls; ALBoysSt; Band; CmntyWkr; CncrtBnd; HonRl; MrchBnd; NHS; SctActv; StuCncl; YthFlsp; LetterFtbl; AmLegAwd; College; History.

MAY, Jeffrey A; Mauston Area HS; Mauston, WI; ALBoysSt; Band; Chrs; CncrtBnd; HonRl; MrchBnd; NHS; SchMus; SchPl; LetterFtbl; Technical College; Refrigeration.

MAY, Karen M; Minonk Dana Rutland HS; Minonk, IL; 1/81 AFS; Chrs; CncrtBnd; HonRl; MrchBnd; PepBnd; VP4-H; SecSpnCl; PpCl; AmLegAwd; Secretarial Field.

MAY, Laurie; Oregon Sr HS; Oregon, WI; Chrs; HonRl; HospAde; Mdrgl; PresNHS; SchMus; RptrYrbk; 4-H; SpnCl; 4-HAwd; Univ Of Wi Eau Claire.

MAY, Mary E; Lapel HS; Lapel, IN; 23/88 VPJrCls; TrsSrCls; Band; HonRl; JrNHS; NHS; OffAde; TchrAde; CaptBsktbl; CaptTrk; Ball State U; Spec Ed.

MAY, Mary M; Holy Child HS; Waukegan, IL; VPFrshCls; PresSrCls; SchMus; SchPl; StuCncl; StuGov; TchrAde; Bsbl; Bsktbl; CchngActv; VPGAA; IMSpt; RotaryAwd; College Of Lake County; Airline Stewardess.

MAY, Phillip; Peshtigo HS; Peshtigo, WI; 5/90 HonRl; NHS; SctActv; LetterFtbl; Wrstlng; Uw Mad;pharmacist.

MAY, Sharon J; Waukegan HS; Waukegan, IL; HonRl; JCC; LbryAde; Trk; GAA; IMSpt; Univ Of Il; Architecture.

MAY, Susan J; Switz Co HS; Veray, IN; 13/105 Band; Chr; HonRl; MrchBnd; NHS; PepBnd; SchMus; SchPl; Twrl; SpnCl; Hanover Clg; Teacher.

MAY, Susan J; Frankfort HS; Frankfort, MI; 2/66 PresSrCls; HonRl; NHS; NatlMeritCmnd; SchPl; TreasStuCncl; TchrAde; EdYrBk; Yrbk; TreasSciCl; Coll; Med Tech.

MAYALL, Marla J; Astoria HS; Astoria, IL; 8/50 Band; CncrtBnd; HonRl; HospAde; JrNHS; MrchBnd; NHS; Graham Hosp Sch; Registered Nurse.

MAYBER, Kenneth P; Niles West HS; Morton Grove, IL; 11/666 CmntyWkr; HonRl; NHS; SchPl; StuGov; KeyCl; GerCl; CaptSwmmng; CchngActv; University; Medicine.

MAYBERRY, Brian K; Abraham Lincoln HS; Council Bluffs, IA; 61/444 Chrs; HonRl; RptrYrbk; SciCl; LetterBsktbl; LetterTennis; IMSpt; KiwanAwd; OptClAwd; RotaryAwd; Iowa State Univ; Veterinarian.

MAYBERRY, Debbie J; Emerson Hubbard HS; Emerson, NE; 7/56 Band; Chr; Chrl; Chrs; ChrhWkr; CncrtBnd; HonRl; MrchBnd; PepBnd; SchPl; 4-H; SpnCl; College; Broadcasting.

MAYBERRY, Gregory M; Lake Ville HS; Columbiaville, MI; 4/183 Band; ChrhWkr; CmntyWkr; HonRl; NHS; SchPl; TchrAde; SptEdYrbk; FTA; LetterWrstlng; U Of Mich; Dentist.

MAYBERRY, Kathy; Pender Public HS; Pender, NE; ALAGirlsSt; Chr; Chrs; HonRl; 4-H; FHA; PpCl; 4-HAwd; Trade School; Vocation.

MAYBERRY, Madelyn P; E P Community HS; East Peoria, IL; 68/451 ChrhWkr; CmntyWkr; HonRl; NHS; StuCncl; StuGov; RptrSchPpr; FrCl; PpCl; GAA; Minneapolis Schl Art&design; Fashion Design.

MAYBERRY, Teddie L; Dora R Iii HS; Dora, MO; HstSrCls; CmntyWkr; HonRl; NHS; SchPl; Yrbk; FFA; SciCl; Bsbl; CaptBsktbl; College; Agriculture.

MAYCAN, James M; Palatine HS; Palatine, IL; 85/464 HonRl; NHS; StuCncl; StuGov; YthFlsp; PpCl; Bsbl; Bsktbl; Ftbl; Northwestern Univ; Coaching.

MAYCHRZAK, Edna I; Scranton Public HS; Scranton, ND; 5/27 SecJrCls; Chr; ChrhWkr; HonRl; NHS; SchPl; EdSchPpr; AmLegAwd; Mary Clge; Free Lance Artist.

MAYER, Barbara A; Wausau East HS; Wausau, WI; 11/337 CmntyWkr; CncrtBnd; HonRl; MrchBnd; NHS; PepBnd; RptrSchPpr; FrCl; SciCl; University; Vet.

MAYER, Bruce J; Marcus Comm HS; Marcus, IA; TrsSrCls; Band; Chr; Chrs; ChrhWkr; CncrtBnd; HonRl; Mdrgl; MrchBnd; NHS; PepBnd; SchMus; SchPl; LetterFtbl; Wrstlng; College; Professional.

MAYER, Caril; Council Grove HS; Alta Vista, KS; Band; Chrs; HonRl; SchMus; Yrbk; RptrSchPpr; 4-H; FHA; Bsbl; Bsktbl; College.

MAYER, Clara L; Medina Public HS; Jamestown, ND; TrsSophCls; Band; Chr; Chrs; ChrhWkr; CncrtBnd; DrmMjrt; HonRl; Bsktbl; Chrldr; Trade Sch; Music.

MAYER, Donald; Grafton HS; Grafton, WI; 9;220 ALBoysSt; NHS; NatlMeritCmnd; NatlThespSoc; SchMus; SchPl; StuCncl; PresSciCl; Uw Madison;biechemist.

MAYER, Ellen M; Mt Assisi Acad; Oaklawn, IL; HonRl; NHS; StuCncl; RptrSchPpr; Univ; Medicine, Labratory Technicican.

MAYER, James B; Memorial HS; Beloit, WI; 42/480 ChrhWkr; HonRl; LitMag; NatlFornLg; NHS; IMSpt; JAAwd; Pacific Univ; Medicine.

MAYER, James P; Cumberland HS; Cumberland, WI; 7/107 Band; ChrhWkr; CncrtBnd; HonRl; MrchBnd; NatlFornLg; NatlMeritSF; PepBnd; Sacrstn; SchPl; Ftbl; Glf; LetterTrk; Wrstlng; Marquette; Law.

MAYER, Janet M; Maine South HS; Park Ridge, IL; Chr; Chrl; Chrs; ChrhWkr; HonRl; Mdrgl; NHS; SchPl; PpCl; Univ Of Illinois.

MAYER, Jerry E; Southern Wells HS; Keystone, IN; PresSrCls; ChrhWkr; HonRl; StuCncl; YthFlsp; LetterBsktbl; LetterFtbl; Trade Or Business School.

MAYER, Marlin J; Streeter Public HS; Streeter, ND; 4/21 PresJrCls; ALBoysSt; Band; Chrs; HonRl; SchPl; RptrYrbk; SchPpr; Trk; Nd State Univ.

MAYER, Mary E; Mother Of Sorrows HS; Chicago, IL; 23/115 HonRl; SchAde; StuCncl; TchrAde; FrCl; MthCl; PpCl; Bsktbl; GAA; Loyola U; Accounting.

MAYER, Patrice; Westville Twp HS; Danville, IL; Chrs; HonRl; LbryAde; TchrAde; FHA; St Elizabeth Sch Nursing; Rn.

MAYER, Patricia A; Elk Grove HS; Elk Grove Village, IL; 60/505 Chr; Chrs; HonRl; NHS; SchMus; SctActv; KeyCl; Trk; Eastern Il Univ; Elementary Ed.

MAYER, Richard V; Pekin Comm HS; Marquette Hts, IL; 4/1003 Univ Of Illinois; Engineer.

MAYER, Sally A; Willowbrook HS; Lombard, IL; 27/824 HonRl; IntrClCncl; ModUN; NHS; NatlMeritCmnd; NatlMeritSchl; StuCncl; LetterTennis; College; Law.

MAYER, Sharon A; Kiel HS; Kiel, WI; AFS; HonRl; SctActv; StuCncl; TreasPpCl; CaptChrldr; Univ; Nursing.

MAYER, Steven A; Campion Jesuit HS; Prairie Du Chien, WI; 3/75 ChrhWkr; HonRl; StuGov; LetterFtbl; LetterGlf; JCAwd; College; Professional.

MAYER, Susan J; Ernest W Seaholm HS; Birmingham, MI; CmntyWkr; Antioch Univ; Education.

MAYERS, Laurie T; Bishop Dwenger HS; Fort Wayne, IN; Band; Chrs; HonRl; TreasJA; Quill&Scroll; SchMus; SchPpr; FrCl; JAAwd; Univ; Journalism.

MAYES, Jeffrey W; Lew Wallace HS; Gary, IN; HonRl; VPNHS; NatlMeritSF; SchPl; RusCl; Clge; Law.

MAYES, Ricky L; Ellis HS; Ellis, KS; HonRl; StuCncl; 4-H; KeyCl; LetterFtbl; LetterTrk; CaptWrstlng; College ;hs.

MAYES, Thomas E; Winner Senior HS; Ideal, SD; 4-H; Bsktbl; Ftbl; College; Agriculture.

MAYFIELD, Connie E; Pleasant Hill Sr HS; Pleasant Hill, MO; 1/111 ALAGirlsSt; Band; ChrhWkr; HonRl; NHS; NatlMeritCmnd; SchMus; SecSpnCl; VPSciCl; College; Engineering.

MAYFIELD, John E; Bishop Ward HS; Kansas, KS; 19/195 ChrhWkr; HonRl; NHS; PolWkr; SctActv; StuCncl; SptEdSchPpr; FrCl; Bsbl; Donnelly College; Accounting.

MAYFIELD, Patricia A; Granite City Sr HS; Granite City, IL; 32/630 Band; CncrtBnd; HonRl; MrchBnd; NHS; PepBnd; SchMus; SpnCl; GAA; Siu Carbondale; Medicine.

MAYFIELD, Richard; Lodi HS; Lodi, WI; 9/122 Aud/Vis; Band; NHS; StuCncl; SchPpr; SpnCl; Ftbl; Winona State College; Medicine.

MAYFIELD, Roger W; Lamar HS; Lamar, MO; AFS; ChrhWkr; HonRl; JrNHS; NHS; NatlMeritSchl; PolWkr; ROTC; PresStuCncl; StuGov; Vocation.

MAYHALL, Michael L; Madison Consolidated HS; Madison, IN; 32/325 HstFrshCls; TrsSophCls; PresJrCls; HonRl; NatlMeritSchl; StuCncl; GerCl; LetterBsbl; LetterSwmmng; CaptIMSpt; Armed Serv Acad; Math.

MAYHEW, Monte N; Marysville HS; Marysville, KS; TrsJrCls; Band; ChrhWkr; CncrtBnd; HonRl; MrchBnd; PepBnd; StuCncl; YthFlsp; SpnCl; Armed Forces.

MAYHEW, Susan V; Palco HS; Palco, KS; Band; Chr; ChrhWkr; HonRl; SchPl; StuCncl; EdYrBk; 4-H; Bsktbl; Trk; Collge; Professional.

MAYHEW, Teresa M; St Elizabeth Acad; St Louis, MO; 2/116 Chrs; ChrhWkr; HonRl; HospAde; SecNHS; NatlMeritSF; SchMus; StuCncl; VPFrCl; Rockhurst; Social Work.

MAYHOE, Kathalene; West Side Sr HS; Gary, IN; 7/845 VPBand; SecChrs; VPCncrtBnd; HonRl; JrNHS; NHS; MrchBnd; NHS; RptrYrbk; VPFrCl; LatCl; AmLegAwd; Marquette Univ; Nurse.

MAYLE, Mark M; St Viator HS; Mt Prospect, IL; 1/245 HonRl; SctActv; GerCl; MthCl; SciCl; LetterTennis; Univ Of Illinois; Computer Engineering.

MAYMON, Douglas D; Charlestown HS; Charlestown, IN; SctActv; TchrAde; Bsbl; Bsktbl; Ftbl; Trk; College; Phy Ed Teacher.

MAYNARD, Bruce C; Delwood Comm HS; Elwood, IA; 12/29 Band; CncrtBnd; HonRl; MrchBnd; Orch; PepBnd; SchMus; SctActv; University Of Iowa; Professional Astronomy.

MAYNARD, Constance Y; Hesperia HS; Bitely, MI; 10/85 TrsFrshCls; ALAGirlsSt; Band; HonRl; NHS; StuCncl; FNA; SpnCl; CaptTrk; U Of Mi; Nursing.

MAYNARD, Gregory A; Central HS; Camp Point, IL; 4/74 VPSrCls; HonRl; NHS; NatlThespSoc; Western Ill Univ; Environmental Engineer.

MAYNARD, Joel R; Hampshire HS; Hampshire, IL; 7/70 VPFrshCls; ALBoysSt; NHS; SchMus; StuCncl; SciCl; CaptBsbl; LetterBsktbl; CaptFtbl; CaptTrk; Air Force; Areo Engineering.

MAYNARD, Karen N; Kickapoo HS; Springfield, MO; 1/350 HonRl; LitMag; LbryAde; NatlMeritSF; CivCl; SecEngCl; GerCl; Univ; Writer.

MAYNARD, Mary; Wahoo HS; Wahoo, NE; CmntyWkr; HonRl; JA; OffAde; ROTC; FHA;.

MAYNARD, Micheline A; Ypsilanti HS; Ypsilanti, MI; Band; Chr; ChrhWkr; CmntyWkr; HonRl; ModUN; OffAde; Orch; PepBnd; PolWkr; Quill&Scroll; SchMus; LetterTennis; Univ; Advertizing.

MAYNARD, Murray K; E Prairie HS; East Prairie, MO; RptrYrbk; FFA; LetterBsbl; Bsktbl; Ftbl; Univ Of Mo.

MAYO, Gregory P; Cavalier Public HS; Cavalier, ND; TrsSrCls; ALBoysSt; Band; Chrs; ChrhWkr; MrchBnd; SchPl; SptEdSchPpr; ChmnBsktbl; CaptFtbl; Nd State Univ; Engr.

MAYO, Marla G; Bradley Bourbonnais Comm HS; Bradley, IL; DrlTm; HonRl; HospAde; SchAde; TchrAde; YthFlsp; FBLA; FSA; Swmmng; GAA; Parkland Comm Clge; Dental Hygiene.

MAYO, Steven A; Bryan Sr HS; Omaha, NE; Band; CncrtBnd; HonRl; MrchBnd; NHS; PepBnd; Bsbl; Bsktbl; LetterSwmmng; LetterTrk; IMSpt; PresAwd; Trade Schl; Vocation.

MAYO, Thomas B; Culver Military Acad; Chicago, IL; 2/168 HonRl; NatlMeritCmnd; SchPl; StuGov; RptrSchPpr; KeyCl; SpnCl; LetterSocr; LetterTrk; IMSpt; Nc U; Acntg.

MAYOR, Laura L; Adelphian Acad; Pontiac, MI; Chr; CmntyWkr; CncrtBnd; NHS; SchPl; EdSchPpr; Andrews Univ; Dental Hygenist.

MAYOTTE, Kathleen L; Lake Linden Hubbell HS; Hubbell, MI; 22/59 Band; Chr; HonRl; NatlMeritSchl; NatlMeritSF; Yrbk; LetterBsktbl; LetterChrldr; 4-HAwd; PresAwd; College; Accountant.

MAYS, Carlotta M; Horace Mann HS; Gary, IN; ALAGirlsSt; ChmnDrlTm; JrNHS; NHS; NatlMeritCmnd; ROTC; StuCncl; TchrAde; LetterSwmmng; CaptChrldr; J Hopkins; Pre Med.

MAYS, Deborah A; Cass Technical HS; Detroit, MI; HonRl; SctActv; TchrAde; Univ Of Michigan; Psychology.

MAYS, Debra I; Jefferson Sr HS; Alexandria, MN; 106/342 AFS; ChrhWkr; HonRl; LitMag; NatlFornLg; SchPl; StuCncl; TchrAde; FTA; College; Prof Teaching.

MAYS, Debra J; Redford HS; Detroit, MI; TrsSrCls; Chrs; HospAde; SchMus; Twrl; Mi St Univ; Advertising.

MAYS, Debra L; High School; Aurora, NE; 20/94 Band; ChrhWkr; CncrtBnd; HonRl; HospAde; MrchBnd; NHS; Teen; SciCl; Nebr Methodist Hosp; Nursing.

MAYS, Kathy; St James Senior HS; St James HS, MN; PresSrCls; Band; CncrtBnd; DrlTm; HonRl; MrchBnd; PepBnd; SchPl; StuCncl; Trk; College; Pro.

MAYSKENS, Deborah J; Kanawha Comm HS; Kanawha, IA; 1/20 Aud/Vis; Band; Chrs; CncrtBnd; HonRl; MrchBnd; NHS; NatlMeritSF; SchPl; Northwestern Col Ia; Music.

MAYSON, Heather K; Cass Tech HS; Detroit, MI; Chr; Chrs; HonRl; NHS; NatlMeritSF; OffAde; Orch; SchMus; StuGov;.

MAZA, Debbie S; Lake Central HS; Schererville, IN; 53/430 Band; CncrtBnd; HonRl; MrchBnd; NHS; PepBnd; SchAde; TchrAde; CitAwd; Bus School; Vocational.

MAZANEK, Richard C; Loyola HS; Lincolnwood, IL; 10/442 HonRl; NHS; NatlMeritCmnd; StuCncl; StuGov; RptrSchPpr; Trk; IMSpt; Northwestern Univ; Doctor.

MAZANEK, Susan E; Kinmundy Alma HS; Alma, IL; 1/56 PresFrshCls; PresSophCls; TrsJrCls; Band; SecNHS; NatlMeritCmnd; TreasStuCncl; EdYrBk; FHA; DARAwd; Eastern Illinois Univ; Music.

MAZANOWICZ, Catherine A; Jefferson HS; Rockford, IL; 48/370 Band; Chr; Chrs; HonRl; Mdrgl; NHS; PepBnd; SchMus; SchPl; No Central Bible College; Music.

MAZELLA, Audrey J; St Scholastica HS; Chicago, IL; RptrYrbk; Notre Dame; Psychology Or Special Ed.

MAZES, Barbara J; Wakefield HS; Wakefield, MI; 2/63 SecFrshCls; Band; Chr; HonRl; SecStuCncl; EdYrBk; RptrSchPpr; Tennis; AmLegAwd; Gogebic Comm Clg; Secretarial.

MAZIK, Christine A; Bedford Sr HS; Temperance, MI; 7/418 SecJrCls; Chr; HonRl; NHS; PolWkr; SchMus; SchPl; StuCncl; EdSchPpr; Michigan St University.

MAZOUCH, Marion A; Otis Bison HS; Timken, KS; ALBoysSt; Band; CncrtBnd; HonRl; MrchBnd; NHS; SchPl; LetterBsktbl; LetterTrk; AmLegAwd; College; Liberal Arts.

MAZOUR, Dave G; Lincoln Northeast HS; Lincoln, NE; 78/800 IntrClCncl; VPJA; JrNHS; PresFFA; FrCl; JAAwd; College; Veterenarian.

MAZUR, Cindy A; Good Counsel HS; Chicago, IL; 44/300 HonRl; HospAde; JA; Sacrstn; SctActv; StuCncl; RptrSchPpr; SpnCl; MthCl; GAA; Univ; Rn.

MAZUR, Cynthia K; Carmel HS; Mundelein, IL; 34/173 HospAde; LbryAde; NHS; StuCncl; 4-H; GAA; College Of St Catherine; Child Development.

MAZUR, Veronica T; Riverside Brookfield HS; Riverside, IL; 60/498 HonRl; OffAde; Chicago Conservatory; Piano.

MAZUREK, Joan M; Trinity HS; Chicago, IL; 9/202 HonRl; SctActv; StuCncl; RptrYrbk; FNA; De Paul Univ; Accounting.

MAZUREK, Lucy M; Madonna HS; Chicago, IL; 25/265 NHS; StuCncl; GerCl; MthCl; SciCl; U Of Ill; Mech Engineer.

MAZUREK, Mitchell J; Joliet Township West HS; Joliet, IL; TreasNHS; Orch; SecStuCncl; FTA; Univ Of Ill; Cpa.

MAZZETTA, Joseph; Loyola Academy; Winnetka, IL; 20/465.

MAZZONE, Sally A; St Stanislaus HS; Chicago, IL; 2/64 TrsFrshCls; PresSrCls; Chr; HonRl; LbryAde; NHS; StuCncl; FNA; FTA; BauchLmbAwd; College; Nursing.

MAZZONI, Mary C; Roncalli HS; Greenwood, IN; Chr; Chrl; Chrs; HonRl; SchMus; SchPpr; FrCl; Social Work.

MAZZONI, Michael A; St Xavier HS; Greenwood, IN; HonRl; NHS; OffAde; SchAde; TchrAde; MthCl; LetterFtbl; Rose Hulman Inst Of Tech; Mathematics.

MAZZUCKELLI, Thomas J; Bloom Township HS; Chicago Hts, IL; PresFrshCls; Chrs; HonRl; Teen; LetterTrk; Augustana College; Medical Doctor.

MEACHAM, John A; Millington Community HS; Millington, MI; Band; ChrhWkr; HonRl; MrchBnd; TchrAde; LetterFtbl; LetterTrk; College; Vocation.

MEACHAM, Mary Anne; Greendale HS; Greendale, WI; FrCl; GAA; Coll; Sociology.

MEAD, Bryan J; Roscommon HS; St Helen, MI; 5/106 ALBoysSt; ChrhWkr; CmntyWkr; HonRl; NatlMeritSF; Yrbk; 4-H; LetterBsktbl; LetterFtbl; LetterGlf; Mi St U; Physics.

MEAD, David; York Comm Hs; Elmhurst, IL; 3/1000 Chr; ChrhWkr; HonRl; LitMag; NHS; NHS; NatlThespSoc; Orch; SchMus; SchPl; College; Conductor.

MEAD, David D; Paw Paw HS; Paw Paw, MI; HonRl; NHS; 4-H; Bsbl; Us Military Academy; Army.

MEAD, Jan M; Weston HS; Cazenovia, WI; Band; HonRl; NatlFornLg; NHS; NatlMeritFnl; Quill&Scroll; RptrYrbk; RptrSchPpr; 4-H; FBLA; 4-HAwd; College; History.

MEAD, Jeffrey A; New Palestine HS; Greenfield, IN; Tri State College; Electrical Engineering.

MEAD, Joanne; Marcellus Community HS; Cassopolis, MI; Band; CncrtBnd; HonRl; LbryAde; MrchBnd; NHS; PepBnd; 4-H; 4-HAwd; Sw Mich Col; Accounting.

MEAD, Larry W; Alton Sr HS; Alton, IL; HonRl; NHS; Siue; Law Enforcement.

MEAD, Mark D; Tri Valley HS; Downs, IL; 8/40 PresSrCls; Band; ChrhWkr; CncrtBnd; HonRl; SchMus; SchPl; StuCncl; YthFlsp; LetterBsktbl; Trade; Farming.

MEAD, Mike G; Lakeshore HS; Baroda, MI; Band; ChrhWkr; HonRl; NHS; KeyCl; Bsktbl; Trk; College; Business.

MEAD, Randy G; Dongola Unit HS; Dongola, IL; VPSophCls; Aud/Vis; HonRl; LbryAde; 4-H; PresFFA; SpnCl; PpCl; SciCl; Bsktbl;.

MEAD, Robert P; Paw Paw HS; Paw Paw, MI; Band; Chr; CmntyWkr; HonRl; 4-H; 4-HAwd; Mi State; Agriculture.

MEADE, Donna S; Webster City HS; Webster City, IA; 13/181 Chrs; DrlTm; HonRl; SchPl; 4-H; SciCl; Bsbl; 4-HAwd; College.

MEADE, Martha; Mt Pleasant HS; Mt Pleasant, IA; Chr; HonRl; ModUN; NatlThespSoc; SchMus; SchPl; SpnCl; Luther Coll; History Major.

MEADER, Craig A; Waverly HS; Waverly, KS; 6/23 TrsJrCls; TrsSrCls; CncrtBnd; HonRl; MrchBnd; SchPl; SptEdYrbk; LetterBsktbl; LetterFtbl; LetterTrk; Emporia State Clg; Business Admin.

MEADERS, Ellen J; Okemos HS; Okemos, MI; Band; Chr; MrchBnd; VPNHS; NatlMeritSF; Orch; Teen; PresYthFlsp; PresGerCl; Michigan Tech Univ; Math Ed.

MEADOR, Cheryl A; Hardin Central C 2 HS; Hardin, MO; Chrs; HonRl; NHS; FFA; FHA;.

MEADOWS, Cindy R; Watertown HS; Watertown, SD; Chr; Chrs; ChrhWkr; HonRl; NatlThespSoc; SchMus; SchPl; College.

MEADOWS, Denise L; Bentley HS; Burton, MI; SecJrCls; Band; CncrtBnd; HonRl; MrchBnd; NHS; OffAde; RedCrAde; RptrYrbk; TreasFHA; College; Court Reporting.

MEADOWS, Gail L; Paoli HS; Paoli, IN; 18/118 SecJrCls; HonRl; TreasStuCncl; LatCl; PpCl; SciCl; CaptChrldr; In Univ; Dance & Language.

MEADOWS, Lynn D; Harrisburg HS; Sturgeon, MO; Band; RptrYrbk; Yrbk; RptrSchPpr; SchPpr; FrCl; PpCl; SciCl; Bsktbl; Chrldr; Housewife.

MEADOWS, Michael J; Stanley Boyd HS; Boyd, WI; PresSophCls; ALBoysSt; Sacrstn; StuCncl; SpnCl; Bsktbl; Ftbl; Trk; College.

MEADOWS, Ruth A; Camelot HS; Cairo, IL; SecSophCls; Chrs; HonRl; NHS; SchPl; StuCncl; YthFlsp; EdYrBk; EdSchPpr; FBLA; FrCl; PpCl; PresSciCl; CaptBsktbl; College; Music.

MEAGHER, Chris M; Marmion Military Academy; Aurora, IL; 1/69 PresFrshCls; HonRl; JrNHS; NHS; NatlMeritCmnd; ROTC; SchPl; StuCncl; StuGov; RptrYrbk; Bsktbl; Ftbl; Trk; Notre Dame Univ; Engineering.

MEAKIN, Thomas E; Bishop Borgess HS; Detroit, MI; CmntyWkr; HonRl; LitMag; NatlFornLg; LetterFtbl; LetterTrk; CchngActv; IMSpt; Univ Of Michigan; Law.

MEALMAN, Steven C; Geneua HS; Geneva, IL; 20/220 ChrhWkr; HonRl; JrNHS; NHS; YthFlsp; KeyCl; SpnCl; LetterBsbl; LetterFtbl; LetterWrstlng; College; Conservation.

MEANA, Alan; East Dubuque HS; East Dubuque, IL; HonRl; SchPpr; 4-H; College, Medicine.

MEANS, Karen K; Newkirk HS; Arkansas City, KS; 31/62 Band; CncrtBnd; HonRl; MrchBnd; PepBnd; SchPl; SptEdYrbk; PpCl; Bsktbl; Oklahoma State Univ; Business.

MEANS, Mark; Roxana Sr Hs; East Alton, IL; 18/271 HonRl; JAAwd; U Of Ill; Veterinary Medicine.

MEANS, Mark A; Spring Valley HS; Spring Valley, MN; Chr; Chrs; HonRl; YthFlsp; YthLg; GerCl; Bsktbl; Glf; College; Cpa.

MEANS, Mark T; Roxana HS; East Alton, IL; HonRl; JA; OffAde; University Of Illinois; Veterinarian.

MEANS, Martha A; Oskaloosa HS; Oskaloosa, KS; 4/36 TrsFrshCls; Chr; Chrs; ChrhWkr; HonRl; SchPl; SecFBLA; FrCl; PpCl; Bsktbl; Southwest Baptist College.

MEANS, Melanie S; Portland Christian HS; Jeffersonville, IN; TrsJrCls; Chrs; ChrhWkr; HonRl; LbryAde; RptrYrbk; RptrSchPpr; SptEdSchPpr; Chrldr; AmLegAwd; Col; Secondary Education.

MEARS, Teresa A; O Hara HS; Kansas City, MO; 6/180 Chrl; HonRl; ModUN; NatlMeritSF; SchMus; SchPl; TchrAde; RptrSchPpr; FrCl; VoiceDemAwd; Western Ky Univ; Journalism.

MEARTZ, Nancy L; Fox Valley Lutheran HS; Neenah, WI; 1/106 Band; HonRl; SchMus; EdYrBk; GAA; VFWAwd; CitAwd; Uw Madison; Pre Med.

MEATLLE, James B; Austin Prep; Grosse Pt Farms, MI; 19/115 HonRl; ModUN; SchMus; SchPl; Teen; RptrYrbk; FrCl; Ftbl; Notre Dame Univ; Business.

MEBRUER, Debby A; Fatima HS; Linn, MO; 9/126 Chrs; HonRl; LbryAde; SchPl; SchPpr; SecFBLA; FHA; PpCl; LetterBsbl; Trk;.

MECCIA, Patricia; Resurrection HS; Chicago, IL; JA; GAA; JAAwd; College; Working In Computors.

MECEY, Donald G; North County R1 HS; Desloge, MO; 9/160 ChrhWkr; HonRl; JrNHS; NHS; TchrAde; MthCl; SciCl; Bsktbl; College; Law.

MECH, Linda L; Assumption HS; Wisconsin Rapids, WI; 6/121 Chrs; HonRl; NHS; StuCncl; TchrAde; RptrYrbk; MthCl; Trk; IMSpt; Univ Of Eau Claire; Business Admin.

MECHA, Leonette M; Bishop Noll Inst; Calumet City, IL; ChrhWkr; CmntyWkr; HonRl; SpnCl; Thorton Comm Coll; Nurse.

MECHEM, Karen J; Union HS; Union, MO; 5/165 PresFrshCls; TrsSrCls; ALAGirlsSt; Band; Chr; CncrtBnd; HonRl; MrchBnd; Orch; PepBnd; SchAde; SchMus; TreasStuCncl; PPFtbl; East Central Jr College; Elem Education.

MECHLER, Brian D; Titonka Cons HS; Titonka, IA; Chr; ChrhWkr; YthFlsp; 4-H; FFA; Bsbl; Trk; College; Agriculture.

MECHLER, Dean E; Titonka HS; Titonka, IA; 14/48 Chrs; HonRl; NHS; SchMus; StuCncl; 4-H; FFA; LetterBsbl; CaptBsktbl; LetterTrk; William Penn; Chemistry.

MECKLEY, Kim M; Colfax HS; Colfax, IA; HonRl; MrchBnd; NHS; Yrbk; Pres4-H; FTA; PpCl; CaptChrldr; 4-HAwd; Beautician.

MECKLIN, Kathleen A; George Rogers Clark HS; Whiting, IN; 6/260 VPFrshCls; Chr; Chrs; DrlTm; HonRl; StuCncl; StuGov; TchrAde; Yrbk; SpnCl; PpCl; Chrldr; GAA; College; Architect.

MECL, Vicky J; Esko HS; Esko, MN; 11/93 SecSophCls; Band; Chr; HonRl; HospAde; NatlFornLg; NHS; OffAde; PepBnd; SchPl; StuCncl; St Lukes Hosp Of Nursing; Nursing.

MECOM, Scott D; Essex Community HS; Essex, IA; Band; ChrhWkr; HonRl; MrchBnd; PolWkr; SchPl; PpCl; SciCl; Ia St Univ; Bus Ad.

MEDANSKY, Cynthia; Munster HS; Fairbanks, IN; 38/440 ChrhWkr; HonRl; LbryAde; SchAde; StuCncl; TchrAde; Univ; Pharmacy.

MEDBERRY, M Scott; Beaman Conrad HS; Beaman, IA; ALBoysSt; Band; Chrs; HonRl; NatlMeritSchl; SchPl; StuCncl; SecYthFlsp; LetterFtbl; LetterWrstlng; AmLegAwd; 4-HAwd; State Univ; Agriculture.

MEDDAUGH, Diane E; Yale HS; Avoca, MI; DrlTm; HonRl; SchPl; TchrAde; College; Medicine.

MEDDAUGH, Loren L; Granton HS; Granton, WI; Band; CncrtBnd; HonRl; MrchBnd; NHS; PepBnd; FFA; LetterBsktbl; Trk; Agriculture.

MEDDERS, Dee A; Houston HS; Houston, MO; VPJrCls; Chrs; CncrtBnd; HonRl; NHS; StuCncl; 4-H; LetterTrk; 4-HAwd; CitAwd; University; Professional.

MEDEMA, Jeffrey M; River Bend Comm HS; Fulton, IL; AFS; HonRl; RptrYrbk; RptrSchPpr; SpnCl; Ftbl; Trk; Wrstlng;.

MEDEMA, Randy; Alcester HS; Alcester, SD; 1/36 PresFrshCls; PresJrCls; PresSrCls; ALBoysSt; TreasNHS; SchPl; Yrbk; EdSchPpr; DanFAwd; VoiceDemAwd; Sd St Univ; Journalism.

MEDEMA, William L; Yankton HS; Kankton, SD; 3 College; Professional.

MEDER, Cynthia L; Thornwood HS; S Holland, IL; ChrhWkr; HonRl; NHS; YthFlsp; Il St Univ; Business Admin.

MEDER, Paul F; Lincoln HS; Manitowoc, WI; 253/636 Chrs; HonRl; YthFlsp; Bsbl; LetterBsktbl; LetterFtbl; Tennis; Trk; CchngActv; College; Professional.

MEDERICH, David J; Sandwich HS; Sandwich, IL; JrNHS; NHS; TreasLatCl; PresPpCl; LetterFtbl; LetterTrk; Trade Schl; Vocation.

MEDERNACH, Darla K; Aurora Central HS; Aurora, IL; 9/164 HonRl; NHS; StuCncl; PpCl; CaptBsktbl; LetterTennis; LetterTrk; CchngActv; GAA; College; Physical Ed.

MEDHURST, Tracey M; Rich South HS; Park Forest, IL; 6/279 CncrtBnd; HonRl; MrchBnd; NHS; SctActv; Colorado State Univ; Forestry.

MEDILL, Michael R; Immaculata HS; Leavenworth, KS; CmntyWkr; HonRl; PolWkr; RedCrAde; StuCncl; LatCl; LetterBsbl; LetterBsktbl; CaptFtbl; Washburn Univ;.

MEDINA, Beatrice M; High School; Chicago, IL; Chrs; HonRl; LbryAde; PpCl; College; Professional.

MEDINA, Silvana A; Plainfield HS; Joliet, IL; 1/297 ALAGirlsSt; HonRl; JrNHS; PresNHS; MthCl; Trk; Chrldr; GAA; DARAwd; Univ Of Ill; Bioengineering.

MEDINA, Vivina A; Waukesha South HS; Waukesha, WI; SctActv; PpCl; LetterTrk; PresAwd; Uw Whitewater.

MEDITZ, Cathleen; Gardner S Wilmington HS; Gardner, IL; 6/62 SecTrsJrCls; HonRl; LbryAde; SchPl; Yrbk; SchPpr; Socr; Chrldr; GAA; Eastern Illinois Univ; Social Worker.

MEDLEN, Sylvia S; Brandon HS; Ortonville, MI; 2/180 PresJrCls; AFS; HonRl; NHS; PolWkr; StuCncl; Yrbk; SchPpr; Trk; VFWAwd; Univ; Journalism.

MEDLEY, Kevin J; Valley HS; Belgrade, MO; HonRl; RptrYrbk; Trade Schl; Professional.

MEDLEY, Leesa J; Wentzville R Iv HS; Wentzville, MO; SecJrCls; HonRl; NHS; StuCncl; TchrAde; PresPpCl; Chrldr; PPFtbl; College; Speech.

MEDLIN, Scot C; Danville HS; Danville, IL; 25/596 HonRl; JA; JCC; NHS; SchPl; RptrSchPpr; Ftbl; LetterGlf; JAAwd; University Of Illinois; Journalism.

MEDLIN, Vicky S; Enfield HS; Enfield, IL; 4/35 VPJrCls; SecSrCls; Band; Chrs; DrmMjrt; HonRl; MrchBnd; YthFlsp; SchPpr; FHA; LetterChrldr; Rend Lake Col; Business.

MEDLIN, Walter; Phillipsburg HS; Phillipsburg, KS; HonRl; SctActv; Bsbl; Bsktbl; Ftbl; Wrstlng; CitAwd; Armed Forces; Career.

MEDNICK, Cary M; Oak Park River Forest HS; River Forest, IL; 194/1012 LbryAde; NatlCathMusEdAsoc; Illinois Inst Tech; Elec Engineering.

MEDOR, Douglas H; Milan HS; Ypsilanti, MI; Band; CncrtBnd; HonRl; MrchBnd; PepBnd; TchrAde; FTA; FrCl; Eastern Mi Univ; Business Management.

MEDOW, Jonathan C; New Trier East HS; Wilmette, IL; 1/847 CmntyWkr; NatlMeritCmnd; PolWkr; StuGov; Yrbk; Univ; Law.

MEDRED, Laurie L; Monroe HS; St Paul, MN; ChrhWkr; LbryAde; SchAde; TchrAde; PresFHA; College; Theology.

MEDUNA, Mary A; Bishop Neuman Central HS; Wahoo, NE; Band; DrmMjrt; MrchBnd; 4-H; PpCl; Se Comm College; Technology.

MEDVE, Gerardette J; Sacred Heart HS; Salina, KS; 2/55 CmntyWkr; RptrYrbk; FHA; Ks St U; Busi Admin.

MEDVICK, Mark A; Marion Community HS; Marion, IL; 21/275 HonRl; NHS; SecKeyCl; MthCl; SciCl; University Of Illinois; Engineering.

MEECE, Candy L; Mt Vernon HS; Mccordsville, IN; ChrhWkr; CmntyWkr; NatlThespSoc; PolWkr; SchPl; Yrbk; In Bloomington Univ; Psychologist.

MEEDER, Lee D; Thornridge HS; South Holland, IL; 6/645 HonRl; NHS; V Of I; Pre Med.

MEEDER, Lee D; Thornrhdge HS; So Holland, IL; 7/675 Chr; Univ Of Ill; Doctor.

MEEDER, Patricia J; Shawnee Mission East HS; Prairie Village, KS; Aud/Vis; Chr; ChrhWkr; HonRl; JrNHS; NHS; YthFlsp; PpCl; Bsbl; University; Education.

MEEHAN, Bill P; Gordon Tech HS; Chicago, IL; 108/619 HonRl; NatlMeritCmnd; PolWkr; SctActv; StuGov; Loyola Univ; Communications.

MEEHAN, Craig; Grace City HS; Grace City, ND; PresSophCls; PresSrCls; ALBoysSt; Chrs; ChrhWkr; HonRl; SchPl; Bsktbl; Trk; Hanson Mech Sch; Mechanics.

MEEHAN, John H; Marshall HS; Marshall, IL; 13/135 VPSrCls; VPChrhWkr; HonRl; NHS; SchPl; StuCncl; Pres4-H; VPSpnCl; VPSciCl; AmLegAwd; Butler Univ; Pharmacy.

MEEHAN, Michael S; Marquette HS; Wood River, IL; 20/145 AFS; HonRl; JA; NHS; NatlThespSoc; SchPl; StuCncl; RptrSchPpr; CivCl; College; Biology.

MEEHAN, Paula; Watseka Community HS; Watseka, IL; 54/128 Band; DrlTm; HonRl; LbryAde; MrchBnd; GAA; IMSpt; Northern Il Univ; Physical Therapy.

MEEHAN, Theresa A; Thornwood HS; Thornton, IL; 154/854 Band; ChrhWkr; HonRl; SctActv; FrCl; GAA; IMSpt; University; Engineering.

MEEK, Esther G; North Platte HS; Edgerton, MO; ChrhWkr; HonRl; SchPl; RptrYrbk; EdSchPpr; FHA; LetterTrk; Northwest Missouri State Univ; English.

MEEK, Glen; Wabash HS; Wabash, IN; NatlMeritFnl; ROTC; SchPl; StuCncl; StuGov; KeyCl; Bsktbl; Ftbl; Trk; RotaryAwd; Purdue Univ; Television Production.

MEEK, Sarah M; Lasalle HS; Cedar Rapids, IA; Chr; Chrs; HonRl; HospAde; ModUN; NHS; SchMus; TchrAde; Col Of Willm & Mary; Busi.

MEEKER, Anne M; Southwest HS; Kansas City, MO; 50/510 TrsFrshCls; TrsSophCls; Chr; ChrhWkr; CmntyWkr; DrlTm; HonRl; HospAde; Mdrgl; NHS; SchMus; StuCncl; YthFlsp; Kansas University.

MEEKER, Woodrow L; Platte Valley Academy; Bison, KS; PresFrshCls; VPJrCls; Band; Chr; HonRl; NatlMeritCmnd; Yrbk; College; Math.

MEEKMA, Patricia K; Beaver Dam Sr HS; Beaver Dam, WI; Band; Chrs; HonRl; SchMus; StuCncl; Tennis; LetterTrk; Chrldr; GAA; IMSpt; Business School; Secretary.

MEEKS, Keith D; L C Mohr HS; South Haven, MI; Band; ChrhWkr; CncrtBnd; HonRl; MrchBnd; PepBnd; TchrAde; RptrSchPpr; SchPpr; Clge; Bus & Law.

MEESE, Scott L; Oblong HS; Oblong, IL; HonRl; NHS; Yrbk; LetterBsktbl; LetterGlf; Lincoln Trail College; Business.

MEETZ, Lynn M; West HS; Green Bay, WI; 30/400 Chr; Chrl; Chrs; HonRl; Mdrgl; SchMus; SchPl; RptrSchPpr; PpCl; St Norberts Coll; Vocal Music.

MEEUSEN, Mark A; Zeeland HS; Zeeland, MI; HonRl; FrCl; College; Accounting.

MEFFORD, Pamela L; Schaumburg HS; Schaumburg, IL; 20/540 ALAGirlsSt; VPBand; Chr; ChrhWkr; CncrtBnd; DrlTm; HonRl; LbryAde; MrchBnd; NHS; Orch; PepBnd; SchMus; StuGov; University Of Illinois; Music.

MEHL, Linda L; Lakeview HS; Battle Creek, MI; HonRl; Orch; SchMus; Michigan St Univ; Catering.

MEHL, Mark A; Drake Public HS; Drake, ND; TrsFrshCls; HonRl; LetterBsbl; LetterBsktbl; College; Professional.

MEHLER, Susann L; Desoto Public HS; De Soto, MO; Band; Chr; ChrhWkr; CncrtBnd; DrlTm; HonRl; JrNHS; Mdrgl; NHS; PepBnd; College; Vocal Music Teacher.

MEHLHAFF, Larry L; Freeman Public HS; Freeman, SD; Band; Chr; CncrtBnd; HonRl; NHS; SchPl; YthFlsp; RptrSchPpr; IMSpt; BttyCrckrAwd; Sd Univ.

MEHLING, Annette L; Morrill HS; Morrill, NE; SecSophCls; Chrs; NatlThespSoc; StuGov; Yrbk; FHA; PpCl; College; Vocation.

MEHLING, Carol A; Forest Park; Ferdinand, IN; 21/124 Chrs; HonRl; NHS; NatlMeritCmnd; PpCl; GAA; CitAwd; Deaconess Hospital School Of Nursing; Nurse.

MEHLING, Charles K; Sidney Public HS; Sidney, NE; Band; ChrhWkr; HonRl; JrNHS; StuCncl; StuGov; Bsktbl; LetterFtbl; LetterGlf; College.

MEHLTRETTER, Louis D; Wautoma HS; Wautoma, WI; Band; HonRl; SctActv; PpCl; Trk; GodCntryAwd; U Of Wi Eau Claire; Bus Admin.

MEHRHOFF, Roberta J; St Mark HS; St Louis, MO; 3/46 HonRl; LbryAde; SchPpr; Clge; History Teacher.

MEHRTENS, Vince C; Gibault Catholic HS; Waterloo, IL; 50/110 Chr; ChrhWkr; LbryAde; StuCncl; StuGov; SptEdSchPpr; PpCl; CaptSocr; Belleville Area Clg.

MEICENHEIMER, Kim W; Litchfield Sr HS; Litchfield, IL; Chrs; SchMus; SchPl; FrCl; SciCl; Chrldr; IMSpt; Southern Ill Univ; Zoology.

MEIDA, Linda M; Harper Woods HS; Harper Woods, MI; HonRl; HospAde; NHS; StuCncl; RptrYrbk; SpnCl; Wayne St U; Denist.

MEIDINGER, Norma; Zeeland Public HS; Zeeland, ND; 7/28 Chr; Chrs; CmntyWkr; HonRl; LbryAde; OffAde; SchPl; TchrAde; PpCl; 4-HAwd; Army.

MEIDINGER, Sherry; Ashley HS; Fredonia, ND; 19/41 Chr; Chrl; Chrs; HonRl; StuCncl; YthFlsp; SchPpr; Trk; PresAwd; Wahpeton Sch Science; Med Secretary.

MEIDL, Julie A; Valders HS; Whitelaw, WI; AFS; Band; ChrhWkr; CncrtBnd; HonRl; MrchBnd; PresPpCl; College; Professional.

MEIDL, Therese M; Lourdes Academy; Oshkosh, WI; 13/140 Chrs; HonRl; Mdrgl; SchMus; KeyCl; GerCl; Socr; Un Of Wi; Special Education Teacher.

MEIENBURG, Lynette M; Heritage HS; Fort Wayne, IN; Band; Chr; CncrtBnd; DrlTm; HonRl; HospAde; MrchBnd; PepBnd; TchrAde; Twrl; Univ; Nursing.

MEIER, Bethanie R; Rolla Public HS; Rolla, ND; 2/35 Band; ChrhWkr; CncrtBnd; HonRl; NHS; SchPl; RptrYrbk; FHA; PpCl; CaptChrldr; University Of North Dakota; Forestry.

MEIER, Charlotte M; Zeeland Public HS; Venturia, ND; 8/28 Chrs; HonRl; SchPl; RptrSchPpr; PpCl; Chrldr; Clge; Med Secretary.

MEIER, Conrad J; Rocori HS; Watkins, MN; 9/167 Chrs; HonRl; NHS; SchMus; StuCncl; St Cloud State Clge; Accounting.

MEIER, David A; Roncalli HS; Omaha, NE; ALBoysSt; HonRl; NHS; EdYrBk; RptrSchPpr; Univ Of Nebraska Omah; Civil Engineering.

MEIER, Lynne M; Lincoln HS; Wisconsin Rapids, WI; ChrhWkr; HonRl; Orch; FrCl; College.

MEIER, Mark A; Charlevoix HS; Charlevoix, MI; Band; CncrtBnd; HonRl; College; Electronics.

MEIER, Mary J; Durant Community HS; Durant, IA; HonRl; JrNHS; LbryAde; TreasNHS; NatlMeritCmnd; PolWkr; Bsbl; LetterBsktbl; LetterTrk; Iowa State Univ; Vet.

MEIER, Michael W; Neillsville HS; Neillsville, WI; 3/110 ALBoysSt; HonRl; NHS; StuCncl; LatCl; Bsktbl; IMSpt; EldAwd; KiwanAwd; Brown Inst; Electronics.

MEIER, Pamela A; Perham HS; Perham, MN; 12/140 HonRl; NHS; RptrYrbk; LatCl; PpCl; LetterGlf; Chrldr; Nd State U; Home Ec.

MEIER, Randall M; Preston Community HS; Bellevue, IA; PresFrshCls; SchPpr; Army.

MEIER, Rochne E; Aquinas HS; Niota, IL; Band; CncrtBnd; MrchBnd; PepBnd; SchMus; SchPl; PpCl; IMSpt;.

MEIER, Rose A; North Boone HS; Capron, IL; VPJrCls; Band; Chrs; ChrhWkr; CncrtBnd; DrmMjrt; Mdrgl; NHS; SchMus; GerCl; College;.

MEIER, Roy; Eureka Public HS; Eureka, SD; /57 ChrhWkr; HonRl; Wrstlng; College; Civil Engr.

MEIER, Sue A; Riceville Comm HS; Elma, IA; Chr; ChrhWkr; CmntyWkr; HonRl; SchAde; RptrSchPpr; Fashon School; Display.

MEIERDIERKS, Karen; Pender Public HS; Pender, NE; Band; Chr; CncrtBnd; MrchBnd; PepBnd; Yrbk; PpCl; Trk; University; Professional.

MEIERDING, Jane L; Morgan Public HS; Morgan, MN; Band; Chrs; HonRl; MrchBnd; TchrAde; EdSchPpr; 4-H; Bsktbl; Trk; 4-HAwd; Univ; Journalism.

MEIERGERD, Roxann; Central Catholic HS; West Point, NE; 18/77 HonRl; SchMus; SchPl; SpnCl; MthCl; PpCl; IMSpt; PPFtbl; 4-HAwd; Lincoln School Of Commerce; Executive Sec.

MEIEROTTO, Sharon; Marquette HS; Hillsboro, IA; Chrs; ChrhWkr; CmntyWkr; LbryAde; 4-H; PpCl; 4-HAwd; Kirkwood; Vocational.

MEIGHAN, Jeffery A; Lancaster Sr HS; Lancaster, WI; 9/164 Chr; CncrtBnd; HonRl; MrchBnd; SchMus; Bsbl; CaptBsktbl; Glf; IMSpt; PresAwd; Clge; Prof.

MEIHOST, Duane P; Tripoli HS; Tripoli, IA; 13/66 HonRl; NHS; PolWkr; SchMus; SchPl; MthCl; Bsbl; Ftbl; Trk; College; Electronics.

MEILAENDER, Natalie R; Hobart Sr HS; Hobart, IN; 1/410 VPSrCls; ALAGirlsSt; SecChrhWkr; HonRl; HospAde; NHS; NatlMeritCmnd; SecStuCncl; TchrAde; SecLatCl; PresSciCl; DARAwd; College; Doctor.

MEILI, Robin C; Whitefish Bay HS; Milwaukee, WI; SecTrsJrCls; AFS; ChrhWkr; CmntyWkr; HonRl; HospAde; NatlMeritCmnd; RedCrAde; StuCncl; StuGov; FrCl; College; Biology.

MEIMANN, Joseph L; Okawville HS; Okawville, IL; VPSrCls; HonRl; ROTC; SctActv; StuCncl; GerCl; PpCl; IMSpt; AmLegAwd; S I U Carbon Dale; Law.

MEINCKE, Lynn A; Durant Comm HS; Durant, IA; 5/74 SecSophCls; VPJrCls; Chr; ChrhWkr; HonRl; LbryAde; NatlFornLg; NHS; SchMus; StuCncl; RptrSchPpr; PresFHA; College; Dietition.

MEINDERTSMA, R Duane; Knoxville Comm HS; Knoxville, IA; 7/125 ALBoysSt; HonRl; TchrAde; PresSciCl; Tennis; University; Pharmacy.

MEINECKE, Becky J; Burwell Jr Sr HS; Burwell, NE; Band; HonRl; StuCncl; 4-H; CaptBsktbl; Swmmng; LetterTrk; LetterWrstlng; GAA; 4-HAwd; College; Biology.

MEINERS, Beth M; Caledonia HS; Caledonia, MN; ChrhWkr; HonRl; SchPl; YthFlsp; College; Psychology.

MEINERT, Dori L; Metamora Twp HS; East Peoria, IL; 41/174 AFS; ALAGirlsSt; DrlTm; HonRl; Quill&Scroll; SchMus; SchPl; SecStuCncl; RptrSchPpr; SecSpnCl; GAA; Northern Univ; Journalism.

MEINERT, Mary A; Durant Community HS; Durant, IA; ALAGirlsSt; PresChrs; HonRl; NHS; SchMus; SchPl; LetterBsbl; Bsktbl; Trk; DARAwd; Univ; Professional.

MEINHARDT, J M; Park Hill HS; Kansas City, MO; ChrhWkr; HonRl; NatlMeritCmnd; Sacrstn; SctActv; EldAwd; GodCntryAwd; College; Law.

MEINHART, Jeanne M; Newton HS; Montrose, IL; 13/180 TrsJrCls; HonRl; JrNHS; NHS; SchPpr; 4-H; GAA; IMSpt; Lakeland Jr Col; Med Technologist.

MEINHART, Paul C; Newton Comm HS; Wheeler, IL; CmntyWkr; JA; 4-H; FFA; LetterBsbl; LetterBsktbl; JAAwd; College.

MEINHART, Shirley; Newton HS; Wheeler, IL; Chr; ChrhWkr; HonRl; NHS; Teen; GAA; IMSpt; 4-HAwd; College; Business Edcuation.

MEINICKE, Nancy C; York Comm HS; Elmhurst, IL; HonRl; LbryAde; NatlMeritCmnd; College; Biology.

MEININGER, Janet L; Powhattan HS; Powhattan, KS; 4/17 SecFrshCls; HstSophCls; Band; Chr; Chrs; CncrtBnd; Bsktbl; Trk; Chrldr; IMSpt; Trade; Vocation.

MEIR, Diane L; Lancaster HS; Lancaster, WI; HonRl; HospAde; VP4-H; FHA; PpCl; IMSpt; Col Or Univ; Pro Nursing.

MEIRESONNE, Robert D; New Trier East HS; Wilmette, IL; 190/850 Bsktbl; Ftbl; Wrstlng; U Of Ind; Banking.

MEIRICK, Donna M; New Hampton HS; Alta Vista, IA; Band; ChrhWkr; CncrtBnd; HonRl; MrchBnd; PepBnd; College.

MEIS, Clyde J; Elgin Public HS; Elgin, NE; CmntyWkr; HonRl; NHS; SchPl; StuCncl; FFA; LetterFtbl; LetterTrk; CaptWrstlng; CchngActv; College; Teach & Coach.

MEISER, Glenn E; Frontier HS; Brookston, IN; 7/67 PresAud/Vis; SchPl; SctActv; Yrbk; SptEdSchPpr; LetterTrk; IMSpt; Ball St Univ; Architecture.

MEISINGER, Katherine A; Plattsmouth HS; Plattsmouth, NE; Band; Chrs; CncrtBnd; MrchBnd; PepBnd; SchMus; 4-H; 4-HAwd;.

MEISINGER, Philip R; Peoria HS; Peoria, IL; HonRl; NHS; SchAde; StuGov; LetterSwmmng; Univ Of Ill; Professional.

MEISINGER, Roger L; Plattsmouth HS; Louisville, NE; 1/133 SecSophCls; ChrhWkr; CmntyWkr; HonRl; NHS; VPStuCncl; StuGov; Pres4-H; MthCl; Bsbl; LetterFtbl; Trk; 4-HAwd; Creighton Univ; Law.

MEISINGER, Terry D; Metropolis HS; Metropolis, IL; Chr; ChrhWkr; CmntyWkr; HonRl; NHS; KeyCl; GerCl; Bsktbl; LetterTrk; Shawnee Community College; Engineer.

MEISNER, Karen A; William Howard Taft HS; Chicago, IL; 8/790 Chrs; VPHonRl; VPNHS; OffAde; SctActv; StuCncl; FrCl; SpnCl; MthCl; GAA; Univ Of Illinois; Mathematics.

MEISNER, Roland; Gering HS; Gering, NE; 23/139 Chrs; HonRl; JrNHS; NHS; YthFlsp; GerCl; Univ Of Wy; Medicine.

MEISSEN, Phillip; Lafollette HS; Madison, WI; 151/550 Band; ChrhWkr; HonRl; TchrAde; 4-H; LetterBsktbl; LetterFtbl; Trk; IMSpt; 4-HAwd; Uw River Falls;phys Educ.

MEISSEN, Richard J; Bradley Bourbonnais Comm HS; Bourbonnais, IL; 66/334 ChrhWkr; CmntyWkr; LbryAde; SchAde; 4-H; PpCl; SciCl; Tennis;.

MEISSERT, Jerene R; Mexico Sr HS; Mexico, MO; Chr; HospAde; JA; NatlFornLg; SchMus; SchPl; SctActv; StuCncl; University Of Missouri; Respiratory Therapy.

MEISSNER, Cynthia S; Sidney HS; Sidney, NE; 5/112 SecChrhWkr; PresHospAde; NHS; SecFHA; PresEngCl; MthCl; EldAwd; Methodist School Of Nursing; Nurse.

MEISSNER, Gabriele L; Maine Twp West HS; Des Plaines, IL; 23/755 AFS; HonRl; JrNHS; NHS; NatlMeritCmnd; Orch; SchMus; RptrYrbk; Yrbk; Univ Of Illinois; Journalism.

MEISTAD, Mary E; Arcadia HS; Arcadia, WI; PresSrCls; ALAGirlsSt; PresBand; NHS; PepBnd; StuCncl; RptrYrbk; RptrSchPpr; SecGAA; BttyCrckrAwd; W Wi Tech Inst La Crosse; Accounting.

MEISTER, Coralyn G; Hammond Baptist HS; Lowell, IN; Chr; Chrl; Chrs; ChrhWkr; HonRl; HospAde; Orch; SchMus; SecYthFlsp; RptrSchPpr; GAA; Tennessee Temple; Nursing.

MEISTER, Darrell S; Wall Lake Community HS; Lake View, IA; 6/32 Band; CncrtBnd; MrchBnd; PepBnd; FFA; College; Accounting.

MEISTER, Jane; Waldron HS; Waldron, MI; 1/48 Band; ChrhWkr; HonRl; NHS; SchPl; StuCncl; TchrAde; YthFlsp; FHA; CitAwd; Elem Education.

MEISTER, Jane R; Waldron HS; Waldron, MI; 1/48 SecFrshCls; SecJrCls; Band; ChrhWkr; CncrtBnd; HonRl; MrchBnd; NHS; PepBnd; SchPl; StuCncl; TchrAde; Twrl; Yrbk; FHA; College; Teacher.

MEISTER, Kurt W; Ypsilanti HS; Ypsilanti, MI; HonRl; NHS; TchrAde; Yrbk; Ftbl; Tennis; Mi State; Art Teacher.

MEITL, Kenneth G; Hoxie HS; Dresden, KS; 6/74 ChrhWkr; HonRl; SchPl; StuCncl; PresFFA; CaptBsktbl; CaptFtbl; LetterTrk; Colby Juco; Electrical Engineering.

MEITNER, Elizabeth M; Appleton East HS; Appleton, WI; 76/500 SecSrCls; HonRl; NHS; PolWkr; Quill&Scroll; StuGov; EdYrBk; EdSchPpr; TreasFrCl; LetterTennis; Marquette U; Lawyer.

MEIWES, Ann M; Marmaton Valley HS; Kincaid, KS; Chr; HonRl; FHA; PpCl; College.

MEJICANO, Maria E; Mt Assisi Academy; Palos Park, IL; HonRl; HospAde; NHS; StuCncl; College; Economics.

MEJSTRIK, Chris L; Howells HS; Jowells, NE; 3/42 ALBoysSt; HonRl; SchPl; StuCncl; StuGov; RptrYrbk; 4-H; FFA; Ftbl; Wrstlng; U Of Nebraska; Pharmacy.

MELANCON, Artie T; College View Academy; Lincoln, NE; Band; Chr; HonRl; NHS; NatlMeritCmnd; RptrYrbk; RptrSchPpr; Trk; IMSpt; PresAwd; Union College; Physician.

MELBERG, Susan J; William Fremd HS; Palatine, IL; 6/607 Chr; HonRl; NHS; SchMus; StuCncl; RptrYrbk; SpnCl; LetterTennis; GAA; DARAwd; De Pauw U; Spanish.

MELBY, Rolf B; Klemme HS; Klemme, IA; 2/32 CncrtBnd; SchMus; SchPl; StuCncl; StuGov; LetterBsbl; LetterBsktbl; LetterFtbl; LetterGlf; Swmmng; Woldorf Junior Clg; Business Administration.

MELCHER, Karla K; Fairbury HS; Fairbury, NE; Band; College; Nursing.

MELCHER, Lisa M; Holy Family HS; Lindsay, NE; ALAGirlsSt; ChrhWkr; CmntyWkr; HonRl; SctActv; 4-H; PpCl; Univ; Vet.

MELCHER, Mary J; Mother Theodore Guerin HS; Chicago, IL; 10/410 Chrl; HonRl; JA; NHS; University Of Illinois; Food & Nutrition.

MELCHER, Thomas J; Lakeview HS; Columbus, NE; Chr; NHS; SchAde; StuCncl; TchrAde; LetterFtbl; Trk; IMSpt; College; Dentistry.

MELCHERT, Glenn D; Glencoe HS; Glencoe, MN; 16/141 Band; ChrhWkr; CncrtBnd; HonRl; MrchBnd; PepBnd; SchMus; SchPl; SpnCl; SciCl; Bsktbl; LetterGlf; IMSpt; Univ Of Minnesota; Biology.

MELCHI, Mona; Herbert Henry Dow Hs; Midland, MI; 83 Band; ChrhWkr; HonRl; HospAde; JrNHS; NHS; PolWkr; SchPl; John Wesley College ; Art Education.

MELCHIOR, Walter; Hortonville HS; Black Creek, WI; 30/154 Band; CncrtBnd; HonRl; RptrSchPpr; IMSpt; DanFAwd; College; Hictory.

MELER, Beth A; Carrier Mills HS; Carrier Mills, IL; 6/31 Band; Chrs; HonRl; SecNHS; SchPl; StuCncl; FHA; MthCl; PpCl; Chrldr; University; Veterinarian.

MELFI, Kathleen M; Vienna Twp HS; Creal Springs, IL; 1/130 Band; CncrtBnd; HonRl; MrchBnd; PepBnd; 4-H; SpnCl; MthCl; University; Doctor.

MELFI, Sheryl A; Lakeview HS; St Clair Shores, MI; CmntyWkr; HonRl; NHS; TchrAde; RptrYrbk; Wayne St Univ; Medicine.

MELHORN, Sara J; Herrin HS; Herrin, IL; 23/216 Chrs; ChrhWkr; DrlTm; OffAde; SchAde; LatCl; Southern Il Univ; Computer Science.

MELIA, Mary A; Dodge City HS; Dodge City, KS; 99/375 Band; CncrtBnd; DrlTm; HonRl; MrchBnd; NHS; StuCncl; Chrldr; Dodge City Comm Clg; Pro Secretary.

MELIN, Susan C; Columbia Hts Sr HS; Columbia Hts, MN; Band; HonRl; JrNHS; MrchBnd; NHS; PepBnd; Swmmng; University.

MELINE, Jeffrey; Webster City HS; Webster City, IA; ALBoysSt; ChrhWkr; HonRl; YthFlsp; Yrbk; MthCl; Bsbl; Glf; GovHonPrgAwd; KiwanAwd; Coll; Engineering.

MELINN, Sharon K; East Kentwood HS; Kentwood, MI; HonRl; NHS; PolWkr; SpnCl; Davenport Col Of Bus; Legal Secretary.

MELINYSHYN, Lev A; Gage Park HS; Chicago, IL; 3/611 HonRl; OffAde; TchrAde; TreasSciCl; Socr; College; Medicine.

MELIUS, Jennifer J; Faulkton HS; Faulkton, SD; PresJrCls; ALAGirlsSt; Band; Chrs; CncrtBnd; HonRl; SchPl; TreasStuCncl; FHA; LetterBsktbl; Sd State Univ; Interior Desinger.

MELIUS, Luan L; Random Lake HS; Adell, WI; 22/100 PresSophCls; HonRl; YthFlsp; 4-H; FHA; Bsktbl; Trk; Chrldr; GAA; 4-HAwd; Lakeshore Tech Instit; Vocation.

MELIUS, Michael M; Faulkton HS; Faulkton, SD; 1/60 HonRl; NatlMeritSF; SchPl; StuCncl; StuGov; EdYrBk; RptrSchPpr; SciCl; Glf; Univ; Astronomy.

MELKO, Joseph; Thornton Fractional South HS; Lansing, IL; 83/552 HonRl; LetterGlf; North Ill Univ; Business.

MELKUS, Brian; Hamtramck HS; Hamtramck, MI; HonRl; JA; NHS; SchPl; Us Nave.

MELLAND, Katherine C; Valley HS; Hoople, ND; 2/31 VPSophCls; ALAGirlsSt; Band; Chrs; HonRl; SchPl; EdSchPpr; Pres4-H; LetterBsktbl; Mayville State College; Elem Education.

MELLEMA, Debra L; Gull Lake HS; Augusta, MI; 14/225 VPSophCls; JrNHS; NHS; SchMus; Bsbl; Bsktbl; Chrldr; GAA; IMSpt; PPFtbl; Michigan State; Special Education.

MELLEN, Patti; Carney Nadeau Public HS; Carney, MI; 1/25 VPFrshCls; TrsSophCls; VPJrCls; Band; Chrs; ChrhWkr; CtyCnl; CmntyWkr; CncrtBnd; GAA; N Mi Univ; Foreign Languages.

MELLENBERNDT, Gala; Central Lyon HS; Rock Rapids, IA; HonRl; Iowa State Univ; Film Production.

MELLER, James E; Anna Jonesboro HS; Anna, IL; 10/147 PresFrshCls; HonRl; SctActv; RptrYrbk; KeyCl; SpnCl; SciCl; Bsktbl; Ftbl; AmLegAwd; Il U; Vet.

MELLHAFF, Charles C; Eureka HS; Eureka, SD; TrsSrCls; ChrhWkr; HonRl; SchMus; SchPl; StuGov; CaptBsktbl; CaptFtbl; CaptTrk; AmLegAwd; Northern State College; Business.

MELLINGER, Mark R; Stephenson HS; Stephenson, MI; HonRl; Bsktbl; Glf; College; Business Administration.

MELLON, Jane M; Immac Heart Of Mary HS; Westchester, IL; 44/250 SecJrCls; FrCl; GAA; IMSpt; Univ Pro.

MELNICK, Elizabeth X; New Trier West HS; Glenview, IL; 27/697 AFS; Chr; Chrs; NatlMeritCmnd; SchMus; EdYrBk; Mt Holyoke College; Political Science.

MELNIK, Marianne K; Lourdes Academy; Oshkosh, WI; 1/125 Chrs; HonRl; JrNHS; NatlFornLg; NHS; SchMus; RptrSchPpr; SchPpr; KeyCl; PresGerCl; LetterTennis; IMSpt; BauchLmbAwd; Univ; Medicine.

MELOCHE, Steven E; Tipton HS; Tipton, IN; 1/172 VPFrshCls; PresJrCls; TrsSrCls; Band; HonRl; NHS; SchPl; StuCncl; PresSciCl; LetterWrstlng; Depauw University; Medicine.

MELODY, Karen M; Ottawa Twp HS; Ottawa, IL; 98/420 CmntyWkr; HonRl; Illinois Valley Comm College; Elem Educ.

MELSEN, Jean A; Assumption HS; Port Edwards, WI; Band; HonRl; PepBnd; RedCrAde; SchMus; StuCncl; Yrbk; PpCl; CaptSwmmng; CchngActv; Clge Of St Catherine; Fashion Designing.

MELSON, Celeste A; Trimont HS; Trimont, MN; TrsSophCls; VPSrCls; Band; LitMag; PepBnd; SchPl; RptrYrbk; SchPpr; FHA; Trk; Iowa Lakes Comm Clg; Nursing.

MELSTAD, Jeanine L; Bismarck HS; Bismarck, ND; 11/588 Chr; HonRl; NatlFornLg; NHS; NatlMeritCmnd; Orch; LatCl; EldAwd; KiwanAwd; PresAwd; Univ Of Nd; Medicine.

MELTABARGER, Dorothy L; S County Technical HS; Lemay, MO; JA; LbryAde; OffAde; FBLA; LatCl; GAA; IMSpt; Secretarial Work.

MELTE, Vickie L; Chillicothe HS; Chillicothe, MO; Chrs; ChrhWkr; HonRl; Quill&Scroll; SchPl; TchrAde; EdSchPpr; FTA; LetterBsktbl; GAA; Central Mo St Univ; Physical Education.

MELTON, Douglas R; Mckinley HS; St Louis, MO; 11/193 ChrhWkr; HonRl; SptEdYrbk; RptrSchPpr; LetterSocr; KiwanAwd; Missouri Univ Of Columbia; Forestry.

MELUM, Karen M; Iola Scandinavia HS; Amherst Junction, WI; 9/46 TrsSrCls; Chrs; HonRl; NHS; SchPl; 4-H; LetterBsktbl; LetterTrk; 4-HAwd; Ambassador Clg; Home Ec.

MELVIN, Diana R; Garden County HS; Oshkosh, NE; Chrs; DrmMjrt; HonRl; HospAde; Quill&Scroll; StuGov; RptrYrbk; EdSchPpr; PpCl; Trk; AmLegAwd; Kearney St College; Journalism.

MELVIN, Joseph A; Murphysboro Township HS; Murphysboro, IL; 24/220 HonRl; TreasKeyCl; Bsktbl; LetterFtbl; LetterTrk; Southern Ill Univ.

MELVIN, Mary K; Plainview HS; Plainview, MN; Band; Chr; CncrtBnd; HonRl; MrchBnd; PepBnd; SchPl; RptrYrbk; Yrbk; 4-H; Rochester Comm Clg; Physics.

MELVIN, Ruth; Bedford Community HS; Blockton, IA; 2/71 NHS; Quill&Scroll; TchrAde; RptrSchPpr; SchPpr; FHA; College; Music.

MEMERING, Kathleen J; Belleville HS; Belleville, MI; 15/525 HonRl; NHS; SchPl; StuGov; RptrSchPpr; SptEdSchPpr; SchPpr; FrCl; SciCl; PPFtbl; Univ Mi.

MEMMER, John A; Princeton Community HS; Princeton, IN; 51/188 ChrhWkr; HonRl; YthFlsp; FFA; Indiana St University; Accounting.

MENACHER, Jay P; Mahomet Seymour HS; Champaign, IL; 5/129 Band; CncrtBnd; HonRl; MrchBnd; NHS; SchMus; StuCncl; 4-H; SpnCl; DanFAwd; 4-HAwd; Univ.

MENACHER, Jo A; Mahomet Seymour HS; Champaign, IL; 6/128 SecSophCls; PresJrCls; PresSrCls; Band; HonRl; PresNHS; 4-H; PresSpnCl; DanFAwd; 4-HAwd; U Of I; Future In 4 H.

MENARD, Brian S; Lincoln HS; Wis Rapids, WI; HonRl; LetterTrk; College; Cpa.

MENARD, Kathryn; St Joseph Acad; De Pere, WI; 30/160 VPSrCls; Chrs; ChrhWkr; HospAde; SchMus; Bsbl; Glf; IMSpt; PresAwd; Univ; Vocation.

MENARD, Raymond E; Hubbard HS; Chicago, IL; 11/431 PresJrCls; PresSrCls; Band; ChrhWkr; HonRl; VPNHS; NatlMeritSchl; Quill&Scroll; SctActv; MthCl; College; Dentist.

MENARD, Raymond J; Wayland Academy; Juneau, WI; 15/71 Chr; TchrAde; MthCl; PresSciCl; LetterTrk; University; Medicine.

MENARY, Jeffrey R; Williamsburg Comm HS; Williamsburg, IA; 16/100 ChrhWkr; HonRl; JrNHS; NHS; LetterBsktbl; LetterFtbl; LetterTrk; College.

MENCINGER, Nicholas; Maine West Hs; Des Plaines, IL; HonRl; LetterSwmmng; College; Bioengineering.

MENDENHALL, Cindy; Wheatland HS; Gove, KS; VPFrshCls; TrsSophCls; TrsJrCls; HonRl; SchMus; SchPpr; FHA; PpCl; LetterTrk; Chrldr; Colby Comm Coll; Sec.

MENDENHALL, David L; Cincinnati Country Day HS; Lawrenceburg, IN; NatlMeritSF; CivCl; SciCl; Hillsdale Coll.

MENDENHALL, Jerry R; Mt Pleasant HS; Mt Pleasant, IA; LetterFtbl; LetterTrk; Bible College; Music.

MENDEY, Jean C; Trinity HS; Chicago, IL; 34/204 Chrs; HonRl; NatlFornLg; NHS; Ill Institute Of Tech; Optometrist.

MENDEZ, Ana C; Wells HS; Chicago, IL; 2/350 Band; CncrtBnd; HonRl; NatlMeritSchl; Orch; EngCl; SpnCl; GAA; AmLegAwd; CitAwd; University.

MENDICINO, Nancy R; Mother Theodore Guerin HS; Chicago, IL; 25/408 HonRl; NHS; StuCncl; Loyola University; Medicine.

MENDOZA, Irene; St Charles HS; St Charles, MO; 65/548 Chrs; ChrhWkr; HonRl; JrNHS; Orch; SchMus; Baptist Bible College; Elem Education.

MENDOZA, Marcus; Kelly HS; Chicago, IL; Band; CmntyWkr; LbryAde; SchMus; SctActv;.

MENDRICK, Mary G; Tomahawk HS; Tomahawk, WI; Chr; CncrtBnd; HonRl; HospAde; MrchBnd; PepBnd; SpnCl; MthCl; GAA; OptClAwd; Coll; Nursing.

MENEGAS, Sam V; Kelly HS; Chicago, IL; 1/552 SecTrsSrCls; HonRl; ModUN; NHS; FDA; MthCl; SciCl; Bsktbl; Ftbl; Loyola University; Doctor.

MENENDEZ, Xiomara; Mundelein HS; Mondelein, IL; 57/386 Chrl; Chrs; HonRl; LitMag; SchAde; SchMus; SchPl; TchrAde; SpnCl; PpCl; College; Medicine.

MENESTRINA, Ricky D; West Vigo HS; W Terre Haute, IN; ALBoysSt; HonRl; YthFlsp; FTA; LetterBsbl; LetterBsktbl; Ftbl; Fl St Univ; Hospital Admin.

MENGARELLI, D Rachelle; Girard HS; Girard, KS; PresChrhWkr; HonRl; SchPl; TchrAde; Yrbk; Pres4-H; PresFHA; LetterBsktbl; LetterTrk; PPFtbl; College; Home Economics.

MENGEL, Alison M; Proviso East HS; Maywood, IL; 13/990 CncrtBnd; HonRl; MrchBnd; NHS; StuGov; Swmmng; Univ Of Illinois; Veterinary Medicine.

MENGELIS, Irisa A; Luther North HS; Chicago, IL; 1/225 ChrhWkr; CmntyWkr; HonRl; SecNHS; NatlMeritCmnd; RptrSchPpr; Northwestern Univ; Medicine.

MENGWASSER, Helen C; Fatima HS; Jefferson City, MO; 8/126 Chrs; HonRl; FBLA; FHA; SpnCl; PpCl; LetterTrk; Lincoln Univ; Accountant.

MENIGOZ, Deborah L; Bradley/bourbonnais Comm HS; Bradley, IL; 59/316 HonRl; SchPl; SctActv; 4-H; TreasFrCl; GAA; Eastern Illinois Univ; Medical Lab Tech.

MENK, Kevin L; New Ulm Sr HS; New Ulm, MN; 3/250 PresSrCls; Chr; HonRl; StuCncl; StuGov; YthFlsp; 4-H; LetterFtbl; LetterTrk; Univ Of Minn; Law.

MENKE, Debra L; Pleasant Hill HS; Rockport, IL; 3/48 SecTrsSophCls; ALAGirlsSt; Band; ChrhWkr; HonRl; PepBnd; TchrAde; 4-H; GAA; Concordia Lutheran; Church Work.

MENKE, Diane M; Sparta HS; Sparta, IL; Chr; ChrhWkr; DrlTm; HonRl; NHS; SchMus; TchrAde; Yrbk; VP4-H; PresFTA; SecLatCl; GAA; 4-HAwd; Eastern Illinois Univ; Teacher.

MENKE, Lynn A; Marquette Schools Inc; West Point, IA; 6/51 Band; DrlTm; MrchBnd; PresNHS; PepBnd; StuCncl; EdSchPpr; SchPpr; Pres4-H; TreasFTA; Creighton U; Nursing.

MENKING, Edward D; Arlington Public HS; Arlington, NE; 13/57 TrsSophCls; HonRl; NHS; RptrYrbk; GerCl; LetterBsktbl; CaptFtbl; LetterGlf; College.

MENNE, Julie A; Neillsville HS; Marshfield, WI; 13/115 HonRl; NatlFornLg; NHS; SchPl; StuCncl; StuGov; SpnCl; Bsktbl; LetterTrk; LetterSt Joseph Hosp; Histology.

MENNEMEYER, Vesta M; East Alton Wood River HS; Hartford, IL; Chr; Chrs; ChrhWkr; HonRl; HospAde; JrNHS; LbryAde; OffAde; StuCncl; TchrAde; Oral Roberts Univ; Religion.

MENNENGA, Ramona M; Rantoul Township HS; Thomasboro, IL; 5/325 VPCncrtBnd; HonRl; MrchBnd; NHS; Orch; PepBnd; SchMus; RptrYrbk; SpnCl; KiwanAwd; Office Work.

MENNENGA, Sandra L; Huron Sr HS; Huron, SD; 16/300 Band; CncrtBnd; JrNHS; MrchBnd; NHS; TchrAde; FHA; GerCl; South Dakota State Univ; Nursing.

MENNINGA, Cathy J; Pella Comm HS; Pella, IA; 14/117 Band; CncrtBnd; DrlTm; HonRl; NHS; NatlThespSoc; SchMus; StuCncl; Trk; Chrldr; College.

MENNINGA, Patricia A; Iowa Grant HS; Rewey, WI; Band; Chrs; ChrhWkr; CncrtBnd; HonRl; Mdrgl; MrchBnd; NatlMeritSF; PepBnd; Bryn Mawr Col; Mathematics.

MENOR, William A; Menominee HS; Menominee, MI; 2/276 ALBoysSt; ChrhWkr; CmntyWkr; HonRl; JA; JrNHS; PresNHS; RptrSchPpr; LetterBsktbl; Trk; Univ; Mech Engr.

MENOWN, Jean A; Kirkwood HS; St Louis, MO; HonRl; SchPpr; PpCl; LetterBsktbl; Swmmng; IMSpt; College; Psychology.

MENSCHER, Sheri L; Wentzville HS; Wentzville, MO; Band; Chr; HonRl; SecNHS; StuCncl; 4-H; AmLegAwd; 4-HAwd; CitAwd; Fontbonne College; Music.

MENSING, Brenda M; Elmore Public HS; Blue Earth, MN; 4/30 Chr; Mdrgl; NHS; SchPl; RptrYrbk; RptrSchPpr; Pres4-H; SecFHA; GerCl; 4-HAwd; CitAwd; VoiceDemAwd; Concordia St Paul; Christian Education.

MENTLEY, Carl R; Ypsilanti HS; Ypsilanti, MI; 1/525 ALBoysSt; HonRl; NHS; NatlMeritSchl; TchrAde; LetterFtbl; Trk; CchngActv; Mich St U; Engineering.

MENTZEL, Dianne M; New Lisbon HS; New Lisbon, WI; 1/57 Band; Chr; ChrhWkr; HonRl; LbryAde; SecNHS; NatlMeritCmnd; EdYrBk; 4-H; BttyCrckrAwd; Univ Of Wisconsin; Engineering.

MENTZER, Milissa S; Morgan Park HS; Chicago, IL; Chr; ChrhWkr; CncrtBnd; HonRl; IntrClCncl; NHS; SchPpr; FrCl; MthCl; Eastern Illinois Univ; Accounting.

MENZEL, Ted M; Newman HS; Mason City, IA; ALBoysSt; Chr; Chrl; Chrs; ChrhWkr; HonRl; PolWkr; SchMus; SchPl; RptrYrbk; Yrbk; SciCl; Jr College; Professional.

MENZIA, Greg; Roscoe HS; Roscoe, SD; TrsSrCls; Band; Chrs; CncrtBnd; MrchBnd; NatlMeritCmnd; PepBnd; SchPl; Trk; Lake Area Vo Tech; Carpentry.

MENZIES, Pamela L; J M Harlan HS; Chicago, IL; 14/707 TrsJrCls; CmntyWkr; HonRl; IntrClCncl; JrNHS; LitMag; NHS; OffAde; Quill&Scroll; SchAde; Univ Il Urbana; Zoology.

MENZL, Judith A; Bishop Noll Institute HS; Hammond, IN; 59/342 ALAGirlsSt; HonRl; NHS; StuCncl; College; Accounting.

MERANDA, Teresa J; Mark Twain HS; Perry, MO; 5/58 HonRl; LbryAde; FHA; BttyCrckrAwd; DARAwd; Coll; Undecided.

MERCADO, Magdalene M; John Glenn HS; Westland, MI; 46/700 NHS; NatlMeritFnl; NatlMeritSchl; NatlMeritSF; SchMus; SchPl; EdSchPpr; SpnCl; PpCl; Madonna College; Professional.

MERCER, Beth E; Cabool HS; Cabool, MO; 6/75 HonRl; LbryAde; NHS; OffAde; SchAde; TchrAde; SchPpr; FBLA; College; Accounting.

MERCER, Edward; Atchison HS; Atchison, KS; PresSophCls; PresJrCls; PresSrCls; Chrs; ChrhWkr; NHS; SchMus; SchPpr; College; Law Enforcement.

MERCER, Nicki A; Van Buren Community HS; Keosauqua, IA; 9/83 JrNHS; MrchBnd; NHS; NatlMeritCmnd; PepBnd; RedCrAde; StuCncl; YthFlsp; LetterBsktbl; LetterTrk; Otteuwa Heights Coll; Radiation Tech.

MERCER, Patricia M; Holy Angels HS; Richfield, MN; 5/106 HonRl; HospAde; NHS; SchMus; SchPl; GAA; LetterPPFtbl; Univ; Communications Engineer.

MERCER, Shelley L; East Kentwood HS; Kentwood, MI; 9/500 Band; Chr; HonRl; MrchBnd; PresNHS; NatlMeritSF; PepBnd; SchMus; SctActv; TchrAde; IMSpt; College; Music.

MERCER, Teresa L; Sully Buttes HS; Blunt, SD; Chrs; OffAde; TchrAde; SpnCl; College; Therpist.

MERCHANT, Gordon C; Onaway Area Community HS; Ocqueoc, MI; 8/96 NatlMeritFnl; NatlMeritCmnd; NatlMeritSF; 4-H; KeyCl; Bsktbl; DanFAwd; 4-HAwd; JAAwd; CitAwd; Mi State Univ; Ag Economics.

MERCIER, Timothy E; Adlai E Stevenson HS; Deerfield, IL; 29/231 VPSophCls; VPJrCls; CmntyWkr; NHS; NatlSciFnd; StuGov; YthFlsp; FBLA; FDA; LetterFtbl; College; Professional.

MERCIL, Mary E; Mt St Benedict HS; Crookstown, MN; TrsJrCls; Chrs; SctActv; Sdlty; SchPpr; College; Social Worker.

MERCK, Shirley M; Bishop Ryan HS; Minot, ND; Chr; DrlTm; SchPl; Yrbk; PpCl; PPFtbl; College; Major Study.

MERCURIO, Philip J; St Ignatius HS; Chicago, IL; 18/156 HonRl; NatlMeritSF; StuCncl; RptrSchPpr; EdSchPpr; 4-H; FTA; FrCl; MthCl; SciCl; Univ; Chemist.

MEREDITH, John; Milan C Ii HS; Milan, MO; Band; CncrtBnd; MrchBnd; SchPl; StuCncl; YthFlsp; Yrbk; 4-H; Northeast Missouri State Univ; Teacher.

MEREDITH, Robert D; Bishop Mark K Carroll HS; Wichita, KS; 44/224 HonRl; ModUN; NHS; NatlMeritSF; PolWkr; TchrAde; RptrSchPpr; SchPpr; LatCl; College; Engineering.

MEREDITH, Shelly J; Rockford East HS; Rockford, IL; 54/665 Band; CncrtBnd; HonRl; MrchBnd; TchrAde; YthFlsp; University; Special Education.

MEREDITH, Vicky L; Grand Ledge HS; Grand Ledge, MI; 16/399 Band; Chr; ChrhWkr; CncrtBnd; HonRl; Mdrgl; MrchBnd; NHS; PepBnd; BttyCrckrAwd; Olivet Clge; Music.

MEREMA, Pamela S; Riverbend Unit #2 HS; Fulton, IL; /135 ALAGirlsSt; Chrs; ChrhWkr; HonRl; NHS; NatlThespSoc; SchMus; VPStuCncl; PresYthFlsp; Trk; College Central Pell Ia.

MERGEL, Kathleen M; Ursuline Academy; St Louis, MO; HonRl; HospAde; LitMag; PresNHS; StuCncl; SpnCl; MthCl; SciCl; GAA; IMSpt; St Louis Univ; Medical Field.

MERGEN, Richard P; Sacred Heart HS; Salina, KS; VPFrshCls; ALBoysSt; JA; Yrbk; FBLA; Bsbl; Bsktbl; Ftbl; Trk; JAAwd; University.

MERICKEL, Becky M; Maplewood Academy; Elysian, MN; 7/63 TrsJrCls; ChrhWkr; HonRl; NatlMeritSchl; OffAde; TchrAde; SchPpr; Union College; Physical Therapy.

MERIDETH, Barbara W; Caruthersville HS; Caruthersville, MO; Band; Chr; ChrhWkr; CmntyWkr; NatlThespSoc; PolWkr; SctActv; YthFlsp; FTA; MthCl; College; Nursing.

MERIL, Karen J; Morton West HS; Stickney, IL; HonRl; HospAde; RptrYrbk; Yrbk; Illinois State U; Social Worker.

MERILA, William D; Hancock Central HS; Hancock, MI; HonRl; RptrSchPpr; LetterFtbl; Trk; NCTE; Mich State; Medicine.

MERING, Kenneth D; Jamestown HS; Jamestown, ND; ChrhWkr; CmntyWkr; HonRl; SchPl; Glf; CaptSwmmng; Clg; Engineering/bus.

MERK, Richard J; Oakfield HS; Oakfield, WI; PresSrCls; ALBoysSt; HonRl; MrchBnd; Orch; StuCncl; RptrSchPpr; 4-H; Bsbl; Wrstlng; Coll; Law.

MERKEL, Carl J; Northwestern Military Academy; Neenah, WI; DrlTm; HonRl; JA; ROTC; Bsktbl;.

MERKEL, Douglas E; Maine West Twp HS; Des Plaines, IL; 1/770 ChrhWkr; HonRl; HospAde; IntrClCncl; NHS; NatlMeritSF; Orch; PolWkr; SchMus; SctActv; MthCl; SciCl; Harvard College; Medicine.

MERKEL, Gayle; Ellendale HS; Forbes, ND; SecSophCls; VPSrCls; Band; SchPl; StuCncl; RptrSchPpr; 4-H; FHA; Chrldr; College; Professional.

MERKEL, Jayne E; O Fallon Township HS; Ofallon, IL; ChrhWkr; HonRl; NHS; SpnCl; PpCl; SciCl; College; Merchandising.

MERKEL, Joan M; Acad Of The Immaculate Concep; Batesville, IN; 26/60 Chrs; HonRl; TchrAde; GerCl; Col; Teacher.

MERKEL, Marilyn L; Southridge HS; Huntingburg, IN; Chr; ChrhWkr; HonRl; SchMus; FHA; PpCl; College; Business.

MERKERT, Edward; Rochester HS; Rochester, IN; PresSrCls; AFS; Band; Chr; HonRl; NHS; SchPl; StuCncl; YthFlsp; Univ; Landscaping Arch.

MERKLE, George; Acad Our Lady Spalding Inst; Peoria, IL; 17/98 HonRl; NHS; SchMus; SchPl; FshEdYrbk; Yrbk; Trk; Illinois Central College; Engineering.

MERKLEIN, Mary K; Phillipsburg HS; Phillipsburg, KS; Band; Chr; Chrs; ChrhWkr; CmntyWkr; CncrtBnd; HonRl; NHS; NatlMeritSchl; NatlSciFnd; PepBnd; TchrAde; Yrbk; 4-H; College; Biology.

MERLAU, Virgil; Hoisington HS; Hoisington, KS; Chr; HonRl; NHS; SctActv; StuCncl; YthFlsp; Bsbl; LetterBsktbl; LetterFtbl; LetterTrk; Kansas Weslyn University; Physical Educ.

MERMAN, Catherine; Homewood Flossmoor Hs; Homewood, IL; RptrSchPpr; College; Elementary Education.

MERRELL, Duane R; Harrison HS; Farmington Hills, MI; Yrbk; SchPpr; Univ Of Michigan Dearborn; Architectural En.

MERRELLI, Bradford J; Austin Catholic Prep; Roseville, MI; 4/115 ChrhWkr; HonRl; VPNHS; SchPl; LetterFtbl; CchngActv; IMSpt; Col; Med.

MERREU, Elizabeth; Noblesville HS; Noblesville, IN; PresSrCls; HonRl; JrNHS; LitMag; NHS; NatlThespSoc; PolWkr; Quill&Scroll;.

MERRICK, Mark F; Northridge HS; Goshen, IN; 1/145 PresSophCls; HonRl; KeyCl; LetterBsbl; LetterFtbl; IMSpt; Coll; Science & Math.

MERRIGAN, Gerianne M; Jefferson HS; Stanberry, MO; TrsSophCls; Band; ChrhWkr; HonRl; StuCncl; RptrSchPpr; 4-H; VPFHA; CchngActv; College; Library Science.

MERRIGAN, Kathleen M; Maysville HS; Maysville, MO; PresSrCls; ALAGirlsSt; Band; Chrs; ChrhWkr; CncrtBnd; HonRl; HospAde; MrchBnd; VPNHS; Warrensburg Univ; Physical Ed Or Music.

MERRIGAN, Phillip; Jefferson HS; Stanberry, MO; PresSophCls; ALBoysSt; Band; Chrs; HonRl; StuCncl; 4-H; Bsktbl; Trk; 4-HAwd;.

MERRILL, Jean; Franklin HS; Riverton, NE; SecFrshCls; Chrs; HonRl; LbryAde; SchPl; 4-H; PpCl; Trk;.

MERRILL, Julie; Geneva Comm Hs; Geneva, IL; SecTrsSrCls; Chr; HonRl; NHS; StuCncl; SchPpr; PpCl; Tennis; GAA; DARAwd; Purdue U;mathematics.

MERRILL, Tom J; Estherville HS; Estherville, IA; Aud/Vis; HonRl; SchMus; YthFlsp; 4-H; Iowa State Univ; Engineering.

MERRILL, William B; Mound Westonka HS; Mound, MN; College.

MERRIMAN, David M; Coldwater HS; Coldwater, MI; College; Professional.

MERRIMAN, Debra A; Ramsey Comm HS; Fillmore, IL; 3/46 Chrs; ChrhWkr; HonRl; LbryAde; StuCncl; RptrYrbk; SchPpr; 4-H; FTA; PpCl; GAA; Western Ill Univ; Physical Ed.

MERRIMAN, Kathy S; Coldwater HS; Coldwater, MI; CmntyWkr; OffAde; PolWkr; 4-H; College; Professional.

MERRIMAN, Lu; Zionsville Comm HS; Zionsville, IN; Chr; 4-H; 4-HAwd; College; Music.

MERRIMAN, Susan K; Nokomis HS; Fillmore, IL; 2/95 PresChrs; HonRl; SchMus; Trk; GAA; BttyCrckrAwd; Western Illinois Univ; Business Admin.

MERRIMAN, Vicki J; Park Tudor HS; Indianapolis, IN; Chr; ChrhWkr; HonRl; NatlMeritSF; PolWkr; SchPl; SctActv; RptrSchPpr; SciCl; Northwestern Univ; Medicine.

MERRITT, Cheryl A; North Platte Sr HS; Wellfleet, NE; HonRl; OffAde; 4-H; FFA;.

MERRITT, Cynthia; Pierce City R 6 HS; Pierce City, MO; SecSophCls; ALAGirlsSt; ChrhWkr; CncrtBnd; HonRl; NHS; StuCncl; FHA; SciCl; Chrldr; College.

MERRITT, Darcia A; Lindblom HS; Chicago, IL; 76/726 SecSophCls; ChrhWkr; HonRl; HospAde; StuCncl; YthFlsp; FDA; MthCl; SciCl; Bsktbl; Socr; University Of Illinois; Doctor.

MERRITT, Karen S; North Chicago Community HS; North Chicago, IL; TrsSrCls; HonRl; StuGov; Chrldr; Il State U.

MERRITT, Karla E; Rich East HS; Park Forest, IL; 47/355 AFS; MrchBnd; NatlMeritCmnd; NatlThespSoc; Orch; SchPl; SchPpr; PresSpnCl; College; Sociology.

MERRITT, Kevin N; Duchesne HS; St Charles, MO; HonRl; Ftbl; LetterTrk; IMSpt; College; Professional.

MERRITT, Laura J; Morton HS; Morton, IL; ChmnDrlTm; HonRl; JA; MrchBnd; Quill&Scroll; SpnCl; Bsbl; Chrldr; 4-HAwd; PresAwd; Southern Univ; Comp.

MERRITT, Lori; Guthrie Center HS; Guthrie Center, IA; Band; CncrtBnd; HonRl; MrchBnd; YthFlsp; RptrSchPpr; FHA; GAA; Trade School; Vocation.

MERRITT, Shellie L; Griswold Comm HS; Griswold, IA; Band; CncrtBnd; HonRl; MrchBnd; PepBnd; RedCrAde; SchMus; SptEdYrbk; Yrbk; LetterBsktbl; Iowa State; Fashion Merch.

MERRITT, Sherri A; Griswold Comm HS; Atlantic, IA; Band; Chrs; CncrtBnd; HonRl; HospAde; MrchBnd; Orch; FHA; Trk; College; Vocation.

MERRY, Margaret J; Effingham HS; Effingham, IL; 13/200 VPFrshCls; Band; HonRl; LbryAde; StuCncl; SpnCl; PpCl; CaptTennis; University Of Illinois; Liberal Arts.

MERRYFIELD, Phoebe A; Newton HS; Newton, KS; 70/294 PresJrCls; PresSrCls; Chrl; Chrs; HonRl; NHS; NatlMeritFnl; NatlMeritSchl; NatlMeritSF; SchMus; EdYrBk; Business School; Secretary.

MERRYMAN, Brenda K; Wamego HS; Wamego, KS; ALAGirlsSt; Band; Chr; CncrtBnd; HonRl; MrchBnd; PepBnd; SchPl; SctActv; Bsktbl; Business Schl; Secretary.

MERSINGER, Dolores; Bishop Du Bourg HS; St Louis, MO; 9/480 HonRl; JA; NHS; OffAde; SchAde; SchMus; SchPl; SctActv; RptrYrbk; Yrbk; Univ; Math.

MERTAUGH, Thomas A; Hackett HS; Kalamazoo, MI; HonRl; JA; NHS; FrCl; College; Science.

MERTENS, Lynn R; Owen Withee HS; Withee, WI; 7/75 CncrtBnd; HonRl; NHS; StuCncl; TchrAde; Yrbk; FHA; Glf; Univ Of Wis; Journalism.

MERTENS, Maureen R; Notre Dame HS; Elm Grove, WI; 9/117 Band; HonRl; NHS; SchMus; StuCncl; StuGov; TchrAde; RptrYrbk; RptrSchPpr; FTA; U Of Wi Milwaukee; Elem Teaching.

MERTENS, Steven R; Carl Junction HS; Carl Junction, MO; 11/99 Band; DrlTm; HonRl; NHS; ROTC; FTA; MthCl; AmLegAwd; DARAwd; CitAwd; Coll.

MERTZ, Garry J; Bowdle HS; Bowdle, SD; PresJrCls; HonRl; StuCncl; TchrAde; RptrSchPpr; SptEdSchPpr; 4-H; PpCl; LetterFtbl; LetterTrk; College; Teaching Profession.

MERTZ, John W; Stevenson HS; Livonia, MI; PresChr; HonRl; Mdrgl; NatlMeritCmnd; SchMus; Yrbk; SchPpr; LatCl; Bsktbl; IMSpt; Michigan State Univ; Broadcasting.

MERTZ, Leslie A; East Detroit HS; E Detroit, MI; Chr; ChrhWkr; CtyCnl; HonRl; JrNHS; LbryAde; NHS; SctActv; TchrAde; PresAwd; Univ; Wildlife.

MERUCCI, Suzanne M; St Agatha HS; Southfield, MI; HonRl; Chrldr;.

MERVAK, Nancy K; Dearborn HS; Dearborn, MI; CchngActv; GAA; IMSpt; PPFtbl; Coll; Medicine.

MERZ, Brenda K; Manchester HS; Manchester, MI; 3/105 Chrs; HonRl; SchMus; TchrAde; University Of Michigan; Dental Hygiene.

MERZ, Jana L; Arkansas City Sr HS; Arkansas City, KS; HonRl; OffAde; StuCncl; TchrAde; 4-H; FBLA; FTA; PpCl; Trk; IMSpt; College; Accounting.

MERZ, Jay A; Elmhurst HS; Fort Wayne, IN; 15/287 Band; ChrhWkr; CmntyWkr; CncrtBnd; HonRl; MrchBnd; Orch; PepBnd; SctActv; YthFlsp; Purdue Univ; Mathematics.

MESARCHIK, Mary L; Lourdes HS; Rochester, MN; Chrs; ChrhWkr; HonRl; TchrAde; FrCl; Coll; Dental Asst.

MESCH, Lana; Wahlert HS; Dubuque, IA; 100/401 ChrhWkr; CmntyWkr; HospAde; PolWkr; SchAde; SchPl; IntrClCncl; TchrAde; Chrldr; College; Home Ec.

MESCHER, Marvonda J; Oak Park HS; Kansas City, MO; 2/602 VPFrshCls; ChrhWkr; HonRl; SchAde; StuCncl; TchrAde; YthFlsp; SchPpr; GerCl; Sw Missouri St Univ; Secondary Educ.

MESEKE, Lori; Saline HS; Saline, MI; Chrs; ChrhWkr; HonRl; NHS; SchPl; TchrAde; FHA; GAA; Concordia Lutheran Jr College; Social Work.

MESENBRING, Kathleen L; North Farmington HS; Farmington Hills, MI; 68/460 ChrhWkr; HonRl; MrchBnd; NatlFornLg; Quill&Scroll; SctActv; RptrSchPpr; SptEdSchPpr; PpCl; GodCntryAwd; Valparaizo Univ; Communications.

MESKA, Gail M; Marquette HS; Mich City, IN; Chrs; SchMus; SchPpr; GAA; Bus School; Legal Secr.

MESKE, Samuel F; Edgeley HS; Egeley, ND; 5/40 SecFrshCls; PresSophCls; TrsJrCls; ALBoysSt; Band; Chr; ChrhWkr; CncrtBnd; HonRl; PepBnd; College; Engineering.

MESKIL, Drew E; Carlyle HS; Keyesport, IL; Chrs; HonRl; NHS; FrCl; College; Professional.

MESLER, Jeanne S; Grand Blanc HS; Grand Blanc, MI; 37/637 CmntyWkr; HonRl; NHS; College; Business Admin.

MESNER, Robert E; Harris Lake Park Comm HS; Lake Park, IA; 9/28 PresFrshCls; Band; HonRl; MrchBnd; PepBnd; StuCncl; LetterBsbl; LetterFtbl; LetterTrk; LetterWrstlng; University.

MESSAMAKER, Kimberly A; Maryville Rii HS; Maryville, MO; 18/129 Band; CncrtBnd; HonRl; MrchBnd; NHS; OffAde; FBLA; Bsbl; Bsktbl; College; Secretarial.

MESSENBRINK, Debra A; Atwater HS; Atwater, MN; Band; CncrtBnd; HonRl; MrchBnd; PepBnd; SchPl; YthFlsp; FHA; PpCl; LetterBsktbl; LetterTrk; IMSpt; PresAwd; College; Professional.

MESSENGER, Anita L; Lawrenceville HS; Lawrenceville, IL; 33/180 ChrhWkr; HonRl; HospAde; RptrYrbk; College; Medical Assistant.

MESSENGER, Julie L; Richmond HS; Richmond, IN; HonRl; JA; Teen; PpCl; Coll; Prof.

MESSER, Beverly; Richardton Public HS; Richardton, ND; 17/40 VPSophCls; Band; HonRl; MrchBnd; ModUN; PepBnd; RptrYrbk; FHA; PpCl; Trk; College; Lpn.

MESSER, Gary L; Waco HS; Wayland, IA; 21/63 ALBoysSt; HonRl; VPStuCncl; Yrbk; EdSchPpr; CaptBsbl; Bsktbl; Ftbl; Trk; 4-HAwd; Wesleyan Coll;.

MESSER, Janet; Lincoln Sr HS; Warren, MI; 7/376 Chrs; HonRl; JrNHS; NHS; OffAde; TchrAde; FrCl; Wayne State Univ; Business.

MESSER, Neal C; Richardton Public HS; Richardton, ND; ALBoysSt; Band; Chrs; CncrtBnd; HonRl; MrchBnd; PepBnd; SchMus; SchPl; RptrSchPpr; Bsbl; Bsktbl; Ftbl; College; Professional.

MESSER, Tammy L; Moscow HS; Moscow, KS; Chrs; HonRl; JrNHS; NHS; PpCl; Bsktbl; LetterTrk; Chrldr; Trade School.

MESSERSCHMIDT, John G; Immaculate Conception HS; Elmhurst, IL; 5/140 VPFrshCls; PresSophCls; PresBand; HonRl; NHS; Orch; PresStuCncl; RptrYrbk; RptrSchPpr; LatCl; Bsktbl; LetterTrk; U S Naval Academy; Engineering.

MESSERSMITH, Timothy; Thomas Jefferson HS; Council Bluffs, IA; 17/460 ALBoysSt; Band; Chr; ChrhWkr; Mdrgl; NHS; Orch; SchMus; StuCncl; YthFlsp; Navy; Nuclear Elect Tech.

MESSIER, Cynthia A; Escanaba HS; Escanaba, MI; 2/383 Chrs; HonRl; NHS; PolWkr; RedCrAde; SchMus; SchPl; StuGov; TchrAde; FTA; Western Mich U; Cpa.

MESSIMER, Donn G; Memorial HS; Joplin, MO; 4/224 Chr; ChrhWkr; PresJrNHS; LitMag; Mdrgl; PresNHS; NatlMeritCmnd; Quill&Scroll; SchPpr; Univ Of Missouri; Music.

MESSINA, Susan C; St Elizabeth Acad; St Louis, MO; 4/115 Band; Chrs; HonRl; HospAde; NHS; Orch; SchMus; Sdlty; TchrAde; FrCl; Fontbonne Coll; Speech.

MESSINGER, Peggy; Avoha Jr Sr HS; Avoca, IA; CncrtBnd; HonRl; SchMus; SchPl; StuCncl; Teen; YthFlsp; Yrbk; Bsktbl; Trk; Beauty School; Beautician.

MESSMER, Joann M; Lead HS; Deadwood, SD; Band; CncrtBnd; HonRl; LbryAde; MrchBnd; PepBnd; Quill&Scroll; StuGov; RptrYrbk; College; Professional.

MESSMER, Mark J; Connersville HS; Connersville, IN; 26/375 CaptBand; CncrtBnd; HonRl; MrchBnd; NHS; PepBnd; GerCl; Purdue Univ; Biochemistry.

MESSMER, Susan K; Burlington Comm HS; Burlington, IA; 1/501 ChrhWkr; HonRl; JA; NHS; SctActv; College; Science.

MESSMORE, Rita; Melvin Sibley HS; Sibley, IL; Band; HonRl; HospAde; PepBnd; Yrbk; SchPpr; FHA; FTA; SpnCl; PpCl; Trade.

MESSNER, Connie J; Sheyenne Public HS; Sheyenne, ND; VPFrshCls; SecTrsSophCls; Chr; Chrs; ChrhWkr; HonRl; SchPl; RptrSchPpr; FHA; PpCl; Bsktbl; Lrjc; Nurse.

MESSNER, Jill R; Lake Linden Hubbell HS; Hubbell, MI; 11/60 SecSophCls; Band; ChrhWkr; HonRl; LbryAde; OffAde; SchPl; StuCncl; Twrl; RptrYrbk; RptrSchPpr; College; Vocation.

MESTELLE, Dan L; Sturgis HS; Sturgis, MI; HonRl; NHS; SctActv; Bsbl; CaptIMSpt; Mi St Univ; Civil Engineer.

METCALF, Douglas L; Baxter Springs HS; Galena, KS; KeyCl; Bsktbl; Ftbl; College; Professional.

METCALF, Lisa A; Robbinsdale Senior HS; Robbinsdale, MN; 256/728 Band; ChrhWkr; OffAde; PpCl; Dunwoody Ind Inst; Archicectural Drafting.

METELAK, Brenda J; Detroit Lakes HS; Detroit Lakes, MN; 3/249 AFS; HonRl; NHS; CaptSwmmng; CaptTrk; U Of Nd; Math Major.

METER, Roxi A; Alliance HS; Alliance, NE; 35/160 VPJrCls; Band; Chr; CncrtBnd; DrlTm; HonRl; MrchBnd; NatlThespSoc; PepBnd; SchPl; Trk; Chrldr; Nebr West Col; Nurse.

METHOD, Pamela J; Warsaw Comm HS; Warsaw, IN; Band; ChrhWkr; CncrtBnd; HonRl; MrchBnd; University; Interior Decorating.

METRO, Susan I; Lake Central HS; Schererville, IN; 12/453 ALAGirlsSt; NHS; Teen; 4-H; FFA; SpnCl; PPFtbl; 4-HAwd; Purdue U; Pharmacy.

METROS, Craig M; Mendel Catholic Prep HS; Calumet Park, IL; 25/192 ChrhWkr; CmntyWkr; HonRl; JrNHS; NHS; Yrbk; SchPpr; KeyCl; MthCl; SciCl; Tennis; CaptWrstlng;.

METSCHKE, Rebecca S; Barrington Community HS; Barrington, IL; CncrtBnd; HonRl; MrchBnd; Orch; Univ Of Iowa; Music.

METSKAS, Susan J; Naperville Central HS; Naperville, IL; 34/844 Band; Chr; Chrl; Chrs; DrlTm; HonRl; JrNHS; Mdrgl; MrchBnd; NHS; NatlThespSoc; Orch; SchMus; StuGov; Augustana College.

METTE, Matthew R; Rochester Adams HS; Rochester, MI; PresJrCls; PresSrCls; StuGov; FrCl; Ftbl; U Of Mich; Professional.

METTE, Melinda; Green Lake HS; Green Lake, WI; 1/34 ALAGirlsSt; HonRl; JA; JrNHS; SchPl; TchrAde; EdYrBk; Chrldr; GAA; PresAwd; College; Professional.

METTE, Melinda L; Green Lake HS; Green Lake, WI; ALAGirlsSt; HonRl; JrNHS; NatlFornLg; NHS; NatlMeritFnl; NatlThespSoc; SchPl; TchrAde; EdYrBk; SpnCl; MthCl; PpCl; College; Professional.

METTE, Robert P; St Antonthy HS; Effingham, IL; Chrs; HonRl; NHS; SchMus; SecStuCncl; KeyCl; Bsktbl; College.

METTLACH, Mary L; Lincoln HS; Wis Rapids, WI; Chrs; Swmmng; La Crosse; Elementary Education.

METTLER, Debra R; Lake Benton Public HS; Lake Benton, MN; HonRl; NHS; Yrbk; SchPpr; FHA; AmLegAwd; College; Animal Health Tech.

METTLER, Linda D; Wessington Spgs HS; Wessington Sprgs, SD; 8/58 Band; Chr; HospAde; NHS; PepBnd; EdYrBk; 4-H; FHA; FNA; Dakota Wesleyan Univ; Nursing.

METTY, John A; Pinckney HS; Pinckney, MI; Bsktbl; Swmmng; Trk; Wrstlng; Coll; Dentist.

METZ, Brenda R; Oblong HS; Oblong, IL; Band; ChrhWkr; CmntyWkr; CncrtBnd; HonRl; MrchBnd; StuCncl; RptrYrbk; SciCl; Marion College; Nursing.

METZ, Curtis L; Brandon Valley HS; Brandon, SD; 2/110 ALBoysSt; HonRl; NHS; LetterBsktbl; LetterFtbl; LetterTrk; College; Business.

METZ, Daniel H; Westview HS; Kankakee, IL; 21/250 ChrhWkr; HonRl; NHS; NatlMeritCmnd; FrCl; MthCl; SciCl; Univ Of Illinois; Civil Engineering.

METZ, Deanna L; Watseka HS; Watseka, IL; 1/138 SecFrshCls; PresAFS; SecNHS; SecQuill&Scroll; StuCncl; RptrYrbk; EdSchPpr; FTA; PresSpnCl; Tennis; DARAwd; Oral Roberts Univ; Journalism.

METZ, Katherine; Calumet HS; Gary, IN; 6/310 LitMag; EdYrBk; SpnCl; Univ; Languages.

METZ, Linda J; Yankton HS; Yankton, SD; Band; Chrs; ChrhWkr; CmntyWkr; CncrtBnd; HonRl; MrchBnd; Orch; Univ Of So Dakota.

METZ, Marci R; Dwight D Eisenhower HS; Blue Island, IL; Chrs; ChrhWkr; HospAde; LbryAde; OffAde; SchPl; TchrAde; YthFlsp; Bsbl; LetterBsktbl; CchngActv; GAA; IMSpt; College; Law.

METZ, Mark T; Wichita Southeast HS; Wichita, KS; 120/604 Band; ChrhWkr; CncrtBnd; HonRl; MrchBnd; RptrYrbk; LetterFtbl; Tennis; IMSpt; Wichita State Univ; Medical.

METZ, Peggy; Flasher HS; Flasher, ND; Band; Chr; CncrtBnd; HonRl; MrchBnd; PepBnd; SchPl; Bsktbl; CchngActv; Mary College; Education.

METZ, Raymond P; St Pius X HS; Kansas City, MO; 30/129 HonRl; SctActv; LetterFtbl; LetterTrk; Wrstlng; GodCntryAwd; Missouri Univ; Architect.

METZ, Renee M; Prairie HS; Cedar Rapids, IA; Chr; Chrs; HonRl; JrNHS; Mdrgl; MrchBnd; SchPl; RptrYrbk; Trk; 4-HAwd; Luther Coll; Vocal Music.

METZ, Robert; Se Warren HS; Locona, IA; .

METZ, Steven R; Fairbury Cropsey HS; Fairbury, IL;

31/103 Band; Chrs; CncrtBnd; PepBnd; SchPl; 4-H; FFA; Ftbl; LetterWrstlng; Isu; Agriculture.

METZ, Valerie; Lakeland Union HS; Woodruff, WI; Band; Chr; Chrs; CncrtBnd; HonRl; MrchBnd; PepBnd; GerCl; PpCl; Uw Lacrosse; Elementary Pe Teacher.

METZGAR, Edward; Blair HS; Blair, NE; Aud/Vis; ChrhWkr; CmntyWkr; LbryAde; SchPl; RptrYrbk; Yrbk; U Of Ne; Teacher Military Pilot.

METZGER, Ann M; Garrigan HS; Whittemore, IA; 3/107 VPFrshCls; Chr; Chrs; DrlTm; HonRl; NHS; SchMus; StuCncl; Yrbk; 4-H; PpCl; IMSpt; College.

METZGER, John O; Frankenmuth HS; Frankenmuth, MI; 5/164 HonRl; JrNHS; NHS; TchrAde; Bsbl; Bsktbl; Ftbl; AmLegAwd; Valparaiso U; Bus Admin Pre Law.

METZGER, Judy K; Cambridge HS; Cambridge, NE; Band; HospAde; MrchBnd; PepBnd; Yrbk; SchPpr; 4-H; FBLA; FHA;.

METZGER, Kay A; Pana HS; Pana, IL; Band; HonRl; MrchBnd; NHS; LetterGlf; LetterTennis; PresGAA; Eastern Illinois University.

METZGER, Maria E; Marian Central Catholic HS; Mchenry, IL; 7/114 Band; ChrhWkr; CncrtBnd; HonRl; NHS; SchMus; Yrbk; College; Elem Education.

METZGER, Marilyn J; Lapel HS; Lapel, IN; 2/82 SecJrCls; SecSrCls; VPNHS; Yrbk; FrCl; PpCl; Bsktbl; GAA; PPFtbl; Homemaker.

METZGER, Mark G; North Boone HS; Capron, IL; 4/101 Band; Chr; Chrs; CncrtBnd; HonRl; Mdrgl; MrchBnd; NHS; PepBnd; SchMus; 4-H; Northwestern Univ; Music.

METZGER, Marshall S; Stoutland Rii HS; Stoutland, MO; 14/47 Band; CmntyWkr; CncrtBnd; RptrYrbk; Yrbk; 4-H; FFA; SpnCl; LetterBsbl; 4-HAwd; Univ Of Mo; Agri Business.

METZGER, Michael; Marshall HS; Marshall, MI; 153/244 ALBoysSt; HonRl; JA; TchrAde; Bsktbl; Ftbl; Glf; IMSpt; Trade School; Architectural Engineering.

METZGER, Michael J; Charleston HS; Charleston, IL; 17/250 HonRl; NHS; 4-H; MthCl; IMSpt; Eastern Illinois University; Business.

METZGER, Mindy A; Papillion HS; Papillion, NE; 19/327 ChrhWkr; HonRl; PolWkr; 4-H; FBLA; FHA; GerCl; PpCl; College.

METZGER, Terri; Plainwell HS; Plainwell, MI; 60/231 RptrSchPpr; SptEdSchPpr; PPFtbl; Suomi College; Cpa.

METZKE, Jean A; Stratford HS; Stratford, WI; 7/90 Band; CncrtBnd; HonRl; MrchBnd; NHS; PepBnd; VPStuCncl; RptrYrbk; FHA; SecFrCl; Univ Of Eau Claire; Social Work.

METZLER, Annette M; Oconto Falls HS; Oconto Falls, WI; 22/153 Band; HonRl; OffAde; StuCncl; Yrbk; FBLA; SpnCl; PpCl; Trk; Chrldr; GAA; Vocational School; Business.

METZLER, Kenneth D; Goshen HS; Goshen, IN; 22/254 ALBoysSt; HonRl; PpCl; LetterFtbl; LetterWrstlng; RotaryAwd;.

MEUERS, Christine L; Derham Hall HS; Roseville, MN; PresJrCls; Band; ChrhWkr; NHS; StuCncl; RptrSchPpr; College; Professional Law.

MEULEMANS, Debra M; Little Chute HS; Little Chute, WI; ChrhWkr; HonRl; SpnCl; College; Professional.

MEURER, Shirley A; Mchenry Comm HS; Mchenry, IL; 32/464 AFS; ChrhWkr; HonRl; SchMus; YthFlsp; RptrYrbk; PpCl; Bsktbl; Trk; Univ Of Ill; Computer Science.

MEUWISSEN, Mary C; Annandale Public HS; Annandale, MN; 7/120 Band; Chr; HonRl; Mdrgl; NHS; Quill&Scroll; SchMus; StuCncl; TchrAde; EdSchPpr; College; Prof.

MEVES, Adrienne T; Brookfield Academy; Brookfield, WI; 2/12 SecSophCls; Chrs; HonRl; LitMag; NatlFornLg; NatlThespSoc; SchMus; SchPl; YthFlsp; CaptBsktbl; College; Music Art Drama.

MEWES, David M; Edwards County HS; W Salem, IL; HonRl; SchMus; SchPl; PresStuCncl; PpCl; College; Law.

MEWS, Renee J; Auburndale HS; Auburndale, WI; 2/92 TrsSrCls; HospAde; NHS; EdSchPpr; FrCl; Technical School; Operating Room Assistant.

MEYER, Alice; Lutheran North HS; Wellston, MO; OffAde; TchrAde; RptrYrbk; FrCl; Coll; French.

MEYER, Amy L; Caledonia HS; Caledonia, MN; SecJrCls; Chrs; CncrtBnd; HonRl; 4-H; GAA; College.

MEYER, Andrea; Highland Park Sr HS; St Paul, MN; Aud/Vis; JA; SchAde; TchrAde; VP4-H; MthCl; 4-HAwd; Trade School; Argicultural Technology.

MEYER, Anita; Hillsboro HS; Hillsboro, IL; Band; Chr; ChrhWkr; HonRl; PepBnd; SchMus; YthFlsp; SpnCl; GAA; IMSpt; College; Vocaion.

MEYER, Ann R; J F K Prep; St Nazianz, WI; ChrhWkr; CmntyWkr; SchPl; TchrAde; Yrbk;.

MEYER, Arthur; Batesville HS; Batesville, IN; 24/148 HonRl; NHS; TchrAde; 4-H; SpnCl; Univ; Radio.

MEYER, Bill C; Wolsey HS; Wolsey, SD; Chrs; DrmMjrt; HonRl; SchMus; TchrAde; YthFlsp; RptrSchPpr; SciCl; CitAwd; Sd St Univ; Sociology.

MEYER, Bonnie K; Weston HS; Loganville, WI; 2/54 PresSophCls; PresJrCls; PresSrCls; Band; DrmMjrt; NHS; Quill&Scroll; StuCncl; SecFBLA; CaptChrldr; U Of Wi La Crosse; Computer Science.

MEYER, Brenda S; Ste Genevieve HS; Ste Genevieve, MO; SecSophCls; HonRl; HospAde; SchMus; SecStuCncl; Yrbk; RptrSchPpr; Tennis; Chrldr; 4-HAwd; College; Dental Tech.

MEYER, Bruce A; Cedarburg HS; Cedarburg, WI; 60/298 Band; CmntyWkr; CncrtBnd; DrmBgl; HonRl; PepBnd; 4-H; Ftbl; Wrstlng; University Of Wisconsin; Accountant.

MEYER, Carol; Tracy HS; Tracy, MN; Band; Chr; SchMus; FHA; FrCl; GAA;.

MEYER, Cathy L; Rochester HS; Springfield, IL; Chr; HonRl; JA; SchPl; Springfield Coll Ill; Music Therapy.

MEYER, Charles F; Le Center HS; Le Center, MN; 2/63 Band; Chrs; HonRl; NHS; SchPl; Yrbk; 4-H; LetterTennis; 4-HAwd; CitAwd; College; Profess.

MEYER, Cynthia L; Downers Grove South HS; Downers Grove, IL; 11/830 HonRl; NHS; SciCl; Manchester College; Biology.

MEYER, Cynthia M; Bergan HS; Peoria, IL; 4/210 HonRl; NHS; NatlMeritCmnd; FrCl; SpnCl; Illinois State University.

MEYER, Daniel P; Dodge HS; Dodge, NE; SecSophCls; ALBoysSt; Chrs; CncrtBnd; MrchBnd; SchPl; StuCncl; LetterBsbl; Bsktbl; Ftbl; Clge; Pro.

MEYER, Danny W; Primghar Comm HS; Primghar, IA; PresSrCls; Band; Chrs; HonRl; NHS; SchPl; StuCncl; 4-H; LetterBsktbl; LetterFtbl; College; Engineering.

MEYER, David; Madison HS; Madison, IN; HonRl; LitMag; SchMus; KeyCl; Bsktbl; Ftbl; Ball Stae Univ; Art.

MEYER, David J; E Dubuque HS; E Dubuque, IL; 3/51 PresSophCls; Band; CncrtBnd; HonRl; MrchBnd; NHS; PepBnd; SptEdYrbk; LetterBsbl; LetterBsktbl; LetterFtbl; College; Actuarial Science.

MEYER, Deborah L; Lourdes HS; Chicago, IL; HonRl; SchPl; SctActv; RptrSchPpr; SpnCl; IMSpt; College.

MEYER, Deborah S; Hoisington HS; Hoisington, KS; 22/108 ChrhWkr; HonRl; FrCl; St Johns College; Social Worker.

MEYER, Debra K; Dodge HS; Dodge, NE; TrsJrCls; SecSrCls; Band; Chr; Chrs; ChrhWkr; CncrtBnd; HonRl; MrchBnd; PepBnd; Trk; IMSpt; PPFtbl; College; Nursing.

MEYER, Diane M; Liberty HS; Liberty, IL; 6/62 TrsSophCls; Chrs; ChrhWkr; HonRl; LbryAde; SchPl; Sdlty; StuCncl; TchrAde; Yrbk; FBLA; FHA; Business Sch; Secretary.

MEYER, Don G; Davenport Comm HS; Davenport, NE; 5/25 SecFrshCls; Band; ChrhWkr; HonRl; PepBnd; SchPl; Bsbl; Ftbl; Trk; Wrstlng; Doane College; History.

MEYER, Donna J; Trico HS; Percy, IL; ChrhWkr; HonRl; SchPl; SctActv; FBLA; FHA; TreasFrCl; PpCl;.

MEYER, Doris M; Fatima HS; Koeltztown, MO; /130 Chr; Chrs; ChrhWkr; HonRl; SchPl; FHA; University; Fasion Design.

MEYER, Dorothy; West Concord HS; West Concord, MN; 1/44 Chr; ChrhWkr; HonRl; LbryAde; NHS; SchAde; SchPl; TchrAde; FTA; GerCl; Univ Of Minnesota; Early Childhood Ed.

MEYER, Douglas R; Oelwein Community HS; Oelwein, IA; 18/186 ALBoysSt; HonRl; JrNHS; TchrAde; SciCl; Ftbl; Trk; Wrstlng; College; Science.

MEYER, Duane; Blair HS; Blair, NE; PresSophCls; HonRl; KeyCl; LetterBsktbl; Coll.

MEYER, Elaine A; Loretto HS; Prairie Village, KS; Chrs; HonRl; HospAde; Quill&Scroll; EdYrBk; College; English.

MEYER, Elizabeth; Warsaw Hs; Warsaw, IL; 5 SecJrCls; AFS; ChrhWkr; DrlTm; LbryAde; NHS; SecStuCncl; Yrbk; VPFBLA; GerCl; College ; Special Education.

MEYER, Elizabeth; Warsaw HS; Warsaw, IL; 5/67 SecJrCls; AFS; DrlTm; NHS; Yrbk; GerCl; GAA; KiwanAwd; Augustana Col; Accounting.

MEYER, Elizabeth A; U Of C Laboratory HS; Chicago, IL; SecJrCls; NatlMeritSF; StuGov; RptrYrbk; GerCl; Univ.

MEYER, Eric T; Elmwood Park HS; Elmwood Park, IL; 8/330 Band; ChrhWkr; CncrtBnd; HonRl; HospAde; MrchBnd; NHS; PepBnd; GerCl; LetterSwmmng; Tennis; Northwestern University; Medicine.

MEYER, Gary D; Blackhawh HS; Apple River, IL; ALBoysSt; Band; Chr; Chrs; ChrhWkr; CncrtBnd; HonRl; MrchBnd; NHS; PepBnd; College; Agriculture.

MEYER, Gene W; Pollock HS; Pollock, SD; Band; Chrs; ChrhWkr; HonRl; MrchBnd; SctActv; PpCl; Ftbl; AmLegAwd; College; Commercial Art.

MEYER, Geraldine M; Marion HS; Birmingham, MI; HonRl; LetterSwmmng; Visual Communication.

MEYER, Gordon S; Beloit Memorial HS; Madison, WI; 35/495 HonRl; NHS; Univ Of Wisc; Physician.

MEYER, Gregory O; Beardstown HS; Beardstown, IL; 4/120 Band; CncrtBnd; HonRl; MrchBnd; NHS; PepBnd; SchMus; SctActv; SpnCl; SciCl;.

MEYER, Gretchen; Fredericktown HS; Fredericktown, MO; Chr; Chrs; DrlTm; HonRl; OffAde; PolWkr; SchMus; Yrbk; SchPpr; Swmmng; College.

MEYER, Irene; Marcus Community HS; Remsen, IA; HonRl; LbryAde; College; Home Ec Teacher.

MEYER, James M; Grand Island HS; Grand Island, NE; 202/486 SpnCl; Bsktbl; Glf; Univ Of Nebraska; Teacher.

MEYER, James M; Premontre HS; Green Bay, WI; 1/156 SecJrCls; PresSrCls; Chrs; CmntyWkr; HonRl; JA; SchPl; SctActv; StuCncl; Yrbk; LetterFtbl; LetterTrk; Col; Civil Engineering.

MEYER, Jane; Jefferson HS; Stanberry, MO; 1/27 PresJrCls; HonRl; StuCncl; EdYrBk; 4-H; PpCl; Chrldr; AmLegAwd; CitAwd; Univ Of Mo; Nursing.

MEYER, Janet S; La Porte HS; La Porte, IN; 6/542 Chr; HonRl; SecNHS; SchMus; SchPl; PresGerCl; PpCl; Trk; GAA; IMSpt; Purdue Univ; Fashion Retailing.

MEYER, Jan P; Willmar HS; Willmar, MN; Band; ChrhWkr; CncrtBnd; MrchBnd; NHS; PpCl; Tennis; Trk; CaptChrldr; PresAwd; Coll; Health Service.

MEYER, Jonathan P; Seymour HS; Seymour, IN; 24/320 ALBoysSt; NatlMeritSF; NatlThespSoc; SchPl; Yrbk; Purdue Univ; Physice & Chemistr.

MEYER, Joseph A; Maryville R Ii HS; Maryville, MO; 13/130 NHS; FBLA; Bsbl; CaptBsktbl; Nw Mo St Univ; Business.

MEYER, Joseph D; Aurora Senior HS; Aurora, IN; ALBoysSt; Band; CncrtBnd; HonRl; MrchBnd; PepBnd; SchMus; LetterBsktbl; LetterTrk; IMSpt; College; Law Enforcement.

MEYER, Joyce D; Sullivan HS; Chicago, IL; Chrs; JA; LitMag; NHS; StuCncl; EdYrBk; SchPpr; KeyCl; PpCl; Trk; University; Communications.

MEYER, Judith A; Warren HS; Warren, IL; 1/58 Chrs; ChrhWkr; CncrtBnd; DrmMjrt; HonRl; NHS; SchMus; VPStuCncl; EdYrBk; FTA; Glf; GAA; AmLegAwd; Carthage College; Music.

MEYER, Julia; Lutheran HS; St Louis, MO; Aud/Vis; Chr; Chrs; HonRl; NatlThespSoc; RedCrAde; SchMus; SchPl; GAA; PPFtbl;.

MEYER, Julie A; Marietta Public HS; Gary, SD; PresFrshCls; PresSophCls; Band; HonRl; PresYthFlsp; RptrSchPpr; FHA; TreasPpCl; LetterBsktbl; LetterTrk; College.

MEYER, Julie K; Tyndall HS; Tyndall, SD; TrsSophCls; PresJrCls; Band; HonRl; MrchBnd; PepBnd; SchPl; StuCncl; LetterTrk; Chrldr; College; Professional.

MEYER, Julie R; Hagerstown HS; Cambridge City, IN; 28/142 HonRl; JA; OffAde; PolWkr; VPFHA; VPLatCl; PresAwd; Business School; Secretary.

MEYER, Karen; Napoleon HS; Clark Lake, MI; 15/107 HonRl; NHS; SchPl; StuCncl; TchrAde; 4-H; PpCl; 4-HAwd; Jcc; Pe Teacher.

MEYER, Karen A; Lewis Central HS; Council Bluffs, IA; 4/161 Band; Chr; DrlTm; HonRl; HospAde; JA; NHS; SchMus; BttyCrckrAwd; Iowa State Univ; Chemical Engineering.

MEYER, Karen S; Coldwater HS; Coldwater, MI; 4/277 Band; ChrhWkr; CmntyWkr; HonRl; NHS; TchrAde; SpnCl; PpCl; IMSpt; Univ Of Michigan; Nursing.

MEYER, Katherine J; Norborne HS; Norborne, MO; 5/22 Band; CncrtBnd; HonRl; MrchBnd; NHS; SchPl; StuCncl; RptrYrbk; FHA; Trk; Nw Missouri St University.

MEYER, Kathleen D; Detroit Lakes HS; Detroit Lakes, MN; HonRl; PpCl; LetterTrk; Chrldr; Univ; Recreation Major.

MEYER, Kathy M; Macksville HS; Macksville, KS; SecTrsFrshCls; SecTrsSophCls; SecJrCls; HstSrCls; Band; Chrs; CmntyWkr; CncrtBnd; DrlTm; HonRl; MrchBnd; Bsbl; Bsktbl; Trk; Correspondence School; Commercial Art.

MEYER, Kenneth A; Hempstead HS; Dubuque, IA; Band; HonRl; Trk; IMSpt; Luther College; Wildlife.

MEYER, Kenneth I; Morgan Park Academy; Chicago, IL; 6/40 HonRl; ModUN; Bsktbl; Univ Of Ill; Law.

MEYER, Kimberlie A; Wayland Academy; Beaver Dam, WI; SchAde; SchPl; SpnCl; PpCl; Bsbl; Tennis; LetterChrldr; IMSpt; College; Interial Design.

MEYER, Laura A; William Horlick HS; Racine, WI; HonRl; NatlFornLg; SctActv; Univ Of Wi; Math.

MEYER, Laura A; Watseka Comm HS; Watseka, IL; Band; CncrtBnd; HonRl; MrchBnd; PepBnd; RptrYrbk; SpnCl; College; Psychology.

MEYER, Lavonne J; Elk Mound HS; Elk Mound, WI; ChrhWkr; HonRl; LbryAde; YthFlsp; RptrYrbk; EdYrBk; RptrSchPpr; Trk; Bible Col; Health Career.

MEYER, Lee P; Downers Grove Comm So HS; Downers Grove, IL; 25/828 HonRl; College; Medicine.

MEYER, Linda J; Napoleon HS; Clark Lake, MI; 7/110 PresFrshCls; PresSophCls; VPJrCls; Band; Chr; CncrtBnd; HonRl; MrchBnd; PresNHS; PepBnd; PolWkr; Western Mi Univ; Secondary Education.

MEYER, Lisa J; New London Sr HS; New London, WI; Chr; HonRl; HospAde; Mdrgl; College.

MEYER, Lois; Valle HS; St Genevieve, MO; 13/80 VPSophCls; TrsJrCls; CmntyWkr; DrmMjrt; HospAde; NHS; 4-H; PpCl; Trk; CchngActv; Jewish Hosp School; Nursing.

MEYER, Lois E; Caledonia HS; Caledonia, MN; Chr; ChrhWkr; HonRl; SchAde; StuGov; SchPpr; GAA; IMSpt; Work;.

MEYER, Lori J; Beardstown HS; Beardstown, IL; 15/136 HonRl; SchAde; SchMus; TchrAde; YthFlsp; RptrYrbk; SchPpr; FTA; IMSpt; 4-HAwd; Il Col; Psychology.

MEYER, Luella M; Ackley Geneva Comm HS; Ackley, IA; Chr; Chrs; ChrhWkr; HonRl; HospAde; RptrSchPpr; 4-H; FHA; 4-HAwd; Palmar Clge; Chiropractor.

MEYER, Lynn C; Louisville HS; Louisville, NE; ChrhWkr; SchPl; SctActv; YthFlsp; Yrbk; FHA; FrCl; PpCl; LetterBsktbl; GAA; Wayne State Clg; Bus Educ.

MEYER, Marcel A; Bern HS; Sabetha, KS; TrsJrCls; HonRl; SchPl; StuCncl; Yrbk; Bsktbl; Trk; Chrldr; Band; CitAwd; Coll; Lab Technology.

MEYER, Mark E; Decatur Community HS; Oberlin, KS; Band; CncrtBnd; HonRl; MrchBnd; NHS; PepBnd; StuGov; SpnCl; University; Professional.

MEYER, Mary C; Spalding Acad; Spalding, NE; TrsFrshCls; Chrs; SchMus; SchPl; SpnCl; MthCl; PpCl; SciCl; Chrldr; 4-HAwd; Kearney St;nursing.

MEYER, Mary E; Fatima HS; Bonnots Mill, MO; Mdrgl; HonRl; NHS; FBLA; SpnCl; SciCl; Univ Of Mo; Veterinary Medicine.

MEYER, Mary L; Mater Dei HS; Carlyle, IL; 1/200 Chrs; HonRl; PresNHS; NatlMeritSF; SchMus; SchPpr; Univ Of Ill; Computer Science.

MEYER, Mary S; Leo HS; Holy Cross, IA; Chr; Chrs; CmntyWkr; HonRl; LbryAde; SchMus; SchPl; TchrAde; RptrYrbk; 4-H; GAA; Kirkwood Comm College; Medicine.

MEYER, Matt L; Forman HS; Manito, IL; 2/51 Chrs; NHS; NatlMeritCmnd; StuCncl; RptrYrbk; 4-H; PresFFA; LetterBsbl; LetterBsktbl; GodCntryAwd; U Of Ill; Agriculture.

MEYER, Maureen C; Rib Lake HS; Rib Lake, WI; SecChr; HonRl; SchPl; VPStuCncl; EdYrBk; RptrSchPpr; PpCl; DARAwd; Eau Claire U; Vocalist.

MEYER, Melita; Waupaca HS; Waupaca, WI; 5/155 ALAGirlsSt; Chr; ChrhWkr; CmntyWkr; HonRl; HospAde; MrchBnd; NHS; RptrSchPpr; LatCl; Univ; Nursing.

MEYER, Michael E; Marquette HS; Michigan City, IN; 2/80 ALBoysSt; Chrs; HonRl; SchMus; StuCncl; Bsktbl; Socr; Tennis; Trk; AmLegAwd; Univ; Md Or Dds.

MEYER, Michele A; Harvard HS; Harvard, IL; 3/180 AFS; ALAGirlsSt; Chr; HonRl; JrNHS; Mdrgl; NHS; SchMus; StuCncl; Yrbk; University; Teacher.

MEYER, Nadine R; Broken Bow HS; Berwyn, NE; TrsSophCls; Chr; HonRl; OffAde; 4-H; FHA; CchngActv; GAA; PresAwd; Kearney State Col6; Teach.

MEYER, Natalie; Emmerich Manual HS; Indianapolis, IN; 35/480 Chr; CmntyWkr; HonRl; HospAde; Mdrgl; NHS; SchMus; EngCl; LatCl; PpCl; Indiana Univ; Doctor.

MEYER, Patricia; St Pius X HS; Festus, MO; TchrAde; PpCl; SciCl; Chrldr; Coll; Field Related To Art.

MEYER, Patricia K; Duluth Central HS; Duluth, MN; 38/438 Chr; HonRl; NHS; SchPl; RptrYrbk; 4-H; FHA; PpCl; IMSpt; 4-HAwd; College Of St Scholatica; Home Economics.

MEYER, Paul J; Warren HS; Warren, IL; 1/64 PresJrCls; Band; Chrs; HonRl; TreasStuCncl; Bsbl; Bsktbl; LetterBsktbl; LetterTrk; AmLegAwd;.

MEYER, Phillip D; Paxton HS; Paxton, IL; HonRl; Mdrgl; NHS; SchPl; EngCl; Bsktbl; LetterTrk; IMSpt; AmLegAwd; Parkland Jr College.

MEYER, Randall S; Albert City Truesdale HS; Storm Lake, IA; 15/49 TrsSrCls; HonRl; StuCncl; 4-H; FFA; Wrstlng; Iowa State Univ; Computer Science.

MEYER, Robert; Alden Hebron HS; Hebron, IL; 2/45 PresJrCls; PresSrCls; ALBoysSt; Aud/Vis; Band; HonRl; NHS; StuCncl; EdYrBk; Bsbl; U S A F A; Air Force Officer.

MEYER, Ronald; Kinmundy Alma Hs; Alma, IL; 5/57 PresJrCls; Band; CncrtBnd; HonRl; NHS; PepBnd; PresStuCncl; PresFFA; CaptBsktbl; CchngActv; Army; Engineer Equipment Repair.

MEYER, Ron D; Davenport Community HS; Davenport, NE; 5/23 HstSrCls; ALBoysSt; Band; HonRl; NatlMeritCmnd; NatlMeritSchl; SchPl; YthFlsp; Bsbl; Ftbl; Trk; Doane College; Physical Education.

MEYER, Ronda C; Delmont Public HS; Delmont, SD; 4/17 SecJrCls; VPSrCls; Chr; ChrhWkr; HonRl; StuCncl; EdYrBk; EdSchPpr; Chrldr; BttyCrckrAwd; Dakota State Coll; Pro.

MEYER, Roy V; North Winneshiek HS; Decorah, IA; 10/40 HonRl; SchPl; FFA; MthCl; PpCl; Bsktbl; Trk; IMSpt; Trade Or Bus Sch; Vocation.

MEYER, Rubi E; Metropolis Comm HS; Metropolis, IL; 9/161 HonRl; NHS; OffAde; TchrAde; FHA; SpnCl; Paducah Tilghman Voc; Operatingroom Tech.

MEYER, Russell W; Edina East HS; Edina, MN; 46/468 Chr; CmntyWkr; PresCncrtBnd; HonRl; LbryAde; MrchBnd; Orch; SchMus; U Of Ia; Music Education.

MEYER, Shalimar C; Mound Westonka HS; Mound, MN; 5/265 Band; CncrtBnd; HonRl; MrchBnd; NHS; PepBnd; SpnCl; CaptBsktbl; Univ Of Mn; Medical Tech.

MEYER, Sharon M; Lyons Township HS; Brookfield, IL; 76/1214 HonRl; GerCl; CchngActv; University Of Illinois; Medical Dietetics.

MEYER, Sheryl K; Arlington HS; Arlington Hts, IL; 83/584 NHS; SchAde; StuCncl; Swmmng; CchngActv; GAA; DARAwd; Univ; Chem Engng.

MEYER, Stephen; Waterford Township HS; Pontiac, MI; 19/440 PresJrCls; PresSrCls; HonRl; NHS; StuCncl; StuGov; OptClAwd; CitAwd; Mi State.

MEYER, Steve M; North HS; Sheboygan, WI; Band; HonRl; Orch; PepBnd; Univ Of Wisconsin; Dentist.

MEYER, Steven; South Knox HS; Vincennes, IN; ALBoysSt; HonRl; YthFlsp; IMSpt; Coll; Optometry.

MEYER, Steven E; Taylorville Sr HS; Taylorville, IL; HonRl; SpnCl; Glf; College; Law.

MEYER, Susan E; Warren Township HS; Wildwood, IL; Chr; HonRl; SchPl; Pres4-H; GerCl; Bsbl; GAA; 4-HAwd;.

MEYER, Susan E; North HS; Wichita, KS; 4/5 HonRl; NHS; OffAde; Yrbk; SpnCl; Bsktbl; University; Professional.

MEYER, Susan G; Jefferson City Sr HS; Jefferson City, MO; 23/502 HonRl; JrNHS; NHS; FBLA; FHA; FTA; SpnCl; Univ Of Mo; Business Admin.

MEYER, Suzanne L; Belding HS; Belding, MI; CncrtBnd; HonRl; MrchBnd; NHS; U Of Michigan; Engineering.

MEYER, Ted P; Fergus Falls Senior HS; Fergus Falls, MN; Band; ChrhWkr; CmntyWkr; CncrtBnd; MrchBnd; PepBnd; 4-H; FFA;.

MEYER, Teresa J; Butterfield Odin HS; Butterfield, MN; VPSophCls; SecJrCls; Band; Chr; HonRl; SchMus; SctActv; StuCncl; EdSchPpr; Chrldr; Coll; English.

MEYER, Teresa M; Holstein HS; Holstein, IA; 6/54 SecSophCls; Band; Chr; ChrhWkr; CncrtBnd; HonRl; MrchBnd; NHS; PepBnd; SchMus; StuCncl; EdYrBk; 4-H; PpCl; CaptBsktbl; Iowa Lutheran School; Nursing.

MEYER, Tricia; Superior HS; Superior, NE; ALAGirlsSt; Chr; Chrs; ChrhWkr; CmntyWkr; Quill&Scroll; Yrbk; RptrSchPpr; College; Music.

MEYER, Vivian R; Lincoln Way HS; New Lenox, IL; 28/625 Chrs; ChrhWkr; HonRl; Mdrgl; NatlThespSoc; StuCncl; 4-H; DanFAwd; 4-HAwd; PresAwd; College; Music.

MEYERAAN, Cynthia L; Worthington Sr HS; Worthington, MN; 73/293 Chr; ChrhWkr; HonRl; NHS; SchMus; TchrAde; YthFlsp; Worthington Comm College; Missionary.

MEYERHOFF, Deborah S; Prospect HS; Arlington Hts, IL; HonRl; PpCl; Miami University.

MEYERHOFF, Nadine; Trico HS; Perc, IL; HonRl; OffAde; SchPl; StuCncl; Yrbk; FBLA; PpCl; SciCl;.

MEYERS, Ann M; Bishop Ward HS; Kansas City, KS; 9/195 ChrhWkr; HonRl; NHS; NatlThespSoc; SchPl; SctActv; StuCncl; StuGov; YthLg; FrCl; MthCl; PpCl; College; English.

MEYERS, Brian D; La Porte HS; La Porte, IN; HonRl; NatlFornLg; NatlMeritSF; Orch; PolWkr; SpnCl; College; Politically Oriented.

MEYERS, Catherine M; Sacred Heart Of Mary HS; Arlington Hts, IL; HonRl; JrNHS; NHS; OffAde; SchMus; SchPl; TchrAde; RptrYrbk; RptrSchPpr; SptEdSchPpr; SchPpr; SciCl; GAA; University; Medicine.

MEYERS, Charles J; Peoria HS; Peoria, IL; 28/450 ChrhWkr; HonRl; JrNHS; NHS; GerCl; PpCl; Bradley U.

MEYERS, Chaundra J; Veblen Public HS; Veblen, SD; 1/17 CncrtBnd; DrlTm; HonRl; SchPl; StuCncl; EdYrBk; Bsktbl; Tennis; LetterTrk; Chrldr; IMSpt; DARAwd; So Dakota St Univ; Dietician.

MEYERS, Christine A; Berkley HS; Berkley, MI; CmntyWkr; StuCncl; TchrAde; YthFlsp; PpCl; SciCl; PresAwd; Oakland U; Rn.

MEYERS, Cynthia J; Coloma HS; Coloma, MI; TrsJrCls; TrsSrCls; HonRl; NHS; StuCncl; TchrAde; PpCl; CaptTrk; Chrldr; Western Mich Univ; Med Tech.

MEYERS, Dave J; Calvin Christian HS; Grand Rapids, MI; HonRl; HospAde; NHS; NatlMeritCmnd; NatlMeritSchl; NatlMeritSF; RedCrAde; MthCl; Coll; Elec Engi.

MEYERS, Diane E; Glenwood City HS; Glenwood City, WI; 4/81 Band; HonRl; MrchBnd; NHS; PepBnd; PresPpCl; LetterBsktbl; LetterTrk; Chrldr; SecGAA; Augsburg Col; Mathematics.

MEYERS, Diane M; Quincy Senior HS; Quincy, IL; SecSrCls; StuCncl; RptrYrbk; Western Illinois Univ; English.

MEYERS, Janet L; Good Counsel HS; Chicago, IL; TrsSrCls; Chr; HonRl; StuCncl; FBLA; Bsktbl; IMSpt; Bus.

MEYERS, Jay; Spring Valley HS; Spring Valley, WI; ChrhWkr; HonRl; YthFlsp; FFA; IMSpt; PresAwd; Service & College.

MEYERS, Jeffrey T; Aurora Central HS; Aurora, IL; 20/165 HonRl; SctActv; TchrAde; SpnCl; LetterBsktbl; LetterGlf; LetterTennis; IMSpt; U Of Il; Pharm.

MEYERS, John I; St Clair HS; St Clair, MI; 19/180 HonRl; SchPl; SptEdYrbk; LetterBsktbl; LetterTrk; Central Michigan University.

MEYERS, Kim; Hilbert HS; Potter, WI; HonRl; YthFlsp; Trk; GAA; IMSpt; Technical School; Secretarial.

MEYERS, Loren C; West HS; Rockford, IL; 1/379 HonRl; NHS; NatlMeritFnl; NatlMeritSF; ROTC; StuCncl; StuGov; College; Law.

MEYERS, Loren C; Rockford West HS; Rockford, IL; 1/379 DrlTm; HonRl; LitMag; NHS; NatlMeritSF; ROTC; StuCncl; StuGov; TchrAde; College; Lawyer.

MEYERS, Mark S; Columbus HS; Marshfield, WI; 27/108 SecTrsJrCls; Aud/Vis; HonRl; SchPl; StuCncl; RptrYrbk; GerCl; LetterFtbl; Trk; IMSpt; College; Science Research.

MEYERS, Martha A; Centerville HS; Centerville, IA; 2/155 VPFrshCls; VPSophCls; DrmMjrt; HonRl; NHS; StuCncl; Twrl; RptrYrbk; Glf; Chrldr; U Of Iowa; Bus Admin.

MEYERS, Mary S; Lake Michigan Catholic HS; St Joseph, MI; 1/89 SecFrshCls; SecSophCls; SecJrCls; ChrhWkr; HonRl; VPJA; NHS; NatlThespSoc; SchAde; SchMus; Univ Of Notre Dame; Psychology.

MEYERS, Michael J; Jacksonville HS; Jacksonville, IL; 110/352 CncrtBnd; MrchBnd; SchMus; Bsktbl; Tennis;.

MEYERS, Roger; Concordia R Ii; Concordia, MO; 16/44 Band; Chrs; CncrtBnd; HonRl; MrchBnd; ModUN; NatlThespSoc; PepBnd; SchMus; College At Cmsu; Lpn.

MEYERS, Sandy L; Pardeeville HS; Rio, WI; PresSrCls; HonRl; LbryAde; NatlFornLg; NatlThespSoc; OffAde; SchAde; TchrAde; RptrYrbk; Univ Of Wisconsin; Veterinarian.

MEYERS, Sharon K; Winnebago HS; Winnebago, IL; 2/108 ChrhWkr; CmntyWkr; SecNHS; NatlMeritCmnd; SchMus; SchPl; RptrYrbk; RptrSchPpr; GerCl; GAA;.

MEYERS, Tilden P; Belvidere HS; Belvidere, IL; 15/350 ChrhWkr; HonRl; JrNHS; NHS; YthFlsp; LetterBsbl; LetterBsktbl; LetterFtbl; SARAwd; Univ Of Wisconsin; Meteorology.

MEYERS, Toni M; Merrill Sr HS; Merrill, WI; 25/428 Chr; HonRl; SchMus; FshEdYrbk; EdSchPpr; MthCl; Trk; Tech School; Accounting.

MEYERSON, William R; Linden HS; Linden, MI; 15/147 SecJrCls; DrlTm; MrchBnd; ROTC; RptrYrbk; RptrSchPpr; SciCl; LetterSwmmng; W Mi Univ; Writer.

MEYLOR, Colleen B; Oconomowoc Sr HS; Okauchee, WI; HstSrCls; ALAGirlsSt; ChrhWkr; HonRl; JrNHS; NHS; StuCncl; PresFrCl; SpnCl; GAA; Univ Of Wisconsin; Engineering.

MEYLOR, Judy K; Mineral Point HS; Mineral Point, WI; Band; CncrtBnd; HonRl; MrchBnd; Twrl; Chrldr; GAA; Madison Area Tech College; Nursing.

MEYLOR, Julia C; Marcus HS; Marcus, IA; TrsFrshCls; Chrs; NHS; SchMus; SchPl; RptrYrbk; RptrSchPpr; Bsbl; Glf; Trk; College; Journalism.

MEYLOR, Priscilla J; Madison HS; Madison, SD; 6/159 Band; Chr; HonRl; NHS; SchPl; FHA; SpnCl; PpCl; Trk; GAA; Univ Of Sd; Biologist.

MEZEL, David L; Lamar HS; Kenoma, MO; AFS; Chrs; HonRl; NHS; College; Chemistry.

MEZO, Marsha G; Herrin HS; Herrin, IL; Chr; Chrs; ChrhWkr; College; Vocation.

MICALLEF, Roseann; Holy Redeemer HS; Detroit, MI; ChrhWkr; CmntyWkr; HonRl; University.

MICEK, Rebecca J; Platte Valley Academy; Omaha, NE; SecTrsFrshCls; Union College.

MICELI, William A; St Ignatius College Prep; Homewood, IL; Chr; HonRl; Trk;.

MICHAEL, Gary A; Cleveland HS; St Louis, MO; 40/600 HonRl; College; Biology.

MICHAEL, Laurie L; Valders HS; St Nazianz, WI; DrlTm; HonRl; StuCncl; YthFlsp; RptrSchPpr; SchPpr; FHA; Lakeshore Inst; Dental.

MICHAEL, Neil A; Fremont HS; Fremont, IN; PresFrshCls; VPJrCls; ALBoysSt; HonRl; 4-H; FFA; MthCl; Bsbl; Bsktbl; Glf; Trk; College; Agriculture.

MICHAEL, Sharon D; Robinson HS; Robinson, IL; HonRl; ModUN; YthFlsp; FHA; Yamhill Carlton HS.

MICHAELS, Gina; George Rogers Clark HS; Hammond, IN; 74/260 Band; ChrhWkr; CncrtBnd; MrchBnd; Orch; PepBnd; SchPl; SctActv; SchPpr; GerCl; Data Processing.

MICHAELS, Thomas E; East Detroit HS; Warren, MI; LetterTrk; IMSpt; CitAwd; Col; Pro.

MICHAELSON, Jacki L; Roland Story Community HS; Story City, IA; PresJrCls; ChrhWkr; CmntyWkr; HonRl; NHS; RedCrAde; SchPl; TchrAde; DanFAwd; CitAwd; Univ Of Iowa; Elementary Education.

MICHAELSON, Julie A; Dekalb HS; Dekalb, IL; 8/350 ChrhWkr; CmntyWkr; HonRl; NHS; SchAde; StuCncl; Univ; Business Adm.

MICHAELSON, Kevin D; Chassell HS; Chassell, MI; VPFrshCls; Band; HonRl; Yrbk; LetterBsktbl; College; Electronic Eng.

MICHAELSON, Steve R; La Salle Peru HS; Peru, IL; 51/500 NHS; SpnCl; LetterBsbl; LetterBsktbl; LetterTrk; IMSpt; College; Engineering.

MICHAL, Julie; Bayard HS; Bayard, NE; PresJrCls; Chr; HonRl; HospAde; LbryAde; SchPl; YthFlsp; Yrbk; FHA; SpnCl; National Colle Of Bus; Computerprogramming.

MICHALAK, Lawrence H; All Saints Central HS; Bay City, MI; 5/140 VPJrCls; VPSrCls; Band; CmntyWkr; HonRl; StuCncl; TchrAde; EdYrBk; Bsktbl; IMSpt; College.

MICHALEK, Anna; St Alphonsus HS; Detroit, MI; 20/109 HonRl; SchMus; Trk; GAA; IMSpt; Nursing School; Nursing.

MICHALES, Judy; Lake Orion HS; Lake Orion, MI; StuGov; Andrews Univ; Social Work.

MICHALIK, Sharon E; Lourdes HS; Chicago, IL; 28/299 HonRl; Col; Pro.

MICHALSKI, Christine C; Bishop Gallagher HS; Detroit, MI; 40/311 CncrtBnd; HonRl; NHS; NatlMeritSchl; SchMus; CaptTrk; Chrldr; PresAwd; Wayne State Univ; Accountant.

MICHALSKI, Kathleen A; Edgar HS; Marathon, WI; 4/84 VPJrCls; ALAGirlsSt; Chr; ChrhWkr; HonRl; PresLbryAde; SchPl; TchrAde; EdSchPpr; TreasFHA; PpCl; U Of Wi Eau Claire; Biology.

MICHAUD, David W; Waukesha South HS; Waukesha, WI; Chrs; CncrtBnd; Mdrgl; MrchBnd; NHS; SchMus; Yrbk; KeyCl; Swmmng; Trk; Carroll College; Law School.

MICHAUD, Terese A; Forest Lake HS; Forest Lake, MN; 82/391 Band; CncrtBnd; HonRl; SchMus; SchPl; Yrbk; FHA; College; Fashion Design.

MICHE, Leland I; Pearl City HS; Pearl City, IL; 12/50 Band; Chrs; HonRl; TreasNHS; SctActv; Pres4-H; SecFFA; Bsktbl; 4-HAwd; Univ Of Wisc; Agricultural Engineer.

MICHEALSON, Kirk A; Plano HS; Plano, IL; 1/94 PresSophCls; PresSrCls; VPBand; CncrtBnd; HonRl; NHS; NatlThespSoc; SchMus; StuGov; SchPpr; Ftbl; Glf; LetterTrk; LetterWrstlng; U S Naval Academy; Nuclear Engineering.

MICHEL, Joann E; Smith Center HS; Smith Center, KS; DrlTm; HonRl; NHS; SchPl; FHA; LetterBsktbl; Trk; College Or Trade School.

MICHELL, Timothy J; Marion HS; Marion, MI; Band; ChrhWkr; HonRl; StuCncl; SptEdSchPpr; 4-H; LetterBsktbl; Ftbl; Trk; IMSpt; 4-HAwd; Michigan Tech Univ; Civil Engineering.

MICHELOTTI, Maria M; Barrington Comm HS; Elgin, IL; 2/652 Chr; HonRl; Mdrgl; NHS; NatlMeritSF; SpnCl; College; Medicine.

MICHELS, Ann D; Horace Mann HS; N Fond Du Lac, WI; 11/92 Chrs; HonRl; NHS; TchrAde; Yrbk; RptrSchPpr; FTA; GAA; IMSpt; College; Elem Education.

MICHELS, Larry E; Clifton HS; Clifton, KS; 2/25 PresFrshCls; PresSophCls; EngCl; MthCl; SciCl; Bsbl; Bsktbl; Ftbl; Trk; PresAwd; Univ; Professional.

MICHELS, Susan G; Fairbury HS; Fairbury, NE; Chrs; HonRl; HospAde; SctActv; FBLA; FHA; GerCl; PpCl; Coll.

MICHELS, Thomas V; Anamosa HS; Anamosa, IA; Band; Chrs; CncrtBnd; SchMus; PresStuCncl; StuGov; LetterBsktbl; LetterFtbl; CaptTrk; LetterPPFtbl;.

MICHELS, Timothy L; Anamosa HS; Anamosa, IA; VPSophCls; PresJrCls; Chr; CncrtBnd; HonRl; StuCncl; LetterBsbl; LetterBsktbl; LetterFtbl; LetterTrk; College; Pharmacy.

MICHELSTETTER, William S; Buhler HS; Hutchinson, KS; HonRl; TchrAde; SpnCl; LetterFtbl; LetterTrk; Hutchinson Comm Jr Clge; Architecture.

MICHLOVICH, Michael S; Marist HS; Crestwood, IL; 29/393 CmntyWkr; HonRl; SciCl; Purdue Univ; Chemical Engineer.

MICHNA, Helenanne; Thornton Twp HS; Dolton, IL; 9/750 CncrtBnd; HonRl; MrchBnd; NHS; NatlMeritCmnd; MthCl; LetterTennis; Augustana College; Medicine.

MICHNIEWICZ, Alice M; St Paul HS; Chicago, IL; Chrs; HonRl; NHS; OffAde; SctActv; StuCncl; Yrbk; GAA; Business School; Accounting.

MICHOLS, Kevin A; Maine Twp North HS; Glenview, IL; HonRl; NHS; LetterSocr; University Of Illinois; Engineering.

MICHONSKI, Cindy L; East Leyden HS; Schiller Park, IL; ChrhWkr; CncrtBnd; HonRl; PpCl; Swmmng; Trk; Chrldr; IMSpt; College; Secretary.

MICHORCZYK, Thaddeus C; St Francis De Sales HS; Chicago, IL; 37/296 HonRl; NHS; SchAde; Bsbl; CchngActv; Loyola Univ; Pharmacy.

MICIC, Dona; River Forest HS; Hobart, IN; ALAGirlsSt; Band; CncrtBnd; HonRl; MrchBnd; NHS; PepBnd; StuCncl; Trk; IMSpt; College;.

MICIUNAS, Perry P; Elgin HS; West Chicago, IL; 1/783 Band; ChrhWkr; HonRl; SctActv; Teen; 4-H; SpnCl; MthCl; Bsktbl; Ill Inst Of Tech; Elec Engineering.

MICK, Carol; Bentley Sr HS; Burton, MI; Band; MrchBnd; NHS; RedCrAde; SchMus; Yrbk; SchPpr; PresFHA; KiwanAwd; CitAwd; E Mich Univ; Caseworker.

MICK, Donna M; New Trier East HS; Wilmette, IL; Chrl; Chrs; ChrhWkr; HonRl; HospAde; OffAde; SctActv; College; History.

MICK, Linda A; St Johns HS; Beloit, KS; VPFrshCls; SecSophCls; SecJrCls; HonRl; TchrAde; Yrbk; LatCl; PpCl; Bsktbl; Trk; College; Professional.

MICK, Perry J; Tipton HS; Tipton, KS; TrsSophCls; HonRl; SchPl; Kansas State Univ; Architecture.

MICKAN, Diana D; South Iron R 1 HS; Annapolis, MO; Chrs; ChrhWkr; Yrbk; VPFHA; VPPpCl; Coll.

MICKE, Steven J; Cloquet Sr HS; Cloquet, MN; 60/273 HonRl; FBLA; Bsbl; Bsktbl; CaptFtbl; Glf; Tennis; Trk; CchngActv; IMSpt; PresAwd; College; Accounting.

MICKE, Susan K; Owensville HS; Owensville, MO; HonRl; FTA; PpCl; Business Sch; Accountant.

MICKELSEN, Barbara A; Forest Lake Sr HS; Forest Lake, MN; Band; ChrhWkr; CmntyWkr; CncrtBnd; HonRl; MrchBnd; NHS; PepBnd; SchMus; StuCncl; RptrSchPpr; GAA; College; Law.

MICKELSON, Barb M; Mobridge Sr HS; Mobridge, SD; 9/75 ALAGirlsSt; ChrhWkr; DrmMjrt; HonRl; NatlThespSoc; SchMus; SchPl; PresFTA; Trk; CaptChrldr; AmLegAwd; University; Special Education.

MICKELSON, Marcia S; Dwight HS; Dwight, IL; 45/111 AFS; DrlTm; HonRl; MrchBnd; SchPl; Yrbk; FHA; FrCl; PpCl; GAA; Joliet Jr Col; Vet Tech.

MICKELSON, Peggy L; Lake Of The Woods HS; Baudette, MN; Band; Chrs; CncrtBnd; HonRl; MrchBnd; NHS; PepBnd; SchPl; YthFlsp; RptrYrbk; LetterBsktbl; Swmmng; GAA; AmLegAwd; College; Professional.

MICKELSON, Rick E; Malven Comm HS; Malvern, IA; Band; CncrtBnd; MrchBnd; SchPl; SctActv; FFA; Bsbl; Bsktbl; CaptFtbl; GodCntryAwd;.

MICKEY, Annette M; Mt Pleasant HS; Mt Pleasant, IA; 22/146 SecTrsSrCls; Band; CncrtBnd; HonRl; MrchBnd; NHS; Twrl; 4-H; SciCl; 4-HAwd; Col; Med Records Tech.

MICKLE, Lawrence E; Lapeer Sr HS; Lapeer, MI; 54/430 PresChr; PresChrs; TreasJA; SchMus; SchPl; SecSctActv; PpCl; LetterTennis; TreasJAAwd; U Mich State; Missionary Work.

MICKLICH, Bradley J; Joliet Catholic HS; Joliet, IL; 3/170 Band; CncrtBnd; HonRl; MrchBnd; NHS; NatlMeritFnl; NatlMeritSF; PepBnd; YthLg; RptrYrbk; RptrSchPpr; LatCl; RusCl; College; Nuclear Research.

MICKNA, Joan; Friend Public HS; Friend, NE; 1/33 PresJrCls; Band; Chrs; HonRl; Yrbk; 4-HAwd; College; Music Drama.

MICKOW, Brenda L; Oregon Davis HS; Hamlet, IN; VPSophCls; Chr; HonRl; YthFlsp; 4-H; PpCl; LetterChrldr; GAA; 4-HAwd; PresAwd; Ball State.

MICOFF, David L; Marine City HS; Marine City, MI; 17/162 HonRl; NHS; SchPl; StuCncl; TchrAde; RptrSchPpr; Trk; Wrstlng; St Clair County Comm College; Communication.

MICOLICHEK, Margie A; St Josephs Academy; De Pere, WI; CmntyWkr; HospAde; RedCrAde; SchAde; SctActv; StuCncl; SptEdSchPpr; LatCl; CaptBsktbl; Trk; GAA; PPFtbl; AmLegAwd; Univ Of Wisconsin; Physical Therapy.

MIDA, Deborah L; Saline HS; Saline, MI; HonRl; SchPl; TchrAde; College; Law.

MIDDAUGH, Gregory H; Crane R 3 HS; Galena, MO; 1/26 HonRl; JrNHS; NHS; NatlThespSoc; SchPl; SctActv; StuCncl; StuGov; TchrAde; BauchLmbAwd; Univ Of Missouri Columbia; Medicine.

MIDDAUGH, Mitzi D; Wabash HS; Wabash, IN; ALAGirlsSt; DrlTm; HonRl; MrchBnd; OffAde; StuCncl; RptrSchPpr; College; Secretary.

MIDDAUGH, Paul; Bremen HS; Bremen, IN; ChrhWkr; HonRl; YthFlsp; Ivy Tech; Bus Adm.

MIDDAUGH, Randall S; Benson HS; Omaha, NE; 10/485 ALBoysSt; Band; CncrtBnd; HonRl; MrchBnd; NatlFornLg; NHS; SchMus; EldAwd; KiwanAwd; Texas Christian U; Biology.

MIDDEN, John; Marquette HS; East Alton, IL; HonRl; NatlThespSoc; SchPl; RptrSchPpr; College; Political Science.

MIDDENDORF, Bobbye J; Academy Of Our Lady HS; Peoria, IL; 6/184 HonRl; LitMag; NHS; NatlMeritCmnd; SchMus; SchPl; Yrbk; College; Social Science.

MIDDENDORF, Bobbye J; Spalding Institute; Peoria, IL; 6/180 HonRl; NHS; NatlMeritCmnd; Quill&Scroll; SchMus; SchPl; Yrbk; SchPpr; AmLegAwd; RotaryAwd; U Of Chicago; Fine Arts.

MIDDENDORF, Bobbye J; Academy Of Our Lady; Peoria, IL; HonRl; NatlMeritCmnd; SchMus; SchPl; Yrbk; University; Journalism.

MIDDENDORF, Ellen; R 111 Central HS; Flat River, MO; 36/165 Band; Chrs; ChrhWkr; HonRl; NHS; RptrYrbk; RptrSchPpr; FTA; FrCl; College; Professional.

MIDDENDORF, Larry A; Lyons HS; Lyons, NE; 2/30 SecSophCls; VPJrCls; Band; Chr; Chrl; Chrs; ChrhWkr; HonRl; StuCncl; StuGov; Bsbl; LetterBsktbl; LetterTrk; Univ Of Ne; Biology.

MIDDENDORF, Matthew; Concordia Acad; St Paul, MN; Band; CncrtBnd; Bsktbl; College; Professional.

MIDDENDORF, Matt J; Concordia Academy; St Paul, MN; Band; CncrtBnd; College; Professional.

MIDDLEKAMP, Brian W; Shawnee Mission South HS; Overland Park, KS; HonRl; JrNHS; NHS; Univ; Math.

MIDDLEKAUFF, Sue J; Mason Consolidated HS; Erie, MI; HonRl; JrNHS; NHS; NatlMeritFnl; NatlMeritSchl; NatlMeritSF; NatlThespSoc; TchrAde; FTA; NCTE; College; Language Teaching.

MIDDLESTADT, Jane L; Owatonna HS; Owatonna, MN; 10/320 ChrhWkr; HonRl; NHS; TchrAde; Yrbk; RptrSchPpr; LatCl; GAA; LionAwd; RotaryAwd; Mankato Clg; Economics & Physical Ed.

MIDDLESTEAD, Sherry L; West Allis Central HS; West Allis, WI; 125/564 Chr; Chrs; ChrhWkr; HonRl; Mdrgl; RptrSchPpr; Univ Of Wi; Major Study.

MIDDLETON, Beth; Beech Grove HS; Beech Grove, IN; 6/219 ALAGirlsSt; Band; CncrtBnd; DrmMjrt; HonRl; NHS; OffAde; Orch; PepBnd; SpnCl; College; Music Teacher.

MIDDLETON, Carroll D; Udall HS; Udall, KS; 3/22 PresFrshCls; VPJrCls; ALBoysSt; Chrs; HonRl; LbryAde; SchPl; StuGov; TchrAde; RptrYrbk; Cowley Co Comm College; Ag Engineering.

MIDDLETON, Charles H; J F Kennedy HS; Taylor, MI; 176/454 Chr; ChrhWkr; HonRl; Tennis; College; Professional.

MIDDLETON, Debra L; North County HS; Bonneterre, MO; ChrhWkr; HonRl; LbryAde; OffAde; Teen; Coll; Major Study.

MIDDLETON, Georgia L; S Iron R1 HS; Vulcan, MO; Chr; Chrs; ChrhWkr; HonRl; OffAde; YthFnd; RptrYrbk; TreasFHA; PpCl; Chrldr; Beauty School; Beautician.

MIDDLETON, James A; Lindblom Tech HS; Chicago, IL; 87/722 Chr; ChrhWkr; HonRl; TchrAde; YthFlsp; SciCl; College; Professional.

MIDDLETON, Jane E; Kinmundy Alma HS; Kinmundy, IL; 4/56 VPSophCls; VPJrCls; Band; HonRl; PresNHS; SchMus; StuCncl; VPFHA; PresPpCl; Bsktbl; GAA; College; Juvenile Law.

MIDDLETON, Kathy; Coopersville HS; Conklin, MI; HonRl; TchrAde; RptrYrbk; EdYrBk; Yrbk; RptrSchPpr; 4-H; FTA; GerCl; PpCl; Aguinas Coll; Art.

MIDDLETON, Lorinda S; South Iron HS; Vulcan, MO; 8/35 SecSophCls; SecSrCls; ChrhWkr; HonRl; SecStuCncl; YthFlsp; Yrbk; PresFHA; PpCl; CaptChrldr; Jr Coll; Dental Assistant.

MIDDLETON, Pamela; Crete Monee HS; Crete, IL; 8/389 ChrhWkr; HonRl; OffAde; Sdlty; YthFlsp; RptrSchPpr; FrCl; College Of St Francis; Medical.

MIDDLETON, Scott A; Twin Lakes HS; Monticello, IN; 15/205 Band; Chrs; HonRl; PepBnd; YthFlsp; LetterBsbl; LetterTennis; IMSpt; Col;.

MIDDLETON, Venenita; Potomac HS; Potomac, IL; TrsSrCls; HonRl; LbryAde; OffAde; TchrAde; EdYrBk; FTA; GAA; CitAwd; Eastern Illinois Univ; Medical Technology.

MIDKIFF, Dawn E; Acad Of Our Lady; Chicago, IL; 2/188 HonRl; HospAde; NHS; RedCrAde; Sdlty; RptrYrbk; PPFtbl; AmLegAwd; College; Law.

MIDTGARD, Cathy J; Camden Frontier HS; Camden, MI; VPSophCls; PresJrCls; PresSrCls; HonRl; SchPl; StuCncl; Yrbk; 4-H; Swmmng; Chrldr; GAA;.

MIDTGARD, Dianne L; Jonesville HS; Jonesville, MI; 4/86 SecJrCls; Band; HonRl; PolWkr; SchPl; VPStuCncl; RptrYrbk; VPFTA; Chrldr; DARAwd; Hillsdale College; Law.

MIDTHUN, Cynthia A; Central HS; Aberdeen, SD; 1/438 AFS; Chr; HonRl; Mdrgl; NHS; NatlMeritSF; Orch; SchPl; Yrbk; DARAwd; Nw Univ; Theatre Arts.

MIDTLYNG, David J; Thornridge HS; Dolton, IL; 6/684 VPChrhWkr; CncrtBnd; HonRl; MrchBnd; NHS; NatlMeritCmnd; Bsktbl; LetterTrk; Drake Univ; Systems Analyst.

MIEDEMA, Jane E; St Anne Community HS; St Anne, IL; Chr; CncrtBnd; HonRl; Mdrgl; MrchBnd; NHS; StuCncl; YthFlsp; FTA; University; Singer.

MIELENHAUSEN, Thomas C; Assumption HS; Davenport, IA; 1/220 HstSophCls; HstJrCls; HstSrCls; ChrhWkr; CmntyWkr; HonRl; LitMag; StuGov; SchPpr; IMSpt; Univ Of Notre Dame; Law.

MIELKE, Claudia M; Mc Donell Central HS; Chippewa Falls, WI; PresChrhWkr; HonRl; ModUN; StuCncl; RptrYrbk; SpnCl; PpCl; Tennis; Chrldr; IMSpt; Univ Of Wisconsin; Physics.

MIELKE, Lori; Swan Valley HS; Saginaw, MI; 5/162 TrsSophCls; TrsJrCls; VPSrCls; HonRl; JrNHS; NHS; YthFlsp; SpnCl; PpCl; JCAwd; Central Michigan Univ; Education Major.

MIELKE, Mark D; Lutheran HS; Racine, WI; PpCl; Bsktbl; Ftbl; AmLegAwd; Coll; Acctng.

MIELKE, Marlon W; Sleepy Eye Public HS; Sleepy Eye, MN; 17/75 Aud/Vis; ChrhWkr; HonRl; SchAde; YthFlsp; PresSciCl; LetterBsktbl; LetterGlf; BauchLmbAwd; Pillsbury Bible Clg; Bible And Science.

MIERITZ, Vicki L; Colby HS; Dorchester, WI; CncrtBnd; HonRl; HospAde; LbryAde; NatlFornLg; Orch; TchrAde; YthFlsp; Bsbl; Bsktbl; Tech Sch; Architectural Design.

MIERS, Judith L; Enterprise Academy; Wichita, KS; Band; Chr; Chrl; Chrs; StuGov; RptrSchPpr; SchPpr; Bsbl; Bsktbl; Sw Union College; Nursing.

MIERZWINSKI, Dianna H; Palatine HS; Palatine, IL; HonRl; JrNHS; NHS; VPStuCncl; RptrSchPpr; SchPpr; FrCl; Trk; GAA; DARAwd; Univ Of Illinois; Journalism.

MIESSNER, Judith A; Edgar HS; Edgar, WI; 13/84 Band; Chr; Chrl; Chrs; ChrhWkr; CncrtBnd; HonRl; LbryAde; MrchBnd; PepBnd; Uw Eau Claire; Med Tech.

MIESSNER, Rebecca S; Alton Sr HS; Godfrey, IL; 17/458 AFS; Band; Chr; Chrs; CncrtBnd; HonRl; Mdrgl; MrchBnd; NHS; Orch; PepBnd; SchMus; SctActv; Ftbl; LetterTrk; Univ Of Missouri; Engineering.

MIESZALA, Mark L; Libertyville HS; Libertyville, IL; 49/458 ChrhWkr; CmntyWkr; HonRl; NHS; Bsbl; Bsktbl; Augustana; Accounting.

MIGHT, M A; Central Noble HS; Albion, IN; 1/111 Band; CncrtBnd; MrchBnd; NHS; PepBnd; StuCncl; Yrbk; 4-H; GAA; 4-HAwd; College; Veterinary.

MIGLIORINO, Marc J; Homewood Flossmoor HS; Chicago Hts, IL; HonRl; JA; JrNHS; NHS; PolWkr; FrCl; College; Science.

MIGNECO, Christine M; St Elizabeth Academy; St Louis, MO; 14/116 HonRl; StuCncl; FrCl; Ftbl; Socr; GAA; IMSpt; PPFtbl; Meramec Comm Col; Accounting.

MIGON, Robert C; Notre Dame HS; Harwood Hts, IL; 1/273 HonRl; NatlMeritSF; StuGov; TchrAde; IMSpt; College; Elec Engineering.

MIH, Alex D; Chanute Sr HS; Chanute, KS; PresFrshCls; PresSophCls; ChrhWkr; HonRl; StuCncl; 4-H; LetterFtbl; LetterGlf; LetterWrstlng; 4-HAwd; College; Doctor.

MIH, Cathy A; Chanute Sr HS; Chanute, KS; CncrtBnd; HonRl; PepBnd; PresStuCncl; RptrYrbk; Pres4-H; SpnCl; MthCl; LetterTennis; LetterTrk; 4-HAwd; University; Music.

MIHALJEVIC, Joan L; Bogan HS; Chicago, IL; 148/678 HonRl; PepBnd; TchrAde; SchPpr; MthCl; PpCl; GAA; Col; Pro.

MIHALOV, Charles G; George Rodgers Clark HS; Whiting, IN; 80/275 CncrtBnd; HonRl; SchPl; SctActv; StuCncl; StuGov; SpnCl; SciCl; Bsktbl; Trk; College; Professional.

MIHAVICS, Kenneth W; Riverside Brookfield HS; Brookfield, IL; 2/483 ChrhWkr; HonRl; JrNHS; NHS; NatlMeritCmnd; PresNatlThespSoc; SchMus; SchPl; TchrAde; EldAwd; College; Medicine.

MIHELICH, Karen A; St Francis Academy; Crest Hill, IL; 19/172 ChrhWkr; CmntyWkr; HonRl; LbryAde; NHS; GerCl; Coll; Med.

MIHM, Randolph J; Turkey Valley HS; Waucoma, IA; Chr; Mdrgl; NHS; NatlMeritCmnd; SchMus; 4-H; LetterFtbl; AmLegAwd; College.

MIHULKA, Frank J; Creighton Prep; Omaha, NE; Band; ChrhWkr; CncrtBnd; HonRl; JA; MrchBnd; Orch; PepBnd; SctActv; Sdlty; IMSpt; Col; Earth Science.

MIILLER, Dianne J; South Newton HS; Kentland, IN; DrlTm; HonRl; MrchBnd; Quill&Scroll; SchPl; Yrbk; 4-H; FHA; LatCl; PpCl;.

MIILU, Debbie L; Ontonagon Area HS; Mass, MI; Band; HonRl; NHS; YthFlsp; Yrbk; LetterTrk; GAA; College; Ecology.

MIKA, Barbara A; Kimball Public HS; Academy, SD; Band; Chr; DrlTm; HonRl; SchPl; RptrSchPpr; Sec4-H; LetterBsktbl; CaptTrk; DanFAwd; 4-HAwd; Univ; Home Economics.

MIKA, Daniel J; Kimball Independent HS; Academy, SD; Band; Chrs; CncrtBnd; HonRl; Mdrgl; PepBnd; SchMus; MthCl; Bsktbl; Trk; College.

MIKEL, Elaine M; Grinnell Community Sr HS; Grinnell, IA; Band; ChrhWkr; ModUN; PolWkr; SchPl; FFA; FTA; SecSophCls; Tennis; RotaryAwd; Col; Bio Sci.

MIKEL, Steve; North Wood HS; Wakarusa, IN; SctActv; 4-H; FFA; PpCl; LetterFtbl; IMSpt; Purdue; Farming.

MIKEWORTH, Lisa K; Palestine HS; Palestine, IL; FHA; FrCl; 4-HAwd; College; Nursing.

MIKICH, Susan M; Edsel Ford HS; Dearborn, MI; HonRl; NHS; NatlMeritCmnd; RptrYrbk; GAA; Mercy Clg; Nursing.

MIKITA, Tammy; Cardinal Ritter HS; Indianapolis, IN; TrsJrCls; HonRl; NHS; SchMus; StuCncl; StuGov; IMSpt; PPFtbl; Univ.

MIKKELSEN, Susan; Anita HS; Anita, IA; ChrhWkr; CncrtBnd; HonRl; MrchBnd; PepBnd; RptrYrbk; FHA; FTA; PpCl; Glf; Coll; Sec.

MIKKELSON, Connie; Appleton Public HS; Louisburg, MN; 18/75 TrsSrCls; Band; HonRl; LbryAde; PepBnd; SchPl; PpCl; Mn Univ; Dental Hygiene.

MIKKELSON, Linda A; Washington Sr HS; Sioux Falls, SD; ALAGirlsSt; Band; HonRl; JA; LitMag; NHS; Quill&Scroll; SctActv; TchrAde; PresFrCl; Trade School; Computer Programming.

MIKLAS, Adrianne C; Regina HS; Detroit, MI; JA; LitMag; PolWkr; SchMus; SchPl; SctActv; RptrSchPpr; SchPpr; Tennis; College; Journalism.

MIKLAS, Ralph M; Southwest HS; St Louis, MO; 150/491 TrsFrshCls; LbryAde; RedCrAde; SctActv; TchrAde; Ftbl; Trk; Wrstlng; CchngActv; IMSpt; Ne Mo State U.

MIKLUSAK, Mary G; George Rogers Clark HS; Whiting, IN; 12/260 Chr; Chrs; HonRl; NHS; YthFnd; FNA; EngCl; SpnCl; PpCl; Bsktbl; GAA; College; Nursing.

MIKOLAJCZAK, David J; Thornridge HS; Dolton, IL; 154/684 HonRl; StuCncl; YthFlsp; Univ Of Illinois; Pharmacy.

MIKOS, Bruce A; Harrison HS; Chicago, IL; 5/300 HonRl; NHS; LetterGlf; Univ Of Ill; Computer Engineer.

MIKOTA, Cindy; Thomas Kelly Hs; Chicago, IL; Chrs; Mdrgl; NatlMeritCmnd; Quill&Scroll; Yrbk; 4-HAwd;.

MIKSANEK, Susan L; Immaculate Heart Of Mary HS; Bellwood, IL; Aud/Vis; NHS; NatlMeritFnl; NatlMeritSchl; SchPpr; FrCl; Northwestern Univ; Law.

MIKULEC, Ann Marie; Riverside HS; Dbn Hts, MI; PresFrshCls; PresJrCls; Chr; HonRl; StuGov; TchrAde; RptrSchPpr; Swmmng; CaptChrldr; GAA; Ferris State College; Dental Assisting.

MIKULICH, Teresa A; Kingsford HS; Kingsford, MI; Chr; Chrs; ChrhWkr; HonRl; LitMag; Tennis; Trk; Chrldr; IMSpt; PPFtbl; CitAwd; College; Liscensed Practical Nurse.

MIKUSCH, David C; Southwest HS; St Louis, MO; ChrhWkr; SctActv; YthFlsp; GodCntryAwd; College; Professional.

MILAKOVIC, Nick; Marie Sklodowska Curie HS; Chicago, IL; PresSrCls; Band; CAP; HonRl; JA; MrchBnd; StuCncl; StuGov; TchrAde; SciCl; Lewis Univ; Commercial Airline Pilot.

MILAN, Dean R; Hill Murray HS; St Paul, MN; HonRl; JrNHS; NHS; LetterBsbl; LetterBsktbl; Ftbl; IMSpt; PresAwd; Trade Or Bus; Vocation.

MILATZ, Janet; Romulus Sr HS; Romulus, MI; 3/282 SecSrCls; ChrhWkr; CncrtBnd; HonRl; HospAde; MrchBnd; StuCncl; JCAwd; KiwanAwd; Eastern Mich Univ; Registered Nurse.

MILBOURNE, Renee A; Portland HS; Grand Ledge, MI; 17/125 CncrtBnd; DrmMjrt; HonRl; JrNHS; LbryAde; MrchBnd; NHS; PepBnd; SchPl; SpnCl; College; Medical Tech.

MILBRANDT, Todd; Logan View Jr Sr HS; Hooper, NE; 28/64 SecSophCls; CmntyWkr; HonRl; StuCncl; TchrAde; SpnCl; SciCl; College.

MILBRATH, Vickie A; Jefferson HS; Sullivan, WI; Chr; ChrhWkr; HonRl; LbryAde; NatlMeritCmnd; SancSoc; SchMus; TchrAde; FBLA; FHA; Bus School; Secretarial Work.

MILDE, Margaret A; Dollar Bay HS; Dollar Bay, MI; 2/24 SecSrCls; Band; HospAde; SchPl; Yrbk; Trk; CchngActv; BttyCrckrAwd; 4-HAwd; VoiceDemAwd; Animal Tech.

MILDEBRANDT, Nancy; So Milw Sr HS; S Milwaukee, WI; 39/480 Band; NHS; NatlThespSoc; Orch; SchPl; VoiceDemAwd; College; Science Fine Arts.

MILDER, Theresa; Davenport West HS; Davenport, IA; Chr; Chrs; ChrhWkr; CmntyWkr; OffAde; College; Social Work.

MILDFELT, Daniel L; Central Heights HS; Richmond, KS; PresJrCls; VPSrCls; Chr; Chrs; ChrhWkr; CmntyWkr; Bsbl; LetterBsktbl; LetterFtbl; LetterTrk; Kansas State Clg Of Pittsburg; Business Fin.

MILERIS, Paul C; Batavia HS; Batavia, IL; HonRl; PresNHS; SchMus; SchPl; TreasLatCl; LetterWrstlng; Creighton University; Medicine.

MILES, Bart A; Nebraska Christian HS; Chambers, NE; ChrhWkr; YthFlsp; 4-H; Ftbl; Trk; Wrstlng; 4-HAwd; Ne Nebraska Tech Univ; Mechanic.

MILES, Bernard A; Ne Christian HS; Chambers, NE; ChrhWkr; NatlMeritCmnd; YthFlsp; 4-H; Bsktbl; Trk; CchngActv; IMSpt; 4-HAwd; College.

MILES, Christopher K; Reitz Mem HS; Evansville, IN; SchPpr; GerCl; Ftbl; CaptWrstlng; IMSpt; PresAwd; College.

MILES, David; Charles City Comm HS; Charles City, IA; 8/250 ALBoysSt; HonRl; NHS; NatlMeritCmnd; Orch; SctActv; Yrbk; 4-H; LetterFtbl; GodCntryAwd; Drake Univ; Law.

MILES, Debra K; Mt Carmel HS; Mt Carmel, IL; 2/183 Chrs; HonRl; NHS; SchAde; SchPl; FTA; SpnCl; KiwanAwd; Wabash Coll; Acct.

MILES, Denise E; Maquoketa Valley HS; Hopkinton, IA; Band; ChrhWkr; CncrtBnd; HonRl; MrchBnd; NatlThespSoc; PepBnd; Quill&Scroll; SchPl; YthFlsp; College.

MILES, Kimi S; Andover HS; Orchard Lake, MI; HonRl; FrCl; Swmmng; College; Prof.

MILES, Lee C; Greenville Rii HS; Patterson, MO; Band; Chrs; ChrhWkr; CncrtBnd; HonRl; MrchBnd; ModUN; PepBnd; SchPl; SpnCl; IMSpt; Ozarks; Industrial Crafrs.

MILES, Mark L; Holland HS; Holland, MI; 51/317 Band; HonRl; MrchBnd; Orch; SctActv; Western Mi Univ; Religion.

MILES, Mary J; Springfield HS; Springfield, IL; 6/585 AFS; ChrhWkr; NHS; SctActv; Pres4-H; VPSpnCl; GAA; IMSpt; 4-HAwd; RotaryAwd; Greenville College; Elem Education.

MILES, Randy H; Juda HS; Juda, WI; Band; Chr; Chrl; Chrs; ChrhWkr; CncrtBnd; MrchBnd; ModUN; NatlMeritSF; Orch; PepBnd; Ftbl; Trk; Wrstlng; U W Platteville; Computer Tech.

MILES, Sarah E; West HS; Madison, WI; 20/583 CncrtBnd; HonRl; HospAde; LbryAde; NHS; NatlMeritSF; Quill&Scroll; SctActv; Yrbk; FrCl; Dartmouth; Business.

MILES, Sharon F; Century HS; Karnak, IL; HonRl; LbryAde; Shawnee Jr Clg.

MILES, Steven W; Lancaster HS; Lancaster, WI; Chrs; HonRl; Mdrgl; SchMus; Yrbk; Bsbl; Bsktbl; Trk; PresAwd; Hertzing Shol ;electronic.

MILES, William; North Putnam HS; Bainbridge, IN; ChrhWkr; HonRl; NHS; SctActv; ModUN; 4-H; CchngActv;.

MILEUR, Deborah K; Murphyboro Township HS; Murphysboro, IL; 5/230 Chrs; ChrhWkr; HonRl; NHS; SctActv; StuCncl; TchrAde; 4-H; SpnCl; College; Teaching.

MILEUR, Edmond C; Du Quoin HS; Du Quoin, IL; HonRl; SchPl; RptrSchPpr; SchPpr; LatCl; VPSciCl; College; Science.

MILEUSNICH, Carlo W; Hot Springs HS; Hot Springs, SD; 7/90 Band; ChrhWkr; CncrtBnd; HonRl; MrchBnd; PepBnd; Bsktbl; University; Professional.

MILEWSKI, Doreen; Amos Alonzo Stagg Hs; Hickory Hills, IL; 13/489 TrsJrCls; TrsSrCls; ChrhWkr; HonRl; NHS; StuCncl; YthFlsp; Yrbk; FrCl; Chrldr; Augustana College; Medicine.

MILEWSKI, Mary A; St Andrew HS; Detroit, MI; 11/108 SecFrshCls; Chr; Chrl; HospAde; NHS; StuCncl; FNA; LetterTrk; LetterChrldr; IMSpt; Mercy College Of Detroit; Rn.

MILEWSKI, Rita C; Taylorville HS; Taylorville, IL; 6/271 Chr; HonRl; NHS; VPNatlThespSoc; SchMus; StuCncl; EdYrBk; FTA; SecLatCl; PpCl; Purdue Univ; Nuclear Pharmacy.

MILHAUPT, Thomas J; Wayland Acad; Madison, WI; PresSophCls; HonRl; PolWkr; PresStuGov; Ftbl; CaptSocr; Beloit; Constitutional Law.

MILKE, Marla J; St Paul J F Kennedy HS; Chicago, IL; HonRl; SchAde; SchPl; StuCncl; TchrAde; Yrbk; 4-H; GAA; 4-HAwd; College; Medical Field.

MILKEY, Michael O; Underwood Public HS; Underwood, ND; SecJrCls; Chrs; ChrhWkr; CmntyWkr; HonRl; SchPl; SchPpr; LetterBsktbl; LetterFtbl; LetterTrk; College; Commercial Art.

MILKINT, Denise T; Evergreen Park Comm HS; Evergreen Park, IL; 50/439 AFS; HonRl; NHS; StuGov; TchrAde; TreasFrCl; MthCl; Univ Of Ill; French.

MILKO, Michelle E; South Lake HS; St Clair Shores, MI; HonRl; SchMus; LetterTennis; PPFtbl; VFWAwd; VoiceDemAwd; Interlocken; Music.

MILLAR, Dorothy L; Libertyville HS; Libertyville, IL; 97/450 Chr; ChrhWkr; HonRl; 4-H; Bsktbl; Swmmng; Gustavus Adolphus College; Biology.

MILLARD, Amy L; Lakeview HS; Trufant, MI; 23/118 ChrhWkr; HonRl; LbryAde; NHS; SchPpr; 4-H; Ferris St College; Dental Asst.

MILLARD, Tammy S; Milton HS; Milton, WI; ChrhWkr; HonRl; LbryAde; NHS; YthFlsp; Milton Coll; Librarian.

MILLBURG, Carl; Marengo HS; Marengo, IL; 13/189 Band; CncrtBnd; HonRl; MrchBnd; PepBnd; Teen; No Illinois Univ; Accounting.

MILLBURG, Katherine R; Nokomis HS; Nokomis, IL; Chrs; College; Law.

MILLBURG, Martin; Nohomis HS; Nakomis, IL; /90 ChrhWkr; PolWkr; RptrYrbk;.

MILLBURN, Karen L; Colfax HS; Colfax, IA; ChrhWkr; CmntyWkr; HonRl; StuCncl; PpCl; Trk; CaptChrldr; Col; Business.

MILLEDGE, Rebecca; Knoxville Sr HS; Knoxville, IA; 4/175 TrsSrCls; Band; ChrhWkr; CncrtBnd; HonRl; NHS; NatlMeritCmnd; YthFlsp; Iowa Wesleyan Coll; Medical Nurse.

MILLER, Alan D; Arsenal Tech HS; Indpls, IN; HonRl; LetterFtbl; Col.

MILLER, Alan J; Granite City South HS; Granite City, IL; 92/630 Univ Of Il; Psychology.

MILLER, Amber L; Mason Senior HS; Erie, MI; Band; Chrs; CncrtBnd; HonRl; MrchBnd; NHS; YthFlsp; SchPpr; Chrldr; GAA; College; Professional.

MILLER, Andrew S; Bourbon HS; Bourbon, MO; ChrhWkr; StuCncl; SpnCl; Bsktbl; U Of Missouri; Game Mgmnt.

MILLER, Angela J; North HS; Hawkeye, IA; 27/105 NatlMeritSF; StuCncl; Ia St Univ; Vet.

MILLER, Anne M; Jasper R 5 HS; Jasper, MO; Band; HonRl; Mdrgl; NHS; SchPl; StuCncl; YthFlsp; FHA; LetterTrk; GAA; Southwest Mo State U; Music.

MILLER, Annette; John Marshall Harlan HS; Chicago, IL; 20/707 Chr; ChrhWkr; HonRl; NHS; OffAde; StuCncl; TchrAde; College; Doctor.

MILLER, Ann M; Thornton Frac South HS; Lansing, IL; AFS; ChrhWkr; HonRl; JrNHS; LbryAde; NatlFornLg; NHS; NatlMeritCmnd; TchrAde; Univ Of Illinois; Genetics.

MILLER, Ann M; Central HS; Evansville, IN; 46/600 HonRl; NHS; SctActv; TchrAde; Col; Ecology.

MILLER, Arden D; Jefferson Sr HS; Alexandria, MN; 81/336 HonRl; LitMag; Orch; SchPl; TchrAde; SecKeyCl; MthCl; Univ Of No Dakota; Electrical Engineer.

MILLER, Arthur; Waseca HS; Waseca, MN; 20/210 AFS; Band; Chr; HonRl; StuCncl; CchngActv; Voc School; Mech.

MILLER, Barbara; St John HS; Independence, IA; Chr; Chrs; CmntyWkr; HonRl; SchMus; SchPpr; FrCl; PpCl; Bsbl; Bsktbl; College; Vocational.

MILLER, Barry W; Chester HS; Ellis Grove, IL; ALBoysSt; CncrtBnd; MrchBnd; SecFrshCls; SchMus; RptrYrbk; Yrbk; PpCl; LetterFtbl; Chrldr; W Point; St Cop.

MILLER, Betty J; Connersville HS; Connersville, IN; 58/380 HstFrshCls; CaptDrlTm; HonRl; Quill&Scroll; StuCncl; TchrAde; FshEdYrbk; FTA; FrCl; PpCl; Vocational.

MILLER, Bobbi S; Kickapoo HS; Springfield, MO; HonRl; LitMag; PresNatlFornLg; NatlMeritFnl; OptClAwd; Abilene Christian Col; Commercial Art.

MILLER, Brenda; Peoria Heights HS; Peoria Heights, IL; 12/99 HonRl; LbryAde; Trk; Chrldr; Icc; Commercial Art.

MILLER, Brenton B; Great Bend HS; Great Bend, KS; 5/335 HonRl; PresNatlFornLg; PresStuCncl; TchrAde; SchPpr; NCTE; OptClAwd; VoiceDemAwd; College; Teacher.

MILLER, Brian K; Batesville HS; Batesville, IN; 17/144 ALBoysSt; Band; ChrhWkr; CncrtBnd; HonRl; MrchBnd; NHS; PepBnd; YthFlsp; LetterBsbl; LetterBsktbl; LetterFtbl; Purdue Univ; Conservation.

MILLER, Brian P; Owen Withee HS; Owen, WI; LetterFtbl; LetterTrk; College; Industrial Engineer.

MILLER, Bruce W; Randolph Southern HS; Winchester, IN; 2/64 PresFrshCls; TrsSophCls; PresJrCls; PresSrCls; ALBoysSt; Band; Chr; Chrs; CncrtBnd; HonRl; MrchBnd; NHS; PepBnd; SchMus; Col; Professional.

MILLER, Caleb D; Haven HS; Partridge, KS; 3/89 ChrhWkr; CmntyWkr; HonRl; NatlMeritCmnd; RptrYrbk; RptrSchPpr; BauchLmbAwd;.

MILLER, Carol J; Leland HS; Leland, IL; TrsSophCls; Chrs; StuCncl; SchPpr; SecFHA; PpCl; GAA; Trade School; Secretary.

MILLER, Carol J; Coal City HS; Coal City, IL; 13/96 ALAGirlsSt; Band; Chrs; DrmMjrt; MrchBnd; NHS; SchMus; SchPl; PpCl; Illinois St Univ; Speech.

MILLER, Catherine J; Belle Plaine HS; Belle Plaine, MN; 13/94 Chr; HonRl; Mdrgl; Quill&Scroll; SchMus; SctActv; TchrAde; Bsktbl; GAA; IMSpt; St Benedicts.

MILLER, Catherine; Queen Of Peace HS; Chicago, IL; HonRl; HospAde; LbryAde; OffAde; SchAde; SchMus; TchrAde; 4-H; FrCl; 4-HAwd; De Paul Univ; Acct.

MILLER, Cathy A; Roseville HS; Roseville, IL; 1/58 Band; CncrtBnd; HonRl; PresNHS; RptrSchPpr; SpnCl; PpCl; LetterBsktbl; Chrldr; TreasGAA; Coll.

MILLER, Cathy L; W Washington HS; Hardinsburg, IN; Chr; ChrhWkr; DrlTm; HonRl; SchMus; Yrbk; 4-H; FHA; Chrldr; 4-HAwd; Trade School; Vocation.

MILLER, C Gail; Virden Comm HS; Virden, IL; SecFrshCls; SecSophCls; SecJrCls; TreasChrs; Mdrgl; NHS; SchMus; SchPl; Sec4-H; TreasSciCl; IMSpt; College; Nurse.

MILLER, Cheri L; Raytown HS; Kansas City, MO; Chr; ChrhWkr; DrlTm; HonRl; HospAde; JrNHS; LitMag; NHS; SchMus; College; Music.

MILLER, Cheri L; Mc Pherson HS; Mc Pherson, KS; 1/222 Chr; ChrhWkr; CmntyWkr; HonRl; NHS; SchMus; YthFlsp; 4-H; FHA; SciCl; Mc Pherson Coll; Math.

MILLER, Cheryl A; Holcomb HS; Holcomb, KS; 2/29 PresFrshCls; VPJrCls; HonRl; SchPl; SecStuCncl; PresFHA; SciCl; Trk; LetterChrldr; PPFtbl; AmLegAwd; 4-HAwd; VoiceDemAwd; Univ Of Kansas; Psychology.

MILLER, Cheryl A; Sargent Central HS; Forman, ND; Band; Chrs; CncrtBnd; HonRl; HospAde; MrchBnd; PepBnd; RptrSchPpr; FHA; 4-HAwd;.

MILLER, Christine L; South Sioux Sr HS; South Sioux City, NE; HonRl; StuGov; Yrbk; PpCl; Togoto College; Home Economics.

MILLER, Christine L; Rock Island HS; Rock Island, IL; Chrs; ChrhWkr; JrNHS; RptrYrbk; College; Occupational Therapy.

MILLER, Christine L; Fowlerville HS; Fowlerville, MI; HonRl; LetterBsktbl; GAA; IMSpt; PPFtbl; College Or Univ; Forestry.

MILLER, Christopher J; Rogers City HS; Mt Clemens, MI; 6/160 VPJrCls; Band; HonRl; NHS; RptrYrbk; KeyCl; CaptBsbl; LetterBsktbl; LetterFtbl; LetterTrk; Univ Of Michigan; Medicine.

MILLER, Cindy A; New London Sr HS; Hortonville, WI; Chr; Chrs; HonRl; NatlFornLg; SchMus; FHA; SciCl; Professional Singing.

MILLER, Cindy J; Norwell HS; Ossian, IN; HonRl; NHS; SchPl; SpnCl; Bsbl; Bsktbl; GAA; IMSpt; PPFtbl; Trade.

MILLER, Clarence J; Johnson Creek HS; Rio, WI; 13/47 TrsSrCls; Band; SchPl; 4-H; FFA; MthCl; Bsbl; Ftbl; Wrstlng; IMSpt; Coll; Acct.

MILLER, Connie L; Northridge HS; Bristol, IN; TrsFrshCls; Chrs; HonRl; MrchBnd; SchAde; Yrbk; VPFTA; PpCl; Trk; GAA; College; Social Work.

MILLER, Craig L; Bentley HS; Burton, MI; 1/200 Band; Chr; ChrhWkr; NHS; NatlMeritSF; SchMus; StuCncl; EdSchPpr; OptClAwd; College; Ministry.

MILLER, Cynthia; Lourdes HS; Chicago, IL; 50/250 HonRl; FrCl; MthCl; IMSpt; Police Woman.

MILLER, Cynthia; Burr Oak HS; Burr Oak, MI; OffAde; SchMus; StuCncl; Twrl; Yrbk; FrCl; PPFtbl; Business School; Entrepreneur.

MILLER, Dale E; Dawson Boyd Public HS; Dawson, MN; Aud/Vis; YthFlsp; Yrbk; SchPpr; Pres4-H; VPFFA; LetterBsktbl; LetterFtbl; Glf; DanFAwd; 4-HAwd; Canby Vo Tech; Automotive Mechanic.

MILLER, Dana L; Pt Washington HS; Saukville, WI; HonRl; TchrAde; MthCl; College; Engineering.

MILLER, Daniel K; Spalding Acad; Spalding, NE; VPFrshCls; SecJrCls; HonRl; NHS; SchPl; StuCncl; LetterBsbl; Bsktbl; LetterFtbl; Trk; Hasting Coll;deisel Mechan.

MILLER, Danny L; Wawasee HS; Warsaw, IN; ChrhWkr; HonRl; Ftbl; Trk; Anderson Coll; Phy Educ & Health.

MILLER, David; Shawnee Hs; Mcclure, IL; 2/60 Chrs; ChrhWkr; HonRl; FFA; IMSpt;.

MILLER, David D; Bremen HS; Bremen, IN; 18/125 ALBoysSt; HonRl; FrCl; MthCl; LetterTrk; IMSpt; Computer Training.

MILLER, David G; Frankton HS; Anderson, IN; SctActv; LetterFtbl; LetterTrk; Wrstlng; CchngActv; Purdue U; Air Force Rotc.

MILLER, David J; Sherrard HS; Milan, IL; Band; CncrtBnd; PepBnd; YthFlsp; EdSchPpr; 4-H; FrCl; Ftbl; Wrstlng; Cllege; Journalism.

MILLER, David J; Cathedral HS; St Cloud, MN; 2/162 PresFrshCls; Chr; HonRl; JrNHS; NHS; StuCncl; StuGov; EdSchPpr; Ftbl; IMSpt; Colorado State U; Law.

MILLER, David J; Marie Curie HS; Chicago, IL; 3/595 Aud/Vis; ChrhWkr; CmntyWkr; HonRl; NHS; TchrAde; SciCl; Ill Inst Of Tech; Engineering.

MILLER, David P; Shawnee HS; Mc Clure, IL; 1/70 Chrs; ChrhWkr; HonRl; FFA; IMSpt; Se Mo;.

MILLER, David W; Benton Consolidated HS; Ewing, IL; 6/160 Aud/Vis; HonRl; NHS; SchMus; Yrbk; SchPpr; FDA; LatCl; MthCl; PpCl; Ftbl; AmLegAwd; Univ Of Illinois; Pharmaceuticals.

MILLER, Dean J; Niles North HS; Morton Grove, IL; 107/632 Aud/Vis; Band; Chr; VPChrhWkr; CncrtBnd; HonRl; MrchBnd; Orch; SchMus; Ftbl; Wrstlng; Washington Univ; Medicine.

MILLER, Dean L; Breken Ridge HS; Breckenridge, MI; 19/96 TrsSophCls; HstJrCls; SecTrsSrCls; HonRl; Bsbl; Bsktbl; Ftbl; Glf; AmLegAwd; ChmbCommrsAwd; John Wesley Clge; Eng.

MILLER, Debbie L; Central HS; Aberdeen, SD; AFS; Band; ChrhWkr; HospAde; SchPl; RptrSchPpr; SpnCl; Trk; PPFtbl; Northern St College; Teacher.

MILLER, Debi M; Ogilvie HS; Ogilvie, MN; Chr; HonRl; Twrl; SchPpr; Glf; Swmmng; LetterTrk; LetterChrldr; PPFtbl; PresAwd; Col; Phy Ed.

MILLER, Deborah C; Luther HS; Chicago, IL; 21/215 HonRl; YthFlsp; GAA; IMSpt; University; Nursing.

MILLER, Deborah R; Fairfax R 3 HS; Fairfax, MO; 5/27 HstFrshCls; SecJrCls; Band; Chrs; CncrtBnd; HonRl; HospAde; MrchBnd; PepBnd; SchMus; SchPl; SctActv; YthFlsp; EdYrBk; FHA;.

MILLER, Debra J; Harrisonville Sr HS; Harrisonville, MO; CmntyWkr; DrmMjrt; HonRl; HospAde; OffAde; RedCrAde; TchrAde; Twrl; FNA; FrCl; CaptChrldr; GAA; IMSpt; Buerge Sch; Nursing.

MILLER, Debra K; Jimtown HS; Elkhart, IN; 5/104 Chr; ChrhWkr; HonRl; LbryAde; NHS; SchMus; 4-H; FHA; PPFtbl; 4-HAwd; Clge; Schl Of Nursing.

MILLER, Dennis R; Burlington HS; Burlington, IA; PolWkr; StuCncl; Bsbl; Bsktbl; College; Business Management.

MILLER, Diane; Blissfield HS; Blissfield, MI; 20/138 Band; ChrhWkr; CncrtBnd; HonRl; HospAde; MrchBnd; RedCrAde; FNA; Toledo Medical Education Center Medical Ass.

MILLER, Diane G; St Edward Public HS; St Edward, NE; Chr; Chrs; ChrhWkr; CmntyWkr; HonRl; LbryAde; NatlThespSoc; SchMus; SchPl; TchrAde; YthFlsp; LetterTrk; CaptChrldr; GAA; College; Special Education.

MILLER, Diane L; Warsaw HS; Warsaw, IL; Chr; HonRl; NHS; Yrbk; FBLA; PresGerCl; Chrldr; GAA; Western Illinois Univ; Accountant.

MILLER, Donald A; Knob Noster HS; Whiteman Afb, MO; HonRl; SciCl; College; Professional.

MILLER, Donna; E Peoria HS; E Peoria, IL; 40/625 ChrhWkr; CmntyWkr; HonRl; NHS; StuGov; RptrYrbk; GerCl; MthCl; SciCl; Ftbl; Bradley; Nursing.

MILLER, Doriane; Elizabeth Seton Hs; Chicago, IL; 20/252 Chrs; HonRl; Mdrgl; NHS; NatlMeritCmnd; SchMus; SchPl; StuCncl; FSA; LatCl; Illinois Institute; Physician.

MILLER, Doug C; Portland HS; Portland, MI; 12/126 HonRl; NHS; TchrAde; LetterBsbl; LetterBsktbl; LetterGlf; LetterTrk; College; Architect.

MILLER, Duane; B G M Community HS; Brooklin, IA; 4/48 HonRl; SchPl; FrCl; PpCl; Univ; Accounting.

MILLER, Duwayne; Arcola HS; Arcola, IL; PresSophCls; HonRl; NHS; YthFlsp;.

MILLER, Earl; Beecher HS; Mount Morris, MI; RptrYrbk; RptrSchPpr; FrCl; Univ Of Mi; Newspaper.

MILLER, Edward; Southern Reynolds HS; Centerville, MO; SchMus; SchPl; StuCncl; 4-H; FFA; Ftbl; Wrstlng; IMSpt; 4-HAwd; RotaryAwd; College; Professional.

MILLER, Eileen M; St Anns HS; Lexington, NE; Band; Chrs; ChrhWkr; HonRl; PepBnd; PolWkr; SchMus; SchPl; SctActv; StuCncl; Swmmng; LetterTrk; Univ Of Ne; Professional.

MILLER, Elaine C; Tremont HS; Tremont, IL; 7/64 HonRl; LbryAde; 4-H; FHA; VPFNA; VPGerCl; BttyCrckrAwd;.

MILLER, Ellen M; Lourdes Academy; Oshkosh, WI; Chrs; EdSchPpr; Vocational Sch; Child Care.

MILLER, Erma; Milford HS; Milford, NE; /47 LbryAde; ;vocation.

MILLER, Gary; Hancock Central HS; Hancock, MI; PresSophCls; HonRl; RedCrAde; SchPl; StuCncl; Yrbk; Ftbl; Trade School; Vocation.

MILLER, Gary L; Wheaton Warrenville HS; Wheaton, IL; 29/212 HonRl; JrNHS; NatlFornLg; NHS; SchMus; SchPl; SctActv; LetterGlf; LetterSocr; Purdue Univ; Mechanical Engineering.

MILLER, Gerald; Superior HS; Guide Rock, NE; 16/96 ChrhWkr; HonRl; SecFFA; Trade Sch; Vet Tech.

MILLER, Gerilyn R; Niles No HS; Skokie, IL; 60/632 CmntyWkr; HonRl; LitMag; NHS; OffAde; SchAde; SchMus; SchPl; TchrAde; University; Art History.

MILLER, Glenn; Marshall University HS; Minneapolis, MN; NatlMeritFnl; PolWkr; Univ Of Mn; Writer.

MILLER, Gregg L; Westview HS; Topeka, IN; Band; CmntyWkr; CncrtBnd; HonRl; MrchBnd; PepBnd; PolWkr; SchPl; RptrSchPpr; GerCl; Trk;.

MILLER, Greg J; Cedarvale HS; Cedarvale, KS; VPFrshCls; VPSophCls; ALBoysSt; SecFrshCls; SchPl; StuCncl; TchrAde; Bsktbl; Ftbl; Trk; Coll.

MILLER, Gregory; Mccluer North HS; Florissant, MO; 84/751 PresFrshCls; HonRl; JrNHS; NHS; NatlMeritSchl; Ftbl; IMSpt; Colleg Univ Of Mo Columbia; General Bus.

MILLER, Gregory A; Maconaquah HS; Peru, IN; 7/259 HonRl; JrNHS; NHS; MthCl; Ftbl; Glf; Swmmng; Trade Schl; Engineer.

MILLER, Gregory S; Watertown HS; Watertown, SD; 5/297 ALBoysSt; Band; Chrs; HonRl; VPNatlFornLg; NHS; NatlMeritSF; Orch; LetterFtbl; BauchLmbAwd; College; Dentist.

MILLER, Greg W; Goshen HS; Goshen, IN; LetterSwmmng; College; Business.

MILLER, Gretchen S; Winfield HS; Winfield, KS; AFS; ChrhWkr; HonRl; LitMag; Orch; 4-H; FrCl; CchngActv; IMSpt; College; Veterinarian.

MILLER, Gwenn C; Wayne Trace HS; Fort Wayne, IN; 5/111 TrsJrCls; SecSrCls; ALAGirlsSt; ChrhWkr; CmntyWkr; HonRl; NHS; OffAde; TchrAde; PresYthFlsp; Pres4-H; PresFTA; PpCl; GAA; College; Professional.

MILLER, Harley; Mc Pherson County HS; Tryon, NE; HonRl; SchPl; StuGov; Bsktbl; Ftbl; Trk; IMSpt; Trade; Vocational.

MILLER, Hazel M; La Moille HS; Arlington, IL; 11/45 Chrs; HonRl; LbryAde; NHS; Yrbk; 4-H; FrCl; PpCl; GAA; PresAwd; College; Cpa.

MILLER, Irene A; Larimore HS; Larimore, ND; ALAGirlsSt; Band; CmntyWkr; CncrtBnd; HonRl; MrchBnd; PepBnd; PolWkr; 4-H; 4-HAwd; Undecided; Conservation.

MILLER, Irvin M; Jefferson HS; Jefferson, WI; Aud/Vis; HonRl; NatlMeritCmnd; FFA; KeyCl; MthCl; Ftbl; University; Professional.

MILLER, James M; Coon Rapids Sr HS; Coon Rapids, MN; 15/732 ALBoysSt; HonRl; JrNHS; LitMag; NatlFornLg; NHS; SchPl; SctActv; StuCncl; StuGov; SchPpr; SpnCl; AmLegAwd; College; Speech.

MILLER, James R; Wahpeton HS; Wahpeton, ND; Band; HonRl; FFA; Wrstlng; College; Agri Business.

MILLER, Janell W; South East Warren HS; Indianola, IA; Chrs; DrlTm; RedCrAde; 4-H; SpnCl; 4-HAwd; Collegef Social Worker.

MILLER, Jane M; Manson HS; Rockwell City, IA; Chrs; CncrtBnd; HonRl; LbryAde; Mdrgl; MrchBnd; NHS; Orch; PepBnd; SchMus; College.

MILLER, Jan M; Moline Sr HS; Coal Valley, IL; 28/845 ChrhWkr; CmntyWkr; HonRl; LitMag; NHS; SctActv; 4-H; LetterTrk; 4-HAwd; Black Hawk Jr College; Accountant.

MILLER, Jean; Central Christian HS; Patridge, KS; 1/22 SecJrCls; TrsSrCls; Chr; Chrs; ChrhWkr; HonRl; BttyCrckrAwd;.

MILLER, Jeffrey; Greenfield HS; Greenfield, IL; 21/57 VPJrCls; VPSrCls; Band; SchMus; SptEdYrbk; FrCl; College; Professional.

MILLER, Jeffrey; Tuttle Public HS; Tuttle, ND; 2/10 VPFrshCls; HonRl; SchPl; SptEdSchPpr; PpCl; Bsktbl; Trk; VoiceDemAwd; Univ Of Nd; Pre Medicine.

MILLER, Jeffrey; South HS; Sheboygan, WI; 35/495 ChrhWkr; CmntyWkr; HonRl; NatlFornLg; NHS; SctActv; StuCncl; StuGov; Swmmng; Carroll Coolege; Pre Med.

MILLER, Jeffrey C; Le Center Public HS; Le Center, MN; Band; CmntyWkr; CncrtBnd; HonRl; MrchBnd; NHS; PepBnd; SchPl; SctActv; YthFlsp; SchPpr; Bsktbl; St Johns Univ.

MILLER, Jerri A; Unity HS; Mendon, IL; 5/87 PresFrshCls; ChrhWkr; HonRl; StuCncl; VPSpnCl; PpCl; Trk; CaptChrldr; TreasGAA; 4-HAwd; College; Teaching.

MILLER, Jerry; North Putnam HS; Roachdale, IN; 29#36#41 JrNHS; NHS; NatlMeritSchl; Bsbl; Bsktbl; Ftbl; Trk; Purdue Univ; Industrial Management.

MILLER, Jnell M; West Smith County HS; Kensington, KS; 3/24 PresSophCls; Chr; HonRl; NHS; SchMus; SchPl; PpCl; CitAwd; College; Business.

MILLER, Joan; Villa Duchesne HS; St Louis, MO; PresJrCls; Chrs; HospAde; JA; ModUN; PolWkr; SchMus; SchPl; StuCncl; StuGov; IMSpt; College; Lawyer.

MILLER, Joan; Acad Of Our Lady; Washington, IL; 9/98 ChrhWkr; CmntyWkr; HonRl; JA; NHS; PolWkr; Sdlty; StuCncl; Yrbk; SchPpr; Illinois Central College; Accounting.

MILLER, Joan M; Joliet Central HS; Joliet, IL; 25/491 Chr; Chrs; HonRl; NHS; OffAde; ROTC; Joliet Jr College; Nursing.

MILLER, Joanne; Milton HS; Janesville, WI; HonRl; TchrAde; FHA; LatCl; Swmmng; Trk; Vocational School; Nursing.

MILLER, Joanne I; Grayslake HS; Grayslake, IL; 10/210 TrsFrshCls; TrsSophCls; TrsJrCls; TrsSrCls; AFS; Band; Chrs; DrlTm; HonRl; NatlMeritCmnd; Illinois State Univ; Special Education.

MILLER, John L; Royall HS; Elroy, WI; 21/106 Band; ChrhWkr; HonRl; MrchBnd; PepBnd; StuGov; Bsktbl; Ftbl; Glf; Trk; U Of Wis La Crosse; Bus Admin.

MILLER, John L; Jackson HS; Jackson, MI; PresFrshCls; HonRl; SchMus; SchPl; StuCncl; StuGov; Michigan State University; Food Science.

MILLER, John M; Dundee HS; Dundee, MI; HonRl; CaptBsbl; CaptBsktbl; LetterFtbl; OptClAwd; Central Mich Univ.

MILLER, John V; Beaman Conrad Liscomb HS; Albion, IA; 35/50 VPFrshCls; Chrs; HonRl; YthFlsp; 4-H; PpCl; LetterBsbl; LetterBsktbl; LetterFtbl; LetterTrk; College; Business Admin.

MILLER, John W; Mt Olive HS; Mt Olive, IL; 7/56 HonRl; StuCncl; Yrbk; PpCl; Univ Of Illinois; Commerce.

MILLER, Jonathan D; Iowa City West HS; Iowa City, IA; Band; CmntyWkr; HonRl; MrchBnd; NHS; NatlMeritCmnd; PepBnd; RptrYrbk; RptrSchPpr; Trk; Carleton Clg.

MILLER, Jordan R; Morgan Park Academy; Chicago, IL; 3/39 SecTrsFrshCls; TrsSophCls; ChrhWkr; CmntyWkr; HonRl; LitMag; ModUN; NHS; NatlMeritCmnd; PolWkr; StuCncl; StuGov; Bsbl; Bsktbl; University; Law.

MILLER, Joyce M; St Patrick HS; Portland, MI; 6/45 Chrs; HonRl; NHS; SchPl; Yrbk; Chrldr; IMSpt; PPFtbl; CitAwd;.

MILLER, Judith K; Beloit Memorial HS; Beloit, WI; 82/549 Band; CncrtBnd; HonRl; MrchBnd; NatlFornLg; YthFlsp; LetterTrk; College; Education.

MILLER, Judy; Holy Family Acad; Chicago, IL; VPSrCls; Chr; DrmMjrt; SchMus; Yrbk; SpnCl; Bsktbl; Chrldr; IMSpt; CitAwd; Chicago Circle Campus; Law Student.

MILLER, Julia E; St Clement HS; Center Line, MI; HonRl; NHS; PpCl; GAA; Coll; Business.

MILLER, Julie A; Delavan Unit Dist #703 HS; Delavan, IL; ChrhWkr; DrlTm; HonRl; NatlThespSoc; SchMus; SchPl; SecStuCncl; RptrYrbk; EdYrBk; RptrSchPpr; George Williams Clg; Social Work.

MILLER, Julie L; Raymond Central HS; Ceresco, NE; VPFrshCls; PresSophCls; PresJrCls; Band; CncrtBnd; HonRl; MrchBnd; NHS; PepBnd; SchPl; StuCncl; TchrAde; RptrYrbk; Yrbk; Chrldr; College; Liberal Arts.

MILLER, Julie M; Jennings County HS; Butlerville, IN; Band; ChrhWkr; CncrtBnd; MrchBnd; OffAde; PepBnd; 4-H; LatCl; 4-HAwd; College; Nursing.

MILLER, Karen J; Harvard HS; Harvard, IL; Band; Chrs; CncrtBnd; MrchBnd; College; Secretarial Science.

MILLER, Karen L; Homewood Flossmoor HS; Olympia Fields, IL; 18/932 CmntyWkr; HonRl; LitMag; NHS; Orch; SctActv; College; Creative Writing.

MILLER, Karen M; Goodrich Public HS; Goodrich, ND; PresJrCls; ALAGirlsSt; Band; Chr; HonRl; NHS; StuCncl; LetterBsktbl; LetterChrldr; LetterGAA; Concordia Coll; Lawyer.

MILLER, Karen P; North Knox HS; Bicknell, IN; 12 130 ChrhWkr; DrlTm; LbryAde; NHS; LatCl; MthCl; Univ Vincennes; Physical Therapy.

MILLER, Karen S; Auburndale HS; Milladore, WI; ChrhWkr; HonRl; NHS; 4-H; FBLA; FHA; PpCl; 4-HAwd; PresAwd; Bus School; Secretary.

MILLER, Katherine I; Pinckney HS; Pinckney, MI; Band; Chr; HonRl; SchPl; SctActv; Trk; GAA; IMSpt; Michigan State Univ; Forest Ranger.

MILLER, Katheryn; Matthews HS; Matthews, MO; Chrs; HonRl; SchPl; Yrbk; FHA; College; Data Processing.

MILLER, Kathleen A; Les Cheneaux Comm HS; Hessel, MI; 2/29 HonRl; NHS; SchPl; TchrAde; LetterTrk; Coll; Med Tech.

MILLER, Kathleen M; Carrollton HS; Carrollton, MO; VPSophCls; ChrhWkr; HonRl; VPNHS; StuCncl; 4-H; TreasFHA; Chrldr; IMSpt; 4-HAwd; College; Bus Acctnt Or Secretary.

MILLER, Kathryn; Heelan HS; Sioux City, IA; 23/247 HonRl; LbryAde; NHS; RedCrAde; TchrAde; SchPpr; FrCl; PpCl; JAAwd; College; Social Work.

MILLER, Kathryn D; Shakamak HS; Jasonville, IN; 15/70 Band; ChrhWkr; DrmMjrt; Quill&Scroll; RptrYrbk; 4-H; PpCl; Bsktbl; Chrldr; GAA; Indiana State Univ; Physical Ed Teacher.

MILLER, Kathy A; Centreville HS; Sturgis, MI; 5/56 Band; HonRl; HospAde; NHS; StuCncl; Yrbk; RptrSchPpr; PresFHA; PpCl; Bsktbl; 4-HAwd; Glen Oaks College; Lpn.

MILLER, Kay A; Otis Bison Sr HS; Bison, KS; Band; Chr; Chrs; ChrhWkr; CmntyWkr; CncrtBnd; HonRl; JA; Mdrgl; MrchBnd; NHS; PepBnd; YthFlsp; Pres4-H; 4-HAwd; College; Music Therapist.

MILLER, Keith J; Omaha Benson HS; Omaha, NE; HonRl; LetterBsbl; Col; Vocation.

MILLER, Kendra K; Harrisonville HS; Harrisonville, MO; AFS; Band; Chrs; HonRl; MrchBnd; SchPl; StuCncl; RptrSchPpr; PpCl; IMSpt; College; Musical Or English Career.

MILLER, Kenneth P; Marquette HS; Marseilles, IL; 4/98 ChrhWkr; CmntyWkr; HonRl; CaptFtbl; College; Business.

MILLER, Kent W; East HS; Wichita, KS; HonRl; LbryAde; OffAde; SctActv; FrCl; LatCl; Glf; Univ; Engineering.

MILLER, Kevin; Macomb Senior Hs; Colchester, IL; Band; ChrhWkr; CncrtBnd; HonRl; MrchBnd; PepBnd; Ftbl; Glf; LetterWrstlng;.

MILLER, Kevin B; Hoover HS; Des Moines, IA; 4/355 HonRl; ModUN; NatlFornLg; SciCl; IMSpt; ChmbCommrsAwd; OptClAwd; Uni; Medicine.

MILLER, Kevin J; Harvard HS; Harvard, IL; 1/185 HonRl; JrNHS; NHS; GerCl; Univ; Vet.

MILLER, Kimberly J; Parshall HS; Parshall, ND; 13/48 Band; Chr; Chrl; Chrs; ChrhWkr; CmntyWkr; CncrtBnd; MrchBnd; Orch; PepBnd; College.

MILLER, Larry E; Bellevue Comm HS; Bellevue, MI; 19/114 ALBoysSt; PresChrhWkr; HonRl; NHS; SctActv; Pres4-H; FFA; SpnCl; CaptTrk; 4-HAwd; Michigan State University; Vet.

MILLER, Larry L; Eisehower HS; Saginaw, MI; 41/365 Band; CncrtBnd; HonRl; MrchBnd; NHS; PepBnd; SctActv; Delta College; Dentist.

MILLER, Laura L; Dodge Public HS; Dodge, NE; RptrSchPpr; 4-H; SpnCl; PpCl; Army.

MILLER, Lauren; Lake Central HS; Schererville, IN; 45/454 NatlThespSoc; SchMus; SchPl; StuCncl; StuGov; TchrAde; FrCl; Indiana U; Physical Therapist.

MILLER, Leisa A; Howell HS; Howell, MI; 26/362 NHS; SchAde; TchrAde; Yrbk; 4-H; Bsbl; Bsktbl; Ftbl; GAA; PPFtbl; Mi State Univ; Computer Programming.

MILLER, Leon; Pewamo Westphalia HS; Eagle, MI; Chrs; HonRl; NHS; SchMus; SchPl; StuCncl; StuGov; TchrAde; Wrstlng; Mich Univ; Microbiology.

MILLER, Lin A; Sparta HS; Sparta, MI; HonRl; LitMag; NHS; StuCncl; StuGov; TchrAde; FTA; PpCl; LetterBsktbl; ChmnFtbl; College; Physical Ed.

MILLER, Lisa; North Knox HS; Bicknell, IN; 1/123 ChrhWkr; DrlTm; HonRl; NHS; OffAde; SchAde; Chrldr; DARAwd; 4-HAwd; CitAwd; Iuput; Nursing.

MILLER, Lori A; Charleston HS; Charleston, IL; 31/262 Band; HonRl; ModUN; NHS; NatlMeritCmnd; PolWkr; RptrSchPpr; Univ; Journalism.

MILLER, Luie; Goshen HS; Goshen, IN; CmntyWkr; IMSpt; College; Professional.

MILLER, Lynn; Sheyenne River Acad; Manfred, ND; TrsJrCls; Band; Chrl; Chrs; ChrhWkr; HonRl; IMSpt; Union Coll; Med.

MILLER, Lynne E; Brimfield HS; Brimfield, IL; Chrs; HonRl; LbryAde; SpnCl; PpCl;.

MILLER, Marc A; Fayette HS; Fayette, IA; PresSophCls; HonRl; NHS; NatlMeritCmnd; FFA; Bsktbl; Iowa State U; Vet.

MILLER, Marc W; Keota Comm HS; Keota, IA; 4/59 Band; ChrhWkr; CncrtBnd; HonRl; SecFrshCls; SctActv; LetterFtbl; LetterTrk; Iowa St Univ; Biologist.

MILLER, Margaret M; Salem Sr HS; Salem, MO; SecJrCls; HonRl; JrNHS; NatlMeritCmnd; SchPl; RptrYrbk; SchPpr; SciCl; PPFtbl; Stephens College; Reading Specialist.

MILLER, Margaret M; Mancelona HS; Mancelona, MI; ChrhWkr; CmntyWkr; HonRl; NHS; OffAde; SchPl; StuGov; Yrbk; 4-H; SpnCl; Community College; Journalism.

MILLER, Maria D; Woodruff HS; Peoria, IL; 19/282 Chr; HonRl; ModUN; NHS; SchMus; StuCncl; FrCl; CaptChrldr; Ohio St U; Psychologist.

MILLER, Marian; Papillion La Vista Sr HS; Papillion, NE; 20/318 ChrhWkr; HonRl; NHS; SchAde; TchrAde; FBLA; FTA; GerCl; PpCl; Kearney St Coll; Elem Teacher.

MILLER, Marianne A; Tri County Area HS; Howard City, MI; 16/94 Band; HonRl; LitMag; OffAde; SchMus; TchrAde; YthFlsp; RptrYrbk; SptEdYrbk; RptrSchPpr; Aquinas Clg; Prof Writer.

MILLER, Mark; Savannah R Iii HS; Savannah, MO; PresFrshCls; VPSrCls; Ftbl; Business.

MILLER, Mark; Platte HS; Platte, SD; ALBoysSt; SecFrshCls; PresSophCls; HonRl; Mdrgl; PepBnd; SctActv; SpnCl; Bsbl; Ftbl; Trk; College; Electrical Eng.

MILLER, Mark A; St Louis Univ HS; Florissant, MO; Band; CncrtBnd; NatlMeritFnl; NatlMeritSchl; SchMus; LetterBsktbl; LetterFtbl; IMSpt; Univ Of Missouri; Medicine.

MILLER, Mark C; South Central HS; Elizabeth, IN; Band; FFA; LetterBsktbl; LetterTrk;.

MILLER, Mark D; Warren HS; Warren, IL; Band; Chrs; CncrtBnd; Mdrgl; MrchBnd; PepBnd; SchMus; SchPl; LetterTrk; Trade School; Home Entertainment Elec.

MILLER, Mark H; Clay Center Public HS; Clay Center, NE; 2/30 TrsFrshCls; TrsSophCls; Band; CncrtBnd; HonRl; MrchBnd; NHS; Bsktbl; Trk; College; Professional.

MILLER, Mark L; Raymond Central HS; Ceresco, NE; VPJrCls; ALBoysSt; HonRl; LetterFtbl; LetterWrstlng; Univ Of Nebraska; Police Officer.

MILLER, Mark W; Central HS; Camp Point, IL; 5/75 ALBoysSt; HonRl; SchPl; SctActv; YthFlsp; SptEdSchPpr; GerCl; LetterFtbl; Glf; LetterTrk; ElDAwd; Central College; Language Specialist.

MILLER, Mary; Bishop Leblond HS; St Joseph, MO; 14/114 SecJrCls; Chrs; HonRl; NatlFornLg; NHS; Quill&Scroll; Yrbk; Mo West State College; Nursing.

MILLER, Mary; Mishawaka Marian HS; Elkhart, IN; 2/117 PresFrshCls; PresJrCls; AFS; HonRl; JrNHS; NHS; NatlMeritCmnd; SchMus; Purdue Univ; Engineering.

MILLER, Mary E; Fall River HS; Fall River, WI; 6/33 SecJrCls; AFS; ALAGirlsSt; Band; HonRl; NatlFornLg; SchPl; TchrAde; 4-H; FHA; Bsktbl; Trk; CaptChrldr; DARAwd; College; Psychology.

MILLER, Mary L; Marian HS; Elkhart, IN; 3/117 PresFrshCls; PresJrCls; HonRl; NHS; NatlMeritCmnd; StuGov; SchPpr; CaptSwmmng; CchngActv; IMSpt; Eng.

MILLER, Mary M; Derham Hall HS; St Paul, MN; HonRl; NHS; StuCncl; StuGov; FrCl; Univ Of Minnesota; Fashion Merchandising.

MILLER, Melinda D; Christopher HS; Christopher, IL; Chr; Chrs; ChrhWkr; HonRl; JrNHS; LbryAde; College; Music.

MILLER, Melledy E; Redfield HS; Redfield, SD; Band; Chrs; ChrhWkr; CncrtBnd; HonRl; Mdrgl; PepBnd; SchMus; SchPl; VPYthFlsp; LetterTennis; College; Music.

MILLER, Mercer W; Downers Grove North HS; Downers Grove, IL; Band; CncrtBnd; HonRl; MrchBnd; NHS; Univ Of Illinois; Lawyer.

MILLER, Michael; Redfield HS; Redfield, SD; ALBoysSt; HonRl; NHS; PolWkr; SchMus; SchPl; StuCncl; TchrAde; RptrYrbk; FTA; Northern State College; Elementary Educaton.

MILLER, Michael D; George Washington HS; Indianapolis, IN; 17/284 VPBand; HonRl; ModUN; NatlSciFnd; SctActv; TchrAde; FSA; SpnCl; MthCl; SciCl; Col; Oceanographer.

MILLER, Michael D; Marian Central HS; Mc Henry, IL; 6/119 HstJrCls; TrsSrCls; HonRl; NHS; NatlMeritCmnd; NatlMeritSF; PolWkr; EdSchPpr; Bsktbl; LetterSocr; Trk; Marquette University; Psychology.

MILLER, Michael E; Mater Dei HS; Evansville, IN; 8/162 PolWkr; StuGov; RptrYrbk; EdSchPpr; SciCl; LetterGlf; Wrstlng; IMSpt; U Of Notre Dame; Engineering.

MILLER, Michael E; Lincoln HS; Manitowoc, WI; HonRl; LetterFtbl; LetterTrk; College; Electronics.

MILLER, Michael J; Brunnerdale Sem HS; S Milwaukee, WI; 3/13 VPSophCls; Chr; HonRl; NHS; PolWkr; SchPl; RptrSchPpr; SciCl; Socr; Univ Of Wisconsin; Special Ed.

MILLER, Michael J; Donnybrook Public HS; Donnybrook, ND; 2/7 TrsFrshCls; SecSophCls; ALBoysSt; Chr; Chrs; ChrhWkr; CmntyWkr; HonRl; Bsbl; Bsktbl; Wahpeton; Diesel Mech & Farming.

MILLER, Michael N; East Rockford HS; Rockford, IL; 30/665 ChrhWkr; HonRl; NatlMeritSF; Orch; SchMus; EdSchPpr; Ill State Univ; Clergy.

MILLER, Michelle A; Fosston HS; Fosston, MN; 7/95 AFS; Chr; ChrhWkr; CncrtBnd; HonRl; HospAde; NHS; SctActv; RptrYrbk; Chrldr; Moorehead State Col;.

MILLER, Mike; Mater Dei HS; Evansville, IN; 8/162 PolWkr; StuGov; RptrYrbk; EdSchPpr; SciCl; LetterGlf; Wrstlng; IMSpt; U Of Notre Dame; Engineering.

MILLER, Mildred L; Beaumont HS; St Louis, MO; 79/800 ChrhWkr; HonRl; OffAde; Quill&Scroll; SchAde; TchrAde; RptrSchPpr; LetterTrk; GAA; College; Psychologist.

MILLER, Nancy M; Carmel Girls HS; Barrington, IL; 11/173 HonRl; NHS; PresStuCncl; StuGov; LatCl; GAA; St Marys College; Liberal Arts.

MILLER, Natalie J; Sac Community HS; Sac City, IA; Band; ChrhWkr; CncrtBnd; HonRl; HospAde; MrchBnd; StuCncl; RptrSchPpr; TreasFHA; PpCl; Clge; Home Ec.

MILLER, Neal A; Wausau West HS; Wausau, WI; StuGov; Technical School; Electronics.

MILLER, Norman A; Burris Laboratory HS; Muncie, IN; LitMag; SctActv; Business.

MILLER, Pahi; Allison Bristow Comm HS; Allison, IA; TrsFrshCls; VPSophCls; VPJrCls; ALAGirlsSt; ChrhWkr; HonRl; SctActv; YthFlsp; PpCl; Jr Coll; Legal Secretary.

MILLER, Pamela R; Newton HS; Willow Hill, IL; Chrs; HonRl; FHA; IMSpt; Col; Bookkeeping.

MILLER, Pamela R; Battle Creek Central HS; Battle Creek, MI; 11/739 VPFrshCls; TrsSophCls; TrsJrCls; Chr; ChrhWkr; CmntyWkr; HonRl; NHS; OffAde; SchMus; SctActv; StuCncl; StuGov; Chrldr; Univ Of Michigan; Medicine.

MILLER, Pamela S; Jefferson Co North HS; Winchester, KS; DrlTm; HonRl; LbryAde; NHS; OffAde; SchMus; FBLA; FHA; PpCl; Modeling Sch; Model.

MILLER, Patricia; Red Bud HS; Red Bud, IL; 15/135 VPSrCls; HonRl; NHS; OffAde; StuGov; PpCl; IMSpt; Bookkeeping.

MILLER, Patricia D; Elkhart Central HS; Elkhart, IN; 1/470 ChrhWkr; HonRl; SecNHS; Teen; YthFlsp; Yrbk; PpCl; JCAwd; Purdue Univ; Mathematics.

MILLER, Patricia L; Columbus HS; Columbus, NE; 26/294 Chr; Chrs; HonRl; SchMus; SchPl; YthFlsp; PpCl; Chrldr; Universtiy; Legal Sec.

MILLER, Patrick R; Kingsford HS; Iron Mountain, MI; 26/165 Band; Chrl; CmntyWkr; CncrtBnd; DrlTm; DrmBgl; HonRl; MrchBnd; NHS; Orch; Mi Tech Univ; Engineering.

MILLER, Patti L; Tonica HS; Tonica, IL; 10/46 SecFrshCls; SecJrCls; HonRl; SchMus; StuCncl; FHA; SpnCl; Chrldr; College; Lawyer.

MILLER, Paula R; West Michigan Christian HS; Muskegon, MI; Band; Chr; HonRl; PresJA; LbryAde; SctActv; PpCl; Bsktbl; Trk; GAA; Muskegon Comm Clge; Secretarial.

MILLER, Paul H; West Platte R Ii HS; Farley, MO; VPSrCls; AFS; ALBoysSt; ModUN; NHS; StuCncl; Yrbk; Bsbl; CaptBsktbl; Ftbl; Trk; College.

MILLER, Pauline A; Morton HS; Hammond, IN; 10/492 ChrhWkr; LbryAde; NHS; NatlMeritSF; StuGov; TchrAde; Purdue U; Veterinarian.

MILLER, Pauline A; Morton Sr HS; Hammond, IN; 10/492 ChrhWkr; HonRl; LbryAde; NHS; NatlMeritFnl; StuGov; Purdue Univ; Veterinarian.

MILLER, Paul K; Douglas Macarthur HS; Decatur, IL; 1/400 CncrtBnd; DrmMjrt; HonRl; LitMag; NHS; NatlSciFnd; NatlThespSoc; SchMus; SchPl; Washington Univ; Medicine.

MILLER, Peggy; Barnum HS; Barnum, MN; 6/58 TrsSrCls; Band; Chr; ChrhWkr; CncrtBnd; HonRl; NHS; PepBnd; Quill&Scroll; SchPl; EdYrBk; RptrSchPpr; 4-H; FTA; FrCl; Coll; Broadcasting.

MILLER, Philip E; Highland Park HS; Fort Sheridan, IL; SctActv; Teen; Bsbl; Bsktbl; LetterFtbl; IMSpt; Purdue Univ; Professional.

MILLER, Phillip A; Spooner HS; Spooner, WI; 6/123 TrsJrCls; CncrtBnd; HonRl; MrchBnd; PepBnd; SchMus; MthCl; SciCl; Glf; Trk; Trade School; Pilot.

MILLER, Phyllis J; Mahnomen HS; Mahnomen, MN; 17/83 VPSrCls; HonRl; NHS; SchMus; YthFlsp; RptrSchPpr; FTA; GAA; 4-HAwd; CitAwd; Trade Schl; Practical Nurse.

MILLER, Ralph; York Community HS; Elmhurst, IL; Chr; HonRl; NHS; NatlMeritCmnd; NatlThespSoc; Orch; SchMus; SchPl; MthCl; University; Cinema Drama.

MILLER, Rebekah L; Indian Creek Sr HS; Trafalgar, IN; Chr; ChrhWkr; SchMus; YthFlsp; 4-H; SpnCl; SciCl; Bsktbl; Chrldr; GAA; PPFtbl; University; Professional.

MILLER, Renee A; Starkweather Public HS; Webster, ND; PresSophCls; SecJrCls; Chrs; HonRl; SchPl; StuCncl; TchrAde; RptrSchPpr; Bsktbl; Chrldr; Coll.

MILLER, Richard; Leroy Ostrander HS; Leroy, MN; ChrhWkr; HonRl; 4-H; FFA; LetterBsktbl; Ftbl; IMSpt; 4-HAwd; PresAwd; Vocational School.

MILLER, Richard D; Midway U S D HS; Denton, KS; VPJrCls; CncrtBnd; HonRl; MrchBnd; PepBnd; RedCrAde; SctActv; Bsktbl; LetterFtbl; Swmmng; Trk; College; Professional.

MILLER, Richard J; Springfield Southeast HS; Springfield, IL; 17/503 HonRl; JrNHS; NHS; KeyCl; CaptFtbl; Glf; CaptWrstlng; CchngActv; GovHonPrgAwd; University.

MILLER, Rita M; Iowa Mennonite HS; Wellman, IA; 5/39 PresSophCls; Chr; Chrs; ChrhWkr; CmntyWkr; HonRl; JrNHS; NHS; OffAde; SchAde; TchrAde; YthFlsp; RptrSchPpr; Bsktbl; College; Nurse.

MILLER, Robert; Volmeyer HS; Valmeyer, IL; 10/59 Chrs; HonRl; NHS; Orch; SchPl; TchrAde; Yrbk; MthCl; Univ Of Ill; Accounting.

MILLER, Robert D; Naperville Central HS; Naperville, IL; PresFrshCls; PresSrCls; HonRl; StuCncl; StuGov; College; Lawyer.

MILLER, Robert E; Normal Comm HS; Normal, IL; LetterFtbl; CaptTrk; Il Wesleyan; Business Administration.

MILLER, Robert L; Benton Cons HS; Benton, IL; 11/168 HonRl; NatlFornLg; NHS; RptrSchPpr; KeyCl; College.

MILLER, Robert W; Streator Township HS; Streator, IL; 131/371 FFA; GerCl; Bsktbl; College; Fish Wildlife Manager.

MILLER, Rue A; Tina Avalon HS; Tina, MO; ChrhWkr; HonRl; NHS; PepBnd; FHA; PpCl; SciCl; LetterBsbl; LetterBsktbl; 4-HAwd; College; Child Development.

MILLER, Russell W; Southport HS; Indianapolis, IN; NatlFornLg; NHS; NatlMeritSF; 4-H; FrCl; MthCl; SciCl; 4-HAwd; OptClAwd; VoiceDemAwd; Indiana Univ; Lawyer.

MILLER, Ruth; Mexico HS; Mexico, MO; 6/248 Band; Chr; CncrtBnd; JrNHS; MrchBnd; NatlFornLg; NHS; SchMus; 4-H; LatCl; College; Medical Technology.

MILLER, Ruth; Evanston Township Hs; Evanston, IL; 2 HonRl; NatlMeritFnl; Quill&Scroll; SchMus; StuCncl; StuGov; Yrbk; CaptSwmmng; Chrldr; CchngActv; U Of Michigan;professional Medicine.

MILLER, Sandra; El Paso HS; El Paso, IL; Chrl; Chrs; LbryAde; FHA; PpCl; IMSpt; Nurses Aid.

MILLER, Sandra S; Jefferson City Sr HS; Jefferson City, MO; Chr; HonRl; JrNHS; NHS; YthFlsp; FHA; MthCl; PpCl; GAA; College; Engineering.

MILLER, Scott J; Lincoln HS; Manitowoc, WI; ALBoysSt; LetterFtbl; LetterTrk; University; Horticulturalist.

MILLER, Sharla L; Iowa Mennonite School; Kalona, IA; SecFrshCls; Chr; ChrhWkr; HonRl; NHS; RptrSchPpr; PpCl; LetterTrk; LetterChrldr; IMSpt; Goshen College.

MILLER, Sheila K; Chaffee HS; Chaffee, MO; Chr; HonRl; SchMus; StuCncl; Col St Univ; Vet Med.

MILLER, Sheila K; Corona HS; Milbank, SD; 1/10 SecJrCls; SecSrCls; ALAGirlsSt; Band; HonRl; LbryAde; SchPl; EdSchPpr; 4-H; PpCl; Coll; Elementary Education.

MILLER, Sheri L; Holly HS; Holly, MI; 6/215 DrmBgl; HonRl; MrchBnd; NatlFornLg; NHS; PepBnd; Yrbk; FrCl; LetterTrk; LetterChrldr; Nursing School; Nurse.

MILLER, Sherrie L; East Grand Forks Central HS; East Grand Forks, MN; Band; HonRl; MrchBnd; NHS; PepBnd; College; Social Worker.

MILLER, Stacy L; Freeport Sr HS; Freeport, IL; 130/550 Chr; HonRl; MrchBnd; Univ Of Illinois; Recreation Admin.

MILLER, Stanley D; Risco HS; Risco, MO; PresSrCls; Chr; ChrhWkr; OffAde; SchMus; SchPl; Yrbk; FFA; Bsbl; Bsktbl; Three Rvrs Comm Clg; Phy Athletic Director.

MILLER, Stanly B; Isle HS; Isle, MN; 2/55 PresJrCls; VPSrCls; Band; HonRl; NHS; StuGov; SptEdSchPpr; CaptFtbl; CaptTrk; CaptWrstlng; Bethel Clge; Elem Ed & Coach.

MILLER, Stefanie; Medford Senior HS; Medford, WI; Chr; HonRl; JrNHS; NHS; SchPl; StuCncl; SpnCl; Univ Of Mn; Clinical Psychology.

MILLER, Stephanie K; Lakeview HS; Decatur, IL; 19/187 AFS; Chr; OffAde; Illinois State Univ; Medical Tech.

MILLER, Stephen; Rockhurst HS; Kansas City, MO; 10/220 HonRl; NatlFornLg; StuCncl; StuGov; SptEdSchPpr; LatCl; Socr; Tennis; IMSpt; College Or Univ; Professional.

MILLER, Stephen S; Parkside HS; Jackson, MI; ChrhWkr; NatlFornLg; Univ Of Michigan; Engineering.

MILLER, Steve L; North HS; Sheboygan, WI; Band; Chr; Chrl; Chrs; ChrhWkr; CncrtBnd; HonRl; Mdrgl; Orch; IMSpt; KiwanAwd; College; Music.

MILLER, Steven; Harper Creek HS; Battle Creek, MI; 52/203 StuGov; College; Photographic.

MILLER, Steven D; Tinley Park HS; Tinley Park, IL; 16/245 CmntyWkr; HonRl; JrNHS; NHS; SctActv; Yrbk; SpnCl; Univ; Wildlife Conservation.

MILLER, Steven D; Dalton Public HS; Dalton, NE; 4/20 PresSophCls; Chrs; ChrhWkr; HonRl; Mdrgl; SchPl; StuCncl; YthFlsp; LetterBsktbl; LetterFtbl; LetterTrk; Univ Of Nebraska.

MILLER, Steven J; Zionsville Comm HS; Zionsville, IN; Band; VPCncrtBnd; HonRl; MrchBnd; NHS; PepBnd; College; Science.

MILLER, Sue J; Wabeno HS; Wabeno, WI; 1/33 Chrs; HonRl; NHS; SchPl; Yrbk; FBLA; FHA; PpCl; LetterBsktbl; BttyCrckrAwd; Uw Of Eau Claire; Special Education.

MILLER, Susan; Taylorville HS; Taylorville, IL; 15/251 Chr; HonRl; SchPl; RptrYrbk; RptrSchPpr; VP4-H; FTA; PresFrCl; PpCl; 4-HAwd; U Of Il; Agriculture.

MILLER, Susan A; Sparta Senior HS; Sparta, WI; Chr; Chrs; ChrhWkr; HonRl; Mdrgl; SchMus; StuCncl; College; Music.

MILLER, Susan E; Pana Sr HS; Pana, IL; 13/149 Chrs; CncrtBnd; HonRl; NHS; OffAde; StuCncl; 4-H; FBLA; Chrldr; GAA; E Il Univ; Mngmnt.

MILLER, Susan E; Lawrenceburg HS; Lawrenceburg, IN; 20/100 Band; CncrtBnd; HonRl; JrNHS; MrchBnd; NHS; FHA; SpnCl; PpCl; Swmmng; University; Pharmacy.

MILLER, Sylvia R; Hirsch HS; Hazel Crest, IL; SecFrshCls; VPSophCls; TrsJrCls; CmntyWkr; HonRl; LbryAde; NatlMeritCmnd; OffAde; Yrbk; Chrldr; Clge; Pro.

MILLER, Tamara A; Blue Valley HS; Stilwell, KS; Chr; DrlTm; HonRl; NHS; RptrYrbk; PpCl; College; Vocation.

MILLER, Tamela M; Lincolnwood HS; Raymond, IL; 1/56 CncrtBnd; HonRl; MrchBnd; NHS; SpnCl; College; Anthropology.

MILLER, Terri L; Bonner Springs HS; Bonner Springs, KS; VPCncrtBnd; HonRl; TreasLatCl; PpCl; RotaryAwd;.

MILLER, Terry; Chysler Hs; New Castle, IN; Band; CncrtBnd; MrchBnd; Pres4-H; SpnCl; 4-HAwd; College; Math Teacher.

MILLER, Terry G; U S D #297 HS; St Francis, KS; VPJrCls; SecSrCls; Chr; Chrs; ChrhWkr; CmntyWkr; HonRl; SchPl; SctActv; StuCncl; Clg; Pharmacy.

MILLER, Terry L; Fairfax Riii HS; Fairfax, MO; 3/25 PresFrshCls; Band; CncrtBnd; HonRl; MrchBnd; PepBnd; SchPl; FHA; PpCl; Chrldr; Business Sch; Receptionist.

MILLER, Terry L; Chrisman HS; Chrisman, IL; 3/41 HonRl; TreasNHS; SchPl; Yrbk; 4-H; SpnCl; Illinois State Univ; Accounting.

MILLER, Terry L; Wayne HS; Ft Wayne, IN; 5/302 Band; ChrhWkr; CmntyWkr; CncrtBnd; HonRl; MrchBnd; Orch; PepBnd; SecKeyCl; ChmbCommrsAwd; Indiana Univ; Law.

MILLER, Terry L; Bremen HS; Bremen, IN; 6/105 ChrhWkr; HonRl; MrchBnd; PresNHS; NatlMeritCmnd; PepBnd; Yrbk; 4-H; FrCl; MthCl; Rose Hulman Inst Of Tech; Engineering.

MILLER, Terry P; Tonganoxie HS; Tonganoxie, KS; ChrhWkr; HonRl; TchrAde; YthFlsp; FFA; SpnCl; Bsbl; Trk; Auto Body Sch; Body Man.

MILLER, Theresa M; Hackett HS; Kalamazoo, MI; ChrhWkr; CmntyWkr; HonRl; JrNHS; LbryAde; NHS; OffAde; RedCrAde; SchAde; Tennis; Kalamazoo Valley Community; Sociologist.

MILLER, Thomas G; Notre Dame HS; Burlington, IA; Band; CncrtBnd; HonRl; JA; MrchBnd; NHS; PepBnd; PolWkr; Iowa State University; Civil Engineering.

MILLER, Thomas H; Ogemaw Heights HS; West Branch, MI; NHS; FFA; KeyCl; Bsktbl; Ftbl; College; Professional.

MILLER, Thomas W; Marist HS; Chicago, IL; 26/393 Aud/Vis; ChrhWkr; HonRl; PolWkr; SpnCl; Tennis; IMSpt; AmLegAwd; College; Business.

MILLER, Timothy L; Jamestown HS; Jamestown, ND; 7/324 Band; Chr; HonRl; NatlFornLg; NHS; NatlMeritCmnd; SchPl; StuCncl; RptrSchPpr; GerCl; St Olaf Clg; Medicine.

MILLER, Toby E; Penny HS; Hamilton, MO; VPSophCls; Band; CncrtBnd; HonRl; JA; MrchBnd; Orch; PepBnd; SchPl; StuCncl; College; Photographer.

MILLER, Tommy J; Welch HS; Chetopa, KS; HstFrshCls; SecTrsSophCls; SecTrsJrCls; SchMus; SchPl; RptrSchPpr; FFA; Bsbl; Bsktbl; Ftbl; Trk; CchngActv; IMSpt; College; Professional.

MILLER, Trisha L; Cambridge HS; Cambridge, NE; VPFrshCls; PresSophCls; VPJrCls; ALAGirlsSt; Band; Chrs; HonRl; PepBnd; 4-H; PpCl; LetterTrk; College; Elementary Teacher.

MILLER, Valerie L; Creston HS; Grand Rapids, MI; 8/430 Chr; ChrhWkr; HonRl; SecJA; JrNHS; NHS; NatlMeritSF; SchMus; SpnCl; IMSpt; JAAwd; Michigan State Univ; Med Technologist.

MILLER, Valrise E; Lindblom HS; Chicago, IL; 22/657 ChrhWkr; HonRl; NHS; OffAde; SchPl; SctActv; TchrAde; FrCl; MthCl; SciCl; Bsktbl; Northern Ill Univ; Medical Tech.

MILLER, Vicki; Mark Twain HS; Hannibal, MO; 2/58 SecJrCls; Band; ChrhWkr; CncrtBnd; HonRl; LbryAde; MrchBnd; PepBnd; Yrbk; FTA; Hannibal Lagrange Coll; Hi Sch English Tea.

MILLER, Virginia A; Round Lake HS; Round Lake, IL; Chrs; VPFTA; PpCl; GAA; Ohio State Univ; Physical Therapy.

MILLER, Walter B; Daleville HS; Daleville, IN; ChrhWkr; HonRl; LbryAde; SctActv; StuCncl; Bsbl; Bsktbl; Trk; College; Accounting.

MILLER, Wanda; Northridge HS; Middlebury, IN; HonRl; HospAde; LbryAde; OffAde; FHA;.

MILLER, William; Covington HS; Couington, IN; 84/90 VPSrCls; Band; HonRl; NHS; SctActv; StuCncl; 4-H; FrCl; Roes Hulman Inst Tech; Electrical Engineeri.

MILLER, William; Northrop HS; Fort Wayne, IN; HonRl; IMSpt; College; Medicine.

MILLER, William D; Dekalb Sr HS; Dekalb, IL; 20/355 HonRl; NHS; NatlMeritCmnd; NatlThespSoc; Orch; SchMus; SchPl; Univ Of Illinois.

MILLER, William K; Mission Valley HS; Eskridge, KS; 5/55 VPSophCls; ALBoysSt; Chrs; PresNHS; SchPl; VPFFA; SpnCl; Ftbl; Glf; Trk; Univ Of Ks; Md.

MILLER, William R; St Viator HS; Mt Prospect, IL; 1/285 HonRl; IMSpt; College.

MILLER III, Jay; Maplewood Acad; Minnetonka, MN; 5/63 PresSrCls; Chr; HonRl; Union College;medicine.

MILLETTE, Marilyn K; Sacred Heart HS; Ege, MN; 14/53 Chr; Chrs; ChrhWkr; SchPl; PpCl; Chrldr; GAA; Vocational School; Medical.

MILLHISLER, Laura S; Perry HS; Perry, MI; 13/123 Band; CncrtBnd; HonRl; MrchBnd; NHS; PepBnd; PpCl; Chrldr; GAA; PPFtbl; Mi St Univ; Criminal Justice.

MILLHOUSE, Phyllis; Chicago Vocational HS; Chicago, IL; 77/788 PresSrCls; NHS; FshEdYrbk; FDA; FTA; Bsbl; Trk; GovHonPrgAwd; LionAwd; PresAwd; Univ; Vocation.

MILLIGAN, Charlotte R; Litchfield Sr HS; Litchfield, IL; 1/137 Chr; HonRl; NHS; Treas-Quill&Scroll; SchMus; YthFlsp; RptrSchPpr; FrCl; GAA; Univ Of Illinois; Mathematics.

MILLIGAN, Denise M; Pekin Comm HS; Pekin, IL; 12/803 Band; Chrs; NHS; SecStuCncl; Northern Illinois Univ; Physical Therapist.

MILLIGAN, Marianne M; New Trier East HS; Wilmette, IL; 127/850 Chr; Chrs; HonRl; LitMag; SchMus; SchPl; LatCl; Univ Of Ill; Journalism.

MILLIGAN, Tammi A; St Elizabeth Academy; St Louis, MO; 5/115 Chrs; HonRl; LitMag; NHS; Orch; SchMus; StuCncl; RptrSchPpr; SpnCl; Bryn Mawr College.

MILLIK, Barbara A; Pawnee HS; Pawnee, IL; 1/39 Band; HonRl; IntrClCncl; JrNHS; TchrAde; YthFlsp; Yrbk; 4-H; PpCl; SciCl; Bsktbl; GAA; Ill College; French.

MILLIKAN, Keith W; St Laurence HS; Bridgeview, IL; 7/400 HonRl; StuCncl; LetterWrstlng; IMSpt; Northwestern Col; Pre Law.

MILLIKAN, Randy E; Burton Bentley HS; Davison, MI; 16/205 ChrhWkr; HonRl; SchMus; SchPl; StuCncl; LetterTrk; VoiceDemAwd; Coll; Teacher.

MILLION, Donald L; Millard Sr HS; Omaha, NE; Band; CncrtBnd; HonRl; MrchBnd; NatlFornLg; NHS; NatlMeritCmnd; NatlThespSoc; SchMus; SchPl; YthFlsp; LetterSwmmng; Univ Of Nebraska; Physics.

MILLIREN, Kathleen A; Arkansaw HS; Arkansaw, WI; SecSrCls; Band; HonRl; NHS; Yrbk; SchPpr; 4-H; FHA; Chrldr; GAA;.

MILLIREN, Patricia M; Arkansaw HS; Arkansaw, WI; TrsJrCls; Band; HonRl; StuCncl; Yrbk; RptrSchPpr; Pres4-H; Chrldr; GAA; 4-HAwd;.

MILLIS, Paul; St Francis De Sales Hs; Chicago, IL; 3/280 HonRl; NHS; NatlMeritCmnd; Yrbk; RptrSchPpr; Michigan State; Radio.

MILLITELLO, Paul G; St Clement HS; Warren, MI; PresFrshCls; ALBoysSt; HonRl; SctActv; StuCncl; StuGov; Bsbl; Ftbl; CchngActv; IMSpt;.

MILLMAN, Martin J; Southwest HS; St Louis, MO; 15/597 HonRl; Quill&Scroll; SctActv; SptEdSchPpr; GerCl; LetterTrk; IMSpt; College; Engineering Or Law.

MILLMAN, Myron M; Kewanee HS; Kewanee, IL; AFS; OffAde; RptrSchPpr; 4-H; KeyCl; SciCl; Wrstlng; Black Hawk East Jr College; Photography.

MILLNER, Arlene F; Virginia HS; Virginia, IL; ChrhWkr; CmntyWkr; HonRl; LbryAde; OffAde; TchrAde; 4-H; SecFHA; DanFAwd; 4-HAwd; Business School; Secretary.

MILLNER, Barb A; Mandan Sr HS; Mandan, ND; Band; CncrtBnd; DrlTm; StuCncl; SpnCl; Trk; Chrldr; GAA; EldAwd; Coll; Prof.

MILLS, Alexis A; Elizabeth Seton HS; S Holland, IL; 50/260 HonRl; OffAde;.

MILLS, Barry R; Newton Senior HS; Newton, IA; HonRl; StuCncl; StuGov; KeyCl; Glf; Iowa St Univ; Agronomy.

MILLS, Curtis L; North Miami HS; Macy, IN; 53/120 ChrhWkr; HonRl; NatlSciFnd; PresFFA; SciCl; Mechanics Training; Mechanic.

MILLS, Cynthia L; Arthur Hill HS; Saginaw, MI; ALAGirlsSt; CncrtBnd; DrmMjrt; NHS; RedCrAde; StuGov; Twrl; SchPpr; DARAwd; Saginaw Vly State College; Elem Education.

MILLS, Daniel P; Marlette HS; Brown City, MI; 21/139 ALBoysSt; ChrhWkr; CncrtBnd; HonRl; MrchBnd; NHS; NatlMeritSF; YthFlsp; LetterFtbl; LetterTrk; Western Michigan Univ; Mathematics.

MILLS, Dawn M; Hancock Public HS; Hancock, MN; VPSophCls; Chrs; ChrhWkr; HonRl; HospAde; SchPl; TchrAde; FHA; FTA; LetterBsktbl; Vocational School; Vocation.

MILLS, James A; Leadwood HS; Leadwood, MO; 1/47 PresJrCls; ALBoysSt; LitMag; NHS; YthFlsp; EdSchPpr; LetterBsktbl; DanFAwd; VoiceDemAwd; U Of Mo; Civil Engineering.

MILLS, Jane A; Hanover HS; Hanover, IL; 2/38 Band; Chrs; ChrhWkr; HonRl; NHS; SchMus; YthFlsp; EdYrBk; SpnCl; VoiceDemAwd; Millikin U; Teaching.

MILLS, Jodie A; Atlanta HS; Atlanta, MI; 1/51 PresJrCls; Band; CncrtBnd; HonRl; MrchBnd; NHS; PepBnd; TchrAde; Yrbk; 4-H; Ferris State College; Pharmacy.

MILLS, Kandis L; Cornell HS; Cornell, IL; 10/29 VPFrshCls; Band; HonRl; SchPl; PresStuCncl; Yrbk; SchPpr; FHA; Chrldr; GAA; Illinois State College; Music Therapist.

MILLS, Kimberly S; Everett HS; Lansing, MI; 38/520 ChrhWkr; HonRl; JrNHS; LbryAde; NHS; OffAde; SchAde; SchPl; TchrAde; YthFlsp; Central Mi U; Medicine.

MILLS, Laura E; Bushnell Prairie City HS; Bushell, IL; 7/98 PresSrCls; Chr; HonRl; NHS; SchMus; StuCncl; Yrbk; SpnCl; PpCl; SciCl; Univ; Professional.

MILLS, Laurie L; St Francis Comm HS; St Francis, KS; 5/52 Chrl; ChrhWkr; CmntyWkr; HonRl; Mdrgl; NatlMeritCmnd; SchPl; TchrAde; 4-H; PpCl; Bsktbl; PPFtbl; Kansas State Univ; Veterinary Pathology.

MILLS, Mark J; Butler R 5 HS; Butler, MO; VPFrshCls; PresSophCls; VPJrCls; AFS; Band; Chrs; CncrtBnd; HonRl; MrchBnd; SchPl; StuCncl; YthFlsp; Yrbk; FBLA; LetterFtbl; College; Broadcasting.

MILLS, Mark S; St Laurence HS; Chicago, IL; SecFrshCls; SecSophCls; HonRl; StuCncl; Ftbl; Trk; IMSpt; Coll; Teach.

MILLS, Marla M; White Bear Sr HS; White Bear Lake, MN; 32/342 St Olaf College; Medicine.

MILLS, Patrick; Andrean HS; Gary, IN; 74/301 ChrhWkr; HonRl; NHS; Quill&Scroll; SchMus; SchPl; SctActv; StuCncl; RptrSchPpr; MthCl; Indiana Univ; Journ.

MILLS, Peggy A; Washington HS; Washington, MO; 8/276 ALAGirlsSt; Band; CncrtBnd; HonRl; JA; MrchBnd; PepBnd; Yrbk; 4-H; SpnCl; Col ; Acct.

MILLS, Rhonda J; Oak Park Acad; Nevada, IA; Band; Chr; CmntyWkr; CncrtBnd; HonRl; SchPpr; Clge; Vocation.

MILLS, Rita A; Bc HS; Denton, IL; 75/185 Chr; ChrhWkr; CmntyWkr; HonRl; LbryAde; OffAde; YthFlsp; FTA; SpnCl; Eastern Ill Univ; Elem Ed.

MILLS, Rosalie; Kingsville R 1 HS; Kingsville, MO; 1/22 Chrs; HonRl; JrNHS; NHS; SchPl; StuCncl; 4-H; PpCl; SciCl; Bsktbl; Longview Comm Coll; Criminology.

MILLS, Ruth E; St Elmo HS; St Elmo, IL; 9/62 TrsSophCls; TrsJrCls; TrsSrCls; Chrs; ChrhWkr; CmntyWkr; HonRl; HospAde; NHS; SchMus; SchPl; StuCncl; BttyCrckrAwd; DARAwd; Vocational School; Nurses Aid.

MILLS, Sharon; Malden HS; Malden, MO; Band; CncrtBnd; HonRl; LbryAde; MrchBnd; NHS; SctActv; TchrAde; Twrl; PresAwd; Coll; Nursing.

MILLS, Sherri L; Anthon Oto HS; Anthon, IA; Band; DrlTm; HonRl; NHS; Orch; SchPl; RptrYrbk; FHA; Bsbl; Trk; College.

MILLS, Sherry J; Triad HS; Marine, IL; 1/164 HonRl; ModUN; NHS; NatlThespSoc; StuCncl; YthFlsp; EdSchPpr; Pres4-H; FFA; GerCl; 4-HAwd; Bradley University; Industrial Engineer.

MILLS, Stacey; Bloomfield Sr HS; Bloomfield, NE; 16/67 ChrhWkr; CmntyWkr; DrlTm; HonRl; NatlThespSoc; SchPl; RptrYrbk; FHA; PpCl; Univ Of Ne; Fashion Merchandising.

MILLS, Terry R; East HS; Rockford, IL; HonRl; LbryAde; LatCl; LetterTennis; College; Librarian.

MILLS, Theresa A; Mulvane HS; Mulvane, KS; SecSrCls; Chrs; ChrhWkr; DrlTm; HonRl; NHS; TchrAde; FHA; PpCl; Chrldr; Hutchinson Jr Coll; Accountant.

MILLS, Toni L; Lansing HS; Leavenworth, KS; 3/98 SecFrshCls; PresSophCls; ChrhWkr; HonRl; PresNHS; PresNatlThespSoc; SchMus; SchPl; Bsktbl; Trk; College; Coaching.

MILLS, Walter A; Torganoxie HS; Tonganoxie, KS; 24/114 HonRl; StuCncl; TchrAde; SpnCl; PresSciCl; Ftbl; Wrstlng; College; Electronics Career.

MILLSAPS, Joseph R; Pacific HS; Pacific, MO; 9/186 ALBoysSt; Band; TreasChr; ChrhWkr; TreasNatlFornLg; PresNatlThespSoc; SchMus; SctActv; YthFlsp; Ftbl; Northwestern Univ; Communcications.

MILLSPAUGH, Chris; Rockville Hs; Rockville, IN; SecFrshCls; SecSophCls; Chr; Chrl; DrlTm; HonRl; MrchBnd; FHA; LatCl; Wrstlng; Business School; Accounting.

MILNER, Donna L; Downers Grove South HS; Downers Grov), IL; Chr; HonRl; NatlThespSoc; Univ Of Illinois; Architecture.

MILOBOSZEWSKI, Zdzislaw J; St Ladislaus HS; Detroit, MI; 20/120 HonRl; SchMus; SchPl; StuGov; FDA; MthCl; PresSciCl; Ftbl; IMSpt; Wayne State Univ; Doctor Of Medicine.

MILOSZEWSKI, Mary Ann; Notre Dame HS; Chicago, IL; 1/303 HonRl; NHS; PolWkr; SchPl; St Mary Of Nazareth; Nursing.

MILROY, Greg M; Toulon HS; Toulon, IL; 15/52 Band; HonRl; SchPl; SptEdSchPpr; LetterBsbl; CaptBsktbl; CaptFtbl; CaptTrk; AmLegAwd; CitAwd; Black Hawk Jr College; Accounting.

MILROY, Janice E; Baldwin HS; Baldwin, KS; Band; CncrtBnd; HospAde; MrchBnd; OffAde; PepBnd; SchMus; SctActv; YthFlsp; RptrYrbk; RptrSchPpr; FHA; PpCl; LetterBsktbl; University; Bookkeeping.

MILSAPS, Phyllis J; Southwestern HS; West Point, IN; 6/108 Band; HonRl; NHS; YthFlsp; RptrYrbk; RptrSchPpr; SpnCl; MthCl; PpCl; SciCl; Campbellsville Clge; Accountant.

MILTENBERGER, Joan M; Marquette HS; Michigan City, IN; VPFrshCls; ChrhWkr; CmntyWkr; HonRl; HospAde; NatlMeritCmnd; SchMus; EdYrBk; Yrbk; Swmmng; Indiana U; Journalism.

MILTENBERGER, Mark A; West Marshall Comm HS; Marshalltown, IA; HonRl; Ia St Univ; Electrical Engineer.

MILTON, Cheryl Y; Wyndmere HS; Mcleod, ND; ALAGirlsSt; Chr; Chrs; ChrhWkr; HonRl; NHS; PolWkr; SchPl; TchrAde; GAA; Bible School; Medical Secretary.

MILTON, Nanci L; Vermillion HS; Vermillion, SD; ALAGirlsSt; Chrs; HonRl; NatlFornLg; NHS; NatlMeritCmnd; NatlThespSoc; SchPl; GerCl; Univ Of So Dakota; Theater.

MILTON, Nancy L; Granite South HS; Granite City, IL; NatlFornLg; SchPl; College.

MILTON, Rebecca; East Lynn Hs; Hoopeston, IL; 12/120 HonRl; PresLbryAde; NatlThespSoc; SchMus; TchrAde; PresYthFlsp; Pres4-H; FTA; SecSciCl; LetterTrk; Illinois State U;home Economics Advisor.

MILUS, Kelly L; Marseilles HS; Marseilles, IL; 3/70 Band; ChrhWkr; HonRl; MrchBnd; NatlFornLg; NHS; NatlThespSoc; SchMus; SchPl; RptrSchPpr; Clarke College; Computer Programmer.

MILWAY, Jeffrey D; Brookfield East HS; Brookfield, WI; Band; ChrhWkr; CncrtBnd; HonRl; NHS; NatlMeritSF; SctActv; MthCl; LetterTennis; Coll; Engr.

MIMICK, Ronald F; Salina South HS; Salina, KS; HonRl; LitMag; PolWkr; SchMus; SchPl; StuGov; TchrAde; PresFTA; Univ Of Ks; Special Ed Learning Disability.

MIMIER, Ann M; Catholic Memorial HS; Hales Corners, WI; HonRl; JrNHS; Univ Of Wisconsin; Special Educ.

MIMS, Terri L; Fremont HS; Fremont, IN; 7/79 PresJrCls; Chr; HonRl; LbryAde; NHS; SchMus; SchPl; EdSchPpr; Trk; LatCl; Univ; Journalism.

MINA, Alan S; Maine Twp East HS; Niles, IL; HonRl; NHS; NatlMeritCmnd; SpnCl; No Illinois Univ; Biology.

MINARDI, Rick L; Cathedral HS; Omaha, NE; ALBoysSt; HonRl; JrNHS; NHS; SctActv; TchrAde; Bsbl; LetterBsktbl; LetterFtbl; LetterTrk; College.

MINARICK, Patrice M; North Bend Central HS; Scribner, NE; 8/56 Band; CncrtBnd; HonRl; MrchBnd; PepBnd; RptrYrbk; FHA; FTA; PpCl; College; Nurse.

MINCHOW, Mark K; Arlington HS; Arlington, NE; Band; Chrs; CncrtBnd; HonRl; MrchBnd; SchMus; SchPl; StuCncl; RptrYrbk; GerCl; Bsktbl; Ftbl; University; Law.

MINDEMAN, Noel R; Wyndmere Public HS; Barney, ND; 6/45 HonRl; NHS; StuCncl; FFA; Collegef Agribusiness.

MINDHAM, Arnold R; Boscobel HS; Gays Mills, WI; HonRl; StuCncl; 4-H; FFA; Wrstlng; 4-HAwd; Trade ; Vocation.

MINDOCK, Brenda K; Westview HS; Kankakee, IL; TrsFrshCls; Band; CncrtBnd; HonRl; HospAde; MrchBnd; NHS; NatlMeritSF; FrCl; Trk; Univ Of Illinois; Medicine.

MINDRUP, Elizabeth M; Lenora HS; Clayton, KS; 2/14 VPFrshCls; PresSophCls; SecJrCls; PresSrCls; Chr; Chrs; ChrhWkr; DrlTm; HonRl; OffAde; SchMus; SchPl; 4-H; PpCl; LetterBsktbl; College; Nursing.

MINEAR, Kathy S; Highland HS; La Belle, MO; SecSophCls; SecJrCls; ALAGirlsSt; HonRl; JrNHS; NHS; StuCncl; FHA; FrCl; PpCl; College; Biology.

MINER, Audrey M; Gregory HS; Gregory, SD; 2/43 Band; Chrs; ChrhWkr; HonRl; MrchBnd; NatlThespSoc; PepBnd; PolWkr; YthFlsp; FBLA; U Of Sd; Dental Hygienist.

MINER, Bobbi; Independence HS; Independence, IA; 5/160 Band; Chrs; HonRl; MrchBnd; NHS; PepBnd; StuCncl; GAA; Iowa State Univ; Chemical Engineering.

MINER, Mark L; Community HS; Marengo, IL; ALBoysSt; HonRl; StuCncl; Yrbk; GerCl; Glf; SARAwd; Western State College Of Co; History.

MINER, Mary K; Gregory Public HS; Gregory, SD; 6/56 PresJrCls; ALAGirlsSt; Band; Chr; CncrtBnd; HonRl; HospAde; NHS; NatlThespSoc; StuCncl; EdSchPpr; FHA; AmLegAwd; 4-HAwd; South Dakota State Univ; Physical Therapy.

MINER, Nancy H; North Shore Country Day HS; Northbrook, IL; Chrl; Chrs; Mdrgl; NHS; NatlMeritSF; SchMus; AmLegAwd; College; Language.

MINER, Tina M; Midway HS; Denton, KS; 24/28 4-H; PpCl; Bsktbl; Trk;.

MINER, Tod; Tippecanoe Valley HS; Mentone, IN; HonRl; JrNHS; NHS; SchPl; StuCncl; SpnCl; MthCl; PpCl; Ball St Coll; Cpa.

MINERT, Rex L; Minden Public HS; Minden, NE; Band; Chr; Chrs; ChrhWkr; CmntyWkr; CncrtBnd; HonRl; MrchBnd; PepBnd; SchMus; SchPl; TchrAde; YthFlsp; LetterGlf; Nebr Wesleyan Univ; Business Admin.

MINGEE, Barbara J; Rantoul Twp HS; Thomasboro, IL; Band; CncrtBnd; HonRl; HospAde; MrchBnd; NHS; PresSpnCl; Bsbl; Bsktbl; U Of Il; Math.

MINGER, Bradley M; Guttenberg Comm HS; Garber, IA; 25/73 Aud/Vis; HonRl; SchPl; SctActv; RptrSchPpr; 4-H;.

MINGO, Julie K; Harrison HS; Farmington, MI; HonRl; LitMag; ModUN; NatlMeritFnl; PolWkr; VPStuCncl; RptrSchPpr; EdSchPpr; BttyCrckrAwd; Wayne State Univ; Social Sciences, Journali.

MINI, Susan M; St Edward HS; Elgin, IL; 21/124 VPBand; CncrtBnd; HonRl; NHS; Orch; SchMus; SptEdSchPpr; SecFSA; LatCl; Trk; College; Professional.

MINICH, Virginia L; Alton HS; Alton, MO; 1/58 TrsFrshCls; SecChrs; CncrtBnd; LbryAde; MrchBnd; NatlMeritCmnd; OffAde; SchPl; StuCncl; TreasFHA; 4-HAwd; Univ Of Missouri; English.

MINKER, Carol J; Oregon Davis HS; Hamlet, IN; 17/64 PresSrCls; VPSrCls; ALBoysSt; ALAGirlsSt; CmntyWkr; HonRl; NHS; StuGov; 4-H; PpCl; GAA; College; Elem Education.

MINKER, Catherine A; Oregon Davis HS; Hamlet, IN; 14/64 Chr; HonRl; NHS; RptrSchPpr; SchPpr; 4-H; PpCl; GAA; College; Special Education.

MINKOWSKI, Jeanine; Rosarian Acad; Kenosha, WI; TrsFrshCls; Chrl; HonRl; NHS; PresStuCncl; SpnCl;.

MINNICK, Kathy; Hardin Central HS; Hardin, MO; ChrhWkr; HonRl; IntrClCncl; SchPl; TchrAde; Yrbk; RptrSchPpr; KeyCl; DanFAwd; 4-HAwd; William Jewell Coll; Elem Ed.

MINO, Stephen M; Stoutland HS; Richland, MO; VPFrshCls; Band; Chrl; Chrs; CncrtBnd; MrchBnd; PepBnd; Bsktbl; Trade Sch; Auto Mech.

MINOR, Courtney B; St Ignatius Coll Prep; Chicago, IL; 61/156 PresCmntyWkr; HonRl; HospAde; StuGov; FrCl; LionAwd; Nw Univ ; Urban Planner.

MINOR, Denise M; Flandreau HS; Flandreau, SD; TrsJrCls; ALAGirlsSt; Chrs; HonRl; NHS; SchPl; PresStuCncl; 4-H; FHA; AmLegAwd; S Dakota State Univ; Nursing.

MINOR, Dorothy L; St Mary Cntr For Learning HS; Chicago, IL; College.

MINOR, Kathy J; Marceline HS; Marceline, MO; AFS; ChrhWkr; HonRl; SchPl; TchrAde; RptrYrbk; 4-H; FHA; LetterBsktbl; LetterTrk; Kirksville State U; Physical Ed Teacher.

MINOR, Kitty E; Marceline HS; Marceline, MO; 3/70 AFS; HonRl; NHS; SchPl; StuCncl; RptrYrbk; 4-H; FHA; LetterBsktbl; LetterTrk; Kirksville State U; Ele Ed.

MINOTIS, Christine A; Bogan HS; Chicago, IL; 36/704 HonRl; JA; NHS; OffAde; SchAde; TchrAde; FrCl; PpCl; GAA; Univ Of Il; Career In Business.

MINSHALL, Roland A; North Nodaway R Vi HS; Pickering, MO; 2/37 HonRl; LbryAde; ModUN; NatlMeritCmnd; Univ; Architecture.

MINSHULL, Lyle B; Sutherland HS; Sutherland, NE; ALBoysSt; Band; CncrtBnd; HonRl; OffAde; PepBnd; SchPl; RptrYrbk; LetterFtbl; LetterTrk;.

MINSON, Stan W; Woodland HS; Glen Allen, MO; Chr; ChrhWkr; JA; YthFnd; FFA; PpCl; Bsbl; Bsktbl; JETSAwd; Seno Coll; Draftsman.

MINTA, James J; Naperville Central HS; Naperville, IL; 89/870 HonRl; YthFlsp; LetterBsktbl; LetterGlf; LetterSwmmng; Notre Dame University; Pre Medicine.

MINTERT, Jean M; Orchard Farm HS; West Alton, MO; 17/120 Chr; HonRl; OffAde; SchMus; SpnCl; PpCl; LetterTrk; Chrldr; CchngActv; IMSpt; College.

MINTLING, Priscilla A; Palisade Public HS; Palisade, NE; 2/12 ALAGirlsSt; Chrs; HonRl; NHS; SchPl; StuCncl; EdSchPpr; PpCl; VFWAwd; College; Communications.

MINTON, John D; Creighton Prep HS; Omaha, NE; 37/249 SecSrCls; HonRl; NatlMeritCmnd; StuCncl; StuGov; Univ; Law.

MINTON, Mark V; Fort Osage HS; Independence, MO; 5/296 HonRl; JrNHS; ModUN; NatlFornLg; NHS; Yrbk; MthCl; SciCl; University; Lawyer.

MIODUS, Paul A; Willowbrook HS; Lombard, IL; 85/865 ChrhWkr; HonRl; Bsktbl; College; Business.

MIONI, Helen T; Ironwood Catholic HS; Ironwood, MI; Chr; Chrs; DrmBgl; HonRl; StuCncl; University; Business.

MIONSKE, Susan; Wauconda Comm HS; Island Lake, IL; 43/201 Chr; CncrtBnd; HonRl; MrchBnd; PepBnd; SctActv; SpnCl; 4-HAwd; Goshen Coll; Pre Med.

MIRABELLI, Mary; Notre Dame Girls HS; Chicago, IL; 6/302 PresJrCls; HonRl; NatlFornLg; NHS; SchMus; SchPl; SctActv; CaptChrldr; JCAwd; U Of Il; Industrial Eng.

MIRANDA, Steven A; Univ Of Detroit HS; Detroit, MI; 15/200 HonRl; ModUN; NatlFornLg; NHS; NatlMeritFnl; NatlMeritCmnd; NatlMeritSF; StuGov; TchrAde; RptrSchPpr; Col; Medicine.

MIRANTI, Christine; Rosary HS; St Louis, MO; 20/350 DrlTm; HonRl; JA; NatlMeritCmnd; TchrAde; PpCl; Mo Univ; Engineer.

MIREK, Robert S; Madison HS; Madison Heights, MI; RptrSchPpr; EdSchPpr; SchPpr; Bsktbl; Fine Arts Degree Painting.

MIRETZKY, David J; Mather HS; Chicago, IL; HonRl; PolWkr; RedCrAde; TchrAde; KeyCl; GerCl; Dartmouth College; Business.

MIRGA, Tomas F; St Andrew HS; Detroit, MI; Chrs; HonRl; NHS; SchPl; Yrbk; University Of Michigan; Medicine.

MIRIANI, Frances; Herrin Hs; Herrin, IL; 2 SecTrsJrCls; SecTrsSrCls; HonRl; NHS; StuCncl; RptrYrbk; RptrSchPpr; SpnCl; Chrldr; AmLegAwd; So Illinois U;certified Public Accountant.

MIRICK, Don G; Clopton HS; Clarksville, MO; 17/57 PresSrCls; Chr; ChrhWkr; StuCncl; StuGov; SciCl; Bsbl; IMSpt; Univ Of Missouri; Engineering.

MIRON, Dave; Peshtigo HS; Peshtigo, WI; 3/90 HonRl; StuGov; Coll; Professional.

MIRON, Jeanne A; Republic Michigamme HS; Republic, MI; 3/42 TrsSophCls; HonRl; NatlFornLg; PolWkr; SctActv; StuCncl; RptrSchPpr; FrCl; Bsktbl; Chrldr; Clge; Lawyer.

MIRT, Sheryl F; Usd #509; South Haven, KS; DrlTm; HonRl; SchPl; PresYthFlsp; EdYrBk; PresFHA; Bsktbl; Trk; 4-HAwd; Salt City Business College; Secretary.

MIRWALDT, Katrina I; Northrop HS; Fort Wayne, IN; HonRl; College; Accounting.

MISAK, James E; Joliet Catholic HS; Joliet, IL; 2/170 ChrhWkr; CmntyWkr; HonRl; JA; LitMag; NHS; NHS; NatlMeritFnl; StuCncl; RptrYrbk; SchPpr; RusCl; Northwestern Univ; Medicine.

MISCHKA, Steven L; Wautoma HS; Wautoma, WI; 1/92 NatlFornLg; NHS; NatlMeritFnl; NatlMeritSchl; NatlThespSoc; PresStuCncl; EdYrBk; Ftbl; CaptTrk; AmLegAwd; CitAwd; Univ Of Wisconsin; Health.

MISCHKE, James B; Crofton HS; Crofton, NE; 17/63 Aud/Vis; Band; HonRl; 4-H; FFA; LetterTrk; Usd At Vermillion Sd.

MISEGADIS, Theresa K; Lodgepole HS; Lodgepole, NE; 2/17 VPFrshCls; TrsJrCls; ALAGirlsSt; HonRl; SchPl; StuCncl; EdYrBk; PpCl; Trk; DanFAwd; Business Sch; Accounting.

MISFELDT, Merri B; Blair HS; Blair, NE; Chr; ChrhWkr; HonRl; FBLA; PpCl; Business Sch; Medical Sec.

MISH, Barbara J; George Rogers Clark HS; Hammond, IN; 16/260 College; Rn.

MISH, David A; Lake Ville HS; Otter Lake, MI; HonRl; MrchBnd; NHS; NatlMeritCmnd; NatlSciFnd; Orch; PepBnd; SchPl; SctActv; Yrbk; Mich St Univ; Medical.

MISHEK, Steve J; Mahtomedi Senior HS; White Bear, MN; Aud/Vis; HonRl; TchrAde; GerCl; Clg; Medicine.

MISHLER, Dennis P; Elkhart Cenral HS; Elkhart, IN; YthFlsp; Trk; CchngActv; IMSpt; College.

MISHLER, Jerold A; Westview HS; Shipshewana, IN; Chr; ChrhWkr; HonRl; SchPl; 4-H; FFA; Bsbl; Bsktbl; IMSpt;.

MISHLER, Mark; Anderson HS; Anderson, IN; Band; CncrtBnd; DrmBgl; HonRl; MrchBnd; NHS; Orch; PepBnd; PolWkr; SchMus; In Univ; Medicine.

MISIAK, Patricia L; Dominican HS; Detroit, MI; LbryAde; OffAde; TchrAde; IMSpt; PPFtbl; College; Professional Nursing.

MISICHKO, Emil W; Plainfield HS; Joliet, IL; ALBoysSt; CncrtBnd; DrmMjrt; NHS; NatlThespSoc; Quill&Scroll; SchMus; StuCncl; Yrbk; RptrSchPpr; Bsktbl; Univ Of Illinois; Engineering.

MISINA, Diane M; Lakeland HS; Lac Du Flambeau, WI; Band; CncrtBnd; HonRl; HospAde; MrchBnd; PepBnd; SpnCl; GAA; University; Nursing.

MISIOLEK, Donna M; St Hedwig HS; Detroit, MI; HonRl; JA; LbryAde; NHS; Sdlty; Yrbk; SchPpr; SpnCl; College; Nursing.

MISKELL, Sheryl A; North Linn HS; Coggon, IA; Band; Chrs; ChrhWkr; HonRl; NHS; SchMus; SchPl; StuCncl; YthFlsp; Bsbl; Bsktbl; University; Elem Ed.

MISKIMEN, Sharon R; St Agnes Academy; Alliance, NE; 1/22 SecFrshCls; ALAGirlsSt; HonRl; VPNHS; StuCncl; RptrYrbk; FrCl; PpCl; SciCl; Chrldr; College.

MISKOWIEC, Linda M; St Agatha HS; Detroit, MI; HonRl; FrCl; College; Professional.

MISTEREK, Rick J; Sisseton HS; Sisseton, SD; ALBoysSt; ChrhWkr; HonRl; SchPl; KeyCl; Bsbl; Glf; IMSpt; College; Vocational.

MISTIATIS, Robert C; Jefferson HS; Monroe, MI; 1/160 VPNHS; StuGov; RptrYrbk; RptrSchPpr; SpnCl; Trk; Wrstlng; Univ Of Michigan; Oceanography.

MISTLEBAUER, Carl; Sevastapol HS; Sturgeon Bay, WI; Band; ChrhWkr; CmntyWkr; CncrtBnd; HonRl; NHS; NatlMeritCmnd; PolWkr; SchPl; SctActv; Coll; Law.

MISTLER, Patti J; Carrollton HS; Carrollton, MO; 28/104 Chrs; CncrtBnd; HonRl; MrchBnd; NHS; NatlThespSoc; SchMus; SchPl; Bsktbl; LetterTennis; LetterTrk; IMSpt; Univ Of Missouri; Medical Technology.

MISUNAS, Marla; Waukegan East HS; Waukegan, IL; HonRl; JrNHS; NatlThespSoc; OffAde; SchMus; SchPl; GAA; College; At History.

MITCHANIS, Mary E; Mother Mc Auley HS; Chicago, IL; 27/486 Chr; Chrs; ChrhWkr; HonRl; NHS; University Of Illinois; Lawyer.

MITCHEL, Henry M; D H Hickmans HS; Columbia, MO; HonRl; NHS; NatlMeritFnl; NatlMeritSF; SctActv; FrCl; LatCl; SciCl; LetterFtbl; AmLegAwd; Univ; Engi.

MITCHELL, Alan R; Triopia HS; Chapin, IL; PresFrshCls; ChrhWkr; HonRl; Ftbl; Univ Of Illinois; Pharmacy.

MITCHELL, Barbara; Washington Catholic HS; Washington, IN; Chrs; HonRl; PpCl; Tennis; Chrldr; Business School.

MITCHELL, Barbara K; Armstrong Comm HS; Armstrong, IA; SecFrshCls; SecJrCls; Chr; CncrtBnd; HonRl; MrchBnd; SchMus; LetterGlf; Swmmng; VoiceDemAwd;.

MITCHELL, Brian L; Hartford HS; Hartford, KS; Chr; Chrl; Chrs; CmntyWkr; SchMus; SchPl; SctActv; KeyCl; Bsktbl; Ftbl; Trk; Us Coast Guard; Marine Biology.

MITCHELL, Carol L; Bgm Community HS; Grinnell, IA; 21/49 HonRl; FrCl; PpCl; Chrldr;.

MITCHELL, Charles; Wellington HS; Hoopeston, IL; TrsJrCls; Chrs; ChrhWkr; CncrtBnd; HonRl; NHS; StuCncl; College; Professional.

MITCHELL, Cindi L; Paris R 2 HS; Holliday, MO; HonRl; LbryAde; SchPl; YthLg; RptrSchPpr; SptEdSchPpr; EngCl; PpCl; LetterBsbl; Bsktbl; AmLegAwd; JCAwd; OptClAwd; Missouri Univ; Journalism.

MITCHELL, Cindy G; Mt Pleasant HS; Mt Pleasant, MI; 26/325 Chr; HonRl; NHS; NatlThespSoc; OffAde; SchPl; TchrAde; RptrYrbk; 4-H; Trk; Central Mich U; Secretarial.

MITCHELL, Daniel; Whiteland Community HS; Whiteland, IN; 5/174 PresFrshCls; HonRl; NHS; NatlMeritCmnd; StuCncl; In Central Univ; Math.

MITCHELL, Darryl; Lindblom HS; Chicago, IL; Univ Of Illinois; Architecture.

MITCHELL, David L; Battle Creek Central HS; Battle Creek, MI; 49/550 HonRl; JA; NHS; SctActv; TchrAde; Navy; Naval Career.

MITCHELL, Debbie L; Usd 462 HS; Burden, KS; 5/34 Band; HonRl; MrchBnd; SchPl; YthFlsp; Yrbk; SchPpr; 4-H; FFA; PpCl; Oral Roberts Univ; Nurse.

MITCHELL, Debbie L; Central Of Burden HS; Burden, KS; 5/35 Band; Chrs; ChrhWkr; CmntyWkr; CncrtBnd; HonRl; HospAde; JA; MrchBnd; PepBnd; SchPl; YthFlsp; Trk; Oral Roberts Univ; Nurse.

MITCHELL, Debra; Mich Center HS; Mich Center, MI; Band; CncrtBnd; DrmMjrt; HonRl; MrchBnd; PepBnd; Michigan State Univ; Horticulture.

MITCHELL, Donell R; Hales Franciscan HS; Chicago, IL; 1/79 HonRl; NHS; GerCl; SciCl; Bsbl; Trk; IMSpt; Harvard Univ; Law.

MITCHELL, Donna M; Enfield HS; Enfield, IL; 3/31 PresFrshCls; PresSophCls; PresJrCls; Band; Chrs; ChrhWkr; HonRl; MrchBnd; RptrYrbk; Pres4-H; VPFHA; KeyCl; Trk; Chrldr; DanFAwd; College; Medical Technologist.

MITCHELL, Donna M; Elmwood HS; Elmwood, IL; 4/53 DrlTm; HonRl; NHS; SchPl; RptrYrbk; PpCl; Bsktbl; Chrldr; VPDARAwd; Ill Central Clg; Phy Ed.

MITCHELL, Doris L; East HS; Wichita, KS; College; Dental Assistant.

MITCHELL, Douglas P; Glenbard East HS; Lombard, IL; 32/700 HonRl; NHS; NatlMeritSF; StuCncl; Univ Of Illinois; Electrical Engineer.

MITCHELL, Gina M; Orchard Farm Sr HS; West Alton, MO; 55/153 Band; CncrtBnd; HonRl; LitMag; LbryAde; MrchBnd; OffAde; SchMus; PpCl; CchngActv; IMSpt; PPFtbl; College; Art.

MITCHELL, Glen A; Holly HS; Holly, MI; 2/232 PresNHS; SchPl; SchPl; StuCncl; PresFrCl; JAAwd; Mich State U; Natural Science.

MITCHELL, Gordon E; Parkway West Sr HS; Ballwin, MO; LetterCaptWrstlng; CchngActv; IMSpt; U Of Missouri; Business.

MITCHELL, Hillman S; Hartford HS; Hartford, KS; Band; HonRl; MrchBnd; SchPl; KeyCl; Bsbl; Bsktbl; Ftbl; Trk; CchngActv; Emporia Kansas St Clge; Pro.

MITCHELL, James W; Proviso East HS; Maywood, IL; 36/1001 Aud/Vis; ChrhWkr; CmntyWkr; HonRl; NHS; NatlMeritSchl; Northwestern Univ; Medicine.

MITCHELL, Janean; Effingham HS; Effingham, IL; Band; HonRl; MrchBnd; Twrl; SpnCl; PpCl; Eastern Il; Social Work.

MITCHELL, Jean A; Newton Community HS; Newton, IL; CmntyWkr; HonRl; NHS; StuCncl; Chrldr; GAA; IMSpt; GovHonPrgAwd; JAAwd; PresAwd; Clge; Physical Therapist.

MITCHELL, Jean S; Negaunee HS; Negaunee, MI; TrsJrCls; Chr; Chrs; ChrhWkr; RptrYrbk; EdSchPpr; Coll; Counseling.

MITCHELL, Jill M; Newton HS; Newton, IL; CmntyWkr; JrNHS; NHS; StuCncl; StuGov; Chrldr; GAA; IMSpt; 4-HAwd; JAAwd; College; Vocation.

MITCHELL, Joellen; Montezuma Comm HS; Malcom, IA; 26/55 Band; Chrs; HonRl; PresFNA; GerCl; LetterBsbl; LetterTrk; LetterChrldr; Mdrgl; MrchBnd; Graceland College; Health.

MITCHELL, Judy A; Rich South HS; Matteson, IL; 1/279 Chr; HonRl; PresNHS; VPStuCncl; Yrbk; North Central College; Business.

MITCHELL, Karen L; Mc Leansboro HS; Mc Leansboro, IL; 1/125 ALAGirlsSt; Band; Chrs; HonRl; HospAde; TreasStuCncl; RptrSchPpr; PresFBLA; PresFNA; MthCl; PpCl; Univ Of Illinois; Law.

MITCHELL, Karen L; Grant Park HS; Grant Park, IL; 1/57 Band; DrmMjrt; HonRl; MrchBnd; NHS; PepBnd; SchMus; Bsktbl; Trk; Chrldr; College; Professional.

MITCHELL, Kathleen A; Mother Mc Auley HS; Chicago, IL; 31/474 Chrs; HospAde; St Xavier College; Speech Therapy.

MITCHELL, Katie A; Central HS; Springfield, MO; 13/279 Chr; Chrl; Chrs; HonRl; OffAde; SchMus; StuCncl; StuGov; PpCl; OptClAwd; Southwest Mo State Univ.

MITCHELL, Kellee A; Harding County HS; Buffalo, SD; 3/27 ALAGirlsSt; Band; Chrs; CncrtBnd; DrlTm; HonRl; MrchBnd; OffAde; Bsktbl; Trk; Chrldr; GAA; AmLegAwd; College; Agriculture.

MITCHELL, Kitty B; Mc Donald County R 1 HS; Noel, MO; ChrhWkr; HonRl; NHS; 4-H; VPFFA; FHA; FTA; Bsbl; College; Business.

MITCHELL, Lashawn; Northern HS; Detrot, MI; PresSrCls; Band; CmntyWkr; HonRl; NHS; OffAde; SchAde; TchrAde; SchPpr; FBLA; Professional Model.

MITCHELL, Margaret M; St Alphonsus HS; Dearborn, MI; Band; Chrl; HonRl; LbryAde; MrchBnd; College.

MITCHELL, Margie M; Flower Voc HS; Chicago, IL; FshEdYrbk; FshEdSchPpr; GAA; Fashion Design School; Professional Designe.

MITCHELL, Marta J; Chester Hubbell HS; Chester, NE; SecFrshCls; VPSophCls; Band; Chr; Chrs; HonRl; SchMus; SchPl; RptrYrbk; Trk; U Of Ne.

MITCHELL, Mary A; Salina Central HS; Salina, KS; TrsFrshCls; DrlTm; HonRl; MrchBnd; TchrAde; RptrSchPpr; SchPpr; PpCl; Tennis; Kansas Univ.

MITCHELL, Mary A; Greenfield HS; Greenfield, WI; 28/348 ChrhWkr; HonRl; NHS; TchrAde; RptrYrbk; Yrbk; GAA; PPFtbl; U Of Wi Milwaukee; Business.

MITCHELL, Mary C; Arlington HS; Indianapolis, IN; 43/500 HonRl; JrNHS; ModUN; NHS; SchPl; StuCncl; Purdue U; Veterinary Medicine.

MITCHELL, Mary R; West Catholic HS; Grand Rapids, MI; Aud/Vis; Chrs; CmntyWkr; HonRl; Mdrgl; RedCrAde; LetterSwmmng; Trk; JAAwd;.

MITCHELL, Matt; Harmony HS; Bonaparte, IA; 13/70 Band; HonRl; NatlCathMusEdAsoc; SchMus; YthFlsp; RptrYrbk; Yrbk; FrCl; Bsktbl; DARAwd; Univ; Spec Educ.

MITCHELL, Melody L; Springfield HS; Springfield, IL; 5/535 Chr; ChrhWkr; CmntyWkr; CncrtBnd; MrchBnd; NHS; OffAde; SctActv; YthFlsp; 4-H; SpnCl; SciCl; Trk; Bradley Univ; Chemistry.

MITCHELL, Michele A; Valders HS; Valders, WI; 28/113 AFS; ALAGirlsSt; CaptDrlTm; HonRl; HospAde; Yrbk; PpCl; LetterBsktbl; LetterTrk; GAA; PPFtbl; College; Legal Secretary.

MITCHELL, Pamela S; Dupree HS; Dupree, SD; 4/17 Chrs; DrlTm; HonRl; SchAde; SchPl; RptrYrbk; EdYrBk; EdSchPpr; PpCl; Bsbl; CaptBsktbl; IMSpt; Business School; Secretarial Field.

MITCHELL, Philip W; East Richland HS; Olney, IL; 4/250 Band; JrNHS; NHS; MthCl; LetterTennis; Univ Of Illinois; Petroleum Engineer.

MITCHELL, Phillip A; Blackford HS; Hartford City, IN; Band; ChrhWkr; CncrtBnd; HonRl; LbryAde; MrchBnd; PepBnd; 4-H; FFA; Trk;.

MITCHELL, Randall N; Cowan HS; Muncie, IN; ALBoysSt; Band; HonRl; NHS; SchPl; SctActv; StuCncl; StuGov; Pres4-H; Bsktbl; Purdue U; Vet.

MITCHELL, Roger R; La Plata R Ii HS; La Plata, MO; 4/41 HonRl; PpCl; College; Math Major.

MITCHELL, Ronald G; Grand Blanc Community HS; Grand Blanc, MI; HonRl; NHS; NatlMeritSF; Tennis; Trk; Univ Mi; Med Dr.

MITCHELL, Ronald L; Meridian HS; Sanford, MI; 9/125 HonRl; NHS; YthFlsp; RptrSchPpr; SptEdSchPpr; FrCl; LetterBsbl; Glf; VFWAwd; Mi State Univ; Professional.

MITCHELL, Sheila L; Valley HS; Crystal, ND; 1/23 PresSophCls; PresJrCls; ALAGirlsSt; Band; Chrs; ChrhWkr; VPYthFlsp; RptrYrbk; Pres4-H; VPPpCl; College;.

MITCHELL, Shirley A; Kewanee HS; Kewanee, IL; 100/220 HstSophCls; TrsJrCls; HstJrCls; TrsSrCls; HstSrCls; ChrhWkr;.

MITCHELL, Susan L; South Ripley HS; Versailles, IN; 5/105 SecJrCls; TrsSrCls; DrmMjrt; HonRl; NHS; Quill&Scroll; PresStuCncl; Twrl; PresSciCl; 4-HAwd; Purdue Univ; Fashion Retailing.

MITCHELL, Terry L; Galena HS; Galena, MO; PresJrCls; Chrs; HonRl; StuCncl; FHA; Bsktbl; Trk; Chrldr; GAA; PresAwd; S M S University; Vocational.

MITCHELL, Theodore; Flint Central HS; Flint, MI; 99/421 HonRl; NHS; NatlMeritCmnd; PolWkr; StuCncl; StuGov; TchrAde; Bsktbl; Ftbl; IMSpt; Western Mich Univ; Public Admin.

MITCHELL, Thomas A; Saline HS; Saline, MI; HonRl; TchrAde; Bsbl; Bsktbl; College; Physical Ed.

MITCHELL, Thomas P; Cathedral HS; Omaha, NE; PresSophCls; ALBoysSt; HonRl; NHS; SciCl; Trk; CchngActv; University Of Nebraska.

MITCHELL, Timothy A; Frankfort Community HS; West Frankfort, IL; 1/175 PresFrshCls; NHS; NatlMeritSF; StuCncl; SecKeyCl; SpnCl; LetterBsktbl; LetterFtbl; LetterTrk; BauchLmbAwd; Univ Of Illinois; Medicine.

MITCHELL, Tom D; Marion C Early HS; Aldrich, MO; HstFrshCls; HstSophCls; ChrhWkr; SchPl; StuCncl; Yrbk; SchPpr; FFA; PresFrCl; PpCl; University; Vocation.

MITCHELL, Vincent E; Enfield Comm HS; Enfield, IL; 7/33 TrsFrshCls; PresSrCls; Band; Chr; Chrs; ChrhWkr; CncrtBnd; HonRl; NHS; LetterBsbl; Rend Lake Jr Col; Professional.

MITCHELL, William C; Francis W Parker HS; Chicago, IL; SchMus; SchPl; RptrYrbk; SchPpr; VPFrCl; Trk; IMSpt; College; Law.

MITCHELL, William D; Murphysboro HS; Murphysboro, IL; HonRl; StuCncl; TchrAde; KeyCl; PpCl; LetterBsbl; Bsktbl; LetterFtbl; IMSpt; PresAwd; State Police Training Academy; Policeman.

MITCHELL, Zander; Chicago Vocational HS; Chicago, IL; HonRl; Univ; Chemistry.

MITCHUM, Charles J; Mendel Catholic Prep HS; Chicago, IL; HonRl; PepBnd; RptrSchPpr; SchPpr; PpCl; Tennis; Trk; College; Cpa.

MITCHUM, Juanita J; Orchard Farm HS; St Charles, MO; 13/140 CmntyWkr; HonRl; HospAde; JA; NHS; PolWkr; StuCncl; PpCl; IMSpt; College; Teacher.

MITERKO, Lisa A; George Rogers Clark HS; Whiting, IN; 19/260 Chr; Chrl; Chrs; Quill&Scroll; StuCncl; RptrYrbk; EdYrBk; SecFNA; SpnCl; Calumet College; Medical Tech.

MITES, Margie K; Columbia HS; Columbia, IL; HonRl; Yrbk; FBLA; Trk; GAA; Patricia Stevens; Legal Secretarial Course.

MITRENGA, Jane; Alvernia Hs; Chicago, IL; 4/283 Chr; NHS; TchrAde; Trk; CchngActv; College; Psychology.

MITRISIN, Jeff W; Eddyville Comm HS; Eddyville, IA; VPJrCls; Quill&Scroll; SchPl; RptrSchPpr; LetterBsbl; Bsktbl; LetterFtbl; Trk; College; Business Administration.

MITROPOULOS, Demetra C; River Rouge HS; River Rouge, MI; TreasBand; SecChr; ChrhWkr; CmntyWkr; CncrtBnd; StuCncl; TchrAde; RptrSchPpr; SecMthCl; Bsktbl; Univ Of Mich; Math/science.

MITSCHELEN, Charles L; Northwood HS; Nappanee, IN; HonRl; TchrAde; YthFlsp; PpCl; Bsbl; Tennis; Wrstlng; IMSpt; Trade School; House Construction.

MITSOS, Michael R; Forest View HS; Des Plaines, IL; 26/645 HonRl; NHS; Ftbl; Swmmng; LetterTrk; Loyola Univ; Medicine.

MITTELHAUSER, Jeffrey A; Smith Cotton Sr HS; Sedalia, MO; 2/358 Chr; HonRl; PresNatlFornLg; NHS; NatlMeritFnl; SctActv; TchrAde; EdSchPpr; VP4-H; GerCl; Trk; IMSpt; VFWAwd; Central Missouri State Col; Journalism.

MITTEN, Stephen F; Zion Benton Twp HS; Zion, IL; 46/430 ALBoysSt; HonRl; NHS; SctActv; GerCl; SciCl; Trk; CitAwd; Coll; Zoology.

MITTLER, Max B; Wright City HS; Wright City, MO; HonRl; NHS; SchPl; StuCncl; Bsbl; CaptBsktbl; Trk; CitAwd; College; Basketball Coach.

MITTLESTAEDT, Erika; Little Falls Comm HS; Little Falls, MN; 6/272 Band; Chrs; CncrtBnd; HonRl; Mdrgl; SchMus; SchPl; TchrAde; Chrldr; GAA; Concordia College; Teaching.

MITTS, Sherri E; Bonner Springs HS; Bonner Springs, KS; 17/179 ALAGirlsSt; PresBand; Chr; Chrs; ChrhWkr; CncrtBnd; HonRl; MrchBnd; PepBnd; SchMus; SchPl; SecStuCncl; PPFtbl; AmLegAwd;.

MITZEL, Lori; Fruitport HS; Muskegon, MI; ChrhWkr; HonRl; NHS; Yrbk; Ferris St Coll; Pre Science.

MITZEL, Myron J; Wolford Public HS; York, ND; PresFrshCls; PresSophCls; HonRl; StuCncl; EdYrBk; Bsktbl; Coll; Vocation.

MITZELFELT, Jeffrey D; Tremont HS; Pekin, IL; 4-H; LetterFtbl; LetterWrstlng; University; Medicine.

MIURA, Sandra; Roosevelt HS; Chicago, IL; HonRl; NHS; TchrAde; GerCl; Trk; Seattle Univ; Phd Oceanography.

MIXON, Deborah R; Marshall HS; Marshall, IL; ChrhWkr; CmntyWkr; DrmMjrt; HospAde; JA; OffAde; SchPl; TchrAde; YthFlsp; College; Vocation.

MIYAHARA, Patrick; Morrill HS; Morrill, NE; 4/46 Band; Chrs; HonRl; SchMus; StuCncl; DanFAwd; EldAwd; Nebraska Western Jr Col; Medical Technology.

MIZE, Donald P; Godwin Heights HS; Wyoming, MI; 32/186 HonRl; NHS; NatlMeritCmnd; Michigan Tech; Chem Engr.

MIZEN, Sharon L; Morgan Park Academy; Chicago, IL; SecJrCls; Chrs; HonRl; ModUN; NHS; NatlThespSoc; SchMus; YthLg; Chrldr; College; Nursing.

MIZENER, Bette; Charleston Hs; Charleston, IL; VPSrCls; HonRl; NatlMeritCmnd; TchrAde; 4-H; PpCl; Trk; Chrldr; GAA; 4-HAwd; Illinois State University; Business.

MIZERA, Christopher T; Weber HS; Chicago, IL; 45/192 ChrhWkr; HonRl; Yrbk; LatCl; Loyola University; Lawyer.

MIZIA, Rita L; Superior HS; Superior, WI; Band; MrchBnd; Orch; PepBnd; TchrAde; Coll; Dietetics.

MIZINIAK, Zofia; Bloom Township HS; Chicago Heights, IL; 9/1018 HonRl; NHS; TchrAde; U I C C; Medicine.

MIZZI, Cecelia A; Edsel Ford HS; Dearborn, MI; AFS; NatlFornLg; Quill&Scroll; SchMus; StuCncl; StuGov; FrCl; IMSpt; Central Michigan Univ; Law.

MLADY, Sandra; Bloomfield HS; Bloomfield, NE; 2/45 PresFrshCls; SecSrCls; HonRl; NHS; NatlMeritCmnd; TchrAde; PpCl; Chrldr; 4-HAwd; Business School; Executive Sec.

MLINEK, Wendi E; St Francis Comm HS; St Francis, KS; 12/51 Band; ChrhWkr; CncrtBnd; HonRl; LbryAde; MrchBnd; PepBnd; SchPl; TreasFHA; PpCl; PPFtbl; CitAwd; Kansas State Univ; Home Economics.

MLYNEK, Deborah J; James B Conant HS; Hoffman Estates, IL; HonRl; University Of Wyoming; Geology.

MNISZEWSKI, Edmund T; Mount Carmel HS; Chicago, IL; 2/203 HonRl; PresNHS; SciCl; IMSpt; Purdue Univ; Chemical Engineer.

MOAKE, Trina I; Vienna HS; Cypress, IL; VPJrCls; 4-H; FHA; FNA; PpCl; Bsktbl; Trk; Chrldr; College; Professional.

MOATS, Geri L; Marseilles HS; Marseilles, IL; NatlThespSoc; SchPl; StuCncl; YthFlsp; RptrYrbk; RptrSchPpr; LetterBsktbl; LetterSocr; LetterChrldr; GAA; IMSpt; PresAwd; College; Law.

MOATS, Linda; Granite City HS; Granite City, IL; NHS; StuCncl; FBLA; SpnCl; PpCl; Chrldr; CchngActv; GAA; IMSpt; Siv Edwardsville Il; Busi Mark.

MOATS, Virginia A; Prospect HS; Mt Prospect, IL; 53/614 Chrs; CmntyWkr; CncrtBnd; HonRl; MrchBnd; NatlFornLg; PepBnd; SchMus; VPSctActv; StuCncl; College; Social Science.

MOBERG, Marla R; Powers Lake HS; Battle View, ND; ALAGirlsSt; Band; Chr; CncrtBnd; MrchBnd; PepBnd; SchPl; FHA; EngCl; LetterBsktbl; Trinity School; Nursng.

MOBERLY, Linda L; Brown County HS; Nashville, IN; 7/169 ChrhWkr; PresNHS; StuCncl; SecLatCl; PpCl;.

MOBLEY, Deborah K; Brookville HS; Brookville, IN; HonRl; VP4-H; SpnCl; 4-HAwd; Bus Sch; Vocation.

MOBLEY, Jerri K; Brown County HS; Nashville, IN; 13/190 HonRl; HospAde; NHS; SchPl; SctActv;

TchrAde; FHA; FrCl; PpCl; GAA; College; Nursing.

MOBLEY, Thomas E; Southport HS; Indianapolis, IN; 52/430 PresSrCls; ALBoysSt; ALAGirlsSt; HonRl; NHS; NatlMeritCmnd; StuCncl; YthFlsp; KeyCl; LetterTennis; Hanover; Business Or Teaching.

MOBURG, John G; Yorkwood HS; Kirkwood, IL; Band; Chrs; HonRl; Mdrgl; StuCncl; PresYthFlsp; Yrbk; SecFFA; Ftbl; LetterWrstlng; Univ Western Ill; Indus Tech.

MOCA, Steve M; Addison Trail HS; Addison, IL; 10/600 Aud/Vis; HonRl; NHS; StuCncl; College; Medicine.

MOCAN, John; Cass City HS; Cass City, MI; 57/158 HonRl; SchPl; SctActv; TchrAde; Yrbk; SchPpr; SpnCl; IMSpt; Col; Forestry.

MOCARSKI, Steven G; Premontre HS; Green Bay, WI; 8/143 TrsFrshCls; TrsSophCls; TrsJrCls; Chrs; HonRl; ROTC; SctActv; StuCncl; RptrYrbk; SptEdYrbk; LetterBsbl; LetterBsktbl; CaptCol; Law.

MOCK, Erika; Owen Withee HS; Owen, WI; 1/98 Band; ChrhWkr; CncrtBnd; HonRl; MrchBnd; NHS; TchrAde; Yrbk; 4-H; TreasFHA; College; Music Therapy.

MOCK, Nancy J; Medora HS; Medora, IN; PresFrshCls; VPJrCls; TrsSrCls; Band; SchPl; StuCncl; Yrbk; 4-H; SpnCl; Bsktbl; Col ; Archit.

MOCOGNI, Frida H; Carmel Girls HS; Highwood, IL; 1/193 ChrhWkr; HonRl; NHS; College; Special Education.

MOCZULSKI, Sue; Pinconning Area HS; Pinconning, MI; 31/249 Band; CncrtBnd; HonRl; MrchBnd; NHS; PepBnd; SchPl; FNA; PPFtbl; VoiceDemAwd; Micigan State Univ; Medical Nursing.

MODAFF, Robert C; Lisle Sr HS; Lisle, IL; 12/170 PresAFS; Chr; HonRl; Mdrgl; NHS; NatlThespSoc; SchMus; SchPl; SpnCl; Southern Illinois Univ; Theater.

MODAHL, Debra R; Badger HS; Badger, MN; 3/23 PresFrshCls; PresSophCls; SecJrCls; TrsSrCls; Chr; HonRl; StuCncl; FshEdYrbk; FHA; GAA; Concordia Col; Social Work.

MODDERMAN, Joni S; Albert Lea Sr HS; Albert Lea, MN; U Of Minn; English Education.

MODDERMAN, Kelle S; Cal Community HS; Alexander, IA; Band; Chrs; ChrhWkr; CncrtBnd; HonRl; MrchBnd; PepBnd; 4-H; Bsktbl; Chrldr; U Of Northern Iowa; Art Teacher.

MODERT, Ted A; Bronson HS; Bronson, MI; 21/135 PresSophCls; HonRl; NHS; SchPl; VPStuCncl; Bsbl; Bsktbl; College; Business.

MODGLIN, Betsy L; Century 100 HS; Ullin, IL; 2/56 TrsJrCls; HonRl; Yrbk; RptrSchPpr; FHA; Shawnee Jr Col; Secretarial.

MODICA, William J; Girard HS; Walnut, KS; PresJrCls; PresSrCls; HonRl; NHS; SchPl; RptrYrbk; RptrSchPpr; 4-H; FFA; LetterFtbl; Ks St Univ ENGNG.

MODIN, Gaylord L; Magic City Campus HS; Minot, ND; Chr; Chrs; HonRl; NatlThespSoc; SchMus; SchPl; RptrYrbk; EdSchPpr; Univ Of Nd; Sociology.

MODLINSKI, Greg; Greenfield HS; Greenfiekd, WI; Band; ChrhWkr; HonRl; PolWkr; StuCncl; StuGov; PresJrCls; VPJrCls; Ftbl; Tennis; College.

MODRALL, Laurie; Arthur Hill HS; Saginaw, MI; HonRl; HospAde; MrchBnd; FrCl; PpCl; University; Doctor.

MOE, Cheri L; Hanson Indt #40 HS; Alexandria, SD; 7/44 Aud/Vis; Band; ChrhWkr; CncrtBnd; DrlTm; HonRl; LbryAde; MrchBnd; PepBnd; Quill&Scroll; University; Marine Biology.

MOE, Keith V; Carbondale Comm HS; Carbondale, IL; Orch; College; Archaeology.

MOE, Pamela D; Dell Rapids Public HS; Dell Rapids, SD; Band; Chrs; ChrhWkr; CmntyWkr; HonRl; NatlThespSoc; SchMus; SchPl; StuCncl; Chrldr; Trade School.

MOE, Patricia K; Hanson Ind #40 HS; Alexandria, SD; Chr; Chrs; ChrhWkr; CmntyWkr; HonRl; LbryAde; Mdrgl; Quill&Scroll; SchAde; SchMus; Chrldr; Business School; Vocation.

MOE, Paul D; Dell Rapids Public HS; Dell Rapids, SD; 7/50 PresSophCls; Band; Chr; ChrhWkr; HonRl; NHS; SchMus; SchPl; StuCncl; Coll; Professional.

MOE, Victoria A; St Mary HS; Suttons Bay, MI; 3/14 VPJrCls; Chr; HonRl; Yrbk; 4-H; Bsbl; CaptBsktbl; Chrldr; Northwestern Mich College; Secretary.

MOECKEL, Debra K; Grass Lake Jr Sr HS; Grass Lake, MI; 19/94 Chrs; HonRl; TchrAde; FHA; Jackson Comm College; Child Services.

MOEDE, Barbara K; New Holstein HS; New Holstein, WI; 19/181 Band; Chrs; CncrtBnd; HonRl; MrchBnd; PepBnd; SctActv; TchrAde; YthFlsp; SchPpr; College;.

MOEDER, Michael D; Central HS; Cape Girardeau, MO; 67/450 ALBoysSt; HonRl; LitMag; NHS; Orch; SchPl; Coll.

MOEDING, Lori J; Manson Community HS; Manson, IA; SecFrshCls; PresSophCls; ALAGirlsSt; ChrhWkr; CncrtBnd; HonRl; MrchBnd; NHS; PepBnd; SchMus; LetterTrk; College; Teaching.

MOEHLE, Normz; Mt Pleasant HS; Mount Pleasant, IA; Band; Chrs; CncrtBnd; MrchBnd; PepBnd; YthFlsp; 4-H; Jr College; Dental Assist.

MOEHN, Mary F; Stockbridge HS; Hilbert, WI; Band; Chrs; CncrtBnd; HonRl; MrchBnd; Orch; PepBnd; SchPl; PpCl; University.

MOELLER, Carol A; Scribner HS; Hooper, NE; Band; Chr; Chrs; ChrhWkr; CncrtBnd; DrlTm; DrmMjrt; HonRl; MrchBnd; NHS; Orch; PepBnd; LetterBsbl; LetterTrk; College; Banking.

MOELLER, Clair J; Denison Comm HS; Denison, IA; Band; Chr; Chrs; HonRl; NatlFornLg; NHS; SchMus; LetterFtbl; U Of Ia; Elec Engr.

MOELLER, Debra A; Badger HS; Lake Geneva, WI; Chr; CmntyWkr; HonRl; SchMus; TchrAde; Twrl; PpCl; Glf; GAA; VoiceDemAwd; Career College; Fashion Modeling.

MOELLER, Gregory F; Hemingford HS; Hemingford, NE; 11/42 VPFrshCls; PresSophCls; VPSrCls; ALBoysSt; PresChrs; PresNHS; PresFFA; CaptBsktbl; CaptFtbl; Trk; Ne Western Coll; Business Administration.

MOELLER, William D; Durant HS; Stockton, IA; 8/78 TrsFrshCls; Band; Chrs; MrchBnd; NatlFornLg; NHS; SchMus; SchPl; VPStuCncl; RptrSchPpr; College.

MOELLER, William J; Joliet Catholic HS; Romeoville, IL; 20/170 HstFrshCls; HstSophCls; HstJrCls; SecSrCls; JA; JrNHS; NHS; StuCncl; StuGov; RptrYrbk; FshEdSchPpr; CaptBsbl; Ftbl; Dartmouth Univ; Architecture.

MOELLERS, Carol M; Mineral Point HS; Mineral Point, WI; 9/98 HonRl; Vocation School; Nursing.

MOELLERS, Coral M; Mineral Point HS; Mineral Point, WI; 11/98 HonRl; LbryAde; Vocational School; Nursing.

MOELLERS, Mayve A; Fayette Comm HS; Fayette, IA; 2/40 VPJrCls; PresSrCls; PresBand; CncrtBnd; HonRl; PresNHS; SchPl; PresSpnCl; Trk; BttyCrckrAwd; Univ Of Ia ;teacher.

MOELLING, Scott P; Jennings HS; Jennings, MO; HonRl; SctActv; Ftbl; College.

MOEN, Debbie K; Irene HS; Volin, SD; 2/33 Band; Chrs; ChrhWkr; CncrtBnd; HonRl; NHS; SchPl; Business School; Secretary.

MOEN, Janelle R; Richland #44 HS; Colfax, ND; Band; Chrs; MrchBnd; PepBnd; SchPl; StuCncl; RptrYrbk; RptrSchPpr; SecFHA; Chrldr; College.

MOEN, Jeri L; Watertown Sr HS; Watertown, SD; Chr; Chrs; HospAde; NatlMeritCmnd; GerCl; Univ Of North Dakota; Nursing.

MOEN, Jon T; Regis HS; Eau Claire, WI; 10/142 HonRl; NatlFornLg; NHS; SpnCl; Col; Business Admin.

MOEN, Luann K; Hendricks HS; Astoria, SD; SecTrsSophCls; Band; Chr; Chrs; CncrtBnd; HonRl; HospAde; MrchBnd; PepBnd; SchPl; YthFlsp; EdSchPpr; Bsktbl; College; Special Education.

MOEN, Valerie J; Madison Public HS; Madison, MN; 4/86 Band; HonRl; HospAde; TchrAde; FHA; PpCl; LetterTrk; GAA; IMSpt; PPFtbl; Moorhead State; Nuclear Medical Technology.

MOENCH, Juliann K; Humboldt HS; Humboldt, IA; TrsJrCls; Band; Chr; ChrhWkr; HonRl; NHS; StuCncl; 4-H; Chrldr; PPFtbl; Iowa State U; Home Economics.

MOENS, Theresa M; Atkinson HS; Atkinson, IL; SecSophCls; HonRl; Yrbk; FHA; SpnCl; Bsbl; Bsktbl; Chrldr; GAA; 4-HAwd; Western U Of Il; Special Education.

MOERER, Janette L; Richland Center HS; Richland Center, WI; 3/183 TrsSrCls; Band; HonRl; MrchBnd; NHS; StuCncl; RptrYrbk; SchPpr; FTA; SpnCl; Vocational School; Legal Sec.

MOES, Jayne A; Osmond Community HS; Osmond, NE; 22/44 LetterBand; CncrtBnd; HonRl; MrchBnd; PepBnd; SchPl; TchrAde; Pres4-H; SecFBLA; PpCl; College; Secretary.

MOFFAT, Lisa A; Sparta HS; Sparta, IL; 5/165 SecFrshCls; SecJrCls; Band; Chr; ChrhWkr; CncrtBnd; HonRl; HospAde; MrchBnd; PepBnd; SchMus; SchPl; SctActv; Swmmng; Stephens College; Theatre.

MOFFATT, Eda A; Parkview HS; Springfield, MO; Chr; Chrs; DrmBgl; HonRl; Mdrgl; NatlFornLg; SchMus; SctActv; StuGov; TchrAde; College; Professional.

MOFFATT, Keith E; Marinette Catholic Centrl HS; Marinette, WI; 5/90 SchAde; SchPl; TchrAde; Bsktbl; Ftbl; Glf; CchngActv; IMSpt; Marquette College; Dentist.

MOFFATT, Kim I; Big Foot HS; Shron, WI; LbryAde; 4-H; FBLA; FFA; FHA; PpCl; 4-HAwd; Gti Vocational School; Pre School Teacher.

MOFFETT, Cheryl J; Windsor HS; Windsor, IL; 1/56 PresSophCls; HonRl; NHS; SchPl; StuCncl; Yrbk; FHA; SpnCl; College; Nursing.

MOFFETT, Mark W; Memorial HS; Beloit, WI; Band; CncrtBnd; Orch; SchPpr; Beloit College; Zoology.

MOFFITT, Gwen J; Stuart Menlo HS; Stuart, IA; SecJrCls; SecSophCls; Chr; CncrtBnd; HonRl; MrchBnd; NHS; NatlThespSoc; SchMus; SchPl; Univ; Home Ec.

MOFFITT, Murial V; Washington HS; Washington, KS; Chrs; ChrhWkr; HonRl; SchMus; SciCl; Mc Pherson College; Biology.

MOGAB, Karen; Winfield HS; Winfield, KS; SecTrsSrCls; AFS; CAP; CmntyWkr; HonRl; HospAde; JA; PolWkr; TchrAde; SchPpr; College; Certified Reg Nurse Anesthetist.

MOGLER, Lynette C; Rutland HS; Colman, SD; HonRl; NHS; OffAde; SchAde; RptrYrbk; RptrSchPpr; FHA; PpCl; Bsbl; Bsktbl; Business School.

MOHAN, Christine M; Marian HS; Birmingham, MI; 33/178 HonRl; NHS; Teen; FTA; MthCl; Bsktbl; College; Engineering.

MOHAN, David J; Springfield HS; Springfield, IL; NatlMeritCmnd; NatlMeritSF; PolWkr; StuCncl; StuGov; RptrSchPpr; SchPpr; LatCl; Ftbl; Univ Of Illinois; Law.

MOHERMAN, Roxann; Wellsville HS; Wellsville, KS; Band; Chr; ChrhWkr; HonRl; HospAde; SchAde; TchrAde; Trk; GAA; Univ Of No Colorado; Nurse.

MOHIT, Julie R; Hays HS; Hays, KS; HonRl; NatlMeritCmnd; Orch; PpCl; College; Business.

MOHLER, John A; Yorktown HS; Yorktown, IN; 8/181 ChrhWkr; NHS; TchrAde; SpnCl; LetterBsbl; LetterBsktbl; LetterFtbl; Ollivet Nazarene College; Ministry.

MOHLKE, Sally L; La Crosse HS; Wanatah, IN; 2/48 SecFrshCls; PresSophCls; ALAGirlsSt; Band; HonRl; NHS; SchMus; TchrAde; Bsktbl; Trk; College; Special Ed.

MOHN, Lavonne; Lakeville HS; Lakeville, MN; VPSophCls; Chr; Chrs; ChrhWkr; HonRl; Mdrgl; NHS; OffAde; StuCncl; St Olaf College; Psychology.

MOHNEN, Debra A; St Mary Central HS; Neenah, WI; 1/102 Chrs; DrlTm; HonRl; NatlFornLg; NatlThespSoc; StuCncl; RptrSchPpr; MthCl; DARAwd; OptClAwd; Coll; Med.

MOHNI, Lanette M; Hartley Comm HS; Hartley, IA; ChrhWkr; CmntyWkr; HonRl; LbryAde; SchPl; YthFlsp; FHA; GerCl; PpCl; Bsktbl; Hairstylist.

MOHNING, Cheryl A; Kingsley Pierson HS; Kingsley, IA; 12/60 PresSrCls; HonRl; NHS; PolWkr; ROTC; StuCncl; RptrYrbk; RptrSchPpr; IMSpt; Tech; Secretary.

MOHOREK, Ronald E; St Laurence HS; Chicago, IL; 4/389 HonRl; PolWkr; LetterBsktbl; Coll; Law.

MOHR, Annetta J; Laharpe Comm HS; Lomax, IL; Chrs; HonRl; NHS; NatlMeritSF; SchMus; Twrl; SptEdSchPpr; 4-H; GAA; PPFtbl; DanFAwd; Univ; Home Economics.

MOHR, David G; South West HS; Green Bay, WI; 1/427 HonRl; NHS; SchPl; LetterTrk; BauchLmbAwd; Mass Inst Of Tech; Physics.

MOHR, Eunice E; Neillsville HS; Neillsville, WI; HonRl; SecNHS; StuGov; SecPpCl; GAA; Secretary At Univ Extension Office Courthou.

MOHR, James A; St Laurence HS; Chicago, IL; 38/380 CmntyWkr; HonRl; StuCncl; TchrAde; PpCl; LetterWrstlng; IMSpt; College; Medicine.

MOHR, John D; Rock Island HS; Coal Valley, IL; NatlThespSoc; SchPl; StuGov; SchPpr; GerCl; SciCl; CaptSwmmng; LetterTrk; Illinois State Univ; Law.

MOHR, John L; Park Sr HS; Cottage Grove, MN; 83/664 Band; CncrtBnd; HonRl; JA; MrchBnd; NHS; NatlMeritSF; PepBnd; RedCrAde; SctActv; GerCl; LetterSwmmng; Tennis; College; Professional.

MOHR, Karen A; Norris HS; Roca, NE; ALAGirlsSt; Band; CncrtBnd; HonRl; MrchBnd; PepBnd; SchPl; TchrAde; 4-H; SecFrCl; U Of Ne; Art.

MOHR, Mark; Andale HS; Wichita, KS; VPJrCls; CmntyWkr; PolWkr; SchPl; StuCncl; StuGov; Yrbk; SchPpr; IMSpt; College; Professional.

MOHR, Mark A; Markesan HS; Fairwater, WI; 40/120 LetterFtbl; LetterWrstlng; Moraine Park Tech; Machine Tooling Tech.

MOHR, Nancy O; Trego Community HS; Collye, KS; HonRl; SchPl; 4-H; FHA; PpCl; SciCl; LetterChrldr; 4-HAwd; Navy.

MOHR, Sandra N; Southeast HS; Wichita, KS; 11/670 Chr; HonRl; PresJA; NatlMeritFnl; NatlMeritSchl; GerCl; Wichita State Univ; Medicine Physician.

MOHR, Steven J; Southern Door HS; Brussels, WI; HonRl; SchPpr; FFA; Bsktbl; Wrstlng; IMSpt; Trade School.

MOHRHAUSER, Luann R; Fremont Sr HS; Fremont, NE; Chr; HonRl; PolWkr; SchMus; TchrAde; GerCl; Technical College; Medicine.

MOHROR, Kelly R; Watertown HS; Watertown, SD; HonRl; LetterFtbl; LetterTrk; LetterWrstlng; IMSpt; Sd State Univ; Wildlife & Fisheries Science.

MOHS, Roberta K; Wahpeton Sr HS; Wahpeton, ND; ChrhWkr; HospAde; LbryAde; 4-H; University; Accounting.

MOKATE, Karen M; Prospect HS; Mt Prospect, IL; 59/610 AFS; Band; ChrhWkr; HonRl; MrchBnd; PresNatlFornLg; NHS; NatlMeritCmnd; YthLg; Univ Of Illinois; Government.

MOKLESTAD, Larry L; Thompson Comm HS; Thompson, IA; VPSophCls; HonRl; NHS; SchPl; YthFlsp; 4-H; FFA; LetterBsbl; LetterBsktbl; LetterFtbl; Iowa St Univ; Physical Ed.

MOLACEK, Ardene R; Howells Public HS; Howells, NE; 4/44 HstJrCls; HonRl; LbryAde; StuGov; TchrAde; 4-H; PpCl; LetterGAA; 4-HAwd; JAAwd; CitAwd; Business School; Vocation.

MOLACEK, Susan J; Schuyler Central HS; Schuyler, NE; 7/84 Band; CncrtBnd; HonRl; MrchBnd; NHS; PepBnd; TchrAde; PpCl; School Of Commerce; Medical Secretary.

MOLANDER, John C; Marian Catholic HS; Homewood, IL; HonRl; NHS; NatlMeritCmnd; PolWkr; SchPl; RptrSchPpr; Wrstlng; University; Engineering.

MOLCYK, Kathryn A; Kearney HS; Kearney, NE; 4/254 HonRl; RedCrAde; TchrAde; FHA; VPSpnCl; PpCl; LetterTrk; CaptIMSpt; EldAwd; College; Veterinarian.

MOLDAN, Lavonne T; St Marys HS; Sleepy Eye, MN; Band; ChrhWkr; CmntyWkr; CncrtBnd; MrchBnd; OffAde; Sdlty; TchrAde; Work.

MOLDEN, Barbara A; Fairbury HS; Fairbury, NE; Band; Chr; Chrs; ChrhWkr; CncrtBnd; DrmMjrt; HonRl; MrchBnd; PepBnd; SchMus; Twrl; YthFlsp; 4-H; Business School; Interior Decorating.

MOLDEN, Carleen M; Milan HS; Milan, MN; 6/31 Band; Chr; ChrhWkr; CncrtBnd; HonRl; PepBnd; SchPl; TchrAde; Yrbk; FHA; Willimar Comm College.

MOLDENHAUER, Karla Y; Milbank HS; Twin Brooks, SD; 18/123 Chrs; PresCncrtBnd; HonRl; Mdrgl; MrchBnd; NHS; SchMus; StuGov; GerCl; Col; Musci.

MOLDENHAUER, Susan L; Jefferson Sr HS; Jefferson, WI; Band; Chr; Chrs; ChrhWkr; CncrtBnd; HonRl; HospAde; MrchBnd; Bsktbl; Swmmng; U Of Wi Lacrosse; Therapeutic Recreation.

MOLDOVAN, Daniel G; Herbert Henry Dow HS; Midland, MI; HonRl; JrNHS; NHS; 4-H; Bsbl; LetterFtbl; IMSpt; ChmbCommrsAwd; 4-HAwd; PresAwd; U Of Mich; Medicine.

MOLE, Stephen J; Big Foot HS; Fontana, WI; Chr; ChrhWkr; LitMag; NatlMeritFnl; PepBnd; Milwaukee Conservatory; Prof Guitarist.

MOLENAAR, Mary; Danube HS; Renville, MN; 2/43 TrsSrCls; Band; Chrs; ChrhWkr; AmLegAwd; DARAwd; CAP; College.

MOLES, Margaret J; Mundelein HS; Mundelein, IL; Band; Chr; Chrs; ChrhWkr; CncrtBnd; HonRl; LitMag; MrchBnd; SctActv; 4-H; FTA; Univ Of Illinois; Writing.

MOLEY, Janet; Morton HS; Morton, IL; DrlTm; HonRl; Yrbk; GAA; Ill State Univ; Elementary Teacher.

MOLGREN, Lisa; Orono HS; Wayzata, MN; 46/206 ChrhWkr; CmntyWkr; HonRl; Yrbk; SpnCl; PpCl; IMSpt; PPFtbl; PresAwd; Univ; Nurse.

MOLGREN, Philip M; Lane Technical HS; Chicago, IL; 108/1463 ChrhWkr; NatlMeritSF; OffAde; PolWkr; SchPl; SctActv; StuCncl; KeyCl; College; Law.

MOLINA, Paul L; Brown Deer HS; Brown Deer, WI; 2/300 ALBoysSt; NHS; StuCncl; EdYrBk; CaptMthCl; LetterBsbl; LetterBsktbl; LetterTrk; BauchLmbAwd; EldAwd; John Hopkins Univ; Medical Doctor.

MOLINARI, Margaret M; Queen Of Peace HS; Chicago, IL; ChrhWkr; HonRl; NHS; NatlMeritCmnd; PolWkr; TchrAde; Yrbk; SpnCl; Univ Of Illinois; Biochemistry.

MOLINARO, Anthony T; Morton West HS; Berwyn, IL; 60/740 Band; HonRl; JA; LitMag; MrchBnd; PresNHS; Quill&Scroll; SchPpr; Trk; Univ Of Chicago; Biology.

MOLINARO, Michael L; Notre Dame HS; Chicago, IL; 23/280 HonRl; NHS; LetterBsbl; IMSpt; St Josephs College; Law.

MOLINE, Deborah L; Durand Area HS; Durand, MI; 30/202 HonRl; HospAde; SchPl; RptrSchPpr; 4-H; FFA; Olivet Nazarene College; Zoology.

MOLITOR, Kenneth B; Mater Dei HS; Germantown, IL; 8/182 Band; ChrhWkr; CmntyWkr; HonRl; NHS; Univ Of Illinois; Engineering.

MOLITOR, Peter F; Notre Dame HS; Park Ridge, IL; 23/280 SecSrCls; HonRl; SchPl; StuCncl; StuGov; Ftbl; University Of Notre Dame; Coporate Lawyer.

MOLITOR, Susan T; Lyons Township HS; Brookfield, IL; SchAde; Mac Cormac Jr Coll; Secretary.

MOLL, Randall R; Lane Technical HS; Chicago, IL; 8/1160 SecTrsSrCls; CmntyWkr; LbryAde; NHS; OffAde; StuGov; YthFnd; KeyCl; JCAwd; USJCAwd; Northwestern Univ; Neurobiology Research.

MOLL, Scott A; Columbus HS; Columbus, WI; 3/150 LetterTrk; IMSpt; Milwaukee Sch Of Engineering; Engineering.

MOLL, Shelley A; Shannon HS; Shannon, IL; VPFrshCls; SecSophCls; HonRl; PresSctActv; SecStuCncl; RptrSchPpr; Pres4-H; FFA; DanFAwd; 4-HAwd; College.

MOLLA, David G; Herrin HS; Herrin, IL; NatlMeritCmnd; So Illinois Univ; Accounting.

MOLLER, Julie A; Crystal Lake Comm HS; Crystal Lake, IL; 82/477 Band; HonRl; MrchBnd; SptEdYrbk; FTA; TreasLatCl; Tennis; CaptChrldr; College; Advertising.

MOLLER, Susan A; Sturden Jeffers Public HS; Windom, MN; 8/50 Band; HonRl; MrchBnd; NHS; OffAde; Orch; PresStuCncl; TchrAde; FHA; MthCl; Worthington Comm Coll; Math.

MOLLET, Richard S; Green Bay Southwest HS; Green Bay, WI; HonRl; StuCncl; LetterFtbl; LetterTrk; LetterWrstlng; College; Political Science.

MOLLETT, Roger W; Hillsboro HS; Hillsboro, IL; 1/180 HonRl; GerCl; Wrstlng; Computer Prog.

MOLLINGER, Therese M; Pius Xi HS; Milwaukee, WI; 21/380 ALAGirlsSt; TreasJA; NHS; StuCncl; College; Med Tech.

MOLLISON, Danny P; Northrop HS; Ft Wayne, IN; Band; Chr; ChrhWkr; ROTC; SchPpr; 4-H; SpnCl; Ftbl; College.

MOLLOY, Cindy M; Dexter HS; Dexter, MO; Chr; NHS; Quill&Scroll; SchPl; SchPpr; FTA; PpCl; Bsktbl; Ftbl; GovHonPrgAwd; Univ; Psychology.

MOLLOY, James L; Badger HS; Lake Geneva, WI; 3/248 ALBoysSt; CmntyWkr; HonRl; NHS; SchPl; Glf; University Of Wisconsin.

MOLLOY, Joseph M; Marquette HS; Alton, IL; ChrhWkr; HonRl; NHS; NatlThespSoc; SchPl; StuGov; RptrYrbk; St Louis University.

MOLLOY, Kevin L; St Rita HS; Chicago, IL; 150/500 HonRl; Trk; Univ Of Illinois; Pharmacy.

MOLLOY, Sheryl L; Trenton HS; Trenton, MO; 30/163 Chrs; HonRl; NHS; SctActv; RptrSchPpr; FHA; SpnCl; Ne Missouri Univ; Art Major.

MOLLUS, Doni S; Lafayette HS; St Joseph, MO; 3/300 HonRl; JA; LitMag; OffAde; SecFTA; SpnCl; JAAwd; NCTE; College; English.

MOLNAR, Christine L; St Marys Acad; Aurora, IL; PresSrCls; JrNHS; NHS; RedCrAde; EdYrBk; Swmmng; AmLegAwd; USJCAwd; CitAwd; VoiceDemAwd; College; Comm Artist.

MOLO, Steven F; A A Stagg HS; Palos Hills, IL; HonRl; NHS; StuCncl; RptrYrbk; Bsktbl; College.

MOLSON, Barbara A; Jefferson HS; Rockford, IL; 21/355 VPSrCls; HonRl; NHS; SchMus; SchPl; StuGov; PpCl;.

MOLSON, Sandra L; Whiting HS; Whiting, IN; ALAGirlsSt; HonRl; NHS; StuCncl; SpnCl; Univ Purdue; Professional.

MOLTER, Ronald G; Monroe HS; Monroe, MI; Chrs; Bsbl; Ftbl; Northwood Inst Midland Mi; Bus.

MOLTZAN, Jacquelyn S; Willowbrook HS; Lombard, IL; 60/814 Chr; HonRl; NHS;.

MOLTZEN, Melisa A; Rock Island Sr HS; Rock Island, IL; 22/688 ChrhWkr; CmntyWkr; SecHospAde; StuCncl; Yrbk; PresMthCl; CchngActv; Augustana College; Mathematics.

MOLUMBY, Daniel J; St Marys HS; Burlington, WI; PresFrshCls; HonRl; SpnCl; MthCl; Bsbl; College; Professional.

MOLUMBY, Daniel J; Saint Marys HS; Burlington, WI; PresFrshCls; HonRl; SctActv; SpnCl; Bsbl; College; Professional.

MOMA, Alicia A; Blue Mound HS; Blue Mound, IL; SecFrshCls; SecSophCls; VPJrCls; HonRl; NHS; SchPl; StuCncl; YthFlsp; FHA; FTA; GAA; DARAwd; PresAwd; Richland Comm Coll; Undecided.

MOMSEN, Amy M; Ogorman HS; Sioux Falls, SD; DrlTm; NHS;.

MONACHINO, Christine; Harrisonville Sr HS; Harrisonville, MO; VPSophCls; Chr; HonRl; SchPl; StuCncl; SpnCl; PpCl; IMSpt; Umkc; Doctor.

MONACO, Helen C; John F Kennedy HS; Chicago, IL; CmntyWkr; HonRl; St Xavier Coll; Audiologist.

MONAGHAN, Brian E; Homewood Flossmoor HS; Flossmoor, IL; 105/950 HonRl; LatCl; LetterSwmmng; University; Management.

MONAGHAN, Daniel H; Humboldt HS; Humboldt, IA; 12/150 TrsJrCls; Chr; HonRl; NHS; StuCncl; YthFlsp; Bsbl; Bsktbl; Ftbl; BauchLmbAwd; Iowa State; Industrial Admin.

MONAGHAN, Nancy K; Superior Sr HS; Superior, WI; 50/527 HonRl; HospAde; StuCncl; 4-H; FrCl; Trk; Marquette Univ; Liberal Arts.

MONAHAN, Bradley R; Hyannis HS; Hyannis, NE; 4/28 PresJrCls; Band; ChrhWkr; CncrtBnd; HonRl; MrchBnd; NHS; StuCncl; Ftbl; LetterTrk; College; Aviation.

MONAHAN, Joan M; Le Sueur HS; Le Sueur, MN; 6/112 Band; HonRl; HospAde; JA; NHS; SchPpr; SpnCl; CaptBsktbl; GAA; IMSpt; PPFtbl; JAAwd; College; Health.

MONAHAN, John E; Austin Catholic Prep; Grosse Pt Shores, MI; 48/115 Ftbl; LetterTrk; Univ Of Michigan; Business.

MONAHAN, Kimberly; South Shore Ind HS; South Shore, SD; 2/8 DrlTm; DrmMjrt; HonRl; SchPl; YthFlsp; FBLA; PpCl; DanFAwd; Business.

MONAHAN, Robert H; Wisconsin Dells HS; Wisconsin Dells, WI; 21/150 VPFrshCls; HonRl; NatlFornLg; StuCncl; StuGov; KeyCl; Bsktbl; Ftbl; Glf; LetterTrk; College; Law.

MONCHER, Dawna; Solomon Juneau HS; Milwaukee, WI; 20/231 Chr; ChrhWkr; HonRl; OffAde; SctActv; SpnCl; PpCl; GAA; Trad Or Bus Sch; Voc.

MONCION, Monique L; Ladywood HS; Livonia, MI; VPChr; CncrtBnd; HonRl; NHS; PresOrch; SchPl; FNA; FrCl; LetterTrk; Madonna Col; Pre Med.

MONCRIEF, Amy S; Elwood HS; Elwood, NE; Band; ChrhWkr; CncrtBnd; MrchBnd; PepBnd; YthFlsp; 4-H; FHA; PpCl; Business School; Accounting.

MONDAY, June E; Woodruff HS; Peoria, IL; ChrhWkr; HonRl; Trk; College; Professional.

MONDINO, Sally J; Frankfort Comm HS; West Frankfort, IL; Band; Chrs; HonRl; MrchBnd; NHS; SchPl; StuCncl; YthFlsp; SpnCl; PpCl; Southern Ill Univ; Music.

MONDRALA, Mark A; Marist HS; Chicago, IL; 29/393 HonRl; CmntyWkr; Socr; IMSpt; College.

MONDUL, Mark M; Guilford HS; Rockford, IL; HonRl; SchAde; Bsbl; Ftbl; Socr; Ill State Univ; Business Adm.

MONEN, James P; Creighton Prep; Omaha, NE; 40/249 Chr; HonRl; NHS; Quill&Scroll; SchMus; SptEdSchPpr; Socr; CchngActv; IMSpt; College; Medicine.

MONER, Susan; Taylor Center HS; Inkster, MI; 38/413 Band; ChrhWkr; CncrtBnd; HonRl; HospAde; MrchBnd; NatlThespSoc; PepBnd; RedCrAde; SchPl; Wayne St Univ; Physician.

MONETTE, Manuel S; Carter H Harrison HS; Chicago, IL; 35/408 VPSrCls; HonRl; LbryAde; OffAde; PepBnd; StuCncl; RptrYrbk; Yrbk; Bsbl; IMSpt; Northern Ill U; Baseball.

MONETTE, Ronald R; St Agata HS; Detroit, MI; HonRl; NatlSciFnd; Bsktbl; College; Sports Representative.

MONEY, Cheryl M; Adrian HS; Adrian, MI; ChrhWkr; TchrAde; Malone College; Child Care.

MONEY, Mechelle J; Meridian HS; Mounds, IL; CmntyWkr; HonRl; RptrSchPpr; 4-H; FHA; LatCl; 4-HAwd; Academy; Police Career.

MONFRE, Tamara E; St Teresa HS; Decatur, IL; ChrhWkr; HonRl; Sacrstn; RptrYrbk; GerCl; MthCl; PpCl; Chrldr; GAA; College; Physical Ed.

MONIAK, Mary L; Saint Augustine HS; Chicago, IL; SecSrCls; Chrs; NHS; SctActv; RptrYrbk; Maccormac Jr Col; Secretary.

MONICKEN, Michella D; Minot HS; Minot, ND; ALAGirlsSt; Chr; ChrhWkr; HonRl; NHS; NatlThespSoc; SchMus; SchPl; StuCncl; FrCl; Minot State Clge; Music Or Drama.

MONIER, Alice M; Henry Senachwine HS; Henry, IL; 5/73 HonRl; NHS; TreasFHA; PpCl; Illinois State Univ; Accountant.

MONIER, Mark L; Sparland HS; Sparland, IL; 2/21 PresSophCls; ALBoysSt; HonRl; NHS; EdYrBk; 4-H; FFA; LetterBsktbl; Trk; DanFAwd; University Of Illinois; Farming.

MONK, Carolyn L; Northern HS; Flint, MI; 7/635 CncrtBnd; MrchBnd; TreasNHS; Orch; YthFlsp; SpnCl; College; Special Edu.

MONK, Jinelle; Greendale HS; Greendale, WI; Chr; ChrhWkr; HonRl; Mdrgl; NHS; SchMus; SchPl; College Brigham Young U; Fine Arts.

MONKE, Cynthia J; Arlington HS; Arlington, NE; Chrs; HonRl; PresYthFlsp; 4-H; GerCl; PpCl; Trk; Chrldr; 4-HAwd; LionAwd; College; Teach Music.

MONKMAN, James A; Brainerd HS; Brainerd, MN; 30/461 AFS; NHS; NatlMeritCmnd; RedCrAde; SchPl; SecLatCl; LetterSwmmng; LetterTrk; CchngActv; IMSpt; Univ Of Minnesota; Medicine.

MONKS, Mary K; Polo HS; Polo, MO; 2/28 PresFrshCls; VPSophCls; VPJrCls; Band; Chr; ChrhWkr; DrmMjrt; HonRl; PpCl; LetterBsktbl; College; Major Study.

MONNAHAN, Mitchell R; Everly HS; Everly, IA; 1/34 VPFrshCls; TrsSophCls; PresJrCls; PresSrCls; ALBoysSt; HonRl; NHS; SctActv; Bsbl; Bsktbl; U Of Ia;.

MONNIER, Donna L; Raymond Central HS; Raymond, NE; ALAGirlsSt; Band; Chrs; HonRl; PepBnd; FBLA; FHA; PpCl; Trk; College; Secretary.

MONNIER, Nancy J; Carthage Comm HS; Basco, IL; 5/88 ALAGirlsSt; ChrhWkr; CmntyWkr; JA; NHS; NatlMeritFnl; NatlSciFnd; PolWkr; StuCncl; Yrbk; Bsktbl; West Il Univ; Medical Tech.

MONNINGER, Michelle; Baldwin HS; Baldwin City, KS; SecJrCls; ALAGirlsSt; Band; Chr; Chrl; Chrs; ChrhWkr; Tennis; Chrldr; 4-HAwd; Coll; Mus.

MONROE, Brian J; Central Community HS; De Witt, IA; ALBoysSt; Chr; Chrs; HonRl; NHS; SchMus; StuCncl; SchPpr; SciCl; University; Professional.

MONROE, Carol A; Shenandoah HS; Shenandoah, IA; 14/94 Chrs; HonRl; OffAde; RedCrAde; Teen; YthFlsp; FNA; PpCl; School Of Commerce; Med Secretary.

MONROE, Leanna M; Franklin HS; Waverly, IL; 1/42 HonRl; SecNHS; SecStuCncl; TchrAde; SchPpr; FHA; SecSpnCl; PpCl; Trk; GAA; College; Mathematics.

MONROE, Mark J; Niagara HS; Niagara, WI; 13/59 PresSrCls; NHS; StuCncl; FBLA; PpCl; LetterBsktbl; LetterFtbl; LetterTrk; Devry Inst Of Tech; Elec Eng.

MONROE, Marlissa I; Webberville HS; Webberville, MI; Band; Chr; ChrhWkr; CncrtBnd; HonRl; NHS; PepBnd; 4-H; GAA; 4-HAwd; Clge; Social Work.

MONROE, Maureen E; Shorewood HS; Milwaukee, WI; 21/212 AFS; HonRl; NatlThespSoc; SchMus; RptrYrbk; PpCl; LetterSwmmng; Chrldr; College; Law.

MONROE, R; Richmond Burton C HS; Richmond, IL; ALBoysSt; HonRl; NHS; MthCl; SciCl; IMSpt; Air Force Acad; Military Service.

MONSER, Robert L; Richwoods HS; Peoria, IL; Band; CncrtBnd; HonRl; MrchBnd; PepBnd; SchMus; Univ Of Illinois; Engineer.

MONSHAU, Monique; St Francis Academy; Joliet, IL; Chrs; DrlTm; HonRl; SchMus; TchrAde; SchPpr; University; Health.

MONSON, Carolyn S; Lane Technical HS; Chicago, IL; 9/1213 Band; Chrs; CncrtBnd; DrmBgl; HonRl; JrNHS; MrchBnd; NHS; NatlMeritCmnd; College; Music.

MONSON, Connie M; Merrill HS; Midland, MI; PresSophCls; HonRl; StuCncl; TchrAde; 4-H; FHA; Bsbl; Bsktbl; Trk; CchngActv; GAA; IMSpt; College Central Michigan; Teaching Pe.

MONSON, Deborah J; Walnut Grove HS; Walnut Grove, MN; 9/50 Band; Chr; ChrhWkr; CncrtBnd; HonRl; SchMus; StuCncl; TchrAde; TreasFHA; SpnCl; College; Medicine.

MONSON, Donna; Frost Public HS; Bricelyn, MN; 2/17 TrsSophCls; PresJrCls; Band; Chrs; ChrhWkr; CncrtBnd; Bsktbl; Trk; Chrldr; GAA; College; Profesional.

MONSON, Echo J; New Town HS; New Town, ND; ALAGirlsSt; Chrs; ChrhWkr; CmntyWkr; HonRl; SchPl; 4-H; FHA; GerCl; North Dakota St Univ; Veterinarian.

MONSON, Gregory L; Winola HS; New Windsor, IL; 4/67 SecSophCls; VPJrCls; PresSrCls; HonRl; NHS; StuCncl; SpnCl; LetterBsktbl; LetterFtbl; LetterTrk;.

MONSON, Kendra J; Stratford Comm HS; Stratford, IA; SecSophCls; Band; Chr; Chrs; HonRl; Mdrgl; MrchBnd; Bsbl; Bsktbl; LetterTrk;.

MONSON, Kerry; Rockford East Sr Hs; Rockford, IL; 50/660 ChrhWkr; CmntyWkr; HonRl; NHS; PolWkr; SctActv; StuGov; LetterFtbl; LetterGlf; Socr; College; Engineer.

MONSON, Lynette M; Brady HS; Brady, NE; 7/17 Band; CmntyWkr; HonRl; PepBnd; SchPl; Yrbk; 4-H; Trk; GAA; DARAwd; Coll; Lab Tech.

MONSON, Raymond E; Evanston Twp HS; Evanston, IL; HonRl; TchrAde; Wrstlng; Milliken Univ; Engineering.

MONSON, Raymond E; Evanston Township HS; Evanston, IL; HonRl; TchrAde; College; Engineering.

MONSON, Ronald D; Alden HS; Alden, MN; 4/45 SecSophCls; HonRl; NHS; SctActv; LetterBsbl; LetterBsktbl; LetterFtbl; CaptGlf; Univ; Golf Course Management.

MONSRUD, Sheryl K; Horace Mann HS; Biwabik, MN; Band; CmntyWkr; HonRl; SchPl; RptrSchPpr; GerCl; PpCl; VFWAwd; CitAwd; VoiceDemAwd; College; Professional.

MONTAG, Jeri A; Brookville HS; Brookville, IN; ChrhWkr; HonRl; NHS; NatlMeritCmnd; NatlThespSoc; SchPl; 4-H; FHA; SpnCl; 4-HAwd; College; Art.

MONTAGUE, Elisabeth; Grosse Pointe South HS; Grosse Pointe, MI; 1/650 DrlTm; HonRl; NHS; NatlMeritSF; Chrldr; GAA; College; Medicine.

MONTALBANO, Gina M; Downers Grove North HS; Downers Grove, IL; 41/500 Chr; CmntyWkr; HonRl; NHS; Bsktbl; College; Horticulture.

MONTALBANO, Michael J; St Patrick HS; Chicago, IL; 21/427 HonRl; SpnCl; MthCl; PpCl; Loras College; Business Admin.

MONTANO, Roger J; Hammond Gavit HS; Hammond, IN; 11/328 ChrhWkr; HonRl; NHS; Socr; College; Industrial Eng.

MONTEITH, Eugene P; Elkhart Central HS; Bristol, IN; Chr; HonRl; NHS; NatlThespSoc; SchPl; StuCncl; RptrYrbk; RptrSchPpr; Trk; LetterWrstlng; Indiana U; Writer Or Journalist.

MONTEMAYOR, Alex; Mundelein HS; Mundelein, IL; 7/400 HonRl; NHS; RptrYrbk; LetterTrk; IMSpt; College; Fine Arts Commercial Arts.

MONTER, Douglas L; Arapahoe HS; Arapahoe, NE; TrsFrshCls; PresSophCls; ALBoysSt; SchPl; YthFlsp; 4-H; CaptBsktbl; LetterFtbl; LetterTrk; 4-HAwd; College; Agriculture.

MONTGOMERY, April; Harvard St George HS; Chicago, IL; 1/19 SecJrCls; SecSrCls; CmntyWkr; NHS; SctActv; YthLg; Yrbk; LetterBsktbl; Chrldr; IMSpt; JCAwd; CitAwd; Univ Of San Francisco; International Law.

MONTGOMERY, Audrey J; Immaculata HS; Detroit, MI; ChrhWkr; CmntyWkr; LbryAde; NHS; SchPl; SctActv; FTA; Wayne St Univ; Accounting.

MONTGOMERY, Brett K; Granton HS; Granton, WI; 6/37 VPFrshCls; VPJrCls; HonRl; TchrAde; FFA; Bsktbl; Glf; LetterTrk; Univ Of Wisconsin; Optometrist.

MONTGOMERY, Carolyn S; Robinson HS; Robinson, IL; 9/186 ChrhWkr; HonRl; 4-H; PresFHA; PpCl; GAA; Southern Illinois Univ; Speech Pathology.

MONTGOMERY, Christie D; Baxter Community HS; Baxter, IA; Band; ChrhWkr; DrlTm; HonRl; MrchBnd; NatlThespSoc; SchMus; StuCncl; Twrl; RptrYrbk; Marshalltown Comm College; Lpn.

MONTGOMERY, Cyndi L; Daleville HS; Daleville, IN; 3/72 Chr; Chrl; Chrs; HonRl; JA; NHS; OffAde; SchPl; Yrbk; FrCl; Clg; Business.

MONTGOMERY, Dennis L; Woodland HS; Hiram, MO; HonRl; FFA; PpCl; Trade School; Vocation.

MONTGOMERY, Donna J; Greenview HS; Greenview, IL; Band; Chrs; HonRl; SchMus; TchrAde; 4-H; FHA; FSA; FTA; College; Professional.

MONTGOMERY, Douglas B; R 4 Public School HS; Greenfield, MO; 2/38 Band; CncrtBnd; HonRl; MrchBnd; PepBnd; SchPl; StuCncl; FTA; MthCl; Univ Of Mo; Engineering.

MONTGOMERY, James M; Hiawatha HS; Kirkland, IL; 8/57 PresFrshCls; PresSophCls; Band; Chrs; HonRl; NHS; FFA; LetterBsbl; Bsktbl; LetterFtbl; Ill St Univ; Comm.

MONTGOMERY, Janice L; Wykoff Public HS; Wykoff, MN; 5/32 Band; Chrs; HonRl; NHS; StuGov; PresYthFlsp; RptrYrbk; TreasFHA; PresFTA; SecGAA; Rochester Voc Tech Inst; Accounting.

MONTGOMERY, Jeanette O; Chaffee HS; Chaffee, MO; 1/65 SecFrshCls; ChrhWkr; CncrtBnd; HonRl; OffAde; YthFlsp; FHA; FrCl; CaptBsbl; CchngActv; Coll; Doctor.

MONTGOMERY, Jeanne M; Bishop Ryan HS; Minot, ND; 1/89 ChrhWkr; CmntyWkr; HonRl; JrNHS; NHS; Sdlty; RptrYrbk; RptrSchPpr; GerCl; PpCl; Univ; Professional.

MONTGOMERY, Joyce K; Porta HS; Petersburg, IL; 14/118# DrlTm; HonRl; JA; JrNHS; MrchBnd; SchPpr; GAA; IMSpt; Business School; Secretary.

MONTGOMERY, Kim C; Faulkner HS; Chicago, IL; 3/9 SecSophCls; SecTrsSrCls; Chrs; HonRl; SchPl; StuGov; RptrYrbk; SchPpr; Glf; Univ; Professional.

MONTGOMERY, Laura L; Glenwood HS; Chatham, IL; 9/143 AFS; ChrhWkr; HonRl; NHS; TchrAde; YthFlsp; RptrYrbk; EdSchPpr; FHA; FrCl; Eastern Ill Univ; Med.

MONTGOMERY, Lester R; Guide Rock Public HS; Guide Rock, NE; TrsFrshCls; SecSophCls; SchPl; 4-H; LetterBsbl; LetterBsktbl; LetterFtbl; LetterTrk; AmLegAwd; Peru State Univ; Business Adm.

MONTGOMERY, Lisa; Hempstead HS; Dubuque, IA; 167/5089 Chr; Swmmng; Trade School.

MONTGOMERY, Monica L; Oakland HS; Oakland, IL; 4/48 TrsSophCls; Chr; ChrhWkr; HonRl; NHS; StuCncl; Yrbk; FHA; MthCl; PPFtbl; Ne Mo; Home Economics.

MONTGOMERY, Robert A; Washington HS; Washington, IL; 4/365 HonRl; NHS; StuCncl; FFA; Bsktbl; IMSpt; JETSAwd; Univ Il; Ag Engr.

MONTGOMERY, Robert M; Benton Consolidated HS; Benton, IL; Chrs; SecFrshCls; HonRl; NatlFornLg; SctActv; YthFlsp; LetterTrk; IMSpt; LionAwd; Olivet Nazerene Coll; Math.

MONTGOMERY, Susan K; Sabetha HS; Sabetha, KS; TrsJrCls; ALAGirlsSt; CncrtBnd; HonRl; NHS; 4-H; FFA; College; Animal Care.

MONTGOMERY, Valarie D; No Chicago Comm HS; North Chicago, IL; 31/275 Chr; Chrs; ChrhWkr; HonRl; JA; NHS; Quill&Scroll; GAA; College; Professional.

MONTGOMERY, William A; Jerseyville HS; Jerseyville, IL; Band; ChrhWkr; CncrtBnd; MrchBnd; NHS; NatlMeritCmnd; EdSchPpr; University Of Illinois; Liberal Arts.

MONTHEY, Debra K; Kearney Catholic HS; Kearney, NE; VPFrshCls; Band; Chrs; ChrhWkr; CncrtBnd; MrchBnd; PepBnd; SchMus; RptrYrbk; 4-H; SpnCl; PpCl; Bsktbl; Kearney State College; English.

MONTVILLE, Debra L; Jefferson HS; Rockford, IL; 9/335 ChrhWkr; HonRl; HospAde; SchMus; SchPl; College; Vocation.

MONTWILL, Richard J; John F Kennedy HS; Chicago, IL; 26/630 Band; CncrtBnd; HonRl; JrNHS; NHS; NatlMeritSchl; Orch; PepBnd; De Paul University; Finance.

MONYEK, Marcia E; Interlochen Arts Acad; Lake Forest, IL; 27/445 Chrs; HonRl; LitMag; SchAde; RptrYrbk; PpCl; GAA; University; Radio Televison Broadcasting.

MONZU, Deborah A; Paul Vi HS; Omaha, NE; Chrs; HonRl; SchMus; SchPl; PpCl; LetterTrk; Chrldr; IMSpt;.

MOOBERRY, Melody D; Woodruff HS; Peoria, IL; 39/225 SecChrhWkr; HonRl; HospAde; TchrAde; GerCl; LatCl; IMSpt; Illinois Central College; Nursing.

MOODY, Anita S; North Vigo HS; Terre Haute, IN; 72/641 Band; ChrhWkr; CncrtBnd; HonRl; HospAde; MrchBnd; Quill&Scroll; SchPl; RptrYrbk; Indiana St Univ; Medical Tech.

MOODY, Barbara F; Mehlville Sr HS; St Louis, MO; 78/500 HonRl; JA; NHS; RedCrAde; SctActv; UNYO; RptrYrbk; FHA; LetterBsktbl; CchngActv; GAA; BttyCrckrAwd; PresAwd; Sw Missouri St Univ; Home Economics.

MOODY, Carol; Millington HS; Millington, MI; 23/168 Chr; CmntyWkr; HonRl; OffAde; FHA; Coll; Bus.

MOODY, Cheryl L; Bogan HS; Chicago, IL; 28/720 Chrs; HonRl; HospAde; JA; NHS; FNA; SpnCl; MthCl; PpCl; GAA; Col Of St Teresa; Nursing.

MOODY, David W; Jo Craig HS; Janesville, WI; HonRl; Bsktbl; LetterFtbl; Tennis; CchngActv; College Major Study.

MOODY, Lawrence S; St Laurence HS; Chicago, IL; HonRl; SchPl; SctActv; SchPpr; Socr; Trk; De Paul University Chicago; Banking.

MOODY, Nancy E; O Fallon Township HS; O Fallon, IL; 51/296 TrsSrCls; Chrs; HonRl; SchMus; SecStuCncl; Yrbk; SchPpr; SpnCl; SecPpCl; Chrldr; Illinois State Univ; Art.

MOODY, Nancy J; Wellington Sr HS; Wellington, KS; ChrhWkr; CmntyWkr; HonRl; PolWkr; SchAde; TchrAde; RptrSchPpr; Washburn U; Law.

MOODY, Sandra; Clarkton HS; Clarkton, MO; Band; ChrhWkr; MrchBnd; PepBnd; SchPl; FHA; PpCl; Chrldr;.

MOODY, Shelley J; Crawford HS; Crawford, NE; SecFrshCls; PresSophCls; Band; Chr; HonRl; Orch; StuCncl; StuGov; LetterTrk; CaptChrldr; Coll; Interior Decorating.

MOODY, Steven B; St Agatha HS; Detroit, MI; 5/105 Chrl; ChrhWkr; CmntyWkr; HonRl; NHS; RptrSchPpr; FrCl; LatCl; MthCl; Bsktbl; LetterTrk; OptClAwd; Univ Of Mich; Internal Medicine.

MOODY, Thomas O; Central HS; Waterloo, IA; CAP; CmntyWkr; SchPl; LetterBsbl; LetterFtbl; LetterTrk; LetterWrstlng; College; Art.

MOODY, Torrence; John Adams HS; S Bend, IN; 144/445 HonRl; NatlMeritSF; Bsktbl;.

MOOHA, Madonna M; Downers Grove North HS; Downers Grove, IL; Chrs; HonRl; LitMag; Mdrgl; NHS; NatlMeritFnl; NatlThespSoc; SchMus; SchPl; SctActv; Isu; Sociology.

MOOMAW, Ann L; River Valley HS; Sawyer, MI; ChrhWkr; HonRl; NHS; SctActv; TchrAde; Trk; College; Accounting.

MOOMAW, Michael R; Romulus HS; Romulua, MI; 12/295 HonRl; NHS; StuGov; SecKeyCl; Ftbl; Tennis; KiwanAwd; College; Nuclear Engineering.

MOON, Carol J; Wykoff Public HS; Wykoff, MN; 3/32 Chrs; ChrhWkr; HonRl; Mdrgl; NHS; TchrAde; YthFlsp; FHA; Rochester Community Col; Nursing.

MOON, Debra S; Lawrenceburg HS; Lawrenceburg, IN; HonRl; NHS; CaptBsktbl; LetterTrk; GAA; Northern Ky State Clg.

MOON, Karl; Motley Public Hs; Pillager, MN; HonRl; 4-H; FFA; Ftbl; Trk; Wrstlng; 4-HAwd; College;physics.

MOON, Linda; Cedar Falls HS; Cedar Falls, IA; 39/423 Band; ChrhWkr; CmntyWkr; CncrtBnd; HonRl; MrchBnd; NatlThespSoc; OffAde; LatCl; Univ Iowa; Bac Science Nursing.

MOON, Marianne E; Eastbrook HS; Van Buren, IN; 3/160 ALAGirlsSt; ChrhWkr; HonRl; MrchBnd; NatlThespSoc; PepBnd; SchMus; SchPl; YthFlsp; 4-H;.

MOON, Mary; Wapello Community HS; Wapello, IA; 30#32#37 HonRl; Mdrgl; MrchBnd; NHS; PepBnd; SchMus; YthFlsp; Chrldr; College; Professional.

MOON, Samuel H; Valley Park HS; Valley Park, MO; VPSophCls; HonRl; StuCncl; LetterBsbl; LetterBsktbl; Clge.

MOON, Timothy D; Naperville Central HS; Naperville, IL; ChrhWkr; HonRl; NHS; StuGov; YthFlsp; KeyCl; Bsbl; LetterFtbl; CaptTrk; Wrstlng;.

MOONEY, Bob D; Forest Lake HS; Hugo, MN; HonRl; Ftbl; LetterTrk; Wrstlng; Univ; Professional.

MOONEY, Carolyn A; O Fallon Township HS; O Fallon, IL; 22/314 ChrhWkr; HonRl; NHS; StuCncl; SpnCl; PpCl; Chrldr; CchngActv; GAA; AmLegAwd; College; Physical Education.

MOONEY, Jeannette L; Stromsburg HS; Stromburg, NE; ChrhWkr; OffAde; YthFlsp; RptrSchPpr; EdSchPpr; SchPpr; 4-H; FHA; 4-HAwd; Air Force; Commercialartist.

MOONEY, Michael G; Pacific HS; Catawissa, MO; ChrhWkr; HonRl; SchMus; SchPl; VPStuCncl; Bsktbl; OptClAwd; College; Liberal Arts.

MOONEY, Michele; Robbinsdale HS; Minneapolis, MN; 5/763 Chr; HonRl; NHS; Quill&Scroll; SchMus; SchPl; StuGov; RptrYrbk; College; Nursing.

MOONEY, William T; Marion HS; Marion, IN; HonRl; Bsbl; Bsktbl; Ftbl; Trk; Prudue U; Chemical Engineering.

MOONEYHAM, Kelly M; Bishop Ward HS; Kansas City, KS; 6/278 ChrhWkr; CmntyWkr; HonRl; ModUN; NatlThespSoc; PolWkr; SchMus; SchPl; StuCncl; TchrAde; Univ Of Kansas; Special Ed Teacher.

MOOR, James D; Steinmetz HS; Chicago, IL; 15/616 HonRl; NHS; OffAde; SchAde; TchrAde; FTA; SpnCl; MthCl; University; Math.

MOORE, Alan R; Ottawa HS; Ottawa, KS; SecJrCls; ALBoysSt; NHS; StuCncl; LetterFtbl; LetterWrstlng; University Of Kansas; Accounting.

MOORE, Anita L; Kent City HS; Casnovia, MI; 43/90 Band; ChrhWkr; CncrtBnd; HonRl; MrchBnd; OffAde; PepBnd; StuCncl; PresYthFlsp; CaptBsktbl;.

MOORE, Ann P; Battle Creek Central HS; Battle Creek, MI; 24/505 Aud/Vis; ChrhWkr; HonRl; HospAde; NatlFornLg; NHS; NatlMeritCmnd; SchMus; SchPl; SpnCl; DARAwd; Albion College; Medical Tech.

MOORE, Barbara L; North Chicago HS; Great Lakes, IL; 73/235 Chrs; CmntyWkr; HonRl; NHS; OffAde; SchAde; TchrAde; Trk; GAA; IMSpt; Austin Peay St Univ; Physical Education.

MOORE, Benjamin F; Niles HS; Dowagiac, MI; Band; HonRl; 4-H; FFA; LetterFtbl; LetterWrstlng; IMSpt; 4-HAwd; JCAwd; OptClAwd; College; Professional.

MOORE, Betty L; Maconaquah HS; Miami, IN; CAP; LbryAde; NatlFornLg; SchPl; SpnCl; VoiceDemAwd; Occupation Therapy.

MOORE, Bonnie S; Virginia HS; Virginia, IL; Chrs; HonRl; SctActv; SecStuCncl; TchrAde; PpCl; Chrldr; GAA; AmLegAwd; GodCntryAwd; Lincoln Land Comm Col; English Teacher.

MOORE, Brad R; Shawnee Mission South HS; Overland Park, KS; 30/800 Chrs; ChrhWkr; HonRl; NHS; Ftbl; Trk; IMSpt; JETSAwd; Univ; Engr.

MOORE, Brian J; Lincolnway HS; Frankfort, IL; HonRl; ModUN; NatlMeritFnl; Knox College; Lawyer.

MOORE, Broderick L; Marmion Military Academy; Chicago, IL; LbryAde; NatlMeritSF; ROTC; SchPl; Ftbl; Trk; Washington Univ St Louis; Medicine.

MOORE, Carol J; U S D #462; Burden, KS; 2/35 Chrs; HonRl; LbryAde; SchPl; TchrAde; RptrSchPpr; Southwestern Col; English.

MOORE, Catherine R; Brown County HS; Nashville, IN; 57/165 HonRl; NHS; OffAde; TchrAde; RptrYrbk; LatCl; PpCl; SciCl; GAA; Univ; Professional.

MOORE, Catherine; Highland HS; Anderson, IN; 26/245 HonRl; NHS; StuGov; LatCl; PpCl; Purude Univ; Pharmacy.

MOORE, Christine S; Stuart Menlo Comm HS; Menlo, IA; ALAGirlsSt; ChrhWkr; HonRl; LbryAde; NHS; TchrAde; FSA; FTA; PpCl; College; Nurse.

MOORE, Christine M; Turner HS; Kansas, KS; Chrs; CaptDrlTm; HonRl; OffAde; SchAde; StuCncl; TchrAde; SpnCl; PpCl; SciCl; Bsktbl; GAA; IMSpt; Providence Radiology Schl; Specl Procedures.

MOORE, Cindy L; Benedict HS; Stromsburg, NE; 2/14 TrsSophCls; HonRl; StuCncl; EdYrBk; PpCl; BttyCrckrAwd; DARAwd; 4-HAwd; VFWAwd; VoiceDemAwd; University; Psychology.

MOORE, Clark B; Fargo North HS; Fargo, ND; Band; HonRl; Univ; Pro.

MOORE, Craig E; Fargo North HS; Fargo, ND; Band; HonRl; JrNHS; LitMag; NHS; SctActv; FrCl; GerCl; KiwanAwd; Univ; Pro.

MOORE, Dale W; Copeland HS; Copeland, KS; PresFrshCls; PresJrCls; Band; HonRl; StuCncl; Yrbk; SptEdSchPpr; 4-H; AmLegAwd; 4-HAwd; Ks State; Engineering.

MOORE, Danette S; Columbia Central HS; Brooklyn, MI; 4/150 TrsJrCls; TrsSrCls; HonRl; SecNHS; OffAde; StuCncl; StuGov; RptrYrbk; Lansing Business U; Secretarial.

MOORE, Daniel P; Proviso West HS; Bellwood, IL; 14/1100 CncrtBnd; MrchBnd; NatlMeritCmnd; PepBnd; University; Mathematics.

MOORE, Darla J; Warsaw HS; Warsaw, IL; SecFrshCls; PresSophCls; ALAGirlsSt; Band; CncrtBnd; HonRl; MrchBnd; NHS; PepBnd; PresStuCncl; Belleville Coll; Computer.

MOORE, David; Holland HS; Holland, MI; Aud/Vis; CmntyWkr; CchngActv; Muskegon Comm Coll; Police Adm.

MOORE, David L; Cassville HS; Cassville, MO; 6/99 HstSophCls; NHS; StuCncl; Yrbk; SchPpr; FFA; SciCl; Univ Of Mo; Agriculture.

MOORE, Deana G; Bellflower Twp HS; Saybrook, IL; 1/19 PresJrCls; Band; Chrs; ChrhWkr; HonRl; LbryAde; StuCncl; EdYrBk; FHA; DARAwd; Lincoln Christian Coll.

MOORE, Deborah; Britton Macon HS; Tecumseh, MI; 23/46 SecSophCls; Chrs; ChrhWkr; HonRl; SchPl; TchrAde; YthFlsp; RptrYrbk; RptrSchPpr;.

MOORE, Deborah K; Norwood HS; Norwood, MO; 2/20 Chr; ChrhWkr; HonRl; SchPl; RptrYrbk; RptrSchPpr; FHA; PpCl; Bsbl; Chrldr; Ozarks; Business.

MOORE, Deborah S; Spokane HS; Highlandville, MO; VPFrshCls; ChrhWkr; HonRl; FHA; PpCl; Vo Tech; Nursing.

MOORE, Debra S; Greenview Community HS; Greenview, IL; 4/23 TrsFrshCls; TrsSophCls; TrsJrCls; TrsSrCls; HonRl; NHS; YthFlsp; FHA; FSA; FTA; Secretary Bookkeeper.

MOORE, Della M; Lyman HS; Vivian, SD; Chr; ChrhWkr; CmntyWkr; CncrtBnd; HonRl; NHS; PolWkr; YthFlsp; 4-H; Bsktbl; GAA; IMSpt; PPFtbl; College; Liberal Arts.

MOORE, Denise; Ozark HS; Ozark, MO; 8/92 Band; Chrs; ChrhWkr; HonRl; Twrl; RptrYrbk; RptrSchPpr; FBLA; PpCl; Chrldr; School Ozarks College; Teaching.

MOORE, Diana S; Waldron HS; Waldron, IN; 4/60 Band; Chr; HonRl; SchAde; RptrYrbk; Pres4-H; LatCl; PpCl; 4-HAwd; Purdue U; Med Tech.

MOORE, Donald R; Zionsville Community HS; Zionsville, IN; 2/125 HonRl; NHS; NatlMeritCmnd; Quill&Scroll; EdSchPpr; LatCl; ChmbCommrsAwd; Univ; Accounting.

MOORE, Gary; Cedar Springs HS; Cedar Springs, MI; CmntyWkr; HonRl; PolWkr; TchrAde; RptrSchPpr; SchPpr; Muskegon Bus Col; Architectural Drafting.

MOORE, Gary W; Liberal HS; Liberal, KS; ChrhWkr; HonRl; TchrAde; RptrSchPpr; SptEdSchPpr; SpnCl; Ftbl; Wrstlng; CchngActv; College.

MOORE, Gene E; John F Kennedy Prep; Milwaukee, WI; PresFrshCls; HonRl; NatlFornLg; StuCncl; StuGov; Bsktbl; LetterFtbl; Trk; Wrstlng; IMSpt; CitAwd; Yale Univ; Lawyer.

MOORE, Gene E; J F K Prep; Milwaukee, WI; PresFrshCls; HonRl; NatlFornLg; NHS; NatlMeritSchl; SchPl; ChmnFtbl; LetterTrk; Yale; Economics.

MOORE, George E; Appleton West HS; Appleton, WI; 70/640 CncrtBnd; HonRl; LitMag; PolWkr; Quill&Scroll; StuGov; YthFlsp; Bsktbl; Wrstlng; ChmbCommrsAwd; Univ Wi Madison; Actuary Science.

MOORE, Ginevera K; Ames Senior HS; Ames, IA; 18/394 Chr; HonRl; NatlMeritSF; SchMus; SchPl; StuCncl; RptrYrbk; Yrbk; Univ.

MOORE, Howard T; Lawrence HS; Lawrence, KS; NatlMeritSF; SciCl; Univ Of Ca; Biology.

MOORE, James R; North Callaway R1 HS; Auxvasse, MO; VPSophCls; Chrs; StuCncl; Bsktbl; Ftbl; Trk;.

MOORE, Janet E; R 1 North Callaway HS; Auxvasse, MO; SecJrCls; Chrs; HonRl; SchMus; SchPl; StuCncl; TchrAde; Yrbk; FHA; FrCl; PresPpCl; CitAwd;.

MOORE, Janet L; Civic Memorial HS; Bethalto, IL; HonRl; NHS; FrCl; PpCl; GAA; So Illinois Univ; Lab Technology.

MOORE, Janet L; F L Schlagle HS; Kansas City, KS; 3/500 HonRl; NHS; Quill&Scroll; StuCncl; SptEdYrbk; PpCl; SciCl; CaptBsktbl; GAA; IMSpt; PPFtbl; College; Business Admin.

MOORE, Janice; Battle Creek Central HS; Battle Creek, MI; 30/505 HonRl; NatlFornLg; NHS; Univ Of Mich; Lawyer.

MOORE, Jeffrey; Homestead Jr Sr HS; Fort Wayne, IN; CncrtBnd; HonRl; MrchBnd; NHS; PepBnd; Yrbk; SchPpr; Trade School; Professional Or Vocation.

MOORE, Jeri; Argonia HS; Argonia, KS; Band; Chr; Chrs; ChrhWkr; DrmMjrt; HonRl; SctActv; LionAwd; College; Music Major.

MOORE, Joe M; Hurley HS; Marionville, MO; HonRl; SchPl; RptrYrbk; S Missouri St Univ; Writer.

MOORE, John K; Chippewa Valley HS; Mt Clemens, MI; 6/310 HonRl; NHS; NatlMeritFnl; NatlMeritCmnd; NatlMeritSchl; SpnCl; Tennis; Wayne St Univ; Aerospace Eng.

MOORE, John R; Richmond Sr HS; Richmond, MO; Band; CncrtBnd; HonRl; MrchBnd; SchPl; LetterTrk; Univ Of Missouri; Aerospace Tech.

MOORE, John R; Gordon Tech HS; Chicago, IL; 52/690 Band; CncrtBnd; HonRl; JrNHS; MrchBnd; Orch; PepBnd; StuCncl; SpnCl; College; Professional.

MOORE, Joni L; Bazine HS; Bazine, KS; 1/9 SecJrCls; Chrs; HonRl; OffAde; SchPl; RptrYrbk; Yrbk; FHA; PpCl;.

MOORE, June; East Catholic HS; Detroit, MI; SecSrCls; ChrhWkr; HonRl; LbryAde; PolWkr; StuCncl; Yrbk; PpCl; Michigan State Univ; Law.

MOORE, Karen S; Greenview HS; Greenview, IL; 4/42 ALAGirlsSt; Chrs; ChrhWkr; HonRl; HospAde; LbryAde; NHS; Yrbk; FSA; TreasFTA; Trinity College; Doctor.

MOORE, Kathy; East Monona HS; Moorhead, IA; Band; CncrtBnd; HonRl; MrchBnd; PepBnd; SchPl; FHA; Nursing School.

MOORE, Kathy S; Richland HS; Richland, MO; 5/65 TchrAde; Twrl; RptrYrbk; RptrSchPpr; FHA; FTA; MthCl; PpCl; Trk; Chrldr; Cox Medical Center; X Ray Tech.

MOORE, Kelly L; Bedford Comm HS; Bedford, IA; PresFrshCls; SecSrCls; Band; CncrtBnd; HonRl; MrchBnd; NHS; PepBnd; SchPl; StuCncl; Nw Mo St Univ; Social Science.

MOORE, Kevin D; Southwest HS; Saint Louis, MO; Aud/Vis; HonRl; NatlMeritSchl; Quill&Scroll; SctActv; SptEdSchPpr; SchPpr; GerCl; LetterTrk; Georgia Inst Of Tech; Engineering.

MOORE, Kevin D; Southwest HS; St Louis, MO; HonRl; NatlMeritSF; Quill&Scroll; SptEdSchPpr; GerCl; LetterTrk; Gmi; Electronic Engineering.

MOORE, Kevin R; Flora HS; Xenia, IL; ChrhWkr; HonRl; NHS;.

MOORE, Kimberly; Warren HS; Sterling Heights, MI; Chrs; ChrhWkr; HonRl; JrNHS; NHS; FFA; PpCl; Chrldr;.

MOORE, Kimberly C; Elk Grove HS; Elk Grove, IL; HonRl; TreasNHS; StuCncl; GerCl; Chrldr; GAA; Univ Of Ill; Teach.

MOORE, Laura A; Ouid Elsie HS; Elsie, MI; Chrl; Chrs; HonRl; Mdrgl; NHS; NatlMeritCmnd; SchMus; SchPl; FFA; BauchLmbAwd; Michigan State Univ; Conservation.

MOORE, Laura J; Proviso East HS; Melrose Park, IL; 1/1001 Chr; Chrl; ChrhWkr; HonRl; HospAde; Mdrgl; NHS; SctActv; StuGov; YthFlsp; U Of Iowa; Pedeatrics.

MOORE, Lesia D; Topeka HS; Topeka, KS; Chrl; ChrhWkr; HonRl; SchMus; YthFlsp; FHA; PpCl; Trk; College; Prof Speech Therapy.

MOORE, Linda M; Winchester Community HS; Winchester, IN; Band; CncrtBnd; MrchBnd; NHS; Orch; SchPl; FHA; PresFTA; SpnCl; Ball State Univ; Teach Biology.

MOORE, Linda S; Sandusky HS; Sandusky, MI; 35/114 Chr; ChrhWkr; HonRl; SctActv; TchrAde; YthFlsp; 4-H; FBLA; FrCl; 4-HAwd; St Clair County Comm Coll.

MOORE, Lynn M; H L Richards HS; Oak Lawn, IL; 5/826 CmntyWkr; HonRl; JrNHS; LitMag; NHS; NatlMeritSchl; OffAde; Orch; TchrAde; No Ill Univ; Professional.

MOORE, Mark E; Prospect HS; Mt Prospect, IL; 181/600 Aud/Vis; ChrhWkr; HonRl; Purdue Univ; Civil Engineering.

MOORE, Mark F; Illiopolis HS; Illiopolis, IL; ALBoysSt; HonRl; NatlThespSoc; Sacrstn; SctActv; LetterBsbl; LetterBsktbl; LetterFtbl; IMSpt; AmLegAwd; Millikin U; Medic.

MOORE, Martha M; Eastern HS; Lansing, MI; 8/540 Chr; ChrhWkr; HonRl; JrNHS; NHS; NatlMeritCmnd; SchMus; YthFlsp; GerCl; LetterTennis; GAA; Michigan St Univ; Nursing.

MOORE, Mary S; Monett HS; Monett, MO; ALAGirlsSt; Band; ChrhWkr; DrmMjrt; HonRl; MrchBnd; NHS; Orch; PepBnd; SctActv; Se Ma State Univ; Speech Therapy.

MOORE, Matthew S; Lacrosse Central HS; Lacrosse, WI; 10/534 Band; Chr; Chrl; CncrtBnd; HonRl; VPJrNHS; TreasNHS; NatlMeritSF; PepBnd; StuCncl; St Olaf Coll; Chem Engr.

MOORE, Melinda G; Lake Forest Ferry Hall HS; Chicago, IL; CmntyWkr; HonRl; LitMag; SchMus; SchPl; StuGov; SchPpr; Chrldr; IMSpt; University; University Education.

MOORE, Michael; Appleton West HS; Appleton, WI; 1/643 Univ; Biochemistry.

MOORE, Michael D; Cisne Comm HS; Cisne, IL; 15/62 HonRl; NatlMeritCmnd; StuCncl; SptEdYrbk; Yrbk; SchPpr; LatCl; MthCl; Washington Univ; Medicine.

MOORE, Michael E; Fenton HS; Fenton, MI; 3/283 HonRl; NHS; Bsbl; CaptBsktbl; Ftbl; Mi St U; Acct.

MOORE, Michael G; Mason City HS; Mason City, IA; ChrhWkr; HonRl; ModUN; NHS; PolWkr; StuGov; RptrSchPpr; AmLegAwd; University; Business Admin.

MOORE, Michael L; Rose Hill HS; Augusta, KS; 15/59 Band; LetterChr; LetterCncrtBnd; HonRl; PepBnd; TchrAde; SpnCl; LetterBsbl; LetterFtbl; LetterTrk; Wichita State Univ; Law.

MOORE, Michele M; Carrollton HS; Saginaw, MI; CmntyWkr; HonRl; NatlFornLg; NHS; OffAde; SchMus; SchPl; TchrAde; RptrSchPpr; College; Radiologic Tech.

MOORE, Mike L; Princeton HS; Princeton, MO; ChrhWkr; CmntyWkr; HonRl; SchAde; StuGov; Bsktbl; Ftbl; Trade.

MOORE, Nancy L; Maine South HS; Park Ridge, IL; Chrs; SecChrhWkr; JrNHS; NatlFornLg; NatlMeritCmnd; NatlThespSoc; CaptChrldr; DARAwd; College; Communications.

MOORE, Patricia S; Oak Park & River Forest HS; River Forest, IL; 20/1007 Chr; TreasChrhWkr; HonRl; HospAde; College.

MOORE, Pete N; Jimtown HS; Elkhart, IN; ChrhWkr; HonRl; JA; PolWkr; Trk; IMSpt; Navy; Radio And Electronics.

MOORE, Phyllis L; Madison HS; Madison, IL; HonRl;.

MOORE, Rebecca; Springfield Southeast HS; Springfield, IL; ChrhWkr; IntrClCncl; JA; SchMus; SchPl; StuCncl; StuGov; FrCl; PpCl; Southern Il; Professional.

MOORE, Rebecca M; Shawnee HS; Mc Clure, IL; Chr; Chrs; HonRl; Mdrgl; SchPl; PpCl; Chrldr; IMSpt; College; Social Work.

MOORE, Renette S; Abraham Lincoln HS; Council Bluffs, IA; 7/440 AFS; Chr; Chrs; HonRl; JA; Mdrgl; NHS; OffAde; SchAde; SchMus; SchPl; TchrAde; LetterGlf; IMSpt; College; School Teacher.

MOORE, Richard E; North Chicago HS; N Chicago, IL; 10/263 HonRl; NHS; NatlMeritSF; SciCl; LetterTrk; SARAwd; Augustana Coll.

MOORE, Rick E; Lawton Bronson Comm HS; Bronson, IA; 4-H; LetterBsbl; LetterFtbl; LetterTrk; LetterWrstlng; PresAwd; College; Professional.

MOORE, Rick S; Sarcoxie HS; Sarcoxie, MO; ALBoysSt; PresBand; ChrhWkr; CncrtBnd; HonRl; PresNHS; PepBnd; SchPl; VPStuCncl; FTA; CaptMthCl; Bsktbl; Ftbl; Us Air Force Academy; Mathematics.

MOORE, Robert; Green Mountain Ind HS; Marshalltown, IA; 2/22 VPFrshCls; TrsSophCls; PresJrCls; ALBoysSt; SctActv; StuCncl; Bsbl; Bsktbl; College; Professional.

MOORE, Roberta A; Carmel HS; Algonquin, IL; 3/195 HonRl; JrNHS; OffAde; RptrSchPpr; FrCl; Creighton Univ; Business Management.

MOORE, Ronnie C; Dallas City HS; Dallas Cty, IL; 2/31 Band; Chrl; Chrs; CncrtBnd; HonRl; MrchBnd; NHS; PepBnd; SchMus; SchPl; Bsktbl; LetterTrk; IMSpt; AmLegAwd; College; Music.

MOORE, Ruth A; Paxton HS; Paxton, IL; 1/130 PresSophCls; ALAGirlsSt; Band; SecNHS; NatlMeritCmnd; SecStuCncl; TchrAde; LetterBsktbl; CaptTennis; AmLegAwd; Eastern Illinois Univ; Music.

MOORE, Scott L; East Richland HS; Olhey, IL; 68/255 SpnCl; The Citadel; Engineering.

MOORE, Shawn A; Brookfield R Iii HS; Brookfield, MO; HonRl; LetterFtbl; CaptTennis; CaptIMSpt; Us Navy.

MOORE, Sheila S; Effingham HS; Effingham, IL; 3/220 PresJrCls; CncrtBnd; HonRl; MrchBnd; SchMus; 4-H; GAA; Mckendree College; Public Relations.

MOORE, Steve R; Randolph S HS; Lynn, IN; 6/60 HonRl; NHS; StuCncl; TchrAde; YthFlsp; FFA; Trk; CaptWrstlng; IMSpt; Purdue; Farmer.

MOORE, Susan A; Mercy HS; Omaha, NE; Chrs; SchMus; SchPl; SctActv; Sdlty; SpnCl; PpCl; Bsbl; Bsktbl; Trk; Univ Of Nebraska; Dental Hygiene.

MOORE, Susan R; Griggsville HS; New Salem, IL; 2/24 Chrs; HonRl; NHS; NatlThespSoc; SchPl; Yrbk; FHA; SpnCl; PpCl; GAA; Bus School; Horology.

MOORE, Susie M; Van Far Ri HS; Vandalia, MO; 4/92 Chrs; HonRl; JrNHS; NHS; YthFlsp; 4-H; FHA; SecFTA; SpnCl; DARAwd; Culver Stockton College; Elem Teacher.

MOORE, Terence D; Northwest HS; Indianapolis, IN; Band; CncrtBnd; DrmMjrt; HonRl; MrchBnd; NatlMeritSF; PepBnd; StuCncl; Yrbk; Bsktbl; College; Industrial Engineering.

MOORE, Teresa M; Bishop Du Bourg HS; St Louis, MO; 50/473 HonRl; HospAde; NHS; SchAde; StuGov; RptrSchPpr; Chrldr; GAA; Fontbonne College; Home Economics.

MOORE, Timothy J; Dodgeville HS; Dodgeville, WI; 8/130 HonRl; LetterBsktbl; LetterFtbl; Glf; IMSpt; U Of Wi; Major In Accounting.

MOORE, Valerie G; Jennings HS; Jennings, MO; SecSophCls; Band; HonRl; StuCncl; YthFlsp; Swmmng; Chrldr; GAA; IMSpt;.

MOORE, Wanda; Mulberry Grove HS; Smithboro, IL; Band; Chrs; CncrtBnd; HonRl; PepBnd; Yrbk; SchPpr; PpCl; GAA; Business.

MOORE, William E; Bartley Public HS; Bartley, NE; 3/20 PresFrshCls; ALBoysSt; ChrhWkr; HonRl; ModUN; SchPl; YthFlsp; LetterBsktbl; LetterFtbl; LetterTrk; College; Agriculture.

MOORE, William L; Rantoul Township HS; Rantoul, IL; 12/398 Aud/Vis; HonRl; VPJrNHS; NHS; NatlMeritSF; SchPl; TchrAde; University Of Alabama; Physics.

MOORE, William M; Charleston HS; Charleston, IL; Band; CncrtBnd; HonRl; MrchBnd; PepBnd; SchPl; SctActv; StuCncl; StuGov; RptrSchPpr; LetterBsktbl; LetterFtbl; LetterTrk; E Illinois University.

MOOREHEAD, John M; Highland HS; Highland, IN; 255/575 SctActv; Yrbk; KeyCl; Trk; IMSpt; College; Forest Ranger.

MOORE NOLLER, Tamara E; Marshall HS; Marshall, IL; 17/125 ChrhWkr; CmntyWkr; MrchBnd; NatlMeritSchl; TchrAde; YthFlsp; Yrbk; 4-H; GAA; DanFAwd; 4-HAwd; College; Professional.

MOORKAMP, William B; Chaminade HS; Ballwin, MO; 61/113 HonRl; StuCncl; SpnCl; LetterFtbl; LetterSocr; LetterTrk; IMSpt; College; Dentistry.

MOORMAN, Annette; Blackford HS; Hartford, IN; 31/200 ChrhWkr; CncrtBnd; MrchBnd; NHS; PepBnd; RptrYrbk; RptrSchPpr; SpnCl; Chrldr; GAA; College; Physical Therapist.

MOORMEIER, Jill A; Harry A Burke HS; Omaha, NE; 1/630 ChrhWkr; HonRl; NHS; NatlMeritSF; YthFlsp; SpnCl; PpCl; Trk; GAA; Univ; Pre Med.

MOOS, Jeffrey W; Greenfield HS; Greenfield, WI; HonRl; Yrbk; SchPpr; PpCl; CaptBsbl; LetterBsktbl; LionAwd; Marquette University; Dentist.

MOOTHART, Michael W; Waterford Mott HS; Pontiac, MI; CmntyWkr; HonRl; SchAde; StuGov; TchrAde; YthLg; Bsbl; Ftbl; Tennis; U Of Mi; Engineering.

MOOTY, Barbara; Grundy Community HS; Grundy Centre, IA; 13/78 Band; Chrs; ChrhWkr; HonRl; NHS; RptrYrbk; RptrSchPpr; PpCl; Glf; Ia Univ; Account.

MOOTZ, Vicki A; East Dubuque HS; East Dubuque, IL; Band; DrlTm; HonRl; MrchBnd; OffAde; PepBnd; SchPl; StuGov; FHA; GAA; Secretarial Area.

MORA, Armando G; Bishop Noll HS; Gary, IN; 46/347 HonRl; Socr; Trk; LetterWrstlng; Purdue Univ; Engineering.

MORALES, Antionette J; St Alphonsus HS; Dearborn, MI; 5/115 HonRl; NatlFornLg; NHS; NatlMeritSF; RptrYrbk; LatCl; VoiceDemAwd; U Of Detroit; Pre Law.

MORALES, Valerie; Holy Family Acad; Chicago, IL; VPSrCls; Aud/Vis; HonRl; LbryAde; RedCrAde; StuCncl; StuGov; Bsktbl; Chrldr; College; Nursing.

MORAMARCO, Joseph E; De Smet Jesuit HS; Berkeley, MO; 1/172 Chrs; HonRl; HospAde; NHS; NatlMeritSF; StuGov; RptrSchPpr; Univ; Chemical Eng.

MORAMARCO, Marie J; St Thomas Aquinas HS; Berkeley, MO; 4/325 ChrhWkr; HonRl; TreasNHS; SchMus; SchPl; Univ; Education.

MORAN, Carol L; Flat Rock HS; Flat Rock, MI; Band; CncrtBnd; DrlTm; HonRl; LbryAde; MrchBnd; PepBnd; RptrYrbk; Yrbk; PpCl; Comm Coll & Univ; Writing.

MORAN, Cheryl A; Washington HS; Chicago, IL; HonRl; LbryAde; NHS; RptrYrbk; Tennis; Trk; University; Art.

MORAN, Cynthia A; Newton HS; Ste Marie, IL; 22/180 Band; Chr; Chrs; CncrtBnd; HonRl; Mdrgl; MrchBnd; NHS; NatlMeritCmnd; PepBnd; SchMus; Chrldr; AmLegAwd; Eastern Ill Univ; Med Technology.

MORAN, Frederick M; Pekin Comm HS; Pekin, IL; 1/840 HonRl; JrNHS; NHS; NatlMeritCmnd; LetterBsktbl; LetterFtbl; Harvard College; Law.

MORAN, James P; Dundee Comm HS; W Dundee, IL; HonRl; NHS; NatlThespSoc; SchMus; SchPl; University Of Notre Dame; Lawyer.

MORAN, Judith; Waukesha South HS; Waukesha, WI; 1/600 Aud/Vis; HonRl; NHS; NatlMeritCmnd; PolWkr; StuCncl; FBLA; MthCl; PpCl; Univ Of Wisconsin; Engineering.

MORAN, Lisa A; Rantoul HS; Thomasboro, IL; 33/300 ALAGirlsSt; Band; VPCncrtBnd; HonRl; MrchBnd; NHS; Orch; SchMus; SctActv; TreasStuCncl; RptrYrbk; EdSchPpr; Trk; AmLegAwd; Univ Of Illinois; Psychology.

MORAN, Marilyn J; Salem Central HS; Antioch, IL; Chr; ChmnChrs; HonRl; Mdrgl; VPNatlThespSoc; SchMus; SchPl; Yrbk; PpCl; LetterGAA; Univ Of Wi; Vocal Music Major.

MORAN, Mary T; North Platte Sr HS; North Platte, NE; HonRl; 4-H; SpnCl; PpCl; Tennis; Trk; GAA; IMSpt; PPFtbl; PresAwd; Mid Plains Voch Tech; Secratary.

MORAN, Michael E; Bradley Bourbonnais HS; Bradley, IL; 11/360 HonRl; NHS; CaptWrstlng; AmLegAwd; GovHonPrgAwd; College; Osteopath.

MORAN, Michael G; Holy Cross HS; Chicago, IL; 24/308 TrsSophCls; HonRl; NHS; SchPl; SptEdYrbk; Loyola Univ; Accounting.

MORAN, Michael J; Holy Cross HS; Chicago, IL; NatlMeritCmnd; IMSpt; Loyola U;pre Med.

MORAN, Nancy K; East Noble HS; Kendallville, IN; 2/250 Band; ChrhWkr; CmntyWkr; HonRl; MrchBnd; NHS; NatlThespSoc; SchMus; PresStuCncl; EdYrBk; 4-HAwd; Purdue Univ; Medicine.

MORAN, Patrick; Lane Technical Hs; Chicago, IL; LbryAde; NatlMeritCmnd;.

MORAN, Richard A; Sault Area HS; Sault Ste Marie, MI; HonRl; IMSpt; Coll; Voc.

MORAN, Susan M; Auburndale HS; Arpin, WI; 6/95 SecJrCls; Band; CncrtBnd; HonRl; MrchBnd; NHS; PepBnd; TchrAde; Trk; EldAwd; Rochester Jr Col; Nursing.

MORAST, Dallas; Zap HS; Zap, ND; 2/12 VPSophCls; Chrs; HonRl; SchPl; StuCncl; TchrAde; KeyCl; Bsktbl; CitAwd;.

MORAST, Dean K; Zap Public HS; Zap, ND; 5/11 VPSrCls; Chrs; ChrhWkr; HonRl; SchAde; SchPl; GerCl; Bsbl; College; Electrical Lineman.

MORAVA, Steve M; Hemingford HS; Marsland, NE; HonRl; Quill&Scroll; StuCncl; StuGov; TchrAde; EdSchPpr; 4-H; SciCl; Bsktbl; Ftbl; College; Professional.

MORAVEC, Luann; Aquinas HS; David City, NE; Band; ChrhWkr; SchMus; SecTrsFrshCls; SpnCl; MthCl; Glf; Trk; Chrldr; 4-HAwd; U Of Neb; Secretarial.

MORAVEC, Mimi M; Ladysmith HS; Ladysmith, WI; 6/143 HonRl; VPLbryAde; NHS; RptrYrbk; VPFHA; PpCl; GAA; Uw Stout Clge; Applied Math.

MORAVEC, Nancy; Geneva Public HS; Geneva, NE; 12/59 Chr; Chrs; ChrhWkr; CmntyWkr; HonRl; Mdrgl; SchAde; SchMus; SchPl; TchrAde; College; Professional.

MORDEN, Natalie J; Arthur Hill HS; Saginaw, MI; Chr; Chrs; DrlTm; HonRl; Mdrgl; NHS; SchMus; GerCl; Saginaw Valley State College; Vocation.

MORDT, Susan; St Charles HS; St Charles, MO; CmntyWkr; HonRl; IntrClCncl; Mdrgl; NHS; Quill&Scroll; TreasYthFlsp; EdYrBk; SecKeyCl; Schof Journ; Journ.

MORE, Lucius E; Taft HS; Chicago, IL; 67/816 HonRl; NatlMeritCmnd; StuCncl; College; Artist.

MORE, Roy A; Huron HS; Ann Arbor, MI; 26/570 HonRl; NatlMeritCmnd; SctActv; StuCncl; StuGov; EdYrBk; RusCl; MthCl; SciCl; Wrstlng; College; Phd Physics.

MOREAU, Bradley D; Cowden Herrick HS; Lakewood, IL; VPFrshCls; PresSophCls; SchPl; StuGov; PresFFA; LetterBsktbl; Univ Or Coll; Agriculture Or Business.

MOREAU, Cheryl A; Edison Sr HS; East Gary, IN; 14/203 Band; Chr; ChrhWkr; CmntyWkr; CncrtBnd; JrNHS; Mdrgl; MrchBnd; SchMus; Univ; Radiology Tech.

MOREAU, Roland J; Kearney Catholic HS; Kearney, NE; PresSophCls; CncrtBnd; Mdrgl; MrchBnd; SchPl; PresStuCncl; CaptBsktbl; Ftbl; Trk; AmLegAwd; Kearney State Col; Medical.

MOREFIELD, Judy L; Reavis HS; Burbank, IL; 17/676 Chr; HonRl; JrNHS; MrchBnd; NHS; SecFrCl; College; Journalism.

MOREHEAD, Cheryl L; Fort Scott HS; Fort Scott, KS; Chrs; DrlTm; HonRl; HospAde; RptrSchPpr; PpCl; Chrldr; Fort Scott Jr College; Nurse.

MOREHEAD, Nancy J; Twin Rivers HS; Broseley, MO; Chrs; ChrhWkr; DrlTm; SchMus; SctActv; Yrbk; FHA; MthCl; PpCl; Chrldr; College; Professional.

MOREHEAD, Neal J; Mt Pulaski Township HS; Mt Pulaski, IL; 4/83 HonRl; PresNHS; StuCncl; LetterTennis; LetterWrstlng; University; Medicine.

MOREHEAD, Nelson K; Mark Twain HS; New London, MO; Band; CncrtBnd; HonRl; MrchBnd; PepBnd; StuCncl; FTA; Bsktbl; LetterFtbl; LetterTrk; College; Major Study.

MOREHOUSE, Dianne M; Pacelli HS; Austin, MN; HonRl; Bsktbl; Trk; Chrldr; IMSpt; Bus Schl; Model Or Office Work.

MOREHOUSE II, Paul; Concord HS; Spring Arbor, MI; TrsSophCls; HonRl; OffAde; SchAde; StuGov; RptrSchPpr; SptEdSchPpr; SchPpr; Tri State College; Engineering.

MOREILLON, Lisa R; Switzerland County HS; Bennington, IN; Band; CncrtBnd; MrchBnd; OffAde; PepBnd; SctActv; 4-H; FHA; SpnCl; PpCl; Bsbl; Swmmng; GAA; Purdue Univ; Interior Decorating.

MOREL, David A; Reese HS; Munger, MI; 19/126 Band; CncrtBnd; HonRl; MrchBnd; NHS; 4-H; Bsbl; CaptGlf; LetterTennis; CitAwd; Univ; Cpa.

MOREL, Dayleen K; Wheatland HS; Girainfield, KS; Chr; Chrs; HonRl; SchMus; SchPl; TchrAde; RptrYrbk; FHA; PpCl; Bsktbl; LetterTrk; Chrldr; GAA; Kansas State Univ; Speech Therapist.

MORELAND, Gary L; Normal Community HS; Bloomington, IL; HonRl; NHS; MthCl; Ftbl; Swmmng; LetterTrk; Southern Illinois University.

MORELAND, Jay C; Harrisonville HS; Harrisonville, MO; 16/175 HonRl; 4-H; FFA; SpnCl; LetterFtbl; Wrstlng; 4-HAwd; Mo U; Ag.

MORELAND, Kathy; Seneca HS; Seneca, MO; AFS; HonRl; LbryAde; TchrAde; FTA; MthCl; PpCl; Chrldr; GAA; Crowder College; School Teacher.

MORELAND, Lamar D; Chadsey HS; Detroit, MI; HonRl; JA; NatlMeritSF; FDA; FFA; FSA; FTA; Bsktbl; Trk; Siena Heights College; Business Admin.

MORELAND, Lois E; Ridge Farm HS; Indianola, IL; VPFrshCls; VPJrCls; Band; CmntyWkr; HonRl; Mdrgl; PepBnd; StuCncl; CaptChrldr; 4-HAwd; College; Art.

MORELAND, Mark D; Madison HS; Madison, KS; PresJrCls; HonRl; NatlMeritSchl; SchPl; TchrAde; LetterFtbl; College.

MORELAND, Mary A; El Dorado HS; El Dorado, KS; 2/184 VPFrshCls; Chrs; ChrhWkr; HonRl; NatlFornLg; PolWkr; SchMus; StuCncl; RptrYrbk; EldAwd; College; Speech.

MORELLO, Elizabeth A; Sts Peter & Paul Area HS; Saginaw, MI; Chrs; HonRl; Mdrgl; NHS; FrCl; GAA; College; Sports Writer.

MORELLO, Merrie T; Forest Lake HS; Forest Lake, MN; HonRl; LbryAde; StuCncl; Yrbk; FFA; FHA; College; Airlines.

MORELOCK, Lisa J; Virden HS; Thayer, IL; 5/90 HonRl; NHS; RptrSchPpr; FHA; PpCl; Coll; Pro.

MOREM, David N; Lesueur HS; Le Sueur, MN; 38/110 HonRl; NHS; YthFlsp; 4-H; Univ Of Minnesota; Law.

MORENCY, Jacklynn; Durand Area HS; Durand, MI; 9/168 VPFrshCls; Band; Chr; CncrtBnd; HonRl; Mdrgl; MrchBnd; NHS; StuCncl; PpCl; Mi St Univ; Animal Tech.

MORESI, Christine C; Taft HS; Chicago, IL; 10/790 Band; CncrtBnd; LbryAde; NHS; Orch; Ripon College; Physical Therapy.

MORET, Loren J; Mankato East HS; Mankato, MN; HonRl; LitMag; StuCncl; SchPpr; PpCl; Bsbl; Chrldr; IMSpt; Coll; Philosophy.

MOREY, Judy I; Rockville HS; Rockville, IN; Chr; ChrhWkr; HonRl; SchPpr; FHA; Army; Medical Specialist.

MOREY, Kimberly K; Sutherland Public HS; Sutherland, NE; 3/26 TrsFrshCls; PresSrCls; HonRl; HospAde; NHS; YthFlsp; RptrSchPpr; PresGAA; BauchLmbAwd; DanFAwd; College; Biological Science.

MOREY, Michael A; Pittsburg HS; Pittsburgh, KS; Band; CncrtBnd; JCC; MrchBnd; Orch; PepBnd; SchMus; StuCncl; TchrAde; Bsktbl; Ks State Clg Of Pittsburgh; Arshitectural.

MOREY, Ruby I; Avon HS; Avon, IL; Band; CncrtBnd; MrchBnd; SchMus; SchPl; Yrbk; 4-H; FrCl; Trk; GAA; Col;.

MORFEY, Brian E; Rantoul Twp HS; Thomasboro, IL; Band; ChrhWkr; CmntyWkr; CncrtBnd; HonRl; MrchBnd; Bsktbl; LionAwd; CitAwd; Jr Coll; Firefighting.

MORFFI, Irene M; Bishop Ward HS; Kansas City, KS; 88/192 JA; SchPl; StuCncl; SpnCl; PpCl; Glf; Swmmng; Chrldr; College; Liberal Arts.

MORGAN, Anita; Decatur Public HS; Macy, NE; 2/16 SecFrshCls; SecSophCls; TrsJrCls; NHS; PepBnd; RptrYrbk; Yrbk; Chrldr; Business School; Prof.

MORGAN, Bonnie E; Edwardsburg HS; Elkhart, IN; 2/135 PresSrCls; ChrhWkr; HonRl; NHS; TchrAde; RptrSchPpr; DARAwd; EldAwd; Ferris State Col; Med Lab Tech.

MORGAN, Carolyn L; Blissfield HS; Blissfield, MI; ChrhWkr; NHS; TchrAde; EdYrBk; RptrSchPpr; FTA; Adrian Clge; English.

MORGAN, Cheryl; Dalton HS; Dalton, NE; 3/20 Chrs; CtyCnl; HonRl; HospAde; PepBnd; RptrYrbk; SpnCl; PpCl; SciCl; Nursing School; Professional Nursing.

MORGAN, Cynthia E; Benton Central HS; Fowler, IN; OffAde; StuCncl; RptrYrbk; FrCl; Swmmng; Hanover College; Professional.

MORGAN, Dawn R; Medford Public HS; Morristown, MN; SecFrshCls; TrsSophCls; HonRl; NHS; SchPl; EdYrBk; FTA; GAA; IMSpt; 4-HAwd; PresAwd; College; Professional.

MORGAN, Denise R; Oak Park And River Forest HS; Oak Park, IL; Band; CmntyWkr; CncrtBnd; HonRl; U Of Il.

MORGAN, Donald B; Waltonville Comm Unit #1 HS; Bonnie, IL; HonRl; GerCl; PpCl; Bsbl; IMSpt; Revel Lake College; Psychology.

MORGAN, Douglas; Concordia R 2 HS; Concordia, MO; Band; CncrtBnd; HonRl; MrchBnd; PepBnd; SchMus; StuCncl; Trk; Cmsu; Electrician.

MORGAN, Gale; Okawville HS; Okawvlle, IL; SecFrshCls; Band; HonRl; NHS; SchPl; StuCncl; GerCl; PpCl; Chrldr; Natural Sci.

MORGAN, Helen; Rock Island HS; Rock Island, IL; 25/622 Band; CmntyWkr; NHS; PepBnd; SpnCl; Augustana College; Medical Technology.

MORGAN, Jeanne M; Ft Zumwalt HS; Ofallon, MO; HonRl; StuCncl; SptEdYrbk; RptrSchPpr; PpCl; CaptChrldr; IMSpt; PPFtbl;.

MORGAN, John S; Clinton HS; Clinton, MO; 46/151 ALBoysSt; HonRl; LbryAde; StuCncl; Bsbl; LetterFtbl; Trk; CchngActv; BauchLmbAwd; PresAwd; College; Computer Science.

MORGAN, Judith A; George Rogers Clark HS; Hammond, IN; LbryAde; OffAde; SchPl; StuCncl; StuGov; Yrbk; SchPpr; PpCl; IMSpt; Art School; Art Teacher.

MORGAN, Judy A; Hoxie HS; Hoxie, KS; ALAGirlsSt; HonRl; StuCncl; TchrAde; 4-H; FHA; SpnCl; PpCl; 4-HAwd;.

MORGAN, Julie A; Saunemin HS; Cullom, IL; 1/24 PresSrCls; HonRl; LitMag; MrchBnd; NHS; SchPl; TchrAde; Yrbk; Trk; AmLegAwd; College Of Engineering; Meteorology.

MORGAN, Karen J; Walthill Public HS; Walthill, NE; 8/24 SecTrsFrshCls; SecTrsSophCls; VPJrCls; Band; Chrs; CncrtBnd; HospAde; MrchBnd; NHS; Nebraska Methodist School; Nursing.

MORGAN, Kathryn G; Redford Union HS; Detroit, MI; HonRl; NHS; SctActv; TchrAde; LetterSwmmng; John Wesleycoll; Spanish.

MORGAN, Kelly A; Seymour HS; Payson, IL; 20/65 PresJrCls; Chr; Chrl; Chrs; ChrhWkr; DrlTm; HonRl; Mdrgl; SchMus; SchPl; StuCncl; StuGov; Ill State Univ; Elem Ed.

MORGAN, Kevin; Northwestern HS; Mellette, SD; VPSrCls; ALBoysSt; Band; Chr; Chrs; ChrhWkr; CncrtBnd; HonRl; MrchBnd; NatlThespSoc; Trade School; Mechanical Draftsmen.

MORGAN, Lana J; Thompson HS; Thompson, ND; 4/19 VPJrCls; ALAGirlsSt; Band; HonRl; SchPl; RptrYrbk; 4-H; Concordia College; Professional.

MORGAN, Lee; Whitefish Bay HS; Milwaukee, WI; 19/336 ChrhWkr; CmntyWkr; CncrtBnd; HonRl; NHS; PepBnd; SchMus; Swmmng; Tennis; IMSpt; Millikin Univ;music.

MORGAN, Linda M; N Decatur HS; St Paul, IN; ChrhWkr; HonRl; LbryAde; NHS; OffAde; YthFlsp; RptrSchPpr; SchPpr; PpCl; GAA; Purdue Univ.

MORGAN, Lita; Chippewa Hills HS; Barryton, MI; 9/150 Band; HonRl; StuCncl; StuGov; TchrAde; Yrbk; RptrSchPpr; SchPpr; FrCl; SciCl; Ferris Coll; Graphic Arts.

MORGAN, Lonie; Northwestern HS; Mellette, SD; ALAGirlsSt; ChrhWkr; CncrtBnd; HonRl; NHS; StuCncl; EdSchPpr; Swmmng; Chrldr;.

MORGAN, Luanne; Keokuk Senior HS; Keokuk, IA; DrlTm; HonRl; StuCncl; SpnCl; KiwanAwd; Patricia Stevens College; Retailing.

MORGAN, Margaret J; Chamberlain HS; Chamberlain, SD; CmntyWkr; HonRl; HospAde; LbryAde; PolWkr; Quill&Scroll; SchPl; TchrAde; EdSchPpr; JCAwd; College; Nurse.

MORGAN, Michael; Shelby Public HS; Shelby, NE; 4/25 PresFrshCls; PresSophCls; VPJrCls; HonRl; Yrbk; SptEdSchPpr; Trk; PresAwd;.

MORGAN, Michael C; Marian Catholic HS; Chicago Hts, IL; 35/360 PresFrshCls; PresSophCls; PresJrCls; HonRl; NHS; SchMus; SctActv; StuCncl; RptrYrbk; LetterBsktbl; LetterFtbl; LetterTrk; University; Professional.

MORGAN, Michael R; Turner HS; Kansas City, KS; 17/300 ChrhWkr; CncrtBnd; HonRl; JrNHS; MrchBnd; NHS; PepBnd; SchMus; StuCncl; Mid America Nazarene College; Mech Engineer.

MORGAN, Pamela; Burke Central HS; Portal, ND; PresJrCls; ALAGirlsSt; Band; HonRl; Twrl; EdYrBk; 4-H; PpCl; Bsktbl; Trk;.

MORGAN, Pamela C; Edwardsburg HS; Niles, MI; 5/126 HonRl; LbryAde; NHS; FrCl; W Kentucky University.

MORGAN, Phillip D; North Vermillion HS; Newport, IN; ALBoysSt; Band; CncrtBnd; HonRl; MrchBnd; NHS; Purdue Univ; Engineering.

MORGAN, Rene A; Academy Of Our Lady; Chicago, IL; 12/188 Chr; Chrs; ChrhWkr; HonRl; LbryAde; NatlFornLg; NHS; RedCrAde; SchMus; SchPl; YthFlsp; RptrYrbk; RptrSchPpr; College; Teacher.

MORGAN, Robert E; Knightstown HS; Knightstown, IN; 3/136 ALBoysSt; HonRl; NHS; SctActv; StuCncl; SpnCl; LetterBsktbl; LetterTennis; AmLegAwd; EldAwd; Purdue University; Engineering.

MORGAN, Robert E; Caruthersville HS; Caruthersville, MO; Band; ChrhWkr; CmntyWkr; CncrtBnd; MrchBnd; PepBnd; FFA; MthCl; College.

MORGAN, Robert W; North Knox HS; Oaktown, IN; ChrhWkr; LbryAde; FrCl; IMSpt; Trade; Voc.

MORGAN, Roger P; West Chicago Comm HS; West Chicago, IL; 53/321 HonRl; LetterBsktbl; LetterGlf; College.

MORGAN, Russell A; Maine East HS; Niles, IL; Band; CncrtBnd; HonRl; HospAde; MrchBnd; NHS; PepBnd; SchMus; Loyola; Medicine.

MORGAN, Sally A; Woodruff HS; Peoria, IL; Band; CncrtBnd; HonRl; MrchBnd; PepBnd; TchrAde; YthFlsp; GerCl; Coll; Teaching.

MORGAN, Sherry G; Senath Hornersville HS; Senath, MO; Chr; Chrs; ChrhWkr; HonRl; SchMus; VPFHA; PpCl; SciCl; College.

MORGAN, Steven B; Havana HS; Havana, IL; 9/94 Band; NHS; StuCncl; Bsbl; Bsktbl; Ftbl; Monmouth Coll; Pre Law.

MORGAN, Tony D; Northwest HS; St Louis, MO; 86/570 HonRl; JA; LetterFtbl; LetterTrk; IMSpt; College; Lawyer.

MORGAN, Tracy; Bayard HS; Bayard, NE; VPSophCls; TrsJrCls; Chrs; HonRl; NHS; SchPl; PpCl; Trade School.

MORGAN, Valerie J; Grant Park HS; Grant Park, IL; 4/50 TrsSrCls; CncrtBnd; HonRl; NHS; OffAde; TchrAde; Yrbk; SecSpnCl; AmLegAwd; DARAwd; Trevecca Nazarene College; Pharmacy.

MORGAN, Virginia A; Stratford Comm HS; Stratford, IA; HonRl; SchPl; FTA; PpCl; LetterBsktbl; LetterTrk;.

MORGAN, William A; Naperville Central HS; Naperville, IL; ChrhWkr; YthFlsp; Illinois Wesleyan Univ; Law.

MORGAN, William P; North Central HS; Indianapolis, IN; 3/1157 HonRl; JA; NHS; NatlMeritSF; SctActv; StuCncl; Yrbk; FrCl; Mich State Univ; Math.

MORGANELLI, Cynthia L; Thornwood HS; South Holland, IL; 13/852 SecCncrtBnd; HonRl; JrNHS; LetterMrchBnd; SpnCl; Ill State Univ; Special Education.

MORGANO, John M; Bishop Foley HS; St Charles, IL; Chrs; CmntyWkr; HonRl; SchMus; SctActv; LatCl; Bsktbl; Ftbl; Marketing.

MORGANTI, Lyneen T; Rich East HS; Park Forest, IL; Chr; ChrhWkr; YthFlsp; GerCl; GAA; IMSpt; PresAwd; College; Md.

MORGEN, Melanie; East Charles Mix HS; Wagner, SD; 1/56 PresJrCls; HonRl; NHS; StuCncl; RptrYrbk; FHA; PpCl; Bsktbl; Chrldr; VoiceDemAwd; Univ Sd; Computer Sci.

MORGEN, Paul D; New Holtein HS; New Holstein, WI; Band; HonRl; MrchBnd; PepBnd; 4-H; SciCl; Bsktbl; IMSpt; Collegef Scientific.

MORGENSTERN, Pamela S; Hoisington HS; Hoisington, KS; Chr; Chrl; ChrhWkr; HonRl; LbryAde; OffAde; SchAde; TchrAde; FHA; GAA; Ks State U; Elementary Ed.

MORGHEIM, Curtis A; Lyman HS; Lyman, NE; Chrs; SchMus; SchPl; SctActv; TchrAde; PresFFA; Bsbl; CaptBsktbl; LetterFtbl; LetterTrk; College; Physical Educ.

MORHARDT, Darby J; Lanark HS; Milledgeville, IL; SecSophCls; Aud/Vis; ChrhWkr; CncrtBnd; DrmMjrt; MrchBnd; SchMus; StuCncl; Twrl; FHA; Col; Professional.

MORIAK, Rollan P; Clayton HS; Clayton, WI; 4/28 Band; Chr; HonRl; Mdrgl; SptEdYrbk; 4-H; FFA; Bsbl; Bsktbl; 4-HAwd;.

MORIARTY, Eileen M; Resurrection HS; Chicago, IL; Chr; NatlSciFnd; StuCncl; TchrAde; SpnCl; SciCl; GAA; IMSpt; De Paul; Nursing.

MORIARTY, Patricia A; Mother Mc Auley HS; Evergreen Park, IL; HonRl; NHS; RptrSchPpr; Northern Illinois Univ; Nurse.

MORIELLO, Karen A; William Howard Taft HS; Chicago, IL; 19/800 CmntyWkr; HonRl; NHS; PolWkr; SpnCl; MthCl; Eastern Illinois Univ; Veterinarian.

MORIN, Debra J; Oscoda Area HS; Oscoda, MI; 29/235 HonRl; NHS; NatlMeritSF; PpCl; LetterChrldr; PPFtbl; CitAwd; Northern Mich Univ; Psychology.

MORIN, Michael E; Lamar HS; Lamar, MO; Band; CncrtBnd; HonRl; MrchBnd; Orch; PepBnd; YthFlsp; Bsbl; Bsktbl; Ftbl; College; Accountant.

MORIN, Michael L; Fairmont HS; Fairmont, MN; Band; Chr; CncrtBnd; HonRl; LitMag; MrchBnd; NatlMeritSF; PepBnd; SchMus; FrCl; College; Law.

MORIN, Sandra K; Brainerd Sr HS; Brainerd, MN; 26/460 SecTrsFrshCls; Chr; HonRl; SchMus; SctActv; PpCl; CaptBsktbl; Swmmng; GAA; IMSpt; Jr College; Aero Mechanical Engineer.

MORISCHE, Gwendolyn; Osage Comm HS; Osage, IA; Band; ChrhWkr; CncrtBnd; MrchBnd; NHS; Trk; College; Major In Biology.

MORISETTE, David R; Cottonwood HS; Marshall, MN; SecSrCls; HonRl; Bsktbl; IMSpt; College; Professional.

MORITZ, Craig C; St Johns HS; Beloit, KS; VPFrshCls; VPSophCls; VPJrCls; VPSrCls; ALBoysSt; ChrhWkr; HonRl; StuCncl; Yrbk; Bsktbl; Ftbl;.

MORITZ, Debra S; Spring Valley Public HS; Spring Valley, WI; CmntyWkr; HonRl; LbryAde; SchPl; TchrAde; RptrYrbk; RptrSchPpr; FHA; College; Law Enforcement.

MORITZ, Julianna M; St Scholastica HS; Chicago, IL; Loyola Univ; Accountant.

MORK, Beth L; Marion HS; Marion, IA; HonRl; Yrbk; PpCl; LetterBsbl; LetterBsktbl; LetterTrk; Univ Of N Ia; Acct Or Cpa.

MORK, First; Manning Community HS; Manning, IA; ALBoysSt; Band; ChrhWkr; CncrtBnd; HonRl; VPStuCncl; Yrbk; Bsktbl; Ftbl; Coll; Bus Admin.

MORK, Jorn L; Renville HS; Renville, MN; 7/54 Band; Chrs; HonRl; LitMag; NHS; SchPl; 4-H; FFA; FTA; GerCl; Univ Of Minn Morris; Art/german.

MORK, Michelle M; O Gorman HS; Sioux Falls, SD; ALAGirlsSt; Chrs; CncrtBnd; MrchBnd; PepBnd; StuGov; EdSchPpr; Coll; Elem Ed.

MORK, Shirley J; Central HS; Aberdeen, SD; 4/421 Chr; ChrhWkr; VPDrlTm; HonRl; Mdrgl; PresNHS; NatlMeritCmnd; SchMus; StuGov; Pres4-H; Univ Of South Dakota; Professional.

MORKEN, Susan L; Central HS; Devils Lake, ND; HonRl; TchrAde; Lake Region Jr College.

MORLAN, Karen K; Green City HS; Green Castle, MO; 4/38 ALAGirlsSt; Band; ChrhWkr; CmntyWkr; HonRl; NHS; StuCncl; EdYrBk; Bsbl; Bsktbl; Univ.

MORLAN, Susan; North Putnam Jr Sr HS; Roachdale, IN; HonRl; NatlFornLg; SchPl; LatCl; SpnCl; MthCl; Ball State Univ; Study Law.

MORLANG, Travis E; Ainsworth HS; Ainsworth, NE; 16/68 TrsJrCls; ALAGirlsSt; Chr; Chrs; HonRl; NatlThespSoc; SchMus; SchPl; SctActv; FHA; College; Professional.

MORLEN, Rick A; Granite City HS; Granite City, IL; 18/350 PresFrshCls; ALBoysSt; Chr; ChrhWkr; NHS; StuCncl; SciCl; LetterTrk; LetterWrstlng; College; Dentist.

MORLEY, Debra J; Alpena HS; Alpena, MI; ALAGirlsSt; Chr; HonRl; Mdrgl; NatlMeritCmnd; SchPl; SctActv; RptrSchPpr; GerCl; College; Biology.

MORLEY, Donivan S; Thomas Jefferson HS; Rockford, IL; 5/351 SecFrshCls; VPSophCls; PresJrCls; PresSrCls; CmntyWkr; HonRl; NHS; NatlThespSoc; SancSoc; StuGov; Coll; Anthropology.

MORLEY, Lois E; Ryan HS; Omaha, NE; Chrs; SchMus; SchPl; PpCl; Bsktbl; Chrldr; Technical School.

MORLOCK, Paul J; St Charles HS; St Charles, IL; 70/465 PresSophCls; VPJrCls; Chr; HonRl; NHS; StuCncl; PresKeyCl; LetterBsktbl; Ftbl; LetterTrk; AmLegAwd; SARAwd; RotaryAwd; Luther College; Medicine.

MORLOCK, Susan L; Glenbard West HS; Glen Ellyn, IL; 103/526 Band; CncrtBnd; MrchBnd; OffAde; PepBnd; University; Zoology.

MORNING, Patricia A; Bloomer Sr HS; Bloomer, WI; SecFrshCls; AFS; MrchBnd; OffAde; StuCncl; PresFBLA; PresFHA; Bsktbl; Chrldr; GAA; Business School; Vocation.

MORNINGSTAR, Jean M; Keokuk Sr HS; Keokuk, IA; 1/192 PresAFS; HonRl; HospAde; NHS; SecStuCncl; EdYrBk; SpnCl; Tennis; KiwanAwd; Univ Of Iowa; Medicine.

MORNINGSTAR, Marjorie A; T F South HS; Lansing, IL; 27/583 AFS; Chr; HonRl; NHS; RptrSchPpr; Univ Of Ill; Veterinarian.

MORONI, Michael A; Advance Riv HS; Painton, MO; PresSophCls; HonRl; SctActv; PresFFA; LetterBsbl; College; Agriculture.

MORR, Garry E; Central Noble HS; Albion, IN; PolWkr; StuCncl; Glf; Tennis; College; Accounting.

MORREN, Sue A; Vicksburg HS; Fulton, MI; 47/159 HonRl; NHS; OffAde; SchMus; FFA; SecPpCl; Tennis; PPFtbl;.

MORRESE, Steven C; O Fallon Township HS; O Fallon, IL; 19/300 Aud/Vis; Chrs; HonRl; Mdrgl; NHS; Us Air Force Academy; Computer Sciences.

MORRETT, Kent E; Connersville HS; Connersville, IN; 31/380 HonRl; NHS; SctActv; StuCncl; GerCl; SciCl; LetterFtbl; LetterWrstlng; IMSpt; DARAwd; Anderson Coll; Engng.

MORRICAL, Gregory W; Lincoln HS; Beverly, KS; 9/60 VPJrCls; PresSrCls; ALBoysSt; CncrtBnd; HonRl; MrchBnd; PepBnd; 4-H; GerCl; LetterFtbl; College; Agriculture.

MORRICK, Pamela A; Oregon HS; Madison, WI; TrsSrCls; Chrs; CncrtBnd; HonRl; MrchBnd; Orch; SchPl; GerCl; LetterTrk; PPFtbl; College; Nursing.

MORRILL, Myra J; Morrill HS; Morrill, NE; 5/40 TrsFrshCls; Chrs; LbryAde; NHS; NatlThespSoc; SchMus; SchPl; Twrl; YthFlsp; RptrYrbk; PresFHA; Chrldr; PPFtbl; MasAwd; College; Science.

MORRILL, Robert J; St Agnes HS; Alliance, NE; PresSophCls; DrmBgl; HonRl; StuCncl; CivCl; FSA; SpnCl; Bsktbl; Ftbl; Trk;.

MORRIN, Ronald M; Mason Senior HS; Erie, MI; HonRl; NHS; SchPl; LetterBsbl; CaptBsktbl; CaptGlf; College; Engineering.

MORRIS, Agnes R; Austin HS; Austin, IN; ChrhWkr; HospAde; NHS; OffAde; SchAde; TchrAde; 4-H; FTA; 4-HAwd; Ivy Tech; Licensed Practical Nurse.

MORRIS, Alice A; Columbus North HS; Columbus, IN; 128/500 ChrhWkr; HonRl; NatlFornLg; PolWkr; SchMus; YthFlsp; YthFnd; CaptSwmmng; LetterTrk; AmLegAwd; Albion Col; Biology Major.

MORRIS, Amanda S; Jefferson City HS; Jefferson City, MO; Chr; ChrhWkr; HonRl; HospAde; FrCl; PpCl; Chrldr; GAA; Univ.

MORRIS, Anne K; Loy Norrix HS; Kalamazoo, MI; 1/500 TrsSophCls; Chr; ChrhWkr; CmntyWkr; NatlMeritSF; PolWkr; SchMus; StuCncl; YthFlsp; SchPpr; GerCl; Trk; NCTE; Duke Univ; Law.

MORRIS, Ann S; Evanston Township HS; Evanston, IL; Chr; HonRl; NatlMeritSF; IMSpt; Brown Univ.

MORRIS, Beverly; Huron HS; Ann Arbor, MI; HonRl; Orch; RptrYrbk; Yrbk; SchPpr; SpnCl; GAA; Univ Of Chicago; Eng.

MORRIS, Bradley K; Mc Leansboro HS; Mc Leansboro, IL; 10/126 HonRl; LbryAde; RptrSchPpr; EdSchPpr; FBLA; Univ Of Ill; Business Administration.

MORRIS, Cathleen A; Waukesha North HS; Waukesha, WI; 66/330 Band; CncrtBnd; Mdrgl; NHS; Orch; SchMus; SecStuCncl; 4-H; SecGAA; CitAwd; Univ Of Wi; Physical Ed Teacher.

MORRIS, Craig; Winterset Community HS; Winterset, IA; ALBoysSt; HonRl; MrchBnd; PepBnd; YthFlsp; 4-H; Bsktbl; Ftbl; Trk; 4-HAwd; Univ.

MORRIS, Cynthia A; Marshall HS; Marshall, MI; 153/253 ALAGirlsSt; CmntyWkr; HonRl; JA; NHS; NatlMeritSchl; RedCrAde; StuGov; TchrAde; Kellogg Community College; Pe Teacher.

MORRIS, Dale C; Winnetonka HS; Kansas City, MO; 7/517 HonRl; NatlMeritCmnd; TchrAde; LatCl; SciCl; Umkc; Elec Engr.

MORRIS, Deann R; Sublette HS; Sublette, KS; Band; ChrhWkr; CncrtBnd; HonRl; MrchBnd; PepBnd; Yrbk; PpCl;.

MORRIS, Debra L; Pekin Comm HS; Pekin, IL; 76/865 Chr; Chrs; HonRl; NHS; NatlMeritCmnd; StuCncl; TchrAde; W Illinois Univ; Journalism.

MORRIS, Donald; St Clair HS; Grubville, MO; 10/162 HonRl; NHS; Sacrstn; 4-H; KeyCl; Bsbl; IMSpt; Coll.

MORRIS, Elizabeth M; East Buchanan HS; Quasqueton, IA; 6/67 ALAGirlsSt; Band; Chrs; HonRl; NHS; Quill&Scroll; SchMus; EdSchPpr; GodCntryAwd; CitAwd;.

MORRIS, Gary J; Gillespie HS; Benld, IL; 28/130 Band; CncrtBnd; HonRl; MrchBnd; PepBnd; PresYthFlsp; RptrYrbk; Bsktbl; LetterFtbl; LetterTrk; Rose Holman Inst Of Tech; Engineering.

MORRIS, Jan; Rose Hill HS; Rose Hill, KS; 1/59 HonRl; NatlFornLg; SchPl; RptrSchPpr; SpnCl; PpCl; Trk; PPFtbl; CitAwd; Butler Coll; Computer Analyst.

MORRIS, John M; North Side HS; Ft Wayne, IN; AFS; LitMag; NatlFornLg; NatlMeritSF; SchPl; StuCncl; StuGov; RptrYrbk; KeyCl; College.

MORRIS, Joseph E; Logan Magnolia HS; Council Bluffs, IA; 3/52 HonRl; NHS; Iowa St Univ; Veterinarian.

MORRIS, Karen A; Eisenhower HS; Decatur, IL; 8/301 Chr; HospAde; SecNHS; SchMus; Yrbk; GerCl; PpCl; Augustana Col; Physical Therapy.

MORRIS, Karla K; Ash Grove R 4 HS; Ash Grove, MO; HstFrshCls; ChrhWkr; HonRl; HospAde; ModUN; SecNHS; StuCncl; Twrl; Pres4-H; PPFtbl; 4-HAwd; Burge Schl; Nursing.

MORRIS, Kathy J; Green Ridge R 8 HS; Sedalia, MO; 1/34 PresFrshCls; Band; Chrs; ChrhWkr; HonRl; EdYrBk; 4-H; PresFHA; BttyCrckrAwd; DARAwd; College.

MORRIS, Kay C; Meservey Thornton HS; Clear Lake, IA; Chr; Chrs; HonRl; PresStuCncl; 4-H; LetterChrldr;.

MORRIS, Kris L; Williamsfield HS; Dahinda, IL; 3/32 Chrs; HonRl; LbryAde; NHS; YthFlsp; YthLg; 4-H; Bsbl; Chrldr; GAA; DARAwd; Illinois St Univ; Accounting.

MORRIS, Laurie L; Prophetstown HS; Prophetstown, IL; 1/100 AFS; Band; CncrtBnd; HonRl; HospAde; MrchBnd; NHS; PepBnd; StuCncl; RptrSchPpr; 4-H; FTA; PresSpnCl; PpCl; Illinois State Univ.

MORRIS, Lori D; Newark Comm HS; Newark, IL; VPSophCls; Band; Chrs; HonRl; SctActv; FHA; FTA; FrCl; GAA; College.

MORRIS, Mary; Fair Grove HS; Sgtraffod, MO; SecTrsJrCls; ChrhWkr; HonRl; SchAde; StuCncl; TchrAde; FHA; FTA; SpnCl; CitAwd; Burge School Of Nursing; Nurse.

MORRIS, Mary Y; Du Quoin HS; Du Quoin, IL; Chrs; DrlTm; HonRl; Yrbk; FHA; FTA; SpnCl; GAA; College; Accounting.

MORRIS, Melissa; Emporia HS; Allen, KS; /320 Chrs; HonRl; PpCl; Trk; Coll; Home Ec.

MORRIS, Michael A; Flushing HS; Flushing, MI; HonRl; NatlMeritSF; TchrAde; Bsbl; LetterGlf; IMSpt; Michigan State Univ; Physics.

MORRIS, Michael J; Carbondale Comm HS; Carbondale, IL; 16/280 ChrhWkr; CmntyWkr; HonRl; ModUN; NHS; PolWkr; StuCncl; StuGov; SpnCl; PpCl; SciCl; So Illinois Univ; Lawyer.

MORRIS, Monica A; Whiteland Comm HS; Franklin, IN; 9/187 CncrtBnd; MrchBnd; PepBnd; SchMus; RptrYrbk; FTA; FrCl; Bsktbl; CaptTrk; SecGAA; Indiana U; Music Or Psychology.

MORRIS, Rebecca; Mt Vernon Township Hs; Mt Vernon, IL; 7/433 HonRl; JrNHS; NHS; SchPl; Yrbk; FrCl; U Of Illinois; Pharmicist.

MORRIS, Rhonda J; Warsaw HS; Warsaw, IN; SecSrCls; Chrs; CmntyWkr; SctActv; StuCncl; YthFlsp; 4-H; PpCl; Swmmng; College; Business.

MORRIS, Robert G; Woodland HS; Streator, IL; HonRl; NHS; KeyCl; GerCl; LetterBsbl; LetterFtbl; Univ Il; Architecture.

MORRIS, Roger C; Southwest HS; St Louis, MO; PresJrCls; CmntyWkr; IntrClCncl; PolWkr; SchPl; PresStuCncl; StuGov; YthLg; AmLegAwd; GodCntryAwd; MasAwd; CitAwd; University; Professional.

MORRIS, Roxanne K; Belmond Community HS; Belmond, IA; Band; HonRl; MrchBnd; OffAde; YthFlsp; 4-H; FHA; PpCl; Chrldr; 4-HAwd; Spencer Sch Of Business; Admin Asst.

MORRIS, Sandra; Chicago Vocational HS; Chicago, IL; HonRl; College; Teacher.

MORRIS, Sandra L; Limestone Comm HS; Peoria, IL; 63/396 ChrhWkr; HonRl; Mdrgl; TchrAde; Ill Central College; Data Processing.

MORRIS, Scott A; St Pius X HS; Kansas City, MO; 70/130 Chr; Chrs; Bsbl; LetterBsktbl; LetterFtbl; CchngActv; IMSpt; College.

MORRIS, Sheryl A; Monrovia HS; Monrovia, IN; 15/100 Band; CncrtBnd; HonRl; MrchBnd; 4-H; PpCl; LetterTrk; Chrldr; College.

MORRIS, Steven P; Thornridge HS; Dolton, IL; HonRl; NHS; Univ.

MORRIS, Susan A; Sherwood Public HS; Tolley, ND; SecSophCls; Chrs; HonRl; MrchBnd; SchPl; Yrbk; SchPpr; PpCl; LetterBsktbl; Chrldr; IMSpt; Minot State College; Biology.

MORRIS, Teresa M; O Fallon Twp HS; O Fallon, IL; HonRl; JrNHS; NHS; StuCncl; Business School; Vocation.

MORRIS, Theresa M; Wyandotte HS; Seneca, MO; HonRl; RptrYrbk; RptrSchPpr; FHA; Neo A&m College.

MORRIS, Vickie A; Chicago Vocational HS; Chicago, IL; 61/700 LbryAde; StuCncl; CchngActv; College; Professional.

MORRIS, Wayne R; Kearney HS; Kearney, MO; 15/86 Band; CncrtBnd; HonRl; MrchBnd; NHS; SctActv; TchrAde; Bsktbl; Trk; Col; Veterinary Science.

MORRIS, William E; Eldorado HS; Eldorado, IL; 4/110 ChrhWkr; CmntyWkr; HonRl; SchMus; Yrbk; SpnCl; CaptBsktbl; LetterFtbl; Trk; Graceland College; Psychology.

MORRIS, William S; North HS; Des Moines, IA; HonRl; JrNHS; NatlMeritCmnd; NatlMeritSchl; NatlMeritSF; PolWkr; StuGov; SchPpr; SpnCl; PpCl; CaptFtbl; Wrstlng; KiwanAwd; Univ Of Iowa; Law.

MORRISETT, Marilyn M; Springfield HS; Springfield, IL; NHS; StuCncl; Eastern Illinois University; Teaching.

MORRISON, Beverly J; Missouri Valley HS; Honey Creek, IA; Chr; Chrs; DrlTm; HonRl; NHS; StuCncl; TchrAde; 4-H; Chrldr; 4-HAwd;.

MORRISON, David R; St Joe Senior HS; Saint Joseph, MI; 76/350 HospAde; VPOrch; SchMus; FDA; Olivet Nazarene College; Doctor.

MORRISON, Deborah A; New Berlin HS; New Berlin, IL; 3/63 HstSrCls; NHS; SchMus; SchPl; RptrYrbk; 4-H; SpnCl; VPPpCl; LetterTrk; SecGAA; DanFAwd; 4-HAwd; River Forest Luth College; Speech Ed.

MORRISON, Debora L; Hume R 8 HS; Hume, MO; 4/16 Band; Chrs; CncrtBnd; HonRl; MrchBnd; ModUN; PepBnd; FHA; LetterBsktbl; LetterSciCl; Univ; Major Study.

MORRISON, Diana; Hume R 8 HS; Hume, MO; SecJrCls; Chrs; DrmMjrt; HonRl; SchPpr; Pres4-H; FHA; PpCl; LetterBsktbl; Chrldr;.

MORRISON, Donna M; Spalding HS; Chicago, IL; 1/70 PresSrCls; Band; Chrs; HonRl; NHS; StuCncl; RptrYrbk; EdYrBk; RptrSchPpr; SchPpr; Loyola Univ; Medical Tech.

MORRISON, Joann; Aurora Central Catholic HS; Aurora, IL; Chr; Chrs; ChrhWkr; HonRl; NHS; RedCrAde; SctActv; Aurora Col; Elementary Education.

MORRISON, Joetta M; Lansing HS; Lansing, KS; SctActv; SpnCl; PpCl; SciCl; LetterTrk; GAA; IMSpt;.

MORRISON, Jonathan J; Minot HS; Minot, ND; 54/649 Chr; Chrs; ChrhWkr; HonRl; NHS; SchMus; StuGov; GerCl; CaptTrk; College; Social Science.

MORRISON, Joseph T; Loyola Academy; Deerfield, IL; 40/442 HonRl; NHS; NatlMeritCmnd; Sdlty; RptrSchPpr; RusCl; CaptBsktbl; College; Medicine.

MORRISON, Kim R; Ellendale Public HS; Ellendale, ND; 16/44 ALAGirlsSt; NHS; SchPl; StuCncl; 4-H; Bsktbl; Trk; Chrldr; IMSpt; College; Dental Hygienist.

MORRISON, Martha M; Oscoda HS; Glennie, MI; Band; ChrhWkr; CncrtBnd; DrlTm; MrchBnd; PepBnd; SchAde; TchrAde; SchPpr; Bsktbl; PPFtbl; Central Mich; Accounting.

MORRISON, Mary; Stuart Menlo HS; Stuat, IA; 3/52 Band; Chrs; CncrtBnd; HonRl; MrchBnd; NHS; SchMus; SchPl; YthFlsp; FSA; Iowa Stae Univ; Elem Teacher.

MORRISON, Patricia A; Cavalier HS; Cavalier, ND; 1/78 VPSophCls; ALAGirlsSt; HonRl; StuCncl; YthFlsp; RptrYrbk; RptrSchPpr; FshEdSchPpr; GAA; BauchLmbAwd; North Dakota State Univ; Home Economics.

MORRISON, Randall W; Harper Creek HS; Battle Creek, MI; HonRl; StuGov; 4-H; SpnCl; Glf; College.

MORRISON, Ray E; Gregory HS; Gregory, SD; Band; Chrs; ChrhWkr; CncrtBnd; HonRl; MrchBnd; NatlFornLg; NatlThespSoc; Orch; PepBnd; LetterTrk; College.

MORRISON, Rochelle; Thorp HS; Thorp, WI; TrsJrCls; Band; Chrs; CncrtBnd; MrchBnd; PepBnd; SchMus; GAA; College; Major Study.

MORRISON, Scott B; Stillman Valley HS; Stillman Valley, IL; Chrs; HonRl; SchMus; SchPl; SctActv; TchrAde; FTA; LetterBsbl; Ftbl; Wrstlng; College; Architecture.

MORRISON, Terri A; Pekin Community HS; Pekin, IL; Chrs; ChrhWkr; HonRl; NHS; YthFlsp; SecGerCl; PpCl; GAA; Ill State Univ; Environmental Science.

MORRISON, Tony E; Southmont HS; Ladoga, IN; HonRl; NHS; StuCncl; EdYrBk; LetterBsbl; LetterFtbl; LetterWrstlng; IMSpt; Indiana State University; Accounting.

MORRISON, William; Rockhurst HS; Leawood, KS; Chr; HonRl; NHS; SchPl; IMSpt; Rockhurst College; Certified Public Acct.

MORRISS, Jeannette M; Pennfield HS; Battle Creek, MI; Band; CncrtBnd; HonRl; MrchBnd; NHS; PepBnd; SctActv; YthFlsp; LetterTennis; GAA; Western Mi Univ; Med Tech.

MORRISSEY, Ann; Marquette HS; Alton, IL; AFS; HonRl; JrNHS; NHS; NatlThespSoc; SchPl; PresStuCncl; EdSchPpr; CaptBsktbl; TrsSophCls; GAA; Denison University; Botany.

MORRISSEY, Bernie; West Chicago Comm HS; West Chicago, IL; Chrs; HonRl; College; Draftsman.

MORRONE, Kyle L; Clawson HS; Clawson, MI; AFS; Band; ChrhWkr; DrlTm; HonRl; HospAde; JrNHS; MrchBnd; SpnCl; PpCl; Hope College; Veterinary Medicine.

MORROW, Audrey L; Hays HS; Hays, KS; Chr; Chrs; ChrhWkr; DrlTm; HonRl; Mdrgl; SchMus; PpCl; College; Music.

MORROW, Bruce D; Greenway HS; Marble, MN; 25/175 Band; CncrtBnd; HonRl; MrchBnd; NHS; PepBnd; SchPl; MthCl; SciCl; LetterWrstlng; College; Computer Science.

MORROW, Deborah E; Kenwood HS; Chicago, IL; 6/462 CmntyWkr; HonRl; HospAde; NHS; NatlMeritFnl; TchrAde; College; Language.

MORROW, Eric J; Maine East HS; Morton Grove, IL; HonRl; SchPpr; Bsktbl; LetterFtbl; College; Law.

MORROW, Gretchen M; Armour HS; Armour, SD; PresJrCls; Band; Chrs; ChrhWkr; PresNHS; SchMus; SchPl; TreasFHA; GerCl; AmLegAwd; Coll; Music.

MORROW, Laurel E; Angola HS; Angola, IN; Band; Chr; CncrtBnd; HospAde; NatlMeritCmnd; NatlThespSoc; Orch; 4-H; LatCl; Purdue Univ; Nursing.

MORROW, Michael; St Marys HS; O Neill, NE; 5/35 Chrs; CmntyWkr; PolWkr; SctActv; StuCncl; Yrbk; CchngActv; Trade School; Profession.

MORROW, Nancy L; Southwest HS; Green Bay, WI; 61/420 Chrs; HonRl; LbryAde; SchPl; FFA; SpnCl; PpCl; LetterTrk; CchngActv; College; Professional.

MORROW, Peggy L; Sullivan HS; Chicago, IL; HonRl; JA; LitMag; VPNHS; StuCncl; TchrAde; RptrYrbk; RptrSchPpr; KeyCl; TrsSophCls; Northern Illinois Univ; Journalism.

MORROW, Richard L; Turkey Run HS; Waveland, IN; 1/63 HonRl; PresNHS; NatlMeritSF; Quill&Scroll; SchPl; StuCncl; Yrbk; Sec4-H; SpnCl; PresSciCl; Wrstlng; IMSpt; 4-HAwd; Wabash College; Law.

MORROW, Richard P; Lincoln Comm HS; Lincoln, IL; ChrhWkr; CncrtBnd; HonRl; MrchBnd; Eastern Ill Univ; Medical Technologist.

MORROW, Scott C; Doniphan HS; Doniphan, NE; 1/37 PresSophCls; Band; Chrs; HonRl; PepBnd; SchPl; VPYthFlsp; SptEdYrbk; 4-H; LetterBsktbl; Hastings College; Medicine.

MORSCH, Brad A; Donovan HS; Donovan, IL; 7/56 SecTrsFrshCls; Band; Chrs; CncrtBnd; HonRl; Quill&Scroll; SchMus; SchPl; RptrYrbk; Univ Of Illinois; Medicine.

MORSCH, Penny; Hinckley Big Rock; Hinckley, IL; 38/77 ALAGirlsSt; Band; ChrhWkr; CncrtBnd; PepBnd; SctActv; TreasVPSophCls; Sec4-H; VPFHA; 4-HAwd; College; Home Economics Ed.

MORSCHING, Lynn M; Waterville Elysian HS; Waterville, MN; Band; Chrs; ChrhWkr; CncrtBnd; HonRl; MrchBnd; SchMus; CaptChrldr; GAA; LionAwd; PresAwd; Jr College; Special Educ.

MORSE, Cynthia F; Harbor Springs HS; Harbor Springs, MI; 4/75 Chrs; CncrtBnd; HonRl; LbryAde; NatlMeritCmnd; PepBnd; SchPl; TchrAde; SpnCl; IMSpt; Clg; Law.

MORSE, Janet L; Kirksville Senior HS; Kirksville, MO; DrlTm; HonRl; NHS; StuCncl; Yrbk; 4-H; SpnCl; LetterTennis; DanFAwd; 4-HAwd; Northeast Missouri State Univ.

MORSE, John R; St Paul Public HS; St Paul, NE; 11/72 PresSrCls; Band; Chr; CncrtBnd; HonRl; MrchBnd; NatlThespSoc; PepBnd; SchMus; EdYrBk; RptrSchPpr; College; Accounting.

MORSE, Kathlene M; Tecumseh HS; Tecumseh, MI; 60/239 Band; ChrhWkr; CncrtBnd; MrchBnd; YthFlsp; SchPpr; 4-H; 4-HAwd; MasAwd; Eastern Michigan Univ; Interior Design.

MORSE, Kendall G; Rice Lake HS; Rice Lake, WI; ChrhWkr; HonRl; YthFlsp; Univ; Professional.

MORSE, Lee J; Hill Mc Cloy HS; Montrose, MI; 18/150 PresFrshCls; Band; HonRl; NHS; StuCncl; Bsktbl; CaptTrk; AmLegAwd; VoiceDemAwd; Northern Mi Clge; Computer Electronics.

MORSE, Lisa M; West HS; Davenport, IA; CncrtBnd; DrlTm; HonRl; MrchBnd; StuCncl; FrCl; Bsbl; LetterBsktbl; LetterTrk; College; Languages.

MORSE, Montgomery A; Oak Park HS; Kansas City, MO; 13/602 HonRl; PpCl; Bsbl; Ftbl; College; Aeronautical Engineer.

MORSE, Peggy R; Central Cass HS; Wheatland, ND; VPJrCls; ALAGirlsSt; Band; Chrs; HonRl; NHS; SchPl; StuCncl; 4-H; FHA; LetterBsktbl; GAA; 4-HAwd; CitAwd; University Of North Dakota; Home Ec.

MORSE, Peter R; Paw Paw HS; Paw Paw, MI; SecFrshCls; PresSophCls; Band; Chr; Chrl; ChrhWkr; CncrtBnd; HonRl; MrchBnd; NHS; Spring Arbor Col; Music Ed.

MORSE, Steven J; La Crescent HS; Dakota, MN; HonRl; NatlMeritCmnd; StuCncl; SchPpr; 4-H; GerCl; SciCl; Wrstlng; University; Biological Sciences.

MORSE, Stewart F; Onsted HS; Onsted, MI; VPSophCls; ALBoysSt; HonRl; SchPl; SctActv; LetterBsbl; LetterBsktbl; Glf; Trk; College; Engineering.

MORTENSEN, Craig L; Raymond Central HS; Raymond, NE; ChrhWkr; HonRl; SctActv; TreasYthFlsp; FFA; Bsktbl; Trk; Se Comm Clg; Welder.

MORTENSEN, Diane M; Alta Community HS; Alta, IA; VPChrhWkr; HonRl; Pres4-H; FHA; PpCl; Chrldr; 4-HAwd; Ellsworth Community Coll; Human Services.

MORTENSEN, John P; Premontre HS; Green Bay, WI; 5/162 VPJrCls; Band; CncrtBnd; HonRl; MrchBnd; NatlCathMusEdAsoc; NHS; NatlMeritSF; PepBnd; ROTC; SchMus; SctActv; TreasStuCncl; LetterTrk; IMSpt; Univ Of Wi; Law.

MORTENSON, Betty; Kimball County HS; Kimnall, NE; SecTrsSophCls; Band; Chrs; HonRl; MrchBnd; PepBnd; SchMus; StuGov; PpCl; Business School; Professional Midical Sec.

MORTH, Patricia A; Fingal Public HS; Fingal, ND; 7/21 SecSrCls; Chrs; HonRl; MrchBnd; PepBnd; SchPl; Sdlty; RptrSchPpr; SchPpr; Bsktbl; Nd State U; Univ Studies.

MORTIERE, Michael D; St Florian HS; Detroit, MI; ChrhWkr; HonRl; SchMus; EdYrBk; RptrSchPpr; FrCl; SciCl; BauchLmbAwd; RotaryAwd; CitAwd; Wayne State Univ; Biology.

MORTON, Caroline E; Dupo Community HS; E Carondelet, IL; SecSophCls; VPSrCls; HonRl; SecStuCncl; TchrAde; RptrYrbk; EdYrBk; SecFTA; PpCl; SciCl; Glf; College; Elementary Ed.

MORTON, Debra S; Lanphier HS; Springfield, IL; 5/473 PresJrCls; PresSrCls; NHS; SchPl; StuCncl; PpCl; SecGAA; Western Illinois Univ; Education.

MORTON, Denise; Ar We Va Comm HS; Vail, IA; 8/42 HonRl; LbryAde; MrchBnd; NHS; Yrbk; Des Moines Area Comm Coll; Physical Therapy.

MORTON, Gerald J; Harding HS; St Paul, MN; 12/725 AFS; Band; CncrtBnd; HonRl; MrchBnd; NHS; PepBnd; SctActv; SciCl; Socr; St Paul Tech Voc; Computer Prog.

MORTON, Jonathan S; Freeport HS; Freeport, IL; 30/500 ALBoysSt; HonRl; Orch; SchMus; SchPl; Bsbl; Ftbl; Glf; Wrstlng; Highland Comm College; Computer Programming.

MORTON, Kenneth L; Salem HS; Salem, MO; 9/173 Chr; Chrs; ChrhWkr; HonRl; FFA; SciCl; Univ Of Mo; Engineering.

MORTON, Kenneth L; Salem Sr HS; Salem, MO; Chr; Chrs; HonRl; SchMus; SchPl; FFA; Univ Of Missouri; Nuclear Physicist.

MORTON, Margaret R; Orangeville HS; Orangeville, IL; 15/60 SecFrshCls; SecSophCls; HonRl; Yrbk; 4-H; FBLA; FHA; FrCl; IMSpt; 4-HAwd; Clg; Physical Therapy.

MORTON, Robert B; New Trier West HS; Glencoe, IL; 12/694 CmntyWkr; HonRl; NatlFornLg; NatlMeritCmnd; PolWkr; StuGov; University; Law.

MOSBRUCKER, Cathy A; Saint Marys Central HS; Bismarck, ND; OffAde; SchPl; SctActv; TchrAde; LetterBsktbl; GAA; University Of Nd; Law.

MOSBY, Judith A; Litchville Public HS; Litchville, ND; Band; Chrs; HonRl; SchMus; YthFlsp; RptrYrbk; RptrSchPpr; Bsktbl; LetterTrk; GovHonPrgAwd; University; Nursing.

MOSBY, Mary A; Rensselaer HS; Rensselaer, IN; HonRl; SchMus; SchPl; SctActv; FTA; LatCl; PpCl; SciCl; St Josephs Coll; Social Work.

MOSCINSKI, Amy S; West Leyden HS; Melrose Park, IL; 37/475 SecFrshCls; SecSophCls; HonRl; NHS; SchPpr; Swmmng; Northeastern Illinois Univ; Veterinarian.

MOSE, Marilyn D; Chesaning HS; St Charles, MI; Band; HonRl; SpnCl; Bus Schl.

MOSE, Sheree C; Streator Twp HS; Streator, IL; 6/400 HonRl; NHS; StuCncl; RptrSchPpr; Illinois State Univ; English.

MOSENG, Marcia R; Milan Public HS; Appleton, MN; HonRl; SchPl; TchrAde; Yrbk; TreasFHA; PpCl; GAA; PresAwd; Work.

MOSER, Anne G; Hiawatha HS; Hiawatha, KS; SecTrsSophCls; Band; HonRl; JrNHS; MrchBnd; FHA; PpCl; Bsktbl; Trk; Chrldr; Kansas State University; Dentistry.

MOSER, Becky; Manistee Catholic Central HS; Manister, MI; 3 Band; CncrtBnd; HonRl; MrchBnd; Swmmng; IMSpt; VoiceDemAwd; Coll; Major Sutdy.

MOSER, Connie M; Medina Public HS; Medina, ND; TrsJrCls; ALAGirlsSt; ChrhWkr; CncrtBnd; HonRl; SchPl; SptEdSchPpr; FFA; FHA; LetterBsbl; LetterTrk; LetterChrldr; GAA; College.

MOSER, Gregg M; Milbank HS; Milbank, SD; CmntyWkr; HonRl; Yrbk; Trade School.

MOSER, Lynne M; Richwoods HS; Peoria, IL; Chr; Chrl; Chrs; ChrhWkr; CmntyWkr; HonRl; PolWkr; TchrAde; YthFlsp; Trinity College; Education.

MOSER, Marilyn A; Durand HS; Durand, IL; 5/60 TrsFrshCls; ALAGirlsSt; HonRl; StuCncl; RptrYrbk; FHA; GerCl; Ill State Univ; Accounting.

MOSER, Marvin; Hoffman Public HS; Hoffman, MN; TrsJrCls; ALBoysSt; Band; HonRl; Orch; SchPl; RptrYrbk; 4-H; AmLegAwd; BauchLmbAwd; Univ; Research Physicist.

MOSER, Mary L; North Central Area HS; Wilson, MI; 1/54 SecSrCls; HonRl; RptrYrbk; Northern Michigan Univ; Political Science.

MOSER, Mary L; Adrian Public HS; Wilmont, MN; Chr; HonRl; NHS; RptrYrbk; Yrbk; 4-H; College; Registered Nurse.

MOSER, Mike R; South Adams HS; Berne, IN; 48/125 ALBoysSt; Chr; StuCncl; RptrSchPpr; FrCl; CaptBsktbl; College; Accounting.

MOSER, Patricia J; Marysville HS; Marysvlle, KS; SecJrCls; Chrl; HonRl; SchPl; CchngActv; IMSpt; Col; Acct.

MOSER, Rick L; West Lyon HS; Larchwood, IA; 29/81 Chrs; HonRl; SchPl; StuCncl; Yrbk; 4-H; FFA; Bsktbl; Ftbl; 4-HAwd; College; Agriculture.

MOSER, Sandra S; Scotland HS; Scotland, SD; 8/45 ALAGirlsSt; HonRl; OffAde; PepBnd; SchPl; FHA; GerCl; PpCl; Univ Of Sd Vermillion; Med Labrotory Tech.

MOSER, Ted D; Warsaw HS; Warsaw, IN; ALBoysSt; Band; CncrtBnd; HonRl; LetterFtbl; College.

MOSER, Wes W; West Lyon Comm HS; Lester, IA; 19/81 Chr; Chrs; HonRl; NHS; SchPl; RptrYrbk; Yrbk;.

MOSES, Betty; Central HS; Omaha, NE; 1/576 ALAGirlsSt; Chr; HonRl; LitMag; NHS; NatlMeritFnl; NatlMeritSF; TchrAde; GerCl; AmLegAwd; Univ; Pharmacist.

MOSES, Dennis; Lake Fenton HS; Fenton, MI; 14/143 ChrhWkr; CmntyWkr; HonRl; NatlFornLg; NHS; NatlThespSoc; StuCncl; TchrAde; Yrbk; Glf; College; Franciscan Brother.

MOSES, Gwendolyn A; John Marhsall HS; Chicago, IL; Chrs; HonRl; JrNHS; NHS; OffAde; SchAde; TchrAde; TreasFrCl; GAA; PPFtbl; College; Physician.

MOSES, Jerry M; Rush City HS; Rush City, MN; 1/65 ChrhWkr; HonRl; NHS; NatlMeritFnl; SchPl; TchrAde; FTA; PpCl; LetterBsbl; LetterBsktbl; St Cloud State Coll; Business Admin.

MOSES, Mathew R; Berkley HS; Oak Park, MI; HonRl; SctActv; StuCncl; StuGov; RptrYrbk; RptrSchPpr; SchPpr; Wrstlng; IMSpt; University Of Detroit; Dentist.

MOSES, Paul; Hays HS; Has, KS; Band; Chr; ChrhWkr; CmntyWkr; CncrtBnd; HonRl; MrchBnd; Orch; PepBnd; SchMus; LetterTrk; College; Music.

MOSES, Richard L; Port Huron Northern HS; Port Huron, MI; 65/432 ChrhWkr; HonRl; NHS; NatlMeritSF; StuCncl; College; Architecture.

MOSHER, Gail; Prospect Hs; Mt Prospect, IL; FTA; FrCl; Moser School; Business Secretarial Course.

MOSHER, Janet D; Clifford Galesburg HS; Clifford, ND; 4/21 VPFrshCls; PresSophCls; Band; Chr; ChrhWkr; DrlTm; HonRl; NHS; PepBnd; CaptBsktbl; Trinity Western; Journalism & Phy Ed.

MOSHER, Jeanette L; Prospect HS; Mt Prospect, IL; 1/614 Band; HonRl; MrchBnd; NatlFornLg; NHS; Orch; SchMus; TchrAde; RusCl; SciCl; U Of Ill; Chemisty Biology.

MOSHER, Michael J; Loyola Academy; Northbrook, IL; 59/442 CmntyWkr; HonRl; LetterFtbl; LetterTrk; CchngActv; IMSpt; St Louis University.

MOSHER, Stacy A; Webberville HS; Webberville, MI; 1/60 PresSophCls; Band; Chr; HonRl; MrchBnd; PepBnd; StuCncl; 4-H; Trk; Univ; Creative Arts.

MOSIER, Karen; Edinburg HS; Edinburg, IN; Chr; HonRl; VPStuCncl; TchrAde; YthFlsp; FrCl; PpCl; LetterBsktbl; LetterTrk; GAA; AmLegAwd; Lindsey Wilson;secondary Art Ed.

MOSKAL, John T; Clayton HS; Clayton, WI; 5/31 PresFrshCls; ChrhWkr; HonRl; Teen; 4-H; FFA; PpCl; LetterBsktbl; LetterFtbl; Trk; 4-HAwd; Univ Of Minn; Journalism.

MOSKAL, Patricia E; Lourdes HS; Chicago, IL; 42/276 HonRl; JA; NHS; Quill&Scroll; SchPpr; GerCl; Chicago Circle; English.

MOSKALICK, Mariann T; Morton Sr HS; Hammond, IN; 70/492 Chr; Quill&Scroll; Twrl; RptrSchPpr; FshEdSchPpr; SciCl; GAA; Purdue Univ; Home Economics.

MOSKALIK, Susan M; Benilde St Margarets HS; Minneapolis, MN; CmntyWkr; HonRl; JA; SchMus; SchPl; StuCncl; RptrSchPpr; SpnCl; JAAwd; OptClAwd; College Of St Cahterines; Business Adm.

MOSKAU, Annette; Usd #406 HS; Wathena, KS; TrsJrCls; PresSrCls; Chrs; HonRl; LbryAde; SchPl; StuCncl; 4-H; Trk; 4-HAwd; Mo Western State Coll.

MOSKOWITZ, Debra E; Niles North HS; Skokie, IL; 24/641 HonRl; NHS; NatlMeritCmnd; PolWkr; Quill&Scroll; SchPl; Yrbk; SchPpr; Univ Of Illinois; Political Science.

MOSLEY, Douglas D; Derby HS; Derby, KS; ChrhWkr; ROTC; SchMus; SctActv; StuGov; YthFlsp; SecTrsSophCls; LetterFtbl; Trk; LetterWrstlng; Clg; Comm In Air Force.

MOSLEY, Gwendolyn J; Beaumont HS; St Louis, MO; 5/800 ChrhWkr; CmntyWkr; HonRl; VPNHS; OffAde; TchrAde; FrCl; SpnCl; College; Medicine.

MOSLEY, Michael E; Dongola Unit HS; Dongola, IL; 4/30 Aud/Vis; Band; CncrtBnd; DrlTm; HonRl; LbryAde; MrchBnd; PepBnd; StuCncl; SpnCl; PpCl; SciCl; Trade Or Bus Sch; Vocation.

MOSNER, Mary B; Yates City HS; Maquon, IL; 5/22 ALAGirlsSt; Band; ChrhWkr; HonRl; MrchBnd; PepBnd; SchPl; StuCncl; TchrAde; RptrYrbk; College; Professional.

MOSQUERA, James P; James B Conant HS; Elk Grove, IL; 67/621 Chr; Chrs; HonRl; NHS; SchMus; SchPl; PresSpnCl; Bsktbl; LetterTennis; Trk; Univ Of Illinois; Nuclear Engineer.

MOSS, Barbara A; Carroll HS; Bringhurst, IN; Chr; Chrs; LbryAde; NatlFornLg; OffAde; StuCncl; FTA; SpnCl; Purdue Univ; Elementary Education.

MOSS, Caron D; Westport HS; Kansas City, MO; SecFrshCls; SecJrCls; VPSrCls; AFS; ChrhWkr; HonRl; NHS; OffAde; StuGov; Univ Of Missouri; Psychology.

MOSS, Cheryl L; Marquette Sr HS; Marquette, MI; 29/382 Chr; ChrhWkr; SctActv; StuCncl; TchrAde; GerCl; LatCl; Glf; College; Veterinarian.

MOSS, Edward J; Pittsfield HS; Pittsfield, IL; TrsSrCls; ChrhWkr; HonRl; Bsbl; Bsktbl; LetterFtbl;.

MOSS, Janet L; Granite City HS; Granite City, IL; 54/630 NatlFornLg; NHS; SchMus; SchPl; YthFlsp; GerCl; PpCl; GAA; Clge;.

MOSS, Jill A; Wethersfield HS; Kewanee, IL; HstSophCls; Chr; Chrs; ChrhWkr; HonRl; OffAde; SchMus; StuCncl; YthFlsp; EdYrBk; RptrSchPpr; FrCl; PpCl;.

MOSS, Jo A; Whitmore Lake HS; Whitmore Lake, MI; 7/76 TrsJrCls; PresSrCls; ChrhWkr; HonRl; NHS; OffAde; TreasStuCncl; PresYthFlsp; EdSchPpr; SptEdSchPpr; PpCl; Bsktbl; Trk; GAA; Michigan State Univ; Journalism.

MOSS, Kevin M; Northwest HS; High Ridge, MO; ALBoysSt; Chr; ChrhWkr; CmntyWkr; HonRl; Mdrgl; NHS; OffAde; PolWkr; SchPl; Bsktbl; LetterGlf; Trk; PresAwd; Columbia Univ; Political Science.

MOSS, Linda L; Lamar R 1 HS; Lamar, MO; Band; Chrs; ChrhWkr; HonRl; NHS; SchPl; Twrl; RptrYrbk; Chrldr; BttyCrckrAwd;.

MOSS, Mike; Poplar Bluff Senior HS; Poplar Bluff, MO; ChrhWkr; StuCncl; 4-H; Ftbl; Trk; Univ Of Mo; Prof Football.

MOSS, Tami J; Rvi Tipton HS; Tipton, MO; AFS; ChrhWkr; CmntyWkr; HonRl; SchPl; RptrYrbk; RptrSchPpr; SptEdSchPpr; PresFHA; PresPpCl; College.

MOSS, Thomas A; Bismarck Henning HS; Danville, IL; 1/68 Band; CncrtBnd; HonRl; MrchBnd; NHS; NatlMeritCmnd; PepBnd; David Lipscomb College; Geology.

MOSS, William F; Albion HS; Albion, MI; 8/250 NHS; TchrAde; SpnCl; Ftbl; Tennis; Purdue Univ; Engineering.

MOSSER, Douglas; Usd 486 HS; Elwood, KS; 2/19 TrsSophCls; PresJrCls; Band; HonRl; RptrYrbk; AmLegAwd; Highland Jr; Engineering.

MOSSER, Mary L; Velva Public HS; Bergen, ND; 6/50 VPJrCls; Chrs; ChrhWkr; CncrtBnd; HonRl; MrchBnd; NHS; Yrbk; LetterChrldr; University; Interior Decorating.

MOSSETT, Amy J; Halliday Public HS; Halliday, ND; HonRl; SchPl; RptrYrbk; RptrSchPpr; SchPpr; PpCl; Chrldr; Univ Of N Dakota; Nursing.

MOSSYGE, James D; Leroy Ostrander HS; Leroy, MN; TrsFrshCls; SecJrCls; Aud/Vis; Band; Chr; Chrl; Chrs; ChrhWkr; HonRl; Mdrgl; SchPl; CaptBsbl; CaptFtbl; Trk; Jr College; Football.

MOST, Clark F; Bullock Creek HS; Midland, MI; 37/170 TrsFrshCls; TrsSophCls; HstSrCls; HonRl; StuCncl; Bsktbl; Trk; Delta Junior Clg; Pre Dental.

MOSTEIKA, Anita M; St Augustine HS; Chicago, IL; 2/85 Chrs; HonRl; NHS; RptrYrbk; RptrSchPpr; College; Professional.

MOSTER, Joyce A; Acad Of Immaculate Conception; Brookville, IN; Chr; HonRl; NHS; Orch; Quill&Scroll; SchMus; StuCncl; RptrYrbk; RptrSchPpr; 4-H; Bsbl; GAA; College; Education.

MOTEBERG, Ladawna A; Lake Of The Woods HS; Baudette, MN; Chrs; ChrhWkr; HonRl; LbryAde; SctActv; RptrSchPpr; SchPpr; LetterBsktbl; Trk; Trade School; Law Enforcement.

MOTHERSHEAD, Russ A; Kelly HS; Benton, MO; 33/54 Band; CncrtBnd; HonRl; MrchBnd; SctActv; TreasStuCncl; 4-H; PresFFA; PpCl; CaptBsktbl; College; Agriculture.

MOTIFF, Michelle M; Middleton HS; Pioneer Place, WI; ALAGirlsSt; Band; Chr; HonRl; MrchBnd; NatlMeritCmnd; PepBnd; SchMus; SpnCl; SciCl; U Of Wisconsin; Dietetics.

MOTIFF, Nancy A; West HS; Green Bay, WI; 20/390 ChrhWkr; DrlTm; HonRl; Yrbk; RptrSchPpr; FrCl; Chrldr; Univ Of Wisc; Business Adm.

MOTISI, Nancy B; Deforest HS; Deforest, WI; Band; HonRl; Mdrgl; PepBnd; SchPl; StuCncl; Yrbk; MthCl; SciCl; LetterSwmmng; Univ; Music Therapy.

MOTKOWICZ, Stephen F; Bishop Noll Institute HS; Hammond, IN; Band; CncrtBnd; HonRl; MrchBnd; PepBnd; College; Professional.

MOTLEY, Karen L; Williamsville HS; Sherman, IL; 1/60 TrsJrCls; Band; Chr; HonRl; NHS; SchPl; StuCncl; RptrYrbk; 4-H; 4-HAwd; University.

MOTOIKE, Patricia Y; Robert A Waller HS; Chicago, IL; 3/214 HonRl; NHS; OffAde; RptrYrbk; RptrSchPpr; KeyCl; PpCl; IMSpt; Clge; Chem Eng.

MOTT, Deann L; Southeast Polk HS; Runnells, IA; 1/240 ChrhWkr; HonRl; NHS; OffAde; StuCncl; RptrYrbk; SptEdYrbk; Bsktbl; LetterTennis; PPFtbl; College; Elementary Educ.

MOTT, Mary Jo E; Holland HS; Holland, MI; ChrhWkr; HonRl; TchrAde; Yrbk; GerCl; SciCl; Western Mich Univ; Special Ed.

MOTT, Steve M; Endora HS; Endora, KS; 4/56 Band; ChrhWkr; HonRl; MrchBnd; SchPl; YthFlsp; GerCl; LetterFtbl; LetterTrk; LetterWrstlng; U Of Ks; Mathematics.

MOTTE, Denise R; Port Huron Northern HS; Jeddo, MI; ChrhWkr; HonRl; College; Nursing.

MOTTET, Diane M; Oskaloosa Sr HS; Oskaloosa, IA; HonRl; NHS; PolWkr; StuCncl; RptrYrbk; SptEdYrbk; RptrSchPpr; SpnCl; SecPpCl; LetterSwmmng; LetterTrk; Chrldr; IMSpt; Univ Of Iowa; Dental Hygiene.

MOTTET, Mary A; Fairfield HS; Richland, IA; ChrhWkr; HonRl; NHS; FrCl; PpCl; College.

MOTTLEY, Carol; Darlington Hs; Darlington, WI; 1/122 TrsSrCls; AFS; ALAGirlsSt; Band; Chrs; HonRl; RptrYrbk; 4-H; Chrldr; 4-HAwd; Uw Platteville; Math Major.

MOTULSKY, Sue L; Danville HS; Danville, IL; 14/613 AFS; CmntyWkr; HonRl; HospAde; LbryAde; SctActv; TchrAde; Indiana Univ; Social Worker.

MOTYCKA, Elaine D; Lincoln Southeast HS; Lincoln, NE; Chr; ChrhWkr; CmntyWkr; HonRl; NHS; TchrAde; 4-H; PpCl; SciCl; College; Forestry.

MOUGHLER, Craig A; Hamilton HS; Waterloo, IN; 8/75 PresJrCls; ALBoysSt; Chr; HonRl; NHS; SchMus; SchPl; RptrSchPpr; Wrstlng; IMSpt; Purdue Univ; Eng.

MOUIS, Scott L; Aurora Central Catholic HS; Aurora, IL; 2/162 HonRl; StuCncl; StuGov; College.

MOULDEN, Jeffery T; Washburn Rural HS; Wakarusa, KS; VPFrshCls; Aud/Vis; Band; HonRl; PolWkr; FBLA; Bsbl; LetterBsktbl; LetterFtbl; Tennis; College; Banking.

MOULDS, Ladell K; Wapsie Valley HS; Fairbank, IA; 6/94 HonRl; SchPl; PpCl; Bsktbl; Trk; Iowa State Univ; Art Major.

MOULLIET, Michele A; Fenton HS; Fenton, MI; 45/307 Aud/Vis; HonRl; PresJA; NHS; TchrAde; PresFrCl; PPFtbl; JAAwd; Univ Of Michigan; Elementary Education.

MOULTON, Cindy; Ankeny HS; Ankeny, IA; Chrs; ChrhWkr; HonRl; JCC; LbryAde; OffAde; SchMus; 4-H; CchngActv; Ankeny Community Col; Speech Therapist.

MOULTON, Mark P; Aberdeen Central HS; Aberdeen, SD; ALBoysSt; HonRl; VPGerCl; College; Lawyer.

MOULTON, Nance; Fonda Community HS; Fonda, IA; PresFrshCls; Band; Chr; CncrtBnd; HonRl; NHS; SchPl; EdSchPpr; Univ; Music.

MOULTON, Sandra M; Sycamore HS; Genoa, IL; 3/220 Band; CncrtBnd; HonRl; MrchBnd; SchMus; YthFlsp; 4-H; SecSpnCl; PpCl; Bsbl; Swmmng; Tennis; GAA; College; Special Educ.

MOULTON, Teresa F; Franklin Center HS; Lee Center, IL; 1/32 SecJrCls; HonRl; NHS; SchMus; StuCncl; RptrYrbk; LetterTrk; GAA; IMSpt; 4-HAwd; College; Phy Ed.

MOULTON, Thomas A; Brimfield HS; Brimfield, IL; 1/54 Chrs; HonRl; PresNHS; Yrbk; EdSchPpr; Trk; Case Western Reserve Univ; Pre Med.

MOUNT, Rhonda M; St Elizabeth Academy; St Louis, MO; HonRl; LbryAde; SchMus; SchPl; TchrAde; Yrbk; PpCl;.

MOUNTFORD, Lois; Triplains HS; Winona, KS; CncrtBnd; HonRl; MrchBnd; SchPl; YthFlsp; EdYrBk; PpCl; Univ; Prof.

MOUNTIN, Lois A; Lincoln HS; Lake City, MN; 23/137 Band; Chr; ChrhWkr; CncrtBnd; HonRl; MrchBnd; NHS; PepBnd; Quill&Scroll; Winona State College; Special Education.

MOUNTS, Jeffrey W; St Louis University HS; St Louis, MO; CmntyWkr; PolWkr; StuCncl; StuGov;

RptrSchPpr; SptEdSchPpr; Bsbl; LetterFtbl; CchngActv; IMSpt; College; Special Ed.

MOURADIAN, Daniel S; Lyons Township HS; La Grange, IL; 365/1214 SchAde; Univ Of Illinois; Computer Science.

MOURNING, Gregory A; Papillion HS; Papillion, NE; NatlMeritCmnd; RptrSchPpr; SpnCl; IMSpt; Univ Of Neb; Mech Engineer.

MOUSEL, Mary J; Heelan HS; Sioux City, IA; 10/247 Chrs; HonRl; NHS; SchMus; SchPl; StuGov; PpCl; CchngActv; IMSpt; ChmbCommrsAwd; College; Vocation.

MOUSER, Kevin L; Franklin HS; Franklin, IL; TreasFFA; Lincoln Land Jr Clg; Farming.

MOUSER, Sheryl A; Woodland R Iv HS; Lutesville, MO; 9/79 Band; CncrtBnd; HonRl; MrchBnd; PepBnd; StuCncl; FHA; PpCl; Coll; Med.

MOUTRAY, Marilyn G; Southwest HS; St Louis, MO; Band; CncrtBnd; HonRl; MrchBnd; Orch; PepBnd; SchMus; TchrAde; William Wood Clge; Engl & Equestrian Study.

MOUW, Cindy; Maurice Orange City Comm HS; Orange City, IA; Band; Chr; Chrs; CncrtBnd; HonRl; MrchBnd; TchrAde; FTA; PpCl; Trk; Coll.

MOUW, Mary A; Sioux Center Comm HS; Sioux Center, IA; 3/80 SecTrsFrshCls; VPJrCls; NHS; NatlMeritCmnd; VPNatlThespSoc; SchPl; SecFFA; PresFHA; VPGAA; BttyCrckrAwd; Iowa State U; Pre Vet.

MOWAT, Suzanne R; Bellevue Comm HS; Bellevue, IA; Aud/Vis; SchMus; RptrYrbk; 4-H; LetterBsktbl; LetterTrk; CchngActv; GAA; AmLegAwd; 4-HAwd; College; Professional.

MOWATT, Frank S; Forest View HS; Mt Prospect, IL; 55/675 Band; ChrhWkr; CncrtBnd; HonRl; MrchBnd; NHS; PepBnd; TchrAde; FrCl; College; Vocation.

MOWCOMBER, Karen M; St Francis HS; Lombard, IL; 11/121 Chr; HonRl; NHS; SchMus; SchPl; StuGov; TchrAde; PpCl; LetterTennis; Chrldr; St Teresa Clge; Physical Therapy.

MOWERS, Linda; Mc Pherson County HS; Tryon, NE; 4/12 TrsSophCls; TrsJrCls; ALAGirlsSt; Chrs; HonRl; JA; SchPl; 4-H; PpCl; College; Teacing Economics And Business.

MOWERY, John W; Dongola HS; Dongola, IL; Band; Chrs; ChrhWkr; HonRl; MrchBnd; 4-H; FFA; SciCl; Murray St Univ; Professional.

MOWERY, Judith; Porta Hs; Petersburg, IL; Chrs; ChrhWkr; HonRl; NHS; NatlMeritCmnd; SchMus; 4-H; GAA; BttyCrckrAwd; College Quincy;music.

MOWERY, Kevin M; Southwest HS; St Louis, MO; 1/600 ChrhWkr; HonRl; SchPpr; LetterBsbl; IMSpt; JETSAwd; College; Engineering.

MOWERY, Penny S; Hillsdale HS; Hillsdale, MI; SecSophCls; Chr; HonRl; SchPl; StuCncl; Teen; RptrSchPpr; SptEdSchPpr; PpCl; Chrldr; University; Professional.

MOWRIS, Kathryn E; George S Parker HS; Janesville, WI; 6/387 PresFrshCls; TrsSophCls; HonRl; NHS; StuCncl; Bsktbl; DanFAwd; EldAwd; University; Civil Engineering.

MOWRY, Bonnie K; Mcpherson County HS; Scottsbluff, NE; Chrs; ChrhWkr; HonRl; SchPl; YthFlsp; SptEdYrbk; 4-H; Trk; Chrldr; PresAwd; College; Teacher Major Math Minor Phy Ed.

MOWRY, Kristy J; Akron Fairgrove HS; Fairgrove, MI; 7/80 Band; ChrhWkr; CmntyWkr; HonRl; NHS; PepBnd; StuGov; TchrAde; GAA; IMSpt; John Wesley Clg; Special Education.

MOWRY, Stanley A; Morton HS; Pekin, IL; 66/292 HonRl; SciCl; CaptBsbl; IMSpt; College; Mathematics.

MOWRY, Todd I; St Joe Ogden HS; St Joseph, IL; 20/104 Band; ChrhWkr; NatlThespSoc; SchPl; SctActv; SptEdSchPpr; SpnCl; PpCl; LetterFtbl; LetterWrstlng; Univ Of Il;.

MOX, Scott W; Glenbrook South HS; Glenview, IL; 9/589 NHS; NatlMeritCmnd; StuCncl; StuGov; TreasKeyCl; SciCl; Glf; Univ Of Illinois; Medicine.

MOY, Cynthia L; Stoughton Sr HS; Stoughton, WI; 20/200 HonRl; 4-H; FTA; Madison Area Tech College; Court Reporter.

MOY, Edmund C; Waukesha North HS; Waukesha, WI; Yrbk; SchPpr; KeyCl; MthCl; Tennis; Univ Wi Madison; Pre Medicine.

MOY, Freeman W; Lane Tech HS; Chicago, IL; 74/1213 JrNHS; NHS; SchAde; StuCncl; StuGov; SchPpr; College; Computer Design.

MOY, Peter; Osborn HS; Detroit, MI; .

MOY, Theresa M; Proviso East HS; Maywood, IL; HonRl; LbryAde; NHS; Univ Of Illinois; Engineering.

MOY, Wanda D; Lindblom Tech; Chicago, IL; 13/650 HonRl; OffAde; SchAde; TchrAde; Yrbk; SchPpr; GerCl; MthCl; GAA; JETSAwd; Il Inst Of Tech; Accountant.

MOY, Wendy; Grosse Pointe North HS; Grosse Point Woods, MI; HonRl; LitMag; LbryAde; SchPl; StuGov; YthFlsp; RptrSchPpr; Mich St U; Social Work.

MOYER, Glenda K; Coleman HS; Coleman, MI; 11/84 Band; CncrtBnd; HonRl; MrchBnd; NHS; PepBnd; SchPl; RptrSchPpr; 4-H; 4-HAwd; Mi St U; Vet.

MOYER, Jeffrey; Golden City HS; Golden City, MO; 3/20 ChrhWkr; CncrtBnd; HonRl; MrchBnd; StuCncl; YthFlsp; EdSchPpr; FSA; Bsktbl; Trk; Southwest Mo State Univ; Professional.

MOYER, Kim A; John Marshall HS; Indianapolis, IN; StuCncl; Chrldr; Univ.

MOYER, Lorie F; Galena HS; Galena, IL; 7/104 AFS; Band; ChrhWkr; CncrtBnd; HospAde; MrchBnd; NatlMeritCmnd; Orch; PepBnd; SchMus; TchrAde; RptrYrbk; College; Medical Technology.

MOYER, Paul K; Alvarado HS; Alvarado, MN; 1/23 Band; Chr; ChrhWkr; HonRl; NatlMeritCmnd; SchPl; TreasStuCncl; Yrbk; Bsktbl; AmLegAwd; Bethel College.

MOYER, Peggy F; Clearwater R 1 HS; Piedmont, MO; 3/98 Band; ChrhWkr; HonRl; JrNHS; MrchBnd; NHS; StuCncl; FHA; SpnCl; PpCl; Southeast Missouri State Univ; Social Work.

MOYER, Sam; Wood River Rural HS; Wood River, NE; TrsFrshCls; VPSrCls; HonRl; NHS; FFA; FrCl; Bsktbl; Ftbl; Tennis; IMSpt; Univ Of Ne; Law.

MOYERS, Mary A; Notre Dame HS; Burlington, IA; 12/75 HonRl; LbryAde; Yrbk; SchPpr; IMSpt; U Of Ia; Computer Programmer.

MOYERS, Randal E; Hays HS; Hays, KS; ChrhWkr; CmntyWkr; HonRl; Orch; YthFlsp; LetterTennis; IMSpt; College; Vet.

MOYLE, Laura M; Nerinx Hall HS; Webster Groves, MO; Chr; Chrs; ChrhWkr; CmntyWkr; HonRl; OffAde; SchAde; SchMus; SchPl; SctActv; College; Photographer.

MOYLE, Sue A; Calumet HS; Calumet, MI; Chrl; CncrtBnd; HonRl; MrchBnd; NHS; SchMus; Yrbk; PpCl; IMSpt; 4-HAwd; Michigan State Univ; Animal Technology.

MOYNIHAN, James; La Salle HS; Fairfax, IA; PresSrCls; VPSrCls; CtyCnl; JA; NHS; NatlSciFnd; NatlThespSoc; PolWkr; StuCncl; StuGov; Air Force.

MOZINGO, Vengi V; North Decatur HS; Greensburg, IN; 13/104 VPSophCls; Band; CncrtBnd; DrlTm; DrmMjrt; HonRl; MrchBnd; NHS; PepBnd; RptrSchPpr; Iupui Univ; Medical Technologist.

MRACHEK, Patricia A; Winona HS; Winona, MN; Chr; ChrhWkr; NHS; PolWkr; SchMus; StuCncl; SptEdYrbk; FrCl; Swmmng; CaptChrldr; Clge; Science Or Social Related.

MRAZEK, Stephen J; Alleman HS; Rock Island, IL; ChrhWkr; HonRl; NHS; NatlMeritCmnd; SchMus; SctActv; FrCl; Univ Of Ill; Civil Engineering.

MRKVA, Kip J; Dearborn HS; Dearborn, MI; Band; CncrtBnd; HonRl; MrchBnd; Orch; PepBnd; SchMus; Glf; LetterTennis; IMSpt; Michigan State Univ; Veterinarian.

MRKVICKA, Ramona L; Loup City HS; Ashton, NE; 9/63 Chr; Chrs; HonRl; LbryAde; NHS; TchrAde; RptrYrbk; PpCl; Bsbl; Kearney State College; Elementary Teacher.

MRKVICKA, Steven R; Glenbard West HS; Glen Ellyn, IL; 55/522 ChrhWkr; HonRl; MthCl; College; Professional.

MRNAK, Gay A; Stevens HS; Rapid City, SD; 84/413 Band; ChrhWkr; CmntyWkr; CncrtBnd; HonRl; MrchBnd; Orch; PepBnd; StuGov; TchrAde; Univ Of Ut; Pro Dancer.

MROCH, Debbie S; Sparta Sen HS; Sparta, WI; HonRl; OffAde; TchrAde; Trade School; Professional.

MROCZEK, David J; North Huron HS; Kinde, MI; 11/43 NHS; StuCncl; FFA; CaptTrk; Msu.

MROCZKA, Katherine; Lumen Christi HS; Jackson, MI; 3/223 HonRl; NatlMeritCmnd; SchMus; SchPl; RptrYrbk; RptrSchPpr; NCTE; Univ Of Michigan; Technical Theatre.

MROCZKIEWICZ, Carol R; North Liberty HS; North Liberty, IN; SecSrCls; HonRl; NHS; Yrbk; 4-H; PresSpnCl; 4-HAwd; CitAwd; In Univ South Bend; Special Ed.

MROCZKOWSKI, Daniel J; Highland HS; Highland, IN; 20/573 Band; CncrtBnd; MrchBnd; PepBnd; TchrAde; PresKeyCl; CaptFtbl; LetterTrk; CitAwd; Purdue Univ; Pharmacy.

MROCZKOWSKI, Paul J; Rosary HS; St Louis, MO; 11/460 Aud/Vis; HonRl; NHS; Univ Of Mo St Louis; Science.

MROCZKOWSKI, Susan; St Marys Acad; West Allis, WI; 5/156 Aud/Vis; Chrs; HonRl; NHS; Orch; SchMus; StuCncl; SpnCl; BauchLmbAwd; U Of Wis Milw; Chem.

MROGENSKI, John M; Benton Consolidated HS; Benton, IL; VPChrs; HonRl; Mdrgl; NHS; NatlThespSoc; SchMus; SchPl; StuCncl; VPKeyCl; Ftbl;.

MROZ, John M; Rochester Adams HS; Rochester, MI; NHS; Ftbl; Az St Univ; Cpa.

MROZEK, David D; Cathedral HS; Waite Park, MN; 21/175 VPFrshCls; TrsJrCls; HonRl; JCC; NatlCathMusEdAsoc; NHS; NatlSciFnd; StuGov; FBLA; LetterWrstlng; Vo Tech Sch; Draftsman.

MROZEK, Lawrence J; Divine Child HS; Dearborn Hts, MI; PresJrCls; Chrl; NHS; NatlThespSoc; SchMus; SchPl; StuCncl; FrCl; Michigan St Univ; Veterinarian.

MROZEK, Leslie A; Sault Area HS; Sault Ste Marie, MI; Band; Chr; CncrtBnd; HonRl; MrchBnd; PepBnd; Tennis; Trk; GAA; IMSpt; Coll; Air Force.

MROZEK, Therese A; Lourdes HS; Chicago, IL; PresSrCls; Band; HonRl; NHS; PresStuCncl; PresStuGov; FSA; FrCl; Bsbl; Univ Of Chicago; Law.

MROZINSKI, Geri L; Ss Peter & Paul HS; Freeland, MI; Chrs; DrlTm; HonRl; NHS; SchMus; RptrYrbk; SecPpCl; Bsbl; LetterBsktbl; LetterChrldr; College; Professional.

MRUGALA, Christine; St Joseph HS; Chicago, IL; 9/121 Chr; HonRl; LbryAde; SchMus; SchPl; 4-H; FHA; SpnCl; Bsktbl; IMSpt; College; Professional.

MRUZEK, Michael T; Monroe Catholic Central HS; Monroe, MI; 6/106 HonRl; NHS; NatlMeritSF; SchMus; SchPl; U Of Mi; Astronomy.

MRZLACK, Robert B; Twin Lakes HS; Monticello, IN; 17/206 ChrhWkr; HonRl; JrNHS; StuCncl; StuGov; YthFlsp; LetterBsbl; LetterSwmmng; Trk; Indiana Univ; Medicine.

MRZLAK, Elaine; Irving Crown HS; Carpentersville, IL; ChrhWkr; HonRl; SctActv; TchrAde; SciCl; College; Nutritional Studies.

MUCCI, Michael L; North Greene HS; White Hall, IL; 12/104 ALBoysSt; Band; CncrtBnd; MrchBnd; OffAde; PepBnd; TchrAde; YthFlsp; Trk; MasAwd; Univ; Pro.

MUCH, Sandra L; Sparta Sr HS; Sparta, WI; 18/203 Chrs; HonRl; Mdrgl; NHS; SchMus; Sec4-H; LetterTrk; CaptIMSpt; 4-HAwd; Palmer College; Chiropractor.

MUCHA, Richard J; Benet Academy; Westchester, IL; Band; CncrtBnd; HonRl; MrchBnd; SctActv; Illinois Benedictine College; Business Mgmt.

MUCK, Kaye M; Bonduel Comm HS; Cecil, WI; ChrhWkr; CmntyWkr; CncrtBnd; JA; Yrbk; Pres4-H; FBLA; FHA; GAA; DanFAwd; 4-HAwd; JAAwd; Technical School; Secretary.

MUCKENHIRN, James; Larimore HS; Larimore, ND; HonRl; SchPl; Ftbl; Wrstlng; AmLegAwd; College; Professional.

MUCKERHEIDE, Karen; Notre Dame HS; Milwaukee, WI; 2/117 DrmBgl; HonRl; PpCl; SciCl; Marquette Univ; Law.

MUCKLOW, Valerie; Superior HS; Superior, NE; Band; ChrhWkr; CmntyWkr; CncrtBnd; MrchBnd; PepBnd; FHA; PpCl; Trade Or Bus Sch; Secretary.

MUDD, Brenda S; Mexico HS; Mexico, MO; CncrtBnd; JrNHS; VPNatlFornLg; VPNHS; SchPl; StuCncl; VP4-H; VPLatCl; PpCl; 4-HAwd; College; Speech.

MUDD, Kathleen M; Grand Blanc HS; Flint, MI; 22/635 HonRl; NHS; NatlMeritCmnd; TchrAde; PpCl; Michigan St Univ; Medical Tech.

MUDD, Linda; Lincoln County R Ii Hs; Elsberry, MO; 5/60 HonRl; HospAde; NHS; OffAde; TchrAde; FBLA; FHA; PpCl; Trk; GAA;.

MUDD, Patrick H; Dupo Comm HS; Dupo, IL; 1/121 HonRl; ModUN; NHS; SctActv; TchrAde; MthCl; LetterFtbl; CaptTrk; Univ Of Missouri; Engineering. .

MUDD, Steven W; Lincoln Co HS; Silex, MO; VPSophCls; PresSrCls; HonRl; JrNHS; NHS; StuCncl; FFA; Bsbl; Bsktbl; Trk; Univ Of Mo; Agriculture.

MUDDER, Christie; Hastings HS; Hastings, NE; Chr; HonRl; IntrClCncl; NatlFornLg; NatlMeritSF; Orch; SchPl; StuCncl; 4-H; PpCl; AmLegAwd; DARAwd; OptClAwd; Hastings College.

MUDGETT, Kent J; Moorhead Sr HS; Moorhead, MN; HonRl; StuGov; KeyCl; Tennis; College; Medical Technician.

MUDRA, Alfred A; Lyle Public HS; Glenville, MN; ALBoysSt; Band; HonRl; MrchBnd; StuCncl; Pres4-H; SecFFA; LetterFtbl; IMSpt; Junior College; Agriculture.

MUEHE, Tim C; Langdon HS; Langdon, ND; 9/135 HonRl; NHS; NatlMeritCmnd; SciCl; CaptBsktbl; CaptGlf; CaptTrk; Univ Of Nd; Computer Programmer.

MUEHLBAUER, Judy A; Prairie Du Chien Sr HS; Prairie Du Chien, WI; 55/140 ChrhWkr; HonRl; VPLbryAde; NatlFornLg; OffAde; TreasFHA; SpnCl; GAA; Univ Of Wisconsin; Food Service.

MUEHLBAUER, Kurt T; Glenbrook South HS; Glenview, IL; 65/600 CncrtBnd; HonRl; MrchBnd; NHS; PepBnd; SctActv; RptrYrbk; Yrbk; Univ Of Ill; Engineering.

MUEHLBERG, Craig D; Mound Westonka HS; Spring Park, MN; HonRl; NHS; LetterFtbl; Coll; Lawyer.

MUEHLEISEN, Mary B; Bradley HS; Bradley, SD; Chrs; HonRl; RptrYrbk; Yrbk; College; Special Ed Teacher.

MUEHLEMAN, Julianne M; Alton Senior HS; Godfrey, IL; Band; HonRl; VPJA; NHS; OffAde; Orch; PepBnd; TchrAde; LatCl; SciCl; Southern Ill Univ; Wildlife Conservation.

MUEHLENKAMP, Jayne E; Sparta Senior HS; Norwalk, WI; 28/192 Band; HonRl; LbryAde; NHS; OffAde; Orch; PepBnd; SchMus; Technical School; Medical Lab Tech.

MUEHLER, Melody L; Underwood Public HS; Dalton, MN; 6/47 ChrhWkr; CmntyWkr; HonRl; LbryAde; SchAde; StuCncl; Twrl; YthFlsp; FFA; FHA; Fergus Falls Jr Clg; Probation Officer.

MUEHLFELT, Jean C; Palatine HS; Palatine, IL; 15/455 Band; CncrtBnd; HonRl; MrchBnd; NHS; PepBnd; SchMus; StuCncl; YthFlsp; Southern Illinois Univ; Wildlife Mgmt.

MUEHLING, Brian K; Ofallon Township HS; Ofallon, IL; 7/294 HonRl; SecNatlFornLg; VPNHS; PolWkr; FrCl; SciCl; LetterBsktbl; Univ Of Wisc; Environmental Sciences.

MUEKLHAUSER, Ryan J; Sandstone HS; Sandstone, MN; 1/43 PresJrCls; Chrs; ChrhWkr; HonRl; NHS; SchPl; SctActv; StuGov; YthFlsp; 4-HAwd; Univ;.

MUELL, Jean M; Logan Magnolia Comm HS; Missouri Valley, IA; 1/54 VPSophCls; VPChrs; HonRl; VPNHS; Yrbk; FHA; VPSciCl; Iowa Western Comm College; Child Care.

MUELLER, Anthony M; Milbank HS; Big Stone City, SD; ALBoysSt; Band; HonRl; NHS; StuCncl; College; Engineering.

MUELLER, Barbara M; Ada HS; Ada, MN; Band; CncrtBnd; MrchBnd; NatlThespSoc; PepBnd; SchMus; RptrYrbk; FHA; PpCl; Chrldr; College.

MUELLER, Brad R; Rockridge HS; Taylor Ridge, IL; 2/145 HonRl; NHS; YthFlsp; EdYrBk; 4-H; SpnCl; Trk; Univ Of Ill; Engineering.

MUELLER, Carl W; Marquette HS; West Point, IA; Aud/Vis; Band; CtyCnl; CmntyWkr; CncrtBnd; DrlTm; RedCrAde; SchPl; StuCncl; StuGov; College; Vocational.

MUELLER, Daniel R; Central Community HS; Donnellson, IA; PresFrshCls; PresJrCls; HonRl; LbryAde; NHS; SchMus; SchPl; SctActv; LetterGlf; College.

MUELLER, Daniel R; H L Richards HS; Oak Lawn, IL; 58/1035 ChrhWkr; HonRl; NatlFornLg; SchPl; YthFlsp; FrCl; Univ Of Illinois; Engineering.

MUELLER, Dave L; Morton HS; Morton, IL; HonRl; StuCncl; SpnCl; LetterBsbl; Ftbl; LetterWrstlng; Univ Of Illinois; Architecture.

MUELLER, David J; Chippewa Falls Sr HS; Chippewa Falls, WI; 49/359 Chrs; Mdrgl; NatlFornLg; NHS; NatlThespSoc; SchMus; SchPl; Tennis; Trk; Univ Of Wisconsin; Transportation.

MUELLER, Doug J; Sevastopol HS; Sturgeon Bay, WI; 10/99 PresSrCls; Chrs; HonRl; NHS; 4-H; LetterFtbl; LetterTrk; LetterWrstlng; JCAwd;.

MUELLER, Gary R; Norway Vulcan HS; Norway, MI; TrsJrCls; ChrhWkr; CmntyWkr; HonRl; StuCncl; StuGov; 4-H; Bsktbl; Trk; 4-HAwd; Clge; Biological Sci.

MUELLER, Gary R; Warren County R Iii HS; Warrenton, MO; 4/99 VPJrCls; ALBoysSt; HonRl; VPNHS; VPYthFlsp; VP4-H; LetterBsktbl; LetterFtbl; Univ Mo; Eng.

MUELLER, George C; Brookfield East HS; Brookfield, WI; 13/523 ChrhWkr; HonRl; NHS; NatlMeritSF; PolWkr; Sacrstn; MthCl; IMSpt; U Of Wi; Pharmacist.

MUELLER, Glenn A; Maine West HS; Des Plaines, IL; HonRl; NHS; Bsktbl; Inst Of Tech; Electronics.

MUELLER, Gregory A; Sidney HS; Sidney, NE; Band; Chr; Chrs; ChrhWkr; CncrtBnd; Mdrgl; MrchBnd; PepBnd; SchMus; SciCl; Ricks College; Science.

MUELLER, Gregory G; Rockridge HS; Taylor Ridge, IL; 30/145 Band; ChrhWkr; CncrtBnd; HonRl; NatlThespSoc; StuCncl; SptEdYrbk; FTA; CaptFtbl; DanFAwd; Univ Of Illinois; Recreation Mgmt.

MUELLER, Heidi J; Greendale HS; Greendale, WI; AFS; Chr; CmntyWkr; CncrtBnd; HospAde; MrchBnd; PepBnd; SctActv; GerCl; College; Lawyer.

MUELLER, James A; Clarion Community HS; Clarion, IA; 12/92 ChrhWkr; HonRl; ROTC; StuCncl; TchrAde; RptrSchPpr; SciCl; Bsktbl; Ftbl; Trk; IMSpt; Florida Institute Of Tech; Marine Biology.

MUELLER, Jeffery S; South HS; Shebygan, WI; CmntyWkr; HonRl; NHS; SctActv; TchrAde; Yrbk; SchPpr; GerCl; IMSpt; U Of Wi Madison; Pharmacist.

MUELLER, Jeff P; Marquette HS; Bellevve, IA; 11/70 Chrs; PpCl; LetterBsbl; LetterBsktbl; LetterGlf; College; Business Electronics.

MUELLER, Jeffrey L; Chisago Lakes HS; Lindstrom, MN; 19/137 Chr; Chrs; ChrhWkr; HonRl; SchMus; FrCl; Glf; IMSpt; College; Engineering.

MUELLER, Judith L; Chisago Lakes Sr HS; Lindstrom, MN; Chr; Chrs; HonRl; SchMus; TchrAde; College; Home Economist.

MUELLER, Julie E; United Township HS; East Moline, IL; 140/638 HonRl; RedCrAde; SctActv; 4-H; LatCl; Black Hawk Jr College; Secretary.

MUELLER, Karen K; Milwaukee Lutheran HS; Brookfield, WI; 27/229 AFS; Chr; ChrhWkr; HonRl; NatlThespSoc; RedCrAde; Pres4-H; Swmmng; LetterTennis; IMSpt; Stevens Point Univ; Medicine.

MUELLER, Karen K; Sully Buttes HS; Onida, SD; Chr; Chrs; HonRl; SpnCl; Trk; Trade Sch.

MUELLER, Karl F; Roncalli HS; Indianapolis, IN; .

MUELLER, Kim; Grinnell Comm HS; Grinnell, IA; 1/180 Chr; CmntyWkr; ModUN; PolWkr; UNYO; SchPpr; College; Professional.

MUELLER, Laurie; Southwest HS; Green Bay, WI; 18 SctActv; GerCl; LatCl; Univ Of Wi River Falls; Veterinary Medicine.

MUELLER, Linda S; Lasalle Peru Township HS; Peru, IL; SecJrCls; SecSrCls; HonRl; NHS; PpCl; Illinois Valley Comm College; Pre Medicine.

MUELLER, Lyle K; Arapahoe HS; Arapahoe, NE; Band; Chrs; ChrhWkr; CncrtBnd; HonRl; MrchBnd; PepBnd; LetterFtbl; LetterGlf; LetterWrstlng; U S Naval Academy; Navy.

MUELLER, Mark A; Steeleville HS; Steeleville, IL; 4/55 TrsSrCls; Band; ChrhWkr; CmntyWkr; HonRl; NHS; NatlMeritCmnd; SchPl; FBLA; Univ Of Ill; Electrical Engineer.

MUELLER, Mark M; West HS; Minneapolis, MN; Band; Chrs; CncrtBnd; HonRl; MrchBnd; PepBnd; SchMus; SchPl; StuCncl; StuGov; Bsktbl; Ftbl; Gustavus Adolphus College; Medicine.

MUELLER, Mary A; Carmel HS; Hawthrn Wds, IL; 6/174 HonRl; NHS; StuCncl; PpCl; Chrldr; GAA; St Marys Coll; Biology.

MUELLER, Mary H; Jackson HS; Jackson, MO; Band; Chr; ChrhWkr; CncrtBnd; HonRl; SctActv; StuCncl; RptrSchPpr; LetterTrk; Chrldr; Coll; Media.

MUELLER, Mary K; Madison Sr HS; E St Louis, IL; 1/117 PresNHS; StuCncl; Yrbk; 4-H; VPLatCl; SciCl; BauchLmbAwd; Univ Of Il; Chemical Engineering.

MUELLER, Mary T; Kiel HS; Newton, WI; AFS; HonRl; SchMus; SchPl; SpnCl; PpCl; GAA; IMSpt; Lakeshore Technical; Dental Assistant.

MUELLER, Michelle; Crofton HS; Crofton, NE; 5/63 SecJrCls; PresSrCls; HonRl; Univ Of Nebraska; Registered Nurse.

MUELLER, Nancy L; Parkway Central Sr HS; Chesterfield, MO; NatlMeritSF; Univ Of Missouri; Accounting.

MUELLER, Nathan S; Milbank HS; Big Stone City, SD; ALBoysSt; ChrhWkr; HonRl; NatlSciFnd; NHS; 4-H; KeyCl; LetterFtbl; IMSpt; Rapid City School Of Mining; Engr.

MUELLER, Paula A; Sherwood HS; Creighton, MO; 12/65 ChrhWkr; HonRl; NHS; TchrAde; Yrbk; FHA; PpCl; Bsbl; LetterBsktbl; GAA; PPFtbl; College; Vocation.

MUELLER, Paul M; Michigan Lutheran Seminary; Owosso, MI; PresJrCls; Chrs; HonRl; NHS; SchAde; StuCncl; StuGov; LatCl; LetterTrk; IMSpt; Northwestern Coll;.

MUELLER, Rita L; Rockridge HS; Reynolds, IL; 8/140 HonRl; HospAde; LbryAde; NHS; StuCncl; EdYrBk; FTA; LatCl; Chrldr; College.

MUELLER, Sheryl L; Edgar HS; Edgar, WI; 1/84 PresSrCls; HonRl; FHA; Trk; DARAwd; Univ Of Wis Stevens Point; Science.

MUELLER, Stephen P; St Edward HS; Elgin, IL; 17/130 PresJrCls; HonRl; NHS; StuCncl; StuGov; LatCl; MthCl; LetterBsktbl; LetterFtbl; Air Force Academy; Pilot.

MUELLER, Steven J; Harlan Community HS; Harlan, IA; 1/250 ALBoysSt; ChrhWkr; HonRl; NHS; NatlThespSoc; SchPl; AmLegAwd; Military Acad; Engineering.

MUELLER, Susan; Lewiston HS; Utica, MN; 3/87 Band; CncrtBnd; HonRl; MrchBnd; NHS; PepBnd; SchPl; 4-H; FTA; 4-HAwd; Rochester Community Col; Registered Nurse.

MUELLER, Susan E; Valmeyer HS; Valmeyer, IL; 2/40 PresFrshCls; PresSrCls; HonRl; NHS; SchPl; StuCncl; TchrAde; RptrSchPpr; FHA; MthCl; College; Special Education.

MUELLER, Susan M; Kiel HS; Kiel, WI; Band; CncrtBnd; HonRl; NHS; PepBnd; YthFlsp; PpCl; Trade Schl; Rn.

MUELLER, Suzanne M; Downers Grove North HS; Downers Grove, IL; 18/537 SecFrshCls; PresSophCls; PresJrCls; PresSrCls; HonRl; JrNHS; NHS; NatlMeritCmnd; SctActv; SecFNA; Northern Il U; B S Nursing.

MUELLER, Teresa C; Maria HS; Burbank, IL; 4/335 Chrs; HonRl; JrNHS; LitMag; NHS; RptrYrbk; Yrbk; LatCl; Beloit College; Anthropology.

MUELLER, Thomas E; Fenton HS; Bensenville, IL; Band; CncrtBnd; PresNatlThespSoc; PepBnd; PolWkr; SchPl; Bsktbl; VoiceDemAwd; College; Politics.

MUELLER, Wesley J; Abbotsford HS; Abbotsford, WI; AFS; HonRl; NHS; MthCl; Bsktbl; Air Force; Electrician.

MUENCH, Mark R; Loyola Academy; Chicago, IL; 95/442 HonRl; RptrYrbk; GerCl; LetterSwmmng; IMSpt; University Of Notre Dame; Biology.

MUENKS, Frances; Fatima HS; Bonnots Mill, MO; ChrhWkr; HonRl; LbryAde; ModUN; SchPl; FBLA; FHA; SpnCl; PpCl; BttyCrckrAwd; Lincoln Univ; Elementary Education.

MUENKS, Frances A; Fatima HS; Bonnots Mill, MO; 23/126 Band; ChrhWkr; CmntyWkr; HonRl; MrchBnd; FBLA; FHA; SpnCl; PpCl; BttyCrckrAwd; Lincoln Univ; Elem Ed.

MUENZENBERGER, Randy M; Cashton HS; Coon Valley, WI; HonRl; FFA; CaptBsbl;.

MUESKE, Penny J; Marion HS; Big Falls, WI; Band; Chrs; ChrhWkr; HonRl; Mdrgl; NHS; StuCncl; 4-H; FHA; GAA; Military.

MUETH, Debbie A; Bishop Dubourg HS; St Louis, MO; Band; CncrtBnd; HonRl; JA; JrNHS; NHS; 4-H; IMSpt; St Louis Univ.

MUETH, Roberta A; Mascoutah HS; Mascoutah, IL; 8/251 DrlTm; HonRl; JA; ModUN; NHS; OffAde; Quill&Scroll; TchrAde; EdYrBk; LetterTennis; William Woods College; Law.

MUETING, Timothy R; Norfolk Catholic HS; Norfolk, NE; 5/50 HonRl; NHS; NatlThespSoc; SchMus; SchPl; EdYrBk; LetterBsktbl; Ftbl; GodCntryAwd; CitAwd; College; Arts.

MUETZEL, Denise; Belview HS; Belview, MN; 10/21 SecFrshCls; SecSophCls; SecJrCls; Chr; HonRl; LbryAde; SchPl; StuCncl; StuGov; YthFlsp;.

MUETZEL, Douglas W; Ogeman Heights HS; West Branch, MI; CncrtBnd; HonRl; PresNHS; LetterBsbl; CaptFtbl; LetterWrstlng; College.

MUETZEL, Katherine I; Springfield Catholic HS; Springfield, MO; 10/63 HonRl; CaptBsbl; LetterBsktbl; Tennis; Trk; GAA; IMSpt; 4-HAwd; OptClAwd; CitAwd; Drury Coll; English.

MUEVHOFF, Steven F; Aguinas HS; Ft Madison, IA; 7/48 Band; CncrtBnd; MrchBnd; PepBnd; SchPl; IMSpt; Devry Inst Tech; Electronics.

MUFF, Debora J; Ventura Comm HS; Ventura, IA; Band; Chrs; CmntyWkr; CncrtBnd; HonRl; MrchBnd; NHS; Twrl; LetterTrk; LetterChrldr; Ellsworth College; Social Work.

MUFFLER, Eileen M; Larkin HS; Elgin, IL; HonRl; NatlMeritSF; NatlThespSoc; PepBnd; FrCl; College; Journalism.

MUFFOLETTO, Anthony V; Andrean HS; Merrillville, IN; 47/250 HonRl; NHS; PresStuCncl; MthCl; Bsktbl; LetterTennis; IMSpt; Institution; Business.

MUGERDITCHIAN, Mark; Waukegan HS; Waukegan, IL; HonRl; NHS; SchMus; GerCl; Univ Of Ill; Dentistry.

MUGOODWIN, William D; Westside Senior HS; Gary, IN; HonRl; NatlMeritCmnd; SciCl; College; Chemical Engineer.

MUHA, Mark R; Bishop Noll HS; St John, IN; Socr; LetterWrstlng; Ball State U; Dentistry.

MUHLBAUER, Dale J; Manning Comm HS; Manning, IA; ChrhWkr; HonRl; Sacrstn; TchrAde; YthFlsp; CaptFtbl; CchngActv; IMSpt;.

MUHLENBRUCK, Cynthia S; Greene Community HS; Greene, IA; 1/72 Band; ChrhWkr; HonRl; LbryAde; NHS; NatlMeritFnl; SctActv; Yrbk; LetterBsktbl; LetterTrk; EldAwd; Univ; Bus Educ.

MUHLIG, Nancy L; Joliet West HS; Joliet, IL; 17/547 TrsSrCls; Chr; HonRl; Mdrgl; NHS; SchMus; StuCncl; FrCl; Illinois Wesleyan Univ; Veterinarian.

MUHM, Michael T; Ballard HS; Muxley, IA; HonRl; LetterFtbl; Trk; IMSpt; Ia State Univ.

MUHR, Timothy D; Bayard HS; Bayard, NE; PresJrCls; Band; PepBnd; SchPpr; Ftbl; Trk; Univ Of Nebraska; Medicine.

MUHS, Vicky K; Calamus Community HS; Ccalamus, IA; ChrhWkr; SchAde; SchPl; GerCl; Iowa State Univ; Elementary Teacher.

MUIR, Dana M; Brown City HS; Brown City, MI; SecFrshCls; HonRl; NHS; TchrAde; 4-H; Univ Of Chicago; Science Major.

MUIR, Jim E; Midway HS; Inkster, ND; TrsSophCls; VPJrCls; PresSrCls; Chrs; NatlMeritSchl; SchMus; SchPl; StuCncl; TchrAde; LetterBsbl; Bsktbl; CaptFtbl; College; Coaching.

MUIR, Rick B; West Bloomfield HS; W Bloomfield, MI; Chr; HonRl; Bsktbl; LetterFtbl; CchngActv; IMSpt; University; Dentistry.

MUKAI, William T; Maine Township HS; Des Plaines, IL; CmntyWkr; HonRl; NHS; RptrSchPpr; LetterBsktbl; University Of Southern Calif; Chem Engineer.

MUKAND, John; Lafayette HS; Red Lake Falls, MN; 1/80 HonRl; LitMag; SchPpr; SpnCl; CitAwd; College; Science.

MULCAHEY, Theresa A; Abl HS; Allerton, IL; TrsSophCls; VPJrCls; Band; ChrhWkr; CncrtBnd; RptrYrbk; FFA; FHA; SciCl; CaptChrldr; Southern Il U; Law Research.

MULCAHY, Gail A; Sacred Heart Of Mary HS; Mt Prospect, IL; ChrhWkr; HonRl; NHS; Yrbk; Bsktbl; IMSpt; Univ Of Ia; Physical Therapist.

MULCAHY, Linda M; Audubon Public HS; Audubon, MN; 3/34 Band; Chr; Chrs; DrmMjrt; HonRl; MrchBnd; NHS; OffAde; PepBnd; SchPl;.

MULDER, Cheryl A; Zeeland HS; Zeeland, MI; 17/180 HonRl; YthFlsp;.

MULDER, Craig; Lowell HS; Ada, MI; 10/197 ALBoysSt; ChrhWkr; HonRl; NHS; NatlMeritSchl; SctActv; YthFlsp; SptEdSchPpr; FrCl; Central Michigan Univ; History.

MULDER, Donn M; Maurice Orange City Comm HS; Maurice, IA; 1/76 Band; CncrtBnd; HonRl; MrchBnd; NHS; LetterBsktbl; LetterFtbl; GovHonPrgAwd; College; Electrical Engineering.

MULDER, Eldon P; Sioux Center Community HS; Sioux Center, IA; PresFrshCls; Chrs; HonRl; NHS; NatlThespSoc; StuCncl; 4-H; Bsbl; Bsktbl; Ftbl; Nw Mo St U; Radio & Tv Announcer.

MULDER, Vicki K; Norris Dist 160 HS; Adams, NE; SchPl; SctActv; TchrAde; 4-H; 4-HAwd; Trade School; Assist Vet.

MULDOON, Gary J; Lancaster Sr HS; Lancaster, WI; AFS; CmntyWkr; CncrtBnd; HonRl; MrchBnd; NatlFornLg; SchPl; SctActv; 4-H; Wrstlng; College; Computer Tech.

MULFORD, Jane A; Mt Pleasant Community HS; Mt Pleasant, IA; Band; CncrtBnd; MrchBnd; PepBnd; StuCncl; StuGov; RptrYrbk; RptrSchPpr; College; Ventinery Technician.

MULHALL, Richard C; Monroe Senior HS; Monroe, WI; 97/250 KeyCl; FrCl; Tennis; IMSpt; College; Optometry.

MULHEARN, Marykay; St Paul Kennedy HS; Chicago, IL; PresSophCls; Chrs; HonRl; StuCncl; Yrbk; Chrldr; LetterGAA; IMSpt; College; Teaching.

MULHOLLAND, Richard; Greenville HS; Greenville, MI; HonRl; 4-H; FFA; SpnCl; LetterFtbl; Trk; IMSpt; 4-HAwd; PresAwd; Mi St Univ; Dairy Sci.

MULKEY, Renee; Arkansas City HS; Arkansas City, KS; 11 VPSrCls; Chr; ChrhWkr; HonRl; OffAde; SchMus; SptEdYrbk; FNA; Tennis; 4-HAwd; College; Major Study.

MULL, Brian E; Homer HS; Homer, MI; PresSrCls; Band; HonRl; MrchBnd; PepBnd; SchPl; TchrAde; LatCl; Trk; Wrstlng; University; Professional.

MULL, Dave C; Brown County HS; Versailles, IL; Chrs; HonRl; College; Biology.

MULL, Joellen; Anna Jonesboro HS; Cobden, IL; 4/139 SecSophCls; SecJrCls; VPSrCls; ChrhWkr; HonRl; YthFlsp; VPFTA; FrCl; Southern Illinois University; Biology.

MULLAN, Dianna L; Harvard HS; Harvard, IL; 7/159 Chrs; HonRl; SchMus; GerCl; MthCl; University; Science.

MULLAN, Richelieu J; St Viator HS; Arlington Hts, IL; 35/250 HonRl; JA; College; Professional.

MULLANE, Janet; Dominican Hs; Detroit, MI; TrsJrCls; Band; CncrtBnd; HonRl; NHS; Orch;.

MULLANEY, Mary C; Our Lady Star Of The Sea HS; Gross Pte Shores, MI; PresJrCls; ChrhWkr; HonRl; LbryAde; NHS; SecStuCncl; FrCl; CaptTennis; GAA; IMSpt; Univ; Business.

MULLARKEY, Scott S; Anderson HS; Anderson, IN; CAP; HonRl; ROTC; SctActv; LatCl; SciCl; LetterFtbl; Trk; CaptWrstlng; IMSpt; Purdue Flight School; Airline Pilot.

MULLEN, Debra A; Girard HS; Atwater, IL; 1/69 HonRl; NHS; OffAde; RptrYrbk; FrCl;.

MULLEN, Joseph J; Robbinsdale HS; Golden Valley, MN; HonRl; Swmmng; St Thomas Clg; Chemistry.

MULLEN, Meredithe M; Gilbert Community HS; Gilert, IA; TrsFrshCls; TrsJrCls; Chrs; StuCncl; PpCl; LetterBsbl; U Of Iowa; Nursing.

MULLEN, Neil; Laporte City Hs; Laporte City, IA; 11/71 VPFrshCls; VPSophCls; HonRl; NHS; SchPl; StuCncl; FFA; LetterBsktbl; LetterFtbl; LetterTrk; College; Curriculum Of Major Study.

MULLEN, Sally A; Derham Hall HS; St Paul, MN; 6/127 LbryAde; NHS; NatlMeritFnl; NatlMeritSchl; SchPpr; FrCl; St Catherine Coll; Law.

MULLEN, Theresa A; Benet Academy; Naperville, IL; 37/229 Chrs; HonRl; NHS; NatlMeritCmnd; PPFtbl; Il State U; Special Ed Teacher.

MULLENMEISTER, Mike; Pacelli HS; Austin, MN; HonRl; Tennis; Coll.

MULLER, Anne M; Marillac HS; Northbrook, IL; Chr; ChrhWkr; Sdlty; StuCncl; StuGov; College.

MULLER, Debra J; Washington Comm HS; Washington, IL; 51/345 AFS; Chr; Chrs; CmntyWkr; HonRl; Mdrgl; SchMus; StuCncl; 4-H; KeyCl; Chrldr; DanFAwd; DARAwd; Univ Of Il; Home Economics.

MULLER, Keith L; Fairbury Sr HS; Fairbury, NE; 19/144 HonRl; FBLA; Bsbl; LetterFtbl; Fairbury Se Comm Clg; Mathematics.

MULLER, Lori; Northwest HS; Grand Island, NE; 23/140 Chr; HonRl; SchMus; 4-H; FBLA; GerCl; 4-HAwd;.

MULLER, Marianne R; Cambridge HS; Cambridge, IL; AFS; Chrs; DrmBgl; HonRl; SchPl; FDA; FHA; Chrldr; GAA; Monmouth Coll; Doctor.

MULLER, Mark L; Benton Central HS; Fowler, IN; 81/257 Band; CncrtBnd; HonRl; MrchBnd; SchPl; SctActv; PpCl; Chrldr; IMSpt; Purdue Univ; Industrial Management.

MULLER, Terry L; Howells Public HS; Howells, NE; Chr; Chrl; Chrs; ChrhWkr; SchMus; SchPl; YthFlsp; FFA; LetterBsktbl; LetterFtbl; LetterTrk; College; Farmer.

MULLER, Theresa A; Benton Central HS; Fowler, IN; 20/257 CncrtBnd; MrchBnd; NHS; PepBnd; Quill&Scroll; RptrYrbk; PpCl; GAA; IMSpt; PPFtbl; College; Recreation Management.

MULLET, Margaret E; Superior HS; Superior, NE; 11/78 ALAGirlsSt; HonRl; NHS; NatlMeritFnl; NatlMeritSchl; NatlSciFnd; 4-H; Univ Of Neb; Medicine.

MULLICAN, Timothy J; Reitz Memorial HS; Evansville, IN; 23/220 HonRl; NHS; SchPl; StuCncl; LetterBsktbl; College; Mj In Biology.

MULLICE, Anthony L; Huron HS; Ann Arbor, MI; SchAde; SctActv; StuGov; YthFlsp; Yrbk; EdSchPpr; LetterBsktbl; IMSpt; Eastern Mi Univ; Business.

MULLIGAN, Anne S; Rosati Kain HS; University City, MO; Aud/Vis; NHS; NatlMeritSchl; SctActv; EdSchPpr; SpnCl; MthCl; PpCl; GAA; St Louis Univ; Art.

MULLIGAN, George H; Lyons Township HS; La Grange, IL; HonRl; Univ Ot Tulsa; Accounting.

MULLIGAN, Mary I; Marian Catholic HS; Hazel Crest, IL; HonRl; NHS; NatlMeritCmnd; Quill&Scroll; PresSdlty; SchPpr; SpnCl; Mundelein College; Home Economics.

MULLIGAN, Theresa; Sturgis HS; Sturgis, MI; SchPl; FrCl; PpCl; PPFtbl; Nazareth Coll;teacher.

MULLIKIN, Mark T; Benton HS; Cuba City, WI; Band; Chrs; CmntyWkr; CncrtBnd; HonRl; ModUN; PepBnd; SchPl; Yrbk; LetterFtbl; University; International Study.

MULLIN, Lynn A; Pike HS; Zionsville, IN; 12/262 ALAGirlsSt; Chr; HonRl; JrNHS; LitMag; LbryAde; NHS; SchMus; Univ; English.

MULLIN, Russell J; Douglass HS; Wichita, KS; 15/50 Chr; CmntyWkr; HonRl; SchPl; TchrAde; SptEdSchPpr; LetterBsbl; Bsktbl; Ftbl; Wrstlng; Trade Sch; Professional.

MULLINGS, Christina; Eastern HS; Lansing, MI; HonRl; JA; LitMag; NatlMeritCmnd; NatlMeritSF; PolWkr; SchPl; FBLA; GerCl; Lansing Comm Coll; Social Wrk.

MULLINK, Kathleen; Carrollton HS; Carrollton, IL; 2/88 SecSrCls; HonRl; LbryAde; SchPl; StuCncl; GAA; AmLegAwd; Lewis & Clark Comm Coll; Vocation Business.

MULLINK, Kathleen A; Carrollton HS; Carrollton, IL; 2/87 SecSrCls; HonRl; TreasNHS; SchPl; StuCncl; VPFBLA; VPFTA; LetterBsktbl; GAA; PPFtbl; JAAwd; Lewis & Clarke Comm College; Business.

MULLINK, Patricia D; Carrollton HS; Carrollton, IL; 3/77 HonRl; LbryAde; FBLA; SpnCl; PpCl; LetterBsbl; Bsktbl; Ftbl; GAA; PresAwd;.

MULLINS, Gayla S; Virden HS; Virden, IL; PresSophCls; HonRl; NHS; Quill&Scroll; SchMus; SchPl; StuCncl; RptrSchPpr; SchPpr; PpCl; Trade Sch; Computer.

MULLINS, Judi A; Ypsilanti HS; Ypsilanti, MI; Band; CncrtBnd; HonRl; HospAde; MrchBnd; Cleary Business College; Secretary.

MULLINS, Martha J; Central Heights HS; Lane, KS; VPChrs; HonRl; SchPl; StuCncl; SecFHA; VPPpCl; College.

MULLINS, Mary E; Unionville HS; Livonia, MO; 1/75 TrsJrCls; ChrhWkr; HonRl; NHS; YthFlsp; 4-H; FHA; PpCl; 4-HAwd; Trade School; Clerical Work.

MULLINS, Mary J; Benton Consolidated HS; Benton, IL; 9/168 PresSrCls; ChrhWkr; HonRl; NHS; StuCncl; EdYrBk; Univ Of Ill; Medical Field.

MULLINS, Rita K; Clay City HS; Ingraham, IL; Chr; Chrs; ChrhWkr; HonRl; SchMus; 4-H; PpCl; Bible College; Florist.

MULLINS, Teresa E; Sturgis HS; Sturgis, MI; Band; CncrtBnd; HonRl; MrchBnd; NHS; Orch; PepBnd; TchrAde; SecLatCl; PpCl; Western Mich Univ; Elem Education.

MULLINS, William D; Granite City South HS; Granite City, IL; 43/630 Band; Chrs; CncrtBnd; HonRl; Mdrgl; MrchBnd; NHS; SchMus; SchPl; StuGov; SchPpr; Ftbl; E Illinois Univ; Law.

MULLIS, William H; Mitchell HS; Mitchell, IN; 1/120 HonRl; NHS; VPQuill&Scroll; EdYrBk; LetterFtbl; CaptGlf; BauchLmbAwd; Indiana U; Law.

MULLVAIN, Jeffry A; El Paso HS; El Paso, IL; 2/84 PresJrCls; AFS; ALBoysSt; PresBand; CncrtBnd; NHS; SchPl; StuCncl; PresYthFlsp; PresSpnCl; DARAwd; Illinois Wesleyan Univ; Physician.

MULNIX, Bruce E; Moberly HS; Moberly, MO; 30/214 HonRl; FBLA; SpnCl; LetterBsktbl; LetterGlf; Northeast Mo State; Business Executive.

MULRINE, Patrick G; Onalaska HS; Onalaska, WI; 25/131 ALBoysSt; Chr; ChrhWkr; Mdrgl; Bsbl; Bsktbl; Ftbl; Tennis; Trk; College; Professional Medicine.

MULROE, Stephen M; St Patrick HS; Chicago, IL; 20/427 HonRl; JrNHS; StuCncl; LetterFtbl; Trk; LetterWrstlng; Loyola Univ; Medicine.

MULROE, Thomas P; St Patrick HS; Chicago, IL; HonRl; Ftbl; Loyola Univ.

MULRY, Theresa A; Mother Of Sorrows HS; Chicago, IL; 30/160 CmntyWkr; HonRl; RptrYrbk; FrCl; MthCl; VFWAwd; VoiceDemAwd; Bus Schl; Secretary.

MULVAINE, Deonna L; Battle Creek Acad; Battle Creek, MI; 4/22 SecFrshCls; HonRl; HospAde; NHS; Orch; SchPl; TchrAde; IMSpt; Andrews Univ; Special Ed Teacher.

MULVANEY, James P; Mount St Benedict HS; Crookston, MN; Chr; Chrl; Chrs; SchMus; SchPl; Sdlty; LetterBsbl; LetterFtbl; College.

MULVIHILL, Anne M; Clay HS; South Bend, IN; Chrl; NHS; NatlMeritSF; StuGov; RptrSchPpr; SpnCl; PpCl; Chrldr; NCTE; Univ; Law.

MULVIHILL, Janet M; Forest Lake HS; Stacy, MN; Chrs; HonRl; JA; MrchBnd; 4-H; PpCl; Bsktbl; GAA; College.

MULVIHILL, Rita; Perry Lecompton HS; Perry, KS; ChrhWkr; HonRl; NatlThespSoc; SchPl; StuCncl; RptrSchPpr; 4-H; Bsktbl; 4-HAwd; CitAwd; Coll; Cirr Of Maj Study.

MULVILLE, Marypatricia A; St Mary Of Redford HS; Detroit, MI; 7/166 HonRl; JrNHS; LitMag; NHS; StuGov; RptrYrbk; PpCl; U Of Detroit; English.

MUMA, Gregory P; St Philip Cc HS; Battle Creek, MI; NatlMeritSchl; SctActv; SpnCl; LetterBsbl; LetterFtbl; W Michigan Univ; Aircraft Tech.

MUMAW, Klem J; Northridge HS; Middlebury, IN; Band; CncrtBnd; HonRl; MrchBnd; YthFlsp; 4-H; SpnCl; PpCl; LetterWrstlng; 4-HAwd; Goshen Clge; Math.

MUMM, Cheryl L; Unity HS; Philo, IL; Chr; HonRl; JrNHS; NHS; NatlThespSoc; SchMus; StuCncl; PpCl; Chrldr; IMSpt; College; Social Work.

MUMM, Timothy J; Milwaukee Luth HS; West Bend, WI; AFS; Chr; ChrhWkr; SchMus; SchPl; College; Parochial Ed.

MUMMA, Debra A; Ottawa HS; Ottawa, KS; 16/183 HonRl; NHS; SpnCl; Baker U; Spanish.

MUMMERT, John R; Johnston City HS; Thompsonville, IL; 1/85 VPFrshCls; HonRl; SpnCl; SecMthCl; SecSciCl; LetterFtbl; LetterTrk; IMSpt; AmLegAwd; LionAwd; Univ Of Illinois; Zoology.

MUNAR, Ellen M; Andrews Univ Academy; Berrien Springs, MI; 3/63 SecJrCls; SecSrCls; Chr; NHS; StuCncl; RptrYrbk; SchPpr; Andrews Univ; Medicine.

MUNCH, Russell A; Murdock C 7 HS; Mrudock, NE; 3/20 VPSophCls; VPJrCls; HonRl; SchPl; PresStuCncl; Yrbk; MthCl; LetterBsktbl; LetterFtbl; Trk; Univ Of Ne At Lincoln; Accounting.

MUNCIE, Brenda K; Staunton HS; Cory, IN; 2/60 ChrhWkr; HonRl; LbryAde; NHS; OffAde; SecStuCncl; TchrAde; DARAwd; Olivet Nazarene; Nursing.

MUND, Carol D; North County HS; Bonne Terr, MO; HonRl; HospAde; OffAde; SctActv; FHA; FNA; SpnCl; PpCl; Col; Nursing Sch.

MUNDAHL, Mark E; Fergus Falls HS; Fergus Falls, MN; 7/310 CncrtBnd; HonRl; NHS; NatlThespSoc; ROTC; SchPl; SctActv; 4-H; GerCl; VoiceDemAwd; Macalester Coll; Nuclear Eng.

MUNDELL, John A; Clinton Prairie HS; Frankfort, IN; 2/105 ALBoysSt; ChrhWkr; CmntyWkr; HonRl; NHS; NatlMeritCmnd; PolWkr; SchPl; PresStuCncl; SptEdYrbk; SptEdSchPpr; FTA; CaptFtbl; LetterTrk; Purdue Univ; Engineering.

MUNDELL, Kevin A; Moline HS; Moline, IL; 1/835 Chr; ChrhWkr; HonRl; JrNHS; LitMag; NHS; RptrYrbk; SciCl; Augustana College; History.

MUNDSCHENK, Darla K; Flanagan HS; Long Point, IL; 6/37 Chr; Chrs; ChrhWkr; CncrtBnd; HonRl; Mdrgl; SchMus; YthFlsp; CchngActv; GAA; College; Professional.

MUNDT, Jerry; West Lyon Comm HS; Inwood, IA; ALBoysSt; HonRl; YthFlsp; College.

MUNDWILER, Marise; Kal Central HS; Kalamazoo, MI; HonRl; PPFtbl; Mich State Univ.

MUNDY, Alan L; Mitchell HS; Mitchell, IN; PresSophCls; VPSrCls; ALBoysSt; Band; ChrhWkr; DrmMjrt; PresNHS; NatlThespSoc; Quill&Scroll; SchPl; StuCncl; Purdue Univ; Pharmacy.

MUNDY, Joe; Southridge HS; Huntingburg, IN; 26/172 PresFrshCls; VPSophCls; HonRl; StuCncl; StuGov; Bsktbl; Ftbl; Glf; Trk; College; Education.

MUNDY, Marylee; Belvidere HS; Belvidere, IL; 60/336 HonRl; YthFlsp; Yrbk; SchPpr; SpnCl; GAA; Rockford College; Business Administration.

MUNGO, Mark J; St Joseph HS; Westchester, IL; 15/162 University; Law.

MUNHOLLON, Julie M; Leaf River HS; Egan, IL; SecSrCls; Band; ChrhWkr; CmntyWkr; CncrtBnd; HonRl; MrchBnd; PepBnd; 4-H; HstSrCls;.

MUNIZ, Michael J; Turner HS; Kansas City, KS; Chr; CmntyWkr; HonRl; LbryAde; SchMus; SctActv; TchrAde; FDA; Ftbl; LetterTrk; University; Medicine.

MUNJAK, Claudia S; Bishop Ward HS; Kansas City, KS; HonRl; StuCncl; StuGov; 4-H; FrCl; PpCl; Chrldr; 4-HAwd; Ks Univ; Photo Journalism.

MUNN, Eugene M; Divine Heart Seminary; Detroit, MI; PresFrshCls; PresJrCls; Chr; SchPl; SctActv; StuCncl; RptrYrbk; SptEdYrbk; SptEdSchPpr; Bsbl; Mercy College; Nursing.

MUNN, Kevin M; Bloomingdale HS; Bloomingdale, MI; 10/91 HonRl; LbryAde; ModUN; NatlFornLg; OffAde; SchPl; TchrAde; RptrYrbk; RptrSchPpr; Bsbl; Military Service.

MUNO, Julie A; St Scholastica HS; Evanston, IL; 20/238 NHS; NatlMeritCmnd; RedCrAde; SchAde; SchMus; SchPl; StuCncl; TchrAde; RptrYrbk; Bradley Univ; Chemistry.

MUNOT, Martin P; Notre Dame HS; Niles, IL; 30/260 HonRl; LitMag; Univ Of Notre Dame.

MUNOZ, Michael J; St Anns HS; Lexington, NE; PresSrCls; Chrs; ChrhWkr; HonRl; SchPl; TchrAde; RptrYrbk; SptEdYrbk; LetterBsktbl; LetterFtbl; Clge Of Medicine; Physician Assistant.

MUNRO, John J; Clinton HS; Clinton, IL; 3/154 HonRl; Ftbl; Wrstlng; College; Medicine.

MUNSELL, Debra A; Oskaloosa Senior HS; Oskaloosa, IA; Band; Chr; Chrs; CncrtBnd; HonRl; MrchBnd; SchMus; SchPl; LetterSwmmng; Trk; Trade School; Fashion.

MUNSEN, Cindy A; White Lake HS; White Lake, SD; SecSophCls; CmntyWkr; ChrhWkr; HonRl; SchMus; SecSdlty; Yrbk; PpCl; Trk; Chrldr; College; Nursing Rn.

MUNSON, Mark R; Princeton HS; Princeton, IL; 8/189 Chrs; CncrtBnd; HonRl; MrchBnd; 4-H; FFA; GerCl; LetterWrstlng; 4-HAwd;.

MUNSON, Scott R; Dundee Comm HS; Carpentersville, IL; HstFrshCls; HonRl; SctActv; StuCncl; YthFlsp; GerCl; CaptBsbl; CaptBsktbl; Ftbl; CchngActv; College; Professional.

MUNSTER, Kent A; Ogallala HS; Ogallala, NE; Band; CncrtBnd; HonRl; MrchBnd; PepBnd; Univ Of Nebraska; Medicine.

MUNYON, Robert J; Phillipsburg HS; Phillipsburg, KS; HonRl; SchMus; SchPl; StuCncl; StuGov; TchrAde; Yrbk; LetterFtbl;.

MUNYON, Susan M; Isabel HS; Isabel, SD; 2/12 PresFrshCls; SecSophCls; TrsJrCls; Chr; Chrs; ChrhWkr; CmntyWkr; DrlTm; HonRl; SchPl; StuCncl; PpCl; CaptBsktbl; College; Stewardess.

MUNZ, Ruth E; Highland Public HS; Avoca, WI; 4/50 SecFrshCls; HonRl;.

MURAD, Dan; South Side HS; Ft Wayne, IN; 38/427 AFS; Chr; HonRl; NHS; SchMus; StuCncl; Bsbl; Socr; Wabash Coll; Dentist.

MURDOCH, David P; Kingsley Pierson HS; Remsen, IA; 4/56 Band; Chr; Chrl; Chrs; CncrtBnd; HonRl; Mdrgl; MrchBnd; PepBnd; SchMus; College; Music Ed.

MURDOCK, Cynthia L; New Trier West HS; Glenview, IL; 256/694 Chrs; HonRl; StuCncl; StuGov; Univ Of Utah; Business.

MURDOCK, Leslie M; St Francis HS; Winfield, IL; DrlTm; HonRl; NHS; SchMus; SchPl; RptrYrbk; PpCl; Tennis;.

MURDOCK, Susan M; United Township HS; East Moline, IL; 18/600 Chr; HonRl; LbryAde; NHS; NatlThespSoc; SchMus; SchPl; Teen; YthFlsp; GAA; College; Education.

MURDY, David C; Rock Island HS; Rock Island, IL; Chr; ChrhWkr; NHS; NatlMeritCmnd; SchMus; SchPl; StuCncl; StuGov; TchrAde; SchPpr; Univ Of Chicago; Medicine.

MURFF, Terrill N; Chicago Vocational HS; Chicago, IL; 43/778 DrlTm; HonRl; NHS; Quill&Scroll; ROTC; StuCncl; StuGov; MthCl; LetterFtbl; Trk; CitAwd; College; Engineering.

MURKOWSKI, David M; Marquette Univ HS; Milwaukee, WI; 5/247 PresSrCls; HonRl; SchMus; SchPl; Sdlty; VPStuCncl; SchPpr; PpCl; Chrldr; Marquette Univ; Law.

MURLEY, Susan A; North HS; Eau Claire, WI; Band; HonRl; NHS; Orch; SchMus; TchrAde; Twrl; YthFlsp; PpCl; University Of Wisconsin; Doctor.

MURPHEY, Joe H; Clinton HS; Clinton, MO; HonRl; TchrAde; Bsktbl; IMSpt; Univ.

MURPHY, Ann; Mother Theodore Guerin HS; Elmwood Pk, IL; 30/420 Chr; HonRl; SchMus; SchPl; Illinois State Univ; Professional.

MURPHY, Beth A; Columbus North HS; Columbus, IN; 21/500 ChrhWkr; HonRl; ModUN; NatlMeritCmnd; Orch; PolWkr; YthFlsp; 4-H; GAA; DARAwd; Indiana Univ; Psychology.

MURPHY, Betty J; Rockridge HS; Reynolds, IL; 15/140 Band; CncrtBnd; HonRl; MrchBnd; NHS; PepBnd; 4-H; FTA; LatCl; IMSpt; Col ;med.

MURPHY, Brenda S; Collinsville HS; Caseyville, IL; 9/645 HonRl; JrNHS; NHS; NatlThespSoc; SchPl; StuCncl; RptrYrbk; College; Business Admn.

MURPHY, Brian; Marshall HS; Marshall, IL; 47/115 CmntyWkr; YthFlsp; Bsktbl; Trade; Petroleum Tech.

MURPHY, Cathleen A; South Side HS; Ft Wayne, IN; 5/435 HstFrshCls; TrsJrCls; Chr; HonRl; JA; StuCncl; TchrAde; FrCl; College; Professional.

MURPHY, Charleen P; O Fallon Township HS; O Fallon, IL; DrlTm; HonRl; SpnCl; PpCl; SciCl; IMSpt; College; Major Study.

MURPHY, Charles A; Detroit Country Day HS; Detroit, MI; ALBoysSt; Chr; CmntyWkr; HonRl; NatlMeritCmnd; 4-H; GerCl; Bsbl; Harvard College; Medicine.

MURPHY, Daniel E; Boylan Cntrl Catholic HS; Rockford, IL; 9/396 Chr; ChrhWkr; CmntyWkr; CncrtBnd; HonRl; JrNHS; NHS; SchAde; TchrAde; YthFlsp; RptrSchPpr; LatCl; Bsbl; Loras College; Business.

MURPHY, Daniel E; Edina East HS; Edina, MN; HonRl; PolWkr; YthFlsp; LetterSocr; LetterSwmmng; LetterTrk; West Point.

MURPHY, Daniel P; Port Washington HS; Port Washington, WI; HonRl; NatlMeritSF; RptrSchPpr; LetterBsktbl; College; History.

MURPHY, David G; Sault HS; Slt St Marie, MI; HonRl; NHS; NatlMeritCmnd; OffAde; TchrAde; LetterBsktbl; LetterTrk; IMSpt; College Lk Superior St; Law.

MURPHY, Diane L; South Page HS; Braddyville, IA; 14/38 Band; Chr; CncrtBnd; HonRl; MrchBnd; Orch; PepBnd; SchMus; SchPl; YthFlsp; College; Professional.

MURPHY, Doug; Notre Dame HS; Cresco, IA; VPFrshCls; VPJrCls; ALBoysSt; HonRl; NHS; SchAde; LetterBsbl; LetterBsktbl; CchngActv; IMSpt; College; Physical Education.

MURPHY, Eileen A; Mt Assisi Acad; Chicago, IL; HonRl; LitMag; NHS; SchMus; StuCncl; EdSchPpr; Loyola Univ; Business.

MURPHY, Elizabeth A; Carl Sandburg HS; Palos Heights, IL; Band; CncrtBnd; MrchBnd; SecNHS; NatlMeritFnl; TchrAde; MthCl; PpCl; SciCl; Trk; Northland Coll; Environmental Studies.

MURPHY, Elizabeth; Carl Sandburg HS; Palos Heights, IL; 19/756 CncrtBnd; MrchBnd; NHS; NatlMeritFnl; TchrAde; GerCl; MthCl; PpCl; SciCl; Trk; Northland College; Environmental Studies.

MURPHY, Erin; Barrington HS; Barrington, IL; Band; Chr; CncrtBnd; DrlTm; HonRl; NHS; SptEdYrbk; Yrbk; RptrSchPpr; GerCl; College Or Univ.

MURPHY, Frederick J; Wyandotte HS; Kansas City, KS; ALBoysSt; Band; CncrtBnd; HonRl; MrchBnd; NatlThespSoc; PepBnd; SchPl; SctActv; Ottawa University; Accountant.

MURPHY, Glen; Messmer HS; Milwaukee, WI; 30/211.

MURPHY, Glenda F; Princeton R V HS; Princeton, MO; Chr; ChrhWkr; HonRl; OffAde; SchMus; TchrAde; SchPpr; GerCl; Nemsu; Lawyer.

MURPHY, James T; Naperville Central HS; Naperville, IL; HonRl; NatlMeritCmnd; Univ Of Illinois; Mathematics.

MURPHY, James W; Wheeling HS; Wheeling, IL; Aud/Vis; HonRl; NatlMeritCmnd; SctActv; Univ Of Illinois; Engineering.

MURPHY, Jane A; Waukon HS; Waukon, IA; 7/155 PresSophCls; VPJrCls; HonRl; StuCncl; Yrbk; PpCl; Bsktbl; PPFtbl; Loras Coll; Secondary Education.

MURPHY, Janice K; Seymour HS; Seymour, IN; Band; CncrtBnd; MrchBnd; PepBnd; FTA; GerCl; PpCl; SciCl; Purdue Univ; Pharmacy.

MURPHY, Jeffrey C; Maple Valley HS; Nashville, MI; 3/108 Band; CncrtBnd; HonRl; MrchBnd; NHS; SchPl; TchrAde; 4-H; Ftbl; IMSpt; Michigan State Univ.

MURPHY, Jill A; Normal Community HS; Bloomington, IL; ChrhWkr; HonRl; HospAde; TchrAde; SpnCl; Ill State Univ; Political Science.

MURPHY, Jill E; Holton HS; Twin Lake, MI; Band; Chr; ChrhWkr; HonRl; MrchBnd; NHS; PepBnd; SchPl; TchrAde; College.

MURPHY, John D; Stuart Menlo Comm HS; Stuart, IA; RptrYrbk; RptrSchPpr; Bsbl; Bsktbl; Ftbl; Ellsworth Jr College.

MURPHY, John G; Marist HS; Oak Lawn, IL; 32/393 HonRl; NHS; SchMus; SchPl; StuCncl; Bsktbl; Glf; Trk; IMSpt; Northwestern Univ; Law.

MURPHY, Karen L; Graceville HS; Graceville, MN; Band; HonRl; NHS; SchPl; RptrYrbk; RptrSchPpr; FHA; FrCl; GAA; PresAwd; Clg; Pro.

MURPHY, Karen L; Rosiclare Community HS; Rosiclare, IL; 5/32 VPSrCls; Band; Chrs; ChrhWkr; CncrtBnd; HonRl; JrNHS; MrchBnd; SchPl; Yrbk; Chrldr; Murray St Univ; Surgical Nurse.

MURPHY, Karen L; La Ville HS; Plymouth, IN; SecSophCls; PresJrCls; ALAGirlsSt; MrchBnd; NatlFornLg; NHS; SchPl; Twrl; RptrSchPpr; Indiana St Univ; Broadcasting.

MURPHY, Kevin M; George S Parker HS; Janesville, WI; 18/387 PresJrCls; ALBoysSt; HonRl; NHS; PresQuill&Scroll; StuCncl; SptEdYrbk; Wrstlng; DanFAwd; EldAwd; U Of Wi Whitewater; Accounting.

MURPHY, Kimberley A; Watertown Sr HS; Watertown, SD; HonRl; IntrClCncl; NatlFornLg; NatlMeritSchl; GerCl; LetterGlf; GAA; College; Special Education.

MURPHY, Laurie A; Odell Comm HS; Odell, IL; 4/45 VPJrCls; Chr; CmntyWkr; HonRl; SchPl; StuCncl; 4-H; FrCl; PpCl; GAA; Coll; Pro.

MURPHY, Lisa A; Lincolnwood HS; Farmersville, IL; Band; HonRl; MrchBnd; TchrAde; Yrbk; 4-H; FHA; FTA; PpCl; Western Il Univ;.

MURPHY, Marianna; Princeton Hs; Princeton, IL; 44/178 PresSophCls; PresAFS; Chr; CmntyWkr; CncrtBnd; HonRl; StuCncl; StuGov; LatCl; GAA; U Of Illinois; Social Service.

MURPHY, Marianne; Queen Of Peace HS; Chicago, IL; 8/430 HonRl; NHS; NatlMeritCmnd; Univ Of Ill; Engineering.

MURPHY, Mark W; Atwood Hammond HS; Atwood, IL; Band; Chrs; CncrtBnd; HonRl; Mdrgl; MrchBnd; PepBnd; SchMus; Parkland Coll; Electronic.

MURPHY, Mary A; Marquette HS; Alton, IL; Chrs; HonRl; JA; LbryAde; SctActv; College; Professional.

MURPHY, Mary C; Canton Sr HS; Canton, IL; Chr; CncrtBnd; DrlTm; HonRl; SchMus; College; Pharmacy.

MURPHY, Mary T; Glenbard East HS; Lombard, IL; 15/656 SecTrsSrCls; ChrhWkr; HonRl; IntrClCncl; NHS; StuCncl; RptrYrbk; Yrbk; SpnCl; Purdue Univ; Business Admin.

MURPHY, Maureen G; St Anne HS; Warren, MI; 2/49 SecSophCls; SecJrCls; CmntyWkr; HonRl; NHS; StuGov; PpCl; Chrldr; Univ Of Detroit; Biology.

MURPHY, Maureen M; Regina HS; Mt Clemens, MI; ChrhWkr; HonRl; NHS; NatlMeritSchl; TchrAde; SchPpr; SpnCl; BttyCrckrAwd; Coll; Interpreter.

MURPHY, Meeghan; St Pius X HS; Kansas City, MO; 22/130 HonRl; TchrAde; Col.

MURPHY, Michael; Eldora HS; Eldora, IA; ALBoysSt; Chrs; HonRl; StuCncl; StuGov; Yrbk; SpnCl; Ftbl; Trk; Iowa St Univ; Business.

MURPHY, Michael J; St Johns Prep HS; Glencoe, MN; HonRl; GerCl; Bsktbl; Ftbl; Trk; CchngActv; College.

MURPHY, Michael J; Dunlap Comm HS; Dunlap, IA; 8/56 ALBoysSt; HonRl; JrNHS; NHS; SchPl; 4-H; LetterBsbl; LetterBsktbl; AmLegAwd; 4-HAwd; PresAwd; Business School; Professional.

MURPHY, Noreen; Mother Mcavley Hs; Merrionette Park, IL; Chrs; HonRl; NatlMeritFnl; SchPl; Bsktbl; CaptFtbl; Purdue U; Industrial Technology.

MURPHY, Patricia; Port Huron HS; Smith Creek, MI; CmntyWkr; HonRl; SchAde; TchrAde; Yrbk; FNA; PpCl; GAA; VFWAwd; VoiceDemAwd; College; Social Work.

MURPHY, Patricia A; Des Lacs HS; Burlington, ND; 3/32 ALAGirlsSt; Chrs; HonRl; LbryAde; SchPl; Yrbk; SchPpr; VPPpCl; SciCl; GAA; Minot State College; Nursing.

MURPHY, Patrick; St Marys HS; St Marys, KS; TchrAde; Ftbl; IMSpt; Vocational; Motorcycle Mechanics.

MURPHY, Patrick A; Dike HS; Dike, IA; Band; Chrs; ChrhWkr; CncrtBnd; MrchBnd; PepBnd; TchrAde; Bsbl; Wrstlng; CchngActv; Civil Eng.

MURPHY, Patrick E; Owosso HS; Owosso, MI; 201/452 SctActv; Michigan Tech Univ; Forestry.

MURPHY, Patrick G; Creighton Prep; Omaha, NE; 91/249 HonRl; Sdlty; LetterBsbl; LetterFtbl; Swmmng; Univ; Professional.

MURPHY, Randy A; Fremont HS; Fremont, MI; Band; DrmMjrt; HonRl; MrchBnd; PresNHS; Orch; SchMus; SchPl; SctActv; 4-HAwd; College.

MURPHY, Rian J; Lake Forest HS; Lake Bluff, IL; Aud/Vis; Chr; Chrs; HonRl; LitMag; Mdrgl; NHS; NatlMeritFnl; NatlMeritSF; SchMus; SchPl;.

MURPHY, Robert C; Lane Tech HS; Chicago, IL; 61/1200 HonRl; StuCncl; StuGov; TchrAde; RptrYrbk; RptrSchPpr; U Of Il; Speech & Theatre.

MURPHY, Ron E; New Bloomfield HS; Holts Summit, MO; VPJrCls; Chrs; StuCncl; SciCl; CaptBsktbl; Coll; Criminology.

MURPHY, Rosemary; John M Harlan HS; Chicago, IL; 3/500 ChrhWkr; CmntyWkr; HonRl; JrNHS; NHS; MthCl; PpCl; SciCl; Northwestern Univ; Computer Science.

MURPHY, Sheryl A; Carroll HS; Flora, IN; Chrs; ChrhWkr; CmntyWkr; DrlTm; HonRl; OffAde; SchAde; SctActv; Pres4-H; Indiana State U; Nursing.

MURPHY, Teresa; Raymond Lincolnwood HS; Farmersville, IL; SecFrshCls; Band; CncrtBnd; DrmMjrt; HonRl; PepBnd; FFA; FTA; Chrldr; College; Major Study.

MURPHY, Teri L; Peoria HS; Peoria, IL; 30/481 HonRl; JA; JrNHS; Quill&Scroll; EdYrBk; FrCl; PpCl; Bsbl; Bsktbl; Bradley Univ; Elem Education.

MURPHY, Theresa; O L Of Mt Carmel HS; Southgate, MI; 4/59 Chrl; HonRl; NHS; StuGov; RptrYrbk; RptrSchPpr; PpCl; Chrldr; IMSpt; Eastern Michigan Univ.

MURPHY, Theresa G; Riverview Comm HS; Riverview, MI; 21/249 HonRl; NHS; SctActv; RptrSchPpr; SchPpr; PresFHA; Coll; Nurse.

MURPHY, Timothy J; St Marys Springs HS; Fond Du Lac, WI; VPSophCls; OffAde; StuCncl; RptrSchPpr; FrCl; Bsktbl; Wrstlng; IMSpt; JCAwd; College; Professional.

MURPHY, Valerie; Monroe HS; St Paul, MN; Chr; HonRl; TchrAde; Chrldr; Coll.

MURPHY, Valerie; Randolph Southern HS; Greenwood, IN; Chr; ChrhWkr; HonRl; College; Vocation.

MURPHY, Vincent J; St Louis Priory HS; Dellwood, MO; 13/32 PresSophCls; Aud/Vis; StuGov; Socr; IMSpt; Univ Of Mo Rolla; Electrical Engr.

MURPHY, Wayne H; Macon County R I HS; Macon, MO; 17/117 HonRl; AmLegAwd; Northeast Mo St Univ; Pharmacy.

MURPHY, William R; Parkston HS; Parkston, SD; 14/97 VPFrshCls; Chr; HonRl; PresYthFlsp; PresMthCl; PresSciCl; SecLetterTrk; CchngActv; U Of Sd; Coach Teacher.

MURRAY, Caryn; Nazareth Acad; Westchester, IL; RptrYrbk; Chrldr; Coll; Home Ec.

MURRAY, Catherine T; Homewood Flossmoor HS; Homewood, IL; 53/940 Chr; HonRl; SchMus; SctActv; Indiana University.

MURRAY, Catherine L; Derham Hall HS; St Paul, MN; SecNHS; PresSpnCl; Swmmng; Chrldr; CchngActv; Clg Of St Catherine; Liberal Arts.

MURRAY, Catherine; East Hs; Kansas City, MO; 4/225 HonRl; IntrClCncl; JrNHS; OffAde; SchPl; TreasStuCncl; TchrAde; RptrSchPpr; College; Medical Technologist.

MURRAY, Christina L; Tuscola HS; Tuscola, IL; 17/124 ChrhWkr; CmntyWkr; HonRl; Mdrgl; NHS; SchPl; StuCncl; EdYrBk; DARAwd; St Francis School; Nurse.

MURRAY, David A; Clay Center Comm HS; Clay Center, KS; HonRl; NHS; SctActv; StuCncl; YthFlsp; 4-H; SciCl; Ftbl; Trk; GodCntryAwd; Kansas State U; Professional.

MURRAY, Denise; Covington HS; Covington, IN; 19/99 Band; Chrs; ChrhWkr; HonRl; SchPl; FHA; FTA; PpCl; Bsktbl; IMSpt; Indiana State Univ; Special Teacher.

MURRAY, James D; Crete HS; Crete, NE; ChrhWkr; TchrAde; FBLA; LetterBsktbl; LetterFtbl; LetterSwmmng; LetterTrk; College; Business.

MURRAY, James L; Big Foot HS; Fontana, WI; Bsktbl; LetterFtbl; Trk; Col; Cpa.

MURRAY, Jane E; Fisher HS; Champaign, IL; VPJrCls; AFS; HonRl; JrNHS; PresStuCncl; 4-H; LetterChrldr; GAA; DanFAwd; 4-HAwd; University.

MURRAY, Jeanne M; Proviso West HS; Westchester, IL; Chr; Chrs; ChrhWkr; HonRl; HospAde; NatlMeritCmnd; RedCrAde; YthFlsp; RptrSchPpr; College; Nursing.

MURRAY, Jill D; Mt Zion HS; Mt Zion, IL; 4/168 HonRl; NHS; TchrAde; Eastern Illinois Univ; Accounting.

MURRAY, Joan K; Queen Of Peace HS; Chicago, IL; Chrs; HonRl; NHS; SchPl; SctActv; StuCncl; Yrbk; 4-H; LatCl; 4-HAwd; St Teresa; Dietician.

MURRAY, John R; Crestwood HS; Cresco, IA; 56/171 ALBoysSt; ChrhWkr; HonRl; Ftbl; College.

MURRAY, Joseph; Lemont HS; Lemont, IL; 15/151 HonRl; NHS; Trk; IMSpt; Loras Coll; Accountant.

MURRAY, Julia E; New Trier East HS; Winnetka, IL; Chrs; CmntyWkr; RptrSchPpr; College.

MURRAY, Karen C; Bishop Ward HS; Kansas City, KS; 8/195 ChrhWkr; CmntyWkr; HonRl; HospAde; LitMag; NHS; SecSpnCl; MthCl; College; Bookkeeping.

MURRAY, Kathleen M; Assumption HS; Davenport, IA; 1/225 Band; ChrhWkr; CncrtBnd; DrmMjrt; HonRl; NHS; NatlMeritSF; PepBnd; EdSchPpr; IMSpt; College; Music.

MURRAY, Kathleen M; New Trier East HS; Winnetka, IL; 154/847 Chrs; HonRl; NatlMeritCmnd; PolWkr; SchPl; StuCncl; FrCl; PpCl; Univ Of Ill; Veterinarian.

MURRAY, Kenneth J; East Peoria Community HS; East Peoria, IL; HonRl; LetterBsktbl; LetterGlf; IMSpt; Western Ill Univ; Engineering.

MURRAY, Linda J; Washington HS; Washington, IN; Chr; Chrl; Chrs; ChrhWkr; JA; LbryAde; OffAde; SchAde; SchPl; SctActv; TchrAde; Bsbl; Bsktbl; College; Liberal Arts.

MURRAY, Margaret A; Mother Mc Auley HS; Chicago, IL; 2/480 HonRl; NHS; NatlMeritSF; SchMus; Yrbk; BauchLmbAwd; University; Chemistry.

MURRAY, Mark; Marceline HS; Marceline, MO; AFS; ALBoysSt; Band; CncrtBnd; HonRl; NatlThespSoc; Bsktbl; Univ Of Missouri; Doctor.

MURRAY, Mark G; Kingsford HS; Kingsford, MI; CmntyWkr; HonRl; Trade Sch.

MURRAY, Martha M; Tiskilwa HS; Tiskilwa, IL; HonRl; LbryAde; 4-H; University; Teaching.

MURRAY, Mary; Wahlert HS; Dubuque, IA; 82/450 CmntyWkr; TchrAde; Ia State Univ; Elementary Teacher.

MURRAY, Mary B; Notre Dame HS; Burlington, IA;

35/90 DrlTm; HonRl; JrNHS; NHS; SpnCl; PpCl; College.

MURRAY, Mary E; Lumen Christi HS; Jackson, MI; 4 252 HonRl; NHS; NatlMeritSF; SchAde; SchMus; SchPl; RptrSchPpr; SchPpr; IMSpt; PPFtbl; Ferris St; Pharm.

MURRAY, Michael W; Union HS; Union, MO; ALBoysSt; Band; Chr; ChrhWkr; CncrtBnd; HonRl; JA; MrchBnd; PepBnd; Bsbl; Bsktbl; Ftbl; GodCntryAwd; Univ Of Missouri; Engineering.

MURRAY, Richard A; North Central Area HS; Spalding, MI; 11/56 SecSophCls; HonRl; StuCncl; Bsktbl; Northern Michigan Univ; Accounting.

MURRAY, Ronald J; Monroe City HS; Monroe City, MO; HonRl; StuCncl; LetterFtbl; Coll; Pro.

MURRAY, Tammie A; Waukegan East HS; Waukegan, IL; Brigham Young University.

MURRAY, William M; Oak Park River Forest HS; River Forest, IL; Aud/Vis; HonRl; LbryAde; Ftbl; Trk; College; Medicine.

MURRELL, Lizabeth L; North Fayette County Comm HS; West Union, IA; 10/105 TrsSrCls; DrlTm; HonRl; NHS; NatlThespSoc; YthFlsp; 4-H; LetterGlf; LetterChrldr; 4-HAwd; Coll; Interior Design.

MURREY, Cheryl L; Wing Public HS; Wing, ND; VPJrCls; Band; Chrs; HonRl; LbryAde; SchPl; EdYrBk; RptrSchPpr; Bsbl; Trk; Trade.

MURREY, Colleen M; Wilton Public HS; Wilton, ND; 4/36 Chrs; HonRl; NHS; SchPl; RptrSchPpr; SchPpr; 4-H; PpCl; Chrldr; 4-HAwd; College; Psych.

MURRIN, Maureen A; Willowbrook HS; Villa Park, IL; HonRl; Rockford College; Biology.

MURRISH, Carol J; Highland HS; Highland, IN; 57/543 Chrs; ChrhWkr; Quill&Scroll; StuCncl; TchrAde; Yrbk; PpCl; GAA; Purdue Univ; Home Ec.

MURRY, Madonna T; Mt Assisi Academy; Palos Heights, IL; 12/189 TrsSophCls; ModUN; NHS; StuCncl; RptrYrbk; SpnCl; Loyola University; Nursing.

MURRY, Timothy J; Delavan Public HS; Delavan, MN; Chrs; HonRl; NHS; SchPl; StuCncl; LetterBsbl; CaptBsktbl; CaptFtbl; LetterTrk; Jr College; Teacher.

MURTHA, Robbin; Heelan HS; Sioux City, IA; 24/250 CmntyWkr; HonRl; HospAde; JA; LbryAde; PolWkr; SctActv; FrCl; PpCl; IMSpt; College; Elementary Education.

MURTO, Susan F; Wauwatosa East HS; Wauwatosa, WI; 118/461 Band; Chrs; HonRl; NatlFornLg; PolWkr; TchrAde; FTA; Trk; AmLegAwd; Univ; Mathematics.

MURZYN, Patrick J; Thornton Fractional S HS; Lansing, IL; 50/552 PresBand; NatlFornLg; NHS; StuGov; Univ Of Il; Engineering.

MUSA, Albert J; Jefferson HS; Rockford, IL; 2/335 HonRl; JrNHS; NHS; YthFlsp; LatCl; LetterBsbl; LetterFtbl; GovHonPrgAwd; University Of Illinois; Engineering.

MUSBACH, Janet; Fremont Sr HS; Fremont, NE; TchrAde; YthFlsp; FHA; FNA; FTA; GerCl; IMSpt; GodCntryAwd; College; Architecture.

MUSBACH, Randy A; Chelsea HS; Chelsea, MI; Aud/Vis; CmntyWkr; HonRl; NHS; PolWkr; RptrYrbk; KeyCl; LetterBsbl; LetterBsktbl; PresAwd; Univ; Pre Law.

MUSCAT, Daniel J; Our Lady Of The Lakes HS; Clarkston, MI; TrsFrshCls; PresJrCls; ChrhWkr; HonRl; NHS; SchAde; SctActv; StuGov; Bsbl; College; Law.

MUSCH, Deborah D; St Joseph HS; Chicago, IL; SecJrCls; Chrs; HonRl; Quill&Scroll; SchPl; StuCncl; RptrSchPpr; FNA; Chrldr; College; Nursing.

MUSE, Jacquelynn; Unity HS; Chicago, IL; 1/182 SecSophCls; Chrs; HonRl; NatlMeritCmnd; StuGov; RptrSchPpr; SpnCl; University; Chemical Engineering.

MUSGRAVE, Kim; Oblong HS; Oblong, IL; 21/75 HonRl; NHS; OffAde; PolWkr; StuCncl; Swmmng; Tennis; Trk; GAA; IMSpt; Olney C Col ;social Worker.

MUSGROVE, Misty A; Brown County HS; Nashville, IN; Chr; HonRl; NHS; SchMus; SchPl; Yrbk; SchPpr; FBLA; Chrldr; DARAwd; Clge; Bus.

MUSHILL, Rose; Civic Memorial HS; Bethalto, IL; Chrs; HonRl; NHS; SctActv; FHA; PpCl;.

MUSHITZ, Alice J; New Underwood HS; New Underwood, SD; 3/25 SecJrCls; HonRl; NHS; RptrYrbk; EdYrBk; FFA; FHA; Trade; Vocation.

MUSHKIN, Steven H; Shawnee Mission East HS; Shawnee Mission, KS; 19/576 HonRl; NatlMeritSF; StuGov; SchPpr; PpCl; SciCl; Tennis; Univ; Lawyer.

MUSHRO, Karen M; Our Lady Star Of The Sea HS; Grosse Pt Woods, MI; HonRl; HospAde; NHS; SchPl; GAA; IMSpt; Univ; Health.

MUSICH, Linda A; Arlington HS; Arlington Heights, IL; 3/580 Chr; Chrs; DrlTm; HonRl; JrNHS; NHS; NatlThespSoc; SchMus; SchPl; GerCl; V Of I Champaign; Dietetics.

MUSICK, Elaine C; Central HS; Golden, IL; 1/72 Chrs; ChrhWkr; HonRl; SecNHS; SchPl; EdSchPpr; GerCl; Trk; GAA; DARAwd; St Johns College.

MUSICK, Randall M; Fruitport HS; Muskegon, MI; 45/300 HonRl; SctActv; LetterBsbl; Swmmng; Purdue U; Naval Pilot Engineering.

MUSICK, Roberta S; Worth County R 1 HS; Grant City, MO; 7/40 VPSrCls; Band; CncrtBnd; DrmMjrt; HonRl; Bsbl; LetterBsktbl; LetterTrk; CaptChrldr; PPFtbl; Nw Missouri State Univ; Lpn.

MUSIELAK, Janice M; Downers Grove Comm HS; Downers Grove, IL; 209/830 HonRl; SctActv; FrCl; College; Art.

MUSIL, Dina; Potter Public HS; Potter, NE; 2/18 VPSophCls; Band; Chrs; HonRl; NHS; OffAde; StuGov; RptrSchPpr; PpCl; Midland Lutheran College; Data Processer.

MUSIL, Gregory L; Frankfort HS; Frankfort, KS; 1/45 VPFrshCls; SecTrsSophCls; VPJrCls; ALBoysSt; RptrYrbk; RptrSchPpr; 4-H; LetterBsktbl; LetterFtbl; LetterTrk; Ks St U; Law.

MUSIL, Joann K; Ravenna Sr HS; Ravenna, NE; SecTrsJrCls; SchPl; FHA; Trade Schl; Vocation.

MUSIL, Terri S; Wilber Clatonia HS; Wilber, NE; Band; CncrtBnd; LbryAde; MrchBnd; PepBnd; FBLA; FHA; PpCl; LetterTrk; IMSpt; 4-HAwd; Business School; Vocation.

MUSKE, Laurice A; Notre Dame HS; Chicago, IL; 16/302 Loyola University; Math.

MUSSATT, Thomas L; Riverton HS; Riverton, IL; PresAud/Vis; HonRl; PresNHS; NatlMeritCmnd; EdYrBk; SptEdYrbk; SptEdSchPpr; Bsbl; LetterBsktbl; LetterUniv Of Ill; Electrical Engineering.

MUSSELMAN, Ann M; Lexington HS; Lexington, IL; 12/60 AFS; Chr; CncrtBnd; HonRl; PolWkr; SchPl; TchrAde; RptrYrbk; SciCl; GAA; Ill Wesleyan Univ; Music Education.

MUSSELMAN, Ken W; North Miami HS; Macy, IN; 12/119 PresSophCls; PresJrCls; Aud/Vis; HonRl; NHS; YthFlsp; 4-H; FFA; LetterBsktbl; Trk; Purdue Univ; Farming.

MUSSER, Luann; Clinton HS; Clinton, MI; HonRl; TchrAde; SpnCl;.

MUSSER, William M; Spring Grove HS; Spring Grove, MN; Band; Chr; HonRl; NHS; StuCncl; StuGov; Yrbk; SchPpr; 4-H; SpnCl; College; Teacher.

MUSSMAN, Brenda K; Meridian Public HS; Tobias, NE; Band; Chrs; ChrhWkr; CncrtBnd; HonRl; MrchBnd; PepBnd; SchPl; 4-H; PpCl; College.

MUSSMAN, Michael L; Central Community HS; De Witt, IA; Aud/Vis; ChrhWkr; JA; PolWkr; SctActv; YthFlsp; LetterBsbl; LetterFtbl; JAAwd;.

MUSTOE, Mark M; Elk Valley HS; Elk City, KS; 2/15 ALBoysSt; ChrhWkr; HonRl; MrchBnd; PolWkr; PresStuCncl; PresYthFlsp; Pres4-H; LetterBsbl; LetterBsktbl; LetterFtbl; LetterTrk; Univ Of Kansas; Medicine.

MUSTON, Susanna I; Wesclin HS; New Baden, IL; 6/110 HonRl; JrNHS; NHS; YthFlsp; SchPpr; GerCl; PpCl; College; Professional.

MUSZAR, Michelle A; Heritage Christian HS; Indianapolis, IN; SecTrsFrshCls; Chr; ChrhWkr; HonRl; NHS; SchMus; Yrbk; 4-H; Bob Jones Univ; Music Education.

MUSZYNSKI, Barbara H; N Chicago Comm HS; Great Lakes, IL; 5/257 Chr; Chrs; ChrhWkr; HonRl; NHS; SchAde; StuCncl; TchrAde; SpnCl; PpCl; College; Special Ed.

MUTCH, John C; Larimore HS; Larimore, ND; PresJrCls; ALBoysSt; Band; Chr; CncrtBnd; HonRl; NatlMeritSF; PepBnd; SchMus; LetterWrstlng; AmLegAwd;.

MUTCHLER, Melody A; Lake Central HS; Crown Point, IN; 11/430 ALAGirlsSt; HonRl; NHS; OffAde; University; Mathematics.

MUTER, Deanna; Port Hope Comm HS; Port Hope, MI; 6/17 Chrs; SctActv; RptrSchPpr; SptEdSchPpr; FHA; Bsktbl; College; Vocation.

MUTH, David J; Rockwell Swaledale Comm HS; Mason City, IA; CmntyWkr; HonRl; RptrSchPpr; LetterTrk; Electrician Apprentice; Electrician.

MUTH, Kari L; Forestburg Independent HS; Forestburg, SD; Chrs; HonRl; SchPl; StuCncl; Yrbk; RptrSchPpr; SchPpr; SpnCl; LetterBsktbl; LetterChrldr; Taximeroly.

MUTH, Margaret V; Maplewood Acad; Sanborn, IA; ChrhWkr; HonRl; HospAde; RptrYrbk; RptrSchPpr; Bsktbl; IMSpt; Union Clge; Medicine.

MUTH, Matthew R; Coloma HS; Coloma, MI; HonRl; NHS; TchrAde; RptrSchPpr; LatCl; LetterFtbl; Michigan St University; Law Enforcement.

MUTH, Randy; Britton HS; Britton, SD; 2/85 PresFrshCls; PresSophCls; PresJrCls; PresSrCls; ALBoysSt; Band; HonRl; Univ; Professionsl.

MUTH, Sheryl M; Hartford Union HS; Hubertus, WI; AFS; ChrhWkr; HonRl; JrNHS; LbryAde; NatlFornLg; RptrYrbk; SpnCl; Mount Mary College; Fashion Design.

MUTIS, Paul W; Reavis HS; Chicago, IL; Band; CtyCnl; CncrtBnd; HonRl; MrchBnd; PepBnd; SchMus; SctActv; RptrSchPpr; SptEdSchPpr; GerCl; MthCl; St Xaviers College; Business.

MUTSCHLER, Sally L; Saranac HS; Saranac, MI; 9/78 Band; ChrhWkr; CncrtBnd; HonRl; MrchBnd; NHS; TchrAde; SpnCl; Univ Of Michigan; Law.

MUTZ, Geri J; St Francis Academy; Joliet, IL; ChrhWkr; HonRl; PresJA; PolWkr; SchMus; Yrbk; CchngActv; GAA; IMSpt; PPFtbl; Joliet Jr Clg; Art.

MUTZIGER, Susan M; United Township HS; East Moline, IL; 12/651 Chr; ChrhWkr; HonRl; LbryAde; NHS; YthFlsp; Trk; GAA; ChmbCommrsAwd; College; Science.

MUUR, Kevin; Thomson Hs; Thomson, IL; 11/40 CncrtBnd; HonRl; Mdrgl; MrchBnd; PepBnd; SchMus; YthFlsp; 4-H; FFA; Bsktbl; Wheaton College.

MUUS, Patrick K; Bishop Ryan HS; Minot, ND; ALBoysSt; Band; ChrhWkr; NHS; Orch; PepBnd; Sacrstn; SchPl; Glf; LetterWrstlng; Nd St Univ; Engr.

MUUS, Patrick K; Ryan HS; Minot, ND; Band; Chrs; ChrhWkr; CmntyWkr; CncrtBnd; HonRl; JrNHS; MrchBnd; NHS; PepBnd; SchMus; KeyCl; LetterWrstlng; Univ; Professional.

MUVICH, Carol; George Rogers Clark HS; Whiting, IN; 59/260 ChrhWkr; HospAde; Quill&Scroll; TchrAde; SpnCl; PpCl; GAA; IMSpt; College; Nursing.

MUYLEART, Diane G; Mt Olive Community HS; Staunton, IL; 17/56 Chrs; HonRl; LbryAde; SchPl; SecFHA; PpCl; Socr; LetterTrk; IMSpt; PresAwd; Coll; Self Employ.

MUZZY, Karen; Argyle Public HS; Argyle, MN; 1/31 PresJrCls; VPSrCls; ALAGirlsSt; CncrtBnd; HonRl; SchAde; StuCncl; TchrAde; Bsktbl; GAA; College; Business Educ.

MUZZY, Russell; Corunna HS; Corunna, MI; 60/196 JA; Swmmng; Air Force.

MYCKOWIAK, Antoinette M; St Stephen Area HS; Saginaw, MI; TrsJrCls; CmntyWkr; HonRl; LbryAde; NHS; RptrYrbk; Mi St Univ; Accounting.

MYCKOWIAK, Michael E; St Stephen Area HS; Saginaw, MI; Mich State Univ; Law.

MYDLAND, Gayle; Langford HS; Pierpont, SD; SecTrsFrshCls; HstJrCls; ALAGirlsSt; Band; HonRl; MrchBnd; SchPl; RptrYrbk; PpCl; Chrldr; South Dakota State Univ; Foods.

MYEARS, Helen J; Green Ridge R Viii HS; Green Ridge, MO; 7/34 HonRl; FFA; FHA; Warrensburg.

MYER, Cindy J; Chenoa HS; Chenoa, IL; 12/60 AFS; Chrs; CncrtBnd; HonRl; HospAde; NHS; SchMus; StuCncl; 4-H; SpnCl; GAA; Univ; Nurse.

MYER, Danny R; Cahokia HS; Cahokia, IL; 60/559 Band; HonRl; JA; MrchBnd; PepBnd; PpCl; Bsbl; Tennis; JAAwd; So Il Univ; Bs Of Business.

MYER, Robert S; Harrison HS; Evansville, IN; 69/530 HonRl; NHS; SchAde; LetterBsbl; CaptFtbl; LetterTrk; LetterWrstlng; IMSpt; ChmbCommrsAwd; Univ Of Evansville; Professional.

MYERS, Anna M; Smith Center HS; Gaylord, KS; Chr; ChrhWkr; PresDrlTm; HonRl; FHA; PpCl; College; Home Ec Major.

MYERS, Anne D; Leaf River HS; German Valley, IL; 10/35 Band; Chrs; ALBoysSt; HonRl; StuCncl; 4-H; SpnCl; PpCl; GAA; 4-HAwd; Trade School; Fashion Merchandising.

MYERS, Barbara; Midway Usd 433 HS; Denton, KS; TrsJrCls; Chr; Chrs; CncrtBnd; HonRl; MrchBnd; NHS; SchAde; SctActv; Chrldr; College; Med Tech.

MYERS, Barry L; Jackson HS; Jackson, MI; Band; HonRl; MrchBnd; NHS; Orch; PepBnd; PolWkr; SchMus; GerCl; Western Mich Or Um; Cpa.

MYERS, Brenda; Hyde Co Ind HS; Onida, SD; 4/54 DrlTm; HonRl; NHS; SchPl; EdYrBk; FHA; Bsktbl; GAA; IMSpt; S Dak State Univ; Home Ec.

MYERS, Carla J; E Richland HS; Olney, IL; 9/260 Band; Chrs; ChrhWkr; DrmMjrt; HospAde; Mdrgl; NHS; SchMus; AmLegAwd; College; Nursing.

MYERS, David A; Riceville Community HS; Riceville, IA; SecFrshCls; SecSophCls; VPSrCls; HonRl; LbryAde; LetterFtbl; LetterTrk;.

MYERS, Denise L; Arcadia Valley HS; Arcadia, MO; SecTrsSophCls; Band; Chr; Chrs; ChrhWkr; CmntyWkr; CncrtBnd; HonRl; SchPl;.

MYERS, Diana M; Greenfield Central HS; Greenfield, IN; 33/295 HonRl; NHS; RptrYrbk; FTA; FrCl; CaptBsktbl; Trk; GAA; PPFtbl; Indiana Univ; Physical Education.

MYERS, Donna; Arkansaw HS; Arkansaw, WI; 10/33 Band; Chr; CmntyWkr; CncrtBnd; HonRl; JA; MrchBnd; RptrYrbk; RptrSchPpr; GAA; Nursing.

MYERS, Elizabeth A; Bosworth R V HS; Bosworth, MO; 3/19 Chrs; CncrtBnd; HonRl; OffAde; SchMus; SchPl; YthFlsp; LetterBsbl; LetterBsktbl; 4-HAwd; Trade; Artist.

MYERS, Greg A; Oak Ridge HS; Friedheim, MO; TrsFrshCls; PresSrCls; Band; ChrhWkr; CncrtBnd; HonRl; MrchBnd; SchPl; StuCncl; LetterBsbl; LetterBsktbl; College.

MYERS, Gregory A; Brazil Sr HS; Brazil, IN; 1/160 ALBoysSt; HonRl; NHS; PpCl; LetterTrk; Rose Hulman Inst Of Tech; Engineering.

MYERS, James M; State HS; Terre Haute, IN; 11/53 CmntyWkr; HonRl; NHS; SchAde; KeyCl; Bsbl; Bsktbl; Glf; Trk; AmLegAwd; Trade Sch; Professional.

MYERS, James R; Taylorville HS; Taylorville, IL; HonRl; KeyCl; LetterTrk; Eastern Ill Univ; Engineering.

MYERS, Jimmie B; Slater HS; Marshall, MO; 5/56 PresJrCls; TrsSrCls; HonRl; StuCncl; Yrbk; 4-H; BauchLmbAwd; OptClAwd; College.

MYERS, Jolene P; Winona HS; La Moille, MN; Chr; ChrhWkr; HonRl; College; Elementary Education.

MYERS, Jolynne; Perry Lecompton HS; Perry, KS; 2/66 SecFrshCls; SecSophCls; Chrl; HonRl; NHS; SecNatlThespSoc; SchMus; TchrAde; PpCl; Chrldr; Univ Of Ks; Nursing.

MYERS, Karen S; Oak Park HS; Kansas City, MO; Chr; ChrhWkr; HonRl; Mdrgl; SchMus; SctActv; College; Medicine.

MYERS, Kathleen A; Big Foot HS; Fontana, WI; 10/170 Chrs; HonRl; Orch; SchMus; YthFlsp; SpnCl; LetterTennis; Trk; GAA; IMSpt; College; Medicine.

MYERS, Kathleen J; Colchester HS; Colchester, IL; CmntyWkr; HonRl; HospAde; StuCncl; RptrSchPpr; SchPpr; MthCl; GAA; College; Graphic Arts.

MYERS, Kay L; Plainfield Jr Sr HS; Plainfield, IN; ALAGirlsSt; Chr; HonRl; SchMus; SchPl; FBLA; FHA; FTA; FrCl; Trk; Married.

MYERS, Linda K; Bellmont HS; Decatur, IN; ChrhWkr; HonRl; TchrAde; SpnCl; LetterGAA; PPFtbl; Ball State Univ; Secretary.

MYERS, Linda M; United Township HS; Silvis, IL; Chr; HonRl; SchPl; SctActv; StuCncl; Teen; FrCl; GAA; College.

MYERS, Lisa K; Maroa Forsyth HS; Maroa, IL; PresBand; Chr; Chrs; ChrhWkr; CncrtBnd; HonRl; HospAde; LbryAde; MrchBnd; Chrldr; GAA; PresAwd; College; Nursing.

MYERS, Marcella J; Rushford HS; Rushford, MN; VPJrCls; ALAGirlsSt; Chr; Chrs; HonRl; Mdrgl; NHS; SchPl; YthFlsp; FFA; Business Sch; Legal Sec.

MYERS, Michael B; Barneveld HS; Barneveld, WI; ALBoysSt; Chrs; HonRl; SctActv; Bsbl; Bsktbl; LetterFtbl; LetterGlf; LetterWrstlng; Military Service.

MYERS, Michael S; North Wood HS; Nappanee, IN; 83/200 HonRl; StuCncl; YthFnd; PpCl; LetterFtbl; CaptTrk; IMSpt; JETSAwd; PresAwd; Jr College; Structual Engineering.

MYERS, Mike R; Columbus Public HS; Columbus, ND; PresJrCls; Band; Chr; Chrs; ChrhWkr; CncrtBnd; HonRl; MrchBnd; PepBnd; StuCncl; EdSchPpr; Bsktbl; Ftbl; Univ; Doctor.

MYERS, Norman L; Waldron Area HS; Waldron, MI; 7/51 HonRl; NHS; Univ; Microbiology.

MYERS, Pamela; West Central Hs; Hartford, SD; ChrhWkr; CmntyWkr; HospAde; RedCrAde; RptrSchPpr; EdSchPpr; PresFHA; AmLegAwd; ChmbCommrsAwd;.

MYERS, Pamela L; Vandercook Lake HS; Jackson, MI; 5/92 SecFrshCls; PresSophCls; PresJrCls; PresBand; NHS; SchPl; StuCncl; StuGov; SptEdSchPpr; Trk; Western; Physical Ed.

MYERS, Raymond S; Northeastern HS; Fountain City, IN; 27/130 Band; ChrhWkr; CncrtBnd; MrchBnd; PepBnd; StuCncl; 4-H; FSA; SpnCl; LetterWrstlng; College; Engineering.

MYERS, Regina K; Colchester #180 HS; Plymouth, IL; VPFrshCls; Chrs; ChrhWkr; HonRl; NHS; SchMus; Yrbk; SecGAA; AmLegAwd; DARAwd; Bus Sch; Vocational.

MYERS, Richard J; Faulkton HS; Faulkton, SD; ALBoysSt; Chrs; HonRl; SchPl; RptrSchPpr; 4-H; Bsktbl; Trk; AmLegAwd; Trade School; Accounting.

MYERS, Robert C; Fairview HS; Fairview, MI; ChrhWkr; SchPl; YthFlsp; EdYrBk; College.

MYERS, Robert K; Hinckley Big Rock HS; Hinckley, IL; Band; CncrtBnd; HonRl; MrchBnd; TreasNHS; PepBnd; Sdlty; DanFAwd; Jr Clge; Accntng.

MYERS, Robert L; Warsaw Comm HS; Warsaw, IN; Band; CncrtBnd; JA; MrchBnd; NatlMeritSF; PepBnd; SchMus; RptrSchPpr; JAAwd; Purdue Univ; Elec Engineering.

MYERS, Roy V; Turkey Valley HS; Waucoma, IA; 4/110 HonRl; NatlFornLg; NHS; RptrSchPpr; Iowa State Univ; Computer Science.

MYERS, Serese S; Sunset Hill HS; Kansas City, MO; 11/32 Chr; HonRl; NatlMeritCmnd; SchMus; SchPl; SctActv; PpCl; Chrldr; CchngActv; Univ;.

MYERS, Shirley A; Nokomis HS; Nokomis, IL; Chrldr; GAA; Business Sch; Secretary.

MYERS, Teresa L; Missouri Blind HS; Ozark, MO; 1/15 Chrs; HonRl; PolWkr; SchMus; StuCncl; RptrSchPpr; Swmmng; Univ Mo; Special Education.

MYERS, Terry E; Delta HS; Dunkirk, IN; 21/225 Chrl; ChrhWkr; NHS; StuCncl; PpCl; VPSciCl; LetterBsbl; IMSpt; Purdue U; Computer Science.

MYERS, Thomas B; Columbia City Joint HS; Columbia City, IN; 9/350 HonRl; NHS; 4-H; FrCl; College; Art.

MYERS, Thomas J; Oconomowoc Sr HS; Oconomowoc, WI; AFS; HospAde; NHS; SctActv; StuGov; RptrSchPpr; GerCl; LatCl; SciCl; Univ Wisc; Medicine.

MYERS, Thomas O; Spencer HS; Spencer, IA; LetterFtbl; LetterWrstlng; Iowa Lakes Comm Clg; Auto Mechanics.

MYERS, Verne H; Elmhurst HS; Fort Wayne, IN; 5/400 Band; ChrhWkr; CncrtBnd; HonRl; MrchBnd; Orch; PolWkr; YthFlsp; RptrSchPpr; College.

MYERS, Vicky J; Brown County HS; Nashville, IN; 9/169 HonRl; NHS; NatlThespSoc; LatCl; Indiana Univ; Education.

MYHRE, Sue E; Whitnall HS; Hales Corners, WI; 7/259 Chrs; ChrhWkr; HonRl; NHS; GerCl; MthCl; CaptBsktbl; CchngActv; GAA; IMSpt; Carthage Clg; Phy Ed.

MYKLEBUST, Anna M; Wis Dells HS; Baraboo, WI; AFS; Chrs; CncrtBnd; HonRl; NatlFornLg; NHS; StuCncl; LetterBsktbl; LetterTrk; GAA; College; Pre Med Or Pre Law.

MYRAN, Kim; Hawley HS; Hawley, MN; Band; Chr; ChrhWkr; CncrtBnd; MrchBnd; PepBnd; SchMus; SchPl; StuCncl; SchPpr; College; Architect.

MYRANT, Rog A; Ft Zumwalt HS; O Fallon, MO; 13/354 HonRl; NHS; NatlMeritCmnd; College; Engineering.

MYREN, Douglas A; Somerset Public HS; Somerset, WI; 1/70 CncrtBnd; HonRl; MrchBnd; PepBnd; StuCncl; SchPpr; PpCl; CaptBsbl; CaptBsktbl; CaptFtbl; Coll; Law.

MYREN, Terry J; Holmen HS; Holmen, WI; 12/115 Band; Chr; Chrs; CncrtBnd; HonRl; MrchBnd; PepBnd; LetterFtbl; Trk; College; Teaching.

MYRKLE, Mary L; Durand HS; Bancroft, MI; Band; Chr; MrchBnd; PepBnd; Quill&Scroll; RptrYrbk; RptrSchPpr; SchPpr; Central Mich; Music Ed.

MYROM, Kathryn G; Glenwood Central HS; Glenwood, MN; 18/150 Chr; ChrhWkr; CmntyWkr; CncrtBnd; HonRl; SchMus; SchPl; StuCncl; LetterTennis; Chrldr; IMSpt; PPFtbl; PresAwd; College; Professional.

MYRVOLD, Lynne T; Glenbrook No HS; Northbrook, IL; 26/604 ChrhWkr; HonRl; LitMag; Teen; Socr; Swmmng; Univ; Special Education.

MYSHKA, Ann M; Newman HS; Wausau, WI; 12/130 SecJrCls; Chrs; HonRl; NHS; SchMus; SchPl; StuGov; RptrYrbk; EdYrBk; SciCl; Chrldr; College; Nursing.

MYSZKA, Charles J; Holy Redeemer HS; Detroit, MI; 35/190 HstJrCls; PresSrCls; HonRl; NHS; NatlSciFnd; StuCncl; StuGov; RptrYrbk; FDA; Trk; IMSpt; College; Medicine.

MYSZKOWSKI, Karen; Warren HS; Warren, MN; Chr; Chrs; ChrhWkr; CmntyWkr; HonRl; SchPl; RptrYrbk; RptrSchPpr; FHA; GerCl;.

MYSZKOWSKI, Susan L; Wenona Comm HS; Wenona, IL; 17/42 TrsJrCls; ALAGirlsSt; Chrs; HonRl; LbryAde; SchAde; SchMus; Jr College; Music.

N

NABB, Kevin L; O Fallon Twsp HS; O Fallon, IL; 2/300 PresFrshCls; PresSophCls; PresJrCls; CncrtBnd; HonRl; PepBnd; StuCncl; SchPpr; LetterBsbl; LetterFtbl; College; Commercial Art.

NABER, Helen M; Palatine HS; Palatine, IL; 8/450 Chr; ChrhWkr; CmntyWkr; HonRl; HospAde; SchMus; SchPl; SecYthFlsp; College; Youth Worker.

NABERS, Maribeth; Valmeyer Hs; Walmeyer, IL; 4/66 Band; Chrs; HonRl; NHS; SchMus; SchPl; 4-H; FHA; KeyCl; 4-HAwd; College; Home Economics.

NABITY, Cynthia; Central Catholic HS; Grand Island, NE; SecTrsSophCls; SecTrsSrCls; HonRl; NHS; StuCncl; Yrbk; PpCl; PPFtbl; Hastings College; Art Therapist.

NACE, Vaughn M; Portageville HS; Portageville, MO; 8/74 PresSophCls; PresJrCls; VPSrCls; Band; CncrtBnd; HonRl; MrchBnd; NHS; PepBnd; SchPl; RptrYrbk; EdSchPpr; Univ Of Missouri; Orthopedic Surgery.

NACHAZEL, Ann M; Our Lady Of The Sea HS; Grosse Pointe, MI; PresSophCls; HonRl; HospAde; NatlFornLg; NHS; SchMus; StuCncl; RptrSchPpr; LetterTennis; IMSpt; Univ; Medicine.

NACHBAR, Mark L; Highland Park HS; Highland Park, IL; NatlFornLg; PolWkr; StuCncl; RptrSchPpr; CivCl; Tulane Univ; Lawyer.

NACHMAN, David R; Pembroke Country Day HS; Kansas City, MO; 3/49 HonRl; NatlMeritFnl; NatlMeritSF; SchMus; SchPl; StuGov; RptrYrbk; EdSchPpr; Socr; SARAwd; Stanford.

NACK, Jeffrey J; Lincoln HS; Wis Rapids, WI; HonRl; NHS; LetterTrk; College; Math.

NACKE, Annette M; Duchesne HS; St Charles, MO; HonRl; FrCl; PpCl; IMSpt; Trade School.

NADING, Jeff L; Boone HS; Boone, IA; ALBoysSt; ChrhWkr; HonRl; JrNHS; StuCncl; YthFlsp; SpnCl; Bsktbl; Ftbl; Trk; College; Engineering.

NADLER, Diane; Peotone HS; Peotone, IL; HonRl; LbryAde; 4-H; SpnCl; PpCl; Eastern Ill Univ; Art History.

NADLER, Steve A; Oakville HS; St Louis, MO; Band; CncrtBnd; HonRl; MrchBnd; ChmnSwmmng; College; Biological Science.

NADOLNY, Paul R; Marist HS; Flossmoor, IL; HonRl; NatlMeritFnl; PolWkr; Wrstlng; U Of Chicago; Political Science.

NADOLNY, Susan M; Elizabeth Seton HS; Flossmoor, IL; HonRl; LatCl; Univ; Biology.

NADOLSKI, Connie; Bishop Noll HS; East Chicago, IN; HonRl; HospAde; 4-H; PpCl; Purdue College; Home Ec Teacher.

NADOLSKI, Cynthia A; Waltonville HS; Scheller, IL; 10/38 Band; Chrs; HonRl; LbryAde; SchPl; RptrYrbk; FHA; GerCl; PpCl; GAA; Business School; Vocational.

NAEGER, David J; Valle HS; Ste Genevieve, MO; VPSophCls; Band; Chr; Chrs; CncrtBnd; HonRl; MrchBnd; NHS; SchMus; SctActv; RptrYrbk; Yrbk; College; Professional.

NAEGLE, Gary L; Waterford Township HS; Holly, MI; HonRl; JA; SctActv; LetterTrk; Brigham Young U; Engineering.

NAFFIE, Anne T; Manistee Catholic Central HS; Manistee, MI; 41/69 VPSophCls; Band; CncrtBnd; HonRl; MrchBnd; NHS; Twrl; RptrYrbk; Grand Valley St College; Special Education.

NAFFZIGER, Connie M; Cedar Springs HS; Cedar Springs, MI; HonRl; 4-H; PresFHA; Trk; PPFtbl; Us Air Force; Nurses Corps.

NAFFZIGER, Janet L; Olympia HS; Armington, IL; ALAGirlsSt; HonRl; 4-H; PpCl; GAA; 4-HAwd; JAAwd; Secretary.

NAFFZIGER, Terri L; Deer Creek Mackinaw HS; Mackinaw, IL; 1/60 HonRl; StuCncl; YthFlsp; Yrbk; Illinois Wesleyan Univ; French.

NAFZIGER, Douglas W; Gridley HS; Gridley, IL; Taylor Univ; Systems Analysis.

NAFZIGER, Joyce E; Deer Creek Mackinaw HS; Tremont, IL; 2/65 VPSrCls; Chrs; HonRl; SchPl; YthFlsp; 4-H; PpCl; IMSpt; Goshen College; Counselor.

NAGAKI, Cynthia; Alliance HS; Alliance, NE; 4/154 HonRl; NHS; Quill&Scroll; RptrYrbk; 4-H; College; Elementary Education.

NAGAKI, Linda K; Alliance HS; Alliance, NE; DrlTm; HonRl; NHS; NatlThespSoc; Quill&Scroll; SchPl; UNYO; Yrbk; 4-H; PpCl; Coll; Pro.

NAGEL, Barry T; Rift Valley Academy; Hamilton, IL; Band; Chr; HonRl; FrCl; SciCl; Bsktbl; Socr; College; Medicine.

NAGEL, Brian; William J Bogan Hs; Chicago, IL; 14/704 HonRl; NHS; NatlMeritSchl; OffAde; YthFlsp; RptrSchPpr; PresGerCl; SciCl; U Of Ill; Computer Science.

NAGEL, Doris K; Morrison Comm HS; Morrison, IL; 3/127 SecSophCls; SecJrCls; TrsSrCls; ALAGirlsSt; Band; Mdrgl; NHS; NatlThespSoc; Quill&Scroll; VPStuCncl; Univ; Math Or Acct.

NAGEL, Gary T; Eonnos Central HS; Linton, ND; 5/36 ChrhWkr; CmntyWkr; HonRl; NHS; SchAde; StuCncl; SptEdSchPpr; 4-H; TrsSophCls; LetterFtbl; Coll; Chemistry.

NAGEL, Jeffery J; Providence HS; Lockport, IL; 3/121 TrsFrshCls; Chrs; ChrhWkr; HonRl; NHS; SchMus; StuCncl; RptrSchPpr; SptEdSchPpr; SchPpr; TreasSpnCl; Bsktbl; Ftbl; Tennis; University Of Illinois; Computer Science.

NAGEL, Jennifer S; Ludington HS; Ludington, MI; HonRl; HospAde; PpCl; IMSpt; Clg; Med Lab Tech.

NAGEL, Kathy; St Gertrudes HS; Raleigh, ND; Chr; Chrs; HonRl; SchMus;.

NAGEL, Lorraine; Saint Gertrudes HS; Raleigh, ND; Chr; Chrs; HonRl; SchMus; SchPl;.

NAGEL, Marian J; Immaculata HS; Detroit, MI; Chr; ChrhWkr; HonRl; NHS; SchMus; SchPl; SctActv; John Carroll University; History.

NAGEL, Mark A; Sherburn HS; Sherburn, MN; 27/61 Band; CncrtBnd; HonRl; MrchBnd; PepBnd; LetterBsktbl; LetterTrk; Vocational Sch; Tv Radio Electronics.

NAGEL, Ronald; Warsaw HS; Basco, IL; TrsJrCls; Chr; HonRl; NHS; YthFlsp; FFA; College.

NAGEL, Sally J; Bloomington HS; Bloomington, IL; 1/391 HonRl; NatlMeritSF; FrCl; MthCl; PpCl; LetterTennis; Univ Of Illinois; Law.

NAGEL, Tim J; Dike Community HS; Dike, IA; 2/45 PresFrshCls; ALBoysSt; Band; PresChrhWkr; CncrtBnd; HonRl; MrchBnd; NHS; NatlMeritCmnd; StuCncl; LetterTrk; College.

NAGELE, Mark J; Sheldon HS; Sheldon, IL; 2/26 VPFrshCls; SecJrCls; Band; HonRl; StuCncl; RptrYrbk; FFA; CaptBsbl; CaptBsktbl; LetterTrk; Jr College; Diesel Mechanic.

NAGGATZ, Theodore P; Fairmont HS; Fairmont, ND; PresJrCls; Band; ChrhWkr; CncrtBnd; HonRl; PepBnd; SchPl; SctActv; RptrYrbk; RptrSchPpr; Bsbl; CaptBsktbl; CaptFtbl; Trk; College.

NAGLE, Betsy J; Lake Forest HS; Lake Bluff, IL; 97/435 HonRl; NHS; SchMus; SchPl; PpCl; College; English.

NAGLE, Patricia; Lake Of The Woods HS; Graceton, MN; 9/59 TrsJrCls; Band; Chrs; HonRl; MrchBnd; NHS; RptrSchPpr; SchPpr; FHA; Trk;.

NAGLER, Mary E; Amery HS; Amery, WI; AFS; Band; Chr; HonRl; NHS; NatlMeritSchl; SchPl; EdSchPpr; PpCl; Chrldr; College.

NAGLICH, Dennis M; Worden HS; Worden, IL; 2/20 TrsFrshCls; PresSrCls; University.

NAGORZANSKI, Steven M; Gordon Tech HS; Chicago, IL; 26/584 HonRl; NHS; PolWkr; SctActv; StuCncl; StuGov; SchPpr; Trk; University; Engineering.

NAGRA, David A; Joliet Township HS; Joliet, IL; Band; HonRl; JrNHS; MrchBnd; NHS; Orch; SchMus; GerCl; LetterBsbl; CaptFtbl; College; Science.

NAGY, Martin; Roncalli HS; Beech Grove, IN; TrsSrCls; Band; CncrtBnd; HonRl; MrchBnd; Orch; PepBnd; ROTC; Coll; Journalism.

NAGY, Tibor; Elk Grove HS; Elk Grove Vill, IL; Chr; Chrs; HonRl; NatlFornLg; PolWkr; SctActv; GerCl; Swmmng; LetterTrk; JCAwd; Il State Univ; Pre Law.

NAHIRNIAK, Anne; Immaculate Conception HS; Warren, MI; Chrs; CmntyWkr; HonRl; NHS; RptrSchPpr; Wayne State Univ, Business.

NAHITCHEVANSKY, George H; Loyola Academy; Chicago, IL; 35/442 HonRl; NHS; RptrSchPpr; FrCl; RusCl; SciCl; Georgetown University.

NAIG, Mark A; Osage Community HS; Osage, IA; ChrhWkr; SctActv; Ftbl; Drake Univ; Acct.

NAIMAN, Melody; Fairbury HS; Endicott, NE; ChrhWkr; CmntyWkr; HonRl; SchMus; StuGov; YthFlsp; 4-H; FBLA; GerCl; PresAwd; College; Dentist Assistant.

NAIRN, Pamela A; Van Buren HS; Harmony, IN; 4/75 VPFrshCls; TrsJrCls; TrsSrCls; Band; CncrtBnd; HonRl; MrchBnd; NHS; PepBnd; TchrAde; Yrbk; 4-H; FTA; Chrldr;.

NAKAMURA, Grant Y; Maplewood Academy; New Brighton, MN; ChrhWkr; CmntyWkr; HonRl; SchPl; PresStuGov; TchrAde; RptrYrbk; RptrSchPpr; SciCl; Loma Linda Univ; Medicine.

NAKAZAWA, Susan K; Lane Technical HS; Chicago, IL; 275/1200 LbryAde; SchAde; TchrAde; YthFlsp;.

NAKUTIS, Aldona M; Maria HS; Chicago, IL; SctActv; StuCncl; GerCl; LetterBsktbl; Trk; CchngActv; GAA; IMSpt; College; Medical Tech.

NALL, Thomas; Buffalo Grove HS; Buffalo Grove, IL; 24/280 Band; CncrtBnd; HonRl; MrchBnd; Univ Of Illinois; Electrical Engineer.

NAMANNY, Scott L; Wentworth Military Academy; Denison, IA; HonRl; ROTC; LetterFtbl; LetterGlf; Trade School; Forestry.

NAMYNIUK, Lorraine L; Belfield HS; Belfield, ND; VPFrshCls; SecJrCls; SecSrCls; DrlTm; HonRl; ModUN; TreasStuCncl; Yrbk; SchPpr; FHA; PpCl; VPSciCl; College; Law.

NANCARROW, Kurt W; Cameron HS; Cameron, WI; 3/51 CncrtBnd; NHS; NatlMeritCmnd; SchPl; TreasStuCncl; SptEdYrbk; PresGerCl; CaptBsbl; LetterBsktbl; LetterFtbl; Us Coast Guard Academy; Engineering.

NANCARROW, Leslie S; Brighton HS; Brighton, MI; 5/287 ChrhWkr; HonRl; NHS; SchPl; StuCncl; TchrAde; FrCl; GAA; Michigan State University; Social Science.

NANCE, Betty T; Soldan HS; St Louis, MO; 12/734 ChrhWkr; HonRl; NHS; NatlMeritCmnd; RptrSchPpr; SchPpr; SpnCl; PpCl; Chrldr; PresAwd; Fl St Univ; Education Major.

NANCE, Cynthia L; Maysville R 1 HS; Pattonsburg, MO; 12/67 Chr; Chrs; HonRl; NHS; StuCncl; EdYrBk; RptrSchPpr; FHA; PpCl; 4-HAwd; College; English.

NANCE, Dana W; Phillips Academy; Indianapolis, IN; HonRl; NatlMeritFnl; NatlMeritSF; College.

NANCE, Kathy A; Nevada Sr HS; Nevada, MO; Nursing College; Nursing.

NANCE, Paul A; Crispus Attucks HS; Indianapolis, IN; Band; Chr; HonRl; MrchBnd; Orch; SchPl; KeyCl; LetterBsbl; Bsktbl; LetterFtbl; IMSpt;.

NANCE, Susan; Calhoun HS; Hardin, IL; HonRl; NHS; FHA; PpCl; GAA; Secretarial Trade; Secretary.

NANNETTI, Sheryl M; Libertyville HS; Libertyville, IL; 2/458 HonRl; SecNHS; NatlMeritSF; BauchLmbAwd; College; Medicine.

NANNEY, Rick; Woodland HS; Marble Hill, MO; 2/80 TrsJrCls; ChrhWkr; HonRl; FFA; FrCl; IMSpt; Vocation.

NANNINGA, Gail M; Unity Chr HS; Coopersville, MI; 20/202 Chr; ChrhWkr; HonRl; Mdrgl; StuCncl; Calvin Coll.

NANTZ, Cheryle S; Hubbard HS; Chicago, IL; ChrhWkr; HonRl; StuGov; TchrAde; PpCl; GAA; St Anns Nursing School; Nurse.

NAPIER, Juliet B; Mexico HS; Mexico, MO; Chr; ChrhWkr; HospAde; PresJA; SchMus; SchPl; SctActv; RptrYrbk; PresFrCl; PpCl; College; Theatre Ed.

NAPIER, Robin; Mason Sr HS; Erie, MI; ChrhWkr; HonRl; FTA; GerCl; PPFtbl; VoiceDemAwd; College; Psychology.

NAPIER, Timothy; Osborn HS; Detroit, MI; 11/630 ChrhWkr; CmntyWkr; NHS; SchMus; SchPl; StuCncl; RptrYrbk; KeyCl; LatCl; CitAwd; Hope College; Pediatrician.

NAPIORKOWSKI, Walter C; Little Falls Community HS; Pierz, MN; ChrhWkr; College; Teacher.

NAPLES, Lynn; Kennedy St Paul Hs; Chicago, IL; Chrs; OffAde; StuCncl; 4-H; GAA; 4-HAwd; Triton College; Optemetric Technology.

NAPOLITANO, Phyllis J; Immaculate Heart Of Mary HS; Berwyn, IL; 27/275 RptrSchPpr; Morton College; Art.

NAPPIER, Darrell E; Pacific HS; Gray Summit, MO; 28/186 ChrhWkr; HonRl; YthFlsp; FBLA; Pacific U; Optometrist.

NARAMOR, Craig S; Marshall HS; Marshall, MI; HonRl; LetterBsktbl; Tennis; Trk; IMSpt; Ferris State; Pharmacy.

NARDI, Michael A; Morgan Park Academy; Hickory Hills, IL; Chrs; CtyCnl; HonRl; SchPl; StuGov; YthLg; RptrSchPpr; KeyCl; SpnCl; MthCl; SciCl; CaptTennis; LetterWrstlng; Engineering School; Physics.

NARETTO, Mark M; Gardner So Wilmington HS; Gardner, IL; 5/62 PresJrCls; Band; ChrhWkr; HonRl; MrchBnd; PepBnd; 4-H; MthCl; PpCl; Bsktbl; College; Elec Engineer.

NARHI, Rae M; Baraga HS; Baraga, MI; 17/45 HonRl; LbryAde; NHS; SchPl; RptrYrbk; SchPpr; Sec4-H; PresFHA; Bsktbl; Trk; 4-HAwd; N Mich Univ; Home Economics.

NARHI, Suzanne; Marquette Senior HS; Marquette, MI; 11/374 ChrhWkr; NatlMeritSchl; SctActv; StuCncl; TchrAde; SchPpr; SecFrCl; No Mich Univ; Account.

NARLOCK, Roger M; Midway HS; Inkster, ND; HonRl; SchPl; FFA; Bsbl; Bsktbl; Tennis; Trk; Devils Lake College; Carpentry.

NAROTZKY, Kim G; Ishpeming HS; Ishpeming, MI; 8/199 HonRl; NatlFornLg; NHS; NatlMeritSF; LatCl; Lawrence Univ; Biology.

NARRAGON, Jeffrey L; Vestaburg Community HS; Vestaburg, MI; PresFrshCls; Band; HonRl; MrchBnd; StuCncl; TchrAde; LetterGlf; CchngActv; Central Mich U; Law Enforcement.

NARU, Stephen; Montabella HS; Edmore, MI; 3/100 PresSrCls; ALBoysSt; Band; ChrhWkr; HonRl; MrchBnd; West Point; Army.

NARUP, Rita M; Calhoun HS; Kampsville, IL; Chr; ChrhWkr; CmntyWkr; HonRl; PolWkr; SchAde; TchrAde; FHA; FTA; Business; Vocation.

NARUP, Susan J; Union HS; Union, MO; 9/165 HonRl; LbryAde; NHS; StuCncl; TchrAde; 4-H; FHA; Jr College; Home Ec.

NASE, Beth L; Armour HS; Armour, SD; 6/35 Band; HonRl; SchPl; StuCncl; FHA; LetterBsktbl; Trk; Chrldr; 4-HAwd; College.

NASELLI, Charles; St Rita HS; Chicago, IL; 8/424 Band; CncrtBnd; HonRl; MrchBnd; NHS; NatlMeritCmnd; PepBnd; De Paul University.

NASENBENY, Susan M; Providence HS; Joliet, IL; 14/125 HonRl; JrNHS; NHS; RptrSchPpr; TreasFrCl; MthCl; SciCl; CaptChrldr; IMSpt; KiwanAwd; Eastern Ill Univ; Psychology.

NASER, Terese M; St Marys Acad; Chicago, IL; Chr; Chrs; HonRl; OffAde; SchPl; TchrAde; YthFlsp; SpnCl; Bsktbl; IMSpt; Col; Interior Design.

NASH, Bunny; Whiteland Comm HS; New Whiteland, IN; 17/187 ALAGirlsSt; NHS; NatlThespSoc; SchMus; EdSchPpr; PpCl; GAA; PPFtbl; DARAwd; CitAwd; Ball State Univ; Music Education.

NASH, Carol K; Macomb Sr HS; Macomb, IL; 39/240 Chr; HonRl; NHS; SchPl; SpnCl; Univ; Business Administration.

NASH, Deborah Y; High School; Mineral Point, MO; Band; Chr; CncrtBnd; HonRl; HospAde; JrNHS; MrchBnd; NHS; NatlThespSoc; Orch; PepBnd; SchMus; SchPl; SctActv; RptrYrbk; College; Medicine.

NASH, Donald K; Holcomb HS; Kennett, MO; PresSophCls; PresSrCls; Band; CncrtBnd; HonRl; MrchBnd; PepBnd; SchPl; StuGov; PpCl; College; Mechanical Engineering.

NASH, Grant E; St Joseph HS; St Joseph, MI; LbryAde; NHS; SchAde; StuGov; Lake Michigan Ollege; General Education.

NASH, Kathy M; Benton HS; St Joseph, MO; CmntyWkr; HonRl; LbryAde; ModUN; SchPl; TchrAde; SecFHA; PpCl; Coll; Elem Ed & Spec Ed.

NASH, Laura N; Richwoods HS; Peoria, IL; TrsJrCls; Chr; Chrs; ChrhWkr; CmntyWkr; College; Professional.

NASH, Noreen M; St Clement HS; Center Line, MI; 10/98 SecSophCls; ChrhWkr; HonRl; JrNHS; NHS; OffAde; StuCncl; Teen; FHA; PpCl; Macomb Cty Comm Coll; Sec Studies.

NASH, Patricia; Salem Hs; Salem, MO; 1/170 HonRl; SchMus; SchPl; SpnCl; PpCl; SciCl; PPFtbl;.

NASH, Preston J; Southwestern HS; Flint, MI; ChrhWkr; JA; NatlMeritCmnd; SctActv; YthFlsp; Tuskegee Inst; Architecture.

NASH, Randall R; St Joseph Central HS; St Joseph, MO; CmntyWkr; OffAde; StuGov; YthFlsp; CaptTrk; IMSpt; Sw Mo U.

NASH, Richard A; Sullivan HS; Sullivan, IN; 8/154 Band; CncrtBnd; HonRl; MrchBnd; NHS; Orch; PepBnd; SchMus; 4-H; TreasSpnCl; MthCl; Rose Hulman Inst Tech; Chemistry.

NASH, Steven G; Mason County Eastern HS; Custer, MI; Band; CmntyWkr; CncrtBnd; HonRl; MrchBnd; PepBnd; Yrbk; PpCl; LetterBsbl; LetterBsktbl; West Shore Comm College; Conservation Offcr.

NASH, Vickie L; Wykoff HS; Wykoff, MN; 2/32 Band; Chrs; ChrhWkr; NHS; SchPl; StuGov; EdYrBk; PresFHA; PresFTA; Chrldr; Luther College.

NASHLAND, Gail M; Ewen Trout Creek HS; Ewen, MI; Band; HonRl; LbryAde; PepBnd; SchPl; StuCncl; Chrldr; GAA; IMSpt; LionAwd; Mich Tech U; Pre Med.

NASMAN, Kathryn S; Taylors Falls HS; Shafer, MN; PresSophCls; Band; Chr; Chrs; CncrtBnd; HonRl; MrchBnd; PepBnd; SchPl; StuCncl; RptrYrbk; Bsktbl; Trk; Chrldr; Univ Of Wisconsin; Physical Educ.

NASON, Corinne A; Deer River HS; Ball Club, MN; Chr; HonRl; NHS; Yrbk; RptrSchPpr; GerCl; LetterBsktbl; CaptTrk; GAA; College; Biology.

NASON, Scott T; Pine River HS; Pine River, MN; Band; CncrtBnd; HonRl; LetterTrk; St Cloud State Clg; Electronics.

NASS, James P; Ralston HS; Ralston, NE; Band; ChrhWkr; CAP; CncrtBnd; MrchBnd; SctActv; Wrstlng; Colorado St Univ; Wildlife Mgmt.

NASS, Michael G; Maur Hill Prep; Atchison, KS; 5/50 PresSophCls; ALBoysSt; HonRl; JA; NatlMeritCmnd; PolWkr; StuCncl; StuGov; Bsktbl; CaptFtbl; Ks State Univ; Law.

NASS, Theresa A; Mount Acad; Atchison, KS; PresFrshCls; VPSophCls; Chrs; HonRl; Sdlty; StuCncl; RptrYrbk; SchPpr; Bsktbl; GAA; Coll.

NASSEN, Kent D; Iowa Falls Senior HS; Iowa Falls, IA; 1/148 Band; CncrtBnd; HonRl; MrchBnd; NHS; NatlThespSoc; PepBnd; SchMus; SchPl; Glf; University; Mathematics.

NASSER, Leslie E; Speedway HS; Speedway, IN; 6/191 HonRl; NHS; NatlThespSoc; TchrAde; Yrbk; SpnCl; GAA; Univ; Lawyer.

NASSER, Susan M; Luke M Powers HS; Clio, MI; 5/306 Band; Chr; ChrhWkr; CncrtBnd; HonRl; HospAde; MrchBnd; NHS; Orch; Univ Of Western Mi; Occupational Therapy.

NAST, Daniele B; Oakfield HS; Oakfield, WI; HonRl; JrNHS; RptrSchPpr; EdSchPpr; SciCl; College; Journalism.

NAST, James B; Carl Sandburg HS; Oak Forest, IL; 69/700 HonRl; NatlMeritSF; SpnCl; Univ Of Ill; Lawyer.

NATH, Patricia A; Gretna HS; Waterloo, NE; Chrs; HonRl; NHS; SchMus; TchrAde; VPFHA; PpCl; SciCl; Tech College; Food Service.

NATION, Rita L; Marion Senior HS; Marion, IL; SecJrCls; Chr; CmntyWkr; NHS; PolWkr; StuCncl; CchngActv; PPFtbl; GovHonPrgAwd; KiwanAwd;

LionAwd; RotaryAwd; John A Logan; Management.

NATIONS, Bobbie; Windsor HS; Windsor, MO; 51 Aud/Vis; CtyCnl; CAP; JCC; NHS; RedCrAde; StuCncl; StuGov; FSA; FTA; Work.

NATIONS, Sandy; Mcdonald County HS; Noel, MO; 3/160 VPJrCls; Band; HonRl; NHS; NatlThespSoc; StuCncl; FTA; PpCl; Bsbl; Trk; Oral Roberts Univ; Professional Sciences.

NATTERSTAD, Karen L; Estherville HS; Estherville, IA; 12/182 Chrs; HonRl; Mdrgl; StuCncl; FHA; College; Vocation.

NATTIER, Dina M; Patoka Community #100 HS; Patoka, IL; PresSophCls; ChrhWkr; HonRl; StuCncl; TchrAde; Yrbk; FHA; SpnCl; PpCl; SciCl; Kaskaskia Jr Clg; Elem Education.

NAU, T; Central HS; Salem, WI; 11/208 Band; ChrhWkr; CncrtBnd; HonRl; MrchBnd; NHS; PepBnd; MthCl; SciCl; EldAwd; Carthage College; Law.

NAU, Toni; Central HS; Salem, WI; Band; ChrhWkr; CncrtBnd; HonRl; MrchBnd; PepBnd; Uw Whitewater; Teaching.

NAUER, David J; Lincoln HS; Ypsilanti, MI; HonRl; NatlFornLg; VPNHS; Orch; SchMus; Yrbk; SpnCl; CaptSwmmng; RotaryAwd; U Of Mich; Astronomy.

NAUERT, Christine M; Bishop Du Bourg HS; St Louis, MO; ChrhWkr; HonRl; NHS; StuCncl; EdYrBk; FTA; College; Special Education.

NAUERT, Connie; Larned HS; Larned, KS; 2/97 ALAGirlsSt; HonRl; NHS; TchrAde; PpCl; Tennis; Chrldr; AmLegAwd; Kansas State Univ; Interior Design.

NAUGHTIN, Susan M; Hibbing HS; Hibbing, MN; 20/432 HonRl; JA; NHS; FrCl; PpCl; Bsktbl; Trk; Univ Of Notre Dame; Math.

NAUGHTON, James P; Bogan HS; Chicago, IL; 1/704 HonRl; NHS; NatlMeritCmnd; SchAde; SchPl; RptrSchPpr; SchPpr; GerCl; Univ Of Illinois; Engineering.

NAUGHTON, Kevin J; Brother Rice HS; Chicago, IL; 66/417 ChrhWkr; HonRl; NHS; SchPl; SctActv; RptrYrbk; EdYrBk; CchngActv; St Josephs College; Acc.

NAUGHTON, Martha A; Our Lady Of Grace Academy; Indianapolis, IN; 8/60 Chrs; HonRl; ModUN; NHS; NatlMeritCmnd; SchPpr; IMSpt; College.

NAUGHTON, Michael T; St Patrick HS; Chicago, IL; 37/427 PresSophCls; PresJrCls; ALBoysSt; HonRl; JrNHS; NHS; OffAde; SchAde; StuCncl; TchrAde; De Paul Univ; Accountant.

NAUGHTON, Nancy G; St Scholastica HS; Park Ridge, IL; SecJrCls; TrsSrCls; NHS; StuCncl; University; Law.

NAULT, Linda E; Marshall HS; Marshall, IL; 5/125 NHS; FBLA; Eastern Ill Univ; Research Scientist.

NAULT, Renee R; Ishpeming HS; Ishpeming, MI; 17/200 Chrl; Chrs; CmntyWkr; HonRl; NHS; SchMus; SchPl; StuCncl; CivCl; CitAwd; U Of Mich; Bus Ad.

NAUM, Chris C; Lew Wallace HS; Merrillville, IN; Band; ChrhWkr; CncrtBnd; HonRl; JrNHS; MrchBnd; NHS; Orch; GerCl; Glf; Ind U;pre Med.

NAUMANN, Bonnie J; Bonduel HS; Cecil, WI; 5/123 VPSrCls; Band; PresChrs; ChrhWkr; HonRl; StuCncl; TchrAde; Yrbk; DARAwd; CitAwd; U W Milwaukee; Medicine.

NAUMANN, Deborah L; Winamac Comm HS; Winamac, IN; CncrtBnd; MrchBnd; Orch; PepBnd; StuCncl; Bsktbl; GAA; IMSpt; PPFtbl; CitAwd; Univ; Teach.

NAUMANN, Julie; Elmore Public HS; Elmore, MN; 7/25 HonRl; OffAde; SchPl; Yrbk; FrCl; Vocational Or Trade School; Graphic Designe.

NAUMANN, Robert; Brewster HS; Brewster, MN; HonRl; SchPl; StuCncl; PpCl; Ftbl; Trade School; Vocation.

NAUYOKAS, Nancy A; Franklin HS; Livonia, MI; SecJrCls; VPSrCls; ChrhWkr; HonRl; HospAde; NatlMeritSchl; PolWkr; YthFlsp; LetterBsktbl; GAA;.

NAVARRE, Robert W; Hillsdale HS; Hillsdale, MI; Chrl; Chrs; NHS; TchrAde; KeyCl; SpnCl; LetterBsbl; LetterBsktbl; LetterFtbl; LetterTrk; Coll; Pro.

NAVIN, Susan M; Heelan HS; Sioux City, IA; 109/249 ChrhWkr; HonRl; HospAde; LbryAde; MrchBnd; OffAde; Quill&Scroll; RptrSchPpr; SchPpr; PpCl; College; Social Work.

NAVINE, Marc L; Armstrong HS; Neenah, WI; 24/620 HonRl; Swmmng; PresAwd; Univ Of Wis Oshkosh.

NAVOCK, Deborah A; Port Austin Public HS; Port Austin, MI; 9/39 TrsSrCls; CmntyWkr; HonRl; RedCrAde; SecStuCncl; Yrbk; SchPpr; FHA; PpCl; DARAwd; Business School.

NAWARA, Bruce G; St Laurence HS; Chicago, IL; 22/382 HonRl; Sacrstn; LetterFtbl; LetterSocr; Trk; Univ Of Miami; Architect.

NAWROCKI, Cynthia M; St Clement HS; Center Line, MI; 14/98 HonRl; NatlMeritCmnd; OffAde; StuCncl; SptEdYrbk; Yrbk; FHA; PpCl; Bsktbl; GAA; Eastern Michigan Univ; Accounting.

NAYER, Richard A; Univ Of Chicago HS; Chicago, IL; Orch; TchrAde; LetterTrk; College; Vet.

NAYES, Lee A; Bismarck HS; Bismarck, ND; 10/586 Band; ChrhWkr; CncrtBnd; HonRl; NHS; NatlMeritSF; College; Electrical Engineering.

NAYLON, Michaela; Marian HS; Omaha, NE; DrlTm; HonRl; Trk; IMSpt; Coll; Medical Field.

NAYLOR, Dorothea M; Civic Memorial HS; Bethalto, IL; 17/250 HonRl; NHS; FHA; GAA; PPFtbl; College ; Vocational.

NAYLOR, Kristina L; Stevens HS; Rapid City, SD; 1/415 AFS; Chr; HonRl; NHS; SchMus; SchPl; StuCncl; RptrSchPpr; 4-H; LetterTennis; Sd State Univ; Foreign Language.

NEAGLE, Linda K; Crestland Comm HS; Nemaha, IA; Band; Chr; CncrtBnd; HonRl; MrchBnd; PepBnd; RptrYrbk; 4-H; LetterGlf; Nursing Schl; Nursing.

NEAHRING, John M; Sterling HS; Sterling, IL; 40/407 Aud/Vis; ChrhWkr; HonRl; NHS; OffAde; SchAde; YthFlsp; 4-H; FFA; College; Speech.

NEAL, Brenda K; Lake Central HS; Schererville, IN; 26/453 NHS; Indiana University; Allied Health.

NEAL, Brenda M; Westville HS; Danville, IL; ChrhWkr; HonRl; FHA; PpCl; Junior College; Professional.

NEAL, D A; Raymore Peculiar HS; Peculiar, MO; 10/116 Band; ChrhWkr; CncrtBnd; HonRl; JrNHS; MrchBnd; Orch; PepBnd; SchMus; LionAwd; Med Sch; Physician.

NEAL, Jacki L; Grandview HS; Grandview, MO; SecSrCls; PresChrhWkr; DrlTm; NHS; Quill&Scroll; StuCncl; EdYrBk; SchPpr; FHA; PpCl; Chrldr; PPFtbl; MasAwd; College; English.

NEAL, Joe M; North Knox HS; Oaktown, IN; 3/160 HonRl; JrNHS; StuCncl; VPYthFlsp; 4-H; FFA; LetterBsbl; Bsktbl; LetterFtbl; Purdue Univ ; Agri.

NEAL, Mitzi L; Athens HS; Athens, MI; HonRl; SchPl; TchrAde; PpCl; SciCl; Trk; Chrldr; GAA; College; Officer In Army.

NEAL, Nancy A; Bonner Springs HS; Edwardsville, KS; ChrhWkr; TchrAde; FHA; FrCl; PpCl; School Of The Ozarks; Biology Teacher.

NEAL, Randall E; Brownstown HS; Mdora, IN; 47/143 HonRl; SchPl; TchrAde; FTA; SpnCl; PpCl; College; Teacher.

NEAL, Randi A; Valley Park HS; Valley Park, MO; 16/60 ChrhWkr; VPNatlThespSoc; SchPl; Bsktbl; IMSpt; Meramee Jr Col.

NEAL, Ratina R; Unity HS; Chicago, IL; 89/200 SecFrshCls; Chr; ChrhWkr; OffAde; FHA; SpnCl; Kentucky St Univ; Legal Stenographer.

NEAL, Thomas C; Lake Shore HS; St Clair Shores, MI; 6/781 Band; ChrhWkr; CncrtBnd; HonRl; MrchBnd; NHS; NatlSciFnd; YthFlsp; Bsktbl; Mi Tech Univ; Chemical Engineering.

NEALE, Lori J; Watertown Sr HS; Watertown, SD; 27/326 ALAGirlsSt; CmntyWkr; CncrtBnd; DrlTm; NHS; NatlThespSoc; PolWkr; SchPl; SchPpr; Chrldr; College; Actress.

NEARING, Cherie A; Douglas Mac Arthur HS; Saginaw, MI; VPSrCls; HonRl; NHS; StuCncl; StuGov; PpCl; Trk; Saginaw Valley State Coll; Dental Hygiene.

NEARY, Kathleen J; Tekamah Herman HS; Tekamah, NE; 4/66 Band; Chr; SchMus; SchPl; SctActv; Teen; 4-H; FHA; PpCl; LetterBsktbl; Univ Of Ne Lincoln; Medicine.

NEARY, Rita M; Weston HS; Cazenovia, WI; Chr; HonRl; FHA; PpCl; Wwti Of Lacrosse; Dental Asst.

NEASE, Franklin E; Slater HS; Slater, MO; 15/68 VPJrCls; PresSrCls; HonRl; NHS; NatlMeritCmnd; NatlSciFnd; SchPl; SciCl; CaptWrstlng; GodCntryAwd; Univ Of Nebraska; Dentistry.

NEATON, Dorothy M; Port Huron HS; Port Huro, MI; DrlTm; StuCncl; EdSchPpr; LetterTennis; GAA; Mi St Univ; Journalism.

NEATON, Robert; University Of Detroit HS; Detroit, MI; 18/190 HonRl; NatlFornLg; NHS; PolWkr; SchPpr; LatCl; IMSpt; U Of Detroit; Political Science.

NEATON, William; University Of Detroit HS; Detroit, MI; HonRl; PolWkr; FrCl; Bsbl; IMSpt; University Of Detroit; Business And Adm.

NEBEL, Spencer R; W G Mather HS; Wetmore, MI; Band; CncrtBnd; HonRl; MrchBnd; OffAde; PepBnd; SchAde; LatCl; Biology.

NEBY, Karen S; Cumberland HS; Comstock, WI; Chr; Chrl; ChrhWkr; CmntyWkr; HonRl; Mdrgl; SchMus; PresYthFlsp; RptrSchPpr; Sec4-H; FHA; 4-HAwd; Golden Valley Luth Col; Music.

NECHANICKY, Susan M; Ellendale Geneva HS; Ellendale, MN; ALAGirlsSt; Band; Chr; NHS; EdSchPpr; FHA; St Teresas College; Music.

NECHIPORENKO, Rick J; Velva Public HS; Velva, ND; 40/52 Chr; HonRl; JA; TchrAde; FFA; PresGerCl; LetterFtbl; CaptWrstlng; College; Law Enforcement.

NEDERHOFF, Bruce D; Wellsburg Comm HS; Wellsburg, IA; 9/33 VPSrCls; Chr; ChrhWkr; SchMus; SchPl; StuCncl; YthFlsp; Yrbk; Bsktbl; IMSpt; Agriculture.

NEDRELO, Randy L; Seneca HS; Seneca, WI; 3/40 TrsSophCls; CncrtBnd; HonRl; MrchBnd; PepBnd; SctActv; Bsktbl; LetterFtbl; LetterTrk; CchngActv; University; Physical Education.

NEDVED, David L; Garner Hayfield HS; Garner, IA; FFA; Ftbl; Waldorf College; Industrial Art.

NEDVED, Gregory J; Yankton Sr HS; Yankton, SD; ChrhWkr; HonRl; PolWkr; RptrSchPpr; Ftbl; Trk; University.

NEDVED, Patricia A; East Charles Mix HS; Wagner, SD; ALAGirlsSt; Chrs; ChrhWkr; CmntyWkr; HonRl; SctActv; College.

NEDZA, Susan M; Maria HS; Chicago, IL; 11/365 Aud/Vis; HonRl; LitMag; NHS; TreasStuCncl; StuGov; FrCl; GAA; IMSpt; Biochemistry.

NEEB, Pamela A; Freeland HS; Freeland, MI; 7/115 TrsSrCls; Chr; CncrtBnd; HonRl; MrchBnd; NHS; NatlThespSoc; SchMus; Yrbk; College; Broadcasting.

NEECE, Rebecca; Harmon HS; Kansas City, KS; Chrs; HonRl; NHS; RptrYrbk; PpCl; College; Bus Admin.

NEEDHAM, Carol A; Resurrection HS; Chicago, IL; 7/260 JA; PresLbryAde; SecNatlFornLg; NHS; NatlMeritFnl; RedCrAde; StuCncl; SpnCl; MthCl; GAA; IMSpt; BttyCrckrAwd; Northwestern University.

NEEDHAM, Joseph W; Greene Comm HS; Greene, IA; ChrhWkr; CmntyWkr; CncrtBnd; HonRl; MrchBnd; PolWkr; StuCncl; 4-H; AmLegAwd; 4-HAwd; Iowa State U; Political Leader.

NEEDLES, Carrie L; Catholic Memorial HS; Waukesha, WI; ChrhWkr; HonRl; JrNHS; NHS; SctActv; TchrAde; PpCl; Chrldr; College; Art.

NEELAND, David J; Great Bend HS; Great Bend, KS; HonRl; College; Agriculture.

NEELD, Lisa A; Lawrence Central HS; Indianapolis, IN; CmntyWkr; HonRl; JrNHS; SctActv; TchrAde; Twrl; PpCl; LetterTrk; Chrldr; PPFtbl; College; Interior Decorator.

NEELEY, Loretta J; N Division HS; Milwaukee, WI; SecSrCls; Chr; DrlTm; HonRl; MrchBnd; OffAde; SchPl; PpCl; GAA; Nurse.

NEELEY, Randy W; Meadville R 4 HS; Brookfield, MO; TrsFrshCls; PresSophCls; VPSrCls; ChrhWkr; HonRl; NHS; StuCncl; 4-H; PpCl; Trk; University; Agriculture Major.

NEELY, Curtiss V; Rantoul Twp HS; Rantoul, IL; ROTC; LetterBsbl; IMSpt; Trade School; Teacher.

NEELY, Teri L; Newman Grove HS; Newman Grove, NE; Band; CncrtBnd; HonRl; MrchBnd; OffAde; PepBnd; SchPl; RptrSchPpr; FHA; Wrstlng; Trade Sch; Air Lines.

NEEMANN, Steven R; Nemaha Valley HS; Cook, NE; 14/23 Band; Chrs; SchPl; SptEdYrbk; LetterFtbl; Peru St College; Music.

NEER, David L; North Knox HS; Oaktown, IN; 5/154 HonRl; LbryAde; NHS; YthFnd; 4-H; Bsktbl; Ftbl; College.

NEES, Kolleen K; De Soto HS; De Soto, MO; CncrtBnd; HonRl; NHS; StuCncl; RptrYrbk; FBLA; PpCl; SciCl; LetterChrldr; CitAwd; Business School; Vocation.

NEESE, Cathy A; Owensville R 2 HS; Owensville, MO; Band; SecFrshCls; CncrtBnd; HonRl; LbryAde; MrchBnd; NHS; PepBnd; Yrbk; PpCl; College; Major Study.

NEESE, Teresa L; Randolph HS; Belden, NE; SecTrsFrshCls; Chrs; ChrhWkr; CmntyWkr; CaptDrlTm; HonRl; SchMus; StuCncl; SpnCl; PpCl; Coll; Soc Sci.

NEET, Deborah Y; Effingham HS; Effingham, IL; 10/200 SecFrshCls; VPSophCls; DrlTm; HonRl; TreasJA; SchMus; SchPl; PresStuCncl; SpnCl; PpCl; DARAwd; Washington Univ; Physical Therapy.

NEFF, Darlene L; North Miami HS; Peru, IN; Chr; HonRl; LbryAde; OffAde; 4-H; Business College.

NEFF, David B; Goshen HS; Goshen, IN; HonRl; NatlFornLg; Orch; RedCrAde; SchPpr; PpCl; Bsbl; Ftbl; CaptSwmmng; LetterTennis; College; Marine Science.

NEFF, Debra A; Mater Dei HS; Germantown, IL; 13/185 Chrs; HonRl; NHS; SchMus; SchPl; RptrYrbk;.

NEFF, Janice; Lake Forest Acad; Elmhurst, IL; HonRl; NatlMeritCmnd; OffAde; TchrAde; FrCl; MthCl; Bsktbl; GAA; University; Math.

NEFF, Karen A; Warren HS; Warren, IL; 4/59 Band; CncrtBnd; HonRl; LbryAde; MrchBnd; PepBnd; SchMus; TchrAde; Yrbk; SchPpr; 4-H; GAA; Univ Of Wisconsin; Elem Education.

NEFF, Michael W; Custer HS; Custer, SD; 5/54 HonRl; JrNHS; NHS; SpnCl; Ftbl; College; Physics.

NEGHERBON, Doris; Trinity HS; Hutchinson, KS; ChrhWkr; DrlTm; HonRl; SchPl; StuCncl; RptrSchPpr; LatCl; Chrldr; IMSpt; PPFtbl; Emporia Ks St Coll; Phy Ed.

NEGRONI, Christina; Emerson HS; Gary, IN; 21/225 Band; CncrtBnd; HonRl; HospAde; MrchBnd; TreasNHS; LatCl; SpnCl; Purdue Univ; Business Mgmt.

NEHER, Thomas F; Union HS; Union, MO; 10/165 SecSophCls; VPJrCls; Band; CncrtBnd; HonRl; MrchBnd; Orch; PepBnd; StuCncl; Bsktbl; Ftbl; College; Professional.

NEHMAN, Paul F; Lytton Comm HS; Lytton, IA; Aud/Vis; HonRl; SchPpr; Pres4-H; VPFFA; PpCl; Bsbl; VPJrCls; 4-HAwd; CitAwd; Farming.

NEHMER, Wendy L; Kindred HS; Walcott, ND; ALAGirlsSt; Chr; Chrs; HonRl; NHS; TchrAde; 4-H; FHA; Concordia College; Elem Education.

NEHRBASS, Sherri S; Athens HS; Athens, WI; 4/94 PresSrCls; Band; HonRl; LbryAde; NHS; PepBnd; SptEdSchPpr; FHA; LetterBsktbl; Coll; Teaching.

NEHRING, Pamela; Springfield HS; Springfield, IL; 15/585 ChrhWkr; NHS; TchrAde; FrCl; GerCl; MthCl; SciCl; Trk; Univ Of Illinois; Liberal Arts.

NEHRING, Scott L; Whitewater HS; Elkhorn, WI; 11/187 ALBoysSt; ChrhWkr; HonRl; NHS; StuCncl; YthFlsp; KeyCl; Bsbl; CaptBsktbl; AmLegAwd; Univ; Pre Optometry.

NEHRING, Wayne R; Bloomer HS; Bloomer, WI; JA; SchAde; TchrAde; FFA;.

NEHRING, Wendy; Dekalb Sr Hs; Dekalb, IL; 16 Band; HonRl; IntrClCncl; NHS; StuCncl; Teen; YthFlsp; FNA; Bsbl; GAA; Illinois Wesleyan U ; Nursing.

NEHRT, Cynthia K; Mtrpln Dist Vernon Tnsh HS; Crothersville, IN; HstFrshCls; Band; Chr; ChrhWkr; ChrhWkr; HonRl; NHS; PepBnd; YthFlsp; Trk; GAA;.

NEICE, Thomas E; Oshkosh W HS; Oshkosh, WI; 38/402 Chr; HonRl; Mdrgl; NatlMeritSF; LetterTennis; Univ; Engineering.

NEIDERHAUSER, Mark D; Kimberly HS; Combined Locks, WI; 5/278 ALBoysSt; HonRl; JrNHS; NHS; LetterFtbl; LetterWrstlng; Uw Madison; Engineering.

NEIDERMYER, Paul; Spring Valley HS; Spring Valley, WI; HonRl; FFA; Bsktbl; Trade School; Armed Services.

NEIDHARDT, Richard F; Huron HS; Ann Arbor, MI; HonRl; Tennis; Univ; Lawyer.

NEIDHARDT, Sandy D; Hebron Public HS; Hebron, ND; Band; HonRl; Yrbk; Pres4-H; FFA; FHA; 4-HAwd; North Dakota St Univ; Animal Science.

NEIDINGER, Robert J; Naperville Central HS; Geneva, IL; CmntyWkr; HonRl; NHS; NatlMeritSF; University Of Chicago; Computer Science.

NEIER, Robert I; Usd 424 HS; Mullinville, KS; PresSrCls; Aud/Vis; Band; Chrs; ChrhWkr; SchMus; PresYthFlsp; Pres4-H; DanFAwd; 4-HAwd; Hutchinson Comm Jr College; Agriculture.

NEIER, Stephen G; Valley HS; Caledonia, MO; PresFrshCls; Band; CncrtBnd; HonRl; MrchBnd; NHS; SchPl; RptrSchPpr; LetterBsbl; LetterBsktbl; Phy Ed Tchr.

NEIER, Stephen G; Valley Of Caledonia HS; Caledonia, MO; PresFrshCls; Band; CncrtBnd; HonRl; NHS; PepBnd; StuCncl; RptrSchPpr; 4-H; Bsbl;.

NEIFING, James L; Rock Island HS; Rock Island, IL; JrNHS; PolWkr; VPKeyCl; PpCl; Glf; University; Engineering.

NEIGHBORS, Lori S; Marceline R V HS; Marceline, MO; 11/73 ALAGirlsSt; Band; HonRl; StuCncl; RptrYrbk; RptrSchPpr; VPFHA; LetterBsktbl; IMSpt; DARAwd; Clge; Forestry.

NEIKIRK, Barbara S; Mt Carmel HS; Mt Carmel, IL; 4/185 Band; Chrs; NHS; OffAde; 4-H; PpCl; College; Mathematics.

NEIL, Matthew M; Onaway HS; Onaway, MI; HstSrCls; SchPl; IMSpt; Olivet Col ;journalism.

NEIL, Michael T; Weber HS; Bellwood, IL; 46/206 PresFrshCls; VPChr; CaptDrlTm; HonRl; NHS; NatlMeritCmnd; StuCncl; PresYthFlsp; RptrSchPpr; IMSpt; De Paul Univ; Accounting.

NEILANDS, Rachelle A; Benet Acad; Naperville, IL; 24/230 HonRl; JA; PolWkr; RedCrAde; SchPl; SctActv; RptrSchPpr; FrCl; Swmmng; DARAwd; Univ; Major Study.

NEILL, Laurie D; Hillsdale HS; Hillsdale, MI; HonRl; NHS; Orch; College; Music.

NEILL, Susan A; Joliet West HS; Joliet, IL; ChrhWkr; HonRl; HospAde; GAA; College; Health.

NEILSEN, Kitty A; Waupaca HS; Waupaca, WI; Chr; Chrl; Chrs; HonRl; StuCncl; RptrYrbk; Yrbk; SchPpr; LatCl; SpnCl;.

NEILSON, Dana; Lake City HS; Merritt, MI; Band; CncrtBnd; HonRl; MrchBnd; NatlMeritSchl; PepBnd; College ;math Teacher.

NEIMAN, Barbara A; Resurrection HS; Chicago, IL; 4/261 HonRl; LitMag; NHS; NatlMeritCmnd; Quill&Scroll; RptrSchPpr; Northwestern Univ; Journalism.

NEIS, David A; Beaver Dam Sr HS; Beaver Dam, WI; 1/349 ALBoysSt; Chrs; Sacrstn; University; Medical Engineer.

NEISE, Regina M; Bloomington HS; Bloomington, IL; 164/351 Chr; ChrhWkr; CmntyWkr; HospAde; SchPl; SctActv; YthFlsp; 4-H; LatCl; PpCl; GAA; IMSpt; 4-HAwd; Triton College; Dental Tech.

NEISEN, Cindy M; Liberty HS; Fowler, IL; 3/65 TrsSophCls; SecJrCls; HonRl; StuCncl; SchPpr; Quincy College; Business.

NEISWANGER, Yvonne C; North Daviess HS; Odon, IN; 6/122 Chr; ChrhWkr; HonRl; JrNHS; LbryAde; NHS; YthFlsp; FrCl; SpnCl; Deaconess Hospital; Nursing.

NEITEKE, Michael A; Detroit Lakes Sr HS; Detroit Lakes, MN; Chr; StuCncl; Bsbl; Ftbl; Univ Of No Dakota.

NEITLING, Laurel L; Rantoul Twp HS; Thomasboro, IL; 32/398 HonRl; LbryAde; SecNHS; SchMus; SchPl; StuCncl; TchrAde; FNA; SciCl; Mennonite Hosp; Nursing.

NEITLING, Loretta L; Rantoul Township HS; Thomasboro, IL; HonRl; NHS; SchAde; SchMus; SchPl; StuCncl; TchrAde; SchPpr; PresFHA; Eastern Ill Univ; Teach Mathematics.

NEITZEL, Debra R; Bird City HS; St Francis, KS; Band; Chr; Chrl; Chrs; CncrtBnd; HospAde; MrchBnd; Orch; PepBnd; SchMus; SchPl; LetterBsktbl; LetterTrk; Chrldr; Colby Comm College; Secretary.

NEITZEL, Lois J; Horicon HS; Horicon, WI; SecTrsJrCls; HonRl; NHS; Quill&Scroll; SchMus; SchPl; SchPpr; EngCl; SpnCl; Bsktbl; GAA; Mt Mary Clge; Commericial Art.

NEITZKE, Brenda L; Winona Sr HS; Winona, MN; Band; ChrhWkr; CncrtBnd; HonRl; MrchBnd; Concordia College; Deaconess.

NEITZKE, Debora K; Norfolk HS; Norfolk, NE; Band; Chr; ChrhWkr; CncrtBnd; Mdrgl; MrchBnd; Orch; SctActv; TchrAde; YthFlsp; Bus School; Vocation.

NELIS, Mary K; Edgewood HS; Madison, WI; 44/220 CmntyWkr; HonRl; HospAde; SchMus; SctActv; RptrYrbk; PpCl; Univ Wi Madison; Geology.

NELLE, James M; North Farmington Sr HS; Farmington Hills, MI; Band; CncrtBnd; NatlMeritSchl; StuCncl; Bsbl; Trk; IMSpt; Wmu.

NELLES, Louise A; Newman HS; Wausau, WI; 34/131 SecSophCls; PresJrCls; ALAGirlsSt; HonRl; NHS; SchMus; SchPl; StuGov; DARAwd; VoiceDemAwd; Uw Marathon Co; Teach Handicapped.

NELLIGAN, Anthony G; St Ignatius Coll Prep HS; Glen Ellyn, IL; NHS; GerCl; MthCl; University Of Michigan; Professional.

NELLIS, Margaret; Washburn Rural HS; Topeka, KS; 4/180 Chrs; ChrhWkr; HonRl; OffAde; StuCncl; TchrAde; YthFlsp; PpCl; Kansas Univ; Child Dev.

NELMES, Amy S; Cuba HS; Smithfield, IL; 6/69 PresSrCls; CncrtBnd; HonRl; NHS; PepBnd; TreasStuGov; PresYthFlsp; PresLatCl; PresPpCl; Glf; U Of Il; Interior Design.

NELMS, Casey R; Hayes Center Public HS; Hayes Center, NE; 10/24 Chrs; RptrYrbk; SptEdSchPpr; VP4-H; FFA; Bsbl; LetterBsktbl; LetterFtbl; LetterTrk; 4-HAwd; College; Horse Trainer.

NELMS, Sharon M; Republican Valley HS; Indianola, NE; 2/34 ALAGirlsSt; Band; Chr; CncrtBnd; HonRl; MrchBnd; PepBnd; SchMus; StuCncl; YthFlsp; Yrbk; 4-H; College; Music.

NELMS, Vicki T; Pacific HS; Pacific, MO; PresFrshCls; PresSophCls; Band; HonRl; SctActv; TreasStuCncl; RptrYrbk; SptEdSchPpr; LetterBsktbl; OptClAwd; Arkansas State U; Physical Education.

NELSEN, Edna A; Ft Calhoun HS; Ft Calhoun, NE; SecJrCls; SecSrCls; Chr; ChrhWkr; HonRl; NHS; SchPl; TchrAde; EdYrBk; PpCl; College; Professional.

NELSEN, Elaine M; Luther North HS; Chicago, IL; 119/276 HonRl; HospAde; LbryAde; LatCl; College; Medicine.

NELSEN, Laurie K; Stillwater Sr HS; Stillwater, MN; 99/608 AFS; Chr; HonRl; JA; Orch; SchAde; TchrAde; SciCl; University Od Mn Duluth; Medicine.

NELSEN, Lorri S; Mankato West HS; N Mankato, MN; AFS; HonRl; Col; Acctg.

NELSEN, Roxanne M; Wild Rose HS; Poy Sippi, WI; Chr; Chrs; ChrhWkr; CmntyWkr; HonRl; PresLbryAde; SchPl; StuCncl; StuGov; RptrSchPpr; SchPpr; 4-H; FBLA; FHA; SpnCl; Trade School; Child Care.

NELSEN, Russell B; Missouri Valley HS; Missouri Valley, IA; 15/99 HonRl; NHS; FFA; SciCl; Ftbl; CaptWrstlng; CchngActv; KiwanAwd; Univ; Vocation.

NELSEN, Tobi; Union Star R Ii HS; Union Star, MO; NatlMeritSchl; TchrAde; PpCl; Coll; Rn.

NELSESTUEN, Laurie L; Gale Ettrick Trempealeau HS; Ettrick, WI; 7/114 Band; Chr; CncrtBnd; HonRl; MrchBnd; SecNHS; StuCncl; SchPpr; 4-H; FrCl; Uw Madison; Doctor.

NELSIN, Jay N; Petoskey HS; Petoskey, MI; Band; Chr; CncrtBnd; DrmBgl; Mdrgl; MrchBnd; PepBnd; TchrAde; YthFlsp; Olivet College; Music.

NELSON, Althea E; Balaton HS; Balaton, MN; 3/33 Band; Chr; ChrhWkr; DrlTm; HonRl; SchPl; TchrAde; RptrYrbk; FHA; Chrldr; College; Professional.

NELSON, Amy L; Westby HS; Westby, WI; 2/115 Band; Chr; ChrhWkr; HonRl; NHS; NatlMeritCmnd; SchPl; SctActv; EdSchPpr; BttyCrckrAwd; Univ Of Wis Madison; Lawyer.

NELSON, Anna M; Madison HS; Venice, IL; Chrs; HonRl; RedCrAde; SchPl; StuCncl; 4-H; FHA; PpCl; Trk; GAA; Southern Ill Univ; Stenographer Or Bookkpr.

NELSON, Barb; Amherst Public HS; Amherst, NE; Chrs; HonRl; OffAde; SchAde; SchPl; TchrAde; RptrYrbk; RptrSchPpr; SchPpr; Chrldr; Central Technical Comm College; Secretary.

NELSON, Barb J; Estherville HS; Estherville, IA; 4/189 Band; Chrs; CncrtBnd; HonRl; MrchBnd; PepBnd; StuCncl; SpnCl; College; Teaching.

NELSON, Barry D; Flaxton Public HS; Flaxton, ND; PresSophCls; ALBoysSt; Chrs; ChrhWkr; CmntyWkr; SchPl; StuCncl; StuGov; 4-H; LetterBsktbl; LetterTrk; IMSpt; 4-HAwd; College; Diesel Mechanic.

NELSON, Barton; Baltic HS; Baltic, SD; VPFrshCls; ALBoysSt; Band; Chr; ChrhWkr; HonRl; NHS; SchPl; SctActv; 4-H; College; Professional.

NELSON, Beth; Blue Earth HS; Blue Earth, MN; 5/107 Band; ChrhWkr; HonRl; LbryAde; NHS; OffAde; TchrAde; YthFlsp; Yrbk; GAA; Augustana College; Special Ed.

NELSON, Beth L; Downers Grove North HS; Downers Grove, IL; Chr; ChrhWkr; HonRl; Mdrgl; NHS; NatlThespSoc; Orch; SchMus; Augustana College.

NELSON, Bradley J; Hastings HS; Hastings, NE; Chr; ChrhWkr; HonRl; Bsbl; LetterTennis; IMSpt; Bethany Nazarene College; Physics.

NELSON, Brenda E; North Callaway HS; Auxvasse, MO; 3/69 ChrhWkr; HonRl; LbryAde; SchPl; StuCncl; TchrAde; FHA; FTA; SpnCl; College; Vocational.

NELSON, Brenda E; R1 N Callaway HS; Auxuasse, MO; 5/72 PresFrshCls; ChrhWkr; HonRl; LbryAde; SchPl; TchrAde; 4-H; FHA; FTA; SpnCl; Coll Or Univ ; Pro.

NELSON, Bruce; Clark HS; Clark, SD; 8/50 Band; Chr; Chrs; PepBnd; SchMus; Sd School Of Mines Tech; Engrg.

NELSON, Bruce; Red River HS; Grand Forks, ND; 2/342 ALBoysSt; Chr; CncrtBnd; HospAde; NHS; VPNatlThespSoc; VPStuCncl; FrCl; Coll;.

NELSON, Carol A; Raymore Peculiar HS; Raymore, MO; 17/89 Band; HonRl; NatlFornLg; NatlMeritSF; OffAde; SchPl; StuCncl; RptrYrbk; FrCl; VoiceDemAwd; University; Political Science.

NELSON, Carol J; Southland HS; Rose Creek, MN; Band; Chrs; CncrtBnd; HonRl; MrchBnd; NHS; PepBnd; SchPl; RptrSchPpr; FHA; Concordia College; Medical Technician.

NELSON, Carol J; Benson HS; Omaha, NE; DrlTm; OffAde; StuCncl; FrCl; MthCl; PpCl; Chrldr; GAA; IMSpt; College; Nursing.

NELSON, Carolyn S; J A Craig HS; Janesville, WI; 4/474 AFS; Chr; HonRl; HospAde; NHS; TchrAde; RptrYrbk; Univ Of Wisconsin; Physical Therapy.

NELSON, Carrie D; Plattsmouth HS; Plattsmouth, NE; 15/163 DrlTm; HonRl; NHS; SchAde; TchrAde; YthFlsp; SpnCl; MthCl; PpCl;.

NELSON, Cindy L; Little Falls Community HS; Little Falls, MN; Band; MrchBnd; Sec4-H; Sec4-HAwd; Farmer.

NELSON, Clarise; Gary HS; Gary, MN; 8/22 Band; Chr; HonRl; OffAde; SchAde; TchrAde; RptrYrbk; FHA; GAA; Crookston Sch Nursing; Lpn.

NELSON, Coleen A; Nicollet HS; Nicollet, MN; 16/57 SecJrCls; Chrs; HonRl; StuCncl; TchrAde; Pres4-H; SecFHA; Wrstlng; Pres4-HAwd; Univ; Professnl.

NELSON, Connie L; Flaxton Public HS; Flaxton, ND; SecTrsJrCls; SecTrsSrCls; ALAGirlsSt; Chrs; ChrhWkr; DrlTm; HonRl; SchPl; Yrbk; Bsktbl; College; Pharmacy.

NELSON, Conrad H; Wallace Dist 65r HS; Wallace, NE; PresFrshCls; Band; Chr; Chrl; Chrs; ChrhWkr; CncrtBnd; Bsbl; Bsktbl; Trk; Agriculture Sch; Agriculture.

NELSON, Craig; Springfield Public HS; Springfield, MN; ALBoysSt; ChrhWkr; HonRl; SchPl; StuCncl; RptrSchPpr; Bsbl; Trk; College; Oceanography.

NELSON, Craig C; Dilworth HS; Dilworth, MN; ALBoysSt; Band; Chrs; CncrtBnd; HonRl; NHS; PepBnd; SchPl; StuCncl; Wrstlng; Coll.

NELSON, Cynthia L; Shickley Public HS; Shickley, NE; TrsJrCls; Band; Chrs; PresChrhWkr; CncrtBnd; DrmMjrt; MrchBnd; SchPl; Yrbk; 4-H; PpCl; Trk; 4-HAwd; College; Nursing.

NELSON, Cynthia M; Frazee HS; Frazee, MN; Band; Chrs; CmntyWkr; HonRl; MrchBnd; SchAde; Yrbk; FHA; FTA; PPFtbl; Clge; Teacher Or Accountant.

NELSON, Dana K; Raytown HS; Raytown, MO; AFS; Chrs; HonRl; JrNHS; LitMag; NHS; SecFrCl; SecPpCl; U Of Southwest Mo.

NELSON, Dave B; Ithaca HS; Gotham, WI; 5/28 HonRl; PpCl; CaptBsktbl; LetterFtbl; Jr College; Accounting.

NELSON, David; Hempstead HS; Dubuque, IA; 8/455 TrsFrshCls; HonRl; JA; JCC; NHS; SctActv; StuCncl; PresJrCls; Trk; IMSpt; College; Engineering Degree.

NELSON, David W; Sioux Valley HS; Volga, SD; 32/66 ChrhWkr; HonRl; 4-H; PresFFA; IMSpt; 4-HAwd; University; Animal Science.

NELSON, Debbie S; Norfolk HS; Norfolk, NE; HonRl; PepBnd; StuCncl; PpCl; Glf; Trk; Chrldr; IMSpt; PPFtbl; KiwanAwd; Clge; Nursing.

NELSON, Deborah A; Lake Benton Public HS; Lake Benton, MN; 11/37 SecTrsJrCls; Band; HonRl; NHS; SchPl; StuCncl; SecYrbk; VPFHA; LetterBsktbl; Chrldr; Dakota State Clg; Phys Ed & Biology.

NELSON, Debra D; Stoughton HS; Stoughton, WI; 55/250 Band; CncrtBnd; HonRl; Orch; TchrAde; Yrbk; FNA; PpCl; 4-HAwd; Clge; Nurse.

NELSON, Denise L; Crete HS; Crete, NE; SecFrshCls; ChrhWkr; CncrtBnd; HonRl; HospAde; MrchBnd; SchMus; SchPl; Twrl; PpCl; College.

NELSON, Denise L; Richmond Burton Comm HS; Richmond, IL; 1/70 ALAGirlsSt; Chr; Chrs; ChrhWkr; HonRl; VPLbryAde; NHS; SchMus; SctActv; Yrbk; 4-H; VPPpCl; Chrldr; GAA; Mc Henry County College; Secretary.

NELSON, Diane E; Lakeview HS; Columbus, NE; 2/70 ALAGirlsSt; Band; ChrhWkr; HonRl; Mdrgl; Orch; SchAde; TchrAde; GAA; BttyCrckrAwd; Univ; Nursing.

NELSON, Diann E; Woodland HS; Streator, IL; 5/76 HonRl; LbryAde; NHS; TchrAde; TreasFTA; FrCl; GAA; College; Elem Teacher.

NELSON, Dick A; Fergus Falls HS; Fergus Falls, MN; ChrhWkr; RptrSchPpr; 4-H; LetterBsbl; Bsktbl; IMSpt; 4-HAwd; Austin Vocational Tech Inst; Broadcasting.

NELSON, Donald J; Tomahawk HS; Tomahawk, WI; ChrhWkr; CmntyWkr; SctActv; StuCncl; SptEdSchPpr; LetterFtbl; Trk; CchngActv; IMSpt; AmLegAwd; U Of Minn; Vet Med.

NELSON, Dru A; H L Richards HS; Palos Heights, IL; Band; CncrtBnd; MrchBnd; NHS; PepBnd; TchrAde; SpnCl; College; Engineer.

NELSON, Elizabeth A; Lake Central HS; Schererville, IN; 3/485 HonRl; NHS; SchAde; FrCl; SciCl; LetterBsktbl; Trk; GAA; IMSpt; Purdue Univ; Forestry/conserv.

NELSON, Elizabeth A; Albion Public HS; Albion, NE; 1/97 VPJrCls; Band; CncrtBnd; MrchBnd; NHS; SecStuCncl; VPPpCl; LetterBsktbl; LetterTrk; Chrldr; PPFtbl; 4-HAwd; College; Veterinarian.

NELSON, Evelyn R; Bloomer HS; Bloomer, WI; AFS; Band; SecNHS; SchPl; StuGov; SecYthFlsp; RptrYrbk; SecFrCl; GAA; 4-HAwd; U Of Wisc La Crosse; Nuclear Medtech.

NELSON, Gail L; Richmond Burton HS; Richmond, IL; Chr; Chrs; ChrhWkr; DrlTm; HonRl; LbryAde; SchMus; FHA; GAA; IMSpt; Business School.

NELSON, Gail L; Newton Community HS; Hidalgo, IL; 13/141 HonRl; LbryAde; PresNHS; NatlMeritCmnd; FBLA; JCAwd; College; Business.

NELSON, Garry L; Brewster HS; Brewster, MN; 2/25 Band; Chr; ChrhWkr; HonRl; PresNHS; SchPl; StuGov; EdYrBk; SchPpr; PpCl; Southwest Mn State; Cpa.

NELSON, Gayle L; Dunlap HS; Peoria, IL; 10/90 ALAGirlsSt; ChrhWkr; HonRl; NHS; StuCncl; EdYrBk; EdSchPpr; FBLA; LatCl; Bradley Univ; Art.

NELSON, Gisele M; Cumberland HS; Cumberland, WI; 8/124 HstSophCls; Chr; ChrhWkr; CmntyWkr; HonRl; NHS; TchrAde; Yrbk; RptrSchPpr; 4-H; Uw Barron County; Psychologist.

NELSON, Glenn E; Calumet HS; Gary, IN; 11/364 HonRl; JrNHS; NHS; FrCl; SciCl; CaptWrstlng; BauchLmbAwd; University; Medicine.

NELSON, Glen R; Grand Island Sr HS; Grand Island, NE; AFS; ChrhWkr; CmntyWkr; CncrtBnd; Orch; PolWkr; SctActv; Yrbk; SchPpr; GerCl; Swmmng; Tennis; College; Dentist.

NELSON, Helen M; Milaca Sr HS; Milaca, MN; 3/158 Chr; ChrhWkr; HonRl; HospAde; NHS; TchrAde; VP4-H; FHA; 4-HAwd; College Medical School; Professional.

NELSON, James B; Milbanks HS; Milbank, SD; 13/130 AFS; HonRl; NHS; PpCl; LetterFtbl; LetterTrk; IMSpt; PresAwd; College; Accountant.

NELSON, Jamie R; Brown County HS; Nashville, IN; 36/182 CncrtBnd; HonRl; MrchBnd; PepBnd; LetterBsbl; LetterFtbl; LetterWrstlng; In U; Music.

NELSON, Jane L; Fairfield HS; Turon, KS; ALAGirlsSt; Band; Chr; Chrl; CncrtBnd; HonRl; MrchBnd; NatlMeritSchl; PepBnd; SchPl; College; Business Education.

NELSON, Janelle L; Barrett Public HS; Barrett, MN; Band; Chr; CncrtBnd; HonRl; MrchBnd; NHS; NatlSciFnd; PepBnd; SchPl; RptrYrbk; LetterBsktbl; LetterTrk; Chrldr; Univ Of Minn; Music.

NELSON, Janet A; O Fallon Township HS; Ofallon, IL; 53/316 Chrs; ChrhWkr; CmntyWkr; HonRl; NHS; SctActv; StuCncl; YthFlsp; FrCl; SciCl; U Of Mi; History Teacher.

NELSON, Janis E; Loy Norrix HS; Kalamazo, MI; 83/520 Chr; ChrhWkr; Mdrgl; RedCrAde; SchMus; Trk; IMSpt; Hope College; Medical Tech.

NELSON, Jean L; Benson HS; Omaha, NE; AFS; Chr; HonRl; NHS; NatlMeritFnl; NatlMeritSF; SchMus; SctActv; StuCncl; RptrSchPpr; Univ Ne; Arch.

NELSON, Jeannette; Sweet Springs R 7 HS; Sweet Springs, MO; 4/45 Band; Chrs; HonRl; NHS; StuCncl; TchrAde; YthFlsp; Yrbk; SciCl; Centrl Methodist Coll; Music.

NELSON, Jeffrey A; Center HS; Kansas City, MO; 65/420 Band; ChrhWkr; CncrtBnd; HonRl; MrchBnd; PepBnd; PolWkr; TreasYthFlsp; RptrYrbk; SchPpr; Bsbl; Bsktbl; Kansas State Univ; Science.

NELSON, Jeffrey D; Glenbrook South HS; Glenview, IL; 11/581 CmntyWkr; HonRl; NHS; StuCncl; SecKeyCl; SpnCl; Glf; Swmmng; Univ Of Illinois; Medicine.

NELSON, Jennifer L; Spring Lake Park HS; Minneapolis, MN; 2/300 CncrtBnd; HonRl; Mdrgl; SchMus; RptrSchPpr; Pres4-H; Tennis; GAA; 4-HAwd; LionAwd; Univ Of Minnesota; Journalist.

NELSON, Jill A; Horace Mann HS; Biwabik, MN; ALAGirlsSt; Band; Chr; ChrhWkr; PepBnd; SchPl; StuCncl; TchrAde; RptrYrbk; RptrSchPpr; EdSchPpr; PpCl; LetterSwmmng; LetterTrk; University.

NELSON, John D; Lake Fenton HS; Fenton, MI; 1/160 HonRl; PresNHS; NatlMeritSF; NatlThespSoc; SchPl; SptEdYrbk; PresFrCl; Univ Of Mi; Physicist.

NELSON, Judy L; Broken Bow HS; Broken Bow, NE; Band; HonRl; RptrYrbk; RptrSchPpr; FBLA; VPFHA; PpCl; OptClAwd; PresAwd; RotaryAwd; University; Dietitian.

NELSON, Julia A; Fennimore HS; Fennimore, WI; 1/120 ALAGirlsSt; Chrs; CncrtBnd; HonRl; HospAde; Mdrgl; NHS; NatlMeritSchl; SchMus; GAA; Uw Madison; Medicine.

NELSON, Juliann; Saunemin Hs; Pontiac, IL; 4/24 Chrs; CncrtBnd; HonRl; MrchBnd; PepBnd; SchPl; PresStuCncl; RptrYrbk; 4-H; Trk; U Of Illinois; Mathematics Education.

NELSON, Julie E; Rockford West HS; Rockford, IL; 12/379 Chr; HonRl; NHS; Orch; PresEngCl; GerCl; Univ Of Illinois.

NELSON, Julie R; United Township HS; East Moline, IL; 27/517 Chr; Chrl; Chrs; HonRl; LbryAde; Mdrgl; NHS; NatlMeritCmnd; SecNatlThespSoc; RedCrAde; SchMus; SchPl; TchrAde; FTA; FrCl; Illinois State Univ; Teacher.

NELSON, Karen L; Toivola Meadowlands HS; Meadowlands, MN; 1/19 SecSrCls; ChrhWkr; HonRl; OffAde; TchrAde; EdYrBk; RptrSchPpr; FHA; IMSpt; BttyCrckrAwd; Mesabi Community Col; Liberal Arts.

NELSON, Karen R; Kickapoo HS; Springfield, MO; 1/326 HonRl; NatlFornLg; OffAde; StuCncl; StuGov; DARAwd; KiwanAwd; OptClAwd; William Jewell Col; Rn.

NELSON, Karen W; Wilton HS; Regan, ND; SecSrCls; TrsSrCls; HonRl; NHS; SchPl; StuCncl; RptrSchPpr; PpCl; Trk; University; Occupational Therapy.

NELSON, Kathleen; Hill Murray HS; St Paul, MN; HonRl; PpCl; Bsktbl; College; Home Economics.

NELSON, Kathy K; Barron Area HS; Barron, WI; 3/105 PresSophCls; SecTrsJrCls; Band; Chr; ChrhWkr; CncrtBnd; HonRl; Mdrgl; MrchBnd; NHS; PepBnd; SchMus; AmLegAwd; College; Home Economics.

NELSON, Keith E; Fredericksburg Comm HS; Fredericksburg, IA; HonRl; SchPl; SctActv; StuCncl; YthFlsp; PpCl; Bsbl; Bsktbl; Ftbl; LetterTrk;.

NELSON, Kris K; Watertown HS; Watertown, SD; 42/267 SecSophCls; SecJrCls; Chr; ChrhWkr; HonRl; Mdrgl; SchMus; StuCncl; YthFlsp; LetterChrldr; CchngActv; GAA; IMSpt; University; Liberal Arts.

NELSON, Kristi S; Emerson Hubbard HS; Emerson, NE; 1/58 Chr; Chrs; ChrhWkr; NHS; Yrbk; Univ Of Nebraska Med Center; Nurse.

NELSON, Laurel; Velva HS; Voltaire, ND; 10/4729# Chrs; CncrtBnd; HonRl; MrchBnd; PepBnd; FBLA; SciCl;.

NELSON, Laurie J; St Joseph Acad; Green Bay, WI; Chrs; StuCncl; FrCl; Chrldr; PPFtbl;.

NELSON, Lawrence M; Addison Trail HS; Addison, IL; Aud/Vis; CmntyWkr; NatlMeritSF; NatlThespSoc; SchMus; SchPl; Yrbk; SchPpr; College; Computer Science.

NELSON, Linda M; Chisago Lakes HS; Lindstrom, MN; ALAGirlsSt; ChrhWkr; HonRl; College; Professional.

NELSON, Lisa J; Prairie HS; Swisher, IA; 6/178 Chr; HonRl; Mdrgl; NatlMeritCmnd; Quill&Scroll; SchMus; SchPl; SchPpr; SpnCl; LetterTrk; Iowa St Univ; Mathematics.

NELSON, Lizzie; Chicago Vocational HS; Chicago, IL; 12/700 Chr; ChrhWkr; CmntyWkr; HonRl; StuCncl; TchrAde; YthFlsp; PpCl; Chrldr;.

NELSON, Lois; Gladstone HS; Gladstone, MI; Band; CncrtBnd; DrlTm; HonRl; HospAde; MrchBnd; NHS; RptrSchPpr; SchPpr; FNA; Bay De Noc College; Secretaial Field.

NELSON, Lorelei K; Windom Area HS; Windom, MN; 30/138 PresSrCls; Band; PresDrlTm; PresHospAde; MrchBnd; PepBnd; StuCncl; TchrAde; PpCl; PPFtbl; College; Recreational Therapy.

NELSON, Lori; Ballard Community HS; Slater, IA; 12/82 SecFrshCls; ALAGirlsSt; Chrs; HonRl; NHS; SchMus; YthFlsp; Bsbl; Bsktbl; IMSpt; Iowa State Univ; Criminology.

NELSON, Lori A; Pepin HS; Stockholm, WI; PresBand; PresChrs; HonRl; MrchBnd; SchPl; SchPpr; FHA; PpCl; Chrldr; PresGAA; University.

NELSON, Lori E; Yankton Senior HS; Tabor, SD; DrlTm; HonRl; NHS; StuCncl; Univ Of Vermillion; Art Major.

NELSON, Lorine; Westmer HS; Joy, IL; 5/61 Chrs; CncrtBnd; HonRl; SchMus; StuCncl; YthFlsp; RptrYrbk; Bsbl; Iowa St Univ; Home Economics.

NELSON, Lyle I; Oslo HS; Oslo, MN; SecTrsSophCls; SecTrsJrCls; SecTrsSrCls; Aud/Vis; Band; CncrtBnd; HonRl; Univ Of N Dakota; Electronics.

NELSON, Marcalene M; Alwood HS; Woodhull, IL; 10/71 SecBand; PresChrs; HonRl; HospAde; Mdrgl; NHS; SchMus; StuCncl; PresFTA; CaptBsktbl; Chrldr; West Ill Univ; Teaching.

NELSON, Maren K; Lake Mills Comm HS; Lake Mills, IA; Chr; Chrs; HonRl; Mdrgl; SchMus; SchPl; SctActv; TchrAde; Yrbk; PpCl; Coll; Legal Secretary.

NELSON, Margaret; Sawyer HS; Sawyer, ND; ALAGirlsSt; Chrs; HonRl; LbryAde; MrchBnd; SchPl; RptrSchPpr; Trk; GAA; College; Education.

NELSON, Maria D; Harmony HS; Bonaparte, IA; 8/40 HonRl; LbryAde; SchPl; Pres4-H; FHA; Bsktbl; LetterTrk; LetterChrldr; 4-HAwd;.

NELSON, Mariam; Newark HS; Seneca, IL; Band; HonRl; FFA; FHA; FTA; College; Professional.

NELSON, Mark; Jackson HS; Jackson, MI; Band; CncrtBnd; HonRl; MrchBnd; Orch; PepBnd; Tennis; College; Music Major.

NELSON, Mark A; Rugby HS; Rugby, ND; 6/99 ALBoysSt; Band; ChrhWkr; HonRl; NHS; StuCncl; FFA; Bsbl; Minot State.

NELSON, Mark A; Staunton Military Academy; Kankakee, IL; DrlTm; HonRl; OffAde; ROTC; LetterTrk;.

NELSON, Mark T; Glenbard West HS; Glen Ellyn, IL; 44/545 Chr; HonRl; NatlMeritSF; SchPpr; MthCl; LetterTrk; Stanford; Philosophy & Anthropology.

NELSON, Marnette A; Cedar Valley HS; Rockwell City, IA; 1/27 Band; Chr; ChrhWkr; HonRl; SecNHS; SchPl; Pres4-H; LetterBsktbl; BttyCrckrAwd; 4-HAwd; Ia St Univ; Textiles & Clothing.

NELSON, Mary L; Roland Story HS; Roland, IA; 5/80 Chrs; ChrhWkr; CncrtBnd; HonRl; NHS; SchMus; TchrAde; YthFlsp; RptrSchPpr; FTA; Waldorf Col; Teaching.

NELSON, Melissa; Eagle Grove Comm HS; Eagle Grove, IA; 1/124 Band; ChrhWkr; CncrtBnd; HonRl; NHS; NatlThespSoc; StuCncl; FNA; GAA; MasAwd; U Of Ia; Music.

NELSON, Michele R; Litchfield Public HS; Litchfield, NE; ALAGirlsSt; ChrhWkr; CmntyWkr; HonRl; NHS; SchPl; UNYO; TreasYrbk; PresFHA; Chrldr; College; Dental Hygiene.

NELSON, Michelle D; Ogorman HS; Sioux Falls, SD; Chr; Chrs; LbryAde; SctActv; College; Psychology.

NELSON, Michelle L; Courtland HS; Courtland, KS; TrsFrshCls; Band; Chr; Chrl; Chrs; ChrhWkr; CncrtBnd; HonRl; FHA; College.

NELSON, N; Elk Point HS; Elk Point, SD; HstJrCls; ALBoysSt; ChrhWkr; HonRl; Mdrgl; SchPl; StuCncl; StuGov; Bsktbl; Ftbl; College; Teaching.

NELSON, Nancy A; Trenton HS; Trenton, MI; Chrs; HonRl; JrNHS; NHS; NatlMeritSF; PresAwd; U Of Mi; Biology.

NELSON, Nancy L; Bennington HS; Solomon, KS; 12/20 SecSrCls; Chrs; ChrhWkr; HonRl; SchMus; StuCncl; TchrAde; RptrYrbk; RptrSchPpr; 4-H; LetterBsktbl; LetterTrk; 4-HAwd; Hutchinson Comm Jr College; Home Economics.

NELSON, Nikita L; Douglass HS; Douglass, KS; HonRl; IntrClCncl; SchMus; SchPl; TchrAde; Teen; RptrYrbk; RptrSchPpr; SchPpr; Sec4-H; Southwestern College; Journalist.

NELSON, Patty R; Kimball County HS; Bushnell, NE; SecTrsSrCls; Chr; Chrs; HonRl; SchMus; StuGov; VPYthFlsp; 4-H; PpCl; 4-HAwd; Univ Of Ne; Home Ec.

NELSON, Paul E; High School; Truro, IA; VPFrshCls; HonRl; VPNHS; StuCncl; VPFFA; LetterBsbl; Ftbl; Trk; AmLegAwd; DanFAwd; Farming.

NELSON, Paul W; T L Handy HS; Bay City, MI; HonRl; Bsbl; Bsktbl; LetterFtbl; Central Mich Univ; Business Admin.

NELSON, Peggy I; Wild Rose HS; Pine River, WI; SecJrCls; Band; Chrs; HonRl; LbryAde; MrchBnd; TchrAde; RptrSchPpr; SecFBLA; FHA; College; Nursing.

NELSON, Peggy M; Akeley Public HS; Akeley, MN; 1/16 PresSrCls; ALAGirlsSt; Band; Chr; HonRl; SchPl; RptrSchPpr; EdSchPpr; PresFHA; Chrldr; College; Elem Teacher.

NELSON, Peter G; Maine South HS; Park Ridge, IL; ChrhWkr; CmntyWkr; HonRl; SctActv; StuCncl; StuGov; LetterTrk; LetterWrstlng; Univ Il Champaign.

NELSON, Philip; Newark Hs; Seneca, IL; PresFrshCls; Band; HonRl; SchPl; 4-H; FFA; Bsbl; LetterBsktbl; DanFAwd; 4-HAwd; Joliet Junior College;agriculture.

NELSON, Randall L; Clearfield Community HS; Clearfield, IA; ChrhWkr; HonRl; SchPl; StuCncl; Pres4-H; LetterBsbl; LetterFtbl; LetterTrk; 4-HAwd; Univ Of Ia; Animal Science.

NELSON, Richard F; St Johns Military Academy; Berrien Springs, MI; 4/49 Band; Chr; ChrhWkr; CncrtBnd; HonRl; MrchBnd; ROTC; GerCl; Ftbl; University.

NELSON, Ricky D; Keya Paha Co HS; Springview, NE; 7/26 Band; Chr; Chrl; Chrs; ChrhWkr; CncrtBnd; HonRl; MrchBnd; PepBnd; SchPl; StuCncl; Bsbl; Bsktbl; Nebraska Weslyan; Dentistry.

NELSON, Rita; Dilworth HS; Dilworth, MN; 3/61 CmntyWkr; HonRl; HospAde; NHS; NatlMeritCmnd; TchrAde; EdYrBk; BttyCrckrAwd;.

NELSON, Rita J; West Marshall HS; St Anthony, IA; Band; ChrhWkr; CncrtBnd; HonRl; MrchBnd; SchPl; SecFFA; SecFHA; Clg; Phy Therapy.

NELSON, Roberta; Egf Senior HS; East Grand Fork, MN; Band; CncrtBnd; HonRl; MrchBnd; PepBnd; PpCl; GAA; Businness; Secretarial.

NELSON, Robert D; Galva HS; Galva, IL; HonRl; VPNHS; Ftbl; LetterTrk; Western Ill Univ; Biology Major.

NELSON, Robert J; Toulon HS; Bradford, IL; Band; Chr; Chrs; CncrtBnd; HonRl; Mdrgl; MrchBnd; PepBnd; LetterFtbl; LetterTrk; AmLegAwd; ChmbCommrsAwd; 4-HAwd; College; Chemistry.

NELSON, Rochelle D; Artesian Ind #6 HS; Artesian, SD; 1/25 SecFrshCls; VPSophCls; SecJrCls; SecSrCls; Band; ChrhWkr; HonRl; EdYrBk; LetterBsktbl; LetterTrk; Univ Fo Sd Vermillion; Pre Medicine.

NELSON, Rodney S; Valley City HS; Valley City, ND; HonRl; StuCncl; Bsktbl; Ftbl; Trk; IMSpt;.

NELSON, Rosanne J; Brainerd Senior HS; Brainerd, MN; 26/475 ChrhWkr; HonRl; NHS; RptrSchPpr; TreasFFA; GerCl; 4-HAwd; VoiceDemAwd; Univ Of Minnesota.

NELSON, Ruth D; Downers Grove North HS; Downers Grove, IL; AFS; Band; ChrhWkr; CncrtBnd; HonRl; MrchBnd; NHS; Orch; Gustavus Adolphus College; Foreign Language.

NELSON, Sandra K; St Johns HS; St Johns, MI; 6/319 VPJrCls; ALAGirlsSt; HonRl; MrchBnd; NHS; StuCncl; TchrAde; YthFlsp; Swmmng; Wrstlng; Adrian College.

NELSON, Sandra L; Clifford Galesburg HS; Galesburg, ND; TrsSrCls; Band; Chrs; HonRl; SchPl; YthFlsp; SchPpr; 4-H; FHA; Bsktbl; Mayville State College; Math.

NELSON, Scott M; Pembroke Country Day HS; Leawood, KS; PresFrshCls; VPFrshCls; HonRl; Bsktbl; LetterFtbl; Tennis; LetterTrk; LetterWrstlng; IMSpt; JAAwd; Southern Methodist Univ; Business.

NELSON, Scott M; Falls City Senior HS; Falls City, NE; Band; ChrhWkr; CtyCnl; HonRl; NHS; NatlThespSoc; SchPl; StuCncl; LetterTrk; LetterWrstlng; University; Ecological Science.

NELSON, Shanon A; Twin Valley Public HS; Gary, MN; 3/30 Band; Chr; Chrs; CncrtBnd; HonRl; HospAde; MrchBnd; NHS; PepBnd; StuCncl; TchrAde; RptrYrbk; EdYrBk; Nursing School; Nurse.

NELSON, Sharon L; Elizabeth Seton HS; Calumet Park, IL; HonRl; JrNHS; NHS; NatlMeritCmnd; SchMus; SchPl; RptrYrbk; RptrSchPpr; FrCl; North Ill Univ; Journalism.

NELSON, Sharon M; Newman Grove HS; Newman Grove, NE; 2/40 Chrs; HonRl; SecNHS; OffAde; SchPpr; PpCl; Chrldr; Univ Of Ne;.

NELSON, Sharon S; Thornridge HS; Dolton, IL; AFS; Chrl; HonRl; NHS; TreasFrCl; Univ Of Il; Elementary Teacher.

NELSON, Sherry F; Huron Sr HS; Huron, SD; Band; Chr; Chrs; ChrhWkr; CncrtBnd; Mdrgl; MrchBnd; SchMus; SchPl; College; Vocation.

NELSON, Stephanie L; United Twp HS; East Moline, IL; 1/517 HonRl; NHS; NatlMeritCmnd; NatlThespSoc; SchMus; SchPl; SecGerCl; ChmbCommrsAwd;.

NELSON, Stephanie; United Township HS; East Moline, IL; HonRl; NHS; NatlMeritCmnd; NatlThespSoc; SchMus; SchPl; Univ; Math.

NELSON, Stephen J; Petosky HS; Petoskey, MI; Band; Chr; ChrhWkr; Mdrgl; NHS; PepBnd; SpnCl; Trk; Grace Clg; Preform/teach Music.

NELSON, Steve; Lake Mills Comm HS; Scarville, IA; 10/86 VPJrCls; SchPl; StuCncl; TchrAde; Yrbk; EngCl; IMSpt; College; Journalism.

NELSON, Steve M; Minneapolis Lutheran HS; Mpls, MN; HonRl; Bsktbl; Glf; LetterTrk; Coll; Bus.

NELSON, Steven; Elgin Hs; Elgin, IL; 81/754 Chr; HonRl; Orch; LetterTennis; Millikan University; Law.

NELSON, Steven R; Concordia Acad; St Paul, MN; Band; Chr; CncrtBnd; PepBnd; SchMus; SchPl; LetterTrk; College; Chem.

NELSON, Susan M; Redwood Falls HS; Redwood Falls, MN; Band; Chr; CncrtBnd; HonRl; MrchBnd; NHS; PepBnd; SchMus; RptrSchPpr; PPFtbl; Coll; Music.

NELSON, Tamara I; Dow City Arion Comm HS; Dow City, IA; TrsSophCls; PresJrCls; Chrs; CncrtBnd; HonRl; LbryAde; MrchBnd; PepBnd; StuCncl; TchrAde; Trade Or Bus Sch.

NELSON, Teaira; Monroe HS; St Paul, MN; Chr; Chrs; OffAde; SctActv; TchrAde; Socr; Trade School; Modeling.

NELSON, Teri S; Springs Valley HS; French Lick, IN; Band; ChrhWkr; CncrtBnd; DrmBgl; HonRl; MrchBnd; PepBnd; YthFlsp; FrCl; House Ofjames Beauty College; Professional.

NELSON, Terrea R; Bryant HS; Rich Hill, MO; 9/50 HonRl; LbryAde; SchPl; StuCncl; Yrbk; FBLA; FHA; PpCl; Chrldr; College; Fashion.

NELSON, Terri; Lincoln HS; Lincoln, KS; 8/60 Band; CncrtBnd; HonRl; MrchBnd; PepBnd; SchAde; TchrAde; 4-H; GerCl; Coll; Accounting.

NELSON, Terri L; Long Prairie HS; Long Prairie, MN; 34/120 AFS; Chr; Chrl; Chrs; HonRl; Mdrgl; NHS; SchPl; StuCncl; YthFlsp; St Cloud Univ; Social Worker.

NELSON, Thomas C; Lincoln Sr HS; Thief River Falls, MN; 3/239 TrsSophCls; ALBoysSt; Chr; Mdrgl; NHS; StuCncl; SciCl; LetterGlf; BauchLmbAwd; St Olaf College; Biology.

NELSON, Thomas M; Waterford HS; Union Grove, WI; Band; HonRl; NatlMeritFnl; NatlMeritSF; 4-H; Marquette Univ; Chemist.

NELSON, William J; Moline HS; Moline, IL; SciCl; Trade School; Mechanic.

NELSON, William J; Exira Community HS; Exira, IA; PresSophCls; PresJrCls; ChrhWkr; CmntyWkr; StuCncl; FFA; CaptBsktbl; CaptFtbl; Trk; N W M S U; Business Admin.

NELSON, William P; Iola Scandinavia Public HS; Iola, WI; 1/55 TrsSrCls; Band; Chrs; HonRl; Mdrgl; NHS; RptrSchPpr; MthCl; LetterFtbl; LetterTrk; University Of Stevens Point; Chemistry.

NEMCEK, Linda; Lake Park Hs; Roselle, IL; 9/439 Chr; Chrs; HonRl; NatlMeritSchl; StuGov; YthFlsp; Bsbl; Bsktbl; Tennis; GAA; College;professional.

NEMCEK, Mary; Rolling Meadows HS; Arlington Hts, IL; 7/546 Chrs; HonRl; NatlFornLg; NHS; NatlMeritFnl; NatlMeritCmnd; EngCl; U Of Illinois; Chemical Engineering.

NEMEC, Patti A; Prairie HS; Cedar Rapids, IA; SecJrCls; HospAde; Kirkwood Comm College; Secretary.

NEMETH, Frances L; St Alphonsus HS; Dearborn, MI; 2/115 Chr; Chrl; HonRl; SchMus; SchPl; SchPpr; SecLatCl; PpCl; IMSpt; PPFtbl; Univ; Psychology.

NEMETH, Joseph R; Pine River Jr Sr HS; Tustin, MI; Band; CncrtBnd; PepBnd; Bsktbl; LetterFtbl; Trade School; Tool & Die.

NEMETH, Steven L; Galesburg Sr HS; Galesburg, IL; 53/588 VPSrCls; IntrClCncl; NHS; StuGov; SptEdSchPpr; CaptSocr; College; Journalism.

NEMETH, Susan M; Kingston HS; Kingston, MI; SecTrsFrshCls; TrsSophCls; Band; Chr; HonRl; SchPl; StuCncl; Yrbk; FrCl; GAA;.

NEMGAR, Susan T; Eveleth HS; Eveleth, MN; 14/170 Band; CncrtBnd; MrchBnd; NHS; PepBnd; StuCncl; Yrbk; PpCl; CaptTrk; PPFtbl; Univ Of Nebraska; Microbiology.

NEMITZ, Diane; Fall River Public HS; Fall River, WI; 1/32 SecSophCls; VPJrCls; SecSrCls; PepBnd; Yrbk; Chrldr; BttyCrckrAwd; Uw Eau Claire; Registered Nurse.

NEMMERS, Mary P; St John HS; Bancroft, IA; ChrhWkr; CmntyWkr; HonRl; LbryAde; LetterTennis; Iowa Central Comm College; Community Serv.

NENZEL, Sharon A; Stanley Boyd HS; Stanley, WI; 2/141 Band; ChrhWkr; CncrtBnd; DrlTm; HonRl; MrchBnd; NHS; SctActv; SciCl; St Josephs Hospital; Radiologic Tech.

NEPERUD, Michael A; Amery HS; Amery, WI; 3/130 Band; Chrs; HonRl; NHS; NatlMeritCmnd; PolWkr; SchPl; RptrSchPpr; BauchLmbAwd; BttyCrckrAwd; Univ Of Wis; Bus Mang.

NEPHEW, Michael P; Geneva Public HS; Geneva, IL; College; Medicine.

NEPPER, Lisa M; Lincoln HS; Wi Rapids, WI; Band; CmntyWkr; HonRl; NatlFornLg; NatlMeritSF; NatlThespSoc; SchMus; SchPl; SctActv; SpnCl; College.

NEPRUD, Dean A; Halstad HS; Shelly, MN; PresSophCls; VPJrCls; PresSrCls; HonRl; NatlMeritCmnd; NatlThespSoc; StuCncl; StuGov; RptrYrbk; FFA; LetterBsktbl; LetterFtbl; AmLegAwd; Moorhead State Univ; Pro Law.

NERAT, John R; Stephenson HS; Wallace, MI; Chrs; HonRl; SchPl; SctActv; LetterBsbl; LetterBsktbl; LetterFtbl; LetterTrk; IMSpt; PresAwd; Naval Aviation.

NERE, Russell G; Danube HS; Danube, MN; Band; Chr; Chrs; PresChrhWkr; CncrtBnd; MrchBnd; PepBnd; StuCncl; Treas4-H; TreasFFA; Ftbl; Wrstlng; 4-HAwd; College; Agribusiness.

NEREM, Ronald G; Roland Story HS; Roland, IA; ALBoysSt; Chr; Chrs; ChrhWkr; CmntyWkr; FFA; Ftbl; College; Law Enforcement.

NERENBERG, Curt C; Evanston Township HS; Evanston, IL; HonRl; TchrAde; GovHonPrgAwd; College; Medicine.

NERENHAUSEN, Sara M; Washington Island HS; Washington Island, WI; HstSrCls; ChrhWkr; CmntyWkr; CncrtBnd; LbryAde; NatlFornLg; SchPl; TchrAde; YthFlsp; BttyCrckrAwd; College; Drama.

NERGENAH, Regina M; Triopia Jr Sr HS; Chapin, IL; ALAGirlsSt; Band; Chr; Chrs; HonRl; SchPl; 4-H; PpCl; LetterTrk; Illinois State Univ; Social Worker.

NERGERAH, Mary F; Jacksonville HS; Jacksonville, IL; 6/363 Band; CncrtBnd; HonRl; MrchBnd; PresNHS; Orch; PepBnd; RptrSchPpr; LatCl; IMSpt; Vassar Coll.

NERNESS, Jennifer; United Community HS; Kelley, IA; Band; Chr; CncrtBnd; MrchBnd; SchMus; SchPl; Bsktbl; College; Vocation.

NEROVICH, Janice; Resurrection HS; Chicago, IL; 86/260 Northeastern Il Univ; Certified Accountant.

NERUD, Myla J; Bayard HS; Bayard, NE; TrsSophCls; Band; Chrs; HonRl; SchPl; StuCncl; 4-H; FHA; SpnCl; PpCl; Business School.

NERVIG, Beverly J; Marcus Community HS; Marcus, IA; TrsSophCls; Chr; ChrhWkr; CncrtBnd; HonRl; MrchBnd; SchPl; Chrldr; Univ.

NESBIT, Jeff; Snider HS; Fort Wayne, IN; 12/515 HonRl; NatlMeritCmnd; StuCncl; Bsbl; Duke Univ.

NESBITT, Murlenle; Lilbourn HS; Lilbourn, MO; 9/80 PresSrCls; ChrhWkr; CmntyWkr; HonRl; SchPl; 4-H; FHA; 4-HAwd; U Of Mo Columbia; Physical Therapy.

NESBITT, Randy J; Sturgeon Bay HS; Sturgeon Bay, WI; HonRl; Bsbl; LetterFtbl; LetterSwmmng; LetterTrk; LetterWrstlng; 4-HAwd; College; Pilot.

NESBITT, Richard C; T L Handy HS; Bay City, MI; NHS; NatlMeritCmnd; SchMus; StuCncl; LetterSwmmng; Central Michigan Univ; Professional.

NESBITT, Ruth E; Seymour HS; Liberty, IL; 17/65 Band; Chr; Chrs; CncrtBnd; MrchBnd; PepBnd; SchPl; Pres4-H; FHA; FrCl; Chrldr; 4-HAwd; College; Law.

NESBITT, Scott A; Eastridge HS; Kankakee, IL; HonRl; Univ Of Ill; Civil Engineering.

NESBITT, Sue A; Lawton HS; Lawton, MI; SecJrCls; HonRl; LbryAde; SchPl; StuCncl; RptrSchPpr; 4-H; GAA; Michigan State Univ; Animal Care Tech.

NESLER, Dean E; Elgin HS; Hanover Park, IL; 400/1000 SchAde; StuCncl; TchrAde; Trk; VFWAwd; University; Pschologist.

NESPOR, James G; Fairbury HS; Fairbury, NE; 22/162 PresFrshCls; ChrhWkr; HonRl; NHS; GerCl; Bsbl; Bsktbl; Ftbl; IMSpt; College; Professional.

NESPOR, Robert D; Fairbury HS; Endicott, NE; Aud/Vis; ChrhWkr; HonRl; NHS; SchMus; SchPl; SpnCl; LetterWrstlng; IMSpt; EldAwd; University; Medicine.

NESS, Andrea K; Edmore Public HS; Edmore, ND; Band; Chrs; CncrtBnd; HonRl; MrchBnd; SchPl; StuCncl; RptrYrbk; 4-H; GAA; University; Professional.

NESS, Janet M; Mobridge HS; Mobridge, SD; 1/75 Band; Chrs; ChrhWkr; DrlTm; HonRl; MrchBnd; NatlThespSoc; SchMus; SecStuCncl; DARAwd; Univ; Dental Hygiene.

NESS, Julie A; Ada HS; Ada, MN; Band; Chr; CncrtBnd; DrmMjrt; HonRl; NatlThespSoc; Yrbk; FHA; LetterBsktbl; LetterChrldr; Junior College; Dental Hygienist.

NESS, Julie M; North HS; Eau Claire, WI; 29/382 ChrhWkr; CncrtBnd; HonRl; MrchBnd; NHS; Orch; PepBnd; SchMus; YthFlsp; GerCl; TreasPpCl; Bsktbl; Swmmng; Univ Of Wi; Physical Therapist.

NESS, Lori J; Newark Co HS; Morris, IL; 1/60 ChrhWkr; CmntyWkr; HonRl; LbryAde; Yrbk; College; Business.

NESS, Nolan S; Washington Sr HS; Sioux Falls, SD; NHS; NatlMeritSF; TchrAde; GerCl; Ball State Univ; German.

NESS, Paul A; Oak Lawn HS; Oak Lawn, IL; Chr; Chrs; LetterTrk; College; Oceanography.

NESS, Randy D; Spring Valley HS; Spring Valley, MN; SecSophCls; TrsSrCls; HonRl; NHS; StuGov; LetterBsbl; LetterBsktbl; CaptFtbl; LetterTrk; LetterWrstlng; Col At St Cloud; Teaching.

NESS, Robin R; Hector Community HS; Hector, MN; PresSrCls; Band; Chr; ChrhWkr; CncrtBnd; HonRl; MrchBnd; PepBnd; StuCncl; University; Public Relations.

NESS, Sylvia G; Underwood HS; Underwood, MN; 3/48 VPSophCls; Chr; CncrtBnd; MrchBnd; PepBnd; SchPl; TchrAde; RptrYrbk; FHA; 4-HAwd; Clge.

NESSELER, Molly J; Rock Island HS; Rock Island, IL; PresSrCls; ChrhWkr; HonRl; HospAde; NHS; StuGov; UNYO; EdSchPpr; CivCl; Chrldr; Coll; Linuist.

NESSLER, Gloria G; Good Counsel HS; Chicago, IL; 15/248 HonRl; TreasNHS; TchrAde; RptrYrbk; TreasFTA; VPGerCl; Northern Illinois Univ; Elem Teacher.

NESSNER, Richard C; Grandville HS; Grandville, MI; NatlMeritSF; Ftbl; LetterTennis; IMSpt; Aquinas Coll; Science.

NESTOROVSKI, Zvonko; Southwestern HS; Dearborn Hgts, MI; 1/210 HonRl; NHS; TchrAde; Wayne St Univ; Medicine.

NESWICK, Michael R; Heelan HS; Sioux City, IA; 29/249 HonRl; JrNHS; NHS; NatlMeritFnl; NatlMeritCmnd; NatlMeritSchl; NatlMeritSF; TchrAde; College; Mathematics.

NETA, Vicki R; Lena HS; Lena, WI; ChrhWkr; HonRl; Teen; SchPpr; 4-H; FHA; PpCl; Bsbl; LetterBsktbl; LetterTrk; GAA; 4-HAwd; Business School; Vocation Study.

NETEMEYER, Andrew H; Mater Dei HS; Germantown, IL; ChrhWkr; JrNHS; NHS; 4-H; College; Engineering.

NETH, Steven D; Broken Bow HS; Broken Bow, NE; 10/112 HonRl; NHS; SchPl; SecStuCncl; StuGov; YthFlsp; RptrSchPpr; SchPpr; CaptFtbl; IMSpt; OptClAwd; Univ Of Nebraska; Journalism.

NETT, Myrna L; Ryan HS; Minot, ND; 8/85 VPFrshCls; Chr; Chrs; HonRl; StuCncl; Yrbk; GerCl; PpCl; Bsktbl; Trk; Minot St College; Accountant Sec.

NETTELS, Margaret A; Pittsburg HS; Pittsburg, KS; PresFrshCls; Band; Quill&Scroll; PresStuCncl; SchPpr; FrCl; PpCl; Glf; Chrldr; University; Business.

NETTER, Jeffrey S; Glenbrook North HS; Northbrook, IL; 8/654 HonRl; SctActv; TchrAde; LetterTrk; LetterWrstlng; Univ Of Ill; Marketing.

NETTESHEIM, Allan J; Hamilton HS; Pewaukee, WI; NHS; Bsbl; Bsktbl; Ftbl;.

NETTLESON, Steven L; Iola Scandinavia HS; Scandinavia, WI; 6/54 Band; Chrs; CncrtBnd; HonRl; MrchBnd; NHS; NatlMeritSchl; PepBnd; RptrSchPpr; CaptFtbl; CaptWrstlng; IMSpt; Univ Of Wisconsin; Paper Chemistry.

NETTLETON, Colleen M; Pickford HS; Pickford, MI; HstSrCls; LbryAde; NatlMeritFnl; SchAde; YthFlsp; 4-H; FHA; PpCl; GAA;.

NETTLETON, Kelley J; Wm G Mather HS; Munising, MI; 31/124 Band; CncrtBnd; HonRl; MrchBnd; OffAde; PepBnd; SctActv; 4-H; Coll; Forestry.

NETZEL, Christine M; St Stanislaus Kostka HS; Chicago, IL; 10/63 HonRl; HospAde; NHS; RptrSchPpr; University Of Illinois; Veterinarian.

NETZER, Catherine; Billings HS; Billings, MO; Band; ChrhWkr; CmntyWkr; HonRl; RedCrAde; SchPl; YthFlsp; 4-H; FHA; Chrldr; University; Professional.

NETZKE, Marvel D; Nicollet Public HS; Nicollet, MN; HonRl; Trade Sch; Business Work.

NEU, Lisa J; Geneva Comm HS; Geneva, IL; HonRl; StuCncl; PpCl; Chrldr; W Kentucky Univ; Computer Program.

NEUBAUER, Gary D; Bloomington HS; Bloomington, IL; 20/389 NHS; LetterBsbl; LetterBsktbl; Ftbl; IMSpt; Illinois State Univ; Accounting.

NEUBAUER, Glen A; Radcliffe Community HS; Radcliffe, IA; 3/34 PresSophCls; PresJrCls; ALBoysSt; HonRl; Mdrgl; PresNHS; NatlThespSoc; PolWkr; PresYthFlsp; RptrSchPpr; Univ; Pre Med.

NEUBAUER, Judy M; Fairfield HS; Fairfield, IA; HonRl; NHS; Quill&Scroll; RptrSchPpr; PpCl; College; Agricultural Management.

NEUBAUER, Kenneth P; Beloit Memorial HS; Beloit, WI; 1/350 ALBoysSt; CncrtBnd; HonRl; MrchBnd; NHS; NatlMeritFnl; StuCncl; YthFlsp; LetterGlf; CaptSwmmng; Col; Pilot.

NEUBERGER, Inez; Riverdale Public HS; Hazen, ND; 3/13 VPSophCls; SecJrCls; HonRl; NHS; SchPl; StuCncl; Yrbk; FHA; PpCl; Chrldr;.

NEUBERGER, Timothy J; Parkston HS; Delmont, SD; 10/97 ALBoysSt; ChrhWkr; HonRl; Sdlty; GerCl; MthCl; SciCl; Us Air Force.

NEUENDORF, Betty; Sauk Prairie HS; Prairie Du Sac, WI; HospAde; NHS; Yrbk; Madison General Hospital; Nursing.

NEUENFELDT, Carl W; Freeland HS; Freeland, MI; PresSrCls; HonRl; NHS; SchPl; StuCncl; LetterBsktbl; LetterFtbl; Trk; College; Math.

NEUFELD, Jolene S; Newton HS; N Newton, KS; 17/317 Band; ChrhWkr; CncrtBnd; HonRl; HospAde; MrchBnd; PepBnd; Kansas State Univ; Medical Tech.

NEUFELD, Ruth A; Inman HS; Inman, KS; 2/48 SecSophCls; HonRl; NHS; StuCncl; YthFlsp;

EdSchPpr; FHA; PpCl; PPFtbl; DARAwd; Bethel College; Home Ec.

NEUFELDT, James G; Oak Park River Forest HS; Oak Park, IL; 65/1040 Ftbl; University; Engineer.

NEUHALFEN, Elizabeth A; Cedar Catholic HS; Hartington, NE; 2/67 Band; Chrs; HonRl; NHS; SchMus; TchrAde; EdSchPpr; 4-H; LetterTrk; LetterWrstlng; Chrldr; Col; Medicine.

NEUHARTH, Dwight R; Leola HS; Leola, SD; 2/50 SecFrshCls; TrsFrshCls; SecTrsSophCls; ALBoysSt; Band; Chr; Chrs; ChrhWkr; CmntyWkr; CncrtBnd; HonRl; Mdrgl; Bsktbl; LetterFtbl; Univ Of S D; Government.

NEUHARTH, Katherine K; Leola Independant HS; Leola, SD; 5/50 PresJrCls; Band; Chrs; CncrtBnd; HonRl; MrchBnd; SchMus; StuCncl; RptrYrbk; Yrbk; Brookings Sdsu; Music.

NEUHARTH, Mark; Alpena Public HS; Apena, SD; 2/16 Univ; Professional.

NEUHOFF, Linda S; Jasper HS; Jasper, IN; 35/328 HonRl; HospAde; SchMus; SchPl; SptEdSchPpr; CivCl; 4-H; Indiana Univ; Optometrist.

NEUHOUSER, Frederick W; Carroll HS; Fort Wayne, IN; 2/200 PresFrshCls; PresSophCls; PresJrCls; TrsSrCls; PresNatlFornLg; NHS; NatlMeritSF; TreasStuCncl; SchPpr; FFA; Coll; Professional.

NEUKAM, Leah A; Dubois HS; French Lick, IN; 2/76 Band; ChrhWkr; HonRl; MrchBnd; StuCncl; Yrbk; 4-H; PpCl; GAA; Indiana State Univ; Nurse.

NEUKAM, Terry L; Dubois HS; Dubois, IN; 29/80 VPSophCls; TrsJrCls; StuCncl; PpCl; LetterBsbl; LetterBsktbl; LetterTrk; IMSpt; Vincennes Univ; Business.

NEUMAN, Carole L; Normal Community HS; Normal, IL; 1/450 Chr; HonRl; NHS; MthCl; PpCl; Tennis; Chrldr; GAA; Ill Wesleyan Univ; Medicine.

NEUMAN, Carole L; Normal Comm HS; Normal, IL; 1/438 Chr; HonRl; NHS; PpCl; Tennis; LetterChrldr; GAA; AmLegAwd; Illinois Wesleyan Univ; Medicine.

NEUMAN, Cathy; Mackinaw City HS; Mackinaw City, MI; Band; Chrs; HonRl; SchPl; StuCncl; Bsktbl; Trk; Chrldr; GAA; IMSpt; College; Social Worker.

NEUMAN, Lealor P; Lindblom Technical HS; Chicago, IL; 28/599 ChrhWkr; HonRl; Michigan State University; Special Educ.

NEUMAN, Lealor P; Lindblom Tech HS; Chicago, IL; 28/599 ChrhWkr; HonRl; TchrAde; Michigan State Univ; Special Education.

NEUMANN, Bruce E; Magic City Campus HS; Minot, ND; ALBoysSt; Chr; Chrs; ChrhWkr; HonRl; NHS; PolWkr; SchMus; SctActv; StuGov; University; Law.

NEUMANN, Cathy G; Carmel Girls HS; Palatine, IL; 2/195 HonRl; OffAde; StuCncl; GerCl; LatCl; Trk; Chrldr; College; Science.

NEUMANN, Coleen D; Sauk Centre HS; Sauk Centre, MN; 7/156 ChrhWkr; Chrl; HospAde; JrNHS; MrchBnd; SchPl; TchrAde; RptrYrbk; RptrSchPpr; CaptTrk; College; Veterinary Med.

NEUMANN, Cynthia L; Michigan Lutheran HS; St Joseph, MI; HonRl; PpCl; Bsktbl; Tennis; IMSpt; NCTE; Univ; Literature.

NEUMANN, Dean W; Beaver Dam Sr HS; Beaver Dam, WI; 31/314 HonRl; SctActv; PpCl; Bsbl; Bsktbl; LetterFtbl; IMSpt; University.

NEUMANN, Karen; Cathedral HS; New Ulm, MN; HonRl; HospAde; LbryAde; Sdlty; EdYrBk; PpCl; College.

NEUMANN, Kurt M; Belleville Township East HS; Fairview Hts, IL; 55/680 Band; ChrhWkr; JrNHS; SchPl; TchrAde; SchPpr; Southern Ill Univ; Math Teacher.

NEUMANN, Michael K; St Johns Seminary; Atchison, KS; TrsSrCls; HonRl; SchAde; StuCncl; StuGov; TchrAde; EdYrBk; Bsktbl; Tennis; Trk; Chrldr; Benedictine College; Priest.

NEUMANN, Robert W; St Rita HS; Chicago, IL; 18/424 HonRl; NHS; Trk; U Of Il; Forestry Major.

NEUMAYER, Cindy L; St Bernard HS; Breda, IA; SecFrshCls; PresSophCls; Chr; Chrs; SchPl; StuCncl; RptrYrbk; RptrSchPpr; PpCl; Chrldr; College; Nursing.

NEUMEYER, Brenda S; Western HS; Bay City, MI; Chr; ChrhWkr; HonRl; NHS; PolWkr; GerCl; LetterBsktbl; LetterTrk; CchngActv; GAA; IMSpt; PPFtbl; College; Athletic Director.

NEUPERT, Mary B; St Charles HS; St Charles, MO; 1/547 CncrtBnd; HonRl; MrchBnd; NatlFornLg; SecNHS; NatlMeritCmnd; Orch; EldAwd; Univ Of Missouri; Dietician.

NEUROHR, Debora A; Addison Trail HS; Addison, IL; 6/567 CmntyWkr; HonRl; NHS; NatlMeritSF; NatlThespSoc; PolWkr; SchPl; StuCncl; EdSchPpr; LetterTennis; LetterTrk; PresGAA; Univ Of Wisconsin; Environmental Science.

NEUSCHAFER, Joy A; Mark Twain HS; Center, MO; PresFrshCls; Band; CncrtBnd; HonRl; MrchBnd; PepBnd; StuCncl; FHA; PpCl;.

NEUWAY, Vergi B; Burrton HS; Burrton, KS; HonRl; SchAde; StuCncl; TchrAde; RptrYrbk; EdYrBk; RptrSchPpr; LetterTrk; Chrldr; PPFtbl;.

NEUWEG, Roger L; Marquette HS; West Point, IA; PresSrCls; Bsktbl; IMSpt; Iowa State U; Mortiction.

NEVE, Cindy S; East Kentwood HS; Kentwood, MI; 20/499 Band; CncrtBnd; DrlTm; HonRl; MrchBnd; NHS; OffAde; SchMus; College; Hospitality.

NEVELLS, Janet A; Pontiac Catholic HS; Pontiac, MI; 30/140 Chrl; HonRl; HospAde; PolWkr; TchrAde; PpCl; Trk; Univ Of Michigan; Physical Therapy.

NEVHARTH, Donald L; Wolsey HS; Wolsey, SD; 3/43 SecFrshCls; Aud/Vis; ChrhWkr; HonRl; OffAde; SchAde; YthFlsp; FFA; SciCl; College; Communication.

NEVILLE, Carolyn S; Beaverton HS; Beaverton, MI; 40/132 PresJrCls; PresSrCls; Chr; HonRl; NHS; SchMus; SctActv; StuCncl; SpnCl; CaptChrldr; Ferris St Clg; Pharm.

NEVILLE, Michele; Wateruliet HS; Wateruliet, MI; Chr; HonRl; TchrAde; RptrYrbk; SchPpr; 4-H; FHA; Western Mich Univ.

NEVILLE, Robert; Neillsville HS; Neillsville, WI; HonRl; Ftbl; Univ; Professional.

NEVILLE, Robert C; Vicksburg HS; Scotts, MI; Band; CncrtBnd; JA; MrchBnd; PepBnd; SctActv; Trk; Wrstlng; Law Enforcement.

NEVIN, Marvelene M; Cashton HS; Cashton, WI; 1/67 SecFrshCls; Chr; HonRl; VPNHS; VPStuCncl; Yrbk; EdSchPpr; SecPpCl; CchngActv; GAA; Uw Lacrosse; Therapeutic Reserarch.

NEVINS, Paul; Pecatonica HS; Blanchardville, WI; SecSophCls; Band; HonRl; NatlMeritSF; PolWkr; SchMus; SciCl; College; Professional.

NEVINS, Thomas H; Niles North HS; Skokie, IL; 35/640 HonRl; JrNHS; NHS; SctActv; StuCncl; LetterBsktbl; CaptFtbl; LetterGlf; LetterTrk; Indiana Univ; Dentistry.

NEVITT, Kent; Noblesville HS; Noblesville, IN; 2/250 ALBoysSt; HonRl; NHS; FrCl; MthCl; LetterBsbl; LetterGlf; LetterTennis; Purdue U; Computer Sci.

NEVSIMAL, Kathryn L; Hillsboro HS; Kendall, WI; 4/65 Band; CncrtBnd; HonRl; MrchBnd; NHS; PepBnd; SecFHA; CaptBsktbl; CaptTrk; GAA; Tech Sch; Medical Asst.

NEW, Bonnie R; Mt Vernon Twp HS; Mt Vernon, IL; 5/436 Band; ChrhWkr; HonRl; JrNHS; NHS; SchMus; SchPl; RptrYrbk; Yrbk; Trk; Graceland Coll; High School Teacher.

NEW, Deborah L; Lansing HS; Leavenworth, KS; VPSophCls; HonRl; NatlThespSoc; OffAde; LetterBsktbl; LetterTrk; Chrldr; College.

NEW, Jennifer L; Malden HS; Malden, MO; ChrhWkr; CncrtBnd; MrchBnd; OffAde; PepBnd; Yrbk; RptrSchPpr; FHA; PpCl; College.

NEW, Michael R; Alexandria Monroe HS; Alexandria, IN; HonRl; NHS; CaptTennis; LionAwd; Ball State U; Architecture Study.

NEWBEGIN, Grace; North Branch HS; Clifford, MI; 6/141 ChrhWkr; HonRl; ModUN; NHS; TchrAde; 4-H; SciCl; DanFAwd; 4-HAwd;.

NEWBERGER, Sara; Ida Crown Jewish Acad; Chicago, IL; 1/71 HonRl; NHS; SchPl; StuCncl; University;majors In Biology & Jodaic Studi.

NEWBERRY, Elizabeth M; Oak Park River Forest HS; Oak Park, IL; 14/1012 Chr; ChrhWkr; HonRl; LitMag; NHS; PolWkr; Macalester College; Political Science.

NEWBERRY, Gary A; Coal City HS; Coal City, IL; 4/96 HonRl; NHS; SchPl; StuCncl; Univ Of Illinois; Accounting.

NEWBERRY, Thomas P; Mt Clemens HS; Mt Clemens, MI; Band; CncrtBnd; HonRl; MrchBnd; Orch; PepBnd; SchMus; Coll; Engineering.

NEWBORN, Glenn A; North Chicago Community HS; North Chicago, IL; Band; ChrhWkr; CncrtBnd; HonRl; HospAde; MrchBnd; PepBnd;.

NEWBURY, Philip; John Adams HS; South Bend, IN; 43/440 HonRl; JA; LbryAde; NatlFornLg; NatlThespSoc; PolWkr; SchMus; SchPl; Socr; JAAwd; College; Professional.

NEWBY, James E; Three Rivers HS; Three Rivers, MI; 1/209 PresFrshCls; VPJrCls; VPSrCls; ALBoysSt; HonRl; PresNHS; Bsktbl; Ftbl; CaptTennis; DanFAwd; Mi St Univ; Business Admin.

NEWBY, William E; Parkwood HS; Joplin, MO; PresSrCls; ChrhWkr; CmntyWkr; HonRl; JA; JrNHS; NHS; StuCncl; College; Ministry.

NEWCOM, Andy W; De Soto HS; De Soto, KS; VPSrCls; ChrhWkr; HonRl; JrNHS; LbryAde; NatlFornLg; TreasNHS; NatlThespSoc; SchMus; SchPl; University; Art.

NEWCOM, Karen K; Taylorville HS; Taylorville, IL; 28/250 Chr; HonRl; SchMus; StuCncl; FHA; FrCl; SpnCl;.

NEWCOMB, Anna; Lawrence HS; Paw Paw, MI; 13/50 HonRl; SchMus; StuCncl; FHA; FTA; Bsbl; Bsktbl; Trk; GAA; PPFtbl; Jacksonville Jr Coll;phys Educ.

NEWCOMB, Cheryl L; Wright City HS; Wright City, MO; SecTrsSophCls; TrsJrCls; Band; Chr; ChrhWkr; HonRl; NHS; 4-H; FHA; PpCl; IMSpt; Nursing School; Nurse.

NEWCOMB, Marsha; Pendleton Heights HS; Pendleton, IN; 29/291 HonRl; PpCl; PPFtbl; Business School; Bookkeeping.

NEWCOME, Mark A; Alton Sr HS; Alton, IL; 191/803 Band; Chrs; HonRl; MrchBnd; NatlThespSoc; Orch; PepBnd; SchMus; SchPl; SctActv; St Louis Sch; Pharmacist.

NEWCOMER, Gary; Potosi R 3 HS; Potosi, MO; 1/190 ALBoysSt; Band; CncrtBnd; HonRl; JrNHS; LbryAde; MrchBnd; NHS; NatlMeritCmnd; Bsktbl; Univ Of Mo; Medical School Md.

NEWCOMER, Jean K; Lanark HS; Lanark, IL; 4/58 SecFrshCls; Band; HonRl; SchMus; SchPl; YthFlsp; RptrYrbk; 4-H; Chrldr; GAA; 4-HAwd; Bradley Univ; Accounting.

NEWCOMER, Katherine A; Potosi HS; Potosi, MO; 6/187 Band; Chr; ChrhWkr; Mdrgl; NHS; NatlThespSoc; SchMus; StuCncl; Chrldr; DanFAwd; Clge; Bus.

NEWCOMER, Steve; Monroe HS; Monroe, WI; /250 HonRl; SctActv; KeyCl; Ftbl; Glf; Swmmng; Tennis; Wrstlng; Univ;.

NEWELL, Cynthia S; Hill City HS; Hill City, KS; 11/56 Chrs; DrlTm; HonRl; LbryAde; RptrYrbk; 4-H; PpCl; Chrldr; IMSpt; PPFtbl; Ft Hays Kansas St Univ; Business.

NEWELL, Douglas G; Ogden HS; Ogden, IA; PresSophCls; ALBoysSt; ChrhWkr; HonRl; SctActv; StuCncl; YthFlsp; SptEdSchPpr; LetterBsbl; LetterBsktbl; LetterFtbl; LetterTrk; University; Physical Ed.

NEWELL, Janell G; Neche Public HS; Neche, ND; SecSrCls; ALAGirlsSt; HonRl; EdYrBk; FHA; LetterGAA; AmLegAwd; BttyCrckrAwd; No Dakota St Univ; Home Economics.

NEWELL, Lesa J; Kimball County HS; Kimball, NE; HonRl; Pres4-H; VPFFA; 4-HAwd; CitAwd; Univ Of Nebraska; Veterinarian.

NEWELL, Philip W; Normandy HS; St Louis, MO; NHS; College; Physics.

NEWELL, Robert D; Rolling Meadows HS; Rolling Meadows, IL; Band; CncrtBnd; MrchBnd; SctActv; LetterFtbl; LetterTrk; LetterWrstlng; Harper College.

NEWENHOUSE, Nancy R; Unity Christian HS; Hudsonville, MI; Chr; ChrhWkr; Mdrgl; NatlMeritCmnd; 4-H; IMSpt; Grand Valley State Coll.

NEWGARD, Sonja; Mandan Senior HS; Mandan, ND; 71/293 ChrhWkr; CAP; HonRl; LbryAde; YthFlsp; Yrbk; GerCl; GAA; GovHonPrgAwd; Nbc Rapid City; Airline Worker.

NEWHOUSE, Brian S; North Boone HS; Clinton, WI; 23/101 Band; Chr; Chrs; ChrhWkr; CncrtBnd; HonRl; Mdrgl; SchMus; SchPl; SctActv; Cllege; Music.

NEWHOUSE, Patricia M; Charleston Sr HS; Charleston, IL; 18/247 HonRl; NHS; SptEdSchPpr; LetterTrk; GAA; No Illinois Univ; Journalism.

NEWKIRK, David C; Columbus East HS; Hope, IN; 8/395 Univ; Physical Science.

NEWKIRK, Tami J; Glendale HS; Springfield, MO; CmntyWkr; HonRl; LitMag; ROTC; SctActv; StuGov; Teen; FHA; GerCl; PpCl; Bsbl; LetterTrk; CchngActv; Sw Missouri St University.

NEWLIN, David W; Morton HS; Morton, IL; Band; Chr; ChrhWkr; CncrtBnd; MrchBnd; PepBnd; YthFlsp; SchPpr; Bsbl; LetterBsktbl; Tennis; Junior College; Professional.

NEWLIN, Hollie; Stephenson HS; Wallace, MI; 1/98 VPFrshCls; ChrhWkr; HonRl; NHS; OffAde; SchPl; PpCl; Mi Tech Unic, Acctg.

NEWLIN, Jeffrey; Henryville HS; Henryville, IN; Aud/Vis; Band; Chrs; CncrtBnd; LbryAde; MrchBnd; SchPl; Yrbk; PpCl; Indiana Univ; Music.

NEWLIN, John; Douglas Macarthur HS; Decatur, IL; 1/410 AFS; Band; CncrtBnd; HonRl; MrchBnd; NHS; RptrYrbk; GerCl; SciCl; Ui;premedicine.

NEWLIN, Julie A; Mattoon Sr HS; Mattoon, IL; Chr; Chrs; HonRl; PpCl; LetterGAA; College; Social Work.

NEWLIN, Leah; Newton HS; Newton, IL; HonRl; LbryAde; NHS; Lakeland Jr College; Nursing.

NEWLIN, Mark E; Plainfield HS; Plainfield, IN; Band; HonRl; NHS; LetterFtbl; CaptSocr; Earlham College; Professional.

NEWLUN, James D; Oconto HS; Oconto, WI; 2/141 HonRl; NatlMeritFnl; NatlMeritSF; Sacrstn; SchPl; SctActv; CaptBsktbl; Ftbl; Glf; Univ Of Wisconsin; Law.

NEWMAN, Barbara C; Tulare HS; Tulare, SD; 6/24 SecJrCls; Chrs; ChrhWkr; HonRl; SchPl; RptrYrbk; RptrSchPpr; FHA; Chrldr; Sdsu; Secretarial Science.

NEWMAN, Clarence G; Walker R 4 HS; Walker, MO; 1/11 TrsJrCls; Chr; Chrl; ChrhWkr; CtyCnl; CmntyWkr; HonRl; SchMus; SchPl; StuCncl; TchrAde; Bsktbl; Trk; Sw Baptist College; Music.

NEWMAN, Cynthia L; Rankin Twp HS; Rankin, IL; 6/23 PresSrCls; Chrs; NHS; SchPl; StuCncl; RptrYrbk; RptrSchPpr; FHA; PpCl; Bsktbl; Lakeview School; Nursing.

NEWMAN, Debra S; Highland Park HS; Deerfield, IL; 40/643 SchMus; SchPl; StuGov; RptrYrbk; Yrbk; University; Accountant.

NEWMAN, Delora R; Anthon Oto Comm HS; Anthon, IA; Chrl; Chrs; HonRl; SchPl; TchrAde; Yrbk; SchPpr; FHA; American Inst Of Bussiness ; Acct Major.

NEWMAN, Glinda L; Grandview Senior HS; Grandview, MO; HonRl; NHS; SctActv; StuCncl; RptrSchPpr; College In Texas; German.

NEWMAN, Herbert R; Culver Community HS; Culver, IN; 3/95 ALBoysSt; PresAud/Vis; HonRl; PresIntrClCncl; NHS; Sec4-H; SecFFA; KeyCl; IMSpt; 4-HAwd; Purdue Univ; Diary Sci.

NEWMAN, James; Holly HS; Clarkston, MI; Chr; Mdrgl; SchMus; SchPl; Yrbk; 4-H; East Mich Univ;graphic Design.

NEWMAN, Janet R; Valley Center HS; Wichita, KS; 12/119 SecTrsJrCls; SecTrsSrCls; Band; Chr; HonRl; HospAde; NHS; NatlThespSoc; SchMus; GerCl; TreasPpCl; Bsbl; Bsktbl; Tennis; Univ Of Kansas; Medicine.

NEWMAN, Jean L; Toulon HS; Toulon, IL; Band; HonRl; SchMus; SchPl; StuCncl; RptrYrbk; FHA; Western Illinois Univ; Home Economics.

NEWMAN, John F; Culver Community HS; Culver, IN; 19/101 ALBoysSt; 4-H; FFA; LetterBsktbl; Purdue Univ; Animal Science.

NEWMAN, Lari Y; St Teresas Academy; Kansas City, MO; Chr; Chrs; ChrhWkr; CmntyWkr; HonRl; LitMag; Mdrgl; StuGov; RptrYrbk; Yrbk; U Of Mo; Broadcast Journalism.

NEWMAN, Lee A; Harrisburg HS; Harrisburg, IL; 7/184 HonRl; NHS; OffAde; Yrbk; FHA; FrCl; MthCl; College; Accounting.

NEWMAN, Leslie; Wylie E Groves HS; Bloomfield Hills, MI; 13/700 ALAGirlsSt; ChrhWkr; JrNHS; NHS; SchMus; StuGov; Swmmng; GAA; Michigan State U; Research Nutritionist.

NEWMAN, Linda F; Halter HS; St Louis, MO; 3/52 ChrhWkr; HonRl; TchrAde; RptrYrbk; RptrSchPpr; SptEdSchPpr; FBLA; Chrldr; College; Bookkeeper.

NEWMAN, Marcia A; Juda HS; Juda, WI; TrsFrshCls; Band; Chrs; ChrhWkr; ModUN; SchPpr; 4-H; FHA; Trk; CaptChrldr; College; Education.

NEWMAN, Mike L; Walker HS; Walker, MO; VPSrCls; ChrhWkr; CtyCnl; CmntyWkr; Yrbk; Bsbl; Bsktbl;.

NEWMAN, Nikki M; Mabel Canton HS; Mabel, MN; 2/56 TrsFrshCls; TrsSophCls; Band; Chr; Chrl; ChrhWkr; CncrtBnd; HonRl; MrchBnd; PepBnd; College Or Univ; Science Major.

NEWMAN, Pamela R; Truman HS; Independence, MO; ChrhWkr; HonRl; JrNHS; NHS; YthFlsp; KeyCl; SpnCl; PpCl; College; Professional.

NEWMAN, Peggy G; Albia Community HS; Lorilia, IA; HonRl; OffAde; Business Schl; Secretary.

NEWMAN, Richard L; Cary Grove HS; Fox River Grove, IL; 24/300 ALBoysSt; Chr; HonRl; NHS; SchMus; Bsbl; Us Air Force Academy; Pilot.

NEWMAN, Stanley B; Tarkio HS; Tarkio, MO; Chrs; ChrhWkr; HonRl; NatlMeritCmnd; PolWkr; SchMus; SchPl; KeyCl; LetterGlf; IMSpt; Univ Of Al; Civil Engr.

NEWMAN, Sylvia A; North Division HS; Milwaukee, WI; 7/244 Chr; DrlTm; HonRl; Mdrgl; NHS; SciCl; GAA; JAAwd; Univ Of Wi Milw; Med Tech.

NEWMAN, Timothy G; Juda HS; Juda, WI; ChrhWkr; CmntyWkr; HonRl; SctActv; YthFlsp; FFA; Bsbl; LetterFtbl; LetterGlf; LetterWrstlng;.

NEWMAN, Todd; Sheldon HS; Ashton, IA; 14/149 TrsSrCls; Band; ChrhWkr; CncrtBnd; HonRl; MrchBnd; NHS; PepBnd; IMSpt; Univ Of Northern Iowa; Accounting.

NEWMARCH, Daniel H; Kingsley Area HS; Kingsley, MI; Aud/Vis; Band; CncrtBnd; LbryAde; MrchBnd; Orch; PepBnd; SchMus; StuCncl; Yrbk; 4-H; Ftbl; CaptTrk; 4-HAwd; College; Law Enforcement.

NEWNAM, David; Homestead Jr Sr HS; Ft Wane, IN; 12/243 HonRl; NHS; RedCrAde; SctActv; SpnCl; PpCl; Glf; IMSpt; Marquette Univ; Pre Medicine.

NEWNAM, Elsie M; Fairbury Cropsgy HS; Fairbury, IL; 10/99 Band; Chr; Chrs; CncrtBnd; HonRl; MrchBnd; PepBnd; YthFlsp; 4-H; College; Secretary.

NEWNUM, Ronald L; Turkey Run HS; Bloomingdale, IN; 25/63 Band; CncrtBnd; MrchBnd; PepBnd; StuCncl; Bsbl; LetterBsktbl; CaptFtbl; LetterTrk; LetterWrstlng; College; Farming.

NEWOHNER, Jeff; Osage Community HS; Osage, IA; ALBoysSt; Bsktbl; Ftbl; Trk; College; Vocation.

NEWPORT, Machell R; Perry Lecompton HS; Perry, KS; PresJrCls; DrlTm; HonRl; TchrAde; FHA; PpCl; CaptBsktbl; LetterTrk; PresAwd; College; Business.

NEWPORT, Michael A; Schulte HS; Terre Haute, IN; PresSophCls; PresJrCls; PresSrCls; Chr; StuCncl; KeyCl; LetterBsbl; LetterBsktbl; RotaryAwd; Isu; Teacher Coach.

NEWSOME, Allen L; Emerson HS; Gary, IN; Band; Chr; ChrhWkr; CmntyWkr; HonRl; JA; JrNHS; MrchBnd; NHS; Orch; StuCncl; SchPpr; FrCl; College; Professional.

NEWSOME, Kendall C; Lebanon HS; Lebanon, IL; 3/90 ChrhWkr; HonRl; JrNHS; NHS; NatlMeritCmnd; NatlMeritSF; PresSctActv; YthFlsp; LetterBsktbl; LetterTennis; Trk; CchngActv; DARAwd; Univ Of Il; Dentistry.

NEWSUM, Danny T; Peoria HS; Peoria, IL; Aud/Vis; HonRl; JrNHS; NatlMeritFnl; NatlMeritSF; Yrbk; SpnCl; Univ Of Illinois; Law.

NEWTON, Beverly A; Dickinson HS; Dickinson, ND; PresSophCls; Chrl; CncrtBnd; DrlTm; DrmMjrt; NHS; SchMus; StuCncl; GerCl; Univ Of North Dakota; Journalism.

NEWTON, Dennis W; South Knox HS; Decker, IN; VPSophCls; HonRl; TchrAde; 4-H; FFA; Bsktbl; Trk; IMSpt; Purdue Univ; Agriculture.

NEWTON, Dwight; J C Harmon Sr HS; Kansas City, KS; HonRl; LbryAde; StuCncl; RptrSchPpr; GerCl; SciCl; College; Journalism.

NEWTON, James D; Kirksville Sr HS; Kirksville, MO; HonRl; ROTC; StuCncl; KeyCl; MthCl; Bsktbl; Trk; Northeast Mo State; Dentistry.

NEWTON, Jeffery A; Kokomo HS; Kokomo, IN; ChrhWkr; HonRl; JA; NHS; Quill&Scroll; PresYthFlsp; SchPpr; JAAwd; Indiana Central University.

NEWTON, Jerry; Marshfield HS; Marshfield, MO; ChrhWkr; HonRl; SctActv; Trk; College.

NEWTON, John H; Peoria HS; Peoria, IL; 70/452 HonRl; NatlMeritSF; Yrbk; SchPpr; GerCl; College.

NEWTON, Kenneth E; Connersville HS; Connersville, IN; 40/390 VPBand; CncrtBnd; HonRl; MrchBnd; PepBnd; RusCl; IMSpt; LionAwd; Purdue U; Pharmacy.

NEWTON, Lynn Y; Cass Technical HS; Detroit, MI; ChrhWkr; HonRl; JrNHS; PolWkr; TchrAde; SpnCl; U Of Mich; Lawyer.

NEWTON, Pamela J; Marian Catholic HS; Chicago Hts, IL; 12/328 Chrs; ChrhWkr; CmntyWkr; HonRl; NHS; Yrbk; FrCl; CchngActv; Univ Of Ill; Foreign Language.

NEWTON, Randy L; Vienna HS; Vienna, IL; 10/115 PresFrshCls; Band; HonRl; MrchBnd; NHS; PepBnd; TchrAde; SptEdYrbk; SptEdSchPpr; FTA; SpnCl; LetterBsbl; LetterBsktbl; College.

NEWTON, Richard L; Smithton HS; Sedalia, MO; PresJrCls; ALBoysSt; Band; Chrs; NHS; StuCncl; College; Science.

NEWTON, Susan A; Clear Lake HS; Deer Park, WI; 2/76 SecJrCls; Band; Chr; ChrhWkr; HonRl; SecNHS; StuCncl; TchrAde; PresFHA; GAA; River Falls Univ; Computer Science.

NG, Laura L; Lindblom Tech HS; Chicago, IL; 8/600 HonRl; LbryAde; OffAde; SchAde; TchrAde; GerCl; MthCl; Univ Of Illinois; Computer Science.

NIBARGER, Joy L; Chillicothe HS; Chillicothe, MO; HonRl; OffAde; FBLA; Secretary.

NIBBE, Michael W; Mpls Lutheran HS; Edina, MN; VPSrCls; Band; Chr; YthFlsp; Bsktbl; Ftbl; Trk; Coll; Pre Med.

NIBBELINK, Jeffrey S; Pella Christian HS; Pella, IA; Chr; Chrs; ChrhWkr; HonRl; SchPl; IMSpt; Univ; Business Adm.

NIBEL, Pamela E; Belton HS; Belton, MO; HonRl; JrNHS; NHS; TchrAde; CivCl; SpnCl; PpCl; Clg; Secretary.

NICASTRO, Virginia L; Mercy HS; Overland, MO; 24/175 HonRl; HospAde; JrNHS; NHS; TchrAde; PpCl; Chrldr; Depaul School Of Nursing; Nurse.

NICE, Suzanne A; Leroy HS; Leroy, IL; 10/85 Band; PresChrs; HonRl; HospAde; NHS; SchPl; PresStuCncl; PresYthFlsp; Yrbk; BttyCrckrAwd; Ill Westleyan Univ; Nursing.

NICEWANDER, Edward; Ccc HS; Clay Center, KS; HonRl; YthFlsp; EdSchPpr; FTA; Wrstlng; Vo Tech; Photography.

NICHELS, Garry W; Whitko HS; Pierceton, IN; HonRl; NatlFornLg; NatlThespSoc; SchMus; SchPl; SciCl; Purdue Extension; Management.

NICHELSON, Cathleen S; Blair HS; Blair, NE; HospAde; StuGov; YthFlsp; RptrSchPpr; 4-H; FHA; SpnCl; PpCl; Bsktbl; 4-HAwd; PresAwd; College; Nursing.

NICHOL, Daniel J; Oak Park River Forest HS; Oak Park, IL; 345/1040 HonRl; Illinois Inst Of Tech; Chemistry.

NICHOL, Ross L; Pittsfield HS; Pittsfield, IL; TrsJrCls; NatlThespSoc; SchPl; SpnCl; Ftbl; CaptGlf; Swmmng; Tennis; Drury College; Dentist.

NICHOLAS, Georgina M; York HS; Elmhurst, IL; HonRl; NHS; NatlMeritSF; NatlSciFnd; Quill&Scroll; TchrAde; RptrYrbk; LatCl; Univ; Science.

NICHOLAS, Jandallee; Walled Lake Central HS; West Bloomfield, MI; ChrhWkr; CmntyWkr; JA; NHS; Orch; SchMus; SctActv; TchrAde; JAAwd; CitAwd; Wayne St Univ; Phy Therapy.

NICHOLAS, Lisa K; Shorewood HS; Shorewood, WI; Chr; Mdrgl; NHS; SchMus; StuCncl; StuGov; Tennis; Chrldr; GAA; AmLegAwd; College; Professnl.

NICHOLAS, Mark; Rockford Guilford HS; Rockford, IL; HonRl; FDA; KeyCl; Ftbl; Trk; U Of Ill; Medicine.

NICHOLI, Gay L; Twin Cedar HS; Knoxville, IA; 4/42 PresJrCls; PresBand; Chrs; HonRl; SchMus; StuCncl; YthFlsp; FTA; IMSpt; 4-HAwd; Simpson College; Music.

NICHOLLS, Emily A; Houghton HS; Houghton, MI; VPSrCls; HonRl; HospAde; OffAde; Twrl; RptrSchPpr; Michigan Tech University.

NICHOLS, Amiee; Holy Cross HS; Marine City, MI; PresJrCls; HonRl; NHS; OffAde; StuCncl; TchrAde; EdYrBk; SecTrsSophCls;.

NICHOLS, Catherine A; Knoxville HS; Gilson, IL; HonRl; 4-H; PpCl; LetterTrk; Chrldr; IMSpt; College; Professional.

NICHOLS, Cathy E; Southern Boone Co R 1 HS; Ashland, MO; 5/65 Band; ChrhWkr; DrlTm; HonRl; MrchBnd; PepBnd; SchPl; YthFlsp; PpCl; LetterBsktbl; LetterTrk; Missouri U; Phy Ed.

NICHOLS, Charles E; River Rough HS; River Rouge, MI; ChrhWkr; HonRl; SchAde; TchrAde; SchPpr; SpnCl; SciCl; Trk; College; Vacation.

NICHOLS, Crystal L; Papillion HS; Papillion, NE; 18/317 Band; HonRl; HospAde; 4-H; GerCl; PpCl; IMSpt; 4-HAwd; College; Nurse.

NICHOLS, Darlene P M; Evanston Township HS; Evanston, IL; 60/1100 Chrs; ChrhWkr; HonRl; LbryAde; NatlFornLg; NatlMeritSF; Northwestern Univ; Chemistry.

NICHOLS, David E; Kansas HS; Kansas, IL; 5/26 ChrhWkr; HonRl; NHS; StuCncl; YthFlsp; LetterBsbl; Bsktbl; LetterTrk; IMSpt; AmLegAwd; Lincoln Christian College.

NICHOLS, Debbie L; South Pemiscot HS; Steele, MO; Chr; Chrs; ChrhWkr; CmntyWkr; HonRl; NHS; OffAde; SchPl; YthFlsp; RptrSchPpr; SchPpr;.

NICHOLS, Gary R; Papillion HS; Pappillion, NE; 6/315 HonRl; NHS; SctActv; U Of Ne; Bus Admin.

NICHOLS, Gary W; Franklin Central HS; Indianapolis, IN; CncrtBnd; Mdrgl; NatlMeritCmnd; SchPl; LetterBsbl; LetterGlf; CaptTennis; GodCntryAwd; PresAwd; Coll; Prof.

NICHOLS, Janis E; Otsego HS; Otsego, MI; HonRl; NHS; TreasStuCncl; SptEdYrbk; LetterBsktbl; CaptTennis; CaptTrk; TreasGAA; DARAwd; Western Michigan Univ; Social Work.

NICHOLS, Jean E; Covington Community HS; Covington, IN; TrsFrshCls; TrsSophCls; VPJrCls; CncrtBnd; DrlTm; HonRl; MrchBnd; PpCl; Chrldr; Business School; Vocation.

NICHOLS, Jennifer S; Melbeta HS; Melbeta, NE; 1/13 SecSophCls; VPJrCls; Chrs; ChrhWkr; HonRl; StuCncl; 4-H; LetterTrk; Chrldr; College; Data Processing.

NICHOLS, Karl C; Cretin HS; Minneapolis, MN; ChrhWkr; CmntyWkr; ROTC; StuGov; College; Law.

NICHOLS, Ken N; Mesick HS; Mesick, MI; 6/51 VPFrshCls; TrsJrCls; VPSrCls; Band; Chr; HonRl; SchMus; TchrAde; Bsktbl; Northern Michigan Univ; Music.

NICHOLS, Linda D; Lexington HS; Lexington, MO; 9/97 SecFrshCls; SecSophCls; TrsSrCls; NHS; PresNatlThespSoc; EdSchPpr; PresFrCl; Swmmng; Tennis; Chrldr; Central Missouri St Coll; Public Relations.

NICHOLS, Linda L; Osborn HS; Osborn, MO; 3/12 SecTrsSrCls; HonRl; LbryAde; NatlMeritCmnd; SchPl; Yrbk; SchPpr; LetterBsktbl; IMSpt; College; Journalism.

NICHOLS, Lynne; Warsaw Comm HS; Warsaw, IN; Band; CncrtBnd; MrchBnd; PepBnd; SchMus; SchPl; Univ; Professional.

NICHOLS, Michael E; Cumberland HS; Toledo, IL; 14/103 PresStuCncl; LetterBsbl; LetterBsktbl; LetterTrk; AmLegAwd; College; Engineer.

NICHOLS, Nancy J; Jefferson HS; Lafayette, IN; 7/591 ALAGirlsSt; Chr; HonRl; SecNHS; SchMus; StuCncl; RptrYrbk; GerCl; 4-HAwd; RotaryAwd; Indiana Univ; Professional.

NICHOLS, Pamela J; Mc Kinley HS; Eminence, MO; 4/180 TrsJrCls; SecTrsSrCls; HonRl; OffAde; TchrAde; Yrbk; PpCl; Chrldr; DARAwd; KiwanAwd; College; Physical Education.

NICHOLS, Pamela S; Edinburg HS; Edinburg, IL; 13/31 MrchBnd; OffAde; PepBnd; SchAde; YthFlsp; EdYrBk; RptrSchPpr; 4-H; FHA; Bsktbl; Business School; Exxecutive Secretary.

NICHOLS, Paula S; Willard HS; Springfield, MO; HstFrshCls; Chr; HonRl; SchMus; SctActv; StuCncl; Twrl; Trk; Chrldr; MasAwd; Sw Mo St Univ; Social Worker Or Teacher.

NICHOLS, Pennie A; Waynesville Sr HS; Waynesville, MO; Band; ChrhWkr; CncrtBnd; HonRl; JrNHS; MrchBnd; NHS; Univ; Chemical Engineer.

NICHOLS, Roxanne M; Southern Boone Co HS; Ashland, MO; DrlTm; DrmMjrt; HonRl; LbryAde; NHS; SchPl; Twrl; 4-H; FHA; SpnCl; College; Education.

NICHOLS, Steven; Winterset Community HS; Winterset, IA; PresSrCls; ALBoysSt; HonRl; SchMus; StuGov; Bsbl; Bsktbl; Ftbl; Trk; AmLegAwd; U Of Iowa; Medicine.

NICHOLS, Thomas K; Unity HS; Ursa, IL; ChrhWkr; JCC; RedCrAde; ROTC; SchAde; StuGov; YthFlsp; AmLegAwd; GodCntryAwd; JAAwd; Vocational.

NICHOLS, Tommy G; Dixon HS; Dixon, MO; 17/65 NatlMeritCmnd; StuCncl; SptEdSchPpr; LetterBsbl; CaptBsktbl; Trk; CchngActv; University; Coaching.

NICHOLSD, Cynthia D; West Washington HS; Salem, IN; 16/81 Band; CmntyWkr; CncrtBnd; HonRl; MrchBnd; PepBnd; SchPl; TchrAde; 4-H; FHA; PpCl; DanFAwd; Purdue University.

NICHOLSON, Debbi J; North Nodaway Riii HS; Hopkins, MO; 7/40 Band; Chrs; HonRl; LbryAde; SchPl; EdSchPpr; PresFHA; PpCl; OptClAwd; Nw Mo St Univ; Speech.

NICHOLSON, Donna J; Colby HS; Colby, KS; 45/92 Band; HonRl; MrchBnd; SchPl; SctActv; StuCncl; TchrAde; FTA; SpnCl; PpCl; U Of Ks; Fashion Design.

NICHOLSON, Douglas G; East Richland HS; Olney, IL; 14/260 Chrs; ChrhWkr; CncrtBnd; Mdrgl; MrchBnd; NHS; NatlMeritCmnd; PepBnd; SchMus; University.

NICHOLSON, John; Danville Sr Hs; Danville, IL; 30/629 Band; HonRl; MrchBnd; Orch; PepBnd; SchMus; RptrSchPpr; SchPpr; University Of Illinois; Political Science.

NICHOLSON, John T; Desoto Senior HS; Sunflower, KS; HonRl; SchPpr; Bsbl; Bsktbl; College; Nuclear Engr.

NICHOLSON, Karey A; Lake Orion HS; Pontioc, MI; 9/350 HospAde; NHS; StuCncl; RptrYrbk; RptrSchPpr; LetterChrldr; Oakland U.

NICHOLSON, Lawrence C; Churubusco HS; Churubusco, IN; ChrhWkr; CtyCnl; CmntyWkr; HonRl; NHS; SchMus; StuGov; YthLg; PpCl; LetterBsbl; LetterFtbl; Univ; Teaching.

NICHOLSON, Mary Jo; St Marys HS; Burlington, WI; 2/73 Chr; HonRl; SctActv; PpCl; SciCl; Chrldr; Univ Of Wisconsin.

NICHOLSON, Patrick H; Wakefield HS; Emerson, NE; VPSrCls; Chr; Chrs; SchPl; StuCncl; TchrAde; Ftbl; Trk; Wrstlng; CchngActv; College.

NICHOLSON, Scott G; Concordia HS; Concordia, KS; ALBoysSt; Aud/Vis; HonRl; TchrAde; LetterFtbl; Trk; Wrstlng; IMSpt; Coll; Pharmacy.

NICHOLSON, Sheila K; Springs Valley HS; French Lick, IN; 9/83 VPSophCls; PresJrCls; ChrhWkr; NHS; StuCncl; Yrbk; 4-H; FHA; FrCl; PpCl; Trk; Chrldr; College; Vocation.

NICHOLSON, Tammy L; Potosi R 3 HS; Potosi, MO; Band; Chr; CncrtBnd; HonRl; MrchBnd; Orch; PepBnd; StuCncl; Mac College; Bookkeeper.

NICHOLSON, Vera Z; E St Louis Sr HS; Centerville, IL; 66/731 SecSrCls; Chrl; ChrhWkr; CmntyWkr; HonRl; StuGov; RptrSchPpr; EdSchPpr; FshEdSchPpr; SptEdSchPpr; Northern Illinois Univ; Journalist.

NICHTING, Joseph J; Marquette HS; Pilot Grove, IA; PresSophCls; ALBoysSt; Aud/Vis; HonRl; Sdlty; StuCncl; StuGov; SchPpr; PpCl; IMSpt; Creighton Univ; Accounting.

NICKEL, Alfred J; Pardeeville HS; Wyocena, WI; Band; HonRl; PepBnd; Bsbl; Bsktbl; Ftbl; Armed Service And College.

NICKEL, Ann L; Ida HS; Monroe, MI; 7/147 Band; CncrtBnd; HonRl; MrchBnd; NHS; SchMus; IMSpt; Adrian College; Political Science Major.

NICKEL, Donna M; Ida HS; Temperance, MI; SecFrshCls; Band; HonRl; NHS; OffAde; StuGov; TchrAde; PpCl; Chrldr; PPFtbl; Jr College; Respiratory Therapy.

NICKEL, Earlita; Winfield Senior HS; Winfield, KS; 15/181 ChrhWkr; HonRl; LbryAde; College; Teaching.

NICKEL, Karen J; Reese HS; Reese, MI; Chr; ChrhWkr; HonRl; NHS; NatlMeritSF; StuCncl; TchrAde; YthFlsp; LetterTrk; Central Mi Univ; Teacher.

NICKEL, Marianne S; Belding Central Jr Sr HS; Belding, MI; SecJrCls; TrsJrCls; Chr; ChrhWkr; HonRl; NHS; StuCncl; YthFlsp; PpCl; Chrldr; College; Professional.

NICKELE, Christopher J; Notre Dame For Boys HS; Chicago, IL; 3/283 HonRl; JA; NatlMeritCmnd; College; Medicine.

NICKELE, Janet M; Resurrection HS; Chicago, IL; 27/294 HonRl; HospAde; NHS; PolWkr; SecRedCrAde; College; Science.

NICKELL, Mark D; Boone Valley HS; Renwick, IA; ChrhWkr; HonRl; SchPl; SptEdYrbk; PpCl; Bsbl; Bsktbl; CaptFtbl; Trk; Northwestern Clg; Teaching.

NICKELS, Darrol S; Henryville HS; Henryville, IN; VPFrshCls; TrsSophCls; TrsJrCls; StuCncl; Bsbl; Bsktbl;.

NICKELS, Dianna N; Stanley County HS; Fort Pierre, SD; 1/52 SecTrsJrCls; ALAGirlsSt; Band; HonRl; JrNHS; NHS; NatlSciFnd; 4-H; LetterBsktbl; GAA; PPFtbl; 4-HAwd; MasAwd; College; Special Education.

NICKELS, Mark; Brookfield Central HS; Brookfield, WI; 13/487 CmntyWkr; NatlFornLg; NHS; GerCl; Bsbl; Bsktbl; Tennis; University Of Wisconsin; Pre Med.

NICKELSON, Debra; Hill Murray HS; St Paul, MN; 4/248 Chr; Chrs; ChrhWkr; HonRl; JrNHS; NHS; PolWkr; SchMus; Coll; Major Biology.

NICKELSON, Gaye D; Valley Center HS; Valley Center, KS; 30/125 VPSophCls; Chr; SecFrshCls; HonRl; NatlThespSoc; SchMus; StuCncl; RptrYrbk; RptrSchPpr; 4-H; Wichita St Univ; Dental Hygiene.

NICKELSON, Mary E; W Chicago Comm HS; West Chicago, IL; VPSrCls; ChrhWkr; HonRl; StuCncl; RptrSchPpr; 4-H; PpCl; Bsktbl; Swmmng; CaptChrldr; Univ; Professional.

NICKENS, Gary E; Tamaroa HS; Tamoroa, IL; 1/26 TrsSrCls; Chrs; HonRl; SchMus; VPFFA; LetterBsbl; College; Professional.

NICKERSON, Dianne; Cloverdale HS; Cloverdale, IN; TrsJrCls; HonRl; StuCncl; SpnCl; PpCl; GAA; Business School; Business.

NICKERSON, Elaine C; Yale HS; Yale, MI; Band; Chr; Chrs; ChrhWkr; CncrtBnd; DrmMjrt; HonRl; LbryAde; MrchBnd; Orch; PepBnd; SchMus; College; Dental Assisting.

NICKLESS, Kenneth; Herculaneum HS; Pevely, MO; 1/99 Band; ChrhWkr; CncrtBnd; HonRl; JA; NHS; PepBnd; StuCncl; JAAwd; Col.

NICKLESS, Melyssa L; Shakamak HS; Lewis, IN; 13/75 ALAGirlsSt; DrlTm; StuCncl; TchrAde; FHA; LatCl; PpCl; Chrldr; College; Art.

NICKMAN, Barbara S; Northwest HS; Grand Island, NE; HonRl; OffAde; StuGov; Teen; FHA; PpCl; Bsbl; College; Stewardess.

NICKODEMUS, Mary A; Reese HS; Richville, MI; 7/127 ALAGirlsSt; Band; Chr; ChrhWkr; CncrtBnd; HonRl; MrchBnd; NHS; PepBnd; Western Michigan Univ; Art Education.

NICKOLAI, Laura E; Regina HS; Detroit, MI; Aud/Vis; CmntyWkr; HonRl; LitMag; OffAde; PolWkr; SctActv; SchPpr; FTA; Wayne State; Instructing The Blind.

NICKOLAY, Pat; New Prague HS; New Prague, MN; 95/194 HonRl; NHS; GerCl; Glf; Uermilion St Jr College; Field Of Science.

NICKRENT, Kathleen M; St Josephs Academy; Florissant, MO; 2/128 ChrhWkr; HonRl; LitMag; NHS; NatlMeritFnl; NatlMeritSchl; NatlMeritSF; LatCl; SecMthCl; PresAwd; Washington University; Art.

NICKS, Darryl R; Gasconade Co R 2 HS; Owensville, MO; Band; HonRl; PepBnd; YthFlsp; 4-H; LetterFtbl; LetterTrk; DanFAwd; 4-HAwd; VoiceDemAwd; E Central Jr Clge Union Mo; Drafting.

NICODEMUS, Charlotte A; Whitko HS; Columbia City, IN; 18/153 Band; Chr; CncrtBnd; HonRl; HospAde; MrchBnd; NatlFornLg; Orch; SchMus; SchPl; StuCncl; Trk; Chrldr;.

NICOL, David B; No Farmington HS; Farmington Hills, MI; ChrhWkr; Orch; SchMus; GerCl; Adrian College.

NICOL, Douglas; Northland HS; Remer, MN; 2/57 HonRl; JrNHS; NHS; SchPl; SctActv; YthFlsp; RptrYrbk; EdYrBk; SptEdYrbk; SciCl; Univ; Doctor.

NICOL, James A; Kingston HS; Deford, MI; Aud/Vis; HonRl; SchPl; SchPpr; FrCl; Business School; Professional.

NICOLAI, Paul M; Milnor HS; Milnor, ND; 7/25 VPFrshCls; VPSophCls; ALBoysSt; Band; Chrs; HonRl; SchPl; StuCncl; TchrAde; 4-H; KeyCl; Bsbl; Bsktbl; CaptFtbl; College; Professional.

NICOLAI, Susan J; Immaculate Heart Of Mary HS; Broadview, IL; 70/250 Chrl; ChrhWkr; SchMus; SchPl; Teen; Western Ill Univ; English.

NICOLAOU, Andrew P; Charlotte HS; Charlotte, MI; OffAde; PresSctActv; StuCncl; CaptTennis; Northwood Inst; Prof.

NICOLAS, Michael P; Aquinas HS; Bellwood, NE; 86/99 LbryAde; OffAde; SchAde; StuGov; TchrAde; SciCl; Wrstlng; CchngActv; Platte College; Mechanical Drawing.

NICOLET, Cathy; Memorial HS; Eau Claire, WI; HonRl; 4-H; FrCl; College.

NICOLETTI, Patti L; Columbus Unified HS; Columbus, KS; ALAGirlsSt; Band; HonRl; HospAde; NHS; NatlThespSoc; StuCncl; Chrldr; PPFtbl; College; Nursing.

NICOLI, David P; Valley City HS; Valley City, ND; HonRl; PolWkr; PresStuCncl; RptrSchPpr; SptEdSchPpr; Wrstlng; IMSpt; U Of Nd; Lawyer.

NICOLINI, Mary B; Marian HS; Mishawaka, IN; 3/118 HonRl; SchPl; StuGov; EdYrBk; RptrSchPpr; Northwestern Univ; Lawyer.

NICOLL, Janet; Dominican Hs; Detroit, MI; Band; StuCncl; LetterBsbl; LetterBsktbl;.

NICOSIA, Virginia M; Glenbard South HS; Glen Ellyn, IL; 5/305 Band; CtyCnl; NHS; NatlMeritCmnd; StuCncl; StuGov; YthLg; AmLegAwd; Northwestern Univ; Computer Science.

NICOSON, Chere M; Waterman HS; Waterman, IL; 16/36 Chr; HonRl; OffAde; Pres4-H; FHA; FrCl; Socr; GAA; 4-HAwd; Du Page College; Fashion Design.

NICOTRA, Thomas W; Bremen HS; Markham, IL; HonRl; NHS; Ftbl; Wrstlng; Univ Of Illinois; Computer Science.

NIDEK, Terry L; Bedford HS; Temperance, MI; 11/421 HonRl; NHS; StuCncl; RptrSchPpr; PpCl; GAA; IMSpt; Michael J Owen Tech Coll; Rn.

NIEBERLE, Susanna G; Wheeling HS; Arlington Hts, IL; 7/446 HonRl; JrNHS; NHS; University; Professional.

NIEBUHR, Kurt W; Lutheran HS; Norwood, MN; TrsSophCls; Band; Chr; HonRl; NHS; StuCncl; PresSciCl; LetterBsbl; LetterBsktbl; LetterFtbl; Trk; College.

NIEBUR, Paula S; Granite HS; Granite, IL; Chr; StuCncl; 4-H; SpnCl; PpCl; Chrldr; GAA; College.

NIECE, Paul A; Green City R I HS; Green Castle, MO; PresSophCls; VPJrCls; SchPl; PresStuCncl; 4-H; FBLA; PpCl; CaptBsbl; CaptBsktbl; Trk; IMSpt; University; Professional.

NIEDER, Rick W; St Louis University; St Louis, MO; StuCncl; StuGov; Ftbl; Trk; IMSpt; AmLegAwd; College; Lawyer.

NIEDERER, Tina M; High School; Bath, IL; SecFrshCls; SecSophCls; SecJrCls; SecSrCls; Band; Bsktbl; GAA; DARAwd; 4-HAwd; JAAwd; Legal Secretary.

NIEDERGESES, William J; Heelan HS; Sioux City, IA; 35/249 Chr; Chrs; CmntyWkr; HonRl; LbryAde; NHS; NatlThespSoc; SchPl; SctActv; StuCncl; College; Vocational.

NIEDERHAUSER, Guy; Macon Jr Sr HS; Macon, MO; 5/117 ALBoysSt; Band; Chrs; ChrhWkr; PresCncrtBnd; HonRl; PepBnd; SchMus; StuCncl; LetterGlf; Univ Of Mo.

NIEDERMAN, Joleen; Elgin Public HS; Morristown, SD; TrsFrshCls; PresSrCls; CncrtBnd; HonRl; MrchBnd; PepBnd; SchPl; RptrSchPpr; FHA; PpCl; Bismarck Jr College; Legal Secretary.

NIEDERMEIER, Lisa E; Airport Community HS; Newport, MI; 1/240 HstSophCls; HstJrCls; HstSrCls; TreasBand; HonRl; NHS; RptrYrbk; 4-H; FrCl; LetterTrk; Univ; Forestry.

NIEDERT, Debra K; Sumner HS; Sumner, IA; Chr; Chrs; ChrhWkr; HonRl; HospAde; SchMus; SchPl; YthFlsp; FHA; GAA; PPFtbl; University Of N Iowa; Art.

NIEDFELDT, Alice A; Wamego HS; Paxico, KS; Band; HonRl; YthFlsp; PpCl; Business School; Secretarial.

NIEDFELDT, Cynthia J; Lakeview HS; Columbus, NE; 1/68 VPFrshCls; SecJrCls; TreasBand; HonRl; MrchBnd; PresNHS; SecStuCncl; RptrYrbk; 4-H; PpCl; Platte College; Math.

NIEDFELDT, Donnalee A; Bangor HS; Bangor, WI; 1/74 ALAGirlsSt; Band; Chrs; HonRl; HospAde; LbryAde; 4-H; DARAwd; 4-HAwd; College; Elem Education.

NIEDMAYER, Roberta; Proviso West Hs; Berkley, IL; 25 HonRl; JrNHS; NHS; U;computer Science.

NIEDZWIECKI, Judith K; East Detroit HS; East Detroit, MI; CmntyWkr; HonRl; StuGov; CivCl; FBLA; IMSpt; VoiceDemAwd;.

NIEHAUS, Brenda; Heritage Hills HS; St Meinrad, IN; 6/147 HonRl; Yrbk; FrCl; PpCl; GAA; OptClAwd; Univ Of Evansville; Math Education.

NIEHAUS, Cindy A; Connersville HS; Connersville, IN; 15/317 SecSophCls; ALAGirlsSt; ChrhWkr; DrlTm; HonRl; NatlMeritSchl; StuCncl; StuGov; RptrYrbk; Yrbk; Cornell U; Home Ec.

NIEHAUS, Jeffrey J; Edgewood Colesburg HS; Edgewood, IA; StuCncl; FFA; SpnCl; Bsktbl; Trade; Vocation.

NIEHAUS, Katherine J; Routt HS; Jacksonville, IL; HospAde; JA; SctActv; StuCncl; SchPpr; SpnCl; IMSpt;.

NIEHAUS, Kristy; Rosary HS; Florissant, MO; Chrs; HonRl; NHS; NatlMeritCmnd; PolWkr; SchMus; StuCncl; RptrYrbk; PpCl; GAA; Univ Of Detroit; Lawyer.

NIEHAUS, Mary A; Allison Bristow Comm HS; Allison, IA; 1/39 SecTrsFrshCls; VPJrCls; Chr; Chrs; ChrhWkr; HonRl; Mdrgl; EdYrBk; DanFAwd; 4-HAwd; Wartburg Clg; Music.

NIEHAUS, Suzanne M; Routt HS; Jacksonville, IL; 2/61 VPSrCls; Band; DrmMjrt; HonRl; StuCncl; Yrbk; SchPpr; FrCl; MthCl; AmLegAwd; Il St U; Accounting.

NIELAND, James K; Sisseton HS; Sisseton, SD; Band; HonRl; NHS; SchPl; Ftbl; Trk; College; Engineer.

NIELSEN, Barb A; Johnston HS; Des Moines, IA; 2/80 VPJrCls; Band; CncrtBnd; HonRl; MrchBnd; NHS; SchPl; StuGov; Tennis; Ia St Univ; Veterinary Medicine.

NIELSEN, Cindy; Tri Center HS; Neoia, IA; 8/76 Chrs; ChrhWkr; CmntyWkr; HonRl; NHS; StuCncl; PpCl; Chrldr; College; Nursing.

NIELSEN, Coleen K; Montabella HS; Blanchard, MI; 10/95 TrsFrshCls; TrsSophCls; TrsJrCls; TrsSrCls; Band; ChrhWkr; CncrtBnd; HonRl; MrchBnd; OffAde; Montcalm Community College.

NIELSEN, Daniel C; Forest Hills Central HS; Grand Rapids, MI; 3/183 NHS; NatlMeritCmnd; NatlMeritSF; Yrbk; College; Structural Engineer.

NIELSEN, David; Lakeview HS; Trufant, MI; HonRl; TchrAde; FTA; Bsbl; Central Michigan U;physical Education Major.

NIELSEN, Diane J; Rushford HS; Rushford, MN; AFS; Chrs; CncrtBnd; HonRl; NHS; PepBnd; SctActv; RptrSchPpr; FHA; IMSpt; Winona State Col; Band Director.

NIELSEN, Erik C; Lexington Comm HS; Lexington, IL; 8/49 TrsSophCls; AFS; Band; CncrtBnd; HonRl; LbryAde; MrchBnd; PepBnd; SchPl; RptrYrbk; 4-H; FFA; SciCl; Univ Of Illinois; Veterinarian.

NIELSEN, James W; Roosevelt Theodore HS; Des Moines, IA; ChrhWkr; CmntyWkr; SchMus; SctActv; StuCncl; LatCl; Bsktbl; LetterTrk; IMSpt; Luther College; Psychology.

NIELSEN, Judith D; New England Public HS; New England, ND; 1/50 PresSophCls; PresSrCls; ALAGirlsSt; ChrhWkr; DrlTm; HonRl; NHS; StuCncl; PresFHA; LetterTrk; Univ; Professional.

NIELSEN, Julie A; Unity HS; Balsam Lake, WI; 17/107 Chr; PresChrhWkr; HonRl; SchMus; 4-H; VPFHA; VPPpCl; College; Art.

NIELSEN, Linda M; Abraham Lincoln HS; Council Bluffs, IA; 21/444 PresBand; CncrtBnd; JrNHS; MrchBnd; NHS; PepBnd; VPRedCrAde; Pres4-H; GerCl; 4-HAwd; U Of Northern Iowa; Accounting.

NIELSEN, Mark W; Minden HS; Minden, NE; PresSophCls; Chr; NHS; SchMus; SchPl; LetterBsktbl; Ftbl; College.

NIELSEN, Ran; Plattsmouth HS; Plattsmouth, NE; Band; ChrhWkr; HstFrshCls; CncrtBnd; MrchBnd; SctActv; MthCl; Trk; CitAwd; Univ Nebraska; Professional.

NIELSEN, Roxanne H; Powers Lake HS; Powers Lake, ND; ALAGirlsSt; ChrhWkr; HonRl; 4-H; PpCl; IMSpt; Undecided;.

NIELSEN, Susan J; Traverse City HS; Traverse City, MI; 8/650 Band; CncrtBnd; DrlTm; HonRl; MrchBnd; NHS; Orch; PepBnd; TchrAde; FshEdSchPpr; Central Mich Univ; Elem Educ.

NIELSEN, Valerie; South Side HS; Ft Wayne, IN; 22/426 HonRl; StuCncl; TchrAde; YthFlsp; SchPpr; SpnCl; NCTE; CitAwd; Purdue Univ; Home Ec.

NIELSEN, Vicki A; Western Comm HS; Buda, IL; Band; ChrhWkr; CmntyWkr; SchPl; StuCncl; Yrbk; SchPpr; FHA; Trk; GAA;.

NIEMAH, Lawrence E; South Decatur HS; Greensburg, IN; HonRl; 4-H; FFA; KeyCl; Bsktbl; LetterTrk; PresAwd; Farming.

NIEMAN, Cynthia B; Pekin Comm HS; Pekin, IL; Chr; Chrl; Chrs; ChrhWkr; HonRl; NHS; SchMus; SchPl; Illinois Wesleyan Univ; Music.

NIEMAN, Karen; Woden Crystal Lake HS; Britt, IA; 4/30 ChrhWkr; HonRl; RptrYrbk; RptrSchPpr; FNA; PpCl; Bsktbl; IMSpt; Luther Coll; Anthropology.

NIEMAN, Sheila K; Guttenberg Comm HS; Guttenberg, IA; 13/72 VPFrshCls; PresSophCls; TrsJrCls; Chrs; HonRl; NHS; TchrAde; RptrYrbk; Yrbk; FHA; Business Office.

NIEMANN, Amy C; Lincoln HS; Wisconsin Rapids, WI; PresChr; TreasChrs; HonRl; MrchBnd; NHS; NatlThespSoc; Orch; SchMus; SchPl; SecStuCncl; Ripon College.

NIEMANN, Barbara A; Underwood HS; Underwood, IA; 6/60 SecJrCls; TrsSrCls; HonRl; FHA; Bsbl; Bsktbl; IMSpt; PPFtbl; Univ Of Northern Ia; Phy Ed Or Elem.

NIEMANN, James J; St Anthony HS; Effingham, IL; Chrs; ChrhWkr; SchMus; SchPl; College; Psychology.

NIEMANN, Jill S; Quincy Notre Dame HS; Quincy, IL; TrsFrshCls; Chr; Chrs; HonRl; Orch; SchMus; StuCncl; RptrYrbk; SpnCl; CaptChrldr; IMSpt; College; Nursing.

NIEMANN, Lynn; Buckley Loda Hs; Buckley, IL; Chr; Chrs; HonRl; NHS; SchPl; YthFlsp; RptrSchPpr; SecFHA; PresMthCl; Trk;.

NIEMANN, Sheryl L; John Hersey HS; Arlington Hts, IL; 48/739 Chrs; ChrhWkr; HonRl; NHS; StuCncl; YthFlsp; Adrian College; Christian Education.

NIEMANN, Thomas A; Saint Thomas HS; Ann Arbor, MI; 3/79 HonRl; NHS; OffAde; StuGov; SpnCl; PpCl; LetterBsbl; LetterFtbl; SARAwd; KiwanAwd; Univ Of Mi; Physical Theraphy.

NIEMANN, Wayne W; New Haven HS; Mt Clemens, MI; HonRl; TchrAde; 4-H; Macomb Co Comm College; Carpenter.

NIEMETSCHEK, Roland S; Brookfield East HS; Brookfield, WI; 5/512 Band; ChrhWkr; HonRl; NHS; StuCncl; SptEdYrbk; MthCl; Sch Of Engin; Med Elec Tech.

NIEMEYER, Carol J; Heritage HS; Fort Wayne, IN; 20/160 ALAGirlsSt; Chr; ChrhWkr; NHS; OffAde; TchrAde; PresPpCl; Trk; Chrldr; GAA; Indiana Purdue; Health Field.

NIEMI, Alan D; Ontonagan HS; Ontonagan, MI; Band; HonRl; SctActv; Michigan Tech Univ; Electronics.

NIEMI, Brian L; J F Kennedy HS; Embarrass, MN; 3/145 HonRl; NHS; Trk; Univ Of Mn; Civil Engineering.

NIEMI, Margaret R; John F Kennedy HS; Taylor, MI; 13/400 SecJrCls; SecSrCls; HonRl; NHS; StuCncl; RptrYrbk; LetterSwmmng; PPFtbl; Ferris State College; Med Lab Technology.

NIEMI, Marlene S; Owen Withee HS; Withee, WI; 11/102 Band; ChrhWkr; HonRl; NHS; SctActv; RptrYrbk; Pres4-H; FHA; PpCl; LetterBsktbl; Trk; GAA; College; Music.

NIEMIEC, Ted R; St Bonaventure Prep; Hammond, IN; 1/25 HonRl; NHS; NatlMeritCmnd; SchPl; EdYrBk; In U Bloomington; Medicine.

NIEMIEROWICZ, Mary; Manistee Cath Cen HS; Manistee, MI; 35/76 HonRl; TchrAde; FrCl; PpCl; IMSpt; Coll; Spec Ed.

NIEMOELLER, John A; Lindbergh Sr HS; St Louis, MO; 11/900 HonRl; NHS; NatlMeritFnl; NatlThespSoc; SchPl; Univ; Professional.

NIEMUTH, Douglas J; Oakville Sr HS; St Louis, MO; ChrhWkr; HonRl; LbryAde; YthFlsp; MthCl; LetterFtbl; LetterSocr; CaptTennis; IMSpt; College; Accounting.

NIEMZYK, Ronald C; Hartford Union HS; Hubertus, WI; HonRl; JrNHS; NHS; NatlMeritCmnd; Univ Of Wi; Hotel Management.

NIENAS, Jonathan W; Northwood HS; Thompson, ND; 5/44 PresFrshCls; ALBoysSt; Band; ChrhWkr; HonRl; FFA; LetterBsktbl; LetterFtbl; LetterTrk; 4-HAwd; Nd St Univ; Bus Admin.

NIENAS, Ronald F; Catholic Memorial HS; Brookfield, WI; TchrAde; LetterFtbl; Trk; Wrstlng; Univ; Professional.

NIENBURG, Karen E; Chaska HS; Excelsior, MN; VPJrCls; HonRl; JA; NHS; SchMus; SchPl; TreasStuCncl; RptrYrbk; EdYrBk; LetterTrk; U Of Ca Irvine; Environmental Sci.

NIENHUESER, Jill A; Union HS; Beaufort, MO; ALAGirlsSt; Band; HonRl; NatlFornLg; NatlMeritSchl; SchPl; Pres4-H; PPFtbl; AmLegAwd; 4-HAwd; University Of Missouri; Veterinarian.

NIENHUESER, Pamela L; Adams Central HS; Juniata, NE; 4/54 VPFrshCls; Chr; Chrs; CmntyWkr; NHS; SchMus; SchPl; RptrSchPpr; LetterTrk; 4-HAwd; Midland Lutheran; Crim Just.

NIENSTEDT, Corinne M; Our Lady Star Of The Sea HS; Grosse Pointe, MI; 15/65 HonRl; NatlFornLg; SchMus; SchPl; RptrYrbk; FrCl; GAA; College; Fashion Design.

NIENSTEDT, William B; Hartford HS; Neosho Rapids, KS; VPFrshCls; VPSophCls; Band; Chr; HonRl; MrchBnd; PepBnd; Bsktbl; LetterFtbl; University; Broadcasting.

NIERE, Carol J; Valley Park HS; Valley Park, MO; ChrhWkr; HonRl; NHS; Yrbk; VPFHA; PpCl; Univ; Accountant.

NIERGARTH, Steven P; Brighton HS; Brighton, MI; Band; CncrtBnd; HonRl; MrchBnd; NHS; PepBnd; SchMus; SctActv; LetterBsktbl; LetterTrk; Schoolcraft Coll; Biomed Electronics.

NIERMEYER, David H; Clarence Lowden HS; Lowden, IA; PresFrshCls; PresJrCls; ALBoysSt; Band; Chrs; ChrhWkr; CncrtBnd; HonRl; Mdrgl; MrchBnd; Cornell College; Medicine.

NIERODZIK, Henry E; Lincoln Northeast HS; Lincoln, NE; 23/556 HonRl; JrNHS; NHS; NatlMeritCmnd; TchrAde; GerCl; LetterFtbl; Neb Wesleyan Univ; Chem Eng.

NIES, Douglas E; Downers Grove Comm HS; Woodridge, IL; ChrhWkr; CmntyWkr; HonRl; PolWkr; SctActv; LetterBsktbl; AmLegAwd; Devry Institute Of Tech; Electronics Eng.

NIES, Kevin; Seneca HS; Seneca, WI; ALBoysSt; Band; CncrtBnd; MrchBnd; Orch; StuCncl; StuGov; RptrYrbk; Wrstlng; AmLegAwd; Uw Lacrosse; Lawyer.

NIES, Kristie J; Wyoming Park HS; Wyoming, MI; TrsSophCls; PresJrCls; Band; CncrtBnd; HonRl; NHS; SchMus; PpCl; Chrldr; GAA; U Of Mich; Art.

NIES, Scott A; Cambridge Sr HS; Cambridge, MN; Band; ChrhWkr; CncrtBnd; PepBnd; SchMus; SchPpr; Glf; IMSpt;.

NIESS, Donna J; Osage Community HS; Osage, IA; Band; ChrhWkr; CncrtBnd; HonRl; MrchBnd; PepBnd; Bus Sch; Medical Secretary.

NIESS, Timothy; Osage Community HS; Osage, IA; VPFrshCls; PresSrCls; ALBoysSt; Band; StuCncl; SchPpr; Trk; Wrstlng; AmLegAwd; College; English Teacher.

NIESSINK, Thomas A; Jackson HS; Jackson, MI; 1#16#29# Chr; HonRl; NHS; StuCncl; StuGov; Coll; Aerospace Engi.

NIESSNER, Corinne; Wheeling HS; Wheeling, IL; Chr; HonRl; NatlFornLg; NatlThespSoc; Quill&Scroll; SchPl; Illinois State University; Acting.

NIESTVCHOWSKI, Valerie A; Mason Sr HS; Erie, MI; 14/122 HonRl; JrNHS; NHS; NatlMeritCmnd; FHA; FNA; GerCl; Bsktbl; CaptTrk; VPGAA; Owens Tech College; Nurse.

NIETERS, Douglas J; St Louis Univ HS; St Louis, MO; Chr; ChrhWkr; HonRl; JA; SchMus; StuCncl; Yrbk; College; Botany.

NIETFELD, Cindy M; Marysville HS; Marysville, KS; Band; MrchBnd; StuCncl; SchPpr; FHA; PpCl; Trk; IMSpt; College; Professional.

NIETFELD, Patricia; Delavan Community HS; Delavan, IL; ChrhWkr; StuCncl; RptrSchPpr; 4-H; PpCl; Trk; IMSpt; Judson College; Pharmacy.

NIETZEL, Robert W; St Laurence HS; Oak Lawn, IL; HonRl; PolWkr; SchAde; Glf; Business Administration.

NIEVEEN, Kelvin P; Sterling Public HS; Sterling, NE; PresSophCls; Band; ChrhWkr; CncrtBnd; MrchBnd; PepBnd; SchAde; SchPl; TchrAde; Trk;.

NIEVINSKI, Peggy S; Muskego HS; Hales Corners, WI; 1/341 PresJrCls; PresSrCls; HonRl; NatlFornLg; NHS; NatlThespSoc; StuCncl; PresSpnCl; GAA; IMSpt; VoiceDemAwd; College; Medicine.

NIEWALD, Gail L; Maries County R Ii HS; Belle, MO; Band; HonRl; StuCncl; Twrl; FBLA; FHA; LetterBsktbl; Trk; CaptChrldr; College; Liberal Arts.

NIEWOEHNER, Roland E; Willow City HS; Willow City, ND; 1/17 PresFrshCls; ALBoysSt; Chrs; HonRl; SchPl; StuCncl; YthFlsp; SptEdYrbk; Yrbk; RptrSchPpr; SptEdSchPpr; SchPpr; FFA; SciCl; Univ Of North Dakota; Accounting.

NIEWOLD, Douglas W; Paxton HS; Loda, IL; AFS; Band; ChrhWkr; CmntyWkr; CncrtBnd; HonRl; MrchBnd; TreasNHS; PepBnd; YthFlsp; College; Farming.

NIFONG, Cindy; Argos Community HS; Argos, IN; 12/74 Band; Chr; HonRl; NHS; 4-H; PpCl; Purdue Univ; Pharmacy.

NIGG, Joel T; Wahlert HS; Dubuque, IA; 5/433 HstSophCls; SctActv; StuCncl; SchPpr; Ftbl; Trk; Wrstlng; University.

NIGG, Joey M; Dubois HS; Jasper, IN; 12/85 CmntyWkr; HonRl; NHS; YthFlsp; 4-H; Bsbl; LetterBsktbl; LetterTrk; Evansville Univ; Electrical Engineering.

NIGGEMAN, Charlene J; Adrian HS; Adrian, MI; 22/390 HonRl; NHS; TchrAde; GAA; Siena Heights College; Business Ed.

NIGHBERT, Debra E; Madison HS; Madison, SD; Band; ChrhWkr; CncrtBnd; HonRl; MrchBnd; NHS; PepBnd; RotaryAwd; Coll; Teaching.

NIGHSWONGER, Kim D; Hill City HS; Hill City, KS; SecSrCls; Band; Chrs; CncrtBnd; DrlTm; HonRl; MrchBnd; PepBnd; FHA; PpCl; College.

NIGHSWONGER, Ronald N; Torrington HS; Morrill, NE; 4-H; Bsbl; Ftbl; College; Professional.

NIGHTENGALE, Carol L; Chase County HS; Cedar Point, KS; SecJrCls; TrsJrCls; Band; ChrhWkr; DrlTm; HonRl; MrchBnd; PepBnd; SchPl; PpCl; LetterBsktbl; LetterTrk; Emporia State University.

NIGHTENGALE, Cathy L; Peabody HS; Burns, KS; 3/35 Band; Chr; HonRl; MrchBnd; NHS; OffAde; YthLg; FHA; CaptBsktbl; Trk; Kansas State U; Chemical Engr.

NIGHTENGALE, Janet L; Chase County HS; Cedar Point, KS; PresJrCls; Band; DrlTm; HonRl; MrchBnd; PepBnd; SchPl; PpCl; LetterBsktbl; LetterTrk; CitAwd; Kansas State University.

NIGON, Thomas E; Lourdes HS; Rochester, MN; PresJrCls; VPSrCls; Chr; Chrs; HonRl; NHS; SchMus; StuCncl; Bsktbl; LetterFtbl; Clge.

NIGRO, James D; Watervliet HS; Watervliet, MI; VPFrshCls; Band; CncrtBnd; DrmMjrt; HonRl; LetterBsbl; Bsktbl; Wrstlng; IMSpt; 4-HAwd; College; State Police.

NIGRO, Mary R; Harrison HS; Harrison, MI; 6/140 VPFrshCls; HonRl; StuCncl; College; Lawyer.

NIKITUK, Sonya E; Breck HS; South Saint Paul, MN; Chrs; HonRl; HospAde; Yrbk; CaptBsktbl; Socr; University; Medicine.

NIKOLEIT, Jill; Von Steuben Hs; Chicago, IL; 20/230 ChrhWkr; HonRl; NHS; OffAde; SchAde; SctActv; TchrAde; Swmmng; Trk; GAA;.

NIKSCH, Louis J; Hobaut HS; Hobart, IN; Band; CncrtBnd; HonRl; JrNHS; MrchBnd; PepBnd; SctActv; StuCncl; GerCl; SciCl; In Univ; Med Doctor.

NIKURS, Andrejs R; Stephen T Mather HS; Chicago, IL; 8/411 ALBoysSt; Chr; Chrs; ChrhWkr; HonRl; PresMdrgl; NatlFornLg; NHS; SchMus; SchPl; StuCncl; StuGov; KeyCl; PresMthCl; College; Medicine.

NILA, Brett E; Marmion Military Academy; Bristol, IL; ChrhWkr; HonRl; ROTC; EdYrBk; RptrSchPpr; SpnCl; Loyola Univ; Lawyer.

NILES, Chad S; Fargo North HS; Fargo, ND; ROTC; Glf; IMSpt; College; Professional.

NILHAS, Steve L; Trego Community HS; Ellis, KS; ChrhWkr; HonRl; Pres4-H; VPFFA; PresSciCl; 4-HAwd; University; Agriculture.

NILLES, Bret A; Hempstead HS; Dubuque, IA; 43/528 ALBoysSt; CmntyWkr; HonRl; ModUN; NHS; PolWkr; SctActv; StuGov; UNYO; AmLegAwd; University.

NILLES, Deborah K; Central Cass HS; Durbin, ND; 2/57 Band; Chr; CncrtBnd; HonRl; NHS; PepBnd; SchPl; 4-H; 4-HAwd; Mary College; Medical Tech.

NILLISSEN, Larry L; Bowler HS; Wittenberg, WI; VPFrshCls; ALBoysSt; HonRl; StuCncl; EdYrBk; MthCl; LetterBsbl; LetterBsktbl; LetterFtbl; LetterTrk; Marquette Univ; Doctor.

NILSON, Nancy J; Blair Jr/sr HS; Blair, NE; 6/139 Band; HonRl; NatlThespSoc; SchPl; RptrYrbk; FBLA; FrCl; PpCl; PresAwd; Col; Busi Or French.

NIMMO, Johnny R; Anna Jonesboro HS; Anna, IL; Chrs; ChrhWkr; CmntyWkr; RptrYrbk; FTA; KeyCl; Bsbl; Bsktbl; CaptFtbl; Trk; Eastern Illinois University; Music.

NIMMO, Johnny R; Anna Jonesboro C HS; Anna, IL; Chr; ChrhWkr; CmntyWkr; PepBnd; RptrYrbk; FTA; KeyCl; PpCl; Bsktbl; East Illinois Univ; Music.

NIMZ, Mark W; Trego Community HS; Wakeeney, KS; CmntyWkr; HonRl; SchPl; VPSctActv; YthFlsp; Bsktbl; LetterTrk; LionAwd; VFWAwd;.

NINHAM, Paul K; West Depere HS; Depere, WI; 87/218 PresSophCls; ChrhWkr; SchPl; StuCncl; Yrbk; FTA; LetterBsktbl; LetterFtbl; LetterTrk; IMSpt; College; Teacher.

NINNEMAN, Dean G; Lowell P Goodrich HS; Fond Du Lac, WI; CmntyWkr; 4-H;.

NINO, Jose F; Kelvyn Park HS; Chicago, IL; 137/300 CmntyWkr; HonRl; SchAde; TchrAde; KeyCl; CaptFtbl; LetterWrstlng; College; Professional.

NIPPLE, Kurt; Brodhead HS; Brodhead, WI; PresFrshCls; VPJrCls; Band; CncrtBnd; HonRl; MrchBnd; PepBnd; College; Professional.

NIQUETTE, Perry S; Southwest HS; Green Bay, WI; HonRl; Bsktbl; Ftbl; LetterTrk; IMSpt;.

NISBET, Bert; Troy HS; Troy, MI; 30/525 HonRl; NHS; TchrAde; LetterTrk; General Motors Institute; Industrial Admin.

NISBET, Nancy; Fisher HS; East Grandforks, MN; 4/28 Band; HonRl; SchPl; StuCncl; FHA; Bsktbl; Chrldr; GAA; College.

NISBET, Thomas A; Troy HS; Troy, MI; 30/525 HonRl; NHS; TchrAde; LetterTrk; General Motors Inst; Industrial Admin.

NISH, John E; Clarke Community HS; Weldon, IA; 1/105 ChrhWkr; HonRl; NHS; SptEdSchPpr; SpnCl; LetterBsktbl; LetterFtbl; JETSAwd; Iowa State U; Ceramic Engineering.

NISONGER, William R; Cranbrook HS; Bloomfield Hills, MI; 9/111 Chrs; ChrhWkr; YthFlsp; Univ Of Michigan; Law.

NISSEN, Debbie K; St Francis HS; Humphrey, NE; 1/34 Band; ChrhWkr; CncrtBnd; HonRl; LbryAde; NHS; PepBnd; TchrAde; Yrbk; LetterTrk; College; Biology.

NISSEN, Evette S; Wetmore HS; Wetmore, KS; 4/24 Band; CncrtBnd; HonRl; MrchBnd; NHS; SchMus; SchPl; StuCncl; RptrYrbk; RptrSchPpr; Clge; Bus Admin.

NISSEN, Jay R; Larimore HS; Mc Canna, ND; HonRl; SctActv; StuCncl; YthFlsp; FFA; Bsbl; Bsktbl; CaptFtbl; LetterTrk; Trade School.

NISSEN, Joella S; Chadron HS; Chadron, NE; Band; Chr; ChrhWkr; HonRl; StuCncl; Sec4-H; PpCl; LetterTrk; Chrldr; GAA; College; Medicine.

NISSEN, Mary Clare; St Francis HS; Humphrey, NE; 11/48 Chrs; HonRl; LbryAde; TchrAde; VPJrCls; LetterTrk; IMSpt; Business School.

NISSEN, Robert B; Oneill Public HS; Page, NE; 3/66 PresJrCls; ALBoysSt; NHS; NatlMeritCmnd; EdYrBk; 4-H; LetterBsbl; LetterBsktbl; EldAwd; Univ; Computer Science.

NISSLEY, Brenda V; Iowa Mennonite HS; Williamsburg, IA; 2/37 ChrhWkr; HonRl; JrNHS; StuCncl; YthFlsp; Yrbk; GerCl; CaptChrldr; Coll; Home Econ.

NISTLER, Janel A; Trinity HS; Dickinson, ND; 9/140 ChrhWkr; DrlTm; HonRl; HospAde; MrchBnd; SchMus; SchPl; 4-H; PpCl; 4-HAwd; Mary Coll; Accounting.

NITKA, Charles A; East De Pere HS; De Pere, WI; 11/195 HonRl; RedCrAde; MthCl; LetterWrstlng; IMSpt; St Norbert College; Accounting.

NITKA, David M; Waterford HS; Waterford, WI; 2/208 ALBoysSt; ChrhWkr; CmntyWkr; HonRl; MrchBnd; NHS; NatlMeritFnl; NatlMeritSF; PolWkr; SchMus; StuCncl; PpCl; LetterGlf; Chrldr; University; Chemistry.

NITKA, Doris A; Pacelli HS; Stevens Point, WI; 1/113 Chrs; HonRl; NHS; SchAde; StuCncl; TchrAde; Bsktbl; VPGAA; BauchLmbAwd; College; Pharmacy.

NITSCHKE, Patricia M; Ashley HS; Ashley, ND; VPSrCls; Chr; ChrhWkr; CncrtBnd; HonRl; PepBnd; SchPl; RptrYrbk; SchPpr; Univ Of No Dakota; Pre Medicine.

NITSCHKE, Ralph R; Milwaukee Lutheran HS; Milwaukee, WI; 40/235 Band; Chr; ChrhWkr; CncrtBnd; DrmMjrt; MrchBnd; Trk; IMSpt; Military Academey Or Marquette; Riminology.

NITZ, Cathy L; Lakeshore HS; Baroda, MI; CncrtBnd; HonRl; MrchBnd; PepBnd; SchAde; SchPl; TchrAde; 4-H; 4-HAwd; Central Michigan Univ; Teaching.

NITZ, William A; Clio Area HS; Flint, MI; 28/399 HonRl; JrNHS; NHS; SctActv; LatCl; SpnCl; JETSAwd; Rensselaer Poly Inst; Electrical Engineer.

NITZSCHE, Cinda K; Sparta HS; Evansville, IL; 25/170 Band; ChrhWkr; HonRl; MrchBnd; Yrbk; Sec4-H; PresFNA; PresPpCl; Bsktbl; PresGAA; Se Mo St; Soc Wrkr.

NITZSCHKE, Carol J; St Marys HS; Remsen, IA; 9/60 Chrs; HonRl; SchMus; RptrYrbk; RptrSchPpr; PpCl; LetterGlf; IMSpt; Bus Sch; Accounting.

NIVA, Beth M; Winston-Churchill HS; Livonia, MI; 3/861 SecSrCls; HonRl; MrchBnd; NatlSciFnd; SchMus; RptrYrbk; EdYrBk; RptrSchPpr; EdSchPpr; IMSpt; Boston Univ; Medicine.

NIXA, John M; Macomb Sr HS; Macomb, IL; ALBoysSt; ChrhWkr; HonRl; IntrClCncl; StuCncl; LetterGlf; LetterWrstlng; IMSpt; Az State U; Cpa.

NIXON, Elaine L; Southwestern HS; Medora, IL; 67/173 Chr; ChrhWkr; CmntyWkr; HospAde; PolWkr; RedCrAde; SchMus; SchPl; 4-H; FHA; PpCl; Ftbl; Jr College.

NIXON, Gregory L; Oxford HS; Oxford, KS; Chr; Chrs; HonRl; SchPl; YthFlsp; Yrbk; SchPpr; 4-H; SpnCl; Bsktbl; Cowley County Comm College; Journalism.

NIXON, James D; Springfield Catholic HS; Springfield, MO; 24/67 Band; CncrtBnd; HonRl; StuCncl; SptEdYrbk; SpnCl; LetterBsbl; CaptBsktbl; LetterTennis; Spring Hill Col, Mobile Al; Acctg & Sales.

NIXON, Julie A; Glenwood Community HS; Glenwood, IA; 21/115 SecFrshCls; Chrs; HonRl; SchMus; SchPl; RptrYrbk; 4-H; FHA; LetterBsbl; Bsktbl; LetterTrk; Ia State; Teacher.

NIXON, Melinda H; Strafford HS; Springfield, MO; 2/66 HonRl; PresNHS; Pres4-H; FTA; LetterTrk; CaptChrldr; 4-HAwd; Sw Mo St Univ; Agriculture.

NOACK, Carol L; Coloma HS; Coloma, MI; 9/172 HonRl; NHS; Lake Michigan College; Chemical Engineering.

NOACK, Ralph W; Appleton HS; Appleton, WI; Chr; Chrl; Chrs; ChrhWkr; NatlMeritSF; College; Aeronautical Engineering.

NOAH, Cheryl L; James B Conant HS; Hoffman Ests, IL; 77/621 CmntyWkr; HonRl; JrNHS; MrchBnd; NHS; StuCncl; YthFlsp; RptrYrbk; LetterTennis; IMSpt; PPFtbl; St Olaf College; Music.

NOAH, Jacalyn Y; Maryville R Ii HS; Maryville, MO; SpnCl; Trade School; Beautician.

NOAH, Nancy H; Charles City Community HS; Charles City, IA; 1/227 Chrs; HonRl; NHS; NatlMeritCmnd; SchPl; SctActv; StuCncl; GerCl; MthCl; PpCl; The Co College.

NOAH, Rhonda; Bucklin R Ii HS; Bucklin, MO; PresFrshCls; PresSrCls; HonRl; HospAde; MrchBnd; Yrbk; SchPpr; SciCl; Arizona State U; Athropologist.

NOASCONI, Doreen A; Stephenson HS; Stephenson, MI; 5/99 ALAGirlsSt; HonRl; NHS; RedCrAde; StuCncl; Yrbk; 4-H; SpnCl; Ferris St College; Nursing.

NOBBE, David E; Litchfield HS; Litchfield, IL; ALBoysSt; HonRl; SpnCl; Bsktbl; Ftbl; Glf; IMSpt; U Of Ill; Architecture.

NOBLE, Alice M; Woodstock HS; Wonder Lake, IL; 10/266 HonRl; NHS; TchrAde; EdSchPpr; Southern Ill Univ; Registered Nurse.

NOBLE, Bryan A; Garber HS; Essexville, MI; HonRl; Bsktbl; Trk; CitAwd; Coll; Math/bus.

NOBLE, Deloris R; Woodstock Community HS; Woodstock, IL; 24/174 ChrhWkr; CncrtBnd; HonRl; MrchBnd; NHS; NatlMeritCmnd; SchMus; Sec4-H; 4-HAwd; Millikin Univ; Music.

NOBLE, Diane K; Fennimore HS; Stitzer, WI; Chrl; Chrs; SecChrhWkr; HonRl; LbryAde; NatlFornLg; SchMus;.

NOBLE, James R; Harlan Comm HS; Harlan, IA; 26/256 AFS; HonRl; NHS; LetterBsktbl; LetterFtbl; Tennis; Trk; Iowa St University; Accounting.

NOBLE, Kathleen E; Hillcrest HS; Springfield, MO; AFS; Chr; Chrs; ChrhWkr; HonRl; LbryAde; SchMus; YthFlsp; VPFHA; PpCl; Sw Missouri St Univ; Home Economics.

NOBLE, Kristine; Westmer HS; Joy, IL; 2/61 PresFrshCls; Chrs; HonRl; SchMus; YthFlsp; RptrYrbk; FTA; SciCl; Chrldr; BttyCrckrAwd; Western Ill Univ; Bs Adm.

NOBLE, Laura E; Springfield HS; Springfield, MI; 17/84 HonRl; NHS; OffAde; StuGov; FHA; Tennis; Kellogg Community College.

NOBLE, Mary A; Jefferson Sr HS; Jefferson, WI; HonRl; PolWkr; SchMus; SchPl; SctActv; PpCl; College; Fashion.

NOBLE, Roberta D; Frontenac HS; Frontenac, KS; HonRl; HospAde; SchPl; SpnCl; Army; Biomedical Elec Tech.

NOBLE, Teresa; Rapid City Stevens HS; Rapid City Stevens, SD; 8/413 AFS; ALAGirlsSt; HonRl; NHS; University; Pro.

NOBLE, Todd A; Holdrege HS; Holdrege, NE; 5/108 PresJrCls; Chrs; ChrhWkr; HonRl; NatlSciFnd; SchMus; StuGov; 4-H; Bsktbl; Trk; U Of Ne; Med.

NOBLES, Denise; Thornwood HS; Markham, IL; 83/852 CncrtBnd; HonRl; MrchBnd; Michigan State Univ; Medical Tech.

NOCITA, Cheryl A; Lourdes Central HS; Nebraska City, NE; 2/36 Band; ChrhWkr; HonRl; StuGov; EdYrBk; TreasSpnCl; SecMthCl; VoiceDemAwd; Nebraska Univ Lincoln; Med Tech.

NOCKELS, Patrick J; St Patrick HS; Chicago, IL; 40/425 Aud/Vis; HonRl; HospAde; JrNHS; NatlMeritCmnd; NatlMeritSF; OffAde; PepBnd; SchAde; SchPl; PpCl; SciCl; Loyola Univ; Doctor.

NOCKELS, Russell P; St Patricks HS; Chicago, IL; 5/377 JrNHS; SchMus; SchPl; StuCncl; StuGov; TchrAde; GerCl; PpCl; SciCl; IMSpt; Loyola Univ; Doctor.

NOE, Glenn E; Richland HS; Richland, MO; PresFrshCls; PresSophCls; PresJrCls; ChrhWkr; HonRl; SchPl; PresStuCncl; LetterBsktbl; LetterTrk; U Of Mo Rdla; Engineering.

NOE, Mark D; Richland HS; Richland, MO; ChrhWkr; FFA;.

NOECKER, Ronald J; Cedar Catholic HS; Hartington, NE; PresFrshCls; PresSophCls; PresJrCls; Band; Chr; Chrl; Chrs; ChrhWkr; CncrtBnd; HonRl; JrNHS; Orch; PepBnd; SchMus; College; Teacher.

NOEHRENBERG, Lisa L; Luther HS; Oak Lawn, IL; 2/217 HonRl; GerCl; Tennis; Concordia Teachers College; Secondary Educ.

NOEL, Anna M; Logan HS; Logan, KS; 1/43 PresJrCls; ALAGirlsSt; HonRl; NHS; Yrbk; RptrSchPpr; Business School; Data Processing.

NOEL, Gayle J; Mason Senior HS; Erie, MI; 5/121 HonRl; TreasNHS; OffAde; SchPl; TchrAde; TreasRptrYrbk; SchPpr; LetterBsktbl; GAA; PPFtbl; College; Data Processing.

NOEL, Gregory B; Cardinal Ritter HS; Indianapolis, IN; 50/165 ChrhWkr; HonRl; StuCncl; SpnCl; Bsbl; Bsktbl; Ftbl; Glf; IMSpt; Ball State U; Bus Admin.

NOEL, Jill M; Laplata R 2 HS; Laplata, MO; Band; ChrhWkr; CncrtBnd; DrmMjrt; HonRl; MrchBnd; NHS; PepBnd; SchMus; SchPl; SctActv; Twrl; FHA; PpCl; LetterChrldr; Univ Of Missouri; Teach Music.

NOEL, John P; Wahlert HS; Dubuque, IA; 20/442 ChrhWkr; NHS; StuGov; TchrAde; Ftbl; Trk; IMSpt; Ia St Univ; Physical Sciences.

NOEL, Margaret A; York Community HS; Elmhurst, IL; HonRl; SecJrNHS; NHS; NatlMeritCmnd; SchPl; StuCncl; EdSchPpr; CivCl; VPSpnCl; Tennis; Davidson College; Medicine.

NOEL, Mary K; Sheldon HS; Sheldon, IL; 9/32 Chrl; Chrs; CmntyWkr; HonRl; NHS; Quill&Scroll; SchPl; RptrSchPpr; 4-H; 4-HAwd; Bus Sch; Secretary.

NOELL, Scott J; Plattsmouth HS; Murray, NE; HonRl; TchrAde; FrCl; Bsktbl; LetterFtbl; Trk; Wrstlng; IMSpt; University; Professional.

NOETHE, Wayne J; Beckman HS; Dyersville, IA; 65/146 NHS; NatlMeritSchl; NatlSciFnd; SchAde; StuCncl; StuGov; FBLA; PpCl; LetterFtbl; LetterWrstlng; Coll.

NOFFSINGER, Robin; Marian HS; Elkhart, IN; 12/118 ChrhWkr; HonRl; JA; PolWkr; Ball State Univ; Social Work.

NOFFZIGER, Terri L; Deer Creek Mackinaw HS; Mackinaw, IL; 1/60 Band; Chrs; ChrhWkr; CncrtBnd; HonRl; MrchBnd; PepBnd; StuCncl; Yrbk; Illinois Wesleyan; French.

NOFSINGER, Gary L; Washington Community HS; Washington, IL; ALBoysSt; Chr; Chrl; ChrhWkr; YthFlsp; 4-H; VPFFA; LetterBsktbl; LetterTrk; JCAwd; Clge; Math.

NOFTSGER, Amy R; Grand Valley HS; Kellerton, IA; 4/27 Chrs; HonRl; MrchBnd; SchPl; StuCncl; Yrbk; SptEdSchPpr; FHA; LetterBsktbl; LetterTrk; Iowa State U; Vet.

NOGGLE, Malynda K; Kennedy HS; Cedar Rapids, IA; Chr; Chrs; JA; Orch; SchMus; YthFlsp; College; Music.

NOKES, Deborah S; Highland HS; Highland, IN; 138/538 Chr; Chrs; ChrhWkr; LitMag; SchMus; PpCl; GAA; College; Professional.

NOLAN, Brenda K; Van Far HS; Vandalia, MO; 2/90 SecJrCls; SecSrCls; ChrhWkr; HonRl; JrNHS; NHS; SchPl; StuCncl; PresFBLA; FHA; VPFrCl; Ne Missouri St Univ; Accounting.

NOLAN, Christopher W; Waukegan HS; Waukegan, IL; 6/1040 HonRl; TreasJrNHS; NHS; NatlMeritSF; LetterTennis; Univ; Physicist.

NOLAN, Denise L; Omaha Central HS; Omaha, NE; ALAGirlsSt; HonRl; JA; NHS; OffAde; TchrAde; MthCl; Univ Of Ne; Genetic Research.

NOLAN, Janet M; Our Lady Of Grace HS; Indianapolis, IN; Chrs; CmntyWkr; HonRl; JA; ModUN; RptrSchPpr; SchPpr; PpCl; IMSpt; PPFtbl; Indiana U; Nursing.

NOLAN, John O; St Louis HS; Richmond Heights, MO; ChrhWkr; CmntyWkr; HonRl; YthFlsp; Bsktbl; Trk; College; Professional.

NOLAN, Juanita J; Proviso East HS; Maywood, IL; Chrs; Western Illinois University; Social Work.

NOLAN, Karen S; Belvidere HS; Belvidere, IL; 63/364 HonRl; NHS; PresStuCncl; FNA; SpnCl; PpCl; Chrldr; GAA; PPFtbl; VoiceDemAwd; St Anthonys Schl Of Nursing; Nursing.

NOLAN, Linda M; Harvard HS; Harvard, IL; 4/170 SecTrsSrCls; Chr; Chrs; HonRl; Mdrgl; VPNHS; SchMus; RptrYrbk; SpnCl; GAA; Northern Ill Univ; Mathematics.

NOLAN, W; Griffin HS; Springfield, IL; 1/155 PresFrshCls; PresSophCls; VPJrCls; PresSrCls; NHS; NatlMeritFnl; EdYrBk; EdSchPpr; Western Ill Univ; Law Enforcement.

NOLAND, Wilma C; Royal Valley HS; Hoyt, KS; Chrs; LbryAde; TchrAde; Yrbk; FHA; PpCl; Bus Schl; Key Punch Acad.

NOLD, Elizabeth S; Tomah HS; Tomah, WI; 18/270 ALAGirlsSt; Chr; CaptDrlTm; HonRl; Mdrgl; NHS; OffAde; SchMus; StuCncl; GAA; Col; Professional.

NOLD, Gregory C; Freeburg Comm HS; Freeburg, IL; 2/120 ALBoysSt; HonRl; ModUN; NHS; NatlThespSoc; SchPl; RptrYrbk; Swmmng; DARAwd; Univ; Law.

NOLD, Shauna L; Owosso HS; Owosso, MI; 13/452 CncrtBnd; LbryAde; MrchBnd; NHS; PepBnd; SchPl; TchrAde; EdYrBk; EdSchPpr; Univ Of Mi; Advertising.

NOLIN, Carol J; Topeka West HS; Topeka, KS; TchrAde; SchPpr; GerCl; Univ Of Ksnsas; Architecture.

NOLL, Byron; Ransom HS; Ransom, KS; 1/25 TrsJrCls; CncrtBnd; HonRl; PepBnd; SchPl; SptEdSchPpr; BauchLmbAwd; CitAwd; Kansas State Univ; Electrical Engineering.

NOLL, Gregory; Jefferson County North HS; Winchester, KS; PresSrCls; DrmMjrt; NHS; SchMus; RptrYrbk; RptrSchPpr; RptrSchPpr; LetterBsktbl; LetterFtbl; LetterTrk; College.

NOLL, Gretchen A; Cassville HS; Cassville, WI; VPSophCls; PresJrCls; PresSrCls; ALAGirlsSt; HonRl; NHS; StuCncl; EdYrBk; GAA; DARAwd; Coll; Psychology.

NOLL, Jerald K; North Putnam HS; Coatsville, IN; 20/137 HonRl; SctActv; StuGov; 4-H; CaptFtbl; Wrstlng; IMSpt; 4-HAwd; GovHonPrgAwd; MasAwd; Purdue Univ; Biomedical Engineer.

NOLLEN, Diana M; Mediapolis Comm HS; Mediapolis, IA; 3/74 ALAGirlsSt; Band; Chrs; ChrhWkr; HonRl; NatlThespSoc; SchMus; EdYrBk; 4-H; FHA; 4-HAwd; University; English Teacher.

NOLLES, Patricia M; Rock County HS; Bassett, NE; 9/48 Chr; Chrs; ChrhWkr; HonRl; SchMus; UNYO; Yrbk; SchPpr; PresFHA; PpCl; 4-HAwd; Lincoln Sch Of Commerce; Accounting.

NOLLETTE, Linda L; Cody Kilgore Unified HS; Nenzel, NE; 2/20 ChrhWkr; HonRl; NHS; SchPl; PresStuGov; PresFFA; PresFHA; Trk; Chrldr; DanFAwd; Univ; Curr Of Major Study.

NOLTE, Dan F; Malcolm HS; Lincoln, NE; 4/27 ChrhWkr; CmntyWkr; HonRl; PolWkr; 4-H; Doane College; Political Science.

NOLTE, Diana L; Santa Fe HS; Blackburn, MO; Chrs; CncrtBnd; MrchBnd; NHS; StuCncl; YthFlsp; 4-H; FHA; Avila College; Nursing.

NOLTE, Marilyn K; Incarnate Academy; Olivette, MO; PresSophCls; HonRl; NHS; PolWkr; StuCncl; Bsktbl; Univ Of Colorado; Teacher.

NOLTE, Mary E; Mac Arthur HS; Decatur, IL; 118/411 Chr; ChrhWkr; HonRl; HospAde; SchMus; SctActv; TchrAde; PresYthFlsp; BttyCrckrAwd; College Of Dupage; Fashion Design.

NOLTE, Rick D; Nehawka Cons HS; Nehawka, NE; 3/15 VPSrCls; ALBoysSt; Band; Chrs; HonRl; PepBnd; SchPl; PresStuCncl; StuGov; PresFFA; Bsktbl; Ftbl; AmLegAwd; Univ Of Nebraska; Agriculture.

NOLTON, Karen B; Brown County HS; Nashville, IN; TrsFrshCls; Chr; HonRl; NHS; NatlThespSoc; SchMus; SchPl; StuCncl; TchrAde; 4-H; FrCl; SpnCl; Tennis; Univ Of Florida; Interpreter.

NOMMAY, Daniel E; Elkhart Central HS; Elkhart, IN; Bsbl; Ftbl; IMSpt; College; Dentist.

NOMMENSEN, Cathy A; Amos Alonzo Stagg HS; Palos Hills, IL; 70/468 Chr; ChrhWkr; CmntyWkr; HonRl; StuCncl; YthLg; SpnCl; SciCl; CaptSwmmng; GAA; Univ Of Ill; Business Admin.

NOOK, Mark A; Holstein Comm HS; Holstein, IA; ALBoysSt; CmntyWkr; SctActv; StuCncl; Yrbk; LetterBsbl; Ftbl; Trk; LetterWrstlng; GodCntryAwd; University; Science.

NOON, Jo Ann E; Elkhorn Kimballton HS; Walnut, IA; SecSrCls; Band; Chr; CncrtBnd; Mdrgl; MrchBnd; PepBnd; SchPl; FHA; BttyCrckrAwd; Col; Special Ed.

NOONAN, Ann C; Sunset Hill HS; Kansas City, MO; Chrl; Mdrgl; Quill&Scroll; SchPl; EdSchPpr; LatCl; Bsbl; Bsktbl; University.

NOONAN, Erin P; Waukesha South HS; Waukesha, WI; Chrs; CAP; DrlTm; Mdrgl; MrchBnd; Orch; SchMus; SchPl; StuCncl; GAA; Coll; Midwife.

NOONAN, Geri L; Ayrshire Consolidated HS; Ayrshire, IA; VPFrshCls; SecSrCls; Chr; ChrhWkr; CncrtBnd; HonRl; MrchBnd; StuCncl; FHA; Chrldr; Coll; Secretary.

NOONAN, Joyce; St Francis HS; Humphrey, NE; Band; Chr; Chrs; ChrhWkr; CmntyWkr; CncrtBnd; HonRl; Bsbl; Trk; GAA; Platte Coll; Bus.

NOONAN, Kathleen M; Lincoln Way HS; Frankfort, IL; 34/498 VPSrCls; Chr; HonRl; HospAde; NHS; NatlThespSoc; StuCncl; TchrAde; GAA; Purdue Univ; Computer Tech.

NOONAN, Mary E; Central City Comm HS; Anamosa, IA; ChrhWkr; HonRl; OffAde; College; Professional.

NOONAN, Nancy J; Ayrshire Consolidated HS; Ayrshire, IA; VPFrshCls; SecJrCls; ChrhWkr; HonRl; MrchBnd; SchMus; 4-H; FHA; Bsktbl; Chrldr; 4-HAwd;.

NOONAN, Patricia A; St Mary Of Perpetual Help HS; Chicago, IL; 1/100 Chrs; HonRl; PepBnd; SchPl; Sdlty; RptrSchPpr; SpnCl; BttyCrckrAwd; Il Inst Of Technology; Engineering.

NOONAN, Therese; Incarnate Word Acad; St Louis, MO; 12/120 HonRl; NatlMeritSchl; SchMus; RptrSchPpr; GAA; St Louis Univ; Pre Law.

NOONE, Timothy C; Roncalli HS; Beech Grove, IN; 28/168 ROTC; Bsktbl; LetterFtbl; Trk; Iupui; Electronics.

NOORDHOEK, Victor L; Campus HS; Haysville, KS; TchrAde; Bsktbl; Trk; Wichita St Univ; Cpa.

NOORDOVER, John A; John F Kennedy Prep; Sheyboygan, WI; CAP; HonRl; SchPl; SctActv; StuGov; EdYrBk; Yrbk; Bsktbl; LetterFtbl; LetterTennis; Eng.

NORAMCZYK, James V; St Bede HS; Spring Valley, IL; Band; CmntyWkr; CncrtBnd; HonRl; MrchBnd; PepBnd; SchAde; TchrAde; SpnCl; Ftbl; College; Professional.

NORBERG, Brian J; Dilworth HS; Dilworth, MN; ChrhWkr; HonRl; NHS; SchPl; SctActv; TreasStuCncl; LetterFtbl; LetterWrstlng; College.

NORBERG, Janis C; Waterford Mott HS; Drayton Plains, MI; 1/500 HstFrshCls; SecSrCls; Band; Chr; Chrs; ChrhWkr; CmntyWkr; CncrtBnd; HonRl; LbryAde; MrchBnd; OffAde; Orch; PepBnd; Michigan State; Mathematics.

NORBERG, Tereda J; Barnum HS; Barnum, MN; Chr; HospAde; NHS; PolWkr; SchPl; Yrbk; EdSchPpr; 4-H; Trk; GAA; U Of Duluth; Pre Med.

NORBUT, Catherine C; Naperville Central HS; Naperville, IL; 75/820 HonRl; JrNHS;.

NORBUT, Cynthia L; Lockport Central HS; Lockport, IL; 77/600 HonRl; JA; NHS; PolWkr; SchMus; StuGov; FNA; FTA; Trk; GAA; College; Pre School Educ.

NORBY, Barclay; Mandan Senior HS; Mandan, ND; 23/293 ALBoysSt; ChrhWkr; HonRl; Bsbl; Bsktbl; Ftbl; Coll; Dental.

NORBY, Sara A; Battle Creek Central HS; Battle Creek, MI; Band; ChrhWkr; CncrtBnd; HonRl; MrchBnd; NHS; Orch; PepBnd; SchMus; YthFlsp; GAA; Clge; Pro Pre Med.

NORBY, Terri L; Walker Sr HS; Walker, MN; HonRl; NatlFornLg; SchAde; SchPl; RptrYrbk; RptrSchPpr; SptEdSchPpr; Trk; GAA; College; Biology.

NORD, Joni S; Raymond Central HS; Valparaiso, NE; Band; Chr; Chrs; ChrhWkr; CncrtBnd; HonRl; SchMus; TchrAde; 4-H; 4-HAwd; Univ; Bus Ed.

NORDBERG, Clark D; Cambridge HS; Cambridge, MN; Chr; ChrhWkr; CncrtBnd; Mdrgl; NatlThespSoc; SchMus; Ftbl; Glf;.

NORDBERG, Jackie M; Roosevelt HS; Marenisco, MI; PresJrCls; Band; Chr; Chrs; ChrhWkr; CncrtBnd; HonRl; LbryAde; MrchBnd; NatlFornLg; College.

NORDBY, Daniel V; Menahga Public HS; Menahga, MN; 8/52 PresSophCls; TrsSrCls; HonRl; SchPl; StuCncl; Yrbk; 4-H; CaptBsbl; LetterBsktbl; LetterTrk; Fergus Falls Comm College.

NORDELL, Beverly; Notre Dame Acad; Omaha, NE; Chr; Chrs; HonRl; SchMus; StuCncl; Chrldr; Business School.

NORDEN, Cheryl A; Corunna HS; Corunna, MI; 23/232 ChrhWkr; CmntyWkr; HonRl; NHS; SchPl; EdYrBk; GAA; Central Mi U; Sociology.

NORDEN, Jeri; West Smith County HS; Kensington, KS; Chr; Chrs; ChrhWkr; HonRl; SchMus; SchPl; StuCncl; PpCl; Trk; GAA; Brown Mackie Bus School; Vocation.

NORDEN, Jeri L; West Smith County HS; Kesington, KS; Chr; Chrs; ChrhWkr; HonRl; SchMus; SchPl; StuCncl; StuGov; PpCl; LetterTrk; Fort Hays Ks State Coll; Prof Secretary.

NORDER, Rodney A; Crescent Iroquois HS; Crescent City, IL; PresSophCls; VPJrCls; TrsSrCls; Chrs; HonRl; NHS; PresStuCncl; LetterBsbl; Bsktbl; College; Engineering.

NORDGAARD, Cynthia K; Rothsay HS; Rothsay, MN; Band; ChrhWkr; CncrtBnd; HonRl; Mdrgl; PepBnd; Yrbk; RptrSchPpr; PpCl; GAA; College.

NORDHAUSEN, Sharla R; Wauneta HS; Wauneta, NE; Chr; HonRl; LbryAde; SchMus; StuCncl; RptrYrbk; RptrSchPpr; PpCl; LetterTrk; Chrldr; College; Professional.

NORDHUES, Steven J; Norfolk Catholic HS; Norfolk, NE; SchPl; RptrSchPpr; LetterFtbl; LetterWrstlng; University; Forestry.

NORDIN, Galen; Lancaster Cons HS; Lancaster, MN; PresSophCls; PresJrCls; ALBoysSt; HonRl; NHS; SchPl; StuCncl; PpCl; IMSpt; Voc; Agriculture.

NORDMAN, Carol; North Boone HS; Belvidere, IL; SecSrCls; Chrs; SchMus; SchPl; RptrYrbk; EdYrBk; FshEdYrbk; Yrbk; 4-H; FHA; Junior College; Conservation.

NORDMEYER, Jerold A; Hamilton Usd #390 HS; Eureka, KS; SecSrCls; CmntyWkr; HonRl; SptEdYrbk; Bsktbl; Trk; CchngActv; Trade Sch.

NORDSTRAND, Scott J; Hudson Sr HS; Hudson, WI; HonRl; JA; PolWkr; SctActv; RptrSchPpr; Glf; Law School; Lawyer.

NORDSTROM, Charles M; Moline Sr HS; Moline, IL; Chr; ChrhWkr; HonRl; KeyCl; LetterBsktbl; LetterTrk; College.

NORDSTROM, Dwight E; Lyons Township HS; Western Springs, IL; Chr; Chrl; Chrs; ChrhWkr; HonRl; JrNHS; NatlMeritSF; GerCl; Bsktbl; IMSpt; Coll ; Missionary.

NORDSTROM, Lauri; Cavalier Public HS; Hamilton, ND; 8/84 VPSrCls; ALAGirlsSt; Chr; Chrs; ChrhWkr; HonRl; SciCl; Trk; Chrldr; DanFAwd; Nd St Unive; Home Ec.

NORDSTROM, Susan M; Melrose Mindoro HS; Melrose, WI; 1/88 SecFrshCls; Band; HonRl; SchPl; StuCncl; FHA; Trk; Chrldr; GAA; DARAwd; Univ; Engineering.

NORDWIG, Thomas L; Bowler Public HS; Bowler, WI; 5/39 PresSrCls; CAP; CncrtBnd; HonRl; RptrYrbk; PpCl; SciCl; Bsktbl; Glf; Trk; Uw Oshkosh; Broadcast Technician.

NORDWIG, Tina M; Clintonville Sr HS; Clintonville, WI; Chr; HonRl; HospAde; NHS; VPStuCncl; IMSpt; RotaryAwd; Univ Of Wi Madison.

NORDYKE, Annette M; Lake Central HS; Dyer, IN; 10/450 HonRl; HospAde; NHS; PresFNA; FTA; SpnCl; SciCl; Marion Cty Nur Sch; Nursing.

NORDYKE, Judy L; Pekin Community HS; Richland, IA; 2/57 TrsFrshCls; HonRl; MrchBnd; SchPl; RptrYrbk; RptrSchPpr; Pres4-H; PresFNA; PpCl; LetterBsbl; Bsktbl; Trk; Pres4-HAwd; College; Medicine.

NOREEN, Jennifer A; Lincoln Sr HS; Bloomington, MN; AFS; Chr; HonRl; ModUN; NHS; NatlMeritSF; SchMus; EdYrBk; College; Lawyer.

NOREEN, Jerald K; Von Steuben HS; Chicago, IL; 12/231 Aud/Vis; Band; ChrhWkr; CncrtBnd; HonRl; JrNHS; YthFlsp; RptrSchPpr; SptEdSchPpr; Bsktbl; North Park College; Psychology.

NORFLEET, Douglas W; Franklin HS; Alexander, IL; 7/42 ALBoysSt; HonRl; NHS; SchPl; SecFFA; LetterBsktbl; LetterTrk; Univ Of Il; Agriculture.

NORFLEET, Julia J; Columbus HS; Marshfield, WI; Chrs; HonRl; JrNHS; NHS; StuCncl; Yrbk; SpnCl; PpCl; Bsktbl; Glf; Chrldr; Col; Psychology.

NORFOLK, Steve; Spencer Ind HS; Spencer, SD; 3/8 VPJrCls; PresSrCls; Chrs; HonRl; SchMus; StuCncl; SptEdYrbk; Bsktbl; Ftbl; Trk; Sd St Univ.

NORGAARD, Dwight A; Finley Public HS; Finley, ND; CncrtBnd; HonRl; PepBnd; SchPl; RptrSchPpr; SptEdSchPpr; Bsbl; Bsktbl; Trk; University; Law.

NORGARD, Linda B; La Follette HS; Madison, WI; HonRl; NatlMeritSF; SchPl; Yrbk; Univ; English.

NORGRANT, Jodell; Lakefield HS; Lakefield, MN; Band; Chrs; CncrtBnd; HonRl; Mdrgl; MrchBnd; PepBnd; Trk; Chrldr; PPFtbl; Mankato Avti; Data Processing.

NORHEIM, Sandra L; North Central HS; Rock Lake, ND; 12/26 Chrs; ChrhWkr; HonRl; LbryAde; NatlMeritSchl; SchPl; RptrYrbk; RptrSchPpr; FHA; LetterTrk; Coll; Med Or Fashion.

NORMAN, Barbara K; Holy Trinity HS; Winsted, MN; 6/56 ChrhWkr; HonRl; SchPl; TchrAde; Bsktbl; Trk; Chrldr; GAA; IMSpt; PPFtbl; St Cloud St Univ; Phy Ed.

NORMAN, Carl A; Pembine HS; Dunbar, WI; 3/32 TrsFrshCls; TrsSophCls; TrsJrCls; HonRl; NatlThespSoc; RptrYrbk; RptrSchPpr; 4-H; Bsktbl; Ftbl; Glf; Stevens Point.

NORMAN, Carol A; Pembine HS; Dunbar, WI; 8/30 Chrs; ChrhWkr; HonRl; SchMus; SchPl; StuCncl; RptrYrbk; Bsktbl; Glf; Trk; College.

NORMAN, Chris A; Fisher HS; Fisher, IL; PresBand; PresChrs; HonRl; PresNatlThespSoc; SchPl; SpnCl; LetterTennis; GAA; Trinity Clge; Elem Ed.

NORMAN, Debbie A; St Frances Cabrini HS; Allen Park, MI; 70/167 HonRl; RptrSchPpr; LetterBsbl; CaptBsktbl; Swmmng; Mechanics.

NORMAN, Dennis A; Pekin Comm HS; Pekin, IL; 35/800 ALBoysSt; HonRl; NHS; NatlMeritCmnd; Univ Of Illinois; Computer Science.

NORMAN, Donald K; Rich Hill HS; El Dorado, MO; LetterChrhWkr; Univ; Agri Business.

NORMAN, Edward M; Schuyler R 1 HS; Lancaster, MO; 11/85 PresSophCls; ALBoysSt; HonRl; NHS; SchPl; TchrAde; FFA; Bsbl; Bsktbl; College; Lawyer.

NORMAN, Gregg S; Pekin Comm HS; Pekin, IL; 22/875 HonRl; NHS; YthFlsp; CaptBsktbl; Trk; AmLegAwd; College; Business Admin.

NORMAN, Janet; Richmond Senior HS; Richmond, IN; Chr; HonRl; JA; LbryAde; NHS; OffAde; SchMus; PpCl; Trk; JAAwd; Indiana Univ.

NORMAN, Jennifer; Kearney Sr HS; Kearney, NE; Chr; HonRl; HospAde; SchPl; FrCl; PpCl; Midland Lutheran College; Nursing.

NORMAN, Linda; Hoffman Public HS; Hoffman, MN; VPSophCls; PresJrCls; Band; Chrs; HonRl; MrchBnd; SchPl; Yrbk; PresFHA; Moorhead State College; Registered Nurse.

NORMAN, Lisa M; Naperville Central HS; Naperville, IL; 12/850 Chrs; HonRl; HospAde; NHS; College; Physician.

NORMAN, Mary S; Erie HS; Erie, IL; Band; ChrhWkr; HonRl; StuCncl; PresYthFlsp; EdYrBk; 4-H; FHA; GAA; BttyCrckrAwd; DARAwd; 4-HAwd; Lutheran Hospital; Nursing.

NORMAN, Sherry L; Franklin Central HS; Indianapolis, IN; 28/221 ChrhWkr; HonRl; NHS; OffAde; TreasYthFlsp; 4-H; FHA; PpCl; IMSpt; 4-HAwd; College.

NORMAN, Steve; Northfield HS; Wabash, IN; PresFrshCls; PresSophCls; ALBoysSt; NHS; YthFlsp; SciCl; Bsbl; Trk; Wrstlng; College; Engineer Designer.

NORMANDIN, Becki J; Quincy HS; Quincy, MI; 1/116 Chr; HonRl; SecNHS; YthLg; Yrbk; SecFrCl; SpnCl; LetterBsktbl; GAA; IMSpt; Grand Rapids Baptist College; Elem Teacher.

NORMANDT, Peter; Arl Heights Hs; Mt Prospect, IL; 147/650 Chr; Chrs; HonRl; Mdrgl; NHS; SchMus; Iowa State U; Florist.

NOROBY, Anna L; Powers Lake HS; White Earth, ND; PresJrCls; ALAGirlsSt; Band; Chr; ChrhWkr; HonRl; SchPl; StuCncl; RptrYrbk; Univ Of North Dakota; Interior Decorating.

NORQUEST, Teresa J; Mc Cool Public HS; Mc Cool Jct, NE; Chr; Chrs; ChrhWkr; CmntyWkr; HonRl; LbryAde; StuCncl; YthFlsp; SchPpr; PpCl; Univ; Music.

NORRIS, Barbara R; Lake Mills Comm HS; Scarville, IA; 6/84 Band; ChrhWkr; CncrtBnd; HonRl; MrchBnd; PepBnd; SchPl; TchrAde; RptrYrbk; GAA; Waldorf Coll; Elem Educ.

NORRIS, Cathy S; Waltonville HS; Waltonville, IL; SecFrshCls; Band; CncrtBnd; HonRl; Twrl; 4-H; FHA; PpCl; Chrldr; GAA; Business Profession.

NORRIS, Christy M; St Mary Academy; Indianapolis, IN; ChrhWkr; CmntyWkr; HonRl; OffAde; SchAde; YthFlsp; FNA; CaptTrk; PresAwd; College; Professional.

NORRIS, Clay A; Virginia HS; Virginia, IL; 2/46 HonRl; Illinois College.

NORRIS, Cynthia L; Divernon HS; Auburn, IL; 1/24 VPJrCls; HonRl; SchPl; StuGov; RptrYrbk; SchPpr; VPFHA; SciCl; LetterTrk; CaptChrldr; Univ; Major Study.

NORRIS, David D; River Rouge HS; River Rouge, MI; HonRl; NHS; GerCl; MthCl; SciCl; OptClAwd; CitAwd; Oakland Univ; Engineering.

NORRIS, James D; Highland HS; Highland, IN; 200/580 Aud/Vis; StuCncl; Bsbl; Bsktbl; Ftbl; Trk; CchngActv; Mechanical Trade School; Mechanic.

NORRIS, James M; Oak Lawn Community HS; Hometown, IL; HonRl; OffAde; PolWkr; SchAde; TchrAde; SchPpr; MthCl; LetterBsktbl; Trk; University Of Illinois; Pre Med.

NORRIS, Janelle A; Millington HS; Millington, MI; 16/210 Chr; CmntyWkr; HonRl; Quill&Scroll; SchPl; TchrAde; YthFlsp; Yrbk; Coll At C S Mott; Business Administration.

NORRIS, Joseph S; Daniel J Gross HS; Bellevue, NE; NHS; StuCncl; Bsktbl; CaptFtbl; LetterTrk; RotaryAwd; Hastings College; Law.

NORRIS, Karen; New Palestine HS; New Palestine, IN; Chr; ChrhWkr; HonRl; TchrAde; Yrbk; FNA; LatCl; SpnCl; PpCl; Bsbl; Nursing.

NORRIS, Kent M; Grandview HS; Grandview, MO; Band; CncrtBnd; HonRl; MrchBnd; NHS; OffAde; College; Electrical Engineering.

NORRIS, Mark J; Carter County R I HS; Van Buren, MO; VPFrshCls; CmntyWkr; HonRl; SchPl; StuCncl; PpCl; LetterBsktbl; School Of The Ozarks; Athletic Coach.

NORRIS, Robert A; Indian Creek HS; Trafalgar, IN; 5/122 NatlMeritCmnd; Quill&Scroll; RptrSchPpr; FTA; LatCl; Purdue U; Eng.

NORRIS, Susan L; Newton Community HS; Newton, IL; 29/187 Chr; Chrs; ChrhWkr; CmntyWkr; HonRl; LbryAde; Mdrgl; NHS; YthFlsp; 4-H; College; Social Work.

NORRIS, Teresa A; Sterling HS; Sterling, IL; Band; CncrtBnd; HonRl; NHS; NatlMeritCmnd; SchPl; Community College; Med Lab Tech.

NORRIS, Warren E; Joliet East HS; Elwood, IL; 51/488 ALBoysSt; HonRl; LbryAde; NHS; SctActv; RptrYrbk; 4-H; LetterBsbl; LetterBsktbl; LetterFtbl; College; Chemist.

NORTH, David; River Valley HS; Harbert, MI; CmntyWkr; HonRl; OffAde; SchAde; SctActv; TchrAde; RptrYrbk; SptEdSchPpr; Bsbl; Bsktbl; Coll.

NORTH, Gary L; Mio Ausable HS; Lewiston, MI; StuCncl; SchPl; SchPpr; Univ; English.

NORTH, James; Dexter HS; Ann Arbor, MI; 4/176 VPFrshCls; HonRl; NHS; AmLegAwd; Univ Of Mi; Engineering.

NORTH, Sheryl L; Center HS; Kansas City, MO; 28/431 Chrl; CncrtBnd; HonRl; SecNatlFornLg; NHS; SchMus; SchPl; PpCl; Trk; College; Medicine.

NORTHCUTT, Richard E; Bridgeport Senior HS; Saginaw, MI; HonRl; NHS; NatlMeritFnl; RotaryAwd; Michigan Tech Univ; Mech Engineering.

NORTHEN, Cathy D; Santa Fe HS; Alma, MO; 6/47 SecSophCls; ALAGirlsSt; Band; Chrs; CncrtBnd; HonRl; MrchBnd; NHS; PepBnd; TreasStuCncl; Central Mo State Univ; Accounting.

NORTHINGTON, Glyn R; Malden HS; Malden, MO; 1/115 Band; Chrs; ChrhWkr; HonRl; TreasNHS; StuCncl; YthFlsp; RptrSchPpr; SchPpr; Pres4-H; VPFrCl; DanFAwd; 4-HAwd; Univ Of Missouri; Journalism.

NORTHRIP, Rebecca L; Parkview HS; Springfield, MO; Chr; Chrs; ChrhWkr; HonRl; Mdrgl; SchMus; YthLg; PpCl; Trk; College; Home Economics.

NORTHRUP, Randall J; Shelbyville Senior HS; Shelbyville, IN; PolWkr; RptrSchPpr; FshEdSchPpr; SptEdSchPpr; SchPpr; LetterTennis; Chrldr; IMSpt; College; Journalism.

NORTON, Bruce C; Winona Sr HS; Winona, MN; 120/430 HonRl; Bsbl; Ftbl; Univ Of Minnesota.

NORTON, Cynthia M; Casey HS; Casey, IL; 5/97 Chr; HonRl; NatlThespSoc; OffAde; SchAde; SchMus; SchPl; TchrAde; RptrSchPpr; PpCl; Lakeland College; Data Processing.

NORTON, Julie; Earlville Comm HS; Earlville, IL; Band; Chrs; HonRl; Mdrgl; NHS; SchMus; StuCncl; FrCl; Socr; Chrldr; College; Art.

NORTON, Kathy; Atwater Public HS; Atwater, MN; ChrhWkr; CmntyWkr; HonRl; SchPl; TchrAde; Trk; Vocational School.

NORTON, Kelly D; Clinton Prairie HS; Colfax, IN; 4/105 SecSophCls; CaptDrmMjrt; HonRl; NHS; Twrl; RptrSchPpr; FTA; SpnCl; AmLegAwd; DARAwd; Indiana Univ; Nursing.

NORTON, Kimberly J; Deckerville Comm HS; Deckerville, MI; Band; ChrhWkr; CmntyWkr; HospAde; NatlMeritSchl; RptrYrbk; FNA; FTA; SpnCl; Central Michigan Univ; Elem Teacher.

NORTON, Mark A; Marshall HS; Marshall, IL; 18/115 Band; ChrhWkr; CncrtBnd; MrchBnd; PepBnd; SctActv; LetterBsbl; Bsktbl; LetterGlf; Tennis; Coll; Bus Mgmt.

NORTON, Mark D; Neponset HS; Neponset, IL; 1/20 TrsFrshCls; ALBoysSt; Band; Chrs; CncrtBnd; HonRl; MrchBnd; PepBnd; VPStuCncl; FrCl; LetterFtbl; LetterTrk; AmLegAwd; Eastern Il Univ.

NORTON, Maureen A; Louisville HS; Louisville, NE; Chrs; LbryAde; TchrAde; EngCl; FrCl; PpCl; Army; Operating Rm Ass.

NORTON, Patricia L; Barry Comm HS; Barry, IL; 11/46 Band; Chrs; CncrtBnd; MrchBnd; NHS; PepBnd; SchPl; YthFlsp; VP4-H; PresFHA; FrCl; SciCl; Chrldr; 4-HAwd; College; Science.

NORTON, Ruth A; Sevastopol HS; Sturgeon Bay, WI; Band; Chr; Chrs; CncrtBnd; MrchBnd; OffAde; PepBnd; SchMus; TchrAde; School; Nurse.

NORTON, Steven C; Yuton Public HS; Yutan, NE; 4/25 PresSophCls; PresSrCls; HonRl; Mdrgl; Bsbl; Bsktbl; Ftbl; Trk; IMSpt; Univ Of Nebraska.

NORTON, Thomas K; Wilton Community HS; Tipton, IA; ALBoysSt; Band; Chr; ChrhWkr; HonRl; Mdrgl; NHS; Bsktbl; Ftbl; CitAwd; Ia State Univ; Pre Vet.

NORTON, Timothy J; Gordon Tech HS; Chicago, IL; 8/618 HonRl; NHS; KeyCl; Northwestern Univ; Medicine.

NORTON, Tom E; Central Sr HS; Clifton, IL; ALBoysSt; HonRl; NHS; EdYrBk; FrCl; MthCl; Bsbl; LetterBsktbl; LetterFtbl; Trk; Univ Of Il; Medicine.

NORTON, Toni L; Berkley HS; Berkley, MI; TrsFrshCls; HonRl; StuCncl; TchrAde; LetterBsbl; Bsktbl; College; Nursing.

NORWINE, Susan E; Bradleyville HS; Bradleyville, MO; SecFrshCls; SecTrsSophCls; SecJrCls; ChrhWkr; NHS; StuCncl; Pres4-H; Chrldr; DanFAwd; 4-HAwd; Sw Mo St Univ ;interior Desing.

NORWOOD, Robert E; Minonk Dana Rutland HS; Rutland, IL; Band; Chr; Chrs; CncrtBnd; Mdrgl; MrchBnd; NatlMeritCmnd; PepBnd; SchPl; FrCl; PpCl; Bsbl; Illinois St Univ; Commercial Art.

NOSAL, James; Glenbard Wes Hs; Glenn Ellyn, IL; 17/522 HonRl; NatlMeritCmnd; YthFlsp; Yrbk; CivCl; LatCl; MthCl; LetterBsktbl; LetterFtbl; LetterTrk; Washington U; Professional.

NOSBISCH, Kenneth L; New Hampton Comm HS; New Hampton, IA; 14/180 HonRl; NHS; 4-H; LetterBsktbl; LetterTrk; 4-HAwd; Trade School.

NOSBISCH, Lynn K; Dieterich HS; Teutopolis, IL; 3/45 Chrs; HonRl; SecStuCncl; 4-H; FBLA; SpnCl; PpCl; CaptChrldr; PresGAA; 4-HAwd; Eiu; Teach.

NOSBISH, Daniel J; La Salle HS; Cedar Rapids, IA; CtyCnl; HonRl; ModUN; StuCncl; RptrYrbk; PpCl; Coll; Banker.

NOSEK, Nancy L; Oak Lawn Comm HS; Oak Lawn, IL; 8/686 HonRl; LbryAde; NHS; OffAde; PolWkr; Moraine Valley Comm Colllege; Medicine.

NOSKO, Peggy A; Owen Withee HS; Owen, WI; 9/98 Band; HonRl; NHS; PepBnd; SctActv; TchrAde; Pres4-H; FrCl; Trk; 4-HAwd; Coll; Equestrian Studies.

NOSS, Jacqueline; Parkview HS; Beloit, WI; 7/165 HonRl; NHS; TchrAde; FBLA; FHA; MthCl; PpCl; GAA; IMSpt;.

NOSS, Marilyn T; Hatton Public HS; Hatton, ND; SecSophCls; TrsJrCls; TrsSrCls; Chrs; HonRl; MrchBnd; SchPl; Yrbk; SecFHA; GAA; BttyCrckrAwd; N Dakota St Schl Of Science; Occup Therapy.

NOTBOHM, Thomas N; Oconomowoc HS; Oconomowoc, WI; 1/260 Band; CncrtBnd; HonRl; JrNHS; MrchBnd; NHS; PepBnd; SchMus; RptrYrbk; Univ Of Wisconsin; Engineering.

NOTCH, Sherri J; Anoka HS; Anoka, MN; HonRl; HospAde; JrNHS; NatlFornLg; NHS; NatlMeritSF; StuCncl; Pres4-H; CaptPpCl; 4-HAwd; College; Business Admin.

NOTESTINE, Kerry E; West Lafayette HS; West Lafayette, IN; 15/220 ALBoysSt; HonRl; NHS; Bsbl; Ftbl; GodCntryAwd; Depauw Univ; Psychology.

NOTTINGHAM, Debi R; North Posey HS; Cynthiana, IN; 18/168 Band; Chr; ChrhWkr; CncrtBnd; DrlTm; HonRl; HospAde; MrchBnd; GAA; PPFtbl; U Of In; Doctor.

NOTY, Richard K; Harvard St George HS; Chicago, IL; TrsFrshCls; TrsSophCls; NatlMeritCmnd; StuCncl; LetterBsbl; LetterBsktbl; College.

NOVAC, Michael F; St Viator HS; Arlington Hts, IL; 10/245 HonRl; FshEdYrbk; Bsktbl; Bradley University; Law.

NOVACEK, Linda; Roseau HS; Roseau, MN; 2/128 Band; Chrs; ChrhWkr; CncrtBnd; HonRl; MrchBnd; PepBnd; RptrYrbk; SptEdYrbk; College; Pharmacy.

NOVACHCOFF, Marisa; Riverside HS; Dearborn Hts, MI; Chrs; ChrhWkr; CmntyWkr; VPJA; PresNatlThespSoc; HonRl; Quill&Scroll; SchMus; FrCl; University; Library Science.

NOVAK, Anita M; Pershing HS; Brooks, MN; 1/15 Band; Chr; ChrhWkr; CmntyWkr; CncrtBnd; HonRl; HospAde; MrchBnd; OffAde; PepBnd; Quill&Scroll; RedCrAde; SchMus; SchPl; StuCncl; North Dakota State Univ; Nursing.

NOVAK, Catherine; Aquinas HS; Surprise, NE; Chrs; NHS; NatlThespSoc; SchMus; TchrAde; SpnCl; PpCl;.

NOVAK, David; Crete Public HS; Crete, NE; Band; Chr; Chrl; Chrs; ChrhWkr; CtyCnl; CncrtBnd; Mdrgl; MrchBnd; Orch; College; Conservation.

NOVAK, Diane L; Chesaning HS; Chesaning, MI; ChrhWkr; HonRl; TchrAde; PpCl; Bsktbl; Trk; GAA; PPFtbl; Trade School; Photography.

NOVAK, Jeffrey P; Douglas Macarthur HS; Saginaw, MI; VPFrshCls; CncrtBnd; HonRl; Orch; SchPl; StuGov; Mi State Univ; Pro.

NOVAK, Lisa M; St Martins Academy; Rapid City, SD; ALAGirlsSt; Chr; Chrl; Chrs; ChrhWkr; CmntyWkr; IntrClCncl; Mdrgl; ModUN; NatlFornLg; NHS; Socr; Creighton Univ; Law.

NOVAK, Mark C; John F Kennedy HS; Cedar Rapids, IA; ALBoysSt; Chr; JA; IMSpt; Clg; Natural Sciences.

NOVAK, Mary; Bishop Noll Inst; E Chicago, IN; 93/347 HonRl; JA; OffAde; Quill&Scroll; SchMus; SchPl; RptrSchPpr; FrCl; MthCl; Loyola Univ; Pre Med.

NOVAK, Mike H; Green Lake Public HS; Green Lake, WI; 6/40 ALBoysSt; Band; HonRl; NHS; PresStuCncl; LetterBsktbl; LetterFtbl;.

NOVAK, Nadine W; Niles West HS; Lincolnwood, IL; HonRl; CchngActv; Univ Of Michigan; Business.

NOVAK, Nancy A; Centre HS; Lost Springs, KS; ALAGirlsSt; Band; Chr; CmntyWkr; HonRl; OffAde; PolWkr; SchMus; StuCncl; RptrYrbk; Emporia Ks State Clge; Social Work.

NOVAK, Pamela K; Harlem North HS; Loves Park, IL; Band; CncrtBnd; HonRl; HospAde; MrchBnd; Quill&Scroll; TchrAde; RptrYrbk; University; Elementary Educ.

NOVAK, Paul; Brainerd Sr HS; Brainerd, MN; 27/475 Chr; HonRl; Univ Of Minn Minneapolis.

NOVAK, Phillip E; East Richland HS; Olney, IL; ALBoysSt; FFA; LetterBsbl; LetterFtbl; Olney Central; Biology.

NOVAK, Phillip M; Central HS; Saint Joseph, MO; 8/550 HonRl; YthLg; GerCl; MthCl; SciCl; Tennis; Cal Tech; Physics.

NOVAK, Robert A; St Joseph HS; Chicago, IL; 1/109 HonRl; NHS; SchPpr; College; Mathematics.

NOVAK, Robert G; Leigh Comm HS; Leight, NE; VPSophCls; PresJrCls; Band; Chr; ChrhWkr; HonRl; MrchBnd; SchPl; Pres4-H; GerCl; Coll; Music.

NOVAK, Shea M; Pinckney HS; Pinckney, MI; ChrhWkr; HonRl; NatlMeritCmnd; SctActv; TchrAde; FrCl; Bsktbl; Trk; CchngActv; PresAwd; Msu Clge; Teacher & Coach.

NOVAK, Stephen D; Lincoln Way HS; Frankfort, IL; 16/500 HonRl; NHS; PolWkr; StuGov; RptrSchPpr; EdSchPpr; Swmmng; Tennis; AmLegAwd; PresAwd; Univ Of Illinois; Law.

NOVAK, Steven; Yankton Senior HS; Yankton, SD; 43/239 ChrhWkr; CmntyWkr; HonRl; JrNHS; NHS; StuGov; TchrAde; Sd St Univ; Vet.

NOVAK, Wendy L; Antigo HS; Gleason, WI; SecFrshCls; LitMag; Pres4-H; GerCl; PpCl; IMSpt; U Of Wi; Md.

NOVAKOSKI, Anthony; Oblong HS; Robinson, IL; 21/71 ChrhWkr; CmntyWkr; HonRl; SchAde; StuGov; EdYrBk; SchPpr; FBLA; FTA; LatCl; College; Missionary.

NOVAKOW, Linda L; Morton HS; Morton, IL; Band; HonRl; NHS; SchMus; YthFlsp; RptrSchPpr; 4-H; GAA; 4-HAwd; PresAwd; Olivet Nazarene Coll; Special Education.

NOVALES, Nancy A; Evanston Township HS; Evanston, IL; NatlMeritCmnd; Univ; Liberal Arts.

NOVEL, Nancy C; Morton HS; Morton, IL; HonRl; OffAde; PpCl; LetterBsktbl; LetterTennis; GAA; Univ Of New Mexico; History.

NOVICH, Chuck A; Plattsmouth HS; Plattsmouth, NE; CmntyWkr; SctActv; StuCncl; Yrbk; 4-H; Swmmng; 4-HAwd; Univ Of Nebraska.

NOVICH, Susanna M; Plattsmouth HS; Plattsmouth, NE; HospAde; 4-H; SpnCl; PpCl; College; Commercial Art.

NOVICK, Teri M; Mather HS; Chicago, IL; 81/442 HonRl; NatlMeritCmnd; TchrAde; Univ Of Illinois; Communications.

NOVITSKY, Leslie; Elmhurst HS; Fort Wayne, IN; PresFrshCls; VPSophCls; ALBoysSt; PolWkr; Quill&Scroll; StuCncl; Yrbk; VoiceDemAwd; Law.

NOVOA, Janet L; Calumet HS; Gary, IN; 10/336 TrsSophCls; DrmMjrt; HonRl; JrNHS; MrchBnd; NHS; OffAde; SchAde; StuCncl; TchrAde; ChmnTeen; Chrldr; GAA; Bus School; Vocational.

NOVO GRADAC, Kevin J; Bishop Ward HS; Kansas City, KS; 12/195 HonRl; ModUN; NHS; NatlThespSoc; SchMus; SchPl; TchrAde; Yrbk; SchPpr;.

NOVOSAD, Michael; West Chicago HS; West Chicago, IL; 70/350 ChrhWkr; HonRl; TchrAde; Ftbl; Trk; RotaryAwd; VFWAwd; CitAwd; U Of Illinois; Architecture.

NOVOTNY, Annette; Acad Of Our Lady; Bartonville, IL; Chr; Chrs; HonRl; JA; NHS; PpCl; College; Com Art.

NOVOTNY, Bradlee N; Pender Public HS; Pender, NE; 6/51 SecTrsFrshCls; VPSrCls; Chr; Chrs; HonRl; HospAde; NatlMeritCmnd; Yrbk; PpCl; SciCl; LetterBsktbl; LetterFtbl; University Of Nebraska; Medicine.

NOVOTNY, Carol L; Kewaunee HS; Kewaunee, WI; 17/167 PresFrshCls; TrsJrCls; VPSrCls; CmntyWkr; HonRl; PresFHA; LetterBsktbl; LetterTrk; PresAwd; VFWAwd;.

NOVOTNY, Joanne G; Divine Savior Holy Angels HS; Milwaukee, WI; 29/121 HonRl; Mdrgl; NHS; SchMus; SchPl; StuGov; Yrbk; SchPpr; FTA; IMSpt; Marquette Univ; Medical Technology.

NOVOTNY, Linda R; Raymond Central HS; Valparaiso, NE; Band; CncrtBnd; HonRl; LbryAde; MrchBnd; NHS; PepBnd; FBLA; FHA; Lincoln School; Accounting.

NOVOTNY, Michael; Bennett County HS; Balesland, SD; ALBoysSt; ChrhWkr; HonRl; JrNHS; NHS; FFA; Bsktbl; IMSpt; College; Vocation.

NOWACK, Mark G; Nemaha Valley HS; Brock, NE; PresFrshCls; PresJrCls; Band; CncrtBnd; HonRl; MrchBnd; PepBnd; SchPl; YthFlsp; Yrbk; University.

NOWACZYK, Mary; Hill Mccloy HS; Flushing, MI; 14/138 DrmMjrt; HonRl; HospAde; MrchBnd; NHS; OffAde; Twrl; PpCl; Glf; Univ; Political Science.

NOWAK, Donna M; Notre Dame For Girls HS; Chicago, IL; 24/302 Chrs; ChrhWkr; HonRl; NHS; SchAde; RptrSchPpr; SchPpr; Loyola University; Optometry.

NOWAK, Gregory S; Elmhurst HS; Fort Wayne, IN; HonRl; JA; PolWkr; University; Business.

NOWAK, Joseph B; George Washington HS; Chicago, IL; 8/481 HonRl; NHS; NatlMeritCmnd; Purdue Univ; Engi.

NOWAK, Lauren G; Belleville HS; Belleville, MI; 70/525 HonRl; TreasNHS; StuCncl; StuGov; GerCl; SciCl; Ftbl; Wrstlng; E Mich U; Engineering.

NOWAK, Michael E; Muskegon Catholic Central HS; Muskegon, MI; HonRl; NatlMeritSchl; Bsbl; Ftbl; IMSpt; Ferris St College; Pharmacy.

NOWAK, Susan M; Thornton Twp HS; Posen, IL; 11/750 HonRl; HospAde; JrNHS; NHS; Sdlty; CaptTwrl; PpCl; College; Nursing.

NOWAKOWSKI, Jill A; Rochester Adams HS; Rochester, MI; Band; HonRl; LbryAde; MrchBnd; OffAde; SctActv; Northern Michigan Univ; Accountant.

NOWAKOWSKI, Mary L; Highland HS; Highland, IN; 184/543 Chrs; ChrhWkr; CncrtBnd; MrchBnd; TchrAde; FrCl; College; Professional Interior Decorator.

NOWARD, Clinton B; Pinckneyville Comm HS; Pinckneyville, IL; 4/112 HonRl; NHS; PpCl; SciCl; Univ Of Missouri; Engineer.

NOWICKI, Maryann; Elizabeth Seton HS; Chicago, IL; 10/252 Chrl; HonRl; NHS; SctActv; RptrYrbk; RptrSchPpr; College; Economics.

NOWISKI, Mary; P H Northern HS; Port Huron, MI; HonRl; NHS; St Clair County Community College;.

NOWLAN, Richard R; Hot Springs HS; Hot Springs, SD; PresJrCls; HonRl; NHS; StuCncl; YthFlsp; CaptBsbl; CaptBsktbl; LetterTrk; AmLegAwd; MasAwd; U Of Sd; Medicine.

NOWLING, Linda J; Turkey Run HS; Marshall, IN; 2/63 TrsJrCls; TrsSrCls; ALAGirlsSt; Band; Chr; ChrhWkr; HonRl; NHS; PepBnd; StuCncl; YthFlsp; Yrbk; FTA; Anderson College; Foreign Languages.

NOWOTNY, Kevin J; White Lake HS; White Lake, SD; HonRl; RptrYrbk; LetterBsbl; LetterBsktbl; LetterFtbl; LetterTrk; IMSpt; Coll; Business.

NOYES, Marilyn M; Glenbard West HS; Wheaton, IL; 69/512 HonRl; NHS; TreasSctActv; PresSpnCl; GAA; Augustana College; Mathematics.

NUDELMAN, Alan H; Rich Township HS; Park Forest, IL; PresBand; CncrtBnd; MrchBnd; NHS; NatlMeritFnl; StuCncl; SchPpr; BttyCrckrAwd; Northwestern University.

NUEHRING, Cheryl A; Klemme Comm HS; Klemme, IA; 1/35 Band; DrmMjrt; HonRl; NHS; StuCncl; Yrbk; FTA; LetterBsktbl; LetterGlf; LetterChrldr; Col; Theatre Arts.

NUERNBERGER, Jean L; Oak Park HS; Kansas City, MO; 24/557 Band; Chr; CncrtBnd; HonRl; Orch; PepBnd; SchMus; YthFlsp; LetterTennis; BttyCrckrAwd; University Of Missouri; Physical Therapy.

NUERNBERGER, Jerry L; Hinsdale Central HS; Hinsdale, IL; 1/608 ChrhWkr; HonRl; NHS; StuGov; YthFlsp; Bsbl; Bsktbl; Univ Of Ill; Corporate Lawyer.

NUERNBERGER, Joan E; Medford HS; Medford, WI; Band; HonRl; NHS; SpnCl; PpCl; Math.

NUETZMAN, Cathleen; Wall Lake Community HS; Wall Lake, IA; Chr; Chrs; DrlTm; HonRl; NatlFornLg; SchPl; RptrYrbk; SchPpr; Bsktbl; Trk; Morningside College; Nursing.

NUGER, Philip L; Elmwood Park HS; Elmwood Park, IL; 10/306 CncrtBnd; HonRl; MrchBnd; Orch; VPGerCl; LetterSwmmng; LetterTennis; Univ Of Illinois; Chemical Engineering.

NUGTEREN, Sharon M; Prairie Ciyt HS; Prairie City, IA; 7/49 HonRl; NHS; TchrAde; Yrbk; U Of Northern Ia; Elementary Teaching.

NUHLICEK, Regina L; Kewaunee HS; Kewanunee, WI; HonRl; NHS; Yrbk; RptrSchPpr; FHA; GAA; IMSpt; Vocation.

NULL, Steven R; Centerville Public HS; Centerville, SD; 3/40 PresJrCls; Band; Chrs; HonRl; SchPl; StuCncl; FFA; Bsktbl; Ftbl; South Dakota State Univ; Engineering.

NULSEN, David J; Cahokia Sr HS; Cahokia, IL; 10/55 Band; CncrtBnd; HonRl; JA; MrchBnd; NHS; PepBnd; SctActv; University; Chemical Engineer.

NULTON, Mike T; Hoisington HS; Hoisington, KS; TrsFrshCls; HonRl; NHS; StuCncl; TchrAde; LetterBsktbl; Ftbl; LetterTrk; College; Biology.

NULTY, Maureen; Plymouth Canton HS; Plymouth, MI; HonRl; OffAde; Univ Of Mi; Mathematics.

NULU, Deborah L; White Pine HS; White Pine, MI; VPSophCls; PresSrCls; Band; HonRl; NHS; Orch; StuCncl; RptrYrbk; Yrbk; Chrldr; Univ; Prof.

NUNEZ, Thomas A; Edsel Ford HS; Dearborn, MI; Chr; Chrl; Chrs; Mdrgl; NatlThespSoc; SchMus; Olivet College; Music.

NUNGESTER, Marva J; Raytown HS; Kansas City, MO; 17/600 Chr; ChrhWkr; HonRl; HospAde; JrNHS; NHS; Orch; SchMus; PpCl; College; Music Teacher.

NUNLEY, Robert; Mclouth Hs; Mclouth, KS; 4/39 TrsJrCls; HonRl; ModUN; NHS; SchPl; PresStuCncl; RptrYrbk; LetterFtbl; LetterTrk; OptClAwd; CitAwd; U Of Kansas; Political Science.

NUNLEY, Robert E; Mc Louth HS; Mc Louth, KS; 4/44 TrsJrCls; HonRl; ModUN; NHS; SchPl; StuCncl; StuGov; LetterFtbl; OptClAwd; CitAwd; Ks Univ; Lawyer.

NUNN, Alma L; East Prairie HS; East Prairie, MO; 7/77 HonRl; NHS; SchPl; StuCncl; RptrSchPpr; FHA; PpCl; SciCl; DARAwd;.

NUNN, Kent G; Lincoln HS; Lincoln, KS; 3/60 SecSophCls; ALBoysSt; ChrhWkr; CmntyWkr; HonRl; StuCncl; StuGov; YthFlsp; 4-H; GerCl; Ks St Univ; Law.

NUNNELLY, Paul D; University HS; Cape Girardeau, MO; 1/40 NatlFornLg; NHS; StuCncl; EdSchPpr; SpnCl; MthCl; PpCl; LetterBsktbl; LetterTrk; Us Air Force.

NUNNIKHOVEN, Sandra K; Oskaloosa HS; Leighton, IA; 28/195 Chr; HonRl; HospAde; LbryAde; NHS; YthFlsp; St Lukes Meth Schl Of Nrsng; Nursing.

NUNNIKLOVEN, Alice; Pella Christian HS; Oskaloosa, IA; RedCrAde; SchPl; YthFlsp; RptrYrbk; RptrSchPpr; 4-H; FHA; GerCl; PpCl; IMSpt; Tech Sch; Nursing.

NURCZYK, Donna R; Joliet Twp Central HS; Joliet, IL; 6/491 Chr; ChrhWkr; HonRl; NHS; NatlMeritCmnd; SchMus; TchrAde; GerCl; MthCl; Univ Of Ill; Math.

NURHADI, Haryanto H; Northwestern HS; Good Hope, IL; PresJrCls; AFS; Chr; NHS; SctActv; PresStuGov; MthCl; SciCl; Ftbl; Tennis; University; Liberal Arts.

NURRENBERN, James D; Gibson Southern HS; Ft Branch, IN; 60/229 VPSophCls; ChrhWkr; SctActv; StuCncl; PpCl; SciCl; LetterBsktbl; LetterFtbl; Trk; LetterWrstlng; IMSpt; Purdue Univ; Pharmacy.

NUSH, Charles S; East Gary Edison HS; East Gary, IN; 96/158 CmntyWkr; StuCncl; LetterBsbl; LetterFtbl; IMSpt; College; Sports.

NUSS, Cynthia M; Paxton HS; Paxton, IL; AFS; Chrs; CmntyWkr; HonRl; Mdrgl; SchPl; Twrl; 4-H; LetterBsbl; LetterBsktbl; GAA; IMSpt; 4-HAwd; Business School; Secretary.

NUSS, Esther L; Ness City HS; Ness City, KS; Band; MrchBnd; PepBnd; SchMus; FHA; College; Special Ed.

NUSSBAUM, Frederic J; C S Mott Sr HS; Warren, MI; PresSrCls; Aud/Vis; ChrhWkr; HonRl; NHS; StuCncl; Oakland Univ; Engineering.

NUSSEL, John R; Staunton HS; Brazil, IN; HonRl; 4-H; KeyCl; MthCl; Indiana State University; Accounting.

NUSSEV, Gail; Public HS; Brewster, MN; VPFrshCls; HonRl; NHS; SchPl; StuCncl; FHA; Chrldr; BttyCrckrAwd; DARAwd; Patricia Stevens; Fasion Merch.

NUTT, Sherrie; Bad Axe Hs; Bad Ate, MI; Band; CmntyWkr; HonRl; JA; OffAde; SchPpr; 4-H; GAA; 4-HAwd; College; Professional.

NUTT, Thomas; Washington HS; Valparaiso, IN; 3/27 HonRl; StuCncl; FFA; Bsbl; College; Computors.

NUTTER, Linda K; Morton HS; Morton, IL; Chr; Chrs; ChrhWkr; JA; OffAde; FBLA; FHA; Bible College.

NUTTING, Daniel A; Glenwood Comm HS; Glenwood, IA; HonRl; Ftbl; Trk; IMSpt; Trade School; Aeronatical Mechanic.

NUTTY, David A; Wentworth Military Academy; Vienna, IL; Band; CncrtBnd; HonRl; MrchBnd; Quill&Scroll; ROTC; Yrbk; RptrSchPpr; 4-H; College; Engineering.

NUTZ, Patricia E; North Central HS; Haddam, KS; VPSrCls; Band; Chrs; ChrhWkr; HonRl; SchPl; StuCncl; RptrYrbk; EdSchPpr; PpCl; Beloit Vo Tech;nursing.

NUWASH, Kathryn L; Silver Lake Public HS; Silver Lake, MN; 6/57 HonRl; SchPl; TchrAde; YthFlsp; Yrbk; 4-H; FFA; FHA; Chrldr; GAA; Univ.

NUYEN, Joseph G; Comstock HS; Kalamazoo, MI; 3/252 Chr; CncrtBnd; MrchBnd; NHS; SchMus; SctActv; VPStuCncl; LetterBsbl; LetterBsktbl; LetterGlf; Trk; Kalamazoo College; Chemistry.

NUZZO, Frank; Lew Wallace HS; Gary, IN; 18/513 HonRl; JrNHS; Purdue Univ; Dentist.

NWESE, Gerald; Hendricks Public HS; Hendricks, MN; 7/50 PresFrshCls; ALBoysSt; HonRl; StuCncl; FFA; PpCl; Bsktbl; Ftbl; Trk; AmLegAwd; Trade School Coll; Electic.

NYBERG, Cynthia J; Gridley HS; Gridley, IL; VPAFS; PresBand; PresChrs; PresCncrtBnd; HonRl; PresMrchBnd; NHS; PresPepBnd; VPStuCncl; Swmmng; VPGAA; DARAwd; Milliken Univ; Surgical Nurse.

NYBERG, Karl; Wichita Heights HS; Wichita, KS; 20/372 HonRl; NHS; NatlMeritCmnd; NatlSciFnd; SctActv; StuGov; LatCl; College; Computer Science.

NYDAM, Mark A; Dakota Christian HS; Corsica, SD; Chr; HonRl; ModUN; NHS; StuCncl; Yrbk; LetterBsktbl; LetterTrk; IMSpt; CitAwd; College.

NYDEGGER, Gregg A; Clinton Prairie HS; Colfax, IN; 8/103 ChrhWkr; HonRl; YthFlsp; LatCl; SciCl; LetterBsbl; Bsktbl; Trk; Indiana Univ; Languages.

NYDEREK, Ann M; Maria HS; Chicago, IL; 78/300 HospAde; TreasNatlThespSoc; SchMus; SchPl; Univj Of Ill; General Classes.

NYE, Nancy R; Bourbon HS; Bourbon, MO; RptrSchPpr; University; Writer.

NYE, Susan; Acad Of The Holy Angels; Minneapolis, MN; 10/112 SecFrshCls; SecTrsJrCls; Chr; NHS; SchPl; StuCncl; Yrbk; JAAwd; College Of St Benedict; Accounting.

NYGAARD, Betty; Wildrose Public HS; Wildrose, ND; 2/14 PresFrshCls; PresSophCls; SecJrCls; PepBnd; Trk; Chrldr; BttyCrckrAwd; 4-HAwd; VFWAwd; Univ Of Nd.

NYGAARD, Ken B; Littlefork Big Falls HS; Big Falls, MN; HonRl; SchPl; Bsktbl; Ftbl; College.

NYGAARD, Nancy A; Cambridge HS; Cambridge, WI; PresJrCls; AFS; Band; HonRl; SchPl; StuCncl; RptrYrbk; Yrbk; RptrSchPpr; SchPpr; Madison Area Tech College; Legal Stenogrphy.

NYGARD, Allen L; St Marys Central HS; Bismarck, ND; Band; CncrtBnd; HonRl; MrchBnd; PepBnd; SchPl; 4-H; PpCl; Bsbl; Bsktbl; LetterFtbl; Tennis; LetterTrk; College; Architecture.

NYGARD, Cindy L; Garrison HS; Roseglen, ND; 3/30 Band; Chr; Chrl; Chrs; CncrtBnd; HonRl; RptrSchPpr; SchPpr; FHA; AmLegAwd; College; Legal Secretary.

NYGARD, Shane D; Grafton Central HS; Grafton, ND; VPBand; Chrs; HonRl; NHS; SchMus; StuCncl; SciCl; Bsbl; IMSpt; DanFAwd; Concordia College; Medicine.

NYGREN, Laura K; Mead Public HS; Wahoo, NE; 1/27 SecFrshCls; TrsFrshCls; PresSophCls; VPJrCls; Band; Chr; Chrs; ChrhWkr; CncrtBnd; HonRl; NHS; PepBnd; YthFlsp; Trk; Chrldr; Univ Nebr; Animal Science.

NYHOLM, Diana J; Forest Park HS; Crystal Falls, MI; 16/84 TrsFrshCls; TrsSrCls; Band; Chrs; ChrhWkr; HonRl; HospAde; PepBnd; SchPl; FNA; Univ; Professional.

NYKAMP, Charlene; Holland Christian HS; Zeeland, MI; 6/265 Chr; ChrhWkr; HonRl; NHS; YthFlsp; GerCl; Bsktbl; IMSpt; Calvin College; Health Career.

NYKAMP, Thomas L; Holland Christian HS; Zeeland, MI; Chr; ChrhWkr; HonRl; Mdrgl; NatlMeritCmnd; FDA; Calvin Col; Doctor Of Pediatrics.

NYLAND, Nancy A; Anna Jonesboro HS; Anna, IL; 25/137 ChrhWkr; HonRl; LbryAde; RptrYrbk; RptrSchPpr; VP4-H; FTA; TreasSpnCl; DanFAwd; 4-HAwd; E Ill Univ; Elementary Ed.

NYLAND, Nancy A; Anna Jonesboro C HS; Anna, IL; ChrhWkr; HonRl; LbryAde; NHS; Quill&Scroll; RptrYrbk; SchPpr; FTA; TreasSpnCl; DanFAwd; Eastern Ill Univ; Elementary Education.

NYLUND, Jeaneen A; Menominee HS; Menominee, MI; ALAGirlsSt; DrlTm; JrNHS; NHS; Quill&Scroll; StuCncl; RptrYrbk; RptrSchPpr; FrCl; DARAwd; Michigan State University.

NYLUND, Kim E; Menominee HS; Menominee, MI; 22/275 HonRl; JrNHS; NHS; Orch; TchrAde; Yrbk; SpnCl; PpCl; College; Special Education.

NYQUIST, Janice L; Northville HS; Northville, MI; 16/320 Chr; ChrhWkr; CncrtBnd; HospAde; MrchBnd; NHS; NatlMeritCmnd; SchPl; RptrSchPpr; Grand Rapids Baptist Coll; Communications.

NYQUIST, Jean; Midland HS; Midland, MI; 4/433 HstFrshCls; NHS; NatlMeritSchl; FrCl; MthCl; Swmmng; JCAwd; JAAwd; Univ Of Mi; Math And Computer Science.

NYQUIST, Jean S; Midland HS; Midland, MI; 3/450 HstFrshCls; HonRl; JA; NHS; NatlMeritSF; SctActv; StuCncl; YthFlsp; SecPpCl; Swmmng; U Of Mich; Math Comp Science.

NYQUIST, Larry K; Bemidji HS; Bemidji, MN; 57/338 Orch; SchMus; LetterTrk; College; Accounting.

NYREN, Charlene; Greendale HS; Greendale, WI; Chr; HonRl; NatlFornLg; RptrYrbk; PpCl; Trade School; Actress.

NYSTROM, David D; Antioch Comm HS; Lake Villa, IL; 26/358 ChrhWkr; College; Chemistry.

NYSTROM, Don J; Kimball Area HS; Kimball, MN; TchrAde; Bsktbl; Ftbl; Undecided.

NYSTUEN, Jeffrey A; Pioneer HS; Ann Arbor, MI; 1/641 Band; CncrtBnd; HonRl; MrchBnd; NatlMeritCmnd; Yrbk; MthCl; SciCl; U Of Mi; Teacher.

O

O BANION, Cindy L; Falls City HS; Falls City, NE; 8/90 Chrs; DrlTm; HonRl; NHS; SecNatlThespSoc; OffAde; SchMus; SchPl; Yrbk; IMSpt; Peru State College; Major In Music.

O BANNON, Allen R; Pillager HS; Pillager, MN; Band; ChrhWkr; CncrtBnd; MrchBnd; PepBnd; SchPl; LetterTrk; BttyCrckrAwd; Univ Of Minnesota; Crop Prod.

O BOYLE, Marybeth; Mother Mcauley HS; Chicago, IL; 52/474 Chrs; HonRl; NHS; Quill&Scroll; RedCrAde; SchPpr; University Of Illinois; Communications.

O BOYLE, Robert M; Parchment HS; Parchment, MI; Chr; Chrl; HonRl; NHS; NatlMeritSF; SchMus; StuCncl; TreasSpnCl; Ftbl; TreasTennis; Kalamazoo Coll; Prof.

O BOYLE, Rosemary; St Teresas Acad; Kansas City, MO; 15/109 VPJrCls; PresSrCls; Chrs; HonRl; LitMag; SchPl; StuGov; LatCl; PPFtbl; Rockhurst College; Dramatics.

O BRIAN, Beth A; Barr Reeve HS; Montgomery, IN; VPFrshCls; Chr; ChrhWkr; DrlTm; HonRl; JrNHS; NHS; SchPl; SctActv; VPFHA; SpnCl; PpCl; Indiana St University.

O BRIEN, Bridget M; Academy Of Sacred Heart; Birmingham, MI; HonRl; HospAde; PolWkr; RedCrAde; SchAde; TchrAde; Saint Marys College; Biology.

O BRIEN, Daniel W; Carlinville HS; Arlinville, IL; SecSrCls; ALBoysSt; PolWkr; SchPl; SchPpr; FrCl; LetterFtbl; Socr; LetterWrstlng; IMSpt; Il St U; Psycology Major.

O BRIEN, Dean A; Ellendale Public HS; Ellendale, ND; Chrs; SchPl; Ftbl; CaptWrstlng; IMSpt; Univ; Professional.

O BRIEN, Denise; St Francis Academy; Joliet, IL; SecSophCls; CmntyWkr; HonRl; LitMag; Quill&Scroll; StuCncl; Yrbk; Joliet Jr College; Special Ed.

O BRIEN, Dixon E; Arlington HS; Arlington Heights, IL; HonRl; Univ Of Illinois; Civil Engineer.

O BRIEN, James B; Big Foot HS; Fontana, WI; ALBoysSt; HonRl; StuCncl; StuGov; MthCl; Glf; University; Professional.

O BRIEN, James D; Davison HS; Davison, MI; 66/428 HonRl; FBLA; Ftbl; IMSpt; Univ Of Mi; Accounting.

O BRIEN, James M; St Laurence HS; Oak Lawn, IL; 172/380 HonRl; LbryAde; Glf; Tennis; Wrstlng; College; Law.

O BRIEN, James P; Pacelli HS; Stevens Point, WI; HonRl; NHS; SctActv; StuCncl; SptEdYrbk; SchPpr; Ftbl; College; Law.

O BRIEN, Janice T; Finney HS; Detroit, MI; Chr; Chrs; SchAde; SchMus; SchPl; SciCl; CitAwd; Fashion Designer.

O BRIEN, Joseph F; Belleville HS; Belleville, WI; FFA; LetterFtbl; LetterWrstlng; Army; Civil Eng.

O BRIEN, Karen M; Belding HS; Belding, MI; VPFrshCls; VPSophCls; VPJrCls; Band; HonRl; NHS; StuCncl; TchrAde; FTA; SpnCl; College; Professional.

O BRIEN, Kathleen J; Superior Sr HS; Superior, WI; HonRl; NHS; SchAde; SctActv; RptrSchPpr; PpCl; Trk; Chrldr; GAA; College Of St Scholastica; Medicine.

O BRIEN, Kathy S; Cambridge Public HS; Cambridge, NE; 8/33 Band; Chrs; CncrtBnd; HonRl; MrchBnd; PepBnd; SchPl; EdYrBk; FBLA; FHA; North Platte Jr College; Secretary.

O BRIEN, Kerry D; Morton Senior HS; Hammond, IN; 18/492 PresSrCls; CncrtBnd; HonRl; MrchBnd; NHS; Orch; StuCncl; StuGov; TchrAde; YthFlsp; College; Pre Law.

O BRIEN, Larry W; East Richland HS; Olney, IL; CmntyWkr; SchAde; 4-H; Bsktbl; CchngActv; 4-HAwd; CitAwd; Olney Central College; Pharmacy.

O BRIEN, Mariellen E; Marian HS; Birmingham, MI; PresSrCls; HonRl; JA; ModUN; NHS; NatlMeritFnl; NatlMeritSchl; StuGov; College; Professional.

O BRIEN, Mark E; Austin Prep; Mount Clemens, MI; PresFrshCls; HonRl; NHS; StuGov; Bsktbl; Michigan St Univ; Business Law.

O BRIEN, Mark M; Marist HS; Palos Heights, IL; 40/360 ChrhWkr; CmntyWkr; HonRl; IntrClCncl; NHS; SchAde; TchrAde; RptrSchPpr; SciCl; Bsbl; Glf; Univ Of Illinois; Veterinarian.

O BRIEN, Mark T; St Mary Of Redford HS; Detroit, MI; PresSophCls; VPSrCls; Aud/Vis; HonRl; JA; StuCncl; StuGov; SciCl; Michigan State University; Medicine.

O BRIEN, Mary C; Duchesne HS; St Charles, MO; 32#50#72 PresSpnCl; VPPpCl; Nursing School; Nursing.

O BRIEN, Maureen A; Mount Assisi Academy; Oak Lawn, IL; 8/194 HonRl; NHS; TchrAde; RptrSchPpr; FrCl; St Marys College.

O BRIEN, Michael B; Assumption HS; Davenport, IA; 19/219 ChrhWkr; HonRl; JrNHS; LitMag; NHS; NatlMeritCmnd; RptrYrbk; Yrbk; CaptGlf; IMSpt; University Of Notre Dame; Electrical Eng.

O BRIEN, Michael G; St Marys Springs HS; Fond Du Lac, WI; VPSrCls; SchPl; StuCncl; RptrSchPpr; SchPpr; TreasKeyCl; SpnCl; LetterTrk; IMSpt; College; Communication.

O BRIEN, Patricia L; Franklin Center HS; Franklin Grove, IL; 5/36 TrsSophCls; VPJrCls; Chrs; DrlTm; HonRl; NHS; StuCncl; RptrSchPpr; PpCl; PPFtbl; Legal Secretary.

O BRIEN, Patricia M; Rice Lake HS; Rice Lake, WI; HonRl; SctActv; RptrSchPpr; GerCl; LetterBsktbl; LetterTrk; GAA; Univ; Professional.

O BRIEN, Richard D; University City HS; University City, MO; Aud/Vis; CmntyWkr; HonRl; LitMag; LbryAde; SchMus; StuCncl; StuGov; Trk; Wrstlng; Col; Writer.

O BRIEN, Rick D; Vandercook Lake HS; Jackson, MI; 10/98 SecJrCls; Band; CncrtBnd; HonRl; JA; MrchBnd; NHS; Orch; PepBnd; PolWkr; LetterBsktbl; LetterFtbl; LetterTrk; College; Lawyer.

O BRIEN, Ronald C; Ontonagon Area HS; Ontonayon, MI; 16/106 Band; HonRl; NHS; LetterFtbl; LetterTrk; IMSpt; Naval Academy Annapolis.

O BRIEN, Sandra A; Cambridge Sr HS; Cambridge, MN; Art Schl; Art.

O BRIEN, Suzanne M; Mercy HS; St Louis, MO; CncrtBnd; HonRl; SchMus; IMSpt; College.

O BRIEN, Thomas R; Mora HS; Mora, MN; 8/140 Chr; CncrtBnd; HonRl; MrchBnd; NHS; NatlThespSoc; Quill&Scroll; SchMus; EdYrBk; RptrSchPpr; U Of Mn; Music.

O BRIEN, Timothy J; Schleswig Comm HS; Schleswig, IA; 6/50 ALBoysSt; HonRl; NHS; PresStuCncl; EdSchPpr; PresFTA; Bsbl; Bsktbl; Ftbl; LetterGlf; College; Journalism.

O BRYAN, Shelly J; Monroe City R 1 HS; Monroe City, MO; ALAGirlsSt; ChrhWkr; CmntyWkr; HonRl; JrNHS; NHS; PolWkr; ROTC; YthFnd; PresAwd; Univ Kirksville; Py Ed Teacher.

O BRYANT, Renee L; Delta HS; Albany, IN; HonRl; JrNHS; NHS; OffAde; YthFlsp; FrCl; PpCl; SciCl; Fashion Merchandising.

O CALLAGHAN, Linda A; Mother Of Sorrows HS; Chicago, IL; 8/120 SecSophCls; HonRl; NHS; PolWkr; StuCncl; TchrAde; PpCl; Marquette University; Physical Therapy.

O CALLAGHAN, Mary A; St Josephs Academy; Green Bay, WI; Band; Chrl; Chrs; ChrhWkr; CncrtBnd; MrchBnd; NHS; Orch; SchMus; College; Music.

O CALLAGHAN, Terese M; Alcona HS; Lincoln, MI; 15/113 OffAde; TchrAde; Bsbl; LetterBsktbl; PPFtbl; Lake Superior State College; Accounting.

O CLAIR, Joel A; Clay Central HS; Royal, IA; Band; Chr; Chrs; CncrtBnd; HonRl; MrchBnd; PepBnd; SchPl; SctActv; UNYO; LetterBsbl; LetterFtbl; LetterTrk; Ilcc; Engine Mechanic.

O CONNELL, Christine M; Calumet HS; Laurium, MI; SecTrsFrshCls; SecSrCls; Band; Chr; CncrtBnd; HonRl; NHS; StuCncl; Yrbk; FNA; PpCl; Univ Of Mich; Medicine.

O CONNELL, Diane K; Senn HS; Chicago, IL; 10/386 Chrs; HonRl; JrNHS; NHS; SchMus; SctActv; TchrAde; College; Medicine.

O CONNELL, Kathleen M; Convent Of The Visitation HS; Hopkins, MN; 2/31 SecJrCls; Chr; Chrl; Chrs; Mdrgl; SchMus; SchPl; Yrbk; FrCl; St Catherine Clge;.

O CONNELL, Kevin M; Munter HS; Munster, IN; SchMus; Ftbl; Socr; IMSpt; College; Marine Biology.

O CONNELL, Mary E; Mother Of Sorrows HS; Chicago, IL; 1/115 HonRl; NHS; StuCncl; St Xavier College; Mathematics.

O CONNELL, Patricia A; Elizabeth Seton HS; Chicago, IL; 19/252 Chrl; HonRl; NHS; RptrYrbk; RptrSchPpr; College; Biology.

O CONNELL, Patricia F; Forest View HS; Des Plaines, IL; ChrhWkr; OffAde; SpnCl; LetterTrk; Chrldr; CchngActv; GAA; IMSpt; Univ; Vocation.

O CONNELL, Tim L; Anthon Oto HS; Smithland, IA; Band; HonRl; SchPl; Yrbk; 4-H; PpCl; Bsbl; Bsktbl; LetterFtbl; Trk; LetterWrstlng; 4-HAwd; College; Professional.

O CONNOR, Beth A; Laker HS; Elkton, MI; HonRl; HospAde; NatlFornLg; NHS; StuCncl; FHA; PpCl; Bsktbl; Trk; Chrldr; GAA; IMSpt; Albion College; Medicine.

O CONNOR, Brian E; Delavan Darien HS; Delavan, WI; ALBoysSt; HonRl; PresNHS; NatlMeritSF; StuCncl; Trk; IMSpt; Ma Inst Of Tech; Chem Engineer.

O CONNOR, Daniel J; Marist HS; Chicago, IL; ChrhWkr; CmntyWkr; HonRl; NHS; LetterFtbl; LetterSocr; LetterTennis; Trk; IMSpt; Ill Inst Of Tech; Computer Science.

O CONNOR, Daniel P; Aquin Central Catholic HS; Freeport, IL; PresFrshCls; Chrs; HonRl; Mdrgl; NHS; SchMus; RptrSchPpr; SchPpr; SciCl; Ftbl; AmLegAwd;.

O CONNOR, Erin M; Barr Reeve HS; Montgomery, IN; Band; HonRl; LbryAde; OffAde; 4-H; FHA; SpnCl; PpCl; Chrldr; IMSpt; College.

O CONNOR, Grace M; T L Handy HS; Bay City, MI; 23/375 HonRl; NHS; 4-H; FrCl; IMSpt; 4-HAwd; Mich State U; Child Psychology.

O CONNOR, Irene; Mexico HS; Mexico, MO; Band; CncrtBnd; MrchBnd; PepBnd; PresSctActv; SchPpr; SpnCl; PresPpCl; Bsktbl; LetterTennis; Univ; Curriculum Of Major Study.

O CONNOR, James M; St Mary Of Redford HS; Detroit, MI; 75/190 PresFrshCls; TrsSophCls; PresJrCls; ChrhWkr; StuCncl; StuGov; Bsktbl; CaptFtbl; Trk; IMSpt; Univ Of Michigan; Professional.

O CONNOR, James T; Marian Catholic HS; Lansing, IL; PresBand; ChrhWkr; CncrtBnd; DrmBgl; HonRl; MrchBnd; PepBnd; StuCncl; Teen; SchPpr; College; Journalism Or Biologist.

O CONNOR, Jimalee; Plattsburg HS; Plattsburg, MO; 6/53 VPJrCls; ChrhWkr; HonRl; ModUN; NHS; OffAde; 4-H; SpnCl; Benedictine College; Political Science.

O CONNOR, Joanne M; Homewood Flossmoor HS; Glenwood, IL; Chrs; SctActv; TchrAde;.

O CONNOR, John C; Forest View HS; Des Plaines, IL; 6/640 Band; CncrtBnd; HonRl; MrchBnd; PresNatlFornLg; NHS; NatlMeritCmnd; PepBnd; SchMus; RotaryAwd; Augustana Clge; Pre Med.

O CONNOR, Kevin M; Oak Grove R Vi HS; Oak Grove, MO; HonRl; NHS; SctActv; Bsktbl; Ftbl; College; Engineering.

O CONNOR, Laurie M; Marian Central HS; Algonquin, IL; 23/115 Chrs; CmntyWkr; HonRl; OffAde; PolWkr; SchPl; Yrbk; College; Journalism.

O CONNOR, Linda M; John F Kennedy HS; Chicago, IL; 56/610 NHS; OffAde; SchAde; PresStuCncl; SpnCl; MthCl; SciCl; LetterGAA; Ill Institute Of Tech; Medical Engineer.

O CONNOR, Margaret M; St Louise De Marillac HS; Chicago, IL; 24/252 Chrs; NatlMeritFnl; Orch; SchMus; SctActv; GerCl; Purdue Univ; Chemical Engineer.

O CONNOR, Mark T; Marist Of Chicago HS; Chicago, IL; 81/365 ChrhWkr; HonRl; NHS; PolWkr; Glf; LetterTrk; Univ Of Illinois; Lawyer.

O CONNOR, Marni; Immaculate Heart Of Mary; Westchester, IL; 9/244 Chrl; ChrhWkr; HonRl; HospAde; NHS; RptrYrbk; Yrbk; PpCl; IMSpt; Coll; Psychology.

O CONNOR, Marni J; Immaculate Heart Of Mary HS; Westchester, IL; 11/244 Chrl; HospAde; RptrYrbk; Yrbk; PpCl; CaptChrldr; GAA; College; Psychology.

O CONNOR, Mary M; Heelan HS; Sioux City, IA; 7/250 Chrs; ChrhWkr; CmntyWkr; HonRl; JA; NHS; PolWkr; SchMus; StuCncl; PpCl; College; Law.

O CONNOR, Michael J; Watertown HS; Watertown, SD; 5/320 ALBoysSt; HonRl; JrNHS; NHS; PolWkr; GerCl; Ftbl; Glf; IMSpt; RotaryAwd; ;law.

O CONNOR, Michael P; Fenwick HS; River Forest, IL; 33/230 HonRl; JrNHS; NHS; CaptBsbl; LetterBsktbl; LetterFtbl;.

O CONNOR, Noreen H; Bethlehem Academy; Faribault, MN; 10/84 DrlTm; HonRl; NHS; SchPl; TchrAde; 4-H; SpnCl; Bsbl; College Of St Benedicts; Teacher.

O CONNOR, Patrice C; St Marys HS; Kansas City, MO; SecSophCls; Chrs; HonRl; JrNHS; NHS; PolWkr; SchMus; SctActv; StuCncl; PpCl; College; Professional.

O CONNOR, Patrick M; St Vincent De Paul HS; Chicago, IL; VPSophCls; Chr; ChrhWkr; HonRl; Sacrstn; SchMus; SchPl; StuCncl; RptrSchPpr; LetterBsktbl; CaptSocr; LetterTennis; LetterTrk; College; Vocational.

O CONNOR, Patrick M; St Vincent De Paul Seminary; Chicago, IL; 1/9 VPSophCls; Chr; ChrhWkr; HonRl; Sacrstn; SchMus; SchPl; StuCncl; RptrSchPpr; Bsktbl; Socr; Tennis; College; Professional.

O CONNOR, Peggy; Seymour HS; Seymour, IN; 7/325 OffAde; HonRl; NatlThespSoc; SchMus; SchPl; Yrbk; SpnCl; Tennis; GAA; Purdue Univ, Veterinarian Or Wildlife Mange.

O CONNOR, Rita A; Maria HS; Chicago, IL; 25/335 CmntyWkr; HonRl; HospAde; TreasNHS; TchrAde; GerCl; LionAwd; Hospital School; X Ray Technician.

O CONNOR, Robert; Saint Laurence HS; Chicago, IL; HonRl; NHS; NatlMeritFnl; NatlMeritSchl; NatlMeritSF; CivCl; FBLA; FSA; IMSpt; College; Navy Rotc And Computerscience.

O CONNOR, Scott M; St Edward HS; Carpentersville, IL; 5/140 ChrhWkr; CtyCnl; HonRl; NHS; NatlThespSoc; SchMus; StuCncl; StuGov; LatCl; MthCl; LetterBsbl; Bsktbl; LetterFtbl; College; Doctor.

O CONNOR, Steven R; Concordia HS; Concordia, KS; Chr; Chrl; ChrhWkr; HonRl; HospAde; MrchBnd; NatlFornLg; Orch; SchPl; College; Music.

O CONNOR, Timothy V; Milbank HS; Milbank, SD; 3/135 LbryAde; PolWkr; Sacrstn; LatCl; Ftbl; Glf; IMSpt; OptClAwd; PresAwd; Military.

O CROTTY, Linda L; Engadine HS; Naubinway, MI; 5/40 HonRl; SchPl; SchPpr; FrCl; LetterTrk; IMSpt; CitAwd; Secretary.

O DANIEL, James T; Normandy Sr HS; St Louis, MO; Band; ChrhWkr; CncrtBnd; HonRl; JrNHS; PolWkr; OptClAwd; CitAwd; Univ; Law.

O DANIEL, Mary E; Northwestern HS; Athol, SD; ALAGirlsSt; Band; Chrs; HonRl; HospAde; PepBnd; SchPl; RptrSchPpr; SchPpr; PpCl; Stewarts Sch Of Hairstyling; Hairstylist.

O DANIELL, Michael W; Central HS; St Joseph, MO; JA; NatlMeritSF; Univ Of Mo; Civil Engineering.

O DAY, Kelly B; Merrill Sr HS; Merrill, WI; 5/358 Chr; HonRl; NatlMeritCmnd; SchMus; SchPl; StuCncl; SpnCl; Ftbl; Wrstlng; Univ Of Wisconsin; Psychology.

O DAY, Stephen M; Edsel Ford HS; Dearborn, MI; CmntyWkr; HonRl; PolWkr; Swmmng; U Of Michigan; Mathematics.

O DEA, James A; Bridgeport HS; Bridgeport, NE; 11/62 Band; CncrtBnd; HonRl; MrchBnd; NHS; PepBnd; PresStuCncl; YthFlsp; 4-H; LetterBsktbl; LetterFtbl; LetterTrk; College.

O DEA, Thomas J; Cedar Lake H S; Cedar Lake, IN; 9/140 HonRl; JrNHS; NHS; FrCl; SpnCl; MthCl; SciCl; Bsbl; Bsktbl; LetterWrstlng; College.

O DELL, Becky; Bellmont HS; Monroeville, IN; HonRl; College; Art.

O DELL, Catherine L; Waterloo Public HS; Fults, IL; ChrhWkr; HonRl; NatlFornLg; OffAde; SchAde; SchPl; StuCncl; TchrAde; FHA; SpnCl; SciCl; GAA; College; Speech.

O DELL, Cindy L; Palestine HS; Palestine, IL; Chrs; ChrhWkr; OffAde; PolWkr; StuCncl; TreasYthFlsp; TreasFHA; PpCl; GAA; College; Medical Tech.

O DELL, Elizabeth F; Stephen Decatur HS; Decatur, IL; 4/368 Band; Chr; CncrtBnd; HospAde; MrchBnd; NHS; NatlMeritCmnd; Orch; SchPl; College; Nursing.

O DELL, Elizabeth E; Roxana HS; East Alton, IL; 37/275 Chrs; HonRl; JA; OffAde; SchMus; RptrYrbk; Yrbk; PpCl; Southern Ill Univ; Business Adm.

O DELL, Kimberly L; North Clay Comm HS; Louisville, IL; 7/55 Band; Chrs; ChrhWkr; CncrtBnd; HonRl; MrchBnd; NHS; PepBnd; SchPl; SctActv; Yrbk; RptrSchPpr; Olney Central College; Psychology.

O DELL, Nancy K; Lawrence Central HS; Florissant, MO; 236/732 HonRl; RptrSchPpr; SchPpr; University.

O DOHERTY, Terry M; Creighton Prep HS; Omaha, NE; 90/229 ALBoysSt; ChrhWkr; CmntyWkr; HonRl; JA; LbryAde; ROTC; SchAde; Sdlty; Teen; SptEdSchPpr; Bsbl; Bsktbl; College; Professional.

O DONNELL, Ann; Mt Carmel HS; Mt Carmel, IL; Band; Chr; Chrs; CncrtBnd; DrlTm; MrchBnd; Quill&Scroll; SchMus; SchPl; EdYrBk; College; Biology.

O DONNELL, Ann F; Belleville East HS; Fairview Hgts, IL; 50/700 HonRl; University.

O DONNELL, Ann L; Marillac HS; Glenview, IL; SchMus; SchPl; St Norberts College; Lawyer.

O DONNELL, Catherine S; St Bede HS; Peru, IL; 10/120 ChrhWkr; CncrtBnd; HonRl; IntrClCncl; OffAde; SchMus; SchPl; StuGov; Tennis; Trk; University; Professional.

O DONNELL, Cheryl M; Mercy HS; Omaha, NE; JA; SchMus; SchPl; StuGov; TreasSpnCl; GAA; College; Elem Ed.

O DONNELL, Dolores A; Pontiac Township HS; Pontiac, IL; HonRl; SctActv; Twrl; 4-H; PpCl; Trk; Chrldr; GAA; IMSpt; JCAwd; USJCAwd; LionAwd; College; Model.

O DONNELL, Helen M; Woodstock Community HS; Wonder Lake, IL; 11/264 HonRl; College; Elementary Education.

O DONNELL, James J; William J Bogan HS; La Grange, IL; 71/704 Aud/Vis; NHS; SchAde; TchrAde; SciCl; De Paul; Political Science.

O DONNELL, James L; St Laurence HS; Chicago, IL; 69/572 Band; HonRl; JA; NHS; StuCncl; StuGov; LetterBsbl; Bsktbl; LetterFtbl; Chrldr; CchngActv; Ill State Univ; Pro Baseball.

O DONNELL, John D; Ste Genevieve Sr HS; Ste Genevieve, MO; 9/196 ALBoysSt; HonRl; HospAde; LbryAde; SchMus; SctActv; StuCncl; LetterBsbl; Bsktbl; LetterFtbl; Trk; Wrstlng; VoiceDemAwd; University; Nursing.

O DONNELL, John M; Immaculate Conception HS; Elmhurst, IL; 10/160 NHS; NatlMeritCmnd; SchPl; SpnCl; SciCl; Bsbl; CaptBsktbl; CchngActv; IMSpt; VoiceDemAwd; University Of Notre Dame; Journalist.

O DONNELL, Kirk; Mason City HS; Mason City, IA; Band; CncrtBnd; HonRl; MrchBnd; Orch; PepBnd; SctActv; Tennis; GodCntryAwd; Univ Of Iowa; Engineering.

O DONNELL, Linda C; St Thomas Aquinas HS; Ferguson, MO; 16/349 CmntyWkr; HonRl; NHS; SchMus; SchPl; SctActv; Sw Missouri St Univ; Medical Technology.

O DONNELL, Mary; Carroll HS; Camden, IN; VPFrshCls; PresSrCls; Chrs; HonRl; NHS; NatlThespSoc; SchPl; StuCncl; SpnCl; RotaryAwd;.

O DONNELL, Maureen; Queen Of Apostles HS; Monona, WI; ChrhWkr; JA; SchPl; RptrYrbk; RptrSchPpr; LetterBsktbl; Glf; Chrldr; IMSpt; PPFtbl; College Wisc Univ; Business Major.

O DONNELL, Michael J; Morgan Park HS; Chicago, IL; DrlTm; NHS; Illinois Inst Tech; Engineering.

O DONNELL, Patrick G; St Francis De Sales HS; Chicago, IL; 23/294 HonRl; JrNHS; NHS; StuCncl; Bsktbl; LetterTrk; Univ Of Illinois; Priesthood.

O DONNELL, Sharon J; Columbus HS; Marshfield, WI; Band; CncrtBnd; HonRl; LbryAde; MrchBnd; NHS; SchMus; Yrbk; FrCl; Coll; Dentist.

O DONNELL, Susan M; Bishop Noll Institute; Highland, IN; 76/360 Chrl; HonRl; GAA; University; Nursing.

O DONNELL, William M; Loyola Academy; Chicago, IL; 100/442 HonRl; LetterBsbl; LetterFtbl; College; Law.

O DONOGHUE, Sharon K; St Mary Academy; Indianapolis, IN; 2/34 SecSophCls; SecJrCls; Chrs; HonRl; NHS; SchAde; SchPl; PresStuCncl; PresSpnCl; GAA; IMSpt; DARAwd; Regis Univ; Political Science.

O DRISCOLL, Richard J; Mehlville Sr HS; St Louis, MO; 47/537 HonRl; JrNHS; NHS; LetterFtbl; LetterWrstlng; Southeast Missouri College; Business Mgmt.

O FARRELL, Richard R; Bay City Central HS; Bay City, MI; Chr; HonRl; SchMus; StuGov; Michigan State University; Biology.

O FLAHERTY, Bridget V; Queen Of Peace HS; Hickory Hills, IL; 15/429 Chrs; CmntyWkr; HonRl; JA; LbryAde; StuCncl; FrCl; LatCl; PpCl; Circle Col; Veterinarian.

O FLAHERTY, Mary B; Queen Of Peace HS; Hickory Hills, IL; 8/429 Chrs; CmntyWkr; HonRl; JA; LbryAde; FrCl; PpCl; GAA; Northern Illinois Univ; Medicine.

O FLANAGAN, La Donna C; Serena HS; Ottawa, IL; 14/72 ChrhWkr; CmntyWkr; HonRl; NHS; OffAde; YthFlsp; Yrbk; 4-H; GAA; JAAwd; Ill Valley Comm Coll; Computer Programming.

O GRADY, Mary T; Holy Child HS; Waukegan, IL; HstJrCls; SchPl; StuGov; GAA; IMSpt; College Of St Teresa; Nursing.

O HANLON, John A; Potosi HS; Potosi, MO; Band; CncrtBnd; HonRl; MrchBnd; NHS; SchPl; College.

O HARA, Kathleen A; Greendale HS; Greendale, WI; 20/380 VPIntrClCncl; LbryAde; ModUN; OffAde; TchrAde; RptrYrbk; SpnCl; GAA; Univ; Nurse.

O HARA, Margaret M; St Mary Acad; Indianapolis, IN; SecFrshCls; Chrs; HonRl; LbryAde; SchPl; SpnCl; Chrldr; GAA; Clg; Nursing.

O HARA, Mary M; So Fork Comm HS; Kincaid, IL; 1/50 Band; HonRl; SchPl; TchrAde; SchPpr; FHA; SpnCl; CaptTrk; Chrldr; BttyCrckrAwd; W Illinois Univ; Med Tech.

O HARA, Thomas R; Edison HS; East Gary, IN; Aud/Vis; HonRl; JrNHS; FrCl; SciCl;.

O KANE, Julie; Mercy HS; Omaha, NE; NatlFornLg; SchPl; FrCl; Bsktbl; College.

O KANE, Reid J; Sycamore HS; Sycamore, IL; Chr; ChrhWkr; CmntyWkr; CncrtBnd; HonRl; Mdrgl; NHS; NatlThespSoc; SchMus; TchrAde; Univ; Theatre.

O KEEFE, Dan T; Hudson Sr HS; Hudson, WI; VPFrshCls; ChrhWkr; CmntyWkr; HonRl; SchPl; SctActv; StuCncl; RptrYrbk; SptEdYrbk; Bsbl; Ftbl; Wrstlng; Trade Schl; Vocation.

O KEEFE, Dianne C; Newton HS; Newton, KS; ChrhWkr; CmntyWkr; HonRl; TchrAde; SpnCl; PpCl; Wichita St U; Chemistry.

O KEEFE, Mary K; Iola Scandinavia HS; Iola, WI; HonRl; JrNHS; Western Wis Tech Inst; Legal Secretary.

O KEEFE, Patrick J; Oak Park River Forest HS; Oak Park, IL; 46/1012 HonRl; StuCncl; PpCl; LetterTrk; Univ Of Illinois; Dentistry.

O KEEFFE, Marian C; Catholic Memorial HS; Wauwatosa, WI; HonRl; RptrSchPpr; LetterTennis; IMSpt; PresAwd; Marquette Univ; Professional.

O KELLY, Kathryn M; Oak Park & River Forest HS; Oak Park, IL; 141/1100 Chr; HonRl; NatlFornLg; NatlThespSoc; SchMus; SchPl; Il State U; Professional Actress.

O LAUGHLIN, Michael W; South Shelby HS; Shelbina, MO; HonRl; Ftbl; Trk; IMSpt; College; Professional.

O LEARY, Corby D; Marshall HS; Marshall, MI; 101/254 Band; HonRl; YthFlsp; LetterBsktbl; LetterFtbl; CaptTennis; Coll; Air Cond Refrig.

O LEARY, Kathleen; Antigo HS; Antigo, WI; Band; HonRl; MrchBnd; ModUN; PepBnd; SctActv; 4-H; GerCl; GAA; IMSpt; 4-HAwd; College; Aerospace Engineer.

O LEARY, Margaret M; Sacred Heart Of Mary HS; Arlington Hgts, IL; PresJrCls; HonRl; LitMag; NHS; SchMus; SchPl; FrCl; SciCl; Socr; IMSpt; De Paul Univ; Marine Biology.

O LEARY, Susan; Andrean HS; Merrillville, IN; 24/250 HonRl; NHS; Quill&Scroll; SchPl; RptrSchPpr; SchPpr; FrCl; GAA; IMSpt; PPFtbl; College; Liberal Arts And Science.

O LOUGHLIN, Michael D; St Laurence HS; Chicago, IL; 61/372 HonRl; StuCncl; LetterFtbl; College; Business.

O MALLEY, John T; Marist HS; Palos Hts, IL; 39/365 HonRl; NatlMeritSF; Glf; Univ Of Illinois; Business Admin.

O MALLEY, Kathleen A; Luke M Powers HS; Flint, MI; LbryAde; NHS; Univ Of Mich; Chemistry.

O MALLEY, Patrick M; Brown City HS; Brown City, MI; 13/95 CmntyWkr; StuCncl; 4-H; Bsbl; Michigan Tech Univ; Engineer.

O MALLEY, Thomas P; Marist HS; Chicago, IL; 9/400 HonRl; University; Psychology.

O MALLEY, Thomas W; York HS; Elmhurst, IL; Univ Of Illinois; Civil Engineer.

O MARA, James E; Lakewood HS; Lake Odessa, MI; 20/225 ALBoysSt; HonRl; NHS; EdYrBk; EdSchPpr; LetterWrstlng; IMSpt; PresAwd; Ferris St College; Business Admin.

O MARA, Mary E; Immac Heart Of Mary HS; Oak Park, IL; 9/250 TrsSrCls; NatlMeritCmnd; StuGov; RptrYrbk; RptrSchPpr; Northwestern Univ; Journalism.

O MARA, Patrick A; Arthur County HS; Arthur, NE; 5/12 HonRl; IntrClCncl; YthFlsp; Yrbk; CivCl; 4-H; KeyCl; CaptBsktbl; CaptFtbl; IMSpt; Trade School; Professional.

O MEARA, Anne E; Wheaton Warrenville HS; Wheaton, IL; HonRl; NatlFornLg; SchPl; StuCncl; TchrAde; PpCl; Eastern Ill Univ; Child Development.

O MEARA, Kathy; Galva Comm HS; Galva, IA; Chrs; CncrtBnd; DrlTm; HonRl; MrchBnd; SchPl; 4-H; Bsktbl; Chrldr; Des Moines Area Comm College; Medical Asst.

O MEARA, Mary C; Dowling HS; Des Moines, IA; SecFrshCls; CmntyWkr; HonRl; UNYO; LatCl; PpCl; Chrldr; Creighton Univ; Nursing.

O NEAL, Denise I; Chicago Vocational HS; Chicago, IL; 32/778 HonRl; NHS; TchrAde; GAA; Northwestern; Journalist.

O NEAL, Jon T; Lawrence HS; Lawrence, KS; 1/550 ALBoysSt; Band; CncrtBnd; HonRl; MrchBnd; PolWkr; SchMus; StuCncl; Trk; LionAwd; Kansas U; Pre Med.

O NEAL, Kathleen M; Clarkson HS; Clarkson, NE; 2/39 Band; HonRl; SchPl; StuCncl; Twrl; PpCl; LetterTrk; Chrldr; GAA; LionAwd; U Of Indiana; Dancer Singer.

O NEAL, Mark S; Downers Grove No HS; Woodridge, IL; 35/509 Band; CncrtBnd; HonRl; MrchBnd; NHS; Orch; PepBnd; LetterTrk; West Point; Engineering.

O NEAL, Melinna M; North Miami HS; Denver, IN; 5/119 Band; CncrtBnd; HonRl; MrchBnd; NHS; SpnCl; PpCl; SciCl; Chrldr; PPFtbl; Purdue Univ; Secretary.

O NEAL, Rockey J; Chicago Vocational HS; Chicago, IL; 4/770 HonRl; JrNHS; NHS; Quill&Scroll; SchAde; PresStuCncl; MthCl; PpCl; Bsbl; LetterFtbl; University; Professional.

O NEAL, Shirley J; Civic Memorial HS; Cottage Hills, IL; 1/203 ChrhWkr; HonRl; JrNHS; NHS; RptrSchPpr; SchPpr; Evangel College; Religion.

O NEAL, Terry L; T C Howe HS; Indianapolis, IN; Aud/Vis; ChrhWkr; HonRl; NHS; StuCncl; SciCl; Rose Hulman; Chem Engr.

O NEAL, Todd S; Angola HS; Angola, IN; ALBoysSt; ChrhWkr; NatlMeritFnl; GerCl; SciCl; Indiana University; Chemistry.

O NEAL, Vicki; Rosati Kain HS; St Louis, MO; NatlMeritCmnd; StuCncl; RptrSchPpr; PresGAA; IMSpt; PPFtbl; College; Electrical Engineering.

O NEIL, Cindy L; Evergreen Park HS; Evergreen Park, IL; 36/439 PresAFS; CmntyWkr; HonRl; NHS; StuGov; PpCl; Bsktbl; GAA; College; Nursing.

O NEIL, Cole P; Grayslake Comm HS; Lake Villa, IL; Aud/Vis; Band; CAP; CncrtBnd; HonRl; MrchBnd; PepBnd; Yrbk; Trk; Lake Forest College; Pro Pilot.

O NEIL, Dennis J; Newman Central Catholic HS; Sterling, IL; ALBoysSt; Chr; Chrl; Chrs; ChrhWkr; HonRl; Mdrgl; NHS; NatlMeritFnl; NatlMeritCmnd; LetterBsktbl; CaptTrk; IMSpt; College; Business.

O NEIL, Karen M; St Francis HS; Glen Ellyn, IL; Chrs; HonRl; HospAde; JrNHS; SchMus; SchPl; RptrYrbk; RptrSchPpr; Bsktbl; LetterTennis; Marquette Univ; Medical Tech.

O NEIL, Keith C; S Newton HS; Goodland, IN; 5/110 Band; CncrtBnd; MrchBnd; PepBnd; StuCncl; RptrYrbk; EdSchPpr; VPFTA; VPLatCl; Bsktbl; LetterFtbl; Col; Science.

O NEIL, Tony J; St Marys HS; St Louis, MO; HonRl; HospAde; LitMag; RedCrAde; SciCl; LetterBsktbl; LetterFtbl; CchngActv; CitAwd; VoiceDemAwd; St Louis Univ; Medical Field.

O NEILL, Cindy L; Heelan HS; Sioux City, IA; ChrhWkr; DrlTm; HonRl; OffAde; RedCrAde; StuCncl; PpCl; Bsktbl; Chrldr; PPFtbl; College; Nursing.

O NEILL, Daryl T; Jefferson County North HS; Winchester, KS; 5/50 Chrl; CmntyWkr; ModUN; NHS; StuCncl; StuGov; YthFlsp; FBLA; LetterFtbl; Trk; Univ; Radio/tv.

O NEILL, Elaine D; Tescott HS; Barnard, KS; HonRl; OffAde; SchAde; SchPl; TchrAde; SecPpCl; BttyCrckrAwd; MasAwd; Wichita State; Registered Nurse.

O NEILL, Frank P; Carlyle HS; Carlyle, IL; 6/143 PresBand; CncrtBnd; HonRl; Mdrgl; NHS; PepBnd; SchMus; SchPl; SpnCl; BauchLmbAwd; Univ Of Illinois; Professional.

O NEILL, Gene M; Oaklawn Comm HS; Oak Lawn, IL; CmntyWkr; HonRl; SchPpr; LetterBsktbl; Tennis; SecTrsSrCls; Coll; Prof.

O NEILL, James J; Creighton Prep HS; Omaha, NE; Band; CncrtBnd; HonRl; MrchBnd; Orch; PepBnd; SchMus; College; Engineering.

O NEILL, James T; Evergreen Park Comm HS; Evergreen Park, IL; HonRl; NHS; NatlMeritCmnd; PolWkr; GerCl; MthCl; University; Political Science.

O NEILL, Paul; Sumner Dist HS; Sumner, NE; 3/19 TrsFrshCls; PresJrCls; PresSrCls; CncrtBnd; HonRl; Bsktbl; Trk; AmLegAwd; Kerney St Coll; Business.

O NEILL, Randall L; Tri Center Comm HS; Logan, IA; ChrhWkr; CmntyWkr; HonRl; FFA; Bsbl; Bsktbl; College.

O NEILL, Richard; Nathan Hale HS; West Allis, WI; Band; CncrtBnd; HonRl; MrchBnd; NatlMeritCmnd; PepBnd; Trk; Lawrence Univ; Music Education.

O NEILL, Timothy P; Mayo HS; Rochester, MN; ChrhWkr; NHS; UNYO; SpnCl; SciCl; LetterTrk; IMSpt; Us Military Acad; Military.

O REILLY, Colleen M; Irving Crown HS; Lake In The Hills, IL; 5/370 HonRl; NHS; Univ; Professional.

O REILLY, Daniel S; Orchard Farm HS; West Alton, MO; 6/121 PresJrCls; PresSrCls; HonRl; NHS; SchPl; StuCncl; Teen; Bsbl; Col.

O REILLY, Karen M; Mc Auley Reg HS; Joplin, MO; PresSophCls; HospAde; ModUN; NHS; RptrYrbk; RptrSchPpr; MthCl; Chrldr; AmLegAwd; Missouri So State Univ; Nursing.

O REILLY, Maureen G; Marshfield Senior HS; Marshfield, WI; S28#41#6 PresFrshCls; StuCncl; PresFBLA; FrCl; PpCl; IMSpt; N Central Tech Inst; Computer Programming.

O REILLY, Maureen M; Arlington HS; Arlington Hts, IL; 59/581 HonRl; JA; RptrYrbk; RptrSchPpr; 4-H; LatCl; PpCl; LetterBsbl; 4-HAwd; Northwestern Univ; Engineering.

O REILLY, Michael G; Immaculate Conception HS; Elmhurst, IL; 12/166 Aud/Vis; HonRl; PresNHS; StuGov; RptrYrbk; RptrSchPpr; SpnCl; IMSpt; University; Professional.

O REILLY, Patrice M; Mother Of Sorrows HS; Blue Island, IL; Chrl; JA; SchPl; SctActv; StuCncl; PpCl; SciCl; GAA; U Of Il; Health Prof.

O ROURKE, Dennis M; Marist HS; Worth, IL; SecSrCls; HonRl; JrNHS; NHS; NatlMeritSF; StuCncl; LatCl; MthCl; IMSpt; University; Management Engineering.

O ROURKE, Mark S; Waubun HS; Waubun, MN; 2/60 Band; CncrtBnd; HonRl; MrchBnd; NHS; PepBnd; Bemidji State College; Computer Programing.

O ROURKE, Mary J; St Augustine HS; Chicago, IL; SecSophCls; DrlTm; HonRl; JA; SchPl; Teen; RptrYrbk; RptrSchPpr; CitAwd; Univ Of Ill.

O ROURKE, Thomas R; Marian Catholic HS; Dolton, IL; PresChr; CmntyWkr; HonRl; Mdrgl; SchMus; SchPl; South Ill Univ; Theatre.

O RYAN, Irene R; St Paul Kennedy HS; Chicago, IL; ChrhWkr; HonRl; OffAde; Sacrstn; StuCncl; Yrbk; Swmmng; GAA; IMSpt; College; Special Education.

O SHANNA, Richard J; Maine Township East HS; Niles, IL; HonRl; LetterSocr; Illinois State Univ; Accounting.

O SHANNA, Richard J; Maine Twp East HS; Niles, IL; HonRl; LetterSocr; Coll; Acct.

O SHEA, Kathleen A; Elizabeth Seton HS; Chicago, IL; 32/252 IntrClCncl; RptrYrbk; PresLatCl; MthCl; SciCl; Loyola Univ; Medicine.

O SHEA, Maurita; St Francis HS; Winfield, IL; 1/119 Chrs; HonRl; NHS; SchMus; Univ Of Illinois; Accountant.

O SHEA, Sally A; White Shield HS; Emmet, ND; SecTrsSophCls; Band; Chr; Chrs; CncrtBnd; HonRl; Trade School.

O SULLIVAN, Linda S; Parkway West Senior HS; Manchester, MO; 128/742 ALAGirlsSt; ModUN; NatlFornLg; NHS; PolWkr; SchAde; TchrAde; University Of Missouri; Law.

O TOOLE, Ann M; Naperville Central HS; Naperville, IL; 39/820 Band; Chr; HonRl; Mdrgl; NHS; College; Medical Technology.

O TOOLE, Jaime D; Valley HS; Crystal, ND; 1/24 PresFrshCls; VPJrCls; Chrs; CncrtBnd; HonRl; PepBnd; SctActv; 4-H; Bsktbl; Ftbl; Nd U ;farmer.

O TOOLE, Julie A; Wahlert HS; East Dubuque, IL; Band; Chr; CncrtBnd; HonRl; MrchBnd; SchMus; RptrSchPpr; FshEdSchPpr; University; Art.

O TOOLE, Kathleen J; Gage Park HS; Chicago, IL; 26/463 HonRl; StuCncl; TchrAde; PpCl; Tennis; Chrldr; College; Criminology.

O TOOLE, Marilyn R; Girard HS; Girard, KS; 7/98 ChrhWkr; HonRl; JrNHS; MrchBnd; NHS; PepBnd; SchPl; Twrl; 4-H; PpCl; Trk; College.

O TOOLE, Timothy E; Merrill HS; Merrill, MI; 7/100 VPSophCls; HonRl; NHS; NatlMeritCmnd; TchrAde; LetterBsktbl; LetterFtbl; LetterTrk; U Of Michigan; Mechanical Engineering.

OAKES, David C; Beloit Memorial HS; Beloit, WI; 48/500 PresSrCls; TrsSrCls; HonRl; NHS; NatlMeritFnl; NatlMeritSchl; Quill&Scroll; StuCncl; Bsktbl; LetterFtbl; LetterSwmmng; Trk; IMSpt; College; Mathematics.

OAKES, David M; Cloquet HS; Cloquet, MN; HonRl; NHS; SchMus; SctActv; TreasStuCncl; LetterBsbl; LetterFtbl; LetterTennis; CchngActv; NCTE; College; Chemist.

OAKES, David W; Cairo HS; Cairo, IL; HonRl; Ftbl; IMSpt; College.

OAKES, Lori L; Robbinsdale Senior HS; Golden Valley, MN; Band; CncrtBnd; HonRl; LbryAde; MrchBnd; PepBnd; SchPpr; FrCl; Swmmng; Trade School; Fashion Merchandising.

OAKES, Sarah D; Hillsboro HS; Hillsboro, MO; TrsSrCls; HonRl; NHS; StuCncl; SptEdYrbk; SchPpr; PpCl; Bsktbl; College; Journalism.

OAKES, Thomas J; Tri County HS; Pierson, MI; 9/94 HonRl; NHS; SctActv; Glf; Tennis; Trk; Univ Of Michigan; Aerospace Engineering.

OAKESON, Mark W; Jenison HS; Jenison, MI; TrsSrCls; ALBoysSt; HonRl; StuCncl; StuGov; LetterBsktbl; CaptFtbl; CaptTennis; IMSpt; EldAwd; Coll; Engi.

OAKLAND, Darlys R; Clarkfield HS; Clarkfield, MN; 2/46 Chr; CncrtBnd; HonRl; MrchBnd; PepBnd; RptrYrbk; RptrSchPpr; FTA; Chrldr; GAA; Univ; Business Education.

OAKLAND, Deborah E; Rock Lake HS; Rock Lake, ND; 1/26 SecTrsJrCls; Band; Chrs; HonRl; SptEdSchPpr; SecFHA; CaptBsktbl; Chrldr; BttyCrckrAwd; EldAwd; No Dakota State University; Pharmacy.

OAKLAND, Jaci A; Bisbee HS; Bisbee, ND; 2/7 PresSrCls; Chrs; HonRl; SchPl; EdSchPpr; FHA; LetterSciCl; LetterTrk; Chrldr; BttyCrckrAwd; DanFAwd; Lake Region Jr College; Speech.

OAKLAND, Margo J; Storden Teffers Public HS; Jeffers, MN; 8/51 Band; Chr; ChrhWkr; CncrtBnd; HonRl; MrchBnd; PepBnd; StuGov; FHA; GerCl; Augustana College Sioux Falls Sd; Special E.

OAKLEY, Cheri L; Heyworth HS; Heyworth, IL; Band; Chrs; ChrhWkr; HonRl; NHS; SchMus; SchPl; SpnCl; SciCl; Trk; Mennonite School; Nursing.

OAKLEY, Daniel T; Cedarburg HS; Cedarburg, WI; PresJrCls; ALBoysSt; ChrhWkr; HonRl; SchMus; StuGov; LetterFtbl; Trk; LetterWrstlng; PPFtbl; Wakeforest U; Pre Law.

OAKLEY, David W; Newton HS; Newton, IL; Chr; Chrs; ChrhWkr; HonRl; Mdrgl; NHS; NatlMeritSF; SchMus; Eastern Illinois Univ; Physics.

OAKLEY, Karen; Lake City HS; Lake City, MI; 4/62 ChrhWkr; HonRl; NHS; OffAde; SchAde; SchPl; TchrAde; RptrYrbk; RptrSchPpr; Trk; Central Mi U; Teach Mentally Handicapped.

OAKLEY, Robert C; Waterford Mott HS; Pontiac, MI; SecSophCls; VPSrCls; SchPl; StuGov; Trk; Mich State; Theater.

OAKLEY, Sandy S; North Decatur HS; Greensburg, IN; 13/104 PresJrCls; Chr; DrlTm; HonRl; NHS; SchPl; StuCncl; RptrSchPpr; GAA; OptClAwd; Cincinnati U; Nurse.

OAKLEY, Thomas J; Rogers HS; Michigan City, IN; 80/546 Band; ChrhWkr; HonRl; JrNHS; MrchBnd; YthFlsp; MthCl; Trk; CchngActv; IMSpt; Lee College; Dentist.

OAKLUND, Susan; Elwood HS; Elwood, NE; /21 SecJrCls; ChrhWkr; CmntyWkr; NHS; SchPl; StuCncl; FHA; PpCl; Trk; Chrldr; Univ Of Ne; Paramedics.

OAKMAN, Julie; Liberty Hs; Liberty, IL; 1/62 Band; Chr; ChrhWkr; HonRl; NHS; StuCncl; EdYrBk; 4-H; SciCl; AmLegAwd; Northeast Missouri State U;elementary Educa.

OARD, Pamela S; Abilene HS; Abilene, KS; SecSophCls; TrsSrCls; Chrs; DrlTm; HonRl; Quill&Scroll; RptrYrbk; 4-H; 4-HAwd; KiwanAwd; Secretarial Work.

OASE, Harvey; Reeder Public HS; Reeder, ND; 3/16 TrsJrCls; ALBoysSt; HonRl; SctActv; StuCncl; Bsbl; Trk; IMSpt; Ndsu; Mechanical Eng.

OATES, Barbara J; Waldron HS; Waldron, MI; 4/44 VPJrCls; Chrs; HonRl; StuCncl; Yrbk; RptrSchPpr; FHA; Trk; Chrldr;.

OATES, Betty; Waldron HS; Waldron, MI; HstSrCls; ChrhWkr; HonRl; OffAde; SchAde; TchrAde; Trk; Secretary.

OBBINK, Brian D; Unity Christian HS; Hawarden, IA; VPFrshCls; HonRl; PresStuCncl; MthCl; Bsktbl; Trk; IMSpt; Carpentry.

OBEJAS, Mario J; Michigan City Rogers HS; Michigan City, IN; PresJrCls; HonRl; NHS; SchPl; StuGov; SchPpr; MthCl; Swmmng; RotaryAwd; College; Electronics Engineer.

OBERBROECKLING, Mark D; Garnavillo HS; Garnavillo, IA; 12/50 TrsSophCls; ALBoysSt; HonRl; StuCncl; Pres4-H; PresFFA; Bsktbl; 4-HAwd; Calmar Area I; Ag.

OBERDIEAR, Kenneth C; Nashua HS; Nashua, IA; 11/70 HonRl; SctActv; FrCl; SciCl; Ftbl; Trk; College; Vocation.

OBERDIEK, Gary D; West Platte HS; Platte City, MO; AFS; Band; CncrtBnd; HonRl; MrchBnd; NHS; SciCl; Bsktbl; Ftbl; Trk; Univ.

OBERG, Debra J; Rock Falls Twp HS; Rock Falls, IL; AFS; HonRl; MrchBnd; SecNHS; SchPl; StuCncl; RptrYrbk; RptrSchPpr; AmLegAwd; No Illinois Univ; French.

OBERG, Debra M; Central Valley HS; Reynolds, ND; Chrs; ChrhWkr; CncrtBnd; HonRl; LbryAde; NatlMeritCmnd; PepBnd; SchPl; LetterBsktbl; Trk; Univ Of No Dakota.

OBERGFELL, James A; Bishop Dwenger HS; Ft Wayne, IN; 11/234 ChrhWkr; HonRl; StuCncl; PresKeyCl; LetterBsbl; LetterFtbl; LetterTrk; IMSpt; ChmbCommrsAwd; JETSAwd; RotaryAwd; Rose Hulman Inst; Engineering.

OBERHAUSER, Amy K; Clintonville HS; Clintonville, WI; Band; HonRl; MrchBnd; NHS; StuCncl; LetterTrk; GAA; IMSpt; Carleton Coll.

OBERHAUSER, Michael E; 200 Adams HS; Laporte City, IA; Band; Chr; Chrs; CncrtBnd; HonRl; MrchBnd; PepBnd; StuCncl; FFA; Clge; Priesthood.

OBERHEIDE, Heide L; Harrison HS; Evansville, IN; 48/430 ChrhWkr; HonRl; NHS; SchMus; StuGov; YthFlsp; College; Art.

OBERLANDER, Cora A; Lemmon HS; Lemmon, SD; 6/69 SecSrCls; HonRl; LbryAde; NHS; SchMus; SchPl; Bsbl; LetterBsktbl; LetterTrk; IMSpt; Music.

OBERLANDER, Mary; Watertown Senior HS; Watertown, SD; ALAGirlsSt; Chr; Chrs; HonRl; NatlFornLg; NHS; Orch; SchMus; SctActv; South Dakota St U; Nutritionist.

OBERLE, John C; Thorp HS; Stanley, WI; 16/75 PresFrshCls; ALBoysSt; HonRl; SchMus; StuCncl; FBLA; SpnCl; Univ Of Wi Eau Claire; Professional.

OBERLIES, James J; Carthage Community HS; Carthage, IL; 2/102 TrsJrCls; PresSrCls; ALBoysSt; Chr; CncrtBnd; HonRl; NHS; NatlMeritCmnd; SctActv; Univ Of Illinois; Medicine.

OBERLIN, Tina M; Lockport Central HS; Crest Hill, IL; Chrs; HonRl; JA; LbryAde; NatlThespSoc; RptrSchPpr; SchPpr; Bsktbl; LetterTrk; CchngActv; College; Radio Broadcaster.

OBERMAN, Mike C; Mediapolis Comm HS; Yarmouth, IA; 5/74 HonRl; 4-H; FFA; Bsbl; Bsktbl; Ftbl; Trk; Central College; Coaching.

OBERMEIER, Sondra L; Aurora Sr HS; Aurora, NE; 15/125 Band; DrmMjrt; HonRl; NHS; PepBnd; 4-H; FBLA; FHA; PpCl; Trk; Ucla Univ; Physical Therapist.

OBERMILLER, Karen; J C Senior HS; Jefferson City, MO; 2/501 Chr; HonRl; JrNHS; NHS; SchMus; StuCncl; YthFlsp; PresSpnCl; MthCl; PpCl; GAA; AmLegAwd; College.

OBERMOLLER, Gary H; Brewster HS; Brewster, MN; SchPl; 4-H; FFA; Bsbl; Trk;.

OBERNBERGER, Melody J; Lincoln HS; Park Falls, WI; Band; ChrhWkr; CncrtBnd; DrmBgl; MrchBnd; SchPl; SctActv; StuCncl; Trade School; Interior Design.

OBERNDORFER, Charlene; Potter HS; Potter, NE; 1/20 TrsJrCls; Band; Chrs; HonRl; NHS; SchPl; YthFlsp; Yrbk; Chrldr; AmLegAwd;.

OBERST, Lawrence J; Parkside HS; Jackson, MI; 9/440 Band; ChrhWkr; CncrtBnd; HonRl; MrchBnd; PepBnd; SctActv; SchPpr; Mich State Univ; Accounting.

OBERT, John E; Shanley HS; Fargo, ND; 24/120 HonRl; SchMus; SctActv; Yrbk; KeyCl; Trk; IMSpt; Moorhead State College; Graphic Artist.

OBERT, Melody J; Lockwood R 1 HS; Lockwood, MO; 5/44 ALAGirlsSt; HonRl; ModUN; SchPl; StuCncl; Yrbk; EdSchPpr; FHA; FTA; PPFtbl; Mo Southern St; Psychology.

OBEY, Jay P; Wausau West HS; Wausau, WI; Trk; IMSpt; U Of Wi; Medical Field.

OBIDZINSKI, Vivian M; St Clare Acad; Detroit, MI; 2/11 PresFrshCls; Chrs; ChrhWkr; HonRl; SchPl; VPStuCncl; Yrbk; EdSchPpr; FrCl; DanFAwd; Univ Of Detroit; Social Work.

OBLENESS, Michael; Keokuk Senior HS; Keokwk, IA; 8/214 ALBoysSt; HonRl; JrNHS; NHS; Bsbl; Bsktbl; Ftbl; Trk; IMSpt; PresAwd; College; Math And Science.

OBORIS, Debra J; Wis Dells HS; Lake Delton, WI; 13/150 Band; CncrtBnd; HonRl; MrchBnd; PepBnd; RptrSchPpr; SpnCl; LetterBsktbl; Tennis; LetterTrk; Uw Madison; Biology Major.

OBREMSKI, Cynthia M; Pulaski HS; Milwaukee, WI; 5/750 ALAGirlsSt; Chr; HonRl; HospAde; JrNHS; NatlMeritSF; OffAde; PresRedCrAde; Marquette Univ; Physician.

OBRIEN, Julie; Bethlehem Acad; Faribault, MN; ALAGirlsSt; Chrs; HonRl; NHS; StuCncl; RptrSchPpr; LetterBsktbl; Glf; Trk; GAA;.

OBRIEN, Margaret; Quincy Notre Dame HS; Quincy, IL; 35/82 DrlTm; StuCncl; RptrYrbk; College; Reg Physical Therapist.

OBRITSCH, Jerry M; South Heart HS; Dickinson, ND; ALBoysSt; HonRl; ModUN; StuCncl; College; Animal Science.

OBUKOWICZ, Timothy P; Greenfield HS; Greenfield, WI; 4/400 HonRl; NHS; ChmnSwmmng; University; Professional.

OCHA, Rhonda A; Osborn HS; Detroit, MI; HonRl; NHS; PolWkr; FrCl;.

OCHAB, Dawn G; Resurrection HS; Norridge, IL; 22/216 CmntyWkr; HonRl; NHS; NatlMeritSF; FrCl; Univ Of Illinois; Business.

OCHOA, Marizza; Raymond & Tirza Martin HS; Litchfield, MN; Band; HonRl; JrNHS; SpnCl; Univ Of Minnesota.

OCHOA, Noe; Bonner Springs HS; Edwardsville, KS; 18/178 CmntyWkr; HonRl; TchrAde; PpCl; Bsbl; College; Art.

OCHOA, Pearl A; Holy Family Academy; Chicago, IL; VPSophCls; SecJrCls; Chrs; CmntyWkr; HonRl; HospAde; NatlMeritSchl; NatlSciFnd; RedCrAde; StuGov; College; Biology.

OCHOA, Peggy S; Bayard HS; Bayard, NE; SecSophCls; SecJrCls; Band; Chrs; ChrhWkr; HonRl; NHS; OffAde; FHA; College; Science.

OCHOCINSKI, Kathy L; St Paul HS; Chicago, IL; HonRl; NHS; Yrbk; GAA; Loyola Univ; Nurse.

OCHOCKI, Carol L; William Howard Taft HS; Chicago, IL; Chrs; HonRl; NHS; StuCncl; Yrbk; SciCl; Trk; GAA; IMSpt; BauchLmbAwd; Northeastern; Veternariam.

OCHOCKI, Kevin J; Canby HS; Canby, MN; Chr; ChrhWkr; HonRl; FFA; Ftbl; Trade Schl; Police Officer.

OCHS, Carol R; Newton HS; West Liberty, IL; Chrs; 4-H; FNA; LatCl; DanFAwd; 4-HAwd; Nurses Training.

OCHS, Cynthia S; Newton HS; Newton, IL; 1/187 Chr; Chrs; NHS; FNA; MthCl;.

OCHS, Jeff; Jennings County Hs; North Vernon, IN; ChrhWkr; SctActv; TchrAde; SpnCl; LetterBsbl; LetterBsktbl; LetterFtbl; College ; Lawyer.

OCKERT, Wanda; South Western HS; Flint, MI; 150/600 Band; Chrs; CmntyWkr; HonRl; HospAde; JA; NHS; RedCrAde; SctActv; YthFlsp; Mott Community Coll; Lpn.

OCKNER, Lee; Ofallon Township Hs; Ofallon, IL; 18 HonRl; JrNHS; ModUN; SctActv; SpnCl; CaptTrk; College;physician.

OCKNER, Samuel; Ofallon Township Hs; Ofallon, IL; 8/311 HonRl; JrNHS; SctActv; SpnCl; SciCl; Bsbl; Bsktbl; Trk; College; Professional.

OCONNELL, Larry; Brother Rice Hs; Chicago, IL; 17/416 CmntyWkr; HonRl; NHS; FrCl; MthCl; SciCl; CaptSwmmng; CchngActv; Loyola U; Psychiatry.

OCONNOR, Jeri; Wentzville Senior HS; Lake St Louis, MO; HonRl; SchAde; TchrAde; PpCl; Chrldr; CitAwd; Lindenwood.

OCONNOR, Joan; Oaklawn Community Hs; Oak Lawn, IL; 9/686 HonRl; JrNHS; NHS; TchrAde; 4-H; MthCl; GAA; 4-HAwd; College; Accounting.

OCONNOR, Mary C; Assumption HS; Wisconsin Rapids, WI; Chr; Chrs; HonRl; SchMus; SctActv; RptrSchPpr; FTA; PpCl; GAA; Col ; Bio.

ODASH, Susan L; Rice Lake HS; Rice Lake, WI; Aud/Vis; FBLA; GAA; Trade School; Vocation.

ODAU, Julie A; Kohler Public HS; Kohler, WI; SecSrCls; Band; Chrs; HonRl; HospAde; NHS; StuCncl; TchrAde; Yrbk; Chrldr; Valparaiso Univ; Rn.

ODDAN, Mary L; Milan HS; Milan, MN; HonRl; 4-H; FHA; BttyCrckrAwd; 4-HAwd; Univ Mn Morris.

ODDEN, Mark G; Lake Preston HS; Lake Preston, SD; SecJrCls; TrsJrCls; Band; Chr; Chrs; ChrhWkr; CncrtBnd; LbryAde; Mdrgl; MrchBnd; Bsbl; LetterFtbl; Trk; LetterWrstlng; South Dakota St Univ; Zoology.

ODDEN, Ronald L; Staples HS; Staples, MN; 20/150 HonRl; YthFlsp; Ftbl; LetterTrk; IMSpt; College; Professional.

ODEEN, Linda R; Lincoln Comm HS; Stanwood, IA; 9/64 DrmMjrt; HonRl; MrchBnd; NHS; StuCncl; Twrl; YthFlsp; FFA; PpCl; Bsktbl; LetterTrk; PPFtbl; CitAwd; Iowa St Univ; Agriculture.

ODEGARD, Joan; Regis HS; Eau Claire, WI; 25/138 CncrtBnd; HonRl; HospAde; MrchBnd; Orch; PepBnd; SchMus; RptrSchPpr; SpnCl; GAA; Univ; Social Work.

ODEGARD, Lynn M; Waukon Sr HS; Waukon, IA; 3/155 Chr; Chrs; ChrhWkr; NHS; NatlThespSoc; Quill&Scroll; SchMus; SchPl; StuCncl; EdSchPpr; GAA; IMSpt; Luther College; Journalism.

ODEGARD, Rayeann; Rhinelander HS; Rhinelander, WI; 7/400 HonRl; NHS; PresSpnCl; PpCl; CaptChrldr; College.

ODELL, Catherine; Community Dist HS; Fults, IL; 7/144 ChrhWkr; HonRl; NHS; NatlThespSoc; OffAde; SchAde; SchMus; SchPl; StuCncl; GAA; College; Speech And Drama Insti.

ODEN, Cheryl J; Centerville HS; Exline, IA; CmntyWkr; HonRl; YthLg; 4-H; PpCl; Bsktbl; LetterTrk; CitAwd; College.

ODEN, Vickie J; Centerville HS; Exline, IA; ChrhWkr; CmntyWkr; HonRl; NHS; OffAde; 4-H; Bsktbl; Trk; 4-HAwd; Northeast Mo State Univ; Nursing.

ODGERS, Charles M; Sublette HS; Sublette, KS; Chr; Chrs; HonRl; Yrbk; 4-H; Bsktbl; CchngActv; DanFAwd; 4-HAwd; Farmer.

ODLAND, Kathryn M; Scott Community HS; Scott City, KS; 16/111 Band; Chr; Chrl; Chrs; ChrhWkr; CmntyWkr; HonRl; LbryAde; MrchBnd; PepBnd; PolWkr; SchMus; TchrAde; LetterTennis; Chrldr; College; Special Ed.

ODLE, Deborah S; Seeger Memorial HS; Williamsport, IN; 4/116 ChrhWkr; HonRl; NHS; 4-H; FHA; Tennessee Temple College; Accountant.

ODLE, Julaine K; Chase County HS; Cedar Point, KS; HonRl; SchPl; Teen; SpnCl; PpCl; Wichita State Univ; Foregn Languages.

ODLE, Marilyn J; Holden HS; Holden, MO; Aud/Vis; ChrhWkr; HonRl; NHS; SchAde; SchPl; FHA; DARAwd; VoiceDemAwd; College; Home Ec.

ODOM, Frances C; Caruthersville HS; Caruthersville, MO; HonRl; NHS; NatlThespSoc; SchPl; FTA; FrCl; College; Teach Deaf & Blind.

ODOM, Gregory W; Crab Orchard HS; Stonefort, IL; HonRl; HospAde; RptrSchPpr; PpCl; Bsbl; Bsktbl; Trk; College; Professional.

ODVODY, Sherry; Seward Sr HS; Seward, NE; Band; CncrtBnd; HonRl; MrchBnd; PepBnd; 4-H; FBLA; FHA; PpCl; 4-HAwd; Neb Tech Coll; Dentist.

OECHSLE, Debra; Fennimore HS; Stitzer, WI; Band; ChrhWkr; CncrtBnd; HonRl; HospAde; MrchBnd; NHS; PepBnd; College; Nursing.

OEHL, Christina M; St Agatha HS; Detroit, MI; HonRl; SpnCl; PpCl; College.

OEHLER, Anne J; Okemos HS; Okemos, MI; 1/285 HospAde; JrNHS; NHS; LatCl; Swmmng; Univ Of Michigan; Nursing.

OEHLER, Daniel A; John Marshall HS; Milwaukee, WI; 12/750 CncrtBnd; HonRl; MrchBnd; NHS; NatlMeritFnl; ROTC; SctActv; VPMthCl; LetterSocr; LetterTennis; Univf Electrical Engineering.

OEHLERKING, Diana K; Waverly HS; Alvo, NE; 22/104 PresSrCls; ALAGirlsSt; ChrhWkr; HonRl; MrchBnd; NHS; TchrAde; YthFlsp; PpCl; DanFAwd; Secretary.

OEHRING, Judith K; Appleton City HS; Rockville, MO; 11/44 SecSrCls; Band; CncrtBnd; HospAde; MrchBnd; PepBnd; 4-H; LetterBsktbl; 4-HAwd; OptClAwd; Lpn Sch; Nursing.

OELERICH, David J; Cedarburg HS; Cedarburg, WI; Chr; Chrs; HonRl; SchMus; YthFlsp; LetterTrk; Wrstlng; IMSpt; Univ Wi.

OELFKE, Jill M; Southwest HS; Minneapolis, MN; 35/397 Band; ChrhWkr; CncrtBnd; MrchBnd; PepBnd; Teen; College; Nursing.

OELKE, Ronald P; East Chain Cons HS; Blue Earth, MN; 4/29 PresJrCls; TrsSrCls; ALBoysSt; ChrhWkr; VPNHS; StuCncl; SptEdYrbk; LetterBsktbl; LetterFtbl; LetterTrk; Us Coast Guard Academy; Elec Engineer.

OELKERS, Shelley; Lacrosse HS; Mccracken, KS; 2/35 VPFrshCls; VPJrCls; Band; Chr; HonRl; LbryAde; ModUN; Orch; PepBnd; Trk; Kansas State Univ; Vet Science.

OELKERS, Shelley J; La Crosse HS; Mccracken, KS; 2/35 VPFrshCls; VPJrCls; Band; Chr; CncrtBnd; HonRl; LbryAde; Mdrgl; MrchBnd; ModUN; Orch; PepBnd; SchMus; YthFlsp; Kansas State Univ; Accounting.

OELRICHS, Brenda; Smithton R Vi HS; Mora, MO; 11/40 VPSrCls; Band; CncrtBnd; HonRl; MrchBnd; NHS; SchPl; StuCncl; 4-H; FBLA; St Fair Comm College; Business Teacher.

OELSCHLAEGER, Gary; Tonganorie; Tonganoxie, KS; 3/120 HonRl; JrNHS; 4-H; FrCl; SpnCl; KiwanAwd; Univ; Ag Econ.

OELSCHLAEGER, John M; Minneapolis Lutheran HS; Edina, MN; 1/38 ALBoysSt; ChrhWkr; HonRl; NHS; PresStuCncl; Bsbl; Ftbl;.

OELTJEN, Ora Mae L; Freeburg Comm HS; Freeburg, IL; 7/135 Band; HonRl; NHS; SecStuCncl; TchrAde; Twrl; EdYrBk; FNA; PpCl; CaptChrldr; Belleville Area College; Nursing.

OEMIG, Sheila; Cornell HS; Cornell, WI; TrsJrCls; HonRl; StuCncl; FHA; Trade School; Vocation.

OEMING, Elizabeth J; Arthur Hill HS; Saginaw, MI; Band; HospAde; NHS; EdSchPpr; PpCl; Univ Of Mi; Pre Architecture.

OESCH, Debra S; Northridge HS; Middlebury, IN; ChrhWkr; HonRl; SchMus; SchPl; TchrAde; YthFlsp; 4-H; SpnCl; Chrldr; 4-HAwd; Voluntary Service.

OESCH, Jennifer L; Hazelwood Central HS; Florissant, MO; 30#33#41 PpCl; Chrldr; GAA; IMSpt; CitAwd; College; Dental Hygenist.

OESTERLING, Mary; Jac Cen Del HS; Osgood, IN; SchPpr; FHA; GAA; Art School; Artist.

OESTERREICHER, Jeff E; Chesaning Union HS; Chesaning, MI; Band; CncrtBnd; HonRl; MrchBnd; FFA; Michigan State Univ; Elevator & Farm Supply.

OESTMANN, Sally; Auburn HS; Auburn, NE; Band; Chr; Chrl; CtyCnl; CncrtBnd; HonRl; MrchBnd; OffAde; YthFlsp; SpnCl; Norhtwest Mo St Univ; Elem Ed.

OESTREICH, Debra L; Neillsville HS; Neillsville, WI; SecJrCls; HonRl; NHS; SchPl; YthFlsp; PpCl; LetterBsktbl; LetterTrk; Chrldr; Vocational School; Vocation.

OESTREICH, Gretchen L; Hudson Sr HS; Hudson, WI; AFS; Band; CncrtBnd; HonRl; MrchBnd; PepBnd; SctActv; GerCl; LetterSwmmng; Univ Of Minn; Forestry.

OESTREICH, Heiden E; Galena HS; Galena, IL; 19/107 AFS; HonRl; HospAde; SchPl; Yrbk; SchPpr; 4-H; FHA; PpCl; LetterTrk; School Nursing; Rn.

OETH, David R; Dowling HS; Des Moines, IA; 60/370 NatlFornLg; NatlMeritCmnd; StuCncl; YthLg; Tennis; IMSpt; AmLegAwd; KiwanAwd; Univ; Law.

OETH, Ronald; Fairfield HS; Fairfield, IL; Chrs; CmntyWkr; HonRl; 4-H; FFA; LatCl; SciCl; LetterFtbl; 4-HAwd; College; Chiropractor.

OETKEN, Beverly; Emerson Hubbard HS; Emerson, NE; 8/55 TrsSrCls; HonRl; NHS; PpCl; Business School; Secretarial.

OETKING, Maude M; Hinsdale Township HS; Hinsdale, IL; 1/608 PresSophCls; HonRl; HospAde; TreasNHS; NatlMeritCmnd; RptrSchPpr; Dartmouth Clge; Journalism.

OETTEL, Pamela A; Dwight D Eisenhower HS; Utica, MI; 2/550 ChrhWkr; HonRl; NHS; NatlMeritCmnd; Quill&Scroll; EdSchPpr; GerCl; LetterSwmmng; Adrian Coll.

OETTING, Rose M; Concordia HS; Concordia, MO; 3/50 HonRl; NHS; SchMus; SchPl; StuCncl; PresPpCl; Chrldr; PPFtbl; PresAwd; College.

OFFENHEISER, Leslie A; Elizabeth HS; Elizabeth, IL; Band; Chrs; HonRl; SchMus; StuCncl; YthFlsp; 4-H; LetterBsktbl; LetterTrk; PresGAA; Wartburg College; Physical Education.

OFFERMANN, Susan L; Southwest HS; Green Bay, WI; 104/420 TrsSrCls; HonRl; PpCl; CaptTennis; LetterTrk; IMSpt; College; Xray Technician.

OFFICER, Jerry W; Archie HS; Harrisonville, MO; 28/42 CncrtBnd; MrchBnd; SchMus; SchPl; YthFlsp; RptrYrbk; Bsbl; Bsktbl; Ftbl; Trk; Warrensburg Univ; Ag.

OFFNER, Joan; Incarnate Word Acad; St Louis, MO; Chrl; HonRl; NHS; SchMus; IMSpt; PPFtbl; Univ; Law.

OFFUTT, Peter W; Geneva Comm HS; Geneva, IL; College; Science.

OGAR, Barbara A; Henry Ford Ii HS; Sterling Hts, MI; 15/297 VPSrCls; CncrtBnd; NHS; VPStuCncl; GAA; DanFAwd; DARAwd; Wayne State Univ; Music.

OGAR, Vincent W; Mexico HS; Mecico, MO; Chr; Chrs; ChrhWkr; CmntyWkr; SchMus; SchPl; SctActv; LatCl; LetterFtbl; Trk; College.

OGAWA, Linda M; Lane Technical HS; Chicago, IL; CncrtBnd; DrmBgl; MrchBnd; NHS; OffAde; ROTC; Univ; Education.

OGBORN, Carolyn J; Omaha Central HS; Omaha, NE; 10/572 ALAGirlsSt; Chr; ChrhWkr; HonRl; LitMag; Mdrgl; NatlMeritSF; SchMus; YthFlsp; FrCl; Ne Wesleyan U; Physician.

OGBURN, Landis W; Colfax HS; Colfax, IA; 4/58 ALBoysSt; HonRl; StuCncl; FTA; SpnCl; LetterFtbl;.

OGDEN, Christopher W; Herrin HS; Herrin, IL; 6/211 HonRl; NatlMeritCmnd; SctActv; TchrAde; S I U; Engineering.

OGDEN, Dean; Parkwood HS; Joplin, MO; Bsktbl; Ftbl; Trk; Coll; Pro.

OGDEN, Kevin C; Monroe Sr HS; Monroe, WI; CAP; HonRl; NatlMeritSF; SctActv; FrCl; SciCl; Ftbl; Wrstlng; Univ; Engineering.

OGINSKI, Cheryl L; Pine River Area HS; Leroy, MI; HonRl; RptrYrbk; 4-H; SpnCl; 4-HAwd; College; Lawyer.

OGLAND, Carolyn J; Hudson HS; Hudson, WI; SecSophCls; AFS; Chr; Chrs; ChrhWkr; HonRl; SchMus; SchPl; SchPpr; College; Medicine.

OGLE, Amy E; Litchfield HS; Litchfield, IL; 23/149 SecSophCls; Chr; Chrs; HonRl; RedCrAde; SchMus; SchPl; SpnCl; College; Professional.

OGLE, Edward; Marquette Senior HS; Marquette, MI; 58/388 Chrl; Chrs; NatlMeritCmnd; Bsbl; Ftbl; College; Professional.

OGLE, James A; Centralia HS; Centralia, MO; HstSophCls; CncrtBnd; DrmMjrt; HonRl; JA; NHS; StuCncl; FFA; SciCl; LetterBsktbl; Missouri University; Mathematics.

OGLE, Kathleen S; Lakeview HS; St Clair Shores, MI; 7/660 HonRl; JrNHS; LbryAde; NHS; NatlMeritCmd; SchPl; VPSpnCl; Michigan State; Social Work.

OGLE, Michael J; Kirksville Sr HS; Kirksville, MO; HonRl; StuCncl; College; Art.

OGLESBY, Anthony R; Charlestown HS; Charlestown, IN; 43/225 Band; ChrhWkr; CncrtBnd; HonRl; JA; MrchBnd; PepBnd; TchrAde; YthFlsp; Trk; Univ; Med Tech.

OGLESBY, Sandy L; Perry Lecompton HS; Lawrence, KS; SecTrsJrCls; DrlTm; HonRl; NHS; StuCncl; RptrSchPpr; SchPpr; PpCl; LetterBsktbl; LetterTrk; University; Teacher.

OGOR, Pamela M; Thornton Twp HS; Riverdale, IL; 5/727 HonRl; HospAde; LbryAde; NHS; OffAde; SancSoc; SchAde; StuGov; TchrAde; IMSpt; Southern Ill; Medicine.

OGREN, Edward; Langford Ind HS; Langford, SD; PresSrCls; ALBoysSt; Chrs; CncrtBnd; HonRl; MrchBnd; StuCncl; 4-H; Bsktbl; Ftbl; Col; Science Ed.

OHAGAN, Mary L; Marian HS; Mishawaka, IN; SecSophCls; SecJrCls; SecSrCls; HonRl; NHS; SchPl; StuCncl; RptrSchPpr; IMSpt; Notre Dame.

OHAVER, Mary M; Farmington East HS; Farmington, IL; 5/126 VPJrCls; Band; Chrs; CncrtBnd; HonRl; MrchBnd; NHS; PepBnd; RptrYrbk; EdYrBk; RptrSchPpr; FTA; FrCl; Central College; French.

OHI, Diane S; Rolling Meadows HS; Arlington Heights, IL; AFS; Chr; ChrhWkr; DrlTm; HonRl; SchMus; SchPl; YthFlsp; Univ Of Illinois; Medical Lab Research.

OHL, Lori L; Oelwein Community HS; Oelwein, IA; AFS; HospAde; JrNHS; SctActv; RptrYrbk; RptrSchPpr; College; Social Work.

OHL, Mary D; Assumption HS; Tower Hill, IL; Chrs; CmntyWkr; HonRl; SchAde; TchrAde; RptrYrbk; SchPpr; FHA; PpCl; GAA; College; Teacher.

OHLAND, Duane E; Northwestern Prep; Hartford, WI; Yrbk; LetterFtbl; Tennis; IMSpt; College; Teacher.

OHLAU, Daniel J; Chester HS; Chester, IL; HonRl; NHS; Bsktbl; Trk; AmLegAwd; EldAwd; U Of Il; Agriculture.

OHLGREN, Betty; Wahpeton HS; Wahpeton, ND; AFS; ALAGirlsSt; Chr; ChrhWkr; HonRl; NatlThespSoc; SchPl; StuCncl; TchrAde; KeyCl; Golden Valley Lutheran Col; Therapist.

OHLSON, Loretta C; St Francis HS; Joliet, IL; CmntyWkr; NatlThespSoc; SchMus; SchPl; StuCncl; LetterBsktbl; LetterTennis; CchngActv; GAA; IMSpt; College; Transportation.

OHLY, Stephen; Laurdes HS; Rochester, MN; ALBoysSt; HonRl; NHS; AmLegAwd; Coll; Vocation.

OHM, Carolyn H; Grant Park HS; Grant Park, IL; TrsSophCls; ChrhWkr; CmntyWkr; HonRl; NHS; 4-H; SpnCl; Bsbl; CaptBsktbl; Trk; GAA; 4-HAwd; JAAwd; College.

OHM, Karen S; Oconomowoc Sr HS; Oconomowoc, WI; 6/212 ALAGirlsSt; Band; Chr; ChrhWkr; CncrtBnd; HonRl; SecJrNHS; MrchBnd; NHS; PepBnd; SchMus; SchPl; DARAwd; College; Fine Arts.

OHMART, Jeffrey; Saunemin HS; Saunemin, IL; PresSophCls; PresJrCls; Band; Chrs; HonRl; StuCncl; RptrYrbk; Bsbl; Bsktbl; Univ; Professional.

OHNEMUS, Michael A; Indianola HS; Indianola, IA; Bsktbl; Ftbl; LetterTennis; IMSpt; Drake Univ; Pharmacy.

OHNSTAD, Lynae; Summit HS; Summit, SD; 2/23 PresSrCls; HonRl; CncrtBnd; HonRl; MrchBnd; StuCncl; StuGov; YthFlsp; FNA; GAA; VoiceDemAwd; Stewart School Of Hairstyling ;cosmotology.

OHRT, Debra K; Hudson HS; Hudson, WI; Chrs; ChrhWkr; HonRl; HospAde; RedCrAde; SchMus; SchPl; GerCl; IMSpt; Univf Prof.

OHRTMAN, Frank; Pomeroy Comm HS; Pomeroy, IA; TrsSophCls; Band; ChrhWkr; CmntyWkr; CncrtBnd; HonRl; PepBnd; RptrSchPpr; 4-H; Trk; Iowa State Univ; Lawyer.

OJANEN, Elizabeth M; Escanaba Area HS; Escanaba, MI; 18/382 Chr; Chrs; HospAde; JrNHS; NHS; StuGov; YthLg; RptrYrbk; 4-H; Trk; Bay De Nac Comm Clge; Speech Therapy.

OJSTERSEK, Joann; La Salle Peru HS; Oglesby, IL; 37/490 VPAFS; Band; HonRl; MrchBnd; Stanford Univ; Political Science.

OKADA, David J; Appleton HS W; Appleton, WI; 20/640 PresFrshCls; TrsSrCls; AFS; ALBoysSt; ChrhWkr; HospAde; SctActv; CaptSwmmng; Tennis; KiwanAwd; Un Of Wisc Madison; Pre Medicine.

OKERBLAD, Denise; Grand Community HS; Ogden, IA; 1/23 SecFrshCls; Band; Chrs; CncrtBnd; HonRl; MrchBnd; NHS; PepBnd; SchMus; Dmacc; Spec Ed.

OKERBLAD, Denise D; Grand Comm HS; Ogden, IA; 1/23 SecFrshCls; Band; Chrs; CncrtBnd; HonRl; MrchBnd; NHS; PepBnd; RptrYrbk; RptrSchPpr; 4-H; SciCl; LetterGlf; 4-HAwd; College; Special Ed.

OKHUYSEN, Nicholas H; Rockford HS; Rockford, MI; 25/289 Chr; HonRl; Mdrgl; NHS; PolWkr; SchMus; SchPl; SciCl; Central Mi Univ.

OKONEK, Anne E; Stevens Point Area Sr HS; Stevens Point, WI; ChrhWkr; NHS; SptEdSchPpr; SciCl; LetterBsktbl; LetterTennis; LetterTrk; GAA; IMSpt; PPFtbl; Univ Of Wis Stevens Point.

OKSENDAHL, Donna L; Hancock Public HS; Hancock, MN; Band; Chr; CncrtBnd; HospAde; PepBnd; TchrAde; SptEdSchPpr; 4-H; FHA; LetterBsktbl; Trk; 4-HAwd; Alexandria Tech; Secretary.

OKUNOWSKI, Mary; St Stanislaus Kostka HS; Chicago, IL; 12/64 TrsFrshCls; SecSrCls; HonRl; RedCrAde; Yrbk; FNA; FTA; VoiceDemAwd; Nursing School; Nurse.

OLAWSKY, Randy M; Corsica HS; Armour, SD; Band; Chr; HonRl; SchMus; StuCncl; YthFlsp; Yrbk; Bsktbl; Ftbl; Trk; School; Engineering.

OLBERDING, Holly D; Randolph Public HS; Randolph, NE; 17/69 Chrs; HonRl; NHS; NatlThespSoc; SchMus; StuCncl; EdSchPpr; Pres4-H; PresFHA; Chrldr; Wayne State Col; Music Major Pe Minor.

OLBERDING, Janet M; B & B HS; Seneca, KS; VPSrCls; Band; HonRl; 4-H; FHA; PpCl; LetterTrk; Chrldr; GAA; CAP; Coll; Art.

OLBERDING, Leanne M; Stuart HS; Stuart, NE; 1/18 Band; Chrs; ChrhWkr; CncrtBnd; HonRl; MrchBnd; StuCncl; SchPl; PpCl;.

OLBINA, Mark R; Pike HS; Indianapolis, IN; Band; HonRl; SchPl; SctActv; StuCncl; YthFlsp; LetterSwmmng; Tennis; IMSpt; College; Dentist.

OLD, Kathleen S; Bucklin HS; Bucklin, KS; Aud/Vis; HonRl; HospAde; LbryAde; StuCncl; TchrAde; RptrSchPpr; PpCl; Wichita St Univ.

OLDAKOWSKI, Malgorzata M; Riverside HS; Dearborn Heights, MI; Chrs; HonRl; NHS; FHA; FrCl; SciCl; GAA; U Of Mi; Biochemist.

OLDAKOWSKI, Mary; Healy HS; Royalton, MN; 1 Band; Chrs; ChrhWkr; CncrtBnd; HonRl; MrchBnd; NatlMeritCmnd; PepBnd; TchrAde; 4-H; College; Teacher Math.

OLDENKAMP, John A; Marshalltown HS; Marshalltown, IA; ALBoysSt; Chrs; CmntyWkr; JA; SchPl; EdSchPpr; College; Meteorology And Sci Ed.

OLDFATHER, Sheilah A; Gasconade R 2 HS; Owensville, MO; HonRl; NHS; OffAde; Quill&Scroll; TchrAde; RptrYrbk; FTA; SpnCl; PpCl; Chrldr; East Central Junior College; Secretarial Ad.

OLDHAM, Jannifer D; Lincoln Community HS; Lincoln, IL; 28/255 ChrhWkr; CtyCnl; CmntyWkr; HonRl; HospAde; NHS; PolWkr; RedCrAde; StuCncl; YthFlsp; 4-H; College; Christian Education.

OLDS, Deborah S; Sturgis HS; Sturgis, MI; HonRl; NatlMeritCmnd; NatlMeritSF; TchrAde; Glen Oaks Community Clg; Accounting.

OLEARY, Colleen M; Browns Valley HS; Beardsley, MN; ALAGirlsSt; Band; HonRl; NHS; RptrSchPpr; Chrldr; GAA; VoiceDemAwd; College; Professional.

OLEARY, Margaret A; Sacred Heart HS; East Grand Forks, MN; Chr; Chrs; CncrtBnd; SchPl; Yrbk; SchPpr; SciCl; LetterBsktbl; LetterTrk; Chrldr; Univ; Nursing.

OLEARY, Michael J; Galva HS; Galva, IL; HonRl; NHS; NatlThespSoc; SchPl; SctActv; RptrYrbk; Univ Of Illinois; Architecture.

OLENA, Cheryl; Geneva HS; Geneva, NE; 14/67 PresFrshCls; Aud/Vis; Band; Chr; HonRl; MrchBnd; StuCncl; StuGov; TchrAde; PPFtbl; Ks Wesleyan Salina; Home Ec.

OLERICH, June M; Wall Lake Comm HS; Breda, IA; 2/30 DrlTm; HonRl; RptrYrbk; Art School; Artist.

OLES, Lou Ann; St Clair HS; St Clair, MI; 44/191 TrsJrCls; HonRl; NatlMeritCmnd; SchPl; FrCl; Wilson Coll; Psychology.

OLESEN, David J; Crystal Lake Community HS; Crystal Lake, IL; 3/476 Band; HonRl; LitMag; NHS; NatlMeritFnl; SchMus; SctActv; LatCl; BauchLmbAwd; NCTE; Univ Of Montana; Wildlife Biology.

OLESEN, Floyd P; Petersburg Porta HS; Tallula, IL; 22/140 Chrs; HonRl; JrNHS; SchMus; StuCncl; Yrbk; 4-H; FFA; KeyCl; 4-HAwd; College; Prof Architect.

OLESEN, Kimberly L; Deer River HS; Deer River, MN; 13/83 ChrhWkr; HonRl; JrNHS; NHS; Quill&Scroll; SchPl; TchrAde; Bsktbl; AmLegAwd; CitAwd; Busi Sch; Med Sec.

OLESKI, Denise M; Pershing; Detroit, MI; 1/477 HonRl; NHS; OffAde; TchrAde; Macomb Comm College; Accountant.

OLESN, Joseph A; William A Wirt HS; Gary, IN; HonRl; Bsbl; Bsktbl; College; Electrician.

OLESNICZAK, Kathleen; St Ladislaus HS; Hamtramck, MI; HonRl; NHS; SchPl; SchPpr; FBLA; FrCl; Trk; GAA; Macomb Cnty Coll; Medical Tech.

OLESON, Brenda K; Le Roy HS; Leroy, IL; CncrtBnd; DrlTm; HonRl; Mdrgl; MrchBnd; NHS; PepBnd; StuCncl; YthFlsp; FHA; Illinois State Univ.

OLESON, Bruce A; Newton HS; Newton, IA; PresJrCls; ChrhWkr; HonRl; JCC; JrNHS; SchPl; YthFlsp; RptrYrbk; EngCl; LetterBsbl; Univ; Philosophy.

OLESON, Kristin; Elkhorn Area Hs; Elkhorn, WI; 60/167 AFS; ChrhWkr; CmntyWkr; SctActv; Yrbk; SchPpr; FHA; Trk; GAA; 4-HAwd; Uw Eau Claire; Elementary Education.

OLESON, Pamela J; Cambridge HS; Isanti, MN; 34/112 Band; Chr; ChrhWkr; CncrtBnd; LbryAde; MrchBnd; NHS; NatlThespSoc; PepBnd; SchMus; College.

OLESZKIEWICZ, Vincent S; De La Salle HS; Chicago, IL; 16/258 ChrhWkr; CmntyWkr; HonRl; NHS; SctActv; StuCncl; StuGov; Bsktbl; Ftbl; Michigan State Univ; Law.

OLEXA, Donald S; Adlai E Stevenson HS; Lincolnshire, IL; VPSrCls; HonRl; NHS; StuGov; RptrSchPpr; Bsktbl; Ftbl; CaptTrk; College; Law.

OLIENYK, Deborah L; Belfield HS; Belfield, ND; 1/57 ALAGirlsSt; DrlTm; HonRl; ModUN; NHS; PolWkr; SchPl; StuCncl; StuGov; FrCl; PpCl; N Dakota S Univ; Wildlife Manager.

OLIGER, Jon A; Mt Vernon Twp HS; Belle Rive, IL; 34/388 ALBoysSt; ChrhWkr; CmntyWkr; DrlTm; HonRl; LbryAde; NHS; TchrAde; Southern Illinois Univ; Law.

OLIGMUELLER, Linda M; Central Catholic HS; West Point, NE; Chrs; HonRl; JrNHS; RedCrAde; SchMus; SchPl; StuCncl; LatCl; PpCl; IMSpt; Business School; Medical Sec.

OLIGSCHLAEGER, Clyde L; Mexico HS; Mexico, MO; ALBoysSt; Band; PepBnd; StuCncl; LatCl; SpnCl; Bsktbl; LetterFtbl; LetterGlf; Univ Of Missouri; Geology.

OLINGER, Wayne W; Forest Park HS; Ferdinand, IN; 2/124 TrsSrCls; Band; HonRl; NHS; SchPl; StuCncl; RptrSchPpr; LetterGlf; IMSpt; VoiceDemAwd; Univ; Prof.

OLINZOCK, Sue R; St Agatha HS; Detoirt, MI; HonRl; OffAde; SchPl; StuCncl; SchPpr; FDA; FTA; PpCl; Chrldr; VoiceDemAwd; Business School; Vocation.

OLIPHANT, Janet K; East Prairie HS; East Prairie, MO; 23085 SecJrCls; Band; ChrhWkr; Bsktbl; Tennis; Trk; CchngActv; IMSpt; PPFtbl; CitAwd; Univ; Teaching Pe.

OLIPHANT, Teresa; Hartville HS; Hartville, MO; 15/64 ALAGirlsSt; Chrs; ChrhWkr; HonRl; OffAde; SchAde; StuCncl; TchrAde; FFA; PpCl; Southwest Miss St U.

OLISZEWICZ, Mark; St Laurence; Chicago, IL; 39/372 HonRl; GovHonPrgAwd; Illinois Inst Of Tech; Engineering.

OLIVA, Sandra R; Wilber Clatonia HS; Western, NE; Band; CncrtBnd; SchPl; StuGov; 4-H; FBLA; FHA; PpCl; Swmmng; Trk; Business Sch; Business.

OLIVA, Vincent W; Notre Dame HS; Niles, IL; 17/266 HonRl; NatlMeritSchl; TchrAde; Northwestern Univ; Medicine.

OLIVARES, Dora M; Lyman HS; Lyman, NE; SecJrCls; Band; Chr; CncrtBnd; HonRl; PepBnd; VPStuCncl; Yrbk; FHA; PpCl; LetterTrk; LetterChrldr; Chadron State Col; Music.

OLIVAREZ, Josefina; St Casimir Parish HS; Chicago, IL; VPSrCls; SchPl; De Paul Univ; Psychology.

OLIVAS, Johnnie J; Sioux County HS; Crawford, NE; 2/18 TrsSophCls; ALBoysSt; Chrs; HonRl; NHS; Yrbk; SciCl; College; Professional.

OLIVE, Cynthia D; North Mahaska HS; Barnes City, IA; HonRl; LbryAde; NHS; RptrYrbk; RptrSchPpr; FBLA; FTA; GerCl; LetterTrk; Chrldr; Bus Sch; Acct.

OLIVE, Deborah L; Edwardsville HS; Edwardsville, IL; 10/461 Chrs; HonRl; NHS; StuCncl; YthFlsp; 4-H; FHA; GerCl; Univ Of Ill; Biochemistry.

OLIVEIRA, Cynthia M; J D Darnall HS; Geneseo, IL; 34/212 Chr; HonRl; HospAde; NatlThespSoc; SchMus; SchPl; YthLg; Univ Of Illinois; Business.

OLIVER, Christine M; Wilber Clatonia HS; Wilber, NE; TrsJrCls; TrsSrCls; HonRl; SchAde; TchrAde; FHA; PpCl;.

OLIVER, Clay A; Campus HS; Wichita, KS; 10/400 Chr; Chrl; Chrs; HonRl; LbryAde; Mdrgl; StuGov; YthLg; LetterTrk; College; Advertising.

OLIVER, Connie R; Bedford N Lawrence HS; Bedford, IN; 9/397 HonRl; PresNatlFornLg; NHS; TchrAde; VPLatCl; Indiana Univ; Accounting.

OLIVER, David M; Vienna HS; Belknaw, IL; ChrhWkr; ModUN; NatlThespSoc; SchPl; SctActv; TchrAde; YthFlsp; 4-H; FTA; Trk; Coll; Prof.

OLIVER, Debora S; Carroll HS; Fort Wayne, IN; 40/206 Band; CncrtBnd; HonRl; MrchBnd; NHS; SctActv; Sdlty; TchrAde; Bus Sch; Secretary.

OLIVER, Dwight H; Richwoods HS; Peoria, IL; 20/449 HonRl; NHS; IMSpt; Univ Of Illinois; Chemical Engineer.

OLIVER, Ella R; Campbell HS; Campbell, MO; Chr; Chrs; ChrhWkr; SchPl; FHA; PpCl; College; Modeling.

OLIVER, Jeffrey D; Sioux Center HS; Sioux Center, IA; 2/81 ALBoysSt; Band; Chr; ChrhWkr; HonRl; NHS; NatlMeritCmnd; NatlThespSoc; SchPl; Yrbk; Central College; Pre Med.

OLIVER, Joanna S; Cassville HS; Shell Knob, MO; 3/108 DrlTm; JrNHS; FHA; PpCl; SciCl; GAA; IMSpt; College; Pro.

OLIVER, Kathy L; Metropolis Community HS; Metropolis, IL; 34/141 ChrhWkr; CmntyWkr; HonRl; OffAde; SpnCl; PpCl; U Of S Il; Social Worker.

OLIVER, Kellie; Corunna HS; Corunna, MI; 30/250 Coll; Art Enterior Design.

OLIVER, Kim L; Corunna HS; Corunna, MI; 31/208 HonRl; NHS; SchPl; YthFlsp; RptrYrbk; 4-H; Chrldr; GAA; 4-HAwd; Ferris State Coll; Legal Asst.

OLIVER, Larry W; Louisiana HS; Louisiana, MO; AFS; ALAGirlsSt; Chr; Chrs; HonRl; Mdrgl; NatlMeritFnl; NatlMeritCmnd; NatlMeritSF; SchMus; LetterFtbl; LetterTrk; IMSpt; University Of Missouri; Physics.

OLIVER, Lawrence D; Illini Bluffs HS; Mapleton, IL; Band; CncrtBnd; Mdrgl; MrchBnd; PepBnd; SctActv; Bsbl; Catter Pillar.

OLIVER, Lisa J; Lutheran HS; Dearborn, MI; 64/184 ChrhWkr; HonRl; OffAde; PolWkr; SchAde; SctActv; TchrAde; YthFlsp; PresLatCl; CchngActv; College; Business.

OLIVER, Luanna L; Cassville HS; Shell Knob, MO; 4/108 DrlTm; SchPl; SctActv; PpCl; SciCl; GAA; IMSpt; College; Prof.

OLIVER, Mary; Kickapoo HS; Viola, WI; 1/53 PresJrCls; ALAGirlsSt; HonRl; SchPl; StuCncl; RptrYrbk; EdSchPpr; GAA; Viterbo College; Medical Records Admin.

OLIVER, Timothy; Saint Johns HS; Bancroft, IA; Band; Chr; Chrs; HonRl; MrchBnd; College.

OLIVER, Verna; Thomas M Cooley HS; Detroit, MI; HonRl; OffAde; Trk; Detroit College; Business Admin.

OLIVERO, Lisa M; Lasalle Peru HS; Peru, IL; 4/516 PresSophCls; AFS; Band; ChrhWkr; NHS; PresStuCncl; SecLatCl; PpCl; CitAwd; VoiceDemAwd; Univ Of Illinois; Lawyer.

OLK, Cynthia M; Carmel HS; Mundelein, IL; 18/173 Chrs; HonRl; SchMus; MthCl; Chrldr; U Of Il; Bio Chem.

OLK, Daniel; Clintonville Senior HS; Clintonville, WI; 9/17829# CncrtBnd; HonRl; MrchBnd; PepBnd; SchPl; IMSpt; U W Madison; Earth Science.

OLK, Laurie S; Cal Comm HS; Latimer, IA; TrsSophCls; TrsJrCls; Chr; Chrs; HonRl; SecYthFlsp; 4-H; SecFHA; LetterGlf; 4-HAwd; Ia St Univ; Interior Design.

OLKOWSKI, Carole A; Pinckney HS; Brighton, MI; 13/238 SecFrshCls; HonRl; HospAde; SchAde; RptrSchPpr; 4-H; LetterBsktbl; LetterChrldr; PresAwd; CitAwd; Nursing School; Nurse.

OLLAYOS, Roberta; St Edward Central Catholc Hs; Elgin, IL; 3 TrsJrCls; TrsSrCls; HonRl; NHS; NatlMeritCmnd; NatlThespSoc; SchMus; RptrYrbk; MthCl; SciCl; College;occupational Therapy.

OLLER, David H; Lyman HS; Vivian, SD; ALBoysSt; TchrAde; LetterFtbl; LetterWrstlng; Trade School; Professional.

OLLER, Lucinda; Williamsville HS; Riverton, IL; 4/62 Band; Chrs; HonRl; Mdrgl; NHS; SchPl; 4-H; FTA; PpCl; 4-HAwd; Coll.

OLLHOFF, Mary L; Bethlehem Acad; Fairbault, MN; 3/91 Chrs; ChrhWkr; HonRl; HospAde; NHS; SchPl; StuCncl; TchrAde; RptrYrbk; RptrSchPpr; Winona St Coll; Busi Admin.

OLM, Paul J; J F K Prep; Appleton, WI; HonRl; College; Law.

OLMSCHEID, Elaine B; Paynesville HS; Paynesville, MN; CmntyWkr; NatlMeritSchl; ROTC; StuGov; 4-H; Swmmng; GAA; GovHonPrgAwd; JAAwd; VoiceDemAwd; College; Vocation.

OLMSTEAD, Danita M; Fort Dodge Sr HS; Fort Dodge, IA; HonRl; SctActv; RptrSchPpr; GodCntryAwd; College; Art Teacher.

OLMSTEAD, Karen; Galien HS; Galien, MI; SecFrshCls; Band; HonRl; StuCncl; GAA;.

OLMSTEAD, Wiletta A; Alburnett HS; Toddville, IA; Band; Chr; ChrhWkr; HonRl; SchMus; Yrbk; Pres4-H; FTA; Bsktbl; 4-HAwd; College; Journalism.

OLMSTED, Diane C; Downers Grove HS; Woodridge, IL; HonRl; LitMag; ModUN; NHS; NatlMeritCmnd; SchMus; StuGov; YthLg; RptrYrbk; LetterTennis; University Of Kansas; State Dept.

OLMSTED, Russell N; Coldwater HS; Coldwater, MI; Band; HonRl; MrchBnd; NHS; StuGov; GerCl; LetterGlf; LetterTennis; LetterTrk; IMSpt; Central Mi Univ; Medical Field.

OLNEY, Linda J; Clarkston HS; Clarkston, MI; SecSrCls; ChrhWkr; HonRl; NHS; StuGov; TchrAde; SecRusCl; DARAwd; Albion College; Doctor.

OLRY, Catherine M; North Side HS; Fort Wayne, IN; 25/475 ALAGirlsSt; NHS; CaptBsktbl; Chrldr; GAA; IMSpt; PPFtbl; Indiana University.

OLSEN, Alfred G; J B Conant HS; Hoffman, IL; 13/627 HonRl; NHS; NatlSciFnd; Quill&Scroll; RptrSchPpr; SptEdSchPpr; SciCl; Yale Univ; Science.

OLSEN, Barbara; Laurel Public HS; Laurel, NE; 8/61 CncrtBnd; HonRl; MrchBnd; OffAde; SchMus; Twrl; 4-H; PpCl; Chrldr; IMSpt; Coll; Teacher Spec Ed.

OLSEN, Christy; Libertyville HS; Libertyville, IL; 46/431 Chr; Chrl; Chrs; HonRl; College; Speech Pathologist.

OLSEN, David A; Falls Sr HS; International Fall, MN; ChrhWkr; Bsbl; College; Coaching.

OLSEN, Debi; Escanaba Public HS; Escanaba, MI; CtyCnl; CncrtBnd; HonRl; NatlFornLg; NHS; PepBnd; StuGov; SchPpr;.

OLSEN, Eunice F; Black Hawk HS; Argyle, WI; 1/70 PresBand; HonRl; PresNHS; OffAde; PepBnd; EdYrBk; FHA; PpCl; GAA; DARAwd; Stout Uw; Home Economics.

OLSEN, Gregory G; Lahser HS; Bloomfield Hills, MI; 23/470 HonRl; JrNHS; NHS; YthLg; Bsbl; Glf; Socr; CchngActv; IMSpt; PresAwd; Univ Of Notre Dame; Architecture.

OLSEN, Joel; Nicollet Public HS; Nicollet, MN; 6/55 ALBoysSt; Band; Chrs; HonRl; MrchBnd; NHS; SchPl; StuCncl; SptEdSchPpr; 4-H; Bsbl; Bsktbl; Ftbl; College.

OLSEN, Julie A; St Paul HS; St Paul, NE; 3/73 PresSophCls; ALAGirlsSt; ChrhWkr; CncrtBnd; NHS; SchMus; SchPl; SctActv; EdYrBk; Chrldr; Kearney State College; Speech Pathology.

OLSEN, Leslie; Lake Zurich Sr Hs; Kildeer, IL; 7 AFS; Band; JrNHS; LbryAde; NHS; NatlThespSoc; SchMus; SchPl; StuGov; Lawrence U;engineering.

OLSEN, Nancy R; Kinsley HS; Kinsley, KS; CmntyWkr; CncrtBnd; HonRl; Mdrgl; SchPl; Teen; RptrYrbk; Bsktbl; 4-HAwd; JAAwd; Clge.

OLSEN, Sheryl A; Forest Lake Sr HS; Scandia, MN; Chr; ChrhWkr; HonRl; HospAde; JrNHS; LbryAde; Mdrgl; NHS; OffAde; SchMus; SchPl; TchrAde; YthFlsp; College; Medical Sec.

OLSEN, Timothy P; Lake Mills HS; Joice, IA; ModUN; NatlMeritSF; SchMus; SctActv; StuCncl; Yrbk; SchPpr; LetterFtbl; LetterWrstlng; GodCntryAwd; Coll; Engng.

OLSEN, Tracy L; Polo Comm HS; Polo, IL; 4/89 ALAGirlsSt; SecChr; HonRl; NHS; PresStuCncl; Pres4-H; GAA; AmLegAwd; DARAwd; 4-HAwd; College; Accounting.

OLSEN, Valerie A; Bogan HS; Chicago, IL; 45/700 ALAGirlsSt; Band; CmntyWkr; CncrtBnd; HonRl; HospAde; JrNHS; LitMag; NHS; Orch; PepBnd; SchMus; SctActv; College; Music.

OLSGAARD, Mary L; West Fargo HS; West Fargo, ND; Band; Chr; CncrtBnd; HonRl; MrchBnd; NHS; NatlThespSoc; Orch; PepBnd; SchPl; Trade Sch; Barber.

OLSHEFSKI, Marion J; Mercy HS; St Louis, MO; CncrtBnd; NHS; TchrAde; SciCl; BttyCrckrAwd; Barnes Hosp; Nursing.

OLSON, Ann M; Axtell HS; Axtell, KS; VPSophCls; PresJrCls; Band; Chrs; HonRl; SecStuCncl; Yrbk; Pres4-H; TreasPpCl; 4-HAwd; College.

OLSON, Barbara B; Ada HS; Ada, MN; Band; Chr; ChrhWkr; CncrtBnd; HonRl; NHS; FHA; LetterTrk; Chrldr; IMSpt; College.

OLSON, Barbara J; Taylor HS; Melrose, WI; 2/25 TrsSrCls; Chrs; ChrhWkr; HonRl; SchPl; TchrAde; EdYrBk; FHA; GAA; DARAwd; Wi Technical Institute; Technical Nurse.

OLSON, Beth A; Senior HS; Superior, WI; 86/540 HonRl; Clge; Special Ed.

OLSON, Blaine A; Almont HS; Almont, ND; 2/10 PresSophCls; ALBoysSt; ChrhWkr; HonRl; SchPl; SctActv; StuCncl; StuGov; RptrYrbk; EdYrBk; PpCl; Bsktbl; Trk; Trade Schl; Mechanical Engineering.

OLSON, Bonnie L; Winona Sr HS; La Moille, MN; Chrs; ChrhWkr; CmntyWkr; HonRl; RptrYrbk; RptrSchPpr; SciCl; Tennis; LetterTrk; GAA; College; Vet.

OLSON, Bradley D; South Hamilton HS; Story City, IA; Band; Chrs; HonRl; NHS; Orch; SchMus; StuCncl; FFA; Bsbl; Bsktbl; LetterFtbl; LetterTrk; IMSpt; College; Agriculture.

OLSON, Catherine M; Stoughton HS; Stoughton, WI; ALAGirlsSt; TreasChrhWkr; HonRl; PresStuCncl; PresGerCl; PpCl; SecGAA; Voc Sch; Art.

OLSON, Christine A; Garden County HS; Oshkosh, NE; 3/42 PresJrCls; ALAGirlsSt; Band; Chr; Chrs; HonRl; JrNHS; LitMag; MrchBnd; NHS; NatlMeritSF; OffAde; PepBnd; Trk; College; Professional.

OLSON, Christine K; Mills HS; Lakevlle, MN; SecTrsFrshCls; Band; CncrtBnd; HonRl; MrchBnd; NatlMeritSF; PolWkr; StuGov; Tennis; Chrldr; Univ; Public Admin.

OLSON, Cindy L; Parkview HS; Footville, WI; 29/163 VPSophCls; PresJrCls; Band; Chrs; CncrtBnd; HonRl; PepBnd; StuCncl; Twrl; Yrbk; Chrldr; GAA; IMSpt; College; Journalism.

OLSON, Craig L; Holdrege HS; Holdrege, NE; Band; Chr; Chrl; Chrs; CncrtBnd; HonRl; MrchBnd; PepBnd; LetterFtbl; Bsktbl; LetterTrk; Grace Bible Inst; Ministry.

OLSON, Cyndi A; West Lyon Comm HS; Inwood, IA; Band; Chr; Chrs; ChrhWkr; CncrtBnd; HonRl; IntrClCncl; MrchBnd; PepBnd; SchPl; YthFlsp; Sioux Falls College.

OLSON, Cynthia A; Thompson Comm HS; Thompson, IA; PresSophCls; Band; Chrs; ChrhWkr; CncrtBnd; HonRl; LbryAde; MrchBnd; OffAde; PepBnd; Secretarial Work.

OLSON, Darlene M; Chaska HS; Chaska, MN; Chr; HonRl; JA; JrNHS; NatlFornLg; NHS; StuCncl; GerCl; PresAwd; Coll; Medical Profession.

OLSON, Darrell L; Parker Public HS; Chancellor, SD; ALBoysSt; Band; HonRl; NHS; FFA; Bsbl; Bsktbl; Trk; CaptWrstlng; 4-HAwd; Mitchel Area Vo Tech; Agriculture.

OLSON, Dave; Esterville HS; Esterville, IA; Mdrgl; StuCncl; SptEdYrbk; RusCl; LetterTrk; Coll; Dr.

OLSON, David J; Calamus Comm HS; Grand Mound, IA; TrsFrshCls; Band; NHS; SchMus; SchPl; Pres4-H; Glf; Trk; 4-HAwd; PresAwd; Coll; Archi.

OLSON, David P; Hiawatha HS; Kirkland, IL; PresJrCls; VPSrCls; HonRl; NatlMeritCmnd; PresStuCncl; FFA; LetterBsbl; LetterBsktbl; LetterFtbl; LetterWrstlng; Univ Of Il; Business Admin.

OLSON, Debra; Annandale HS; Annandale, MN; 2/125 Band; Chr; DrlTm; HonRl; NHS; PepBnd; SchPl; PpCl; Bsktbl; St Cloud State U; Business Relations.

OLSON, Debra; Reeths Puffer HS; Muskegon, MI; ChrhWkr; HonRl; HospAde; NHS; OffAde; SpnCl; Bible Col; Religion And Pe.

OLSON, Debra; Altoona Public HS; Altoona, WI; ChrhWkr; SchPl; RptrSchPpr; PpCl; Trk; Chrldr; GAA; Univ Of Wi Eau Claire; Communicative Disord.

OLSON, Debra A; Thompson Public HS; Thompson, ND; Band; Chr; ChrhWkr; HospAde; PepBnd; SchMus; SchPl; TchrAde; RptrYrbk; RptrSchPpr;.

OLSON, Dianne L; Osmond Community HS; Mc Lean, NE; 7/44 Chr; Chrs; DrlTm; HonRl; MrchBnd; NHS; SchPl; VP4-H; FBLA; PpCl; Univ; Computer Science.

OLSON, Disa A; West Holt HS; Atkinson, NE; 2/80 SecFrshCls; Band; ChrhWkr; DrmMjrt; HonRl; NHS; Yrbk; PpCl; Chrldr; Ne Christian Col; Deaf Missions Secretarial.

OLSON, Duane A; Amery HS; Amery, WI; 8/125 ChrhWkr; NHS; NatlMeritCmnd; LetterTrk; Band; Chr; CncrtBnd; HonRl; MrchBnd; Bible College; Aviation.

OLSON, Eddy; Midway HS; Forest River, ND; CmntyWkr; HonRl; SchPl; SctActv; Bsktbl; Trk; Bismark; Marketing.

OLSON, Erica M; Omaha Central HS; Omaha, NE; ALAGirlsSt; Chr; Chrl; Chrs; ChrhWkr; CmntyWkr; HonRl; HospAde; Trk; IMSpt; Colorado Coll; Writer.

OLSON, Floyd B; Trenton HS; Williston, ND; PresFrshCls; ALBoysSt; Band; Chrs; HonRl; PepBnd; Bsktbl; Ftbl; Trk; College; Vocation.

OLSON, Forrest B; Detroit Lakes Sr HS; Detroit Lakes, MN; 25/260 HonRl; NHS; VPSctActv; CivCl; Bsktbl; CaptGlf; CaptIMSpt; Concordia College; Dentistry.

OLSON, Gary L; Fairmont HS; Fairmont, MN; HonRl; KiwanAwd; Bemidji St Clg; Arch Engr.

OLSON, Geraldine L; North HS; Eau Claire, WI; 12/360 Chr; ChrhWkr; HonRl; HospAde; PpCl; AmLegAwd; U Of Wi Eau Claire; Nurse.

OLSON, Glendon A; Wildrose HS; Wildrose, ND; PresJrCls; Band; Chr; CncrtBnd; HonRl; PepBnd; SchPl; StuCncl; Yrbk; SchPpr; 4-H; Bsktbl; Trk; College.

OLSON, Gregory J; West HS; Green Bay, WI; Aud/Vis; HonRl; Univ; Accounting.

OLSON, Jacqueline K; Parkview HS; Orfordville, WI; 23/165 ChrhWkr; CmntyWkr; HonRl; NHS; TchrAde; PpCl; CaptBsktbl; GAA; IMSpt; PresAwd; Univ Of Wisc; Physical Ed.

OLSON, James D; Lincoln HS; Thief River Falls, MN; 21/239 Band; CncrtBnd; NHS; Orch; PepBnd; RptrYrbk; RptrSchPpr; LetterGlf; DanFAwd; Clge; Dentistry.

OLSON, James J; Loyola Academy; Lake Bluff, IL; College.

OLSON, Jamie L; Kindred HS; Kindred, ND; VPJrCls; Chr; PresChrhWkr; CncrtBnd; HospAde; NHS; StuCncl; RptrSchPpr; SecFHA; PpCl; College; Psychology.

OLSON, Janet L; Bristol HS; Bristol, SD; PresJrCls; Band; Chrs; ChrhWkr; CncrtBnd; HonRl; HospAde; LbryAde; MrchBnd; Chrldr;.

OLSON, Jay H; Alwood HS; Oneida, IL; 1/75 Chrs; HonRl; LbryAde; NHS; SchMus; SchPl; PresFFA; LetterBsktbl; Univ Of Illinois; Agriculture.

OLSON, Jeffrey R; Sparta Sr HS; Sparta, WI; ALBoysSt; Band; CncrtBnd; HonRl; MrchBnd; NHS; Quill&Scroll; SctActv; StuCncl; StuGov; SptEdSchPpr; LetterBsktbl; College; Doctor.

OLSON, Jenny L; Parkview HS; Orfordville, WI; 13/161 VPJrCls; Band; HonRl; MrchBnd; StuCncl; TchrAde; Twrl; EdYrBk; SpnCl; Col; Vocation.

OLSON, Jo Ann C; Edmore Public HS; Webster, ND; 13/23 Band; Chr; Chrs; ChrhWkr; CmntyWkr; CncrtBnd; PepBnd; RptrYrbk; EdSchPpr; FHA; Minot State Clg; Rn.

OLSON, John B; Shabbona HS; Shabbona, IL; 5/44 VPSrCls; CncrtBnd; HonRl; NHS; StuCncl; StuGov; FFA; Glf; Socr; College; Farming.

OLSON, John M; St Rita HS; Chicago, IL; 38/425 SecJrCls; LetterBsktbl; IMSpt; Lewis Univ; Elec Engr.

OLSON, Joleen L; Welcome Comm HS; Welcome, MN; 10/19 VPJrCls; PresSrCls; Band; Chrs; MrchBnd; PepBnd; SchPl; TchrAde; RptrYrbk; CaptChrldr; Marriage Work.

OLSON, Jon R; Hibbing HS; Hibbing, MN; Band; Chr; HonRl; NatlFornLg; NHS; YthFlsp; GerCl; Glf; IMSpt; PresAwd; College; Lawyer.

OLSON, Julie; Platte Valley Acad; Rapid City, SD; HonRl; TchrAde; College; Medicine.

OLSON, Julie A; Maine East HS; Niles, IL; Chr; CmntyWkr; HonRl; JrNHS; Mdrgl; SecNHS; SchMus; StuCncl; Swmmng; Chrldr; Univ Of Iowa; Nursing.

OLSON, Julie A; Black River Falls Sr HS; Black River Falls, WI; Band; Chr; Chrs; CncrtBnd; HonRl; LbryAde; MrchBnd; PepBnd; SchMus; TreasStuCncl; Bsbl; Trk; Chrldr; GAA; College; Veterinarian.

OLSON, Karen A; Wm G Mather HS; Minising, MI; Band; ChrhWkr; CncrtBnd; HonRl; MrchBnd; PepBnd; SchPl; RptrYrbk; RptrSchPpr; Swmmng; Mi State; Corporate Lawyer.

OLSON, Karen S; Eat Chain HS; Fairmont, MN; 3/22 PresJrCls; Band; Chrs; PresNHS; Sec4-H; PresFHA; CaptChrldr; BttyCrckrAwd; 4-HAwd; VoiceDemAwd; Augustana College; Elementary Ed & Music.

OLSON, Kari J; Winnebago HS; Amboy, MN; VPFrshCls; TrsJrCls; ALAGirlsSt; Band; Chr; HonRl; SchPl; FHA; GerCl; PpCl; College; Nursing.

OLSON, Kathleen J; Hector Comm HS; Hector, MN; 10/48 Chr; DrmMjrt; HonRl; NHS; Twrl; FHA; LetterBsktbl; LetterTrk; LetterChrldr; College; Home Economics.

OLSON, Kathryn J; La Crescent HS; La Crescent, MN; HonRl; NatlThespSoc; PolWkr; StuCncl; YthFlsp; FrCl; AmLegAwd; Uw La Crosse; Secondary Educ.

OLSON, Keith A; East Troy HS; Eagle, WI; VPSophCls; ALBoysSt; CncrtBnd; HonRl; MrchBnd; NHS; PepBnd; Yrbk; SchPpr; Supermarket Mgmnt.

OLSON, Kenneth P; Lincoln HS; Bloomington, MN; HonRl; NHS; Glf; U Of Mn; Marine Biology.

OLSON, Kenneth R; Hill City HS; Hill City, MN; 1/28 PresSophCls; PresSrCls; HonRl; PresStuCncl; PresYthFlsp; SptEdYrbk; SptEdSchPpr; Bsbl; Bsktbl; AmLegAwd; College; Accountant.

OLSON, Kurt A; South Milwaukee HS; South Milwaukee, WI; HonRl; SchAde; SchPl; TchrAde; Ftbl; Trk; Wrstlng; AmLegAwd; College; Pro.

OLSON, Laura M; Lincoln HS; Bloomington, MN; HonRl; Orch; FBLA; College; Professional.

OLSON, Laurel M; Gillett Public HS; Gillett, WI; Band; Chr; Chrs; CncrtBnd; MrchBnd; SchPl; TchrAde; YthFlsp; FHA; PpCl; U Of Wi Stevens Point; Home Econ Teach.

OLSON, Lauri L; Richwoods HS; Peoria, IL; 80/480 SecBand; Chr; SecCncrtBnd; DrlTm; HonRl; SecMrchBnd; NHS; SecPepBnd; Quill&Scroll; Yrbk; Iowa St Univ; Child Development.

OLSON, Lee F; Clara City HS; Clara City, MN; ChrhWkr; HonRl; NHS; NatlMeritCmnd; CivCl; LetterBsktbl; LetterFtbl; LetterTrk; West Point Academy.

OLSON, Lesley C; George E Thompson HS; St Charles, IL; 19/450 AFS; Chr; PresCncrtBnd; HonRl; NHS; NatlMeritCmnd; Orch; SchMus; Univ Of Illinois; Music.

OLSON, Lisa M; Bemidji HS; Cass Lake, MN; PresChr; HonRl; NatlThespSoc; SchMus; StuGov; RptrYrbk; IMSpt; Clge; Music & Int Design.

OLSON, Lynette S; Mineral Point HS; Mineral Point, WI; Band; Chr; Chrs; ChrhWkr; CncrtBnd; HonRl; Mdrgl; MrchBnd; PepBnd; SchMus; SchPl; YthFlsp; FHA; Bsktbl; Business College; Secretary.

OLSON, Margaret A; Pocahontas Comm HS; Pocahontas, IA; 29/70 LetterBand; ChrhWkr; DrlTm; HonRl; MrchBnd; PepBnd; RptrSchPpr; 4-H; FHA; PresFTA; LetterTrk; College; Fashion Merchandising.

OLSON, Maribeth L; Montello HS; Montello, WI; 20/70 Band; Chrs; CncrtBnd; HonRl; MrchBnd; PepBnd; SchMus; SchPl; FHA; PpCl; University Of Wisconsin Madison; Music.

OLSON, Marlys E; Rush City HS; Rush City, MN; 5/61 PresChr; CncrtBnd; HonRl; NHS; RptrYrbk; Pres4-H; Chrldr; LetterGAA; 4-HAwd; VoiceDemAwd; St Olaf College; Rn.

OLSON, Mary J; Oakes Public HS; Oakes, ND; 1/63 Band; ChrhWkr; HonRl; HospAde; MrchBnd; PepBnd; SchPl; VPSrCls; U Of Nd; Physical Therapy.

OLSON, Monica D; Perry HS; Baylis, IL; Band; Chrs; HonRl; JA; MrchBnd; SchPl; VP4-H; FHA; Bsktbl; 4-HAwd; University.

OLSON, Nadine M; Souris Public HS; Souris, ND; 3/13 SecFrshCls; Band; HonRl; LbryAde; SchMus; StuCncl; RptrSchPpr; 4-H; SciCl; Chrldr; Univ Of Nd; Math.

OLSON, Nancy; Watertown HS; Watertown, SD; 34/326 Chr; Chrs; ChrhWkr; HonRl; NatlFornLg; NatlThespSoc; SchMus; SchPl; GAA; IMSpt; College; Professional.

OLSON, Nancy J; Hendricks HS; Astoria, SD; PresFrshCls; Band; Chr; Chrs; CncrtBnd; HonRl; MrchBnd; PepBnd; StuCncl; PpCl; College.

OLSON, Pam; Shawneetown HS; Shawneetown, IL; SecTrsSrCls; HonRl; StuCncl; StuGov; RptrYrbk; Yrbk; RptrSchPpr; Southern Illinois Univ; Pediatrician.

OLSON, Pamela R; Kensington Public HS; Farwell, MN; Band; Chr; ChrhWkr; Pres4-H; Bsbl; Bsktbl; Trk; Chrldr; PresGAA; 4-HAwd; CitAwd; Fergus Falls Jr College; Physical Educ.

OLSON, Philip D; Arkansas City HS; Arkansas City, KS; 5/271 PresSrCls; HonRl; NHS; StuCncl; FFA; FTA; SciCl; LetterFtbl; LetterGlf; CaptWrstlng; Kansas State U; Pre Vet.

OLSON, Phillip A; Newman Grove Public HS; Newman Grove, NE; 4/40 VPJrCls; TrsSrCls; HonRl; NHS; NatlMeritCmnd; SchPl; YthFlsp; Pres4-H; SecFFA; LetterFtbl; LetterWrstlng; Kearney St College.

OLSON, Ramona C; Wahpeton HS; Mooreton, ND; HstSrCls; AFS; Band; HonRl; JrNHS; SchPl; TchrAde; Yrbk; FHA; RotaryAwd; U Of N D.

OLSON, Randy C; Becker HS; Becker, MN; PresJrCls; Band; Chrs; ChrhWkr; HonRl; SchPl; TchrAde; Bsktbl; Trk; CchngActv; North Central Bible College; Agri Business.

OLSON, Rebecca J; Spencer Community HS; Spencer, IA; 13/166 VPFrshCls; HonRl; Quill&Scroll; SchPl; RptrYrbk; LatCl; Bsktbl; Trk; IMSpt; KiwanAwd; Iowa State Univ; Journalism.

OLSON, Richard H; Central HS; St Paul, MN; 5/332 HonRl; NatlMeritSF; Univ Of Mn; Accounting.

OLSON, Ricky C; Southern HS; Stronghurst, IL; ChrhWkr; HonRl; LbryAde; SctActv; Western Illinois Univ; Accounting.

OLSON, Robert J; Little Falls Comm HS; Little Falls, MN; Band; ChrhWkr; CmntyWkr; HonRl; MrchBnd; ModUN; Orch; StuCncl; LetterBsbl; LetterBsktbl; LetterFtbl; College; Pharmacy.

OLSON, Robyn L; St Charles HS; Wasco, IL; 23/450 Chr; Chrl; ChrhWkr; CncrtBnd; HonRl; HospAde; MrchBnd; NHS; Orch; Univ Of Iowa; Nursing.

OLSON, Ronald L; Langdon HS; Langdon, ND; 17/109 HonRl; 4-H; University Of North Dakota.

OLSON, Roy J; Mount Carmel HS; Chicago, IL; 13/197 HonRl; NHS; College.

OLSON, Sara B; Viroqua HS; Viroqua, WI; Band; ChrhWkr; CncrtBnd; NatlFornLg; Orch; Sec4-H; FHA; 4-HAwd; St Paul Bible College; Special Education.

OLSON, Scott L; Pecatonica HS; Blanchardville, WI; 2/58 VPSrCls; Band; Chr; CmntyWkr; CncrtBnd; HonRl; NatlMeritCmnd; SchMus; YthFlsp; CaptBsktbl; College; Business Administration.

OLSON, Sharon A; Magic City Campus HS; Minot, ND; ALAGirlsSt; Chr; Chrs; ChrhWkr; HonRl; NHS; TreasSpnCl; PpCl; IMSpt; College; Professional.

OLSON, Sheila; Fennimore HS; Fennimore, WI; Chrs; HonRl; SchMus; GAA; Vocational Tech School; Professional.`

OLSON, Shelley R; Wildrose Public HS; Wildrose, ND; Band; Chr; Chrs; ChrhWkr; CncrtBnd; HonRl; PepBnd; SchPl; StuCncl; Bsktbl; Trk; Chrldr; GAA; Univ Of North Dakota.

OLSON, Sonja L; Poynette HS; Poynette, WI; 4/99 AFS; Band; HonRl; NatlFornLg; NHS; SchPl; Sdlty; RptrYrbk; 4-H; Trk; Madison; Nursing.

OLSON, Steven R; Butterfield Odin HS; Odin, MN; 3/28 TrsSophCls; TrsJrCls; VPSrCls; Chr; HonRl; SchPl; StuCncl; Yrbk; RptrSchPpr; Glf; Univ Of S Dak; Electrical Engin.

OLSON, Susan M; Amos Alonzo Stagg HS; Hickory Hills, IL; ChrhWkr; HonRl; LbryAde; RptrYrbk; Moraine Valley Comm College; Elem Education.

OLSON, Susan M; Kadoka HS; Kadoka, SD; 1/29 SecTrsFrshCls; SecTrsJrCls; PresBand; Chrs; CaptDrlTm; RptrYrbk; EdSchPpr; PresPpCl; DARAwd; So Dakota State University.

OLSON, Terese M; St Joseph HS; South Bend, IN; 8/270 HonRl; NHS; RptrSchPpr; Trk; Engineering.

OLSON, Terry; Arlington HS; Arlington, SD; Band; Chr; ChrhWkr; Mdrgl; SchPl; 4-H; Bsktbl; 4-HAwd; Vocational School; Farming.

OLSON, Thomas J; Saint Teresa HS; Decatur, IL; NatlMeritSF; LetterFtbl;.

OLSON, Thonias E; Riverdale HS; Avoca, WI; ChrhWkr; HonRl; PepBnd; RptrYrbk; 4-H; FFA; SciCl; Ftbl; Trk; Wrstlng;.

OLSON, Timothy W; Coon Rapids Sr HS; Coon Rapids, MN; 21/738 ChrhWkr; HonRl; JrNHS; NHS; NatlMeritSF; Univ Of Minnesota; Science.

OLSON, Todd C; Westview HS; Braham, MN; TchrAde; LetterFtbl; LetterGlf; Arizona State Univ; Bartender.

OLSON, Todd E; Taylor HS; Taylor, WI; 2/27 Chrs; CncrtBnd; HonRl; MrchBnd; VP4-H; TreasFFA; GerCl; LetterBsktbl; Trk; CchngActv; Trade School; Agricultural Mech.

OLSON, Toni R; Logan Magnolia HS; Logan, IA; 2/52 Chrs; HonRl; NHS; Yrbk;.

OLSON, Verne J; Roseau HS; Roseau, MN; ChrhWkr; SchAde; StuCncl; TchrAde; RptrSchPpr; 4-H; Tennis; U Of Minn; Engineering.

OLSON, Warren G; Prairie Community HS; Gowrie, IA; 9/78 ALBoysSt; HonRl; NHS; SchMus; MthCl; Bsktbl; Ftbl; Trk; CchngActv; DanFAwd; Central Coll; Coaching.

OLSSON, Kristine M; Arlington HS; Arlington Hts, IL; Chr; Chrs; HonRl; NatlThespSoc; SchAde; College; Theatre.

OLSVIG, Marla; Prairie Farm HS; Clayton, WI; TrsFrshCls; TrsSophCls; SecJrCls; Band; HonRl; LbryAde; NHS; EdYrBk; 4-H; FHA; College; Teacher.

OLTMAN, Pamela M; Joliet West HS; Joliet, IL; 30/495 HonRl; HospAde; NHS; StuCncl; Northern Ill Univ; Medical Technology.

OLTMAN, Randy R; Woodland HS; Streator, IL; ChrhWkr; HonRl; SchAde; SchPl; StuCncl; StuGov; FBLA; FTA; KeyCl; GerCl; Navy; Aviations Machinist Mate.

OLTMAN, Sandra K; Tri Mont Public HS; Trimont, MN; 2/27 SecJrCls; ALAGirlsSt; PresBand; Chrs; ChrhWkr; CncrtBnd; HonRl; MrchBnd; IMSpt; BttyCrckrAwd; Bemidiji State Col; Music Teacher.

OLTMANNS, Merri K; Lockport Central HS; Lockport, IL; 190/540 Band; CncrtBnd; DrlTm; HonRl; MrchBnd; PepBnd; LetterTrk; GAA; IMSpt; Joliet Jr College; Dental Asst.

OLTMANS, Debra K; Lamberton Public School; Lamberton, MN; 6/45 Chr; CncrtBnd; DrlTm; MrchBnd; SchPl; RptrSchPpr; 4-H; FHA; FTA; BttyCrckrAwd; U Of Minn St Paul College; Home Econmics.

OLVERA, Jose M; Harrison HS; Chicago, IL; 3/408 HonRl; PresNHS; Orch; RptrYrbk; RptrSchPpr; Loyola Univ; Doctor.

OMAN, Patrick A; Redwood Falls HS; Redwood Falls, MN; Chr; HonRl; NatlFornLg; NHS; NatlMeritSF; SchMus; SchPl; Yrbk; Univ Of Wisc; Law Enforcement.

OMDAHL, Daphne J; Fordville HS; Fordville, ND; 2/15 PresFrshCls; VPSophCls; VPJrCls; ChrhWkr; HonRl; SchMus; EdYrBk; 4-H; Trk; Chrldr; Mayville State Clg; Home Ec.

OMMEN, Jean M; Leroy HS; Arrowsmith, IL; 1/85 PresSrCls; Chrs; Mdrgl; NHS; SctActv; StuCncl; RptrYrbk; 4-H; Chrldr; GAA; U Of Il; Biology.

OMO, Lucy; Good Counsel HS; Chicago, IL; CmntyWkr; HonRl; NatlFornLg; NatlSciFnd; StuCncl; RptrSchPpr; SciCl; Univ Of Chicago; Biology Research.

OMODT, Linda M; Aberdeen Central HS; Aberdeen, SD; 11/413 AFS; Band; Chr; ChrhWkr; HonRl; 4-H; SpnCl; SciCl; Bsktbl; GAA; Vetrinary Medicine.

OMSTEAD, Luann L; Malcom Price Lab HS; Cedar Falls, IA; Band; CncrtBnd; DrlTm; MrchBnd; Teen; Twrl; PpCl; LetterSwmmng; Business School; Legal Secretary.

ON, Maria M; Roger C Sullivan HS; Chicago, IL; VPFrshCls; TrsSophCls; PresJrCls; Chr; HonRl; StuCncl; Yrbk; Univ Of Illinois; Foreign Languages.

ONAK, Lynette M; Thornridge HS; Harvey, IL; 1/684 HonRl; LitMag; NatlFornLg; SecNHS; OffAde; PpCl; BttyCrckrAwd; Ill State Univ; Special Education Major.

ONDA, Robert J; Andrean HS; Merrillville, IN; 5/300 TrsSrCls; HonRl; NHS; StuCncl; Bsktbl; LetterTennis; IMSpt; RotaryAwd; Univ Of Notre Dame; Lawyer.

ONDERAK, John; Beloit Catholic HS; Beloit, WI; 8/86 Aud/Vis; ChrhWkr; HonRl; NHS; SchMus; SchPl; Yrbk; RptrSchPpr; IMSpt; Loras College; Dentistry.

ONDRA, Stephen L; Bradley Bourbonnais HS; Bourbonnais, IL; 5/385 ALBoysSt; HonRl; IntrClCncl; NHS; NatlThespSoc; SchAde; SchPl; SctActv; StuGov; TchrAde; FrCl; SciCl; Ftbl; University; Professional.

ONDRACEK, Brian D; J S Morton HS; Berwyn, IL; Band; ChrhWkr; CncrtBnd; HonRl; JrNHS; MrchBnd; NHS; PepBnd; Moody Bible Institute; Ministry.

ONEAL, Gayle; Rich South Hs; Park Forest, IL; HonRl; IntrClCncl; NatlMeritSchl; OffAde; SchAde; RptrSchPpr; SpnCl; Chrldr; Northern Illinois; Teacher.

ONG, Charles L; La Crosse HS; Rush Center, KS; PresFrshCls; VPSophCls; Band; Chr; HonRl; PepBnd; SchPl; FFA; PpCl; LetterBsktbl; Ksu; Engineering.

ONION, David D; Industry HS; Table Grove, IL; PresFrshCls; HonRl; SchPl; YthFlsp; Bsktbl; LetterFtbl; Glf; Trk; IMSpt; PresAwd; Bradley U; Business.

ONION, Melanie S; Abingdon HS; Abingdon, IL; Band; HonRl; NHS; PresStuCncl; Pres4-H; LetterBsktbl; GAA; DanFAwd; 4-HAwd; KiwanAwd; College; Professional.

ONKEN, Dean R; Carroll Community HS; Glidden, IA; 13/102 HonRl; StuCncl; YthFlsp; Yrbk; 4-H; Bsktbl; College.

ONNEN, Janet L; Benson HS; Omaha, NE; 2/402 Band; CncrtBnd; DrlTm; HonRl; MrchBnd; NHS; PepBnd; MthCl; PpCl; GAA; Univ Ne; Chem Engr.

ONNEN, Neal; Fairbury HS; Hebron, NE; 7/140 TrsJrCls; ALBoysSt; ChrhWkr; HonRl; NHS; 4-H; Ks St U.

ONOPA, Susan B; Wausau East HS; Wausau, WI; 8/297 SecTrsSrCls; DrmMjrt; NHS; Quill&Scroll; RedCrAde; StuCncl; EdYrBk; SchPpr; MthCl; Bsktbl; Swmmng; Trk; GAA; Marquette Univ; Nursing.

ONORATO, Michael J; Coal City HS; Coal City, IL; 15/96 PresSrCls; Band; CncrtBnd; HonRl; MrchBnd; NHS; Orch; PepBnd; SchMus; SchPl; StuGov; RptrYrbk; Univ Of Illinois; Lawyer.

ONWILER, Helen K; Franklin Public HS; Franklin, NE; 15/54 Band; Chrs; ChrhWkr; CncrtBnd; HonRl; MrchBnd; PepBnd; 4-H; FHA; PpCl; Univ; Marine Biol.

OOSTING, Cloyd; Adams HS; Adams, NE; 10/26 VPSrCls; ChrhWkr; HonRl; SchPl; Ftbl; Un Of Nebr; Forestry.

OPAL, Thomas N; Manchester HS; Manchester, MI; 4/100 ALBoysSt; Chr; Chrs; ChrhWkr; StuCncl; YthFlsp; GerCl; Bsktbl; LetterTrk; Eastern Mi U; Structural Engi.

OPBROEK, Carla A; Gregory HS; Gregory, SD; Chr; Chrs; ChrhWkr; HonRl; Quill&Scroll; StuCncl; RptrSchPpr; FBLA;.

OPEL, Douglas J; John Marshall HS; Indianapolis, IN; HonRl; JrNHS; NHS; StuCncl; KeyCl; SpnCl; Glf; Tennis; IMSpt; Clg; Prof.

OPELT, Wayne A; Neillsville HS; Neillsville, WI; TrsFrshCls; ChrhWkr; HonRl; StuCncl; FFA; PpCl; Ftbl; Trk; CaptWrstlng; IMSpt;.

OPENSHAW, Karen L; Chippewa Valley HS; Mt Clemens, MI; 1/310 HonRl; JrNHS; NatlFornLg; NHS; NatlMeritFnl; NatlMeritCmnd; NatlMeritSchl; OffAde; SctActv; RptrYrbk; LetterTennis; IMSpt; DARAwd; Wayne State Univ; Pre Medicine.

OPHEIM, Janice E; Mason City HS; Mason City, IA; Band; PresJA; MrchBnd; NHS; SctActv; YthFlsp; Chrldr; IMSpt; EldAwd; GovHonPrgAwd; Coll; Business Ed.

OPHEIM, Jeffrey R; Dows Comm HS; Dows, IA; 4/30 ALBoysSt; Band; CncrtBnd; HonRl; MrchBnd; VPStuCncl; Bsbl; Bsktbl; Ftbl; Glf; College; Banking.

OPILA, Anne M; Immaculate Heart Of Mary HS; Riverside, IL; 2/275 NatlMeritSF; SchPl; SctActv; FrCl; Univ Of Ill.

OPOIEN, David C; Dell Rapids Public HS; Dell Rapids, SD; 13/50 ChrhWkr; CncrtBnd; MrchBnd; NatlThespSoc; SchMus; SchPl; SctActv; SptEdYrbk; Ftbl; Trade School.

OPOLSKI, Kathy P; Calumet HS; Griffith, IN; HonRl; NHS; TchrAde; FrCl; Bsktbl; Trk; GAA; IMSpt; PPFtbl; Ball St Uni; Teacher.

OPP, Brian; Albert Lea Sr HS; Albert Lea, MN; HonRl; YthFlsp; GerCl; IMSpt; Univ Of Minnesota; Law.

OPP, Georgetta J; Glen Ullin HS; Glen Ullin, ND; 3/40 PresJrCls; PresSrCls; ALAGirlsSt; HonRl; HospAde; SchPl; PpCl; SciCl; Trk; Mary College; Work Handicapped.

OPP, Michael; Eureka HS; Eureka, SD; 15;57 Chrs; HonRl; SchMus; SchPl; StuGov; LetterBsbl; LetterBsktbl; LetterFtbl; LetterTrk; VoiceDemAwd; College;bus.

OPPE, Pamela A; Bergan HS; Peoria Heights, IL; 30/230 DrlTm; HonRl; PpCl; Special Educ.

OPPENHEIM, Judith L; University City HS; University City, MO; 6/538 AFS; Band; Chr; ChrhWkr; HonRl; NatlMeritCmnd; Orch; SctActv; SciCl; College; Clinical Pharmacy.

OPPERMAN, Jimmy S; Springfield HS; Springfield, IL; 66/550 Band; College; Electrical Engineering.

OPPERMAN, Jon E; Senior HS; Dubeuque, IA; ALBoysSt; Chr; Chrs; Ftbl; Trk; Wrstlng; IMSpt; AmLegAwd; JCAwd; PresAwd; Col.

OPPERMANN, Mark G; Rolla HS; Lecoma, MO; HonRl; PresNatlFornLg; TchrAde; PresGerCl; PresLatCl; IMSpt; CitAwd; Georgetown College Ky; German.

OPRISH, Sue E; Lew Wallace HS; Gary, IN; Chr; HonRl; NHS; College; Secretary.

OPSAHL, Marsha A; Austin HS; Austin, MN; 3/493 AFS; Chr; ChrhWkr; CmntyWkr; CncrtBnd; HonRl; NHS; Orch; StuCncl; 4-H; Trk; Austin Community College; Elem Education.

OPSAL, Betty; Mt Horeb HS; Mt Horeb, WI; 40/132 Chr; SchMus; SchPl; FrCl; PpCl; Bsktbl; Trk; Chrldr; GAA; Coll; English Ed.

ORAM, Priscilla J; Allegan HS; Allegan, MI; HonRl; NHS; SchPl; SchPpr; CivCl; 4-H; 4-HAwd; Trade; Outdoor Survival.

ORBAN, Alexander A; Gordon Tech HS; Chicago, IL; 45/618 CAP; HonRl; StuCncl; GerCl; MthCl; SciCl; Loyola; Biology.

ORBAN, Kenneth D; Warren Mott HS; Warren, MI; TrsFrshCls; VPBand; CncrtBnd; HonRl; MrchBnd; NHS; PepBnd; SchPl; TreasStuGov; FrCl; Tennis; Trk; Us Air Force Academy; Engineering & Pilot.

ORBAN, Randal D; Brown City HS; Brown City, MI; PresSophCls; CmntyWkr; HonRl; Yrbk; FFA; LetterBsktbl; IMSpt;.

ORCHARD, Gwendolyn K; Forest Park HS; Crystal Falls, MI; Chr; Chrs; CncrtBnd; HonRl; MrchBnd; 4-H; LetterTrk; IMSpt; PresAwd; Bus Sch; Major Acctg.

ORCHARD, Lauren W; Magic City Campus HS; Minot, ND; 117/656 Chr; ChrhWkr; HonRl; ROTC; YthFlsp; SpnCl; AmLegAwd; Col; Chaplaincy.

ORCUTT, Mark J; J C Harmon HS; Kansas City, KS; ALBoysSt; CncrtBnd; HonRl; MrchBnd; Orch; PepBnd; SchPl; StuGov; TchrAde; SciCl; Univ; Mechanical Engineer.

ORCUTT, Richard; Doniphan Public HS; Doniphan, NE; 5/38 TrsFrshCls; TrsSophCls; TrsJrCls; TrsSrCls; ALBoysSt; ChrhWkr; DrmBgl; HonRl; SchPl; 4-H; Ag School; Farmer.

ORCUTT, Venetta L; Lasalle Peru Twp HS; Peru, IL; PresAFS; Band; HonRl; MrchBnd; NHS; NatlMeritCmnd; StuCncl; FrCl; PpCl; College; Pharmacist.

ORDAZ, Steven P; Oak Forest HS; Oak Forest, IL; 7/326 JA; JCC; PolWkr; RedCrAde; StuCncl; StuGov; UNYO; YthFlsp; YthFnd; YthLg; Bsktbl; Augustana College; Law.

OREBAUGH, Allan K; Daleville HS; Daleville, IN; 7/92 Aud/Vis; NHS; 4-H; LetterTrk; 4-HAwd; Purdue University; Agriculture.

OREHEL, Rosemarie F; Riverside Brookfield HS; N Riverside, IL; 3/488 HospAde; NHS; SctActv; SecStuCncl; FrCl; GAA; Univ Of Ill; Engineering.

OREL, Elaine M; Colome HS; Hamill, SD; 3/34 DrlTm; OffAde; SchPl; EdSchPpr; PpCl; Bsktbl; AmLegAwd; DanFAwd; CitAwd; VoiceDemAwd; Vocational School; Vocation.

OREN, Dan A; Nicolet HS; Glendale, WI; 7/503 Band; CncrtBnd; MrchBnd; NHS; NatlMeritSF; PepBnd; StuGov; TchrAde; FrCl; College; Mathematics.

OREN, Marce; Shepherd HS; Shepherd, MI; 9/125 TrsSophCls; Band; HonRl; NHS; NatlMeritCmnd; NatlMeritSchl; Yrbk; LatCl; OptClAwd; Univ; Speech Pathology.

ORENDER, James P; St Laurence HS; Chicago, IL; 25/372 HonRl; SciCl; Univ Of Illinois; Pharmacy.

ORENIC, Christopher J; Joliet Catholic HS; Joliet, IL; 45/170 PresBand; MrchBnd; SchMus; RusCl; LetterBsktbl; College; Law.

ORF, Russell; St Dominic HS; O Fallon, MO; Chrl; HonRl; NatlMeritFnl; SchMus; StuGov; RptrSchPpr; FrCl; IMSpt; Drake Univ; Music Educ.

ORGANS, Harry; John Hersey HS; Arlington Hts, IL; 1/957 TrsFrshCls; SecSophCls; VPJrCls; PresSrCls; ALBoysSt; Aud/Vis; Band; ChrhWkr; CncrtBnd; HonRl; PPFtbl; BttyCrckrAwd; 4-HAwd; MasAwd; Univ Of So Palatine; Librarian.

ORI, Deborah L; Highland Park HS; Highland Park, IL; ChrhWkr; CmntyWkr; College; Secretary.

ORILLION, John S; Glenbard North HS; Bloomingdale, IL; 28/398 HonRl; SpnCl; LetterFtbl; LetterTrk; LetterWrstlng; Illinois Inst Of Tech; Engineering.

ORISON, Kathy J; Ponca HS; Ponca, NE; 4/36 CaptBand; Chrs; DrmMjrt; HonRl; NHS; SchPl; StuCncl; EdSchPpr; LetterTrk; Chrldr; Business School; Vocation.

ORKE, Cheryl A; Bottineau HS; Bottineau, ND;

Band; CncrtBnd; HonRl; HospAde; 4-H; FFA; Bsktbl; Trk; Chrldr; 4-HAwd; College.

ORKEGREN, Lynette; Palmer Public HS; Palmer, NE; Chrs; ChrhWkr; CncrtBnd; HonRl; MrchBnd; NHS; PepBnd; SchPl; PpCl; Chrldr; College; Legal Secretary.

ORLANDO, Annette R; Mason Sr HS; Mason, MI; 10/238 HonRl; JrNHS; NHS; NatlMeritCmnd; OffAde; SctActv; 4-H; PpCl; CaptTennis; Lansing Comm College; Secretary.

ORLOS, Michael; Roosevelt HS; Wyandotte, MI; Band; CncrtBnd; IMSpt; Trade School; Professional.

ORLOWSKI, Anthony A; Marquette HS; Michigan City, IN; HonRl; JA; OffAde; SchMus; StuCncl; Tennis; AmLegAwd; Purdue North Central; Fine Arts.

ORLOWSKI, Mark R; Menomonee Falls N HS; Menomonee Falls, WI; HonRl; NHS; NatlMeritFnl; GerCl; Ripon College; Medicine.

ORMAN, Alice F; Clay City HS; Cory, IN; 11/64 Band; CncrtBnd; DrlTm; HonRl; LbryAde; MrchBnd; NHS; TchrAde; FHA;.

ORMAN, Kimberly J; Linton Stockton HS; Linton, IN; 4/89 SecFrshCls; SecSophCls; SecJrCls; Band; Chr; HonRl; TreasNHS; SchPl; Yrbk; PresSpnCl; Butler U; Music.

ORMBERG, Kenneth; Nicollet Public HS; Nicollet, MN; HonRl; SchPl; SptEdYrbk; 4-H; Bsbl; Ftbl; Trk; College.

ORME, Sandra L; Williamsfield HS; Williamsfied, IL; 2/32 ALAGirlsSt; Chrs; HonRl; LbryAde; NHS; OffAde; SchPpr; GAA; CitAwd; Carl Sandburg Coll; Nurse.

ORNER, Cheryl L; Twin Valley HS; Bennington, KS; 2/20 Band; CmntyWkr; HonRl; NatlThespSoc; SchMus; SchPl; StuCncl; EdYrBk; RptrSchPpr; 4-H; Kansas St Univ; Research Chemistry.

ORNS, Veronica L; Gull Lake HS; Hickory Corners, MI; Band; ChrhWkr; HonRl; PepBnd; PolWkr; RptrSchPpr; 4-H; FrCl; PpCl; University; Psychology.

OROS, Cheryl M; Divine Child HS; Dearborn, MI; SecSrCls; HonRl; NHS; Quill&Scroll; StuCncl; RptrSchPpr; FrCl; Chrldr; Univ Of Michigan; Math Teacher.

OROSZ, Joel J; Portage No HS; Portage, MI; 13/380 HonRl; NHS; NatlMeritSF; TchrAde; SchPpr; PresLatCl; LetterFtbl; LetterTrk; CaptIMSpt; Kalamazoo Col; English.

OROURKE, Robert; Collinsville Hs; Collinsville, IL; HonRl; College; Accountant.

OROZCO, Rosa; Ellsworth HS; Kanopolis, KS; 12/69 ChrhWkr; HonRl; StuCncl; SpnCl; BttyCrckrAwd; Wichita St Univ; Nursing.

ORR, Christine L; Unity HS; Lima, IL; SecJrCls; Band; Chrs; CncrtBnd; HonRl; MrchBnd; PepBnd; YthFlsp; RptrSchPpr; 4-H; College.

ORR, Daniel; Houston HS; Houston, MN; ChrhWkr; HonRl; LbryAde; 4-H; FFA; 4-HAwd; Tech Coll; Nursery Management.

ORR, Jacquelyn M; Ritenour Sr HS; St Louis, MO; 50/900 ChrhWkr; JrNHS; NHS; StuCncl; LetterBsbl; LetterBsktbl; LetterSwmmng; LetterTennis; GAA; PresAwd; Univ Of Missouri; Physical Education.

ORR, Linda; Oak Park HS; Kansas City, MO; Chr; Chrs; DrlTm; HonRl; SchMus; SchPl; StuCncl; TchrAde; PpCl; Bsktbl; Trk; Chrldr; GAA; College; Computer Programming.

ORR, Louisa F; Parkway Central HS; Chesterfield, MO; ALAGirlsSt; Chr; ChrhWkr; NHS; YthFlsp; SptEdYrbk; PpCl; Chrldr; PPFtbl; Southern Methodist U; Professional.

ORR, Patrick N; Sabetha HS; Sabetha, KS; ALBoysSt; Chr; ChrhWkr; HonRl; YthFlsp; FBLA; Coll; Pro.

ORR, Paula J; Granite City North HS; Granite City, IL; 18/375 Chrs; NHS; PpCl; Univ; Business Adm.

ORR, Ruth E; Oakville HS; St Louis, MO; 7/338 Chrs; HonRl; LitMag; NHS; NatlMeritCmnd; SchMus; 4-H; PpCl; IMSpt; 4-HAwd; St Louis U; Speech Pathology.

ORRIS, Michael; Benson HS; Omaha, NE; Chr; ChrhWkr; HonRl; LbryAde; SchAde; TchrAde; College; Lab Tech.

ORSBORN, Lyle D; O Meill Public HS; O Meill, NE; PresSophCls; Chrl; Chrs; HonRl; SchMus; StuCncl; LetterFtbl; LetterTrk; LetterWrstlng; College; Teaching.

ORSHEK, Cynthia; Cedar Rapids HS; Cedar Rapids, NE; 2/32 HstFrshCls; SecSophCls; CncrtBnd; HonRl; MrchBnd; PepBnd; SchMus; YthFlsp; Yrbk; College.

ORSINGER, Jack A; Benet Academy; Naperville, IL; HonRl; NHS; Bsbl; LetterBsktbl; Ftbl; College; Accounting.

ORSTED, Michele J; Gibraltar HS; Fish Creek, WI; 17/67 CmntyWkr; CncrtBnd; NatlFornLg; NHS; StuGov; UNYO; YthFnd; FBLA; Trk; GAA; U W Eau Claire; Special Educ.

ORTBALS, Joann D; Fatima HS; Argyle, MO; Chr; Chrs; Univ Of Missouri; Biology.

ORTEGA, Yvonne C; Pius X HS; Lincoln, NE; 12/160 HonRl; NHS; RptrYrbk; FBLA; LatCl; SpnCl; MthCl; SciCl; Chrldr; GAA; University; Medicine/surgeon.

ORTEL, Thomas L; New Palestine HS; New Palestine, IN; 10/146 HonRl; NHS; TchrAde; Yrbk; 4-H; KeyCl; LatCl; Wrstlng; Indiana Univ; Physician.

ORTGIESEN, John W; Dixon HS; Dixon, IL; 41/352 ALBoysSt; Band; CncrtBnd; NHS; PepBnd; RptrYrbk; 4-H; Bsktbl; Trk; Univ Of Ill; Animal Science.

ORTH, Daniel A; Central HS; Evansville, IN; 21/650 HonRl; JA; NHS; Indiana St Univ; Accounting.

ORTH, Margaret A; Fairbury Cropsey HS; Fairbury, IL; Band; CncrtBnd; HonRl; MrchBnd; NatlMeritCmnd; PepBnd; Quill&Scroll; RptrYrbk; SchPpr; Illinois Wesleyan; English.

ORTH, Matthew T; Thomas Carr Howe HS; Indianapolis, IN; 13/616 DrlTm; HonRl; NHS;.

ORTHMANN, Cindy; Decatur Community HS; Oberlin, KS; SecSrCls; ALAGirlsSt; Chr; Chrl; Chrs; CmntyWkr; HonRl; SchMus; SchPl; Bus Sch.

ORTIQUE, Althea L; Emil G Hirsch HS; Chicago, IL; VPJrCls; HonRl; JrNHS; LbryAde; NHS; SctActv; MthCl; University; Civil Engineering.

ORTISI, Joann; Our Lady Star Of The Sea HS; Grosse Pointe Wood, MI; 4/65 SecSrCls; HonRl; LbryAde; NHS; SchMus; StuCncl; StuGov; SpnCl; GAA; IMSpt; Univ Mi; Education.

ORTIZ, Joyce A; Edison Sr HS; East Gary, IN; HstJrCls; VPSrCls; MrchBnd; StuCncl; RptrSchPpr; SchPpr; SpnCl; PpCl; GAA; College; Nurse.

ORTIZ, Sandy M; Shawnee Mission South HS; Overland Park, KS; HonRl; HospAde; NatlFornLg; PolWkr; SctActv; PpCl; SciCl; Univ; Eng Or Law.

ORTMAN, Lizanne L; Huron HS; Huron, SD; ChrhWkr; CaptBsktbl; Tennis; Trk; GAA; IMSpt; Coll.

ORTMAN, Paula A; Brookville HS; Brookville, IN; HonRl; OffAde; StuCncl; FHA; SpnCl; PpCl; LetterTrk; Chrldr; GAA; College.

ORTMANN, Barbara; St Marys HS; Remsen, IA; 12/47 TrsFrshCls; TrsSophCls; Chrs; HonRl; SchMus; SchPl; StuCncl; RptrSchPpr; 4-H; Glf; St Josephs Mercy Hosp; Radiologic Tech.

ORTMANN, Michael J; St Clement HS; Center Line, MI; 3/105 CmntyWkr; HonRl; NHS; SpnCl; SciCl; IMSpt; JETSAwd; Univ; Science Engineering Area.

ORTMEIER, Timothy M; Luther North HS; Chicago, IL; VPFrshCls; SchAde; SctActv; TchrAde; KeyCl; Ftbl; Trk; Wrstlng; Iowa State Univ; Electrical Engineer.

ORTMEIER, Warren A; Central Catholic HS; West Point, NE; PresJrCls; Chrl; HonRl; NHS; VPLatCl; Bsbl; Bsktbl; CaptFtbl; Trk; CchngActv; University; Business Finance.

ORTNER, Kathryn; Pittsville HS; Pittsville, WI; 4/84 SecSophCls; VPJrCls; NHS; StuCncl; RptrSchPpr; FBLA; FHA; FTA; PpCl; GAA; Technical School; Medical.

ORTON, Lisa R; West HS; Green Bay, WI; ChrhWkr; HonRl; LbryAde; NHS; OffAde; TchrAde; Yrbk; FrCl; SpnCl; PpCl; LetterSwmmng; Chrldr; Eau Claire Univ Wis; Sec Science.

ORTON, Luann P; Martin Hughes HS; Britt, MN; Band; Chr; HonRl; NHS; RptrYrbk; EdSchPpr; FHA; PpCl; Community Coll.

ORTON, Lynn D; West Sioux HS; Hawarden, IA; 6/79 Chrs; ChrhWkr; HonRl; LbryAde; NHS; SchMus; Wartburg College; Psychology.

ORTQUIST, Rise; Dassel Cokato HS; Cokato, MN; 19/122 ALAGirlsSt; Band; Chr; CtyCnl; DrmMjrt; HonRl; Mdrgl; MrchBnd; NHS; Chrldr; St Cloud Hospital School Of Nursing; Nurse.

ORVIS, Kevin L; Wilsonville HS; Wilsonville, NE; VPSophCls; Chrs; HonRl; SchPl; StuCncl; EdYrBk; RptrSchPpr; Ftbl; Nebraska Univ; Business.

ORZEL, Ronald B; St Patrick HS; Chicago, IL; 57/425 Loyola Univ; History.

OSAFORT, Joyce A; Edgerton Public HS; Woodstock, MN; HonRl; LbryAde; TchrAde; 4-H; FTA; College.

OSANTOWSKE, Debbie; Reese HS; Fairgrove, MI; 33/128 HonRl; NatlThespSoc; SchPl; TchrAde; RptrSchPpr; Trade School; Lpn Nurse.

OSBORN, Cynthia J; Affton HS; Affton, MO; Chr; Chrs; ChrhWkr; HonRl; HospAde; NatlMeritFnl; NatlMeritCmnd; NatlMeritSchl; StuGov; TchrAde; Wash Univ; Pre Med.

OSBORN, Cynthia J; Affton Sr HS; St Louis, MO; 37/387 Chr; Chrs; ChrhWkr; HonRl; HospAde; NatlMeritCmnd; NatlMeritSF; StuGov; TchrAde; SpnCl; College; Physician.

OSBORN, Denise L; Missouri Valley HS; Missouri Valley, IA; Chr; ChrhWkr; MrchBnd; StuCncl; 4-H; PpCl; CaptBsktbl; CaptSwmmng; CaptTrk; MasAwd; College; Professional.

OSBORN, Fred G; Kokomo HS; Kokomo, IN; 2/358 ALBoysSt; HonRl; JrNHS; NHS; NatlMeritSF; StuCncl; RptrSchPpr; SpnCl; LetterOptClAwd; In Univ; Medical Research.

OSBORN, Jeffrey S; Winnetonka Sr HS; Kansas City, MO; 11/517 CmntyWkr; HonRl; StuGov; TchrAde; SchPpr; GerCl; LatCl; MthCl; VPSciCl; Univ Of Missouri; Psychiatry.

OSBORN, Julie L; Quincy Comm HS; Coldwater, MI; TrsSophCls; TrsJrCls; TrsSrCls; OffAde; StuCncl; TchrAde; Yrbk; FTA; PresSpnCl; LetterTrk; Chrldr; GAA; IMSpt; College; Liberal Arts.

OSBORN, Marilyn R; Central HS; Burden, KS; 1/35 Chrs; ChrhWkr; HonRl; HospAde; OffAde; SchPl; TchrAde; Yrbk; 4-H; Oklahoma Baptist Univ; Nurse.

OSBORN, Marilyn R; Central Usd #462 HS; Burden, KS; Band; Chr; ChrhWkr; HonRl; NHS; OffAde; TchrAde; Yrbk; 4-H; Okla Baptist Univ; Nursing.

OSBORN, Morris E; Thomas A Edison Sr HS; East Gary, IN; VPSophCls; Band; ChrhWkr; CncrtBnd; HonRl; JrNHS; MrchBnd; PepBnd; SctActv; StuCncl; FrCl; Bsbl; Bsktbl; Univ; Physician.

OSBORN, Rebecca L; Kirksville Senior HS; Kirksville, MO; SecTrsJrCls; Band; Chrs; DrlTm; HonRl; NHS; RedCrAde; SchMus; PresStuCncl; FrCl; LetterTennis; Chrldr; GAA; College; Social Work.

OSBORN, Robert W; Alton Senior HS; Godfrey, IL; 326/803 Band; Chr; Chrs; ChrhWkr; HonRl; NatlThespSoc; SchMus; SchPl; SctActv; YthFlsp; Ill State Univ; Bus Admin & Law.

OSBORN, Sondra; Switzerland County Jr Sr Hs; Vevay, IN; 1/110 Band; HonRl; NHS; SchPl; StuCncl; YthFnd; 4-H; PpCl; GAA; 4-HAwd; College; Wildlife & Forestry Fields.

OSBORN, Theresa I; Ottawa HS; Ottawa, IL; 5/527 HonRl; NHS; NatlMeritSF; TchrAde; GerCl; Illinois Valley Comm College; Pharmacy.

OSBORN, Timothy E; Culver Comm HS; Culver, IN; Band; CncrtBnd; MrchBnd; PepBnd; SctActv; TchrAde; YthFlsp; 4-H; Bsbl; Bsktbl; IMSpt; University; Professional.

OSBORN, Vicky S; Prairie City Comm HS; Prairie City, IA; Band; Chrs; SchPl; TchrAde; RptrYrbk; RptrSchPpr; Bsbl; Area Xi Community College.

OSBORNE, Deborah A; Kinmundy Alma HS; Alma, IL; SecTrsFrshCls; SecSophCls; Band; SecChrs; HonRl; NHS; PresFHA; University; Nursing.

OSBORNE, Jamie M; Camelot Parochial HS; Cairo, IL; 3/16 TrsFrshCls; TrsSophCls; Chr; HonRl; StuCncl; RptrYrbk; RptrSchPpr; FrCl; Bsktbl; CaptChrldr; IMSpt; College; Engineering Technology.

OSBORNE, Jill E; Garretson Public HS; Garretson, SD; 11/50 Band; CncrtBnd; HonRl; MrchBnd; NatlFornLg; SchMus; SchPl; Yrbk; College; Medicine.

OSBORNE, Jo E; Central HS; Linton, IN; 4/47 TrsFrshCls; TrsJrCls; TrsSrCls; Band; HonRl; SecNHS; Orch; YthFlsp; 4-H; LetterBsktbl; Indiana University; Dental Hygiene.

OSBORNE, John A; Finlayson HS; Finlayson, MN; 1/14 TrsFrshCls; HonRl; SchPl; TreasStuCncl; LetterBsbl; LetterBsktbl; PresAwd;.

OSBORNE, Kimberly; Chaparral HS; Danville, KS; VPJrCls; Band; CncrtBnd; HonRl; MrchBnd; NHS; PepBnd; FHA; PpCl; College; Psychologist.

OSBORNE, Mark E; Chaminade Col Prep; Alton, IL; 18/116 Band; CncrtBnd; HonRl; NHS; StuCncl; Ftbl; Socr; Trk; IMSpt; AmLegAwd; St Mary Univ; Pro.

OSBOURN, Lori L; Monroe City R 1 HS; Monroe City, MO; SecFrshCls; SecBand; HonRl; PresNHS; VPStuCncl; RptrSchPpr; VPFHA; PpCl; PresSciCl; Bsktbl; Univ Of Mo At Columbia; Medicine.

OSBURN, Randall D; Centura HS; Cairo, NE; ALBoysSt; NHS; SctActv; Bsbl; LetterBsktbl; LetterFtbl; LetterTrk; Wrstlng;.

OSCARSON, Renee A; Richland HS; Wahpeton, ND; 1/28 CncrtBnd; HonRl; SchPl; RptrYrbk; EdSchPpr; Sec4-H; FHA; BttyCrckrAwd; 4-HAwd; Free Lutheran Bible School; Medical Tech.

OSCHWALD, Jeffrey A; Centennial HS; Champaign, IL; 1/355 Band; Chr; ChrhWkr; CncrtBnd; NHS; NatlMeritSF; Bsktbl; LetterFtbl; CchngActv; IMSpt; College; Minister.

OSCHWALD, Joseph M; St Johns Prep HS; Minneapolis, MN; HonRl; JrNHS; LbryAde; NHS; RptrYrbk; Bsbl; Bsktbl; Univ Of Minnesota; Engineering.

OSE, Susan I; Coon Rapids HS; Coon Rapids, MN; Chr; ChrhWkr; HonRl; LbryAde; Mdrgl; Orch; SchMus; RptrSchPpr; 4-H; GerCl; O Roberts Univ; Music.

OSER, Dennis O; New Franklin HS; New Franklin, MO; 3/35 HonRl; JrNHS; StuCncl; SpnCl; Bsbl; Bsktbl; IMSpt; U Of Mo; Agriculture.

OSER, Renae; Homestead HS; Ft Wayne, IN; 25/230 ChrhWkr; HonRl; NHS; TchrAde; SpnCl; Fort Wayne Bible Coll; Elementary Educ.

OSETH, Merilee J; Oslo Public HS; Oslo, MN; 3/53 SecTrsSophCls; Band; Chrs; ChrhWkr; HonRl; SchAde; SchPl; SchPpr; PresFHA; PpCl; Coll;sec.

OSGOOD, Monica A; Chase County HS; Cedar Point, KS; SecTrsSophCls; Band; CncrtBnd; HonRl; LbryAde; MrchBnd; PepBnd; SchPl; PpCl; Bsktbl; Dental Assistant.

OSHEA, Teresa; Jetmore HS; Jetmore, KS; 0/36 SecTrsSrCls; HonRl; RptrYrbk; SecTrsSophCls; College; Business.

OSHIRO, Kevin S; Elk Grove HS; Elk Grove Vlg, IL; 8/547 Band; HonRl; MrchBnd; NHS; NatlMeritCmnd; Quill&Scroll; SchMus; University; Music.

OSIP, Thomas; Riverside HS; Dearborn Heights, MI; Aud/Vis; ChrhWkr; HonRl; OffAde; SctActv; SpnCl; Swmmng; Tennis; Msu; Bus Adm.

OSKANDY, Maureen E; Oswego HS; Oswego, IL; 1/241 PresCncrtBnd; HonRl; LitMag; MrchBnd; NHS; Orch; VPCivCl; SpnCl; MthCl; DARAwd; Case Western Res Univ; Pre Medicine.

OSKEY, Jean M; Random Lake HS; Random Lake, WI; 5/99 HonRl; StuGov; SchPpr; FBLA; PpCl; LetterBsktbl; GAA; U W Oskosh; Letters And Science.

OSMER, Carol L; East Detroit HS; East Detroit, MI; HonRl; TchrAde; College; Dentistry.

OSOWSKI, David B; Thorp HS; Thorp, WI; ChrhWkr; CmntyWkr; HonRl; SchPl; SpnCl; LetterBsbl; LetterBsktbl; LetterFtbl; 4-HAwd; Us Army; Law Layer.

OSOWSKI, Pamela; Thorp HS; Thorp, WI; 18/75 SecSrCls; HonRl; SchMus; StuCncl; TchrAde; Yrbk; 4-H; PpCl; GAA; 4-HAwd; Coll; Fashion Design.

OSOWSKI, Theodore E; Flushing HS; Flushing, MI; PresJrCls; CAP; HonRl; Ftbl; Swmmng; Trk; University; Engineering.

OSOWSKI, Twyla; Oslo HS; Oslo, MN; 8/47 HonRl; SchPl; RptrYrbk; Yrbk; RptrSchPpr; PpCl; Chrldr; Moorhead St Coll.

OSOWSKI, Victor; Herrin Hs; Herrin, IL; PresSophCls; SctActv; PresStuCncl; StuGov; Ftbl; Wrstlng; AmLegAwd; U Of Illnois; Civil Engineering.

OSSEFOORT, James N; Edgerton Public HS; Woodstock, MN; 17/35 CmntyWkr; HonRl; 4-H; Bsbl; Ftbl; Trk; IMSpt; College.

OSSIAN, Michael S; Novi HS; Novi, MI; PresFrshCls; HonRl; NatlSciFnd; Orch; SchMus; TchrAde; RptrSchPpr; PresSciCl; AmLegAwd; Michigan State Univ; Doctor.

OSSMANN, William J; Brandywine HS; Niles, MI; HonRl; VPNHS; NatlMeritSF; PresNatlThespSoc; PresOrch; SchPl; RotaryAwd; University; Experimental Scienc.

OST, Holly J; Highland Community HS; Riverside, IA; 3/50 Chrs; HonRl; NHS; SchMus; SchPl; StuCncl; PresSpnCl; PpCl; Univ Of Iowa; Pharmacist.

OST, Holly J; Highland Comm HS; Riverside, IA; 2/48 Chrs; HonRl; NHS; SchMus; StuCncl; PresSpnCl; U Of Iowa; Engineering.

OST, Kelly D; Highland Community HS; Riverside, IA; 11/60 Chrs; HonRl; SchMus; LetterFtbl; LetterTrk; IMSpt; U Of Ia; Business.

OST, Linda C; Beulah HS; Beulah, ND; Band; Chr; ChrhWkr; CncrtBnd; SchMus; SctActv; YthFlsp; SchPpr; FHA; PpCl; Capital Commercial College.

OSTBY, Michael L; New Glarus HS; Monticello, WI; Band; CncrtBnd; MrchBnd; PepBnd; FFA; Wrstlng; Farming.

OSTENDORF, John; Okawville HS; Nashville, IL; Band; CncrtBnd; HonRl; MrchBnd; PepBnd; YthFlsp; 4-H; GerCl; PpCl; Kaskaskia Jr Coll; Plt & Soil.

OSTENDORF, Marsha D; Okawville HS; Nashville, IL; 4/65 Band; CncrtBnd; HonRl; MrchBnd; NHS; PepBnd; YthFlsp; RptrSchPpr; GerCl; Bsktbl; IMSpt; Kaskaskie Jr College; Pharmacist.

OSTER, Catherine A; Brookfield Academy; Wauwatosa, WI; 2/13 TrsJrCls; HonRl; SchPl; Yrbk;.

OSTER, Jolene K; Velva Public HS; Velva, ND; HonRl; TchrAde; FHA; GerCl; SciCl; GAA; Clge; Psychology.

OSTER, Peggy K; Midland Comm HS; Center Jct, IA; SecJrCls; HonRl; TchrAde; EdSchPpr; FHA; FTA; LetterTrk; Secretary;.

OSTER, Todd D; Ipswich Public HS; Ipwsich, SD; Aud/Vis; HonRl; PresNHS; SchMus; SchPl; PresStuCncl; RptrYrbk; LetterBsktbl; LetterFtbl; LetterTrk; Sd St Univ ;vet.

OSTERBERG, Debra L; Florence HS; Iron Mountain, MI; Band; Chr; Chrs; HonRl; Quill&Scroll; RptrYrbk; FTA; PpCl; Chrldr; College; Professional.

OSTERBY, Krisan L; Wayzata HS; Wayzata, MN; ChrhWkr; CmntyWkr; HonRl; HospAde; LitMag; NHS; NatlMeritSF; College;social Or Historic Res.

OSTERHAUS, Rebecca A; Bloomington HS; Bloomington, WI; 1/49 PresFrshCls; VPBand; Chrs; NHS; SecStuCncl; EdYrBk; Bsktbl; GAA; IMSpt; BttyCrckrAwd; Viterbo College; Nursing.

OSTERHOLT, Julie; Heelan HS; Sioux City, IA; 6/249 Chrs; HonRl; JA; NHS; NatlThespSoc; SchMus; SchPl; StuCncl; SpnCl; IMSpt; College; Business Admin.

OSTERLOH, Kevin; Glenbard North HS; Carol Stream, IL; SpnCl; LetterBsbl; LetterFtbl; Univ; Biological Sciences.

OSTERMAN, Joy L; Pekin Comm HS; Pekin, IL; Chrs; HonRl; HospAde; LbryAde; NHS; OffAde; StuCncl; Illinois Cntrl College; Data Processing.

OSTEROOS, Garnet; United HS; Des Lacs, ND; 2/38 ALAGirlsSt; Band; Chrs; CtyCnl; HonRl; SchPl; EdSchPpr; 4-H; 4-HAwd; Coll; Nurse.

OSTGARD, Daniel J; Paxton HS; Paxton, IL; 23/157 HonRl; SctActv; 4-H; FFA; Bsktbl; Ftbl; Trk; Univ Of Illinois; Teacher.

OSTGARDEN, Mark A; Lincoln HS; Thief River Falls, MN; 147/255 ChrhWkr; HonRl; SctActv; RptrSchPpr; SptEdSchPpr; GerCl; SpnCl; Ftbl; PPFtbl; Univ Of N Dak; Econ/law.

OSTLIE, Kirsten; Larimore HS; Northwood, ND; TrsJrCls; Chr; Chrs; HonRl; LitMag; SchMus; SchPl; StuCncl; StuGov; Coll; Art Studey.

OSTOICH, Thomas A; Morton Sr HS; Hammond, IN; ALBoysSt; HonRl; NHS; TchrAde; LetterBsktbl; Trk; Indiana Univ; Medicine.

OSTRAND, Deborah J; Gibraltar HS; Egg Harbor, WI; Chr; Chrs; LbryAde; 4-H; FHA;.

OSTRANDER, Dale P; Central City HS; Central City, NE; 5/92 PresSrCls; HonRl; PresNHS; RptrSchPpr; CaptBsbl; Bsktbl; CaptFtbl; LetterGlf; Trk; Wrstlng; Ne Univ; Teacher.

OSTRANDER, James W; Adlai E Stevenson HS; Deerfield, IL; 12/237 CAP; HonRl; NHS; StuGov; LetterBsbl; LetterBsktbl; LetterFtbl; Wrstlng; AmLegAwd; College; Professional.

OSTRANDER, Susan K; Manson Comm HS; Manson, IA; Band; CncrtBnd; HonRl; LbryAde; MrchBnd; Orch; PepBnd; SchPl; Trk; IMSpt; College; Computer Science.

OSTRANDER, Teri L; Central City HS; Central City, NE; Band; Chr; Chrs; CncrtBnd; HonRl; MrchBnd; PepBnd; StuGov; Bsktbl; LetterTrk; Coll; Pro.

OSTREM, Philip M; Eldora HS; Eldora, IA; VPSrCls; Band; HonRl; PepBnd; 4-H; MthCl; SciCl; Bsktbl; 4-HAwd; VFWAwd; Univ; Agribusiness.

OSTROM, Randy D; Patoka HS; Patoka, IL; 8/27 SchPl; StuCncl; TchrAde; YthFlsp; RptrSchPpr; PresFFA; PresFTA; SpnCl; LetterBsbl; LetterFtbl; College; Teacher.

OSTROSKY, Micki M; Glenbard South HS; Glen Ellyn, IL; 49/350 ChrhWkr; DrlTm; HonRl; HospAde; HstFrshCls; SchPl; PpCl; GAA; IMSpt; DARAwd; College; Social Work.

OSTROWSKI, Donald J; Oak Lawn HS; Oak Lawn, IL; HonRl; NatlMeritCmnd; StuCncl; TchrAde; KeyCl; College; Professional.

OSTROWSKI, Sandra J; Westview HS; Kankakee, IL; 10/270 JrNHS; NHS; SchMus; Bsbl; Swmmng; Tennis; Univ Of Ill; Physical Therapy.

OSTRUM, Dave; Saint Croix Central HS; New Richmond, WI; TrsSophCls; FFA; Wrstlng; Univ; Professional.

OSTRUSKA, Kathy L; Resurrection HS; Niles, IL; 29/260 CmntyWkr; HonRl; HospAde; NHS; SchMus; SchPl; SctActv; StuCncl; TchrAde; GAA; St Norbert Col; Elementary Ed.

OSTRUSZKA, Ellen S; Coloma HS; Coloma, MI; HonRl; NHS; TchrAde; RptrYrbk; PresLatCl; PpCl; Bsktbl; LetterTennis; BttyCrckrAwd; Michigan State Univ; Medical Tech.

OSWALD, Jeffrey S; Roncalli HS; Manitowoc, WI; 3/141 Aud/Vis; VPNHS; VPStuCncl; StuGov; RptrSchPpr; KeyCl; MthCl; LetterBsktbl; LetterTennis; LetterTrk; Military Academy; Medicine.

OSWALD, Kay J; Gary HS; Gary, SD; 1/16 SecTrsSrCls; ALAGirlsSt; Band; HonRl; SchPl; EdYrBk; Bsktbl; Trk; Chrldr; College.

OSWALD, Marilyn K; Southland HS; Adams, MN; 2/122 HonRl; NHS; Sdlty; StuCncl; GerCl; LetterTrk; U Of Mn Morris; Physical Ed Teacher.

OSWALD, Mark E; Gary HS; Gary, SD; VPSophCls; ALBoysSt; HonRl; Sacrstn; SchPl; StuCncl; SptEdYrbk; LetterBsktbl; LetterFtbl; LetterTrk; College.

OSWALD, Mark W; Arapahoe HS; Arapahoe, NE; VPFrshCls; ChrhWkr; CmntyWkr; HonRl; JCC; RedCrAde; StuCncl; StuGov; SchPpr; CivCl; Arizona State College; Baseball.

OSWALD, Susie; Memorial HS; Evansville, IN; CmntyWkr; HonRl; TchrAde; FrCl; University; Special Education.

OSWALL, Mary F; Edgewood HS; Madison, WI; Chrs; HonRl; HospAde; NHS; SchMus; PpCl; Marquette Univ; Dental Hygiene.

OSWALT, David A; Southern Wells HS; Bluffton, IN; 9/100 VPFrshCls; ALBoysSt; ChrhWkr; HonRl; NHS; SchAde; TchrAde; YthFlsp; LetterBsktbl; LetterGlf; Col; Professional.

OSWALT, Rebecca; Collins Community HS; Colo, IA; Chrs; CncrtBnd; HonRl; Yrbk; SpnCl; IMSpt; PPFtbl; Univ Of Northern Ia; Elementary Education.

OSWEILER, Andy M; Tri County HS; Webster, IA; ALBoysSt; Band; ChrhWkr; CmntyWkr; HonRl; MrchBnd; SchPl; 4-H; Bsbl; 4-HAwd; College; Farmer.

OSWEILER, Thomas J; English Valley HS; Webster, IA; 1/65 PresSophCls; ALBoysSt; HonRl; NHS; SctActv; StuCncl; TchrAde; FTA; SpnCl; PpCl; Univ Of Iowa; Educ.

OTEY, Dennis H; Woodruff HS; Peoria, IL; 17/275 HonRl; SctActv; TchrAde; KeyCl; GerCl; Bradley U; Elec Eng.

OTIS, Phillip E; Haslett HS; Haslett, MI; 41/147 ChrhWkr; CncrtBnd; LbryAde; MrchBnd; PepBnd; SctActv; TchrAde; LetterFtbl; Swmmng; LetterTrk; College; Physics.

OTLOSKI, Elizabeth L; Luke M Powers HS; Flint, MI; 8/306 NHS; RedCrAde; SchMus; TchrAde; U Of Mi; Chemistry.

OTT, Don A; Deerfield HS; Deerfield, IL; ChrhWkr; HonRl; Calvin College; Pharmacy.

OTT, Gregory A; Central HS; Waterloo, IA; SecFrshCls; ALBoysSt; Chr; HonRl; NHS; SchMus; SchPl; LetterBsbl; LetterFtbl; LetterWrstlng; Clg In Iowa; Music & Sports.

OTT, John C; Toulon HS; La Fayette, IL; 4/58 CmntyWkr; HonRl; SchAde; TchrAde; Pres4-H; FFA; KeyCl; LetterBsktbl; DanFAwd; 4-HAwd; JAAwd; College; Farming.

OTT, Judith A; Roanoke Benson HS; Roanoke, IL; Chr; Chrl; Chrs; HonRl; LbryAde; OffAde; 4-H; FHA; Chrldr; IMSpt; Ill Central Coll; Science.

OTT, Julie A; Mitchell HS; Bedford, IN; 2/150 HonRl; NHS; Quill&Scroll; 4-H; FHA; GAA; DanFAwd; 4-HAwd; Purdue Univ.

OTT, Kathy A; New Glarus HS; New Glarus, WI; 25/58 VPSophCls; Band; CncrtBnd; PepBnd; SchPl; PresStuCncl; EdSchPpr; PresPpCl; Trk; LetterChrldr; GAA; CitAwd; Trade School; Florist.

OTT, Matthew; Naperville Central Hs; Naperville, IL; 107 HonRl; NHS; NatlMeritCmnd; TreasYthFlsp; College;chemistry.

OTT, Nancy L; North HS; Fargo, ND; ChrhWkr; NatlFornLg; NatlThespSoc; SchMus; SchPl; StuCncl; RptrSchPpr; CivCl; Chrldr; U Of Nd; Medicine.

OTT, O William; East HS; Waterloo, IA; 2/340 Band; Chr; HonRl; NHS; Orch; StuCncl; EdSchPpr; Bsbl; Bsktbl; Ftbl; College.

OTT, Robert E; Avon HS; Avon, IL; PresFrshCls; Band; CncrtBnd; HonRl; JrNHS; MrchBnd; PepBnd; FrCl; LetterFtbl; IMSpt; University; Professional.

OTT, Susan E; Quincy Sen HS; Quincy, IL; AFS; ChrhWkr; CmntyWkr; HonRl; HospAde; SctActv; Yrbk; PresGerCl; LatCl; Trk; Ill State Univ; Sociology.

OTT, Timothy M; Madison HS; Lamont, KS; PresFrshCls; ALBoysSt; Band; CncrtBnd; HonRl; MrchBnd; PresStuCncl; Treas4-H; LetterBsktbl; CaptFtbl; Kansas State University.

OTT, William; East HS; Waterloo, IA; 4/340 ALBoysSt; Band; ChrhWkr; CncrtBnd; HonRl; TchrAde; EdSchPpr; Bsbl; Bsktbl; Ftbl; Iowa State.

OTTE, Brenda D; Downs HS; Cawker City, KS; SecSrCls; ALAGirlsSt; Chr; HonRl; SchPl; RptrSchPpr; FHA; PpCl; Bsktbl; Trk; Dordt College ;education.

OTTE, Daniel R; Oostburg HS; Oostburg, WI; 5/70 ChrhWkr; HonRl; StuGov; YthFlsp; Yrbk; SptEdSchPpr; LetterBsktbl; Glf; IMSpt; College.

OTTE, Doris L; Seymour HS; Seymour, IN; 10/325 Chr; HonRl; HospAde; SchMus; 4-H; PpCl; Trk; GAA; Iupui Indianapolis; Nursing.

OTTE, Jean M; Chesaning Union HS; Chesaning, MI; HonRl; JrNHS; NHS; RedCrAde; StuGov; TchrAde; PresTeen; YthFlsp; Pres4-H; TreasFrCl; Computers.

OTTE, Marianne E; Southeast HS; Wichita, KS; 128/466 Band; ChrhWkr; CmntyWkr; MrchBnd; Orch; RedCrAde; SchMus; UNYO; EdSchPpr; CivCl; College; Music Performance.

OTTE, Teresa L; South Page HS; Clarinda, IA; 8/36 Chr; ChrhWkr; Mdrgl; SchMus; RptrYrbk; RptrSchPpr; FHA; PpCl; College; Medicine.

OTTEN, Conny M; Mattawan HS; Texas Corners, MI; 17/108 Chrl; HonRl; HospAde; NHS; SchAde; StuCncl; RptrYrbk; FHA; IMSpt; 4-HAwd; Western Mi U; Hs Choir Director.

OTTENBACHER, Arlene M; Eureka HS; Eureka, SD; 1/57 Chr; HonRl; SchMus; SchPl; YthFlsp; Yrbk; SchPpr; FHA; PpCl; GAA; N State Clge; Business.

OTTENSMANN, Peggy A; Coon Rapids HS; Coon Rapids, MN; HonRl; NHS; TchrAde; LetterSwmmng; College; Professional Engineer.

OTTERNESS, Craig A; Spring Grove HS; Spring Grove, MN; PresSophCls; PresJrCls; PresSrCls; HonRl; StuCncl; 4-H; LetterBsbl; Wrstlng; 4-HAwd; Col; Architect.

OTTERSON, David J; Caledonia HS; Caledonia, MN; 1/152 ALBoysSt; Band; Chrs; HonRl; NHS; NatlMeritCmnd; StuCncl; LetterBsbl; LetterBsktbl; LetterFtbl; VFWAwd; Us Naval Academy; Engineering.

OTTERSON, Keith E; Benton HS; Benton, IL; Band; Chr; Chrs; CmntyWkr; CncrtBnd; MrchBnd; PepBnd; SchMus; 4-H; MthCl; 4-HAwd; Rend Lake Col; Music.

OTTERSON, Tammy A; Mapleton Public HS; Mapleton, ND; SecTrsFrshCls; SecTrsSophCls; Band; Chr; Chrs; PepBnd; SchMus; SchPl; YthFlsp; Bsktbl;.

OTTIS, Mark; Kindred HS; Kindred, ND; ALBoysSt; Band; Chr; CncrtBnd; SctActv; FFA; 4-HAwd; Trade; Farming.

OTTMAN, Robert A; Rhinelander HS; Rhinelander, WI; Bsktbl; LetterFtbl; LetterTrk; Machinist.

OTTO, Cecile M; Holy Trinity HS; Lester Prairie, MN; 2/56 Chrs; HonRl; LbryAde; SchMus; TchrAde; RptrYrbk; 4-H; EngCl; MthCl; College Of St Katherine; Home Economics.

OTTO, Christopher P; Campion HS; Carroll, IA; 6/100 SecSrCls; CncrtBnd; ModUN; NatlMeritCmnd; PepBnd; SchPl; StuGov; RptrSchPpr; LetterFtbl; LetterTennis;.

OTTO, Judy; Nicollet Public HS; Nicollet, MN; TrsSrCls; ChrhWkr; HonRl; FHA; PpCl; SciCl; Coll; Majory Study.

OTTO, Kristina E; Herbert Henry Dow HS; Midland, MI; ChrhWkr; HonRl; NHS; Orch; EngCl; Swmmng; IMSpt; Alma College; English.

OTTO, Lynn M; Assumption HS; Davenport, IA; 5/204 AFS; Band; HonRl; NHS; NatlMeritSF; NatlThespSoc; SchMus; SchPl; StuCncl; LetterSwmmng; Univ;foreign Lang.

OTTO, Mark A; Heyworth HS; Heyworth, IL; Chrs; CmntyWkr; HonRl; SchMus; EngCl; SpnCl; LetterBsbl; Bsktbl; LetterFtbl; LetterTrk; Univ; Behavioral Sciences.

OTTO, Randall G; Sheboygan Falls HS; Sheboygan Falls, WI; ALBoysSt; Band; CncrtBnd; HonRl; MrchBnd; NHS; PepBnd; RptrSchPpr; GerCl; Ftbl; Uw Sheyb; Mass Comm.

OTTO, William B; Northwestern Preparatory HS; Montello, WI; Yrbk; SchPpr; SciCl; Tennis; IMSpt; Dr Martin Luther Col; Professional Teacher.

OTTO, William L; Milwaukee Lutheran HS; Menomonee Falls, WI; LetterBsbl; IMSpt; Trade School.

OTTOSON, Rebecca J; Monroe Sr HS; Monroe, WI; ChrhWkr; CmntyWkr; HonRl; LitMag; StuCncl; TchrAde; YthFlsp; SchPpr; 4-H; Tennis; Trk; GAA; Trinity College; Religion.

OTZENBERGER, Theresa M; St Anthony HS; St Louis, MO; 15/72 Chrs; HonRl; HospAde; JA; LbryAde; SchMus; SctActv; SciCl; IMSpt; 4-HAwd; Clge; Lawyer.

OUDENHOVEN, Kathryn L; Saint Joseph Academy; De Pere, WI; Chrl; Chrs; JA; NatlThespSoc; OffAde; SchAde; SchMus; SchPl; StuGov; Yrbk; SpnCl; PpCl; Tennis; College; Law.

OUELLETTE, Ann C; Sacred Heart HS; Dearborn, MI; HonRl; LetterTrk; LetterSwmmng; College.

OUELLETTE, Gary L; Holy Redeemer HS; Detroit, MI; 8/186 PresAud/Vis; HonRl; NHS; SchPl; Yrbk; CaptTrk; Mi Tech U; Conservation Officer.

OUELLETTE, Nancy; Washington HS; Washington, KS; HonRl; FBLA; FFA; FHA; PpCl; Coll.

OUJIRI, Timon M; Lasalle HS; Cedar Rapids, IA; ALBoysSt; Aud/Vis; Chr; ChrhWkr; Mdrgl; SchMus; SchPl; StuCncl; PpCl; LetterFtbl; College; Business.

OURADA, Bill T; Elm Creek HS; Elm Creek, NE; 9/30 PresJrCls; PresSrCls; HonRl; NHS; Bsbl; LetterBsktbl; LetterFtbl; LetterTrk; College; Vocation.

OUREN, Renae L; Pelican Rapids HS; Rothsay, MN; Band; ChrhWkr; CncrtBnd; HonRl; MrchBnd; PepBnd; Vo Tech School; Bookkeeping.

OURSBOURN, Debra S; Stoutland HS; Richland, MO; 1/38 Chrs; ChrhWkr; CncrtBnd; HonRl; LitMag; LbryAde; MrchBnd; VPFHA; PpCl; Bsbl; Sw Mo St Univ; Business.

OURSO, Susan A; Lee M Thurston HS; Detroit, MI; ChrhWkr; CmntyWkr; HospAde; JrNHS; NHS; SchMus; TchrAde; RptrYrbk; GerCl; Spring Arbor Coll; Spec Ed.

OVELLETTE, Gary L; Holy Redeemer HS; Detroit, MI; 15/188 PresAud/Vis; NHS; SptEdYrbk; CaptTrk;.

OVERBERG, Teresa A; Marquette HS; Salem, IA; 4/49 TrsFrshCls; Chr; Chrs; DrlTm; HonRl; NHS; SchPl; StuCncl; FTA; College.

OVERBEY, Jackie D; E St Louis Sr HS; E St Louis, IL; 32/691 ChrhWkr; HonRl; LbryAde; NHS; SchPl; StuCncl; StuGov; RptrYrbk; Air Force; Aircraft Maintenance.

OVERBY, Brian J; Shabbona HS; Shabbona, IL; 9/44 TrsSrCls; CncrtBnd; HonRl; MrchBnd; SctActv; StuCncl; LetterBsbl; LetterSocr; Kishwaukee Jr College; History.

OVERCASH, Timothy J; Eastside HS; Butler, IN; HonRl; StuCncl; SpnCl; SciCl; LetterFtbl; LetterWrstlng; Purdue U; Elec Engr.

OVERCASHIER, John R; Holly HS; Holly, MI; CmntyWkr; HonRl; JA; NatlFornLg; NHS; PolWkr; SchMus; SchPl; StuCncl; Wrstlng; U Of Mich; Lawyer.

OVERFELT, Lynda K; Boone County HS; Centrlia, MO; 21/90 CncrtBnd; HonRl; MrchBnd; NHS; PepBnd; SchMus; YthFlsp; FHA; LetterBsktbl; LetterTrk; Univ.

OVERFIELD, Charlene M; Tri Central HS; Sharpsville, IN; 7/85 Band; ChrhWkr; HonRl; JrNHS; NHS; TchrAde; YthFlsp; PpCl; Trk; Chrldr;.

OVERGAARD, Kaj K; Austin Central HS; Austin, MN; Chr; ChrhWkr; SchPpr; CaptBsktbl; LetterTrk; Lutheran School; Religion.

OVERGAARD, Marcia L; Luverne HS; Luverne, MN; 1/130 ALAGirlsSt; CncrtBnd; HonRl; MrchBnd; NatlFornLg; NHS; PepBnd; SpnCl; Chrldr; PresAwd; Ks State Univ; Biology.

OVERGAARD, Steven R; Central HS; Albert Lea, MN; 20/496 VPJrCls; HonRl; SctActv; StuCncl; StuGov; KeyCl; LetterFtbl; Glf; Austin Jr College; Mech Engineer.

OVERHOLT, Debra K; Pellston HS; Levering, MI; 1/50 TrsSrCls; Band; HonRl; SchPl; 4-H; N Michigan Univ; Secretarial Admin.

OVERHOLTZER, Bretton C; Lewis Central HS; Council Bluffs, IA; 6/182 PresFrshCls; PresSophCls; PresJrCls; ALBoysSt; Band; HonRl; NHS; SctActv; StuCncl; Bsktbl; Ia State U; Civil Engr.

OVERLEY, Sherri; St Mary Acad; Indianapolis, IN; 2/33 HstJrCls; SecSrCls; Chr; CmntyWkr; HonRl; NHS; StuCncl; StuGov; GerCl; GovHonPrgAwd; Ind Central Univ; Law.

OVERLEY, Sherri L; St Mary Academy; Indianapolis, IN; 2/34 HstJrCls; SecSrCls; Chr; Chrs; ChrhWkr; HonRl; JA; JrNHS; PresNHS; VPGerCl; PPFtbl; JAAwd; Col; Law.

OVERMAN, Robert E; St Rita HS; Chicago, IL; 140/400 EdYrBk; SchPpr; De Paul Univ; Doctor.

OVERMILLER, Karma J; Smith Center HS; Bellaire, KS; 13/61 ChrhWkr; HonRl; NHS; StuGov; EdYrBk; RptrSchPpr; 4-H; FHA; AmLegAwd; Kansas State University; Home Economics.

OVERMILLER, Pamela J; Smith Center Jr Sr HS; Bellaire, KS; TrsJrCls; Chrs; ChrhWkr; CmntyWkr; HonRl; MrchBnd; StuCncl; FHA; Chrldr; 4-HAwd;.

OVERMILLER, Teresa A; Smith Center HS; Smith Center, KS; 7/75 Band; Chrl; ChrhWkr; HonRl; MrchBnd; NHS; StuCncl; PresYthFlsp; LetterPpCl; AmLegAwd;.

OVERMYER, Linda S; Culver Comm HS; Monterey, IN; 4/100 ALAGirlsSt; Band; IntrClCncl; MrchBnd; NHS; RptrYrbk; 4-H; FTA; SpnCl; PpCl; Purdue Univ; Mathematics.

OVERMYER, Suzanne M; Rantoul Township HS; Rantoul, IL; CmntyWkr; LbryAde; SchAde; SchPl; SchPpr; SpnCl; VoiceDemAwd; Clg; Interior Decorater.

OVERPECK, Eddie R; Van Buren HS; Centerpoint, IN; ChrhWkr; SctActv; Teen; YthFlsp; FrCl; Ftbl; Trk; KiwanAwd; U S Marines; Auto Mechanics.

OVERSON, Bruce R; Mound Westonka HS; Mound, MN; Band; HonRl; StuGov; LetterFtbl; LetterTennis; College; Forestry.

OVERTON, Judith L; Gibson Southern HS; Fort Branch, IN; VPFrshCls; SecSophCls; ALAGirlsSt; SchPpr; FHA; LatCl; College; Political Journalism.

OVERTON, Rhonda C; Corydon Central HS; Corydon, IN; 7/134 HonRl; NHS; TchrAde; FTA; FrCl; PpCl; Se Indiana Univ.

OVERTON, Ronald E; Stevens HS; Rapid City, SD; 25/425 ALBoysSt; ChrhWkr; CmntyWkr; HonRl; PolWkr; StuCncl; TchrAde; YthFlsp; Ftbl; Glf; College; Major Study.

OVERTON, Samuel E; Shiloh HS; Hume, IL; ChrhWkr; CmntyWkr; HonRl; TchrAde; YthFlsp; Yrbk; SecFFA; LetterBsbl; LetterBsktbl; Trk; College; Vocation.

OVERTON, Sheila M; Stevens HS; Rapid City, SD; 29/410 NHS; OffAde; PpCl; S Dakota St Univ; Nursing.

OVERTURF, Diane R; Sparta Senior HS; Sparta, WI; Chr; Chrs; ChrhWkr; HonRl; NHS; YthFlsp; RptrSchPpr; MthCl; Christian College; Gospel Singer.

OVERTURF, Susan; Centerville HS; Richmond, IN; /120 HonRl; SchPl; StuGov; TchrAde; Teen; FTA; PpCl; Trk; GAA; IMSpt; Indiana Univ; Business.

OVERVIG, Brian J; Rosemount Sr HS; Inver Grove Hts, MN; HonRl; JA; NatlFornLg; TchrAde; RptrSchPpr; SpnCl; Tennis; CchngActv; IMSpt; College; Business.

OWCZARZAK, Milissa M; St Florian HS; Detroit, MI; 15/126 SecFrshCls; SecSophCls; SecJrCls; SecSrCls; HonRl; NHS; StuCncl; StuGov; RptrYrbk; CaptChrldr; Eastern Mi Univ; Psychology.

OWDZIEJ, Mary; Our Lady Of Mercy HS; Lathrup Village, MI; CmntyWkr; ModUN; NatlFornLg; TchrAde; RptrSchPpr; GerCl; Univ Of Mi; Law.

OWEN, Karen A; Britton HS; Britton, SD; Chr; Chrs; ChrhWkr; HonRl; MrchBnd; NHS; PolWkr; SchPl; StuCncl; TchrAde; Chrldr; CchngActv; Univ Of South Dakota; Business Admin.

OWEN, Laurel A; Proviso West HS; Westchester, IL; 45/950 Band; ChrhWkr; CncrtBnd; HonRl; HospAde; MrchBnd; NHS; NatlMeritCmnd; Orch; PepBnd; YthLg; GerCl; Univ Of Illinois; Music.

OWEN, William J; Central HS; Flint, MI; 30/480 Aud/Vis; HonRl; NHS; NatlThespSoc; SchPl; StuCncl; EdSchPpr; Mi State Univ; Social Science.

OWENS, Anne E; John Adams HS; Suth Bend, IN; 2/450 Chr; HonRl; NatlMeritSF; NatlThespSoc; SchMus; SchPl; RptrSchPpr; SchPpr; U Of Chicago; Pre Med.

OWENS, Ann M; Bishop Du Bourg HS; St Louis, MO; HonRl; NHS; OffAde; SchAde; GAA; IMSpt; PPFtbl; CitAwd; Col;.

OWENS, Billy J; Tipton HS; Tipton, IN; HonRl; NHS; TchrAde; SciCl; LetterGlf; Trk; IMSpt; Ball State University; Accounting.

OWENS, Carmen M; Shawano HS; Shawano, WI; Chrs; CmntyWkr; HonRl; LbryAde; NHS; NatlMeritCmnd; Treas4-H; FrCl; 4-HAwd; JAAwd; Univ Of Wisconsin; Horsemanship.

OWENS, Dale K; Crab Orchard HS; Marion, IL; HstJrCls; Band; ChrhWkr; CmntyWkr; HonRl; HospAde; PepBnd; SctActv; SptEdSchPpr; SchPpr; Trade School; Mechanic On Diesels.

OWENS, Dana S; O Fallon HS; Fairview Hts, IL; 10/314 ChrhWkr; CmntyWkr; HonRl; NHS; PepBnd; SctActv; StuCncl; 4-H; FrCl; PpCl; Chrldr; JAAwd; College; Mathematics.

OWENS, Deborah J; Hoopeston East Lynn HS; Hoopeston, IL; 24/127 ChrhWkr; LbryAde; NHS; GAA; Col; Ct Steno.

OWENS, Diane J; Roosevelt HS; Minneapolis, MN; ChrhWkr; TchrAde; PpCl; RptrYrbk; Swmmng; GAA; PPFtbl; MasAwd; PresAwd; College; Para Medic.

OWENS, Douglas W; Mitchell HS; Mitchell, IN; ALBoysSt; ChrhWkr; CmntyWkr; HonRl; NatlThespSoc; SchPl; SctActv; EdSchPpr; Glf; RotaryAwd; Indiana University; Doctor Of Dental Serv.

OWENS, Elizabeth N; Walled Lake Central HS; W Bloomfield, MI; 2/367 Chr; Chrs; HonRl; ChmnModUN; PresNHS; SchMus; SctActv; StuGov; YthFlsp; SciCl; Wittenberg Univ; Biology Major.

OWENS, Gregory; Dexter HS; Dexter, MO; 12/140 Chr; ChrhWkr; CmntyWkr; HonRl; NHS; NatlThespSoc; SchPl; FBLA; Tennis; EldAwd; Mid America Nazarene; Business.

OWENS, Howard S; La Salle HS; St Ignace, MI; ALBoysSt; Band; CmntyWkr; NHS; KeyCl; MthCl; SciCl; CaptBsktbl; LetterFtbl; IMSpt; Navy; Elec Entr.

OWENS, Jeri E; St Elmo Comm HS; St Elmo, IL; HonRl; NHS; SctActv; FHA; College.

OWENS, Joellen; Springfield HS; Springfield, IL; ChrhWkr; Lincolland Comm College; Sociology.

OWENS, John P; St Bede Academy; Bradford, IL; PresFrshCls; ALBoysSt; HonRl; NatlMeritCmnd; PolWkr; SchPl; StuGov; SpnCl; Creighton Univ; Physician.

OWENS, Karen A; Fennimore HS; Fennimore, WI; Band; CncrtBnd; HonRl; HospAde; MrchBnd; NHS; SchPl; SctActv; 4-H; LetterTrk; Coll; Chemist.

OWENS, Kent A; Elgin HS; Elgin, IL; 16/784 HonRl; NatlMeritCmnd; StuGov; LatCl; Univ Of Denver; Doctor.

OWENS, Marilyn; Bernie HS; Bernie, MO; 8/52 PresJrCls; Chrs; CncrtBnd; HonRl; MrchBnd; TchrAde; Twrl; FHA; Chrldr; BttyCrckrAwd;.

OWENS, Mary P; O Hara HS; Raytown, MO; 1/200 ALAGirlsSt; Chrs; HonRl; NHS; RptrSchPpr; SchPpr; FrCl; PpCl; Chrldr; IMSpt; College; Social Worker.

OWENS, Nancy R; R 1 North Callaway HS; Auxvasse, MO; 4/77 ChrhWkr; HonRl; TreasNHS; OffAde; SchPl; Twrl; FshEdYrbk; TreasFHA; FrCl; TreasPpCl; Ne Missouri State Univ; Medical Secretary.

OWENS, Patricia A; Paxton HS; Paxton, IL; 8/137 TrsSophCls; AFS; NHS; NatlMeritCmnd; NatlThespSoc; SchPl; StuCncl; TchrAde; PresEngCl; LetterTennis; Univ Of Illinois; Law.

OWENS, Sally J; New Trier East HS; Winnetka, IL; 70/841 Band; ChrhWkr; CncrtBnd; HonRl; Orch; YthFlsp; Colorado College; Veterinary Medicine.

OWENS, Sharron A; Madison HS; Madison Heights, MI; 25/264 HonRl; NHS; SpnCl; PpCl; Bsbl; Bsktbl; Swmmng; LetterTennis; LetterTrk; GAA; Mi St Univ; Veterinarian.

OWENS, Susan L; Kewanee HS; Kewanee, IL; 4/216 AFS; Chrs; HonRl; LbryAde; SchPl; SctActv; RptrYrbk; GerCl; Ill Wesleyan Univ; Biology.

OWENS, Tammy; Onalaska HS; Onalaska, WI; TrsJrCls; ALAGirlsSt; Band; HonRl; HospAde; NHS; StuCncl; FrCl; Chrldr; Viterbo Coll; Nursing.

OWENS, Teri L; Manhattan HS; Manhattan, KS; AFS; Band; Chr; CncrtBnd; MrchBnd; PepBnd; 4-H; PpCl; University; Nursing.

OWENS, Thomas E; Wamego HS; Wamego, KS; ALBoysSt; ChrhWkr; HonRl; SchAde; SctActv; TchrAde; SciCl; College; Business.

OWENS, Vicki L; New Berlin HS; New Berlin, IL; 5/63 Band; Chr; HonRl; JrNHS; SchMus; SchPl; StuCncl; Yrbk; FHA; PpCl; Trk; Univ Of Illinois; Social Work.

OWENS, Wes L; Marengo Comm HS; Marengo, IL; Band; Chr; Chrl; Chrs; CncrtBnd; HonRl; Mdrgl; MrchBnd; NatlThespSoc; PepBnd; LetterTrk; Wrstlng; BttyCrckrAwd; U S Armed Service.

OWERS, Linda J; Huron HS; Ann Arbor, MI; ChrhWkr; CmntyWkr; HonRl; HospAde; LitMag; NatlMeritSF; RedCrAde; SchPl; YthFlsp; RptrYrbk; University Of Michigan; Biochemistry.

OWINGS, Kendrick H; Ann Arbor Pioneer HS; Ann Arbor, MI; Band; Chr; CncrtBnd; HonRl; MrchBnd; NatlMeritSF; Orch; SctActv; YthFlsp; FrCl; Univ.

OWNBEY, James M; Maconaquah HS; Grissom Afb, IN; 53/217 NatlThespSoc; SchMus; SchPl; StuGov; TchrAde; YthFlsp; LatCl; SpnCl; LetterWrstlng; Us Air Force Acad; Political Sci.

OWSEN, David P; Chippewa Valley HS; Mt Clemens, MI; HonRl; SchAde; TchrAde; SchPpr; IMSpt; Ferris State College.

OWSLEY, Stephen K; Marquette HS; Michigan City, IN; TreasChr; SchMus; SchPl; LetterBsbl; LetterBsktbl; LetterTrk; College; Coach.

OXFORD, Jaricia L; John Glenn HS; Westland, MI; SecFrshCls; HstSrCls; Chr; Chrl; ChrhWkr; HonRl; HospAde; JrNHS; NHS; SchMus; SchPl; SctActv; LetterSwmmng; Trk; GAA; John Wesley College; Research Biologist.

OXFORD, Morey; Manhattan HS; Manhattan, KS; 6#36#41# TchrAde; Teen; CaptSocr; Swmmng; Trk; IMSpt; University; Orthopedic Surgeon.

OXMAN, Lisa A; Hibbing HS; Hibbing, MN; Chr; LitMag; NatlFornLg; NatlThespSoc; SchMus; SchPl; TchrAde; Univ Of Wisconsin; Communications.

OYER, Brenda; Gridley HS; Gridley, IL; Band; Chrs; CncrtBnd; HonRl; PepBnd; SchMus; PpCl; GAA; PPFtbl; Beauty School; Vocation.

OYER, Kathleen L; St Agatha HS; Detroit, MI; 11/99 Chrl; HonRl; NHS; StuCncl; Mercy Coll;art Major.

OYGARD, Brynhild; North Winneshiek HS; Decorah, IA; HonRl; StuCncl; Bsktbl; College; Professional.

OYLER, James M; Hardin Central HS; Hardin, MO; Aud/Vis; Band; Chr; Chrs; CncrtBnd; HonRl; JA; MrchBnd; PepBnd; SchMus; StuCncl; StuGov; Pres4-H; TreasFFA; Ftbl; Missouri Valley College; Mathematics.

OYLER, William K; Central HS; St Joseph, MO; Band; HonRl; MrchBnd; SctActv; YthFnd; YthLg; SciCl; LetterFtbl; Tennis; IMSpt; College; Doctor Specialist.

OYSTER, Michael C; Cass Midway HS; Freeman, MO; VPFrshCls; SecJrCls; Band; ChrhWkr; HonRl; LbryAde; PresNHS; Quill&Scroll; PresStuCncl; StuGov; Ftbl; Trk; AmLegAwd; 4-HAwd; College; Mechanical Engineering.

OZIER, Eric W; Arthur HS; Arthur, IL; VPFrshCls; PresSophCls; StuCncl; Forestry.

OZMUN, David N; Washington Comm HS; Washington, IL; 44/345 ALBoysSt; HonRl; GerCl;.

OZURISIN, Jean A; Streator Twp HS; Streator, IL; HonRl; 4-H; GerCl; College; Pharmacy.

P

PAAVOLA, Jeffrey; Bayfield Public HS; Bayfield, WI; Aud/Vis; Chr; Chrl; Chrs; ChrhWkr; SchMus; Bsktbl; Trk; College; Professional.

PABIAN, Beverly A; Ravenna Senior HS; Ravenna, NE; Band; Chrs; ChrhWkr; CncrtBnd; Mdrgl; NHS; PepBnd; StuCncl; TreasFBLA; FHA; College; Professional.

PABICH, Maureen A; All Saints Central HS; Bay City, MI; 17/140 HonRl; OffAde; SctActv; RptrSchPpr; SchPpr; PpCl; Michigan Tech Univ; Communication.

PABICH, Paul J; Owen Withee Sr HS; Owen, WI; 6/98 HonRl; NHS; SchPl; StuCncl; StuGov; RptrSchPpr; EdSchPpr; FrCl; Bsktbl; Ftbl; Military Academy; Mathematics.

PACE, David D; Oskaloos Senior HS; Oskaloosa, IA; HonRl; StuCncl; Ftbl; LetterTennis; Trk; LetterWrstlng; University; Professional.

PACE, John T; Elwood Comm HS; Elwood, IN; ALBoysSt; HonRl; SctActv; SpnCl; PpCl; Ftbl; Wrstlng; Iupui; Dr Medicine.

PACE, Lawrence A; St Pius X HS; Kansas City, MO; Band; HonRl; Orch; PepBnd; SchMus; StuCncl; YthLg; Col; Pro.

PACE, Mary J; Tipton HS; Tipton, IN; 21/172 HonRl; TchrAde; SecFTA; PpCl; In U Kokomo; Education.

PACE, Michael J; Lawrenceville HS; St Francisville, IL; 5/178 PresFrshCls; ALBoysSt; HonRl; NHS; SchPl; StuCncl; LetterTrk; LetterWrstlng; EldAwd; GodCntryAwd; Southern Ill Univ; Med.

PACE, Penny A; St Mary Academy; Indianapolis, IN; 10/43 Chrs; HonRl; LbryAde; PolWkr; SchPl; TreasRptrYrbk; RptrSchPpr; PresGerCl; PpCl; JAAwd; Marion College; Drama.

PACHA, Sandy J; Fairfield HS; Richland, IA; HonRl; RptrYrbk; RptrSchPpr; FBLA; SpnCl; PpCl; LetterTrk; IMSpt; Technical School.

PACHAY, Amy; Decatur Jr Sr HS; Decatur, MI; 6/75 SecSrCls; HonRl; NHS; SchPl; StuCncl; RptrYrbk; CivCl; PpCl; Tennis; Chrldr; W Mi Univ; Education.

PACHOLKE, Paula J; Dwight D Eisenhower HS; Saginaw, MI; 26/364 Chr; HonRl; LbryAde; NHS; SchMus; SchPl; SctActv; GerCl; Univ Of Mich; Med Doc.

PACIORKA, Kevin M; Lyons Township HS; Lagrange Park, IL; 260/1300 Band; CncrtBnd; HonRl; MrchBnd; PolWkr; StuGov; College; Accounting.

PACK, Linda S; John Marshall HS; Milwaukee, WI; StuCncl; TchrAde; PpCl; Chrldr; PresAwd; Coll; Medicine.

PACKARD, Debra S; Wheatland HS; Gove, KS; Band; Chr; Chrs; HonRl; MrchBnd; SchMus; SchPl; TreasYthFlsp; 4-H; 4-HAwd; College; Music.

PACKARD, Julie K; Huron Sr HS; Huron, SD; 64/301 Band; Chrs; CncrtBnd; MrchBnd; Orch; SctActv; TchrAde; YthFlsp; SpnCl; College; Professional.

PACKARD, Stanley A; Dundee Comm HS; Carpentersville, IL; 108/377 Band; MrchBnd; SctActv; YthFlsp; Trk; Wrstlng; Military Academy; Pilot.

PACKINGHAM, Susan A; Edwardsburg HS; Edwardsburg, MI; Chr; Chrl; ChrhWkr; CmntyWkr; LbryAde; Sacrstn; SancSoc; Sdlty; TchrAde; YthFlsp; College; Beautician.

PACZAS, Cynthia; Hazel Park HS; Hazel Park, MI; 10/410 DrlTm; HonRl; JrNHS; NHS; Michigan State Univ; Professional.

PADDING, William C; Holland Christian HS; Zeeland, MI; Chr; HonRl; LetterMdrgl; Orch; GerCl; IMSpt; Calvin Coll; Secondary Ed English Music.

PADEN, Sara L; Ell Saline HS; Salina, KS; Chrl; Chrs; ChrhWkr; HonRl; LitMag; OffAde; SchPl; RptrYrbk; RptrSchPpr; PpCl; Secretarial.

PADGETT, Brian V; Carl Sandburg HS; Tinley Park, IL; 169/619 Chr; Chrl; CaptBsbl; Bsktbl; Ftbl; Isu Clge; Pro.

PADGETT, Byron P; Custer HS; Milwaukee, WI; Chr; SchMus; StuCncl; Bsktbl; Ftbl; U W M; Phy Ed Teacher.

PADGETT, Jeff; Marion Adams Hs; Sheridan, IN; TchrAde; VPFFA; FSA;.

PADGETT, Jill L; New Harmony HS; New Harmony, IN; 1/23 PresJrCls; PresSrCls; ALAGirlsSt; NHS; Quill&Scroll; YthFlsp; Yrbk; EdSchPpr; College; Teaching.

PADGETT, Judy K; Austin HS; Austin, IN; 3/65 VPJrCls; HonRl; NHS; OffAde; SchMus; SchPl; StuCncl; FTA; SpnCl; GAA; In Uni ;math.

PADGETT, Patricia L; Scecina Memorial HS; Indianapolis, IN; DrlTm; MrchBnd; Chrldr; GAA; IMSpt; Legal Secretary.

PADGETT, Stephen M; Albion HS; Albion, MI; NatlMeritFnl; NatlMeritSF; PolWkr; RptrSchPpr;.

PADGETT, Suetta L; South Newton HS; Brook, IN; 38/97 Chr; ChrhWkr; MrchBnd; SctActv; YthFlsp; 4-H; FHA; LatCl; PpCl; 4-HAwd; Ball State Univ; Elementary Education.

PADILLA, Alice J; Aurora Central HS; Aurora, IL; 34/175 Chrs; SchPl; TchrAde; College; Curriculm Of Major Study.

PADILLA, Elsie; Spalding HS; Chicago, IL; VPSrCls; Chrs; HonRl; NHS; OffAde; SchPl; StuCncl; EdYrBk; EdSchPpr; LatCl; De Paul; Business.

PADOLAK, Donna L; Munster HS; Munster, IN; 53/400 DrlTm; HonRl; MrchBnd; ModUN; RptrYrbk; PpCl; GAA; IMSpt; College; Nursing.

PAGANINI, Mark W; Annapolis HS; Drbn Hgts, MI; 9/435 Band; CncrtBnd; HonRl; JrNHS; MrchBnd; NHS; NatlMeritCmnd; NatlMeritSchl; PepBnd; Clg; Medicine.

PAGE, Ann L; Plankinton Independent HS; Plankinton, SD; Band; Chrs; DrlTm; HonRl; NHS; OffAde; SchPl; EdYrBk; RptrSchPpr; FHA; Augustana College; Music Education.

PAGE, Benita L; Lindblom Technical HS; Chicago, IL; 37/600 SecJrCls; ChrhWkr; HonRl; IntrClCncl; JA; ROTC; StuCncl; StuGov; TchrAde; CchngActv; GAA; AmLegAwd; College.

PAGE, Darlene V; Oregon HS; Oregon, IL; Band; CncrtBnd; HonRl; MrchBnd; PepBnd; SctActv; Illinois State Univ; Business.

PAGE, Deborah J; Slater HS; Slater, MO; 6/56 ALAGirlsSt; Chrs; ChrhWkr; HonRl; OffAde; SchAde; SchPl; StuCncl; TchrAde; RptrYrbk; Chrldr; GAA; College; Elementary Teacher.

PAGE, Jeanne E; Holden R Iii HS; La Tour, MO; 15/90 Band; CncrtBnd; DrlTm; HonRl; MrchBnd; NHS; 4-H; LetterTennis; IMSpt; PresAwd; University; Conservation.

PAGE, Jo A; Hancock Public HS; Hancock, MN; Band; Chrs; HonRl; MrchBnd; PepBnd; FHA; Bsktbl; Trk; Chrldr; Winina State Coll; Nursing.

PAGE, Kathryn C; Ermest W Seaholm HS; Birmingham, MI; VPJrCls; Band; ChrhWkr; MrchBnd; ModUN; SctActv; StuGov; LetterBsbl; LetterBsktbl; Univ; Physical Ed And Recreation.

PAGE, Keith A; Belleville East HS; Fairview Hgts, IL; 29/667 HonRl; JrNHS; NHS; EdYrBk; FrCl; LetterTrk; College; Business Admin.

PAGE, Kevin P; Gobles Public HS; Gobles, MI; 3/65 PresFrshCls; HonRl; NHS; NatlMeritSchl; StuCncl; MthCl; SciCl; LetterBsbl; LetterFtbl; IMSpt; Ferris St Col; Pharmacist.

PAGE, Leslie J; Emil Hirsch HS; Chicago, IL; 3/269 VPSrCls; Chr; HonRl; JrNHS; LbryAde; Mdrgl; NHS; NatlMeritSF; FrCl; GAA; Fisk Univ; Lawyer.

PAGE, Nancy R; Levington HS; Lexington, NE; 13/147 HonRl; SchPl; Sec4-H; TreasFHA; FTA; PpCl; Trk; IMSpt; AmLegAwd; Univ Of Ne; Medicine.

PAGE, Randy L; Tower Hill HS; Tower Hill, IL; VPFrshCls; PresSophCls; TrsJrCls; HonRl; SpnCl; PpCl;.

PAGE, Robert K; Elgin HS; Elgin, IL; 1/749 PresBand; CncrtBnd; HonRl; MrchBnd; Orch; PepBnd; SpnCl; MthCl; Ill Wesleyan Univ; Math.

PAGE, Scott; Mona Shores HS; Muskegon, MI; CncrtBnd; HonRl; MrchBnd; PepBnd; SctActv; LetterBsbl; LetterGlf; Cntrl Mich; Business Admin.

PAGE, Susie; Otterville HS; Otterville, MO; SecSophCls; Chrs; HonRl; Yrbk;.

PAGEL, Karen M; Forest Park HS; Amasa, MI; 2/91 Band; ChrhWkr; HonRl; NatlFornLg; SchPl; 4-H; New College; Child Psychology.

PAGEL, Kathleen A; Forest Park HS; Amasa, MI; 1/91 TrsFrshCls; Band; ChrhWkr; CncrtBnd; HonRl; MrchBnd; NatlFornLg; PepBnd; SchPl; 4-H; Michigan Tech Univ; Civil Engineering.

PAGEL, Lois; Wonewoc Center HS; Wonewoc, WI; 3/44 SecFrshCls; TrsSophCls; TrsJrCls; TrsSrCls; Band; NHS; PepBnd; StuCncl; Yrbk; Chrldr; W Wisc Tech School; Medical Records Tech.

PAGEL, Patricia A; Rockwell City HS; Rockwell City, IA; PresFrshCls; ALAGirlsSt; CmntyWkr; HonRl; StuCncl; TchrAde; RptrYrbk; Bsbl; Bsktbl; Trk; Army National Guard; Nursing.

PAGEL, Suzanne M; Lincoln HS; Wisconsin Rapids, WI; Band; ChrhWkr; CncrtBnd; HonRl; MrchBnd; PepBnd; SchAde; SchPl; TchrAde; Lakeshore Technical College; Opt Asst.

PAGELS, Ronald E; Luther South HS; Chicago, IL; 34/207 HonRl; Univ Of Il Urbana Champaign; Electrical Eng.

PAGLIA, David J; St Clement HS; Center Line, MI; 30/97 HonRl; Bsbl; Bsktbl; Ftbl; IMSpt; Macomb County College; Business Admin.

PAGLIARINI, Shawn E; Eveleth HS; Eveleth, MN; 17/162 Chr; ChrhWkr; CmntyWkr; NHS; Orch; SchMus; SchPl; SctActv; EdYrBk; Augsburg College; Music.

PAHL, Allan J; Aguinas HS; Lacrosse, WI; 31/191 RptrYrbk; SptEdYrbk; RptrSchPpr; SptEdSchPpr; Ftbl; Tennis; IMSpt; VoiceDemAwd; College; Sports Journalism.

PAHL, Douglas J; Crandon HS; Crandon, WI; Band; ChrhWkr; CmntyWkr; CncrtBnd; HonRl; MrchBnd; Orch; PepBnd; Teen; MthCl; Tec School; Electronics.

PAHLMAN, Lynn D; Warren Twp HS; Wildwood, IL; Band; ChrhWkr; HonRl; MrchBnd; NHS; SctActv; RptrYrbk; SptEdYrbk; GAA; Evanston Hospital; Nursing.

PAHLMANN, Cheri E; Jacksonville HS; Murrayville, IL; 69/363 Band; CncrtBnd; HonRl; MrchBnd; PepBnd; SchMus; SchPl; Pres4-H; FrCl; DanFAwd; 4-HAwd; Illinois College; Business.

PAHLMEYER, Charles L; Regent Public HS; Regent, ND; 1/21 TrsSophCls; ALBoysSt; Band; Chrs; ChrhWkr; HonRl; NatlMeritCmnd; College; Engineer.

PAHNKE, Nancy D; Denmark HS; Green Bay, WI; AFS; HonRl; FHA; SpnCl; PpCl; Trk; Univ Of Wisconsin; Data Processing.

PAICE, Judith A; Proviso West HS; Hillside, IL; Chr; HospAde; Elmhurst College; Nursing.

PAINE, Robert; Carbondale Community HS; Carbondale, IL; 31/323 HonRl; NatlMeritCmnd; NatlMeritSF; GerCl; Univ Of Il; Law.

PAINO, James M; St Louis University HS; St Louis, MO; Band; OffAde; Bsbl; Bsktbl; College; Professional Accountant.

PAINTER, Darrell L; Lincoln County R 2 HS; Elsberry, MO; 18/62 PresSrCls; ALBoysSt; HonRl; StuCncl; Yrbk; RptrSchPpr; SptEdSchPpr; PresSciCl; Bsbl; Bsktbl; College; Major Study.

PAINTER, Jeannie L; Davison Sr HS; Davison, MI; 12/436 Chr; Mdrgl; MrchBnd; NHS; VPNatlThespSoc; PresOrch; SchMus; SchPl; Univ Of Michigan; English.

PAINTER, Phil L; Morton West HS; Berwyn, IL; HonRl; JrNHS; NHS; NatlMeritCmnd; NatlSciFnd; StuGov; LetterBsbl; LetterBsktbl; LetterGlf; CchngActv; Col; Professional.

PAINTER, Valerie A; Bellmont HS; Decatur, IN; 1/251 HonRl; NHS; Quill&Scroll; Twrl; EdYrBk; GerCl; Purdue Univ; Veterinarian.

PAINTER, Victoria L; Bellmont HS; Decatur, IN; 2/251 HonRl; NHS; VPQuill&Scroll; Twrl; EdYrBk; GerCl; RotaryAwd; Purdue Univ; Physical Education.

PAINTER, William D; Winchester Community HS; Ridgeville, IN; VPFrshCls; HonRl; StuCncl; Bsbl; LetterWrstlng; Trade Schl; Carpenter.

PAITZ, Janet M; Pleasanton HS; Hazard, NE; PresFrshCls; ALAGirlsSt; Chr; Chrs; ChrhWkr; HonRl; Mdrgl; SchPl; LetterTrk; Chrldr; College.

PAITZ, Robert F; Amherst Public HS; Amherst, NE; 2/19 ChrhWkr; CmntyWkr; HonRl; NHS; SchPl; College; Ind Arts Teacher.

PAJAK, Jacqueline A; Thorp HS; Thorp, WI; 7/74 Band; ChrhWkr; CncrtBnd; HonRl; NHS; PepBnd; StuCncl; Yrbk; Trk; Chrldr; U Of W; Nursing.

PAJAK, Phillip E; Gordon Tech HS; Chicago, IL; 2/618 HonRl; NatlMeritCmnd; GerCl; MthCl; Northwestern Univ; Elec Engineer.

PAKIER, Rochelle C; Peoria HS; Peoria, IL; 21/450 ChrhWkr; HonRl; JrNHS; LbryAde; NHS; OffAde; GerCl; PpCl; Univ Of Illinois; Accountant.

PAKZYGNAT, Kathy; Madonna HS; Chicago, IL; 7/274 Chrs; HonRl; GAA; IMSpt; Northern Ill Univ; Accounting.

PAL, Judith M; Taft HS; Chicago, IL; HonRl; NHS; NatlMeritCmnd; OffAde; SchPl; StuCncl; Teen; PpCl; College; Medical Technology.

PALACHECK, Christine M; Lincoln HS; Park Falls, WI; HonRl; StuCncl; CivCl; RptrSchPpr; PpCl; Trk; Chrldr; GAA; College; Nurse.

PALADIN, Leslie S; Nerinx Hall HS; St Louis, MO; SecJrCls; SecSrCls; HonRl; SchMus; SchPl; StuCncl; RptrSchPpr; PresPpCl; GAA; IMSpt; University Of Missouri.

PALAN, Amy M; Highland Public HS; Highland, WI; VPFrshCls; Band; Chr; CncrtBnd; MrchBnd; NatlFornLg; StuCncl; TchrAde; FHA; LetterTrk; Chrldr; GAA; College.

PALARDY, Antoinette M; Bishop Foley HS; Madison Heights, MI; 3/176 CmntyWkr; HonRl; PolWkr; RptrYrbk; SchPpr; FrCl; PpCl; Oakland U; Medical Technology.

PALEN, Kathleen M; Derham Hall HS; St Paul, MN; SecJrCls; Chrs; PresChrhWkr; CmntyWkr; HospAde; SchMus; StuCncl; SpnCl; Chrldr; GAA; St Benedicts College; Social Work.

PALERMO, Diane M; State Univ Campus HS; Cape Girardeau, MO; 4/39 HonRl; NHS; SecFTA; SpnCl; PpCl; SciCl; IMSpt; AmLegAwd; RotaryAwd; Se Missouri St Univ; Botanical Research.

PALERMO, Susan J; Andrean HS; Schererville, IN; CmntyWkr; RedCrAde; SchAde; SchPl; StuCncl; SchPpr; LatCl; SpnCl; Trk; GAA; College; Professional.

PALETA, Roy J; William Fremd HS; Palatine, IL; HonRl; NHS; Univ; Elec Engineering.

PALID, Mari B; Holly HS; Holly, MI; Chr; Chrl; SchMus; SchPl; SpnCl; Coll; Fine Arts.

PALIK, Autumn M; Ithaca HS; Ithaca, MI; HonRl; StuCncl; TchrAde; FTA; PresFrCl; PresSpnCl; MthCl; PresPpCl; CaptBsktbl; GAA; Ferris Coll; Dental Hygiene.

PALKOWSKI, Nancy; Cochrane Fountain City HS; Cochrane, WI; FHA; 4-HAwd; Vocational School; Nurse.

PALL, Joanne M; Mother Of Sorrows HS; Chicago, IL; 10/143 CmntyWkr; HonRl; HospAde; JrNHS; LbryAde; PolWkr; StuCncl; StuGov; FrCl; MthCl; SciCl; VFWAwd;.

PALLACH, Susan; Imlay City Comm HS; Lum, MI; 8/140 Band; HonRl; NHS; PepBnd; RedCrAde; FSA; SciCl; Mi State Univ; Nursing.

PALLER, Harry H; Holy Cross HS; River Grove, IL; 22/300 HonRl; RptrSchPpr; IMSpt; Il Institute Of Tech; Mechanical Engineer.

PALLISTER, Charles T; Sturgeon Bay HS; Sturgeon Bay, WI; PresSrCls; Band; ChrhWkr; HonRl; NatlFornLg; NHS; Bsbl; Bsktbl; IMSpt; LionAwd; Tech Sch; Accountant.

PALMA, Julianne; Washburn Rural HS; Topeka, KS; ALAGirlsSt; Chr; HonRl; MrchBnd; SchMus; StuCncl; RptrSchPpr; PpCl; Chrldr; PPFtbl; Coll;.

PALMATIER, Julie A; Coopersville Public HS; Coopersville, MI; Band; CncrtBnd; HonRl; MrchBnd; NHS; PepBnd; StuCncl; FBLA; GerCl; PpCl; Bsktbl; Davenport College; Accounting.

PALMEN, Michael; Stoughton HS; Stoughton, WI; /226 HonRl; NHS; Yrbk; RptrSchPpr; PresFrshCls; SecSophCls; Ftbl; LetterWrstlng; Arch Or Carpentry;pro.

PALMER, Beverly S; Leadwood HS; Irondale, MO; 14/47 HonRl; LitMag; LbryAde; NHS; FHA; Mineral Area College; Nursing.

PALMER, Brian D; Huron HS; Ann Arbor, MI; HonRl; GerCl; MthCl; SciCl; IMSpt; U Of Mi; Engineering.

PALMER, Darcy L; Limestone Comm HS; Bartonville, IL; 16/396 Band; ChrhWkr; CncrtBnd; HonRl; HospAde; MrchBnd; PepBnd; SchMus; SctActv; TchrAde; Mou; Deitetics.

PALMER, David T; Austin Catholic Prep; Grosse Pt, MI; 39/115 VPFrshCls; PresSophCls; HstSrCls; ALBoysSt; HonRl; NatlFornLg; SchMus; SchPl; StuCncl; LetterFtbl; AmLegAwd; Michigan State Univ; Business.

PALMER, Debra L; Ubly HS; Ubly, MI; ChrhWkr;

CmntyWkr; HonRl; HospAde; RedCrAde; SchPl; TchrAde; Univ; Medicine.

PALMER, Diana M; Trinity HS; Melrose Park, IL; 25/204 ChrhWkr; HonRl; HospAde; NHS; Ne Illinois Univ; Special Educ Teacher.

PALMER, Dwight R; Wichita Southeast HS; Wichita, KS; 1/671 Chr; Chrs; ChrhWkr; HonRl; LitMag; LbryAde; NatlMeritSF; SctActv; RptrYrbk; SpnCl; Ks St U; Electrical Engineering.

PALMER, Elaine A; Morrill HS; Morrill, NE; 1/43 ChrhWkr; NHS; FTA; Eastern Wyoming Coll; Secretarial.

PALMER, Elizabeth; Jacksonville Hs; Jacksonville, IL; 9/363 TrsSrCls; Chr; HonRl; LitMag; StuGov; YthFlsp; FrCl; SpnCl; LetterSwmmng; EldAwd;.

PALMER, Joellyn; Rock Bridge HS; Columbia, MO; Band; Chrs; ChrhWkr; PepBnd; StuCncl; PpCl; SciCl; GAA; Stephens College; Phy Ed.

PALMER, Karla; Rushville HS; Rushville, NE; Chrs; ChrhWkr; LbryAde; Mdrgl; OffAde; YthFlsp; FHA; FTA; PpCl; Chrldr; Coll; Teach.

PALMER, Lynn S; New Trier East HS; Winnetka, IL; 190/847 PresFrshCls; AFS; ChrhWkr; CmntyWkr; LitMag; PolWkr; Vassar College; Internatl Business.

PALMER, Marcia L; Lees Summit HS; Lees Summit, MO; ALAGirlsSt; HonRl; NatlFornLg; NHS; RedCrAde; StuCncl; TchrAde; YthFlsp; Chrldr; PPFtbl; Missouri Univ Columbia; Busines.

PALMER, Sheryl A; Mormon Trail Community HS; Garden Grove, IA; 8/35 TrsJrCls; Band; Chr; HonRl; MrchBnd; PepBnd; YthFlsp; Yrbk; FHA; PpCl;.

PALMER, Susan M; Westport HS; Kansas City, MO; Chrs; NHS; LatCl;.

PALMER, Terry J; Eloquet HS; Cloquet, MN; CmntyWkr; HonRl; SctActv; MthCl; Trk; U Of Mn At Duluth; Eng.

PALMISANO, Diane; Southwest HS; St Louis, MO; Chr; LitMag; Quill&Scroll; SchMus; SchPl; StuGov; RptrYrbk; Chrldr; Dance Ther.

PALMORE, Patricia L; Minonk Dana Rutland HS; Dana, IL; 5/60 SecJrCls; AFS; Chrs; HonRl; NatlMeritCmnd; SchPl; StuCncl; TchrAde; FHA; FrCl; PpCl; CaptChrldr; PresGAA; University; Professional.

PALMQUIST, Clayton H; Stanton Community HS; Stanton, IA; Chr; Chrs; HonRl; 4-H; FFA; Bsktbl; Col ; Voc.

PALMQUIST, Jonathan R; Glenwood Comm HS; Glenwood, IA; 15/109 Band; Chrs; ChrhWkr; CncrtBnd; Mdrgl; MrchBnd; PresNHS; SchMus; VPStuCncl; LetterTrk; Ne Christian Col; Ministry.

PALMREUTER, Lynne; Reese HS; Reese, MI; VPSrCls; Chr; ChrhWkr; ModUN; OffAde; SchPl; RptrSchPpr; GerCl; PpCl; Chrldr; College; Barber.

PALOMBI, Annette M; Oak Park River Forest HS; Oak Park, IL; 32/1012 Chrs; HonRl; NHS; Rosary College; Foreign Languages.

PALOMBO, Carmella G; De Land Weldon HS; De Land, IL; AFS; Band; Chrs; HonRl; LbryAde; MrchBnd; SchMus; SchPl; StuCncl; GAA; College; Legal Secretary.

PALOPOSKI, Seija S; Centralia HS; Centralia, MO; AFS; HonRl; JA; SchPl; StuCncl; EngCl; FrCl; SpnCl; GAA; Univ; Medicine.

PALOUMPIS, Thomas D; Minonk Dana Rutland HS; Minonk, IL; 6/81 AFS; Band; Chrs; HonRl; SchPl; FrCl; PpCl; SciCl; AmLegAwd; U Of I; Medicine.

PALS, Cedrick H; Maurice Orange City HS; Orange City, IA; 6/76 PresSophCls; Band; CncrtBnd; HonRl; NHS; StuCncl; YthFlsp; LetterFtbl; LetterTrk; IMSpt; Bethel College; Antheriologist.

PALSMA, Byron; Tyndall HS; Tyndall, SD; Band; Chrs; MrchBnd; PepBnd; StuCncl; Bsbl; LetterBsktbl; LetterFtbl; LetterGlf; LetterTrk; Coll.

PALUCH, Theresa M; Steinmetz HS; Chicago, IL; 7/616 HospAde; NHS; OffAde; SecStuCncl; TchrAde; MthCl; Loyola University; Science.

PALUMBO, Frank A; Bellevue HS; Omaha, NE; ALBoysSt; HonRl; LetterFtbl; Trk; Eastern Mich Univ.

PALUMBO, Karen K; Bishop Dwenger HS; Grabill, IN; HonRl; JA; PolWkr; SchMus; RptrYrbk; KeyCl; FrCl; PpCl; Chrldr; GAA; College; Secretary.

PALUMBO, Robert D; Superior Senior HS; Superior, WI; HonRl; NHS; StuCncl; FrCl; Ftbl; University; Lawyer.

PALUMBO, Suzanne R; Southwest O Fallon Tech; St Louis, MO; ChrhWkr; CmntyWkr; CncrtBnd; HonRl; MrchBnd; SchMus; YthFlsp; FBLA; Business Clg; Data Processing.

PALUTA, Roman M; Mt Carmel HS; Chicago, IL; 8/197 ChrhWkr; HonRl; NHS; SctActv; StuCncl; StuGov; SchPpr; RusCl; Univ; Professional.

PALY, Oleh S; Grant Comm HS; Ingleside, IL; 1/270 ChrhWkr; HonRl; JrNHS; NHS; PolWkr; VPStuCncl; EdSchPpr; SchPpr; VPSciCl; IMSpt; Univ; Medicine.

PAMBIANCO, Dan M; St Bede Academy; Spring Valley, IL; Band; CncrtBnd; HonRl; MrchBnd; PepBnd; SchMus; StuGov; Ftbl; College; Conservation.

PAMPERIN, Cindy M; Lomira HS; Theresa, WI; 9/82 VPSrCls; Chrs; HonRl; NHS; SchMus; YthFlsp; SchPpr; 4-H; FrCl; AmLegAwd; Technical School; Accounting.

PANASKY, Mary Rose; Maria HS; Chicago, IL; 66/301 ChrhWkr; HonRl; HospAde; JA; LitMag; NatlThespSoc; SchAde; SchMus; SchPl; SctActv; StuCncl; RptrSchPpr; SptEdSchPpr; GAA; Univ Of Ill; Accounting.

PANCHUK, Christine Z; Regina Dominican HS; Chicago, IL; 16/207 HonRl; LatCl; Univ Of Illinois; Pharmacy.

PANCOAST, Charlene J; Harper Creek HS; Battle Creek, MI; 6/221 ChrhWkr; HonRl; NHS; NatlMeritCmnd; RedCrAde; FTA; College; Rn.

PANCRATZ, Joan M; Prospect HS; Mt Prospect, IL; HonRl; NatlMeritCmnd; SchMus; Moser Business School; Retail Management.

PANE, Mike J; Creighton Prep HS; Omaha, NE; 21/250 HonRl; NHS; NatlMeritCmnd; Bsktbl; Creighton Univ; Psychology.

PANEK, Donna M; William Howard Taft HS; Chicago, IL; 12/790 Chrs; HonRl; JrNHS; NHS; OffAde; TchrAde; KeyCl; FrCl; MthCl; GAA; U Of Ill; Lawyer.

PANEK, Richard J; St Patrick HS; Chicago, IL; 5/427 ChrhWkr; CmntyWkr; HonRl; NatlMeritSF; PolWkr; TchrAde; RptrSchPpr; FTA; Northwestern Univ; Journalist.

PANEK, Timothy J; Carman HS; Flint, MI; NHS; Hope College; Medicine.

PANGALLO, Frank J; Center Grove HS; Greenwood, IN; 21/235 HonRl; NHS; SctActv; StuCncl; PresFrCl; PpCl; LetterBsbl; LetterBsktbl; CchngActv; AmLegAwd; Marian College; Biology.

PANGBORN, Julie M; Bullock Creek HS; Midlad, MI; 1/175 Band; CncrtBnd; HonRl; NHS; NatlMeritSF; Orch; StuCncl; EdYrBk; PpCl; Chrldr; Mi St U; Vet Med.

PANGER, Nanette H; Thorton Fractional So HS; Lansing, IL; 129/552 Chr; Chrl; Chrs; ChrhWkr; HonRl; SctActv; FrCl; PpCl; College; Music.

PANGMAN, Mary H; Waterford HS; Waterford, WI; Chr; HonRl; HospAde; Mdrgl; NatlFornLg; SchMus; SchPl; StuCncl; RptrYrbk; EdYrBk; LatCl; PpCl; LetterGlf; LetterTrk; University; Physician.

PANGRAZIO, Margo; Plainfield HS; Joliet, IL; 50/291 HonRl; LbryAde; GAA; IMSpt; PPFtbl; Nohrtern Ill Univ; Medical Technician.

PANKE, Cynthia G; Frankfort Sr HS; Frankfort, IN; ChrhWkr; DrmMjrt; SchPl; RptrYrbk; Glf; Swmmng; Chrldr; GAA; 4-HAwd; College; Law.

PANKEY, Shannon L; Grand Blanc HS; Grand Blanc, MI; 96/637 ChrhWkr; HospAde; JA; Trk; PPFtbl; Evangel Col; Elementary Teaching.

PAN KOP, Robert A; Churubusco HS; Churubusco, IN; HonRl; StuCncl; FFA; PpCl; Ftbl; Trk;.

PANKOW, Sherry M; Magic City Campus HS; Minot, ND; ALAGirlsSt; HonRl; SctActv; EdYrBk; RptrSchPpr; GerCl; LetterSwmmng; LetterTrk; GAA; College; Physical Ed.

PANKRATZ, Jan M; Staples HS; Staples, MN; 14/149 Chr; HonRl; LbryAde; NHS; SctActv; SciCl; LetterGAA; IMSpt; St Cloud State U; Accountant.

PANKRATZ, Jeanette K; Buhler HS; Buhler, KS; Band; ChrhWkr; CncrtBnd; HonRl; MrchBnd; PepBnd; TchrAde; YthFlsp; Bsbl; College; Accounting.

PANKRATZ, Kimberly A; Carpio HS; Carpio, ND; HonRl; SchPl; SptEdSchPpr; PpCl; LetterBsktbl; LetterTrk; IMSpt;.

PANNEBECKER, Elizabeth D; De Soto Sr HS; De Soto, MO; Band; Chrs; CncrtBnd; HonRl; JrNHS; NHS; StuCncl; Yrbk; PpCl; LetterBsktbl; LetterTennis; LetterChrldr; IMSpt; College; Physical Ed.

PANNELL, Barbara L; Brown County HS; Morgantown, IN; 9/170 HonRl; NatlThespSoc; SchPl; SctActv; StuCncl; 4-H; FHA; FrCl; SpnCl; PpCl; Ind State U; Computer Programming.

PANNING, Wendy J; Central HS; Green Isle, MN; 6/94 Band; ChrhWkr; CncrtBnd; HonRl; LbryAde; MrchBnd; NHS; PepBnd; YthFlsp; PresAwd; Clg; Elem Educ.

PANOS, Lynne M; Foreman HS; Chicago, IL; 5/354 TrsSrCls; Chrs; HonRl; NHS; NatlMeritSF; Quill&Scroll; RptrSchPpr; SchPpr; VPGerCl; Tennis; Northeastern Il U; Teacher.

PANOSH, Nancy R; Kewaunee HS; Kewaunee, WI; Band; Chrs; HonRl; NatlThespSoc; PepBnd; StuCncl; StuGov; RptrSchPpr; FHA; SciCl; Univ Of Wisconsin.

PANOZZO, Michael E; Campion Jesuit HS; Flossmoor, IL; CmntyWkr; HonRl; StuGov; RptrSchPpr; SptEdSchPpr; SchPpr; LetterTennis; IMSpt; College; Professional.

PANSIER, Mary; Medford HS; Faribault, MN; Band; Chrs; CncrtBnd; HonRl; MrchBnd; TchrAde; FHA; FTA; 4-HAwd; CitAwd; Coll; Professional.

PANTAGES, Lori S; Woodruff HS; Peoria, IL; TrsFrshCls; SecSophCls; TreasAFS; Chr; HonRl; HospAde; TchrAde; RptrSchPpr; KeyCl; FrCl; Northern Il Univ; Medical Technology.

PANTALEONE, James T; East HS; Coal City, IL; 5/95 LetterTrk; ALBoysSt; Band; HonRl; NatlMeritSF; Yrbk; 4-H; LetterTrk; U Of Il; Physics.

PANUSKA, Mary Joan; Kouts HS; Kouts, IN; 11/53 Band; CncrtBnd; HonRl; HospAde; MrchBnd; NHS; SchPl; TchrAde; Yrbk; FTA; PresSciCl; LetterBsktbl; Swmmng; University; Medicine.

PANZER, Scott R; Wheaton North HS; Carol Stream, IL; 39/308 Band; CncrtBnd; HonRl; MrchBnd; NHS; Orch; PepBnd; LetterFtbl; IMSpt; So Illinois Univ; Medicine.

PANZICA, Paul G; Princeton HS; Princeton, IL; HonRl; TchrAde; SpnCl; Bsktbl; Ftbl; Glf; Jr College; Business Adm Accounting.

PAOLETTI, Ann M; Iron Mountain HS; Iron Mountain, MI; 20/157 ChrhWkr; HospAde; NHS; StuCncl; 4-H; FHA; FNA; SpnCl; 4-HAwd; Mi Tech Univ; Obstetrition & Pediatrition.

PAOLETTI, Marisa A; Notre Dame HS; Chicago, IL; 15/302 HonRl; NHS; NatlMeritCmnd; NatlMeritSF; VPRedCrAde; Tennis; CchngActv; AmLegAwd; DARAwd; University; Elem Education.

PAONESSA, Karen A; John Glenn HS; Belleville, MI; 18/673 Band; CncrtBnd; HonRl; JrNHS; MrchBnd; NHS; Orch; PepBnd; FTA; FrCl; Wayne St Univ; Psychology.

PAPADAKIS, Michael C; Spalding HS; Chicago, IL; Chrs; HonRl; Univ Of Chicago; Sociology.

PAPAMARCOS, Paula; Barrington HS; Barrington, IL; HonRl; NHS; U Of Illinois;elementary Education.

PAPAMARCOS, Paula C; Barrington HS; Barrington, IL; ChrhWkr; HonRl; NHS; CchngActv; College; Education.

PAPARELLA, Susan M; Catholic Central HS; Muskegon, MI; 7/215 DrlTm; HonRl; JA; NHS; NatlMeritCmnd; PolWkr; SchMus; StuCncl; TchrAde; Yrbk; Muskegon Comm College; Elementary Education.

PAPE, Eileen L; Pius Xi HS; West Allis, WI; 33#41#54 PolWkr; SctActv; FTA; GerCl; MthCl; BauchLmbAwd; Mt Mary Col; Science.

PAPENDICK, Michael S; Warren Township HS; Gurnee, IL; VPSrCls; AFS; HonRl; NHS; SchAde; StuCncl; LetterFtbl; CaptWrstlng; Northern Ill Univ.

PAPENFUSS, Diane K; Cavalier Public HS; Cavalier, ND; ALAGirlsSt; Chrs; ChrhWkr; CmntyWkr; HonRl; OffAde; YthFlsp; PpCl; SciCl; GAA; College.

PAPENHAUSE, Susan M; Tremont HS; Tremont, IL; 8/80 AFS; Band; CncrtBnd; HonRl; MrchBnd; PepBnd; Yrbk; College; Computer Programer.

PAPIER, Paul A; R N Snider HS; Ft Wayne, IN; HonRl; NatlMeritSF; YthFlsp; RptrSchPpr; College; Journalism.

PAPIER, Paul A; R Nelson Snider HS; Fort Wayne, IN; HonRl; NatlMeritFnl; College; Journalism.

PAPIERSKI, Karen R; Maine East HS; Niles, IL; Chr; DrlTm; HonRl; HospAde; Mdrgl; MthCl; CaptTrk; CchngActv; Jr College; Physical Ed.

PAPINEAU, Clement J; Ontonagon Area HS; Ontonagon, MI; 59/107 Aud/Vis; DrmBgl; HonRl; MrchBnd; NatlMeritFnl; NatlMeritSchl; SchMus; LetterFtbl; LetterTrk; CaptIMSpt; College; Law.

PAPINEAU, William M; Grosse Pointe North HS; Grosse Pointe, MI; HonRl; NatlMeritCmnd; SchPl; StuCncl; U Of Mi.

PAPINI, Dennis R; Orion HS; Orion, IL; HonRl; StuGov; YthFlsp; RptrSchPpr; FrCl; Bsbl; Ftbl; LetterTrk; LetterWrstlng; IMSpt; College; Prof.

PAPKE, Jeff A; East Central HS; Miles, IA; ALBoysSt; Band; Chrs; CncrtBnd; HonRl; MrchBnd; NHS; SchMus; GerCl; Bsktbl; College.

PAPLOW, Ronald; Westbrook HS; Minnesota, MN; 15/40 HonRl; FFA; Vocational School.

PAPPAGEORGE, Vicki G; Maine South HS; Park Ridge, IL; 95/820 Chr; HonRl; LitMag; NHS; NatlMeritCmnd; VPFDA; VPFrCl; CaptBsktbl; Tennis; ChmbCommrsAwd; Loyola Univ; Medicine.

PAPPAS, Helen R; Wausau East HS; Wausau, WI; 25/297 HonRl; NHS; SctActv; RptrSchPpr; GAA; Univ Wi; Nursing.

PAPPAS, Nicholas; Lyons Township HS; Hinsdale, IL; PolWkr; SchAde; StuCncl; YthFlsp; Texas Christian Univ; Business Accounting.

PAPPAS, William J; Gage Park HS; Chicago, IL; 21/461 Aud/Vis; HonRl; NatlMeritCmnd; TchrAde; SptEdSchPpr; Bsbl; Roosevelt Univ; Accounting.

PAPPENFUS, Dianne; Foley HS; Foley, MN; 9/127 Chr; Chrs; HonRl; NHS; PepBnd; SchPl; StuCncl; PpCl; Moorhead State; Premedicine.

PAPSDORF, Shelly; Waverly HS; Lansing, MI; 96/378 Chr; NHS; SchMus; FrCl; College; Dance.

PAQUET, Brenda L; Mackinaw City HS; Macinaw, MI; 3/21 PresSophCls; Band; HonRl; PepBnd; SchPl; StuCncl; EdYrBk; PpCl; Bsktbl; Chrldr; University; Undecided.

PAQUIN, Jill R; Vanderbilt HS; Vanderbilt, MI; PresFrshCls; StuCncl; RptrYrbk; RptrSchPpr; 4-H; PpCl; Bsktbl; Trk; Chrldr; 4-HAwd; Clg; Prof.

PAQUIN, Teresa A; Casey HS; Greenup, IL; 2/89 Band; CncrtBnd; HonRl; MrchBnd; NHS; NatlMeritCmnd; Orch; RptrYrbk; Lake Land Jr College; Accounting.

PARACHINI, Edward A; Garden County HS; Oshkosh, NE; CAP; HonRl; ROTC; RptrYrbk; Yrbk; SpnCl; SciCl; Trk; Wrstlng; U Of Nebraska Sch Of Tec Agr; Horticulture.

PARADIS, Robert J; Holy Trinity HS; Winsted, MN; 6/54 PresJrCls; HonRl; NHS; FshEdYrbk; Trk; Wrstlng; CchngActv; Willmar Comm Clg; Law Enforcement.

PARADISE, Terrance W; Alcona HS; Black River, MI; HonRl; TchrAde; LetterBsbl; LetterBsktbl; LetterFtbl; LetterTrk; Forris State Coll; Accounting.

PARAS, Donald K; Loyola Academy; Deerfield, IL; HonRl; NHS; Univ Of Ill; Engineering.

PARCEL, Denise L; Winamac Community HS; Winamac, IN; Band; CncrtBnd; MrchBnd; PepBnd; StuCncl; SpnCl; CaptBsktbl; Tennis; LetterTrk; VPGAA; IMSpt; College; Physical Education.

PARCELLS, Frederick R; Adlai E Stevenson HS; Deerfield, IL; 25/235 HonRl; LitMag; TchrAde; LetterBsbl; LetterBsktbl; College.

PARDE, Darryl D; Auburn HS; Auburn, NE; 32/90 CmntyWkr; JA; SctActv; TchrAde; YthFlsp; Pres4-H; LetterBsktbl; LetterFtbl; 4-HAwd; JAAwd; College; Teaching Biology.

PAREIGAT, Monica M; Forest Lake HS; Hugo, MN; 22/353 Chr; ChrhWkr; HonRl; JrNHS; Mdrgl; NHS; Yrbk; SpnCl; Coll; Nursing.

PARENT, Carol L; Saint Agatha HS; Detroit, MI; SecFrshCls; SecSophCls; HonRl; NHS; PpCl; Bsbl; Chrldr; Coll; Teacher.

PARENT, Frances M; St Agatha HS; Detroit, MI; SecFrshCls; HonRl; HospAde; JA; OffAde; RptrSchPpr; PPFtbl; Schoolcraft College; Registered Nurse.

PARENT, Nancy G; Wayland Acad; Beaver Dam, WI; VPFrshCls; PresSophCls; HonRl; NatlThespSoc; Orch; SchMus; SchPl; SctActv; Yrbk; FrCl; Oberlin Clge; Music.

PARENT, Philip R; Graceville HS; Graceville, MN; 3/54 PresFrshCls; PresSophCls; HonRl; NHS; NatlMeritSF; StuCncl; FrCl;.

PARFEN, Deborah A; St Alphonsus HS; Dearborn, MI; StuCncl; PpCl; Trk; Chrldr; GAA; IMSpt; PPFtbl; PresAwd; Coll; Mathematics.

PARIS, Beverly J; Whiteland Community HS; Whiteland, IN; 27/180 ChrhWkr; HonRl; NHS; VPYthFlsp; 4-H; FTA; KeyCl; SpnCl; Trk; PPFtbl; 4-HAwd; Indiana University; Physical Therapist.

PARIS, Karen K; Hale HS; Hale, MO; Band; Chrs; CncrtBnd; HonRl; NatlFornLg; NatlThespSoc; SchPl; TreasFHA; PpCl; Chrldr;.

PARIS, Nancy S; Woodruff HS; Peoria, IL; 12/281 SecAFS; Chrs; HonRl; SecJA; Pres4-H; FrCl; VPGerCl; Trk; 4-HAwd; JAAwd; Illinois St U; German.

PARIS, Susan E; Sidney Public HS; Sidney, NE; HonRl; JrNHS; NHS; FBLA; EngCl; PpCl; Business School; Vocational.

PARISH, David; Rockville HS; Rockville, IN; ALBoysSt; TreasNHS; SctActv; YthFlsp; SptEdSchPpr; SciCl; Ftbl; Trk; Wrstlng; Depaw Univ; Pro.

PARISH, Rebecca B; South Decatur HS; Westport, IN; SecSophCls; VPJrCls; Chr; DrlTm; HonRl; HospAde; NatlThespSoc; PepBnd; SchMus; PpCl;.

PARISH, Rene; Derby Senior HS; Derby, KS; Chr; ChrhWkr; JrNHS; NHS; Orch; SchMus; StuCncl; RptrYrbk; 4-H; PpCl; College; Chemistry.

PARISH, Robert M; Hinsdale South HS; Darien, IL; 29/448 HonRl; NHS; StuCncl; StuGov; Glf; Univ Of Ill; Dentistry.

PARISH, Ronda L; Riverdale HS; Muscoda, WI; AFS; Band; Chrs; HonRl; Mdrgl; SchMus; StuCncl; YthFlsp; TreasFHA; PpCl; Vocational Schl; Child Development.

PARISH, Stewart A; Brimley HS; Brimley, MI; HonRl; StuCncl; FTA; Bsktbl; Ftbl; IMSpt; Mich St Police; Police Force.

PARISH, Susan D; Kewanee HS; Kewanee, IL; AFS; DrlTm; SchMus; SchPl; StuCncl; Twrl; FTA; GerCl; PpCl; GAA; College; Elem Sch Teacher.

PARISH, Wally M; Macksville HS; St John, KS; TrsFrshCls; Band; Chr; CncrtBnd; SctActv; Bsktbl; Ftbl; Trk; CchngActv; CitAwd; Ft Hays Ks St College.

PARISI, James A; Madison West HS; Madison, WI; 107/582 StuCncl; YthFlsp; SpnCl; LetterWrstlng; University Of Wisconsin; Political Science.

PARISOT, Carol A; Alleman HS; Rock Island, IL; HonRl; NHS; FrCl; College; Business.

PARK, Claudia G; Mt Morris HS; Mt Morris, IL; AFS; Band; Chr; Chrs; ChrhWkr; CmntyWkr; CncrtBnd; HonRl; MrchBnd; SecNHS; GAA; IMSpt; College; Business Admin.

PARK, Collin; Plainwell HS; Plainwell, MI; 7/211 Band; HonRl; MrchBnd; NHS; PepBnd; SchMus; SchPl; Mich State Univ; Biophysics.

PARK, Daniel P; Dell Rapids Public HS; Dell Rapids, SD; 18/56 Band; ChrhWkr; CncrtBnd; HonRl; MrchBnd; NatlThespSoc; PepBnd; SchMus; SchPl; Ftbl; College; Engineer.

PARK, James E; Lincoln Sr HS; Sioux Falls, SD; ALBoysSt; ChrhWkr; HonRl; JA; NatlMeritSF; StuCncl; FBLA; GerCl; Mass Inst Of Tech; Management.

PARK, James R; De Kalb HS; Auburn, IN; 9/276 HstSrCls; Chr; Chrs; HonRl; NHS; SchMus; TchrAde; LatCl; LetterBsbl; Swmmng; De Pauw U; Law.

PARK, Kay F; Mexico HS; Mexico, MO; Band; ChrhWkr; MrchBnd; YthFlsp; FrCl; PpCl; Chrldr; U Of Mo; Prof.

PARKE, Jacquelyn D; Perry Meridian HS; Indianapolis, IN; 47/573 ALAGirlsSt; Chr; HonRl; NHS; PolWkr; SchMus; VPStuCncl; Yrbk; 4-H; Indiana University; English Physical Ed.

PARKE, Steve A; Lead HS; Lead, SD; 2/168 Band; ChrhWkr; CncrtBnd; HonRl; NHS; VPFrshCls; SctActv; YthFlsp; Bsktbl; Trk; College; Statistician.

PARKER, Allison; Jackson HS; Jackson, MI; Chr; HonRl; JA; College; Nursing.

PARKER, Brenda; Heritage Christian HS; Noblesville, IN; Chr; ChrhWkr; HonRl; SchMus; Yrbk; RptrSchPpr; Bsktbl; GAA; Business School; Legal Secr.

PARKER, Carol S; Eminence HS; Quincy, IN; 9/32 HonRl; OffAde; SchAde; EdYrBk; Treas4-H; FHA; Bsktbl; GAA; IMSpt; 4-HAwd; U Of In; Medicine.

PARKER, Christopher R; Plainfield HS; Plainfield, IL; Band; Chr; CmntyWkr; CncrtBnd; MrchBnd; PepBnd; SchMus; SchPl; SciCl; University; Chemistry.

PARKER, Cinda K; Steelville R 3 HS; Steelville, MO; 8/79 Band; ChrhWkr; CmntyWkr; HonRl; HospAde; NHS; 4-H; FHA; Bsktbl; 4-HAwd; Umkc; Medicine.

PARKER, Dale; Waukesha North HS; Waukesha, WI; 3/352 HonRl; NHS; MthCl; IMSpt; BauchLmbAwd; Marquette Univ; Major In Physics.

PARKER, Doretta; Gering HS; Gering, NE; 1/j35 Band; DrlTm; HonRl; NHS; PepBnd; StuCncl; Twrl; RptrYrbk; PpCl; Nebraska Western Col; Business.

PARKER, Gary; Twin Cedars HS; Bussey, IA; PresSophCls; TrsSrCls; ALBoysSt; HonRl; PolWkr; SchMus; StuCncl; EdSchPpr; SciCl; Ftbl; Berkly University; Law.

PARKER, Geffrey; Astoria HS; Astoria, IL; 5/45 PresFrshCls; VPSophCls; VPJrCls; HonRl; NHS; SchPl; YthFlsp; Bsktbl; Ftbl; Trk; Univ Of Il; Math And Computer Sci.

PARKER, George L; Shawnee Mission East HS; Shawnee Mission, KS; JA; NatlMeritSF; Bsbl; College; Psychology.

PARKER, Gregg M; East Leyden HS; Schiller Park, IL; 50/700 Band; ChrhWkr; CmntyWkr; HonRl; NHS; SctActv; TchrAde; RptrSchPpr; SciCl; Swmmng; Triton College; Mechanical Engineer.

PARKER, Harlan D; Ness City HS; Ness City, KS; 6/58 TrsJrCls; Band; Chrs; ChrhWkr; CncrtBnd; HonRl; MrchBnd; NHS; NatlThespSoc; PepBnd; Emporia Ks State Clg; Professional.

PARKER, James D; Lockwood HS; Lockwood, MO; 15/44 Band; HonRl; RptrSchPpr; FFA; LetterBsktbl; LetterFtbl; LetterTrk; College.

PARKER, Jeffrey A; Fulton HS; Albany, IL; VPJA; NatlThespSoc; SctActv; PresStuCncl; Ftbl; College; Radio Announcer.

PARKER, Jerry; Waterford Mott Hs; Pontiac, MI; HonRl; U Arizona; Secondary Art Ed.

PARKER, John; Hononegah Community HS; Roscoe, IL; 13/217 HonRl; SchMus; SchPl; Yrbk; SchPpr; LetterFtbl; Wrstlng;.

PARKER, John T; Springfield HS; Springfield, IL; 117/535 LetterFtbl; Tennis; Augustana College; Dentist.

PARKER, Kathleen D; Centralia HS; Centralia, KS; 10/40 PresSophCls; HonRl; LbryAde; TchrAde; Yrbk; PpCl; SciCl; LetterBsktbl; LetterTrk; Kansas State University; Teaching.

PARKER, Kenneth; East Kentwood HS; Kentwood, MI; Aud/Vis; LbryAde; NatlFornLg; NatlMeritCmnd; RptrSchPpr; SchPpr; Grand Rapids Jr College; Journalism.

PARKER, Kimberly B; Hanover Central HS; Cedar Lake, IN; 4/144 ALBoysSt; ALAGirlsSt; CmntyWkr; HonRl; HospAde; JrNHS; NHS; RedCrAde; StuCncl; Merriville Beauty Coll; Beautician.

PARKER, Lynette M; St Mark HS; St Louis, MO; 3/36 HonRl; LitMag; NHS; SchPl; Sdlty; Yrbk; Fontbonne College; Mentally Retarded.

PARKER, Lynette M; St Mark HS; Pine Lawn, MO; 5/36 HonRl; SchPl; Sdlty; FshEdYrbk; Fontbonne College; Special Ed.

PARKER, Michael G; Indian Creek HS; Martinsville, IN; 4/110 ALBoysSt; Chr; HonRl; NHS; SchMus; StuCncl; PresLatCl; Bsktbl; LetterFtbl; LetterTrk; University; Professional.

PARKER, Mickey J; Manhattan HS; Manhattan, KS; 39/400 Chr; SctActv; Kansas State Univ; Engineering.

PARKER, Mike R; Waynesville HS; Waynesville, MO; Chr; HonRl; JrNHS; NHS; GerCl; LetterFtbl; LetterTrk; College; Law.

PARKER, Nancy L; Kingston HS; Kingston, MI; VPFrshCls; VPJrCls; Band; HonRl; MrchBnd; VPStuCncl; TchrAde; SchPpr; FrCl; CaptBsktbl; Nursing.

PARKER, Peggy A; Stockbridge HS; Munith, MI; 3/123 ALAGirlsSt; Band; HonRl; NHS; 4-H; SciCl; Mich Tech; Engr.

PARKER, Peggy A; Murray Community HS; Murray, IA; Chr; HonRl; SchPl; StuCncl; FHA; FNA; LetterBsbl; LetterTrk; College; Journalism.

PARKER, Philip L; Nebraska Christian HS; Chambers, NE; TrsFrshCls; PresJrCls; Band; Chr; Chrl; ChrhWkr; CncrtBnd; PepBnd; SchMus; SchPl; SctActv; CaptBsktbl; Tennis; LetterTrk; Grace Bible Inst; Music.

PARKER, Robert J; Jackson HS; Jackson, MI; ALBoysSt; Band; CncrtBnd; HonRl; MrchBnd; PresNHS; PepBnd; SchMus; SchPl; GerCl; Univ Of Michigan; Physical Science.

PARKER, Sally L; Benkelman HS; Benkelman, NE; 1/31 HonRl; LbryAde; NHS; Yrbk; 4-H; FHA; SciCl; Trk;.

PARKER, Sharon; Holy Redeemer HS; Detroit, MI; 24/190 HonRl; JA; SctActv; Bsktbl; Coll.

PARKER, Stanley M; Golden City HS; Golden City, MO; PresFrshCls; TrsSrCls; HonRl; StuCncl; Bsktbl; Ftbl; Trk; Univ; Law.

PARKER, Stephan M; St Mary Of Redford HS; Detroit, MI; PresJrCls; JrNHS; SchPl; StuGov; Sacred Heart Seminary; Philosophy.

PARKER, Stephen L; Northrop HS; Fort Wayne, IN; 97/643 Band; ChrhWkr; CncrtBnd; HonRl; MrchBnd; 4-H; Bsbl; CchngActv; IMSpt; College; Engineering.

PARKER, Thomas A; Niles HS; Niles, MI; 75/364 Chrl; HonRl; SchMus; SchPl; YthFlsp; John Wesley College; U S History.

PARKER, Thomas F; Reeths Puffer HS; Muskegon, MI; 35/265 Band; HonRl; MrchBnd; NHS; SctActv; College; Engineering.

PARKER, Thomas G; Creighton Prep; Omaha, NE; 26/250 HstFrshCls; ChrhWkr; CmntyWkr; HonRl; JrNHS; NHS; StuCncl; Bsktbl; LetterGlf; IMSpt; University; Professional.

PARKER, Thomas K; St Joseph Ogden HS; St Joseph, IL; TrsFrshCls; PresSophCls; PresSrCls; HonRl; NHS; StuGov; FrCl; Ftbl; Ill State U; Business Admn.

PARKER, Valerie J; Carmel Girls HS; Mundelein, IL; 12/173 Chrs; HonRl; LitMag; TreasNHS; RedCrAde; SchMus; StuCncl; MthCl; Univ Of Illinois; Computer Science.

PARKEY, Bruce E; Highland HS; Highland, IN; 113/538 Band; CncrtBnd; MrchBnd; NatlThespSoc; PepBnd; SchPl; StuCncl; College; Business Administration.

PARKHURST, Brenda J; Maysville R I HS; Weatherby, MO; 11/71 Band; Chr; CncrtBnd; HonRl; MrchBnd; PepBnd; SchMus; SpnCl; JAAwd; PresAwd; Nw Col & Medical Ctr; Registered Nurse.

PARKIN, Joy C; Forman HS; Manito, IL; 3/45 PresJrCls; NHS; NatlMeritCmnd; SchPl; StuCncl; EdYrBk; 4-H; Bsktbl; Trk; Trk; Ill State Univ; Accounting.

PARKINS, Kathy A; Bloomington HS; Glen Haven, WI; Band; Chrs; MrchBnd; Yrbk; FHA; PpCl; Bsktbl; GAA; IMSpt; PresAwd; College; Physica Ed Major.

PARKINS, Kenneth R; Chanute HS; Chanute, KS; Band; ChrhWkr; CncrtBnd; HonRl; MrchBnd; YthFlsp; University; Ministry.

PARKINS, Rose M; Mead Public HS; Mead, NE; Band; Chrs; CncrtBnd; MrchBnd; NatlThespSoc; PepBnd; YthFlsp; 4-H; FHA; PpCl; College; Professional.

PARKINSON, Craig L; Oakville Sr HS; St Louis, MO; HonRl; IntrClCncl; SchPl; SctActv; KeyCl; MthCl; Swmmng; College; Scientist.

PARKINSON, Michael; St Louis University HS; St Louis, MO; Glf; Socr; College; Dentistry.

PARKINSON, Randal L; Calhoun HS; Hardin, IL; Band; CncrtBnd; PepBnd; SctActv; FFA; Bsktbl; LetterFtbl; IMSpt; Military Academy; Officer.

PARKINSON, Teresa J; Freeport HS; Freeport, IL; 11/507 CncrtBnd; HonRl; LbryAde; MrchBnd; NatlMeritCmnd; Orch; 4-H; FTA; MthCl; 4-HAwd; College; Elementary Educ.

PARKISON, Kathy; Rensselaer Central HS; Rensselaer, IN; 6/175 Chrl; ChrhWkr; HonRl; NHS; NatlMeritCmnd; SchMus; SchPl; RptrYrbk; FrCl; Urdue U; Medicine.

PARKS, Debra A; Sweet Springs HS; Sweet Springs, MO; HonRl; FHA; SciCl; College.

PARKS, Delea A; Mc Henry Comm HS; Mc Henry, IL; 151/477 AFS; Chr; HonRl; LbryAde; Mdrgl; NatlMeritCmnd; SchMus; SchPl; TchrAde; RptrYrbk; FBLA; Univ Of Illinois; Animal Science.

PARKS, Denise; Hill City HS; Hill City, KS; Band; Chrs; DrmBgl; HonRl; MrchBnd; PepBnd; YthFlsp; PpCl; PPFtbl;.

PARKS, Frank L; Whitewater HS; Whitewater, WI; 9/191 Band; PresChr; HonRl; Mdrgl; NHS; NatlMeritCmnd; NatlThespSoc; Orch; VPKeyCl; PresFrCl; LetterFtbl; Univ Of Wis; Medicine.

PARKS, John H; Beatrice HS; Beatrice, NE; Band; Chr; CncrtBnd; PepBnd; Bsbl; Bsktbl; LetterFtbl; Glf; University.

PARKS, Linda S; Ldf Comm HS; Le Grand, IA; VPFrshCls; Chrs; ChrhWkr; HonRl; NHS; SchPl; RptrYrbk; 4-H; FTA; PPFtbl; 4-HAwd; Iowa St University; Sociology.

PARKS, Mark; Henry Co R I HS; Windsor, MO; 20/56 PresFrshCls; ALBoysSt; HonRl; Bsbl; Ftbl; IMSpt; AmLegAwd; VFWAwd; Central Mo St Univ; Buss Adm.

PARKS, Michael; Bishop Dwenger HS; Fort Wayne, IN; StuCncl; KeyCl; Ftbl; Coll; Mechanical.

PARLEE, Andrew; Arlington HS; Arlington Hts, IL; 1/585 HonRl; LitMag; NHS; NatlMeritSchl; SctActv; RotaryAwd; Univ Of Illinois; Architect.

PARLEE, Andrew D; Arlington HS; Arlington Hts, IL; 1/581 HonRl; JrNHS; NHS; Univ Of Illinois; Architecture.

PARLI, Joe D; Sabetha HS; Sabetha, KS; TrsFrshCls; PresJrCls; SecBand; ChrhWkr; HonRl; NHS; PepBnd; StuCncl; VPYthFlsp; LetterWrstlng; Coll; Research Chemist.

PARMAN, Richard F; Benkelman HS; Benkelman, NE; 3/45 Band; HonRl; PresNHS; SchPl; StuCncl; SchPpr; 4-H; Ftbl; DanFAwd; 4-HAwd; Nebraska University; Farmer.

PARMELEY, Cynthia; Desoto HS; Desoto, MO; 34/224 Chr; CmntyWkr; HonRl; LbryAde; PolWkr; SchPpr; AmLegAwd; VFWAwd; CitAwd; VoiceDemAwd; Jefferson Coll; Pre Medicicine.

PARN, Joseph B; Monroe R I HS; Monroe City, MO; HonRl; SchPl; Trade School.

PARON, Nicholas G; Douglas Mac Arthur HS; Saginaw, MI; 41/294 ChrhWkr; HonRl; NHS; NatlMeritSF; SctActv; LetterBsbl; LetterBsktbl; LetterFtbl; Alma Coll; Pre Med.

PARR, Dan J; La Farge HS; La Farge, WI; Chrs; EngCl; FrCl; MthCl; PpCl; SciCl; LetterBsbl; Bsktbl; LetterFtbl; IMSpt; U Of Wi; Phy Ed Teacher.

PARR, Keith D; Hillsboro HS; Donnellson, IL; 1/184 ALBoysSt; HonRl; IntrClCncl; NHS; SchMus; StuCncl; StuGov; 4-H; FFA; Ftbl; LetterTrk; AmLegAwd; DanFAwd; 4-HAwd; Univ Of Illinois; Professional.

PARR, Kent C; Snider HS; Fort Wayne, IN; 69/500 Band; CncrtBnd; HonRl; MrchBnd; Orch; PepBnd; SchMus; IMSpt; U Of Evansville; Music.

PARR, Steven E; Sturgis HS; Sturgis, MI; HonRl; IMSpt; Mi Tech Univ; Forestry.

PARRENT, Mary F; Dearborn HS; Dearborn, MI; AFS; Chrs; HonRl; Orch; Chrldr; AmLegAwd; College; Lawyer.

PARRIGON, Susan M; Mc Auley Regional HS; Pierce City, MO; SecSophCls; SecJrCls; Chrs; DrmBgl; HonRl; NHS; SchMus; StuCncl; 4-H; PpCl; College; Secretarial Work.

PARRIS, Janni G; Chippewa Valley HS; Mt Clemens, MI; Band; HonRl; OffAde; PolWkr; ROTC; StuCncl; StuGov; RptrYrbk; FDA; Trk; LetterWrstlng; GAA; PPFtbl; Macomb Comm College; Physician.

PARRISH, Becky S; Carbondale Comm HS; Carbondale, IL; HonRl; University; Business Teacher.

PARRISH, Beverly K; Falls City HS; Falls City, NE; LetterBand; ChrhWkr; DrlTm; HonRl; NHS; SchMus; StuCncl; TchrAde; YthFlsp; Yrbk; 4-H; GerCl; PpCl; Univ Of Nebraska; Business.

PARRISH, James D; Jefferson 'S; Rockford, IL; HonRl; NHS; Trk; College; Architect.

PARRISH, John W; Crocker Rii HS; Crocker, MO; VPFrshCls; TrsSophCls; NHS; StuCncl; SpnCl; PpCl; Bsbl; Bsktbl; Trk; AmLegAwd; College; Pro Baseball.

PARRISH, Mark; Warren Hs; Menmouth, IL; 2/42 PresFrshCls; VPJrCls; Band; Chrs; HonRl; PepBnd; PresStuCncl; Ftbl; Trk; DARAwd; U Of Illinois; Agriculture.

PARRISH, Michael L; Moberly HS; Moberly, MO; ChrhWkr; HonRl; SchPl; StuGov; PresYthFlsp; RptrSchPpr; PresKeyCl; Bsbl; Bsktbl; Ftbl; Moberly Jr College; Journalism.

PARRISH, Rebecca A; Walnut Grove HS; Walnut Grove, MO; 3/18 SecJrCls; TrsSrCls; HonRl; OffAde; SchPl; TchrAde; FHA; PpCl; Swbc ;secretary.

PARRISH, Terry L; Attica HS; Attica, IN; 15/81 PresSrCls; Chr; HonRl; SchPl; FFA; LetterBsbl; CaptBsktbl; LetterFtbl; IMSpt; Trade School; Professional.

PARRO, Kathleen M; Eliz Seton HS; Dolton, IL; 158/250 Chrs; DrmBgl; HonRl; Mdrgl; NatlThespSoc; SchMus; SchPl; VFWAwd; VoiceDemAwd; Co Univ; Spec Educ.

PARROTT, Barbara C; Waterloo HS; Red Bud, IL; 2/146 HonRl; JrNHS; Nursing School; Nurse.

PARROTT, Craig H; Adair Casey HS; Adair, IA; 11/48 ALBoysSt; ChrhWkr; HonRl; NHS; Quill&Scroll; SchMus; SchPl; EdSchPpr; Bsbl; DanFAwd; Concordia Col; Ministry.

PARROTT, Dennis M; Annapolis HS; Dearborn Heights, MI; 68/435 JA; StuCncl; SchPpr; JAAwd; U Of Mi; Electronic Engineering.

PARROTT, Leslie; Danville Comm; Danville, IA; 3/35 TrsSrCls; VPBand; CncrtBnd; HonRl; MrchBnd; PepBnd; SchMus; SchPl; SecStuGov; Sec4-H; College; Medicine.

PARROTT, Mark A; Northwest HS; House Springs, MO; 40/369 CmntyWkr; HonRl; SchAde; LetterBsktbl; LetterTrk; CitAwd; Graceland College; Recreation.

PARROTT, Sharon K; Portage HS; Endeavor, WI; 3/210 VPSrCls; HonRl; Mdrgl; MrchBnd; NHS; PepBnd; SchMus; YthFlsp; SpnCl; GAA; U Of Wi Eau Claire; Accounting.

PARROTT, Terry R; Clarinoa HS; Clarinda, IA; HonRl; Ftbl; Trk; IMSpt; Willmar Comm Coll; Conservatn.

PARRY, Daniel E; Warsaw Comm HS; Winona Lake, IN; SchPl; RptrYrbk; College; Christian Service.

PARRY, Linda R; Genoa Public HS; Monroe, NE; 3/46 SecJrCls; ALAGirlsSt; Chrl; Chrs; ChrhWkr; HonRl; LbryAde; NHS; SchPl; PpCl; LetterTrk; PPFtbl; University Of Nebraska; Teaching.

PARRY, Mary; Rolla HS; St James, MO; 18/217 ALAGirlsSt; Chr; Chrs; HonRl; TchrAde; 4-H; FHA; PpCl; Chrldr; 4-HAwd; College; Veterinary Medicine.

PARSEL, William M; Hayden HS; Topeka, KS; 32/209 SchMus; StuCncl; Ftbl; LetterWrstlng; Benedictine College; Engineering.

PARSELL, Barry; Jersey Com HS; Jerseyville, IL; Band; Chr; Chrl; Chrs; CncrtBnd; HonRl; MrchBnd; SchMus; TchrAde; YthFlsp; Judson Coll; Music.

PARSONS, Carla J; Jasper HS; Jasper, MO; ChrhWkr; HonRl; NHS; YthFlsp; Bsktbl; Trk; CaptChrldr; GAA; PPFtbl; Ozark Bible College; Music.

PARSONS, Gayle A; Magic City Campus HS; Minot Air Force B, ND; 54/656 Chr; ChrhWkr; CmntyWkr; HonRl; JrNHS; NHS; NatlThespSoc; PresSchMus; SchPl; SchPpr; Univ; Nursing.

PARSONS, Jan; Amos Alonzo Stagg Hs; Hickory Hills, IL; 3/480 Chr; HonRl; NHS; NatlMeritCmnd; Quill&Scroll; RptrYrbk; RptrSchPpr; GerCl;.

PARSONS, Mary B; Pekin Community HS; Richland, IA; 6/50 Band; Chrs; ChrhWkr; CncrtBnd; HonRl; LbryAde; NHS; PepBnd; SchMus; SchPl; Northwest Missouri St U; Child Developement.

PARSONS, Richard J; Auburndale HS; Auburndale, WI; VPJrCls; HonRl; Yrbk; FBLA; Bsktbl; Ftbl; Univ; Dentist.

PARSONS, Ruena L; Harrisburg R Viii HS; Rocheport, MO; 3/20 ChrhWkr; HonRl; JrNHS; StuCncl; RptrYrbk; RptrSchPpr; PpCl; Trk; CaptChrldr; CitAwd; Air Force; Nurse Or Medical Field.

PARSONS, Teresa; Winfield Sr HS; Burden, KS; FHA; PpCl; Coll; Nursing.

PARSONS, William; Eudora HS; Eudora, KS; Band; CncrtBnd; HonRl; MrchBnd; PepBnd; Mo Inst Of Tech; Bs Elecrtonic Eng Tech.

PARTIPILO, Petronilla L; Josephinum HS; Chicago, IL; 3/100 HonRl; LbryAde; Business School; Secretary.

PARTON, Frances E; Crab Orchard HS; Stonefort, IL; 1/25 PresSrCls; HonRl; StuCncl; SchPpr; PpCl; Univ Of Illinois; Engineer.

PARTON, Ronald; City HS; Iowa City, IA; 1/276 Chrs; NatlFornLg; NHS; SchMus; SchPl; Tennis; ChmbCommrsAwd; GovHonPrgAwd; OptClAwd; Ma Inst Of Tech; Medicine.

PARTRIDGE, Dane M; Clio HS; Clio, MI; 6/360 LitMag; NHS; NatlMeritCmnd; SchMus; EdSchPpr; Ftbl; Michigan St Univ; Political Science.

PARTRIDGE, Linda J; Paxton HS; Paxton, IL; 6/128 Band; Chr; Chrs; CncrtBnd; HonRl; Mdrgl; NHS; NatlThespSoc; GAA; U Of Il; Education.

PARTRIDGE, William D; Collins HS; Collins, IA; 3/15 SecJrCls; PresSrCls; Band; Chrs; CncrtBnd; HonRl; MrchBnd; PepBnd; SchPl; RptrYrbk; RptrSchPpr; SchPpr; 4-H; Area Xi Comm College; Electronic Tech.

PARTYKA, Cindy M; Thornton Fractional No HS; Calumet City, IL; 17/433 ALAGirlsSt; HonRl; NHS; Quill&Scroll; Eastern Illinois Univ; Speech Pathology.

PARTYKA, Diane; St Paul Kennedy HS; Chicago, IL; Band; CncrtBnd; HonRl; MrchBnd; SchAde; 4-H; Chrldr;.

PARULSKI, Kenneth A; Oconomowoc Sr HS; Oconomowoc, WI; JrNHS; NatlMeritCmnd; NatlMeritSF; SchMus; SchPl; Yrbk; SchPpr; College; Elec Engineering.

PASCHAL, Dirk W; Savanna HS; Savanna, IL; 4/66 VPSophCls; VPSrCls; HonRl; 4-H; SpnCl; LetterGlf; Univ Of Illinois; Computer Science.

PASCHALL, Mark R; Detroit Country Day HS; Detroit, MI; PresChr; ChrhWkr; HonRl; FDA; VPFrCl; Bsbl; Bsktbl; Ftbl; LetterTrk; College; Medical.

PASCHEN, John N; Milton HS; Milton, WI; 68/185 Band; CncrtBnd; HonRl; MrchBnd; PepBnd; PpCl; Trk; College; Business.

PASCHEN, Marie; Oregon Davis HS; Walkerton, IN; Chr; HonRl; PepBnd; 4-H; FHA; PpCl; College; Business.

PASCHKE, Paul E; Bishop Mc Namara HS; Kankakee, IL; 42/173 HonRl; Ftbl; LetterTennis; IMSpt;.

PASHOS, Demetrius L; Southwest HS; St Louis, MO; ALBoysSt; HonRl; ModUN; PolWkr; Quill&Scroll; SctActv; RptrYrbk; SpnCl; LetterSwmmng; OptClAwd; U Of Missouri Columbia; Political Science.

PASISINIC, Jeanie; Lakeview HS; Decatur, IL; Aud/Vis; Southern Ill Univ; Science.

PASKACH, David M; Spencer HS; Spencer, IA; 10/200 PresFrshCls; VPJrCls; Chr; ChrhWkr; HonRl; JrNHS; NatlFornLg; NHS; SchMus; LetterTrk; Univ ;acct.

PASKE, Brenda A; Heights HS; Wichita, KS; HonRl; NatlMeritFnl; StuGov; Univ; Genetic Research.

PASKE, Michael; Sheboygan South HS; Sheboygan, WI; 28/540 CncrtBnd; HonRl; LbryAde; MrchBnd; NatlFornLg; PolWkr; IMSpt; Univ; Engineering.

PASKE, Richard R; East Kentwood HS; Kentwood, MI; 7/389 PresBand; ChrhWkr; CncrtBnd; HonRl; MrchBnd; NHS; NatlMeritCmnd; SchMus; Ftbl; LetterTrk; Hope College; Physician.

PASKER, Sandra M; W Delaware HS; Manchester, IA; Chrs; HonRl; PpCl; GAA; PPFtbl;.

PASLAWSKI, Sharon L; Frank Cody HS; Detroit, MI; TrsJrCls; JrNHS; MrchBnd; NHS; StuGov; Yrbk; KeyCl; Tennis; GAA; Business Clg; Executive Secretary.

PASLEY, Charles D; Richland HS; Richland, MO; ChrhWkr; CmntyWkr; SchPl;.

PASLEY, Marilyn R; Rock Bridge HS; Columbia, MO; SecTrsFrshCls; HonRl; NHS; SchPl; SecStuGov; RptrYrbk; 4-H; PresPpCl; GAA; 4-HAwd; Stephens College; Fashion Design.

PASMINSKI, Richard J; St Patrick HS; Chicago, IL; 41/377 HonRl; University; Liberal Arts.

PASQUALUCCI, Tina; J E Murphy HS; Montreal, WI; 5/119 Band; CncrtBnd; HonRl; MrchBnd; NHS; SchMus; SchPl; RptrYrbk; PpCl; Chrldr; College; Counseling.

PASS, Vickie L; Peoria HS; Peoria, IL; 52/450 ChrhWkr; HonRl; NHS; OffAde; RedCrAde; TchrAde; YthFlsp; SchPpr; Blackburn Univ; Elem Education.

PASSIG, Carolyn; Watertown HS; Watertown, SD; Chrs; ChrhWkr; 4-H; Coll; Biology.

PASSINI, Barry T; Newman Cen HS; Rock Falls, IL; HonRl; NHS; Bsbl; CaptFtbl; CaptWrstlng; College; Professional.

PASSMORE, Jim; Concordia HS; Concordia, KS; Band; CncrtBnd; MrchBnd; RptrYrbk; Ftbl; Glf; IMSpt; Junior College; Farmer.

PASTEL, Kenneth D; Proviso West HS; Berkeley, IL; 5/1181 CmntyWkr; HonRl; JrNHS; NHS; SctActv; Purdue Univ; Engineering.

PASTERCZYK, Gail A; St Scholastica HS; Skokie, IL; Chrs; SchPl; TchrAde; GAA; IMSpt; De Paul Univ; Science.

PASTERNAK, Mary E; St Francis Acad; Joliet, IL; 9/186 HonRl; NHS; NatlMeritSF; FrCl; PresSciCl; Coll;physics Or French.

PASTERNAK, Mary E; St Francis Academy; Joliet, IL; 8/178 HonRl; NHS; NatlMeritFnl; NatlMeritSF; FrCl; PresSciCl; College; Physics.

PASTIR, Mark; St Marys Of Redford Hs; Livonia, MI; 30/166 VPJrCls; PresSrCls; HonRl; IntrClCncl; SchMus; Bsbl; Bsktbl; Trk; Um Dearborn;business Adm.

PASTORI, Cindy; Phelps Union Free HS; Phelps, WI; 4;14 PresSrCls; HonRl; StuCncl; StuGov; RptrYrbk; PpCl; DARAwd; CitAwd; Uw;artist.

PASTUCHA, Linda L; Mona Shores HS; Muskegon, MI; Chrs; HonRl; ModUN; NHS; RptrYrbk; FHA; VPFrCl; LetterTennis; Chrldr; GAA; College; Medicine.

PASTUSZYN, Dorothy H; Notre Dame HS; Chicago, IL; VPFrshCls; Chr; HonRl; NatlFornLg; SecNHS; SchPl; StuCncl; StuGov; Bsktbl; Loyola Univ; Psychology.

PASUIKA, Irene M; Alvernia HS; Chicago, IL; VPSophCls; VPSrCls; ChrhWkr; NHS; Coll.

PASYK, Rodney M; Bishop Noll Inst HS; Hammond, IN; 1/360 HonRl; NHS; PresMthCl; Bsbl; IMSpt; College; Math.

PATAI, Mary E; Morton Sr HS; Hammond, IN; 4/492 HonRl; JrNHS; NatlFornLg; NHS; VPQuill&Scroll; StuGov; EdSchPpr; Univ Of Notre Dame; Engineer.

PATAPACK, Albert J; Harlem HS; Rockford, IL; 91/526 PresSophCls; NHS; VPStuCncl; CaptFtbl; Trk; CaptWrstlng; Ill State Univ; Chemistry.

PATCH, Randy L; South Adams HS; Geneva, IN; .

PATE, Cynthia J; Larkin HS; Elgin, IL; Chr; HonRl; TchrAde; SpnCl; LetterSwmmng; College; Aas In Child Care.

PATE, Cynthia S; Madison Consolidated HS; Madison, IN; TrsSrCls; ChrhWkr; CmntyWkr; PolWkr; StuGov; 4-H; GerCl; PpCl; SciCl; GAA; In Univ Southeast; Nursing.

PATE, James R; Bloomington HS; Bloomington, IL; HonRl; SctActv; SchPpr; PpCl; LetterFtbl; CaptTrk; IMSpt; College; Business.

PATEJDL, Carol A; Morgan Park Academy; Chicago, IL; Chrs; HonRl; ModUN; NHS; NatlThespSoc; SchMus; YthLg; FrCl; SpnCl; Trk;.

PATEK, David C; Randolph HS; Randolph, WI; 6/60 PresJrCls; AFS; ALBoysSt; Band; HonRl; NHS; StuCncl; Yrbk; LetterFtbl; LetterTrk; College; Professional.

PATER, Karen; Holy Family Acad; Chicago, IL; TrsSophCls; Chrs; HonRl; NHS; StuCncl; Bsktbl; College; Professional.

PATER, Robert G; Holy Trinity HS; Chicago, IL; 16/178 HonRl; JrNHS; NHS; OffAde; StuCncl; TchrAde; LetterBsbl; Bsktbl; Loyola Univ; Bus Mngmnt.

PATEREK, Kurt R; Luther South HS; Chicago, IL; HonRl; Tennis; Univ Il Chicago Cir; Accounting.

PATERSON, Benjamin L; New Trier East HS; Wilmette, IL; 34/849 CmntyWkr; Orch; SchMus; SctActv; YthFlsp; Northwestern Univ; Professional.

PATINKIN, Gary; Yeshiva Hs; Chicago, IL; 1 StuCncl; RptrYrbk; CaptBsbl; College ; Mathemetician.

PATINO, Linda M; James B Conant; Hoffman Est, IL; HonRl; StuCncl; Chrldr; LetterGAA; IMSpt; AmLegAwd; University; Physical Therapy.

PATNOE, James M; Milbank HS; Milbank, SD; HonRl; KeyCl; LetterBsbl; LetterBsktbl; LetterFtbl; LetterGlf; LetterTrk; College; Professional.

PATNOUDES, Bruce A; Joliet Central HS; Joliet, IL; 24/549 HonRl; NHS; LetterFtbl; LetterTrk; IMSpt; College.

PATRIARCA, Alberta; Northwest HS; High Ridge, MO; 46/382 Band; HonRl; LbryAde; TchrAde; SchPpr; Trade Or Bus School; Professional.

PATRIC, Leslie A; Galien HS; Galien, MI; VPSophCls; TrsSrCls; HonRl; NHS; StuCncl; 4-H; LetterTrk; University; Professional.

PATRICK, Constance A; Martin Luther HS; West Allis, WI; 16/87 ChrhWkr; CncrtBnd; HonRl; NHS; SchMus; SchPl; RptrYrbk; Yrbk; RptrSchPpr; Univ Of Wisconsin; Nuclear Med Tech.

PATRICK, Debbie R; Immaculata HS; Highland Park, MI; CmntyWkr; LbryAde; Orch; Univ Mi St; Aaccountant.

PATRICK, Donald G; Carsonville Port Sanilac HS; Carsonville, MI; 6/53 Band; CncrtBnd; HonRl; MrchBnd; SecNHS; PepBnd; SchPl; SptEdSchPpr; SciCl; LetterFtbl; Grand Rpds Sch Of The Bible; Law Enforcemnt.

PATRICK, Franklin E; Mitchell HS; Mitchell, IN; 2/130 TrsFrshCls; PresSrCls; HonRl; NHS; StuCncl; LetterBsktbl; LetterFtbl; LetterTrk; RotaryAwd; College; Chem.

PATRICK, Jocelyn D; St Francis De Sales HS; Chicago, IL; 30/294 Chrs; HonRl; JA; NHS; NatlMeritCmnd; TchrAde; Marquette Univ; Criminal Law.

PATRICK, Julia L; Seymour HS; Seymour, IN; 1/315 CmntyWkr; HonRl; PolWkr; SchPl; Yrbk; RptrSchPpr; SpnCl; PpCl; Swmmng; DARAwd; Univ; Math.

PATRICK, Mary; Aquinas HS; Bridgeton, MO; AFS; Band; Chrs; ChrhWkr; CmntyWkr; CncrtBnd; HonRl; MrchBnd; Orch; PepBnd; Univ.

PATRICK, Mary S; Carthage Sr HS; Carthage, MO; 5/209 TrsSophCls; TrsJrCls; Chr; MrchBnd; NHS; StuCncl; LatCl; MthCl; LetterTennis; BttyCrckrAwd; Univ Of Missouri; Lawyer.

PATRICK, Michael C; Edgewood HS; Spencer, IN; 1/167 NHS; SchPl; PresStuCncl; 4-H; PresWrstlng; Hanover Coll.

PATRICK, Ronald L; Pratt HS; Pratt, KS; 11/143 Chr; Chrl; HonRl; Orch; SchMus; SchPl; Kansas Tech Inst; Elec & Computer Science.

PATRICK, Ron J; High School; Milwaukee, WI; 5/103 CncrtBnd; MrchBnd; NHS; Orch; PepBnd; SchPl; TchrAde; Yrbk; MthCl; Tennis; U Of Wi Milwaukee; Mathematics.

PATRICK, Shari L; Lincoln East HS; Lincoln, NE; 4/407 Chr; HonRl; LitMag; ModUN; NatlMeritSF; SchMus; StuGov; College; Law.

PATRICOSKI, Ann T; Mt Assisi Academy; Palos Park, IL; 1/129 PresFrshCls; TrsSophCls; HonRl; LitMag; NHS; SchMus; SchPl; StuCncl; StuGov; TchrAde; AmLegAwd; VFWAwd; College; Medicine.

PATRIKUS, Helen M; Fairmont HS; Fairmont, MN; 1/259 CncrtBnd; MrchBnd; NatlMeritCmnd; PepBnd; LetterBsktbl; LetterTrk; GAA; College; Business Admin.

PATTEE, Kim A; Evart HS; Evart, MI; ChrhWkr; CmntyWkr; HonRl; JrNHS; NatlFornLg; NHS; SchPl; 4-H; SpnCl; PpCl; LetterBsbl; Bsktbl; LetterFtbl; Univ Of Michigan; Architecture.

PATTEN, Steve; Elgin HS; West Chicago, IL; SchPl; SctActv; Ftbl; Tennis; College; Doctor.

PATTENAUDE, Celeste G; Mother Of Sorrows HS; Blue Island, IL; 16/150 Chrs; HonRl; HospAde; LbryAde; StuCncl; VPFNA; PresFrCl; Ill Wesleyan Univ; Nursing.

PATTERMANN, Linda M; Hilbert HS; Hilbert, WI; 1/67 ALAGirlsSt; HonRl; NatlFornLg; NHS; SchPl; TchrAde; EdYrBk; Chrldr; DARAwd; GovHonPrgAwd; Tech Schl; Med Lab Tech.

PATTERMANN, Randy W; Hilbert HS; Hilbert, WI; HonRl; RptrYrbk; RptrSchPpr; Ftbl; IMSpt; Tech Schl; Diesel Mechanic.

PATTERSON, Alan D; Adelphian Academy; Holly, MI; HstSrCls; CncrtBnd; StuGov; FrCl; IMSpt; Univ; Biology Teacher.

PATTERSON, Angela C; Concordia Lutheran HS; Fort Wayne, IN; Chrs; ChrhWkr; CmntyWkr; HonRl; NatlThespSoc; PolWkr; SchMus; SchPl; StuCncl; YthFlsp; SchPpr; FrCl; Taylor Univ; Medicine.

PATTERSON, Bradley; East Richland HS; Olney, IL; ChrhWkr; SchAde; YthFlsp; RptrYrbk; SptEdSchPpr; Bsktbl; College; Communications.

PATTERSON, Bruce D; St Johns Military HS; Topeka, KS; Chr; DrlTm; HonRl; MrchBnd; NatlThespSoc; ROTC; SchMus; SchPl; LetterTrk; LetterWrstlng; Coll; Law.

PATTERSON, Charles K; St Charles HS; Saginaw, MI; CncrtBnd; HonRl; MrchBnd; Coll; Graphic Arts.

PATTERSON, Cheryl A; Saline HS; Saline, MI; TrsFrshCls; Band; HonRl; HospAde; VPNHS; PresFrCl; College; Nursing.

PATTERSON, Cheryl A; Washington Catholic HS; Washington, IN; CmntyWkr; JCC; JrNHS; NatlCathMusEdAsoc; NHS; NatlMeritSF; PolWkr; RedCrAde; StuCncl; RptrSchPpr;.

PATTERSON, Connie S; Barr Reeve HS; Cannelburg, IN; SecSophCls; TrsSrCls; Band; ChrhWkr; DrmMjrt; HonRl; MrchBnd; Twrl; YthFlsp; Vincennes Univ; Physical Therapy.

PATTERSON, Darlene M; Waterford Mott HS; Pontiac, MI; TrsJrCls; TrsSrCls; ChrhWkr; CmntyWkr; HonRl; PresJA; OffAde; SchAde; SchPl; StuCncl; TchrAde; YthFlsp; PpCl; Bsktbl; University Of Michigan; Attorney.

PATTERSON, Donald A; Remington HS; Whitewater, KS; VPJrCls; Band; Chrs; ChrhWkr; HonRl; NatlThespSoc; SchMus; SchPl; StuCncl; 4-H; Bethel College; Architect.

PATTERSON, James L; North Mahaska HS; New Sharon, IA; 6/43 Band; CncrtBnd; HonRl; MrchBnd; NHS; 4-H; FFA; LetterFtbl; Wrstlng; 4-HAwd; Iowa State Univ; Vet.

PATTERSON, James T; Culver Military Academy; Evanston, IL; 76/166 DrlTm; HonRl; LbryAde; ROTC; StuGov; Trk; Miami Univ; Lawyer.

PATTERSON, John M; Mendel Catholic Prep; Riverdale, IL; HstFrshCls; HstSophCls; HstJrCls; HonRl; LbryAde; SchPpr; Bsktbl; Ftbl; Tennis; Trk; Western Il; Law Enforcement.

PATTERSON, Karen S; El Dorado Sr HS; El Dorado, KS; 4/182 HonRl; StuCncl; TchrAde; Yrbk; PpCl; CaptBsktbl; LetterTennis; LetterTrk; GAA; EldAwd; Kansas State College; Pe Instructor.

PATTERSON, Katherine F; Adelphian Academy; Holly, MI; Band; Chr; ChrhWkr; CmntyWkr; CncrtBnd; HonRl; NHS; SchMus; StuCncl; YthFlsp; IMSpt; College; Nursing.

PATTERSON, Kathleen S; South Knox HS; Vincennes, IN; 15/100 ChrhWkr; CncrtBnd; HonRl; JA; MrchBnd; PepBnd; TchrAde; YthFlsp; CaptBsktbl; Trk; Univ; Physical Ed.

PATTERSON, Kathy D; Stewardson Strasburg HS; Strasburg, IL; Chrs; ChrhWkr; HonRl; NHS; SchPl; 4-H; FHA; AmLegAwd;.

PATTERSON, Lisa; Corunna HS; Owosso, MI; HonRl; LbryAde; StuCncl; 4-H; GAA; Working In Business Office.

PATTERSON, Mark E; Parkside HS; Jackson, MI; TrsFrshCls; PresChr; HonRl; SchMus; StuGov; TreasGerCl; Bsktbl; LetterTrk; IMSpt; MasAwd; Alma College; Business Admin.

PATTERSON, Martha J; East Noble HS; Kendallville, IN; 99/278 Band; CncrtBnd; HonRl; MrchBnd; SpnCl; St Francis College; Elementary Ed.

PATTERSON, Mary A; Unity HS; Chicago, IL; Chr; NHS; RedCrAde; StuGov; SchPpr; FrCl; SciCl; CitAwd; Univ; Eviron Engr.

PATTERSON, Michael J; Roncalli HS; Omaha, NE; Chrs; ChrhWkr; HonRl; JA; NHS; PolWkr; RptrYrbk; SptEdYrbk; RptrSchPpr; Tennis; Univ Of Ne; Newspaper Reporter.

PATTERSON, Nikki A; Copeland HS; Copeland, KS; 1/12 PresJrCls; PresSrCls; ChrhWkr; DrlTm; HonRl; PresStuCncl; TchrAde; EdYrBk; LetterBsktbl; LetterTrk; Chrldr; BttyCrckrAwd; Wichita State Univ; Secretarial.

PATTERSON, Paula J; Carson City HS; Crystal, MI; 6/114 TrsJrCls; ALAGirlsSt; HonRl; NHS; PolWkr; RptrYrbk; FHA; IMSpt; BttyCrckrAwd; Montcalm Comm Col; Social Service.

PATTERSON, Philip M; Blair HS; Blair, NE; 18/139 ALBoysSt; PresBand; Chrs; NHS; StuCncl; PresYthFlsp; RptrYrbk; LetterFtbl; LetterTrk; GodCntryAwd; West Point; Military.

PATTERSON, Ramona G; Palestine HS; Palestine, IL; 10/42 HonRl; MrchBnd; OffAde; StuGov; FHA; Lincoln Trail Jr College; Secretary.

PATTERSON, Randy L; Cave In Rock HS; Cave In Rock, IL; VPFrshCls; Band; CncrtBnd; MrchBnd; OffAde; PolWkr; StuCncl; MthCl; Gonzaga Univ; Political Science.

PATTERSON, Rodney D; Osborne HS; Osborne, KS; 6/69 HonRl; LbryAde; SchPl; LetterWrstlng; CitAwd; Coll; Biology.

PATTERSON, Romona J; Harper Creek HS; Battle Creek, MI; 5/280 Chr; HonRl; NHS; College; Art.

PATTERSON, Sally B; Semco Community HS; Gilman, IA; SecFrshCls; SecJrCls; ALAGirlsSt; ChrhWkr; HonRl; NHS; NatlThespSoc; StuCncl; YthFlsp; LetterBsktbl; Univ; Scie.

PATTERSON, Sharon K; North Winneshiek HS; Decorah, IA; 13/34 TrsFrshCls; DrlTm; LbryAde; Yrbk; 4-H; FHA; Bsktbl; Chrldr; 4-HAwd; PresAwd; Coll; Teacher.

PATTERSON, Sherrie E; Airport Community HS; Carleton, MI; 1/220 PresSophCls; TrsJrCls; CncrtBnd; DrmMjrt; HonRl; NHS; 4-H; FrCl; Trk; 4-HAwd; Univ; Med Tech.

PATTERSON, Sherri K; Guthrie Center HS; Guthrie Center, IA; 12/56 ALAGirlsSt; Chr; ChrhWkr; HonRl; Mdrgl; SchMus; StuCncl; TchrAde; 4-H; Chrldr; College; Elem Education.

PATTERSON, Sherry L; Ellington HS; Ellington, MO; SecTrsFrshCls; SecSophCls; TrsJrCls; TrsSrCls; Chr; OffAde; SchPl; EdYrBk; RptrSchPpr; VPFHA; PpCl; Southwest Baptist College; Mission Work.

PATTERSON, Steven L; Hillsdale HS; Hillsdale, MI; 8/180 VPSrCls; Band; CmntyWkr; CncrtBnd; HonRl; JrNHS; MrchBnd; NHS; PepBnd; FTA; Mich State Univ; Accounting.

PATTERSON, Ted D; Cozad Sr HS; Cozad, NE; Band; Chrs; ChrhWkr; CncrtBnd; MrchBnd; 4-H; LetterFtbl; Trk; Wrstlng; IMSpt; 4-HAwd; Trade College; Vocation.

PATTERSON, Teresa L; East Jackson HS; Jackson, MI; 5/125 Band; HonRl; NHS; LetterBsktbl; LetterTrk; PresAwd; CitAwd; Jackson Community Clg; Nursing.

PATTILLO, David K; La Salle HS; South Bend, IN; 10/503 HonRl; NHS; NatlMeritSF; LetterTennis; KiwanAwd; Manchester College; Accounting.

PATTINSON, Catherine E; Pt Huron Central HS; Port Huron, MI; 4/225 SecSophCls; PresJrCls; CtyCnl; NHS; SchPl; PresStuCncl; TreasFrCl; Socr; GAA; IMSpt; Univ Of Michigan; Pre Law Studies.

PATTON, Angela G; Casey HS; Casey, IL; Lakeland Jr College; Data Processing.

PATTON, David D; Gibson City HS; Gibson City, IL; VPFrshCls; VPSophCls; Band; CncrtBnd; HonRl; StuCncl; LetterBsbl; LetterBsktbl; LetterFtbl; Univ; Pro.

PATTON, Donna M; St Pius X HS; Parkville, MO; 15/132 Band; ChrhWkr; HonRl; SecFrshCls; OffAde; PepBnd; SchMus; SchPl; PpCl; GAA; College;.

PATTON, Douglas A; Fullerton HS; Fullerton, NE; VPSrCls; Chrs; ChrhWkr; SchPl; TchrAde; PresYthFlsp; Pres4-H; VPFFA; Bsktbl; Ftbl; Univ Of Nebraska ; Farming.

PATTON, Fred C; Northeastern HS; Detroit, MI; Chr; ChrhWkr; CncrtBnd; LbryAde; OffAde; SchMus; SchPl; StuCncl; YthFlsp; JAAwd; Clge; Lawyer.

PATTON, James A; Rosiclare HS; Elizabethtown, IL; PresJrCls; Band; ChrhWkr; CncrtBnd; MrchBnd; SchPl; StuCncl; Bsktbl; AmLegAwd; SARAwd; College; Minister.

PATTON, James G; Willmar Sr HS; Willmar, MN; Chr; Orch; SchPl; GerCl; Bsktbl; LetterFtbl; LetterGlf; PresAwd; University; Professional.

PATTON, James P; Andover HS; Birmingham, MI; 1/420 HonRl; NHS; NatlMeritSF; GerCl; Bsktbl; Glf; IMSpt; RotaryAwd; Univ Mi; Med.

PATTON, Karen S; Kickapoo HS; Springfield, MO; 75/338 DrmBgl; HonRl; LitMag; LbryAde; NatlFornLg; TchrAde; GerCl; Southwest Missouri State University; German.

PATTON, Kevin T; Bishop Dubourg HS; Saint Louis, MO; 20/406 HonRl; NHS; SctActv; RptrYrbk; Yrbk; RptrSchPpr; University; Veterinarian.

PATTON, Linda D; Delta HS; Muncie, IN; VPJrCls; HospAde; SchPl; 4-H; FHA; FrCl; SpnCl; Bsbl; Bsktbl; Registered Nurse.

PATTON, Luther C; Lindblom Tech HS; Chicago, IL; 6/657 Chr; ChrhWkr; HonRl; NHS; TchrAde; YthFlsp; MthCl; Trk; Morehouse Col; Elec Engineer.

PATTON, Michael R; Calhoun Comm HS; Hardin, IL; 17/77 Band; CncrtBnd; HonRl; PepBnd; SctActv; FFA; LetterFtbl; Trade; Professionl.

PATTON, Paul E; Ashwaubenon HS; Green Bay, WI; Band; HonRl; StuCncl; U Of Wi; Physics.

PATTON, Sharon K; Osceola HS; Osceola, MO; CmntyWkr; HonRl; NHS; StuCncl; FBLA; FSA; SpnCl; GovHonPrgAwd; PresAwd; Bible Coll; Missionary To Mexico Or Teach.

PATTON, Steven J; Berkley HS; Berkley, MI; 13/500 Band; Chr; ChrhWkr; CncrtBnd; HonRl; MrchBnd; PepBnd; PolWkr; YthFlsp; IMSpt; Wayne State U; Eng.

PATTON, Steven L; Humboldt HS; Humboldt, IA; 1/132 ALBoysSt; Band; Chrs; HonRl; NHS; StuCncl; Yrbk; Bsktbl; Ftbl; LetterTrk; College; Science.

PATTON, Valerie E; Normandy Sr HS; Northwoods, MO; 100/514 PresSophCls; HonRl; PresNatlThespSoc; Quill&Scroll; SchPl; StuCncl; Yrbk; FBLA; DARAwd; CitAwd; Howard Univ; Business Admin.

PATTYN, Lynn M; Ladywood St Agnes HS; Indianapolis, IN; 27/124 HonRl; StuGov; TchrAde; SpnCl; MthCl; Tennis; Trk; CchngActv; GAA; IMSpt; Purdue Univ; Mathematics.

PATZELL, Christopher D; Thomas More Prep; Manhattan, KS; VPFrshCls; VPSophCls; VPJrCls; PresSrCls; ALBoysSt; HonRl; NatlMeritSF; SchPl; StuCncl; VPLatCl; Univ.

PATZER, James R; Benton Harbor HS; Benton Harbor, MI; 10/419 HonRl; JrNHS; NHS; MthCl; BauchLmbAwd; EldAwd; Univ Of Michigan; Computer Engineering.

PATZLOFF, Judith R; Edina East HS; Edina, MN; 14/450 Band; ChrhWkr; HonRl; HospAde; MrchBnd; PepBnd; SchMus; StuCncl; TchrAde; Unif Of Mn; Medicine.

PATZMAN, Laurence S; Mt Horeb HS; Mt Horeb, WI; 14/135 ALBoysSt; NHS; Glf; Wrstlng; IMSpt; U Of Wis Madison; Business.

PATZNER, Daniel J; Potosi HS; Potosi, WI; ALBoysSt; CmntyWkr; LetterBsktbl; LetterFtbl;.

PAUCAK, Denise M; Whiting HS; Whiting, IN; 8/94 HonRl; HospAde; NHS; RptrSchPpr; FTA; SpnCl; PpCl; Chrldr; GAA; College; Nursing.

PAUGH, Gary L; Northrop HS; Fort Wayne, IN; 89/578 Band; CncrtBnd; HonRl; MrchBnd; Orch; PepBnd; SchMus; TchrAde; SchPpr; Trk; Purdue Univ Ft Wayne; Archetectural Tech.

PAUKEN, Teresa E; Onsted HS; Onsted, MI; VPSrCls; Aud/Vis; HonRl; NHS; 4-H; SpnCl; LetterBsktbl; CaptTrk; GAA; 4-HAwd; Col; Lab Animal Science Tech.

PAUL, Andrew; Joliet Catholic Hs; Joliet, IL; 16 HonRl; NHS; NatlMeritCmnd; YthLg; RptrYrbk; RptrSchPpr; LatCl; RusCl; U Of Illinois;computer Science.

PAUL, Barbara L; Hinsdale South HS; Clarendon Hills, IL; 41/428 VPChr; Chrs; HonRl; HospAde; NHS; NatlThespSoc; SchMus; SchPl; YthFlsp; U Of Ill.

PAUL, Daryl R; Stanton Community HS; Stanton, IA; Chrs; HonRl; FFA; LetterBsbl; LetterFtbl;.

PAUL, John D; Swea City Comm HS; Swea City, IA; 11/33 HonRl; FFA; Bsbl; Bsktbl; Ftbl; Iowa State; Animal Science.

PAUL, Judith A; Bishop Dwenger; Hs; Fort Wayne, IN; TrsSophCls; TrsSrCls; HonRl; StuGov; 4-H; Bsktbl; IMSpt; 4-HAwd; College; Nursing.

PAUL, Kenneth L; Charlevois HS; Charlevoix, MI; ALBoysSt; Band; CncrtBnd; MrchBnd; PepBnd; TchrAde; Trk; College; Professional Field.

PAUL, Mark S; Auburndale HS; Auburndale, WI; Chrs; HonRl; NHS; SchPl; RptrSchPpr; FBLA; GerCl; Bsktbl; Ftbl; Glf; Trk; LionAwd; Univ; Medicine.

PAUL, Michael S; Foreman HS; Chicago, IL; 5/355 CncrtBnd; HonRl; TreasNHS; Quill&Scroll; SchMus; StuCncl; SchPpr; SecKeyCl; TreasGerCl; VPSciCl; Arizona State Univ; Chemical Engineering.

PAUL, Nancy R; Southwest HS; St Louis, MO; 3/500 Chrl; HonRl; SctActv; YthFlsp; SpnCl; GAA; College; Special Education.

PAUL, Rebecca E; Oregon Davis HS; Grovertown, IN; ALAGirlsSt; Chr; HonRl; NHS; 4-H; PpCl; Trk; Chrldr; GAA; Business School; Vocation.

PAUL, Roberta L; Joliet Central HS; Joliet, IL; 4/497 PresJrCls; AFS; HonRl; NHS; Quill&Scroll; SchPl; StuCncl; EdSchPpr; FrCl; GAA; U Of Ill; English Teacher.

PAUL, Robert S; Malden HS; Malden, MO; ChrhWkr; CmntyWkr; HonRl; NHS; NatlThespSoc; SchPl; StuGov; YthFlsp; FrCl; LetterTennis; Bible College; Minister.

PAUL, Steven J; Limestone Comm HS; Bartonville, IL; 22/396 Chr; ChrhWkr; CncrtBnd; HonRl; LbryAde; Mdrgl; NHS; SchMus; SchPl; College; Chemical Engineering.

PAUL, Susan C; Fremont HS; Fremont, NE; 74/425 ChrhWkr; CmntyWkr; HonRl; JrNHS; LbryAde; NatlFornLg; GerCl; MthCl; HstSophCls; Trk; Sd School Of Mines & Tech; Electronical Eng.

PAUL, Tamra S; Pontiac Northern HS; Pontiac, MI; Chr; ChrhWkr; HonRl; LbryAde; RptrSchPpr; 4-H; FTA; Cincinnati Bible Clg; Music.

PAUL, Thomas A; Hope HS; Hope, ND; PepBnd; StuCncl; Yrbk; SchPpr; 4-H; Bsktbl; Ftbl; Tennis; Trk; Fargo Univ; Counselor.

PAUL, Valerie J; Eldora HS; Eldora, IA; 1/66 ChrhWkr; HonRl; NHS; NatlThespSoc; SchPl; YthFlsp; RptrYrbk; EdSchPpr; SpnCl; Chrldr; N Ia Univ; Computer Sci.

PAUL, Victor M; Grinnell Sr HS; Grinnell, IA; 5/190 HonRl; College; Electronics Engineering.

PAULE, Dawn E; Downers Grove North HS; Downers Grove, IL; 35/524 Chr; Chrl; Chrs; HonRl; LbryAde; NHS; SchMus; SchPl; EngCl; College; International Business.

PAULEY, Clovetta; Central Of Argyle Comm HS; Argyle, IA; SchPl; PpCl; Chrldr; Bus Sch; Pro.

PAULEY, Craig E; Norwalk HS; Norwalk, IA; PresSophCls; ALBoysSt; Band; ChrhWkr; CmntyWkr; CncrtBnd; HonRl; SciCl; CaptFtbl; Trk;.

PAULEY, Elizabeth A; Harvard Public HS; Harvard, NE; Band; Chr; Chrs; CncrtBnd; Mdrgl; MrchBnd; PepBnd; SchPl; YthFlsp; Yrbk; 4-H; LetterTrk; BttyCrckrAwd; Doane College; Veterinarian.

PAULFREY, Joe; Wood River HS; Wood River, IL; 13/300 ChrhWkr; HonRl; JrNHS; NHS; SctActv; LatCl; Siu Edwardsville; Pre Med.

PAULFREY, Joe C; East Alton Wood River HS; Wood River, IL; 11/300 HonRl; JrNHS; Southern Illinois Univ; Medicine.

PAULIK, George F; Manistee Catholic Central HS; Manistee, MI; 1 88 HonRl; NHS; NatlMeritFnl; StuCncl; StuGov; Clg; Physics.

PAULING, Judi J; De Kalb HS; De Kalb, IL; 75/370 Band; ChrhWkr; CmntyWkr; CncrtBnd; HonRl; MrchBnd; PepBnd; StuCncl; StuGov; YthFlsp; 4-H; LetterBsbl; GAA; IMSpt; College.

PAULINSKI, Diane R; Maria HS; Chicago, IL; 84/299 HonRl; HospAde; GerCl; SciCl; Loyola Univ; Biology Major.

PAULK, Nina; Central Comm HS; Flint, MI; Chr; DrlTm; HonRl; HospAde; RedCrAde; TchrAde; YthFlsp; Mid Michigan Comm; Lp Nurse.

PAULL, Lynn; Whitefish Bay HS; Milwaukee, WI; Band; CncrtBnd; HonRl; MrchBnd; Twrl; SpnCl; Uw Madison; Medical School.

PAULL, Melinda J; Coldwater HS; Coldwater, MI; VPSophCls; VPSrCls; ALAGirlsSt; Chr; CncrtBnd; NHS; StuCncl; LetterBsktbl; IMSpt; DARAwd; Nursing; Rn.

PAULMAN, Roric R; Hershey HS; Hershey, NE; TrsJrCls; Chrs; ChrhWkr; HonRl; PepBnd; SchMus; TchrAde; LetterBsktbl; LetterFtbl; IMSpt; Trade Sch; Mechanic.

PAULS, Jeffrey D; Naperville Central HS; Naperville, IL; 15/800 HonRl; NHS; NatlMeritCmnd; LetterFtbl; LetterWrstlng; Northwestern Univ; Engineering.

PAULS, Linda J; Riverdale HS; Muscoda, WI; 13/75 ChrhWkr; HonRl; NHS; FFA; FHA; PpCl; GAA; Uw Center Richland; English Teacher.

PAULS, Tim; Richland Center HS; Richland Center, WI; MrchBnd; Orch; PepBnd; FFA; MthCl; Trk; Wrstlng; Vocational Tech School; Auto Mechanic.

PAULSEL, George A; Lapel HS; Lapel, IN; 25/90 Band; Chr; Chrs; CncrtBnd; HonRl; MrchBnd; PolWkr; SchMus; SchPl; RptrYrbk; Ball State U; Singer.

PAULSEN, David A; Freind Public HS; Friend, NE; VPSophCls; SchAde; SchMus; StuCncl; TchrAde; LetterGlf; LetterWrstlng; Fairbury Jr Clg; History.

PAULSEN, Jeffrey F; Brother Rice HS; Birmingham, MI; HonRl; NHS; SchPpr; CaptTrk; IMSpt; PresAwd; Col; Pre Med.

PAULSEN, Jeffrey T; Holdrege Sr HS; Holdrege, NE; Band; CncrtBnd; HonRl; MrchBnd; PepBnd; Kearney St College; Biology.

PAULSEN, Jill L; Delwood HS; Delmar, IA; SecTrsSophCls; Band; ChrhWkr; HonRl; NHS; RptrYrbk; RptrSchPpr; FNA; Bsktbl; Trk; Vocation.

PAULSEN, Jim W; Durant Community HS; Durant, IA; ALBoysSt; ChrhWkr; CmntyWkr; HonRl; SctActv; LetterBsktbl; LetterFtbl; Glf; Swmmng; Wrstlng; Univ; Soc Wrkr.

PAULSEN, Laurie A; Wausau East HS; Wausau, WI; 8/338 SecTrsSrCls; Chr; CncrtBnd; MrchBnd; NatlFornLg; NHS; NatlMeritCmnd; NatlSciFnd; SecStuGov; EdSchPpr; U Of Wi; Law.

PAULSEN, Linda M; Luther South HS; Chicago, IL; HonRl; NHS; OffAde; GerCl; Business School; Accounting.

PAULSEN, Lisa A; Grandview HS; Grandview, MO; Chr; HonRl; HospAde; JrNHS; VPRptrYrbk; PresFrCl; Col.

PAULSEN, Lori J; Crawford HS; Crawford, NE; PresSophCls; Chrs; ChrhWkr; HonRl; JrNHS; NHS; OffAde; SchPl; YthFlsp; FshEdYrbk; Coll.

PAULSEN, Mark A; Exira Comm HS; Exira, IA; 17/46 PresFrshCls; VPJrCls; ALBoysSt; Chrs; ChrhWkr; HonRl; SchMus; SchPl; FFA; CaptBsbl; College; Teaching.

PAULSEN, Michael A; Wausau East HS; Wausau, WI; Band; ChrhWkr; CncrtBnd; MrchBnd; NatlFornLg; PepBnd; StuGov; RptrSchPpr; MthCl; VoiceDemAwd;.

PAULSON, Anthony E; Cavalier HS; Cavalier, ND; HonRl; HospAde; SchPl; SctActv; Yrbk; VPSciCl; Trk; IMSpt; JETSAwd; College; Electrical Engineering.

PAULSON, Bradley A; Oak Grove Lutheran HS; Moorhead, MN; 3/50 Band; Chr; HonRl; Mdrgl; NHS; NatlMeritCmnd; SctActv; SchPpr; LetterFtbl; Wrstlng; Concordia Coll; Engineering.

PAULSON, Charles A; Gorham HS; Gorham, KS; 1/12 PresJrCls; Band; Chr; ChrhWkr; HonRl; SchPl; SctActv; PresStuCncl; CaptBsktbl; CaptFtbl; Kansas State Univ; Civil Engineering.

PAULSON, Craig J; Hanson HS; Alexandria, SD; NatlFornLg; SchMus; SchPl; SptEdSchPpr; 4-H; FFA; LetterBsktbl; LetterFtbl; Trk; CchngActv; College; Agriculture.

PAULSON, Dave G; Bristol Independant HS; Conde, SD; Chrs; HonRl; NatlMeritCmnd; LetterFtbl; LetterTrk; IMSpt; TIMEAwd; Col; Vocation.

PAULSON, Glory; Brooten HS; Brooten, MN; 3/45 SecSophCls; Band; Chr; HonRl; HospAde; NatlThespSoc; SchPl; RptrSchPpr; 4-H; Chrldr; Concordia Moorhead; Registered Nurse.

PAULSON, Hugh A; Pecatonica Area HS; Blanchardville, WI; VPSophCls; HonRl; SchPl; LetterBsbl; LetterBsktbl; ChmnFtbl; LetterGlf; Navy.

PAULSON, Julie; Canton HS; Canton, SD; Band; CncrtBnd; HonRl; MrchBnd; PepBnd; SchPl; RptrYrbk; Coll; Political Science.

PAULSON, Martin P; Campion Jesuit HS; Waukegan, IL; 8/98 TrsJrCls; TrsSrCls; CmntyWkr; ModUN; SchPl; StuCncl; StuGov; RptrYrbk; SptEdSchPpr; Bsbl; LetterBsktbl; Ftbl; Glf; Univ Of Notre Dame.

PAULSON, Peggy J; Tomahawk HS; Tomahawk, WI; 30/155 ALAGirlsSt; CncrtBnd; HonRl; Twrl; Yrbk; PresPpCl; Bsktbl; Socr; Chrldr; Western Wi Tech Sch; Commercial Art.

PAULSON, Rodney A; Huron HS; Huron, SD; 59/305 ALBoysSt; Chr; Chrs; ChrhWkr; CncrtBnd; PepBnd; KeyCl; GerCl; Bsktbl; LetterFtbl; Ia State Univ; Architectural Eng.

PAULSON, Rodney J; Roosevelt HS; Carson, ND; 8/26 PresSrCls; AFS; HonRl; SchPl; StuCncl; RptrYrbk; SptEdSchPpr; Bsbl; Bsktbl; Trk; College; Accounting.

PAULSON, Sally A; Central Cass HS; Casselton, ND; Band; Chrs; CncrtBnd; HonRl; MrchBnd; NHS; PepBnd; SchPl; GAA; Univ; Cytotechnologist.

PAULUS, Lynn A; Holy Family Acad; Manitowoc, WI; Chr; ChrhWkr; CmntyWkr; NatlFornLg; SchMus; SchPl; RptrYrbk; SchPpr; FrCl; VFWAwd; College; Psychology.

PAULY, George G; North Side HS; Fort Wayne, IN; NatlMeritSF; Orch; SchMus; I U Ft Wayne;music.

PAULY, Kathleen M; Wahpeton HS; Wahpeton, ND; Band; Chr; CncrtBnd; HonRl; JrNHS; LbryAde; MrchBnd; PepBnd; SpnCl; IMSpt; PPFtbl; Jr College; Nursing.

PAULY, Liz M; Owen Withee HS; Withee, WI; 5/98 Chrs; HonRl; NHS; SchPl; Yrbk; FrCl; Univ; Dramatics.

PAULY, Mark A; Springville HS; Springville, IA; PresBand; PresChr; HonRl; SchMus; TchrAde; LetterBsktbl; LetterTrk; AmLegAwd; College; Vocation.

PAULY, Mary J; Jordan HS; Jordan, MN; Band; ChrhWkr; NatlMeritSF; SchPl; SctActv; College Of St Benedict; Art.

PAULY, Robert C; Premontre HS; Green Bay, WI; Chrs; HonRl; SchMus; VPKeyCl; Bsktbl; Ftbl; Drake Univ.

PAULY, William H; Immaculate Conception HS; Hillside, IL; 13/174 CmntyWkr; HonRl; NHS; SchPl; VPLatCl; IMSpt; College; Medicine.

PAUNESCU, Anita; Mchenry Hs; Mchenry, IL; 7 CncrtBnd; HonRl; MrchBnd; NHS; Orch; SchMus; RptrYrbk; GAA; College;foreign Language Professor.

PAUSBACK, Ron J; Notre Dame HS; Park Ridge, IL; 6/276 HonRl; NHS; NatlMeritCmnd; SchMus; LetterTennis; IMSpt; Univ; Professional.

PAUSTIAN, Roberta L; Bloomfield HS; Bloomfield, NE; 1/45 HonRl; NHS; NatlThespSoc; SchAde; SchMus; SchPl; TchrAde; 4-H; FHA; PpCl; Clge; Elem Ed.

PAUTSCH, Suzan; Cedarburg HS; Cedarburg, WI; HonRl; NHS; Quill&Scroll; SchPl; SchPpr; FNA; GAA; Uw La Crosse; Mass Communications.

PAVEK, Christine E; Steinmetz HS; Chicago, IL; 12/616 Chrs; HonRl; HospAde; LbryAde; NHS; OffAde; SchMus; TchrAde; KeyCl; GerCl; MthCl; Loyola Univ; Mathematics.

PAVEL, Sharon K; Bishop Miege HS; Prairie Village, KS; 3/220 PresChrl; ChrhWkr; DrlTm; HonRl; NHS; SchMus; SchPl; StuCncl; Kansas Univ; Secondary Education.

PAVEL, Suzette L; Rochester Adams HS; Rochester, MI; ChrhWkr; HonRl; JA; NHS; Orch; TchrAde; FDA; GerCl; SpnCl; GAA; Oakland U; Pharmacy.

PAVELKA, Jim C; Hobart Sr 'S; Hobart, IN; ChrhWkr; CncrtBnd; NatlMeritFnl; StuCncl; TchrAde; PresFTA; Swmmng; LetterTennis; BauchLmbAwd; GovHonPrgAwd; LionAwd; OptClAwd; Andrews Univ; Medicine.

PAVESICH, Anton R; Lockport Central HS; Crest Hill, IL; 23/550 HonRl; MthCl; LetterBsbl; Bradley Univ; Chemistry.

PAVICH, Christine N; Lead HS; Lead, SD; 17/168 Chr; Chrs; ChrhWkr; CmntyWkr; DrlTm; HonRl; Quill&Scroll; RptrSchPpr; Chrldr; PresAwd; College; Business.

PAVINATO, Eugene A; St Bede Academy; Oglesby, IL; 2/125 HonRl; Bsbl; Ftbl; AmLegAwd; College; Accounting.

PAVLICK, Gary A; West Lafayette HS; West Lafayette, IN; SctActv; Tennis; LetterTrk; IMSpt;.

PAVLIK, Anne M; Verdigre HS; Verdigre, NE; 4/42 PresJrCls; PresSrCls; ALAGirlsSt; HonRl; HospAde; VPNHS; OffAde; SchPl; SctActv; PresStuCncl; PPFtbl; CitAwd; Kearny St College; Business Ed.

PAVLIK, David M; Bloomington HS; Bloomington, IL; 32/391 HonRl; NHS; TchrAde; Bsbl; Bsktbl; Ftbl; Glf; Socr; Swmmng; Tennis; Trk; College; Accounting.

PAVLIK, Donna L; Verdigre Public HS; Verdigre, NE; Band; Chrs; CncrtBnd; HonRl; MrchBnd; PepBnd; SchPl; PpCl; College; Vets Assistant.

PAVLIK, Dorothy; Verdigre Public HS; Verdigre, NE; SecSophCls; Chrs; HonRl; SchPl; PpCl; Business School; Legal Secretary.

PAVLINAC, Cindy A; Pontiac Northern HS; Pontiac, MI; 5/404 Chr; ChrhWkr; HonRl; Mdrgl; NHS; LetterOrch; SchPl; FSA; Kalamazoo Coll; Aerospace Engr & Photograph.

PAVLOCK, Joy S; John Marshall HS; Milwaukee, WI; Chr; DrlTm; HonRl; NatlMeritCmnd; SchMus; SctActv; 4-H; Chrldr; AmLegAwd; 4-HAwd; Univ Of Wis Madison; Professional Law.

PAVLOVICH, Andrew S; West Lafayette HS; West Lafayette, IN; ALBoysSt; HonRl; NHS; StuCncl; CaptBsbl; Bsktbl; CaptFtbl; Swmmng; DanFAwd; Wabash College; Medicine.

PAVLOVICH, Mark; Geo Rogers Clark HS; Whiting, IN; 32/260 ChrhWkr; CmntyWkr; HonRl; MrchBnd; NatlThespSoc; Orch; SchPl; StuCncl; Bsktbl; Purdue Univ; Psychology.

PAVLOVICH, Mark G; Ironwood Catholic HS; Ironwood, MI; VPJrCls; Chrs; ChrhWkr; HonRl; NHS; SchMus; StuGov; TchrAde; PpCl; Gogebic College; Law.

PAVOLKO, David T; Nokomis HS; Nokomis, IL; 23/105 ALBoysSt; ChrhWkr; HonRl; Bsktbl; LetterFtbl; LetterTrk; College; Vocation.

PAVON, Ricardo M; St Rita HS; Chicago, IL; 105/590 Aud/Vis; VPChrhWkr; CmntyWkr; HonRl; JrNHS; SancSoc; SpnCl; IMSpt; College; Architect.

PAWER, Terri A; East Appleton HS; Appleton, WI; 1/523 Chrl; HonRl; Mdrgl; NHS; NatlMeritCmnd; SchMus; StuCncl; PpCl; LetterBsktbl; LetterTrk; Chrldr; GAA; AmLegAwd; Univ; Accountant.

PAWL, Michelle M; Regina HS; Roseville, MI; NatlFornLg; SchMus; SchPl; StuCncl; Northwood Business Inst; Business Admin.

PAWLAK, Mary A; All Saints Central HS; Bay City, MI; 4/140 Band; DrlTm; HonRl; NatlCathMusEdAsoc; NHS; NatlMeritCmnd; PepBnd; SchMus; TchrAde; PpCl; Saginaw Vly State Coll; Computer Math.

PAWLAK, Peggy S; Owen Withee HS; Withee, WI; 4/75 Band; ChrhWkr; CncrtBnd; HonRl; MrchBnd; NHS; PepBnd; Yrbk; FHA; Trk; Chrldr; Univ Of Wisconsin; Accounting.

PAWLES, Jennifer L; Holy Redeemer HS; Detroit, MI; 11/190 HonRl; LbryAde; NHS; Yrbk; Arch.

PAWLIAS, Susan E; Macomb HS; Macomb, IL; CncrtBnd; HonRl; LbryAde; NHS; Orch; PepBnd; SctActv; TchrAde; FrCl; SpnCl; Drake U; International Rel.

PAWLICKI, Mark J; St Vincent De Paul HS; Chicago, IL; 2/9 SecSophCls; PresJrCls; HonRl; SchPl; StuCncl; EdSchPpr; LetterBsktbl; LetterSocr; Louisiana State; Engineering.

PAWLIK, Christine M; St Alphonsus HS; Dearborn, MI; 6/145 ChrhWkr; HonRl; Sacrstn; SchPl; Sdlty; PpCl; College; Professional.

PAWLIK, Donna J; St Michael Cen HS; Chicago, IL; 1/37 PresFrshCls; VPSophCls; PresJrCls; Chr; ChrhWkr; HonRl; NHS; StuCncl; RptrSchPpr; College; Accounting.

PAWLIK, Donna J; St Michael Central HS; Chicago, IL; 1/37 PresFrshCls; VPSophCls; PresJrCls; Chr; Chrs; ChrhWkr; HonRl; NHS; Yrbk; RptrSchPpr; PpCl; University; Accounting.

PAWLIK, Linda S; Sts Peter & Paul Area HS; Saginaw, MI; CmntyWkr; NHS; SchMus; StuCncl; PpCl; LetterBsbl; LetterBsktbl; Trk; CaptChrldr; IMSpt; College; Vocation.

PAWLING, Kathy S; Logan View HS; Hooper, NE; 12/54 ALAGirlsSt; Band; Chr; Chrs; ChrhWkr; CmntyWkr; CncrtBnd; HonRl; MrchBnd; NHS; PepBnd; TchrAde; CaptTrk; IMSpt; Wayne State College; Physical Educ.

PAWLISCH, Curt F; Whitefish Bay HS; Milwaukee, WI; 25/350 HonRl; LitMag; SchPpr; GerCl; Univ Of Iowa; English.

PAWLISCH, Debra; Brodhead Hs; Brodhead, WI; 3/112 SecFrshCls; PresJrCls; ALAGirlsSt; ChrhWkr; HonRl; HospAde; PresNHS; SecFrCl; LetterBsktbl; Trk; University; Nursing.

PAWLITSCHEK, Virginia E; Underwood HS; Dalton, MN; 6/41 HonRl; MrchBnd; SchAde; SchPl; TchrAde; Twrl; Bsktbl; Chrldr; College.

PAWLOW, Alan; Niles North Hs; Skokie, IL; 8 CmntyWkr; HonRl; NHS; Bsbl; Socr; U;chemistry Premedicine.

PAWLOWSKI, Joanne; Royal Oak HS; Royal Oak, MI; PresNHS; PresNatlThespSoc; OptClAwd; Princeton Univ.

PAWLOWSKI, Mary J; Goodman HS; Armstrong Creek, WI; 1/36 Band; Chrs; ChrhWkr; HonRl; MrchBnd; PepBnd; RptrSchPpr; SpnCl; Bsbl; LetterBsktbl; Uw Stout; Poss.

PAWLOWSKI, Paul K; St Clement HS; Center Line, MI; 5/98 PresHonRl; PresNHS; StuCncl; VPSciCl; Bsbl; Ftbl; IMSpt; Univ Of Michigan; Engineering.

PAWLOWSKI, Renee A; Wm H Taft HS; Chicago, IL; Chr; Chrs; HonRl; HospAde; LitMag; SchMus; SchPl; StuCncl; TchrAde; KeyCl; PpCl; Illinois Wesleyan; Grand Opera.

PAWLUKIEWICZ, Michael J; St Andrew HS; Detroit, MI; Chr; ChrhWkr; HonRl; SchPl; SctActv; Yrbk; IMSpt; Math.

PAWLUS, James M; Gavit Jr Sr HS; Hammond, IN; 6/341 HonRl; LitMag; NHS; Bsbl; LetterSwmmng; College; Engineer.

PAX, Robert J; Belvidere HS; Belvidere, IL; 39/343 Aud/Vis; ChrhWkr; HonRl; NHS; Quill&Scroll; SchMus; TchrAde; YthFlsp; Yrbk; RptrSchPpr; SptEdSchPpr; Bsktbl; LetterTrk; CchngActv; Northern Illinois Univ; Coach.

PAXSON, John; Bluffton HS; Bluffton, IN; 1/138 Band; HonRl; NHS; NatlThespSoc; PepBnd; StuCncl; SchPpr; CivCl; Butler Univ; Bio Chemical Research.

PAYANT, Patricia L; St Josephs Acad; Green Bay, WI; SecTrsFrshCls; Band; Chrs; HonRl; HospAde; Mdrgl; RptrSchPpr; SpnCl; Swmmng; Trk; College; Professional.

PAYLO, Barbara; Thomas Kelly Hs; Chicago, IL; 4/550 HonRl; JrNHS; NHS; TchrAde; Yrbk; FTA; SpnCl; GAA; Junior College; Business.

PAYNE, Bonita; Gresham Public HS; Grasham, NE; SecFrshCls; TrsJrCls; Chrs; DrmMjrt; HonRl; MrchBnd; RptrYrbk; PpCl; Chrldr; Bus Sch; Stenographer.

PAYNE, Carin L; Paw Paw HS; Paw Paw, MI; 1/170 Chrl; ChrhWkr; NHS; NatlMeritSF; Quill&Scroll; SchMus; StuCncl; PresYthFlsp; RptrSchPpr; DARAwd; Adrian Clge; Botany.

PAYNE, Cheryl L; Walled Lake Western HS; Union Lake, MI; 8/400 Chr; CncrtBnd; HonRl; Mdrgl; MrchBnd; VPNHS; NatlMeritSF; Orch; LetterTennis; CaptChrldr;.

PAYNE, Cornelia W; Marquette Sr HS; Marquette, MI; 62/386 Band; ChrhWkr; CmntyWkr; CncrtBnd; HonRl; LitMag; MrchBnd; NatlFornLg; Orch; PepBnd; PolWkr; Trk; Chrldr; Michigan St Univ; Social Work.

PAYNE, Dana; Plainfield Hs; Plainfield, IL; 38/297 Chr; Chrl; Chrs; HonRl; NatlMeritCmnd; SchMus; SchPl; GAA; College; Psychologist.

PAYNE, De Anna M; St Paul Public HS; St Paul, NE; 25/72 Chr; Chrs; ChrhWkr; CmntyWkr; HonRl; IntrClCncl; OffAde; StuCncl; FFA; Bsktbl; College; Lab Tech.

PAYNE, Debbie L; Pontiac Northern HS; Pontiac, MI; 63/397 ChrhWkr; HospAde; NHS; Yrbk; Northern Mi U; Nursing.

PAYNE, Edward C; Swea City Comm HS; Ledyard, IA; 19/33 ALBoysSt; Chrs; FFA; Bsktbl; College; Accounting.

PAYNE, Jackie L; Cleveland HS; St Louis, MO; 11/639 Chrs; DrlTm; HonRl; NHS; SchPl; PpCl; PresAwd; St Louis Univ.

PAYNE, James F; Blackford County HS; Hartford City, IN; 4-H; Bsbl; LetterFtbl; Chrldr; IMSpt; College; Business.

PAYNE, Joellen I; Cardinal HS; Batavia, IA; TrsSophCls; TrsJrCls; TrsSrCls; Chrs; HonRl; SchPl; TreasStuCncl; RptrYrbk; RptrSchPpr; 4-H; LetterBsktbl; CaptTrk; PPFtbl; Business School; Secretary.

PAYNE, John S; Brazil HS; Brazil, IN; 57/175 Aud/Vis; ChrhWkr; HonRl; VPStuCncl; YthFlsp; PpCl; LetterBsbl; LetterFtbl; LetterWrstlng;.

PAYNE, Karen S; St Peter & Paul HS; Saginaw, MI; Chrs; ChrhWkr; HonRl; NHS; OffAde; SchAde; SchMus; TchrAde; PpCl; Bsktbl; Ferris State College; Optometry.

PAYNE, Kelly R; St Pius X HS; Gladstone, MO; 19/130 HonRl; Bsbl; Bsktbl; U Of Ut; Meteorology.

PAYNE, Kimberly; Maroa Forsyth HS; Maroa, IL; HonRl; YthFlsp; PpCl; GAA; Decatur Comm Coll; Business.

PAYNE, Linda G; Galien HS; Galien, MI; TrsFrshCls; SecSophCls; SecJrCls; HonRl; NHS; StuCncl; PpCl; GAA; PresAwd; CitAwd; College.

PAYNE, Linda K; Huntley HS; Lyman, NE; 1/13 PresJrCls; Band; Chrs; ChrhWkr; NHS; TreasStuCncl; Yrbk; Pres4-H; VPFHA; Trk; Chrldr; GAA; BauchLmbAwd; Colo State Univ; Med Technician.

PAYNE, Michael E; Allendale HS; Allendale, IL; TrsSophCls; Band; Chrs; ChrhWkr; CncrtBnd; HonRl; NatlMeritSchl; SchPl; StuCncl; StuGov; YthFlsp; LetterBsktbl; AmLegAwd; 4-HAwd; College; Business.

PAYNE, Patricia A; Sacred Heart Of Mary HS; Mt Prospect, IL; HonRl; JrNHS; NHS; SchPl; StuGov; TchrAde; EdSchPpr; SchPpr; Northwestern Univ; Medicine.

PAYNE, Patty A; Hastings Sr HS; Hastings, NE; 4/329 ALAGirlsSt; ChrhWkr; CmntyWkr; DrmMjrt; NatlThespSoc; SchPl; Teen; Twrl; PpCl; EldAwd; Hastings College; Medical Career.

PAYNE, Peggy J; Woodruff HS; Peoria, IL; 7/281 HonRl; SchPl; TchrAde; FrCl; C Of I Cen; Pre Law.

PAYNE, Phillip; Blackford HS; Hartford City, IN; 7/260 ALBoysSt; HonRl; NHS; SchAde; StuGov; YthLg; 4-H; Bsbl; Bsktbl; Ftbl; Univ; Prof.

PAYNE, Regina K; La Porte City HS; La Porte City, IA; LetterBand; Chr; LetterChrs; ChrhWkr; CncrtBnd; HonRl; MrchBnd; PepBnd; RedCrAde; SchMus; PresYthFlsp; PpCl; College; Physical Therapy.

PAYNE, Terry L; Zalma HS; Kinder, MO; PresSrCls; Chrs; CmntyWkr; HonRl; PolWkr; ROTC; SchPpr; FFA; Ftbl; JCAwd; Navy.

PAYNE, Thomas E; New Berlin HS; Loami, IL; Yrbk; SptEdSchPpr; LetterTrk; College.

PAYNE, William T; Lexington Comm Unit HS; Lexington, IL; 3/62 AFS; Chr; HonRl; NHS; SchPl; TchrAde; RptrYrbk; SptEdYrbk; FTA; SpnCl; VPSciCl; Bsktbl; Ftbl; Univ Of Illinois; Physician.

PAYONK, James J; Lake Central HS; St John, IN; 13/450 HonRl; NHS; NatlThespSoc; SchPl; GerCl; College; Engineering.

PAYTON, Arlene R; Stanton Public HS; Stanton, ND; VPJrCls; Chrs; ChrhWkr; HonRl; MrchBnd; RedCrAde; SchMus; RptrYrbk; RptrSchPpr; 4-H; Minot Business; Dental Assist.

PAYTON, Karlene; Vanderbilt HS; Vanderbilt, MI; SecJrCls; HonRl; StuCncl; TchrAde; YthFlsp; Yrbk; FNA; Univ; Modeling.

PAYTON, Robert T; Kingman HS; Kingman, KS; Band; Chr; Chrs; HonRl; NatlMeritSF; SpnCl; Coll; Astronomy.

PAZOUR, Diane M; Kimball HS; Pukwana, SD; VPSophCls; PresJrCls; ALAGirlsSt; Band; HonRl; NHS; SchPl; RptrYrbk; EdYrBk; PpCl; Univ; Professional.

PEABODY, Charles L; Portland HS; Portland, MI; 16/131 HonRl; NHS; Quill&Scroll; EdSchPpr; SptEdSchPpr; FrCl; LetterBsbl; LetterBsktbl; IMSpt; Michigan State U; Televiosion & Radio.

PEACH, Anthony W; Gibson Southern HS; Owensville, IN; Band; Chr; Chrs; CncrtBnd; MrchBnd; SchMus; PpCl; LetterBsbl; Bsktbl; LetterFtbl; Tech School; Oil Production.

PEACHER, Brenda S; Crispus Attucks HS; Indianapolis, IN; 5/245 VPJrCls; VPSrCls; ChrhWkr; HonRl; MrchBnd; NHS; StuCncl; StuGov; RptrYrbk; RptrSchPpr; All St Univ ; Acct Or Law.

PEACOCK, Allan E; Chase County HS; Strong City, KS; HonRl; PolWkr; SchPl; StuCncl; LetterBsbl; CaptFtbl; CaptWrstlng; Cloud Co Jr Col; Civil Engrng.

PEACOCK, Annette M; Fulton HS; Fulton, IL; 1/125 Chr; Chrs; ChrhWkr; HonRl; HospAde; NHS; SecNatlSciFnd; TreasNatlThespSoc; SchPl; FHA; GAA; College; Science.

PEACOCK, Ann Lee R; Winfield HS; Winfield, KS; Chrs; SchMus; TchrAde; PpCl; Chrldr; CchngActv; Kansas State Teachers Coll; Special Ed.

PEACOCK, Cynthia; Coal City Hs; Morris, IL; 3 Band; CncrtBnd; HonRl; MrchBnd; PepBnd; Yrbk; 4-H; FHA; BttyCrckrAwd; U Of Illinois;medical Field.

PEACOCK, Deborah; Hartland HS; Brighton, MI; Band; NHS; PepBnd; TchrAde; FrCl; PpCl; Wrstlng; IMSpt; Central Mich Iuniv; Medicine.

PEACOCK, Mark E; Lakewood HS; Lake Odessa, MI; 31/204 TrsFrshCls; HonRl; NatlFornLg; SctActv; Michigan State Univ; Elec Engineering.

PEACOCK, Paula R; Paw Paw HS; Paw Paw, MI; 8/168 HonRl; NHS; Teen; 4-H; Western Michigan Univ; Spanish.

PEAK, Bobby; Pope County HS; Golconda, IL; ChrhWkr; SchPl; TchrAde; FFA; PpCl; S Eastern South Ill Univ Ag Mac.

PEAK, Julie M; J D Darnall HS; Geneseo, IL; 67/218 Chrs; HospAde; NatlThespSoc; SchMus; Univ Of Ill; Engineering.

PEAK, Mark S; Girard HS; Girard, KS; SchPl; Ftbl; LetterGlf; Kansas State Voc Tech School; Mechanics.

PEAKE, Alan; Waukon Senior HS; Waukon, IA; Band; Chr; ChrhWkr; HonRl; Mdrgl; PepBnd; SchMus; Bsktbl; Trk;.

PEARCE, Debra G; Clay City HS; Clay City, IL; Chr; Chrs; ChrhWkr; HonRl; SchMus; StuCncl; Yrbk; 4-H; FHA; Chrldr; GAA; College; Music.

PEARCE, Debra G; Clay City Comm HS; Clay City, IL; Chrs; ChrhWkr; HonRl; SchMus; SchPl; StuCncl; Yrbk; SchPpr; 4-H; FHA; PpCl; LetterChrldr; GAA; 4-HAwd; College; Music Instructor.

PEARCE, James; Burrton HS; Burrton, KS; SecSophCls; PresJrCls; ALBoysSt; Chr; CmntyWkr; HonRl; StuCncl; SptEdYrbk; Bsktbl; College; Medicial Technician.

PEARCE, Kathy S; Big Foot HS; Walworth, WI; 17/152 SecSophCls; SecJrCls; Chr; HonRl; SchMus; 4-H; FFA; Chrldr; DanFAwd; 4-HAwd; Madison Univ; Meat Animal Science.

PEARCE, Laura A; Ofallon Township HS; Ofallon, IL; 52/327 Chr; PresChrs; CmntyWkr; HonRl; LitMag; Mdrgl; SchMus; SchPl; Yrbk; SchPpr; Murray St Univ; Music Ed.

PEARCE, Mary E; Academy Of Our Lady; Chicago, IL; 17/180 SecJrCls; SecSrCls; Chr; HonRl; HospAde; JrNHS; NHS; SchMus; SchPl; SctActv; StuGov; PpCl; College; Law.

PEARCE, Shelli J; Woodruff HS; Peoria, IL; 11 275 ChrhWkr; HonRl; NHS; KeyCl; SpnCl; Illinois Central Clg; Business.

PEARCE, Thomas M; Bentley Sr HS; Burton, MI; HonRl; NHS; SctActv; Bsktbl; Ftbl; University; Economics.

PEARCE, Timothy H; Flora HS; Flora, IL; 29/145 Chr; SecChrhWkr; HonRl; YthFlsp; VP4-H; SpnCl; SciCl; DanFAwd; 4-HAwd; Mc Kendree Col; Ministry.

PEARCY, Elizabeth A; Marion HS; Marion, IN; SecFrshCls; Chr; HonRl; HospAde; NHS; NatlMeritSF; SchMus; StuCncl; TchrAde; 4-H; GerCl; College; Science.

PEARD, Jan L; Homewood Flossmoor HS; Homestead, IL; CncrtBnd; HonRl; HospAde; MrchBnd; Orch; PepBnd; FrCl; Univ.

PEARL, Walter M; Fordson HS; Dearborn, MI; HonRl; Quill&Scroll; SchAde; LetterTrk; IMSpt; Henry Ford Comm Clg; Electronics Technician.

PEARLMAN, Alan D; James B Conant HS; Hoffman Estates, IL; ChrhWkr; HonRl; NHS; NatlMeritCmnd; Univ Of Ill; Prof.

PEARMAN, Vicki K; Blue Valley HS; Stilwell, KS; Band; Chr; DrlTm; HonRl; LbryAde; MrchBnd; OffAde; PpCl; LetterBsktbl; Chrldr; GAA; College; Vocation.

PEARRE, Cynthia N; New Bloomfield Riii HS; New Bloomfield, MO; TrsFrshCls; Band; Chrs; HonRl; NHS; TreasStuCncl; EdSchPpr; PpCl; Bsktbl;.

PEARRE, Gregg A; New Bloomfield HS; New Bloomfield, MO; Chrs; ChrhWkr; HonRl; SchPl; TchrAde; RptrSchPpr; PpCl; SciCl; Bsktbl; Trk; College; Accounting.

PEARSON, Alan; Reavis Hs; Burbank, IL; 56/676 LetterSwmmng; LetterTrk; College; Technical.

PEARSON, Brenda S; Marion Adams HS; Sheridan, IN; ChrhWkr; RptrYrbk; VPFHA; PpCl; Chrldr; GAA; PPFtbl; 4-HAwd;.

PEARSON, Carleen; Shenandoah HS; Shenandoah, IA; Chr; Chrs; ChrhWkr; SchMus; Teen; SpnCl; PpCl; Tennis; Chrldr; IMSpt; Business School;.

PEARSON, Carol A; Boone HS; Boone, IA; 3/202 TreasChrs; HonRl; LitMag; NHS; NatlThespSoc; Quill&Scroll; Pres4-H; PresLatCl; CaptChrldr; DanFAwd; Iowa St U;journalism.

PEARSON, Cindy; Raymond Central HS; Ceresco, NE; Chr; Chrs; CncrtBnd; HonRl; MrchBnd; PepBnd; SchPl; 4-H; PpCl; Trk; Univ; Cytotechnologist.

PEARSON, Claudia J; Plainfield HS; Plainfield, IN; 4/265 TrsSrCls; Band; JrNHS; NHS; NatlMeritCmnd; StuCncl; 4-H; PresSpnCl; PpCl; 4-HAwd; General Motors Inst; Engineering & Patent L.

PEARSON, Debbie L; Forest Park HS; Crystal Falls, MI; SecSophCls; Chr; ChrhWkr; CncrtBnd; HonRl; MrchBnd; SchPpr; FNA; College; Social Work.

PEARSON, Deborah K; Wakonda Public HS; Wakonda, SD; SecFrshCls; SecSophCls; Band; Chrs; ChrhWkr; CncrtBnd; HonRl; LbryAde; MrchBnd; PepBnd; Swmmng; Army; Chemistry Lab Ass.

PEARSON, Denise R; Northrop HS; Ft Wayne, IN; 62/568 Band; ChrhWkr; CncrtBnd; HonRl; LbryAde; MrchBnd; PepBnd; Iu Pu Ext; Elem Ed.

PEARSON, Diane M; Homer Comm HS; Hubbard, NE; CncrtBnd; HonRl; JrNHS; MrchBnd; StuCncl; Yrbk; SpnCl; LetterBsktbl; LetterTrk; CaptChrldr; College; Professional.

PEARSON, Donald J; Fargo North HS; Fargo, ND; ChrhWkr; RptrYrbk; RptrSchPpr; IMSpt; College; Law.

PEARSON, Dorothy; Ozark Acad; Ft Scott, KS; HonRl; OffAde; StuCncl; StuGov; TchrAde; RptrSchPpr; Union Coll; Music Education.

PEARSON, Douglas R; Genoa HS; Genoa, NE; 2/27 PresJrCls; ALBoysSt; CncrtBnd; HonRl; MrchBnd; NHS; NatlMeritFnl; NatlMeritCmnd; SctActv; RptrSchPpr; College; Biological Sciences.

PEARSON, Eric M; Stevens HS; Rapid City, SD; 4/413 ALBoysSt; NatlFornLg; NatlThespSoc; SchMus; SchPl; StuCncl; StuGov; University; Physics Degree.

PEARSON, Eurestine S; Beaumont HS; St Louis, MO; CmntyWkr; DrlTm; HonRl; JA; JrNHS; NHS; StuGov; TchrAde; LatCl; GAA; Univ; Professional.

PEARSON, Gary D; Cobden HS; Cobden, IL; SchPl; StuCncl; StuGov; RptrSchPpr; Bsbl; Bsktbl; CchngActv; Coll.

PEARSON, Huey L; Wayne HS; Ft Wayne, IN; ChrhWkr; CmntyWkr; HonRl; NatlMeritSF; PolWkr; StuCncl; StuGov; RptrSchPpr; IMSpt; College; Law.

PEARSON, James L; Lyons Twshp HS; Western Springs, IL; 25/1250 Chr; Chrs; HonRl; JrNHS; Mdrgl; NHS; NatlMeritSF; SchMus; StuGov; MthCl; Northwestern U;medical Reasearch.

PEARSON, Jane L; Logan Rogersville HS; Turners, MO; 23/89 Chrl; Chrs; ChrhWkr; HonRl; NHS; SchPl; PpCl; SciCl; Evangel College; English.

PEARSON, Jan L; Newcastle Public HS; Newcastle, NE; 3/24 TrsSophCls; Band; HonRl; MrchBnd; NatlMeritCmnd; PepBnd; TchrAde; RptrSchPpr; PpCl; Chrldr; College; Mathematics.

PEARSON, Jay D; Dickinson HS; Dickinson, ND; 5/204 ALBoysSt; Aud/Vis; HonRl; NHS; SctActv; GerCl; Bsktbl; BauchLmbAwd; NCTE; College; Teach College Biology.

PEARSON, Jean; Webb HS; Reedsburg, WI; VPJrCls; Band; ChrhWkr; CmntyWkr; CncrtBnd; MrchBnd; StuCncl; StuGov; Airline School; Legal Sec.

PEARSON, Jeffrey D; George Washington HS; Chicago, IL; ALBoysSt; Chr; ChrhWkr; CmntyWkr; CncrtBnd; MrchBnd; NHS; TchrAde; YthFlsp; LatCl; CchngActv; College; Professional.

PEARSON, Jeffrey E; Plainfield HS; Plainfield, IL; 21/297 Band; HonRl; GerCl; LetterGlf; Augustana College; Engineering.

PEARSON, Jeri L; Lohrville Comm HS; Lohrville, IA; 5/29 PresSrCls; VPBand; Chrs; HonRl; SchMus; PresYthFlsp; RptrYrbk; SchPpr; LetterBsktbl; Univ; Art Teacher.

PEARSON, Jocelyn; Harlem Hs; Loves Park, IL; 4/550 TrsSrCls; Chr; ChrhWkr; HonRl; Mdrgl; NHS; NatlThespSoc; SchMus; SchPl; StuCncl; College;professional Musician.

PEARSON, John C; Stevens HS; Rapid City, SD; 13/431 ALBoysSt; Band; CncrtBnd; HonRl; NatlFornLg; NatlMeritFnl; NHS; NatlSciFnd; PepBnd; Trk; Univ ;physics.

PEARSON, Joseph L; Jordan HS; Jordan, MN; Band; CncrtBnd; 4-HAwd; U Of Mn; Physicist.

PEARSON, Kathleen; Moline Sr Hs; Moline, IL; 1 HonRl; NHS; NatlMeritCmnd; StuCncl; RptrSchPpr; LatCl; Bsbl; LetterBsktbl; CaptTennis; PresGAA; U Illimois ; Education.

PEARSON, Kris K; Lancaster HS; Lancaster, MN; Chr; Chrs; ChrhWkr; CmntyWkr; HonRl; SchPl; Yrbk; SchPpr; FHA; PpCl; Rochester Vo Tech; Medical Clerical.

PEARSON, Kristie D; Holdrege Senior HS; Holdrege, NE; Band; Chrs; ChrhWkr; CncrtBnd; MrchBnd; PepBnd; SchMus; FBLA; PpCl; Bsktbl;.

PEARSON, Paula E; Adel HS; Adel, IA; Chrs; HonRl; NatlThespSoc; Quill&Scroll; RptrYrbk; SchPpr; College; Liberal Arts.

PEARSON, Richard B; Lasalle HS; South Bend, IN; 1/500 HonRl; College; Pharmacy.

PEARSON, Ronald L; Adair County R Ii HS; Brashear, MO; PresJrCls; PresSrCls; Band; ChrhWkr; CncrtBnd; HonRl; MrchBnd; NHS; PepBnd; SctActv; StuGov; EdSchPpr; Bsktbl; Trk; Northwestern Univ; Medicine.

PEARSON, Rosella; Prairie Comm HS; Moorland, IA; 15/78 ALAGirlsSt; Band; Chrs; CncrtBnd; HonRl; MrchBnd; SchMus; SchPl; StuCncl; RptrYrbk; Ia St U; Home Ec Ed.

PEARSON, Sheila L; Churubussco HS; Churubusco, IN; RptrSchPpr; SchPpr; 4-H; FHA; LatCl; PpCl; College; Medicine.

PEARSON, Susan; Clinton Comm HS; Clinton, IL; 35/156 Chrs; SpnCl; PpCl; College; Law.

PEARSON, Therese J; Pawnee HS; Pawnee, IL; 2/53 SecJrCls; Band; Chrs; ChrhWkr; CncrtBnd; DrmMjrt; HonRl; LbryAde; MrchBnd; NHS; YthFlsp; RptrYrbk; GAA; College; Education.

PEARSON, Thomas; Toulon HS; Toulon, IL; HonRl; NHS; SchPl; FFA; Bsbl; Bsktbl; Ftbl; Trk;.

PEARSON, Timothy J; Kankakee Westview HS; Kankakee, IL; HonRl; NHS; MthCl; SciCl; Univ Of Illinois; Business Admin.

PEART, Debra A; Mitchell Senior HS; Mitchell, SD; Band; HonRl; GAA; IMSpt; College; Nursing.

PEASE, Michael J; Saint Johns HS; Saint Johns, MI; HonRl; College; Writer.

PEASE, Teresa J; Climax Scotts HS; Scotts, MI; Band; CncrtBnd; HonRl; MrchBnd; NHS; OffAde; EdYrBk; 4-H; FHA; Bsktbl;.

PEASLEY, Julie; Fairfield HS; Fairfield, IA; Chr; ChrhWkr; HonRl; OffAde; SchMus; RptrYrbk; FrCl; PpCl; IMSpt; College.

PEAVLER, Patricia; Leroy HS; Leroy, IL; 6/95 HonRl; HospAde; FHA; PpCl; GAA; Mennonite Hosp; Nursing.

PEAVLER, Teresa J; Leroy HS; Leroy, IL; 10/84 SecSrCls; Chr; HonRl; NHS; OffAde; SchAde; TchrAde; 4-H; FHA; PpCl; Parkland Coll; Legal Sec.

PECH, Diane R; Necedah Area HS; Necedah, WI; 2/38 SecFrshCls; PresSophCls; Band; CncrtBnd; HonRl; LbryAde; PepBnd; FHA; PpCl; Bsbl; Bsktbl; GAA; IMSpt; Univ; Law.

PECH, Thomas R; Lincoln Comm HS; Lincoln, IL; Chrs; CmntyWkr; HonRl; Mdrgl; Orch; PolWkr; SchMus; 4-H; Illinois Wesleyan Univ; Business Admin.

PECHTER, Tammy; Stephen T Mather HS; Chicago, IL; 44/421 HonRl; JA; LbryAde; NHS; SecOrch; VPGerCl; GAA; Northeastern Ill Univ; Liberal Arts Science.

PECINOVSKY, Kim D; Lancaster Sr HS; Lancaster, WI; HstFrshCls; Chr; Chrs; ChrhWkr; HonRl; NatlFornLg; NHS; OffAde; SctActv; Bsktbl; Trk; GAA; IMSpt; Univ; Prof.

PECK, Douglas L; Saline HS; Ann Arbor, MI; 7/180 VPJrCls; PresSrCls; Chrs; HonRl; PresNHS; SchMus; StuCncl; LetterBsbl; Bsktbl; CaptFtbl; Trk; Hillsdale College; Law.

PECK, John E; Parkwood HS; Joplin, MO; AFS; Aud/Vis; ChrhWkr; CmntyWkr; HonRl; HospAde; JrNHS; YthFlsp; FrCl; Bsktbl; Columbia Univ; Doctor.

PECK, Julie A; Tekamah Herman HS; Tekamah, NE; ALAGirlsSt; Band; CncrtBnd; DrlTm; HonRl; MrchBnd; NatlThespSoc; SchMus; PpCl; Swmmng; LetterTrk; CaptChrldr; 4-HAwd; University Of Nebraska; Music.

PECK, Lyle; Battle Creek Central HS; Battle Creek, MI; NatlFornLg; NHS; NatlMeritFnl; NatlMeritCmnd; StuGov; Univ Of Michigan; Law.

PECK, Peter F; Lutheran North HS; St Louis, MO; Chr; HonRl; JrNHS; NHS; SchMus; SctActv; StuCncl; Trk; GodCntryAwd; College; Chemistry.

PECK, Steven D; Glenburn Public HS; Glenburn, ND; 2/29 VPFrshCls; ALBoysSt; Band; Chrs; CncrtBnd; HonRl; StuCncl; EdYrBk; 4-H; Bsktbl; Trk; N D St Univ; Agricultural Econ.

PECKENPAUGH, Scott D; Maine West HS; Des Plaines, IL; ChrhWkr; HonRl; JrNHS; NatlFornLg; NatlThespSoc; SchPl; SctActv; StuCncl; StuGov; College; Communications.

PECKHAM, James D; Harper Creek HS; Battle Creek, MI; 11/225 HonRl; SctActv; StuCncl; TchrAde; LetterBsbl; LetterBsktbl; LetterFtbl; Michigan State Univ; Business Management.

PECKHAM, Jerry L; Corning Comm HS; Corning, IA; 8/73 SecJrCls; CmntyWkr; HonRl; NHS; Bsbl; Bsktbl; Ftbl; Trk; AmLegAwd; DanFAwd; Luther College ;math.

PECKMAN, Paul E; Paola HS; Paola, KS; 1/162 Band; ChrhWkr; CncrtBnd; HonRl; MrchBnd; PepBnd; SchMus; SctActv; YthFlsp; SciCl; Bsbl; Bsktbl; LetterFtbl; Trk; College; Medicine.

PECKWORTH, Margaret; Rolla HS; Rolla, MO; 5/217 HonRl; NatlMeritCmnd; SchAde; SchMus; StuGov; TchrAde; FTA; LatCl; PpCl; Depauw Univ.

PECORARO, Donna M; Mercy HS; Omaha, NE; Chr; Chrs; HonRl; NHS; SchMus; SchPl; FrCl; Creighton Univ; Nursing.

PECORD, Angela K; Anna Jonesboro C HS; Mill Creek, IL; 2/137 HonRl; ModUN; Quill&Scroll; StuCncl; EdYrBk; Southern Il Univ; Fine Arts.

PECORD, Angela K; Anna Jonesboro HS; Mill Creek, IL; 2/137 HonRl; ModUN; Quill&Scroll; StuCncl; RptrYrbk; EdYrBk; Yrbk; 4-H; SpnCl; PpCl; SciCl; GAA; South Ill Univ; Fine Arts.

PECORD, William M; Cairo HS; Cache, IL; VPJrCls; HonRl; SchPl; TchrAde; RptrYrbk; SptEdSchPpr; PpCl; Bsbl; Bsktbl; Vienna Voc Scho ;water Treatmen.

PECORD, William M; Camelot HS; Cache, IL; TrsFrshCls; VPJrCls; CmntyWkr; HonRl; Quill&Scroll; SchAde; TchrAde; RptrYrbk; SptEdSchPpr; PpCl; Bsbl; Bsktbl; Vienna Voc School; Water Purification.

PEDE, Linda R; Waverly Shell Rock HS; Waverly, IA; Chrs; CncrtBnd; HonRl; HospAde; MrchBnd; TchrAde; Twrl; VPFSA; LetterTrk; Chrldr; U Of North Dakota; Major In Nursing.

PEDELTY, Gregory; Newaygo Public HS; Newaygo, MI; Band; HonRl; JrNHS; NHS; NatlMeritSF; PepBnd; SchPl; RptrYrbk; Yrbk; CivCl; Col; Pro.

PEDELTY, Jeffrey; Mason City HS; Mason City, IA; HonRl; Univ; Engineering.

PEDELTY, Ronald R; Newaygo HS; Newaygo, MI; VPFrshCls; Band; ChrhWkr; CncrtBnd; HonRl; MrchBnd; VPNHS; PepBnd; SchPl; Yrbk; Tennis; Albion College; Religion.

PEDELTY, Sharon M; Streator Town HS; Ransom, IL; Chr; HonRl; OffAde; Univ; Vocation.

PEDEN, Kathryn J; Brookings HS; Brookings, SD; 1/192 VPSophCls; ALAGirlsSt; TreasChr; CncrtBnd; HonRl; NatlFornLg; NHS; NatlMeritSF; NatlThespSoc; SchPl; Coll; Prof.

PEDERSEN, Alan; Exira Comm HS; Exira, IA; 8/45 TrsJrCls; ChrhWkr; HonRl; RptrSchPpr; FFA; Trk; LetterWrstlng; Ia St Univ; Vet.

PEDERSEN, Donna; Guthrie Center Comm HS; Guthrie Center, IA; 7/66 TrsFrshCls; VPJrCls; CncrtBnd; MrchBnd; NHS; PepBnd; FHA; FTA; Glf; 4-HAwd; College; Prof.

PEDERSEN, Douglas J; Campbell Tintah HS; Fergus Falls, MN; HonRl; RptrSchPpr; College; Agriculture.

PEDERSEN, Janis R; East Monona HS; Moorhead, IA; Band; CncrtBnd; HonRl; MrchBnd; NHS; RptrYrbk; 4-H; FHA; LetterTrk; Chrldr; Bus Schl; Vocation.

PEDERSEN, Jon P; Kenmare HS; Kenmare, ND; 4/55 Chr; Chrs; ChrhWkr; HonRl; FFA; Univ Of North Dakota; Business.

PEDERSEN, Karen L; E Peoria Community HS; Creve Coeur, IL; 6/480 TreasChr; HonRl; JA; Mdrgl; NatlFornLg; NHS; PolWkr; SecGerCl; MthCl; Bradley U; Engineering.

PEDERSEN, Patrick A; York Community HS; Elmhurst, IL; 90/963 HonRl; NHS; MthCl; Bsbl; Ftbl; University; Engineering.

PEDERSEN, Robert G; Tomah Senior HS; Tomah, WI; HonRl; College; Computer Programmer.

PEDERSEN, Roger A; Randolph Public HS; Belden, NE; 8/69 PresSrCls; Chrs; HonRl; SctActv; SchPpr; LetterFtbl; LetterWrstlng; Univ Of Nebraska; Architecture.

PEDERSEN, Ruth; Luck Public HS; Luck, WI; 7/55 Band; Chr; HonRl; PepBnd; SchPl; YthFlsp; EdYrBk; FHA; GAA; BttyCrckrAwd; Stout Univ; Dietetics.

PEDERSON, Alan W; Westhope Public HS; Westhope, ND; VPJrCls; Chrs; ChrhWkr; CmntyWkr; HonRl; SchPl; FFA; Bsbl; LetterSwmmng; LetterTrk; N Dakota State U; Agricultural Engineer.

PEDERSON, Barbara J; Drayton HS; Drayton, ND; 10/34 SecJrCls; Chrs; ChrhWkr; HonRl; HospAde; StuCncl; RptrYrbk; FHA; Trk; BttyCrckrAwd; U Of North Dakota; Special Ed Teacher.

PEDERSON, Diane C; New Effington HS; New Effington, SD; ALAGirlsSt; Band; Chrs; CncrtBnd; HonRl; SchMus; SchPl; Yrbk; SchPpr; Chrldr; College; Curriculum Of Major Study.

PEDERSON, Jeffrey J; Westby HS; Coon Valley, WI; Band; Chrs; ChrhWkr; HonRl; LbryAde; SchPl; CaptBsbl; Ftbl; LetterTrk; CaptWrstlng; Univ Of Wi Platteville; Criminal Justice.

PEDERSON, Joan M; Rutland HS; Nunda, SD; 8/22 TrsJrCls; Band; Chr; HonRl; TreasStuCncl; Yrbk; FHA; PpCl; Chrldr; Secretary.

PEDERSON, Judy E; Williston Sr HS; Williston, ND; Chr; HospAde; PpCl; SciCl; IMSpt; PPFtbl; Trade School; Prof Photographer.

PEDERSON, Robin J; Burnsville HS; Burnsville, MN; 10/650 ChrhWkr; HonRl; NHS; NatlMeritSF; StuGov; LetterTrk; Chrldr; CchngActv; Coll; Orthodontistry.

PEDERSON, Ronda J; Hatton Public HS; Hatton, ND; 11/27 VPSrCls; Band; Chrs; ChrhWkr; PepBnd; SchPl; Yrbk; FHA; PpCl; Mayville State College; Elementary Educ.

PEDERSON, Sandra; Milbank HS; Milbank, SD; 4-H; PpCl; Trk;.

PEDERSON, Sheila; Glenwood HS; Glenwood, MN; 13/132 VPJrCls; SecSrCls; Chr; ChrhWkr; HonRl; StuGov; TchrAde; 4-H; Bsktbl; Trk; Univ Of Minn Morris; Graphics.

PEDERSON, Stuart M; Bridgeport HS; Bridgeport, NE; 4/64 Band; CncrtBnd; HonRl; NHS; SctActv; StuCncl; YthFlsp; FrCl; LetterFtbl; LetterWrstlng; U Of Nebraska; Mathmatics.

PEDIGO, Margaret L; Wayland Academy; Horicon, WI; Chr; NatlThespSoc; SchMus; SchPl; StuGov; TchrAde; Yrbk; Swmmng; CchngActv; IMSpt; Univ Of Ia Ames; Biology.

PEDLER, Lisa A; Reeths Puffer HS; Muskegon, MI; 12/280 CmntyWkr; HonRl; NHS; StuCncl; SchPpr; Muskegon Comm Coll; Housewife.

PEDRETTI, Julie J; Holmen HS; Holmen, WI; 1/118 SecFrshCls; SecJrCls; HonRl; NHS; RptrYrbk; FHA; PpCl; LetterTrk; Chrldr; U Of Wis; History Teaching.

PEDRICK, Kathleen L; Van Buren Comm HS; Douds, IA; 1/90 ALAGirlsSt; Chrs; ChrhWkr; HonRl; NHS; 4-H; SpnCl; LetterBsktbl; LetterTrk; DARAwd; 4-HAwd; Central College; Education.

PEECHER, Mary L; Louisiana HS; Louisiana, MO; 17/88 TrsFrshCls; Chrs; HonRl; HospAde; StuCncl; FTA; SpnCl; LetterBsktbl; LetterTrk; IMSpt; University; Phy Educ.

PEEK, Jan; Medora HS; Medora, IN; 7/31 HstFrshCls; HstJrCls; SecSrCls; HonRl; MrchBnd; SchPl; Yrbk; SchPpr; IMSpt;.

PEEK, Janelle D; Huron HS; Huron, SD; ALAGirlsSt; Band; JrNHS; OffAde; PresSctActv; Teen; YthFlsp; SpnCl; PpCl; VPSciCl; College Or Univ; Chemistry Biology Orientat.

PEEL, Julie L; Plainfield HS; Joliet, IL; Chr; HonRl; HospAde; OffAde; 4-H; FNA; Nursing School.

PEELEN, Scott B; East Grand Rapids HS; East Grand Rapids, MI; Band; ChrhWkr; CncrtBnd; HonRl; NHS; PolWkr; StuCncl; Tennis; Wrstlng; College; Lawyer & Politics.

PEERBOLTE, Gregory J; Eastridge HS; Kankakee, IL; 2/225 Band; CncrtBnd; HonRl; MrchBnd; NHS; PepBnd; Trinity Christian College; Business.

PEERY, David; Benson HS; Omaha, NE; AFS; PolWkr; EdSchPpr; FrCl; SciCl; JAAwd; Doane College; Psychologist.

PEERY, David V; Benson HS; Omaha, NE; AFS; HonRl; JA; NatlMeritCmnd; Quill&Scroll; RptrSchPpr; SchPpr; Antioch Coll; Journalism.

PEETERS, Joseph D; New York Mills HS; Menahga, MN; TrsFrshCls; SecSophCls; HonRl; TchrAde; 4-H; FFA; LetterBsktbl; LetterFtbl; 4-HAwd; U Of Mn Crookston; Mech Engineer Or Farmer.

PEETERS, Mary B; West De Pere HS; De Pere, WI; Chrs; HonRl; NHS; SctActv; Twrl; FrCl; PpCl; GAA; IMSpt; Technical School; Operating Room Asst.

PEETZ, Denise A; Burke HS; Omaha, NE; Chr; ChrhWkr; DrlTm; HonRl; NHS; PpCl; LetterTrk; Chrldr; Univ Of Ne.

PEETZ, Diane L; Burke HS; Omaha, NE; Chr; ChrhWkr; HonRl; NHS; StuGov; PpCl; LetterTrk; Chrldr; Secretary.

PEETZ, Diane M; Carsonville Port Sanilac HS; Carsonville, MI; 2/55 ChrhWkr; HonRl; HospAde; NHS; OffAde; SchPl; TchrAde; FHA; SciCl; Chrldr; Northern Michigan Univ; Registered Nursing.

PEETZ, Jeffery T; Sidney HS; Sidney, NE; PresSrCls; HonRl; NHS; Quill&Scroll; StuGov; SptEdSchPpr; MthCl; Bsktbl; Ftbl; Glf; Univ; Law.

PEFER, Russell; Jackson HS; Alpha, MN; IMSpt; Univ Of Mn Morris; Mechanical Engineer.

PEFFER, Sandra K; Pine River HS; Le Roy, MI; 14/80 HonRl; LbryAde; NHS; SpnCl; Ferris State Coll; Med Tech.

PEFLEY, Albert H; Centerville HS; Centerville, IA; 15/200 Chr; ChrhWkr; HonRl; TchrAde; YthFlsp; RptrSchPpr; 4-H; SciCl; Bsbl; Bsktbl; Swmmng; IMSpt; Trade School; Electronics.

PEGOUSKIE, Debora S; Lincoln Consolidated HS; Willis, MI; 18/165 ChrhWkr; HonRl; NHS; Quill&Scroll; SctActv; TchrAde; SptEdSchPpr; FHA; BttyCrckrAwd; Grand Valley St Coll.

PEHRSON, Connie S; Mason County Central HS; Scottville, MI; 13/135 Chr; ChrhWkr; HonRl; StuCncl; StuGov; TchrAde; RptrYrbk; 4-H; FrCl; PpCl; Ferris State Coll; Accounting.

PEIER, Jeffrey; Hays HS; Hays, KS; 5/231 PresSophCls; PresJrCls; PresSrCls; ALBoysSt; ChrhWkr; HonRl; CivCl; Bsktbl; Tennis; Coll; Corporate Law.

PEIRANO, Mary L; Conway HS; Conway, MO; 28/68 SecJrCls; Chr; ChrhWkr; HonRl; Mdrgl; SchMus; StuCncl; TchrAde; RptrSchPpr; FNA; Southwest Mo St U; Business.

PEIRCE, Terri L; Central HS; Burden, KS; 3/35 SecFrshCls; TrsJrCls; TrsSrCls; Chrs; ChrhWkr; NHS; SchPl; EdSchPpr; FFA; OptClAwd; Cowley County Juco; Business.

PEIRCE, Terri L; Central U S D 462 HS; Burden, KS; 3/34 SecFrshCls; TrsJrCls; TrsSrCls; HonRl; NHS; SchPl; Yrbk; EdSchPpr; FFA; PpCl; Cowley County Ju Co; Business.

PEIRICK, Jerome M; St Francis Borgia HS; Union, MO; 3/120 HonRl; NHS; Sacrstn; SchPl; TchrAde; EdSchPpr; FrCl; IMSpt; Coll; Engr.

PEITZ, Julianne C; Marquette HS; Hillsboro, IA; 4/55 PresSophCls; Chr; Chrs; DrlTm; NHS; StuCncl; TchrAde; RptrYrbk; FTA; PpCl; College.

PEJSA, Peter M; Riverside Brookfield HS; Brookfield, IL; 37/489 HonRl; NHS; SciCl; LetterTennis; Trk; Univ Of Ill; Chemical Engineering.

PEKAREK, Patricia M; Our Lady Of Grace Academy; Indianapolis, IN; 1/60 Chrs; ChrhWkr; HonRl; NHS; SchMus; Yrbk; 4-H; SpnCl; IMSpt; Marian College; Biology Major.

PEKARSKE, Diane A; Valders Public HS; Valders, WI; Chrs; HonRl; NatlFornLg; SchPl; 4-H; FHA; PpCl; Chrldr; IMSpt; PPFtbl; Tech Institute; Medical Assistant.

PEKOW, Charles; University HS; Hoghland Park, IL; Chr; PolWkr; RptrYrbk; RptrSchPpr; SchPpr; RusCl; Georgetown Univ.

PELATE, Curtis B; Dupo Comm HS; Dupo, IL; LbryAde; PresYthFlsp; Pres4-H; SciCl; LetterBsbl; LetterBsktbl; LetterFtbl; LetterGlf; College; Professional.

PELC, Loretta E; Homewood Flossmoor HS; Glenwood, IL; 187/910 AFS; Chrs; CmntyWkr; HonRl; Mdrgl; OffAde; Orch; SchMus; Trinity Univ; Accounting.

PELC, Philip P; Howells Public HS; Dodge, NE; .

PELC, Philip P; Howells HS; Dodge, NE; Band; CncrtBnd; MrchBnd; PepBnd; SchPl; StuCncl; Bsktbl; Trade School; Radio.

PELECH, Mark H; Marist HS; Palos Heights, IL; 63/365 HonRl; Bsktbl; LetterFtbl; LetterTrk; Drake Univ; Business Administration.

PELECKIS, Debbie A; Oak Lawn Comm HS; Hometown, IL; 24/676 HonRl; NHS; SchPpr; Swmmng; Univ Of Illinois; Political Science.

PELISSERO, Paul D; A D Johnston HS; Bessemer, MI; 14/104 ALBoysSt; HonRl; ROTC; EdYrBk; LetterBsbl; LetterBsktbl; LetterFtbl; Trk; IMSpt; AmLegAwd; Us Military Academy; Engineer.

PELKIE, Margaret; Negaunee HS; Negaunee, MI; 2/145 PresFrshCls; PresSophCls; VPSrCls; Chrs; HonRl; NHS; Orch; StuCncl; RptrSchPpr; Chrldr; Univ; Mental Retardation.

PELKOFER, Steve G; Whitnall HS; Hales Corner, WI; HonRl; CaptBsktbl; CchngActv; IMSpt; College; Broadcasting.

PELL, Andy J; Western Mi Chr HS; Fremont, MI; Band; ChrhWkr; CncrtBnd; HonRl; MrchBnd; SchPl; LetterIMSpt; Univ; Engr.

PELL, Jeanne A; Avon HS; Plainfield, IN; HonRl; HospAde; LbryAde; ModUN; OffAde; SchPl; EdYrBk; SecGerCl; DanFAwd; Pres4-HAwd; Purdue U; Home Ec.

PELL, Mary A; Van Buren HS; Brazil, IN; 10/70 Band; CncrtBnd; HonRl; MrchBnd; NHS; PepBnd; SchPl; StuCncl; EdYrBk; 4-H; FTA; SciCl; Chrldr; College; Professional.

PELL, Mary R; Rogers HS; Wyoming, MI; Chr; HonRl; NHS; SchMus; Chrldr; HospAde; SchPl; KeyCl; PpCl; Aquinas College; Medicine.

PELLAK, Diane H; Evergreen Park Comm HS; Evergreen Park, IL; 39/452 AFS; NHS; OffAde; TchrAde; FrCl; SecRusCl; PpCl; IMSpt; Illinois State University.

PELLEGRINI, Cindy J; Marseilles HS; Marseilles, IL; Band; ChrhWkr; CncrtBnd; HonRl; MrchBnd; NatlThespSoc; OffAde; RptrYrbk; LetterBsktbl; LetterSocr; Jr College Nursing ; Nursing.

PELLEGRINO, Kareen; Cherry Hill HS; Inkster, MI; CmntyWkr; HonRl; NHS; NatlMeritCmnd; SchMus; SchPl; PpCl; IMSpt; Wayne Univ; Commercial Art.

PELLETT, Todd C; Atlantic HS; Atlantic, IA; ALBoysSt; CncrtBnd; HonRl; NatlFornLg; NHS; PolWkr; StuCncl; SchPpr; Ftbl; LetterTennis; Univ; Dentistry.

PELLEYMOUNTER, Charles R; Osage Comm HS; Osage, IA; SecJrCls; DrmBgl; Ftbl; College; Musician.

PELLIKKA, Patricia A; Ely Memorial HS; Ely, MN; 1/130 AFS; CncrtBnd; HonRl; NHS; NatlMeritCmnd; NatlThespSoc; PepBnd; PolWkr; SchPl; StuGov; MasAwd; Gustavus Adolphus Coll; Pre Med.

PELLUM, Janis K; East Richland HS; Olney, IL; Band; CncrtBnd; MrchBnd; PepBnd; RptrYrbk; RptrSchPpr; FrCl; PpCl; Trk; Chrldr; College.

PELLUM, Martin W; Marshall HS; Marshall, IL; 20/126 ALBoysSt; ALBoysSt; CtyCnl; CncrtBnd; StuGov; YthFlsp; FSA; SciCl; Bsktbl; Trk; Lincoln Trail Jr College.

PELMORE, Dorothy Y; J M Harlan HS; Chicago, IL; 16/707 Chr; Chrs; HonRl; HospAde; NHS; SchMus; StuCncl; TchrAde; FrCl; Swmmng; Purdue Univ; Cpa.

PELOWSKI, Lona J; Benkelman HS; Benkelman, NE; 6/33 Band; Chrs; CncrtBnd; HonRl; HospAde; MrchBnd; PepBnd; FHA; PpCl; Chrldr; 4-HAwd; Univ Of Ne; Acct.

PELOWSKI, Paula A; Falls HS; Intl Falls, MN; 16/260 Chrs; HonRl; NHS; StuCncl; RptrYrbk; RptrSchPpr; PpCl; LetterTrk; Chrldr; GAA; College; Nutrition & Dietetics.

PELSTER, Jane; Dalton Public HS; Dalton, NE; VPJrCls; Chrs; DrmMjrt; HonRl; StuCncl; 4-H; FHA; LetterTrk; Chrldr; 4-HAwd; Nebraska Univ; Physicians Assistant.

PELSTER, Sandra; Pope John Xxiii HS; Bartlett, NE; NatlMeritCmnd; SchMus; StuCncl; StuGov; EdSchPpr; 4-H; PpCl; BttyCrckrAwd; 4-HAwd; VoiceDemAwd; Univ Of Nebr Lincoln.

PELTIER, Deborah K; Carrollton HS; Carrollton, MO; Chrs; HonRl; RptrSchPpr; SchPpr; 4-H; FHA; SpCl; IMSpt; 4-HAwd; Training; Conservation Worker.

PELTIER, Suzette K; Dakota HS; Arthur, ND; 2/25 SecSophCls; PresSrCls; ALAGirlsSt; Band; Chrs; HonRl; HospAde; TreasNHS; PepBnd; SchPl; StuCncl; PresYthFlsp; Yrbk; PresFHA; University.

PELTON, Jim V; Holly HS; Holly, MI; Chr; HonRl; SchPl; RptrSchPpr; Bell & Howell Or Control Data; Comp Program.

PELTON, Nancy K; East HS; Waterloo, IA; Aud/Vis; ChrhWkr; HonRl; Orch; LetterSwmmng; LetterTennis; LetterTrk; Trade School; Retailing.

PELTZ, Vernon R; Glen Ullin HS; New Salem, ND; 2/40 ALBoysSt; HonRl; ModUN; NHS; SchMus; SchPl; StuGov; LetterBsktbl; LetterTrk; DanFAwd;.

PELUSO, Michele F; Greenway HS; Coleraine, MN; VPFrshCls; VPSophCls; Band; CmntyWkr; CncrtBnd; HonRl; MrchBnd; OffAde; StuCncl; StuGov; Yrbk; SchPpr; 4-H; PpCl; CaptBsbl; College.

PELZ, Lori S; Minonk Dana Rutland HS; Minonk, IL; 2/62 HonRl; MrchBnd; NHS; StuCncl; Twrl; Pres4-H; Chrldr; SecGAA; PPFtbl; Clge ; Acntg.

PELZER, Patricia A; Plattsmouth HS; Plattsmouth, NE; 16/138 HonRl; NHS; FHA; MthCl; PpCl; Chrldr; College; Sec Science.

PELZER, Randall; Griswold Community HS; Griswold, IA; ALBoysSt; Band; CmntyWkr; HonRl; TchrAde; FTA; SciCl; Ftbl; Glf; AmLegAwd; Univ; Animal Science.

PELZER, Rebecca J; Griswold HS; Griswold, IA; 2/86 Chrs; HonRl; LbryAde; NHS; SchMus; SchPl; FHA; LetterTrk; Iowa State Univ Ames; Vet Med.

PELZL, Laurence P; Maine South HS; Park Ridge, IL; 14/100 NHS; Yrbk; SchPpr; Univ Of Ill; Fine Arts.

PELZL, Lorry L; Ellendale HS; Ellendale, MN; TrsFrshCls; Chr; Chrs; ChrhWkr; CmntyWkr; HonRl; Bsbl; LetterBsktbl; LetterFtbl; Trk;.

PEMBER, Janice J; Hale HS; Hale, MI; 14/65 ALAGirlsSt; Chr; CncrtBnd; MrchBnd; NHS; RedCrAde; StuCncl; RptrSchPpr; Bsktbl; Chrldr; AmLegAwd; 4-HAwd; Central Michigan Univ; Teaching.

PEMBERTON, Cathy L; Pacific HS; Pacific, MO; VPJrCls; HonRl; LitMag; StuCncl; RptrYrbk; College; Nursing.

PEMBERTON, Jennifer K; High School; Connersville, IN; 8/371 HonRl; NHS;.

PEMBERTON, Timothy J; Normal Comm HS; Normal, IL; Band; Chr; CncrtBnd; HonRl; NatlMeritSF; SctActv; StuCncl; RptrSchPpr; Univ Of Illinois; Liberal Arts.

PEMBROOK, Richard W; Greenfield HS; Greenfield, IL; 7/77 Chr; ChrhWkr; CmntyWkr; HonRl; YthFlsp; 4-H; FrCl; CaptBsktbl; Ftbl; LetterTrk; DARAwd; College; Math.

PENALVER, Oremia; Kirksville HS; Kirksville, MO; Band; Chrs; DrlTm; HonRl; HospAde; Orch; SchMus; SchPl; SctActv; SciCl; Med Dr.

PENAS, Julie A; Park River HS; Park River, ND; Band; Chrs; HonRl; MrchBnd; PepBnd; SchPl; RptrYrbk; FrCl; PpCl; Trk; GAA; Mayville State Clg; French.

PENCAK, Carol M; Genoa Public HS; Genoa, NE; Chr; HonRl; SchAde; StuCncl; TchrAde; RptrSchPpr; SchPpr; 4-H; FHA; PpCl; Chrldr; PPFtbl; College; Secretary.

PENCE, Christopher M; Lees Summit HS; Lees Summitt, MO; HonRl; NHS; NatlMeritCmnd; StuGov; Univ; Engineering.

PENCE, Donna; Westmer HS; Keithsburg, IL; FBLA; FHA; FTA; GAA; IMSpt; 4-HAwd; PresAwd; Clericl Work.

PENCE, John D; Charleston HS; Charleston, IL; 25/237 Chrs; HonRl; NHS; Bsktbl; Trk; CchngActv; Eastern Il Univ.

PENCE, Thomas J; Linden; Linden, MI; CncrtBnd; HonRl; LitMag; NHS; Orch; TreasSpnCl; SciCl; IMSpt; Mich State University; Engineering.

PENCE, Tina L; Rantoul Township HS; Rantoul, IL; Chrs; CmntyWkr; SchMus; CivCl; FrCl; U Of Il; Occupational Therapy.

PENDER, Michele; Presentation Acad; Jeffersonville, IN; TrsFrshCls; Chr; Chrl; HospAde; JA; RedCrAde; YthFlsp; FrCl; SciCl; Swmmng; Yavier Univ; Pre Medical.

PENDERGRAPH, Cheryl L; Marion C Early HS; Morrisville, MO; 4/45 ChrhWkr; CncrtBnd; HonRl; ModUN; TchrAde; RptrSchPpr; EdSchPpr; FHA; FrCl; SciCl; Bsbl; University; Counselor.

PENDERGRASS, Karen G; Robichaud; Inkster, MI; 8/153 Chrs; ChrhWkr; HonRl; NHS; SchMus; StuCncl; Teen; PpCl; Eastern Michigan Univ; Fashion.

PENDERGRASS, Marc R; Lakeshore HS; St Joseph, MI; JA; SchMus; Bsbl; JAAwd; Trade Or Bus School; Vocation.

PENDLETON, David A; Frankenmuth HS; Frankenmuth, MI; ALBoysSt; Band; CncrtBnd; HonRl; MrchBnd; StuCncl; LetterBsbl; LetterBsktbl; LetterFtbl; Ferris St; Criminology.

PENDLEY, Jennifer S; Anderson HS; Anderson, IN; Band; Chr; LitMag; MrchBnd; Orch; SchMus; SctActv; TreasYthFlsp; SpnCl; Swmmng; College; Teacher.

PENDOLA, Janet M; Proviso West HS; Hillside, IL; 57/1086 ChrhWkr; HonRl; LitMag; NHS; Illinois State Univ; Art.

PENDZISZEWSKI, Thomas J; St Charles Borromeo Seminary; Lockport, IL; 1/13 PresFrshCls; PresSophCls; PresJrCls; PresSrCls; Chr; Chrl; Chrs; ChrhWkr; HonRl; NatlMeritCmnd; EdYrBk; EdSchPpr; LetterBsktbl; College Of St Thomas; Priesthood.

PENELTON, Lesley N; Crispus Attucks HS; Indianapolis, IN; HonRl; VPJA; NHS; PresNatlThespSoc; StuCncl; EdYrBk; Yrbk; VPLatCl; PpCl; JAAwd; CitAwd; Indiana Central Schl; Nursing.

PENFOLD, Steven; Onaway HS; Onaway, MI; Band; ChrhWkr; HonRl; NatlMeritFnl; NatlMeritSF; BauchLmbAwd; NCTE; PresAwd; CitAwd; VoiceDemAwd; Central Mich Univ; Accounting.

PENGELLEY, Rodney A; Mt Vernon Twp HS; Belle Rive, IL; 125/388 DrlTm; LbryAde; Southern Illinois Univ; Electronic Tech.

PENKIVICH, Michaeline; Round Lake Community HS; Round Lake Beach, IL; 25/204 Chrs; HonRl; RedCrAde; SchAde; GAA; CitAwd; Nursing School; Nursing.

PENMAN, Stacey A; Mt Vermon HS; Greenfield, IN; 2/120 ChrhWkr; DrlTm; HonRl; LbryAde; NHS; OffAde; SchMus; SchPl; TchrAde; Indiana State Univ; Law.

PENN, Cynthia L; Coldwater HS; Coldwater, MI; Chr; YthFlsp; Yrbk; FrCl; Swmmng; CaptChrldr; Nursing School; Registered Nurse.

PENNAMON, Rodney E; Bremen HS; Markham, IL; Chrs; ChrhWkr; HonRl; SpnCl; SciCl; Illinois St Univ; Medicine.

PENNE, Mary K; Timothy Christian HS; La Grange, IL; 1/82 Band; Chr; ChrhWkr; CmntyWkr; HonRl; Orch; SchMus; StuCncl; LatCl; Wheaton College; Physical Therapist.

PENNEBECKER, Ronald E; Mellen Public HS; Mellen, WI; 1/42 ALBoysSt; Band; CncrtBnd; MrchBnd; PepBnd; SchPl; TchrAde; SpnCl; MthCl; Navy; Nuclear Field.

PENNELL, Kathleen A; Wesclin Jr Sr HS; Trenton, IL; 10/100 Aud/Vis; Chr; Chrl; Chrs; HonRl; HospAde; JrNHS; NHS; NatlThespSoc; OffAde; SchMus; SchPl; GAA; 4-HAwd; St Johns Hosp Sch; Nurse.

PENNER, Carole; Tri County HS; Beatrice, NE; 3/63 TrsSophCls; ChrhWkr; HonRl; PresNHS; YthFlsp; EdYrBk; RptrSchPpr; Pres4-H; GerCl; SecPpCl; Nebr Westeyan Univ; Phy Ther.

PENNER, Kimberly J; Fremont HS; Fremont, IN; SecJrCls; VPBand; SecChr; HonRl; SchMus; SchPl; Sec4-H; FHA; FrCl; SecPpCl; Trk; College; Professional.

PENNER, Marlene A; Ingalls HS; Ingalls, KS; 1/24 Chr; ChrhWkr; CncrtBnd; HonRl; PepBnd; SchPl; PresYthFlsp; RptrYrbk; EdSchPpr; CaptBsktbl; Tabor College; Music.

PENNER, Michael A; Burrton HS; Burrton, KS; 3/25 VPSrCls; Band; CncrtBnd; HonRl; MrchBnd; PepBnd; SchPl; LetterBsktbl; Bethel College; Engineer.

PENNER, Yvonne R; Cascade HS; Clayton, IN; 1/152 ALAGirlsSt; Band; ChrhWkr; CmntyWkr; HonRl; NHS; TchrAde; FrCl; PpCl; 4-HAwd; College; Nursing.

PENNERTZ, Marlys D; Litchfield Sr HS; Litchfield, MN; Chr; HonRl; NHS; SchPl; RptrSchPpr; 4-H; FHA; DARAwd; 4-HAwd; College; Elementary Education.

PENNING, Helen A; Marquette HS; Alton, IL; 1/123 HonRl; JrNHS; LbryAde; NHS; NatlMeritCmnd; SchMus; YthFnd; RptrSchPpr; 4-H; Illinois State Univ; Medicine.

PENNINGS, Clark B; Maurice Orange City HS; Orange City, IA; Band; ChrhWkr; CncrtBnd; HonRl; MrchBnd; PepBnd; YthFlsp; 4-H; Ftbl; Glf; College; Pre Med.

PENNINGS, Daniel J; Premontre HS; Green Bay, WI; Chrs; HonRl; SchMus; RptrYrbk; SchPpr; SecKeyCl; LetterFtbl; Trk; IMSpt;.

PENNINGTON, James B; H L Richards HS; Worth, IL; 140/1100 ChrhWkr; CncrtBnd; HonRl; OffAde; Concordia Tchrs Coll; Lutheran Mnst Rlgn.

PENNINGTON, Jeffrey M; Marquette Manor Christian HS; Plainfield, IL; ChrhWkr; HonRl; JrNHS; LbryAde; NHS; IMSpt; Air Force Acad; Air Force.

PENNINGTON, Keith D; Plano HS; Plano, IL; Band; CncrtBnd; HonRl; MrchBnd; LetterBsbl; LetterBsktbl; College; Prof Lawyer.

PENNINGTON, Laura L; Bishop Mcnamara HS; Kankakee, IL; 44/173 HonRl; FrCl; GAA; IMSpt; Univ; Professional.

PENNINGTON, Mark A; Central HS; Easton, MO; 32/505 Chr; CmntyWkr; JrNHS; Mdrgl; NHS; SchPl; StuCncl; TchrAde; AmLegAwd; CitAwd; Kansas State U; Architecture.

PENNINGTON, Mary J; Silver Creek HS; Sellersburg, IN; 2/136 ALAGirlsSt; CmntyWkr; HonRl; NHS; 4-H; SpnCl; PpCl; AmLegAwd; 4-HAwd; Indiana Univ Se; Business.

PENNINGTON, Michael E; Bishop Mc Namara HS; Kankakee, IL; Band; CncrtBnd; HonRl; StuCncl; RptrSchPpr; EdSchPpr; SptEdSchPpr; LetterTrk; University; Elec Engineer.

PENNINGTON, Molly E; Wesclin HS; Trenton, IL; 9/110 Band; Chr; Chrl; Chrs; ChrhWkr; CmntyWkr; CncrtBnd; HonRl; JrNHS; MrchBnd; NHS; NatlThespSoc; Orch; PepBnd; RptrSchPpr; College; Law.

PENNINGTON, Richard D; S Milw HS; S Milwaukee, WI; Band; CncrtBnd; MrchBnd; NatlMeritSF; StuCncl; StuGov; Trk; Univ; History.

PENNINGTON, Teresa L; Paris HS; Paris, IL; 1/240 ChrhWkr; HonRl; LbryAde; NHS; SctActv; Eastern Illinois Univ; Elem Education.

PENNISTON, Greg K; Raytown HS; Kansas City, MO; ChrhWkr; CncrtBnd; HonRl; Ftbl; Wrstlng; Univ Of Mo; Environmental Sciences.

PENNOCK, Leonard; Berkley HS; Berkley, MI; Center For Creative Studies.

PENNOCK, Melinda L; Jennings Sr HS; Jennings, MO; 35/250 CmntyWkr; HonRl; NHS; StuCncl; TchrAde; TreasYthFlsp; EdYrBk; FHA; Swmmng; GAA; College; Law Enforcement.

PENNY, Linda S; Oak Ridge HS; Oak Ridge, MO; 9/22 Chrs; HonRl; OffAde; SchPl; College; Secretary.

PENNY, Tanya Y; Christian Fenger HS; Chicago, IL; 1/700 DrmMjrt; HonRl; IntrClCncl; NHS; NatlMeritCmnd; Quill&Scroll; StuCncl; TchrAde; RptrSchPpr; SchPpr; FrCl; Bsktbl; GAA; Stanford University; Communications.

PENPRAZE, Cheryl A; Coldwater HS; Coldwater, MI; 3/250 ALAGirlsSt; Band; CncrtBnd; HonRl; MrchBnd; NatlMeritSF; PepBnd; TchrAde; SchPpr; VPFrCl; PpCl; IMSpt; University.

PENQUITE, Ruth E; Canton Galva Sr HS; Canton, KS; Band; Chr; Chrs; HonRl; SchMus; PpCl; IMSpt; Us Army.

PENROD, Faith A; Hale HS; Hale, MI; PresSophCls; Chr; HonRl; NatlMeritCmnd; NatlMeritSF; SchPl; StuCncl; TchrAde; RptrSchPpr; SchPpr; Ferris St Coll; Microbiologist.

PENROD, Shelby K; New Ulm HS; New Ulm, MN; PresFrshCls; TrsSophCls; PresJrCls; Band; HonRl; LetterBsbl; Bsktbl; LetterFtbl; CchngActv; IMSpt; College; Social Service/medicine.

PENROSE, John F; Central R Iii HS; Flat River, MO; 10/150 HonRl; NHS; SctActv; SciCl; University; Professional.

PENTECOST, Gary; Hammond Baptist Hs; Hammond, IN; 19/88 VPFrshCls; VPJrCls; Band; NHS; LetterBsbl; CaptBsktbl; LetterFtbl;.

PENTIS, Charles J; Austin Catholic Prep; Grosse Pt Woods, MI; 27/115 HonRl; NatlFornLg; SchMus; SchPl; Univ Of Michigan; Law.

PENTON, Roma; Liberty Senior HS; Liberty, MO; 27/279 AFS; HonRl; HospAde; JrNHS; NHS; OffAde; SctActv; GAA; AmLegAwd; MasAwd; Nw Mo State Univ; Dential Hygiene.

PENTON, Virginia K; Lu Verne HS; Lu Verne, IA; 2/17 SecJrCls; SecSrCls; Chrs; HonRl; Yrbk; LetterBsbl; Bsktbl; Trk; CchngActv; GovHonPrgAwd; U Of Ia; Computer Programming.

PENWARDEN, Julia A; Hononegah HS; Rockton, IL; 26/211 Chrs; HonRl; RptrSchPpr; SchPpr; 4-H; PpCl; Bsbl; Bsktbl; GAA; Rock Valley College.

PENZENIK, Richard D; Howe Military HS; South Bend, IN; 2/43 TrsSrCls; DrlTm; HonRl; NatlFornLg; NHS; ROTC; StuCncl; StuGov; LetterFtbl; LetterTrk; Notre Dame; Medicine.

PENZENSTADLER, Sharon I; Lourdes Academy; Oshkosh, WI; 2/125 PresFrshCls; SecSophCls; VPJrCls; PresSrCls; NHS; StuGov; YthLg; KeyCl; AmLegAwd; DARAwd; Carroll Col; Medical Technology.

PENZIEN, Donald B; Reeths Puffer HS; Muskegon, MI; 20/286 HonRl; NHS; LatCl; LetterFtbl; LetterTrk; Hopo College; Medicine.

PEONI, Charles A; Roncalli HS; Indianapolis, IN; .

PEOPLES, Deborah A; Harper HS; Chicago, IL; 9/286 ChrhWkr; CmntyWkr; NHS; NatlMeritSchl; OffAde; RptrSchPpr; SpnCl; Bsbl; GAA; Univ Of Urbana; Social Working.

PEOPLES, Nujya A; St Anne HS; Momence, IL; 7/103 PresFrshCls; PresSrCls; Aud/Vis; Band; Chr; Chrs; CmntyWkr; CncrtBnd; HonRl; LbryAde; Mdrgl; MrchBnd; NHS; NatlMeritSF; PepBnd; Drake Univ; Law.

PEOT, Susanne M; Benet Academy; Naperville, IL; 10/242 Chrs; HonRl; NHS; SctActv; StuCncl; PpCl; Swmmng; IMSpt; Georgetown University; Foreign Service.

PEOTTER, Jeffrey D; Palatine HS; Palatine, IL; 104/441 HonRl; SctActv; RptrSchPpr; Bsbl; Trk; Wrstlng; Univ Of Illinois; Engineer.

PEPER, Robyn C; Homewood Flossmoor HS; Homewood, IL; 6/900 AFS; ChrhWkr; CncrtBnd; MrchBnd; NHS; NatlMeritCmnd; Univ Of Illinois; Business.

PEPIN, Donna D; Hillsdale HS; Hillsdale, MI; 10/180 HonRl; JrNHS; NHS; TchrAde; PresLatCl; Sw Michigan College; Nurse.

PEPIN, Michael K; Gladstone Area Public HS; Gladstone, MI; Band; Chr; Chrl; CncrtBnd; HonRl; MrchBnd; Orch; PepBnd; SchMus; SchPl; College.

PEPIN, Susan G; Custer HS; Custer, SD; HonRl; LbryAde; GerCl; Trade School; Assistant Veterenian.

PEPP, Mark M; Saint Laurence HS; Burbank, IL; 12/396 HonRl; SciCl; Univ Of Michigan; Psychology.

PEPPER, Dawn; Huntington North HS; Andrews, IN; LbryAde; Ball State; Accounting.

PEPPER, Debra; Sioux Rapids Comm HS; Webb, IA; TrsSrCls; ChrhWkr; NHS; CncrtBnd; MrchBnd; PepBnd; SchPl; YthFlsp; Yrbk; SpnCl; AmLegAwd; Northwestern College; Sociology Major.

PEPPER, Karla M; East Pike HS; Pearl, IL; HonRl; SchPl; 4-H; FHA; 4-HAwd;.

PEPPER, Kelly L; Warren HS; Apple River, IL; Chrs; HonRl; JrNHS; FHA; GAA; Baptist Coll.

PEPPLE, Diane; Ccr 1 HS; Revere, MO; 1/93 Band; CmntyWkr; DrmMjrt; LbryAde; NHS; SchPl; AmLegAwd; DARAwd; 4-HAwd; CitAwd; College; Librarian.

PEPPLE, Jo A; Pittsford HS; Osseo, MI; HonRl; College.

PEPPLE, Karen J; Cathay HS; Cathay, ND; 8/11 Chrs; ChrhWkr; NHS; SchAde; SchPl; Yrbk; SchPpr; 4-H; CaptBsktbl; IMSpt; 4-HAwd; Freemen Jr College; Nursing.

PEPPLE, Lannette; Steele HS; Steele, ND; 7/33 ALAGirlsSt; Band; Chr; Chrs; MrchBnd; PepBnd; SchMus; SchPl; Bsktbl; PPFtbl; Bismarck Junior Coll; Airline Hostess.

PERABEAU, Vicki V; Jacksonville HS; Jacksonville, IL; Band; Chr; CmntyWkr; CncrtBnd; HonRl; MrchBnd; PepBnd; SchMus; SchPl; StuCncl; Bsktbl; Tennis; CaptChrldr; PPFtbl; Univ Of Illinois; Graphic Designer.

PERADOTTI, Donna R; Morris Comm HS; Morris, IL; 39/240 Band; CaptDrlTm; TreasNatlThespSoc; PepBnd; SchPl; Yrbk; PpCl; BttyCrckrAwd; So Illinois Univ; Dental Hygiene.

PERAICA, Tony J; Cathedral HS; Chicago, IL; Band; CmntyWkr; CncrtBnd; Orch; SchPl; StuGov; SchPpr; FSA; Ftbl; Socr; College; Major Study.

PERALTA, Bonnie J; Southport HS; Southport, IN; 49/446 Chrs; HonRl; NatlMeritFnl; NatlMeritCmnd; NatlMeritSchl; NatlMeritSF; RptrSchPpr; College; Nursing.

PERAULT, Michael D; Kadoka HS; Belvidere, SD; 2/37 ALBoysSt; HonRl; 4-H; Bsktbl; Trk; Trade School; Agriculture.

PERCIFIELD, Deanna L; Brown County HS; Nashville, IN; 10/206 SecJrCls; HonRl; LbryAde; StuCncl; 4-H; SpnCl; In Univ; Professional.

PERCIFIELD, Julie A; Brown County HS; Helmsburg, IN; 48/204 ChrhWkr; DrlTm; HonRl; SchPl; SctActv; YthFlsp; Yrbk; 4-H; FrCl; SpnCl; Business College; Secretary.

PERCIVAL, Everett E; Alliance HS; Alliance, NE; 97/160 HonRl; Quill&Scroll; StuCncl; StuGov; TchrAde; SptEdSchPpr; LatCl; Ftbl; Swmmng; Trk; Wrstlng; University Of Nebraska; Railroad Officer.

PERCIVALL, Jessie K; Belleville East HS; Belleville, IL; Orch; Tennis; IMSpt; PPFtbl;.

PERCY, Cindy; Walled Lake Central HS; Union Lake, MI; 13/363 Chrl; HonRl; Mdrgl; VPModUN; SchMus; StuCncl; StuGov; Grand Valley State Coll; Child Psych.

PERCZAK, Carol; Fordson HS; Dearborn, MI; Chrs; ChrhWkr; HonRl; LitMag; NHS; SchMus; StuCncl; SchPpr; Univ Of Mich; Humanities.

PERDUE, Judith; Morton HS; Morton, IL; 32/286 SecTrsFrshCls; ChrhWkr; HospAde; MrchBnd; StuCncl; YthFlsp; 4-H; PpCl; GAA; PPFtbl; College; Registered Nurse.

PERDUE, Sheila A; North Huron HS; Kinde, MI; 1/45 TrsSophCls; SecJrCls; PresSrCls; HonRl; PresNHS; SchAde; StuCncl; RptrYrbk; DARAwd; 4-HAwd; Eastern Michigan Univ; Speech Therapy.

PEREKRESTENKO, Myrna F; Magic City Campus HS; Minot, ND; ChrhWkr; HonRl; No American Baptist Col; Home Economics.

PERENCHIO, Regina L; Harvard HS; Harvard, IL; Band; CncrtBnd; HonRl; MrchBnd; SchMus; SecStuCncl; 4-H; PpCl; Chrldr; 4-HAwd; W Ill Univ; Bus Admin.

PEREZ, Barbara J; Lakeview HS; Battle Creek, MI; HonRl; NHS; OffAde; Quill&Scroll; Yrbk; SchPpr; SpnCl; PpCl; Kellogg Comm Col; Dental Assistant.

PEREZ, Carmen M; Josephinum HS; Chicago, IL; PresJrCls; VPJrCls; TrsJrCls; HonRl; HospAde; LbryAde; StuCncl; RptrSchPpr; EdSchPpr; Augustana Hospital; Nursing.

PEREZ, Cyndi M; Morton West HS; Berwyn, IL; HonRl; OffAde; Orch; SchMus; SctActv; TchrAde; Swmmng; KiwanAwd; College; Physician.

PEREZ, Elizabeth; Jesse Spalding HS; Chicago, IL; TrsJrCls; Chrs; HonRl; SchPl; StuCncl; LatCl; AmLegAwd; De Paul; Nursing.

PEREZ, Felix; Lakeview HS; Lakeview, MI; PresFrshCls; HonRl; StuCncl; TchrAde; FTA; SpnCl; LetterBsbl; CaptFtbl; CaptWrstlng; IMSpt; Grand Rapids Jr College.

PEREZ, Julia; Holland HS; Holland, MI; 5/317 HonRl; NHS; Yrbk; FrCl; LetterBsktbl; College; Chemistry.

PEREZ, Marvin; Harrison HS; Chicago, IL; 6/400 ChrhWkr; HonRl; JrNHS; StuCncl; Ftbl; IMSpt; College; Computer.

PEREZ, Paulino; Harrison HS; Chicago, IL; DrlTm; HonRl; LbryAde; NHS; ROTC; SchPl; StuCncl; LetterSwmmng; LetterTrk; College; Computers.

PEREZ, Rebecca M; Parsons HS; Parsons, KS; 35/165 VPJrCls; Chr; HonRl; IntrClCncl; NHS; OffAde; StuCncl; PresPpCl; Chrldr; PPFtbl; College; Accounting.

PERGAMS, Oliver R; Albert G Lane Tech HS; Chicago, IL; 22/1213 CmntyWkr; JA; NatlMeritSF; SctActv; StuCncl; StuGov; TchrAde; RptrSchPpr; College; Biological Science.

PERGANDE, Albert N; Wisconsin Lutheran HS; Milwaukee, WI; HonRl; NHS; College; Electrical Engineer.

PERIARD, Amy J; Birch Run HS; Burt, MI; HonRl; LbryAde; NatlFornLg; NatlThespSoc; SchPl; StuCncl; SchPpr; LetterTrk; CaptChrldr; PresAwd; College; Theatre Arts.

PERIASWAMY, Cecilia N; St Stanislaus Kostka HS; Des Plaines, IL; 4/64 TrsJrCls; ChrhWkr; HonRl; NHS; Orch; TchrAde; RptrYrbk; RptrSchPpr; FNA; Loyola Univ; Biology.

PERILLO, Edward M; Prosser HS; Chicago, IL; NHS; NatlMeritFnl; NatlMeritCmnd; NatlMeritSchl; NatlMeritSF; NatlSciFnd; FDA; FSA; MthCl; SciCl; College; Professional.

PERINE, Patricia E; Highland Park HS; Topeka, KS; 10/350 SecFrshCls; Chr; Chrs; ChrhWkr; HonRl; NHS; StuGov; YthFlsp; Swmmng; Chrldr; Kansas University.

PERINI, Christine; Madison HS; Madison Heights, MI; Chrs; ChrhWkr; CmntyWkr; HonRl; RedCrAde; YthFlsp; PpCl; Bsbl; Chrldr; W M V College; Social Science.

PERISHO, Janie; Nesco HS; Zearing, IA; Chr; Chrs; HonRl; NHS; SchMus; EdYrBk; Yrbk; PpCl; IMSpt; Trade School; Vocation.

PERIUS, David J; Langdon Public HS; Langdon, ND; VPSrCls; SptEdYrbk; Bsbl; Bsktbl; Ftbl; Glf; Swmmng; Tennis; AmLegAwd; PresAwd; Drafting Trade.

PERK, John L; Crofton Public HS; Crofton, NE; 19/69 SecSrCls; Band; Chrs; CncrtBnd; MrchBnd; SchPl; StuCncl; StuGov; LetterBsktbl; LetterTrk; College; Atheltic Teacher.

PERKINS, Brenda E; Coldwater HS; Coldwater, MI; 11/271 Chr; HonRl; Mdrgl; NHS; SchMus; SchPl; StuCncl; YthFlsp; Store Manager.

PERKINS, Brian N; Louisa Muscatine HS; Muscatine, IA; 4/51 PresSrCls; ALBoysSt; NatlSciFnd; NHS; Quill&Scroll; SchPl; Twrl; EdSchPpr; Wrstlng; Us Military Acad; Civil Engineer.

PERKINS, Calvin L; Stamford Public HS; Stamford, NE; 6/13 TrsFrshCls; TrsJrCls; Chrs; ChrhWkr; HonRl; SchPl; StuCncl; Bsktbl; Ftbl; Trade School.

PERKINS, Carol L; Lake Shore HS; St Clair Shores, MI; HonRl; JrNHS; NHS; NatlMeritSchl; PolWkr; Quill&Scroll; SchPpr; Wayne St U; Pharmacy.

PERKINS, Cotriece; Eisenhower HS; Decatur, IL; Chr; NatlMeritCmnd; StuCncl; SpnCl; Chrldr; Notre Dame Col; Pre Law.

PERKINS, Cynthia J; Dallas Comm HS; Dallas Center, IA; TreasChr; ChrhWkr; CncrtBnd; HonRl; Mdrgl; SchMus; TchrAde; YthFlsp; EdYrBk; Chrldr; PPFtbl; College; Teacher.

PERKINS, Daniel B; Anderson HS; Anderson, IN; 76/576 HonRl; JrNHS; NHS; FSA; SciCl; Bsktbl; Ftbl; Glf; IMSpt; Purdue Univ; Geoscience.

PERKINS, Daniel L; Estherville HS; Estherville, IA; 35/189 Band; HonRl; MrchBnd; PepBnd; SchMus; SchPl; SctActv; FFA; LetterFtbl; Trk; Agricultural Sch; Farmer.

PERKINS, James K; Thomas Jefferson HS; Council Bluffs, IA; 3/450 Band; HonRl; NatlFornLg; NHS; NatlMeritCmnd; PepBnd; VPStuCncl; ChmnSwmmng; IMSpt; Univ Of Ia; Elec Engr.

PERKINS, Jeffery W; Donovan HS; Iroquois, IL; 5/51 HonRl; NHS; Quill&Scroll; SchPpr; FTA; GerCl; SciCl; Bsktbl; University; Professional.

PERKINS, Kathy; West Elk Hs; Howard, KS; 1/45 Band; DrlTm; HonRl; NHS; PolWkr; SchPl; SptEdSchPpr; LetterBsktbl; Trk; AmLegAwd; University; Professional.

PERKINS, Levon; Cathedral HS; Chicago, IL; PresSrCls; Band; HonRl; SchMus; SchPl; StuCncl; StuGov; YthLg; SchPpr; Trk; Illinois Institute Tech; Architect.

PERKINS, Pamela B; Crawford HS; Crawford, NE; SecJrCls; Chrs; ChrhWkr; CmntyWkr; HonRl; SchPl; StuGov; SchPpr; PpCl; College; Journalism.

PERKINS, Paul S; Clarksville HS; Clarksville, IN; 5/200 Band; CncrtBnd; HonRl; MrchBnd; PepBnd; PolWkr; SchAde; SctActv; GerCl; LetterTennis; University.

PERKINS, Priscilla; Horton Watkins HS; St Louis, MO; Band; CncrtBnd; MrchBnd; Orch; SchMus; TchrAde; FTA; Mount Holyoke Coll.

PERKINS, Rita; Hallsville HS; Hallsville, MO; 4/45 Chr; Chrs; ChrhWkr; HonRl; SchPpr; BttyCrckrAwd; Coll.

PERKINS, Steven; Cassville HS; Eagle Rock, MO; 27/108 CmntyWkr; HonRl; Vocational.

PERKINS, Susan S; North Shore Country Day HS; Winnetka, IL; PresJrCls; Chrl; Chrs; Mdrgl; PolWkr; SchMus; SchPl; StuGov; Bsktbl; Tennis; College; Professional.

PERKINS, Tami L; Fremont Mills HS; Tabor, IA; PresJrCls; ALAGirlsSt; HonRl; NHS; PresNatlThespSoc; PolWkr; SchPl; StuCncl; RptrYrbk; RptrSchPpr; University; Professional.

PERKKIO, Cindy L; Cloquet HS; Cloquet, MN; Band; CncrtBnd; MrchBnd; NHS; PepBnd; Twrl; PpCl; IMSpt; PPFtbl; Mn School Of Business; Fashion Merchandisin.

PERLEWITZ, Phillip C; Negaanee HS; Negaanee, MI; 15/150 HonRl; Tennis; Coll; Eng.

PERLINGER, Douglas W; Paxton HS; Paxton, NE; 3/16 TrsFrshCls; VPSophCls; PresJrCls; PresSrCls; HstSrCls; ALBoysSt; Chr; Chrs; HonRl; Mdrgl; NHS; CaptBsbl; CaptBsktbl; Ftbl; Kearney State College.

PERLINGER, Laure J; Paxton Consolidated HS; Paxton, NE; 1/15 PresFrshCls; PresJrCls; HonRl; Mdrgl; NHS; OffAde; SchPpr; LetterBsktbl; Swmmng; LetterTrk; Univ Of Nebraska; Major Study.

PERLMAN, Scott D; Rich South HS; Park Forest, IL; PresJrCls; Quill&Scroll; SchPl; PresStuCncl; SchPpr; KeyCl; LetterBsbl; LetterBsktbl; Trk; College; Doctor.

PERLOW, Steven P; Niles North HS; Skokie, IL; 43/632 HonRl; NHS; Bsktbl; LetterSocr; Washington Univ; Professional.

PERNICE, Phillip J; St Pius X HS; Kc, MO; 14/132 ALBoysSt; Chrs; HonRl; NHS; StuCncl; SptEdSchPpr; SchPpr; LetterFtbl; LetterTennis; Univ; Pharmacy Or Med.

PERNICKA, Debra K; La Salle HS; Cedar Rapids, IA; Chrs; HonRl; ModUN; PolWkr; Yrbk; PpCl; Univ Of Iowa; Computer Science.

PERNOT, Diane M; Girard HS; Mulberry, KS; 2/89 ChrhWkr; HonRl; NHS; SchPl; Teen; RptrYrbk; SecFHA; SecSpnCl; PpCl; LetterTrk; Chrldr; PPFtbl; AmLegAwd; Ks State Col Of Pittsburg; Accounting.

PERON, Lori J; Woodhaven HS; Woodhaven, MI; Chrl; HonRl; NHS; NatlMeritSchl; FrCl; Ferris State Clge; Dental Hygiene.

PERONA, Lou A; Harvard HS; Harvard, IL; Band; Chrs; CncrtBnd; HonRl; MrchBnd; SchMus; Yrbk; FrCl; PpCl; Chrldr; Univ; Vocation.

PERONI, Madelyn M; Davison Sr HS; Davison, MI; 34/433 CmntyWkr; HonRl; JA; JrNHS; MrchBnd; NatlFornLg; NHS; RptrSchPpr; SchPpr; IMSpt; Ohio State U; Journalism.

PERRIER, Nanette; North Polk HS; Shedahl, IA; 4/35 SecSophCls; SecJrCls; SecSrCls; VPFrshCls; ChrhWkr; HonRl; NHS; SchPl; YthFlsp; Yrbk; PpCl; Western Baptist Bible College; Rn.

PERRIGO, David A; Arrowhead HS; Pewaukee, WI; HstSophCls; Chr; HonRl; StuCncl; StuGov; YthLg; CchngActv; University; Lawyer.

PERRIN, David E; Gull Lake HS; Richland, MI; ChrhWkr; SctActv; StuCncl; YthFlsp; 4-H; SpnCl; SciCl; Bsbl; Bsktbl; Glf; College; Biology.

PERRINE, Brent E; Monroe City HS; Monroe City, MO; 11/92 ALBoysSt; PresBand; CncrtBnd; HonRl; MrchBnd; NHS; PepBnd; PresSciCl; CaptTrk; DanFAwd; Ne Mo State U; Environmental Sce.

PERRINE, Debra J; Saline HS; Stevensville, MI; 2/196 HonRl; LbryAde; SecNHS; StuCncl; GerCl; Western Michigan Univ; Business Admin.

PERRINE, Patrick J; Mc Gregor HS; Mc Gregor, MN; 5/53 PresSrCls; ALBoysSt; Band; HonRl; NHS; SchMus; SchPl; StuCncl; RptrYrbk; CaptFtbl; St Cloud State Clge; Mass Communications.

PERRINE, Rita M; Welcome Comm HS; Fairmont, MN; Band; Chrs; DrmMjrt; HonRl; SchPl; RptrYrbk; 4-H; FHA; Bsktbl; LetterTrk; Chrldr; GAA; IMSpt; Inver Hills Comm College; Nursing.

PERRINE, Timothy; Mc Gregor HS; Mc Gregor, MN; 15/70 PresFrshCls; Band; CncrtBnd; HonRl; JrNHS; SchPl; StuGov; RptrSchPpr; Coll.

PERRINO, Anthony J; Grass Lake HS; Grass Lake, MI; 22/94 NatlMeritSF; RptrYrbk; SptEdSchPpr; LatCl; PpCl; Bsbl; Bsktbl; Ftbl; Wrstlng; CchngActv; Albion College; Medical Tech Ed.

PERRONNE, Kathleen; Plymouth HS; Plymouth, WI; 5/234 Band; Chr; Chrs; CncrtBnd; HonRl; MrchBnd; NHS; SchMus; SchPl; VoiceDemAwd; Lakeland Coll; Medical Technology.

PERROT, Joseph G; Fatima HS; Bonnots Mill, MO; Band; HonRl; FrCl; SciCl; Univ; Professional.

PERROW, Wendy L; Morton HS; Morton, IL; 38/286 Chr; Chrl; Chrs; HonRl; Mdrgl; SchMus; PresAwd; College; Elementary Teacher.

PERRY, Belinda S; Brown County HS; Timewell, IL; ALAGirlsSt; Chr; Chrs; TreasChrhWkr; HonRl; TreasNHS; OffAde; TchrAde; YthFlsp; Yrbk; GAA; IMSpt; 4-HAwd; College; Special Education.

PERRY, Carol L; Mendota HS; Mendota, IL; 76/187 ChrhWkr; HonRl; OffAde; SchPl; TchrAde; RptrSchPpr; College; Girls Pe Teacher.

PERRY, Christopher R; Watseka Community HS; Watseka, IL; 3/125 TrsFrshCls; TrsSophCls; ALBoysSt; HonRl; NHS; RedCrAde; RptrYrbk; SpnCl; LetterBsktbl; LetterTrk; Un Of Il; Architecture.

PERRY, David A; Nevada HS; Nevada, MO; StuCncl; LatCl; College; Conservation.

PERRY, Debra A; West Iron County HS; Iron River, MI; Band; HonRl; LbryAde; MrchBnd; NHS; PepBnd; 4-H; LatCl; PpCl; LetterBsktbl; LetterTrk; GAA; BauchLmbAwd; Michigan State University; Vet.

PERRY, Denise A; Hillcrest HS; Country Club Hills, IL; TrsFrshCls; Chr; SpnCl; PpCl; Chrldr; GAA; IMSpt; PPFtbl; Univ; Professnl.

PERRY, Edward G; Austin Catholic Prep; East Detroit, MI; 27/115 HstSrCls; SchMus; SchPl; StuCncl; Bsbl; LetterFtbl; Central Michigan Univ; Business.

PERRY, Flora J; Austin HS; Chicago, IL; 23/527 Chr; Chrs; ChrhWkr; HonRl; HospAde; LbryAde; NHS; PresAwd; CitAwd; VoiceDemAwd; Univ.

PERRY, James; Jonesville Hs; Jonesville, MI; Chr; Chrs; YthFlsp; 4-H; Bsktbl; Trk; 4-HAwd; College; Computer Law.

PERRY, James R; Marine City Ward Cottrell HS; Marine City, MI; PresFrshCls; PresSophCls; ChrhWkr; HonRl; StuCncl; StuGov; TchrAde; PresYthFlsp; SchPpr; LetterBsbl; Cedarville College; Business Adm.

PERRY, Jane E; Marshall HS; Marshall, IL; 11/115 Band; ChrhWkr; CncrtBnd; MrchBnd; OffAde; FHA; SciCl; GAA; 4-HAwd; PresAwd; College; Psychologist.

PERRY, Jeanne E; Southside HS; Ft Wayne, IN; 85/435 Chr; HonRl; SchMus; SctActv; StuCncl; FrCl; IMSpt; OptClAwd; In Tech; Commercial Art.

PERRY, Jonathan T; Schulte HS; Terre Haute, IN; 17/96 TrsSrCls; ALBoysSt; HonRl; KeyCl; LetterFtbl; Trk; Rose Hulman Institute Of Tech; Engineer.

PERRY, Joyce E; Cowan HS; Muncie, IN; Band; CncrtBnd; MrchBnd; PepBnd; SctActv; YthFlsp; 4-H; College; Nursing.

PERRY, Kathleen A; Warroad HS; Warroad, MN; HonRl; HospAde; SchPl; SctActv; FNA; FrCl; PpCl; Bsktbl; GAA; IMSpt; Medical School; Professional.

PERRY, Marianne S; Bevier Public HS; Bevier, MO; 1/29 ALAGirlsSt; ChrhWkr; HonRl; JrNHS; PolWkr; TchrAde; 4-H; LatCl; Bsbl; Bsktbl; Univ; Elementary Ed.

PERRY, Mary Ann; Roncalli HS; Indianapolis, IN; ChrhWkr; HonRl; SctActv; RptrSchPpr; FrCl;.

PERRY, Nina K; Edinburg Comm HS; Edinburg, IN; 3/75 PresFrshCls; LitMag; TreasNHS; SecTrsFrshCls; EdYrBk; RptrSchPpr; TreasFrCl; PresPpCl; LetterTrk; Chrldr; Ball St Univ; Special Ed.

PERRY, Patti J; Saline Area HS; Saline, MI; Chrs; HonRl; HospAde; NatlFornLg; NHS; NatlMeritCmnd; SchMus; SchPl; PresStuCncl; VPSciCl; U Of Mi; Medicine/doctor.

PERRY, Reid A; Barron HS; Barron, WI; Band; Chr; Mdrgl; MrchBnd; NHS; StuCncl; YthFlsp; SchPpr; GerCl; LetterGlf; U W; Pro.

PERRY, Roy; Cooley HS; Detroit, MI; HonRl; NatlMeritSchl; OffAde; SchAde; StuCncl; TchrAde; FBLA; Ftbl; Detroit Inst Of Tech; Mech Engineering.

PERRY, Sue E; Pana Sr HS; Pana, IL; AFS; ChrhWkr; HonRl; JrNHS; StuCncl; YthFlsp; RptrSchPpr; 4-H; FNA; LetterTennis; GAA; AmLegAwd; BttyCrckrAwd; Univ Of Ill; Interpreteur.

PERRY, Susan C; Barrington Consol HS; Barrington, IL; 14/652 AFS; ChrhWkr; HonRl; JrNHS; MrchBnd; NHS; SpnCl; CchngActv; GAA; Univ Of Il; Liberal Arts.

PERRY, Susan L; St Francis Academy; Joliet, IL; 12/190 Chrs; HonRl; NHS; StuCncl; Yrbk; FrCl; Chrldr; CchngActv; IMSpt; PPFtbl; College; Law.

PERS, Bill F; George Rogers Clark HS; Hammond, IN; 8/260 VPJrCls; ALBoysSt; NHS; Quill&Scroll; StuCncl; RptrSchPpr; SpnCl; PpCl; Tennis; Trk; University; Elec Engineer.

PERSCHBACHER, Mark W; Hillsdale HS; Hillsdale, MI; ChrhWkr; NHS; RptrSchPpr; SchPpr; KeyCl; SpnCl; SciCl; LetterTrk; University Of Michigan.

PERSCHBACHER, Mary J; Murphysboro Township HS; Murphysboro, IL; HonRl; NHS; Business School; Professional.

PERSCHBACHER, Philip; Ofallon Township HS; Ofallon, IL; Aud/Vis; Band; CncrtBnd; MrchBnd; PepBnd; SchMus; SchPl; SpnCl; IMSpt; Coll; Business Management.

PERSCHNICK, Mary E; J D Darnall HS; Geneseo, IL; 20/212 HonRl; SchPl; Blackhawk College.

PERSENAIRE, Patricia; Unity Christian HS; Hudsonville, MI; 1/197 Chr; HonRl; Mdrgl; SchPpr; IMSpt; Calvin College; German Teacher.

PERSHING, Jeanne M; Notre Dame HS; Burlington, IA; 11/78 ChrhWkr; HonRl; HospAde; SchMus; SctActv; EdSchPpr; SpnCl; Marycrest College; Nursing.

PERSHING, Leslie; Notre Dame HS; Burlington, IA; 1/63 DrlTm; HonRl; HospAde; ModUN; NHS; PolWkr; RptrYrbk; EdSchPpr; DARAwd; Drake Univ; Law.

PERSICO, Angila; Joliet East HS; Joliet, IL; 20/409 Chr; Chrs; HonRl; SchMus; StuCncl; RptrSchPpr; PpCl; GAA; PresAwd; College; Physical Education Teacher.

PERSIN, Cathy A; Morton West HS; Berwyn, IL; 20/755 Chrs; HonRl; LbryAde; NHS; NatlMeritCmnd; College; Attorney.

PERSINGER, Debra J; Medora HS; Medora, IN; 1/13 TrsFrshCls; Band; Chr; ChrhWkr; HonRl; StuCncl; TchrAde; YthFlsp; PpCl; Bsktbl; Ball State Univ; Elem Teacher.

PERSOHN, Kaye A; Dubois HS; Jasper, IN; 18/80 VPFrshCls; SecSrCls; Chrs; HonRl; SchPl; FHA; PpCl; Chrldr; Indiana Univ; Nursing.

PERSON, Brian L; Glenburn HS; Minot, ND; PresJrCls; Band; CncrtBnd; HonRl; MrchBnd; PepBnd; SchPl; StuCncl; 4-H; PpCl; Bsktbl; Ftbl; College.

PERSON, Lorrie R; Spring Grove Public HS; Spring Grove, MN; 5/48 SecJrCls; TrsSrCls; Chr; ChrhWkr; HonRl; NHS; NatlThespSoc; GerCl; Northwestern Bible; Legal Secretary.

PERSON, Sheree G; Ft Dodge Sr HS; Fort Dodge, IA; Chr; CncrtBnd; HonRl; MrchBnd; PolWkr; SchMus; SchPl; StuCncl; FTA; PpCl; Iowa Central Comm Clg; Musical Therapy.

PERSONS, Janalee; St Charles HS; St Charles, MN; 36/86 Chr; Chrl; Chrs; ChrhWkr; HonRl; LbryAde; OffAde; SchAde; FHA; Northwestern College; Rn.

PERSONS, Kim D; Brentwood HS; Brentwood, MO; 5/117 CtyCnl; CmntyWkr; HonRl; PolWkr; StuCncl; StuGov; TchrAde; SpnCl; PpCl; College; Law.

PERSONS, Laura J; Kelliher HS; Waskish, MN; 2/31 PresJrCls; Band; Chr; HonRl; OffAde; SchPl; EdYrBk; Bsktbl; Trk; IMSpt; Bemidji State Univ; Mathematics.

PERSSON, Dan A; Markoma Bible Academy; Washburn, MO; PresSophCls; PresSrCls; Band; Chr; Chrl; Chrs; HonRl; StuCncl; LetterBsbl; LetterBsktbl; CaptSocr; IMSpt; College; Coach.

PERSZYK, Kenneth; Marquette U Hs; Milwaukee, WI; 7 HonRl; ModUN; NHS; KeyCl; LatCl; Marquette U;law School.

PERTEL, Karen M; Rolling Meadows HS; Arlington Heights, IL; 7/648 HonRl; HospAde; NatlFornLg; NHS; SchMus; FrCl; IMSpt; Univ; Physician.

PERTEL, Richard; Forest View HS; Arlington Hts, IL; 17/583 HonRl; NatlMeritCmnd; Tennis; Univ; Medicine.

PERTMER, Roberta J; Pius Xi HS; West Allis, WI; 2/375 Band; HonRl; LbryAde; NHS; OffAde; Orch; SchAde; TchrAde; FTA; MthCl; U Of Wisc Mil; Biology.

PERUSKI, Catherine M; Clawson Sr HS; Clawson, MI; SchMus; SchPl; SciCl; PPFtbl; Oakland Univ; Nursing.

PERZ, Robert; Bay City Central HS; Bay City, MI; HonRl; NHS; NatlMeritCmnd; Bsbl; Ftbl; Saginaw Valley State College; Lawyer Prelaw.

PERZYNSKI, Elizabeth M; Riceville Comm HS; Riceville, IA; 9/79 SecJrCls; Band; CncrtBnd; HonRl; MrchBnd; SchPl; RptrSchPpr; 4-H; PpCl; Chrldr; TreasGAA;.

PESAVENTO, Linda S; Lockport Central HS; Crest Hill, IL; 20/536 DrlTm; HonRl; NHS; NatlMeritFnl; PolWkr; StuCncl; StuGov; RptrYrbk; FTA; PresGAA; College; Social Work.

PESCH, Brian J; Greenfield HS; Greenfield, WI; JrNHS; NHS; LetterTrk; IMSpt; Marquette Univ; Lawyer.

PESCH, Kathleen S; James Madison HS; Milwaukee, WI; Band; CncrtBnd; HonRl; MrchBnd; NatlMeritSF; Orch; SchAde; SctActv; GerCl; College Or Univ; Professional.

PESCHEL, Mary F; Waterloo Public HS; Waterloo, WI; 13/77 Band; ChrhWkr; HonRl; NHS; SchPl; TchrAde; RptrSchPpr; PpCl; AmLegAwd; LionAwd; Wi Univ Madison; Physical Therapy.

PESEK, Jane A; Tyndall HS; Tyndall, SD; Chrs; ChrhWkr; SchPl; FHA; PpCl; Bsktbl; Trk; Chrldr; Navy; Communications Tech.

PESHKIN, Michael A; York Community HS; Elmhurst, IL; HonRl; NHS; NatlMeritSF; TchrAde; MthCl;.

PESHKIN, Michael A; York Comm HS; Elmhurst, IL; HonRl; NHS; NatlMeritSF; TchrAde; College; Science.

PESKE, Mark I; Lutheran HS; Mayer, MN; 1/64 AFS; Chrs; HonRl; NHS; SchPl; StuCncl; 4-H; SciCl; LetterTennis; LetterWrstlng; IMSpt; College; Religion.

PESKO, Kevin M; Hillsboro HS; Taylor Springs, IL; 11/190 ALBoysSt; ChrhWkr; HonRl; StuCncl; SpnCl; Bsbl; CaptBsktbl; CaptFtbl; CchngActv; College.

PESTKA, John; Loyola HS; Mankato, MN; Band; Chr; HonRl; MrchBnd; NatlMeritSchl; SchMus; StuCncl; Bsktbl; Ftbl; Trk; Vo Tech; Restaurant.

PETEK, Paula; Nazareth Academy; Riverside, IL; 19/154 HonRl; NHS; StuCncl; GerCl; Tennis; Univ Of Il; German.

PETELLE, Stephanie A; Proviso East HS; Maywood, IL; Chrs; ChrhWkr; NHS; StuCncl; College; Education.

PETER, Charlton A; Forest View HS; Mt Prospect, IL; 8/645 ChrhWkr; HonRl; NHS; SctActv; TchrAde; LetterFtbl; LetterTrk; Loyola Univ; Medicine.

PETER, Douglas A; Garner Hayfield Comm HS; Garner, IA; VPJrCls; Band; Chrs; ChrhWkr; HonRl; PolWkr; StuCncl; 4-H; FFA; LetterFtbl; Technical School; Electronics.

PETER, John J; Athens HS; Athens, WI; 2/66 PresFrshCls; ALBoysSt; PresBand; ChrhWkr; HonRl; NHS; SchPl; StuCncl; MthCl; PresPpCl; U Of Wisc; Business Administration.

PETER, Theresa A; Caledonia Public HS; Caedonia, MN; 22/147 ALAGirlsSt; Band; CncrtBnd; HonRl; MrchBnd; PepBnd; Yrbk; Viterbo Clg; Dietician.

PETEREIN, Pamela S; St Pius X HS; Festus, MO; HonRl; LbryAde; NHS; College; Nursing.

PETEREK, Heidi P; River Valley HS; Harbert, MI; SecSophCls; SecJrCls; SecSrCls; HonRl; JrNHS; NHS; TchrAde; FHA; GerCl; Business School; Secretary.

PETERIE, Terry L; Livingston Co R4 HS; Chillicothe, MO; 4/13 SecSophCls; SecJrCls; TrsSrCls; Chrs; HonRl; LbryAde; SchPl; StuCncl; RptrYrbk; RptrSchPpr; Business School; Vocation.

PETERKA, Kimberly; Kapaun Mt Carmel HS; Wichita, KS; HonRl; NHS; SchMus; SctActv; StuCncl; Yrbk; PpCl;.

PETERMAN, Debra A; Appleton East HS; Appleton, WI; 1/523 Chrl; NatlMeritCmnd; SchMus; PpCl; Univ Of Wi; Pharmacy.

PETERMAN, Mary M; Cedarbury HS; Cedarburg, WI; 43/298 AFS; HonRl; FBLA; GerCl; Uw Stevens Point; Business Admin.

PETERMAN, Melinda K; Cobden Unit HS; Cobden, IL; Chrs; ChrhWkr; HonRl; SchMus; RptrYrbk; 4-H; PpCl; Nursing School; Nurse.

PETERMAN, Michael L; Angola HS; Angola, IN; 5/195 ALBoysSt; Band; Chr; NHS; NatlMeritSF; StuCncl; SpnCl; Bsbl; Bsktbl; AmLegAwd; Tri State College; Engineering.

PETERMAN, Raymond W; Ruskin HS; Kansas City, MO; 12/392 ALBoysSt; ChrhWkr; HonRl; JA; NHS; Orch; PolWkr; StuCncl; MthCl; Northwestern Univ; Engineering.

PETERMAN, Robin; Saint Francis HS; Trauerse City, MI; 16/84 HonRl; HospAde; ModUN; NHS; StuCncl; SptEdYrbk; PpCl; IMSpt; RotaryAwd; Univ Of Michigan; Doctor.

PETERMAN, Sheila R; Bowdle HS; Bowdle, SD; Band; Chrs; ChrhWkr; HonRl; LbryAde; NatlMeritCmnd; SchPl; TchrAde; SptEdSchPpr; Business School; Vocation.

PETERMANN, Janet E; Holdrege HS; Holdrege, NE; Chrs; HonRl; SchMus; Teen; YthFlsp; PpCl; Trk; PresAwd; Trade Or Bus School; Sec.

PETERS, Aleta; Ubly Community HS; Ubly, MI; HonRl; NHS; SchPl; TchrAde; FHA; PpCl; Nursing School; Nursing.

PETERS, Anita; West Central Hs; Hartford, SD; ALAGirlsSt; Band; HonRl; MrchBnd; NHS; SchPl; RptrYrbk; FHA; LetterTrk; BttyCrckrAwd; College; Accounting.

PETERS, Ann F; Arthur Hill HS; Saginaw, MI; Chr; HospAde; NHS; NatlThespSoc; SchMus; SctActv; RptrYrbk; PpCl; Us Air Force.

PETERS, Ann M; Marian HS; Omaha, NE; SecSophCls; HonRl; VPNatlFornLg; NHS; SchPl; StuCncl; StuGov; LatCl; MthCl; College; Professional.

PETERS, Beverly A; Huntington North HS; Andrews, IN; Band; CncrtBnd; HonRl; MrchBnd; PepBnd; RptrYrbk; PpCl; GAA; PPFtbl; College; Teach Art.

PETERS, Brad D; Dexter HS; Dexter, MI; ALBoysSt; HonRl; TchrAde; CaptBsbl; AmLegAwd; University Of Michigan; Engineering.

PETERS, Bradley D; Taylorville HS; Taylorville, IL; 16/271 Band; PresChr; ChrhWkr; HonRl; Mdrgl; NatlMeritCmnd; NatlThespSoc; SchMus; SchPl; KeyCl; Univ Of Illinois; Natural Science.

PETERS, Brian G; Pepin HS; Pepin, WI; 3/44 PresFrshCls; PresSophCls; PresJrCls; PresSrCls; Band; Chr; Chrs; CncrtBnd; HonRl; PresStuCncl; PresBsktbl; CchngActv; Uw Stevens Pt; Wildlife Mngmt.

PETERS, Calvin J; Alleman HS; Orion, IL; LetterBsbl; LetterFtbl; Oru.

PETERS, Cathy J; Lakeland HS; La Grange, IN; 10/148 ChrhWkr; HonRl; StuCncl; PresTeen; YthFlsp; FNA; SpnCl; PpCl; PPFtbl; MasAwd;.

PETERS, Craig H; Pierce HS; Pierce, NE; Band; ChrhWkr; CmntyWkr; HonRl; YthFlsp; FFA; PpCl; Bsbl; LetterFtbl; Trk;.

PETERS, Cynthia J; East HS; Kansas City, MO; 3/220 Chr; Chrl; HonRl; JrNHS; NHS; StuCncl; RptrSchPpr; SchPpr; LetterTennis; GAA; Faith Baptist Bible Col; Teach.

PETERS, Cynthia L; Carrollton HS; Carrollton, MO; Band; DrlTm; HonRl; NHS; SctActv; Twrl; GerCl; PpCl; Trk; Business School; Accounting.

PETERS, Cynthia M; Leopold HS; Lutesville, MO; VPJrCls; Chr; HonRl; SchPl; SptEdYrbk; SptEdSchPpr; PpCl; CaptChrldr; IMSpt; Bus School; Secretary.

PETERS, David; Mercy HS; Olivette, MO; ChrhWkr; HonRl; NHS; TchrAde; MthCl; SciCl; College; Pharmacy.

PETERS, David A; Warsaw Senior HS; Warsaw, IN; StuCncl; PpCl; LetterGlf; College; Business Adm.

PETERS, David C; Marissa HS; Marissa, IL; Aud/Vis; Band; ChrhWkr; CncrtBnd; LitMag; SchMus; SctActv; YthFlsp; FFA; MthCl; SciCl; Trk; Univ.

PETERS, David K; Prospect HS; Mt Prospect, IL; 184/610 HonRl; Univ Of Illinois; Veterinarian.

PETERS, David L; Big Foot HS; Walworth, WI; ALBoysSt; Band; CncrtBnd; HonRl; MrchBnd; PepBnd; SchPl; SctActv; Trk; College; Engineering.

PETERS, David S; Lake View Auburn HS; Lake View, IA; Band; Chr; ChrhWkr; CncrtBnd; HonRl; MrchBnd; SchMus; SchPl; PpCl; Ftbl; College; Vocation.

PETERS, Debbie K; Kapaun Mt Carmel HS; Wichita, KS; Aud/Vis; HonRl; SchPl; Swmmng; University; Professional.

PETERS, Debra M; Hastings HS; Hastings, MN; CtyCnl; HstFrshCls; HonRl; RedCrAde; StuCncl; RptrYrbk; SchPpr; IMSpt; VFWAwd; VoiceDemAwd;.

PETERS, Denise; North Boone Hs; Poplar Grove, IL; CmntyWkr; HonRl; SchMus; 4-H; FHA; SpnCl; PpCl; GAA; 4-HAwd;.

PETERS, Diana J; South Shore HS; Chicago, IL; 4/500 Chr; CncrtBnd; HonRl; NHS; NatlMeritCmnd; ROTC; TchrAde; Teen; GAA; JETSAwd; U Of Il; Architecture.

PETERS, Dolores; Ladywood St Agnes HS; Indianapolis, IN; HonRl; NHS; SchMus; StuGov; RptrYrbk; Yrbk; FrCl; MthCl; SciCl; Tennis; Spring Hill Col; Biology Med.

PETERS, Edward N; Chaminade HS; St Louis, MO; 27/107 Band; CncrtBnd; HonRl; NatlFornLg; Orch; PepBnd; SchPl; SctActv; LetterTrk; St Louis University; Pre Med.

PETERS, Elizabeth A; North Callaway HS; Kingdom City, MO; 14/77 Band; Chr; HonRl; MrchBnd; NatlMeritCmnd; PepBnd; SchMus; SchPl; Yrbk; RptrSchPpr; College; Law.

PETERS, Francine L; Harvard Community HS; Harvard, IL; Chr; Chrl; Chrs; OffAde; PpCl; Chrldr; GAA; College; Missionary Work.

PETERS, Glen T; Tipton HS; Tipton, IA; Aud/Vis; HonRl; SctActv; StuCncl; Trk; Trade Sch; Automotive Field.

PETERS, Jeffrey A; York HS; Elmhurst, IL; 175/950 HonRl; Univ Of Illinois; Law.

PETERS, Joe A; Brookville HS; Brookville, IN; 44/190 ChrhWkr; HonRl; NHS; StuCncl; KeyCl; SpnCl; LetterBsbl; LetterBsktbl; LetterFtbl; Swmmng; Tennis; Trk; College; Business.

PETERS, Julia L; Belleville Twp HS; Belleville, IL; 1/677 PresNHS; StuCncl; PresYthFlsp; EdYrBk; PresGerCl; DARAwd; Millikin University; Physician.

PETERS, Julie N; West Pike HS; Hull, IL; 3/43 TrsFrshCls; Band; CncrtBnd; HonRl; HospAde; MrchBnd; NHS; PepBnd; 4-H; LatCl; N M S U; Medicine.

PETERS, Kent V; Avo Ha HS; Avocal, IA; ALBoysSt; Chrs; ChrhWkr; HonRl; SchMus; SchPl; SctActv; StuCncl; Swmmng; Wrstlng; Military.

PETERS, Linda J; Alma HS; Alma, MI; 24/269 VPJrCls; PresSrCls; Band; CncrtBnd; HonRl; MrchBnd; NHS; Sacrstn; StuCncl; YthFlsp; Mi St Univ; Rn With Bs.

PETERS, Marjo A; Streator Township HS; Streator, IL; 91/365 Band; CncrtBnd; HonRl; HospAde; MrchBnd; PepBnd; StuCncl; College; Nursing.

PETERS, Mark S; Mason HS; La Salle, MI; Chrs; CmntyWkr; HonRl; RedCrAde; SctActv; StuCncl; GerCl; Ftbl; Mi State U; Engineering.

PETERS, Mary K; Mother Of Sorrows HS; Chicago, IL; 52/143 HonRl; StuCncl; PpCl; GAA; Coll; Nursing.

PETERS, Michael; Madison Consolidated HS; Madison, IN; 17/300 Band; HonRl; NHS; NatlThespSoc; PepBnd; StuCncl; IMSpt; ChmbCommrsAwd; Rose Holman Inst Of Tech; Engineering.

PETERS, Michael F; Creighton Prep; Omaha, NE; 7/249 ChrhWkr; HonRl; JrNHS; NatlMeritSF; SctActv; MthCl; Bsbl; Bsktbl; Trk; IMSpt; Notre Dame Univ; Pre Med.

PETERS, Norris F; Brownstown Central HS; Vallonia, IN; 20/146 Chr; HonRl; NHS; Quill&Scroll; EdSchPpr; FTA; LatCl; PpCl; SciCl; Franklin Clg; Elementary Ed.

PETERS, Pamela S; Clay Center HS; Clay Center, NE; 9/28 VPJrCls; Chrs; CncrtBnd; HonRl; MrchBnd; StuCncl; VPTeen; PpCl; LetterTrk; Chrldr; College; Major Study.

PETERS, Patty; Powers Lake HS; Powers Lake, ND; Chr; HonRl; LbryAde; SchPl; TchrAde; PpCl; Coll; Correctional Officer.

PETERS, Perry L; Hartley Comm HS; Hartley, IA; Chr; Chrs; ChrhWkr; HonRl; SchPl; LetterBsktbl; LetterFtbl; Trk; Control Data Inst; Computer Tech.

PETERS, Randy C; Homer HS; Homer, IL; 1/38 TrsJrCls; ALBoysSt; Chrs; HonRl; VPNHS; SchPl; Yrbk; PresFSA; Glf; BttyCrckrAwd; SARAwd; Univ Of Illinois; Aviation.

PETERS, Regina; Midway HS; Leona, KS; Chrs; HonRl; TchrAde; PpCl; Bsktbl; Trk; Ricks Junior College; Social Work.

PETERS, Roberta L; Dixon HS; Dixon, MO; Chr; ChrhWkr; DrlTm; HospAde; LbryAde; SchPl; YthFlsp; RptrYrbk; FHA; PpCl; Mo Univ; Veterinary Medicine.

PETERS, Scott R; Gallatin R 5 HS; Gallatin, MO; Band; ChrhWkr; CncrtBnd; MrchBnd; NHS; StuCncl; 4-H; FFA; Bsktbl; Ftbl; College.

PETERS, Sharon M; Marian HS; Troy, MI; Band; HonRl; LbryAde; ModUN; PolWkr; StuGov; Yrbk; College; Communications.

PETERS, Steven G; Bisbee HS; Perth, ND; 1/7 PresFrshCls; SecSophCls; TrsSophCls; PresJrCls; SecSrCls; TrsSrCls; Chrs; HonRl; SchPl; EdYrBk; Yrbk; FFA; CaptBsktbl; CaptFtbl; Trk; College; Professional.

PETERS, Steven J; Broken Bow HS; Broken Bow, NE; CmntyWkr; HonRl; VPStuCncl; LetterBsktbl; LetterFtbl; LetterTrk; CchngActv; University Of Nebraska.

PETERS, Sue M; Central Comm HS; Breese, IL; 2/129 Band; Chr; Chrs; CncrtBnd; HonRl; Quill&Scroll; SchPl; TchrAde; RptrSchPpr; MthCl; College; Accounting.

PETERS, Susan M; Merrillville HS; Merrillville, IN; Chr; ChrhWkr; CmntyWkr; HonRl; NHS; StuCncl; FTA; Swmmng; Chrldr; Olivet Nazarene College; Music.

PETERS, Theresa J; Notre Dame HS; Quincy, IL; ALAGirlsSt; Chr; FrCl; LetterChrldr; S I U; Recreation.

PETERS, Tracy L; Stephen Decatur HS; Decatur, IL; Southern Illinois Univ; Engineering.

PETERS, V; Carrollton HS; Waverly, MO; 15/101 Band; ChrhWkr; CmntyWkr; CncrtBnd; HonRl; MrchBnd; NHS; TchrAde; IMSpt; College; Business.

PETERS, Walter R; Macomb Sr HS; Macomb, IL; 1/242 Chr; ChrhWkr; PresCncrtBnd; HonRl; Mdrgl; MrchBnd; NHS; EldAwd; GodCntryAwd; SARAwd; Western Il Univ; Pre Medicine.

PETERSBURG, Kevin; North Central HS; Hanlontown, IA; ALBoysSt; ChrhWkr; CncrtBnd; HonRl; MrchBnd; NHS; PolWkr; FrCl; SciCl; Ia St Univ; Vet.

PETERSEN, Cathy J; Irene HS; Irene, SD; 1/28 ALAGirlsSt; Band; Chrs; CncrtBnd; HonRl; MrchBnd; NHS; PepBnd; SchPl; EdYrBk; South Dakota State Univ.

PETERSEN, Cynthia L; Cedar Valley HS; Farnhamville, IA; SecSrCls; Band; Chr; ChrhWkr; CncrtBnd; HonRl; HospAde; MrchBnd; LetterBsktbl; Trk; Clge; Nursing.

PETERSEN, Daina A; Rockwell Swaledale HS; Rockwell, IA; PresJrCls; ChrhWkr; CmntyWkr; HonRl; TchrAde; SchPpr; FNA; FTA; LetterBsbl; LetterBsktbl; LetterGlf; 4-HAwd; College.

PETERSEN, Debra; Rutland HS; Madison, SD; 5/15 ALAGirlsSt; Chrs; ChrhWkr; HonRl; SchPl; RptrYrbk; EdSchPpr; FHA; FrCl; DARAwd; Coll; Profess.

PETERSEN, Donna J; Southridge HS; Holland, IN; Band; ChrhWkr; HonRl; HospAde; YthFlsp; GerCl; PpCl; University.

PETERSEN, Edwin; Crawford HS; Crawford, NE; ChrhWkr; HonRl; StuCncl; TchrAde; YthFlsp; 4-H; Bsktbl; 4-HAwd; Usaf; State Patrol.

PETERSEN, Gary L; Mc Cool Junction Public HS; Mc Cool Junction, NE; PresSophCls; ALBoysSt; CncrtBnd; HonRl; MrchBnd; Yrbk; RptrSchPpr; 4-H; LetterBsktbl; LetterFtbl;.

PETERSEN, Guy A; Burlington HS; Burlington, WI; 12/300 VPFrshCls; VPSophCls; HonRl; NHS; NatlMeritCmnd; 4-H; FrCl; LetterFtbl; Glf; BttyCrckrAwd; Beloit Col; Chemistry.

PETERSEN, Jeffrey J; Durand HS; Durand, WI; 9/147 Band; Chr; HonRl; JrNHS; NatlFornLg; NHS; NatlMeritSF; PolWkr; Bsbl; Bsktbl; Univ; Broadcast Journalism.

PETERSEN, Jodi R; Hillcrest HS; Hazel Crest, IL; PresFrshCls; TrsJrCls; VPChr; PresChrs; LitMag; PresStuCncl; LetterSwmmng; LetterTennis; LetterTrk; Chrldr; Univ; Pre Med.

PETERSEN, Joel W; Schleswig HS; Schleswig, IA; 8/50 Band; Chrs; CmntyWkr; HonRl; NHS; SctActv; YthFlsp; LetterBsktbl; LetterFtbl; LetterGlf; Wrstlng; College.

PETERSEN, John W; Forest Lake Sr HS; Forest Lake, MN; 19/360 VPSrCls; NHS; CaptBsbl; Bsktbl; CaptFtbl; CchngActv; College; Dentistry.

PETERSEN, Kelly S; Western Dubuque HS; Bernard, IA; 18/243 Chrs; HonRl; MrchBnd; ModUN; NHS; RptrSchPpr; 4-H; Bsktbl; University Of Iowa; Medical Technology.

PETERSEN, Kenneth L; Pella Christian HS; Pella, IA; 3/95 PresJrCls; ChrhWkr; HonRl; NHS; StuCncl; RptrSchPpr; LetterTrk; IMSpt; BauchLmbAwd; Dordt College; Forestry.

PETERSEN, Kevin L; Pine City HS; Rock Creek, MN; 3/117 TrsJrCls; VPAFS; HonRl; NHS; SchPl; PresStuCncl; StuGov; Pres4-H; 4-HAwd; VoiceDemAwd; Univ Of Minnesota.

PETERSEN, Kim R; Rockwell Swaledale HS; Rockwell, IA; TrsFrshCls; TrsSophCls; HonRl; 4-H; PpCl; LetterBsktbl; Swmmng; LetterTrk; Chrldr; 4-HAwd; Business School.

PETERSEN, L Chris; Graettinger Comm HS; Graettinger, IA; PresFrshCls; HonRl; VPNHS; PolWkr; SecStuCncl; Bsbl; LetterFtbl; LetterGlf; LetterTrk; GovHonPrgAwd; Washington Univ; Business.

PETERSEN, Mark M; Galesburg Senior HS; Galesburg, IL; 18/659 CncrtBnd; HonRl; MrchBnd; NHS; NatlMeritCmnd; YthFlsp; SchPpr; LetterBsbl; Bsktbl; Socr; Univ; Engineering.

PETERSEN, Marlene K; Medicine Valley Jr/sr HS; Curtis, NE; 4/32 SecTrsFrshCls; Chrs; CncrtBnd; HonRl; MrchBnd; NHS; PepBnd; SchMus; RptrYrbk; RptrSchPpr; U Of Ne Lincoln; Legal Secretary.

PETERSEN, Marty R; North Clay County HS; Louisville, IL; HonRl; LbryAde; SchPpr; FFA;.

PETERSEN, Mary; Kent School; Northville, MI; HonRl; OffAde; SchPpr; Bsktbl; Socr; College; Pro.

PETERSEN, Michael K; Irene HS; Irene, SD; ALBoysSt; HonRl; NHS; SchPl; Yrbk; Bsktbl;.

PETERSEN, Michael S; Newaygo HS; Newaygo, MI; 15/93 HonRl; LetterTrk; Bus Sch; Curr Of Study.

PETERSEN, Nancy; Bancroft HS; Lyons, NE; SecTrsSrCls; Band; ChrhWkr; MrchBnd; SctActv; StuCncl; EdYrBk; RptrSchPpr; Univ Of Nebr; Police Work.

PETERSEN, William; Tri County HS; Dewitt, NE; Karney State; Business Admin.

PETERSILIE, Kathy L; Ness HS; Ness City, KS; HstFrshCls; PresSophCls; MrchBnd; NHS; NatlThespSoc; SecStuCncl; TreasYthFlsp; EdYrBk; FHA; SecPpCl; University Of Kansas; Research Scientist.

PETERSON, Ann R; Osmond Community HS; Osmond, NE; 3/42 Band; Chrs; ChrhWkr; CncrtBnd; HonRl; MrchBnd; SchPl; StuCncl; 4-H; 4-HAwd; Univ.

PETERSON, Avis D; Windom Area HS; Windom, MN; 47/145 Chr; ChrhWkr; HonRl; HospAde; OffAde; TchrAde; YthFlsp; 4-H; FFA; FHA; FTA; College; Secretary.

PETERSON, Beth A; Lancaster HS; Orleans, MN; PresSrCls; ALAGirlsSt; Chrs; HonRl; SchPl; PresStuCncl; RptrYrbk; EdSchPpr; PresFHA; U Of Nd; Rn.

PETERSON, Bradley E; Guthrie Center Community HS; Guthrie Center, IA; ALBoysSt; Band; Chrs; ChrhWkr; CmntyWkr; HonRl; PepBnd; SchMus; Bsktbl; LetterFtbl; LetterTrk; CchngActv; Coll; Ag.

PETERSON, Brenda L; Grundy R V HS; Trenton, MO; 1/36 VPFrshCls; TrsSophCls; HstJrCls; Band; HonRl; NHS; StuCncl; Pres4-H; TreasFHA; LetterBsktbl; Nemsu;.

PETERSON, Brent G; Aurelia HS; Cherokee, IA; Band; Chr; Chrl; CncrtBnd; HonRl; MrchBnd; ModUN; PepBnd; SchPl; RptrYrbk; Drake Univ; Law.

PETERSON, Carol L; Berkeley HS; Berkeley, MO; 4/287 HonRl; NHS; NatlMeritSF; Washington U; Engineering.

PETERSON, Christine D; Joliet Twp HS; Joliet, IL; 18/491 HonRl; NHS; OffAde; PresSctActv; TchrAde; GAA; Illinois State Univ; Art.

PETERSON, Cindy; Dassel Cokato HS; Cokato, MN; Chr; ChrhWkr; HonRl; SctActv; FHA; PpCl; GAA; St Cloud College; Kindergarten Teacher.

PETERSON, Connie L; Union HS; Oquawka, IL; 30/74 HonRl; SchAde; SchPl; TchrAde; 4-H; FHA; FTA; PpCl; 4-HAwd; GovHonPrgAwd; College; Nursing.

PETERSON, Connie L; Forest Lake Sr HS; Forest Lake, MN; Chr; Chrl; HonRl; HospAde; LitMag; Mdrgl; SchMus; SchPl; TchrAde; RptrSchPpr; LetterTennis; 4-HAwd; Tech Voc Inst; Med Lab Assistant.

PETERSON, Corey A; Parkview HS; Orfordville, WI; HonRl; Trk; Wrstlng; Trade Or Bus; Vocational.

PETERSON, Craig; Redfield HS; Redfield, SD; AFS; HonRl; NHS; PepBnd; PresFrshCls; SchPl; RptrSchPpr; KeyCl; Bsbl; College; Professional.

PETERSON, Curt N; West HS; Sioux City, IA; 14/270 TrsSrCls; Chr; Chrs; ChrhWkr; HonRl; SchMus; SchPl; StuCncl; StuGov; EdSchPpr; Iowa State U; Indstrl Admin.

PETERSON, Cynthia L; Rushford HS; Rushford, MN; 2/63 PresJrCls; Chr; HonRl; JrNHS; NHS; Twrl; EdSchPpr; PresFHA; Chrldr; VFWAwd; St Olaf College; Nursing.

PETERSON, Daniel; Osceola HS; Osceola, WI; SchPl; Voc Tech School; Dramatic Arts & Design.

PETERSON, Daryl M; Danville HS; Danville, IL; 19/700 DrlTm; HonRl; OffAde; Orch; SchMus; TchrAde; RptrYrbk; RptrSchPpr; SchPpr; Swmmng; Indiana Univ; Education.

PETERSON, David B; William A Wirt HS; Gary, IN; NHS; Bsbl; VPJrCls; Ftbl; AmLegAwd; LionAwd; OptClAwd; Valparaiso Univ; Accounting.

PETERSON, David J; Guilford HS; Rockford, IL; HonRl; SchAde; Bsbl; Univ Of Il; Law.

PETERSON, Dean A; Marinette HS; Marinette, WI; 33/231 Band; MrchBnd; Bsbl; Ftbl; Trk; LetterWrstlng; Trade School.

PETERSON, Deborah A; Glenbrook North HS; Northbrook, IL; 200/670 AFS; Aud/Vis; ChrhWkr; HonRl; SchPpr; GAA; IMSpt; Carthage College; Special Education.

PETERSON, Deborah K; Marenisco HS; Marenisco, MI; 4/19 Band; Chrs; ChrhWkr; HonRl; SchPl; SchPpr; VPFrshCls; Bsbl; Chrldr; BttyCrckrAwd; College; Gogebic Community.

PETERSON, Debra J; Cooper Senior HS; Brooklyn Park, MN; 23/640 Band; CncrtBnd; DrmMjrt; HonRl; MrchBnd; NHS; OffAde; PepBnd; SchMus; Twrl; Gustavus Adolphus Clg; Medical Tech.

PETERSON, Debra J; Dumont Community HS; Dumont, IA; PresJrCls; Chrs; HonRl; HospAde; StuCncl; RptrSchPpr; 4-H; Bsktbl; Chrldr; GodCntryAwd; Child Care.

PETERSON, Delayne; Wahoo Public HS; Malma, NE; ChrhWkr; CmntyWkr; HonRl; HospAde; 4-H; PpCl; 4-HAwd; Univ; Rn.

PETERSON, Dennis C; Menominee HS; Menominee, MI; 15/275 ChrhWkr; HonRl; TrsFrshCls; SctActv; SchPpr; Wrstlng; Michigan Tech Univ; Chemistry.

PETERSON, Donna S; North Winneshiek HS; Decorah, IA; 2/34 Band; Chrs; ChrhWkr; NHS; EdYrBk; LetterBsbl; LetterBsktbl; LetterTrk; BttyCrckrAwd; EldAwd; Waldorf College; Ecology.

PETERSON, Douglas R; Loyola HS; N Mankato, MN; 1/74 PresJrCls; PresSrCls; ALBoysSt; NatlFornLg; NHS; NatlMeritSF; StuCncl; LetterBsbl; LetterFtbl; BauchLmbAwd; College; Law.

PETERSON, Eleanor K; Lanse HS; Pelkie, MI; 5/88 HonRl; 4-H; PpCl; 4-HAwd; Gogebic Community Clg; Secretarial.

PETERSON, Elna; Mankato East HS; Mankato, MN; 14/212 AFS; Chr; Chrl; ChrhWkr; NHS; NatlThespSoc; SchMus; StuCncl; RptrYrbk; GAA; Private Coll; Natural Science.

PETERSON, Eric J; Wausau East HS; Wausau, WI; Band; TchrAde; MthCl; Glf; CaptSwmmng; IMSpt; University; Forestry.

PETERSON, Gail R; Northwestern HS; Poplar, WI; SecFrshCls; Chr; HonRl; Mdrgl; OffAde; SchPl; SctActv; RptrSchPpr; 4-H; EngCl; College; Social Worker.

PETERSON, Gary E; Centerville Public HS; Centerville, SD; VPFrshCls; VPJrCls; Chrs; LbryAde; SchPl; RptrYrbk; SptEdYrbk; FFA; Ftbl; Vocational Sch; Agribus.

PETERSON, Gerald E; Centreville Public HS; Centreville, MI; 11/54 HonRl; NHS; TchrAde; 4-H; TreasFFA; 4-HAwd; Vocational School; Accountant.

PETERSON, Glen T; New Trier East HS; Wilmette, IL; 48/847 AFS; HonRl; IntrClCncl; U Of Co; Archit.

PETERSON, Greg J; Conde HS; Conde, SD; 4/21 VPFrshCls; PresSophCls; PresSrCls; ALBoysSt; HonRl; OffAde; SchPl; StuCncl; RptrYrbk; Trk; Sd State U; Mechanized Agriculture.

PETERSON, Heidi; Southwest HS; Kansas City, MO; 37/505 AFS; ChrhWkr; CmntyWkr; HonRl; NHS; StuCncl; Glf; Trk; IMSpt; PPFtbl;.

PETERSON, Jan; Big Foot Hs; Walworth, WI; 9/175 PresSophCls; PresJrCls; CncrtBnd; HonRl; MrchBnd; SchMus; YthFlsp; 4-H; Chrldr;.

PETERSON, Janet F; Parkview HS; Janesville, WI; 18/125 SecJrCls; AFS; Band; ChrhWkr; CncrtBnd; DrlTm; HonRl; MrchBnd; StuCncl; StuGov; TchrAde; Twrl; Yrbk; SpnCl; Wisconsin State College; Teacher.

PETERSON, Janice; Keokuk HS; Keokuk, IA; 6/196 AFS; ChrhWkr; HonRl; NHS; NatlMeritSchl; StuCncl; SpnCl; PpCl; IMSpt; Univ Iowa; Undecided.

PETERSON, Jeff A; Bristol HS; Bristol, SD; TrsFrshCls; TrsJrCls; ALBoysSt; HonRl; SctActv; StuCncl; YthFlsp; Bsktbl; Ftbl; University Of South Dakota.

PETERSON, Jeffery; Alpena HS; Alpena, MI; Aud/Vis; NatlMeritCmnd; TchrAde; Ftbl; Trk; IMSpt; Clge; Mass Communications.

PETERSON, Jeffrey B; Michigan Public HS; Michigan, ND; 5/25 ALBoysSt; EdYrBk; Bsktbl; AmLegAwd; Navy; Air Traffic Controller.

PETERSON, Jeffrey F; Oconto Falls HS; Oconto Falls, WI; 4/147 PresSophCls; ALBoysSt; ChrhWkr; HonRl; PresNHS; FBLA; PresKeyCl; LetterBsbl; LetterFtbl; AmLegAwd; KiwanAwd; Wartburg Col; Business Admin.

PETERSON, Joe D; Lanesboro HS; Lanesboro, MN; ChrhWkr; CmntyWkr; 4-H; FFA; PpCl; LetterBsktbl; LetterFtbl; LetterTrk; Agriculture.

PETERSON, John G; Auburndale HS; Arpin, WI; HonRl; StuCncl; TchrAde; FFA; Trk; College; Professional.

PETERSON, John W; Ladysmith HS; Ladysmith, WI; Aud/Vis; Chr; HonRl; SchMus; SctActv; RptrSchPpr; 4-H; SpnCl; Ftbl; 4-HAwd; College ; Computers.

PETERSON, Karna M; Unity HS; Luck, WI; Band; CncrtBnd; HonRl; HospAde; MrchBnd; PepBnd; SchMus; SctActv; Yrbk; SchPpr; 4-H; FBLA; FHA; Bsktbl; Uw Stevens Point; Foods.

PETERSON, Kelly R; Burke Central HS; Flaxton, ND; 1/20 Chrs; ChrhWkr; HonRl; SchPl; StuCncl; 4-H; Bsktbl; Trk; Chrldr; IMSpt; College.

PETERSON, Kimberly R; Wheeling HS; Wheeling, IL; PresSrCls; HonRl; NHS; NatlMeritSchl; Quill&Scroll; StuCncl; EdYrBk; EdSchPpr; DanFAwd; DARAwd; College; Education.

PETERSON, Kristine M; Danville HS; Danville, IL; VPSophCls; Chr; HonRl; JA; SchMus; TreasStuCncl; RptrSchPpr; FrCl; CaptChrldr; University; Professional.

PETERSON, Larry L; Kearney HS; Kearney, NE; ALBoysSt; ChrhWkr; HonRl; OffAde; NatlFornLg; Quill&Scroll; StuCncl; SptEdSchPpr; SciCl; Bsbl; Coll; Law Or Engr.

PETERSON, Lee A; Barrett Public HS; Barrett, MN; VPFrshCls; PresSophCls; TrsJrCls; Band; Chr; NHS; EdYrBk; SecSophCls; LetterBsktbl; Coll; Med.

PETERSON, Lela; Eldora HS; Eldora, IA; HonRl; YthFlsp; SpnCl; Bsktbl; Univ.

PETERSON, Lilliam; Bigfork HS; Bigfork, MN; Chrs; HonRl; HospAde; LbryAde; SchMus; SchPl; YthFlsp; EdSchPpr; Bsktbl; College; Interior Decorating.

PETERSON, Linda M; Eden Prairie HS; Eden Prairie, MN; 13/140 Band; Chr; ChrhWkr; HonRl; NHS; SchMus; SchPl; SctActv; Univ Of Minnesota; Horticulture.

PETERSON, Lorence E; Archie Rv HS; Archie, MO; TrsJrCls; Band; CmntyWkr; CncrtBnd; HonRl; PepBnd; YthFlsp; FFA; Bsbl; LetterFtbl; College; Farming.

PETERSON, Margie S; Rockford Lutheran HS; Rockford, IL; VPSophCls; TrsSrCls; Chr; LbryAde; OffAde; SchPl; Yrbk; PpCl; Chrldr; GAA; Clge; Secretarial.

PETERSON, Marie A; Underwood HS; Erhard, MN; Chr; LetterTrk; Trade School.

PETERSON, Mark A; Tri Valley HS; Colton, SD; Band; HonRl; NatlFornLg; NHS; SchPl; Trk; South Dakota State Univ; Agronomy Or Eng.

PETERSON, Mark L; Catholic Memorial HS; Waukesha, WI; HonRl; PresJA; NHS; Bsktbl; Chemistry.

PETERSON, Marlene E; Cosmos HS; Cosmos, MN; 6/35 SecSophCls; Band; ChrhWkr; HonRl; SchPl; Yrbk; 4-H; FHA; Bsktbl; LionAwd; Mankato St Clg.

PETERSON, Martha L; Rich Central HS; Country Club Hills, IL; 3/400 Chr; HonRl; Mdrgl; NHS; NatlMeritCmnd; SchMus; YthFlsp; MthCl; GAA; Coll; Biology.

PETERSON, Mary E; Glenville HS; Glenville, MN; 2/49 Band; Chrs; ChrhWkr; CncrtBnd; HonRl; OffAde; RptrYrbk; EdSchPpr; FHA; IMSpt; Vocational Scl; Office & Secretarial.

PETERSON, Mary J; Morris Sr HS; Morris, MN; HonRl; NHS; RptrSchPpr; PpCl; CaptBsktbl; IMSpt; Univ Of Minnesota; Physical Education.

PETERSON, Mary M; West Chicago Comm HS; West Chicago, IL; Chr; HonRl; Mdrgl; NatlFornLg; NHS; NatlMeritCmnd; NatlThespSoc; Orch; SchMus; SchPl; SecLatCl; College.

PETERSON, Maureen L; Lincoln Way HS; Joliet, IL; 74/566 HonRl; TchrAde; 4-H; FFA;.

PETERSON, Max; Centennial HS; Waco, NE; 15/58 VPFrshCls; PresSophCls; YthFlsp; 4-H; FFA; Farming.

PETERSON, Melanie S; Ferndale HS; Ferndale, MI; ChrhWkr; HonRl; NHS; NatlMeritCmnd; TchrAde; U Of Mi; Major Spanish Profession Law Or Ed.

PETERSON, Michael D; Finley HS; Finley, ND; PresJrCls; ALBoysSt; HonRl; NatlMeritFnl; NatlMeritCmnd; PepBnd; SchPl; LetterBsbl; LetterBsktbl; LetterFtbl; LetterTrk; College; Medicine.

PETERSON, Michael R; Pembroke Country Day HS; Kansas City, MO; ALBoysSt; Chrs; CmntyWkr; CaptDrmBgl; HonRl; StuCncl; StuGov; SchPpr; Bsktbl; Ftbl; ChmbCommrsAwd; MasAwd; OptClAwd; College; Dentist.

PETERSON, Michele; Sargent HS; Sargent, NE; 1/43 Band; Chrs; ChrhWkr; CmntyWkr; CncrtBnd; HonRl; MrchBnd; PepBnd; YthFlsp; PpCl; College; Veterinary Med.

PETERSON, Mindy A; United Township HS; Carbon Cliff, IL; PresSrCls; HonRl; NatlThespSoc; SchPl; StuCncl; YthFlsp; RptrSchPpr;.

PETERSON, Nan L; Rock Island HS; Rock Island, IL; 6/685 AFS; HonRl; LitMag; NHS; NatlMeritCmnd; FrCl; Univ Of Illinois; Biology.

PETERSON, Norman K; Mt Pleasant HS; Mt Pleasant, IA; 16/170 ChrhWkr; HonRl; LetterBsbl; Univ Ia; Engr.

PETERSON, Patrice J; Harry A Burke HS; Omaha, NE; 54/594 Chr; Chrs; ChrhWkr; HonRl; Orch; YthFlsp; GerCl; PpCl; Univ; Med Tech.

PETERSON, Patrick N; Watersmeet Twp HS; Watersmeet, MI; 3/15 PresSrCls; ALBoysSt; Band; Chr; Chrs; CncrtBnd; HonRl; MrchBnd; NHS; PepBnd; StuCncl; RptrSchPpr; SptEdSchPpr; LetterBsbl; Michigan Tech Univ; Medicine.

PETERSON, Paul E; Glenbrook South HS; Glenview, IL; HonRl; NatlFornLg; NatlMeritCmnd; StuCncl; Eastern Illinois Univ; Chemistry.

PETERSON, Richard L; Woodstock HS; Woodstock, IL; 8/274 ChrhWkr; HonRl; NHS; NatlMeritSF; StuCncl; LetterFtbl; LetterTrk; College; Biology.

PETERSON, Robert G; Lake Mills Comm HS; Lake Mills, IA; Chr; Chrl; Chrs; CmntyWkr; SchPl; LetterFtbl; LetterWrstlng; IMSpt; College; Law Enforcement.

PETERSON, Robert H; Ridgewood HS; Norridge, IL; HonRl; NHS; PolWkr; SctActv; PresStuCncl; EdSchPpr; De Paul Univ; Accounting.

PETERSON, Robert J; Clifton HS; Clifton, KS; VPJrCls; Band; CncrtBnd; DrmBgl; HonRl; MrchBnd; PepBnd; Bsbl; LetterFtbl; Vo Tech School.

PETERSON, Ronald A; Wauwatosa East HS; Wauwatosa, WI; HonRl; NatlMeritCmnd; MthCl; SciCl; Lawrence Univ; Computer Elec.

PETERSON, Roy R; Kewaskum HS; West Bend, WI; PresSophCls; ChrhWkr; HonRl; NHS; SchPl; StuCncl; 4-H; FFA; MthCl; Bsktbl; IMSpt; University; Agriculture.

PETERSON, Ruth E; Guilford HS; Rockford, IL; 40/656 Chrs; ChrhWkr; HonRl; LbryAde; NatlMeritCmnd; SctActv; SecYthFlsp; North Park College; Medical Technician.

PETERSON, Scott T; Mounds View HS; St Paul, MN; Chr; JrNHS; NatlMeritSF; Bsktbl; Michigan State Univ.

PETERSON, Sherlyn L; Rushford HS; Peterson, MN; Band; ChrhWkr; CncrtBnd; HonRl; NHS; SchPl; RptrSchPpr; FFA; FHA; FTA; Vocational; Art.

PETERSON, Stephen S; Princeton HS; Princeton, IL; 12/183 HonRl; PolWkr; SchPl; SctActv; StuGov; GerCl; Bsktbl; College; Law.

PETERSON, Steve L; Paynesville HS; Paynesville, MN; 6/130 PresSrCls; Band; Chr; HonRl; MrchBnd; SchMus; StuGov; LetterBsktbl; CaptFtbl; LetterTrk; College; Professional.

PETERSON, Sue Ellen; River Valley HS; Three Oakes, MI; 7/154 HonRl; NHS; OffAde; TchrAde; Ferris St Col; Dentistry.

PETERSON, Susan M; Albert City Truesdale HS; Albert City, IA; TrsFrshCls; Chr; HonRl; NHS; SchPl; StuCncl; RptrSchPpr; LetterTrk; Chrldr; Univ.

PETERSON, Suzanne; Michigan Center HS; Jackson, MI; Chrs; HonRl; StuCncl; StuGov; RptrSchPpr; FHA; FNA; SpnCl; SciCl; Trk; Clge; Lpn Training.

PETERSON, Tamera S; Brady HS; Brady, NE; 6/16 VPJrCls; VPSrCls; Chrs; ChrhWkr; SchPl; StuCncl; Yrbk; SchPpr; 4-H; Chrldr; College; Vocation.

PETERSON, Tammie S; Big Springs HS; Brule, NE; Band; Chrs; CncrtBnd; HonRl; PepBnd; SchPl; TchrAde; YthFlsp; FHA; PpCl; Col; Home Economics.

PETERSON, Tammy A; York Comm HS; Elmhurst, IL; 221/912 Chrs; CmntyWkr; HonRl; SchPl; StuCncl; TchrAde; Univ Of Illinois; Psychology.

PETERSON, Theresa A; Ellsworth HS; Bay City, WI; 9/154 ALAGirlsSt; HonRl; NHS; StuCncl; Bsktbl; Trk; Chrldr; GAA; IMSpt; PPFtbl; Vocational School; Lab Tech.

PETERSON, Thomas A; Milwaukee Lutheran HS; Milwaukee, WI; 39/231 ChrhWkr; YthFlsp; Yrbk; SchPpr; Ftbl; Trk; Wrstlng; CchngActv; Trade Schl; Pro.

PETERSON, Thomas J; Valders HS; Valders, WI; SecFrshCls; VPJrCls; AFS; HonRl; RptrSchPpr; EdSchPpr; IMSpt; College; Professional.

PETERSON, Thomas K; Lincoln HS; Thief River Falls, MN; Band; CncrtBnd; HonRl; MrchBnd; PepBnd; University Of Minnesota; Law.

PETERSON, Timothy S; Northwest HS; Fenton, MO; 5/390 HonRl; NHS; RptrSchPpr; SptEdSchPpr; Trk; College; Professional.

PETERSON, Todd; Glenbard West HS; Glen Ellyn, IL; 234/517 StuGov; YthLg; SchPpr; Bsbl; Bsktbl; CchngActv; Luther College; Sports Admin.

PETERSON, Tom L; Wausau West HS; Wausau, WI; TchrAde; Yrbk; SchPpr; KeyCl; LetterBsktbl; LetterFtbl; Trk; IMSpt; College Eau Clair; Professional.

PETERSON, Valerie A; Huron HS; Huron, SD; 72/301 Band; CncrtBnd; DrlTm; MrchBnd; NatlFornLg; TchrAde; SpnCl; Business School; Business Management.

PETERSON, Vercle S; Mnpl Area Vocational Tch Inst; Minneapolis, MN; 14/313 Chr; HonRl; JrNHS; LbryAde; StuGov; TchrAde; U Of Mn; Art.

PETERSON, William C; Cambridge Sr HS; Isanti, MN; 1/212 NHS; NatlMeritSF; StuCncl; SchPpr; GerCl; LetterBsbl; IMSpt; AmLegAwd; College; Lawyer.

PETESCH, Mary Beth; Ozaukee HS; Belgium, WI; 1/84 VPSophCls; TrsJrCls; ALAGirlsSt; Band; HonRl; NHS; StuCncl; 4-H; PpCl; CaptBsktbl; Trk; Uw Steven Point; Natural Resources.

PETET, Debra K; Overton Public HS; Elm Creek, NE; 1/21 SecSophCls; SecJrCls; HonRl; SchPl; VPFHA; PpCl; Trk; Chrldr; College.

PETET, Pamela J; Overton Public HS; Elm Creek, NE; 1/20 Chrs; HonRl; SchPl; VPStuCncl; EdYrBk;

4-H; VPFHA; PresPpCl; College; Home Economics.

PETIGNA, Lucrezia; Shawnee Mission South HS; Overland Park, KS; HonRl; Coll.

PETITJEAN, Leanne L; Bronson HS; Bronson, MI; 1/140 Band; HonRl; PresLbryAde; MrchBnd; NHS; OffAde; PepBnd; RptrYrbk; FTA; PpCl; Ferris State Coll; Court Reporter.

PETITO, Guy T; Macon Sr HS; Luna Pier, MI; 11/121 ALBoysSt; HonRl; NatlFornLg; NHS; SchPl; GerCl; Bsktbl; Ftbl; LetterGlf; Michigan State Univ; Veterinary Science.

PETKEVICH, Anne M; J F Kennedy HS; Chicago, IL; 45/610 CncrtBnd; MrchBnd; NHS; NatlMeritFnl; NatlMeritCmnd; NatlMeritSchl; NatlMeritSF; Orch; SchMus; SchPl; Illinois State Univ; Medical Admin.

PETKUS, Judith; Bogan Hs; Chicago, IL; 98/700 Chr; ChrhWkr; HonRl; LbryAde; FrCl; SciCl; GAA;.

PETKUS, Loretta; Mt Assisi Academy; Orland Park, IL; 61/189 LbryAde; Illinois Bene College; Medical Tech.

PETLICK, C J; Lake Mich Catholic HS; Benton Harbor, MI; PresJrCls; Band; HonRl; SchMus; SchPl; Bsktbl; Tennis; IMSpt; VFWAwd; VoiceDemAwd; Univ.

PETONKE, Arthur R; Danville HS; Danville, IL; CncrtBnd; MrchBnd; SctActv; U Of Illinois; Electronics.

PETRACCO, Debra A; Rezin Orr HS; Chicago, IL; 1/334 HonRl; NHS; OffAde; StuCncl; TchrAde; RptrSchPpr; GAA; University; Professional.

PETRAK, Richard A; Brother Rice HS; Evergreen Pk, IL; PresSrCls; HonRl; NHS; StuCncl; SchPpr; Bsbl; LetterFtbl; Tennis; Wrstlng; AmLegAwd; Carleton College; Professional.

PETRAKIS, Mary D; Freeport HS; Freeport, IL; CmntyWkr; HonRl; HospAde; SchMus; North Ill Univ; Biology.

PETRI, Paul D; Kewaskum HS; Kewaskum, WI; 44/180 HonRl; SchPpr; Bsktbl; KiwanAwd; Trade Sch; Auto Mech.

PETRIC, Katharine J; Providence HS; Joliet, IL; 25/121 Chrs; ChrhWkr; HonRl; NHS; SecStuCncl; RptrSchPpr; SpnCl; Bsktbl; Tennis; Trk; GAA; College; Elem Teacher.

PETRICK, Diane; Jefferson Sr HS; Johnson Creek, WI; 8/172 CmntyWkr; HonRl; TchrAde; RptrSchPpr; FTA; SciCl; Bsktbl; GAA; IMSpt; Univ; Prof Physical Educ.

PETRIE, Kenneth J; Marist HS; Oak Lawn, IL; 53/400 HonRl; NHS; CaptBsbl; IMSpt; AmLegAwd; N Il U; Business.

PETRIE, Kevin F; Hinsdale Central HS; Hinsdale, IL; Univ Of Ill; Engineering.

PETRIK, Kim; Parkway Central Sr HS; Chesterfield, MO; Chr; NHS; IMSpt; PPFtbl; College.

PETRIK, Thomas C; Forest View HS; Des Plaines, IL; Band; CncrtBnd; HonRl; MrchBnd; PepBnd; SchMus; RusCl; College; Medicine.

PETRO, Beth A; Grand Blanc HS; Grand Blanc, MI; PresJrCls; PresSrCls; TreasBand; PresChrhWkr; MrchBnd; NatlFornLg; NHS; NatlThespSoc; SchMus; TreasStuCncl; U Of Mi Flint; English.

PETRO, Lynne M; South Side HS; Fort Wayne, IN; HonRl; SctActv; StuCncl; FrCl; College; Physician.

PETROELJE, Nancy K; Holland Christian HS; Holland, MI; 23/260 ChrhWkr; HonRl; NHS; Orch; SchPl; SpnCl; IMSpt; Calvin College; Spec Education.

PETRON, Theodore L; High School; Breckenridge, MN; Band; Chrs; CncrtBnd; HonRl; MrchBnd; PepBnd; Bsbl; Bsktbl; College.

PETRON, Thomas L; Breckenridge HS; Breckenridge, MN; 29#32#37 HonRl; PepBnd; Bsbl; Univ; Engineering.

PETRONE, Lucille M; Notre Dame HS; Chicago, IL; 17/313 TrsJrCls; Chrs; HonRl; NHS; VPFTA; Univ Of Ill; Secondary Education.

PETRONIS, Karen L; Maria HS; Chicago, IL; 44/335 HonRl; RptrSchPpr; GerCl; College; Journalism.

PETROSHA, Luba; Athens HS; Troy, MI; 1/250 HonRl; NHS; TchrAde; SchPpr; Univ; Medicine.

PETROSKI, Tony; Benilde HS; Minneapolis, MN; JrNHS; Mn Univ; Teach.

PETROVISH, Debra E; Summerfield HS; Petersburg, MI; Chr; LetterChrs; ChrhWkr; HonRl; SchPl; TchrAde; Trk; 4-HAwd; College; Teacher.

PETROVSKY, Darlene K; Fordson HS; Dearborn, MI; PresSrCls; HonRl; NHS; OffAde; StuCncl; LetterTennis; CaptChrldr; GAA; IMSpt; EldAwd; Secretarial.

PETROWITZ, Sharon R; Fingal Public HS; Ringal, ND; 8/21 SecJrCls; Band; Chrs; HonRl; NHS; SchPl; EdYrBk; RptrSchPpr; LetterBsktbl; Chrldr; College; Speech Pathology.

PETROWSKE, Nancy J; Chester HS; Chester, IL; 2/100 VPJrCls; HonRl; NHS; PpCl; Chrldr; College; Physical Therapist.

PETRY, Rebecca S; O Fallon Township HS; O Fallon, IL; 10/310 ChrhWkr; HonRl; NHS; SctActv; TchrAde; Purdue University; Physics.

PETSCHE, Susan; Warren HS; Scales Mound, IL; ChrhWkr; HonRl; HospAde; NHS; StuCncl; FHA; BttyCrckrAwd; DARAwd; CitAwd; Trade School; Registered Nurse.

PETSEL, Sharon K; Plainfield HS; Plainfield, IN; 46/260 ChrhWkr; CncrtBnd; HonRl; MrchBnd; PepBnd; StuCncl; FBLA; FHA; SpnCl; GAA; Purdue U; Nursing.

PETSINGER, Terry; Larimore HS; Arvilla, ND; 18/66 JA; PresSrCls; ALBoysSt; HonRl; 4-H; Bsbl; Bsktbl; Ftbl; Trade Sch; Electrical.

PETT, Ann E; High School; Pleasant Dale, NE; 4/27 ALAGirlsSt; SchPl; TchrAde; RptrYrbk; EdYrBk; FshEdYrbk; SptEdYrbk; Yrbk; 4-H; PpCl;.

PETT, Sally M; Malcolm HS; Malcolm, NE; Chrs; Mdrgl; TchrAde; 4-H; PpCl; Marine Biology.

PETTEGREW, Mark H; Galva HS; Galva, IL; 10/75 TrsFrshCls; PresSophCls; VPJrCls; HonRl; TreasNHS; Yrbk; Ftbl; Trk; Bradley University; Accounting.

PETTENGILL, Paul; Libertyville Hs; Libertyville, IL; 46/458 Band; CncrtBnd; HonRl; MrchBnd; NatlMeritCmnd; SchMus; Universtiy; Electrical Engineering.

PETTERSON, Nathan P; Ankeny HS; Ankeny, IA; 15/260 HonRl; JrNHS; NHS; PresSpnCl; Bsktbl; CchngActv; College; Social Sciences.

PETTERSON, Wayne C; Beloit HS; Beloit, KS; 34/68 VPJrCls; VPSrCls; Band; StuCncl; Yrbk; SchPpr; Bsbl; Ftbl; Trk; College; Professional.

PETTIJOHN, Jeffrey; Lafayette HS; St Joseph, MO; HonRl; ModUN; StuCncl; Coll.

PETTINGER, Cari L; Owen Gage HS; Cass City, MI; HonRl; NatlFornLg; NHS; OffAde; SchAde; TchrAde; GAA; Business School; Business.

PETTIS, James L; Charlevoix HS; Charlevoix, MI; 29/148 ALBoysSt; Band; ChrhWkr; HonRl; MrchBnd; PepBnd; StuGov; TchrAde; YthFlsp; Bsktbl; Michigan Tech Univ; Civil Engineer.

PETTIS, Kevin G; Maple Wood Academy; Long Lake, MN; Band; Chr; Chrl; ChrhWkr; CncrtBnd; SchPl; StuGov; SptEdSchPpr; Bsbl; Bsktbl; Ftbl; Glf; Tennis; College; Business.

PETTIS, Shawn J; Creighton Prep HS; Omaha, NE; 2/214 ChrhWkr; HonRl; Sdlty; MthCl; Univ; Medicine.

PETTIT, Marcia K; Fairfield HS; Fairfield, IA; ChrhWkr; CmntyWkr; HonRl; HospAde; NHS; SchPl; SecYthFlsp; 4-H; SpnCl; PpCl; U Of Ia; Social Welfare.

PETTIT, Nancy L; Custer HS; Custer, SD; Chr; HonRl; NHS; YthFlsp; RptrYrbk; EdSchPpr; FTA; Bsktbl; Chrldr; GAA; University; Professional.

PETTIT, Vickie; Riverview Gardens Senior HS; St Louis, MO; 6/728 HonRl; NHS; NatlMeritCmnd; Orch; SchAde; SchPl; TchrAde; RptrSchPpr; SecTrsSophCls; PPFtbl; St Louis Univ; Physical Therapy.

PETTITT, Pamela E; Spring Hill HS; Spring Hill, KS; 5/59 VPFrshCls; SecSophCls; Band; Chr; Chrs; CncrtBnd; HonRl; MrchBnd; NHS; PepBnd; RedCrAde; CaptBsktbl; Trk; GAA; AmLegAwd; College; Vocation.

PETTUS, Timothy W; North County HS; Bonne Terre, MO; HonRl; SctActv; 4-H; FrCl; SciCl; LetterTrk; College; Professional.

PETTY, Brenda L; Salem Comm HS; Salem, IL; 8/204 HospAde; JrNHS; NatlFornLg; NHS; SchMus; SchPl; 4-H; SecFrCl; SpnCl; University Of Illinois.

PETTY, Elizabeth; Richland HS; Essex, MO; VPJrCls; Band; ChrhWkr; CncrtBnd; HonRl; MrchBnd; PepBnd; SctActv; StuCncl; Mc Pherson Col; Social Work.

PETTY, Gary L; Union County HS; Liberty, IN; HonRl; NHS; StuCncl; FDA; FSA; FrCl; Swmmng; Tennis; JAAwd; Indiana Univ; Physician.

PETTY, Jack S; Griswold Comm HS; Elliott, IA; 15/86 PresSophCls; ALBoysSt; Chrs; HonRl; NHS; VPStuCncl; 4-H; LetterBsbl; LetterFtbl; 4-HAwd; College; Natural Science.

PETTY, Janice L; Cassville HS; Cassville, MO; 39/103 ChrhWkr; RptrSchPpr; FHA; FTA; Burge Sch Of Nursing; Nurse.

PETTY, Jo L; Garden County HS; Oshkosh, NE; SecJrCls; Band; Chr; Chrs; ChrhWkr; HonRl; SchMus; RptrYrbk; PpCl; LetterTrk; College; Professional.

PETTY, Linda D; Salem Comm HS; Salem, IL; 9/204 HospAde; JrNHS; NatlFornLg; NHS; SchMus; SchPl; RptrSchPpr; 4-H; FrCl; University Of Illinois; Physician.

PETTY, Michael C; Garber HS; Essexville, MI; Chr; HonRl; SchMus; SchPl; TchrAde; Mi State Univ; Doctor Vet Med.

PETTY, Shannon D; Protection HS; Protection, KS; SecSophCls; DrmMjrt; HonRl; PolWkr; SchMus; EdYrBk; SecPpCl; LetterGlf; Chrldr; PPFtbl; University; Major Study History.

PETTYGROVE, Lynne; Concordia HS; Concordia, KS; 15/141 Band; Chr; Chrs; ChrhWkr; CncrtBnd; HonRl; MrchBnd; PepBnd; StuCncl; Twrl; Kansas State Univ;.

PETTYS, Harlan F; Minot HS; Minot, ND; Band; CncrtBnd; MrchBnd; RedCrAde; TchrAde; LetterSwmmng; College; Hospital Admin.

PETZING, Dale R; Tonica HS; Tonica, IL; 2/45 Band; ChrhWkr; CncrtBnd; HonRl; JrNHS; PepBnd; Illinois Valley Comm College.

PETZING, Janice E; Tonica HS; Tonica, IL; 2/50 Band; ChrhWkr; CncrtBnd; HonRl; NHS; PepBnd; SchMus; RptrYrbk; SpnCl; Ill Valley Comm College; Data Processing.

PEUSTER, Pamela S; Slater HS; Slater, MO; SecSophCls; Band; ChrhWkr; CncrtBnd; HonRl; MrchBnd; PepBnd; TchrAde; 4-H; FHA; IMSpt; College; Home Economics.

PEUTERBAUGH, Randy L; Calhoun HS; Hamburg, IL; HonRl; JA; SctActv; 4-H; FFA; PpCl; LetterFtbl; LetterTrk; IMSpt; 4-HAwd; JAAwd; College; Vocation.

PEW, Kathy A; Tri HS; Spiceland, IN; 11/95 NHS; RptrYrbk; 4-H; FHA; SpnCl; PpCl; SciCl; GAA; 4-HAwd; College; Speech Therapy.

PEW, Thomas H; Le Mars Gehlen HS; Le Mars, IA; PresJrCls; ALBoysSt; Band; HonRl; NHS; SchMus; StuCncl; Bsktbl; Ftbl; College; Professional.

PEYTON, Brad R; North Linn HS; Walker, IA; 3/55 PresFrshCls; PresSophCls; Band; NHS; SchMus; PresStuCncl; Pres4-H; PresFFA; Bsbl; Bsktbl; University; Agriculture.

PEYTON, Cynthia O; Highland Park Sr HS; St Paul, MN; Chr; ChrhWkr; HonRl; HospAde; LbryAde; Orch; College; Professional.

PEYTON, Linda M; Theodore Roosevelt HS; Wyandotte, MI; CncrtBnd; DrmBgl; TchrAde; LetterBsktbl; LetterTrk; GAA; College; Mathematics.

PEYTON, Valerie D; Auburn HS; Rockford, IL; HonRl; NHS; NatlMeritFnl; NatlMeritCmnd; NatlMeritSchl; OffAde; Rock Valley College; Law.

PFAB, Linda L; Hempstead HS; Dubuque, IA; CmntyWkr; JA; SchAde; JAAwd;.

PFAFF, Debra; Melrose Mindoro HS; Mindoro, WI; 7/84 CncrtBnd; HonRl; SctActv; StuGov; RptrYrbk; Chrldr; GAA; AmLegAwd; Univ Wisc; Physical Ed.

PFAFF, Eric R; Green Lake HS; Green Lake, WI; VPJrCls; HonRl; NHS; Bsktbl; College.

PFAFF, Rita A; Sauk Prairie HS; Sauk City, WI; 14/225 VPJrCls; ALAGirlsSt; Chrs; CncrtBnd; HonRl; HospAde; NHS; SchMus; SchPl; CaptChrldr; Clg; Nursing.

PFANDER, Michael B; Nixa HS; Nixa, MO; VPSophCls; Band; ChrhWkr; CncrtBnd; HonRl; MrchBnd; NHS; SchMus; SchPl; StuCncl; IMSpt; DanFAwd; 4-HAwd; Univ Of Mo; Medicine.

PFANNENSTIEL, Edie J; Campus HS; Haysville, KS; Chr; HonRl; NatlFornLg; NatlThespSoc; SchPl; TchrAde; College.

PFANNENSTIEL, Mark J; Ness City HS; Ness City, KS; 3/56 Band; LetterChr; Chrl; Chrs; ChrhWkr; CncrtBnd; LetterHonRl; MrchBnd; LetterNHS; NatlThespSoc; LetterBsktbl; LetterFtbl; LetterTrk; Hutchinson Comm Jr College; Mass Media.

PFANNENSTIEL, Mary J; Marian HS; Hays, KS; 4/61 VPFrshCls; HonRl; JrNHS; ModUN; NHS; TchrAde; LatCl; PpCl; CaptBsktbl; LetterTrk; Kansas State Univ; Recreation.

PFANNER, Janet D; Monroe City R I HS; Monroe City, MO; PresSophCls; ALAGirlsSt; Band; Chrs; CncrtBnd; HonRl; MrchBnd; NHS; PepBnd; StuCncl; RptrSchPpr; FHA; College; Pharmacy.

PFANTZ, Tamara J; West Marshall HS; State Center, IA; 2/90 TrsJrCls; Chrs; HonRl; NHS; TreasStuCncl; SecYthFlsp; LetterBsbl; LetterBsktbl; LetterTrk; CitAwd;.

PFAU, Mary A; Esmond Public HS; Esmond, ND; Band; Chrs; HonRl; SchPl; 4-H; EngCl; MthCl; Bsktbl; Trk; Chrldr; College; Phy Ed.

PFEFFER, Carol L; Union Grove HS; Union Grv, WI; Chr; Chrs; ChrhWkr; HonRl; NHS; GAA;.

PFEFFER, Karen F; Malden HS; Malden, MO; 33/102 Band; ChrhWkr; CncrtBnd; HonRl; LbryAde; MrchBnd; FrCl; Murray U; Home Ec.

PFEFFERKORN, Troy G; Eisenhower HS; New Berlin, WI; SctActv; SchPpr; Wrstlng; IMSpt; Marquette Univ; Pre Med.

PFEIFER, Beverly L; Southwest HS; St Louis, MO; 11/538 Chr; HonRl; ModUN; NatlMeritCmnd; Quill&Scroll; SchMus; StuCncl; EdSchPpr; FrCl; GAA; U Of Mo; Journalism.

PFEIFER, Donald R; Spalding Acad; Spalding, NE; HonRl; FFA; Ftbl; Trk; Coll; Farming.

PFEIFER, Donna M; Hays HS; Hays, KS; Band; Chr; CncrtBnd; HonRl; HospAde; LbryAde; MrchBnd; OffAde; PpCl; College; Fashion Merchandising.

PFEIFER, Gina K; Gardner So Wilmington HS; Gardner, IL; 1/60 ALAGirlsSt; Band; HonRl; LbryAde; NatlMeritCmnd; SchPl; EdYrBk; RptrSchPpr; SpnCl; MthCl; Eastern Il Univ; Accounting & Math.

PFEIFER, Janice; Morland HS; Morland, KS; 4/21 PresFrshCls; Band; Chr; Chrs; ChrhWkr; HonRl; RptrYrbk; PpCl; PPFtbl; College;.

PFEIFER, Kathy A; St Francis HS; Humphrey, NE; Chrs; HonRl; LbryAde; NHS; StuGov; TchrAde; RptrSchPpr; 4-H; PpCl; Business School; Office Work.

PFEIFER, Linda L; Alton Sr HS; Godfrey, IL; HonRl; NHS; Orch; SctActv; GerCl; LetterBsktbl; PPFtbl; Valparaiso Univ; Business.

PFEIFER, Merlin C; Langdon HS; Langdon, ND; 40/109 Band; CncrtBnd; HonRl; MrchBnd; PepBnd; StuGov; FFA; Trade; Communications Servicing.

PFEIFER, Patrick J; Spalding Academy; Spalding, NE; 4/26 SecJrCls; HonRl; NHS; SchPl; TchrAde; LetterFtbl; Tennis; LetterTrk; LetterWrstlng; College; Aviation.

PFEIFER, Randy F; Holy Family HS; Lindsay, NE; 9/33 VPJrCls; HonRl; NatlMeritSchl; StuCncl; College; Business Management.

PFEIFER, Reginald; Lakeside Lutheran HS; Lake Mills, WI; 13/79 PresFrshCls; Chr; HonRl; StuCncl; YthFlsp; GerCl; Univ; Coaching.

PFEIFF, Doreen F; North Central Area HS; Wilson, MI; 2/54 HonRl; SchPl; TchrAde; Teen; RptrSchPpr; 4-H; Central Michigan Univ; Special Ed.

PFEIFFER, Joan; Tipton HS; Tipton, KS; 5/22 TrsFrshCls; Chrs; HonRl; StuCncl; Yrbk; 4-H; PpCl; 4-HAwd; College; Business & Economics.

PFEIFFER, Karl T; Lake Forest HS; Lake Forest, IL; 62/420 Chr; ChrhWkr; CmntyWkr; HonRl; Mdrgl; NHS; NatlMeritCmnd; SctActv; Loyola University; Psychology.

PFEIFFER, Monte J; Winside Public HS; Winside, NE; 21/45 PresStuCncl; Ftbl; LetterWrstlng; Trade Sch; Prof.

PFEIFFER, Robin L; Hammond Baptist HS; Hammond, IN; PresSrCls; Band; Chr; ChrhWkr; HonRl; NHS; PepBnd; RptrSchPpr; GerCl; Bob Jones University; Cinema.

PFEIL, Mark P; Truman Public HS; Lewisville, MN; ALBoysSt; Chr; ChrhWkr; HonRl; TchrAde; FFA; FTA; LetterBsbl; LetterBsktbl; LetterFtbl; College; Mathematics.

PFEILER, Jane E; Leo HS; Holy Cross, IA; 6/38 SecSrCls; Chrs; HonRl; SchMus; SchPl; EdYrBk; RptrSchPpr; LatCl; PpCl; TreasSciCl; Loras College; Child Care.

PFINGSTEN, Craig D; Racine Lutheran HS; Racine, WI; HonRl; LbryAde; SciCl; LetterBsbl; LetterFtbl; CaptWrstlng; IMSpt; Uw Platteville; Eng.

PFINGSTEN, Lynn A; Racine Lutheran HS; Racine, WI; 6/83 CmntyWkr; HonRl; NHS; OffAde; PolWkr; SchPl; Yrbk; RptrSchPpr; PpCl; Bsbl; Bsktbl; SecGAA; Univ Of Wisconsin; Veterinarian.

PFISTER, Carl E; Munster HS; Munster, IN; ChrhWkr; HonRl; PresJrCls; Bsktbl; Ftbl; JCAwd; PresAwd; College; Architect.

PFISTER, Carmon J; Bluffton Allen HS; Bluffton, IN; 40/139 HonRl; LbryAde; Quill&Scroll; SchPl; Teen; Yrbk; RptrSchPpr; SpnCl; PpCl; Ball State University; English.

PFISTER, Daniel W; Goddard HS; Goddard, KS; 1/146 SecFrshCls; SecSophCls; SecJrCls; SecSrCls; NatlFornLg; NHS; NatlMeritSF; SpnCl; SciCl; Trk; College; Law Or Politics.

PFISTER, Joseph D; Jasper HS; Jasper, IN; 21/295 Band; CtyCnl; DrmMjrt; HonRl; NHS; Quill&Scroll; SchMus; StuCncl; Yrbk; KeyCl; Univ Of Indiana; Law.

PFISTER, Joy E; Washington HS; Hubertus, WI; 1/215 NHS; GerCl; MthCl; LetterSwmmng; LetterTennis; LetterTrk; AmLegAwd; PresAwd; VFWAwd; Air Force College; Accounting & Math.

PFISTER, Linda L; Sevastopol HS; Sturgeon Bay, WI; TrsSrCls; Chr; Chrs; CmntyWkr; UNYO; YthFnd; 4-H; GAA; IMSpt; Professional.

PFISTER, Patti L; Newcastle Public HS; Newcastle, NE; SecSophCls; TrsJrCls; TrsSrCls; Band; CncrtBnd; HonRl; MrchBnd; CaptBsktbl; Chrldr; IMSpt; Sch Of Commerce.

PFISTER, Steven B; Roanoke Benson HS; Roanoke, IL; 10/97 Band; CncrtBnd; HonRl; MrchBnd; PepBnd; IMSpt; 4-HAwd; College; Vocation.

PFLASTERER, Christina; Winchester Comm HS; Ster, IN; ChrhWkr; HonRl; NHS; TchrAde; RptrSchPpr; 4-H; FHA; PpCl; Anderson College; Nursing.

PFLAUM, Karen M; St Peter HS; St Peter, MN; PresBand; Chr; DrmMjrt; Mdrgl; NHS; VPNatlThespSoc; PepBnd; LetterBsktbl; LetterTennis; Col; Elementary Education.

PFLEGER, Gary; Center Public HS; New Salem, ND; TrsJrCls; Band; HonRl; SchPpr; FFA; GerCl; Ftbl; Army; Electronics.

PFLEGHAAR, Jeaninne M; Mason Sr HS; Erie, MI; Band; CncrtBnd; HonRl; MrchBnd; NHS; PepBnd; RptrSchPpr; FHA; Tech Sch; Medical.

PFLEIDERER, Janie L; Lafayette HS; St Joseph, MO; 17/450 HonRl; LitMag; StuCncl; TchrAde; VPFTA; North West Mo.

PFLEIDERER, John M; Whitefish Bay HS; Whitefish Bay, WI; VPBand; CncrtBnd; NatlMeritCmnd; Orch; LatCl; IMSpt; College; Socio Environmental Studies.

PFLIGER, Douglas A; Azen HS; Hazen, ND; 10/38 PresSophCls; VPSrCls; HonRl; SchPl; SctActv; StuCncl; Yrbk; SchPpr; Bsktbl; Ftbl; LetterTrk; CitAwd; Bismarck College; Advertising Arts.

PFLUEGER, Burton W; Wisner Pilger HS; Wisner, NE; Band; CncrtBnd; HonRl; MrchBnd; NHS; FFA; CaptBsktbl; Univ Of Neb; Agricultural Employ.

PFLUEGER, Laurie A; Salem Central HS; Salem, WI; PresChrs; VPLetterTrk; Business School; Court Reporter.

PFLUGHAUPT, Cabrina M; Central City HS; Central City, IA; PresSrCls; HonRl; NHS; TchrAde; RptrYrbk; 4-H; Bsktbl; Trk; Chrldr; 4-HAwd; Iowa; Pharmacy.

PFLUGI, Matt J; Hill Murray HS; St Paul, MN; HonRl; SchMus; StuCncl; Ftbl; Trk; Wrstlng; IMSpt; College; Engineering.

PFLUMM, Lisa A; Saint Joseph HS; Shawnee, KS; HonRl; LitMag; OffAde; StuCncl; RptrSchPpr; SchPpr; PpCl; Chrldr; IMSpt; College; Phy Education.

PFORTMILLER, Gary G; Thomas More Prep HS; Hays, KS; 1/80 CmntyWkr; HonRl; JA; OffAde; PolWkr; SchAde; TchrAde; RptrYrbk; RptrSchPpr; FDA; EngCl; Ftbl; Trk; Kansas Univ; Doctor.

PFOTENHAUER, David L; Sgt Bluff Luton Comm HS; Sgt Bluff, IA; Band; CncrtBnd; MrchBnd; PepBnd; SctActv; LetterFtbl; LetterTrk; CitAwd; Trade School; Vocation.

PFRIMMER, John L; Mormon Trail HS; Derby, IA; Band; CmntyWkr; CncrtBnd; HonRl; MrchBnd; SchMus; YthFlsp; Bsktbl; LetterFtbl; Trade Schl; Mechanic.

PFUND, Julie A; Monroe Sr HS; Monroe, WI; HonRl; YthFlsp; FrCl; PpCl; College.

PHALEN, Kathleen L; Shawano HS; Shawano, WI; 2/247 NHS; NatlMeritCmnd; PolWkr; SchMus; SchPl; SctActv; TchrAde; RptrYrbk; RptrSchPpr; FBLA; Beloit Coll; Social Studies.

PHEBUS, Charles E; Plano HS; Plano, IL; ChrhWkr; College; Professional.

PHEBUS, Dan E; Rossville HS; Frankfort, IN; 2/65 ALBoysSt; HonRl; NHS; TchrAde; 4-H; Bsbl; Bsktbl; Glf; College; Engineer.

PHEGLEY, Glenn S; Red Bud HS; Prairie Du Rocher, IL; 4/95 Band; HonRl; JrNHS; MthCl; LetterBsbl; Bsktbl; U Of Mo; Engineering.

PHEGLEY, Mary A; St Joseph Academy; Warson Woods, MO; 1/124 Chr; Chrl; Chrs; ChrhWkr; HonRl; HospAde; NHS; NatlMeritCmnd; SchMus; SctActv; TreasStuCncl; GAA; IMSpt; St Louis Univ; Dietician.

PHEGLEY, Richard B; Arcadia Valley HS; Ironton, MO; 26/87 HonRl; JrNHS; NHS; SchPl; PpCl; Bsbl; Mineral Area College.

PHEIFER, Patricia A; Lesueur HS; Lesueur, MN; AFS; Band; ChrhWkr; CmntyWkr; HonRl; HospAde; Yrbk; RptrSchPpr; 4-H; 4-HAwd; Univ Of Mn; Literature.

PHELAN, Donald M; Cathedral HS; Indianapolis, IN; 12/121 HonRl; NHS; PolWkr; RptrYrbk; Yrbk; FrCl; IMSpt; Depauw University.

PHELAN, Myra B; Tracy HS; Currie, MN; Band; Chr; Chrl; Chrs; HospAde; RptrYrbk; RptrSchPpr; FHA; GAA; PPFtbl; University; Hotel Mgmt.

PHELPS, Dale E; Center HS; Kansas City, MO; HonRl; NatlFornLg; RptrYrbk; RptrSchPpr; KeyCl; LetterFtbl;.

PHELPS, Jay C; Shortridge HS; Indianapolis, IN; HonRl; NHS; University; Professional.

PHELPS, John; Whittemore Prescott HS; Whittmore, MI; 10 80 VPFrshCls; PresSophCls; PresJrCls; PresStuCncl; LetterBsbl; LetterFtbl; Central Mi Univ; Accounting.

PHELPS, Kathleen; Colchester HS; Colchester, IL; Chrs; HonRl; YthFlsp; 4-H; FHA; College; History Major.

PHELPS, Kathleen; Calumet Senior HS; Chicago, IL; 5/832 HonRl; JA; OffAde; TchrAde; SchPpr; GAA; JAAwd; CitAwd;.

PHELPS, Ronald C; Northwest HS; Ribes Junction, MI; 1/265 Band; CncrtBnd; HonRl; MrchBnd; NHS; SchPl; StuGov; CaptBsktbl; Trk; RotaryAwd; Univ Of Michigan; Business Administration.

PHELPS, Ruth A; Marlette Comm HS; Marlette, MI; 18/140 ALAGirlsSt; HonRl; NHS; TchrAde; Yrbk; FBLA; Bsktbl; Wrstlng; Macomb County Comm College; Dental Asst.

PHELPS, Suzanna; Marissa Unit Dist #40 HS; Marissa, IL; 1/66 DrlTm; HonRl; NHS; SchMus; StuCncl; VPYthFlsp; VPFBLA; VPPpCl; CaptChrldr; Belleville Area Col; Business Ed.

PHEND, Rebecca A; Whitko HS; South Whitley, IN; HonRl; NHS; RptrSchPpr; 4-H; FFA; University; Veterinarian.

PHENIS, Leda J; Richmond Senior HS; Richmond, IN; HonRl; NHS; Teen; College; Elementary Education.

PHERIGO, Nancy J; Waverly HS; Waverly, KS; HonRl; MrchBnd; OffAde; 4-H; LetterBsktbl; 4-HAwd; Kansas St University.

PHILGREEN, Daniel I; Downers Grove Comm HS; Downers Grove, IL; Chr; Chrs; HonRl; YthFlsp; RptrYrbk; Bob Jones Univ; Communications.

PHILIPP, Jacqueline M; Benet Academy; Downers Grove, IL; 48/270 SecSrCls; ChrhWkr; CmntyWkr; HonRl; NatlMeritCmnd; StuGov; RptrSchPpr; EngCl; PpCl; Univ Of Miami Of Ohio.

PHILIPP, Stacy N; Sturgeon Bay HS; Sturgeon Bay, WI; PresFrshCls; Chrl; HonRl; NHS; Quill&Scroll; SchMus; EdYrBk; RptrSchPpr; SpnCl; Chrldr; Unviersity; Language.

PHILIPPART, Nancy L; Bishop Borgess HS; Detroit, MI; 1/366 ChrhWkr; HonRl; HospAde; NHS; NatlMeritSF; RptrYrbk; Yrbk; FDA; LatCl; IMSpt; Wayne State U; Engineer.

PHILIPPE, Michael; Gordon Tech; Chicago, IL; 15/591 CmntyWkr; HonRl; NHS; StuCncl; SptEdSchPpr; SchPpr; PpCl; IMSpt; ChmbCommrsAwd; JCAwd; Univ; Medicine.

PHILLIPS, Alice J; Valley Falls HS; Valley Falls, KS; 8/56 HonRl; NHS; NatlMeritSchl; SchPl; TchrAde; Pres4-H; FHA; PpCl; Trk; 4-HAwd; Kansas St Univ; Child Development.

PHILLIPS, Allison R; Woodruff HS; Peoria, IL; 13/275 Chrs; CmntyWkr; HonRl; OffAde; SctActv; TchrAde; KeyCl; Illinois Central College; Computer Technolo.

PHILLIPS, Andrea M; Tecumseh Senior HS; Tecumseh, MI; 6/240 Band; ChrhWkr; CncrtBnd; HonRl; MrchBnd; NHS; PepBnd; SchMus; SpnCl; University Of Michigan; Doctor.

PHILLIPS, Belinda K; Vienna HS; Vienna, IL; HonRl; TchrAde; PresFHA; PpCl; Chrldr; GAA;.

PHILLIPS, Bradley J; Newton HS; Willow Hill, IL; Aud/Vis; LbryAde; NHS; NatlMeritCmnd; Sec4-H; MthCl; Rose Hulman Inst Of Tech; Mathematics.

PHILLIPS, Bradley J; Catholic Boys HS; Quincy, IL; 13/75 HonRl; SchPl; StuCncl; RptrSchPpr; KeyCl; EngCl; Bsktbl; Illinois State Univ; Mathematics.

PHILLIPS, Brenda S; Midland HS; Midland, MI; 92/433 ChrhWkr; HonRl; NHS; Mi Christian Jr Clg; Secretarial Field.

PHILLIPS, Brian H; Ogemaw Heights HS; West Branch, MI; 30/286 Chr; Chrs; Mdrgl; SchMus; SchPl; YthFlsp; Bsktbl; Ftbl; LetterTrk; IMSpt; College.

PHILLIPS, Bruce A; Willow Run HS; Ypsilanti, MI; Aud/Vis; Chrs; ChrhWkr; CmntyWkr; CncrtBnd; HonRl; JA; MrchBnd; PepBnd; SchMus; College; Attorney.

PHILLIPS, Bryan K; West Vigo HS; W Terre Haute, IN; 28/194 HonRl; FTA; KeyCl; MthCl; Rose Hulman Clg; Engineering.

PHILLIPS, Carol A; Marion Senior HS; Marion, IL; SecChrhWkr; DrlTm; HonRl; HospAde; NHS; EdYrBk; PresFBLA; PpCl; PPFtbl; CitAwd; John A Logan Jr College; Executive Sec.

PHILLIPS, Carolyn K; Elston Sr HS; Michigan City, IN; PresSophCls; StuGov; Bsbl; LetterTennis; Chrldr; CchngActv; IMSpt; College; Journalism.

PHILLIPS, Charles D; Cambridge Sr HS; Cambridge, MN; 1/246 Band; Chr; ChrhWkr; CncrtBnd; Mdrgl; MrchBnd; NHS; PepBnd; SchMus; SchPl; StuCncl; LetterGlf; IMSpt; Air Force Academy; Math.

PHILLIPS, Charles K; Northern University HS; Cedar Falls, IA; Band; Orch; State Univ Of Iowa; Law.

PHILLIPS, David S; Mason City HS; Mason City, IA; Band; Chr; Chrl; ChrhWkr; PepBnd; YthFlsp; 4 Yr State U; Computer Programming.

PHILLIPS, Debra; West Liberty HS; West Libery, IA; Band; HonRl; MrchBnd; NHS; Univ Of Ia; Nursing.

PHILLIPS, Deena; Mt Vernon Sr HS; Mt Vernon, IN; Chr; ChrhWkr; CmntyWkr; SchMus; SchPl; StuCncl; YthFlsp; CivCl; GAA; Brooks College; Fashion Merch.

PHILLIPS, Donna C; Northwood HS; Nappanee, IN; 14/197 SecBand; DrmMjrt; HonRl; MrchBnd; TreasNHS; OffAde; StuCncl; SecPpCl; Trk; GAA; Univ Of In; Biological Sciences.

PHILLIPS, Douglas M; Dowagiac Union HS; Dowagiac, MI; 32/215 AFS; HonRl; Kendall School Of Design; Illustrator.

PHILLIPS, Dwight E; Griggsville HS; Pittsfield, IL; Chrs; HonRl; SchPl; 4-H; FFA; LetterBsktbl; 4-HAwd; College; Veterinarian.

PHILLIPS, Elaine M; Perry Community HS; Perry, IA; Band; ChrhWkr; CncrtBnd; HonRl; MrchBnd; NatlThespSoc; PepBnd; PolWkr; SchMus; SchPl; University; English.

PHILLIPS, Elizabeth A; Pana Senior HS; Pana, IL; SecFrshCls; TrsFrshCls; SecTrsFrshCls; Chrs; RedCrAde; StuCncl; RptrSchPpr; LetterTennis; LetterTrk; GAA; St Josephs College; Political Science.

PHILLIPS, Frances; Arthur Hill HS; Saginaw, MI; Band; Chr; HospAde; Mdrgl; NHS; Univ Of Michigan.

PHILLIPS, Gregory J; Carterville HS; Carteville, IL; VPJrCls; VPSrCls; Aud/Vis; ChrhWkr; HonRl; NHS; SchPl; Yrbk; LetterBsktbl; Ftbl; Southern Il Univ; Forestry.

PHILLIPS, Jeanie B; Mundelein HS; Mundelein, IL; 29/364 HonRl; HospAde; NHS; TchrAde; PresLatCl; SpnCl; Bsktbl; Univ Of Illinois; Pediatrician.

PHILLIPS, Jean M; Valley Falls HS; Valley Falls, KS; 3/38 Band; HonRl; LbryAde; NHS; PepBnd; TchrAde; Sec4-H; PpCl; Trk; 4-HAwd; Vo Tec; Florist.

PHILLIPS, Jeffrey L; Lanphier HS; Springfield, IL; 33/473 NHS; College; Professional.

PHILLIPS, Joanne; Urbana HS; Urbana, IL; VPSophCls; CmntyWkr; SchPl; StuCncl; StuGov; YthLg; RptrYrbk; IMSpt; Southern Ill Univ, Rn.

PHILLIPS, Joanne M; Owosso HS; Owosso, MI; 5/452 JA; NHS; TchrAde; LatCl; GAA; E Michigan Univ; Physical Therapy.

PHILLIPS, John F; East Pike HS; Pittsfield, IL; VPFrshCls; PresSophCls; TrsJrCls; ChrhWkr; HonRl; StuCncl; Yrbk; 4-H; FFA; Technical School; Diesel Mechanic.

PHILLIPS, Kathy R; Tri County HS; Delta, IA; Band; Chr; CmntyWkr; CncrtBnd; IntrClCncl; LbryAde; PresFrshCls; SchMus; StuGov; Bsbl; Bsktbl; Trk; IMSpt; Col; Pro.

PHILLIPS, Kathy S; Clinton Prairie HS; Frankfort, IN; 12/100 HonRl; HospAde; NHS; OffAde; SchPl; StuCncl; TchrAde; EdSchPpr; SpnCl; College; Professional.

PHILLIPS, Kim M; Mazon Verona Kinsman HS; Morris, IL; 3/39 TrsFrshCls; VPSophCls; TrsJrCls; HonRl; LbryAde; NHS; Quill&Scroll; SchPl; Yrbk; SchPpr; 4-H; FHA; Chrldr; SecGAA; TIMEAwd; Univ Of Utah; Communications.

PHILLIPS, Linnae K; Atwater Public HS; Atwater, MN; Band; Chrs; HonRl; PepBnd; YthFlsp; Sec4-H; SpnCl; GAA; IMSpt; 4-HAwd; College; Professional.

PHILLIPS, Mark A; Dearborn HS; Dearborn, MI; TrsSophCls; TrsJrCls; TrsSrCls; CmntyWkr; CncrtBnd; HonRl; StuCncl; StuGov; Yrbk; LetterSwmmng; College; Professional.

PHILLIPS, Michael; Elwood HS; Elwood, NE; HstSophCls; Band; Chrl; Chrs; CncrtBnd; HonRl; MrchBnd; Univ Of Ne; Doctor Of Medicine.

PHILLIPS, Michaela M; Southwest HS; St Louis, MO; 114/490 SecJrCls; SecSrCls; HonRl; HospAde; RedCrAde; SchAde; Chrldr; Missouri Univ; Special Ed.

PHILLIPS, Michael J; Norway Vulcan HS; Loretto, MI; RptrSchPpr; SptEdSchPpr; 4-H; CchngActv; IMSpt; 4-HAwd; Mi Tech U; Civil Engr.

PHILLIPS, Michael L; Decatur Central HS; Indianapolis, IN; 4/317 HonRl; NHS; StuCncl; YthFlsp; SciCl; LetterTrk; IMSpt; Purdue Univ; Chemistry.

PHILLIPS, Michael T; Manning Community HS; Manning, IA; 10/60 Band; Chrs; CncrtBnd; SchMus; StuCncl; Bsbl; Bsktbl; Ftbl; Glf; Swmmng; College; Business.

PHILLIPS, Patrick E; Elwood HS; Elwood, NE; PresSophCls; Band; Chrs; CncrtBnd; HonRl; MrchBnd; NHS; Orch; PepBnd; SchPl; LetterFtbl; LetterTrk; LetterWrstlng; Army; Vet.

PHILLIPS, Penny S; Rossville HS; Rossville, IN; VPSrCls; Chrs; DrlTm; SchPl; TchrAde; FHA; PpCl; LetterTrk; Chrldr; GAA; Vocation;.

PHILLIPS, Randall E; Gordon HS; Gordon, NE; 4/70 Band; Chrs; HonRl; OffAde; SctActv; TchrAde; YthFlsp; LetterBsktbl; Anderson Clg; Theology/psychology.

PHILLIPS, Robert J; Milan C 2 HS; Green City, MO; ChrhWkr; CncrtBnd; MrchBnd; SctActv; YthFlsp; 4-H; Bsbl; Bsktbl; LetterFtbl; LetterTrk; Missouri Univ; Veterinary Medicine.

PHILLIPS, Scooter; Homestead HS; It Wayne, IN; 10/240 TrsFrshCls; TrsSophCls; VPJrCls; ChrhWkr; HonRl; NHS; StuCncl; TrsSophCls; HstFrshCls; Ftbl; Wrstlng; College; Professional.

PHILLIPS, Spencer F; Interlochen Arts Acad; Freeport, IL; ALBoysSt; Band; CncrtBnd; HonRl; MrchBnd; NatlMeritCmnd; Orch; SchMus; StuCncl; GerCl; Duke U; Medicine.

PHILLIPS, Susan C; Pleasantville Comm HS; Pleasantville, IA; 5/60 Band; Chrs; HonRl; NHS; SctActv; YthFlsp; FBLA; Bsktbl; Glf; Iowa State Univ; Psychology.

PHILLIPS, Susan G; Lawrence Central HS; Indianapolis, IN; 11/699 Chr; ChrhWkr; NatlMeritSF; SchMus; SchPl; SctActv; StuGov; PPFtbl;.

PHILLIPS, Susan J; Arthur Hill HS; Saginaw, MI; ChrhWkr; CmntyWkr; HonRl; YthFlsp; FrCl; PpCl; Trk; Chrldr; IMSpt; College.

PHILLIPS, Susan M; Orchard View HS; Muskegon, MI; 9/200 Band; HonRl; MrchBnd; NHS; VPStuCncl; Yrbk; SchPpr; Swmmng; Trk; KiwanAwd; Univ Of Mich; Psychology.

PHILLIPS, Suzanne L; Mercy HS; Omaha, NE; 8/75 JA; NatlFornLg; NatlMeritCmnd; PolWkr; SchMus; Sdlty; FrCl; PpCl; Chrldr; JAAwd; Creighton Univ; Pre Law.

PHILLIPS, Wyatt J; Pilot Grove HS; Pilot Grove, MO; VPFrshCls; VPSophCls; PresJrCls; Chrs; SchPl; StuCncl; FFA; Bsbl; Bsktbl; Umc College; Engineering.

PHILLIS, James W; E Peoria Comm HS; E Peoria, IL; 67/484 VPCncrtBnd; DrmMjrt; Mdrgl; MrchBnd; NatlFornLg; NHS; Orch; Quill&Scroll; SchMus; SptEdSchPpr; Bsbl; College; Music.

PHINNEY, Scot A; Paris HS; Paris, IL; HonRl; NHS; SctActv; SpnCl; College.

PHIPPS, Beverly; Mullen HS; Mullen, NE; Chr; HonRl; MrchBnd; SchMus; SchPl; EdYrBk; 4-H; PpCl; LetterTrk; IMSpt; Coll; Clothing & Textiles.

PHIPPS, Bryan D; Junction Senior HS; Junction, KS; VPFrshCls; Band; StuCncl; TchrAde; RptrYrbk; RptrSchPpr; SptEdSchPpr; Bsbl; LetterFtbl; LetterTrk; IMSpt; CitAwd; College In Kansas; English.

PHIPPS, Doris L; Oxford HS; Belle Plaine, KS; 2/39 Chrs; NatlMeritSF; SchPl; StuCncl; SchPpr; 4-H; PresSpnCl; MthCl; PpCl; College.

PHIPPS, Edna M; Mahomet Seymour HS; Seymour, IL; 26/132 ALAGirlsSt; CncrtBnd; DrlTm; HonRl; NatlThespSoc; SchMus; StuCncl; KeyCl; Eastern Illinois University; Recreation.

PHIPPS, Laura J; Andrean HS; Merrillville, IN; 19/250 HonRl; MthCl; GAA; College.

PHIPPS, Robert M; Grosse Ile HS; Grosse Ile, MI; Chr; PresJA; Mdrgl; PresNHS; NatlMeritSF; TreasNatlThespSoc; SchPl; YthFlsp; Computer Science.

PHIPPS, Scott B; Riverton HS; Riverton, KS; Band; CncrtBnd; HonRl; MrchBnd; NHS; StuCncl; SpnCl; Bsktbl; Ftbl; College.

PHIPPS, Sheila R; Sioux Rapids Comm HS; Sioux Rapids, IA; SecTrsJrCls; Chr; HonRl; NHS; SchPl; StuCncl; Trade; Broadcasting.

PHIPPS, Teresa G; Warsaw Sr HS; Warsaw, IN; College.

PHLYPO, Linda R; Grosse Pointe North HS; Grosse Pointe Wood, MI; 115/626 Chr; HonRl; HospAde; JA; NHS; NatlMeritSchl; NatlMeritSF; JAAwd; Clge; Nursing.

PIASECKI, Jean A; Marquette HS; Marquette, MI; 13/400 Band; CncrtBnd; HonRl; MrchBnd; PepBnd; CchngActv; Northern Mi Univ; Business Admn.

PIASECKI, Paula; Maine Township South HS; Park Ridge, IL; 92/860 HonRl; LbryAde; NHS; NatlThespSoc; Orch; Quill&Scroll; SchMus; RptrSchPpr; EdSchPpr; FrCl; Univ Of Iowa; Physical Therapy.

PIASECKI, Sandra A; All Saints HS; Bay City, MI; CmntyWkr; HospAde; NHS; StuCncl; YthFlsp; EdYrBk; FNA; FrCl; Bsktbl; CchngActv; College; Nursing.

PIATCHEK, Mark; Oakville HS; St Louis, MO; HonRl; StuCncl; Socr; Swmmng; Wrstlng; OptClAwd; Univ; Professional.

PIAZZI, Michelle T; St Louise De Marillac HS; Niles, IL; Chr; Chrs; ChrhWkr; LitMag; NHS; NatlMeritSF; Orch; SchMus; SchPl; TchrAde; Northwestern Univ; Musician.

PIC, Anita R; Michigan Public HS; Whitman, ND; SecTrsJrCls; Band; Chr; Chrs; CncrtBnd; HonRl; MrchBnd; PepBnd; StuCncl; RptrSchPpr; 4-H; FHA; PpCl; University; Teaching.

PICARDAT, Connie A; Manistee Catholic Cen HS; Manistee, MI; 15/75 SecFrshCls; SecSophCls; HonRl; PpCl; Business School.

PICARDAT, Robert; Manistee Catholic Central HS; Manistee, MI; TrsFrshCls; ALBoysSt; Band; CncrtBnd; HonRl; MrchBnd; PepBnd; StuGov; Glf; IMSpt; Coll; Curriculum Of Study.

PICCIONE, Louis; St Laurence HS; Hickory Hills, IL; HonRl; Bsbl; Trk; AFS; College; Law.

PICCO, Christian A; Lincoln HS; Lake City, MN; NatlMeritFnl; Band; Chr; CncrtBnd; HonRl; MrchBnd; NHS; StuCncl; GerCl; Trk; University; Professional.

PICCOLO, Joann E; Hill Murray HS; St Paul, MN; Chr; HospAde; SchMus; SchPl; SchPpr; University; Music.

PICEK, Linda R; Kimball Independent HS; Pukwana, SD; ALAGirlsSt; Chr; Chrs; ChrhWkr; HonRl; LbryAde; SchMus; 4-H; FHA; PpCl; LetterTrk; Wrstlng; Chrldr; College; Veterinarian.

PICHA, Edward J; Riverside Brookfield HS; Riverside, IL; 59/498 HonRl; NHS; SpnCl; SchPl; SctActv; EdYrBk; Yrbk; University Of Illinois; Law.

PICHEA, Beth D; Hillsdale HS; Hillsdale, MI; Band; ChrhWkr; CncrtBnd; HonRl; MrchBnd; NatlMeritSF; OffAde; PepBnd; YthFlsp; FrCl; Business School; Accounting.

PICHEN, Sheila J; Cary Grove HS; Cary, IL; CncrtBnd; HonRl; MrchBnd; NHS; NatlMeritCmnd; OffAde; SchMus; SchPl; TchrAde; Yrbk; Il Wesleyan Univ; Biology.

PICHLA, Doreen E; Ubly HS; Bad Axe, MI; 12/132 VPJrCls; SecSrCls; Band; ChrhWkr; HonRl; JrNHS; NHS; LetterTrk; Chrldr; 4-HAwd; Delta Univ; Secretary.

PICKARD, Diane E; Millington HS; Millington, MI; SecJrCls; Band; DrmMjrt; HonRl; HospAde; NHS; TchrAde; YthFlsp; FNA; FrCl; College; Nursing.

PICKARD, Kevin B; Lawrence Central HS; Lawrence, IN; 34/732 Chr; ChrhWkr; NHS; SchMus; YthFlsp; Butler Univ; Biology.

PICKART, Andrew P; Norway Community HS; Norway, IA; 7/40 PresFrshCls; Chrs; HonRl; MrchBnd; SchPl; PresStuCncl; SptEdSchPpr; LetterBsbl; LetterBsktbl; College.

PICKEN, Linda; Annandale HS; Annandale, MN; 20/120 HonRl; LbryAde; NHS; SchPl; StuCncl; TchrAde; YthFlsp; FHA; PpCl; Chrldr; PPFtbl; Univ Of Mn Morris; Business.

PICKENS, Anita J; Highland HS; Highland, IN; 243/538 VPSrCls; StuCncl; SpnCl; PpCl; Chrldr; University; Business.

PICKENS, Arthus C; Newton HS; Wheeler, IL; 10/200 HonRl; StuGov; LatCl; MthCl; SciCl; LetterGlf; AmLegAwd; Rose Hulman Inst Of Tech; Engineering.

PICKENS, Ernest S; Newton Comm HS; Wheeler, IL; ChrhWkr; StuGov; Yrbk; 4-H; MthCl; Ftbl; College; Forestry.

PICKENS, Gayle E; Huntley HS; Huntley, IL; 7/54 Chr; HonRl; NHS; NatlMeritSchl; StuCncl; EdYrBk; 4-H; LatCl; LetterTrk; Chrldr; AmLegAwd; Northern Illinois Univ; Journalism.

PICKERING, Bonnie L; Gallatin R V HS; Gallatin, MO; 2/42 Band; Chr; CmntyWkr; HonRl; NHS; Yrbk; FFA; PpCl; LetterBsktbl; DARAwd; 4-HAwd; College; Professional.

PICKERING, Mary E; South Callaway Rii HS; Mokone, MO; SecJrCls; HonRl; StuCncl; Yrbk; PpCl; Bsbl; Trk; Chrldr; College; Journalism.

PICKERING, Patricia L; Frankton HS; Anderson, IN; 8/136 TrsJrCls; TrsSrCls; HonRl; JA; TchrAde; 4-H; SpnCl; PpCl; GAA; Business Schl; Business.

PICKERING, Robert B; St Thomas Aquinas HS; Florissant, MO; HonRl; RptrSchPpr; Bsktbl; CchngActv; Univ Of Mo; Bus Admn.

PICKERING, Scott; Thomas Jefferson HS; Bloomington, MN; HonRl; NHS; StuGov; SpnCl; Bsktbl; Ftbl; Trk; University Of Kansas; Accounting.

PICKERING, Suzanne; Morton Sr HS; Hammond, IN; Chr; Chrl; ChrhWkr; HonRl; StuCncl; TchrAde; FTA; Business College; Medical Secretary.

PICKETT, Angela; Southeast Senior HS; Kansas City, MO; DrlTm; HonRl; NHS; ROTC; StuCncl; StuGov; RptrSchPpr; SpnCl; PpCl; Northwestern; Lawyer.

PICKETT, Beverly; Eastbrook Hs; Van Buren, IN; ChrhWkr; TreasYthFlsp; FBLA; TreasFHA;.

PICKETT, Jay A; Anna Jonesboro Comm HS; Anna, IL; 9/138 PresJrCls; HonRl; StuCncl; RptrYrbk; FTA; KeyCl; SpnCl; SciCl; Bsktbl; Ftbl; CchngActv;.

PICKETT, Jeffrey D; Kirksville HS; Kirksville, MO; 56/198 PresJrCls; HonRl; StuCncl; Bsbl; LetterFtbl; LetterTrk; LetterWrstlng; Clge; Athletics.

PICKETT, John R; Waterford Mott HS; Pontiac, MI; HonRl; TchrAde; LetterBsktbl; U Of Mi; Criminal Justice.

PICKETT, Karen L; Elkhart Central HS; Elkhart, IN; 22/470 Band; CncrtBnd; HonRl; JA; MrchBnd; Orch; SchMus; SchPl; YthFlsp; Yrbk; Purdue U; Civil Engineering.

PICKETT, Kathy J; Battle Creek Central HS; Battle Creek, MI; StuCncl; SptEdYrbk; PpCl; Coll; Court Reporter.

PICKETT, Kay E; Mehlville HS; St Louis, MO; Band; Chr; Chrs; ChrhWkr; CncrtBnd; HonRl; MrchBnd; NHS; Orch; Univ Of Missouri; Psychology.

PICKETT, Marcia A; Incarnate Word Acad; Florissant, MO; HonRl; Quill&Scroll; SchMus; SctActv;

RptrSchPpr; EdSchPpr; GAA; PPFtbl; College; Special Education.

PICKETT, Ronda; Grandview Senior HS; Grandview, MO; AFS; Band; DrmMjrt; HonRl; HospAde; OffAde; SpnCl; TreasPpCl; PPFtbl; Coll Or Bus Sch; Account Bus.

PICKFORD, Mary; Jenison HS; Jension, MI; Chr; ChrhWkr; HonRl; LbryAde; SchMus; RptrSchPpr; Tennis; College; Doctor.

PICKFORD, Sandy A; Waldron HS; Pittsford, MI; 5/51 Band; Chrs; CncrtBnd; HonRl; MrchBnd; NHS; PepBnd; SchPpr; 4-H; FTA; Bsktbl; Trk;.

PICKLE, Judith; Mexico HS; Mexico, MO; DrmMjrt; LbryAde; FrCl; LatCl; College.

PICKRELL, Rochelle M; Bridgewater Fontanelle HS; Fontanelle, IA; 1/42 SecFrshCls; PresSophCls; ALAGirlsSt; Band; Chr; Chrs; ChrhWkr; CncrtBnd; HonRl; MrchBnd; NHS; PepBnd; SchMus; SchPl; Simpson College; Music.

PICKUP, Michael A; Hazelwood W Sr HS; Hazelwood, MO; 2/372 HonRl; NatlMeritSF; PolWkr; SchAde; TchrAde; Yrbk; SchPpr; MthCl; Washington Univ; Physics.

PICL, Raymond; Peoria Heights HS; Peoria Heights, IL; 3/99 VPSrCls; Band; ChrhWkr; CmntyWkr; HonRl; NHS; NatlThespSoc; PolWkr; SchPl; Bradley Univ; Computer Sci.

PICONE, Joseph W; Fenwick HS; Oak Park, IL; 3/230 HonRl; NHS; TchrAde; LatCl; Bsbl; Univ Of Chicago; Physicist.

PICTON, Kathy J; Lewistown HS; Lewistown, IL; Band; Chrs; CncrtBnd; DrmMjrt; HonRl; MrchBnd; Twrl; RptrSchPpr; FHA; SpnCl; College; Secretary.

PICUS, Joel; Guilford HS; Rockford, IL; 3/650 Band; CncrtBnd; HonRl; MrchBnd; NatlMeritSF; PepBnd; SctActv; StuCncl; Tennis;.

PIECHAN, Mary A; Lutheran West HS; Detroit, MI; 3/145 ChrhWkr; HonRl; NHS; SchPl; YthFlsp; LatCl; PpCl; Wayne St Univ; Med Tech.

PIECHOWSKI, Kathryn A; Wautoma HS; Redgranite, WI; HonRl; MrchBnd; PepBnd; StuCncl; TreasFrCl; PpCl; LetterTrk; CaptChrldr; Univ Of Wi Madison; Physical Therapist.

PIECZYRAK, Constance A; Lourdes HS; Chicago, IL; 76/277 HonRl; LbryAde; SchMus; SchPl; TchrAde; 4-H; FrCl; SciCl; CaptChrldr; 4-HAwd; College Of St Teresa; Dietetics.

PIEGOLS, Joan L; Hart HS; Hart, MI; 1/116 Band; ChrhWkr; CncrtBnd; HonRl; LbryAde; NHS; NatlMeritFnl; NatlThespSoc; SchPl; RptrSchPpr; Msu Honors College.

PIEHL, Bradley T; Hector Comm HS; Hector, MN; 13/60 Band; Chr; CncrtBnd; HonRl; MrchBnd; Orch; PolWkr; Bsktbl; Ftbl; Trk; South Dakota State Univ; Engineering.

PIEKARCZYK, Danette M; Madonna HS; Chicago, IL; 7/265 HonRl; NHS; StuCncl; RptrSchPpr; FrCl; University; Creative Writing.

PIEKARSKI, Virginia L; Thornton Twp HS; Harvey, IL; HonRl; NHS; Illinois State Univ; Veterinarian.

PIEKIELNIAK, Doris E; Rolla HS; Rolla, MO; 7/292 HonRl; NatlMeritSF; SchPl; KeyCl; GerCl; LetterBsktbl; Trk; IMSpt; PresAwd; Univ; Biology.

PIEL, Cindy L; Winfield HS; Winfield, KS; CmntyWkr; DrlTm; HonRl; OffAde; TreasStuCncl; StuGov; TchrAde; College; Art.

PIELSTICK, Ellen K; Gering HS; Gering, NE; 1/136 Band; Chr; Chrs; CncrtBnd; HonRl; JrNHS; LbryAde; MrchBnd; NHS; PepBnd; Oral Roberts U; Music.

PIEMONTE, Joann S; St Stanislaus Kostka HS; Chicago, IL; 7/64 VPSrCls; LbryAde; StuGov; SpnCl; Chrldr; Wilbur Wright; Medical Profession.

PIEPER, Caroline L; Luther HS; La Crescent, MN; 5/75 Chr; HonRl; MrchBnd; NHS; Orch; RptrYrbk; EdSchPpr; LetterBsktbl; IMSpt; Bus Sch; Cosmotologist.

PIEPER, Christopher; Stoughton Senior HS; Stoughton, WI; AFS; CncrtBnd; HonRl; MrchBnd; PepBnd; SchMus; SchPl; StuCncl; Yrbk; SciCl; Univ Of Wi; Engrg.

PIEPER, Gregg A; Marquette School Inc; W Point, IA; 4/35 NHS; StuCncl; EdSchPpr; College; Med.

PIEPER, Gregory J; Mitchell HS; Mitchell, NE; 1/52 ALBoysSt; HonRl; NHS; SchMus; StuCncl; TchrAde; Bsktbl; LetterFtbl; VoiceDemAwd; College; Engineering.

PIEPER, Margaret; Aquinas HS; Wever, IA; PresFrshCls; PresSophCls; ChrhWkr; OffAde; PolWkr; RptrYrbk; SpnCl; PpCl; Creighton Univ; Elem Ed.

PIEPER, Pamela J; Hallock HS; Hallock, MN; Chr; CncrtBnd; HonRl; SchPl; SptEdSchPpr; FHA; SciCl; LetterBsktbl; GAA; IMSpt;.

PIEPER, Patricia A; Glenwood HS; Springfield, IL; CmntyWkr; HonRl; IntrClCncl; SctActv; FHA; FNA; GerCl; Nurses Training.

PIEPER, Steven M; Stewardson Strasburg HS; Strasburg, IL; Band; ChrhWkr; CncrtBnd; MrchBnd; SchPl; 4-H; FFA; PpCl; Bsbl; Bsktbl; Jr College; Farmer.

PIEPGRAS, Lois M; St Croix Lutheran HS; St Paul, MN; 1/53 Band; Chr; CncrtBnd; HonRl; MrchBnd; StuCncl; LetterBsktbl; CaptChrldr; College.

PIER, Peggy S; Venice HS; Venice, IL; 1/45 Band; TreasChrs; ChrhWkr; HonRl; OffAde; SchPl; StuCncl; YthFlsp; TreasFHA; AmLegAwd; College; Liberal Arts.

PIERCE, Christina P; Cass City HS; Cass City, MI; HonRl; LbryAde; TchrAde; SpnCl; PpCl; College; Professional.

PIERCE, Daniel J; Marian Central HS; Woodstock, IL; 3/135 Aud/Vis; ChrhWkr; HonRl; NHS; SciCl; BauchLmbAwd; Northwestern; Liberal Arts.

PIERCE, David M; Woodstock HS; Woodstock, IL; Band; Chr; CncrtBnd; HonRl; MrchBnd; NHS; NatlMeritCmnd; NatlThespSoc; SchMus; SchPl; Univ Of Illinois; Music.

PIERCE, David R; St Stephen Area HS; Saginaw, MI; 13/104 Band; CmntyWkr; CncrtBnd; MrchBnd; SchPl; Tennis; Mi St Univ; Liberal Arts.

PIERCE, Dianna J; New Palestine HS; Greenfield, IN; HonRl; Yrbk; SpnCl; Trade School; Interior Decorator.

PIERCE, Donald E; Shakamak HS; Jasonville, IN; 26/70 Aud/Vis; CchngActv; IMSpt; Us Air Force; Electronics.

PIERCE, Gregory W; Latin School Of Inddls; Indianapolis, IN; ALAGirlsSt; NHS; PepBnd; SchMus; StuCncl; EdYrBk; RptrSchPpr; IMSpt; College.

PIERCE, Jan E; Sparta HS; Sparta, IL; Band; CncrtBnd; HonRl; HospAde; MrchBnd; PepBnd; Yrbk; FBLA; PpCl; College; Medical Field.

PIERCE, Janice B; St Alphonsus HS; Dearborn, MI; HonRl; NatlMeritSchl; NatlMeritSF; SchMus; SctActv; Bsbl; CaptBsktbl; GAA; IMSpt; PPFtbl; KiwanAwd; PresAwd; Central Michigan Univ; Medical Tech.

PIERCE, Jan M; Gibbon HS; Gibbon, NE; 10/59 VPSrCls; HonRl; StuGov; TchrAde; Yrbk; LetterBsktbl; Trk; IMSpt; AmLegAwd; CitAwd; Kearney St Coll; Bus Ed.

PIERCE, Jo Ann L; Indianola Sr HS; Indianola, IA; HonRl; HospAde; NatlMeritCmnd; SctActv; Trk; IMSpt; College; Physician.

PIERCE, John M; North Knox HS; Bruceville, IN; Band; CncrtBnd; PepBnd; LetterFtbl; LetterWrstlng; University; Professional.

PIERCE, Larry R; Bayard HS; Bayard, NE; ChrhWkr; Univ Of Nebraska.

PIERCE, Lori L; Clay Center Public HS; Clay Center, NE; 3/25 VPJrCls; Band; Chr; Chrs; ChrhWkr; HonRl; NHS; SchPl; TchrAde; EdSchPpr; LetterTrk; Chrldr; PresAwd; Univ Of Ne; Teaching.

PIERCE, Marilyn E; Peoria Hgts HS; Peoria, IL; 17/93 Chr; Chrs; HonRl; 4-H; FrCl; Coll; Law.

PIERCE, Mark A; Webber Township HS; Bluford, IL; PresStuCncl; 4-H; FFA; PpCl; Bsktbl; Swmmng; Trk; 4-HAwd; VoiceDemAwd; College; Electrician.

PIERCE, Mary C; Ladywood HS; Livonia, MI; 15/90 Chr; ChrhWkr; CmntyWkr; HonRl; NatlFornLg; NHS; TrsSophCls; MthCl; Coll; Nurse.

PIERCE, Michael S; Minooka Comm HS; Minooka, IL; 1/106 PresFrshCls; Chrs; HonRl; Mdrgl; NHS; NatlMeritCmnd; StuCncl; MthCl; Bsbl; Bsktbl; Ftbl; College.

PIERCE, Patrick E; Carterville HS; Carterville, IL; PresSophCls; ChrhWkr; CmntyWkr; NHS; SchMus; TreasStuCncl; PpCl; SciCl; Bsbl; Bsktbl; Ftbl; Trk; Southern Illinois Univ.

PIERCE, Patti; Delta HS; Gaston, IN; Chrs; HonRl; FHA; FrCl; PpCl; Chrldr;.

PIERCE, Phyllis J; Tomah Sr HS; Tomah, WI; TrsJrCls; TrsSrCls; Band; Chr; CncrtBnd; DrmMjrt; MrchBnd; StuCncl; Twrl; Chrldr; GAA;.

PIERCE, Randall W; Iron Mountain HS; Iron Mountain, MI; AFS; KeyCl; Ftbl; Trk; Wrstlng; No Michigan Univ; Accounting.

PIERCE, Robert L; Glenbard West HS; Glen Ellyn, IL; CncrtBnd; HonRl; MrchBnd; PresOrch; PepBnd; SchMus; StuCncl; SchPpr; GerCl; IMSpt; Univ Of Il; Pro Pre Med.

PIERCE, Sherri J; Tri County HS; Keswick, IA; 2/46 HonRl; MrchBnd; PpCl; LetterTrk; Chrldr;.

PIERCE, Sylvia; Dixon Hs; Dixon, IL; Chr; ChrhWkr; CmntyWkr; HonRl; HospAde; SchMus; SchPl; YthFlsp;.

PIERCE, William R; Bentley HS; Burton, MI; HonRl; NHS; Yrbk; SchPpr; Trk; Mich St Univ; Eng.

PIERCY, David L; Mt Vernon Twp HS; Mt Vernon, IL; 1/395 ChrhWkr; HonRl; PresNHS; Quill&Scroll; EdSchPpr; AmLegAwd; LionAwd; Univ Of Illinois; Lawyer.

PIERCY, Laura L; Waterman HS; Waterman, IL; DrlTm; HonRl; LbryAde; OffAde; 4-H; FrCl; GAA;.

PIERCY, Noel A; Edwards County HS; Ellery, IL; Band; NatlMeritSF; PepBnd; SchPpr; Augustana College; Music.

PIERCY, Phyllis S; Fairbury Cropsey HS; Fairbury, IL; 7/100 HonRl; NatlMeritCmnd; BttyCrckrAwd; U Of Il; Photo.

PIERI, Frank J; Cary Grove HS; Fox River Grove, IL; 9/263 HonRl; LitMag; PresNHS; SchMus; PresSchPl; SpnCl; Ill Wesleyan University; Medicine.

PIERICK, Patty A; Maple Valley Comm HS; Danbury, IA; 15/99 Chrs; HonRl; LbryAde; NHS; 4-H; Bsktbl; LetterTrk; 4-HAwd; College; Teacher.

PIERMARINI, Charles N; Elk Grove HS; Elk Grove Village, IL; 4/504 HonRl; NHS; StuCncl; Bsktbl; Ftbl; University; Medicine.

PIERRE, Adrian G; Emerson HS; Gary, IN; ChrhWkr; HonRl; NatlMeritCmnd; SchPl; RptrSchPpr; FrCl; PpCl; CaptGlf; Tennis; Purdue University; Chemical Engineer.

PIERRE, Frederique G; St Francis Academy; Bolingbrook, IL; 57/172 HonRl; StuCncl; Yrbk; FrCl; College; Foreign Languages.

PIERSCINSKI, Joyce; Griffith Senior HS; Griffith, IN; Chrs; HonRl; SchMus; SchPl; SctActv; StuCncl; StuGov; RptrSchPpr; PpCl; PPFtbl; College; Psychology.

PIERSKI, Mark A; Tri City HS; Mechanicsburg, IL; 6/50 HonRl; SchPl; StuCncl; FTA; PresSpnCl; PpCl; LetterBsbl; LetterTrk; Univ Of Illinois; Civil Engineering.

PIERSMA, Daniel R; Western Michigan ChristianHS; Grand Haven, MI; ChrhWkr; CmntyWkr; HonRl; NatlMeritFnl; SctActv; MthCl; SciCl; Swmmng; Tennis; JETSAwd; United Elec Inst; Electronics.

PIERSOL, David S; Lahser HS; Bloomfield Hills, MI; Band; CncrtBnd; HonRl; MrchBnd; NHS; FrCl; LetterSocr; U Of Mi; Lawyer.

PIERSON, Debra R; Wellcome Memorial HS; Lake Crystal, MN; TrsSrCls; Chrs; HonRl; SchPl; TreasStuCncl; RptrYrbk; RptrSchPpr; GerCl; LetterChrldr; GAA; Vocational School.

PIERSON, Gary H; Notre Dame HS; Chicago, IL; 15/276 PresSrCls; CtyCnl; NatlMeritFnl; PolWkr; RedCrAde; ROTC; EdSchPpr; Ftbl; Swmmng; IMSpt; University Of Miami; Biology.

PIERSON, Julie; Ewing Public HS; Page, NE; 4/28 Band; Chrs; HonRl; MrchBnd; NHS; PepBnd; SchPl; TchrAde; EdYrBk; 4-H;.

PIERSON, Julie K; Hillsboro HS; Hillsboro, IL; Band; CncrtBnd; HonRl; JrNHS; MrchBnd; PepBnd; StuCncl; SpnCl; Chrldr; TreasGAA; College; Lab Technician.

PIERSON, Karen M; Stephen T Mather HS; Chicago, IL; 35/442 Band; CmntyWkr; HonRl; HospAde; NHS; NatlMeritSF; TchrAde; SpnCl; Knox College; Business Admin.

PIERSON, Patty L; Oakland HS; Oakland, IL; 2/43 HonRl; VPNHS; EdYrBk; MthCl; DARAwd; Univ Of Ill; Pharmacy.

PIERSON, Scott C; Kirkwood HS; Kirkwood, MO; Aud/Vis; Band; CmntyWkr; CncrtBnd; HonRl; LbryAde; Orch; RedCrAde; SctActv; StuCncl; Northeast Mo State U; Indust Arts.

PIERUCCI, Angelo P; Gordon Tech HS; Chicago, IL; 42/618 College; Mathematics.

PIERUCKI, Cynthia A; Coldwater HS; Coldwater, MI; SecFrshCls; Chr; CmntyWkr; CncrtBnd; OffAde; SchMus; PpCl; Bsbl; Trk; PPFtbl; Western Mi Univ; Retailing Field.

PIESZCHALA, Tim A; La Porte HS; La Porte, IN; VPFrshCls; PresSophCls; CmntyWkr; HonRl; RedCrAde; StuCncl; StuGov; RptrYrbk; Bsktbl; Purdue University; Biology.

PIETENPOL, David J; New Trier West HS; Winnetka, IL; SctActv; StuCncl; LetterSwmmng; University; Geology.

PIETERICK, Susan; Regis HS; Eau Claire, WI; 42/140 Band; Chr; CncrtBnd; HonRl; Orch; PepBnd; SchMus; StuCncl; SpnCl; GAA; Univ Of Wi; Physical Therapy.

PIETERS, Kimberly A; George Rogers Clark HS; Whiting, IN; ALAGirlsSt; HonRl; Sdlty; StuCncl; SpnCl; PpCl; LetterBsktbl; GAA; IMSpt; College; Athletic Trainer.

PIETRON, Claudia P; Larimore HS; Larimore, ND; Band; Chrs; DrmMjrt; HonRl; 4-H; FHA; PpCl; LetterBsktbl; LetterTrk; 4-HAwd; College; Professional.

PIETROWIAK, Cheryl L; Muskego HS; Hales Corners, WI; Chr; HonRl; NHS; NatlMeritFnl; SchPl; PresStuCncl; Swmmng; GAA; College; Psychology.

PIETROWSKI, Denise M; Bark River Harris HS; Bark River, MI; ChrhWkr; CncrtBnd; HonRl; MrchBnd; PepBnd; RptrYrbk; Bsbl; LetterBsktbl; LetterTrk; 4-HAwd; College; Architecture.

PIETRUSZEWSKI, Cathy L; Kennedy Public HS; Donaldson, MN; PresJrCls; Chrs; HonRl; SpnCl; PpCl; Business School; Vocation Secretary.

PIETRUSZKA, Cynthia A; T F South HS; Lansing, IL; HonRl; HospAde; NHS; PresFNA; SpnCl; S Chicago School Of Nursing; Nurse.

PIETRUSZKA, Jolanta I; Goodrich HS; Grand Blanc, MI; VPSrCls; Chr; HonRl; NHS; OffAde; SchPl; SctActv; SchPpr; 4-H; College; Anaesthesiologist.

PIETRYKOWSI, Patrick M; Madison Cons HS; Madison, IN; 69/296 Band; CncrtBnd; HonRl; MrchBnd; PepBnd; StuGov; TchrAde; 4-H; LetterBsbl; LetterFtbl; College; Professional.

PIETRZAK, Dorothy A; St Florian HS; Hamtramck, MI; 1/126 SecFrshCls; HonRl; NHS; SchMus; StuCncl; RptrYrbk; RptrSchPpr; FBLA; IMSpt; RotaryAwd; Univ Of Mi Dearborn; Eng & Math.

PIETRZAK, Jacqueline A; Donald E Gavit HS; Hammond, IN; 33#36#41 SctActv; College; Radiology.

PIETSCH, William; Whitnall HS; Greenfield, WI; Band; Chrs; CncrtBnd; HonRl; MrchBnd; PepBnd; SchMus; TchrAde; MthCl; College; Music.

PIETZ, John M; Lakefield HS; Lakefield, MN; VPFrshCls; SecSophCls; SecJrCls; PresSrCls; HonRl; SctActv; SciCl; University; Professional.

PIETZ, Velda M; Pillager Public HS; Pillager, MN; 4/36 TrsFrshCls; Chr; HonRl; StuCncl; Trk; Voc Tech School.

PIFER, Peter A; Larimore HS; Arvilla, ND; PresSophCls; ALBoysSt; HonRl; PresStuCncl; 4-H; Bsbl; Bsktbl; CaptFtbl; Trk; 4-HAwd; College; Professional.

PIFKO, Duane J; St Francis De Sales HS; Dolton, IL; 32/296 HonRl; NHS; SchMus; University Of Illinois; Accounting.

PIGHINI, Claudette A; Marillac HS; Niles, IL; PresSophCls; Chrs; NHS; SctActv; Chrldr; College; Social Worker.

PIGNATARO, Karen S; Prospect HS; Mt Prospect, IL; 15/614 HonRl; NatlMeritCmnd; TreasFBLA; Univ Of Illinois; Education.

PIGULA, Mary Ann V; Cass Technical HS; Detroit, MI; 3/1000 HonRl; NHS; SctActv; Wayne State Univ; English.

PIHA, Cathy A; Lincoln Way HS; Frankfort, IL; 8/498 HonRl; NatlMeritCmnd; PresStuCncl; TchrAde; LetterChrldr; Univ Of Notre Dame.

PIHL, Lori J; Marshall Sr HS; Marshall, MN; 91/240 Chr; HospAde; SchMus; StuGov; YthFlsp; 4-H; FHA; LetterChrldr; 4-HAwd; JAAwd; College; Dentistry.

PIHLAJA, Cindy M; Ontonagon Area HS; Mass, MI; SecFrshCls; ChrhWkr; DrmBgl; HonRl; StuCncl; SchPpr; 4-H; PpCl; Trk; Chrldr; College; Business.

PIJUT, Daniel T; Vianney HS; St Louis, MO; 1/170 HonRl; PresNHS; StuGov; LetterFtbl; LetterSocr; IMSpt; St Marys Univ; Accounting.

PIKE, Bobbi J; Dexter HS; Dexter, MO; SecJrCls; Band; HonRl; YthFlsp; FHA; FTA; PpCl; PPFtbl; Se Ms St Col.

PIKE, Susan E; Plainwell HS; Plainwell, MI; 22/211 Band; Chr; HonRl; MrchBnd; NHS; PepBnd; SchMus; SctActv; TreasYthFlsp; LetterTennis; College Or Trade School; Art & Music.

PIKE, Warren A; Girard Usd 248 HS; Girard, KS; 13/97 VPJrCls; ChrhWkr; CmntyWkr; HonRl; NHS; SchPl; YthFlsp; Bsbl; LetterFtbl; CchngActv; College.

PIKKA, Mary E; Wakefield HS; Wakefield, MI; 9/63 HonRl; NatlFornLg; OffAde; TchrAde; RptrYrbk; RptrSchPpr; 4-H; SpnCl; Gogebic Comm College; Secretary.

PIKUL, Janet C; Assumption HS; St Louis, IL; Chr; Chrs; HonRl; ModUN; SctActv; Bradley Univ; Civil Engineering.

PIKULA, Renetta; St Mary Hs; Chicago, IL; 8/100 VPSrCls; Chrs; HonRl; LbryAde; OffAde; SchAde; Sdlty; StuCncl; StuGov; Southwest College; Data Processing.

PILARSKI, Janice; St Marys Acad; Milwaukee, WI; 1/150 PresSrCls; NHS; StuGov; RptrYrbk; RptrSchPpr; NCTE; VoiceDemAwd; Univ Notre Dame; Pre Med.

PILARSKI, Karen L; Brandywine HS; Niles, MI; TrsJrCls; Band; PresChr; HonRl; Mdrgl; MrchBnd; NHS; SchMus; OptClAwd; St Marys Col; Vocal Music.

PILARSKI, Karen S; Wethersfield HS; Kewanee, IL; 8/88 VPFrshCls; VPSophCls; SecJrCls; SchMus; RptrSchPpr; Chrldr; GAA; Laboratory Xray Technician.

PILAT, Diana L; Alvernia HS; Chicago, IL; 22/225 NHS; RptrYrbk; Loyola U; Dentistry.

PILCHER, Cheryl D; Civic Memorial HS; Bethalto, IL; 16/221 ChrhWkr; HonRl; Evangel College; Speech Therapy.

PILCHER, Randy L; Fairfield Comm HS; Cisne, IL; 22/165 HonRl; SpnCl; Ftbl; Glf; Univ Of Illinois; Chemical Engineering.

PILE, Kathryn E; Morton HS; Morton, IL; 10/312 ChrhWkr; HonRl; NHS; OffAde; YthFlsp; 4-H; PpCl; LetterBsktbl; LetterTennis; GAA; 4-HAwd; Univ Of Missouri; Accounting.

PILGER, Barbara K; Beardstown HS; Beardstown, IL; 3/140 TrsFrshCls; TrsSophCls; Band; HonRl; NHS; EdYrBk; FTA; SciCl; IMSpt; Univ Of Illinois; Computer Programming.

PILKINGTON, Randy R; English Valley HS; North English, IA; SecFrshCls; HstJrCls; Band; CaptBsbl; Bsktbl; CaptFtbl; Swmmng; Trk; CchngActv; IMSpt; Univ Of N Ia; Education Guidance.

PILLE, Martha E; Farmington East HS; Trivoli, IL; 8/130 Chr; HonRl; NHS; NatlMeritCmnd; RedCrAde; TchrAde; 4-H; GAA; DanFAwd; 4-HAwd; U Of Il; Bus.

PILLING, James; Mediapolis Community Hs; Mediapolis, IA; 15/85 VPSophCls; Aud/Vis; ChrhWkr; HonRl; NatlThespSoc; SchMus; StuGov; 4-H; FFA; SciCl; Iowa State U; Ag Mechanization.

PILLION, Mary E; Marquette HS; Ottawa, IL; TrsSrCls; HonRl; NHS; StuCncl; RptrSchPpr; PpCl; TreasGAA; St Francis Hospital; X Ray Technician.

PILLSBURY, Rhoda E; Lanark HS; Lanark, IL; 8/56 Chrs; HonRl; SchMus; SchPl; 4-H; FHA; SpnCl; GAA; IMSpt; College; Professional.

PILOT, Timothy J; Standish Sterling Central HS; Bentley, MI; 22/170 Band; HonRl; Bsbl; Ftbl; IMSpt; Delta Col; Archetecture.

PILOTTE, Catherine; Benton Central HS; Fowler, IN; TrsSrCls; Chr; Chrs; HonRl; PolWkr; Quill&Scroll; SchMus; SchPl; Yrbk; SchPpr; IMSpt; Herron School Of Art Adv.

PILOTTE, Marilyn E; Grant Park HS; Grant Park, IL; 3/54 Chrs; HonRl; Mdrgl; NHS; SchMus; SchPl; StuCncl; SchPpr; 4-H; SpnCl; MthCl; PpCl; Bsktbl; Univ Of Illinois; Business Admin.

PINDAK, Janet; Notre Dame Hs; Chicago, IL; 10/262 HonRl; NatlFornLg; NHS; 4-H; MthCl; GAA; 4-HAwd;.

PINDELL, Lee M; Dallas City HS; Niota, IL; Band; ChrhWkr; CmntyWkr; CncrtBnd; HonRl; LbryAde; MrchBnd; NHS; Orch; PepBnd; Bsbl; Bsktbl; Trk; Tech School; Agriculture.

PINE, Daniel T; South Shore HS; Cornucopia, WI; VPSophCls; VPSrCls; Chr; HonRl; StuCncl; Yrbk; RptrSchPpr; 4-H; Bsktbl; Trk; Vocational Sch.

PINE, Kathleen L; Routt HS; Jacksonville, IL; 2/61 HonRl; SctActv; StuCncl; RptrSchPpr; FrCl; LatCl; VoiceDemAwd; U Of I; Law Major/political Science.

PINE, Regina L; Marshall HS; Marshall, IL; 50/115 Band; CncrtBnd; MrchBnd; PepBnd; SchPl; TchrAde; FHA; LatCl; SciCl; Indiana State Univ; Secretary.

PINE, Stanley; Marquette Inc HS; West Point, IA; /49 StuCncl; EdYrBk; PpCl; LetterBsbl; Bsktbl; Trk; Ottumwa Hts Coll;bus.

PINEDA, Roberto; St Gregory; Chicago, IL; 14/129 Chrs; NHS; SchPl; SctActv; StuGov; Yrbk; Swmmng; Tennis; Univ Of Il Circ Campus; Veterinarian.

PINEGAR, Robert; Dixon HS; Dixon, IL; 89/332 ALBoysSt; CchngActv; North Central College; Engineering.

PING, Anita J; Huntington North HS; Warren, IN; ALAGirlsSt; ChrhWkr; GAA; Huntington College; Business Career.

PINGER, Peggy M; Holy Family HS; Lindsay, NE; 2/33 HonRl; NHS; RptrSchPpr; PpCl; Coll; Wildlife.

PINGREE, Teena M; Louisville HS; Louisville, NE; Band; Chr; CncrtBnd; FHA; FrCl; PresPpCl; GAA; College; Doctor.

PINGSTERHAUS, Mike F; Mater Dei HS; Germantown, IL; 6/182 Band; CncrtBnd; HonRl; MrchBnd; NHS; PepBnd; PresAwd; College;engineering.

PINGSTERHAUS, Ruth A; Central Community HS; Germantown, IL; HonRl; FHA; Kaskasia C Col ;data Processing.

PINKERMAN, Revona F; Bevier HS; Bevier, MO; 5/29 PresBand; ChrhWkr; CncrtBnd; HonRl; OffAde; SchPl; StuCncl; RptrYrbk; RptrSchPpr; Chrldr; University; Journalism.

PINKERT, Gene R; Milbank HS; Big Stone, SD; HonRl; NHS; StuGov; 4-H; SecFFA; KeyCl; Wrstlng; CchngActv; Sd State U; Chemistry.

PINKHAM, Kay L; West Marshall HS; State Center, IA; TrsJrCls; Band; Chrs; CncrtBnd; HonRl; MrchBnd; NHS; PepBnd; PpCl; LetterBsbl; Uni; Professional.

PINKSTER, Michael; Parchment HS; Kalamazoo, MI; ChrhWkr; TchrAde; SpnCl; PpCl; Trk; Coll; Phys Educ Or Bus Admin.

PINKSTON, Christine L; Pc HS; Pekin, IL; 58/803 Chr; Chrs; HonRl; JA; SchPl; TchrAde; 4-H; 4-HAwd; Purdue Univ; Pharmacy.

PINKSTON, Herbert M; West Ricland HS; Noble, IL; ChrhWkr; HonRl; LetterBsbl; Southern Il Univ; Accounting.

PINKSTON, Tricia; North St Francois County HS; Desloge, MO; 16/175 HonRl; JrNHS; LbryAde; NHS; OffAde; FNA; PpCl; Coll; Business.

PINKUS, Kay E; Highland Park HS; Highland Park, IL; SchPl; College; Lawyer.

PINNEY, Jack T; H H Dow HS; Midland, MI; 3/490 HonRl; JrNHS; NHS; OffAde; PolWkr; LetterBsbl; Bsktbl; LetterFtbl; Tennis; CchngActv; Michigan State Univ; Medicine.

PINNICK, Trudi A; North Knox HS; Bicknell, IN; 11/155 HonRl; NHS; SchPl; EdSchPpr; 4-H; FHA; LatCl; AmLegAwd; Col; Psychiatry Social Worker.

PINO, Connie J; Bonner Springs HS; Edwardsville, KS; 3/190 SecSophCls; SecJrCls; Chr; ChrhWkr; HonRl; SchMus; SchPl; LatCl; PpCl; SciCl; Coll; Pharmacist.

PINO, Robert S; Highland HS; Highland, IN; 22/587 ChrhWkr; HonRl; NHS; TchrAde; GerCl; Trk; Indian Univ; Medicine.

PINSKI, Patricia J; Arlington Hts HS; Arlington Hts, IL; 26/593 CncrtBnd; HonRl; MrchBnd; NHS; NatlMeritCmnd; PepBnd; LetterBsktbl; LetterTennis; LetterTrk; GAA; Winona St College; Physical Therapist.

PINTARO, Josephine R; St Marys Of P H HS; Chicago, IL; CmntyWkr; HospAde; NatlMeritSchl; OffAde; PolWkr; StuCncl; FBLA; FNA; FTA; VoiceDemAwd; College; Professional.

PINTER, Jeffrey A; Abbotsford Public HS; Abbotsford, WI; 5/70 HonRl; 4-H; FFA; MthCl; Bsbl; CaptTrk; EldAwd; Univ Of Wis River Falls; Agriculture.

PINTER, Lori A; Malden HS; Malden, IL; TrsSrCls; Chr; Chrs; ChrhWkr; CmntyWkr; HonRl; HospAde; StuCncl; RptrSchPpr; 4-H;.

PINTER, Mark A; La Moille Comm HS; Arlington, IL; 8/40 HonRl; NHS; SchMus; Yrbk; SchPpr; FFA; Illinois Vly Comm College; Accounting.

PINTER, Michael R; La Moille Unit HS; Arlington, IL; 12/40 HonRl; SchPl; TreasFFA; PpCl; Bsktbl; CaptIMSpt; College; Vocational.

PINTER, Suzanna; Morton HS; Hammond, IN; HonRl; Quill&Scroll; TchrAde; RptrYrbk; University; Chemistry.

PINTO, Cecilia A; Woodlands Sacred Heart Acad; Hinsdale, IL; 27/64 Chrs; LitMag; SchMus; SchPl; SchPpr; College.

PIONK, Kevin L; Denby HS; Detroit, MI; 49/657 VPFrshCls; Band; HonRl; JrNHS; SctActv; SptEdSchPpr; SpnCl; Bsbl; Wayne State Univ.

PIONK, Mary Jane; Ubly HS; Ruth, MI; ChrhWkr; HonRl; HospAde; NHS; RedCrAde; StuCncl; 4-H; FFA; PpCl; Trk; Chrldr; 4-HAwd; College; Medicine.

PIONTEK, Gregory R; Wabeno HS; Wabeno, WI; SchPpr; FFA; PpCl; Rhinelander Tech Instit; Heavy Duty Machine.

PIONTKOWSKI, Tim R; Loup City HS; Loup City, NE; 25/67 HonRl; NHS; Bsbl; LetterBsktbl; LetterFtbl; LetterTrk; College; Professional.

PIORKOWSKI, Donna M; St Thomas Aquinas HS; Florissant, MO; HonRl; Twrl; SpnCl; College; Doctor.

PIOTROWSKI, Anna M; Pittsville HS; Marshfield, WI; TrsSophCls; Band; Chrs; HonRl; JrNHS; Mdrgl; NHS; FrCl; SciCl; EldAwd; Coll; Nursng.

PIOTROWSKI, Mary M; Little Falls Comm HS; Little Falls, MN; AFS; Chr; HonRl; HospAde; SchMus; StuCncl; TchrAde; Yrbk; FrCl; College; Medicine.

PIOTROWSKI, Philip J; Flushing Sr HS; Mt Morris, MI; 57/460 Univ Of Michigan; Scientist.

PIOTTER, Steven W; Blissfield HS; Blissfield, MI; ALBoysSt; HonRl; Bsktbl; LetterGlf; Univ Mi; Business.

PIPER, Gary F; Johnson Brock HS; Brock, NE; 1/25 SecTrsSrCls; Band; Chrs; HonRl; RptrYrbk; LetterFtbl; LetterTrk; CchngActv; 4-HAwd; Univ Of Nebraska; Pilot.

PIPER, Laura M; Whitko HS; Claypool, IN; 1/152 ChrhWkr; HonRl; MrchBnd; TreasNatlFornLg; StuCncl; TchrAde; Yrbk; SchPpr; FTA; PpCl; Grace College; Elementary Educ.

PIPER, Mary K; Davis County Comm HS; Bloomfield, IA; ALAGirlsSt; HonRl; NHS; NatlThespSoc; EdSchPpr; PresSpnCl; Bsbl; Bsktbl; Trk; Chrldr; GAA; VoiceDemAwd; College; Professional.

PIPER, Rex S; Cedarburg HS; Cedarburg, WI; 15/315 ChrhWkr; HonRl; NHS; TchrAde; YthFlsp; GerCl; LetterTrk; IMSpt; U Of Wi Mad; Engineering.

PIPER, Todd G; H H Dow HS; Midland, MI; 50/460 HonRl; NHS; NatlMeritSF; SchPl; YthFlsp; Swmmng; LetterTennis; Kalamazoo Clge; Science.

PIPER, Travis A; Mexico HS; Mexico, MO; PresBand; StuCncl; KeyCl; LetterBsktbl; LetterTrk; College; Professional.

PIPKIN, Katherine A; Southeast HS; Springfield, IL; PresFrshCls; SecSophCls; Chr; ChrhWkr; CmntyWkr; HonRl; JA; SchMus; SchPl; SctActv; StuCncl; StuGov; TchrAde; GAA; College; Medicine.

PIPKIN, Pamela J; Lafayette HS; St Joseph, MO; ChrhWkr; HonRl; HospAde; VPJA; Quill&Scroll; StuCncl; RptrSchPpr; LetterBsktbl; GAA; IMSpt; College; Health Field.

PIPKINS, Mark L; Gideon HS; Gideon, MO; ALBoysSt; PresBand; CncrtBnd; MrchBnd; StuCncl; FrCl; PpCl; LetterBsbl; LetterBsktbl; College; Professional.

PIPO, Melody A; Brandon Public HS; Farwell, MN; 10/39 Band; CncrtBnd; HonRl; MrchBnd; SchPl; TchrAde; RptrSchPpr; 4-H; FHA; 4-HAwd; U Of Mn; Elem Education.

PIPPERT, Steven; Dysart Geneseo Hs; Dysart, IA; 10/53 HonRl; NHS; YthFlsp; RptrYrbk; FFA; Wrstlng; Iowa State U; Farmer.

PIPPIN, Donald L; Southside HS; Fort Wayne, IN; Band; ChrhWkr; CncrtBnd; HonRl; PolWkr; TchrAde; Bsbl; Wrstlng; IMSpt; PresAwd; College; Educator.

PIPPIN, Judith; Stoutland HS; Stoutland, MO; HonRl; LitMag; Yrbk; FHA; PpCl; College; Journalism.

PIPPIN, Sylvia; Union County HS; Liberty, IN; HonRl; MrchBnd; NHS; Orch; PepBnd; SchMus; SchPl; FHA; College; Social Worker.

PIPYNE, Markus; Wheaton North Hs; Wheaton, IL; University; Engineering.

PIRC, Pamela J; St Francis Academy; Joliet, IL; 53/172 SecSophCls; VPSrCls; HonRl; HospAde; StuCncl; StuGov; RptrSchPpr; Trk; IMSpt; University.

PIRLOT, Brenda J; William G Mather HS; Munising, MI; 9/127 Band; Chrs; ChrhWkr; CncrtBnd; HonRl; MrchBnd; NHS; PepBnd; 4-H; PpCl; Northern Mich Univ; Elem Ed Learning Disabi.

PIROCHTA, Tamara L; Chesaning Union HS; Chesaning, MI; TrsFrshCls; ALAGirlsSt; VPChr; NHS; NatlMeritCmnd; SchMus; YthFlsp; FrCl; Chrldr; RotaryAwd; Alma College.

PIROK, Cheryl A; Roxana Sr HS; E Alton, IL; 2/275 HonRl; NHS; OffAde; RptrYrbk; PpCl; Tennis; So Illinois Univ; Business.

PIROLO, Linda J; Manistique HS; Manistique, MI; HonRl; HospAde; NatlMeritSF; Mi Technoligical Univ; Engineering.

PIROTTE, Patrick J; Carroll HS; Wichita, KS; 28/260 ALBoysSt; HonRl; Mdrgl; ModUN; NatlFornLg; NHS; Quill&Scroll; StuCncl; EdSchPpr; LetterTennis; College; Law.

PIRSIG, Susan C; Elmore Public HS; Elmore, MN; ALAGirlsSt; HonRl; SchPl; RptrYrbk; CaptBsktbl; CaptChrldr; GAA; IMSpt; PresAwd; Junior College; Business.

PIRTLE, Charles E; Brebeuf Prep HS; Carmel, IN; 18/120 VPJrCls; LitMag; NatlMeritSF; PolWkr; SchPl; StuCncl; TchrAde; RptrSchPpr; EdSchPpr; PresFrCl; Trk; Wabash Col; Journalism.

PIRTLE, Jon S; Davis County HS; Bloomfield, IA; TrsFrshCls; TrsSophCls; HonRl; LetterBsbl; LetterFtbl; LetterTrk; Trade School; Vocation.

PISAREK, Theresa M; Maria HS; Chicago, IL; 81/300 HonRl; HospAde; OffAde; SctActv; SpnCl; MthCl; GAA; IMSpt; College; General Studies.

PISCATOR, Kevin K; Worthington Sr HS; Worthington, MN; 9/286 JrNHS; NHS; SctActv; StuCncl; PpCl; SciCl; College; Chemistry.

PISCHEL, Robin E; Albion Senior HS; Albion, MI; 4/204 HonRl; JrNHS; SecNHS; NatlMeritCmnd; OffAde; SchAde; KeyCl; FrCl; SecSciCl; Central Michigan Univ; Accounting.

PISEL, Bruce E; Roanoke Benson HS; Roanoke, IL; 11/97 TrsFrshCls; HonRl; RptrSchPpr; SpnCl; MthCl; Univ Of Illinois; Journalism.

PISKE, Theresa M; Albion Sr HS; Albion, MI; 11/204 Band; CncrtBnd; HonRl; HospAde; MrchBnd; NHS; SciCl; Ferris State College; Phamacist.

PISSIOS, Louis M; Maine Twp East HS; Niles, IL; 233/1000 HonRl; LitMag; NatlFornLg; StuGov; GerCl; Socr; Univ Of Illinois; Biology.

PISTILLO, Bernie J; Creighton Prep HS; Omaha, NE; 21/249 Chrs; ChrhWkr; CmntyWkr; HonRl; NHS; NatlMeritCmnd; PolWkr; SchPl; Sdlty; StuGov; MthCl; College; Professional.

PISTONE, Julie R; Palatine HS; Palatine, IL; Chrl; Chrs; ChrhWkr; HonRl; Chrldr; College; Psychologist.

PISZCZEK, Susan M; Norton Communtity HS; Norton, KS; 3/83 Chr; DrlTm; HonRl; NatlFornLg; NatlThespSoc; PolWkr; SchAde; StuCncl; RptrYrbk; GAA; U Of Arizona; Physical Therapy.

PITCHER, Barbara; St James Senior HS; St James, MN; PresSrCls; Chr; HospAde; Mdrgl; NHS; PepBnd; SchMus; StuCncl; PresSwmmng; PresGAA; St Olaf Coll.

PITCHER, Shannon J; Newton HS; Montrose, IL; Band; ChrhWkr; HonRl; MrchBnd; NHS; 4-H; GAA; IMSpt; 4-HAwd; PresAwd; College; Vocation.

PITCHERS, David L; High School; Virden, IL; ALBoysSt; Chrs; HonRl; Mdrgl; SchMus; StuCncl; SciCl; Bsbl; LetterBsktbl; LetterFtbl; LetterTrk; College; Respiratory Therapy.

PITCHFORD, Deborah D; Lincolnwood HS; Raymond, IL; 10/60 SecJrCls; Band; CncrtBnd; HonRl; MrchBnd; PepBnd; TchrAde; FHA; PresFTA; PpCl;.

PITCHFORD, Jo A; Franklin HS; Waverly, IL; 1/39 Band; Chrs; HonRl; HospAde; MrchBnd; NHS; SchPl; 4-H; GAA; DARAwd; Legal Assistant.

PITCOCK, Cathy A; Earlham Community HS; Earlham, IA; DrlTm; HonRl; NHS; TreasStuCncl; PresTeen; Pres4-H; Bsktbl; Trk; DanFAwd; 4-HAwd; Area Xi Ankeny Ia; Med Assistant.

PITMAN, Thomas D; Monrovia HS; Mooresville, IN; 37/102 Chr; Chrs; CmntyWkr; HonRl; LitMag; LbryAde; OffAde; Quill&Scroll; SchMus; SctActv; Indiana State Univ; Special Edu.

PITNEY, Jennifer M; Kirksville HS; Kirksville, MO; ALAGirlsSt; ChrhWkr; HonRl; MrchBnd; NHS; PepBnd; FTA; FrCl; PresPpCl; University; Medicine.

PITRAK, Karen D; Oak Lawn Community HS; Oak Lawn, IL; TrsSrCls; ChrhWkr; HonRl; JrNHS; NHS; NatlMeritSF; TchrAde; RptrSchPpr; Bsktbl; Bryn Mawr; Md.

PITSOR, Kyle; Hampton Community HS; Hampton, IA; 2/111 PresFrshCls; HonRl; ModUN; NHS; StuCncl; EdSchPpr; LetterGlf; IMSpt; BauchLmbAwd; 4-HAwd; Ia St Univ; Math And Physical Science.

PITSTICK, Donna R; Moline Sr HS; Moline, IL; ChrhWkr; LitMag; 4-H; Univ Of Illinois; History.

PITSTICK, Paul V; Serena HS; Serena, IL; 14/85 PresSophCls; PresJrCls; Chrs; SchPl; StuCncl; StuGov; 4-H; FFA; Socr; Wrstlng; College; Vocational.

PITT, Layne L; Bonduel Community HS; Bonduel, WI; 32/122 Band; CncrtBnd; MrchBnd; Orch; SchPl; Yrbk; 4-H; SciCl; Milwaukee Area Tech College; Photography.

PITT, Leonard B; Roeper City & Country HS; Farmington Hills, MI; NatlMeritFnl; NatlMeritSF; RptrYrbk; SptEdYrbk; RptrSchPpr; SptEdSchPpr; LetterFtbl; LetterTrk; IMSpt; Harvard College; Clinical Psychology.

PITT, Rebecca D; Nicolet HS; Milwaukee, WI; 38/504 Band; CncrtBnd; MrchBnd; NHS; SchPpr; U Of Wisconsin.

PITTERLE, James F; Aquin Central Catholic HS; Freeport, IL; 4/45 HonRl; JA; SchMus; FrCl; MthCl; Bsbl; Bsktbl; Ftbl; LetterGlf; Trk; U Of Il; Math.

PITTMAN, Becky S; Chase County HS; Cottonwood Falls, KS; HonRl; SchAde; EdYrBk; RptrSchPpr; SpnCl; PpCl; Bsktbl; Trk; Emporia Kansas St College; Physical Educ.

PITTS, Cathy J; Riverton HS; Springfield, IL; 5/62 Band; Chrs; CncrtBnd; HonRl; MrchBnd; NatlFornLg; PepBnd; SchMus; StuGov; PresFHA; GAA; IMSpt; College; Architect.

PITTS, Debra; Washington HS; Chicago, IL; 78/481 HonRl; LbryAde; NHS; SchAde; GAA; PresAwd; College; Major Study.

PITTS, Diane M; St Alphonsus HS; Detroit, MI; ChrhWkr; HonRl; NatlMeritSF; PolWkr; SchPl; Yrbk; FrCl; PpCl; IMSpt; PPFtbl; Mi State U; Med Tech.

PITTS, Donna R; Emil G Hirsch HS; Chicago, IL; 16/280 HonRl; HospAde; JrNHS; SchMus; YthFlsp; SchPpr; PresGAA; IMSpt; CitAwd; Northwestern U; Speech Therapist.

PITTS, Douglas J; Olympia HS; Mc Lean, IL; 15/246 ALBoysSt; HonRl; NHS; FrCl; MthCl; PpCl; SciCl; CaptFtbl; LetterTrk; Wrstlng; Univ.

PITTS, Joseph L; Toluca HS; Toluca, IL; 12/42 ALBoysSt; Band; Chrs; CncrtBnd; HonRl; Orch; PepBnd; SctActv; SptEdSchPpr; PpCl; SciCl; Bsktbl; Illinois Valley Comm College; Engineer.

PITTS, Michael J; Schulte HS; Terre Haute, IN; Aud/Vis; ChrhWkr; HonRl; SchPl; RptrSchPpr; KeyCl; OptClAwd; Col; Astronautics.

PITTS, Sally T; Winona Sr HS; Winona, MN; 36/438 Aud/Vis; Chrs; HonRl; NHS; SchPl; StuCncl; TchrAde; YthLg; SchPpr; FrCl; SciCl; Swmmng; JCAwd; College Of St Teresa; Astronomy.

PITTS, Teresa L; Chippewa Hills HS; Sears, MI; Band; ChrhWkr; CncrtBnd; HonRl; MrchBnd; PepBnd; 4-H; FTA; College; Elem Teacher.

PITTS, Trinette D; University HS; Milwaukee, WI; PresSophCls; AFS; ChrhWkr; CmntyWkr; HonRl; NatlMeritCmnd; SchPpr; MthCl; PpCl; CaptTrk; CaptChrldr; PresAwd; Marquette Univ; Attorney.

PITTSENBARGER, Debi J; Highland HS; Anderson, IN; 19/243 ALAGirlsSt; Chr; HonRl; LitMag; NatlThespSoc; Quill&Scroll; SchPl; Yrbk; SchPpr; CaptGlf; Womens Coll.

PITZ, Paula; St Mary Central HS; Neenah, WI; 6/121 HonRl; JrNHS; LbryAde; Univ; Professional.

PITZER, Vicki L; Coon Rapids Community HS; Coon Rapids, IA; ALAGirlsSt; HonRl; TreasNHS; TchrAde; EdYrBk; RptrSchPpr; FHA; CaptChrldr; DanFAwd; DARAwd; Trade Sch; Voc.

PITZL, Mary Jo; Mercy HS; Omaha, NE; 4/75 HonRl; NHS; Quill&Scroll; SchMus; SchPl; StuCncl; RptrSchPpr; EdSchPpr; FrCl; Trk; U Lincoln; Jounalism.

PIUCA, Laura M; Steinmetz HS; Chicago, IL; 49/700 Chrs; CmntyWkr; HonRl; OffAde; SchAde; TchrAde; CivCl; LatCl; GAA; Univ Of Ill; Social Worker.

PIUNTI, Andrew; Adlai Stevenson HS; Livonia, MI; AFS; CmntyWkr; HonRl; NatlMeritCmnd; PolWkr; StuCncl; Univ Of Southern California; History.

PIVAC, Michael T; Pattonville Sr HS; Bridgeton, MO; Band; CmntyWkr; CncrtBnd; HonRl; MrchBnd; PepBnd; SctActv; StuCncl; EdSchPpr; University; Journalist.

PIVONKA, Myra A; Hoisington HS; Hoisington, KS; CmntyWkr; HonRl; SchAde; TchrAde; SpnCl; TreasPpCl; Bsktbl; LetterGlf; GAA; PPFtbl; Fort Hays Kansas St; Special Ed.

PIZAREK, Beth A; Taylor HS; Kokomo, IN; JA; NHS; StuCncl; Yrbk; SecFrCl; PpCl; Glf; CchngActv; PresJAAwd; Vocational Schl; Industrial Admin.

PIZAREK, Cherie R; Marquette HS; Laporte, IN; 17/80 ChrhWkr; CmntyWkr; HonRl; SchMus; Yrbk; RptrSchPpr; SchPpr; 4-H; Tennis; Purdue Univ; Conservation.

PIZAREK, Steven E; Taylor HS; Kokomo, IN; NHS; NatlThespSoc; SctActv; Bsktbl; LetterFtbl; LetterGlf;.

PIZZATO, Michael S; Bloom Township HS; Glenwood, IL; 42/980 HonRl; Univ Of Illinois; Medical Lab Sciences.

PIZZUTO, Marie A; J S Morton East HS; Cicero, IL; 4/771 SecSrCls; Band; CncrtBnd; HonRl; VPJrNHS; MrchBnd; VPNHS; Orch; SchMus; StuCncl; GAA; Purdue Univ; Medicine.

PLACE, Carolyn S; Bladen Public HS; Bladen, NE; 2/11 SecSophCls; SecSrCls; Band; Chrs; CncrtBnd; HonRl; StuCncl; TchrAde; Twrl; RptrYrbk; PresPpCl; LetterTrk; 4-HAwd; Tech School; Business.

PLACE, Michael B; Abilene HS; Abilene, KS; HonRl; SchPl; TchrAde; SchPpr; LetterTrk; Wrstlng; IMSpt; PresAwd; Fort Hays Kansas State Clg; Arch Engr.

PLACEK, Christine S; Loup City HS; Rockville, NE; 25/67 Band; ChrhWkr; CmntyWkr; Pres4-H; Bsktbl; LetterTrk; Chrldr; PPFtbl; DanFAwd; 4-HAwd; Kearney St College; Nurse.

PLACHETKA, Catherine F; Lumen Christi HS; Jackson, MI; 12/220 Chr; ChrhWkr; CmntyWkr; HonRl; NHS; LatCl; Univ Of Michigan; Nursing.

PLACHTA, Walter J; Gaylord HS; Gaylord, MI; HonRl; GerCl; Bsktbl; Mich State Univ; Anthropology.

PLACHY, Rick L; Johnson Brock HS; Brock, NE; Chrs; StuCncl; StuGov; Ftbl; Trk; College; Coach Or Electrician.

PLACK, Laura A; St Mark HS; St Ann, MO; 3/38 Chrs; ChrhWkr; HonRl; LitMag; PolWkr; SchMus; Sdlty; RptrYrbk; RptrSchPpr; PpCl; Hickey Business Col; Management.

PLACKE, Jennifer L; Norborne HS; Norborne, MO; VPSophCls; Band; Chr; CncrtBnd; HonRl; MrchBnd; SchPl; SctActv; RptrSchPpr; Bsktbl; College; Child Psychology.

PLACKE, Laurie A; St Paul HS; St Libory, NE; Chrs; DrlTm; HonRl; SchMus; FHA; SpnCl; PpCl; Trk; 4-HAwd; PresAwd; Beautician Sch; Beautician.

PLACKE, Rochelle M; St Paul HS; St Libory, NE; Chr; HonRl; NHS; NatlThespSoc; SchMus; SchPl; StuCncl; 4-H; VPFHA; PpCl; College; Elementary Teacher.

PLAG, Mark D; Kirkwood HS; Kirkwood, MO; ChrhWkr; HonRl; NatlMeritSF; SctActv; YthFlsp; LetterBsbl; College; Engineer.

PLAGER, Kenneth W; Ballard HS; Cambridge, IA; 3/75 Chrs; HonRl; NHS; NatlThespSoc; SchMus; DARAwd; College; Architect.

PLAGGE, Jolene J; Cal Community HS; Latimer, IA; 10/34 PresFrshCls; Band; Chrs; ChrhWkr; HonRl; PolWkr; StuCncl; YthFlsp; 4-H; FHA; LetterBsktbl; Glf; Trk; 4-HAwd; College; Medical Assistant.

PLAGMAN, Arleatta F; Irwin Community HS; Irwin, IA; Band; Chrs; HonRl; MrchBnd; PepBnd; SchMus; SchPpr; FHA; GerCl; LetterTrk; Uni; Registered Nurse.

PLAKUT, Carol J; Little Falls Community HS; Little Falls, MN; Chr; Chrs; HospAde; SchMus; Yrbk; College; Prof.

PLAMANN, Amy S; Appleton West HS; Appleton, WI; StuCncl; Yrbk; SchPpr; GerCl; PpCl; Bsktbl; Trk; University.

PLAMBECK, Maurice; Bancroft HS; Lyons, NE; 1/32 PresSophCls; TrsJrCls; ALBoysSt; Band; Chrs; HonRl; NHS; SchPl; Ftbl; Trk; Univ Nebr; Architecture.

PLANK, Becky J; Buena Vista HS; Saginaw, MI; Band; CncrtBnd; HonRl; MrchBnd; PepBnd; SctActv; TchrAde; University; Physical Educ.

PLANT, Renae L; Hanover Central HS; Cedar Lake, IN; 4/140 VPFrshCls; VPSophCls; HonRl; JrNHS; OffAde; StuCncl; PpCl; Wrstlng; Business Sch; Secretarial.

PLANT, Steven G; Hanover Central HS; Cedar Lake, IN; 20/130 ALBoysSt; ChrhWkr; HonRl; JrNHS; NHS; LetterWrstlng; AmLegAwd; Elec Trade Sch; Vocation.

PLANTE, Andrea K; Waterford Mott HS; Pontiac, MI; 67/375 HonRl; HospAde; OffAde; SchAde; College; Medicine.

PLANTE, Laurie; St Francis HS; Little Falls, MN; 1/27 PresSrCls; Chrs; NatlMeritSF; SchMus; SchPl; StuCncl; Yrbk; St Benedicts Col; Pathology.

PLANTENGA, Paul E; Bentley Senior HS; Bunton, MI; VPFrshCls; CmntyWkr; HonRl; PolWkr; PresStuCncl; Bsktbl; Glf; OptClAwd; College; Economics.

PLANTZ, Frederick; Ripon Senior HS; Pickett, WI; Chr; HonRl; Mdrgl; NHS; 4-H; GovHonPrgAwd; Uw Madison; Computer Sciences.

PLAPP, Sharon L; Weston HS; Cazenovia, WI; SecBand; VPChrs; Quill&Scroll; StuCncl; TchrAde; RptrYrbk; RptrSchPpr; Chrldr; GAA; IMSpt; U Of Wi La Crosse; Phy Ed.

PLASENCIA, Maria; Andrean HS; Gary, IN; 80/250 ChrhWkr; CmntyWkr; HonRl; Bsbl; CchngActv; Coll; Acc.

PLASKETT, Pamela D; Ruskin HS; Kansas City, MO; DrlTm; HonRl; HospAde; JrNHS; NHS; NatlThespSoc; OffAde; SchPl; FrCl; Trk; College; Law.

PLASSMEYER, Harold J; St Marys HS; St Louis, MO; 59/237 PresFrshCls; HonRl; StuCncl; RptrSchPpr; Bsbl; LetterBsktbl; LetterFtbl; PPFtbl; U Of Mo Columbia; Veterinarian.

PLASSMEYER, John H; Fatima HS; Loose Creek, MO; Chrs; HonRl; FFA; Trk; Trade School; Professional.

PLASTERER, Richard W; Bishop Dwenger HS; Fort Wayne, IN; Trk; Trade School; Vocation.

PLATH, Gail; University HS; Champaign, IL; SecTrsSrCls; JrNHS; SchMus; StuCncl; Yrbk; College; Architech.

PLATHE, Denise R; Bellingham HS; Bellingham, MN; PresFrshCls; VPJrCls; Band; HonRl; Twrl; EdSchPpr; FHA; LetterBsktbl; LetterTrk; Chrldr; Clge; Nursing.

PLATKO, David P; Arthur Hill HS; Saginaw, MI; Aud/Vis; NHS; Yrbk; College; Industrial Arts.

PLATO, Danny A; Eastwood HS; Correctionville, IA; 2/44 Band; Chr; HonRl; NHS; NatlMeritSF; Orch; SchPl; Bsktbl; College; Teaching.

PLATSKE, Christine M; Ewen Trout Creek HS; Ewen, MI; 20/70 HonRl; SchPl; College; Secretary.

PLATT, Amy; Harvard HS; Harvard, IL; 32/156 Chr; Chrs; HonRl; NatlThespSoc; SchMus; SchPl; YthFlsp; Yrbk; PpCl; Bsktbl; Univ; Social Worker.

PLATT, Cindy L; Columbia City Joint HS; Columbia City, IN; 20/290 Band; Chr; ChrhWkr; CncrtBnd; MrchBnd; OffAde; YthFlsp; 4-H; GAA; 4-HAwd;.

PLATT, Craig A; Morton HS; Morton, IL; ALBoysSt; Band; CncrtBnd; HonRl; NHS; NatlMeritSF; Orch; EdSchPpr; Bsktbl; AmLegAwd; U Of Il; Audio Visual.

PLATT, James B; Lincoln Sr HS; Sioux Falls, SD; ALBoysSt; VPBand; HonRl; JA; NatlFornLg; YthFlsp; GerCl; AmLegAwd; Iowa State Univ; Corporate Law.

PLATT, Michael; Alma HS; Alma, NE; VPFrshCls; PresJrCls; ALBoysSt; Band; HonRl; Bsktbl; Glf; Univ Of Neb; Pro.

PLATT, Teresa Y; Knoxville HS; Maquon, IL; 11/95 Band; HonRl; JrNHS; MrchBnd; NHS; Orch; SchPl; LatCl; Bsktbl; GAA; Monmouth Clg; Fine Arts.

PLATTER, Michael A; Hancock HS; Lemay, MO; VPFrshCls; PresSophCls; VPJrCls; ALBoysSt; ChrhWkr; NHS; VPStuCncl; AmLegAwd; OptClAwd; Mid American Nazarene College; Psychology.

PLATZMAN, Kenneth R; St Ignatius C P HS; Chicago, IL; NHS; PolWkr; StuCncl; Carleton College.

PLAZA, Deborah; Cody HS; Detroit, MI; Band; HonRl; MrchBnd; SchAde; FNA; PpCl; GAA; U Of Detroit; Dental Hygenist.

PLAZA, Gwen M; Carmel Girls HS; Palatine, IL; Chrs; HonRl; NHS; SchMus; SchPl; RptrSchPpr; TreasSpnCl; College; Fine Arts.

PLEBANEK, Kimberly; St Edward Public HS; St Edward, NE; Chrl; Chrs; HonRl; LbryAde; NatlThespSoc; SchPl; FHA; PpCl; SciCl; Chrldr; Hastings Tech College; Dental Assistant.

PLECHASH, Steven; Oak Park River Forest HS; Oak Park, IL; ALBoysSt; HonRl; NatlMeritFnl; NatlMeritSF; Orch; Yale College; Law.

PLEMEL, Joseph R; Cardinal Muench Seminacy HS; Starkweather, ND; PresSophCls; PresJrCls; PresSrCls; Sacrstn; StuCncl; CaptBsktbl; CaptFtbl; CaptTrk; DanFAwd; GodCntryAwd; North Dakota Univ; Law.

PLENCNER, Debbie K; Warren HS; Warren, MN; Chr; HonRl; HospAde; SctActv; RptrSchPpr; GerCl; SciCl; LetterBsktbl; PresGAA; CaptIMSpt; College; Medicine.

PLENDL, Bruce R; Hinton Comm HS; Hinton, IA; 1/45 VPJrCls; HonRl; NHS; PpCl; Trade School; Agriculture.

PLEOTIS, Lydia A; Wm Fremd HS; Palatine, IL; 1/588 ALAGirlsSt; HonRl; JrNHS; PresNHS; NatlMeritFnl; NatlMeritSchl; PresNatlThespSoc; SchPl; SchPpr; Nw Univ; Medicine.

PLESE, Annette C; Benet Academy; Lisle, IL; HonRl; StuCncl; College; Professional.

PLESHA, Carrie J; Horace Mann HS; Biwabik, MN; Band; Chr; MrchBnd; SchPl; StuCncl; SchPpr; PpCl; LetterSwmmng; LetterChrldr; Business School; Accounting.

PLESHA, Julie A; J Sterling Morton West HS; Lyons, IL; 3/755 Chr; HonRl; JrNHS; LitMag; NHS; SchPpr; GAA; St Marys College; Primatologist.

PLETAN, Kevin D; Flasher Public HS; Flasher, ND; 5/39 TrsFrshCls; HonRl; SchPl; RptrYrbk; Yrbk; SciCl; LetterFtbl; North Dakota State Univ.

PLETT, Susan G; Antioch Comm HS; Antioch, IL; 97/321 HonRl; NHS; OffAde; SchMus; SchPl; SctActv; FTA; LetterGAA; Lake Cnty College; Secretary.

PLETTNER, Jane M; Sutton Public Sr HS; Sutton, NE; 1/66 Chr; Chrs; ChrhWkr; HonRl; NHS; SchMus; YthFlsp; EdSchPpr; DARAwd; Hastings College; Music.

PLICHTA, Lori A; Wheaton North HS; Wheaton, IL; Chr; HonRl; NatlFornLg; NHS; SchMus; SchPl; StuCncl; Chrldr; Univ Of Ill; Theatre.

PLINER, Kent; Richland Center HS; Richland Center, WI; 9/185 Band; CncrtBnd; PepBnd; SciCl; Uwc Richland; Medicine.

PLISZKA, Janet M; Normandy HS; St Louis, MO; 2/600 HonRl; LbryAde; MrchBnd; TreasNHS; NatlMeritSF; Orch; PepBnd; SchMus; FrCl; Univ; Com Sci.

PLIZGA, Glenn J; Waukegan East HS; Waukegan, IL; RptrSchPpr; GerCl; Bsbl; Bsktbl; LetterFtbl; Carthage Col; Business Admin.

PLOCK, Pamela R; Harvard Public HS; Harvard, NE; TrsJrCls; Band; DrmMjrt; HonRl; SchPl; Yrbk; GerCl; PpCl; LetterTrk; Chrldr;.

PLOEGER, Cindy R; Schaller Comm HS; Schaller, IA; TrsJrCls; ChrhWkr; CmntyWkr; HonRl; SchPl; YthFlsp; Bsbl; Bus Sch.

PLOEN, Kris Ann; Columbus HS; Marshfield, WI; 17/104 Chrs; HonRl; HospAde; LbryAde; RptrYrbk; VPFrCl;.

PLOESSL, Juliann M; Wahlert HS; Dubuque, IA; ChrhWkr; SecSctActv; TchrAde; RptrYrbk; RptrSchPpr; SpnCl; IMSpt; Trade Sch; Vocation.

PLOETZ, Jennifer E; Hanover Central HS; Cedar Lake, IN; PresSophCls; HonRl; NHS; OffAde; SchAde; StuCncl; Twrl; Pres4-H; CaptChrldr; SecGAA; 4-HAwd; Indiana Univ; Medicine.

PLONA, Christopher D; Oak Park & River Forest HS; Oak Park, IL; HonRl; NatlFornLg; NatlMeritSF; StuGov; SchPpr; LatCl; MthCl; SprCl; SciCl; Socr; Coll; Government.

PLOOF, Shellaine D; Paw Paw HS; Paw Paw, MI; Band; Chr; HonRl; SctActv; StuCncl; Teen; YthFlsp; SchPpr; 4-H; Bsktbl; University; Professional.

PLOOG, Thomas E; George Washington HS; Chicago, IL; HonRl; NHS; NatlMeritCmnd; StuCncl; De Paul Univ; Business.

PLOOSTER, Rhonda L; Platte Public HS; Platte, SD; VPFrshCls; ALAGirlsSt; Chr; Chrs; ChrhWkr; CmntyWkr; DrlTm; HonRl; HospAde; LbryAde; Trade; Professional.

PLOTKIN, Debra A; Niles Township East HS; Skokie, IL; 32/581 TrsSophCls; SecJrCls; PresSrCls; AFS; HonRl; LitMag; NHS; Univ Of Illinois; Education.

PLOTNER, Eric G; St Joseph Ogden HS; Ogden, IL; VPFrshCls; PresSophCls; Band; Chrs; CncrtBnd; HonRl; MrchBnd; NHS; PepBnd; SpnCl;.

PLOTNER, Greg A; Lincoln HS; Lincoln, IL; CmntyWkr; HonRl; PolWkr; TchrAde; SpnCl; PpCl; Bsktbl; LetterGlf; Southern Ill Univ; Commercial Recreation.

PLOTZ, Steven G; Lasalle HS; Cedar Rapids, IA; Chr; HonRl; ModUN; PresNHS; SchPl; StuCncl; StuGov; Bsbl; CaptFtbl; Trk; University Of Iowa.

PLOUCHE, Cynthia R; Clinton HS; Clinton, IA; TrsJrCls; ALAGirlsSt; Band; Chr; Chrs; ChrhWkr; CncrtBnd; HonRl; JrNHS; MrchBnd; NHS; NatlThespSoc; PPFtbl; College; Medicine.

PLOUFF, Gregg A; Homestead HS; Mequon, WI; 20/400 TrsJrCls; VPSrCls; HonRl; NHS; StuCncl; IMSpt; LionAwd; Univ; Engineering.

PLOUZEK, John M; Washington Community HS; Washington, IL; PresFrshCls; TrsSophCls; PresJrCls; HonRl; NHS; StuCncl; FrCl; Ftbl; IMSpt; SARAwd; Univ; Engineer.

PLUCINSKI, Donna; Amos Alonzo Stagg HS; Palos Hills, IL; 29/463 ChrhWkr; CmntyWkr; HonRl; NHS; YthLg; SpnCl; Moraine Valley College; Social Worker.

PLUDE, Keith D; Menominee HS; Menominee, MI; NHS; RedCrAde; YthFlsp; FDA; FSA; LetterFtbl; Trk; CchngActv; PresAwd;.

PLUDE, Maureen L; Linden HS; Swartz Creek, MI; 4/145 HonRl; NHS; NatlMeritSF; TchrAde; FTA; SpnCl; SciCl; LetterTrk; PPFtbl; University; Professional.

PLUFF, Sharon L; Airport HS; South Rockwood, MI; 47/200 HstJrCls; Chrs; HonRl; LbryAde; SchPl; 4-H; PpCl; 4-HAwd; Business Field.

PLUGGE, Ramona L; Arlington HS; Arlington, NE; 15/62 Band; Chrs; CncrtBnd; HonRl; MrchBnd; PepBnd; SchPl; Teen; FBLA; GerCl; PpCl; College; Journalism.

PLUKE, Jean M; Lincoln HS; Wisconsin Rapids, WI; 9/532 Chr; ChrhWkr; HonRl; Mdrgl; NHS; PolWkr; Univ Of Wisconsin; Math.

PLUM, Larry K; Semco HS; Gilman, IA; PresFrshCls; PresSophCls; VPSrCls; Chrs; NatlThespSoc; SchMus; SchPl; StuCncl; Bsktbl; Ftbl; Trade School.

PLUMB, William T; Andrean HS; Merrillville, IN; 45/250 HonRl; NHS; Quill&Scroll; SchMus; SchPl; College; Fine Arts.

PLUMLEE, Anita M; Clinton HS; Brownington, MO; Chr; ChrhWkr; HospAde; RptrSchPpr; Trade School; Cosmetology.

PLUMLEY, Mark; Rochelle Township HS; Rochelle, IL; HonRl; SctActv; Swmmng; Trk; Wrstlng; DARAwd; PresAwd; VFWAwd; College; Vocation.

PLUMMER, Ceresa K; Circle HS; Eldorado, KS; Band; Chrs; ChrhWkr; CncrtBnd; HonRl; MrchBnd; PepBnd; SchMus; PpCl;.

PLUMMER, Dorothy M; Wamego HS; Wamego, KS; Band; CncrtBnd; MrchBnd; PepBnd; SchPl; SctActv; TchrAde; FBLA; PpCl; Business School; Professional.

PLUMMER, Gina L; Lindblom Technical HS; Chicago, IL; 9/722 CmntyWkr; HonRl; NHS; TchrAde; PresFrshCls; FDA; MthCl; University Of Tulsa; Lawyer.

PLUMMER, John L; Pittsfield HS; Baylis, IL; Aud/Vis; Chrl; Chrs; HonRl; NatlMeritCmnd; SchAde; SchMus; SctActv; TchrAde; YthFlsp; VPLatCl; Quincy College.

PLUMMER, Peggy; Laville HS; Lakeville, IN; SecJrCls; SecSrCls; Band; NHS; YthFlsp; PpCl; Trk; GAA; AmLegAwd; Manchester Coll; Bus Acct.

PLUMMER, Robert W; Bloomfield HS; Bloomfield, MO; 5/60 Chr; HonRl; SecFFA; PpCl; LetterBsktbl; IMSpt; Clg; Veterinarian.

PLUNGER, Mark A; North Central HS; Hermansville, MI; 19/54 VPSophCls; LbryAde; SchPl; TchrAde; Bsktbl; Ftbl; LetterTrk; College; Marine Biology.

PLUNILEY, Steven J; Rochelle Twnship HS; Rochelle, IL; ChrhWkr; HonRl; SctActv; LatCl; Bsktbl; Ftbl; Northern Illinois Univ; Doctor.

PLUNKETT, Michael B; St Thomas Acad; St Paul, MN; 3/101 SecFrshCls; SecSophCls; HonRl; LitMag; NatlFornLg; ROTC; StuCncl; RptrYrbk; RptrSchPpr; Ftbl; St Thomas College; Medicine.

PLUNKETT, Paul B; St Thomas Acad; St Paul, MN; SecFrshCls; SecSophCls; SecJrCls; VPSrCls; ROTC; StuCncl; StuGov; Yrbk; SchPpr; IMSpt; Univ Of Minnesota; Law.

PLUNKETT, Susan J; Hillsboro HS; Hillsboro, IL; 60/182 Band; Chrs; CncrtBnd; HonRl; MrchBnd; SchPl; YthFlsp; SchPpr; FHA; PresAwd; Col; Elem Ed.

PLUTOWSKI, Cynthia A; Minto HS; Minto, ND; 1/23 ALAGirlsSt; Band; Chr; HonRl; NHS; SchPl; RptrYrbk; RptrSchPpr; MthCl; Chrldr; GAA; Univ Of N Dakota; Medicine.

PLUTOWSKI, Debra K; Minto HS; Minto, ND; TrsFrshCls; SecTrsSophCls; VPJrCls; Band; Chr; Chrs; CncrtBnd; HonRl; LbryAde; MrchBnd; PepBnd; SchPl; StuCncl; Chrldr; Univ Of N Dakota; Medicine.

PLUYM, Donna K; Wahlert HS; E Dubuque, IL; Band; CncrtBnd; DrmBgl; HonRl; HospAde; MrchBnd; NHS; PepBnd; SchAde; TchrAde; Trade School.

PLYMALE, Jon E; Lebanon HS; Lebanon, IL; Band; CncrtBnd; HonRl; JrNHS; MrchBnd; VPNHS; StuGov; YthFlsp; LetterTrk; Eastern Il Univ; Engineering.

PLZAK, Bonnie L; Balaton HS; Balaton, MN; ALAGirlsSt; Chr; HonRl; RedCrAde; SchPl; 4-H; FHA; KeyCl; GAA; 4-HAwd; Univ Mn Morris; Math/psychology.

POAGE, Cheryl A; Harper HS; Chicago, IL; 27/274 Band; CmntyWkr; HonRl; JrNHS; NatlMeritSF; StuCncl; StuGov; UNYO; YthFnd; EdYrBk; RptrSchPpr; SpnCl; MthCl; University Of Illinois; Ceramic Engineer.

POAGE, Julie A; Clarkston HS; Clarkston, MI; 28/430 JrNHS; NHS; StuGov; EdYrBk; PPFtbl; University Of Mich; Med.

POAT, Marjorie; Anderson HS; Anderson, IN; 6/600 ALAGirlsSt; HonRl; HospAde; NHS; OffAde; PolWkr; Quill&Scroll; StuCncl; EdSchPpr; PpCl; Univ; Medicine.

POBANZ, Jill M; Sturgis HS; Sturgis, MI; Band; ChrhWkr; CncrtBnd; HonRl; MrchBnd; Orch; SctActv; Pres4-H; KeyCl; SecFrCl; Trk; 4-HAwd; College; Teacher.

POBANZ, Michelle L; Galva HS; Cambridge, IL; 5/81 Chrs; ChrhWkr; DrlTm; HonRl; LbryAde; NatlThespSoc; PepBnd; SchMus; SchPl; 4-H; FHA; FrCl; GAA; College; English.

POBANZ, Patty L; United Township HS; E Moline, IL; Chr; HonRl; OffAde; Teen; LetterGlf; GAA; College Or University.

POBST, Gina L; Oran HS; Oran, MO; 3/35 SecFrshCls; HonRl; LbryAde; SchPl; StuCncl; EdYrBk; RptrSchPpr; FHA; CaptChrldr; BttyCrckrAwd; U Of Mo; Social Serv.

POBUDA, Mary P; Harper Creek HS; Ceresco, MI; 12/221 HonRl; NHS; StuGov; SpnCl; PpCl; Bsbl; Bsktbl; ChmnChrldr; PPFtbl; OptClAwd; College.

POCHYLA, Karen M; Shelby HS; Shelby, MI; 2/124 Band; ChrhWkr; CncrtBnd; HonRl; JrNHS; MrchBnd; StuCncl; FrCl; LetterBsktbl; GAA; OptClAwd; College; Social Work.

PODANY, Frank; Clarkson Public HS; Clarkson, NE; 10/35 PresSophCls; Band; HonRl; SchPl; StuCncl; RptrSchPpr; EdSchPpr; Univ;law.

PODEY, Karen M; Perry Community HS; Perry, IA; 4/145 Chr; HonRl; Twrl; FrCl; PpCl; University; Accounting.

PODKOWSKI, Richard J; Brother Rice HS; Chicago, IL; 103/487 HonRl; PpCl; University; Dentistry.

PODOLL, Monte L; Frederick HS; Westport, SD; SecTrsSophCls; HonRl; SchPl; TchrAde; Bsbl; LetterBsktbl; LetterTrk;.

PODOLSKI, Tam J; Bishop Ryan HS; Minot, ND; 15/85 PresJrCls; ALAGirlsSt; Chrs; CmntyWkr; HonRl; PpCl; Trk; IMSpt; PPFtbl; CitAwd; College; Law And Politics.

PODULKA, Karen M; Millington HS; Millington, MI; ALAGirlsSt; Band; ChrhWkr; CncrtBnd; HonRl; MrchBnd; NHS; PepBnd; FNA; Coll; Lawyer.

PODVOYSKI, Karen A; Cabrini HS; Allen Park, MI; 28/167 Chr; ChrhWkr; CmntyWkr; CncrtBnd; HonRl; HospAde; Yrbk; RptrSchPpr; SchPpr; FNA; GAA; Mercy Clg Of Detroit; Nursing.

POE, Candace A; Dexter HS; Dexter, MO; 2/150 Band; ChrhWkr; HonRl; TreasNHS; NatlThespSoc; SchPl; EdSchPpr; FrCl; SpnCl; GodCntryAwd; Univf Journalism.

POE, Diana R; Alton HS; Alton, MO; ALAGirlsSt; Chr; Chrs; HonRl; LbryAde; PolWkr; RedCrAde; SchPpr; FNA; SpnCl; IMSpt; Trade School; Vocation.

POE, Jay D; Huntington North HS; Huntington, IN; ChrhWkr; CmntyWkr; HonRl; TreasJrNHS; TchrAde; YthFlsp; KeyCl; SpnCl; IMSpt; Purdue; Civil Engineer.

POEHLING, Joseph; Aquinas HS; Lacrosse, WI; 48/204 PresJrCls; TrsSrCls; HonRl; NHS; StuCncl; StuGov; LetterBsktbl; LetterFtbl; LetterTrk; IMSpt; Uw Mil;md.

POESE, Bruce A; Lutheran N HS; Ferguson, MO; Aud/Vis; ChrhWkr; SchAde; TchrAde; RptrSchPpr; LetterTennis; LetterCchngActv; IMSpt; Northeast Univ Of Missouri; Chemistry.

POFAHL, Jean G; Lincoln HS; Wis Rapids, WI; Chr; HonRl; PolWkr; Quill&Scroll; SchPl; RptrYrbk; RptrSchPpr; SchPpr; SpnCl; CaptChrldr; Univ Of Madison; Law.

POFF, Karen I; River Falls Sr HS; River Falls, WI; Band; Chr; HonRl; SchPl; 4-H; GerCl; Trk; Univ Of Wisconsin.

POFF, Linda L; Stanberry R Ii HS; Gentry, MO; SecJrCls; HonRl; SchPl; RptrSchPpr; FHA; SpnCl; PpCl; Trk; Chrldr; Undecided;.

POFF, Mark W; River Falls Sr HS; River Falls, WI; 19/186 ChrhWkr; NatlMeritCmnd; StuGov; GerCl; LetterBsktbl; Univ Of Minn; Architect.

POFFENBERGER, Barbara A; Adel HS; Adel, IA; Chrs; NatlThespSoc; RptrYrbk; RptrSchPpr; College; Nursery School.

POGATSHNIK, Peter J; Lakota HS; Lakota, ND; /42 PresJrCls; ALBoysSt; SecSophCls; Chr; Chrs; CncrtBnd; Bsbl; LetterBsktbl; LetterFtbl; LetterTrk; U; Teach Or Law.

POGGE, Steve J; Tri Center HS; Minden, IA; Band; ChrhWkr; CncrtBnd; HonRl; MrchBnd; PresFFA; Wrstlng; College; Agribusness.

POGUE, Gary D; Puxico HS; Puxico, MO; 4/51 VPJrCls; VPSrCls; MrchBnd; Orch; StuCncl; CaptBsbl; CaptBsktbl; LetterTennis; CchngActv; IMSpt; College; Professional.

POGUE, Michael A; York Comm HS; Elmhurst, IL; Band; CncrtBnd; HonRl; MrchBnd; NHS; NatlMeritSF; PepBnd; Univ Of Illinois; Elec Engineer.

POHL, Kathleen M; Dominican HS; Detroit, MI; Chrl; Chrs; JrNHS; NHS; SchMus; College; Drama.

POHL, Patricia; Marysville HS; Marysville, MI; 6/170 Band; CncrtBnd; HonRl; MrchBnd; NHS; NatlMeritCmnd; Quill&Scroll; SchPl; SctActv; FFA; St Clair County Comm College, Legal Sec.

POHL, Scott E; Concord HS; Albion, MI; PresSophCls; Band; CncrtBnd; HonRl; MrchBnd; Sdlty; TchrAde; EdSchPpr; Bsbl; Bsktbl; Jackson Col; Broadcasting.

POHL, Terri S; Sparta Sr HS; Sparta, WI; Band; CncrtBnd; MrchBnd; GAA; IMSpt; Trade Sch; Lab Technition.

POHLMAN, Cheryl A; Novi HS; Novi, MI; VPSophCls; ALAGirlsSt; HonRl; NHS; NatlMeritSchl; NatlMeritSF; Coll; Math.

POHLMANN, Julianne C; Pella Comm HS; Pella, IA; 51/113 AFS; Band; ChrhWkr; CncrtBnd; MrchBnd; PepBnd; Quill&Scroll; RptrYrbk; PpCl; LetterGlf; Iowa St Univ; Interior Decorator.

POHLMANN, Lorraine; William Howard Taft HS; Chicago, IL; 138/800 Band; Chrs; CncrtBnd; HonRl; Orch; PepBnd; SctActv; Univ Of Ill; Forestry.

POI, Kevin M; Lake Central HS; St John, IN; 69/485 HstSophCls; HstJrCls; HstSrCls; HonRl; SchMus; StuCncl; StuGov; TchrAde; GerCl; SciCl; Ftbl; Wrstlng; Indiana Univ; Lawyer.

POINDEXTER, Brigitte; Delta C 7 HS; Bragg City, MO; CmntyWkr; HonRl; PolWkr; ROTC; StuCncl; Bsktbl; Chrldr; GAA; IMSpt; CitAwd; Coll; Professional.

POINDEXTER, Carol J; Tina Avalon HS; Tina, MO; 1/22 TrsSophCls; Chrs; ChrhWkr; CmntyWkr; HonRl; NHS; StuCncl; EdYrBk; SchPpr; 4-H; FHA; PpCl; LetterBsbl; LetterChrldr; Nmsu Kirksville; Business.

POINDEXTER, Steven S; Breckenridge HS; Breckenridge, MI; 3/102 HonRl; NHS; StuCncl; 4-H; FFA; Bsktbl; Ftbl; Trk; CchngActv; 4-HAwd; Mich State U; Vetenarian.

POINEAU, Theodore; Saginaw HS; Saginaw, MI; 9/435 HonRl; JrNHS; Mich State Univ; Engineering.

POINTS, Elizabeth G; Derby Sr HS; Derby, KS; 34/375 ChrhWkr; HonRl; JrNHS; NatlFornLg; NHS; OffAde; SchMus; Teen; Yrbk; 4-H; Oklahoma State Univ; Liberal Arts.

POIROT, Jonathan; Miller HS; Golden City, MO; Band; CncrtBnd; HonRl; MrchBnd; NHS; FFA; College; Agriculture.

POJAR, Carol E; North Bend Central HS; North Bend, NE; SecFrshCls; PresSophCls; VPJrCls; Chr; Chrs; CncrtBnd; HonRl; MrchBnd; StuCncl; Chrldr; Tech School; Dental Asst.

POKACH, Tamela R; Seaman HS; Topeka, KS; Chr; ChrhWkr; CmntyWkr; HonRl; NatlThespSoc; SchAde; SchMus; 4-H; FrCl; University; Nurse.

POKEYWCZYNSKI, James V; George Washington HS; Chicago, IL; 32/497 Band; HonRl; RptrSchPpr; SpnCl; Northwestern Univ; Newswriting.

POKOJOWCZYK, Jean C; Holy Family Academy; Chicago, IL; 1/75 TrsFrshCls; PresSophCls; PresJrCls; HonRl; SchPl; StuCncl; RptrSchPpr; MthCl; De Paul University; Medical Technology.

POKORNY, Karen J; Wahoo Public HS; Wahoo, NE; Chrs; ChrhWkr; CmntyWkr; HonRl; YthFlsp; 4-H; FHA; SpnCl; PpCl; 4-HAwd; Teacher.

POKORNY, Mary; Schuyler Central HS; Schuyler, NE; HonRl; SchPl; 4-H; FSA; GerCl; PpCl; Trk; Univ Of Ne; Social Work.

POKORNY, Philip A; Harlan Comm HS; Harlan, IA; 10/256 HonRl; NHS; NatlMeritCmnd; SctActv; LetterTrk; GodCntryAwd; College; Chemistry.

POKRAL, Lorelei R; Lake Forest HS; Lake Forest, IL; 16/443 Band; HonRl; MrchBnd; NHS; NatlMeritCmnd; Orch; SchMus; TchrAde; Butler Univ; Music.

POKRYWCAYNSKI, James; George Washington HS; Chicago, IL; 32/495 Band; HonRl; NHS; NatlMeritCmnd; SchPpr; SpnCl; Univ; Newswriter Broadcaster.

POLACEK, Patricia A; Neumann HS; Prague, NE; Band; CncrtBnd; MrchBnd; PepBnd; RptrYrbk; PpCl; BttyCrckrAwd; Univ Of Ne; Psycology.

POLACEK, Robert J; John F Kennedy HS; Chicago, IL; 1/610 HonRl; NHS; StuCncl; CaptTennis; LetterTrk; JCAwd; Loyola Univ; Psychiatry.

POLAK, Gary E; Proviso West HS; Berkeley, IL; PresChrhWkr; CmntyWkr; JrNHS; NHS; Univ; Medicine.

POLAK, Joseph E; Oswego HS; Oswego, IL; HonRl; NatlMeritSF; LetterBsbl; LetterBsktbl; AmLegAwd; DARAwd; S Illinois Univ; Biologist.

POLAK, Margaret M; Cardinal Ritter HS; Indianapolis, IN; 7/165 SecFrshCls; HonRl; NHS; StuCncl; SpnCl; CchngActv; IMSpt; College; Criminal Lawyer.

POLAND, Carol J; Nauvoo Colusa HS; Nauvoo, IL; Band; ChrhWkr; CncrtBnd; HonRl; LbryAde; MrchBnd; PepBnd; SchPl; SctActv; 4-H; FHA; GAA;.

POLAND, Cindy N; Greensburg HS; Greensburg, KS; 2/43 ALAGirlsSt; Band; ChrhWkr; CncrtBnd; HonRl; LbryAde; MrchBnd; NHS; YthFlsp; SchPpr; FHA; SpnCl; PpCl; College.

POLANSKI, Steven J; Allen Park HS; Allen Park, MI; 19/517 CmntyWkr; HonRl; JrNHS; Socr; IMSpt; KiwanAwd; U Of Mi; Professional.

POLASEK, Leandra M; Lourdes HS; Chicago, IL; 7/299 Band; HonRl; LitMag; TchrAde; PpCl; De Paul University; Math Teacher.

POLASKY, Alan S; Huron HS; Ann Arbor, MI; 19/600 Band; CncrtBnd; HonRl; MrchBnd; PepBnd; SchMus; StuGov; RusCl; LetterTrk; Chrldr; College; Social Science Math.

POLCYN, Gregory J; John Hersey HS; Mt Prospect, IL; HonRl; JrNHS; NHS; Bsbl; LetterSwmmng; University.

POLCYN, Thomas C; Green Lake HS; Ripon, WI; 4/36 TrsSophCls; ALBoysSt; ChrhWkr; HonRl; NHS; NatlMeritCmnd; StuCncl; SptEdSchPpr; LetterBsbl; LetterBsktbl; Trade School; Vocation.

POLEGA, Irene F; Harbor Beach Comm HS; Filion, MI; 24/136 HonRl; HospAde; NHS; OffAde; SchMus; TreasStuCncl; 4-H; FHA; FNA; FTA; Coll; Nursing.

POLENSKA, Judy A; Markesan HS; Markesan, WI; PresSrCls; CmntyWkr; HonRl; LitMag; NHS; NatlMeritSchl; PolWkr; FshEdYrbk; FshEdSchPpr; FBLA; Univ; Comm Art.

POLENZ, Melissa; Memorial HS; Eau Claire, WI; Chr; ChrhWkr; LitMag; PolWkr; 4-H; PpCl; IMSpt; 4-HAwd; Univ Wi;dentist.

POLHEMUS, Karen D; Oscoda Area HS; Wurtsmith Afb, MI; Chr; ChrhWkr; CAP; HonRl; PolWkr; StuCncl; YthFlsp; FNA; Trk; Michigan State Univ; Biology.

POLHILL, Connie K; Freeport Sr HS; Freeport, IL; AFS; HonRl; NatlSciFnd; OffAde; SciCl; Ripon College; Ecology.

POLHILL, Thomas A; Peoria Heights HS; Peoria Hts, IL; 28/95 HonRl; TchrAde; SpnCl; Bsbl; LetterBsktbl; LetterTennis; Trk; Univ Of Ia; Pharmacist.

POLI, Kevin W; H H Dow HS; Midland, MI; 62/430 HonRl; NHS; LetterFtbl; Western Michigan Univ; Architecture.

POLICANDRIOTES, Mary V; Joliet West Twp HS; Joliet, IL; HonRl; StuCncl; Jr College; X Ray Tech.

POLICKY, Sandy K; East Butler HS; Bee, NE; Chr; Chrl; Chrs; ChrhWkr; CmntyWkr; HonRl; NHS; NatlMeritCmnd; OffAde; Yrbk; Southeast Comm Coll; Computer Programming.

POLIPNICK, Judith A; Sauk Centre HS; Sauk Center, MN; 21/158 SecFrshCls; Band; CncrtBnd; HonRl; StuCncl; EdYrBk; Bsktbl; CaptGlf; Chrldr; GAA; College; Music.

POLITANO, Michael J; Marist HS; Chicago, IL; 1/393 HonRl; SecSpnCl; PpCl; IMSpt; College; Mathematics.

POLITES, George E; Lane Tech HS; Northbrook, IL; ALBoysSt; ChrhWkr; HonRl; JrNHS; LbryAde; NHS; ROTC; StuCncl; StuGov; TchrAde; Northwestern University; Medicine.

POLITIS, Constantine L; Oak Park River Forest HS; River Forest, IL; Chr; Chrl; Chrs; ChrhWkr; HonRl; LitMag; SchMus; StuGov; TchrAde; MthCl; LetterWrstlng; Loyola Univ; Dentistry.

POLITOWICZ, Michael J; Quigley North HS; Marcellus, MI; HonRl; SctActv; Swmmng; Trk; Wrstlng; IMSpt; Davenport College; Accounting.

POLITTE, Joyce A; Herculaneum HS; Pevely, MO; 6/101 CaptDrlTm; HonRl; ChmnNatlFornLg; VPNHS; ChmnNatlThespSoc; SchPl; FBLA; PresFNA; TreasSpnCl; Jefferson College; Lawyer.

POLITTE, Madge L; Sullivan HS; Sullivan, MO; 33/159 HonRl; JrNHS; NHS; RedCrAde; StuCncl; YthFlsp; 4-H; FTA; IMSpt; CitAwd; Jr College; File Clerk.

POLITTE, Preston R; Bismarck R 5 HS; Bismarck, MO; 3/42 Band; HonRl; NHS; SctActv; LetterBsbl; LetterBsktbl; LetterTrk; College; Doctor.

POLIVKA, Delora J; Williston HS; Williston, ND; 8/268 ChrhWkr; CmntyWkr; HonRl; HospAde; LbryAde; NatlMeritFnl; SchPpr; U Of Nd; Nursng.

POLKING, Carol; St Bernards HS; Breda, IA; Chr; Chrs; HonRl; RptrYrbk; PpCl; Chrldr; IMSpt; Coll; Nursing.

POLKOWSKI, Dennis R; West Catholic HS; Grand Rapids, MI; 1/330 HonRl; NHS; LatCl; IMSpt; Univ; Dentistry.

POLL, Corla; Hamilton HS; Hailton, MI; 7/125 TrsJrCls; Chrs; SecFrshCls; PresFrshCls; NHS; TchrAde; YthFlsp; SpnCl; Tennis; Chrldr; Ferris St Coll;x Ray Tech.

POLLA, Dennis L; Lincoln HS; Floodwood, MN; 1/42 PresFrshCls; TrsSrCls; HonRl; NatlFornLg; NHS; RptrYrbk; EdSchPpr; LetterBsbl; LetterBsktbl; LetterFtbl; Mass Inst Of Tech; Physics.

POLLACK, Daniel B; Central HS; Omaha, NE; HonRl; ModUN; NatlMeritCmnd; SctActv; StuGov; TchrAde; University.

POLLACK, Gary M; Downers Grove North HS; Downers Grove, IL; 2/510 HonRl; NHS; NatlMeritSF; Bsktbl; Grinnell College; Physician.

POLLACK, Gregory; Aquinas HS; Allen Park, MI; VPFrshCls; HonRl; SchPpr; IMSpt; VoiceDemAwd; Rotc College; Military.

POLLACK, Gregory W; Aquinas HS; Alen Park, MI; VPFrshCls; HonRl; SchPpr; LetterTrk; AFS; VoiceDemAwd; College; Army Officer.

POLLAN, Alan R; Holdrege HS; Holdrege, NE; PresFrshCls; Band; Chrs; CncrtBnd; HonRl; PepBnd; SchMus; StuCncl; Univ Of Nebraska; Business Admin.

POLLAN, Jim L; Holdrege HS; Holdrege, NE; Chr; Chrs; SchMus; LetterFtbl;.

POLLARD, Connie S; Allendale HS; Allendale, IL; Band; CmntyWkr; HonRl; LitMag; ModUN; NatlMeritSchl; OffAde; SchPl; StuGov; UNYO; Yrbk; Univ Of Il; Medicine.

POLLARD, Linda E; Danville HS; Danville, IL; 7/684 Band; Chr; HonRl; NHS; SchMus; SchPl; SecStuCncl; RptrYrbk; SchPpr; PpCl; CaptChrldr; Purdue University.

POLLARD, Martha; Allendale HS; Allendale, IL; Band; ChrhWkr; PolWkr; FHA; PpCl; Chrldr; College; Professional.

POLLARD, Mary M; Woodlands Academy; Winnetka, IL; ChrhWkr; CmntyWkr; SchMus; SchPl; SctActv; StuCncl; StuGov; TchrAde; Bsktbl; Socr; College.

POLLARD, Pamela S; Galesburg HS; Galesburg, IL; 65/629 College; Foreign Languages.

POLLEY, Melinda L; Northrop HS; Ft Wayne, IN; 21/568 HonRl; JA; LatCl; Indiana University; Economics.

POLLICK, Deborah A; Frankenmuth HS; Frankenmuth, MI; 58/159 DrmBgl; HonRl; JA; RedCrAde; EdYrBk; GAA; College; Medical Assistnat.

POLLICK, Patricia A; Chesaning HS; Oakley, MI; SecSophCls; Band; CncrtBnd; DrlTm; HonRl; MrchBnd; NHS; 4-H; Chrldr; College; Professional.

POLLITT, J Douglas; Danville HS; Danville, IL; 82/629 EdSchPpr; SptEdSchPpr; Ftbl; Univ Of Ill; Professional Law.

POLLOCK, Cindy S; Oakwood HS; Oakwood, IL; Chr; Chrs; HonRl; HospAde; LbryAde; NHS; OffAde; SchPl; RptrSchPpr; 4-H; FHA; LatCl; PpCl; Mac Murray College; Medicine.

POLLOCK, Diana L; Webster Groves HS; Webster Groves, MO; Chr; HonRl; NatlMeritSF; Univ; Physician.

POLLOCK, Douglas D; Wawasee HS; Syracuse, IN; Chr; HonRl; JrNHS; LetterBsbl; Bsktbl; Law Enforcement.

POLLOCK, Kathy S; Northridge HS; Goshen, IN; HonRl; SctActv; 4-H; PpCl; Bsktbl; Trk; College; Teacher.

POLLOCK, Nan A; St Louise De Marillac HS; Park Ridge, IL; ChrhWkr; CmntyWkr; HonRl; SchPl; StuCncl; StuGov; SchPpr; Bsktbl; College; Education.

POLLOCK, Patrick A; Litchfield Senior HS; Darwin, MN; VPSrCls; HonRl; Sdlty; Teen; Trade School; Vocation.

POLLREISZ, Susan; Stoutland HS; Richland, MO; VPSrCls; Chr; Chrl; Chrs; HonRl; LbryAde; NHS; TchrAde; FHA; SpnCl; Navy; Nursing.

POLLY, Jerry D; Watertown Senior HS; Watertown, SD; 16/325 ALBoysSt; Band; CncrtBnd; HonRl; JrNHS; MrchBnd; LetterBsktbl; LetterTennis; College; Engineer Or Math.

POLMAN, Sheryl A; Sebeka Public HS; Sebeka, MN; 6/66 ALAGirlsSt; Band; Chr; HonRl; SchPl; RptrYrbk; RptrSchPpr; FHA; LetterGAA; AmLegAwd; College; Accounting.

POLNASEK, Gregory W; Union HS; Union Grove, WI; PresSophCls; TrsSrCls; HstFrshCls; ChrhWkr; HonRl; StuCncl; LetterBsbl; LetterBsktbl; LetterSocr; U Of Wis Eau Claire; Accountat.

POLNASZEK, Jane M; Abbotsford Sr HS; Abbotsford, WI; SecFrshCls; ALAGirlsSt; Band; HonRl; HospAde; NHS; Twrl; EdSchPpr; LetterBsktbl; Chrldr; GAA; Nursing Schl; Nurse.

POLOWSKI, Patricia M; Port Austin HS; Port Austin, MI; 5/39 LbryAde; StuCncl; FHA; Grace Nursing School; Nurse.

POLRIES, Peggy L; Sykeston HS; Sykeston, ND; Band; Chr; ChrhWkr; HonRl; StuCncl; SchPpr; SciCl; LetterBsktbl; Chrldr; ChmbCommrsAwd; Minto State Clg; Special Education.

POLSGROVE, Vicky G; Campbell HS; Campbell, MO; Chr; ChrhWkr; CncrtBnd; HonRl; LbryAde; Mdrgl; MrchBnd; SctActv; PpCl; College; English.

POLSON, Paula E; Nevada HS; Nevada, MO; TrsSophCls; LbryAde; NHS; StuCncl; Yrbk; SecSpnCl; PpCl; Chrldr; GAA; IMSpt; Civil Service.

POLSTON, Diana M; Hope HS; Hope, KS; 2/25 HonRl; StuCncl; TreasFHA; SecPpCl; Bsbl; CaptBsktbl; LetterTrk; Chrldr; Kansas State Univ; Home Economics.

POLYAK, Delphina M; Plainfield HS; Joliet, IL; ChrhWkr; CmntyWkr; HonRl; NHS; Marriage.

POLZIEN, Patricia; Crestland Community HS; Sac City, IA; 1/28 Band; Chr; Chrs; ChrhWkr; CncrtBnd; HonRl; NHS; RptrYrbk; 4-H; Glf; College.

POLZIN, Douglas L; Brownton Public HS; Brownton, MN; SecFrshCls; Chrs; HonRl; SchPl; SctActv; FFA; EngCl; PpCl; LetterFtbl; CitAwd; Trade School; Vocation.

POLZIN, Jodi M; Forest Lake HS; Forest Lake, MN; ChrhWkr; CmntyWkr; CncrtBnd; HospAde; MrchBnd; NHS; PepBnd; SchPl; RptrSchPpr; 4-H; College; Mathematics.

POMA, Nancy M; Blair HS; Blair, NE; 47/135 Chr; LitMag; TchrAde; VPPpCl; LetterBsktbl; LetterTrk; CchngActv; Kearney State Clg; Physical Education.

POMERANKE, Gary; Putnam County HS; Magnolia, IL; ALBoysSt; Band; CncrtBnd; MrchBnd; NHS; OffAde; PresFrshCls; StuCncl; FrCl; MthCl; Univ; Earth Sci.

POMERANTZ, Ruth E; Harbor Beach Comm HS; Port Hope, MI; Band; Chr; Chrs; CncrtBnd; HonRl; HospAde; MrchBnd; NHS; SchMus; SctActv; StuCncl; LetterBsktbl; LetterTrk; Mich State Univ; Vet.

POMERENKE, David L; Okabena HS; Okabena, MN; ALBoysSt; Band; HonRl; NHS; SchPpr; FFA; MasAwd; Jackson Vocational; Farming.

POMERLEAU, Nancy L; Lewis Central HS; Council Bluffs, IA; 15/165 ChrhWkr; HonRl; HospAde; NHS; OffAde; SchMus; FNA; SpnCl; Nursing Schl; Nurse.

POMEROY, Brian B; Jefferson HS; Cedar Rapids, IA; Aud/Vis; Band; StuGov; RptrSchPpr; Bsbl; Ftbl; U Of Iowa; Medicine.

POMEROY, Dan M; Carroll Community HS; Dedham, IA; 1/104 PresFrshCls; SecSophCls; ModUN; NatlFornLg; NatlMeritCmnd; PolWkr; StuCncl; StuGov; RptrYrbk; RptrSchPpr; College Univ Of Iowa; Liberal Arts.

POMEROY, Deborah L; Plainfield HS; Plainfield, IL; 10/297 Band; Chr; NHS; NatlThespSoc; SchMus; SchPl; RptrYrbk; 4-H; GAA; Univ Of Minn; Court Reporting.

POMIERSKI, Michelle M; Woodlands Academy; Chicago, IL; 10/64 Chrs; SchMus; College; Liberal Arts.

POMMERENKE, Kay; Unionville Sebewaing HS; Sebewaing, MI; 40/125 Chrs; ChrhWkr; CmntyWkr; HonRl; HospAde; NHS; OffAde; RptrYrbk; Bsktbl; GAA;.

POMMREHN, Mark R; Valley HS; West Des Moines, IA; 15/440 Band; Chr; CncrtBnd; HonRl; MrchBnd; NatlFornLg; NHS; NatlMeritFnl; SchMus; GerCl; Iowa State Univ; Engineering.

POMMREHN, Mark R; Valley HS; W Des Moines, IA; 15/436 Band; Chr; CncrtBnd; HonRl; MrchBnd; NHS; NatlMeritFnl; PepBnd; SchMus; GerCl; Ia State Univ; Electrical Engineer.

POMPER, Rudy W; Catholic Central HS; Muskegon, MI; 2/224 ChrhWkr; HonRl; NHS; SchPl; Univ Of Michigan; Chemical Engineer.

PONADER, Carl W; Lawrence Central HS; Indianapolis, IN; 42/750 ChrhWkr; CncrtBnd; HonRl; JA; MrchBnd; PepBnd; SchMus; SchPl; SctActv; CaptSocr; Trk; College; Science.

PONCE, Christine; Westview HS; Middleburg, IN; Chr; HonRl; VPStuCncl; Taylor Univ; Social Work.

PONCIROLI, Jan M; St Elizabeth Acad; St Louis, MO; 3/117 HonRl; NHS; SchMus; VPSpnCl; GAA; U Of Miami; Mathematics Teacher.

POND, Jean A; New Haven HS; New Haven, IN; Band; CncrtBnd; HospAde; JA; MrchBnd; NatlFornLg; SctActv; EdYrBk; 4-H; GerCl; University; Physical Therapy.

PONDEL, Anthony D; Notre Dame HS; Des Plaines, IL; 60/300 HonRl; EdYrBk; De Paul University; Accounting.

PONDELL, Stephen M; Garden City East HS; Garden City, MI; 2/500 PresSophCls; VPJrCls; PresSrCls; Chr; NatlFornLg; NatlMeritSF; NatlThespSoc; SchMus; SchPl; LetterFtbl; Clge Of Engineering; Chemical Engineer.

PONDER, Anita J; John M Harlan HS; Chicago, IL; VPSrCls; HonRl; NHS; StuCncl; MthCl; SciCl; CchngActv; GAA; College; Psychology.

PONDER, David G; Newton HS; Newton, IA; SecTrsJrCls; Chr; Chrs; ChrhWkr; HonRl; Orch; SchMus; SchPl; SciCl; Swmmng; College; Music.

PONDER, Jay W; North Central HS; Indianapolis, IN; 20/1168 HonRl; JA; NHS; NatlMeritFnl; NatlMeritSF; GerCl; Glf; College; Chemistry.

PONDER, Julia C; Fountain Central HS; Veedersburg, IN; Band; CncrtBnd; HonRl; MrchBnd; TchrAde; YthFlsp; 4-H; PpCl; University; Liberal Arts.

PONGONIS, Janet M; Fitzgerald HS; Warren, MI; HonRl; NHS; SctActv; SpnCl; Bsbl; GAA; Macomb County Comm Clg; Computer Sciences.

PONGRATZ, Peggy; Caledonia Public HS; Caledonia, MN; CncrtBnd; HonRl; MrchBnd; NHS; Yrbk; Glf; IMSpt; CitAwd; Wi Univ; Secondary Ed.

PONIATOWSKI, Karen Sue; Lourdes HS; Chicago, IL; 10/276 CmntyWkr; HonRl; JA; NHS; PolWkr; TchrAde; SpnCl; PpCl; Univ Of Il; Physical Therapist.

PONSONBY, James M; North Miami HS; Macy, IN; 9/123 HonRl; NHS; SchMus; TchrAde; TrsFrshCls; EdYrBk; FTA; SpnCl; SciCl; Wrstlng; Burlter U; Chemistry.

PONT, Dianne K; St Edward Public HS; St Edward, NE; Chrs; CncrtBnd; HonRl; MrchBnd; NatlThespSoc; StuCncl; RptrSchPpr; FFA; FHA; Yankton College; Lawyer.

PONTIER, Anthony L; Clarke Community HS; Osceola, IA; 17/110 PresFrshCls; AFS; HonRl; ROTC; StuCncl; FFA; FTA; LetterFtbl; Wrstlng; JAAwd; Clge; Vocation.

PONTIOUS, Linda A; Lasalle Peru Township HS; Peru, IL; Band; CncrtBnd; DrlTm; HonRl; MrchBnd; PepBnd; SchMus; SpnCl; PpCl; Univ Of Illinois; Medicine.

PONTIOUS, Valeda R; Salem Community HS; Salem, IL; 15/213 ChrhWkr; HonRl; JrNHS; NHS; SchPl; Yrbk; 4-H; LatCl; Bsbl; LetterTennis; Trk; 4-HAwd; Valparaiso University; Medical Tech.

PONTIUS, Donna J; Edwardsville Sr HS; Edwardsville, IL; HonRl; NatlFornLg; EdSchPpr; SchMus; SchPl; GerCl; Wester Ill Univ; Teach Theatre.

POOCK, Sandra S; Wapsie Valley HS; Readlyn, IA; 8/95 LetterBand; LetterChr; ChrhWkr; CncrtBnd; HonRl; Mdrgl; MrchBnd; NHS; PepBnd; LetterGAA; Clge; Tchng Music.

POOL, Charles; Avon HS; Roseville, IL; Band; Chrs; PepBnd; SchPl; FFA; Ftbl; Bus Sch; Bus Mngmnt.

POOL, Cindy D; Meredosia Chambersburg HS; Chambersburg, IL; 1/44 VPNHS; SchPl; SecStuCncl; EdYrBk; VPFHA; SecSciCl; DARAwd; EldAwd; CitAwd; Millikin Univ; Elementary Ed.

POOL, Mark G; Quincy Sr HS; Quincy, IL; South Ill Univ; Medicine.

POOL, Pamela; Peotone Community Hs; Peotone, IL; 43/100 Chrs; Mdrgl; SchMus; SpnCl;.

POOLE, Alvin; Fremont Sr HS; Fremont, NE; Chr; ChrhWkr; CmntyWkr; SchMus; SchPl; YthFlsp; CivCl; Bsktbl; Swmmng; CitAwd; Milford Trade School; Business Study.

POOLE, Dale R; Vienna HS; Vienna, IL; 18/101 CmntyWkr; SctActv; FFA; PpCl; LetterBsktbl; College; Professional.

POOLE, Deborah S; Northwest HS; Jackson, MI; CaptDrlTm; HonRl; NHS; SecStuGov; GerCl; MasAwd; Mi St U; Bs In Nursing.

POOLE, Geraldine L; Morton HS; Hammond, IN; 4/492 CncrtBnd; HonRl; JrNHS; MrchBnd; NHS; Orch; SchPl; FTA; Brigham Young Univ; Elem Ed.

POOLE, Kathleen M; Marian Catholic HS; Homewood, IL; 21/328 Chr; HonRl; NHS; Quill&Scroll; SchMus; RptrYrbk; RptrSchPpr; SchPpr; SpnCl; Knox College; Sociology.

POOLE, Lawrence W; Morton HS; Hammond, IN; 23/492 Band; Chr; CncrtBnd; HonRl; JrNHS; LbryAde; MrchBnd; NHS; PresNatlThespSoc; SchMus; SchPl; StuGov; Brigham Young Univ; Communications.

POOLE, Samuel J; Henderson HS; Henderson, MN; Band; HonRl; PepBnd; SchPl; SctActv; TreasStuCncl; LetterBsbl; LetterBsktbl; LetterFtbl; IMSpt; College.

POOLE, Sandra; Reavis Hs; Burbank, IL; 10/676

HonRl; JrNHS; NHS; TchrAde; RusCl; College;special Education.

POOLEY, Julie; Carthage Public HS; Fesbra, SD; /23 Band; Chrs; HonRl; LbryAde; MrchBnd; RptrYrbk; Trk; IMSpt; AmLegAwd; Coll Or Army;music Or Photography.

POOR, Julia K; Greencastle HS; Greencastle, IN; 13/162 Band; Chr; HonRl; NHS; NatlThespSoc; SchMus; RptrSchPpr; 4-H; FTA; GAA; Western Ky Univ; Home Ec And Music.

POORE, Curtis A; Tri Jr/sr HS; New Lisbon, IN; Aud/Vis; Band; ChrhWkr; SctActv; FFA; Ftbl; Trade Sch; Farming & Woodworking.

POORE, Shirley E; Lawton HS; Lawton, MI; DrlTm; HonRl; LbryAde; TchrAde; YthFlsp; PresAwd; Parsons Business School; Legal Secretary.

POORMAN, Kevin L; Terre Haute North Vigo HS; Terre Haute, IN; Chr; ChrhWkr; HonRl; NHS; TchrAde; LatCl; SciCl; BauchLmbAwd; Indiana Univ; Medical.

POORMAN, Richard D; Hutsonville HS; West Union, IL; 8/40 PresSrCls; Band; CncrtBnd; HonRl; MrchBnd; NHS; PepBnd; SchPl; StuCncl; Yrbk; SchPpr; PpCl;.

POPE, Colleen V; North County R 1 HS; French Village, MO; 19/165 CmntyWkr; HonRl; LbryAde; NHS; TchrAde; FHA; SecSpnCl; PpCl; SciCl; RotaryAwd; College; Elem Educ Home Ec.

POPE, Frances; Columbia HS; Columbia, IL; HonRl; Yrbk; FHA; GerCl; PpCl; GAA; PresAwd;.

POPE, Janet M; Fatima HS; Freeburg, MO; 4/126 Chr; HonRl; Sdlty; SchPpr; FBLA; Business School; Vocational.

POPE, Julie M; De Soto Sr HS; Desoto, MO; ALAGirlsSt; HonRl; NHS; SctActv; StuCncl; RptrYrbk; PpCl; SciCl; CaptChrldr; College; Professional.

POPE, Kim E; North County R I HS; Bonne Terre, MO; 8/170 Band; CncrtBnd; HonRl; MrchBnd; PresNHS; OffAde; StuCncl; Swmmng; IMSpt; Clge; Business.

POPE, Marcia; Newton Senior HS; Newton, IA; 8/320 Chr; ChrhWkr; HonRl; NHS; SpnCl; North Central Bible Coll; Business.

POPE, Nikki D; Francis W Parker HS; Chicago, IL; Chr; Chrs; CmntyWkr; PolWkr; SchMus; SchPl; StuGov; RptrSchPpr; Bsktbl; Carleton College; Political Science.

POPEJOY, Peggy J; Fairfield HS; Brighton, IA; HonRl; FBLA; College; International Trade.

POPEJOY, Steven L; Excelsior Springs HS; Excelsior Springs, MO; 1/240 VPJrCls; VPSrCls; ALBoysSt; Band; NHS; StuCncl; StuGov; TchrAde; EdSchPpr; SciCl; LetterFtbl; Glf; AmLegAwd; William Jewell College; Law.

POPELKA, Judith; Glencoe HS; Glencoe, MN; 11/143 DrlTm; HonRl; SchPl; 4-H; FHA; IMSpt; PPFtbl; 4-HAwd; VoiceDemAwd; College Of St Benedict; Business.

POPELKA, Linda A; Drummond HS; Cable, WI; SecSophCls; SecJrCls; Chr; HonRl; NHS; SchPl; Twrl; GerCl; LetterTrk; Chrldr; College.

POPESCU, Dolores; Palatine Hs; Palatine, IL; 88/560 Chrs; ChrhWkr; HonRl; LbryAde; NatlThespSoc; RptrYrbk; FrCl; College; Business Administration.

POPIL, Olga T; Josephinum HS; Chicago, IL; 2/101 HonRl; NHS; Orch; SchPl; TreasStuCncl; StuGov; RptrYrbk; EdYrBk; Bsktbl; GAA; JCAwd; Univ Of Ill; Pharmacy.

POPKEN, Barbara K; Logan View HS; Uehling, NE; 17/54 SecFrshCls; ChrhWkr; SchAde; SchPl; StuCncl; TchrAde; YthFlsp; 4-H; PpCl; LetterBsktbl; Univ Of Neb; Pe.

POPLETT, Paul W; Gibson City HS; Gibson City, IL; Chrs; HonRl; SchMus; SctActv; FFA; PpCl; Bsktbl; LetterFtbl; LetterTrk; LetterWrstlng; Univ; Professional.

POPOVITCH, Catherine L; Northwest HS; Cedar Hill, MO; Chr; RptrYrbk; RptrSchPpr; LetterTrk; Jefferson Cty Jr Coll.

POPP, Christine M; L C Mohr HS; So Haven, MI; Band; Chr; Chrl; Chrs; HonRl; SchPl; SctActv; TchrAde; 4-H; FrCl; IMSpt; 4-HAwd; Business School.

POPP, Christopher P; Aurora Cental Catholic HS; Aurora, IL; 48/123 ChrhWkr; HonRl; JA; PolWkr; SctActv; LetterGlf; IMSpt; JAAwd; Northern Illinois Univ; Business.

POPP, David E; Pontiac Twp HS; Pontiac, IL; 9/200 Chr; Chrs; HonRl; Mdrgl; NHS; SchMus; 4-H; KeyCl; LatCl; LetterBsbl; 4-HAwd; Ill State Univ; Mathematics.

POPP, Nancy; Lincoln Park HS; Lincoln Park, MI; 8/557 TrsSrCls; NHS; StuCncl; LetterTrk; LetterGAA; PPFtbl; Michigan State Univ; Math.

POPP, Phyllis I; Ionia HS; Ionia, MI; 5/224 ALAGirlsSt; ChrhWkr; CmntyWkr; HonRl; HospAde; MrchBnd; NHS; OffAde; PolWkr; YthFlsp; SchPpr; FDA; Bsktbl; Michigan St Univ; Medicine.

POPPE, Charlene J; West Point HS; West Point, NE; 1/59 TrsSrCls; Chrl; Chrs; ChrhWkr; HonRl; NatlMeritCmnd; Quill&Scroll; SchPl; SchPpr; PresFHA; Midland Lutheran Coll; Nursing.

POPPE, Janelle K; Tri Valley HS; Colton, SD; 5/63 Band; Chrs; HonRl; NHS; StuCncl; RptrYrbk; RptrSchPpr; CaptTrk; LetterChrldr; Sd State Univ; Microbiology.

POPPE, Karl A; Lutheran West HS; Detroit, MI; AFS; HonRl; NHS; NatlThespSoc; StuCncl; IMSpt; Wayne State U; Medicine.

POPPE, Lisa M; Wellcome Memorial HS; Good Thunder, MN; TrsFrshCls; Chrs; CmntyWkr; DrlTm; HospAde; LbryAde; RedCrAde; 4-H; FFA; FHA; Trade School; Secretary.

POPPEN, Craig D; Manson HS; Manson, IA; ALBoysSt; Chrs; ChrhWkr; HonRl; SchMus; SchPl; LetterBsbl; LetterBsktbl; LetterFtbl; LetterTrk;.

POPPEN, Richard P; Milbank HS; Milbank, SD; 32/123 TrsSophCls; ALBoysSt; PresChrhWkr; NHS; TreasStuCncl; TchrAde; SecKeyCl; GerCl; LetterBsktbl; LetterFtbl; CaptTrk; IMSpt; Augustana College.

POPPENS, Deanne P; Princeton HS; Princeton, IL; CmntyWkr; HonRl; MrchBnd; OffAde; PolWkr; TchrAde; SptEdYrbk; SchPpr; PpCl; Bradley University; Nursing.

POPPENS, Larry W; Lennox HS; Lennox, SD; ALBoysSt; Band; Chrl; Chrs; CncrtBnd; HonRl; MrchBnd; PepBnd; SchPl; Trk; Sd Univ; Medicine.

POPPY, Cheryl A; Columbus HS; Marshfield, WI; Chrs; HonRl; FrCl; MthCl; PpCl; LetterBsktbl; Swmmng; Trk; Chrldr; GAA; Coll; Nursing.

POPPY, Gerald D; Kalkaska HS; Kalkaska, MI; 10/156 VPJrCls; HonRl; NHS; PepBnd; SecSchPl; 4-H; Ftbl; CaptWrstlng; University; Veterinarian.

POPSON, Lyle L; Holly HS; Holly, MI; 39/219 HonRl; NHS; SchMus; SctActv; SciCl; LetterBsktbl; LetterFtbl; Trk; College; Doctor.

POQUETTE, Valerie; Pulaski HS; Pulaski, WI; HonRl; SchAde; Sdlty; TchrAde; FHA; Trk; GAA; College; Vocation Professional.

POREDA, Joyce A; Madonna HS; Chicago, IL; 23/273 PresSrCls; HonRl; NatlFornLg; NHS; OffAde; StuCncl; FBLA; LetterChrldr; GAA; College; Professional.

POREMBA, Gregory A; Northland HS; Longville, MN; 4/57 Aud/Vis; HonRl; NHS; TchrAde; SciCl; Trk; AmLegAwd; Coll; Dr.

PORKARSKI, Scarlet; Mason Senior HS; Lasalle, MI; HonRl; NHS; FTA; EngCl; GerCl; School Of Nursing; Rn.

PORRITT, Ruth H; Suttons Bay HS; Traverse City, MI; 1/50 SecFrshCls; SecJrCls; ChrhWkr; HonRl; RptrYrbk; Yrbk; 4-H; Trk; 4-HAwd; VFWAwd; College.

PORSTMANN, Jill E; Davenport West HS; Blue Grass, IA; ALAGirlsSt; ChrhWkr; HonRl; LbryAde; 4-H; CaptBsbl; CaptBsktbl; GAA; AmLegAwd; 4-HAwd; Keypunch.

PORTELL, Angela; Potosi HS; Potosi, MO; HonRl; LbryAde; SpnCl; Military.

PORTELL, Donald J; N St Francois County HS; Desloge, MO; 13/175 VPSophCls; PresSrCls; Band; CncrtBnd; HonRl; JrNHS; Mdrgl; NHS; SctActv; FrCl; College; Pre Med.

PORTER, Ann; Crystal Lake Community Hs; Crystal Lake, IL; 17 ChrhWkr; HonRl; NHS; FTA; U Of Illinois;home Economics.

PORTER, Beth E; Douglas Mac Arthur HS; Decatur, IL; 10/403 AFS; Chr; Chrs; ChrhWkr; HonRl; NHS; SchMus; SchPl; RptrSchPpr; IMSpt; Southern Illinois Univ; Journalism.

PORTER, Bruce J; Central HS; Bloomfield, IN; Band; CncrtBnd; HonRl; MrchBnd; PepBnd; StuCncl; PpCl; LetterBsbl; LetterBsktbl; LetterTrk; State Police.

PORTER, Bruce R; Lincoln HS; Bloomington, MN; HonRl; SchAde; SpnCl; LetterTrk; CchngActv; IMSpt; College; Professional Hockey Player.

PORTER, Carol L; Edgewood HS; Madison, WI; Band; CncrtBnd; HospAde; NatlFornLg; OffAde; PepBnd; SchMus; RptrSchPpr; SciCl; Univ Of Madison; Nursing.

PORTER, Cheryl; Oakley HS; Oakley, KS; Band; ChrhWkr; CncrtBnd; MrchBnd; PepBnd; SchMus; SctActv; TchrAde; FHA; PpCl; St Marys Of The Plains; Lic Practical Nurse.

PORTER, Christina L; North Salem HS; North Salem, IN; 7/42 SecJrCls; SecSrCls; ALAGirlsSt; CncrtBnd; MrchBnd; NHS; Quill&Scroll; SchPl; EdSchPpr; PpCl; Ball State University; Business Teacher.

PORTER, David; Wausau West HS; Wausau, WI; Band; ChrhWkr; CncrtBnd; MrchBnd; PepBnd; KeyCl; GerCl; Trk; PresAwd; Trade School; Vocational.

PORTER, David; Kelloggsville HS; Kentwood, MI; Band; Chrs; ChrhWkr; CncrtBnd; HonRl; MrchBnd; PepBnd; Bsktbl; SecTrsSophCls; Bible Or Law School; Ministry Or Politics.

PORTER, Debra; Nokomis HS; Nakomis, IL; Chr; Chrs; ChrhWkr; CmntyWkr; HonRl; LbryAde; SchMus; GAA; Coll; Child Care.

PORTER, Debra L; La Salle Peru Twp HS; Oglesby, IL; 9/511 Band; Chr; HonRl; MrchBnd; SchAde; YthFlsp; SpnCl; PpCl; AmLegAwd; College; Music Teacher.

PORTER, Dennis; St Bede Acad; Lasalle, IL; 40/89 CmntyWkr; HonRl; OffAde; TchrAde; Yrbk; IMSpt; College; Accounting.

PORTER, Donna S; Brown County HS; Nineveh, IN; 5/169 SecSrCls; HonRl; SecNHS; Quill&Scroll; Yrbk; FrCl; PresPpCl; Trk; GAA; International Jr Col; Fashion Merchandising.

PORTER, Gregory B; Momence HS; Momence, IL; 10/130 ChrhWkr; HonRl; NHS; SchPl; SctActv; LetterGlf; Purdue Univ; Professional.

PORTER, James W; Beatrice HS; Beatrice, NE; AFS; Band; CncrtBnd; HonRl; MrchBnd; Orch; PepBnd; Yrbk; SchPpr; GerCl; Nebraska Wesleyan; Doctor.

PORTER, Jim T; Kennett HS; Kennett, MO; Chr; Chrs; HonRl; RptrYrbk; KeyCl; SciCl; Bsbl; Ftbl; LetterTrk; Chrldr; Bus Schl; Computer Analyst.

PORTER, John; Greenfield Central HS; Greenfield, IN; 23/257 ChrhWkr; HonRl; NHS; SchMus; SchPl; YthFlsp; Ball St Univ; Arch.

PORTER, John H; New Trier East HS; Wilmette, IL; 164/847 HonRl; TchrAde; Univ; Professional.

PORTER, Karen N; Duquoin HS; Duquoin, IL; 30/119 Chrs; HonRl; SchPl; StuCncl; Yrbk; FTA; PpCl; GAA; Murray St Univ; Theater.

PORTER, Laura; University HS; Champaign, IL; SecFrshCls; LitMag; SchAde; SchMus; SchPl; Sdlty; StuGov; RptrYrbk; RptrSchPpr; EdSchPpr; Smith Coll; Profesional.

PORTER, Lisa A; North Putnam Jr/sr HS; Roachdale, IN; 7/131 Band; ChrhWkr; HonRl; PresNHS; NatlThespSoc; SchMus; StuCncl; 4-H; PresLatCl; Chrldr; Indiana U; Psychology & Business.

PORTER, Marilyn S; Covington Community HS; Veedersburg, IN; 1/92 Chr; NHS; Quill&Scroll; RptrSchPpr; Pres4-H; VPFHA; TreasPpCl; DanFAwd; DARAwd; 4-HAwd; Purdue Univ; Home Economics.

PORTER, Mary L; Shawnee Mission East HS; Prairie Village, KS; PresSophCls; HonRl; NHS; StuGov; RptrYrbk; PpCl; Swmmng; Tennis; Trk; Chrldr; College.

PORTER, Melissa J; Knightstown HS; Kennard, IN; 14/135 Chr; ChrhWkr; HonRl; NHS; NatlThespSoc; SchMus; StuCncl; SpnCl; Ball State Univ; Nurse.

PORTER, Michelle E; Lawrence Central HS; Indianapolis, IN; 61/780 Chr; HonRl; OffAde; SctActv; TchrAde; 4-H; IMSpt; 4-HAwd; KiwanAwd; Bulter U; English Ed.

PORTER, Myron T; Thater Senior HS; Thayer, MO; Chr; Chrs; ChrhWkr; HonRl; SchPl; Yrbk; SpnCl; LetterTennis; Journalism.

PORTER, Nancy D; Rockford HS; Rockford, MI; ChrhWkr; NatlMeritSF; PolWkr; Medical Assitant.

PORTER, Patti J; Bentley Senior HS; Burton, MI; ChrhWkr; CmntyWkr; HonRl; SchAde; SchMus; SchPl; SctActv; TchrAde; College; Cosmetology.

PORTER, Russell D; Ansley Public HS; Mason City, NE; Band; CncrtBnd; HonRl; Mdrgl; SchMus; SchPl; PresFFA; LetterBsktbl; LetterFtbl; LetterTrk; Nebraska Univ; Professional.

PORTER, Russell M; West Harrison HS; Modale, IA; 2/50 PresSrCls; Band; Chrs; ChrhWkr; CmntyWkr; HonRl; PresNHS; PresStuCncl; StuGov; YthFlsp; LetterFtbl; LetterTrk; LetterWrstlng; University Of Iowa.

PORTER, Sarah L; Vienna Township HS; Vienna, IL; Band; HonRl; StuCncl; Twrl; EdYrBk; VPSpnCl; PpCl; Univ Of Illinois.

PORTER, Stephen R; Monroe City R I HS; Monroe City, MO; HonRl; StuCncl; SpnCl; LetterTrk; College; Law.

PORTER, Terry R; Plattsmouth HS; Plattsmouth, NE; 21/133 HonRl; MthCl; Bsbl; LetterFtbl; LetterGlf; CchngActv; College; Optometrist.

PORTER, Todd M; Plattsmouth HS; Plattsmouth, NE; 30/160 TrsJrCls; Chrs; HonRl; SchMus; SctActv; StuCncl; TchrAde; YthFlsp; CaptBsbl; LetterFtbl; LetterGlf; LetterWrstlng; CchngActv; College.

PORTERFIELD, Jill A; Van Horn HS; Independence, MO; Chr; HonRl; JrNHS; NHS; SchMus; TchrAde; SpnCl; PpCl; Chrldr; College.

PORTH, Andrew V; Barrington HS; Barrington, IL; 35/672 HonRl; NHS; NatlMeritSF; SchPl; StuGov; RptrSchPpr; SchPpr; Socr; IMSpt; Clge; Enterpreneur.

PORTICE, Linda E; Pickford Public HS; Pickford, MI; 4/50 Chr; HonRl; SchPl; StuCncl; YthFlsp; EdYrBk; Pres4-H; PresFHA; BttyCrckrAwd; 4-HAwd; Univ Of Michigan; Med Tech.

PORTNER, Dorothy A; Cathedral HS; New Ulm, MN; ChrhWkr; CmntyWkr; HonRl; HospAde; LbryAde; PpCl; Voc Techn Ins; Med Lab Aid Or Tech.

PORTWOOD, Debra D; Bowling Green R 1 HS; Bowling Green, MO; 8/128 PresFrshCls; ALAGirlsSt; Chr; HonRl; NHS; OffAde; SctActv; StuCncl; FHA; Chrldr; Ne Missouri St University; Business.

PORZEL, Cathleen A; Richmond Burton HS; Spring Grove, IL; Chrs; ChrhWkr; DrlTm; HonRl; SchMus; SchPl; Yrbk; RptrSchPpr; FrCl; Trk; Chrldr; GAA; 4-HAwd; College; Theatre.

PORZUCZEK, Jean A; George Washington HS; Chicago, IL; HonRl; HospAde; NatlMeritCmnd; OffAde; RedCrAde; TchrAde; SpnCl; CaptChrldr; GAA; Jr College; Professional.

POSEY, Roger D; Ava HS; Ava, MO; 16/134 HonRl; VPFBLA; PresSpnCl; Bsbl; Bsktbl;.

POSHARD, Katherine E; Octavia HS; Colfax, IL; Band; CncrtBnd; HonRl; MrchBnd; YthFlsp; 4-H; SecFFA; Trk; 4-HAwd; University Of Illinois; Veterinarian.

POSKIN, Joseph E; Rockhurst HS; Kansas City, MO; 20/183 HonRl; NHS; StuCncl; StuGov; TchrAde; Bsbl; LetterBsktbl; LetterFtbl; Swmmng; Trk; CchngActv; IMSpt; University Of Missouri; Engineer.

POSKO, Mary; George Washington HS; Chicago, IL; 12/481 HonRl; StuCncl; GAA; Loyola Univ; Nursing.

POSLUSZNY, Mark D; De La Salle Institute; Chicago, IL; 2/258 VPBand; CncrtBnd; HonRl; MrchBnd; NHS; Orch; PepBnd; SchMus; StuGov; MthCl; CaptTennis; BauchLmbAwd; Technological Training; Computer Technician.

POSNER, Cheryl A; Appleton West HS; Appleton, WI; AFS; HonRl; College; Astronaut.

POSPISCHIL, William A; Aquin Central Catholic HS; Freeport, IL; Band; Chr; HonRl; Mdrgl; PepBnd; SchMus; SptEdSchPpr; MthCl; LetterBsktbl; CaptFtbl; Coll; Phy Ed.

POSPISIL, Debra L; Eville HS; Esthervill, IA; Band; CtyCnl; HonRl; MrchBnd; StuCncl; Yrbk; Chrldr; EldAwd; MasAwd; VoiceDemAwd; Coll; Psych.

POSPISIL, Debra L; Estherville HS; Estherville, IA; 10/157 HonRl; NatlMeritCmnd; Teen; YthFlsp; RptrYrbk; SpnCl; Chrldr; EldAwd; MasAwd; VoiceDemAwd; Simpson Coll; Psycology.

POSPISIL, Susan G; Oak Park River Forest HS; Oak Park, IL; 63/1012 ChrhWkr; HonRl; Sdlty; TchrAde; VPFHA; Northern Ill Univ; Fashion Merchandising.

POSS, Janet A; Angola HS; Angola, IN; Chr; Chrs; HonRl; NatlMeritCmnd; PolWkr; SchPl; LatCl; Ft Lewis College; English.

POSS, Lawrence D; Garnett HS; Richmond, KS; Chr; HonRl; JA; SchPl; StuCncl; StuGov; TchrAde; 4-H; FFA; Bsktbl; Trk; 4-HAwd; Kansas State Univ; Extension Worker.

POSSEHL, Debra; Arcadia HS; Arcadia, WI; 2/95 Band; CncrtBnd; DrlTm; HonRl; MrchBnd; NHS; PepBnd; SchMus; RptrSchPpr; GAA; Luther College; Accounting Major.

POSSLEY, Marie C; Marillac HS; Mt Prospect, IL; Chrs; St Norberts College; Business.

POSSO, William M; Spooner HS; Spooner, WI; 25/128 ALBoysSt; Band; CncrtBnd; HonRl; PepBnd; PolWkr; Ftbl; BttyCrckrAwd; Univ; Pro Law.

POST, Becky J; West HS; Sioux City, IA; HonRl; College; Medical Tech.

POST, Gerald; Rockford HS; Rockford, MI; 2/289 Chr; HonRl; MrchBnd; NHS; Orch; SchMus; SchPl; 4-H; SciCl; IMSpt; Central Mi Univ; Music Ed.

POST, Kevin B; Chandler Lake Wilson HS; Pipestone, MN; 14/41 Band; Chr; Chrs; CncrtBnd; HonRl; MrchBnd; PepBnd; StuCncl; CaptBsktbl; IMSpt; College; Computer Programming.

POST, Marcia L; Coopersville HS; Marne, MI; Chr; ChrhWkr; HonRl; NHS; NatlMeritSF; SchMus; SchPl; YthFlsp; FBLA; PpCl; Mi State U; Computer.

POST, Mark E; Midland HS; Midland, MI; Band; CncrtBnd; HonRl; MrchBnd; PepBnd; Swmmng; Trk; U Of Mi; Med.

POST, Merna K; Sandy Creek Jr Sr HS; Fairfield, NE; 29/51 Band; Chrs; ChrhWkr; CmntyWkr; RptrYrbk; RptrSchPpr; 4-H; PpCl; 4-HAwd; PresAwd; Bethany Naz College; Computer Science.

POST, Paul W; Box 430 Bridgeport HS; Bridgeport, NE; PresJrCls; ALBoysSt; Band; ChrhWkr; CmntyWkr; CncrtBnd; HonRl; NHS; SchMus; SchPl; Bsktbl; Ftbl; LetterTrk; AmLegAwd; Wesleyan Univ; Medicine.

POST, Peggy L; Southside HS; Ft Wayne, IN; 91/411 HonRl; Chrldr; Medical; Nursing.

POST, Richard A; Parkway West HS; Ballwin, MO; Band; HonRl; TchrAde; LetterBsbl; LetterBsktbl; LetterFtbl; College; Business.

POST, Steven; Mt Horeb HS; Mount Horeb, WI; VPJrCls; ALBoysSt; Chr; RedCrAde; SchMus; SctActv; Trk; IMSpt; Univ Of Wi; Natural Resources Sch Of Agric.

POSTAL, Debra; Libertyville Hs; Libertyville, IL; 11/458 TrsSrCls; HonRl; NHS; NatlMeritCmnd; SchPl; StuCncl; TreasSpnCl; PpCl;.

POSTEL, Christine A; Grayville Comm HS; Grayville, IL; 2/31 ALAGirlsSt; Band; Chrs; CmntyWkr; HonRl; StuCncl; RptrYrbk; EdSchPpr; PresFHA; GAA; Murray St Univ; Nurse.

POSTER, Debra A; Healy HS; Pierz, MN; 9/117 HonRl; OffAde; Vocational School; Practical Nursing.

POSTLEWAITE, Barbara L; Palestine HS; Palestine, IL; ALAGirlsSt; Band; Chr; Chrs; ChrhWkr; MrchBnd; SecYthFlsp; 4-H; LatCl; GAA; University; Liberal Arts.

POSTMA, Donna M; Platte HS; Platte, SD; 3/46 Band; Chrs; DrlTm; HonRl; MrchBnd; EdYrBk; RptrSchPpr; FHA; FNA; PpCl; Col; Professional.

POSTMA, Jo A; Platte HS; Platte, SD; 9/54 SecTrsJrCls; Band; Chrs; DrlTm; HonRl; LbryAde; RptrYrbk; EdSchPpr; FHA; FNA; Col;.

POSZ, Patricia A; Sanborn Public HS; Sanborn, MN; Band; Chr; Chrs; CncrtBnd; HospAde; PepBnd; YthFlsp; RptrYrbk; RptrSchPpr; Trk; LetterChrldr; Vocational Sch; Nursing.

POTAKIS, Effie A; Highland Park HS; Highwood, IL; College; Professional.

POTEET, Carol S; Nokomis HS; Nokomis, IL; 1/100 Chrs; HonRl; Business.

POTEMPA, Leonard D; Lake Park HS; Bloomingdale, IL; 12/510 Band; CncrtBnd; HonRl; MrchBnd; NatlMeritCmnd; Univ; Professional.

POTEMPA, Ronald A; St Rita HS; Chicago, IL; 160/424 Aud/Vis; Chrs; ChrhWkr; CmntyWkr; Bradley Univ; Biochemistry.

POTRAMENT, Lois A; Lancaster HS; Lancaster, MN; SecFrshCls; TrsSophCls; HonRl; NHS; SchPl; StuCncl; TchrAde; FHA; PpCl; CaptBsktbl; Chrldr; Univ Of Minnesota; Accounting.

POTRZUSKI, Robert D; Ferndale HS; Ferndale, MI; HonRl; NHS; StuGov; LetterBsbl; CaptBsktbl; Glf; University; Professional.

POTTEBAUM, Sheila M; Spalding HS; Granville, IA; SecFrshCls; Chrs; DrlTm; MrchBnd; Quill&Scroll; RptrSchPpr; Glf; Trk; IMSpt; College; Journalsim.

POTTER, Brian E; Pleasant Ridge HS; Atchison, KS; ChrhWkr; HonRl; Farming.

POTTER, Carmen; Lyman Independent HS; Presho, SD; Band; CncrtBnd; DrlTm; HonRl; MrchBnd; NHS; PepBnd; Yrbk; SchPpr; GerCl; Coll.

POTTER, Carrie F; Lancaster HS; Lancaster, WI; AFS; LbryAde; FHA; PpCl; College.

POTTER, Curtis W; Griswold HS; Griswold, IA; 27/85 Band; CncrtBnd; MrchBnd; PepBnd; SchMus; SchPl; YthFlsp; 4-H; 4-HAwd; College.

POTTER, Dan; Washington HS; Gremantown, WI; ALBoysSt; CncrtBnd; HonRl; MrchBnd; NHS; Tennis; Trk; RotaryAwd; College; Ministry.

POTTER, David B; Douglas Mac Arthur HS; Saginaw, MI; ALBoysSt; Band; CncrtBnd; HonRl; JrNHS; MrchBnd; NHS; Orch; PepBnd; SchMus; Kendall Sch Of Design; Comm Art.

POTTER, David D; Caledonia Public HS; Caledonia, MN; 12/152 Band; Chr; Chrl; CncrtBnd; HonRl; NHS; Bsktbl; Ftbl; Trk; 4-HAwd; Coll; Music.

POTTER, Dawn L; Otsego HS; Kalamacoo, MI; 24/235 HonRl; NHS; OffAde; StuCncl; Yrbk; 4-H; LatCl; Grad Rapids Baptist Col ;lawyer.

POTTER, Deanne S; Charlevoix HS; Charlevoix, MI; CncrtBnd; HonRl; MrchBnd; Business.

POTTER, Edwin L; Crossville HS; Crossville, IL; NatlMeritFnl; NatlMeritCmnd; PolWkr; SchPl; RptrSchPpr; SchPpr; GerCl; MthCl; SciCl; AmLegAwd; Univ Of Ill; Electrical Engineering.

POTTER, Gregory J; Assumption HS; Wisconsin Rapids, WI; TrsSophCls; TreasKeyCl; LetterFtbl; LetterTrk; LetterWrstlng; IMSpt; College; Professional.

POTTER, Julie A; Walthill Public HS; Pender, NE; 1/29 SecTrsJrCls; SecTrsSrCls; Chrs; HonRl; LbryAde; NHS; PpCl; Univ Of Ne; Chemistry.

POTTER, Kaye; Danube HS; Danube, MN; 3/43 SecJrCls; HonRl; NHS; SchMus; YthFlsp; SchPpr; 4-H; FHA; GAA; Willmar Voc Tech Inst; Leagal Secretary.

POTTER, Mary A; Bismarck Henning HS; Danville, IL; Band; Chrs; CncrtBnd; HonRl; NatlThespSoc; PepBnd; SchPl; RptrYrbk; PpCl; SciCl; Clge; Voc.

POTTER, Matthew N; South Milwaukee HS; South Milwaukee, WI; 73/460 Aud/Vis; TchrAde; Ftbl; Trk; IMSpt; U W Platteville; Radio & Tv Broadcasting.

POTTER, Michael T; Truman HS; Independence, MO; Band; ChrhWkr; CmntyWkr; CncrtBnd; NatlThespSoc; SchMus; SchPl; StuCncl; SpnCl; LetterFtbl; College.

POTTER, Peggy M; Corunna HS; Corunna, MI; CncrtBnd; HonRl; MrchBnd; 4-H; LetterBsbl; Business School; Secretarial Work.

POTTER, Penny M; Princeton HS; Princeton, IL; 15/217 HonRl; PolWkr; StuCncl; TchrAde; LatCl; SpnCl; PpCl; CaptBsktbl; Trk; LetterGAA; Univ Of Illinois; Physical Education.

POTTER, Rene L; Clear Creek HS; Tiffin, IA; HonRl; MrchBnd; RptrYrbk; Yrbk; FBLA; SpnCl; Trade Sch; Vocation.

POTTER, Ronald L; Routt HS; Jacksonville, IL; HonRl; Illinois College.

POTTER, Steven J; Trimont HS; Ormsby, MN; Band; CncrtBnd; HonRl; MrchBnd; PepBnd; RptrSchPpr; SchPpr; LetterBsktbl; LetterFtbl; LetterTrk; College; Biology.

POTTER, Steven L; Armada HS; Armada, MI; 5/95 TrsSrCls; ALBoysSt; ChrhWkr; HonRl; VPNHS; NatlMeritCmnd; SchMus; LetterBsktbl; LetterFtbl; CaptIMSpt; Mi State Univ; Accounting.

POTTER, Tonjia D; Golden City R Iii HS; Golden City, MO; SecFrshCls; SecSophCls; SecJrCls; HonRl; StuCncl; FHA; Chrldr; GAA; PPFtbl; S M S U; English.

POTTHOFF, Brigitta A; Mccook HS; Mccook, NE; 6/162 AFS; HonRl; NHS; 4-H; FTA; MthCl; PpCl; DARAwd; 4-HAwd; Mccook Community Clg; Pol Science Lawyer.

POTTHOFF, Dennis; Palisade Public HS; Palisade, NE; 1/10 PresFrshCls; VPSophCls; VPSrCls; ALBoysSt; Band; HonRl; NHS; NatlMeritFnl; SptEdYrbk; Ftbl; EldAwd; Univ Of Nebraska; History.

POTTHOFF, Jeffrey D; Patoka Unit 100 HS; Patoka, IL; 8/25 VPSophCls; PresSrCls; HonRl; SchPl; StuCncl; FFA; SciCl; Bsbl; Bsktbl; College.

POTTORF, Tina L; Easton Comm Unit HS; Easton, IL; 2/19 SecJrCls; Band; CncrtBnd; HonRl; SchPl; EdSchPpr; FHA; Bsktbl; Trk; Chrldr; GAA; Lincoln Land Comm College.

POTTS, Cathy L; Lake Central HS; Dyer, IN; SecSophCls; VPJrCls; PresSrCls; Band; CncrtBnd; HonRl; MrchBnd; StuCncl; TchrAde; Teen; Don Roberts Beauty Schl; Beautician.

POTTS, Charlene M; Crofton Public HS; Crofton, NE; Chrs; ChrhWkr; DrlTm; HospAde; SchMus; TchrAde; RptrYrbk; LetterTrk; Univ Of Ne Lincoln; Psychology.

POTTS, Janet L; John Marshall Jr Sr HS; Milwaukee, WI; ChrhWkr; HonRl; OffAde; SchAde; StuCncl; TchrAde; PpCl; Work.

POTTS, Janice L; Jefferson HS; Independence, IA; Chr; ChrhWkr; CncrtBnd; HospAde; SchMus; SchPl; RptrYrbk; RptrSchPpr; GAA; PPFtbl; College; Nursing.

POTTS, Joanne; Dixon Hs; Dixon, IL; 54/334 HonRl; RptrSchPpr; EdSchPpr; Chrldr; Ui;art.

POTTS, Kenneth S; Beaverton HS; Hope, MI; 20/130 Band; CncrtBnd; HonRl; LbryAde; NHS; SpnCl; College; Electrical Engineering.

POTTS, Rhonda G; Chandlerville HS; Chandlerville, IL; VPJrCls; ALAGirlsSt; Band; CncrtBnd; HonRl; MrchBnd; NHS; RptrSchPpr; FHA; PpCl; College; Professional.

POTTS, Sheryl D; Holland Christian HS; Holland, MI; 16/261 Chr; ChrhWkr; HonRl; NHS; SchPl; SpnCl; PpCl; LetterBsktbl; LetterTrk; IMSpt; Calvin College; Elem Education.

POTTS, Tim L; Lakeview HS; Decatur, IL; 14/240 HonRl; NHS; GerCl; LetterTrk; Illinois Wesleyan.

POTTS, William H; Brown HS; Sturgis, SD; Chr; ChrhWkr; HonRl; Mdrgl; SchMus; SchPl; Teen; YthFlsp; Trk; IMSpt; College.

POTWARDSKI, Gregory P; Detour Area HS; Goetzville, MI; TrsSrCls; HonRl; SctActv; StuGov; TchrAde; 4-H; Bsbl; Bsktbl; Ftbl; 4-HAwd; Michigan State Univ; Professional.

POULER, Patrick J; Central HS; Trevov, WI; 7/200 ALBoysSt; HonRl; NatlFornLg; NHS; SchPl; SchPpr; MthCl; PpCl; SciCl; LetterGlf; Univ Of Notre Dame; Chemical Engineering.

POULIOT, Jocelyn M; Theodore Roosevelt HS; Wyandotte, MI; 10/550 HonRl; HospAde; LbryAde; NHS; SctActv; TchrAde; College; Chemical Engineering.

POULSON, Lorean; Ashwaubanon HS; Green Bay, WI; 16 ChrhWkr; HonRl; NHS; PpCl; Univ; Computer Programmer.

POULTER, Bradley W; Liberty HS; Liberty, IL; 10/58 PresFrshCls; PresBand; CmntyWkr; HonRl; TreasNHS; SchPl; VPStuCncl; FFA; LetterBsktbl; LetterTrk; Quincy Coll; Biology.

POULTER, David; Anamosa Community HS; Anamosa, IA; AFS; Chrs; CncrtBnd; HonRl; SchMus; StuCncl; SecTrsSophCls; College; Professional.

POUSSON, James M; Duchesne HS; Saint Charles, MO; Chr; Chrs; HonRl; NHS; SchMus; SchPl; 4-H; College; Social Work.

POUST, David W; Orion HS; Orion, IL; 4/125 Chrs; ChrhWkr; CmntyWkr; HonRl; NHS; YthFlsp; LatCl; LetterBsktbl; LetterFtbl; LetterTrk; IMSpt; LionAwd; College; Engineering.

POUTANEN, Robert B; Negaunee HS; Palmer, MI; Band; CncrtBnd; HonRl; MrchBnd; Orch; PepBnd; Northern Mi Univ; Accounting.

POVLICH, James J; S Milwaukee HS; South Milwaukee, WI; 41/480 HonRl; NHS; StuCncl; Univ Of Wisconsin; Accounting.

POWE, Kenneth A; Assumption HS; Fairview Heights, IL; Chrs; HonRl; SchPl; LetterWrstlng; Univ Of Illinois; Biochemistry.

POWELL, Betty J; Lansing HS; Lansing, KS; Chr; ChrhWkr; HospAde; OffAde; PolWkr; RptrYrbk; PpCl; LetterBsktbl; LetterTrk; IMSpt; PPFtbl;.

POWELL, Bill A; Kingsley Pierson HS; Kingsley, IA; 11/68 ChrhWkr; HonRl; NHS; YthFlsp; FTA; KeyCl; MthCl; LetterBsktbl; LetterFtbl; LetterGlf; C; Curriculum Of Major Study.

POWELL, Brian E; Cambridge HS; Cambridge, MN; Aud/Vis; Chr; SchMus; SchPl; LetterBsktbl; Glf; College; Airplane Pilot.

POWELL, Charlotte A; Moulton Udell Community HS; Udell, IA; 1/32 CmntyWkr; HonRl; LbryAde; SchMus; SchPl; YthFlsp; RptrSchPpr; 4-H; 4-HAwd; GovHonPrgAwd; Faith Baptist Bible Col; Christian Work.

POWELL, Cheryl; South Pemiscot HS; Steele, MO; 11/45 Band; HonRl; NHS; PepBnd; StuCncl; RptrYrbk; RptrSchPpr; FHA; SpnCl; PpCl; Nursing School.

POWELL, Cheryl E; Lincoln HS; Kansas City, MO; 1/235 CncrtBnd; HospAde; JrNHS; MrchBnd; NHS; NatlMeritCmnd; Orch; PresStuCncl; Chrldr; Miami Univ; Doctor.

POWELL, Christa; Mineral Point HS; Mineral Point, WI; 4/94 CncrtBnd; HonRl; MrchBnd; NHS; PepBnd; SchMus; SctActv; YthFlsp; Yrbk; FHA; College; Nursing.

POWELL, Christine A; Annawan HS; Annawan, IL; 3/51 Band; HonRl; NHS; SchPl; StuCncl; FHA; FTA; CaptChrldr; GAA; DARAwd; Augustana College; Speech Pathology.

POWELL, Daniel; Kirksville Sr HS; Kirksville, MO; Aud/Vis; HonRl; StuCncl; StuGov; IMSpt; College; Professional.

POWELL, Debra; Knoxville HS; Galesburg, IL; 30/98 Band; Chr; CncrtBnd; MrchBnd; OffAde; SchPl; YthFlsp; 4-H; FHA; IMSpt;.

POWELL, Eva; Brunswick R Ii Hs; Brunswick, MO; Band; Chrs; CncrtBnd; HonRl; LbryAde; OffAde; SchPl; FHA; Bsbl; BttyCrckrAwd; U Mo Rolla;geological Engineer.

POWELL, Gregory D; Big Fork HS; Big Fork, MN; 9/33 PresFrshCls; Band; HonRl; StuCncl; YthFlsp; RptrYrbk; Bsbl; Bsktbl; Ftbl; Trk; CchngActv; Itasca Comm College.

POWELL, Jane E; Morgan Park HS; Chicago, IL; 22/554 HonRl; JrNHS; ModUN; NHS; StuCncl; YthFlsp; EdSchPpr; FTA; MthCl; Univ Of Ill; Elem Teacher.

POWELL, Jayleen R; Parkway Central HS; Chesterfield, MO; 3/450 AFS; HonRl; SecJA; LitMag; Mdrgl; NHS; Orch; StuCncl; PresSpnCl; GAA; Duke University; Foreign Relations.

POWELL, Jolene A; Verdi Public HS; Verdi, MN; 7/12 Band; ChrhWkr; DrmMjrt; HonRl; OffAde; PepBnd; SptEdYrbk; RptrSchPpr; Bsktbl; LetterTrk; Pipestone Voc Sch; Sec.

POWELL, Jolene M; Marcus HS; Pierson, IA; Band; ChrhWkr; CncrtBnd; HonRl; MrchBnd; PepBnd; Twrl; 4-H; LetterBsktbl; LetterTrk; PPFtbl; 4-HAwd; PresAwd; College; Nursing.

POWELL, Karin L; Tri County HS; Sand Lake, MI; 3/93 SecSophCls; TrsJrCls; TrsSrCls; TreasBand; CncrtBnd; HonRl; MrchBnd; NHS; PepBnd; 4-HAwd; Mi Univ; Chemical Engineering.

POWELL, Kenneth E; Hutchinson HS; Hutchinson, KS; Band; CncrtBnd; DrmBgl; HonRl; MrchBnd; NatlMeritSF; Orch; PepBnd; SciCl; Ks St U; Chemistry.

POWELL, Kimberly K; Maconaquah HS; Peru, IN; 6/200 ALAGirlsSt; JrNHS; NHS; StuCncl; Yrbk; VPFrCl; TreasMthCl; Tennis; Purdue Univ.

POWELL, Kip; Eddyville HS; Eddyville, IA; 7/50 Band; CncrtBnd; HonRl; MrchBnd; PepBnd; Ftbl; Trk; Univ Of Northern Iowa; Business.

POWELL, La Donna M; Cass Technical HS; Detroit, MI; ChrhWkr; CmntyWkr; DrlTm; ROTC; StuCncl; TchrAde; SciCl; Wayne Univ; Med Doctor.

POWELL, Linda L; East Prairie HS; East Prairie, MO; Chr; CmntyWkr; CncrtBnd; HonRl; MrchBnd; NHS; SchMus; PpCl; Chrldr; IMSpt; Semo State U.

POWELL, Linda L; Elston HS; Michigan City, IN; 24/336 Aud/Vis; Chr; HonRl; NHS; Orch; SchMus; SchPl; StuGov; TchrAde; SciCl; Purdue U; Art Ed.

POWELL, Lisa G; St Francis HS; St Francis, KS; HonRl; Mdrgl; StuGov; FHA; Bsbl; LetterTrk; Chrldr; PPFtbl; PresAwd; CitAwd; College; Professional.

POWELL, Lorna L; Riverton HS; Riverton, IL; 4/75 HonRl; NHS; OffAde; PpCl; GAA; College; Teaching.

POWELL, Lowell K; Clay City HS; Clay City, IL; 12/41 PresFrshCls; SecSophCls; Band; CncrtBnd; HonRl; PepBnd; StuCncl; FFA; Bsbl; Wabash Vly Jr College.

POWELL, Pamela S; Manual HS; Peoria, IL; 8/329 Band; DrlTm; HonRl; SchPl; VPKeyCl; LetterTennis; GAA; University; Spanish.

POWELL, Peggy S; Weeping Water Public HS; Weeping Water, NE; Band; Chrs; HonRl; SchMus; TchrAde; FHA; PpCl; LetterBsktbl; LetterTrk; GAA; Work; Marriage.

POWELL, Phoebe X; Macon Jr/sr HS; Macon, MO; 12/117 Chr; DrlTm; HonRl; SchMus; SchPl; SctActv; StuCncl; SpnCl; Chrldr; PresAwd; College; Architecture.

POWELL, Rebecca L; James H Bowen HS; Chicago, IL; 94/614 SecChr; ChrhWkr; HonRl; PolWkr; StuCncl; TreasFDA; MthCl; Chrldr; LetterGAA; IMSpt; Bradley University; Medicine.

POWELL, Sara F; Pittsburg HS; Pittsburg, KS; 24/280 SecSrCls; HonRl; Orch; Quill&Scroll; SctActv; StuCncl; YthFlsp; RptrYrbk; FrCl; PpCl; Clge; Fashion Design.

POWELL, Sharon K; Manton HS; Manton, MI; TrsSophCls; TrsJrCls; TrsSrCls; SecBand; HonRl; MrchBnd; PepBnd; EdYrBk; RptrSchPpr; TreasSchPpr; Bapt Coll; Youth For Christ Staff.

POWER, Chip; Monroe HS; Monroe, WI; Band; CncrtBnd; HonRl; PepBnd; KeyCl; SchPl; LetterGlf; Univ; Eng Or Architecture.

POWER, Kathie K; South Harrison HS; Bethany, MO; 5/79 ALAGirlsSt; HonRl; NHS; FHA; FTA; BttyCrckrAwd; Coll; Bookkeeper.

POWER, Mary J; Chenoa HS; Chenoa, IL; AFS; HonRl; MrchBnd; NHS; SchMus; EdYrBk; SpnCl; Bsbl; Chrldr; GAA; Marquette University; Physical Therapy.

POWER, Nancy J; North Decatur HS; Greensburg, IN; SecChrhWkr; DrlTm; HonRl; MrchBnd; TreasStuCncl; VP4-H; LetterTrk; Chrldr; GAA; 4-HAwd; University; Dental Hygienist.

POWER, Robert J; Marquette HS; Fox Point, WI; 16/260 CmntyWkr; HonRl; SchPl; StuCncl; Bsbl; CchngActv; Craighton; Psy.

POWER, William N; Langdon Public HS; Langdon, ND; 24/109 HonRl; FFA; Wrstlng; Trade School; Vocation.

POWERS, Carolyn D; Raytown HS; Raytown, MO; 27/625 HonRl; SecJrNHS; LitMag; NHS; NatlMeritSF; SchPl; SchPpr; University Of Kansas; Data Processing.

POWERS, Christine S; Mt Clemens HS; Selfridge Ang Base, MI; 3/400 Band; DrlTm; HonRl; JrNHS; LitMag; MrchBnd; NHS; SchPl; YthFlsp; LatCl; Mi State Univ; Language Major.

POWERS, Cindy J; Mulvane Sr HS; Mulvane, KS; SecFrshCls; Band; CncrtBnd; DrlTm; HonRl; MrchBnd; PepBnd; StuCncl; PpCl; Chrldr; U Of Kansas; Music Ed.

POWERS, Cindy L; Guil Lake HS; Hickory Corners, MI; 4/228 HonRl; JA; SecNHS; NatlMeritSchl; NatlSciFnd; PolWkr; 4-H; SpnCl; SciCl; IMSpt; Michigan State; Dairy Science.

POWERS, Coleen D; Monroe Sr HS; Monroe, MI; Chr; ChrhWkr; HonRl; JA; NHS; NatlMeritCmnd; NatlThespSoc; Orch; SchMus; SchPl; StuCncl; FrCl; College; Biology.

POWERS, Dennis R; O Fallon Twp HS; Belleville, IL; 1/327 HonRl; NHS; YthFlsp; FrCl; MthCl; University.

POWERS, Diane M; Maryville Rii HS; Maryville, MO; Chr; HospAde; LbryAde; NHS; SchMus; SchPl; PresFBLA; FHA; FNA; PpCl; Nw Missouri St Univ; Speech.

POWERS, Donna J; Northwest Webster HS; Fort Dodge, IA; VPSophCls; VPJrCls; Chrs; ChrhWkr; CmntyWkr; PolWkr; TchrAde; YthFlsp; RptrSchPpr; 4-H; College; Registered Nurse.

POWERS, Dorothy M; Mt Assisi Academy; Chicago, IL; 20/194 ChrhWkr; HonRl; HospAde; NatlFornLg; NHS; SchPl; StuCncl; RptrYrbk; Yrbk; SpnCl; Univ Of Illinois; Nursing.

POWERS, Elaine A; Woodruff HS; Peoria, IL; 2/268 AFS; Chr; HonRl; Orch; SchMus; SctActv; YthFlsp; GerCl; U Of F St; Marine Biology.

POWERS, Jill L; Beardsley HS; Beardsley, MN; SecSophCls; VPJrCls; ALAGirlsSt; Chrs; ChrhWkr; HonRl; LbryAde; SchPl; StuCncl; Bsktbl; LetterTrk; GAA; IMSpt; PPFtbl; Trade Schl; Fashion Merchandise.

POWERS, Kit K; Ames Community HS; Ames, IA; Band; ChrhWkr; CmntyWkr; TreasCncrtBnd; HonRl; MrchBnd; NatlMeritSF; Orch; PepBnd; SchMus; YthFlsp; Bsbl; Wrstlng; IMSpt; Univ; Engineering.

POWERS, Lucinda; Marissa HS; Marissa, IL; 9/63 HonRl; NHS; Quill&Scroll; SchMus; RptrSchPpr; FHA; MthCl; GAA;.

POWERS, Nicholas; Columbus HS; Columbus, WI; 7/130 Chrs; CmntyWkr; Mdrgl; 4-H; Univ; Veterarian.

POWERS, Patricia; Kimball HS; Kimball, SD; ChrhWkr; HonRl; FHA; PpCl; Bus Sch.

POWERS, Paul O; Berkeley Sr HS; Berkeley, MO; Band; CncrtBnd; HonRl; MrchBnd; NHS; SchMus; SchPl; LetterSwmmng; LetterTennis; College; Architecture.

POWERS, Rod R; United Community HS; Boone, IA; PresSophCls; Aud/Vis; Band; SchMus; SchPl; StuGov; RptrSchPpr; 4-H; PpCl; Bsktbl; LetterFtbl; Iowa St Univ; Education.

POWERS, Sharon M; Manlius Community Unit HS; Walnut, IL; 5/20 Band; Chr; HonRl; NHS; Yrbk; SchPpr; 4-H; FHA; CaptChrldr; PresAwd; College; Teaching.

POWERS, Vickie J; North Platte HS; North Platte, NE; DrlTm; HonRl; Pres4-H; PpCl; Bsbl; LetterTrk; PresGAA; IMSpt; PPFtbl; College.

POWLESS, Berle G; Clinton HS; Clinton, IL; HonRl; EngCl; PpCl; Ftbl; LetterTrk; IMSpt; VFWAwd; College.

POWLESS, John A; Milwaukee Lutheran HS; Milwaukee, WI; 63/240 Ftbl; CaptUniv; Law.

POWNELL, Cindy R; Leeds Public HS; York, ND; ALAGirlsSt; Band; Chr; HonRl; HospAde; SchMus; SchPl; RptrYrbk; EdSchPpr; FHA; Jr College; Acct.

POYNOR, Sally A; New Madrid HS; Kewanee, MO; HonRl; TreasFBLA; FHA; PpCl; CaptChrldr; IMSpt; College; Major In Business Admin.

POYNTER, Gary L; North Salem HS; Lizton, IN; 2/60 Band; CncrtBnd; HonRl; JrNHS; MrchBnd; NHS; PepBnd; Trade School; Vocation.

POYNTER, Larry; Montague HS; Montague, MI; HonRl; NatlMeritSF; StuCncl; Michigan State Univ; Ornithology.

POYNTER, Michael J; Avon HS; Danville, IN; 7/150 HonRl; NHS; LatCl; Bsktbl; Ftbl; Purdue Univ; Engineering.

POZARNIUK, Ann; Queen Of Peace HS; Burbank, IL; Chrs; HonRl; LitMag; NHS; Univ Of Ill; Architecture.

POZEGA, Debra A; Grand Ledge HS; Lansing, MI; 7/400 SecSrCls; HonRl; JrNHS; PresNHS; Quill&Scroll; StuCncl; SptEdYrbk; EdSchPpr; SptEdSchPpr; SchPpr; 4-H; LatCl; CaptTrk; Michigan State Univ; Journalism.

POZNICH, Charles R; Southeast HS; Weir, KS; 3/70 PresFrshCls; PresSophCls; SecSrCls; ALBoysSt; HonRl; NHS; NatlSciFnd; SchPl; StuCncl; PresFFA; Kansas State Clg; Astrophysicist.

POZOLO, Gary T; Roseville HS; Roseville, MI; 35/500 Aud/Vis; HonRl; NHS; PpCl; CaptBsktbl; Mich St Univ; Acct.

PRACHEIL, Michael J; Exeter Public HS; Exeter, NE; 1/21 SecSrCls; ALBoysSt; Band; HonRl; NatlMeritCmnd; StuCncl; EdYrBk; MthCl; CaptFtbl; CitAwd; University.

PRAHL, Bob R; Brillion HS; Brillion, WI; 4/84 NHS; StuCncl; YthFlsp; SciCl; LetterBsktbl; Ftbl; LetterTrk; CchngActv; Fox Valley Tech College; Electronics.

PRAHL, John W; Mahomet Seymour HS; Mahomet, IL; Band; ChrhWkr; CncrtBnd; HonRl; MrchBnd; Orch; PepBnd; SchMus; SchPl; YthFlsp; College; Probation Officer.

PRAHL, Rick; Waterville Elysian HS; Waterville, MN; Chr; Chrs; ChrhWkr; HonRl; SchPl; SctActv; YthFlsp; Bsbl; Bsktbl; Ftbl; College; Professional.

PRAHM, Susan C; Slayton HS; Slayton, MN; PresJrCls; Band; Chr; HonRl; SchPl; GerCl; PpCl; GAA; IMSpt; PPFtbl; College.

PRAISA, Nancy E; Immaculate Heart Of Mary HS; Westchester, IL; RptrSchPpr; Univ Of Ill; Accounting.

PRAISWATER, Deborah; Odessa HS; Odessa, MO; 33/113 Chr; ChrhWkr; HonRl; SctActv; FTA; MthCl; SciCl; IMSpt; PresAwd; Trade School; Professional.

PRAMBERG, Sandra; Gothenburg HS; Gotherburg, NE; 16#32#41 NHS; SchAde; SchMus; TchrAde; 4-H; PpCl; 4-HAwd; College.

PRANGE, Carla; Seward Senior HS; Seward, NE; / 145.

PRANGE, Dorothy L; North Shelby HS; Shelbyville, MO; 2/55 SecJrCls; DrlTm; HonRl; PresNHS; SchPl; EdYrBk; RptrSchPpr; VPFHA; SecPpCl; DARAwd; U Of Mo Columbia; Business Administration.

PRANGE, Rebecca J; Macomb HS; Macomb, IL; 20/250 HonRl; NHS; NatlMeritFnl; NatlMeritSF; 4-H; VPSciCl; Swmmng; 4-HAwd; Michigan State University; Veterinarian.

PRANGER, Dawn M; Carrollton HS; Carrollton, IL; 9/95 HonRl; NHS; FHA; PpCl; Ftbl; Tennis; Trk; Chrldr; GAA; Nursing School; Nursing.

PRANKE, Susan A; De Pere HS; De Pere, WI; 41#77#93 Bsbl; Bsktbl; Trk; CchngActv; PresGAA; IMSpt;.

PRANULIS, Trudy; Marissa HS; Marissa, IL; 1/75 Band; CncrtBnd; HonRl; MrchBnd; NHS; NatlMeritSF; PepBnd; SchMus; PpCl;.

PRASCH, Catherine M; Lockport Central HS; Lockport, IL; 37/550 HonRl; NHS; Lewis University; Nursing.

PRASSER, Gary; Hamilton HS; Menomonee Falls, WI; 72/296 ChrhWkr; HonRl; SctActv; YthFlsp; Ftbl; Wrstlng; Coll; Architect.

PRATER, Brenda C; Tippecanoe Valley HS; Akron, IN; LbryAde; MrchBnd; SchPl; FNA; SpnCl; MthCl; PpCl; SciCl; Chrldr; Ball State Univ; Nurse.

PRATHER, Charles R; Catlin HS; Atlin, IL; ChrhWkr; HonRl; SchPl; SchPpr; PpCl; Johnson Bible Coll; Minister.

PRATHER, Cheryl A; Eastern HS; Pekin, IN; TrsJrCls; TchrAde; RptrYrbk; SpnCl; PpCl; GAA; Indiana Univ Southeast.

PRATHER, Dennis; Bigfork HS; Effie, MN; VPSophCls; PresJrCls; Chrs; RptrYrbk; RptrSchPpr; Bsktbl; College; Proffessional.

PRATHER, Greg A; East HS; Sioux City, IA; YthFlsp; LetterBsbl; LetterFtbl; LetterWrstlng; PPFtbl; College; Professional.

PRATHER, Jeffrey A; Wheatland HS; Gore, KS; SecFrshCls; VPJrCls; Chr; HonRl; FFA; LetterBsktbl; Ftbl; LetterTrk; College.

PRATHER, John; Rockford West HS; Rockford, IL; 63/347 Chr; CmntyWkr; HonRl; IntrClCncl; Orch; SchMus; StuCncl; StuGov; Socr; College; Dteacher.

PRATHER, Robert A; Pike HS; Indpls, IN; TrsFrshCls; TrsSophCls; HonRl; StuGov; ALBoysSt; LetterBsktbl; AmLegAwd; Col; Lawyer.

PRATHER, Todd M; Glenwood Sr HS; Glenwood, IA; 24/110 VPFrshCls; CmntyWkr; HonRl; YthFlsp; FrCl; LetterBsbl; LetterBsktbl; LetterFtbl; LetterGlf; LetterTrk; CchngActv; IMSpt; College.

PRATT, Diana J; Harmony Comm HS; Keosauqua, IA; Band; Chrs; CncrtBnd; LbryAde; Mdrgl; MrchBnd; PepBnd; SchPl; Yrbk; 4-H; FHA; College; Professional.

PRATT, Frank; Bath HS; Bath, MI; 18/120 HonRl; RptrSchPpr; Lansing Community College; Engineer.

PRATT, Lynn C; Northridge HS; Middlebury, IN; Chr; ChrhWkr; NHS; SchMus; EdYrBk; SchPpr; 4-H; Chrldr; 4-HAwd; Purdue U; 4 H Youth Extension Agent.

PRATT, Michael R; Greensburg HS; Greensburg, IN; 35/200 VPJrCls; HonRl; JrNHS; StuCncl; YthFlsp; SptEdYrbk; LatCl; LetterBsbl; Bsktbl; LetterFtbl; College; Education.

PRATT, Rodger R; Wonewoc Center HS; Mauston, WI; SctActv; 4-H; FFA; Bsbl; Bsktbl; Ftbl; Trk; Professional Cop.

PRATT, Roxanne M; Sauk Rapids HS; Sauk Rapids, MN; 12/164 CncrtBnd; DrlTm; HonRl; MrchBnd; NHS; RptrYrbk; Yrbk; RptrSchPpr; SchPpr; 4-H; Trk; Montana St Univ; Nuclear Engineering.

PRATT, Sandra K; Muskego HS; Muskego, WI; TrsJrCls; VPSrCls; HonRl; OffAde; StuCncl; 4-H; SpnCl; PpCl; CaptChrldr; GAA; University; Physical Education.

PRATT, Teresa; Muskego HS; Muskego, WI; 61/329 ChrhWkr; HonRl; NatlFornLg; NHS; SchPl; SctActv; StuCncl; 4-H; FHA; 4-HAwd; Univ Wi Green Bay; Commun.

PRATT, Teri L; Forrest Strawn Wing HS; Cropsey, IL; 2/42 SecTrsFrshCls; AFS; DrlTm; HonRl; NHS; OffAde; SchPl; StuCncl; Yrbk; Pres4-H; TreasFFA; FHA; SpnCl; Trk; Junior College; Accounting.

PRAUS, Marlene; South Heart HS; South Heart, ND; 7/25 HonRl; LbryAde; SchPl; FHA;.

PRAVECEK, Debra M; Mitchell HS; Mitchell, SD; Band; DrlTm; NHS; SctActv; FBLA; FHA; PpCl; Bsktbl; Trk; IMSpt; Northern St Clge; Business.

PRAWL, Phyllis; Wathena HS; Wathena, KS; 2/40 SecJrCls; ALAGirlsSt; HonRl; SchPl; EdYrBk; PpCl; DanFAwd; Benedictine Col Atchison Ks; Language Major.

PREDIGER, Christine A; Collinsville HS; Collinsville, IL; 51/674 HonRl; NHS; OffAde; EdSchPpr; FHA; LatCl; SpnCl; PpCl; S Illinois Univ; English.

PREDIGER, Steven C; Mona Shores HS; Muskegon, MI; PresJrCls; PresSrCls; NHS; NatlMeritCmnd; StuCncl; LetterBsktbl; LetterFtbl; LetterTrk; Hope Coll; Mathematics.

PREDKO, Jean K; Catholic Central HS; Muskegon, MI; SecSophCls; HonRl; SchAde; SchMus; SchPl; StuGov; Yrbk; SpnCl; Bsktbl; Chrldr; Clg; Pro Design Of Acct.

PREDMORE, Terry L; Wethers Field HS; Kewanee, IL; HonRl; SchPl; Illinois St Univ; Business Admin.

PREEDY, Nancy K; Satanta HS; Satanta, KS; SecJrCls; Band; Chr; ChrhWkr; CncrtBnd; HonRl; MrchBnd; NHS; PepBnd; StuCncl; LetterBsktbl; CaptChrldr; PPFtbl; 4-HAwd; Business School; Secretary.

PREFFS, Judy; St Marys Cathedral HS; Gaylord, MI; 18/53 HonRl; NHS; SchAde; Yrbk; LatCl; PpCl; College; Family Relation & Human Behavior.

PREHEIM, Jill R; Freeman HS; Freeman, SD; 1/52 Chrs; SecFrshCls; HonRl; TreasNHS; SchMus; YthFlsp; RptrSchPpr; FHA; PpCl; Trk; Freeman Jr Coll; Child Psychology.

PREHN, James E; Mc Bain Public HS; Mc Bain, MI; ALBoysSt; Band; ChrhWkr; MrchBnd; NHS; NatlMeritCmnd; PepBnd; SchPl; YthFlsp; 4-H; PpCl; Michigan State Univ; Anthropology.

PREHODA, Valerie E; Calumet Public HS; Lake Linden, MI; HonRl; NatlFornLg; NHS; NatlMeritCmnd; OffAde; RptrSchPpr; LetterBsktbl; LetterTrk; Univ; Geological Engineer.

PRELL, Renae D; Catholic Memorial HS; Elm Grove, WI; CmntyWkr; HospAde; JrNHS; NHS; SchMus; SchPl; RptrYrbk; Yrbk; Univ Wis Stevens Point; Natural Resourses.

PRELLWITZ, Bruce E; Kearney Catholic HS; Kearney, NE; TrsSophCls; ALBoysSt; HonRl; MrchBnd; SctActv; StuCncl; SpnCl; LetterFtbl; LetterWrstlng; GodCntryAwd; College; Medical.

PRELLWITZ, Randy S; Fairbury HS; Reynolds, NE; PresJrCls; ChrhWkr; CmntyWkr; HonRl; RedCrAde; SctActv; StuCncl; IMSpt; OptClAwd; RotaryAwd; Milford Tech Clge; Auto Tech.

PREMACK, Paul; Central HS; Aberdeen, SD; AFS; Chr; ChrhWkr; HonRl; Mdrgl; NatlFornLg; SchMus; SchPl; DARAwd; Univ; Prof.

PREMEAU, Chad P; Medford HS; Greenwood, WI; 1/238 CncrtBnd; HonRl; MrchBnd; NHS; NatlMeritFnl; PepBnd; StuCncl; TchrAde; SciCl; Trk; College; Teacher.

PREMO, Dennis M; Adams Friendship HS; Westfield, WI; HonRl; SctActv; TchrAde; 4-H; FFA; Bsktbl; Ftbl; Wrstlng; PPFtbl; Tech School; Commercial Art.

PREMO, Susan J; Libertyville HS; Libertyville, IL; 74/431 AFS; ChrhWkr; HonRl; SchPl; YthFlsp; PresFrCl; University Of Illinois.

PRENDERGAST, Sharon E; Sisseton HS; Sisseton, SD; 1/96 TreasALAGirlsSt; Band; Chrs; HonRl; HospAde; NHS; NatlThespSoc; SecStuCncl; SecPpCl; LetterBsktbl; Sd St U;teaching.

PRENDIVILLE, Kerry L; St Marys HS; Ralph, SD; 3/50 PresJrCls; Band; ChrhWkr; CncrtBnd; HonRl; MrchBnd; PepBnd; SchPl; StuCncl; SptEdYrbk; University.

PRENGER, Beatrice M; Macon County R 1 HS; Macon, MO; Chr; ChrhWkr; DrlTm; HonRl; SchMus; FrCl; TreasPpCl; LetterTennis; Trk; KiwanAwd; College; Special Education.

PRENGER, Loran E; Jefferson City HS; Jefferson City, MO; 5/488 HonRl; NHS; Sdlty; 4-H; LatCl; Univ Of Missouri; Medicine.

PRENGER, Loran E; Jefferson HS; Jefferson City, MO; 15/502 HonRl; NHS; Sdlty; 4-H; LatCl; College; Professional.

PRENTICE, Peggy A; Cornell HS; Cornell, WI; Band; HonRl; SchPl; PresYthFlsp; RptrYrbk; RptrSchPpr; PpCl; LetterBsktbl; LetterTrk; GAA; IMSpt; University; Medical Technology.

PRENTISS, Tyrone E; Southeastern HS; Detroit, MI; 6/113 Chr; ChrhWkr; HonRl; Univ Of Mich; Business Adm.

PRENTLER, Stacey A; Leslie HS; Mason, MI; 6/99 Chr; HonRl; NHS; OffAde; SchMus; StuCncl; Univ; Mgmt Position In Data Processing.

PRESAR, Jeffrey D; New Trier West HS; Winnetka, IL; Aud/Vis; HonRl; SctActv; StuCncl; StuGov; TchrAde; Bsbl; Wrstlng; Ohio Univ; Business.

PRESCOTT, Mary; Divine Savior Holy Angels HS; Wauwatosa, WI; 1/140 HonRl; IntrClCncl; JrNHS; NatlMeritSF; Quill&Scroll; SchMus; TchrAde; RptrYrbk; EdSchPpr; University; Md Radiology.

PRESCOTT, Ralph A; Hononegah HS; Rockton, IL; 10/185 Band; CncrtBnd; HonRl; MrchBnd; NHS; Orch; PepBnd; SchMus; StuCncl; 4-H; SpnCl; LetterBsktbl; LetterFtbl; JETSAwd; Michigan Tech Univ; Engineer.

PRESCOTT, Valarie A; Imlay City HS; Imlay City, MI; 10/150 HonRl; HospAde; NHS; RedCrAde; TchrAde; RptrYrbk; 4-H; FSA; LetterBsktbl; GAA; Kalamazoo Col; Med Doctor.

PRESCOTT, William J; Broken Bow HS; Broken Bow, NE; 41/109 SecTrsSophCls; Band; Chr; Chrl; Chrs; ChrhWkr; CmntyWkr; CncrtBnd; HonRl; MrchBnd; PepBnd; Bsktbl; LetterFtbl; Trk; College; Music.

PRESIDIO, Derrick R; Beaverton HS; Beaverton, MI; 7/135 PresFrshCls; VPSophCls; VPSrCls; HonRl; JrNHS; NHS; NatlMeritCmnd; StuCncl; Central Michigan University; Computer.

PRESLER, Kenda L; Humboldt HS; Thor, IA; Chrs; ChrhWkr; HonRl; OffAde; SchMus; SchPl; TchrAde; 4-H; Trk; 4-HAwd; Bus Sch; Secretary.

PRESLER, Randy; Wilsonville Hs; Wilsonville, NE; VPSophCls; VPBand; HonRl; MrchBnd; SchPl; RptrYrbk; RptrSchPpr; LetterBsktbl; LetterFtbl; LetterTrk; College ; Vocation.

PRESPERIN, Jessica J; Prospect HS; Mt Prospect, IL; Chr; CmntyWkr; HonRl; Harper Jr Col; Math.

PRESS, Randy J; Quinter HS; Quinter, KS; PresFrshCls; HonRl; JrNHS; NHS; StuCncl; StuGov; RptrYrbk; SptEdYrbk; Bsktbl; Ftbl; Univ; Chem Or Computer Engin.

PRESSLEY, Karen; Mother Of Sorrows HS; Alsip, IL; 10/147 Chr; Chrs; ChrhWkr; HonRl; JA; NHS; SchMus; TchrAde; FrCl; VFWAwd; VoiceDemAwd; College; Paramedic Of Trauma Nurse.

PRESSWOOD, Randall L; Wentz HS; Wentzville, MO; Band; ChrhWkr; CncrtBnd; HonRl; MrchBnd; PepBnd; SchMus; SchPl; SctActv; StuCncl; College; Theatre.

PRESTAY, Helen C; North Central Area HS; Powers, MI; 4/56 Band; Chrs; ChrhWkr; HonRl; LbryAde; SchPl; StuCncl; Teen; RptrSchPpr; 4-H; KeyCl; Mi Tech Univ; Chemical Engineering.

PRESTEBAK, Jane L; Goodridge HS; Goodridge, MN; PresSophCls; PresJrCls; HonRl; StuCncl; RptrYrbk; RptrSchPpr; 4-H; Bsktbl; Chrldr; GAA; Clge.

PRESTEGARD, Pauline A; Bricelyn Public HS; Bricelyn, MN; 7/29 VPSophCls; CncrtBnd; HonRl; NHS; PepBnd; PresStuCncl; YthFlsp; CaptBsktbl; LetterTrk; PresGAA; College; Special Ed Teacher.

PRESTON, Amy L; Elk Grove HS; Elk Grove Vlg, IL; ChrhWkr; HonRl; NHS; NatlMeritCmnd; Quill&Scroll; StuCncl; StuGov; RptrYrbk; Yrbk; CaptChrldr; Northern Il Univ; Journalism.

PRESTON, Denise A; Missouri Valley HS; Missouri Valley, IA; DrlTm; Yrbk; Pres4-H; FHA; PpCl; Chrs; Bsktbl; Ftbl; Trk; 4-HAwd; Trade School; Vocatior.

PRESTON, Guadalupe; The Immaculata HS; Chicago, IL; 11/201 HonRl; NHS; RptrYrbk; RptrSchPpr; Northwestern Univ; Diplomatic Law.

PRESTON, Jill A; Watseka Comm HS; Watseka, IL; VPAFS; Band; Chr; HonRl; RusCl; Bsbl; LetterTennis; LetterTrk; VP4-HAwd; Coll; Phy Educ.

PRESTON, Kandis A; Haven HS; Mt Hope, KS; Band; Chr; ChrhWkr; HonRl; HospAde; Mdrgl; PepBnd; SchMus; TchrAde; YthFlsp; Friends U; Music.

PRESTON, Kristi L; Rosalie Public HS; Rosalie, NE; SecSophCls; PresJrCls; Chrs; HonRl; SchMus; SchPl; PpCl; Chrldr; Lincoln School Of Commerce; Secretary.

PRESTON, Randy L; Camden Frontier HS; Frontier, MI; ChrhWkr; CmntyWkr; HonRl; SchPl; TchrAde; YthFlsp; 4-H; FFA; Bsbl; Bsktbl; College; Vocational.

PRESTON, Robin P; Unity HS; Chicago, IL; PresFrshCls; VPSophCls; PresJrCls; Chr; YthFlsp; RptrYrbk; RptrSchPpr; SchPpr; PpCl; CitAwd; College.

PRESTON, Tomie A; Lenox Community HS; Lenox, IA; 12/47 CaptFtbl; College.

PRESUHN, Randall M; Fergus Falls HS; Fergus Falls, MN; 4/303 AFS; ChrhWkr; NHS; NatlMeritSF; NatlThespSoc; SchPl; SctActv; GerCl; Coll.

PRESUILL, William I; Highland Park HS; Highland Park, IL; NatlFornLg; Orch; PolWkr; SchMus; SchPl; TchrAde; College; History.

PRETNAR, Alan A; Nokomis HS; Nokomis, IL; 21/98 ALBoysSt; HonRl; FFA; LetterBsbl; LetterFtbl; Tennis; LetterWrstlng; University; Professional.

PRETTI, Gerald; J E Murphy HS; Montreal, WI; 3/120 Band; HonRl; NHS; NatlMeritFnl; SchPl; Yrbk; SptEdSchPpr; AmLegAwd; Usma West Point; Nuclear Engineering.

PRETTI, Gerald L; J E Murphy HS; Montreal, WI; 3/120 Band; HonRl; NatlMeritSF; SchMus; SchPl; Yrbk; SptEdSchPpr; LetterTrk; LetterWrstlng; IMSpt; College; Engineering.

PRETTYMAN, Gerald R; Rosemounst HS; Apple Valley, MN; Chr; HonRl; LbryAde; TchrAde; University; Biology.

PRETTYMAN, Glenn C; Central HS; Omaha, NE; Band; Chr; CncrtBnd; MrchBnd; PepBnd; SchMus; YthFlsp; GerCl; MthCl; Glf; IMSpt; GodCntryAwd; University Of Nebraska; Architecture.

PRETTYMAN, Timothy L; Terumieh HS; Tecumseh, MI; 1/244 ALBoysSt; NHS; NatlMeritFnl; NatlMeritCmnd; SchPl; YthFlsp; SpnCl; Ftbl; U Of Mi; Engineering.

PRETZER, Sherie J; Velva Public HS; Velva, ND; 9/47 Band; CmntyWkr; HonRl; NHS; PolWkr; StuCncl; FBLA; GerCl; SciCl; LetterBsktbl; GAA;.

PREUSCH, Connie M; Marian Catholic HS; Chicago Hts, IL; 65/336 ChrhWkr; CmntyWkr; HonRl; NHS; Sdlty; StuCncl; LatCl; Prairie State College; Nursing.

PREUSS, Charlene R; Manistee HS; Manistee, MI; Band; Chr; CncrtBnd; HonRl; MrchBnd; Yrbk; RptrSchPpr; GAA; PPFtbl; Trade Sch; Vocation.

PREUSS, Margaret; Alexander Hamilton HS; Milaukee, WI; HonRl; MrchBnd; EdYrBk; RptrSchPpr; PpCl; GAA; IMSpt; PPFtbl; Wu Madison.

PREWETT, Jennie R; Marshall HS; Marshall, IL; 6/115 CncrtBnd; MrchBnd; PepBnd; FFA; FHA; SciCl; U Of Illinois; Agriculture.

PREWITT, Regina C; St John Cathedral HS; Milwaukee, WI; Band; CncrtBnd; JrNHS; MrchBnd; Orch; SchMus; Univ; Music.

PREYER, Herbert M; Malden HS; Malden, MO; Band; CncrtBnd; HonRl; MrchBnd; PepBnd; FrCl; Bsktbl; Tennis; College.

PRIBBENO, Michael S; Chase County HS; Imperial, NE; YthFlsp; CaptBsktbl; CaptFtbl; LetterTrk; CchngActv; College.

PRIBBENOW, Mark D; Denver Community HS; Denver, IA; VPFrshCls; VPSophCls; ALBoysSt; Chrs; HonRl; PepBnd; StuCncl; LetterBsktbl; LetterFtbl; PresAwd; College; Accountant.

PRIBBENOW, Paul P; Denver HS; Denver, IA; ALBoysSt; Band; Chr; ChrhWkr; HonRl; NHS; SchMus; YthFlsp; Yrbk; DanFAwd; Luther Col; Ministry.

PRIBBENOW, Toyia A; Haven HS; Sedgwick, KS; 5/92 Band; Chr; Chrl; CncrtBnd; HonRl; MrchBnd; PepBnd; SchPl; 4-H; 4-HAwd; Emporia Ks State Clge; Certified Pub Accoun.

PRIBBLE, Holly A; Mt Assisi Academy; Summit, IL; HonRl; JrNHS; LitMag; ModUN; NHS; Yrbk; Loyola Univ; Artist.

PRICCO, Martin F; Hall HS; Ladd, IL; 2/134 HonRl; Yrbk; PpCl; Glf; Univ Of Ill.

PRICE, Angela; Northwest HS; University City, MO; 8/389 ChrhWkr; HonRl; JA; MrchBnd; NHS; GAA; IMSpt; JAAwd; PresAwd; CitAwd; U Of Kansas; Architectural Engineer.

PRICE, Bradley E; Benton Cone HS; Benton, IL; Band; ChrhWkr; CmntyWkr; NHS; SchMus; StuCncl; YthFlsp; FFA; Bsktbl;.

PRICE, Charles E; Malden HS; Malden, MO; 7/104 HonRl; NatlMeritCmnd; StuCncl; Yrbk; RptrSchPpr; FFA; LetterBsktbl; Glf; University Of Missouri; Agriculture.

PRICE, Cheryl L; Paseo HS; Kansas City, MO; AFS; Chr; CmntyWkr; HonRl; JA; SctActv; PresStuCncl; RptrYrbk; RptrSchPpr; SciCl; Carleton Clg; Peditrician.

PRICE, Cindy J; Mt Pleasant Sr HS; Mt Pleasant, MI; HonRl; TchrAde; Central Michigan University; Teacher.

PRICE, Clifford R; Lindblom Tech HS; Chicago, IL; TchrAde; YthFnd; FBLA; LetterBsbl; LetterBsktbl; CaptFtbl; LetterTrk; LetterWrstlng; CchngActv; IMSpt; Tn St Univ; Busi Admin.

PRICE, David D; Cook HS; Cook, MN; PresFrshCls; PresSophCls; PresSrCls; Band; HonRl; StuCncl; RptrYrbk; SptEdSchPpr; Ftbl; Trk; VoiceDemAwd; U Of Minnesota; Tela Communications.

PRICE, Donald; Rolling Meadows HS; Arlington Heights, IL; HonRl; Quill&Scroll; RptrSchPpr; SchPpr; Univ Of Urbana Ill; Diving Instructor.

PRICE, Donald W; St Elmo HS; St Elmo, IL; 1/56 PresSophCls; Band; Chrs; HonRl; University Of Illinois; Accounting.

PRICE, Geania E; Chicago Vocational HS; Chicago, IL; 71/667 HonRl; LbryAde; SchPl; StuCncl; TchrAde; GAA; N Ill U; Professional.

PRICE, Greg R; Harrisonville HS; Harrisonville, MO; 29/146 DrmBgl; HonRl; NatlFornLg; SctActv; GodCntryAwd; U Of Columbia; Science.

PRICE, G S; So Soo HS; So Sioux City, NE; Band; CncrtBnd; HonRl; MrchBnd; PepBnd; SchMus; YthFlsp; SpnCl; PpCl; Nursing School; Nurse.

PRICE, Jennifer L; Edwardsville Senior HS; Edwardsville, IL; Chr; CmntyWkr; HonRl; NHS; PresStuCncl; StuGov; YthFlsp; GerCl; PPFtbl; AmLegAwd; College; Nurse.

PRICE, Joyce Y; Lindblum Technical HS; Chicago, IL; 45/695 HonRl; NHS; NatlMeritSF; SchAde; TchrAde; RptrYrbk; FrCl; Univ Of Southern Cal; Psychology.

PRICE, Joyce Y; Lindblom Tech HS; Chicago, IL; HonRl; SchAde; TchrAde; RptrYrbk; Yrbk; Univ Of Illinois; Psychology.

PRICE, Karen K; Broken Bow HS; Broken Bow, NE; CncrtBnd; HonRl; LbryAde; MrchBnd; PepBnd; RedCrAde; FHA; PpCl; Trk; PresAwd; College; Vocation.

PRICE, Karen L; Hillsdale HS; Hillsdale, MI; Chr; HonRl; NHS; NatlMeritSchl; SchMus; StuCncl; StuGov; Yrbk; 4-H; 4-HAwd;.

PRICE, Kathryn L; Onarga HS; Onarga, IL; HonRl; OffAde; Trade Schl; Auto Mechanic.

PRICE, Kathy L; Stevenson HS; Livonia, MI; College; Business Acctg.

PRICE, Kenneth S; Houghton HS; Houghton, MI; Band; Chrs; CncrtBnd; HonRl; MrchBnd; NatlMeritFnl; Orch; SctActv; Coll.

PRICE, Kevin M; Fenton HS; Holly, MI; Chr; Trk; IMSpt; Univ; Architect.

PRICE, Ki A; Springfield HS; Springfield, IL; 48/550 Chr; Chrs; HonRl; TchrAde; RptrSchPpr; Sec4-H; PpCl; Bsktbl; Trk; GAA; Community College; Architectural Draftsman.

PRICE, Lawrence T; Lake Forest HS; Lake Forest, IL; CaptBsbl; LetterBsktbl; CaptGlf; Univ; Golf Professional.

PRICE, Margaret; Manhattan HS; Manhatten, KS; ChrhWkr; HonRl; HospAde; NatlThespSoc; Orch; SchMus; SchPl; PpCl; College; English Drama.

PRICE, Mary Jean G; Cor Jesu Academy; St Louis, MO; Chrl; HonRl; JA; LitMag; RptrYrbk; SpnCl; IMSpt; College.

PRICE, Mary L; Muskegon Catholic Central HS; Muskegon, MI; 28/209 TrsSrCls; HonRl; NHS; StuCncl; Swmmng; IMSpt; St Marys Of Notre Dame; Math.

PRICE, Mary R; Hilbert HS; Hilbert, WI; 4/70 HonRl; LbryAde; NHS; TchrAde; Yrbk; LetterBsktbl; LetterTrk; GAA; IMSpt; U Of Oshkosh ;acct.

PRICE, Melinda A; Valley Park HS; Valley Park, MO; Chrs; HonRl; NHS; SchMus; VPStuCncl; FHA; FrCl; CaptChrldr; GAA; AmLegAwd; Meramec Community College; Accounting.

PRICE, Merrie B; Jefferson HS; Rockford, IL; AFS; HonRl; NHS; TchrAde; RptrSchPpr; Univ Of Texas; Social Worker.

PRICE, Michael T; Berkley HS; Berkley, MI; Band; Chr; JA; Mdrgl; MrchBnd; PepBnd; RptrYrbk; Yrbk; College; Business Admins.

PRICE, Robin L; Waverly HS; Waverly, IL; Band; NHS; NatlThespSoc; SchPl; YthFlsp; 4-H; FHA; FTA; PpCl; Bsbl; Trk; IMSpt; College; Liberal Arts.

PRICE, Roger; Highland HS; Monticello, MO; 1/129 VPSophCls; PresSrCls; Band; ChrhWkr; CncrtBnd; HonRl; NHS; PepBnd; StuCncl; FSA; College; Biology.

PRICE, Sharyn A; Traverse City Senior HS; Traverse City, MI; ChrhWkr; HonRl; HospAde; PolWkr; StuCncl; StuGov; RptrSchPpr; PpCl; Bsktbl; GAA; Oakland University; Business Management.

PRICE, Sheryl F; Roosevelt HS; Gary, IN; 56/623 Band; CncrtBnd; HonRl; JrNHS; MrchBnd; NatlMeritCmnd; OffAde; Orch; ROTC; SchMus; Ball St U; Broadcasting.

PRICE, Terry L; Norfolk Catholic HS; Norfolk, NE; HonRl; NHS; PpCl; BttyCrckrAwd; Northeast Nebr Tech Comm Clg; Auto Mechanic.

PRICE, Thomas M; Milbank HS; Milbank, SD; ALBoysSt; Chrs; Mdrgl; StuGov; KeyCl; Bsbl; Bsktbl; Ftbl; Trk; Wrstlng; CchngActv; IMSpt; Northern St College; Recreation.

PRICE, Timothy A; Norfolk Catholic HS; Norfolk, NE; HonRl; NHS; SptEdSchPpr; SchPpr; LetterFtbl; LetterWrstlng; College.

PRICH, Gerry R; Owen Gage HS; Gagetown, MI; PresSrCls; Chr; HonRl; SchPl; RptrYrbk; RptrSchPpr; Central Mi Univ; Journalism.

PRICHARD, Dennis L; Meramec Valley R Iii HS; Pacific, MO; 26/182 PresSrCls; Band; CncrtBnd; DrmMjrt; HonRl; MrchBnd; Bsbl; Bsktbl; Ftbl; Trk; IMSpt; JCAwd; Bradley Univ; Engineering.

PRICHARD, Elizabeth A; Douglass HS; Douglass, KS; 10/45 DrlTm; HospAde; Band; PresNatlThespSoc; SchPl; StuCncl; TchrAde; RptrYrbk; SchPpr; PpCl; Sw Univ; Theater Arts.

PRICHARD, James; Storm Lake HS; Storm Lake, IA; 1/140 AFS; ALBoysSt; Band; ChrhWkr; CncrtBnd; MrchBnd; NHS; IMSpt; KiwanAwd; Lib Arts College; Liberal Arts.

PRICHARD, Susan; Oxford HS; Oxford, KS; 4/39 Band; HonRl; NHS; PepBnd; SctActv; EdYrBk; RptrSchPpr; PpCl; LetterTrk; BttyCrckrAwd; Cowley Cnty Coll; Accounting.

PRICKETT, Barbara S; Mt Pleasant HS; Salem, IA; Chr; ChrhWkr; HonRl; YthFlsp; FHA; Vocation.

PRICKETT, Donna J; Stillman Valley HS; Davis Junction, IL; Band; CncrtBnd; HonRl; MrchBnd; NHS; PepBnd; SchMus; RptrSchPpr; FHA; FTA; Col.

PRIDAVKA, Gary M; Niles HS; Niles, MI; 11/364 VPJrCls; PresSrCls; HonRl; NHS; SchPl; RptrYrbk; PresLatCl; CaptFtbl; LetterTrk; CaptWrstlng; Calamazoo Clge; Bus Admin.

PRIDDY, Lisa; Junction City Senior HS; Junction City, KS; DrlTm; HonRl; HospAde; PolWkr; SchMus; SctActv; RptrYrbk; SptEdYrbk; PpCl; PPFtbl; Kansas St Univ.

PRIDE, Dale R; Eisenhower HS; Decatur, IL; 16/301 HonRl; NHS; Milwaukee School Of Eng; Engineering.

PRIDE, Linda; Springfield Southeast Hs; Springfield, IL; Chr; PresCncrtBnd; HonRl; LbryAde; MrchBnd; NatlThespSoc; PepBnd; SchPl; StuCncl; PresFrCl; College; Environmental Studies.

PRIDE, Michael K; Castle HS; Newburgh, IN; 25/284 Band; CncrtBnd; HonRl; LatCl; Indiana Univ; Medicine.

PRIDE, Steven; Maryville HS; Maryville, MO; 21/128 ALBoysSt; Band; CncrtBnd; MrchBnd; NHS; PepBnd; SchMus; StuCncl; SciCl; GodCntryAwd; Northwest Mo State Univ; Music.

PRIDE, Steven D; Maryville HS; Maryville, MO; 21/114 Band; CncrtBnd; MrchBnd; NHS; PepBnd; SchMus; StuCncl; SciCl; Northwest Mo State University; Music.

PRIDE, Vernon R; Oak Park Academy HS; Nevada, IA; VPFrshCls; Bsbl; Bsktbl; Ftbl; Swmmng; Trk; Walla Walla College; Nurse.

PRIDIE, Jeanne R; Akron Comm HS; Akron, IA; Chr; Chrs; HonRl; NHS; StuCncl; 4-H; FHA; FrCl; PpCl; Chrldr; College; Home Economics.

PRIDJIAN, Ara K; Morgan Park Academy; Palos Hts, IL; HonRl; JrNHS; LitMag; ModUN; NHS; NatlThespSoc; SchMus; SchPl; StuCncl; KeyCl; LetterTrk; College; Medicine.

PRIEB, Robert C; Hillsboro HS; Hillsboro, KS; 5/66 PresSophCls; PresSrCls; ChrhWkr; HonRl; StuCncl; Yrbk; SchPpr; Bsktbl; CaptFtbl; LetterGlf; College; Math Computor Area.

PRIEBE, David L; Maynard Public HS; Maynard, MN; 2/26 VPSrCls; Band; Chrs; ChrhWkr; CncrtBnd; HonRl; NHS; PepBnd; SchPl; StuCncl; Univ Of Mn Morris; Med Field.

PRIEFERT, Mary E; Fairmont Public HS; Fairmont, NE; Band; Chr; Chrs; ChrhWkr; CncrtBnd; HonRl; LbryAde; MrchBnd; PepBnd; SchPl; Peru State Clg.

PRIEM, Charles I; Arthur Hill HS; Saginaw, MI; Aud/Vis; Band; Chr; ChrhWkr; CncrtBnd; MrchBnd; PepBnd; SctActv; YthFlsp; College; Dentistry.

PRIEN, Cheryl A; Monroe HS; Monroe, WI; ChrhWkr; HonRl; SpnCl; PpCl; Trk; College; Pharmacy.

PRIESS, Linda J; Carmel HS; Lake Zurich, IL; 31/173 Univ Of Illinois; Journalism.

PRIEST, David E; Heritage HS; Ft Wayne, IN; Band; CncrtBnd; DrmMjrt; PresNHS; PresYthFlsp; Trk; College; Professional.

PRIEST, Gale D; Kinsley HS; Kinsley, KS; 1/78 Chr; HonRl; NatlMeritCmnd; SchMus; PpCl; Bsktbl;.

PRIEST, Jolene R; Wauneta HS; Hamlet, NE; Chr; SchMus; SchPl; StuCncl; YthFlsp; Yrbk; Pres4-H; FHA; PpCl; LetterTrk; College; Nurse.

PRIEST, Roxanna; North Putnam HS; Roachdale, IN; ChrhWkr; DrlTm; HonRl; NHS; CaptSwmmng; Indiana Bus Clg.

PRIESTLEY, Beth A; Libertyville HS; Libertyville, IL; 86/431 Chrs; ChrhWkr; HonRl; NHS; NatlMeritCmnd; SchMus; SchPl; SctActv; Trk; College; Commercial Art.

PRIEUR, Diana M; Alpena Senior HS; Alpena, MI; HonRl; Orch; SchMus; RptrYrbk; RptrSchPpr; GerCl; SciCl; College; Forest Technology.

PRIEVE, Kathleen; Hutchinson HS; Hutchinson, MN; 6/187 AFS; Chr; HonRl; NHS; NatlThespSoc; SchMus; YthFlsp; FBLA; JCAwd; Hamlin Univ; Biochem.

PRIKAZSKY, Wencelaus; St Ignatius HS; Berwyn, IL; 21/155 JrNHS; NHS; StuGov; CaptSocr; Illinois Inst Of Tech; Engineering.

PRIM, Dale L; Poplar Bluff HS; Poplar Bluff, MO; 70/400 HonRl; YthFlsp; SciCl; Bsbl; Ftbl; LetterSwmmng; IMSpt; EldAwd; CitAwd; College; Professional Architecture.

PRINC, Elaine K; Lucas HS; Lucas, KS; 1/13 PresFrshCls; TrsJrCls; SecSrCls; HonRl; NHS; SchPl; StuCncl; EdYrBk; Pres4-H; PresPpCl; Fort Hays Kansas State Clg; Home Ec.

PRINCE, Barbara J; Tinley Park HS; Tinley Park, IL; 9/304 TrsJrCls; SecSrCls; HonRl; NHS; TchrAde; PpCl; Thornton Community College.

PRINCE, Betty A; Covert HS; South Haven, MI; CncrtBnd; HonRl; MrchBnd; OffAde; PepBnd; TchrAde; RptrYrbk; Yrbk; FHA; SpnCl; Ferris St Coll; Data Processing Bus.

PRINCE, Charles S; Elmhurst HS; Fort Wayne, IN; Chr; ChrhWkr; CmntyWkr; HonRl; YthFlsp; LatCl; SpnCl; LetterBsbl; Taylor University.

PRINCE, Richard; Faulkton HS; Faulkton, SD; CmntyWkr; HonRl; LbryAde; SchPl; RptrSchPpr; 4-H; Bsbl; Glf; College.

PRINDLE, Don A; Sweet Springs HS; Sweet Springs, MO; 2/62 VPFrshCls; VPSophCls; ALBoysSt; ChrhWkr; HonRl; NHS; 4-H; SciCl; LetterBsktbl; LetterTrk; Col; Pro.

PRING, Cynthia K; Centennial HS; Champaign, IL; Chr; Chrs; ChrhWkr; DrlTm; HospAde; NatlThespSoc; SchMus; SchPl; SctActv; PpCl; GAA; Coll; Oceanography.

PRINGLE, Barbara J; Yates Center HS; Yates Center, KS; Band; Chr; Chrl; Chrs; ChrhWkr; CncrtBnd; HonRl; LbryAde; MrchBnd; NHS; PepBnd; 4-H; FHA; Jr College; Home Economics.

PRINGLE, Joseph B; Hinsdale Central HS; Hinsdale, IL; 135/600 HonRl; Yrbk; SchPpr; LetterSwmmng; College; Business.

PRINGNITZ, Tami D; Kanawha HS; Kanawha, IA; Band; Chrs; ChrhWkr; CncrtBnd; HonRl; Mdrgl; MrchBnd; Bsktbl; Univ; Physical Therapy.

PRIOR, Cynthia K; Dupo Comm HS; Dupo, IL; TrsJrCls; HonRl; NHS; StuCncl; TchrAde; MthCl; Chrldr; PPFtbl; Professional.

PRIORE, Anthony; Glenbrook South HS; Glenview, IL; 41/600 HonRl; JrNHS; NHS; PolWkr; StuGov; VPKeyCl; LetterSocr; LetterTrk; Northwestern U; Lawyer.

PRISTO, Lori A; Hinsdale Central HS; Oakbrook, IL; 56/584 Chrs; ChrhWkr; HonRl; College; Architect.

PRITCHARD, Michael; Spalding Acad; Spalding, NE; ChrhWkr; SctActv; StuCncl; StuGov; FFA; Bsbl; Ftbl; Trk; Wrstlng; IMSpt; Trade; Farmer.

PRITCHARD, Stephanie J; Superior Senior HS; Superior, WI; 31/590 Chrs; CmntyWkr; HonRl; HospAde; NatlMeritSF; SchPl; YthLg; College; Professional.

PRITCHARD, Wayne D; Bloomer HS; Bloomer, WI; AFS; Aud/Vis; Chrs; SchPl; StuCncl; SptEdYrbk; FFA; PpCl; LetterBsbl; LetterFtbl; IMSpt; College; Computer Operator.

PRITCHETT, Karen E; Holly Sr HS; Holly, MI; 4/225 Chr; Mdrgl; NHS; SchMus; PresFrCl; LetterBsktbl; LetterTrk; IMSpt; Central Mich U; Science.

PRITCHETT, Rodney R; Goreville HS; Goreville, IL; 5/30 Band; CncrtBnd; HonRl; MrchBnd; StuCncl; StuGov; RptrYrbk; FFA; Technical Sch; Electr Engineer.

PRITCHETT, Timothy M; Bloomington HS; Bloomington, WI; 1/55 ALBoysSt; Band; Chrs; Mdrgl; NHS; SchMus; RptrYrbk; Bsktbl; LetterTrk; 4-HAwd; College; Physical Sciences.

PRIVETT, Debra L; Duluth Central HS; Duluth, MN; 47/440 Chr; HonRl; NatlFornLg; NHS; SchMus; SchPl; RptrSchPpr; Umd; Medicine Pediatrician.

PRIVETTE, Steve A; Willow Springs HS; Willow Springs, MO; StuCncl; VPFFA; LetterWrstlng;.

PRIVITOR, Jim F; Southwest HS; St Louis, MO; PresSrCls; HonRl; NatlMeritSchl; TchrAde; SptEdSchPpr; MthCl; Bsbl; Socr; IMSpt; College; Electrician.

PRIZANT, Paula; Von Steuben Hs; Chicago, IL; 9/231 Band; CncrtBnd; HonRl; NHS; TchrAde; RptrSchPpr; GAA; Northwestern U; Medicine.

PROBST, Angela J; Teutopolis HS; Sigel, IL; TrsJrCls; DrlTm; HonRl; FHA; GerCl; PpCl; GAA; Nursing School; Nurse.

PROBST, John S; St Mary Central HS; Menasha, WI; HonRl; StuCncl; RptrSchPpr; SptEdSchPpr; SpnCl; LetterBsbl; LetterBsktbl; Ftbl; LetterTrk; College; Liberal Arts.

PROBST, Lucinda K; Northwestern HS; Palmyra, IL; 7/58 DrlTm; HonRl; SchPl; TchrAde; FHA; FTA; Trk; Chrldr; GAA; Western Il Univ; Elem Ed.

PROBST, Nancy G; Newton Comm HS; Wheeler, IL; 7/182 HonRl; NHS; 4-H; Univ Of Illinois; Computer Science.

PROBST, Pamela J; Our Lady Of Peace HS; St Paul, MN; 7/135 HstFrshCls; Chrs; CmntyWkr; HonRl; HospAde; SchMus; SchPl; StuCncl; StuGov; SpnCl; MthCl; College; Nurse.

PROBST, Theresa H; Newton HS; Wheeler, IL; Chrs; HonRl; JrNHS; StuCncl; 4-H; FBLA; PpCl; GAA; 4-HAwd; Lakeland Jr Col; Secretarial.

PROCHASKA, Sandra D; Good Counsel HS; Chicago, IL; 13/285 Chrs; SchMus; SchPl; StuCncl; SciCl; GAA; College Or Univ.

PROCHAZKA, Dudley M; Hemingford HS; Hemingford, NE; HonRl; NHS; SchPl; TchrAde; Yrbk; SciCl; Ftbl;.

PROCHNOW, Suzanne J; Bellevue Senior HS; Bellevue, NE; 1/660 HonRl; JrNHS; LitMag; NHS; SchMus; GerCl; PpCl; Trk; U Of Ne; English.

PROCHOVNICK, Ora S; Kenwood HS; Chicago, IL; 2/461 ChrhWkr; CmntyWkr; CncrtBnd; HonRl; NHS; NatlMeritFnl; Quill&Scroll; SchPpr; GerCl; MthCl; College; Mathematics.

PROCKNOW, Linda S; Jefferson HS; Jefferson, WI; SecJrCls; ChrhWkr; HonRl; SchMus; SchPl; PPFtbl; Col Or Univ; Veterinarian.

PROCTOR, Amanda A; Rochester HS; Rochester, MI; Chr; Chrs; ChrhWkr; HonRl; LbryAde; NatlMeritSF; SchMus; SchPl; RptrYrbk; Yrbk; Hillsdale Coll; Medicine.

PROCTOR, Brian D; Washington Senior HS; Washington, IA; 8/174 HonRl; NatlMeritSF; TchrAde; RptrSchPpr; FrCl; SpnCl; SciCl; LetterFtbl; Westmar College; Marine Biology.

PROCTOR, Brian D; Washington HS; Washington, IA; 7/172 HonRl; NHS; NatlMeritFnl; NatlMeritSchl; PolWkr; FrCl; TrsSophCls; SciCl; Ftbl; BauchLmbAwd; College; Marine Biologist.

PROCTOR, Diane P; Immaculata HS; Detroit, MI; Chr; ChrhWkr; CmntyWkr; HonRl; JA; NHS; PolWkr; SchMus; SchPl; StuGov; Spelman College; Journalism.

PROCTOR, Jody M; Mayville HS; Mayville, MI; 22/116 Band; ChrhWkr; CncrtBnd; HonRl; NHS; SchPl; Yrbk; RptrSchPpr; EdSchPpr; FHA; Bible Inst; Communications.

PROCTOR, Steven J; Montague HS; Montague, MI; 3/144 Chrs; ChrhWkr; HonRl; LbryAde; NHS; NatlMeritSF; SctActv; DanFAwd; Baptist Bible Coll; Pastorate.

PRODANOVICH, Gordana; Osseo Fairchild HS; Fairchild, WI; Aud/Vis; ChrhWkr; HonRl; NatlFornLg; NHS; NatlMeritCmnd; FHA; GerCl; LetterGAA; IMSpt; University; Biological Science.

PROEHL, Robert W; Braham HS; Raham, MN; TchrAde; Ftbl; Trk; LetterWrstlng; Vo Tech Sch; Vocational.

PROFFITT, Elizabeth A; Lisbon Community HS; Lisbon, IA; 2/36 Chrs; CncrtBnd; HonRl; HospAde; MrchBnd; NHS; SchMus; YthFlsp; 4-H; Bsktbl; LetterTrk; 4-HAwd; College; Nursing.

PROFFITT, Mary J; Waterford Township HS; Union Lake, MI; ChrhWkr; TchrAde; Michigan Christian Clg; Special Ed Teacher.

PROFFITT, Susan E; Waterford Township HS; Union Lake, MI; 8/414 ChrhWkr; HonRl; Geneal Motors Inst; Engineering.

PROFILET, Suzanne M; Bloomington HS; Bloomington, IL; 68/390 HonRl; JrNHS; NHS; SctActv; FrCl; PpCl; GAA; IMSpt; AmLegAwd; Illinois St Univ; Business.

PROFIT, Ricky; Ypsilanti HS; Ypsilanti, MI; 1/507 HonRl; NHS; YthFlsp; Bsbl; Mi Univ.

PROGAR, Donna; Kapaun Mt Carmel HS; Wichita, KS; 15/127 CmntyWkr; HonRl; RptrYrbk; RptrSchPpr; SpnCl; PpCl; Univ; Majorin Biology.

PROHASKA, Kathryn; Hiawatha HS; Hiawatha, KS; 7/99 PresFrshCls; VPSophCls; HonRl; NHS; NatlMeritCmnd; NatlThespSoc; OffAde; SchMus; SchPl; Bsktbl; Benedictine Coll; Medical Technology.

PROHASKA, Richard F; Morton West HS; Berwyn, IL; 75/800 HonRl; JrNHS; NHS; Sacrstn; SctActv; MthCl; SciCl; University; Bio Eng.

PROKASH, Jackie M; Assumption HS; Wis Rapids, WI; Band; CncrtBnd; HonRl; MrchBnd; PepBnd; SchPl; StuCncl; Twrl; RptrYrbk; RptrSchPpr; SpnCl; College.

PROKOP, Arlie; Friend Public HS; Friend, NE; 1/40 ChrhWkr; CmntyWkr; CncrtBnd; HonRl; Mdrgl; SchMus; SchPl; YthFlsp; SchPpr; LetterTrk; Coll; Major Englis Ele Ed.

PROKOP, Mary E; St Hedwig HS; Detroit, MI; 14/76 SecFrshCls; TrsSophCls; HonRl; NHS; StuCncl; Yrbk; Chrldr; VoiceDemAwd; Clge; Secretary.

PROKOP, Wendie L; Hay Springs HS; Hay Springs, NE; Chr; DrlTm; HonRl; LbryAde; SchPl; LetterTrk; PPFtbl; PresAwd; Gering Beatuy School; Beautician.

PROKOPOVITZ, Laura J; Pulaski HS; Pulaski, WI; 3/200 Band; ChrhWkr; CncrtBnd; HonRl; JrNHS; PepBnd; SpnCl; PpCl; GAA; Uw Stevens Point; Business.

PROKOPY, Lydia M; Lutheran West HS; Detroit, MI; ChrhWkr; CmntyWkr; HonRl; StuCncl; GerCl; PpCl; LetterBsktbl; GAA; Akland Comm Col; Medical Secretary.

PROM, Marijo; Cedar Grove HS; Belgium, WI; 14/82 VPJrCls; VPSrCls; Chrs; HonRl; SchPl; StuCncl; EdSchPpr; Chrldr; GAA; Columbia Hospital; Registered Nurse.

PROMBO, Michael J; Morris Community HS; Morris, IL; 17/230 HonRl; NHS; MthCl; LetterBsktbl; Ftbl; LetterTrk; Trade School.

PRONSCHINSKE, Cheryl; Cochrane Fountain City HS; Fountain City, WI; Aud/Vis; Band; CncrtBnd; MrchBnd; NHS; PepBnd; Yrbk; FBLA; GAA; Voc Sch; Bus.

PRONSCHINSKE, Rochelle A; Arcadia Public HS; Arcadia, WI; Band; HonRl; MrchBnd; NHS; PepBnd; SchMus; FHA; GAA; Univ Of Wi Stout; Fashion Merchandising.

PROOST, Jean L; Duchesne HS; St Charles, MO; Chrs; HonRl; HospAde; NHS; NatlMeritSchl; OffAde; StuCncl; UNYO; College; Professional.

PROPER, Sharon; Ontonagon Area HS; Ontonagon, MI; 30/107 Band; HonRl; PresHospAde; MrchBnd; PpCl; LetterBsktbl; LetterGlf; GAA; Northern Mich; Rn.

PROPP, Kathleen J; Minatare HS; Minatare, NE; 2/32 ALAGirlsSt; Band; Chrs; HonRl; NHS; SecStuCncl; PresPpCl; BttyCrckrAwd; DARAwd; EldAwd; Chadron St Clg; Music Teacher.

PROSHEK, W S; New Prague HS; New Prague, MN; 74/197 VPFrshCls; ALBoysSt; SctActv; StuCncl; CaptBsktbl; Coll Of St Thomas; Coaching.

PROSISE, William L; Durand HS; Durand, IL; Chr; CncrtBnd; HonRl; MrchBnd; PepBnd; SchMus; SpnCl; Bsktbl; Trk; College; Youth Minister.

PROSSER, Chuck B; Springs Valley HS; West Baden, IN; 3/80 SecJrCls; Aud/Vis; HonRl; LbryAde; 4-H; PpCl; Ftbl; Glf; Trk; IMSpt; Univ; Vocation.

PROSSER, Donn A; Maplewood Acad; Northome, MN; Chr; HonRl; StuCncl; Yrbk; College; Professional.

PROSSER, Ron E; Spring Valley HS; W Bden, IN; 3/80 Aud/Vis; HonRl; LbryAde; 4-H; PpCl; CaptTrk; CaptWrstlng;.

PROST, Warren G; St Thomas Seminary; Jefferson City, MO; 5/11 VPFrshCls; Chrs; HonRl; SchMus; SchPl; StuCncl; PpCl; Bsktbl; Socr; Chrldr; Seminary College; Priest.

PROSZOWSKI, Richard S; St Patrick HS; Chicago, IL; 1/375 HonRl; MthCl; Tennis; University; Math.

PROTEXTER, Lori M; Aberdeen Central HS; Aberdeen, SD; AFS; ChrhWkr; HonRl; SpnCl; PpCl; Trk; PPFtbl; College; Professional.

PROTHE, Darryl E; Paola HS; Paola, KS; 43/140 ChrhWkr; CmntyWkr; HonRl; StuCncl; 4-H; Bsbl; LetterBsktbl; LetterFtbl; LetterTrk; IMSpt; 4-HAwd; Kansas State Univ; Electronics.

PROTHE, James R; Paola HS; Paola, KS; 28/140 ALBoysSt; ChrhWkr; CmntyWkr; HonRl; 4-H; GerCl; Bsbl; LetterFtbl; Trk; LetterWrstlng; 4-HAwd; Allen Co Comm Jr College; Engineer.

PROTHE, Melissa M; Wabash HS; Wabash, IN; HonRl; NatlFornLg; NHS; NatlThespSoc; PolWkr; SchMus; SctActv; 4-H; GerCl; Chrldr; Univ; Pro.

PROUD, Lynette J; Hanover Central HS; Cedar Lake, IN; 8/140 HonRl; JrNHS; College; Professional.

PROUGH, Karolynn; Prairie Heights HS; Wolcottville, IN; 8/107 HonRl; LitMag; NHS; SchPl; Yrbk; Goshen Coll; Illustrator And Author.

PROULX, Denice E; Au Gres Sims HS; Au Gres, MI; 5/38 Band; ChrhWkr; CncrtBnd; HonRl; MrchBnd; NatlMeritCmnd; Orch; PepBnd; SchPl; YthFlsp; RptrYrbk; SptEdYrbk; RptrSchPpr; Bsbl; College; Data Processing.

PROUT, Kim A; Seymour HS; Seymour, IN; 60/300 Chr; ChrhWkr; HonRl; SchMus; SchPl; Sdlty; StuCncl; GerCl; LatCl; Trk; IMSpt; Hanover Clg; Pre Med.

PROUT, Lynda R; East Troy HS; Elkhorn, WI; AFS; Chr; Chrs; HonRl; NatlFornLg; NHS; SchPl; SpnCl; PPFtbl; Univ Of Wi; Music Education.

PROUTY, Denise; Hamlin HS; Bryant, SD; 2/66 VPFrshCls; Band; Chrs; CncrtBnd; HonRl; MrchBnd; PepBnd; SchPl; RptrYrbk; BttyCrckrAwd; Sd State Univ; Pre Law.

PROVANCE, Cindy; Malden HS; Malden, MO; Band; Chr; Chrs; ChrhWkr; CncrtBnd; DrmMjrt; HonRl; YthFlsp; FrCl; Chrldr; College; Counseling Or Music Theory.

PROVANCE, David R; Glendale HS; Springfield, MO; Ftbl; Wrstlng; IMSpt; Univ Of Mo; Vet.

PROVANCE, Keith R; E Alton Woodriver HS; Hartford, IL; ChrhWkr; JA; College; Business.

PROVANCHA, Louis E; Hallsville HS; Columbia, MO; ChrhWkr; HonRl; HospAde; NHS; SchAde; SchPl; TchrAde; RptrYrbk; AmLegAwd; Columbia School Of Nursing; Nursing.

PROVAZNIK, Richard F; Bishop Dubourg HS; Richmond Heights, MO; 2/450 ALBoysSt; ChrhWkr; CmntyWkr; HonRl; NHS; PolWkr; Bsbl; Bsktbl; College; Law.

PROVEN, Martha A; Lutheran East HS; Detroit, MI; ChrhWkr; CmntyWkr; CncrtBnd; HonRl; HospAde; NHS; NatlMeritSchl; StuCncl; GerCl; GAA; U Of Mi; Math.

PROVENCE, Timothy D; Noblesville HS; Noblesville, IN; Band; CncrtBnd; MrchBnd; Orch; PepBnd; SchMus; LatCl; LetterTrk; LetterWrstlng; University; Music.

PROVENCHER, Judith A; Dassel Cokato HS; Dassel, MN; 9/117 TrsSrCls; Band; CncrtBnd; HonRl; LbryAde; MrchBnd; NHS; PepBnd; SchMus; Yrbk; SchPpr; SecFHA; Vocational School; Practical Nursing.

PROVENZANO, Judy A; Mount Assisi Acad; Oak Lawn, IL; 26/145 PresJrCls; HonRl; StuCncl; GAA; IMSpt; Business School; Medical Ass Or Med Sec.

PROVENZANO, Mary L; Mount Assisi Academy; Oak Lawn, IL; 31/197 SecSophCls; Chrs; HonRl; NHS; SchMus; SecStuCncl; GAA; IMSpt; St Xavier College; Nursing.

PROVOST, Elizabeth A; Wayland Academy; Mackinaw City, MI; PresFrshCls; HonRl; NHS; NatlThespSoc; Quill&Scroll; StuCncl; SecStuGov; Yrbk; GAA; Albion College; Management.

PROW, Patricia; Central HS; Evansville, IN; 9/650 SecFrshCls; VPSophCls; Band; CtyCnl; HonRl; MrchBnd; NHS; StuCncl; PPFtbl; Univ; Medical Eng.

PRUEMER, Jane M; Teutopolis HS; Teutopolis, IL; 1/116 HonRl; HospAde; NHS; NatlMeritCmnd; 4-H; FHA; PpCl; GAA; BttyCrckrAwd; Univ Of Illinois; Pharmacy.

PRUENTE, Beth C; Verona R 7 HS; Verona, MO; 2/16 TrsSophCls; PresJrCls; PresSrCls; DrlTm; SecNHS; StuCncl; TchrAde; Yrbk; PresFBLA; Chrldr; Smsu University; Special Education.

PRUETT, Sarah C; Springfield Catholic HS; Springfield, MO; VPJrCls; HonRl; ModUN; OffAde; SctActv; TreasLatCl; MthCl; Chrldr; VFWAwd; VoiceDemAwd;.

PRUGH, Rickey L; Salem HS; Salem, MO; 6/161 Chr; ChrhWkr; HonRl; SchMus; StuGov; FFA; PpCl; LetterBsbl; Bsktbl; LetterFtbl; U Of Mo; Journalism.

PRUITT, Daniel W; Philomath HS; Whitman, NE; PresFrshCls; PresSophCls; IntrClCncl; PolWkr; StuCncl; RptrSchPpr; FshEdSchPpr; SchPpr; Trk;.

PRUITT, Janice J; Columbus North HS; Columbus, IN; 19/468 HonRl; MthCl; Indiana Central Univ; Nursing.

PRUITT, Joseph M; Kapaun Mt Carmel HS; Wichita, KS; 1/140 HstSrCls; Chrs; ChrhWkr; CmntyWkr; HonRl; NHS; StuCncl; StuGov; SpnCl; Bsbl; University; Professional.

PRUITT, Joy L; Carrollton HS; Eldred, IL; 7/85 SecJrCls; NHS; NatlThespSoc; FBLA; TreasFHA; TreasFTA; SpnCl; SecPpCl; GAA; AmLegAwd; Eastern Illinois University.

PRUITT, Laura G; Chillicothe HS; Chillicothe, MO; 19/195 Chrs; HonRl; FBLA; FrCl; MthCl; College.

PRUITT, Nancy L; Raymore Peculiar HS; Raymore, MO; HonRl; SpnCl; PpCl; Chrldr; GAA; College.

PRUITT, Patricia L; Oak Park & River Forest HS; Oak Park, IL; 5/1012 HonRl; JrNHS; NHS; NatlMeritCmnd; StuCncl; CaptChrldr; AmLegAwd; Univ Of Illinois; Veterinarian.

PRULLAGE, Paula F; Reitz Memorial HS; Evansville, IN; 9/211 NHS; TchrAde; SciCl; Trk; Purdue Univ; Engineering.

PRUNTY, Laura; Auburn Sr Hs; Rockford, IL; HonRl; JrNHS; NHS; Rockford College; Display Design.

PRUNTY, Mary Therese; Lourdes HS; Chicago, IL; 50/299 HonRl; IMSpt; PPFtbl; Business School; Accountant.

PRUS, Sharon R; Lincoln Park HS; Lincoln Park, MI; 2/576 SecNHS; StuCncl; StuGov; TchrAde; FTA; GAA; Mi St Univ; Math Computer Sci.

PRUSA, Kenneth J; Claflin Rural HS; Claflin, KS; 4/51 HonRl; PresNHS; StuCncl; FFA; LetterBsktbl; LetterFtbl; LetterTrk; Fort Hays St College; Biology.

PRUSER, Diane F; Clifton HS; Clifton, KS; 3/21 ALAGirlsSt; DrmMjrt; HonRl; VPStuCncl; Twrl; EdYrBk; PresPpCl; Chrldr; BttyCrckrAwd; EldAwd; College.

PRUSER, Sheryl K; Farmer City Mansfield HS; Farmer City, IL; PresSrCls; AFS; Band; Chr; Chrs; CncrtBnd; HonRl; MrchBnd; SchMus; PpCl;.

PRUSIS, Allen W; Marist HS; Chicago, IL; 12/393 HonRl; PresNHS; SchPpr; SecFrCl; PpCl; Univ; Architecture.

PRUSS, Laura C; Plainfield HS; Plainfield, IL; Chr; DrlTm; HonRl; NHS; SpnCl; Jol Jr College; Teacher.

PRUTER, Daniel; Rosemount HS; Rosemount, MN; 6/348 HonRl; SchPl; StuGov; Wrstlng; Univ Of Minn; Engineering.

PRUTZ, Stanley J; Newman HS; Mosinee, WI; Band; CncrtBnd; HonRl; PepBnd; SpnCl; MthCl; LetterWrstlng; College; Engineering.

PRYBYSZ, Linda; St Francis Academy; Joliet, IL; 6/186 ChrhWkr; HonRl; NHS; PolWkr; StuCncl; RptrSchPpr; FrCl; Northwestern; Law.

PRYOR, Barbara S; Belton HS; Richards Gebaur, MO; 3/282 Chr; Chrl; Chrs; ChrhWkr; CmntyWkr; HonRl; HospAde; IntrClCncl; JrNHS; Mdrgl; NatlFornLg; NHS; NatlSciFnd; NatlThespSoc; PolWkr; Univ Of Texas; Surgeon.

PRYOR, Barbara S; Belton HS; Richards Gebaurafb, MO; 3/280 Chr; HonRl; JrNHS; NHS; NatlThespSoc; RedCrAde; StuCncl; FDA; KeyCl; PPFtbl; U Of Tx; Surgery.

PRYOR, Patricia J; York Community HS; Elmhurst, IL; 25/950 Chr; HonRl; NHS; Northern Illinois Univ; Art.

PRYOR, Wendy; Maria HS; Chicago, IL; 44/335 Chrs; HonRl; NHS; NatlThespSoc; SchMus; SchPl; SctActv; StuCncl; RptrSchPpr; College; Theatre.

PRYSTALSKI, Alice L; Elizabeth Seton HS; So Holland, IL; 30/260 Chr; HonRl; SecNHS; SchMus; SchPl; StuCncl; MthCl; SciCl; Ill State U; Spec Ed.

PRZEDWOJEWSKI, James L; Armada HS; Armada, MI; HonRl; FrCl; PpCl; Bsbl; Bsktbl; Ftbl; AmLegAwd; College; Education.

PRZEPIORA, Denise M; All Saints Central HS; Bay City, MI; 8/138 VPFrshCls; CtyCnl; JrNHS; NHS; NatlMeritSchl; NatlMeritSF; SchMus; SctActv; TchrAde; College; Medicine.

PRZYBILLA, Laura; Healy HS; Pierz, MN; 1/119 NatlMeritCmnd; TchrAde; BttyCrckrAwd; CitAwd; Bus College; Private Secretary.

PRZYBYL, Diane; Shelbyville HS; Shelbyville, IL; 5/133 Chrs; HonRl; NHS; SchMus; TchrAde; FHA; Lake Land Jr College; Elem Education.

PRZYGODA, Annamaria; Jennings Sr HS; Jennings, MO; 16/253 HonRl; LbryAde; NHS; TchrAde; Yrbk; FTA; EngCl; Webster College; Commercal Artsist.

PRZYGODA, Cheryl A; Granite City HS; Granite City, IL; Chr; Chrs; CmntyWkr; JA; LbryAde; NatlSciFnd; RedCrAde; UNYO; SchPpr; College; Veterinarian.

PRZYTULSKI, Denise A; St Clare Academy; Detroit, MI; 1/11 PresFrshCls; PresSrCls; Chr; Chrs; HospAde; SchPl; StuCncl; StuGov; RptrSchPpr; SchPpr; FrCl; Trk; Lourdes College; Liberal Arts.

PTACEK, Mark J; Aquinas HS; Bruno, NE; TrsFrshCls; VPSophCls; Band; Chrs; HonRl; MrchBnd; NHS; SchPl; SpnCl; LetterFtbl; Music.

PTAK, Maria; Marian Catholic HS; Chicago Hts, IL; 48/328 Band; ChrhWkr; CncrtBnd; HonRl; MrchBnd; NHS; PepBnd; SchMus; Univ Of Chicago Cc; Environmental Chemistry.

PTASNIK, David B; Richwoods HS; Peoria, IL; 15/475 ChrhWkr; HonRl; HospAde; NatlFornLg; Univ Of Ill; Medicine.

PUCCI, Anne H; Kingsford HS; Kingsford, MI; HonRl; CaptBsktbl; LetterTrk; IMSpt; St Norbert College; Phy Ed Teacher.

PUCEL, Victor; Joliet Catholic Hs; Joliet, IL; 38 ALBoysSt; Band; CncrtBnd; HonRl; JrNHS; MrchBnd; PepBnd; SchMus; FrCl;.

PUCHALSKI, Cynthia I; Resurrection HS; Chicago, IL; 30/261 SpnCl; College; Professional.

PUCHALSKI, Paul A; Thorton Fractional North HS; Calumet City, IL; Aud/Vis; HonRl; NatlMeritSF; TchrAde; LetterTrk; College; Aerospace Engineering.

PUCHER, Karen A; Bishop Luers HS; Ft Wayne, IN; HonRl; GAA; PPFtbl; Indiana U; Secretarial.

PUCIN, Lynne M; Waukegan HS; Waukegan, IL; 7/1000 SecJrCls; HospAde; JrNHS; NHS; NatlMeritCmnd; StuCncl; EdYrBk; GerCl; Glf; Univ Of Iowa; Nursing.

PUCINSKIS, Angela M; John F Kennedy HS; Glenwood, IL; 23/610 SecJrCls; TrsJrCls; HonRl; NHS; NatlMeritCmnd; SchMus; So Ill Univ; Broadcast.

PUCKETT, Doris; Girard HS; Walnut, KS; ALAGirlsSt; DrlTm; HonRl; NHS; College; Business.

PUCKETT, Jackie S; Eastern HS; Solsberry, IN; TchrAde; PpCl;.

PUCKETT, Jo Ann L; Waldron HS; Waldron, IN; Band; CncrtBnd; HonRl; MrchBnd; Orch; PepBnd; RptrYrbk; 4-H; Chrldr; IMSpt; College; Certified Public Accountant.

PUCKETT, Pamela S; Franklin Central HS; Indianapolis, IN; 47/221 ChrhWkr; HonRl; TchrAde; YthFlsp; RptrSchPpr; FHA; Trade School; Window Display.

PUCKETT, Susan L; Rock Co HS; Bassett, NE; 3/35 SecFrshCls; PresJrCls; Band; Chr; Chrs; ChrhWkr; CncrtBnd; HonRl; MrchBnd; PepBnd; SchMus; LetterTrk; GAA; Univ Of Nebraska; Journalism.

PUDLINER, John H; Okemos HS; Okemos, MI; TchrAde; RptrYrbk; GerCl; CaptBsbl; CaptBsktbl; LetterFtbl; Thiel College; Liberal Arts.

PUDLITZKE, Gale; Howard Lake Waverly HS; Howard Lake, MN; 25/88 HonRl; RptrYrbk; RptrSchPpr; PpCl; IMSpt; BttyCrckrAwd; Medical Inst Of Minn; Medical Assistant.

PUDWILL, Peggy L; Pollock HS; Herreid, SD; ALAGirlsSt; Band; Chrs; DrlTm; HonRl; Pres4-H; PresFHA; BttyCrckrAwd; DARAwd; 4-HAwd; Pierre Sch Of Nursing; Prac Nurse.

PUEPPKE, David D; Hanson Ind #40 HS; Farmer, SD; Chr; Chrs; ChrhWkr; HonRl; LitMag; SchMus; SchPl; SchPpr; Bsktbl; Trk; College; Professional.

PUESCHNER, Shane E; Columbus HS; Marshfield, WI; Chrs; HonRl; FrCl; Bsktbl; College; Medicine.

PUETZ, Janet A; Resurrection HS; Chicago, IL; 3/261 SecFrshCls; SecSrCls; Chrs; HonRl; NHS; NatlMeritCmnd; StuCncl; Loyola Univ; Early Childhood Education.

PUETZ, Rosemary J; Streator HS; Streator, IL; Band; CncrtBnd; MrchBnd; PepBnd; 4-H; SpnCl; 4-HAwd; JAAwd; St Francis College; Registered Nurse.

PUFALL, Kevin E; Minot Sr HS; Minot, ND; Aud/Vis; HonRl; JrNHS; LitMag; NHS; NatlMeritSF; SchPl; TchrAde; Univ Of North Dakota; Communications.

PUFFER, Andrew J; United Township HS; East Moline, IL; ALBoysSt; Band; CncrtBnd; HonRl; MrchBnd; SchMus; SchPl; StuCncl; Trk; LetterWrstlng;.

PUFFER, Andrew J; United Twp HS; East Moline, IL; 51/517 ALBoysSt; Band; Chr; CncrtBnd; HonRl; MrchBnd; PepBnd; SchMus; StuCncl; StuGov; Ftbl; College.

PUGH, David T; Jasper HS; Jasper, IN; 30/300 Band; ChrhWkr; CncrtBnd; HonRl; MrchBnd; FrCl; LetterFtbl; LetterTennis; Purdue Univ.

PUGH, Ralph A; Alpena Senior HS; Alpena, MI; VPJrCls; HonRl; Orch; SchMus; SchPl; StuCncl; EdSchPpr; LatCl; OptClAwd; RotaryAwd; Kalamazoo Clg; Historical Research.

PUGH, Robert S; Rapid City Central HS; Rapid City, SD; ALBoysSt; Band; CncrtBnd; HonRl; MrchBnd; NHS; PepBnd; SchPl; KeyCl; SciCl; Sd Schl Of Mines & Tech; Retail Bus.

PUGH, Timothy C; Stonington HS; Stonington, IL; PresSophCls; PresJrCls; Band; EdYrBk; Bsbl; Bsktbl; Trk; West Point Military Academy; Nuclear Physic.

PUGH, William; Rossville HS; Rossville, KS; HonRl; NatlMeritCmnd; TchrAde; SptEdYrbk; RptrSchPpr; Trk; Kaw Area Voc Tech; Tech Draft.

PUGLIESE, Sandy D; James B Conant HS; Schaumburg, IL; CmntyWkr; HonRl; HospAde; NHS; RedCrAde; TchrAde; PpCl; CaptChrldr; CchngActv; GovHonPrgAwd; College; Physical Therapy.

PUKALL, Marsha K; Lakeland Union HS; Arbor Vitae, WI; Band; DrmMjrt; HonRl; Twrl; GerCl; SpnCl; SciCl; Col; Pro.

PULASKI, Sue E; Grant Park HS; Grant Park, IL; Band; ChrhWkr; DrlTm; LbryAde; Yrbk; SchPpr; 4-H; FHA; GAA; College; Interior Decorating.

PULC, Edward; St Patrick HS; Chicago, IL; 4/400 HonRl; JA; RptrSchPpr; GerCl; PpCl; JAAwd; Univ; Psychiatrist.

PULKKINEN, John; Cherry HS; Mt Iron, MN; TrsJrCls; Band; CncrtBnd; HonRl; NHS; StuCncl; StuGov; Univ Of Minn; Natural Resourcestech.

PULKOWNIK, Lawrence J; Plymouth Salem HS; Plymouth, MI; ALBoysSt; NHS; PolWkr; SchAde; SctActv; StuCncl; StuGov; YthLg; LetterFtbl; LetterSwmmng; AmLegAwd; OptClAwd; College; Engineering.

PULKRABEK, Jodi L; Northern University HS; Cedar Falls, IA; Band; Chr; Chrs; HonRl; SchMus; SchPl; PpCl; LetterSwmmng; LetterChrldr; IMSpt; University.

PULL, Jeff; Bismarck HS; Bismarck, ND; LetterFtbl; Bismarck Jr Col; Engineering.

PULLEN, Deana; Oakland Comm HS; Oakland, IA; 10/48 TrsJrCls; Chr; HonRl; NHS; RptrYrbk; RptrSchPpr; FNA; LionAwd; Univ Northern Ia; Geography Major.

PULLEN, Kathleen M; Pine River HS; Tustin, MI; SecFrshCls; Chr; HonRl; NHS; SchPl; YthLg; Yrbk; FrCl; SpnCl; LetterTrk; College; Professional.

PULLEN, Marcia A; Harrisonville Sr HS; Harrisonville, MO; 14/145 AFS; Band; ChrhWkr; CncrtBnd; HonRl; NatlFornLg; Quill&Scroll; SchPl; Yrbk; Southern Mo State; Speech.

PULLES, Alexander J; Maine Township East HS; Niles, IL; HonRl; NatlMeritSF; SciCl; Ftbl; Univ Of Illinois; Mechanical Engineer.

PULLEY, Sheryl K; Maysville HS; Clarksdale, MO; ChrhWkr; HonRl; StuCncl; FHA; PpCl; Chrldr;.

PULLIAM, David K; Kirksville HS; Greentop, MO; 14/188 ALBoysSt; Band; ChrhWkr; HonRl; MrchBnd; NHS; 4-H; FFA; LetterBsktbl; DanFAwd; U Of Mo; Agriculture.

PULLIAM, David W; Fox HS; Arnold, MO; Band; ChrhWkr; CmntyWkr; HonRl; OffAde; SchMus; CaptBsbl; CaptFtbl; Trk; College; Pe.

PULLIAM, Debbie S; Carrier Mills HS; Stonefort, IL; Band; Chrs; ChrhWkr; MrchBnd; NHS; PepBnd; SchPl; YthFlsp; RptrSchPpr; PpCl; Univ; Pharmacist.

PULLIAM, Jeannie L; Jackson HS; Burfordville, MO; PpCl; Secretarial Bus School; Ex Sec.

PULLIAM, Karla L; Smithville R2 HS; Smithville, MO; 6/76 SecTrsSrCls; ALAGirlsSt; Band; ChrhWkr; CmntyWkr; CncrtBnd; HonRl; MrchBnd; TreasNHS; SecFHA; VPPpCl; Chrldr; IMSpt; Col; Biology.

PULLIAM, Susan; Oregon Davis HS; Walkerton, IN; Band; Chr; HonRl; PepBnd; SchMus; SchPl; 4-H; PpCl; GAA; DARAwd;.

PULLIN, Mark B; Beach HS; Beach, ND; 5/39 VPSophCls; Band; Chr; Chrs; CncrtBnd; MrchBnd; SchPl; StuCncl; StuGov; FFA; Bsbl; Ftbl; College; Medicine.

PULS, Kevin; Union HS; Union, MO; 15/167 Band; ChrhWkr; CncrtBnd; HonRl; JA; MrchBnd; Bsbl; Ftbl; Trk; College; Engineer.

PULSE, Peggy; Southern HS; Stronghurst, IL; HonRl; RptrSchPpr; FHA; FTA; PpCl; Bsktbl; Chrldr; GAA; IMSpt; PresAwd; Bus School; Vocation.

PULTER, Kim M; Harry S Truman HS; Taylor, MI; 7/461 Band; ChrhWkr; CncrtBnd; HonRl; MrchBnd; NatlFornLg; NHS; TchrAde; SpnCl; Henry Ford Comm Col; Legal Secretary.

PUMMILL, Le Ann; Le Roy HS; Le Roy, IL; ChrhWkr; HonRl;.

PUMP, Sharon J; Venango Consolidated HS; Venango, NE; 4/11 PresFrshCls; Band; CncrtBnd; MrchBnd; PepBnd; SchPl; 4-H; PresPpCl; LetterTrk; DARAwd; Business School; Executive Secretary.

PUNDMANN, Joel; St Charles HS; St Charles, MO; 27/547 Chr; HonRl; Mdrgl; NHS; SchMus; Univ Of Missouri.

PUNT, Janice K; Chicago Christian HS; Evergreen Park, IL; ChrhWkr; HonRl; NHS; RptrYrbk; Trk; College.

PUNT, Terry L; Maurice Orange City Comm HS; Orange City, IA; Band; CncrtBnd; HonRl; MrchBnd; PepBnd; LetterFtbl; IMSpt; Sioux Falls College; Management.

PURCELL, Ellen E; Streator Township HS; Streator, IL; HonRl; HospAde; SpnCl; LetterBsktbl; Tennis; College.

PURCELL, Jane E; Derham Hall HS; St Paul, MN; 1/150 Aud/Vis; ChrhWkr; NHS; SctActv; Yrbk; RusCl; GAA; Univ Of Mn Cla; Russian & Chinese Languages.

PURCELL, Margaret M; Derham Hall HS; St Paul, MN; 1/126 Chrs; CmntyWkr; NatlMeritSF; SchPl; SctActv; FrCl; BauchLmbAwd; Univ Mn; Computer Sci.

PURCELL, Mark A; Washington HS; Washington, IL; 34/340 ChrhWkr; CtyCnl; CmntyWkr; HonRl; NHS; PolWkr; StuGov; CivCl; GerCl; IMSpt; Butler Univ; Pharmacy.

PURCELL, Teresa R; Holdrege HS; Holdrege, NE; Chr; Chrl; Chrs; ChrhWkr; HonRl; SchMus; YthFlsp; FBLA; PpCl; Chrldr; Kearney State College; Business.

PURCELL, Tim E; Goldfield Comm HS; Goldfield, IA; CmntyWkr; HonRl; SchMus; Yrbk; Bsbl; Bsktbl; Glf; Trk; Webster City Jc.

PURCELL, Timothi A; Lakeland HS; La Grange, IN; 36/138 HonRl; SchMus; SchPl; PpCl; College; Computer Technology.

PURCHASE, Pam S; Pine River Area HS; Luther, MI; Chr; ChrhWkr; HonRl; LbryAde; NHS; FHA; FrCl; Bsktbl; Trk; Chrldr; College; Vocation.

PURDY, Eric P; Porta HS; Petersburg, IL; 7/143 Band; Chrs; CncrtBnd; HonRl; JrNHS; Mdrgl; MrchBnd; NHS; Orch; PepBnd; SchMus; College; Air Force.

PURDY, Jerry E; Oskaloosa HS; Aloosa, IA; 7/189 HonRl; Bsbl; William Penn Coll; Math.

PURINTON, Martha E; Sturgeon Bay HS; Sturgeon Bay, WI; 1/140 Band; CncrtBnd; HonRl; JrNHS; NHS; PepBnd; SpnCl; GAA; Univ; Naval Architect.

PURKAPILE, Elaine; Orient Macksburg HS; Winterset, IA; TrsJrCls; SecSrCls; Band; Chrs; ChrhWkr; CmntyWkr; HonRl; YthFlsp; RptrYrbk; 4-H; Nurses Training.

PURKAPILE, Krista M; George S Parker HS; Janesville, WI; 2/387 ChrhWkr; CncrtBnd; LbryAde; NHS; SchPl; StuCncl; TchrAde; VPSpnCl; SecGAA; EldAwd; Univ Of Wisconsin; Special Educ.

PURKEL, Arthur W; Mascoutah HS; Mascoutah, IL; Band; Chrs; Mdrgl; ModUN; NatlMeritSF; SchPl; StuCncl; StuGov; RptrSchPpr; MthCl; College; Psychiatry.

PURKHISER, Marvin L; West Washington HS; Salem, IN; Band; Chrs; CncrtBnd; HonRl; MrchBnd; NHS; 4-H; FFA; IMSpt; Trade School; Diesel Mechanics.

PURKHISER, Ralph E; Springs Valley HS; W Baden Springs, IN; 1/75 ALBoysSt; ChrhWkr; NHS; SchAde; PresYthFlsp; Pres4-H; PresLatCl; Bsktbl; Ftbl; Tennis; 4-HAwd; Indiana Central Univ; English.

PUROL, Marie; Monroe Ri HS; Monroe City, MO; PresJrCls; PresSrCls; CmntyWkr; HospAde; RptrYrbk; EdYrBk; Bsktbl;.

PUROL, Patrick J; Round Lake Comm HS; Round Lake, IL; HonRl; PolWkr; LetterBsktbl; Ftbl; LetterGlf; CchngActv; IMSpt; College; Business Admin.

PUROL, Thomas; Posen Consolidated HS; Posen, MI; 4/56 PresFrshCls; PresSophCls; ALBoysSt; Chr; HonRl; NHS; RptrYrbk; SchPpr; AmLegAwd;.

PURPURA, Gregory M; Plymouth Canton HS; Plymouth, MI; HonRl; TchrAde; Eastern Michigan Univ; Scientific Field.

PURSCELL, Sally; Spencer Comm Hs; Spencer, IA; Band; Chr; ChrhWkr; CncrtBnd; HonRl; MrchBnd; PepBnd; SchMus; YthFlsp; RptrYrbk; University; Socil Psychologist.

PURSIFULL, Debbie J; Community R 6 HS; Martinsburg, MO; 18/76 TrsJrCls; VPBand; NHS; Quill&Scroll; SchPl; StuCncl; Yrbk; LetterBsbl; LetterBsktbl; Trk; PresGAA; IMSpt; University Of Missouri; Marine Biology.

PURSLEY, David E; St Clair HS; St Clair, MO; ChrhWkr; HonRl; SctActv; YthFlsp; KeyCl; PpCl; LetterBsbl; LetterFtbl; Wrstlng; IMSpt; CitAwd; College; Professional.

PURSLEY, Michael J; Benkelman HS; Benkelman, NE; TrsJrCls; StuCncl; 4-H; Bsktbl; Ftbl; College; Vocation.

PURVES, Julie A; Clarkston Sr HS; Clarkston, MI; Coll.

PURVIS, Michael; Wabasha Kellogg HS; Wabasha, MN; HonRl; SchPl; RptrSchPpr; Rochester Comm College.

PURVIS, Nancy A; St Bernards HS; St Paul, MN; Chr; HonRl; PpCl; Chrldr; St Marys Jr College; Nurse.

PUSARA, John; Geo Washington HS; Chicago, IL; 2/481 ChrhWkr; HonRl; NHS; TchrAde; EdSchPpr; LatCl; VoiceDemAwd; St Vladimirs Orthodox Seminary;priest.

PUSCHAK, Ellen J; Atkinson HS; Atkinson, IL; 6/33 VPSophCls; PresJrCls; HonRl; SecStuCncl; Yrbk; VPFHA; SpnCl; Bsktbl; Chrldr; GAA; 4-HAwd; Univ Of Iowa; Nursing.

PUSCZEK, Eugene J; Riverview Gardens HS; St Louis, MO; Band; CncrtBnd; HonRl; MrchBnd; NHS; NatlMeritCmnd; Quill&Scroll; SptEdSchPpr; Ftbl; College; Journalism.

PUSKALA, David B; Hibbing HS; Hibbing, MN; ChrhWkr; HonRl; NatlCathMusEdAsoc; NHS; SchMus; SchPl; SctActv; YthLg; GerCl; MthCl; Col.

PUSZYNSKI, Marsia A; Resurrection HS; Chicago, IL; 55/261 SecFrshCls; AFS; HonRl; LitMag; Quill&Scroll; SchPl; SctActv; StuCncl; RptrSchPpr; AmLegAwd; Northern Ill Univ; Major In Journalism.

PUTJENTER, Jennifer J; Mercy HS; Omaha, NE; 15/75 HonRl; NatlFornLg; NHS; SchPl; StuCncl; SpnCl; SciCl; Bsbl; Bsktbl; Trk; Univ; Speech Therapist.

PUTMAN, William D; Libertyville HS; Libertyville, IL; 61/450 Band; CncrtBnd; HonRl; MrchBnd; Carthage College; Business Admin.

PUTNAM, Brett J; Sycamore HS; Sycamore, IL; 26/226 HonRl; SctActv; 4-H; LetterBsktbl; 4-HAwd; Univ Of Illinois; Pilot.

PUTNAM, Diane L; Richwoods HS; Peoria, IL; 29/454 Chrs; HonRl; SchPpr; Illinois St University.

PUTNAM, Gayle L; Carthage Comm HS; Carthage, IL; Band; Chrs; CncrtBnd; HonRl; MrchBnd; NatlMeritCmnd; SchMus; RptrSchPpr; SchPpr; FHA; Ne Missouri St U; Business.

PUTNAM, Michael; Vassar HS; Vassar, MI; NatlThespSoc; SchMus; SchPl; TchrAde; RptrYrbk; RptrSchPpr; SchPpr; GerCl; SpnCl; PpCl; E Michigan U; Cinematic Arts.

PUTNAM, Patrick J; Fraser HS; Fraser, MI; CmntyWkr; HonRl; SpnCl; Bsbl; LetterBsktbl; Glf; College; Professional.

PUTNEY, George F; Bishop Dubourg HS; St Louis, MO; 17/430 ALBoysSt; HonRl; LetterBsktbl; IMSpt; CitAwd; U; Science.

PUTSKEY, Thomas; Lincoln HS; Wis Rapids, WI; HonRl; GerCl; Socr; CchngActv; IMSpt; Univ.

PUTT, Larry R; Garrett HS; Auburn, IN; 12/150 SchMus; SchPl; SpnCl; Trk; IMSpt; Univ; Engineering.

PUTT, Roger; Midland HS; Midland, MI; 11/460 ChrhWkr; CmntyWkr; HonRl; JA; NHS; TchrAde; Tennis; Coll; Chem Engrg.

PUTTMANN, Kay; Kingsley Pierson HS; Kingsley, IA; 2/66 ChrhWkr; HonRl; ModUN; SchMus; TchrAde; EdYrBk; RptrSchPpr; U Northern Iowa; Elem Education.

PUTTONEN, Sandra L; Cotton HS; Cotton, MN; 2/25 SecTrsFrshCls; PresSrCls; HonRl; NHS; SecStuCncl; RptrYrbk; GAA; U Of Mn; Medical.

PUTZ, Jeff L; Howe Military HS; Michigan City, IN; 1/40 PresFrshCls; VPJrCls; VPSrCls; Band; CncrtBnd; HonRl; JrNHS; MrchBnd; NatlFornLg; NHS; CaptBsbl; CaptBsktbl; Ftbl; Socr; Univ; Professional.

PUZA, Beverly K; Cabrini HS; Allen Park, MI; 6/167 HonRl; LetterTrk; Trade School; Vocation.

PUZON, Therese S; George WashingtonHS; Chicago, IL; 65/481 CmntyWkr; DrmBgl; HonRl; JrNHS; NHS; StuCncl; TchrAde; Chrldr; GAA;.

PYATT, Kevin R; Pinckneyville HS; Pinckneyville, IL; HonRl; StuCncl; StuGov; SpnCl; PpCl; LetterBsbl; LetterBsktbl; LetterFtbl; U Of Mississippi; Law.

PYELL, Susan E; Stamford Public HS; Stamford, NE; 2/6 SecFrshCls; SecSophCls; PresJrCls; CmntyWkr; YthFlsp; RptrYrbk; 4-H; PresPpCl; Trk; University; Elementary Education.

PYETT, Nicholas J; Northville HS; Northville, MI; HonRl; JA; NHS; GerCl; IMSpt; College; Business.

PYGMAN, Gayle; Monrovia HS; Mooresville, IN; 1/94 ALAGirlsSt; Band; CncrtBnd; HonRl; LbryAde; MrchBnd; PepBnd; EdYrBk; SpnCl; University Of Evansville; Rn.

PYGMAN, Gayle M; Monrovia HS; Mooresville, IN; 1/96 ALAGirlsSt; Band; CncrtBnd; HonRl; LbryAde; PresNHS; PepBnd; SecYthFlsp; EdYrBk; SpnCl; Evansville U; Rn.

PYLE, Donald P; Girard Usd 248 HS; Girard, KS; 8/98 Band; ChrhWkr; CmntyWkr; CncrtBnd; HonRl; MrchBnd; NHS; PepBnd; SchPl; SpnCl; College; Accounting.

PYLE, Kathy L; Nevada Sr HS; Nevada, MO; 2/180 Chrs; ChrhWkr; CtyCnl; NatlThespSoc; SchMus; SchPl; StuCncl; RptrYrbk; LatCl; GAA; U Of Mo; Vet.

PYLE, Kaye L; Pomeroy Community HS; Jolley, IA; SecJrCls; Band; HonRl; NHS; PepBnd; RptrSchPpr; FHA; PpCl; LetterBsktbl; LetterTrk; Iowa Central Comm College; Nursing.

PYLE, Kent C; Huntington Catholic HS; Huntington, IN; 1/36 VPJrCls; Chrs; ChrhWkr; HonRl; SchPl; Yrbk; Bsbl; CaptBsktbl; Glf; Trk; Notre Dame; Business.

PYLE, Randall S; Marshall Co Central HS; Newfolden, MN; ChrhWkr; PresStuCncl; StuGov; TchrAde; Ftbl; Trk; Wrstlng; College; Electronic Engineer.

PYLE, Ronald C; Ridgway HS; New Haven, IL; 1/43 PresJrCls; VPSrCls; StuCncl; SptEdYrbk; Yrbk; FFA; AmLegAwd; BttyCrckrAwd; Army; Law Enforcement.

PYLE, Shirley E; Wyoming Park HS; Wyoming, MI; 44/238 HonRl; NHS; SchPl; RptrSchPpr; EdSchPpr; GerCl; PpCl; Grand Rapids Jr College; Journalism.

PYNE, Richard J; University HS; Normal, IL; HonRl; StuCncl; SchPpr; PpCl; LetterFtbl; LetterTrk; College; Prof.

PYNER, Raymond R; Wayne Community HS; Corydon, IA; 33/74 Chrs; HonRl; NHS; FTA; SciCl; LetterBsbl; Bsktbl; LetterFtbl; Glf; Trk; Junior College; Biology.

PYPSKY, Marianne; Thornwood HS; Calumet City, IL; 29/582 HonRl; Jr College; Business.

PYRZEWSKI, William J; Morley Stanwood HS; Morley, MI; 2/80 PresFrshCls; Band; HonRl; VPNHS; SciCl; LetterBsbl; LetterBsktbl; LetterFtbl; LetterTrk; CitAwd; West Point University; Business.

PYSH, Thomas W; Edison Sr HS; East Gary, IN; HonRl; JrNHS; StuCncl; FrCl; Bsktbl;.

PYTLESKI, Lori; East Chain HS; Fairmont, MN; 1/22 Band; Chr; ChrhWkr; HonRl; HospAde; LbryAde; MrchBnd; NHS; OffAde; Orch; College Of St Teresa;bi Lingualelementary E.

PYZIK, Christopher J; Bentley HS; Livonia, MI; PolWkr; U Of Mi; Environmenta Researcher.

Q

QUACKENBUSH, Jeffrey L; Tri County HS; De Witt, NE; 6/64 Chrl; Chrs; HonRl; Mdrgl; NHS; NatlThespSoc; SchPl; LetterFtbl; LetterWrstlng; University Of Nebraska; Engineering.

QUADE, Diane M; St Pauls HS; Edwardsville, IL; HonRl; LbryAde; SctActv; Southern Ill Univ; Librarian.

QUADE, Gregory; Prospect Hs; Arlington Hts, IL; VPFrshCls; HonRl; JrNHS; NHS; Bsbl; Bsktbl; Ftbl; College;accounting Or Journalism.

QUADE, Joan; Healy HS; Peirz, MN; VPSrCls; HonRl; TchrAde; Yrbk; FHA; PpCl; SciCl; Coll; Nurse.

QUADERER, Lucinda A; New Lothrop HS; New Lothrop, MI; OffAde; SchAde; TchrAde; Yrbk; RptrSchPpr; FHA; Bsbl; Bsktbl; Cenral Mich U; Teacher.

QUAGLIATO, Sandra; Osborn HS; Detroit, MI; 50/660 Aud/Vis; ChrhWkr; HonRl; LitMag; NHS; SchPl; TchrAde; RptrSchPpr; CitAwd; Marygrove College; Broadcasting Major.

QUAIL, Crystal R; Deubrook HS; Brandt, SD; SecSophCls; SecSrCls; Band; HonRl; SchMus; Yrbk; RptrSchPpr; FHA; LetterBsktbl; LetterTrk; College; Professional.

QUAITE, Michael R; Pekin Comm HS; Pekin, IL; 120/803 Bradley Univ; Electrical Engineering.

QUALE, Jeffery W; Summit HS; Summit, SD; VPSrCls; Chrs; HonRl; StuGov; LetterBsktbl; LetterFtbl; LetterTrk;.

QUALE, Jo Ann C; New Town Public HS; New Town, ND; Band; Chr; MrchBnd; NatlMeritFnl; 4-H; FHA; SciCl; LetterBsktbl; GAA; PPFtbl; Concordia College; Computer Science.

QUALE, Joann C; New Town HS; New Town, ND; Chr; CncrtBnd; MrchBnd; NatlMeritSF; 4-H; FHA; PpCl; VPSciCl; LetterBsktbl; GAA; PPFtbl; 4-HAwd; College; Computer Science.

QUAM, Dean A; De Forest HS; De Forest, WI; Band; ChrhWkr; CncrtBnd; HonRl; MrchBnd; PepBnd; LetterWrstlng; College; Accounting.

QUAM, Stephen L; Ashby HS; Ashby, MN; 6/24 VPSophCls; PresSrCls; ALBoysSt; Chr; ChrhWkr; HonRl; NHS; SchPl; TchrAde; SptEdYrbk; LetterBsbl; LetterBsktbl; LetterFtbl; College.

QUAN, James M; Elk Grove HS; Elk Grove Village, IL; 72/505 HonRl; Columbia College; Filmmaking.

QUANDT, Gwen J; Stewart Public HS; Stewart, MN; 8/37 Chrs; HonRl; SchPl; RptrYrbk; RptrSchPpr; FHA; GAA; Voc Sch; Vocation.

QUANDT, Linda J; Warren Central HS; Indianapolis, IN; ChrhWkr; VPJA; GerCl; SciCl; Indiana Univ; Nurse.

QUANTIVS, Susan E; Homestead HS; Thiensville, WI; 1/410 ALAGirlsSt; ChrhWkr; CmntyWkr; HonRl; Mdrgl; NatlFornLg; NHS; NatlMeritSF; StuCncl; PresFrCl; DARAwd; College; Lawyer.

QUARBERG, Timothy D; Lancaster Sr HS; Lancaster, WI; Chr; Chrl; Chrs; ChrhWkr; HonRl; SchMus; StuCncl; RptrYrbk; Yrbk; LetterBsbl; CaptGlf; CchngActv; IMSpt; Drake University; Pharmacy.

QUARFOOT, Robert W; Schaumburg HS; Schaumburg, IL; 33/549 HonRl; RptrSchPpr; SciCl; Harper Jr College; Business Field.

QUARTON, Laura D; Kingswood Cranbrook HS; Lincoln Park, MI; SecSophCls; CmntyWkr; LitMag; NatlMeritSF; PolWkr; StuGov; LatCl; Tennis; Col; La.

QUARTUCCIO, Anthony A; Marquette HS; Michigan City, IN; 25/60 HonRl; JA; Tennis; Purdue North Central; Computer Technology.

QUASNY, Rodney M; George Washington HS; Chicago, IL; 75/450 HonRl; NatlMeritCmnd; SchAde; SctActv; TchrAde; LetterBsktbl; Trk; Univ Of Illinois; Liberal Arts.

QUASTAD, Marjean E; Armstrong Comm HS; Armstrong, IA; 2/27 Band; Chr; Chrs; ChrhWkr; CncrtBnd; HonRl; SecStuCncl; EdYrBk; VPFHA; BttyCrckrAwd; Central Coll; Home Ec.

QUATTROCCHI, Julie A; Hannibal Senior HS; Hannibal, MO; Chr; Chrs; CmntyWkr; SchAde; SchMus; PpCl; Chrldr; GAA; IMSpt; Special Ed Teacher.

QUATTROCKI, Anthony J; Brother Rice HS; Oak Lawn, IL; 184/445 Aud/Vis; LbryAde; OffAde; SchPl; TchrAde; 4-H; St Marys College; Pre Medicine.

QUECK, Nancy L; Orient Macksburg Comm HS; Orient, IA; 2/42 Chr; Chrs; DrlTm; HonRl; NHS; SchMus; SchPl; Teen; YthLg; Business School.

QUELLER, Katherine A; Centennial HS; Champaign, IL; 1/350 CmntyWkr; HonRl; JrNHS; NHS; NatlMeritSF; PolWkr; SchMus; Trk; U Of Il.

QUELLHORST, Julie A; Boscobel HS; Boscobel, WI; SecFrshCls; Chrs; DrlTm; HonRl; HospAde; FHA; PpCl; Trk; GAA; College; Professional Teaching.

QUENOY, Diann M; Frontenac HS; Frontenac, KS; ALAGirlsSt; ChrhWkr; CmntyWkr; HonRl; OffAde; PolWkr; FHA; SpnCl; MthCl; College; Business Admin.

QUERY, Marlon; Owen Valley HS; Coal City, IN; 2/192 Band; ChrhWkr; NHS; NatlFornLg; SpnCl; ChmbCommrsAwd; Northwestern Univ; Chemival.

QUESTAD, Deanna L; Tri Valley HS; Baltic, SD; 1/62 Band; Chr; Chrs; ChrhWkr; HonRl; NatlFornLg; NHS; PolWkr; RptrSchPpr; VoiceDemAwd; Uniiv Of Sd; Pre Med.

QUICK, David H; Midland HS; Midland, MI; Ftbl; Socr; Trk; CchngActv; Univ Of Mich; Architecture/coaching.

QUICK, Kathryn A; St James Public HS; St James, MN; 19/150 Band; Chr; ChrhWkr; CmntyWkr; CncrtBnd; HonRl; HospAde; MrchBnd; PepBnd; RedCrAde; College; Special Ed.

QUICK, Linda K; Greenfield Central HS; Greenfield, IN; 2/260 NHS; NatlMeritCmnd; SctActv; TchrAde; SchPpr; FSA; MthCl; EldAwd; KiwanAwd; RotaryAwd; Butler U; Pharmacology.

QUICK, Melody C; Taylorville HS; Taylorville, IL; 52/271 Band; Chrs; CncrtBnd; HonRl; Mdrgl; MrchBnd; TreasNatlThespSoc; Orch; PepBnd; SecYthFlsp; Univ Of Illinois; Education.

QUICK, Robert D; Waynesville HS; Waynesville, MO; 4/250 HonRl; JrNHS; NHS; Trk; Wrstlng; Univ Of Mo Columbia; Medicine.

QUICK, Scott; Laker Hs; Bay Port, MI; 15/141 Band; ChrhWkr; CncrtBnd; HonRl; MrchBnd; NHS; PepBnd; SctActv; TreasYthFlsp;.

QUIGG, Lorraine S; Guilford HS; Rockford, IL; 53/650 SecChr; ChrhWkr; HonRl; HospAde; Mdrgl; Orch; SchAde; SchPl; SctActv; YthFlsp; College; Music.

QUIGG, Mary K; Regis HS; Eau Claire, WI; 3/119 HonRl; Orch; SchMus; RptrYrbk; LetterBsktbl; Tennis; Chrldr; GAA; IMSpt;.

QUIGGLE, Julie G; New Ulm Sr HS; New Ulm, MN; 10/250 Chr; Chrl; ChrhWkr; HonRl; HospAde; SchPl; PresYthFlsp; Pres4-H; PpCl; LetterTrk; 4-HAwd; Westmar College; Christian Ed.

QUIGGLE, Julie G; New Ulm HS; New Ulm, MN; 10/250 Chr; Chrl; Chrs; ChrhWkr; HonRl; HospAde; SchPl; YthFlsp; 4-H; PpCl; LetterTrk; 4-HAwd; Westmar College; Christian Educ.

QUIGLEY, John B; Griffin HS; Springfield, IL; 22/190 HonRl; HospAde; SchPpr; Bsbl; Bsktbl; LetterFtbl; Socr; LetterTrk; IMSpt; Springfield Jr College; Medicine.

QUIGLEY, Margie A; Tripoli Community HS; Ionia, IA; PresSrCls; Chr; HonRl; JrNHS; StuCncl; RptrYrbk; CivCl; Ftbl; GovHonPrgAwd; CitAwd; Bus Sch.

QUIGLEY, Theresa M; St Francis HS; St Francis, KS; 1 52 Band; ChrhWkr; CmntyWkr; CncrtBnd; HonRl; MrchBnd; NatlMeritSF; PepBnd; SchPl; FHA; Clg; Math.

QUIGLEY, Timothy T; Republican Valley HS; Indianola, NE; PresSophCls; Band; Chr; Chrs; CncrtBnd; MrchBnd; SchMus; StuCncl; FFA; LetterFtbl; LetterTrk; College; Professional.

QUILLEN, Katherine; Lew Wallace Hs; Gary, IN; 23/513 HonRl; NHS; TchrAde; Purdue Or Indiana U;secretary.

QUILLER, Jill A; Calhoun HS; Hamburg, IL; VPSophCls; HonRl; NHS; SchPl; FrCl; PpCl; Chrldr; GAA; AmLegAwd; Blessing Hosp; X Ray Tech.

QUINCE, Carlotta A; Pontiac Central HS; Pontiac, MI; Band; Chr; Chrl; Chrs; ChrhWkr; CncrtBnd; DrlTm; HonRl; HospAde; Mdrgl; College; Secondary Ed.

QUINLAN, Anna M; Sevastopol HS; Sturgeon Bay, WI; 24/100 SchPl; RptrSchPpr; SchPpr; SpnCl; College; Professional.

QUINLAN, Brian J; Bellevue HS; Omaha, NE; 23/706 Band; CmntyWkr; HonRl; JrNHS; NatlMeritSF; PolWkr; Bsbl; IMSpt; College; Engineering.

QUINLAN, Catherine M; Sevastopol HS; Sturgeon Bay, WI; Band; LitMag; MrchBnd; SchMus; SchPl; StuCncl; SpnCl; IMSpt; Univ Of Madison; Professional.

QUINLAN, Jo El S; St Francis De Sales HS; Chicago, IL; 39/297 PresSophCls; DrlTm; HonRl; JrNHS; NHS; SchMus; SchPl; StuCncl; Trk; Western Illinois Univ; Business Admin.

QUINLAN, Rita C; Paxton HS; Ludlow, IL; AFS; HonRl; SchAde; SchPl; TchrAde; 4-H; LatCl; TreasGAA; IMSpt; 4-HAwd; College; Special Education.

QUINLEY, Denise D; New Franklin HS; New Franklin, MO; 17/50 SecBttyCrckrAwd; Chr; CncrtBnd; HonRl; MrchBnd; NatlMeritSchl; PepBnd; YthFlsp; LetterBsbl; Chrldr; Univ Of Mo; Music.

QUINN, Alice J; Humboldt HS; St Paul, MN; ALAGirlsSt; CncrtBnd; HonRl; StuCncl; YthFlsp; FHA; FrCl; Glf; Chrldr; AmLegAwd; College; Theatre.

QUINN, Carol; Ventura Community HS; Ventura, IA; Band; CncrtBnd; HonRl; MrchBnd; SchPl; Bsbl; Bsktbl; Swmmng; Chrldr; PPFtbl;.

QUINN, Charles H; Harvard St George HS; Chicago, IL; HonRl;.

QUINN, Christopher; Marmion Military Acad; Dundee, IL; 13/90 HonRl; Quill&Scroll; ROTC; EdYrBk; RptrSchPpr; Trk; JAAwd; West Point Usma; Military Off.

QUINN, Daniel R; Franklin HS; Westland, MI; 179/779 ALBoysSt; HonRl; HospAde; StuCncl; Ftbl; CaptTrk; Wayne State Univ; Medicine.

QUINN, Kari A; Atwater HS; Atwater, MN; 2/52 SecTrsSrCls; Chr; HonRl; JA; LbryAde; NHS; Orch; SchAde; TchrAde; DARAwd; MasAwd; Moorhead State College; Medical Technician.

QUINN, Mark M; St Ignatius HS; Chicago, IL; 3/158 VPSrCls; ChrhWkr; NHS; NatlMeritSF; StuCncl; IMSpt; Univ Il; Lawyer.

QUINN, Mary; Rantoul Twp HS; Rantow, IL; ChrhWkr; HonRl; Bsbl; Bsktbl; Swmmng; Tennis; Trk; GAA; IMSpt; PPFtbl; Eastern Ill Univ; Physical Theraphy.

QUINN, Rebecca J; Litchfield Sr HS; Litchfield, IL; 20/150 CmntyWkr; HonRl; NatlSciFnd; RedCrAde; StuCncl; FDA; FNA; FSA; SciCl; Tennis; Eastern Illinois Univ; Md.

QUINN, Roger S; Abl HS; Sidney, IL; 2/23 TrsFrshCls; HonRl; NHS; StuCncl; LetterFtbl; AmLegAwd; BauchLmbAwd; Parkland Jr Clg; Accounting.

QUINN, Sally A; Jacksonville HS; Jacksonville, IL; 24/352 ALAGirlsSt; HonRl; HospAde; NHS; YthFlsp; FrCl; SciCl; St Louis Coll Of Pharm; Pharmacist.

QUINN, Sandra J; Hamilton Southeastern HS; Noblesville, IN; 21/131 Band; NHS; SchMus; Treas4-H; SpnCl; PpCl; CaptSwmmng; CaptTrk; GAA; College; Business.

QUINN, Stanley B; Elk Grove HS; Elk Grove, IL; 5/600 Band; CAP; CmntyWkr; CncrtBnd; HonRl; JrNHS; LitMag; MrchBnd; NatlFornLg; NHS; NatlMeritFnl; NatlMeritCmnd; NatlMeritSF; Univ Of Illinois; Musician.

QUINN, Steven J; St Pius HS; Kansas City, MO; 18/137 HonRl; RptrSchPpr; LetterTennis; Wrstlng; Univ Of Missouri; Professional.

QUINN, Timothy J; Spalding Institute; Peoria, IL; CmntyWkr; HonRl; NHS; OffAde; FBLA; KeyCl; LetterTrk; IMSpt; Augustana Clge; Dentistry.

QUINN, Wanda C; Chicago Vocational HS; Chicago, IL; 64/649 ChrhWkr; OffAde; SchAde; SchPl; TchrAde; GAA; Night Sch.

QUINNELL, Steven E; Spring Grove Public HS; Spring Grove, MN; Band; CncrtBnd; MrchBnd; PepBnd; SchPl; 4-H; FFA; Bsktbl; Agriculture School; Farmer.

QUINT, Frank R; Lake Central HS; Crown Point, IN; NHS; FDA; Indiana Univ; Doctor.

QUINT, Julie A; Nerinx Hall HS; St Louis, MO; 25/99 SchMus; Music Therapy.

QUINT, Roger L; Hill City HS; Hill City, KS; HonRl; StuCncl; TchrAde; SchPpr; FFA; IMSpt; CitAwd; Trade School; Vocation.

QUINTANILLA, Monica; Center Grove HS; Greenwood, IN; 5/235 ALAGirlsSt; Chr; HonRl; HospAde; JrNHS; NHS; SpnCl; PpCl; JCAwd; Franklin College; Spanish.

QUIRING, Greg L; Hampton Public HS; Hampton, NE; Chrs; LbryAde; FFA; Ftbl; Univ Nebr; Ag Education.

QUIRING, Nyla J; Mt Lake Public HS; Mt Lake, MN; ALAGirlsSt; Chr; SchMus; Twrl; YthFlsp; PpCl; Chrldr; GAA; Vocational School; Rec Or Secretary.

QUIRK, Patrick B; Wauwatosa West HS; Wauwatosa, WI; 48/432 AFS; Band; CncrtBnd; HonRl; MrchBnd; NHS; PepBnd; MthCl; Socr; Uw Madison; Engineer.

QUIROZ, Luis A; Divine Heart Seminary; Chicago, IL; 3/16 PresFrshCls; VPSophCls; VPJrCls; HonRl; NHS; SctActv; StuCncl; RptrSchPpr; LetterBsktbl; LetterSoc; Illinois Inst Of Tech; Commercial Art.

QUISH, Theresa A; Prophetstown HS; Prophetstown, IL; 9/98 AFS; Chrs; ChrhWkr; HonRl; JrNHS; NHS; SchPl; 4-H; VPSpnCl; GAA; Il St Univ.

QUIST, Rochelle A; Blair HS; Blair, NE; DrmMjrt; HospAde; PepBnd; 4-H; FNA; PpCl; LetterBsktbl; LetterTrk; CaptChrldr; 4-HAwd; Midland Luth Clg; Nursing.

QUIVEY, Marilyn K; La Ville HS; Plymouth, IN; 4/164 Band; VPNatlFornLg; NHS; SecNatlThespSoc; PresYthFlsp; Pres4-H; 4-HAwd; VoiceDemAwd; Univ; Speech.

R

RAAB, Gerald M; Dickinson HS; Dickinson, ND; 99/186 Chr; HonRl; TchrAde; Electronics.

RAAB, Virginia K; Stockton HS; Stockton, IL; HonRl; LbryAde; FBLA; FHA; GAA;.

RAABE, Joan K; North Greene HS; Hillview, IL; HonRl; SecNHS; MthCl; VPGAA; Med Tech.

RAAP, Denise L; Tolley Public HS; Tolley, ND; 4/11 HonRl; LbryAde; OffAde; SchPl; RptrYrbk; RptrSchPpr; GerCl; Bsktbl; Trk; PresAwd; College; Vocation.

RAASCH, Carol L; Kewaunee HS; Kewaunee, WI; 1/155 VPAFS; Band; Chr; Chrs; NHS; PepBnd; TchrAde; EdYrBk; SciCl; LetterBsktbl; Trk; Chrldr; GAA; College; Accounting.

RAASCH, James P; Oconomowoc Sr HS; Okauchee, WI; 14/223 HonRl; JrNHS; College; Veterinarian.

RAASCH, Patricia E; Harlem HS; Rockford, IL; 39/520 Rock Valley Jr College; Dental Asst.

RABADUEX, Nancy A; North County HS; Desloge, MO; 20/175 Band; Chr; HonRl; Mdrgl; MrchBnd; NHS; PepBnd; RedCrAde; StuCncl; PpCl; Coll;prof Musician.

RABADUEX, Nancy A; North County R I HS; Desloge, MO; 20/174 Chr; ChrhWkr; PresCncrtBnd; HonRl; Mdrgl; MrchBnd; NatlFornLg; PepBnd; SchPl; SecStuCncl; Clg; Pro Musician.

RABAS, Sue M; Kewaunee HS; Kewaunee, WI; VPJrCls; SecAFS; Band; HospAde; VPNHS; TreasStuCncl; SecSciCl; Bsktbl; Trk; Chrldr; Coll; Elementary Teacher.

RABBERS, Jodi L; Lake Shore HS; Stevensville, MI; Band; CncrtBnd; HonRl; MrchBnd; PepBnd; SchMus; SchPl; PpCl; CaptBsktbl; Western Mich; Pro Basketball.

RABBITT, Richard D; Harper Creek HS; Battle Creek, MI; PresJrCls; HonRl; NHS; StuCncl; StuGov; YthFlsp; MthCl; LetterFtbl; LetterTennis; Mi State; Engineering.

RABE, Barry G; Willowbrook HS; Villa Park, IL; 58/822 ChrhWkr; HonRl; ModUN; NHS; PolWkr; Quill&Scroll; EdSchPpr; Carthage College; Secondary Education.

RABE, Bruce K; Seymour HS; Payson, IL; Band; Chrs; SchMus; StuCncl; TreasYthFlsp; VP4-H; Trk; Univ Of Illinois; Agriculture.

RABE, Daniel J; Oconomowoc HS; Oconomowoc, WI; 12/250 AFS; Chrs; HonRl; NHS; SchMus; Univ; Theatre Arts.

RABE, Randy S; Valders HS; Valders, WI; TrsFrshCls; PresJrCls; AFS; HonRl; NHS; YthFlsp; Bsbl; Bsktbl; Ftbl; CchngActv; College; Professional.

RABE, Sue A; Iowa Falls HS; Iowa Falls, IA; 17/149 VPJrCls; TrsSrCls; HonRl; NHS; StuCncl; YthFlsp; EdYrBk; SecFFA; LetterBsktbl; 4-HAwd; Iowa State Univ; Agriculture Business.

RABE, Susan M; Gladbrook Community HS; Gladbrook, IA; PresSophCls; Band; ChrhWkr; CncrtBnd; MrchBnd; ModUN; TreasNHS; NatlMeritSF; PepBnd; SchPl; Ia St U; Anthropology.

RABELHOFER, Alice E; Richmond Burton HS; Spring Grove, IL; Chr; Chrs; CmntyWkr; DrlTm; HonRl; SchMus; SchPl; TchrAde; FrCl; GAA; College; Airline Stewardess.

RABENHORST, Karl; Senior HS; Markesan, WI; 27/116 MrchBnd; PepBnd; SchMus; 4-H; 4-HAwd; KiwanAwd; CitAwd; Univ Of Wi Madison; Us Navy Pilot.

RABER, Kristin M; Goshen HS; Goshen, IN; 3/252 Band; CncrtBnd; MrchBnd; NHS; NatlMeritCmnd; Orch; SchMus; SchPl; LetterSwmmng; GAA; DARAwd; Goshen College; Medicine.

RABIDEAU, Sandra; Saint Charles HS; Saint Charles, MI; SecSophCls; SecJrCls; Band; HonRl; PepBnd; GAA; IMSpt; 4-HAwd; Us Air Force.

RABINAK, Glenn C; Brother Rice HS; Evergreen Park, IL; 2/431 ChrhWkr; HonRl; NatlFornLg; PresNHS; NatlMeritSF; IMSpt; AmLegAwd; Il Tech; Chem Engr.

RABINAK, Glenn C; Brother Rice HS; Evergreen Pk, IL; 2/412 ChrhWkr; HonRl; NatlFornLg; PresNHS; NatlMeritFnl; NatlMeritSF; Ill Inst Of Tech; Chemical Engr.

RABINOWITZ, Arthur P; Highland Park HS; Highland Park, IL; FDA; Univ Of Illinois; Doctor.

RABINOWITZ, Jeff W; Southfield Lathrup HS; Southfield, MI; 69/683 AFS; HonRl; Univ Of Mi; Biomedical Eng.

RABIOLA, Annette; St Mary Of Perpetual Help HS; Chicago, IL; Chrs; HonRl; LbryAde; Yrbk; College; Professnl.

RABISH, Kent J; Pinconning Area HS; Pinconning, MI; FrCl; IMSpt; RotaryAwd; Mi State U; Pre Med.

RABOIN, Carilyn A; Niagara HS; Niagara, WI; 6/58 SecLbryAde; NHS; EdYrBk; RptrSchPpr; PpCl; LetterTrk; CaptChrldr; IMSpt; Univ Of Wisconsin; Psychology.

RABOINE, David R; Saint Marys HS; Kansasville, WI; HonRl; LetterFtbl; IMSpt; Clge; Ag.

RACE, Karen E; Goodridge HS; Goodridge, MN; Band; Chrs; HonRl; YthFlsp; RptrYrbk; Pres4-H; FHA; FTA; PpCl; GAA; 4-HAwd; College; Math.

RACE, Mimi; Grosse Pointe South HS; Grosse Point Farms, MI; Chr; ChrhWkr; HonRl; HospAde; NHS; NatlThespSoc; SchPl; Yrbk; FrCl; IMSpt; Univ; Major Study.

RACEK, Karen; Luther High South HS; Oak Lawn, IL; 17/135 ChrhWkr; HonRl; NHS; SchPpr; Tennis; GAA; IMSpt; Trinity Christian College; Undecided.

RACEY, C Karen M; Trenton HS; Trenton, MI; 40/581 JrNHS; NHS; Swmmng; Eastern Michigan Univ; Medical Tech.

RACHAS, Barbara J; St Anthony HS; St Louis, MO; PresJrCls; HonRl; SecLbryAde; NHS; SchMus; PresSctActv; PresStuCncl; TchrAde; RptrSchPpr; LatCl; Chrldr; Rockhurst College; Teaching.

RACHEL, Vonda L; Wing HS; Arena, ND; PresSophCls; ALAGirlsSt; Band; Chr; Chrs; ChrhWkr; CncrtBnd; HonRl; LbryAde; MrchBnd; PepBnd; SchAde; CaptBsktbl; Trk; IMSpt; College.

RACHMACIEJ, Rosemary A; Good Counsel HS; Chicago, IL; 40/275 VPJrCls; Chr; Chrl; Chrs; HonRl; SchMus; SchPl; JAAwd; College; Business.

RACICKI, Marlene A; New Haven HS; New Haven, MI; 10/110 DrmMjrt; JA; OffAde; Yrbk; SchPpr; FrCl; PpCl; LetterChrldr; College.

RACICOT, Larry D; Bark River Harris HS; Bark River, MI; 15/56 HonRl; SchPl; TchrAde; YthLg; RptrYrbk; EdYrBk; LetterBsktbl; CchngActv; CaptIMSpt; Armed Services.

RACINE, Joseph; Greenlake HS; Greenlake, WI; Band; CncrtBnd; HonRl; MrchBnd; PepBnd; 4-H; Univ; Conservation.

RACINE, Thomas L; Naperville Central HS; Naperville, IL; 29/844 HonRl; JrNHS; NHS; LetterTrk; Univ Of Southern Calif; Architecture.

RACKERS, Charles L; Senior HS; Holt Summit, MO; HonRl; JrNHS; LitMag; NatlMeritCmnd; Univ Of Mo; Computer Science.

RACKERS, Cheryl A; Fatima HS; Bonnots Mill, MO; Chrs; HonRl; SchPl; FBLA; FHA; SpnCl; Social Work.

RACKOUSKI, Brian V; Lincoln Way HS; New Lenox, IL; 134/500 HonRl; NHS; OffAde; Bsbl; CaptBsktbl; Ftbl; LetterTrk; Illinois State College; Business Admin.

RACOP, Carol E; Lawrenceville HS; Flat Rock, IL; 13/180 HonRl; NHS; SchMus; SchPl; Pres4-H; FNA; GAA; DanFAwd; 4-HAwd; JAAwd; Lincoln Trail Clg; English Educ.

RADACHI, Mark J; Creighton Prep; Omaha, NE; 42/218 VPSophCls; HonRl; JA; PolWkr; Sdlty; StuCncl; RptrYrbk; IMSpt; JAAwd; College; Psycology.

RADANDT, Sheryl K; North HS; Eau Claire, WI; 85/362 Chr; HonRl; FHA; PpCl; GAA; IMSpt; Voc Tech Sch; Degree In Accounting.

RADCLIFF, Cathy L; Madison HS; Madison, IL; HonRl; LbryAde; StuCncl; YthFlsp; SecFBLA; SciCl; Business School; Secretary.

RADCLIFFE, Elizabeth E; East Noble HS; Kendallville, IN; 12/270 Chr; NHS; NatlThespSoc; SchMus; SchPl; StuCncl; RptrSchPpr; LetterBsktbl; LetterGlf; 4-HAwd; Ball U; Radio Broadcasting.

RADECHEL, Krista A; Clarion Community HS; Clarion, IA; 5/94 Band; CncrtBnd; HonRl; MrchBnd; NHS; StuCncl; Twrl; LetterBsbl; CaptBsktbl; Chrldr; Wartburg; Biology.

RADEK, Matthew G; John F Kennedy HS; Chicago, IL; 45/610 PresFrshCls; PresSophCls; Band; Chrs; CmntyWkr; CncrtBnd; HonRl; MrchBnd; NHS; PepBnd; SchMus; StuCncl; CaptFtbl; Swmmng; Air Force Academy; Chemical Eng.

RADEL, Sherri L; Wabasso Public HS; Wabasso, MN; Band; Chr; HonRl; HospAde; TchrAde; RptrYrbk; PpCl; Chrldr; College; Nursing.

RADEMACHER, Bruce E; Central HS; Evansville, IN; 6/600 ChrhWkr; CmntyWkr; HonRl; JA; NHS; PolWkr; StuGov; YthFlsp; Purdue Univ; Pharmacy.

RADEMACHER, Janet K; Southridge HS; Holland, IN; ChrhWkr; HonRl; HospAde;.

RADEMACHER, Sandra L; Berthold Public HS; Foxholm, ND; 2/15 VPSophCls; TrsJrCls; ALAGirlsSt; Band; DrlTm; DrmMjrt; HonRl; SchPl; VPYthFlsp; Yrbk; PpCl; Chrldr; U Of Nd; Medicine.

RADEMACHER, Valerie L; Prospect HS; Mt Prospect, IL; 95/610 NHS; NatlThespSoc; SchMus; University Of Missouri; Journalism.

RADEMAKER, Randall J; Woodruff HS; Peoria, IL; ChrhWkr; HonRl; NHS; SctActv; VPStuCncl; KeyCl; Bsbl; Wrstlng; University Of Illinois; Law.

RADER, Carolyn A; Carroll HS; Burlington, IN; 39/132 HonRl; LbryAde; 4-H; Indiana University; Nurse.

RADER, John W; Waunakee Community HS; Waunakee, WI; 35/144 AFS; Band; Chrs; CncrtBnd; HonRl; MrchBnd; PepBnd; SchPl; SctActv; LetterBsktbl; U Of Wi Madison; Civil Engineer.

RADER, Mark; Three Rivers HS; Three Rivers, MI; 9/210 HonRl; SctActv; 4-H; LatCl; Univ; Electrical Engineer.

RADERS, Dean A; West HS; Sioux City, IA; HonRl; RptrYrbk; Yrbk; SchPpr; College; Med.

RADETIC, Joan M; Mercy HS; St Louis, MO; 3/180 HonRl; NHS; TchrAde; EdYrBk; SecSpnCl; PpCl; St Louis Univ; Accounting.

RADFORD, Andrea L; C V S HS; Chicago, IL; 66/889 TreasBand; CncrtBnd; HonRl; LbryAde; MrchBnd; NHS; OffAde; PepBnd; TreasStuCncl; TchrAde; EngCl; MthCl; GAA; University; Teacher Of Mathematics.

RADFORD, Andrea L; Cvs HS; Chicago, IL; 41/668 TreasBand; CncrtBnd; HonRl; JrNHS; LbryAde; MrchBnd; TreasStuCncl; TchrAde; EngCl; MthCl; Univ; Pro.

RADFORD, Darrel K; Blue River Valley HS; Mooreland, IN; 9/94 HonRl; NHS; SchPl; RptrYrbk; RptrSchPpr; SchPpr; LatCl; Bsbl; Bsktbl; IMSpt; Ball State Univ; Broadcasting.

RADFORD, Joyce M; Dupo HS; Dupo, IL; Band; Chr; Chrl; Chrs; ChrhWkr; HonRl; LbryAde; NHS; OffAde; Orch; TchrAde; YthFlsp; College; Accountant.

RADICE, Venise L; Proviso East HS; Elmhurst, IL; 34/990 Chrs; HonRl; NHS; NatlThespSoc; SchPl; RptrYrbk; RptrSchPpr; PresTrk; Univ; Professional.

RADIN, Amelia A; Campbell HS; Campbell, MO; HonRl; CivCl; 4-H; FHA; 4-HAwd; Business School; Clerical Work.

RADKE, Joan B; West Liberty HS; W Liberty, IA; SecSophCls; CmntyWkr; Yrbk; Pres4-H; FHA; CaptGlf; 4-HAwd; College; Radiology.

RADKE, Ronald; Balaton HS; Balaton, MN; 8/33 PresSrCls; HonRl; SchPl; Mankato State Coll; Recreation Park Adm.

RADKE, Ruth; East Greene Community HS; Grand Junction, IA; 9/43 Band; Chr; HospAde; MrchBnd; RedCrAde; SchAde; SchMus; TchrAde; RptrYrbk; FHA; Univ Of Northern Ia; Spanish Teacher.

RADLER, Robert J; Brookfield East HS; Brookfield, WI; Aud/Vis; HonRl; LbryAde; SctActv; StuCncl; KeyCl; CaptSwmmng; Trk; Wrstlng; Ia St Univ.

RADLOFF, Ronald; Mattoon Senior Hs; Mattoon, IL; ChrhWkr; HonRl; NHS; NatlMeritFnl; StuCncl; KeyCl; SciCl; Bsktbl; Trk; AmLegAwd; College; Lawyer.

RADLOFF, Steven E; Mattoon Sr HS; Mattoon, IL; HonRl; JrNHS; NHS; SctActv; KeyCl; Bsbl; Bsktbl; Ftbl; College; Professional.

RADMER, Ronnie C; Lafayette HS; St Joseph, MO; Band; CncrtBnd; MrchBnd; Orch; PepBnd; SchMus; SchPl; Ftbl; Glf; Free Lance Artist.

RADOSEVICH, Cheryl L; Ondossagon HS; Mason, WI; SecFrshCls; TrsSrCls; Chrs; HonRl; SchPl; StuCncl; Yrbk; SchPpr; FHA; SecPpCl; Uw Superior; Bus Admin.

RADS, Debra A; Immaculate Heart Of Mary HS; Lyons, IL; Chrl; Chrs; ChrhWkr; CmntyWkr; SctActv; College; History.

RADTKE, Heidi L; Oconomowoc HS; Oconomowoc, WI; 5/212 Chr; ChrhWkr; HonRl; NHS; RptrYrbk; 4-H; SpnCl; PpCl; GAA; 4-HAwd; U Of Wis Madison; Major Study.

RADTKE, Richard; Kennedy HS; Chicago, IL; TchrAde; College; Electronice Engineering.

RADTKE, Tom W; Fremont HS; Fremont, NE; CmntyWkr; RptrYrbk; RptrSchPpr; Bsbl; Ftbl; Trk; IMSpt; Midland Coll; Professional.

RADZICKI, Michael J; North HS; Sheboygan, WI; 18/537 HonRl; NHS; SctActv; PresStuCncl; KeyCl; LetterWrstlng; GodCntryAwd;.

RAEBEL, David A; Lafayette Of Red Lake Fls HS; Red Lake Falls, MN; Band; Chr; CncrtBnd; HonRl; SchPl; SpnCl; LetterBsbl; Bsktbl; Ftbl; Univ; Computer Analysis.

RAEBURN, Teresa M; Octavia HS; Cooksville, IL; 6/45 Band; Chrs; ChrhWkr; HonRl; NHS; SchMus; StuCncl; RptrSchPpr; Trk; IMSpt; Harding College; Nursing.

RAEDER, Beverly; Wahpeton Sr HS; Wahpeton, ND; HonRl; StuCncl; RptrYrbk; KeyCl; PpCl; Bsktbl; Trk; GAA; IMSpt; Sss Teacher In Phy Ed.

RAEDER, Doreen; Elkhart Lake Glenbeulah HS; Glenbeulah, WI; 7/60 SecJrCls; AFS; Band; Chrs; CncrtBnd; HonRl; MrchBnd; PepBnd; RptrYrbk; Part Time Col Student; Craftsman Ceramics.

RAES, Bart E; Lawrence HS; Lawrence, NE; ChrhWkr; SchPl; TchrAde; SchPpr; Bsktbl; Ftbl; University; Medicine.

RAES, Lu Ann; Missouri Valley HS; Honey Creek, IA; SecJrCls; Chr; Chrs; HonRl; Mdrgl; NHS; FNA; College; Professional.

RAESCHEN, Susan I; Wm Horlick HS; Racine, WI; 58/600 ChrhWkr; HonRl; StuCncl; Univ Of Wisconsin; Medical Technology.

RAESLY, Bradley J; Carthage HS; Carthage, SD; Band; Chrs; CncrtBnd; HonRl; SchPl; RptrYrbk; LetterBsktbl; LetterFtbl; LetterTrk; IMSpt; College.

RAFA, Maria L; Alvernia HS; Chicago, IL; 12/225 Band; NHS; RedCrAde; StuGov; EngCl; University; Medical Technology.

RAFALSKI, Robert H; Ottawa HS; Ottawa, IL; 10/420 ALBoysSt; HonRl; NHS; LetterBsktbl; LetterFtbl; LetterTennis; College; Engineering.

RAFFIN, Christina; Holly HS; Holly, MI; HonRl; JrNHS; NHS; OffAde; SchMus; FrCl; Eastern Mi Univ; Elementary Education.

RAFTERY, Maureen P; So Bo Co R 1 HS; Hartsburg, MO; Band; Chr; HonRl; OffAde; Sms; Music.

RAGAINS, Kevin G; Springs Valley HS; French Lick, IN; 15/90 TrsSophCls; ALBoysSt; ChrhWkr; CmntyWkr; HonRl; JrNHS; NHS; PpCl; LetterBsktbl; LetterFtbl; LetterTrk; CchngActv; AmLegAwd; College; Vocation.

RAGAN, Rise S; North Kansas City HS; North Kansas City, MO; AFS; HonRl; SchMus; StuCncl; TchrAde; VPTeen; PresGerCl; YthFlsp; PpCl; Chrldr; Col; Theatre & Dance.

RAGAN, Tamara L; Seymour HS; Payson, IL; 9/68 Band; CmntyWkr; HonRl; SchMus; StuCncl; 4-H; Bsbl; Chrldr; College.

RAGAN, Thomas; Mendel C HS; Chicago, IL; HonRl; SctActv; MthCl; PpCl; IMSpt; Devry Inst Of Tech; Oceanography.

RAGATZ, Virginia K; Potosi HS; Potosi, WI; 1/70 VPSophCls; ChrhWkr; CmntyWkr; HonRl; NHS; OffAde; FBLA; LetterBsktbl; Swmmng; Trk; College.

RAGAUSS, Peter; Catholic Central HS; Grand Rapids, MI; NatlMeritCmnd; Michigan State U; Engineer.

RAGER, Mary A; Wabash HS; Wabash, IN; HonRl; StuCncl; StuGov; GerCl; PpCl; Chrldr; Purdue Univ; Physical Therapy.

RAGIAS, Theodore S; Pekin Comm HS; Pekin, IL; 44/759 HonRl; NHS; LetterBsbl; LetterBsktbl; LetterTrk; Univ Of Ill; Data Processing.

RAGINS, Tammie; Delta C7 HS; Gobler, MO; 2/30 SecTrsFrshCls; SecTrsSophCls; HonRl; StuCncl; Yrbk; FHA; FTA; PpCl; Chrldr; College; Vocation.

RAGOS, Michael A; Bolingbrook HS; Bolingbrook, IL; 110/350 HonRl; Yrbk; Glf;.

RAGSDALE, Amy W; West HS; Madison, WI; 4/650 HonRl; NHS; NatlMeritSF; SchMus; RptrSchPpr; SchPpr; LetterSwmmng; College; Dance Choreographer.

RAGSDALE, Lisa L; Normal Community HS; Carlock, IL; SecFrshCls; SecSophCls; SecJrCls; SecSrCls; ALAGirlsSt; NHS; PolWkr; StuCncl; GAA; RotaryAwd; U Of Alabama; Pre Law.

RAGSDALE, Michael; St Marys HS; Kansas City, MO; Chr; Chrl; Chrs; ChrhWkr; HonRl; PolWkr; SchMus; SchPl; TchrAde; Bsktbl; Ftbl; Rockhurst Coll; Funeral Director.

RAGSDALE, Rockne; Century HS; Ullin, IL; ChrhWkr; HonRl; SchPl; SchPpr; FFA; PpCl; Bsbl; Swawnee Coll; Wildlife Tech.

RAGSDELL, Philip B; Farmington HS; Farmington, MO; 2/289 Band; Chr; HonRl; NHS; NatlThespSoc; SchMus; StuCncl; Yrbk; SpnCl; SciCl; LetterFtbl; Tennis; College; Nuclear Engineering.

RAHAM, Roger M; Saline HS; Saline, MI; TrsSrCls; HonRl; VPNHS; NatlMeritSF; TchrAde; Bsktbl; Ftbl; Trk; Univ Of Michigan; Accounting.

RAHE, Daniel O; Valmeyer HS; Valmeyer, IL; 14/59 TrsSophCls; PresSrCls; Chr; HonRl; SchMus; RptrYrbk; 4-H; FFA; PpCl; Bsktbl; U Of Il; Agriculture.

RAHE, David; Beckman HS; Earlville, IA; ChrhWkr; CmntyWkr; HonRl; PolWkr; SchPl; RptrSchPpr; SptEdSchPpr; FrCl; Bsktbl;.

RAHE, Donna; Academy Of Immaculate HS; Batesville, IN; 13/67 HonRl; SchMus; GerCl; Marian College; Accountant.

RAHE, Joyce A; Monticello HS; Monticello, IA; HonRl; FHA; SpnCl; Mount Mercy Coll; Accounting.

RAHEL, Patrice K; Westside HS; Omaha, NE; ChrhWkr; CmntyWkr; HonRl; StuCncl; 4-H; FrCl; LatCl; Chrldr; PPFtbl; 4-HAwd; College; Business.

RAHM, George A; Doland HS; Doland, SD; Chrs; HonRl; SchMus; SchPl; StuCncl; TchrAde; FFA; Bsktbl; Ftbl; Trk; Univ; Farmer.

RAHMEIER, Larry E; Salina Central HS; Salina, KS; 19/329 HonRl; RptrYrbk; SchPpr; RusCl; Trk; Univ Of Ks; Elec Eng.

RAHN, Gary R; Gibault Catholic HS; Red Bud, IL; 1/90 Band; HonRl; LitMag; PresNHS; SctActv; StuCncl; SchPpr; St Louis Univ; Accounting.

RAHN, Judith; Foreman Hs; Chicago, IL; 6/355 CncrtBnd; HonRl; NHS; SchPl; TchrAde; PresGerCl; PresMthCl; SciCl; GAA; Florida Southern College; Accountint.

RAHN, Paul A; Lincoln Sr HS; Bloomington, MN; HonRl; NHS; Trk; IMSpt; College; Science.

RAHN, Robert F; Hazen HS; Hazen, ND; 3/38 PresFrshCls; ALBoysSt; Chr; Chrs; HonRl; SchPl; StuCncl; StuGov; RptrYrbk; Ftbl; Nd State Univ; Gen Studies.

RAHNKE, Lynn A; Andover HS; W Bloomfield, MI; HonRl; HospAde; RedCrAde; SchMus; SchPl; SctActv; FSA; University; Medical.

RAHOY, Pamela L; Cassville HS; Cassville, MO; 18/108 ALAGirlsSt; DrlTm; NatlFornLg; PolWkr; SchPl; StuCncl; FBLA; LetterBsktbl; GAA; IMSpt; Univ Of Mo Columbia; Psychology.

RAHTER, Karen M; Liberty HS; Liberty, MO; PresAFS; HonRl; JrNHS; NHS; Yrbk; SpnCl; PresPpCl; Col; Nursing.

RAICA, Marie A; Josephinum HS; Chicago, IL; SecFrshCls; TrsSophCls; PresJrCls; HonRl; StuCncl; StuGov; Yrbk; SchPpr; Bsktbl; CchngActv; GAA; Business School; Accounting.

RAICHE, Rosemary A; St Mary Central HS; Neenah, WI; Chrs; CmntyWkr; HonRl; HospAde; SchMus; StuCncl; RptrYrbk; LetterTennis; Trk; GAA; College.

RAIHALA, William K; Aurora Hoyt Lakes HS; Makinen, MN; 6/227 ALBoysSt; CncrtBnd; HonRl; MrchBnd; NHS; PepBnd; MthCl; LetterBsbl; BauchLmbAwd; DanFAwd; Univ Of Minnesota; Engineering.

RAIKES, Linda; Porta HS; Oakford, IL; 43/97 Band; MrchBnd; NatlThespSoc; PepBnd; SchMus; TchrAde; Yrbk; 4-H; PpCl; College; Voc.

RAILE, Brenda A; Goodland HS; Edson, KS; 1/132 TrsFrshCls; Chr; ChrhWkr; CmntyWkr; HonRl; IntrClCncl; JrNHS; NHS; Pres4-H; PpCl; CaptBsktbl; Chrldr; GAA; DARAwd; Kansas State Univ; Medical Technology.

RAILE, Cynthia M; Wishek HS; Wishek, ND; 15/40 HonRl; NHS; OffAde; StuCncl; StuGov; FDA; PresAwd; College; Secretary Medical.

RAIMONDI, Josephine A; Our Lady Of Grace Academy; Indianapolis, IN; 5/56 Chrs; HonRl; TreasJA; NHS; SchMus; EdYrBk; SecSpnCl; GAA; JAAwd; College; Accounting.

RAINE, Douglas; T Roosevelt HS; Wyandotte, MI; Aud/Vis; HonRl; Bsktbl; Wrstlng; Univ; Curriculum Of Major Study.

RAINES, Cheryl A; Roxana Sr HS; Wood River, IL; 108/275 Chr; Chrs; ChrhWkr; DrlTm; HospAde; JA; OffAde; SchMus; YthFlsp; Yrbk; FHA; Western Ill Univ; Home Economics.

RAINES, Kevin C; Notre Dame HS; Illmo, MO; Band; HonRl; SchMus; SctActv; IMSpt; Se Mo St U; Wildlife Conserv.

RAINES, Maribeth A; Bishop Mcnamara HS; Bourbonnais, IL; 2/187 HonRl; NHS; RptrYrbk; FrCl; LetterBsktbl; LetterTrk; GAA; IMSpt; PPFtbl; Medical Technologist.

RAINEY, Janice M; Laura Speed Elliot HS; Boonville, MO; NHS; YthFlsp; SpnCl; PpCl; LetterBsktbl; Trk; Chrldr; IMSpt; College; Medical Secretary.

RAINEY, Lee A; Metropolis Comm HS; Joppa, IL; 15/161 PresSrCls; HonRl; HospAde; MrchBnd; NHS; NatlMeritCmnd; OffAde; StuCncl; StuGov; SpnCl; PpCl; Univ Of Ill; Professional.

RAINEY, Marjorie M; Tri County HS; Jamesport, MO; Band; Chr; Chrl; Chrs; CncrtBnd; DrmBgl; HonRl; 4-H; FHA; Trade School; Vocation.

RAINFORD, Gary D; South Newton HS; Kentland, IN; PresSophCls; ALBoysSt; ChrhWkr; HonRl; NHS; YthFlsp; 4-H; Bsktbl; Ftbl; 4-HAwd; Coll; Vocation.

RAINFORTH, Jon D; New Market Comm HS; Gravity, IA; VPJrCls; ALBoysSt; Chrl; Chrs; HonRl; LbryAde; StuCncl; FFA; PpCl; Ftbl; Ia Western Comm College; Vocal Education.

RAINS, Beth G; Desoto Sr HS; Desoto, KS; SecJrCls; Band; HonRl; NHS; StuCncl; Yrbk; VPFBLA; FHA; College; Advertising.

RAIRICK, Linda M; Fraser HS; Ypsilanti, MI; 9/565 TrsSophCls; Band; ChrhWkr; CncrtBnd; HonRl; MrchBnd; NHS; StuCncl; PPFtbl; Eastern Mi Univ; Med Technology.

RAISANEN, Diane L; Annandale Public HS; Annandale, MN; 4/124 PresSophCls; Band; Chr; ChrhWkr; HonRl; Mdrgl; StuCncl; 4-H; Chrldr; IMSpt; St Cloud State Col; Music Major.

RAISANEN, Marty J; Calumet HS; Calumet, MI; 2/170 CncrtBnd; HonRl; MrchBnd; NHS; Chrldr; PresAwd; Coll; Pro.

RAISLEGER, Michael L; Kewaunee HS; Denmark, WI; HonRl; FFA; SciCl; Ftbl;.

RAITT, Susan A; So Bo Co HS; Hartsburg, MO; Band; CmntyWkr; CncrtBnd; HonRl; MrchBnd; NHS; PepBnd; PolWkr; SchPl; TchrAde; FHA; PpCl; Bsbl; College; Nursing.

RAJALA, Anne M; Big Fork HS; Big Fork, MN; Band; Chr; SchMus; SchPl; StuCncl; EdYrBk; Chrldr; Hasca Comm Clg; Secretarial.

RAJALA, Neil S; Marquette HS; Marquette, MI; 32/384 HonRl; GerCl; N Mich U; Commercial Art.

RAJKOWSKI, Barbara; Good Counsel HS; Chicago, IL; Chrs; HonRl; SchMus; SchPl; Coll; Ed.

RAJMAIRA, Salil; Lane Tech HS; Chicago, IL; 37/1162 DrlTm; HonRl; NHS; OffAde; ROTC; SchAde; SctActv; TchrAde; RptrSchPpr; Socr; Northwestern Univ; Medicine.

RAJU, Alexander; Southeastern HS; Detroit, MI; 2/110 HonRl; TreasNHS; FDA; CitAwd; Univ Of Mi; Physician.

RAKERS, Teri L; Wesclin HS; New Baden, IL; SchPpr; FBLA; FHA; FrCl; LetterTrk; PresAwd; Busi Coll; Prof.

RAKESTRAW, Barbara; Arkansas City HS; Arkansas, KS; VPFrshCls; HonRl; HospAde; LbryAde; StuCncl; SpnCl; PpCl; Trk; Chrldr; GAA; College.

RAKOCZY, Mary; Central Valley HS; Reynolds, ND; 7/24 Band; ChrhWkr; PepBnd; SchPl; Yrbk; SchPpr; Bsktbl; BttyCrckrAwd; Aakers Business Coll; Secretarial.

RAKOCZY, Melvin; Valparaiso HS; Valparaiso, IN; 53/419 HonRl; SciCl; Bsbl; Valparaiso U; Business.

RAKOV, Elizabeth R; Verdigre HS; Verdigre, NE; 2/42 Chrs; HonRl; NHS; SchPl; TchrAde; Twrl; Yrbk; EdSchPpr; LetterTrk; IMSpt; PPFtbl; Cornell Univ; Law.

RAKOW, Debra; Richland Center HS; Richland Center, WI; Aud/Vis; ChrhWkr; HonRl; NHS; PpCl; SciCl; Univ; Vet.

RALEY, David P; Union HS; Grand Rapids, MI; LetterTrk; IMSpt; Grand Rap Jr Coll.

RALITZ, Cynthia J; Mosinee HS; Mosinee, WI; 14/170 Chr; HonRl; NatlFornLg; Twrl; YthFlsp; FrCl; U Of Wi Madison; Physical Therapy.

RALLINS, Clifford R; Maine North HS; Des Plaines, IL; CmntyWkr; HonRl; OffAde; TchrAde; Teen; Bsbl; Bsktbl; CchngActv; College.

RALLO, John L; St Catherines HS; Racine, WI; SchPl; StuCncl; TchrAde; SpnCl; Ftbl; Milwaukee Sch Of Engineering; Architect.

RALPH, Carl E; St Agnes HS; Springfield, MO; HonRl; LitMag; SctActv; Twrl; RptrYrbk; EdSchPpr; Ftbl; Tennis; Trk; VoiceDemAwd; Smsu Springfield Mo; Writer.

RALPH, Joan R; Girard HS; Farlington, KS; Band; Chrs; CncrtBnd; HonRl; MrchBnd; NHS; PepBnd; PolWkr; SchPl; Twrl; LetterTrk; PPFtbl; 4-HAwd; Col; Medical Tech.

RALPH, Michael J; Wenona Comm HS; Streator, IL; Chrs; ChrhWkr; CmntyWkr; HonRl; SchMus; SchPl; Bsbl; Bsktbl; Univ Of Ill; Phy Ed Teacher.

RALSON, Joan M; Mt Assisi HS; Chicago Ridge, IL; 74/189 HonRl; SchPl; SctActv; Teen; Glf; Work In Accounting.

RALSTON, Jane A; Oblong HS; Oblong, IL; 1/72 Chrs; ChrhWkr; HonRl; NHS; NatlMeritCmnd; RptrYrbk; EdSchPpr; FrCl; GAA; Cottey College.

RALSTON, Sherrie L; Nokomis HS; Fillmore, IL; 24/92 Chrs; HonRl; GAA; Secretarial Training.

RALSTON, Sherry M; Bruning Public HS; Bruning, NE; 7/15 Band; Chrs; HonRl; SchPl; YthFlsp; 4-H; PpCl; LetterTrk; College; Accounting.

RAMACKER, Joseph R; Fremont HS; Fremont, NE; CmntyWkr; HonRl; NHS; GerCl; MthCl; LetterFtbl; IMSpt; KiwanAwd; Midland Lutheran Coll; Bus Admin.

RAMAEKER, Joseph; Fremont Senior HS; Fremont, NE; 12/425 CmntyWkr; HonRl; NHS; GerCl; MthCl; IMSpt; KiwanAwd; Midland Lutheran College; Bus Administrati.

RAMAEKERS, Roxane R; Genoa Public HS; Genoa, NE; Chrl; CmntyWkr; HonRl; LbryAde; MrchBnd; OffAde; SchPl; FHA; PpCl; Chrldr; Col; Keeping Hosp Records.

RAMAGE, Patti J; Dupo Comm HS; Dupo, IL; HonRl; NHS; OffAde; TchrAde; PpCl; CaptChrldr; PPFtbl; College; Secretary.

RAMAGE, Sharon; Century HS; Perks, IL; ChrhWkr; TchrAde; FHA; PpCl; Marion Beauty Sch.

RAMBECK, Elizabeth; Cavalier Public HS; Hensel, ND; ALAGirlsSt; Band; HonRl; HospAde; SchPl; StuCncl; SciCl; GAA; PPFtbl; 4-HAwd; Univ; Nurse.

RAMBIS, Teresa E; Sparta Senior HS; Sparta, WI; TrsFrshCls; Band; CncrtBnd; HonRl; NHS; StuCncl; Twrl; PpCl; Trk; Chrldr; Univ Of Wis Eau Claire; Math.

RAMBO, Richard; Bellmont HS; Decatur, IN; 49/251 HonRl; NHS; LatCl; MasAwd; Ball State Univ; Archetic.

RAMBOW, Brenda L; Willmar Sr HS; Willmar, MN; Band; CncrtBnd; MrchBnd; NatlFornLg; PepBnd; SchPl; College.

RAMEY, Cheryl A; Jackson HS; Jackson, MI; CmntyWkr; HospAde; NHS; StuGov; RptrSchPpr; FNA; Bsbl; Swmmng; PPFtbl; College; Physical Therapy.

RAMEY, Rebecca L; Northeastern HS; Williamsburg, IN; Band; ChrhWkr; CncrtBnd; HonRl; MrchBnd; NHS; PepBnd; SchMus; YthFlsp; 4-H; Ohio State University; Medicine.

RAMEY, Sharon; Shelby HS; Shelby, MI; Band; ChrhWkr; CncrtBnd; HonRl; LbryAde; MrchBnd; RedCrAde; SctActv; YthFlsp; FNA; Trade; Vocation.

RAMEYER, Marcia; Ackley Geneva HS; Ackley, IA; 8/56 SecSophCls; CncrtBnd; HonRl; MrchBnd; PepBnd; Teen; Twrl; RptrYrbk; Bsktbl; Chrldr; Ellsworth Jr Col; Medical Sec.

RAMFJORD, Per A; Pioneer HS; Ann Arbor, MI; College.

RAMIG, Paul N; Gering HS; Gering, NE; 11/139 SecSophCls; VPJrCls; TrsSrCls; ALBoysSt; Pres-Band; PresChr; HonRl; PresJrNHS; NHS; PepBnd; Bsktbl; Tennis; Coll; Bus Admin.

RAMILO, Carlos E; Maine Twp West HS; Des Plaines, IL; 98/800 HonRl; NatlSciFnd; MthCl; SciCl; Bsktbl; IMSpt; Coll; Math/engr.

RAMIREZ, Deborah R; Junction City HS; Ft Riley, KS; HonRl; SctActv; StuCncl; StuGov; SpnCl; PpCl; Tennis; Chrldr; IMSpt; Kansas Univ; Interior Design.

RAMIREZ, Gloria J; Southwest HS; Kansas City, MO; DrlTm; HonRl; JrNHS; SecNHS; PepBnd; SecLatCl; RusCl; College; Political Science.

RAMIREZ, Mark D; Loyola Academy; Northfield, IL; 20/442 HonRl; NHS; NatlMeritFnl; SchMus; SciCl; LetterFtbl; LetterWrstlng; Univ Of Chicago; Vet Medicine.

RAMIREZ, Michael J; Bay City Central HS; Bay City, MI; HonRl; Bsktbl; LetterFtbl; Trk; Alma College; Social Worker.

RAMIREZ, Terry J; Lourdes HS; Rochester, MN; ChrhWkr; CncrtBnd; MrchBnd; SctActv; SpnCl; SciCl; Bsktbl; Ftbl; Trk; Univ Of Minnesota; Lawyer.

RAMLET, James; Naperville Central Hs; Naperville, IL; Chr; Chrl; HonRl; NatlFornLg; NatlThespSoc; SchMus; SchPl; Indiana U.

RAMOLD, Carolyn; Ewing HS; Inman, NE; Band; HonRl; LbryAde; MrchBnd; SchPl; TchrAde; Yrbk; EdSchPpr; IMSpt; PPFtbl; Trad; Journalism.

RAMOS, Joseph A; Frankfort HS; Frankfort, IN; NHS; SchPl; StuCncl; TchrAde; KeyCl; SpnCl; LetterFtbl; Trk; IMSpt; Butler; Medicine.

RAMOS, Pamela A; Mehlville HS; St Louis, MO; 94/500 JA; PresFHA; PresSpnCl; College; Lawyer.

RAMOS, Timothy; United Township Hs; East Moline, IL; 10 ALBoysSt; Chr; HonRl; PresLbryAde; VPNHS; NatlThespSoc; PolWkr; SchPl; StuCncl; Wrstlng; Augustana College ; Music.

RAMSAY, Ann R; East Gary Edison HS; East Gary, IN; SecFrshCls; Chr; JrNHS; Mdrgl; OffAde; SchMus; StuCncl; College; Music.

RAMSAY, Brenda K; Elmwood HS; Elmwood, IL; Band; Chrs; DrlTm; RptrSchPpr; PpCl; SciCl; LetterBsktbl; Chrldr; GAA; IMSpt; College; Graphic Arts.

RAMSAY, Gregory A; Illinois Valley Central HS; Chillicothe, IL; 11/229 HonRl; NHS; LetterGlf; Augustana College; Physics.

RAMSDEN, Diane M; Forest Lake HS; Circle Pines, MN; HonRl; NHS; Vocation Sch; Cosmetology.

RAMSDEN, Jill; Annandale Public HS; Annandale, MN; TrsFrshCls; VPSophCls; TrsJrCls; TrsSrCls; HonRl; NHS; TchrAde; RptrYrbk; EdYrBk; Coll; Art.

RAMSEY, Carl T; Griffith HS; Griffith, IN; Chr; Chrs; CmntyWkr; HonRl; SctActv; FTA; Bsktbl; Trk; IMSpt; College; Study.

RAMSEY, Chris A; Vincennes Lincoln HS; Vincennes, IN; 106/400 HonRl; IntrClCncl; NatlFornLg; PolWkr; YthLg; Indiana Univ; Law.

RAMSEY, Debra L; Eastern Hancock HS; Greenfield, IN; TrsFrshCls; Band; TreasChrhWkr; TreasJA; StuCncl; TreasYthFlsp; VP4-H; Chrldr; GAA; 4-HAwd; Dental Clg; Dental Hygienist.

RAMSEY, Dianna M; La Plata Rii HS; La Plata, MO; 1/33 Band; ChrhWkr; CmntyWkr; CncrtBnd; DrlTm; HonRl; MrchBnd; NHS; PepBnd; SchMus; SchPl; SctActv; Bsbl; University Of Missouri; Dentist.

RAMSEY, Joan; Dawson Verdon Cons; Dawson, NE; Band; Chr; Chrs; ChrhWkr; Bsbl; Bsktbl; Trk; Chrldr; CchngActv; 4-HAwd; College; Nurse.

RAMSEY, Joan; Arlington Hs; Arlington Hts, IL; Chr; CmntyWkr; HonRl; Mdrgl; NatlMeritCmnd; NatlThespSoc; SchMus; StuCncl; StuGov; TchrAde; Illinois State U;deaf Education.

RAMSEY, Lois; Marquette Hs; Marquette, KS; 2/17 ALAGirlsSt; Band; Chrs; HonRl; SchPl; TreasStuCncl; RptrYrbk; SchPpr; BttyCrckrAwd; 4-HAwd; Fort Hays State College; Accounting.

RAMSEY, Lynda K; Newkirk HS; Arkasas City, KS; Band; ChrhWkr; CncrtBnd; MrchBnd; Orch; TchrAde; PpCl; MasAwd; Housewife.

RAMSEY, Mark B; Bloomington HS; Bloomington, IL; PresSrCls; AFS; Chr; HonRl; IntrClCncl; NHS; NatlMeritCmnd; OffAde; SchAde; StuCncl; StuGov; JCAwd; University Of Virginia; Philosophy.

RAMSEY, Rex A; Daleville HS; Daleville, IN; 12/70 PresFrshCls; VPSophCls; PresJrCls; PresSrCls; Band; NHS; SchPl; 4-H; LetterBsktbl; DanFAwd; University; Law.

RAMSEY, Richard; Neosho HS; Joplin, MO; 45/250 Chr; HonRl; LbryAde; TchrAde; 4-H; Trk; IMSpt; DanFAwd; 4-HAwd; Missouri Southern State Col; Accounting.

RAMSEY, Ruth A; Doniphan HS; Doniphan, MO; 5/132 Band; ChrhWkr; CncrtBnd; HonRl; MrchBnd; PepBnd; SecStuCncl; PpCl; LetterBsktbl; Anderson College.

RAMSEY, Sandra R; Park River HS; Park River, ND; ALAGirlsSt; HonRl; HospAde; NHS; StuCncl; EdYrBk; 4-H; FHA; Trk; GAA; FFA; University.

RAMSEY, Susan R; Republic R 3 HS; Republic, MO; 15/113 Chr; Chrs; ChrhWkr; HonRl; Mdrgl; NHS; TchrAde; FTA; PpCl; Sw Baptist Clge Bolivar Mo; Christianity.

RAMSEY, William A; Elkhart Central HS; Elkhart, IN; CmntyWkr; HonRl; StuCncl; YthFlsp; LetterBsktbl; CchngActv; Army; Private Investigation.

RAMSEY, William R; Oelwein HS; Oelwein, IA; ALBoysSt; Aud/Vis; Band; CncrtBnd; HonRl; JrNHS; MrchBnd; PepBnd; PolWkr; SchMus; SctActv; StuCncl; LetterBsktbl; LetterWrstlng; Univ Of Iowa.

RAMSOUR, Stephen E; Memorial HS; Joplin, MO; 1/229 AFS; ALBoysSt; HonRl; JrNHS; LitMag; StuGov; SptEdYrbk; KeyCl; Univ Of Notre Dame; Business.

RAMSTAD, Elaine G; Climax HS; Shelly, MN; 1/26 Chrs; CncrtBnd; HonRl; NHS; SchPl; EdYrBk; FHA; GerCl; SciCl; LetterBsktbl; Moorhead St Coll; Bio Med.

RAMSTEIN, Richard R; Crawford County Ri HS; Bourbon, MO; Band; HonRl; SchPl; SctActv; StuCncl; StuGov; SpnCl; MthCl; Bsktbl; Trk; Univ Of Missouri; Dvm.

RAMTHUN, Brian; D C Everest HS; Rothschild, WI; 59/344 College; Accounting.

RAMTHUN, Marsha A; Triopia HS; Chapin, IL; VPFrshCls; Chr; Chrs; ChrhWkr; CmntyWkr; DrlTm; HonRl; HospAde; LbryAde; SchPl;.

RAMTHUN, Randy R; Rockwell City Comm HS; Rockwell City, IA; VPSrCls; HonRl; PolWkr; StuGov; LetterBsktbl; College; Computer Electronics.

RAMUS, Dennis M; Cousino HS; Warren, MI; VPJrCls; PresSrCls; HonRl; JrNHS; NHS; SctActv; StuCncl; LatCl; MthCl; LetterFtbl; Wayne St Univ; Accounting.

RANALLETTA, Vanice M; Sacred Heart Academy; Springfield, IL; ChrhWkr; NatlMeritCmnd; NatlMeritSF; StuCncl; 4-H; PpCl; Western Illinois Univ; Accounting.

RANCK, Kiplin M; Springs Valley HS; Dubois, IN; Band; HonRl; TchrAde; Yrbk; FrCl; LatCl; LetterTrk; Indiana Univ; Bio Chemistry.

RANCOUR, Marie L; Divine Child HS; Dearborn Heights, MI; 33/170 HonRl; JA; OffAde; Quill&Scroll; SchAde; TchrAde; RptrSchPpr; GerCl; PPFtbl; JAAwd; Univ Of Mi; Business Admn.

RAND, Craig A; Greendale HS; Greendale, WI; CmntyWkr; HonRl; NHS; StuGov; LetterTennis; LetterWrstlng; College;.

RAND, Terri L; Southwest HS; Green Bay, WI; 84/427 Chr; ChrhWkr; HonRl; JA; LitMag; SecStuCncl; RptrYrbk; SpnCl; PpCl; Clge; Home Ec Teacher.

RAND, Tracey D; Melrose Mindoro HS; Melrose, WI; 16/84 HonRl; SchPl; RptrYrbk; GerCl; GAA; Uw Of Eau Claire; Theatre.

RANDA, Jeffrey C; Broad Ripple HS; Indianapolis, IN; 22/330 HonRl; NHS; TreasQuill&Scroll; SchPl; EdSchPpr; LetterBsktbl; LetterTrk; Univ; Industrial Manag.

RANDA, Roberta L; Mc Gregor HS; Mc Gregor, MN; 12/60 SecSophCls; Band; CncrtBnd; HonRl; MrchBnd; NHS; SchPl; StuGov; EdYrBk; PpCl; GAA; St Scholastica; Registured Nurse.

RANDALL, Alison E; Central HS; St Joseph, MO; 58/490 SecTrsJrCls; HonRl; HospAde; LitMag; NHS; GerCl; SciCl; LetterSwmmng; University; Professional.

RANDALL, Andrea S; Athens HS; Athens, MI; TrsJrCls; Band; ChrhWkr; CncrtBnd; HonRl; MrchBnd; NHS; Trk; Univ.

RANDALL, Curt J; Bath HS; Bath, MI; 6/95 Band; CncrtBnd; HonRl; JA; MrchBnd; NHS; TchrAde; Trk; Wrstlng; Naval Academy; Marine Biologist.

RANDALL, Daniel E; Gull Lake HS; Richland, MI; 16/220 HonRl; NHS; NatlMeritFnl; NatlMeritCmnd; NatlMeritSchl; NatlMeritSF; TchrAde; CaptFtbl; CaptTrk; IMSpt; Kalamazoo Clg; Accounting Cpa.

RANDALL, Jason L; Springfield HS; Springfield, IL; 49/535 SctActv; KeyCl; GerCl; Ftbl; Glf; Univ Of Ill; Veterinarian.

RANDALL, Kathy M; Roland Story Comm HS; Story City, IA; 3/90 Chrs; CncrtBnd; HonRl; MrchBnd; StuCncl; Yrbk; Treas4-H; PresFTA; LetterGlf; 4-HAwd; Iowa St Univ; Computer Science.

RANDALL, Leah L; Willmar Sr HS; Willmar, MN; ChrhWkr; CncrtBnd; DrmMjrt; HonRl; MrchBnd; Orch; Quill&Scroll; EdSchPpr; GerCl; Swmmng; LetterTrk; College; Science Research.

RANDALL, Louise E; Ft Atkinson HS; Fort Atkinson, WI; 10/249 PresSrCls; ALAGirlsSt; Band; ChrhWkr; CncrtBnd; HonRl; HospAde; MrchBnd; NHS; EldAwd; Uw Oshkosh; Nursing.

RANDALL, Lydia L; Zionsville Comm HS; Zionsville, IN; 2/125 Band; CncrtBnd; HonRl; NHS; NatlMeritSF; SctActv; TchrAde; 4-H; Purdue Univ; Physician.

RANDALL, Lynn; Lidgerwood HS; Lidgerwood, ND; ALBoysSt; Band; Chr; ChrhWkr; CncrtBnd; HospAde; JrNHS; MrchBnd; NHS; PepBnd; Brigham Young Univ;rn.

RANDALL, Mark K; Pioneer HS; Ann Arbor, MI; College.

RANDALL, Mary F; Wisconsin Heights HS; Mazomanie, WI; 13/109 PresJrCls; PresSrCls; ALAGirlsSt; Band; Chr; NHS; SchMus; SchPl; CaptChrldr; GAA; Univ Of Wisconsin; Elementary Education.

RANDALL, Nancy A; Lewistown Community HS; Lewistown, IL; ALAGirlsSt; Band; CncrtBnd; HonRl; MrchBnd; SctActv; Yrbk; PpCl; GAA; Jr College; Secretary.

RANDALL, Philip M; Wawasee HS; Warsaw, IN; 35/213 Band; ChrhWkr; CncrtBnd; HonRl; MrchBnd; YthFlsp; FTA; SciCl; LetterGlf; Indiana Univ; Journalsim.

RANDALL, Ronald L; Rolla Sr HS; Rolla, MO; Aud/Vis; SctActv; FTA; FrCl; Bsbl; Bsktbl; Ftbl; CchngActv; IMSpt; College; Psychology.

RANDALL, Samuel K; Elm Creek Public HS; Elm Creek, NE; 4/28 HonRl; SchPl; TchrAde; Trk; Armed Services; Mechanic.

RANDALL, Terry L; Chamberlain Public HS; Chamberlain, SD; VPJrCls; VPSrCls; ALBoysSt; Band; NHS; StuCncl; Bsbl; CaptBsktbl; Ftbl; LetterTrk; South Dakota State Univ; Optometry.

RANDEL, Elizabeth G; Central Catholic HS; West Point, NE; Band; Chr; Chrs; HonRl; PepBnd; SchMus; SchPl; StuCncl; 4-H; Trk; Univ; Phy Therapy.

RANDERSON, Jo A; Freedom HS; Appleton, WI; 3/108 PresFrshCls; PresSophCls; ALAGirlsSt; Band; Chr; Chrs; Trk; Chrldr; GAA; IMSpt; Professional.

RANDICH, Barbara; Mother Mc Auley Lib Arts HS; Oak Lawn, IL; 75/484 HonRl; TchrAde; FTA; Purdue Univ; Civil Engineer.

RANDICH, Barbara J; Mother Mcauley HS; Oak Lawn, IL; 74/474 Chrs; CmntyWkr; HonRl; SchMus; TchrAde; Purdue Univ; Engineering.

RANDOLPH, Eric; Roosevelt HS; Des Moines, IA; 76/439 LatCl; Socr; KiwanAwd; Univ Of Iowa; Accounting And Law.

RANDOLPH, James L; Farmington HS; Farmington Hills, MI; SctActv; SchPpr; PpCl; Wrstlng; Univ Of Mi; Dentistry.

RANDOLPH, Mary C; Macomb Senior HS; Macomb, IL; 1/240 TrsFrshCls; Chr; HonRl; PresNHS; NatlMeritCmnd; SchMus; RptrYrbk; SchPpr; FrCl; Univ Of Illinois; Biology.

RANDOLPH, Robert F; Kirkwood HS; Kirkwood, MO; AFS; HonRl;.

RANDOLPH, Roxanne F; Valley HS; W Des Moines, IA; 135/450 HonRl; LbryAde; ModUN; SchMus; SchPl; Pres4-H; SciCl; Bsktbl; CaptSocr; LetterTrk; CchngActv; 4-HAwd; Iowa State Univ; Animal Science.

RANDS, David W; Collinsville HS; Collinsville, IL; 12/700 NatlMeritSF; SchPl; YthFlsp; SchPpr; Knox College; Law.

RANEK, Jerome M; O Borman HS; Sioux Falls, SD; Band; ChrhWkr; CmntyWkr; NatlFornLg; NHS; StuCncl; College; Priesthood.

RANEY, Barbara A; Farmer City HS; Farmer City, IL; SecFrshCls; Chrs; CncrtBnd; HonRl; MrchBnd; NHS; StuCncl; SptEdYrbk; LetterBsktbl; GAA; S Illinois University.

RANEY, Linda L; Barr Reeve HS; Loogootee, IN; 12/67 JrNHS; NHS; RptrYrbk; FHA; LatCl; PpCl; Indiana University; Biology.

RANG, Morris E; Southeastern HS; Augusta, IL; 4/50 SecSophCls; Chrs; HonRl; VPNHS; SchPl; 4-H; SpnCl; PpCl; VPSciCl; LetterGlf; Western Il Univ; Dentistry.

RANGE, Joan E; Granite City South HS; Granite City, IL; 15/630 Chrs; LitMag; Mdrgl; NHS; PpCl; Southern Illinois Univ; Music.

RANGE, Merrilee D; White Lake HS; White Lake, SD; 11/27 Chrs; CncrtBnd; HonRl; TchrAde; YthFlsp; RptrYrbk; RptrSchPpr; SchPpr; LetterBsktbl; LetterTrk; Dakota St Coll; Tchr.

RANGEN, Kristin K; Maddock Public HS; Maddock, ND; TrsFrshCls; HstSophCls; Band; Chrs; ChrhWkr; CncrtBnd; HonRl; PepBnd; RptrSchPpr; SptEdSchPpr; 4-H; FHA; PpCl; LetterChrldr; 4-HAwd; College; Professional.

RANGER, Kristine; Alcona HS; Barton City, MI; 11/140 HonRl; JrNHS; NHS; 4-H; FFA; Mich State Univ; Veterinarian.

RANGER, Sherry L; Harper Creek HS; Battle Creek, MI; VPChr; Chrl; Chrs; HonRl; NHS; YthFlsp; SpnCl; Kellogg Comm Col; Music.

RANK, Gail A; Jefferson Sr HS; Cedar Rapids, IA; 4/451 TrsFrshCls; Chr; HonRl; PresNHS; RedCrAde; SchMus; StuCncl; FBLA; CaptTrk; Cornell College; Psychology.

RANKIN, Carol A; Ankeny HS; Bondurant, IA; 10/300 Band; CncrtBnd; HonRl; JrNHS; MrchBnd; FHA; Bsktbl; LetterTrk; IMSpt; University; Physical Education.

RANKIN, Catherine A; Dundee HS; Dundee, MI; 3/128 Band; Chr; ChrhWkr; CncrtBnd; HonRl; JrNHS; MrchBnd; NHS; SchPl; GerCl;.

RANKIN, Charles W; Fisher HS; Foosland, IL; 7/56 PresFrshCls; PresSophCls; ALBoysSt; HonRl; StuCncl; LetterBsktbl; LetterFtbl; Illinois State Univ; Physics.

RANKIN, Douglas; Monmouth Hs; Monmouth, IL; 8/150 ChrhWkr; HonRl; JrNHS; NHS; Quill&Scroll; SchPl; RptrYrbk; RptrSchPpr; SpnCl; Bsbl; Monmouth College; Theatre.

RANKIN, Jeffrey D; Monmouth HS; Monmouth, IL; 3/150 AFS; ChrhWkr; HonRl; NHS; Quill&Scroll; SchPl; StuCncl; EdSchPpr; LatCl; SpnCl; St Lawrence U; Journalism.

RANKIN, Marcia J; St Joseph HS; St Joseph, MI; RptrSchPpr; Lake Michigan College; Accountant.

RANKIN, Tamora J; Pope Co HS; Golconda, IL; TrsSophCls; ChrhWkr; CncrtBnd; HonRl; RptrYrbk; EdYrBk; 4-H; FHA; SpnCl; GAA; University.

RANKIN, Therese R; Alexis HS; Alexis, IL; 11/43 Band; Chr; Chrs; CmntyWkr; CncrtBnd; HonRl; HospAde; MrchBnd; NHS; SchPl; TchrAde; YthFlsp; Bsbl; College; Physical Therapy.

RANKL, Robert; Midland HS; Midland, MI; 16/434 HonRl; SchAde; StuCncl; StuGov; TchrAde; Michigan Tech Univ; Chemical Engineer.

RANNALS, William; Clear Lake HS; Clear Lake, IA; HonRl; NHS; YthFlsp; Bsbl; Bsktbl; Glf; Trk; CitAwd; Iowa State; Business.

RANNEY, Richard F; Brookfield Central HS; Brookfield, WI; 32/479 NatlMeritSF; University.

RANNEY, Steven P; Nebraska Christian HS; Central City, NE; 5/35 HstJrCls; ChrhWkr; HonRl; RptrYrbk; LetterBsktbl; LetterFtbl; LetterTrk; College; Professnl.

RANS, Wanda K; Bremen Senior HS; Bremen, IN; Chr; HonRl; StuCncl; TchrAde; PresYthFlsp; Sec4-H; PresFTA; SpnCl; PpCl; IMSpt; Manchester College; Early Childhood Ed.

RANSHAW, Maeila S; Lapeer HS; Metamora, MI; 25/426 Band; HonRl; MrchBnd; NHS; NatlMeritSchl; NatlThespSoc; RedCrAde; SchPl; StuCncl; StuGov; Ferris St; Med Tech.

RANTA, Pamela A; Chester HS; Chester, IL; Chrl; HonRl; NHS; NatlThespSoc; SchPl; RptrYrbk; SchPpr; PresSciCl; College; Medicine.

RANTALA, Caroline M; Greenway HS; Nashwauk, MN; Band; Chr; HonRl; MrchBnd; PepBnd; StuGov; PpCl; Swmmng; Chrldr; College; Communications.

RANTALA, Karen A; South Shore HS; Iron River, WI; 5/38 Band; Chr; CncrtBnd; HonRl; PepBnd; RptrYrbk; EdYrBk; RptrSchPpr; SchPpr; 4-H; PresFHA; Bsktbl; 4-HAwd;.

RANTALA, Lori K; Proctor HS; Proctor, MN; 2/200 Chr; ChrhWkr; HonRl; NHS; Quill&Scroll; SchMus; EdYrBk; RptrSchPpr; FTA; GerCl; College; Elementary Ed.

RANTZ, Peter R; Whitko HS; Pierceten, IN; PresSophCls; PresJrCls; PresSrCls; SchPl; StuCncl; SchPpr; FFA; SpnCl; LetterBsktbl; LetterFtbl; Ivy Tech; Own Auto Body Shop.

RANWEILER, Jean M; Cathedral HS; New Ulm, MN; HonRl; LbryAde; RptrSchPpr; PpCl; College.

RANZENBERGER, Larry D; Caledonia HS; Caledonia, MN; HonRl; 4-H; LetterFtbl; Wrstlng; Tech Sch; Meat Cutting Or Marketing.

RAPACZ, Paul M; Lane Tech HS; Chicago, IL; 50/1200 Illinois Inst Of Tech; Aerospace Engineer.

RAPAGNANI, Steven G; Springfield Catholic HS; Springfield, MO; PresFrshCls; Band; CncrtBnd; Orch; StuCncl; StuGov; YthLg; LatCl; SciCl; RotaryAwd; Clge; Medicine.

RAPALA, Therese A; Sacred Heart Of Mary HS; Mt Prospect, IL; ChrhWkr; HonRl; NHS; StuGov; Yrbk; Univ Of Notre Dame; Chemical Engineering.

RAPER, Jacquelin; Colfax HS; Colfax, IA; HonRl; StuCncl; TchrAde; FTA; PpCl; Bsktbl; CchngActv; GAA; IMSpt; College; Counseling.

RAPER, Ralph W; Inter City Christian HS; Allen Park, MI; 1/42 TrsSrCls; ChrhWkr; HonRl; NHS; SchPl; StuCncl; EdYrBk; AmLegAwd; U Of Mich; Pre Med.

RAPKIN, Jeffrey S; Jean Nicolet HS; Glendale, WI; HonRl; NatlFornLg; NatlMeritCmnd; SchPl; Yrbk; SchPpr; Univ Of Wisconsin; Medicine.

RAPLINGER, Jane; Lexington HS; Lexington, MO; Band; Chrs; CncrtBnd; HonRl; Orch; FrCl; SpnCl; Unvi Mo; Music.

RAPP, Barbara; Niantic Harristown HS; Decatur, IL; Band; HonRl; MrchBnd; SchPl; Twrl; FTA; SpnCl; Trk; Chrldr; GAA; Coll; Professional.

RAPP, Cheryl L; Trico HS; Percy, IL; PresJrCls; Chrs; HonRl; YthFlsp; RptrYrbk; FBLA; FHA; PpCl; TreasSciCl; GAA; Eastern Ill Univ; Mathematics.

RAPP, Gilbert; Morton HS; Morton, IL; HonRl; NHS; YthFlsp; SchPpr; 4-H; LetterBsktbl; LetterFtbl; LetterTrk; TIMEAwd; PresAwd;.

RAPP, Lynn; Ogilvie HS; Dalbo, MN; Band; ChrhWkr; HonRl; HospAde; LbryAde; SchAde; SchMus; SctActv; TchrAde; YthFlsp; Trade School; Professional.

RAPPOLD, Susan D; Lancaster HS; Lancaster, WI; 8/157 ChrhWkr; HonRl; RedCrAde; RptrSchPpr; 4-H; 4-HAwd; U W Platteville; Veterinary Medicine.

RAQUEPAW, Collin; Hale HS; Hale, MI; PresFrshCls; PresSophCls; PresJrCls; PresSrCls; JA; ROTC; EdYrBk; 4-H; Bsbl; DARAwd;.

RARDIN, Larry A; Oakland HS; Hindsboro, IL; 1/43 HonRl; MrchBnd; NatlMeritSchl; PepBnd; SchPl; StuCncl; MthCl; SciCl; Bsbl; Ftbl; Yale Univ; Architect.

RARDIN, Thomas; Albia Comm HS; Albia, IA; 11/150 HstSrCls; Chrs; HonRl; NatlMeritCmnd; SchPl; RptrYrbk; SpnCl; Univ Of Ia; Specialized Dentistry.

RARIDEN, Tim L; Brown County HS; Nashville, IN; HonRl; NHS; LetterBsbl; LetterBsktbl; LetterTrk; Purdue Univ; Civil Engineer.

RARL, Brad D; Buhler HS; Hutchinson, KS; PresFrshCls; ChrhWkr; HonRl; StuCncl; TchrAde; YthFlsp; SptEdYrbk; SpnCl; Ftbl; Trk; College; Major Study.

RASCHE, Mary A; Dubois HS; Dubois, IN; SecJrCls; TrsSrCls; Band; Chrs; HonRl; Sdlty; 4-H; FHA; LetterTrk; GAA;.

RASCHKA, Bill; Rogers HS; Michigan City, IN; ChrhWkr; PolWkr; GerCl; IMSpt; College; Law.

RASCHKE, Kathleen J; Columbus HS; Marshfield, WI; 14/117 ALAGirlsSt; Band; NHS; SchPl; RptrYrbk; RptrSchPpr; TreasSpnCl; LetterBsktbl; Trk; TreasGAA; Marquette Univ; Biology.

RASEMAN, Steven J; Gull Lake HS; Augusta, MI; 4/260 PresSophCls; VPJrCls; HonRl; PresNHS; StuCncl; FrCl; Swmmng; CitAwd; Univ; Marine Biology.

RASH, Lori J; Moline Sr HS; Moline, IL; 62/845 ALAGirlsSt; Chr; HonRl; NHS; StuCncl; SecYthFlsp; EdYrBk; Univ Of Arkansas; Secretarial.

RASHID, James M; J W Sexton HS; Lansing, MI; 12/447 HonRl; NHS; SctActv; LetterBsbl; LetterWrstlng; College; Accountant.

RASK, Cindy A; Alliance HS; Alliance, NE; Band; ChrhWkr; CncrtBnd; MrchBnd; PepBnd; PpCl; JCAwd;.

RASK, Kim P; Pekin Comm HS; Pekin, IL; 114/759 Band; CncrtBnd; HospAde; MrchBnd; PepBnd; YthFlsp;.

RASK, Meryl; Pelican Rapids HS; Vergas, MN; SecSrCls; Chr; HonRl; StuCncl; Bsbl; Bsktbl; Ftbl; College; Profesional.

RASK, Michael; Horace Mann HS; Gilbert, MN; Band; Chr; Chrs; CncrtBnd; MrchBnd; PepBnd; SctActv; Mesabi; Forestry.

RASKA, Jerome A; Armada HS; Armada, MI; 23/110 VPSrCls; Chr; Chrs; HonRl; JA; SchMus; SchPl; 4-H; KeyCl; 4-HAwd; College; Retailing.

RASKY, Mitchell B; Niles North HS; Skokie, IL; 16/641 CmntyWkr; HonRl; NHS; StuGov; TchrAde; Glf; Socr; U Of I; Accounting.

RASMUSEN, Eric B; University HS; Urbana, IL; Orch; College; Prof.

RASMUSON, Luann K; Magic City Campus; Minot, ND; 16/656 TrsJrCls; SecSrCls; ALAGirlsSt; Chrs; ChrhWkr; DrlTm; HonRl; NatlFornLg; NHS; StuCncl; SpnCl; PpCl; University; Law.

RASMUSSEN, Brian J; Tomah HS; Tomah, WI; 4/283 ALBoysSt; Chr; HonRl; NHS; VPStuCncl; FFA; Bsktbl; College; Dairy Farmer.

RASMUSSEN, Carol J; Chetek HS; Chetek, WI; 4/85 ALAGirlsSt; Band; Chr; PresChrhWkr; HonRl; JrNHS; Mdrgl; NHS; FBLA; FHA; Univ Of Wisconsin; Education.

RASMUSSEN, Cathy L; Polo Community HS; Polo, IL; 27/84 Band; Chr; Chrs; CncrtBnd; HonRl; MrchBnd; Orch; PepBnd; SchPl; FHA; W Illinois Univ; Music.

RASMUSSEN, Corine A; Big Bay De Noc HS; Garden, MI; CncrtBnd; HonRl; PepBnd; TchrAde; 4-H; Chrldr; 4-HAwd; Mich St Univ; General.

RASMUSSEN, Craig M; Harlan Comm HS; Harlan, IA; 2/259 HonRl; NatlMeritCmnd; SctActv; YthFlsp; Swmmng; IMSpt; GodCntryAwd; Iowa State University; Chemical Engineering.

RASMUSSEN, Dean; Fertile Beltrami HS; Fertile, MN; Band; Chr; Chrs; CncrtBnd; HonRl; Mdrgl; MrchBnd; PepBnd; SchPl; University; Music Major.

RASMUSSEN, Deborah C; Salem Central HS; Bristol, WI; Chrs; HonRl; Business School; Data Processing.

RASMUSSEN, Jean M; Columbus HS; Marshfield, WI; 22/120 Chrs; CmntyWkr; HonRl; NHS; SchMus; SchPl; StuCncl; FrCl; GAA; St Josephs Sch Of Nursing; Nursing.

RASMUSSEN, Kim; Hamlin HS; Hazel, SD; 6/66 VPJrCls; PresSrCls; ALAGirlsSt; HonRl; RptrSchPpr; EdSchPpr; SchPpr; Chrldr; DARAwd; Sd State Univ.

RASMUSSEN, Lorraine; Marquette HS; Michigan City, IN; SecJrCls; Chrs; CmntyWkr; SchMus; TchrAde; SpnCl; Swmmng; Tennis; Notre Dame; Law.

RASMUSSEN, Marialene; Hamlin HS; Bryant, SD; 13/66 ALAGirlsSt; Band; Chrs; ChrhWkr; HonRl; Yrbk; GerCl; PpCl; Bsktbl; Trk; South Dakota State Univ; Music.

RASMUSSEN, Mark A; Spirit Lake HS; Spirit Lake, IA; 2/92 Chrs; HonRl; NatlMeritFnl; TchrAde; Bsktbl; Ia Univ; Engineer.

RASMUSSEN, Merle M; Underwood Community HS; Council Bluffs, IA; Chr; Chrs; ChrhWkr; HonRl; NHS; SchMus; SctActv; Yrbk; PresSciCl; Ia St U; Civil Engi.

RASMUSSEN, Myra M; Crystal Lake Community HS; Crystal Lake, IL; 28/477 ChrhWkr; DrlTm; HonRl; Northern Illinois Univ; Computer Science.

RASMUSSEN, Nels P; Rossville Alvin HS; Alvin, IL; 2/39 ChrhWkr; HonRl; VPNHS; NatlMeritCmnd; VPNatlThespSoc; SchPl; RptrYrbk; PresFTA; VPSciCl; Trk; Univ; History.

RASMUSSEN, Randy L; Osmond Community HS; Osmond, NE; 8/42 PresSophCls; PresJrCls; ALBoysSt; Chrs; HonRl; StuCncl; TchrAde; LetterBsktbl; LetterFtbl; LetterTrk; AmLegAwd; Univ Of Nebraska; Engineering.

RASMUSSEN, Robert H; Herbert Hoover HS; Des Moines, IA; JA; PolWkr; RedCrAde; SctActv; StuCncl; YthFlsp; RptrSchPpr; 4-H; LetterFtbl; Swmmng; CchngActv; College; Forestry.

RASMUSSEN, Scott W; Columbus HS; Marshfield, WI; PresSophCls; Aud/Vis; HonRl; NatlThespSoc; SchMus; SchPl; StuCncl; Bsktbl; IMSpt; Trade; Tv.

RASMUSSEN, Wayne A; East Central #12 HS; Egeland, ND; TrsJrCls; Chr; HonRl; SchPl; YthFlsp; SchPpr; PpCl; Bsktbl; 4-HAwd; CitAwd; Bible School; Professional.

RASMUSSON, Ann M; Magic City HS; Minot, ND; 1/700 CncrtBnd; MrchBnd; NHS; NatlMeritSF; PolWkr; StuCncl; SpnCl; CchngActv; College; Special Education.

RASMUSSON, Beth; Nevada Community HS; Nevada, IA; 6/117 Band; Chr; CncrtBnd; HonRl; MrchBnd; NHS; PepBnd; RptrSchPpr; SchPpr; Univ North Ia; Music Major.

RASNER, Dennis P; Stephenson HS; Wallace, MI; 7/99 ALBoysSt; HonRl; NHS; SchPl; SctActv; No Michigan Univ; Law Enforcement.

RASP, Betty J; Ofallon HS; Ofallon, IL; ChrhWkr; CmntyWkr; YthFlsp; SchPpr; SpnCl; College.

RASP, John M; Roxana HS; East Alton, IL; 1/300 NHS; NatlMeritSF; TreasNatlThespSoc; SchPl; StuCncl; GerCl; PresRusCl; TreasMthCl; Mit; Mathematics.

RASSBACH, Karen S; Memorial HS; Eau Claire, WI; HstSophCls; ChrhWkr; HospAde; StuCncl; YthFlsp; College.

RASSEL, Paul J; Garrett HS; Garrett, IN; PresSophCls; ALBoysSt; HonRl; NHS; NatlThespSoc; SchMus; StuCncl; SpnCl; Ftbl; Glf; IMSpt; DanFAwd; Ball State U; Business.

RASSEL, Walter; Garrett HS; Garrett, IN; 7/165 SecFrshCls; PresSophCls; ALBoysSt; HonRl; NHS; Yrbk; Ftbl; CitAwd; In Univ;.

RASSET, Patty A; Annandale HS; Annandale, MN; Chr; Chrs; HonRl; Quill&Scroll; SchMus; SchPl; TchrAde; SpnCl; PpCl; IMSpt; College Of St Benedict; Psychology Major.

RASSI, Dennis D; Morton HS; Morton, IL; 5/310 HonRl; Il Central Col; Building Contractor.

RASSLER, Le Anne; Centennial HS; Cushing, MN; Band; ChrhWkr; CmntyWkr; JA; LbryAde; MrchBnd; OffAde; PepBnd; Yrbk; Vo Tec; Accountant.

RASTALL, Lorene; Saugatuck HS; Saugatuck, MI; SecSophCls; Chrs; HonRl; SchPl; StuCncl; TchrAde; Bsbl; Chrldr; BttyCrckrAwd; Air Force.

RASURE, Nora B; Auburn HS; Auburn, IL; HonRl; JA; MrchBnd; NHS; StuCncl; YthFlsp; Yrbk; Sec4-H; PpCl; LetterTrk; SecGAA; 4-HAwd; College.

RATCLIFF, Earl J; North Mahaska Comm HS; New Sharon, IA; PresSophCls; HonRl; StuCncl; YthFlsp; RptrSchPpr; FTA; SciCl; LetterBsktbl; LetterFtbl; IMSpt; College; Missionary.

RATH, Dianne; Leola Public HS; Leola, SD; 1/50 VPSophCls; ALAGirlsSt; ChrhWkr; HonRl; StuCncl; Sec4-H; PresFBLA; PresFHA; LetterTrk; 4-HAwd; National Coll Business; Computer Programmer.

RATH, Jody; Potosi HS; Cadet, MO; HonRl; Trk; Coll.

RATH, Patricia A; Dundee HS; Dundee, IL; 19/370 Band; ChrhWkr; HonRl; NHS; Orch; SchMus; TchrAde; SecFTA; PresSpnCl; PresSciCl; Coll; Med Research.

RATH, Robert; Rushville HS; Rushville, NE; Chrs; HonRl; Mdrgl; SchMus; FFA; GerCl; Bsktbl; Sidney Tech Sch; Diesel Mech.

RATHBUN, Joseph E; Charlotte HS; Charlotte, MI; 14/280 NHS; SciCl; Bsktbl; LetterTrk; IMSpt; Mich St Univ; Limnologist.

RATHBUN, Richard C; Daleville HS; Muncie, IN; Band; Chr; CncrtBnd; HonRl; JA; MrchBnd; SchMus; TchrAde; 4-H; PpCl; Ball State Univ; Music Teacher.

RATHBURN, Judie A; St Joseph Academy; Green Bay, WI; Chrs; ChrhWkr; JA; LitMag; Mdrgl; NHS; FTA; MthCl; Bsktbl; College; Teacher.

RATHBURN, Patty J; Maple Valley HS; Vermontville, MI; 17/118 HonRl; OffAde; SchAde; SchPl; SctActv; StuCncl; Bsbl; Chrldr; GAA; PPFtbl; Alma Or Western Mi College; Pro In Business.

RATHEL, Michelle R; Lindblom Tech HS; Chicago, IL; 16/599 Chr; ChrhWkr; HonRl; YthFlsp; FDA; LatCl; SciCl; College; Medicine.

RATHER, Linda J; Waupun HS; Waupun, WI; 19/259 Band; ChrhWkr; CncrtBnd; HonRl; MrchBnd; NHS; OffAde; PepBnd; TchrAde; YthFlsp; College.

RATHGEBER, Gail; Lake Park Hs; Roselle, IL; 19/500 ChrhWkr; HonRl; NatlMeritCmnd; StuCncl; RptrYrbk; Chrldr;.

RATHJE, Connie J; Arthur Hill HS; Saginaw, MI; ChrhWkr; HonRl; JA; PolWkr; StuCncl; TchrAde; Chrldr; CchngActv; Delta College; Interior Decorator.

RATHKE, Rick A; Northern HS; Flint, MI; HonRl; PolWkr; GerCl; MthCl; CaptWrstlng; CchngActv; Michigan St Univ; Engineering.

RATHMANN, Karen M; Preble HS; Green Bay, WI; HonRl; LbryAde; NatlFornLg; NHS; OffAde; Orch; SchPl; StuCncl; PpCl; College; Soil Science.

RATHS, Martin G; Eden Prairie HS; Eden Prairie, MN; PresJrCls; TrsSrCls; NHS; SchMus; StuCncl; CaptBsktbl; Ftbl; CaptTrk; Carleton Clg; Professional Biology.

RATHWELL, Mary Jo; Edsel Ford HS; Dearborn, MI; CmntyWkr; HonRl; NHS; StuCncl; RptrYrbk; PpCl; Bsktbl; GAA; IMSpt; PPFtbl; Univ Of Detroit; Chemical Engineer.

RATICAN, Patricia M; Carmel Girls HS; Mundelein, IL; 21/173 Chrs; ChrhWkr; HonRl; LbryAde; RedCrAde; 4-H; GAA; College; Business Admin.

RATLIFF, Cynthia; Immaculata HS; Detroit, MI; 24/106 PresJrCls; TrsSrCls; CmntyWkr; HonRl; NHS; PolWkr; StuCncl; YthFlsp; RptrYrbk; Swmmng; Kalamazoo Coll; Pre Law.

RATLIFF, Cynthia A; Immaculata HS; Detroit, MI; 25/106 TrsJrCls; TrsSrCls; AFS; ChrhWkr; CmntyWkr; HonRl; NHS; PolWkr; StuCncl; RptrYrbk; LetterSwmmng; Kalamazoo College; Lawyer.

RATLIFF, Sandra J; U 238 HS; Kensington, KS; 1/27 PresSrCls; Band; HonRl; NHS; SecStuCncl; LetterTrk; Chrldr; AmLegAwd; BttyCrckrAwd; Wichita State Univ; Math.

RATLIFF, Susan R; Rock County HS; Bassett, NE; 2/48 Band; Chrs; DrmMjrt; NHS; SchMus; StuCncl; EdYrBk; FHA; Chrldr; Univ Of Nebraska; Home Economics.

RATTER, Michael L; Maplewood Acad; Hutchinson, MN; 1/63 Aud/Vis; ChrhWkr; Loma Linda Univ; Med.

RATTS, Barbara J; Eastern HS; Pekin, IN; 16/77 DrlTm; HonRl; NHS; StuCncl; TchrAde; RptrYrbk; RptrSchPpr; SpnCl; PpCl; GAA;.

RATZ, Karen M; Brookville HS; Brookville, IN; 20/169 Band; CncrtBnd; HonRl; MrchBnd; SchAde; SchMus; SctActv; 4-H; FHA; PpCl; Business School; Accounting.

RAU, Debra J; Ashley HS; Ashley, ND; 29#30#33 CmntyWkr; HonRl; Mdrgl; PepBnd; CchngActv; North Dakota State; Nursing.

RAU, John E; Hudson HS; Hudson, SD; 3/15 PresFrshCls; VPSophCls; VPJrCls; Band; Chrs; HonRl; Mdrgl; MrchBnd; SchMus; SchPl; Tech; Metallurgical Engin.

RAU, Jolene K; Perkins Co HS; Grant, NE; Chr; HonRl; NHS; 4-H; PpCl; LetterTrk; BttyCrckrAwd; Mc Cook Com Clg; Business.

RAU, Mary K; Meremec Valley Riii HS; Pacific, MO; Band; CncrtBnd; HonRl; MrchBnd; YthFlsp; Univ Of Mo; Math.

RAUCH, Kim R; Warren Co Riii HS; Warrenton, MO; 16/112 Chr; HonRl; NHS; Yrbk; RptrSchPpr; PpCl; LetterBsktbl; LetterTrk; Chrldr; IMSpt; U Of Missouri; Veterinarian.

RAUCH, Kristin A; Lafayette County C I HS; Higginsville, MO; AFS; ALAGirlsSt; CncrtBnd; DrlTm; HonRl; MrchBnd; NHS; PpCl; SciCl; Univ Of Missouri; Medicine.

RAUCH, Lois E; Healy HS; Pierz, MN; 29/118 PresSrCls; HonRl; StuCncl; TchrAde; LetterTrk; Alexandria Area Voc Tech Schl; Med Lab Asst.

RAUCH, Randi S; Dearborn HS; Dearborn, MI; PresSophCls; Band; CmntyWkr; HonRl; JrNHS; NatlMeritCmnd; StuCncl; 4-H; SecGAA; IMSpt; 4-HAwd; Univ Of Michigan; Social Work.

RAUCH, Teresa J; Mason Cons HS; La Salle, MI; RptrSchPpr; FNA; FTA; GerCl; Bsbl; LetterBsktbl; LetterTrk; GAA; PPFtbl; Nursing.

RAUEN, Matthew A; St Laurence HS; Burbank, IL; HonRl; StuCncl; Christian Brothers College; Engineering.

RAUENHORST, Michael G; St Thomas Academy; Edina, MN; PresFrshCls; VPJrCls; Chr; ChrhWkr; CmntyWkr; StuCncl; RptrSchPpr; FrCl; LetterSocr; Tennis; OptClAwd;.

RAUGELLIS, Paula F; Lakeview HS; Decatur, IL; 15/184 PresSophCls; TrsJrCls; AFS; HonRl; HospAde; RptrYrbk; LatCl; SciCl; Bsktbl; LetterTennis; Trk; GAA; Southern Ill Univ; Doctor.

RAUH, Carol; Hinsdale Central HS; Hinsdale, IL; 7/608 HonRl; NHS; U Of Illinois; Lawyer.

RAUH, Maryjane; Gilbert HS; Gilbert, MN; 3/80 Band; Chr; HonRl; Mdrgl; NatlThespSoc; SchMus; SchPl; SctActv; FHA; Chrldr; Misabi.

RAUK, John N; Caledonia HS; Caledonia, MN; HonRl; NatlMeritFnl; NatlMeritSchl; NatlMeritSF; SchPl; College; Literature.

RAUKER, Julia K; Lawton HS; Lawton, MI; SecFrshCls; Chr; HonRl; NHS; OffAde; SchAde; SchPl; StuCncl; TchrAde; Chrldr; Junion College Kalamazoo; Medicine.

RAULAND, Scott M; Big Foot HS; Walworth, WI; 2/175 Band; Chr; CncrtBnd; HonRl; Mdrgl; SchMus; SchPl; YthFlsp; Tennis; IMSpt; College; Physics.

RAUMAN, Mark A; Lockport Central HS; Lockport, IL; 17/550 HonRl; NHS; TchrAde; LetterBsbl; LetterBsktbl; LetterFtbl; College.

RAUN, Gail R; Webster City HS; Webster City, IA; 3/200 PresFrshCls; Chrs; ChrhWkr; HonRl; Mdrgl; NatlMeritSF; SchMus; FTA; FrCl; SciCl; Iowa State Univ; Architect.

RAUPP, Douglas R; Harvard HS; Harvard, IL; 20/160 ChrhWkr; HonRl; GerCl; Bsbl; Mchenry Cnty College; Accounting.

RAUSCH, Dorothy L; New Franklin HS; New Franklin, MO; HonRl; SecNHS; SchPl; SpnCl; PpCl; Trk; PresAwd; Trade Schl; Dental Asst.

RAUSCH, Linda K; Turkey Valley Comm HS; Ft Atkinson, IA; Band; Sdlty; RptrSchPpr; 4-H; LetterBsktbl; LetterTrk; GAA; IMSpt; 4-HAwd;

GodCntryAwd; JAAwd; CitAwd; Iowa St Univ; Nursing.

RAUSCHER, James; Medford Senior HS; Medford, WI; 1/205 ALBoysSt; Band; ChrhWkr; NHS; NatlMeritCmnd; StuCncl; LetterSwmmng; KiwanAwd; VFWAwd; Uw Eau Claire; Music.

RAUTERKUS, Dale R; New Richmond HS; New Richmond, WI; LetterBsktbl; College; Professional.

RAUTIO, Julie; South Shore HS; Iron River, WI; Band; Chr; Chrs; CncrtBnd; HonRl; MrchBnd; PepBnd; RptrYrbk; Yrbk; RptrSchPpr;.

RAUWERDINK, Kenneth; Oostburg HS; Oostburg, WI; VPJrCls; TrsSrCls; Chrs; HonRl; YthFlsp; RptrYrbk; College, Accounting.

RAVANELLI, Priscilla; Ad Johnston HS; Bessemer, MI; 1/104 HonRl; SchPl; StuGov; PpCl; N Mi Univ; Medicine.

RAVEILL, Mary A; St Marys HS; Kansas City, MO; 6/75 VPSrCls; Chrs; ChrhWkr; HonRl; NHS; NatlMeritFnl; OffAde; SchMus; StuCncl; SciCl; St Lukes Sch Of Radiological; X Ray Tech.

RAVENBERG, Debbie M; Ramona HS; Winfred, SD; VPFrshCls; ALAGirlsSt; Chrs; DrmMjrt; HonRl; SchMus; SchPl; EdYrBk; VPFHA; Chrldr; AmLegAwd; Beauty Acad; Beauty.

RAVENBERG, Sharrie L; Ramona Public HS; Winfred, SD; PresSophCls; PresJrCls; HonRl; MrchBnd; SchPl; StuCncl; EdYrBk; EdSchPpr; Trk; Chrldr; College; Medicine Or Secretary.

RAVENSCRAFT, Dorothy; Otterville Public HS; Syracuse, MO; 4/24 TrsSophCls; VPSrCls; HonRl; EdYrBk; RptrSchPpr; FBLA; PpCl; Chrldr; S M S U; Business Education.

RAVER, Clark A; North White HS; Mondon, IN; 5/111 ChrhWkr; HonRl; LbryAde; NHS; NatlThespSoc; SchMus; SchPl; SctActv; SchPpr; 4-H; College.

RAW, Jeremy J; University City HS; University City, MO; NatlMeritSF; EdSchPpr; College; Linguistics.

RAWAL, Upma K; York Comm HS; Elmhurst, IL; 12/900 Band; HonRl; LbryAde; NHS; Medical College; Doctor.

RAWE, Sharon Y; Carrollton HS; Carrollton, IL; 5/85 HonRl; LbryAde; NHS; NatlThespSoc; SchPl; TchrAde; FBLA; FTA; SpnCl; Lewis And Clark; Accounting.

RAWE, Theresa E; Routt HS; Carrollton, IL; 4-H;.

RAWERS, Lynn M; Morton West HS; Stickney, IL; PresSophCls; PresJrCls; PresSrCls; HonRl; NHS; SctActv; StuCncl; Swmmng; AmLegAwd; KiwanAwd; College; Business Admin.

RAWHOUSER, Kent J; La Crosse Central HS; Lacrosse, WI; HonRl; StuCncl; LetterFtbl; LetterTrk; LetterWrstlng; IMSpt; PresAwd; College; Professional.

RAWLEY, Paula J; Clay City HS; Clay City, IN; Band; CncrtBnd; MrchBnd; TchrAde; FrCl; College; Nursing.

RAWLINGS, Diane M; Union HS; Modoc, IN; 3/55 HstJrCls; ChrhWkr; HonRl; NHS; OffAde; Yrbk; FHA; SpnCl; Chrldr; DARAwd; Taylor Univ; Guidance Counselor.

RAWLINGS, Richard S; Northern Valley HS; Almena, KS; SchPl; StuCncl; Yrbk; SchPpr; 4-H; FFA; Bsbl; LetterFtbl; LetterTrk; 4-HAwd; Univ; Biology.

RAWLINGS, Tamie K; Kingsley Area HS; Kingsley, MI; 9/45 HonRl; NatlMeritCmnd; SchMus; SchPl; StuCncl; TchrAde; RptrYrbk; RptrSchPpr; Chrldr; Nw Michigan College; Elementary Teacher.

RAWLINS, Eric C; Eminence HS; Monrovia, IN; VPBand; CncrtBnd; HonRl; NHS; SctActv; Yrbk; FFA; Business School; Accounting.

RAWLINS, Randa C; Hale R1 HS; Hale, MO; 1/19 SecSrCls; Band; HonRl; NatlFornLg; StuCncl; StuGov; RptrYrbk; LetterBsktbl; LetterTrk; BttyCrckrAwd; Nemsu; Political Sci Or Law Enforcement.

RAWLINS, Thomas E; Henry Ind HS; Henry, SD; PresFrshCls; Band; Chrs; CmntyWkr; HonRl; Quill&Scroll; StuGov; EdYrBk; Bsbl; LetterBsktbl; LetterTrk; College.

RAWOT, Debbie L; Carl Sandburg HS; Palos Park, IL; CmntyWkr; HonRl; TchrAde; YthFlsp; FHA; FTA; SpnCl; MthCl; PpCl; GAA; Olivet Nazarene Coll; Home Econ.

RAWSKI, Daniel J; Reavis HS; Burbank, IL; 86/758 Aud/Vis; CmntyWkr; HonRl; SctActv; IMSpt; Business; Professional.

RAWSON, Melissa L; North County HS; Desloge, MO; 12/170 Band; CncrtBnd; DrlTm; HonRl; JrNHS; NHS; SctActv; Yrbk; EdSchPpr; PpCl; Coll.

RAWSON, Ronald C; Carlisle Comm HS; Carlisle, IA; ALBoysSt; Chrs; HonRl; SchMus; SctActv; YthFlsp; Yrbk; SpnCl; Bsktbl; Glf; U Of Northern Ia; Accounting.

RAWSON, Ronald L; Geneva Comm HS; Geneva, IL; 2/243 Band; Chrs; Mdrgl; MrchBnd; SchMus; StuCncl; Yrbk; SchPpr; FrCl; Western Illinois Univ; Photography.

RAY, Cindy C; St Mary Cathedral HS; Saginaw, MI; 11/76 TrsSophCls; HonRl; LbryAde; NHS; Twrl; LatCl; PpCl; Chrldr; St Thomas Aquinas Clg; Phy Ed.

RAY, Cynthia J; Shenandoah Community HS; Shenandoah, IA; 3/95 AFS; Band; Chr; HonRl; MrchBnd; NHS; Quill&Scroll; SchMus; RptrSchPpr; EdSchPpr; LetterGlf; U Of Iowa; Pre Law.

RAY, Diana J; Jennings Co HS; Seymour, IN; 107/382 LbryAde; SchAde; TchrAde; 4-H; FrCl; CchngActv; 4-HAwd; Bus School; Exe Sec.

RAY, Jama L; Central HS; St Joseph, MO; 2/505 Chr; ChrhWkr; HospAde; JA; NHS; LatCl; MthCl; SciCl; LetterBsktbl; LetterTrk; Tulane Univ New Orleans; Medicine.

RAY, Janice; Madison HS; Madison, NE; PresFrshCls; PresSophCls; Band; Chr; ChrhWkr; HonRl; LbryAde; NHS; YthFlsp; PpCl; Beauty School; Beautician.

RAY, Jeffery W; Homestead HS; Fort Wayne, IN; CncrtBnd; HonRl; MrchBnd; PepBnd; SctActv; StuCncl; GerCl; LetterFtbl; LetterWrstlng; IMSpt; Us Military Academy; Business.

RAY, John H; Avon HS; Avon, IL; CncrtBnd; HonRl; MrchBnd; PepBnd; SchPl; University; Astromomer.

RAY, Kevin D; West Plains HS; West Plains, MO; 45/261 HonRl; NHS; VPStuCncl; YthFlsp; SptEdYrbk; Ftbl; Trk; Wrstlng; EldAwd; Southwest Mo State U; Veterinarian.

RAY, Larry D; Superior HS; Superior, NE; FFA; Trade Sch; Mechanic Or Electronics.

RAY, Mary A; Billings HS; Billings, MO; ALAGirlsSt; Chrs; ChrhWkr; HonRl; FshEdYrbk; 4-H; FHA; PpCl; University; Home Economics.

RAY, Melissa A; Bunker Hill HS; Bunker Hill, IL; 11/81 HonRl; NHS; FHA; Siue Col; Secretarial Studies.

RAY, Ola J; Northrop HS; Fort Wayne, IN; 213/568 ChrhWkr; HonRl; JA; NatlFornLg; Orch; SchMus; Purdue Univ; Speech.

RAY, Patricia; Granite City South HS; Granite City, IL; JA; ModUN; Quill&Scroll; RptrSchPpr; SpnCl; PpCl; Univ; Social Sciences.

RAY, Paul C; Van Tar HS; Vandalia, MO; 33/92 PresFrshCls; TrsSophCls; Band; ChrhWkr; CncrtBnd; HonRl; MrchBnd; StuCncl; 4-H; FrCl; 4-HAwd; Missouri Univ; Public Relations.

RAY, Rita J; Preston HS; Preston, MN; 8/54 Band; Chr; Chrs; ChrhWkr; CmntyWkr; HonRl; NHS; SchPl; RptrSchPpr; 4-HAwd; Univ Of Mn; Med Tech.

RAYBOURN, Mary J; Appleton HS; Butler, MO; 2/44 VPSophCls; ChrhWkr; HonRl; LbryAde; Yrbk; RptrSchPpr; SecPpCl; BttyCrckrAwd; CitAwd; Secretarial Work.

RAYBURN, Mike K; United Township HS; East Moline, IL; 67/687 Trade; Tool & Die.

RAYCROFT, Patrick M; George Rogers Clark HS; Whiting, IN; 2/261 PresJrCls; ALBoysSt; HonRl; NHS; Quill&Scroll; VPStuCncl; StuGov; RptrYrbk; RptrSchPpr; SpnCl; CaptTennis; Trk; IMSpt; University; Professional.

RAYE, Frank W; Crystal Lake HS; Crystal Lake, IL; 34/477 ChrhWkr; HonRl; NHS; LetterBsbl; LetterBsktbl; LetterFtbl; Col.

RAYFIELD, Theresa A; St Anthony Of Padua HS; St Louis, MO; 8/72 Chrl; Chrs; HonRl; NHS; SchMus; SchPl; TchrAde; RptrSchPpr; College; Secretarial.

RAYHEL, Brenda; Hutsonville HS; West Union, IL; Band; Chrs; HonRl; MrchBnd; NHS; PepBnd; Yrbk; MthCl; SciCl; Wabashvalley Junior College; Bus. Clerical.

RAYMAN, Barbara J; Frontier HS; Chalmers, IN; SecSrCls; Band; HonRl; NHS; TchrAde; 4-H; FrCl; PpCl; Sch Of Nursing; Prof.

RAYMER, Debra J; Atkinson West Holt HS; Stuart, NE; 4-H; College; Veterinarian Asst.

RAYMO, Paul C; Madison Public HS; Madison, MN; PresSophCls; Aud/Vis; Chr; Chrs; ChrhWkr; SchPl; TchrAde; YthFlsp; LetterBsbl; LetterFtbl; Wrstlng; IMSpt; Austin Vocational School; Broadcasting.

RAYMOND, Christopher J; White Pine HS; White Pine, MI; 4/40 ALBoysSt; ChrhWkr; HonRl; NHS; RptrYrbk; FrCl; LetterGlf; LionAwd; Michigan Tech Univ; Elec Engineer.

RAYMOND, Helena B; Herscher HS; Kankakee, IL; 4/158 TrsFrshCls; Chrs; HonRl; SctActv; TchrAde; 4-H; PpCl; Bsbl; Chrldr; Kankakee Comm College; Accounting.

RAYMOND, Janet L; Gurdon S Hubbard HS; Chicago, IL; 4/431 VPChrs; HonRl; LbryAde; NHS; TchrAde; SchPpr; RusCl; PpCl; GAA; Univ Of Ill; Special Education.

RAYMOND, Jeffrey C; Spoon River Valley HS; Ellisville, IL; 9/60 Chrs; CmntyWkr; HonRl; SchMus; SctActv; StuCncl; YthFlsp; Treas4-H; FFA; CaptFtbl; Wrstlng; 4-HAwd; SARAwd; Western Ill Univ; Agriculture Mach Tech.

RAYMOND, Jill L; Clare Public HS; Clare, MI; DrmMjrt; HonRl; MrchBnd; NHS; Twrl; 4-H; GAA; Univ; French Major Russian Minor.

RAYMOND, Julia L; Harper Creek HS; Ceresco, MI; Band; CncrtBnd; HonRl; MrchBnd; PepBnd; RptrYrbk; 4-H; SpnCl; Calvin College; Teach.

RAYMOND, Margaret H; Notre Dame De Sion HS; Kansas City, MO; 1 35 Chrl; HonRl; NHS; NatlSciFnd; NatlThespSoc; PolWkr; SchPl; StuCncl; BauchLmbAwd; DARAwd; Univ; Engin.

RAYMOND, Mary A; Rich Central HS; Olympia Fields, IL; 80/400 ChrhWkr; HonRl; Orch; FHA; SciCl; Lewis Univ; Nursing.

RAYMOND, Michael J; Ogemaw Heights HS; West Branch, MI; Band; ChrhWkr; CmntyWkr; HonRl; MrchBnd; YthFlsp; College; Christian Minister.

RAYMOND, Philp R; Niles North HS; Skokie, IL; Chrs; CmntyWkr; HonRl; LitMag; NatlThespSoc; SchMus; SchPl; StuCncl; StuGov; Cornell University; Electrical Engineering.

RAYMOND, Robert; Liberty HS; Mtn View, MO; Chr; Chrl; HonRl; Mdrgl; NHS; SchMus; SchPl; YthFlsp; PpCl; Bsktbl; School Of Ozarks; Mathematics.

RAYMOND, Terri; Lancaster Sr HS; Lancaster, WI; TrsSrCls; Band; ChrhWkr; HonRl; Orch; SchPl; StuCncl; RptrSchPpr; FHA; Vocational School; Accounting.

RAYNER, Robert A; Beloit Memorial HS; Beloit, WI; 105/549 Band; HonRl; LbryAde; SctActv; StuCncl; Glf; Univ Of Wisconsin; Veterinarian.

RAYNER, Susan M; Queen Of Peace HS; Chicago, IL; HonRl; NatlMeritFnl; NatlMeritSF; StuCncl;.

RAYOME, Kathleen A; Assumption HS; Port Edwards, WI; VPBand; CncrtBnd; HonRl; MrchBnd; Orch; PepBnd; SchMus; PresSdlty; TchrAde; RptrYrbk; TreasFNA; PpCl; CaptGAA; Univ Of Wisc; Medical Techn.

RAZAK, Brian W; Nickerson HS; Hutchinson, KS; 17/107 HonRl; NHS; SchPl; StuCncl; TchrAde; LetterBsktbl; LetterFtbl; Ks Wesleyan Univ; Sports Trainer.

RAZAK, Renate; Hays HS; Hays, KS; 94/238 Chrs; ChrhWkr; CmntyWkr; HonRl; HospAde; PolWkr; IMSpt; College; Professional.

RAZUMICH, Maria; George Rogers Clark HS; Whiting, IN; 27 HonRl; StuCncl; SchPpr; FrCl; PpCl; GAA; IMSpt; College; Maw Major.

RAZZANO, Dana L; Watseka Comm HS; Watseka, IL; Band; HonRl; NHS; StuCncl; SpnCl; LetterBsbl; LetterBsktbl; LetterFtbl; LetterGlf; LetterTrk; College; Dentist.

REA, Dixie L; Nauvoo Colusa HS; Niota, IL; PresFrshCls; PresSophCls; StuCncl; FHA; Bsbl; Bsktbl; Chrldr;.

REA, Michael J; Ralston HS; Ralston, NE; 11/213 HonRl; NHS; StuCncl; LetterBsktbl; U Of Ne; Chemicla Engineering.

READ, Kelly J; Aurora HS; Aurora, NE; HonRl; SecYthFlsp; 4-H; FBLA; FHA; PpCl; 4-HAwd; Business School; Secretary.

READ, Patricia G; Blair HS; Blair, NE; Band; Chr; ChrhWkr; CncrtBnd; DrlTm; HonRl; HospAde; MrchBnd; NHS; PepBnd; SchMus; SchPl; YthFlsp; Yrbk; College; Professional.

READ, Rita M; Chambers HS; Chambers, NE; TrsSophCls; Band; Chrs; ChrhWkr; CncrtBnd; HonRl; MrchBnd; NHS; PepBnd; SchPl; TchrAde; Twrl; 4-H; FHA; Trade School.

READUS, Mache; Lindblom Tech HS; Chicago, IL; 72/722 ChrhWkr; HonRl; TchrAde; SpnCl; MthCl; College; Architecture.

READY, Myra J; Giltner Public HS; Giltner, NE; 1/15 SecFrshCls; PresSophCls; Band; Chrs; ChrhWkr; CncrtBnd; HonRl; MrchBnd; PepBnd; SchAde; SchPl; YthFlsp; Hastings College; Business Admin.

READY, Susan L; Pike HS; Indianapolis, IN; HonRl; JA; Purdue Univ; Interior Design.

REAGAN, Lawrence P; Belvidere HS; Belvidere, IL; 23/333 AFS; HonRl; SchPl; SctActv; StuCncl; YthFlsp; GerCl; Tennis; Air Force Academy; Aerospace Engineering.

REAGAN, Nancy A; Mccluer North HS; Florissant, MO; HonRl; LbryAde; SchMus; SchPl; StuCncl; StuGov; TchrAde; PresAwd; Florissant Vly Comm Clg; Computer Programmg.

REAGAN, Nancy L; Maine Twp South HS; Park Ridge, IL; ChrhWkr; HonRl; NHS; PolWkr; Sdlty; GerCl; PpCl; St Marys College; Biology.

REAM, Anne C; Thayer R 2 HS; Thayer, MO; PresJrCls; Band; CncrtBnd; HonRl; MrchBnd; PepBnd; StuCncl; ChmnBsktbl; LetterTennis; College; Optometry.

REAM, Gregory L; Hamilton HS; Hamilton, IN; 10/60 VPFrshCls; HonRl; Bsbl; LetterSwmmng; Glf; HstSophCls; PresAwd; Coll; Conservation.

REAMANN, James A; Braddock Public HS; Braddock, ND; VPFrshCls; TrsSrCls; ALBoysSt; HonRl; SchPl; Yrbk; SchPpr; 4-H; Bsbl; LetterBsktbl; Bismarck Jr Clg; Mechanics.

REAMER, Michelle R; Marshall Sr HS; Marshall, WI; Band; CncrtBnd; HonRl; NHS; PepBnd; FrCl; LetterBsktbl; LetterTrk; GAA; PPFtbl; Business School.

REAMES, Carolyn N; Pinckneyville Community HS; Pinckneyville, IL; Chrs; ChrhWkr; DrlTm; HonRl; MrchBnd; NHS; SchMus; SchPl; FHA; FrCl; Central College Of Iowa; Teacher.

REAMES, Curtis A; Jamestown HS; Jamestown, KS; PresFrshCls; PresSophCls; VPJrCls; Band; Chr; ChrhWkr; SchMus; SchPl; StuCncl; CaptBsktbl; Ftbl; CaptTrk; CitAwd; VoiceDemAwd; College; Psychology.

REANDEAU, Debora A; Archbishop Bergan HS; Fremont, NE; PresJrCls; CAP; HonRl; SchPl; StuCncl; Yrbk; PpCl; Chrldr; Univ Of Ne; Bus Ad.

REAR, Rebecca A; Valley Comm HS; Clermont, IA; VPSrCls; Band; Chr; Chrs; ChrhWkr; CmntyWkr; CncrtBnd; DrmMjrt; HonRl; HospAde; LbryAde; Trk; CaptChrldr; Loras College.

REARDEN, Cheryl L; Pekin Community HS; Pekin, IL; JA; NHS; NatlMeritSchl; NatlMeritSF; SchAde; StuCncl; FTA; IMSpt; 4-HAwd; GovHonPrgAwd; JAAwd; NCTE; College; Teaching.

REARDEN, Timothy P; N County R I HS; Desloge, MO; 11/180 Chr; CncrtBnd; HonRl; JrNHS; NHS; SctActv; StuCncl; TchrAde; FrCl; SciCl; LetterFtbl; LetterGlf; Univ Of Mo; Medicine.

REARDON, Charles E; Oak Lawn Comm HS; Oak Lawn, IL; 35/660 HonRl; NHS; SchMus; TchrAde; MthCl; Tennis; Univ Of Illinois; Engineering.

REARDON, Patrick; Seneca HS; Seneca, IL; Chr; Chrs; FFA; Bsktbl; Ftbl; Trk; Coll; Pilot/mechanic.

REARS, Donna J; Southeast Nebraska Con HS; Stella, NE; 9/36 DrlTm; HonRl; MrchBnd; SchPl; Twrl; Yrbk; RptrSchPpr; College; Vocational.

REASON, Beverly D; Spencer HS; Spencer, IA; Chr; DrlTm; HonRl; JrNHS; NHS; YthFlsp; RptrYrbk; SpnCl; American Inst Of Business; Computer Prog.

REASON, Linda J; Kewanna HS; Kewanna, IN; SecJrCls; Band; HonRl; PepBnd; EdYrBk; Chrldr; GAA; Business Sch; Secretary.

REAU, Phyllis L; Blissfield HS; Blissfield, MI; 3/140 ALAGirlsSt; Chr; HonRl; NHS; SchMus; TchrAde; FBLA;.

REAUME, Mark A; Ida HS; Ida, MI; 37/160 HonRl; NHS; NatlMeritFnl; NatlMeritSF; SchAde; RptrYrbk; Yrbk; KeyCl; LetterTrk; IMSpt; Trade Sch; Elect.

REAVES, Blake; Northwestern HS; Flint, MI; 48/540 CncrtBnd; HonRl; JA; NHS; Orch; KeyCl; IMSpt; JAAwd; Georgia Tech; Electrical Engineer.

REAVES, Elizabeth A; Alton R 4 HS; Alton, MO; 4/57 Band; Chr; Chrs; CncrtBnd; HonRl; LbryAde; MrchBnd; OffAde; SchMus; SchPl; FHA; PpCl; GAA; University; Professional.

REAVES, Lieschen A; Hazelwood West HS; Bridgeton, MO; ChrhWkr; HonRl; NHS; YthFlsp; PpCl; CaptChrldr; GAA; IMSpt; PPFtbl; College; Teaching.

REAVIS, Allen B; Platte County R Iii HS; Parkville, MO; AFS; Band; CmntyWkr; HonRl; LbryAde; StuCncl; Yrbk; RptrSchPpr; FrCl; SciCl; Nw Missouri State Univ; Med Doctor.

REBA, Peter J; Andrean HS; Crown Point, IN; Chrl; HonRl; NHS; MthCl; LetterFtbl; LetterTrk; College; Medicine.

REBEL, Debbie A; Heritage Hills HS; Chrisney, IN; 26/200 VPJrCls; HonRl; NHS; StuCncl; EdSchPpr; FHA; LetterChrldr; JCAwd; KiwanAwd; OptClAwd; Business School; Professional Secretary.

REBEL, Sherrie A; South Harrison HS; Bethany, MO; Band; ChrhWkr; NatlFornLg; StuCncl; RptrSchPpr; VPFHA; FTA; PpCl; Col; Vocation.

REBER, Carol; Newton HS; Newton, KS; Chrs; HonRl; NatlFornLg; SchMus; TchrAde; YthFlsp; FFA; PpCl; Chrldr; PPFtbl; Ks State University.

REBER, Laurel A; Fairview HS; Fairview, MI; Chr; ChrhWkr; NatlFornLg;.

REBERGER, Cheryl L; Van Buren HS; Brazil, IN; 3/67 SecSophCls; SecJrCls; ALAGirlsSt; Band; CncrtBnd; NHS; PepBnd; PresSpnCl; Chrldr; GAA; U Of In.

REBERGER, Lisa R; Van Buren HS; Brazil, IN; 14/72 Band; CncrtBnd; MrchBnd; PepBnd; TchrAde; SpnCl; PpCl; GAA; Business College; Accounting.

REBHUHN, James; Albert City Truesdale HS; Albert City, IA; 11/50 CncrtBnd; MrchBnd; PepBnd; 4-HAwd; Ia St Univ; Agronomy.

REBICH, Robert P; Lutheran North HS; Florissant, MO; Band; ChrhWkr; CmntyWkr; CncrtBnd; PepBnd; SchMus; YthFlsp; Bsbl; Bsktbl; Ftbl; PPFtbl; College; Professional.

REBSAMEN, Trudi L; Prospect HS; Mt Prospect, IL; HonRl; NatlMeritCmnd; Quill&Scroll; RptrYrbk; FshEdYrbk; Yrbk; PpCl; CaptTrk; GAA; IMSpt; PPFtbl; Iowa State; English.

REBSCH, Charles L; Northwood HS; Thompson, ND; 12/44 Band; Chr; ChrhWkr; CmntyWkr; Wrstlng; Univ Nd; Architectual.

REC, Annmarie; Port Huron Northern HS; Port Huron, MI; HonRl; NatlMeritCmnd; PolWkr; SctActv; RptrSchPpr; Central Mich U; Journalism.

RECHENMACHER, Janet; Benet Acad; Naperville, IL; 53/230 Band; CncrtBnd; HonRl; MrchBnd; OffAde; PpCl; College; Business.

RECHNER, Lisa A; Sacred Heart Academy; Springfield, IL; 14/146 Chrl; Chrs; HonRl; SchMus; StuCncl; Yrbk; FrCl; MthCl; PpCl; Univ Of Illinois; Pharmacist.

RECHTENBACH, Lynn A; Milford HS; Milford, NE; Chr; Chrs; ChrhWkr; CmntyWkr; HonRl; HospAde; RedCrAde; 4-H; Marriage&work.

RECHTIEN, Michael W; Rolla HS; Rolla, MO; HonRl; RptrSchPpr; LetterFtbl; IMSpt; Minister.

RECHTZIGEL, Susan K; Rosemount HS; Rosemount, MN; 30/347 PresFrshCls; ALAGirlsSt; Band; ChrhWkr; HonRl; PresNHS; StuCncl; 4-H; PPFtbl; 4-HAwd; Univ Of Mn; Biology.

RECK, Janet L; Mendota Township HS; Mendota, IL; 45/201 ALAGirlsSt; Band; DrlTm; HonRl; MrchBnd; RptrSchPpr; SchPpr; U Of Ill; Horticulture.

RECKAMP, Maureen P; St Elizabeth Acad; St Louis, MO; 5/120 SecJrCls; ChrhWkr; CmntyWkr; HonRl; NHS; NatlMeritCmnd; StuCncl; RptrSchPpr; FrCl; Socr; College; Professional.

RECKAMP, Sharon A; Harvard HS; Harvard, IL; Band; Chrs; HonRl; JrNHS; FrCl; Chrldr; College; Special Ed.

RECKAMP, Wayne E; Marian Central HS; Harvard, IL; HonRl; SchPl; StuGov; SciCl; Ftbl; IMSpt; U Of Il; Vet Dr.

RECKER, Jean A; Leo HS; Holy Cross, IA; 5/38 Chrs; ChrhWkr; HonRl; LbryAde; SchMus; SchPl; RptrYrbk; 4-H; LatCl; PpCl; SciCl; Univ; Home Economics.

RECKER, Julie E; Appleton East HS; Appleton, WI; 28/523 HonRl; HospAde; Yrbk; FDA; Trk; GAA; IMSpt; Marquette U; Dental Hygiene.

RECKERT, Carolyn J; Maine South HS; Niles, IL; NHS; PolWkr; Quill&Scroll; SchPl; RptrSchPpr; EdSchPpr; Northern Illinois Univ; Journalism.

RECKERT, Meredith; Central Lyon HS; Rock Rapids, IA; 18/100 CncrtBnd; HonRl; Mdrgl; SchMus; SchPl; RptrSchPpr; IMSpt; JETSAwd; Iowa State Univ; Civil Engineering.

RECKLEY, Karen R; Homewood Flossmoor HS; Glenwood, IL; 15/910 CmntyWkr; HonRl; NHS; AmLegAwd; 4-HAwd; PresAwd; Prairie State College; Dental Hygiene.

RECKLING, Beth A; Chamberlain HS; Chamberlain, SD; 1/97 ALAGirlsSt; Band; Chr; ChrhWkr; CncrtBnd; CaptDrlTm; HonRl; MrchBnd; NHS; PepBnd; Sd State U; Pharmacy.

RECKMEYER, Andrew W; Mt Morris HS; Mt Morris, IL; 3/80 VPFrshCls; Band; Chrs; HonRl; PresNHS; SchPl; StuCncl; GerCl; LetterBsktbl; Univ; Professional.

RECLA, Lori A; Niagara HS; Niagara, WI; 3/59 ALAGirlsSt; NHS; RptrSchPpr; EdSchPpr; PpCl; Trk; Chrldr; DARAwd; CitAwd; Bellin School Of Nursing; Regiastered Nurse.

RECORDS, Elizabeth; Central HS; Elnora, IN; 1/47 TrsFrshCls; SecSophCls; PresSrCls; Band; CncrtBnd; HonRl; MrchBnd; PresNHS; PepBnd; PresStuCncl; GAA; DARAwd; Purdue Univ; Forestry.

RECTOR, Daniel J; Highland HS; Anderson, IN; 9/264 HonRl; NHS; TchrAde; Ftbl; Gmi; Engineering.

RECTOR, Douglas A; Warren Township HS; Waukegan, IL; HonRl; NHS; Trk; Accounting.

RECTOR, Karen L; Truman HS; Independence, MO; OffAde; SptEdYrbk; PpCl; CaptChrldr; Kansas Cy College; Shorthand Reporting.

RECTOR, Lynn M; Waverly HS; Waverly, IL; 1/30 ChrhWkr; HonRl; NHS; EdYrBk; 4-H; FTA; SpnCl; Business School; Secretary.

RECTOR, Sandra; Fremont Senior HS; Fremont, NE; CmntyWkr; HonRl; Bsktbl; Swmmng; GAA; IMSpt;.

RECZEK, Michael J; Thornton Fractional No HS; Calumet City, IL; 6/447 Band; CncrtBnd; HonRl; JrNHS; MrchBnd; NHS; PepBnd; Univ Of Ill; Math.

REDA, John; Maine South HS; Park Ridge, IL; HonRl; NatlMeritCmnd; PolWkr; University Of Illinois; Economics.

REDDEMAN, Leslie J; Chadsey HS; Detroit, MI; Band; CmntyWkr; CncrtBnd; HonRl; MrchBnd; NHS; OffAde; PepBnd; RedCrAde; SchAde; LetterSwmmng; Trk; CchngActv; GAA; University; Athletics.

REDDEN, Lola A; Palisade Public HS; Palisade, NE; 3/10 PresSrCls; Band; Chrs; HonRl; NHS; SecStuCncl; PresPpCl; BttyCrckrAwd; EldAwd; CitAwd; Methodist Hosp Sch Of Nursing; Nursing.

REDDIN, Steven J; Mexico HS; Mexico, MO; HonRl; NatlFornLg; NHS; NatlMeritCmnd; PolWkr; SchMus; StuCncl; StuGov; Ftbl; Univ; Economics.

REDDING, Debbie A; Millington HS; Millington, MI; 8/165 Band; CncrtBnd; HonRl; MrchBnd; NHS; PepBnd; TchrAde; College.

REDDING, Jane A; Rich South HS; Park Forest, IL; Chr; HonRl; HospAde; StuCncl; GerCl; RusCl; Bus Schl; Accounting.

REDDING, Jonathon M; Woodstock HS; Woodstock, IL; Chrs; CncrtBnd; HonRl; NHS; SchMus; StuCncl; College; Business Admin.

REDDING, Thomas A; Holy Cross HS; Chicago, IL; 23/306 HonRl; St Marys College; Law.

REDDING, Valencia B; West Side HS; Coury, IN; 45/889 DrlTm; HonRl; NHS; ROTC; SchAde; PpCl; Coll; Computer Tech.

REDDRICK, Wayne S; Luther South HS; Crete, IL; 65/204 Chr; Chrs; ChrhWkr; LbryAde; NatlMeritCmnd; OffAde; SchMus; SchPl; Northwestern Univ; Speech.

REDDY, Bridget A; Pecatonica HS; Pecatonica, IL; VPSrCls; Band; Chrs; HonRl; HospAde; JrNHS; PresNHS; Quill&Scroll; TchrAde; EdYrBk; College.

REDDY, Jacqulin; Ishpeming HS; Ighpeming, MI; 13/201 HonRl; NatlFornLg; NHS; Yrbk; SchPpr; FHA; Mich Tech Univ; Bus Ad.

REDDY, Janet; St Francis Acad; Joliet, IL; 1/174 HonRl; NHS; RptrYrbk; RptrSchPpr; FrCl; GAA; IMSpt; Univ.

REDDY, Patricia J; St Scholastica HS; Chicago, IL; Chrl; ChrhWkr; HospAde; LbryAde; SchPl; St Teresa; Nursng.

REDEKOP, Bill; Bethany Christian HS; Goshen, IN; Bsbl; Bsktbl; College.

REDEL, Cynthia A; Helias HS; Jefferson City, MO; 1/182 Chrs; HonRl; NHS; NatlMeritSF; SchMus; AmLegAwd; Stephens Coll Of Mo; Computer Science.

REDEL, Kenneth C; St Louis University HS; St Louis, MO; Chrl; ChrhWkr; HonRl; SchPl; SctActv; UNYO; EngCl; Bsbl; CaptFtbl; CaptIMSpt; St Louis U; Business.

REDENBAUGH, Robert; John Marshall HS; Rochester, MN; LetterTrk; Coll.

REDENIUS, Candy; Tri Point HS; Ashkum, IL; 6/32 Chrs; ChrhWkr; HonRl; NHS; SchPl; EdYrBk; RptrSchPpr; 4-H; FFA; GAA; Kankakee Comm College; Accounting.

REDER, Martin; All Saints Western HS; Bay City, MI; PresSophCls; ALBoysSt; Band; CtyCnl; HonRl; StuCncl; StuGov; Bsktbl; Ftbl; Trk; College; Engineering.

REDFEARN, Phyllis; Spokane; Highlandville, MO; 1/24 Chrs; HonRl; SchPl; FHA;.

REDFIELD, Lisa J; South Barber HS; Hardtner, KS; Band; Chr; Chrs; ChrhWkr; HonRl; FHA; FTA; PpCl; LetterBsktbl; LetterTrk; College; Professional.

REDFORD, Douglas S; Macarthur HS; Decatur, IL; 5/410 ChrhWkr; HonRl; NHS; SctActv; PresStuCncl; YthFlsp; GerCl; Tennis; Washington Univ; Environmental Law.

REDFORD, Larry J; Lyons HS; Lyons, KS; 18/97 Band; HonRl; OffAde; TchrAde; KeyCl; LetterBsktbl; LetterTrk; LetterWrstlng; CchngActv; College.

REDHAIR, Kathryn J; Solon Comm HS; Solon, IA; 1/69 Band; Chrs; HonRl; SecQuill&Scroll; SchPpr; William Jewell Coll; Elem Ed.

REDICK, Edward L; Shawneetown HS; Shawneetown, IL; 1/35 HonRl; StuCncl; RptrYrbk; Yrbk; SchPpr; Jr College; Business Administration.

REDIGER, Lynn M; Crown Point HS; Crown Point, IN; HonRl; HospAde; GAA; Indiana University; Nursing.

REDIGER, Steven R; Northrop HS; Fort Wayne, IN; Aud/Vis; HonRl; MrchBnd; OffAde; SctActv;.

REDIKER, Karen K; Council Grove HS; Council Grove, KS; 6/108 PresJrCls; ALAGirlsSt; Chrs; ChrhWkr; HonRl; NHS; Yrbk; RptrSchPpr; 4-H; LetterGlf; 4-HAwd; Emporia Ks St Col; Business.

REDINBAUGH, Les; Tri Center HS; Neola, IA; HonRl; StuCncl; StuGov; 4-H; FFA; Wrstlng; 4-HAwd; Dana Univ; Mec Engineer.

REDING, Gerilanne; Saint Louise De Marillac HS; Des Plaines, IL; Chrs; CmntyWkr; SchPl; StuCncl; TchrAde; PpCl; Tennis; College; Veternarian Medicine.

REDINGER, Rhonda L; Phillipsburg HS; Phillipsburg, KS; HonRl; SchAde; TchrAde; FHA; PpCl; Coll; Teach.

REDINGTON, Patty J; Clayton HS; Clayton, MO; 31/201 HospAde; ModUN; NatlMeritSF; PolWkr; SctActv; Bradley Univ; Home Economics.

REDINGTON, Thomas P; Galesburg Sr HS; Galesburg, IL; TrsJrCls; VPSrCls; ChrhWkr; CmntyWkr; HonRl; PolWkr; SctActv; StuCncl; StuGov; YthLg; RptrSchPpr; SchPpr; FrCl; Bsktbl; Northern Illinois Univ; Law.

REDLIN, Rita R; Lamoure HS; Ellendale, ND; 10/48 SecTrsSophCls; ALAGirlsSt; Chrs; CncrtBnd; HonRl; MrchBnd; PepBnd; GerCl; PpCl; North Dakota St Univ; Nursing.

REDLIN, Sandra J; Watertown Sr HS; Watertown, SD; 20/326 Chr; Chrs; ChrhWkr; DrlTm; HonRl; NatlThespSoc; SchMus; Chrldr; Trade School; Vocation.

REDMON, Debra K; Monroe Senior HS; Monroe, MI; 1/523 VPChr; ChrhWkr; HonRl; VPJA; NHS; Monroe Co Comm Clg; Algebra Teacher.

REDMON, Lullaby; Roosevelt HS; Gary, IN; TrsFrshCls; HonRl; NHS; NatlMeritSchl; Bsktbl; GAA; JAAwd; NCTE; CitAwd; Trade School.

REDMOND, Kevin P; Athens HS; Athens, MI; Band; Chr; HonRl; JA; NHS; SchPl; SctActv; Bsktbl; Trk; IMSpt; College; Landscape Architect.

REDPATH, David J; Eden Prairie HS; Eden Prairie, MN; HonRl; NatlMeritSF; StuCncl; Bsktbl; Ftbl; CchngActv; College; Law.

REDPATH, Karen E; St Thomas The Apostle HS; Ann Arbor, MI; 6/79 HonRl; VPNHS; NatlMeritSF; StuGov; TchrAde; SchPpr; FrCl; MthCl; PpCl; SciCl; Mich St U; Math.

REDUME, Mark A; Ida HS; Ida, MI; ChrhWkr; HonRl; NHS; NatlMeritSF; RptrYrbk; Yrbk; RptrSchPpr; SchPpr; LetterTrk; College.

REDWANZ, Wendy M; Reese HS; Reese, MI; Chr; ChrhWkr; HonRl; SchPl; YthFlsp; FHA; College Ferris State; Conference Room Repor.

REDWINE, Charles P; Vienna HS; New Burnside, IL; PresSophCls; ChrhWkr; PpCl; Bsktbl; Trade Sch; Voc.

REDWINE, Lisa P; Dillsboro HS; Dillsboro, IN; 1/30 VPJrCls; ALAGirlsSt; Chrs; ChrhWkr; HonRl; NHS; SchPl; Yrbk; Bsktbl; Purdue Univ; Industrial Mgmt.

REDWING, Valerie J; Watertown HS; Watertown, SD; 23/326 ChrhWkr; CmntyWkr; HonRl; YthFlsp; Northern State; Math.

REECE, Cindy L; Maplewood Richmond Hts Sr HS; Maplewood, MO; 12/170 VPJrCls; SecSrCls; HonRl; NHS; Quill&Scroll; StuGov; Yrbk; SchPpr; FrCl; GAA; Univ; Professional.

REECE, Edward L; Santa Fe Trail HS; Overbrook, KS; PresFrshCls; HonRl; SchAde; StuCncl; StuGov; TchrAde; LetterBsktbl; LetterFtbl; LetterGlf; LetterTrk; College.

REECE, John; Salina Central HS; Salina, KS; HonRl; MrchBnd; NHS; PepBnd; StuCncl; YthFlsp; Bsktbl; Trk; PresAwd; Univ Of Tulsa; Electrical Engineering.

REED, Barbara S; Waverly HS; Waverly, KS; 4/24 ALAGirlsSt; HonRl; HospAde; SchPl; StuCncl; YthFlsp; Yrbk; PresPpCl; IMSpt; PPFtbl; Allen County Comm Clg; Elem Educ.

REED, Beth E; Lagrove Comm HS; Loogootee, IL; 1/34 Chrs; HonRl; JA; NHS; SchMus; 4-H; FBLA; FHA; DanFAwd; 4-HAwd; Coll; Business.

REED, Brent W; South Iron HS; Vulcan, MO; SecTrsSophCls; VPJrCls; Chrl; Chrs; HonRl; NHS; Bsktbl; College; Professional.

REED, Carl A; Flora HS; Flora, IL; 10/140 HonRl; NHS; SpnCl; SciCl; Ftbl; Tennis; College; Engineering.

REED, Cathy L; St Elmo HS; St Elmo, IL; 7/54 HstSrCls; ChrhWkr; CncrtBnd; HonRl; MrchBnd; PepBnd; SctActv; FHA; PpCl; College Lakeland; Child Care.

REED, Charles F; Rolling Meadows HS; Arlington Hts, IL; 9/581 HonRl; LbryAde; NHS; OffAde; FrCl; MthCl; SciCl; Ftbl; Swmmng; Loyola Univ; Physician.

REED, Charles F; Rolling Meadows HS; Arlington Hgts, IL; 6/575 CmntyWkr; HonRl; NHS; OffAde; FDA; FrCl; MthCl; SciCl; LetterFtbl; LetterSwmmng; Loyola U; Medicine.

REED, Darrel R; Doniphan HS; Doniphan, MO; 15/173 HonRl; NHS; SchPl; StuCncl; StuGov; TchrAde; KeyCl; LetterBsktbl; LetterFtbl; LetterTrk; Ms U; Law.

REED, David B; Niantic Harristown HS; Mt Auburn, IL; 3/50 HonRl; StuCncl; StuGov; RptrYrbk; Yrbk; SpnCl; LetterBsbl; LetterBsktbl; CaptFtbl; LetterTrk; College; Veterinarian.

REED, Dawn; Harlan Community HS; Harlan, IA; 24/256 VPSophCls; AFS; DrlTm; HonRl; NHS; StuCncl; YthFlsp; PpCl; Univ; Bus Administration.

REED, Debbie A; Wyoming Park HS; Wyoming, MI; 15/252 Band; CncrtBnd; HonRl; MrchBnd; NHS; PepBnd; SchMus; StuCncl; TchrAde; GerCl; College; Music.

REED, Debbie De A; Willmar Sr HS; Willmar, MN; Chr; HonRl; PpCl; CaptChrldr; College; Professional.

REED, Deborah L; Normal Comm HS; Normal, IL; ChrhWkr; CncrtBnd; DrmMjrt; HonRl; MrchBnd; NHS; Orch; PepBnd; PolWkr; StuCncl; Univ Of Illinois; Psychology.

REED, Debra; Beecher HS; Flint, MI; 5/250 HonRl; HospAde; JrNHS; NHS; FNA; FrCl; Hurley School Of Nursing; Nurse Or X Ray Te.

REED, Debra K; West Delaware Senior HS; Manchester, IA; Aud/Vis; Band; Chrs; CncrtBnd; DrmMjrt; HonRl; MrchBnd; NatlThespSoc; PepBnd; RedCrAde; Junior College; Vocation.

REED, Debra L; Parker HS; Janesville, WI; 11/382 ChrhWkr; CmntyWkr; HonRl; HospAde; LbryAde; NHS; Bsktbl; LetterTrk; GAA; IMSpt; Uw Whitewater; Journalism.

REED, Denise K; Highland HS; Highland, IN; 22/538 ChrhWkr; HonRl; SctActv; YthFlsp; RptrYrbk; Yrbk; FHA; SpnCl; PpCl; Tennis; GAA; College; Professional.

REED, Denise L; Greenfield Central HS; Greenfield, IN; 11/286 CaptBand; CaptCncrtBnd; HonRl; LbryAde; CaptMrchBnd; NHS; NatlThespSoc; CaptOrch; CaptPepBnd; SchMus; SchPl; VPLatCl; MthCl; Manchester College; Chemistry.

REED, Dolores A; Waverly Consolidated HS; Lincoln, NE; CncrtBnd; HonRl; MrchBnd; TchrAde; RptrYrbk; 4-H; GerCl; PpCl;.

REED, Douglas; Lyons HS; Lyons, KS; VPFrshCls; VPSophCls; HonRl; 4-H; IMSpt;.

REED, Douglas; Saydel HS; Des Moines, IA; 15/161 TrsSophCls; ALBoysSt; CncrtBnd; HonRl; NHS; StuCncl; Yrbk; SchPpr; Tennis; College; Professional.

REED, Douglas E; Centreville HS; Constantine, MI; HonRl; SctActv; YthFlsp; Hope College; Biochemist.

REED, Evelyn D; Flower Voc HS; Chicago, IL; PresFrshCls; Band; Chr; ChrhWkr; CmntyWkr; LbryAde; SchPl; 4-H; FBLA; GAA; Mudelin; News Media.

REED, Gae P; Century HS; Karnak, IL; 5/60 SecBand; ChrhWkr; HonRl; SchPl; PresStuCncl; PresYthFlsp; Yrbk; VPFHA; SecPpCl; IMSpt; Shawnee Jr Coll; Social Work.

REED, Gary L; Huntington North HS; Huntington, IN; CncrtBnd; DrmMjrt; JrNHS; MrchBnd; SchMus; SctActv; StuCncl; PresYthFlsp; 4-H; GerCl; Col Or Univ; Engineer Law Or Medicine.

REED, Grace M; Soldan HS; St Louis, MO; 4/734 CmntyWkr; HonRl; NHS; StuCncl; Univ; Psychologist.

REED, Jacqueline; Southwest HS; St Louis, MO; 39/617 HonRl; StuCncl; Univ; Vet.

REED, Jane A; Thomas Jefferson HS; Council Bluffs, IA; CmntyWkr; HonRl; HospAde; JA; LbryAde; NHS; NatlMeritCmnd; PolWkr; College; Special Ed.

REED, Jean M; Winfield HS; Winfield, KS; Band; CncrtBnd; HonRl; MrchBnd; PepBnd; FrCl; PpCl; Trk; College; Professional.

REED, Jennifer L; Centerville Sr HS; Centerville, IN; 1/131 ChrhWkr; HonRl; NHS; NatlMeritCmnd; NatlThespSoc; Yrbk; Pres4-H; FrCl; PpCl; LetterTennis; College; Commercial Artist.

REED, Joy A; South Knox HS; Monroe City, IN; 20/130 ALAGirlsSt; Band; ChrhWkr; CmntyWkr; HonRl; NHS; StuCncl; YthFlsp; PpCl; GAA; 4-HAwd; Vincennes Univ; Fashion Coordinator.

REED, Karen K; Maple Valley HS; Castana, IA; ChrhWkr; HonRl; 4-H; Amer Inst Of Busi; Court Reporter.

REED, Kathleen; Southeast Of Saline HS; Assaria, KS; VPJrCls; Bsbl; Bsktbl; Trk; GAA; 4-HAwd; CitAwd; Kansas State Univ; Physical Education.

REED, Laura L; Fremont Sr HS; Fremont, MI; 10/205 ChrhWkr; CmntyWkr; HonRl; HospAde; JA; JrNHS; NHS; UNYO; YthFlsp; Muskegon Com Col; History.

REED, Laurie G; Eau Claire HS; Eau Claire, MI; HonRl; SchPl; TchrAde; SpnCl; SciCl; DARAwd; U Of Mich; Archaeologist.

REED, Lorrie K; Joliet West HS; Joliet, IL; 47/495 Chr; HonRl; NHS; GAA; Joliet Jr Coll; Accounting.

REED, Louis R; Pomona HS; Pomona, KS; Band; ChrhWkr; CmntyWkr; HonRl; MrchBnd; PepBnd; SchPl; SctActv; Trk; College; Liberal Arts.

REED, Marianne; Copeland HS; Copeland, KS; 3/12 VPJrCls; VPSrCls; ALAGirlsSt; Band; Chrs; ChrhWkr; CmntyWkr; DrlTm; HonRl; MrchBnd; PepBnd; SchPl; StuCncl; Yrbk; College; Oceanography.

REED, Marsha G; Circle HS; Towanda, KS; TrsSrCls; Band; HonRl; LbryAde; MrchBnd; OffAde; PepBnd; PpCl; SciCl; IMSpt; Butler County Comm Jr Clg; Secretary.

REED, Mary J; Pacelli HS; Stevens Point, WI; ChrhWkr; HonRl; SchPl; StuCncl; StuGov; SchPpr; LetterChrldr; AmLegAwd; OptClAwd; Vocational School; Nursing.

REED, Mary K; Escanaba Area HS; Escanaba, MI; 20/393 Chrl; CtyCnl; CncrtBnd; MrchBnd; NHS; Orch; SchMus; StuCncl; StuGov; No Michigan Univ; Music.

REED, Mary K; Joseph A Craig Sr HS; Janesville, WI; Chr; DrmBgl; HonRl; NatlThespSoc; SchMus; SchPl; StuCncl; Teen; RptrYrbk; RptrSchPpr; 4-H; VPFHA; Swmmng; GAA; University Of Wisconsin; Home Economics.

REED, Michael I; Centralia HS; Centralia, IL; HonRl; Kaskaskla Jr College; Journalism.

REED, Michael J; Crane HS; Crane, MO; 5/25 PresJrCls; PresSrCls; Band; ChrhWkr; NHS; StuCncl; RptrYrbk; LetterBsbl; LetterBsktbl; LetterTrk; Sw Missouri St Univ.

REED, Michael P; Indian Creek HS; Trafalgar, IN; Band; CncrtBnd; MrchBnd; PepBnd; SchMus; SciCl; LetterTrk; Clg; Marine Biologist.

REED, Mitch M; Cannelton HS; Cannelton, IN; 4/25 PresSophCls; ChrhWkr; HonRl; NHS; SctActv; StuCncl; 4-H; 4-HAwd; Farming.

REED, Patricia A; Crown Point HS; Crown Point, IN; 9/582 Band; CncrtBnd; HonRl; LitMag; MrchBnd; Quill&Scroll; Yrbk; SchPpr; 4-H; LatCl; 4-HAwd; College; Journalism.

REED, Patricia J; Columbus North HS; Columbus, IN; 6/465 AFS; HonRl; SecSdlty; StuCncl; StuGov; YthFlsp; PpCl; LetterBsktbl; DARAwd; OptClAwd; Purdue Univ; Math.

REED, Patricia K; Highland HS; Highland, IN; 34/583 Band; Chr; Chrs; MrchBnd; NatlFornLg; PepBnd; SchPl; GerCl; University; Special Edu Teacher.

REED, Peggy L; Northern HS; Port Huron, MI; 20/430 ChrhWkr; HonRl; HospAde; StuCncl; Mich State U; Medicine.

REED, Peter M; Mendel C HS; Chicago, IL; HonRl; OffAde; StuCncl; LetterBsktbl; LetterFtbl; IMSpt; Bradley Univ; Professional.

REED, Robert C; Marquette Manor HS; Downers Grove, IL; PresSrCls; Chr; ChrhWkr; HonRl; StuGov; RptrSchPpr; Bsktbl; Socr; Bob Jones Univ; Evangelism.

REED, Robert L; Overton Public HS; Overton, NE; 4/21 ChrhWkr; HonRl; SchPl; RptrYrbk; SptEdYrbk; LetterBsktbl; LetterFtbl; LetterTrk; Trade School; Vocation.

REED, Robin; Southern Door HS; Brussels, WI; PresJrCls; PresSrCls; HonRl; SchMus; SchPl; StuCncl; StuGov; EdSchPpr; PpCl; Travel.

REED, Rose M; Soldan HS; St Louis, MO; 15/734 CmntyWkr; HonRl; StuCncl; PpCl; Chrldr; Univ;psychology.

REED, Rusty R; Taylorville Sr HS; Taylorville, IL; Band; CncrtBnd; HonRl; MrchBnd; KeyCl; Univ Of Illinois; Civil Engineer.

REED, Sally R; Parkwood HS; Joplin, MO; ChrhWkr; HonRl; NHS; Teen; Yrbk; Glf; Missouri So State College.

REED, Sean M; Bellmont HS; Decatur, IN; HonRl; NatlMeritSchl; SchPl; LatCl; Trk; Ind Univ; Industrial Chemistry.

REED, Sherri J; Abraham Lincoln HS; Council Bluffs, IA; HonRl; ModUN; Univ; Elem Education.

REED, Sherrill L; Fruitport HS; Muskegon, MI; Band; CncrtBnd; HonRl; MrchBnd; OffAde; SchPl; SptEdYrbk; Yrbk; 4-H; College; Professional.

REED, Susan K; Macksville HS; Seward, KS; HonRl; 4-H; Trk;.

REED, Susan L; Puxico R8 HS; Puxico, MO; TrsSophCls; SecJrCls; Band; Chr; HonRl; JrNHS; FTA; PpCl; SciCl; PresAwd; College; Math & Science.

REED, Sylvia; Mother Mcauley HS; Chicago, IL; 3/484 NHS; NatlMeritSF; Orch; PolWkr; SchMus; SctActv; TchrAde; FTA; IMSpt; Univ; Physician.

REED, Wanda J; Tippecanoe Valley HS; Akron, IN; HonRl; NHS; RptrSchPpr; 4-H; GerCl; LatCl; MthCl; PpCl; SciCl; GAA; Univ; Engineering.

REED, Zebbie S; Marseilles HS; Marseilles, IL; Illinois Valley Comm College; Math.

REEDER, Brian D; Ottawa HS; Ottawa, IL; 30/420 HonRl; NHS; SciCl; Ftbl; LetterTennis; Creighton Univ; Medicine.

REEDER, Cindy G; Decatur Central HS; Indianapolis, IN; 13/319 HonRl; NHS; OffAde; TchrAde; LatCl; PpCl; Bus Sch, Ind Bus College; Accounting.

REEDER, Dale W; Carterville HS; Cambria, IL; PresBand; PresCncrtBnd; HonRl; PresMrchBnd; PepBnd; SchPl; RptrYrbk; RptrSchPpr; 4-H; SciCl; Univ; Law.

REEDER, Jefferson L; Smithville HS; Smithville, MO; 5/75 PresFrshCls; HonRl; JrNHS; VPNHS; SchPl; TreasStuCncl; LetterBsktbl; ChmnFtbl; LetterTrk; AmLegAwd; College; Professional.

REEDER, Sam R; Washington Community HS; Washington, IL; HonRl; Illinois Cntrl College; Electrician.

REEDER, Teresa R; Mt Pleasant HS; Mount Pleasant, IA; 11/170 SecTrsSophCls; Chrs; HonRl; NHS; RptrYrbk; 4-H; LetterBsktbl; IMSpt; 4-HAwd;.

REEDER, Thomas J; Riverside Brookfield HS; Riverside, IL; 43/488 ChrhWkr; HonRl; NHS; NatlMeritFnl; StuGov; Yrbk; FrCl; Univ Of Michigan; Economics.

REEDY, Ann E; Lovington HS; Lovington, IL; TrsSophCls; Band; Chrs; HonRl; StuCncl; FHA; PpCl; Chrldr; GAA; College.

REEDY, Becky A; Hanover HS; Hanover, KS; SecSophCls; Chrs; HonRl; VPNHS; PpCl; TreasSciCl; Marymount College; Medicine.

REEDY, Cathy; J D Darnall Hs; Geneseo, IL; 13/207 HonRl; VPJA; NHS; Yrbk; SecTreasLatCl; Bsbl; GAA; JAAwd; Clarke College; Computer Science.

REEDY, Stephen E; Humboldt Sr HS; Hardy, IA; 45/147 Chrl; ChrhWkr; HonRl; SchMus; SchPl; StuCncl; VP4-H; PresFFA; Trk; 4-HAwd; Univ; Agricultural Education.

REEHM, Mary A; Mc Donald HS; Pineville, MO; 8/176 Chrs; ChrhWkr; CmntyWkr; DrlTm; HonRl; SecNHS; SctActv; StuCncl; EdSchPpr; Bsktbl; LetterTrk; CchngActv; Missouri Valley College; Physician.

REEKS, Mike A; Bremen HS; Midlothian, IL; 35/427 HonRl; NHS; GerCl; MthCl; LetterWrstlng; Univ Of Illinois; Economics.

REEL, Cherri J; Holcomb HS; Holcomb, MO; 5/33 SecSophCls; VPJrCls; Chr; Chrs; ChrhWkr; HonRl; LbryAde; SchMus; SchPl; SctActv; StuGov; 4-H; FHA; PpCl; College; Professional.

REEL, Mike A; Munster HS; Munster, IN; HonRl; SchMus; TchrAde; Ftbl; Wrstlng; IMSpt; In Central U; Sales.

REEL, Phillip H; Tri County HS; Remington, IN; TrsSophCls; Band; CncrtBnd; HonRl; MrchBnd; PepBnd; StuCncl; RptrSchPpr; SpnCl; Indiana St Univ; Accountant.

REEL, Vickie K; Holcomb HS; Holcomb, MO; 3/36 HonRl; SchAde; SchPl; StuCncl; StuGov; TchrAde; 4-H; FHA; MthCl; PpCl; Se Mo Univ; Pharamicist.

REELING, Patrick J; Waterford Twp HS; Drayton, MI; Central Michigan Univ; Marketing.

REENERS, Scott R; Green Bay Sw HS; Green Bay, WI; HonRl; JA; StuCncl; RptrYrbk; RptrSchPpr; FFA; FrCl; LetterGlf; IMSpt; Univ Of Wisconsin; Agronomy.

REENTS, Timothy E; Litchfield HS; Litchfield, IL; 38/165 ALBoysSt; SchPl; TreasKeyCl; FrCl; PpCl; Bsktbl; LetterFtbl; IMSpt; Siu Edwardsville; Dentistry.

REES, David S; Du Quoin HS; Du Quoin, IL; 2/143 PresFrshCls; PresSophCls; PresJrCls; PresSrCls; Band; HonRl; SchPl; LatCl; BttyCrckrAwd; College.

REES, Ginger L; Houston HS; Houston, MO; 5/114 Band; CncrtBnd; HonRl; HospAde; MrchBnd; NHS; OffAde; PepBnd; StuCncl; TchrAde; Twrl; RptrYrbk; RptrSchPpr; Chrldr; Sw Missouri St Univ; Accounting.

REES, La Nelle R; Burwell HS; Burwell, NE; 1/37 TrsSophCls; ChrhWkr; HonRl; NHS; VPYrbk; RptrSchPpr; PresSpnCl; SecMthCl; Chrldr; Univ Of Ne; Pre Med.

REES, Mary; Yankton Senior HS; Yankton, SD; Band; CncrtBnd; HonRl; MrchBnd; NHS; Orch; Quill&Scroll; RptrSchPpr; Univ; Nursing.

REES, Roger A; Golden City R 3 HS; Jasper, MO; 1/25 PresJrCls; VPSrCls; Band; HonRl; SchPl; StuCncl; 4-H; FFA; MthCl; LetterBsktbl; LetterFtbl; LetterTrk; 4-HAwd; Univ Of Missouri; Vet.

REESE, Debra; Wautoma HS; Wautoma, WI; Aud/Vis; Chr; LbryAde; PepBnd; CivCl; PpCl; Bsbl; Bsktbl; GAA; Vocational.

REESE, Joann; Rosati Kain HS; St Louis, MO; ChrhWkr; LbryAde; NatlMeritCmnd; TchrAde; UNYO; College; Special Education.

REESE, Jody M; Lodi HS; Lodi, WI; SecSophCls; TrsJrCls; Band; CmntyWkr; StuCncl; RptrSchPpr; SpnCl; PpCl; Chrldr; College; Spanish Interpreter.

REESE, John W; Estherville HS; Estherville, IA; Band; CncrtBnd; MrchBnd; NatlFornLg; Orch; PepBnd; SchPl; SctActv; YthFlsp; RptrSchPpr; College.

REESE, Julie; Avondale HS; Troy, MI; Chr; Chrs; ChrhWkr; HonRl; Trk; GAA; IMSpt; PPFtbl; College; Curriculum.

REESE, Laura A; Dearborn HS; Dearborn, MI; AFS; Band; ChrhWkr; CncrtBnd; HonRl; MrchBnd; Orch; PepBnd; SctActv; College; Music.

REESE, Lois A; Tekonsha HS; Tekonsha, MI; 5/40 TrsJrCls; HonRl; TchrAde; 4-H; DARAwd; 4-HAwd; Coll; Law.

REESE, Mark W; Columbus HS; Columbus, WI; 13/130 Aud/Vis; ChrhWkr; SchMus; SchPl; TchrAde; Ftbl; Wrstlng; College; Professional.

REESE, Paul C; Perry HS; Griggsville, IL; TrsSophCls; Band; Chr; Chrs; ChrhWkr; CmntyWkr; CncrtBnd; HonRl; MrchBnd; PepBnd; College; Engineering.

REESE, Rita A; Sioux Valley Comm HS; Peterson, IA; PresFrshCls; TrsJrCls; Band; Chrs; CncrtBnd; Mdrgl; NHS; NatlMeritCmnd; SchMus; SchPl; StuCncl; College.

REESE, Tom A; Ledyard Community HS; Ledyard, IA; VPJrCls; ALBoysSt; Band; HonRl; SchPl; StuCncl; YthFlsp; Yrbk; Bsbl; Trade School; Vocation.

REESTMAN, Karen; Elgin Public HS; Elgin, NE; /26 VPJrCls; NHS; 4-H; PpCl; Trk; Coll.

REETHS, Steven P; Orchard View HS; Muskegon, MI; Band; HonRl; MrchBnd; NHS; StuGov; Yrbk; SchPpr; Swmmng; LetterGlf; CchngActv; Muskegon Comm Coll; Photojournalist.

REETZ, Randall S; Oak Park River Forest HS; Oak Park, IL; 57/1012 Chr; HonRl; NHS; StuGov; PresPpCl; Southern Methodist Univ; Business Admin.

REEVE, Kent V; Walker HS; Walker, MN; Band; Chr; CncrtBnd; MrchBnd; PepBnd; Yrbk; Ftbl; Wrstlng; Trade School; Law Enforcement.

REEVE, Patricia A; East Lansing HS; E Lasning, MI; OffAde; SctActv; Bsktbl; Michigan State Univ; Engineering.

REEVE, Ronda; Douglas Mac Arthur HS; Saginaw, MI; Chr; ChrhWkr; HonRl; PolWkr; SchPl; TchrAde; PPFtbl; Univ.

REEVER, Delores R; Golva Public HS; Golva, ND; 5/10 TrsFrshCls; ChrhWkr; HonRl; HospAde; SchPl; RptrSchPpr; College; Veterinary Asst.

REEVES, Clinton W; Madison HS; Madison, NE; SecSophCls; TrsJrCls; HonRl; LbryAde; NHS; SchPl; YthFlsp; RptrYrbk; RptrSchPpr; College; Optomitrist.

REEVES, Daniel A; New Monroe Comm HS; Monroe, IA; Chr; HonRl; TchrAde; YthFlsp; LetterTrk; Coll; Prof.

REEVES, Daniel L; St Clair HS; St Clair, MI; 39/191 ALBoysSt; Band; ChrhWkr; CncrtBnd; HonRl; MrchBnd; PepBnd; TchrAde; CaptBsbl; E Michigan Univ; Music.

REEVES, David R; Clinton HS; Clinton, IL; 4/153 Chr; HonRl; PresNHS; SchMus; SchPl; StuCncl; FrCl; LetterFtbl; Glf; IMSpt; Eastern Illinois Univ; Dentist.

REEVES, Deborah A; Wheaton Central HS; Wheaton, IL; 7/317 ChrhWkr; HonRl; NHS; NatlMeritCmnd; SchPl; TchrAde; YthFlsp; College; Education.

REEVES, Herbert A; Wichita HS; Wichita, KS; JA; SctActv; FrCl; JAAwd; Wichita State Univ; Computer Sciences.

REEVES, Jamie R; Newton HS; Newton, KS; 46/285 ChrhWkr; HonRl; LbryAde; TchrAde; YthFlsp; FrCl; PpCl; Wichita St Univ; Engineer.

REEVES, Kathleen R; Carlisle Community HS; Carlisle, IA; 9/95 Chr; ChrhWkr; HonRl; LitMag; LbryAde; NHS; Yrbk; RptrSchPpr; BttyCrckrAwd; College; Journalism.

REEVES, Kaye M; Pewaukee HS; Pewaukee, WI; CncrtBnd; HonRl; NHS; NatlMeritSF; SchPl; SchPpr; Carroll College; Writer.

REEVES, Kristy A; Riverdale HS; Muscoda, WI; Band; Chr; ChrhWkr; HonRl; HospAde; NatlFornLg; SctActv; RptrYrbk; SchPpr; GodCntryAwd; U Of Wi Platteville; Biology.

REEVES, Norma J; Creston Comm HS; Creston, IA; 34/170 CmntyWkr; HonRl; HospAde; RedCrAde; TchrAde; Yrbk; SpnCl; Nw Mo St Univ; Rn.

REEVES, Teresa; Tri Jr Sr HS; Knightstown, IN; Chr; ChrhWkr; HonRl; NHS; 4-H; FHA; SpnCl; GAA; College; Forrestry.

REEVIS, Monte A; Southeast HS; Springfield, IL; 8/550 Band; NHS; StuCncl; YthFlsp; 4-H; KeyCl; FrCl; Bsbl; CaptFtbl; Socr; Trk; Wrstlng; 4-HAwd; Univ; Medical.

REFFNER, Jessica; Lincoln Sr HS; Junction City, WI; Chrl; Chrs; HonRl; MrchBnd; Orch; PepBnd; SchMus; 4-H; SciCl; 4-HAwd; Army Band.

REFNER, Ken R; Oak Lawn Community HS; Oak Lawn, IL; Band; HonRl; SctActv; Bsbl; Bsktbl; Ftbl; Trk; College; Business Administration.

REFNER, Michael K; Dekalb HS; Waterloo, IN; NHS; GerCl; LetterFtbl; IMSpt; Purdue U; Engineering.

REGAL, Jeffrey A; South Lake HS; Detroit, MI; HonRl; Lawerence Inst Tech; Mech Engineer.

REGAN, Barb; Crete Monee HS; Crete, IL; SecSophCls; TrsJrCls; Chr; LitMag; Quill&Scroll; SchMus; TchrAde; Yrbk; LetterBsktbl; Tennis; College; Art.

REGAN, Dolores T; Notre Dame HS; Chicago, IL; PresJrCls; HonRl; NHS; StuCncl; College; Liberal Arts.

REGAN, E Quinn; Loyola Academy; Deerfield, IL; 36/442 CmntyWkr; HonRl; NHS; NatlMeritCmnd; SchMus; SchPl; LetterFtbl; Northwestern Univ; Doctor.

REGEHR, Richard L; Iola HS; Iola, KS; VPFrshCls; HonRl; Bsktbl; Ftbl; College ;rotc.

REGELIN, Mary J; Loomis Public HS; Loomis, NE; CmntyWkr; HonRl; SchPl; Teen; PpCl; Trk; Col; Professional.

REGENSCHEID, Ronald E; Le Sueur HS; St Peter, MN; HonRl; NHS; College; Acricultural.

REGENT, Nancy C; Alexander Hamilton HS; Milwaukee, WI; 8/78628# Aud/Vis; HonRl; LbryAde; NatlMeritFnl; RptrSchPpr; SchPpr; MthCl; VPSciCl; College; Police Lab Chem.

REGER, Kevin M; Sun Prairie Sr HS; Sun Prairie, WI; 1/350 CncrtBnd; MrchBnd; ModUN; NatlMeritSF; PepBnd; SctActv; Univ Of Wi; Advertising.

REGGIO, Christopher T; Dwight D Eisenhower HS; Utica, MI; 44/535 CmntyWkr; HonRl; LbryAde; NHS; Quill&Scroll; SchPl; TchrAde; EdYrBk; SchPpr; GerCl; Oakland Univ; Secondary Education.

REGIER, Myron T; Frederic Remington HS; Newton, KS; Band; ChrhWkr; CncrtBnd; MrchBnd; StuCncl; StuGov; TchrAde; RptrYrbk; RptrSchPpr; College; Law.

REH, Karen R; Rockford Sr HS; Rockford, MI; Band; Chr; ChrhWkr; HonRl; LbryAde; Grand Rapids Bap Clg; Special Ed Teacher.

REHA, David A; Dodge Center HS; Dodge Center, MN; 2/53 SecTrsSrCls; Aud/Vis; ChrhWkr; CncrtBnd; HonRl; NHS; SchPl; SptEdSchPpr; Tennis; Trade School; Bachelor Degree In Electronic.

REHBEIN, Rita K; Forest Lake HS; Forest Lake, MN; CncrtBnd; HonRl; NatlFornLg; Yrbk; Engr.

REHBEIN, Robyn L; Forest Lake Sr HS; Lino Lakes, MN; 17/428 Band; CncrtBnd; PepBnd; StuCncl; Twrl; TreasSpnCl; PpCl; Tennis; GAA; Univ; Fashion Merch.

REHBERG, Jeanmarie; Burlington HS; Burlington, WI; 1/285 Band; ChrhWkr; CncrtBnd; HonRl; MrchBnd; NatlFornLg; SchMus; YthFlsp; Sec4-H; 4-HAwd; Lawrence Univ; Elementary Teacher.

REHFELDT, Peggy A; West Central HS; Sioux Falls, SD; TrsSophCls; Chr; Chrs; ChrhWkr; HonRl; HospAde; MrchBnd; SchMus; SchPl; StuCncl; 4-H; FHA; PpCl; LetterTrk; Trade School.

REHKOP, Janet K; Concordia HS; Concordia, MO; 11/44 VPJrCls; VPSrCls; HonRl; ModUN; SchPl; RptrYrbk; SptEdSchPpr; FHA; PpCl; PresAwd; Univ; Nursing.

REHLING, Alan; William Howard Taft Hs; Chicago, IL; 118/800 Band; CncrtBnd; HonRl; Orch; RptrSchPpr; GerCl; Ii.

REHM, Katherine A; Round Lake Sr HS; Round Lake, IL; HonRl; LitMag; NHS; Quill&Scroll; SctActv; StuCncl; Yrbk; SchPpr; GAA; College; English.

REHM, Sheryl J; Advance Riv HS; Advance, MO; 5/46 SecTrsJrCls; Band; HonRl; MrchBnd; SchPl; FHA; PpCl; GAA; CitAwd; Clge; Medical Doctor.

REHMERT, Richard L; Frederic Remington HS; Whitewater, KS; ALBoysSt; Chrl; HonRl; NHS; NatlThespSoc; SchMus; StuCncl; TchrAde; YthFlsp; Ftbl; College; Minister.

REHMKE, Denise M; Oxford Junction Cons HS; Oxford Junction, IA; 1/26 SecJrCls; Band; Chrs; HonRl; LbryAde; NHS; 4-H; LetterTrk; ChmnChrldr; 4-HAwd; U Of Iowa; English.

REHRAUER, Matthew J; St Josephs Prep; Whitewater, WI; 2/14 PresSophCls; ChrhWkr; CncrtBnd; HonRl; NHS; SchPl; VPStuCncl; SchPpr; LatCl; CaptIMSpt;.

REIBER, Karla J; Chesaning HS; Oakley, MI; Band; CncrtBnd; HonRl; MrchBnd; NHS; PepBnd; SciCl; Delta Clg; Interior Design.

REIBER, Michelle A; Chesaning Union HS; Chesaning, MI; PresJrCls; Chr; HonRl; NHS; SchPl; FrCl; PpCl; Western Mi Univ; Art.

REIBERT, Gary D; Streator Twp HS; Streator, IL; 29/400 ALBoysSt; ChrhWkr; CncrtBnd; HonRl; GerCl; PpCl; LetterBsktbl; LetterTennis; Bradley Univ.

REICH, Barbara J; Proviso East HS; Melrose Park, IL; 49/1001 Chrs; HonRl; Univ; Business.

REICH, Carol J; Lourdes HS; Chicago, IL; 7/372 HstSrCls; SecBand; ChrhWkr; CncrtBnd; HonRl; MrchBnd; NHS; NatlThespSoc; VPStuCncl; PresLatCl; Bsktbl; Ftbl; De Paul Univ; Music.

REICH, Michael W; Tomahawk HS; Tomahawk, WI; 13/150 HonRl; NHS; StuCncl; StuGov; RptrSchPpr; VPMthCl; Ftbl; Tech Insti; Architecture.

REICHARD, Dale E; Williamsburg HS; Williamsburg, KS; 8/28 Band; Chr; Chrs; ChrhWkr; CncrtBnd; HonRl; MrchBnd; NHS; PepBnd; YthFlsp; SchPpr; 4-H; FFA; College; Liberal Arts.

REICHARDT, Linda K; Pacific HS; Union, MO; Chr; ChrhWkr; HonRl; JA; TchrAde; YthFlsp; SchPpr; SpnCl; PpCl; Mo U; Medical.

REICHART, Gerald A; Plattsmouth HS; Plattsmouth, NE; 1/133 Band; HonRl; NHS; SctActv; FBLA; MthCl; Bsbl; Bsktbl; LetterFtbl; LetterTrk; Peru St Col; Accountant.

REICHART, Lawrence J; Plattsmouth HS; Plattsmouth, NE; Band; CncrtBnd; MrchBnd; NHS; PepBnd; StuCncl; VPFBLA; FrCl;.

REICHEN, Debra R; Henry Senschwine HS; Henry, IL; 1/73 SecBand; HonRl; JrNHS; SecNHS; PepBnd; CivCl; VP4-H; VPFHA; PpCl; 4-HAwd; Eastern Ill Univ; Medical Technology.

REICHENBERG, Mary A; Center HS; Hannover, ND; SecTrsSophCls; SecSrCls; ALAGirlsSt; Chrs; HonRl; MrchBnd; SchPpr; 4-H; FHA; BttyCrckrAwd; Minot St; Secretarial.

REICHERT, Brent L; Central HS; Crookston, MN; 1/205 Chr; CncrtBnd; NHS; Orch; SchMus; SctActv; CaptBsktbl; CaptFtbl; LetterTennis; EldAwd; LionAwd; RotaryAwd; College; Law.

REICHERT, Carol A; Catholic Memorial HS; Elm Grove, WI; 44/160 CmntyWkr; HonRl; HospAde; NatlThespSoc; SchMus; SchPl; PpCl; Chrldr; PPFtbl; Clge Of Saint Benedicts; Psychology.

REICHERT, Janet M; Brunswick R Ii HS; Brunswick, MO; 4/46 VPSophCls; Band; NHS; TreasStuCncl; SchPpr; Pres4-H; PresFHA; PresPpCl; LetterBsbl; CaptChrldr; SecGAA; DanFAwd; College; Accountant.

REICHERT, Jolene M; Clifton Central HS; Ashkum, IL; Chrs; HonRl; NatlFornLg; NatlThespSoc; SchMus; SchPl; StuCncl; RptrYrbk; 4-H; GAA; Parkland Jr Clg; Business.

REICHERT, Nancy A; Rocori HS; Richmond, MN; VPFrshCls; TrsSophCls; VPSrCls; NHS; Swmmng; Trk; Chrldr; GAA; IMSpt; PPFtbl; College; Therapy.

REICHERT, Scott B; Thomas More HS; Milwaukee, WI; 33/155 Chrs; HonRl; SctActv; University Of Wisconsin; Accounting.

REICHERT, Steve; St Pius X HS; Kansas City, MO; 11/139 Chrs; HonRl; SchMus; SchPl; College.

REICHMANN, Randall D; Carlinville HS; Carlinville, IL; 70/175 HonRl; SchPl; StuCncl; SchPpr; FrCl; Bsktbl; Ftbl; Trk; Univ Of Il; Agriculture.

REICHMEIER, Julie A; St Teresas Academy; Leawood, KS; 1/117 Chrs; HonRl; LitMag; Mdrgl; NHS; StuCncl; Chrs; LatCl; PresSciCl; IMSpt; Rockhurst Clg; Medicine.

REICHMUTH, Joyce; St Francis HS; Humphrey, NE; PresFrshCls; HonRl; NHS; StuCncl; TchrAde; SchPpr; 4-H; PpCl; Chrldr; College; Professional.

REICHMUTH, Julie R; Leigh Comm HS; Leigh, NE; 3/39 HonRl; SchPl; StuCncl; LetterBsktbl; LetterTrk; CchngActv; PPFtbl; College; Mathematics.

REICHTER, Lynn C; Tremont Comm HS; Tremont, IL; 5/76 CmntyWkr; HonRl; NHS; GAA; Secretary.

REICKS, Henry; Turkey Valley HS; Lawler, IA; VPFrshCls; Chr; ChrhWkr; HonRl; Mdrgl; NHS; SchMus; StuCncl; StuGov;.

REICKS, Mary J; New Hampton Comm HS; Alta Vista, IA; 15/180 VPFrshCls; Chrs; HonRl; NHS; 4-H; Bsktbl; Glf; Trk; College.

REID, Charles J; Yale HS; Avoca, MI; 14/139 PresJrCls; HonRl; SchPl; StuCncl; 4-H; LetterBsbl; LetterFtbl; IMSpt; 4-HAwd; Coll;.

REID, Debora S; Shabbona HS; Shabbona, IL; 7/44 Band; CncrtBnd; HonRl; LbryAde; MrchBnd; PepBnd; SchPl; Yrbk; FrCl; SciCl; Bsktbl; GAA; Northern Ill Univ; Medical Technology.

REID, Diane S; Tri County HS; Plainfield, WI; Chr; HonRl; LbryAde; NHS; PresYthFlsp; RptrYrbk; FHA; SpnCl; SciCl; 4-HAwd; Col.

REID, Eric; Gull Lake HS; Richland, MI; 4/235 Aud/Vis; Band; CncrtBnd; DrmMjrt; HonRl; JA; MrchBnd; PepBnd; SchMus; SchPl; FrCl; Public Univ; Computer Programming.

REID, Gail; Lincoln East HS; Lincoln, NE; Band; CncrtBnd; HonRl; JA; MrchBnd; PepBnd; RptrSchPpr; Tennis; College; Journalist.

REID, Janet G; Cassville HS; Cassville, MO; Chr; ChrhWkr; CmntyWkr; DrlTm; OffAde; PolWkr; TchrAde; PresPpCl; Trk; Chrldr; Oral Roberts U; Social Work.

REID, Kathleen; Sts Peter & Paul HS; Saginaw, MI; ChrhWkr; HonRl; JrNHS; NatlFornLg; SchAde; SchMus; GAA;.

REID, Linda C; Holly HS; Holly, MI; Band; CncrtBnd; MrchBnd; NHS; Orch; PepBnd; FrCl; SpnCl; Oakland University.

REID, Ricky S; Washington HS; Germantown, WI; 55/115 HonRl; SchPl; EdYrBk; U Of Wi; Professional.

REID, Steven D; Parker HS; Janesville, WI; HonRl; LetterTrk; IMSpt; College; Accountant.

REID, Susan K; Norway HS; Vulcan, MI; HonRl; RptrSchPpr; 4-H; FHA; LetterBsktbl; GAA; 4-HAwd; Ferris State College; Fashion Merchandising.

REIDMEYER, Carole R; Hannibal Sr HS; Hannibal, MO; 2/266 Aud/Vis; HonRl; LbryAde; NHS; RedCrAde; YthFnd; 4-H; SpnCl; College; Chemical Engineering.

REIDT, Jena L; Pacific HS; Pacific, MO; Band; CncrtBnd; HonRl; MrchBnd; OffAde; SchMus; YthFlsp; SpnCl; PpCl; CaptChrldr; DARAwd; PresAwd; Meramec Comm Col; Nursing.

REIER, Ann M; Aurora Central Catholic HS; Aurora, IL; 12/190 HonRl; LetterBsktbl; CaptTrk; College; Coach.

REIER, Jim; Cozad HS; Cozad, NE; JCC; SchPl; StuCncl; StuGov; FBLA; FSA; SpnCl; Ftbl; Trk; IMSpt; College; Prof.

REIF, Susan K; Hoisington HS; Claflin, KS; TrsFrshCls; Chr; Chrs; HonRl; NatlFornLg; SchPpr; PpCl; PPFtbl; Dental Tech School; Dental Asst.

REIFENSTUHL, Robert A; Thornridge HS; Dolton, IL; 110/684 Aud/Vis; HonRl; HospAde; Univ Of Illinois; Physical Therapist.

REIFF, Gary W; Twin Lakes HS; Burnettsville, IN; 1/204 Band; NatlFornLg; NHS; NatlMeritSF; FFA; LetterTrk; LetterWrstlng; 4-HAwd; Univ; Engineering.

REIFF, Ralph V; Wawasee HS; Warsaw, IN; PresSophCls; ALBoysSt; ChrhWkr; HonRl; StuCncl; StuGov; 4-H; FFA; KeyCl; Bsktbl; Ftbl; Trk; 4-HAwd; College; Management.

REIFSCHNEIDER, David L; Hubbard HS; Hubbard, IA; VPFrshCls; PresSophCls; YthFlsp; StuCncl; 4-H; Ftbl; Trk; 4-HAwd; Isu.

REIFSTECK, Annette S; Bellmont HS; Ossian, IN; Chr; HonRl; NHS; Quill&Scroll; Twrl; Yrbk; 4-H; GerCl; PpCl; LetterTrk; College; Dental Assistant.

REIFSTECK, Charles R; Unity HS; Tolono, IL; ALBoysSt; Chrs; ChrhWkr; HonRl; NHS; NatlThespSoc; SchMus; StuCncl; YthFlsp; University Of Illinois; Architecture.

REIFSTECK, Debra L; Bismarck Henning HS; Potomac, IL; Band; Chrs; ChrhWkr; CmntyWkr; CncrtBnd; HonRl; LbryAde; MrchBnd; NHS; NatlThespSoc; PepBnd; SchMus; GAA; Univ Of Ill; Broadcasting.

REIGEL, Laura C; Kal Loy Norrix S; Kalamazoo, MI; Chr; NatlFornLg; Orch; SchMus; RptrSchPpr; SchPpr; PpCl; Trk; Alma Coll; Med Tech.

REIGHARD, Shari R; Wentzville HS; Foristell, MO; 2/233 ChrhWkr; HonRl; NHS; TchrAde; PpCl; Col; Busi Admn.

REIGLE, Julie K; Madison HS; Madison, NE; ALAGirlsSt; Chr; ChrhWkr; HonRl; NHS; SchPl; PpCl; College; Vocation.

REIGSTAD, Marvin J; Kerkhoven Sunburg HS; Sunburg, MN; 5/49 PresFrshCls; TrsJrCls; Band; HonRl; NHS; NatlMeritCmnd; StuCncl; YthFlsp; Bsktbl; CaptTrk; Willmar Comm Coll; Law.

REIHER, Todd C; Allison Bristow HS; Allison, IA; 4/51 PresJrCls; ALBoysSt; Chr; VPFrshCls; HonRl; PpCl; Bsbl; Bsktbl; Ftbl; Trk; Col; Law.

REIHLE, Jeffrey G; New Hampton Comm HS; New Hampton, IA; 36/190 Chrs; NatlMeritSF; SchMus; SchPl; Bsktbl; Univ Of Iowa; Physics.

REIHMAN, Dave; Connersville HS; Connersville, IN; 11/386 ALBoysSt; ChrhWkr; CmntyWkr; HonRl; NatlFornLg; NHS; YthFlsp; CivCl; GerCl; Purdue Univ; Engineer.

REIKOFSKI, Jeanne; Neligh Public HS; Oakdale, NE; 4/60 Chrs; ChrhWkr; HonRl; YthFlsp; SchPpr; Trade School; Vocation.

REILING, Barbara A; Albany Senior HS; Albany, MN; 25/129 Band; Chrs; CncrtBnd; HonRl; MrchBnd; PepBnd; SchPl; Yrbk; FHA; LetterChrldr; St Cloud School Of Nursing; Registered Nurs.

REILING, Mark; St Thomas Academy; St Paul, MN; ROTC; SchPl; RptrYrbk; Yrbk; RptrSchPpr; SchPpr; PpCl; Socr; Tennis; Univ Of Notre Dame; Finaance.

REILING, Mary L; Duchesne HS; St Charles, MO; 35/195 HonRl; StuCncl; StuGov; PpCl; CaptBsktbl; GAA; IMSpt; PPFtbl; College; Business Administration.

REILLEY, Dawn R; Carlinville HS; Carlinville, IL; 7/167 VPJrCls; ALAGirlsSt; ChrhWkr; HonRl; JrNHS; NHS; SctActv; StuCncl; VPFrCl; GAA; Univ Of Ill; Law.

REILLY, Anne; John Marshall Jr Sr HS; Milwaukee, WI; 41#65#66 Yrbk; PpCl; Marquette Univ; Biology.

REILLY, Charles H; Marist HS; Palos Hts, IL; 27/374 HonRl; FrCl; LetterBsbl; St Norbert College; Intl Business.

REILLY, Charles O; Thornton Fractional N HS; Calumet City, IL; 33/447 CncrtBnd; HonRl; HospAde; JrNHS; MrchBnd; NHS; Univ Of Illinois; Medicine.

REILLY, Lynn; Big Bay De Noc HS; Garden, MI; Band; Chr; ChrhWkr; CncrtBnd; HonRl; LbryAde; PepBnd; SchPl; Bsktbl; Univ; Christian Nursing.

REILLY, Nancy M; Mother Mcauley HS; Chicago, IL; CmntyWkr; HonRl; Ftbl; CchngActv; Western Ill Univ; Urban Planning.

REILLY, Robert; Scotus Central Catholic HS; Columbus, NE; 45/62 SchPl; IMSpt; College; Medicine.

REILLY, Timothy; Greendale HS; Greendale, WI; MthCl; College; Professional.

REILY, Daniel L; Forest View HS; Des Plaines, IL; 1/650 Chr; HonRl; JrNHS; NHS; TchrAde; PresGerCl; University; Dancer.

REIMAN, Lois G; Ayrshire Cons HS; Ayrshire, IA; 1/16 Band; HonRl; PepBnd; StuCncl; RptrYrbk; 4-H; FHA; LetterBsktbl; BttyCrckrAwd; 4-HAwd; Mt Marty Coll; Nursing.

REIMAN, Mark D; Adrian HS; Adrian, MO; Band; CncrtBnd; HonRl; MrchBnd; PepBnd; SchMus; Univ Of Mo Ks City; Musician.

REIMAN, Robert K; Clinton Community HS; Clinton, IL; 10/190 NHS; StuCncl; SpnCl; LetterFtbl; LetterTrk; IMSpt; College; Professional.

REIMAN, Trisha; Princeton Sr HS; Princeton, MN; HonRl; NHS; GAA; Hospital Sch; X Ray Tech.

REIMANN, Rachel; St Francis HS; Isanti, MN; 10 SecJrCls; Band; Chr; Chrs; HonRl; NatlMeritSchl; Orch; PepBnd; SchPl; SciCl; Concordia College; Music.

REIMANN, Susan J; Big Foot HS; Fontana, WI; AFS; Chrs; HonRl; SchMus; StuCncl; PpCl; Tennis; LetterTrk; GAA; IMSpt; Univ; Education.

REIMEL, Garth A; Fenton HS; Bensenville, IL; 13/409 ChrhWkr; HonRl; LitMag; NHS; Quill&Scroll; SctActv; YthFlsp; EdSchPpr; SchPpr; Bsbl; College; Business Administration.

REIMER, Barbara J; Jetmore HS; Spearville, KS; Chrs; ChrhWkr; HonRl; SchPl; TchrAde; YthFlsp; College; Physical Therapy.

REIMER, Billie E; Centerville HS; Centerville, IN; ChrhWkr; HonRl; TchrAde; 4-H; CchngActv; Asbury Univ; Elem Education.

REIMER, Cindy K; Wallace County HS; Sharon Spgs, KS; Chr; Chrs; ChrhWkr; CmntyWkr; HonRl; NHS; YthFlsp; PpCl; College; Liberal Arts.

REIMER, Duveen A; Tri County HS; Beatrice, NE; 1/63 SecFrshCls; TrsSrCls; PresCncrtBnd; HonRl; NHS; OffAde; PepBnd; StuCncl; SecYthFlsp; SecGerCl; Univ Of Ne; Library Science.

REIMER, Gerald W; Guttenberg Comm HS; Garnavillo, IA; 4/70 SecSrCls; HonRl; NHS; Trk; Loras Coll; Voc.

REIMER, Vickie L; North Boone HS; Roscoe, IL; Chrs; HonRl; Yrbk; 4-H; GerCl; PpCl; GAA; 4-HAwd; College; Vocation.

REIMERS, James L; Sauk Prairie HS; Lodi, WI; Ftbl; Tennis; Trk; IMSpt; Coll; Landsacpe Arch.

REIMERS, Pamela; Calamus HS; Calamus, IA; 1/27 PresJrCls; CncrtBnd; HonRl; NHS; SchPl; StuCncl; EdYrBk; Bsktbl; CitAwd; Mount Mary Coll; Nursing.

REIMERS, Randy; Sioux Valley HS; Lake Park, IA; HonRl; SchPl; Bsktbl; Ftbl; Trade School; Electronics Technition.

REIMERS, Roxanne; Grand Community HS; Ogden, IA; 7/24 PresSophCls; VPJrCls; Band; Chrl; Chrs; CncrtBnd; DrmMjrt; HonRl; Bsbl; Bsktbl; Iowa State Univ; Textiles And Clothing.

REIMERS, Roxanne J; Grand Comm HS; Ogden, IA; 7/23 PresSophCls; Band; Chrs; CncrtBnd; DrmMjrt; HonRl; MrchBnd; PepBnd; SchMus; SchPl; StuCncl; Bsktbl; Iowa St College; Home Economics.

REIMERS, Thomas K; Ogallala HS; Ogallala, NE; 8/127 PresJrCls; HonRl; NHS; StuCncl; TchrAde; Bsktbl; LetterFtbl; LetterTrk; Clg; Engineering.

REIMINK, Timothy J; Grand Haven Sr HS; West Olive, MI; TrsSrCls; Chr; HonRl; Mdrgl; NHS; NatlMeritCmnd; NatlThespSoc; SchMus; StuCncl; College.

REIN, Alison M; Kimberly HS; Menasha, WI; Band; DrlTm; HonRl; NHS; StuCncl; YthFlsp; GAA; Clge; Textiles.

REIN, Nancy L; Cary Grove HS; Cary, IL; PresJrCls; CncrtBnd; HonRl; MrchBnd; NHS; PepBnd; SchMus; StuCncl; SpnCl; Western Ill; Airlines Stewardess.

REINART, Marlene A; Browns Valley HS; Browns Valley, MN; VPSophCls; VPSrCls; HonRl; StuCncl; RptrYrbk; RptrSchPpr; FHA; PpCl; GAA; IMSpt; Willmar Vo Tech Inst; Chef.

REINARTS, Mary S; Winona Sr HS; Winona, MN; 31/430 HonRl; NHS; VPSpnCl; LetterSwmmng; CchngActv; Texas Christian Univ; Math.

REINBOLD, Rita K; Heelan HS; Sioux City, IA; 4/267 Aud/Vis; ChrhWkr; CmntyWkr; HonRl; LbryAde; NHS; Sacrstn; SctActv; TchrAde; Teen; SchPpr; Swmmng; Chrldr; College; Professional.

REINCE, Mary J; Kewaunee HS; Kewaunee, WI; 10/144 SecBand; HonRl; NHS; PepBnd; SctActv; StuCncl; TchrAde; Yrbk; SciCl; La Crosse Univ; Physical Therapy.

REINCKE, Robert G; Mercy HS; St Louis, MO; 20/178 PresSrCls; HonRl; SchPl; StuCncl; GerCl; PpCl; LetterFtbl; IMSpt; Univ Of Missouri; Journalism.

REINDERS, Mark A; Mallard Community HS; Curlew, IA; 4/37 PresJrCls; PresSrCls; ALBoysSt; ChrhWkr; HonRl; LbryAde; SchPl; EdYrBk; EdSchPpr; Ftbl; Clge; Pro English.

REINDERS, Steve; Homestead HS; Mequon, WI; Univ Of Dayton; Cybernetics Study.

REINEBACH, Kathy J; Seymour HS; Payson, IL; 1/65 HonRl; FHA; PpCl; Western Ill Univ.

REINEKE, Lawrence G; Browns Valley HS; Beardsley, MN; Chr; Chrl; Chrs; HonRl; SchMus; SchPl; Moorhead St College; Air Force.

REINERS, Andrew T; South Adams HS; Berne, IN; 3/125 Band; CncrtBnd; MrchBnd; NatlMeritCmnd; Orch; PepBnd; SchMus; LatCl; Glf; Depauw Univ; Medicine.

REINERS, Lori R; Hartsburg Emden HS; Hartsburg, IL; Band; Chrs; ChrhWkr; CncrtBnd; HonRl; SchMus; StuCncl; YthFlsp; EdSchPpr; Bsktbl; GAA; DARAwd; College; Accounting.

REINERT, Lori A; Oconto Falls HS; Oconto Falls, WI; ChrhWkr; HonRl; NatlFornLg; SchPl; SpnCl; Tennis; Wrstlng; GAA; AmLegAwd; Univ Wi Eau Claire; Psychology.

REINERTSEN, David A; Canton Sr HS; Canton, IL; 52/275 ALBoysSt; Band; ChrhWkr; HonRl; NHS; SctActv; RptrYrbk; GerCl; LetterWrstlng; Augustana College; Liberal Arts.

REINHARD, James S; Greenville HS; Greenville, IL; HonRl; JA; MrchBnd; NHS; PepBnd; SchMus; StuGov; LetterBsktbl; CaptFtbl; LetterTennis; Med School; Medicine Or Math.

REINHARD, Jennifer C; Niles Township West HS; Lincolnwood, IL; Chr; Chrs; HonRl; NHS; SpnCl; Northwestern University; Psychology.

REINHARD, Shawn C; Central HS; West Point, IA; 9/91 HonRl; JrNHS; SchPl; SctActv; SpnCl; LetterBsktbl; Trk; IMSpt; Iowa State Univ; Engineering.

REINHARDT, Colleen I; Zap Public HS; Zap, ND; 5/12 VPJrCls; SecTrsSrCls; Band; Chrs; ChrhWkr; SchMus; SchPl; TchrAde; Chrldr; GAA; Nd State U; Social Service Aide.

REINHARDT, Dee A; Alton Sr HS; Godfrey, IL; 98/803 Chr; Chrs; ChrhWkr; HonRl; HospAde; NHS; SctActv; Southern Ill Univ; Elem Counselling.

REINHARDT, Karen D; Carl Schurz HS; Chicago, IL; Chr; ChrhWkr; CmntyWkr; HonRl; NHS; NatlMeritCmnd; College; Physical Sciences.

REINHARDT, Mark E; Central HS; Evansville, IN; PresFrshCls; Band; ChrhWkr; CncrtBnd; HonRl; MrchBnd; PolWkr; RedCrAde; ROTC; SchMus; SchPl; Glf; Swmmng; Trk; Ball St Univ; Psychology.

REINHARDT, Melody A; Ansley Public HS; Ansley, NE; 2/31 SecFrshCls; SecSophCls; Band; Chrs; ChrhWkr; HonRl; OffAde; SchPl; LetterTrk; Chrldr; 4-HAwd; Nebr Christian College; Professional.

REINHARDT, Terri S; Erie HS; Erie, KS; 2/65 ALAGirlsSt; Band; Chr; Chrs; ChrhWkr; CmntyWkr; CncrtBnd; HonRl; MrchBnd; NHS; OffAde; PepBnd; SchAde; Kansas State Univ; Music.

REINHART, Barbara A; Villa Grove HS; Pesotum, IL; 9/83 TrsSophCls; VPJrCls; ChrhWkr; HonRl; NHS; ChmnBsktbl; Trk; Chrldr; GAA; Il State University.

REINHART, Jean A; Bishop Dwenger HS; Ft Wayne, IN; 10/250 Chrs; HonRl; VPJA; NatlMeritSF; PolWkr; RptrSchPpr; GerCl; IMSpt; Purdue Univ; Engineering.

REINHOLD, Charlene; John Hersey Hs; Arlington Hts, IL; AFS; Chr; HonRl; Mdrgl; NHS; PolWkr; SchMus; SchPl; StuCncl; SchPpr; University; Lawyer.

REINHOLD, Sherry L; Winnebago Lutheran HS; Van Dyne, WI; Band; Chrs; ChrhWkr; HonRl; SchPpr; 4-H; Tennis; Trk; Business Schl; Vocation.

REINHOLTZEN, Sanna; North Boone HS; Caledonia, IL; 7/80 SecSrGls; Band; Chr; Chrs; Mdrgl; NHS; SchMus; EdYrBk; Bsktbl; Trk; College; Veterinary Medicine.

REINIG, Joan; Harlan Community HS; Portsmouth, IA; ChrhWkr; HonRl; NHS; FHA; FrCl; Tennis; ChmbCommrsAwd; Amer Inst Of Business; Accounting.

REINKE, Douglas A; Bottineau Public HS; Bottineau, ND; SecFrshCls; ALBoysSt; Chr; CncrtBnd; MrchBnd; PresFrshCls; SchPl; SctActv; LetterFtbl; College; Heavy Construction.

REINKE, Timothy W; Davenport Community HS; Davenport, NE; 10/23 ALBoysSt; ChrhWkr; HonRl; SchPl; PresStuCncl; StuGov; YthFlsp; LetterBsktbl; LetterTrk; Univ Of Nebraska; Science.

REINKER, Donna J; Lincoln County R 2 HS; Elsberry, MO; 13/57 TrsJrCls; ChrhWkr; HonRl; LbryAde; NHS; FHA; College; Professional.

REINSCH, Linda S; Oak Park Sr HS; Kansas City, MO; Chr; Chrl; Chrs; HonRl; SchMus; SchPl; 4-H; FHA; IMSpt; College; History.

REINSCH, Ranee; Geneva HS; Geneva, NE; 2/65 ChrhWkr; HonRl; NHS; StuCncl; YthFlsp; 4-H; FBLA; PpCl; IMSpt; Lincoln School Of Comm; Data Processing.

REINTS, Connie E; Genoa Kingston HS; Genoa, IL; Band; CncrtBnd; HonRl; MrchBnd; 4-H; SciCl; LetterTrk; GAA; 4-HAwd; College; Park Ranger.

REIS, Carolyn A; Nerimx Hall HS; Webster Groves, MO; 1/93 HonRl; NatlMeritSF; TchrAde; GAA; Univ; Science.

REIS, Cindy L; Chamberlain HS; Pukwana, SD; 10/97 Aud/Vis; Chr; HonRl; SchPl; FHA; SpnCl; PpCl; SciCl; PresAwd; Med Inst Mn; Veterinary Asst.

REIS, Ronald L; Fonda Comm HS; Fonda, IA; Band; CncrtBnd; HonRl; MrchBnd; NatlMeritCmnd; College; Professional.

REIS, Ted C; Fremont HS; Fremont, NE; 80/420 HonRl; GerCl; LetterFtbl; IMSpt; PresAwd; College.

REIS, Teresa M; Notre Dame HS; Quincy, IL; SecSrCls; Chrs; HonRl; StuCncl; PpCl; IMSpt; Quincy Coll; Accounting.

REISCHEL, Joan M; Morton HS; Hammond, IN; 50/499 HonRl; JrNHS; Quill&Scroll; StuGov; TchrAde; Yrbk; PpCl; University; Professional.

REISCHL, Sharon A; Manning HS; Manilla, IA; TrsFrshCls; PresSophCls; VPSrCls; Chr; HonRl; OffAde; TchrAde; PpCl; IMSpt;.

REISDORFER, Sharon M; Marshall Senior HS; Marshall, MN; 10/200 Band; Chr; CncrtBnd; HonRl; MrchBnd; PepBnd; YthFlsp; RptrSchPpr; FHA; LetterChrldr; College; Home Ec.

REISDORPH, Roberta L; Morgan Public HS; Morgan, MN; Band; Chr; Chrs; ChrhWkr; HonRl; MrchBnd; EdYrBk; RptrSchPpr; FTA; College; Interior Design.

REISER, Judith E; St Marys Academy; Milwaukee, WI; Chr; CncrtBnd; HonRl; MrchBnd; PepBnd; TreasPolWkr; SchMus; TchrAde; CchngActv; GAA; Milw Area Tech Clg; Radiological Tech.

REISER, Michael W; Kirksville HS; Kirksville, MO; ALBoysSt; Band; Chr; HonRl; MrchBnd; NHS; NatlMeritCmnd; SchMus; SchPl; RptrYrbk; LetterTrk; College; Medical Field.

REISER, Susan K; Valentine HS; Valentine, NE; Chrs; HospAde; SctActv; Sdlty; TchrAde; YthFlsp; FTA; PpCl; SciCl; College; Professional.

REISETTER, Steven P; Roland Story HS; Story City, IA; 3/80 Band; CncrtBnd; HonRl; MrchBnd; VPNHS; NatlMeritSchl; NatlMeritSF; PepBnd; SchMus; LetterFtbl; LetterTrk; CaptWrstlng; College.

REISNER, Mike R; Waukon Sr HS; Waukon, IA; 20/167 PresFrshCls; SecSophCls; VPJrCls; ALBoysSt; HonRl; NHS; StuCncl; LetterBsktbl; LetterFtbl; LetterGlf; College.

REISS, Kim; Western HS; Bay City, MI; CmntyWkr; PolWkr; Saginaw Valley State Col; Data Processing.

REISS, Leonard J; Meade HS; Meade, KS; Band; Chr; Chrs; ChrhWkr; CncrtBnd; HonRl; Mdrgl; MrchBnd; PepBnd; Bible College; Social Worker.

REISTER, Debra; Brookville HS; Brookville, IN; 24/175 HonRl; NHS; RedCrAde; SchPl; TchrAde; EdYrBk; FTA; SpnCl; PpCl; Colle; Nursing.

REISWIG, David L; Mc Clusky HS; Mc Clusky, ND; Band; PepBnd; SctActv; YthFlsp; LetterBsbl; Col; Ins.

REITAN, Julia L; University HS; Normal, IL; 4/125 PresJrCls; Chrs; HonRl; NatlFornLg; NHS; NatlMeritFnl; NatlThespSoc; SchPl; FrCl; DARAwd; College; Professional.

REITER, Deborah A; Ankeny HS; Ankeny, IA; 5/237 Chr; CncrtBnd; HonRl; LitMag; NHS; Orch; SchPl; SpnCl; EldAwd; Drake Univ; Music.

REITHMAIER, Tina M; Lincoln Way HS; Frankfort, IL; CmntyWkr; HonRl; IntrClCncl; NHS; PresNatlThespSoc; Orch; PolWkr; SchPl; TchrAde; FrCl; PpCl; University; Professional.

REITSMA, Robert S; Bird Island Lk Lillian HS; Lake Lillian, MN; ALBoysSt; ChrhWkr; StuCncl; FFA; LetterBsktbl; AmLegAwd; Vocational Tech School; Agri Business.

REITZ, Teresa A; Effingham HS; Effingham, IL; 4-H; FrCl; PpCl; 4-HAwd; College; Art.

REKAS, Virginia H; Nazareth Academy; Chicago, IL; 16/154 ChrhWkr; HonRl; NHS; NatlMeritCmnd; TchrAde; University; Professional.

REKEMEYER, Randall; Bennett Community HS; Bennett, IA; 4/32 ALBoysSt; Band; CncrtBnd; HonRl; NHS; PepBnd; StuCncl; Bsbl; Bsktbl; Trk; College; Business.

REKKEDAL, Darleen M; Minnewaukan Public HS; Minnewaukah, ND; VPFrshCls; PresSrCls; Chr; HonRl; SchPl; 4-H; FHA; Bsktbl; Trade School; Professional.

REKOW, Veronica M; Lower Brule HS; Lower Brule, SD; 2/12 ALAGirlsSt; Band; SchPl; StuCncl; EdYrBk; RptrSchPpr; SchPpr; Bsktbl; South Dakota State University; Law.

REKOWSKI, Elaine A; Stevens Point Area Sr HS; Stevens Point, WI; 6/520 ALAGirlsSt; NHS; Quill&Scroll; EdSchPpr; SciCl; AmLegAwd; DARAwd; EldAwd; OptClAwd; VFWAwd; Viterbo College; Rn.

REKRUCIAK, Mary E; Mt Assisi HS; Palos Heights, IL; 11/190 ChrhWkr; HonRl; JrNHS; ModUN; NHS; OffAde; SchPl; TchrAde; SpnCl; GAA; Jr Coll; Radiological Tech.

RELIHAN, Dayne E; Smith Center HS; Smith Center, KS; PolWkr; LetterBsktbl; LetterFtbl; IMSpt; College; Professional.

RELTMEYER, John D; Heyworth HS; Mc Lean, IL; HstJrCls; HonRl; SchPl; StuCncl; StuGov; 4-H; SpnCl; Bsbl; Bsktbl; LetterFtbl; LetterTrk; 4-HAwd; W Illinois Univ; Science.

REMALY, Donna A; Franklin Public HS; Franklin, NE; 6/32 TreasBand; SecChrhWkr; HonRl; NHS; TchrAde; Twrl; RptrYrbk; FHA; VPPpCl; SciCl; Chrldr; 4-HAwd; Kearney State College; Education.

REMER, Cynthia A; Central HS; Burlingtn, WI; ChrhWkr; CmntyWkr; HonRl; JA; SchMus; SchPl; 4-H; SpnCl; 4-HAwd;.

REMER, Janice G; Winnebago HS; Winnebago, IL; Chrs; ChrhWkr; CAP; HonRl; SchMus; SctActv; YthFlsp; 4-H; SpnCl; PpCl; GAA; Rock Valley College; Liberal Arts.

REMICK, Richard L; Monsignor Hackett HS; Kalamazoo, MI; TrsJrCls; PresSrCls; Band; ChrhWkr; HonRl; NHS; PresStuCncl; FrCl; Bsktbl; LetterFtbl; CaptTrk; IMSpt; Univ; Law.

REMINGTON, Kevin L; Barrington Cons HS; Barrington, IL; 97/700 CncrtBnd; MrchBnd; PepBnd; College.

REMINGTON, Linda R; Beloit Memorial HS; Beloit, WI; Band; HonRl; HospAde; JA; 4-H; GAA; College; Special Education Teacher.

REMINGTON, Scott I; Barrington Community HS; Barrington, IL; 29/642 HonRl; Univ Of Illinois; Engineering.

REMKE, Jean A; Forest Park HS; Ferdinand, IN; DrlTm; HonRl; StuCncl; EdYrBk; SchPpr; PpCl;.

REMKUS, Susan Ta; West Allis Central HS; West Allis, WI; 2/465 HonRl; JA; NHS; SchMus; StuGov; TchrAde; ChmnBsbl; ChmnBsktbl; LetterTrk; GAA; Marquette; Physics Math.

REMMENGA, Patricia K; Elwood HS; Elwood, NE; Chrs; HonRl; Twrl; YthFlsp; RptrYrbk; FHA; PpCl; Trk; Chrldr; Kearney State; Home Economics.

REMMEREID, Mark C; Petersburg Public HS; Petersburg, NE; SecFrshCls; ALBoysSt; Band; Chr; ChrhWkr; HonRl; SchPl; StuCncl; RptrSchPpr; Ftbl; Technical Col; Agricultural Production.

REMMEREID, Mark C; Petersburg HS; Petersburg, NE; 5/15 SecTrsFrshCls; ALBoysSt; Band; Chrs; HonRl; SchMus; SchPl; StuCncl; RptrSchPpr; 4-H; Bsbl; Bsktbl; Ftbl; Univ Of Ne; Vet Medicine.

REMPALA, Barbara A; Lourdes HS; Chicago, IL; 62/299 HonRl; LbryAde; Quill&Scroll; RptrSchPpr; PpCl; IMSpt; PPFtbl; Univ; Journalism.

REMPE, James H; Superior HS; Superior, NE; ChrhWkr; CncrtBnd; HonRl; SancSoc; Teen; FFA; KeyCl; Swmmng; Wrstlng; 4-HAwd; Unsta Curtis; Agriculture.

REMPEL, Donald J; Diller Community HS; Diller, NE; Band; Chrs; CncrtBnd; HonRl; MrchBnd; SchPl; Yrbk; FFA; CaptBsktbl; LetterFtbl; LetterTrk; College; Agri Business.

REMUND, Karen A; Corona HS; Corona, SD; VPFrshCls; PresSophCls; ALAGirlsSt; Band; Chrs; ChrhWkr; CmntyWkr; CncrtBnd; HonRl; LbryAde; MrchBnd; PepBnd; SchPl; StuCncl; EdYrBk; South Dakota State Univ; Social Worker.

REMUND, Susan K; Mitchell Sr HS; Mitchell, SD; ALAGirlsSt; DrlTm; DrmMjrt; HonRl; NHS; StuCncl; Twrl; PpCl; Trk; College; Liberal Arts.

REMUS, Kenneth P; Forest View HS; Des Plaines, IL; 68/640 HonRl; NatlMeritCmnd; College; Business.

REMUS, Rhonda K; Maywood HS; North Platte, NE; PresJrCls; Band; Chrs; HonRl; JrNHS; SchPl; 4-H; PpCl; Bsktbl; College; Teacher.

REMUS, Sandra J; Maywood HS; North Platte, NE; 1/23 SecJrCls; TrsSrCls; Chrs; DrmMjrt; NHS; NatlMeritSF; 4-H; Trk; Chrldr; College; Professional.

REMUS, Sandra J; Maywood HS; No Platte, NE; 1/22 SecJrCls; TrsSrCls; Band; DrmMjrt; NHS; NatlMeritSchl; 4-H; Trk; Chrldr; BttyCrckrAwd; Univ Of Chic; Law.

REMY, Kimberly; Albia Community HS; Albie, IA; 10/165 VPJrCls; Aud/Vis; Band; Chrs; CncrtBnd;

HonRl; MrchBnd; 4-H; Bsktbl; 4-HAwd; Aib; Court Reporter.

REMY, Teresa D; Tippecanoe Valley HS; Warsaw, IN; 28/145 Chr; CncrtBnd; LbryAde; MrchBnd; NHS; SchPpr; FHA; FTA; SecSpnCl; PpCl; College; Secratary.

RENAKER, Deborah E; Brookville HS; Brookville, IN; Band; Chr; ChrhWkr; CncrtBnd; DrmMjrt; MrchBnd; PepBnd; YthFlsp; 4-H; GAA; Miami Univ; Stewardess.

RENAUD, Keith A; Mehlville HS; St Louis, MO; Band; CncrtBnd; Orch; PepBnd; Mechanical Trade; Mechanical Engineer.

RENAUER, Sandra L; St Andrew HS; Detroit, MI; 3/110 TrsFrshCls; TrsSophCls; Chrl; HonRl; JA; NHS; NatlMeritCmnd; StuGov; Yrbk; FNA; Mercy Coll; Reg Nurse.

RENBERGER, Randy W; Northfield HS; Wabash, IN; PresJrCls; VPSrCls; HonRl; 4-H; FFA; PpCl; Bsktbl; Ftbl; IMSpt; 4-HAwd; Farm.

RENCHOF, Sharon A; St Francis Acad; Joliet, IL; 1/174 HonRl; NHS; Sdlty; RptrYrbk; RptrSchPpr; SchPpr; PresLatCl; MthCl; GAA; IMSpt; Univ; Law Or Medicine.

RENDALL, Mary B; Almond HS; Almond, WI; Band; Chrs; HonRl; NHS; SctActv; StuCncl; Yrbk; FshEdSchPpr; Trk; GAA; College; Occupational Therapy.

RENDEK, Peter M; Downers Grove North HS; Downers Grove, IL; 38/524 Aud/Vis; HonRl; NHS; NatlMeritCmnd; Quill&Scroll; RptrSchPpr; SchPpr; Arizona State Univ; Engineering.

RENDINA, Elizabeth L; Andrean HS; Merrillville, IN; 37/301 HonRl; Quill&Scroll; RptrSchPpr; SchPpr; MthCl; PpCl; Purdue Univ; Communications.

RENDLEMAN, Shelba K; Wesclin HS; Trenton, IL; 5/110 Band; ChrhWkr; CncrtBnd; HonRl; HospAde; JrNHS; MrchBnd; NHS; TchrAde; RptrYrbk; LatCl; PpCl; College; Professional.

RENEBERG, Perry G; West Smith County HS; Kensington, KS; PresFrshCls; VPJrCls; Chrs; HonRl; Mdrgl; SchMus; SchPl; FFA; Bsktbl; Ftbl; Saprtan Sch Aero;.

RENER, William H; Schulte HS; Terre Haute, IN; 22/99 CmntyWkr; HonRl; SchPl; GerCl; Ftbl; Trk; Wrstlng; Service; Air Force.

RENFREE, Mark D; Reavis HS; Burbank, IL; 79/676 HonRl; MthCl; Glf; Swmmng; Univ Of Arizona; Accounting.

RENFRO, Brent A; Taylor HS; Kokomo, IN; 4/157 Chr; Chrs; ChrhWkr; HonRl; NHS; NatlMeritFnl; NatlMeritSF; NatlThespSoc; IMSpt; GovHonPrgAwd; LionAwd; Wabash College; Lawyer.

RENFRO, Michael D; Central HS; Cap Girardeau, MO; 17/323 HonRl; NatlFornLg; NHS; PolWkr; SchPl; RptrSchPpr; LionAwd; RotaryAwd; VoiceDemAwd; Southeast Mi St Univ; Attorney.

RENFROE, James; Adlai E Stevenson Hs; Lincolnshire, IL; HonRl; SptEdSchPpr; LetterFtbl; Trk; U Of Illinois; Law.

RENFROE, Jeff D; Coon Rapids HS; Coon Rapids, MN; 59/739 HonRl; NHS; TchrAde; LetterBsbl; College; Professional.

RENFROW, Carol L; Olympia HS; Atlanta, IL; 100/230 Band; Chrs; ChrhWkr; CncrtBnd; HonRl; MrchBnd; Orch; PepBnd; SchMus; SchPl; TreasFHA; PpCl; GAA; Business School; Vocation.

RENFROW, Darlisa J; Cassville HS; Shell Knob, MO; 6/108 NHS; OffAde; SciCl; U Of Mo; Med.

RENGSTORF, Di Anne P; South Division HS; Milwaukee, WI; Chrs; HonRl; OffAde; Quill&Scroll; RptrSchPpr; EdSchPpr; FTA; GerCl; MthCl; PpCl; Univ Of Wisconsin; Nurse.

RENICHE, Theresa L; Normal Community HS; Towanda, IL; 63/454 HonRl; JA; OffAde; SctActv; PresLatCl; Univ Of Illinois; Veterinarian.

RENICK, Glenda E; Sullivan HS; Sullivan, MO; 14/159 Chrs; HonRl; SchMus; SchPl; TchrAde; FHA; FTA; RotaryAwd; E Central Jr Clg; Math.

RENK, Jean; Kee HS; New Albin, IA; 17/70 SecFrshCls; SecJrCls; Chrs; HonRl; NHS; Quill&Scroll; SchMus; SchPl; SchPpr; Techicolor Trade; Medical Assistant.

RENKEN, Sharon A; Flasher HS; Flasher, ND; Chrs; OffAde; SchPl; Yrbk; FHA; PpCl; SciCl; Bsktbl; Trk; GAA; Ndsu Fargo; Social Worker.

RENKES, Jason J; Morrison Comm HS; Morrison, IL; ALBoysSt; HonRl; Ftbl; Glf; LetterWrstlng; College; Professional.

RENKOSIK, Douglas G; La Salle Peru HS; Peru, IL; HonRl; LetterFtbl; LetterTrk; LetterWrstlng; U Of I; Engineer.

RENNE, Lynn K; Chippewa Hills HS; Rodney, MI; 4/150 HonRl; NHS; TchrAde; FHA; Ferris St Coll; Accountant.

RENNECKAR, William R; Flint Southwestern HS; Flint, MI; Band; ChrhWkr; CmntyWkr; NHS; SchMus; SctActv; YthFlsp; GerCl; LetterFtbl; OptClAwd; College.

RENNER, Debra L; Farmington East HS; Farmington, IL; 7/131 Band; Chr; Chrs; HonRl; Mdrgl; NHS; StuCncl; TchrAde; FTA; Illinois State Univ; French.

RENNER, Douglas H; Adams Frienship HS; Adams, WI; HonRl; Bsbl; Ftbl;.

RENNER, Gary L; Gibault HS; Evansville, IL; VPSrCls; HonRl; PolWkr; StuCncl; PpCl; CchngActv;.

RENNER, Jackie A; Glen Ullin HS; Glen Ullin, ND; Chrs; CmntyWkr; MrchBnd; SchPl; StuCncl; FHA; PpCl; Chrldr; Airline Stewardess.

RENNER, Joe J; Tyndall HS; Tabor, SD; HonRl; Bsbl; Trk; Trade School; Mechanics.

RENNER, Karen S; Pekin Comm HS; Pekin, IL; 47/500 Chrs; HonRl; TreasJA; TchrAde; SpnCl; TreasJAAwd;.

RENNER, Kathy L; Dickinson HS; Dickinson, ND; 5/216 TrsFrshCls; TrsSophCls; TrsJrCls; ChrhWkr; HonRl; JrNHS; NatlThespSoc; OffAde; SchMus; SchPl; Yrbk; SchPpr; FFA; VPFHA; Chrldr; College; Veterinarian.

RENNER, Laverne M; Detroit Lakes HS; Detroit Lakes, MN; 1/251 4-H; 4-HAwd; College.

RENNER, Mary E; Lakeville HS; Burnsville, MN; 1/200 HonRl; LbryAde; NHS; TchrAde; BttyCrckrAwd; Uw Stout; Math.

RENNER, Mary Kay; Mardan Sr HS; Mardan, ND; ALAGirlsSt; Band; CncrtBnd; HonRl; HospAde; MrchBnd; Bismarck Jr College; Nursing.

RENNHACK, Linda J; Coloma HS; Coloma, MI; Band; HonRl; NHS; NatlMeritCmnd; SctActv; TchrAde; FTA; LatCl; Tennis; College; Math.

RENNICH, Steven D; Harrisburg HS; Harrisburg, SD; 5/36 ALBoysSt; VPBand; Chr; CncrtBnd; HonRl; MrchBnd; PepBnd; SchMus; Pres4-H; VPFFA; Vocational; Agribusiness.

RENNISON, Eugene W; Braymer C 4 HS; Braymer, MO; 10/38 Chrs; ChrhWkr; CmntyWkr; HonRl; SctActv; FFA; LetterBsbl; LetterBsktbl; LetterFtbl; LetterTrk; Auctioneering; Farming.

RENO, Daniel C; Muncie Northside HS; Muncie, IN; 10/316 ChrhWkr; HonRl; NHS; YthFlsp; LatCl; Bsbl; Bsktbl; Ftbl; Trk; Indiana University; Dentistry.

RENSINK, Gary M; Sioux Center Comm HS; Sioux Center, IA; 6/79 Chr; Chrs; HonRl; NHS; Northwestern College; Elec Engineer.

RENSTROM, Cindy J; Evansville Public HS; Elbow Lake, MN; Band; Chr; HonRl; LbryAde; SchPl; RptrSchPpr; FFA; FHA; Fergus Falls Comm Clg; Secretarial.

RENTEL, Kurt R; West HS; Sioux City, IA; 1/268 Band; Chr; Chrs; CncrtBnd; HonRl; MrchBnd; NatlMeritSF; Orch; StuCncl; NatlThespSoc; Iowa U; Engineering.

RENTMEESTER, Timothy J; East Depere HS; Depere, WI; 12/200 JA; NHS; RptrYrbk; Glf; Swmmng; Trk; Wrstlng; IMSpt; Carroll Coll; Pre Med.

RENTNER, Joann M; O Fallon Twp HS; O Fallon, IL; 38/316 CmntyWkr; HonRl; PolWkr; SchMus; SchPl; 4-H; VPFHA; College; Business Mgmt.

RENTSCHLER, Teresa A; Mexico HS; Mexico, MO; VPFrshCls; TrsSophCls; PresJrCls; SecSrCls; ALAGirlsSt; Band; NHS; LatCl; Bsktbl; Chrldr; Coll; Biology.

RENTZ, Laurie A; Ferndale HS; Ferndale, MI; Chr; ChrhWkr; CmntyWkr; HonRl; PolWkr; TchrAde; LatCl; Marygrove College; Social Work.

RENUSCH, Suellen; East Detroit HS; East Detroit, MI; Band; HonRl; SchPl; College; Professional.

RENWICK, Lawson; Batesville HS; Batesville, IN; Chrs; HonRl; SchPl; StuCncl; SpnCl; Trk; GAA; College; Animal Related Study.

RENZ, Danny J; Ruskin Public HS; Ruskin, NE; SecSophCls; PresJrCls; ALBoysSt; SchMus; StuCncl; Trade School.

RENZ, Steven R; Superior HS; Nora, NE; ChrhWkr; HonRl; StuCncl; RptrSchPpr; 4-H; TreasFFA; LetterFtbl; LetterTrk; Univ Of Nebraska; Agronomy.

REOPELLE, Pamela; Gresham HS; Gresham, WI; 2/30 PresFrshCls; SecSophCls; TrsSrCls; CncrtBnd; NHS; LetterBsktbl; LetterTrk; CaptChrldr; GAA; 4-HAwd; St Josephs School; Nursing.

REPA, Cynthia A; Josephinum HS; Chicago, IL; PresFrshCls; ALAGirlsSt; HonRl; LitMag; NHS; SchMus; StuGov; RptrYrbk; Bsktbl; Chrldr; Loyola University.

REPETSKY, Jan A; Morgan Park HS; Chicago, IL; 17/559 HonRl; NHS; OffAde; YthFlsp; Yrbk; 4-H; TreasSpnCl; TreasMthCl; SecGAA; Eastern Illinois Univ; Home Economics.

REPKING, Cathy L; St Anthony HS; Effingham, IL; 5/79 Band; ChrhWkr; CncrtBnd; HonRl; MrchBnd; NHS; PepBnd; StuCncl; RptrYrbk; 4-H; FTA; Eastern Ill Univ.

REPLOGLE, Steven B; Harper Creek HS; Battle Creek, MI; LbryAde; SchPl; Yrbk; EdSchPpr; SchPpr; Mich St Univ; English.

REPPER, Mona J; Raytown South HS; Raytown, MO; 81/540 VPAFS; Chr; JA; RptrYrbk; JAAwd; College; Acctg Cpa.

REPPERT, Muriel A; Coldwater HS; Coldwater, MI; Band; Chr; ChrhWkr; CncrtBnd; DrmMjrt; HonRl; MrchBnd; PepBnd; SchMus; TchrAde; Graceland Clge; Computer Tech.

REPROGLE, Michael J; Tri Central HS; Greentown, IN; 1/98 HonRl; NHS; StuCncl; LetterFtbl; LetterWrstlng; Gmi; Engineering.

REQUEJO, Thomas; St Agnes Acad; Alliance, NE; SecSophCls; Chrs; ChrhWkr; StuCncl; StuGov; FSA; SciCl; Bsktbl; Ftbl; DARAwd; College.

RESCH, Karen; Broad Ripple HS; Indianapolis, IN; 11/340 HonRl; HospAde; NHS; Quill&Scroll; EdYrBk; SpnCl; Purdue Univ;.

RESCH, Mark A; Maine Twp HS; Park Ridge, IL; HonRl; NatlMeritCmnd; GerCl; SpnCl; LetterSwmmng; Loyola Univ; Medicine.

RESCH, Thomas E; Jackson HS; Spirit Lake, IA; 6/113 TrsJrCls; PresSrCls; HonRl; SchAde; StuCncl; TchrAde; SptEdSchPpr; 4-H; FFA; Ftbl; Chrldr; DanFAwd; 4-HAwd; University Of Minnesota; Teacher.

RESCH, Thomas E; Jackson Sr HS; Spirit Lake, IA; HonRl; StuCncl; TchrAde; 4-H; FFA; DanFAwd; Univ Of Minnesota; Agriculture.

RESCH, Thomas E; Jackson HS; Spirit Lake, IA; 5/112 HonRl; StuCncl; 4-H; FFA; Ftbl; PPFtbl; DanFAwd; 4-HAwd; JAAwd; CitAwd; U Of Mn; Ag Ed.

RESCHAK, Debra A; Willowbrook HS; Lombard, IL; 33/825 Chr; HonRl; NHS; SciCl; Bsktbl; Trk; Univ Of Illinois; Nursing.

RESCHKA, Martin; Interlocken Arts Acad; Mt Clemens, MI; /278 HonRl; SctActv; Yrbk; GerCl; Socr; Univ Of Mich; Med Tech.

RESCHKE, Dean A; Naperville Central HS; Naperville, IL; 60/820 Chr; Chrl; Chrs; ChrhWkr; HonRl; Mdrgl; SchMus; SctActv; YthFlsp; College; Sociology.

RESCHKE, Vickie S; Chapman HS; Enterprise, KS; 7/145 TreasAFS; Chr; LitMag; MrchBnd; SchPl; StuCncl; Teen; Sec4-H; SecPpCl; 4-HAwd; Emporia Ks State Clg; Engl Or Speech Teach.

RESCIGNO, Jodi M; West Bend East HS; West Bend, WI; Chr; SchAde; StuCncl; StuGov; RptrYrbk; PpCl; Bsbl; LetterChrldr; GAA; College.

RESEIGH, Philip M; Redford Union HS; Redford Twp, MI; 12/608 VPJrCls; Chr; CncrtBnd; HonRl; MrchBnd; NHS; Wrstlng; IMSpt; Gen Motors Inst; Electrical Engineering.

RESHEL, Sue M; Pittsville HS; Pittsville, WI; ChrhWkr; CmntyWkr; NatlFornLg; SchPl; TchrAde; Yrbk; SchPpr; FBLA; PpCl; Trk; Chrldr; GAA; College Social Worker.

RESIDE, David K; Jacksonville HS; Jacksonville, IL; 38/380 HonRl; NatlMeritCmnd; NatlMeritSF; SctActv; LetterSocr; LetterWrstlng; IMSpt; Univ Of Illinois; Medicine.

RESNIK, Carolyn R; St Josephs HS; South Bend, IN; HonRl; RedCrAde; SctActv; 4-H; 4-HAwd; College.

RESNIK, Marla B; Mather HS; Chicago, IL; 33/442 Chrs; HonRl; JA; JrNHS; LbryAde; NHS; SchAde; StuCncl; TchrAde; FTA; SpnCl; University Of Illinois; Accounting.

RESSEGIEU, Matthew V; St Agnes HS; Alliance, NE; PresFrshCls; ALBoysSt; ChrhWkr; NatlSciFnd; SchPl; SctActv; Sdlty; StuCncl; StuGov; 4-H; Bsktbl; LetterFtbl; LetterTrk; AmLegAwd; College; Ranching.

RESSLER, Dennis E; Tipton HS; Tipton, IN; 10/175 HonRl; StuCncl; StuGov; 4-H; PpCl; Bsktbl; Ftbl; Indiana Univ; Law.

RESSLER, Lori; Binford Public HS; Jessie, ND; SecJrCls; ALAGirlsSt; HonRl; NHS; StuCncl; EdYrBk; PpCl; Chrldr; BttyCrckrAwd; North Dakota State Univ; Pre Veterinary.

RESSLER, Randall J; Western Dubuque HS; Epworth, IA; 4/243 Chr; NHS; NatlMeritCmnd; StuCncl; Ftbl; LetterTrk; U Of Ia; Psychology.

RETHERFORD, Gary D; Brookville HS; Brookville, IN; ALBoysSt; Band; CncrtBnd; MrchBnd; PepBnd; StuCncl; 4-H; KeyCl; Bsktbl; LetterFtbl; LetterTrk; Trade School.

RETHMEIER, Timothy J; Newton HS; Laurel, IA; ChrhWkr; HonRl; YthFlsp; FFA; College; Agriculture.

RETLEWSKI, Sharon R; All Saints Central HS; Bay City, MI; Chrl; HonRl; NHS; StuCncl; StuGov; SchPpr; IMSpt; University Of Michigan A A; Physical Therpy.

RETT, Mary S; Lamoille HS; Arlington, IL; SecFrshCls; Chrs; HonRl; NHS; SchPl; SchPpr; 4-H; FrCl; PpCl; Trk; Univ.

RETTER, Kenneth W; Castle HS; Chandler, IN; HonRl; JrNHS; TreasNHS; SctActv; SptEdYrbk; LetterBsktbl; University.

RETTERATH, Jeannie M; Lidgerwood Public HS; Lidgerwood, ND; 4/49 PresSrCls; Band; Chr; Chrl; Chrs; ChrhWkr; CmntyWkr; CncrtBnd; HonRl; HospAde; CaptSwmmng; Trk; CaptChrldr; PPFtbl; Col; Dental Hygiene.

RETTERATH, Linda; Riceville HS; Chester, IA; Chrs; CmntyWkr; HonRl; HospAde; PepBnd; RedCrAde; StuCncl; UNYO; 4-H; FHA; Trade School; Child Care.

RETTERATH, Rosalie; Stanton Public HS; Stanton, ND; 5/16 PresFrshCls; PresJrCls; PresSrCls; StuCncl; RptrYrbk; SptEdYrbk; Yrbk; Bsktbl; Trk; PresAwd; Bismarck Jr Coll; Med Sec.

RETTERER, Linda A; Amos Alonzo Stagg HS; Palos Hills, IL; 36/480 HonRl; JrNHS; OffAde; TchrAde; Monmouth College; Dental Hygiene.

RETTINGER, Roger K; Triton HS; Bourbon, IN; Band; Chrs; HonRl; NHS; SchMus; YthFlsp; Yrbk; 4-H; SpnCl; 4-HAwd;.

RETTLER, Luke; Hartford Union HS; Hartford, WI; VPFrshCls; HonRl; JrNHS; NHS; Sacrstn; LatCl; SpnCl; SciCl; Univ Oshkosh; Broadcasting.

RETTMANN, Douglas; Premontre HS; Green Bay, WI; 33/141 Aud/Vis; ChrhWkr; CmntyWkr; HonRl; JA; StuCncl; StuGov; SchPpr; KeyCl; IMSpt; U Of Wis Green Bay; Business.

RETZ, Susan K; Anita HS; Anita, IA; PresSophCls; Chrs; ChrhWkr; HonRl; Quill&Scroll; StuCncl; Yrbk; PpCl; LetterBsktbl; Trk; Coll; Fine Arts.

RETZER, Daniel; Jacksonville HS; Ashland, IL; 56/352 ChrhWkr; Illinois College; Veternarian.

RETZER, Gail L; Calhoun HS; Hardin, IL; 2/90 Chrs; HonRl; NHS; TchrAde; FTA; FrCl; GAA; Univ Of Il; Fine Arts.

RETZER, Patrick J; James Madison HS; Milwaukee, WI; ALBoysSt; HonRl; JA; LitMag; NHS; NatlMeritSF; StuCncl; SpnCl; MthCl; Wrstlng; Marquette Univ; Accounting.

RETZLAFF, James R; Tigerton HS; Tigerton, WI; 7/36 VPFrshCls; PresJrCls; ALBoysSt; HonRl; NHS; SchPl; StuCncl; CaptBsktbl; CaptFtbl; CaptTrk; Air Force.

RETZLAFF, Kathy L; Waverly HS; Lincoln, NE; 20/103 HonRl; TchrAde; RptrYrbk; 4-H; FHA; GerCl; PpCl; Coll; Nurse.

RETZLAFF, Stephen C; Ralston HS; Ralston, NE; ChrhWkr; CmntyWkr; HonRl; NHS; SchMus; SchPl; SctActv; Ftbl; Swmmng; AmLegAwd; Univ Of Ne At Omaha; Electrical Engineering.

RETZLAFF, Susan; Palmer Public HS; Plamer, NE; Band; CncrtBnd; DrmMjrt; HonRl; JrNHS; MrchBnd; PepBnd; RptrYrbk; RptrSchPpr; Chrldr; College; Nurse.

RETZLAFF, Teresa; Palmer Public HS; Palmer, NE; SecTrsSophCls; Band; ChrhWkr; CmntyWkr; CncrtBnd; HonRl; MrchBnd; PepBnd; Chrldr; College; Interior Art Home Ec Major.

REUER, Gary G; Hoven HS; Hoven, SD; Chr; Chrl; HonRl; Mdrgl; StuGov; PresFFA; PpCl; LetterBsktbl; LetterFtbl; Trk; Clg; Vocation.

REUER, Roderick; Napoleon HS; Dawson, ND; VPSrCls; Chr; Chrs; StuCncl; Bsktbl; Ftbl; Trk; College; Vocation.

REUL, Jane E; Beloit Memorial HS; Beloit, WI; ChrhWkr; HonRl; SchMus; RptrSchPpr; GAA; College.

REUMANN, Carol; Lyman Independant HS; Presho, SD; SecFrshCls; SecJrCls; ChrhWkr; CncrtBnd; HonRl; NHS; Bsbl; Chrldr; College; Biologist.

REUSS, John L; Pope John Xxiii HS; Elgin, NE; CmntyWkr; TchrAde; CaptBsktbl; LetterFtbl; CchngActv; IMSpt; University Of Nebraska; Coaching.

REUTEMANN, Karen D; Taylor HS; Kokomo, IN; 8/189 HonRl; HospAde; NHS; 4-H; 4-HAwd; LionAwd; Purdue U; Veterinarian.

REUTER, Barbara J; Riverside HS; Dearborn Heights, MI; 1/269 ChrhWkr; CncrtBnd; HonRl; MrchBnd; NHS; PepBnd; StuCncl; CaptTwrl; FrCl; GAA; University.

REUTER, John R; Marist HS; Oak Lawn, IL; 10/393 HonRl; NHS; SpnCl; Ftbl; IMSpt; Univ.

REUTER, John T; Centerville HS; Richmond, IN; HonRl; LitMag; SctActv; RptrSchPpr; Management Training.

REUTER, Laura B; Unity Of Tolono HS; Tolono, IL; 2/154 Chr; HonRl; LitMag; NHS; NatlThespSoc; SchPl; SchPpr; LetterBsbl; Univ Of Illinois; Journalism.

REUTER, Nancy J; New Glarus HS; New Glarus, WI; 10/58 VPSrCls; Band; CncrtBnd; HonRl; MrchBnd; NatlFornLg; NHS; YthFlsp; EdSchPpr; Chrldr;.

REUTER, Vickie L; Peru HS; Peru, IN; 26/191 ChrhWkr; HonRl; JrNHS; NHS; OffAde; RptrYrbk; Yrbk; SpnCl; GAA; Purdue Univ; Reg Nurse.

REUTTER, Juli M; Grand Comm HS; Ogden, IA; SecSophCls; PresSrCls; Band; Chrs; CncrtBnd; HonRl; MrchBnd; OffAde; SchMus; SchPl; StuCncl; Twrl; Yrbk; RptrSchPpr; College; Secretary.

REUTTER, Ruth A; Immaculata HS; Detroit, MI; HonRl; NatlMeritSF; StuGov; FrCl; College.

REVELAND, Janice K; Bethlehem Academy; Faribault, MN; 4/83 ALAGirlsSt; HonRl; NHS; SchPl; StuCncl; Yrbk; EdSchPpr; Chrldr; AmLegAwd; DARAwd; Coll; English.

REVELLE, George S; Poplar Bluff HS; Poplar Bluff, MO; 9/396 HonRl; JrNHS; NHS; NatlMeritCmnd; SctActv; StuCncl; CivCl; FBLA; SpnCl; Bsbl; Bsktbl; Culver Stockton College; Accounting.

REVLING, Lester D; Auburndale HS; Auburndale, WI; 7/96 ALBoysSt; Chrs; ChrhWkr; HonRl; NHS; SchPl; SctActv; StuCncl; RptrSchPpr; FBLA; GerCl; PpCl; Trk; College; Accounting.

REVORD, Mary E; Marillac HS; Glenview, IL; 3/252 Chrs; Mdrgl; NHS; Orch; SchMus; Sdlty; StuCncl; College; Speech Therapist.

REWALD, Margaret; Waukesha South HS; Waukesha, WI; AFS; MrchBnd; NHS; NatlMeritCmnd; Orch; SchMus; Bsktbl; GAA; IMSpt; Uw Eau Claire; Zoology.

REWERS, Ralph; George Rogers Clark HS; Hammond, IN; 54/250 HonRl; NHS; StuCncl; SpnCl; Trk; Purdue; Pharmacy.

REWERTS, Debra L; Guilford HS; Rockford, IL; 51/658 CmntyWkr; HonRl; JA; TchrAde; LatCl; PpCl; LetterBsbl; Bsktbl; GAA; JAAwd; College; Elem Education Teacher.

REX, Judy; Clinton Prairie Hs; Mulberry, IN; 3/86 SecJrCls; CncrtBnd; HonRl; MrchBnd; Twrl; FNA; TreasSpnCl; PpCl; Trk; Chrldr; College; Professional Nursing.

REXROAT, Barbara J; Downs HS; Downs, KS; 4/26 TrsSrCls; Band; HonRl; LitMag; SchPl; Yrbk; EdSchPpr; Trk; Chrldr;.

REYBURN, Dean L; Grand Ledge HS; Grand Ledge, MI; 32/400 Band; ChrhWkr; CmntyWkr; CncrtBnd; NHS; SctActv; TchrAde; Tennis; Wrstlng; MaSAwd; Moody Bible Inst; Minister.

REYER, Janet M; Highland HS; Highland, KS; Band; HonRl; LbryAde; MrchBnd; PepBnd; RptrSchPpr; 4-H; PpCl; GAA; College; Cosmetology.

REYES, Awilda; Jones Commercial HS; Chicago, IL; 64/437 HonRl; NHS; Coll;grad Nurse.

REYES, Michael F; Gordon Technical HS; Chicago, IL; HospAde; LbryAde; OffAde; Sacrstn; SchAde; StuCncl; RptrSchPpr; KeyCl; FrCl; SpnCl; Spertus College; Religion.

REYES, Rebbecca S; Summerfield HS; Riga, MI; HonRl; College; Professional.

REYES, Virginia J; Mitchell HS; Mitchell, NE; Band; CncrtBnd; DrlTm; HonRl; MrchBnd; PepBnd; PpCl; Chrldr; GAA; U Of Ne; Secretary.

REYNEBEAU, Becky; Little Chute HS; Little Chute, WI; ALAGirlsSt; HonRl; NHS; OffAde; TchrAde; PpCl;.

REYNEBEAU, Stephen J; Little Chute HS; Little Chute, WI; 35/112 HonRl; RptrSchPpr; Ftbl; LetterTrk; Army.

REYNEN, Kathleen M; Wm Howard Taft HS; Chicago, IL; 33/815 HonRl; JrNHS; NHS; TchrAde; Loyola Univ; Nursing.

REYNOLDS, Charlene F; George Rogers Clark HS; Hammond, IN; LbryAde; GerCl; Trade Schl; Admin Secretary.

REYNOLDS, Coleen K; Holt HS; Dimondale, MI; HonRl; NHS; SchPl; TchrAde; SpnCl; Mi State U; Dramatics.

REYNOLDS, David J; Boylan Central Catholic HS; Rockford, IL; 37/357 ChrhWkr; NHS; StuGov; LatCl; Bsbl; LetterFtbl; Wrstlng; Loras College; Biology.

REYNOLDS, Deborah R; Mounds View Senior HS; St Paul, MN; PresJA; OffAde; RedCrAde; TchrAde; EdYrBk; FNA; PpCl; JAAwd; University Of Minnesota; Accounting.

REYNOLDS, Deborah S; Greenfield HS; Greenfield, WI; ChrhWkr; HonRl; LbryAde; GAA; Trade Schl; Accountant.

REYNOLDS, Edward J; Richwoods HS; Peoria, IL; 90/449 CmntyWkr; StuCncl; TchrAde; SpnCl; PpCl; Univ Of Ill; Engineering.

REYNOLDS, Gerald W; Gordon HS; Merriman, NE; Aud/Vis; LitMag; SchPl; Bsktbl; Ftbl; Glf; U Of Ne; Creative Writing.

REYNOLDS, Jeffrey G; Cheboygan Area HS; Cheboygan, MI; Band; Chr; ChrhWkr; CAP; CmntyWkr; StuCncl; StuGov; RptrYrbk; PpCl; Univ; Journalism.

REYNOLDS, Jona L; Farmer City Mansfield HS; Farmer City, IL; 15/75 AFS; Band; HonRl; NHS; Yrbk; 4-H; GAA; IMSpt; AmLegAwd; DARAwd; Parkland Jr College; Radiological Tech.

REYNOLDS, Joseph R; Battle Creek Central HS; Battle Creek, MI; 102/498 Band; Chr; Chrl; CncrtBnd; LitMag; MrchBnd; PepBnd; SchMus; SchPl; LetterTrk; Michigan St Univ; Medicine.

REYNOLDS, Jovita J; Winfield HS; Winfield, KS; 15/177 HonRl; SchAde; PpCl; Wichita State U; Pharmacy.

REYNOLDS, Kathy R; Liberal HS; Liberal, MO; Band; Chr; CncrtBnd; HonRl; SchPl; EdYrBk; RptrSchPpr; 4-H; FHA; PpCl; Mo S St; Bus.

REYNOLDS, Kenneth A; Mexico HS; Mexico, MO; 21/270 Band; PepBnd; SctActv; LatCl; College; Engineer.

REYNOLDS, Leonard D; Rochelle Twp HS; Rochelle, IL; ChrhWkr; HonRl; College; Professional.

REYNOLDS, Martin R; Kingsville HS; Pleasant Hill, MO; Band; Chr; ChrhWkr; CncrtBnd; HonRl; EdYrBk; College; Archaeology.

REYNOLDS, Pamela K; Grundy Ctr Comm HS; Grundy Center, IA; SecTrsJrCls; Band; Chrs; ChrhWkr; HonRl; NHS; Yrbk; PresPpCl; CaptBsktbl; LetterGlf; Iowa Methodist Schl Nursing; Rn.

REYNOLDS, Randy; Springs Valley HS; French Lick, IN; 11/75 HstSrCls; HonRl; NHS; FrCl; PpCl; Bsktbl; IMSpt; Vincennes Univ; Forestry & Conservation.

REYNOLDS, Rebecca A; Bedford HS; Lambertville, MI; 1/424 Chr; ChrhWkr; HonRl; LbryAde; NHS; SchPl; PresLatCl; Bob Jones Univ; Music.

REYNOLDS, Ricky L; Dexfield HS; Redfield, IA; ChrhWkr; CmntyWkr; StuCncl; YthFlsp; 4-H; FFA; Bsbl; Bsktbl; LetterFtbl; Trk; Wrstlng; 4-HAwd;.

REYNOLDS, Rita K; Alexis HS; Alexis, IL; Band; Chrl; Chrs; ChrhWkr; CncrtBnd; HonRl; Mdrgl; MrchBnd; PepBnd; SchPl; Augustana Col; Speech Therapist.

REYNOLDS, Robert; Elgin Hs; Streamwood, IL; 26/986 HonRl; JA; NatlMeritSF; SpnCl; PpCl; Bsktbl; Ftbl; Trk; U Of Southern Ill; Computer Programmer.

REYNOLDS, Ruth A; Tri Central HS; Sharpsville, IN; 1/100 SecJrCls; Band; Chrs; TreasNHS; PolWkr; RedCrAde; 4-H; PresFrCl; PpCl; LetterTrk; Indiana Univ; Medicine.

REYNOLDS, Susan K; Hays HS; Hays, KS; HonRl; ModUN; NatlFornLg; NatlMeritSF; SchMus; SchPl; StuCncl; Washington Univ; Medicine.

REYNOLDS, Tammy S; Marceline HS; Marceline, MO; Band; CncrtBnd; HonRl; MrchBnd; PepBnd; 4-H; FHA; 4-HAwd; Arm Forces Clge; Lawyer.

REYNOLDS, Teri L; Morton HS; Morton, IL; 45/292 ChrhWkr; HonRl; OffAde; Tennis; GAA; IMSpt; 4-HAwd; Illinois St Univ; Special Educ.

REYNOLDS, Thomas; Oconomowoc Senior Hs; Oconomowoc, WI; 5/223 Band; CmntyWkr; HonRl; PresJrNHS; PresNHS; PepBnd; SchMus; SchPl; StuCncl; RptrSchPpr; College; Music Teacher Comductor.

REYNOLDS, Vivian M; Galena HS; Galena, MO; Band; Chrs; CmntyWkr; SctActv; 4-H; FHA; PpCl; Bsbl; Swmmng; College; Art.

REYZER, Tamera; Gilman Public HS; Lublin, WI; ChrhWkr; HonRl; NatlFornLg; NHS; OffAde; SchPl; StuCncl; RptrYrbk; Bsktbl; GAA; Lakeland Med Den Acad;med Lab Tech.

REYZLIK, Randy F; Tekamah Herman HS; Herman, NE; PresSrCls; HonRl; NHS; NatlThespSoc; StuCncl; StuGov; CaptWrstlng; AmLegAwd; Purdue University; Lawyer.

REZAB, Linda; Macomb HS; Macomb, IL; 1/244 Chr; HonRl; Mdrgl; NHS; NatlThespSoc; Orch; SchMus; SchPl; SctActv; YthFlsp; College; Chemistry.

REZELMAN, Ann M; Lapeer Sr HS; Lapeer, MI; 9/426 SecSrCls; CmntyWkr; HonRl; NHS; NatlThespSoc; SchPl; RptrYrbk; PresSpnCl; PpCl; Tennis; College.

REZICH, Barbara A; Academy Of The Visitation; St Louis, MO; 3/41 Chr; NHS; SchPl; StuCncl; Univ Of Virginia; Veterinarian.

REZNICEK, Joan M; Dodge HS; Dodge, NE; 19/38 Chrs; HonRl; SchMus; SchPl; TchrAde; Yrbk; SpnCl; LetterTrk; IMSpt; PPFtbl; Kearney State College; Recreation.

REZNICEK, Joni M; Daniel J Gross HS; Omaha, NE; 7/169 HonRl; NHS; OffAde; PpCl; Bsbl; Bsktbl; IMSpt; St Marys Univ; Medical Technology.

REZNICEK, Susan E; Ottawa HS; Ottawa, KS; Chrs; HonRl; HospAde; TchrAde; Pres4-H; VPFBLA; 4-HAwd; Kansas State University; Social Work.

RHEA, Karla D; Topeka HS; Topeka, KS; ALAGirlsSt; Chr; Chrl; Chrs; VPChrhWkr; NatlFornLg; NatlThespSoc; SchMus; SchPl; Trk; Univ; Writer.

RHEAUME, Craig; Larimore HS; Emerado, ND; HonRl; Ftbl; Wrstlng; Coll; Farm & Tradesman.

RHEAUME, Martin J; St Catherines HS; Racine, WI; SctActv; SchPpr; RusCl; CchngActv; IMSpt; College; Engineering.

RHEE, Albert S; Concordia Lutheran HS; Fort Wayne, IN; ChrhWkr; HonRl; StuCncl; StuGov; LatCl; LetterTennis; College.

RHEE, Hyun A; St Mary Academy; Monroe, MI; HonRl; GAA; University; Doctor.

RHEM, Dennis; N Christian HS; Kalamazoo, MI; JA; NatlMeritCmnd; Albion College; Engineer.

RHEUBLE, William D; Centerville HS; Richmond, IN; Chrs; HonRl; JrNHS; Mdrgl; NHS; SchAde; SchMus; SchPl; Bsktbl; Ftbl; Coll; Doctor.

RHEW, Perry; Holcomb HS; Holcomb, MO; 2/47 TrsSrCls; RptrYrbk; EdYrBk; Yrbk; SpnCl; Bsbl; Bsktbl; IMSpt; University; Medical Research.

RHINE, Diann; North Miami HS; Mexico, IN; 8/120 PresFrshCls; Chr; DrlTm; HonRl; Mdrgl; MrchBnd; NHS; OffAde; SchMus; SctActv; College; Nursing.

RHINE, Jane L; Manhattan HS; Manhattan, KS; Chr; Chrs; PolWkr; SctActv; SecStuCncl; PpCl; Swmmng; University; Botanical Sciences.

RHINER, Becky; Poynette HS; Arlington, WI; 4/98 Band; Chrs; ChrhWkr; HonRl; NHS; PepBnd; 4-H; FHA; PpCl; IMSpt; Uw Madison; X Ray Technologist.

RHINES, Lorelei J; Maine West HS; Des Plaines, IL; Chr; Chrl; ChrhWkr; HonRl; NatlMeritCmnd; NatlMeritSF; Orch; RedCrAde; SchMus; RptrSchPpr; Word Of Life Bible Inst; Camp Work.

RHINES, Renee; Marseilles HS; Marseilles, IL; HonRl; NHS; NatlThespSoc; SchPl; PpCl; GAA; Eastern Illinois Univ; Elementary Education.

RHOADES, Dawn C; Okemos HS; Mason, MI; 11/280 PresSophCls; PresHospAde; NHS; StuGov; YthFlsp; Treas4-H; LatCl; Bsktbl; DARAwd; Univ Of Michigan; Nursing.

RHOADES, Denise A; Guthrie Center HS; Guthrie Center, IA; 16/70 Band; Chr; Chrs; CncrtBnd; LbryAde; MrchBnd; SchMus; TchrAde; RptrSchPpr; PpCl; LetterChrldr; Northwest Missouri State Univ; Music.

RHOADES, Gerald L; Monticello HS; White Heath, IL; 99/168 HonRl; Univ Of Illinois; Chemical Engineering.

RHOADES, Kathleen L; Muskegon HS; Muskegon, MI; 10/590 HonRl; NHS; TchrAde; Mi St U; Work With People.

RHOADES, Lori L; Lincoln County HS; Elsberry, MO; 7/60 SecJrCls; HonRl; NHS; StuCncl; TchrAde; FHA; College; Nursing.

RHOADES, Mark L; Lincoln County R Ii HS; Elsberry, MO; 15/64 PresFrshCls; ALBoysSt; HonRl; NHS; SchPl; RptrYrbk; Yrbk; RptrSchPpr; SptEdSchPpr; LetterBsktbl; LetterTrk; College; Drafting.

RHOADES, Teresa; Waldron HS; Waldron, IN; Chr; CncrtBnd; MrchBnd; PepBnd; TchrAde; YthFlsp; Yrbk; 4-H; PpCl; Business School; Secretary.

RHOADS, Angela L; South Newton HS; Goodland, IN; 7/94 Band; CncrtBnd; MrchBnd; NHS; PepBnd; GerCl; LatCl; SciCl; Purdue University; Vet.

RHOADS, Dustin D; North HS; Wichita, KS; Band; ChrhWkr; CmntyWkr; CncrtBnd; MrchBnd; StuCncl; YthFlsp; MthCl; Glf; Swmmng; Coll; Chem/physics.

RHOADS, Keith L; Southmont Jr Sr HS; Ladoga, IN; 69/164 ALBoysSt; StuCncl; TchrAde; YthFlsp; Pres4-H; PresFFA; PpCl; Bsktbl; Trk; 4-HAwd; Purdue University; Farming.

RHOADS, Marcia M; Fredericktown HS; Bridgeton, MO; HonRl; PpCl; LetterTennis; Trk; Coll; Journalism.

RHOADS, Russell C; Rockford West Jr HS; Rockford, IL; HonRl; Quill&Scroll; SctActv; RptrYrbk; EdYrBk; RptrSchPpr; Bsbl; Ill State Univ; Neurosurgeon.

RHOADS, Samuel K; Carlinville Comm HS; Carlinville, IL; Chrs; HonRl; IntrClCncl; LetterBsktbl; LetterFtbl; LetterTrk; Eastern Illinois Univ; Law.

RHODE, Ann M; Roncalli HS; Mankowoc, WI; Band; ChrhWkr; CmntyWkr; HonRl; TchrAde; PpCl; LetterBsktbl; LetterTennis; CchngActv; PresAwd; College; Coaching.

RHODE, Kaylyn; Ford Central HS; Piper City, IL; HonRl; StuCncl; YthFlsp; RptrYrbk; FHA; SpnCl; PpCl; Trk; Chrldr; GAA; College; Vocation.

RHODE, Lynn E; Oconto Falls HS; Suring, WI; 7/154 Chrs; NHS; PresFTA; IMSpt; Uw Eau Claire; Elementary Ed.

RHODE, Sandra; Belvidere HS; Belvidere, IL; 56/340 SecSophCls; HonRl; HospAde; StuCncl; 4-H; SpnCl; PpCl; PPFtbl; College; Professional.

RHODEN, Don B; Plattsmouth HS; Plattsmouth, NE; 10133 Chr; HonRl; NHS; SchMus; TreasStuCncl; PresMthCl; Ftbl; DARAwd; VoiceDemAwd; Univ Of Nebraska; Medicine.

RHODES, Carol E; Prairie Hts HS; Dresden, KS; CmntyWkr; HonRl; PolWkr; SchPl; TchrAde; RptrYrbk; GerCl; University.

RHODES, Dawn; Jimtown HS; Elkhart, IN; 30/96 Band; Chr; ChrhWkr; HonRl; NatlThespSoc; PepBnd; GAA; IMSpt; PPFtbl; University; Medicine.

RHODES, Diana L; Lincoln County R 2 HS; Elsberry, MO; 7/62 SecJrCls; SecSrCls; ChrhWkr; HonRl; PresNHS; PresFBLA; SecGAA; BttyCrckrAwd; College; Teaching.

RHODES, Doran L; North Platte Sr HS; North Platte, NE; ChrhWkr; College; Professional.

RHODES, Doris J; Williamsville Comm HS; Williamsville, IL; ChrhWkr; HonRl; TchrAde; FHA; Lincoln Christian College.

RHODES, Doug K; Wichita East HS; Wichita, KS; PresFrshCls; VPSophCls; ChrhWkr; CmntyWkr; HonRl; IntrClCncl; SchMus; SchPl; StuCncl; StuGov; RptrSchPpr; SptEdSchPpr; CaptBsktbl; LetterGlf; CitAwd; Tcu; Medicine.

RHODES, Gregory P; Gibson City HS; Gibson City, IL; 30/90 AFS; Chr; Chrs; ChrhWkr; CmntyWkr; HonRl; Mdrgl; SchMus; SchPl; SctActv; YthFlsp; Bsktbl; Ftbl; College; Science.

RHODES, Nancy J; Anna Jonesboro HS; Jonesboro, IL; SecSophCls; HonRl; StuCncl; FHA; FrCl; PpCl; ChmnChrldr; VPGAA; Southern Ill Univ; Art.

RHODES, Paul; Usd 237 HS; Gaylord, KS; 5/61 Band; ChrhWkr; CncrtBnd; HonRl; IntrClCncl; MrchBnd; StuCncl; EdYrBk; EdSchPpr; Ks St Univ; Journalism.

RHODES, Paula J; Bridgeport HS; Bridgeport, NE; 2/62 HonRl; LbryAde; SchPl; StuGov; TchrAde; RptrYrbk; FFA; PresFHA; VPFrCl; VoiceDemAwd; U Of Neb; Home Ec Educ.

RHODES, Rick A; Gibson City HS; Gibson City, IL; 17/90 PresBand; PresChrs; HonRl; Mdrgl; NHS; NatlMeritCmnd; NatlMeritSF; SchMus; SchPl; YthFlsp; Bsbl; LetterBsktbl; LetterFtbl; Eastern Ill University; Music.

RHODES, Robert J; Lakeshore HS; Stevensville, MI; 33/250 HonRl; JA; NHS; NatlThespSoc; SchPl; FDA; GerCl; VPMthCl; TreasSciCl; LetterTrk; College; Marine Biologist.

RHODES, Robert S; Paris HS; Paris, IL; SecSophCls; Band; Chr; Chrs; CncrtBnd; Mdrgl; MrchBnd; PepBnd; SchMus; SchPl; StuCncl; RptrSchPpr; SchPpr; 4-H; South Ill Univ; Photography.

RHODES, Sharon K; St Elmo Comm HS; St Elmo, IL; 8/56 SecFrshCls; ChrhWkr; HonRl; NHS; SctActv; FHA; PpCl; Eastern Il Univ; Mathematics.

RHOMBERG, Mark; Wahlert HS; Dubugg, IA; HonRl; PolWkr; StuCncl; StuGov; YthLg; College;.

RHOTEN, Don C; Brown Deer HS; Brown Deer, WI; CmntyWkr; NatlMeritCmnd; Quill&Scroll; RptrSchPpr; SchPpr; LetterFtbl; LetterTrk; LetterWrstlng; IMSpt; JCAwd; Univ Of Wi; Psychology.

RHOTON, Karen J; Santa Fe HS; Waverly, MO; Chr; Chrs; HonRl; SchPl; PpCl; Trk; Coll; Counsler.

RHUE, Deborah J; Eisenhower HS; Decatur, IL; 18/309 Band; ChrhWkr; CncrtBnd; HonRl; HospAde; MrchBnd; NHS; Orch; PepBnd; College; Pharmacy.

RHYMER, Sonia S; Dongola HS; Dongola, IL; Band; HonRl; HospAde; StuCncl; FHA; VPFTA; SecSpnCl; GAA; 4-HAwd; College; Nurse.

RHYNER, Michael J; Newman HS; Schofield, WI; CncrtBnd; HonRl; MrchBnd; SchMus; SctActv; SptEdSchPpr; MthCl; SciCl; CaptWrstlng; BauchLmbAwd; College; Engineering.

RIAN, Cathy M; Niles East HS; Skokie, IL; 39/583 Chr; HonRl; NatlMeritCmnd; Northern Il Univ; Occupational Therapy.

RIBAUDO, Judith M; St Anthony HS; St Louis, MO; 7/72 Chrl; Chrs; HonRl; SchMus; SchPl; TchrAde; TreasRptrSchPpr; SpnCl; GAA;.

RIBBENS, David; Holland Christian HS; Holland, MI; ALBoysSt; Band; Chr; ChrhWkr; CncrtBnd; MrchBnd; Bsktbl; Socr; Trk; IMSpt; Calvin College.

RIBOLZI, Patricia L; La Salle Peru Twp HS; Oglesby, IL; 38/485 Chrs; HonRl; 4-H; SpnCl; Jr College; Music.

RIBSKIS, Al A; De La Salle HS; Chicago, IL; 2/258 CmntyWkr; HonRl; NHS; StuCncl; EdYrBk; LetterTennis; U Of Il; Art Design.

RICARD, Betty J; Thornwood HS; South Holland, IL; 64/865 HonRl; NHS; Thornton Comm College; Accounting.

RICARD, Gary R; Stevens HS; Rapid City, SD; 96/413 Col; Curriculum Of Major Study.

RICCA, Steven T; Limestone Comm HS; Bartonville, IL; 1/396 ChrhWkr; HonRl; JA; NHS; Univ Of Ill; Elec Engineering.

RICCA, William; Bergan HS; West Peoria, IL; 75/200 HonRl; Bsktbl; Bradley University; Accounting.

RICCI, Cynthia; St Stanislaus Kostka HS; Chicago, IL; 9/64 SecSrCls; Chr; HonRl; NHS; StuCncl; RptrYrbk; RptrSchPpr; College; Lab Technician.

RICCI, James; Civic Memorial HS; Bethalto, IL; 12/221 PresJrCls; HonRl; NHS; StuCncl; SptEdYrbk; PpCl; Washington U; Pre Med.

RICE, Barbara J; Milton Sr HS; Milton Jct, WI; Band; ChrhWkr; HonRl; LbryAde; MrchBnd; StuCncl; RptrYrbk; Yrbk; FrCl; SpnCl; PpCl; Swmmng; Business School; Med Secretary.

RICE, Beth; Northwest HS; Dittmer, MO; 1/379 Chr; HonRl; Mdrgl; NHS; NatlMeritSchl; Univ Of Mo; Biochemistry.

RICE, Brenda C; Winston Churchill HS; Livonia, MI; CncrtBnd; MrchBnd; Orch; PepBnd; TchrAde; Adrian College; Law.

RICE, Catherine E; Joliet Twp West Campus HS; Joliet, IL; 74/580 Chr; Chrs; ChrhWkr; HonRl; NHS; SchMus; FrCl; Trk; College Of St Francis; Medical Technologist.

RICE, Cathy D; Borden HS; Borden, IN; 1/78 Band; ChrhWkr; HonRl; MrchBnd; NHS; StuCncl; TchrAde; Yrbk; FHA; College; Cpa.

RICE, Daniel L; Montague Sr HS; Montague, MI; ALBoysSt; ChrhWkr; HonRl; LetterTrk; Bob Jones Univ; Chemistry.

RICE, David A; Morton HS; Morton, IL; 7/292 ChrhWkr; NHS; SctActv; TchrAde; SpnCl; SciCl; CaptBsktbl; Glf; U Of Il; Dentist.

RICE, David A; Union City Community HS; Union City, IN; 3/95 LbryAde; NHS; NatlMeritSF; StuCncl; FrCl; Rose Hulman Inst Of Tech; Chemical Engineer.

RICE, David A; Morton HS; Morton, IL; 7 292 ChrhWkr; HonRl; NHS; SctActv; TchrAde; SpnCl; SciCl; CaptBsktbl; Glf; U Of I; Dentistry.

RICE, Deborah E; St Ann HS; Chicago, IL; VPSophCls; VPJrCls; Chr; Chrs; HonRl; NHS; OffAde; SchMus; SchPl; StuGov; MthCl; College; Music.

RICE, Elton R; South Central HS; Laconia, IN; Chrs; SchPl; FFA; Bsktbl; Trade School; Vocation.

RICE, Gail S; Lutheran East HS; Detroit, MI; 21/129 ChrhWkr; HonRl; JA; NHS; StuCncl; LetterBsktbl; Trk; GAA; Univ Of Mi; Architect.

RICE, Gary L; Knightstown HS; Knightstown, IN; 2/136 ALBoysSt; HonRl; LbryAde; NHS; SpnCl; Tennis; Miami U; Accounting.

RICE, Gary R; N Central HS; Indianapolis, IN; ChrhWkr; CmntyWkr; JA; NatlMeritCmnd; SchPl; StuCncl; StuGov; Univ Of So Calif; Architect.

RICE, Jana M; Hays HS; Hays, KS; 30/238 Band; CncrtBnd; HonRl; MrchBnd; PepBnd; SchMus; IMSpt; U Of Ks; Botany.

RICE, Joel W; Hobart HS; Hobart, IN; HonRl; NHS; NatlMeritCmnd; OffAde; GerCl; Wrstlng; College; Biology.

RICE, John R; Joseph A Craig Sr HS; Janesville, WI; 43/474 HonRl; NHS; Orch; TchrAde; GerCl; LetterTrk; Univ Of Wisc Madison; Physician.

RICE, Jon K; Smithville HS; Kansas City, MO; 6/73 HonRl; JrNHS; NHS; Ftbl; Trk; Univ; Architecture.

RICE, Karen M; Plainfield HS; Joliet, IL; 23/284 Chr; ChrhWkr; CmntyWkr; HonRl; OffAde; SchMus; SchPpr; 4-H; Joliet Jr College; Nursing.

RICE, Kenneth A; Belfield HS; Belfield, ND; HonRl; Bsktbl; Ftbl; Trk; IMSpt; Clge; Office Job Business.

RICE, Kenneth A; Catholic Central HS; Southfield, MI; CncrtBnd; HonRl; MrchBnd; NatlFornLg; NHS; NatlMeritSF; Orch; PepBnd; StuCncl; EdSchPpr; IMSpt; University.

RICE, Kris; Harrisonville Sr HS; Harrisonville, MO; 15/143 ChrhWkr; DrmBgl; HonRl; SchPl; StuCncl; Yrbk; MthCl; Ftbl; Glf; Wrstlng; U Of Mo; Doctor Of Medicine.

RICE, L David; Winneconne Comm HS; Winneconne, WI; 9/130 AFS; Band; ChrhWkr; CmntyWkr; HonRl; NHS; SctActv; SpnCl; PpCl; SciCl; Bsktbl; Ftbl; Univ Of Wisconsin; Engineering.

RICE, Lisa J; Greenville HS; Greenville, MI; 7/220 Band; ChrhWkr; CncrtBnd; HonRl; MrchBnd; NatlFornLg; PepBnd; FrCl; Glf; GAA; Univ; Microbiology.

RICE, Margaret J; Maddock Public HS; Maddock, ND; 5/38 Band; ChrhWkr; CncrtBnd; HonRl; PepBnd; SchPl; StuCncl; EdYrBk; FHA; Chrldr; Univ; Clinical Psychologst.

RICE, Mark J; Paul C Schulte HS; Terre Haute, IN; HonRl; Bsbl; College; Professional.

RICE, Michael D; Hillsboro Comm HS; Hillsboro, IL; HonRl; TchrAde; College; Ecological Work.

RICE, Nancy L; Negounee HS; Negaunee, MI; 13/143 VPFrshCls; TrsSophCls; ChrhWkr; HonRl; NHS; Orch; YthFlsp; RptrYrbk; FTA; PPFtbl; Lake Superior St College; Accounting.

RICE, Pamela J; Casey Jr Sr HS; Casey, IL; 6/89 HonRl; Mdrgl; VPNatlThespSoc; SchMus; SchPl; SpnCl; PpCl; Trk; LetterChrldr; GAA; College.

RICE, Rebecca S; Sisseton HS; Sisseton, SD; 3/106 SecFrshCls; SecSrCls; ALAGirlsSt; Chr; Chrs; HonRl; NHS; StuCncl; GerCl; GAA; Concorida Col;.

RICE, Rick L; Chillicothe HS; Chillicothe, MO; 50/190 Chr; Chrs; CmntyWkr; HonRl; NHS; Quill&Scroll; RptrSchPpr; SchPpr; LetterBsktbl; Trk; CchngActv; IMSpt; Missouri Western College; Engineering.

RICE, Robert J; Jac Cen Del HS; Osgood, IN; 4/89 ALBoysSt; CncrtBnd; HonRl; MrchBnd; NHS; PepBnd; TchrAde; VP4-H; LetterGlf; LetterTrk; Purdue; Aerospace Engr.

RICE, Shirley L; St Ann HS; Chicago, IL; PresSophCls; PresJrCls; Chr; HonRl; NHS; OffAde; VPStuCncl; MthCl; SciCl; JAAwd; Coll; Anthropology Theatre.

RICE, Tamika L; Stillman Valley HS; Stillman Valley, IL; SecJrCls; Chrs; DrlTm; HonRl; SchMus; SchPl; StuCncl; Yrbk; SpnCl; PpCl; 4-HAwd; Univ Of Okla; Spec Educ.

RICE, William T; Gordon Technical HS; Chicago, IL; VPSrCls; ChrhWkr; CmntyWkr; HonRl; LitMag; StuCncl; YthFnd; MthCl; PpCl; LetterBsktbl; CchngActv; IMSpt; Northwestern University; Medicine.

RICH, Barbara M; Rock Island HS; Rock Island, IL; 150/670 Chr; Chrs; ChrhWkr; PolWkr; SchMus; SchPl; YthFlsp; RptrSchPpr; SchPpr; SciCl; College; Professional.

RICH, Carl L; Morton HS; Morton, IL; HonRl; NHS; LetterBsktbl; College; Math.

RICH, Dale T; Woodbury Central HS; Moville, IA; 5/60 ALBoysSt; Band; ChrhWkr; NHS; PepBnd; ROTC; SctActv; MthCl; LetterBsktbl; LetterFtbl; Univ; Wildlife Mgmt.

RICH, Dixon M; Park Tudor HS; Indianapolis, IN; ChrhWkr; CtyCnl; HonRl; PolWkr; SctActv; Sdlty; Swmmng; Brigham Young University.

RICH, Janis A; Oblong HS; Robinson, IL; ChrhWkr; HonRl; StuCncl; RptrYrbk; RptrSchPpr; FTA; FrCl; SecSciCl; Chrldr; IMSpt; Lincoln Trail Jr College; English.

RICH, Joann R; Ottawa HS; Williamsburg, KS; Band; CncrtBnd; MrchBnd; OffAde; PepBnd; SctActv; TchrAde; 4-H; FrCl; PpCl; Coll; Vet.

RICH, John C; Brown County HS; Nashville, IN; 35/206 Band; CncrtBnd; MrchBnd; NatlThespSoc; PepBnd; SchMus; SchPl; LatCl; Ingiana U; Doctor.

RICH, Judy; Wild Rose Public HS; Pine River, WI; SecSophCls; Band; Chrs; CncrtBnd; HonRl; MrchBnd; SchMus; FHA;.

RICH, Leta R; Anna Jonesboro HS; Cobden, IL; 5/137 ALAGirlsSt; Band; CncrtBnd; HonRl; NHS; StuCncl; 4-H; FTA; LatCl; SciCl; Southern Il Univ; Elementary Ed.

RICH, Mark D; Ottawa HS; Ottawa, KS; NatlFornLg; SchPl; TchrAde; College.

RICHARD, Betty M; South Spencer HS; Rockport, IN; 27/131 Band; Chr; Chrs; CncrtBnd; HonRl; MrchBnd; NatlThespSoc; SchMus; SchPl; PpCl; Chrldr; LetterGAA; Univ Of Evansville; Respiratory Therapy.

RICHARD, Daniel L; Thomson Com HS; Thomson, IL; 9/39 Band; Chrl; Chrs; ChrhWkr; CncrtBnd; HonRl; MrchBnd; PepBnd; StuCncl; TchrAde; Faith Baptist Bible College; Theology.

RICHARD, Joseph; Buffalo Grove Hs; Arlington Heights, IL; 14/300 Band; Chr; HonRl; LbryAde; NatlFornLg; NHS; SchMus; StuCncl; YthFlsp; GodCntryAwd; U Of Illinois; Study Botany.

RICHARD, Lysette C; John Marshall Harlan HS; Chicago, IL; 1/800 HonRl; ModUN; NHS; StuCncl; RptrSchPpr; LatCl; Socr; SecChrldr; LetterGAA; Northwestern Univ; Lawyer.

RICHARD, Michael L; St Francis Comm HS; St Francis, KS; CmntyWkr; HonRl; SchAde; SctActv; YthFlsp; Trk; PresAwd; CitAwd; Kansas State U; Architecture.

RICHARD, Raymond P; Crestwood HS; Dearborn Hts, MI; CncrtBnd; JA; MrchBnd; SchMus; SctActv; Wayne St Univ; Medicine.

RICHARDS, Anne M; Allen Park HS; Allen Park, MI; Chr; Chrl; LbryAde; NHS; SchMus; TchrAde; RptrSchPpr; FrCl; GerCl; SpnCl; Univ; Sci Res.

RICHARDS, Barry F; Hayes Center HS; Hayes Center, NE; Chrs; ChrhWkr; YthFlsp; 4-H; FFA; LetterBsktbl; LetterFtbl; IMSpt; Ag College; Farmer.

RICHARDS, Betty L; Prescott Comm HS; Corning, IA; Chrs; HonRl; LetterTrk;.

RICHARDS, Bonita M; Naperville Central HS; Wheaton, IL; TrsSophCls; HospAde; GerCl; University; Nursing.

RICHARDS, David; Cheboygan HS; Cheboygan, MI; Band; Chr; CncrtBnd; HonRl; MrchBnd; PepBnd; SchPl; TchrAde; Tennis; College; Prof Bus Ins.

RICHARDS, David A; New Madrid County HS; Matthews, MO; Band; Chr; ChrhWkr; HonRl; MrchBnd; PepBnd; SchPl; StuCncl; FFA; LetterBsbl; College; Agricultural Field.

RICHARDS, David A; Griffith HS; Griffith, IN; 1/300 HonRl; JrNHS; NHS; SctActv; PresStuCncl; RptrYrbk; RptrSchPpr; FDA; Swmmng; BauchLmbAwd; Purdue; Engineering.

RICHARDS, Debbie J; Center HS; Center, ND; Band; Chr; Chrs; CncrtBnd; HonRl; MrchBnd; PepBnd; SchPl; SctActv; TchrAde; LetterTrk; Chrldr; GAA; PresAwd; Air Force; Accountant.

RICHARDS, Debora E; Saint Anthony HS; Effingham, IL; Chr; Chrl; Chrs; ChrhWkr; HospAde; SchMus; SchPl; SctActv; RptrSchPpr; SchPpr; FTA; PpCl; College; Nurse.

RICHARDS, Deborah; Laville HS; Plymouth, IN; Band; CncrtBnd; MrchBnd; NHS; NatlMeritCmnd; StuCncl; RptrYrbk; Yrbk; SchPpr; Tennis; Bus School; Secretary.

RICHARDS, Deborah A; Whitehall HS; Whitehall, MI; 12/165 HonRl; JrNHS; NHS; StuCncl; RptrSchPpr; Michigan State University; Interior Design.

RICHARDS, Debra L; Baraga Twp HS; Baraga, MI; 9/47 Chrs; ChrhWkr; CncrtBnd; HonRl; LbryAde; NHS; SchMus; Yrbk; 4-H; Michigan Tech Univ; Elec Engineer.

RICHARDS, Dixie; Geneva Public Senior HS; Geneva, NE; VPFrshCls; SecSophCls; PresJrCls; Band; Chr; Chrldr; GAA; IMSpt; 4-HAwd; College; Medicine.

RICHARDS, Joan L; Cal Comm HS; Alexander, IA; 4/34 VPFrshCls; TrsSrCls; NHS; NatlMeritCmnd; SchMus; SchPl; StuCncl; 4-H; CaptBsbl; Glf; Chrldr; DanFAwd; 4-HAwd; Univ Of No Iowa; Guidance Counselor.

RICHARDS, Kathleen E; Wayland Academy; Beaver Dam, WI; Aud/Vis; HonRl; RptrYrbk; Yrbk; SchPpr; SpnCl; LetterSwmmng; LetterTennis; U Of Wis; Physical Ed.

RICHARDS, Lynae D; Sac Community HS; Sac City, IA; Chr; ChrhWkr; CncrtBnd; HonRl; HospAde; Mdrgl; MrchBnd; SchMus; YthFlsp; FHA; College; Professional.

RICHARDS, Margaret A; Windsor HS; Windsor, IL; 1/56 TrsSophCls; Band; HonRl; NHS; SchPl; TreasStuCncl; EdYrBk; FHA; PresSpnCl; BttyCrckrAwd; Lakeland Jr College.

RICHARDS, Mark A; North Montgomery HS; Crawfordsville, IN; 31/191 Band; CncrtBnd; HonRl; MrchBnd; PepBnd; LatCl; MthCl; Bsbl; College; Engineering.

RICHARDS, Mary A; Cresbard HS; Cresbard, SD; HstSophCls; Band; Chrs; HonRl; JrNHS; StuCncl; EdSchPpr; Chrldr; JAAwd; VoiceDemAwd; Sd Univ Brookings; Med Tech.

RICHARDS, Michael; Henry Ford HS; Detroit, MI; StuGov; Swmmng; Univ; Cpa.

RICHARDS, Mindy L; Bath HS; Dewitt, MI; 3/80 HonRl; NHS; OffAde; SchAde; StuCncl; TchrAde; RptrYrbk; SchPpr; Bsktbl; GAA; Michigan State Univ; Doctor In Medicine.

RICHARDS, Monica; Taylor HS; Kokomo, IN; 48/178 HonRl; NatlThespSoc; SchAde; SchPl; StuCncl; StuGov; TchrAde; PpCl; Chrldr; PPFtbl; Indiana Univ; Education.

RICHARDS, Nancy L; Berkeley Sr HS; Berkeley, MO; CncrtBnd; HonRl; NHS; StuCncl; Swmmng; Sw Missouri State Univ.

RICHARDS, Pamela J; Nashville Comm HS; Nashville, IL; 20/180 Band; Chrs; CncrtBnd; HonRl; MrchBnd; PepBnd; StuCncl; Twrl; PpCl; University; Science.

RICHARDS, Robert P; Fenwick HS; Berwyn, IL; 65/222 CAP; CmntyWkr; GerCl; SciCl; Bsktbl; CchngActv; IMSpt; College; Physical Geographer.

RICHARDS, Scott T; Big Fork HS; Effie, MN; Band; Chrs; CncrtBnd; HonRl; MrchBnd; PepBnd; StuCncl; RptrYrbk; Bsbl; College; Accounting.

RICHARDS, Thomas N; I F Community HS; Iowa Falls, IA; 6/150 Band; Chr; Chrs; CncrtBnd; HonRl; MrchBnd; NHS; PepBnd; GerCl; Ellsworth Jr Coll; Music.

RICHARDSON, Benita J; West Side Sr HS; Gary, IN; ChrhWkr; CmntyWkr; SecCncrtBnd; NHS; Orch; StuGov; SecFrCl; PpCl; Indiana Univ; Accounting.

RICHARDSON, Betty; Charlestown HS; Charlestown, IN; VPJrCls; HonRl; TchrAde; YthFlsp; FHA; SpnCl; PpCl; GAA; Univ; Professional.

RICHARDSON, Charlotte M; Merrill Sr HS; Merrill, WI; Chr; ChrhWkr; CncrtBnd; HonRl; MrchBnd; NatlFornLg; NatlMeritCmnd; PepBnd; MthCl; GAA; Univ Of Wi At Milwaukee; Engineering.

RICHARDSON, Cornel C; Union Star Rii HS; Union Star, MO; TrsSophCls; PresJrCls; CncrtBnd; HonRl; SchPl; SctActv; LetterFtbl; Trk; CchngActv; College; Vocation.

RICHARDSON, David M; Winfield HS; Winfield, KS; 28/193 VPSophCls; PresJrCls; ALBoysSt; HonRl; IntrClCncl; StuCncl; KeyCl; LetterBsktbl; Socr; LetterTennis; Univ.

RICHARDSON, Denise C; Reavis HS; Burbank, IL; 13/676 HonRl; JrNHS; NHS; NatlMeritCmnd; Blackburn College; Biology.

RICHARDSON, Diana L; Davis Co Comm HS; Bloomfield, IA; PresChrhWkr; HonRl; HospAde; VPNHS; OffAde; SchAde; SchPl; PresYthFlsp; Pres4-H; 4-HAwd; CitAwd; College; Medicine.

RICHARDSON, Dorothy B; Ann Arbor Huron HS; Ypsilanti, MI; Chr; NatlMeritSF; StuCncl; Yrbk; Trk; College; Interior Design.

RICHARDSON, Ellen; Laurens Community HS; Laurens, IA; 29/47 Chrs; HonRl; SchPl; Teen; Yrbk; Bsktbl; Chrldr; Ankeny Des Moines Area Comm Coll; Lab Tech.

RICHARDSON, Ginger K; Orrick HS; Orrick, MO; 15/47 Band; Chrs; CncrtBnd; HonRl; MrchBnd; PepBnd; TchrAde; RptrYrbk; SchPpr; FHA; PpCl; Trk; Chrldr; College; Professional.

RICHARDSON, Irving R; Simeon Vocational HS; Chicago, IL; 3/316 HonRl; NHS; Ill St Univ; Acct.

RICHARDSON, James A; Cadillac HS; Cadillac, MI; HonRl; NHS; SctActv; YthFlsp; Bsbl; LetterBsktbl; LetterFtbl; Trk; IMSpt; Mi St Univ; Medicine.

RICHARDSON, James H; Prospect HS; Arlington Hts, IL; 1/614 ChrhWkr; NHS; NatlMeritCmnd; Univ Of Illinois; Liberal Arts.

RICHARDSON, Joel A; Benedict HS; Benedicz, NE; 1/14 VPJrCls; PresSrCls; HonRl; TchrAde; 4-H; LetterBsktbl; LetterFtbl; LetterTrk; U Of Neb; Business.

RICHARDSON, Judith; West Side HS; Gary, IN; 1/700 Band; CncrtBnd; HonRl; MrchBnd; NHS; NatlMeritSF; SchPl; Indiana Univ; Law.

RICHARDSON, Judith L; West Side HS; Gary, IN; Band; HonRl; JrNHS; MrchBnd; NHS; NatlMeritSF; SchPl; Univ; Law.

RICHARDSON, Kathleen M; Beaver Dam Senior HS; Beaver Dam, WI; 56/310 AFS; Band; Chrs; CncrtBnd; HonRl; MrchBnd; Orch; PepBnd; SchMus; StuCncl; GAA; College; Early Childhood Education.

RICHARDSON, Kimberly D; Rochester HS; Rochester, IN; 31/154 HonRl; LbryAde; NHS; Teen; CivCl; FHA; GerCl; Nursing School; Nursing.

RICHARDSON, Kristine; Burt Township HS; Munising, MI; Chr; DrmBgl; LbryAde; SchAde; StuCncl; YthLg; 4-H; FHA; FNA; College; Vocation.

RICHARDSON, Laurie A; Mason Co Central HS; Pentwater, MI; HonRl; TchrAde; FHA; Coll; Psych.

RICHARDSON, Loretta M; Beaver Dam Sr HS; Beaver Dam, WI; 8/316 SecTrsSophCls; Band; Chrs; CncrtBnd; MrchBnd; PepBnd; SchMus; StuCncl; College; Nursing.

RICHARDSON, Loretta M; Beaver Dam Senior HS; Beaver Dam, WI; 6/349 SecTrsSophCls; Band; Chrs; CncrtBnd; MrchBnd; PepBnd; SchMus; College; Nursing.

RICHARDSON, Mareta M; Bishop Dwenger HS; Fort Wayne, IN; HonRl; HospAde; SpnCl; PpCl; College; Registered Nurse.

RICHARDSON, Mark; Kingsley Pierson HS; Kingsley, IA; Band; HonRl; 4-H; Ftbl; 4-HAwd; Coll; Ag Ed.

RICHARDSON, Mark D; Ernest W Seaholm HS; Birmingham, MI; 43/750 ChrhWkr; CmntyWkr; PresJrNHS; NatlMeritSF; PresSctActv; StuGov; YthFnd; IMSpt; GodCntryAwd; GovHonPrgAwd; Albion College; Medicine.

RICHARDSON, Mary J; Alton HS; Alton, MO; 6/55 SecBand; CncrtBnd; HonRl; MrchBnd; Twrl; RptrYrbk; RptrSchPpr; PresPpCl; Bsbl; LetterBsktbl; W Plains Residence Ctr; Elementary Educatio.

RICHARDSON, Michelle R; Trinity HS; Hutchinson, KS; ALAGirlsSt; HonRl; HospAde; NHS; RptrYrbk; CaptTrk; Chrldr; GAA; 4-HAwd; PresAwd; Fort Hays St Coll; Art.

RICHARDSON, Peggy J; Magic City Campus HS; Minot, ND; 139/656 Chrs; ChrhWkr; HonRl; NHS; SchAde; YthFlsp; FHA; PpCl; Nd St Univ ; Home Ec.

RICHARDSON, Rexann; Columbus North HS; Columbus, IN; 17/490 HonRl; ModUN; VPQuill&Scroll; EdYrBk; MthCl; PpCl; OptClAwd; Ball St Univ; Math.

RICHARDSON, Richard A; Canton Senior HS; Canton, IL; 14/257 ALBoysSt; CncrtBnd; DrmMjrt; HonRl; MrchBnd; NHS; YthFlsp; SptEdYrbk; Bsktbl; Glf; Purdue U; Eng.

RICHARDSON, Roberta M; John Hersey HS; Arlington Hts, IL; 1/606 Band; CncrtBnd; HonRl; MrchBnd; NHS; Orch; PepBnd; SchMus; Butler Univ; Medicine.

RICHARDSON, Robert H; Fonda Comm HS; Fonda, IA; VPJrCls; Chr; LbryAde; ModUN; RptrYrbk; RptrSchPpr; College; Law.

RICHARDSON, Robert J; Ashton HS; Ashton, IL; VPSrCls; HonRl; IntrClCncl; SchPl; StuCncl; RptrSchPpr; PresSciCl; LetterFtbl; CaptTrk; LetterWrstlng; Insrnc Salesman; Professional.

RICHARDSON, Ruben H; Emerson HS; Gary, IN; ALBoysSt; Band; CncrtBnd; HonRl; MrchBnd; PresNHS; Orch; PepBnd; FTA; CitAwd; Trade School; Computer Science.

RICHARDSON, Sara; New Haven HS; New Haven, IN; Band; CncrtBnd; HonRl; MrchBnd; StuCncl; StuGov; TchrAde; YthFlsp; FrCl; GAA; Oral Roberts U; Phys Ed.

RICHARDSON, Sara J; Monrovia HS; Monrovia, IN; 15/93 VPJrCls; SecBand; CncrtBnd; HonRl; MrchBnd; NHS; OffAde; SecStuCncl; TchrAde; SpnCl;.

RICHARDSON, Scott E; Lake Central HS; St John, IN; 3/420 ALBoysSt; HonRl; NHS; VPNatlThespSoc; SchMus; SchPl; SpnCl; SciCl; Bsktbl; Northwestern U; Comp Tech.

RICHARDSON, Susan D; Superior HS; Superior, NE; ChrhWkr; CncrtBnd; HonRl; MrchBnd; PepBnd; Teen; YthFlsp; 4-H; PpCl; DARAwd; Clg; Pro.

RICHARDSON, Terry L; Maysville HS; Pattonsburg, MO; 24/60 ChrhWkr; HonRl; OffAde; TchrAde; College; Art.

RICHARDSON, Thomas J; Galena HS; Galena, IL; Band; CncrtBnd; MrchBnd; PepBnd; PolWkr; StuCncl; StuGov; LetterFtbl; Trk; University; Attorney.

RICHARDSON, Vicki L; Yankton HS; Yankton, SD; Band; Chrs; CncrtBnd; DrlTm; HonRl; MrchBnd; NatlFornLg; NHS; RptrYrbk; College; Professional.

RICHARDT, Nancy; Summit Independent HS; Summit, SD; 7/21 Band; Chrs; CmntyWkr; CncrtBnd; HonRl; MrchBnd; PepBnd; RptrYrbk; RptrSchPpr; Bsktbl; Univ; Med Secretary.

RICHART, Teresa; Our Lady Of Grace HS; Indianapolis, IN; Chr; Chrl; Chrs; ChrhWkr; SchMus; SchPl; StuCncl; PpCl; Chrldr; Butler Univ Jordan Coll Music;.

RICHER, Stacy L; Triton HS; Bourbon, IN; Chr; HonRl; PpCl; Bsktbl; GAA; PresAwd; University; Medicine.

RICHERSON, Mary; Marshfield HS; Fair Grove, MO; 2/136 ChrhWkr; HonRl; HospAde; NHS; OffAde; Yrbk; DARAwd; CitAwd; St Johns School Of Nursing; Regnurse.

RICHERT, James J; Winamac Comm HS; Winamac, IN; TrsFrshCls; HonRl; NHS; NatlMeritCmnd; PolWkr; StuCncl; Yrbk; SchPpr; Trk; VoiceDemAwd; Coll; Architecture.

RICHERT, Penny; Stillwater Sr HS; Stillwater, MN; HonRl; JrNHS; TchrAde; Univ Of Minn; Doctor Gp.

RICHERT, Valerie; Eastern HS; Salem, IN; 6/74 Band; ChrhWkr; HonRl; NHS; StuCncl; TchrAde; SpnCl; Indiana U Southeast; Elementary Education.

RICHES, John C; Humboldt HS; Humboldt, IA; 37/140 ALBoysSt; Aud/Vis; Chr; Chrl; Chrs; ChrhWkr; HonRl; LbryAde; OffAde; Quill&Scroll; Iowa Central Comm College; Journalism.

RICHEY, David A; Southeast HS; West Mineral, KS; 11/60 ALBoysSt; Band; HonRl; PepBnd; SchPl; StuCncl; SciCl; LetterFtbl; AmLegAwd; Kansas St College; Business Admin.

RICHEY, Jackie L; Cardinal Ritter HS; Indianapolis, IN; Chr; Chrs; HonRl; NHS; SchMus; StuCncl; Twrl; FrCl; Iu Sch Of Nursing ; Nursing.

RICHEY, James A; Greenfield Central HS; Greenfield, IN; 92/285 Chr; JA; NatlThespSoc; SchMus; SctActv; YthFlsp; LatCl; SciCl; Ftbl; Wrstlng; JAAwd; MasAwd; University; Engineering.

RICHEY, Janelle K; N Platte Senior HS; North Platte, NE; 17/397 Chr; CmntyWkr; CncrtBnd; HonRl; Mdrgl; MrchBnd; PepBnd; RedCrAde; SchMus; YthFlsp; College; Art Major.

RICHEY, Julee K; Maryville R Ii HS; Maryville, MO; 12/129 SecFrshCls; Chr; Chrs; MrchBnd; NHS; StuCncl; Twrl; Yrbk; FTA; College; Business.

RICHEY, Marianne F; Mother Mc Auley Lib Arts HS; Chicago, IL; VPFrshCls; Chrs; HospAde; NatlMeritCmnd; Chr; SchMus; SchPl; StuGov; SecFrCl; Bsbl; Univ Ed; Clinical Psychologist.

RICHEY, Robert S; Grayville Community HS; Grayville, IL; 4/40 SecFrshCls; SecSophCls; Band; 4-H; FrCl; Bsktbl; Trk; University; Doctor.

RICHEY, Rodney P; Madison Hts HS; Anderson, IN; 78/404 HonRl; JA; LitMag; Quill&Scroll; StuCncl; TchrAde; EdSchPpr; Ball St Univ; Writer.

RICHEY, Scott D; West Lafayette HS; W Lafayette, IN; ChrhWkr; HonRl; JA; PolWkr; SctActv; LetterTrk; IMSpt; Purdue Univ; Md.

RICHEY, Thomas D; Crab Orchard ;hs; Pittsburg, IL; 2/26 PresSophCls; ChrhWkr; HonRl; SchPl; StuCncl; RptrYrbk; Bsbl; CaptBsktbl; Trk; CchngActv; University; Professional.

RICHEY, Victoria A; Fremont HS; Fremont, IN; HonRl; TchrAde; FrCl; College; Professional.

RICHGELS, Julie M; Richland Center HS; Richland Center, WI; Band; 4-H; U Of Wi; English.

RICHGRUBER, Rhonda M; Rhinelander HS; Rhinelander, WI; SecTrsSrCls; Band; Chr; CncrtBnd; HonRl; MrchBnd; StuCncl; PresGerCl; PpCl; LetterTrk; College; Teaching.

RICHIE, Michael G; Hudson HS; Hudson, WI; 4/231 ChrhWkr; CmntyWkr; HonRl; StuCncl; StuGov; RptrSchPpr; GerCl; LetterBsbl; LetterBsktbl; LetterFtbl; Univ; Prof.

RICHMOND, Ann E; Hartford HS; Watervlier, MI; 1/90 TrsSrCls; ALAGirlsSt; Band; ChrhWkr; HonRl; NHS; SchPl; 4-H; PpCl; College.

RICHMOND, Anne M; East Gary Edison Sr HS; East Gary, IN; 48/179 Aud/Vis; Chr; LbryAde; OffAde; SchMus; TchrAde; SpnCl; GAA; IMSpt; PPFtbl; University; Lawyer.

RICHMOND, Cindy J; High School; Algoma, WI; SecJrCls; TrsSrCls; HonRl; NHS; SctActv; StuGov; Glf; College.

RICHMOND, Julie A; Desoto Senior HS; Desoto, KS; HonRl; FBLA; FHA; PpCl; College; Professional.

RICHMOND, Lester; Simeon Vocational HS; Chicago, IL; 17/319 HstSrCls; Band; Chr; HonRl; JA; JrNHS; NHS; RptrSchPpr; Central State Univ; Management.

RICHMOND, Mike A; Brookfield East HS; Brookfield, WI; HonRl; MthCl; LetterTrk; Wrstlng; Wi St Univ; Landscape Architect.

RICHMOND, Regina M; Manistee Catholic HS; Bear Lake, MI; ChrhWkr; HonRl; HospAde; NHS; StuCncl; PpCl; LetterTrk; CaptChrldr; VoiceDemAwd; College; Business.

RICHMOND, Rhonda R; Marion HS; Marion, KS; Band; Chrl; CncrtBnd; DrmMjrt; LbryAde; MrchBnd; PepBnd; SchMus; FHA; Bsktbl; Trade Sch; Florist.

RICHMOND, Richard C; Avon HS; Danville, IN; 14/142 HonRl; SctActv; Yrbk; LatCl; Glf; Trk; IMSpt; University; Science.

RICHMOND, Ruby E; Fulton HS; Fulton, MO; College.

RICHMOND, Shelley J; Eastside HS; Butler, IN; 2/116 TrsJrCls; Chrl; CncrtBnd; DrmMjrt; HonRl; NHS; PresNatlThespSoc; SchMus; FrCl; CitAwd; Indiana Univ; Music.

RICHMOND, Steven G; Fayette HS; Fayette, IA; 17/37 Aud/Vis; CncrtBnd; MrchBnd; PepBnd; RptrYrbk; Kirkwood College.

RICHNAK, Colleen M; Merrill HS; Merrill, MI; 7/107 VPSrCls; Band; CncrtBnd; HonRl; SecNHS; StuCncl; TchrAde; VPFHA; Chrldr; GAA;.

RICHSTEIN, Nancy L; Garden County HS; Oshkosh, NE; VPJrCls; Band; Chrs; HospAde; OffAde; PepBnd; 4-H; FHA; PpCl; Nursing School; Professional.

RICHT, Richard P; Wm J Bryan HS; Omaha, NE; 1/360 HonRl; NHS; NatlMeritCmnd; TchrAde; Bsbl; Bsktbl; College; Professional.

RICHTARIK, Patrice A; Wilber Clatonia HS; Wilber, NE; 1/33 PresSophCls; ALAGirlsSt; Band; HonRl; VPNHS; SchPl; StuCncl; SecYthFlsp; EdYrBk; VPFHA; Ne Wesleyon U; Med Tech.

RICHTER, Annette J; Gresham HS; Gresham, NE; 1/13 VPFrshCls; Band; Chrs; HonRl; SchPl; SecStuCncl; RptrYrbk; EdSchPpr; Sec4-H; PpCl; Univ Nebraska; Home Economics.

RICHTER, Bruce H; Brookfield East HS; Brookfield, WI; Band; ChrhWkr; HonRl; MrchBnd; NatlMeritSF; PepBnd; LetterFtbl; Wrstlng; IMSpt; Medical School; Medicine.

RICHTER, Charlene K; North Knox HS; Edwardsport, IN; 3/130 PresSophCls; ALAGirlsSt; Band; Chr; CmntyWkr; HonRl; HospAde; StuCncl; TchrAde; YthFlsp; Bsktbl; Chrldr; GAA; Univ Of Evansville; Nurse.

RICHTER, Cheryl M; Republican City HS; Naponee, NE; 2/6 SecTrsSrCls; Band; Chr; HonRl; LbryAde; SchPl; EdYrBk; 4-H; Kearney State Col; Lab Technician.

RICHTER, Cindy; Adair Casey HS; Adair, IA; 17/48 CncrtBnd; HonRl; StuCncl; RptrSchPpr; 4-H; Trk; AmLegAwd; 4-HAwd; College; Nursing.

RICHTER, David E; Sheldon Community HS; Sheldon, IA; Bsktbl; Ftbl; College; History.

RICHTER, David P; Fergus Falls HS; Fergus Falls, MN; Chr; ChrhWkr; Orch; SchMus; SchPl; IMSpt; College; Teacher.

RICHTER, Debbie L; Boscobel HS; Boscobel, WI; HonRl; NHS; RptrSchPpr; SecFrCl; Trk; GAA; College; Professional.

RICHTER, Debra; Jamaica HS; Fairmount, IL; 4/48 HonRl; NHS; TchrAde; RptrSchPpr; PpCl; Eastern Il Univ; Teacher.

RICHTER, Jill M; Frederic HS; Frederic, WI; HonRl; LbryAde; Bus School; Vocation.

RICHTER, Kevin L; Bishop Mc Namara HS; Kankakee, IL; 11/162 HonRl; NHS; Yrbk; RptrSchPpr; Lewis University; Mech Engineer.

RICHTER, Kristine L; Oswego Sr HS; Aurora, IL; Chr; HonRl; TchrAde;.

RICHTER, Larry L; Central HS; Norwood, MN; HonRl; LetterTrk; College.

RICHTER, Marshall; Mather HS; Chicago, IL; Aud/Vis; Chr; CmntyWkr; HonRl; HospAde; LbryAde; StuCncl; Ill State Univ; Marine Biology.

RICHTER, Paul D; Collinsville Sr HS; Collinsville, IL; 21/670 Chrs; HonRl; JrNHS; LbryAde; NHS; NatlMeritCmnd; VPLatCl; TreasMthCl; SciCl; Univ Of Illinois; Medicine.

RICHTER, Randy C; Hayes County HS; Hayes Center, NE; VPSophCls; VPJrCls; 4-H; FFA; Bsbl; Ftbl; Glf; Trk; Univ Of Ne; Agriculture.

RICHTER, Steven C; Niles Sr HS; Niles, MI; Band; CncrtBnd; HonRl; MrchBnd; NatlMeritSF; PepBnd; SchMus; SctActv; StuCncl; Msu; Music.

RICHTER, Steven J; Central Noble HS; Albion, IN; PresJrCls; PresSrCls; ALBoysSt; HonRl; NHS; LetterBsktbl; LetterTennis; LetterTrk; PresAwd; Coll; Math.

RICHTER, Steven R; Brookfield Central HS; Brookfield, WI; 31/430 Band; CncrtBnd; PepBnd; SchMus; KeyCl; Bsktbl; College.

RICHTER, Wayne D; Ash Grove HS; Ash Grove, MO; 1/55 Band; ChrhWkr; CncrtBnd; HonRl; MrchBnd; NHS; PepBnd; SecFFA; MthCl; Univ Of Missouri; Chemical Engineer.

RICHTERS, Michael G; Centennial HS; Beaver Crossing, NE; 4/68 ALBoysSt; Band; CncrtBnd; MrchBnd; NHS; PepBnd; SchPl; StuCncl; University; Medical Technology.

RICHTSMEIER, Gloria A; Ackley Geneva HS; Ackley, IA; 1/55 VPSophCls; SecSrCls; TrsSrCls; CncrtBnd; HonRl; MrchBnd; NHS; OffAde; StuCncl; PresYthFlsp; Univ Of Northern Iowa.

RICHWALSKI, Daniel C; Lake Central HS; St John, IN; 19/453 ALBoysSt; Aud/Vis; HonRl; NHS; OffAde; SchAde; TchrAde; CaptBsktbl; LetterFtbl; Trk; College; Radio Television Prod.

RICK, Brian N; Hutchinson HS; Hutchinson, MN; 3/220 Band; Chr; Chrs; CncrtBnd; HonRl; MrchBnd; NatlThespSoc; PepBnd; SchMus; SchPl; College; Professional.

RICKABY, Duane; Stephenson HS; Stephenson, MI; HonRl; SctActv; StuCncl; Bsbl; Bsktbl; Ftbl; Tennis; Wrstlng; CchngActv; IMSpt; PPFtbl; College; Professional.

RICKABY, Michael J; Premontre HS; Green Bay, WI; 9/150 Band; CncrtBnd; HonRl; NatlMeritSF; NatlSciFnd; PepBnd; Univ; Physician.

RICKARD, Deana J; Eastern HS; Pekin, IN; 3/90 SecSrCls; HonRl; NHS; StuCncl; EdYrBk; 4-H; FHA; SpnCl; PpCl; GAA; Purdue; Engineering.

RICKARD, Karen L; Jimtown HS; Elkhart, IN; 1/97 ChrhWkr; HonRl; LbryAde; NHS; SctActv; RptrSchPpr; FHA; FTA; Bsktbl; Tennis; Purdue U; Wildlife Cons.

RICKE, Cheryl M; Sharon HS; Sharon, KS; Band; SecChrs; HonRl; VPStuCncl; Yrbk; PpCl; LetterBsktbl; LetterTrk; College; Medicine.

RICKE, Kevin J; Kuemper HS; Westside, IA; ALBoysSt; ChrhWkr; HonRl; 4-H; LatCl; SciCl; IMSpt; AmLegAwd; 4-HAwd;.

RICKE, Steven C; Ramsey HS; Bingham, IL; 5/46 HonRl; LbryAde; SchPl; StuCncl; Yrbk; 4-H; FTA; FrCl; DanFAwd; College; Veterinary.

RICKE, Tom C; Greensburg HS; Greensburg, IN; 67/226 Chr; CmntyWkr; SchPl; VP4-H; PpCl; Bsbl; Bsktbl; Trk; 4-HAwd; College; Agriculture.

RICKELMAN, Debra K; Marquette Inc HS; West Point, IA; 19/49 ChrhWkr; HonRl; LbryAde; 4-H; PpCl; 4-HAwd;.

RICKELMAN, Linda E; Heritage Hills HS; Mariah Hill, IN; Band; HonRl; NHS; SchMus; SctActv; Swmmng; Trk; CaptChrldr; Clg; Certified Pub Accountant.

RICKER, Janis L; Fenton HS; Bensenville, IL; Band; HonRl; HospAde; NHS; PepBnd; YthFlsp; Yrbk; RptrSchPpr; VPGAA; College; Professional.

RICKERS, Debra J; Beatrice Sr HS; Beatrice, NE; ChrhWkr; DrlTm; HonRl; Orch; SctActv; GerCl; PpCl; LetterTrk; Chrldr; Trade School; Computers.

RICKERS, Lorri J; Fairbury HS; Fairbury, NE; 11/140 Chrs; ChrhWkr; HonRl; FBLA; College; History.

RICKERT, Paula J; Normal Community HS; Normal, IL; Chr; DrlTm; HospAde; LbryAde; Mdrgl; SctActv; TchrAde; PresFNA; SpnCl; IMSpt; Mennonite Hosp School; Nursing.

RICKERT, Paul W; Elmwood Park HS; Elmwood Park, IL; 5/305 ChrhWkr; CncrtBnd; HonRl; MrchBnd; NHS; NatlMeritCmnd; Orch; SchMus; GerCl; Univ Of Illinois.

RICKERTSEN, Lori R; Gothenburg HS; Gothenburg, NE; Chrs; ChrhWkr; NatlThespSoc; TchrAde; YthFlsp; 4-H; PpCl; Trk; AmLegAwd; 4-HAwd; Clge.

RICKETTS, Rhonda K; Yorkwood HS; Little York, IL; Chrs; HonRl; YthFlsp; Yrbk; 4-H; LetterBsktbl; GAA; Western Il Univ; Business Education.

RICKEY, Thomas L; James W Riley HS; South Bend, IN; Band; CncrtBnd; DrmBgl; MrchBnd; Orch; PepBnd; SctActv; Berklee College Of Music; Music.

RICKHER, Mark S; Springfield Southeast HS; Springfield, IL; 4/503 JrNHS; NHS; TchrAde; Univ Of Illinois; Architecture.

RICKLEFS, Dianne E; Ayrshire Consolidated HS; Ayrshire, IA; Band; Chr; Chrs; ChrhWkr; CncrtBnd; HonRl; SchPl; FHA; Coll; Secretary.

RICKLEFS, Richard C; Palmyra HS; Palmyra, WI; 2/61 TrsSophCls; ALBoysSt; ChrhWkr; HonRl; NatlMeritCmnd; PolWkr; SchPl; Bsbl; LetterBsktbl; LetterTrk; Ripon College; Chemistry.

RICKLEFS, Ronald S; Midway Usd #433 HS; Bendena, KS; Aud/Vis; Band; CncrtBnd; HonRl; MrchBnd; PepBnd; LetterBsktbl; LetterFtbl; LetterTrk; College; Vocation.

RICKMAN, Brenda A; Mackenzie HS; Detroit, MI; Band; HonRl; LbryAde; NatlThespSoc; OffAde; SchAde; SchPl; StuCncl; TchrAde; YthFlsp; College; Professional.

RICKMAN, Dan S; D C Everest Sr HS; Hatley, WI; Univ Of Wisconsin; Chem Engineering.

RICKMAN, Rodger R; J D Darnall HS; Osco, IL; 87/207 HonRl; YthFlsp; Pres4-H; FFA; LetterFtbl; 4-HAwd;.

RICKS, Lisa J; High School; Holliday, MO; 3/71 TrsSophCls; ChrhWkr; NHS; SchPl; YthFlsp; 4-H; FHA; SpnCl; PpCl; BttyCrckrAwd; Mo St Univ; Speech Pathology.

RIDDELL, Glenn L; Eureka HS; Eureka, IL; 20/100 PresSrCls; Band; Chr; HonRl; MrchBnd; ModUN; PepBnd; PolWkr; SchMus; SchPl; SctActv; StuCncl; StuGov; RptrYrbk; RptrSchPpr; Northwestern Univ; History.

RIDDELL, Laurel D; Center Senior HS; Kansas City, MO; Band; CncrtBnd; HonRl; MrchBnd; NHS; NatlMeritSF; YthFlsp; PpCl; LetterSwmmng; College.

RIDDER, Jeannette M; Alleman HS; Moline, IL; 14/215 NHS; Yrbk; FrCl; GAA; Northern Arizona Univ; Psychologist.

RIDDER, Phillip M; Augusta HS; Augusta, KS; ChrhWkr; HonRl; TchrAde; SchPpr; GerCl; Bsbl; LetterFtbl; LetterTennis; IMSpt; College; Engineering.

RIDDER, William H; Marquette HS; Alton, IL; 35/118 AFS; HonRl; JA; University; Medicine.

RIDDLE, Janis; Grosse Pointe South HS; Grosse Pointe Frms, MI; 28/637 Band; ChrhWkr; CncrtBnd; HonRl; MrchBnd; NHS; NatlMeritCmnd; SctActv; GerCl; PPFtbl; Mich State Univ; Veterinary Medicine.

RIDDLE, Steven; New Palestine HS; Greenfield, IN; 7/170 HonRl; NHS; SctActv; StuCncl; RptrYrbk; SpnCl; Indiana St; Accountant.

RIDDLE, Teresa; Cassville HS; Cassville, MO; 1/101 SecSophCls; VPJrCls; ALAGirlsSt; NHS; StuCncl; StuGov; SciCl; Bsktbl; IMSpt; BttyCrckrAwd; Umkc Med School; Md.

RIDDLE, Terry J; Kearney HS; Kearney, NE; FBLA; Kearney St College; Business Admin.

RIDDLER, Guy S; St Charles HS; St Charles, MO; CmntyWkr; HonRl; PolWkr; EdSchPpr; University; Political Science.

RIDEHOUR, Kristy L; Haslett HS; Williamston, MI; 8/153 ChrhWkr; CmntyWkr; CncrtBnd; SecHospAde; MrchBnd; PepBnd; SchMus; YthFlsp; Swmmng; Msu.

RIDENHOUR, Kirk D; Maries Co R Ii HS; Belle, MO; VPFrshCls; PresSophCls; PresJrCls; HonRl; CncrtBnd; Band; StuCncl; Bsbl; Bsktbl; Trk; College; Professional.

RIDENHOUR, Rachelle R; Maries County Rii HS; Belle, MO; 1/53 HstSophCls; SecJrCls; TrsJrCls; PresSrCls; Band; Chrs; ChrhWkr; HonRl; SchMus; FHA; PpCl; LetterBsktbl; Trk; Chrldr; Southwest Mo State Univ; English.

RIDENOUR, Betty L; Crossville HS; Crossville, IL; Band; Chrs; CncrtBnd; HonRl; HospAde; PepBnd; SecStuCncl; RptrYrbk; FHA; PpCl; Wabash Valley College; Agri Business.

RIDENOUR, Janet F; Harrisburg HS; Harrisburg, IL; 1/180 PresSrCls; NHS; NatlMeritCmnd; PresYthFlsp; EdYrBk; SecFHA; CaptBsktbl; Glf; Trk; PresGAA; DARAwd; Siu; Professional.

RIDENOUR, William E; Huntington North HS; Huntington, IN; SctActv; GerCl; SciCl; LetterFtbl; LetterSwmmng; LetterTrk; College; Marine Corps Officer.

RIDEOUT, Sherrie L; Johnston City HS; Johnston City, IL; 4/84 Chrs; ChrhWkr; HonRl; NHS; SchMus; College; Teacher.

RIDER, Connie R; Century HS; Dongola, IL; 10/57 ChrhWkr; DrmMjrt; HonRl; LbryAde; OffAde; RptrSchPpr; FHA; PpCl; GAA; IMSpt; College.

RIDER, Shelly A; Henry HS; Hazel, SD; PresJrCls; ALAGirlsSt; ChrhWkr; HonRl; HospAde; SchPl; TchrAde; RptrSchPpr; Bsktbl; Trk; CaptChrldr; IMSpt; College.

RIDGELL, Tramell G; Northern HS; Flint, MI; PresFrshCls; TrsJrCls; VPSrCls; HonRl; NHS; NatlMeritCmnd; Univ Of Mi; Political Science.

RIDGEWAY, Scott L; Pekin Community HS; Pekin, IL; CncrtBnd; HonRl; MrchBnd; NHS; Orch; Univ Il; Architect.

RIDGWAY, Cynthia; Resurrection HS; Chicago, IL; 122/294 HonRl; HospAde; NatlThespSoc; FNA; College; Nursing.

RIDGWAY, David; Orchard Farm HS; Saint Charles, MO; HonRl; JA; SctActv; JAAwd; Ranken Tech Inst; Computer Analyst.

RIDGWAY, June M; Southwestern HS; Flint, MI; 28/660 SecFrshCls; Band; ChrhWkr; MrchBnd; NHS; Orch; SchMus; Univ Of Michigan; Medicine.

RIDGWAY, Mitchell; Hallsville R Iv HS; Hallsville, MO; 16/50 HonRl; NHS; YthFlsp; RptrYrbk; Yrbk; Bsbl; Bsktbl; Trk; IMSpt; AmLegAwd; Coll; Teacher.

RIDINGER, Gayle M; Glenbard West HS; Glen Ellyn, IL; 5/530 Chr; HonRl; LitMag; Mdrgl; NatlFornLg; NatlMeritSF; NatlThespSoc; SchMus; SchPl; EdYrBk; Oberlin Coll; English Ba.

RIDINGS, Kathy A; Waverly HS; Waverly, IL; Chrs; HonRl; SchPpr; FHA; CaptTrk; Chrldr; IMSpt; PPFtbl; PresAwd; Lincolnland Comm Clge; Admin Secretary.

RIDLEN, Randy W; Eisenhower HS; Decatur, IL; Aud/Vis; Chr; SchMus; Bsktbl; LetterFtbl; LetterTennis; Wrstlng; Anderson College; Electrical Engineering.

RIDLEY, Jean M; Crary Public HS; Crary, ND; 5/13 SecTrsJrCls; Band; Chr; ChrhWkr; CncrtBnd; HonRl; OffAde; SctActv; RptrYrbk; RptrSchPpr; GAA; Lake Region Jr Col; Retail Merchandising.

RIDLEY, Randy R; Washington HS; Washington, IA; 36/157 HonRl; FrCl; SciCl; Univ Of Iowa; History.

RIDLEY, Robin A; Cuba HS; Cuba, IL; 2/69 TrsSophCls; ChrhWkr; HonRl; VPNHS; SchPl; StuGov; YthFlsp; Yrbk; PresFrCl; Chrldr; Univ Of Iowa; Writer.

RIDNER, Patricia; Monroe HS; Monroe, MI; 28/527 JA; NHS; RedCrAde; SchMus; SchPl; StuCncl; FNA; JAAwd; Monroe County Comm Col; Registered Nurse.

RIEB, Cynthia M; Washington Sr HS; Sioux Falls, SD; Band; Chrs; ChrhWkr; CncrtBnd; HonRl; HospAde; MrchBnd; NHS; PepBnd; SpnCl; Augustana Col; Rn.

RIECHERS, Lynn; Highland HS; Highland, IN; 58/543 HonRl; NHS; Quill&Scroll; SchPl; TchrAde; Yrbk; SchPpr; FTA; GerCl; Coll; Accounting.

RIECHMANN, Eileen; Columbia HS; Columbia, IL; 3/135 ALAGirlsSt; ChrhWkr; HonRl; SecNHS; OffAde; YthFlsp; Yrbk; SecFHA; PresFTA; GerCl; SecMthCl; PresPpCl; Eastern Ill Univ; Elementary Education.

RIECK, Cynthia L; Murray HS; St Paul, MN; 8/173 CncrtBnd; HonRl; NatlFornLg; StuCncl; YthFlsp; RptrSchPpr; GerCl; LetterIMSpt; Univ Mn; Physical Therapy.

RIECK, Kellie L; Marceline R 5 HS; Marceline, MO; 15/74 TrsJrCls; Band; Chrs; CncrtBnd; HonRl; MrchBnd; OffAde; RptrSchPpr; SpnCl; GodCntryAwd; Univ; Prof.

RIECKMANN, Susan; Kennedy St Paul Hs; Chicago, IL; 20/610 HonRl; Orch; 4-H; Il Ins Technology; Math.

RIEDEL, Carla G; West Vigo HS; West Terre Haute, IN; 23/188 Aud/Vis; Chr; HonRl; JA; NHS; OffAde; SchPl; SctActv; FHA; LetterSwmmng; Univ; Nursing Rn.

RIEDEL, Steven; Wheatland HS; Park, KS; 5/42 HonRl; FFA; Bsbl; Bsktbl; AmLegAwd; Trade School; Farmer.

RIEDEMAN, John M; Scecina Memorial HS; Indianpolis, IN; Chrs; HonRl; NHS; SchMus; RptrSchPpr; SchPpr; College.

RIEDEMANN, Dawn; Hartley HS; Hartley, IA; JrNHS; LbryAde; NHS; YthFlsp; FHA; GerCl; PpCl; Glf; Trk; BttyCrckrAwd; Westmar College.

RIEDER, Jill M; Griffith HS; Griffith, IN; PresChrhWkr; HonRl; JrNHS; Mdrgl; Quill&Scroll; SchMus; StuCncl; RptrSchPpr; SchPpr; PpCl; College; Profesionel.

RIEDERER, Paul A; Southern Door HS; Sturgeon Bay, WI; ALBoysSt; Band; CncrtBnd; HonRl; MrchBnd; PepBnd; SchMus; 4-H; Ftbl; Wrstlng; Us Army; Police Work.

RIEDIGER, Kendall C; Hinton Comm HS; Hinton, IA; 4/40 Band; Chrs; CncrtBnd; HonRl; MrchBnd; PepBnd; YthFlsp; RptrYrbk; MthCl; College; Vocation.

RIEDL, Margaret A; Divine Savior Holy Angels HS; Wauwatosa, WI; 2/121 HonRl; OffAde; SchPl; TchrAde; SchPpr; MthCl; Mount Mary College; Dietetics.

RIEDL, Susan; Oak Park River Forest Hs; Oak Park, IL; 141/1107 HonRl; LitMag; SctActv; RptrYrbk; Yrbk; Coe College; Medical.

RIEDLER, Kevin R; Rosemount HS; Apple Valley, MN; ChrhWkr; LbryAde; PolWkr; SchPl; RptrSchPpr; GerCl; LetterBsbl; Bsktbl; Us Military Acad Westpoint;engr.

RIEDY, Susan; Chassell HS; Chassell, MI; HonRl; HospAde; LbryAde; SchPl; Yrbk; Bsbl; IMSpt;.

RIEF, Lynn M; Waconia HS; Waconia, MN; SecFrshCls; TrsJrCls; Chr; ChrhWkr; DrmBgl; HonRl; HospAde; MrchBnd; OffAde; 4-H; FHA; Trk; Chrldr; GAA; St Cloud St College.

RIEGE, Kristi K; Valentine HS; Kilgore, NE; ALAGirlsSt; ChrhWkr; CmntyWkr; HonRl; NHS; RedCrAde; StuGov; 4-H; FBLA; 4-HAwd; Chadron State College; Vocation Bus.

RIEGER, Holly A; Carmel HS; Barrington, IL; PresSophCls; ChrhWkr; HonRl; JrNHS; StuCncl; College; Law.

RIEGER, Julie A; Forrest Strawn Wing HS; Forrest, IL; AFS; ALAGirlsSt; Band; Chrs; NHS; Pres4-H; PresFBLA; SpnCl; Chrldr; TreasGAA; Nursing.

RIEGER, Kathleen I; Wesclin Sr HS; Trenton, IL; PresFrshCls; HonRl; JrNHS; PresStuCncl; YthFlsp; FBLA; FrCl; PresPpCl; LetterTrk; College.

RIEGER, Robert A; Wesclin HS; Trenton, IL; PresSophCls; JrNHS; StuCncl; RptrYrbk; LetterBsbl; LetterBsktbl; College; Business.

RIEGER, Timothy; Eureka Public HS; Eureka, SD; Band; CncrtBnd; HonRl; MrchBnd; StuCncl; Bsktbl; CaptFtbl; Trk; Natl College Of Business; Business Admin.

RIEGLE, Candace D; Wapahani HS; Muncie, IN; Band; MrchBnd; SecNatlFornLg; SecNatlThespSoc; 4-H; AmLegAwd; 4-HAwd; Ball State University; Social Work.

RIEHL, Margaret M; St Gertrudes HS; Raleigh, ND; 1/27 ALAGirlsSt; Chrs; HonRl; NHS; NatlMeritFnl; NatlMeritSF; SchPl; StuCncl; EdSchPpr; LetterTrk; Chrldr; IMSpt; Creighton Univ; Clinical Psychology.

RIEHL, Rita E; St Gertrude HS; Raleigh, ND; SecJrCls; Chr; Chrl; Chrs; ChrhWkr; CmntyWkr; DrlTm; HonRl; JrNHS; NHS; Bsktbl; LetterTrk; Chrldr; 4-HAwd; College.

RIEHL, Tony; St Gertrudes HS; Raleigh, ND; 4/26 ALBoysSt; Chrs; NHS; NatlSciFnd; StuCncl; RptrSchPpr; 4-H; Bsktbl; LetterTrk; BauchLmbAwd; Carroll Coll;engineer.

RIEK, William D; Evanston Township HS; Evanston, IL; Us Air Force; Business Admin.

RIEKE, Susan A; Langdon HS; Langdon, ND; 11/109 ALAGirlsSt; HonRl; NHS; RptrSchPpr; FBLA; FHA; PpCl; LetterBsktbl; LetterTrk; Chrldr; GAA; Wahpeton State School; Legal Secretary.

RIEKENA, Teresa L; Illini Bluffs HS; Mapleton, IL; 6/95 PresJrCls; HonRl; NHS; PresStuCncl; PresStuGov; RptrYrbk; 4-H; CaptBsktbl; Trk; GAA; IMSpt; 4-HAwd; College; Medicine.

RIEKENBERG, Renae; Hanover HS; Hanover, KS; Chr; Chrs; ChrhWkr; CncrtBnd; MrchBnd; PepBnd; SchPl; FHA; PpCl; Chrldr; Cloud Comm Jr Coll; Elementary Educ.

RIEKENBERG, Sharon K; Odell Public HS; Odell, NE; Band; Chrs; HonRl; Mdrgl; SchPl; StuCncl; RptrYrbk; LetterBsktbl; LetterTrk; Chrldr; Data Processing.

RIEKER, Joyce L; Eustis Public HS; Eustis, NE; PresJrCls; Chrs; ChrhWkr; HonRl; YthFlsp; Yrbk; 4-H; PpCl; Trk; 4-HAwd; College; Medical.

RIEKER, Lorri; Gothenburg HS; Gothenburg, NE; 7/85 VPSrCls; Chr; Chrs; ChrhWkr; HonRl; Mdrgl; SchPl; YthFlsp; 4-H; PpCl; Univ; Music.

RIEKER, Mary A; Western HS; Sheffield, IL; Band; Chrs; HonRl; HospAde; NatlThespSoc; FHA; FrCl; PpCl; Chrldr; GAA; Nursing Sch; Nursing.

RIELY, Susan M; Unity Public HS; Petersburg, ND; PresJrCls; ALAGirlsSt; Chr; StuCncl; Twrl; Yrbk; SchPpr; 4-H; PpCl; LetterBsktbl; College; Respiratory Therapist.

RIEMAN, Daniel E; Jennings HS; Jennings, MO; 18/250 Aud/Vis; Chrs; HonRl; TchrAde; Yrbk; Wrstlng; College; Law.

RIEMERSMA, Darlene L; Zeeland HS; Zeeland, MI; Chrs; ChrhWkr; CmntyWkr; JrNHS; NHS; StuCncl; Bsbl; Bsktbl; CchngActv; PPFtbl; ChmbCommrsAwd; JAAwd; Calvin College; Special Educ.

RIENKS, Julie A; Verona HS; Verona, WI; Band; Chrs; CncrtBnd; HonRl; MrchBnd; NHS; GerCl; PpCl; Chrldr; College.

RIENSCHE, Barbara L; Nemaha Valley HS; Tecumseh, NE; 2/33 VPFrshCls; HstJrCls; Band; Chrs; CncrtBnd; HonRl; NHS; RptrYrbk; Yrbk; EdSchPpr; Bsbl; Trk; College; Medical Technology.

RIEPE, Susan B; Arapahoe HS; Arapahoe, NE; 1/34 HstFrshCls; VPSophCls; Band; ChrhWkr; HonRl; SchPl; Yrbk; FHA; BttyCrckrAwd; 4-HAwd; Univ Of Nebr; Music.

RIES, Edward B; High School; Mobridge, SD; 40/73 HonRl; SctActv; StuCncl; StuGov; TchrAde; FTA; Bsbl; LetterFtbl; LetterWrstlng; Trade School.

RIES, William B; Sergeant Bluff HS; Sergeant Bluff, IA; 3/43 Band; CncrtBnd; HonRl; MrchBnd; PepBnd; SchPl; StuCncl; LetterBsbl; LetterBsktbl; LetterFtbl; College; Marine Biology.

RIESE, Lynne M; Colo Comm HS; Colo, IA; 3/34 CncrtBnd; HonRl; NHS; SchMus; YthFlsp; Pres4-H; FHA; LetterBsktbl; LetterTrk; 4-HAwd; University; Teacher.

RIESE, Ruth A; St Mary Central HS; Appleton, WI; 20/104 Band; Chrs; HonRl; NatlFornLg; NHS; NatlThespSoc; EdYrBk; OptClAwd; Lawrence Univ; Journalism.

RIESEN, Dean; Nevada Sr HS; Nevada, IA; 8/120 NHS; NatlThespSoc; PolWkr; SciCl; Cornell College; Medicine.

RIESLAND, Denise K; Danville HS; Danville, IL; 1/629 HonRl; HospAde; NHS; NatlMeritCmnd; OffAde; SpnCl; Univ Of Ill; Chemical Engineer.

RIESTERER, Sandy A; J F K Prep; St Nazianz, WI; HonRl; SctActv; TchrAde; Coll; Busi.

RIETH, Blair A; Goshen HS; Goshen, IN; ALBoysSt; Chr; HonRl; Mdrgl; NHS; SchMus; YthFlsp; PpCl; LetterFtbl; LetterTrk; Wrstlng; IMSpt; Univ; Technical Engineering.

RIETH, Rodney L; Waterford Twp HS; Pontiac, MI; HonRl; JA; Bsbl; Univ; Medicine.

RIETUELD, James; Kimberly Sr HS; Kimberly, WI; Chr; SchMus; SctActv; KeyCl; Trk; CchngActv; IMSpt; College; Professional.

RIETVELD, Jerry; Cary Grove HS; Cary, IL; 1/293 ALBoysSt; HonRl; NHS; RptrSchPpr; SpnCl; CaptTennis; IMSpt; BauchLmbAwd; College; Chemical Oceanography.

RIETVELD, Paul H; Beecher HS; Beecher, IL; Band; CncrtBnd; HonRl; MrchBnd; PepBnd; YthFlsp; FFA; IMSpt; Vocation.

RIETZ, Jay C; Oconto Senior HS; Oconto, WI; Band; CAP; HonRl; PepBnd; TchrAde; United States Air Force; Air Traffic.

RIFE, Daniel J; Stratton Public HS; Stratton, NE; 2/18 VPFrshCls; PresJrCls; ALBoysSt; HonRl; NHS; StuCncl; TchrAde; LetterFtbl; LetterTrk; Univ; Acct.

RIFE, Joan; St Clair HS; St Clair, MI; 17/191 HonRl; NatlMeritSF; SchPl; StuCncl; RptrYrbk; Yrbk; 4-H; Adrian Coll; Lawyer.

RIFE, Mark; Manchester HS; North Manchester, IN; JA; NatlFornLg; NHS; SchPl; RptrSchPpr; FrCl; SciCl; Bsktbl; IMSpt; JAAwd; Indiana Univ; Law.

RIFFEL, Bonnie; Inman HS; Inman, KS; Band; Chr; CncrtBnd; HonRl; MrchBnd; PepBnd; SchPl; StuCncl; FHA; PpCl; Airline Sch; Stewardess.

RIFFEL, Patricia H; Ss Peter & Paul HS; Saginaw, MI; Chrs; DrlTm; HonRl; NHS; OffAde; SchAde; SchMus; SchPl; PpCl; College; Nursing.

RIFFENBURG, Donald A; Northville HS; Northville, MI; Chr; Univ; Medicine.

RIFFER, Charlene; Homewood Flossmoor HS; Homewood, IL; 49/932 Chrl; ChrhWkr; HonRl; TchrAde; Teen; University; Professional.

RIFFLE, Barbara L; Auburn HS; Rockford, IL; 20/300 Chrs; HonRl; Mdrgl; College; Elem Education.

RIFFLE, Patricia A; Pius Xi HS; Milwaukee, WI; StuGov; Twrl; FTA; FrCl; Marquette Univ; Nursing.

RIFFLE, Rebecca E; Washington Comm HS; Washington, IL; 8/345 Chrs; ChrhWkr; HonRl; Mdrgl; NHS; NatlMeritCmnd; SchMus; SchPl; TchrAde; FrCl; Univ Of Ill; Pre Medicine Pediatrician.

RIGDON, Ronald E; Griffin HS; Springfield, IL; NHS; RptrSchPpr; Pres4-H; So Ill Univ; Doctor.

RIGG, Curt A; Colchester Jr Sr HS; Colchester, IL; PresSophCls; Band; Chr; Chrl; Chrs; ChrhWkr; CncrtBnd; HonRl; MrchBnd; SchMus; SchPl; StuCncl; Yrbk; CaptBsktbl; Carl Sandburg Jr College; Mechanics.

RIGGANS, Cynthia R; Rich Central HS; Matteson, IL; 21/416 Chr; HonRl; ModUN; SchPl; VPStuCncl; SchPpr; FrCl; MthCl; PpCl; Univ; Liberal Arts.

RIGGENBACH, Kevin C; East Peoria Comm HS; East Peoria, IL; 31/440 NHS; Orch; IMSpt; Bradley Univ; Mech Engi.

RIGGINS, Anita F; North Davies HS; Odon, IN; 2/115 Band; ChrhWkr; HonRl; LbryAde; VPStuCncl; 4-H; FHA; PpCl; IMSpt; DARAwd; Iupui; Radiologic Tech.

RIGGINS, David L; Industry HS; Industry, IL; 15/36 TrsSrCls; HonRl; OffAde; SchAde; SchPl; SctActv; StuCncl; StuGov; EngCl; SciCl; Clg; Vocation.

RIGGINS, Randall D; Monticello HS; Monticello, IL; Band; CncrtBnd; HonRl; MrchBnd; PepBnd; SchMus; LetterTrk; CaptWrstlng; IMSpt; Univ; Music Elec Major.

RIGGINS, Ruth L; Wichita HS; Wichita, KS; 20/657 Band; Chr; HonRl; Mdrgl; OffAde; Orch; SchMus; StuGov; Twrl; Wichita State University; Music.

RIGGINS, Sally M; Henry Co R 1 HS; Windsor, MO; 8/73 Band; CncrtBnd; DrmMjrt; HonRl; MrchBnd; NHS; PepBnd; FTA; LatCl; LetterTrk; Col; Professional.

RIGGIO, Jim; Mendel Catholic HS; Dolton, IL; TrsSrCls; CmntyWkr; StuGov; KeyCl; IMSpt; KiwanAwd; Coll; Bus Admin.

RIGGIO, Joseph; Du Quoin HS; Du Quoin, IL; 27/143 SciCl; Southern Illinois University; Engineering.

RIGGIO, Patricia A; Murphysboro Township HS; Murphysboro, IL; Chrs; HonRl; SctActv; FHA; SpnCl; Siu C; Lab Technician.

RIGGLE, Karen J; Sullivan HS; Sullivan, IL; 6/104 Chrs; HonRl; Mdrgl; NHS; FrCl; University; Fine Arts.

RIGGLE, Stephen F; D C Everest HS; Mosinee, WI; 6/337 CncrtBnd; MrchBnd; NHS; NatlMeritSF; NatlSciFnd; RotaryAwd; College; Airline Pilot.

RIGGS, Beth A; Danville Comm HS; Danville, IN; TrsJrCls; Band; ChrhWkr; NHS; NatlThespSoc; SchMus; SchPl; 4-H; FHA; Purdue Univ; Home Economics.

RIGGS, Frederick R; Manistee Catholic Cen HS; Manistee, MI; 10/70 Band; HonRl; MrchBnd; StuCncl; Yrbk; SchPpr; IMSpt;.

RIGGS, Leigh A; Bennett County HS; Allen, SD; Chrs; DrlTm; HonRl; NHS; FHA; PpCl; CaptChrldr; College.

RIGGS, Robert A; Westport HS; Kansas City, MO; 1/172 CmntyWkr; NHS; Quill&Scroll; PresStuGov; Yrbk; SchPpr; FTA; PresSpnCl; SciCl; CaptTennis; College; Professional.

RIGGS, Robert E; Southwest HS; St Louis, MO; 35/596 PresBand; PresCncrtBnd; HonRl; PresMrchBnd; PepBnd; SchMus; StuCncl; Wrstlng; IMSpt; LionAwd; Coll; Medicine.

RIGGS, Roger C; Newtown Harris HS; Newtown, MO; ALBoysSt; ChrhWkr; HonRl; NHS; Quill&Scroll; EdYrBk; FBLA; LetterBsbl; LetterBsktbl; LetterTrk; College; Lawyer.

RIGGS, Sandy L; Quinter HS; Quinter, KS; Band; HonRl; MrchBnd; ModUN; NHS; SchPl; StuCncl; Twrl; Chrldr; University Of Kansas; Medicine.

RIGNANESE, Sandy; Bishop Dwenger HS; Fort Wayne, IN; Chrs; HonRl; JA; 4-H; College; Teaching.

RIGONI, Mary A; Decatur Jr Sr HS; Decatur, MI; 11/76 NHS; OffAde; SchPl; StuCncl; Pres4-H; PpCl; Trk; Chrldr; DanFAwd; Michigan State Univ; Art.

RIGONI, Steven D; Decatur Jr Sr HS; Decatur, MI; SchPl; SctActv; StuCncl; 4-H; Trk; AmLegAwd; Mich State Univ; Math.

RIGSBEE, John E; Rushville Consolidated HS; Arlington, IN; AFS; Band; ChrhWkr; NHS; PresYthFlsp; Pres4-H; PresMthCl; Ftbl; 4-HAwd; RotaryAwd; College; Architecture.

RIHA, Carol A; La Salle HS; Cedar Rapids, IA; Chr; Mdrgl; NatlFornLg; NHS; Orch; SchMus; RptrSchPpr; Univ; Pre Med.

RIHARB, Joanne M; Waterford Kettering HS; Drayton Plains, MI; 48/423 Band; CncrtBnd; HonRl; MrchBnd; NHS; SctActv; StuCncl; Univ Of Mich; Medical Tech.

RIHM, Carolyn; Tri Jr Sr High; Straughn, IN; 1/90 Band; HonRl; NHS; PresNatlThespSoc; SctActv; Sec4-H; FHA; FrCl; PpCl; 4-HAwd;.

RIHM, Mary; Lincoln HS; Cambridge City, IN; 3/125 SecFrshCls; SecSophCls; SecJrCls; ALAGirlsSt; Band; NHS; OffAde; Chrldr; GAA; Univ.

RIKER, Timothy R; Washington HS; Montgomery, IN; Aud/Vis; ChrhWkr; SchPl; TchrAde; 4-H; FFA; Trade School; Vocation.

RILETT, Richard B; Clare HS; Clare, MI; ChrhWkr; HonRl; StuCncl; TchrAde; EdSchPpr; LetterBsbl; Ftbl; IMSpt; DanFAwd; 4-HAwd; Central Mich Univ; Sec Educ.

RILEY, Belinda A; Northern HS; Detroit, MI; 4/156 PresFrshCls; SecSophCls; TrsJrCls; CmntyWkr; HonRl; RptrSchPpr; SchPpr; Chrldr; DARAwd; OptClAwd; Virginia Farnell College; Professional.

RILEY, Bradley A; Poplar Bluff Sr HS; Poplar Bluff, MO; 22/407 HonRl; Yrbk; SchPpr; MthCl; SciCl; College; Pharmacy.

RILEY, Carol; Notre Dame HS; Quincy, IL; 3/83 PresJrCls; Band; Chrs; CncrtBnd; MrchBnd; NatlMeritCmnd; PepBnd; StuCncl; RptrSchPpr; College; Education.

RILEY, Carol A; Nevada HS; Nevada, MO; Band; CncrtBnd; MrchBnd; 4-H; PpCl; 4-HAwd; OptClAwd; Bus Sch; Exec Secretary.

RILEY, Catherine E; Mac Arthur HS; Decatur, IL; 25/400 AFS; HonRl; JrNHS; RptrSchPpr; GerCl; University Of Illinois; Lawyer.

RILEY, Eva K; Santa Fe Trail HS; Carbondale, KS; 9/90 ALAGirlsSt; Chr; HonRl; NHS; PpCl; LetterBsktbl; LetterTrk; Chrldr; CchngActv; IMSpt; Kansas State Univ; Coaching.

RILEY, Gary P; Monticello HS; Monticello, IL; 2/168 PresSophCls; ALBoysSt; HonRl; MrchBnd; NHS; StuCncl; Bsktbl; Trk; AmLegAwd; College; Business Admin.

RILEY, Guy L; Crothersville HS; Crothersville, IN; PresStuCncl; Bsbl;.

RILEY, Jeffrey K; Pratt Sr HS; Pratt, KS; 19/149 VPFrshCls; VPSophCls; VPJrCls; ALBoysSt; Band; Chr; CncrtBnd; HonRl; MrchBnd; SchPl; PresStuCncl; StuGov; YthFlsp; LetterFtbl; LetterTrk; Kansas University; Lawyer.

RILEY, Jim B; Mt Carmel HS; Evergreen Park, IL; 8/200 HonRl; NHS; StuCncl; StuGov; RptrSchPpr; Loras College; Law.

RILEY, Karen; Goshen HS; Goshen, IN; Chr; HonRl; Yrbk; RptrSchPpr; SpnCl; Chrldr; PresAwd; College; Legal Secretary.

RILEY, Karen L; Lewistown Comm HS; Liverpool, IL; SecFrshCls; ChrhWkr; HonRl; NHS; SchPl; StuCncl; YthFlsp; FrCl; PpCl; LetterGAA; Coll; Secretary.

RILEY, Kathleen J; Waterford Kettering HS; Drayton Plains, MI; 2/424 HonRl; JA; NatlFornLg; PolWkr; StuGov; UNYO; IMSpt; TIMEAwd; GovHonPrgAwd; VoiceDemAwd; Oakland U; Lawyer Or Judge.

RILEY, Kathleen O; Onsted Comm HS; Onsted, MI; Band; CncrtBnd; DrlTm; HonRl; LitMag; MrchBnd; OffAde; PepBnd; SchPl; PpCl; Az U; Journalism.

RILEY, Laura M; Hanover Horton HS; Clarklake, MI; 1/90 TrsSophCls; HonRl; VPDARAwd; Univ (wmu); Science.

RILEY, Maritha J; Roosevelt HS; Gary, IN; Chr; Chrs; ChrhWkr; HonRl; JA; NHS; OffAde; SchMus; TchrAde; College; Pediatrician.

RILEY, Mary; Wgtn Sr HS; Worthington, MN; 9/290 HonRl; LitMag; NHS; RptrSchPpr; Creighton Unv; Chemical Major.

RILEY, Mary F; Oak Park River Forest HS; Oak Park, IL; CmntyWkr; HonRl; HospAde; PolWkr; RptrSchPpr; SptEdSchPpr; Trk; CchngActv; College; Journalism.

RILEY, Mary P; Appleton West HS; Appleton, WI; Band; CncrtBnd; MrchBnd; SpnCl; College; Dental Hygenist.

RILEY, Patrick D; Madison HS; Madison Hts, MI; 30/242 PresSrCls; HonRl; NHS; StuCncl; StuGov; PpCl; CaptFtbl; LetterTrk; CchngActv; IMSpt; PresAwd; CitAwd; Oakland Community College; Physical Therapy.

RILEY, Ricky L; C Ville HS; Culle, MO; 4-H; FBLA; FFA; Trade School; Vocation.

RILEY, Rita E; Cowden Herrick HS; Cowden, IL; Band; Chr; HonRl; SchPl; StuCncl; Yrbk; FHA; GAA; Business Col; Professional.

RILEY, Rita J; Mother Of Sorrows HS; Alsip, IL; 11/162 HonRl; TchrAde; RptrYrbk; MthCl; St Xavier Col; Mathematics.

RILEY, Shannon M; Grace HS; St Paul, MN; Chrs; JrNHS; TchrAde; Chrldr; College; Professional Phy Ed & Horsemanship.

RILEY, Sharon M; Lindblom Technical HS; Chicago, IL; Chr; ChrhWkr; HonRl; LitMag; Quill&Scroll; TchrAde; RptrSchPpr; MthCl; SciCl; GAA; Pre Med.

RILEY, Susan J; California R1 HS; California, MO; 13/100 Band; Chrs; ChrhWkr; HonRl; Mdrgl; TreasNHS; Yrbk; Pres4-H; AmLegAwd; DanFAwd; 4-HAwd; State Univ; Medicine.

RILEY, Susan M; Highland HS; Highland, WI; TrsFrshCls; Band; Chrs; HonRl; Herzing Institute; Medical Secretary.

RILINGER, Don J; B & B HS; Seneca, KS; HonRl; SchPl; LetterBsbl; CaptBsktbl; CaptFtbl; LetterTrk;.

RIMAS, Audra Ann H; Comfrey Public HS; Comfrey, MN; ALAGirlsSt; CncrtBnd; HonRl; HospAde; MrchBnd; SchPl; RptrSchPpr; SciCl; LetterBsktbl; LetterTrk; College Of St Benedicts; Physical Therapy.

RINARD, Gail; Peotone Hs; Peotone, IL; OffAde; PepBnd; SpnCl; MthCl; PpCl; Millikin U; Accounting.

RINCK, James R; Northview HS; Grand Rapids, MI; 13/235 Band; CncrtBnd; MrchBnd; NHS; NatlMeritSF; SctActv; SchPpr; LetterBsktbl; LetterTrk;.

RINDAL, Abraham E; Rockford East HS; Rockford, IL; 33/665 Band; CncrtBnd; HonRl; MrchBnd; NHS; NatlMeritCmnd; TchrAde; Univ Of Illinois; Elec Engineer.

RINDE, Nancy K; St Thomas Public HS; St Thomas, ND; Chrs; HonRl; LbryAde; SchPl; StuCncl; RptrSchPpr; Bsktbl; GAA; PPFtbl; University; Pharmacy.

RINDFUSZ, Karen P; Pontiac Catholic HS; Pontiac, MI; 1/140 CmntyWkr; HonRl; NHS; PolWkr; SchMus; RptrYrbk; FrCl; SciCl; LetterTennis; GAA; Univ Of Michigan; Medical Technology.

RINDT, Kathy A; Rib Lake HS; Westboro, WI; PresFrshCls; VPSophCls; Band; Chr; PepBnd; StuGov; Yrbk; EdSchPpr; Clge.

RINE, Janet; Brookfield Central HS; Brookfield, WI; 2/473 AFS; CmntyWkr; HonRl; JA; NHS; SchPl; Yrbk; U Of Wisconsin; Engineering.

RINEHART, Cynthia R; Centerville HS; Mystic, IA; DrlTm; NHS; Yrbk; SchPpr; 4-H; PpCl; Bsktbl; LetterTrk; 4-HAwd; Clge; Photo Journalism.

RINEHART, Jimmy D; Moravia Comm HS; Moravia, IA; Aud/Vis; Bsbl; Bsktbl; Trade School; Mechanic.

RINEHART, Joyce A; Worth Co Ri HS; Grant City, MO; Band; CncrtBnd; HonRl; MrchBnd; PepBnd; SchMus; 4-H; FTA; PpCl; SciCl; College; Secretarial Work.

RINEHART, Pansy S; Humboldt HS; Humboldt, KS; 11/62 Chr; Chrl; ChrhWkr; HonRl; PpCl; Bsktbl; Trk; Jr Col; Teaching/english.

RINER, Kimberly A; Richmond Sr HS; Richmond, IN; 138/693 Band; CncrtBnd; HonRl; HospAde; SecJA; MrchBnd; StuCncl; Teen; Swmmng; College; Business.

RINESMITH, Randy A; Paris HS; Vermillion, IL; 13/256 Aud/Vis; Band; Chr; Chrs; ChrhWkr; CncrtBnd; HonRl; Mdrgl; MrchBnd; NHS; Bsbl; Rose Hulman Inst Of Tech; Chemistry.

RING, Brian F; Clarion Comm HS; Clarion, IA; ALBoysSt; RptrSchPpr; Bsbl; Bsktbl; College; Law.

RING, Cynthia K; Virginia HS; Virginia, IL; Band; CncrtBnd; HonRl; MrchBnd; StuCncl; 4-H; PpCl; Trk; Chrldr; Passavant Hosp; Nursing.

RING, Daniel W; Emmons HS; Twin Lakes, MN; 1/21 VPJrCls; Band; CncrtBnd; HonRl; MrchBnd; NHS; PepBnd; SchPl; LetterFtbl; LetterGlf;.

RING, Darla; Mo Valley Comm HS; Missouri Valley, IA; Band; ChrhWkr; CncrtBnd; MrchBnd; PepBnd; 4-H; FHA; FTA; PpCl; IMSpt; Ia State Univ; Home Ec Education.

RING, David M; Emmons HS; Twin Lakes, MN; 2/27 PresFrshCls; PresSophCls; Band; CncrtBnd; HonRl; MrchBnd; NHS; PepBnd; SchPl; StuCncl; Augustana College; Accounting.

RING, Deanne K; Huntley HS; Lyman, NE; PresSophCls; Chrs; HonRl; OffAde; StuCncl; FHA; PpCl; Clge.

RING, Deborah L; Metamora HS; Metamora, IL; 17/175 ChrhWkr; HonRl; JrNHS; NHS; SchPl; YthFlsp; RptrYrbk; PpCl; GAA; IMSpt; Icc Bradley; Engi.

RING, Deborah R; East HS; Des Moines, IA; 27/487 ChrhWkr; HonRl; TreasJA; TreasGerCl; PpCl; Tennis; Concordia Teachers Coll; Math.

RING, Diane; Columbus HS; Columbus, WI; 13/125 Band; ChrhWkr; HospAde; MrchBnd; NHS; OffAde; SchMus; 4-H; Uw Madison; Diplomatic Service.

RING, Margaret R; Carmel Girls HS; Mundelein, IL; 1/183 HonRl; NHS; NatlMeritSF; RptrYrbk; FrCl; College; Medicine.

RING, Randy J; Lincoln HS; Sioux Falls, SD; HonRl; NatlMeritSF; TchrAde; SpnCl; Sd State University.

RING, Rhaelyn M; Lincoln HS; Floodwood, MN; 1/45 ChrhWkr; HonRl; JA; NHS; SchPl; SecStuCncl; TchrAde; RptrSchPpr; FHA; ChmnChrldr; Trade; Medical Tech.

RING, Rita; Paris HS; Paris, IL; 15/236 Tennis; GAA; DanFAwd; DARAwd; 4-HAwd; PresAwd; Univ; Math Accounting.

RING, Suzanne K; Winnebago Lutheran Academy; Oshkosh, WI; Tech School; Medical Sec.

RINGENBERG, Lorie A; Tiskilwa HS; Tiskilwa, IL; PresSrCls; Band; Chr; Chrs; CncrtBnd; HonRl; HospAde; LetterBsktbl; Chrldr; GAA; Goshen College; Nursing.

RINGERS, Kathryn A; Philip HS; Philip, SD; 1/42 ALAGirlsSt; ChrhWkr; CncrtBnd; HonRl; NHS; StuCncl; Yrbk; RptrSchPpr; FrCl; DARAwd; LionAwd; Sd St U; Nurse.

RINGGENBERG, Albert A; Perry Community HS; Perry, IA; Band; HonRl; ModUN; NatlFornLg; PolWkr; SchPl; SctActv; LetterStuCncl; StuGov; SchPpr; Drake Univ; Legal.

RINGLE, Shelley R; Marathon HS; Edgar, WI; 1/98 PresSophCls; TrsJrCls; Band; HonRl; SecStuCncl; TchrAde; RptrSchPpr; SchPpr; GAA; AmLegAwd; DARAwd; CitAwd; Univ Of Wisconsin; Nursing.

RINGLEIN, Sharon M; Luke M Powers HS; Flint, MI; Band; Chr; ChrhWkr; CmntyWkr; HonRl; HospAde; PresJA; PolWkr; SchMus; IMSpt; Nazareth College; Medicine.

RINGLER, Christine D; Lakeshore HS; Stevensville, MI; 22/240 Band; CncrtBnd; HonRl; MrchBnd; NHS; NatlMeritCmnd; PepBnd; SchAde; TchrAde; Yrbk; Central Mi Univ; Commercial Art & Advertise.

RINGLER, Kevin J; Mattawa HS; Kalamazoo, MI; 16/115 Band; JrNHS; NHS; NatlMeritCmnd; LetterFtbl; Western Mich Univ; Medicine.

RINGLING, Charles P; Aquinas HS; Fort Madison, IA; CmntyWkr; TchrAde; RptrSchPpr; PpCl; IMSpt; Jr College; Law.

RINGO, Kerry B; Bremen HS; Bremen, IN; Chr; HonRl; JrNHS; SchMus; SchPl; FrCl; PpCl; Tennis; GAA; University; Theatre.

RINGSTAD, Kristy L; South Hamilton HS; Jewell, IA; 5/91 SecFrshCls; ALAGirlsSt; Band; Chrs; HonRl; Mdrgl; MrchBnd; NHS; PepBnd; SchMus; Univ Of Ia; Nursing.

RINKER, Colleen J; Streator Township HS; Streator, IL; 7/372 Band; SecChrs; CmntyWkr; HonRl; Mdrgl; NHS; SchMus; YthFlsp; 4-H; FTA; GerCl; 4-HAwd; Ill State Univ; Spec Education.

RINKER, Elizabeth A; Streator Twp HS; Streator, IL; 54/383 HonRl; HospAde; OffAde; StuCncl; YthFlsp; 4-H; GerCl; Univ Of Il; Vet Medicine.

RINN, Frances A; Bellevue HS; Bellevue, NE; 19/684 ALAGirlsSt; HonRl; NHS; FHA; IMSpt; PPFtbl; College; Nursing.

RINNE, Bob D; Bern HS; Bern, KS; VPJrCls; Band; Chr; HonRl; SchPl; StuCncl; YthFlsp; Bsktbl; LetterFtbl; IMSpt; Washburn U;math & Sci.

RINNE, Denise L; Jefferson City HS; Holts Summit, MO; 33/486 Band; Chr; Chrl; CncrtBnd; HonRl; JrNHS; MrchBnd; NHS; Quill&Scroll; Yrbk; Mo U; Journ.

RINTA, Ann S; J F Kennedy HS; Babbitt, MN; 27/143 SecSophCls; Band; Chr; HonRl; NHS; Orch; SchMus; SchPl; StuCncl; RptrSchPpr; U M D; Music Therapy.

RIO, Steve; Willowbrook Hs; Villa Park, IL; 120/822 Chr; ChrhWkr; CmntyWkr; HonRl; NHS; NatlThespSoc; SchMus; SchPl; StuCncl; StuGov; College; Psychology Philosophy Theology.

RIOPEL, Cecilia D; Forest Lake Sr HS; Hugo, MN; 44/353 Alexandria Vo Tech; Art.

RIOPELLE, Tim M; Mount Cathedral HS; Crookston, MN; VPFrshCls; VPSophCls; Chr; Chrs; SchMus; StuCncl; SptEdSchPpr; SpnCl; Bsbl; Ftbl; Coll; Prof.

RIORDAN, Michael K; Rapid City Stevens HS; Rapid City, SD; ALBoysSt; ChrhWkr; HonRl; NatlFornLg; NatlThespSoc; SchMus; SchPl; StuCncl; StuGov; College; Law.

RIORDAN, Michael L; Wichita East HS; Wichita, KS; 1/657 VPSrCls; ALBoysSt; CtyCnl; HonRl; ModUN; PolWkr; StuGov; YthFlsp; SpnCl; CaptSwmmng; NCTE; Washington Univ; Chemical Engineer.

RIORDAN, Susan A; Elizabeth Seton HS; Calumet Park, IL; PresSophCls; Chrs; HonRl; HospAde; Mdrgl; NHS; SchMus; SchPl; StuCncl; StuGov; TchrAde; St Xavier College; Nursing.

RIPA, Daniel R; Wilbur/clatonia HS; Wilber, NE; 5/45 PresJrCls; Band; HonRl; SchMus; SchPl; RptrYrbk; RptrSchPpr; Sec4-H; SecFFA; Ftbl; College; Medicine.

RIPBERGER, Richard C; Tri Central HS; Sharpsville, IN; ChrhWkr; SctActv; Teen; YthFlsp; FrCl; Bsbl; LetterBsktbl; LetterTrk; IMSpt; In U; Bus.

RIPP, Donald C; Ravenna HS; Ravenna, NE; ChrhWkr; 4-H; FFA; Wrstlng;.

RIPPA, Cindy M; Proviso East HS; Forest Park, IL; ChrhWkr; CmntyWkr; HonRl; NHS; PolWkr; Quill&Scroll; SctActv; YthFlsp; FrCl; Northwestern Univ; Journalist.

RIPPENKROEGER, Christine L; Aquinas HS; Fort Madison, IA; 3/45 Chr; DrlTm; HonRl; RptrYrbk; RptrSchPpr; FHA; SpnCl; PpCl; Univ Of Northern Ia; Social Work.

RIPPENTROP, Brent L; Titonka HS; Titonka, IA; HonRl; NHS; TreasStuCncl; VPYthFlsp; PresFFA; Bsbl; Ftbl; Trk; College; Agriculture.

RIPPETOE, Deborah L; Shawnee Heights HS; Tecumseh, KS; 13/187 DrlTm; LbryAde; NatlFornLg; NatlThespSoc; SchPl; Ks St Univ; Bio Chem Research.

RIPPEY, Glenda; Maysville R I HS; Amity, MO; 6/71 Chrs; CncrtBnd; HonRl; MrchBnd; NHS; 4-H; PpCl; Bsbl; Trk; PPFtbl; Coll Of Mo; Vet.

RIPPLE, Julie A; Sturgis HS; Sturgis, MI; CncrtBnd; HonRl; NHS; Glen Oaks Comm College; Accounting.

RIPPLE, Mark; Hammond HS; Hammond, IN; 23/250 VPSophCls; ALBoysSt; Band; CncrtBnd; HonRl; JrNHS; NHS; Orch; StuGov; Rose Hulman Inst Of Tech; Mathematician.

RIPPY, Brenda S; Odin Public HS; Odin, IL; 2/26 VPFrshCls; SecSophCls; SecSrCls; Chrs; HonRl; NatlThespSoc; EdYrBk; SchPpr; FHA; PpCl; Kaskaskia Jr C; Secretarial.

RIPPY, Howard E; Southmont Jr Sr HS; Ladoga, IN; ALBoysSt; YthFlsp; Ytrbk; VP4-H; FFA; SpnCl; Ftbl; Trk; AmLegAwd; 4-HAwd; Purdue Univ; Agriculture.

RIPSLINGER, Jane F; West HS; Davenport, IA; 51/828 Band; DrlTm; HonRl; MrchBnd; StuCncl; TchrAde; FrCl; LetterTennis; CchngActv; GAA; College; Teacher.

RIPSTRA, Katie L; Northview HS; Grand Rapids, MI; HonRl; PpCl; PPFtbl; College; Business.

RIQUELME, Brenda M; George Rogers Clark HS; Whiting, IN; Chrs; HonRl; JrNHS; NHS; SctActv; FHA; SpnCl; IMSpt; Military; Professional.

RISCH, Debbie; Lincoln HS; Manitowoc, WI; HonRl; LetterTennis; GAA; IMSpt; Voc Sch; Sec.

RISCH, Peggy; Incarnate Word Acad; Florissant, MO; ; ChrhWkr; HonRl; JrNHS; NHS; OffAde; Sdlty; StuCncl; RptrSchPpr; VoiceDemAwd; Coll; Lawyer.

RISCHE, Martin R; Luther North HS; Harwood Hgts, IL; 75/300 CncrtBnd; SctActv; Trk;.

RISCHER, Cynthia L; Topeka West HS; Topeka, KS; 31/422 HonRl; TchrAde; EdYrBk; LetterBsktbl; LetterTennis; LetterCchngActv; PPFtbl; Col;.

RISCHLING, Steven E; Crete HS; Crete, NE; 15/120 ChrhWkr; HonRl; Mdrgl; MrchBnd; ModUN; SchPl; StuGov; SptEdSchPpr; LetterFtbl; DARAwd; Doane College.

RISINGER, Barbara J; Assumption HS; Wis Rapids, WI; 35/117 ALAGirlsSt; CncrtBnd; HonRl; NHS; StuCncl; Yrbk; FNA; ChmnBsktbl; Trk; DARAwd; Univ Wi; Nursing.

RISK, James; West Bloomfield HS; West Bloomfield, MI; PresSophCls; PresJrCls; CmntyWkr; HonRl; NHS; StuGov; FDA; Bsktbl; Ftbl; Trk; Michigan State U; Psychologist.

RISLER, Kevin P; Gilmanton HS; Alma, WI; Band; ChrhWkr; CmntyWkr; JA; 4-H; FFA; PpCl; Bsbl; 4-HAwd; Trade School; Vocation.

RISLEY, Clifford R; Riverside Brookfield HS; Brookfield, IL; Aud/Vis; Chr; Chrs; ChrhWkr; JA; SchPl; SctActv; PresYthFlsp; GerCl; Parks Univ; Service Aircraft.

RISNER, Daniel W; Penn HS; Mishawaka, IN; 22/504 ALBoysSt; ChrhWkr; NHS; FTA; GerCl; LetterFtbl; Trk; IMSpt; JETSAwd; Rose Hullman Institute; Mech Engineer.

RISS, Beverly J; Dwight HS; Ransom, IL; 2/110 VPSrCls; AFS; Chrs; DrlTm; HonRl; NHS; Yrbk; 4-H; FrCl;.

RISSE, Joseph W; Frankfort HS; Frankfort, IN; PresSophCls; JrNHS; NatlMeritCmnd; NatlMeritSchl; SchMus; SchPl; StuCncl; SptEdSchPpr; FTA; IMSpt; Indiana University; Business Major.

RISSELMAN, Mary J; Connersville HS; Connersville, IN; Band; CncrtBnd; HonRl; JA; LbryAde; MrchBnd; NHS; PepBnd; TchrAde; IMSpt; Trade Schl; Accounting.

RIST, Becky J; Papillion HS; Papillion, NE; DrlTm; YthFlsp; FBLA; FHA; Business School; Secretarial.

RISTAU, Rene L; Kimberly HS; Combined Locks, WI; 17/280 ALAGirlsSt; CmntyWkr; HonRl; NHS; SchPl; EdYrBk; FHA; LetterGlf; Univ; Professional.

RISTER, Steven; Litchfield Sr Hs; Litchfield, IL; ALBoysSt; HonRl; JrNHS; NHS; KeyCl; FrCl; S I U Carbondale; Business.

RISTICH, Samuel M; Thornton Fractional So HS; Lansing, IL; HonRl; NHS; PolWkr; TchrAde; LatCl; LetterBsktbl; CaptTrk; Univ Of Ill; Vet.

RISTOW, Denise; J F K Prep; Kiel, WI; OffAde; StuGov; Yrbk; EdSchPpr; Bsktbl; Marquette U; Pre Med.

RISTOW, Mark R; Aquinas HS; La Crosse, WI; PresJrCls; StuCncl; StuGov; Bsktbl; LetterFtbl; Trk; IMSpt; College; Accounting.

RITALA, Shelley A; Horace Mann HS; Gilbert, MN; Band; Chr; PepBnd; SchPl; RptrYrbk; Treas4-H; 4-HAwd; College; Animal Science.

RITCHAY, William J; Assumption HS; Wisconsin Rapids, WI; HonRl; NHS; StuCncl; RptrSchPpr; KeyCl; Bsbl; LetterBsktbl; LetterFtbl; LetterTrk; Clge.

RITCHEY, Lisa K; Pinckney HS; Pinckney, MI; 4/286 Band; HonRl; NHS; StuCncl; Yrbk; 4-H; Trk; GAA; 4-HAwd; College; Professional.

RITENOUR, Denise L; Maconaquah HS; Grissom Afb, IN; 17/217 LetterBand; CncrtBnd; HonRl; MrchBnd; NatlThespSoc; SchMus; SchPl; FrCl; LetterTrk; College.

RITENOUR, Kimberly; Chadwick Comm HS; Chadwick, IL; SecSophCls; TrsJrCls; Band; Chrs; ChrhWkr; HonRl; SchMus; SchPl; StuCncl; Glf; College; Music.

RITER, Pamela; Platte Valley Acad; Lisco, NE; Chr; ChrhWkr; NHS; NatlMeritCmnd; StuGov; RptrYrbk; RptrSchPpr; CaptBsktbl; Socr; Union College; Mathematics Education.

RITLAND, David P; Whitehall Memorial HS; Whitehall, WI; 4/68 PresSrCls; ALBoysSt; Band; Chrs; CncrtBnd; HonRl; Mdrgl; MrchBnd; PresNHS; Trk; College; Music.

RITLAND, Randy R; Hubbard Comm HS; Hubbard, IA; 3/43 TrsSrCls; Band; Chrs; CncrtBnd; HonRl; MrchBnd; PepBnd; SchMus; Yrbk; Ftbl; Iowa St Niv; Agriculture.

RITONIA, Kathleen L; Grafton HS; Grafton, WI; 36/210 HonRl; NHS; OffAde; SctActv; TchrAde; Yrbk; SpnCl; Bsbl; Chrldr; GAA; Univ Of Wi Oshkosh; Accountin.

RITSCHE, Dan F; Turtle Lake HS; Turtle Lake, WI; 1/60 PresFrshCls; ALBoysSt; CncrtBnd; HonRl; NatlMeritSF; SchPl; StuCncl; SptEdYrbk; 4-H; LetterBsktbl; LetterFtbl; LetterGlf; 4-HAwd; College; Science.

RITSCHER, Kevin N; Alma HS; Alma, WI; PresJrCls; HonRl; LetterBsbl; LetterFtbl; LetterGlf; LetterTrk; AmLegAwd; Trade School; Vocation.

RITSEMA, Liala J; Westview HS; Kankakee, IL; 28/223 TrsJrCls; HonRl; Mdrgl; NHS; NatlThespSoc; VPQuill&Scroll; PresStuCncl; RptrSchPpr; Trk; Augustanna College; Teacher.

RITTENHOUSE, Daniel J; Griffin HS; Springfield, IL; 58/210 SecFrshCls; HonRl; JA; SchMus; SchPl; StuCncl; StuGov; RptrYrbk; SciCl; LetterGlf; College; Veterinarian.

RITTENHOUSE, Dorothy A; St Francis HS; Wheaton, IL; 6/88 Band; Chrs; HonRl; StuCncl; Chrldr; Medicine.

RITTENHOUSE, Julie A; Marian HS; Mishawaka, IN; 15/118 VPJrCls; VPSrCls; HonRl; Mdrgl; NHS; SchPl; StuCncl; RptrYrbk; SchPpr; CchngActv; IMSpt; Univ Of Notre Dame; Law.

RITTENHOUSE, Karin M; Kingsford HS; Kingsford, MI; SecTrsFrshCls; Chrs; HonRl; TchrAde; PpCl; Chrldr; Michigan State University; Special Educ.

RITTENOUR, Timothy M; Maplewood Academy; Cambridge, MN; Band; Chr; ChrhWkr; HonRl; Mdrgl; RptrYrbk;.

RITTER, Anne E; La Salle HS; South Bend, IN; VPJrCls; Chrs; HonRl; NHS; Quill&Scroll; SchMus; StuGov; SptEdSchPpr; 4-H; 4-HAwd; Indiana Univ; Nursing.

RITTER, Bonnie L; Leigh Community HS; Creston, NE; ALAGirlsSt; Band; HonRl; Mdrgl; SecStuCncl; TchrAde; Yrbk; Sec4-H; FHA; Chrldr; Lincoln Bus Schl; Medical Secretary.

RITTER, Brenda J; Avon HS; Plainfield, IN; Band; CncrtBnd; MrchBnd; PepBnd; SchMus; TchrAde; LatCl; Iupui; Lawyer.

RITTER, Dale R; E Waterloo HS; Waterloo, IA; PresFrshCls; ALBoysSt; Band; Chr; CncrtBnd; HonRl; MrchBnd; SchMus; LetterTrk; LetterWrstlng; Iowa State U; Vet.

RITTER, Daniel P; Washington Comm HS; Washington, IL; 19/345 HonRl; NHS; NatlMeritFnl; NatlMeritSF; SchPpr; University; Computer Programming.

RITTER, Gay L; Sherwood Public HS; Sherwood, ND; VPJrCls; Band; Chrs; DrlTm; HonRl; SchPl; StuCncl; EdYrBk; PpCl; Bsktbl; Clge; Business Or Physical Ed.

RITTER, James L; Paris HS; Paris, IL; 21/256 TrsFrshCls; ChrhWkr; HonRl; JA; NHS; NatlMeritCmnd; StuCncl; SpnCl; Bsbl; Bsktbl; CaptSwmmng; Purdue Univ; Nuclear Physics.

RITTER, Joan F; Mt Assisi Academy; Oak Lawn, IL; 20/194 HonRl; EngCl; SpnCl; MthCl; College.

RITTER, Kevin L; Kinmundy Alma HS; Kinmundy, IL; 2/57 TreasBand; NHS; SchPl; StuCncl; Yrbk; Pres4-H; FFA; LetterTrk; DanFAwd; 4-HAwd; University; Professional.

RITTER, Laura M; Reading Community HS; Reading, MI; Band; CncrtBnd; HonRl; LbryAde; MrchBnd; Yrbk; SchPpr; School Of Design; Architecture.

RITTER, Marie G; Decatur Community HS; Oberlin, KS; 3/86 Chr; ChrhWkr; CmntyWkr; HonRl; NatlFornLg; NHS; FTA; SpnCl; Kansas College; Law.

RITTER, Nancy E; Pekin Community HS; Pekin, IL; 18/759 HospAde; Illinois Cntrl College; Ethology.

RITTER, Sheri L; Davis Co Comm HS; Bloomfield, IA; PresSophCls; HonRl; NHS; SecNatlThespSoc; StuCncl; RptrYrbk; EdSchPpr; VPFrCl; VoiceDemAwd; College; Professional.

RITTERBUSCH, Brenda K; Owensville R 2 HS; Owensville, MO; 5/118 DrlTm; HonRl; NHS; NatlThespSoc; SchMus; SchPl; StuCncl; PresYthFlsp; VPLatCl; PresPpCl; College; Dental Hygienist.

RITTGERS, Brian R; Prairie Comm HS; Gowrie, IA; 29/78 PresFrshCls; Band; Chrs; ChrhWkr; CncrtBnd; HonRl; SchMus; Bsktbl; CaptFtbl; Trk; CchngActv; Iowa St Univ; Management.

RITTMANIC, Paula S; Dixon HS; Dixon, IL; 7/350 Band; Chr; Chrs; CncrtBnd; HonRl; Mdrgl; MrchBnd; NHS; University; Social Worker.

RITZ, Carmen; Litchfield HS; Litchfield, IL; VPJrCls; HonRl; StuCncl; Bsbl; Trk; CchngActv; GAA; IMSpt; PresAwd; Coll; Vetrinary Medicine.

RITZ, Daniel; Newton Comm HS; Newton, IL; 56/187 Aud/Vis; HonRl; FFA; Ftbl; Trk; IMSpt; Jr Coll; Mechanic.

RITZDORF, Mary E; Mercy HS; Omaha, NE; TrsSophCls; Chrs; HonRl; NHS; SchPl; Sdlty; FrCl; Bsbl; Bsktbl; IMSpt; College; Major Study.

RITZHEIMER, Tammy M; Highland HS; Highland, IL; 6/179 LetterBand; DrmMjrt; HonRl; NHS; SchMus; SchPl; LetterTennis; LetterTrk; PresGAA; PPFtbl; U Of Il; Law.

RITZMAN, Jeff N; Hempstead HS; Dubuque, IA; 25/540 PresSrCls; HonRl; ModUN; NHS; StuGov; Bsbl; AmLegAwd; College; Law.

RITZMAN, Laura L; Bishop Borgess HS; Detroit, MI; ChrhWkr; CmntyWkr; HonRl; HospAde; NHS; SchMus; SchPl; StuCncl; MthCl; SciCl; Univ Of Mi; Medicine.

RITZWOLLER, Robert M; Carmel HS; Waukegan, IL; 15/172 HonRl; Univ Of Il; Veterinary Med.

RIUS, Richard P; Saint Joseph HS; Bellwood, IL; 4/200 PresSophCls; PresJrCls; HonRl; NatlMeritSF; StuCncl; StuGov; SpnCl; PpCl; LetterBsbl; LetterWrstlng; IMSpt; Notre Dame Univ; Law.

RIVARA, Kathy M; Forest View HS; Mt Prospect, IL; 161/645 HonRl; HospAde; NHS; SctActv; Univ Of Illinois; Accounting.

RIVARD, Jayne; Lake Of The Woods HS; Baudette, MN; 3/60 PresSophCls; ALAGirlsSt; Band; HonRl; ModUN; NHS; Yrbk; SchPpr; College; Nursing.

RIVARD, Susan F; Bay City Central HS; Munger, MI; HonRl; NHS; TchrAde; 4-H; EngCl; PPFtbl; BauchLmbAwd; 4-HAwd; U Of Mi; Nursing Registered.

RIVARO, Raymond T; Glenwood City HS; Glenwood City, WI; 20/85 PresSrCls; HonRl; PolWkr; StuCncl; TchrAde; RptrSchPpr; SptEdSchPpr; LetterBsbl; LetterBsktbl; LetterGlf; St Univ; Teaching.

RIVERS, Kathleen A; High School; Ripon, WI; 20/160 AFS; HonRl; SchPl; RptrYrbk; RptrSchPpr; PresAwd; University; Nursing.

RIVERS, Linnie M; Cass Technical HS; Detroit, MI; NHS; NatlMeritFnl; Oakland U; Mathematics.

RIVERS, Randy G; Central HS; Grenola, KS; ALBoysSt; CmntyWkr; HonRl; JA; JrNHS; NHS; OffAde; PolWkr; SchAde; SchPl; StuCncl; TchrAde; Bsbl; Bsktbl; College; Engineering.

RIVERS, Rocky D; Centralia HS; Hannibal, MO; 3/88 HonRl; JrNHS; LitMag; NHS; SchPl; Yrbk; RptrSchPpr; SchPpr; SpnCl; University; Minister.

RIX, Sandra J; Lytton Comm HS; Fonda, IA; SecJrCls; CncrtBnd; HonRl; MrchBnd; NHS; PepBnd; SchPl; RptrSchPpr; PpCl; LetterBsktbl; College; Court Reporter.

RIZER, Barbara A; Atchison HS; Atchison, KS; HonRl; ModUN; NatlFornLg; SchMus; StuGov; UNYO; YthLg; RptrSchPpr; Univ Of Arizona; Air Force.

RIZZARDI, Cecile M; Catholic Central HS; Marinette, WI; 5/89 VPJrCls; VPSrCls; ALAGirlsSt; ChrhWkr; HonRl; SchMus; TreasStuCncl; SecSciCl; Tennis; EldAwd; St Norberts College; Law.

RIZZO, Jayne; Our Lady Star Of The Sea HS; Grosse Pte Farms, MI; 1/57 PresSophCls; HonRl; NatlFornLg; PresNHS; NatlThespSoc; SchPl; RptrSchPpr; Bsktbl; IMSpt; CitAwd; Univ Of Notre Dame; Business & Law.

RIZZO, Regina M; Carl Brablec HS; Roseville, MI; 13/475 CncrtBnd; HonRl; JrNHS; MrchBnd; NHS; NatlMeritSchl; NatlMeritSF; PepBnd; SchMus; SctActv; TchrAde; EdYrBk; EdSchPpr; Alma College; Journalism.

RIZZO, Virginia A; Arlington HS; Arlington Heights, IL; 6/581 Chrs; HonRl; PresNatlFornLg; PresNHS; StuCncl; PresFrCl; SecPpCl; LetterBsktbl; Swmmng; Trk; College; Law.

RIZZO, Virginia A; Arlington HS; Arlington Hts, IL; 6/585 Chrs; HonRl; PresNatlFornLg; PresNHS; StuCncl; PresFrCl; SecPpCl; LetterBsktbl; GAA; Coll; Pol Sci.

RIZZOLI, Thomas J; East Alton Wood Rvr Comm HS; Wood River, IL; 10/331 PresJrCls; ALBoysSt; HonRl; JrNHS; LitMag; NHS; OffAde; StuCncl; SpnCl; LetterTennis; Drake Univ; Biology Research.

RIZZUTO, John F; Marist HS; Blue Island, IL; 9/365 HonRl; NatlMeritCmnd; Loyola Univ; Teacher.

ROACH, Brian D; Central Cass HS; Wheatland, ND; ChrhWkr; CncrtBnd; HonRl; NHS; 4-H; AmLegAwd; 4-HAwd; LionAwd; VFWAwd; College; Agriculture.

ROACH, James E; Florence HS; Florence, WI; 2/69 PresFrshCls; VPSrCls; Band; HonRl; PresNHS; LetterBsbl; ChmnFtbl; LetterWrstlng; GovHonPrgAwd; PresAwd; U Of Wi; Agricultural Eng.

ROACH, Joseph J; Regis HS; Eau Claire, WI; 65/140 ChrhWkr; CmntyWkr; NatlFornLg; SchMus; SchPl; SpnCl; Bsbl; Bsktbl; LetterFtbl; University; Broadcasting.

ROACH, Karen J; Edgewood HS; Ellettsville, IN; 7/167 HonRl; NHS; SchPl; RptrYrbk; RptrSchPpr; 4-H; GerCl; SciCl; GAA; PPFtbl; Univ; Art.

ROACH, Kathleen; St Anthonys Hs; St Louis, MO; 3/73 SecSophCls; PresSrCls; CncrtBnd; HonRl; HospAde; NHS; NatlFornLg; StuCncl; RptrSchPpr; CchngActv; St Louis U; Math Major.

ROACH, Pamela; Evergreen Park HS; Oak Lawn, IL; Chrs; HonRl; NHS; FNA; GerCl; PpCl; GAA; Loyola; Nursing.

ROACH, Phil C; Northrop HS; Ft Wayne, IN; 22/647 Band; CncrtBnd; HonRl; MrchBnd; StuCncl; IMSpt; ChmbCommrsAwd; Indiana Univ; Dentist.

ROACH, Robert P; Roncalli HS; Greenfield, IN; HonRl; SchMus; SchPl; Ftbl; LetterTrk; Wrstlng; College; Law.

ROADCAP, Sandra J; Lake Forest HS; Lake Forest, IL; 2/435 HonRl; HospAde; NHS; NatlMeritFnl; Orch; Quill&Scroll; SchMus; SctActv; SchPpr; University; Science.

ROAM, Karen A; Lincoln Cnty Rii HS; Elsberry, MO; ChrhWkr; HonRl; NHS; Orch; Gateway College.

ROAM, Kim M; Richland HS; Richland, MO; ChrhWkr; HonRl; YthFlsp; Bsbl; Bsktbl; Trk; College; Law.

ROARTY, Michael; Austin Cath Prep; Grosse Pte Pk, MI; 6/135 HonRl; NHS; Quill&Scroll; SchMus; SchPl; SctActv; RptrSchPpr; IMSpt; Univ Of Mich; Engineering.

ROBACK, Dawn E; Sand Creek HS; Jasper, MI; Band; Chr; CncrtBnd; HonRl; MrchBnd; SchMus; SchPl; YthFlsp; 4-H; 4-HAwd; College.

ROBARGE, Lynn M; Gobles HS; Gobles, MI; TrsJrCls; HonRl; NHS; StuCncl; Yrbk; EdSchPpr; FrCl; Bsktbl; Chrldr; IMSpt; Western Michigan Univ; Stewardess.

ROBARTS, Van E; Franklin Central HS; Indianapolis, IN; Band; Chr; MrchBnd; NHS; Trk; IMSpt; Freed Hardeman Clg; Minister.

ROBB, Brenda K; Big Springs HS; Big Springs, NE; VPFrshCls; Band; VPStuCncl; Twrl; EdYrBk; FHA; LetterTrk; Chrldr; 4-HAwd; Kearney; Elementary Educ.

ROBB, Dan L; Guide Rock Public HS; Guide Rock, NE; VPFrshCls; TrsSophCls; VPJrCls; PresSrCls; Band; Chrs; TchrAde; LetterFtbl; LetterTrk; Central Ne Tech; Ag.

ROBB, Kelly I; University HS; Centerview, MO; 13/47 HonRl; SecNatlFornLg; SecNHS; SchPl; Yrbk; FrCl; PpCl; Chrldr; IMSpt; College; Accountant.

ROBB, Margie; Fowlerville HS; Fowlerville, MI; /115 TrsFrshCls; Chrl; HonRl; NHS; 4-H; SpnCl; Chrldr; GAA; 4-HAwd; Virginia Polytechnical Univ; Dairy Science.

ROBB, Rita F; Edwards Co Sr HS; Albion, IL; SecJrCls; ChrhWkr; HonRl; NHS; OffAde; RptrSchPpr; SchPpr; PpCl; Jr College; Business.

ROBBIE, Robin; Belleville East HS; Belleville, IL; 18/677 HonRl; NHS; GerCl; IMSpt; DARAwd; Upper Iowa Univ; Biology.

ROBBINS, Alan D; Manson HS; Manson, IA; Band; Chr; Chrs; ChrhWkr; CmntyWkr; CncrtBnd; MrchBnd; PepBnd; SchMus; Bsbl; College; Professional.

ROBBINS, Amy J; Winchester Comm HS; Winchester, IN; 1/180 TrsJrCls; TrsSrCls; DrlTm; HonRl; NHS; TchrAde; FHA; FTA; FrCl; LetterGlf; Indiana Univ; Chemistry.

ROBBINS, Bonnie S; Bennett County HS; Martin, SD; 8/65 Band; Chrs; CncrtBnd; HonRl; MrchBnd; NHS; 4-H; SpnCl; Trk; College; Forestry.

ROBBINS, Dena L; Elk Point Public HS; Elk Point, SD; Chr; ChrhWkr; CmntyWkr; HonRl; SchPl; YthFlsp; 4-H; Glf; Chrldr; College.

ROBBINS, Gary A; Kewanee HS; Kewanee, IL; HonRl; SctActv; PresYthFlsp; VPKeyCl; LatCl; Glf; College; Scout Executive.

ROBBINS, Karen K; Warren HS; Warren, IL; CncrtBnd; MrchBnd; Orch; PepBnd; SchMus; RptrSchPpr; Pres4-H; VPFHA; TreasFTA; BttyCrckrAwd; 4-HAwd; Univ Of Wisconsin; Home Economics.

ROBBINS, Kenneth E; Parsons Sr HS; Parsons, KS; HonRl; College; Forestry.

ROBBINS, Linda S; Greencastle HS; Greencastle, IN; 2/162 VPJrCls; CmntyWkr; HonRl; HospAde; NatlThespSoc; SchMus; SchPl; FrCl; JCAwd; KiwanAwd; Miami Univ; Marketing.

ROBBINS, Mark T; Moline HS; Moline, IL; PresFrshCls; HonRl; NHS; StuGov; SptEdSchPpr; KeyCl; Bsbl; Bsktbl; CaptFtbl; Trk; College; Professional Baseball.

ROBBINS, Marshall L; Clarenceville HS; Livonia, MI; 13/231 AFS; Band; CncrtBnd; HonRl; MrchBnd; NHS; NatlMeritCmnd; NatlMeritSF; Orch; SchAde; Bsbl; Ftbl; Trk; United States Air Force; Dentist.

ROBBINS, Richard T; Chelsea HS; Grass Lake, MI; Aud/Vis; HonRl; NHS; NatlMeritCmnd; LetterBsktbl; LetterTrk;.

ROBECK, Patrick; St Michael Albertville HS; St Michael, MN; Band; Chrs; CncrtBnd; HonRl; MrchBnd; TchrAde; Yrbk; SpnCl; SciCl; Trk; Navy; Elec Tech.

ROBEL, Rick W; St Marys HS; Storm Lake, IA; PresFrshCls; PresSrCls; Band; Chrs; CncrtBnd; MrchBnd; PepBnd; SancSoc; StuCncl; RptrYrbk; RptrSchPpr; LetterBsbl; LetterBsktbl; LetterTrk; College.

ROBERSON, Cheryl A; New Hampton Community HS; Elma, IA; Chrl; HonRl; NHS; 4-H; SpnCl; SecTrsSophCls; 4-HAwd; Bethany Lutheran Clg; Library Science.

ROBERSON, Donna M; Gasconade County HS; Bland, MO; 2/18 SecSophCls; TrsJrCls; SecSrCls; Chrs; HonRl; SchPl; StuCncl; Yrbk; SchPpr; Bsktbl; Chrldr;.

ROBERSON, Mona L; Southeastern HS; Detroit, MI; HonRl; OffAde; SchPl; Tennis; Mi St; Legal Secretary.

ROBERSON, Vicki M; Ritenour HS; St Louis, MO; 15/873 VPChrhWkr; HonRl; JrNHS; NHS; RedCrAde; SpnCl; Swmmng; Univ Of Mo; Business.

ROBERT, Carol L; Red Bud HS; Red Bud, IL; 18/141 Band; HonRl; NHS; SchPl; PresYthFlsp; SchPpr; 4-H; FTA; PpCl; DanFAwd; Eastern Ill Univ; Speech Teacher.

ROBERT, Susan M; Springfield HS; Springfield, IL; Chr; CmntyWkr; HonRl; TchrAde; YthFlsp; SciCl; Swmmng; College; Medicine.

ROBERTI, Kathyann E; Glenbrook North HS; Northbrook, IL; 10/640 VPChrl; Chrs; PresChrhWkr; HonRl; Mdrgl; NHS; OffAde; SchMus; TchrAde; GAA; AmLegAwd; College; Special Ed.

ROBERTS, Anita L; Midway HS; Denton, KS; SecFrshCls; Band; Chrs; HonRl; MrchBnd; PresNHS; SchPl; Pres4-H; PpCl; 4-HAwd; Highland Jr Clg; Businss.

ROBERTS, Becky A; East Charles Mix HS; Wagner, SD; 4/66 Band; Chrs; ChrhWkr; HonRl; LbryAde; Mdrgl; NatlFornLg; NHS; SchPl; RptrSchPpr; PpCl; Bsktbl; RotaryAwd; College; Missionary.

ROBERTS, Brenda E; Soldan HS; St Louis, MO; 18/500 VPFrshCls; Chr; ChrhWkr; CmntyWkr; HonRl; JA; SchMus; StuCncl; YthFlsp; PpCl; University; Business Admin.

ROBERTS, Brian; St Francis Seminary; Indianapolis, IN; 3/13 HonRl; Sacrstn; SchPl; RptrYrbk; Yrbk; LatCl; IMSpt; Purdue Univ; Computer Tech.

ROBERTS, Brion A; Tampico HS; Tampico, IL; VPSrCls; Aud/Vis; Band; ChrhWkr; CmntyWkr; HonRl; LbryAde; SchPl; TchrAde; Sauk Valley College; Electronics.

ROBERTS, Bruce G; Burlington Comm HS; Burlington, IA; 35/476 Chr; Chrl; CncrtBnd; HonRl; NHS; SchMus; SctActv; College; Education.

ROBERTS, Cathy L; Fayette HS; Fayette, MO; 2/67 SecTrsJrCls; DrmMjrt; HonRl; SecNHS; SecStuCncl; PresYthFlsp; EdYrBk; AmLegAwd; Univ Of Missouri; Medicine.

ROBERTS, Cheryl A; Pender Public HS; Pender, NE; Aud/Vis; LbryAde; LetterBsktbl; Ftbl; LetterTrk; Univ; Cpa.

ROBERTS, Dale M; Alpena HS; Alpena, MI; Aud/Vis; ChrhWkr; NatlThespSoc; SchPl; RptrSchPpr; SpnCl; SecTrsSophCls; Ftbl; Coll; Chemist.

ROBERTS, Dave; Trego Community HS; Wakeeney, KS; PresSophCls; HstJrCls; StuCncl; SciCl; Bsktbl; Ftbl; Trk; CchngActv; DanFAwd; JCAwd; Colby Jr College; Teacher.

ROBERTS, Deborah K; Frankfort HS; Frankfort, IN; 20/240 DrlTm; LitMag; NHS; ROTC; SchMus; SchPl; RptrYrbk; 4-H; FTA; AmLegAwd; College; Radiologic Tech.

ROBERTS, Debra L; Tri Central HS; Tipton, IN; 4/86 ChrhWkr; CncrtBnd; HonRl; MrchBnd; NHS; VPPolWkr; SchMus; SchPpr; VPFrCl; PpCl; General Motors Inst; Engineering.

ROBERTS, Denise R; Sunnydale Academy; University City, MO; 4/46 SecFrshCls; Chrl; ChrhWkr; HonRl; NHS; OffAde; RedCrAde; EdYrBk; IMSpt; CitAwd; Oakwood College; Pediatrician.

ROBERTS, Diane S; Kent City HS; Kent City, MI; 6/90 SecSophCls; Band; ChrhWkr; HonRl; NHS; Orch; StuCncl; YthFlsp; 4-H; CaptChrldr; Butterworth Hosp Sch Nursing; Rn.

ROBERTS, Ginger K; Lyle Public HS; Austin, MN; 1/30 Chrs; HonRl; NHS; StuCncl; SchPpr; 4-H; FHA; LetterBsktbl; CchngActv; 4-HAwd; Coll; Cpa.

ROBERTS, Glenda S; Falls City Senior HS; Falls City, NE; HonRl; OffAde; College.

ROBERTS, James A; Forest Lake HS; Wyoming, MN; Band; CncrtBnd; HonRl; MrchBnd; College.

ROBERTS, Janet L; Newtrier East HS; Wilmette, IL; 65/847 Chrl; Chrs; HonRl; OffAde; SctActv; GAA; Univ; Prof Medicine.

ROBERTS, Jim C; Highland HS; Ainsworth, IA; Chr; Chrs; HonRl; SchMus; LetterBsbl; LetterBsktbl; LetterFtbl; LetterTrk; 4-HAwd; College.

ROBERTS, Joan E; Davis County HS; Bloomfield, IA; ChrhWkr; HonRl; LbryAde; OffAde; 4-H; SpnCl;.

ROBERTS, Jody D; Baldwin HS; Baldwin, KS; PresFrshCls; ALBoysSt; Band; CncrtBnd; HonRl; MrchBnd; NHS; SchMus; SchPl; SctActv; University; Pre Law.

ROBERTS, Johnnie C; Central HS; St Joseph, MO; 51/505 NHS; SchPl; LatCl; MthCl; Univ Of Missouri; Math.

ROBERTS, John T; Dekalb HS; Dekalb, IL; PresJrCls; HonRl; NHS; StuCncl; YthFlsp; Bsktbl; Tennis; AmLegAwd; College; Professional.

ROBERTS, John W; Yale HS; Yale, MI; 3/150 HonRl; NHS; NatlMeritFnl; StuCncl; SciCl; Bsbl; Ftbl; Tennis; Wrstlng; IMSpt; Georgia Inst Of Tech; Med Engr.

ROBERTS, Jonathan R; Cresbard Ind HS; Cresbard, SD; PresFrshCls; PresSophCls; PresJrCls; SchPl; PpCl; LetterBsbl; LetterBsktbl; LetterFtbl; LetterTrk; College.

ROBERTS, Judi A; Western Community HS; Buda, IL; ALAGirlsSt; Chrs; DrlTm; HonRl; NatlThespSoc; SchPl; SchPpr; SecFHA; Clge.

ROBERTS, Judy; Argos HS; Argos, IN; 10/75 VPFrshCls; PresSophCls; SecJrCls; VPSrCls; Chr; Chrs; Bsktbl; Trk; Chrldr; GAA; Purdue; Home Economics.

ROBERTS, Julie A; Sevastopol HS; Sturgeon Bay, WI; TrsSophCls; VPSrCls; Band; CncrtBnd; MrchBnd; NHS; Quill&Scroll; SchMus; StuCncl; Yrbk; RptrSchPpr; College; Professional.

ROBERTS, Kathleen D; White Pine HS; White Pine, MI; 13/40 Chrs; ChrhWkr; CmntyWkr; HonRl; LbryAde; OffAde; YthFlsp; FHA; Michigan Tech Univ; Nurse.

ROBERTS, Kathleen L; Sullivan HS; Sullivan, MO; 11/151 PresFrshCls; Band; ChrhWkr; CmntyWkr; HonRl; HospAde; StuCncl; RptrSchPpr; FTA; CchngActv; IMSpt; PPFtbl; 4-HAwd;.

ROBERTS, Kathleen L; Oak Park HS; Kansas City, MO; HonRl; NHS; OffAde; College.

ROBERTS, Kathy; Onsted HS; Onsted, MI; HonRl; OffAde; TchrAde; Yrbk; 4-H; FHA; Office Work.

ROBERTS, Kelly D; Gilbert Community HS; Ames, IA; 1/30 Chrs; NHS; NatlMeritCmnd; SchPl; StuCncl; EdYrBk; 4-H; FHA; PresPpCl; Bsktbl; Univ Of Iowa; Journalism.

ROBERTS, Kent H; Campus HS; Cape Girardeau, MO; 1/40 PresSrCls; ChrhWkr; HonRl; NatlMeritCmnd; SctActv; EdSchPpr; PpCl; AmLegAwd; Univ; Phd History.

ROBERTS, Kristi E; Wm M Kelley HS; Finland, MN; 18/152 AFS; HonRl; LbryAde; SchAde; Yrbk; RptrSchPpr; 4-H; PpCl; GAA; PPFtbl; Bemidji St Clg; Phy Ed Maj.

ROBERTS, Lester N; Loup City HS; Ashton, NE; Chrs; ChrhWkr; SchMus; SchPl; Ftbl;.

ROBERTS, Linda F; Harrisburg HS; Clark, MO; TrsFrshCls; PresSophCls; PresSrCls; ALAGirlsSt; HonRl; StuCncl; TchrAde; FrCl; LetterBsktbl; Trk; CitAwd; College; Secondary Education.

ROBERTS, Linda S; West Washington HS; Campbellsburg, IN; Band; ChrhWkr; TreasStuCncl; SptEdSchPpr; FHA; SpnCl; PpCl; Bsktbl; Trk; CaptChrldr; GAA; Indiana Univ; Psychology.

ROBERTS, Loretta A; Mc Cook Sr HS; Mccook, NE; Band; DrmMjrt; HonRl; NHS; PepBnd; StuCncl; 4-H; MthCl; PpCl; College; Professional.

ROBERTS, Margaret R; Marquette HS; Michigan City, IN; 15/60 HonRl; TreasStuCncl; TchrAde; Chrldr; College; Physical Education.

ROBERTS, Mark; Fort Zumwalt HS; O Fallon, MO; 4/340 Chr; Chrs; NHS; NatlMeritCmnd; YthLg; RptrSchPpr; SpnCl;.

ROBERTS, Mark S; Charleston HS; Charleston, IL; Eastern Illinois University.

ROBERTS, Marline A; Lake Central HS; Schererville, IN; 18/453 ALAGirlsSt; PresBand; PresCncrtBnd; HonRl; PresMrchBnd; NHS; NatlThespSoc; PepBnd; SchMus; StuGov; YthFlsp; TreasGerCl; PpCl; Purdue University; Engineering.

ROBERTS, Mary E; Kirksville HS; Kirksville, MO; 2/174 ChrhWkr; HonRl; LbryAde; NatlMeritCmnd; TchrAde; FrCl; PresSciCl; Ne Missouri St; Biology.

ROBERTS, Mary E; Notre Dame HS; Quincy, IL; Chr; Chrs; PpCl; Tennis; College; Elementary Ed.

ROBERTS, Mary J; Monroe City HS; Hunnewell, MO; 16/92 Chr; Chrs; HonRl; NHS; RptrYrbk; Northeast Mo State U; Journalism.

ROBERTS, Mary K; Forest Lake HS; Wyoming, MN; 53/353 Band; CncrtBnd; HonRl; MrchBnd; NatlFornLg; Quill&Scroll; RptrSchPpr; EdSchPpr; SchPpr; VoiceDemAwd; College; Journalism Psychology.

ROBERTS, Melinda K; Northeast HS; Kansas City, MO; 1/385 Baker Univ; Doctor.

ROBERTS, Michael L; Northwestern HS; Ashton, SD; ALBoysSt; Band; Chr; Chrs; CncrtBnd; HonRl; MrchBnd; PepBnd; SctActv; LetterTrk; College.

ROBERTS, Michael N; Brookport HS; Brookport, IL; 3/24 SecSophCls; PresJrCls; PresSrCls; Chrs; ChrhWkr; CmntyWkr; HonRl; OffAde; StuCncl; Yrbk; 4-H; Murray State Univ; Bus Admin.

ROBERTS, Michele; Minooka HS; Minooka, IL; 11/100 ALAGirlsSt; ChrhWkr; CmntyWkr; HonRl; YthFlsp; FrCl; MthCl; LionAwd; Coll; Bio.

ROBERTS, Mona J; Woden Crystal Lake HS; Britt, IA; HstFrshCls; HstSophCls; SecJrCls; Band; ChrhWkr; CncrtBnd; HonRl; MrchBnd; PepBnd; SchPl; RptrSchPpr; 4-H; LetterBsktbl; LetterTrk;.

ROBERTS, Nancy A; Hale Area HS; Hale, MI; 1/65 SecSophCls; SecJrCls; SecSrCls; Chrs; HonRl; HospAde; NHS; NatlMeritSF; SchPl; TchrAde; Northern Mi Univ; Elem Teacher.

ROBERTS, Nancy A; Kenwood HS; Chicago, IL; Band; HonRl; TreasGerCl; CaptSwmmng; GAA; Clge; Pro.

ROBERTS, Nancy J; Willowbrook HS; Villa Park, IL; 6/825 Chrs; HonRl; JrNHS; Univ Of Illinois; Fine Arts.

ROBERTS, Paul M; Hauser HS; Hope, IN; TrsFrshCls; Aud/Vis; ModUN; SchAde; SctActv; YthFlsp; PpCl; Bsktbl; Trk; CchngActv; Technical School; Electronics.

ROBERTS, Peggy J; St Martins Academy; Rapid City, SD; 4/33 PresSophCls; Chr; Chrs; CmntyWkr; HonRl; NHS; PpCl; Chrldr; GAA; IMSpt; Laramie County Comm College; Special Educ.

ROBERTS, Phil W; Menasha HS; Menasha, WI; HonRl; Ftbl; Trk; IMSpt;.

ROBERTS, Raequel; Coon Rapids Sr HS; Coon Rapids, MN; PresJrCls; Chr; ChrhWkr; HonRl; LbryAde; SchMus; SchPl; StuGov; Trk; College; Science.

ROBERTS, Rebecca; Richland HS; Richland, MO; Band; ChrhWkr; CncrtBnd; HonRl; MrchBnd; PepBnd; SchPl; StuCncl; 4-H; Trade Or Business; Vocation.

ROBERTS, Rhonda L; Armstrong HS; Penfield, IL; 1/49 HonRl; NHS; SchPl; StuCncl; SecYthFlsp; Pres4-H; LetterChrldr; LetterGAA; AmLegAwd; 4-HAwd; University; Law.

ROBERTS, Rita L; Central HS; St Joseph, MO; 7/505 ChrhWkr; NHS; PolWkr; SchAde; TchrAde; LatCl; SpnCl; PpCl; SciCl; College; Political Science.

ROBERTS, Robert; Maine West Hs; Des Plaines, IL; 97/800 Band; HonRl; NatlMeritFnl; PolWkr; MthCl; SciCl; LetterWrstlng; Northwestern U; Medicine.

ROBERTS, Robin L; Tri Valley HS; Downs, IL; 5/40 HonRl; VPFFA; Bsbl; Bsktbl; CaptGlf; Trk; SARAwd; Ill State Univ; Business Adm.

ROBERTS, Rodney A; Nesco HS; Zearing, IA; ALBoysSt; HonRl; NHS; SchMus; SchPl; PresStuCncl; YthFlsp; Bsktbl; Trk; University; Social Work.

ROBERTS, Rosemary; York Comm HS; Elmhurst, IL; 4/880 HonRl; ModUN; VPNHS; NatlMeritCmnd; Quill&Scroll; RptrYrbk; Yrbk; GerCl; MthCl; Univ Of Illinois; Civil Engineering.

ROBERTS, Sharon S; Lincoln Co R I HS; Silex, MO; 4/36 SecSophCls; DrlTm; HonRl; OffAde; SchPl; Yrbk; 4-H; FHA; Vocational School; Nursing.

ROBERTS, Sheryl A; Bonner Springs HS; Bonner Springs, KS; 5/175 ChrhWkr; HonRl; StuCncl; FHA; SpnCl; PpCl; SciCl; College; Business.

ROBERTS, Steven A; College HS; Cape Girardean, MO; 3/37 PresJrCls; Chr; NHS; SpnCl; LetterBsktbl; LetterTrk; College; Doctor.

ROBERTS, Susan J; Buffalo Grove HS; Buffalo Grove, IL; HonRl; NHS; RptrYrbk; Illinois State College; Business.

ROBERTS, Susan L; Grosse Pointe South HS; Grosse Pointe, MI; 16/636 ChrhWkr; DrlTm; HonRl; JrNHS; NatlMeritFnl; StuGov; MthCl; PpCl; Bsbl; LetterBsktbl; Chrldr; Univ Of Michigan; Computer Science.

ROBERTS, Susan R; Crandon HS; Hiles, WI; Band; HonRl; MrchBnd; PepBnd; StuCncl; TchrAde; Twrl; Yrbk; RptrSchPpr; Bsktbl; Trade Or Business School.

ROBERTS, Terrell L; Potosi Sr HS; Potosi, MO; 14/250 Chr; HonRl; Mdrgl; NHS; NatlThespSoc; SchMus; SchPl; RptrYrbk; Bsbl; University; Professional Baseball.

ROBERTS, Timothy C; Hackett HS; Kalamazoo, MI; 1/146 Chr; HonRl; SchMus; SchPl; StuCncl; StuGov; SpnCl; LetterBsbl; LetterBsktbl; LetterFtbl; Kalamazoo Col; Psychology.

ROBERTS, Timothy D; Highland HS; Ainsworth, IA; 7/55 Chrs; CmntyWkr; HonRl; NHS; SchMus; PresStuCncl; Bsbl; Bsktbl; Ftbl; Trk; College; Law.

ROBERTS, Timothy R; Elbow Lake HS; Elbow Lake, MN; SecTrsSrCls; HonRl; FFA; U Of Mn Morris; Dvm.

ROBERTS, T Maureen; Ladywood St Agnes HS; Indianapolis, IN; JA; SchMus; SchPl; GAA; IMSpt; Trade Schl.

ROBERTS, Toni R; Ida HS; Ida, MI; HonRl; OffAde; 4-H; PpCl; LetterTrk; GAA; IMSpt; 4-HAwd; E Michigan College; Accounting.

ROBERTS, Valerie; Switzerland County HS; Vevay, IN; CncrtBnd; HonRl; MrchBnd; NHS; PepBnd; 4-H; FHA; SpnCl; PpCl; Coll; Business Or Nursing.

ROBERTS, Velecia A; Northern HS; Flint, MI; Band; CncrtBnd; HonRl; JA; MrchBnd; NHS; Orch; University; Professional.

ROBERTS, Vicki S; Boone County R Vi HS; Centralia, MO; Band; Chr; CncrtBnd; HonRl; MrchBnd; PepBnd; PpCl; Chrldr; GAA; PPFtbl;.

ROBERTSON, Alan D; James Madison HS; Milwaukee, WI; 180/850 ChrhWkr; OffAde; SpnCl; Ftbl; Trk; IMSpt; Univ Of Wi; Business Major.

ROBERTSON, Alice; J S Morton East Hs; Cicero, IL; Band; CncrtBnd; MrchBnd; Orch; PepBnd; GAA; U Of Illinois; Pharmacy.

ROBERTSON, Amy E; Arthur Hill HS; Saginaw, MI; Band; ChrhWkr; CncrtBnd; HonRl; HospAde; MrchBnd; PepBnd; RptrYrbk; RptrSchPpr; FrCl; Univ; Business Administration.

ROBERTSON, Amy M; Central HS; St Joseph, MO; VPSrCls; Chr; Chrs; CmntyWkr; OffAde; SchAde; StuGov; TchrAde; YthLg; Chrldr; M U Columbia; Fashion Merchandizing.

ROBERTSON, Andrea L; Neodesha HS; Neodesha, KS; Band; Chr; Chrl; Chrs; ChrhWkr; HospAde; Tennis; Trk; PPFtbl; 4-HAwd; Murses Aid Sch;.

ROBERTSON, Bruce A; Ritenour HS; Overland, MO; 10/875 JrNHS; NHS; Ftbl; Trk; Col;.

ROBERTSON, Daniel M; Desoto Sr HS; Olathe, KS; 15/94 Chr; Chrs; HonRl; NHS; SchMus; SchPl; SctActv; LetterBsktbl; Trk; Missouri Inst Of Tech; Electronics.

ROBERTSON, Gregory R; Anderson HS; Anderson, IN; 38/569 ChrhWkr; HonRl; NHS; NatlMeritCmnd; GerCl; College.

ROBERTSON, Jill M; Norris #160 HS; Roca, NE; ChrhWkr; StuGov; TchrAde; YthFlsp; 4-H; FBLA; PpCl; Chrldr; PresAwd; Business School; Legal Secretary.

ROBERTSON, Julianna G; Bedford N Lawrence HS; Bedford, IN; 7/395 ALAGirlsSt; NHS; PolWkr; SctActv; StuCncl; TchrAde; FHA; FrCl; LatCl; MthCl; LetterTennis; AmLegAwd; GovHonPrgAwd; Indiana University; Law.

ROBERTSON, Kay L; Harmony HS; Donnellson, IA; 6/40 Band; Chr; CncrtBnd; NHS; StuCncl; Twrl; FHA; Bsktbl; BttyCrckrAwd; Univ; Computer Science.

ROBERTSON, Keith J; Blissfield HS; Blissfield, MI; 10/136 ChrhWkr; HonRl; NatlMeritCmnd; YthFlsp; LetterBsbl; Bsktbl; IMSpt; Univ Of Mi; Business.

ROBERTSON, Kenneth E; Central HS; Linton, IN; 5/47 VPSrCls; ALBoysSt; ChrhWkr; HonRl; NHS; TchrAde; YthFlsp; 4-H; LetterBsbl; LetterBsktbl; Purdue Univ; Pharmacist.

ROBERTSON, Lisa S; Monroe HS; Monroe, MI; 1/570 TrsFrshCls; TrsSophCls; TrsJrCls; TrsSrCls; Chr; ChrhWkr; NHS; NatlMeritCmnd; SchMus; LatCl; Baylor Univ; Medicine.

ROBERTSON, Marcia L; Lake Park HS; Itasca, IL; 35/530 Chr; Chrs; ChrhWkr; HonRl; StuGov; GAA; Augustana College; Physical Education.

ROBERTSON, Merrill L; Glenwood HS; Springfield, IL; Band; CncrtBnd; MrchBnd; VPNHS; PepBnd; SchMus; SchPl; TchrAde; FHA; GerCl; Univ Of Ill; Computer Engineering.

ROBERTSON, Michael; Morrison HS; Morrison, IL; 2/127 PresSophCls; PresJrCls; ALBoysSt; HonRl; NHS; NatlThespSoc; SchPl; StuCncl; YthFnd; FTA; Univ Of Chicago; Literaure Or Law.

ROBERTSON, Myra; Malden HS; Marklen, MO; Band; CncrtBnd; DrlTm; DrmMjrt; HonRl; MrchBnd; SchMus; SctActv; TchrAde; Twrl;.

ROBERTSON, Shelby G; Malden HS; Malden, MO; Band; Chr; Chrs; ChrhWkr; MrchBnd; TchrAde; Yrbk; SchPpr; FHA; PpCl; JCAwd; Military Service; Air Force.

ROBERTSON, Steve C; Boystown HS; Boystown, NE; JA; OffAde; SchAde; SchPl; SchPpr; 4-H; PpCl; LetterFtbl; Trk; Chrldr; College; Actor.

ROBERTSON, Suzanne M; Sauk Prairie HS; Prairie Du Sac, WI; Band; Chr; ChrhWkr; CncrtBnd; HonRl; MrchBnd; SchMus; StuCncl; YthFlsp; 4-H; PpCl; Swmmng; GAA; College; Elementary Education.

ROBERTSON, Tammy; Pike HS; Indianapolis, IN; Band; CncrtBnd; HonRl; MrchBnd; Orch; PepBnd; SchAde; SchMus; 4-H; 4-HAwd;.

ROBERTSON, Timothy; St Philip Catholic HS; Battle Creek, MI; 5/110 SecFrshCls; VPSophCls; SecJrCls; PresSrCls; Chrl; ChrhWkr; CmntyWkr; Bsktbl; Northwood Institute; Doctor Of Chiropratic.

ROBERTSON, Timothy K; Seymour HS; Quincy, IL; 7/65 VPJrCls; ChrhWkr; HonRl; NHS; 4-H; Community College; Agriculture.

ROBERTSON, Tracy; Wabash HS; Wabash, IN; Chr; HonRl; StuCncl; YthFlsp; GAA; Evansville Univ, Law.

ROBERTUS, Carole A; Irondale HS; New Brighton, MN; ChrhWkr; NatlFornLg; NHS; NatlMeritSF; PolWkr; SchPl; StuCncl; EdSchPpr; Univ; Lawyer.

ROBEY, Suzanne; Bloomer HS; Bloomer, WI; TrsSophCls; VPJrCls; VPSrCls; AFS; DrlTm; HonRl; NHS; FBLA; FHA; SpnCl; Voc Tech; Vocation.

ROBIN, Linda K; South Iron HS; Glover, MO; PresSrCls; HonRl; HospAde; PresStuCncl; EdYrBk; RptrSchPpr; 4-H; FHA; PpCl; SecSciCl; Mo Sch For Doctors; Rma.

ROBINETT, Holly A; Glendale HS; Springfield, MO; AFS; HonRl; NatlMeritSF; PolWkr; StuCncl; FrCl; MthCl; PpCl; Bsktbl; Trk; College.

ROBINETT, Larry E; Seymour HS; Seymour, MO; TrsFrshCls; Band; ChrhWkr; HonRl; ModUN; SctActv; StuCncl; TchrAde; 4-H; Bsktbl; Sw Missouri State Univ; Computer Science.

ROBINETTE, Pamela K; South Sioux City HS; South Sioux City, NE; PresFrshCls; PresSophCls; Chr; HonRl; LbryAde; StuCncl; StuGov; RptrYrbk; SpnCl; PpCl; Medical Technology School; Professional.

ROBINS, Jeanelle; West Marshall Hs; Clemons, IA; 7/107 Band; Chrs; CncrtBnd; HonRl; MrchBnd; PepBnd; SchMus; YthFlsp; LetterBsbl; LetterTrk; College;professional.

ROBINS, Kathy S; Woodruff HS; Peoria, IL; 23/281 ChrhWkr; HonRl; Quill&Scroll; SchPl; RptrYrbk; RptrSchPpr; SchPpr; College; Vocation.

ROBINSON, Annie; North Division HS; Milwaukee, WI; ChrhWkr; CmntyWkr; HonRl; PpCl; Trk; CaptChrldr; Collefe; Professional.

ROBINSON, Brad E; Pierre HS; Ogema, MN; ChrhWkr; Bsktbl; Ftbl; Glf; Trk; University; Medical.

ROBINSON, Brian K; North Clay Community HS; Farina, IL; ModUN; NatlSciFnd; RedCrAde; YthFnd; FFA; FHA;.

ROBINSON, Cathy L; Ernest W Seaholm HS; Birmingham, MI; Chr; OffAde; SchAde; SchMus; Univ.

ROBINSON, Charles G; Ravenna HS; Ravenna, MI; 7/110 Band; ChrhWkr; CncrtBnd; HonRl; MrchBnd; NHS; PepBnd; SchPl; StuCncl; TchrAde; LetterBsbl; LetterBsktbl; DanFAwd; Ferris State College; Data Processing.

ROBINSON, Debra L; South Side HS; Fort Wayne, IN; Chr; HonRl; OffAde; TchrAde; 4-H; PPFtbl; 4-HAwd; College; Medical Field.

ROBINSON, Debra L; Manual HS; Peoria, IL; 22/329 Band; CncrtBnd; DrlTm; HonRl; MrchBnd; OffAde; PepBnd; Chrldr; GAA; Bus School; Secretary.

ROBINSON, Diane M; Norfolk Senior HS; Norfolk, NE; ALAGirlsSt; HonRl; MrchBnd; NatlFornLg; Twrl; FrCl; College; Radio.

ROBINSON, Donna M; St Clement HS; Sterling Hgts, MI; HstSophCls; LbryAde; HonRl; NatlFornLg; NHS; StuCncl; Chrldr; CchngActv; IMSpt; JAAwd; U ;po Science.

ROBINSON, Donna M; Aquinas Dominican HS; Chicago, IL; 5/150 HonRl; VPNHS; NatlMeritCmnd; SchPl; FrCl; Univ Of Chicago; Mathematics.

ROBINSON, Edward J; Hannibal HS; Hannibal, MO; ChrhWkr; ROTC; College; Christian Missions.

ROBINSON, Elisabeth A; Ernest W Seanolm HS; Birmingham, MI; 5/725 SecSophCls; CmntyWkr; HonRl; JrNHS; NHS; NatlMeritFnl; NatlMeritSF; StuCncl; StuGov; IMSpt; U Of Mich; Law.

ROBINSON, Eric V; Platteville HS; Platteville, WI; SecTrsFrshCls; PresJrCls; AFS; CncrtBnd; HonRl; Orch; SctActv; YthFlsp; FrCl; Bsktbl; Ftbl; Univ Of Wisconsin; Pre Medicine.

ROBINSON, Frederick D; Mendel Catholic Prep HS; Chicago, IL; SecSophCls; Band; CncrtBnd; JA; MrchBnd; SctActv; StuCncl; Bsbl; College; Computer Programmer.

ROBINSON, Henry W; Cass Tech HS; Detroit, MI; HonRl; JrNHS; SctActv; StuGov; University Of Michigan; Architect.

ROBINSON, Jacki S; Marion HS; Florence, KS; SecJrCls; Band; CncrtBnd; HonRl; MrchBnd; PepBnd; StuCncl; TchrAde; FHA; GerCl; PpCl; Coll; Prof.

ROBINSON, Janice L; Thedford HS; Thedford, NE; ALAGirlsSt; HonRl; RptrYrbk; RptrSchPpr; 4-H; PpCl; Bsktbl; Trk; IMSpt; DanFAwd; College.

ROBINSON, Janice M; Immaculate Heart Of Mary HS; Westchester, IL; VPSophCls; Chrs; SctActv; SpnCl; PpCl; Bsktbl; Trk; Chrldr; GAA; IMSpt; U Of Il Chicago Circle; Nursingor Sports.

ROBINSON, Jeffrey L; Chicago Vocational HS; Chicago, IL; 50/650 Band; Chr; Chrl; ChrhWkr; HonRl; NHS; StuCncl; LetterFtbl; LetterTennis; CchngActv; Western Univ; Bio Tech.

ROBINSON, Jeffry; Luhs HS; Woodruff, WI; Aud/Vis; Band; Us Madison; Doctor.

ROBINSON, Jolene K; Baxter Community HS; Melbourne, IA; 1/32 PresJrCls; Band; HonRl; NHS; NatlThespSoc; SchPl; VPYthFlsp; EdYrBk; CaptBsktbl; LetterTrk; Amer Inst Of Business; Exec Secretary.

ROBINSON, Joseph M; Seymour HS; Barry, IL; NHS; FFA; Bsbl; Bsktbl; Trk; College; Veterinarian.

ROBINSON, Karen M; Lindblom Tech HS; Chicago, IL; 20/656 HonRl; IntrClCncl; LbryAde; SchAde; StuCncl; GAA; College; Chemistry.

ROBINSON, Kimberly A; Holcomb HS; Holcomb, MO; VPFrshCls; Band; HonRl; MrchBnd; NatlFornLg; StuGov; 4-H; PpCl; Chrldr; IMSpt; Coll.

ROBINSON, Lawrence B; De La Salle HS; Chicago, IL; 24/270 HonRl; Northwestern; Psychology.

ROBINSON, Lee M; Soldan HS; St Louis, MO; College; Professional.

ROBINSON, Linda J; Belleville East HS; Belleville, IL; Chrs; HospAde; OffAde; SctActv; TchrAde; YthFlsp; 4-H; Trk; PPFtbl; Northern Illinois Univ; Nursing.

ROBINSON, Lori C; Winola HS; Viola, IL; 3/65 PresFrshCls; SecSrCls; ALAGirlsSt; Band; NHS; EdYrBk; 4-H; FHA; GAA; 4-HAwd; Special Education.

ROBINSON, Lynnette E; United Township HS; Moline, IL; 44/639 Aud/Vis; Chr; HonRl; Mdrgl; FrCl; SpnCl; LetterTennis; GAA; Georgetown Univ; Foreign Service.

ROBINSON, Marcia G; Pinckney HS; Lakeland, MI; TrsSophCls; Band; Chr; CncrtBnd; HonRl; MrchBnd; SchPl; SchPpr; Chrldr; Eastern Mich Univ; Dramatics.

ROBINSON, Mark; Bentley HS; Davison, MI; LbryAde; NHS; SchMus; OptClAwd; College.

ROBINSON, Marlene; Baxter Comm HS; Melbourne, IA; Band; DrlTm; HonRl; MrchBnd; PepBnd; StuCncl; RptrYrbk; PpCl; Bsktbl; Homemaker.

ROBINSON, Marty C; North Linn HS; Coggon, IA; 3/75 PresFrshCls; PresSophCls; PresJrCls; CncrtBnd; MrchBnd; StuCncl; 4-H; FFA; Ftbl; Glf; LetterWrstlng; Iowa State Univ; Agriculture.

ROBINSON, Mary A; Gering HS; Gering, NE; SecJrCls; ChrhWkr; DrlTm; HonRl; StuGov; RptrSchPpr; SpnCl; PpCl; LetterTrk; Chrldr; College; Med Tech.

ROBINSON, Mary K; Garden County HS; Oshkosh, NE; 3/33 Band; HonRl; HospAde; NHS; OffAde; SchMus; SchPl; SpnCl; PpCl; SciCl; GovHonPrgAwd; Univ Of Ne; Med Doctor Pediatrics.

ROBINSON, Michael R; Seymour HS; Barry, IL; 12/65 HonRl; Bsbl; Bsktbl; Univ; Proffesional.

ROBINSON, Michelle L; Interlochen Arts Academy; Farmington, MI; Chr; HonRl; Orch; SchMus; Michigan State Univ; Professional Musician.

ROBINSON, Mona; North Kansas City HS; Kansas City, MO; 2/450 AFS; HonRl; JrNHS; NHS; StuCncl; TchrAde; EdYrBk; FrCl; PpCl; Univ Of Mo;.

ROBINSON, Nicholas F; Holcomb HS; Holcomb, MO; 3/38 ALBoysSt; HonRl; SctActv; VPStuGov; TchrAde; KiwanAwd; University Of Missouri; Orthodontist.

ROBINSON, Nyle D; Knoxville Comm HS; Knoxville, IA; 18/30 ALBoysSt; NHS; PolWkr; SctActv; EdSchPpr; LetterTrk; Iowa St Univ; Journalism.

ROBINSON, Patricia F; Warrensburg HS; Decatur, IL; 8/90 AFS; Band; Chrs; HonRl; HospAde; SctActv; Bsktbl; GAA; IMSpt; PPFtbl; College; Nursing.

ROBINSON, Phillip; Covert HS; South Haven, MI; HonRl; StuCncl; TchrAde; RptrYrbk; Yrbk; SchPpr; PpCl; Bsktbl; Trk; College; Professional.

ROBINSON, Phyllis L; Harrison HS; Chicago, IL; 57/400 TrsSrCls; CmntyWkr; HonRl; Trk; LetterChrldr; College; Special Education.

ROBINSON, Reginald L; Salina HS; Salina, KS; VPSophCls; ALBoysSt; Band; ChrhWkr; CncrtBnd; HonRl; StuCncl; Ftbl; Trk; VoiceDemAwd; Univ Of Ks; Political Science, Law Sch.

ROBINSON, Richard; Blair HS; Blair, NE; 1/150 VPJrCls; ALBoysSt; HonRl; NHS; StuCncl; FSA; FrCl; Coll; Md.

ROBINSON, Richard D; Minot HS; Minot Afb, ND; HonRl; LitMag; MthCl; SciCl; Bsktbl; College; Research Science.

ROBINSON, Richard L; Oswego HS; Oswego, IL; 9/285 College; Engineering.

ROBINSON, Risa R; Calumet HS; Chicago, IL; 1/300 PresSrCls; Chrs; HonRl; PresJrNHS; PresNHS; NatlMeritCmnd; NatlMeritSF; StuGov; SpnCl; SciCl; GAA; IMSpt; Univ Of Chicago; Pediatrician.

ROBINSON, Robert; Ste Gen Sr HS; Ste Genevieve, MO; 14/200 PresSrCls; ALBoysSt; Chr; ChrhWkr; CmntyWkr; HonRl; Mdrgl; Bsbl; Bsktbl; Trk; Ne Mo St; Vet.

ROBINSON, Robert; Englewood HS; Chicago, IL; 176/397 CmntyWkr; IntrClCncl; NatlMeritCmnd; SchAde; SctActv; TchrAde; Ftbl; Trk; IMSpt; Rice Univ; Gym Teacher.

ROBINSON, Robert J; Minot HS; Minot Afb, ND; HonRl; LitMag; Bsktbl; College; Research Science.

ROBINSON, Robin; Moberly HS; Moberly, MO; Band; CncrtBnd; HonRl; MrchBnd; NHS; Ftbl; Trk; IMSpt; Moberly Jr College; Chemical Engr.

ROBINSON, Ron D; U Of Detroit HS; Detroit, MI; ChrhWkr; CmntyWkr; HonRl; NatlMeritSF; StuCncl; LetterBsktbl; CaptFtbl; Trk; Dartmouth College; Pre Med.

ROBINSON, Sarah M; Thomson HS; Thomson, IL; VPJrCls; Band; Chrs; CncrtBnd; MrchBnd; SchMus; StuCncl; FHA; Chrldr; GAA; College; Nursing.

ROBINSON, Sharon J; Jefferson HS; Rockford, IL; 13/361 Rock Valley College.

ROBINSON, Sheri; Swartz Creek HS; Swartz Creek, MI; 14/380 VPSrCls; HonRl; JrNHS; NHS; StuCncl; Chrldr; BttyCrckrAwd; Mott Comm Coll; Medical Tech.

ROBINSON, Susan M; Grand Ledge HS; Grand Ledge, MI; ChrhWkr; HonRl; JA; LbryAde; NatlMeritCmnd; SctActv; YthFlsp; 4-H; FrCl; SpnCl; Adrian College; Psychology.

ROBINSON, Wayne; Calumet HS; Gary, IN; JrNHS; PpCl; Bsbl; Ftbl; IMSpt; Vincennes Univ;.

ROBINSON, Yvette; John Marshall Harlan HS; Chicago, IL; 36/608 ChrhWkr; HonRl; NHS; OffAde; StuCncl; FTA; EngCl; MthCl; Northern Illinois Univ; Statishcian.

ROBISON, Christine L; Byron HS; Byron, MI; Band; CncrtBnd; NHS; 4-H; Bsktbl; LetterTrk; Central Mi U; Landscaping.

ROBISON, David A; Whiteland Comm HS; Greenwood, IN; 40/183 PresJrCls; PresSrCls; ALBoysSt; SctActv; TreasStuCncl; StuGov; 4-H; SecFFA; KeyCl; FrCl; CaptBsbl; Purdue Univ; Farming.

ROBISON, Mark A; Community R 6 HS; Laddonia, MO; PresBand; CncrtBnd; HonRl; MrchBnd; NHS; VPSciCl; CaptBsktbl; Wichita Automitive Inst.

ROBISON, Meg D; Tilihandy HS; Bay City, MI; TrsFrshCls; TrsSophCls; TrsJrCls; SecSrCls; Band; HonRl; MrchBnd; NHS; PepBnd; LetterBsbl; Bsktbl; Swmmng; Tennis; GAA; University Of Michigan.

ROBISON, Stacey R; Rockford East HS; Rockford, IL; 12/665 HonRl; NHS; RedCrAde; PpCl; GAA; No Illinois Univ; Accounting.

ROBITSCHEK, Rex A; John Marshall HS; Mpls, MN; Band; ChrhWkr; CncrtBnd; JA; NatlMeritSF; StuCncl; Yrbk; SchPpr; GerCl; SciCl; Elec Eng.

ROBLEE, Patti S; Trinity HS; Hutchinson, KS; PresFrshCls; TrsSophCls; Chr; ChrhWkr; DrlTm; HonRl; NHS; SchPl; StuCncl; PpCl; LetterBsktbl; Colg; Phys Educ.

ROBLING, Cynthia A; Chaska HS; Chaska, MN; 13/215 HonRl; NHS; SchPl; RptrYrbk; RptrSchPpr; EdSchPpr; LetterChrldr; St Marys Jr Clge; Medical Lab Tech.

ROBNETT, George W; Webster Groves HS; Rock Hill, MO; PresFrshCls; Band; CtyCnl; CmntyWkr; ModUN; Bsbl; Bsktbl; Ftbl; Morehouse College; Accounting.

ROBNETT, Glenn W; Christian Bros Col Mil Inst; St Louis, MO; 20/169 ChrhWkr; CAP; CaptDrlTm; HonRl; NatlMeritCmnd; ROTC; SchPl; IMSpt; College; Science.

ROBNETT, Sherolyn A; Rantoul Twp HS; Rantoul, IL; 140/400 Chr; Chrs; ChrhWkr; Mdrgl; YthFlsp; 4-H; FHA; 4-HAwd; College.

ROBOLD, Edward; Yorktown HS; Yorktown, IN; 12/176 HonRl; NHS; YthFlsp; College; Professional.

ROBSON, Kurt G; John Hersey HS; Arlington Heights, IL; 142/749 AFS; HonRl; HospAde; JrNHS; NHS; NatlMeritFnl; SctActv; SciCl; Univ Of Chicago; Medicine.

ROBSON, Mark E; Clarion Community HS; Clarion, IA; 9/93 HonRl; NHS; SchMus; SchPl; Yrbk; University; Major Study.

ROBSON, Michael T; St Louis U HS; Warson Woods, MO; PresSrCls; HonRl; NatlMeritCmnd; SctActv; MthCl; SciCl; Swmmng; Trk; College; Archiect Or Eng.

ROBSON, Rebecca R; Caledonia HS; Caledonia, MN; Band; Chr; ChrhWkr; CncrtBnd; MrchBnd; PepBnd; 4-H; GAA; Tech Sch; Secretary.

ROBY, Cassandra M; St Elizabeth Academy; St Louis, MO; Chrs; ChrhWkr; HonRl; JA; RedCrAde; SchMus; SctActv; StuCncl; RptrSchPpr; SpnCl; Bsbl; GAA; IMSpt; Boston Univ; Math.

ROBY, Debra A; St Anne Comm HS; St Anne, IL; HonRl; PresFHA; Bsktbl; LetterChrldr; Kankakee Comm Coll; Nursing.

ROBY, Elise R; Kenwood HS; Chicago, IL; 4/38 HonRl; LbryAde; NatlMeritCmnd; Quill&Scroll; SchMus; SctActv; StuCncl; SptEdSchPpr; SchPpr; SciCl; CaptTrk; GAA; IMSpt; Univ Of Tennessee; Engineering.

ROCH, Katrina A; Northside HS; Muncie, IN; 16/350 VPJrCls; HonRl; NHS; VPStuGov; TreasFHA; PresFrCl; PresMthCl; SecSciCl; AmLegAwd; Butler Univ; Chemistry.

ROCHA, Christine; Merrill HS; Merrill, MI; HonRl; SchMus; SchPl; 4-H; PpCl; Central Michigan Univ; Business Education.

ROCHA, Maria V; Bishop Lillis HS; Kansas City, MO; NatlFornLg; NHS; SchPl; StuCncl; StuGov; RptrSchPpr; GerCl; VPLatCl; SpnCl; Trk; Univ Of Ca Berkeley; Theatre Arts & Media.

ROCHE, Claudia A; Saint Francis HS; Wheaton, IL; Chrs; HonRl; NHS; SchMus; StuCncl; Yrbk; Chrldr; St Marys Coll; Business Admin.

ROCHE, Evelyn; Lourdes HS; Chicago, IL; 100/393 SecFrshCls; HonRl; NatlMeritCmnd; SchAde; StuCncl; PresSophCls; SpnCl; PpCl; Chrldr; BttyCrckrAwd; Business Clg; Professional.

ROCHE, Jeffrey A; Maine Twp S HS; Park Ridge, IL; CmntyWkr; HonRl; NHS; CchngActv; Univ Of New Hampshire; Life Science.

ROCHE, Kathleen M; Ryan HS; Omaha, NE; PpCl; College; Professional.

ROCHE, Michael J; Brother Rice HS; Oak Forest, IL; 62/414 HonRl; St Louis Univ; Lawyer.

ROCHEFORT, Rhonda Y; River Valley HS; Sawyer, MI; 21/154 Band; CmntyWkr; HonRl; HospAde; NHS; TchrAde; Bronsons Schl; Nursing.

ROCHELEAU, Marie; Cheb Area HS; Cheboygan, MI; Band; CAP; CncrtBnd; HonRl; MrchBnd; SchMus; SchPl; SctActv; FrCl; Tennis; Ferris State College; Opthalmic Lab Tech.

ROCHNOWSKI, Donna L; La Salle Peru Township HS; Peru, IL; 13/490 HonRl; OffAde; SpnCl; PpCl; Ill Valley Comm College; Community Health.

ROCHON, Mark J; Edsel Ford HS; Dearborn, MI; PresFrshCls; NatlFornLg; NatlMeritFnl; NatlMeritSF; PolWkr; StuCncl; StuGov; IMSpt; Navy; Law.

ROCK, David; Galien HS; Galien, MI; 1/52 ALBoysSt; Band; CncrtBnd; NHS; OffAde; SchPl; StuCncl; SptEdYrbk; Michigan Tech; Computer Science.

ROCK, David; Elmwood Park Hs; Elmwood Park, IL; 2/327 HonRl; NatlMeritCmnd; StuGov; KeyCl; SpnCl; LetterSwmmng; LetterTennis; AmLegAwd; U Of Illinois; Mathematics.

ROCK, David J; Swea City Comm HS; Sewa City, IA; 8/32 HonRl; SchPl; SctActv; FFA; Bsbl; Bsktbl; Ftbl; Glf; Trk; Iowa State; Ag Business.

ROCK, Linda M; Kadoka HS; Kadoka, SD; ALAGirlsSt; Band; Chrs; HonRl; StuCncl; RptrYrbk; RptrSchPpr; Bsktbl; CaptChrldr; GAA; South Dakota St University.

ROCK, Marcella; Mt St Benedict HS; Crookston, MN; TrsFrshCls; HstSophCls; Chr; ChrhWkr; DrmBgl; HospAde; SchMus; Chrldr; Univ; Nurse.

ROCK, Pamela J; Mentor Public HS; Mentor, MN; VPSophCls; SecTrsJrCls; Band; Chrs; HonRl; PepBnd; Teen; RptrSchPpr; 4-H; Trk; Trade Sch; Secretary.

ROCK, Randall W; Hope HS; Hope, KS; 1/25 PresFrshCls; PresSophCls; TrsJrCls; VPSrCls; ALBoysSt; Band; ChrhWkr; CncrtBnd; HonRl; HospAde; University Of Kansas; Medicine.

ROCK, Rhonda Y; Farmington East HS; Farmington, IL; 19/135 HonRl; NHS; TchrAde; FTA; SpnCl; SciCl; CchngActv; GAA; IMSpt; Bradley University; Physical Education.

ROCK, William; Avoca Community HS; Avoca, IA; VPJrCls; Band; Chr; NatlThespSoc; PepBnd; SchMus; StuCncl; FTA; Bsbl; Ftbl; Dana College; Detective.

ROCKAFELD, Ann M; Homestead HS; Mequon, WI; 10/400 HonRl; JrNHS; NHS;.

ROCKEL, Craig A; Senn HS; Chicago, IL; 89/300 PresFrshCls; PresSophCls; HonRl; JrNHS; SchAde; SctActv; StuCncl; StuGov; TchrAde; RptrYrbk; LetterBsbl; LetterBsktbl; LetterFtbl; Glf; Illinois State Univ; Business Admin.

ROCKERS, Christopher J; Garnett HS; Garnett, KS; 27/130 HstJrCls; ALBoysSt; Pres4-H; PresFFA; Ftbl; Trk; 4-HAwd; Kansas State Univ; Agriculture.

ROCKEY, John D; Raytown South HS; Raytown, MO; CAP; HonRl; NHS; LetterTrk; Penn Valley Comm College; Pilot.

ROCKHOLD, Douglas L; Lineville C/10 HS; Lineville, IA; VPSophCls; PresJrCls; CncrtBnd; HonRl; MrchBnd; NatlMeritSchl; ROTC; StuGov; FFA; LetterBsbl;.

ROCKWEILER, Sheila; Weston HS; Cazenovia, WI; SecFrshCls; Band; CncrtBnd; HonRl; MrchBnd; NHS; PepBnd; Chrldr; GAA; IMSpt; College; Journalism.

ROCKWELL, Ned; Wirt HS; Gary, IN; 14/237 Band; CncrtBnd; HonRl; MrchBnd; Orch; PepBnd; GerCl; SciCl; IMSpt; Purdue Univ; Chemistry.

ROCKWOOD, Cheryl A; Dwight D Eisenhower HS; Calumet Park, IL; 10/700 College; Professional.

ROCKWOOD, Gina M; Algonac HS; Algonac, MI; 13/210 VPSrCls; HonRl; NHS; SchPl; StuCncl; LetterBsktbl; GAA; BttyCrckrAwd; DARAwd; CitAwd; VoiceDemAwd; Michigan State University.

ROCKZIEN, Julie A; Olin Consolidated HS; Wyoming, IA; 5/26 Band; CncrtBnd; HonRl; MrchBnd; NHS; PepBnd; SchPl; VPStuCncl; RptrYrbk; RptrSchPpr; College;.

ROCQUE, Michelle A; West HS; Green Bay, WI; 51/390 SecJrCls; HonRl; NHS; StuCncl; LetterSwmmng; LetterTrk; Chrldr; GAA; IMSpt; PresAwd; Madison Clge; Therapy.

ROD, Joe J; St Rita HS; Argo, IL; HonRl; SptEdYrbk; RptrSchPpr; Socr; Trk; Wrstlng; IMSpt; JAAwd; St Scholastica; Electrical Engineer.

ROD, Kathy A; Cassville HS; Glen Haven, WI; Chrs; HonRl; SchMus; StuCncl; TchrAde; Yrbk; EdSchPpr; FHA; IMSpt; PPFtbl; Madison Tech Inst; Nursing.

ROD, Sandra L; Roland Story HS; Story City, IA; 12/80 SecTrsFrshCls; Chr; Chrl; Chrs; HonRl; NHS; SchPpr; FHA; PpCl; CaptChrldr; Iowa Lutheran Hosp School Of Nursing.

RODAHL, Marcia A; Minot HS; Minot, ND; 3/656 Band; CncrtBnd; DrlTm; HonRl; JrNHS; MrchBnd; NHS; PepBnd; College; Veterinary Medicine.

RODAK, Mary K; Kewanee HS; Kewanee, IL; 2/210 TrsSophCls; AFS; OffAde; TreasSchPpr; FrCl; GAA; AmLegAwd; LionAwd; College; Business.

RODAMMER, Jill; Davison Sr HS; Burton, MI; 22/450 CmntyWkr; HonRl; HospAde; NHS; RedCrAde; TchrAde; RptrSchPpr; FNA; SciCl; IMSpt; Univ Of Mich; Nursing.

RODARTE, Dede; Southwest HS; Kansas City, MO; 170/540 Chr; HonRl; NatlFornLg; PresNatlThespSoc; SchMus; SchPl; StuCncl; Swmmng; PPFtbl; Park College; Theatre.

RODBRO, Ryan D; Waukegan HS; Waukegan, IL; HonRl; JrNHS; NHS; NatlMeritSF; StuCncl; U Of Miami; Medicine.

RODDA, Errol M; Urbana HS; Urbana, IL; 60/420 SctActv; Yrbk; SchPpr; Univ Of Illinois; Mech Engineer.

RODDA, Mary E; West Iron County HS; Iron River, MI; TrsFrshCls; SecSophCls; Chrs; HonRl; NHS; NatlMeritSF; SchPl; StuGov; RptrYrbk; Central Michigan Univ; Speech Pathology.

RODDEWIG, Paula J; Sully Buttes HS; Onida, SD; 1/55 SecJrCls; TrsJrCls; ALAGirlsSt; PresNHS; PresQuill&Scroll; EdYrBk; Sec4-H; AmLegAwd; DanFAwd; 4-HAwd; Dakota Weslyan Univ; Study Elementary Ed.

RODDY, Virgil L; Brebeuf Prep; Indianapolis, IN; 13/117 CmntyWkr; HonRl; JA; NHS; NatlMeritCmnd; SchAde; FrCl; Bsbl; Wrstlng; IMSpt; C; Nuclear Engineer.

RODE, Anne C; Acad Of The Holy Angels; Bloomington, MN; Chrs; ChrhWkr; SchPl; TchrAde; LetterGlf; Normandale Jr Coll; Pro Bus.

RODE, Marie C; Bishop Miege HS; Overland Park, KS; Chr; DrlTm; NHS; SchMus; College; Education.

RODECK, Barbara A; East Waterloo HS; Waterloo, IA; Chr; Chrs; ChrhWkr; HonRl; JrNHS; NHS;.

RODECK, Brian D; East Waterloo HS; Waterloo, IA; 41/343 Band; CncrtBnd; HonRl; MrchBnd; SchMus; StuCncl; StuGov; RptrYrbk; Yrbk; LetterTrk; Iowa St U; Aerospace Engr.

RODEHEAVER, Cynthia G; O Fallon Township HS; O Fallon, IL; ChrhWkr; YthFlsp; RptrSchPpr; SpnCl; University; Professional.

RODEN, Susan; Cassville HS; Cassville, MO; 20/103 ChrhWkr; LbryAde; NHS; FHA; FTA;.

RODENBAUGH, Marvin T; Mexico HS; Mexico, MO; 21/248 Band; ChrhWkr; CncrtBnd; MrchBnd; NHS; PepBnd; SctActv; SpnCl; Coll; Ministry.

RODENKIRCH, William M; New Trier East HS; Wilmette, IL; 252/847 ChrhWkr; HonRl; NatlFornLg; NatlMeritCmnd; PolWkr; RedCrAde; SctActv; LetterTrk; Univ Of Washington; Law.

RODENROTH, Susan M; Sault Area HS; Sault Ste Marie, MI; HonRl; HospAde; LbryAde; NatlMeritSF; OffAde; TchrAde; SpnCl; PpCl; Swmmng; GAA; College; Nursing.

RODER, Terry; St Marys HS; Remsen, IA; 8/60 Band; Chrs; CncrtBnd; HonRl; Orch; PepBnd; SchMus; SchPl; RptrSchPpr; Col; Music.

RODERICK, Allan J; Kennedy HS; Cedar Rapids, IA; Band; ChrhWkr; CncrtBnd; MrchBnd; Orch; PepBnd; SchMus; University; Law.

RODERICK, Blake E; Lanphier HS; Springfield, IL; 30/535 NHS; Quill&Scroll; PresStuCncl; RptrYrbk; SchPpr; TreasKeyCl; GerCl; PpCl; Texas A&m Univ; Engineering.

RODGER, Kathleen A; Sheldon HS; Sheldon, IA; 5/112 HonRl; NHS; Quill&Scroll; StuCncl; RptrYrbk; RptrSchPpr; PpCl; Bsktbl; Trk; IMSpt; College; Bus Management.

RODGERS, Bradley D; Kearney Senior HS; Kearney, NE; SecKeyCl; CaptBsktbl; CaptFtbl; Univ Of Nebr Lincoln; Pre Med.

RODGERS, Carl L; Peck HS; Peck, MI; 5/67 ALBoysSt; HonRl; NHS; StuCncl; TchrAde; 4-H; College; Professional.

RODGERS, Cynthia J; Oak Park HS; Kansas City, MO; Chrs; HonRl; NHS; SchMus; TchrAde; College; Professional.

RODGERS, Donna L; Edwardsville HS; Edwardsville, IL; CmntyWkr; IntrClCncl; JrNHS; NHS; PresStuCncl; TchrAde; RptrSchPpr; FBLA; St Louis Univ; Lawyer.

RODGERS, Eric; Richmond Sr HS; Richmond, IN; 75/562 ChrhWkr; HonRl; NHS; NatlMeritCmnd; Quill&Scroll; SptEdYrbk; Tennis; IMSpt; College; Chemistry.

RODGERS, Festus E; Jay HS; Southwest City, MO; ChrhWkr; 4-H; 4-HAwd; Trade School; Horticulture.

RODGERS, Gary A; Lyons Township HS; La Grange Pk, IL; 100/1200 Chr; Chrl; Chrs; HonRl; JrNHS; Mdrgl; NHS; SchMus; SchPl; Swmmng; St Olaf Clg; Dentistry.

RODGERS, Gregory W; Palestine HS; Palestine, IL; SecSrCls; Band; CncrtBnd; HonRl; MrchBnd; PepBnd; ROTC; SchMus; YthFlsp; Yrbk; LatCl; Univ Of Illinois; Medicine.

RODGERS, James P; Academy Of The Holy Angels; Richfield, MN; SciCl; LetterTennis; IMSpt; College; Pro.

RODGERS, Jennifer R; West Vigo HS; West Terre Haute, IN; ALAGirlsSt; Chrl; ChrhWkr; HonRl; TchrAde; RptrYrbk; FTA; GAA; Indiana State Univ; Education.

RODGERS, John R; Eastern Heights HS; Agra, KS; 2/21 Band; Chrs; HonRl; SchMus; SchPl; StuCncl; Yrbk; Bsktbl; Ftbl; Trk; University.

RODGERS, Karen; Van Buren HS; Knightsville, IN; 15;64 TrsSrCls; Band; CncrtBnd; MrchBnd; NHS; PepBnd; PresFBLA; SpnCl; PpCl; GAA; Indiana State University;secre Tarial Cours.

RODGERS, Karen; Sullivan HS; Sullivan, MO; 26/165 ALAGirlsSt; Band; Chrs; NHS; SchMus; StuCncl; EdYrBk; SptEdSchPpr; FHA; FTA; Se Mo State; Teaching Exceptional Children.

RODGERS, Lavonda B; Caledonia HS; Alto, MI; CncrtBnd; DrmMjrt; HonRl; MrchBnd; 4-H; 4-HAwd; MasAwd; College; History.

RODGERS, Marilyn; Williamsville HS; Williamsville, IL; 17/61 HonRl; OffAde; SchAde; SchPl; TchrAde; Vocational.

RODGERS, Marley D; Carmi Comm HS; Carmi, IL; Band; CAP; CncrtBnd; DrmBgl; MrchBnd; PepBnd; Quill&Scroll; SchPl; RptrSchPpr; EdSchPpr; LatCl; MthCl; PresSciCl; IMSpt;.

RODGERS, Marley D; Carmi HS; Carmi, IL; Band; CncrtBnd; DrmBgl; MrchBnd; PepBnd; Quill&Scroll; SchPl; RptrSchPpr; EdSchPpr; PresSciCl;.

RODGERS, Mary L; Flora HS; Flora, IL; Band; CmntyWkr; CncrtBnd; Teen; FBLA; IMSpt; College; Music.

RODGERS, Michael J; Crete Monee HS; Park Forest, IL; HonRl; LetterTrk;.

RODGERS, Pamela K; Clarke Comm HS; Woodburn, IA; Band; Chrs; ChrhWkr; DrlTm; HonRl; PepBnd; YthFlsp; RptrYrbk; RptrSchPpr; 4-H; FHA; FTA; LetterBsktbl; 4-HAwd; Ne Missouri State Univ; Law Enforcement.

RODGERS, Randall D; Montgomery County R Ii HS; Bellflower, MO; 4/94 SecFrshCls; PresJrCls; ChrhWkr; DrmMjrt; NHS; StuCncl; Pres4-H; PresFFA; IMSpt; Univ Of Mi Columbia; Veterinary Medicine.

RODGERS, Theodis; Lindblom Tech HS; Chicago, IL; 124/656 Band; Chr; Chrl; Chrs; ChrhWkr; HonRl; JA; De Paul; Computer Tech.

RODGIS, Janell; West Side HS; Gary, IN; ChrhWkr; CncrtBnd; HonRl; JrNHS; MrchBnd; YthFlsp; Anderson; Sociology.

RODIBAUGH, Margaret A; Goshen HS; Goshen, IN; NatlMeritSchl; College; Nursing.

RODIE, Faye; Otis Bison Senior HS; Timken, KS; Chr; Chrs; ChrhWkr; HonRl; HospAde; YthFlsp; PpCl; Trk; Beloit Vo Tech Sch; Nurse.

RODIGHIERO, Bonnie L; Lasalle Peru Twp HS; Oglesby, IL; 15/516 LitMag; NatlMeritCmnd; StuCncl; RptrSchPpr; VPLatCl; Univ Of Illinois; Math Teacher.

RODINE, Brian D; Gothenburg Public HS; Gothenburg, NE; .

RODINO, Thomas J; Glenbrook North HS; Northbrook, IL; 75/630 University Of Illinois; Art.

RODMAN, Jane A; Springville Community HS; Springville, IA; 14/55 Chr; ChrhWkr; CmntyWkr; HonRl; LbryAde; SchPl; TchrAde; YthFlsp; RptrSchPpr; SptEdSchPpr; PpCl; LetterBsbl; CaptChrldr; College.

RODMAN, Kathleen M; Huron Sr HS; Huron, SD; Chrs; ChrhWkr; DrlTm; Orch; SchMus; 4-H; SpnCl; PpCl; GAA; South Dakota State University.

RODRIGUEZ, Benigna C; Westport HS; Raytown, MO; 6/200 AFS; Chr; ChrhWkr; HonRl; NHS; StuCncl; VPFTA; Author.

RODRIGUEZ, Cristela; Ashton HS; Ashton, IL; 18/43 Chr; HonRl; SchPl; RptrSchPpr; SchPpr; FHA; Northern Illinois University.

RODRIGUEZ, Jenny; St Barbara HS; Chicago, IL; VPSophCls; ChrhWkr; HonRl; ModUN; OffAde; SchPl; StuCncl; StuGov; Northwestern University; Professional.

RODRIGUEZ, Kent A; Elmore Public HS; Elmore, MN; 2/30 VPFrshCls; TrsSophCls; TrsJrCls; TrsSrCls; Band; Chr; ChrhWkr; CncrtBnd; HonRl; MrchBnd; LetterBsbl; LetterFtbl; LetterGlf; Trk; College; Medicine.

RODRIGUEZ, Maria E; Notre Dame Girls HS; Chicago, IL; 22/302 Chr; Loyola Univ; Psychology.

RODRIGUEZ, Mario A; Gordon Technical HS; Chicago, IL; 29/604 HonRl; NHS; SpnCl; Loyola University; Medicine.

RODRIGUEZ, Melinda; Genoa HS; Genoa, NE; Chr; Chrs; HonRl; PepBnd; StuCncl; YthFlsp; Trk; GAA; IMSpt; Trade School; Photographer.

RODRIGUEZ, Timothy A; Moline HS; Moline, IL; CtyCnl; CmntyWkr; NatlSciFnd; PolWkr; SctActv; TchrAde; UNYO; FDA; FFA; FTA; Southern Illinois Univ; Social Studies.

RODRIQUEZ, Deborah A; St Scholastica HS; Chicago, IL; Chrl; JA; SchMus; SchPl; PpCl; JAAwd; Univ; Medical Technology.

RODRIQUEZ, Sharon L; Southeast HS; Weir, KS; HonRl; LbryAde; 4-H; FHA; Kansas State College; Computer Science.

RODVELT, Ronnie L; Atchison County Community HS; Horton, KS; 1/110 ALBoysSt; Chr; HonRl; NHS; SchMus; SecFFA; MthCl; SciCl; LetterBsktbl; Col; Agriculture Engineering.

ROE, Gregory S; Olympia HS; Mc Lean, IL; 75/230 SpnCl; MthCl; PpCl; SciCl; LetterBsktbl; University; Accounting.

ROE, Karen A; Climax Scotts HS; Climax, MI; 9/53 ALAGirlsSt; Band; ChrhWkr; HonRl; HospAde; NHS; TchrAde; LetterBsktbl; LetterTrk; CaptChrldr; College; Landscaping.

ROE, Kathe L; Macon Co HS; Macon, MO; Band; ChrhWkr; CncrtBnd; HonRl; LbryAde; MrchBnd; NHS; NatlMeritSchl; OffAde; PepBnd; RedCrAde; AmLegAwd; Ne Missouri St Univ; Architecture.

ROE, Kirk W; Superior HS; Superior, NE; Band; ChrhWkr; CncrtBnd; MrchBnd; PepBnd; 4-H; FFA; CaptBsktbl; LetterTrk; 4-HAwd; U Of Ne; Animal Science.

ROE, Michael O; Ogemaw Heights HS; West Branch, MI; SchPl; Bsktbl; LetterFtbl; College; Engineering.

ROE, Richard B; Creston HS; Creston, IA; Aud/Vis; Chr; Chrl; Chrs; HonRl; NHS; NatlThespSoc; SchMus; SchPl; RptrYrbk; Yrbk; RptrSchPpr; Bsbl; Bsktbl; Iowa State Univ; Metallurgical Eng.

ROE, Sherrie L; Kirksville HS; Kirksville, MO; 30/174 HonRl; LbryAde; TchrAde; FrCl; University; English.

ROE, William R; Pacific HS; Robertsville, MO; 13/186 Aud/Vis; Chr; Chrs; HonRl; LbryAde; Mdrgl; SchMus; SchPl; SciCl; Us Navy; Electronics Technician.

ROEBBEKE, Daniel M; Ceylon Public HS; Dunnell, MN; VPSophCls; Band; Chr; ChrhWkr; CncrtBnd; MrchBnd; PepBnd; SchPl; StuCncl; LetterBsktbl; Trade School; Agriculture.

ROEBER, Cynthia J; Tulare HS; Redfield, SD; Band; Chrs; Chr; CncrtBnd; LbryAde; PepBnd; SchAde; 4-H; FHA; LetterBsbl; Presentaton Col ;nurse.

ROEBKE, Glen T; Seward HS; Seward, NE; .

ROED, Candace K; Mentor Public HS; Mentor, MN; Band; Chr; ChrhWkr; HonRl; StuCncl; YthFlsp; EdYrBk; 4-H; LetterBsktbl; Chrldr; College.

ROEDER, Cindy L; Andrew Comm HS; Andrew, IA; 3/33 Band; Chrs; HonRl; VPNHS; NatlThespSoc; LetterBsbl; CaptBsktbl; LetterTrk; DanFAwd; 4-HAwd; PresAwd; Wartburg College; English.

ROEDER, Kristine; Bremen HS; Bremen, IN; 30/125 VPSrCls; Chr; ChrhWkr; HonRl; LbryAde; MrchBnd; SchMus; FrCl; PpCl; Work At A Bank.

ROEDER, Linda; Coon Rapids Senior HS; Coon Rapids, MN; 36/738 HonRl; JrNHS; NHS; SchAde; Univ Of Minnesota, Agronomy.

ROEDER, Mark A; Hempstead HS; Dubuque, IA; 55/455 HonRl; NHS; StuGov; Ftbl; IMSpt; PresAwd; Univ Of Ia.

ROEGE, Paul E; Haslett HS; Haslett, MI; 2/155 ALBoysSt; Band; HonRl; NatlMeritSF; SctActv; FrCl; Bsbl; Ftbl; LetterSwmmng; LetterTrk; College; Civil.

ROEGER, Joanne M; Ursuline Academy; St Louis, MO; HonRl; HospAde; LitMag; NHS; RedCrAde; SchPl; StuCncl; SchPpr; PpCl; SciCl; University; Nursing.

ROEGER, Michael D; North Side HS; Ft Wayne, IN; JA; RptrYrbk; Ft Wayne; Magazine Work.

ROEGGE, Frederick J; Mpls Luth HS; Edina, MN; Band; Chr; Chrs; HonRl; PepBnd; StuCncl; SchPpr; LatCl; Bsktbl; LetterTrk; University; Lawyer.

ROEHL, Lou A; Sheyenne River Academy; Hatton, ND; Band; Chrl; Chrs; ChrhWkr; HonRl; TchrAde; Bsktbl; Ftbl; IMSpt; PresAwd; College; Nursing.

ROEHL, Lynne C; Nevis HS; Nevis, MN; ALAGirlsSt; Chr; CncrtBnd; HonRl; StuCncl; Yrbk; 4-H; LetterBsktbl; Chrldr; 4-HAwd; Vocational Schl; Legal Secretary.

ROEHL, Ross; Immanuel Lutheran HS; Eau Claire, WI; VPSophCls; PresJrCls; Chr; StuCncl; GerCl; College; Vocation.

ROEHL, Timothy D; Sleepy Eye Public HS; Sleepy Eye, MN; 1/85 PresSrCls; Band; Chr; HonRl; MrchBnd; NatlMeritCmnd; PepBnd; VPStuCncl; PresYthFlsp; LetterBsbl; College; Professional.

ROEHM, Deveda; Bellmont HS; Decatur, IN; Chrs; ChrhWkr; CmntyWkr; HonRl; SchPl; TchrAde; LatCl; GAA; IMSpt;.

ROEHNER, Linda M; Mona Shores HS; Muskegon, MI; Chrs; NHS; NatlThespSoc; RptrYrbk; PresFrCl; Tennis; Mi State U; Computer Engr.

ROEHR, Barbara; Jennings HS; Jennkngs, MO; Chr; HonRl; SchAde; SctActv; RptrYrbk; GerCl; Bsktbl; GAA; IMSpt; OptClAwd; PresAwd; College; Medicine.

ROEHR, Charlotte L; Central HS; Aberdeen, SD; ChrhWkr; CmntyWkr; PresNatlFornLg; NHS; YthFlsp; VPSpnCl; CaptTrk; GAA; IMSpt; PPFtbl; EldAwd; Univ Of S Dakota; Medicine.

ROEHRS, Dale E; Osceola HS; Osceola, NE; 5/50 ALBoysSt; Chr; Chrs; HonRl; SchPl; CaptFtbl; U Of Nebraska; Accountant.

ROEHRS, Janet; New Richland Hartland HS; New Richland, MN; 18/68 Chr; HonRl; OffAde; SchPl; SchPpr; 4-H; FHA; GerCl; 4-HAwd; St Cloud St; Speech Path.

ROEKER, Ruth E; La Moure HS; Fullerton, ND; 4/48 Chr; HonRl; TchrAde; College; Professional.

ROEKER, Ruth E; Lamoure HS; Fullerton, ND; 1/47 Chr; HonRl; TchrAde; Clge; Pro Nurse.

ROELANT, Susan E; St Mary Academy; Newport, MI; Chrl; HonRl; ModUN; NHS; SchPl; StuCncl; FrCl; DARAwd; Monroe County Comm College; Nursing.

ROELFSEMA, Kirby K; Steamboat Rock Comm HS; Steamboat Rock, IA; 2/14 SecFrshCls; DrmMjrt; VPJrCls; SecSrCls; ALAGirlsSt; Band; Chr; Chrs; ChrhWkr; CmntyWkr; CncrtBnd; University; Speech.

ROELL, Christine M; Our Lady Of Grace HS; Beech Grove, IN; Chr; ChrhWkr; HonRl; ModUN; SpnCl; IMSpt; PPFtbl; College; Airline Stewardess Or Oceanography.

ROELL, Patricia M; Academy Of The Immaculate Con; Batesville, IN; 36/60 VPSrCls; Chrs; HonRl; SchMus; StuCncl; SchPpr; SpnCl;.

ROELLGEN, Beth A; Rivet HS; Vincennes, IN; 4/49 VPJrCls; ALAGirlsSt; HonRl; StuCncl; Bsktbl; Tennis; Trk; PresGAA; IMSpt; BttyCrckrAwd; Vincennes Univ.

ROELOFS, Lu Ann; Danube Public HS; Blomkest, MN; /43 Band; Chr; CmntyWkr; SchMus; SchPl; RptrSchPpr; FHA; FTA; Willmar Area Vo Tech; Lpn.

ROELOFS, Nicolas H; Morgan Park Academy; Worth, IL; HonRl; LitMag; ModUN; NHS; TchrAde; UNYO; YthLg; SchPpr; KeyCl; Bsktbl; Ftbl; LetterTrk; College; Bio Chemistry.

ROEMER, Judy A; Pacific HS; Pacific, MO; Band; CncrtBnd; HonRl; MrchBnd; SchMus; TchrAde; PresFTA; Clge; Teaching.

ROEMER, Margo; Unionville Sebewaing HS; Sebewaing, MI; Chr; ChrhWkr; CmntyWkr; HonRl; LbryAde; OffAde; Yrbk; FHA; LatCl; Bsbl; Delta College; Dental Assistant.

ROEMERMAN, Constance R; Blakesburg Community HS; Blakesburg, IA; 3/17 TrsSophCls; SecJrCls; Band; Chr; ChrhWkr; HonRl; SchMus; SchPl; PresGerCl; SpnCl; LetterBsktbl; LetterTrk; LetterChrldr; College; Music.

ROEMKE, Brian S; Woodlan HS; Grabill, IN; 26/139 ChrhWkr; CmntyWkr; HonRl; JA; NHS; SchPl; FFA; College; Professional.

ROEMMICH, Ross K; New Salem HS; New Salem, ND; TrsFrshCls; Band; Chrs; HonRl; MrchBnd; PepBnd; CaptBsktbl; LetterFtbl; Trk; LionAwd; College; Major Study.

ROENFANZ, Hope I; Ventura Comm HS; Ventura, IA; VPSophCls; Band; ChrhWkr; CncrtBnd; HonRl; MrchBnd; SchPl; YthFlsp; CaptBsktbl; IMSpt; Adams St Coll; Guidance Counselor.

ROENFELD, Tami D; Glenwood Comm HS; Mineola, IA; 10/105 Chr; ChrhWkr; HonRl; LbryAde; NHS; 4-H; Bsktbl; Trk; Business Schl; Secretary.

ROENZ, Carl J; Little Wolf HS; Manawa, WI; SecSrCls; Band; HonRl; SchPl; SctActv; StuGov; RptrSchPpr; LetterBsbl; Bsktbl; CchngActv; U; Professional.

ROEPKE, Lori J; Centennial HS; Circle Pines, MN; 2/217 VPFrshCls; ALAGirlsSt; CncrtBnd; HospAde; TreasNHS; StuCncl; Yrbk; CaptChrldr; VFWAwd; VoiceDemAwd; Gustavus Adolphus; Elementary Teacher.

ROEPKE, Ruth A; Oelwein Comm HS; Aurora, IA; 10/281 Chr; ChrhWkr; HonRl; JrNHS; Mdrgl; OffAde; Waldorf Clg; Business.

ROEPKE, Shelly L; Valley Heights HS; Waterville, KS; ALAGirlsSt; Chr; ChrhWkr; HonRl; MrchBnd; NHS; PepBnd; SctActv; StuCncl; Chrldr; Ks Univ; Med.

ROESCH, Michael T; Fox HS; Arnold, MO; 2/725 CncrtBnd; HonRl; JrNHS; MrchBnd; NHS; YthFlsp; GerCl; LetterFtbl; Trk; Wrstlng; College; Engineer.

ROESCH, Pamela L; Anderson HS; Anderson, IN; 125/656 HonRl; HospAde; RedCrAde; SctActv; YthFlsp; 4-H; GerCl; 4-HAwd; College; Medicine.

ROESCH, Shirley A; Mcleansboro HS; Dahlgren, IL; 23/158 HonRl; OffAde; 4-H; FHA; Trk; 4-HAwd; College; Prof.

ROESCHLEY, Curtis Lee; Flanagan HS; Graymont, IL; 3/38 PresSophCls; Band; Chrs; CncrtBnd; HonRl; Mdrgl; MrchBnd; NHS; PepBnd; SchMus; StuCncl; LetterBsbl; LetterBsktbl; LetterFtbl; College.

ROESE, Janis; Mt Clemens HS; Mt Clemens, MI; 1/417 Chr; HonRl; NHS; SchMus; RptrSchPpr; Univ Of Mi; Music.

ROESLER, Keith R; Junction City HS; Junction City, KS; 2/303 ALBoysSt; TreasNHS; NatlMeritCmnd; 4-H; SciCl; LetterTrk; 4-HAwd; Ks St Univ; Engineering.

ROETHE, Ann; Fort Atkinson HS; Fort Atkinson, WI; 2/235 PresFrshCls; ALAGirlsSt; SchMus; EdSchPpr; Chrldr; DARAwd; GovHonPrgAwd; College; Physician.

ROETHE, Ruth A; Pinckneyville Community HS; Pinckneyville, IL; 2/115 ChrhWkr; HonRl; LitMag; LbryAde; NHS; NatlMeritCmnd; SchPl; Yrbk; SchPpr; FrCl; Ill St U.

ROETHELI, Janice K; St Francis Borgia HS; Washington, MO; 2/95 VPFrshCls; VPSophCls; PresJrCls; HonRl; NHS; StuCncl; TchrAde; RptrYrbk; RptrSchPpr; PpCl; East Central Junior College; Secretary.

ROETHEMEYER, Susan; Maywood HS; Maywood, NE; HstSrCls; SchPl; StuCncl; StuGov; Twrl; RptrYrbk; SchPpr; 4-H; PpCl; Univ Of Nebr; Vocation.

ROETHIG, Larry A; Marshall HS; Marshall, MO; HonRl; StuGov; YthFlsp; SptEdSchPpr; Bsbl; Ftbl; Swmmng; LetterWrstlng; IMSpt; GodCntryAwd; College; Physical Education.

ROETHKE, Mary L; Pecatonica HS; Blanchardville, WI; Band; Chr; CncrtBnd; MrchBnd; PepBnd; SchMus; StuCncl; TchrAde; FHA; CaptTrk; U W Platteville; Phy Ed & Elem Ed.

ROETHLE, Suzanne T; Hartford Union HS; Hartford, WI; TrsJrCls; SecAFS; SecChr; Chrs; HonRl; NHS; StuCncl; Tennis; GAA; GovHonPrgAwd; RotaryAwd; Univ Of Wisconsin; Nursing.

ROETZEL, Larry A; Custer HS; Custer, SD; 19/56 ChrhWkr; HonRl; NHS; Yrbk; RptrSchPpr; SptEdSchPpr; CaptBsktbl; Trk; CchngActv; Black Hills St Coll; Biologist.

ROEWERT, Joy R; Elkhorn Valley HS; Tilden, NE; Band; Chr; Chrs; ChrhWkr; CmntyWkr; CncrtBnd; HonRl; MrchBnd; Orch; PepBnd; SchPl; Swmmng; Tennis; LetterTrk; Norfolk Tech College; Nursing.

ROFFI, Raymond P; Lyons Township HS; Western Springs, IL; 77/1288 Chrl; CmntyWkr; HonRl; JrNHS; NHS; NatlMeritCmnd; YthFlsp; CaptFtbl; Glf; Univ Of So California; Medicine.

ROGALA, Frank; Mackinaw City HS; Mackinaw City, MI; VPSophCls; PresSrCls; ALBoysSt; Band; CmntyWkr; HonRl; PepBnd; SchPl; RptrYrbk; Ftbl; Univ; Professional.

ROGALSKI, Anita M; Thornton Fractional N HS; Calumet City, IL; 57/447 Chr; Chrs; ChrhWkr; HonRl; HospAde; OffAde; SchAde; TchrAde; SchPpr; College; Business Admin.

ROGERS, Albert D; John Marshall HS; Indianapolis, IN; 60/444 Band; HonRl; JrNHS; NHS; SctActv; StuCncl; VPKeyCl; LetterFtbl; LetterTrk; LetterWrstlng; Bradley University; Accounting.

ROGERS, Anita A; Millard M Halter HS; St Louis, MO; Aud/Vis; Band; ChrhWkr; CncrtBnd; HonRl; LitMag; MrchBnd; PepBnd; RptrSchPpr; SecFNA; Nursing School; Medicine.

ROGERS, Ann M; Harrison HS; Farmington Hills, MI; Chr; HonRl; NatlFornLg; NHS; NatlThespSoc; SchPl; LetterChrldr; W Michigan Univ; Aviation.

ROGERS, Carol D; Mt Pleasant HS; Mt Pleasant, IA; 22/180 Band; CncrtBnd; DrlTm; HonRl; MrchBnd; PepBnd; YthFlsp; RptrYrbk; Yrbk; SpnCl; Univ; Interior Design.

ROGERS, Cindy S; Fountain Central HS; Wingate, IN; ALAGirlsSt; ChrhWkr; HonRl; LbryAde; NHS; SctActv; SpnCl; PpCl; SciCl; In State U; Special Ed Teacher.

ROGERS, Cynthia; Lakeview HS; St Clair Shores, MI; 16/660 HonRl; JrNHS; NHS; OffAde; SpnCl; PpCl; Mi State Univ; Business.

ROGERS, David A; Jersey Comm HS; Jerseyville, IL; 11/270 HonRl; NHS; YthFlsp; LetterTrk; College; Mathematics.

ROGERS, David E; Belle Plaine HS; Belle Plaine, KS; 8/40 CncrtBnd; HonRl; Mdrgl; MrchBnd; PepBnd; SchMus; SchPl; CaptFtbl; LetterTrk; DanFAwd; Garden City Coll; Farmer.

ROGERS, Debbie J; Green Valley HS; Green Valley, IL; Chrs; HonRl; LbryAde; SchPl; TchrAde; Social Worker.

ROGERS, Deborah K; Kewanna HS; Kewanna, IN; 2/24 Aud/Vis; HonRl; NatlFornLg; PolWkr; TchrAde; SptEdSchPpr; LetterBsktbl; GAA; BttyCrckrAwd; Washington Univ; Political Science.

ROGERS, Debra; Western HS; Russiaville, IN; 35/165 ChrhWkr; HonRl; SchPl; TchrAde; YthFlsp; PpCl; SciCl; GAA; Indiana Central Coll; Nursing.

ROGERS, Debra S; Richwoods HS; Peoria, IL; 17/449 Chr; HonRl; NHS; Illinois State Univ; Biology.

ROGERS, Denise M; Halter HS; Wellston, MO; 1/54 Aud/Vis; Band; CncrtBnd; HonRl; LitMag; MrchBnd; NHS; TchrAde; College.

ROGERS, Donna; Portland HS; Portland, MI; 53/120 PresJrCls; HonRl; NHS; NatlMeritCmnd; OffAde; StuCncl; TchrAde; EdYrBk; 4-H; Bsktbl; Vocational.

ROGERS, Elizabeth K; George Community HS; George, IA; 6/48 Chr; PresChrhWkr; HonRl; NHS;

SchMus; SchPl; TchrAde; Twrl; RptrSchPpr; FTA; College; Home Ec Teacher.

ROGERS, James O; Memorial HS; Beloit, WI; HonRl; 4-H; Ftbl; Colorado Sch Of Mines; Geophysics.

ROGERS, Janet M; Lanark HS; Lanark, IL; 13/55 VPSrCls; Band; Chr; Chrl; Chrs; ChrhWkr; CncrtBnd; HonRl; HospAde; Mdrgl; MrchBnd; PepBnd; SchMus; SchPl; College; English.

ROGERS, Jeanine M; Stickney HS; Stickney, SD; Band; CncrtBnd; MrchBnd; PepBnd; SchPl; YthFlsp; Yrbk; VPPpCl; Bsktbl; LetterTrk; Sioux Falls College; Art Major.

ROGERS, Jeffrey A; Forest View HS; Des Plaines, IL; 12/645 Band; CncrtBnd; MrchBnd; PresNatlFornLg; NHS; PepBnd; Northwestern Univ; Anthropolgy.

ROGERS, Jennifer; Oak Park HS; Kansas City, MO; HonRl; StuCncl; TchrAde; FrCl; College; Home Economics.

ROGERS, Joann; Leola HS; Leola, SD; 7/50 Band; Chr; Chrs; CncrtBnd; HonRl; Mdrgl; MrchBnd; SchMus; Bsktbl; Trk; College.

ROGERS, Leesa L; Clinton Sr HS; Clinton, IL; 16/180 TrsJrCls; HonRl; SchPl; StuCncl; RptrSchPpr; 4-H; KeyCl; GAA; DanFAwd; Univ; Home Economics.

ROGERS, Lynn W; Arlington HS; Arlington, NE; 3/62 PresFrshCls; PresJrCls; ChrhWkr; CmntyWkr; HonRl; PolWkr; VPStuCncl; YthFlsp; 4-HAwd; CitAwd; U Of Ne; Law.

ROGERS, Marieta J; Nixa HS; Nixa, MO; 3/86 Chrs; ChrhWkr; HonRl; HospAde; TchrAde; FHA; SpnCl; PpCl; Indiana Univ; Nursing.

ROGERS, Marilyn D; Annapolis HS; Dearborn Hts, MI; TrsJrCls; TrsSrCls; CncrtBnd; HonRl; MrchBnd; NHS; StuCncl; Yrbk; LetterBsbl; LetterBsktbl; Business School; Exec Secretary.

ROGERS, Markael G; Blackford HS; Hartford City, IN; Chr; Chrl; Chrs; ChrhWkr; HonRl; NHS; StuCncl; YthFlsp; PpCl; IMSpt; Taylor Univ; Elem Sch.

ROGERS, Mark P; Trenton HS; Trenton, MI; 50/571 ChrhWkr; HonRl; NHS; StuCncl; RptrSchPpr; Trk; Mi St Univ; Pre Dental.

ROGERS, Mary C; Mother Mc Auley HS; Chicago, IL; 21/474 Chrs; HonRl; NHS; TchrAde; Lewis Univ; Business Admin.

ROGERS, Michael G; Blackford HS; Hartford City, IN; Aud/Vis; Chr; Chrl; Chrs; ChrhWkr; YthFlsp; RptrYrbk; SptEdYrbk; RptrSchPpr; IMSpt; Taylor Univ; Teaching Elem Schl.

ROGERS, Norman H; Southmont HS; New Ross, IN; 34/161 ALBoysSt; Band; Chr; ChrhWkr; HonRl; PolWkr; SchMus; LetterTrk; RotaryAwd; University; Medicine.

ROGERS, Pamela; Arcadia Hs; Arcadia, WI; Band; HonRl; NatlFornLg; NHS; NatlThespSoc; Yrbk; FHA; FTA; PresJrCls; AmLegAwd; Uw Eau Claire;special Ed.

ROGERS, Pamela S; H H Dow HS; Midland, MI; 37/467 Band; HonRl; MrchBnd; ModUN; NHS; SpnCl; Tennis; Chrldr;.

ROGERS, Philo A; Knox Co R 1 HS; La Belle, MO; TrsFrshCls; Chrs; HonRl; University Of Missouri; Agriculture.

ROGERS, Randall J; Chapman HS; Junction City, KS; HonRl; LitMag; NatlMeritCmnd; SchPl; TchrAde; Pres4-H; Bsbl; CaptFtbl; LetterTrk; LetterWrstlng; ChmbCommrsAwd; 4-HAwd; Kansas State Univ; Aeronautical Engineer.

ROGERS, Robin K; Maplewood Academy; Afton, MN; HonRl; Union College; Music.

ROGERS, Sandra K; Wahoo HS; Wahoo, NE; Chr; Chrl; Chrs; ChrhWkr; HonRl; SecFHA; University Of Nebraska; Music.

ROGERS, Sandra L; Beardstown HS; Beardstown, IL; 6/122 SecFrshCls; Chrs; HonRl; Mdrgl; NHS; SchMus; SchPl; StuCncl; RptrYrbk; EdYrBk; Trk; BttyCrckrAwd; DanFAwd; Illinois State University; Education.

ROGERS, Sara J; Christopher HS; Mulkeytown, IL; 7/68 Band; HonRl; NHS; TchrAde; Yrbk; College; Accountant.

ROGERS, Shirley I; Nevada HS; Richards, MO; 31/186 AFS; DrlTm; LbryAde; StuCncl; Yrbk; Pres4-H; GAA; IMSpt; 4-HAwd; University Of Missouri; Veterinarian.

ROGERS, Susan K; Northwestern HS; Blandinsville, IL; CmntyWkr; HonRl; NHS; TchrAde; SciCl; GAA; Western Illinois Univ; Law.

ROGERS, Ted L; St Elmo HS; Beecher City, IL; 4/57 VPFrshCls; VPJrCls; VPSrCls; HonRl; NHS; RptrSchPpr; SpnCl; LetterFtbl; Southern Il Univ; Medical Doctor.

ROGERS, Thomas M; Rolling Meadows HS; Arl Hts, IL; 90/581 Northern Ill Univ; Art.

ROGERS, Vicki F; Harrison HS; Chicago, IL; 4/250 PresSrCls; StuCncl; Howard University; Lawyer.

ROGERS, Vicki L; Clarksville Comm HS; Greene, IA; Band; Chrs; HonRl; LbryAde; NHS; SecStuCncl; SecPpCl; Bsbl; Bsktbl; College; Dental Asst.

ROGERS, Wanda F; Northwestern HS; Detroit, MI; HonRl; VPNHS; NatlMeritCmnd; SciCl; DARAwd; Mich State Univ; Pre Medical.

ROGGENBAUER, Thomas G; Central Community HS; Fox Lake, WI; 46/152 ALBoysSt; HonRl; SchAde; Bsbl; AmLegAwd; College; Engine Repair.

ROGGLES, Cheryl L; Waterford Township HS; Pontiac, MI; 20/440 HonRl; OffAde; RptrYrbk; Chrldr; Col; Nursing.

ROGHAIR, Randy L; Clay Central HS; Royal, IA; 10/34 ChrhWkr; CmntyWkr; HonRl; SchPl; Treas4-H; VPFFA; LetterBsktbl; Iowa Col; Agri.

ROGNEBY, Nancy; Willowbrook Hs; Lombard, IL; 50/822 Band; ChrhWkr; CmntyWkr; CncrtBnd; HonRl; MrchBnd; PepBnd; TchrAde; College; Mathematics.

ROGNEY, Shawn M; Osceola HS; Osceola, WI; Chr; HospAde; OffAde; SchPl; SctActv; 4-H; FHA; Trade School; Vocation.

ROGNLI, Judy; Silver Lake Public HS; Silver Lake, MN; /43 ALAGirlsSt; Band; Chrs; HonRl; NHS; SchPl; SchPpr; FHA; SecTrsSophCls; LetterChrldr; Moorehead St Coll;spe Educ.

ROGNLIE, Jon M; Iimmewaukan Public HS; Minnewaukan, ND; SecFrshCls; ALBoysSt; SchPl; Bsktbl; IMSpt; Bible Col; Wildlife Management.

ROGSTAD, Mark R; Belvidere HS; Belvidere, IL; 88/332 Aud/Vis; HonRl; YthFlsp; PpCl; LetterBsktbl; LetterFtbl; LetterTrk; College; Athletic Trainer.

ROGSTAD, Monica; Lake Mills Community HS; Lake Mills, IA; 15/84 VPSophCls; Band; CncrtBnd; HonRl; MrchBnd; PepBnd; SchPl; College.

ROHDE, Karen L; Lomira HS; Theresa, WI; Chrs; HonRl; SchMus; SchPpr; FrCl; Vocational School; Office Work.

ROHDE, Paul F; Emerson Hubbard HS; Hubbard, NE; PresFrshCls; ChrhWkr; CncrtBnd; MrchBnd; PepBnd; SchPl; 4-H; Bsktbl; Ftbl; 4-HAwd; College; Professional.

ROHDER, James T; Lapeer HS; Metamora, MI; Band; Chr; LbryAde; NatlMeritSF; PresNatlThespSoc; PolWkr; RedCrAde; SchMus; SchPl; PresFrCl; Bsktbl; Col; Dramatics.

ROHE, Marlene E; St Agnes HS; St Paul, MN; 1/136 CmntyWkr; HonRl; LbryAde; NatlFornLg; NatlMeritFnl; RptrYrbk; Yrbk; PresGerCl; St Catherine Coll; Occupational Therapist.

ROHE, Mary L; Manning Comm HS; Manning, IA; 16/64 Band; CncrtBnd; HonRl; MrchBnd; OffAde; PepBnd; Quill&Scroll; TchrAde; RptrYrbk; EdYrBk; 4-H; PpCl; 4-HAwd; American Beauty School; Beautician.

ROHERTY, Daniel; Columbus HS; Marshfield, WI; 7/104 HonRl; SpnCl; Trk; IMSpt; Trade Or Bus School.

ROHLEDER, Richard J; Loyola Academy; Northbrook, IL; 72/442 Chrs; ChrhWkr; HonRl; NHS; Indiana Univ; Medicine.

ROHLF, William R; St Thomas HS; Mpls, MN; 11/96 Band; CmntyWkr; HonRl; NatlFornLg; ROTC; StuCncl; RptrYrbk; MthCl; Tennis; IMSpt; U Of Minn; Pre Med.

ROHLIK, Patrick J; Sterling HS; Sterling, IL; NHS; NatlMeritCmnd; SchPl; Augustana College; Physician.

ROHLMAN, Monica; Kingman HS; Kingman, KS; 11/112 Chr; HonRl; SchMus; FTA; Bsktbl; College.

ROHLOFF, Julie A; Rhinelander HS; Rhinelander, WI; 9/356 Chrs; HonRl; Mdrgl; SecNHS; NatlThespSoc; SchPl; RptrSchPpr; PpCl; Chrldr; Univ Of Wisconsin; Elementary Educ.

ROHLOFF, Karen A; West Central HS; Francesville, IN; 9/90 Band; ChrhWkr; CncrtBnd; HonRl; MrchBnd; NHS; YthFlsp; RptrYrbk; 4-H; 4-HAwd; Indiana State U; Accounting.

ROHM, Dale M; Lincoln HS; Rudolph, WI; ALBoysSt; HonRl; JrNHS; NHS; NatlSciFnd; NatlThespSoc; Bsktbl; Ftbl; Trk; AmLegAwd; U W Madison; Teach.

ROHM, Deborah J; Columbus North HS; Columbus, IN; 4/514 AFS; HonRl; ModUN; NatlMeritFnl; NatlMeritSchl; SchMus; Bsktbl; LetterGlf; Swmmng; Trk; In Univ; Accountant.

ROHMILLER, Monica J; Lawton Bronson HS; Lawton, IA; SecFrshCls; TrsSophCls; Chrs; DrlTm; TchrAde; 4-H; PpCl; Bsbl; Chrldr; 4-HAwd; Trade Or Business School.

ROHN, Deanne E; Richland Center HS; Richland Center, WI; Chr; ChrhWkr; DrlTm; HonRl; HospAde; YthFlsp; FBLA; FFA; PpCl; U Of Wi.

ROHR, Glenda L; William Chrisman HS; Independence, MO; AFS; HonRl; JrNHS; NHS; StuCncl; YthFlsp; FTA; FrCl; BttyCrckrAwd; CitAwd; Nwmsu; Teacher.

ROHR, Katharine; Menasha HS; Menasha, WI; 2/303 HonRl; JrNHS; NHS; GovHonPrgAwd; Univ; Math.

ROHR, Mark A; Meridian HS; Tobias, NE; 6/35 ALBoysSt; ChrhWkr; HonRl; MrchBnd; NHS; StuCncl; 4-H; Bsktbl; Ftbl; Trk; University; Vocation.

ROHR, Melinda J; Hanston HS; Hutchinson, KS; PresSrCls; Chr; Chrs; HonRl; SchPl; RptrYrbk; EdYrBk; PpCl; Southwest Area Vo Tech; Florist.

ROHRBACHER, Jody L; Waverly HS; Lansing, MI; SecSophCls; SecJrCls; SecSrCls; HonRl; JA; NHS; StuCncl; TchrAde; SpnCl; JAAwd; General Motors Institute; Engineering.

ROHRER, Brad; Sullivan HS; Sullivan, MO; ALBoysSt; HonRl; NHS; StuCncl; FTA; PpCl; Bsktbl; Ftbl; Glf; Trk; Southwest Missouri State; Lawyer.

ROHRER, Brian P; West Marshall HS; State Center, IA; PresFrshCls; PresSophCls; HonRl; SchAde; StuCncl; StuGov; CaptBsbl; CaptBsktbl; CaptFtbl; CaptTrk; Univ.

ROHRER, Jean M; Serena HS; Sheridan, IL; SecBand; DrmMjrt; NHS; SchPl; StuCncl; Treas4-H; FFA; VPFHA; Socr; DanFAwd; Jr College; Child Care.

ROHRER, Joseph C; Jenning County HS; North Vernon, IN; 6/273 Band; HonRl; NHS; NatlMeritFnl; SctActv; StuCncl; RptrYrbk; TreasLatCl; Tennis; Butler University.

ROHRER, Joseph C; Jennings County HS; North Vernon, IN; 6/273 Band; HonRl; NHS; NatlMeritSF; SctActv; StuCncl; Yrbk; TreasLatCl; PpCl; Tennis; Butler Univ.

ROHRICH, George A; Napoleon HS; Napoleon, ND; 20/75 PresStuCncl; RptrSchPpr; MthCl; SciCl; College; Professional.

ROHRIG, Brad G; Friend HS; Friend, NE; PresJrCls; Band; Chrs; CncrtBnd; HonRl; SchPl; StuCncl; EdYrBk; LetterFtbl; CaptWrstlng; U Of Ne; Journalist.

ROHRSCHEIB, Annilee; Eisenhower HS; Decatur, IL; 1/308 Chr; HonRl; VPNHS; NatlMeritSF; NatlThespSoc; SchMus; StuCncl; College; Chemistry.

ROJAS, Karen K; Collinsville HS; Collinsville, IL; PresSophCls; SecJrCls; Aud/Vis; ChrhWkr; HonRl; HospAde; LbryAde; RedCrAde; SchAde; TchrAde; Teen; YthFlsp; St Lukes Nursing School; Nurse.

ROJEK, Johnny; Tamaroa HS; Tamaroa, IL; PresJrCls; Chrs; HonRl; PolWkr; RedCrAde; StuCncl; StuGov; RptrSchPpr; Bsbl; Bsktbl;.

ROJEK, Monica J; Downers Grove North HS; Downers Grove, IL; 4/524 SecSophCls; Chrs; HonRl; College; Law.

ROJO, Cynthia A; Maria HS; Bridgeview, IL; 59/335 HonRl; StuCncl; SpnCl; GAA; College; Speech Therapy.

ROJOHN, Claire E; Denver HS; Denver, IA; ALBoysSt; LetterBand; LetterChr; HonRl; MrchBnd; PepBnd; SchMus; SctActv; VPTeen; LetterFtbl; College; Veterinary Medicine.

ROKKE, Bruce W; Marshall County Central HS; Newfolden, MN; VPJrCls; HonRl; RptrSchPpr; FFA; SecTrsSophCls; Ftbl; Trk;.

ROKKE, Eunice I; Strandquist HS; Strandquist, MN; 2/21 PresJrCls; Band; Chrs; ChrhWkr; HonRl; SchPl; RptrYrbk; SptEdSchPpr; LetterBsktbl; GAA; College; Medicine.

ROKOSZ, Karen S; Midland HS; Midland, MI; 77/433 Chr; ChrhWkr; CmntyWkr; HonRl; SchAde; TchrAde; Yrbk; SchPpr; PpCl; SciCl; U Of Mi; Medical Technologist.

ROKOSZ, Susan M; St Joseph HS; Chicago, IL; 2/125 HonRl; NHS; College; Secretarial.

ROLAND, Beverly M; Richwoods HS; Peoria, IL; 19/449 DrlTm; HonRl; NatlMeritCmnd; OffAde; Univ; Athletic Training.

ROLAND, Deborah J; Sycamore HS; Sycamore, IL; Chr; Chrs; ChrhWkr; HonRl; LbryAde; TchrAde; PresYthFlsp; FHA; Niu; Religion.

ROLAND, Michelle A; St Pius X HS; Hillsboro, MO; 20/116 Chr; ChrhWkr; CmntyWkr; HonRl; PolWkr; College; Teacher.

ROLEN, Lewis W; Southwest HS; St Louis, MO; 273/597 Ftbl; IMSpt; Univ.

ROLER, Charlene Y; Carroll HS; Cutler, IN; 2/132 SecFrshCls; VPSophCls; Chrs; NHS; OffAde; SecFrCl; PpCl; DanFAwd; DARAwd; Purdue University; Business Data Programng.

ROLF, Merna; Burke HS; Herrick, SD; 5/36 ALAGirlsSt; Band; CmntyWkr; HonRl; StuGov; YthFnd; EdSchPpr; FBLA; FHA; CitAwd; Vo Tech School; Secretarial.

ROLFES, Zara F; Pike HS; Zionsville, IN; HonRl; LitMag; NatlThespSoc; Quill&Scroll; SchMus; SchPl; TreasStuGov; PresMthCl; CaptSwmmng; Purdue U; Mechanical Engineering.

ROLFS, Jolene; Geneseo HS; Geneseo, KS; PresSophCls; HonRl; PpCl; Chrldr; PPFtbl; Bus School; Professional.

ROLFS, Michael; West Bend East HS; West Bend, WI; HonRl; SchPl; GerCl; Bsktbl; LetterFtbl; LetterGlf; Univ Co;econ Or Archit Designs.

ROLIN, Louis J; Joliet Central HS; Joliet, IL; HonRl; JrNHS; NatlMeritSF; ROTC; TchrAde; Univ Of Chicago; Physics.

ROLING, Gloria A; Blair Oak HS; Jefferson City, MO; Band; CmntyWkr; HonRl; SchPl; StuCncl; TchrAde; Yrbk; 4-H; MthCl; AmLegAwd; College; Teaching.

ROLING, Tamela M; Kingsley Pierson HS; Kingsley, IA; Chrs; HonRl; Mdrgl; PpCl; Socr; PPFtbl; Clge.

ROLLAND, Cheri L; Snider HS; Ft Wayne, IN; 30/515 HonRl; Orch; PolWkr; YthFlsp; Bsktbl; Trk; IMSpt; University.

ROLLAND, Katherine S; Theodore Roosevelt HS; East Chicago, IN; 1/217 VPFrshCls; ALAGirlsSt; NHS; StuGov; MthCl; SciCl; Bsktbl; GAA; AmLegAwd; DARAwd; Univ; Spec Ed.

ROLLE, Rhonda J; East Monona Community HS; Moorhead, IA; 2/28 HonRl; LbryAde; NHS; RptrSchPpr; GerCl; College; Professional.

ROLLE, Russell; East Monona Comm HS; Moorhead, IA; 7/28 HonRl; RptrSchPpr; Trk; Iowa St Univ; Proffessional.

ROLLER, Janet A; York Comm HS; Elmhurst, IL; 70/950 HonRl; LitMag; NatlThespSoc; SchMus; SchPl; RptrYrbk; Yrbk; EngCl; GerCl; Bfa Degree; Fine Arts.

ROLLER, Rodney S; Southwest HS; Seligman, MO; 4/50 HstFrshCls; Chrs; HonRl; StuCncl; SptEdYrbk; FFA; FHA; FTA; Bsbl; Bsktbl; College; Speech.

ROLLING, Ann M; Dubuque Senior HS; Dubuque, IA; 25/445 HonRl; HospAde; RedCrAde; SchPpr; Chrldr; College; Secondary Education.

ROLLINS, Angela K; Dixon R 1 HS; Dixon, MO; Band; Chr; HonRl; MrchBnd; PepBnd; SchPl; Yrbk; FHA; PpCl; Business School; Business.

ROLLINS, Diana; Inkstex HS; Inkstek, MI; SecSophCls; TrsJrCls; CmntyWkr; SchAde; SchPl; StuCncl; StuGov; RptrYrbk; Western Mich Univ; Business Manage.

ROLLINS, James A; Satanta HS; Satanta, KS; 1/35 VPFrshCls; HonRl; NHS; PresStuCncl; EdYrBk; EdSchPpr; Bsktbl; LetterFtbl; LetterTrk; CitAwd; Coll; Pro.

ROLLINS, Laura J; Morton Sr HS; Hammond, IN; HonRl; NHS; Purdue Univ; Forestry.

ROLLINS, Randy J; Moores Hill HS; Moores Hill, IN; TrsFrshCls; ALBoysSt; Band; LetterBsbl; LetterGlf; Trk; Trade School.

ROLLINS, Valerie; Highway 19 HS; Owensville, MO; TrsFrshCls; TrsSophCls; Band; CncrtBnd; HonRl; MrchBnd; NHS; PepBnd; StuCncl; Southeast Mo; Music Major.

ROLLO, Russell S; Frederick HS; Frederick, SD; 4/34 VPSophCls; ALBoysSt; Band; Chr; Chrs; CncrtBnd; HonRl; MrchBnd; NatlMeritCmnd; PepBnd; SchPl; StuCncl; College; Law.

ROLOF, Bill C; Baraga HS; Baraga, MI; HonRl; OffAde; SchPl; SctActv; Bsbl; LetterBsktbl; LetterFtbl; LetterTrk; CchngActv; College; Teacher.

ROLWING, Kevin F; Charleston HS; Wyatt, MO; FFA; M U.

ROMAN, Christopher D; Benet Academy; Woodridge, IL; 61/230 Band; CncrtBnd; HonRl; MrchBnd; LetterFtbl; LetterTrk; Univ Of Ill; Engineering.

ROMAN, Leonard W; St Patrick HS; Chicago, IL; 1/421 HonRl; NHS; SctActv; LetterSwmmng; Tennis; Univ Of Notre Dame; Accountant.

ROMAN, Margie; Cathedral HS; Chicago, IL; Chr; HonRl; TchrAde; SpnCl; Swmmng; Trade Or Business School; Professional.

ROMAN, Myrian; Cathedral HS; Chicago, IL; HonRl; NHS; Sacrstn; SpnCl; College.

ROMAN, Richard J; Carmel Boys HS; Buffalo Grove, IL; Chrs; ChrhWkr; HonRl; NHS; SchMus; SchPl; StuCncl; Marquette Univ; Medicine.

ROMANEK, James; St Patrick HS; Chicago, IL; 58/377 HonRl; Teen; FrCl; PpCl; Bsbl; Tennis; IMSpt; Univ Of Notre Dame; Lawyer.

ROMANOW, Amy; All Saints Central HS; Bay City, MI; 3/138 ALAGirlsSt; HonRl; NHS; StuCncl; SpnCl; Glf; DARAwd; OptClAwd; VFWAwd; Univ Of Detroit; Bioly Major.

ROMANOWSKI, Lillian; Osborn HS; Detroit, MI; 9/636 HonRl; HospAde; NHS; OffAde; SchPl; StuCncl; RptrYrbk; FrCl; Wayne State U; Nurse.

ROMEL, Lawrence A; Evergreen Park Comm HS; Evergreen Park, IL; 50/432 NHS; RusCl; LetterSwmmng; Univ Of Illinois; Chemistry.

ROMENS, Randy A; Turkey Valley Comm HS; Protivin, IA; VPSrCls; LetterBsbl; LetterFtbl; LetterWrstlng; CchngActv; College.

ROMES, Terry L; Howell HS; Brighton, MI; 43/375 CtyCnl; CmntyWkr; HonRl; HospAde; RedCrAde; StuGov; EdSchPpr; FBLA; FDA; FSA; College; Accounting.

ROMIG, Ralph W; Southeast Of Saline HS; Assaria, KS; 4/51 Band; CncrtBnd; HonRl; MrchBnd; NatlMeritCmnd; PepBnd; SctActv; FrCl; Ks State Univ; Chem Eng.

ROMINE, John C; Centralia HS; Centralia, MO; HonRl; JA; NHS; LetterBsbl; LetterBsktbl; CaptLetterTrk; PresJAAwd; PresAwd; College; Professnl.

ROMINE, Kevin; Tri Valley HS; Downs, IL; 6/41 Band; ChrhWkr; CncrtBnd; HonRl; MrchBnd; PepBnd; 4-H; FFA; Trk; Wrstlng; Coll; Radiology.

ROMINE, Terri J; Sycamore HS; Sycmore, IL; 11/200 Chrs; HonRl; FrCl; GAA; College.

ROMINSKI, Betty J; Warren HS; Warren, MN; 6/73 SecJrCls; Band; HonRl; SchPl; StuCncl; EdYrBk; GerCl; PpCl; SciCl; GAA; University Of Mankato; Nursing (r.n.).

ROMINSKY, Keith A; Walled Lake Western HS; Union Lake, MI; 17/388 CncrtBnd; HonRl; MrchBnd; NHS; Orch; PepBnd; SchMus; TchrAde; Oakland University; Liberal Arts.

ROMINSKY, Kenneth G; Walled Lake Western HS; Union Lake, MI; Band; CncrtBnd; HonRl; MrchBnd; NHS; Orch; PepBnd; SchMus; Lawrence Inst Of Tech; Architecture.

ROMJO, Debbie D; Hannah Public HS; Hannah, ND; VPFrshCls; PresJrCls; SecTrsSrCls; ALAGirlsSt; Chr; Chrl; ChrhWkr; HonRl; JA; Bsktbl; Nd State Univ; Home Ec.

ROMME, Fran C; Liberal HS; Liberal, KS; HstSrCls; HonRl; College; Secretary.

ROMMELMANN, Douglas W; Carlyle HS; Carlyle, IL; 3/145 Band; ChrhWkr; HonRl; NHS; YthFlsp; 4-H; PpCl; LetterBsbl; Bsktbl; DanFAwd; Jr College; Elec Engineering.

ROMO, Cheryl A; Negaunee HS; Palmer, MI; Orch; Alpena Comm Coll; Law Enforcement.

ROMOHR, Julia; Gresham Public HS; Gresham, NE; 5/13 CncrtBnd; HonRl; SchPl; StuCncl; CchngActv; GAA; Univ Of Ne; Dental Hygiene.

ROMOSER, Craig W; Community HS; Winfield, IL; 7/311 AFS; HonRl; NHS; StuCncl; LetterTrk; Univ Of Washington; Business.

ROMSEK, Deborah J; Concord HS; Jackson, MI; 5 69 Band; CncrtBnd; HonRl; LbryAde; NatlMeritFnl; PresYthFlsp; PpCl; CaptBsktbl; Trk; GAA; College; Special Education.

ROMSOS, Lisa R; Bottineau HS; Bottineau, ND; 14/89 ALAGirlsSt; HonRl; SchPl; TchrAde; FBLA; FHA; PpCl; CaptBsktbl; LetterTrk; Wrstlng; College; Law.

RONAT, William J; Jacksonville HS; Jacksonville, IL; 23/360 Band; Chr; Chrs; CncrtBnd; HonRl; LitMag; MrchBnd; NatlThespSoc; PepBnd; SchMus; SchPl; RptrSchPpr; SchPpr; Univ Of Illinois; English.

RONCANCIO, Silvia M; Sacred Heart Academy; Springfield, IL; VPFrshCls; HonRl; IntrClCncl; SpnCl; MthCl; PpCl; SciCl; Chrldr; Western Illinois University.

RONCONE, Claudia J; Maine Twp West HS; Des Plaines, IL; ChrhWkr; HonRl; IntrClCncl; JrNHS; StuCncl; RptrYrbk; Yrbk; SpnCl; PpCl; PresGAA; Illinois State Univ; Special Education.

RONDEAU, Kathy; Drummond HS; Cable, WI; 2/53 Band; Chr; HonRl; NHS; Yrbk; Trk; Chrldr; GAA; College; Medicine.

RONDEAU, Kathy A; Drummond HS; Cable, WI; 2/56 SecFrshCls; CncrtBnd; HonRl; NHS; PepBnd; 4-H; LetterBsbl; LetterBsktbl; LetterTrk; Chrldr; Univ; Medicine.

RONDOT, Judith M; Bishop Luers HS; Ft Wayne, IN; 28/225 HonRl; TchrAde; FrCl; PpCl; Chrldr; GAA; IMSpt; College; Dental Hygiene.

RONEY, Renee A; H L Richards HS; Oak Lawn, IL; 24/1035 Band; CncrtBnd; DrmMjrt; HonRl; MrchBnd; NHS; NatlMeritCmnd; Orch; PepBnd; SchMus; TchrAde; College; Professional.

RONGITSCH, Michael C; St Thomas Acad; St Paul, MN; HstSrCls; HonRl; NatlMeritCmnd; SchPl; TchrAde; FTA; MthCl; Ftbl; CchngActv; IMSpt; St Thomas Coll; Teacher.

RONKOWSKI, Mark A; Marquette Univ HS; Milwaukee, WI; Marquette Univ; Engineering.

RONNA, Valerie A; Buckley Loda HS; Loda, IL; SecSophCls; CncrtBnd; HonRl; HospAde; SchPl; TreasYthFlsp; Yrbk; TreasFHA; VPSciCl; GAA; Parkland Coll; Dental Assistant.

RONNAU, Kent A; North Bend Central HS; North Bend, NE; Chr; Chrs; ChrhWkr; HonRl; SchMus; SchPl; SctActv; YthFlsp; EdSchPpr; LetterFtbl; College.

RONNING, Barbara F; Raymond HS; Raymond, MN; VPFrshCls; VPSrCls; ALAGirlsSt; Chr; HonRl; LbryAde; NHS; EdYrBk; PPFtbl;.

RONNING, Ruth A; Iola Scandinavia HS; Iola, WI; 3/47 PresSrCls; Chrs; CncrtBnd; Mdrgl; SecNHS; PepBnd; StuCncl; PresFHA; GAA; Concordia College.

RONSICK, Barbara J; Centre HS; Lincolnville, KS; 9/39 ALAGirlsSt; Chr; Chrs; CncrtBnd; DrlTm; HonRl; Mdrgl; SchMus; FHA; PPFtbl; Emporia Kansas St Clg; Secretary.

RONSKE, Lisa M; York Comm HS; Elmhurst, IL; 60/912 Chrs; HonRl; JA; LbryAde; Quill&Scroll; Univ Of Illinois; Journalism.

RONSPIES, Debra; Pierce HS; Pierce, NE; 16/63 SecSophCls; Chr; Chrl; Chrs; HonRl; Mdrgl; NatlThespSoc; 4-H; AmLegAwd; Coll; Nurse.

RONSSE, Scott R; St Marys HS; St Marys, KS; 1/60 Chrl; Chrs; HonRl; NHS; TchrAde; EngCl; FrCl; SpnCl; PpCl; SciCl; Univ; Secondary Education.

RONVIK, Tracy; Evanston Township HS; Evanston, IL; 10/1040 HonRl; PolWkr; YthLg; College; Writing.

ROOD, Scott A; Muskegon Catholic Central HS; Muskegon, MI; 50/210 Band; Chr; ChrhWkr; HonRl; MrchBnd; PolWkr; RedCrAde; SchMus; SctActv; College; Law.

ROOK, Glenda K; Brownstown HS; Brownstown, IL; TrsFrshCls; Chrs; CmntyWkr; CncrtBnd; OffAde; SchPl; RptrYrbk; EdYrBk; GAA; 4-HAwd; Secretary;.

ROOK, Sharon L; Elk Grove HS; Elk Grove Vlg, IL; 94/505 TreasChr; SecChrs; SecDrlTm; NHS; NatlMeritCmnd; PolWkr; PresSctActv; RptrSchPpr; KeyCl; Eastern Ill Univ; Elementary Ed.

ROOKER, Joseph L; John Glenn HS; Bay City, MI; 110356 LetterFtbl; LetterWrstlng; U Of Mi; Med.

ROOKER, Kevin C; Moline HS; Moline, IL; Aud/Vis; CmntyWkr; JA; LbryAde; PresSchPl; SctActv; LetterWrstlng; TreasJAAwd; OptClAwd; Col; Writer.

ROON, Debbie; Unity Christian HS; Allendale, MI; Band; CncrtBnd; HonRl; MrchBnd; 4-H; Chrldr; IMSpt; Univ Of Mich; Journalist.

ROONEY, Ardith R; Satanta HS; Satanta, KS; 1/30 Band; Chrs; DrmMjrt; HonRl; NHS; SchPl; EdYrBk; Bsbl; LetterBsktbl; Trk; Chrldr; CchngActv; PPFtbl; College; Architecture.

ROONEY, Cecile A; Superior Senior HS; Superior, WI; Chr; Chrs; HonRl; JrNHS; OffAde; PpCl; Chrldr; GAA; PresAwd; Clg Of St Scholastica; Rn.

ROONEY, James J; Kaneland HS; Maple Park, IL; 42/166 Chrs; ChrhWkr; HonRl; NatlFornLg; SctActv; StuGov; SchPpr; FSA; FrCl; MthCl; PpCl; Bsbl; Ne Ill Univ; Computer Science.

ROONEY, Robin T; Alpena HS; Alpena, MI; Chr; ChrhWkr; HonRl; NatlMeritCmnd; NatlMeritSchl; NatlMeritSF; NatlThespSoc; SchMus; RptrSchPpr; W Michigan Univ; Communications.

ROONEY, Timothy J; Fenwick HS; Riverside, IL; CmntyWkr; HonRl; NHS; PolWkr; SchPl; RptrYrbk; RptrSchPpr; LetterBsktbl; LetterFtbl; IMSpt; Northwestern Univ; Law.

ROOP, Betty M; Wheaton Christian HS; West Chicago, IL; TrsSophCls; TrsJrCls; TrsSrCls; Band; Chr; HonRl; RptrYrbk; Clge.

ROOP, Jennifer A; Westview HS; Kankakee, IL; 1/230 ALAGirlsSt; Band; CncrtBnd; HonRl; HospAde; MrchBnd; PresNHS; SchMus; YthFlsp; PresFrCl; Univ Of Iowa; Nursing.

ROOP, Karen S; Bellflower Township HS; Bellflower, IL; 2/24 Band; Chrs; ChrhWkr; CmntyWkr; CncrtBnd; HonRl; MrchBnd; OffAde; PepBnd; SchPl; StuCncl; Trk; IMSpt; Wesleyan Univ; Nurse.

ROOP, Melanie; West Washington HS; Campbellsburg, IN; HonRl; NHS; OffAde; FHA; LatCl; PpCl; DARAwd;.

ROORDA, Londa L; Montpelier HS; Ypsilanti, ND; SecJrCls; Chr; ChrhWkr; HonRl; HospAde; RedCrAde; SchPl; StuCncl; StuGov; YthFlsp; Coll; Mdical.

ROOSE, Susan; Ishpeming HS; Ishpeming, MI; 12/199 SecJrCls; Chrs; DrmBgl; HonRl; NHS; StuCncl; Yrbk; SchPpr; Swmmng; Trk; College; Social Worker.

ROOT, Allen J; Sparta HS; Norwalk, WI; 5/192 Chrs; HonRl; NHS; IMSpt; Wheaton Coll; Actuary Science.

ROOT, Beverly A; Pillager HS; Pillager, MN; 1/35 SecJrCls; ALAGirlsSt; Chr; Chrs; ChrhWkr; HonRl; SchPl; FHA; GAA; DARAwd; College;.

ROOT, Bradford G; Saginaw HS; Saginaw, MI; 42/600 Band; CncrtBnd; HonRl; JrNHS; MrchBnd; NHS; SctActv; TchrAde; Swmmng; University Of Hawaii; Nuclear Engineer.

ROOT, Faith; Eastern HS; Solsberry, IN; Chrs; ChrhWkr; HonRl; NHS; SchMus; YthFlsp; PpCl; SciCl; Coll; Christ Educ.

ROOT, Grace A; Alburnett Comm HS; Alburnett, IA; Band; Chrs; LbryAde; SchMus; TchrAde; YthFlsp; 4-H; FHA; FTA; Chrldr;.

ROOT, Karen S; Maple Valley HS; Nashville, MI; HonRl; NHS; StuGov; FHA; SpnCl; College; Engineering.

ROOT, Leslie; Hill City HS; Hill City, KS; Band; CncrtBnd; HonRl; HospAde; PepBnd; PpCl; College; Teaching.

ROOT, Patricia A; Edwards County HS; Bone Gap, IL; 12/104 VPSophCls; SecBand; HonRl; NHS; PepBnd; RptrSchPpr; SchPpr; FTA; PpCl; Olney Central Jr Coll; Elementary Ed.

ROOT, Thatcher W; Lahser HS; Bloomfield Hills, MI; 3/464 ChrhWkr; CncrtBnd; MrchBnd; NHS; NatlMeritSF; PepBnd; SchMus; SctActv; Tennis; RotaryAwd; College; Engineering.

ROOT, Thomas A; Collinsville HS; Collinsville, IL; 28/645 HonRl; LbryAde; NHS; StuGov; MthCl; SciCl; Bsktbl; Glf; Eastern Ill Univ; Business.

ROOTMAN, Clifton; Albia Community HS; Albia, IA; 32/150 VPSophCls; CAP; MrchBnd; EdSchPpr; FSA; RusCl; Socr; College.

ROOZEN, Kimberly S; Gayville Volin HS; Gayville, SD; 6/16 ALAGirlsSt; Chr; ChrhWkr; LbryAde; SchPl; EdYrBk; RptrSchPpr; 4-H; LetterBsktbl; LetterTrk; Clge; Home Ec.

ROOZENBOOM, Gary A; Rock Valley Community HS; Rock Valley, IA; 37/63 CAP; CmntyWkr; HonRl; NatlMeritFnl; FBLA; ChmbCommrsAwd; GovHonPrgAwd; PresAwd; CitAwd; VoiceDemAwd; Trade School; Communictions.

ROPELE, Michael A; Norway Vulcan HS; Norway, MI; VPJrCls; Chr; HonRl; NHS; StuGov; RptrYrbk; SptEdYrbk; 4-H; Bsktbl; Trk; College; Teaching.

ROPELLA, Kent L; St Mary Central HS; Menasha, WI; HonRl; StuCncl; SpnCl; PpCl; Bsbl; Bsktbl; Ftbl; Glf; Trk; IMSpt; Univ; Architect.

ROPER, Brenda; Corunna HS; Corunna, MI; 14/201 SecFrshCls; Band; HonRl; NHS; PepBnd; RptrYrbk; PpCl; College; Creative Writing.

ROPER, Cynthia L; Hobart HS; Hobart, IN; 40/400 VPAFS; ALAGirlsSt; PresCncrtBnd; HonRl; VPJrNHS; MrchBnd; NHS; StuCncl; Pres4-H; PresSpnCl; Clge; Vet Med.

ROPER, John E; Civic Memorial HS; Bethalto, IL; HonRl; StuCncl; RptrYrbk; FrCl; PpCl; LetterBsbl; Wrstlng; Il Univ; Computers.

ROPP, Stephen A; Nevada HS; Nevada, IA; Chrs; CncrtBnd; HonRl; MrchBnd; NHS; PepBnd; YthFlsp; FFA; LetterFtbl; 4-HAwd; College.

ROPPEL, Michael A; Alsen Public HS; Alsen, ND; VPFrshCls; SecTrsJrCls; SchPl; StuCncl; CaptBsktbl; IMSpt; U Of Nd; Professnl.

RORVIG, Dawn R; Binford Public HS; Binfordd, ND; 1/10 PresSophCls; Chrs; HonRl; StuCncl; EdYrBk; RptrSchPpr; SchPpr; TreasPpCl; College.

ROSADO, Edward J; Sycamore HS; Sycamore, IL; 50/250 CncrtBnd; MrchBnd; TreasStuCncl; University.

ROSALES, Jeffry M; Osseo Senior HS; Minneapolis, MN; 30/360 HonRl; Univ Of Mn.

ROSBOROUGH, Kevin L; Mendota HS; Mendota, IL; Band; Chr; ChrhWkr; Mdrgl; MrchBnd; College; Liberal Arts.

ROSCOE, Mark A; Calumet HS; Gary, IN; 14/330 PresSophCls; HonRl; JrNHS; NHS; Quill&Scroll; StuCncl; EdYrBk; SpnCl; AmLegAwd; Valparasiso U; Pre Law.

ROSE, Andrew A; Luther South HS; Chicago, IL; 17/207 Chr; HonRl; NHS; SchMus; SchPl; YthFlsp; Bsbl; Wrstlng; IMSpt; VFWAwd; E Ill Univ.

ROSE, Bobbette L; Peoria HS; Peoria, IL; 42/450 ChrhWkr; HonRl; Quill&Scroll; PresYthFlsp; Yrbk; SchPpr; Treas4-H; LatCl; So Ill Univ; Commercial Design.

ROSE, Bonnie; Gering HS; Mitchell, NE; PresFrshCls; Chrs; HonRl; JrNHS; StuCncl; TchrAde; 4-H; Choolron State; Double Major Inhome Ec Psyc.

ROSE, Cathy A; Resurrection HS; Chicago, IL; 99/294 CmntyWkr; HonRl; SctActv; Bsktbl; CchngActv; GAA; IMSpt; College; Physical Therapy.

ROSE, Cindy M; Brentwood HS; Brentwood, MO; Chr; DrlTm; HonRl; JA; Mdrgl; ModUN; NHS; NatlThespSoc; SchPl; FTA; Coll; Teacher.

ROSE, Cynthia D; Paxton HS; Paxton, IL; Band; CncrtBnd; HonRl; HospAde; MrchBnd; NHS; NatlThespSoc; SchPl; RptrYrbk; 4-H; LatCl; SciCl; GAA;.

ROSE, David A; Mason HS; Erie, MI; ALBoysSt; Band; ChrhWkr; CncrtBnd; HonRl; MrchBnd; NHS; LetterSwmmng; College; Engineering.

ROSE, David J; Clearwater R 1 HS; Piedmont, MO; 1/95 TrsSophCls; Band; Chrs; ChrhWkr; CncrtBnd; HonRl; LbryAde; MrchBnd; StuCncl; Sw Mo St Springfield; Psychology.

ROSE, Deborah; Lomira HS; Lomira, WI; AFS; Chrs; HonRl; NatlFornLg; SchPl; StuCncl; Bsktbl; Ftbl; Trk; GAA;.

ROSE, Dennis; Arthur County HS; Arthur, NE; TrsSophCls; ALBoysSt; SchPl; Yrbk; 4-H; Ftbl; Trk; IMSpt; 4-HAwd; Trade School; Saddle Maker.

ROSE, Donna M; Calhoun HS; Hardin, IL; SecFrshCls; SecSophCls; SecJrCls; Band; CncrtBnd; HonRl; NHS; PepBnd; 4-H; GAA; College; Major Study.

ROSE, John A; Great Bend Sr HS; Great Bend, KS; HonRl; SchPl; FFA; Jr College; Law Enforcement.

ROSE, Kathy; Central Catholic HS; West Point, NE; CmntyWkr; HonRl; SchMus; SchPl; FHA; PpCl; GAA; Univ Sd; Social Work.

ROSE, Kenneth D; Blue Hill Comm HS; Blue Hill, NE; VPFrshCls; PresSophCls; Band; Chrs; Mdrgl; PepBnd; SchPl; SchPpr; 4-H; FFA; LetterBsktbl; LetterFtbl; 4-HAwd; Trade School.

ROSE, Kimberly J; Grace HS; Crystal, MN; JA; SctActv; StuGov; CaptTrk; IMSpt; JAAwd; PresAwd; Coll; Social Welfare.

ROSE, Linda M; Blue Hill Community HS; Blue Hill, NE; 10/40 Band; Chrs; CncrtBnd; MrchBnd; PepBnd; SchPl; YthFlsp; FHA; PpCl; 4-HAwd; Ctcc.

ROSE, Lori L; Springville HS; Springville, IA; 3/58 PresJrCls; Chr; HonRl; NHS; SchPl; TchrAde; RptrYrbk; RptrSchPpr; LetterTrk; CaptChrldr; College.

ROSE, Machelle J; Vassar HS; Vassar, MI; Chr; ChrhWkr; HospAde; NHS; TchrAde; PresFHA; University; Teacher.

ROSE, Mark A; Jackson HS; Alpha, MN; FFA; GerCl; Jackson Voc; Farmer.

ROSE, Michael A; Brookfield Central HS; Brookfield, WI; TrsJrCls; Chr; Chrs; PolWkr; StuCncl; StuGov; RptrYrbk; KeyCl; LetterSwmmng; Coll; Educ.

ROSE, Patricia M; Jacksonville HS; Jacksonville, IL; 15/363 ChrhWkr; HonRl; NHS; PolWkr; SchMus; StuCncl; SpnCl; Ill St Univ.

ROSE, Ruth M; Tri HS; Spiceland, IN; PresJrCls; Chrs; ChrhWkr; HonRl; NHS; SchAde; RptrYrbk; RptrSchPpr; FHA; SpnCl; Ball St Univ; Occup Ther.

ROSE, Sheila M; Calhoun HS; Hardin, IL; Band; ChrhWkr; CmntyWkr; HonRl; NHS; PepBnd; TchrAde; Pres4-H; GAA; 4-HAwd; Quincy Blessing College; Nursing.

ROSEBERRY, Carolyn S; Center Point Cons HS; Center Point, IA; Chr; NHS; SchMus; RptrSchPpr; FNA; BttyCrckrAwd; Coe College; History.

ROSEBERRY, Richard E; Murphysboro Township HS; Murphysboro, IL; College; Professional.

ROSEBERRY, Ronald; Mullen Public HS; Mullen, NE; TrsFrshCls; VPSophCls; Chrs; HonRl; PepBnd; SchMus; 4-H; LetterFtbl; LetterTrk; LetterWrstlng; Coll; Voc.

ROSEBROCK, Janet L; Frederick HS; Frederick, SD; Band; ChrhWkr; CncrtBnd; HonRl; MrchBnd; PepBnd; 4-H; PpCl; College; Professional.

ROSEBROUGH, Linda S; Ft Scott HS; Ft Scott, KS; Chrs; ChrhWkr; CmntyWkr; DrlTm; HonRl; HospAde; RptrSchPpr; College; Nursing.

ROSECRANS, Jo Ann; Elmwood HS; Elmwood, IL; 1/55 SecBand; HonRl; NHS; EdYrBk; SpnCl; PpCl; Chrldr; GAA; University Of Illinois; Political Science.

ROSEDALE, Tracy T; Semco Comm HS; Gilman, IA; Band; Chrs; CncrtBnd; HonRl; MrchBnd; NatlThespSoc; PepBnd; SchMus; SchPl; StuCncl; LetterFtbl; Glf; LetterWrstlng; College; Professional.

ROSEHTRETER, John F; York HS; Elmhurst, IL; University; Forestry.

ROSELL, Tarris D; Parkers Prairie HS; Eagle Bend, MN; 4/74 PresSrCls; ALBoysSt; Band; Chr; ChrhWkr; HonRl; NHS; NatlMeritCmnd; StuCncl; 4-H; Bethel College, St Paul; Theology & Music.

ROSEMA, Debra K; Oakridge HS; Muskegon, MI; 8/117 Band; CncrtBnd; HonRl; LbryAde; MrchBnd; NHS; PepBnd; StuCncl; LetterBsktbl; LetterChrldr; Albion College; Biology.

ROSEMEYER, David W; Fenwick HS; La Grange, IL; HonRl; LitMag; NHS; NatlMeritCmnd; Yrbk; SchPpr; GerCl; PpCl; Ftbl; LetterTrk; Univ Of Notre Dame; Law.

ROSEMEYER, Rick E; Webster Groves HS; Rock Hill, MO; 18/484 HonRl; RptrSchPpr; LetterBsbl; LetterFtbl; LetterGlf; Univ Of Oh; Radio.

ROSEN, Carl F; Metropolitan Studies HS; Chicago, IL; Chrs; SecStuGov; RptrSchPpr; Tennis; University; Economics.

ROSEN, Joyce A; East Peoria Comm HS; East Peoria, IL; 12/450 ChrhWkr; CncrtBnd; HonRl; NHS; Orch; SctActv; Yrbk; PresGerCl; MthCl; TreasSciCl; Cottey College; Mathematics.

ROSEN, Marc J; New Trier East HS; Glencoe, IL; Band; CncrtBnd; Orch; PepBnd; SchMus; SchPl; University; Music.

ROSENAK, Lynn A; Wayland Academy; Eagle River, WI; Band; HonRl; NHS; PepBnd; SctActv; Twrl; Yrbk; 4-H; FrCl; University.

ROSENAK, Steven W; Ofallon Township HS; Ofallon, IL; 136/316 HonRl; SctActv; GerCl; Socr; Us Air Force Academy; Aviation.

ROSENBALM, Larry D; Eminence HS; Martinsville, IN; 1/35 PresSophCls; ALBoysSt; PresNHS; RptrYrbk; Pres4-H; FFA; LetterBsbl; LetterBsktbl; AmLegAwd; 4-HAwd; Purdue Univ; Engineering.

ROSENBARGER, David V; Frontier HS; Brookston, IN; Band; HonRl; MrchBnd; SchAde; TchrAde; FFA; Bsbl; Bsktbl; CaptFtbl; Trk; Business; Vocation.

ROSENBAUGH, Linda J; Smithville HS; Kansas City, MO; HonRl; LitMag; LbryAde; OffAde; PolWkr; RptrYrbk; SchPpr; EngCl; PpCl; JCAwd; William Jewell.

ROSENBAUM, Jay A; Deerfield HS; Deerfield, IL; HonRl; StuGov; TchrAde; LetterBsbl; LetterBsktbl; CchngActv; College; Professional.

ROSENBAUM, Kim; Pratt HS; Pratt, KS; 1/145 Band; CncrtBnd; DrmMjrt; HonRl; MrchBnd; PepBnd; 4-H; 4-HAwd; Sw Oklahoma State U; Pharmacy.

ROSENBAUM, Kimberly; Elk Point HS; Elk Point, SD; Chrs; ChrhWkr; HonRl; SchPl; YthFlsp; Yrbk; PpCl;.

ROSENBAUM, Martin R; Colfax Comm HS; Colfax, IA; 2/57 Band; Chrs; NHS; SchMus; SchPl; Glf; Coe College Cedar Rapids.

ROSENBAUM, Peter J; Whitefish Bay HS; Milwaukee, WI; HonRl; NatlFornLg; NatlMeritCmnd; NatlSciFnd; LatCl; MthCl; Ftbl; Tennis; IMSpt; U Of Mn; Doctor Of Vet Med.

ROSENBERG, Carolyn H; Southfield Lathrup HS; Southfield, MI; 5/683 NatlFornLg; NHS; NatlThespSoc; PolWkr; SchMus; OptClAwd; VoiceDemAwd; U Of Mi; Lawyer.

ROSENBERG, Christine A; Black River Falls HS; Black River Falls, WI; 11/140 Band; Chr; CncrtBnd; DrmMjrt; HonRl; MrchBnd; NHS; SchMus; CaptBsktbl; Glf; Stevens Point U; Music Education.

ROSENBERG, Marc A; Sullivan HS; Chicago, IL; Chrs; HonRl; NHS; OffAde; SchMus; RptrSchPpr; SpnCl; College; Education.

ROSENBERG, Margaret S; Appleton West HS; Madison, WI; CmntyWkr; NatlMeritSF; Coll; Pre Kindergarten Education.

ROSENBERG, Steven J; Roosevelt HS; Des Moines, IA; 29/432 TrsSrCls; CaptTennis; Univ; Medicine.

ROSENBERGER, Cindy K; Guthrie Center Comm HS; Guthrie Center, IA; 1/55 TrsSrCls; Band; Chr; NHS; NatlMeritCmnd; SchMus; SchPl; TchrAde; EdSchPpr; TreasFNA; Nw Mo State; Physical Therapy.

ROSENBERGER, Linda A; Brookville HS; Brookville, IN; 31/190 ALAGirlsSt; HonRl; NHS; SchPl; StuCncl; Yrbk; PpCl; Trk; CaptChrldr; GAA; Univ; Com Prog.

ROSENBERGER, Lisa; Switz Co HS; Vevay, IN; 2/105 Band; HonRl; NHS; PepBnd; PolWkr; SchPl; SpnCl; PpCl; GAA; Franklin Col; Industrial Librarian.

ROSENBLUM, Nita A; Glenbrook North HS; Northbrook, IL; 24/610 CmntyWkr; HospAde; NHS; Oberlin College.

ROSENBURG, Bryan S; Maryville R Ii HS; Maryville, MO; 1/130 Chr; VPCncrtBnd; VPMrchBnd; NHS; NatlMeritFnl; NatlMeritSchl; StuCncl; PresYthFlsp; PresSciCl; OptClAwd; Mich State U; Mathematics.

ROSENCRANS, Rosemary M; Chesaning HS; Chesaning, MI; Band; CncrtBnd; HonRl; MrchBnd; EdYrBk; Yrbk; RptrSchPpr; EdSchPpr; SchPpr; FrCl; College; Broadcast Journalism.

ROSENDAHL, Beth A; Ventura Comm HS; Ventura, IA; Band; CncrtBnd; MrchBnd; PepBnd; YthFlsp; RptrYrbk; EdSchPpr; Tennis; Waldorf Clg; Photography.

ROSENE, Kathy A; Winola HS; New Windsor, IL; SecSophCls; Chr; ChrhWkr; CmntyWkr; HonRl; LbryAde; NHS; SchPl; StuCncl; Yrbk; FshEdSchPpr; SptEdSchPpr; 4-H; GAA; American Floral Art Sch; Florist.

ROSENFELD, Peter M; New Trier East HS; Glencoe, IL; 72/647 AFS; CmntyWkr; HonRl; PolWkr; UNYO; College; Int Relations.

ROSENFELDER, Bruce A; Lane Tech HS; Chicago, IL; 26/1213 HonRl; NatlMeritSF; SchPpr; Carthage College; Math.

ROSENQUIST, Daniel; St Paul HS; Saint Paul, NE; TrsSophCls; Chr; HonRl; OffAde; Yrbk; BauchLmbAwd; College; Pre Med.

ROSENQUIST, Eric W; High School; Ceresco, NE; ChrhWkr; 4-H; FFA; LetterFtbl; LetterWrstlng; 4-HAwd; Ne U; Agriculture.

ROSENSTIEL, Bruce A; Oak Park River Forest HS; Oak Park, IL; 50/1100 PresSophCls; JrNHS; NatlMeritCmnd; StuCncl; StuGov; MthCl; Syracuse Univ; Law.

ROSENTHAL, William N; Central HS; St Joseph, MO; 1/500 Chr; HonRl; NHS; StuGov; YthLg; LatCl; PresSciCl; Swmmng; AmLegAwd; OptClAwd; College; Medicine.

ROSENTRATER, Dianne L; Luther South HS; Merrionette Park, IL; 1/197 Chr; DrlTm; NatlFornLg; NHS; SecSctActv; YthLg; RptrSchPpr; LetterTennis; GAA; St Olaf College; Chemistry.

ROSENTRETER, Denise; Carlinville HS; Carlinville, IL; 22/180 HonRl; JrNHS; SchPl; StuCncl; 4-H; Chrldr; GAA; College; Vocational.

ROSENWINKEL, Betty A; Timothy Christian HS; Cicero, IL; 9/84 ChrhWkr; HonRl; NHS; SchPl; PpCl; Calvin College.

ROSENWINKEL, Mary S; Lyons Township HS; Lagrange, IL; NatlMeritCmnd; OffAde; College.

ROSETTI OLIVEIRA, Marco A; Alton HS; Godgrey, IL; AFS; StuCncl; StuGov; IMSpt; Clg; Medicine.

ROSEVEAR, Terry J; Barrington HS; Barrington, IL; Chrs; ChrhWkr; HonRl; NHS; YthFlsp; Univ Of Ill; Medicine.

ROSFELD, Mary P; Batesville HS; Metamora, IN; 2/150 Chrs; HonRl; NHS; RptrSchPpr; SpnCl; GAA; Univ; Social Work.

ROSHELL, Terri J; Chippewa Falls Sr HS; Chippewa Falls, WI; 14/370 AFS; Chrs; ChrhWkr; Mdrgl; NHS; SchPl; EdSchPpr; SecFrCl; PpCl; Univ Of Wi; Nursing.

ROSIEK, Linda M; St Clement HS; Warren, MI; 15/98 JrNHS; NHS; SchPl; SctActv; PpCl; SciCl; LetterBsbl; LetterChrldr; GAA; Accounting/computer Math.

ROSIEK, Margaret M; Maria HS; Chicago, IL; 115/390 CncrtBnd; DrlTm; HospAde; MrchBnd; Orch; PolWkr; SchMus; SctActv; Sdlty; Univ Of Illinois; Accounting.

ROSIERE, Peter B; Hononegah Comm HS; Roscoe, IL; Band; CncrtBnd; HonRl; JA; MrchBnd; Orch; PepBnd; SchMus; College; Business.

ROSIN, Jeff W; Barrett HS; Barrett, MN; 4/19 SecFrshCls; VPSophCls; SchPl; Yrbk; FFA; LetterBsbl; LetterBsktbl; LetterFtbl; IMSpt; Technical; Vocation.

ROSIN, Jerry A; Mayville HS; Horicon, WI; 7/124 ALBoysSt; HonRl; NHS; StuCncl; SptEdSchPpr; FFA; LetterBsktbl; LetterFtbl; CchngActv; AmLegAwd; U; Pro.

ROSIN, John D; Walther Lutheran HS; River Forest, IL; 1/91 Chr; CncrtBnd; HonRl; LbryAde; MrchBnd; NHS; NatlMeritCmnd; NatlThespSoc; Orch; PepBnd;.

ROSIN, Robert L; Decatur Comm HS; Oberlin, KS; HonRl; NHS; CmntyWkr; NHS; SchPl; VPStuCncl; StuGov; SpnCl; LetterFtbl; LetterWrstlng; Col; Med Dr.

ROSINSKY, Samuel J; Harry A Burke HS; Omaha, NE; 104/496 HonRl; NatlFornLg; LetterGlf; Univ Nebraska Lincoln; Medicine.

ROSIO, Cheryl; Antigo Sr HS; Deerbrook, WI; 7/375 Band; Chr; ChrhWkr; CncrtBnd; HonRl; MrchBnd; PepBnd; Trk; GAA; IMSpt; College; Professional.

ROSKE, Wendy J; Riceville Comm HS; Riceville, IA; 6/65 TrsSophCls; Band; Chrs; DrlTm; NHS; SchPl; 4-H; FNA; Chrldr; GAA; Coll; Pro.

ROSKENS, Sidney H; Everly Community HS; Spencer, IA; HonRl; SchMus; StuCncl; Ftbl; Trade Sch.

ROSKOM, Dale E; Gillett Public HS; Cecil, WI; 4/77 Band; CncrtBnd; MrchBnd; Orch; PepBnd; StuCncl; LetterBsktbl; BttyCrckrAwd; Uw Madison; Actuary.

ROSKOM, Gail M; Gillett HS; Cecil, WI; 5/78 Band; CmntyWkr; CncrtBnd; HonRl; Mdrgl; MrchBnd; PepBnd; RedCrAde; TchrAde; PpCl; U Of Wi; Special Education.

ROSOLEK, Mark; Milwaukee Lutheran HS; Milwaukew, WI; HonRl; Uw; Banking Fincane Economics.

ROSONKE, Susan C; New Hampton Community HS; New Hampton, IA; HonRl; PolWkr; RptrYrbk; Bus Schl; Vocation Secretary.

ROSS, Barbara J; Beach HS; Beach, ND; Chr; CaptDrlTm; HonRl; HospAde; SchPl; FHA; Bsktbl; Trk; Brooks College; Fashion Merchandising.

ROSS, Carolann F; St Agatha HS; Ljuonia, MI; AFS; Chrs; CmntyWkr; HonRl; OffAde; SchMus; SchPl; SctActv; SpnCl; College; Fashion Design.

ROSS, Cathy A; Forreston HS; Egan, IL; 10/69 ChrhWkr; HonRl; Mdrgl; NHS; StuCncl; YthFlsp; Pres4-H; GAA; AmLegAwd; 4-HAwd; Rockford Memorial; Nursing.

ROSS, Charles R; Sedgwick HS; Sedgwick, KS; 1/30 ChrhWkr; HonRl; NatlMeritSF; PepBnd; SctActv; YthFlsp; EdYrBk; Bsktbl; Ftbl; Trk; College; Geology Anthropology.

ROSS, Cindi D; Warsaw Comm HS; Warsaw, IN; ChrhWkr; CmntyWkr; HonRl; YthFlsp; CivCl; PpCl; LetterBsktbl; LetterTrk; CchngActv; TreasGAA; Anderson College; Teaching.

ROSS, Cynthia; Elmhurst HS; Fort Wayne, IN; Chr; Chrs; HonRl; JA; SchPl; StuCncl; SchPpr; College; Medicine.

ROSS, Cynthia A; Evanston Township HS; Evanston, IL; 101/1200 CtyCnl; HonRl; IntrClCncl; SchPl; RptrSchPpr; FrCl; LetterSwmmng; Univ; Chemical Engineer.

ROSS, David A; Hutchinson Jr Sr HS; Hutchinson, MN; HonRl;.

ROSS, David A; Atherton HS; Burton, MI; 5/160 Band; CncrtBnd; HonRl; MrchBnd; NHS; PepBnd; SchPl; StuGov; Tennis; DanFAwd; U Of Mi; Eng.

ROSS, David C; Prospect HS; Mt Prospect, IL; 45/610 HonRl; NatlFornLg; RptrYrbk; Univ Of Illinois; Chemistry.

ROSS, David M; Hartford Union HS; Hubertus, WI; ChrhWkr; HonRl; OffAde; SchAde; IMSpt; College; Business Admin.

ROSS, Debora A; Mt Pleasant HS; Mt Pleasant, IA; 21/160 ChrhWkr; HonRl; HospAde; NHS; SciCl; Mc Neese State Univ.

ROSS, Debra S; Harmony HS; Hillsboro, IA; 1/62 Band; Chr; Chrs; CncrtBnd; HonRl; NHS; SchPl; FHA; LetterBsbl; LetterBsktbl; College.

ROSS, Janice; Northwestern HS; Good Hope, IL; 2/54 Band; HonRl; NHS; SchMus; 4-H; SpnCl; MthCl; SciCl; GAA; MasAwd; College; Prof.

ROSS, Jill; Woodruff Hs; Peoria, IL; 15 HonRl; JrNHS; NHS; OffAde; TchrAde; Yrbk; FrCl; GAA; IMSpt;.

ROSS, Julie A; Lakeside Lutheran HS; Savanna, IL; Band; ChrhWkr; CncrtBnd; MrchBnd; PepBnd; IMSpt; Dr Martin Luther Clg; Parochial Sch Teacher.

ROSS, Karen M; Thornwood HS; So Holland, IL; 4/852 VPAFS; HonRl; JrNHS; NHS; NatlMeritCmnd; RptrYrbk; RptrSchPpr; SchPpr; FrCl; MthCl; College; Engineering.

ROSS, Kathryn G; Hancock Central HS; Hancock, MI; HonRl; SchPl; University; Professional.

ROSS, Kimberly; Sunflower HS; Scottsbluff, NE; 10/20 TrsFrshCls; TrsSophCls; Chrs; HonRl; Mdrgl; SchPl; SptEdYrbk; PpCl; Trk; Chrldr; Coll; Vocation.

ROSS, Laureen G; Chesaning Sr HS; Montrose, MI; 68/241 Chr; CaptChrhWkr; HonRl; NCTE; VoiceDemAwd;.

ROSS, Leslie; Houston HS; Houston, MO; 2/113 PresJrCls; Chrs; CncrtBnd; DrlTm; NHS; SchPl; StuCncl; Twrl; Chrldr; CitAwd; College; Nursing.

ROSS, Linda; Luther HS; Winona, MN; CncrtBnd; HonRl; MrchBnd; OffAde; SchPl; RptrYrbk; Chrldr; IMSpt; Dr Martin Luther Coll; Elem Ed.

ROSS, Linda S; Twin Lakes HS; Monticello, IN; 2/200 Band; Chrs; CncrtBnd; HonRl; JrNHS; MrchBnd; NHS; YthFlsp; PpCl; MasAwd; College; Veterinary Medicine.

ROSS, Lorraine; Haviland HS; Haviland, KS; TrsFrshCls; TrsJrCls; ChrhWkr; HospAde; MrchBnd; PepBnd; YthFlsp; Chrldr; Friends Bible College; Registered Nurse.

ROSS, Melanie W; Lutheran HS; Minneapolis, MN; Band; Chr; Chrs; ChrhWkr; HonRl; NHS; NatlMeritSF; SchPl; StuCncl; RptrSchPpr; SchPpr; Univ Of Minnesota; Nurse.

ROSS, Michael A; Mather HS; Chicago, IL; CmntyWkr; HonRl; NHS; Bsktbl; LetterFtbl; CchngActv; Univ Of Illinois; Physical Education.

ROSS, Michael L; Lindblom Tech HS; Chicago, IL; 40/695 HonRl; SchAde; StuCncl; StuGov; FTA; GerCl; College; Engineering.

ROSS, Michele; Lakeville HS; Columbiaville, MI; 6/183 HstJrCls; Band; ChrhWkr; MrchBnd; NHS; RedCrAde; SchPl; IMSpt; Olivet Nazarene College; Rn.

ROSS, Nancy K; Colby HS; Colby, KS; 9/100 Band; ChrhWkr; CmntyWkr; CncrtBnd; HonRl; MrchBnd; Orch; PolWkr; SchMus; SchPl; Ft Hays St Coll; Art.

ROSS, Paula; Sacred Heart HS; Deerfield, IL; PresFrshCls; PresSrCls; HonRl; PolWkr; StuCncl; RptrSchPpr; GAA; IMSpt; University; Lawyer.

ROSS, Randy A; Triton Central HS; Fairland, IN; PresSophCls; VPJrCls; StuCncl; LetterFtbl; LetterTrk; IMSpt;.

ROSS, Rebecca J; East HS; Waterloo, IA; Band; Chr; ChrhWkr; HonRl; Orch; PolWkr; StuGov; SpnCl; ChmnSwmmng; Tennis; CitAwd; College.

ROSS, Robert J; Marist HS; Palos Hts, IL; ChrhWkr; CmntyWkr; HonRl; Yrbk; RptrSchPpr; SchPpr; Univ Of Ill; Business Adm.

ROSS, Roxanna E; Watervliet HS; Watervliet, MI; ChrhWkr; HonRl; NHS; OffAde; SchAde; SctActv; StuCncl; StuGov; YthFlsp; YthFnd; College; Law Enforcement.

ROSS, Stanley H; Monroe Township HS; Muncie, IN; Aud/Vis; Band; HonRl; MrchBnd; PepBnd; SchMus; SchPl; SctActv; StuCncl; 4-H; Ball St Univ; Organist.

ROSS, Stephanie M; Sturgeon Bay HS; Sturgeon Bay, WI; HonRl; LitMag; StuGov; College; Art.

ROSS, Stephen J; Loyola Academy; Deerfield, IL; 27/442 HonRl; NHS; LetterTrk; College Of Holy Cross; Classics.

ROSS, Steven C; Sullivan HS; Sullivan, MO; Band; Chr; ChrhWkr; CncrtBnd; HonRl; Mdrgl; NatlThespSoc; PepBnd; SchMus; Ftbl; Freed Hardiman Col; Music.

ROSS, Susan R; Faith HS; Faith, SD; 7/37 Band; Chr; Chrs; CncrtBnd; MrchBnd; PepBnd; YthFlsp; Bsktbl; LetterTrk; Chrldr; College; Music.

ROSS, Theresa H; Dexter Sr HS; Dexter, MO; SecFrshCls; SecSophCls; VPJrCls; PresSrCls; HonRl; JrNHS; NHS; StuCncl; TchrAde; VPFHA; PPFtbl; College; Fashion Merchandising.

ROSS, Tina M; Lanphier HS; Springfield, IL; 8/535 HospAde; Univ Of Illinois; Engineering.

ROSS, Tina M; J M Harlan HS; Chicago, IL; Band; HonRl; JA; NHS; SctActv; StuCncl; Cook County School Of Nursing; Reg Nurse.

ROSS, Vicki M; West Vigo HS; West Terre Haute, IN; Band; CncrtBnd; HonRl; MrchBnd; PepBnd; TchrAde; Teen; FBLA; FTA; Coll.

ROSSANDER, Harry V; Stevens HS; Rapid City, SD; SecSophCls; TrsSophCls; HonRl; 4-H; CchngActv; 4-HAwd; Air Force Academy; Air Force Engineer.

ROSSBERG, Cheryl L; Rolling Meadows HS; Rolling Meadows, IL; 262/582 HonRl; OffAde; SchAde; TchrAde; IMSpt; William Rainer Harper Coll; Exec Secretary.

ROSSE, James L; Jennings HS; Saint Louis, MO; Band; CncrtBnd; HonRl; MrchBnd; Orch; PepBnd; LetterBsbl; PresAwd; College; Music Teacher.

ROSSEN, Cheryl R; Crete Monee HS; Park Forest S, IL; 4/382 CmntyWkr; HonRl; NHS; RptrSchPpr; MthCl; Univ; Accountant.

ROSSETTI, Anna M; Toluca HS; Toluca, IL; SecFrshCls; MrchBnd; PepBnd; StuCncl; FHA; SpnCl; PpCl; SciCl; Chrldr; GAA; Jr Coll.

ROSSETTI, Michael J; Campion HS; Mc Henry, IL; PresJrCls; StuCncl; Marquette Univ; Business.

ROSSETTI, Paula J; Marian Central HS; Mc Henry, IL; ChrhWkr; HonRl; LitMag; SchMus; SchPl; Barat College; Business Admin.

ROSSI, Armano J; Thornton Frac S HS; Lansing, IL; 72/586 HonRl; NatlMeritCmnd; GerCl; CaptTrk; College; Sec Education.

ROSSI, Douglas J; Kingsford HS; Kingsford, MI; 20/165 HonRl; NHS; SchPl; University; Professional.

ROSSI, Henry D; Peotone HS; Peotone, IL; 6/110 PresBand; CncrtBnd; HonRl; MrchBnd; NHS; PepBnd; SchAde; FrCl; PresMthCl; LetterFtbl; Denison Univ; Dentist.

ROSSI, Joseph P; Crete Monee HS; Crete, IL; 8/360 PresJrCls; HonRl; NHS; StuGov; Glf; Trk; Illinois Wesylan University; Dentist.

ROSSI, Laura; Fenton Hs; Bensenville, IL; 17/357 Band; College;professional.

ROSSI, Mary Ellen; Notre Dame HS; Chicago, IL; 21/302 HonRl; NHS; StuGov; SpnCl; U Of Ill; Optometrist.

ROSSI, Tina L; Lasalle Peru Twp HS; Oglesby, IL; 1/635 HonRl; NHS; StuCncl; FrCl; PpCl; Trk; Chrldr; IMSpt; Illinois St Univ; Special Educ.

ROSSIER, Jean R; Frankfort Sr HS; Frankfort, IN; CtyCnl; SchMus; SchPl; YthFlsp; Yrbk; SchPpr; FrCl; MthCl; SciCl; KiwanAwd; College; Computer Science.

ROSSIN, Jeanne; University City HS; St Louis, MO; 25/453 Band; HonRl; Orch; SchMus; SchPl; FBLA; Coll; Business.

ROSSMAN, Beth I; Goodrich HS; Goodrich, MI; 1/77 Band; Chr; ChrhWkr; CncrtBnd; HonRl; MrchBnd; NHS; SchMus; YthFlsp; 4-H; College; Music Therapy.

ROSSMAN, Illeen; Otis Bison Senior HS; Albert, KS; VPFrshCls; SecSrCls; Chr; Chrs; HonRl; NHS; PpCl; Bsktbl; Chrldr; Jr College; Business.

ROSSMAN, Larry W; Hammond Baptist HS; Lansing, IL; PresSophCls; Chr; ChrhWkr; SpnCl; SciCl; Bsbl; Bsktbl; Ftbl; Bob Jones Univ; Coaching.

ROSSMILLER, Ann M; Liberty HS; Liberty, IL; 5/56 VPFrshCls; VPSophCls; TrsJrCls; HonRl; NHS; OffAde; SchPl; PresFBLA; SecPpCl; Gem City Bus Coll; Legal Sec.

ROSSMILLER, David W; Okemos HS; Okemos, MI; Band; CmntyWkr; CncrtBnd; HonRl; HospAde; LbryAde; MrchBnd; NHS; Orch; PepBnd; Bsktbl; Ftbl; Univ; International Economics.

ROSSMILLER, Gwen E; Wildrose HS; Wildrose, ND; 3/14 TrsJrCls; ALAGirlsSt; Chr; CncrtBnd; HonRl; LbryAde; SchPl; RptrSchPpr; Univ Of North Dakota; Science.

ROSSMILLER, Mary K; Liberty HS; Liberty, IL; 15/62 TrsFrshCls; HonRl; Sdlty; StuCncl; FBLA; FHA; FTA; GAA; Junior College; Secretary.

ROSSMILLER, Patty H; Liberty HS; Liberty, IL; 16/62 HstJrCls; HonRl; SecStuCncl; Pres4-H; VPFHA; PpCl; Chrldr; PresGAA; College; Special Education.

ROSSO, Mark A; Holy Cross HS; Chicago, IL; 24/314 HonRl; NHS; NatlMeritCmnd; StuCncl; RptrSchPpr; University; Mathematics.

ROSSOL, Ernest R; Roseville HS; Roseville, MI; 1/470 Aud/Vis; Chr; ChrhWkr; HonRl; Mdrgl; NHS; StuGov; PresYthFlsp; Bsktbl; CitAwd; Grand Rapids Baptist Clg; Teaching.

ROSSOW, Charles A; Ind #75 HS; Florence, SD; 3/14 SecJrCls; ALBoysSt; Chrs; ChrhWkr; CmntyWkr; HonRl; SchPl; 4-H; FFA; LetterBsktbl; Vocational Sch; Agriculture.

ROSSTEDT, Lynn; Thornwood Hs; South Holland, IL; 92/962 HonRl; NatlThespSoc; Yrbk; 4-H; GrCl;.

ROST, Bradley S; Weyerhaeuser Public HS; Weyerhaeuser, WI; 3/30 HstSrCls; Chrs; HonRl; SchPl; SecTrsSophCls; Bsktbl; Trk; Coll; Conservation.

ROST, Mary E; J S Morton West HS; Lyons, IL; 5/734 Chr; Chrs; HonRl; JrNHS; NHS; TchrAde; J S Morton; Business Management.

ROST, Stephen W; J A Craig HS; Janesville, WI; 8/474 AFS; HonRl; NHS; StuCncl; MthCl; CaptTennis; Univ Of Ia; Law.

ROSTOLLAN, Daniel J; Waukesha South HS; Waukesha, WI; Band; CncrtBnd; HonRl; MrchBnd; NHS; PepBnd; FrCl; MthCl; Marquette University; Lawyer.

ROSTRON, Bruce W; Gibson Southern HS; Haubstadt, IN; Chr; ChrhWkr; CmntyWkr; CncrtBnd; MrchBnd; PepBnd; SctActv; YthFlsp; 4-H; PpCl; Trade School; Forestry.

ROSTVOLD, Roger; Nashwauk Keewatin HS; Keewatin, MN; SctActv; Bsbl; College; Civil Engineer.

ROSTYNE, Kim S; Carthage Public HS; Carthage, SD; Chr; ChrhWkr; CmntyWkr; HonRl; SchPl; RptrSchPpr; PpCl; IMSpt; AmLegAwd;.

ROSZELL, Nancy; Northside HS; Muncie, IN; 1/319 Band; Chr; NHS; NatlMeritFnl; NatlMeritSchl; StuCncl; LatCl; MthCl; SciCl; JETSAwd; Washington Univ; Chem Engineer.

ROSZELL, Nancy J; Northside HS; Muncie, IN; 1/350 Band; Chr; CncrtBnd; HonRl; MrchBnd; NHS; NatlMeritSF; PepBnd; SchMus; StuGov; SecSciCl; JETSAwd; OptClAwd; Washington U St Louis; Chemical Eng.

ROSZKO, Cindi L; Crystal Lake Comm HS; Crystal Lake, IL; 129/440 University; Professional.

ROSZKO, Cynthia L; Crystal Lake Community HS; Crystal Lake, IL; NatlThespSoc; Ucla; Medicine.

ROSZKOWSKI, Paul J; Gordon Tech HS; Chicago, IL; Aud/Vis; Chr; ChrhWkr; CmntyWkr; SctActv; StuCncl; StuGov; PpCl; Bsktbl; Swmmng; Chrldr; Trade Sch; Carpentry.

ROTERMUND, Jane H; Lincoln HS; Wisconsin Rapids, WI; Chr; ChrhWkr; HonRl; SpnCl; PPFtbl; College; Teaching.

ROTH, Bonnie; Oak Ridge Hs; Oak Ridge, MO; 2 SecSophCls; TrsJrCls; ChrhWkr; HonRl; SchPl; StuCncl; Yrbk; SchPpr; FHA; Chrldr; Business School;vocation.

ROTH, Brian E; Mt Pleasant Community HS; Mt Pleasant, IA; 56/170 Band; HonRl; Quill&Scroll; SchMus; YthFlsp; EdSchPpr; Pres4-H; FBLA; Ftbl; DanFAwd; 4-HAwd; JAAwd; Univ; Professional.

ROTH, Carol S; Harrisonville HS; Harrisonville, MO; Band; Chrs; ChrhWkr; CncrtBnd; HonRl; HospAde; MrchBnd; RedCrAde; SchMus; Twrl; 4-H; FHA; IMSpt; 4-HAwd; Research Hosp; Nurse.

ROTH, Cynthia L; Spash HS; Junction City, WI; 13/525 NHS; Orch; PpCl; SciCl; IMSpt; Univ Of Wisconsin; Medical Tech.

ROTH, Cynthia M; Wood River Rural HS; Wood River, NE; Band; CncrtBnd; HonRl; MrchBnd; PepBnd; SchMus; StuCncl; YthFlsp; FrCl; LetterTrk; Clge; Med Vocation.

ROTH, Gerri P; Hamady HS; Flint, MI; 5/180 Band; CncrtBnd; HonRl; HospAde; MrchBnd; NHS; SchPl; TchrAde; Univ Of Mi Flint; Elem Ed.

ROTH, Glenda K; Glen Ullin HS; Glen Ullin, ND; Chr; ChrhWkr; CmntyWkr; LbryAde; SchPl; Teen; 4-H; PpCl; Chrldr; 4-HAwd; College; Vocation.

ROTH, Jane L; Valle HS; Ste Genevieve, MO; 2/76 HonRl; HospAde; NHS; FHA; MthCl; U Of Mo; Professional.

ROTH, Jeffrey M; Morton HS; Morton, IL; Chrl; Chrs; SchPl; FFA; Jr College; Agri Business.

ROTH, John C; Lawrenceville HS; Lawrenceville, IL; 1/189 HonRl; StuCncl; SpnCl; MthCl; SciCl; LetterGlf; U Of Ill; Computer Engr.

ROTH, John M; St Louis U HS; St Louis, MO; 5/188 TrsSrCls; HonRl; OffAde; TreasStuGov; RptrSchPpr; Ftbl; LetterGlf; Wrstlng; IMSpt; Univ Of Pa; Economics.

ROTH, Kirby G; Gordon HS; Gordon, NE; TchrAde; YthFlsp; 4-H; Ftbl; Wrstlng; Kearney State; Bus Admin.

ROTH, Kirsten A; Antigo HS; Antigo, WI; CncrtBnd; MrchBnd; SchMus; SchPl; RptrSchPpr; KeyCl; GerCl; LatCl; Trk; GAA; Marquette; Dental Hygeine.

ROTH, Leann; Napoleon HS; Kintyre, ND; Band; Chrl; Chrs; ChrhWkr; CmntyWkr; CncrtBnd; MrchBnd; PepBnd; StuCncl; RptrSchPpr; Coll; Music Major.

ROTH, Leslie; Whitefish Bay HS; Milwaukee, WI; HonRl; JrNHS; NHS; NatlMeritFnl; NatlMeritCmnd; NatlMeritSF; SchMus; TchrAde; RptrSchPpr; FrCl; Univ Of Pennsylvania; Medicine.

ROTH, Linda K; Waterville Elysian HS; Waterville, MN; 4/41 Band; Chrs; CncrtBnd; HonRl; MrchBnd; NHS; PepBnd; SchPl; YthFlsp; RptrYrbk; Clge; Pro.

ROTH, Mark A; Fenton HS; Bensenville, IL; 3/350 TreasChr; Chrs; HonRl; NHS; SchMus; University; Computer Science.

ROTH, Marti E; Jamaica HS; Sidell, IL; HonRl; Band; Chrs; NHS; SchMus; SchPl; StuCncl; TchrAde; RptrSchPpr; SciCl; Univ; Doctor.

ROTH, Pamela S; Farmer City Mansfield HS; Mansfield, IL; ALAGirlsSt; Band; CncrtBnd; HonRl; MrchBnd; PepBnd; GAA; Eastern U; Elem Ed.

ROTH, Patricia S; Iowa Mennonite HS; Washington, IA; 1/37 Band; Chr; HonRl; NHS; StuCncl; YthFlsp; Yrbk; SchPpr; IMSpt; BttyCrckrAwd; Goshen Coll; Home Ec.

ROTH, Theodore J; Stonington HS; Stonington, IL; 1/34 VPFrshCls; VPJrCls; PresSrCls; Band; HonRl; 4-H; PresFFA; LetterBsbl; LetterBsktbl; LetterTrk; Univ Of Il; Commerce & Bus Clge.

ROTH, V; Iowa Mennonite HS; Haven, KS; Chr; ChrhWkr; HonRl; SchPl; TchrAde; YthFlsp; RptrSchPpr; SchPpr; FrCl; IMSpt; College; Teach Foreign Languagees.

ROTHE, Dianne; Virden HS; Virden, IL; HonRl; FHA; PpCl;.

ROTHE, Doug; Girard HS; Girard, IL; 3/58 HonRl; Bsktbl; University; Computer Tech.

ROTHENGASS, Cheryl A; Mother Of Sorrows HS; Chicago, IL; ChrhWkr; HonRl; TchrAde; Art School; Commercial Art.

ROTHER, Gregory D; Craig Riii HS; Craig, MO; 2/18 TrsSophCls; PresSrCls; ALBoysSt; Band; CncrtBnd; HonRl; MrchBnd; PepBnd; PresFFA;

LetterTrk; BauchLmbAwd; Univ Of Missouri; Animal Science.

ROTHER, Pam S; Wolbach Public HS; Wolbach, NE; Band; ChrhWkr; CmntyWkr; SchMus; SchPl; Yrbk; CaptBsktbl; Swmmng; LetterTrk; 4-HAwd; Trade School.

ROTHERHAM, Rosemary; Ewing Public HS; Ewing, NE; 1/28 PresSrCls; Chrs; ChrhWkr; HonRl; ModUN; NHS; SchAde; RptrYrbk; PpCl; IMSpt; Lincoln Sch Of Comm; Court Reporting.

ROTHERING, Ann T; St Mary HS; Burlington, WI; Band; Chr; HonRl; LbryAde; SctActv; EngCl; SciCl; Chrldr; IMSpt; PPFtbl; College.

ROTHRING, Lucretia M; Crothersville HS; Crothersville, IN; 3/50 TrsJrCls; Chr; HonRl; ModUN; NHS; PolWkr; SchMus; PpCl; Bsktbl; LetterTrk; LetterChrldr; GAA; Indiana Univ; Med Tech.

ROTHSCHILD, Anthony E; Deerfield HS; Highland Park, IL; 5/550 HonRl; NHS; NatlMeritCmnd; StuCncl; StuGov; RptrSchPpr; CaptSocr; IMSpt; Harvard University.

ROTHSCHILD, Mare; Berkley HS; Huntington Woods, MI; 24/580 NatlMeritCmnd; NatlMeritSchl; PolWkr; StuCncl; Bsbl; IMSpt; Univ Of Mich; Cpa.

ROTHSOLK, Craig N; Manning Comm HS; Manning, IA; Aud/Vis; Band; Chr; CncrtBnd; MrchBnd; NatlFornLg; 4-H; FFA; Band Instrument Repairer.

ROTHWELL, Brian J; Bishop Du Bourg HS; St Louis, MO; 45/475 ALBoysSt; HonRl; VPJA; NHS; NatlMeritCmnd; RptrSchPpr; LetterTrk; IMSpt; JAAwd; VoiceDemAwd; Univf Math.

ROTHWELL, Gail; Medicine Valley HS; Tryon, NE; VPFrshCls; PresSophCls; HonRl; NHS; StuCncl; RptrYrbk; EdSchPpr; 4-H; 4-HAwd; Coll; Vocation.

ROTRAMEL, Ronald L; Jay HS; Southwest City, MO; ChrhWkr; NHS; Vocational School.

ROTRAMEL, Victor G; Waynesville HS; Waynesville, MO; 2/241 PresBand; PresCncrtBnd; HonRl; PresMrchBnd; SecNHS; PresPepBnd; ROTC; StuGov; Teen; EdYrBk; DanFAwd; Texas Tech Univ; Medicine.

ROTT, Laurei; Whitnall HS; Hales Corners, WI; 19/261 HonRl; NHS; PepBnd; SchMus; SchPl; SctActv; MthCl; PpCl; GAA; Univ; Medical Technoligist.

ROTTA, James L; Davison HS; Davison, MI; 87/433 NatlThespSoc; SchMus; SchPl; TchrAde; Yrbk; Mi Univ; Comm Art.

ROTTER, Bruce; Granite City South HS; Granite City, IL; /630 NHS; SctActv; BauchLmbAwd; Southern Il Univ; Dental School.

ROTTER, J; Central Community Of Argyle; West Point, IA; 2/68 ALBoysSt; Band; CmntyWkr; HonRl; NHS; RedCrAde; StuCncl; Glf; 4-HAwd; GovHonPrgAwd; West Point Military Acad; Public Service.

ROTTER, Rebecca; Louisville Public HS; Louisville, NE; 6/38 SecJrCls; Band; Chrs; CncrtBnd; HonRl; MrchBnd; PepBnd; Yrbk; 4-H; FHA; Lincoln Sch Of Commerce; Accounting.

ROTTGER, Donnie J; Lincoln County R Iv HS; Old Monroe, MO; PresSophCls; HonRl; NHS; SchPl; StuCncl; Yrbk; SchPpr; GerCl; Bsbl; Bsktbl; Work; Mechanic.

ROTTINGHAUS, Joseph; Nemaha Valley HS; Corning, KS; TrsJrCls; ALBoysSt; Band; HonRl; MrchBnd; NHS; PepBnd; StuCncl; Yrbk; SciCl; Benedictine College; Science.

ROTTINK, Doreen A; Allison Bristow Comm HS; Allison, IA; Chrs; ChrhWkr; SchMus; SchPl; YthFlsp; Pres4-H; FHA; LetterTrk; 4-HAwd; CitAwd; Business School; Vocation.

ROTTMANN, Larry D; Metropolis HS; Metropolis, IL; 4-H; College.

ROTVOLD, Irvin M; Climax Public HS; Climax, MN; 1/28 PresSophCls; TrsJrCls; ALBoysSt; PresNHS; PresFFA; VPGerCl; PresSciCl; LetterBsbl; Bsktbl; LetterFtbl; IMSpt; Moorhead St Univ; Computer Science.

ROUBAL, Susan J; North Bend Central HS; North Bend, NE; 3/75 ALAGirlsSt; ChrhWkr; NHS; PolWkr; YthFlsp; 4-H; FHA; FTA; Bsktbl; Trk; Univ Of Ne At Lincoln; Secondary Teaching.

ROUBIK, Elizabeth J; Oak Lawn Community HS; Bridgeview, IL; 51/667 CmntyWkr; HonRl; NHS; TchrAde; GAA; College; Legal Research.

ROUCEK, Anita J; Immaculate Heart Of Mary HS; Westchester, IL; 40/275 HonRl; NatlMeritSF; GAA; Mich State; Psychology.

ROUCH, Loraine D; North Ridge HS; Middlebury, IN; ChrhWkr; HonRl; 4-H; LetterSocr; 4-HAwd; Vocation.

ROUDEBUSH, David C; Lutheran HS West; Southgate, MI; StuCncl; YthFlsp; SptEdSchPpr; GerCl; Bsbl; Ftbl; Concordia Teachers College; Biology Teacher.

ROUDEBUSH, Phillip R; Central HS; Worthington, IN; Band; HonRl; JA; NHS; 4-H; SpnCl; Bsbl; Bsktbl; Trk; 4-HAwd; Rose Hulman College; Engineering.

ROUGE, Jerry M; Lake Benton Public HS; Lake Benton, MN; HonRl; SchPl; SptEdYrbk; FFA;.

ROUHANDEH, Steven H; Carbondale Comm HS; Murphysboro, IL; 5/323 HonRl; LitMag; NatlFornLg; PresNHS; NatlMeritCmnd; YthLg; FrCl; Bsktbl; University; Pre Law.

ROUHIB, Margaret A; Servite HS; Detroit, MI; 6/90 HonRl; NHS; TchrAde; AmLegAwd; Univ Of Mi Ann Arbor; Medicine.

ROUINTREE, Kevin P; Anderson HS; Anderson, IN; HonRl; NHS; LetterWrstlng; College; Medicine.

ROULEAU, Michael A; St Charles Borromeo HS; Downers Grove, IL; 3/19 TrsFrshCls; Chrl; CmntyWkr; HonRl; LetterSocr; IMSpt; St Thomas College; Math.

ROULT, Maureen M; Notre Dane De Sion HS; Leawood, KS; 4/32 Chr; Chrs; HonRl; Mdrgl; NHS; NatlMeritFnl; NatlThespSoc; SchMus; SchPl; Swmmng; Univ Of Kansas; Languages.

ROULT, Maureen M; Notre Dame De Sion HS; Leawood, KS; Chrs; HonRl; Mdrgl; NHS; NatlMeritSF; SchMus; SchPl; FrCl; Swmmng; CchngActv; Univ; Vocal Music Or Languages (fr).

ROUMAS, Kevin; Stewartsville Cii HS; Stewartsville, MO; HstFrshCls; VPSrCls; Band; HonRl; EdYrBk; EdSchPpr; DanFAwd; College.

ROUNDS, James K; Harper Creek HS; Battle Creek, MI; HstFrshCls; HstSophCls; HstJrCls; CncrtBnd; JA; LbryAde; MrchBnd; PepBnd; TchrAde; Yrbk; Navy; Photography.

ROUNDTREE, Tom D; Benkelman HS; Parks, NE; 9/45 HonRl; VPNHS; Pres4-H; SciCl; Bsbl; Bsktbl; Ftbl; IMSpt; 4-HAwd; PresAwd; University Of Nebraska; Veterinarian.

ROUNDY, Dina G; Woodbine Comm HS; Woodbine, IA; 8/69 CncrtBnd; HonRl; HospAde; JrNHS; MrchBnd; NHS; YthFlsp; 4-H; FHA; 4-HAwd; Creighton Univ; Dr.

ROUNER, Larry; South Harrison HS; Mcfall, MO; Bsbl; Bsktbl; Trade School; Vocational.

ROUNSVILLE, Jenice M; Ritenour Sr HS; Breckenridge, MO; JA; OffAde; Nursing School; Nurse.

ROUNTREE, Connie J; Ri North Callaway HS; Auxvasse, MO; 4/80 SecFrshCls; Band; Chr; Chrs; HonRl; MrchBnd; PepBnd; SchMus; SchPl; StuCncl; Yrbk; FHA; PpCl; CaptChrldr; PresAwd; Business Sch; Secretarial.

ROUNTREE, Connie J; Ri North Callaway HS; Auxrasse, MO; 4/75 SecFrshCls; Band; Chrl; Chrs; HonRl; MrchBnd; NHS; SchMus; SchPl; StuCncl; Yrbk; Business School; Secretary.

ROUPP, Brad D; Hesston HS; Hesston, KS; SchPl; StuCncl; SptEdYrbk; SptEdSchPpr; Bsktbl; Trk; Col; Pro.

ROURKE, John P; Oskaloosa Sr HS; Oskaloosa, IA; Chr; CmntyWkr; HonRl; NatlFornLg; SctActv; StuCncl; StuGov; U Of Iowa; Biomedical Eng.

ROUSE, Brian D; Plattsmouth HS; Murray, NE; 17/163 HonRl; SctActv; YthFlsp; Pres4-H; Bsktbl; Ftbl; Univ Of Ne; Farming.

ROUSE, Eric V; Mendel Cath Prep; Chicago, IL; CmntyWkr; StuGov; YthFnd; LetterFtbl; CaptTrk; CchngActv; IMSpt;.

ROUSE, Kathryn R; Emerson HS; Gary, IN; 16/223 Aud/Vis; HonRl; JrNHS; LbryAde; NHS; OffAde; SchPl; TchrAde; SchPpr; SpnCl; PpCl; LetterGlf; Tennis; Purdue Univ; Business Admin.

ROUSE, Kathy; Bentley HS; Burton, MI; HonRl; PpCl; Bsktbl; Trk; CchngActv; GAA; College; Professional.

ROUSE, Michael; Creighton Prep; Omaha, NE; 58/249 HonRl; NHS; Sdlty; RptrYrbk; Trk; IMSpt; Creighton U;pre Med.

ROUSE, Randy; Ayrshire Cons HS; Curlew, IA; PresSophCls; SecJrCls; VPSrCls; ALBoysSt; Chrs; HonRl; 4-H; Bsktbl; AmLegAwd; 4-HAwd; Vocational School; Auto Mecanic.

ROUSE, Vickie L; South Newton HS; Kentland, IN; 7/96 Band; ChrhWkr; HonRl; OffAde; Yrbk; FBLA; LatCl; PpCl; PPFtbl; Bus ; Secre.

ROUSH, Barbara; Leaf River HS; Egan, IL; TrsJrCls; Band; Chrs; HonRl; SchPl; SpnCl; GAA; 4-HAwd; Coll; Theater.

ROUSH, Edward W; Truman HS; Independence, MO; 67/614 ChrhWkr; CncrtBnd; HonRl; MrchBnd; PolWkr; VPStuCncl; StuGov; SpnCl; LetterBsktbl; CaptTennis; College; Lawyer.

ROUSH, Jan A; Jefferson HS; La Fayette, IN; 49/609 HonRl; JrNHS; SctActv; Purdue; Accounting.

ROUSH, Tom L; Ash Grove HS; Ash Grove, MO; 16/56 Band; ChrhWkr; ModUN; NatlFornLg; NHS; OffAde; SchPl; Yrbk; SchPpr; FBLA; Sch Of Ozarks; Speach Teacher.

ROUSH, Vicki L; Mendota HS; Mendota, IL; CaptDrlTm; HonRl; HospAde; LbryAde; StuCncl; YthFlsp; Yrbk; FNA; FrCl; College; Vacation.

ROUSSEAU, Elizabeth J; Jeffersonville HS; Jeffersonville, IN; AFS; NHS; SpnCl; Trk; College; Interior Decorator.

ROUSSIN, Richard J; St Pius X HS; Festus, MO; Band; Chrs; CncrtBnd; MrchBnd; PepBnd; SchMus; StuCncl; Trk; Coll; Professional.

ROUTE, Thomas; Whitewater HS; Whitewater, WI; 11/200 ALBoysSt; VPBand; ChrhWkr; HonRl; JrNHS; NHS; PresStuGov; KeyCl; LetterBsktbl; CaptTrk; Univ; Engin.

ROUTH, Dale A; Macks Creek HS; Climax Springs, MO; Aud/Vis; Chrs; CmntyWkr; HonRl; SchPl; StuCncl; 4-H; Bsbl; State University; Public Safety.

ROUTH, Paul; Baldwin HS; Baldwin, KS; PresSophCls; StuCncl; StuGov; YthFlsp; College.

ROUTHIER, John B; Stephenson HS; Stephenson, MI; ALBoysSt; Aud/Vis; ChrhWkr; HonRl; NatlMeritSchl; PolWkr; ROTC; SchPl; SctActv; StuGov; SchPpr; 4-H; CaptFtbl; LetterTrk; U S Coast Guard Academy; Officer.

ROUTIER, Donald; Franklin Comm HS; Franklin, IN; HonRl; JrNHS; NHS; NatlMeritCmnd; IMSpt; College; Art Teacher.

ROUTLEDGE, Cathy; Seneca HS; Joplin, MO; PresSrCls; AFS; StuGov; YthFlsp; SchPpr; FDA; FSA; FTA; Chrldr; CitAwd; College; Major Study.

ROUX, Mark E; Champaign Central HS; Champaign, IL; HonRl; Quill&Scroll; SchMus; SchPl; StuCncl; StuGov; RptrYrbk; RptrSchPpr; FFA; Bsbl; Swmmng; Trk; Univ Of Illinois; Agronomy.

ROVENSKY, Carolyn M; Mt Assisi Acad; Chicago, IL; 5/190 ChrhWkr; HonRl; JrNHS; ModUN; NHS; SchMus; SchPl; SctActv; Sdlty; GAA; U Of Il Chicago; Bus Admin.

ROVIN, Brad H; Maine Twp North HS; Glenview, IL; 1/340 ALBoysSt; HonRl; NatlFornLg; SecNHS; NatlMeritCmnd; Tennis; DARAwd; JETSAwd; Northwestern Univ; Biomedical Engineer.

ROW, Rita M; Desoto Sr HS; De Soto, KS; Band; CncrtBnd; HonRl; NHS; RptrSchPpr; FBLA; PpCl; SciCl; Bsktbl; College; Professional.

ROWAN, Carol A; College Springs HS; Coin, IA; Chr; Chrs; DrlTm; HonRl; NHS; 4-H; FHA; PpCl; Bsktbl; Trk; Nw Mo State Col; Legal Secretary.

ROWAN, Cedric L; Southeast HS; Kansas City, MO; TrsFrshCls; ChrhWkr; HonRl; NHS; StuGov; FrCl; Bsktbl; Ftbl; College; Professional Law.

ROWAN, Jody; Osceola HS; Osceola, NE; SecFrshCls; SecSrCls; Band; Chrs; CncrtBnd; HonRl; MrchBnd; Swmmng; Tennis; Trk; Doane College; Teacher.

ROWAN, Kevin B; Norfolk HS; Norfolk, NE; HonRl; RptrYrbk; LetterTrk; IMSpt; College; Engineering.

ROWAN, Michael L; Gurley Public HS; Gurley, NE; 5/10 VPFrshCls; SecSophCls; Chrs; ChrhWkr; CmntyWkr; HonRl; SchPl; SctActv; Yrbk; SpnCl; College; Agruculture.

ROWAN, Steven R; Ingalls HS; Ingalls, KS; Band; MrchBnd; PepBnd; SchPl; 4-H; LetterBsktbl; DanFAwd; 4-HAwd; Jr College; Irrigation Farming.

ROWCLIFFE, Hazel; Philip HS; Philip, SD; 8/140 ChrhWkr; HonRl; HospAde; SchPl; YthFlsp; RptrSchPpr; FHA; PpCl; Nursing College; Registered Nurse.

ROWDEN, Anne K; Granite City HS; Granite City, IL; 2/485 ALAGirlsSt; Chrs; SecNHS; OffAde; SchMus; SchPl; GerCl; PpCl; Chrldr; CchngActv; Illinois State Univ; Chemistry.

ROWDEN, Sandy J; Dixon HS; Dixon, MO; Band; Chr; Chrs; ChrhWkr; CncrtBnd; HonRl; MrchBnd; PepBnd; SchMus; StuCncl; VPFBLA; FHA; FTA; PpCl; Business School; Secretary.

ROWDON, Gregory A; Northrop HS; Ft Wayne, IN; 30/648 HonRl; LetterBsbl; LetterFtbl; Wrstlng; IMSpt; College; Math & Science.

ROWE, Dana P; Lawrence Public HS; Lawrence, MI; 16/50 HonRl; SchPl; TchrAde; RptrSchPpr; 4-H; FTA; LetterBsbl; LetterBsktbl; LetterFtbl; LetterTrk; DanFAwd; 4-HAwd; Kucc; Auto Maechanics.

ROWE, Ernestine; Winfield HS; Winfield, KS; 51/176 ChrhWkr; DrlTm; HonRl; Orch; StuCncl; TchrAde; Bsbl; Bsktbl; LetterTrk; College; Professional.

ROWE, Gregory G; Sturgis HS; Sturgis, MI; TchrAde; Ftbl; College.

ROWE, Julie; Harding HS; St Paul, MN; 14/724 VPSrCls; HonRl; IntrClCncl; NHS; StuCncl; StuGov; YthFlsp; FrCl; Chrldr; College; Mathematics.

ROWE, Kathryn A; Rice Lake HS; Rice Lake, WI; 5/290 Chr; Chrs; HonRl; NHS; Univ Of Wi; English.

ROWE, Lynn R; Watertown HS; Watertown, SD; 97/297 ChrhWkr; CmntyWkr; HonRl; PresNatlThespSoc; OffAde; SchMus; SchPl; PresFBLA; GAA; Oklahoma Christian College; Secretary.

ROWE, Ruth M; Kaneland HS; Elburn, IL; .

ROWE, Stephen H; Paseo HS; Kansas City, MO; 7/290 HonRl; NHS; SpnCl; SciCl; Ftbl; College; Professional.

ROWE, Sue A; Rova HS; Oneida, IL; 2/72 SecFrshCls; PresJrCls; TrsSrCls; PresChrs; ChrhWkr; CmntyWkr; HonRl; SecNHS; StuCncl; RptrYrbk; SciCl; GAA; DARAwd; Knox College; English.

ROWE, Tonya L; La Ville Jr Sr HS; Lakeville, IN; 11/126 Aud/Vis; ChrhWkr; NHS; SpnCl; PpCl; Chrldr; Business Schl; Secretary.

ROWELL, Bill J; Ft Dodge Sr HS; Ft Dodge, IA; HonRl; NatlMeritCmnd; NatlMeritSF; College; Chemistry.

ROWELLS, Gale S; Lyons Township HS; Lagrange Prk, IL; 98/1214 HonRl; NHS; GerCl; U; Science.

ROWITS, Barbara A; Goshen HS; Goshen, IN; ALAGirlsSt; Chr; HonRl; Mdrgl; NHS; NatlMeritCmnd; SchMus; TreasYthFlsp; EdYrBk; De Pauw U; English.

ROWLAND, Chris; Leaf River HS; Leaf River, IL; Band; Chrs; CncrtBnd; MrchBnd; SchPl; SctActv; RptrSchPpr; GAA; Trade School; Professional Photographer.

ROWLAND, David; Tri County HS; Remington, IN; 17/94 TrsJrCls; Band; HonRl; LitMag; Orch; SchPl; Bsktbl; IMSpt; Indiana Univ; Md.

ROWLAND, David L; Riverside Brookfield HS; Brookfield, IL; 21/480 Band; ChrhWkr; CncrtBnd; HonRl; MrchBnd; NHS; PepBnd; SchMus; SctActv; Us Merchant Marine Academy.

ROWLAND, John F; Roosevelt HS; Wyandotte, MI; ChrhWkr; CmntyWkr; HonRl; LbryAde; PolWkr; SchAde; TchrAde; SchPpr; LetterSwmmng; CitAwd; Coll; Med.

ROWLAND, Karen D; Holden HS; Holden, MO; 26/98 HonRl; SchPl; PpCl; SciCl; Tennis; Nursing Schl; Nursing.

ROWLAND, Martha L; Shawnee Mission South HS; Overland Park, KS; HonRl; OffAde; PpCl; Chrldr;.

ROWLAND, Terry J; Fitzgerald HS; Warren, MI; HstSrCls; Band; ChrhWkr; CncrtBnd; HonRl; MrchBnd; NHS; NatlMeritSF; StuCncl; TchrAde; Swmmng; CaptTrk; OptClAwd; Univ Of Mich; Dentistry.

ROWLES, Craig J; East Greene HS; Grand Junction, IA; 1/43 TrsJrCls; Band; Chr; HonRl; NHS; SchMus; SchPl; 4-H; FFA; LetterBsktbl; 4-HAwd; Iowa State Univ; Veterinarian.

ROWLES, Rochelle Y; Southeast Sr HS; Kansas City, MO; Chrs; HonRl; HospAde; JA; StuCncl; StuGov; FNA; PpCl; LetterTrk; PPFtbl;.

ROWLEY, Barbara J; Mineral Point HS; Mineral Point, WI; 12/94 VPFrshCls; SecSrCls; Chr; HonRl; NHS; SchMus; RptrYrbk; RptrSchPpr; FHA; SpnCl; Chrldr; PPFtbl; College; Journalism.

ROWLEY, Lila J; Clio Area HS; Clio, MI; Chr; HonRl; SctActv; YthFlsp; 4-H; Business School; Accounting.

ROWLEY, Marcia R; Mineral Point HS; Mineral Point, WI; VPJrCls; ALAGirlsSt; HonRl; SchMus; RptrYrbk; LetterBsktbl; College; Art.

ROWLEY, Terri; Addison HS; Addison, MI; 15/107 Chrs; CmntyWkr; HonRl; NHS; SctActv; GAA; PPFtbl; 4-HAwd; Siena Heights College; Special Education.

ROY, Cynthia K; Ashland HS; Ashland, IL; HonRl; SchPl; StuCncl; TchrAde; Yrbk; RptrSchPpr; PresFHA; PpCl; VPGAA;.

ROY, Gina M; Triton HS; Bourbon, IN; ALAGirlsSt; HonRl; StuCncl; YthFlsp; Yrbk; FTA; SpnCl; PpCl; SciCl; GAA; Univ.

ROY, Janet S; Carmel Girls HS; Libertyville, IL; 4/183 Chrs; HonRl; NatlMeritCmnd; StuCncl; SecMthCl; Univ Of Illinois; Medicine.

ROY, Jennifer J; Central Catholic HS; Grand Island, NE; DrlTm; HonRl; TreasNHS; OffAde; Quill&Scroll; SchAde; SecStuCncl; StuGov; TchrAde; Yrbk; College; Vocation.

ROY, Jon F; Bishop Dwenger HS; Ft Wayne, IN; CtyCnl; HonRl; JA; PolWkr; StuCncl; StuGov; FDA; Ftbl; Trk; IMSpt; Univ Of In; Doctor.

ROY, Paul J; Calumet HS; Gary, IN; 21/315 HonRl; NHS; SctActv; Bsbl; LetterTrk; IMSpt; Coll Marine Corp; Mechcnl Elec Eng.

ROY, Robert J; Adams Friendship HS; Friendship, WI; HonRl; HospAde; PolWkr; StuCncl; TchrAde; FrCl; Bsbl; Bsktbl; Ftbl; CchngActv; IMSpt; Tech Sch Then Coll; De Teacher.

ROYALTY, Stanley P; Montague HS; Montague, MI; Band; CncrtBnd; MrchBnd; 4-H; 4-HAwd; Coll; Bus Admin.

ROYCE, Nancy G; Eastbrook HS; Upland, IN; HonRl; JA; NHS; NatlThespSoc; SchPl; SctActv; StuCncl; RptrYrbk; GerCl; PpCl; Nursing School; Nurse.

ROYER, Galen R; Elkhart Central HS; Elkhart, IN; Band; ChrhWkr; CmntyWkr; CncrtBnd; HonRl; MrchBnd; PepBnd; SchMus; YthFlsp; Mcpherson College; Business Admin.

ROYER, Kurt D; Otis Bison HS; Otis, KS; Band; ChrhWkr; CncrtBnd; HonRl; Mdrgl; PepBnd; SchPl; LetterFtbl; VFWAwd; CitAwd; VoiceDemAwd; Kansas University; Biology.

ROYER, Nancy J; Springs Valley HS; French Lick, IN; 9/73 HonRl; VPNHS; PresYthFlsp; PresYthFnd; FrCl; PpCl; LetterTrk; In Univ; Coaching Or Athletic Straing.

ROYLE, Michael J; Truman HS; Independence, MO; 17/600 ALBoysSt; HonRl; JrNHS; NHS; StuCncl; LetterBsbl; LetterBsktbl; LetterFtbl; Trk; University; Law.

ROYS, Ronald A; Coopersville HS; Grand Rapids, MI; CncrtBnd; NatlMeritSF; PepBnd; SctActv; StuCncl; Sacrstn; GerCl; Ftbl; LetterTrk; RotaryAwd; Grand Valley College; Electronics.

ROYSE, Janice E; Noble HS; Noble, IL; SecTrsFrshCls; SecTrsSophCls; PresJrCls; Band; Chrs; HonRl; JA; OffAde; PepBnd; SchMus; SchPl; YthFlsp; 4-H; Chrldr; Beauty School; Beautician.

ROYSE, Martin J; W Washington HS; Fredericksburg, IN; Band; CncrtBnd; HonRl; MrchBnd; NHS; PepBnd; Purdue Univ; Electrical Engineering.

ROZAK, Victoria; Weyerhaeuser HS; Weyerhaeuser, WI; PresSophCls; ALAGirlsSt; HonRl; MrchBnd; PepBnd; StuCncl; 4-H; PpCl; Bsktbl; Univ; Home Economist.

ROZANSKI, Beth A; A Hamilton HS; Milwaukee, WI; 26/800 Chrs; ChrhWkr; CmntyWkr; HonRl; NatlMeritCmnd; RedCrAde; SchPpr; GerCl; Trk; Marquette U; Eng.

ROZANSKI, Thomas A; St Patrick HS; Chicago, IL; 7/427 HonRl; SctActv; SpnCl; Loyola Univ; Lawyer.

ROZELLA, Debra J; Mosinee HS; Mosinee, WI; CncrtBnd; HonRl; LbryAde; MrchBnd; PepBnd; TchrAde; RptrSchPpr; FHA;.

ROZGONYI, Barbara J; Danville HS; Danville, IL; 49/629 Band; ChrhWkr; CncrtBnd; HonRl; JA; MrchBnd; Orch; PepBnd; SchMus; SchPl; University; Business Admin.

ROZIER, Cindy L; R 1 North Callaway HS; Kingdom City, MO; PresFrshCls; PresSophCls; PresJrCls; PresSrCls; CtyCnl; StuCncl; TchrAde; FHA; Chrldr; DanFAwd; Univ Of Mo; Vocation.

ROZMAN, Zvonka A; St Ann HS; Chicago, IL; Chr; Chrs; HonRl; MthCl; College; Major Study.

RUANO, Michael S; South Beloit HS; South Beloit, IL; HonRl; NHS; NatlMeritSF; TchrAde; FrCl; Ftbl; Illinois State Univ; Biology.

RUARK, Robin A; Mitchell Sr HS; Pierre, SD; 9/294 Band; Chrs; JrNHS; LitMag; LbryAde; NatlFornLg; NHS; SchMus; GerCl; VoiceDemAwd; Sd State Univ; Medicine.

RUBACH, Cindy S; Trico HS; Percy, IL; ALAGirlsSt; Chrs; HonRl; SchMus; SchPl; RptrYrbk; FBLA; FHA;.

RUBBELKE, Deborah; Derham Hall HS; Saint Paul, MN; VPSrCls; StuCncl; SpnCl; Chrldr;.

RUBEL, Larry S; Bloomfield Hills HS; Bloomfield Hills, MI; 92/510 NHS; NatlMeritSF; PolWkr; SchAde; TchrAde; YthFlsp; Bsbl; Michigan State University; Computer.

RUBENACKER, Patrick F; Melvin Sibley HS; Sibley, IL; 1/23 PresJrCls; PresSrCls; HonRl; NHS; SchPl; StuCncl; Yrbk; SciCl; AmLegAwd; Univ Of Illinois; Engineering.

RUBENDALL, Richard A; Hyde Co HS; Highmore, SD; 8/54 PresChrhWkr; CmntyWkr; HonRl; PresNHS; SchPl; RptrSchPpr; FBLA; MthCl; SciCl; LetterBsktbl; LetterFtbl; LetterTrk; College; Professional.

RUBENSTEIN, Barbara L; Hubbard HS; Chicago, IL; 2/400 SecAud/Vis; Chrs; NHS; Quill&Scroll; SchMus; StuCncl; SchPpr; MthCl; PresPpCl; SecSciCl; Univ Of Illinois; Law.

RUBENTHALER, Dean; Gothenburg HS; Brady, NE; Chrs; ChrhWkr; HonRl; SchMus; 4-H; FFA; KeyCl; Ftbl; Wrstlng; 4-HAwd; Univ Of Neb; Pro.

RUBEUKING, Raleigh; Adair Casey HS; Adair, IA; SecTrsFrshCls; ChrhWkr; HonRl; StuCncl; PpCl; AmLegAwd; BttyCrckrAwd; Trade School; Broadcasting Engineer.

RUBEY, Kevin V; Milnor Public HS; Cayuga, ND; PresSrCls; Chrs; HonRl; SchPl; RptrYrbk; Yrbk; SchPpr; Trk; College; Architect.

RUBIN, Glenn R; Marist HS; Palos Hts, IL; 65/365 HonRl; StuCncl; Trk; St Xavier College; Mathematics.

RUBIN, Michael P; Beach Public HS; Beach, ND; 1/39 PresFrshCls; VPSophCls; PresJrCls; PresSrCls; ALBoysSt; VPBand; VPCncrtBnd; HonRl; NatlMeritFnl; VPStuCncl; Pres4-H; Bsktbl; Ftbl; Trk; North Dakota State Univ; Engineering.

RUBINGH, Glenn A; Ellsworth Community HS; Ellsworth, MI; VPSophCls; PresJrCls; ChrhWkr; SchPl; TchrAde; YthFlsp; RptrYrbk; RptrSchPpr; 4-H; KeyCl; Bsktbl; LetterFtbl; Ferris College; Radio Television.

RUBINSTEIN, Scott A; Niles Township HS; Skokie, IL; 137/632 Aud/Vis; Band; CmntyWkr; CncrtBnd; MrchBnd; NatlThespSoc; SchMus; SchPl; Coll; Physician.

RUBISH, Jeff R; Richland Center HS; Richland Center, WI; 53/185 Band; CncrtBnd; HonRl; MrchBnd; ModUN; SchPl; LatCl; College; Pathology.

RUBLE, Karen L; Harper Creek HS; Battle Creek, MI; 2/280 Chr; Chrl; HonRl; NHS; SpnCl; Michigan State; Secondary Educ.

RUBLEE, Anne M; Hartford Union HS; Hartford, WI; Band; CncrtBnd; HonRl; MrchBnd; Orch; PepBnd; StuCncl; Tennis; Chrldr; GAA; College; Professional.

RUBOW, Jennifer L; New Richmond HS; New Richmond, WI; ChrhWkr; HonRl; SchMus; SchPl; Yrbk; Bsktbl; IMSpt; Univ; Prof.

RUBSAM, Kim E; Sanborn Comm HS; Sanborn, IA; Band; Chrs; CncrtBnd; HonRl; MrchBnd; NHS; SchPl; YthFlsp; LetterBsktbl; LetterTrk; College; Medical Field.

RUBY, Randy J; North Mahaska HS; New Sharon, IA; HonRl; SchPl; FFA; SciCl;.

RUBY, Rebecca S; Seymour HS; Payson, IL; 6/65 Band; CncrtBnd; HonRl; MrchBnd; PepBnd; SchMus; 4-H; PpCl; Western Illinois Univ; Liberal Arts.

RUCH, Kathleen M; Eastridge HS; Kankakee, IL; 21/255 HonRl; Glf; LetterTennis; GAA; Univ; Aviation.

RUCH, Kevin M; Clinton Prairie HS; Mulberry, IN; 4/88 NHS; StuCncl; SptEdSchPpr; Pres4-H; FFA; SciCl; Bsktbl; LetterFtbl; Trk; College; Law.

RUCH, Robert R; Morton West HS; Berwyn, IL; 40/750 SecSrCls; NatlSciFnd; Quill&Scroll; YthFlsp; EdYrBk; FBLA; EngCl; GerCl; NHS; LetterBsktbl; Norther Il Univ ;bus Act.

RUCH, Virginia M; Britton Public HS; Britton, SD; 10/75 SecSophCls; VPJrCls; ALAGirlsSt; Chrs; ChrhWkr; NHS; SchPl; SctActv; SecStuCncl; EdYrBk; College; Occup Therapist.

RUCHOTZKE, Betty L; East Central HS; Sabula, IA; VPFrshCls; ALAGirlsSt; ChrhWkr; HonRl; LbryAde; NHS; EdSchPpr; GerCl; PpCl; Trk; Aib In Des Moines; Executive Legal Sec.

RUCINSKI, Elaine M; St Ladislaus HS; Hamtramck, MI; HonRl; JA; FBLA; FNA; FrCl; FrCl; MthCl; PpCl; SecSciCl; CitAwd; University; Mathematics.

RUCKER, Arthur L; Paseo HS; Kansas City, MO; 32/300 NHS; SchPpr; GerCl; LetterBsktbl; LetterTrk; CitAwd; Millikin U; Law.

RUCKER, Karen J; Northeast Nodaway R V HS; Ravenwood, MO; VPJrCls; HonRl; RedCrAde; LetterBsbl; LetterBsktbl; Swmmng; Chrldr; Univ.

RUCKER, Mary K; Trinity HS; Hutchinson, KS; Chr; ChrhWkr; DrlTm; HonRl; NHS; SchPl; StuCncl; PpCl; Bsbl; Bsktbl; College; Psychology.

RUCKER, Patricia A; East Catholic HS; Detroit, MI; VPJrCls; VPSrCls; NHS; StuCncl; Chrldr; Univ Of Detroit; Accounting.

RUCKERT, Margaret L; Chase HS; Chase, KS; 1/31 Band; CncrtBnd; HonRl; HospAde; Tennis; BttyCrckrAwd; 4-HAwd; LionAwd; VFWAwd; VoiceDemAwd; Fort Hays Clg Ks; Nursing.

RUCKL, Judy; South HS; Omaha, NE; ChrhWkr; CmntyWkr; HonRl; JA; NHS; NatlMeritCmnd; EngCl; College; Economics And Business.

RUD, Joni A; Sheyenne Public HS; Sheyenne, ND; Band; Chr; ChrhWkr; HonRl; SchPl; 4-H; FHA; LetterBsktbl; 4-HAwd; GodCntryAwd; N Dakota State Sch Of Science; Data Proc.

RUDD, Judith; Les Cheneaux HS; Cedarville, MI; Chr; ChrhWkr; CmntyWkr; HonRl; SchPl; StuCncl; RptrYrbk; 4-H; Bsktbl; College; Social Work.

RUDD, Peggy S; Seneca HS; Seneca, MO; 33/99 Chrs; HonRl; RptrSchPpr; EdSchPpr; 4-H; FHA; FrCl; GAA; College; Journalism.

RUDD, Terri L; Niles North HS; Skokie, IL; 4/631 HonRl; JrNHS; NHS; StuCncl; University; Liberal Arts.

RUDDY, Robert J; Hill Mccloy HS; Flushiny, MI; ChrhWkr; CmntyWkr; CncrtBnd; NHS; Orch; PolWkr; AmLegAwd; GodCntryAwd; CitAwd; VoiceDemAwd; College; Landscape Architect.

RUDDY, T E; Schaumburg HS; Schaumburg, IL; Chr; NatlMeritCmnd; Orch; Quill&Scroll; SchMus; SptEdSchPpr; GerCl; PpCl; CaptWrstlng; Us Naval Academy; Science.

RUDE, Nancy A; Redfield Independent HS; Redfield, SD; SecAFS; ALAGirlsSt; Chrs; PresChrhWkr; HonRl; LbryAde; SchAde; SchPl; TchrAde; VPPpCl; College; Nursing.

RUDEBUSCH, George H; Tosa East HS; Wauwatosa, WI; 14/416 NHS; NatlMeritSF; Orch; Tennis; Concordia Milwaukee; Theology.

RUDEN, Joyce M; Western Dubuque HS; Bernard, IA; 11/243 Band; Chrs; CncrtBnd; HonRl; MrchBnd; PresNHS; PolWkr; SchMus; EdSchPpr; SecFTA; Univ Of Iowa; Journalism.

RUDER, Lisa; Hays HS; Kansas, KS; DrlTm; HospAde; NatlFornLg; TchrAde; Yrbk; PpCl; IMSpt; College; Professional.

RUDICH, Renee A; New Haven HS; Washington, MI; 7/135 Band; CncrtBnd; HonRl; MrchBnd; NHS; PepBnd; StuCncl; Yrbk; Chrldr;.

RUDIE, Pauline R; Wahpeton Sr HS; Wahpeton, ND; HonRl; HospAde; SchPl; GerCl; PpCl; N D St Univ; Education.

RUDIN, Kathy J; Washington HS; Cedar Rapids, IA; 10/463 SecFrshCls; NHS; RedCrAde; StuGov; PpCl; Bsktbl; LetterSwmmng; IMSpt; Iowa State Univ; Veterinary Medicine.

RUDIN, Thomas W; Lincoln Way HS; New Lenox, IL; 32/500 CmntyWkr; HonRl; NHS; OffAde; RptrSchPpr; SptEdSchPpr; Purdue Univ; Communications.

RUDIS, Joseph G; Rhinelander HS; Rhinelander, WI; 15/335 ALBoysSt; HonRl; NHS; LatCl; Uw Stevens Point; Eng.

RUDKIN, David R; Peru HS; Peru, IN; 6/253 ALBoysSt; HonRl; NatlFornLg; NHS; StuCncl; VPStuGov; SpnCl; LetterFtbl; LetterTrk; Wrstlng; IMSpt; College; Engineering.

RUDNICKI, Timothy; Waconia HS; St Bonifacius, MN; Chrs; CncrtBnd; HonRl; MrchBnd; NHS; PepBnd; SchMus; Coll; Pol Sci.

RUDO, Dianne S; Highland Park HS; Highland Pk, IL; HonRl; NHS; StuGov; FrCl; SpnCl; PpCl; Swmmng; CchngActv; Univ; Diplomat.

RUDOLPH, Daniel C; Camtom HS; Camtom, SD; Band; CncrtBnd; HonRl; NHS; SciCl; Ftbl; LetterWrstlng; DanFAwd; Schl Of Mines; Eng.

RUDOLPH, Donald R; Savannah R Iii HS; Savannah, MO; 10/159 ALBoysSt; Chr; HonRl; NHS; PolWkr; StuCncl; Trk; Wrstlng; Univ Of Mo Columbia; Engineering.

RUDOLPH, Earlene G; Eastern HS; Palmyra, IN; HonRl; TreasNHS; OffAde; SchAde; TreasStuCncl; TchrAde; YthFlsp; RptrYrbk; RptrSchPpr; FHA;.

RUDOLPH, Jean L; Macomb Sr HS; Macomb, IL; SecFrshCls; VPSrCls; Chr; HonRl; NHS; SchMus; StuCncl; SchPpr; FrCl; De Paul University.

RUDOLPH, Kim; Grafton HS; Grafton, WI; HonRl; SchMus; RptrYrbk; Yrbk; SpnCl; PpCl; IMSpt; Univ Of Wis; Occupational Therapy.

RUDOLPH, Linda S; Marine City Ward Cottrell HS; Marine City, MI; HonRl; NHS; NatlMeritCmnd; NatlMeritSF; VPStuGov; RptrSchPpr; EdSchPpr; 4-H; KeyCl; LetterBsktbl;.

RUDOLPH, Mary K; Morton HS; Morton, IL; Band; CncrtBnd; HonRl; JA; MrchBnd; GerCl; PpCl; GAA; University; Psychology.

RUDOLPH, Stephen B; St Teresa HS; Decatur, IL; 6/119 VPSrCls; AFS; CmntyWkr; NatlMeritCmnd; StuCncl; RptrYrbk; CivCl; Bsbl; LetterBsktbl; LetterTrk; College; Computer Science.

RUDOLPH, Tamara S; Rockridge HS; Muscatine, IA; 1/140 SecBand; CncrtBnd; HonRl; LitMag; NHS; StuCncl; Pres4-H; FTA; LatCl; 4-HAwd; College; Music Education.

RUDY, Susan K; Goshen HS; Goshen, IN; 15/262 PresJrCls; Chr; NatlFornLg; NHS; NatlThespSoc; StuCncl; FrCl; Earlham College; Law.

RUDZINSKI, Mary I; Oak Park River Forest HS; Oak Park, IL; ChrhWkr; CmntyWkr; HonRl; Orch; SchAde; SchMus; SchPl; TchrAde; Univ Of Illinois; Music.

RUDZINSKI, Susan D; Downers Grove South HS; Woodridge, IL; 23/849 ChrhWkr; HonRl; JrNHS; NHS; NatlMeritFnl; NatlMeritSchl; NatlMeritSF; OffAde; FTA; FrCl; GAA; College.

RUEB, Marsha E; Streeter Public HS; Streeter, ND; 5/21 CncrtBnd; HonRl; MrchBnd; PepBnd; SchPl; YthFlsp; SchPpr; 4-H; PpCl; 4-HAwd;.

RUEBE, Richard H; Brother Rice HS; Chicago, IL; 12/415 HonRl; JrNHS; NHS; TchrAde; Univ Of Illinois; Accounting.

RUEBLING, Mark R; West HS; Davenport, IA; AFS; Band; Chrs; HonRl; LitMag; NatlThespSoc; SchPl; RptrYrbk; SchPpr; College; Professional.

RUED, Thomas C; Iola Scandinavia HS; Iola, WI; 5/61 ALBoysSt; Chrs; ChrhWkr; HonRl; Mdrgl; NatlFornLg; NHS; StuCncl; LetterFtbl; IMSpt; University; Science.

RUEDEBUSCH, Charles A; Mayville HS; Mayville, WI; 7/130 HonRl; JA; NHS; NatlMeritSF; StuGov; LetterGlf; Univ Of Wisconsin.

RUEDEBUSCH, Mary J; St Marys HS; Burlington, WI; TrsFrshCls; PresSophCls; SecTrsJrCls; Band; Chrs; HonRl; SchPl; Twrl; Yrbk; PpCl; Gateway Tech Schl; Secretary.

RUEFF, Ronda K; Cary Grove HS; Crystal Lake, IL; Band; Chr; CncrtBnd; HonRl; LitMag; MrchBnd; PepBnd; SchMus; College.

RUEGE, Elizabeth A; Northwestern Prep; Oakfield, WI; SecTrsJrCls; Chr; Chrs; SchPl; RptrYrbk; RptrSchPpr; PPFtbl; College; Teacher.

RUEGG, Jadene C; Big Foot HS; Walworth, WI; AFS; Chr; HonRl; NHS; NatlThespSoc; Orch; SchMus; PpCl; LetterTrk; SecCollege; Physical Therapy.

RUEGGE, Arlene; Civic Memorial HS; Bethalto, IL; 14/203 ChrhWkr; HonRl; HospAde; JrNHS; NHS; OffAde; RptrSchPpr; SchPpr; FrCl; Nursing School; Nurse.

RUEGGER, Deborah L; Beloit Memorial HS; Beloit, WI; /465 ChrhWkr; CncrtBnd; HonRl; MrchBnd; NHS; PepBnd; SchPpr; SpnCl; GAA; Beloit College; Spanish And Music Major.

RUEGSEGGER, Peter; Prospect Hs; Mt Prospect, IL; 14 HonRl; NHS; StuCncl; StuGov; Bsktbl; Trk; U Of Illinois;business Economics.

RUEHR, Beth S; South HS; Sheboygan, WI; 69/549 Chr; NHS; Riverview Hosp; Lab Assistant.

RUEHR, Stephen N; York Comm HS; Oak Brook, IL; Medical School; Medicine.

RUEMENAPP, Kenneth J; South Lake HS; St Clair Shores, MI; 19/533 PresSrCls; HonRl; NHS; StuCncl; StuGov; SciCl; Bsktbl; LetterFtbl; CaptTennis; IMSpt; Mich St U; Prof.

RUEMMELE, Bridget; Hudson Senior Hs; Hudson, WI; RptrSchPpr; SchPpr; 4-H; 4-HAwd; Uw River Falls;math Or Speech.

RUEMMELE, Bridget A; Hudson Senior HS; Hudson, WI; HonRl; RptrSchPpr; EdSchPpr; SchPpr; 4-H; 4-HAwd; College; Speech Math Or Aagriculture.

RUEMMELE, Larry E; Hudson Sr HS; Hudson, WI; 14/220 ChrhWkr; HonRl; RptrSchPpr; VP4-H; FFA; Bsbl; LetterWrstlng; Univ Of Wisconsin; Agriculture.

RUEMMELE, Sheryl A; Hill Murray HS; White Bear Lk, MN; ChrhWkr; HonRl; NHS; College; Dental Hygiene.

RUESCH, Fay A; Medford Sr HS; Medford, WI; 9/212 Band; HonRl; MrchBnd; NHS; TchrAde; FrCl; PpCl; LetterSwmmng; Trk; PresGAA; IMSpt; Univ Of La Crosse; Physical Ed.

RUESCH, Gayle L; Worthington HS; Worthington, MN; SchPpr; Voc Sch; Sec Legal.

RUESINK, Diane K; Spring Valley HS; Spring Valley, MN; Chr; ChrhWkr; HospAde; OffAde; SchPl; TchrAde; PresYthFlsp; 4-H; GerCl; 4-HAwd; Vocational Sch; Operating Rm Tech.

RUETER, Jean M; Mater Dei HS; Carlyle, IL; 6/190 PresSophCls; VPJrCls; Chr; Chrs; ChrhWkr; HonRl; LbryAde; NHS; SchMus; SecStuCncl; RptrSchPpr; 4-HAwd; Illinois State.

RUETTEN, Michael G; Sparta HS; Sparta, WI; 17/197 HonRl; NHS; LetterFtbl; LetterTrk; IMSpt; Univ Wi; Mining Engr.

RUETTGERS, Donna S; Linn R 2 HS; Linn, MO; Band; Chrs; CncrtBnd; MrchBnd; StuCncl; TchrAde; PpCl; LetterBsktbl; LetterTrk; Chrldr; Nursing.

RUETZ, Kevin P; St Croix Central HS; Hammond, WI; HonRl; SctActv; RptrSchPpr; SptEdSchPpr; SchPpr; LetterBsbl; LetterBsktbl; Ftbl; CchngActv; College.

RUF, Cynthia A; Wilsonville HS; Wilsonville, NE; PresSophCls; SecBand; Chrs; HonRl; SchPl; SecStuCncl; 4-H; PpCl; Bsktbl; LetterTrk; Chrldr; IMSpt; 4-HAwd; Univ Of Ne.

RUFEDER, Joann K; Monroe HS; Monroe, WI; 84/255 PresFrshCls; SecSophCls; SecJrCls; HonRl; PolWkr; 4-H; FHA; LetterTrk; CaptChrldr; 4-HAwd;.

RUFF, Andrew T; Bloomer HS; Bloomer, WI; HonRl; StuCncl; Pres4-H; FFA; Ftbl; 4-HAwd; Univ; Engr.

RUFF, Bradley R; Academy Of The Holy Angels; Richfield, MN; SciCl; Bsbl; LetterFtbl; LetterWrstlng; College.

RUFF, Catherine M; Bloomer HS; Bloomer, WI; 4/122 AFS; MrchBnd; NHS; 4-H; FHA; LetterBsktbl; LetterTrk; GAA; 4-HAwd; University Of Wisconsin; Secondary Educ.

RUFF, Cindy J; Woodland HS; Streator, IL; 1/74 ALAGirlsSt; NHS; StuCncl; 4-H; AmLegAwd; DARAwd; Univ Of Illinois; Veterinarian.

RUFF, Darcy D; Lehr HS; Lehr, ND; SecSophCls; VPJrCls; ALBoysSt; Band; Chr; Chrs; ChrhWkr; HonRl; PepBnd; StuCncl; 4-H; Bsbl; College; Professional.

RUFF, Denette D; Bismarck HS; Bismarck, ND; 1/588 HonRl; LitMag; NHS; EdSchPpr; EldAwd; Univ Of Nd; Journalism.

RUFF, Edmund F; Garnaville Community HS; Farmersburg, IA; HonRl; SchPl; StuCncl; 4-H; FFA; Bsbl; Iowa St Univ; Agriculture.

RUFF, Gary C; Wahlert HS; Dubuque, IA; HonRl; StuCncl; StuGov; Bsktbl; Ftbl; Trk; IMSpt; Coe Col; Engineering.

RUFF, Heidi K; Amana HS; South Amana, IA; 1/24 Chrs; HonRl; JA; JrNHS; NHS; SchMus; StuCncl; Central College; Language.

RUFF, Janice K; Stewardson Strasburg HS; Strasburg, IL; Chrs; HonRl; LbryAde; SchPl; Yrbk; FHA; College; Math.

RUFF, Judy K; Greendale HS; Greendale, WI; SecJrCls; Chr; Chrl; Chrs; ChrhWkr; CncrtBnd; NHS; StuGov; GAA; College; Nursing.

RUFF, Lonnie L; Hanston HS; Hanston, KS; 7/15 Chr; Chrs; ChrhWkr; CmntyWkr; HonRl; SchMus; SchPl; YthFlsp; RptrYrbk; Bsktbl; Panhanle St ;farmer Or Rancher.

RUFF, Ossie; Hayti HS; Hayti, MO; VPJrCls; Band; CncrtBnd; HonRl; MrchBnd; NHS; StuCncl; Chrldr; GAA; IMSpt; Univ.

RUFF, Rhonda S; South Harrison R 2 HS; Bethany, MO; Chr; ChrhWkr; SchPl; SctActv; FHA; PpCl; EldAwd; Chrldr; College; Model.

RUFF, Robin L; Lakeshore HS; Stevensville, MI; HonRl; SpnCl; College; Psychology.

RUFF, Susie C; Alton HS; Birch Tree, MO; 5/95 VPFrshCls; SecJrCls; Chrs; HonRl; MrchBnd; PepBnd; SchPl; SptEdSchPpr; SchPpr; Chrldr;.

RUFFALO, Barbara J; Notre Dame HS; Chicago, IL; 50/261 StuCncl; StuGov; Clge; Nursing.

RUFFING, Julie A; Columbus HS; Marshfield, WI; 11/118 HonRl; NHS; SchMus; SchPl; EdYrBk; 4-H; FrCl; PpCl; GAA; College.

RUFKAHR, Jane M; Saint Thomas Aquinas HS; Florissant, MO; 21/349 HonRl; NHS; NatlMeritCmnd; SctActv; TchrAde; Yrbk; LatCl; CitAwd; College; Engineering Management.

RUGEN, Lewis L; Prairie Home HS; Priarie Home, MO; 3/16 TrsJrCls; Band; HonRl; SchPl; Yrbk; SchPpr; LetterBsbl; LetterBsktbl; Trk; BttyCrckrAwd; Sch Of The Ozarks; Math & Chem.

RUGG, David J; Buffalo Grove HS; Buffalo Grove, IL; 23/290 Chr; ChrhWkr; HonRl; NHS; NatlMeritFnl; NatlMeritSchl; NatlMeritSF; Michigan St U; Zoology.

RUGGIERO, Janice A; St Marys Of Perpetual HelpHS; Chicago, IL; 430/100 Chrs; SchMus; SchPl; StuCncl; YthFnd; Yrbk; RptrSchPpr; PpCl; Chrldr; Carthage Col; Dance.

RUGH, Linda M; Highland HS; Highland, IN; 9/585 Chr; Chrs; ChrhWkr; CncrtBnd; MrchBnd; NatlMeritCmnd; SchMus; 4-H; KeyCl; 4-HAwd; Drake Univ; Pharmacist.

RUHBUSCH, Vicki A; Gresham HS; Gresham, WI; 1/31 PresSophCls; ALAGirlsSt; ChrhWkr; CncrtBnd; HonRl; NHS; SecStuCncl; EdYrBk; 4-H; PresFTA; DARAwd; College; Office Work.

RUHE, Mary K; Forest Park HS; Ferdinand, IN; 15/124 HonRl; SecNHS; SchPl; StuCncl; PresPpCl; LetterTrk; GAA; IMSpt; CitAwd; Indiana U; Accounting.

RUHL, Sharon A; Grayling HS; Grayling, MI; 8/145 TrsJrCls; HonRl; Yrbk; 4-H; Lake Superior St College; Mathematics.

RUHLIG, Susan M; Buena Vista HS; Saginaw, MI; ChrhWkr; HonRl; OffAde; College; Dental Assisting.

RUHLMAN, Dennis E; Faulkton HS; Faulkton, SD; 4/65 PresSrCls; ALBoysSt; HonRl; SchPl; StuCncl; EdSchPpr; Bsktbl; Ftbl; Glf; South Dakota State Univ.

RUHLMAN, Joseph A; North Branch HS; North Branch, MI; 15/141 PresJrCls; Band; ChrhWkr; CncrtBnd; HonRl; MrchBnd; NHS; StuCncl; StuGov; Ftbl; E Michigan Univ; Business Accounting.

RUHOLL, Jane; Teutopolis Hs; Teutopolis, IL; 15/115 HonRl; HospAde; NatlMeritFnl; NatlMeritSchl; RptrSchPpr; 4-H; FHA; PpCl; Bsbl; GAA; College; Vocational.

RUHR, Byron J; Castlewood Ind Con HS; Castlewood, SD; 10/30 HonRl; RptrYrbk; IMSpt; S Dakota State Univ; Engineering.

RUHR, Kay M; Castlewood HS; Castlewood, SD; 1/22 Band; CncrtBnd; HonRl; MrchBnd; PepBnd; EdYrBk; LetterBsktbl; LetterTrk; IMSpt; PresAwd; College; Music.

RUHS, Sue M; La Salle HS; Cedar Rapids, IA; Aud/Vis; Chr; HospAde; NatlFornLg; SchMus; SchPl; PpCl; Univ Of Iowa; Pharmacy.

RUIGH, Karen E; Pine River HS; Pine River, MN; 6/70 Band; CncrtBnd; HonRl; NHS; PresStuCncl; EdSchPpr; EldAwd; 4-HAwd; College; Law.

RUIZ, Daniel J; Gordon Tech HS; Chicago, IL; 68/640 Band; College; Lawyer.

RUIZ, Gloria M; Brentwood HS; Brentwood, MO; DrlTm; HonRl; HospAde; ModUN; NHS; StuCncl; FrCl; PpCl; GAA; PresAwd; College; Math.

RUIZ, Minerva; Jefferson Senior HS; Jefferson, WI; CmntyWkr; HonRl; OffAde; RedCrAde; StuGov; FrCl; SpnCl; Bsktbl; Swmmng; Tennis; Univ; Executive Secretary.

RUKAMP, Kathy L; Denmark HS; Greenbay, WI; Chrs; HonRl; GAA;.

RULAND, Joseph J; University City HS; University City, MO; AFS; Band; CncrtBnd; MrchBnd; Orch; PepBnd; SchMus; FrCl; LatCl; Macalester Col.

RULE, Derrick; East St Louis Senior HS; East Saint Louis, IL; 11/650 Band; ChrhWkr; HonRl; JA; JrNHS; NHS; StuCncl; 4-H; FrCl; MthCl; Univ Of Illinois; Engineering.

RULE, Edwin K; Central HS; Montrose, IA; HonRl; JrNHS; NHS; NatlMeritSchl; SchPl; FBLA; FFA; Bsbl; Bsktbl; Ftbl; College; Auto Mechanic.

RULE, Mary C; Springfield HS; Springfield, IL; 31/535 Chr; NHS;.

RUMAGE, Sherrie M; Parkview HS; Beloit, WI; Band; Chr; Chrs; CncrtBnd; DrlTm; DrmBgl; DrmMjrt; HonRl; Mdrgl; MrchBnd; College; Music.

RUMAN, Mary B; Marquette Sr HS; Marquette, MI; 89/388 ALAGirlsSt; Band; ChrhWkr; CmntyWkr; HonRl; MrchBnd; NatlThespSoc; PepBnd; SchPl; TchrAde; University; Special Ed.

RUMBLE, Ann M; Princeton Comm HS; Princeton, IN; 30/212 Aud/Vis; ChrhWkr; StuCncl; StuGov; RptrYrbk; EdSchPpr; 4-H; FFA; KeyCl; Purdue Univ; Agriculture.

RUMMEL, Kim D; Holdrege Sr HS; Holdrege, NE; 9/121 Chrs; HonRl; HospAde; NatlFornLg; NatlThespSoc; Teen; 4-H; PpCl; Chrldr; University Of Nebraska.

RUMMEL, Tammie L; Glendale HS; Springfield, MO; AFS; Chrs; ChrhWkr; CmntyWkr; HonRl; OffAde; FHA; KeyCl; Chrldr; IMSpt; Univ; Home Ec Archtect.

RUMPLE, Robert B; Adair Casey HS; Casey, IA; PresSophCls; VPJrCls; Band; CmntyWkr; HonRl; StuCncl; StuGov; 4-H; FFA; PpCl; Des Moines Comm Clg.

RUMPTZ, Patrick J; Bishop Borgess HS; Detroit, MI; StuCncl; Teen; SchPpr; IMSpt; Mercy Clge Of Detroit; Social Work.

RUMREICH, Sandra J; Mound Westonka HS; Mound, MN; Chr; Chrl; HonRl; Mdrgl; NatlFornLg; NatlThespSoc; SchPl; StuCncl; YthFlsp; PpCl; College; Professional.

RUMSCHLAG, Paul A; Bellmont HS; Decatur, IN; Band; CncrtBnd; MrchBnd; NHS; NatlMeritSF; PepBnd; VPQuill&Scroll; RptrYrbk; EdSchPpr; SptEdSchPpr; LetterFtbl; Trk; LetterWrstlng; In Univ; Journalism.

RUNBOM, Dennis E; Rockridge HS; Reynolds, IL; 41/141 ALBoysSt; HonRl; LbryAde; TchrAde; 4-H; FTA; SpnCl; LetterBsktbl; LetterFtbl; LetterTrk; IMSpt; Iowa Wesleyan College; Teacher.

RUNDALL, John M; Aquin Cen Catholic HS; Freeport, IL; Chr; Chrl; Chrs; HonRl; Mdrgl; SchMus; SchPl; SctActv; PpCl; Ftbl; Devry Tech Inst; Electronics.

RUNDE, David G; Duchesne HS; St Charles, MO; 54/186 Band; CncrtBnd; MrchBnd; SchMus; KeyCl; LatCl; Socr; Tennis; KiwanAwd; U Of Mo; Biology.

RUNDE, Jeffrey M; Kennedy Sr HS; Cedar Rapids, IA; 31/455 NHS; SciCl; LetterBsbl; LetterBsktbl; Univ; Pro.

RUNDE, Tina J; Teutopolis HS; Teutopolis, IL; TrsFrshCls; HonRl; HospAde; SchPl; StuCncl; FHA; PpCl; Chrldr; GAA; 4-HAwd; Eastern Ill Univ; Accounting.

RUNDIKS, Emilija L; Niantic Harristown HS; Niantic, IL; SecSrCls; Band; HonRl; SchPl; SctActv; StuCncl; YthFlsp; PpCl; Chrldr; Milikin University; Vocation.

RUNDLE, Kimberly A; Smith Center HS; Smith Center, KS; Band; CncrtBnd; HonRl; HospAde; MrchBnd; Orch; PepBnd; SchAde; StuGov; TchrAde; Twrl; FHA; University; Teaching.

RUNGE, Dale A; Milbank HS; Twin Brooks, SD; 19/123 ALBoysSt; Aud/Vis; Chrs; HonRl; NatlFornLg; RptrYrbk; Trade Schl; Photography.

RUNGE, Valerie A; Warsaw HS; Warsaw, IL; SecSophCls; NHS; StuCncl; GerCl; SpnCl; GAA; Bus Shcool; Vocation.

RUNIA, Beverly A; Balaton Public HS; Balaton, MN; Chr; HonRl; LbryAde; SchPl; Sec4-H; FFA; FHA; CaptBsktbl; GAA; IMSpt; Univ Of Mn; Phy Ed.

RUNION, Rebecca N; Alexis HS; North Henderson, IL; Chr; Chrs; HonRl; SchPl; FHA;.

RUNT, James L; Oconomowoc HS; Oconomowoc, WI; 19/234 Band; ChrhWkr; CncrtBnd; HonRl; JrNHS; SctActv; LatCl; LetterFtbl; Trk; IMSpt; 4-HAwd; College.

RUNYAN, James B; Elwood Community HS; Elwood, IN; 11/223 Aud/Vis; HonRl; NHS; PresStuCncl; SptEdYrbk; VP4-H; SpnCl; LetterFtbl; LetterTrk; LetterWrstlng; College.

RUNYON, Bruce A; West Richland HS; Olney, IL; PresSrCls; Band; HonRl; SchMus; SchPl; StuCncl; EdYrBk; FrCl; University.

RUNYON, Catherine A; Morton HS; Morton, IL; 4/300 DrlTm; HonRl; NHS; YthFnd; EdYrBk; GAA; Univ Of Ill; Physical Therapy.

RUNYON, David E; Edwardsville Sr HS; Edwardsville, IL; 65/454 Band; Chrs; HonRl; Mdrgl; RptrSchPpr; EngCl; Southern Illinois University.

RUNYON, Janet S; Green Valley HS; Green Valley, IL; 5/25 VPFrshCls; Band; ChrhWkr; HonRl; JrNHS; NHS; PepBnd; SchPl; StuCncl; EdSchPpr;.

RUNYON, Norman K; Chatsworth HS; Chatsworth, IL; 4/46 ChrhWkr; HonRl; YthFlsp; 4-H; FFA; LetterFtbl; Trk; 4-HAwd; College; Conservation.

RUNYON, Pamela S; West Richland HS; Noble, IL; SecTrsFrshCls; VPSophCls; SecTrsJrCls; HonRl; SchMus; SchPl; EdYrBk; Yrbk; LetterChrldr; BttyCrckrAwd; College; Curriculum Of Major Study.

RUNYON, Paul; Morton HS; Morton, IL; HonRl; Cenweral Motors Inst; Vocational.

RUNYON, Ruby N; Pine River HS; Tustin, MI; TrsFrshCls; TrsSrCls; Chr; LbryAde; NHS; StuCncl; RptrYrbk; SpnCl; PresPpCl; PPFtbl; University; Professional.

RUNZHEIMER, Mark A; Colby HS; Colby, WI; 27/136 ChrhWkr; HonRl; SctActv; StuCncl; StuGov; RptrYrbk; CivCl; 4-H; FFA; Bsktbl; Uw Menomomie; Auto Mechanics.

RUOTSALAINEN, Jodi J; Rosemount Sr HS; St Paul, MN; SchPpr; 4-H; College.

RUPAR, Mary J; Josephinum HS; Chicago, IL; 3/104 HstFrshCls; VPNHS; StuCncl; StuGov; Yrbk; College; Mathematics.

RUPE, Carla J; Cardinal HS; Eldon, IA; SecSrCls; Band; Chrs; ChrhWkr; CmntyWkr; HonRl; MrchBnd; OffAde; 4-H; 4-HAwd; Executive Sec.

RUPINSKI, Timothy E; Thomas More HS; Milwaukee, WI; Chrs; HonRl; LbryAde; U Of Wi Milwaukee; Math.

RUPLINGER, Eileen; Marathon HS; Marathon, WI; 8/98 ALAGirlsSt; CncrtBnd; HonRl; MrchBnd; PepBnd; SchMus; Yrbk; RptrSchPpr; FHA; GAA; Technical; Architectural Res Design.

RUPLINGER, Paul J; Tomahawk HS; Tomahawk, WI; ChrhWkr; CmntyWkr; HonRl; 4-H; LatCl; LetterBsbl; LetterBsktbl; Glf; Trk; Wrstlng; IMSpt; 4-HAwd; College; Priest.

RUPP, Anthony F; Thomas More Prep; Hays, KS; 14/75 HonRl; PolWkr; LetterBsktbl; CchngActv; IMSpt; Coll; Coach.

RUPP, Cindy J; Mevidian HS; Sanford, MI; ChrhWkr; CmntyWkr; HonRl; HospAde; SchMus; SchPl; FrCl; Bsktbl; VoiceDemAwd; College; Dietetics.

RUPP, Cynthia L; Diamond R #4 HS; Diamond, MO; 8/60 Band; ChrhWkr; HonRl; Mdrgl; ModUN; NHS; OffAde; PepBnd; SchPl; TreasFHA; PpCl; College; Education.

RUPP, Robert L; Medicine Valley HS; Curtis, NE; ChrhWkr; HonRl; StuCncl; StuGov; YthFlsp; CaptBsbl; CaptBsktbl; CaptFtbl; Swmmng; Tennis; LetterTrk; CchngActv; College; Professional.

RUPP, William K; Quincy Sr HS; Quincy, IL; 1/836 CncrtBnd; HospAde; NHS; NatlMeritCmnd; Orch; SctActv; TchrAde; YthLg; Southern Illinois Univ; Psychology.

RUPPERT, Susan M; Nokomis HS; Nokomis, IL; Chrs; ChrhWkr; HonRl; TchrAde; 4-H; KeyCl; LetterTrk; DanFAwd; PresAwd; CitAwd; Western Ill U; Biological Sce.

RUPPERT, William L; Wayland Academy; Iowa City, IA; 8/74 VPJrCls; HonRl; Mdrgl; NatlMeritCmnd; StuCncl; GerCl; LetterBsbl; LetterBsktbl; LetterFtbl; Chrldr; U Of Ia; Lawyer.

RUPPRECHT, Hannalore; Midland HS; Midland, MI; ChrhWkr; CncrtBnd; HonRl; JA; MrchBnd; NHS; PepBnd; SctActv; YthFlsp; JAAwd; Alma College; Biology.

RUPRIGHT, Nora; Millington HS; Clio, MI; ChrhWkr; HonRl; HospAde; NHS; YthFlsp; FrCl; Coll; Nrsng.

RUS, David; Pella Christian HS; Pella, IA; Band; CncrtBnd; HonRl; MrchBnd; PepBnd; Yrbk; IMSpt; Univ; Science.

RUSCH, Lori L; Valders HS; Valders, WI; Band; PresChrs; CncrtBnd; HonRl; Mdrgl; MrchBnd; PepBnd; SchPl; 4-H; FHA; Technical School; Optomotrist Assistant.

RUSCH, Mark A; De La Salle HS; Roseville, MI; 18/125 HonRl; JA; StuCncl; RptrSchPpr; SpnCl; IMSpt; JAAwd; Univ Of Detroit; Accounting.

RUSCH, Randi L; Valders HS; Valders, WI; TrsJrCls; Chr; Chrs; ChrhWkr; HonRl; Mdrgl; YthFlsp; Chrldr; GAA; PPFtbl; College.

RUSCH, Richard; Laona HS; Laona, WI; 2/37 VPSophCls; Chrs; HonRl; SchPl; StuCncl; Uw Milwaukee; Biol.

RUSCH, Thomas D; Wauwatosa West HS; Wauwatosa, WI; 12/436 Chrs; HonRl; MrchBnd; NHS; NatlThespSoc; Orch; SchPl; TchrAde; FTA; Univ Of Wisconsin; Foreign Language.

RUSCHE, Kathryn A; Smithton HS; Sedalia, MO; 10/41 Band; Chr; Chrs; HonRl; Mdrgl; SchMus; SchPl; StuCncl; 4-H; Chrldr; College.

RUSH, Harlan E; Ida Crown Jewish Academy; Chicago, IL; ChrhWkr; HonRl; NHS; SancSoc; SchPl; TreasStuCncl; YthFnd; RptrSchPpr; Trk; College.

RUSH, Jaclyn L; Smith Center HS; Smith Center, KS; ALAGirlsSt; ChrhWkr; CmntyWkr; HonRl; NHS; StuCncl; EdYrBk; FBLA; FTA; GAA; PPFtbl; Hays College; Elementary Teacher.

RUSH, Marc; Niles East HS; Skokie, IL; 72/540 VPSrCls; Chr; Chrs; NHS; NatlThespSoc; SchMus; Cornell University; Engineering.

RUSH, Marc C; Harris Lake Park Comm HS; Lake Park, IA; ALBoysSt; Aud/Vis; HonRl; Mdrgl; SchPl; FFA; LetterBsbl; LetterBsktbl; LetterFtbl; LetterGlf; Coll; Professional.

RUSH, Michael; Duluth Central HS; Duluth, MN; 5/486 Band; CmntyWkr; CncrtBnd; HonRl; JrNHS; ModUN; StuGov; UNYO; PpCl; Trk; College; Doctor Md.

RUSH, Michael S; Shawnee Mission North HS; Mission, KS; 145/636 LetterBand; DrmBgl; SctActv; SciCl; Ftbl; Socr; Wrstlng; CchngActv; IMSpt; PPFtbl; GodCntryAwd; College; Biology.

RUSH, Richard G; Sidney HS; Sidney, NE; Band; HonRl; NHS; Quill&Scroll; SchPl; StuCncl; RptrYrbk; RptrSchPpr; 4-H; MthCl; College; Actuarial Sciences.

RUSH, Tim; Galatia Hs; Galatia, IL; TrsFrshCls; Band; HonRl; Bsktbl;.

RUSHTON, Steven A; Carlinville Comm HS; Carlinville, IL; 6/156 Aud/Vis; JrNHS; TreasNHS; PolWkr; RptrYrbk; EdYrBk; FrCl; Tennis; College; Mathematics.

RUSINEK, Carol S; Marian HS; S Bend, IN; Chrs; HonRl; NHS; SchPl; SchPpr; DARAwd; Coll; Foreign Language.

RUSINEK, Carol S; Marian HS; Southbend, IN; 3/110 Chrs; HonRl; NHS; SchMus; SchPl; RptrSchPpr; SchPpr; DARAwd; College St Marys; French.

RUSK, Cheryl A; Ozark Academy; Carterville, MO; PresFrshCls; PresSophCls; PresJrCls; PresSrCls; ChrhWkr; HonRl; EdYrBk; EdSchPpr; Bsbl; Bsktbl; Southwestern Union Clg; Dental Hygenist.

RUSK, John S; Mount Ayr Community HS; Mount Ayr, IA; Band; CncrtBnd; MrchBnd; PepBnd; StuCncl; LetterBsktbl; Swmmng; AmLegAwd; College; Professional.

RUSK, Kathy; Clifton Central HS; Chebanse, IL; 1/145 ALAGirlsSt; HonRl; 4-H; SciCl; GAA; Coll; Math.

RUSK, Terry; Cedar Lake Acad; Berrien Springs, MI; 11/72 ChrhWkr; NatlMeritSF; SchMus; SchPl; StuCncl; StuGov; Ftbl; IMSpt; BttyCrckrAwd; Andrews Univ; Medicine.

RUSKAMP, Donna M; Dodge HS; Dodge, NE; ALAGirlsSt; CmntyWkr; HonRl; JA; JrNHS; NatlMeritSchl; TchrAde; UNYO; EdSchPpr; PpCl; Col Of Saint Mary; Pro.

RUSKAMP, Jeanette E; Dodge HS; Dodge, NE; 5/38 Band; Chr; Chrs; HonRl; PepBnd; SchMus; SchPl; 4-H; PpCl; 4-HAwd; College Of St Mary; Nursing.

RUSKELL, Richard D; Chosen Valley HS; Chatfield, MN; Band; Chr; ChrhWkr; CmntyWkr; CncrtBnd; HonRl; Mdrgl; NatlThespSoc; PepBnd; SchMus; SchPl; Viterbo College; Theatre.

RUSKUSKY, Rita A; Peoria Heights HS; Peoria Heights, IL; Chr; HonRl; NHS; Quill&Scroll; RptrYrbk; EdYrBk; Yrbk; RptrSchPpr; SchPpr; SpnCl; Icc Jr College; Nursing.

RUSKY, William M; Comstock Park HS; Comstock Park, MI; HonRl; TchrAde; 4-H; LetterWrstlng; 4-HAwd; CitAwd; College; Engineering.

RUSLEY, Diane M; Lake Mills Comm HS; Leland, IA; Band; Chr; Chrs; ChrhWkr; CncrtBnd; DrlTm; HonRl; MrchBnd; PepBnd; SchMus; SchPl; TchrAde; Bsktbl; Chrldr; Iowa State Univ; Veterinarian.

RUSNOK, Ken L; Wheaton Christian HS; West Chicago, IL; Aud/Vis; College; Electrician.

RUSS, Deborah L; Pembine HS; Pembine, WI; ALAGirlsSt; HonRl; NatlFornLg; SchMus; SchPl; PresStuCncl; Yrbk; RptrSchPpr; GAA; CitAwd; Trade School.

RUSS, Michael M; Guilford HS; Roscoe, IL; 50/658 Chr; ChrhWkr; HonRl; JrNHS; NHS; NatlMeritFnl; NatlMeritSF; YthFlsp; Bsktbl; LetterTrk; Univ Of Ill; Law.

RUSSELL, Anne M; Greeley County HS; Tribune, KS; VPSophCls; Chr; HonRl; SchPl; TchrAde; YthFlsp; College; Artist.

RUSSELL, Beverly J; Boscobel HS; Boscobel, WI; 24/112 Band; ChrhWkr; CncrtBnd; HonRl; MrchBnd; NHS; PepBnd; SchMus; 4-H; Calvary Bible Clge; Missions.

RUSSELL, Bobby D; Muskegon Catholic Central HS; Muskegon Hts, MI; 446/215 Band; Chr; ChrhWkr; CncrtBnd; HonRl; JA; MrchBnd; NHS; Orch; SchMus; SchPl; Muskegon Comm College; Medicine.

RUSSELL, Carole A; Canton Senior HS; Canton, IL; Chrs; DrlTm; HonRl; HospAde; OffAde; TchrAde; RptrSchPpr; GerCl; PpCl; LetterBsbl; College; Nursing Degree.

RUSSELL, Curtis A; Uniontown HS; Redfield, KS; ALBoysSt; HonRl; StuCncl; TchrAde; 4-H; FFA; LetterFtbl; Ks State U; Ag Ed.

RUSSELL, Cynthia A; Normandy Sr HS; St Louis, MO; 3/493 Chr; Chrs; HonRl; NHS; SchMus; LatCl; SpnCl; IMSpt; NCTE; Southeast Mo State; Secondary Ed.

RUSSELL, Cynthia C; Mercy HS; Omaha, NE; Chr; Chrs; HonRl; NatlFornLg; SchMus; SctActv; Sdlty; 4-H; SciCl; GAA; University; Medicine.

RUSSELL, Debbie A; Norris HS; Hickman, NE; TrsFrshCls; Band; Chrs; CncrtBnd; DrmMjrt; MrchBnd; PepBnd; SchPl; TchrAde; YthFlsp; Univ; Music.

RUSSELL, Deborah; Our Lady Acad; Chicago, IL; 42/160 Chrs; HonRl; HospAde; SchPl; RptrSchPpr; FNA; St Xavier College; Registered Nurse.

RUSSELL, Donna L; West Leyden HS; Melrose Pk, IL; 11/422 HonRl; NHS; StuCncl; Triton Jr College; Accounting.

RUSSELL, Edmund P; Creighton Prep; Omaha, NE; 6/249 PresSrCls; PresBand; CncrtBnd; HonRl; NatlFornLg; NHS; NatlMeritSF; SchPl; SctActv; Sdlty; Umiv.

RUSSELL, Edmund P; Creighton Preparatory; Omaha, NE; 4/249 PresSrCls; PresBand; HonRl; NatlFornLg; NHS; NatlMeritFnl; NatlMeritSchl; SchPl; Sdlty; StuCncl; IMSpt; AmLegAwd; Stanford University.

RUSSELL, John P; Cobden Comm HS; Cobden, IL; SecSophCls; SecJrCls; PresSrCls; HonRl; NHS; SchMus; SchPl; RptrYrbk; College; English.

RUSSELL, Kristy L; Sterling HS; Sterling, IL; 12/450 SecSophCls; Chr; Chrs; ChrhWkr; HonRl; NHS; StuCncl; FNA; GAA; Southern Calif Coll; Special Education.

RUSSELL, Pamela S; Pacific HS; Robertsville, MO; Chr; HonRl; Mdrgl; TchrAde; 4-H; PpCl; So Missouri Univ; Teaching.

RUSSELL, Paul P; Carthage Sr HS; Carthage, MO; 4/206 AFS; ChrhWkr; CmntyWkr; HonRl; HospAde; NHS; OffAde; RedCrAde; SchAde; YthFlsp; MthCl; SciCl; Univ Of Missouri; Ceramic Engineer.

RUSSELL, Philip P; Beatrice HS; Beatrice, NE; 17/223 Band; ChrhWkr; CncrtBnd; HonRl; MrchBnd; NatlMeritCmnd; PepBnd; KeyCl; LetterTrk; IMSpt; Nebraska Wesleyan Univ; Chemistry.

RUSSELL, Randy R; Richland Senior HS; Dexter, MO; 7/33 VPFrshCls; VPSophCls; PresJrCls; PresSrCls; Band; PepBnd; StuCncl; LetterBsbl; LetterBsktbl; DanFAwd; Southeast Mo Univ; Law Enforcement.

RUSSELL, Ronald; Morrill HS; Mitchell, NE; Chrs; HonRl; NHS; StuCncl; StuGov; RptrSchPpr; Bsktbl; Ftbl; Trk; RotaryAwd; Montana State Univ; Agriculture.

RUSSELL, Steve G; Streator Twp HS; Streator, IL; 28/382 StuCncl; Univ Of Illinois; Teacher.

RUSSELL, Steven H; Columbia Heights HS; Columbia Heights, MN; HonRl; NatlFornLg; NHS; NatlMeritFnl; NatlMeritSF; StuCncl; SchPpr; Univ; History.

RUSSELL, Susan E; Edgewood HS; Spencer, IN; 16/161 Band; CncrtBnd; HonRl; MrchBnd; PepBnd; FBLA; FHA; Bus Sch; Pro.

RUSSELL, Susan G; Alton Senior HS; Alton, IL; AFS; HonRl; NHS; NatlThespSoc; Orch; SchMus; SchPl; SctActv; SecGerCl; Southern Illinois University; Teacher.

RUSSELL, Susan P; Downers Grove North HS; Downers Grove, IL; 5/509 Univ Of Illinois; Journalism.

RUSSELL, Toby L; Galatia HS; Galatia, IL; VPSophCls; ChrhWkr; CmntyWkr; HonRl; SchPl; YthFlsp; LetterBsbl; CaptBsktbl; Trk; College; Business Admin.

RUSSELL, Todd S; Lansing HS; Lansing, KS; SecFrshCls; ALBoysSt; HonRl; NHS; Bsbl; LetterBsktbl; LetterFtbl; CchngActv; University; Professional Rotc.

RUSSELL, Tracey L; Wyaconda Cl HS; Wyaconda, MO; PresFrshCls; Band; Chrs; ChrhWkr; CmntyWkr; HonRl; SchPl; StuGov; Bsktbl; IMSpt; Trade Schl.

RUSSELL, Valerie; Elkhart Memorial HS; Elkhart, IN; Band; CncrtBnd; HonRl; MrchBnd; NHS; NatlThespSoc; SchMus; SchPl; RptrYrbk; RptrSchPpr;.

RUSSETT, David C; Wahlert HS; Dubuque, IA; SctActv; SciCl; Univ.

RUSSMANN, Ellen R; Walnut Comm HS; Avoca, IA; Band; Chrs; ChrhWkr; CncrtBnd; HonRl; NHS; SchPpr; FHA; PpCl; SciCl; Iowa St Univ; Interior Decorator.

RUSSO, Christina; Wells Easton HS; Wells, MN; 25/111 SecSrCls; SchPl; StuCncl; GAA; College; Medical Technology.

RUSSO, Julianne B; Addison Trail HS; Addison, IL; 1/510 HonRl; NHS; Orch; Quill&Scroll; RptrYrbk; KeyCl; Ill St Univ; Elem Tchr.

RUSSO, Paul H; St Paul John F Kennedy HS; Chicago, IL; 5/610 CncrtBnd; HonRl; MrchBnd; Univ Of Illinois; Biochemistry.

RUSSOW, Edward J; Gordon Tech HS; Chicago, IL; 59/604 HonRl; PolWkr; LetterWrstlng; IMSpt; Us Naval Acadmey.

RUSSOW, Laura A; Cornell HS; Odell, IL; Chrs; HonRl; OffAde; SchPl; StuCncl; StuGov; RptrYrbk; RptrSchPpr; FHA; GAA; U Of Il; Nursing.

RUST, David L; St Ansgar Senior HS; St Ansgar, IA; 26/115 VPSrCls; ALBoysSt; HonRl; JrNHS; College; Professional.

RUST, Gary D; Goodland HS; Goodland, KS; 19/133 ALBoysSt; HonRl; NHS; Quill&Scroll; YthFlsp; RptrSchPpr; Univ Of Kansas; Architecture.

RUST, Martin; Subiaco Acad; Greensburg, IN; Band; Chrs; HonRl; StuCncl; EdSchPpr; Bsbl; Notre Dame.

RUST, Priscilla M; Sheffield Chapin HS; Sheffield, IA; 3/46 SecSrCls; ChrhWkr; HonRl; YthFlsp; EdYrBk; Bsbl; Bsktbl; Trk; CchngActv; Niacc; P E Major.

RUST, Sarah L; Jacksonville HS; Jacksonville, IL; AFS; LitMag; NHS; Orch; 4-H; FrCl; St Louis Univ.

RUST, Susan J; Dearborn HS; Dearborn, MI; HonRl; NHS; NatlMeritCmnd; GAA; IMSpt; Ma Inst Tech; Biomedical Engineering.

RUSTAD, Melissa K; Fostton HS; Fosston, MN; Chr; HonRl; MrchBnd; PepBnd; RedCrAde; FHA; PpCl; Chrldr; GAA; IMSpt; Voctational School; Secretary.

RUSTAD, Roger A; Iola Scandinavia HS; Iola, WI; 1/50 ALBoysSt; Band; HonRl; NHS; NatlMeritSF; PolWkr; StuCncl; MthCl; LetterBsbl; LetterBsktbl; Univ Of Wi Stevens Point; Law.

RUSTAN, Jean E; Oklee Public HS; Oklee, MN; 1/37 PresJrCls; ALAGirlsSt; Band; Chrs; HonRl; SchPl; StuCncl; EdYrBk; RptrSchPpr; FHA; GAA; Northland Comm College; Business.

RUSTAND, Patricia A; Marian HS; Omaha, NE; 8/153 Chr; HonRl; JrNHS; LitMag; NHS; NatlMeritSF; SchPl; FBLA; College; Nursing.

RUSTHOVEN, Donald M; Thornwood HS; South Holland, IL; 33/852 HonRl; NHS; LatCl; MthCl; U Of Il; Dentistry.

RUSTIN, Susan R; East Monona HS; Soldier, IA; 6/29 SecJrCls; VPSrCls; Band; Chr; HonRl; NHS; SchAde; EdYrBk; FHA; Chrldr; Commercial Extension; Medical Secretary.

RUTH, Donna J; Normandy Sr HS; St Louis, MO; 18/610 Chrl; Chrs; HonRl; HospAde; PolWkr; SctActv; RptrYrbk; University; Nursing.

RUTH, Donna L; Pinckney HS; Howell, MI; ChrhWkr; CmntyWkr; HonRl; HospAde; OffAde; SchAde; StuCncl; TchrAde; YthFlsp; YthLg; LatCl; Bsbl; Bsktbl; Univ Of Mich; Medicine.

RUTHENBECK, Jon F; Okabena HS; Okabena, MN; PresFrshCls; TrsSophCls; VPJrCls; LetterBsktbl; LetterFtbl; Tennis; LetterTrk; IMSpt; AmLegAwd; 4-HAwd; Univ Of Minn; Agricultural Educ.

RUTHERFORD, Jim D; Pacific HS; Villa Ridge, MO; PresChr; Chrs; ChrhWkr; HonRl; Mdrgl; StuCncl; FTA; PpCl; CaptFtbl; Trk; LetterWrstlng; Chrldr; College; Physical Ed.

RUTHERFORD, Katherine A; Hudson Sr HS; Hudson, WI; ChrhWkr; HospAde; LbryAde; SctActv; YthFlsp; College; Foreign Language.

RUTHERFORD, Margaret L; Wahpeton Sr HS; Wahpeton, ND; SecSophCls; TrsJrCls; Band; HonRl; MrchBnd; StuGov; Yrbk; KeyCl; LetterBsbl; GAA; IMSpt; PPFtbl; College; Nursing.

RUTHERFORD, Regina; Benton Central HS; West Lafayette, IN; 9/258 TrsJrCls; Chr; Chrs; HonRl; NHS; NatlThespSoc; SchPl; YthFlsp; BauchLmbAwd; Indiana Univ; Math Teacher.

RUTHERFORD, Walter E; De Soto Sr HS; Desoto, KS; ALBoysSt; HonRl; NHS; FBLA; College.

RUTHERMAN, Laura G; Metropolis Community HS; Metropolis, IL; ChrhWkr; CmntyWkr; CaptDrlTm; HonRl; NatlFornLg; NHS; NatlThespSoc; SchMus; SpnCl; MthCl; Ky U.

RUTKOWSKI, Cynthia A; Joliet West HS; Joliet, IL; 12/537 HonRl; NHS; Lewis Univ; Medicine.

RUTLEDGE, Jean; Adel HS; Adel, IA; VPJrCls; Band; CncrtBnd; HonRl; MrchBnd; Yrbk; SchPpr; FrCl; Glf; Univ; Natural Sciences.

RUTLEDGE, Joseph L; North Greene HS; White Hall, IL; Chrs; CmntyWkr; PolWkr; SchMus; Mac Murray; Chemistry.

RUTLEDGE, Pamela; Excelsior Springs West HS; Kansas City, MO; 8/225 Chr; HonRl; JrNHS; NHS; PolWkr; Quill&Scroll; StuCncl; EdYrBk; FrCl; College.

RUTLEDGE, Steven R; Kickapoo HS; Springfield, MO; ChrhWkr; HonRl; OffAde; SchMus; SctActv; KeyCl; Bsktbl; LetterFtbl; IMSpt; CitAwd; Clge; Civil Eng.

RUTLEDGE, Timothy C; Clearwater Pub HS; Clearwater, NE; 2/14 PresSrCls; ALBoysSt; Chr; HonRl; SctActv; StuCncl; StuGov; LetterFtbl; LetterTrk; LetterWrstlng; College; Civil Engineering.

RUTT, Leslea C; Metropolis Comm HS; Metropolis, IL; Band; HonRl; HospAde; SchPl; SctActv; Yrbk; GerCl; MthCl; PpCl; Us Air Force; Photography.

RUTTAN, Cheryl; Dondero HS; Royal Oak, MI; 2/540 HonRl; LbryAde; ModUN; NHS; NatlThespSoc; PolWkr; SchPl; BttyCrckrAwd; Oakland Univ; Librarian.

RUTTENBERG, Donna L; Maine Twp East HS; Morton Grove, IL; CmntyWkr; HonRl; NatlMeritCmnd; SchMus; StuGov; TchrAde; National College Of Educ; Teacher.

RUTZEN, Janel E; Hubbard Comm HS; Hubbard, IA; 6/43 HonRl; JA; NHS; NatlMeritSF; StuCncl; RptrYrbk; FBLA; Chrldr; 4-HAwd; JAAwd; American Inst Of Bus; Accountant.

RUUD, Mitchell T; Northwood Public HS; Northwood, ND; ALBoysSt; ChrhWkr; CmntyWkr; HonRl; StuCncl; LetterFtbl; CchngActv; Univ; Business Admin.

RUYLE, Enid G; Berkeley Sr HS; Berkeley, MO; ChrhWkr; HonRl; NatlFornLg; NHS; SchPl; StuCncl; StuGov; Twrl; FNA; College; Biology.

RUZEVICH, Donna J; J S Morton East HS; Cicero, IL; 34/771 Chr; HonRl; JrNHS; NHS; Orch; SchMus; SchPl; 4-H; Univ Of Ill; Hs Orchestra Director.

RUZIC, David N; Rogers HS; Beverly Shores, IN; ALBoysSt; Band; Chr; HonRl; JrNHS; NHS; NatlMeritSF; Orch; SchPl; SctActv; Ftbl; LetterSwmmng; Purdue University; Physicist.

RUZICH, Cynthia G; Pittsfield HS; Pittsfield, IL; Band; Chrs; CncrtBnd; HonRl; LbryAde; MrchBnd; PepBnd; SchMus; StuGov; LatCl; College; Nursing.

RUZICH, Jeffery V; Libertyville HS; Libertyville, IL; 28/485 ChrhWkr; HonRl; JrNHS; ChmnNHS; SchPl; VPStuCncl; PresYthFlsp; Swmmng; United State Naval Academy; Engineering.

RUZICKA, Douglas J; Silver Lake HS; Silver Lake, MN; 10/56 Band; CncrtBnd; HonRl; MrchBnd; PepBnd; Vocational Schl; Technician.

RUZICKA, James P; Scottsbluff Senior HS; Scottsbluff, NE; LetterLetterTrk; LetterWrstlng; Dickinson State College; Physical Education.

RUZICKA, Karen; Rosati Kain HS; St Louis, MO; 1/112 Chrs; NHS; NatlThespSoc; SchMus; SchPl; Yrbk; St Louis Univ; Biology Ecology.

RUZICKA, Theresa; Acad Of The Visitation; St Louis, MO; 6/41 NHS; HstFrshCls; SchPl; StuCncl; Yrbk; PpCl; Bsktbl; GAA; IMSpt; St Louis Univ; Account.

RYALS, Racinda L; Southern Boone R 1 HS; Hartsburg, MO; 3/44 SecJrCls; TrsJrCls; Chr; HonRl; NHS; OffAde; Quill&Scroll; SchPl; StuCncl; YthFlsp; EdYrBk; PpCl; LetterTrk; Chrldr; Central Missouri St University.

RYAN, Anna M; Maple Lake HS; Maple Alke, MN; 9/57 SecSrCls; Chrs; HonRl; MrchBnd; NHS; StuCncl; SchPpr; FHA; PpCl; PPFtbl; St Cloud Bus Col; Court Reporting.

RYAN, Barbara J; Horace Mann HS; Biwabik, MN; Band; Chr; ChrhWkr; MrchBnd; NatlFornLg; PepBnd; SchPl; RptrYrbk; EdSchPpr; Business College; Court Reporting.

RYAN, Blane P; North Side HS; Ft Wayne, IN; AFS; CmntyWkr; HonRl; JrNHS; ModUN; NHS; NatlMeritCmnd; StuCncl; UNYO; YthLg; Indiana U; Medicine.

RYAN, Cynthia K; Oak Park HS; Kansas City, MO; 5/602 HonRl; StuCncl; TchrAde; Univ Of Missouri; Medical Technology.

RYAN, Daniel E; Kewaskum HS; Kewaskum, WI; Chrs; HonRl; SchMus; SchPl; RptrYrbk; RptrSchPpr; SchPpr; Bsktbl; Ftbl; Glf; U Of Wi Oshkosh; Professnl.

RYAN, David J; Plattsmouth HS; Murray, NE; Band; CncrtBnd; MrchBnd; PepBnd; SchMus; TchrAde; FBLA; MthCl; College; Accounting.

RYAN, Diane G; Pontiac HS; Pontiac, IL; 20/194 ChrhWkr; CmntyWkr; HonRl; IntrClCncl; StuCncl; Teen; Yrbk; FTA; SpnCl; MthCl; PpCl; Northern Ill Univ; Interior Designer.

RYAN, Douglas R; Lawton Bronson Comm HS; Bronson, IA; .

RYAN, James; Oak Lawn Comm HS; Oak Lawn, IL; College; Business.

RYAN, James F; Winola HS; Viola, IL; 16/65 ChrhWkr; CmntyWkr; HonRl; Sacrstn; SctActv; SptEdSchPpr; SchPpr; 4-H; FFA; PpCl; Bsktbl; Ftbl; IMSpt; College; Agriculture.

RYAN, Jeffrey R; Alton Senior HS; Alton, IL; Band; Chrs; CncrtBnd; HonRl; MrchBnd; NHS; Coe College Afrotc; Air Force Officer.

RYAN, John; Marist Hs; Oak Lawn, IL; 30 ChrhWkr; CmntyWkr; HonRl; NHS; NatlMeritCmnd; SchMus; Teen; SchPpr; PresFrCl; Trk; U Of Notre Dame;business Administration.

RYAN, Kathleen R; Campbellsport HS; Campbellsport, WI; 11/150 AFS; CmntyWkr; HonRl; NHS; RptrSchPpr; SchPpr; SpnCl; LetterTrk; GAA; Morane Park Tech; Accountant.

RYAN, Linda K; Palestine HS; Palestine, IL; 1/48 SecTrsSophCls; SecSrCls; Band; Chr; Chrs; ChrhWkr; IMSpt; ChmbCommrsAwd; DanFAwd; 4-HAwd; University.

RYAN, Lisa A; Elmhurst HS; Fort Wayne, IN; JA; TchrAde; College; Social Work Field.

RYAN, Lori L; Larimore HS; Emerado, ND; Chrs; ChrhWkr; HonRl; HospAde; MrchBnd; SchAde; YthFlsp; 4-H; SpnCl; PpCl; Univ Of North Dakota; Physical Therapist.

RYAN, Mary; Richland Center HS; Richland Center, WI; Band; CncrtBnd; DrmMjrt; HonRl; StuCncl; Twrl; RptrYrbk; PpCl; Trk; Chrldr; College; Prof.

RYAN, Mary A; Webster City HS; Webster City, IA; SchPl; Sec4-H; FHA; PpCl; Glf; 4-HAwd; College.

RYAN, Mary E; St Edmond HS; Fort Dodge, IA; TrsFrshCls; StuCncl; YthFlsp; PresSpnCl; PpCl; Chrldr; IMSpt; BttyCrckrAwd; Creighton Univ; Social Work.

RYAN, Mary T; Elizabeth Seton HS; Thornton, IL; 37/250 HonRl; VPNHS; Orch; SchMus; SchPl; StuCncl; FrCl; Art Institute Of Chgo; Art.

RYAN, Michael C; Kingsford HS; Kingsford, MI; 23/160 HonRl; Bsbl; LetterBsktbl; LetterFtbl; LetterTennis; Ferris State College; Pharmacy.

RYAN, Michele; Hillsdale HS; Hillsdale, MI; TrsSophCls; Band; HonRl; MrchBnd; NHS; Orch; StuCncl; PpCl; GAA; Business School; Executive Secretary.

RYAN, Monica A; Carmel Girls HS; Lake Forest, IL; 8/190 Chrs; HonRl; NHS; StuCncl; St Marys Of Notre Dame; Business.

RYAN, Myrtle K; Soldan HS; St Louis, MO; 6/607 Chrs; ChrhWkr; CmntyWkr; DrlTm; HonRl; NHS; FBLA; PpCl; College; Nursing.

RYAN, Pat T; Drummond HS; Cable, WI; 37#39#41 MrchBnd; NHS; Bsktbl; Ftbl; Trk; Wrstlng; IMSpt; Coll; Med.

RYAN, Paula R; East Chanas Mix HS; Wagner, SD; Chrs; DrlTm; FHA; LetterBsktbl; LetterTrk; South Dakota St Univ; Law.

RYAN, Randy L; Casey Junior Senior HS; Casey, IL; 1/96 HonRl; JrNHS; RptrYrbk; Treas4-H; VPFFA; IMSpt; DanFAwd; 4-HAwd; Lake Land Junior Clg; Agriculture Manage.

RYAN, Renee K; Prairie Community HS; Gowrie, IA; Chrs; ChrhWkr; HonRl; VPFrshCls; StuCncl; FrCl; Bsktbl; Glf; College; English.

RYAN, Robert C; West Chicago Comm HS; Winfield, IL; 77/311 HonRl; 4-H; FrCl; CaptTennis; Northern Illinois Univ; Accountant.

RYAN, Susan A; Fonda Comm HS; Fonda, IA; CncrtBnd; MrchBnd; PepBnd; SchPl; Twrl; 4-H; FHA; GerCl; IMSpt; PPFtbl; University; Accounting.

RYAN, Susan M; Marquette Sr HS; Marquette, MI; 10/450 Band; ChrhWkr; CncrtBnd; HonRl; MrchBnd; Northern Michigan Univ; Chemistry.

RYAN, Vincent A; Glencoe HS; Glencoe, MN; 9/141 ALBoysSt; HonRl; NatlMeritCmnd; PresStuCncl; SciCl; LetterFtbl; LetterTrk; LetterWrstlng; IMSpt; Univ; Aeronautical Engineering.

RYAN, Warren; Haven HS; Haven, KS; 8/93 ALBoysSt; Band; Chr; Chrl; Chrs; CncrtBnd; HonRl; SchMus; SchPl; Widhita State Univ; Psychology.

RYBA, Christine C; Our Lady Of Mercy HS; Detroit, MI; ModUN; NatlFornLg; NHS; NatlMeritSchl; SchMus; SchPl; RptrSchPpr; LatCl; SciCl; VoiceDemAwd; U Of Mich; Law.

RYBA, Michael C; Michigan HS; Michigan, ND; Band; CncrtBnd; MrchBnd; PepBnd; FFA; LetterFtbl; Trk;.

RYBACK, Kenneth; Holy Cross Hs; Franklin Park, IL; 8/342 HonRl; NHS; RptrSchPpr; LatCl; Bsbl; Tennis; AmLegAwd; St Marys College; Medicine.

RYBACKI, Susan C; Nicolet HS; Milwaukee, WI; 66/529 ChrhWkr; NHS; TchrAde; Univ Of Wis Milwaukee; Sociology.

RYBAK, Sandra; Nazareth Academy; Brookfield, IL; LbryAde; NHS; Yrbk; FrCl; University; Law.

RYBICKI, Richard L; Roosevelt HS; Wyandotte, MI; HonRl; NatlMeritCmnd; SchPl; Tennis; Univ Mi; Doctor.

RYBIN, Janice; Daniel J Gross HS; Bellevue, NE; 12/163 CmntyWkr; HonRl; NHS; SchAde; SciCl; IMSpt; Univ Of Neb; Photo.

RYBINSKI, Susan L; Frank Cody HS; Detroit, MI; ChrhWkr; HonRl; LbryAde; NHS; OffAde; SchAde; MthCl; SciCl; Henry Ford Comm Coll.

RYBKA, Sophie; Notre Dame HS; Chicago, IL; HonRl; College; Medicine.

RYBURN, Kimberly J; Leroy HS; Ellsworth, IL; 3/68 VPJrCls; SecSrCls; Chrs; HonRl; JrNHS; NHS; StuCncl; 4-H; 4-HAwd; Arizona State Univ; Maj In Social Welfare.

RYCHWALSKI, Kenneth M; Austin Catholic Prep; St Clair Shores, MI; 32/115 HonRl; LetterTennis; College; English.

RYCKMAN, Debra K; Laurel HS; Laurel, IN; SecTrsFrshCls; Chrs; DrlTm; HonRl; StuCncl; TchrAde; Twrl; RptrSchPpr; PpCl; Dancing Instructor.

RYCZEK, Shirley; All Saints Central HS; Bay City, MI; CmntyWkr; HonRl; SchMus; SchPl; SctActv; SpnCl; PpCl; College; Medicine.

RYDEN, Beth J; Kennedy Public HS; Kennedy, MN; 4/27 PresJrCls; Chrs; HonRl; RptrYrbk; FHA; Univ Of North Dakota; Stewardess.

RYDEN, Nancy L; Neenah Armstrong HS; Neenah, WI; 10/600 HonRl; LitMag; NatlMeritFnl; SchMus; SchPl; RptrSchPpr; Coll; Soc Sci.

RYDER, Frank W; Libertyville HS; Libertyville, IL; HonRl; SctActv; GerCl; Bsktbl; Univ Of Ill; Lawyer.

RYE, Brian G; Baltic HS; Renner, SD; HstJrCls; Chrs; ChrhWkr; CmntyWkr; LbryAde; SchMus; StuCncl; PresFFA; LetterTrk; Carpentry.

RYE, Pamela J; Minnesota Public HS; Porter, MN; Band; HonRl; MrchBnd; RptrSchPpr; EdSchPpr; FHA; Vocational Schl; Medicine.

RYE, Timothy W; Stephenson HS; Wallace, MI; ChrhWkr; HonRl; NatlMeritSchl; Bay Denoc College; Electric Engineer.

RYERSON, Dave A; Ripon HS; Ripon, WI; HonRl; Bsbl; Bsktbl; Ftbl; College.

RYGH, Annette K; Turtle Lake Mercer Public HS; Turtle Lake, ND; SecSophCls; ALAGirlsSt; Chrl; HonRl; SchPl; SecStuCncl; YthFlsp; EdYrBk; PpCl; Trk; College; Medical Secretary.

RYGIEL, Richard J; Univ Of Detroit HS; Dearborn Hts, MI; 13/203 Chrs; CmntyWkr; HonRl; NatlFornLg; NHS; StuGov; EdSchPpr; SciCl; IMSpt; Medical School; Medicine.

RYHERD, Sandra K; Sullivan HS; Sullivan, IL; 26/106 Band; Yrbk; FTA; Lakeland College; Dental Hygienist.

RYKAL, Douglas A; Cadott HS; Cadott, WI; TrsJrCls; VPSrCls; ALBoysSt; Band; CncrtBnd; MrchBnd; PepBnd; CaptBsbl; CaptBsktbl; U Of Wi; Teaching.

RYKER, Chris A; Batesville HS; Oldenburg, IN; 25/160 HonRl; NHS; SciCl; Univ; Business.

RYKOVICH, Susan M; Andrean HS; Gary, IN; 4/250 ChrhWkr; CmntyWkr; HonRl; StuCncl; StuGov; RptrYrbk; MthCl; GAA; IMSpt; PPFtbl; University; Mathematics.

RYLANDER, Dave J; Rova HS; Oneida, IL; Band; Chr; HonRl; MrchBnd; PepBnd; 4-H; College; Agriculture.

RYLANDER, Debora K; Onarga HS; Onarga, IL; 3/22 VPJrCls; Chrs; HonRl; NHS; NatlThespSoc; SchPl; Yrbk; FHA; Trk; CaptChrldr; University; Professional.

RYLKO, Edward M; Gordon Tech HS; Chicago, IL; 11/661 ChrhWkr; CncrtBnd; HonRl; MrchBnd; NHS; SchMus; SctActv; Northwestern Univ; Math Major.

RYMARCZYK, Ellen S; T F South HS; Lansing, IL; 3/565 Chr; HonRl; JrNHS; NHS; OffAde; LetterTennis; PresGAA; Univ Of Illinois; Law.

RYMISZEWSKI, Theresa A; St Ladislaus HS; Detroit, MI; 7/127 CmntyWkr; HonRl; JA; SctActv; SecStuCncl; FBLA; FNA; LetterTrk; Chrldr; JAAwd; College.

RYMPH, Carol; El Dorada HS; El Dorado, KS; 8/182 Band; ChrhWkr; HonRl; VPFrshCls; NatlFornLg; YthFlsp; FHA; GerCl; PpCl; VoiceDemAwd; Southwestern Col; Medicine.

RYNAZEWSKI, Joyce M; Daniel J Gross HS; Omaha, NE; 21/170 HonRl; NHS; Nursing Schl; Nursing.

RYNER, Anthony J; Waterford Twnsp HS; Pontiac, MI; HstSophCls; HstJrCls; HonRl; RptrYrbk; Glf; VoiceDemAwd; U Of Mi; Law.

RYNISH, Karen P; Carmel For Girls HS; Round Lake, IL; 8/173 HonRl; LbryAde; NHS; FrCl; VPMthCl; Marquette University; Speech Pathology.

RYSAVY, Renee; Owatonna HS; Owatonna, MN; 34/317 Chr; Chrs; HonRl; Orch; Quill&Scroll; SchPl; TchrAde; RptrSchPpr; SchPpr; SpnCl; Mankato St Coll; Mass Communications.

RYSCHON, Kay L; Valentine HS; Valentine, NE; 1/75 SecJrCls; TrsJrCls; HonRl; NHS; StuCncl; YthFlsp; SpnCl; PpCl; SciCl; IMSpt;.

RYSTROM, Lynne B; Frederick HS; Frederick, SD; ChrhWkr; HonRl; StuCncl; Bsktbl; Chrldr; College; Professional.

RYSTROM, Nancy A; Anoka Sr HS; Anoka, MN; Chr; CncrtBnd; HonRl; JrNHS; MrchBnd; NHS; NatlMeritSF; Orch; PepBnd; SchMus; EdSchPpr; 4-H; 4-HAwd; College.

RYTERSKI, James R; St John The Baptist HS; St Louis, MO; 11/88 ChrhWkr; CmntyWkr; HonRl; SchMus; TchrAde; IMSpt; CitAwd; Univ Of Mo; Vet.

RYTI, Valerie K; Cosmos HS; Cosmos, MN; TrsFrshCls; Band; Chr; Chrs; ChrhWkr; CncrtBnd; HonRl; 4-H; FHA; PpCl; Bsktbl; CaptTrk; Chrldr; GAA; Willmar Comm College; Music.

RZEPCZYNSKI, Mark S; Marist HS; Chicago, IL; 7/390 HonRl; NHS; SchMus; SchPl; Yrbk; RptrSchPpr; 4-H; 4-HAwd; Purdue U; Chemical Engineer.

RZEPINSKI, Jeffrey J; St John Cathedral HS; Milwaukee, WI; Chrs; ChrhWkr; HonRl; Sacrstn; SctActv; YthFnd; RptrSchPpr; Ftbl; CchngActv; College; Professional.

RZEPKA, Cynthia M; Lourdes HS; Chicago, IL; HonRl; SctActv;.

RZEPKA, Gregory S; St Clement HS; Centerline, MI; 8/97 HonRl; SciCl; Bsbl; Bsktbl; IMSpt; OptClAwd; College; Chem Engr.

RZEPKA, Michael M; St Patrick HS; Chicago, IL; 31/441 HonRl; JrNHS; SciCl; LetterTrk; Univ Of Ill; Med Tech.

RZYHAK, Suzanne G; Port Austin Public HS; Port Austin, MI; 3/39 SecJrCls; VPSrCls; HonRl; SchMus; VPStuCncl; YthFnd; Yrbk; SchPpr; FHA; Bsktbl; LetterChrldr;.

S

SAAGER, Laura L; Bloomington HS; Bloomington, IL; 33/391 Chr; HonRl; Mdrgl; NHS; StuCncl; TchrAde; LatCl; MthCl; PpCl; Chrldr; Ill Wesleyan University; Medicine.

SAALE, Mary A; Chillicothe HS; Chillicothe, MO; ChrhWkr; HonRl; FTA; LatCl; LetterTrk; Chrldr; GAA; IMSpt; GodCntryAwd; PresAwd; University; Pharmacist.

SAALE, Thomas C; Marquette HS; Alton, IL; 3/116 HonRl; JrNHS; NHS; CaptBsbl; Bsktbl; Ftbl; CaptTrk; CaptWrstlng; Washington University; Medicine.

SAALFELD, Kelly D; Lakeview HS; Columbus, NE; TrsSophCls; Chrl; ChrhWkr; HonRl; Mdrgl; TchrAde; MthCl; LetterBsktbl; LetterFtbl; LetterTrk; Univ Of Ne; Agricultural Ec.

SAATHOFF, Daniel L; Amherst Public HS; Miller, NE; Band; Chr; Chrs; ChrhWkr; CncrtBnd; HonRl; MrchBnd; NHS; PepBnd; SchMus; CaptBsbl; Bsktbl; CaptFtbl; Swmmng; College.

SAATHOFF, Steve M; Norris HS; Cortland, NE; ALBoysSt; Band; ChrhWkr; CmntyWkr; CncrtBnd; MrchBnd; PepBnd; SchPl; TchrAde; Ftbl; College; Professional.

SABANSKI, Brenda K; Eastbrook HS; Fairmount, IN; 11/169 HstSrCls; TreasBand; ChrhWkr; HonRl; MrchBnd; NHS; 4-H; SpnCl; PpCl; Chrldr; College; Special Ed Teacher.

SABATKE, Robin K; Lakeland HS; Lac Du Flambeau, WI; Band; Chr; CmntyWkr; CncrtBnd; NHS; RptrSchPpr; SpnCl; Trk; Chrldr; GAA;.

SABEL, Betsy; Shawnee Mission South HS; Leawood, KS; HonRl; OffAde; SchMus; TchrAde; PpCl; Trk; IMSpt; PPFtbl; Kansas Univ;.

SABEL, Charles; New Holstein HS; Malone, WI; 4-H; Wrstlng; Univ Of Wi; Agriculture.

SABEL, Joanne M; Lowell P Goodrich HS; Fond Du Lac, WI; Aud/Vis; Chrs; CmntyWkr; HonRl; JA; NHS; 4-H; GerCl; TIMEAwd; JAAwd; U Of Wis Oshkosh; Spec Ed Tchr.

SABEL, Mark H; Ripon 'S; Ripon, WI; 4-H; FFA; Trade School; Vocation.

SABEL, Michael A; Ripon Senior HS; Ripon, WI; 7/173 ChrhWkr; HonRl; NatlFornLg; NHS; TreasYthFlsp; PresFFA; LetterBsbl; Bsktbl; KiwanAwd; CitAwd; U Of Wi Madison; Agriculture Teacher.

SABELL, Robert G; Taylor Center HS; Taylor, MI; ChrhWkr; HonRl; NHS; CitAwd; Coll; Engi.

SABIN, Kenneth; Armstrong Comm HS; Armstrong, IA; TrsFrshCls; HonRl; SchPl; SctActv; StuCncl; CchngActv; IMSpt; Service.

SABIN, Tammy L; Malden HS; Princeton, IL; 1/15 ChrhWkr; CmntyWkr; HonRl; HospAde; RedCrAde; StuCncl; YthFlsp; 4-H; PpCl; GAA; University; Nursing.

SABINA, Mary Ann E; Marian Heights Acad; Marion, IN; PresSrCls; Chrs; HonRl; NHS; SchMus; SchPl; Sdlty; StuCncl; Tennis; GAA; St Joseph Sch Of Nur; Nurse.

SABLICH, Kathryn M; Muskego HS; Hales Corners, WI; TrsSrCls; AFS; NHS; SchPl; SctActv; StuCncl; RptrYrbk; SciCl; U Of Wis Milwakee; Art.

SABLICH, Michael L; Muskego HS; Hales Corners, WI; Glf; LetterSwmmng; Clg; Forestry.

SABOURN, Scott; Bay City Central HS; Bay City, MI; Band; HonRl; Teen; Central Mi Univ; Medicine.

SABRES, Cynthia A; Resurrection HS; Chicago, IL; 59/294 CmntyWkr; HonRl; HospAde; CchngActv; GAA; Col; Pro.

SABYAN, Elyssa A; Herbert Henry Dow HS; Midland, MI; CmntyWkr; OffAde; SchAde; TchrAde; VPEngCl; Swmmng; Trk; PPFtbl; Mich State U.

SACEVIC, Carol A; Mt Assisi Acad; Chicago, IL; ChrhWkr; CmntyWkr; HonRl; JrNHS; NHS; StuCncl; StuGov; SchPpr; SpnCl; GAA; St Xavier College; Surgical Nursing.

SACEVIC, Carol A; Mt Assisi Academy; Chicago, IL; TrsJrCls; SecSrCls; Chr; Chrs; ChrhWkr; CmntyWkr; HonRl; HospAde; JrNHS; NHS; SchAde; SchMus; SchPl; StuCncl; StuGov; St Xavier College; Nursing.

SACHA, Cynthia M; St Andrew HS; Detroit, MI; 4/110 PresSophCls; HonRl; NHS; SecStuCncl; StuGov; Yrbk; PpCl; LetterBsktbl; IMSpt; OptClAwd; Bus Admin.

SACHS, Edward A; Plattsmouth HS; Plattsmouth, NE; 8/133 Chr; Chrs; ChrhWkr; HonRl; SchPl; YthFlsp; YthLg; 4-H; MthCl; Bsbl; Bsktbl; IMSpt; Univ Of Nebraska; Mechanical Engineer.

SACHS, Jean L; Plattsmouth HS; Plattsmouth, NE; 11/163 DrlTm; HonRl; OffAde; YthFlsp; Pres4-H; FTA; SpnCl; PpCl; Glf; PPFtbl; DARAwd; 4-HAwd; MasAwd; College; Art.

SACHS, Kathleen M; Wentzville HS; Wentzville, MO; Band; Chrs; HonRl; NHS; StuCncl; RptrSchPpr; PpCl; Trk; GAA; OptClAwd; Clge; Music Or Language.

SACHSE, Mary H; Immaculata HS; Leavenworth, KS; 3/55 SecJrCls; Chr; HonRl; PresStuCncl; RptrSchPpr; 4-H; SecPpCl; 4-HAwd; CitAwd; VoiceDemAwd; Benedictine College; Special Education.

SACIA, Denise K; Holmen HS; Holmen, WI; 6/98 Band; Chr; Chrs; ChrhWkr; CncrtBnd; HonRl; MrchBnd; NHS; PepBnd; FHA; Western Wisconsin Tech Inst; Retailing.

SACIA, Mary J; Gale Eltmek Trempeauliau HS; Galesville, WI; Chr; ChrhWkr; HonRl; SctActv; YthFlsp; FrCl; SciCl; LetterTrk; Chrldr; GAA; U Of Wi; Therapeutical Recreation.

SACK, Paula; Sully Buttes HS; Onida, SD; 5/55 Chr; ChrhWkr; HonRl; NHS; Quill&Scroll; SchPl; StuCncl; RptrSchPpr; PpCl; Chrldr; College.

SACKETT, Dave L; Menasha HS; Menasha, WI; Aud/Vis; Quill&Scroll; SchPpr; SpnCl; MthCl; SciCl; LetterFtbl; Tech Inst; Police.

SACKETT, Mark; Grand Rapids Senior HS; Grand Rapids, MN; 42/377 Band; Chr; ChrhWkr; HonRl; PepBnd; SchPl; StuGov; TchrAde; IMSpt; Itasca Jr College; Medicine.

SACKMAN, Ricky L; South County Tech HS; St Louis, MO; Aud/Vis; HonRl; SctActv; Bsbl; Socr; PresAwd; Bell And Howell Sch; Electronics.

SACKS, Jeffrey A; Roger C Sullivan HS; Chicago, IL; 56/276 HonRl; OffAde; StuCncl; RptrYrbk; RptrSchPpr; SptEdSchPpr; CivCl; KeyCl; Tennis; Univ Of Ill; Law.

SADE, Marcus; Churubusco HS; Churubusco, IN; PresSrCls; HonRl; StuCncl; Wrstlng; IMSpt; Univ; Life Science.

SADEK, Joseph P; North Central HS; Rogers, ND; 14/30 Band; Chr; CmntyWkr; HonRl; LetterBsktbl; LetterFtbl; LetterTrk; North Dakota State Univ; Electrical Eng.

SADEK, Paul C; Stillwater HS; Stillwater, MN; 10/603 ALBoysSt; Chr; CncrtBnd; SecTrsFrshCls; HonRl; JrNHS; NHS; NatlMeritCmnd; Socr; Tennis; OptClAwd; Carleton Col; Research Chemist.

SADLER, Amy L; Cobden HS; Cobden, IL; Chrs; ChrhWkr; LbryAde; OffAde; TchrAde; FHA; PpCl; Socr; Coll; Secretary.

SADLER, Cathy; Chaffee HS; Chaffee, MO; 17/70 TrsFrshCls; Chr; HonRl; NHS; FHA; PpCl; Chrldr; Univ; Professional.

SADLER, Jack W; Valley HS; Belgrade, MO; PresSrCls; Band; Chrs; CncrtBnd; HonRl; NHS; PepBnd; TchrAde; Mineral Area Col; Radio Broadcasting.

SADLER, Marla M; Maysville HS; Amity, MO; 15/73 Chr; ChrhWkr; HonRl; NHS; OffAde; SchPl; 4-H; FHA;.

SADLER, Sandra L; Maine West HS; Des Plaines, IL; DrlTm; HonRl; NatlThespSoc; OffAde; SchMus; SchPl; StuCncl;.

SADOWSKI, Theresa; Regina HS; Detroit, MI; ALAGirlsSt; ChrhWkr; DrlTm; HonRl; IntrClCncl; PolWkr; SctActv; TchrAde; RptrSchPpr; EdSchPpr;.

SADOWY, Carol A; Sandusky HS; Applegate, MI; 23/114 CtyCnl; CAP; HospAde; RedCrAde; StuGov; UNYO; Bsktbl; Chrldr; 4-HAwd; GovHonPrgAwd; Ferris State College; Medical Assistant.

SADZAK, Kathleen M; Thornton Fractional South HS; Lansing, IL; 19/552 HonRl; NHS; OffAde; SchAde; FrCl; College; Professional.

SAEGER, Martha A; Northwest HS; House Springs, MO; 2/375 Chr; ChrhWkr; LitMag; LbryAde; NHS; TchrAde; RptrYrbk; RptrSchPpr; TreasFBLA; EldAwd; St Pauls College; Business.

SAETHRE, David H; Maine East HS; Niles, IL; ChrhWkr; HonRl; Trk; CchngActv; University; Directing.

SAFFOLD, David J; North Divison HS; Milwaukee, WI; VPBand; CncrtBnd; HonRl; VPJA; MrchBnd; ℥AAwd; Coll; Prof.

SAFFOLD, Venettia E; Proviso East HS; Maywood, IL; 166/1001 HonRl; TchrAde; KiwanAwd; U Of Ill; Microbiogist.

SAGAMI, Donna E; Rich South HS; Richton Park, IL; 29/285 VPSophCls; Chr; HonRl; NatlFornLg; PolWkr; Quill&Scroll; StuCncl; RptrSchPpr; SchPpr; Univ Of Illinois.

SAGATAW, Connee A; Bark River Harris HS; Harris, MI; 10/55 SecFrshCls; SecJrCls; HonRl; JA; NHS; SchPl; Yrbk; 4-H; FrCl; PpCl; Bsbl; Bsktbl; College; Social Work.

SAGE, Laura K; Waukegan HS; Park City, IL; ChrhWkr; HonRl; LitMag; NatlFornLg; 4-H; FTA; LatCl; AmLegAwd; College; Teacher.

SAGE, Melissa J; Denver Community HS; Waterloo, IA; 1/78 PresFrshCls; ChrhWkr; HonRl; NatlMeritFnl; NatlMeritSchl; YthFlsp; Yrbk; 4-H; BauchLmbAwd; 4-HAwd; Iowa St Univ; Math.

SAGE, Randall L; Bradley Bourbonnais Comm HS; Bourbonnais, IL; 7/369 Chr; Chrs; HonRl; JrNHS; Mdrgl; NHS; SchMus; RptrSchPpr; SpnCl; Univ Of Ill; Astrophysics.

SAGER, Brian D; High School; New Richmond, WI; AFS; Aud/Vis; ChrhWkr; CmntyWkr; LbryAde; NatlMeritSchl; SchPl; StuCncl; StuGov; RptrYrbk; Univ Of Wisconsin; Business.

SAGER, Darlene F; Orangeville Community HS; Dakota, IL; Chrs; HonRl; SchMus; TreasYthFlsp; Sec4-H; FBLA; 4-HAwd; Collge; Occupational Therapist.

SAGER, Julie; Cahokia HS; Cahokia, IL; TrsJrCls; Band; HonRl; JrNHS; Quill&Scroll; StuCncl; StuGov; PpCl; Chrldr; PPFtbl; College; Vocation.

SAGER, Lora L; Paris HS; Paris, IL; 67/232 CncrtBnd; JA; SchPl; RptrYrbk; College; Sciences.

SAGER, Paul K; Deerfield HS; Highland Park, IL; Bsbl; Bsktbl; Socr; Swmmng; Trk; Wrstlng; CchngActv; IMSpt; JCAwd;.

SAGER, Shelly L; Savanna HS; Savanna, IL; 5/83 Band; CncrtBnd; DrmMjrt; HonRl; MrchBnd; PepBnd; SpnCl; PpCl; GAA; College; Music Teacher.

SAGGAU, Peter R; Grosse Pointe South HS; Grosse Pointe, MI; GerCl; LetterSwmmng; Trk; Wrstlng; Mich State U; Liberal Arts.

SAGMAN, Barbara S; Zeeland HS; Zeeland, MI; Chr; HonRl;.

SAGORSKI, Jean M; Cedar Springs HS; Cedar Springs, MI; CmntyWkr; HonRl; JrNHS; NHS; NatlMeritSF; TchrAde; FHA; Mercy Central; Nurse.

SAGORSKI, Mary R; Tri County HS; Sand Lake, MI; 2/95 SecJrCls; SecSrCls; CncrtBnd; MrchBnd; NHS; PepBnd; StuCncl; Yrbk; Bsktbl; IMSpt; College; Mathematics.

SAHA, Julie A; Pinconning HS; Pinconning, MI; HonRl; SctActv; FNA; FTA; FrCl; LetterTrk; PPFtbl; College; Nursing.

SAHLI, Julia A; Sauk Centre Sr HS; Sauk Centre, MN; 7/160 Band; CncrtBnd; HonRl; MrchBnd; Yrbk; RptrSchPpr; LetterTrk; GAA; IMSpt; PresAwd; College; Professional.

SAHLI, Teresa J; Napoleon HS; Napoleon, ND; 4/61 ALAGirlsSt; CmntyWkr; HonRl; NHS; StuCncl; EdYrBk; RptrSchPpr; 4-H; PpCl; LetterBsktbl; Univ; Prof.

SAHNOW, Kenneth A; Hudson HS; Hudson, WI; Band; ChrhWkr; CncrtBnd; HonRl; LbryAde; MrchBnd; PepBnd; SctActv; VPGerCl; Swmmng; College.

SAHR, Gayle S; Reese HS; Saginaw, MI; 1/127 Band; ChrhWkr; NHS; NatlMeritSF; PepBnd; SchPl; RptrYrbk; Trk; ChmnChrldr; DARAwd; Ferris State; Respiratory Therapy.

SAILER, Joan M; Hill City HS; Hill City, MN; 7/28 ALAGirlsSt; Band; ChrhWkr; CncrtBnd; HonRl; PepBnd; RedCrAde; StuCncl; TchrAde; Bsktbl; St Cloud St Univ; Phy Educ.

SAILER, Shelly J; Perry Comm HS; Perry, IA; 1/160 Band; CncrtBnd; HonRl; MrchBnd; NHS; NatlThespSoc; SchMus; SchPl; SpnCl; KiwanAwd; College; Phy Science.

SAILER, Thomas L; Stanton HS; Stanton, ND; 1/17 HonRl; NHS; RptrYrbk; RptrSchPpr; LetterFtbl; Tech; Electronics.

SAILOR, Connie J; Frankfort Sr HS; Frankfort, IN; 36/242 DrlTm; ROTC; RptrYrbk; VPFHA; SpnCl; Ball State University; Home Economics.

SAILOR, Scott D; Albia Comm HS; Albia, IA; 3/150 PresFrshCls; SecJrCls; ALBoysSt; Aud/Vis; HonRl; Quill&Scroll; SchPl; StuCncl; EdYrBk; Bsbl; Bsktbl; Ftbl; College; Journalism.

SAILORS, Cindy A; Falls City HS; Falls City, NE; SecFrshCls; Chr; Chrs; ChrhWkr; DrlTm; NatlThespSoc; SchMus; YthFlsp; 4-H; GerCl; Trade Sch; Voc.

SAILORS, Randall E; Falls City HS; Falls City, NE; GerCl; Bsbl; Bsktbl; Ftbl; Trk; Southeast Comm College; Auto Body Tech.

SAILY, Darcy L; A D Johnston HS; Bessemer, MI; Band; Chr; ChrhWkr; HonRl; PepBnd; RptrYrbk; Yrbk; RptrSchPpr; 4-H; IMSpt; Suomi Clge In Hancock.

SAINE, Susan J; Ishpeming HS; Ishpeming, MI; 65/204 Band; ChrhWkr; Bsktbl; Swmmng; Trk; PPFtbl; Northern Mi U; Nurse.

SAJDAK, Margaret M; John F Kennedy HS; Chicago, IL; 15/610 ChrhWkr; HonRl; HospAde; PresNHS; OffAde; SchAde; TchrAde; 4-H; FrCl; 4-HAwd; Loyola Univ; Nursing.

SAJKO, Annette; Andrean HS; Gary, IN; ChrhWkr; CmntyWkr; HonRl; College; Business Field.

SAKAI, Daniel; Columbus North HS; Columbus, IN; 30/513 HonRl; ModUN; StuGov; SptEdSchPpr; SciCl; Ftbl; Glf; Socr; Swmmng; IMSpt; Pordue Univ; Act Scie Or Fin.

SAKARI, June; Hancock Central HS; Hancock, MI; ChrhWkr; HonRl; TchrAde; Business School; Secretary.

SAKO, Kenneth; Highland HS; Highland, IN; 120/600 Chrl; HonRl; ROTC; TchrAde; Trk; College; Engineering.

SAKOWSKY, Valerie M; Fitzgerald Sr HS; Warren, MI; Harper Hospital School; Nurse.

SALA, Lori L; Godwin Heights HS; Wyoming, MI; 7/186 ChrhWkr; HonRl; NHS; TchrAde; GAA; Col; Missions.

SALADA, David A; Lake Shore HS; St Clair Shores, MI; 7/741 CncrtBnd; HonRl; LbryAde; MrchBnd; NHS; TchrAde; FrCl; BauchLmbAwd; College; Engineering.

SALADINO, Mark J; Hononegah Comm HS; Roscoe, IL; 2/198 PresFrshCls; CncrtBnd; HonRl; NHS; PresNatlThespSoc; SchMus; SchPl; TreasStuCncl; Yrbk; SchPpr; Univ Of Ill; Commerce & Business Admin.

SALADINO, Sam J; Griffin HS; Springfield, IL; 45/192 SecJrCls; VPSrCls; HonRl; StuCncl; StuGov; KeyCl; Bsbl; Ftbl; CchngActv; Univ.

SALAK, Sheldon E; Rock Island HS; Rock Island, IL; 6/667 ChrhWkr; HonRl; NHS; Orch; SchMus; RptrSchPpr; FrCl; SciCl; Tennis; IMSpt; Augustana Coll; Acct.

SALAS, Sharlene J; Freeland HS; Freeland, MI; 5/123 Band; CncrtBnd; HonRl; MrchBnd; NHS; Orch; PepBnd; SchMus; SctActv; TchrAde; IMSpt; University; Music.

SALATA, Rosemarie D; Madonna HS; Chicago, IL; 67/273 ChrhWkr; HonRl; LbryAde; NatlFornLg; PolWkr; Loyola Univ; Business Admin.

SALATA, Wayne F; Gordon Technical HS; Chicago, IL; 71/661 HonRl; StuCncl; RptrSchPpr; MthCl; PpCl; SciCl; IMSpt; Devry Institute Of Tech; Elect Engineer.

SALAVA, Julie A; Grant Comm HS; Ingleside, IL; 2/199 Band; Chr; HonRl; Mdrgl; MrchBnd; NHS; NatlThespSoc; PepBnd; SchMus; SchPl; StuGov; GAA; North Ill Univ; Systems Analysis.

SALAY, Roberta A; Watervliet HS; Watervliet, MI; PresJrCls; PresSrCls; PresBand; CncrtBnd; HonRl; NHS; CaptBsbl; CaptBsktbl; Trk; Chrldr; U Of Mi; Architecture & Design.

SALBER, Doris J; Petersburg HS; Petersburg, NE; 4/25 VPFrshCls; Band; Chrs; HonRl; TchrAde; Yrbk; SchPpr; PpCl; LetterTrk; 4-HAwd; Tech Sch.

SALBERG, Karan R; Yankton Senior HS; Yankton, SD; Band; Chrs; CncrtBnd; MrchBnd; NatlThespSoc; SchPl; IMSpt; Orch; PepBnd; Chr; University; Professional.

SALDA, Michael; William Jennings Bryan HS; Omaha, NE; 2/403 ALBoysSt; CmntyWkr; HonRl; ModUN; NatlFornLg; NHS; StuCncl; Yrbk; SchPpr; Coll; Physics.

SALDIVAR, Raul; Axtell Comm HS; Axtell, NE; Bsbl; Ftbl; Trk; Wrstlng; Coll; Phy Ed.

SALE, Ann E; Manlius HS; Manlius, IL; 3/27 PresBand; Chrs; HonRl; NHS; Quill&Scroll; RptrYrbk; RptrSchPpr; VP4-H; PresFHA; TreasFrCl; Chrldr; GAA; 4-HAwd; Western Illinois Univ; Music.

SALE, Craig L; Moline HS; Moline, IL; 13/822 Band; Chr; NatlFornLg; NHS; NatlThespSoc; Orch; PolWkr; SchMus; SchPl; SchPpr; Northwestern U; Music.

SALEM, Doris P; Butterfield Odin HS; Butterfield, MN; S9#t16#2 SecSophCls; ChrhWkr; CmntyWkr; HonRl; LbryAde; SchPl; EdYrBk; FHA; Sioux Falls St; Nurse.

SALEMI, Daniel; Sycamore Hs; Sycamore, IL; 12/200 HonRl; LitMag; TchrAde; SpnCl; Bsktbl; U Of Illinois; Pharmacist.

SALEN, William T; Rich South HS; Park Forest, IL; 60/289 Band; HonRl; MrchBnd; Quill&Scroll; SchAde; TchrAde; Yrbk; RptrSchPpr; SptEdSchPpr; PresKeyCl; SpnCl; Bsbl; Bsktbl; Ftbl; Univ Of Illinois; Liberal Arts.

SALERNO, Chris J; Creighton Prep HS; Omaha, NE; HonRl; Bsktbl; College; Professional.

SALERNO, Mark A; Creighton Prep; Omaha, NE; HonRl; LetterWrstlng; College; Professional.

SALERNO, Martha A; Chippewa Valley HS; Mt Clemens, MI; Chr; CncrtBnd; DrmMjrt; HonRl; MrchBnd; ModUN; NHS; PepBnd; College; Pharmacy.

SALES, Cheryl A; Valley Falls HS; Valley Falls, KS; 1/38 SecSophCls; Band; Chrs; CncrtBnd; DrlTm; HonRl; MrchBnd; NHS; PepBnd; StuCncl; Teen; Pres4-H; CaptBsktbl; CchngActv; University; Business.

SALESIN, Cynthia; Southfield Lathrup HS; Southfield, MI; 70/670 HonRl; HospAde; NatlMeritCmnd; Univ; Nursing.

SALEWSKE, Sue; Redwood Falls HS; Redwood Falls, MN; 5/125 Band; CncrtBnd; HonRl; MrchBnd; NHS; PepBnd; SchMus; SchPl; Yrbk; GerCl; Mankato State College; Professional.

SALIKLIS, Dana M; Maria HS; Chicago, IL; 3/301 Chr; HonRl; NHS; SchPpr; VPFrCl; Univ Of Ill; Dentist.

SALINAS, Marie L; Bishop Noll Institute; East Chicago, IN; HonRl; VPJA; OffAde; SchAde; StuGov; YthFnd; IMSpt; Purdue Univ; Teacher.

SALINGER, Stephen F; Niles West HS; Morton Grove, IL; 20/676 Band; CncrtBnd; HonRl; MrchBnd; NHS; Orch; PepBnd; Northwestern Univ; Professional.

SALISBURY, Anne F; The Barstow HS; Kansas City, MO; Chr; Chrs; LitMag; NHS; SchPpr; Swmmng; DARAwd; Univ Of Denver; Interior Designer.

SALISBURY, Dean A; Pawnee HS; Pawnee, IL; 5/47 ChrhWkr; HonRl; SctActv; TchrAde; YthFlsp; FrCl; SciCl; Bsktbl; Trk; IMSpt; College; Doctor.

SALISBURY, Devin H; Gordon HS; Gordon, NE; SctActv; Trk; Mc Cook Junior College; Business.

SALKOWSKI, Thomas M; Premontre HS; Kewaunee, WI; Aud/Vis; HonRl; JA; ROTC; SchMus; SchPl; SctActv; Yrbk; SchPpr; PpCl; Univf Science Of Communication.

SALL, Jessica A; Marian HS; Omaha, NE; HonRl; LitMag; NatlFornLg; NHS; IMSpt; AmLegAwd; Univ Of Montana; Forestry.

SALLA, Nancy L; Benton Central HS; Earl Park, IN; 7/258 ALAGirlsSt; PresChrhWkr; HonRl; NHS; Pres4-H; FHA; FTA; LatCl; SciCl; IMSpt; 4-HAwd; Purdue Univ; Pharmacy.

SALLACH, Lisa L; Bluffton HS; Bluffton, IN; 3/136 Band; Chr; ChrhWkr; HonRl; NHS; SecStuCncl; YthFlsp; RptrYrbk; RptrSchPpr; LatCl; Ball State Univ; Math.

SALLADAY, Sandy L; Jamaica HS; Fairmount, IL; Band; ChrhWkr; HonRl; NHS; StuCncl; SpnCl; Chrldr; Jr College; X Ray Tech.

SALLANS, Larry; Fitzgerald HS; Warren, MI; 5/418 HonRl; NHS; NatlMeritSchl; NatlSciFnd; SctActv; StuGov; TchrAde; CaptSwmmng; CchngActv; Wayne State Univ; Nuclear Chemistry.

SALLEE, Kenneth S; Troy HS; Troy, KS; Chr; Chrs; HonRl; YthFlsp; 4-H; CaptBsbl; LetterFtbl; 4-HAwd; Wesburn Univ; Lawyer.

SALLEE, Meredith L; Stephen Decatur HS; Decatur, IL; ChrhWkr; CncrtBnd; MrchBnd; NHS; NatlMeritSF; Orch; Yrbk; Univ; Math Engineering.

SALLEE, Robin A; Troy HS; Troy, KS; Chr; Chrs; HonRl; LbryAde; SchMus; SchPl; TchrAde; YthFlsp; RptrYrbk; 4-H; FHA; PpCl; College; Buyer.

SALLEN, James; Aquinas HS; Fort Madison, IA; Aud/Vis; ChrhWkr; CmntyWkr; SchMus; SchPl; SctActv; SpnCl; PpCl; IMSpt; GodCntryAwd; St Ambrose College; Tv Production.

SALLEY, Darla R; Guilford HS; Caledonia, IL; 137/672 ChrhWkr; HonRl; TchrAde; 4-H; Wrstlng; Peru State College; Accounting.

SALLEY, Tamia K; Waterford Mott HS; Drayton Plains, MI; Chr; ChrhWkr; HonRl; HospAde; JA; RedCrAde; SctActv; TchrAde; 4-HAwd; U; Med Tech.

SALLIE, Pamela S; Hammond Baptist HS; Merrillville, IN; 4/88 Chr; ChrhWkr; HonRl; NHS; OffAde; SchPl; StuGov; TchrAde; Teen; RptrSchPpr; SchPpr; College; English Teacher.

SALLMAN, Terrie K; Concordia HS; Aurora, KS; HonRl; PpCl; College; Chemical Engineering.

SALMEN, Linda S; Woodstock HS; Wonder Lake, IL; ALAGirlsSt; HonRl; NHS; Medical Inst Of Minn; Veterinarian.

SALMON, Janice E; T H North Vigo HS; Terre Haute, IN; 1/520 HonRl; NatlFornLg; NHS; StuCncl; FrCl; PpCl; Chrldr; GAA; Purdue U; Computer.

SALMON, Sheryl L; Reeder Public HS; Reeder, ND; PresFrshCls; SecSophCls; TrsSophCls; VPJrCls; ALAGirlsSt; Chrs; HonRl; StuGov; EdYrBk; SchPpr; College; Nursing.

SALMONSON, Rebecca; Frazee HS; Osage, MN; VPSophCls; Chrs; ChrhWkr; HonRl; JrNHS; NHS; OffAde; Yrbk; FHA; FTA; PPFtbl; College; Lab Technician.

SALO, Darwin E; High School; Biwabik, MN; HonRl; Ftbl; Trk; Trade School; Vocational.

SALO, Faith E; Cloquet Sr HS; Cloquet, MN; TrsSrCls; DrlTm; MrchBnd; NHS; NatlMeritCmnd; StuCncl; RptrYrbk; PpCl; PPFtbl; Augsburg College; Juvenile Corr Counselng.

SALO, Karla; Houghton HS; Houghton, MI; SctActv; TchrAde; Yrbk; 4-H; 4-HAwd; LionAwd; Suomi College; Liberal Arts.

SALOIS, Joseph; Bowling Green R1 HS; Bowling Green, MO; HonRl; Quill&Scroll; RptrYrbk; FrCl; SciCl; LetterFtbl; Coll; Medical.

SALOIS, Suzanne M; St Andrew HS; Detroit, MI; Chrs; HonRl; SchMus; SchPl; PpCl; Bsktbl; IMSpt; Pharmicist.

SALOMO, Bethany P; Southwest HS; Kansas City, MO; 47/500 Chr; HonRl; NHS; SchMus; StuCncl; StuGov; TchrAde; PpCl; IMSpt; Univ Mo;.

SALOMON, Joyce R; West Bloomfield HS; West Bloomfield, MI; 27/450 HonRl; JrNHS; LbryAde; NHS; RptrSchPpr; SpnCl; LetterBsktbl; IMSpt; U Of Mich; Professional.

SALOMONS, Julie B; Sterling Public HS; Sterling, NE; 1/22 SecSophCls; Band; ChrhWkr; HonRl; PepBnd; SchPl; EdSchPpr; Sec4-H; SecPpCl; LetterTrk; Nebr Western U; Medical Technician.

SALONE, Lynn; Lindblom Technical Hs; Chicago, IL; 31/722 Band; HonRl; NHS; Quill&Scroll; TchrAde; RptrSchPpr; SchPpr; MthCl; VPGAA; Northwestern U; Lawyer.

SALSBERRY, Bobby G; Novinger R 1 HS; Novinger, MO; 2/29 ALBoysSt; HonRl; NHS; LetterTrk;.

SALSBERY, Teresa; Tri Central HS; Tioton, IN; Band; HospAde; LbryAde; NHS; NatlMeritSchl; OffAde; Twrl; FNA; PpCl; PPFtbl; Ball State Univ; Nursing.

SALTER, Steven J; Slinger HS; Slinger, WI; VPSophCls; PresJrCls; HonRl; StuCncl; StuGov; SchPpr; SpnCl; MthCl; LetterBsbl; Bsktbl; LetterFtbl; Tennis; College; Teaching.

SALTER, Terri L; Livingston HS; Livingston, IL; 2/21 HonRl; SecSchAde; VPStuCncl; FHA; PpCl; CaptChrldr; Coll.

SALTSGAVER, Linda M; Allendale HS; Allendale, IL; 4/19 ChrhWkr; CmntyWkr; HonRl; LbryAde; NHS; SchPl; Teen; YthFlsp; Yrbk; 4-H; Clge; Prof.

SALTWELL, Cairy A; Maine South HS; Park Ridge, IL; 797/849 HonRl; NHS; FrCl; PpCl; Ill State Univ; Nursing.

SALTZGABER, Susan L; Tekonsha HS; Tekonsha, MI; 5/58 Chr; VPStuCncl; TchrAde; PresFHA; VPPpCl; Trk; Chrldr; 4-HAwd; College; Marine Biologist.

SALTZMAN, Alisa E; Sullivan Public HS; Sullivan, MO; 35/159 ALAGirlsSt; ChrhWkr; HonRl; StuCncl; StuGov; FHA; FTA; Bsbl; Bsktbl; College; Business Admin.

SALTZMAN, Bonnie; Niles Township Hs; Skokie, IL; PresFrshCls; PresSophCls; NHS; NatlMeritCmnd; NatlThespSoc; SchMus; YthFnd; GAA;.

SALTZMAN, Deanna K; Ridgeway Rv HS; Ridgeway, MO; 2/10 SecSophCls; PresJrCls; HonRl; StuCncl; DARAwd; Central Methodist College; Physical Therapy.

SALTZMAN, Kevin W; Marshall HS; Marshall, MI; 16/273 Band; CncrtBnd; HonRl; JA; JrNHS; MrchBnd; NHS; YthFlsp; LatCl; JAAwd; W Mi St Univ; Paper Sci.

SALTZMAN, Michael B; Buffalo Grove HS; Buffalo Grove, IL; 77/290 HonRl; LetterGlf; LetterSwmmng; Univ Of Iowa; Dentist.

SALTZMAN, Paul; Niles East Hs; Skokie, IL; NatlMeritFnl; PolWkr; RptrSchPpr; Macalester College; Journalism.

SALVA, Mary F; Bullock Creek HS; Merrill, MI; 3/170 HonRl; JrNHS; NHS; PolWkr; StuCncl; TchrAde; 4-H; FrCl; IMSpt; Grand Valley Clg; Med Tech.

SALVERDA, Julie R; Forest Lake HS; Forest Lake, MN; 4-H; FFA; 4-HAwd; PresAwd;.

SALVINO, Michele M; Hillcrest HS; Hazel Crest, IL; 7/474 HonRl; SecNHS; OffAde; StuCncl; PresFrCl; MthCl; LetterTennis; Knox College; Mathematics And French.

SALVINO, Renee M; Mother Theodore Guerin HS; Elmwood Park, IL; HonRl; Bsktbl; Illinois State Univ; Special Education.

SALVO, Victor A; Willowbrook HS; Villa Park, IL; 36/822 PresSrCls; Chr; HonRl; JrNHS; NHS; NatlMeritCmnd; NatlThespSoc; SchMus; SchPl; Univ Of Illinois; Architectural Design.

SALWAY, Kathy S; R L Nelson Snider HS; Fort Wayne, IN; Chr; HonRl; JA; IMSpt; Indiana Univ; Engineer.

SALYER, Janette; Wauneta Public HS; Wauneta, NE; Band; CncrtBnd; HonRl; MrchBnd; PepBnd; SctActv; YthFlsp; PpCl; Trk; GAA; College.

SALYER, Richard L; Sarcoxie R2 HS; Sarcoxie, MO; Band; CncrtBnd; HonRl; MrchBnd; PepBnd; TchrAde; Trade; Professional.

SALYERS, Sherry G; Bluffton HS; Bluffton, IN; 10/139 HonRl; SchPl; TchrAde; Teen; RptrYrbk; RptrSchPpr; SpnCl; PpCl; Univ; Nursing.

SALZ, Karen A; East Chain HS; Fairmont, MN; 1/22 PresSrCls; Chr; ChrhWkr; HonRl; NHS; StuCncl; YthFlsp; RptrYrbk; FHA; CaptBsktbl; Coll; Prof.

SALZ, William A; Streator HS; Streator, IL; Chr; Chrs; ChrhWkr; HonRl; Mdrgl; SchMus; SchPl; College; Music.

SALZMAN, Beth A; Niles West HS; Skokie, IL; 155/626 Chr; CmntyWkr; LitMag; NatlThespSoc; PolWkr; SchMus; Univ Of Wisc; Sociology.

SALZMAN, Steven S; Evanston Township HS; Skokie, IL; University Of Illinois; Architecture.

SALZMAN, Valerie K; Sheldon Community HS; Sheldon, IA; HonRl; SchMus; RptrYrbk; FHA; FTA; PpCl; College; English Education.

SALZMANN, Carolyn E; Maine Twp South HS; Park Ridge, IL; ChrhWkr; HonRl; NHS; NatlMeritSF; GerCl; IMSpt; Unin; Chemical Engi.

SALZMANN, Nancy B; Auburndale HS; Milladore, WI; TrsSophCls; ChrhWkr; DrlTm; HonRl; JA; MrchBnd; NHS; StuCncl; RptrSchPpr; 4-H; FBLA; PpCl; Univ Of Wis; Special Education.

SAMA, Desiree; West Washington HS; Campbellsburg, IN; HonRl; SchMus; StuCncl; RptrYrbk; 4-H; LatCl; Pe Teacher.

SAMARZA, Alane M; Maplewood Acad; Mound, MN; SecFrshCls; Band; Chr; Chrs; CncrtBnd; HonRl; OffAde; SchMus; SchPl; Yrbk; Columbia Union College; Medicine.

SAMBOL, David H; Roncalli HS; Omaha, NE; HonRl; NHS; StuCncl; LetterTrk; Coll; Prof.

SAMBORN, Cynthia L; Bay City Western HS; Auburn, MI; Chr; Chrs; ChrhWkr; HonRl; OffAde; SchAde; SchMus; YthFlsp; FTA; Central Michigan Univ; Psychology.

SAMIEC, Anthony J; Homewood Flossmoor HS; Homewood, IL; HonRl; OffAde; Cornell Univ; Chef.

SAMMARCO, Anthony; St Ignatius Prep HS; Chicago, IL; 52/151 HonRl; Sacrstn; SchAde; Tennis; De Paul Univ; Dentistry.

SAMMATARO, Peter A; Beaver Dam Sr HS; Beaver Dam, WI; 8/347 ALBoysSt; ChrhWkr; CAP; PolWkr; TchrAde; Trk;.

SAMMET, Cheryl E; Princeville HS; Princeville, IL; 6/74 VPNHS; OffAde; RedCrAde; StuCncl; Yrbk; PresPpCl; Ftbl; TreasGAA; DARAwd; Univ Of Illinois; Mathematics.

SAMMONS, Donna J; Mercy HS; St Louis, MO; Chrs; HonRl; JrNHS; SchMus; TchrAde; RptrYrbk; College; Psychology.

SAMMONS, Mark W; West Holt HS; Atkinson, NE; ALBoysSt; HonRl; NHS; SchPl; 4-H; GerCl; CaptWrstlng; University.

SAMMUT, Evelyn; Annapolis HS; Deerborn Heights, MI; Aud/Vis; ChrhWkr; CmntyWkr; HonRl; HospAde; JA; NatlFornLg; NHS; RedCrAde; College; Nursing.

SAMP, Jayne; Kearney Sr HS; Kearney, NE; ChrhWkr; HonRl; HospAde; LbryAde; YthFlsp; PpCl; Coll; Med Tech.

SAMP, Michael K; Morton HS; Morton, IL; 21/292 AFS; Aud/Vis; HonRl; JA; OffAde; YthFlsp; Yrbk; CivCl; SciCl; University Of Illinois; Engineer.

SAMP, Thomas C; Forest View HS; Mt Prospect, IL; 29/625 HonRl; NatlMeritCmnd; SchPl; TchrAde; GerCl; IMSpt; Univ Of Iowa; Broadcasting.

SAMPAIR, Scott; Mahtomedi HS; Mahtomedi, MN; HonRl; StuCncl; TchrAde; Coll.

SAMPAIR, Stephen; Mahtomedi HS; Mahtomedi, MN; HonRl; TchrAde; PresAwd; Coll.

SAMPEN, Kurt A; El Paso HS; El Paso, IL; 1/92 AFS; ALBoysSt; CncrtBnd; HonRl; MrchBnd; NHS; SchPl; StuCncl; EdSchPpr; LetterWrstlng; IMSpt; Univ; Education.

SAMPEY, Dennis A; Fowlerville HS; Fowlerville, MI; CmntyWkr; HonRl; SchPl; SctActv; StuCncl; 4-H; FFA; Bsktbl; LetterTrk; 4-HAwd; Michigan State U; Electrical Engr.

SAMPO, Dennis; Lamoille HS; Lamoille, IL; 5/44 TrsSrCls; Chrs; HonRl; SchMus; SchPl; StuCncl; StuGov; Yrbk; Bsktbl; Glf; Coll; Pre Law.

SAMPSON, Gregg O; Estherville HS; Estherville, IA; 5/189 PresSophCls; HonRl; SctActv; SpnCl; SciCl; LetterBsktbl; LetterFtbl; Univ Of Iowa; Medicine.

SAMPSON, Karen A; New Trier East HS; Wilmette, IL; 193/847 Chr; HonRl; SctActv; YthFlsp; LetterBsktbl; LetterTrk; Illinois St Univ; Physical Educ.

SAMPSON, Kurtis B; Bettendorf HS; Bettendorf, IA; SciCl; Coll; Pro.

SAMPSON, Larry; La Salle Peru Township HS; Peru, IL; HonRl; Illinois State University; Accounting Major.

SAMPSON, Lee E; Belview Public HS; Belview, MN; Band; Chrs; CncrtBnd; SctActv; StuCncl; Bsktbl; Trk; College; Funeral Director.

SAMPSON, Leslie R; United Community HS; Madrid, IA; Band; Chr; CncrtBnd; MrchBnd; RptrSchPpr; 4-H; PpCl; 4-HAwd; U Of N Ia; Psychologist.

SAMPSON, Michael J; Chippewa Valley HS; Mt Clemens, MI; HonRl; NHS; LetterTrk; University; Aero Engineering.

SAMPSON, Sally A; Clay Center Public HS; Clay Center, NE; PresAud/Vis; CmntyWkr; HonRl; RedCrAde; SctActv; Pres4-H; TreasPpCl; Bsbl; Trk; PresAwd; Kearney St Coll; Phy Educ.

SAMPSON, Steven J; University Milwaukee HS; Milwaukee, WI; PresSophCls; PresJrCls; ALBoysSt; Chrs; NatlMeritSchl; StuCncl; EdYrBk; SchPpr; Bsktbl; Socr; Harvard University; Law.

SAMPSON, Toni M; Windom Area HS; Windom, MN; ChrhWkr; HonRl; HospAde; OffAde; SptEdSchPpr; Pres4-H; FHA; FTA; 4-HAwd; Clge.

SAMPSON, Toni R; Oakland HS; Oakland, IL; 3/49 Band; CncrtBnd; HonRl; MrchBnd; PepBnd; Yrbk; PresMthCl; PPFtbl; Parkland College; Nursing.

SAMPY, Teresa L; Ansley Public HS; Ansley, NE; 4/31 TrsJrCls; SecSrCls; DrlTm; HonRl; PpCl; LetterBsktbl; LetterTrk; State College; Business.

SAMS, Lea A; Cooper HS; Minneapolis, MN; 94/653 Chr; ChrhWkr; HonRl; Mdrgl; NHS; SchMus; SchPl; GerCl; Col; Music.

SAMS, Marlene; Roosevelt HS; Gary, IN; Chr; ChrhWkr; HonRl; Mdrgl; TchrAde; FHA; College.

SAMS, Patricia C; Kirksville Sr HS; Kirksville, MO; Band; Chrs; Mdrgl; OffAde; SchMus; StuCncl; RptrYrbk; 4-H; FBLA; Ne Missouri St Univ; Music.

SAMSON, Jane M; Blair Community HS; Blair, NE; 10/151 PresBand; Chr; HonRl; MrchBnd; NHS; PresNatlThespSoc; PepBnd; SchMus; SchPl; PpCl; College; Music,math Minor.

SAMSON, Julie A; Marian HS; Omaha, NE; CmntyWkr; HonRl; NHS; PolWkr; StuGov; PresSpnCl; MthCl; LetterBsktbl; GAA; IMSpt; Univ Of Nebraska; Special Education.

SAMSON, Linda; Malta Bend R 5 HS; Malta Bend, MO; SecFrshCls; TrsSophCls; HstJrCls; ALAGirlsSt; Band; Chr; Bsbl; Bsktbl; Trk; Chrldr; Kentucky State Univ; Home Economics.

SAMSON, Mary T; Shell Lake HS; Shell Lake, WI; 12/66 PresJrCls; HonRl; LbryAde; TchrAde; Yrbk; RptrSchPpr; 4-H; FHA; U Of Wis Stout; Day Care Teacher.

SAMSON, Vikki L; Maryville HS; Maryville, MO; 31/129 ALAGirlsSt; NHS; SchPl; StuCncl; EdYrBk; PpCl; College; Teach.

SAMUEL, Douglas P; Rochester HS; Rochester, IL; 33/82 Band; Chr; Chrs; ChrhWkr; CncrtBnd; HonRl; Mdrgl; PepBnd; SchMus; SchPl; SctActv; Bsbl; Bsktbl; Univ; Marine Biologist.

SAMUEL, Julie; Wapella HS; Wapella, IL; VPFrshCls; Band; HonRl; SchMus; SchPl; VPStuCncl; Pres4-H; PresFFA; Bsktbl; Trk; CaptChrldr; GAA; Western Illinois Univ; Agriculture.

SAMUEL, Wendell; Paseo HS; Kansas City, MO; Chr; ChrhWkr; HonRl; JA; MthCl; College; Professional.

SAMUELS, Valerie A; Pittsburg HS; Pittsburg, KS; Band; StuCncl; PpCl; FHA; CaptTwrl; Swmmng; LetterTrk; LetterChrldr; GAA; CaptIMSpt; Kansas State College Of Pitts.

SAMUELSON, Curtis A; Wallace County HS; Sharon Springs, KS; PresSophCls; VPJrCls; Chrs; HonRl; NHS; StuCncl; TchrAde; Ftbl; Ft Hays Ks State Col; Business.

SAMUELSON, Kathy R; Adams Public HS; Adams, ND; 9/25 PresSrCls; ALAGirlsSt; Chrs; HonRl; SchPl; TchrAde; RptrYrbk; RptrSchPpr; SchPpr; 4-H; Winfield Manor Sch; Horsemanship.

SAMUELSON, Michael L; Ottawa Township HS; Ottawa, IL; Band; Chr; DrmBgl; HonRl; NHS; SctActv; VPYthFlsp; Ftbl; Swmmng; Oral Roberts College; Christian Education.

SANBORN, Dirk K; Rolla Senior HS; Rolla, MO; 26/217 CncrtBnd; HonRl; MrchBnd; SctActv; StuCncl; LetterTrk; Missouri Univ; Mechanical Engineering.

SANBORN, Gayle L; Alpena Sr HS; Lachine, MI; Band; CncrtBnd; MrchBnd; PepBnd; SchMus; SchPl; RptrSchPpr; 4-H; GerCl; PpCl; Central Mich Univ; Journalism.

SANCHEZ, John P; St Xaviers HS; Junction City, KS; 1/36 PresFrshCls; ALBoysSt; Band; Chrs; HonRl; NatlMeritSF; SchPl; StuCncl; StuGov; EdYrBk; LetterTrk; CitAwd; University Of Kansas; Geology.

SANCHEZ, Jorge E; Nicholas Senn HS; Chicago, IL; LetterBsbl; Bsktbl; IMSpt; University; Professional.

SANCHEZ, Marilyn E; Adrian HS; Adrian, MI; ChrhWkr; CmntyWkr; OffAde; SpnCl; College; International Business.

SANCHEZ, Patricia D; Lourdes HS; Chicago, IL; 37/299 HonRl; NHS; SchMus; FrCl; PpCl; SciCl; Northwestern Univ; Medicine.

SANCKEN, Thomas; Pontiac Hs; Pontiac, IL; 1/199 CncrtBnd; HonRl; Mdrgl; MrchBnd; NHS; PepBnd; Sec4-H; VPLatCl; Ftbl; LetterWrstlng; Iwu;chemistry & Biology.

SAND, Connie J; Warsaw HS; Warsaw, IN; 4/371 ChrhWkr; HonRl; TreasYthFlsp; Yrbk; FHA; College; Accounting.

SAND, Larry D; St Francis HS; Humphrey, NE; 2/30 HonRl; FFA; LetterFtbl; IMSpt; Trade Schl.

SAND, Shavonne M; New Town HS; New Town, ND; 10/42 VPFrshCls; VPSophCls; VPSrCls; HonRl; StuCncl; EdYrBk; FFA; FHA; GerCl; Chrldr; College; Nursing.

SAND, William H; Langdon HS; Langdon, ND; ALBoysSt; Band; Chr; PepBnd; SchMus; SchPl; StuCncl; YthFlsp; PpCl; Ftbl; College; Vocational.

SANDA, Jayme M; Velva Public HS; Velva, ND; HonRl; HospAde; LbryAde; SctActv; TchrAde; FBLA; FHA; College; Nursing.

SANDAGE, Jeffrey A; Jefferson Comm HS; Scranton, IA; 5/96 HonRl; Sec4-H; PresFFA; Iowa State Univ; Agricultural Educ.

SANDAHL, Bruce E; Lincoln Northeast HS; Lincoln, NE; 23/580 Chr; ChrhWkr; HonRl; NHS; SchAde; SchMus; TchrAde; SptEdSchPpr; CaptSwmmng; CchngActv; College; Physical Ed Teacher.

SANDBORG, Rebecca R; Galesburg Senior HS; Galesburg, IL; 29/642 Chr; HonRl; LitMag; Mdrgl; NHS; SchMus; TchrAde; FTA; LatCl; SciCl; Univ Of Il; Biology/chemistry.

SANDBORG, Rebecca R; Galesburg HS; Galesburg, IL; 30/629 Chr; HonRl; Mdrgl; NHS; SchMus; TchrAde; FTA; LatCl; SciCl; Univ Of Il; Pharmacy.

SANDBORN, Nancy A; Saranac HS; Saranac, MI; 12/78 Band; Chrs; HonRl; NHS; SchMus;.

SANDEL, Elizabeth J; Homewood Flossmoor HS; Homewood, IL; 18/940 Chr; Chrs; CncrtBnd; HonRl; LitMag; NHS; NatlMeritSF; NatlThespSoc; Orch; SchMus; College.

SANDEL, Karin G; University City Senior HS; University City, MO; Chr; SctActv; TchrAde; Washington Univ; Veterinary Medicine.

SANDER, Bryan; Hays HS; Hays, KS; HonRl; Bsbl; IMSpt; College; Business.

SANDER, Martha A; Dubois HS; Jasper, IN; 4/76 PresSophCls; Chrs; HonRl; StuCncl; RptrSchPpr; SchPpr; FHA;.

SANDER, Michael R; Jasper HS; Jasper, IN; KeyCl; LetterFtbl; LetterTennis; College; Professional.

SANDER, Pamela A; Catholic Central HS; Muskegon, MI; 3/215 SecJrCls; Band; HonRl; MrchBnd; NHS; PepBnd; PolWkr; SchMus; TchrAde; Nazareth College; Nursing.

SANDER, Rick M; Notre Dame HS; Burlington, IA; 19/80 Aud/Vis; HonRl; Ftbl; Trk; Junior College; Mech Engineer.

SANDER, Shaw E; St Mary Center For Learning; Chesterton, IN; PolWkr; SchPl; StuCncl; University; Fine Arts.

SANDER, Shaw E; St Mary Center For Learn HS; Chesterton, IN; SchPl; StuGov; Univ; Working In Womens Issues.

SANDERHOLM, Kathy J; Arkansas City HS; Arkansas City, KS; 3/223 HonRl; StuCncl; FBLA; FTA; PpCl; GAA; Southwestern College; Gymnastics Coach.

SANDERS, Beverly A; Glasgow Rii HS; Armstrong, MO; 2/60 SecJrCls; Band; CncrtBnd; HonRl; MrchBnd; NHS; PepBnd; Yrbk; FHA; PpCl; Northeast Mo; Nursing.

SANDERS, Carol J; St Francis HS; Wheaton, IL; 2/88 Chr; Chrs; HonRl; HospAde; JA; JrNHS; NHS; PolWkr; SchMus; LatCl; PpCl; College; Music.

SANDERS, Carolyn J; Deerfield HS; Deerfield, IL; 2/561 AFS; ModUN; NatlFornLg; NHS; NatlMeritFnl; NatlMeritSchl; SchPl; EdYrBk; FrCl; Stanford University.

SANDERS, Charlene L; Mitchell HS; Mitchell, IN; HonRl; Vincennes Univ; Nursing.

SANDERS, Charles W; Elhurst & Leo HS; Fort Wayne, IN; Bsktbl; Ftbl; Swmmng; Anderson College.

SANDERS, Chris A; Nevada HS; Nevada, MO; Chrs; StuCncl; FTA; LatCl; PpCl; Swmmng; Chrldr; GAA; Univ Of Ar; Teachr.

SANDERS, Christine L; North Knox HS; Sandborn, IN; 1/144 HonRl; NHS; SchPl; 4-H; FHA; FTA; FrCl; MthCl; College.

SANDERS, David L; Naperville Central HS; Naperville, IL; HonRl; LbryAde; PresQuill&Scroll; StuCncl; EdSchPpr; Univ Of South Al; Law.

SANDERS, Dean E; Glenwood City HS; Downing, WI; 3/78 TrsSophCls; ALBoysSt; Chr; HonRl; NHS; SchPl; FBLA; LetterBsktbl; LetterFtbl; Coll; Broadcasting.

SANDERS, Ellen S; Goodridge HS; Goodridge, MN; 1/33 Chr; HonRl; LbryAde; NHS; OffAde; Yrbk; FHA; PpCl; Trk; GAA; Morehead Coll; Computer Science.

SANDERS, Harvey B; Bishop Noll Institute; East Chicago, IN; Band; CncrtBnd; JA; MrchBnd; PepBnd; SchMus; SchPl; StuCncl; MthCl; Swmmng; Ga Tech; Engi.

SANDERS, James D; Edinburg Comm HS; Edinburg, IN; 2/81 Band; ChrhWkr; CncrtBnd; HonRl; NatlMeritFnl; StuCncl; LetterBsktbl; LetterFtbl; LetterTrk; Ball St Univ; Honors Program.

SANDERS, Janice A; Josephinum HS; Chicago, IL; CmntyWkr; HonRl; HospAde; SchAde; SciCl; Nursing School; Intensive Care Nursing.

SANDERS, Jeffrey C; Parkway West HS; Manchester, MO; 278/794 Chr; HonRl; TchrAde; Bsbl; Bsktbl; College.

SANDERS, John E; Maries Co Rii HS; Belle, MO; 4/50 VPSophCls; VPJrCls; HonRl; NHS; VPStuCncl; LetterBsbl; LetterBsktbl; Trk; IMSpt; Math.

SANDERS, Kristin G; Delavan HS; Delavan, IL; 25/76 Band; ChrhWkr; CncrtBnd; MrchBnd; SecYthFlsp; GAA; IMSpt; Millikin Univ; Merchandising.

SANDERS, Lauri M; Aquinas Dominican HS; Chicago, IL; Band; ChrhWkr; CmntyWkr; HonRl; HospAde; Orch; SchMus; SchPl; StuCncl; RptrYrbk; 4-H; Spelman College; Medicine.

SANDERS, Melissa A; Columbus HS; Marshfield, WI; Chr; CmntyWkr; HonRl; HospAde; SchPl; StuCncl; StuGov; EdSchPpr; FrCl; PpCl; College; Professional.

SANDERS, Michele; Cahokia Senior HS; Cahokia, IL; 88/532 Chr; TchrAde; FTA; PpCl; Coll; Med Record Admin.

SANDERS, Monte M; Taylor HS; Kokomo, IN; 7/150 Band; ChrhWkr; CncrtBnd; HonRl; MrchBnd; NHS; PepBnd; SpnCl; Indiana University; Lawyer.

SANDERS, Norma J; North Knox HS; Sandborn, IN; 4/136 Band; CncrtBnd; HonRl; MrchBnd; NHS; TreasPepBnd; FrCl; Business Col; Accounting.

SANDERS, Patricia A; St Louise De Marillac HS; Northbrook, IL; Chrl; Chrs; CmntyWkr; NatlMeritCmnd; SchMus; College; Theatre/dance.

SANDERS, Paula M; W J Brown HS; Piedmont, SD; 31/204 Chr; ChrhWkr; CmntyWkr; HonRl; Mdrgl; SchMus; TchrAde; FTA; AmLegAwd; 4-HAwd; School Nursing; Rn.

SANDERS, Raymond A; Griffith HS; Griffith, IN; 3/309 HonRl; JrNHS; VPNHS; Quill&Scroll; TchrAde; SptEdYrbk; Yrbk; SchPpr; Valparaiso Technical Inst; Electronics.

SANDERS, Rebecca; Central HS; St Joseph, MO; 10/500 ChrhWkr; HonRl; LitMag; TchrAde; YthFlsp; RptrYrbk; FrCl; GodCntryAwd; College; Elementary Teacher.

SANDERS, Robin M; Albert Lea HS; Albert Lea, MN; Band; CncrtBnd; MrchBnd; Swmmng; Univ Of Minn; Veterinary Med.

SANDERS, Sandra K; Wichita West HS; Wichita, KS; 15/604 HonRl; NHS; Quill&Scroll; RptrSchPpr; EdSchPpr; SchPpr; Wichita State U; Journalism.

SANDERS, Sandra K; Venice HS; Madison, IL; 12/44 VPFrshCls; SecSophCls; SecJrCls; SecSrCls; Chr; SchPl; StuCncl; FHA; Bsbl; CaptChrldr; College; Secretarial Studies.

SANDERS, Susan A; Thornton Township HS; Riverdale, IL; 4/800 HonRl; NHS; Swmmng; AmLegAwd; U Of Il; Engi.

SANDERS, Thomas J; Thorton Fractional South HS; Lansing, IL; HonRl; LetterTennis; Valparaiso Univ; Lawyer.

SANDERS, Thomas R; Loyola Academy; Glenview, IL; 43/461 Chrs; HonRl; SchAde; StuCncl; LetterTrk; CitAwd; Us Air Force Academy; Military Career.

SANDERS, Vernon J; Montezuma Comm HS; Montezuma, IA; 6/57 HonRl; NatlMeritCmnd; NatlThespSoc; ROTC; StuCncl; MthCl; Bsbl; Bsktbl; Ftbl; Glf; Ia St Univ; Physical Science.

SANDERS, William J; St Marys HS; Independence, MO; TrsSrCls; ALBoysSt; Band; HonRl; NHS; SchPl; StuCncl; Ftbl; Trk; LetterWrstlng; University; Engineer.

SANDERSFELD, Paul K; Cal Community HS; Latimer, IA; VPSophCls; VPJrCls; ALBoysSt; HonRl; 4-H; FFA; IMSpt; AmLegAwd; 4-HAwd; College; Vocation.

SANDERSON, Michael A; Grandview HS; Grandview, MO; Band; Chr; CncrtBnd; HonRl; MrchBnd; SchMus; SchPl; SptEdYrbk; SchPpr; University; Engineering.

SANDERSON, Patricia L; Conde Public HS; Conde, SD; 1/21 VPJrCls; Band; CncrtBnd; HonRl; Quill&Scroll; StuCncl; FHA; LetterBsktbl; Trk; AmLegAwd; Northern St Clg; Elem Education.

SANDERSON, Susan F; Canton HS; Canton, SD; Band; HonRl; SchPl; YthFlsp; Yrbk; RptrSchPpr; VPFHA; Business School; Legal Secretary.

SANDGREN, Susan; Joseph Craig Sr Hs; Janesville, WI; Band; Chr; HonRl; LbryAde; Orch; Quill&Scroll; SchMus; RptrYrbk; Yrbk; FrCl; University; Interpretor Or Translator.

SANDIFER, Caren E; Blakesburg Comm HS; Blakesburg, IA; Band; Chrs; ChrhWkr; CncrtBnd; HonRl; MrchBnd; PepBnd; SchMus; SchPl; SctActv; College; Social Welfare.

SANDMAN, Edward L; Bishop Dwenger HS; Ft Wayne, IN; Chrs; HonRl; JrNHS; NHS; SchMus; SchPl; SptEdSchPpr; LetterTrk; Purdue Univ; Engineering.

SANDMAN, Mark A; Bishop Ryan HS; Minot Afb, ND; 19/89 HonRl; NHS; StuCncl; SptEdYrbk; KeyCl; CaptBsktbl; LetterFtbl; LetterTrk; IMSpt; PresAwd; College; Medicine.

SANDNER, Karen L; Macon R 1 HS; Macon, MO; 76/119 ChrhWkr; HonRl; HospAde; OffAde; FBLA; FHA; FNA; Trenton Jr Clge; Nursing Career.

SANDONA, Cheryl; St Francis De Sales HS; Valparaiso, IN; HonRl; NHS; NatlMeritCmnd; SchAde; SchMus; TchrAde; Purdue Univ; Veterinarian.

SANDONA, Paula M; St Francis De Sales HS; Chicago Heights, IL; 5/297 HonRl; JrNHS; NHS; GAA; Univ Of Il; Interior Design.

SANDOR, Charles S; Marian HS; South Bend, IN; HonRl; Mdrgl; SchPl; RptrYrbk; SchPpr; Bsktbl; ChmnFtbl; Trk; IMSpt;.

SANDOVAL, Patti; United Township HS; Silvis, IL; 17/638 ChrhWkr; CmntyWkr; HonRl; LbryAde; FrCl; ChmbCommrsAwd; Physics.

SANDQUIST, Kevin J; Adel HS; Adel, IA; PresSophCls; ALBoysSt; HonRl; NHS; PresStuCncl; PresYthFlsp; FTA; LetterFtbl; LetterWrstlng; College; Law.

SANDQUIST, Marianne; Northwestern HS; Mellette, SD; ChrhWkr; CncrtBnd; HonRl; MrchBnd; PepBnd; SchPl; RptrYrbk; PpCl; College.

SANDROCK, Catharine M; Prophetstown HS; Propheststown, IL; Band; Chr; Chrs; ChrhWkr; CncrtBnd; MrchBnd; PepBnd; 4-H; FTA; GAA; Dana Coll; Music.

SANDRY, Diane L; Streator Twp HS; Streator, IL; Band; CncrtBnd; HonRl; HospAde; MrchBnd; PepBnd; SchMus; FTA; GerCl; PpCl; Univ; Professional.

SANDS, Elizabeth J; Minot HS; Minot, ND; Chrs; HonRl; HospAde; JrNHS; NHS; NatlMeritSF; NatlThespSoc; SchPl; FrCl; Univ Of N Dakota; Law.

SANDS, Jo Deen M; West Aurora Sr HS; North Aurora, IL; 13/625 Chr; ChrhWkr; HonRl; NHS; NatlMeritCmnd; SchAde; Brigham Young Univ; Nursing.

SANDSTROM, Donna; Toivola Meadowlands HS; Meadowlands, MN; 3/19 SecSophCls; VPSrCls; Chr; ChrhWkr; HonRl; LbryAde; SchPl; StuCncl; FHA; GAA; Mesabi Comm College; Undecided.

SANDSTROM, Jane E; Cambridge HS; Stanchfield, MN; 2/210 ALAGirlsSt; ChrhWkr; PresNHS; StuCncl; Pres4-H; GerCl; PpCl; IMSpt; 4-HAwd; MasAwd; Coll; Engi.

SANDVEN, Luann J; Milan HS; Monteideo, MN; 9/31 TrsSrCls; Band; Chr; HonRl; LbryAde; PepBnd; SchPl; Yrbk; FHA; PpCl; Trade Sch; Voc.

SANDY, Bradley J; Indianola HS; Indianola, IA; 71/225 HonRl; RptrSchPpr; Ftbl; Trk; IMSpt; Simpson College; History.

SANDY, Christine; Audubon Public HS; Audubon, MN; SecSophCls; Chr; Chrs; HonRl; Mdrgl; NHS; SchPl; RptrYrbk; FHA; Chrldr; College; Professional.

SAN FILIPPO, Jill G; Greenfield HS; Greenfield, WI; Band; Chrs; CncrtBnd; Mdrgl; MrchBnd; PepBnd; FTA; PpCl; IMSpt; College; Music.

SANFILIPPO, Mary E; St Thomas Aquinas HS; Florissant, MO; ChrhWkr; HonRl; SchMus; SchPl; SctActv; IMSpt; Univ Of Missouri; Mathematics.

SANFORD, Diana L; Abraham Lincoln Senior HS; Bloomington, MN; AFS; Chrs; HonRl; NHS; GerCl; Tennis; Trade School Or College; Vocation.

SANFORD, Mark D; Lakeshore HS; Stevensville, MI; Band; NHS; NatlMeritSchl; SchMus; SchPl; PresStuCncl; PresKeyCl; MthCl; Tennis; Trk; Adrian Col; Law Advertising.

SANFORD, Peter J; Assumption HS; Wisconsin Rapids, WI; Aud/Vis; ChrhWkr; RedCrAde; SchPl; College; Design Electronics.

SANFORD, Richard B; Glendale HS; Springfield, MO; ChrhWkr; HonRl; Orch; SchMus; Evangel Coll; Public Accountant.

SANGER, Debra; Franklin Public HS; Franklin, NE; 2 SecSophCls; PresBand; PresNHS; StuCncl; Twrl; PresFHA; SecSciCl; CaptChrldr; VoiceDemAwd; Kearney St College;.

SANGER, Debra J; Franklin Public HS; Franklin, NE; 2/32 SecSophCls; SecJrCls; ALAGirlsSt; PresBand; Chrs; HonRl; NHS; VPStuCncl; PresFHA; ChmnChrldr; Kearney Coll; Sociology.

SANGREGARIO, John W; Notre Dame HS; Sterling Hgts, MI; Macomb Community College; Communications.

SANGREN, Judy A; Willow River HS; Willow River, MN; 4/41 Band; Chrs; NHS; OffAde; SchPl; RptrSchPpr; 4-H; FHA; LetterBsktbl; LetterTrk; GAA; College; Accounting.

SANKEN, Brenda J; Brownton Public HS; Brownton, MN; TrsSrCls; Chr; ChrhWkr; HonRl; HospAde; YthFlsp; EdSchPpr; FHA; GerCl; PpCl; Col ; Music.

SANKO, Mary Carol; Hillcrest HS; Hazel Crest, IL; 5/450 JrNHS; NHS; StuCncl; SpnCl; PpCl; Chrldr; GAA; IMSpt; ALBoysSt; Medicine.

SANKOWSKI, Kathryn S; Clark HS; Hammond, IN; 68/260 HonRl; NHS; Sdlty; StuCncl; SchPpr; FNA; FrCl; PpCl; IMSpt; University; Marine Archeology.

SANNEMAN, Arlyn L; Clifton HS; Palmer, KS; 2/26 PresJrCls; HonRl; SptEdYrbk; Yrbk; Bsbl; College; Architecture.

SANNERUD, Paul D; Blaine HS; Noka, MN; CmntyWkr; CncrtBnd; HonRl; JrNHS; TchrAde; SchPpr; Pres4-H; Socr; DanFAwd; 4-HAwd; College; Psychology.

SANREGRET, Debra A; Hazel Park HS; Hazel Park, MI; 3/426 ChrhWkr; HonRl;.

SANSONE, James F; Divine Child HS; Dearborn Heights, MI; PresSrCls; HonRl; NHS; PolWkr; SchPl; StuGov; SchPpr; PpCl; LetterFtbl; CchngActv; U Of Mi; Chem Eng.

SANSONE, Paula J; Lafayette HS; St Joseph, MO; 26/254 Chr; HonRl; JA; JrNHS; LitMag; SchMus; GAA; Coll; Archeology.

SANTALA, Jeanne M; Waterford Mott HS; Pontiac, MI; 311/365 Chr; Chrs; ChrhWkr; HonRl; Oakland Univ; Medicine.

SANTANDREA, Margaret R; Proviso East HS; Melrose Park, IL; 86/1001 CmntyWkr; HonRl; LbryAde; NatlMeritFnl; NatlMeritCmnd; SchAde; SctActv; Univ Of Ill; Doctor.

SANTANGELO, Jean M; Mother Guerin HS; Chicago, IL; 14/409 Chrs; HonRl; NHS; NatlMeritSF; MthCl; GAA; Collge; Math Major.

SANTARELLI, James R; Rivertone HS; Riverton, IL; VPFrshCls; HstSophCls; HstJrCls; HonRl; StuCncl; StuGov; Bsbl; Bsktbl; Glf; IMSpt; College; Dentist.

SANTARELLI, Nancy R; Riverton HS; Riverton, IL; 1/77 SecTrsFrshCls; HonRl; StuCncl; PpCl; CaptChrldr; GAA; IMSpt; DARAwd; 4-HAwd; Business School; Liberal Arts.

SANTEE, Edward R; Alton HS; Alton, IL; Band; Chr; Chrs; CncrtBnd; HonRl; MrchBnd; NHS; Orch; SchMus; MthCl; Univ Of Il; Physics.

SANTEL, Barbara A; Wesclin HS; New Baden, IL; 8/100 HonRl; JrNHS; NHS; RptrSchPpr; EdSchPpr; FBLA; FHA; GerCl; Bus School; Vocation.

SANTHUFF, Barbara A; Clearwater R 1 HS; Piedmont, MO; HonRl; JrNHS; SpnCl; U Of Arkansas.

SANTILLI, Michael A; Cousino HS; Warren, MI; Chr; HonRl; JrNHS; Mdrgl; NHS; TchrAde; MthCl; SciCl; CaptSocr; Wrstlng; U Of Az; Astronomy.

SANTIONI, Doreen; Edsel Ford HS; Dearborn, MI; /520 NatlFornLg; NatlMeritSF; IMSpt; Coll;pro.

SANTMAN, Dawn A; Dysart Geneseo HS; Dysart, IA; 5/68 SecSophCls; Band; CncrtBnd; DrmMjrt; HonRl; MrchBnd; NHS; PepBnd; Yrbk; Pres4-H; TreasFFA; Bsktbl; Trk; College; Liberal Arts.

SANTORO, Kathryn A; O Fallon Twnshp HS; Ofallon, IL; Business School; Secretarial Science.

SANTORO, William D; Fraser HS; Fraser, MI; Aud/Vis; ChrhWkr; HonRl; NHS; OffAde; StuCncl; TchrAde; YthFlsp; Bsbl; Bsktbl; Ftbl;.

SANTY, Lisa A; Mc Auley Regional HS; Carthage, MO; 4/34 VPSophCls; PresJrCls; Chrl; HonRl; ModUN; NatlFornLg; PresNHS; PolWkr; SchMus; SchPl; Music.

SANZONE, Rosemarie A; Evergreen Park HS; Evergreen Park, IL; 33/439 AFS; Aud/Vis; HonRl; NHS; NatlThespSoc; Quill&Scroll; SchPl; Sdlty; SchPpr; College; Engineer.

SAPA, Allan E; Brookfield East HS; Brookfield, WI; EldAwd; KeyCl; Ftbl; Trk; CchngActv; IMSpt; JCAwd; College; Professional.

SAPENARO, Lisa D; St Marys HS; Independence, MO; CaptDrlTm; OffAde; SchMus; SchPl; RptrYrbk; PpCl; IMSpt; PresAwd; Business Sch; Secretary.

SAPIENZA, Thomas; Bishop Du Bourg HS; St. Louis, MO; 55,470 Band; CncrtBnd; JA; PepBnd; IMSpt; JAAwd; Univ. Of Missouri; Engineering.

SAPP, Jeanne L; Southern Boone County R 1 HS; Ashland, MO; 2/65 HospAde; NHS; Quill&Scroll; SchPl; YthLg; Yrbk; RptrSchPpr; FHA; SpnCl; IMSpt; College.

SAPP, Kathryn L; Reading HS; Reading, KS; Band; Chrs; HonRl; SchAde; SchPl; SecStuCncl; RptrYrbk; RptrSchPpr; Bsktbl; LetterTrk; Voc Or Tech Schl; Secretarial.

SAPP, Lee A; Burke HS; Omaha, NE; 160/560 Ftbl; KiwanAwd; Univ; Prof.

SAPP, Linda R; Hazen Public HS; Hazen, ND; Chrs; SchPl; SctActv; YthFlsp; 4-H; FHA; College; Vocation.

SAPP, Paul J; Sioux Valley HS; Bruce, SD; 35/67 PresSrCls; ChrhWkr; HonRl; SchPl; StuCncl; StuGov; YthFlsp; FFA; Ftbl; Trk; Wrstlng; College; History.

SAPP, Rebecca L; Roanoke Benson HS; Roanoke, IL; Band; HonRl; HospAde; LbryAde; OffAde; SctActv; SecMthCl; Il Central Col; Major Music.

SAPP, Terry; Southern Boone County HS; Ashland, MO; HonRl; JrNHS; NHS; SchPl; StuCncl; YthLg; 4-H; GerCl; SpnCl; Univ; Professsional.

SAPUTO, Mary F; St Marys HS; Kansas City, MO; 29/115 HonRl; PolWkr; SchMus; EngCl; GerCl; MthCl; PpCl; CaptChrldr; Art Institute; Artist.

SARAFA, Haithem K; Brother Rice HS; Southfield, MI; 9/210 ChrhWkr; HonRl; ModUN; Teen; RptrSchPpr; FBLA; University Of Michigan; Lawyer.

SARAFINY, Cindy A; West Iron County HS; Caspian, MI; VPFrshCls; VPSophCls; Band; HonRl; MrchBnd; EdYrBk; 4-H; FrCl; GAA; Michigan Tech University; Medical Tech.

SARANG, Kathy M; Morton Sr HS; Hammond, IN; 1/492 HonRl; JrNHS; NHS; TchrAde; Univ; Professional.

SARAUER, Bonnie; Bloomer Sr HS; Bloomer, WI; HonRl; NHS; OffAde; SchPl; TchrAde; RptrSchPpr; SchPpr; FBLA; Bus School; Clerical Work.

SARBACKER, Thomas A; Belleville HS; Belleville, WI; 4-H; FFA; LetterFtbl; CaptWrstlng; CchngActv; 4-HAwd; KiwanAwd; Univ Of Wisconsin; Dairy.

SARGEANT, Ann E; Forest Lake HS; Forest Lake, MN; ChrhWkr; HonRl; JA; RptrYrbk; FrCl; Tennis; Trk; GAA; IMSpt; PPFtbl; College; Professional Architect.

SARGEANT, Mary; Milton Senior Hs; Milton Junction, WI; TrsSophCls; ChrhWkr; HonRl; StuCncl; SchPpr; 4-H; FrCl; Swmmng; Trk; 4-HAwd; College; Nursing & Art.

SARGENT, Barbara A; Tuscola HS; Tuscola, IL; Chrs; CncrtBnd; MrchBnd; StuCncl; YthFlsp; 4-H; LatCl; PpCl; Chrldr; E Illinois Univ; Teacher.

SARGENT, Marsha J; Sturgeon Bay HS; Sturgeon Bay, WI; Band; Chr; CncrtBnd; HonRl; PepBnd; PpCl; IMSpt; Interior Decorator.

SARGENT, Patricia A; Ransom HS; Ransom, KS; PresJrCls; Band; DrmMjrt; HonRl; PresStuCncl; PpCl; LetterBsktbl; LetterTrk; CaptChrldr; PresAwd; Bethel College; Teaching.

SARGENT, Patrick C; Kapaun Mt Carmel HS; Wichita, KS; 13/125 PresFrshCls; PresSophCls; PresJrCls; HonRl; ModUN; NHS; StuCncl; RptrSchPpr; Ftbl; LetterWrstlng; Kansas State U; Professional.

SARNA, Thomas; Akron Fairgrove HS; Caro, MI; ChrhWkr; HonRl; JA; ModUN; NHS; RedCrAde; SctActv; StuCncl; YthFnd; 4-H; United Elect Inst; Technition Or Engin.

SARNACKI, Mark S; Our Lady Of Mt Carmel HS; Wyandotte, MI; 13/60 PresFrshCls; PresSophCls; VPJrCls; HonRl; StuCncl; StuGov; Bsbl; Bsktbl; Ftbl;.

SARNECKI, Anita M; Bishop Noll HS; E Chicago, IN; 184/360 SpnCl; Col; Vocation.

SARNICKI, Joseph M; Lane Technical HS; Chicago, IL; HonRl; PresJA; LbryAde; NHS; SctActv; TreasKeyCl; MthCl; Ftbl; Wrstlng; JAAwd; De Paul U.

SARNO, Angela M; Proviso East HS; Melrose Park, IL; HonRl; NHS; Univ Of Ill; Occupational Therapy.

SAROCH, Emil E; Rolla HS; Rolla, MO; 55/217 Band; HonRl; SctActv; GerCl; LetterBsbl; LetterBsktbl; LetterTrk; GodCntryAwd; College; Business.

SAROKIN, Steven; Pontiac Central HS; Pontiac, MI; HonRl; LitMag; NHS; Swmmng; W Mi Univ; Engineering.

SARRO, Tom L; Taft HS; Chicago, IL; 42/790 HonRl; NHS; PolWkr; SctActv; Ill Inst Of Tech; Engineering.

SARSANY, Helen A; Witt Public HS; Witt, IL; 1/24 SecFrshCls; SecSophCls; SecJrCls; Chrs; HonRl; SchPl; Yrbk; FTA; MthCl; Col; Math Or Phy Ed.

SARTO, Anthony F; Marist HS; Lansing, IL; 3/393 HonRl; SctActv; MthCl; Univ; Engineering.

SARTORE, Linda S; Marian Heights Academy; Evansville, IN; TrsJrCls; TrsSrCls; HonRl; NatlFornLg; NHS; SchPl; StuCncl; EdYrBk; RptrSchPpr; Tennis; Hanover College; Psychology.

SARTZ, Jon; Central HS; Lacrosse, WI; 7/530 ChrhWkr; HonRl; LitMag; GovHonPrgAwd; Uw Madison; Environmental Science.

SARUSSI, Julianne V; Argo Comm HS; Bridgeview, IL; 5/502 HonRl; NHS; NatlMeritCmnd; Yrbk; SciCl; LetterTrk; Univ Of Ill; Vet.

SARVER, Christel; Dekalb Sr HS; Dekalb, IL; 49/350 Chrs; ChrhWkr; HonRl; StuCncl; TchrAde; Teen; 4-H; FrCl; GAA; 4-HAwd;.

SARVER, Dawn M; Ramsey HS; Ramsey, IL; 6/48 VPFrshCls; ChrhWkr; CmntyWkr; HonRl; LbryAde; SchPl; StuCncl; RptrYrbk; FTA; SecFrCl; PpCl; LetterTrk; LetterChrldr; Eastern Illinois University; Psychology.

SARVER, Dawn M; Ramsey Comm HS; Ramsey, IL; 7/49 VPFrshCls; ChrhWkr; HonRl; NHS; SchPl; StuCncl; FrCl; Trk; Chrldr; GAA; Psychologist.

SARVER, Janice E; Griggsville HS; Griggsville, IL; 4/24 Chr; HonRl; LbryAde; NHS; SchPl; LatCl; Olivet Nazarene College; Medicie.

SASH, Bette J; Maplewood Academy; Brownsdale, MN; VPSophCls; TrsJrCls; Band; Chr; Chrl; Union College; Physical Therapy.

SASH, Robert C; Western Community HS; Buda, IL; HstSophCls; PresJrCls; TrsSrCls; HonRl; NHS; StuCncl; TchrAde; SchPpr; FTA; AmLegAwd; Northern Il Univ; Business.

SASS, Carol A; Douglas Mac Arthur HS; Saginaw, MI; 9/293 CmntyWkr; HonRl; NHS; StuCncl; PpCl; Tennis; Mi State U; Bio Chem.

SASS, Lisa V; Basehor HS; Tonganoxie, KS; VPFrshCls; SecTrsSophCls; DrlTm; HonRl; SchPl; 4-H; SpnCl; PpCl; 4-HAwd; PresAwd; College; Prof.

SASS, Mary B; Woodland HS; Ancona, IL; 3/63 SecFrshCls; ChrhWkr; CmntyWkr; HonRl; LbryAde; NHS; SchMus; SchPl; TchrAde; YthFlsp; Yrbk; Chrldr; GAA; Ill State Univ; Home Economics.

SASS, Michael A; Downers Grove Comm HS; Downers Grove, IL; 11/827 HonRl; NHS; NatlMeritSF; SchPl; Univ; Medicine.

SASSACK, Martha; Aquinas HS; Lincoln Park, MI; 1/220 HonRl; JA; NHS; PpCl; Bsbl; PPFtbl; BauchLmbAwd; VoiceDemAwd; Merry College Of Detroit; Nursing.

SASSE, Bonnie; Golden Valley HS; Golden Valley, ND; 5/12 PresSrCls; Band; Chr; Chrs; LbryAde; OffAde; Orch; PepBnd; SchPl; EdYrBk;.

SASSE, Debra A; Gordon HS; Gordon, NE; 1/67 Chrs; HonRl; StuCncl; TchrAde; 4-H; FHA; PpCl; 4-HAwd; Creighton Univ; Law.

SASSEEN, Kimberly A; Cairo HS; Cairo, IL; PresJrCls; ChrhWkr; DrlTm; HonRl; NHS; StuCncl; RptrSchPpr; PpCl; Collgeg.

SASSEN, Ruth E; Grand Island Sr HS; Grand Island, NE; 14/432 DrlTm; HonRl; OffAde; TchrAde; PpCl; LetterTrk; Chrldr; GAA; IMSpt; PresAwd; College; Fashion Design.

SASSENBERG, Dale B; Gibbon HS; Winthrop, MN; Band; MrchBnd; PepBnd; Vocational Schl; Agriculture.

SATHER, Brian L; Gilmanton HS; Mondovi, WI; VPJrCls; Band; HonRl; StuCncl; 4-H; TreasFFA; LetterBsbl; LetterBsktbl; Trk; LetterWrstlng;.

SATHER, Kent P; Madison HS; Madison, MN; 13/89 PresJrCls; ALBoysSt; NHS; Trk; IMSpt; College; Agriculture.

SATHRE, Brenda J; Tuttle Public HS; Tuttle, ND; 4/10 TreasBand; Chrs; HonRl; SchPl; RptrYrbk; RptrSchPpr; PpCl; Bsktbl; GAA; Nd State U.

SATINOFF, Abbey L; Highland Park HS; Highland Park, IL; HonRl; NatlMeritCmnd; StuGov; Univ Of Il; Law.

SATKO, Cynthia R; Prospect HS; Arlington Hts, IL; 4/600 HonRl; NHS; Quill&Scroll; StuCncl; SchPpr; PpCl; Bsktbl; Trk; Northwestern Univ; Biology.

SATKO, Margaret; Aquinas HS; Taylor, MI; HonRl; NatlFornLg; PpCl; Bsbl; Bsktbl; Chrldr; PPFtbl; Univ Of Mi; Lawyer.

SATO, Marc G; Lake Central HS; St John, IN; 7/453 PresFrshCls; ALBoysSt; Chr; HonRl; Mdrgl; NHS; NatlMeritCmnd; NatlThespSoc; SchMus; SchPl; Univ; Para Psy.

SATO, Peggy D; Nicholas Senn HS; Chicago, IL; 1/386 HonRl; JA; NHS; OffAde; TchrAde; KeyCl; SecFrCl; Loyola Univ; Business.

SATORIUS, Vicki J; Porta HS; Petersburg, IL; 13/98 Band; Chrs; ChrhWkr; HonRl; Mdrgl; NatlThespSoc; SchMus; EdYrBk; Chrldr; IMSpt; Univ; Nursing.

SATTERFIELD, Gwendolyn F; Lindblom Tech HS; Chicago, IL; 63/600 Chr; ChrhWkr; HonRl; LitMag; OffAde; SchMus; SchPl; SctActv; StuCncl; SecYthFnd; CaptTrk; CaptChrldr; GAA; Bradley; Artist.

SATTERFIELD, Kevin K; Olympia HS; Mc Lean, IL; 48/192 ALBoysSt; Band; CncrtBnd; HonRl; Mdrgl; MrchBnd; PepBnd; SchMus; FrCl; MthCl; SciCl; LetterFtbl; College; Hotel Management.

SATTERFIELD, Phyllis A; St Marks HS; St Louis, MO; SecFrshCls; Chrs; HonRl; LbryAde; SchPl; Sect Sch; Language.

SATTERLUND, Bonnie; Amery HS; Amery, WI; Band; Chr; CncrtBnd; HonRl; MrchBnd; PepBnd; Twrl; PpCl; Trk; CitAwd; Uw Lacrosse; Physical Therapy.

SATTLER, Gail A; Menasha HS; Menasha, WI; 27/310 TrsSrCls; AFS; Band; JA; NHS; StuCncl; LetterBsktbl; LetterTennis; OptClAwd; VoiceDemAwd; Univ; Bus Admin.

SATTLER, Ronald L; D C Everest HS; Rothschild, WI; 25/337 HonRl; Bsktbl; LetterFtbl; IMSpt; Technical School; Vocation In Machine Desig.

SATURDAY, Rita; Sturgis HS; Sturgis, MI; Band; HonRl; MrchBnd; NatlFornLg; NHS; PepBnd; Quill&Scroll; SchMus; RptrYrbk; Glen Oaks Comm Col; Journalism.

SAUCEDO, Anita C; Holland Senior HS; Holland, MI; Chr; HonRl; YthFlsp; SpnCl; College; Receptionist Typist.

SAUCEDO, Sylvia; Holy Family Academy; Chicago, IL; Chrs; HonRl; FrCl; SpnCl; MthCl; SciCl; College.

SAUDER, Doug F; Roanoke Benson HS; Roanoke, IL; Chr; HonRl; NHS; SchPl; StuCncl; SpnCl; IMSpt; U Of Il; Accounting.

SAUDER, John D; Roanoke Benson HS; Eureka, IL; 20/100 MthCl; LetterBsbl; LetterBsktbl; LetterTrk; College; Accounting.

SAUDER, Marilyn; Petoskey Sr HS; Petoskey, MI; Band; Chr; Chrs; ChrhWkr; CncrtBnd; HonRl; MrchBnd; NHS; TchrAde; SpnCl; Grand Rapids Baptist College; Secondary Ed.

SAUENHAGE, Sharon K; Sparta HS; Evansville, IL; ChrhWkr; 4-H; 4-HAwd;.

SAUER, Bruce W; Fulda Jr Sr HS; Fulda, MN; 13/85 ALBoysSt; ChrhWkr; CmntyWkr; HonRl; NHS; 4-H; FFA; PpCl; Bsbl; CaptBsktbl; CaptFtbl; LetterTrk; CchngActv; Worthington Jr College; Agriculture.

SAUER, Kim M; Omro HS; Omro, WI; Band; CncrtBnd; HonRl; MrchBnd; NHS; NatlMeritFnl; NatlMeritSF; PepBnd; Yrbk; 4-H; FHA; Northwestern University; Studio Art.

SAUER, Scott G; West De Pere HS; De Pere, WI; 35/187 Band; HonRl; SchPl; StuCncl; PresFrCl; LetterFtbl; CaptGlf; Trk; IMSpt; OptClAwd; U Of Whitewater; Accounting.

SAUER, Sheila M; Incarnate Word Academy; St Louis, MO; 5/111 Chrl; HonRl; LitMag; NHS; SchMus; StuCncl; PpCl; Bsktbl; GAA; PPFtbl; University; Architecture.

SAUER, Terry S; Valley City HS; Valley City, ND; PresFrshCls; Band; HonRl; PepBnd; SchPl; StuCncl; UNYO; 4-H; Bsktbl; Ftbl; College; Professional.

SAUERBRUNN, Cindy A; Anna Jonesboro Cath HS; Jonesboro, IL; 1/131 ALAGirlsSt; Band; Chrs; ChrhWkr; CmntyWkr; HonRl; HospAde; NHS; FNA; DARAwd; Wesleyan Univ; Nursing.

SAUERS, Rhonda L; Julesburg HS; Big Springs, NE; 14/42 Band; CncrtBnd; HonRl; MrchBnd; SchAde; RptrYrbk; FBLA; FHA; Vocation.

SAUKSTELIS, Laura L; Maria HS; Chicago, IL; HospAde; Sdlty; TchrAde; Teen; SpnCl; Trade School; Modeling.

SAUL, Marita N; Harvard HS; Harvard, IL; Band; CncrtBnd; MrchBnd; SchPpr; MthCl; LetterTrk; PPFtbl; College; Computer Programming.

SAULSBERRY, Thomas C; Normandy Sr HS; Northwoods, MO; Chr; ChrhWkr; HonRl; StuCncl; YthFlsp; Bsktbl; Ftbl; CaptTrk; College; Business Lawyer.

SAULYS, Algirdas V; Marian Catholic HS; Chicago Heights, IL; 25/335 Chr; HonRl; SchPl; Bsktbl; Univ Of Illinois.

SAUM, Brenda L; Davenport Comm HS; Davenport, NE; SecTrsFrshCls; Band; Chr; CncrtBnd; LbryAde; MrchBnd; PepBnd; SctActv; 4-H; College; Nursing.

SAUNDERS, Alan B; Sioux Valley HS; Peterson, IA; VPFrshCls; PresJrCls; ALBoysSt; HonRl; NHS; StuCncl; LetterBsbl; Bsktbl; Ftbl; LetterTrk; Trade School; Vocation.

SAUNDERS, Barbara A; John Glenn HS; Belleville, MI; 25/580 Aud/Vis; Band; ChrhWkr; CncrtBnd; HonRl; LitMag; NHS; TchrAde; RptrYrbk; FrCl; Eastern Mi U; Elementary Education.

SAUNDERS, Gwendolyn J; Edgerton Sr HS; Edgerton, WI; AFS; Chr; HonRl; HospAde; ModUN; SchPl; StuGov; RptrYrbk; 4-H; LetterTennis; Deaconess Hosp Sch Of Nursing; Nurse.

SAUNDERS, Kathy J; St Xaviers HS; Junction City, KS; PresJrCls; HonRl; SctActv; TreasStuCncl; StuGov; 4-H; PpCl; Bsktbl; LetterTrk; Chrldr;.

SAUNDERS, Lucy L; Kingswood Cranbrook HS; Birmingham, MI; CmntyWkr; HonRl; LitMag; LbryAde; NatlMeritFnl; RedCrAde; SchPl; FrCl; OptClAwd; College; Law.

SAUNDERS, Michelle L; Quincy HS; Quincy, MI; 7/116 Band; TreasNHS; OffAde; StuCncl; TchrAde; YthLg; TreasFTA; FrCl; IMSpt; Tri State Coll; Accountant.

SAUNDERS, Philip G; South Shelby HS; Shelbina, MO; PresJrCls; HonRl; StuCncl; StuGov; 4-H; FFA; CaptFtbl; LetterTrk; Wrstlng; IMSpt; Trade School.

SAUNDERS, Robert S; Manilla Community HS; Manilla, IA; 6/47 Chrl; Chrs; ChrhWkr; HonRl; NHS; SchMus; SchPl; YthFlsp; YthFnd; College.

SAUNDERS, Ted L; Huntington North HS; Huntington, IN; ALBoysSt; HonRl; JrNHS; LitMag; YthFlsp; RptrSchPpr; SchPpr; PpCl; Tennis; Wrstlng; I U Purdue; Radiologist.

SAUNDERS, Victoria A; Carl Sandburg HS; Oak Forest, IL; 36/680 PresJrCls; VPSrCls; HonRl; NHS; StuCncl; TreasFrCl; MthCl; SecPpCl; TreasChrldr; GAA; Arizona State Univ; Marketing.

SAURE, Brad S; Amery HS; Amery, WI; VPSrCls; HonRl; SchPl; StuCncl; Bsbl; Bsktbl; Ftbl; Glf; College; Accounting.

SAUSER, Heidi T; Anthon Oto Comm HS; Anthon, IA; 1/33 VPSophCls; DrlTm; HonRl; NHS; SchPl; Yrbk; SptEdSchPpr; FHA; PpCl; LetterBsbl; CaptTrk; Chrldr; Iowa State Univ; Engineering.

SAUSER, Mark J; Roncalli HS; Omaha, NE; College; Professional.

SAUSER, Theresa M; Marian HS; Omaha, NE; College; Languages.

SAUSSER, Linda M; Oak Park Sr HS; Kansas City, MO; Chr; HonRl; SchMus; PpCl; College; English.

SAUSSER, Victoria L; John Marshall HS; Indianapolis, IN; 10/430 ALAGirlsSt; HonRl; JA; LbryAde; NHS; SctActv; CivCl; PPFtbl; Miami Univ; Law.

SAUTER, Carol; Luther L Wright HS; Ironwood, MI; 7/201 ChrhWkr; CmntyWkr; HonRl; HospAde; LbryAde; FHA; College; Medical Tech.

SAUTER, Jack; Flasher Public HS; Flasher, ND; Chrs; SciCl; Trade School; Vocation.

SAUTER, Joseph A; Fairmount Public HS; Fairmount, ND; PresSrCls; ALBoysSt; Band; HonRl; SchPl; EdYrBk; RptrSchPpr; Bsktbl; Ftbl; Trk; Coll; Farmer.

SAUTER, Patricia A; Lourdes HS; Chicago, IL; 30/299 Chr; CmntyWkr; HonRl; SchPl; Sdlty; FrCl; College; Pharmacy.

SAUTER, Renee M; Maria HS; Chicago, IL; 33/301 CmntyWkr; CncrtBnd; MrchBnd; NHS; Orch; 4-H; VPGerCl; SciCl; AmLegAwd; 4-HAwd; GovHonPrgAwd; Univ Of Illinois.

SAUTTER, David J; Mullen HS; Mullen, NE; Band; Chr; ChrhWkr; HonRl; Mdrgl; 4-H; LetterBsktbl; LetterFtbl; Glf; Swmmng; Clge; Pro Sport Or Teaching.

SAUTTER, Elizabeth A; Wall HS; Wall, SD; 6/47 Band; Chr; ChrhWkr; HonRl; OffAde; SchPl; FHA; PpCl; Bsktbl; LetterTrk; Chrldr; Univ Of So Dakota; Medicine.

SAUVE, Michael J; Memorial HS; Eau Claire, WI; LbryAde; ModUN; NatlMeritSF; SchMus; SchPl; Univ Of Mi; Electrical Engineer.

SAVAGE, Brenda R; Le Sueur HS; Le Sueur, MN; 16/110 PresFrshCls; Band; NHS; PepBnd; Twrl; PpCl; CaptBsktbl; Trk; Chrldr; PPFtbl; Univ Of Minnesota; Liberal Arts.

SAVAGE, Gayle; South Haven HS; Lacota, MI; 50/218 Chr; Chrl; Chrs; HonRl; Mdrgl; SchMus; SchPl; StuCncl; StuGov; TchrAde; Kalamazoo Vall Comm Coll; Dent Hyg.

SAVAGE, James; Addison HS; North Adams, MI; 36/108 ALBoysSt; CncrtBnd; HonRl; MrchBnd; PepBnd; StuCncl; PpCl; Bsbl; Wrstlng; Mich State U.

SAVAGE, Julie A; North Miami HS; Macy, IN; Band; ChrhWkr; CncrtBnd; MrchBnd; PepBnd; SchMus; YthFlsp; RptrSchPpr; PPFtbl; 4-HAwd; Trade; Conservationist.

SAVAGE, Kent W; Carrollton Comm Unit HS; Eldred, IL; 1/87 Band; Chrs; HonRl; MrchBnd; NHS; NatlMeritCmnd; PepBnd; FBLA; Ill College; Chemist.

SAVAGE, Michele A; Bishop Hogan HS; Kansas City, MO; 1/119 Chrs; DrlTm; HonRl; HospAde; PolWkr; SchAde; SchMus; SchPl; StuCncl; StuGov; TchrAde; VPYthFnd; RptrYrbk; SpnCl; MthCl; Univ Of Missouri; Engineering.

SAVAGE, Robert J; Bishop Owenger HS; Ft Wayne, IN; HonRl; LitMag; NatlCathMusEdAsoc; NatlMeritCmnd; PresOrch; SchMus; StuCncl; SchPpr; Tennis; LetterTrk; Notre Dame Univ; Law.

SAVAGLIO, Fred; St Josephs HS; Kenosha, WI; ChrhWkr; HonRl; NHS; RptrYrbk; Ftbl; Glf; IMSpt; College; Professional.

SAVARINO, Bruna; Maria HS; Chicago, IL; HonRl; NHS; StuCncl; FrCl; SpnCl; IMSpt; Wiu; Law.

SAVCIC, Vera; Onsted HS; Onsted, MI; VPJrCls; PresSrCls; ALAGirlsSt; HonRl; NHS; SchPl; Yrbk; LetterTrk; LetterChrldr; Col;.

SAVERS, Dennis E; El Paso HS; El Paso, IL; 13/90 PresJrCls; PresSrCls; AFS; HonRl; IntrClCncl; ModUN; NHS; SchPl; StuGov; CaptWrstlng; College; Biology.

SAVILLE, Janelle L; Braddock Public HS; Moffit, ND; 2/13 TrsSophCls; PresJrCls; Chrs; ChrhWkr; CmntyWkr; HonRl; PolWkr; SchMus; SchPl; StuCncl; CaptBsktbl; LetterTrk; LetterChrldr; North Dakota State Univ; Law Enforcement.

SAVILLE, Terry; Lincoln HS; Des Moines, IA; 109/578 Aud/Vis; Des Moines Area Comm Coll;engineering.

SAVINA, Julie E; Rogers City HS; Rogers City, MI; Aud/Vis; Chr; RedCrAde; HonRl; Mdrgl; NHS; PepBnd; RptrYrbk; SciCl; LetterBsktbl; Lake Superior State College; Medical Tech.

SAVINE, Timothy J; Madison HS; Madison Heights, MI; 4/240 HonRl; NHS; NatlMeritCmnd; Quill&Scroll; RptrSchPpr; SciCl; Univ Of Mi; Biological Sciences.

SAWDON, Marianne M; Douglas Mac Arthur HS; Saginaw, MI; 7/274 HonRl; LitMag; NHS; SchPl; StuGov; TchrAde; FrCl; PpCl; LetterTrk; St Olaf Coll; Nursing.

SAWER, Deanna J; Owosso HS; Henderson, MI; 9/452 ChrhWkr; CncrtBnd; HonRl; MrchBnd; NHS; NatlMeritFnl; PepBnd; 4-H; GAA; CitAwd; Central Mich; Bus Educ Teacher.

SAWHILL, Bruce K; Rochester Adams HS; Rochester, MI; LitMag; NHS; NatlMeritSF; SchMus; SctActv; GerCl; SciCl; LetterSwmmng; Tennis; Univ; Physics.

SAWICKI, Halina A; Madonna HS; Chicago, IL; HonRl; StuCncl; GerCl; MthCl; U Of Illinois; Pharmacy.

SAWICKI, Marie L; O L Of Mt Carmel HS; Wyandotte, MI; 2/55 VPFrshCls; SecSrCls; Chr; HonRl; NHS; Sdlty; StuCncl; StuGov; RptrYrbk; RptrSchPpr; PpCl; Bsktbl; CaptChrldr; IMSpt; Michigan State; Law Enforcement.

SAWIN, Nancy E; Anthon Oto HS; Anthon, IA; 3/33 VPSophCls; DrlTm; HonRl; JrNHS; NHS; StuCncl; EdYrBk; FHA; LetterBsktbl; LetterTrk; Chrldr; Iowa State Univ; Agriculture.

SAWIN, Scott M; Washington HS; Washington, KS; 14/42 SecSophCls; VPJrCls; PresSrCls; ALBoysSt; HonRl; SchPl; StuCncl; TchrAde; Yrbk; LetterTrk; College; Carpentry.

SAWIN, Valerie A; Anthon Oto HS; Anthon, IA; PresJrCls; Band; Chrs; CncrtBnd; HonRl; NHS; PepBnd; SchPl; StuCncl; EdSchPpr; SchPpr; FHA; Trade School; Vocation.

SAWYER, Brian D; Middleton HS; Middleton, WI; CmntyWkr; Bsbl; Bsktbl; Ftbl; CchngActv; IMSpt; U Of Arizona; Social Work.

SAWYER, Carolyn A; Crothersville HS; Crothersville, IN; SecJrCls; Chr; OffAde; SchMus; StuCncl; PpCl;.

SAWYER, Charles G; Desoto HS; Shawnee, KS; ChrhWkr; HonRl; StuCncl; StuGov; TchrAde; IMSpt; Trade School; Electronics Engineer.

SAWYER, Cynthia A; Rushville HS; Rushville, NE; 4/39 PresSophCls; Chr; HonRl; SchPl; FHA; GerCl; PpCl; 4-HAwd; Clge; Elem Ed.

SAWYER, James C; Gretna Public HS; Gretna, NE; ChrhWkr; HonRl; NHS; TchrAde; RptrYrbk; SchPpr; SciCl; University; Professional.

SAWYER, Jeffrey R; Boone Valley HS; Renwick, IA; HonRl; SchPl; LetterBsbl; LetterBsktbl; LetterFtbl; LetterGlf; IMSpt; Clge; Teaching & Coaching.

SAWYER, John; Gibraltar HS; Egg Harbor, WI; CncrtBnd; Quill&Scroll; SchPl; StuGov; RptrSchPpr; SchPpr; 4-H; Bsbl; Bsktbl; Ftbl; Univ; Professional.

SAWYER, Julie A; Cerro Gordo HS; Hammond, IL; HonRl; SchPl; Yrbk; SpnCl; Chrldr; AmLegAwd; DARAwd; Siu; Interpreter.

SAWYER, Karen D; Naperville Central HS; Naperville, IL; Chr; HonRl; NHS; LetterTrk; Chrldr; GAA; IMSpt; College.

SAWYER, Katherine M; Naperville Central HS; Naperville, IL; ChrhWkr; HonRl; NHS; TchrAde; YthFlsp; Trk; GAA; College; Teaching.

SAWYER, Kevin P; Sparta HS; Sparta, MI; PresBand; HonRl; NHS; NatlMeritFnl; SchPl; Coll; Biochemist.

SAWYER, Michael L; St Laurence HS; Chicago, IL; 32/385 ChrhWkr; CmntyWkr; HonRl; NatlMeritSF; SchPl; SctActv; Bsktbl; CchngActv; Univ Of Il; Pre Medicine.

SAWYER, Michael W; Clarkston HS; Clarkston, MI; 48/430 HonRl; JrNHS; NHS; Bsktbl; Glf; Ferris St College; Pharmacy.

SAWYER, Sarah M; Mt Carmel HS; Mt Carmel, IL; 14/185 TrsSophCls; Band; Chrs; MrchBnd; NHS; SchMus; StuCncl; RptrYrbk; FrCl; Chrldr; Wabash Valley College.

SAWYER, Scott W; Lenox Comm HS; Lenox, IA; 8/50 PresSophCls; Chrs; HonRl; LbryAde; Mdrgl; LetterBsbl; LetterBsktbl; LetterGlf; Univ Ia; Acctng.

SAXE, Kenneth D; Edwards Co HS; Albion, IL; PresFrshCls; HonRl; SctActv; LetterBsbl; LetterBsktbl; Swmmng; LetterTrk; 4-HAwd; College; Dentistry.

SAXON, Bruce; Fenton HS; Bensenville, IL; 87/400 HonRl; Ftbl; Glf; U Of Ill; Engineering.

SAXTON, Michael A; Britton Macon HS; Britton, MI; 2/45 VPFrshCls; Chrs; HonRl; NHS; SchPl; YthFlsp; LetterBsbl; LetterBsktbl; LetterFtbl; VoiceDemAwd; Mi State Univ.

SAYERS, Rhonda C; Coleman HS; Coleman, MI; Chr; ChrhWkr; HonRl; NHS; TchrAde; YthFlsp; Yrbk; Mid Michigan Comm College; Nursing.

SAYLER, Cynthia; Hartley Comm HS; Hartley, IA; 1/69 PresSrCls; Chrs; CncrtBnd; HonRl; MrchBnd; YthFlsp; Drake Univ; Liberal Arts.

SAYLER, Jeanice A; Tripp Public HS; Tripp, SD; Chr; Chrl; Chrs; HonRl; SchPl; YthFlsp; RptrYrbk; Yrbk; RptrSchPpr; SchPpr; FHA; Trk; Nettleton College; Cosmetology.

SAYLER, Todd P; Beulah HS; Beulah, ND; PresSophCls; ALBoysSt; Chr; HonRl; LbryAde; SchPl; SctActv; StuCncl; Yrbk; LetterBsktbl; College; Engineering.

SAYLES, Patrick; Oak Park HS; Oak Park, MI; 6/500 RedCrAde; SchMus; FDA; Bsktbl; Mi St Univ; Vet.

SAYLOR, Daniel S; Waterford Kettering HS; Drayton Plains, MI; 8/425 Band; HonRl; JA; CaptMrchBnd; NatlThespSoc; StuCncl; SptEdSchPpr; Bsbl; CaptFtbl; U Of Mich.

SAYLOR, James; Sweet Springs R Vii HS; Sweet Springs, MO; ChrhWkr; HonRl; FFA; Ftbl; Trade; Auto & Diesel Mechanic.

SAYLOR, Jayne A; Metropolis Comm HS; Metropolis, IL; 30/157 ChrhWkr; HonRl; NatlThespSoc; SchMus; SchPl; RptrSchPpr; EdSchPpr; GerCl; PpCl; GAA; Coll; Nurse.

SAYRE, Christie A; Durand Area HS; Durand, MI; 52/177 Chr; HonRl; MrchBnd; OffAde; Quill&Scroll; SchPl; TchrAde; RptrSchPpr; SchPpr; Central Michigan University; Teaching.

SCABORN, Cynthia D; Ottawa Township HS; Ottawa, IL; HonRl; TchrAde; RptrSchPpr; 4-H; FHA; PpCl; Ill Valley Comm Col; Fashion Merch.

SCAFFIDI, Anthony P; St Johns Cathedral HS; Milwaukee, WI; Chrs; CncrtBnd; HonRl; Sacrstn; SctActv; YthFnd; SpnCl; Bsktbl; CchngActv; College; Accountant.

SCALES, Anthony R; Castle HS; Newburgh, IN; 20/311 PresSrCls; ALBoysSt; ChrhWkr; HonRl; StuCncl; KeyCl; LatCl; LetterBsbl; Bsktbl; Ftbl; Trk; Purdue Univ; Pharmacy.

SCALES, Lynette D; Maplewood Richmond HS; Maplewood, MO; 17/199 ALAGirlsSt; CtyCnl; LbryAde; NHS; VPFTA; FrCl; PpCl; Chrldr; GAA; IMSpt; Columbia Col; Fashion Buying & Merchanding.

SCALES, Monarae; Southridge HS; Huntingburg, IN; 1/185 ALAGirlsSt; PresBand; CncrtBnd; DrlTm; HonRl; MrchBnd; SchMus; SctActv; StuCncl; YthFlsp; FrCl; PpCl; Swmmng;.

SCALETTA, Marilee; Prospect Hs; Mt Prospect, IL; DrlTm; DrmMjrt; HonRl; JrNHS; MrchBnd; NHS; VPMthCl; PpCl; GAA; College;nursing Or Business.

SCALETTA, Susan E; J S Morton West HS; Berwyn, IL; 135/755 University Of Illinois; Vet.

SCALF, Linda J; Lewistown Community HS; Lewistown, IL; ChrhWkr; HonRl; NHS; SchPl; StuCncl; Yrbk; EngCl; SpnCl; PpCl; Trade Schl; Beautician.

SCALISE, Catherine A; Queen Of Peace HS; Chicago, IL; 13/416 Chrs; HonRl; NHS; SchPl; VPStuCncl; FrCl; De Paul Univ; Marketing.

SCALPONE, Stephen; Oshkosh North HS; Oshkosh, WI; ALBoysSt; Aud/Vis; StuGov; EdSchPpr; Coll; Computer Engineering.

SCAMAHORN, Ellen B; South Spencer HS; Rockport, IN; Chrs; ChrhWkr; CmntyWkr; HonRl; PolWkr; SchMus; SchPl; TchrAde; RptrYrbk;.

SCANLAN, Brian E; Oaklawn Comm HS; Hometown, IL; 1/667 HonRl; PresNHS; NatlMeritFnl; TchrAde; MthCl; Univ Of Ill; Medicine.

SCANLAN, Brian E; Oak Lawn Community HS; Hometown, IL; 1/667 HonRl; NatlMeritSF; TchrAde; MthCl; U Of Il; Pre Med.

SCANLAN, Deborah A; Almond HS; Bancroft, WI; 4/38 ALAGirlsSt; Band; HonRl; LbryAde; NHS; VPFrshCls; RptrYrbk; RptrSchPpr; LetterTrk; GAA; U Of W; Vet Medicine.

SCANLAN, Joli F; Williston HS; Epping, ND; 19/276 ChrhWkr; HonRl; LbryAde; FFA; PpCl; LetterBsktbl; Trk; GAA; Und Williston; Art.

SCANLAN, Mark K; Abilene HS; Abilene, KS; 20/129 PresSrCls; HonRl; NatlFornLg; NatlMeritSchl; 4-H; Ftbl; IMSpt; 4-HAwd; Kansas State University; Agriculture.

SCANLON, Bruce A; Cheasning HS; Allan Rd, MI; 82/249 Band; CncrtBnd; HonRl; MrchBnd; SchPl; SctActv; Ftbl; Trk; IMSpt; 4-HAwd; Western Mich U; Wildlife Mgmt.

SCANLON, Catherine B; Ladywood St Agnes HS; Indianapolis, IN; Chrs; SctActv; Yrbk; RptrSchPpr; SchPpr; Ball State University; Home Ec.

SCANLON, George P; St Laurence HS; Chicago, IL; 33/376 HonRl; NatlMeritCmnd; SchAde; StuCncl; LetterBsbl; Bsktbl; Glf; Univ Of Notre Dame; Lawyer.

SCANLON, Kathleen M; Bishop Borgess HS; Detroit, MI; 3/500 HonRl; JrNHS; NatlFornLg; NHS; GAA; Univ; Law.

SCANLON, Laurie; Pennfield HS; Battle Creet, MI; CmntyWkr; HonRl; VPSophCls; TchrAde; SpnCl; Univ; Design.

SCANLON, Leslie K; Grand Rapids HS; Grand Rapids, MN; 2/377 AFS; HonRl; ModUN; NatlMeritCmnd; SchMus; SchPl; Yrbk; RptrSchPpr; KiwanAwd; RotaryAwd; Coll Of St Cartherine; Journalism.

SCANLON, Maureen; Mother Mcauley Hs; Chicago, IL; 68/484 HonRl; SchMus; MthCl; Bsbl; Bsktbl; College; Medical Technology.

SCANLON, Randy J; Proviso West HS; Berkeley, IL; 50/1086 Band; CncrtBnd; HonRl; MrchBnd; NHS; PepBnd; RptrSchPpr; PpCl; LetterTrk; U S Naval Academy; Meteorology.

SCANLON, Todd R; St Louis Comm HS; St Louis, MO; ChrhWkr; CmntyWkr; HonRl; SchMus; SchPl; YthFlsp; Wrstlng; IMSpt; College; Professional.

SCANNELL, Sharon R; William Fremd HS; Palatine, IL; Band; Chr; HonRl; LitMag; NHS; NatlThespSoc; SchMus; CaptTwrl; College; Law.

SCARAMUCCI, Paul; Fordson HS; Dearborn, MI; HonRl; NHS; StuCncl; StuGov; RptrYrbk; Ftbl; CitAwd; Henry Ford Comm Coll; Wildlife Biology.

SCARBOROUGH, Shayla S; Valley HS; West Des Moines, IA; 48/435 AFS; CncrtBnd; HonRl; MrchBnd; NatlFornLg; NHS; NatlThespSoc; PepBnd; LatCl; RotaryAwd; U Of Iowa; Speech Pathology.

SCARBROUGH, Linda L; Dearborn HS; Dearborn, MI; TreasAFS; Chr; Chrs; ChrhWkr; HonRl; HospAde; TchrAde; YthFlsp; IMSpt; University; Medicine.

SCARBROUGH, Robert W; Farmer City Mansfield HS; Farmer City, IL; AFS; ALBoysSt; ChrhWkr; HonRl; SchPl; YthFlsp; LetterBsbl; Bsktbl; IMSpt; College; Professional.

SCARNAVACK, Mary C; Maine North HS; Des Plaines, IL; Chr; HonRl; SchMus; SchPl; Eastern Illinois Univ; Psychology.

SCARNECCHIA, Suellyn; Pioneer HS; Ann Arbor, MI; HonRl; NatlMeritFnl; NatlMeritSchl; NatlMeritSF; Orch; SchMus; StuCncl; StuGov; Northwestern Univ; Law.

SCARROW, Thad; Ventura Comm HS; Clear Lake, IA; Band; Chrs; Mdrgl; NHS; SchMus; StuCncl; Ftbl; Trk;.

SCARROW, Thad E; Ventura Community HS; Clear Lake, IA; Band; Chrs; HonRl; Mdrgl; NHS; SchMus; StuCncl; FTA; Ftbl; Trk;.

SCATES, Geron D; Civic Memorial HS; Bethalto, IL; ChrhWkr; HonRl; SctActv; GerCl; PpCl; Bsbl; Coll; Teacher.

SCATURRO, Jefferson M; Plattsmouth HS; Plattsmouth, NE; LetterWrstlng; College; Civil Service.

SCERING, Julee D; Covington HS; Covington, IN; 17/106 Band; ChrhWkr; CncrtBnd; HonRl; HospAde; MrchBnd; StuCncl; Yrbk; PpCl; College; Public Relations.

SCHAACK, Bonnie V; Grace City HS; Grace City, ND; 1/9 Chrs; ChrhWkr; HonRl; PepBnd; SchPl; YthFlsp; SchPpr; 4-H; PpCl; College; Accounting.

SCHAACK, Laura; Sykeston HS; Sykeston, ND; 1/18 PresFrshCls; VPJrCls; Band; Chrs; ChrhWkr; HonRl; StuCncl; RptrSchPpr; 4-H; BttyCrckrAwd; Us Navy; Communications.

SCHAACK, Michael B; Lewis Central HS; Council Bluffs, IA; Band; CncrtBnd; HonRl; NHS; StuCncl; StuGov; LetterBsbl; LetterBsktbl; CchngActv; OptClAwd; University; Professional.

SCHAAD, Janet L; Leigh Community HS; Leigh, NE; SecJrCls; Band; Chrs; HonRl; Mdrgl; PepBnd; SchPl; FHA; PpCl; PPFtbl; Platte Tech Comm Clg; Stenographic Secty.

SCHAAF, Keith A; Mc Bain Public HS; Mc Bain, MI; VPFrshCls; Band; CncrtBnd; HonRl; NHS; SchPl; LetterBsbl; LetterBsktbl; LetterFtbl; LetterTrk; Lake Superior St College; Engineer.

SCHAAF, Margaret R; Superior HS; Superior, NE; 3/92 SecSophCls; VPJrCls; Band; Chrs; CncrtBnd; DrmMjrt; HonRl; NHS; 4-H; PpCl; College; Teacher.

SCHAAF, Mark H; Sidney Comm HS; Randolph, IA; ALBoysSt; Band; CncrtBnd; MrchBnd; StuCncl; 4-H; FFA; LetterBsktbl; LetterFtbl; 4-HAwd; Col; Vocation.

SCHAAF, Robert; Central HS; St Joseph, MO; ALBoysSt; DrmBgl; HonRl; NHS; ROTC; TchrAde; LatCl; MthCl; SciCl; JCAwd; Coll; Math.

SCHAAF, Vivian K; Mc Bain Public HS; Mc Bain, MI; TrsSophCls; Band; HonRl; NHS; PepBnd; SchPl; TchrAde; YthFlsp; CaptBsktbl; Trk; Central Mi Univ; Physical Educ.

SCHAAFSMA, Gerald A; St Anne HS; St Anne, IL; HonRl; VPNHS; FFA; Univ; Engineering.

SCHAAFSMA, James F; St Anne HS; St Anne, IL; HonRl; NHS; FFA; LetterBsktbl; LetterTrk; Univ; Engineering.

SCHAAN, Cindy; Balta HS; Balta, ND; 2/10 SecSophCls; TrsSrCls; Chrs; HonRl; SchPl; RptrYrbk; RptrSchPpr; 4-H; Bsktbl; N D State Univ; Home Economics.

SCHAAR, Lance A; Scranton HS; Scranton, ND; Chr; Chrs; CmntyWkr; YthFlsp; 4-H; SciCl; Ftbl; LetterTrk; IMSpt; Trade School.

SCHAAR, Neil L; Scranton Public HS; Scranton, ND; HonRl; NHS; YthFlsp; 4-H; LetterTrk; IMSpt; Univ; Vet.

SCHAAR, Steven R; Oak Lawn Comm HS; Oak Lawn, IL; 85/686 SctActv; StuGov; Univ Of Illinois; Accountant.

SCHABEN, Jack G; Wentworth Military Academy; Dunlap, IA; HonRl; PolWkr; ROTC; SchPpr; Ftbl; Trade School; Auctioneer.

SCHABEN, Larry J; Harlan Comm HS; Panama, IA; HonRl; LetterTennis; IMSpt; JAAwd; Air Force & Bus Sch; Acctg Or Electronics.

SCHABER, Roberta A; Fraser HS; Fraser, MI; ChrhWkr; FrCl; GAA; IMSpt; Mercy Clge Of Detroit; Nursing.

SCHABES, Karin L; Bogan HS; Chicago, IL; 3/704 Chrs; HonRl; NHS; NatlMeritCmnd; SchMus; RptrYrbk; GerCl; MthCl; SciCl; St Xavier College; Nursing.

SCHACHER, Becky; Carrollton HS; Carrollton, IL; 15/98 TrsJrCls; TrsSrCls; LbryAde; NHS; SchPl; FBLA; PpCl; Trk; Chrldr; GAA; College; Art Field.

SCHACHER, Thomas E; Brandon HS; Ortonville, MI; 1/170 HonRl; NHS; NatlMeritSF; SctActv; TchrAde; GerCl; LetterTrk; DanFAwd; Michigan Technological Univ; Forestry.

SCHACHERBAUER, Diana L; Thayer HS; Thayer, MO; Band; CncrtBnd; JA; MrchBnd; PepBnd; Yrbk; FHA; LetterBsbl; LetterBsktbl; Trk; Beauty School.

SCHACHET, Deborah A; Parkway North HS; Creve Coeur, MO; 6/465 Chr; Chrs; ChrhWkr; CmntyWkr; HospAde; JrNHS; NHS; NatlMeritSF; SctActv; FrCl; College; French & German.

SCHACHNER, Cheryl A; Althoff Catholic HS; O Fallon, IL; 14/316 HonRl; NHS; Yrbk; SpnCl; College; Accounting.

SCHACHT, Cynthia L; Rogers HS; Michigan City, IN; 12/440 Chrs; HonRl; NHS; NatlMeritCmnd; 4-H; GerCl; 4-HAwd; Purdue Univ; Humanities.

SCHACHT, Vivian L; Kewaskum HS; West Bend, WI; 36/177 Chr; HonRl; NatlFornLg; NHS; SchMus; SchPl; TchrAde; VPFTA; Bsktbl; Glf; Trk; Chrldr; PresGAA; Military; Physical Education.

SCHACHTNER, Michael; Sts Peter Paul Area HS; Saginaw, MI; Chr; ChrhWkr; Mdrgl; PepBnd; SchPl; Saginaw Valley St Coll; Music Ed.

SCHACHTNER, William J; Somerset HS; Somerset, WI; 6/60 HonRl; NHS; NatlMeritCmnd; StuCncl; College; General Practitioner.

SCHAD, Donna D; Purdy R Ii HS; Purdy, MO; 1/48 SecTrsFrshCls; ChrhWkr; CmntyWkr; NHS; StuCncl; EdYrBk; FHA; Bsktbl; JAAwd; CitAwd; Smsu; Nursing & Biology.

SCHAD, John P; Marissa HS; Marissa, IL; 1/75 VPSophCls; PresSrCls; PresBand; ChrhWkr; CncrtBnd; HonRl; MrchBnd; PresNHS; PepBnd; Quill&Scroll; SchMus; StuCncl; LetterBsbl; College; Business.

SCHAD, Julie A; St Xaviers HS; Milford, KS; HonRl; StuCncl; YthFlsp; Yrbk; FBLA; TreasFHA; FrCl; PresPpCl; Ks State Univ; Clge Of Ed.

SCHADEWALT, Heidi K; Darlington HS; Argyle, WI; Chrs; DrlTm; Yrbk; 4-H; FHA; SpnCl; Vocational Sch; Secretary.

SCHAECHER, Dan J; Scotus Central HS; Columbus, NE; 11/78 Chrs; HonRl; StuGov; LetterBsktbl; LetterFtbl; LetterTrk; IMSpt; College; Professional.

SCHAECHER, Susan; Scotus Central Catholic HS; Columbus, NE; SecFrshCls; SecJrCls; Chrs; HonRl; RedCrAde; RptrSchPpr; IMSpt; AmLegAwd; Univ Of Ne; Journ.

SCHAEFER, Barbara A; Incarnate Word Academy; Florissant, MO; HonRl; TreasNHS; SchMus; SchPl; TchrAde; CchngActv; IMSpt; College.

SCHAEFER, Cynthia A; Mater Dei HS; Albers, IL; 8/188 Band; Chrs; CncrtBnd; DrmMjrt; HonRl; MrchBnd; NHS; PepBnd; SchMus; SchPl; FrCl; College; Music.

SCHAEFER, David J; Wakonda Public HS; Wakonda, SD; 3/22 ALBoysSt; MrchBnd; NHS; RptrYrbk; SptEdYrbk; 4-H; LetterBsktbl; LetterGlf; LetterTrk; BauchLmbAwd; Sd State U; Electrical Engineering.

SCHAEFER, Deborah L; Edwardsville Sr HS; Edwardsville, IL; 18/430 Band; ChrhWkr; CncrtBnd; DrlTm; HonRl; MrchBnd; NHS; PepBnd; Yrbk; SecGerCl; GAA; Concordia Teachers Coll; Elem Teacher.

SCHAEFER, Denna M; Faulkton Ind HS; Seneca, SD; ALAGirlsSt; Chrs; DrlTm; HonRl; NatlCathMusEdAsoc; SchPl; RptrYrbk; 4-H; Bsktbl; Swmmng; College; Vocation.

SCHAEFER, Gerard T; Platteville HS; Platteville, WI; 58/196 Aud/Vis; Band; CncrtBnd; HonRl; LitMag; MrchBnd; ModUN; PepBnd; FSA; Swmmng; College; Professional Engineering.

SCHAEFER, Gregory L; Arcadia HS; Arcadia, WI; 4/100 Chr; ChrhWkr; CncrtBnd; NatlFornLg; NHS; NatlThespSoc; Orch; SchPl; StuCncl; St Olaf College; Music.

SCHAEFER, Greg W; Oregon Consolidated HS; Oregon, WI; Aud/Vis; HonRl; SchMus; VPFrshCls; Yrbk; Tech College; Accounting.

SCHAEFER, Janet K; Wakonda Public HS; Wakonda, SD; 3/19 HonRl; NHS; TchrAde; Bsbl; Bsktbl; Glf; Swmmng; Tennis; Trk; Chrldr; U Of Sd; Rn.

SCHAEFER, Jonathan P; Notre Dame HS For Boys; Park Ridge, IL; 8/284 HonRl; NHS; NatlMeritCmnd; SchMus; SctActv; StuGov; TchrAde; PpCl; Bsktbl; Trk; Depaul U; Law.

SCHAEFER, Kristine J; Nicollet HS; Nicollet, MN; SecFrshCls; ChrhWkr; HonRl; SchPl; TchrAde; 4-H; PpCl; 4-HAwd; Mn Univ.

SCHAEFER, Mary J; Stormlake Comm HS; Storm Lake, IA; Chr; Chrs; ChrhWkr; HospAde; YthFlsp; College; Vocation.

SCHAEFER, Randy J; Ann A Jonesboro C HS; Jonesboro, IL; Band; IntrClCncl; MrchBnd; Yrbk; SchPpr; LatCl; PpCl; SciCl; Bsktbl; Ftbl; Vocational Tech Inst; Mechanical Engineer.

SCHAEFER, Richard N; Milbank HS; Twin Brooks, SD; Aud/Vis; Band; CncrtBnd; HonRl; MrchBnd; NatlMeritSF; Univ; Computer Science.

SCHAEFER, Rick R; Anna Jonesboro HS; Jonesboro, IL; CmntyWkr; HonRl; IntrClCncl; NatlMeritCmnd; SctActv; FBLA; LatCl; SciCl; Bsbl; Ftbl; Trk; CchngActv; College; Business.

SCHAEFER, Rita; Montrose Ind HS; Montrose, SD; Band; ChrhWkr; CncrtBnd; DrlTm; MrchBnd; RptrYrbk; EdYrBk; RptrSchPpr; Trk; Radiology School; Reg Radiologist.

SCHAEFER, Rita L; Hartford HS; Emporia, KS; Chrs; CncrtBnd; HonRl; MrchBnd; SchMus; FBLA; SpnCl; Bsbl; Bsktbl; Trk; Clge; Music Teacher.

SCHAEFER, Susan L; Holly Senior HS; Fenton, MI; TrsJrCls; TrsSrCls; Chr; ChrhWkr; OffAde; SchMus; SctActv; College; Education.

SCHAEFER, Susan M; St Josephs Academy; St Louis, MO; 4/125 PresSophCls; Chrs; HonRl; NHS; SchMus; SecStuCncl; MthCl; IMSpt; St Louis Univ; Medical Technolgist.

SCHAEFER, Virginia G; Newberry HS; Mcmillan, MI; 4/141 ALAGirlsSt; Band; NHS; TchrAde; YthFlsp; KeyCl; PPFtbl; EldAwd; 4-HAwd; CitAwd; Northern Mich U; Home Ec.

SCHAEFFER, Janice I; E A Johnson HS; Flint, MI; 4/271 Band; Chr; HonRl; NHS; PresStuCncl; Yrbk; FHA; LetterTrk; LetterChrldr; DARAwd; U Of Mi Flint; Math.

SCHAEFFER, Jerry R; Weyanwega HS; Weyanwega, WI; Band; CncrtBnd; HonRl; JA; MrchBnd; StuCncl; LetterBsbl; LetterBsktbl; LetterFtbl; LetterTrk; Stevens Point Univ; Biological Science Acct.

SCHAEFFER, Kathy A; M D S Of Fremont HS; Fremont, IN; 5/64 ChrhWkr; HonRl; NHS; SchMus; SchPl; StuCncl; RptrSchPpr; PresFHA; GAA; BttyCrckrAwd; International Junior College; Accounting.

SCHAEFFER, Rex L; Woodruff HS; Peoria, IL; 8/269 ALBoysSt; TreasBand; TreasCncrtBnd; HonRl; TreasMrchBnd; NHS; Orch; PepBnd; Glf; Swmmng; Ill State U; Accounting.

SCHAETZ, Naomi A; Brookfield Central HS; Brookfield, WI; 18/460 AFS; NHS; FrCl; PpCl; PresAwd; College.

SCHAFBUCH, Paul; Iowa Valley HS; Marengo, IA; 2/73 PresSrCls; Band; HonRl; NatlMeritFnl; NatlThespSoc; PepBnd; SchPl; YthFlsp; FTA; KiwanAwd; Ia Univ; Research Engineer.

SCHAFENACKER, Ann; Concordia Lutheran HS; Ft Wayne, IN; 1/250 Chrs; CtyCnl; HonRl; NHS; Quill&Scroll; RedCrAde; FshEdSchPpr; ChmbCommrsAwd; Kalamazoo Coll; Physician.

SCHAFER, Charles J; Greene Community HS; Dougherty, IA; 8/72 TrsFrshCls; PresJrCls; PresSrCls; Band; HonRl; NHS; 4-H; Trk; Wrstlng; North Ia Area Comm Coll; Accountant.

SCHAFER, Cheryl L; Seymour HS; Liberty, IL; 9/65 Chrs; CmntyWkr; DrlTm; HonRl; NHS; SecStuCncl; TchrAde; 4-H; FHA; VPFTA; TreasPpCl; VPGAA; IMSpt; Quincy College.

SCHAFER, David J; Flasher HS; Flasher, ND; 4/39 ALBoysSt; Chrs; ChrhWkr; HonRl; NHS; Sacrstn; SchPl; StuCncl; StuGov; DanFAwd; Bjc; Agricultural Engr.

SCHAFER, Dennis R; Flasher Public HS; Flasher, ND; 1/42 PresJrCls; Chr; ChrhWkr; HonRl; SchPl; StuCncl; EdYrBk; SciCl; LetterFtbl; College; Architectural Drafting.

SCHAFER, Diane M; Bath HS; Dewitt, MI; 13/78 VPSrCls; Band; CncrtBnd; HonRl; MrchBnd; OffAde; StuCncl; TchrAde; Yrbk; Bsktbl;.

SCHAFER, Jane A; Notre Dame Girls HS; Chicago, IL; 17/303 Chrs; HonRl; LitMag; NHS; Quill&Scroll; RptrSchPpr; EdSchPpr; Triton Comm College; Restaurant Mgmt.

SCHAFER, Janet K; Clay City HS; Coal City, IN; 8/65 Chr; Chrs; ChrhWkr; HonRl; NHS; YthFlsp; 4-H; VPFrCl; PpCl; Bsktbl; University.

SCHAFER, John; Columbus North HS; Columbus, IN; 30/469 TrsSrCls; CmntyWkr; HonRl; LitMag; SctActv; StuGov; Ftbl; Swmmng; Us Army; Md In Toxicology.

SCHAFER, Judith C; Notre Dame HS; Chicago, IL; 17/262 Chr; Chrl; HonRl; LitMag; NHS; RptrSchPpr; FrCl; Coll; Commericial Art.

SCHAFER, Jyme H; Mundelein HS; Mundelein, IL; 18/371 HonRl; SchPl; LetterTennis; Chrldr; GAA; IMSpt;.

SCHAFER, Karen M; East Leyden HS; Schiller Pk, IL; 122/567 HonRl; JA; LitMag; EngCl; JAAwd;.

SCHAFER, Kris G; Griffin HS; Springfield, IL; 50/172 CncrtBnd; DrlTm; College; Law Enforcement.

SCHAFER, Lisa S; Lutheran HS; Mayer, MN; SecJrCls; Chr; ChrhWkr; SchAde; SchPl; RptrSchPpr; SchPpr; 4-H; FTA; Bsktbl; Ftbl; Trk; CchngActv; College; Teaching.

SCHAFER, Mark S; Scottsbluff HS; Scottsbluff, NE; 88/279 Aud/Vis; Chr; Chrs; HonRl; Mdrgl; NatlMeritSF; NatlThespSoc; SchMus; StuGov; KeyCl; College; Tentative Psychology.

SCHAFER, Michael M; Porta HS; Petersburg, IL; JA; SchMus; Yrbk; RptrSchPpr; KeyCl; Bsbl; Ftbl; University Of Missouri; Professional.

SCHAFER, Nickie A; Dickinson HS; Dickinson, ND; 37/203 DrlTm; HonRl; HospAde; NatlFornLg; NatlThespSoc; SchMus; SchPl; RptrYrbk; RptrSchPpr; FNA; GerCl; Tennis; LetterTrk; Grand Forks Univ; Medicine.

SCHAFER, Patrick B; Perry Lecompton HS; Perry, KS; Band; Chrs; CncrtBnd; HonRl; MrchBnd; NatlThespSoc; PepBnd; SchMus; SchPl; 4-H; Univ; Ag Engineering.

SCHAFER, Regina M; Andrean HS; Crown Point, IN; 21/301 CmntyWkr; HonRl; Quill&Scroll; Yrbk; MthCl; Purdue U; Eng.

SCHAFER, Robert; Mt Ayr Comm HS; Mt Ayr, IA; 20/74 HonRl; StuCncl; 4-H; FFA; Ftbl; Wrstlng; 4-HAwd; Univ; Business Study.

SCHAFER, Susan; New Leipzig HS; New Leipzig, ND; TrsFrshCls; ALAGirlsSt; Band; Chr; Chrs; CncrtBnd; PepBnd; Yrbk; SchPpr; Bsktbl; Coll; Curriculum Of Major Study.

SCHAFER, Veronica S; Gothenburg HS; Gothenburg, NE; Band; CncrtBnd; HospAde; MrchBnd; PepBnd; SctActv;.

SCHAFER, Vickie L; Pewamo Westphalia HS; Pewamo, MI; HonRl; VPStuCncl; TchrAde; CaptChrldr; Business School; Accountant.

SCHAFF, Annette C; Flasher Public HS; Shields, ND; SecTrsFrshCls; Band; Chrs; HonRl; SchPl; StuCncl; RptrSchPpr; SciCl; Trk; University; Professional.

SCHAFFER, Cathy A; Redfield HS; Ashton, SD; 5/92 Band; Chrl; Chrs; ChrhWkr; CncrtBnd; HonRl; MrchBnd; PepBnd; SchMus; PpCl; College; Accounting.

SCHAFFER, David L; University Liggett HS; Detroit, MI; 1/77 TrsSophCls; PresJrCls; HonRl; NatlMeritSchl; Orch; EdSchPpr; TreasSpnCl; LetterFtbl; LetterTrk; BauchLmbAwd; Swarthmore Coll.

SCHAFFER, Jacqueline A; Homewood Flossmoor HS; Flossmoor, IL; HonRl; LitMag; NHS; NatlMeritCmnd; TchrAde; YthFlsp; Univ Of Illinois; Medical Illustrator.

SCHAFFER, James W; Orion HS; Orion, IL; 1/120 HonRl; StuCncl; LetterFtbl; Univ Of Illinois; Engineer.

SCHAFFER, June M; Xavier Girls HS; St Louis, MO; Chrl; LitMag; NatlMeritFnl; SchMus; SchPl; RptrSchPpr; SchPpr; FrCl; NCTE; St Louis U; English.

SCHAFFER, Karen M; Heron Lake Public HS; Heron Lake, MN; SecChrs; HonRl; LbryAde; MrchBnd; NHS; TchrAde; Yrbk; SchPpr; Sec4-H; 4-HAwd; College; Elementary Teacher.

SCHAFFER, Kenneth J; Guttenberg Comm HS; Colesburg, IA; 5/73 CncrtBnd; HonRl; Mdrgl; MrchBnd; NHS; PepBnd; SchMus; Yrbk; FTA; MthCl; U Of Iowa; Doctor.

SCHAFFER, Stanley L; Western Comm Unit #306 HS; Neponset, IL; HonRl; NatlThespSoc; SchPl; Yrbk; FFA; FrCl; Ftbl; College.

SCHAFFNER, Delores M; Leeland Public HS; Leeland, ND; 3/28 PresJrCls; ChrhWkr; HonRl; SchPl; StuCncl; TchrAde; EdSchPpr; Bsktbl; Chrldr; LionAwd; Bjc Col; Data Procssing Curriculum.

SCHAFFTER, Michael D; Tipton HS; Tipton, MO; 12/84 VPFrshCls; PresSophCls; ALBoysSt; CncrtBnd; MrchBnd; NHS; YthFlsp; CaptBsktbl; CaptFtbl; Glf; College; Agriculture.

SCHAKEL, Ann K; Delta HS; Muncie, IN; 1/275 ALAGirlsSt; NHS; RptrYrbk; U Of N Carolina; Lawyer.

SCHALBLEY, James R; Marquette HS; Streator, IL; 30/98 ALBoysSt; SchPpr; LetterBsbl; CaptBsktbl; LetterFtbl; Trk; CitAwd; Monmouth Coll; Engi.

SCHALL, Tammy; Broken Bow HS; Broken Bow, NE; Band; Chrs; CncrtBnd; HonRl; MrchBnd; PepBnd; StuCncl; YthFlsp; Yrbk; Chrldr; College; Nursing.

SCHALLER, James R; Logan Sr HS; La Crosse, WI; 10/230 CtyCnl; HonRl; JrNHS; LbryAde; NHS; SctActv; PpCl; LetterBsktbl; IMSpt; ChmbCommrsAwd; Univ Of Wisconsin; Engineering.

SCHALLER, Katherine A; Pope County HS; Rosebud, IL; Band; CncrtBnd; HonRl; MrchBnd; PepBnd; TchrAde; RptrSchPpr; 4-H; 4-HAwd; Trade Sch; Forestry.

SCHALLER, Margaret A; Newman HS; Wausau, WI; 25/130 ChrhWkr; CncrtBnd; HonRl; MrchBnd; SecNHS; PepBnd; RptrSchPpr; Pres4-H; BttyCrckrAwd; 4-HAwd; Univ; Medical.

SCHALLHORN, Valerie R; Lamoille Community HS; Lamoille, IL; SecSophCls; Chrs; ChrhWkr; SchMus; SchPl; YthFlsp; 4-H; FHA; PpCl; GAA; Medical Or Dental Assistant.

SCHAMBER, Joanne M; Kent City HS; Casnovia, MI; 13/90 SecJrCls; ALAGirlsSt; HonRl; Yrbk; RptrSchPpr; PPFtbl; Grand Rapids Jr Clg; Elem Education.

SCHAMBERGER, Jeanne M; Hoxie HS; Hoxie, KS; 2/57 Band; CncrtBnd; HonRl; MrchBnd; FHA;.

SCHAMBURECK, Michael G; Valders HS; Whitelaw, WI; 4/113 VPSrCls; Band; Chrs; HonRl; Mdrgl; MrchBnd; Swmmng; Univ; Computer Programmer.

SCHAMENS, Clarice J; Sparta HS; Sparta, WI; 9#37#38# HonRl; LbryAde; MrchBnd; PepBnd; SchMus; SchPpr; Pres4-H; Tech Inst; Secretarial.

SCHAMENS, David W; O Fallon Twp HS; O Fallon, IL; ChrhWkr; CncrtBnd; HonRl; MrchBnd; Orch; PepBnd; SchMus; University; Law.

SCHANTZ, Marilyn L; Wisner Pilger HS; Wisner, NE; 3/74 TrsJrCls; ChrhWkr; HonRl; LbryAde; VPNHS; PresFHA; DanFAwd; Hesston Coll; Home Ec.

SCHANUEL, Jeffrey L; Bths West HS; Belleville, IL; 55/806 ChrhWkr; NHS; Wrstlng; Col; Engineering.

SCHAPER, Brenda; Halliday Public HS; Halliday, ND; 8/30 HonRl; SchPl; StuCncl; RptrYrbk; FHA; PpCl; SciCl; College; Regustered Nurse.

SCHAPER, Brenda R; Halliday Public HS; Halliday, ND; 4/31 PresJrCls; Band; Chr; Chrs; CncrtBnd; DrlTm; HonRl; MrchBnd; LetterFtbl; LetterTrk; CaptChrldr; SecGAA; Dickinson St Col; Nursing.

SCHAPER, Edwin H; Beulah HS; Beulah, ND; TrsSophCls; Chr; Chrl; Chrs; ChrhWkr; HonRl; LetterBsktbl; LetterTrk; Univ Of North Dakota; Professional.

SCHAPER, Linda K; Notre Dame HS; St Louis, MO; Chr; Chrs; HonRl; JA; NHS; PolWkr; SchMus; GAA; IMSpt; University; Medical Tech.

SCHAPPAUGH, Kathleen A; Pekin HS; Pekin, IL; 32/803 Chr; NHS; LetterBsktbl; LetterTennis; CchngActv; PresGAA; Univ Of Illinois; Corrections.

SCHAPPE, Cathy A; Edgewood HS; Madison, WI; 1/140 VPFrshCls; VPSophCls; VPJrCls; HonRl; JA; StuCncl; College; Math.

SCHARDT, Lucinda R; Davenport Community HS; Davenport, NE; 3/23 PresSrCls; Band; ChrhWkr; HonRl; MrchBnd; PepBnd; SchPl; YthFlsp; 4-H; PpCl; Concordia Tchr College.

SCHARENBERG, Bonnie; Oran HS; Oran, MO; 9/49 TrsSophCls; TrsJrCls; Chr; Chrs; HonRl; SchAde; SchPl; TchrAde; SchPpr; College; Remidial Math Tea Ele.

SCHARF, Antoinette L; Gregory Sr HS; Gregory, SD; 9/456 Chrs; HonRl; HospAde; LbryAde; NatlThespSoc; College.

SCHARF, Danny L; Scottsbluff Senior HS; Scottsbluff, NE; HonRl; Ftbl; IMSpt; Univ; Professional.

SCHARF, Debra; Medicine Valley HS; Curtis, NE; 2/32 HonRl; MrchBnd; NHS; OffAde; StuCncl; YthFlsp; Chrldr; 4-HAwd; PresAwd; Univ Of Neb; Interior Design.

SCHARF, Gary E; Medicine Valley HS; Curtis, NE; Band; CncrtBnd; HonRl; MrchBnd; NHS; PepBnd; 4-H; FFA; Bsktbl; LetterFtbl; 4-HAwd; PresAwd; College; Farming.

SCHARLAU, Vicky L; Arcadia HS; Independence, WI; ChrhWkr; DrlTm; HonRl; NatlFornLg; SecStuCncl; Yrbk; Pres4-H; FHA; LetterTrk; GAA; 4-HAwd; Univ Of Wi; Agriculture.

SCHARNHORST, Douglas J; Catholic Boys HS; Quincy, IL; 1/72 PresBand; CncrtBnd; HonRl; MrchBnd; SctActv; EngCl; Univ Of Illinois; Business Administration.

SCHARNOWSKE, Jeffery D; River Valley HS; Sawyer, MI; 2/154 HonRl; NHS; Michigan State Univ; Accounting.

SCHARNOWSKE, Lyle J; Highland HS; Anderson, IN; 47/247 HstFrshCls; HstSophCls; HstJrCls; StuCncl; Bsktbl; Ftbl; Trk; OptClAwd; RotaryAwd;.

SCHARP, Dennis L; Shenandoah HS; Shenandoah, IA; TrsFrshCls; ALBoysSt; JrNHS; StuCncl; FFA; KeyCl; CaptBsktbl; LetterTrk; AmLegAwd; KiwanAwd; RotaryAwd; Trade School.

SCHARPING, Gary S; William Horlick HS; Racine, WI; 201/525 ChrhWkr; SchAde; LetterTrk; College.

SCHARRER, Alan J; Slinger HS; Allenton, WI; Band; Chrs; CncrtBnd; MrchBnd; PepBnd; StuCncl; Glf; LetterSwmmng; Tennis; RotaryAwd; Univ Of Wisconsin; Medicine.

SCHARTNER, Cindy A; Sevastopol HS; Egg Harbor, WI; SecJrCls; SecSrCls; Chrs; SchPpr; 4-H; FHA; PpCl; Bsktbl; College; Child Care Assistant.

SCHARTZ, Jan M; Larned Sr HS; Larned, KS; VPFrshCls; VPSophCls; Band; ChrhWkr; CmntyWkr; HonRl; NHS; 4-H; Bsbl; LetterBsktbl; LetterTrk; GAA; PPFtbl; 4-HAwd; St Marys Of The Plains; Medical Tech.

SCHARTZ, Jorja K; Liberal HS; Liberal, KS; Chr; ChrhWkr; HonRl; LitMag; SchPl; SpnCl; Junior College; Art.

SCHATZ, Blaine G; Balfour Public HS; Balfour, ND; PresFrshCls; PresSophCls; VPJrCls; SchPl; SchPpr; LetterBsktbl; Trade Sch.

SCHATZ, Carol J; Maine East HS; Des Plaines, IL; HonRl; JrNHS; NatlMeritCmnd; Swmmng; Trk; Washington Univ; Engr.

SCHATZ, Dinah L; Marian Heights Acad; St Meinrad, IN; Band; Orch; SchMus; SchPl; Sdlty; 4-H; Trk; CitAwd; U Of Evansville; Music.

SCHAU, Millie C; Tarkio HS; Tarkio, MO; ChrhWkr; CmntyWkr; HonRl; HospAde; MrchBnd; SchPl; YthFlsp; RptrSchPpr; FHA; IMSpt; Univ Of Mo; Elementary Art.

SCHAU, Susan M; Mchenry HS; Wonder Lake, IL; 4-H; FBLA;.

SCHAUB, Gary J; St Mary HS; Suttons Bay, MI; 2/16 VPJrCls; Chr; HonRl; SctActv; Yrbk; Bsbl; Bsktbl; College; Biology.

SCHAUBERT, David L; Bowdon Public HS; Bowdon, ND; ALBoysSt; HonRl; EdYrBk; Yrbk; 4-H; LetterBsktbl; LetterFtbl; LetterTrk; North Dakota State Univ; Agricultural Eng.

SCHAUBERT, Penney L; Rowdon Public HS; Rowdon, ND; SecFrshCls; TrsSophCls; SecJrCls; Band; Chrs; HonRl; 4-H; LetterBsktbl; LetterTrk; LetterChrldr; University; Teacher.

SCHAUBERT, Steven; Bowdon HS; Heaton, ND; JA; SchMus; SchPl; YthFlsp; RptrSchPpr; 4-H; 4-HAwd; St Sch Of Sci; Auto Mech.

SCHAUDER, Martin; Harper Creek HS; Battle Creek, MI; HonRl; LbryAde; College; Chemistry.

SCHAUER, David J; Southwest HS; Green Bay, WI; HonRl; KeyCl; University; Professional.

SCHAUER, Dawn M; Bismarck HS; Bismarck, ND; HospAde; NHS; OffAde; SchPl; TchrAde; GerCl; Kansas State Univ; Vet Medicine.

SCHAUF, Kimberly J; Bishop Miege HS; Overland Park, KS; 2/199 Chr; HonRl; Co State College; Forestry.

SCHAUNAMAN, Pearl L; Frederick HS; Westport, SD; SecTrsSrCls; HonRl; YthFlsp; 4-H; LetterTrk; Coll; Professional.

SCHAUS, Susan M; Nazareth Academy; La Grange, IL; TrsSrCls; Chrs; OffAde; SchAde; SchMus; SchPl; SctActv; StuCncl; StuGov; Yrbk; Tennis; GAA; Illinois State Univ; Biology.

SCHAWL, Vicki L; Centralia HS; Centralia, MO; Band; HonRl; NHS; SchMus; SctActv; FSA; SpnCl; SciCl; Chrldr; GAA; U Of Missouri; Medicine.

SCHEBERL, Susan K; Lomira HS; Lomira, WI; ALAGirlsSt; Band; CncrtBnd; HonRl; MrchBnd; NatlFornLg; NHS; PepBnd; CaptChrldr; GAA; College; Art.

SCHECHINGER, Lee M; Harlan Community HS; Harlan, IA; LetterFtbl; Swmmng; LetterTrk; LetterWrstlng; IMSpt; KiwanAwd; PresAwd; College; Vocation.

SCHECK, Joel C; Unionville Sebewaing HS; Seewaing, MI; 31/125 Chrs; ChrhWkr; HonRl; YthFlsp; 4-H; LatCl; Bsbl; 4-HAwd; Coll; Conservation.

SCHECK, Patrice R; Salem Central HS; Salem Oaks, WI; PresFrshCls; PresJrCls; Band; ChrhWkr; RptrYrbk; SpnCl; Trk; Chrldr; College; Journalism.

SCHECKEL, Debra A; Central HS; Kenosha, WI; 11/208 Band; CncrtBnd; HonRl; MrchBnd; NHS; PepBnd; SchMus; Uw Parkside; Music.

SCHECKLMAN, Bonnie D; Columbus HS; Marshfield, WI; 13/117 HonRl; NHS; Yrbk; SchPpr; GerCl; College; Elem Education.

SCHEEL, Curtis J; Ladysmith HS; Ladysmith, WI; PresBand; ChrhWkr; CncrtBnd; HonRl; MrchBnd; NHS; PepBnd; SchMus; LetterFtbl; LetterTrk; CaptIMSpt; PresAwd; Univ; Medical.

SCHEEL, Susan E; Airport HS; Flat Rock, MI; HstSophCls; HonRl; NHS; StuCncl; Yrbk; FrCl; LetterBsktbl; Chrldr; University.

SCHEEL, Tammy S; Turner HS; Kansas City, KS; ChrhWkr; LbryAde; NatlThespSoc; PolWkr; SchMus; SchPl; SctActv; TchrAde; College; English.

SCHEEN, Delynn J; Alpena HS; Lachine, MI; 11/725 SecJrCls; ChrhWkr; CncrtBnd; HonRl; NatlMeritCmnd; Orch; SchMus; 4-H; DanFAwd; EldAwd; Eastern Mich Univ; Med Tech.

SCHEER, Gary J; Maple Valley HS; Mapleton, IA; 1/100 ChrhWkr; ModUN; NatlMeritSF; PolWkr; SchPl; RptrYrbk; FSA; FTA; College; Aerospace Engineering.

SCHEERES, David E; G P South HS; Grosse Pte Farms, MI; 22/627 Aud/Vis; Band; Chr; HonRl; NHS; NatlMeritSF; TchrAde; PresGerCl; Trk; IMSpt; Calvin College; Medicine.

SCHEETZ, Barbara K; Clear Creek Comm HS; Oxford, IA; 1/66 VPSrCls; Band; CncrtBnd; HonRl; LbryAde; MrchBnd; ModUN; NHS; LetterBsbl; CaptBsktbl; U Of Ia; Medicine.

SCHEFDORE, Lynn M; Oconto Falls HS; Stiles, WI; Chr; Chrs; CaptDrlTm; HonRl; OffAde; SchAde; TchrAde; RptrSchPpr; SchPpr; CchngActv; Univ Of Wisconsin; Advertising.

SCHEFELKER, Judy S; Little Wolf HS; Manawa, WI; 24/79 VPSrCls; ALAGirlsSt; VPBand; Chr; SecChrs; ChrhWkr; CncrtBnd; HonRl; LetterBsbl; LetterBsktbl; Techanical School; Lp Nursing.

SCHEFFEL, Robin; Maine Twp Hs; Des Plaines, IL; HonRl; NHS; NatlMeritCmnd; PpCl; GAA; Luther College; Biology.

SCHEFFLER, Kenneth J; Gabriel Richard HS; Trenton, MI; 3/155 PresFrshCls; ALBoysSt; HonRl; NHS; PolWkr; SchMus; SchPl; StuCncl; StuGov; RptrSchPpr; Grand Valley State Col; Attorney.

SCHEFFLER, Lynn M; Wheaton North HS; Wheaton, IL; 60/290 Chr; DrlTm; HonRl; Mdrgl; VPNatlFornLg; NatlThespSoc; SchMus; SchPl; TchrAde; Clge; Pro Actress.

SCHEFFLER, Michael A; Alex Hamilton HS; Milwaukee, WI; 113/700 Aud/Vis; SchAde; Yrbk; SpnCl; MthCl; LetterBsbl; LetterBsktbl; IMSpt; Univ Of Wi Milwaukee; Accounting.

SCHEFKE, John; Mercy HS; Overland, MO; 40/180 Band; CncrtBnd; HonRl; NHS; PepBnd; SchMus; SciCl; College; Accounting.

SCHEIBER, Phillip M; Huntington Catholic HS; Huntington, IN; 11/40 SecFrshCls; Chrs; HonRl; SchMus; SchPl; StuCncl; Bsbl; Bsktbl; Notre Dame Univ; Writer.

SCHEIBLE, Daniel W; Norborne HS; Norborne, MO; VPFrshCls; ALBoysSt; SchPl; PresStuCncl; FFA; FrCl; LetterFtbl; LetterTrk; Wrstlng; Col; Coach.

SCHEIBMEIR, Monica S; Sacred Heart HS; Salina, KS; PresSophCls; ALAGirlsSt; SecStuCncl; SecFBLA; SecFHA; Chrldr; College; Nurse.

SCHEID, Diane K; Greendale HS; Greendale, WI; 3/338 Chr; HonRl; HospAde; ModUN; NHS; PresPpCl; GAA; College; Physical Therapy.

SCHEID, Douglas K; Frankfort HS; Frankfort, IN; 9/274 Band; CmntyWkr; HonRl; HospAde; JrNHS; NHS; RedCrAde; SchMus; SchPl; YthFlsp; Swmmng; Tennis; Wabash College; Medicine.

SCHEID, Kenneth J; Belding Central HS; Belding, MI; CncrtBnd; HonRl; MrchBnd; NHS; NatlMeritSF; 4-H; PpCl; IMSpt; U Of Mi;.

SCHEID, Kenneth O; Colo Comm HS; Nevada, IA; Band; Chr; ChrhWkr; CmntyWkr; CncrtBnd; MrchBnd; SchMus; YthFlsp; 4-H; FFA; Iowa State Univ; Agricultural Business.

SCHEIDLER, Andrew D; Roncalli HS; Indianapolis, IN; ALBoysSt; HonRl; GerCl; MthCl; Ftbl; LetterWrstlng; Rose Hulman Inst Of Tech; Chemical Engineer.

SCHEIDLER, Mary Ann R; Academy Of The Immaculate Con; Greensburg, IN; TrsSophCls; ChrhWkr; CmntyWkr; PolWkr; SecStuCncl; RptrYrbk; Pres4-H; SpnCl; CaptBsbl; Bsktbl; SecGAA; 4-HAwd; Univ Of Indiana; Social Worker.

SCHEIDT, Catherine M; Joliet East HS; Joliet, IL; 131/381 Chr; Chrs; ChrhWkr; HonRl; JA; SchMus; StuCncl; 4-H; Trade School; Nursing.

SCHELDRUP, Chris; Washington HS; Washington, IA; SecFrshCls; ALBoysSt; NatlFornLg; FTA; Trk; IMSpt; Drake U Or U Of Northern Iowa; History, Law.

SCHELFHOUT, Sharon M; Necedah HS; Necedah, WI; 4/42 SecSrCls; ALAGirlsSt; Chrs; HonRl; NHS; VPFHA; CaptChrldr; GAA; BttyCrckrAwd; DARAwd; Tech Sch; Interior Decorator.

SCHELFHOUT, Stephen J; Joliet Township W HS; Joliet, IL; 68/508 PresSrCls; HonRl; NHS; StuCncl; StuGov; FrCl; LetterFtbl; LetterSwmmng; IMSpt; College; Medicine.

SCHELFHOUT, Stephen J; Joliet Twp West HS; Joliet, IL; 54/495 PresSrCls; HonRl; NHS; StuCncl; StuGov; FrCl; Bsbl; Bsktbl; Ftbl; University; Medicine.

SCHELHAAS, Alan D; Edgerton Public HS; Edgerton, MN; Chrs; ChrhWkr; SchPl; StuCncl; 4-H; FTA; GerCl; LetterBsbl; LetterBsktbl; LetterFtbl; College;.

SCHELHAAS, Marsha J; Edgerton Public HS; Edgerton, MN; SecFrshCls; SecJrCls; CmntyWkr; SchPl; Twrl; EdSchPpr; FHA; GerCl; Bsktbl;.

SCHELICH, Chris; Duchesne HS; St Charles, MO; 9/145 Band; Chrs; CncrtBnd; DrmMjrt; HonRl; MrchBnd; NHS; TchrAde; LatCl; College; Math.

SCHELL, Gail L; Lasalle Peru Twp HS; Peru, IL; 83/490 AFS; Band; ChrhWkr; CncrtBnd; HonRl; MrchBnd; PepBnd; SchMus; YthFlsp; SpnCl; College; Music.

SCHELL, Jayne M; Blair Oaks HS; Jefferson City, MO; 25/51 Band; CncrtBnd; HonRl; MrchBnd; PepBnd; RptrSchPpr; 4-H; FBLA; FHA; PpCl;.

SCHELL, Linda L; Lewiston HS; Minneiska, MN; PresChrs; HonRl; SchPl; StuCncl; TchrAde; Yrbk; 4-H; FTA; PresGAA; 4-HAwd; Winona Vocational Tech; Farming.

SCHELLENBERG, Terry L; Nekoma HS; Nekoma, ND; PresFrshCls; HonRl; CivCl; 4-H; SpnCl; LetterBsktbl; LetterChrldr; GAA; 4-HAwd; Art Institute; Art Instructor.

SCHELLENTRAGER, Joyce L; Glenbrook North HS; Northbrook, IL; 51/610 SecAFS; HonRl; NHS; GAA; IMSpt; Univ Of Illinois; English.

SCHELLENTRAYER, Joyce L; Glenbrook North HS; Northbrook, IL; 51/610 SecAFS; HonRl; NHS; GAA; Univ Of Ill; English.

SCHELLER, Steve L; Waupaca HS; Waupaca, WI; Chr; Chrs; HonRl; SchMus; PresYthFlsp; Treas4-H; TreasFFA; KeyCl; IMSpt; 4-HAwd; Coll; Agriculture.

SCHELLHAS, Julie A; Frankenmuth HS; Vassar, MI; 39/158 SecChr; ChrhWkr; SchMus; College; Vocation.

SCHELLINGEIHOUT, Tom N; Crystal City HS; Crystal City, MO; 21/85 ALBoysSt; ChrhWkr; HonRl; NHS; Orch; SctActv; Trk; IMSpt; Westminster College; History Major.

SCHELP, Monica L; Union HS; Union, MO; 1/165 ALAGirlsSt; Chr; ChrhWkr; HonRl; LitMag; NHS; SchMus; YthFlsp; SpnCl; PPFtbl; Se Missouri State Univ; Computer Science.

SCHELSKE, Cynthia A; Ann Arbor Pioneer HS; Ann Arbor, MI; Orch; SpnCl; Univ; Math Or Law.

SCHEMEL, Kathy R; Oak Ridge HS; Perryville, MO; 2/21 VPSophCls; PresJrCls; TrsSrCls; HonRl; SchPl; Treas4-H; TreasPpCl; DARAwd; Browns Bus School; Secretary.

SCHEMM, Paula; Appleton East HS; Appleton, WI; 63/525 AFS; ChrhWkr; PpCl; GAA; Bellin Mem Hosp Sch Of Nrsng; Rn.

SCHEMP, Patty L; Leola Public HS; Leola, SD; Band; Chr; Chrl; Chrs; ChrhWkr; CmntyWkr; CncrtBnd; HonRl; Mdrgl; MrchBnd; PepBnd; SchMus; SchPl; RptrYrbk; EdYrBk; Sdsu; Nurse.

SCHEMPP, Delayne; Montpelier Public HS; Montpelier, ND; /21 HonRl; SchPl; RptrYrbk; RptrSchPpr; State School Of Science In Wahpeton General.

SCHENCK, Gordon L; Algona HS; Algona, IA; 7/128 ALBoysSt; Band; Chrs; CncrtBnd; HonRl; NHS; PepBnd; RptrSchPpr; CaptFtbl; LetterWrstlng; Drake Univ; Pharmacy.

SCHENCK, Kenneth A; Andrew Jackson HS; South Bend, IN; Band; CncrtBnd; HonRl; MrchBnd; NHS; NatlMeritSF; PepBnd; SchMus; College; Accountant.

SCHENCK, Sandra K; Nauvoo Clousa HS; Nauvoo, IL; ALAGirlsSt; Aud/Vis; Chr; ChrhWkr; CmntyWkr; HonRl; LbryAde; TchrAde; YthFlsp; FBLA; Bus Sch; Prof.

SCHENK, Diane L; Lisbon Community HS; Lisbon, IA; Chrs; HonRl; SchMus; SchPl; StuCncl; RptrYrbk; Bsktbl; Col; Nursing.

SCHENK, Diane R; Windom Area HS; Windom, MN; Band; Chr; ChrhWkr; CncrtBnd; HonRl; MrchBnd; PepBnd; 4-H; FTA; Business School; Secretarial.

SCHENK, Krista J; Lincoln HS; Rudolph, WI; 32/570 Chr; HonRl; NHS; NatlMeritCmnd; College; Math.

SCHENK, Mark G; Thomas More Prep HS; Olmitz, KS; 4/63 CncrtBnd; HonRl; MrchBnd; ModUN; NatlMeritCmnd; PepBnd; SchPl; SecStuCncl; YthFlsp; PpCl; IMSpt; St Fidelis Seminary; Math.

SCHENK, Mary A; Marquette HS; Alton, IL; Chrs; HonRl; JrNHS; LitMag; NatlThespSoc; SchPl; RptrSchPpr; LatCl; PpCl; Univ; Home Econ.

SCHENK, Nancy; Tankton HS; Mission Hill, SD; HonRl; NHS; Quill&Scroll; RptrSchPpr; SptEdSchPpr; Univ; Professional Medicine.

SCHENK, Steve R; Otis Bison Sr HS; Olmitz, KS; Band; CncrtBnd; HonRl; MrchBnd; NHS; SchPl; Bsbl; Bsktbl; Ftbl; Trk; Service; Electronics.

SCHEPERLE, Susan E; Cole R 1 HS; Lohman, MO; 3/68 SecFrshCls; VPSophCls; Chrs; HonRl; LbryAde; NHS; FHA; Central Missouri State Univ; Business.

SCHEPERS, Keith R; Dubois HS; Jasper, IN; 6/79 HonRl; College; Professional.

SCHEPERS, Lyle H; Delwood Community HS; Lost Nation, IA; Chr; Chrl; Chrs; ChrhWkr; HonRl; Mdrgl; SchPl; Univ Of Dubuque; Special Educ.

SCHEPERS, Robert A; Chaminade College Prep; St Louis, MO; 18/107 HonRl; NHS; IMSpt; College; Accounting.

SCHEPPLER, Jill I; Ankeny Senior HS; Ankeny, IA; 25/214 Chr; ChrhWkr; CncrtBnd; HonRl; LitMag; MrchBnd; NHS; OffAde; PepBnd; PolWkr; Yrbk; Des Moines Area Comm College; Literature.

SCHER, Christine M; Huntington Catholic HS; Huntington, IN; 10/40 VPFrshCls; PresSophCls; Chrs; SchMus; SchPl; RptrYrbk; RptrSchPpr; 4-H; Bsktbl; Trk; Public Relations.

SCHER, Julia; Huntington Catholic Hs; Huntington, IN; 4/36 SecJrCls; HonRl; SchPl; StuCncl; Yrbk; PpCl; CaptBsktbl; Glf; GAA; 4-HAwd; College; Writer.

SCHERBARTH, Janene A; Hay Springs HS; Hay Springs, NE; 20/40 HstSrCls; LbryAde; 4-H; PpCl; 4-HAwd; College; Med Secretary.

SCHERBRING, Laura J; Beckman HS; Dyersville, IA; Band; Chr; Chrs; CncrtBnd; MrchBnd; Orch; PepBnd; SchMus; SchPl; SctActv; Central Col Pella; Art.

SCHERDT, Patricia J; Saline HS; Saline, MI; HonRl; SctActv; TchrAde; YthFlsp; FHA; Eastern Mi U; Bus Ed.

SCHERER, Anthony J; Lincoln HS; Manitowoc, WI; PresJrCls; ALBoysSt; Chrs; HonRl; StuCncl; LetterBsbl; LetterBsktbl; LetterFtbl; College; Accounting.

SCHERER, Gary W; University HS; Centerview, MO; TrsSrCls; ChrhWkr; HonRl; NHS; RptrYrbk; SptEdYrbk; PresFFA; Bsbl; CaptFtbl;.

SCHERER, James F; Loyola Academy; Deerfield, IL; HonRl; NatlMeritFnl; NatlMeritSF; PolWkr; SchPpr; LetterSocr; Swmmng; Univ Of Notre Dame; Medicine.

SCHERER, Jean D; Richwoods HS; Peoria, IL; 4/449 Chrs; HonRl; LbryAde; TchrAde; SchPpr; GAA; College.

SCHERER, Karen A; Bishop Dwenger Catholic HS; Columbia City, IN; Chr; Chrs; ChrhWkr; HonRl; GerCl; College; Social Worker.

SCHERER, Pamela S; Holly Senior HS; Holly, MI; Chrl; Chrs; HonRl; Mdrgl; SchMus; SchPl; TchrAde; RptrSchPpr; FTA; College; Education.

SCHERER, Peter A; Lakeview Sr HS; Battle Creek, MI; HonRl; SctActv; StuCncl; StuGov; Socr; Kellogg Comm College; Law.

SCHERESKY, Kimberly A; United Public HS; Des Lacs, ND; Chrs; ChrhWkr; LbryAde; OffAde; SchMus; RptrSchPpr; SciCl; Bsktbl; Trk; GAA; Coll; Major Study.

SCHERF, Jordan T; Evanston Township HS; Evanston, IL; ChrhWkr; HonRl; Orch; SchMus; College; Sciences.

SCHERI, Susan M; La Salle Peru Twn HS; Oglesby, IL; 25/400 DrlTm; HonRl; FrCl; PpCl; No Illinois Univ; Physical Therapy.

SCHERLING, Faith E; Hanover HS; Hollenberg, KS; Chrs; HonRl; OffAde; TchrAde; YthFlsp; PresFHA; SciCl; LetterBsktbl; Chrldr; College; Vocational Home Economics.

SCHERMERHORN, John P; Loyola Academy; Deerfield, IL; 62/442 HonRl; NHS; LetterSwmmng; Univ Of Wisconsin; Medicine.

SCHERMERHORN, Thomas R; Ripon Sr HS; Ripon, WI; 7/180 ALBoysSt; HonRl; NHS; StuCncl; Bsktbl; LetterFtbl; Trk; Univ; Engineer.

SCHERR, Connie M; Trego Comm HS; Collyer, KS; Band; Chr; ChrhWkr; HonRl; Orch; Yrbk; 4-H; SecSciCl; Bsbl; Bsktbl; Fort Hays Ks State Col6; Nursing.

SCHERR, David A; Cardinal Muench Seminary; Napoleon, ND; PresJrCls; PresSrCls; Band; Chr; Chrs; ChrhWkr; SchPl; SctActv; StuCncl; StuGov; SptEdSchPpr; CaptTrk; Mary College; Accounting.

SCHERR, Mark; South Tech HS; St Louis, MO; Band; CncrtBnd; HonRl; JA; PepBnd; 4-H; FFA; CchngActv; IMSpt; Coll; Forestry.

SCHERR, Michelle M; Hazelwood Central HS; Florissant, MO; SecTrsJrCls; DrlTm; HonRl; NHS; SctActv; RptrYrbk; RptrSchPpr; EdSchPpr; PpCl; College; Jounralism.

SCHERRER, Donald H; Salem Central HS; New Munster, WI; 13/214 HonRl; RptrSchPpr; FFA; College; Applied Science.

SCHERRER, Maureen L; Highland Comm HS; Riverside, IA; 8/50 SecTrsSophCls; SecTrsSrCls; CmntyWkr; HonRl; SecNHS; RptrYrbk; EdYrBk; SchPpr; LetterBsbl; College.

SCHERSCHEL, Sharon L; Mitchell HS; Mitchell, IN; ChrhWkr; CmntyWkr; HonRl; NHS; Quill&Scroll; RptrSchPpr; Pres4-H; DanFAwd; DARAwd; 4-HAwd; Purdue Univ; Fashion Merchandising.

SCHERTZ, April R; El Paso HS; El Paso, IL; 4/89 SecFrshCls; PresAFS; HonRl; NHS; SchPl; YthFlsp; Sec4-H; SecFFA; SecSpnCl; Univ; Prof Doctor.

SCHERTZ, Debra S; Metamora Township HS; Metamora, IL; 11/171 AFS; Band; HonRl; NHS; PresYthFlsp; 4-H; GAA; AmLegAwd; Goshen College.

SCHERTZ, Nancy L; Wheaton Warrenville HS; Wheaton, IL; 5/212 AFS; Band; CncrtBnd; HonRl; MrchBnd; PresNHS; StuCncl; TchrAde; Yrbk; PpCl; Trk; LetterChrldr; GovHonPrgAwd; Univ Of Iowa; Dental Hygienist.

SCHETTLER, Robert N; Iron Mountain HS; Iron Mountain, MI; HonRl; NHS; CaptBsktbl; Michigan Tech Univ; Mechanical Engineering.

SCHEU, Jean M; Rice Lake HS; Rice Lake, WI; 8/280 Band; Chr; HonRl; LbryAde; MrchBnd; NHS; NatlMeritSF; PepBnd; GAA; PresAwd; Univ; Nursing.

SCHEUER, Christopher J; St Clair HS; St Clair, MI; 32/190 PresFrshCls; ALBoysSt; HonRl; SchPl; StuCncl; StuGov; TchrAde; Bsktbl; LetterTrk; IMSpt; Oakland Univ; Civil Engr.

SCHEUER, Robert F; Holy Cross HS; River Grove, IL; 30/340 HonRl; GerCl; MthCl; Glf; Loyola Univ; Pharmacy.

SCHEUERN, Mark G; Clarkston HS; Clarkston, MI; Aud/Vis; HonRl; Mi State U; Astrophysics.

SCHEUFLER, Greta; Usd 351 HS; Belpre, KS; Chrs; ChrhWkr; CmntyWkr; CncrtBnd; HonRl; MrchBnd; PepBnd; SchPl; PpCl; Tennis; Ks St Univ; Air Line Steward.

SCHEUMANN, Debra; Heritage Hs; Hoagland, IN; TrsSophCls; Chr; ChrhWkr; CmntyWkr; HospAde; MrchBnd; NatlFornLg; SchMus; YthFlsp; GAA; Nursing Rn.

SCHEURICH, Anne M; Academy Of Our Lady HS; Chicago, IL; 8/180 HonRl; VPNHS; StuGov; GAA; IMSpt; Carleton College; Doctor.

SCHEURING, Karen M; Monroe HS; St Paul, MN; StuCncl; Yrbk; SchPpr; Chrldr; Col;.

SCHEVE, Rita T; St Elizabeth Academy; St Louis, MO; 6/116 ChrhWkr; HonRl; NHS; SchPl; StuCncl; GAA; IMSpt; College; Theology.

SCHEWE, Carol A; Mother Of Sorrows HS; Chicago, IL; 1/165 Chrl; ChrhWkr; HonRl; NHS; StuCncl;

TchrAde; FNA; PpCl; GAA; VoiceDemAwd; College; Nursing.

SCHEWE, Kevin L; Riverview Gardens HS; St Louis, MO; 40/733 CtyCnl; HonRl; NHS; StuCncl; LetterFtbl; Univ Of Missouri; Medicine.

SCHEY, Tim S; Niles West HS; Skokie, IL; NHS; KeyCl; LetterSocr; LetterTennis; IMSpt; University Of Illinois.

SCHIAPPACASSE, Mary H; Immaculata HS; Detroit, MI; 1/105 Chrl; CmntyWkr; CncrtBnd; HonRl; NHS; SchAde; StuGov; EdYrBk; SptEdYrbk; SpnCl; LetterBsbl; CaptBsktbl; IMSpt; University Of Mich; Medicine.

SCHIAVO, Jon; Forest Park HS; Crystal Falls, MI; 8/81 Band; ChrhWkr; CncrtBnd; HonRl; MrchBnd; Univ, Biology.

SCHIAVO, Julie; Forest Park HS; Crystal Falls, MI; 2/81 Chrs; CncrtBnd; HonRl; HospAde; Mdrgl; MrchBnd; PepBnd; StuCncl; FNA; College, Nursing.

SCHICK, Patricia A; Menominee HS; Menominee, MI; 27/278 Chr; HonRl; NHS; OffAde; SchPl; FrCl; Univ Of Wi; Civil Engineering.

SCHIEBER, Cindy C; Maryville R Ii HS; Maryville, MO; Chrs; ChrhWkr; HonRl; StuCncl; 4-H; FHA; PpCl; Bsbl; Bsktbl; Trk; Nwms Univ; Vocation.

SCHIEBER, Judith A; Eureka HS; Eureka, IL; Band; Chr; VPChrl; CaptDrlTm; NHS; NatlMeritSF; SchMus; SchPl; StuCncl; EdSchPpr; Pres4-H; SecFrCl; DARAwd; College; Journalism.

SCHIEBER, Mark; Jefferson HS; Stanberry, MO; 1/22 PresSophCls; PresSrCls; ALBoysSt; HonRl; StuCncl; StuGov; Bsktbl; Trk; IMSpt; Coll.

SCHIEBER, Paul W; Maryville HS; Maryville, MO; HonRl; NHS; SctActv; LetterWrstlng; University; Accounting.

SCHIEBERL, Jeffrey S; Bettendorf HS; Bettendorf, IA; Chrs; SchMus; SchPpr; Saint Ambrose College; Computer Sciences.

SCHIEF, David S; Muskego HS; Hales Corners, WI; 89/328 Band; HonRl; IMSpt; College; Accounting.

SCHIEFELBEIN, Bruce; Clear Lake HS; Clear Lake, SD; Band; Chr; Chrl; Chrs; ChrhWkr; CncrtBnd; Bsbl; Bsktbl; Ftbl; Trk; Sdsu; Curriculum Of Major Study.

SCHIEL, Linda; Marquette HS; Michigan City, IN; Chr; ChrhWkr; HonRl; HospAde; Mdrgl; SchMus; SchPl; Yrbk; Trk; GAA; Notre Dame; Computer Science.

SCHIELD, Gregory R; Merrill Sr HS; Merrill, WI; Band; Chr; HonRl; SchMus; 4-H; FFA; Tennis; North Central Tech Inst; Mechanic.

SCHIELDT, Scott L; La Follette HS; Madison, WI; 95/558 ChrhWkr; HonRl; SctActv; Bsbl; Bsktbl; LetterFtbl; Trk; LetterWrstlng; IMSpt; OptClAwd; Univ Of Wis.

SCHIELE, Kathy; Karlsrohe Public HS; Balfour, ND; 3020 VPFrshCls; PresSophCls; PresJrCls; SecSrCls; HonRl; SchPl; StuCncl; Yrbk; RptrSchPpr; PpCl; Univ; Child Dev & Family Relations.

SCHIELE, Wanda P; Drake Public HS; Drake, ND; Chrs; DrmMjrt; HonRl; LbryAde; MrchBnd; SchAde; TchrAde; Yrbk; SchPpr; Bsktbl; Beauty School; Beautician.

SCHIELEIN, Diana L; Illinois Valley Central HS; Chillicothe, IL; TrsSophCls; TrsJrCls; TrsSrCls; ChrhWkr; HonRl; LitMag; NHS; Quill&Scroll; RptrSchPpr; 4-H; Chrldr; GAA; DanFAwd; Eastern Illinois University; Home Economics.

SCHIERENBECK, Paul R; Fox Valley Lutheran HS; New London, WI; 3/109 Chr; CncrtBnd; HonRl; NatlMeritSF; SchMus; SchPl; RptrSchPpr; SchPpr; FTA; College; Music.

SCHIERL, Jean M; St Marys Central HS; Neenah, WI; VPJrCls; SchMus; StuCncl; SpnCl; PpCl; Trade School; Art.

SCHIESS, Janis A; Stockton HS; Stockton, IL; 5/88 TrsSophCls; PresJrCls; AFS; Chr; HonRl; SchPl; FFA; Iowa State Univ; Veterinarian.

SCHIESS, Sandra K; Hickman HS; Columbia, MO; NatlThespSoc; SchPl; StuGov; Stephens College; Theater.

SCHIESSER, Jeffrey G; Southern Door HS; Forestville, WI; ALBoysSt; HonRl; FFA; University; Electronics.

SCHIESSER, Kathy; Northern Heights HS; Allen, KS; TrsSrCls; ALAGirlsSt; Band; Chrs; HonRl; NHS; PpCl; AmLegAwd; Vo Tec School; Secretarial.

SCHIEVENIN, Karen A; Eisenhower HS; Utica, MI; 2/541 Chr; ChrhWkr; HonRl; NHS; YthFlsp; EdSchPpr; GerCl; Bsktbl; Chrldr; PPFtbl; Adrian Cl; Missionary Teacher.

SCHIFERL, Lee W; Jefferson HS; Jefferson, WI; 43/164 AFS; Chr; HonRl; SchMus; StuCncl; FFA; Ftbl; Trk; LetterWrstlng; IMSpt; University; Business Management.

SCHIFFEL, Debbie A; Comstock HS; Kalamozoo, MI; HonRl; StuCncl; Yrbk; FrCl; PpCl; Trk; Mich St Univ; Journalism.

SCHIFFELBEIN, Eric A; Lakin HS; Lakin, KS; VPSrCls; HonRl; SchPl; StuGov; PpCl; Bsbl; LetterGlf; MasAwd; Junior College; Vocation.

SCHIFFER, Barbara J; Cabrini HS; Allen Park, MI; 66/167 Chrs; ChrhWkr; HonRl; Bus Sch.

SCHIFTER, Teresa A; Fordson HS; Dearborn, MI; HonRl; NHS; NatlMeritSF; Orch; GerCl; GAA; IMSpt; U Of Mi; Electricial Engineer.

SCHIK, Charlene J; Derham Hall HS; St Paul, MN; 5/136 Aud/Vis; HonRl; LbryAde; PolWkr; SchPpr; FrCl; Col; Commercial Pilot.

SCHILB, Russell; Otterville Hs; Otterville, MO; TrsFrshCls; PresSophCls; PresJrCls; ChrhWkr; HonRl; StuCncl; PpCl; LetterBsbl; CaptBsktbl; LetterTrk; Southwest Baptist College; Phy Ed.

SCHILB, Russell L; Otterville R Vi HS; Otterville, MO; 6/24 TrsFrshCls; PresSophCls; PresJrCls; Chrs; ChrhWkr; HonRl; PpCl; Bsbl; CaptBsktbl; Trk; Sw Baptist College; Physical Educ.

SCHILD, Becky K; Quincy Sr Ii HS; Quincy, IL; 65/690 DrlTm; HonRl; NHS; StuCncl; YthFlsp; 4-H; FrCl; LetterSwmmng; IMSpt; 4-HAwd; Univ Of Iowa; Pharmacist.

SCHILD, Diane E; Greenfield HS; Greenfield, IL; Chrs; ChrhWkr; CmntyWkr; CncrtBnd; HonRl; Mdrgl; SchMus; Yrbk; FHA; Chrldr; Business School; Professional.

SCHILD, Leslie A; Morton HS; Morton, IL; 30/287 SecTrsSrCls; DrlTm; HonRl; NHS; StuCncl; PpCl; Univ Of Illinois; Business Administration.

SCHILDER, Bruce E; Faulkton HS; Faulkton, SD; Band; Chr; Chrs; HonRl; MrchBnd; SchPl; StuCncl; 4-H; Bsktbl; 4-HAwd; Col; Major Study.

SCHILDGEN, Elaine C; Lancaster Senior HS; Lancaster, WI; Chrs; HonRl; Treas4-H; SpnCl; PpCl; Bsbl; IMSpt; Uw Platteville; Elem Education.

SCHILDKNECHT, Cathy A; Orchard Farm HS; St Charles, MO; SecSrCls; Band; CncrtBnd; DrmMjrt; HonRl; MrchBnd; PepBnd; SchMus; FSA; PpCl; Meramec Community Clg; Data Processing.

SCHILEY, Debora J; Holdredge Sr HS; Holdrege, NE; HospAde; LbryAde; 4-H; FNA; PpCl; 4-HAwd; College; Professional.

SCHILL, Claire D; Le Sueur HS; Le Sueur, MN; 27/110 Band; HonRl; NHS; PepBnd; Yrbk; SchPpr; Bsbl; Bsktbl; Ftbl; IMSpt; Univ;.

SCHILL, Debra L; Auburndale HS; Auburndale, WI; VPFrshCls; SecJrCls; DrlTm; HonRl; JrNHS; SchPl; 4-H; FBLA; PpCl; Bsktbl; Coll; Nursing.

SCHILL, Karen M; Auburndale HS; Arpin, WI; VPJrCls; HonRl; NHS; StuCncl; SptEdYrbk; FBLA; PpCl; Trk; 4-HAwd; College; Nursing.

SCHILL, Linda G; Crothersville HS; Crothersville, IN; 9/55 Chr; HonRl; NHS; SchPl; StuCncl; YthFlsp; 4-H; SpnCl; VPPpCl; Bsktbl; LetterTrk; LetterChrldr; GAA; College; Language.

SCHILL, Paul J; Auburndale HS; Arpin, WI; HonRl; NHS; MthCl; CchngActv; Trade School; Vocation.

SCHILL, Sandy Y; South Knox HS; Vincennes, IN; 4/104 HstJrCls; CmntyWkr; HonRl; HospAde; NHS; SchAde; TchrAde; RptrSchPpr; 4-H; PpCl;.

SCHILLEMAN, Mark D; East Troy HS; Waterford, WI; 22/123 Chrs; HonRl; Trk; College; Education.

SCHILLER, Kenneth R; Holdingford Public HS; Freeport, MN; 41/98 VPSophCls; HonRl; NHS; NatlThespSoc; SchMus; SchPl; StuCncl; FFA; PpCl; LetterFtbl; Vocational Sch; Computer Programming.

SCHILLER, Nancy; George S Parker Sr HS; Janesville, WI; HonRl; NHS; Quill&Scroll; Yrbk; Swmmng; Steamstress.

SCHILLER, Sharon S; Chelsea HS; Chelsea, MI; 21/195 Chr; DrlTm; HonRl; HospAde; NHS; NatlMeritCmnd; NatlMeritSF; TchrAde; KiwanAwd; College; Pre Law.

SCHILLING, Brenda J; Mocksville HS; Seward, KS; Band; CncrtBnd; HonRl; MrchBnd; NHS; PepBnd; SchPl; StuCncl; TchrAde; PpCl; Bargon County Comm Clg.

SCHILLING, Karen R; Brownstown HS; Vandalia, IL; ChrhWkr; HonRl; LbryAde; SchPl; FHA; Business Trade; Secretary.

SCHILLING, Peggy A; Luck Public HS; Luck, WI; 3/56 TrsJrCls; TrsSrCls; Aud/Vis; Chr; ChrhWkr; HonRl; NHS; TchrAde; 4-H; FHA; PpCl; Tech Institute; Vocation.

SCHILLING, Stephen R; Regis HS; Eau Claire, WI; PresSophCls; PresJrCls; HonRl; FrCl; Bsktbl; Ftbl; LetterWrstlng; Wi U; Bus Mngmnt.

SCHILLING, Susan M; Canby HS; Canby, MN; VPSrCls; HonRl; HospAde; AmLegAwd; University; Math Teacher.

SCHILLINGER, Terry; Campbell Tintah HS; Campbell, MN; 2/35 Band; CncrtBnd; HonRl; MrchBnd; PepBnd; SchPpr; FFA; Mankate Avti; Computer Technician.

SCHILTZ, Rhonda M; Tomahawk HS; Tomahawk, WI; 1/150 VPFrshCls; VPSophCls; ALAGirlsSt; Chr; CncrtBnd; HonRl; NHS; Twrl; RptrYrbk; Technical School; Secretary.

SCHILZ, Linda; St Patricks HS; Sidney, NE; SchPl; RptrYrbk; EdYrBk; RptrSchPpr; EdSchPpr; PpCl; GAA; Business College; Secretarial.

SCHILZ, Michael T; Muskego HS; Hales Corners, WI; 27/350 Band; CAP; CncrtBnd; DrlTm; HonRl; MrchBnd; NHS; PepBnd; EdYrBk; GerCl; Ftbl; Glf; LetterTrk; Military Academy; Pilot.

SCHILZ, Robert J; Oconomowoc HS; Oconomowoc, WI; HonRl; HospAde; NHS; NatlMeritCmnd; TchrAde; FDA; MthCl; LetterGlf; College; Doctor.

SCHIMKAT, Lori J; Parker HS; Parker, SD; 13/45 Chr; Chrs; ChrhWkr; CmntyWkr; HonRl; HospAde; StuCncl; FHA; Univ Of South Dakota; Business Admin.

SCHIMKE, Faye I; Wess Sprgs HS; Wessington Spgs, SD; 6/52 Band; Chr; Chrs; ChrhWkr; CncrtBnd; MrchBnd; PepBnd; YthFlsp; College; Engineer.

SCHIMMEL, Brian D; Lake Central HS; Crown Point, IN; 35/453 Aud/Vis; HonRl; JrNHS; NHS; SchAde; TchrAde; GerCl; Bsbl; Ftbl; CitAwd; Col Radio Disc Jocky.

SCHIMMING, Denver K; Hammond Baptist HS; Hammond, IN; PresFrshCls; Chr; ChrhWkr; HonRl; TchrAde; RptrYrbk; GerCl; Bsbl; LetterBsktbl; Ftbl; LetterSocr; Trk; College; Preacher.

SCHIMONITZ, Thomas E; Creighton Prep; Omaha, NE; Band; CncrtBnd; HonRl; MrchBnd; Orch; PepBnd; SchPpr; Socr; Univ Of Ne Omaha; Electronical Engineer.

SCHIMWEG, Mark; Duchesne HS; St Charles, MO; Chrs; CmntyWkr; HonRl; SchMus; KeyCl; KiwanAwd;.

SCHINDEL, Harald P; Sullivan HS; Chicago, IL; NHS; College; Medicine.

SCHINDEL, Kornelia E; Lake View HS; Chicago, IL; 12/360 SecSrCls; HonRl; OffAde; TchrAde; GerCl; Trk; SecGAA; AmLegAwd; DARAwd; Northeastern Univ; Mathematics.

SCHINDERLE, Mary A; Kingsford HS; Kingsford, MI; HonRl; LbryAde; NatlFornLg; SchPl; TchrAde; SchPpr; College; Lawyers Assistant.

SCHINDERLE, Mary E; Plainfield HS; Plainfield, IL; HonRl; HospAde; StuCncl; RptrYrbk; Yrbk; TreasFNA; LatCl; PpCl; LetterChrldr; GAA; Nursing Sch; Nurse.

SCHINDLER, Daniel G; Port Huron Northern HS; North St, MI; 246/520 ChrhWkr; HonRl; YthFlsp; 4-H; Bsbl; LetterFtbl; Trk; Wrstlng; 4-HAwd; College; Conservation.

SCHINDLER, Gary L; Egf Senior HS; E Grand Forks, MN; 14/157 VPSrCls; Band; Chr; HonRl; NHS; SchPl; Yrbk; SchPpr; University Of North Dakota; History Teacher.

SCHINK, Myra; East Depere HS; Depere, WI; Band; CncrtBnd; MrchBnd; PepBnd; Yrbk; IMSpt; 4-HAwd; U W Stevens Point; Major In Biology.

SCHINKER, Janet L; Wahoo HS; Wahoo, NE; Band; CncrtBnd; HonRl; IntrClCncl; MrchBnd; PepBnd; RptrYrbk; RptrSchPpr; 4-H; SpnCl; Coll; Bus.

SCHINZEL, Betty M; Wenona HS; Lostant, IL; SecFrshCls; SecSophCls; SecJrCls; ChrhWkr; DrmMjrt; HonRl; VPNHS; TchrAde; Chrldr; VPGAA; Collge; Vocation.

SCHIPPER, Daniel R; Loy Norrix HS; Kalamozoo, MI; 49/451 Band; ChrhWkr; HonRl; Orch; SctActv; Bsktbl; Tennis; IMSpt; Mi St ;preveterinary.

SCHIPPER, Lynn; Fulton HS; Albany, IL; Chr; Chrs; HonRl; Mdrgl; SchMus; YthFlsp; Bsbl; Glf; College; Sports Or Mathematics.

SCHIPPER, Marcia L; George Comm HS; George, IA; 10/45 Chrs; ChrhWkr; HonRl; NHS; SchMus; Twrl; RptrSchPpr; FTA; LetterGlf; LetterChrldr; College.

SCHIPULL, Larry D; Boone Valley Comm HS; Renwick, IA; 1/26 Band; Chrs; HonRl; SchPl; StuCncl; PresYthFlsp; RptrYrbk; VPSciCl; Glf; Drake University; Music.

SCHIRER, Myron E; Roanoke Benson HS; Roanoke, IL; 12/90 ChrhWkr; HonRl; NHS; StuCncl; 4-H; FFA; CaptWrstlng; GovHonPrgAwd; David Lipscomb College.

SCHIRMER, James R; Joliet Central HS; Joliet, IL; 53/500 HonRl; NHS; TchrAde; LetterFtbl; LetterSwmmng; LetterTrk; Univ Of Illinois; Electrical Engineer.

SCHISLER, Debbie K; Industry HS; Vermont, IL; Band; Chrs; ChrhWkr; CncrtBnd; HonRl; LbryAde; OffAde; RptrSchPpr; 4-H; FHA; GAA; 4-HAwd;.

SCHISLER, Susan K; Vit Jr Sr HS; Ipava, IL; 2/60 HstFrshCls; TrsSophCls; ChrhWkr; HonRl; LbryAde; SecStuCncl; FHA; Trk; Chrldr; IMSpt;.

SCHISSEL, Jacque A; Mabel Canton HS; Mabel, MN; Chr; Chrs; HonRl; HospAde; SchPl; SchPpr; FHA; FNA; SpnCl; GAA; Collge; Associate Degree Nursing.

SCHIWAL, Deborah A; Lefor Public HS; Lefor, ND; 1/7 PresFrshCls; PresSrCls; HonRl; StuCncl; Yrbk; RptrSchPpr; LetterBsktbl; Trk; Chrldr; GAA; Mary College; Business.

SCHIWAL, Nancy K; Lefor HS; Lefor, ND; 1/8 VPFrshCls; TrsJrCls; ALAGirlsSt; HonRl; SchPl; TchrAde; RptrSchPpr; PresPpCl; LetterBsktbl; GAA; IMSpt; College; Nurse.

SCHIWITZ, Susan E; Thomas W Kelly HS; Benton, MO; ALAGirlsSt; Band; CncrtBnd; HonRl; MrchBnd; FHA; College.

SCHJERVHEIM, Gail L; Onarga HS; Onarga, IL; 4/24 PresJrCls; PresSrCls; ALAGirlsSt; Band; HonRl; Chrldr; GAA; AmLegAwd; BttyCrckrAwd; 4-HAwd; University; Fashion Merchandising.

SCHLABACH, John C; Macomb HS; Macomb, IL; VPSophCls; Band; PresChr; ChrhWkr; CncrtBnd; HonRl; Mdrgl; MrchBnd; NHS; Orch; PepBnd; RptrYrbk; LetterBsbl; LetterSwmmng; College; Professional.

SCHLACK, Dian M; Fennville HS; South Haven, MI; ChrhWkr; CmntyWkr; HonRl; LbryAde; RedCrAde; YthFlsp; 4-H; FrCl; 4-HAwd; CitAwd; Mich St Univ.

SCHLACKS, Steven C; Downers Grove South HS; Downers Grove, IL; 44/887 HonRl; JrNHS; Glf; Coll; Accountant.

SCHLAFKE, Theodore F; Wabeno HS; Wabeno, WI; 3/40 VPSophCls; Chrs; CncrtBnd; HonRl; MrchBnd; NHS; PepBnd; CaptBsktbl; CaptFtbl; CaptGlf; U W Stevens Point; Paper Sci.

SCHLAFLY, Phyllis D; Mary Inst; Alton, IL; 1/60 AFS; Chr; CmntyWkr; HonRl; LbryAde; ModUN; NatlMeritSF; PolWkr; RptrSchPpr; EdSchPpr; Univ; Law.

SCHLAGEL, Barbara; Cambridge HS; Cambridge, NE; 1/32 PresSrCls; ALAGirlsSt; Band; HonRl; PepBnd; StuCncl; PpCl; Kearney State College.

SCHLAGENHAFT, Julie A; Columbus HS; Marshfield, WI; 26/106 VPSophCls; HonRl; HospAde; SchPl; StuCncl; RptrSchPpr; FrCl; PpCl; Trk; GAA; Voc Sch; Nursing.

SCHLAKE, Denise; Southern HS; Blue Springs, NE; 1/43 SecSrCls; ALAGirlsSt; HonRl; SecNHS; SchPl; Teen; Pres4-H; SpnCl; PpCl; Bsktbl; University Of Ne; Home Ec.

SCHLAKE, Frances; Goreville Hs; Goreville, IL; Band; Chrs; HonRl; MrchBnd; SchPpr; Pres4-H; SecFHA; PpCl; DanFAwd; 4-HAwd; Shawnee Jr Coll;registered Nurse.

SCHLANGEN, Sue; St Thomas Aquinas HS; Hazelwood, MO; CmntyWkr; HonRl; HospAde; SchMus; StuGov; SchPpr; FNA; Chrldr; CchngActv; Nursing School; Rn.

SCHLANGER, Joseph W; Maine North HS; Glenview, IL; Band; Chr; Chrs; HonRl; JrNHS; NHS; VPNatlThespSoc; SchMus; SchPl; Univ Of Illinois; Music.

SCHLAPKOHL, David A; High School; Durant, IA; 7/68 HonRl; JrNHS; ModUN; NHS; StuCncl; LetterBsbl; CaptBsktbl; College; Conservation.

SCHLAPPI, James G; Blackhawk HS; Browntown, WI; HonRl; 4-H; TreasFFA; Bsktbl; Trk; 4-HAwd; Dairy Farmer.

SCHLARB, Ruth A; Ewen Trout Creek HS; Ewen, MI; 3/85 Chrs; NatlFornLg; NHS; SchPl; Northern Mi Univ; Pre Law.

SCHLATT, Debra A; Mexico HS; Mexico, MO; HospAde; RptrSchPpr; FBLA; LatCl; PpCl; Burge School; Nursing.

SCHLATTEN, Tim W; Waco HS; Wayland, IA; ALBoysSt; Chrs; ChrhWkr; PresFrshCls; RptrYrbk; SptEdYrbk; LetterBsbl; Bsktbl; Ftbl; Trk; Col; Architect.

SCHLATTER, Ann E; Bethlehem Academy; Faribault, MN; SecTrsJrCls; Chrs; HonRl; HospAde; SchMus; SchPl; SpnCl; PpCl; Trk; Chrldr; College; English.

SCHLATTER, Kristine A; Pearl City HS; Pearl City, IL; 2/49 College; Equestrian Studies.

SCHLATTERER, Robert G; Arlington HS; Arlington Hts, IL; 2/585 HonRl; NHS; SchPl; TchrAde; Northwestern Univ; Bio Medical Engineer.

SCHLATTMANN, Craig H; Atchison HS; Atchison, KS; 3/164 ALBoysSt; Band; CncrtBnd; HonRl; MrchBnd; ModUN; NHS; PepBnd; SchMus; SchPl; LatCl; College; Engineering.

SCHLAUTMAN, Martin F; Howells Public HS; Clarkson, NE; 1/44 TrsFrshCls; Aud/Vis; HonRl; StuGov; RptrSchPpr; 4-H; FFA; Bsktbl; LetterFtbl; LetterTrk; College; Professional.

SCHLAUTMAN, Peggy S; Howells Public HS; Howells, NE; SecSophCls; ChrhWkr; HonRl; LbryAde; SchPl; TchrAde; RptrSchPpr; SchPpr; 4-H; PpCl; Business School.

SCHLAX, Ellen; Regina Dominican HS; Northbrook, IL; 10/207 Aud/Vis; HonRl; LitMag; Mdrgl; SchMus; StuCncl; GerCl;.

SCHLEAPPE, Alvin E; Fox Senior HS; Imperial, MO; Chr; NHS; SchMus; SchPl; GerCl; LetterBsbl; LetterBsktbl; Trk; IMSpt; Air Force Academy; Professional.

SCHLEBEN, James E; Western HS; Bay City, MI; NatlMeritCmnd; LetterBsktbl; LetterFtbl; LetterTennis; CchngActv; Central Mich Univ; Lawyer.

SCHLECHT, Bruce K; Medina HS; Medina, ND; SecFrshCls; VPJrCls; TrsSrCls; Band; Chr; Chrs; ChrhWkr; CncrtBnd; HonRl; MrchBnd; PepBnd; SchPl; LetterBsktbl; LetterTrk; College; Agriculture.

SCHLECHT, Carla J; Canby HS; Porter, MN; ChrhWkr; HonRl; SchAde; 4-H; GerCl; LetterTrk; GAA; 4-HAwd; Bethel College; Elementary Education.

SCHLECHT, Cynthia R; Central Catholic HS; Beemer, NE; 12/65 Chrs; HonRl; NHS; SchMus; PresSophCls; PpCl; Trade Sch; Sec.

SCHLECHT, Kathy; Bowdle Public HS; Bowdle, SD; HonRl; YthFlsp; Yrbk; RptrSchPpr; PpCl; College; Prof.

SCHLEDER, Rayna M; Ithaca HS; Ithaca, MI; Chr; ChrhWkr; CncrtBnd; HonRl; Mdrgl; MrchBnd; NHS; SchMus; YthFlsp; 4-HAwd; College; Major In Music.

SCHLEGEL, Jacklyn; Naperville Central HS; Naperville, IL; ChrhWkr; HonRl; HospAde; YthFlsp; PpCl; GAA; University Of Iowa; Nursing.

SCHLEGEL, Kurt C; Romeoville HS; Bolingbrook, IL; 71/293 HonRl; ROTC; Ftbl; Glf; IMSpt; Us Marine Corps; Vocational.

SCHLEGEL, Teresa J; Clay City HS; Clay City, IN; SecFrshCls; SecSophCls; Band; HonRl; MrchBnd; StuCncl; TchrAde; Yrbk; 4-H; PpCl; Employment; Work With Children.

SCHLEGELMILCH, Daniel O; Lewis Cass HS; Walton, IN; Band; ChrhWkr; CncrtBnd; HonRl; PepBnd; SctActv; YthFlsp; 4-H; FFA; Purdue University.

SCHLEICH, Gloria; Emery HS; Emery, SD; ALAGirlsSt; Band; DrlTm; HonRl; MrchBnd; PepBnd; Sdlty; RptrSchPpr; FHA; Bsktbl; Comm Coll; Professional.

SCHLEICH, Gloria J; Emery HS; Emery, SD; Band; DrlTm; HonRl; MrchBnd; PepBnd; Sdlty; RptrSchPpr; 4-H; FHA; PpCl; Bsktbl; LetterTrk; College; Professional.

SCHLEICHER, Allen A; Plattsmouth HS; Plattsmouth, NE; YthFlsp; FBLA; FrCl; SpnCl; Clg; Business.

SCHLEICHER, Carol J; Central HS; St Joseph, MO; 43/528 Chrs; HonRl; NHS; SchMus; SchPl; TchrAde; Yrbk; Pres4-H; 4-HAwd; College; Math.

SCHLEICHER, Jane; Cambridge Senior HS; Cambridge, MN; Band; Chr; ChrhWkr; HonRl; NHS; SchMus; StuCncl; RptrYrbk; RptrSchPpr; PresAwd; College.

SCHLEICHER, Kimberley A; Spring Hill HS; Spring Hill, KS; Chrs; HonRl; LbryAde; NHS;.

SCHLEICHER, Linda J; Wheaton Warrenville HS; Wheaton, IL; HonRl; NHS; NatlMeritSchl; SctActv; StuGov; EdYrBk; RptrSchPpr; Chrldr; University Of Illinois; Chemical Engineer.

SCHLEICHER, Matthew L; Spring Hill HS; Spring Hill, KS; VPJrCls; Chr; HonRl; Mdrgl; NHS; SchMus; SchPl;.

SCHLEICHER, Susan M; Addison Trail HS; Addison, IL; 42/597 NatlThespSoc; KeyCl; GerCl; N Ill Univ; Nursng.

SCHLEIERMACHER, Kathy L; Marion County R 2 HS; Ewing, MO; SecJrCls; ALAGirlsSt; Chrs; ChrhWkr; HonRl; LbryAde; FHA; LetterBsktbl; AmLegAwd; CitAwd; College; Art.

SCHLEINZ, Tony J; Antigo HS; Aniwa, WI; Band; SctActv; Bsbl; Glf; Univ Of Wi St; Pro.

SCHLEMMER, Betty J; Centralia Boone HS; Centralia, MO; 6/88 Band; CncrtBnd; HonRl; MrchBnd; NHS; NatlSciFnd; OffAde; PepBnd; SchMus; SchPl; FHA; St Johns; Registered Nurse.

SCHLEMMER, Michael J; West Noble HS; Ligonier, IN; 10/123 ALBoysSt; NHS; LetterBsktbl; LetterTrk; Tri State Clg; Chemistry.

SCHLEMPER, Deborah E; Pacific HS; Pacific, MO; Band; ChrhWkr; CncrtBnd; HonRl; MrchBnd; PepBnd; SchMus; FHA; SpnCl; PpCl; Southwest Baptist; Nursing.

SCHLENKER, Chris K; Berkley HS; Huntington Woods, MI; NatlMeritCmnd; LetterTrk; U Of Mi.

SCHLENKER, Kathryn G; Forbes Public HS; Forbes, ND; Chrs; HonRl; SchPl; YthFlsp; Yrbk; RptrSchPpr; SchPpr; 4-H; Bsktbl; Aberdeen Schl Of Commerce; Accounting.

SCHLENKER, Terry; Ashley HS; Ashley, ND; Band; Chr; ChrhWkr; CncrtBnd; HonRl; HospAde; PepBnd; SchPl; Med Tech.

SCHLENKER, Thomas; Carman HS; Flint, MI; Band; CAP; HonRl; Michigan U Flint; Business Administration.

SCHLENSKER, Christine S; Central HS; Evansville, IN; 31/650 ChrhWkr; CncrtBnd; HonRl; NHS; PolWkr; SctActv; StuCncl; TchrAde; LetterTennis; ChmbCommrsAwd; Univ; Md Tech.

SCHLEPER, Theresa; Albany Area HS; Albany, MN; SecSophCls; Band; Chrs; HonRl; MrchBnd; PepBnd; RptrYrbk; FHA; GAA; College; Social Work.

SCHLEPP, Susan L; Francis HS; Kanorado, KS; HonRl; SchPl; Teen; TreasFHA; PpCl; Bsktbl; Trk; PPFtbl; University; Professional.

SCHLESINGER, Keith R; Cranbrook Boys HS; Bloomfield Hls, MI; HonRl; LbryAde; NatlFornLg; NatlMeritSF; SchPl; SctActv; StuCncl; TchrAde; Oberlin Univ; Education.

SCHLESINGER, Laura J; Woodruff HS; Peoria, IL; 2/281 AFS; Band; CncrtBnd; HonRl; Orch; SchPl; SctActv; YthFlsp; SecKeyCl; PresGerCl;.

SCHLESSELMAN, Kathryn; Concordia R2 HS; Concordia, MO; 12/43 TrsSophCls; TrsJrCls; ALAGirlsSt; ChrhWkr; HonRl; ModUN; NHS; NatlThespSoc; RptrYrbk; EdSchPpr; Univ; Teacher.

SCHLESSER, Pamela E; Adlai E Stevenson HS; Prairie View, IL; 1/230 Band; CncrtBnd; HonRl; MrchBnd; NHS; Bradley Univ; Biology.

SCHLESSER, Sennen R; Cudahy HS; Cudahy, WI; AFS; HonRl;.

SCHLETER, Harvey A; Gibson Southern HS; Fort Branch, IN; Band; CncrtBnd; HonRl; MrchBnd; SchMus; SciCl; LetterTrk; LetterWrstlng; Indiana U; Law.

SCHLEUSENER, Randy L; Stevens HS; Rapid City, SD; 7/426 PresFrshCls; Band; ChrhWkr; CncrtBnd; HonRl; NatlFornLg; NatlMeritSF; LetterBsktbl; LetterFtbl; EldAwd;.

SCHLEY, Jacqueline A; Brainerd HS; Brainerd, MN; 50/475 Chr; PresFrshCls; SchPl; VP4-H; FHA; PpCl; IMSpt; Brianerd Vo Tech; Dental Asst.

SCHLEY, Mary A; Denmark HS; Maribel, WI; AFS; Chr; ChrhWkr; HonRl; YthFlsp; 4-H; FHA; SpnCl; IMSpt; 4-HAwd; Technical School.

SCHLEY, Wanda A; Theodore Roosevelt HS; Wyandotte, MI; Band; Chr; CncrtBnd; HonRl; MrchBnd; NHS; StuGov; TchrAde; SchPpr; VPFTA; Mi Univ; Occupational Therapy.

SCHLEYHAHN, Ellen J; Lanphier HS; Springfield, IL; 1/451 HonRl; NHS; SchPl; StuCncl; Springfield College; Medical Technologist.

SCHLICHER, John F; Wayland Academy; Beaver Dam, WI; 12/75 HonRl; NatlMeritSF; SchPl; SchPpr; KeyCl; LetterBsbl; LetterFtbl; LetterSwmmng; LetterTrk; LetterWrstlng; Chrldr; College; Natural Resources.

SCHLICHTER, George J; Bremen HS; Midlothian, IL; 47/403 HonRl; NHS; NatlThespSoc; SchMus; SchPl; StuCncl; RptrYrbk; EdYrBk; Thornton Comm College; Theatre.

SCHLICHTING, Deborah A; Sauk Centre Sr HS; Sauk Centre, MN; 2/156 PresSophCls; Chr; HonRl; HospAde; ModUN; SecStuCncl; Trk; CaptChrldr; LetterGAA; University; Psychology.

SCHLICHTMANN, Kathy; Potosi HS; Potosi, WI; Band; Chrs; CncrtBnd; DrmMjrt; HonRl; HospAde; MrchBnd; RptrYrbk; RptrSchPpr; PpCl; Viterbo Col Lacrosse; Nursing.

SCHLIENTZ, Debbie R; Stapleton Public HS; Stapleton, NE; Chrs; HonRl; SchPl; Yrbk; FHA; PpCl; Trade School; Vocation.

SCHLIEP, David L; Appleton HS; Holloway, MN; Band; CncrtBnd; HonRl; MrchBnd; PepBnd; SchAde; TchrAde; Pres4-H; TreasFFA; Wrstlng; 4-HAwd; Univ; Agriculture.

SCHLIES, Al B; Kewaunee HS; Kewaunee, WI; LetterBsktbl; LetterFtbl; LetterTrk; College; Professnl.

SCHLIES, Theresa A; Kewaunee HS; Denmark, WI; PresSrCls; AFS; ALAGirlsSt; Chr; Chrs; HonRl; LbryAde; NHS; PresFBLA; TreasFHA; Bsktbl; Trk; Chrldr; GAA; Col; Nursing.

SCHLIESMAN, Teresa A; Milbank HS; Milbank, SD; 14/113 DrlTm; HonRl; PolWkr; FBLA; PresFHA; GerCl; PpCl; College.

SCHLIEWE, Darlene H; Lakeside Lutheran HS; Beaver Dam, WI; PpCl; IMSpt;.

SCHLINSOG, Ben A; Granton Public HS; Granton, WI; 10/40 HonRl; StuCncl; StuGov; LetterBsbl; Glf; LetterTrk; Eau Clair Tech; Air Conditioning.

SCHLOBOHM, Susan; Civic Memorial HS; Bethalto, IL; 71/270 Chr; ChrhWkr; CncrtBnd; DrmBgl; HonRl; MrchBnd; SchMus; StuCncl; RptrSchPpr; PpCl; Coll; Social Work.

SCHLOESSER, Lori J; Lakeside Lutheran HS; Jefferson, WI; RptrYrbk; IMSpt; Coll.

SCHLOMANN, Linda R; Prospect HS; Mt Prospect, IL; NatlThespSoc; HonRl; NatlThespSoc; SchMus; SchPl; IMSpt; BttyCrckrAwd; William Rainey Harper; Work With Children.

SCHLORHOLTZ, Scott; Newman HS; Rockwell, IA; CmntyWkr; HonRl; Ftbl; Wrstlng; College; Physical Science.

SCHLOSS, Jerry P; St Vincent HS; Perryville, MO; 61/81 VPSophCls; ChrhWkr; HonRl; NHS; SctActv; RptrYrbk; Bsbl; Ftbl; IMSpt; College; Engineering.

SCHLOSSER, Cindy M; Frederick HS; Frederick, SD; Band; Chr; HonRl; MrchBnd; PepBnd; SchPl; StuCncl; TchrAde; RptrYrbk; PpCl; Northern State Coll; Elementary Education.

SCHLOSSER, Francine L; Braddock Public HS; Braddock, ND; 3/13 PresFrshCls; SecJrCls; Chrs; ChrhWkr; HonRl; PolWkr; SchPl; Sdlty; StuCncl; SptEdYrbk; EdSchPpr; LetterBsktbl; LetterChrldr; 4-HAwd; North Dakota St Univ; Law Enforcement.

SCHLOTTERBACK, Janet K; Chester Area HS; Madison, SD; 1/32 VPSophCls; SecJrCls; ALAGirlsSt; Chrs; CncrtBnd; HonRl; NHS; SchPl; SptEdSchPpr; Trk; Univ Sdsu; Nursing.

SCHLOTTERBECK, Timothy C; Centerville Sr HS; Richmond, IN; ALBoysSt; Chr; ChrhWkr; HonRl; NHS; Bsbl; Bsktbl; Ftbl; Ball State Univ; Actuarial Science.

SCHLOTZHAVER, Kathy S; New Franklin HS; New Franklin, MO; 7/48 VPFrshCls; Chr; Chrs; ChrhWkr; CmntyWkr; HonRl; JA; NHS; SchPl; YthFlsp; LetterBsbl; LetterBsktbl; LetterTrk; Chrldr; College; Police.

SCHLOUGH, Cindy; Menomonie Jr Sr HS; Menomonie, WI; Band; Chr; MrchBnd; SctActv; StuCncl; Yrbk; FrCl;.

SCHLUCKEBIER, Paul; Frankenmuth HS; Saginaw, MI; ChrhWkr; HonRl; NHS; Michigan State U; Veterinary Medicine.

SCHLUCKEHIER, Brian L; Reese HS; Frankenmath, MI; 21/128 Chr; HonRl; NHS; SchPl; 4-H; FFA; GerCl; IMSpt; 4-HAwd; CitAwd; College; Auto Mechanic Or Writer.

SCHLUENDER, Mary E; St Francis HS; Zimmerman, MN; 6/148 HonRl; RptrSchPpr; FFA; PpCl; SciCl; Col St Cloud; Accountant.

SCHLUETER, Dean; Rockford East Hs; Rockford, IL; 72/665 HonRl; JrNHS; CaptFtbl; Trk; College; Physical Therapy.

SCHLUETER, Jennifer M; Wahlert HS; Dubuque, IA; LetterBsktbl; GAA; IMSpt; College; Professional.

SCHLUETER, Lynn M; Mercy HS; Omaha, NE; Chr; TreasJA; RedCrAde; SchMus; SctActv; Sdlty; TchrAde; EdSchPpr; SchPpr; SpnCl; JAAwd; Omaha College; Elementary Educ.

SCHLUETER, Tom W; Solomon Juneau HS; Milwaukee, WI; 5/232 Aud/Vis; Band; CncrtBnd; HonRl; MrchBnd; NHS; Orch; PepBnd; SchMus; IMSpt; College; Musician.

SCHLUETER, Valarie J; Superior HS; Hardy, NE; ALAGirlsSt; Band; CncrtBnd; HonRl; MrchBnd; PepBnd; FBLA; PpCl; Trk; Bus School; Business.

SCHLUETER, Valerie L; West Sioux HS; Hawarden, IA; Chrs; HonRl; HospAde; MrchBnd; Twrl; FrCl; Nursing Sch; Nursing.

SCHLUMBOHM, Renae L; West Sioux HS; Ireton, IA; Chr; Chrs; ChrhWkr; HonRl; SchPl; RptrSchPpr; 4-H; PpCl; Bsktbl; 4-HAwd; College Or Trade School; Physical Therapy A.

SCHLUMP, Karen; Ida HS; Ida, MI; 3/150 ALAGirlsSt; Band; CncrtBnd; HonRl; MrchBnd; NatlThespSoc; SchMus; PPFtbl; Mi St Univ; Rn.

SCHLUTER, Kathy A; Dongola Unit HS; Dongola, IL; Band; Chrs; ChrhWkr; CncrtBnd; MrchBnd; PepBnd; StuCncl; TchrAde; 4-H; FHA; FTA; PpCl; SecSciCl; GAA; Shawnee Jr College; Case Worker.

SCHLUTTENHOFER, Linda L; Benton Central HS; Earl Park, IN; 17/250 ChrhWkr; CmntyWkr; HonRl; LbryAde; NHS; OffAde; Sdlty; TchrAde; YthFlsp; 4-H; FrCl; Trk; VPGAA; PPFtbl; Indiana Univ; Physical Therapy.

SCHMADEKE, Rochelle J; Prairie Community HS; Callender, IA; Band; CncrtBnd; HonRl; MrchBnd; Yrbk; SchPpr; 4-H; FHA; Bsktbl; Spencer School Of Business; Airlines.

SCHMAHL, Daniel K; Elkhart Lake HS; Elkhart Lake, WI; 1/65 ALBoysSt; Band; CncrtBnd; HonRl; NHS; PepBnd; SchPl; RptrYrbk; FFA; LetterTrk; Trade; Farming.

SCHMALE, Barry A; Fredericktown HS; Fredericktown, MO; 9/160 ALBoysSt; Band; HonRl; PpCl; LetterTennis; IMSpt; College; Engr Or Accounting.

SCHMALE, Richard J; Oregon Senior HS; Brooklyn, WI; Aud/Vis; HonRl; NHS; RptrSchPpr; FFA; Bsktbl; Trk; Univ Of Wi; Architecture.

SCHMALFELDT, Joseph G; Center HS; Center, ND; ALBoysSt; HonRl; StuCncl; SptEdSchPpr; GerCl; PpCl; Bsktbl; Ftbl; Nd State Univ; Coach.

SCHMALHAUSEN, H; East Richland HS; Olney, IL; Band; MrchBnd; RptrSchPpr; Bsktbl; Trk; Tech; Computer Puogramer.

SCHMALING, Joyce E; Delavan Darien HS; Delavan, WI; 4/230 AFS; ChrhWkr; HonRl; JrNHS; Quill&Scroll; VPStuCncl; EdYrBk; Pres4-H; Trk; Chrldr; GAA; 4-HAwd; College.

SCHMALSHOF, Andy; Avon HS; Avon, IL; 14/47 Band; Chrs; CmntyWkr; SctActv; SptEdSchPpr; PresFFA; LetterBsktbl; CaptFtbl; LetterGlf; LetterTrk; University; Agriculture.

SCHMALSHOF, Lois; Liberty Hs; Liberty, IL; CncrtBnd; HonRl; LbryAde; MrchBnd; SchPl; 4-H; FHA; SciCl; GAA; School Of Nursing.

SCHMALTZ, Cindy M; Bottineau Public HS; Bottineau, ND; Chr; Chrs; CncrtBnd; MrchBnd; PepBnd; Twrl; SciCl; Bsktbl; Trk; Chrldr; College; Professional.

SCHMALTZ, Lorraine C; Balta Public HS; Balta, ND; VPFrshCls; Chrs; SchPl; TchrAde; Yrbk; 4-H; 4-HAwd;.

SCHMALTZ, Stephen P; Huron HS; Ann Arbor, MI; Band; NatlCathMusEdAsoc; NatlFornLg; SchMus; SchPl; SctActv; FDA; FrCl; Tennis; JETSAwd; U Of Mi; Medicine.

SCHMALZ, Deborah L; St Croix Falls HS; St Croix Falls, WI; 2/84 Band; Chr; ChrhWkr; HonRl; NatlFornLg; NHS; EdYrBk; RptrSchPpr; FHA; Valparaiso Univ; Medical Tech.

SCHMALZ, Kathy A; Immaculate Heart Of Mary HS; Cicero, IL; SchPl; SctActv; Sdlty; Rosary College; Writer.

SCHMALZ, Michael J; John Marshall Jr Sr HS; Milwaukee, WI; Aud/Vis; HonRl; NHS; SchMus; SchPl; Marquette Univ; Medicine.

SCHMALZ, Randle C; Westbrook HS; Westbrook, MN; 1/40 TrsFrshCls; PresSophCls; Chr; NHS; NatlMeritSF; SchPl; RptrSchPpr; LetterFtbl; LetterTrk; LetterWrstlng; College; Psychology.

SCHMANDT, Linda M; West HS; Davenport, IA; 1/750 AFS; HonRl; NatlMeritFnl; Quill&Scroll; StuCncl; Yrbk; RptrSchPpr; PresFrCl; SpnCl; Coll; Foreighn Lang.

SCHMEICHEL, Joan M; Freeman Public HS; Freeman, SD; Chrs; DrlTm; HonRl; SchMus; SchPl; Yrbk; Pres4-H; FHA; GerCl; 4-HAwd; College; Physical Therapy.

SCHMEIDLER, Frank A; Thomas More Prep; Hays, KS; Chrs; CncrtBnd; HonRl; MrchBnd; Orch; PepBnd; SchMus; SchPl; EdSchPpr; SpnCl; Univ; Music.

SCHMEIDLER, Joyce E; Hays HS; Victoria, KS; 4/188 Chrs; HonRl; LbryAde; TchrAde; EdSchPpr; SchPpr; SecFNA; PpCl; College; Registered Nurse.

SCHMEITS, Rose E; Spalding Acad; Spalding, NE; 2/17 SecFrshCls; Chrs; HonRl; SecNHS; SecStuCncl; TchrAde; RptrYrbk; EdSchPpr; 4-H; VPPpCl; St Mary Coll; Spanish.

SCHMELING, Lorchelle E; Cosmos HS; Cosmos, MN; 4/35 PresSrCls; ALAGirlsSt; Chrs; HonRl; MrchBnd; NHS; SchPl; EdYrBk; FHA; Chrldr; Willmar Voc; Cosmetologist.

SCHMELTER, Pamela M; Hobart Senior HS; Hobart, IN; HonRl; NHS; StuCncl; TchrAde; 4-H; GerCl; LetterTennis; GAA; CaptPPFtbl; Isu Notre Dame; Art.

SCHMELTER, Philip A; Lowell Sr HS; Lowell, IN; HonRl; LetterBsbl; Ftbl; Wrstlng; College; Computer Science.

SCHMELZER, Joanna D; Hayes County HS; Maywood, NE; 4/25 Band; Chr; HonRl; MrchBnd; StuCncl; UNYO; 4-H; 4-HAwd; LionAwd; CitAwd; Music/home Economicis.

SCHMELZER, Joseph G; Highland Public HS; Highland, WI; SecJrCls; HonRl; StuCncl; FFA; LetterFtbl; LetterTrk; Vocational School; Mechanic.

SCHMERBAUCH, John P; Chester HS; Chester, IL; 23/122 ALBoysSt; HonRl; LetterBsbl; College; Professional.

SCHMICH, Nancy A; Incarnate Word HS; Florissant, MO; 25/111 Chr; SchMus; SchPl; SctActv; GAA; Ne Mo Univ; Medical Tech.

SCHMID, Joyce A; Fairbury Cropsey HS; Chenoa, IL; Chrs; HonRl; HospAde; LbryAde; MrchBnd; SctActv; RptrYrbk; 4-H; FHA; Nursing School; Practical Nurse.

SCHMID, Judy J; West Allis Central HS; West Allis, WI; 1/469 CncrtBnd; Orch; PepBnd; SchMus; FBLA; Bookkeeping Plans.

SCHMID, Laurie A; Albany Senior HS; Avon, MN; Chrs; DrlTm; HonRl; NatlFornLg; SchPl; StuCncl; RptrYrbk; EdYrBk; College; Biology.

SCHMID, Michael; Monroe Sr HS; Monroe, WI; HonRl; SctActv; YthFlsp; KeyCl; Bsbl; Ftbl; Wrstlng; IMSpt; GodCntryAwd; Coll; Prof.

SCHMID, Patricia; Attica HS; Attica, IN; TrsSophCls; TrsSrCls; Chr; Mdrgl; ModUN; SchPl; TchrAde; FTA; PpCl; SciCl; Indiana St Univ; Music.

SCHMID, Rebecca L; Shelby Public HS; Shelby, NE; SecFrshCls; SecSophCls; SecJrCls; Band; Chrs; ChrhWkr; CncrtBnd; MrchBnd; SchPl; Chrldr; Univ Of Ne; Music.

SCHMID, Roland D; St James HS; St James, MN; ALBoysSt; Chr; DrmMjrt; NHS; SchPl; Bsktbl; Ftbl; Glf; Trk; GodCntryAwd; Col; Math Or Physics.

SCHMIDGALL, Dawn E; Hancock Public HS; Hancock, MN; SecJrCls; Chrs; HonRl; HospAde; LbryAde; SchPl; YthFlsp; EdSchPpr; SchPpr; FHA; LetterBsktbl; Trk; Alexandria Voc Tech; Art.

SCHMIDGALL, Nancy J; Hancock HS; Hancock, MN; CncrtBnd; HonRl; LbryAde; PepBnd; SchPl; Twrl; RptrYrbk; LetterBsktbl; LetterTrk; LetterChrldr; Tech; Bookkeeping.

SCHMIDLIN, Jenny A; Lakeview HS; Lakeview, MI; 6/120 ALAGirlsSt; ChrhWkr; NHS; PepBnd; StuCncl; RptrYrbk; RptrSchPpr; 4-H; Bsktbl; Trk; Michigan State U; Veterinary Medicine.

SCHMIDT, Alan C; Marissa Unit Dist #40 HS; Marissa, IL; PresFrshCls; HonRl; NHS; YthFlsp; FFA; Bsbl; LetterBsktbl; Trk; Univ Of Illinois; Agriculture.

SCHMIDT, Ann M; Marietta HS; Marietta, MN; 7/19 Band; ChrhWkr; DrmMjrt; HonRl; StuCncl; Yrbk; FHA; PpCl; CaptBsktbl; Chrldr; College;.

SCHMIDT, Barbara A; Deshler Public HS; Davenport, NE; 1/26 SecJrCls; ChrhWkr; HonRl; Mdrgl; SecStuCncl; TchrAde; 4-H; LetterTrk; Chrldr; 4-HAwd; U Of Nebraska; Mathematics.

SCHMIDT, Barbara J; Jackson HS; Jackson, MI; Band; Chr; CncrtBnd; HonRl; MrchBnd; NHS; Orch; SchMus; College; Music Performance.

SCHMIDT, Bonnie; Bellevue Community HS; Bellevue, IA; 6/45 Chrs; HonRl; HospAde; ModUN; SchPl; FHA; College; Vocation.

SCHMIDT, Bruce E; Max Public HS; Max, ND; 2/13 PresFrshCls; VPSophCls; PresJrCls; Band; CncrtBnd; HonRl; PepBnd; StuCncl; SptEdYrbk; SptEdSchPpr; 4-H; Ndsu; Agriculture.

SCHMIDT, Caryl J; East HS; Waterloo, IA; Band; Chrs; ChrhWkr; HonRl; HospAde; College; Doctor.

SCHMIDT, Catherine; Kapaun Mt Carmel HS; Wichita, KS; CmntyWkr; HonRl; NatlMeritCmnd; PolWkr; EdYrBk; EdSchPpr; BttyCrckrAwd; Benedictine Coll; Creative Writing.

SCHMIDT, Cheryl L; South Sioux HS; South Sioux City, NE; 36/145 PresJrCls; SecBand; HonRl; MrchBnd; PepBnd; SptEdYrbk; Swmmng; Trk; Chrldr; IMSpt; Univ; Prof.

SCHMIDT, Chris G; Reitz Memorial HS; Evansville, IN; 47/225 ChrhWkr; HonRl; SchMus; LetterWrstlng; IMSpt; Purdue; Mechanical Engineer.

SCHMIDT, Clynt R; Jr Reedsville HS; Buckley, IL; Band; 4-H; FFA; Glf;.

SCHMIDT, Coleen R; Fairbury HS; Fairbury, NE; 30/132 Band; Chrs; ChrhWkr; CncrtBnd; HonRl; PepBnd; StuCncl; 4-H; TreasPpCl; IMSpt; 4-HAwd; Lincoln Schl Of Commerce; Clerical.

SCHMIDT, Colleen E; Immanuel Lutheran HS; Valentine, NE; Chr; ChrhWkr; Yrbk; RptrSchPpr; GerCl; PpCl; CaptBsktbl; CchngActv; GAA; IMSpt; College.

SCHMIDT, Colleen K; Grundy Center HS; Grundy Center, IA; Band; Chrs; CncrtBnd; DrmMjrt; HonRl; Mdrgl; MrchBnd; PepBnd; EdSchPpr; Univ Of N Ia; English.

SCHMIDT, Connie L; Willow Lake Public HS; Willow Lake, SD; Band; Chrs; ChrhWkr; CncrtBnd; HonRl; LbryAde; OffAde; FHA; PpCl; Chrldr; College; Music.

SCHMIDT, Curtis C; Rosemount HS; Apple Valley, MN; 90/355 HonRl; Univ; Engi.

SCHMIDT, Danna K; Memorial HS; Joplin, MO; HonRl; NatlFornLg; NHS; StuGov; RptrYrbk; EdYrBk; MthCl; Glf; Chrldr; Duke Univ; Language.

SCHMIDT, David A; Wausau East HS; Wausau, WI; NatlMeritCmnd; YthFlsp; PpCl; Bsktbl; Ftbl; IMSpt; Univ; Computer Science.

SCHMIDT, David A; Antigo HS; Antigo, WI; Wrstlng; Vocational Sch.

SCHMIDT, David E; Crescent Iroquois HS; Crescent City, IL; 3/23 SecFrshCls; TrsSophCls; HonRl; LbryAde; NHS; SchPl; Univ Of Illinois; Accounting.

SCHMIDT, David L; Up 237 HS; Smith Center, KS; 6/76 PresFrshCls; PresSophCls; ALBoysSt; HonRl; StuCncl; YthFlsp; SchPpr; Bsbl; College.

SCHMIDT, Deborah A; Shawnee Mission South HS; Overland Park, KS; Chr; HonRl; OffAde; StuCncl; PpCl; CaptChrldr; Kansas Univ; School Counselor.

SCHMIDT, Debra; Clinton Prairie Hs; Mulberry, IN; 1/84 PresJrCls; ALAGirlsSt; Band; HonRl; YthFlsp; LatCl; SciCl; LetterBsktbl; AmLegAwd; 4-HAwd;.

SCHMIDT, Denise A; Buhler HS; Buhler, KS; HonRl; TchrAde; PpCl; LetterTrk; PresAwd; College Social Work.

SCHMIDT, Dennis J; Northwestern HS; Bennett, WI; Univ; Science.

SCHMIDT, Diana S; Seymour HS; Payson, IL; TrsJrCls; Band; Chrs; ChrhWkr; CncrtBnd; HonRl; Mdrgl; SchMus; SchPl; StuCncl; 4-H; Western Il Univ.

SCHMIDT, Edward L; Evart HS; Evart, MI; 7/90 VPSrCls; CncrtBnd; HonRl; MrchBnd; VPNHS;

PepBnd; SchPl; LetterBsbl; LetterBsktbl; LetterFtbl; No Michigan Univ; Elec Technician.

SCHMIDT, Elaine M; Milwaukee Lutheran HS; Milwaukee, WI; AFS; Chr; CncrtBnd; DrmMjrt; HospAde; MrchBnd; NatlThespSoc; SchMus; SchPl; GerCl; Univ Of Wis; Music.

SCHMIDT, Ellen L; Gillespie HS; Gillespie, IL; 10/130 Band; HonRl; NHS; Yrbk; RptrSchPpr; VPFrCl; Trk; GAA; Illinois Wesleyan College; Nursing.

SCHMIDT, Frederic W; Abbot Pennings HS; Green Bay, WI; 12/92 ChrhWkr; HonRl; NHS; NatlMeritCmnd; RptrYrbk; RptrSchPpr; KeyCl; GerCl; LetterFtbl; LetterTennis; Marquette U; Prof.

SCHMIDT, Jacqueline; Muskego HS; Hales Corners, WI; 6/330 PresJrCls; HonRl; StuCncl; TchrAde; SpnCl; PpCl; GAA; Univ Of Wi At Stev Pt; Psych.

SCHMIDT, James A; Thorp HS; Thorp, WI; HonRl; StuCncl; Yrbk; Bsbl; Bsktbl; Ftbl; Wrstlng; IMSpt; College; Vocation.

SCHMIDT, James H; Riverview Gardens HS; St Louis, MO; 13/779 HonRl; NHS; NatlMeritSF; SctActv; Clge; Military Or Civilian Police Career.

SCHMIDT, James L; North HS; Evansville, IN; 94/428 Chr; NHS; SchMus; CaptBsbl; CaptBsktbl; CaptFtbl; LetterTrk; KiwanAwd;.

SCHMIDT, James M; Sparta HS; Sparta, WI; 1/192 PresJrCls; Chrs; CncrtBnd; HonRl; MrchBnd; NHS; StuCncl; RptrYrbk; FFA; SciCl; West Point; Engineering.

SCHMIDT, Jamie M; Klemme Community HS; Garner, IA; VPFrshCls; PresJrCls; Band; Chrs; ChrhWkr; CncrtBnd; HonRl; Mdrgl; MrchBnd; NHS; Iowa State Univ; General Ag.

SCHMIDT, Janet; Spalding Acad; Spalding, NE; PresJrCls; Chrs; HonRl; Yrbk; SpnCl; PpCl; Chrldr; Trade School; Professional.

SCHMIDT, Janice L; Alton Sr HS; Alton, IL; 55/803 Band; Chrs; ChrhWkr; CncrtBnd; HonRl; MrchBnd; Orch; SchAde; TchrAde; YthFlsp; SchPpr; South Ill Univ; Biology.

SCHMIDT, Jayne; D C Everest HS; Rothschild, WI; 29/346 Band; ChrhWkr; HonRl; MrchBnd; NHS; MthCl; Swmmng; Trk; IMSpt; Uw Marathon County; Computer Science.

SCHMIDT, Jeff P; Sleepy Eye Public HS; Sleepy Eye, MN; Band; Chrs; ChrhWkr; CncrtBnd; HonRl; MrchBnd; VPNatlThespSoc; SchMus; SchPl; VPSciCl; College; Optometrist.

SCHMIDT, Jennifer L; Garner Hayfield HS; Garner, IA; Chrs; CncrtBnd; HonRl; MrchBnd; PepBnd; SctActv; FHA; PpCl; Chrldr; PPFtbl; College; Physical Educ.

SCHMIDT, Jerome F; Franklin Center HS; West Brooklyn, IL; 15/50 ALAGirlsSt; HonRl; LbryAde; SchMus; SchPl; PpCl; LetterFtbl; Trk; College; Major.

SCHMIDT, Jo Ann M; Immaculate Conception Acad; South Bend, IN; 35/60 TrsJrCls; Chrs; SchMus; SchPl; StuCncl; StuGov; RptrYrbk; RptrSchPpr; SpnCl; Bsktbl; GAA; Univ; Special Education.

SCHMIDT, Joann M; St Mary HS; Sleepy Eye, MN; 26/84 ChrhWkr; LitMag; Quill&Scroll; TchrAde; SchPpr; GAA; Mankato State Clg; Law Enforcement.

SCHMIDT, Joann M; Columbus HS; Marshfield, WI; 43/104 CtyCnl; CmntyWkr; HospAde; JA; NHS; PolWkr; RedCrAde; StuCncl; YthLg; FNA; Trade School; Professional.

SCHMIDT, Joseph A; Osage Comm HS; Osage, IA; 9/175 PresJrCls; ALBoysSt; Band; CncrtBnd; HonRl; MrchBnd; TreasNHS; PepBnd; Bsbl; Bsktbl; LetterTrk; College; Professional.

SCHMIDT, Joyce R; Buffalo Sr HS; Buffalo, MN; 44/217 Chr; ModUN; StuCncl; RptrYrbk; Pres4-H; GerCl; PpCl; LetterTrk; LetterWrstlng; GAA; 4-HAwd; No Hennepin College; Accounting.

SCHMIDT, Judith A; Canton Sr HS; Canton, IL; 14/257 Chr; Chrs; CmntyWkr; HonRl; LbryAde; NHS; Yrbk; SchPpr; Spoon River College; Medicine.

SCHMIDT, Julia L; Cardinal Ritter HS; Indianapolis, IN; HonRl; VPJA; JrNHS; NHS; SchPl; SctActv; RptrYrbk; Purdue Univ; Pharmacy.

SCHMIDT, Julie M; Forest Lake HS; Wyoming, MN; Band; Chr; CncrtBnd; DrlTm; HonRl; MrchBnd; PepBnd; SctActv; RptrYrbk; Trade Schl; Secretary.

SCHMIDT, Karen C; Parkston HS; Parkston, SD; Chr; Chrl; Chrs; ChrhWkr; HonRl; OffAde; SchPpr; 4-H; FHA; Trk; St Lukes Schl; Nurse.

SCHMIDT, Katherine A; Belview Public HS; Belview, MN; 4/21 SecSrCls; ChrhWkr; HonRl; LbryAde; NHS; SchPl; StuGov; YthFlsp; RptrYrbk; DARAwd; Employment At Nursing Home.

SCHMIDT, Kathryn A; Carmel For Girls; Waukegan, IL; 21/195 Chrs; DrmBgl; HonRl; IntrClCncl; JrNHS; OffAde; SchMus; GerCl; Bsbl; Accounting.

SCHMIDT, Kerry L; Norris HS; Panama, NE; PresFrshCls; VPJrCls; Chr; ChrhWkr; NHS; SchPl; 4-H; PpCl; LetterTrk; Chrldr; U Of Ne Lincoln; Fashion Design.

SCHMIDT, Krist J; Pekin Community HS; Pekin, IL; 32/744 HonRl; NHS; Illinois Central College; Data Processing.

SCHMIDT, Lois E; Thorp HS; Thorp, WI; /74 TrsJrCls; TrsSrCls; Band; CncrtBnd; HonRl; NHS; StuCncl; Yrbk; SchPpr; FBLA; Univ.

SCHMIDT, Lynden D; Farmington East HS; Elmwood, IL; 3/144 Chr; Chrs; HonRl; LitMag; LbryAde; NHS; SchMus; SchPl; StuGov; Bradley Univ; English.

SCHMIDT, Margaret K; A Hamilton HS; Milwaukee, WI; 146/786 HonRl; StuGov; Trk; CchngActv; GAA; IMSpt; U Of Wis Mil; Professional Business.

SCHMIDT, Margorie F; Grundy Center Comm HS; Holland, IA; Chrs; HonRl; LbryAde; NHS; YthFlsp; LetterBsktbl;.

SCHMIDT, Marie A; Elgin Millville HS; Elgin, MN; 5/50 Chrs; HonRl; StuCncl; RptrYrbk; RptrSchPpr; 4-H; SpnCl; Trk; GAA; 4-HAwd; Concordia Col; Biology.

SCHMIDT, Mark A; Centura HS; Cairo, NE; VPFrshCls; PresSophCls; Aud/Vis; Band; CncrtBnd; MrchBnd; PepBnd; StuCncl; FBLA; Coll; Pro.

SCHMIDT, Mark A; Milford Community HS; Milford, IA; 1/65 ALBoysSt; Band; Chrs; HonRl; NHS; RptrYrbk; SciCl; Bsbl; Glf; College; Professional.

SCHMIDT, Mark E; Marquette HS; Godfrey, IL; HonRl; RptrSchPpr; LatCl; LetterBsbl; LetterFtbl; IMSpt; Univ Of Ill; Biology.

SCHMIDT, Mark E; Rapid City Central HS; Rapid City, SD; 26/583 ALBoysSt; Band; Chrl; LitMag; MrchBnd; NatlFornLg; NHS; NatlMeritFnl; SchMus; SchPl; SctActv; Univ; Pre Med.

SCHMIDT, Marlene A; Gaylord Public HS; Gaylord, MN; 3/67 Chr; ChrhWkr; CncrtBnd; HonRl; PepBnd; SchMus; FHA; BauchLmbAwd; Gustavus Adolphus College; Nursing.

SCHMIDT, Mary A; Franklin Center HS; West Brooklyn, IL; 3/31 HonRl; LbryAde; NHS; SchPl; StuCncl; VPFHA; FrCl; PpCl; GAA; College; Nursing.

SCHMIDT, Mary C; Incarnate Word Acad; Florissant, MO; 20/111 HonRl; NatlThespSoc; Quill&Scroll; StuCncl; MthCl; PpCl; Swmmng; GAA; IMSpt; PPFtbl; U Of Mo At St Louis; Speech Therapy.

SCHMIDT, Mary E; Mercy HS; St Louis, MO; 32/166 CmntyWkr; HonRl; JrNHS; NHS; TchrAde; IMSpt; Avila College; Montessori Teacher.

SCHMIDT, Michael; Taft Hs; Chicago, IL; 70/816 ALBoysSt; Band; CncrtBnd; HonRl; IntrClCncl; SchAde; SchPl; StuCncl; FDA; SpnCl;.

SCHMIDT, Michael A; Pinckneyville Comm HS; Pinckneyville, IL; 9/120 HonRl; SchMus; SpnCl; MthCl; PpCl; SciCl; LetterFtbl; LetterWrstlng; Univ Of Il; Veterinarian Med.

SCHMIDT, Nancy E; New Holstein HS; New Holstein, WI; SecBand; Chr; LitMag; LbryAde; NatlFornLg; PepBnd; SchPpr; Sec4-H; FHA; GAA;.

SCHMIDT, Pamela; Billings HS; Billings, MO; Chr; Chrs; ChrhWkr; CncrtBnd; HonRl; MrchBnd; SchPl; YthFlsp; RptrYrbk; 4-H; Sw Missouri St Univ; Teacher.

SCHMIDT, Patricia L; Adlai E Stevenson HS; Mundelein, IL; 17/237 Band; Chr; CmntyWkr; CncrtBnd; HonRl; NHS; Orch; RedCrAde; SchMus; Trk; GAA; Indiana Univ; Science.

SCHMIDT, Paula F; Sullivan HS; Sullivan, MO; 3/159 VPSophCls; SecTrsSrCls; CncrtBnd; DrlTm; HonRl; NHS; PepBnd; StuCncl; SpnCl; Rockhurst College; Dental Hygiene.

SCHMIDT, Randy J; Bishop Mcnamara HS; Aroma Park, IL; 8/180 HonRl; NHS; TreasStuCncl; RptrYrbk; IMSpt; AmLegAwd; University; Biologist.

SCHMIDT, Rebecca L; Lyons Township HS; La Grange, IL; SecFrshCls; AFS; HonRl; NHS; Lawrence Univ; International Business.

SCHMIDT, Robert A; Cosmos Public HS; Cosmos, MN; SchPl; 4-H; SpnCl; 4-HAwd; Trade School; Cabinet Maker.

SCHMIDT, Robert A; Marquette HS; Godfrey, IL; 10/119 HonRl; JrNHS; NHS; SptEdYrbk; SptEdSchPpr; LatCl; LetterBsbl; LetterBsktbl; LetterFtbl; LetterTrk; Clge.

SCHMIDT, Roberta L; Oakfield HS; Oakfield, WI; Band; CncrtBnd; HonRl; MrchBnd; PepBnd; TchrAde; FBLA; SciCl; Bsktbl; Trk; College; Marine Biologist.

SCHMIDT, Robert C; Tripp HS; Tripp, SD; 2/36 HonRl; NHS; NatlMeritSF; Univ; Math.

SCHMIDT, Robert L; Lincoln Comm HS; Lincoln, IL; 29/273 ChrhWkr; HonRl; NHS; PolWkr; Ftbl; Wrstlng; U Of Ill; Doctor.

SCHMIDT, Rocky L; Edmore Public HS; Edmore, ND; 1/24 Band; Chrs; VPChrhWkr; HonRl; PepBnd; SchPl; Yrbk; EdSchPpr; SciCl; BttyCrckrAwd; U Of Nd; Journalism.

SCHMIDT, Ronald D; Newton HS; Newton, KS; 41/275 HonRl; TchrAde; Univ Of Kansas; Astronomy.

SCHMIDT, Ronald H; Menominee HS; Menominee, MI; ALBoysSt; CmntyWkr; HonRl; JrNHS; NHS; SciCl; Mi Tech U; Engineering.

SCHMIDT, Russell L; Chester Area HS; Chester, SD; VPFrshCls; VPSophCls; CmntyWkr; SchPl; YthFnd; FFA; Ftbl; LetterTrk; LetterWrstlng; College; Pilot.

SCHMIDT, Sandra D; New England Public HS; New England, ND; PresFrshCls; SecTrsJrCls; Band; Chr; Bsbl; LetterBsktbl; LetterTrk; Chrldr; IMSpt; 4-HAwd; Dickinson St Teachers Col; Professional.

SCHMIDT, Sandra S; Jackson HS; Jackson, MN; 21/108 AFS; Band; Chr; ChrhWkr; CncrtBnd; HospAde; Mdrgl; SchPl; StuGov; SchPpr; College; Deaf Education.

SCHMIDT, Sherry L; Oakfield HS; Oakfield, WI; Band; ChrhWkr; CncrtBnd; MrchBnd; PepBnd; FBLA; Bsktbl; Trk; GAA; IMSpt; College; Veterinarian.

SCHMIDT, Sheryl I; Bennington HS; Bennington, KS; Band; Chrs; HonRl; NatlFornLg; PepBnd; SchMus; SchPl; Twrl; PpCl; Bsktbl; Kansas State Univ; Zoology Major.

SCHMIDT, Shirley; Kewaskum HS; Kewaskum, WI; 34/172 MrchBnd; NHS; Orch; PepBnd; SchMus; SchPl; 4-H; FTA; GerCl; Trk; Uw Washington County; Criminal Justice.

SCHMIDT, Shirley J; Dominican HS; Detroit, MI; Chrl; HonRl; JA; NHS; SchMus; StuGov; Yrbk; Trk; IMSpt; Michigan State Univ; Dentist.

SCHMIDT, Steven N; Flasher HS; Berien, ND; VPJrCls; HonRl; SchPl; 4-H; Bsktbl; Ftbl; 4-HAwd; Waheton; Electronic Engr.

SCHMIDT, Tammy L; Reese HS; Fairgrove, MI; 14/126 Band; CmntyWkr; HonRl; ModUN; NHS; SctActv; StuGov; YthFlsp; FBLA; CitAwd; Delta Clge Bay City; Dental Assisting.

SCHMIDT, Thomas A; Proviso East HS; Maywood, IL; 110/1000 Band; ChrhWkr; CmntyWkr; CncrtBnd; HonRl; NatlMeritCmnd; PepBnd; SctActv; RptrSchPpr; Univ Of Illinois; Social Science.

SCHMIDT, Tim J; Clinton Prairie HS; Mulberry, IN; 1/103 ChrhWkr; HonRl; NHS; NatlMeritCmnd; YthFlsp; PresSciCl; AmLegAwd; Univ Purdue; Science.

SCHMIDT, Tina M; Marietta Public HS; Marietta, MN; 4/19 VPSophCls; VPJrCls; ALAGirlsSt; Band; ChrhWkr; HonRl; SchPpr; FHA; LetterTrk; Chrldr;.

SCHMIDT, Todd A; Mound Westonica HS; Mound, MN; 9/215 Chr; ChrhWkr; HonRl; Mdrgl; NHS; LetterBsktbl; LetterGlf; LetterTrk; IMSpt; AmLegAwd; College; Medicine.

SCHMIDT, Tom R; Gibault HS; Waterloo, IL; 11/88 Chrs; HonRl; RptrYrbk; RptrSchPpr; Bsbl; Bsktbl; College; Professional.

SCHMIDT, Victoria M; Flasher Public HS; Flasher, ND; 15/39 PresSophCls; ALAGirlsSt; Chr; Chrs; HonRl; SchPl; StuCncl; 4-H; CaptBsktbl; Trk; College; Professn.

SCHMIDTBAUER, Carol; Hutchinson Sr HS; Hutchinson, MN; AFS; Chr; MrchBnd; OffAde; SchPl; SchPpr; SpnCl; Trk; 4-HAwd; Coll; Police Woman.

SCHMIDTBAUER, John; Hutchinson HS; Hutchinson, MN; ALBoysSt; Chr; Chrs; HonRl; NatlThespSoc; OffAde; Sdlty; SchPl; Bsktbl; DARAwd; Business; Government.

SCHMIDTBERGER, John F; Victoria HS; Victoria, KS; 5/45 HonRl; NHS; NatlMeritCmnd; Sacrstn; SctActv; StuCncl; LetterBsbl; LetterBsktbl; LetterFtbl; Trk; Notre Dame Univ; Math.

SCHMIDTKE, Julie; Humboldt HS; Humboldt, IA; Band; Chr; ChrhWkr; CncrtBnd; DrmMjrt; HonRl; MrchBnd; PepBnd; StuCncl; Chrldr; College; Major Study.

SCHMIDTKNECHT, Steven A; La Crosse Logan HS; La Crosse, WI; 23/225 VPFrshCls; HonRl; JrNHS; NHS; StuCncl; StuGov; Bsbl; Bsktbl; LetterFtbl; IMSpt; KiwanAwd; U W Platteville; Civil Engineering.

SCHMIEDEN, Jean M; Elkhorn Area HS; Elkhorn, WI; AFS; ALAGirlsSt; HonRl; NHS; NatlMeritSF; RptrYrbk; RptrSchPpr; FHA; SpnCl; College; Math Teacher & Government.

SCHMIEDER, Tom L; Albany HS; Brooklyn, WI; 6/36 VPFrshCls; HonRl; NHS; TchrAde; SptEdSchPpr; FrCl; MthCl; CaptBsktbl; Trk; Trade School; Electronics.

SCHMIEG, Steven; Bedford HS; Lambertville, MI; 6/420 HonRl; NHS; NatlMeritCmnd; SchAde; Ftbl; Adrian Col; Mathematics.

SCHMIEGE, Aurthur L; Chesaning Union HS; Chesaning, MI; ChrhWkr; HonRl; 4-H; FFA; Wrstlng; 4-HAwd; Farming.

SCHMIEGE, Karen A; Memorial HS; Ely, MN; 2/135 PresAFS; Band; ChrhWkr; CncrtBnd; NHS; NatlMeritCmnd; NatlThespSoc; SchPl; StuGov; KiwanAwd; Valparaiso U; Social Work.

SCHMIERBACH, Renee B; Belleville Twp West HS; Millstadt, IL; 38/755 SecSrCls; Chrs; ChrhWkr; JrNHS; NHS; StuCncl; College; Accounting.

SCHMIESS, Vicki L; Alsen Public HS; Munich, ND; ChrhWkr; HospAde; PolWkr; EngCl; GerCl; GAA; BttyCrckrAwd; GodCntryAwd; CitAwd; VoiceDemAwd; College; Relgion.

SCHMIG, Darwin D; Groton Central HS; Groton, SD; 1/58 HonRl; NatlFornLg; NHS; PolWkr; SchPl; YthFlsp; RptrSchPpr; SptEdSchPpr; IMSpt; JCAwd; Univ Of Sd; Business Accountant.

SCHMILL, Greg R; Manitowoc Lutheran HS; Manitowoc, WI; 2/81 PresFrshCls; Chr; ChrhWkr; PolWkr; PresStuCncl; RptrSchPpr; SptEdSchPpr; CaptBsktbl; Trk; CchngActv; RotaryAwd; College; Math.

SCHMILLEN, Karen M; Toluca HS; Rutland, IL; TrsJrCls; Band; ChrhWkr; HonRl; NHS; Yrbk; 4-H; FHA; Bsktbl; TreasGAA; Il Valley Comm Coll; Accounting.

SCHMIT, Diana; Potosi HS; Potosi, WI; SecSrCls; Chrs; HonRl; NatlFornLg; OffAde; StuCncl; TchrAde; 4-HAwd; Farming.

SCHMIT, Joanna M; Kensal Public HS; Bordulac, ND; 9/17 Chr; Chrs; HonRl; NatlMeritSchl; OffAde; SchPl; TchrAde; RptrSchPpr; 4-H; Trk; College; Vocation.

SCHMIT, Joanne R; Randolph Public HS; Randolph, NE; Chr; Chrs; SchAde; FBLA; PresFHA; LetterPpCl; Chrldr; Business School; Vocation.

SCHMIT, Karen M; Dundee Comm HS; Carpentersville, IL; 14/360 HonRl; SctActv; Yrbk; FTA; Elmhurst College; Pediatric Nurse.

SCHMIT, Susan M; Catholic Memorial HS; Elm Grove, WI; SecSophCls; ALAGirlsSt; HospAde; NatlFornLg; NHS; SctActv; SecStuCncl; TchrAde; DARAwd; OptClAwd; College; English.

SCHMIT, Tom C; Fosston HS; Trail, MN; StuCncl; FFA; College.

SCHMITKE, Kevin E; Chelsea HS; Chelsea, MI; 40/198 CAP; CncrtBnd; DrmMjrt; HonRl; MrchBnd; NHS; PepBnd; SchMus; TchrAde; Bsbl; Western Mi U; Aviation Tech & Mgmt.

SCHMITT, Anthony E; Lohrville Comm HS; Churdan, IA; 2/29 PresFrshCls; Aud/Vis; Band; HonRl; ModUN; SchMus; RptrYrbk; 4-H; FFA; Bsbl; U Of Northern Iowa; Music.

SCHMITT, Catherine A; Sauk Centre Public HS; Sauk Centre, MN; 14/156 ChrhWkr; HonRl; HospAde; LbryAde; RedCrAde; TchrAde; SchPpr; Trk; GAA; MrchBnd; Hamlin U ;pre Vet.

SCHMITT, Cornella M; St Marys New England HS; New England, ND; 10/52 SecTrsFrshCls; Chr; Chrs; HonRl; SchMus; SchPl; 4-H; PpCl; LetterChrldr; IMSpt; Armed Forces; Speech Specialist.

SCHMITT, Daniel A; Somerset HS; Somerset, WI; 2/57 PresFrshCls; ALBoysSt; Chr; ChrhWkr; StuCncl; SptEdYrbk; GerCl; LetterBsktbl; LetterTrk; Univ Of Wisconsin; Teaching.

SCHMITT, David J; Laporte HS; La Porte, IN; HonRl; College; Mechanical Engineering.

SCHMITT, David L; St Francis Borgia HS; Washington, MO; TrsSrCls; HonRl; SchPl; FrCl; CchngActv; Junior College; Air Cond, Heating, & Refrig.

SCHMITT, Dean; Jasper HS; Jasper, IN; 14/290 ChrhWkr; HonRl; CchngActv; Univ; Bus Acct.

SCHMITT, Julie M; Lomira HS; Lomira, WI; 1/80 SecFrshCls; SecSophCls; SecSrCls; Band; HonRl; SecNHS; FHA; FrCl; GAA; BttyCrckrAwd; U Of Wisc; Cpa.

SCHMITT, Kathleen; Madison Public HS; Madison, MN; AFS; HonRl; HospAde; TchrAde; FHA; GerCl; Bsktbl; Mankato State; Busness Teacher.

SCHMITT, Kathy J; Mabel Canton HS; Mabel, MN; 2/57 TrsSophCls; ALAGirlsSt; Chr; HonRl; HospAde; NHS; SctActv; RptrYrbk; RptrSchPpr; FHA; Rochester Comm College; Nursing.

SCHMITT, Kimbra L; Scott Community HS; Scott City, KS; 25/124 Band; ChrhWkr; CncrtBnd; MrchBnd; OffAde; PepBnd; SchMus; SctActv; PpCl; LetterGlf; College; Art.

SCHMITT, Linda K; Bad Axe HS; Bad Axe, MI; 4/152 HonRl; NHS; TchrAde; SpnCl; Mi State Univ; Elementary Ed.

SCHMITT, Lois C; Highmore HS; Highmore, SD; 1/63 Chrs; ChrhWkr; HonRl; LbryAde; Mdrgl; NHS; YthFlsp; FHA; SciCl; Augustana College; Medicine.

SCHMITT, Marion I; Hartford Union HS; Colgate, WI; 1/360 HonRl; HospAde; NatlFornLg; NHS; SctActv; StuGov; YthFlsp; Yrbk; LatCl; DARAwd; Marquette U; Physician.

SCHMITT, Mark; Turkey Valley HS; Fort Atkinson, IA; 9/111 PresSrCls; Chr; HonRl; NHS; SchMus; StuCncl; SchPpr; Ia State Univ; Liberal Arts.

SCHMITT, Mary J; Saydel HS; Des Moines, IA; SecJrCls; Band; Chrs; CncrtBnd; HonRl; MrchBnd; NHS; PepBnd; PolWkr; SchMus; 4-H; FTA; Univ; Elementary Teacher.

SCHMITT, Michael A; Somerset Public HS; Somerset, WI; 2/72 PresFrshCls; Band; HonRl; MrchBnd; VPStuCncl; VPGerCl; LetterBsktbl; LetterTrk; CchngActv; College; Professional.

SCHMITT, Michael P; St Patrick HS; Chicago, IL; 3/422 HonRl; NatlMeritCmnd; PpCl; Trk; Univ Of Illinois; Engineering.

SCHMITT, Nancy J; O Fallon Twp HS; O Fallon, IL; HonRl; ModUN; NHS; FHA; College; Business Admin.

SCHMITT, Paula A; Chaffee HS; Chaffee, MO; ChrhWkr; CmntyWkr; HospAde; StuCncl; YthFnd; 4-H; FSA; Swmmng; USJCAwd;.

SCHMITT, Peter M; De La Salle HS; Mpls, MN; Chrs; JrNHS; NHS; SctActv; Univ Of Mn; Environmental Concern.

SCHMITT, Randal L; Jasper HS; Jasper, IN; Chr; HonRl; Orch; SchMus; 4-H; KeyCl; Univ; Physics & Mathmatics.

SCHMITT, Ruth E; Bergan HS; Edwards, IL; 21/208 Chr; ChrhWkr; CmntyWkr; HonRl; TchrAde; 4-H; FrCl; DanFAwd; Eastern Illinois Univ; Home Economics.

SCHMITT, Sidney R; Harmony HS; Farmington, IA; Chr; HonRl; Mdrgl; Yrbk; 4-H; PresFFA; Bsktbl; LetterFtbl; 4-HAwd; College; Welder.

SCHMITT, Steven J; Warren HS; Warren, IL; 5/60 SecJrCls; Chrs; HonRl; SchMus; Bsbl; Bsktbl; Ftbl; Trk; CchngActv; College; Computers.

SCHMITT, Terri; English Valleys HS; Wellman, IA; 10/62 Band; Chr; Chrs; CncrtBnd; HonRl; MrchBnd; SchMus; Glf; Univ Of Iowa.

SCHMITT, Thomas J; Marquette HS; Cottage Hills, IL; Chr; Chrs; ChrhWkr; HonRl; JrNHS; NatlThespSoc; RptrSchPpr; College; Music.

SCHMITTER, Craig S; High School; Manawa, WI; 9#33#37# HonRl; MrchBnd; PepBnd; MthCl; Bsktbl; Ftbl; Trk;.

SCHMITTER, Joel S; Little Wolf HS; Manawa, WI; 8/80 Band; ChrhWkr; CncrtBnd; HonRl; MrchBnd; NHS; 4-H; MthCl; Trk; Wrstlng; Uw Oshkosh Wi; Teacher.

SCHMITTGENS, Eugene P; Rich East HS; Park Forest, IL; Chr; ChrhWkr; HonRl; NatlFornLg; Natl-

ThespSoc; TchrAde; TreasGerCl; LetterBsbl; Macmurray College; Lawyer.

SCHMITZ, Alice L; Petersburg HS; Petersburg, NE; SecTrsSophCls; Band; Chrs; HonRl; PepBnd; SchPl; Yrbk; SchPpr; PpCl; LetterTrk; College; Science.

SCHMITZ, Audrey; Fatima Hs; Argyle, MO; 5/126 Band; CncrtBnd; HonRl; NHS; SchPl; RptrYrbk; RptrSchPpr; 4-H; FHA; PpCl; Lincoln U; Art.

SCHMITZ, Barbara J; Tower Hill HS; Tower Hill, IL; SecSophCls; PresJrCls; Chrs; HonRl; NHS; StuCncl; PpCl; Trk; Coll; Dental Hygienist & Beautician.

SCHMITZ, Dee A; F J Reitz HS; Evansville, IN; 57/432 ChrhWkr; HonRl; HospAde; JA; JrNHS; Quill&Scroll; SchPl; RptrSchPpr; FFA; College; Respiratory Therapy.

SCHMITZ, Denise; Central HS; Norwood, MN; 11/94 Band; Chr; Chrs; DrlTm; Mdrgl; MrchBnd; Orch; PepBnd; SchPl; GAA; College; Music.

SCHMITZ, Diane M; Ithaca HS; Hillpoint, WI; 2/30 Band; CncrtBnd; HonRl; MrchBnd; PepBnd; EdYrBk; RptrSchPpr; FBLA; PpCl; DARAwd; Sw Wisconsin Voc Tec; Business Admin.

SCHMITZ, John G; Brookfield East HS; Brookfield, WI; CmntyWkr; SctActv; ChmnKeyCl; LatCl; Bsktbl; Glf; Trk; IMSpt; College; Study Accounting.

SCHMITZ, Julie A; Northeast Nodaway Rv HS; Parnell, MO; 1/24 PresSophCls; PresSrCls; Chrs; HonRl; NHS; SchMus; SchPl; StuCncl; PpCl; Bsbl; CaptBsktbl; LetterTrk; College; Liberal Arts.

SCHMITZ, Lawrence G; Axtell Public HS; Axtell, KS; VPSrCls; ALBoysSt; Chrs; ChrhWkr; CmntyWkr; HonRl; SchPl; StuCncl; RptrYrbk; Trk; Usn; Mechanic.

SCHMITZ, Lori; Don Bosco HS; Gilbertville, IA; 13/57 ChrhWkr; HonRl; NHS; OffAde; RptrYrbk; SchPpr; PpCl; IMSpt; Business; Secretary.

SCHMITZ, Lori A; New Holstein Sr HS; St Cloud, WI; SecSophCls; SecJrCls; SecSrCls; Band; HonRl; NHS; OffAde; 4-H; PpCl; Chrldr; College; Teaching.

SCHMITZ, Marita A; Montevideo Sr HS; Montevideo, MN; AFS; ChrhWkr; HonRl; GerCl; Coll; Nurse.

SCHMITZ, Nancy; Don Bosco HS; Jesup, IA; 4/57 SecTrsSrCls; Chrs; HonRl; HospAde; JrNHS; NHS; OffAde;.

SCHMITZ, Nicholas R; B & B HS; Baileyville, KS; HonRl; SchPl; StuCncl; 4-H; LetterFtbl; College; Pro.

SCHMITZ, Reuben; Northwestern Prep; Watertown, WI; Band; ChrhWkr; CncrtBnd; HonRl; PepBnd; StuCncl; Ftbl; IMSpt; College; Professional.

SCHMITZ, Ronald L; Central HS; Evansville, IN; HonRl; SpnCl; Indiana Univ; Physical Therapy.

SCHMITZ, Sandy G; Lake Central HS; Dyer, IN; 34/500 Chr; ChrhWkr; HonRl; Mdrgl; NHS; SchMus; SchPl; TchrAde; GerCl; Indiana Univ; Physical Therapy.

SCHMITZ, Sue M; Don Bosco HS; Jesup, IA; 3/57 Band; Chr; Chrs; CncrtBnd; HonRl; NHS; PepBnd; TchrAde; PpCl; Bsktbl; Univ; Earth Sci.

SCHMITZER, Joann; Marquette HS; Alton, IL; 22/116 Chrs; HonRl; LitMag; RptrYrbk;.

SCHMITZER, Joel R; Frankenmuth HS; Frankenmuth, MI; HonRl; OffAde; SchPl; SctActv; TchrAde; IMSpt; Trade Sch; Construction.

SCHMOKER, David P; Mullen HS; Mullen, NE; 10/38 Band; Chr; Chrs; CncrtBnd; HonRl; Mdrgl; MrchBnd; PepBnd; SchMus; RptrYrbk; Coll; Music.

SCHMOLESKY, Debra S; Winnebago Lutheran HS; N Fond Du Lac, WI; 5/44 Band; ChrhWkr; CncrtBnd; MrchBnd; NatlFornLg; NatlMeritCmnd; PepBnd; RptrYrbk; Yrbk; EdSchPpr; Dr Martin Luther College; Elementary Ed.

SCHMOLKE, Karen L; Onamia HS; Carrison, MN; 7/70 Band; Chr; ChrhWkr; CncrtBnd; HonRl; MrchBnd; PepBnd; StuCncl; LetterTrk; PPFtbl; Vocational Sch; Med Field.

SCHMOLL, Robert; Shiocton HS; Fremont, WI; 8/75 PresJrCls; ALBoysSt; Chrs; ChrhWkr; HonRl; NHS; SchPl; EdYrBk; Us Coast Guard.

SCHMOLZE, Karen E; Glenbrook So HS; Glenview, IL; 102/579 AFS; Chr; HonRl; NatlThespSoc; PolWkr; SchMus; SchPl; SctActv; PpCl; College; Nursing.

SCHMUCK, Craig A; Pipestone HS; Pipestone, MN; Band; CncrtBnd; HonRl; MrchBnd; PepBnd; TchrAde; LetterBsbl; Bsktbl; LetterFtbl; University; Professional.

SCHMUCKIE, Barbara A; Dixon HS; Dixon, IL; 2/337 HonRl; JA; NHS; NatlMeritCmnd; NatlThespSoc; SchMus; StuCncl; RptrYrbk; EdYrBk; Univ Of Illinois; Mathematics.

SCHMUHL, Cynthia; Ripon HS; Brandon, WI; ChrhWkr; CmntyWkr; CncrtBnd; HonRl; NatlThespSoc; PepBnd; SchMus; SchPl; YthFlsp; GerCl; College; Legal Secretary.

SCHMUHL, Kathryn L; Coloma HS; Coloma, MI; Band; HonRl; NHS; TchrAde; Yrbk; Pres4-H; KeyCl; LetterBsktbl; LetterTrk; 4-HAwd; Mi State U; Medical Technology.

SCHMUKE, Debbie G; Union HS; Union, MO; ChrhWkr; HonRl; OffAde; EdYrBk; PpCl; CchngActv; PPFtbl; E Central Jr College; Nursing.

SCHMUKE, Kathy M; Union HS; Union, MO; 12/165 ALAGirlsSt; Chrs; HonRl; JA; NatlFornLg; College; Health.

SCHMUTTE, Mary E; Cardinal Ritter HS; Indianapolis, IN; 18/151 SecJrCls; HonRl; NHS; SchPl; StuCncl; Indiana University; Doctor.

SCHMUTZ, Fred; Mooseheart HS; Mooseheart, IL; 2,18 VPSophCls; ALBoysSt; HonRl; ROTC; StuCncl; EdYrBk; SptEdSchPpr; Bsktbl; Ftbl; Trk; College; Vocation.

SCHMUTZLER, Jane L; Watertown HS; Watertown, WI; TrsSophCls; VPJrCls; VPSrCls; AFS; HospAde; StuCncl; YthFlsp; LatCl; SpnCl; SecTrsSophCls; Univ Of Wisconsin; Nursing.

SCHNAARE, Carol A; Trico HS; Murphysboro, IL; SecFrshCls; TrsJrCls; Band; ChrhWkr; CncrtBnd; HonRl; HospAde; Pres4-H; FBLA; TreasFHA; SecSciCl; GAA; College; Medical Lab Technologist.

SCHNABEL, Karen; Eureka HS; Eureka, SD; 4/56 PresFrshCls; Band; Chrs; JA; NatlMeritCmnd; SchMus; SchPl; Trk; GAA; DARAwd; College; Professional Possibly Phy Therapy.

SCHNABEL, Kristie; Tripp Public HS; Tripp, SD; 13/36 Chrs; ChrhWkr; DrlTm; HonRl; NHS; StuCncl; RptrYrbk; RptrSchPpr; Trk; Nettleton Coll; Account.

SCHNABL, Barbara; Newtrier East HS; Wilmette, IL; HonRl; HospAde; TchrAde; FSA; LatCl; SciCl; GAA; Univ; Biologist.

SCHNABL, Christine M; Riverside Brookfield HS; Brookfield, IL; 23/489 HonRl; JrNHS; NHS; Yrbk; CaptChrldr; GAA; Loyola; Nursing.

SCHNAGL, Pamela J; Merrill HS; Merrill, WI; 1/334 Band; CncrtBnd; HonRl; MrchBnd; NatlFornLg; PepBnd; SchMus; GerCl; GovHonPrgAwd; RotaryAwd; Carthage Col;.

SCHNAKE, Richard; Mt Vernon HS; Mt Vernon, MO; 6/95 ALBoysSt; ChrhWkr; CmntyWkr; HonRl; ModUN; NatlMeritCmnd; Yrbk; Sw Mo Univ; Law.

SCHNARRE, Thomas D; Nakomis HS; Nakomis, IL; 12/89 ALBoysSt; Band; Chrl; Chrs; HonRl; SchMus; Yrbk; VP4-H; SciCl; 4-HAwd; College; Occupational Therapy.

SCHNAUS, Vicki L; Jasper HS; Jasper, IN; 15/332 VPJrCls; VPSrCls; ChrhWkr; HonRl; StuCncl; PpCl; Chrldr; Brymines; Medical Assistant.

SCHNECK, Kent J; Wausau West HS; Wausau, WI; 129/425 LetterBsbl; LetterLetterFtbl; AmLegAwd; U W Stevens Point; Business Administration.

SCHNECKLOTH, Mary M; Winola HS; Viola, IL; Chr; ChrhWkr; LbryAde; StuCncl; Teen; SchPpr; FHA; Bsbl; GAA; IMSpt; Blackhawk Clg; English/history.

SCHNEEMAN, Julia; Visitation HS; Saint Paul, MN; PresFrshCls; SecSophCls; SecJrCls; StuCncl; SchPpr; Bsbl; Bsktbl; Tennis; KiwanAwd; RotaryAwd; St Marys College At Notre Dame; Nursing.

SCHNEEMAN, Nicholas J; St Thomas Academy; St Paul, MN; TrsSophCls; SecJrCls; HonRl; StuCncl; StuGov; LatCl; SciCl; CaptUniv Of Notre Dame; Medicine.

SCHNEIDER, Andrew; Jasper HS; Jasper, IN; 4/290 Chr; HonRl; NHS; NatlMeritCmnd; SchMus; StuCncl; 4-H; Ftbl; Tennis; Purdue; Engineer.

SCHNEIDER, Cathy M; Proviso West HS; Westchester, IL; 150/1000 HonRl; GerCl; Triton Coll; Spec Ed Tchr.

SCHNEIDER, Cheryl A; Merrill HS; Midland, MI; 4-H; GAA; VoiceDemAwd; Clge; Pro.

SCHNEIDER, Cheryl L; East Central HS; Sunman, IN; HonRl; NHS; SpnCl; PpCl; GAA;.

SCHNEIDER, Cindy M; Sevastopol HS; Egg Harbor, WI; SecFrshCls; SecSophCls; NHS; SchPl; SctActv; TchrAde; FHA; LatCl; Chrldr; IMSpt;.

SCHNEIDER, Clinton C; Goodrich HS; Goodrich, ND; 2/21 HstFrshCls; VPSophCls; HstJrCls; HstSrCls; Band; ChrhWkr; CmntyWkr; CncrtBnd; HonRl; MrchBnd; CaptBsktbl; Ftbl; Swmmng; Trk; Univ Of Minnesota; Law.

SCHNEIDER, Daniel F; Campbellsport HS; St Cloud, WI; 29/153 ALBoysSt; FFA; LetterFtbl; Army.

SCHNEIDER, David H; Taft HS; Chicago, IL; TchrAde; RptrSchPpr; Bsktbl; U Of Ill; Business Management.

SCHNEIDER, Dawn M; Owen Withee HS; Owen, WI; 4/98 VPFrshCls; HonRl; NHS; 4-H; FHA; LetterBsktbl; Glf; LetterTrk; GAA; 4-HAwd; Col;nur.

SCHNEIDER, Debora S; Jefferson City Sr HS; Jefferson City, MO; 32/486 Band; ChrhWkr; CncrtBnd; HonRl; JrNHS; MrchBnd; NHS; SctActv; PresYthFlsp; FTA; TreasLatCl; PpCl; Southwest Mo State Univ; English.

SCHNEIDER, Debra R; Whitefish Bay HS; Whitefish Bay, WI; Band; CncrtBnd; HonRl; MrchBnd; NatlMeritCmnd; RptrSchPpr; SchPpr; GerCl; Swmmng; IMSpt; Univ Of Wi River Falls; Horse Science.

SCHNEIDER, Diane; Chilton Public HS; Chilton, WI; ChrhWkr; HonRl; NHS; TchrAde; FHA; Fox Valley Tech; Occupational Therapy.

SCHNEIDER, Doug P; Southland HS; Taopi, MN; TrsSophCls; Chr; Chrs; HonRl; NHS; SchPl; Sdlty; 4-H; FFA; LetterBsbl; LetterFtbl; LetterTrk; 4-HAwd; Univ Of Minnesota; Agriculture.

SCHNEIDER, Eileen; Southland HS; Adams, MN; 18/123 HonRl; NHS; Yrbk; FHA; GerCl; Rochester Comm Coll; Writer.

SCHNEIDER, Gary; Roncalli HS; Manitowoc, WI; 25/300 Aud/Vis; Chrs; HonRl; JrNHS; NHS; StuCncl; TchrAde; IMSpt; College; Natural Resources.

SCHNEIDER, Heidi A; Windom Area HS; Windom, MN; 2/138 VPSophCls; CncrtBnd; HonRl; NatlFornLg; NHS; Orch; SchPl; StuCncl; RptrYrbk; Carleton College; Journalism.

SCHNEIDER, John; Bishop Dwenger HS; Fort Wayne, IN; 25/245 HonRl; NHS; SchMus; SchPl; KeyCl; IMSpt; Univ; Actuarial Science.

SCHNEIDER, John A; Cape Central HS; Cape Girardeau, MO; 85/500 HonRl; NHS; SctActv; CivCl; Bsbl; Ftbl; LetterWrstlng; PresAwd; Military Academy; Engineering.

SCHNEIDER, Julie A; Minden HS; Heartwell, NE; CncrtBnd; Teen; MrchBnd; NHS; SecFHA; GerCl; PresPpCl; Bsktbl; LetterGlf; Kearney State College; Medical Technology.

SCHNEIDER, Karen M; St Teresa HS; Decatur, IL; 8/118 AFS; HonRl; HospAde; NHS; Sacrstn; SctActv; Yrbk; 4-H; PpCl; DanFAwd; Univ Of Illinois; Home Economics.

SCHNEIDER, Laurie K; Okawville HS; Venedy, IL; SecFrshCls; SecSophCls; HonRl; LbryAde; VPNHS; SecStuCncl; SecYthFlsp; RptrSchPpr; VPPpCl; College; Pharmacist.

SCHNEIDER, Lawrence M; New Holstein HS; Mt Calvary, WI; 11/196 HonRl; LbryAde; NHS; TchrAde; SecSpnCl; Univ Of Wi; Cpa.

SCHNEIDER, Madonna; Jefferson County North HS; Nortonville, KS; 1/48 SecJrCls; HonRl; LbryAde; NHS; SchPl; RptrSchPpr; FBLA; PpCl; College Nights; Computer Programming.

SCHNEIDER, Mary; Langdon HS; Langdon, ND; 8/107 HonRl; HospAde; NHS; RptrYrbk; RptrSchPpr; FFA; GerCl; PpCl; Univ Nd; Psychology.

SCHNEIDER, Mary A; North HS; Sheboygan, WI; ChrhWkr; HonRl; HospAde; LbryAde; SchAde; SctActv; FrCl; Coll; Teaching.

SCHNEIDER, Mary E; Forest Lake HS; Forest Lake, MN; Band; CncrtBnd; DrlTm; HonRl; MrchBnd; NHS; FHA; Chrldr; GAA; IMSpt; Coll.

SCHNEIDER, Mary M; Red Wing Central HS; Red Wing, MN; HonRl; NHS; Orch; GAA; PPFtbl; College Of St Benedict; Spanish Bus Govt.

SCHNEIDER, Mich; Duchesne HS; Saint Charles, MO; HonRl; PolWkr; IMSpt; Univ Of Mo; Chem Engrg.

SCHNEIDER, Michael; Avon HS; Plainfield, IN; HonRl; YthFlsp; Ind St Univ; Criminology.

SCHNEIDER, Nancy A; Red Wing Central HS; Red Wing, MN; 2/319 Chr; ChrhWkr; HonRl; PresNHS; NatlMeritCmnd; RptrYrbk; GerCl; CaptChrldr; College; Vocation.

SCHNEIDER, Nicholas M; Appleton East HS; Appleton, WI; 1/523 ALBoysSt; NatlFornLg; NatlMeritSF; NatlThespSoc; SchMus; SchPl; SctActv; StuCncl; RptrYrbk; RptrSchPpr; Dartmouth College; Science.

SCHNEIDER, Pamela; Liberty Hs; Liberty, IL; 1/56 HonRl; SecLbryAde; PresNHS; SchPl; DrlTm; FNA; PresSpnCl; VPPpCl; LetterTrk; BttyCrckrAwd; Quincy College; Teacher.

SCHNEIDER, Patricia A; Maria HS; Oak Lawn, IL; NatlThespSoc; SctActv; Sdlty; StuCncl; SpnCl; Bsktbl; Tennis; Trk; IMSpt; College; Dental Hygiene.

SCHNEIDER, Paul E; Bayard HS; Bayard, NE; VPSophCls; ALBoysSt; Band; Chrl; Chrs; HonRl; NHS; OffAde; SchMus; SchPl; College.

SCHNEIDER, Raymond M; St Johns HS; St Johns, MI; 80/325 ChrhWkr; HonRl; NHS; YthFlsp; Bsktbl; LetterFtbl; LetterTennis; IMSpt; Lansing Comm College; Statistician.

SCHNEIDER, Richard; Laboratory HS; Terre Haute, IN; Coll; Comm Art.

SCHNEIDER, Rissa K; Central HS; St Joseph, MO; Chr; Chrs; HonRl; NHS; Orch; SchMus; LatCl; PpCl; College; Music.

SCHNEIDER, Rita; Otis Bison Sr HS; Olmitz, KS; VPJrCls; Band; Chr; Chrs; ChrhWkr; CncrtBnd; HonRl; MrchBnd;.

SCHNEIDER, Rita M; Lefor HS; Lefor, ND; 2/8 PresJrCls; Chr; ChrhWkr; HonRl; SchPl; TchrAde; 4-H; LetterBsktbl; GAA; 4-HAwd; College; Xray Technician.

SCHNEIDER, Sharon A; Rich Central HS; Matteson, IL; MthCl; Eastern Ill Univ; Accounting.

SCHNEIDER, Stephen E; New Trier HS; Wilmette, IL; 9/847 HonRl; NatlSciFnd; MthCl; Univ; Research Scientist.

SCHNEIDER, Stephen L; St Marys HS; Burlington, WI; 3/73 VPFrshCls; HonRl; StuCncl; LetterFtbl; Trk; College; Chemistry.

SCHNEIDER, Thomas A; Bismarck HS; Bismarck, ND; 15/650 HonRl; NHS; GerCl; Bsktbl; Ftbl; Tennis; IMSpt; College; Engineering.

SCHNEIDER, Timothy J; Scotus Central Catholic HS; Columbus, NE; SchPl; Bsktbl; LetterFtbl; Trk; Navy.

SCHNEIER, Cheri K; Duchesne HS; St Charles, MO; 4/135 Chrs; HonRl; NHS; NatlMeritCmnd; OffAde; RptrYrbk; FrCl; College; Accounting.

SCHNEITER, Marilyn; Lomira Community HS; Lomira, WI; HonRl; FHA; Technical School; Nursing.

SCHNELL, Lori A; Bishop Mcnamara HS; Bourbonnais, IL; 22/161 HonRl; HospAde; FrCl; Jr College.

SCHNELL, Patricia; Bradley Bourbonnais HS; Bradley, IL; Band; ChrhWkr; CmntyWkr; HospAde; Orch; StuCncl; YthFlsp; EngCl; FrCl; GerCl; Airline Training Sch; Airlines.

SCHNELL, Patricia L; Jfk Prep; Kiel, WI; Chr; Yrbk; Bsktbl; Marquette Univ Wi; Medical Tech.

SCHNELL, Sharon A; Valders HS; Manitowoc, WI; 3/110 Chr; Chrs; ChrhWkr; HonRl; StuCncl; EdYrBk; 4-H; PresFHA; PpCl; DARAwd; Secretarial.

SCHNELL, Shirley A; Kiel HS; Kiel, WI; Chr; HonRl; JA; NHS; 4-H; GerCl; Bsktbl; Trk; GAA; Technical Schl; Data Processing.

SCHNELL, Shirley K; Dubois HS; Birdseye, IN; 6/80 Chrs; NHS; College; Business.

SCHNELL, Thomas E; Hastings HS; Hastings, MN; PresFrshCls; VPFrshCls; PresSophCls; VPSophCls; PresJrCls; VPJrCls; SecJrCls; PresSrCls; VPSrCls; SecSrCls; EdYrBk; LetterBsbl; Ftbl; IMSpt; College; Bus.

SCHNELLE, Kaylyn J; Lockwood R1 HS; Lockwood, MO; 4/45 HonRl; NHS; SchPl; StuCncl; Yrbk; RptrSchPpr; TreasFHA; PpCl; IMSpt; CaptPPFtbl; Smsu; Business.

SCHNELLENBERGER, Patricia A; Southridge HS; Huntingburg, IN; 9/133 ALAGirlsSt; ChrhWkr; HonRl; 4-H; FrCl; 4-HAwd; College; Business.

SCHNEPP, Catherine M; Huntington Catholic HS; Huntington, IN; 2/39 HonRl; NHS; Pres4-H; GAA; 4-HAwd; KiwanAwd; RotaryAwd; Huntington Coll; Acct.

SCHNEPP, David; Northrop Senior HS; Ft Wayne, IN; 31/642 Band; CncrtBnd; HonRl; MrchBnd; PepBnd; Iu Law Sch; Probate Court Law.

SCHNEPPER, Erin L; Lancaster Senior HS; Lancaster, WI; 47/155 Chr; CmntyWkr; CncrtBnd; HonRl; JrNHS; ModUN; NatlMeritSchl; StuCncl; TchrAde; YthFlsp; Business College; Stewardess.

SCHNERRE, Susan; Bluffton Allen HS; Bluffton, IN; 7/139 HonRl; NHS; NatlMeritFnl; TchrAde; Univ; Veterinary Medicine.

SCHNIRRING, Carolyn B; Springfield HS; Springfield, IL; 49/580 Chr; Chrl; ChrhWkr; HonRl; StuGov; Trk; Purdue Univ; Interior Design.

SCHNIRRING, Jane M; Pacelli HS; Austin, MN; PresSophCls; Chrs; ChrhWkr; HonRl; Chrldr; Coll; Prof.

SCHNITZ, Randy J; Oswego Sr HS; Oswego, IL; 149/250 ChrhWkr; CmntyWkr; HonRl; Pres4-H; FFA; KeyCl; GerCl; Bsbl; Ftbl; DanFAwd; 4-HAwd; CitAwd; Joliet Jr College; Business.

SCHNOBRICH, Vicky; St Francis HS; Bethel, MN; ChrhWkr; HonRl; TchrAde; Vocational Technical Schoo.

SCHNOEBELEN, Jamie C; Macksville HS; Macksville, KS; ChrhWkr; CmntyWkr; StuGov; YthFnd; Yrbk; PpCl; Bsktbl; Ftbl; Trk; GAA; Marymount Clg; Registered Nurse.

SCHNOLL, Steven R; Glendale Nicolet HS; Milwaukee, WI; 100/530 HonRl; NatlFornLg; RptrSchPpr; MthCl; FrCl; GerCl; SciCl; Glf; U Of Wisc Madison; Chem Eng.

SCHNUETTGEN, Janet L; Dow City Arion HS; Dow City, IA; 2/39 HonRl; LbryAde; NHS; SchPl; TchrAde; FTA;.

SCHNULLE, Marlys A; Polo Comm HS; Polo, IL; Chr; Chrs; HonRl; SchMus; SpnCl; PpCl; Chrldr; GAA; 4-HAwd; Business School.

SCHNUR, David C; Reitz Memorial HS; Evansville, IN; 5/211 Aud/Vis; CmntyWkr; HonRl; NHS; 4-H; SciCl; LetterBsbl; LetterBsktbl; Ftbl; IMSpt; ChmbCommrsAwd; 4-HAwd; Purdue Univ; Agriculture.

SCHNUR, Marilyn A; Reitz Memorial HS; Evansville, IN; 1/212 HonRl; HospAde; NHS; TchrAde; Yrbk; Pres4-H; SpnCl; PresSciCl; IMSpt; 4-HAwd; Purdue Univ; Biology.

SCHNURPEL, Charles C; Brazil HS; Brazil, IN; 6/204 HonRl; NHS; SctActv; StuCncl; LetterWrstlng; Rose Human Inst; Engineering.

SCHOB, Christine M; St Thomas Aquinas HS; Florissant, MO; 25/325 NHS; SchMus; SchPl; Yrbk; IMSpt; Medicine.

SCHOCH, Amelia C; Pioneer HS; Ann Arbor, MI; 61/678 Chr; Chrl; SchMus; Hillsdale College; Fine Art Or Com Art.

SCHOCH, James; Central HS; Aberdeen, SD; HonRl; IMSpt; College; Accounting.

SCHOCK, Beverly A; Glidden Public HS; Glidden, WI; 2/30 PresSrCls; Chr; HonRl; StuCncl; RptrYrbk; EdYrBk; PpCl; LetterBsbl; LetterBsktbl; CaptChrldr; River Falls Univ; Phy Ed.

SCHODER, Andrew O; New Trier HS; Winnetka, IL; 109/700 VPStuGov; YthFlsp; CaptTrk; Dartmouth College; Business.

SCHOEBERL, Anthony R; Rush City HS; Rush City, MN; TrsJrCls; ALBoysSt; ChrhWkr; HonRl; JrNHS; 4-H; FFA; PpCl; LetterFtbl; Trk; Voc; Farmer/mechanic.

SCHOEBERL, Suzanne; Memorial HS; Joplin, MO; ChrhWkr; HonRl; HospAde; JrNHS; NHS; OffAde; Sdlty; TchrAde; Teen; Yrbk; CivCl; Tennis; Chrldr; College.

SCHOEDER, Rosamary C; St Marys HS; Reeder, ND; ALAGirlsSt; HonRl; PolWkr; Yrbk; PpCl; Trk; Chrldr; N Dakota State Univ; Lawyer.

SCHOEDER, Teresa E; St Marys HS; Reeper, ND; 14/44 Chr; HonRl; PolWkr; TchrAde; RptrYrbk; PpCl; North Dakota State Univ; Law.

SCHOEFF, Nancy E; Eastbrook HS; Marion, IN; 19/170 Chrs; HonRl; SchMus; SchPl; YthFlsp; RptrYrbk; 4-H; PpCl; College; Business.

SCHOEMANN, Jane L; St Marys HS; St Marys, KS; 13/67 PresJrCls; Chrs; HonRl; OffAde; PolWkr; TchrAde; PresFHA; PpCl; Trk; BttyCrckrAwd; Brown Mackie Bus Coll; Medical Sec.

SCHOEN, Bruce H; Oak Ridge HS; Oak Ridge, MO; PresFrshCls; Band; CncrtBnd; MrchBnd; PepBnd; StuCncl; 4-H; Bsktbl; Trk; Coll; Ag.

SCHOEN, Kathleen M; Sacred Heart Of Mary HS; Arlington Hts, IL; 6/136 HonRl; HospAde; PresNHS; StuGov; Marycrest College; Science.

SCHOEN, Mary L; Derham Hall HS; St Paul, MN;

HospAde; LbryAde; StuGov; RptrYrbk; Yrbk; SpnCl; College; Police Career.

SCHOEN, Paul W; Naperville Central HS; Naperville, IL; 20/844 AFS; ChrhWkr; HonRl; NHS; FrCl; MthCl; SciCl; Tennis; University Of Illinois; Mathematics.

SCHOEN, Teresa; Oak Ridge HS; Oak Ridge, MO; Band; Chrs; ChrhWkr; HonRl; MrchBnd; PepBnd; StuCncl; 4-H; FHA; 4-HAwd; Southeast Missouri Univ; Agriculture.

SCHOENBEIN, Gregory D; Abingdon Comm HS; Maquon, IL; Band; ChrhWkr; MrchBnd; PepBnd; YthFlsp; 4-H; FFA; Carl Sandburg College; Agriculture.

SCHOENBURG, Harry D; Niles North HS; Skokie, IL; 7/600 CmntyWkr; JrNHS; LitMag; NatlFornLg; NHS; NatlMeritSF; NatlSciFnd; NatlThespSoc; StuCncl; StuGov; Oberlin Coll; Rabbi.

SCHOENDIENST, Eileen; St Joseph Academy; St Louis, MO; VPSrCls; Chr; Chrs; SchMus; SchPl; SpnCl; PpCl; GAA; St Louis Univ; Communications.

SCHOENE, Virginia L; Wesclin Jr Sr HS; Trenton, IL; 7/100 Band; HonRl; NHS; SecNatlThespSoc; EdYrBk; SptEdSchPpr; SecGerCl; LetterTrk; GAA; DARAwd; Siu Carbondale; Music.

SCHOENECKER, Karen S; Oak Forest HS; Oak Forest, IL; 18/346 Band; HonRl; NHS; PepBnd; RptrYrbk; PpCl; Trk; Univ.

SCHOENEFELD, Joyce G; Grant Deuel HS; Altamont, SD; Chr; Chrs; ChrhWkr; HonRl; TchrAde; YthFlsp; FHA; PpCl; College; Rn.

SCHOENER, Catherine; Cosmos HS; Cosmos, MN; /45 SecTrsJrCls; Band; Chr; CncrtBnd; DrmMjrt; HonRl; SchPl; PresSctActv; LetterBsktbl; LetterChrldr; College; Phy Ed.

SCHOENFELDER, Jolene M; Parkston Public HS; Dimock, SD; 1/98 Chrs; ChrhWkr; CmntyWkr; LbryAde; StuCncl; FTA; Univ Of Sd; Accounting Cpa.

SCHOENFELDER, Linda; Parkston HS; Dimock, SD; 3/98 Chrs; CmntyWkr; HonRl; LbryAde; NHS; PolWkr; 4-HAwd; University; Dental Hygiene.

SCHOENFELDT, Marti; D C Everest Sr HS; Schofield, WI; 61/360 Band; CncrtBnd; HonRl; MrchBnd; PepBnd; SchMus; Ftbl; Glf; College.

SCHOENHALS, Victor L; Lawrence HS; Lawrence, NE; SecTrsSophCls; Chrs; SchPl; RptrSchPpr; SptEdSchPpr; 4-H; Bsktbl; Ftbl; Trk; 4-HAwd; Coll; Broadcasting.

SCHOENHERR, John E; Southeastern HS; Bowen, IL; 15/55 VPFrshCls; ChrhWkr; CmntyWkr; HonRl; SchPl; LatCl; MthCl; PpCl; Swmmng; IMSpt; Western Il Univ; Dentist.

SCHOENHERR, Kent R; Wausau West HS; Wausau, WI; Band; CncrtBnd; MrchBnd; OffAde; PepBnd; SchAde; Bsktbl; LetterFtbl; Wrstlng; IMSpt; College State System; Grade Arts.

SCHOENHOLZ, Kim R; Bruning Public HS; Bruning, NE; VPSophCls; Band; Chrs; CmntyWkr; CncrtBnd; MrchBnd; PepBnd; SchPl; TchrAde; Teen; LetterBsktbl; Ftbl; Milford Trade Schl; Agriculture Tech.

SCHOENI, Jean L; Slinger Sr HS; Slinger, WI; HonRl; TchrAde; EdSchPpr; VP4-H; PpCl; LetterBsktbl; LetterTrk; LetterChrldr; 4-HAwd; CitAwd; Uw Madison; Doctor.

SCHOENIKE, Jenny A; South HS; Sheboygan, WI; 9/496 TrsSrCls; Band; HonRl; MrchBnd; NatlFornLg; NHS; StuGov; Bsbl; LetterSwmmng; CaptTrk; Uw Madison; Pharmacey.

SCHOENKIN, Marsha J; North HS; Sheboygan, WI; Chrs; PresChrhWkr; HonRl; SecFrshCls; PolWkr; SchPl; SchPpr; OptClAwd; University; Journalism.

SCHOENKNECHT, Alison L; Lincoln Sr HS; Wisconsin Rapids, WI; 56/516 Aud/Vis; Band; HonRl; Quill&Scroll; SchAde; TchrAde; RptrSchPpr; SchPpr; SciCl; Tennis; U Of Wi Eau Claire; Pre Med.

SCHOENLAUB, Susan L; Central HS; St Joseph, MO; 62/520 Chr; Chrs; ChrhWkr; HonRl; NHS; PolWkr; SchMus; YthFlsp; SpnCl; College; Forestry Or Conservation.

SCHOENMANN, Jeff; River Valley HS; Spring Green, WI; 30/182 Chr; Chrs; CncrtBnd; HonRl; MrchBnd; SchMus; StuGov; Bsktbl; Ftbl; Glf; Platteville Univ.

SCHOENROCK, Mary; Fairbury Senior HS; Fairbury, NE; Chrs; CncrtBnd; HonRl; OffAde; PepBnd; SchMus; Pres4-H; FBLA; IMSpt;.

SCHOENROCK, Ramona J; Fairbury HS; Fairbury, NE; 9/147 Chrs; HonRl; JCC; NHS; OffAde; 4-H; SecFBLA; TreasGerCl; PpCl; EldAwd; Clg; Business Teacher.

SCHOENTHAL, Nadine L; Lake View Auburn HS; Lake View, IA; HonRl; Lamson Business College; Accounting.

SCHOENWALD, Mary M; Bishop Ryan HS; Minot, ND; 25/85 Band; Chr; CncrtBnd; HonRl; MrchBnd; Orch; PepBnd; SchMus; FHA; PpCl; Chrldr; GAA; University.

SCHOENWANDT, Margaret A; Creston HS; Grand Rapids, MI; HonRl; JA; JrNHS; NHS; NatlMeritSF; SchPl; RptrSchPpr; SciCl; Univ; Veterinary Med.

SCHOENWETTER, Alan R; Klemme Comm HS; Garner, IA; ChrhWkr; CmntyWkr; CncrtBnd; MrchBnd; PepBnd; YthFlsp; 4-H; FFA; Bsktbl; College.

SCHOENWETTER, Laurie M; Beaver Dam Sr HS; Beaver Dam, WI; 7/314 Chrs; ChrhWkr; HonRl; HospAde; OffAde; StuCncl; PpCl; GAA; KiwanAwd; College; Accountant.

SCHOEPF, Cindy E; Rutland HS; Ruthland, SD; 1/22 ALAGirlsSt; Aud/Vis; CmntyWkr; HonRl; LbryAde; NHS; EdYrBk; RptrSchPpr; SchPpr; LetterBsktbl; Dakota Wesleyan Univ; Medicine.

SCHOEPKE, John; Nicolet HS; Glendale, WI; 40/500 JA; NatlFornLg; NatlMeritCmnd; PolWkr; TchrAde; GerCl; Northwestern U; Law.

SCHOETTLER, Bill G; Marist HS; Oak Lawn, IL; 60/375 HonRl; NatlMeritSchl; NatlMeritSF;.

SCHOETTMER, Larry F; Columbus North HS; Columbus, IN; 77/500 HonRl;.

SCHOFFELMAN, Daniel; Mt Pleasant Hs; Mt Pleasant, IA; 1/170 CncrtBnd; MrchBnd; ModUN; NatlFornLg; SchMus; TreasYthFlsp; 4-H; SpnCl; MthCl; 4-HAwd; College; Computer Programmer.

SCHOFFMANN, Albert B; West Vigo HS; W Terre Haute, IN; 1/250 HonRl; PresKeyCl; LetterTrk; Rose Hulman Inst Tech; Computer Science.

SCHOFIELD, Annette; Wichita East HS; Wichita, KS; CmntyWkr; HonRl; LitMag; ModUN; NatlFornLg; NatlMeritFnl; NatlSciFnd; StuGov; TchrAde; JAAwd; NCTE; College.

SCHOFIELD, Rita K; Midland Independent HS; Ottumwa, SD; SecTrsJrCls; PresSrCls; Chr; HonRl; NHS; SchMus; StuCncl; SptEdSchPpr; SchPpr; 4-H; PpCl; LetterBsktbl; LetterTrk; Chrldr; Trade School.

SCHOFIELD, Timothy J; Muskegon Sr HS; Muskegon, MI; PresJrCls; PresSrCls; NHS; StuCncl; LetterFtbl; Tennis; Trk; U Of Mi; Medicine.

SCHOL, Nancy L; Northwood Public HS; Northwood, ND; Band; HonRl; MrchBnd; PepBnd; SchMus; Twrl; RptrYrbk; FHA; Bsktbl; Trk; Mayville State;.

SCHOLAND, Joyce; Mayville Portland HS; Buxton, ND; 11/82 Chr; ChrhWkr; HonRl; NatlFornLg; NatlThespSoc; SciCl; VoiceDemAwd;.

SCHOLES, Cheryl; Fairfield HS; Sylvia, KS; Band; Chr; Chrs; ChrhWkr; CncrtBnd; HonRl; Mdrgl; MrchBnd; PepBnd; Teen; Sterling Coll; Elem Ed.

SCHOLES, Michelle E; Virginia HS; Virginia, IL; ChrhWkr; HonRl; HospAde; LbryAde; TchrAde; SchPpr; PpCl; GAA; St Johns Hosp; Medical Tech.

SCHOLL, Mary Y; Healy HS; Pierz, MN; HonRl; TchrAde; FHA; CaptBsktbl; GAA; College; Physical Education.

SCHOLL, Rebecca A; Lyons Township HS; La Grange, IL; HonRl; NHS; SchMus; SecFrCl; Univ Of Illinois; Biology.

SCHOLLAERT, Stephen M; Avon HS; Plainfield, IN; 30/155 VPJrCls; ModUN; GerCl; Purdue; Transportation Engineering.

SCHOLPP, Janet L; Lockwood HS; Golden City, MO; 1/48 PresFrshCls; PresBand; ChrhWkr; HonRl; MrchBnd; PepBnd; SchPl; EdYrBk; Yrbk; SecFHA; U Of Mo; Med Res.

SCHOLTEN, Alan L; Armour HS; Armour, SD; 5/31 VPSrCls; ALBoysSt; ChrhWkr; HonRl; NHS; StuCncl; SptEdYrbk; 4-H; Bsktbl; Ftbl;.

SCHOLTEN, Debra M; East Kentwood HS; Kentwood, MI; CmntyWkr; HospAde; PolWkr; RptrSchPpr; SptEdSchPpr; LetterBsktbl; GAA; IMSpt; Calvin College; Law.

SCHOLTEN, Gary P; West Lyon Community HS; Larchwood, IA; PresSophCls; HonRl; NHS; SchPl; StuCncl; LetterBsbl; LetterBsktbl; LetterFtbl; LetterGlf; LetterTrk; College; Computer Programming.

SCHOLTEN, Lorraine K; Vicksburg HS; Vicksburg, MI; 2/165 Band; CncrtBnd; MrchBnd; NatlMeritCmnd; Orch; SchMus; FshEdSchPpr; FTA; DanFAwd; CitAwd; Calvin Clg; Elem Ed.

SCHOLTES, Charles E; Ains HS; Ainsworth, NE; Aud/Vis; Band; CncrtBnd; SchMus; StuGov; TchrAde; RptrYrbk; Yrbk; SciCl; LetterBsktbl; Ftbl; Swmmng; Trk; Univ Of Nebraska; Medicine.

SCHOLTZ, Sheri; Harbor Beach Community HS; Harbor Beach, MI; 4/135 Band; CncrtBnd; HonRl; MrchBnd; NatlMeritCmnd; IMSpt; College.

SCHOLZ, Debra K; West Platte HS; Weston, MO; HonRl; NHS; Yrbk; FBLA; FrCl; PpCl; RotaryAwd; Military Service; Accountant.

SCHOLZEN, Betty; Washington Park HS; Racine, WI; /475 AFS; HonRl; JA; ModUN; RedCrAde; SchPl; TchrAde; CchngActv; GAA; PresAwd; Tech Schooling; Clerk Typist Or Stenographe.

SCHOMACKER, Lorinda L; Cheney HS; Murdock, KS; PresSophCls; Band; Chr; ChrhWkr; CncrtBnd; HonRl; Mdrgl; MrchBnd; PepBnd; SchMus;.

SCHOMAKER, John B; Wesclin Sr HS; New Baden, IL; 2/111 TrsSophCls; Aud/Vis; HonRl; LbryAde; NHS; Yrbk; SchPpr; College; Business.

SCHOMMER, Paul M; Holy Trinity HS; Winsted, MN; 1/50 Aud/Vis; Band; HonRl; SchAde; TchrAde; RptrSchPpr; 4-H; Bsbl; Bsktbl; LetterWrstlng; College.

SCHONE, Brenda K; Bluffs HS; Bluffs, IL; SchMus; VPStuCncl; Yrbk; Sec4-H; FHA; Chrldr; Business College.

SCHONE, Craig W; Triopia HS; Chapin, IL; Band; ChrhWkr; HonRl; JrNHS; MrchBnd; NHS; 4-H; Ftbl; Univ Of Illinois; Medicine.

SCHONE, Denise S; Aberdeen Central HS; Aberdeen, SD; AFS; Chr; HonRl; FHA; PpCl; Northern State; Special Ed.

SCHONEBOOM, Bruce A; Ash Grove HS; Bois D Are, MO; Chr; HonRl; NHS; StuCncl; FSA; MthCl; SciCl; LetterFtbl; College.

SCHONEGG, Joan M; Lawrence Central HS; Indianapolis, IN; HonRl; JA; TchrAde; RptrYrbk; University; Social Work.

SCHONEICH, Elizabeth M; Queen Of Peace HS; Chicago, IL; Chrs; HonRl; LbryAde; NHS; Yrbk; SpnCl; U Of Il; Pre Pharmacy & Chemistry Major.

SCHONEWEIS, Doreen; Adams Public HS; Adams, NE; Chr; Chrs; DrmMjrt; PresFrshCls; SchPl; StuCncl; StuGov; Twrl; YthFlsp; 4-H; Univ.

SCHONEWEIS, Marlys J; Manhattan HS; Manhattan, KS; HonRl; MrchBnd; PpCl; LetterTrk; Kansas State Univ; Medical Technologist.

SCHONEWILL, Mark; Sioux Valley HS; Volga, SD; 2/66 ALBoysSt; Chrs; CncrtBnd; HonRl; Mdrgl; MrchBnd; PepBnd; SchMus; Bsktbl; College; Engineering.

SCHONHORST, Mary; North Polk HS; Slater, IA; 5/34 HonRl; NHS; SchMus; RptrYrbk; Bsktbl; Chrldr; DanFAwd; 4-HAwd; KiwanAwd; Lbi Seattly Wa; Undecided.

SCHONHORST, Roger D; North Polk HS; Slater, IA; Band; CncrtBnd; MrchBnd; SchAde; SchMus; SchPl; 4-H; Bsktbl; Ftbl; College; Agribusiness.

SCHOOB, Kathleen L; Joliet Central HS; Joliet, IL; 61/491 Chrs; HonRl; Joliet Jr College; Legal Secretary.

SCHOOF, Val E; Council Grove HS; Council Grove, KS; HonRl; Yrbk; 4-H; FFA; 4-HAwd; Univ Of Ks State; Medicine.

SCHOOFS, Andrew J; Hartford Union HS; Hartford, WI; HonRl; NHS; SctActv; StuCncl; Bsktbl; LetterFtbl; LetterTrk; CchngActv; IMSpt; RotaryAwd; Uw Wash Co & Stevens Point; Natural Resourc.

SCHOOLEY, Bart; Central HS; Cambridge, KS; 12/54 Band; HonRl; SchPl; TreasStuCncl; VPFFA; Ftbl; Wrstlng; Furrir School;horse Shoser.

SCHOOLEY, Teresa L; Bluffton HS; Bluffton, IN; 5/140 Chr; Chrs; ChrhWkr; HonRl; NHS; Teen; YthFlsp; 4-H; SpnCl; Milligan College; Elementary Ed.

SCHOON, Carol A; Haven HS; Haven, KS; 29/94 Band; Chr; HonRl; PepBnd; SchMus; StuGov; TchrAde; YthFlsp; PpCl; LionAwd; St Johns Winfield; Secretarial.

SCHOON, Kelvin K; Pocahontas Comm HS; Pocahontas, IA; ALBoysSt; Band; ChrhWkr; CmntyWkr; CncrtBnd; HonRl; MrchBnd; PepBnd; SchMus; SctActv; PpCl; Ftbl; Trk; University.

SCHOON, Steven; Manson Comm HS; Manson, IA; PresFrshCls; Band; HonRl; NHS; PepBnd; SchMus; StuCncl; Trk; Coll.

SCHOONMAKER, Lorainne; Elk Grove Hs; Elk Grove, IL; 17/505 Chr; HospAde; LitMag; Mdrgl; NHS; NatlThespSoc; PolWkr; SchMus; RptrSchPpr; FrCl; College; Psychology.

SCHOONOVER, Barbara A; Willow City HS; Willow City, ND; 4/18 SecFrshCls; SecSophCls; VPJrCls; ALAGirlsSt; Band; Chrs; HonRl; PepBnd; SchPl; Yrbk; College; Lpn Curriculum.

SCHOONOVER, Jeffrey D; Wood Memorial HS; Oakland City, IN; 1/118 ALBoysSt; HonRl; NHS; SchAde; Bsbl; Bsktbl; Wrstlng; College; Professional.

SCHOONOVER, Linda M; Richland Center HS; Richland Center, WI; HonRl; 4-H; FFA; Cur Of Major Study.

SCHOONOVER, Ruanne R; Black River Falls HS; Black River Falls, WI; 2/139 Band; Chr; HonRl; PresNHS; Orch; SchPl; YthFlsp; RptrSchPpr; SeLatCl; LionAwd; Uw Platteville; Chemical Eng.

SCHOOP, Christine L; Taft HS; Chicago, IL; 45/816 Chrs; ChrhWkr; HonRl; NHS; StuCncl; TchrAde; SpnCl; PpCl; TreasChrldr; Resurrection Hosp; Respiratory Therapist.

SCHOOP, Lori J; Rockwell City Community HS; Rockwell City, IA; 11/71 SecSrCls; Band; Chrs; ChrhWkr; HonRl; TchrAde; YthFlsp; FHA; Chrldr; MasAwd; Iowa Central Comm College; Secretary.

SCHOOSE, Keith J; Nw Military & Naval Academy; Schiller Park, IL; 1/33 HstJrCls; DrmBgl; HonRl; Quill&Scroll; ROTC; SchPl; StuGov; RptrYrbk; EdSchPpr; LetterTennis; University; Law.

SCHOPP, Charles T; Pontiac HS; Pontiac, IL; ChrhWkr; CmntyWkr; HonRl; OffAde; PolWkr; SchAde; SctActv; TchrAde; MthCl; PpCl; Western Ill; Biology.

SCHOPP, Kathleen M; Olympia HS; Bloomington, IL; Chrs; HonRl; Yrbk; SpnCl; PpCl; LetterBsktbl; Swmmng; LetterGAA; 4-HAwd; College.

SCHOPPER, Cynthia A; Muskego HS; Hales Corners, WI; ChrhWkr; HonRl; NatlFornLg; NHS; StuCncl; TchrAde; LetterBsktbl; LetterTrk; PresGAA; IMSpt; William Penn Coll; Physical Education Teach.

SCHORFHEIDE, Alan K; Moweaqua HS; Moweaqua, IL; 1/50 PresFrshCls; PresSophCls; HonRl; NHS; SctActv; RptrYrbk; SpnCl; Ftbl; Trk; GodCntryAwd; U Of Ill; Civil Engr.

SCHORN, Margaret; Stuart Public HS; Stuart, NE; 9/32 Band; Chrs; CncrtBnd; HonRl; StuCncl; 4-H; BttyCrckrAwd;.

SCHORN, Marilyn T; R O Dondero HS; Royal Oak, MI; 13/532 Chr; HonRl; NHS; TchrAde; PresFrCl; Bsbl; GAA; Mich St Univ; Spec Ed.

SCHORNACK, David J; New York Mills HS; New York Mills, MN; 26/71 PresFrshCls; TrsJrCls; VPSrCls; Chr; VPNHS; StuCncl; FFA; CaptFtbl; Trk; Wrstlng; Univ Of Mn; Farming.

SCHORR, Teresa A; Raytown HS; Kansas City, MO; Chr; HonRl; JCC; SctActv; Teen; FHA; PpCl; SciCl; Penn Valley Jr Clg; Dental Lab Tech.

SCHORZMAN, Danny D; Haigler Public Dist 7 A HS; Haigler, NE; 3/9 HonRl; SchPl; VPStuCncl; RptrYrbk; SptEdYrbk; SptEdSchPpr; LetterBsktbl; LetterFtbl; Southeast Comm Clg; Air Conditioning Tec.

SCHOSSMAN, Dwight A; New Holstein HS; Maline, WI; 78/196 ChrhWkr; TchrAde; YthFlsp; SchPpr; 4-H; FFA; 4-HAwd; U Of Wis; Agriculture.

SCHOSSOW, Darwin L; Pocahontas Comm HS; Laurens, IA; 3/75 Band; CncrtBnd; HonRl; NHS; NatlMeritSchl; EdSchPpr; PpCl; GovHonPrgAwd; PresAwd; CitAwd; Midland Luthern Coll; Respritory Therapy.

SCHOTT, Donna K; Marissa HS; Marissa, IL; 27/64 SecSrCls; Band; CncrtBnd; HonRl; MrchBnd; YthFlsp; 4-H; FHA; PpCl; IMSpt; Coll; Piano.

SCHOTT, Michael W; Clarenceville HS; Livonia, MI; Band; CncrtBnd; DrmBgl; JrNHS; NHS; NatlMeritFnl; NatlMeritSchl; TIMEAwd; GovHonPrgAwd; PresAwd; Col Mi St; Musician Literature.

SCHOTT, Robert J; Gull Lake HS; Richland, MI; 3/230 HonRl; JrNHS; NHS; StuGov; Univ Of Mich; Medicine.

SCHOTTHOFER, Stephen M; Illinois Valley Central HS; Chillicothe, IL; 50/226 RptrSchPpr; Bradley Univ; Construction.

SCHOTTLAND, Deborah L; Ida Crown Jewish Academy; Chicago, IL; HonRl; NHS; OffAde; SchMus; PresStuCncl; StuGov; RptrYrbk; RptrSchPpr; BttyCrckrAwd; University; Social Work.

SCHOUN, Daniel; Cedar Lake Academy; Coleman, MI; 8/73 Chr; ChrhWkr; CmntyWkr; HonRl; NHS; StuGov; TchrAde; IMSpt; Andrews Univ; Science Teacher.

SCHOUTEN, Garry L; Mendel HS; Chicabgo, IL; 15/191 SecJrCls; SecSrCls; NHS; StuCncl; StuGov; KeyCl; LetterFtbl; ChmnTrk; CchngActv; IMSpt; College; Engineer.

SCHOUTEN, Garry L; Mendel HS; Chicago, IL; 15/191 SecJrCls; SecSrCls; HonRl; NHS; StuCncl; StuGov; LetterFtbl; Tennis; CaptTrk; CchngActv; IMSpt; CitAwd; University; Engineer.

SCHOWALTER, Ann Marie F; St Joseph Ogden HS; St Joseph, IL; 6/103 TrsSophCls; TrsSrCls; HonRl; NHS; NatlThespSoc; SpnCl; LetterBsbl; CaptBsktbl; SecGAA; College; Health.

SCHRADER, Eugene; Emery HS; Emery, SD; 2/25 ALBoysSt; HonRl; SchPl; AmLegAwd; College; Teacher.

SCHRADER, George E; Centreville HS; Centreville, MI; 15/55 HonRl; SctActv; FrCl; LetterBsktbl; Ftbl; LetterTrk; Michigan State University; Engineer.

SCHRADER, Julie A; Benkelman HS; Benkelman, NE; 8/30 Band; Chr; Chrs; CncrtBnd; HonRl; LbryAde; MrchBnd; NHS; OffAde; PepBnd; SchPl; YthFlsp; 4-H; FHA; No Platte Vo Tec; Nursing.

SCHRAEDER, Renee R; Jetmore HS; Jetmore, KS; 3/42 SecJrCls; ChrhWkr; HonRl; HospAde; SchPl; SctActv; YthFlsp; FFA; PpCl; PPFtbl; Fort Hays State; Nurse.

SCHRAG, Catherine B; Moundridge HS; Moundridge, KS; SecJrCls; Band; Chr; Chrs; CncrtBnd; HonRl; Mdrgl; MrchBnd; NHS; PepBnd; SchMus; Chrldr; IMSpt; Univ.

SCHRAG, Connie F; Moundridge HS; Moundridge, KS; Band; Chrs; HonRl; NatlFornLg; SchMus; SchPl; StuCncl; VPFHA; IMSpt; PPFtbl; College.

SCHRAG, Lynnette; Moundridge HS; Moundridge, KS; Band; Chr; Chrs; ChrhWkr; CmntyWkr; HonRl; NHS; PepBnd; SchMus; StuCncl; College; Business.

SCHRAG, Rebecca S; Rose Hill HS; Rose Hill, KS; 15/60 Chr; Chrs; CmntyWkr; HonRl; SchPl; TchrAde; RptrSchPpr; EdSchPpr; FHA; PpCl; Western Bible Coll; Nurse.

SCHRAGE, Buzz; Wheaton Warrenville HS; Wheaton, IL; HonRl; LetterBsbl; LetterBsktbl; LetterFtbl; College; Professional.

SCHRAGE, John L; St Laurence HS; Chicago, IL; 19/396 ChrhWkr; HonRl; SctActv; LatCl; MthCl; SciCl; Trk; IMSpt; Univ; Engineering.

SCHRAM, Catherine L; Lakeview HS; St Clair Shores, MI; 8/620 HonRl; NHS; SpnCl; College; Accountant.

SCHRAM, Debra; Oxford HS; Lakeville, MI; 50/205 ChrhWkr; TchrAde; RptrSchPpr; GerCl; PpCl; IMSpt; PPFtbl; Western Mich Univ; Occupational Therapy.

SCHRAM, Joanne; High School; Livonia, MI; 6/97 PresFrshCls; Chr; Chrl; Chrs; HonRl; IntrClCncl; JrNHS; NHS; NatlMeritSF; PolWkr; Quill&Scroll; SchMus; StuCncl; Bsktbl; Michigan State Univ; Law.

SCHRAM, Laureen J; Bay View HS; Milwaukee, WI; HonRl; StuGov; SciCl; Univ; Biology.

SCHRAMER, Mark F; Kaneland HS; Maple Park, IL; 19/168 Band; DrlTm; HonRl; NHS; SchMus; PpCl; LetterFtbl; CaptWrstlng; IMSpt; College; Farming.

SCHRAMKA, Eugene R; Marquette HS; Milwaukee, WI; 3/270 CmntyWkr; HonRl; TchrAde; PpCl; Bsktbl; LetterSocr; GovHonPrgAwd; College; Accountant.

SCHRAMKE, Anna M; Ondossagon HS; Ashland, WI; 1/59 Chr; HonRl; LbryAde; SchPl; RptrSchPpr; FHA; Trk; EldAwd; 4-HAwd; RotaryAwd; College; Business Administration.

SCHRAMM, Bradley R; O Neill Public HS; O Neill, NE; 9/66 PresSrCls; Band; Chr; HonRl; NHS; SchMus; SchPl; PresStuCncl; LetterBsktbl; CaptFtbl; Univ; Business Administration.

SCHRAMM, Jodi; Norris HS; Hallam, NE; Chrs; ChrhWkr; CncrtBnd; NHS; PepBnd; 4-H; FBLA; PpCl; Chrldr; Business Sch; Accountant.

SCHRAMM, Keith M; Rogers City HS; Rogers City, MI; .

SCHRAMM, Martin W; Marion HS; Marion, IN; 1/850 Chrl; ChrhWkr; HonRl; NHS; StuGov; RusCl; LetterBsbl; LetterFtbl; Naval Academy; Naval Officer.

SCHRAMSKI, Mary M; St Clement HS; Center Line, MI; 11/97 TrsSophCls; HonRl; NatlMeritCmnd; OffAde; SptEdYrbk; FHA; PpCl; LetterBsbl; ChmnBsktbl; GAA; Oakland Univ; Med Tech.

SCHRANG, Stephen J; St Marys Central HS; Neenah, WI; NatlFornLg; NatlMeritCmnd; FrCl; SpnCl; MthCl; JAAwd; College; Lawyer.

SCHRANK, Michael J; Brookville HS; Brookville, IN; 24/190 HonRl; NHS; SciCl; LetterBsbl; LetterBsktbl; LetterTrk; Purdue Univ; Aeronautical Engineer.

SCHRANK, Randy D; Webb HS; Loganville, WI; 7/220 HonRl; KeyCl; SpnCl; Bsktbl; LetterFtbl; LetterTrk; IMSpt; Uw La Crosse; Accounting.

SCHRANK, Robert; Milton Senior HS; Milton Jct, WI; 18/175 Band; Chr; ChrhWkr; CncrtBnd; HonRl; NHS; SchMus; TchrAde; KiwanAwd; Univ Of Wis; Professional Music.

SCHRANK, William A; Naperville Central HS; Naperville, IL; 92/864 HonRl; Bsbl; LetterFtbl; LetterGlf; College; Business.

SCHRANZ, Thomas J; Northside HS; Muncie, IN; 54/320 ALBoysSt; HonRl; NHS; PolWkr; Sacrstn; SctActv; StuCncl; StuGov; TchrAde; SpnCl; Bsktbl; LetterFtbl; Glf; Purdue Univ; Engineering.

SCHRAUBEN, Kathleen L; St Patricks HS; Portland, MI; 4/45 TrsSophCls; Chrs; ChrhWkr; CmntyWkr; HonRl; NHS; SchPl; RptrYrbk; FrCl; CaptChrldr;.

SCHRECK, Gregory; Lincoln HS; Lake City, MN; 295/144 HonRl; NHS; SctActv; RptrYrbk; Bsktbl; College U Of W Stout; Proffessional.

SCHRECK, Jane R; High School; Durant, IA; 13/68 SecFrshCls; VPSrCls; HonRl; Bsktbl; PPFtbl; DARAwd; U Of Iowa; Mathematics.

SCHRECK, John A; Kuemper Catholic HS; Dedham, IA; 1/281 TrsJrCls; Chrs; HonRl; Mdrgl; SchMus; LatCl; MthCl; BauchLmbAwd; RotaryAwd; CitAwd; U Of Northern Ia; Math Physics.

SCHRECK, Ronald; Wayne Community Hs; Chariton, IA; CmntyWkr; TchrAde; PresFFA; FTA; SpnCl; SciCl; Bsbl; Bsktbl;.

SCHRECK, Susan L; Douglas Macarthur HS; Saginaw, MI; HonRl; NHS; SchPl; StuCncl; StuGov; RptrYrbk; Delta College; Med Tech.

SCHREDER, Brenda K; Gibault HS; Hecker, IL; Band; Chrs; ChrhWkr; CmntyWkr; HonRl; HospAde; CivCl; 4-H; GAA;.

SCHREDER, Carleen; Gibault Hs; Hecker, IL; 4/101 SecJrCls; PresSrCls; Chrl; Chrs; HonRl; NHS; PolWkr; SchMus; StuCncl; StuGov; College; Political Science.

SCHREFFLER, Rita M; Ravanna R 4 Public HS; Mercer, MO; 1/10 HstFrshCls; SecSophCls; HstJrCls; Chrs; ChrhWkr; HonRl; OffAde; SchMus; TreasStuCncl; LetterBsbl; LetterBsktbl; LetterTrk; Chrldr; Trenton Jr College; Secretary.

SCHREIBER, Alan D; Aquinas HS; David City, NE; Band; CmntyWkr; CncrtBnd; MrchBnd; PepBnd; SchMus; LatCl; MthCl; SciCl; LetterWrstlng; Technical College; Business.

SCHREIBER, Karen; Campbell Tintah HS; Campbell, MN; Band; Chr; Chrs; CncrtBnd; HonRl; MrchBnd; FHA; GAA; 4-HAwd; Nd State School Of Science; Accounting.

SCHREIBER, Karen L; Robinson HS; Speedway, IN; Band; CncrtBnd; HonRl; MrchBnd; University; Medicine.

SCHREIBER, Margaret; Lfch; Little Falls, MN; Chr; HospAde; SchMus; TchrAde; FHA; PpCl; GAA; PPFtbl; Voc Sch; Nurse Lpn.

SCHREIBER, Mary A; St Francis HS; Wheaton, IL; 16/121 HonRl; SecJA; NHS; SchMus; PpCl; BttyCrckrAwd; Bradley University.

SCHREIER, Chris; Verdigre Public HS; Verdigre, NE; HonRl; SchPl; SpnCl; Ftbl; Trk; Trade Sch Or Military; Voc.

SCHREIER, Lisa A; Niles West HS; Morton Grove, IL; 145/626 HonRl; Northeastern Ill Univ.

SCHREIFELS, Diane M; Round Lake Sr HS; Round Lake, IL; Chrs; HonRl; NHS; SchMus; SchPl; FHA; College; Special Education.

SCHREIFELS, Michael M; Round Lake HS; Round Lake Beach, IL; HonRl; NHS; Lake County College; Accounting.

SCHREIMAN, Harriet M; High School; Alma, MO; SecTrsSophCls; Chr; HonRl; OffAde; StuCncl; RptrYrbk; FHA; PpCl; Trk; Chrldr;.

SCHREIMAN, Nancy A; Resurrection HS; Chicago, IL; 7/260 HonRl; NHS; SchPl; GAA; IMSpt; College; Advertising Art.

SCHREIMAN, Nancy A; Santa Fe HS; Waverly, MO; CncrtBnd; HonRl; MrchBnd; Twrl; Yrbk; FHA; PpCl; Bsbl; LetterTrk; LetterChrldr; College; Teaching.

SCHREINER, Barbara E; Rib Lake HS; Rib Lake, WI; 4/60 Band; Chr; CmntyWkr; CncrtBnd; HonRl; PepBnd; RptrSchPpr; 4-H; IMSpt; 4-HAwd; Uw Eau Claire; Medical Technology.

SCHREINER, Glen C; Elizabeth HS; Elizabeth, IL; YthFlsp; FFA; Bsktbl; Trk; IMSpt; College; Auto Mechanics.

SCHREINER, Judith; Bayard HS; Bayard, NE; Band; Chrs; CncrtBnd; HonRl; MrchBnd; PepBnd; SchPl; StuGov; SpnCl; PpCl; Pro.

SCHREINER, Laura E; Larned Senior HS; Larned, KS; Chrs; PresYthFlsp; FHA; SpnCl; PpCl; College; Business.

SCHREINER, Lynn R; Sioux Valley Comm HS; Peterson, IA; ALAGirlsSt; SchPl; Twrl; Pres4-H; TreasFrCl; LetterBsktbl; LetterTrk; Art School.

SCHREINER, Mark; Emmons Central HS; Strasburg, ND; ChrhWkr; JrNHS; NHS; RptrSchPpr; SptEdSchPpr; Bsktbl; Ftbl; Coll; Marine Biology.

SCHREINER, Sheri; Milbank HS; Milbank, SD; 3/121 AFS; Chrs; DrlTm; HonRl; StuCncl; TchrAde; Trk; Chrldr; IMSpt; PPFtbl; College;vocation.

SCHREINER, Susan K; Rib Lake HS; Rib Lake, WI; PresJrCls; PresSrCls; Band; Chr; ChrhWkr; HonRl; 4-H; LetterBsktbl; IMSpt; 4-HAwd;.

SCHREINER, Susannah J; Shelbyville HS; Shelbyville, IN; 65/350 ChrhWkr; CncrtBnd; MrchBnd; NatlThespSoc; SchPl; SecStuCncl; YthFlsp; 4-H; 4-HAwd; LionAwd; Purdue U; Vet Assistant.

SCHREMP, Bill J; Mosinee HS; Mosinee, WI; PresFrshCls; Band; Chr; HonRl; StuCncl; FrCl; LetterBsbl; CaptBsktbl; CaptFtbl; LetterGlf; U Of La Crosse; Phy Ed Teacher.

SCHREMS, Susan M; Frankenmuth HS; Saginaw, MI; HonRl; JA; 4-H; FrCl; GAA; 4-HAwd; College; Nursing.

SCHRENK, Lawrence P; Cuanbrook HS; St Joseph, MI; NatlFornLg; PresSchPl; IMSpt; U Of Mi.

SCHREUR, Bonnie; Floyd Valley HS; Alton, IA; 4/46 HonRl; PpCl; GAA; 4-HAwd; Northwestern Coll; Elem Ed.

SCHREUR, Edward H; Maurice Orange City Com HS; Orange City, IA; Band; Chr; Chrl; Chrs; CncrtBnd; MrchBnd; SchMus; StuGov; YthFlsp; LetterFtbl; College; Professional.

SCHREYER, Dorothy C; North Platte Sr HS; North Platte, NE; 57/397 Chr; ChrhWkr; HonRl; OffAde; Quill&Scroll; SchPl; YthFlsp; YthLg; Yrbk; PpCl; U Of Co Greely; Law.

SCHRIEVER, Anna E; Superior HS; Superior, NE; 7/79 ChrhWkr; DrlTm; MrchBnd; NHS; SchPl; StuGov; YthFlsp; 4-H; FHA; 4-HAwd; College; Medical Field.

SCHRIEVER, Gaye L; Central HS; Aberdeen, SD; SecTrsJrCls; ChrhWkr; HonRl; RedCrAde; YthFlsp; 4-H; PpCl; LetterTrk; Chrldr; GAA; Comm Col Glendale Az; Recreation.

SCHRITTER, Neil H; Goodland HS; Kanorado, KS; FFA;.

SCHROCK, Bradley A; Goshen HS; Goshen, IN; Band; ChrhWkr; CncrtBnd; MrchBnd; Orch; PepBnd; SchMus; SctActv; YthFlsp; Yrbk; SciCl; Trk; GodCntryAwd; College; Music.

SCHROCK, David P; Lowpoint Washburn HS; Washburn, IL; 15/60 Chr; Chrs; HonRl; JA; SchMus; SchPl; 4-H; FFA; 4-HAwd; JAAwd; Coll; Animal Cience.

SCHROCK, Deirdre A; Central Cass HS; Casselton, ND; SecFrshCls; DrmMjrt; HonRl; HospAde; SchPl; TchrAde; YthFlsp; Yrbk; LetterBsktbl; Chrldr; Bus School; Secretary.

SCHROCK, Lu Ann K; Metamora Township HS; Metamora, IL; 6/180 AFS; Band; CncrtBnd; HonRl; MrchBnd; NHS; Orch; PepBnd; SchMus; YthFlsp; FTA; GerCl; Western Ill Univ; Music.

SCHROCK, Rhonda R; Lakeland HS; Wolcottville, IN; 5/145 ALAGirlsSt; Band; CncrtBnd; HonRl; MrchBnd; SecNHS; SctActv; MthCl; PpCl; GAA; PPFtbl; College.

SCHRODER, Nathaniel L; Moorhead HS; Moorhead, MN; Band; ChrhWkr; HonRl; Ftbl; Trk; Grand Rapids Bible College.

SCHRODER, Phyllis A; Marshall HS; Marshall, MI; 14/273 SecFrshCls; SecSophCls; HonRl; JrNHS; NHS; SecStuGov; PpCl; Glf; CaptSwmmng; GAA; PPFtbl; CitAwd; Univ Of Colorado.

SCHRODER, Ruth A; Palmyra HS; Palmyra, NE; 3/36 SecFrshCls; VPSophCls; PresSrCls; ALAGirlsSt; ChrhWkr; HonRl; SchPl; StuCncl; 4-H; FHA; PpCl; Business College.

SCHRODER, Susan K; Warsaw HS; Warsaw, MO; 11/65 Band; ChrhWkr; HonRl; JrNHS; NHS; StuCncl; TchrAde; 4-H; FHA; Chrldr; Univ; Major Study.

SCHRODT, Joseph K; St Thomas Aquinas HS; Berkeley, MO; ChrhWkr; HonRl; NHS; SchMus; Yrbk; SciCl; Univ Of Missouri; Geophysicist.

SCHROECKENTHALER, Todd A; Wisconsin Academy; Sussex, WI; Band; Chr; ChrhWkr; HonRl; LitMag; Mdrgl; SpnCl; Tennis; IMSpt; College; Music.

SCHROEDER, Anita L; Martin Hughes HS; Mt Iron, MN; 3/38 Chr; HonRl; LbryAde; NHS; TchrAde; RptrSchPpr; EdSchPpr; Pres4-H; SecFHA; PpCl; Hibbing Community Clg; Mathematics.

SCHROEDER, Aubrey L; Tecumseh HS; Tecumseh, MI; ALBoysSt; ChrhWkr; CmntyWkr; LitMag; NHS; PolWkr; SchPl; PresStuCncl; RptrSchPpr; KeyCl; College; Professional.

SCHROEDER, Craig L; Tri County HS; Howard City, MI; 4/94 PresSophCls; PresJrCls; PresSrCls; CncrtBnd; DrmMjrt; HonRl; MrchBnd; NHS; NatlMeritCmnd; BttyCrckrAwd; Univ; Music Ed.

SCHROEDER, Cynthia M; Eisenhower HS; Utica, MI; 29/500 VPJrCls; Chrl; HonRl; NHS; SchMus; StuCncl; EngCl; FrCl; GAA; PPFtbl; General Motors Inst; Engineering.

SCHROEDER, Debra E; Alma HS; Alma, WI; 3/39 SecFrshCls; SecJrCls; VPSrCls; ALAGirlsSt; Chr; Chrs; ChrhWkr; CmntyWkr; HonRl; NHS; SchMus; CaptChrldr; GAA; DARAwd; Univ Of Mn; Social Worker.

SCHROEDER, Gail D; Buhler HS; Inman, KS; Chrs; ChrhWkr; HonRl; TchrAde; RptrSchPpr; FHA; PpCl; Bsbl; Bsktbl; Trk; Tabor College; Accountant.

SCHROEDER, Gary P; La Harpe HS; La Harpe, IL; 5/56 Pres4-H; VPFFA; CaptFtbl; Wrstlng; 4-HAwd; College; Farming.

SCHROEDER, Gene R; Gibraltar HS; Ephraim, WI; 9/65 VPSrCls; Band; HonRl; NHS; Bsktbl; Ftbl; Trk; CchngActv; IMSpt; DanFAwd; Milw School Of Engingeering; Biomedical Eng.

SCHROEDER, James; Goodland HS; Goodland, KS; 9/133 CncrtBnd; HonRl; MrchBnd; ModUN; NatlFornLg; NHS; NatlMeritCmnd; Quill&Scroll; RptrSchPpr; EdSchPpr; Washburn Univ; Journalism.

SCHROEDER, James W; Bellflower Twp HS; Bellflower, IL; 4/21 PresFrshCls; Band; HonRl; PresStuCncl; PresYthFlsp; VP4-H; FFA; SciCl; Bsbl; CaptBsktbl; Trk; Univ Of Ill; Agriculture.

SCHROEDER, Jane A; Giltner HS; Giltner, NE; TrsSrCls; CmntyWkr; HonRl; OffAde; RptrSchPpr; FNA; Bsbl; LetterTrk; PPFtbl; PresAwd; Trade School; Nurse.

SCHROEDER, Jane D; Harlan Comm HS; Harlan, IA; 63/252 SecBand; CncrtBnd; HonRl; MrchBnd; NHS; PepBnd; PresYthFlsp; FNA; FrCl; GAA; IMSpt; Iowa Western Comm Coll; Med Techinician.

SCHROEDER, Janet; Wm Horlick HS; Racine, WI; 94/603 CncrtBnd; HonRl; LbryAde; PolWkr; GAA; Univ Of Wi Eau Claire; Law Enforcement.

SCHROEDER, Janet M; Springfield Catholic HS; Springfield, MO; Chrs; HonRl; SchPl; YthLg; LatCl; MthCl; GAA; IMSpt; Clge; Bus.

SCHROEDER, Janice K; Effingham HS; Effingham, IL; 8/212 HonRl; 4-H; FHA; DanFAwd; Eastern Ill Univ; Zoology.

SCHROEDER, Jeffrey C; Bridgeport HS; Saginaw, MI; Chr; ChrhWkr; CmntyWkr; HonRl; RedCrAde; SctActv; YthFlsp; KeyCl; PresAwd; Mich St Univ; Instrum Perform.

SCHROEDER, John; Zionsville Community HS; Zionsville, IN; 14/152 CncrtBnd; HonRl; MrchBnd; NHS; PepBnd; SctActv; 4-H; LatCl; Trk; College; Electrical Engineering.

SCHROEDER, Joyce; Hanover HS; Hanover, KS; 5/38 Chrs; HonRl; HospAde; NHS; SchMus; SchPl; PpCl; SciCl; Cloud County Comm Coll; Account.

SCHROEDER, Julie A; Southridge HS; Huntingburg, IN; Band; Chr; DrlTm; MrchBnd; SecYthFlsp; Pres4-H; SecFHA; PpCl; Trk; PPFtbl;.

SCHROEDER, Kathrine K; Worthington Sr HS; Worthington, MN; ALAGirlsSt; Band; Chr; JrNHS; Mdrgl; NHS; SchMus; Sec4-H; FFA; LetterTrk; Univ Of Minnesota; Veterinarian.

SCHROEDER, Keith L; Crescent Iroquois HS; Milford, IL; 1/28 PresFrshCls; ALBoysSt; Band; Chrs; ChrhWkr; NHS; SchPl; StuCncl; PresFFA; LetterBsktbl;.

SCHROEDER, Kevin D; Greensburg Comm HS; Greensburg, IN; 3/191 ALBoysSt; HonRl; NHS; KeyCl; PpCl; LetterBsbl; LetterFtbl; LetterWrstlng; IMSpt; RotaryAwd; Indiana Univ; Public Accountant.

SCHROEDER, Linda L; Leo HS; Holy Cross, IA; 1/45 SecJrCls; Chrs; HonRl; OffAde; SchAde; SchMus; RptrYrbk; RptrSchPpr; PpCl; BauchLmbAwd; Business School; Medical Career.

SCHROEDER, Lowell; Bloomfield HS; Bloofield, NE; Band; ChrhWkr; HonRl; LbryAde; NHS; PepBnd; Yrbk; 4-H; FFA; IMSpt; Univ Of Ne; Agricultural Ed And Economics.

SCHROEDER, Michael R; Altoona Public HS; Altoona, WI; 1/60 VPJrCls; HonRl; PresStuCncl; Ftbl; Wrstlng; University; Electronics.

SCHROEDER, Paula; Cal Community HS; Latimer, IA; CncrtBnd; HonRl; NHS; PepBnd; SchPl; 4-H; IMSpt; 4-HAwd; College; Medical Technology.

SCHROEDER, Paul K; Fergus Falls Senior HS; Fergus Falls, MN; Chrs; ChrhWkr; CmntyWkr; JA; RedCrAde; 4-H; FFA; Wrstlng; University; Agriculture.

SCHROEDER, Richard E; Morton West HS; Berwyn, IL; 125/900 Band; Chr; Chrs; CncrtBnd; HonRl; MrchBnd; ModUN; PepBnd; SchMus; Illinois Inst Tech; Chemical Engineer.

SCHROEDER, Rusty W; Tipton HS; Tipton, IA; 22/98 SecFrshCls; Band; CncrtBnd; HonRl; MrchBnd; PepBnd; FFA; LetterBsktbl; LetterFtbl; College; Vocation.

SCHROEDER, Sandra K; Viroqua HS; Viroqua, WI; Band; Chrs; HonRl; NatlMeritSF; RptrSchPpr; FrCl; University Of Wisconsin; Pre Med.

SCHROEDER, Scott; Kearney HS; Kearney, NE; Band; Chr; ChrhWkr; MrchBnd; LetterFtbl; LetterTennis; IMSpt; College; Professional.

SCHROEDER, Shari J; Valley Center HS; Valley Center, KS; Band; Chr; HonRl; LitMag; NatlFornLg; NHS; TchrAde; Kansas St University; Veterinary Medicine.

SCHROEDER, Sharleen R; Hector Community HS; Hector, MN; 5/49 SecFrshCls; DrlTm; HonRl; MrchBnd; SchPl; TchrAde; RptrYrbk; Yrbk; RptrSchPpr; FHA; SciCl; GAA; Alexandria Area Voc Tech; Medical Lab Tech.

SCHROEDER, Stacy; Beecher HS; Beecher, IL; 12/63 Band; CncrtBnd; HonRl; MrchBnd; PepBnd; SchPl; Yrbk; GAA; Junior College; Legal Secretary.

SCHROEDER, Stacy A; Allegan HS; Allegan, MI; 1/204 Band; HonRl; MrchBnd; NHS; NatlMeritSF; TchrAde; VPSpnCl; Western Mi Univ; Bus Admin.

SCHROEDER, Steven; Sheffield Capin Community Hs; Sheffield, IA; 4/50 Chrs; CncrtBnd; HonRl; MrchBnd; PepBnd; SchPl; YthFlsp; 4-H; FTA; 4-HAwd; Iowa State U; Architecture.

SCHROEDER, Susan L; Nicollet Public HS; Nicollet, MN; Chr; HonRl; GAA; Vocational School; Secretarial.

SCHROEDER, Susan P; Niles West HS; Skokie, IL; Chr; ChrhWkr; HonRl; Bsktbl; Swmmng; CaptTrk; IMSpt; University.

SCHROEDER, Susan R; Glenbard East HS; Lombard, IL; CmntyWkr; HonRl; NHS; NatlMeritFnl; NatlMeritSchl; PolWkr; SchMus; StuGov; Teen; YthFnd; Southern Ill Univ; Medicine.

SCHROEDER, Thomas C; Prophetstown HS; Prophetstown, IL; 26/100 PepBnd; SchPl; SctActv; StuCncl; SpnCl; SciCl; LetterFtbl; LetterGlf; Trk; LetterWrstlng; Coll; Veterinary Medicine.

SCHROEN, Barbara E; Chatsworth HS; Chatsworth, IL; 3/48 VPSophCls; PresAFS; HonRl; LbryAde; Mdrgl; SchPl; YthFlsp; EdYrBk; Chrldr; GAA; Parkland Junior College; Law Enforcement.

SCHROEPFER, Beth A; St Marys HS; Sleepy Eye, MN; Chr; Chrs; SchMus; StuGov; RptrYrbk; Yrbk; LatCl; MthCl; Worthington Com College; Nursing.

SCHROER, Debra L; Potosi HS; Potosi, MO; 11/185 VPSrCls; ChrhWkr; CmntyWkr; HonRl; JrNHS; NHS; NatlThespSoc; PolWkr; IMSpt; PPFtbl; College; Secretary.

SCHROER, Michael S; Pattonville HS; Bridgeton, MO; 6/800 ALBoysSt; HonRl; NHS; NatlMeritSF; OffAde; SctActv; TchrAde; College; Medicine.

SCHROER, Peter M; Washington HS; South Bend, IN; 1/320 ChrhWkr; HonRl; NHS; YthFlsp; DARAwd; Wabash Clge; History.

SCHROERING, Marcia K; Dubois HS; Jasper, IN; 8/80 Chrs; ChrhWkr; CmntyWkr; HonRl; RptrSchPpr; SchPpr; 4-H; FHA; Trk; College; Health.

SCHROETER, Debra A; Newman Grove Public HS; Lindsay, NE; PresFrshCls; SecSrCls; Band; Chr; CncrtBnd; HonRl; LbryAde; MrchBnd; NHS; PepBnd; Marriage.

SCHROETER, Neal J; Random Lake Comm HS; Random Lake, WI; 9/101 VPFrshCls; VPSophCls; VPJrCls; VPSrCls; Chr; CncrtBnd; HonRl; SchMus; LetterFtbl; GovHonPrgAwd; College; Math.

SCHROETER, Susan E; Marian HS; Bloomfield Hills, MI; HonRl; ModUN; NHS; StuCncl; LetterTennis; Univ; Foriegn Service.

SCHROETLIN, Denise; Butte Public HS; Butte, NE; Chrs; HonRl; LbryAde; SchPl; RptrSchPpr; PpCl; Bsktbl; Nce School Commerce; Accounting.

SCHROETTER, Anita B; Jacksonville HS; Jacksonville, IL; 4/363 CncrtBnd; DrmMjrt; MrchBnd; NHS; StuGov; FrCl; Tennis; Chrldr; Univ Of Iowa; Pharmacy.

SCHROFF, Karen J; Glendale HS; Springfield, MO; PresSophCls; ChrhWkr; HonRl; HospAde; StuCncl; StuGov; SpnCl; PpCl; Chrldr; GAA; University; Nursing.

SCHROFF, Reiko L; South Harrison HS; Bethany, MO; PresJrCls; Band; HonRl; NHS; FFA; LetterBsktbl; LetterTrk; IMSpt; 4-HAwd; PresAwd; Col; Business.

SCHROLL, Sandra L; Chatham Glenwood GS; Pawnee, IL; Chr; HonRl; OffAde; SchMus; SchPl; TchrAde; VPFHA; VPFNA; PresFTA; Community Hosp; Payroll Clerk.

SCHROLL, Scott A; Amundsen HS; Chicago, IL; Yrbk; RptrSchPpr; LetterBsbl; Bsktbl; LetterFtbl; College; Professional Baseball.

SCHROWANG, Brian L; Putnam Co HS; Granville, IL; 10/70 ALBoysSt; Band; VPCncrtBnd; MrchBnd; PepBnd; StuCncl; 4-H; VPFFA; LetterBsbl; 4-HAwd; Univ Of Ill; Agronomy.

SCHROYER, Linda K; Gideon School District #37; Gideon, MO; 6/39 Chrs; ChrhWkr; HonRl; MrchBnd; OffAde; StuCncl; FHA; PpCl; GAA;.

SCHUB, Linda G; Von Steuben HS; Chicago, IL; 2/257 Aud/Vis; Band; CncrtBnd; HonRl; JA; LbryAde; NHS; NatlMeritSF; SchPpr; College; Environmental Engineer.

SCHUBERT, Karen L; Manistee Catholic HS; Manistee, MI; 15/69 HonRl; NHS; StuCncl; Yrbk; RptrSchPpr; PpCl; CaptBsktbl; CaptChrldr; VoiceDemAwd; Secretary.

SCHUBERT, Lucinda A; Elkhart Lake Glenbeulah HS; Glenbeulah, WI; 7/60 PresSrCls; AFS; ALAGirlsSt; HonRl; SchPl; RptrYrbk; RptrSchPpr; U Of Wisc.

SCHUBERT, Regina M; Maria HS; Chicago, IL; 20/335 SecFrshCls; Chrl; HonRl; NHS; SecNHS; Orch; SchMus; Sdlty; GerCl; SciCl; Univ Of Illinois; Accounting.

SCHUCH, Arlene K; Tyndall HS; Tyndall, SD; 1/58 Band; Chrs; CncrtBnd; HonRl; Mdrgl; MrchBnd; PepBnd; SchPl; RptrSchPpr; EdSchPpr; Univ Of South Dakota; Medical Tech.

SCHUCH, Debra A; Southridge HS; Huntingburg, IN; Band; Chr; DrlTm; HonRl; SchMus; StuCncl; VPYthFlsp; Yrbk; LetterSwmmng; CaptTrk; GAA; PPFtbl; 4-HAwd; Indiana University; Nursing.

SCHUCH, Diane M; Lincolnway HS; Mokena, IL; 15/545 Chrs; HonRl; TchrAde; CaptBsktbl; Trk; GAA; IMSpt; Univ Of Illinois; Science.

SCHUCHARD, Bruce G; Naperville Central HS; Naperville, IL; ChrhWkr; HonRl; NHS; Sacrstn; Sdlty; YthFlsp; Tennis; Trk; Iowa State Univ; Marine Science.

SCHUCHART, Linda M; Marinette Sr HS; Marinette, WI; Band; Chrs; HospAde; NHS; PpCl; Swmmng; Trk; GAA; IMSpt; Bay De Noc Comm Clg; Nursing.

SCHUCHART, Marie E; Mayo HS; Rochester, MN; 9/469 ChrhWkr; HonRl; HospAde; JrNHS; NatlFornLg; NHS; NatlThespSoc; SpnCl; SciCl; LetterTrk; Univ Of Mn; General Phys.

SCHUCK, Carolynn M; Benson HS; Omaha, NE; AFS; HonRl; JA; LbryAde; NatlMeritSF; SctActv; FrCl; GerCl; KiwanAwd; Univ; Foreign Languages.

SCHUCK, Heidi M; Regina HS; East Detroit, MI; Band; Chr; DrlTm; Chrldr; GAA; PPFtbl; Oakland Univ.

SCHUCKMAN, Samuel; Victoria HS; Victoria, KS; 3/51 NatlMeritSchl; StuCncl; 4-H; Bsktbl; LetterFtbl; Univ; Professional.

SCHUDA, Mary B; Brule HS; Brule, NE; 1/17 PresJrCls; ALAGirlsSt; NHS; OffAde; TreasStuCncl; EdYrBk; LetterTrk; PresGAA; Univ Of Nebraska; Home Economics.

SCHUELE, Cathy A; Mount Acad; Atchison, KS; 14#33#41 NHS; Sdlty; StuCncl; PpCl; LetterTrk; CaptChrldr; GAA;.

SCHUELER, Anne M; Winneconne HS; Winneconne, WI; 5/120 Band; Chrs; HonRl; Mdrgl; MrchBnd; NHS; PepBnd; EdYrBk; RptrSchPpr; ChmnTrk; Clge; Music Ed Degree.

SCHUELER, Karl F; Rushford HS; Rushford, MN; HonRl; SchMus; SchPl; Voc Tech; Electronic Comm.

SCHUELER, Matthew; Our Lady Of Providence HS; New Albany, IN; 6/135 ChrhWkr; HonRl; Sacrstn; Bsbl; Bsktbl; Ftbl; CchngActv; OptClAwd; VFWAwd; Purdue U; Engineering.

SCHUELKE, Susan L; Murdock Cons HS; Alvo, NE; SecTrsJrCls; Band; Chrs; CncrtBnd; HonRl; MrchBnd; OffAde; PepBnd; SchMus; TchrAde; YthFlsp; EdSchPpr; 4-H; PpCl; Trade School; Secretary.

SCHUELLER, Douglas R; Hermantown HS; Duluth, MN; 4/137 Aud/Vis; Chr; HonRl; NHS; NatlMeritCmnd; StuCncl; PresFrCl; DanFAwd; RotaryAwd; College; Computer Tech.

SCHUELLER, James A; Jfk Prep; Belgium, WI; Band; CncrtBnd; SancSoc; SchPl; StuGov; Bsbl; Bsktbl; LetterTrk; IMSpt; College; Business Admin.

SCHUENEMEYER, Michael D; Union HS; Union, MO; ALBoysSt; Band; Chr; Chrs; ChrhWkr; CncrtBnd; HonRl; JA; MrchBnd; PepBnd; LetterBsbl; LetterBsktbl; LetterFtbl; East Central Jr College; Law.

SCHUESSLER, Colleen K; Potter HS; Potter, NE; 29#50#61 PepBnd; SchPl; StuGov; RptrYrbk; EdYrBk; 4-H; PpCl; Coll; Nursing.

SCHUESSLER, Neal M; Taft HS; Chicago, IL; 66/800 ChrhWkr; HonRl; NatlMeritCmnd; SchAde; TchrAde; GerCl; LetterBsktbl; College; Dentistry.

SCHUETT, Connie S; Centura HS; Cairo, NE; Band; ChrhWkr; CncrtBnd; MrchBnd; NHS; PepBnd; YthFlsp; SecGerCl; College.

SCHUETTE, Alice J; Civic Memorial HS; Bethalto, IL; 3/292 Chr; PresChrhWkr; CncrtBnd; HonRl; MrchBnd; NHS; TchrAde; FTA; PresGerCl; PpCl; Concordia Teachers Coll; Elem Educ.

SCHUETTE, David T; St Anthony HS; Effingham, IL; HstJrCls; CmntyWkr; SchAde; SchMus; SchPl; YthFlsp; KeyCl; PpCl; Trk; JCAwd; College; Vocation.

SCHUETTE, Donna; Nazareth Acad; Bellwood, IL; 26/154 NHS; SecSophCls; GerCl; Tennis; GAA; Western Illinois U;law Enforcement.

SCHUETTE, Janice; Elkton Pigeon Bay Port HS; Pigeon, MI; 5/146 HonRl; NHS; NatlMeritCmnd; GerCl; Univ Of Michigan; Professional Nursing.

SCHUETTE, Jeffrey S; Central HS; Flint, MI; TreasNHS; LetterSwmmng; Michigan State Univ; Veterinarian.

SCHUETZ, Evelyne G; Duchesne HS; St Charles, MO; 8/185 Chrs; HonRl; TreasNHS; SchMus; RptrYrbk; LatCl; PpCl; CitAwd; University; Professional.

SCHUETZ, Lois C; Hays HS; Catherine, KS; HonRl; Fort Hays State College; Business.

SCHUETZ, Sherri A; North Bend Central HS; North Bend, NE; 5/69 Band; CncrtBnd; HonRl; LbryAde; MrchBnd; NHS; PepBnd; FTA; College;.

SCHUETZ, Terri B; North Bend Central HS; North Bend, NE; 4/69 Band; CncrtBnd; HonRl; LbryAde; MrchBnd; NHS; PepBnd; FTA; College;.

SCHUH, Mervin K; Edwards County Sr HS; Albion, IL; 1/102 PresSophCls; PresJrCls; HonRl; StuCncl; 4-H; PpCl; LetterBsktbl; LetterTrk; AmLegAwd; 4-HAwd;.

SCHUH, Nancy; Cedarburg HS; Cedarburg, WI; Band; CncrtBnd; HonRl; MrchBnd; Orch; PepBnd; SchMus; FBLA; PpCl; GAA; Milwaukee Area Tech College; Computer Prog.

SCHUHLER, David A; Bishop Luers HS; Ft Wayne, IN; HonRl; NHS; LetterBsktbl; LetterTrk; IMSpt; In Univ Bloom; Accounting.

SCHUHMACHER, Peggy L; Glenwood HS; Glenwood, MN; VPBand; CncrtBnd; HonRl; MrchBnd; PepBnd; Yrbk; 4-H; PPFtbl; 4-HAwd; St Cloud St Coll; Med Tech.

SCHULD, Debra L; Edgerton Public HS; Edgerton, MN; TrsJrCls; Band; Chr; ChrhWkr; CncrtBnd; HonRl; LbryAde; MrchBnd; PepBnd; SchPl; Trade School; Vocation.

SCHULD, Diane M; Ursuline Academy; St Louis, MO; Chrl; Chrs; HospAde; SchAde; SchMus; SchPl; RptrSchPpr; SpnCl; SciCl; Fontbone College; Special Ed.

SCHULDT, James T; Dundee Comm HS; Carpentersville, IL; 116/375 HonRl; SciCl; LetterBsbl; LetterBsktbl; LetterFtbl; Coll; Forestry.

SCHULDT, Patti J; Stickney Public HS; Stickney, SD; 1/36 ALAGirlsSt; Band; Chrs; HonRl; LbryAde; NatlMeritCmnd; SchPl; Yrbk; EdSchPpr; VoiceDemAwd; College; Music.

SCHULENBERG, Barbara A; Lincoln Northeast HS; Lincoln, NE; 20/589 Chr; ChrhWkr; HonRl; HospAde; NHS; OffAde; SchMus; TchrAde; Teen; PpCl; GAA; Nebraska Wesleyen Univ; Medical Tech.

SCHULER, Claire S; Homewood Flossmoor HS; Homewood, IL; 97/940 ChrhWkr; HonRl; NatlMeritSF; StuCncl; RptrSchPpr; FHA; Univ Of Chicago; Doctor.

SCHULER, Debra M; Tuttle HS; Tuttle, ND; 1/10 PresSophCls; TrsJrCls; SecSrCls; Chrs; SchPl; VPSophCls; LetterTrk; BttyCrckrAwd; Univ Nd;.

SCHULER, Donna V; Lidgerwood HS; Lidgerwood, ND; Chrs; SchPl; RptrYrbk; RptrSchPpr; SchPpr; TreasFHA; Moorehead State Univ.

SCHULER, Pamela; Lyman HS; Morril, NE; 5/19 Chr; ChrhWkr; HonRl; NHS; SctActv; StuCncl; YthFlsp; EdYrBk; 4-H; PPFtbl; Kearney State College; Sociology.

SCHULER, Steve J; Chaska HS; Chaska, MN; Aud/Vis; Band; CncrtBnd; DrlTm; HonRl; PolWkr; SchPl; Bsktbl; Ftbl; Trk; College; Professional.

SCHULER, Tonya M; Campbell Tintah HS; Campbell, MN; SecTrsFrshCls; SecTrsSophCls; SecTrsJrCls; Band; Chr; ChrhWkr; CmntyWkr; CncrtBnd; HonRl; PepBnd; CaptBsktbl; CaptTrk; CaptChrldr; GAA; Arizona State; Registered Nurse.

SCHULER, William M; Corona Ind HS; Twin Brooks, SD; VPSrCls; SchPl; StuCncl; CaptBsktbl; LetterTrk; IMSpt; Farming.

SCHULIST, Diana L; Whitefish Bay HS; Whitefish Bay, WI; Chr; ChrhWkr; JA; LbryAde; SchPpr; FHA; GerCl; IMSpt; JAAwd; Uwm Milwaukee; Pro Business Field.

SCHULJAK, Robert J; Lake Central HS; Crown Point, IN; 85/453 VP4-H; GerCl; SciCl; 4-HAwd; Purdue Calumet; Conservation.

SCHULKE, Richard H; Almond HS; Almond, WI; ChrhWkr; HonRl; NatlFornLg; SctActv; RptrYrbk; RptrSchPpr; Technical Sch; Pro.

SCHULLER, Carol; Southern HS; Wymore, NE; TrsSrCls; Chr; CmntyWkr; PresFrshCls; SchMus; TchrAde; FBLA; PpCl; PPFtbl;.

SCHULT, Cynthia J; Iowa Grant HS; Montfort, WI; 13/120 SecSophCls; SecSrCls; Band; CmntyWkr; HonRl; NHS; SchPl; RptrYrbk; EdSchPpr; Bsktbl; IMSpt; PPFtbl; Univ Of Wisconsin; Nuclear Med Tech.

SCHULT, Joel L; Eldora HS; Eldora, IA; 6/64 VPSophCls; PresSrCls; HonRl; MthCl; SciCl; LetterTrk; Northern Iowa; Teacher.

SCHULT, Linda; Mt Horeb HS; Mt Horeb, WI; AFS; Chrs; ChrhWkr; FHA; PpCl; GAA; Dental Hygiene.

SCHULTA, Linda S; Grundy Center Comm HS; Grundy Center, IA; 22/75 Band; Chr; ChrhWkr; CncrtBnd; HonRl; MrchBnd; PepBnd; PpCl; Bsktbl; Wilma Boyd Airline Schl; Professional.

SCHULTE, Barbara L; Corona HS; Twin Brooks, SD; ChrhWkr; CncrtBnd; HonRl; MrchBnd; PepBnd; YthFlsp; RptrYrbk; 4-H; PpCl; Trk;.

SCHULTE, Catherine A; St Mark HS; St Ann, MO; 1/38 SecSrCls; HonRl; SchMus; Sdlty; StuCncl; PpCl; CchngActv; IMSpt; BttyCrckrAwd; TIMEAwd; Busi; Computer Prog.

SCHULTE, Charles J; Mc Cluer North HS; Florissant, MO; 335/751 CmntyWkr; HonRl; HospAde; St Louis Jewish Hos School; Anesthetist.

SCHULTE, Clare A; Norton Comm HS; Norton, KS; Chrs; ChrhWkr; CmntyWkr; HonRl; LbryAde; NatlThespSoc; SchMus; StuCncl; FFA; FHA; Fort Hays St College; Business.

SCHULTE, Claudia A; Notre Dame HS; Quincy, IL; PresSrCls; Chrs; CmntyWkr; HonRl; HospAde; JA; StuCncl; RptrSchPpr; 4-H; PpCl; Bsktbl; Blessing Hosp; Nursing.

SCHULTE, David E; Gasconade County HS; Owensville, MO; Band; Chr; CncrtBnd; HonRl; MrchBnd; NHS; YthFlsp; RptrYrbk; MthCl; SciCl; College; Engineering.

SCHULTE, Diana L; Nemaha Valley HS; Cook, NE; 8/33 Chrs; ChrhWkr; HonRl; SchPl; 4-H; GerCl; PpCl; 4-HAwd; Coll; Special Ed.

SCHULTE, Eric F; Niles West HS; Morton Grove, IL; 5/650 HonRl; NHS; NatlMeritSF; SctActv; StuCncl; StuGov; GodCntryAwd; Univ; Medicine.

SCHULTE, Gerald; Watertown HS; Watertown, SD; TrsFrshCls; PresSophCls; PresJrCls; ALBoysSt; Band; Chr; HonRl; MrchBnd; Bsktbl; Ftbl; Trk; College; Professional.

SCHULTE, Jane M; Emery HS; Emery, SD; PresFrshCls; PresSophCls; Chrs; HonRl; SchPl; Sdlty; VPStuCncl; Yrbk; SecFHA; LetterTrk; Bus School; Vocation.

SCHULTE, Joan M; Mss Acad; Grinnell, KS; Band; HonRl; NHS; PresStuCncl; RptrSchPpr; PpCl; GAA; PPFtbl; CitAwd; Rockhurst College; Account.

SCHULTE, Karen E; Waukon HS; Dovchester, IA; 13/155 TrsSophCls; HonRl; NHS; StuCncl; StuGov; FNA; KiwanAwd; PresAwd; Rochester Comm College; Registered Nurse.

SCHULTE, Karen M; New Salem HS; New Salem, ND; TrsSophCls; TrsJrCls; Band; CncrtBnd; HonRl; SchPl; Yrbk; LetterBsktbl; LetterTrk; GAA; Monot St College; Phy Ed.

SCHULTE, Kevin J; La Salle HS; Cedar Rapids, IA; HonRl; ModUN; SctActv; Ftbl; IMSpt; Law.

SCHULTE, Lou Ann; St Bernard HS; Breda, IA; Chrs; HonRl; SchPl; RptrYrbk; RptrSchPpr; PpCl; Iowa Lakes Comm Coll; Photography.

SCHULTE, Marilyn M; St Josephs HS; Kenosha, WI; 4/160 Chr; HonRl; NHS; SchAde; StuCncl; YthFnd; RptrSchPpr; SchPpr; LetterTrk; IMSpt; College; Psychology.

SCHULTE, Pamela S; Nemaha Valley HS; Seneca, KS; VPJrCls; Band; ChrhWkr; HospAde; NatlFornLg; NHS; SchPl; StuCncl; Chrldr; Clge; Nursing.

SCHULTE, Paul R; So Spencer HS; Rockport, IN; 23/139 ChrhWkr; HonRl; Sacrstn; College; Accountant.

SCHULTE, Philip D; Plymouth Canton HS; Plymouth, MI; CAP; DrlTm; HonRl; ModUN; NHS; NatlMeritSF; TchrAde; GerCl; SciCl; LetterTrk; Univ; Nuclear Eng.

SCHULTE, Robert J; Creighton Preparatory HS; Omaha, NE; Band; CncrtBnd; HonRl; JA; MrchBnd; PepBnd; SctActv; University Of Nebraska; Architecture.

SCHULTE, Teresa J; Portland HS; Portland, MI; 5/130 SecJrCls; SecSrCls; HonRl; NHS; GAA; PPFtbl; Mich State U; Computer Science.

SCHULTE, Theresa M; Brussels Comm HS; Golden Eagle, IL; ALAGirlsSt; HonRl; LbryAde; SchPl; Yrbk; 4-H; FHA; PresFTA; PpCl; Chrldr; Southern Il University; Medical Doctor.

SCHULTES, Lisa M; Springfield Catholic HS; Springfield, MO; 1/50 TrsFrshCls; TrsSophCls; Chrs; HonRl; Sacrstn; SecStuCncl; RptrSchPpr; LatCl; MthCl; SciCl; Sw Mo St U; Education.

SCHULTHEIS, Angela M; Reitz Memorial HS; Evansville, IN; 18/225 DrlTm; HonRl; NHS; OffAde; SchMus; SctActv; StuCncl; 4-H; PpCl; OptClAwd; U Of Evansville; Nursing.

SCHULTHEIS, Dorothy; Valmeyer Public HS; Prairie Du Rocher, IL; VPJrCls; Chr; HonRl; LbryAde; TchrAde; RptrSchPpr; 4-H; FHA; MthCl; 4-HAwd; Coll; Professional.

SCHULTHEIS, Lisa; Heritage Christian HS; Indpls, IN; TrsJrCls; Chr; SchMus; TchrAde; YthFlsp; Chrldr; Taylor Univ; Nursing.

SCHULTHEIS, Sandra M; Walled Lake Central HS; Union Lake, MI; CmntyWkr; HonRl; NHS; SchMus; Yrbk; FTA; Col; Pro.

SCHULTHEISS, Edward H; Abingdon HS; Abingdon, IL; PresFrshCls; PresSophCls; ALBoysSt; Chrs; HonRl; NatlMeritSF; YthLg; FTA; Univ Of Ill; Medicine.

SCHULTZ, Andrew; Lane Tech Hs; Chicago, IL; 147/940 Chrs; CncrtBnd; Orch; SchAde; SchPl; Depaol College; Music Compositoin&orchestra.

SCHULTZ, Audrey B; Lomira HS; Knowles, WI; 13/78 AFS; Chrs; HonRl; NHS; FHA; Tech School; Vocation.

SCHULTZ, Audrey M; Wonewoc Center HS; Wonewoc, WI; SecJrCls; Band; CncrtBnd; DrmMjrt; HonRl; MrchBnd; PepBnd; Twrl; EdYrBk; Chrldr; Univ Of Wisconsin; Nursing.

SCHULTZ, Becky L; Williston HS; Williston, ND; TrsJrCls; TrsSrCls; CmntyWkr; HospAde; StuGov; Private School; Fashion.

SCHULTZ, Bradley; Forest Park HS; Crystall Falls, MI; 11/89 CmntyWkr; HonRl; SchPl; College; Forestry.

SCHULTZ, Brenda; Lakeview HS; Lakeview, MI; HonRl; HospAde; Twrl; RptrYrbk; FNA; PpCl; Chrldr; GAA; St Lukes School Of Nursing; Nursing.

SCHULTZ, Carl W; Naperville Central HS; Naperville, IL; ChrhWkr; PolWkr; U Of Ill; Horticulture.

SCHULTZ, Carol W; Maria HS; Chicago, IL; 62/335 HonRl; JA; SctActv; RptrSchPpr; SpnCl; IMSpt; College.

SCHULTZ, Cathy S; Pekin Comm HS; Ollie, IA; 20/46 HonRl; HospAde; SchMus; StuCncl; YthFlsp; 4-H; FNA; Bsktbl; LetterTrk; PresAwd;.

SCHULTZ, Cynthia A; Sioux Rapids Comm HS; Sioux Rapids, IA; 4/19 PresFrshCls; PresJrCls; Band; Chrs; CncrtBnd; HonRl; MrchBnd; NHS; PepBnd; SchPl; LetterBsktbl; LetterTrk; LetterChrldr; Des Moines Area Comm College; Secretary.

SCHULTZ, Dave L; Columbus HS; Marshfield, WI; 25/120 ALBoysSt; HonRl; MthCl; Trk; Uw; Accounting.

SCHULTZ, David; Kingsford HS; Kingsford, MI; HonRl; Tennis; College.

SCHULTZ, Deborah A; Watervliet HS; Watervliet, MI; HonRl; NHS; TchrAde; Trk; LetterChrldr; College; Vocation.

SCHULTZ, Debra; Hamlin Ind 1 HS; Lake Norden, SD; TrsFrshCls; Band; Chr; HonRl; SchPl; RptrSchPpr; FHA; PpCl; Trk; IMSpt; University; Teach Music And Drama.

SCHULTZ, Diane R; South Milwaukee HS; South Milwaukee, WI; 37/435 HonRl; JA; OffAde; FBLA; Tennis; Univ; Acctg Cpa.

SCHULTZ, Diane V; Wadena Sr HS; Wadena, MN; Chrs; HonRl; SchMus; StuCncl; University; Psychology.

SCHULTZ, Donald F; Joliet Catholic HS; Lockport, IL; 26/168 GerCl; LatCl; S Illinois Univ; Engineering.

SCHULTZ, Gary; Neodesha HS; Neodesha, KS; 4/57 SecTrsJrCls; SecTrsSrCls; HonRl; SchPl; LetterBsktbl; CaptFtbl; Coll Icjc;accounting.

SCHULTZ, Gary L; Onsted HS; Onsted, MI; ALBoysSt; HonRl; SchPl; YthFlsp; VP4-H; FFA; LetterFtbl; CaptTrk; IMSpt; 4-HAwd; Trade School; Professional Machinist.

SCHULTZ, Glenn L; Normal Comm HS; Normal, IL; 34/443 ChrhWkr; HonRl; JA; NHS; 4-H; LatCl; MthCl; Bsktbl; Socr; Univ Of Illinois; Business Admin.

SCHULTZ, Greg; Washington HS; Two Rivers, WI; 70/222 ChrhWkr; HonRl; StuCncl; RptrSchPpr; KeyCl; SpnCl; University; Business Administration.

SCHULTZ, Henry; Arcadia HS; Arcadia, WI; 1/92 ALBoysSt; CncrtBnd; HonRl; NHS; NatlMeritFnl; NatlMeritSF; SchPl; Ftbl; Glf; Univ Wisc; Law.

SCHULTZ, James R; Dundee HS; Carpentersville, IL; 33/362 ChrhWkr; HonRl; SchAde; SctActv; StuGov; YthFlsp; College.

SCHULTZ, Janet M; Arlington Green Isle Pub HS; Arlington, MN; VPBand; Chr; HonRl; NHS; StuCncl; YthFlsp; EdYrBk; FHA; PpCl; LetterBsktbl; Swmmng; LetterTrk; GAA; College; Medicine.

SCHULTZ, Jerry R; Kelly HS; Chicago, IL; 6/475 PresJrCls; PresSrCls; Band; CncrtBnd; IntrClCncl; NHS; PolWkr; SchPl; StuCncl; Illinois Inst Of Tech; Bio Medical Engineer.

SCHULTZ, Jo Ann; Tecumseh Public HS; Tecumseh, NE; Chr; Chrs; HonRl; LbryAde; SchMus; SchPl; RptrSchPpr; 4-H; PpCl; College; Elementary Teacher.

SCHULTZ, Jody L; Postville Comm HS; Postville, IA; 21/93 Chr; Chrs; ChrhWkr; HonRl; TchrAde; SchPpr; FTA; LetterTrk; PresAwd; CitAwd; Wartburg Coll; Religion.

SCHULTZ, John F; E C Memorial HS; Eau Claire, WI; HonRl; NHS; NatlMeritSF; Orch; SchMus; SctActv; LetterTennis; IMSpt; College; Medicine.

SCHULTZ, John F; Marist HS; Tinley Park, IL; 13/404 ChrhWkr; HonRl; NHS; PolWkr; PresStuCncl; RptrSchPpr; Bsktbl; LetterTrk; IMSpt; CitAwd; Univ; Medicine.

SCHULTZ, John M; Lake Holcombe HS; Holcombe, WI; 2/42 VPSophCls; TrsJrCls; PresSrCls; HonRl; StuGov; 4-H; FFA; GerCl; LetterBsbl; CaptBsktbl; Univ Of Wis; Architecture.

SCHULTZ, Karen A; Carl Sandburg HS; Orland Park, IL; 42/730 PresSophCls; VPJrCls; SecSrCls; HonRl; VPNHS; RedCrAde; SchPl; StuCncl; TchrAde; RptrSchPpr; VPFrCl; MthCl; Bsktbl; CaptChrldr; College; Vocation.

SCHULTZ, Karen B; Thornwood HS; So Holland, IL; 30/842 AFS; CncrtBnd; MrchBnd; NHS;.

SCHULTZ, Kathleen; Tiskilwa HS; Princeton, IL; Chrs; HonRl; LbryAde; RptrYrbk; RptrSchPpr; SchPpr; 4-H; FFA; GAA; 4-HAwd; Norhtern Ill Univ; Graphic Art.

SCHULTZ, Keith L; Mendota HS; Compton, IL; Band; Chr; Chrs; ChrhWkr; CncrtBnd; MrchBnd; PepBnd; SchPl; Tennis; Wrstlng; Air Force; Pilot.

SCHULTZ, Kenneth; Newman HS; Schofield, WI; ChrhWkr; HonRl; Bsktbl; Ftbl; Trk; CchngActv; IMSpt; Trade School; Machine Tool Operator.

SCHULTZ, Kenneth E; Burligton HS; Burlington, KS; Band; Chrs; ChrhWkr; CncrtBnd; HonRl; MrchBnd; PepBnd; SchMus; TchrAde; 4-HAwd; College.

SCHULTZ, Kevin E; Williamsville HS; Williamsville, IL; PresFrshCls; HonRl; NHS; SchPl; StuCncl; LetterBsbl; LetterFtbl; College; Business Administration.

SCHULTZ, Kevin T; Ruskin HS; Superior, NE; 2/9 PresJrCls; ALBoysSt; ChrhWkr; CmntyWkr; SchPl; StuCncl; YthFlsp; LetterBsktbl; CaptFtbl; LetterTrk; Ellsworth Comm Coll; Agriculture.

SCHULTZ, Linda; Waterford Township HS; Union Lk, MI; 6/414 HonRl; NHS; StuGov; Chrldr; Oakland Univ; Cpa.

SCHULTZ, Linda C; Sts Peter & Paul Area HS; Saginaw, MI; VPBand; CmntyWkr; HonRl; MrchBnd; NHS; SchMus; SctActv; Yrbk; GerCl; GAA; Saginaw Valley Clg; Sp Ed.

SCHULTZ, Lisa M; Pawnee City HS; Pawnee City, NE; 4/37 Band; Chr; Chrs; ChrhWkr; CncrtBnd; HonRl; HospAde; MrchBnd; PepBnd; SchPl; StuCncl; Univ; Nursing.

SCHULTZ, Lynn M; Walther Lutheran HS; Maywood, IL; 14/91 HonRl; LbryAde; NHS; YthLg; EdYrBk; SchPpr; LetterBsktbl; LetterTennis; TreasGAA; College; Journalism.

SCHULTZ, Marcy L; Deerfield HS; Deerfield, IL; AFS; HonRl; NHS; SchPpr; FTA; FrCl; GerCl; PpCl; Western Ill Univ; Math.

SCHULTZ, Margaret A; Macksville HS; Haviland, KS; ChrhWkr; TchrAde; YthFlsp; Yrbk; FrCl; LetterBsktbl; Swmmng; Tennis; Trk; PPFtbl; 4-HAwd; Kansas State Univ; Zoology.

SCHULTZ, Michael A; Plymouth HS; Plymouth, IN; Band; Chr; CmntyWkr; CncrtBnd; LitMag; MrchBnd; Orch; PolWkr; SchMus; TchrAde; Ancilla Col; Music/politics/journalsim.

SCHULTZ, Michael A; Kankakee Eastridge HS; Kankakee, IL; HonRl; RptrSchPpr; PpCl; Bsktbl; Glf; CchngActv; Clge; Business.

SCHULTZ, Michael B; Clayton HS; Clayton, MO; StuGov; PpCl; LetterFtbl; LetterGlf; LetterTrk; Coll; Bus Admin.

SCHULTZ, Monica L; Concord Comm HS; Goshen, IN; Band; HonRl; JrNHS; MrchBnd; NHS; Orch; PepBnd; SchMus; RptrSchPpr; FrCl; Indiana St U; Music Major.

SCHULTZ, Nancy; New Trier Township Hs; Glenview, IL; 129/694 Chrs; ChrhWkr; HonRl; OffAde; TchrAde; Bethel College; General Education.

SCHULTZ, Nancylee M; Elizabeth Seton HS; Riverdale, IL; 40/240 Chr; Chrs; HonRl; Mdrgl; Tennis; Depaul Univ; Psychosciences.

SCHULTZ, Neil T; Harvard Unit Dist 50 HS; Harvard, IL; 23/158 ALBoysSt; ChrhWkr; CncrtBnd; Mdrgl; NHS; NatlThespSoc; StuCncl; Ftbl; Trk; Wrstlng; Carthage College; Music.

SCHULTZ, Pamela; Plainview HS; Plainview, MN; 1/91 Band; HonRl; PepBnd; StuCncl; RptrSchPpr; GerCl; GAA; Drake Univ; Government Or Law.

SCHULTZ, Rachel; Hillsboro HS; Hillsboro, KS; Band; Chr; Chrs; HonRl; TchrAde; PpCl; Tabor College; Teacher.

SCHULTZ, Richard C; Arcadia HS; Arcadia, WI; 5/102 PresJrCls; Chrs; HonRl; NHS; NatlMeritCmnd; NatlThespSoc; SchMus; LetterBsktbl; LetterFtbl; LetterTrk; Univ; Bus.

SCHULTZ, Roger; Council Grove HS; Council Grove, KS; /120 Kansas State Univ; Pre Med.

SCHULTZ, Roger R; St Croix Central HS; Roberts, WI; 4-H; FFA; LetterBsbl; LetterFtbl; Wrstlng;.

SCHULTZ, Russell R; Northland HS; Remer, MN; 13/57 VPSrCls; HonRl; NHS; Bsbl; Bsktbl; Ftbl; College; Accounting.

SCHULTZ, Sandra; Medicine Valley HS; Curtis, NE; 4/32 Band; Chrs; FDA; DrmMjrt; HonRl; MrchBnd; NHS; StuCncl; LetterTrk; PPFtbl; Coll; Voc.

SCHULTZ, Sandra L; De Witt HS; De Witt, MI; 7/126 ChrhWkr; HonRl; LbryAde; NHS; OffAde; SchAde; VPFrshCls; TchrAde; YthFlsp; MthCl; Lansing Comm; Busi Management.

SCHULTZ, Scott A; Fenwick HS; Melrose Park, IL; 6/223 HonRl; Marquette Univ; Accounting.

SCHULTZ, Sharrill; Benton County R1 HS; Cole Camp, MO; 8/42 Chr; ChrhWkr; CtyCnl; HonRl; NatlThespSoc; UNYO; EdSchPpr; TIMEAwd; PresAwd; CitAwd; University; Law.

SCHULTZ, Stephanie; Whitehall HS; Monxague, MI; 20/170 Band; CncrtBnd; HonRl; MrchBnd; VPFrshCls; TchrAde; GerCl; PPFtbl; Univ Of Michigan; Physical Therapy.

SCHULTZ, Susan; Dundee HS; Dundee, MI; 9/128 HonRl; LbryAde; TchrAde; FTA; GerCl; Tennis; Coll; Dentist Assistant.

SCHULTZ, Susan K; Racine Lutheran HS; Racine, WI; HonRl; StuCncl; TchrAde; SptEdSchPpr; PpCl; LetterBsbl; LetterBsktbl; Trk; CaptChrldr; GAA; College; Professional.

SCHULTZ, Suzanne M; Carmel Girls HS; Mundelein, IL; 18/195 PresChrs; HonRl; NHS; OffAde; SchMus; SchPl; C/llege; Drama.

SCHULTZ, Tammie J; Crete HS; Crete, NE; 13/123 Chr; Chrs; HonRl; NHS; SchMus; SchPl; FHA; FTA; PpCl; Chrldr; Elementary Teacher.

SCHULTZ, Ted; Fairfield HS; Sylvia, KS; 24/80 SecTrsJrCls; HstSrCls; CmntyWkr; SctActv; YthFlsp; 4-HAwd; Hutchinson Juco College; Agric.

SCHULTZ, Thomas; Rockridge HS; Reynolds, IL; ALBoysSt; HonRl; NHS; FTA; SpnCl; Mathmatics.

SCHULTZ, Valerie J; West HS; Davenport, IA; AFS; HonRl; NatlMeritSF; NatlThespSoc; Orch; SchMus; SchPl; StuCncl; PpCl; IMSpt; U Of Iowa; Political Sci.

SCHULTZ, Wayne L; New Lisbon HS; New Lisbon, WI; 3/70 Band; Chr; ChrhWkr; HonRl; NHS; SchMus; University; Accounting.

SCHULTZ, William E; Whiting HS; Whiting, IN; 20/102 CmntyWkr; HonRl; SchAde; TchrAde; SptEdSchPpr; SpnCl; Bsbl; Bsktbl; Glf; CchngActv; College; Mathematics.

SCHULTZE, June K; Ceylon Public HS; Fairmont, MN; SecTrsSophCls; Chr; Chrs; HonRl; SchPl; EdYrBk; RptrSchPpr; PpCl; Bsktbl; Vocational School; Secretary.

SCHULTZE, Katherine A; Keokuk HS; Keokuk, IA; 1/206 DrlTm; HonRl; PresNHS; StuCncl; EdYrBk; PpCl; Knox Clge;.

SCHULTZE, Laurie L; Ceylon Public HS; Ceylon, MN; 2/28 PresSophCls; TrsSrCls; Aud/Vis; Chrs; HonRl; NHS; SchPl; RptrYrbk; RptrSchPpr; Trk; Wadena Av Ti; Electronics.

SCHULZ, Alice K; Community Unit 6 HS; Pontiac, IL; 3/23 Chrs; HonRl; NHS; StuCncl; SchPpr; 4-H; PpCl; Chrldr; College; Professional.

SCHULZ, Carolyn M; Hanson Ind #40 HS; Fulton, SD; 1/45 PresJrCls; Band; Chrs; HonRl; Mdrgl; Quill&Scroll; RptrYrbk; RptrSchPpr; AmLegAwd; 4-HAwd; U Of Sd.

SCHULZ, Christine R; New Buffalo HS; New Buffalo, MI; 11/88 HonRl; NHS; TchrAde; LetterChrldr; IMSpt; PPFtbl; College; Nursing.

SCHULZ, Craig A; Grayslake Comm HS; Grays Lake, IL; 5/219 HonRl; PresNHS; NatlMeritCmnd; StuCncl; RptrSchPpr; PpCl; Bsbl; LetterFtbl; AmLegAwd; University; Law.

SCHULZ, David S; Hill City HS; Hill City, KS; Chrs; SchMus; SchPl; SctActv; LetterFtbl; College.

SCHULZ, Deborah; Edgeley Public HS; Edgeley, ND; 3/47 Chr; Chrs; HonRl; RptrYrbk; Yrbk; FBLA; FHA; PpCl; Chrldr; Colege Ndsss; Business Management.

SCHULZ, Debra R; Salem Central HS; New Munster, WI; Chrs; ChrhWkr; CmntyWkr; HonRl; SecNHS; TchrAde; Yrbk; SecFrCl; PpCl; Trade School; Professional.

SCHULZ, Gerald A; Fatima HS; Westphalia, MO; 12/120 Chrs; CncrtBnd; HonRl; MrchBnd; PepBnd; SchPl; PpCl; SciCl; Bsktbl; Trade School; Vocation.

SCHULZ, Geralyn M; Alvernia HS; Chicago, IL; 16/285 HonRl; HospAde; LitMag; NHS; StuCncl; StuGov; TchrAde; EdSchPpr; Bsktbl; Ftbl; Tennis; GAA; Univ Of Wisc; Professional.

SCHULZ, Joann L; Muskego HS; Muskego, WI; Aud/Vis; ChrhWkr; CmntyWkr; OffAde; TchrAde; VPFTA; PresAwd; College; Professional.

SCHULZ, Marjorie S; Harold L Richards HS; Palos Heights, IL; 87/977 HonRl; LitMag; MrchBnd; VPNHS; Orch; TchrAde; YthFlsp; FrCl; GAA; Knox College; Geology Or Biology.

SCHULZ, Mark W; Fargo North HS; Fargo, ND; DrmMjrt; NatlFornLg; SpnCl; Wrstlng;.

SCHULZ, Nancy C; Charles S Mott HS; Warren, MI; HonRl; PresNHS; StuGov; EdYrBk; SpnCl; LetterSwmmng; Mi St Univ; Veterinary Medicine.

SCHULZ, Peggy; Mediapolis Comm HS; Burlington, IA; 1/85 Chrs; HonRl; HospAde; 4-H; FHA; SpnCl; College; Medical Assistant.

SCHULZ, Steven A; West Point Public HS; Beemer, NE; HonRl; SchAde; SchPl; TchrAde; RptrSchPpr; 4-H; FFA; CaptFtbl; LetterTrk; CaptWrstlng; Univ Of Ne; Agricultural Business.

SCHULZ, Verna J; Albia Comm HS; Pleasantville, IA; 18/150 Chrs; HonRl; Quill&Scroll; SchMus; SchPl; EdYrBk; FFA; FTA; LetterTrk; Trade Schl; Lab Tech.

SCHULZ, Wesley M; Shawnee HS; Grand Tower, IL; 41/60 HonRl; FBLA; PpCl; LetterBsbl; LetterBsktbl; IMSpt; PresAwd; Univ Or College; Professional.

SCHULZ, William C; Loyola Academy; Niles, IL; 36/442 Chr; Chrs; HonRl; SchMus; StuCncl; FrCl; Glf; Univ Of Illinois; Medicine.

SCHULZ, William J; Plymouth Canton HS; Plymouth, MI; HonRl; JrNHS; LbryAde; ModUN; NHS; TchrAde; LatCl; SciCl; LetterTennis; IMSpt; Eastern Mi U; Chemistry.

SCHULZE, Julie A; Central Catholic HS; Bloomington, IL; 8/94 HonRl; YthFnd; 4-H; FrCl; PpCl; IMSpt; College.

SCHUM, Patricia L; Heritage Hills HS; Dale, IN; Chrs; HonRl; MrchBnd; SctActv; TchrAde; Twrl; RptrSchPpr; PpCl; Chrldr; GAA; Business School; Secretary.

SCHUMACHER, Algerd J; Amos Alonzo Stagg HS; Hickory Hills, IL; Univ Of Ill; English Teacher.

SCHUMACHER, Cindy; St Edmond HS; Duncombe, IA; 14/113 Chr; Chrs; ChrhWkr; HonRl; HospAde; NHS; StuCncl; LatCl; SpnCl; Chrldr; College; Biology.

SCHUMACHER, Cindy K; Arthur Hill HS; Saginaw, MI; 48/683 HonRl; NHS; SciCl; Michigan St Univ; Medicine.

SCHUMACHER, Cloris K; Bowdle HS; Jaua, SD; Band; Chrs; HonRl; LbryAde; SchPl; RptrSchPpr; 4-H; LetterBsktbl; LetterTrk; 4-HAwd; College; Home Ec.

SCHUMACHER, Debora R; Garrigan HS; Whittemore, IA; 7/106 SecJrCls; CaptDrlTm; HonRl; NHS; NatlMeritSF; StuCncl; SpnCl; PpCl; Iowa Lakes Comm College; Secretary.

SCHUMACHER, Debra K; Central Comm HS; Trenton, IL; 6/129 Band; HonRl; NHS; FHA; College.

SCHUMACHER, Debra L; Cumberland HS; Barronett, WI; 12/126 HonRl; LbryAde; StuCncl; RptrSchPpr; PpCl; Clge; Rn.

SCHUMACHER, Elaine F; Morton West HS; Berwyn, IL; 16/775 HonRl; JrNHS; NatlFornLg; SecNatlThespSoc; OffAde; SchMus; SchPl; FNA; NCTE; Univ Of Illinois; Animal Biology.

SCHUMACHER, Elaine F; J Sterling Morton West HS; Berwyn, IL; 16/775 HonRl; JrNHS; NatlFornLg; SecNatlThespSoc; OffAde; SchMus; SchPl; FNA; Univ Of Illinois; Animal Science.

SCHUMACHER, James; St Pius X HS; Kansas City, MO; 10/130 Band; CmntyWkr; CncrtBnd; HonRl; Orch; PepBnd; Ftbl; Trk;.

SCHUMACHER, James R; St Pius X HS; Kansas City, MO; 8/137 Band; CncrtBnd; HonRl; PepBnd; SchMus; SchPl; SctActv; StuCncl; MthCl; College.

SCHUMACHER, Jane; Holy Family HS; Lindsay, NE; 15/33 Chrs; HonRl; SchMus; StuCncl; PpCl; Chrldr; College; Vocation.

SCHUMACHER, Janice C; Teutopolis HS; Teutopolis, IL; 1/115 DrlTm; HonRl; NatlMeritCmnd; EdYrBk; 4-H; FHA; GerCl; GAA; EldAwd; Indiana State Univ; Nurse.

SCHUMACHER, Joy E; Lewiston HS; Rollingstone, MN; TrsSrCls; Chr; ChrhWkr; HonRl; YthFlsp; FHA; GAA; Vocational Technical; Medical Secretary.

SCHUMACHER, Julia A; Elk Mound HS; Elk Mound, WI; 4/43 Band; Chrs; DrmMjrt; NatlFornLg; PepBnd; RptrYrbk; RptrSchPpr; 4-H; 4-HAwd; Col; Nursing.

SCHUMACHER, Julie A; St Francis HS; Humphrey, NE; Chrs; HonRl; LbryAde; NHS; TchrAde; PpCl; Col; Pro.

SCHUMACHER, Kathleen M; Beresford Independent HS; Beresford, SD; Chr; Chrs; ChrhWkr; HonRl; SchMus; TchrAde; 4-H; FHA; PpCl; College; Nursing.

SCHUMACHER, Kent J; Hempstead HS; Dubuque, IA; 11/455 HonRl; NHS; KeyCl; IMSpt; ChmbCommrsAwd; EldAwd; Iowa State University; Engineering.

SCHUMACHER, Linda K; Teutopolis HS; Sigel, IL; HonRl; StuCncl; FHA; PpCl; Trk; Chrldr; College; Teaching.

SCHUMACHER, Marla R; Clarence Lowden HS; Clarence, IA; 1/45 TrsSophCls; VPSrCls; Band; Chrs; Mdrgl; NHS; NatlMeritCmnd; SchMus; StuCncl; Yrbk; Iowa St; Med Tech.

SCHUMACHER, Mary; Plymouth HS; Plymouth, WI; 18/236 Chrs; CmntyWkr; HonRl; HospAde; NHS; SchMus; RptrYrbk; FNA; GerCl; PpCl; U Of Wis Oshkosh; Nursing.

SCHUMACHER, Pamela R; Lacrescent Jr Sr HS; Lacrescent, MN; HonRl; EdSchPpr; FHA; Tech School; Accounting.

SCHUMACHER, Patricia; Napoleon HS; Napoleon, ND; 10/61 AFS; CtyCnl; CmntyWkr; JA; ModUN; StuCncl; StuGov; UNYO; YthFlsp; YthLg; Bus Sch;data Proc.

SCHUMACHER, Rebecca S; Lowpoint Washburn HS; Toluca, IL; 7/68 AFS; Band; Chrs; CncrtBnd; ModUN; PepBnd; SchMus; SchPl; EdSchPpr; SchPpr; St Olaf Coll; Music.

SCHUMACHER, Richard A; Memorial HS; Eau Claire, WI; LitMag; ModUN; NatlMeritFnl; NatlMeritSF; SciCl; Caltech; Astronomy.

SCHUMACHER, Robert G; Downers Grove S HS; Downers Grove, IL; HonRl; RptrSchPpr; LetterFtbl; College; Law.

SCHUMACHER, Scott R; Leola HS; Leola, SD; 14/50 ALBoysSt; Band; Chr; Chrs; ChrhWkr; CmntyWkr; CncrtBnd; HonRl; MrchBnd; PepBnd; SchMus; LetterBsktbl; LetterFtbl; LetterTrk; S Dakota St Univ; Agriculture.

SCHUMACHER, Susan; St Joseph HS; Kenosha, WI; 35/150 HonRl; HospAde; StuCncl; RptrSchPpr; SchPpr; PpCl; Bsbl; Trk; Parkside; Psych.

SCHUMACHER, William G; Wautoma HS; Wautoma, WI; 12/93 Aud/Vis; Chr; Chrl; Chrs; ChrhWkr; CmntyWkr; HonRl; LbryAde; Mdrgl; NatlCathMusEdAsoc; OffAde; SchAde; SchMus; SchPl; Univ Of Wisconsin; Music.

SCHUMAIER, Cynthia; Max Public HS; Benedict, ND; 1/29 Band; Chrs; CncrtBnd; HonRl; PepBnd; RptrYrbk; RptrSchPpr; PpCl; Bsktbl; Chrldr; Univ Of N Dak.

SCHUMAKER, Lisa A; West Catholic HS; Grand Rapids, MI; 2/314 ChrhWkr; HonRl; NHS; Grand Rapids Jr College; Interior Design.

SCHUMAKER, Susan E; Lakeview HS; Decatur, IL; AFS; Chr; ChrhWkr; HonRl; HospAde; Mdrgl; NHS; TchrAde; RptrSchPpr; Grand Rapids Bible Col; Christian Ed.

SCHUMAN, Aaron J; Southfield Lathrup HS; West Bloomfield, MI; 5/683 PresModUN; NHS; NatlMeritFnl; NatlSciFnd; PolWkr; StuGov; SciCl; Brown U.

SCHUMAN, Glenn M; Niles West HS; Morton Grove, IL; 65/626 HonRl; NatlMeritCmnd; SctActv; Socr; Univ Of Illinois; Medicine.

SCHUMAN, Johanna D; Tinley Park HS; Tinley Park, IL; 1/275 ChrhWkr; HonRl; NHS; PolWkr; TreasStuCncl; StuGov; SecPpCl; LetterTennis; College; Law.

SCHUMAN, Michael L; Lisbon HS; Lisbon, ND; AFS; HonRl; SctActv; IMSpt; North Dakota St Univ; Pharmacy.

SCHUMAN, Stephen J; Shawnee Mission North HS; Shawnee Mission, KS; 14/603 Chr; Chrl; HonRl; NHS; Quill&Scroll; SchPpr; LetterTrk; Univ; Engineering.

SCHUMAN, Vicki L; Milton HS; Milton Jct, WI; 10175 PresSrCls; SecAud/Vis; CncrtBnd; HonRl; MrchBnd; NHS; PepBnd; LetterTrk; LetterChrldr; KiwanAwd; Uw; Acct.

SCHUMANN, Bobbi J; Riceville Community HS; Leroy, MN; Band; Chrs; CncrtBnd; DrlTm; HonRl; MrchBnd; SchPl; StuCncl; LetterBsktbl; IMSpt; Airline School; Stewardess.

SCHUMANN, Jennie M; Wisconsin Heights HS; Mazomanie, WI; 1/104 VPSophCls; ALAGirlsSt; Chr; ChrhWkr; HonRl; NHS; PolWkr; SchMus; StuCncl; YthFlsp; Univ Of Wisc; Teacher.

SCHUMANN, Kevin P; Merrill HS; Brainerd, MN; 14/350 ALBoysSt; Band; Chr; Chrl; ChrhWkr; NatlFornLg; PepBnd; SchMus; YthFlsp; AmLegAwd; VFWAwd; North Western College; Professional.

SCHUMANN, Lori J; Fonda Comm HS; Albert City, IA; SecJrCls; Band; ChrhWkr; HonRl; JrNHS; SchPl; TchrAde; SchPpr; 4-H; PresFHA; LetterBsktbl; IMSpt; PPFtbl; 4-HAwd; College.

SCHUMANN, Paula A; Paul K Cousino HS; Warren, MI; HonRl; Coll; Prof.

SCHUMER, Ellen J; Glenbrook North HS; Northbrook, IL; CmntyWkr; NHS; NatlMeritCmnd; College.

SCHUNCK, Jan M; St Clair HS; St Clair, MI; 4/191 VPSrCls; ChrhWkr; HonRl; NatlMeritCmnd; SchPl; StuGov; TchrAde; Chrldr; PresAwd; Oakland Univ; Liberal Arts.

SCHUNEMAN, Mary C; Bradford HS; Bradford, IL; 3/48 AFS; Band; Chrs; CncrtBnd; HonRl; NHS; SchPl; SchPpr; 4-H; Chrldr; GAA; IMSpt; Illinois St Univ; Spanish.

SCHUNTER, Nancy J; Central Community HS; Dewitt, IA; AFS; HonRl; RptrSchPpr; SchPpr; FTA; PpCl; Grand View College; Journalism.

SCHUPFER, Patricia C; Spencer HS; Spencer, IA; 4/166 ChrhWkr; JrNHS; NHS; NatlMeritCmnd; NatlMeritSF; StuCncl; RptrYrbk; SpnCl; Chrldr; IMSpt; Creighton Univ; Biological Research.

SCHUPP, Angela C; Jennings HS; Jennings, MO; 28/245 Chr; ChrhWkr; CncrtBnd; HonRl; NHS; StuCncl; FNA; EngCl; PpCl; GAA; Nursing School; Registered Nurse.

SCHUPPENER, Mark O; Platteville Jr Sr HS; Platteville, WI; 14/196 HonRl; Bsbl; Bsktbl; Flight School; Flight Instructor.

SCHUPPENHAUER, Steven P; Winona Senior HS; Winona, MN; ChrhWkr; HonRl; NHS; Winona St Univ; Engineer.

SCHUREMAN, Jean A; Morton HS; Morton, IL; 28/287 Chr; Chrs; ChrhWkr; HonRl; YthFlsp; 4-H; FHA; GAA; College.

SCHURING, Julie; Larkin HS; Elgin, IL; Band; Chr; Chrl; Chrs; ChrhWkr; CmntyWkr; HonRl; StuGov; TchrAde; Stetson Florida Univ; Liberal Arts.

SCHURMAN, Cindy M; Southeast Warren HS; Milo, IA; 8/64 CtyCnl; CmntyWkr; NHS; StuCncl; EdYrBk; Yrbk; RptrSchPpr; Business School; Secretary.

SCHURMAN, Julie A; Greenview HS; Greenview, IL; 9/50 VPFrshCls; VPSophCls; Chrs; LbryAde; SchMus; RptrSchPpr; FHA; FSA; PpCl; Glf; Univ Of Il; Physical Therapist.

SCHURMEIER, Mark E; Wheaton North HS; Wheaton, IL; 11/390 ALBoysSt; NHS; NatlMeritSF; SchMus; SchPl; YthFlsp; EdYrBk; RptrSchPpr; LetterSocr; Wake Forest Univ; Journalism.

SCHURR, S S; Springfield HS; Springfield, IL; NatlMeritFnl; NatlMeritCmnd; GerCl; MthCl; SciCl; Reed College; Physics.

SCHURTTER, Joyce A; Edgewood HS; Bloomington, IN; HonRl; JrNHS; MrchBnd; StuCncl; YthFlsp; EdYrBk; FHA; LetterTrk; GAA; 4-HAwd; PresAwd; CitAwd; University; Nursing.

SCHUSSLER, Craig A; Libertyville HS; Mundelein, IL; 30/431 ChrhWkr; HonRl; StuCncl; SchPpr; Carthage College; Dentistry.

SCHUSSLER, Kay F; Deepwater HS; Deepwater, MO; 1/12 Band; HonRl; SchPl; EdYrBk; Pres4-H; PresFHA; PpCl; Bsktbl; Chrldr; BttyCrckrAwd; 4-HAwd; Cntrl Mo St Univ.

SCHUSTER, Audrey; Chokio Alberta HS; Chokio, MN; PresSrCls; Chrs; HonRl; SchPl; 4-H; SpnCl; Chrldr; Fergus Falls Community College; Lpn.

SCHUSTER, Daniel L; Maryville R Ii HS; Maryville, MO; TrsFrshCls; PresJrCls; HonRl; NHS; StuCncl; YthFlsp; KeyCl; PpCl; SciCl; Bsktbl; Ftbl; DARAwd; Hospital Training; Nurse.

SCHUSTER, Gary P; Bishop Dwenger HS; Fr Wayne, IN; 39/243 Band; CncrtBnd; HonRl; MrchBnd; Orch; PepBnd; SchMus; SctActv; U Of Notre Dame; Electrical Engineering.

SCHUSTER, James N; Willow City Public HS; Willow City, ND; 2/18 SecTrsSophCls; PresJrCls; Chrl; HonRl; PolWkr; SchPl; EdYrBk; SchPpr; SciCl; LetterBsktbl; University; Law.

SCHUSTER, Janet F; Immaculate Heart Of Mary HS; Westchester, IL; Aud/Vis; Band; CmntyWkr; HospAde; SchMus; SchPl; SctActv; RptrYrbk; Yrbk; RptrSchPpr; Marquette; Communications.

SCHUSTER, Laura J; Aurora HS; Phillips, NE; 8/90 Band; CncrtBnd; HonRl; MrchBnd; NHS; SecStuCncl; StuGov; Yrbk; Pres4-H; CaptTrk; Wayne State College; Physical Education Tea.

SCHUSTER, Lawrence E; Pilot Grove HS; Pilot Grove, MO; 6/36 TrsFrshCls; Chrs; ChrhWkr; SchPl; TchrAde; FFA; PpCl; LetterTrk; Univ Of Missouri; Agriculture.

SCHUSTER, Mark A; Pilot Grove HS; Pilot Grove, MO; 1/38 TrsJrCls; Chrs; HonRl; SchPl; TreasFFA; LetterBsbl; Bsktbl; LetterTrk; Univ Of Missouri; Agriculture.

SCHUSTER, Nancy; Harper Woods HS; Harper Woods, MI; 4/158 HonRl; NHS; StuCncl; Swmmng; IMSpt; AmLegAwd; CitAwd; Univ Detroit; Dental Assistant.

SCHUSTER, Ronald L; Phillipsburg HS; Phillipsburg, KS; 2/86 Band; ChrhWkr; CncrtBnd; HonRl; MrchBnd; PepBnd; Bsbl; Ftbl; Trk; Ks St Univ; Nuclear Eng.

SCHUSTER, Shari L; Wahlert HS; Dubuque, IA; 37/480 HonRl; HospAde; ModUN; NatlMeritSF; PolWkr; SctActv; RptrYrbk; SchPpr; 4-H; College; Journalism.

SCHUSTER, Vicky L; East Buchanan C 1 HS; Gower, MO; 4/62 PresSrCls; ALAGirlsSt; Band; Chrs; ChrhWkr; HonRl; NHS; SecQuill&Scroll; Sec4-H; VPFHA; St Lukes Hospital; Nurse.

SCHUTTE, Diane K; Mexico Sr HS; Mexico, MO; TrsSrCls; NatlSciFnd; ChrhWkr; MrchBnd; NHS; PepBnd; TchrAde; 4-H; LatCl; Univ Missouri Columbia; Veterinary Med.

SCHUTTE, John P; Creighton Prep; Omaha, NE; 7/249 HonRl; NatlFornLg; NHS; NatlMeritFnl; NatlThespSoc; SchPl; Sdlty; StuCncl; MthCl; SciCl; Northwester University; Law.

SCHUTTE, Michelle M; Onsted Community HS; Adrian, MI; Band; HonRl; FHA; Trade School; Air Line Hostess.

SCHUTZ, Sandra; Houghton HS; Houghton, MI; Aud/Vis; Chrs; DrlTm; HonRl; 4-H; SpnCl; 4-HAwd; Western Michigan Univ; Special Education.

SCHUVER, Debra J; Ogorman HS; Sioux Falls, SD; ALAGirlsSt; ChrhWkr; CmntyWkr; NHS; StuCncl; StuGov; CitAwd; College; Professional.

SCHUYLER, Joyce M; Centura HS; Cairo, NE; SecFrshCls; Band; CncrtBnd; DrmMjrt; MrchBnd; PepBnd; StuCncl; TchrAde; VP4-H; LetterTrk; Hastings Tech; Dental Asst.

SCHUYTEN, Mary E; Rockford HS; Rockford, MI; 4/289 ChrhWkr; HonRl; NHS; NatlMeritCmnd;

RedCrAde; SchMus; SchPl; Calvin Coll; French Teach.

SCHWAB, Ann M; Assumption HS; Davenport, IA; 18/205 HonRl; JA; NHS; RptrSchPpr; JAAwd; Univ; Geneticist.

SCHWAB, Christine A; Potosi HS; Potosi, WI; 10/70 Band; Chrs; ChrhWkr; CmntyWkr; HonRl; MrchBnd; ModUN; NatlFornLg; NHS; SchPl; TchrAde; Bsktbl; Trk;.

SCHWAB, Connie J; Vassar HS; Vassar, MI; 5/146 Band; CncrtBnd; HonRl; MrchBnd; NHS; Orch; Saginaw Valley College; Med Tech.

SCHWAB, Debra A; Rockford HS; Rudd, IA; 21/76 Band; Chrs; CncrtBnd; HonRl; SchPl; Twrl; RptrSchPpr; Trk; Chrldr; IMSpt; U Of Ia; Bsn.

SCHWAB, Diane K; Prairie HS; Swisher, IA; 9/197 HonRl; JrNHS; NHS; TchrAde; College; X Ray Tech.

SCHWAB, Elaine M; Ionia HS; Lyons, MI; SecTrsFrshCls; Chr; ChrhWkr; DrmBgl; HonRl; OffAde; StuCncl; StuGov; TchrAde; Bsktbl; Trk; PresPresAwd; Central Michigan Univ; Physical Therapy.

SCHWAB, Eliazbeth; Holy Redeemer HS; Detroit, MI; Chr; HonRl; HospAde; LbryAde; OffAde; SchPl; FrCl; Coll; Nurse.

SCHWAB, Gail A; Truman HS; Independence, MO; JrNHS; NHS; Quill&Scroll; StuCncl; FHA; PpCl; Chrldr; Coll.

SCHWAB, Gregory K; Tolna Public HS; Tolna, ND; PresFrshCls; PresSophCls; PresJrCls; HonRl; NHS; SchPl; StuCncl; PpCl; LetterBsbl; LetterBsktbl;.

SCHWAB, Gregory M; Mandan Sr HS; Mandan, ND; ALBoysSt; ChrhWkr; HonRl; NHS; NatlMeritCmnd; SchPl; PresStuCncl; EdYrBk; CivCl; EldAwd; Carroll College; Religion.

SCHWAB, Joseph J; Potosi HS; Potosi, WI; 15/64 VPFrshCls; HonRl; NHS; Tennimore Vo Tec School.

SCHWAB, Kathy; Millington HS; Millington, MI; HonRl; OffAde; TchrAde; RptrYrbk; Trk; CchngActv; IMSpt; Business College; Vocational.

SCHWAB, Kenneth J; Manchester HS; Manchester, MI; VPSrCls; Chr; Chrs; CncrtBnd; MrchBnd; PepBnd; GerCl; LetterBsbl; Wrstlng; Coll; Eletronics.

SCHWAB, Mary; St Marys Central HS; Bismarck, ND; SptEdSchPpr; PpCl; CchngActv; GAA;.

SCHWAB, Paul J; Naperville Central HS; Naperville, IL; YthFlsp; YthLg; LetterTennis; College; Lawyer.

SCHWAB, Ronald F; Larkin Sr HS; Elgin, IL; 18/593 CmntyWkr; HonRl; Illinois Inst Of Tech; Elec Engineer.

SCHWAB, Steven L; Richardton Public HS; Richardton, ND; HonRl; SchPl; SctActv; LetterBsbl; Bsktbl; LetterFtbl; Trk; College; Accountant.

SCHWABE, Daniel J; St Bernards HS; Carroll, IA; VPFrshCls; PresSophCls; HonRl; LetterBsktbl; College; Professional.

SCHWABENLANDER, Kathy A; Hilbert Public HS; Wilbert, WI; 8/67 VPSrCls; ALAGirlsSt; HonRl; NHS; SchPl; TchrAde; FshEdYrbk; LetterBsktbl; GAA; AmLegAwd; Lake Shore Tech Inst ;nurse.

SCHWALB, Laurie K; Marissa HS; Marissa, IL; 4/74 Band; CncrtBnd; HonRl; MrchBnd; SecNHS; NatlMeritCmnd; PepBnd; Quill&Scroll; SchMus; SctActv; SecStuCncl; College; Architecture.

SCHWALBE, Cynthia J; Glencoe Sr HS; Glencoe, MN; ALAGirlsSt; Band; Chr; ChrhWkr; CmntyWkr; CncrtBnd; HonRl; HospAde; LbryAde; MrchBnd; PepBnd; RptrYrbk; College; Audiology.

SCHWANINGER, Denise; Norris HS; Cortland, NE; 7/77 Band; ChrhWkr; CncrtBnd; MrchBnd; PepBnd; PpCl; Univ Of Ne; Bus Secretary.

SCHWANTES, Constance L; Sevastopol HS; Sturgeon Bay, WI; Chrs; ChrhWkr; SchAde; SchMus; SchPl; SctActv; TchrAde; Bsbl; Bsktbl; 4-HAwd; College.

SCHWARCK, Rick A; Riceville Comm HS; Riceville, IA; HonRl; SchPl; Ftbl; College.

SCHWARK, Bonnie J; Green Lake HS; Green Lake, WI; HonRl; NHS; OffAde; RptrSchPpr; SchPpr; GAA;.

SCHWARK, Van R; Herscher HS; Herscher, IL; 12/179 Band; CncrtBnd; HonRl; MrchBnd; Pres4-H; PresFFA; AmLegAwd; DanFAwd; 4-HAwd; College; Livestock Farmer.

SCHWARM, Nancy A; Southwestern HS; Hanover, IN; 2/109 SecJrCls; PresSrCls; HonRl; NHS; NatlMeritCmnd; PresNatlThespSoc; SchMus; EdYrBk; FHA; SecPpCl; Purdue U; Engineering.

SCHWARM, Russell S; Brownstown Comm HS; Loogootee, IL; HonRl; StuCncl; FFA; Lakeland Clg; Ag Prod.

SCHWARTING, Julie; Neligh Public HS; Oakdale, NE; Band; Chrs; HonRl; NHS; PepBnd; Quill&Scroll; SchMus; SchPl; StuCncl; EdSchPpr; School Of Nursing; Nursing.

SCHWARTZ, Albert; South Adams HS; Berne, IN; Band; Chr; ChrhWkr; CncrtBnd; MrchBnd; StuCncl; SpnCl; PpCl; Bsktbl; IMSpt; Fort Wayne Bible Coll; Mission.

SCHWARTZ, Carol L; Lutheran High West; Detroit, MI; Chr; ChrhWkr; CmntyWkr; HonRl; NHS; OffAde; StuCncl; PpCl; GAA; IMSpt; U Of Mi; Dr.

SCHWARTZ, Constance M; Blue Valley HS; Bucyrus, KS; 4/94 Chr; Chrl; Chrs; HonRl; NHS; SchPpr; FTA; PpCl; BauchLmbAwd; College; Professional.

SCHWARTZ, Cynthia; Marquette Inc; West Point, IA; Chr; ChrhWkr; StuCncl; PpCl;.

SCHWARTZ, Daniel J; Hoisington HS; Hoisington, KS; HonRl; ModUN; CivCl; GerCl; LetterBsktbl; IMSpt; Kansas State University; Conservaton.

SCHWARTZ, Dorothy F; Cass City HS; Cass City, MI; 37/141 ALAGirlsSt; ChrhWkr; HonRl; JrNHS; NHS; PresSpnCl; PpCl; Chrldr; GAA; AmLegAwd;.

SCHWARTZ, Edward G; Cass City HS; Cass City, MI; HonRl; SctActv; Bsktbl; Swmmng; Trade; Tool & Dye.

SCHWARTZ, Gerard J; Saint Mary HS; Burlington, WI; VPJrCls; HonRl; PpCl; Schooling; Botany.

SCHWARTZ, Grant F; Chippewa Valley HS; Utica, MI; HonRl; Mich Tech; Sci.

SCHWARTZ, Joanna M; Nerinx Hall HS; Webster Grove, MO; 3/84 Chrl; CmntyWkr; HonRl; SchMus; TchrAde; RptrYrbk; SchPpr; College; Science.

SCHWARTZ, John K; Adrian HS; Adrian, MI; 25/400 Aud/Vis; ChrhWkr; NHS; NatlMeritCmnd; PolWkr; StuCncl; SciCl; IMSpt; EldAwd; RotaryAwd; Univ Of Mi; Law.

SCHWARTZ, Kara L; Kenmare Public HS; Kenmare, ND; Chrs; CncrtBnd; MrchBnd; SchPl; PresSctActv; RptrYrbk; VPFHA; PpCl; Wrstlng; Chrldr; College; Professional.

SCHWARTZ, Laurie L; Corunna HS; Vernon, MI; 29/202 ChrhWkr; HonRl; JA; LbryAde; YthFlsp; 4-H; Trk; Commercial Horticulture.

SCHWARTZ, Lori J; Willmar Sr HS; Willmar, MN; NatlFornLg; NHS; PolWkr; SchPl; SchPpr; Pres4-H; PresFHA; 4-HAwd; VoiceDemAwd; Univ Of Minnesota; Home Ec.

SCHWARTZ, Mark J; Berkley HS; Huntington Woods, MI; Chr; Mdrgl; SctActv; University; Professional.

SCHWARTZ, Mark L; Niles West HS; Lincolnwood, IL; RptrYrbk; VPBsbl; IMSpt; College; Law.

SCHWARTZ, Mary K; St Joseph Academy; Green Bay, WI; Chr; Chrs; ChrhWkr; LbryAde; TchrAde; Sec4-H; FrCl; Univ At Green Bay; Business.

SCHWARTZ, Nancy J; Marion HS; Marion, SD; 1/36 TrsJrCls; Band; Chrs; HonRl; SchPl; Yrbk; RptrSchPpr; FHA; SciCl; College; Mathematics.

SCHWARTZ, Steven R; Liberty HS; Liberty, IL; 14/62 Band; ChrhWkr; CncrtBnd; HonRl; SchMus; SchPl; 4-H; FFA; PpCl; 4-HAwd; Unvi; Elec Eng.

SCHWARTZ, Theresa J; Seymour HS; Liberty, IL; 21/70 Band; CncrtBnd; HonRl; MrchBnd; PepBnd; StuCncl; FHA; Trade School; Vocation.

SCHWARTZ, Thomas; Tecumseh HS; Tecumseh, MI; ALBoysSt; YthFlsp; EdYrBk; Univ; Professional.

SCHWARTZ, Todd E; Pringhar Comm HS; Pringhar, IA; VPSophCls; TrsSrCls; Band; MrchBnd; 4-H; Bsbl; Bsktbl; Ftbl; Trk; College.

SCHWARTZ CROMWELL, Peggy S; La Moille Comm HS; La Moille, IL; Chr; ChrhWkr; LbryAde; YthFlsp; RptrSchPpr; 4-H; FrCl; PpCl; College.

SCHWARTZE, Barbara M; Freeman HS; Freeman, SD; Chrs; HonRl; SchPl; SctActv; TchrAde; SpnCl; University; Lawyer.

SCHWARTZE, John A; Helias HS; Jefferson City, MO; 6/186 ALBoysSt; HonRl; VPNHS; SchMus; StuCncl; LetterBsktbl; Missouri Univ; Engineer.

SCHWARTZE, Mary A; Fatima HS; Argyle, MO; 44/121 Band; Chr; CncrtBnd; HonRl; MrchBnd; SchPl; FrCl; SpnCl; SciCl; 4-HAwd; Florissant Valley Com; Advertising Design.

SCHWARTZE, Susan; Southwest HS; Kansas City, MO; 34/475 Band; ChrhWkr; CncrtBnd; HonRl; JA; MrchBnd; NHS; StuCncl; IMSpt; JAAwd; Kansas City Business Col; Accountant.

SCHWARTZFISHER, Alice R; Petoskey HS; Petoskey, MI; Chr; SchMus; SchPl; Yrbk; SchPpr; 4-H; FFA; Trk; 4-HAwd; KiwanAwd; Coll; Voc.

SCHWARTZKOPF, Cindy S; Red Bud C U HS; Baldwin, IL; 25/125 TreasYthFlsp; Pres4-H; AmLegAwd; 4-HAwd; Work.

SCHWARTZKOPF, Lee A; Ness City HS; Ness City, KS; 2/54 VPChrhWkr; VPNHS; NatlThespSoc; PolWkr; 4-H; FHA; LetterBsktbl; LetterTennis; Chrldr; 4-HAwd; Kansas State Univ; Home Economics.

SCHWARZ, Carolyn E; Ursuline Academy; St Louis, MO; ChrhWkr; HonRl; HospAde; JA; FrCl; PPFtbl; St Louis Univ; Med Technology.

SCHWARZ, Edward W; Lanphier HS; Springfield, IL; 15/535 HonRl; PresNHS; NatlMeritSF; OffAde; KeyCl; VPGerCl; Il U; Elec Eng.

SCHWARZ, Eunice J; St Ann HS; Lexington, NE; 1/19 SecJrCls; CncrtBnd; HonRl; VPNHS; NatlMeritCmnd; SecStuCncl; Yrbk; EdSchPpr; EldAwd; VFWAwd; Hastings Tech; Business.

SCHWARZ, Karen E; Mother Of Sorrows HS; Blue Island, IL; 20/115 Aud/Vis; HonRl; LbryAde; FNA; FrCl; College; Translator Of French.

SCHWARZ, Katherine M; Ford Central HS; Roberts, IL; PresFrshCls; Band; Chrs; CncrtBnd; HonRl; MrchBnd; StuCncl; TchrAde; SchPpr; FTA; PpCl; CaptChrldr; GAA; PresAwd; Trade School; Vocation.

SCHWARZ, Kevin H; Woodbury HS; Moville, IA; ALBoysSt; ChrhWkr; HonRl; RptrSchPpr; SptEdSchPpr; 4-H; PpCl; St Johns College; Ministry.

SCHWARZ, Michael; Winston Churchill HS; Livonia, MI; 22/830 HonRl; Orch; SchMus; Univ Of Mi; Dds.

SCHWARZ, Rhonda S; Central City HS; Palmer, NE; 1/74 SecSophCls; SecJrCls; Chrs; ChrhWkr; HonRl; Mdrgl; NHS; OffAde; SpnCl; PpCl; College.

SCHWARZ, Susan M; Ofallon Township HS; Lebanon, IL; 1/310 ChrhWkr; HonRl; JrNHS; Pres4-H; 4-HAwd; Business School; Computer Science.

SCHWARZENBERGER, Serena I; Trego Community HS; Collyer, KS; 4/80 Chrs; ChrhWkr; HonRl; Yrbk; FHA; PpCl; SciCl; LetterTrk; Ks State U; Interior & Landscapedesigner.

SCHWARZKOPF, Paula; St Bernard HS; Wall Lake, IA; 4/18 PresSrCls; Band; Chrs; CncrtBnd; HonRl; JrNHS; PepBnd; Yrbk; PpCl; Bsktbl; College; Nursing.

SCHWARZKOPF, Sandra L; Becker Public HS; Becker, MN; 1/44 TrsFrshCls; Chr; Chrl; Chrs; ChrhWkr; HonRl; LbryAde; OffAde; SchAde; SchPl; TchrAde; Bsktbl; GAA; College; Vocation.

SCHWEBACH, Mark J; Dell Rapids Public HS; Dell Rapids, SD; HonRl; SchMus; SchPl; StuCncl; StuGov; GerCl; PpCl; Bsbl; National Clg Of Business Rapid City Sd.

SCHWEFEL, Laura R; Watertown Sr HS; Watertown, WI; 15/310 Band; ChrhWkr; HospAde; JrNHS; NHS; OffAde; EdSchPpr; FHA; Uw Milwaukee; Nursing.

SCHWEFEL, Susan A; Kewanee HS; Kewanee, IL; 17/210 HonRl; StuCncl; StuGov; GerCl; Chrldr; Black Hawk Jr Clg; Undecided.

SCHWEGEL, Pamela J; Alton Sr HS; Alton, IL; 28/865 CmntyWkr; College; Physical Therapist.

SCHWEHR, Michael J; North Central Of Barnes HS; Sanborn, ND; PresFrshCls; SecTrsSophCls; SecTrsJrCls; ALBoysSt; HonRl; SchPl; StuCncl; Bsbl; LetterBsktbl; LetterFtbl; College; Business.

SCHWEICKERT, Stephanie M; Academy Of Our Lady; E Peoria, IL; 3/100 Chrs; ChrhWkr; HonRl; NHS; SchMus; SchPl; Yrbk; SchPpr; Univ Of Notre Dame; Pre Medicine.

SCHWEIER, Peter; Bellmont HS; Decatur, IN; 10/374 HonRl; NHS; SctActv; TchrAde; RptrSchPpr; FrCl; College; Curriculum Of Major Study.

SCHWEIFLER, Mary; Grand Haven HS; Grand Haven, MI; 4/388 ALAGirlsSt; HonRl; HospAde; JrNHS; NHS; Bsbl; Bsktbl; Trk; GAA; Grand Vly St Coll;psychology.

SCHWEIGERDT, Richard L; Raytown HS; Aytown, MO; ALBoysSt; HonRl; JrNHS; Bsbl; Ftbl; College.

SCHWEIGERT, Keith; Zeeland HS; Zeeland, ND; 1/28 Band; Chr; ChrhWkr; HonRl; Mdrgl; MrchBnd; SchPl; StuCncl; SchPpr; Nd St Univ; Pharmacy.

SCHWEIGERT, Susan; Kensal Public HS; Kensal, ND; 2/17 VPSrCls; Band; CncrtBnd; HonRl; LbryAde; SchPl; RptrSchPpr; Univ Of N Dak; Nursing.

SCHWEIKART, Joan M; Homewood Flossmoor HS; Homewood, IL; 31/910 NHS; NatlMeritCmnd; SchAde; LatCl; SpnCl; LetterBsktbl; CchngActv; IMSpt; Creighton Univ; Lawyer.

SCHWEIKL, Jay J; Columbus HS; Marshfield, WI; 19/118 HonRl; PresNHS; NatlMeritCmnd; SctActv; SptEdYrbk; SptEdSchPpr; LetterTrk; CchngActv; CaptIMSpt; PresAwd; La Crosse Univ; Business Admin.

SCHWEIKL, Scott M; Columbus HS; Marshfield, WI; 32/104 HonRl; StuCncl; LetterTrk; IMSpt; College.

SCHWEINEBART, Teresa I; Baxter Community HS; Baxter, IA; Band; HonRl; NatlThespSoc; PolWkr; SchPl; StuCncl; RptrYrbk; RptrSchPpr; PpCl; Central College; Elementary Teacher.

SCHWEINZGER, Sara J; Niles HS; Niles, MI; Chr; HonRl; SchMus; SctActv; StuGov; YthFlsp; Bsktbl; Chrldr; IMSpt; OptClAwd; College; Major Study.

SCHWEISS, Brenda S; Valle HS; Ste Genevieve, MO; Band; HonRl; NHS; SchMus; StuCncl; PpCl; Chrldr; IMSpt; PPFtbl; Med Sch; Medical Field.

SCHWEISS, Sandy L; Rockridge HS; Taylor Ridge, IL; HonRl; JrNHS; NHS; 4-H; FrCl; SpnCl; 4-HAwd; Blackhawk Jr Col; Accountant.

SCHWEITZER, Herbert L; Cumberland HS; Cumberland, WI; 2/126 TrsSophCls; Band; ChrhWkr; CncrtBnd; HonRl; YthFlsp; RptrSchPpr; SchPpr; Bsktbl; Glf; Bsnss Sch; Accting.

SCHWEITZER, Kenneth A; Halliday HS; Dodge, ND; 5/30 PresSrCls; ALBoysSt; HonRl; NHS; StuCncl; Bsktbl; Ftbl; Trk; AmLegAwd; Univ; Mech Engr.

SCHWEITZER, Rod R; Poplar Bluff HS; Poplar Bluff, MO; Band; CmntyWkr; CncrtBnd; PepBnd; Ftbl; Trk; Wrstlng; IMSpt; Coll.

SCHWENDEMAN, John C; Desmet Jesuit HS; St Louis, MO; 65/180 Chr; ChrhWkr; PolWkr; StuGov; LetterBsktbl; LetterFtbl; LetterTrk; IMSpt; University; Law.

SCHWENDINGER, Donna; Hempstead HS; Peosta, IA; 9/455 4-H; 4-HAwd; Loras Coll; Rn.

SCHWENKE, Roy A; Cumberland & Massena Comm HS; Massena, IA; 412/30 HonRl; SctActv; Pres4-H; Bsktbl; 4-HAwd; Iowa State Univ; Forestry.

SCHWENNINGER, Sharlette A; Elwood HS; Elwood, NE; 2/18 PresFrshCls; VPSophCls; Band; Chr; CncrtBnd; HonRl; MrchBnd; NHS; NatlMeritCmnd; PepBnd; Univ Of Nebraska.

SCHWENNSEN, Katherine L; Dubuque Senior HS; Dubuque, IA; 6/370 Band; Chr; Chrl; Chrs; ChrhWkr; CmntyWkr; CncrtBnd; HonRl; HospAde; JrNHS; NHS; Mdrgl; Swmmng; Tennis; Iowa State Univ; Architecture.

SCHWER, Darlene; Carl Sandburg Hs; Tinley Park, IL; 30/700 HonRl; NHS; 4-H; GerCl; MthCl; PpCl; SciCl; LetterBsbl; GAA; IMSpt; University; Professional.

SCHWERHA, Kristin D; Elkhart Central HS; Elkhart, IN; SecSophCls; Chr; HonRl; NHS; PresNatlThespSoc; SchMus; SchPl; TchrAde; Purdue Univ; Biology.

SCHWERING, Karen A; South Decatur HS; Greensburg, IN; ChrhWkr; CmntyWkr; HonRl; LbryAde; FHA; SpnCl; St Elizabeth School Of Nursing; Nursing.

SCHWERMANN, Rita M; St Johns HS; Beloit, KS; 2/21 SecSrCls; Chrs; CmntyWkr; HonRl; StuCncl; TchrAde; RptrYrbk; Trk; EldAwd; CitAwd; Univ Ks St; Doctor Of Vet Med.

SCHWERT, Michael A; Forest View HS; Mt Prospect, IL; 31/670 HonRl; NatlFornLg; NHS; StuGov; KeyCl; SciCl; Northwestern Univ; Medicine.

SCHWERY, Meg R; Harlan Comm HS; Panama, IA; 43/256 VPSrCls; Chr; ChrhWkr; HonRl; NHS; SchPl; Yrbk; 4-H; HstJrCls; Tennis; Nursing Training;.

SCHWIEBERT, Susan M; Center Point Cons HS; Center Point, IA; 1/45 VPSophCls; Band; Chr; Chrs; ChrhWkr; HonRl; NHS; LetterBsbl; LetterBsktbl; LetterTrk; St Lukes Sch; Nurse.

SCHWIEN, Fred L; Trego Comm HS; Wakeeney, KS; VPSrCls; ALBoysSt; HonRl; NHS; RedCrAde; TchrAde; VPSciCl; Bsktbl; Trk; GodCntryAwd; West Point Academy; Military.

SCHWIER, Sandra J; North Decatur HS; Greensburg, IN; 4/104 Chr; HonRl; LbryAde; NHS; SctActv; YthFlsp; LatCl; SpnCl; IMSpt; Ball State U; Elem Ed.

SCHWIESOW, Rebecca R; West Sioux Comm HS; Hawarden, IA; Chrs; SctActv; StuGov; RptrYrbk; SchPpr; FTA; PpCl; Trk; Chrldr; IMSpt; Univ; Major Study.

SCHWIESOW, Richard E; Ponca Public HS; Ponca, NE; 5/36 ALBoysSt; Chr; SchPl; Teen; SptEdSchPpr; Bsbl; LetterFtbl; Glf; Swmmng; IMSpt;.

SCHWIMMER, Celia; Evanston Township HS; Evanston, IL; HonRl; Mdrgl; Orch; SchMus; Univ; Prof Cellist.

SCHWINCK, Jayne A; West Point HS; West Point, NE; Chr; ChrhWkr; HonRl; SchPl; SctActv; RptrYrbk; EdSchPpr; 4-H; FHA; 4-HAwd; Clge.

SCHWINDEL, Dianne M; Derham Hall HS; St Paul, MN; CmntyWkr; HospAde; LbryAde; SchPl; StuCncl; SpnCl; St Marys Jr College; Medicine.

SCHWINDT, Cynthia E; Salina Central HS; Salina, KS; 7/313 Chr; Chrl; ChrhWkr; HonRl; NatlThespSoc; SchMus; SchPl; SctActv; TchrAde; College; Music.

SCHWINDT, Randy M; Utica HS; Utica, KS; VPJrCls; Band; CncrtBnd; HonRl; SchPl; StuCncl; StuGov; Yrbk; RptrSchPpr; LetterBsktbl; Jr Clg; Photographer.

SCHWINGLE, Sara; Riverdale HS; Boscobel, WI; HonRl; MrchBnd; NHS; Twrl; FHA; GerCl; SciCl; Vocational School; Nursery School Teacher.

SCHWOCH, Terri L; Merrill HS; Merrill, WI; 15/334 HonRl; HospAde; NatlFornLg; SchMus; SchPl; StuCncl; YthFlsp; RptrYrbk; RptrSchPpr; Lawrence Univ; Journalism.

SCHWYN, Patricia A; Northside HS; Fr Wayne, IN; 91/438 AFS; HospAde; LetterSwmmng; PPFtbl; Ball State Univ; Nursing.

SCHYMANSKI, John J; Washington HS; South Bend, IN; 1/325 HonRl; JrNHS; NHS; EdYrBk; RptrSchPpr; Northwestern Univ; Dentist.

SCIACERO, Mark L; Clark HS; Hammond, IN; 21/245 ALBoysSt; Band; CncrtBnd; MrchBnd; NHS; Orch; PepBnd; GerCl; PpCl; Ftbl; Purdue Univ; Statistics.

SCIORTINO, Rosellen; Villa Duchesne HS; St Louis, MO; 2/50 CmntyWkr; HonRl; ModUN; NHS; Yrbk; SchPpr; LatCl; Chrldr; IMSpt; University; Pre Med.

SCITTERS, John D; Davison HS; Davison, MI; 15/433 NHS; SctActv; IMSpt; Univ Of Mi; Engineering.

SCOBY, James A; Sabetha Sr HS; Sabetha, KS; TrsSrCls; HonRl; YthFlsp; YthLg; KeyCl; LetterTrk; IMSpt; College; Chemistry.

SCOFIELD, Don L; High School; Kirksville, MO; Nmsu Kcom; Physcian.

SCOGGIN, Deborah J; Douglas Macarthur HS; Saginaw, MI; 4/280 CncrtBnd; HonRl; MrchBnd; VPNHS; NatlMeritCmnd; GerCl; LetterBsbl; Bsktbl; CaptTrk; Albion College; Biology.

SCOGGIN, Donna M; Hartford HS; Hartford, KS; 2/33 Chrs; HonRl; OffAde; SchPl; EdYrBk; FBLA; PpCl; Trk; CchngActv; 4-HAwd; College; Accounting.

SCOGGIN, Larry J; Buchan HS; Buchanan, MI; TchrAde; FFA; Trk; LetterWrstlng; Tech School; Electrician.

SCOGGIN, Tamara R; Highland HS; Labelle, MO; Band; Chr; JrNHS; NHS; StuCncl; VPStuCncl; FSA; PresPpCl; Chrldr; Nursing School.

SCOGGINS, Felicia; Hauser HS; Columbus, IN; 12/85 ChrhWkr; HonRl; HospAde; JrNHS; NHS; OffAde; SchPl; TchrAde; FTA; GAA; Evansville Univ; Law.

SCOGGINS, Helen D; Greenfield HS; Greenfield, IL; HstJrCls; Chr; Chrs; ChrhWkr; HonRl; LbryAde; OffAde; SchMus; TreasFHA; GAA; Business School; Vocation.

SCOTT, Andre K; Roosevelt HS; Gary, IN; 50/608 HonRl; JrNHS; NHS; SchPl; EngCl; SpnCl; MthCl; Ftbl; Ftbl; CitAwd; Univ; Accntg.

SCOTT, Barbara A; Joliet East HS; Joliet, IL; 17/381 HonRl; SchMus; SchPl; SchPpr; PpCl; SciCl; GAA; VoiceDemAwd; Joliet Jr Clg; Nursing.

SCOTT, Barbara J; Kirksville HS; Greentop, MO; 49/188 Ne Missouri St College; Business.

SCOTT, Basil; Chelsea HS; Chelsea, MI; HonRl; NatlMeritSF; StuCncl; TchrAde; Michigan State; Psychology.

SCOTT, Becky J; Three Rivers HS; Three Rivers, MI; 11/210 HonRl; JrNHS; NHS; NatlMeritCmnd; SchAde; LatCl; PpCl; CaptBsktbl; CaptTrk; Kalamazoo Vly Comm College; Dental Hygiene.

SCOTT, Bradley L; Chaska HS; Exc, MN; University; Law.

SCOTT, Brenda; Proviso West Hs; Bellwood, IL; 99/1200 Chrs; ChrhWkr; HonRl; HospAde; LbryAde; NHS; StuCncl; TchrAde; FTA; SpnCl; Rosary College; Elementary Education.

SCOTT, Brian A; Appleton West HS; Appleton, WI; Chrs; HonRl; Mdrgl; PolWkr; SchMus; StuGov; KeyCl; LetterTennis; IMSpt; Auburn Univ; Veterinarian.

SCOTT, Brian D; Streator Twp HS; Streator, IL; VPFrshCls; PresSophCls; Band; PresChrhWkr; HonRl; MrchBnd; NatlThespSoc; SchMus; SchPl; SchPpr; Ivcc; Mass Communications.

SCOTT, Brian K; Mt Vernon HS; Mt Vernon, MO; Band; CncrtBnd; MrchBnd; NatlThespSoc; PepBnd; SchMus; SchPl; SctActv; StuCncl; RptrSchPpr; SchPpr; Univ Of Missouri; Forestry.

SCOTT, Bridget M; Luke M Powers HS; Flint, MI; 17/305 Band; CncrtBnd; HonRl; HospAde; MrchBnd; NHS; SchMus; Charles Stewart Mott; Nursing.

SCOTT, Carla M; Maine Twp HS; Park Ridge, IL; HonRl; JA; NHS; PolWkr; FrCl; College.

SCOTT, Cassius A; Marquette HS; Michigan City, IN; PresSophCls; ALBoysSt; HonRl; SchMus; SchPl; StuCncl; College; Medicine.

SCOTT, Cinda R; Bradford HS; Bradford, IL; Chrs; HonRl; LbryAde; YthFlsp; 4-H; FHA; 4-HAwd; Black Hawk East; Accounting.

SCOTT, Claudia; Sullivan HS; Sullivan, MO; Band; ChrhWkr; CncrtBnd; HonRl; MrchBnd; PepBnd; PolWkr; FTA; SpnCl; PpCl; College.

SCOTT, Colby N; Hillsboro Sr HS; De Soto, MO; VPJrCls; Band; MrchBnd; PepBnd; SctActv; PpCl; LetterBsbl; LetterBsktbl; Trk; College; Forestry.

SCOTT, Daniel J; Lourdes Acad; Oshkosh, WI; Band; HonRl; SctActv; RptrYrbk; Yrbk; SchPpr; Trk; Wrstlng; College; Medical Field.

SCOTT, Daniel K; Hinsdale South HS; Hinsdale, IL; 12/460 HonRl; NHS; SctActv; College; Science.

SCOTT, David L; Central HS; Springfield, MO; 22/279 ChrhWkr; CmntyWkr; HonRl; StuCncl; StuGov; MthCl; Bsktbl; LetterTennis; GodCntryAwd; KiwanAwd; Drury Clge; Md.

SCOTT, Denise K; U S D 399 Natoma HS; Waldo, KS; Band; ChrhWkr; HonRl; NHS; NatlMeritFnl; NatlMeritCmnd; NatlMeritSchl; NatlMeritSF; StuCncl; LetterTrk; Chrldr; PPFtbl; CitAwd; Ft Hays St Univ; Occup Theraphy.

SCOTT, Donnell L; Yale Jamaica Bagley HS; Yale, IA; 2/23 PresJrCls; Chrs; HonRl; NHS; StuCncl; Pres4-H; FTA; PpCl; LetterBsktbl; LetterTrk;.

SCOTT, Douglas E; Arlington HS; Arl Hgts, IL; 21/588 CncrtBnd; HonRl; MrchBnd; NHS; PepBnd; Bsktbl; LetterTennis; Univ; Law.

SCOTT, Ellen; Holt HS; Holt, MI; 20/300 Band; Chr; CncrtBnd; HonRl; MrchBnd; NHS; PepBnd; SchMus; FrCl; LetterTennis; University; Performance Piano.

SCOTT, Eugene F; Lakeshore HS; Stevensville, MI; 41/240 VPJrCls; HonRl; NHS; MthCl; Michigan Tech Univ; Civil Engineer.

SCOTT, Gary W; Muscatine HS; Muscatine, IA; 1/377 CncrtBnd; DrmMjrt; MrchBnd; ModUN; NatlFornLg; NHS; PepBnd; 4-H; GerCl; Iowa State Univ; Physics.

SCOTT, Ginger; Castle HS; Newburgh, IN; 30/292 Chr; NHS; NatlThespSoc; SchMus; SctActv; FTA; GAA; Murray State Univ; Elem Teaching.

SCOTT, Gregg E; Brownstown Central HS; Brownstown, IN; ALBoysSt; HonRl; SchPl; LatCl; PpCl; SciCl; LetterBsbl; IMSpt; University Of Evansville; Accountant.

SCOTT, Henry A; Collinsville HS; Collinsville, IL; TrsFrshCls; Band; CncrtBnd; HonRl; MrchBnd; PpCl; LetterBsbl; Bsktbl; LetterFtbl; Washington Univ; Architecture.

SCOTT, James E; Greenfield HS; Rockbridge, IL; PresFrshCls; PresSophCls; PresJrCls; ChrhWkr; HonRl; LetterBsktbl; LetterTrk; IMSpt; 4-HAwd; Wi U; Electronics Or Ag.

SCOTT, Jean L; Lake View Auburn HS; Lake View, IA; ALAGirlsSt; SecBand; ChrhWkr; SecCncrtBnd; HonRl; NatlThespSoc; PresStuCncl; LetterBsbl; LetterChrldr; PresAwd; Iowa State Univ; Elementary Teaching.

SCOTT, Jean M; Sullivan HS; Sullivan, MO; 9/165 CmntyWkr; HonRl; LbryAde; NHS; SchAde; SchPl; StuCncl; RptrYrbk; RptrSchPpr; SpnCl; Coll; Journalism.

SCOTT, Jeffrey G; Union HS; Grand Rapids, MI; HonRl; NHS; LetterTrk; Coll; Biological Science.

SCOTT, Jenny C; Marshall HS; Marshall, IL; 19/115 VPJrCls; VPSrCls; ChrhWkr; ModUN; OffAde; StuCncl; FBLA; FHA; PpCl; CaptChrldr; Inst U;bus Ed.

SCOTT, John D; Pioneer HS; Logansport, IN; 30/90 HonRl; NHS; SchAde; StuCncl; YthFlsp; SpnCl; Bsbl; Bsktbl; Trk; Wrstlng; In State; Teacher.

SCOTT, Judson R; Brebeuf Prep HS; Indianapolis, IN; PresFrshCls; PresSophCls; HonRl; NHS; SctActv; SecStuCncl; TchrAde; LetterFtbl; LetterTrk; CaptWrstlng; College; Medicine.

SCOTT, Keith A; Northrop HS; Fort Wayne, IN; 181/643 ALBoysSt; Aud/Vis; Band; HonRl; MrchBnd; SchAde; VPStuCncl; SchPpr; LetterTrk; IMSpt; College; Lawyer.

SCOTT, Kimra; Monticello HS; Monticello, IL; 43/136 Chr; Chrs; CncrtBnd; HonRl; HospAde; Mdrgl; MrchBnd; SchMus; 4-H; GerCl; Jr College; Nurse.

SCOTT, Laurie B; Mahomet Seymour HS; Mahomet, IL; 1/124 PresSophCls; SecJrCls; Band; Mdrgl; NHS; NatlThespSoc; SchMus; StuCncl; Pres4-H; Trk; Univ Of Illinois; Architect.

SCOTT, Lisa A; Lathrop HS; Lathrop, MO; 3/38 Chr; Chrs; HonRl; ModUN; NatlMeritCmnd; SchPl; EdYrBk; RptrSchPpr; SecFTA; SpnCl; PpCl; IMSpt; Univ; Political Science.

SCOTT, Lori S; Tecumseh Public HS; Tecumseh, NE; PresJrCls; HonRl; NHS; RedCrAde; StuCncl; Bsktbl; LetterTrk; Chrldr; CchngActv; IMSpt; 4-HAwd; College; Social Worker.

SCOTT, Lynda L; Bradford HS; Bradford, IL; 1/47 TrsSophCls; ALAGirlsSt; ChrhWkr; HonRl; NHS; RptrSchPpr; FHA; Bsktbl; Chrldr; Business School; Vocational.

SCOTT, Margaret; St Marys HS; Storm Lake, IA; 2/40 Chr; Chrs; HonRl; NatlMeritCmnd; SchMus; StuCncl; Twrl; PpCl;.

SCOTT, Margaret L; Richland Center HS; Richland Center, WI; 17/184 Chr; ChrhWkr; CncrtBnd; HonRl; Mdrgl; NHS; SchPpr; LatCl; TreasPpCl; LetterBsktbl; SecGAA; U Of Wi Eau Clair; Special Ed.

SCOTT, Marquita L; Southeast HS; Kansas City, MO; 2/350 HonRl; JrNHS; NHS; NatlMeritCmnd; NatlMeritSchl; SchMus; SpnCl; SciCl; Research Med Ctr; Rn.

SCOTT, Marsha; Memorial HS; Joplin, MO; 25/225 HonRl; HospAde; NHS; OffAde; SctActv; StuGov; GAA; IMSpt; Univ Of Ark; Lawyer.

SCOTT, Michael D; Carrollton HS; Carrollton, MO; 2/104 Band; ChrhWkr; CncrtBnd; HonRl; MrchBnd; NHS; PepBnd; SchMus; SctActv; YthFlsp; SpnCl; SciCl; LetterBsktbl; LetterFtbl; University Of Missouri; Business Agri.

SCOTT, Michael R; Plainfield HS; Joliet, IL; 3/297 HonRl; SecNHS; SpnCl; MthCl; LetterBsktbl; LetterFtbl; LetterTrk; College; Business Administration.

SCOTT, Pamela S; East Charles Mix #102 HS; Wagner, SD; DrlTm; LbryAde; RptrSchPpr; PpCl; LetterBsktbl; Chrldr; Sioux Falls College; Physical Ed.

SCOTT, Peggy S; Batavia HS; Batavia, IL; 1/220 CmntyWkr; CncrtBnd; LitMag; NHS; Orch; StuCncl; MthCl; Trk; GAA; IMSpt; Univ Of Illinois; Music.

SCOTT, Quintin D; East Richland HS; Olney, IL; PresFrshCls; StuCncl; StuGov; Ftbl; Trk; IMSpt; Coll; Pro.

SCOTT, Rebecca; Larned HS; Larned, KS; Band; Chrs; CmntyWkr; CncrtBnd; HonRl; MrchBnd; SchMus; Twrl; PpCl; Chrldr; College; Early Childhood Develop.

SCOTT, Rebecca K; Pleasant Hill HS; Pleasant Hill, IL; 8/48 Band; Chr; HonRl; PepBnd; SctActv; PresFNA; PpCl; GAA;.

SCOTT, Roger D; University HS; Normal, IL; ALBoysSt; HonRl; SchPl; StuCncl; RptrYrbk; Yrbk; RptrSchPpr; SchPpr; FrCl; PpCl; LetterBsbl; LetterBsktbl; LetterFtbl;.

SCOTT, Sandra L; Mc Donald Co HS; Rocky Comfort, MO; ChrhWkr; HonRl; FHA; FTA; PpCl; College; Lab Technician.

SCOTT, Sherryl; Maine Township West Hs; Des Plaines, IL; HonRl; NHS; FrCl; Northern University; Acting.

SCOTT, Stephanie D; St Anthony Village HS; Minneapolis, MN; 32/197 ALAGirlsSt; Band; Chrs; CncrtBnd; HospAde; PresJA; MrchBnd; NatlMeritCmnd; PepBnd; SctActv; RptrYrbk; LetterTennis; GAA; IMSpt; College; Medicine.

SCOTT, Steven C; Adlai E Stevenson HS; Lincolnshire, IL; Band; CncrtBnd; DrmMjrt; MrchBnd; NHS; NatlMeritCmnd; NatlMeritSF; PepBnd; SctActv; Univ Of Colorado; Business.

SCOTT, Steven M; Lindblom Tech HS; Chicago, IL; 38/657 VPJrCls; PresSrCls; Chr; HonRl; IntrClCncl; Mdrgl; NHS; NatlMeritCmnd; OffAde; Quill&Scroll; Howard Univ; Medicine.

SCOTT, Sue E; Gaylord HS; Gaylord, MI; PresJrCls; SecJrCls; PresSrCls; Chr; HonRl; NHS; KeyCl; FrCl; LatCl; SpnCl; College; Rn & Foreign Language.

SCOTT, Teresa R; Broadripple HS; Indiannapolis, IN; 166/495 ChrhWkr; HonRl; JA; OffAde; SchAde; FDA; FHA; Iupui; Pedetrician.

SCOTT, Vernon L; East Prairie HS; East Prairie, MO; HonRl; Yrbk; SchPpr; FFA; LetterBsbl; Air Force Academy; Air Force.

SCOTT, Virginia M; Beaumont HS; St Louis, MO; HonRl; NHS; Arizona State; Psychology.

SCOTT, William W; Hartville R 2 HS; Hartville, MO; VPFrshCls; Chr; ChrhWkr; SchPl; Bsktbl; Clge; Vocation.

SCOVEL, Susan E; Derby Sr HS; Wichita, KS; 18/371 Band; Chr; ChrhWkr; CncrtBnd; JrNHS; NatlFornLg; NHS; NatlMeritCmnd; Orch; PepBnd; SchMus; SctActv; YthFlsp; FrCl; Univ; Biologist.

SCOVILL, Mary L; Maine Township East HS; Des Plaines, IL; HonRl; HospAde; JrNHS; NatlMeritCmnd; SchPl; SctActv; College; Liberal Arts.

SCOW, Robert M; Whitehall HS; Whitehall, WI; HonRl; SpnCl; LetterBsbl; LetterBsktbl; LetterFtbl; Eau Claire Tech Institute; Police Science.

SCRANTON, Eula G; J D Darnall HS; Geneseo, IL; 13/250 ChrhWkr; HonRl; NHS; SchPl; Yrbk;.

SCRIBNER, Leslie; Macarthur Hs; Decatur, IL; Chr; Chrs; Southern Illinois; Psychology.

SCRIPPS, Dave J; Hesperia HS; Hesperia, MI; Chr; ChrhWkr; CncrtBnd; HonRl; MrchBnd; PepBnd; SchMus; TchrAde; Ftbl; Trk; Cedarville College; Music.

SCRIPSICK, Mark A; Burlington HS; Kiowa, KS; ALBoysSt; Chrs; HonRl; SancSoc; SchPl; SctActv; Sdlty; FFA; LetterBsbl; LetterBsktbl; GovHonPrgAwd; Oklahoma St Univ; Arts.

SCRIPTURE, Maureen K; Central Catholic HS; Grand Island, NE; CtyCnl; DrlTm; HonRl; JCC; NatlMeritFnl; NatlMeritSchl; NatlMeritSF; RedCrAde; SchAde; YthLg; College; Human Development.

SCRIVANO, Mary E; West HS; Rockford, IL; 16/379 Chr; CncrtBnd; HonRl; NHS; NatlThespSoc; Orch; SchMus; SchPl; TchrAde; Rock Valley College; Music.

SCROGGIN, Doreen K; Rockwell City HS; Rockwell City, IA; 11/72 TrsJrCls; Chr; Chrs; ChrhWkr; HonRl; JrNHS; Mdrgl; NHS; OffAde; SchMus; 4-H; FHA; LetterBsktbl; LetterTrk; Business School; Secretary.

SCROGGINS, Steven K; Glendale HS; Springfield, MO; ChrhWkr; HonRl; SctActv; StuCncl; MthCl; CchngActv; IMSpt; U Of Mo; Engineering.

SCROGGINS, Ted W; Bunker Hill HS; Bunker Hill, IL; 5/90 SecSrCls; ALBoysSt; HonRl; NHS; SpnCl; College; Coast Guard.

SCRUGGS, Marilyn E; East HS; Kansas City, MO; 20/230 HonRl; LbryAde; NatlMeritCmnd; RptrSchPpr; PpCl; Tennis; Trk; IMSpt; Univ; Psych.

SCULLEY, Vida R; Badger HS; Lake Geneva, WI; 3/200 ALAGirlsSt; Aud/Vis; HonRl; NHS; NatlMeritSF; SchAde; SchMus; VPSctActv; PresStuCncl; RptrSchPpr; Univ; Zoologist.

SCULLY, William; Paul Schulte HS; Terre Haute, IN; 13/88 VPSophCls; VPJrCls; ALBoysSt; NHS; StuCncl; EngCl; Swmmng; AmLegAwd; OptClAwd; Indiana Univ; Diplomatic Corps.

SCULTHORPE, Michael J; Rochester Adams HS; Rochester, MI; Aud/Vis; SctActv; StuGov; Bsktbl; Trk; IMSpt; Oakland Community Clg; Electronics.

SCWAEGEL, Christine R; O Fallon Township HS; O Fallon, IL; Band; CncrtBnd; MrchBnd; PepBnd; SchMus; 4-H; Bsktbl; IMSpt; Brigham Young Univ; Music.

SCZGELSKI, Sidney C; Merrill HS; Merrill, WI; 37/360 Band; CncrtBnd; HonRl; MrchBnd; PepBnd; SchMus; U Of Wi; Business.

SEABAUGH, Kimberly A; Woodland HS; Lutesville, MO; 12/65 PresSophCls; SecSophCls; HstSophCls; PresJrCls; SecJrCls; TrsJrCls; PresSrCls; Aud/Vis; Band; Chr; Chrl; Bsbl; Glf; Swmmng; College; Liberal Arts.

SEABOLT, Loretta D; Virden HS; Virden, IL; CncrtBnd; HonRl; MrchBnd; NHS; PepBnd; SchMus; EdYrBk; RptrSchPpr; PpCl; SciCl; Coll; Pharmacist.

SEABURG, David L; Dilworth Public HS; Dilworth, MN; PresFrshCls; Band; Chr; HonRl; SchMus; SchPl; StuCncl; Trk; Wrstlng; VoiceDemAwd; Moorhead State; Theatre.

SEAGO, Sean W; Liberal HS; Liberal, KS; 2/235 PresSophCls; VPSophCls; HonRl; LitMag; PresNHS; NatlMeritCmnd; SchPpr; Un;physics.

SEAGRAVES, Pamela; Schafer HS; Southgate, MI; 28/290 HonRl; JA; OffAde; TchrAde; Detroit Clge Of Business; Executive Sec.

SEAL, Gary G; Portland HS; Portland, MI; PresFrshCls; HonRl; StuCncl; LetterBsbl; ChmnBsktbl; ChmnFtbl; LetterTrk; CchngActv; IMSpt; PPFtbl; College; Journalism Writing.

SEAL, James F; Clearwater R 1 HS; Piedmont, MO; PresFrshCls; PresSophCls; Band; ChrhWkr; CncrtBnd; HonRl; MrchBnd; College; History.

SEAL, John D; Anderson HS; Anderson, IN; 18/569 ChrhWkr; CmntyWkr; HonRl; LitMag; NHS; PolWkr; Quill&Scroll; SchPl; TchrAde; YthFlsp; FrCl; PpCl; Bsbl; CaptFtbl; Indiana Univ; Optometry.

SEAL, Kenneth H; Barr Reeve HS; Cannelburg, IN; 21/66 ChrhWkr; HonRl; NHS; EdSchPpr; PpCl; Bsktbl; LetterTrk; IMSpt; Us Marine.

SEAL, Thomas; Barr Reeve HS; Montgomery, IN; SecSophCls; HstSrCls; HonRl; SchPl; StuGov; EdSchPpr; 4-H; LatCl; IMSpt; Us Air Force; Legal Profession.

SEAMAN, Millard T; Sunshine Bible Academy; Wichita, KS; 2/29 PresFrshCls; PresSophCls; ALBoysSt; Band; Chr; Chrl; Chrs; ChrhWkr; CncrtBnd; HonRl; Mdrgl; Bsktbl; Ftbl; Trk; Sterling College; Music.

SEAMAN, Thomas A; Palatine HS; Palatine, IL; ALBoysSt; Chr; HonRl; NHS; StuCncl; U Of Il; Law.

SEAMANN, Eugene E; Spalding Academy; Albion, NE; PresFrshCls; TrsSophCls; HonRl; NHS; SchPl; TchrAde; LetterWrstlng; Col; Veterinarian.

SEAMON, Russell E; Hillsboro Comm HS; Hillsboro, IL; 62/180 ChrhWkr; YthFlsp; Jr College; Law Enforcement.

SEAR, Tim J; Stephen Hempstead HS; Dubuque, IA; 90/500 Band; CncrtBnd; MrchBnd; ModUN; PepBnd; SctActv; LetterTennis; CchngActv; IMSpt; GodCntryAwd; College; Elementary Education.

SEARBY, Charles C; Wayne Community HS; Corydon, IA; 2/73 CmntyWkr; HonRl; SpnCl; SciCl; U Of Iowa; Engineer.

SEARCY, Esther D; Kirksville Sr HS; Kirksville, MO; 8/174 ChrhWkr; HonRl; HospAde; NHS; OffAde; StuCncl; YthFlsp; PresFHA; SpnCl; SciCl; LetterTrk; GAA; DanFAwd; Ne Missouri St Univ; Osteopathy.

SEARLE, Kathleen A; J D Darnall HS; Colona, IL; 29/212 SecTrsSrCls; SecCncrtBnd; HonRl; PresJA; NHS; TreasStuCncl; LetterBsktbl; LetterTrk; SecGAA; 4-HAwd; Univ Of Il; Biology.

SEARLES, Mark N; Avon HS; Indianapolis, IN; ModUN; LetterFtbl; LetterTrk; IMSpt; University.

SEARLES, Pamela J; Metropolis Comm HS; Metropolis, IL; ChrhWkr; HonRl; HospAde; NHS; NatlThespSoc; PolWkr; SchMus; SchPl; MthCl; PpCl; Coll; Maj Study.

SEARLES, Susan; Liberal HS; Iantha, MO; SchPl; 4-H; FHA; PpCl;.

SEARS, Becky L; Garden County HS; Lisco, NE; 2/33 VPSrCls; ALAGirlsSt; Chrs; ChrhWkr; HonRl; JrNHS; StuCncl; YthFlsp; LetterTrk; 4-HAwd; PresAwd; Eastern Wyoming College; Veterinarian.

SEARS, Catherine A; Albia Comm HS; Melrose, IA; Chr; HonRl; SchPl; FTA; SpnCl; Clge; Speech.

SEARS, Penny L; Southwest Ri HS; Utica, MO; 4/25 StuGov; FBLA; FDA; FFA; FHA; FNA; FSA; FTA; CitAwd; VoiceDemAwd; Clge; Prof.

SEARS, Sarona; Woodward Granger Comm HS; Woodward, IA; 6/60 Band; ChrhWkr; CncrtBnd; HonRl; MrchBnd; NHS; PepBnd; PolWkr; Bsktbl; Univ Of Iowa; Lawyer.

SEARS, Trudy A; Atkinson HS; Atkinson, IL; 10/31 Chrs; DrmMjrt; HonRl; MrchBnd; SctActv; StuCncl; Twrl; Yrbk; 4-H; SecFHA; SpnCl; Bsbl; LetterBsktbl; GAA; Black Hawk College.

SEARS, William R; Rockville HS; Rockville, IN; HonRl; NHS; SciCl; LetterBsbl; LetterBsktbl; LetterFtbl; Valparasio U; Engineer.

SEASTONE, Vicky E; Holdrege HS; Grand Island, NE; Band; ChrhWkr; CncrtBnd; MrchBnd; PepBnd; 4-H; PpCl; Bsbl; Trk; 4-HAwd; College; Psychiatrist.

SEATON, Jay; Waterford Mott Hs; Pontiac, MI; HonRl; SctActv; U; Engineer.

SEATON, Nancy R; La Salle Peru Twp HS; La Salle, IL; 8/505 Chr; ChrhWkr; HonRl; LbryAde; Mdrgl; NHS; SchAde; SchMus; YthFlsp; Northern Illinois Univ; Med Tech.

SEAVECKI, Debra J; Hartford Union HS; Rubicon, WI; AFS; CmntyWkr; HonRl; JA; YthFlsp; RptrSchPpr; FrCl; LatCl; JAAwd; Univ; Sociology.

SEAVERSON, Wanda L; Chicago Vocational HS; Chicago, IL; HonRl; Nursing School; Nurse.

SEAY, George A; Excelsior Springs HS; Excelsior Springs, MO; 32/240 ALBoysSt; Chr; ChrhWkr; HonRl; JrNHS; NHS; CaptBsktbl; LetterFtbl; LetterGlf; Univ Of Miss; Doctor.

SEAY, John W; Community R 6 HS; Benton City, MO; 30/85 HonRl; JA; JrNHS; OffAde; RptrYrbk; RptrSchPpr; PpCl; College; Business Admin.

SEBACHER, Carol; Duchesne HS; St Charles, MO; Chr; HonRl; PpCl; IMSpt; College; Home Economics.

SEBACHER, Susan L; Duchesne HS; St Charles, MO; 32/182 Chrs; HonRl; SchMus; RptrSchPpr; PpCl; CitAwd; College; Home Economics.

SEBASTIAN, Sherry; Jackson Sr HS; Jackson, MO; Band; CncrtBnd; HonRl; MrchBnd; PepBnd; StuCncl; 4-H; FHA; PpCl; Southeast Mo St Univ; Art.

SEBASTIANI, Alan E; Bishop Mc Namara HS; Kankakee, IL; 1/161 CmntyWkr; HonRl; NHS; NatlMeritCmnd; SchPl; StuCncl; StuGov; RptrYrbk; Univ Of Illinois; Law.

SEBBY, Steven D; Sandwich HS; Sandwich, IL; Jr College; Business.

SEBERG, Lance A; Hastings HS; Hastings, NE; HonRl; RedCrAde; SctActv; SpnCl; Ftbl; Swmmng; PresAwd; Univ; Business Adm.

SEBERT, Rod; Clarion Hs; Clarin, IA; 23/82 PresFrshCls; VPSophCls; HonRl; StuCncl; VP4-H; FFA; Bsbl; Ftbl; LetterWrstlng; 4-HAwd; University; Civil Engineering.

SEBREE, Roderick; Western HS; Spring Arbor, MI; ChrhWkr; CmntyWkr; HonRl; NatlFornLg; SctActv; TchrAde; FrCl; Socr; PresAwd; VoiceDemAwd; Spring Arbor Col; Minister.

SECAN, Mark E; Manhattan HS; Manhattan, KS; AFS; Band; CncrtBnd; HonRl; Orch; PepBnd; PresGerCl; Socr; Tennis; Trk; Univ; Architecture.

SECKER, Jeffrey R; Freeport HS; Freeport, IL; 10/530 Band; CncrtBnd; HonRl; MrchBnd; NatlFornLg; NatlMeritCmnd; PepBnd; VPGerCl; MthCl; LetterTennis; Univ Of Il; Nuclear Engineering.

SECOR, Dale; Kewaskum HS; Kewaskum, WI; 4/196 ALBoysSt; CncrtBnd; HonRl; PepBnd; SchMus; KiwanAwd; Ripon Col; Marine Biology.

SECOR, Deborah A; Grafton HS; Grafton, WI; Band; HonRl; MrchBnd; NHS; Orch; PepBnd; YthFlsp; SchPpr; Wheaton Coll; Chemistry.

SECOR, Nancy J; Carson City Crystal HS; Carson City, MI; HonRl; NHS; OffAde; SchPl; StuCncl;

TchrAde; 4-H; Trk; Chrldr; 4-HAwd; Mich State Univ; Psychology.

SECOR, Susan; Bremen HS; Bremen, IN; 27/125 TrsSrCls; HonRl; OffAde; SchPl; 4-HAwd; U; Home Economics.

SECOY, Debra J; East Prairie HS; East Prairie, MO; Chr; ChrhWkr; CncrtBnd; HonRl; NHS; Yrbk; SchPpr; SciCl; IMSpt; PresAwd; College; Professional.

SEDAITIS, Judith B; Hubbard HS; Chicago, IL; 16/400 Chr; LitMag; NHS; Quill&Scroll; SchPl; StuGov; Yrbk; RptrSchPpr; Univ Of Illinois; Journalism.

SEDBROOK, Dale J; Potosi HS; Potosi, WI; 4-H; FFA; Bsktbl; Trk; 4-HAwd; Vocational Schl; Meat Cutter.

SEDDON, Judy A; Hartford HS; Hartford, MI; Band; ChrhWkr; HonRl; MrchBnd; Yrbk; 4-H; PpCl; IMSpt; Coll; Comm.

SEDIVY, Karen; Verdigre HS; Verdigre, NE; 5/38 CmntyWkr; HonRl; StuCncl; StuGov; TchrAde; YthFlsp; SchPpr; FFA; Chrldr; Univ Of Neb; Journalism.

SEDLACEK, Gary L; Dexter HS; Dexter, MO; HonRl; NatlMeritFnl; NatlMeritSchl; TchrAde; Yrbk; SchPpr; FrCl; SciCl; LetterWrstlng; Univ Of Mo At Rolla.

SEDLACEK, Gary L; Dexter Senior HS; Dexter, MO; HonRl; NatlMeritSF; SctActv; TchrAde; Yrbk; SchPpr; FrCl; MthCl; SciCl; Glf; CaptWrstlng; Univ Of Missouri; Medicine.

SEDLACEK, Jerry J; Hanover HS; Hanover, KS; Band; Chr; HonRl; SchMus; StuCncl; SpnCl; Bsbl; LetterBsktbl; LetterFtbl; LetterTrk; College.

SEDNEK, Amelia R; Rushville Consolidated HS; Rushville, IN; 54/268 Chr; HonRl; NHS; OffAde; SchPl; RptrYrbk; RptrSchPpr; PpCl; Tennis; Chrldr; In State U; Child Development.

SEE, Charlotte M; Our Lady Of Lourdes HS; Chicago, IL; HonRl; LitMag; SchMus; SchPl; StuGov; SpnCl; CaptBsktbl; LetterFtbl; IMSpt; PresAwd; Northwestern Univ; Psychology.

SEE, Kathryn; Lake Orion HS; Pontiac, MI; 10/400 ALAGirlsSt; Chrs; HonRl; LbryAde; SctActv; College, Poli Sci.

SEE, Michael; North Miami Hs; Denver, IN; 22/119 Chr; HonRl; 4-H; FFA;.

SEE, William C; Knox County HS; Rutledge, MO; HonRl; 4-H; Jr College; Agriculture.

SEEBA, Kris L; Nemaha Valley HS; Cook, NE; 6/34 Chr; Chrs; ChrhWkr; CmntyWkr; HonRl; PolWkr; SchMus; SchPl; YthFlsp; 4-H; EngCl; PpCl; LetterTrk; PresAwd; Univ Of Ne; Nursing.

SEEBER, Cynthia D; Richwoods HS; Peoria, IL; 17/449 ChrhWkr; HonRl; NHS; TchrAde; CaptBsbl; CaptBsktbl; GAA; IMSpt; Bradley Univ; Computer Science.

SEEBERG, Cynthia J; Ashton HS; Ashton, IL; 2/41 TrsSrCls; HonRl; NHS; RptrSchPpr; Tennis; Trk; Chrldr; GAA; So Illinois Univ; Photography.

SEEFELDT, Karen L; Oakes HS; Oakes, ND; 7/61 ALAGirlsSt; Band; ChrhWkr; CmntyWkr; HonRl; HospAde; MrchBnd; OffAde; FHA; Trk; College; Computer Programmer.

SEEFELDT, Kristine; Northwestern Preparatory; Hartford, WI; TrsFrshCls; Chrs; ChrhWkr; SchPl; Coll; Professional.

SEEGER, Christopher; Catholic Memorial HS; Brookfield, WI; 13/147 ALBoysSt; HonRl; NHS; CchngActv; KiwanAwd; OptClAwd; CitAwd; College; Natural Resources.

SEEGER, Joyce A; Hill City HS; Hill City, KS; 13/54 Band; Chrs; CncrtBnd; HonRl; MrchBnd; PepBnd; StuCncl; FHA; PpCl;.

SEEGER, Sarah L; Bath HS; Bath, MI; 1/95 TrsJrCls; Band; HonRl; NHS; OffAde; PepBnd; StuCncl; TchrAde; 4-H; 4-HAwd; Mich State U; Teacher.

SEEHAFER, Julie J; Columbus HS; Marshfield, WI; 1/105 Band; CncrtBnd; DrmMjrt; HonRl; MrchBnd; PepBnd; SchMus; RptrSchPpr; FrCl; LetterBsktbl; LetterTrk; GAA; EldAwd; Univ Of Wi; Zoology.

SEEHAUSEN, Dirk V; W Rockford HS; Rockford, IL; PresJrCls; CtyCnl; HonRl; NHS; NatlMeritCmnd; StuCncl; KeyCl; GerCl; LetterSwmmng; Tennis; Washington Univ; Accounting.

SEEHAVER, Thomas C; Colfax HS; Colfax, WI; 15/60 TrsJrCls; Band; CncrtBnd; MrchBnd; SchPl; StuCncl; MthCl; Bsktbl; Ftbl; Tennis; Tech Sch; Professional.

SEELA, Melanie; Dickinson HS; Dickinson, ND; 9/180 Chrl; CncrtBnd; HonRl; NHS; PepBnd; SchMus; RptrYrbk; RptrSchPpr; GerCl; BttyCrckrAwd; Dickinson State College.

SEELEY, Debbie J; Fenton HS; Fenton, MI; Chrl; HonRl; TchrAde; Coll; Bus.

SEELEY, F L; Lindbergh HS; St Louis, MO; 15/946 HonRl; NHS; Univ; Food Tech.

SEELEY, Juliann; Fordson HS; Dearborn, MI; TrsJrCls; HonRl; LbryAde; NHS; StuCncl; TchrAde; Yrbk; PpCl; Tennis; IMSpt; Eastern Mi Univ; Public Accountant.

SEELEY, Sherry L; Van Far HS; Farber, MO; Chrs; DrlTm; HonRl; TchrAde; FHA; PpCl; Chrldr; Kansas Airline Sch; Stewardess.

SEELMAN, Richard L; North Clay Comm HS; Louisville, IL; SecTrsFrshCls; ChrhWkr; CmntyWkr; HonRl; NHS; SchPl; SctActv; RptrYrbk; 4-H; KeyCl; LetterBsbl; LetterBsktbl; Glf; AmLegAwd; College; Lawyer.

SEELYE, Blake A; Henery Ford HS; Sterling Heights, MI; 93/353 HonRl; NatlMeritSchl; OffAde; SchAde; SchPl; TchrAde; GerCl; Univ; Business.

SEELYE, Margaret S; Pekin Comm HS; Pekin, IL; 268/750 AFS; StuCncl; TchrAde; YthFlsp; Yrbk; GerCl; Tennis; Illinois St Univ; Psychology.

SEELYE, Roger; Marcellus HS; Marcellus, MI; 19/82 PresFrshCls; HonRl; NHS; 4-H; FFA; KeyCl; DanFAwd; 4-HAwd; Mi State Univ; Animal Husbandry.

SEES, Donald J; Irene HS; Irene, SD; ChrhWkr; SchPl; TchrAde; 4-H; MthCl; Trk; IMSpt; Air Force Academy; Pilot.

SEES, Richard G; Marshfield HS; Marshfield, MO; HonRl; TchrAde; SecFFA; FTA; SciCl; Univ Of Mo; Agriculture.

SEEVER, Linda L; Oak Park HS; Gladstone, MO; Band; CncrtBnd; HonRl; MrchBnd; Orch; TchrAde; 4-H; University; Business.

SEEVERS, Boyd V; Oneill Public HS; Oneill, NE; 1/87 PresSophCls; HonRl; NHS; StuCncl; Bsktbl; Ftbl; Swmmng; LetterTrk; 4-HAwd; GodCntryAwd; University; Aviator.

SEFCIK, Mary; Providence HS; Joliet, IL; 9/121 HonRl; JrNHS; NHS; SchPl; StuCncl; RptrSchPpr; LatCl; MthCl; SciCl; Tennis; Eastern Il Univ; Medical Dietetics.

SEFFRIN, Martin P; Connersville HS; Connersville, IN; 7/381 HonRl; NHS; GerCl; SciCl; Bsbl; IMSpt; LionAwd; RotaryAwd; Rose Hulman Inst Of Tech; Engineering.

SEFTON, James; East Central HS; Guilford, IN; 3/210 TrsSophCls; ALBoysSt; MrchBnd; NHS; YthFlsp; SpnCl; Bsktbl; LetterFtbl; Trk; IMSpt; Purdue U; Argriculture.

SEFTON, Nancy L; Kingston HS; Kingston, MI; HonRl; TchrAde; RptrYrbk; Yrbk; LetterBsktbl; IMSpt;.

SEGAFREDO, Chris L; Cahokia HS; Cahokia, IL; 59/559 HonRl; SctActv; MthCl; Bsktbl; College; Professional.

SEGEBART, Steve E; Northwest Webster HS; Clare, IA; ChrhWkr; CmntyWkr; HonRl; NatlMeritSF; SchPl; StuCncl; YthFlsp; Bsktbl; LetterTrk; 4-HAwd; University; Science.

SEGELHORST, Celeste E; Okawville HS; Addieville, IL; 6/58 HonRl; SchPl; VPFHA; PpCl; Nursing Sch; Nurse.

SEGER, Cathryn M; Milaca HS; Milaca, MN; Chrs; HonRl; Mdrgl; NHS; SchMus; StuCncl; FHA; CaptChrldr; Northwestern Bible Clg.

SEGER, John M; Lakeview Auburn HS; Lakeview, IA; Band; ChrhWkr; CncrtBnd; HonRl; MrchBnd; NatlMeritCmnd; PepBnd; PolWkr; SctActv; Bsktbl; Briar Cliff College; Law.

SEGER, Mark S; Gordon HS; Gordon, NE; TrsFrshCls; VPJrCls; CmntyWkr; HonRl; YthFlsp; LetterBsktbl; LetterFtbl; LetterTrk; IMSpt; ChmbCommrsAwd; Undecided.

SEGER, Martha E; Liberty HS; Liberty, IL; 1/64 Band; Chrs; HonRl; SchPl; TreasStuCncl; Yrbk; FHA; PpCl; SciCl; 4-HAwd; University; Journalism.

SEGER, Thomas; Jasper HS; Jasper, IN; CmntyWkr; PolWkr; StuGov; CchngActv; Indiana Univ; Professional Business Politic.

SEGERT, Sandra L; Crete Monee HS; Crete, IL; 3/382 VPChr; ChrhWkr; HonRl; NHS; SchMus; SchPl; SecYthFlsp; Yrbk; LatCl; Bsbl; Bsktbl; Chrldr; Univ Of Illinois.

SEGHERS, Paula D; St Marys Academy; Lasalle, IL; 7/27 Chrs; HonRl; SchPl; StuCncl; StuGov; PpCl; Bsktbl; Swmmng; U S Air Force Academy; Law.

SEGOBIANO, Michael E; Central Catholic HS; Bloomington, IL; 11/93 VPFrshCls; PresJrCls; HonRl; VPNHS; PolWkr; StuCncl; FrCl; LetterFtbl; LetterTrk; Wrstlng; Univ; Professional.

SEGOVIA, Jimmy; Saginaw HS; Saginaw, MI; ALBoysSt; HonRl; NHS; FrCl; CitAwd; Mi St; Pharmacist.

SEGOVIANO, Fernando; Holy Cross HS; Chicago, IL; 14/308 ChrhWkr; HonRl; NHS; TreasSpnCl; Wrstlng; Rosary College; Priest.

SEGRE, Alberto M; Urbana HS; Urbana, IL; 17/428 Band; ChrhWkr; CncrtBnd; HonRl; MrchBnd; NatlMeritSF; Orch; PepBnd; TreasStuCncl; RptrSchPpr; SARAwd; University Of Illinois; Sciences.

SEGRETI, Fabio M; Cathedral HS; Chicago, IL; 6/106 VPJrCls; HonRl; NHS; EdYrBk; Loyola Univ; Psychology.

SEGRIFF, James D; Washington HS; Cedar Rapids, IA; 142/470 SchMus; SchPl; Bsbl; Glf; IMSpt; OptClAwd; U Of Ia; Law.

SEGVICH, Maria M; Mother Mc Auley HS; Oak Lawn, IL; ChrhWkr; HonRl; OffAde; RedCrAde; Moraine Valley Comm Coll; Business Admin.

SEHORN, Carol E; Raymore Peculiar HS; Raymore, MO; Band; ChrhWkr; CncrtBnd; HonRl; MrchBnd; Chrldr; GAA; PPFtbl; College.

SEHORN, David G; Raymore Peculiar HS; Ramore, MO; ChrhWkr; CaptBsktbl; CaptFtbl; LetterTrk; Missouri Western; Recreation.

SEHUBERT, Sheryl; Wilcox Public HS; Wilcox, NE; 6/26 Band; Chrs; ChrhWkr; HonRl; NHS; RptrSchPpr; PpCl; LetterBsktbl; LetterTrk; Colle; Phy Ed.

SEHUFMAN, Susan; Derham Hall HS; St Paul, MN; Chrs; LbryAde; SchMus; Yrbk; FrCl; GAA; Coll; Professional.

SEIB, Larry R; Gibson Southern HS; Fort Branch, IN; ChrhWkr; RptrSchPpr; SchPpr; PpCl; LetterFtbl; LetterTrk; IMSpt; College; Vocation.

SEIB, Ronald W; Metamora Twp HS; East Peoria, IL; 13/179 Chrs; HonRl; NHS; NatlMeritCmnd; StuCncl; VPGerCl; LetterBsbl; LetterBsktbl; LetterFtbl; DARAwd; Augustana College; Math.

SEIBEL, David E; Arkansas City HS; Arkansas City, KS; 2/200 AFS; Band; CncrtBnd; MrchBnd; NatlMeritCmnd; Orch; PresSciCl; Tennis; CitAwd; VoiceDemAwd; Southwestern Col; Ornithology.

SEIBEL, Joan M; Somerset Public HS; Somerset, WI; PresJrCls; Band; Chr; HonRl; MrchBnd; NatlFornLg; SchPl; StuCncl; RptrYrbk; GerCl; College; Major Study.

SEIBEL, Judith K; Goodrich HS; Fond Du Lac, WI; ChrhWkr; CmntyWkr; HonRl; College; Nursing.

SEIBERT, Julie A; Clinton Comm HS; Clinton, IL; Chrs; HonRl; OffAde; PolWkr; Yrbk; SpnCl; PpCl; Univ Of Ill; Journalism.

SEIBERT, Melanie K; Mt Vernon Senior HS; Mt Vernon, IN; 1/224 SecSrCls; VPAFS; SecBand; CncrtBnd; HonRl; MrchBnd; VPNHS; SchMus; SecLatCl; Butler University; Pharmacy.

SEIBERT, Patricia A; Harrisonville HS; Harrisonville, MO; 6/150 Band; CncrtBnd; HonRl; HospAde; MrchBnd; PepBnd; SchPl; 4-H; 4-HAwd; Clge; Medical Technology.

SEID, Jean M; Ontonagon Area HS; Ontonagon, MI; DrmBgl; RedCrAde; ROTC; StuCncl; SptEdYrbk; SptEdSchPpr; Bsbl; LetterBsktbl; CchngActv; GAA; College.

SEID, Mae; Cairo HS; Cairo, IL; 1/95 PresSophCls; HstJrCls; HonRl; LbryAde; NHS; Yrbk; SecFrCl; Univ; Bus Admin.

SEIDEI, Kathleen A; Alexander Hamilton HS; Milwaukee, WI; 22/756 Band; CncrtBnd; HonRl; MrchBnd; SctActv; Trk; Chrldr; CchngActv; Treas-GAA; IMSpt; Uw Eau Claire; Acct.

SEIDEL, Ann Marie K; Bishop Borgess HS; Detroit, MI; Chrl; HonRl; HospAde; NHS; SchMus; SpnCl; Chrldr; GAA; Mi Univ; Medical Technology.

SEIDEL, Cheryl P; Jefferson City Sr HS; Lohman, MO; 14/486 Chrs; HonRl; JrNHS; NHS; Quill&Scroll; SchMus; YthFlsp; SchPpr; LatCl; PpCl; Sw Mo State Univ; English.

SEIDEL, Karen A; John F Kennedy HS; Chicago, IL; ChrhWkr; DrmMjrt; HonRl; NHS; SchMus; SchPl; PresFBLA; MthCl; PpCl; GAA; Moser Bus School; Secretary.

SEIDEL, Paula; Harry A Burke HS; Omaha, NE; 8/590 ALAGirlsSt; Band; NHS; NatlMeritCmnd; Orch; Quill&Scroll; StuGov; EdSchPpr; LatCl; KiwanAwd; Umiv; Iundecided.

SEIDEL, Steven R; Saint Patricks HS; Sidney, NE; SchPl; RptrYrbk; IMSpt; Trade School; Electronics Technician.

SEIER, Dave G; Petersburg Public HS; Petersburg, NE; Chr; Chrs; StuCncl; StuGov; LetterBsktbl; LetterFtbl; Trk; Trade; Vocation.

SEIERSTAD, Rita; Luck HS; Cumberland, WI; 14/54 SecSrCls; ChrhWkr; HonRl; FHA; PpCl; Trk; College; Home Economics.

SEIERSTAD, Rita K; Luck HS; Cumberland, WI; 14/54 SecSrCls; ChrhWkr; FHA; College; Home Economics.

SEIFERT, Carol J; Cathedral HS; New Ulm, MN; HonRl; LbryAde; NHS; Yrbk; PpCl; Mankato Area Voc; Sec.

SEIFERT, Cheryl L; Amos Alonzo Stagg HS; Hickory Hills, IL; 3/468 PresFrshCls; PresSophCls; PresJrCls; PresSrCls; ChrhWkr; HonRl; NHS; StuCncl; EdYrBk; CaptChrldr; GAA; College.

SEIFERT, Gary H; Midland HS; Midland, MI; Bsktbl; Ftbl; RotaryAwd; Central Mi Univ; Business Administration.

SEIFERT, Jean; Bishop Noll Institute; Highland, IN; 33/342 HonRl; NHS; NatlMeritCmnd; SchAde; FrCl; John Carroll Univ;.

SEIFERT, Lucinda E; Pepin HS; Pepin, WI; 4/45 VPFrshCls; ChrhWkr; HonRl; NHS; SchPl; StuCncl; RptrYrbk; SchPpr; FHA; Chrldr; Univ; Biology.

SEIFERT, Mark E; St Marys Central HS; Menasha, WI; ALBoysSt; ChrhWkr; JA; NatlFornLg; Sacrstn; SctActv; RptrSchPpr; Ftbl; JAAwd; OptClAwd; College; Professional.

SEIFERT, Rhonda M; Otterville HS; Otterville, MO; VPSophCls; Band; Chrs; EdSchPpr; FBLA; PpCl; Bsbl; Trk; Chrldr; State Fair Comm Col; Librarian.

SEIFERT, Thomas F; Mercy HS; St Louis, MO; VPJrCls; ChrhWkr; CmntyWkr; StuGov; Bsbl; Ftbl; Socr; IMSpt; Univ; Accounting.

SEIFERT, Victor; Sumner HS; Sumner, NE; DrlTm; ROTC; StuGov; Ftbl; Trk; Wrstlng;.

SEIGO, Victoria L; Portland HS; Eagle, MI; 3/139 ChrhWkr; HonRl; SchPl; TchrAde; YthFlsp; College; Medicine.

SEIJAS, Laura M; Southwestern HS; Flint, MI; SecSrCls; CtyCnl; HonRl; NHS; StuCncl; StuGov; College; Professional.

SEILE, Janette; Regina HS; East Detroit, MI; Chrl; DrlTm; HonRl; LbryAde; College; Business.

SEILER, Lori R; Southern Door HS; Sturgeon Bay, WI; Band; Chrs; CncrtBnd; HonRl; MrchBnd; PepBnd; SchMus; Bsktbl; LetterTrk; IMSpt; Coll;.

SEILER, Sarah J; Pana Sr HS; Pana, IL; 16/150 Band; Chrs; HonRl; NHS; NatlMeritSF; RedCrAde; TchrAde; EdYrBk; LetterTennis; LetterTrk; GAA; Univ Of Illinois; Teacher.

SEILER, Wayne J; St Gertrude HS; Raleigh, ND; 1/26 TrsJrCls; Chrs; HonRl; NHS; SchPl; LetterTrk; Us Air Force Acad.

SEILS, Cynthia A; Hanover Central HS; Dyer, IN; 10/140 SecFrshCls; HonRl; JrNHS; NHS; OffAde; StuCncl; TchrAde; PpCl; Chrldr; College.

SEIM, Robert A; Bison HS; Shate Hill, SD; TrsSrCls; ALBoysSt; Chrs; HonRl; NHS; SchPl; 4-H; SpnCl; LetterFtbl; CaptWrstlng; Agriculture.

SEIPEL, Anita L; Pepin HS; Stockholm, WI; 4/45 SecJrCls; SecSrCls; Band; CncrtBnd; HonRl; MrchBnd; StuCncl; SchPpr; VPFHA; DARAwd; Secretary.

SEIPEL, Brenda J; Athens HS; Springfield, IL; 2/51 SecTrsSrCls; HonRl; NHS; StuCncl; RptrSchPpr; 4-H; FHA; FTA; Bsktbl; IMSpt; DARAwd; College; Business.

SEIPELT, Gregory M; Taylor Center HS; Taylor, MI; Auto Mech.

SEISTRUP, Chris T; Mendota Township HS; Mendota, IL; 10/187 AFS; ChrhWkr; CmntyWkr; HonRl; NHS; PolWkr; StuCncl; StuGov; YthFlsp; FrCl; MthCl; LetterBsktbl; CaptTennis; Northern Ill Univ; Business.

SEITER, Sheila M; Benilde St Margarets HS; Minneapolis, MN; CmntyWkr; NHS; SctActv; College; Law Enforcement.

SEITTER, Scott E; Blue Valley HS; Leawood, KS; Band; ChrhWkr; CncrtBnd; HonRl; MrchBnd; NHS; Orch; PepBnd; SctActv; YthFlsp;.

SEITZ, Andrea K; Sullivan HS; Sullivan, IL; 7/115 Band; Chr; HonRl; MrchBnd; SecYthFlsp; Yrbk; FTA; FrCl; PresGerCl; Illinois Wesleyan U; Jouralism.

SEITZ, Anna M; St Paul HS; Highland, IL; 1/55 ChrhWkr; HonRl; PepBnd; SchMus; Yrbk; 4-H; Trk; GAA; AmLegAwd; 4-HAwd; Univ; Math.

SEITZ, David; Thomas More HS; Oak Creek, WI; Band; HonRl; NHS; PepBnd; Yrbk; Ill Institute Of Technocgy; Chemistry.

SEITZ, Mary A; Academy Of Our Lady; Peoria, IL; 1/89 HonRl; NHS; NatlMeritFnl; NatlMeritSF; SancSoc; SchMus; RptrYrbk; FTA; Univ Of Illinois; Veterinarian.

SEITZ, Michael E; Bellmont HS; Decatur, IN; 20/255 ALBoysSt; HonRl; NHS; GerCl; LetterFtbl; LetterWrstlng; CchngActv; In Univ; Teaching.

SEITZ, Nancy; Kee HS; Lansing, IA; HonRl; SchAde; SchPpr; 4-H; Chrldr; Technical School; Ward Clerk.

SEITZ, Pamela; Elwood Public HS; Elwood, NE; VPSophCls; Band; Chr; ChrhWkr; CncrtBnd; HonRl; JrNHS; MrchBnd; NHS; OffAde;.

SEITZ, Terry R; Dubois HS; Jasper, IN; 4/81 Aud/Vis; Band; ChrhWkr; CmntyWkr; CncrtBnd; DrmBgl; HonRl; MrchBnd; NatlMeritCmnd; Orch; LetterBsbl; BttyCrckrAwd; Vincenne Univ; Professional.

SEIVER, James L; Freeport Senior HS; Freeport, IL; 51/504 ChrhWkr; HonRl; JA; MthCl; Univ Of Ill; Electrical Engineering.

SEIWALD, Clair L; Tonganoxie HS; Lawrence, KS; 5/115 Chrl; HonRl; NHS; OffAde; TchrAde; FHA; SpnCl; PpCl; SciCl; KiwanAwd; Coll; Med Pro.

SEIZINGER, Catherine H; Trenton HS; Trenton, MI; CmntyWkr; HonRl; NHS; StuCncl; GerCl; GAA; PPFtbl; U Of Mich; Architecture.

SELANDER, Linda S; Prairie Community HS; Gowrie, IA; 5/78 Chrl; Chrs; ChrhWkr; HonRl; NHS; SchMus; RptrSchPpr; EdSchPpr; FrCl; Bsktbl; Bus Sch; Medical Secretary.

SELBEE, Dawn; Athens HS; Athens, MI; 1/100 VPJrCls; HonRl; HospAde; NHS; OffAde; StuCncl; PpCl; Bsktbl; Ftbl; Trk;.

SELBERG, Victoria A; Stevens HS; Rapid City, SD; 15/413 Chr; ChrhWkr; CmntyWkr; HonRl; PolWkr; College; History.

SELBO, Steven P; Fargo North HS; Fargo, ND; PresSophCls; StuCncl; EdSchPpr; KeyCl; LetterSwmmng; Univ; Professnl.

SELBY, Bruce D; Paxton HS; Paxton, IL; 3/150 Band; HonRl; NHS; LetterBsktbl; Trade School; Automotive Technician.

SELBY, Cathy J; Lawrenceville HS; Lawrenceville, IL; Chrs; ChrhWkr; HonRl; HospAde; SctActv; TchrAde; YthFlsp; FNA; LatCl; PpCl; Barnes Hosp School; Nursing.

SELBY, Debra; Cass City HS; Cass City, MI; SecSophCls; Band; HonRl; JrNHS; NHS; RedCrAde; SchPl; TchrAde; GAA; PPFtbl; Ferris State College; Dental Lab Technology.

SELBY, Debra J; Adair County Rii HS; Brashear, MO; TrsSophCls; Band; Chrs; HonRl; MrchBnd; PepBnd; SchAde; YthFlsp; 4-H; FHA; LetterBsktbl; LetterTrk; Northeast Mo St Univ; Accounting.

SELBY, Diane; Portage Northern HS; Portage, MI; ChrhWkr; NHS; SctActv; FrCl; West Mich Univ;social Sciences.

SELBY, Kati; Williamsburg HS; Parnell, IA; 7/94 HstJrCls; HonRl; StuCncl; HstFrshCls; GerCl; GAA; PPFtbl; KiwanAwd; Army.

SELBY, Melissa K; Dewitt Central HS; Delmar, IA; Chrs; ChrhWkr; HonRl; 4-H; PpCl; Trk; Voca ;beauty.

SELCHOW, Wanda L; Minneapolis Lutheran HS; Richfield, MN; 10/37 Chr; HonRl; SchPl; RptrSchPpr; LetterTrk; LetterChrldr; Golden Valley Luth Coll; Acctg Bus Adm.

SELCK, Sandy L; Boonville HS; Boonville, MO; ALAGirlsSt; Band; Chr; Chrs; CncrtBnd; MrchBnd; PepBnd; SchPl; PresFrCl; PpCl; Unif Of Missouri; Pe Teacher.

SELENKE, Karen; Winfield Sr HS; Winfield, KS; Chrs; DrlTm; HonRl; JA; OffAde; SchPl; TchrAde; FHA; Glf; Chrldr; Emporia Teachers Coll; Phy Ed.

SELF, Charles H; Alexander Ramsey HS; Roseville, MN; 32/577 ChrhWkr; CncrtBnd; MrchBnd; NHS; PepBnd; PolWkr; TreasStuGov; IMSpt; St Olaf Col; Law.

SELFRIDGE, Heather L; Shawnee Mission South HS; Overland Park, KS; Chr; CmntyWkr; HonRl; SchMus; SchPl; YthFlsp; PpCl; College; Therapist For Deaf & Blind.

SELIG, Craig; Lawrenceville HS; Lawerenceville, IL; 4/175 HonRl; NHS; Univ Of Michigan; Actuarial.

SELIG, David J; Meridian HS; Alexandria, NE; 1/33 PresJrCls; Band; CncrtBnd; HonRl; NHS; SchMus; LetterFtbl; LetterTrk; LetterWrstlng; College; Professional.

SELINE, Lynne E; Rockford East HS; Rockford, IL; HonRl; JrNHS; NHS; NatlMeritCmnd; Yrbk; FTA; PpCl; Illinois State Univ; Education.

SELINE, Nancy A; East HS; Rockford, IL; HonRl; NHS; FTA; PpCl; GAA; Northern Ill Univ; Industry.

SELINGER, Robert; Springfield Hs; Springfield, IL; 8/535 NatlMeritCmnd; SecMass Insttitue Ot Tech; Computer Engineerin.

SELINGER, Sharon; St Marys HS; New England, ND; 18/46 Band; Chr; CncrtBnd; DrlTm; HonRl; PepBnd; SchAde; StuCncl; RptrSchPpr; Chrldr;.

SELK, Clarice A; Everly Comm HS; Everly, IA; Chr; HonRl; Mdrgl; NatlThespSoc; SchMus; SchPl; EdSchPpr; FTA; LetterBsktbl; IMSpt; College; Journalism.

SELKE, Gregory L; Connersville HS; Connersville, IN; 43/371 PresSrCls; HonRl; StuCncl; StuGov; PresSpnCl; SciCl; IMSpt; Purdue Univ; Pharmacy.

SELKO, John T; Lincoln East HS; Lincoln, NE; LetterBsktbl; LetterFtbl; LetterTrk; U Of Nebraska; Dentistry.

SELL, Christine M; Streator Twp HS; Streator, IL; 1/385 HonRl; NHS; StuCncl; StuGov; St Teresa College; Dance.

SELL, Cindy S; Triton Jr Sr HS; Bourbon, IN; ALAGirlsSt; Band; Chr; DrlTm; MrchBnd; NHS; SchMus; StuCncl; 4-H; FTA; College; Special Education.

SELL, Linda L; Concordia Academy; Eagan, MN; 13/51 Chr; HonRl; NHS; College; Vocation.

SELL, Michelle K; Burlington HS; Middletown, IA; 4/501 AFS; Band; Chr; CncrtBnd; HonRl; ModUN; NHS; Orch; PresStuCncl; SecYthFlsp; LetterTennis; DARAwd; College; Music.

SELL, Sandra L; Weeping Water HS; Weeping Water, NE; 16/40 Chrs; HonRl; SchPl; TchrAde; FHA; Trk; Army; Nursing.

SELL, Walter E; Pioneer HS; Royal Center, IN; 2/114 PresFrshCls; ALBoysSt; Band; ChrhWkr; HonRl; NHS; SchMus; 4-H; Trk;.

SELLAND, Mark A; Magic City Campus HS; Minot, ND; 68/660 ALBoysSt; HonRl; NHS; StuCncl; GerCl; LetterFtbl; IMSpt; Univ Of Nd; Medicine.

SELLARS, Renee D; Cobden Community HS; Cobden, IL; 2/43 Chr; HonRl; OffAde; SchMus; SctActv; StuCncl; YthFlsp; EdYrBk; University; Vet.

SELLE, David M; Fair Grove HS; Strafford, MO; SchPl; FTA; SpnCl; SciCl; IMSpt; Smsu Springfield Mo; Speech Theatre.

SELLEN, John M; East HS; Sioux City, IA; 4/346 ALBoysSt; Chr; Chrs; ChrhWkr; HonRl; SchMus; StuCncl; RptrSchPpr; LetterWrstlng; IMSpt; Coll ; Law.

SELLERS, Cynthia J; Rossville Alvin HS; Alvin, IL; 5/39 SecSophCls; ChrhWkr; HonRl; NHS; Yrbk; SchPpr; FTA; GAA; IMSpt; BttyCrckrAwd; Jr Coll Then College; English Teacher.

SELLERS, Dianna; Mt Vernon Senior HS; Mt Vernon, IN; 7/235 HonRl; Mdrgl; NHS; SchMus; SchPl; FshEdYrbk; SpnCl; PpCl; Prudue Univ; Pharmacy.

SELLERS, Patricia J; Corunna HS; Corunna, MI; 1/200 Band; ChrhWkr; CncrtBnd; HonRl; MrchBnd; NHS; PepBnd; SpnCl; JCAwd; PresAwd; University; Music Ed.

SELLEY, Michael L; St Marys HS; Saginaw, MI; TrsFrshCls; CmntyWkr; HonRl; NatlMeritSF; PolWkr; Michigan St Univ; Art.

SELLHAUSEN, Stephen; Menomonee Falls HS; Menomonee Falls, WI; PresSophCls; ALBoysSt; HonRl; NHS; StuCncl; Trk; Wrstlng; AmLegAwd;.

SELLHORN, Mary D; Tecumseh Public HS; Tecumseh, NE; 3/58 Chrs; HonRl; LbryAde; NHS; SchMus; Teen; Yrbk; Bsktbl; College; Business Admin.

SELLHORST, Janice M; Howells HS; Howells, NE; 11/42 Band; CncrtBnd; HonRl; MrchBnd; SchPl; PpCl; Chrldr; Lincoln Sch Of Commerce; Medical Secty.

SELLIN, Kathleen A; Waupaca HS; Waupaca, WI; 1/154 ALAGirlsSt; TreasBand; Chr; ChrhWkr; Mdrgl; SecNHS; NatlMeritCmnd; Quill&Scroll; SchPpr; DARAwd; Lawrence University; Music.

SELLMAN, James C; Metamora Township HS; Metamora, IL; CncrtBnd; HonRl; JrNHS; MrchBnd; NHS; NatlMeritSF; SchMus; SctActv; RptrSchPpr; LetterTrk;.

SELLMEYER, Lisa K; Cameron HS; Cameron, MO; 27/140 Chrs; ChrhWkr; HonRl; JrNHS; NHS; NatlThespSoc; Tennis; Chrldr; IMSpt; PPFtbl; Rockhurst; Journalism.

SELLNER, Bradley; Saint Marys HS; Sleepyeye, MN; 5/85 ChrhWkr; HonRl; NHS; LatCl; PpCl; Bemidji State; Business Management Marketin.

SELLNER, Carol H; St Marys HS; Sleepy Eye, MN; 4/84 Band; Chrs; CncrtBnd; LbryAde; MrchBnd; TchrAde; SchPpr; GAA; St Cloud State Clg; Accounting.

SELLNER, Marjorie C; Saint Marys HS; Sleepy Eye, MN; 1/84 ALAGirlsSt; SecBand; Chrs; HonRl; NHS; SchPl; Sec4-H; LatCl; 4-HAwd; LionAwd; Mankato St Clg; Music Teacher.

SELLNER, Susan A; St Marys HS; Comfrey, MN; 11/84 Chrs; SchPl; TchrAde; GAA; Vocational Schl; Legal Secretary.

SELLON, Terri; Osage Community HS; Nora Springs, IA; 4/157 HonRl; NHS; FFA; RotaryAwd; Iowa State U; Chemistry.

SELLS, Donna J; West Side Sr HS; Gary, IN; CmntyWkr; CncrtBnd; HonRl; JrNHS; MrchBnd; NHS; Quill&Scroll; RptrSchPpr; LatCl; MthCl; Univ; Journalism.

SELLS, Jeffery S; Ida HS; Petersburg, MI; Chr; HonRl; NatlThespSoc; RedCrAde; SchMus; SchPl; RptrYrbk; SptEdSchPpr; Wrstlng; Monroe Co & Comm Clg; English.

SELLS, Nancy J; Clio HS; Clio, MI; VPFrshCls; VPSophCls; VPJrCls; HonRl; NHS; SchPl; StuCncl; FrCl; Chrldr; IMSpt; U Of Mi Coll; Work For Un.

SELMECKI, James S; Pacelli HS; Austin, MN; HonRl; SctActv; SchPpr; MthCl; LetterBsktbl; LetterGlf; ChmnIMSpt; Univ Of Minnesota; Multi Millionaire.

SELMECKI, Jon; Pacelli HS; Austin, MN; HonRl; IMSpt; Univ Of Mn; Pre Law.

SELNESS, Mark R; Spring Grove Public HS; Minneapolis, MN; 6/48 TrsFrshCls; TrsSophCls; VPJrCls; ALBoysSt; Chr; HonRl; NHS; PolWkr; StuGov; 4-H; Univ Mn; Cpa.

SELTZER, Ann M; Goodrich HS; Grand Blanc, MI; 5/77 TrsJrCls; TrsSrCls; HonRl; NHS; SchPl; StuCncl; RptrSchPpr; LetterBsbl; LetterBsktbl; CaptChrldr; GAA; Central Michigan Univ; Social Work.

SELVES, Sharon K; Granton Public HS; Granton, WI; 2/26 PresFrshCls; TreasBand; TreasChrs; CncrtBnd; HonRl; MrchBnd; SchMus; TchrAde; Yrbk; FHA; Trade Sch; Business Management.

SELVEY, Thelma E; Aurora R 8 HS; Aurora, MO; 9/150 Band; CncrtBnd; HonRl; MrchBnd; NHS; PepBnd; StuGov; FBLA; FHA; Chrldr; GAA; Nursing School; Anesthesiology.

SELVIG, Loren L; Blue Earth HS; Blue Earth, MN; 30/106 PresSrCls; ALBoysSt; ChrhWkr; HonRl; NHS; StuCncl; Bsbl; Bsktbl; Ftbl; CitAwd; Northewestern Clg; Accounting.

SELZER, Jerry D; Schuyler Central HS; Schuyler, NE; VPSrCls; HonRl; StuGov; RptrYrbk; Yrbk; LetterBsbl; LetterBsktbl; LetterFtbl; LetterTrk; U Of Ne; Architecture.

SEM, Claude D; Powers Lake Public HS; Powers Lake, ND; 9/30 PresFrshCls; Band; ChrhWkr; CncrtBnd; HonRl; StuCncl; YthFlsp; PresFFA; Bsbl; Bsktbl; Nd S U Bottineau; Veterinary.

SEM, Merlyn J; Powers Lake HS; Powers Lake, ND; SchPl; TchrAde; YthFlsp; FFA; PpCl; Bsktbl; Ftbl; Trk; IMSpt; College; Wildlife Managment.

SEMENIUK, Camille G; Homewood Flossmoor HS; Flossmoor, IL; AFS; ChrhWkr; HonRl; NatlFornLg; NatlMeritSchl; NatlThespSoc; PolWkr; SchAde; SchMus;.

SEMISCH, Douglas R; Lakeview HS; Decatur, IL; 20/200 Band; CncrtBnd; HonRl; MrchBnd; NHS; SctActv; RptrSchPpr; KeyCl; GerCl; SciCl; CaptBsktbl; Swmmng; LetterTennis; Creighton Univ; Law.

SEMPEK, Janice M; Genoa Public HS; Genoa, NE; Chrs; HonRl; RptrSchPpr; FHA; PpCl;.

SEMPEK, Susan A; Genoa Public HS; Genoa, NE; 6/43 Chrs; HonRl; FHA; PpCl; IMSpt;.

SEMPERT, Bekki S; St Joseph Sr HS; St Joseph, MI; Band; CncrtBnd; MrchBnd; NHS; Orch; SchMus; SchPl; SctActv; StuCncl; YthFlsp; 4-H; SpnCl; College; Accounting.

SEMPLE, Paul E; Newton HS; West Liberty, IL; Aud/Vis; ChrhWkr; HonRl; JA; LbryAde; StuGov; YthFlsp; CivCl; 4-H; IMSpt; 4-HAwd; College; Professional.

SEMPLE, Valerie A; Rolling Meadows HS; Rolling Meadows, IL; 9/546 Chr; ChrhWkr; HonRl; HospAde; NHS; PresQuill&Scroll; EdYrBk; Yrbk; FrCl; Purdue University; Pharmacy.

SEMRAU, Barbara A; Marinette Sr HS; Marinette, WI; Band; Chrs; ChrhWkr; OffAde; SctActv; StuCncl; LetterBsktbl; LetterTrk; GAA; IMSpt; 4-HAwd; Lake Land Medical Dental Acad; Med Asst.

SEMROSKA, Milesa M; Edgemont HS; Edgemont, SD; SecAFS; Chrs; DrlTm; HonRl; SchPl; StuCncl; YthFlsp; EdYrBk; PpCl; Chrldr; College.

SENAC, Denise E; Kapaun Mt Carmel HS; Wichita, KS; CmntyWkr; HonRl; PolWkr; SchMus; College; Law.

SENAGORE, Anthony; Austin Prep; Grosse Pte Farm, MI; 6/145 HonRl; NHS; Quill&Scroll; EdSchPpr; SciCl; Bsbl; Mich Univ; Medicine.

SENART, Michael E; Romulus HS; Romulus, MI; 72/295 HonRl; FrCl; LetterTennis; Lake Superior State College; Management.

SENDEK, Daniel S; Kimball HS; Royal Oak, MI; HonRl; NHS; Quill&Scroll; RptrSchPpr; SchPpr; Clge; Medicine.

SENDELBACH, Betty J; Arcadia HS; Cochrane, WI; 25/99 CncrtBnd; HonRl; LbryAde; MrchBnd; NHS; PepBnd; SchPl; Yrbk; RptrSchPpr; Technical School; Nurse.

SENDZIK, Judy; Goodman HS; Goodman, WI; 2/21 CncrtBnd; HonRl; NHS; PepBnd; StuCncl; TchrAde; EdYrBk; SchPpr; PpCl; Vocational School; Accountant.

SENECZKO, Cynthia L; Harold L Richards HS; Oak Lawn, IL; 17/977 Chrl; ChrhWkr; HonRl; NatlMeritCmnd; TreasSctActv; FrCl; Trk; GAA; College; Professional.

SENF, Barbara; Trenton Senior HS; Trenton, MO; LbryAde; MrchBnd; NHS; StuCncl; PpCl; Ftbl; Tennis; Trk; Chrldr; GAA; Evangel Coll; Math.

SENFF, Dean; Hampton Public HS; Hampton, NE; VPJrCls; Chr; Chrs; ChrhWkr; SchPl; StuGov; TchrAde; FFA; Bsktbl; IMSpt; Trade School; Farmer.

SENG, Daniel P; South Milwaukee HS; South Milwaukee, WI; LetterFtbl; LetterTrk; LetterWrstlng; IMSpt; College.

SENGER, Bonita I; Anamoose HS; Orrin, ND; 1/19 VPFrshCls; Chrs; HonRl; NatlThespSoc; SchPl; StuCncl; StuGov; EdYrBk; RptrSchPpr; PpCl; VFWAwd; Mary College; Special Education.

SENGSTOCK, Paul W; Bloom Township HS; Steger, IL; 100/903 ChrhWkr; CncrtBnd; HonRl; MrchBnd; NHS; Orch; PepBnd; College; Electrical Engineerin.

SENIUTA, Orest S; Gordon Tech HS; Chicago, IL; 19/584 SecTrsFrshCls; HonRl; StuGov; FrCl; PpCl; SciCl; Tennis; College; Medicine.

SENKA, Elizabeth A; Kennedy St Paul HS; Chicago, IL; PresSrCls; Chrs; HonRl; StuCncl; TchrAde; Yrbk; 4-H; PpCl; GAA; IMSpt; Business School.

SENN, Mary B; Campbellsport HS; Campbellsport, WI; VPBand; CncrtBnd; HonRl; MrchBnd; NHS; PepBnd; StuCncl; VP4-H; KiwanAwd; Univ Of Wisconsin; Home Economics.

SENN, Teresa M; Valley Falls HS; Valley Falls, KS; 5/52 Band; Chrs; HonRl; NHS; OffAde; SchPl; TchrAde; RptrYrbk; RptrSchPpr; LetterTrk; Clarks Business Schl; Accounting.

SENNEFF, Rosemary E; Thomson HS; Mt Carroll, IL; 7/40 Aud/Vis; Band; Chrs; HonRl; NHS; SchMus; VPFHA; SecFTA; Bsktbl; GAA; College; Journalism.

SENNENMOSER, Rosanne M; West Platte HS; Weston, MO; AFS; Chr; Chrs; HonRl; ModUN; NatlMeritCmnd; TchrAde; DanFAwd; DARAwd; RotaryAwd; College; History Teacher.

SENNHENN, Jacalyn S; Columbus HS; Columbus, WI; Band; Chrs; Mdrgl; MrchBnd; NatlFornLg; NHS; PepBnd; SchMus; GAA; PPFtbl; U Of Wi Madison; Engineering.

SENNOTT, Bonita S; Glenbard No HS; Glendale Hts, IL; 9/371 Band; CncrtBnd; HonRl; MrchBnd; NatlThespSoc; OffAde; PepBnd; SchMus; SchPl; SchPpr; De Paul University; Professional Musician.

SENSENBAUGH, Sue E; Kingsley HS; Kingsley, MI; SecJrCls; Band; Chr; ChrhWkr; HonRl; RptrYrbk; Yrbk; FHA; LetterTrk; GAA; Bible College; Biological Science.

SENSION, Mark S; Elmwood HS; Elmwood, WI; Aud/Vis; Chr; CmntyWkr; HospAde; SchMus; StuCncl; FFA; LetterFtbl; IMSpt; College.

SENSTAD, Allen L; Jefferson HS; Carlos, MN; 39/330 ChrhWkr; HonRl; ModUN; NatlFornLg; NHS; NatlMeritCmnd; NatlThespSoc; SchMus; SchPl; SchPpr; U Of Mn; Law.

SENTER, Denise A; Crispus Attucks HS; Indianapolis, IN; SecFrshCls; PresJrCls; Chr; ChrhWkr; HonRl; NHS; Orch; SchMus; StuCncl; RptrYrbk; DARAwd; College; Medicine.

SENYK, Borys S; Imaculate Concptn UkranianHS; Detroit, MI; 2/34 Aud/Vis; HonRl; NHS; NatlMeritCmnd; Yrbk; University; Elec Engr.

SENYK, Roma M; Ukrainian Catholic HS; Detroit, MI; Chr; HonRl; NHS; RptrSchPpr; Wayne State Univ.

SENYK, Stephen G; Hill Murray HS; St Paul, MN; ChrhWkr; HonRl; YthFnd; RptrSchPpr; GerCl; LetterBsktbl; Ftbl; Trk; IMSpt;.

SENZIG, Marie S; Mauston Area HS; Lyndon Station, WI; Band; CmntyWkr; CncrtBnd; HonRl; MrchBnd; NHS; PepBnd; RptrSchPpr; LatCl; Nursing Schl; Nurse.

SEPKA, Tom; St Patrick HS; Chicago, IL; HonRl; SciCl; IMSpt; Iit; Electronics.

SEPPALA, Bryan R; Stewartville HS; Stewartsville, MN; 11/98 HonRl; SchPl; SctActv; TchrAde; RptrSchPpr; SptEdSchPpr; Bsbl; Ftbl; U Of Mn; Chemical Engineering.

SEPPALA, John W; Lawton HS; Lawton, MI; 10/53 Band; Chr; ChrhWkr; HonRl; PepBnd; SchMus; TchrAde; CaptTrk; Kvcc Them Wmu; Music Education.

SEPRODI, John A; Schulte HS; Terre Haute, IN; 16/96 ALBoysSt; Chr; HonRl; StuCncl; University; Professional.

SEPRODI, Mary K; Schulte HS; Terre Haute, IN; 9/88 VPSrCls; ChrhWkr; CmntyWkr; HonRl; IntrClCncl; JA; OffAde; PolWkr; SctActv; StuCncl; StuGov; Teen; RptrSchPpr; SptEdSchPpr; Indiana State University; Special Educ.

SEPULVEDA, Eva; St Augustine HS; Chicago, IL; VPSrCls; HonRl; JrNHS; NHS; SchAde; SchPl; StuCncl; EdYrBk; Yrbk; JCAwd; De Paul U; Pharmacist.

SERA, Arleen K; Lake View HS; Chicago, IL; Chrs; HonRl; TchrAde; FrCl; MthCl; De Paul Univ; Accounting.

SERBAN, Daniel E; St Josephs HS; S Bend, IN; 29/240 HonRl; NHS; NatlMeritSF; StuGov; LetterFtbl; CaptWrstlng; Univ Of Notre Dame; Lawyer.

SERBINSKI, Debra L; West Iron County HS; Stambaugh, MI; Band; NHS; StuCncl; RptrYrbk; SptEdSchPpr; LatCl; PpCl; LetterTrk; Chrldr; SecGAA; College; Physical Education.

SERBOUSEK, Mark W; West Holt HS; Atkinson, NE; Band; HonRl; NHS; StuCncl; Yrbk; Bsktbl; CaptFtbl; Trk; Kearney St Coll.

SERBUS, Teri L; Forest Lake Sr HS; Forest Lake, MN; Chr; HonRl; FHA; FrCl; PpCl; GAA; College; Professional.

SERDAR, David; Farmington Dist 324 HS; Trivoli, IL; 5/150 Band; MrchBnd; NHS; StuCncl; 4-H; SciCl; Bsbl; Bsktbl; Ftbl; Trk; JETSAwd; College; Electrical Engineering.

SERDAR, Erin M; Warren Township HS; Gurnee, IL; VPSophCls; Chr; HonRl; MrchBnd; SchMus; StuCncl; 4-H; FrCl; College; Physical Therapy.

SEREIKA, Mark J; Brother Rice HS; Oak Lawn, IL; HonRl; NHS; SctActv; RptrSchPpr; SptEdSchPpr; PpCl; Univ Of Illinois; Engineering.

SERETNY, Andrew W; Scecina Memorial HS; Indianapolis, IN; ChrhWkr; CmntyWkr; HonRl; SctActv; YthFnd; 4-H; CaptBsbl; Wrstlng; CchngActv; 4-HAwd; Purdue Univ; Mechanical Engineer.

SERGO, Liisa M; Wautoma HS; Redgranite, WI; TrsFrshCls; TrsSophCls; TrsJrCls; ALAGirlsSt; Band; HonRl; NHS; NatlThespSoc; RptrYrbk; Chrldr; College; Physical Therapy.

SERIE, Cindy L; Hamilton HS; Hamilton, MI; 8/125 VPSophCls; HonRl; NHS; TchrAde; YthFlsp; RptrSchPpr; GerCl; PpCl; CaptChrldr; PPFtbl; Ferris St Clg; Radiologic Tech.

SERNETT, Kathleen A; Laurens Comm HS; Lourens, IA; 5/52 PresFrshCls; SecJrCls; PresSrCls; Band; HonRl; Mdrgl; NHS; StuCncl; GerCl; LetterBsktbl; College; Psychology.

SEROOGY, Kim B; West Depere HS; De Pere, WI; 1/200 HonRl; NHS; SciCl; Bsktbl; Glf; IMSpt; College Uw Eau Claire; Biology.

SERRANO, Joaquin P; La Crosse HS; La Crosse, KS; HonRl; ModUN; NHS; RptrYrbk; Yrbk; SpnCl; Univ Of Kansas; Medicine.

SERRITELLA, Laura L; Harold L Richards HS; Oak Lawn, IL; 54/1084 HonRl; JrNHS; NHS; TchrAde; PpCl; KiwanAwd; Evangelical Sch Of Nursing.

SERSCH, Randall F; Black Hawk HS; Apple River, IL; 7/81 PresFrshCls; VPSophCls; HonRl; SctActv; StuCncl; FFA; LetterBsbl; LetterBsktbl; CaptFtbl; LetterTrk;.

SERSHEN, Daniel J; North HS; Fargo, ND; Chr; Chrl; NatlFornLg; NHS; NatlThespSoc; SchMus; SchPl; StuCncl; Ftbl; Swmmng; Wrstlng; College; Broadcasting.

SERUP, Don L; Woodruff HS; Peoria, IL; 31/290 Band; CncrtBnd; HonRl; MrchBnd; SctActv; KeyCl; GerCl; Ftbl; Glf; IMSpt; University.

SERVA, Raylene M; Lourdes HS; Chicago, IL; ChrhWkr; LbryAde; TchrAde; College; Nursing.

SERVAIS, Cheryl A; Luxemburg Casco HS; New Franken, WI; 12/170 ALAGirlsSt; HonRl; NatlSciFnd; SchMus; SchPl; StuCncl; StuGov; Yrbk; DARAwd; CitAwd; Uw Whitewater; Elem Ed.

SERVAIS, Stephen B; Union HS; Franksville, WI; 1/250 VPFrshCls; PresSophCls; PresJrCls; ALBoysSt; ChrhWkr; HonRl; NHS; StuCncl; StuGov; 4-H; College; Engineer.

SERVENT, Kim; Three Lakes HS; Rhinelander, WI; TrsSophCls; AFS; ChrhWkr; CmntyWkr; HospAde; RedCrAde; StuCncl; YthFlsp; FBLA; CitAwd;.

SERVEY, Beth E; Decatur Central HS; Indianapolis, IN; 4/358 HonRl; NHS; TchrAde; Marian College; Education.

SERVI, Lawrence J; Highland Pk HS; Highland Pk, IL; Band; CncrtBnd; MrchBnd; NatlMeritSF; PepBnd; SchMus; LatCl; MthCl; SciCl; Northwestern Univ; Biomedical Engineering.

SERVINE, Beverly D; Emerson Hubbard HS; Waterbury, NE; 4/55 Chr; Chrs; LbryAde; SchPl; SpnCl; College; Professional.

SERVISS, Arnell B; Mc Pherson Senior HS; Mc Pherson, KS; 30/228 ChrhWkr; HonRl; SciCl; Kansas St U; Gen Engineering.

SERVOSS, Michael L; Britton Macon Area HS; Britton, MI; 3/46 PresFrshCls; ALBoysSt; HonRl; NHS; SchPl; StuCncl; TchrAde; EdYrBk; Bsbl; Ftbl; Eastern Mich Univ; Physical Education.

SERWISE, Cheryl A; Farmington East HS; Trivoli, IL; 3/131 HonRl; NHS; OffAde; RptrSchPpr; SchPpr; FHA; GAA; Business Secretarial.

SESKO, Ann M; Sacred Heart HS; Dearborn, MI; VPJrCls; HonRl; HospAde; NHS; RedCrAde; StuCncl; StuGov; EdYrBk; PresFNA; PresFrCl; Swmmng; DARAwd; Univ Of Mich; Medical Doctor.

SESSING, Brenda M; Jefferson HS; Rockford, IL; 34/363 HonRl; HospAde; TchrAde; Rock Valley Jr College; Exec Secretary.

SESSIONS, Charles E; Farmer City Mansfield HS; Farmer City, IL; 19/74 ALBoysSt; NHS; 4-H; FFA; LetterBsktbl; Ftbl; LetterTrk; AmLegAwd; DanFAwd; 4-HAwd; Kansas St Univ; Agriculture.

SESSO, Cindy A; Taft HS; Chicago, IL; 24/843 HonRl; LitMag; LbryAde; NHS; TchrAde; SpnCl; Mac Cormac Jr College; Court Reporter.

SESTAK, Vicki A; Sacred Heart Academy; Springfield, IL; 6/147 Chr; ChrhWkr; CmntyWkr; HonRl; IntrClCncl; NHS; PolWkr; Sdlty; StuCncl; StuGov; SchPpr; LatCl; MthCl; Junior College; Nursing.

SESTERHENN, Steven E; Libertyville HS; Libertyville, IL; HonRl; Orch; Loras College; Genetics Research.

SESVOLD, Ann L; Central HS; La Crosse, WI; Chrs; HonRl; HospAde; YthFlsp; Pres4-H; FrCl; PpCl; GAA; 4-HAwd; College; Nursing.

SESVOLD, Karen E; Central HS; La Crosse, WI; 54/530 Chrs; HonRl; JrNHS; NHS; SchPl; StuCncl; VPYthFlsp; RptrSchPpr; VP4-H; FrCl; 4-HAwd; Univ Of Wisconsin; Elem Education.

SETEN, Kelli J; Mahomet Seymour HS; Mahomet, IL; ALAGirlsSt; HonRl; NHS; Quill&Scroll; Yrbk; RptrSchPpr; VP4-H; VPFFA; SciCl; 4-HAwd; U Of Il; Agricultural Comm.

SETHALER, Anne M; Carrollton HS; Carrollton, IL; 4/77 ChrhWkr; CmntyWkr; HonRl; TreasLbryAde; NHS; SecOffAde; FBLA; PpCl; Junior College; Bookkeeper.

SETHNA, Michael P; Alexander Ramsey HS; St Paul, MN; 3/557 NHS; NatlMeritSF; PolWkr; StuCncl; GerCl; MthCl; SciCl; IMSpt; University.

SETINA, Sally S; Joliet West HS; Joliet, IL; Chr; HonRl; NHS; SchPl; StuCncl; Yrbk; FrCl; GAA; Ill State Univ; Business.

SEUBERT, Ronald; Marathon HS; Marathon, WI; 7/100 HonRl; TchrAde; MthCl; Univ Of Wis Wau Claire; Certified Pub Acct.

SEUFERT, Sheila M; Forest Park HS; Ferdinand, IN; ChrhWkr; HonRl; NHS; SchPl; PpCl; LetterTrk; GAA; IMSpt; Notre Dame Univ; Medicine.

SEUFFERLEIN, Paul W; West View HS; Lake City, IA; 11/61 Aud/Vis; Chr; Chrl; Chrs; ChrhWkr; LbryAde; Mdrgl; NHS; PolWkr; SchMus; SchPl; College.

SEVART, Carol M; Kapaun Mt Carmel HS; Wichita, KS; Chrs; CmntyWkr; HonRl; HospAde; SchMus; SchPl; SctActv; GerCl; PpCl; College; Special Education.

SEVCIK, Bruce M; Montgomery HS; Lonsdale, MN; TrsJrCls; Band; Chr; ChrhWkr; CncrtBnd; HonRl; LbryAde; Orch; StuGov; FFA; Business School; Technition.

SEVCIK, James J; Fullerton HS; Fullerton, NE; PresSrCls; HonRl; NHS; StuCncl; SptEdYrbk; LetterBsktbl; LetterTrk; CitAwd; Nebraska Wesleyan U; Law Or Athletic Traing.

SEVCIK, Margaret; North Tama Comm HS; Traer, IA; 5/73 TrsFrshCls; ALAGirlsSt; Band; Chrs; MrchBnd; NHS; PepBnd; StuCncl; AmLegAwd; Ia State Univ; Pro.

SEVCIK, Patricia J; Immaculate Heart Of Mary HS; Bellwood, IL; College; Business Administration.

SEVELA, Jeffrey J; Bedford HS; Lambertville, MI; 1/434 HonRl; TreasNHS; NatlMeritSF; PolWkr; Chr; Univ; Natural Sciences.

SEVER, Byron; East Alton Wood River HS; Wood River, IL; 1/275 Band; ChrhWkr; CncrtBnd; HonRl; MrchBnd; NHS; Orch; PepBnd; GerCl; OptClAwd; College; Professional.

SEVER, Sheryl R; Lasalle Peru Twp HS; Peru, IL; 31/490 AFS; Band; CncrtBnd; HonRl; MrchBnd; Orch; PepBnd; SchMus; SpnCl; PpCl; Ill State Univ; English Teacher.

SEVERANCE, Nanci L; Loy Norrix HS; Kalamazoo, MI; Chr; Chrl; Chrs; HonRl; Mdrgl; NHS; Orch; SchMus; YthFlsp; Oberlin Clge; Viola/music.

SEVERE, Kurt A; West Chicago Comm HS; W Chicago, IL; 58/311 HonRl; TchrAde; CivCl; University; Elec Engineering.

SEVERSON, Douglas J; East Monona HS; Soldier, IA; Chr; Chrs; ChrhWkr; HonRl; 4-H; FFA; Bsbl; Bsktbl; College; Agriculture.

SEVERSON, Gregory A; Columbus HS; Columbus, WI; 24/153 ChrhWkr; StuCncl; SciCl; LetterFtbl; Trk; University; Professional.

SEVERSON, Keith A; Ogorman HS; Sioux Falls, SD; Bsbl; CaptBsktbl; CaptFtbl; CaptTrk; University; Major Study.

SEVERSON, Marilyn; Long Prairie HS; Long Prairie, MN; 4/119 ALAGirlsSt; HonRl; MrchBnd; NHS; StuCncl; StuGov; YthFlsp; Chrldr; BauchLmbAwd; St Cloud State Coll; Nursing.

SEVERSON, Steven G; Bonduel Community HS; Cecil, WI; 32/127 ChrhWkr; HonRl; HospAde; IntrClCncl; NatlFornLg; StuCncl; StuGov; RptrSchPpr; SchPpr; Ftbl; Uw Milwau ;pharmacist.

SEVERSON, Tanna K; Argyle HS; Argyle, WI; Chrs; HonRl; OffAde; 4-H; SecFHA; PpCl; Trk; 4-HAwd; Southwest Wisconsin Tech Institute; Sales.

SEVERSON, Thomas; Cal Community HS; Coulter, IA; Band; Chrs; HonRl; Mdrgl; SchPl; YthFlsp; SchPpr; Univ Of Ia; X Ray Technician.

SEVERSON, Tom S; West Salem HS; West Salem, WI; Aud/Vis; Chr; Chrl; Chrs; ChrhWkr; HonRl; SchMus; SchPl; StuCncl; StuGov; University; Agriculture.

SEVERT, Linda; Lincoln HS; Wisconsin Rapids, WI; 44/532 HonRl; NHS; PpCl; SciCl; EldAwd; Medical Institute Of Minn; Veterinary.

SEVIGNY, Nora; Brandon HS; Ortonville, MI; TrsJrCls; HonRl; NHS; OffAde; StuCncl; RptrYrbk; EdSchPpr; Chrldr; PPFtbl;.

SEWARD, Gregory S; Hillsboro HS; Butler, IL; 29/185 HonRl; NatlMeritCmnd; SctActv; 4-H; LetterBsktbl; LetterFtbl; LetterTrk; Macmurray College; Engineering.

SEWARD, Lou; Rockville Consolidated Hs; Rockville, IN; HonRl; 4-H; FHA; LatCl; SpnCl; SciCl; Bsktbl; Trk; GAA; Purdue U; Home Economics Design.

SEWELL, Allen K; Acc HS; Lancaster, KS; 8/92 PresSophCls; HonRl; NHS; NatlMeritCmnd; NatlMeritSchl; StuCncl; RptrYrbk; RptrSchPpr; EdSchPpr; LetterBsktbl; Univ.

SEWELL, Cynthia F; Corunna HS; Vernon, MI; Chr; HonRl; College; Model.

SEWELL, Pamela J; La Plata R Ii HS; Atlanta, MO; 3/33 TrsSophCls; SecJrCls; Band; CncrtBnd; HonRl; MrchBnd; NHS; PepBnd; SchPl; EdSchPpr; 4-H; Bsktbl; DanFAwd; Univ Of Missouri; Business Administration.

SEWING, Brenda; Mt Olive HS; Litchfield, IL; 11/54 TrsJrCls; SecBand; SecChrs; ChrhWkr; HonRl; NHS; Yrbk; FHA; Chrldr; PresGAA; Belleville Area Coll;phys Ther Assist.

SEWING, Linda; Mt Olive Public HS; Litchfield, IL; 6/54 VPSophCls; SecJrCls; VPBand; TreasChrs; ChrhWkr; DrmMjrt; NHS; SchPl; SecStuCncl; VPGAA; Trade Sch;sec.

SEWING, Linda L; Comm HS; Litchfield, IL; 6/54 VPSophCls; SecJrCls; VPBand; TreasChrs; ChrhWkr; DrmMjrt; SecStuCncl; Pres4-H; LetterTrk; VPGAA; Lewis & Clark Jr College; Med Lab Tech.

SEWNIG, Timothy J; Mendel HS; Chicago, IL; 17/180 TrsSophCls; HonRl; IntrClCncl; RptrYrbk; RptrSchPpr; KeyCl; Trk; Wrstlng; IMSpt; AmLegAwd; College; Lawlyer.

SEXTON, Ann M; Crystal Lake Community HS; Crystal Lake, IL; 42/447 Chr; HonRl; Mdrgl; NatlThespSoc; OffAde; SchMus; SchPl; SchPpr; Chrldr; PPFtbl; U Of Iowa; Accountant.

SEXTON, Brett C; Southeast Polk Jr Sr HS; Mitchellville, IA; NHS; SctActv; VPStuCncl; Bsbl; Wrstlng; Univ; Banker.

SEXTON, Deborah V; Porta HS; Tallula, IL; 9/135 HonRl; LbryAde; Mdrgl; MrchBnd; NHS; RptrYrbk; 4-H; IMSpt; DanFAwd; 4-HAwd; Coll; Spanish.

SEXTON, Jerome; New London Sr HS; New London, WI; ALBoysSt; ChrhWkr; HonRl; 4-H; IMSpt; 4-HAwd; JAAwd;.

SEXTON, Mary; Howard Lake Waverly HS; Waverly, MN; 2/88 TrsJrCls; Aud/Vis; HonRl; RptrYrbk; RptrSchPpr; PpCl; Chrldr; GAA; Coll Of St Catherine; Physical Ed.

SEXTON, Michael F; Rochester HS; Rochester, IL; 3/82 Band; CncrtBnd; HonRl; Cornell Univ; Professor Of Medieval History.

SEXTON, Tammy L; Edison Sr HS; East Gary, IN; ChrhWkr; HonRl; Business School; Business.

SEXTON, Virginia A; St Louise De Marillac HS; Glenview, IL; 30/252 Chrl; Chrs; NatlMeritCmnd; SchMus; University; Journalism.

SEXTON, Virginia A; Marillac HS; Glenview, IL; 26/240 Chrl; Chrs; NatlMeritCmnd; SchMus; RptrSchPpr; College; Journalism.

SEYBOLD, Terry; Benkelman HS; Benkelman, NE; VPJrCls; HonRl; OffAde; SctActv; YthFlsp; Yrbk; PpCl; Trk; Chrldr; PresAwd;.

SEYDEL, Dale E; Regina HS; Iowa City, IA; StuCncl; LetterBsbl; LetterBsktbl; LetterFtbl;.

SEYER, Kathleen S; St Pius X HS; Arnold, MO; 26/127 Band; ChrhWkr; CncrtBnd; MrchBnd; PepBnd; SctActv; Coll; Vocation.

SEYER, Melissa L; Lincoln Community HS; Lincoln, IL; NHS; SecNatlThespSoc; FrCl; Illinois St Univ; Communications.

SEYFERT, Cindy K; Claflin HS; Claflin, KS; 1/51 Band; Chrs; CncrtBnd; NHS; StuCncl; FHA; PpCl; LetterBsktbl; LetterTennis; LetterTrk; Univ; Natural Sciences.

SEYFRIED, Philip F; Cardinal Ritter HS; Indianspolis, IN; Chrs; HonRl; NHS; SchMus; SchPl; Ftbl; Wrstlng; Clg; Marine Biologist.

SEYLLER, Michael C; Kewanee HS; Kewanee, IL; 3/200 AFS; ChrhWkr; HonRl; SchMus; SchPl; StuCncl; TchrAde; Teen; KeyCl; GerCl; Bsktbl; Trk; Univ Of Il; Engineering.

SEYMOUR, Cheryl L; John Glenn HS; Westland, MI; 16/673 TrsCncrtBnd; TreasMrchBnd; NHS; NatlMeritSF; PepBnd; SchMus; StuCncl; Yrbk; SchPpr; DARAwd; Wayne St Univ; Medical Tech.

SEYMOUR, Debra A; Greendale HS; Greendale, WI; Chr; HonRl; NHS; StuGov; Yrbk; ChmnPpCl; U F Wis; Home Ec.

SEYMOUR, Julie A; Clinton HS; Clinton, IL; 16/160 Band; Chrs; ChrhWkr; CncrtBnd; HonRl; MrchBnd; NHS; SchMus; SchPl; 4-H; SpnCl; PpCl; College; Special Educ.

SEYMOUR, Linda S; Athens HS; East Leroy, MI; 10/90 ChrhWkr; HonRl; JrNHS; NHS; OffAde; StuCncl; PpCl; Trk; Chrldr; 4-HAwd; Kellogg Community Coll; Med Tech.

SEYMOUR, Patrick E; New Trier East HS; Wilmette, IL; 196/847 Trk; U Of Il; Forest Science.

SEYMOUR, Terri L; Northwestern HS; Mellette, SD; SecTrsJrCls; Band; Chrs; CncrtBnd; HonRl; MrchBnd; PepBnd; SchPl; StuCncl; YthFlsp; College; Phy Ed.

SHABAZ, Susan M; Morton Sr HS; Hammond, IN; 21/529 ChrhWkr; CmntyWkr; HonRl; NHS; Orch; SchMus; TchrAde; Swmmng; College.

SHACKELFORD, Jacqueline R; Stanberry HS; Stanberry, MO; 10/47 Chr; HonRl; HospAde; LbryAde; NatlMeritSchl; TchrAde; FTA; Clge.

SHACKELFORD, James L; Castle HS; Newburgh, IN; ALBoysSt; Band; CncrtBnd; HonRl; MrchBnd; NHS; PepBnd; SchMus; KeyCl; Purdue; Electrical Engineer.

SHACKLEY, Connie M; Streator Twp HS; Streator, IL; VPJrCls; ChrhWkr; CmntyWkr; HonRl; NHS; StuCncl; GerCl; SciCl; College; Medicine.

SHACKTER, Eric R; Glendale HS; Springfield, MO; VPFrshCls; PresSophCls; PresJrCls; PresSrCls; HonRl; NatlFornLg; NatlMeritSF; ROTC; Wrstlng; BttyCrckrAwd; College; Medicine.

SHADDEN, Carl C; Eddyville Comm HS; Eddyville, IA; 1/65 Aud/Vis; Chr; Chrs; ChrhWkr; HonRl; TchrAde; LetterBsktbl; LetterTrk; College; Physics.

SHAFER, Cynthia M; Saline HS; Saline, MI; HonRl; Bsktbl; GAA; College; Professional.

SHAFER, Daniel L; North Greene HS; Hillview, IL; Band; ChrhWkr; CncrtBnd; DrlTm; MrchBnd; Orch; PepBnd; YthFlsp; 4-H; CitAwd; Trade Schl; Pro.

SHAFER, Frank E; Saint Edmond HS; Fort Dodge, IA; 7/114 VPJrCls; HonRl; JA; ModUN; NHS; SchPl; StuCncl; EdYrBk; SpnCl; Bsktbl; Ftbl; Trk; Creighton University; Biology.

SHAFER, Kerri A; Laf Co C 1 HS; Higginsville, MO; SecSrCls; Band; HonRl; JA; RedCrAde; LetterSwmmng; LetterTrk; Chrldr; GAA; College; Commercial Artist.

SHAFER, Mark A; Rantoul Township HS; Rantoul, IL; 49/398 Band; ChrhWkr; CmntyWkr; CncrtBnd; DrmMjrt; HonRl; JrNHS; NHS; Orch; PepBnd; SchMus; StuCncl; Univ Of Ill; Math.

SHAFER, Melissa A; Fairfield HS; Fairfield, IA; ChrhWkr; HonRl; YthFlsp; FNA; SpnCl; College; Veterinarian.

SHAFER, Nancy A; Holbrook Public HS; Holbrook, NE; 1/13 SecFrshCls; PresSophCls; SecJrCls; Band; Chr; ChrhWkr; CncrtBnd; HonRl; LbryAde; MrchBnd; PepBnd; SchMus; StuCncl; TchrAde; Yrbk; College; Nutrition.

SHAFER, Timothy P; Gering HS; Gering, NE; Band; Chrs; DrmMjrt; HonRl; PepBnd; SchMus; SctActv; StuCncl; GerCl; GodCntryAwd; Ne W Coll; Psychology.

SHAFER, Vivian C; Chippewa Falls Sr HS; Jim Falls, WI; 1/351 AFS; ModUN; PresNatlFornLg; NHS; NatlMeritCmnd; NatlThespSoc; SchPl; FrCl; AmLegAwd; BauchLmbAwd; University; Medicine.

SHAFFER, Betty; Arapahoe Public HS; Edison, NE; 6 Chrs; ChrhWkr; CmntyWkr; HonRl; SchPl; SchPpr; 4-H; PpCl; GAA; College; Teaching Spanish.

SHAFFER, Carol J; Shelbyville HS; Shelbyville, IL; 7/135 CncrtBnd; MrchBnd; NHS; SchMus; SchPl; YthFlsp; Yrbk; 4-H; PpCl; Il Wesleyan Univ; Theatre.

SHAFFER, Charles W; Kinmundy Alma HS; Kinmundy, IL; TrsSophCls; PresSrCls; Band; HonRl; Pres4-H; PresFFA; LetterBsktbl; CchngActv; DanFAwd; 4-HAwd; Kaskaskia Jr College; Farmer.

SHAFFER, Cynthia B; Mankato West HS; North Mankato, MN; 35/281 Chr; ChrhWkr; CncrtBnd; DrlTm; HonRl; NHS; Orch; SchMus; StuCncl; PpCl; St Cloud State Coll; Spec Ed.

SHAFFER, Denise C; Whiteland Comm HS; New Whiteland, IN; 39/215 Band; CncrtBnd; DrlTm; HonRl; MrchBnd; TchrAde; 4-H; FBLA;.

SHAFFER, George F; West Washington HS; Milltown, IN; 5/86 PresSrCls; HonRl; StuCncl; 4-H; FFA; LatCl; Bsbl; Bsktbl; CaptFtbl; Trk; Indiana Central Univ; Marine Biology.

SHAFFER, Kimbra A; Du Quoin HS; Du Quoin, IL; 4/145 PresFrshCls; VPSophCls; DrmMjrt; HonRl; StuCncl; Twrl; Yrbk; FTA; SpnCl; University Of Illinois.

SHAFFER, Nancy; Udall HS; Udall, KS; 4/22 Band; Chrs; CncrtBnd; DrlTm; HonRl; SchMus; SchPl; RptrSchPpr; EdSchPpr; FHA; Patricia Stevans Ne; Legal Secretary.

SHAFFER, Rebecca J; Nevada HS; Nevada, MO; 67/173 SpnCl; Marketing.

SHAFFER, Richard S; Camden Frontier HS; Hillsdale, MI; 1/44 HonRl; SchMus; SchPl; TchrAde; FFA; LetterBsktbl; LetterFtbl; CaptTrk; IMSpt; BauchLmbAwd; Vocation.

SHAFFER, Terina K; Junction City Sr HS; Junction City, KS; 30/309 Chr; HonRl; NHS; SchMus; TchrAde; SecPpCl; LetterTennis; College; Animal Health.

SHAFFER, Twyla; Culver Community HS; Culver, IN; 14/110 Band; HonRl; MrchBnd; NHS; StuCncl; YthFlsp; EdYrBk; FFA; Trk; Chrldr; Purdue Univ; Med Tech.

SHAFFER, Vicky L; Mt Vernon HS; Bluford, IL; Band; Chr; Chrs; ChrhWkr; HonRl; HospAde; NHS; PepBnd; Teen; SpnCl; College.

SHAFFER, William E; Central Of Burden HS; Atlanta, KS; 12/54 TrsFrshCls; Band; CncrtBnd; HonRl; MrchBnd; PepBnd; SchPl; StuCncl; FFA; LetterBsbl; LetterBsktbl; LetterFtbl; LetterTrk; College; Engineer.

SHAFRANSKI, Nancy A; Whitefish Bay HS; Milwaukee, WI; 21/340 HonRl; NHS; NatlMeritCmnd; PolWkr; TchrAde; FTA; VPGerCl; College; Political Science.

SHAFT, Beverly J; Bluffton HS; Bluffton, IN; SctActv; YthFlsp; LatCl; Univ; Accountant.

SHAGENE, Beth A; Cass City HS; Cass City, MI; 4/150 ChrhWkr; CmntyWkr; NHS; StuGov; College; Commercial Art.

SHAGER, Kevin L; Blackhawk HS; South Wayne, WI; Band; CmntyWkr; CncrtBnd; HonRl; MrchBnd; PepBnd; 4-H; FFA; LetterBsktbl; LetterFtbl; Vocational; Farming.

SHAHEEN, Kenneth W; De La Salle Collegiate HS; Grosse Pte Pk, MI; CmntyWkr; HonRl; SchMus; Bsktbl; IMSpt; Univ Mi;md.

SHAHIN, Richard P; Midland HS; Midland, MI; PresFrshCls; PresSrCls; IntrClCncl; NatlMeritFnl; NatlMeritSF; StuCncl; RptrSchPpr; EdSchPpr; SchPpr; FrCl; Univ; Law.

SHAHIN, Ric P; Midland HS; Midland, MI; Band; ChrhWkr; JA; NatlMeritFnl; PolWkr; StuCncl; StuGov; FrCl; College; Law.

SHAIN, Barry I; Ida Crown HS; Chicago, IL; 16/71 HonRl; ModUN; NHS; NatlMeritSF; RptrYrbk; RptrSchPpr; University; Professional.

SHAIN, Pamela A; Freeburg HS; Freeburg, IL; 8/124 HonRl; LbryAde; NHS; NatlMeritCmnd; TchrAde; RptrYrbk; SecFHA; FTA; College; Professional.

SHALDA, Ann M; Glen Lake HS; Empire, MI; 3/60 Chrs; HonRl; NHS; Quill&Scroll; SchPl; TchrAde; RptrYrbk; EdYrBk; FTA; FrCl; PpCl; Chrldr; GAA; Central Michigan Univ; Home Economist.

SHALINSKY, Debra L; Shawnee Mission South HS; Overland Park, KS; CmntyWkr; HonRl; PolWkr; SctActv; StuCncl; EdSchPpr; SecSpnCl; SciCl; PresAwd; Univ; Social Sci.

SHALLA, Rebecca A; Highland HS; Riverside, IA; HonRl; PpCl; Chrldr; Kirkwood Community; Secretarial Sciences.

SHALLBETTER, Keith D; St Patrick HS; Chicago, IL; 53/377 HonRl; SctActv; IMSpt; Northwestern Univ ;law.

SHALLENBERGER, Ralph E; Clinton HS; Clinton, IL; 49/189 HonRl; NatlThespSoc; SchMus; SchPl; SctActv; StuCncl; YthFlsp; Bsbl; LetterFtbl; LetterWrstlng; IMSpt; Knox College; Theater.

SHALLOW, Laura; Mother Mc Auley HS; Chicago, IL; 35/474 ChrhWkr; HonRl; NHS; RedCrAde; TchrAde; RptrSchPpr; SchPpr; FTA; SpnCl; De Paul Univ; Business.

SHALOWITZ, Deborah H; New Trier West HS; Glencoe, IL; 47/700 ChrhWkr; HonRl; LitMag; NatlMeritCmnd; SchMus; StuGov; FrCl; Univ; Attorney Of Law.

SHALOWITZ, Nancy; New Trier West Hs; Wimmetka, IL; 55 NatlFornLg; PolWkr; SecStuCncl; StuGov; RptrYrbk; FrCl; SciCl;.

SHALZ, Mary; Usd#406 HS; Wathena, KS; 8/34 Chrs; HonRl; LbryAde; Mdrgl; EdYrBk; 4-H; SpnCl; PpCl; Chrldr; 4-HAwd; St Mary College;med Tech.

SHAMBAUGH, Clarenda S; Cerro Gordo HS; Cerro Gordo, IL; 7/78 Chrs; HonRl; OffAde; SchPl; StuCncl; TchrAde; RptrSchPpr; SptEdSchPpr; FFA; SpnCl; Ftbl; Trk; AmLegAwd; University; Veterinarian.

SHAMP, Mary L; St Anthony Village HS; Minneapolis, MN; 21/192 PresJrCls; TrsSrCls; AFS; ChrhWkr; DrmMjrt; NHS; SchPl; StuCncl; VPPpCl; PPFtbl; U Of Mn; Nursing.

SHANAHAN, Jeffrey M; Berlin HS; Berlin, WI; 22/175 ALBoysSt; Band; HonRl; KeyCl; LetterFtbl; IMSpt; Ripon College; History.

SHANDROSS, Richard A; Mather HS; Chicago, IL; 26/442 Aud/Vis; HonRl; JA; LitMag; NHS; NatlMeritSF; SchAde; SchPl; RptrSchPpr; College; Environmental Engineer.

SHANE, Lori S; West Holt HS; Atkinson, NE; HonRl; StuGov; RptrSchPpr; EdSchPpr; 4-H; FHA; Trk; Chrldr; AmLegAwd; 4-HAwd; Coll; Professnl.

SHANEBROOK, Kerry L; Woodlan HS; Woodburn, IN; 17/150 ALBoysSt; ChrhWkr; HonRl; JrNHS; NHS; NatlThespSoc; SchMus; SchPl; RptrSchPpr; FFA; GerCl; LetterFtbl; LetterTrk; IMSpt; Purdue Univ; Agriculture.

SHANER, Lee A; Lanark HS; Lanark, IL; 15/54 Chrs; HonRl; Mdrgl; YthFlsp; FHA; GAA; IMSpt; PPFtbl; 4-HAwd; College; Professional.

SHANEYFELT, Lynne M; St George HS; St George, KS; 1/25 PresSophCls; VPSrCls; ALAGirlsSt; Chr; StuCncl; RptrYrbk; PpCl; LetterBsktbl; BttyCrckrAwd; DARAwd; Univ; Veterinary Medicine.

SHANHOLTZ, Wendy L; Plattsmouth HS; Plattsmouth, NE; 9/133 Band; HonRl; SecNHS; SecStuCncl; SecYthFlsp; Pres4-H; MthCl; SecPpCl; PPFtbl; DARAwd; Nebraska Wesleyan Uni; Physicaltherapy.

SHANK, Robin L; Carthage Sr HS; Carthage, MO; AFS; Band; ChrhWkr; CncrtBnd; MrchBnd; OffAde; FrCl; PpCl; College.

SHANK, Tamela J; Ashland HS; Ashland, IL; 3/36 TrsSophCls; SecBand; Chrs; SecCncrtBnd; HonRl; MrchBnd; NHS; SchMus; SchPl; GAA; College.

SHANKLE, Dexter W; Flint Southwestern HS; Flint, MI; Bsbl; Ftbl; Trk; Univ; Professional.

SHANKS, Laura J; Sauk Prairie HS; Merrimac, WI; Band; ChrhWkr; CncrtBnd; HonRl; MrchBnd; Orch; SchMus; VPFrCl; OptClAwd; Uw Stevens Point; Communications.

SHANKS, Linda G; Wisconsin Dells HS; Lake Delton, WI; 19/156 TrsJrCls; AFS; Band; ChrhWkr; CncrtBnd; HonRl; MrchBnd; NHS; PepBnd; RptrSchPpr; SchPpr; SpnCl; PpCl; No Dakota State Univ; Pharmacy.

SHANKS, Marcia J; Villa Grove HS; Villa Grove, IL; TrsSrCls; HonRl; NHS; PresYthFlsp; FHA; PpCl; Bsktbl; Chrldr; GAA; Methodist Hosp Schl Of Nursing; Nurse.

SHANKS, Norma J; North Platte HS; Dearborn, MO; Chrs; OffAde; SchPl; PpCl; SciCl; Trk; CitAwd; Legal Sec.

SHANKS, Phillip J; Brazil Senior HS; Brazil, IN; Chr; Chrl; Chrs; ChrhWkr; HonRl; ModUN; NHS; NatlThespSoc; SchMus; SchPl; PresKeyCl; LetterFtbl; LetterTrk; Purdue; Industrial Management.

SHANLE, Jean E; Lincoln Community HS; Lincoln, IL; 27/272 PresSophCls; HonRl; NHS; StuCncl; StuGov; FTA; SpnCl; PpCl; St Johns School; Nurse.

SHANLE, Joan K; Holy Family HS; Genoa, NE; Chrs; HonRl; NHS; 4-H; PpCl; 4-HAwd;.

SHANN, Mary L; Holy Rosary HS; Flint, MI; 9/58 HonRl; LbryAde; NHS; SchPl; RptrYrbk; LetterBsktbl; Mott Community Clge; Bus Data Processing.

SHANNON, John R; Marshall HS; Napton, MO; 5/154 Chrs; ChrhWkr; HonRl; PresStuCncl; EdYrBk; RptrSchPpr; SchPpr; DARAwd; Univ; Political Analyst,teacher,broadcastin.

SHANNON, Mary F; Mercy HS; Omaha, NE; 25/70 TrsFrshCls; CmntyWkr; PolWkr; RedCrAde; SchMus; SchPl; Bsktbl; GAA; College; Business.

SHANNON, Mary Jo; West Ottawa HS; Holland, MI; ChrhWkr; Glf; Trk; Muskegon Comm College; Dental Asst.

SHANNON, Pamela; Englewood HS; Chicago, IL; Chr; ChrhWkr; HonRl; JrNHS; StuCncl; TchrAde; PpCl; University; Pharmacy.

SHANNON, Sean J; Mauston Area HS; Mauston, WI; PresSophCls; AFS; Chr; HonRl; Mdrgl; SchMus; SchPl; FrCl; LetterBsktbl; LetterFtbl; CaptTrk; University; Criminal Justice.

SHANNON, Sherry M; Freeburg Comm HS; Freeburg, IL; 4/124 Band; Chrs; ChrhWkr; CmntyWkr; CncrtBnd; HonRl; LbryAde; MrchBnd; South Ill Univ; Medical Tech.

SHANNON, Steven R; Dundee Community HS; Carpentersville, IL; Band; Chrs; CncrtBnd; HonRl; Mdrgl; MrchBnd; NatlMeritSF; Orch; SchMus; IMSpt; Coll; Nuclear Engineering.

SHANNON, Terri; Jefferson Senior HS; Jefferson, WI; Band; Chr; CncrtBnd; DrlTm; HonRl; MrchBnd; PepBnd; SchMus; StuCncl; PPFtbl; Univ; Nursing.

SHAPE, Steven M; Glenbrook North HS; Northbrook, IL; 97/699 Band; HonRl; Bsktbl; Univ Of Illinois; Elec Engineering.

SHAPIRO, Daniel P; Glen Brook South HS; Glenview, IL; HonRl; NatlMeritCmnd; PolWkr; SchPpr; Univ Of Illinois; Law.

SHAPIRO, Hershel J; Gering HS; Gering, NE; 8/139 PresFrshCls; Band; HonRl; NHS; StuCncl; KeyCl; Bsktbl; Ftbl; Glf; Wrstlng; Denver Univ; Law.

SHAPLAND, Janice M; Dighton HS; Shields, KS; 9/47 Chr; Chrs; HonRl; NHS; SctActv; PresYthFlsp; Yrbk; PpCl; Dodge Cty Comm Coll; Dietetic Tech.

SHAPPELL, Kim E; Wabash HS; Wabash, IN; Chr; Chrs; HonRl; 4-H; GerCl; University; Anthropologist.

SHARER, Kimberly J; Yorkwood Senior HS; Little York, IL; 4/52 SecJrCls; Aud/Vis; HonRl; NHS; SctActv; TchrAde; YthFlsp; RptrYrbk; PresFHA; PpCl; Midstate College; Medical Sectrtary.

SHARKEY, Robert R; Westhope HS; Westhope, ND; VPFrshCls; VPSophCls; PresJrCls; CncrtBnd; HonRl; PepBnd; SchPl; EdSchPpr; FFA; Univ Of Nd; Law.

SHARKO, Susan M; Vassar HS; Millington, MI; HospAde; TchrAde; Business School.

SHARMAN, Gary W; Sidney HS; Sidney, NE; Chr; Chrl; Chrs; ChrhWkr; HonRl; JrNHS; Mdrgl; TchrAde; SchPpr; EngCl; Seward Ctc; Dce.

SHARON, Sharon J; Nazareth Academy; Westchester, IL; 12/161 NHS; SchMus; StuCncl; TchrAde; RptrSchPpr; GAA; Drake Univ.

SHARP, Barbara K; Bethany HS; Bethany, IL; 4/30 Band; Chrs; HonRl; Mdrgl; NHS; SchMus; YthFlsp; RptrYrbk; Trk; 4-HAwd; College; P E Teacher.

SHARP, Brenda J; Raymore Peculiar HS; Raymore, MO; HonRl; FHA; FTA; PpCl; Trk; Chrldr; GAA; PPFtbl; College; Registered Nurse.

SHARP, Dannie E; Mark Twain HS; Perry, MO; Chrs; HonRl; SctActv; YthFlsp; 4-H; FFA; Bsbl; Bsktbl; GodCntryAwd; CitAwd; Trade School; Farming.

SHARP, Deanna L; Marceline R V HS; Marceline, MO; 9/70 HonRl; OffAde; RptrSchPpr; PpCl; LetterBsktbl; College.

SHARP, Deborah; Regina; Warren, MI; HonRl; StuCncl; Vocational Ed; Horticulture.

SHARP, Elizabeth A; Billings HS; Billings, MO; 4/35 SecJrCls; Band; Chrs; HonRl; MrchBnd; PepBnd; Twrl; 4-H; FHA; PpCl; Draughon Bus Col; Med Rectp.

SHARP, Janet S; Earlville Comm HS; Earlville, IL; 5/45 Band; Chrs; NHS; SchMus; StuCncl; Yrbk; SchPpr; SciCl; CaptSoc; CaptChrldr; Univ.

SHARP, Kristie L; Melvin Sibley HS; Melvin, IL; 6/24 VPSrCls; HonRl; Quill&Scroll; YthFlsp; Yrbk; RptrSchPpr; FHA; PpCl; SciCl; Chrldr; Parkland Comm Col; Bus Management.

SHARP, Kurtis L; Dwight D Eisenhower HS; Decatur, IL; 17/301 HonRl; NHS; NatlMeritCmnd; NatlThespSoc; SchMus; SchPl; Illinois State University; Liberal Arts.

SHARP, Marilyn K; Wathena HS; Wathena, KS; HstSrCls; Chr; Chrs; ChrhWkr; HonRl; SchPl; PpCl; Platt Coll Of Commerce; Vocation.

SHARP, Mark; Providence HS; Lackport, IL; 9/125 CtyCnl; HonRl; StuCncl; LatCl; SciCl; Glf; Wrstlng; College; Dentist.

SHARP, Mary A; Lasalle Peru HS; La Salle, IL; Band; CncrtBnd; HonRl; MrchBnd; PepBnd; FrCl; College; Music.

SHARP, Mary J; Troy HS; Troy, MO; HonRl; HospAde; College; Professional.

SHARP, Nancy; Woodhaven HS; Woodhaven, MI; 1/140 NatlMeritSF; PolWkr; TchrAde; Yrbk; PpCl; Univ Of Mich; Pharmacy.

SHARP, Patricia; Dodgeland HS; Juneau, WI; 3/77 AFS; ChrhWkr; HonRl; LbryAde; SecNHS; SchPl; RptrYrbk; Yrbk; SpnCl; BttyCrckrAwd; U Of Wi Whitewater; Psychology.

SHARP, Phillip O; Daleville HS; Daleville, IN; Band; Chrs; ChrhWkr; HonRl; MrchBnd; TchrAde; Bsbl; LetterTrk; LetterWrstlng; IMSpt; University; Vocation.

SHARP, Sally L; St Marys HS; St Marys, KS; VPFrshCls; SecJrCls; Band; Chrs; CncrtBnd; MrchBnd; OffAde; PepBnd; SctActv; YthFlsp; College; Music.

SHARP, Samuel R; Dixon HS; Dixon, MO; HonRl; LetterBsktbl; Trk; Trade; Professional.

SHARP, Sara S; Connersville HS; Falmouth, IN; 15/381 Chr; DrmMjrt; JrNHS; LbryAde; NatlThespSoc; SchMus; SchPl; SecYthFlsp; FrCl; 4-HAwd; KiwanAwd; College; Music Or Math.

SHARP, Susan E; Nebraska City Sr HS; Nebraska City, NE; Band; CmntyWkr; CncrtBnd; HonRl; MrchBnd; PepBnd; FBLA; FHA; SpnCl; PpCl; SciCl; Univ Of Nebraska; Medical Tech.

SHARPE, Kathleen M; La Salle Peru HS; Oglesby, IL; Band; CncrtBnd; HonRl; MrchBnd; PepBnd; StuCncl; RptrSchPpr; FrCl; SpnCl; College.

SHARPE, Margaret D; Columbus North HS; Taylorsville, IN; 98/480 SecSrCls; CmntyWkr; HonRl; MrchBnd; ModUN; OffAde; RedCrAde; SctActv; StuGov; CaptTwrl; GerCl; Purdue Univ; Biology.

SHARPE, Martha Q; Sumner HS; St Louis, MO; 37/447 HonRl; Southeast Mo State Univ; Medical Tech.

SHARPE, Susan E; Braymer C 4 HS; Braymer, MO; 1/31 SecSophCls; SecSrCls; HonRl; SecStuCncl; RptrYrbk; EdSchPpr; 4-H; FHA; SecPpCl; N W M S U; Business.

SHARPIN, Kathleen L; Elmhurst HS; Fort Wayne, IN; PpCl; IMSpt; College;.

SHARPING, Marjean; Kimball HS; Pukwana, SD; Band; HonRl; MrchBnd; PepBnd; SchMus; SchPpr; Trk; Chrldr; AmLegAwd; College; Professional.

SHARRETT, Mari L; West HS; Davenport, IA; College; Teaching.

SHASKY, Mary J; Wahpeton HS; Wahpeton, ND; AFS; HonRl; SpnCl; PpCl; LetterBsktbl; LetterTrk; GAA; IMSpt; PPFtbl;.

SHASTEEN, Gary W; Collinsville HS; Collinsville, IL; ChrhWkr; LetterBsktbl; Coll; Cpa.

SHATEK, Ann B; Turkey Valley HS; Fort Atkinson, IA; Chr; CncrtBnd; HonRl; PepBnd; SchMus; PresSdlty; Twrl; Pres4-H; LetterGlf; 4-HAwd; GodCntryAwd; College.

SHATEK, Kenneth L; Mew Hampton Community HS; Elma, IA; 3/170 HonRl; NHS; SecFFA; GodCntryAwd; Area I Vocational School; Farming.

SHATTUCK, Sherri; Belvidere HS; Belvidere, IL; 43/366 Chr; Chrs; HonRl; SchMus; StuCncl; YthFlsp; SpnCl; PpCl; Chrldr; PPFtbl; Eastern Illinois Univ; Elementary Education.

SHATZER, Dale M; Jesup Comm HS; Jesup, IA; 1/85 PresFrshCls; ALBoysSt; HonRl; NatlMeritCmnd; PresStuCncl; FrCl; LetterBsbl; Bsktbl; LetterFtbl; LetterGlf; Luther Clg.

SHAUGHNESSY, Adrienne; Sacred Heart Acad; Springfield, IL; HospAde; JA; SchPpr; 4-H; PpCl; College; Professional.

SHAUGHNESSY, April M; Mt Assisi Academy; Chicago, IL; TrsSophCls; CmntyWkr; HonRl; SchMus; StuCncl; SpnCl; CaptCchngActv; GAA; IMSpt; Creighton Univ; Pharmacy.

SHAUGHNESSY, Judy K; St Mary Of Redford HS; Detroit, MI; 3/175 VPSophCls; HonRl; JrNHS; PresNHS; RptrSchPpr; PpCl; DARAwd; Univ Of Mich; Engineering.

SHAUGHNESSY, Rita A; Lumen Christi HS; Jackson, MI; 35/233 Band; CmntyWkr; CncrtBnd; HonRl; JrNHS; MrchBnd; NHS; PepBnd; EdSchPpr; SchPpr; Tennis; College; Professional.

SHAUL, Kevin W; Ainsworth HS; Ainsworth, NE; TrsFrshCls; Bsbl; LetterFtbl; LetterTrk; CaptWrstlng; Trade School.

SHAUM, Donita L; Engadine Consolidated HS; Engadine, MI; Chr; HonRl; TchrAde; College; Medicine.

SHAVER, Stephen R; Hartville HS; Grovespring, MO; 1/62 HonRl; StuCncl; PresFFA; College; Ag Business.

SHAVLIK, Jude W; Premontre HS; Green Bay, WI; 5/130 HonRl; NatlMeritSF; StuCncl; StuGov; IMSpt; Col; Science.

SHAW, Charlotte P; Rogers HS; Michigan City, IN; AFS; ChrhWkr; HonRl; NHS; SchPl; SpnCl; PpCl; Coll; Special Education Teacher.

SHAW, Clayton; Oelrichs HS; Oerichs, SD; 1/9 SecTrsFrshCls; PresJrCls; ALBoysSt; Chrs; HonRl; SchPl; StuCncl; Yrbk; Univ; Professional.

SHAW, Debra D; Mason HS; Erie, MI; 6/121 Band; HonRl; HospAde; MrchBnd; NHS; TchrAde; YthFlsp; FHA; FNA; Owens Tech Coll; Nurse.

SHAW, Denise S; Ashley Comm HS; Ashley, MI; 9/42 TrsFrshCls; HonRl; NHS; NatlThespSoc; SchPl; StuCncl; Twrl; Bsbl; LetterBsktbl; IMSpt; Anderson Col; Mathematics Computer.

SHAW, Donald W; Homewood Flossmoor HS; Flossmoor, IL; 72/914 CncrtBnd; HonRl; MrchBnd; Orch; Purdue; Engineering.

SHAW, Edward G; Glenbrook North HS; Northbrook, IL; 202/610 CmntyWkr; TchrAde; RptrSchPpr; University; Medicine.

SHAW, Gene R; Faribault HS; Faribault, MN; PresJrCls; AFS; CmntyWkr; NatlMeritSF; StuCncl; YthFlsp; SptEdSchPpr; Trk; Wrstlng; University; Physical Sciences.

SHAW, Gordon R; Kirkwood HS; Kirkwood, MO; ChrhWkr; CncrtBnd; MrchBnd; Orch; PepBnd; College; Engineering.

SHAW, Jill; Dix HS; Potter, NE; 1/19 TrsSophCls; ALAGirlsSt; Band; Chrs; EdYrBk; Univ Of Nebraska; Journalism.

SHAW, Joel L; Oskaloosa Sr HS; Oskaloosa, IA; PresAud/Vis; HonRl; StuCncl; Pres4-H; FFA; Wrstlng; IMSpt; 4-HAwd; Ryder Tech; Auto Mechanic.

SHAW, Jon R; Abraham Lincoln HS; Council Bluffs, IA; AFS; Chr; Chrs; HonRl; PolWkr; SchMus; KeyCl; SciCl; Iowa State Univ; Physics.

SHAW, Julie B; J D Darnall HS; Geneseo, IL; Band; CncrtBnd; HonRl; JA; LbryAde; MrchBnd; PepBnd; 4-H; Trk; GAA; IMSpt; PPFtbl;.

SHAW, Karen A; Lancaster Sr HS; Lancaster, WI; 1/158 AFS; Chrs; CncrtBnd; HonRl; NHS; NatlMeritCmnd; Orch; SchMus; RptrSchPpr; SpnCl; College; Spanish.

SHAW, Karla J; Johnston City HS; Johnston City, IL; 2/85 Band; ChrhWkr; CncrtBnd; HonRl; MrchBnd; TreasNHS; TchrAde; SpnCl; MthCl; LionAwd; John A Logan Col; Business.

SHAW, Kevin J; St Marys Springs HS; Fond Du Lac, WI; PresFrshCls; PresSrCls; StuCncl; Yrbk; RptrSchPpr; VPKeyCl; TreasSciCl; CaptBsktbl; Trk; St Norbert College.

SHAW, Kim L; Guide Rock HS; Guide Rock, NE; 2/14 TrsJrCls; ALBoysSt; Band; CncrtBnd; ModUN; PepBnd; SchPl; SctActv; Bsktbl; Univ Of Nebraska; Civil Engineering.

SHAW, Larry R; Roseland Public HS; Roseland, NE; VPSophCls; TrsJrCls; SecSrCls; ALBoysSt; Chrs; HonRl; IntrClCncl; StuCncl; YthFlsp; RptrYrbk; LetterBsktbl; LetterFtbl; LetterTrk; College; Professional.

SHAW, Larry T; Streator Twp HS; Streator, IL; 21/420 HonRl; NHS; StuCncl; StuGov; College; Sociology.

SHAW, Leigh A; Lapel HS; Lapel, IN; 7/84 Band; CncrtBnd; HonRl; MrchBnd; NHS; NatlMeritCmnd; OffAde; RptrYrbk; Yrbk; TreasPpCl; Purdue Univ; Business Management.

SHAW, Lisa; Bentley HS; Livonia, MI; HonRl; LitMag; ModUN; PolWkr; Mi Univ; Eng.

SHAW, Marietta L; Frankfort HS; Frankfort, IN; Chr; Chrs; HonRl; NatlMeritCmnd; OffAde; SchMus; StuCncl; TchrAde; VP4-H; FBLA; Trade Sch; Interior Decorator.

SHAW, Mark A; Delavan Darien HS; Delavan, WI; RptrSchPpr; LetterBsbl; Bsktbl; CaptFtbl; IMSpt; College; Professional.

SHAW, Michael H; Cotter HS; Winona, MN; VPSrCls; ALBoysSt; HonRl; LbryAde; NHS; NatlThespSoc; SchMus; SchPl; Yrbk; Ftbl; Col Of St Teresa; Physical Therapy.

SHAW, Mike A; Centralia HS; Centralia, IL; HonRl; College; Professional.

SHAW, Nancy J; Alma HS; Alma, MI; 4/267 SecJrCls; CncrtBnd; HonRl; MrchBnd; NHS; PepBnd; StuGov; SpnCl; PpCl; SciCl; Mi St Univ; Pre Veterinary.

SHAW, Pamela S; Fairfax R 3 HS; Fairfax, MO; 7/27 VPFrshCls; PresJrCls; Chr; Chrs; ChrhWkr; HonRl; LbryAde; SchPl; StuCncl; Yrbk; FHA; PpCl; Bsktbl; College; Chemistry.

SHAW, Patrick; Menasha HS; Menasha, WI; Band; ChrhWkr; CncrtBnd; DrmBgl; HonRl; MrchBnd; PepBnd; YthFlsp; Trk; Uw Stevens Point.

SHAW, Penny E; Ashley HS; Ashley, MI; 6/44 ChrhWkr; CmntyWkr; HonRl; NHS; YthFlsp; 4-H; FHA; KeyCl; LetterChrldr; CitAwd; Lansing Comm College; Commercial Art.

SHAW, Sally D; Shelbyville HS; Shelbyville, IL; ChrhWkr; HonRl; NHS; SchMus; StuCncl; FrCl; PpCl; Trk; Chrldr; SecGAA; Il State; French Teacher.

SHAW, Sherm E; High School; La Moille, IL; Aud/Vis; ChrhWkr; CmntyWkr; OffAde; SchAde; SchPl; SctActv; StuGov; YthFlsp; Yrbk; RptrSchPpr; SptEdSchPpr; SchPpr; CaptGlf; IMSpt; Morrison Inst Of Tech; Drafting.

SHAW, Sonya C; Broken Bow HS; Broken Bow, NE; HonRl; MrchBnd; SchMus; StuGov; RptrYrbk; Yrbk; RptrSchPpr; SchPpr; 4-H; LionAwd; College; Professional.

SHAW, Stewart; Onaway Area Community HS; Onaway, MI; Band; CncrtBnd; HonRl; MrchBnd; PepBnd; SctActv; PpCl; Bsktbl; Ftbl; IMSpt; Coll; Engineering.

SHAW, Susan; Kent City HS; Casnovia, MI; 1/90 SecFrshCls; NatlMeritCmnd; PepBnd; SchPl; RptrYrbk; 4-H; PPFtbl; 4-HAwd; Western Mich Univ.

SHAW, Susan L; Leroy Ostrander Public HS; Ostrander, MN; 7/36 ChrhWkr; HonRl; LbryAde; NHS; SchAde; TchrAde; FTA; Benidji State Clge; Biology.

SHAW, Susan V; St Scholastica HS; Park Ridge, IL; 67/233 Chr; Chrs; ChrhWkr; CmntyWkr; SctActv; RptrYrbk; Yrbk; Purdue Univ; Microbiology.

SHAW, Teresa D; Sedan HS; Sedan, KS; Chrs; ChrhWkr; HonRl; MrchBnd; NHS; OffAde; YthFlsp; PpCl; 4-HAwd; LionAwd; Okla Baptist U; Counseling.

SHAW, Vicki L; Dewitt HS; Dewitt, MI; 6/123 HonRl; JrNHS; NHS; PolWkr; SchAde; SchPl; TchrAde; SpnCl; SciCl; PresAwd; Lansing Comm Clg; Computer.

SHAW, Victoria M; Warren HS; Monmouth, IL; OffAde; SchPl; RptrYrbk; Pres4-H; SecFFA; KeyCl; DanFAwd; 4-HAwd; Junior College; Nutrition & Health.

SHAWHAN, Timothy A; Spalding Inst HS; Peoria, IL; 8/100 HonRl; JA; NHS; Bradley Univ; Geology.

SHAY, Clifton; St Bede Academy; Chicago, IL; Chrs; CmntyWkr; HonRl; LbryAde; MrchBnd; OffAde; SchAde; SchMus; SchPl; StuCncl; Ftbl; Swmmng; CaptTrk; CchngActv; Mac Murray College; Business Admin.

SHAY, Denise E; Winfield HS; Winfield, KS; CmntyWkr; HonRl; LitMag; NatlMeritSF; SctActv; TchrAde; RptrSchPpr; PpCl; College.

SHAY, Donald J; Arthur Hill HS; Saginaw, MI; ChrhWkr; HonRl; PresNHS; SctActv; StuCncl; StuGov; CaptBsktbl; CchngActv; Central Mich Univ.

SHAY, Joy R; New Ulm Senior HS; New Ulm, MN; 5/250 Band; TreasCncrtBnd; HonRl; MrchBnd; PepBnd; SctActv; Yrbk; SchPpr; SpnCl; PpCl; GAA; College; Home Economics.

SHCROEDER, Jay T; Central Lyon HS; Doon, IA; 1/96 SecTrsFrshCls; PresJrCls; ALBoysSt; Band; HonRl; NHS; KeyCl; SpnCl; Wrstlng; Briar Cliff Coll.

SHEA, Julie A; Regis HS; Eau Claire, WI; HonRl; FrCl; Northern Arizona University.

SHEA, Maureen; Whitnall HS; Hales Corners, WI; HonRl; NHS; RptrSchPpr; U W Eau Claire.

SHEA, Patricia A; Knoxville HS; Knoxville, IL; 2/96 Chrs; HonRl; NHS; OffAde; SchPl; TchrAde; FrCl; PpCl; Knox College; Science.

SHEA, Thomas E; Assumption HS; Nekoosa, WI; Band; CncrtBnd; MrchBnd; PepBnd; Yrbk; LetterTennis; Trk; IMSpt; U W Stevens Point; Art.

SHEA, William J; Sacred Heart HS; Salina, KS; ALBoysSt; CmntyWkr; HonRl; NHS; StuCncl; TchrAde; YthFlsp; FBLA; PresKeyCl; Bsbl; LetterBsktbl; LetterFtbl; LetterTrk; Kansas University; Business.

SHEADE, Wynn; York Comm HS; Elmhurst, IL; 27/912 HonRl; JrNHS; NHS; Quill&Scroll; RptrSchPpr; LetterSoc; Univ Of Illinois; Medicine.

SHEAHON, Mike K; Sacred Heart HS; Salina, KS; TrsSophCls; VPJrCls; HonRl; StuGov; FBLA; KeyCl; Bsktbl; Ftbl; Trk; College; Pre Law.

SHEAKLEY, Cindy A; Algona HS; Algona, IA; 5/125 PresAFS; Band; Chr; Chrl; CncrtBnd; DrlTm; DrmBgl; DrmMjrt; HonRl; MrchBnd; NHS; Twrl; Univ Of Ia; Physicians Assistant.

SHEAR, John K; Columbia Central HS; Brooklyn, MI; 42/152 Band; Chr; CncrtBnd; DrmMjrt; Mdrgl; MrchBnd; PepBnd; SchMus; SchPl; LetterTrk; Central Michigan Univ; Park Ranger.

SHEARER, Arnold D; Macon Co R 1 HS; Excello, MO; ChrhWkr; CmntyWkr; HonRl; LbryAde; RedCrAde; SchPl; FFA; Ftbl; PresAwd; Trade School.

SHEARER, Valerie J; St Joseph HS; St Joseph, MI; 11/330 Chr; HonRl; NHS; NatlMeritCmnd; SchAde; StuCncl; YthFlsp; Yrbk; MthCl; CaptTrk; Michigan St Univ; Medicine.

SHEARRER, Susan C; Normandy HS; St Louis, MO; Chr; HonRl; Mid America Nazarene College; Music.

SHEBENECK, Paul R; Racine Lutheran HS; Racine, WI; 11/72 ChrhWkr; CmntyWkr; HonRl; NHS; StuCncl; TchrAde; RptrYrbk; RptrSchPpr; Bsktbl; Tennis; Concordia Coll; Accounting.

SHECKLER, Holly S; Milan Jr/sr HS; Dillsboro, IN; Chr; Chrs; HonRl; LitMag; NHS; OffAde; RptrYrbk; SchPpr; LatCl; MasAwd; College; Biochemistry.

SHEDELBOWER, Patricia; Washington Catholic HS; Washington, IN; 2/33 Chrs; HonRl; NHS; 4-H; PpCl; Tennis; AmLegAwd; 4-HAwd; Univ Of Evansville; Nursing.

SHEEDY, Joseph H; Austin Pacelli HS; Austin, MN; HonRl; NHS; LetterBsbl; IMSpt; Ia State U; Ag Eng.

SHEEHAN, Kathleen A; Carroll HS; Carroll, IA; 9/104 Chrl; Chrs; CmntyWkr; HonRl; ModUN; PolWkr; Quill&Scroll; SchMus; SchPl; EdYrBk; EdSchPpr; PpCl; Glf; Univ Of Notre Dame; Journalism.

SHEEHY, Francis X; Griffin HS; Springfield, IL; Band; CncrtBnd; HonRl; MrchBnd; Orch; PepBnd; College; Chemical Engineering.

SHEELER, Julie A; South East Polk HS; Des Moines, IA; Chr; SchMus; SchPl; StuGov; YthFlsp; 4-H; Bsktbl; LetterTrk; PPFtbl; 4-HAwd; College; Interior Design.

SHEELEY, Rachel; Atchison County Community HS; Nortonville, KS; 13/86 Band; ChrhWkr; CncrtBnd; HonRl; MrchBnd; NHS; TchrAde; FHA; MthCl; Kansas State U; Pre Veterinary Medicine.

SHEELY, Linda G; Chester HS; Chester, IL; Chrs; HonRl; LbryAde; Yrbk; FHA; Southern Il U; Major.

SHEERAN, Anne E; Andrean HS; Merrillville, IN; 36/250 SecFrshCls; SecSophCls; SecJrCls; VPSrCls; HonRl; NHS; Quill&Scroll; SchMus; EdSchPpr; College; Communication.

SHEETS, Carol A; Lewistown Comm HS; Lewistown, IL; 15/120 ChrhWkr; HonRl; StuCncl; RptrYrbk; Yrbk; RptrSchPpr; FHA; FTA; SpnCl; PpCl;.

SHEETS, Daniel J; Warren Cousino HS; Warren, MI; PresFrshCls; Band; CncrtBnd; LetterBsktbl; CaptTrk; Hillsdale College; State Police.

SHEETS, Ester K; Britt HS; Britt, IA; Chrs; HonRl; PolWkr; SchPl; Yrbk; RptrSchPpr; 4-H; PpCl; LetterTrk; 4-HAwd; U Of Iowa; Physical Ed.

SHEETS, Karen C; Illiopolis Com HS; Illiopolis, IL; SecSophCls; Band; Chrs; DrmMjrt; HonRl; LbryAde; SchPl; TchrAde; Twrl; PresFHA; GAA; Richland Comm College; Lab Tech.

SHEFCIK, Barbara S; St Paul John F Kennedy HS; Chicago, IL; 24/610 Chrs; HonRl; JrNHS; SecNHS; OffAde; Orch; Pres4-H; GAA;.

SHEFFERLY, Claire P; Grosse Pointe South HS; Grosse Pte Farms, MI; HonRl; Northern Mi College; Medical Lab Tech.

SHEFFIELD, John W; Axtell Comm HS; Wilcox, NE; PresFrshCls; Chrs; HonRl; Mdrgl; NHS; SchPl; StuCncl; Bsbl; LetterBsktbl; LetterFtbl; Kearney St; Bookkeeper.

SHEFFIELD, Margaret J; St Scholastica HS; Chicago, IL; 25/230 HstJrCls; HstSrCls; HonRl; NHS; SchAde; SchMus; SchPl; StuCncl; StuGov; Yrbk; CchngActv; Loyola Univ; Theatre.

SHEFFLER, Deborah S; Sullivan HS; Sullivan, IN; 16/139 Chr; HonRl; NHS; YthFlsp; 4-H; SpnCl; MthCl; PpCl; Bsbl; ChmnBsktbl; Isu; Dental Hygienist.

SHEFFOLD, Janet; Westville Twp HS; Westville, IL; 6/104 CncrtBnd; HonRl; MrchBnd; NHS; PepBnd; SctActv; RptrYrbk; Yrbk; SpnCl; PpCl; Junior College.

SHEFSKY, Jay S; Evanston Twp HS; Skokie, IL; VPSrCls; ALBoysSt; HonRl; PolWkr; SchPl; StuCncl; StuGov; Univ Of Illinois.

SHEHI, Darlene R; Luckey HS; Manhattan, KS; 4/31 VPSrCls; HonRl; ModUN; SchPl; StuCncl; EdYrBk; SptEdYrbk; Yrbk; RptrSchPpr; SchPpr; Bsktbl; College; Accounting.

SHEILDS, Michael P; St Bede Academy; Ladd, IL; HonRl; Bsbl; Bsktbl; Ftbl; College; Pharmacy.

SHEKLETON, Maureen; Richwoods HS; Peoria, IL; 44/449 HonRl; LbryAde; NatlMeritFnl; TchrAde; Univ Of Iowa; Journalism.

SHELBURNE, Mark R; Zionsville Comm HS; Zionsville, IN; Band; CncrtBnd; DrlTm; MrchBnd; PepBnd; 4-H; FFA; 4-HAwd; Purdue Univ; Veteranarian.

SHELBY, Kathryne; South Harrison HS; Bethany, MO; HonRl; MrchBnd; ModUN; NHS; SchMus; SctActv; StuCncl; YthFlsp; FHA; GodCntryAwd; College.

SHELBY, Lynn A; Abl HS; Broadlands, IL; SecSophCls; SecJrCls; SctActv; VPFHA; Trk; Chrldr; GAA; College; Professional.

SHELBY, Melissa K; Edwards County Sr HS; West Salem, IL; ChrhWkr; LbryAde; NHS; OffAde; FHA; PpCl; Bus School; Secretary.

SHELDON, Ann; Battle Creek Lakeview HS; Waukegan, IL; HonRl; NHS; NatlMeritCmnd; Iit; Engineer Science.

SHELDON, Debbie E; North Loup Scotia HS; North Loup, NE; 4/22 Chrs; ChrhWkr; HonRl; SchMus; SchPl; StuCncl; StuGov; YthFlsp; Yrbk; Chrldr;.

SHELDON, Kathryn S; Yale HS; Yale, MI; 11/145 Chr; ChrhWkr; HonRl; StuCncl; TchrAde; YthFlsp; Yrbk; 4-H; PresSpnCl; SciCl; College; Office Admin.

SHELDON, Kevin A; Lane Tech HS; Chicago, IL; 109/1200 CmntyWkr; HonRl; JA; PolWkr; StuCncl; StuGov; TchrAde; Yrbk; College; Political Science.

SHELDON, Mary L; New Providence Comm HS; Eldora, IA; 3/19 Chr; DrmMjrt; HonRl; SchMus; SchPl; TchrAde; YthFlsp; Pres4-H; Bsktbl; 4-HAwd; Jr College; Secretary.

SHELDON, Steven E; Lost Nation Community HS; Lost Nation, IA; ALBoysSt; HonRl; MrchBnd; CchngActv; IMSpt; Palmer Coll; Chiropractor.

SHELDRICK, Margaret A; Bellevue Sr HS; Bellevue, NE; Band; Chr; ChrhWkr; HonRl; JrNHS; LitMag; NHS; NatlMeritCmnd; SchMus; University Of Nebraska; English.

SHELEMI, Steven E; Ridgewood HS; Norridge, IL; 10/369 Band; CncrtBnd; MrchBnd; NHS; SchMus; Univ Of Notre Dame; Accounting.

SHELEY, Colleen K; Westview Jr Sr HS; Topeka, IN; 4/65 HonRl; NHS; SchPl; StuCncl; RptrSchPpr; SecFHA; FTA; PpCl; CaptChrldr;.

SHELHAMMER, James L; Wabeno HS; Laona, WI; HonRl; LbryAde; FBLA; PpCl; LetterBsktbl; LetterFtbl; Blue Collar Worker; Industrial Mech.

SHELITE, Rockne A; Sharon HS; Sharon, KS; Band; Chrs; ChrhWkr; CmntyWkr; HonRl; SchPl; Bsbl; LetterBsktbl; LetterFtbl; LetterTrk; Coll.

SHELL, Dotta; Woodland R4 HS; Lutesville, MO; 3/61 Band; ChrhWkr; HonRl; MrchBnd; NHS; StuCncl; Yrbk; SchPpr; FHA; PpCl; Univ; Pre Med.

SHELLEY, Gregory V; Colchester HS; Plymouth, IL; LetterBsktbl; Carl Sandburg Coll.

SHELLEY, Kenneth W; Breckenridge Jr Sr HS; Breckenridge, MI; Aud/Vis; HonRl; LbryAde; FFA;.

SHELLY, Karen E; Mt Morris HS; Mt Morris, IL; 5/80 AFS; ChrhWkr; HonRl; LbryAde; NHS; NatlMeritCmnd; SchPl; SctActv; SecYthFlsp; GerCl; LetterTrk; GAA; Eastern Il Univ; Elementary Education.

SHELQUIST, Marilyn L; Moravia Community HS; Moravia, IA; 3/42 Band; Chrs; HonRl; NHS; SchMus; EdSchPpr; Pres4-H; FHA; BttyCrckrAwd; DanFAwd; Central College; Teaching.

SHELTEL, Nancy L; Wyanet HS; Princeton, IL; 2/30 PresSophCls; Band; CncrtBnd; HonRl; MrchBnd; NHS; NatlMeritCmnd; NatlThespSoc; SchPl; StuCncl; 4-H; SpnCl; PpCl; Chrldr; University Of Illinois.

SHELTERS, Joanna J; Concord HS; Albion, MI; Chr; ChrhWkr; HonRl; TchrAde; YthFlsp; RptrSchPpr; Bsktbl; Trk; GAA; IMSpt; Trade Sch; Pro Photo.

SHELTON, Barbara J; Richland HS; Richland, MO; TrsJrCls; Band; CncrtBnd; HonRl; MrchBnd; PepBnd; FHA; PpCl; Trk; Chrldr;.

SHELTON, David; Harlan Comm HS; Harlan, IA; Utah St Univ; Forest Recreation.

SHELTON, Deborah R; Anna Jonesboro C HS; Anna, IL; 9/146 VPJrCls; SecBand; CncrtBnd; HonRl; MrchBnd; PepBnd; Quill&Scroll; Yrbk; RptrSchPpr; SchPpr; FTA; Chrldr; Murray St Univ; Mathematics.

SHELTON, Donald B; High School; Creston, IA; Band; ChrhWkr; CmntyWkr; DrlTm; MrchBnd; YthFlsp; 4-H; Glf; Trk; IMSpt;.

SHELTON, Jay L; Jewell HS; Randall, KS; ALBoysSt; Band; Chr; Chrs; CncrtBnd; MrchBnd; PepBnd; SchPl; StuCncl; YthFlsp; University; Professional.

SHELTON, John B; New Bloomfield HS; New Bloomfield, MO; PresJrCls; Band; Chrs; CncrtBnd; MrchBnd; PepBnd; StuCncl; StuGov; LetterBsbl; LetterBsktbl; LetterTrk; University; Professional.

SHELTON, John C; Huron HS; Ann Arbor, MI; CncrtBnd; SctActv; LetterFtbl; Univ Of Michigan; Medicine.

SHELTON, Karen L; Bucklin R Ii HS; Bucklin, MO; HonRl; HospAde; Yrbk; PpCl; Bsbl; Chrldr;.

SHELTON, Kris A; Richland Center HS; Richland Center, WI; Band; CncrtBnd; HonRl; LitMag; MrchBnd; NHS; PepBnd; Pres4-H; LatCl; 4-HAwd;.

SHELTON, Lisa K; Pittsburg Sr HS; Pittsburg, KS; ALAGirlsSt; ChrhWkr; CncrtBnd; HospAde; MrchBnd; PepBnd; StuCncl; PresFHA; PpCl; MasAwd; Kansas State College; Math Or Teaching.

SHELTON, Marc E; Rolla HS; Rolla, MO; 3/307 VPFrshCls; PresSophCls; Band; CncrtBnd; HonRl; NatlFornLg; PolWkr; SchMus; StuGov; VPKeyCl; College; Medicine.

SHELTON, Marina L; Northern HS; Detroit, MI; 23/179 CmntyWkr; HonRl; HospAde; OffAde; PolWkr; SchPl; TchrAde; PpCl; SciCl; Chrldr; Msu; Pediatrian.

SHELTON, Mark M; Barr Reeve HS; Loogootee, IN; LatCl; Indiana University; Chemist.

SHELTON, Michael; Fargo North HS; Fargo, ND; AFS; CncrtBnd; HonRl; MrchBnd; ModUN; NHS; NatlMeritCmnd; Orch; LatCl; EldAwd; Carleton College; Medical.

SHELTON, Yolanda K; Iberia HS; Iberia, MO; 5/44 PresSrCls; Band; HonRl; MrchBnd; PepBnd; StuCncl; PpCl; Central Missouri St Univ; Social Work.

SHEMAK, Patrick; Highland HS; Highland, WI; 12/50 Chr; Chrs; ChrhWkr; SchMus; SchPl; TchrAde; YthFlsp; FFA; LionAwd; Univ Of Wi; Ag Ed.

SHENEMAN, Nancy J; North Liberty HS; North Liberty, IN; Chrs; ChrhWkr; HonRl; NHS; OffAde; SchAde; SchPl; RptrSchPpr; SpnCl; Valparaiso University; Communications.

SHEPANIK, Robert L; D C Everest HS; Schofield, WI; Band; CncrtBnd; DrmBgl; HonRl; Orch; SchMus; Ftbl; Swmmng; LetterTrk; IMSpt; OptClAwd; College; Percussion.

SHEPARD, Alan J; Oak Forest HS; Oak Forest, IL; 4/346 ChrhWkr; HonRl; JrNHS; LitMag; NHS; YthFlsp; LetterBsbl; Bsktbl; CchngActv; AmLegAwd; University; Basketball.

SHEPARD, Tracy M; Bloomington HS; Bloomington, IL; 77/391 PresJrCls; HonRl; NHS; SchPl; SctActv; StuCncl; TchrAde; YthFlsp; FrCl; Tennis; U Of Il.

SHEPECK, Maria R; Cloquet HS; Cloquet, MN; 8/475 HonRl; NHS; LetterTrk; Umd; Mathematics.

SHEPERDIGIAN, Douglas V; M P HS; Mt Pleasant, MI; Band; Chr; CncrtBnd; HonRl; Mdrgl; MrchBnd; NHS; NatlMeritSF; NatlThespSoc; PepBnd; SchMus; SchPl; LetterTennis; IMSpt;.

SHEPHARD, David B; Paseo HS; Kansas City, MO; VPFrshCls; Chr; ChrhWkr; HonRl; JA; NHS; FrCl; Bsbl; Bsktbl; Ftbl; IMSpt; ChmbCommrsAwd; College; Professional.

SHEPHERD, David; Grant Community Hs; Ingleside, IL; 20/208 Band; Chr; CncrtBnd; HonRl; Orch; PepBnd; SchMus; Junior College; Law Enforcement.

SHEPHERD, Denice; Holdrege HS; Holdrege, NE; Chr; HonRl; NatlFornLg; OffAde; RptrYrbk; Yrbk; RptrSchPpr; Univ; Journalism.

SHEPHERD, Douglas A; Harrisburg HS; Harrisburg, IL; LetterBsktbl; LetterFtbl; Swmmng; LetterTrk; CchngActv; College; Engineer.

SHEPHERD, Gary K; Robinson HS; Robinson, IL; 15/180 ALBoysSt; HonRl; ModUN; Quill&Scroll; SchPl; StuCncl; SchPpr; FrCl; LatCl; SciCl; Ftbl; Glf; College; Archeologist.

SHEPHERD, James D; Hillcrest HS; Country Club Hills, IL; 20/500 ChrhWkr; HonRl; LbryAde; NHS; NatlThespSoc; PolWkr; SchMus; SchPl; SctActv; TchrAde; SchPpr; Ftbl; LetterSwmmng; LetterTrk; College; Attorney.

SHEPHERD, Judith L; West Chicago Community HS; West Chicago, IL; 13/321 Band; CncrtBnd; HonRl; MrchBnd; NHS; Orch; PepBnd; SchMus;.

SHEPHERD, Julia; Circle HS; Benton, KS; Chrs; HonRl; Mdrgl; SchMus; Yrbk; SciCl; IMSpt; PresAwd; Univ; Teaching.

SHEPHERD, Karen M; Platteville HS; Platteville, WI; HonRl; HospAde; LitMag; LbryAde; RptrSchPpr; FHA; FNA; FSA; FrCl; JCAwd; College; Interior Decorator.

SHEPHERD, Kent M; Marietta HS; Gary, SD; 13/20 HstFrshCls; HstSophCls; ALBoysSt; HonRl; SchPl; StuGov; YthFlsp; RptrSchPpr; 4-H; Bsktbl; College.

SHEPHERD, Maxine; Oak Park Acad; Pierre, SD; SecFrshCls; Chr; ChrhWkr; CmntyWkr; HonRl; Trade; Professional.

SHEPHERD, Nancy S; Central Catholic HS; Bloomington, IL; 9/81 SecFrshCls; CmntyWkr; HonRl; SchPl; Yrbk; FHA; FrCl; PpCl; Il Wesleyan Univ; Special Ed.

SHEPHERD, Paula; Herbert Henry Dow HS; Midland, MI; 33/433 HonRl; NHS; SpnCl; Trk; Mich St Univ.

SHEPHERD, Rebecca S; Hamilton HS; Hamilton, IN; 2/75 SecSrCls; HonRl; NHS; SchMus; 4-H; SpnCl; PresPpCl; LetterBsktbl; Swmmng; Trk; Indiana Univ; Medicine.

SHEPHERD, Warren D; Garden County HS; Oshkosh, NE; Chrs; HonRl; SchPl; SctActv; 4-H; PresSpnCl; Bsbl; Bsktbl; LetterFtbl; LetterTrk; University; Engineer.

SHEPHERD, William H; Broad Ripple HS; Indianapolis, IN; 14/300 ChrhWkr; HonRl; NHS; NatlMeritSF; Univ Of Georgia; Music.

SHEPPARD, Barbara A; Cheboygan Area HS; Cheboygan, MI; 47/200 Band; HonRl; PolWkr; SchPl; StuGov; FrCl; SpnCl; PpCl; Tennis; Trk; Northwestern Mich.

SHEPPARD, Garry G; Lesterville HS; Boss, MO; PresFrshCls; PresSophCls; PresJrCls; PresSrCls; Band; ChrhWkr; SchPl; Bsbl; Bsktbl; MasAwd; Rankan Trade.

SHEPPARD, Jeff A; Cary Grove HS; Cary, IL; 44/280 ChrhWkr; SctActv; SchPpr; College; Engineering.

SHEPPARD, Julie A; Riggs HS; Pierre, SD; 18/250 CmntyWkr; HonRl; HospAde; YthFlsp; FBLA; SpnCl; PpCl; IMSpt; PPFtbl; U Of Sd; Special Education Teacher.

SHEPPARD, Thomas A; Pittsfield HS; Pittsfield, IL; Band; ChrhWkr; CncrtBnd; HonRl; MrchBnd; PepBnd; 4-H; FFA; KeyCl; LatCl; College; Agriculture.

SHEPPELMAN, Rebecca S; Ford Central HS; Loda, IL; AFS; Band; Chrs; HonRl; MrchBnd; SpnCl; PpCl; LetterBsktbl; LetterTrk; Chrldr; JCAwd; PresAwd; College; Professional.

SHEPPERD, Edna M; Ursuline Acad; Kirkwood, MO; CmntyWkr; HonRl; JA; NatlMeritCmnd; SchMus; SchPl; TchrAde; FrCl; GAA; JAAwd; Medical Sch; Psychoanalysist.

SHEPUTIS, Lynn; South Haven HS; South Haven, MI; ChrhWkr; HonRl; NHS; StuGov; TchrAde; YthFlsp; Swmmng; College; Psychotherapy.

SHERA, Barbara J; Laurel HS; Laurel, IN; 2/45 ALAGirlsSt; DrlTm; HonRl; NHS; Twrl; EdSchPpr; 4-H; PpCl; Chrldr; DARAwd; Ball St Univ; Teaching.

SHERBON, Mary A; North Linn HS; Center Point, IA; Chrs; ChrhWkr; HonRl; JrNHS; LbryAde; SchMus; FBLA; Coll; Med.

SHERBURN, Cynthia J; Berrien Springs HS; Berrien Center, MI; 2/115 SecFrshCls; TrsSrCls; NHS; NatlMeritSF; NatlThespSoc; PresMthCl; PresSciCl; LetterTrk; Chrldr; GAA; DARAwd; College; Medical Doctor.

SHERBURN, Mary J; Britton HS; Britton, SD; 15/75 Chr; PresHonRl; LbryAde; SchPl; YthFlsp; RptrSchPpr; Pres4-H; PresFNA; VoiceDemAwd; College; Nursing.

SHERCK, Richard M; Lakeland HS; La Grange, IN; 24/125 AFS; ChrhWkr; StuCncl; YthFlsp; MthCl; PpCl; LetterGlf; Coll; Bus.

SHERE, Mark E; Malvern Comm HS; Malvern, IA; Band; CncrtBnd; MrchBnd; PepBnd; SciCl; LetterBsbl; Bsktbl; LetterFtbl; LetterTrk; College; Vocation.

SHERF, Melissa M; Shawnee Mission South HS; Leawood, KS; ChrhWkr; DrlTm; HonRl; HospAde; NHS; StuCncl; SpnCl; PpCl; College.

SHERIDAN, Dana D; Rosiclare HS; Elizabethtown, IL; HonRl; SctActv;.

SHERIDAN, Joan; E J HS; East Jordan, MI; 5/75 Band; NHS; PepBnd; SchPl; SctActv; StuCncl; EdYrBk; EdSchPpr; Trk; Us Navy; Journalism.

SHERIDAN, Patricia A; Joliet West HS; Joliet, IL; ChrhWkr; CmntyWkr; HospAde; StuCncl; StuGov; SchPpr; Bsbl; LetterBsktbl; LetterTrk; GAA; IMSpt; St Joseph Hosp; Nursing.

SHERIDAN, Peter D; Gibson Southern HS; Haubstadt, IN; 3/230 VPFrshCls; VPJrCls; VPSrCls; ChrhWkr; PpCl; SciCl; LetterFtbl; LetterWrstlng; BttyCrckrAwd; KiwanAwd; Clge; Medicine.

SHERIDAN, Philip E; Merrill HS; Merrill, MI; HonRl; SchPl; CmntyWkr; TchrAde; Bsbl; Glf; LetterWrstlng; W Mi Univ; Pre Med.

SHERIDAN, Sally J; Newton HS; Ste Marie, IL; 10/200 HonRl; NHS; MthCl; PpCl; PresGAA; IMSpt; Eastern Il Univ; Math Teacher.

SHERIDAN, Sheri L; Lincoln Co R 2 HS; Elsberry, MO; 6/70 CncrtBnd; HonRl; NHS; SchPl; RptrYrbk; RptrSchPpr; FBLA; St Louis College; Pharmacist.

SHERIDAN, Teresa A; Jayhawk Linn HS; Mound, KS; Chrs; CmntyWkr; SctActv; RptrYrbk; Yrbk; RptrSchPpr; SchPpr; 4-H; FHA; Trk; Xray Tech.

SHERIDAN, Terri A; St Mary S Springs HS; Fon Du Lac, WI; ChrhWkr; CmntyWkr; LbryAde; PolWkr; SchPl; StuCncl; StuGov; TchrAde; RptrYrbk; LetterBsbl; Uw La Crosse; Physical Education.

SHERIDAN, Thomas; Marist Hs; Chicago, IL; HonRl; LetterBsktbl; LetterFtbl; Western Illinois U; Accounting.

SHERIFF, Randy D; R 7 HS; Sweet Springs, MO; TrsSophCls; HonRl; NHS; SciCl; Bsktbl; College; Professional.

SHERLOCK, Dennis E; Hemingford HS; Hemingford, NE; Band; Chr; CncrtBnd; MrchBnd; PepBnd; SchMus; Yrbk; LetterBsktbl; LetterFtbl; LetterTrk; College; Athletic Trainer.

SHERLOCK, E Todd; St Francis Comm HS; St Francis, KS; 20/55 HonRl; JA; SchPl; EdSchPpr; Pres4-H; Bsktbl; LetterTrk; DanFAwd; 4-HAwd; CitAwd; Oklahoma State Univ; Broadcasting.

SHERMAN, Anne M; Duchesne HS; St Charles, MO; 13/134 Chrs; HonRl; NHS; NatlMeritCmnd; Sacrstn; StuCncl; RptrYrbk; CitAwd; VoiceDemAwd; St Louis Univ; Nursing.

SHERMAN, Barbara; Maine West Hs; Des Plaines, IL; HonRl; LbryAde; StuCncl; RptrSchPpr; Western Ill U; Business Education.

SHERMAN, Bradley S; Glenbard North HS; Lombard, IL; Illinois St Univ; Business.

SHERMAN, Brian; Colomus Community HS; Colomus, IA; 4/28 VPFrshCls; ChrhWkr; HonRl; NHS; SchPl; GerCl; SciCl; AmLegAwd; Acad Of Radio & Television; Broadcasting.

SHERMAN, Daniel J; Clear Lake HS; Goodwin, SD; PresFrshCls; HonRl; SchPpr; Ftbl; Trk; College; Professional.

SHERMAN, Daniel W; South Haven HS; South Haven, MI; 3/219 ChrhWkr; NHS; StuGov; TchrAde; RptrYrbk; Bsbl; Bsktbl; Ftbl; AmLegAwd; KiwanAwd; College; Teaching.

SHERMAN, David J; Hannibal Sr HS; Hannibal, MO; Band; CncrtBnd; HonRl; MrchBnd; NHS; StuCncl; LetterBsbl; Univ Of Mo Columbia; Chemistry Major.

SHERMAN, Diane K; Harvard HS; Harvard, IL; VPJrCls; Chr; Chrl; Chrs; HonRl; StuCncl; Yrbk; VPFrCl; Coll; Business.

SHERMAN, Frances M; Valentine HS; Valentine, NE; Chr; HonRl; LbryAde; SchMus; StuCncl; YthFlsp; 4-H; FHA; LetterTrk; IMSpt; Clge; Pro.

SHERMAN, James B; Winona Senior HS; Minnesotacity, MN; Chr; HonRl; Mdrgl; SchMus; SchPl; College; Music.

SHERMAN, Julie K; Dickinson HS; Dickinson, ND; ALAGirlsSt; Chrl; ChrhWkr; HonRl; ModUN; NatlFornLg; NHS; NatlThespSoc; SchMus; SchPl; College.

SHERMAN, Karl D; Marquette HS; Marquette, NE; 8/16 VPSophCls; Band; CAP; CncrtBnd; MrchBnd; NatlThespSoc; PepBnd; YthFlsp; LetterFtbl; 4-HAwd; U Of Ne Lincoln; Ag.

SHERMAN, Kathy C; Boone Grove HS; Valparaiso, IN; 1/64 TreasBand; HonRl; SecNHS; OffAde; YthFlsp; RptrYrbk; RptrSchPpr; Pres4-H; PresSpnCl; VPGAA; 4-HAwd; Valparaiso Univ; Teacher.

SHERMAN, Mark C; North Side HS; Ft Wayne, IN; 10/438 Chr; CncrtBnd; HonRl; JA; Mdrgl; SecTrsFrshCls; NHS; PepBnd; StuCncl; IMSpt; Manchester Ciollege; Accounting.

SHERMAN, Mark J; Carthage HS; Carthage, IL; 3/95 PresJrCls; ChrhWkr; HonRl; NHS; LetterBsbl; Bsktbl; CaptFtbl; Western Ill Univ; Business Management.

SHERMAN, Mary; Rbc HS; Richmond, IL; HonRl; ModUN; PepBnd; PpCl; Chrldr; PresAwd; Coll; Professional.

SHERMAN, Milli J; Bloomington HS; Bloomington, WI; 4/60 ALAGirlsSt; Band; Chrs; Mdrgl; NatlFornLg; NHS; SchMus; SchPl; Bsktbl; Trk; Chrldr; GAA; University; Special Ed.

SHERMAN, Pamela A; Central Cass HS; Amenia, ND; Chr; Chrs; HonRl; NHS; SchPl; Yrbk; LetterTrk; GAA; College; Professional.

SHERMAN, Patricia; St Charles HS; St Charles, MI; /150 Coll; Prof.

SHERMAN, Robert V; St Johns Prep HS; Apple Valley, MN; HonRl; SchPl; StuCncl; Yrbk; SchPpr; GerCl; Bsktbl; Trk; Denver Univ; Biology.

SHERMAN, Timothy V; Mt Carmel HS; Mt Carmel, IL; Band; Quill&Scroll; Yrbk; 4-H; LatCl; SciCl; U Of Evansville; Radiologic Tech.

SHERRARD, Charles; West Washington HS; Fredericksburg, IN; 5/78 HonRl; NHS; NatlThespSoc; TchrAde; Yrbk; LatCl; Indiana Univ; Medical Doctor.

SHERRELL, Carla J; Crispus Attucks HS; Indianapolis, IN; 4/230 Chr; ChrhWkr; CmntyWkr; HonRl; NHS; NatlMeritSF; Orch; SchMus; StuGov; Ball State Univ; Music.

SHERRILL, Debbie S; South Iron HS; Annapolis, MO; 1/32 SecJrCls; Chrs; ChrhWkr; NatlMeritSF; 4-H; PpCl; AmLegAwd; Coll; Prof.

SHERRILL, Donald A; Poplar Bluff Sr HS; Poplar Bluff, MO; ChrhWkr; HonRl; NatlMeritCmnd; SchPl; SciCl; Univ Of Mo; Computer Science.

SHERROD, Carmen L; Arlington HS; Indianapolis, IN; 64/478 Chr; Chrs; DrlTm; HonRl; JA; NatlMeritCmnd; College; Accounting.

SHERRY, Kristi; Onalaska HS; Onalaska, WI; 7/130 Chr; HonRl; NHS; GAA;.

SHERRY, Michael; New Lothrop HS; New Lothrop, MI; ChrhWkr; NatlFornLg; NatlMeritSF; SchPl; TchrAde; RptrYrbk; RptrSchPpr; SptEdSchPpr; Olivet Coll Olivet Mi; State Police Admin.

SHERRY, Thomas E; Mt Carmel HS; Crestwood, IL; 23/225 HonRl; JrNHS; NHS; Lewis University; Lawyer.

SHERWIN, Gary; North Greene HS; Roodhouse, IL; College; Vocation.

SHERWIN, Kristine; Missouri Valley HS; Missouri Valley, IA; RptrSchPpr; 4-H; FNA; FTA; PpCl; College; Religion.

SHERWIN, Rhonda J; Ness City HS; Beeler, KS; ALAGirlsSt; Band; HonRl; NHS; NatlThespSoc; 4-H; SecFHA; Bsbl; LetterBsktbl; AmLegAwd; 4-HAwd; College; Professional.

SHERWOOD, Barbara J; Nerinx Hall HS; Webster Groves, MO; HonRl; JA; OffAde; StuCncl; CivCl; RotaryAwd; Southeast Missouri State U; Bus Admin.

SHERWOOD, Carol A; Shelbyville HS; Shelbyville, IL; 27/150 SecTrsFrshCls; VPSophCls; Band; ChrhWkr; SchMus; SecStuCncl; 4-H; PpCl; CaptTrk; CaptChrldr; Southern Il Univ; Phy Ed.

SHERWOOD, Jane M; Breckenridge HS; Breckenridge, MI; 2/94 VPJrCls; HonRl; NHS; EdYrBk; PpCl; Chrldr; DARAwd; Journalism.

SHERWOOD, Leslie M; Mobridge HS; Mc Laughlin, SD; Band; CncrtBnd; HonRl; MrchBnd; OffAde; PepBnd; TchrAde; 4-H; FTA; Northern State College; Elementary Educ.

SHERWOOD, Linda M; Burlington Comm HS; Burlington, IA; 41/456 VPFrshCls; Chr; HonRl; NHS; StuCncl; ChmnPpCl; Trk; LetterChrldr; IMSpt; KiwanAwd; Southeastern Community; Secretarial.

SHERWOOD, Mary E; Pittsville HS; Pittsville, WI; Chr; Chrl; HonRl; Mdrgl; FBLA; PpCl; LetterChrldr; Mid State Tech Institute; Medical Asst.

SHERWOOD, Steve D; St Marys HS; St Louis, MO; 44/198 ChrhWkr; JA; SchPl; SctActv; Sdlty; StuCncl; Ftbl; IMSpt; Univ Of Mo At Rolla; Computer Programer.

SHETLEY, Kevin L; Riverton HS; Galena, KS; 19/51 VPSrCls; HonRl; Mdrgl; ModUN; NHS; Orch; SchMus; SchPl; Yrbk; SchPpr; Kscp; Prof.

SHEVLIN, Elizabeth A; Immaculate Conception HS; Elmhurst, IL; 45/184 Aud/Vis; HonRl; FrCl; PpCl; Bsktbl; GAA; IMSpt; Coll; Health Ser.

SHEWAN, Eleanore J; Valparaiso HS; Valparaiso, IN; Band; CncrtBnd; MrchBnd; PepBnd; Valparaiso Univ; Professional.

SHEWMAKE, James W; Lyons Twp HS; Western Springs, IL; Indiana Univ; Biology.

SHEWMAKER, Lloyd; Western Christian College HS; Grand Forks, ND; Chrs; ChrhWkr; HonRl; College; Computers.

SHEY, Jane E; Garrigan HS; Algona, IA; 24/103 VPJrCls; Band; Chr; Chrs; ChrhWkr; CncrtBnd; HonRl; MrchBnd; OffAde; PepBnd; CaptBsktbl; LetterTennis; Trk; 4-HAwd; College; Guidance Counseling.

SHEYER, Susan E; Whitefish Bay HS; Milwaukee, WI; 7/325 HonRl; NHS; NatlMeritCmnd; StuCncl; RptrYrbk; EdYrBk; FrCl; Univ; Teacher.

SHEZAK, Gerald D; Milligan Public HS; Milligan, NE; PresSrCls; ALBoysSt; Chrs; HonRl; SchMus; SchPl; StuCncl; LetterBsktbl; LetterTrk; Univ Of Nebr; Agriculture.

SHIDE, Georgiann; South Newton HS; Brook, IN; Chr; ChrhWkr; CmntyWkr; LbryAde; OffAde; Quill&Scroll; SchMus; SchPl; SctActv; Yrbk; RptrSchPpr; 4-H; PPFtbl; Indiana University.

SHIDE, Patricia; Larimore HS; Larimore, ND; VPJrCls; CncrtBnd; HonRl; MrchBnd; StuCncl; SptEdYrbk; SpnCl; MthCl; PpCl; Ndsu; Computer Programmer.

SHIELD, Gary W; Holdrege HS; Holdrege, NE; Chrs; SchMus; Yrbk; Univ Of Ne; Zoology.

SHIELDS, Beth A; Eastbrook HS; Marion, IN; 4-H; SpnCl; PpCl; Chrldr; GAA; 4-HAwd; In Comm Col; Physical Therapy.

SHIELDS, Charles A; Cheboygan Area HS; Cheboygan, MI; 11/219 HonRl; NHS; LetterBsktbl; LetterFtbl; Ferris St College; Auto Service.

SHIELDS, Darlene; Roger C Sullivan HS; Chicago, IL; PresSrCls; VPSrCls; Band; CtyCnl; CncrtBnd; HonRl; NHS; NatlMeritFnl; OffAde; StuCncl; YthFnd; SchPpr; FBLA; FDA;.

SHIELDS, Mary; Iowa Grant HS; Cobb, WI; 6/120 PresJrCls; ChrhWkr; CncrtBnd; HonRl; NHS; NatlThespSoc; SchPl; StuCncl; Bsktbl; Chrldr; Univ Of Wis Platteville; Broadcasting.

SHIELDS, Sally J; Springs Valley HS; West Baden, IN; SecJrCls; HonRl; NHS; StuCncl; Yrbk; PpCl; Bsktbl; Trk; Indiana St Univ.

SHIELDS, Sarita A; Maplewood Acad; Minneapolis, MN; 4/67 Band; ChrhWkr; HonRl; LbryAde; SchPl; RptrYrbk; Bsbl; So Missionary Coll; History.

SHIELDS, Shonda W; Cathedral HS; Chicago, IL; 36/128 PresSrCls; JrNHS; NHS; NatlMeritFnl; NatlMeritSchl; EdYrBk; FBLA; CaptBsktbl; CaptChrldr; JAAwd; VoiceDemAwd; University; Professional.

SHIELDS, Sue; Oakland HS; Hindsboro, IL; 2/64 HospAde; NHS; PolWkr; RedCrAde; SchAde; TchrAde; SpnCl; SciCl; U Of Illinois; Professional Medical.

SHIELDS, Susan M; Wahlert HS; Dubuque, IA; Chr; HonRl; LbryAde; NHS; RptrYrbk; EdSchPpr; SecMthCl; Glf; Univ; Pharmacy.

SHIELDS, Walter J; Oakland HS; Hindsboro, IL; 5/42 VPSrCls; Band; CncrtBnd; HonRl; MrchBnd; Orch; PepBnd; SchPl; StuGov; Yrbk; U Of Ill; Engineering.

SHIER, Craig W; Portage Northern HS; Portage, MI; Band; HonRl; NatlMeritSF; Orch; TchrAde; Mi St U; Engineering.

SHIERS, Becky J; Lyman HS; Henry, NE; 2/15 SecSophCls; VPJrCls; Chrs; CaptDrlTm; HonRl; SchMus; EdYrBk; VPFNA; PpCl; Chrldr; Colorado St Univ; Accountan.

SHIERS, Rebecca J; Lyman HS; Henry, NE; 2/16 SecSophCls; VPJrCls; Chrs; ChmnDrlTm; HonRl; SchMus; ChmnRptrYrbk; VPFNA; PpCl; Chrldr; U Of Co; Acct.

SHIEVER, Alan R; Coloma HS; Coloma, MI; 32/172 HonRl; NHS; RedCrAde; LatCl; Bsktbl; W Michigan Univ; Food Distribution.

SHIKOSKI, Barbara L; Green Lake Public HS; Green Lake, WI; 16/45 HonRl; SchPl; RptrSchPpr; LatCl; Vet Assistant; Vocation.

SHILEY, David C; Unity HS; Sidney, IL; 15/143 ALBoysSt; HonRl; MrchBnd; NHS; PepBnd; SctActv; 4-H; FFA; Bsktbl; Trk; Southern Illinois U; Forestry.

SHILLING, Robert W; Thornton Township HS; Riverdale, IL; Aud/Vis; ChrhWkr; CmntyWkr; IntrClCncl; OffAde; PolWkr; SchAde; Trade Schl; Automotive.

SHILLINGTON, Thomas P; Clarion Community HS; Clarion, IA; 1/93 HonRl; NatlMeritCmnd; YthFlsp; 4-H; LetterBsbl; LetterBsktbl; CaptFtbl; LetterTrk; BauchLmbAwd; Air Force Academy; Engineering.

SHILT, Anne D; Appleton West HS; Appleton, WI; SecFrshCls; ChrhWkr; SchAde; SchPl; SchPpr; PpCl; Chrldr; College; Nursing.

SHILT, Jean M; Plymouth HS; Plymouth, IN; 15/221 ALAGirlsSt; Chr; ChrhWkr; HonRl; NHS; SchMus; TchrAde; TreasYthFlsp; FTA; MthCl; PpCl; LetterBsktbl; LetterTennis; Indiana Central Univ; Math.

SHIMER, Pamela K; Wateruliet HS; Wateruliet, MI; 6/96 VPJrCls; Band; HonRl; MrchBnd; NHS; PepBnd; TchrAde; Yrbk; RptrSchPpr; Bsbl; Nm State; Cpa.

SHIMMIN, Celia M; Roseville HS; Roseville, IL; 1/52 Band; HonRl; NHS; YthFlsp; FFA; KeyCl; PpCl; GAA; DanFAwd; VP4-HAwd; U Of Illinois; Homemaker.

SHIMON, Alan J; Pocahontas Community HS; Pocahontas, IA; VPFrshCls; VPSophCls; HonRl; PpCl; LetterBsktbl; LetterFtbl; LetterGlf; Creighton University; Business.

SHIMON, Kay; Reedsville HS; Whitelaw, WI; 3/99 HonRl; NHS; PepBnd; SchPl; EdYrBk; Univ Of Madison; Communicat Art.

SHINABERY, Cindy A; Ovid Elsie HS; Ovid, MI; HonRl; LitMag; NHS; EdYrBk; RptrSchPpr; PpCl; GAA; PPFtbl; College; Journalism.

SHINE, Jeri L; Valley HS; Des Moines, IA; 5/440 Band; ChrhWkr; CncrtBnd; HonRl; MrchBnd; NHS; NatlMeritSF; Orch; PepBnd; YthFlsp; Univ.

SHINN, Donald E; Pawnee City HS; Du Bois, NE; 2/31 ALBoysSt; HonRl; RptrSchPpr; EdSchPpr; PresFFA; Univ; Mech Engin.

SHINN, Lyle R; Northridge HS; Bristol, IN; HonRl; NHS; 4-H; KeyCl; PpCl; LetterFtbl; LetterTrk; IMSpt; College.

SHINNESS, Nancy; Richmond Senior HS; Richmond, IN; 218/634 HonRl; JA; PolWkr; StuGov; Teen; 4-H; PpCl; In Univ; Teacher.

SHINNICK, Daniel L; Madison West HS; Madison, WI; HonRl; LetterBsktbl; Ftbl; U Of Wi; Law.

SHINNICK, Peggy F; St Bede Academy; Peru, IL; Chrs; HonRl; SchMus; TchrAde; Trk; Chrldr; College.

SHIPBAUGH, Calvin L; Huntington North HS; Huntington, IN; Aud/Vis; SchPpr; SciCl; College; Physicist.

SHIPLEY, Connie S; Archie HS; Archie, MO; 13/36 CmntyWkr; JrNHS; NatlMeritSchl; RedCrAde; StuGov; UNYO; DARAwd; GodCntryAwd; CitAwd; VoiceDemAwd; Univ.

SHIPLEY, David O; Jefferson City HS; Jefferson City, MO; 6/502 CncrtBnd; HonRl; JA; NatlMeritSF; Orch; StuCncl; LatCl; MthCl; SciCl; JAAwd; Bus Admin.

SHIPLEY, Lynnette J; Jennings HS; Jennings, KS; 2/22 PresJrCls; TrsSrCls; HonRl; Yrbk; FFA; FHA; PpCl; LetterBsktbl; LetterTrk; Chrldr; College; Secretarial.

SHIPLEY, Richard; Unity HS; Tolono, IL; LbryAde; SctActv; GerCl; SciCl;.

SHIPLEY, Terry J; Whiteland Comm HS; Whiteland, IN; 25/184 HonRl; FTA; ChmnKeyCl; FrCl; LetterFtbl; LetterWrstlng; Col; English.

SHIPMAN, Wilma J; Bernie HS; Bernie, MO; 3/56 SecSophCls; ChrhWkr; HonRl; Quill&Scroll; SchAde; SchPl; StuCncl; StuGov; RptrYrbk; FshEdSchPpr; Oral Roberts Univ; Study Pre Law.

SHIPPEN, Larry J; Friend Public HS; Friend, NE; Band; ChrhWkr; CncrtBnd; MrchBnd; PepBnd; LetterTrk; LetterWrstlng; IMSpt; Southeast Comm College; Carpenter.

SHIREK, Patricia J; Michigan HS; Lankin, ND; SecFrshCls; VPSophCls; Band; Chrs; CncrtBnd; HonRl; MrchBnd; PepBnd; RptrSchPpr; EdSchPpr; PpCl; LetterTrk; Chrldr; Univ Of North Dakota.

SHIREY, Jamie R; Pittsford HS; Osseo, MI; Band; CncrtBnd; HonRl; MrchBnd; OffAde; Bsktbl; Trk; Chrldr; GAA; PresAwd; Coll; Pro.

SHIRK, Kevin W; Highland HS; Chesterfield, IN; 52/260 CmntyWkr; HonRl; PolWkr; FDA; KeyCl; LatCl; SciCl; Bsbl; LetterFtbl; LetterTrk; Indiana University; Denistry.

SHIRLEY, Denise; North Platte Sr Hs; North Platte, NE; 46/393 CncrtBnd; HonRl; MrchBnd; VPYthFlsp; YthLg; 4-H; VPFHA; Trk; GAA; 4-HAwd; University Of Nebraska; Home Economics.

SHIRLEY, Jerry W; Ruskin HS; Kansas City, MO; 38/394 HonRl; MthCl; JETSAwd; Longview Comm College; Professional.

SHIRLEY, Lee A; Laville Jr Sr HS; Lakeville, IN; Aud/Vis; Band; ChrhWkr; CncrtBnd; MrchBnd; NHS; SpnCl; PpCl; LetterTennis; School Of Nursing; Nursing.

SHIRLEY, Lou A; Laville Jr Sr HS; Lakeville, IN; ChrhWkr; CncrtBnd; HonRl; NHS; Orch; 4-H; SpnCl; Chrldr; 4-HAwd; PresAwd; College.

SHIRLEY, Mark D; Maywood HS; Maywood, NE; 3/23 VPFrshCls; VPSophCls; VPJrCls; VPSrCls; ALBoysSt; Band; Chr; Chrs; ChrhWkr; CncrtBnd; HonRl; LetterBsktbl; LetterFtbl; LetterTrk; Hastings College.

SHIRLEY, Michael H; Evanston Township HS; Evanston, IL; HonRl; LbryAde; NatlMeritSF; GerCl; College; Teaching.

SHIRLEY, Nancy J; South Side HS; Fort Wayne, IN; 58/438 AFS; CmntyWkr; HonRl; LbryAde; NatlFornLg; SchMus; SctActv; RptrSchPpr; Trk; GAA; College; Theatre.

SHIRLEY, Pamela A; M D R HS; Minonk, IL; 4/59 ALAGirlsSt; HonRl; OffAde; SchPl; SecStuCncl; SpnCl; PpCl; GAA; PPFtbl; College; Professional.

SHIRLEY, Sandra L; Athens HS; Athens, MI; ChrhWkr; CmntyWkr; NHS; OffAde; Quill&Scroll; SchPl; StuCncl; YthFlsp; Yrbk; RptrSchPpr; SptEdSchPpr; Treas4-H; LetterTrk; Chrldr; Business School; Secretary.

SHIRLEY, Valoree L; Perry Community HS; Perry, IA; 29/145 HonRl; IntrClCncl; LbryAde; NatlFornLg; TchrAde; Art School; Artist.

SHIVELY, Carmen M; Monroe City R 1 HS; Hunnewell, MO; 3/93 HonRl; SecNHS; RptrYrbk; RptrSchPpr; PresFHA; FSA; Univ Of Mo At Columbia; Accountancy.

SHIVELY, Linda S; Oregon Davis HS; Hamlet, IN; Aud/Vis; ChrhWkr; HonRl; Sec4-H; FHA; PpCl; 4-HAwd; Univ; Dietitian.

SHIVELY, Mary Jo; Manistee Catholic Central HS; Manistee, MI; 12/70 Chr; ChrhWkr; CmntyWkr; HonRl; LbryAde; NHS; RedCrAde; TchrAde; EdYrBk; PpCl; College; Special Education.

SHIVELY, Steven D; North Wood HS; Nappanee, IN; 60/198 ChrhWkr; CmntyWkr; 4-H; PpCl; Ftbl; Trk; Wrstlng; 4-HAwd; Ball State University; Industrial Arts.

SHIVERDECKER, Georgann; Van Far R 1 HS; Vandalia, MO; 9/92 SecFrshCls; TrsSophCls; TreasNHS; FHA; TreasFTA; Mid American Nazarene Clg; Accountant.

SHIVERS, Douglas R; Richland HS; Richland, MO; ChrhWkr; HonRl; StuCncl; FFA; College; Minister.

SHIVERS, Robert L; Lindblom Tech HS; Chicago, IL; 346/695 LetterDrlTm; DrmBgl; LitMag; NatlMeritCmnd; ROTC; SchAde; Trk; Yale Univ; Law.

SHIVES, Aaron B; Milbank HS; Milbank, SD; 1/127 PresSrCls; HonRl; NHS; YthFlsp; PresFFA; PresKeyCl; LetterFtbl; AmLegAwd; Univ; Chemistry.

SHLAY, Judith C; Homewood Flossmoor HS; Flossmoor, IL; 165/940 AFS; Band; CmntyWkr; CncrtBnd; HonRl; LitMag; MrchBnd; PepBnd; Univ Of Illinois; Doctor.

SHMIGELSKY, Bruce A; Lane Tech HS; Chicago, IL; 540/1267 De Paul U; Business.

SHOAF, Norman L; Mc Kinley HS; St Louis, MO; 1/223 TrsSophCls; ALBoysSt; HonRl; RptrYrbk; RptrSchPpr; FTA; SciCl; Tennis; BauchLmbAwd; DanFAwd; Ambasador Col; Communications.

SHOBE, Alan W; Brainerd HS; Brainerd, MN; 54/465 Chr; ChrhWkr; HonRl; NHS; Quill&Scroll; SctActv; YthFlsp; SchPpr; University Of Montana; Forestry.

SHOBE, Georgia A; Hannibal Sr HS; Hannibal, MO; 26/277 ChrhWkr; HonRl; LbryAde; NHS; SpnCl; LetterBsktbl; GAA; IMSpt; Univ Of Missouri; Law.

SHOBERG, David J; Kenyon HS; Kenyon, MN; Chr; ChrhWkr; HonRl; 4-H; FFA; FrCl; Ftbl; Wrstlng; College; Porfessional Pilot.

SHOBERG, Thomas G; Roncalli HS; Omaha, NE; HonRl; JA; NHS; StuGov; SciCl; U Of Ne; Astrophysics.

SHOCK, Christopher D; Linden HS; Linden, MI; 37/154 CmntyWkr; TchrAde; SciCl; Bsbl; Glf; Mi St Univ; Natural Science.

SHOCKEY, David D; Dakota Comm HS; Ridott, IL; 1/78 PresFrshCls; PresSophCls; PresJrCls; Band; SchPl; PresStuCncl; EdSchPpr; 4-H; FFA; DanFAwd; Univ Of Illinois; Economics.

SHOCKLEY, Beth A; Winchester Comm HS; Winchester, IN; Chr; Chrs; SchMus; YthFlsp; FBLA; FHA; FNA; PpCl; 4-HAwd; Asbury Col; Mission Field.

SHOCKLEY, Mark H; Pike HS; Indianapolis, IN; 38/268 Band; CncrtBnd; HonRl; JrNHS; MrchBnd; SchMus; Glf; CaptTennis; IMSpt;.

SHOCKMAN, Kevin; Lamoore Hs; La Moure, ND; 7/45 ALBoysSt; HonRl; SptEdSchPpr; FFA; LetterBsbl; CaptBsktbl; CaptFtbl; Trk; CitAwd;.

SHOCKMAN, Phyllis A; La Moure Public HS; Lamoure, ND; VPSrCls; Band; Chr; Chrs; CncrtBnd; HonRl; Bsktbl; Trk; Chrldr; GAA; Nd St U ; Med.

SHOEMAKER, Anne L; Dakota HS; Dakota, IL; 4/76 TrsSophCls; SecJrCls; SecSrCls; ChrhWkr; CmntyWkr; HonRl; StuCncl; TchrAde; YthFlsp; Yrbk; SchPpr; College; Social Work.

SHOEMAKER, Cynthia A; West Sioux Comm HS; Hawarden, IA; Band; Chr; Chrs; ChrhWkr; CncrtBnd; HonRl; MrchBnd; Orch; PepBnd; SchMus;.

SHOEMAKER, Deborah K; Carroll HS; Bringhurst, IN; 33/136 HonRl; LbryAde; RptrSchPpr; PpCl; LetterBsktbl; Tennis; LetterTrk; GAA; IMSpt; PPFtbl; Ball State Univ; Physical Ed Teacher.

SHOEMAKER, Kimberly A; Vienna HS; Vienna, IL; VPFrshCls; SecTrsJrCls; HonRl; Twrl; Yrbk; 4-H; PpCl; DanFAwd; College.

SHOEMAKER, Lisa G; Brownstown Central HS; Vallonia, IN; 1/143 VPSophCls; SecSrCls; Chr; HonRl; SecNHS; SchMus; Pres4-H; FTA; PresLatCl; SciCl; College; Teacher.

SHOEMAKER, Robert J; Winner Sr HS; Winner, SD; 10/133 ALBoysSt; HonRl; NatlThespSoc; SchMus; SchPl; PresSciCl; Bsbl; Bsktbl; Tennis; Wrstlng; IMSpt; AmLegAwd; Kansas St Univ; Veterinarian.

SHOEMAKER, Sarah K; Bentley HS; Livonia, MI; VPFrshCls; Chr; Chrs; ChrhWkr; HonRl; NHS; OffAde; SchPl; StuGov; TchrAde; College; Teacher.

SHOEMAKER, Timothy V; William Fremd HS; Palatine, IL; 24/558 ChrhWkr; HonRl; NHS; Triton College; Business Management.

SHOENHAIR, Daniel R; Winnebago HS; Rockford, IL; 5/120 Band; Chrs; CncrtBnd; HonRl; MrchBnd; NHS; Orch; PepBnd; SchMus; Glf; Univ; Pro.

SHOENHAIR, Karla A; Martensdale St Marys HS; Prole, IA; 5/36 Chr; Chrs; DrlTm; HonRl; ModUN; SchMus; SchPl; Teen; UNYO; RptrYrbk; Bsbl; Trk; Iowa Trade School; Medical.

SHOENHAIR, Susan J; Swea City Comm HS; Bancroft, IA; 3/30 TrsSophCls; PresJrCls; Band; Chrs; DrmMjrt; MrchBnd; NHS; SchMus; LetterBsktbl; Trk; Iowa St Univ; Phy Ed.

SHOFROTH, Robert C; Hammond Baptist HS; St John, IN; SecFrshCls; TrsFrshCls; ChrhWkr; HonRl; SpnCl; Bsbl; Bsktbl; Hyles Anderson; Christian Ed.

SHOGER, Gordon L; Princeton HS; Princeton, MO; Chr; Chrl; ChrhWkr; HonRl; JA; NHS; NatlMeritSF; SchPl; 4-H; SciCl; University; Veterinarian.

SHOHOLM, Karen A; Harvard Comm HS; Harvard, IL; 18/160 SecTrsJrCls; SecTrsSrCls; HonRl; OffAde; StuCncl; RptrYrbk; RptrSchPpr; SpnCl; Business;.

SHOICHET, Andria L; Ida Crown Jewish Academy; Chicago, IL; 6/72 HonRl; NHS; Yrbk; College.

SHOLTS, Janice M; Oregon HS; Oregon, WI; TrsSophCls; ChrhWkr; HonRl; NatlMeritCmnd; StuCncl; Trade School; Medicine.

SHOLTZ, Mark; Guide Rock Public HS; Guide Rock, NE; SchMus; SchPl; StuCncl; RptrSchPpr; SptEdSchPpr; FBLA; Bsbl; Bsktbl; Ftbl; Trk; Univ; Business Education.

SHONK, Mark A; Hutsonville HS; Annapolis, IL; HonRl; StuCncl; SptEdSchPpr; SchPpr; FFA; IMSpt; DanFAwd; 4-HAwd; College; Teaching.

SHONKWILER, Barbara J; North Vermillion HS; Perrysville, IN; 13/71 Band; Chrs; ChrhWkr; HonRl; NHS; OffAde; VPYthFlsp; SecSpnCl; PresPpCl; GAA; Univ; Phy Educ.

SHONKWILER, Cindy K; Arcola HS; Arcola, IL; 4/63 ALAGirlsSt; HonRl; NHS; TchrAde; YthFlsp; SpnCl; CaptBsktbl; LetterFtbl; CaptTrk; PresGAA; Eastern Il Univ; Phys Ed.

SHONKWILER, Jeffery W; Centerville HS; Richmond, IN; 13/132 HonRl; NHS; YthFlsp; Ftbl; Glf; Ball State Univ; Political Science.

SHOOK, Randal; Northwestern HS; Lake Nebagamon, WI; CmntyWkr; HonRl; SctActv; Wrstlng; College; Professional.

SHOOK, Sara L; Lake Orion HS; Lake Orion, MI; PresFrshCls; TrsJrCls; TrsSrCls; CmntyWkr; HonRl; HospAde; LbryAde; NHS; NatlMeritSF; Chrldr; Mi State Univ.

SHOOKMAN, Ellis R; Huntington North HS; Huntington, IN; Ftbl; Coll; Law.

SHOOP, Linda K; Neodesha HS; Neodesha, KS; Chrs; ChrhWkr; HonRl; OffAde; Teen; SchPpr; FHA; PresFrCl; SpnCl; PpCl;.

SHOPE, John C; Barrington HS; Barrington, IL; 39/642 CmntyWkr; HonRl; JrNHS; NHS; NatlMeritCmnd; SchPl; StuCncl; RptrSchPpr; Univ Of Alabama; Medicine.

SHORB, Dava L; Enfield HS; Enfield, IL; 2/35 Chr; ChrhWkr; HonRl; FHA; Milligan Col; Teaching.

SHORE, Allan; Belding HS; Belding, MI; ALBoysSt; Aud/Vis; HonRl; SctActv; Tennis; CitAwd; Univ Of Nich; Law.

SHORE, Julia; Gasconade R 2 HS; Owensville, MO; CmntyWkr; HonRl; HospAde; NHS; SctActv; StuCncl; StuGov; YthFlsp; 4-H; FNA; Nursing School.

SHOREY, Ken A; Rosemount Senior HS; Apple Valley, MN; ChrhWkr; HonRl; SctActv; StuCncl; StuGov; YthFlsp; Ftbl; LetterSwmmng; College; Business Administration.

SHORMA, Thomas D; Wahpeton HS; Wahpeton, ND; Band; Chr; CncrtBnd; HonRl; NatlThespSoc; SchPl; KeyCl; Bsktbl; Ftbl; Tennis; College; Prof.

SHORT, Janet M; Brimfield HS; Brimfield, IL; 12/50 SecSrCls; Chrs; HonRl; NHS; NatlMeritCmnd; NatlMeritSchl; OffAde; StuCncl; Yrbk; SpnCl; Caterpiller Office Worker.

SHORT, Jay M; Randolph Southern HS; Lynn, IN; 3/55 HonRl; NHS; SchAde; Yrbk; 4-H; Col; Science.

SHORT, John A; Hackett HS; Portage, MI; HonRl; IMSpt; Western Mich Univ; Lawyer.

SHORT, Kenneth L; Crispus Attucks HS; Indianapolis, IN; 13/232 PresJrCls; ChrhWkr; HonRl; JA; NHS; StuCncl; LetterBsbl; IMSpt; JAAwd; Olivet Nazarene Col; Accountant.

SHORT, Kevin L; Crispus Attucks HS; Indianapolis, IN; ChrhWkr; HonRl; LetterBsbl; LetterBsktbl; Olivet Nazarene College; Business.

SHORT, Linda; Platteville Hs; Platteville, WI; Band; Chr; ChrhWkr; CmntyWkr; HonRl; Mdrgl; NatlMeritCmnd; PolWkr; SchMus; UNYO; Carleton Grinnell; Work At United Nations.

SHORT, Mark C; Garner Hayfield HS; Garner, IA; Chrs; ChrhWkr; CncrtBnd; HonRl; NHS; PepBnd; SchPl; StuGov; RptrYrbk; FDA; College; Gen Physician.

SHORT, Peggy S; Goodland HS; Goodland, KS; VPFrshCls; HstSophCls; Chr; Chrs; OffAde; Quill&Scroll; SchMus; StuCncl; Yrbk; Pres4-H; LetterBsktbl; LetterTrk; Chrldr; GAA; College; Teaching.

SHORT, Rick A; Farmer Cy Mansfield HS; Farmer City, IL; TrsFrshCls; TrsJrCls; TrsSrCls; AFS; Band; ChrhWkr; CncrtBnd; HonRl; MrchBnd; NHS; University.

SHORT, Susan M; Huron HS; Milwaukee, WI; 25/600 DrlTm; HonRl; PresJA; RptrYrbk; VPFrCl; JAAwd; University; Interior Design.

SHORT, Tamara J; Lapeer West HS; Lapeer, MI; 97/426 HospAde; MrchBnd; RedCrAde; Twrl; 4-H; PpCl; LetterTennis; IMSpt; 4-HAwd; Coll; Pro.

SHORTER, Rosemarie; Winamac Community HS; Winamac, IN; ; SecJrCls; SecSrCls; PresFrshCls; NHS; Yrbk; AmLegAwd; Coll; Dress Designs.

SHOTSBERGER, Gerald; Schaumburg HS; Schaumburg, IL; 13/537 HonRl; GerCl; IMSpt; Purdue Univ; Engineering.

SHOTT, Nancy L; Rich Township HS; Park Forest, IL; 12/326 PresJrCls; MrchBnd; NHS; StuCncl; FTA; Chrldr; Purdue Univ; Med/bio.

SHOTTON, Vicki L; Franklin HS; Livonia, MI; DrmBgl; HonRl; MrchBnd; OffAde; StuGov; Twrl; Bsbl; GAA; IMSpt; CitAwd; Coll; Professnl.

SHOUKLETOVICH, Susan D; Marion HS; Marion, IL; Band; ChrhWkr; CmntyWkr; DrlTm; HonRl; HospAde; IntrClCncl; JA; MrchBnd; VPNHS; Murray Univ; Nursing.

SHOULDERS, Charles R; Centerville HS; Richmond, IN; 10/128 HonRl; JrNHS; NHS; PresStuGov; SpnCl; Bsktbl; Trk; College; Wildlife Mgr.

SHOULTS, Cindy L; West Washington HS; Campbellsburg, IN; 11/84 HonRl; NHS; OffAde; Yrbk; 4-H; FHA; Bsktbl; Trk; GAA; Bus School; Vocation.

SHOULTZ, Janice K; Delavan HS; Delavan, IL; 20/68 SecFrshCls; Chr; Chrl; Chrs; HonRl; PpCl; Bsktbl; Chrldr; GAA; IMSpt; Business School; Secretary.

SHOUP, Barbara M; Carthage Community HS; Carthage, IL; Chrs; ChrhWkr; HonRl; LbryAde; PresNHS; NatlThespSoc; SecStuCncl; EdSchPpr; FrCl; PpCl; CaptBsktbl; DARAwd; KiwanAwd; Western Illinois Univ; Teaching.

SHOUP, Jeffrey; Harvard HS; Harvard, IL; Band; Chrs; CncrtBnd; MrchBnd; PepBnd; SchMus; Ill Univ; Engineering Physics.

SHOUSE, John; Mexico HS; Mexico, MO; Band; CncrtBnd; MrchBnd; PepBnd; TchrAde; JETSAwd; University Of Mo; Engineering.

SHOUSE, Mary A; North Vigo HS; Terre Haute, IN; 1/650 NatlMeritCmnd; Quill&Scroll; StuCncl; Teen; EdYrBk; CaptBsktbl; CaptTennis; PresGAA; DARAwd; NCTE; CitAwd; Auburn Univ; English.

SHOUSE, Susan K; Gladbrook Community HS; Gladbrook, IA; 1/46 SecTrsSophCls; PresAFS; SecChr; Chrs; CncrtBnd; DrmMjrt; NHS; 4-H; CchngActv; CitAwd; St Lukes Sch; Rn.

SHOUSH, Diane E; Macon County R1 HS; Macon, MO; 2/117 Band; CncrtBnd; HonRl; MrchBnd; PepBnd; SctActv; SpnCl; PpCl; LetterBsktbl; LetterTennis; Univ Of Mo Columbia; Med.

SHOVAN, Michael J; Arthur Hill HS; Saginaw, MI; Band; HonRl; MrchBnd; NHS; PepBnd; SctActv; Bsbl; CaptSwmmng; Alma College; Pre Med.

SHOWALTER, Anthony R; Barr Reeve HS; Montgomery, IN; 20/65 VPJrCls; ALBoysSt; ChrhWkr; HonRl; LbryAde; PresStuCncl; SpnCl; PpCl; Bsbl; Bsktbl; Trk; Evansville Univ; Civil Engineering.

SHOWALTER, Bruce; Fairfield HS; Goshen, IN; 4-H; FFA; Bsktbl; 4-HAwd; Agriculture.

SHOWALTER, Buster C; Sherman Comm HS; Goodland, KS; Band; Chr; Chrl; ChrhWkr; CmntyWkr; CncrtBnd; HonRl; JA; JrNHS; NHS; Bsktbl; Ftbl; Trk; College; Vet.

SHOWALTER, Lisa M; Barr Reeve HS; Montgomery, IN; SecChrhWkr; HonRl; JrNHS; MrchBnd; StuCncl; FHA; VPSpnCl; PpCl; CaptBsktbl; GAA; IMSpt; Indiana State Univ; Sociology.

SHRADER, Julie; Tri Valley HS; Colton, SD; Band; DrlTm; HonRl; NHS; SchAde; SchPl; TchrAde; PpCl;.

SHREVE, Tama M; Maysville HS; Maysville, MO; Band; DrmMjrt; HonRl; MrchBnd; NHS; PepBnd; SchAde; 4-H; SpnCl; Trk; Univ; Music.

SHREVE, Thomas W; North HS; Fargo, ND; ChrhWkr; HonRl; NatlFornLg; NHS; NatlMeritSF; YthFlsp; YthLg; FrCl; OptClAwd; College; Political Science.

SHROBA, Louis L; Joliet Twp East HS; Joliet, IL; SchPl; StuCncl; RptrSchPpr; KeyCl; GerCl; LetterFtbl; LetterTrk; IMSpt; Milwaukee School; Engineering.

SHROBA, Patricia H; Joliet West HS; Joliet, IL; 10/499 HonRl; JrNHS; NHS; SchAde; TchrAde; GerCl; AmLegAwd; Joliet Jun Coll; Optometrist.

SHROKA, Jayne A; Hanover Central HS; Cedar Lake, IN; DrlTm; HonRl; JrNHS; NHS; OffAde; StuCncl; TchrAde; Yrbk; 4-H; PpCl; Bsnss Sch; Secretary.

SHROUT, Jeffrey L; Maysville HS; Maysville, MO; PresSophCls; VPJrCls; ALBoysSt; Chr; SchPl; StuCncl; 4-H; Bsbl; Bsktbl; Ftbl; Trk; U Of Mo; Vet Med.

SHROYER, Douglas L; Twin Lakes HS; Monticello, IN; 26/202 Band; ChrhWkr; HonRl; NHS; YthFlsp; LetterBsktbl; LetterTrk; Clge; Tchng.

SHROYER, Kimberlee; Wethersfield HS; Kewanee, IL; 10/65 AFS; Band; HonRl; PepBnd; SchMus; SchPl; TchrAde; RptrSchPpr; FTA; GAA; Western Il Univ;psych.

SHROYER, Lola L; Hillsboro HS; Hillsboro, IL; Band; ChrhWkr; DrmMjrt; HonRl; Twrl; GerCl; Navy; Electrical Engineering.

SHRUM, Debbie S; Roosevelt HS; St Louis, MO; 1/520 ALAGirlsSt; Chr; Chrs; Swmmng; GAA; IMSpt; DanFAwd; PresAwd; RotaryAwd; CitAwd; Clge; Pre Med.

SHRYOCK, Sharon C; Riverton HS; Springfield, IL; 2/60 Chr; Chrs; ChrhWkr; HonRl; NHS; SchMus; RptrYrbk; RptrSchPpr; 4-H; FHA; PpCl; Illinois State Univ; Education.

SHUBERG, Thomas M; Wesclin HS; New Baden, IL; 16/99 Band; HonRl; RedCrAde; SctActv; UNYO; RptrSchPpr; SchPpr; LetterTrk; IMSpt; Coll; Forestry.

SHUBITOWSKI, Pamela; Arthur Hill HS; Saginaw, MI; ALAGirlsSt; ChrhWkr; CmntyWkr; HonRl; LitMag; TchrAde; 4-H; PpCl; Ftbl; 4-HAwd;.

SHUBITOWSKI, Yvonne; Arthur Hill HS; Saginaw, MI; ChrhWkr; CmntyWkr; HospAde; JA; NatlSciFnd; NatlMeritSchl; Quill&Scroll; RptrSchPpr; 4-H; Chrldr; Univ Of Mich;doctor.

SHUCK, Elaine F; Jefferson HS; Rockford, IL; 28/335 Band; CncrtBnd; HonRl; JA; JrNHS; MrchBnd; NHS; SchMus; SchPl; RptrSchPpr; LatCl; Illinois State Univ; Medical Record Admini.

SHUCK, Karen L; Sandwich HS; Sandwich, IL; 2/127 TreasAFS; ChrhWkr; HonRl; SecNHS; SctActv; RptrSchPpr; Pres4-H; LatCl; PpCl; 4-HAwd; University; Accounting.

SHUE, Terry W; Chaparral HS; Harper, KS; VPSrCls; Chrl; Chrs; ChrhWkr; HonRl; SchMus; YthFlsp; LetterFtbl; Wrstlng; Hesston College; Vocational.

SHUFELDT, Barbara A; Arlington HS; Arlington Hts, IL; 16/550 HonRl; NatlFornLg; Beloit College; Anthropology.

SHUFELDT, Llaina R; Royal Valley HS; Hoyt, KS; Chrs; HonRl; SchPl; FHA; PpCl; Kaw Area Voc Tec.

SHUK, Barbara C; Stanley Boyd HS; Stanley, WI; 1/109 ALAGirlsSt; PresDrlTm; HonRl; NatlFornLg; SptEdYrbk; FHA; SpnCl; BttyCrckrAwd; Us Air Force.

SHULAR, Rebecca A; Dixon HS; Dixon, IL; 1/337 VPJrCls; ALAGirlsSt; HonRl; PresNHS; NatlMeritCmnd; StuCncl; Chrldr; GAA; DARAwd; EldAwd; Univ Of Illinois; Medicine.

SHULAW, Thomas D; Robinson HS; Robinson, IL; 83/198 VPSrCls; SctActv; KeyCl; LatCl; LetterBsbl; LetterFtbl; Jacksonville College; Petroleum Engineer.

SHULER, Jeri L; Alpena HS; Alpena, MI; Chr; ChrhWkr; HospAde; NatlSciFnd; SchMus; SchPl; YthLg; 4-H; PpCl; GAA; Northern Mi Univ; Rn.

SHULER, John H; Seaholm HS; Bloomfield Hills, MI; Band; CncrtBnd; JrNHS; MrchBnd; NatlMeritSF; Orch; PepBnd; StuCncl; StuGov; UNYO; U Of Mi; Music.

SHULER, Kathy A; Tri County HS; Jamesport, MO; Chr; Chrs; ChrhWkr; CmntyWkr; HonRl; SchMus; LetterBsbl; LetterBsktbl; LetterTrk; 4-HAwd; Trenton Jr Coll; Mid Mgmt.

SHULER, Yonna M; Switz Co HS; Vevay, IN; TrsSophCls; PresJrCls; HonRl; NHS; StuCncl; TchrAde; 4-H; FFA; FHA; GAA; Trade.

SHULL, Tamara L; Effingham HS; Effingham, IL; 8/212 Band; HonRl; MrchBnd; NatlMeritCmnd; SctActv; RptrYrbk; FTA; LatCl; PpCl; LetterTennis; LetterTrk; GAA; Univ Of Ill; Aeronautical Eng.

SHULMAN, Daniel; University HS; Champaign, IL; TrsJrCls; Aud/Vis; Chrs; LitMag; MrchBnd; SchPl; YthLg; RptrYrbk; RptrSchPpr; Wrstlng; Univ Of Il; Writing.

SHULMAN, Michael S; New Trier West HS; Glencoe, IL; 139/694 NatlMeritCmnd; TchrAde; Washington Univ; Audio Engineering.

SHULTHEIS, Martha A; Lincoln Sr HS; Bloomington, MN; NHS; Trk; CaptChrldr; College; Professional.

SHULTZ, Brian R; Parsons Sr HS; Parsons, KS; Band; CncrtBnd; HonRl; MrchBnd; PepBnd;.

SHULTZ, Eric; Parson Senior HS; Parsons, KS; Orch; YthFlsp; Tennis; CchngActv; Southwest Missouri State Univ; Fish & Game.

SHULTZ, James D; Mormon Trail Comm HS; Weldon, IA; SecFrshCls; TrsSrCls; Band; CncrtBnd; HonRl; MrchBnd; PepBnd; SchMus; SchPl; FFA; Ia St Univ; Farm Mgmnt.

SHULTZ, Mary A; Warsaw Sr HS; Warsaw, IN; YthFlsp; 4-H; Bsktbl; Trk; GAA; 4-HAwd;.

SHUMAKER, Christine M; Gull Lake HS; Augusta, MI; SecJrCls; Band; DrlTm; HonRl; StuCncl; TchrAde; 4-H; PpCl; PPFtbl; 4-HAwd; College; Professional.

SHUMAN, Katherine M; University HS; Normal, IL; TrsJrCls; HonRl; SchMus; SctActv; StuCncl; VPSpnCl; PpCl; ChmnChrldr; GAA; Univ; Prof.

SHUMAN, Robert E; Downers Grove North HS; Downers Grove, IL; 8/535 HonRl; NHS; SctActv; FSA; SecSciCl; AmLegAwd; GodCntryAwd; JETSAwd; Univ Of Illinois; Elec Engineer.

SHUMARD, Jo A; Lumen Christi HS; Jackson, MI; 21/223 ChrhWkr; CmntyWkr; VPNHS; NatlThespSoc; OffAde; PolWkr; SchMus; SecStuCncl; RptrSchPpr; VoiceDemAwd; Central Michigan Univ; Law.

SHUMSKI, David J; East Chain HS; Fairmont, MN; ChrhWkr; HonRl; SchPl; SctActv; VPYthFlsp; LetterFtbl; Trk; IMSpt;.

SHUSTER, Robert E; Rensselaer Central HS; Brook, IN; PresFrshCls; ALBoysSt; HonRl; StuCncl; RptrSchPpr; Bsbl; Ftbl; LetterWrstlng; CaptIMSpt; St Francis College; Business Administration.

SHUTE, Sharon A; Wheaton Central HS; Wheaton, IL; ChrhWkr; HonRl; NHS; OffAde; John Brown University; Business.

SHUTES, Carol J; Brown City HS; Brown City, MI; 2/96 HonRl; TchrAde; YthFlsp; FTA; Christian College; Vocational.

SHUYA, George B; Hammond HS; Hammond, IN; Chr; SchAde; SchMus; SchPl; StuGov; TchrAde; PpCl; Ftbl; Socr; Swmmng; Indiana Univ; Dentist.

SHWERY, Margaret K; Hempstead HS; Dubuque, IA; 1/455 Chr; HonRl; ModUN; NHS; StuCncl; StuGov; PpCl; Glf; LetterSwmmng; AmLegAwd; ChmbCommrsAwd; U Of N Ia; Teaching.

SHYKER, Howard K; Horton Watkins HS; St Louis, MO; 142/434 Band; CncrtBnd; MrchBnd; Orch; PepBnd; SchMus; Indiana Univ; Pre Med.

SHYMANSKI, Henry J; Sacred Heart HS; Dearborn, MI; HonRl; JA; JrNHS; NHS; NatlMeritCmnd; Bsktbl; Glf; IMSpt; U Of Mich; Law.

SHYNE, Laurie D; Roger C Sullivan HS; Chicago, IL; 28/278 SecFrshCls; VPSophCls; JA; NHS; TreasStuCncl; CaptChrldr; Northwestern Univ; Teacher.

SHYNK, Susan E; Brimfield HS; Edwards, IL; HonRl; OffAde; SchAde; TchrAde; YthFlsp; Yrbk; RptrSchPpr; FHA; SpnCl; PpCl; Clg; Legal Sec.

SIAMA, Susan L; Proviso West HS; Bellwood, IL; ChrhWkr; HonRl; NatlMeritCmnd; SchPl; Trk; Univ Of Illinois; Accounting.

SIBAL, Virginia A; Lumen Christi HS; Jackson, MI; VPJrCls; HonRl; NHS; PolWkr; SchAde; SchPl; StuCncl; RptrSchPpr; LatCl; IMSpt; Mi State U; Medical Doctor.

SIBBING, Jeffrey M; Seymour HS; Quincy, IL; Band; Chrs; CncrtBnd; HonRl; Mdrgl; MrchBnd; PepBnd; SchMus; SchPl; Trk; St Univ; Electronic Engineer.

SIBEL, Jerri; Lutheran West HS; Detroit, MI; Tennis; Coll;arch/medical.

SIBERT, Heidi L; Illinois Valley Central HS; Chillicothe, IL; 11/230 VPJrCls; NHS; SptEdYrbk; Yrbk; SchPpr; PpCl; Univ Of Illinois; Landscape Architect.

SIBERT, Larry J; Superior HS; Superior, NE; HonRl; Quill&Scroll; Yrbk; RptrSchPpr; KeyCl; College; Aviation.

SIBERY, Douglas E; Wheaton Warrenville HS; Wheaton, IL; 13/242 HonRl; JrNHS; NHS; SchPl; TchrAde; 4-H; CaptFtbl; Trk; Wrstlng; CchngActv; 4-HAwd; RotaryAwd; CitAwd; Purdue Univ; Veterinarian.

SIBLEY, Jeffrey A; Prophetstown HS; Prophetstown, IL; 16/100 PresFrshCls; VPSophCls; AFS; Band; CncrtBnd; HonRl; NHS; PepBnd; StuCncl; RptrSchPpr; 4-H; FrCl; Univ Of Illinois; Liberal Arts.

SIBLEY, Julie A; Kaneland Sr HS; Elburn, IL; 30/162 Chr; PresChrs; HonRl; Mdrgl; MrchBnd; NatlFornLg; NHS; NatlMeritCmnd; TreasNatlThespSoc; SchMus; SchPl; SctActv; Trk; GAA; Northern Illinois Univ; Vocal Music.

SICHAK, Stephen; Mt Carmel HS; Dalton, IL; 5/197 HonRl; NHS; NatlMeritCmnd; RptrSchPpr; MthCl; St Louis University; Chemistry.

SICHKO, Paul M; Senior HS; Albert Lea, MN; 7/526 HstSrCls; Aud/Vis; HonRl; NHS; StuCncl; KeyCl; GerCl; LetterFtbl; LetterGlf; LetterSocr; LetterSwmmng; LetterTennis; Augustana College; Pilot.

SICK, Cynthia; Lodgepole HS; Lodgepole, NE; SecTrsFrshCls; SecTrsSophCls; SecTrsJrCls; Band; DrmMjrt; JrNHS; YthFlsp; GAA; 4-HAwd; CitAwd;.

SICKEL, Glenda L; Dist #56 Falls City HS; Falls City, NE; Chrs; HonRl; SchMus; Sec4-H; PpCl; Bsktbl; Trk; GAA; 4-HAwd; JAAwd; College; Nurse.

SICKELS, David L; Grand Valley Community HS; Kellerton, IA; 5/28 SecTrsFrshCls; VPSophCls; PresBand; Chr; HonRl; PresMrchBnd; SchPl; StuCncl; LetterBsbl; LetterTrk; College; Vocation.

SICKINGER, Debra R; Valders HS; Cato, WI; PresSophCls; VPAFS; HonRl; NHS; SchPl; 4-H; PresFFA; VPPpCl; LetterTrk; Chrldr; GAA; IMSpt; PPFtbl; College; Business.

SICKLE, Peter R; Highland Park HS; Highland Park, IL; CmntyWkr; StuGov; Socr; Wrstlng; College; Veternarian.

SICKLESMITH, Linda; Clarksville HS; Clarksville, IN; SecJrCls; SecSrCls; Chr; Mdrgl; NHS; Quill&Scroll; Yrbk; FTA; PpCl; Chrldr; Indiana University.

SIDDELL, Janice L; Carlyle HS; Huey, IL; 1/150 SecJrCls; SecSrCls; DrlTm; NHS; StuCncl; YthFlsp; RptrYrbk; FBLA; KeyCl; FrCl; DanFAwd; Western Illinois Univ; Accountant.

SIDDELL, Phyllis R; Maquoketa Valley HS; Delhi, IA; ALAGirlsSt; ChrhWkr; HonRl; MrchBnd; TchrAde; YthFlsp; GerCl; PpCl; LetterTrk; IMSpt; Col; Rn.

SIDDONS, Virginia E; St Mary Academy; Indianapolis, IN; Chr; Chrs; HonRl; NHS; YthFlsp; EdSchPpr; PresGerCl; College; Teaching.

SIDES, David A; Lew Wallace HS; Gary, IN; HonRl; TchrAde; LetterBsbl; Univ; Math.

SIDMORE, Mardell A; Allison Bristow HS; Bristow, IA; Chr; Chrs; HonRl; Yrbk; Trade Sch; Sec Work.

SIDNEY, Paul J; De La Salle Institute; Chicago, IL; 66/258 PresSophCls; ChrhWkr; CmntyWkr; HonRl; IntrClCncl; OffAde; SchAde; SctActv; StuCncl; StuGov; Teen; Bsbl; Bsktbl; CchngActv; College; Engineer.

SIDOR, Stanley; Kingsley Area HS; Kingsley, MI; Band; HonRl; IntrClCncl; LbryAde; MrchBnd; PepBnd; PpCl; SciCl; CaptTrk; CaptCchngActv; College; Marine Biologist.

SIDWELL, Bill; Tri HS; Straughn, IN; 25/86 HonRl; NHS; SciCl; Bsktbl; College; Professional.

SIEBECKER, Steven L; Superior HS; Superior, NE; VPFrshCls; TrsSophCls; SchPl; TreasKeyCl; FrCl; Bsbl; LetterBsktbl; CaptFtbl; LetterTrk; Morningside College; Business Admin.

SIEBEL, Kerri L; Bennett Community HS; Bennett, IA; PresJrCls; PresSrCls; ALAGirlsSt; ChrhWkr; CncrtBnd; HonRl; NHS; StuCncl; CaptBsbl; CaptBsktbl; Trk; AmLegAwd; 4-HAwd; Trade Schl; Cosmetology.

SIEBELS, Steve; St Louis HS; St Louis, MO; CmntyWkr; HonRl; PolWkr; Bsbl; Ftbl; Socr; IMSpt; Univ; Business.

SIEBEN, Deborah K; Grafton Central HS; Grafton, ND; Chrs; CmntyWkr; SchPl; StuCncl; RptrSchPpr; FBLA; SpnCl; PpCl; Trk; Chrldr; College; Nursing.

SIEBEN, Lisa J; Hastings Senior HS; Hastings, MN; ALAGirlsSt; HonRl; PolWkr; StuCncl; RptrYrbk; FBLA; LetterChrldr; GAA; College; Home Economics.

SIEBEN, Susan A; Mattoon Senior HS; Mattoon, IL; 20/397 AFS; Chr; Chrs; HonRl; HospAde; JrNHS; NHS; 4-H; FTA; GAA; College; Nursing.

SIEBENALER, Carol L; Random Lake HS; Random Lake, WI; 5/95 TrsSophCls; TrsJrCls; ALAGirlsSt; ChrhWkr; HonRl; PepBnd; FBLA; Univ Of Whitewater; Accountant.

SIEBENS, Carolyn A; Akron Community HS; Akron, IA; Chrs; HonRl; PresLbryAde; TchrAde; RptrSchPpr; FHA;.

SIEBERS, Becky L; Unity HS; Ursa, IL; 1/77 Band; Chrs; HonRl; HospAde; PresYthFlsp; RptrYrbk; PresFHA; MthCl; SciCl; GAA; BttyCrckrAwd; DARAwd; 4-HAwd; College; Nursing.

SIEBERS, David B; Northview HS; Grand Rapids, MI; 5/235 LitMag; ModUN; NHS; NatlMeritFnl; NatlMeritSF; SctActv; TchrAde; SpnCl; Trk; CchngActv; West Point; Military.

SIEBERS, Janice M; Liberty Comm HS; Liberty, IL; ChrhWkr; HonRl; NHS; OffAde; SchPl; Yrbk; SptEdSchPpr; FBLA; VPFHA; Trk; 4-HAwd; Business School; Business.

SIEBERT, Cheryl; Lasalle Peru Township HS; Lasalle, IL; 20/505 HonRl; LbryAde; NHS; SpnCl; PpCl; College; Education.

SIEBERT, Judith; Granite City South Hs; Granite City, IL; 18/630 Chrs; HospAde; NHS; PpCl; GAA;.

SIEBERT, Kyle; Wallace County HS; Sharon Springs, KS; 12/41 PresJrCls; CmntyWkr; HonRl; NHS; OffAde; StuCncl; Bsktbl; Ftbl; Trk; Fort Hays Kansas State; Industrial Arts.

SIEBERT, Laura L; Lake Central HS; Schereville, IN; 21/453 NHS; Quill&Scroll; StuCncl; Teen; Yrbk; 4-H; SpnCl; PpCl; GAA; PPFtbl; Purdue Univ; Medical Technology.

SIEBERT, Mary L; Bergan HS; Peoria, IL; 49/203 CmntyWkr; HonRl; SchAde; TchrAde; SchPpr; FrCl; LetterTennis; Univ Of Illinois; Recreation.

SIEBOLD, David E; Hannibal Sr HS; Hannibal, MO; ALBoysSt; ChrhWkr; HonRl; NHS; KeyCl; Bsktbl; U Of Mo Rolla; Elec Eng.

SIEBRASS, Janet K; Mankato West HS; Mankato, MN; 3/340 Band; CncrtBnd; HonRl; MrchBnd; PepBnd; SchPl; StuCncl; PpCl; SciCl; IMSpt; College.

SIEBRASSE, Jon D; Truman HS; Independence, MO; ChrhWkr; HonRl; IMSpt; College.

SIEBURG, Susan A; St Benedict HS; Chicago, IL; 8/188 Chrs; HonRl; NHS; GAA; Univ Of Illinois; Sociology.

SIECK, Tony R; Goodland HS; Goodland, KS; 24/133 HonRl; VP4-H; VPFFA; Ftbl; Trk; 4-HAwd;.

SIECKMAN, Lynne D; Riverview Gardens HS; St Louis, MO; 1/779 Band; CncrtBnd; DrmMjrt; HonRl; MrchBnd; NHS; CaptBsbl; GAA; IMSpt; U Of Mo Columbia; Physcial Therapy.

SIEDHOFF, Janet L; Crete HS; Milford, NE; TrsFrshCls; Chrs; CncrtBnd; HospAde; SchMus;

TchrAde; 4-H; TreasFBLA; PresFTA; PpCl; IMSpt; College; Accounting.

SIEDLECKI, Ellen M; Queen Of Peace HS; Chicago, IL; 11/420 Chrs; HonRl; LitMag; StuCncl; Yrbk; SpnCl; Chrldr; GAA; IMSpt; Harvard;.

SIEDLECKI, Martin F; St Laurence HS; Chicago, IL; 5/379 Band; CncrtBnd; HonRl; JrNHS; LitMag; MrchBnd; NatlCathMusEdAsoc; NHS; SchPl; Univ Of Chicago; Medicine.

SIEFERT, Charles S; Du Quoin HS; Du Quoin, IL; 9/143 HonRl; SciCl; Bsbl; University.

SIEFERT, Cheryl A; Goreville HS; Goreville, IL; 1/4/28 HstFrshCls; HstSophCls; Chrs; ChrhWkr; CncrtBnd; HonRl; VPHospAde; StuCncl; RptrYrbk; FHA; University Of Evansville; Rn.

SIEFERT, Lynn L; Oconto Falls HS; Oconto Falls, WI; 4/154 TrsJrCls; TrsSrCls; ALAGirlsSt; Band; ChrhWkr; HonRl; TreasNHS; SchPl; StuCncl; Yrbk; University; General Practitioner.

SIEFERT, Sue M; Academy Immaculate Conception; Batesville, IN; 8/67 PresSrCls; HonRl; NHS; Orch; Quill&Scroll; StuCncl; RptrYrbk; RptrSchPpr; GerCl; SpnCl; Marian College; Spanish Interpretor.

SIEFKES, Kent D; Comfrey Public HS; Comfrey, MN; TrsJrCls; Band; CncrtBnd; HonRl; PepBnd; StuCncl; SptEdSchPpr; SciCl; Bsktbl; Ftbl; Univ Of Wisconsin River Falls; Sstatisticn.

SIEG, Jeff R; Larimore HS; Emerado, ND; SecFrshCls; PresJrCls; HonRl; NatlMeritSchl; 4-H; Bsbl; LetterBsktbl; LetterFtbl; LetterTrk; PresAwd; College; Agriculture.

SIEGAL, Susan J; Ida Crown Jewish Academy; Chicago, IL; SecSophCls; ChrhWkr; CmntyWkr; HonRl; JrNHS; NHS; NatlMeritFnl; StuCncl; StuGov; SchPpr; Swmmng; College; School Admin.

SIEGEL, Amy I; Shawnee Mission S HS; Overland Park, KS; Chr; VPHonRl; VPHospAde; SchPl; TchrAde; SpnCl; University; Medical Illustration.

SIEGEL, Andrew J; J Sterling Morton East HS; Cicero, IL; 71/771 PresJrCls; PresSrCls; HonRl; PresJA; LitMag; NatlFornLg; NatlThespSoc; SchPl; RptrYrbk; IMSpt; JAAwd; University Of Illinois; Law.

SIEGEL, Ellyn S; Niles East HS; Skokie, IL; 19/581 University Of Illinois.

SIEGEL, Vicky L; Fremont HS; Fremont, IN; Band; CncrtBnd; LbryAde; MrchBnd; PepBnd; SchPl; SctActv; TchrAde; 4-H; FHA; Bsktbl; Trk; GAA; College; Professional.

SIEGER, Becky S; Lawton Bronson Comm HS; Lawton, IA; VPSophCls; PresJrCls; VPJrCls; Chrs; ChrhWkr; CmntyWkr; SchMus; StuCncl; Bsktbl; Trk; College; Major Study.

SIEGERT, Lisa K; Grayville HS; Grayville, IL; 3/50 Band; ChrhWkr; HonRl; StuCncl; Pres4-H; FHA; SecFrCl; Chrldr; GAA; AmLegAwd; DanFAwd; 4-HAwd; CitAwd; College; Vocation.

SIEGLE, Deborah; Divine Child HS; Dearborn Heights, MI; VPSophCls; HonRl; MrchBnd; NHS; Yrbk; FTA; FrCl; DARAwd; Univ Of Mich; Political Science.

SIEGLER, Donna M; Necedah HS; Necedah, WI; ALAGirlsSt; Band; HonRl; PepBnd; FHA; PpCl; LetterBsktbl; LetterTrk; GAA; IMSpt; PresAwd; VoiceDemAwd; College; Home Economics.

SIEGLER, Mary L; Assumption HS; Wisconsin Rapids, WI; Band; Chrs; CncrtBnd; HonRl; SchMus; RptrYrbk; RptrSchPpr; PpCl; LetterTrk; LetterChrldr; College.

SIEGRIST, Brett; St Alberts HS; Council Bluffs, IA; MthCl; Ftbl; Wrstlng; IMSpt; Iowa St Univ; Veterinary Science.

SIEGRIST, Cynthia; Catholic Central HS; Grand Rapids, MI; CmntyWkr; NHS; NatlMeritSchl; PolWkr; StuGov; SchPpr; Grand Valley College; Occupational Therapy.

SIEGWART, Martin G; Gaylord HS; Gaylord, MI; HonRl; StuCncl; Ftbl; Wrstlng; IMSpt; PresAwd; College; Professional.

SIEH, Carolyn D; Leola HS; Leola, SD; Band; Chrs; CncrtBnd; HonRl; StuCncl; Yrbk; SchPpr; FHA; PpCl; Trk; Univ; Optometry.

SIEHLING, Barbara; Marywood Acad; Grand Rapids, MI; 2/27 PresJrCls; Chr; NHS; NatlMeritCmnd; Orch; SchMus; PPFtbl; College; Elementary Teaching.

SIEJA, Joanne; Weyerhaeuser Public HS; Weyerhaeuser, WI; SecTrsJrCls; Chr; HonRl; RptrSchPpr; Pres4-H; SecFHA; SecPpCl; LetterTrk; LetterChrldr; 4-HAwd; College; Police Science Or Phy Ed Teacher.

SIEKOWSKI, Barbara A; Resurrection HS; Park Ridge, IL; 25/261 College.

SIELING, Don J; East Charles Mix #102 HS; Wagner, SD; TrsFrshCls; Chrs; RptrYrbk; SptEdYrbk; 4-H; FFA; Bsbl; Bsktbl; Ftbl; Wrstlng; Coll; Voc.

SIELOFF, Stephen D; Lisle Senior HS; Lisle, IL; 17/210 HonRl; NHS; NatlMeritCmnd; SchPl; StuCncl; TchrAde; YthFlsp; LetterBsktbl; LetterFtbl; CchngActv; Eastern Ill U; Computer Prog.

SIELSKI, Ronda M; Clio HS; Clio, MI; 36/364 Chr; Chrl; LitMag; SchMus; LatCl; Chrldr;.

SIEMASZKE, Konstanty B; St Ignatius College Prep HS; Chicago, IL; PolWkr; SctActv; SchPpr; Swmmng; IMSpt; PPFtbl; College.

SIEMENS, Kay C; Buhler HS; Buhler, KS; ChrhWkr; DrlTm; HonRl; SchPl; TreasYthFlsp; FHA; PpCl; LetterTennis; LetterChrldr; PPFtbl; Univ; Home Ec.

SIEMER, Carolyn J; Brussels Comm HS; Meppen, IL; Chr; Chrs; ChrhWkr; CmntyWkr; HonRl; SchMus; SchPl; StuCncl; EdYrBk; FHA; Chrldr; IMSpt; 4-HAwd; Belleville Dist College; Physical Therapy.

SIEMER, Michael B; Brussels Comm HS; Brussels, IL; 2/29 SecSophCls; TrsJrCls; Band; HonRl; StuGov; SchPpr; LetterBsbl; LetterBsktbl; IMSpt; CitAwd; Univ; Med.

SIEMERS, Kent H; Bowbells HS; Bowbells, ND; SecFrshCls; SecSophCls; SecSrCls; ALBoysSt; Band; Chrs; ChrhWkr; CncrtBnd; HonRl; MrchBnd; PepBnd; Bsbl; LetterBsktbl; CaptFtbl; University; Professional.

SIEMIANOWSKI, Nancy M; Morton East HS; Cicero, IL; HonRl; JrNHS; NHS; TchrAde; CaptChrldr; IMSpt;.

SIEMIENIEWSKI, Diane; Lidgerwood Public HS; Geneseo, ND; ChrhWkr; HonRl; SchPl; SpnCl;.

SIEMONSMA, Anna M; Baltic HS; Sioux Falls, SD; HonRl; LbryAde; NHS; OffAde; FHA; PpCl; Bsktbl; Trk; College.

SIEMSEN, Deborah; Holyrood HS; Holyrood, KS; 1/15 PresJrCls; ALAGirlsSt; HonRl; NatlMeritFnl; AmLegAwd; BttyCrckrAwd; DanFAwd; 4-HAwd; LionAwd; Emporia Kansas St Col; Teach Home Economics.

SIEMSEN, Deborah L; Holyrood HS; Holyrood, KS; 1/15 VPFrshCls; SecSophCls; PresJrCls; PresBand; Chrs; HonRl; NatlMeritSF; SecPresYthFlsp; Pres4-H; Emporia Kansas St; Music.

SIEMSEN, Linda G; Peotone HS; Peotone, IL; 1/99 Band; Chrs; HonRl; NHS; RptrSchPpr; 4-H; SpnCl; MthCl; DanFAwd; Univ; Psychology.

SIENKIEWICZ, Meta E; Minot HS; Minot Afb, ND; Chr; HonRl; JrNHS; NatlMeritSF; SctActv; StuGov; TchrAde; RptrSchPpr; SchPpr; GerCl; MthCl; Texas A&m Univ; Meteorology.

SIENKO, Mary T; Acad Of The Holy Angels; Richfield, MN; 27/110 Chr; Chrs; ChrhWkr; CmntyWkr; Bsbl; LetterBsktbl; LetterFtbl; IMSpt; PPFtbl; Moorhead Clge Moorhead Mn.

SIEPEL, Randall; Plymouth Dist 319 HS; Plymouth, IL; 1/24 Band; CncrtBnd; HonRl; MrchBnd; PepBnd; ROTC; RptrSchPpr; SchPpr; U Of Il; Prof Pilot.

SIEPEL, Randall C; Plymouth HS; Plymouth, IL; Band; CncrtBnd; HonRl; MrchBnd; Orch; PepBnd; ROTC; SchMus; RptrSchPpr; LetterBsktbl; Univ Of Illinois; Air Force Pilot.

SIEPKER, Deborah A; Lewis Central HS; Council Bluffs, IA; 2/167 ALAGirlsSt; ChrhWkr; CmntyWkr; HonRl; LbryAde; NHS; NatlMeritCmnd; TchrAde; FNA; Tennis; Coll; Medicine.

SIERAKOWSKI, Donna L; Lapeer Sr HS; Metamora, MI; HonRl; HospAde; RedCrAde; FHA; Baker Business Schl; Accounting.

SIERECKI, Cheryl L; Lourdes HS; Chicago, IL; HonRl; HospAde; GerCl; Medical; Professional.

SIEREN, Anita J; Tri County Comm HS; Keswick, IA; Band; Chrs; ChrhWkr; HonRl; SchPl; Twrl; Bsktbl;.

SIEREN, Charles E; Tri County Community HS; Keswick, IA; Chrs; ChrhWkr; HonRl; SchPl; StuCncl; 4-H; FFA; LetterBsbl; CaptFtbl; LetterTrk; CaptWrstlng; Trade School; Vocation.

SIEREN, Cheryl A; Keota Comm HS; Sigourney, IA; 1/58 LetterBand; CncrtBnd; HonRl; MrchBnd; PepBnd; Iowa State Univ; Interior Design.

SIESS, Mary J; B&b HS; Seneca, KS; CmntyWkr; HonRl; OffAde; StuCncl; 4-H; FHA; Bsktbl; Trk; GAA; 4-HAwd; Coll; Prof.

SIESS, Trude I; Union HS; Union, MO; 26/174 ChrhWkr; HonRl; HospAde; JA; TchrAde; RptrYrbk; 4-H; LetterBsktbl; IMSpt; PPFtbl; JAAwd; PresAwd; University; Elementary Teacher.

SIETSEMA, Jacqueline K; Danube Public HS; Danube, MN; 17/43 LbryAde; YthFlsp; TchrAde; Yrbk; SchPpr; Bsktbl; LetterTrk; GAA; Nettleton Comm Col; Fashion Merch.

SIETSEMA, Jeffrey M; Northwood Kensett HS; Northwood, IA; PresJrCls; PresSrCls; PresBand; PresCncrtBnd; HonRl; MrchBnd; PepBnd; SchPl; StuCncl; YthFlsp; LetterBsbl; LetterBsktbl; LetterFtbl; Coe College; Medicine.

SIEVE, Daniel; St Francis Borgia HS; Washington, MO; 8/95 CncrtBnd; HonRl; MrchBnd; NHS; SchPl; RptrSchPpr; FrCl; LionAwd; CitAwd; E Central Jr Coll; Bus.

SIEVE, Randy M; Worthington Sr HS; Worthington, MN; TrsFrshCls; TrsSophCls; CmntyWkr; HonRl; JrNHS; Sacrstn; FrCl; LetterBsbl; Bsktbl; IMSpt; College.

SIEVERDING, Ann E; Andrew Comm HS; Lamotte, IA; 8/40 PresSophCls; Aud/Vis; Chrs; HonRl; TreasNatlThespSoc; SchPl; TreasStuCncl; Yrbk; VP4-H; GerCl; 4-HAwd; Univ Of Iowa; Professional.

SIEVERDING, Mark A; Andrew Comm HS; Lamotte, IA; 11/33 SecSophCls; PresJrCls; PresSrCls; Aud/Vis; Chrs; HonRl; LbryAde; NatlThespSoc; SchPl; StuCncl; 4-H; DanFAwd; Iowa State Univ; Elec Engineering.

SIEVERS, Alan F; Albert City Truesdale HS; Storm Lake, IA; 1/48 VPFrshCls; Chr; NHS; SchMus; SchPl; YthFlsp; Bsktbl; Ftbl; Univ Of Morris; Science.

SIEVERS, Kurt W; Gridley Comm Unit 10 HS; Gridley, IL; 21/40 Chrs; SchMus; SchPl; StuCncl; LetterBsbl; CaptBsktbl; LetterFtbl; LetterTrk; College; Coach.

SIEVERS, Lisa A; Avoha Community HS; Avoca, IA; 1/55 PresJrCls; HonRl; NHS; NatlThespSoc; Quill&Scroll; StuCncl; Yrbk; EdSchPpr; GerCl; Pres4-HAwd; Univ Of Ia; Pre Law.

SIEVERS, Peggy L; Cotter HS; Winona, MN; 4/106 DrlTm; HonRl; SchPpr; SpnCl; Winona St Clg.

SIEVERT, Kathleen L; Lakeside Lutheran HS; Fort Atkinson, WI; TrsFrshCls; TrsJrCls; TrsSrCls; ALAGirlsSt; Band; CmntyWkr; YthFlsp; EdSchPpr; 4-H; Bsktbl; IMSpt; Martin Luther College; Elem Christian Ed.

SIEVERT, Timothy J; Manitowoc Lutheran HS; Manitowoc, WI; 11/79 Chr; ChrhWkr; StuCncl; 4-H; MthCl; Bsktbl; LetterFtbl; LetterTrk; Coll; Dr Of Med.

SIEVWRIGHT, Gail M; Arkansaw HS; Arkansaw, WI; PresJrCls; HonRl; SchPl; StuCncl; EdSchPpr; PresSpnCl; Chrldr; GAA; University; Foriegn Languages.

SIEWERT, Julie J; Mc Intosh Independent HS; Mc Intosh, SD; SecJrCls; ChrhWkr; DrlTm; HonRl; LbryAde; SchPl; YthFlsp; FHA; PpCl; College; Nursing.

SIEWERT, Kari L; Gaylord HS; Gaylord, MN; 1/67 Band; Chr; ChrhWkr; HonRl; SchMus; SchPl; SctActv; RptrYrbk; EdSchPpr; FDA; Chrldr; Rochester Comm College; Medicine.

SIEWERT, Kim M; Lake Michigan Catholic HS; Coloma, MI; HonRl; OffAde; SctActv; 4-H; LatCl; PpCl; Bsbl; Chrldr; CchngActv; IMSpt; Michigan State Univ; Animal Tech.

SIFFERMANN, Patricia M; Harillac HS; Des Plaines, IL; 26/257 SecTrsJrCls; HospAde; NHS; SchPl; StuCncl; Chrldr; College; Business.

SIFFORD, Mary; Puxico HS; Puxico, MO; Band; Chr; HonRl; SchPl; TchrAde; Yrbk; FHA; FTA; PpCl; College; Special Education.

SIFNER, Thomas A; Kennedy St Paul HS; Chicago, IL; Aud/Vis; HonRl; NHS; KeyCl; LetterSwmmng; LetterTrk; IMSpt; University Of Illinois; Physical Therapy.

SIGEL, Robert I; Homewood Flossmoor HS; Flossmoor, IL; 14/917 HonRl; NatlFornLg; NHS; NatlMeritCmnd; StuGov; IMSpt; U Of Mich; Doctor.

SIGG, Julie L; Mona Shores HS; Muskegon, MI; HospAde; NatlThespSoc; SctActv; StuCncl; RptrYrbk; FHA; FrCl; PpCl; Chrldr; Hackley Hosp Sch; Registered Nursing.

SIGLER, Andrew H; Barstow HS; Kansas City, MO; PresFrshCls; PresJrCls; AFS; Chr; PolWkr; SchMus; SchPl; PresStuCncl; StuGov; RptrYrbk; EdYrBk; RptrSchPpr; Bsktbl; CaptGlf; College; Law.

SIGLER, John M; Lincoln HS; Cambridge City, IN; ALBoysSt; Band; CncrtBnd; HonRl; MrchBnd; PolWkr; SchMus; StuCncl; KeyCl; LetterFtbl; LetterTrk; IMSpt; Indiana University; Accounting.

SIGMON, Larry A; Rock Island HS; Rock Island, IL; HonRl; Physics.

SIGMON, Timothy; Brown County Hs; Mt Sterling, IL; 6 Band; CncrtBnd; NHS; PepBnd; FFA; U Illinois ; Vetinarian.

SIGMUND, Michael A; Plainfield HS; Indianapolis, IN; 14/259 ALBoysSt; Chr; Chrs; HonRl; JrNHS; Mdrgl; NHS; SchMus; SchPl; SctActv; Ftbl; Swmmng; LetterTrk; AmLegAwd; Rose Hulman Inst Tech; Engineering.

SIGNOR, David B; East Kentwood HS; Kentwood, MI; CncrtBnd; MrchBnd; NHS; Michigan St Univ; Engineering.

SIGO, Belinda A; Frontier HS; Brookston, IN; SecSophCls; HonRl; YthFlsp; SpnCl; SecPpCl; GAA;.

SIGRIST, Jodi L; Brookfield East HS; Elm Grove, WI; Chr; HonRl; LitMag; NHS; NatlMeritSF; Quill&Scroll; SchMus; SchPl; StuCncl; StuGov; RptrSchPpr; SchPpr; MthCl; Univ Of Wisc.

SIGRIST, Michael D; Arthur HS; Arthur, IL; HonRl; NHS; SctActv; FFA; MthCl; LetterBsbl; CaptBsktbl; CaptFtbl; SARAwd; U Of Illinois; Chemical Engineer.

SIGRIST, Jr,Charles; Springfield HS; Springfield, IL; 117/535 VPSrCls; CncrtBnd; MrchBnd; PepBnd; PolWkr; SctActv; Trk; Wrstlng; CchngActv; Univ; Civil Engineer.

SIKKEMA, Paul H; Fulton HS; Fulton, IL; Band; Chr; CncrtBnd; HonRl; Mdrgl; MrchBnd; PepBnd; YthFlsp; Bsktbl; College; Professional.

SIKKEMA, Shawn K; Northern Christian HS; Mc Bain, MI; 7/42 Band; Chr; Chrs; ChrhWkr; CncrtBnd; HonRl; MrchBnd; NatlMeritCmnd; PepBnd; SchMus; College.

SIKKEMA, Wm; Riverbend Unit Dist HS; Fulton, IL; ALBoysSt; Chr; HonRl; TchrAde; Glf; IMSpt; Dordt Coll; Bus Adm.

SIKKENGA, Carolyn J; West Michigan Christian HS; Rothbury, MI; Chr; ChrhWkr; HonRl; NatlMeritSchl; SchMus; RptrYrbk; PpCl; GAA; Calvin College.

SIKKENGA, Shirley J; Western Mich Christian HS; Montague, MI; Chr; ChrhWkr; SchAde; SchPl; Yrbk; RptrSchPpr; 4-H; FNA; GAA; IMSpt; Mi State U; Floriculturist.

SIKKILA, Mark; L Anse HS; Lanse, MI; ChrhWkr; DrmBgl; HonRl; N Mich Univ; Teacher.

SIKORA, Corinne A; Dominican HS; Detroit, MI; SchMus; College; Dental Assistant.

SIKORA, Kathleen V; Dominican HS; Grosse Pt Woods, MI; NHS; OffAde; SchMus; SchPl; StuGov; PpCl; Michigan State Univ; Business.

SIKORA, Michelle M; George Rogers Clark HS; Whiting, IN; Chr; OffAde; StuCncl; FrCl; PpCl; GAA; College; Social Worker.

SILAGI, Susan L; Dondero HS; Royal Oak, MI; TreasBand; LitMag; MrchBnd; NHS; NatlMeritSF; PepBnd; TchrAde; GerCl; Oberlin College; English.

SILARSKI, Robert E; Eisenhower HS; Utica, MI; 25/500 VPJrCls; HonRl; IntrClCncl; NatlMeritSF; StuCncl; StuGov; GerCl; PpCl; Tennis; IMSpt; Univ Mi; Archi.

SILAS, Lynne; Durand HS; Durand, MI; Chrs; HonRl; College; Vocational.

SILBERNAGEL, Teresa A; Mt Horeb HS; Verona, WI; 12/130 SecSophCls; Band; Chrs; MrchBnd; NHS; YthFlsp; FrCl; Trk; IMSpt; St Olaf College; Psychologist.

SILFIES, Syndi L; La Moille Comm HS; La Moille, IL; 9/45 Band; MrchBnd; PepBnd; SchMus; Yrbk; RptrSchPpr; FHA; PpCl; GAA; Collge; Music Teacher Or Accounting.

SILHAVY, Mark M; Alma HS; Alma, MI; TchrAde; Pres4-H; FFA; DanFAwd; Mich State Univ; Production Agriculture.

SILKA, Antoinette; Divine Child HS; Dearborn Heights, MI; HonRl; NHS; NatlThespSoc; SchMus; SchPl; StuCncl; StuGov; FrCl; Chrldr; EldAwd; Univ Of Mich; Pre Med.

SILKMAN, Karman J; Hettinger HS; Reeder, ND; ChrhWkr; HonRl; StuCncl; 4-H; FFA; PpCl; Bsktbl; GAA; College; Vocation.

SILL, Cathy J; Cumberland HS; Cumberland, WI; PresFrshCls; Band; Chr; ChrhWkr; CncrtBnd; DrmMjrt; HonRl; HospAde; MrchBnd; PepBnd; College; Professional Nursing.

SILL, Rachel; Triton HS; Tippecanoe, IN; VPJrCls; Band; Chr; DrmMjrt; HonRl; NHS; SchMus; StuCncl; YthFlsp; DARAwd;.

SILL, Rick M; Carl Junction HS; Joplin, MO; 6/99 HonRl; ModUN; NHS; OffAde; TchrAde; MthCl; Bsbl; Ftbl; Wrstlng; Mi Southern St College.

SILLARS, Tina M; D C Everest HS; Schofield, WI; 37/318 Chr; Chrs; ChrhWkr; HonRl; Mdrgl; NHS; SchMus; SctActv; PpCl; North Central Tech Inst; Legal Secretary.

SILLINGS, Mary A; Floyd Central HS; Georgetown, IN; 50/264 VPSophCls; VPJrCls; Chr; HonRl; NHS; OffAde; PolWkr; SchAde; Yrbk; TreasFTA; PpCl; Trk; CaptChrldr; DARAwd;.

SILLIVEN, Cynthia J; Hillsdale HS; Hillsdale, MI; HstFrshCls; HstSophCls; SecJrCls; CncrtBnd; NHS; StuCncl; LatCl; Trk; Chrldr; College; Biology.

SILLMAN, Bruce W; Millard Sr HS; Omaha, NE; 13/318 HonRl; ModUN; NHS; NatlMeritFnl; NatlMeritSchl; FrCl; MthCl; IMSpt; College; Medicine.

SILLS, Geoffrey A; Elmhurst HS; Fort Wayne, IN; Band; CncrtBnd; HonRl; MrchBnd; PepBnd; SchPl; Indiana Univ; Pre Law.

SILVA, Nanette M; Queen Of Peace HS; Chicago, IL; 2/415 Chrs; ChrhWkr; CncrtBnd; NHS; SpnCl; Chrldr; Rosary College; Psychology.

SILVER, Martin J; Seeger Memorial HS; Williamsport, IN; 6/120 VPSophCls; PresSrCls; Band; HonRl; PresNHS; StuCncl; MthCl; Bsktbl; 4-HAwd; SARAwd; Purdue Univ; Elec Enf.

SILVER, Patrick T; Tracy HS; Tracy, MN; VPSophCls; Chr; SchMus; StuCncl; RptrSchPpr; Ftbl; Trk; LetterWrstlng; Alexandria Votec; Computer Maintenance.

SILVER, Thomas R; Taylor HS; Kokomo, IN; Band; MrchBnd; NHS; PepBnd; SctActv; Purdue Univ; Pharmacy.

SILVERMAN, Robert K; Oak Park River Forest HS; Chicago, IL; 90/1300 HonRl; NHS; StuCncl; StuGov; SchPpr; MthCl; SciCl; LetterFtbl; LetterTrk; DanFAwd; Col; Pre Med.

SILVERS, Thomas E; Albany HS; Albany, MN; HonRl; SciCl; Bsktbl; Trk; IMSpt; Trade Sch; Vocation.

SILVERSTEIN, Rachel A; Niles West HS; Lincolnwood, IL; 45/666 ChrhWkr; HonRl; NatlMeritSF; SchAde; TchrAde; Univ; Gerontology.

SILVERSTRINI, Dino F; West Iron County HS; Iron River, MI; 23/180 ChrhWkr; HonRl; NHS; NatlMeritFnl; NatlMeritCmnd; Sacrstn; Sdlty; RptrYrbk; LatCl; Bsktbl; St Francis De Sales; Priesthood.

SILVERTHORN, Donald L; St Joseph HS; St Joseph, MI; ChrhWkr; SctActv; Bsbl; Ftbl; Trk; IMSpt; Engineering College; Engineering.

SILVERTHORN, Michael J; Yale HS; Yale, MI; 3/144 Band; ChrhWkr; CncrtBnd; HonRl; MrchBnd; YthFlsp; RptrSchPpr; SptEdSchPpr; Bsbl; LetterBsktbl; St Clair County Comm College; Journalism.

SILVIUS, Jean; Belvidere Senior Hs; Rockford, IL; ChrhWkr; CmntyWkr; CncrtBnd; LbryAde; MrchBnd; SchMus; 4-H; FrCl; Trk; College; Music.

SILVOLA, Ruth A; Warren HS; Gurnee, IL; 2/300 HonRl; NHS; OffAde; StuCncl; Univ Of Wisconsin; Nursing.

SIM, Donna; Evergreen Park Community Hs; Evergreen Park, IL; 29/439 AFS; SchPpr; SpnCl; MthCl; U Of Illinois; Dental Assistant.

SIMANEK, Joseph M; St Catherines HS; Racine, WI; 6/262 HonRl; ModUN; NHS; Sacrstn; PresSpnCl; LetterBsbl; Bsktbl; CchngActv; IMSpt; GovHonPrgAwd; St Norbert College; Accounting.

SIMBOB, Cheryll K; Forest Park HS; Crystal Falls, MI; 6/89 SecSrCls; CncrtBnd; MrchBnd; PepBnd; RptrYrbk; RptrSchPpr; VPFNA; IMSpt; Ferris State College; Medical Tech.

SIME, Glenda J; Northwood Kensett HS; Northwood, IA; Band; Chr; Chrl; HonRl; RedCrAde; SchMus; FrCl; LetterTrk; LetterChrldr; PresAwd; Mankato St U; Business Admin.

SIMEK, Karen L; Jefferson HS; Lafayette, IN; 7/592 ChrhWkr; CmntyWkr; HonRl; JrNHS; NHS; Orch;

SchMus; TchrAde; GerCl; JAAwd; Washinton U; Med.

SIMENSON, Robert C; Chisago Lakes HS; Lindstrom, MN; 16/134 ALBoysSt; HonRl; SchPl; StuCncl; EdSchPpr; LetterGlf; College; Bus Admin.

SIMERMAN, Debbie K; North Side HS; Ft Wayne, IN; SchAde; TchrAde; Iu Pu Ext Ft Wayne; Clinical Psy.

SIMES, Elizabeth A; St Marys Central HS; Bismarck, ND; College; Professional.

SIMET, Joel R; Bloomer HS; Bloomer, WI; HonRl; Univ Wi; Mech Engr.

SIMGRO, Robert; Jefferson HS; Cedar Rapids, IA; 40/500 PresFrshCls; Chr; Chrs; HonRl; NHS; SchMus; Trk; Univ Of Ia; Law.

SIMILUK, Martin; Our Lady Of Lakes HS; Drayton Plains, MI; 16/63 TrsJrCls; Aud/Vis; HonRl; NatlMeritCmnd; SchAde; StuCncl; FrCl; Ftbl; IMSpt; College; Architecture.

SIMISON, Theodore P; Danville HS; Danville, IL; 18/629 HonRl; IntrClCncl; NatlMeritSF; EdYrBk; LetterSwmmng; RotaryAwd; Purdue Univ; Chemical Engineering.

SIMMELINK, Ross M; Maurice Orange City HS; Orange City, IA; ChrhWkr; PresStuCncl; PresYthFlsp; Bsbl; LetterFtbl; IMSpt; Northwestern Coll; Bus Exec.

SIMMELINK, Scott D; Lebanon HS; Lebanon, KS; SecJrCls; SecSrCls; StuCncl; FFA; Bsktbl; Ftbl; Trk; College; Vocation.

SIMMERMAN, Keri D; Elm Creek Public HS; Elm Creek, NE; Band; Chrs; DrmMjrt; HonRl; HospAde; NHS; StuCncl; 4-H; PpCl; Bsktbl; 4-HAwd; Medical Inst Of Mn; Med Lab Tech.

SIMMERMEYER, Mary Beth; Acad Of The Immaculate Concep; Oldenburg, IN; 9/69 ALAGirlsSt; Chrs; HonRl; Mdrgl; NHS; Orch; Quill&Scroll; EdSchPpr; Swmmng; VoiceDemAwd; College; Registered Nurse.

SIMMERMEYER, Sharon; Brookville Hs; Brookville, IN; HonRl; NHS; OffAde; SchPl; TchrAde; FHA; FTA; PpCl; Trade School ; Interior Decorator.

SIMMERT, Robert L; Downers Grove So HS; Downers Grove, IL; 129/879 Chr; HonRl; NatlMeritCmnd; SchAde; RptrSchPpr; FrCl; Bsktbl; LetterFtbl; CaptTrk; College; Elementary Education.

SIMMET, Mark A; Cathedral HS; New Ulm, MN; Band; ChrhWkr; CncrtBnd; HonRl; MrchBnd; SchPl; RptrSchPpr; Dramatics.

SIMMONDS, Laura A; West Allis Central HS; West Allis, WI; 8/426 ChrhWkr; CncrtBnd; HonRl; MrchBnd; SchPl; StuCncl; SecStuGov; YthFlsp; RptrYrbk; EdYrBk; College; Model Physics.

SIMMONDS, Scott; Daleville HS; Daleville, IN; HonRl; TchrAde; College; Attorney.

SIMMONS, Billie J; Hauser HS; Columbus, IN; 2/83 HonRl; NHS; Quill&Scroll; YthFlsp; RptrYrbk; RptrSchPpr; FTA; PpCl; GAA; DanFAwd; Indiana U; Elem Ed.

SIMMONS, Bonnie S; Hauser Jr Sr HS; Columbus, IN; 20/83 DrlTm; HonRl; NHS; Quill&Scroll; RptrYrbk; 4-H; FFA; FTA; GAA; 4-HAwd;.

SIMMONS, Brad A; Glendale HS; Springfield, MO; LetterBsbl; LetterBsktbl;.

SIMMONS, Bradley M; Brother Rice HS; Birmingham, MI; 21/213 Band; ChrhWkr; CncrtBnd; HonRl; MrchBnd; NHS; PepBnd; SctActv; RptrYrbk; Univ Of Detroit; Finance.

SIMMONS, Cathy E; Woodland R 4 HS; Glen Allen, MO; ChrhWkr; HonRl; LbryAde; OffAde; StuCncl; TchrAde; RptrSchPpr; FHA; FrCl; PpCl; Univ; Bus.

SIMMONS, Douglas D; Huron HS; Huron, SD; Band; ChrhWkr; CncrtBnd; MrchBnd; PepBnd; KeyCl; LetterFtbl; Trk; Wrstlng; Trade School.

SIMMONS, Edward J; Ozark HS; Rogersville, MO; 6/91 HonRl; NatlFornLg; SchPl; SctActv; MthCl; PpCl; LetterFtbl; LetterWrstlng; IMSpt; Col; Chemistry.

SIMMONS, Freda L; King City HS; King City, MO; ALAGirlsSt; HonRl; NHS; Twrl; FHA; SpnCl; PpCl; Bsktbl; LetterTrk; 4-HAwd; College; Design.

SIMMONS, James J; Creston HS; Grand Rapids, MI; 106/440 Band; Chr; ChrhWkr; CncrtBnd; JrNHS; MrchBnd; Orch; PepBnd; ROTC; Grand Rapids Junior College; Music.

SIMMONS, Jan E; Maconaquah HS; Grissom Afb, IN; 58/200 HonRl; SchPl; StuCncl; GAA; Indiana Univ; Special Educ.

SIMMONS, Joan A; Thornton Fractional South HS; Lansing, IL; 63/589 HonRl; NatlMeritCmnd; OffAde; SchAde; FrCl; PpCl; GAA; University; Law.

SIMMONS, Joan M; Highland HS; Highland, IN; 64/538 SctActv; TchrAde; FBLA; FDA; FNA; PpCl; CchngActv; GAA; PPFtbl; LionAwd; Coll; Teacher.

SIMMONS, Joann E; Waldron Area HS; Waldron, MI; 7/42 TrsFrshCls; Band; ChrhWkr; CncrtBnd; LbryAde; MrchBnd; OffAde; PepBnd; SchPl; VPTeen; LetterTrk; GAA; College; Business.

SIMMONS, Judy K; Lanark HS; Lanark, IL; Band; Chr; Chrs; ChrhWkr; CncrtBnd; HonRl; MrchBnd; PepBnd; Teen; YthFlsp; Olivet College; Religion.

SIMMONS, Judy M; New Underwood HS; New Underwood, SD; HonRl; NHS; SchPl; Yrbk; SptEdSchPpr; TreasFHA; TreasPpCl; Bsktbl; Trk; Chrldr; Sd State; Comput.

SIMMONS, Kathleen J; Palatine HS; Palatine, IL; 37/440 Chrs; HonRl; StuGov; RptrYrbk; College; Elem Ed.

SIMMONS, Kathy J; Mt Vernon Township HS; Mt Vernon, IL; 10/436 HonRl; JrNHS; SecNHS; Orch; SchMus; TchrAde; YthFlsp; RptrSchPpr; 4-H; FrCl; 4-HAwd; Univ Of Illinois; Psychology.

SIMMONS, Kevin G; Larned HS; Larned, KS; 30/100 ChrhWkr; RptrYrbk; Bsktbl; LetterFtbl; Glf; LetterTrk; IMSpt; VoiceDemAwd; Dodge City Comm College; Business.

SIMMONS, Linda A; Ben Davis HS; Indianapolis, IN; Band; Chr; Chrl; Chrs; ChrhWkr; CmntyWkr; CncrtBnd; DrlTm; MrchBnd; OffAde; College; Professional.

SIMMONS, Marilynn N; Sumner HS; St Louis, MO; 66/600 ChrhWkr; HonRl; SchMus; SchPl; StuCncl; Trk; Chrldr; GAA; College; Nursing.

SIMMONS, Mark E; Centerville HS; Centerville, IA; 11/147 Aud/Vis; ChrhWkr; HonRl; NHS; Loma Linda Univ; Madicine.

SIMMONS, Mary E; Maryville R Ii HS; Maryville, MO; 20/121 Chr; OffAde; Northwest Missouri State Univ; Nursing.

SIMMONS, Micheal C; Colonial HS; Muscatine, IA; 48/785 JA; NatlMeritCmnd; GerCl; MthCl; Rose Hulman Inst Of Tech; Math.

SIMMONS, Renald A; Saranac Comm HS; Saranac, MI; 1/82 ChrhWkr; CncrtBnd; HonRl; MrchBnd; PresNHS; NatlMeritSF; SctActv; YthFlsp; LetterTrk; BauchLmbAwd; Mi State Univ; Mathematics.

SIMMONS, Rhonda L; Minooka HS; Channahon, IL; 10/99 Chr; Chrs; ChrhWkr; HonRl; Mdrgl; NHS; PepBnd; IMSpt; LionAwd; Eastern Ill U; Med Tech.

SIMMONS, Samuel G; Roosevelt HS; Gary, IN; 1/668 ALBoysSt; ChrhWkr; HonRl; PolWkr; StuGov; TchrAde; FTA; KeyCl; IMSpt; Us Marines; Law.

SIMMONS, Sandra K; Duchesne HS; St Charles, MO; 19/184 SecJrCls; ChrhWkr; HonRl; NHS; StuCncl; Chrldr; CitAwd; Univ; Professional.

SIMMONS, Sheila J; Clarion Community HS; Clarion, IA; 3/96 Chrs; HonRl; NHS; SchPl; TchrAde; PresFTA; GovHonPrgAwd; RotaryAwd; VFWAwd; University Of Northern Iowa; Speech.

SIMMONS, Stacy S; Madison Heights HS; Anderson, IN; 2/465 ALAGirlsSt; NHS; PresNatlThespSoc; Quill&Scroll; TchrAde; YthLg; Yrbk; LetterTennis; Trk; GAA; AmLegAwd; DARAwd; NCTE; Ball State Univ; French.

SIMMS, Doris E; North Side HS; Ft Wayne, IN; AFS; HonRl; FrCl; PpCl; Col; Art.

SIMMS, Jayne L; Plano HS; Plano, IL; 10/95 SecSophCls; AFS; Band; Chr; Chrs; CncrtBnd; HonRl; HospAde; Mdrgl; MrchBnd; PepBnd; Bsktbl; CaptSocr; CaptTrk; East Ill Univ; Tv Radio Broadcasting.

SIMMS, Katherine A; Macomb HS; Macomb, IL; 21/235 Band; Chr; CncrtBnd; DrmMjrt; HonRl; HospAde; MrchBnd; NHS; VPOrch; GAA; 4-HAwd; Western Illinois Univ; Interior Design.

SIMON, Alan M; Francis W Parker HS; Chicago, IL; TrsFrshCls; Aud/Vis; LitMag; NatlMeritSF; Orch; PolWkr; StuCncl; StuGov; RptrYrbk; SchPpr; Univ; Oceanography.

SIMON, Bryan R; Saint Patricks HS; Portland, MI; 10/46 VPFrshCls; HonRl; StuCncl; LetterBsbl; Bsktbl; LetterFtbl; Air Force; Trade.

SIMON, Cheryl D; School Of The Osage HS; Lake Ozark, MO; 1/59 SecTrsSrCls; ALAGirlsSt; TreasStuCncl; EdYrBk; VPPpCl; Chrldr; AmLegAwd; DARAwd; LionAwd; CitAwd; U Of Mo Columbia; Bus Ed.

SIMON, Connie L; Princeton HS; Princeton, IL; PresJrCls; Band; CncrtBnd; HonRl; MrchBnd; StuGov; Twrl; VP4-H; Chrldr; 4-HAwd; College; Ecology.

SIMON, Deanna M; Lake View Auburn Comm HS; Lake View, IA; TreasBand; PresChrs; ChrhWkr; CncrtBnd; Mdrgl; MrchBnd; PepBnd; SchMus; TreasYthFlsp; RptrSchPpr;.

SIMON, Debra K; Cassville HS; Shell Knob, MO; DrlTm; NHS; OffAde; SchPl; TchrAde; FBLA; FTA; PpCl; SciCl; Chrldr; GAA; IMSpt; College; Elementary Education.

SIMON, Joan E; Cuba City HS; Cuba City, WI; VPJrCls; HonRl; NHS; StuCncl; RptrYrbk; RptrSchPpr; SecPpCl; Trk; Chrldr; PresGAA; Vo Tec College; Operating Rm Technician.

SIMON, John J; Precious Blood Seminary; Sedalia, MO; 1/8 Chr; HonRl; NHS; Yrbk; EdSchPpr; Pres4-H; IMSpt; 4-HAwd; Univ Of Missouri; Agriculture.

SIMON, Joyce M; Calhoun HS; Hardin, IL; VPJrCls; PresSrCls; Band; HonRl; NHS; PepBnd; StuCncl; Western Ill Univ; English Ed.

SIMON, Julie A; St Joseph Acad; Green Bay, WI; ChrhWkr; HospAde; VPNHS; EdYrBk; LatCl; U Of Wis Oshkosh; Nurse.

SIMON, Leon; Highland Hs; Riverside, IA; 11/50 PresSrCls; HonRl; NHS; StuCncl; 4-H; CaptIMSpt; 4-HAwd;.

SIMON, Linda L; Chelsea HS; Chelsea, MI; 17/184 Chrs; HonRl; NHS; StuCncl; LatCl; SpnCl; Clge; Biology Or Medicine.

SIMON, Linda M; Tecumseh Sr HS; Adrian, MI; 24/240 CmntyWkr; HonRl; JrNHS; OffAde; SchAde; SctActv; 4-H; FBLA; University; Business Admin.

SIMON, Lucille M; Lomira HS; Lomira, WI; Chrs; HonRl; NHS; SctActv; Yrbk; FHA; Work.

SIMON, Mark A; Truman HS; Independence, MO; Bsbl; Bsktbl; Ftbl; CchngActv; College; Professnl.

SIMON, Mary A; Delta HS; Albany, IN; 3/262 Chr; HonRl; JrNHS; NHS; SchMus; StuCncl; PresYthFlsp; RptrYrbk; College; Mental Health Techniccian.

SIMON, Nancy; Montabella HS; Edmore, MI; Band; CncrtBnd; MrchBnd; NHS; PepBnd; TchrAde; Yrbk; SpnCl; PpCl; PPFtbl; Grand Valley State College; Psychology.

SIMON, Ora T; Highland Park HS; Highland Park, IL; 59/648 ChrhWkr; HonRl; NHS; PolWkr; Univ Of Illinois; Geography.

SIMON, Paul J; Creighton Prep HS; Omaha, NE; CmntyWkr; Sdlty; RptrSchPpr; SptEdSchPpr; LetterFtbl; LetterTrk; LetterWrstlng; IMSpt; College; Management.

SIMON, Paul R; Joliet Central HS; Joliet, IL; 51/491 HonRl; College; Law.

SIMON, Philip F; Carbondale Comm HS; Carbondale, IL; 12/330 ChrhWkr; CmntyWkr; HonRl; LitMag; NatlMeritSF; PolWkr; YthLg; FrCl; VPMthCl; CaptIMSpt; College; Lawyer.

SIMON, William A; Maine Twp East HS; Morton Grove, IL; HonRl; StuCncl; StuGov; MthCl; Swmmng; Univ Of Illinois; Dentistry.

SIMONDS, Nancy A; Hackett HS; Kalamazoo, MI; 18/160 VPFrshCls; VPSophCls; HstSrCls; Chr; ChrhWkr; HonRl; NHS; StuCncl; ChmnBsktbl; GAA; West Mi Univ; Physical Ed.

SIMONET, Mary; Derham Hall HS; St Paul, MN; HospAde; StuCncl; SpnCl; Tennis; CchngActv; Clg; Councelor.

SIMONETTA, Joann K; Lutheran West HS; Detroit, MI; HonRl; NHS; OffAde; StuCncl; RptrYrbk; GerCl; Clge; Medicine Or Social Work.

SIMONIC, Mark; Menominee HS; Menominee, MI; /279 HonRl; 4-H; Bsbl; Bsktbl; Ftbl; Trk; 4-HAwd; Lake Superior St Coll;elect Res.

SIMONIS, Laurie J; St Mary Central HS; Neenah, WI; SecSophCls; Chrs; HonRl; OffAde; StuCncl; TchrAde; FrCl; Stout University; Fashion Field.

SIMONIS, Rose M; Villa De Chantal HS; Rock Island, IL; 1/12 TrsFrshCls; SecSophCls; PresSrCls; ChrhWkr; HonRl; RptrYrbk; RptrSchPpr; PresFrCl; Augustana College; Marine Biology.

SIMONITSCH, Pamela; St Marys HS; Independence, MO; Band; ChrhWkr; HonRl; NHS; SchMus; PpCl; Bsktbl; Trk; GAA;.

SIMONITSCH, Patricia; St Marys HS; Independence, MO; Band; HonRl; NHS; StuCncl; StuGov; Bsktbl; Trk; GAA; IMSpt; Univ; Chemical Engineering.

SIMONS, Carl; Caledonia Public HS; Caledonia, MN; HonRl; SchPl; RptrYrbk; RptrSchPpr; Glf; College; Prof.

SIMONS, Jimmy D; Jayhawk Linn HS; Mound City, KS; SecFrshCls; Band; CmntyWkr; CncrtBnd; HonRl; MrchBnd; SchPl; 4-H; Glf; Trade Or Bus; Professional.

SIMONS, Joan K; Marcus Comm HS; Marcus, IA; Band; CncrtBnd; MrchBnd; PepBnd; YthFlsp; PPFtbl;.

SIMONS, Kerry J; Parkside HS; Jackson, MI; ChrhWkr; CncrtBnd; HonRl; JA; MrchBnd; SchMus; SctActv; Yrbk; GerCl; JAAwd; Michigan State Univ; Advertising.

SIMONS, Linda M; Glencoe HS; Glencoe, MN; TrsJrCls; Band; CncrtBnd; HonRl; MrchBnd; PepBnd; StuCncl; RptrYrbk; RptrSchPpr; LetterChrldr; Jr Coll; Pro.

SIMONS, Linda M; Woodland HS; Streator, IL; 7/76 TrsSrCls; HonRl; LbryAde; NHS; OffAde; YthFlsp; RptrYrbk; GerCl; Patricia Stevens Career College.

SIMONS, Marjorie A; Bellevue HS; Bellevue, NE; Chr; Chrl; Chrs; SchMus; College; Music.

SIMONS, Patti; Pelican Rapids HS; Pelican Rapids, MN; Chr; ChrhWkr; HonRl; HospAde; OffAde; SchMus; FHA; Voc School; Home Econ.

SIMONS, Penny L; St Charles Comm HS; St Charles, MI; 2/126 VPJrCls; HonRl; HospAde; NHS; StuCncl; TchrAde; CaptBsktbl; PresGAA; IMSpt; VoiceDemAwd; Michi State Univ; Accounting.

SIMONS, Rosanne H; Edgemont HS; Edgemont, SD; 2/33 TrsJrCls; AFS; Chrs; HonRl; LbryAde; NHS; SchPl; Yrbk; MthCl; PpCl; South Dakota State U; Chemistry.

SIMONSEN, Cindy S; Pender HS; Pender, NE; Aud/Vis; ChrhWkr; CmntyWkr; HonRl; HospAde; LbryAde; SchMus; SchPl; RptrYrbk; School Of Nursing; Registered Nurse.

SIMONSEN, Janet; Steinmetz Hs; Chicago, IL; 45/617 ChrhWkr; PresCncrtBnd; HonRl; MrchBnd; Orch; TchrAde; KeyCl; GAA; Augustana College; Instrumentalmusic Dir.

SIMONSEN, Kathy K; Pender Public HS; Pender, NE; 4/23 PresSrCls; Chr; ChrhWkr; HonRl; HospAde; Mdrgl; SchAde; SchPl; Glf; Chrldr; Ne Methodist Nursing; Registered Nurse.

SIMONSEN, Leif R; Comstock Park HS; Comstock Park, MI; HonRl; JA; NHS; TchrAde; LetterFtbl; LetterTennis; Coll;sci.

SIMONSON, Alan R; Parkers Prairie HS; Parkers Prairie, MN; 7/72 TrsJrCls; HonRl; NHS; StuCncl; PresFFA; LetterBsbl; Bsktbl; LetterFtbl; LetterWrstlng; Alexandria Vo Tech; Cpa.

SIMONSON, Catherine M; Wanamingo Public HS; Wanamingo, MN; 7/35 Chrs; HonRl; SchPl; StuGov; RptrYrbk; RptrSchPpr; LetterBsktbl; Trk; GAA; IMSpt; U Of M Morris; Physical Education.

SIMONSON, Glenda D; Tuttle Public HS; Arena, ND; TrsSophCls; TrsJrCls; VPSrCls; Band; CmntyWkr; HonRl; RedCrAde; SchPl; FshEdYrbk; RptrSchPpr; SchPpr; PpCl; Chrldr; Business School; Vocation.

SIMONSON, James; Palmer Public HS; Nebr, NE; SecSrCls; ALBoysSt; Band; Chrs; ChrhWkr; HonRl; MrchBnd; Bsktbl; Ftbl; AmLegAwd; Southeast Community College; Social Studies.

SIMONSON, Paul; Thomas Roberts HS; Decorah, IA; 5/128 Band; Chr; ChrhWkr; CmntyWkr; CncrtBnd; HonRl; Mdrgl; MrchBnd; NHS; NatlMeritFnl; NatlMeritSF; SchMus; SchPl; PresStuCncl; IMSpt; College; Math.

SIMONSON, Sarah E; Hillsboro HS; Hillsboro, KS; VPSophCls; ALAGirlsSt; Chrs; CncrtBnd; HonRl; SchMus; StuCncl; University; Teacher.

SIMONSON, Steven D; Parkview HS; Orfordville, WI; 60/170 ALBoysSt; Chr; HonRl; Mdrgl; NatlFornLg; NatlThespSoc; SchMus; SchPl; TchrAde; Ftbl; Trk; Wrstlng; College; Music.

SIMONSON, Steven G; Pleasant Valley HS; Bettendorf, IA; 13/174 CncrtBnd; VPJA; MrchBnd; PolWkr; StuCncl; RptrSchPpr; Bsktbl; LetterGlf; JAAwd; Univ; Medicine Or Architecture.

SIMONSON, Wanda M; Taylor HS; Taylor, WI; Band; Chrs; ChrhWkr; MrchBnd; RptrSchPpr; FHA; GerCl; CaptChrldr; GAA; 4-HAwd; College; Phy Ed Teacher.

SIMPSEN, Cynthia J; Gibson City HS; Gibson City, IL; 10/98 VPJrCls; Chrs; HonRl; NHS; SchMus; StuCncl; EdYrBk; FHA; PpCl;.

SIMPSEN, Denise; Weston HS; Cazenovia, WI; Band; CncrtBnd; HonRl; MrchBnd; PepBnd; RptrSchPpr; FBLA; FHA; PpCl; IMSpt; M A T C; Legal Stenographer.

SIMPSON, Annette E; O Fallon Township HS; O Fallon, IL; 8/301 HonRl; ModUN; NHS; SecGerCl; PpCl; SciCl; CaptChrldr; AmLegAwd; Mc Kendree College; Science.

SIMPSON, Bert E; Topeka HS; Topeka, KS; 38/600 PresSrCls; Band; Chr; ChrhWkr; DrlTm; NatlMeritFnl; SchPl; EdYrBk; Swmmng; Trk; College; Medical Degree.

SIMPSON, Cathy A; Red Cloud Community HS; Red Cloud, NE; Chrs; HonRl; TchrAde; EdYrBk; 4-H; FHA; SpnCl; PpCl; Undecided.

SIMPSON, Cindy L; Alexis HS; Alexis, IL; Band; Chrs; ChrhWkr; HonRl; NHS; SchPl; YthFlsp; EdYrBk; FHA; Bsktbl; College; Pk & Recreation Admin.

SIMPSON, Daniel S; Glendale HS; Springfield, MO; PresSophCls; CmntyWkr; HonRl; NatlMeritSF; PolWkr; SchMus; SchPl; StuGov; CivCl; IMSpt; Univ.

SIMPSON, Dari C; C U HS; Columbus, KS; TrsSophCls; HonRl; LetterBsbl; LetterFtbl; Tennis; LetterWrstlng; College; Vocation.

SIMPSON, David M; Davenport Central HS; Davenport, IA; 60/570 ALBoysSt; CncrtBnd; HonRl; Quill&Scroll; SchPpr; PpCl; CaptBsbl; Bsktbl; Trk; IMSpt; Univ; Journalism.

SIMPSON, Dennis D; Montezuma HS; Montezuma, IA; 10/57 AFS; ChrhWkr; SchPl; StuCncl; GerCl; SecTrsSophCls; LetterBsbl; LetterBsktbl; LetterFtbl; LetterTrk; Central Col; Business.

SIMPSON, Dorice F; John Marshall Harlan HS; Chicago, IL; 19/510 HonRl; NHS; StuCncl; TchrAde; Univ Of Ill; Pharmacist.

SIMPSON, Gary C; Huron HS; Ann Arbor, MI; ALBoysSt; LetterFtbl; CaptSwmmng; College; Engineering.

SIMPSON, Gladys; Chicago Vocational HS; Chicago, IL; 45/735 HonRl; College; Secondary Teacher.

SIMPSON, Harold D; Mitchell HS; Mitchell, NE; 11/55 Chrs; ChrhWkr; CmntyWkr; HonRl; NHS; YthFlsp; GerCl; Bsktbl; Ftbl; Trk; MasAwd; United States Navy; Electronics.

SIMPSON, James; Waterville Elysian HS; Waterville, MN; 10/71 Band; Chrs; NHS; SchMus; SchPpr; FFA; Gustavus Adolphus College; Math.

SIMPSON, James F; Berkeley HS; Berkeley, MO; Band; ChrhWkr; CncrtBnd; HonRl; Orch; 4-H; Univ; Social Worker.

SIMPSON, James J; Huron HS; New Boston, MI; 14/190 PresSophCls; ALBoysSt; Chr; ChrhWkr; HonRl; NHS; StuCncl; StuGov; 4-H; LetterFtbl; LetterWrstlng; 4-HAwd; Adrian College; Law.

SIMPSON, Jeanette M; Tell City HS; Tell City, IN; 7/180 Chrs; CncrtBnd; HonRl; JrNHS; MrchBnd; NatlMeritCmnd; PepBnd; 4-H; Indiana State Univ; History.

SIMPSON, Kent; Fulton HS; Fulton, IL; HonRl; JA; SctActv; Ftbl; Glf; IMSpt; JAAwd; Coll; Lawyer.

SIMPSON, Lorie; Herman Community HS; Chokio, MN; 6/40 Band; ChrhWkr; NHS; RptrYrbk; 4-H; FHA; Chrldr; BttyCrckrAwd; 4-HAwd; PresAwd; U Of Wisc; Home Econ Teach.

SIMPSON, Mari L; Edsel Ford HS; Dearborn, MI; Chr; Chrl; Chrs; HonRl; Mdrgl; NHS; NatlMeritCmnd; VPNatlThespSoc; Orch; SchMus; SchPl; TchrAde; Western Michigan University; Music.

SIMPSON, Mark R; North HS; Evansville, IN; 1/440 ALBoysSt; CncrtBnd; HonRl; MrchBnd; NHS; SctActv; StuCncl; YthFlsp; GerCl; DARAwd; Coll; Physics.

SIMPSON, Mary J; Columbus North HS; Columbus, IN; 96/500 Chr; ChrhWkr; HonRl; Spencer College; Keypunch Operator.

SIMPSON, Norma N; Marshall HS; Marshall, IL; 5/115 ChrhWkr; SecNHS; OffAde; SpnCl; SciCl; GAA; Business Sch; Secretary.

SIMPSON, Ronald L; Dixon HS; Dixon, MO; HonRl; Bsbl; College; Professional.

SIMPSON, Sandra K; Alton Senior HS; Alton, IL; 42/832 Chrs; ChrhWkr; HonRl; JrNHS; NHS; TchrAde; VPFBLA; LatCl; College; Math Teacher.

SIMPSON, Scott A; Casey HS; Casey, IL; 11/95 Band; CncrtBnd; HonRl; MrchBnd; NHS; 4-H; LetterFtbl; IMSpt; College.

SIMPSON, Steven Q; Hesston HS; Hesston, KS; 1/60 ALBoysSt; HonRl; NatlMeritCmnd; SctActv; StuCncl; EdSchPpr; CaptFtbl; LetterWrstlng; NCTE; CitAwd; Baker Univ; Medicine.

SIMPSON, Susan K; Niobrara Public HS; Niobrara, NE; 1/22 DrlTm; HonRl; OffAde; SchPl; VoiceDemAwd; Ne Wesleyan Univ; Risepiratory Therapy.

SIMPSON, Terri L; South Spencer HS; Rockport, IN; 19/136 HonRl; TchrAde; PpCl; Univ Of Evansville; Secondary Ed.

SIMPSON, William A; Lamphere HS; Madison Hts, MI; Band; Chr; HonRl; NHS; NatlMeritSchl; NatlThespSoc; LetterTrk; Mi State Univ; Elec Eng.

SIMS, Barbara A; Waverly HS; Waverly, IL; PresFrshCls; VPSophCls; Chrs; ChrhWkr; HonRl; LbryAde; NHS; OffAde; SchAde; SchPl; StuCncl; 4-H; LatCl; SpnCl; Blackburn College.

SIMS, Candis S; Woodlawn HS; Walnut Hill, IL; PresJrCls; Chrs; ChrhWkr; HonRl; JrNHS; NHS; SchPl; StuCncl; FHA; SpnCl; PpCl; Chrldr;.

SIMS, Carol J; Cloverdale Comm HS; Cloverdale, IN; Band; Chr; Chrl; Chrs; ChrhWkr; CncrtBnd; HonRl; MrchBnd; PepBnd; SchMus; SchPl; Bsktbl; Trk; Indiana St Univ.

SIMS, Cynthia L; Wilcox HS; Republican City, NE; 12/26 TrsFrshCls; Band; Chrs; HonRl; NHS; EdYrBk; 4-H; Bsktbl; Trk; Chrldr; Kearney State Clge; Special Ed.

SIMS, Deborah G; Flower Vocational; Chicago, IL; SecSrCls; Band; HonRl; FshEdSchPpr; FBLA; Bsktbl; GAA; CitAwd; Executive Pro Secretary.

SIMS, Debra J; Girard HS; Girard, KS; 15/98 ChrhWkr; CmntyWkr; NHS; SchMus; SchPl; Teen; PresFrCl; TreasSpnCl; SciCl; LetterBsktbl; LetterTrk; PPFtbl; College; Languages.

SIMS, Demar; Lindblom Tech HS; Chicago, IL; 333/700 ChrhWkr; CmntyWkr; OffAde; SchAde; TchrAde; LetterFtbl; LetterTrk; College; Business.

SIMS, Dondi; Monett HS; Monett, MO; SecSrCls; HonRl; LbryAde; OffAde; TchrAde; FTA; PpCl; GAA; College; Professional.

SIMS, Fred D; Whitfield HS; St Louis, MO; 1/23 VPFrshCls; VPSophCls; VPJrCls; HonRl; ModUN; NHS; NatlMeritCmnd; StuCncl; LetterSocr; Bsktbl; College; Astrophysics.

SIMS, Gary R; Oak Park HS; Kansas City, MO; Band; ChrhWkr; CncrtBnd; HonRl; MrchBnd; Orch; PepBnd; TchrAde; Ftbl; Trk; Univ Of Missouri; Medicine.

SIMS, James; Gary West Side HS; Gary, IN; 30/700 Aud/Vis; ChrhWkr; CncrtBnd; JrNHS; MrchBnd; NHS; PepBnd; FrCl; SciCl; Bsktbl; Valparaiso Univ; Music Educator.

SIMS, Jeff A; Schaller Community HS; Schaller, IA; TrsFrshCls; ALBoysSt; Band; CncrtBnd; HonRl; MrchBnd; PepBnd; SchMus; SchPl; PpCl; LetterBsbl; LetterBsktbl; LetterFtbl; College.

SIMS, Loretta; Tishilwa HS; Tiskilwa, IL; SecJrCls; Chrs; StuCncl; TchrAde; FHA; MthCl; Trk; GAA;.

SIMS, Richard D; Buhler HS; Hutchinson, KS; Band; Chr; DrmBgl; MrchBnd; SchPl; SctActv; TchrAde; YthFlsp; College; Oceanography.

SIMS, Rueben A; John Marshall Harlan HS; Chicago, IL; 87/708 HonRl; SchAde; SctActv; StuCncl; TchrAde; FrCl; MthCl; Univ Of Illinois; Engineering.

SIMS, Sondra W; St Thomas Apostle HS; Chicago, IL; Chr; ChrhWkr; CmntyWkr; HonRl; HospAde; SchPpr; University; Medicine.

SIMS, Wanda L; N Daviess HS; Odon, IN; Chrl; ChrhWkr; HonRl; SchMus; TchrAde; FHA; PpCl;.

SIMUNACI, Janet; Roncalli Hs; Omaha, NE; PresSrCls; HonRl; JrNHS; SchPl; SctActv; StuCncl; RptrSchPpr; MthCl; College; Accountant.

SINACOLA, Cynthia H; Marian HS; Southfield, MI; Chrl; HonRl; NHS; OffAde; SchMus; TchrAde; Secretary.

SINCLAIR, Brad W; Jersey Comm HS; Jerseyville, IL; Western Ill Univ; Engineering.

SINCLAIR, Cynthia L; Petersburg Porta HS; Petersburg, IL; 7/97 SecSrCls; CncrtBnd; HonRl; NHS; NatlThespSoc; SchMus; Yrbk; Trk; CaptChrldr; TreasPPFtbl; Univ Of Il; Theater.

SINCLAIR, Kimberly; Huntington North HS; Huntington, IN; YthFlsp; PPFtbl; Ball State Univ; Elem Education.

SINCLAIR, Margi J; Virginia HS; Virginia, IL; 6/48 PresFrshCls; TrsSophCls; ALAGirlsSt; ChrhWkr; HonRl; NHS; StuCncl; RptrSchPpr; GAA; 4-HAwd; College.

SINCLAIR, Max; Sycamore HS; Sycamore, IL; 10/212 PresJrCls; CncrtBnd; Mdrgl; NHS; NatlMeritCmnd; NatlThespSoc; SchMus; SchPl; RptrSchPpr; LetterTrk; University Of Chicago.

SINCLAIR, Michael D; Hastings HS; Hastings, MI; Band; HonRl; MrchBnd; NatlMeritCmnd; PepBnd; SctActv; LetterFtbl; IMSpt; College; Electronics Engineer.

SINCLAIR, Patricia D; Seneca HS; Seneca, IL; HonRl; LbryAde; GerCl; Chrldr; GAA; IMSpt; College; Professnl.

SINCLAIR, Renee T; Clarkston Sr HS; Clarkston, MI; 22/430 Band; CmntyWkr; CncrtBnd; HonRl; MrchBnd; NHS; PepBnd; SchMus; SchPl; TchrAde; CchngActv; IMSpt; PPFtbl; Barbizon College; Fashion Design.

SINDELAR, Scott S; Richfield HS; Richfield, MN; 8/796 Band; CmntyWkr; CncrtBnd; HonRl; MrchBnd; NHS; NatlMeritSF; PepBnd; PolWkr; LetterFtbl; LetterTrk; IMSpt; College; Biology.

SINDEN, Sharon M; Eisenhower HS; Blue Island, IL; Chr; HonRl; MrchBnd; OffAde; SchAde; Trade School; Paramedics.

SINDICICH, Ed J; Bishop Noll HS; East Chicago, IN; 71/412 TrsJrCls; HonRl; StuCncl; StuGov; Swmmng; Trk; IMSpt; College; Professional.

SINDING, Pamela M; Siren Consld HS; Siren, WI; 6/48 Chr; DrmBgl; HonRl; SchMus; FHA; PpCl; Swmmng; Chrldr; Business School; Court Reporter.

SINDT, Douglas R; Franklin Public HS; Riverton, NE; 2/55 Band; ChrhWkr; HonRl; NHS; SchPl; StuCncl; YthFlsp; LetterBsktbl; LetterFtbl; LetterTrk;.

SINDT, Douglas R; Franklin R 6 HS; Riverton, NE; 2/58 VPSophCls; HonRl; NHS; SchPl; StuCncl; YthFlsp; 4-H; LetterBsktbl; LetterFtbl; LetterTrk; College; History.

SINECKI, Gary W; Duchesne HS; St Charles, MO; 106/220 Chrs; CmntyWkr; HonRl; PolWkr; SchMus; KeyCl; LetterBsbl; LetterBsktbl; CchngActv; College.

SINER, Mark S; Schulte HS; Terre Haute, IN; ChrhWkr; HonRl; PolWkr; Sacrstn; LetterFtbl; LetterTrk; Ind St Univ; Accounting.

SINES, James L; West HS; Iowa City, IA; PresFrshCls; NatlMeritSF; SchPl; StuGov; UNYO; RptrYrbk; SptEdSchPpr; SpnCl; LetterGlf; IMSpt; Clg; Law.

SINGCO, Judy A; Greenfield Central HS; Greenfield, IN; 16/270 VPSophCls; TrsJrCls; ALAGirlsSt; Chrs; HonRl; NHS; NatlThespSoc; OffAde; Sacrstn; SchMus; Indiana Univ; Medical Career.

SINGER, Alex C; New Trier East HS; Wilmette, IL; AFS; Chr; PolWkr; SchMus; Univ Of Wisconsin; African Studies.

SINGER, Deborah; Okemos HS; Okemos, MI; 8/280 ChrhWkr; CmntyWkr; NHS; NatlMeritCmnd; PolWkr; StuGov; TchrAde; RptrYrbk; FrCl; LetterTennis; Mich St Univ; Law.

SINGER, Karen L; Cheboygan Catholic Ctrl HS; Cheboygan, MI; 10/32 HonRl; HospAde; SchAde; SchPl; StuCncl; StuGov; EdYrBk; PpCl; LetterBsktbl; CchngActv; PresAwd; Central Michigan Univ; Physical Education.

SINGER, Nancy R; Daleville HS; Daleville, IN; ChrhWkr; HonRl; SecNHS; TchrAde; YthFlsp; FHA; FrCl; Anderson Clg; Medical Tech.

SINGHURST, Joel C; Sheyenne River Academy; Lemmon, SD; ChrhWkr; HonRl; NatlMeritCmnd; TchrAde; RptrSchPpr; SptEdSchPpr; CaptBsktbl; CchngActv; IMSpt; College; Statistician.

SINGISER, Robert T; Warren Township HS; Gurnee, IL; 3/323 HonRl; NHS; LetterTennis; Purdue Univ; Dentistry.

SINGLETON, Diane M; Lewiston HS; Liberty, NE; 4/23 HonRl; SchPl; RptrYrbk; Yrbk; PpCl; College; Rn.

SINGLETON, Rebecca R; Alpena HS; Alpena, MI; Band; HonRl; HospAde; Orch; SchMus; SchPl; TchrAde; FrCl; Mich State Univ; Audiology.

SINGLEY, Aylesa D; Broad Ripple HS; Indianapolis, IN; SecChr; VPJA; NHS; StuCncl; RptrYrbk; 4-H; 4-HAwd; JAAwd; College; Psychiatry.

SINGSANK, Thomas R; Beckman HS; Dyersville, IA; 3/148 HonRl; NHS; SchMus; SchPl; 4-H; MthCl; Wrstlng; IMSpt; 4-HAwd; St Mary Col; Act.

SINICKI, Mark R; Bay City Central HS; Bay City, MI; CAP; HonRl; LitMag; NHS; StuCncl; SchPpr; Delta College; Pharmacist.

SINISI, Ethna M; Munster HS; Munster, IN; PresFrshCls; LitMag; Quill&Scroll; SchAde; SchPl; TchrAde; Art Institute; Art Design.

SINKEVICS, John H; Grand Haven HS; Grand Haven, MI; 10/397 HonRl; NHS; Quill&Scroll; VPStuCncl; LatCl; RusCl; OptClAwd; RotaryAwd; U Of Mi.

SINKEY, Debra J; Sheldon Comm HS; Ashton, IA; Chr; ChrhWkr; HonRl; NHS; Quill&Scroll; TchrAde; YthFlsp; Yrbk; FTA; PpCl; Northwestern Coll; Social Work.

SINKFIELD, Cecil G; Haworth HS; Kokomo, IN; Band; Chrs; HonRl; SecJrNHS; LbryAde; OffAde; SchAde; LetterBsbl; LetterFtbl; IMSpt; College; Vocation.

SINKS, Rod G; Lindbergh HS; Minnetonka, MN; ChrhWkr; Orch; SctActv; SpnCl; MthCl; Swmmng; College; Engineering.

SINKULE, Jenee L; Crete HS; Crete, NE; Band; Chrs; ChrhWkr; CncrtBnd; MrchBnd; HstFrshCls; PresSophCls; YthFlsp; VPFTA; Univ; Music.

SINN, Jane; Martensdale St Marys Comm Hs; Martensdale, IA; 3 PresSophCls; ChrhWkr; HonRl; NHS; SchPl; Yrbk; PpCl; LetterBsktbl; LetterTrk; Liberal Arts College;dramatics.

SINN, Jeanie K; Olympia HS; Delavan, IL; 22/192 AFS; ChrhWkr; NHS; SchPl; YthFlsp; RptrSchPpr; EdSchPpr; 4-H; FHA; SpnCl; Chrldr; GAA; DanFAwd; Bradley Univ; Journalism.

SINNER, Leslie T; Central Cass HS; Casselton, ND; TrsSrCls; ALAGirlsSt; DrlTm; HonRl; NHS; SchPl; StuCncl; Yrbk; LetterChrldr; GAA; Clge; Math.

SINNER, Paula J; Central Cass HS; Casselton, ND; 4/58 TrsJrCls; ALAGirlsSt; HonRl; NHS; SchPl; EdSchPpr; SchPpr; 4-H; CaptBsktbl; Wrstlng; U Of Nd; Accountant.

SINNES, Susan M; Elgin HS; Bartlett, IL; SecSrCls; Band; Chr; StuCncl; LetterSwmmng; Chrldr; GAA; IMSpt; University; Special Education.

SINNESS, Marilyn J; Minnewaukn Public HS; Minnewaukan, ND; SecTrsSophCls; Chrs; HonRl; SchPl; TchrAde; YthFlsp; EdYrBk; 4-H; FHA; College; Exec Secretary.

SINNING, Allan R; Darlington HS; Darlington, WI; 29/119 ALBoysSt; Band; CmntyWkr; SchPl; StuGov; YthFlsp; 4-H; FFA; KeyCl; LetterBsbl; Uw Lacrosse; Professional.

SINNOTT, Daniel J; St Francis Prep; Ann Arbor, MI; 2/21 HonRl; NHS; RedCrAde; VPStuCncl; EdYrBk; SchPpr; FrCl; LatCl; VPMthCl; CaptTennis; Univ Of Mi; Engineer.

SINNOTT, Jamie A; Belview Public HS; Redwood Falls, MN; 2/21 Band; Chrs; HonRl; LbryAde; NHS; NatlMeritCmnd; SchPl; StuGov; RptrSchPpr; Univ Of Minnesota; Elementary Ed.

SINSABAUGH, Diane; Watervliet HS; Watervliet, MI; 5/96 VPSrCls; ChrhWkr; HonRl; HospAde; NHS; Orch; SchMus; StuCncl; DARAwd; Ferris St Coll; R Ph.

SINSABAUGH, Donna L; Morton Sr HS; Hammond, IN; 4/540 HonRl; NHS; Business College; Aviation Admin.

SINSHEIMER, Janet S; Ann Arbor Pioneer HS; Ann Arbor, MI; Band; CncrtBnd; MrchBnd; NatlMeritSF; NatlSciFnd; Orch; MthCl; SciCl; Biochemistry.

SINSKI, Sheryl; St Mary Of Ph Hs; Chicago, IL; HonRl; NHS; ROTC; ROTC; SctActv; StuCncl; Yrbk; 4-H; FrCl; GAA;.

SINSKI, Sheryl; St Mary Of Ph HS; Chicago, IL; PresSrCls; HonRl; NHS; ROTC; SctActv; StuCncl; StuGov; IMSpt; PresAwd;.

SINTZ, Patti J; Brookville Senior HS; Brookville, IN; Band; ChrhWkr; CncrtBnd; MrchBnd; TchrAde; 4-H; FHA; FTA; Secretarial Job.

SIP, James A; Bow Homme #96 HS; Tyndall, SD; TrsSophCls; VPJrCls; PresSrCls; ALBoysSt; HonRl; StuCncl; StuGov; Ftbl; Wrstlng; Univ Of S Dak; Mechanics.

SIPE, Diane L; Prophetstown HS; Prophetstown, IL; 9/99 SecSrCls; TreasAFS; Chrs; ChrhWkr; HonRl; JrNHS; SecNHS; SctActv; PresYthFlsp; Yrbk; FTA; PresFrCl; PpCl; Knox College; Biology.

SIPE, Gary W; Eastside Jr Sr HS; Butler, IN; ALBoysSt; ChrhWkr; HonRl; YthFlsp; FFA; Bsktbl; LetterFtbl; University.

SIPE, Keven R; Adams Central HS; Monroe, IN; Aud/Vis; HonRl; NHS; SchPpr; FFA; GerCl; SpnCl; Wrstlng; IMSpt; Farmer.

SIPPEL, Kim T; Chippewa Falls HS; Chippewa Falls, WI; 1/358 ALBoysSt; ChrhWkr; HonRl; NHS; StuCncl; YthFlsp; CaptBsbl; CaptBsktbl; LetterFtbl; RotaryAwd; Il Inst Of Tech; Architect.

SIPPEL, Ronald; St Marys Hs; Schaller, IA; 10/45 PresJrCls; Chr; HonRl; NHS; StuCncl; StuGov; Bsbl; Bsktbl; Trk; PresAwd; University; Architect.

SIPPEL, Teresa D; Petoskey HS; Petoskey, MI; 15/375 SpnCl; Lake Superior St Col; Acctg.

SIPPLE, Margaret A; West Senior HS; Garden City, MI; Band; Chrs; CncrtBnd; MrchBnd; PepBnd; College.

SIPPLE, Patricia R; Maine Township West HS; Des Plaines, IL; HonRl; NHS; GerCl; Swmmng; DAAwd; U Of Ill; Medicine.

SIRESS, Katherine; St Pius X HS; Gladstone, MO; 31/129 Band; CncrtBnd; HonRl; JrNHS; ModUN; NHS; OffAde; PepBnd; SchMus; SchPl;.

SIREVICIUS, John A; St Laurence HS; Chicago, IL; 44/372 HonRl; SctActv; Yrbk; SchPpr; SciCl; LetterBsktbl; GovHonPrgAwd; Syracuse Univ; Physics.

SIRHAN, Robert F; Romulus HS; Romulus, MI; 46/300 CmntyWkr; HonRl; NHS; SctActv; SecKeyCl; Bsbl; CaptFtbl; Tennis; Trk; Ferris St Coll; Pharmacy.

SIRKO, Michelle; Merrillville Sr HS; Merrillville, IN; 12/574 HonRl; NHS; SchPl; 4-H; PpCl; GAA; PPFtbl; AmLegAwd; CitAwd; Valparaiso Univ; Law.

SIROIS, Laurena; St Scholastica Hs; Park Ridge, IL; 6/233 Chr; Chrl; CmntyWkr; NHS; NatlMeritCmnd; Yrbk; Purdue U; Professional.

SIRVINSKAS, Alan A; Metro HS; Chicago, IL; College; Business.

SIS, Steve L; Benkelman HS; Benkelman, NE; 12/45 VPJrCls; PresSrCls; Chrs; HonRl; NHS; StuCncl; SciCl; Bsbl; Bsktbl; Ftbl; College.

SISAK, Joanne M; Wm Horlock HS; Racine, WI; 13/525 Band; CncrtBnd; HonRl; HospAde; MrchBnd; PepBnd; SchAde; TchrAde; Univ Wis Parkside; Computer Science.

SISCO, Kenton; Clearwater R I HS; Piedmont, MO; 33/70 SecTrsFrshCls; PresJrCls; Band; CncrtBnd; HonRl; SciCl; Bsbl; Glf; Trk; IMSpt; Coll.

SISK, William D; Worthington Jefferson HS; Worthington, IN; Aud/Vis; LbryAde; OffAde; TchrAde; 4-H; FFA; PpCl; CchngActv; IMSpt; Wabash Valley College; Diesel Specialist.

SISSON, Richard M; Circle HS; Towanda, KS; HonRl; SctActv; SciCl; Bsktbl; Ftbl; Trk; IMSpt; Ks State; Physician.

SISTI, Jon L; Rochester HS; Rochester, IN; 14/168 Band; HonRl; PepBnd; SchPl; StuCncl; RptrYrbk; GerCl; LetterTennis; IMSpt; University; Journalism.

SITAR, Debra J; Seymour Sr HS; Seymour, IN; 97/334 CmntyWkr; NHS; NatlMeritFnl; NatlMeritSchl; NatlMeritSF; NatlSciFnd; RedCrAde; StuGov; FSA; Swmmng; Tennis; Indiana Univ; Bio Science.

SITASZ, John S; St Rita HS; Chicago, IL; 3/424 HonRl; NHS; Univ Of Illinois; Electronics.

SITEK, Mary E; Our Lady Of Mt Carmel HS; Wyandotte, MI; 3/61 VPSophCls; PresJrCls; HonRl; HospAde; NHS; RptrYrbk; SpnCl; Bsktbl; Chrldr; IMSpt; Univ Of Mi; Nursing.

SITKOWSKI, Joy Ann; Glenbard West HS; Glen Ellyn, IL; 73/522 Chrs; HonRl; IntrClCncl; JA; NatlThespSoc; SchPl; StuCncl; GAA; PPFtbl; JAAwd; U Of Ill; Therapist.

SITLINGTON, James R; St Thomas HS; Ann Arbor, MI; PresFrshCls; ChrhWkr; HonRl; NatlMeritSchl; NatlMeritSF; StuCncl; StuGov; RptrYrbk; SptEdYrbk; FrCl; West Point; Pre Law.

SITTER, Rose M; Anna Jonesboro Comm HS; Anna, IL; HonRl; SciCl;.

SITZMAN, Sherry; Table Rock Public HS; Table Rock, NE; 3/25 Chrs; CncrtBnd; HonRl; MrchBnd; NatlMeritCmnd; SchPl; 4-H; PpCl; BttyCrckrAwd; Univ Of Neb; Chem Engin.

SIUBA, Kenneth E; St Francis De Sales HS; Chicago, IL; 16/297 ChrhWkr; HonRl; NHS; Univ Of Illinois; Medicine.

SIUNIAK, Louis G; Waterford Kettering HS; Drayton Plains, MI; 9/450 Band; HonRl; JrNHS; NHS; Univ Of Michigan.

SIVCOVICH, Paul D; Pattonville HS; Bridgeton, MO; 88/800 ChrhWkr; HonRl; NHS; StuCncl; LetterTennis; PresAwd; Sw Mo State Univ.

SIVIA, Tom W; Waukegan E HS; Waukegan, IL; LitMag; RptrYrbk; Yrbk; College.

SIVICEK, David A; Brother Rice HS; Chicago, IL; CmntyWkr; HonRl; SctActv; SciCl; Socr; Wrstlng; College; Liberal Arts.

SIVIER, Katherine A; Mahomet Seymour HS; Mahomet, IL; Band; MrchBnd; NHS; NatlMeritFnl; NatlThespSoc; SchMus; Eastern Ill Univ; Landscape Architecture.

SIVILS, Cotton C; Bryant HS; Rich Hill, MO; PresJrCls; PresSrCls; ALBoysSt; HonRl; StuCncl; FFA; Bsbl; LetterBsktbl; LetterFtbl; LetterTrk; CchngActv; AmLegAwd; Univ Of Missouri.

SIX, Thomas; Underwood HS; Underwood, ND; Band; CncrtBnd; MrchBnd; SchPl; SctActv; SchPpr; Bsbl; Bsktbl; SecJrCls; Trk; Teaching.

SIZER, Karen D; Belton HS; Richard Gebaur Afb, MO; Band; CncrtBnd; HonRl; JA; NHS; TchrAde; FHA; RusCl; SpnCl;.

SJOERDSMA, Ellen J; Central Wisconsin HS; Randolph, WI; Chr; ChrhWkr; HonRl; JrNHS; LbryAde; OffAde; SchPl; StuCncl; TchrAde; Yrbk; SchPpr; PpCl; RotaryAwd; University; Technician.

SJOLANDER, Janet; Bayard HS; Bayard, NE; 8/43 SecSophCls; SecJrCls; SecSrCls; HonRl; NHS; RptrYrbk; FHA; Trk; Chrldr; Chadron St Coll; Elementary Teaching.

SJOMELING, Catherine L; Stevens HS; Rapid City, SD; 75/413 Chr; CmntyWkr; HonRl; HospAde; SchMus; TchrAde; 4-H; PpCl; Tennis; College; Professional.

SJOSTRAND, Faith R; E Grand Forks Sr HS; E Grand Forks, MN; 8/191 CncrtBnd; HonRl; HospAde; NHS; PepBnd; SchPl; TreasFHA; GerCl; Chrldr; GAA; Univ Of Minnesota; Mathematics.

SJOSTROM, Laurel L; St Charles HS; St Charles, IL; 8/465 Chr; NHS; Univ Of Illinois; Biology.

SJULLIE, Dave P; John F Kennedy HS; Cedar Rapids, IA; Band; ChrhWkr; CncrtBnd; DrmBgl; HonRl; MrchBnd; SchPpr; LetterBsbl; IMSpt; Univ Of Mo; Sports Broadcaster.

SJURSON, Gail M; Bristol HS; Butler, SD; 1/30 SecJrCls; ALAGirlsSt; Chrs; ChrhWkr; HonRl; HospAde; LbryAde; StuCncl; PresFNA; PpCl; College; Teacher.

SJURSON, Kristi A; Bristol HS; Butler, SD; Chr; Chrl; Chrs; HonRl; LbryAde; StuCncl; PpCl; Bsktbl; Chrldr; College; Business.

SKAAR, Cherry S; Central HS; Hayward, MN; 32/526 Chr; Chrs; HonRl; SchMus; YthFlsp; CivCl; 4-H; FHA; 4-HAwd; Coll; Animal Sci.

SKAARE, Jerald; Bristol HS; Bristol, SD; PresJrCls; HonRl; StuCncl; IMSpt; EldAwd; JCAwd; Coll; Electronics.

SKAGGS, Cydney R; Fredericktown Ri HS; Fredericktown, MO; 13/170 PresBand; ChrhWkr; CmntyWkr; CncrtBnd; HonRl; MrchBnd; PepBnd; PolWkr; Sdlty; PpCl; University Of Missouri; Child Psychology.

SKAGGS, Dennis F; Seneca HS; Seneca, MO; 4/111 TrsJrCls; HonRl; NHS; StuCncl; TchrAde; FTA; MthCl; LetterBsbl; LetterBsktbl; LetterFtbl; College.

SKAGGS, Grace; Eau Claire HS; Sodus, MI; 18/96 Band; ChrhWkr; CncrtBnd; HonRl; JrNHS; MrchBnd; NHS; PepBnd; Bsbl; Bsktbl; Sw Mich; Bookkeeping.

SKAGGS, Grace M; Eau Claire HS; Sedus, MI; 11/96 PresBand; CncrtBnd; HonRl; MrchBnd; NHS; PepBnd; SchPl; StuGov; YthFlsp; Yrbk; Bsbl; Bsktbl; Univ Of Southwestern Mi; Accounting.

SKAGGS, Jeffrey L; Crocker R Ii HS; Crocker, MO; ALBoysSt; Band; HonRl; SpnCl; PpCl; Bsbl; Bsktbl; College.

SKAGGS, Randy; Van Buren HS; Birmingham, IA; 16/90 Band; Chrs; HonRl; MrchBnd; NHS; SchMus; PpCl; Bsbl; Ftbl; Jr College; Business.

SKAGGS, Robert N; Franklin Central HS; Indianapolis, IN; 44/209 CmntyWkr; HonRl; FSA; LatCl; PpCl; Indiana Univ; Microbiology.

SKAGGS, Sharon K; Viburnum C 4 HS; Viburnum, MO; 18/60 Chrs; ChrhWkr; HonRl; LbryAde; ModUN; SchPpr; 4-H; FHA; PpCl; Tennis; College; Registered Nurse.

SKAGGS, Vickie L; Valley Of Caledonia HS; Belgrade, MO; VPFrshCls; PresJrCls; Band; CncrtBnd; HonRl; PresNHS; PepBnd; SchPl; SecStuCncl; CaptChrldr; DARAwd; CitAwd;.

SKALBECK, Jeffrey P; Sacred Heart Public HS; Sacred Heart, MN; 1/30 Chr; HonRl; NHS; 4-H; FFA; Ftbl; LetterTrk; LetterWrstlng; 4-HAwd; Univ Of Minnesota; Medicine.

SKALITZKY, Elecia I; Platte County R Iii HS; Platte City, MO; Band; CncrtBnd; HonRl; MrchBnd; VPNHS; SchPl; StuCncl; FrCl; SpnCl; Maple Woods Comm Coll; Secretarial Science.

SKALKA, Karen L; Morton Sr HS; Hammond, IN; 47/529 CmntyWkr; HonRl; JrNHS; MrchBnd; StuGov; TchrAde; CivCl; FDA; PpCl; Bsbl; Bsktbl; Ftbl; Purdue Univ; Medical Technology.

SKALSKY, Rita; Beulah HS; Beulah, ND; Band; Chr; HonRl; MrchBnd; PepBnd; SchPl; RptrSchPpr; FHA; EngCl; PpCl; College; Nursong.

SKANDERA, Margaret C; Glenbard West HS; Glen Ellyn, IL; 91/508 Chr; Chrs; HonRl; PresFrCl; GerCl; GAA; Illinois State Univ; Teacher.

SKARBEK, Elizabeth J; Lasalle HS; Cedar Rapids, IA; HonRl; LitMag; ModUN; College; Health.

SKARIE, Mark K; Cardinal Muench Seminary HS; Balfour, ND; Band; ChrhWkr; CncrtBnd; HonRl; MrchBnd; SctActv; StuCncl; FFA; LetterBsktbl; Trk; U Of Nd; Priesthood.

SKARJA, John F; Eveleth HS; Eveleth, MN; 15/161 NHS; NatlSciFnd; SchPl; Yrbk; SchPpr; BauchLmbAwd; Clg Of St Scholistica; Biology Photog.

SKARO, Toni L; Valley HS; Hoople, ND; 1/31 PresJrCls; PresSrCls; Band; Chrs; HonRl; SchPl; EdYrBk; Trk; Chrldr; BttyCrckrAwd; Univ; Phys Therapy.

SKARPHOL, Arlene; Wildrose HS; Mc Gregor, ND; PresJrCls; SecTrsSrCls; Chr; LbryAde; SchPl; RptrYrbk; RptrSchPpr; PpCl; Trk; GAA; Minot State College; Business Admin.

SKARPHOL, Lori; Wildrose Public HS; Mc Gregor, ND; SecFrshCls; VPSophCls; SecJrCls; ALAGirlsSt; Chr; HonRl; SchPl; SchPpr; PpCl; Coll; Voc.

SKATTUM, Jon; Monroe Senior HS; Monroe, WI; HonRl; LitMag; Bsktbl; Tennis; AmLegAwd; Univ; Professional.

SKAU, Chris T; Bishop Ward HS; Kansas City, KS; 1/220 CmntyWkr; HonRl; NHS; NatlThespSoc; 4-H; FrCl; ChmbCommrsAwd; 4-HAwd; College; Music Therapy.

SKAWSKI, Joan E; Resurrection HS; Chicago, IL; HonRl; HospAde; LbryAde; SchPl; SctActv; StuCncl; SpnCl; Bsktbl; GAA; IMSpt; Univ Of Il; Lawyer.

SKEELS, Mark E; Hampshire HS; Hampshire, IL; CncrtBnd; MrchBnd; PepBnd; Jr College; Electronic Tech.

SKELLENGER, Debra J; Orient Macksburg HS; Greenfield, IA; Band; Chrs; DrmMjrt; HonRl; MrchBnd; NHS; SchMus; SchPl; PresStuCncl; Twrl; YthFlsp; LetterBsktbl; LetterTrk; College; Professional.

SKELLEY, Linda K; Van Buren HS; Brazil, IN; ChrhWkr; CmntyWkr; FHA; FTA; SpnCl; SciCl; University Social Work.

SKELLY, Patrick; Mpls Patrick Henry HS; Mpls, MN; 12/389 HonRl; NHS; ROTC; SctActv; Univ Of Min;.

SKELLY, Paul; Illiopolis HS; Illiopolis, IL; 1/43 TrsSophCls; Band; Chrs; CncrtBnd; MrchBnd; SctActv; Univ; Professional.

SKELLY, Susan S; Beloit Catholic HS; Beloit, WI; Chrs; CmntyWkr; HonRl; JA; NHS; OffAde; PolWkr; StuCncl; RptrYrbk; RptrSchPpr; U Of Wi La Crosse; Health Education.

SKELTON, Pamela R; Eastern HS; Salem, IN; 8/76 Band; CncrtBnd; HonRl; MrchBnd; SecNHS; PepBnd; 4-H; SpnCl; PpCl; Trk; GAA; 4-HAwd; Indiana St Univ; Professional.

SKENDER, Christine A; Bergan HS; Peoria, IL; 19/208 HonRl; Univ Of Illinois; Psychology.

SKERRITT, John K; Malvern Community HS; Malvern, IA; 5/33 Band; NHS; PolWkr; SctActv; StuCncl; 4-H; FFA; LetterBsbl; 4-HAwd; GodCntryAwd; College; Agricultural Engineering.

SKERTIC, Robert P; Morton HS; Hammond, IN; 43/492 Band; ChrhWkr; CncrtBnd; MrchBnd; NHS; NatlSciFnd; Orch; PepBnd; SctActv; StuGov; SciCl; Trk; Army Academy; Science.

SKETCH, Michael H; Creighton Prep; Omaha, NE; 25/230 VPSophCls; HonRl; JA; Sdlty; RptrSchPpr; LetterBsktbl; LetterFtbl; Wrstlng; CchngActv; RotaryAwd; College; Professional.

SKEVINGTON, Anthony L; Bishop Luers HS; Ft Wayne, IN; 10/230 ALBoysSt; Aud/Vis; ChrhWkr; HonRl; Yrbk; SchPpr; SecKeyCl; CaptTrk; KiwanAwd; RotaryAwd; Univ Of Notre Dame; Accounting.

SKIBA, Barbara; Madonna HS; Chicago, IL; 45/273 HonRl; SctActv; GAA; Ray Vogue Schools; Commercial Artist.

SKIBA, Mitchell J; Bishop Noll Inst; Calumet City, IL; 20/360 HonRl; PresNHS; StuCncl; Socr; LetterWrstlng; College.

SKIBBA, William J; Assumption HS; Wisconsin Rapids, WI; 86/117 LetterBsbl; LetterBsktbl; LetterFtbl; LetterTennis; LetterTrk; LetterWrstlng; GAA; IMSpt; Technical School; Salesman Sports Field.

SKIBINSKI, David J; Bishop Noll Institute HS; Hammond, IN; ALBoysSt; HonRl; SancSoc; KeyCl; MthCl; Bsbl; Bsktbl; Ftbl; CchngActv; IMSpt; Medical Univ; Medicine.

SKIBINSKI, Jodene M; Lasalle Peru Township HS; Peru, IL; Aud/Vis; HonRl; SecSpnCl; PpCl; U Of Illionis; Registered Nurse.

SKIBO, Karen A; Forest Park HS; Alpha, MI; 5/80 SecJrCls; CncrtBnd; HonRl; HospAde; MrchBnd; PepBnd; SecStuCncl; TchrAde; FNA; Chrldr; IMSpt; CitAwd; College; Medicine.

SKIBO, Rebecca J; Benton Consolidated HS; Benton, IL; Chrs; HonRl; NHS; NatlMeritSF; OffAde; Yrbk; FHA; FNA; FTA; SpnCl; Trk; Southern Ill Univ; Medicine.

SKIDMORE, Beth A; Ottawa HS; Ottawa, KS; 1/187 TrsSrCls; DrlTm; HonRl; NHS; StuCncl; TchrAde; YthFlsp; FrCl; PpCl; ChmbCommrsAwd; Univ; Nursing.

SKIDMORE, Harley; Gregory Hs; Gregory, SD; 5/46 HonRl; NHS; StuGov; LetterBsbl; LetterBsktbl; LetterFtbl; LetterTrk; IMSpt; OptClAwd; PresAwd; Us Navel Academy; Pilot.

SKIDMORE, Lori J; Lawrenceburg HS; Lawrenceburg, IN; HonRl; JrNHS; SctActv; PpCl; Bsktbl; Trk; GAA; IMSpt; AmLegAwd; Business College; Secretarial.

SKILES, Darrell; Salem Senior HS; Salem, MO; FFA; Trk;.

SKILES, Deidra D; Wellsville HS; Wellsville, KS; Chr; Chrl; DrlTm; HonRl; LitMag; NHS; SchMus; EdSchPpr; LetterTrk; Kansas St College; Psychology.

SKILES, Julie L; Beardstown HS; Beardstown, IL; 25/133 Band; CncrtBnd; HonRl; Yrbk; SchPpr; FTA; SpnCl; Univ; English.

SKILES, Kimberly S; Scottsbluff HS; Scottsbluff, NE; 62/272 Chr; Chrs; ChrhWkr; CtyCnl; HonRl; SchPl; SchMus; GerCl; PpCl; Chrldr; Coll; Criminology.

SKILLINGTON, Christopher J; Chaminade College Prep; O Fallon, MO; 6/112 HonRl; NatlFornLg; Sacrstn; RptrSchPpr; 4-H; LetterTrk; AmLegAwd; 4-HAwd; OptClAwd; VoiceDemAwd; Medical Field.

SKILLMAN, Jeanne A; Morristown HS; Shelbyville, IN; Band; SptEdYrbk; SptEdSchPpr; FTA; LetterBsktbl; LetterTrk; CchngActv; GAA; Ball St Univ; Physical Educ.

SKINN, Lorrie L; Magic City Campus HS; Minot, ND; ALAGirlsSt; HonRl; NatlFornLg; NHS; StuCncl; SpnCl; PpCl; SciCl;.

SKINNER, Bradley J; Yankton HS; Yankton, SD; ALBoysSt; Band; NHS; Orch; Quill&Scroll; SptEdSchPpr; Bsbl; Ftbl; Trk; College.

SKINNER, Janet; Hordville Public HS; Clarks, NE; 3/14 TrsFrshCls; TrsJrCls; TrsSrCls; Band; Chrs; ChrhWkr; DrmMjrt; Trk; Chrldr; IMSpt;.

SKINNER, Joe R; Plano HS; Plano, IL; TrsSrCls; CncrtBnd; HonRl; MrchBnd; StuGov; University Of Illinois; Environment.

SKINNER, John D; Benton Central HS; Fowler, IN; ALBoysSt; ChrhWkr; CmntyWkr; HonRl; Bsbl; Bsktbl; Ftbl; Swmmng; IMSpt; AmLegAwd; Univ; Major Study.

SKINNER, Kim A; Bronson HS; Bronson, MI; HonRl; StuCncl; Ftbl; Wrstlng; West Shore Comm College; Auto Technician.

SKINNER, Michael L; Caston HS; Twelve Mile, IN; 2/90 ChrhWkr; CmntyWkr; HonRl; NHS; YthFlsp; 4-H; Yrbk; GerCl; LetterBsbl; CaptFtbl; Rose Hulman Inst Of Tech.

SKINNER, Patrick L; Hale HS; Hale, MI; 20/60 HonRl; LbryAde; SctActv; TchrAde; Ftbl; West Point Military Acad; Military.

SKINNER, Russell D; Nokomis HS; Nokomis, IL; Chrl; Chrs; ChrhWkr; HonRl; MrchBnd; SchMus; LetterFtbl; Trk;.

SKINNER, Steven; Glenwood Hs; Springfield, IL; ChrhWkr; HonRl; TreasNHS; SctActv; GerCl; GodCntryAwd; Ill State U;accounting.

SKINNER, Wendi L; West Harrison HS; Little Sioux, IA; Band; HonRl; LbryAde; YthFlsp; RptrYrbk; 4-H; Glf; Chrldr; IMSpt; Business School; Accountant.

SKIPPER, Brady T; Constantine HS; Vandalia, MI; 51/109 Band; Chr; ChrhWkr; CncrtBnd; HonRl; MrchBnd; Orch; PepBnd; PolWkr; YthFlsp; Mich St U; Attorney.

SKIPTON, Randy L; Wapello Comm HS; Wapello, IA; 2/69 VPFrshCls; HonRl; NHS; SctActv; StuCncl; StuGov; LetterFtbl; LetterTrk; IMSpt; College.

SKIRVIN, Daniel G; Vestaburg HS; Riverdale, MI; 8/64 PresSrCls; Band; ChrhWkr; CncrtBnd; HonRl; NHS; StuCncl; StuGov; SchPpr; SpnCl; Oral Roberts U; Fine Arts.

SKITTONE, Serena M; Elk Grove HS; Elk Grove Village, IL; ChrhWkr; HonRl; NHS; NatlThespSoc; SchMus; SchPl; College.

SKJERVHEIM, Jack L; Nekoma Public HS; Alsen, ND; 1/16 SecFrshCls; VPSophCls; SecJrCls; HonRl; SchPl; SptEdSchPpr; LetterBsktbl; University; Business.

SKNERSKI, Larry C; Morton Sr HS; Hammond, IN; 42/529 HonRl; StuCncl; StuGov; TchrAde; Bsbl; College; Industrial Engineering.

SKOCELAS, Jean M; Manistee Catholic Central HS; Manistee, MI; TrsJrCls; HonRl; FrCl; PpCl; IMSpt; VoiceDemAwd; Bus School; Data Processing.

SKOCIPICK, Loretta A; Mother Mc Auley HS; Oak Lawn, IL; 115/484 Chrs; HonRl; Northern Il Univ; Nursing.

SKOCYPEC, Russell D; Homewood Flossmoor HS; Homewood, IL; 33/910 Chr; Chrs; HonRl; NHS; OffAde; Univ Of Ill; Engineering.

SKOKAN, Sheryl; Niobrara Public HS; Verdigre, NE; 6/30 Coll; Medical.

SKOMAL, Terri A; Cathedral HS; Omaha, NE; 7/87 ALAGirlsSt; HonRl; LitMag; NHS; SchAde; SchMus; SchPl; TchrAde; PpCl; Bsbl; College; Art Major.

SKOOG, Melinda R; Johnson Sr HS; St Paul, MN; Chr; ChrhWkr; NatlFornLg; SchAde; SchMus; SchPl; StuCncl; StuGov; TchrAde; YthFlsp; GerCl; Gustavus Adolphus Col; Theater.

SKOOG, Ruth M; Stratford Comm HS; Stratford, IA; 3/32 TrsSrCls; Chrs; HonRl; JrNHS; SchPl; Yrbk; Bethel College; Art.

SKORHEIM, Rita R; Adams Public HS; Adams, ND; SecSophCls; ALAGirlsSt; Chrs; HonRl; StuCncl; Twrl; EdSchPpr; 4-H; PpCl; LetterBsktbl; 4-HAwd; College; Fashion Merchandising.

SKORNIA, Mark D; Owensville HS; Gerald, MO; CncrtBnd; MrchBnd; PepBnd; SchMus; SctActv; YthFlsp; RptrSchPpr; Bsbl; LetterBsktbl; CaptFtbl; College; Professional.

SKOUBIS, John G; Morton West HS; Berwyn, IL; 21/706 Chr; Chrl; Chrs; HonRl; PresJrNHS; NHS; RptrYrbk; SptEdYrbk; Yrbk; EldAwd; Bradley U; Acct Law.

SKOUG, James G; Eleva Strum Central HS; Strum, WI; 34/73 Chr; ChrhWkr; Orch; SchPl; StuCncl; TchrAde; RptrSchPpr; SchPpr; University Of Wisconsin; Professional.

SKOWERA, Mary Ann; Putnam County HS; Mc Nabb, IL; 1/78 HonRl; PresNHS; OffAde; FrCl; MthCl; GAA; Illinois Valley Comm College; Business.

SKOWRONEK, Russell K; Naperville Central HS; Naperville, IL; NHS; FrCl; Univ; Anthropology.

SKOWRONEK, Thomas D; George Washington HS; Chicago, IL; CAP; HonRl; NHS; NatlMeritFnl; NatlMeritCmnd; NatlMeritSF; OffAde; SchAde; SchPpr; Bsktbl; Tennis; Bradley Univ; Law Enforcement.

SKOWRONSKI, Sally A; St Catherines HS; Racine, WI; HonRl; RedCrAde; SchAde; TchrAde; Yrbk; Work With Children.

SKOY, Debora C; Kennedy HS; Bloomington, MN; 58/660 Chr; HonRl; LbryAde; NHS; Swmmng; College; Nursing.

SKRDLANT, Gary L; Norton Comm HS; Norton, KS; HonRl; Quill&Scroll; Yrbk; RptrSchPpr; SchPpr; University; Wildlife.

SKRIP, Sharon J; Resurrection HS; Des Plaines, IL; 68/261 Band; ChrhWkr; LbryAde; SctActv; TchrAde; Teen; FTA; MthCl; SciCl; Winona State College; Teacher.

SKRIPSKY, Alan J; Omaha South HS; Omaha, NE; ChrhWkr; CmntyWkr; HonRl; StuCncl; SpnCl; LetterTrk; CaptWrstlng; IMSpt; Univ Ne; Professional.

SKROBIAK, L; Bark River Harris HS; Bark River, MI; SecJrCls; Chr; HonRl; RptrYrbk;.

SKROBOT, Katherine M; Highland HS; Highland, IN; TchrAde; Sec4-H; Clge; Nursing.

SKROCH, James E; Neillsville HS; Neillsville, WI; ALBoysSt; HonRl; StuCncl; RptrYrbk; Yrbk; LetterBsktbl; LetterFtbl; LetterGlf; CchngActv; IMSpt; Technical School; Engineer Technology.

SKRODZKI, David; Quigley North HS; Northbrook, IL; 21/66 SecSophCls; Chrs; ChrhWkr; HonRl; StuCncl; SptEdYrbk; SptEdSchPpr; FBLA; IMSpt; St Marys Coll; Business Admin.

SKRZYCKI, Gerald A; John F Kennedy HS; Taylor, MI; Chr; HonRl; NatlFornLg; StuCncl; StuGov; Bsbl; DanFAwd; CitAwd; Clge; Music.

SKRZYPEK, Janice M; George Rogers Clark HS; Hammond, IN; 28/260 NHS; OffAde; SctActv; PpCl; College; Professional.

SKRZYPEK, Linda; Notre Dame HS; Chicago, IL; 34/261 Chrs; ChrhWkr; CmntyWkr; HonRl; College.

SKUBA, Jonathan B; Osseo Fairchild HS; Osseo, WI; 12/88 ALBoysSt; Aud/Vis; HonRl; NHS; SchPl; SctActv; TchrAde; SptEdYrbk; CaptBsktbl; Trk; Uw Madison; Chemistry Law.

SKUBISZEWSKI, Paul C; St Laurence HS; Chicago, IL; 62/372 4-H; Ill Institute Of Tech; Electrical Engineer.

SKULAVIK, Joanne B; Maria HS; Chicago, IL; 3/335 HonRl; NHS; NatlThespSoc; SchMus; SchPl; StuCncl; TchrAde; RptrSchPpr; SpnCl; Univ; Bio.

SKULLY, Susan E; Schaumburg HS; Schaumburg, IL; 21/510 HonRl; JrNHS; NHS; StuCncl; RptrYrbk; W Illinois Univ; Math.

SKUPIEN, Michael A; Gordon Technical HS; Chicago, IL; 48/661 VPJrCls; HonRl; JA; NatlFornLg; StuCncl; RptrSchPpr; GerCl; PpCl; Chrldr; JAAwd; U Of Il Champaign; Biochemist.

SKWIRA, Teresa; Healy Sr HS; Peirz, MN; 6/113 SecTrsSrCls; Chr; Chrs; HonRl; LbryAde; OffAde; TchrAde; IMSpt; PPFtbl; Coll; Mathematics.

SLAATS, Gileen; Whitewater HS; Whitewater, WI; 33/187 ChrhWkr; HonRl; LbryAde; OffAde; PolWkr; 4-H; College; Music Director.

SLABACH, Dorrine M; Adelphian Academy; Pontiac, MI; Chr; TchrAde; College; Special Ed Teacher.

SLABAUGH, Daniel N; Goshen HS; Goshen, IN; ALBoysSt; Band; ChrhWkr; CncrtBnd; HonRl; MrchBnd; Orch; PepBnd; TchrAde; LatCl; Bsktbl; LetterFtbl; RotaryAwd; Ball State University; Business.

SLABAUGH, Stephanie; Mason Senior HS; Mason, MI; SecJrCls; HonRl; JrNHS; OffAde; SchMus; StuGov; EdSchPpr; PpCl; IMSpt; College; Accountant.

SLABBEKOOSH, Richard J; Kelloggsville HS; Wyoming, MI; HonRl; JA; NHS; NatlMeritFnl; NatlMeritSchl; NatlMeritSF; Tennis; Mich St Univ; Nuclear Physics.

SLABY, Chad A; Gibraltar HS; Fish Creek, WI; Band; CncrtBnd; MrchBnd; College; Engineering.

SLACHTA, Richard C; St Stephens HS; Saginaw, MI; PresFrshCls; Band; ChrhWkr; CncrtBnd; HonRl; Mdrgl; NHS; PolWkr; VPStuCncl; StuGov; TchrAde; Bsktbl; IMSpt; Mich St Univ; Music.

SLACK, Gregory E; Newark Comm HS; Newark, IL; 3/53 PresJrCls; Chr; Chrs; ChrhWkr; HonRl; NHS; SchPl; LetterBsbl; LetterBsktbl; LetterSocr; LetterTrk; Southern Ill Univ; Lawyer.

SLACK, Julie A; Waterford Township HS; Pontiac, MI; NHS; SctActv; StuGov; RptrYrbk; Pres4-H; LetterBsbl; LetterBsktbl; LetterTrk; CchngActv; 4-HAwd; Mi St Univ; Nursing.

SLACK, Kevin W; Crystal Lake Community HS; Crystal Lake, IL; SchPl; YthFlsp; SpnCl; Bsktbl; Glf; LetterTennis; IMSpt; Florida St U; Marine Bio.

SLACK, Nancy C; Homewood Flossmoor HS; Flossmoor, IL; Band; ChrhWkr; CncrtBnd; HonRl; MrchBnd; Orch; PepBnd; Univ Of Illinois; Interior Design.

SLACK, Wesley J; Wheeler HS; Valparaiso, IN; SpnCl; Bsbl; Bsktbl; Valparaiso Univ; Professional Major In Hist.

SLADEK, Daniel; Granton HS; Granton, WI; PresJrCls; Chrs; SchAde; SchMus; SchPl; TchrAde; RptrSchPpr; SchPpr; FFA; Bus School.

SLADETZ, Judith L; Morton West HS; Stickney, IL; 74/776 HonRl; HospAde; NatlFornLg; NHS; NatlThespSoc; OffAde; SchAde; SchMus; SchPl; College; Medicine.

SLADKY, Dave W; Catholic Memorial HS; Brookfield, WI; Sacrstn; SctActv; StuCncl; RptrYrbk; Bsktbl; Glf; Trk; IMSpt; Marquette Univ; Medicine.

SLADKY, Ronald B; Neumann HS; Wahoo, NE; 13/50 VPSrCls; ALBoysSt; ChrhWkr; HonRl; StuGov; Teen; 4-H; Bsktbl; IMSpt; 4-HAwd; Trade School; Carpenter.

SLAGA, Marylou A; Elizabeth Seton HS; Chicago, IL; 2/252 HonRl; HospAde; NHS; RptrYrbk; Yrbk; RptrSchPpr; SchPpr; LatCl; MthCl; Loyola Univ; Medical Tech.

SLAGELL, Larry G; St Johns HS; St Johns, MI; Band; ChrhWkr; CncrtBnd; HonRl; MrchBnd; SecTrsFrshCls; PepBnd; YthFlsp; LetterBsbl; IMSpt; College; Social Work.

SLAGER, Laura L; Chicago Christian HS; Tinley Park, IL; 19/165 Chrl; Mdrgl; NHS; StuCncl; GerCl; PpCl; Trk; CaptChrldr; IMSpt; Calvin College; German.

SLAGER, Stephen L; Streator Twp HS; Streator, IL; HonRl; NHS; NatlMeritFnl; NatlMeritCmnd; NatlMeritSchl; NatlMeritSF; SctActv; SpnCl; LetterSwmmng; LetterTennis; University; Medicine.

SLAGG, Val Rae; Washburn HS; Washburn, ND; 3/27 ALAGirlsSt; Band; Chrs; CmntyWkr; CncrtBnd; DrlTm; HonRl; MrchBnd; Chrldr; MasAwd; Minot State College; Speech Pathology.

SLAGH, Betty J; Zeeland HS; Zeeland, MI; Band; ChrhWkr; CncrtBnd; HonRl; MrchBnd; PepBnd; LatCl; College.

SLAGHT, Betty J; Truman HS; Independence, MO; SecCncrtBnd; DrmMjrt; JA; MrchBnd; SecOrch; PepBnd; SchMus; CaptGAA; PresAwd; Graceland College; Special Education.

SLAGLE, Debra; Northeast Nodaway HS; Ravenwood, MO; VPSrCls; Chrs; ChrhWkr; SchPl; YthFlsp; RptrYrbk; PpCl; Bsktbl; Trk; IMSpt; Missouri Univ; Florist.

SLAGLE, Doreen K; Humboldt HS; Humboldt, NE; Chrs; LbryAde; TchrAde; Trade Or Bus; Vocation.

SLAGLE, Karen S; Milan HS; Milan, MI; Chrs; HonRl; StuGov; 4-H; MthCl; SciCl; Mich St U; Pre Vet.

SLAGLE, Tim K; Sargent Public HS; Sargent, NE; Bsktbl; LetterFtbl; Univ Of Nebraska; Agriculture.

SLAGTER, Monica L; Central Minn Christian HS; Prinsburg, MN; SecTrsFrshCls; TrsJrCls; Chr; HonRl; NHS; NatlMeritCmnd; SchMus; EdYrBk; SchPpr; PpCl; Calvin College; Undecided.

SLAGTER, Valerie; Marcus Community HS; Marcus, IA; 11/70 TrsJrCls; ALAGirlsSt; HonRl; JrNHS; NHS; SchPl; RptrYrbk; Swmmng; College; Radio Broadcasting.

SLAMA, Bette R; Boscobel HS; Boscobel, WI; 16/112 Chr; Chrs; ChrhWkr; CmntyWkr; HonRl; NatlFornLg; NHS; OffAde; StuCncl; Yrbk; Clerk For Dept Of Revenue In Wis.

SLAMA, Debra; Potter HS; Potter, NE; 1/15 SecFrshCls; Band; Chrs; HonRl; SchPl; RptrYrbk; RptrSchPpr; AmLegAwd; DanFAwd;.

SLAMA, Janice R; Milton Public HS; Osnabrock, ND; VPSophCls; SecJrCls; HonRl; HospAde; SchMus; SchPl; EdSchPpr; FHA; PpCl; Chrldr; Medical School; Professional.

SLAMA, Mary E; Milton Public HS; Osnabrock, ND; 1/12 Chrs; CmntyWkr; HonRl; SchPl; EdYrBk; SchPpr; PresFHA; SecPpCl; BttyCrckrAwd; Medical Inst Of Minnesota; Medical Tech.

SLAMA, Michael A; Mercy HS; St Louis, MO; 20/193 Band; Chr; Chrl; Chrs; ChrhWkr; HonRl; JrNHS; NHS; SchMus; Ftbl; Coll; Musician.

SLAMKOWSKI, Karen M; Clark HS; Hammond, IN; ChrhWkr; CmntyWkr; DrlTm; OffAde; PolWkr; SchPl; SctActv; SpnCl; Univ; Metalurgical Engr.

SLANIA, Maria E; Conant HS; Hoffman Est, IL; Chr; HonRl; NHS; SchMus; SctActv; RptrSchPpr; FrCl; Bsktbl; GAA; PresAwd; College; Foreign Language.

SLAPAK, Dean; Addison Trail HS; Addison, IL; 25/579 HonRl; Western Illinois U; Certified Public Accoun.

SLASKE, Donna J; Pacelli HS; Stevens Point, WI; Chr; ChrhWkr; HonRl; NHS; StuCncl; 4-H; TreasSpnCl; CaptChrldr; CchngActv; GAA; College; Elementary Teacher.

SLATER, Donald L; East Kentwood HS; Grand Rapids, MI; CncrtBnd; MrchBnd; NatlFornLg; LetterBsbl; Bsktbl; Ftbl; Trk; Central Mi U; Lawyer.

SLATER, Jjean; Cary Grove; Cary, IL; HonRl; NHS; StuCncl; 4-H; KeyCl; SpnCl; DanFAwd;.

SLATER, Jon R; Ogorman HS; Sioux Falls, SD; SchMus; SchPl; TchrAde; Bsktbl; Ftbl; Glf; College; Coach.

SLATER, Karen S; Norton Comm HS; Norton, KS; Band; Chrs; CncrtBnd; HonRl; MrchBnd; PepBnd; SchMus; PpCl; Colby Jr Clg; Nurse.

SLATER, Kenneth M; Southfield Christian HS; Royal Oak, MI; 3/47 ChrhWkr; HonRl; NHS; SchPl; StuCncl; RptrSchPpr; LetterSocr; CchngActv; IMSpt; Wheaton Coll; Med, Biology.

SLATER, Teresa S; East Richland HS; Claremont, IL; 7/264 JrNHS; NHS; RedCrAde; 4-H; SpnCl;.

SLATON, Jeffrey A; Tomahawk HS; Tomahawk, WI; CmntyWkr; CncrtBnd; HonRl; MrchBnd; Orch; PepBnd; SchPpr; GerCl; Bsktbl; Ftbl; Univ; Professional.

SLATTERY, Lynn M; St Thomas Aquinas HS; Ferguson, MO; ChrhWkr; HonRl; NHS; TchrAde; Clerical Job.

SLATTERY, Mary; Central Catholic HS; Grand Island, NE; Chrs; HonRl; Quill&Scroll; SchMus; SchPl; RptrSchPpr; Chrldr; GAA; Univ Of Ne; Undecided.

SLAUGHTER, Connie D; Adel HS; Adel, IA; HonRl; NatlThespSoc; Quill&Scroll; Yrbk; SchPpr; Business School.

SLAUGHTER, James B; Holly HS; Holly, MI; 40/300 NHS; LetterBsbl; LetterBsktbl; LetterFtbl; Col; Law.

SLAUGHTER, Lisa; Cleveland HS; St Louis, MO; 14/560 Band; CncrtBnd; HonRl; NHS; NatlMeritCmnd; Orch; Yrbk; 4-H; PpCl; Bsktbl; Kansas City Mo Univ; Dental Hygienist.

SLAUGHTER, Sherra S; Belle Plaine HS; Belle Plaine, KS; 1/35 HonRl; LbryAde; SchMus; SctActv; StuCncl; TchrAde; RptrYrbk; RptrSchPpr; DARAwd; MasAwd; Emporia Ks State College.

SLAVEN, Karen; Sparta Hs; Sparta, IL; 1/160 Band; ChrhWkr; JrNHS; MrchBnd; NHS; NatlMeritCmnd; PepBnd; SchMus; Yrbk; 4-H; Southern Il U; Social Welfare.

SLAVEN, Mary P; Roncalli HS; Omaha, NE; SecSophCls; Chrs; HonRl; RptrYrbk; RptrSchPpr; FrCl; Univ; Biology.

SLAVEN, Pamela J; North Daviess HS; Odon, IN; Chrs; HonRl; NHS; SchPl; FHA; PpCl;.

SLAVENS, Kevin D; Brazil HS; Brazil, IN; Aud/Vis; ChrhWkr; HonRl; SctActv; Indiana Stae U; Criminology.

SLAVENS, Larry M; Earlham Community HS; Earlham, IA; Chrs; HonRl; NHS; NatlMeritCmnd; SchMus; SchPl; Yrbk; RptrSchPpr; SchPpr; Photography.

SLAVENS, Timothy C; Winterset HS; Cumming, IA; ALBoysSt; HonRl; NatlMeritCmnd; SchPl; StuGov; SchPpr; MthCl; SciCl; LetterFtbl; IMSpt; U Of Ia; Pre Law.

SLAVICK, Allison D; Lincoln Consolidated HS; Belleville, MI; 10/154 HonRl; JA; NHS; E Mi Univ; Art.

SLAVIK, Daniel J; Boys Town HS; Boys Town, NE; 10/65 ChrhWkr; HonRl; RptrSchPpr; KeyCl; SpnCl; LetterTrk; College; Social Worker.

SLAVIK, Steven A; Oakville HS; St Louis, MO; 23/357 HonRl; MrchBnd; NHS; SchMus; SchPl; MthCl; LetterBsbl; Swmmng; Tennis; IMSpt; Coll; Medicine.

SLAWINSKI, Elaine A; Lake View HS; Chicago, IL; 2/365 Chrs; SchMus;.

SLAWINSKI, Robert M; Manistee Catholic Cent HS; Manistee, MI; Aud/Vis; CncrtBnd; MrchBnd; SctActv; RptrYrbk; Bsktbl; LetterFtbl; LetterTrk; IMSpt; Ferris St Coll; Architural Drafting.

SLAWINSKI, Ursula H; Center Line HS; Center Line, MI; HonRl; LitMag; NHS; NatlSciFnd; StuGov; Yrbk; SciCl; Bsktbl; Univ Mi.

SLAY, Gregory D; Cooley HS; Detroi, MI; Aud/Vis; HonRl; PolWkr; StuGov; SpnCl; IMSpt; Shaw College; Biology.

SLAYBAUGH, Janet A; Lakeland R Iii HS; Lowry City, MO; PresFrshCls; SecTrsSophCls; HonRl; ModUN; StuCncl; EdYrBk; FHA; LetterBsbl; LetterBsktbl; Chrldr; Southwest Baptist College; Phy Ed Coach.

SLAYBAUGH, Keith A; Murphysboro Twp HS; Murphysboro, IL; 1/240 HonRl; VPNHS; SchPl; StuCncl; KeyCl; College; Professional.

SLAYMAKER, Dana L; Fulton HS; Fulton, IL; 7/123 TrsSrCls; Chrs; College; Social Welfare.

SLAYMAKER, Kathy L; Erie HS; Erie, IL; 12/81 TrsSrCls; AFS; CncrtBnd; HonRl; YthFlsp; Yrbk; 4-H; FHA; Glf; Northern Ill Univ; Computer Science.

SLAYTON, William M; Northwestern Community HS; Blandinsville, IL; PresSophCls; AFS; ALBoysSt; Band; Chr; ChrhWkr; HonRl; LbryAde; NHS; NatlMeritCmnd; SchMus; Bsbl; Bsktbl; Ftbl; West Point Military Academy; Nuclear Eng.

SLEEMAN, Cindy S; Vicksburg HS; Vicksburg, MI; Band; Chr; ChrhWkr; CmntyWkr; HospAde; JA; SctActv; Teen; YthFlsp; PPFtbl; Clge; Pro.

SLEEP, Kenneth D; Bedford Comm HS; Bedford, IA; RptrYrbk; EdYrBk; SptEdYrbk; RptrSchPpr; EdSchPpr; 4-H; FFA; FTA; Bsbl; Bsktbl; Ftbl; Trk; Wrstlng; William Penn Col; Agribusiness.

SLEETH, Scott A; Chautauqua Co Comm HS; Peru, KS; ChrhWkr; SchPl; SctActv; TchrAde; Bsktbl; LetterGlf; S E K; Welding.

SLEGER, Mark L; Kewaskum HS; Kewaskum, WI; 15/185 Chr; Chrs; Mdrgl; SchAde; SchMus; SchPl; StuCncl; StuGov; Trk; Wrstlng; College; Chem Eng.

SLEIGLE, Autum D; Holden HS; Holen, MO; HonRl; SchPl; SciCl; Trade Sch; Computers.

SLEMP, Debra S; Plymouth HS; Plymouth, IN; ChrhWkr; HonRl; Quill&Scroll; TchrAde; EdYrBk; SpnCl; PpCl; GAA; Ancilla College; Special Educ.

SLENZAK, Mary G; Regina HS; Warren, MI; 25/270 HonRl; JA; LbryAde; NatlThespSoc; SchPl; Teen; Trk; GAA; OptClAwd; Mi State U; Accounting.

SLEPICKA, Colleen L; Wilber Clatonia HS; Wilber, NE; 13/41 VPJrCls; Band; DrmMjrt; HonRl; PepBnd; TchrAde; Twrl; Yrbk; 4-H; 4-HAwd; Business School; Accountant.

SLEPPY, Teresa A; Belleville East HS; Belleville, IL; 1/680 Chr; ChrhWkr; HonRl; SecNHS; NatlMeritSF; SchMus; YthFlsp; VPSpnCl; TreasPpCl; PPFtbl; College; Medicine.

SLEPSKY, Timothy; Saline HS; Saline, MI; 19/200 CmntyWkr; HonRl; NHS; FDA; FSA; FTA; MthCl; LetterBsbl; LetterBsktbl; LetterFtbl; Univ; Medicine.

SLETTEN, Linda S; Pershing HS; Plummer, MN; 3/22 Band; CncrtBnd; HonRl; MrchBnd; PepBnd; SchPl; RptrYrbk; RptrSchPpr; FHA; IMSpt; College; Elementary Education.

SLIBOWSKI, Julie; Lafayette HS; St Joseph, MO; SecSrCls; Chr; NHS; SchMus; SchPl; StuCncl; RptrYrbk; PpCl; Chrldr;.

SLIDER, Laura L; Webberville Community HS; Webberville, MI; 2/60 ALAGirlsSt; Chr; HonRl; PresNHS; SecFHA; GAA; Coll.

SLIGER, Deanna; Houston HS; Licking, MO; 12/125 SecTrsFrshCls; CmntyWkr; HonRl; NHS; OffAde; PolWkr; SchAde; StuCncl; TchrAde; Smsu; Legal Secretary.

SLIKKERS, Francine L; Comstock Park HS; Comstock Park, MI; CmntyWkr; HonRl; NatlFornLg; TchrAde; SchPpr;.

SLIKKERS, George T; Holland HS; Holland, MI; ALBoysSt; HonRl; NatlMeritSF; Univ Of Michigan.

SLIND, Darla K; Plaza HS; Plaza, ND; 4/12 PresJrCls; Band; CncrtBnd; HonRl; MrchBnd; PepBnd; SchPl; StuCncl; Yrbk; 4-H; FHA; PpCl; Bsktbl; Minot State College; Medical Tech.

SLINGER, Joanne M; Edgerton Public HS; Woodstock, MN; 7/35 PresJrCls; HonRl; NHS; OffAde; 4-H; FHA; PpCl; 4-HAwd; College.

SLINKARD, Chris R; Oak Ridge R Vi HS; Oak Rige, MO; 5/21 SecSrCls; DrlTm; HonRl; PresStuCncl; Yrbk; 4-H; FHA; PpCl; Chrldr; Semo University; Womens Physical Educ.

SLINKARD, Lana K; York HS; Elmhurst, IL; HonRl; SchMus; RptrYrbk; College Of Dupage; Nursing.

SLINKER, Ronald M; Lamar R 1 HS; Lamar, MO; 13/86 Chrs; ChrhWkr; CncrtBnd; HonRl; LitMag; LbryAde; MrchBnd; NatlFornLg; PepBnd; SchPl; Bethany Nazarene Clge; Chemistry & Art.

SLINKMAN, Shari K; Manhattan HS; Manhattan, KS; AFS; Chr; ChrhWkr; HonRl; PolWkr; Teen; SpnCl; PpCl; IMSpt; Coll; Teaching.

SLISHER, Devoe R; I C Elston HS; Michigan City, IN; 22/340 Aud/Vis; CncrtBnd; HonRl; MrchBnd; NHS; PepBnd; SchMus; SchPl; SpnCl; AmLegAwd; Ind Univ Nw; Broadcasting.

SLIWA, Debra L; Amos Alonzo Stagg HS; Hickory Hills, IL; 20/468 HonRl; LitMag; LbryAde; College; Elem Education.

SLIWA, Nancy; Marquette HS; Michigan City, IN; 1/60 ChrhWkr; HonRl; HospAde; NHS; Quill&Scroll; Yrbk; SchPpr; SpnCl; KiwanAwd; RotaryAwd; Purdue Univ; Engrg.

SLIWA, Thomas M; Morton Sr HS; Hammond, IN; 23/529 Chr; ChrhWkr; HonRl; NHS; LetterSwmmng; Univ; Architecture.

SLIWA, William G; Loyola Academy; Lincolnwood, IL; Band; CncrtBnd; MrchBnd; NatlFornLg; NHS; SchMus; Sdlty; EdYrBk; College; Medicine.

SLOAN, David W; North Adams HS; North Adams, MI; 6/52 ChrhWkr; HonRl; LitMag; NHS; StuCncl; TchrAde; FFA; FHA; Bsktbl; Ftbl; AmLegAwd; Michigan Tech Univ; Engineering.

SLOAN, Merry; Brentwood HS; Brentwood, MO; 1/125 DrlTm; HonRl; NHS; NatlThespSoc; FrCl; GAA; AmLegAwd; MasAwd; OptClAwd;.

SLOAN, Michael C; Knoxville Comm HS; Knoxville, IA; 25/180 Chrs; HonRl; TchrAde; PpCl; Bsktbl; Ftbl; Glf; IMSpt; PresAwd; College; Professional.

SLOAN, Patrick G; Lowpoint Washburn HS; Washburn, IL; 2/68 Band; CncrtBnd; HonRl; MrchBnd; Orch; PepBnd; Sacrstn; Pres4-H; FFA; Trk; 4-HAwd; Univ Of Illinois; Aerospace Engineering.

SLOAN, Roger D; Luther HS; Onalaska, WI; ChrhWkr; HonRl; GerCl; LatCl; Northwestern College; Lutheran Minister.

SLOAN, Romeyn B; James B Conant HS; Hoffman Estates, IL; 19/620 Band; ChrhWkr; CmntyWkr; HonRl; HospAde; JA; NHS; NatlThespSoc; YthFlsp; JAAwd; Illinois Wesleyan Univ; Engineering.

SLOAN, Shannon M; Hazel Park HS; Hazel Park, MI; 41/426 NHS; StuGov; Bsbl; Swmmng; GAA; IMSpt; Oakland U; Business.

SLOAN, Sharon; Turkey Valley Comm HS; Waucoma, IA; 3/110 Chr; CncrtBnd; Mdrgl; MrchBnd; NHS; PepBnd; SchMus; 4-H; Univ; Music.

SLOAN, William D; Superior Senior HS; Superior, WI; 139/540 Band; CncrtBnd; HonRl; JA; MrchBnd; PepBnd; Ftbl; Trk; JAAwd; Um Duluth Mn; Pre Med.

SLOBIG, Robert; Marian Catholic Hs; Cedarburg, WI; 5/328 Band; HonRl; NHS; NatlMeritCmnd; Quill&Scroll; PresStuCncl; RptrSchPpr; SchPpr; LatCl;.

SLOBIG, Robert J; Marian Catholic HS; Cedarburg, WI; Band; HonRl; IntrClCncl; NHS; NatlMeritCmnd; Quill&Scroll; StuCncl; RptrSchPpr; SchPpr; AmLegAwd; Marquette Univ;.

SLOBODA, Joyce M; Reavis HS; Burbank, IL; 192/758 HonRl; MrchBnd; SchMus; Yrbk; SchPpr; GerCl; MthCl; PpCl; LetterBsktbl; GAA; University; Dental Hygiene.

SLOBODNIK, Stephen P; Mt Pleasant HS; Mount Pleasant, IA; YthFlsp; FFA; LetterBsbl; Ftbl; Trk; IMSpt; Trade School; Mechanic.

SLOCA, Amelia; Fairfield HS; Fairfield, IA; Band; ChrhWkr; CmntyWkr; HonRl; NatlFornLg; SchMus; SchPl; RptrYrbk; EdYrBk; IMSpt; College; Major Study.

SLOCUM, Joan M; Madelia Independent HS; Madelia, MN; VPAFS; Band; Chr; HonRl; HospAde; Yrbk; EdSchPpr; 4-H; 4-HAwd; MasAwd; Deaconess Schl; Nursing.

SLOCUM, Mary; Mt Pleasant HS; Mt Pleasant, MI; 2/332 CmntyWkr; CncrtBnd; HonRl; MrchBnd; NHS; SchMus; FrCl; LetterTrk; EldAwd; VoiceDemAwd; Mich St Univ; App Mus Maj.

SLOCUM, Sara E; Warren Township HS; Grayslake, IL; Band; ChrhWkr; SecFrshCls; HonRl; MrchBnd; NHS; PepBnd; SchPl; RptrSchPpr; FrCl; College; English Major.

SLOGGETT, Steven W; Broken Bow HS; Broken Bow, NE; HonRl; RedCrAde; SchPl; SctActv; StuCncl; YthFlsp; Bsbl; Bsktbl; Ftbl; Glf; Univ Of Nebraska; Physical Therapy.

SLOMAN, Dawn I; Morrisonville HS; Pawnee, IL; 1/60 Band; Chrs; ChrhWkr; HonRl; SchPl; StuCncl; YthFlsp; RptrYrbk; EdSchPpr; DanFAwd; Baylor Univ; Medicine.

SLOMINSKI, Susan M; Bishop Du Bourg HS; St Louis, MO; 19/469 HonRl; NHS; StuCncl; FNA; LatCl; IMSpt; Univf Secretary.

SLONE, Bryan E; Gering HS; Gering, NE; 7/140 Band; Chr; HonRl; MrchBnd; NHS; NatlMeritCmnd; SchMus; CaptBsktbl; CaptFtbl; CaptFtbl; Univ Of Nebraska; Law.

SLONE, Eric; Charlevoix HS; Charlevoix, MI; ALBoysSt; Band; CncrtBnd; HonRl; MrchBnd; SpnCl; Bsktbl; Tennis; IMSpt; Univ; Bus.

SLONE, Nancy E; Century HS; Karnak, IL; 6/60 ChrhWkr; HonRl; LbryAde; OffAde; SchPl; TchrAde; RptrSchPpr; FHA;.

SLOSSER, David J; John Glenn HS; Bay City, MI; 110/335 NatlMeritSF; RedCrAde; SctActv; Mich Tech Univ; Biological Sci.

SLOTARSKI, John A; St Rita HS; Chicago, IL; 20/449 HonRl; College; Professional.

SLOTSEMA, Janyce; Grand Rapids Christian HS; Grand Rapids, MI; Chr; Chrs; CmntyWkr; RptrYrbk; SpnCl; PpCl; Bsbl; Bsktbl; Socr; IMSpt; Calvin College; Coach.

SLOTTEN, Renee A; Verona HS; Verona, WI; TrsSrCls; ChrhWkr; CncrtBnd; DrlTm; HonRl; NatlFornLg; SctActv; Yrbk; TreasFTA; AmLegAwd; U Of Wi; Social Work.

SLOVER, Rodney C; Union HS; Oquawka, IL; StuCncl; Ftbl; Trk; Augustana College.

SLOVINEC, Joseph G; Marist HS; Riverdale, IL; 18/393 PresSophCls; TrsSrCls; HonRl; NHS; PolWkr; StuCncl; YthLg; SchPpr; IMSpt; AmLegAwd; University; Lawyer.

SLOWEY, David E; Crete Monee HS; Park Forest, IL; HonRl; Univ Of Illinois; Doctor.

SLOWINSKI, Karen M; Evergreen Pk C HS; Evergreen Park, IL; 26/442 Band; HonRl; NHS; TchrAde; GerCl; PpCl; Bsktbl; TreasGAA; IMSpt; College; Lab Technician.

SLUITER, Jody; Platte Comm Indep HS; Platte, SD; 12/46 CmntyWkr; CncrtBnd; HonRl; PepBnd; RedCrAde; StuCncl; RptrSchPpr; GerCl; College; Business.

SLUKICH, Richard S; Dodge Center HS; Dodge Center, MN; Aud/Vis; HonRl; RedCrAde; SchPl; TchrAde; RptrSchPpr; FTA; LetterGlf; LetterTrk; CchngActv; Univ Of Wi At La Crosse; Accountant.

SLUSAR, Brian L; Marist HS; Chicago, IL; 4/374 NatlMeritFnl; NatlMeritSF; Illinois Inst Of Tech; Chemical Engineer.

SLUSARSKI, Robert M; Alleman HS; E Moline, IL; LetterFtbl; LetterTrk; Wrstlng; IMSpt; Univ; Vocation.

SLUSHER, Morgan P; Lexington HS; Lexington, MO; 1/100 Chr; HonRl; NHS; NatlMeritSF; NatlThespSoc; SchMus; SchPl; RptrSchPpr; FrCl; CitAwd; Univ ; Scie.

SLUSIEWICZ, Eugene; West Catholic HS; Grand Rapids, MI; 8/322 VPSophCls; VPJrCls; ALBoysSt; HonRl; NatlMeritCmnd; Chrldr; AmLegAwd; EldAwd; General Motors Inst; Engineering.

SLUSSER, Holly M; Lincoln HS; Wisconsin Rapids, WI; 1/610 SecSophCls; PresJrCls; SecTrsSrCls; ALAGirlsSt; HonRl; JrNHS; NatlFornLg; NHS; FDA; GovHonPrgAwd; Clge; Doctor.

SLUSSER, Lisa; Richmond Sr HS; Richmond, IN; 21/570 CncrtBnd; HonRl; LbryAde; MrchBnd; NHS; 4-H; SpnCl; 4-HAwd; College; Language.

SLUZEVICH, David; Benton HS; Benton, IL; 14/168 TrsSophCls; HonRl; NHS; StuCncl; Yrbk; SptEdSchPpr; Bsktbl; Ftbl; Trk; Eastern Illinois U; Accountant.

SLY, Randy L; Dow City Arion Community HS; Dow City, IA; 8/43 VPJrCls; Chrs; ChrhWkr; CmntyWkr; HonRl; NHS; SchPl; RptrYrbk; SptEdSchPpr; PpCl; Univ; Math.

SLYE, Terry L; Crosby Ironton HS; Emily, MN; 1/148 ChrhWkr; HonRl; NHS; NatlMeritFnl; NatlMeritSchl; StuCncl; Yrbk; EdSchPpr; Houghton Coll; Lawyer.

SLYTER, Kenneth D; Spring Hill HS; Spring Hill, KS; 4/59 SecTrsSophCls; PresJrCls; Band; HonRl; MrchBnd; NHS; StuCncl; TchrAde; Bsktbl; Univ Of Kansas; Chemical Engineer.

SMAGACZ, Lori K; Neillsville HS; Neillsville, WI; 11/115 ChrhWkr; NHS; SchPl; Yrbk; RptrSchPpr; SchPpr; FBLA; TreasFHA; PresFTA; PpCl; GAA; Technical School; Secretary.

SMAIL, Carlton R; Usd 463 HS; Udall, KS; Chr; HonRl; SchPl; FFA; Bsktbl; Ftbl; Trk; PresAwd; Coll; Professional.

SMAIL, Jeanne M; Udall HS; Udall, KS; 2/21 PresSophCls; SecJrCls; Chrs; SecStuCncl; YthFlsp; FHA; PresPpCl; LetterTrk; PresAwd; Wichita State U; Social Work.

SMALE, Anita F; Les Cheneaux Comm HS; Cedarville, MI; SecTrsSophCls; VPJrCls; Band; HonRl; VPNHS; OffAde; RptrYrbk; SpnCl; MthCl; PpCl; College; Professional.

SMALEC, Thomas M; St Patrick HS; Chicago, IL; 72/427 HonRl; NatlMeritCmnd; No Illinois Univ; Journalism.

SMALL, Brian; Galatia Hs; Galatia, IL; PresFrshCls; HonRl; Glf; BauchLmbAwd;.

SMALL, Brian P; Marquette HS; Michigan City, IN; Chrl; HonRl; SchMus; LetterBsbl; College; Business Marketing.

SMALL, David; Riverview Comm HS; Riverview, MI; 17/237 CncrtBnd; HonRl; MrchBnd; NHS; PolWkr; SctActv; StuGov; RptrSchPpr; Bsbl; College; Medicine.

SMALL, David T; New Haven HS; Fort Wayne, IN; Band; CncrtBnd; DrlTm; HonRl; MrchBnd; NHS; Orch; PepBnd; ROTC; TchrAde; In U; Music.

SMALL, Gregory N; Warrensburg HS; Warrensburg, MO; TrsFrshCls; Band; Chr; CncrtBnd; MrchBnd; PepBnd; StuCncl; CaptBsktbl; Glf; Swmmng; College; Medical Technology.

SMALL, Lois J; Northwest Ri HS; House Springs, MO; HonRl; NHS; SctActv; StuCncl; YthFlsp; PpCl; LetterTrk; IMSpt; PresAwd;.

SMALL, Marcia L; Unity HS; Chicago, IL; Chr; CmntyWkr; SchMus; StuCncl; TchrAde; University; Professional.

SMALL, Maureen K; Braddock Public HS; Moffit, ND; 5/13 Chr; HonRl; LbryAde; PolWkr; SchPl; Sdlty; StuCncl; Yrbk; RptrSchPpr; PpCl; Mary College; Elementary Ed.

SMALL, Nora P; Deerfield HS; Deerfield, IL; HonRl; NHS; NatlMeritCmnd; Orch; SchMus; SctActv; StuCncl; Univ Of Delaware; Architectural Restoration.

SMALL, Patricia A; Dowagiac Sr HS; Dowagiac, MI; Band; CncrtBnd; HonRl; MrchBnd; NatlFornLg; PepBnd; Teen; 4-H; LetterBsbl; LetterBsktbl; LetterTrk; College; Social Work.

SMALL, Sherie L; Lebo HS; Lebo, KS; 2/14 VPSrCls; ChrhWkr; HonRl; SchPl; YthFlsp; EdYrBk; 4-H; FBLA; PpCl; LetterTrk; Emporia Ks State Clg; Bus.

SMALLBECK, Mona K; St Thomas Public HS; St Thomas, ND; ALAGirlsSt; Chrs; ChrhWkr; HonRl; SchPl; EdSchPpr; Bsktbl; GAA; PPFtbl; Wahpeton Sch Of Science; Legal Secretary.

SMALLEY, Linda; Parchment HS; Kalamazoo, MI; HonRl; NHS; RptrYrbk; LatCl; Kellogg Coll; Physical Therapist.

SMALLEY, Timothy W; Tripoli Community HS; Sumner, IA; HonRl; PresStuCncl; Pres4-H; LetterBsbl; LetterFtbl; LetterTrk; LetterWrstlng;.

SMALLWOOD, Gregory L; Jefferson HS; Rockford, IL; 28/361 Band; HonRl; SchPl; StuCncl; RptrSchPpr; Bsbl; University Of Illinois; Engineering.

SMALLWOOD, Kevin C; Jefferson HS; Lafayette, IN; 22/562 Band; HonRl; JrNHS; NatlFornLg; NHS; Orch; TchrAde; SchPpr; SciCl; College; Computer Science.

SMANIOTTO, Deena M; St Joseph HS; Kenosha, WI; 14/150 Chr; HonRl; HospAde; JrNHS; Mdrgl; StuGov; Yrbk; 4-H; SpnCl; Chrldr; College; Nursing.

SMART, Dale L; Forest View HS; Mt Prospect, IL; ChrhWkr; HonRl; LitMag; RptrYrbk; GAA; College; Elementary Ed.

SMART, Kimberly K; Cameron Ri HS; Cameron, MO; Chrs; CmntyWkr; HonRl; OffAde; RedCrAde; FHA; FTA; Trk; Chrldr; IMSpt; College.

SMART, Lena S; Attica Consolidated HS; Attica, IN; 11/76 Band; CncrtBnd; HonRl; HospAde; MrchBnd; SctActv; FHA; SciCl; Bsktbl; GAA; Indiana Central Coll; Nursing.

SMARZ, Jean S; Beloit Memorial HS; Beloit, WI; HonRl; VPSpnCl; LetterBsktbl; LetterTennis; College; Vocation.

SMAZENKA, Pamela; Summerfield HS; Petersburg, MI; 30/69 CmntyWkr; HonRl; SchPl; StuGov; TchrAde; 4-H; FHA; SpnCl; Bsktbl; GAA; Monroe Comm Coll; Ed.

SMEALL, Benjamin; Central HS; Grand Forks, ND; 29 354 HonRl; NHS; NatlMeritSF; Orch; SchMus; Clg; Profes.

SMEDRA, Kenneth A; Loup City Public HS; Loup City, NE; 15/66 PresJrCls; ALBoysSt; HonRl; JrNHS; NHS; SchPl; SchPpr; Pres4-H; PresFFA; LetterFtbl; U Of Neb; Lawyer.

SMEDSHAMMER, Duane D; Litchville HS; Litchville, ND; Band; Chrs; HonRl; YthFlsp; 4-H; LetterWrstlng; 4-HAwd; University; Wildlife Mgmt.

SMEDSHAMMER, Marlin P; Litchville HS; Litchville, ND; Chrs; HonRl; YthFlsp; 4-H; Wrstlng; North Dakota State Univ; Animal Science.

SMEINS, Darla; Ackley Geneva HS; Ackley, IA; 9/56 Band; Chrs; HonRl; MrchBnd; NHS; PepBnd; SchMus; EdYrBk; Trade School; Vocation.

SMELTER, Jane M; Foley HS; Foley, MN; Chrs; HonRl; LbryAde; Navy Acad; Electronics.

SMERDON, James R; Bangor John Glenn HS; Bay City, MI; Band; Chr; Chrl; Chrs; CmntyWkr; CncrtBnd; HonRl; LbryAde; MrchBnd; College; Conservation.

SMEREK, Janice; St Francis De Sales HS; Chicago, IL; 48/300 Chrs; ChrhWkr; HonRl; NHS; StuCncl; SpnCl; PpCl; Trk; Chrldr; GAA; College.

SMESTAD, Cynthia; Fordville HS; Niagara, ND; VPFrshCls; Band; Chrs; HonRl; SchMus; SchPl; RptrYrbk; RptrSchPpr; 4-H; 4-HAwd; Univ; Journalism.

SMET, Arthur; United Township Hs; E Moline, IL; 2/650 HonRl; NHS; PolWkr; GerCl; Tennis; Wrstlng; BauchLmbAwd; ChmbCommrsAwd; No Illinois U; Mathematics Field.

SMET, Arthur D; United Twp HS; E Moline, IL; 3/650 CmntyWkr; HonRl; NHS; PolWkr; Tennis; Wrstlng; BauchLmbAwd; ChmbCommrsAwd; No Illinois Univ; Mathematics.

SMET, Sandra J; Southwest HS; Green Bay, WI; 34/420 Band; ChrhWkr; HonRl; HospAde; Quill&Scroll; SchMus; EdYrBk; RptrSchPpr; VPSpnCl; TreasPpCl; U Of Wi; Elementary Ed.

SMETTE, De Vonna M; Newburg HS; Newburg, ND; ALAGirlsSt; Band; CncrtBnd; DrmMjrt; HonRl; SchPl; RptrSchPpr; EdSchPpr; PpCl; Chrldr; Univ Nd.

SMIAROWSKI, Mary J; Fenton HS; Fenton, MI; 15/293 Chr; HonRl; Mdrgl; NHS; NatlThespSoc; OffAde; SchPl; TchrAde; Chrldr; PPFtbl; Clge; Computer Science.

SMICK, Peggy A; Geneva Comm HS; Geneva, IL; 42/218 Band; CncrtBnd; HonRl; HospAde; MrchBnd; PepBnd; SchPl; TchrAde; FTA; University; Teaching.

SMID, Margareth M; Maine East HS; Des Plaines, IL; HonRl; NHS; SchAde; Loyola University; Business.

SMIERSKI, James J; East Gary Edison HS; East Gary, IN; 2/175 ALBoysSt; ChrhWkr; HonRl; NHS;.

SMIERTKA, Eric M; Willowbrook HS; Villa Park, IL; 20/822 Aud/Vis; HonRl; JA; NHS; NatlMeritSF; Coll;electronics.

SMIGEL, William R; Thornridge HS; Dolton, IL; Aud/Vis; HonRl; JrNHS; NHS; NatlMeritSF; Yrbk; GerCl; Trk; College; Architecture.

SMILAY, Stephanie B; Carsonville Port Sanilac HS; Applegate, MI; 5/55 HonRl; NHS; SchPl; RptrYrbk; RptrSchPpr; SciCl; Central Mich Univ.

SMILEY, Janet C; Jefferson City HS; Jefferson City, MO; PresNatlThespSoc; Quill&Scroll; SchPl; StuCncl; StuGov; TchrAde; YthLg; SchPpr; Wrstlng; AmLegAwd; U Of Mo; Journalism.

SMILEY, Kathleen D; Lindblom Technical HS; Chicago, IL; 2/656 HonRl; OffAde; TchrAde; CaptGAA; College.

SMIT, Douglas; West Sioux HS; Ireton, IA; Chr; Chrs; ChrhWkr; SchMus; SchPl; 4-H; Univ; Curr Of Major Study.

SMITH, Alan D; Whitmore Lk HS; Whitmore Lake, MI; TrsFrshCls; PresSophCls; PresJrCls; HonRl; JrNHS; NHS; SchPl; SctActv; Ftbl; U Of Mi; Novelist Acting.

SMITH, Alyson J; East Alton Wood River HS; Wood River, IL; 90/275 Chr; ChrhWkr; HonRl; HospAde; MrchBnd; PolWkr; SchPl; RptrYrbk; FNA; PpCl; College; Music.

SMITH, Amy E; Marian HS; Birmingham, MI; HonRl; ModUN; NHS; StuGov;.

SMITH, Amy J; Okemos HS; Okemos, MI; Chr; Mdrgl; NatlFornLg; SchMus; SchPl; Yrbk; BttyCrckrAwd; DanFAwd; EldAwd; Oakland Academy Of Dramatic Art; Actress.

SMITH, Amy L; Sandusky HS; Sandusky, MI; 1/128 PresJrCls; Band; ChrhWkr; SchMus; SchPl; StuCncl; Bsktbl; Trk; GAA; IMSpt; Graceland Coll; Cultural Sci.

SMITH, Andrea L; Harvard HS; Harvard, IL; 1/170 ALAGirlsSt; Band; Chrs; HonRl; NHS; PresStuCncl; CaptBsktbl; CaptChrldr; DARAwd; Univ Of Notre Dame; Mathematics.

SMITH, Anita L; Marine City HS; Marine City, MI; 10/160 VPSophCls; Chrs; HonRl; LbryAde; NHS; NatlMeritFnl; StuGov; RptrYrbk; SptEdYrbk; RptrSchPpr; SpnCl; Bsktbl; Trk;.

SMITH, Ann D; Bridgeport HS; Bridgeport, NE; 5/62 TrsSophCls; VPJrCls; HonRl; PresNHS; Quill&Scroll; SchPl; StuGov; RptrYrbk; RptrSchPpr; GAA; Co St U; Fashion Merchandising.

SMITH, Ann E; Sycamore HS; Sycamore, IL; 7/201 HonRl; NHS; FrCl; College; Liberal Arts.

SMITH, Anthony E; Switz City Central HS; Switz City, IN; FFA; Bsktbl; Farmer.

SMITH, Anthony J; Witt HS; Witt, IL; TrsSophCls; Chrl; Chrs; ChrhWkr; CmntyWkr; HonRl; SchPl; Yrbk; SchPpr; Bsbl; Clg; Teacher.

SMITH, Arthur W; Turner HS; Kansas City, KS; Chr; ChrhWkr; HonRl; NHS; Quill&Scroll; StuCncl; StuGov; YthFlsp; RptrSchPpr; SptEdSchPpr; Business College; Business Management.

SMITH, Augustine; Roosevelt HS; Gary, IN; 3/600 Band; ChrhWkr; CmntyWkr; HonRl; JrNHS; NHS; NatlMeritCmnd; StuCncl; FTA; CitAwd; Purdue U; Veterinarian Medicine.

SMITH, Barbara H; Lumen Christi HS; Jackson, MI; 16/223 HonRl; JA; NHS; SchMus; Jackson Comm College; Radio Broadcasting.

SMITH, Barbara J; R I North Callaway HS; Williamsburg, MO; 3/73 TrsSophCls; VPJrCls; Band; Chrs; ALAGirlsSt; MrchBnd; PepBnd; SchPl; Yrbk; DARAwd; College; Medicine.

SMITH, Barbara J; La Salle Peru Twp HS; Peru, IL; Band; CncrtBnd; HonRl; MrchBnd; RptrSchPpr; FrCl; College; Veterinarian.

SMITH, Barbara J; Brimfield HS; Brimfield, IL; 14/50 Chr; HonRl; HospAde; SpnCl; PpCl; Business School; Vocation.

SMITH, Barbara R; Maconaquah HS; Bunker Hill, IN; 30/261 TrsJrCls; TrsSrCls; ChrhWkr; HonRl; NHS; StuCncl; PresYthFlsp; Yrbk; 4-H; LatCl; MthCl; VPGAA; College; Medical.

SMITH, Barbara S; Melbeta HS; Minatare, NE; PresFrshCls; SecJrCls; HonRl; StuCncl; PpCl; LetterBsktbl; LetterTrk; Chrldr; IMSpt; CitAwd;.

SMITH, Betsy A; Hays HS; Hays, KS; Chr; HonRl; Orch; College; Music.

SMITH, Betty J; Meservey Thornton HS; Thornton, IA; 1/27 TrsJrCls; PresSrCls; Band; Chr; HonRl; LbryAde; MrchBnd; NHS; PepBnd; StuCncl; Yrbk; RptrSchPpr; 4-H; North Iowa Area Comm College; Secretary.

SMITH, Beverly; Brookville HS; Cedar Grove, IN; Chrs; DrlTm; LbryAde; SchPl; Yrbk; College.

SMITH, Blaine; No Platte Senior HS; North Platte, NE; Chr; HonRl; Orch; SchMus; YthFlsp; FrCl; SciCl; Bsktbl; Trk; Wrstlng; College; Ministry.

SMITH, Bonita R; Goshen HS; Goshen, IN; 15/252 Band; Chr; ChrhWkr; HonRl; NatlFornLg; NHS; Orch; PepBnd; YthFlsp; Bethel College; Medical Technology.

SMITH, Bradley; Newell Providence HS; Newell, IA; 6/41 PresFrshCls; Chrs; HonRl; 4-H; FFA; Bsbl; Ftbl; Trk; 4-HAwd; LionAwd; Ia State Univ; Agriculture.

SMITH, Bradley; Waterfod Mott HS; Pontiac, MI; Band; LetterTrk; LetterWrstlng; CchngActv; Michigan State University; Commercial Art.

SMITH, Brady K; Highland Park HS; Topeka, KS; Band; ChrhWkr; CncrtBnd; HonRl; MrchBnd; PepBnd; LetterTrk; IMSpt; College.

SMITH, Brand; Milton Hs; Milton, WI; 25/124 Band; HonRl; NHS; PepBnd; LetterFtbl; LetterSwmmng;.

SMITH, Brenda L; Tri County R 7 HS; Jamesport, MO; PresJrCls; VPSrCls; HonRl; SchMus; StuGov; RptrYrbk; Pres4-H; VPFHA; SecSciCl; Bsktbl; Chrldr; 4-HAwd; Central Missouri State Univ; Home Economics.

SMITH, Brenda R; Alpena HS; Alpena, MI; Band; CncrtBnd; HospAde; MrchBnd; NatlMeritCmnd; PepBnd; SecSpnCl; College; Math.

SMITH, Brian D; Chelsea HS; Chelsea, MI; 1/189 ALBoysSt; Band; HonRl; NHS; RptrSchPpr; SecFrshCls; KiwanAwd; W Mi U; Paper Science & Engineer.

SMITH, Brian J; Mcbain Public HS; Mc Bain, MI; Chr; ChrhWkr; HonRl; NHS; SchPl; 4-H; FFA; PpCl; LetterFtbl; LetterTrk; Mich St U; Veterinary Med.

SMITH, Brian J; Altoona HS; Eau Claire, WI; Band; SctActv; EngCl; MthCl; SciCl; LetterWrstlng; College; Medicine.

SMITH, Brian K; Oak Park River Forest HS; River Forest, IL; 252/1107 HonRl; Univ Of Illinois; Architecture.

SMITH, Brian R; Imlay City HS; Imlay City, MI; 1/130 Chr; SctActv; StuGov; FSA; Ftbl; Tennis; IMSpt; U Of Mi; Physical Science.

SMITH, Bruce A; Thornton Fractional So HS; Lansing, IL; 10/580 Chr; CncrtBnd; JrNHS; MrchBnd; NHS; TreasYthFlsp; LetterFtbl; CaptSwmmng; LetterTrk; Le Tourneau College; Electrical Engineering.

SMITH, Bryan D; South Page HS; College Springs, IA; 10/40 PresFrshCls; CmntyWkr; HonRl; FFA; Bsbl; CaptBsktbl; Ftbl; Trk;.

SMITH, Candace; North Side HS; Ft Wane, IN; 4/438 HonRl; LitMag; NHS; NatlMeritFnl; Orch; SchMus; EngCl; DanFAwd; Wittenberg Univ; Psychology.

SMITH, Candace S; North Side HS; Fort Wayne, IN; PresAFS; ChrhWkr; HonRl; NHS; NatlMeritSF; Orch; SchMus; SctActv; StuCncl; RptrYrbk; SchPpr; EngCl; FrCl; Bsktbl; College; Science.

SMITH, Carl; Hartford Union HS; Hartford, WI; Band; HonRl; NHS; SctActv; StuCncl; Tennis; Univ Of Wisconsin; Acturial Science.

SMITH, Carl L; Ovid Elsie HS; Owosso, MI; Band; ChrhWkr; CncrtBnd; MrchBnd; PepBnd; RptrSchPpr; Ftbl; College; Highway Engineer.

SMITH, Carol A; Lake Orion Comm HS; Pontiac, MI; 14/300 HonRl; NatlFornLg; NatlMeritSF; NatlThespSoc; SchPl; StuCncl; U Of Mi; Broadcasting.

SMITH, Catherine L; York Comm HS; Elmhurst, IL; HonRl; LbryAde; NHS; FrCl; College; Nurse.

SMITH, Charlotte; Mondovi HS; Mondovi, WI; CncrtBnd; HonRl; NHS; StuCncl; RptrYrbk; FrCl; MthCl; Trk; Chrldr; GAA; College; Liberal Arts.

SMITH, Charlotte E; Delta C 7 HS; Steele, MO; 9/29 Band; ChrhWkr; HospAde; StuCncl; Twrl; RptrYrbk; 4-H; FHA; FTA; School Of Ozarks.

SMITH, Charlotte R; Andrews Laboratory HS; Berrien Springs, MI; 4 Chr; ChrhWkr; HospAde; JA; Andrews Univ; Social Work.

SMITH, Cheryl A; Urbana Comm HS; Center Point, IA; 3/20 ALAGirlsSt; Chrs; HonRl; Mdrgl; NHS; EdYrBk; RptrSchPpr; Pres4-H; Trk; AmLegAwd;.

SMITH, Cheryl A; Douglas Macarthur HS; Saginaw, MI; HonRl; HospAde; LitMag; StuCncl; Michigan State University; Medicine.

SMITH, Cheryl D; Campus HS; Wichita, KS; Chr; Chrs; ChrhWkr; HonRl; Mdrgl; NHS; SchMus; SctActv; StuCncl; StuGov; Winfield Kansas; Little Kids.

SMITH, Christine E; Albia Community HS; Albia, IA; Chrs; MrchBnd; Twrl;.

SMITH, Cindi A; Kickapoo HS; Springfield, MO; 66/338 Chr; Chrs; ChrhWkr; DrmBgl; HonRl; SchMus; StuCncl; LatCl; LetterTennis; IMSpt; Smsu; Sec Bus.

SMITH, Cindy; Bradshaw Public HS; Bradshaw, NE; 1/16; Band; DrmMjrt; JrNHS; NHS; TchrAde; 4-H; CitAwd; Univ Of Neb; Professional.

SMITH, Cindy L; Lake Forest Academy; Onalaska, WI; PresJrCls; ChrhWkr; HonRl; SchPl; StuCncl; StuGov; College; Law.

SMITH, Cindy L; Hutchinson Senior HS; Hutchinson, MN; Band; ChrhWkr; CncrtBnd; HonRl; MrchBnd; OffAde; SchMus; Business School; Secretary.

SMITH, Cindy L; North Clay Comm HS; Louisville, IL; Band; CncrtBnd; HonRl; MrchBnd; NHS; SchPl; StuCncl; Yrbk; SchPpr; 4-H; Bsktbl; Trk; Chrldr; College.

SMITH, Claudia L; University HS; Centerview, MO; 3/49 SecSrCls; HonRl; JrNHS; NatlFornLg; NHS; NatlThespSoc; OffAde; StuGov; FBLA; Bsbl; Univ; Business Field.

SMITH, Connie; East HS; Wichita, KS; Band; CncrtBnd; HonRl; TchrAde; PpCl; SciCl; IMSpt; Kansas State; Retail Floriculture.

SMITH, Connie; Sparta HS; Sparta, MI; 7/220 SecFrshCls; HonRl; NHS; StuCncl; SpnCl; PPFtbl; DanFAwd; OptClAwd; Davenport Coll; Secretary.

SMITH, Craig L; Argo Community HS; Argo, IL; 65/450 HonRl; PolWkr; SctActv; Bsbl; Bsktbl; Univ Of Arizona; Law.

SMITH, Craig L; Northwestern HS; Northville, SD; 11/35 ALBoysSt; CncrtBnd; HonRl; PepBnd; SchPl; StuCncl; RptrSchPpr; LetterBsktbl; LetterFtbl; AmLegAwd; Northern St College; Professional.

SMITH, Craig R; West Catholic HS; Grand Rapids, MI; HonRl; Ftbl; College; Professional.

SMITH, Cynthia J; Clarkton HS; Clarkton, MO; Band; ChrhWkr; CncrtBnd; HonRl; MrchBnd; PepBnd; StuCncl; YthFlsp; Three Rivers College; Secretary.

SMITH, Cynthia J; Glenbard So HS; Wheaton, IL; 10/300 CmntyWkr; HonRl; NHS; SchPl; StuCncl; YthFlsp; RptrYrbk; FrCl; PpCl; Jr College; Pharmacist.

SMITH, Cynthia L; La Salle Peru Twp HS; Peru, IL; 14/430 ChrhWkr; HonRl; NHS; SpnCl; Us Army; Interpretor.

SMITH, Cynthia M; Deering HS; Deering, ND; 2/7 Chrs; HonRl; JrNHS; RptrYrbk; RptrSchPpr; LetterBsktbl; Trk; BttyCrckrAwd; DARAwd; Clge; Accounting.

SMITH, Cynthia M; Lakeland Union HS; Minocgua, WI; Band; CncrtBnd; HonRl; NHS; SchPpr; SpnCl; PpCl; Chrldr; Univ Of Wisconsin; Accounting.

SMITH, Cynthia R; Plainview HS; Coolidge, KS; SecTrsSrCls; Band; CmntyWkr; DrmMjrt; HonRl; SchPl; StuCncl; SchPpr; LetterBsktbl; Tennis; LetterTrk; Chrldr; BttyCrckrAwd; Business School; Secretary.

SMITH, Dan D; Prophetstown HS; Prophetstown, IL; 30/105 Chr; HonRl; SctActv; YthFlsp; SptEdYrbk; SptEdSchPpr; FTA; LetterBsktbl; LetterTrk; Carthage College; Medicine.

SMITH, Daniel D; Farmer City Mansfield HS; Farmer City, IL; AFS; Band; Chrs; CncrtBnd; MrchBnd; SchMus; 4-H; Ftbl; LetterTrk; IMSpt; 4-HAwd; Eastern Illinois Univ; Electronics.

SMITH, Daniel D; Gregory HS; Gregory, SD; 2/60 Chrs; HonRl; LbryAde; VoiceDemAwd; College; Secondary Education.

SMITH, Danny; Caruthersville Sr HS; Caruthersville, MO; Band; Chrs; CncrtBnd; DrmBgl; HonRl; MrchBnd; NHS; PepBnd; IMSpt; So East Mo St; Music.

SMITH, Dan R; Abingdon HS; Abingdon, IL; Chr; ChrhWkr; CmntyWkr; HonRl; LbryAde; StuGov; Teen; YthFlsp; YthFnd; FFA; North American School; Motorcycle Mechanic.

SMITH, Darla; Virden HS; Virden, IL; /79 Band; ChrhWkr; CmntyWkr; HonRl; SctActv; YthFlsp; FHA; FTA; 4-HAwd; JCAwd; Coll; Social Worker.

SMITH, Darla J; Manhattan HS; Manhattan, KS; 32/420 Band; ChrhWkr; CmntyWkr; HonRl; MrchBnd; RedCrAde; SctActv; TchrAde; YthFlsp; GodCntryAwd; Kansas State U; Psychologyr Or Pub Rel.

SMITH, Darlene A; Crete HS; Martell, NE; Chr; HonRl; SchMus; SchPl; RptrSchPpr; 4-H; FBLA; FHA; PpCl; College; Accounting.

SMITH, Darrell E; Highland HS; Chesterfield, IN; Chr; HonRl; JA; SctActv; StuCncl; Bsktbl; Ftbl; LetterGlf; Swmmng; JAAwd; Ball State Univ; Architecture.

SMITH, David; Watertown Senior HS; Watertown, SD; 15/330 ALBoysSt; Chrs; HonRl; Mdrgl; NatlFornLg; Ftbl; IMSpt; College; Data Processing.

SMITH, David; Sweet Springs R 7 HS; Sweet Springs, MO; HonRl; ModUN; SctActv; SciCl; CitAwd; Univ Mo Rolla; Nuclear Engineering.

SMITH, David; St Paul Kennedy HS; Chicago, IL; Chrs; Orch; Yrbk; IMSpt; Coll.

SMITH, David E; Unity HS; Ursa, IL; StuCncl; 4-H; LetterBsktbl; CaptFtbl; LetterTrk; Clge; Fish & Game Management.

SMITH, David I; G R Clark HS; Hammond, IN; Aud/Vis; SecSpnCl; Indiana Univ; Professional.

SMITH, David L; Eureka HS; Allenton, MO; ChrhWkr; Trk; Wrstlng;.

SMITH, David S; Ontonagon Area HS; Ontonagon, MI; 14/108 HonRl; Bsbl; Ftbl; Michigan Technological Univ; Civil Engineer.

SMITH, Dawn S; Effingham HS; Effingham, IL; Chrs; HonRl; SchMus; SctActv; YthFlsp; RptrSchPpr; Pres4-H; FrCl; PpCl; Chrldr; GAA; PresAwd; Eastern Illinois Univ; Teacher.

SMITH, Dean M; Epping Public HS; Epping, ND; 1/6 SecTrsJrCls; SctActv; Bsktbl; University; Accounting.

SMITH, Debbie; Scecina HS; Indianapolis, IN; ChrhWkr; CmntyWkr; HonRl; JrNHS; MrchBnd; NHS; RedCrAde; SchMus; SchPl; StuCncl; RptrSchPpr; Marion College; Elem Educa.

SMITH, Debbie A; Morgan Co R Ii HS; Sunrise Beach, MO; Chrs; HonRl; NHS; SchAde; SchPl; TchrAde; RptrYrbk; FrCl; MthCl; PpCl; College; Dentist.

SMITH, Debbie K; Udall HS; Udall, KS; Band; Chr; Chrs; MrchBnd; PepBnd; SchPl; YthFlsp; FHA; PpCl; LetterBsktbl; College.

SMITH, Deborah E; Osawatomie HS; Osawatomie, KS; 15/90 ALAGirlsSt; Band; ChrhWkr; CncrtBnd; HonRl; MrchBnd; PepBnd; YthFlsp; PpCl; Kansas Univ; Lawyer.

SMITH, Deborah J; Hanover Central HS; Cedar Lake, IN; 9/144 SecFrshCls; HonRl; NHS; StuCncl; TchrAde; EngCl; SpnCl; PpCl; GAA;.

SMITH, Deborah L; North Liberty HS; South Bend, IN; 3/90 CncrtBnd; HonRl; MrchBnd; NHS; NatlMeritFnl; NatlMeritSchl; SchMus; 4-H; BttyCrckrAwd; Purdue Univ; Forestry.

SMITH, Deborah L; Cass City HS; Decker, MI; Chr; ChrhWkr; CmntyWkr; HonRl; NHS; OffAde; 4-H; College; Accounting.

SMITH, Debra; Constantine HS; Union, MI; 11/107 Chrs; ChrhWkr; HonRl; NHS; SchPl; YthFlsp; 4-H; SpnCl; PpCl; 4-HAwd; Grand Valley; Biochemistry.

SMITH, Debra A; Morton HS; Hammond, IN; 43/492 HonRl; NatlFornLg; NHS; TchrAde; College.

SMITH, Debra A; Mankato East HS; Mankato, MN; CmntyWkr; HonRl; HospAde; NatlThespSoc; Orch; Mankato State Univ; Speech Pathologist.

SMITH, Debra A; King HS; Detroit, MI; HonRl; CitAwd; Ferris St Col; Accounting.

SMITH, Debra J; Adrian HS; Adrian, MI; 93/361 CmntyWkr; HonRl; NHS; OffAde; SchAde; SctActv; StuGov; TchrAde; College; Secretarial Sciences.

SMITH, Debra L; Paseo HS; Kansas City, MO; ChrhWkr; HonRl; JA; NatlFornLg; SchPl; SctActv; StuCncl; Teen; PpCl; Howard Univ; Medicine.

SMITH, Debra L; North Boone HS; Poplar Grove, IL; Band; Chr; Chrs; CncrtBnd; DrlTm; MrchBnd; PepBnd; SchMus; SchPl; Yrbk; 4-H; FHA; LetterBsktbl; Trk; Rock Vly College.

SMITH, Debra L; Winchester Comm HS; Winchester, IN; DrlTm; DrmMjrt; RedCrAde; StuCncl; PresFHA; SpnCl; PpCl; Asbury Coll; Missionary.

SMITH, Delores J; New Town HS; New Town, ND; 5/46 SecTrsSrCls; ALAGirlsSt; Band; HonRl; StuCncl; Yrbk; GerCl; GAA; BttyCrckrAwd; 4-HAwd; Grandforks Univ; Nursing.

SMITH, Dena L; Suttons Bay HS; Suttons Bay, MI; 3/50 SecBand; Chr; HonRl; EdYrBk; CchngActv; DanFAwd; Univ Of Mi; Oceanographer.

SMITH, Dena L; Addison Trail HS; Lombard, IL; College; Teacher.

SMITH, Denise L; Princeton R V HS; Princeton, MO; 2/53 TrsSophCls; SecJrCls; CncrtBnd; HonRl; NHS; SchPl; Twrl; YthFlsp; FHA; LetterFtbl; Cottey Jr College; Interior Decorator.

SMITH, Dennis L; Morrisonville HS; Morrisonville, IL; 2/55 PresJrCls; Band; Chrs; CncrtBnd; HonRl; MrchBnd; ModUN; PepBnd; SchPl; SctActv; StuCncl; Bradley Univ; Air Force.

SMITH, Diane; Parker HS; Chicago, IL; Chr; ChrhWkr; CncrtBnd; HonRl; Yrbk; C; Curriculum Of Major Study.

SMITH, Dianne M; Parkwood HS; Joplin, MO; SecSophCls; SecJrCls; CmntyWkr; HonRl; Quill&Scroll; StuCncl; Teen; YthFlsp; RptrYrbk; EdYrBk; PpCl; College; Teaching.

SMITH, Dianne M; Mehlville Sr HS; St Louis, MO; Band; Chrs; SecCmntyWkr; CncrtBnd; HonRl; HospAde; OffAde; RedCrAde; SpnCl; College.

SMITH, Donna M; Taylorville HS; Taylorville, IL; HospAde; OffAde; College; Accounting.

SMITH, Donny T; North Winnesheik HS; Decorah, IA; 5/43 Chrs; ChrhWkr; CncrtBnd; HonRl; MrchBnd; RptrYrbk; 4-H; FFA; Bsktbl; Trk; College; Agri And Math.

SMITH, Doreen; Maplewood Richmond Hgts HS; Maplewood, MO; 15/185 CtyCnl; CmntyWkr; CncrtBnd; HonRl; MrchBnd; NHS; PepBnd; Quill&Scroll; SchAde; TchrAde; Coll; Spec Educ.

SMITH, Dorene J; Bird Island Public HS; Bird Island, MN; 4/91 Chr; ChrhWkr; HonRl; NatlFornLg; NHS; SchMus; YthFlsp; RptrYrbk; FHA; Trk; College; Accounting.

SMITH, Duane; Wallace HS; Lincoln, NE; TrsJrCls; TrsSrCls; Band; Chrs; PepBnd; SchPl; StuCncl; RptrYrbk; Bsktbl; Ftbl;.

SMITH, Ellen C; St Clement HS; Center Line, MI; Chrs; HonRl; NHS; OffAde; StuCncl; StuGov; Yrbk; PpCl; SciCl; Chrldr; Central Mi Univ; Accounting.

SMITH, Emily D; Central HS; Detroit, MI; 25/203 ChrhWkr; CmntyWkr; HonRl; SchAde; StuCncl; TchrAde; Yrbk; FrCl; DARAwd; U Of Mi Dearborn; Pediatrician.

SMITH, Frances; Acad Of Our Lady; Chicago, IL; 28/160 Chr; ChrhWkr; HonRl; LitMag; NHS; Quill&Scroll; SchPl; TchrAde; SchPpr; VoiceDemAwd; Mundelein Coll; Art.

SMITH, Galene J; Council Grove HS; Alta Vista, KS; TrsJrCls; Chrs; HonRl; MrchBnd; SchMus; SctActv; PresYthFlsp; Sec4-H; PpCl; 4-HAwd; College; Medicine.

SMITH, Galen L; David City Public HS; David City, NE; Chr; HonRl; Quill&Scroll; Yrbk; Bsktbl; LetterTrk; Wrstlng; RotaryAwd; College; Mechanical Engineer.

SMITH, Gary R; Harrisburg HS; Harrisburg, IL; 15/200 HonRl; NHS; MthCl; Bsbl; Bsktbl; So Illinois Univ; Communications.

SMITH, Geneva G; Galena HS; Galena, MO; SecFrshCls; Band; Chr; Chrs; CmntyWkr; CncrtBnd; HonRl; PepBnd; SchPl; Twrl; LetterBsbl; LetterBsktbl; LetterTrk; Chrldr; College.

SMITH, George W; Thayer HS; Thayer, MO; 13/50 Chr; HonRl; SchPl; SptEdYrbk; Tennis; Trk; IMSpt; DanFAwd; College.

SMITH, Gerald A; St Paul Kennedy HS; Chicago, IL; Chrs; HonRl; Orch; StuCncl; Yrbk; SchPpr; Socr; Trk; IMSpt; Electrical Engr.

SMITH, Gerald W; Normal Comm HS; Normal, IL; PresSrCls; ChrhWkr; CmntyWkr; NHS; SchMus; StuCncl; SchPpr; Trk; Wrstlng; GodCntryAwd; U Of Ill; Law.

SMITH, Glenda D; Central HS; Burden, KS; Band; Chrs; SchPl; Twrl; RptrSchPpr; 4-H; PpCl; Bsktbl; LetterTrk; Chrldr; PPFtbl; 4-HAwd; College; Stenographer.

SMITH, Glenda E; Great Bend HS; Great Bend, KS; 4/335 ChrhWkr; CmntyWkr; HonRl; HospAde; NatlFornLg; NatlMeritSF; YthLg; SchPpr; FHA; PpCl; Mi St U; Economics.

SMITH, Gordon K; Woodstock HS; Woodstock, IL; 17/294 TrsFrshCls; Band; Chrs; DrmMjrt; NHS; SctActv; PresStuCncl; YthFlsp; LetterFtbl; LetterWrstlng; College; Religion.

SMITH, Greg L; Lawton Bronson HS; Lawton, IA; ALBoysSt; HonRl; StuCncl; LetterBsbl; LetterBsktbl; LetterFtbl; LetterTrk; IMSpt; AmLegAwd; PresAwd; College; Agriculture.

SMITH, Gregory; Munster HS; Munster, IN; 7/440 ALBoysSt; HonRl; NHS; TchrAde; Purdue Univ; Elec Engineering.

SMITH, Gregory J; Monticello HS; Monticello, WI; Aud/Vis; Band; Chr; Chrs; ChrhWkr; CncrtBnd; HonRl; MrchBnd; PepBnd; SchPl; FFA; PpCl; LetterGlf; Tech Sch; Agriculture.

SMITH, Gregory K; St Johns Prep HS; Madison, WI; Band; HonRl; NHS; PepBnd; SchPl; TchrAde; RptrSchPpr; GerCl; Wrstlng; College.

SMITH, Gregory S; Naperville Central HS; Naperville, IL; HonRl; College; Medicine.

SMITH, Gynett; Hayti Hs; Hayti, MO; 13/87 SecTrsFrshCls; SecTrsSophCls; ChrhWkr; HonRl; StuCncl; RptrYrbk; RptrSchPpr; FHA; FTA; PpCl; Murray State Univ; Home Economics Teacher.

SMITH, Harold R; Cass Technical HS; Detroit, MI; CncrtBnd; HonRl; NHS; NatlMeritCmnd; PolWkr; Quill&Scroll; SctActv; StuGov; RptrSchPpr; LatCl; Univ Mi; Med.

SMITH, Harold R; Morton East HS; Cicero, IL; 7/771 HonRl; JrNHS; LbryAde; NHS; De Paul Univ; Mathematics.

SMITH, Harry A; Midland HS; Midland, MI; 13/410 HonRl; JA; LbryAde; NatlMeritCmnd; YthFlsp; Univ Of Michigan; Physics.

SMITH, Heidi L; Richland Center HS; Richland Center, WI; Aud/Vis; DrmBgl; HonRl; YthFlsp; FTA; PpCl; Glf; IMSpt; Tech School; Vocational Sec.

SMITH, Helen; North HS; Sheboygan, WI; ChrhWkr; HonRl; NHS; YthFlsp; FTA; Coll; Bio And Art.

SMITH, Howard E; Garrett HS; Garrett, IN; HonRl; NatlMeritCmnd; StuCncl; StuGov; LatCl; Ftbl; LetterTrk; LetterWrstlng; IMSpt; College; Prof Chemical Sci.

SMITH, Ingrid S; H H Dow HS; Midland, MI; 6/440 PresSrCls; HonRl; ModUN; NHS; PolWkr; EngCl; GerCl; Univ Of Michigan; Law.

SMITH, Irene J; Providence St Mel HS; Chicago, IL; 4/52 HonRl; JrNHS; NHS; OffAde; Yrbk; Bsktbl; Trk; Northwestern; Writing.

SMITH, Jacalyn; Vicksburg HS; Leonidas, MI; 26/159 Chr; ChrhWkr; NHS; 4-H; Trk; 4-HAwd; Mi St Univ; Vet Med.

SMITH, Jack W; Western Dubuque HS; Epworth, IA; 12/248 VPSophCls; ALBoysSt; Chr; Chrs; HonRl; StuCncl; SchPpr; 4-H; IMSpt; 4-HAwd;.

SMITH, Jacqueline L; Dundee HS; Milan, MI; 21/117 Band; CncrtBnd; DrlTm; HonRl; MrchBnd; Orch; PepBnd; StuCncl; TchrAde; Twrl; Univ Of Michigan; Physical Therapy.

SMITH, Jacquelyn; Nishna Valley HS; Emerson, IA; 5/30 VPFrshCls; SecSophCls; PresJrCls; TrsSrCls; HonRl; SchPl; DARAwd; 4-HAwd; Univ Of Northern Iowa; Business Education.

SMITH, James D; Pender Public HS; Pender, NE; 10/54 Chr; HonRl; SchPl; Bsktbl; CaptFtbl; Trk; DanFAwd; U S Air Force Academy.

SMITH, James D; Stanberry Ri HS; Gentry, MO; Chrs; HonRl; StuCncl; SptEdYrbk; 4-H; LetterFtbl; LetterTrk; CchngActv; IMSpt; 4-HAwd; College.

SMITH, James G; Abraham Lincoln HS; Bloomington, MN; PresFrshCls; Band; Chr; Chrl; ChrhWkr; CncrtBnd; HonRl; MrchBnd; PepBnd; Embry Riddle Areonaughtics; Pilot.

SMITH, James M; Holland Christian HS; Holland, MI; Band; ChrhWkr; CncrtBnd; MrchBnd; Orch; PepBnd; RptrYrbk; PpCl; LetterBsbl; LetterGlf; Tennis; IMSpt; Calvin College; Health.

SMITH, Jan; Savannah HS; Savannah, MO; VPSophCls; ChrhWkr; HonRl; RptrSchPpr; SchPpr; PpCl; Chrldr; College; Secretary.

SMITH, Janean; Parkview HS; Beloit, WI; 2/150 Chr; ChrhWkr; HonRl; Mdrgl; NatlFornLg; NHS; NatlThespSoc; GAA; Olive Naz Coll; Elementary Educ.

SMITH, Janet; Pittsfield HS; Pittsfield, IL; HonRl; PolWkr; SchPl; Yrbk; SpnCl; PpCl; GAA; Macomb Ill Univ; Psycology.

SMITH, Janet I; Kanawha Community HS; Kanawha, IA; SecSrCls; Band; Chrs; ChrhWkr; CmntyWkr; HonRl; StuCncl; YthFlsp; EdYrBk; 4-H; Business School; Executive Secretary.

SMITH, Janet M; Blair HS; Blair, NE; 17/139 Band; Chr; ChrhWkr; CmntyWkr; CncrtBnd; HonRl; 4-H; FFA; FSA; 4-HAwd; Univ Of Nebraska; Vet.

SMITH, Janet R; Southwest HS; St Louis, MO; Chr; ModUN; PolWkr; Quill&Scroll; SchMus; StuCncl; RptrSchPpr; EngCl; LatCl; GAA; College; Writer.

SMITH, Janice R; Lincoln Comm HS; Lincoln, IL; 5/255 Band; HonRl; JA; NHS; NatlThespSoc; SchMus; SchPl; FrCl; 4-HAwd; College; Veterinarian.

SMITH, Janie F; St Mary HS; Cairo, IL; 10/81 CmntyWkr; HonRl; LbryAde; NHS; OffAde; SchMus; StuCncl; RptrYrbk; RptrSchPpr; FrCl; University; Journalism.

SMITH, Jason M; Manhattan HS; Manhattan, KS; 3/307 ALBoysSt; HonRl; NatlFornLg; NatlMeritSF; StuCncl; EdSchPpr; SciCl; CaptSwmmng; AmLegAwd; Stanford University; Chemical Engineer.

SMITH, Jean E; Richfield HS; Richfield, MN; Band; CncrtBnd; HonRl; JrNHS; NHS; PepBnd; SpnCl; Univ Of Mn; Medical Technology.

SMITH, Jean M; Our Lady Of Good Counsel Acad; Madelia, MN; 14/54 Chr; Chrs; StuCncl; RptrYrbk; Yrbk; SchPpr; St Teresa Coll; Religious Educ.

SMITH, Jean M; West Bend East HS; West Bend, WI; ChrhWkr; CmntyWkr; NatlFornLg; NHS; StuCncl; Bsbl; LetterBsktbl; LetterSwmmng; LetterTrk; CaptChrldr; College; Spanish.

SMITH, Jeanne; Hackett HS; Kalamazoo, MI; Chr; CncrtBnd; HonRl; JrNHS; NHS; TchrAde; FrCl; MthCl; Bsbl; Chrldr; Coll; Professional.

SMITH, Jeff D; Menasha HS; Menasha, WI; 56/325 MthCl; CaptFtbl; Wrstlng; IMSpt; Univ; Professional.

SMITH, Jeffrey A; Mundelein HS; Mundelein, IL; 1/425 PresJrCls; HonRl; NHS; NatlMeritSF; Quill&Scroll; SchPl; StuCncl; RptrSchPpr; EdSchPpr; IMSpt; College; Jorunalism And Writing.

SMITH, Jeffrey H; St Laurence HS; Chicago, IL; 9/475 HonRl; NHS; StuCncl; RptrSchPpr; SptEdSchPpr; Socr; LetterWrstlng; Univ Of Chicago; Medicine.

SMITH, Jeffrey L; Louisiana R Ii HS; Louisiana, MO; 17/88 PresSophCls; ALBoysSt; CncrtBnd; HonRl; MrchBnd; PepBnd; StuCncl; Yrbk; SchPpr; AmLegAwd; University; Professional Engineering.

SMITH, Jeffrey L; Pardeeville HS; Pardeeville, WI; 12/94 VPFrshCls; VPJrCls; Chr; Chrs; HonRl; LbryAde; NatlThespSoc; SchMus; SchPl; SctActv; Bsktbl; Ftbl; Glf; Winona St College; Business Admin.

SMITH, Jennifer L; Adrian HS; Adrian, MI; ChrhWkr; HospAde; TchrAde; SpnCl; PpCl; IMSpt; Adrian College; Psychologist.

SMITH, Jennifer M; St Josephs HS; South Bend, IN; Chrs; ChrhWkr; HonRl; HospAde; JA; SchMus; SchPpr; 4-H; Trk; Clge; Nursing.

SMITH, Jennifer S; Lake Forest Academy; Chillicothe, IL; VPJrCls; HonRl; LitMag; LbryAde; Quill&Scroll; SchAde; StuCncl; TchrAde; RptrSchPpr; EdSchPpr; LetterBsktbl; LetterSwmmng; College; Journalism.

SMITH, Jerry L; Southeastern HS; West Point, IL; CmntyWkr; HonRl; NHS; PolWkr; SctActv; Yrbk; SchPpr; FrCl; Bsktbl; Trade School; Commercial Art.

SMITH, Joann; Parker HS; Chicago, IL; SecTrsJrCls; SecSrCls; HonRl; SchMus; SchPl; Central College; Major Study.

SMITH, Joann; Clare HS; Clare, MI; 27/148 Band; Chr; Chrs; ChrhWkr; HonRl; PepBnd; TchrAde; Grand Rapids Baptist Coll.

SMITH, Joann K; Lovington Jr Sr HS; Lovington, IL; 1/39 HonRl; NHS; PresStuCncl; Pres4-H; GAA; AmLegAwd; BauchLmbAwd; DanFAwd; 4-HAwd; PresAwd; St Louis U; Physical Therapy.

SMITH, Jodi L; Turtle Lake Mercer HS; Coleharbor, ND; SecFrshCls; TrsSophCls; VPJrCls; Yrbk; SptEdSchPpr; 4-H; Bsktbl; Trk; 4-HAwd; PresAwd; College.

SMITH, Joe D; Milltown HS; Milltown, IN; HonRl; LetterBsktbl; LetterTrk; College; Vocation.

SMITH, Joel D; Toluca HS; Toluca, IL; TrsSophCls; HonRl; FFA; PpCl; SciCl; LetterBsktbl; College.

SMITH, John; New Trier East Hs; Wilmette, IL; 101/847 ALBoysSt; Chrs; HonRl; NatlFornLg; SptEdYrbk; LetterFtbl; LetterWrstlng; AmLegAwd; Notre Dame U; Business.

SMITH, John; Mcciver Sr HS; Ferguson, MO; Aud/Vis; JA; Quill&Scroll; StuCncl; StuGov; EdYrBk; SchPpr; MthCl; SciCl; IMSpt; Univ Of Mo St Louis; Engineering.

SMITH, John E; Cent Catholic HS; Bloomington, IL; 10/90 ALBoysSt; HonRl; NHS; StuCncl; PpCl; LetterBsktbl; LetterFtbl; LetterGlf; GovHonPrgAwd; RotaryAwd; University Of Illinois; Lawyer.

SMITH, John P; Comm HS; Pinckneyville, IL; Chrs; HonRl; NHS; 4-H; FFA; PpCl; SciCl; DanFAwd;.

SMITH, John P; East Jordan HS; East Jordan, MI; ChrhWkr; HonRl; U Of Mi; Organic Chemistry.

SMITH, John R; Pardeeville East HS; Pardeeville, WI; YthLg; AmLegAwd; Col; Vocation.

SMITH, John S; Proviso East HS; Maywood, IL; 1/990 Band; HonRl; NHS; NatlMeritSF; Ftbl; CaptWrstlng; BauchLmbAwd; Stanford Univ; Medicine.

SMITH, John W; North HS; Fargo, ND; Concordia College.

SMITH, Joni K; Assumption HS; Wisc Rapids, WI; 5/123 HonRl; NatlMeritCmnd; StuCncl; TchrAde; MthCl; PpCl; Bsktbl; VPChrldr; Uw Madison; Law.

SMITH, Joni K; Assumption HS; Wisconsin Rapids, WI; 4/123 HonRl; NHS; NatlMeritCmnd; StuCncl; TchrAde; MthCl; PpCl; LetterBsktbl; LetterChrldr; DARAwd; Northwestern U; Law.

SMITH, Joyce A; Sommerfield HS; Petersburg, MI; TchrAde; College; Veterinary.

SMITH, Joy M; Stewartville HS; Rochester, MN; ALAGirlsSt; HonRl; LbryAde; MrchBnd; SchPl; YthLg; RptrYrbk; RptrSchPpr; 4-H; LatCl; Rochester Voc Tech; Dental Assistant.

SMITH, Judith A; Southwest Sr HS; Minneapolis, MN; 1/375 AFS; Band; HonRl; MrchBnd; NHS; PepBnd; VPGerCl; Bsktbl; CaptTennis; RotaryAwd; Winona State Univ; Computer Analysis.

SMITH, Judy K; Charleston HS; Charleston, MO; 15/163 Band; Chr; DrlTm; HonRl; Mdrgl; MrchBnd; NHS; SchMus; SctActv; Semo University; Secretarial.

SMITH, Judy K; Robichaud HS; Inkster, MI; 10/232 NHS; Michigan State; Vet.

SMITH, Julia A; Meredosia Chamersburg HS; Meredosia, IL; Band; Chrs; ChrhWkr; CmntyWkr; HonRl; NHS; Pres4-H; FHA; GAA; 4-HAwd; Western Ill Univ; Teaching.

SMITH, Julie Ann J; Mexico HS; Mexico, MO; 17/248 ChrhWkr; CtyCnl; HonRl; LbryAde; TchrAde; SchPpr; Univ Of Missouri; Elementary Education.

SMITH, Julie D; Pittsboro HS; Pittsboro, IN; TrsJrCls; ALAGirlsSt; ChrhWkr; HonRl; NHS; YthFlsp; Bsbl; Bsktbl; Chrldr; GAA; Indiana Univ; Dental Hygienist.

SMITH, Julie M; Tiskilwa HS; Tiskilwa, IL; PresJrCls; Band; DrlTm; HonRl; NHS; SchMus; StuCncl; 4-H; FHA; IMSpt; College; Professnl.

SMITH, Karen A; Southland HS; Adams, MN; 27/122 ChrhWkr; HonRl; NHS; SchPl; TreasSdlty; StuCncl; Yrbk; PpCl; GAA; PresAwd; Trade School; Vocation.

SMITH, Karen D; St Joseph HS; Shawnee, KS; TrsSophCls; TrsJrCls; HonRl; StuCncl; RptrYrbk; RptrSchPpr; PpCl; Swmmng; Chrldr; College; Journalism.

SMITH, Katherine E; Schell City R 1 HS; Harwood, MO; 3/14 Chrs; HonRl; OffAde; SchPl; TchrAde; Yrbk; RptrSchPpr; VPFHA; PpCl; BttyCrckrAwd; DARAwd; Central Missouri State Univ; Psychology.

SMITH, Kathleen D; Bunker Hill HS; Bunker Hill, IL; 4/90 HonRl; NHS; PresStuCncl; Yrbk; CaptChrldr; GAA; Southern Il Univ; Computer Sciences.

SMITH, Kathleen J; Streator Twp HS; Streator, IL; PresBand; CncrtBnd; HonRl; MrchBnd; PepBnd; PpCl; Illinois Valley Comm College; Clerical.

SMITH, Kathryn A; William G Mather HS; Munising, MI; 7/120 Chr; HonRl; OffAde; SchPl; SchPpr; FHA; PpCl; LetterBsktbl; LetterSwmmng; 4-HAwd; College; Professional.

SMITH, Kathy A; Sacred Heart Of Mary HS; Prospect Hts, IL; 231/786 HstFrshCls; HstSophCls; HstJrCls; HstSrCls; DrlTm; HonRl; HospAde; NHS; StuGov; RptrYrbk; Tennis; GAA; IMSpt; University Of Dayton; Medical Technology.

SMITH, Kathy J; Memorial HS; Joplin, MO; SecAFS; ChrhWkr; HonRl; NatlFornLg; NatlThespSoc; SchMus; SchPl; TreasStuCncl; SchPpr; MthCl; College; Law.

SMITH, Kathy R; Bluffton HS; Bluffton, IN; Chr; HonRl; HospAde; JA; PresSctActv; YthFlsp; Pres4-H; SpnCl; GAA; 4-HAwd; Ball State Univ; Social Work.

SMITH, Katrina J; Chesterton HS; Chesterton, IN; Chr; HonRl; NHS; NatlMeritSF; NatlSciFnd; OffAde; Orch; SchMus; LetterTrk; GAA; U Of Va; Pre Med.

SMITH, Keith T; Muncie Northside HS; Muncie, IN; 27/290 ALBoysSt; HonRl; JrNHS; NHS; StuCncl; StuGov; LatCl; Bsbl; Ftbl; IMSpt; Air Force Academy; Prof Pilot.

SMITH, Kelley C; Winner Sr HS; Winner, SD; PresSophCls; CmntyWkr; HonRl; SctActv; StuCncl; Bsktbl; Ftbl; South Dakota State University.

SMITH, Kelly R; Vienna Twp HS; Vienna, IL; 9/102 Band; CncrtBnd; HonRl; MrchBnd; NatlThespSoc; PepBnd; SchAde; SchPl; TchrAde; FHA; FTA; Bsbl; Bsktbl; Murray St Univ; Physical Educ.

SMITH, Kelly R; Vienna Township HS; Vienna, IL; 10/105 Band; ChrhWkr; HonRl; MrchBnd; NatlThespSoc; PepBnd; SchPl; TchrAde; FHA; FTA; VPSpnCl; PresPpCl; Bsbl; Murray State Univ; Physical Education.

SMITH, Kenneth F; Augusta HS; Augusta, WI; HonRl; VPSophCls; FFA; PpCl; Ftbl; Wrstlng; Military.

SMITH, Kenneth L; Troy HS; Troy, MI; JA; NatlMeritCmnd; LetterGlf; JAAwd; U Of Colorado; Social Sciences.

SMITH, Kerry M; Madison Cons HS; Madison, IN; ChrhWkr; HonRl; LbryAde; PolWkr; SpnCl; PpCl; LetterSwmmng; LetterTrk; Ball State Univ; Prelaw Major.

SMITH, Kevin L; Jackson HS; Jackson, MI; University; Professional.

SMITH, Kevin W; West Plains HS; West Plains, MO; ChrhWkr; HonRl; SctActv; LetterFtbl; LetterTrk; LetterWrstlng; GodCntryAwd; Sw Missouri St; Forestry.

SMITH, Kimberly A; Ernest W Seaholm HS; Birmingham, MI; Band; Chrl; Chrs; ChrhWkr; HonRl; JrNHS; ModUN; SchMus; SchPl; StuCncl; U Of Mi; Fashion Merchandizing.

SMITH, Kimberly A; Mancelona HS; Mancelona, MI; Band; HonRl; NHS; SchPl; StuCncl; CitAwd; College; Accounting.

SMITH, Kimberly R; South Decatur HS; Greensburg, IN; 21/87 TrsJrCls; DrlTm; HonRl; SchMus; PresStuCncl; TchrAde; Twrl; SptEdSchPpr; TreasFrCl; LetterTrk; Medical Ass.

SMITH, Kim M; Kapaun Mt Carmel HS; Wichita, KS; 18/130 CmntyWkr; HonRl; HospAde; RedCrAde; StuGov; FNA; SpnCl; Trk; JAAwd; VoiceDemAwd; Wichita St Univ & St Joseph Nur Sch; Rn.

SMITH, Kim W; Monroe HS; Monroe, WI; HonRl; LetterGlf; LetterWrstlng; College.

SMITH, Kip A; Oak Park River Forest HS; Oak Park, IL; 224/1012 HonRl; Illinois State University.

SMITH, Kirby; Port Washington HS; Port Washington, WI; 7/235 HonRl; NatlMeritCmnd; SctActv; TchrAde; MthCl; Bsktbl; IMSpt; KiwanAwd; College; Sciences.

SMITH, Krisanne; English HS; English, IN; 2/36 ALAGirlsSt; Band; ChrhWkr; HonRl; NHS; 4-H; Chrldr; DARAwd; 4-HAwd; College; Professional.

SMITH, Laura J; Crown Point HS; Cedar Lake, IN; HonRl; NHS; CaptChrldr; GAA; IMSpt; USJCAwd; KiwanAwd; MasAwd; RotaryAwd; In State U; Spanish.

SMITH, Laura L; Stephenson HS; Wallace, MI; ChrhWkr; HonRl; NHS; Yrbk;.

SMITH, Laurel E; Medford Senior HS; Medford, WI; Chr; SchPl; SchPpr; 4-H; FHA; SpnCl; PpCl; Business School; Secretary.

SMITH, Laurie A; Pardeeville HS; Pardeeville, WI; VPFrshCls; SecSophCls; VPJrCls; Band; Chr; Chrs; DrmMjrt; HonRl; LbryAde; MrchBnd; NHS; Chrldr; GAA; Madison Area Tech Schl; Dental Hygiene.

SMITH, Lawrence W; Chaminade HS; Bridgeton, MO; 15/107 HonRl; Coe Clg; Accountant.

SMITH, Lea Ann; Strafford Public HS; Strafford, MO; 8/66 HonRl; FHA; FTA; SpnCl; Sw Mo St Univ; Account.

SMITH, Leslie D; Wheaton North HS; Wheaton, IL; Chr; Chrs; HonRl; StuCncl; StuGov; FrCl; IMSpt; Coll; Bus Admin.

SMITH, Linda; Central Wis Chr HS; Waupun, WI; Chr; Chrs; SchPl; Yrbk; GerCl; PpCl; Coll; Lpn.

SMITH, Linda; Charlevoix HS; Charlevoix, MI; ALAGirlsSt; ChrhWkr; HonRl; NatlFornLg; SchMus; SchPl; YthFlsp; Trk; IMSpt; 4-HAwd; Univ Of Mich; Nat Res.

SMITH, Linda G; Columbus North HS; Edinburg, IN; 11/500 ChrhWkr; HonRl; ModUN; TchrAde; YthFlsp; Kentucky Christian College; Religion.

SMITH, Linda L; Mid Buchanan HS; St Joseph, MO; 4/60 Chr; ChrhWkr; DrlTm; HonRl; NHS; SchPl; FHA; PpCl; Chrldr; PPFtbl; Mo Western College; Social Worker.

SMITH, Linda L; Portage Central HS; Portage, MI; 50/331 Band; HonRl; MrchBnd; PepBnd; Kellogg Comm College; Physical Therapy.

SMITH, Lisa K; Whitko HS; South Whitley, IN; ChrhWkr; HonRl; NHS; YthFlsp; RptrYrbk; FHA; Col; Mathematics.

SMITH, Lisa K; Whitko HS; S Whitley, IN; 1/156 ChrhWkr; HonRl; NatlFornLg; NHS; RptrYrbk; EdYrBk; TreasFHA; FTA; SciCl; College.

SMITH, Lisa K; Whitko HS; South Whitely, IN; ChrhWkr; HonRl; NatlFornLg; NHS; RptrYrbk; EdYrBk; TreasFHA; FTA; PpCl; SciCl; Coll; Science.

SMITH, Lise A; Warren Central HS; Indianapolis, IN; 268/650 Chr; Chrl; Chrs; Mdrgl; SchMus; StuCncl; PpCl; Bsktbl; Trk; CaptChrldr; IMSpt; PPFtbl; Purdue Univ; Physical Educ.

SMITH, Liz A; Ladywood St Agnes HS; Carmel, IN; SecJrCls; HonRl; SchMus; StuCncl; FTA; PpCl; LetterTennis; IMSpt; Univ; Ed.

SMITH, Lizette J; Beaumont HS; St Louis, MO; 19/594 HonRl; NHS; University; Psychology.

SMITH, Lorraine L; Carlinville HS; Carlinville, IL; 3/161 HonRl; JrNHS; VPNHS; YthFlsp; RptrYrbk; TreasFNA; FrCl; Tennis; GAA; 4-HAwd; College; Nursing.

SMITH, Mabla J; Trenton Sr HS; Trenton, MO; CncrtBnd; HonRl; HospAde; LbryAde; MrchBnd; NHS; PepBnd; Univ; Professional.

SMITH, Marcia J; Fairmont Public HS; Fairmont, NE; 2/26 PresJrCls; Band; Chrl; ChrhWkr; HonRl; MrchBnd; SchPl; StuCncl; RptrYrbk; PpCl; Bus School; Secreatrial Work.

SMITH, Marcia K; Butterfield Odin HS; Butterfield, MN; SecFrshCls; PresSrCls; Band; CmntyWkr; HonRl; SchPl; RptrYrbk; RptrSchPpr; FHA; Chrldr; Coll; Sp Ed Or Psy.

SMITH, Mareta J; Frontenac HS; Pittsburg, KS; CncrtBnd; HonRl; HospAde; PepBnd; TreasStuCncl; RptrYrbk; RptrSchPpr; VPFHA; College; Business.

SMITH, Margaret A; Borden HS; Borden, IN; 2/64 VPSophCls; HstSrCls; Band; CncrtBnd; HonRl; JrNHS; MrchBnd; SecNHS; PepBnd; SchAde; SecStuCncl; Yrbk; SchPpr; PpCl; Trk; In St Univ; Business Sec.

SMITH, Margaret R; South Iron R 1 HS; Des Arc, MO; CmntyWkr; DrlTm; HonRl; OffAde; ROTC; RptrSchPpr; Bellville Area Col; Lpn.

SMITH, Marianne; Pittsfield HS; Pittsfield, IL; 7/135 HonRl; LbryAde; NHS; SctActv; RptrYrbk; SchPpr; 4-H; VPFHA; SpnCl; College; Spanish.

SMITH, Marianne I; J W Sexton HS; Lansing, MI; 1/450 HonRl; JA; JrNHS; NHS; NatlMeritFnl; NatlMeritSF; Orch; SchMus; StuCncl; RptrYrbk; Yrbk; LetterSwmmng; DARAwd; PresAwd; College; Musical Therapist.

SMITH, Marianne I; Lone Tree Comm HS; Lone Tree, IA; 11/33 Band; Chr; Chrs; ChrhWkr; CncrtBnd; HonRl; Mdrgl; MrchBnd; NatlFornLg; PepBnd; SchPl; LetterBsbl; LetterBsktbl; LetterTrk; Univ Of Iowa; Speech.

SMITH, Mark; Ovid Elsie HS; Ovid, MI; 25/165 CtyCnl; HonRl; SchPl; YthFlsp; EdSchPpr; Trk; Mi St Univ; Electrical Eng.

SMITH, Martha A; Terre Haute North Vigo HS; Terre Haute, IN; 27/656 ChrhWkr; HonRl; GerCl; LatCl; SciCl; Univ; Pro.

SMITH, Martha F; Monett HS; Monett, MO; 15/125 Band; ChrhWkr; CncrtBnd; HonRl; LitMag; MrchBnd; NatlFornLg; PepBnd; SchMus; FrCl; College; Writing Or Music.

SMITH, Marvin; Catholic Boys HS; Quincy, IL; 2/72 VPJrCls; HonRl; StuCncl; StuGov; KeyCl; EngCl; Univ; History.

SMITH, Marvin; Mt Vernon Twp Hs; Ina, IL; 3/420 ChrhWkr; HonRl; JrNHS; NHS; U Of Illinois; Law.

SMITH, Mary; Ashwaubenon HS; Green Bay, WI; 37;238 TrsSophCls; HonRl; NHS; FBLA; GerCl; PpCl; CaptTrk; GAA; Employed At St Howard.

SMITH, Mary; Ionia HS; Ionia, MI; 15/226 HonRl; NHS; StuGov; 4-H; IMSpt; BttyCrckrAwd; 4-HAwd; Ferris St College; Optometry.

SMITH, Mary A; Corydon Central HS; Corydon, IN; 1/150 CncrtBnd; MrchBnd; NHS; NatlMeritSF; SchMus; RptrYrbk; EdYrBk; EdSchPpr; Sec4-H; SpnCl; MthCl; 4-HAwd; Purdue Univ; Engineering.

SMITH, Mary A; Carrollton Comm Unit HS; Carrollton, IL; ALAGirlsSt; Band; Chr; Chrs; ChrhWkr; CncrtBnd; HonRl; MrchBnd; NHS; PepBnd; Patricia Stevens; Music.

SMITH, Mary B; Fonda Comm HS; Fonda, IA; 3/30 Band; Chrs; CncrtBnd; DrmMjrt; HonRl; JrNHS; VPJrCls; Glf; IMSpt; PPFtbl; Business School; Bookkeeper.

SMITH, Mary C; Maine Twnp HS; Park Ridge, IL; HonRl; JrNHS; NatlFornLg; TreasNHS; NatlMeritCmnd; PolWkr; SchPl; StuCncl; College; Law.

SMITH, Mary E; Brownstown HS; Brownstown, IL; 3/38 ChrhWkr; HonRl; SchPl; TchrAde; 4-H; GAA; 4-HAwd; Marriage; Off Mach.

SMITH, Mary Ellen; Wahlert HS; Dubuque, IA; 60/434 Band; ChrhWkr; CncrtBnd; DrmBgl; MrchBnd; TchrAde; IMSpt; DARAwd; Col; Computer Sci.

SMITH, Mary J; Onaga HS; Onaga, KS; 1/43 PresJrCls; PresSrCls; ChrhWkr; CmntyWkr; VPStuCncl; Yrbk; Pres4-H; PresPpCl; DARAwd; 4-HAwd; Kansas St Univ; Journalism.

SMITH, Mary Jo; Lakeville HS; Burnsville, MN; 10/190 PresAFS; Band; Chr; HonRl; PresNatlFornLg; SecNatlThespSoc; SchMus; StuCncl; 4-H; VoiceDemAwd; Uw River Falls; Prof.

SMITH, Mary L; Lourdes HS; Rochester, MN; ALAGirlsSt; Band; Chrl; ChrhWkr; CmntyWkr; CncrtBnd; HonRl; HospAde; JA; JrNHS; Bsktbl; Trk; University; Professional.

SMITH, Mary Lou; Brookfield HS; Brookfield, MO; 6/105 ChrhWkr; HonRl; NHS; Quill&Scroll; TreasStuCncl; RptrSchPpr; FHA; Trk; IMSpt; EldAwd; Baker Univ; Interior Design.

SMITH, Mary S; Ladywood St Agnes HS; Indianapolis, IN; 4/128 ChrhWkr; JA; NatlMeritSF; SctActv; EdYrBk; FrCl; JAAwd; Purdue Univ; Engineering.

SMITH, Matthew J; Murdock HS; Murdock, NE; PresSophCls; HonRl; StuCncl; StuGov; YthFlsp; RptrYrbk; LetterBsbl; LetterBsktbl; LetterGlf; Creighton; Lawyer.

SMITH, Matt N; Escanaba Area HS; Escanaba, MI; 27/382 HonRl; JrNHS; NHS; NatlMeritCmnd; StuGov; Bsktbl; Ftbl; Glf; Trk; U Of Mi; Accounting.

SMITH, Maureen; Pontiac Twp HS; Pontiac, IL; 10/202 CmntyWkr; HonRl; NHS; EdYrBk; SecFrCl; MthCl; PpCl; SciCl; GAA; Ill Wesleyan Univ; Science.

SMITH, Maxine; Cass City HS; Cass City, MI; 13/165 ChrhWkr; CmntyWkr; HonRl; NHS; StuCncl; TchrAde; YthFlsp; Swmmng; CchngActv; IMSpt; College; Teaching.

SMITH, Maxine I; New Glarus HS; New Glarus, WI; Chrs; LbryAde; NHS; SctActv; Bsktbl; GAA;.

SMITH, Melinda J; Franklin HS; Franklin, IL; 3/40 SecFrshCls; Band; Chrs; HonRl; NHS; TchrAde; Yrbk; PresFFA; FHA; PpCl; Trk; Chrldr; GAA; University Of Illinois; Clothing Retail.

SMITH, Melodae D; Park Hill HS; Parkville, MO; HonRl; NHS; OffAde; StuCncl; RptrSchPpr; EdSchPpr; VPFHA; PpCl; Chrldr; PresAwd; College; Law.

SMITH, Merrill H; E Grand Rapids HS; Grand Rapids, MI; HonRl; ModUN; PolWkr; StuCncl; FrCl; Tennis; Kalamazoo Coll; Lawyer.

SMITH, Michael; Our Lady Of The Lakes Hs; Clarkston, MI; 15/69 VPFrshCls; HonRl; NHS; LetterBsbl; LetterBsktbl; LetterFtbl; College;professional.

SMITH, Michael; Divernon HS; Divernon, IL; 23/30 Band; Chr; CncrtBnd; MrchBnd; PepBnd; YthFlsp; SciCl; Trade Sch; Elect Engrg.

SMITH, Michael; St Charles HS; Saginaw, MI; PresSophCls; PresJrCls; Chrs; ChrhWkr; CncrtBnd; HonRl; NHS; SchPl; 4-H; Bsktbl; Trk; IMSpt; Coll; Professional.

SMITH, Michael; Lincoln HS; Wisconsin Rapids, WI; HonRl; SctActv; StuCncl; FrCl; Ftbl; College; Electronics.

SMITH, Michael; Batesville HS; Batesville, IN; ChrhWkr; HonRl; YthFlsp; Coll; Bus.

SMITH, Michael J; Papillion HS; Omaha, NE; ALBoysSt; LetterBsbl; LetterFtbl; Bsktbl; IMSpt; Coll; Law.

SMITH, Mike L; Hoxie HS; Hoxie, KS; 4/77 Band; Chr; Chrs; CncrtBnd; HonRl; Mdrgl; MrchBnd; PepBnd; SchPl; YthFlsp; Nw Christian College; Art.

SMITH, Molly E; Galesburg Sr HS; Galesburg, IL; 32/639 HonRl; NHS; StuCncl; LetterBsktbl; LetterTrk; JCAwd; Univ Of Illinois; Professional.

SMITH, Mona L; Carman HS; Flint, MI; 57/420 Chr; HonRl; HospAde; NatlThespSoc; SchMus; SchPl; Trk; U Of Mi; Criminal Justice Or Theatre Arts.

SMITH, Murray J; Thornton HS; Harvey, IL; Chr; HonRl; NatlFornLg; NatlThespSoc; SchMus; SchPl; StuGov; Ill Wesylan Col; Drama.

SMITH, Nancy E; Gregory Public HS; Dallas, SD; 1/46 TrsFrshCls; Band; Chrs; HonRl; StuCncl; YthFlsp; FHA; PpCl; Trk; IMSpt; Coll; Md Tech.

SMITH, Nancy F; East Pike HS; Pearl, IL; 1/29 CmntyWkr; NHS; PolWkr; SchPl; StuCncl; StuGov; TchrAde; Yrbk; FHA; BttyCrckrAwd; Univ; Home Ec Extension.

SMITH, Nancy K; Lexington HS; Lexington, MO; 14/94 Band; Chr; Chrl; Chrs; ChrhWkr; CncrtBnd; HonRl; MrchBnd; NHS; Orch; PepBnd; SchMus; SctActv; PresFrCl; William Jewell College; Medicine.

SMITH, Naomi R; Berkeley Sr HS; St Louis, MO; 25/265 PresJrCls; VPJrCls; Chr; Chrs; ChrhWkr; CmntyWkr; HonRl; NHS; SchPl; RptrSchPpr; Univ; Law.

SMITH, Neal E; Salem Comm HS; Salem, IL; ChrhWkr; HonRl; IntrClCncl; JrNHS; SctActv; FrCl; PpCl; LetterBsktbl; LetterFtbl; Westpoint; Professional.

SMITH, Nedra J; Avondale HS; Rochester, MI; 3/241 AFS; Chr; ChrhWkr; JrNHS; Mdrgl; NHS; NatlThespSoc; Yrbk; FrCl; CitAwd; College; Pediatrics.

SMITH, Nora A; Elm Creek HS; Elm Creek, NE; Band; HonRl; NHS; SchPl; VPStuCncl; TchrAde; RptrSchPpr; PpCl; CitAwd; Kearney State Coll; Professional.

SMITH, Norman B; Centerville HS; Cincinnati, IA; 19/151 HonRl; ModUN; FFA; LetterBsktbl; College; Vocational.

SMITH, Norman P; Lane Tech HS; Chicago, IL; 303/1208 CmntyWkr; PolWkr; TreasSctActv; LetterFtbl; Univ Of Ill; Chemist.

SMITH, Pamala V; Climax Springs HS; Roach, MO; 1011 SecTrsJrCls; ChrhWkr; CmntyWkr; HonRl; MrchBnd; SchPl; StuCncl; EdYrBk; EdSchPpr; FHA; College; Prof.

SMITH, Pamela A; Bishop Lillis HS; Kansas City, MO; 23/84 SecSophCls; SecJrCls; ChrhWkr; JA; JCC; SchAde; SchPl; StuCncl; StuGov; TchrAde; College; Professional.

SMITH, Pamela S; Ottawa HS; Ottawa, IL; 46/425 SecFrshCls; Chr; HonRl; HospAde; NHS; StuCncl; YthFlsp; Trk; Univ Of Il; Dentistry.

SMITH, Pamela S; Lincoln HS; Thief River Fls, MN; 1/234 Band; Chrs; CncrtBnd; CaptDrlTm; DrmMjrt; HonRl; MrchBnd; ModUN; NHS; PepBnd; Twrl; PpCl; CaptBsktbl; Trk; Univ Of North Dakota; Physical Therapy.

SMITH, Pamela S; Winfield HS; Winfield, KS; 52/176 Chr; Chrs; ChrhWkr; HonRl; SchMus; TchrAde; FHA; PpCl; LetterBsktbl;.

SMITH, Pamela S; Adrian Riii HS; Adrian, MO; 6/55 SecSophCls; ALAGirlsSt; HonRl; NHS; Quill&Scroll; SchMus; SchPl; RptrSchPpr; PresFHA; LetterBsktbl; Smsu.

SMITH, Patricia; Grosse Pte North HS; Grosse Pointe Wood, MI; 96/625 ChrhWkr; HonRl; NHS; YthFlsp; Michigan St Univ; Retail Of Clothing Textil.

SMITH, Patricia A; Colo Community HS; Colo, IA; 6/30 HonRl; NHS; OffAde; SchMus; SchPl; TchrAde; Yrbk; 4-H; FHA; FTA; Trk; PPFtbl; Des Moines College; Computer Operater.

SMITH, Patsy J; Sharon HS; Sharon, KS; VPFrshCls; VPSophCls; VPJrCls; Band; Chrs; HonRl; SchPl; Yrbk; PpCl; LetterBsktbl; LetterTrk; Chrldr; PPFtbl; Trade School; Dental Assistant.

SMITH, Patsy R; Elgin HS; Hanover Park, IL; 63/800 Chrs; SchPl; StuGov; GerCl; LetterBsktbl; LetterTrk; GAA; IMSpt; Clge; Nurse.

SMITH, Paul; Richland HS; Laquey, MO; PresFrshCls; PresJrCls; ChrhWkr; Southwest Baptist; Baptist Minister.

SMITH, Paul A; Chippewa Falls Sr HS; Chippewa Falls, WI; SctActv; Yrbk; Bsbl; Univ Of Alaska; Professional.

SMITH, Paula J; Campbell HS; Campbell, MO; 2/63 Chrs; HonRl; LbryAde; SctActv; TreasStuCncl; SecPpCl; IMSpt; College; Nursing.

SMITH, Paul G; Creighton Prep; Council Bluffs, IA; LetterTrk; RotaryAwd; Coll;law Or Sci.

SMITH, Peggy J; Madrid Community HS; Madrid, IA; Chrs; HonRl; 4-H; FrCl; PpCl; Bsktbl; Ia Lutheran Hosp School Of Nursing; Nursing.

SMITH, Peggy L; Dixon HS; Dixon, IL; SecTrsJrCls; SecTrsSrCls; HonRl; NHS; StuCncl; PpCl; Bsbl; LetterBsktbl; GAA; AmLegAwd; DARAwd; EldAwd; Univ Of Illinois; Commercial Art.

SMITH, Phillip L; Carterville HS; Carterville, IL; 6/100 Aud/Vis; ChrhWkr; HonRl; IntrClCncl; SchPl; StuCncl; StuGov; RptrYrbk; RptrSchPpr; SptEdSchPpr; Bsktbl; Ftbl; LetterTrk; Wrstlng; Southern Illinois Univ; Pre Dentistry.

SMITH, Randall; Parkwood HS; Joplin, MO; Chr; Chrl; Chrs; ChrhWkr; HonRl; ModUN; NHS; StuGov; UNYO; YthLg; Mssc; Law.

SMITH, Randy; Edgewood Sr HS; Bloomington, IN; Aud/Vis; ChrhWkr; TchrAde; Trade School Ele; Vocational.

SMITH, Rebecca; Western HS; Russiaville, IN; 9/155 ChrhWkr; HonRl; NHS; EdYrBk; RptrSchPpr; FHA; Grand Rapids Baptist; Teacher.

SMITH, Rebecca L; Semco Comm HS; Tama, IA; 1/33 TrsSophCls; TrsJrCls; TrsSrCls; Band; Chrs; ChrhWkr; CncrtBnd; HonRl; PresNHS; NatlThespSoc; College; Science.

SMITH, Rebecca R; Excelsior Springs HS; Excelsior Spgs, MO; 13/220 SecSrCls; ALAGirlsSt; Band; Chr; ChrhWkr; CncrtBnd; HonRl; JrNHS; LbryAde; MrchBnd; NHS; OffAde; College; Nursing.

SMITH, Rebecca S; Three Rivers HS; Three Rivers, MI; 1/209 Band; ChrhWkr; CncrtBnd; HonRl; MrchBnd; NHS; PepBnd; SctActv; YthFlsp; Yrbk; LatCl; LetterBsktbl; Ferris State College; Pharmacy.

SMITH, Regina; Marshall HS; Marshall, MI; Band; ChrhWkr; CmntyWkr; HonRl; MrchBnd; 4-H; FrCl; 4-HAwd; Business.

SMITH, Regina D; Lexington Comm HS; Lexington, IL; 16/65 TrsFrshCls; AFS; SchPl; YthFlsp; RptrYrbk; Pres4-H; Bsktbl; Trk; GAA; IMSpt; BttyCrckrAwd; 4-HAwd; Southern Illinois Univ; Journalism.

SMITH, Renee K; Josephinum HS; Chicago, IL; 27/98 PresFrshCls; SecSophCls; TrsJrCls; Chr; Chrs; HonRl; NatlMeritCmnd; SchMus; SchPl; Chrldr; College; Professional.

SMITH, Rhonda E; Rushville HS; Rushville, NE; Band; Chr; Chrs; ChrhWkr; CncrtBnd; HonRl; LbryAde; MrchBnd; PepBnd; SctActv; TchrAde; FTA;.

SMITH, Richard; Pewamo Westphalia HS; Pewamo, MI; HonRl; TchrAde; Bsbl; Bsktbl; Trk; Mi St Univ;acct.

SMITH, Richelle J; Adrian R 3 HS; Adrian, MO; CmntyWkr; HonRl; LbryAde; NatlMeritCmnd; VPQuill&Scroll; SchMus; SchPl; TchrAde; RptrSchPpr; SchPpr; FHA; FTA; PpCl; University; Liberal Arts.

SMITH, Ricky L; Paris HS; Paris, IL; Band; ChrhWkr; CncrtBnd; HonRl; MrchBnd; College; Music.

SMITH, Robbin; Union City HS; Union City, MI; LbryAde; OffAde; SpnCl; PpCl; College; Florist.

SMITH, Robert; Plainfield Hs; Plainfield, IL; 91/298 Band; LetterTrk;.

SMITH, Robin; Potter Public HS; Potter, NE; 6/19 Band; Chrs; HonRl; MrchBnd; 4-H; PpCl; Chrldr; Business School; Secretarial.

SMITH, Robin M; Cahokia HS; Cahokia, IL; 59/532 Chr; ChrhWkr; HonRl; SchMus; SchPl; GerCl; Night School.

SMITH, Robyn V; Duchesne HS; St Charles, MO; 10/200 Chr; HonRl; NHS; SchMus; SctActv; Yrbk; SpnCl; PpCl; GAA; University; Speech.

SMITH, Rod; Monticello HS; Monticello, IL; CmntyWkr; SchPpr; PpCl; Bsktbl; Ftbl; CchngActv; IMSpt; University; Sports Broadcasting.

SMITH, Roger C; Cavalier HS; Cavalier, ND; Aud/Vis; HonRl; SchPl; SctActv; StuCncl; StuGov; RptrSchPpr; SptEdSchPpr; FrCl; SciCl; Ftbl; University; Professional.

SMITH, Roger L; Puxico R 8 HS; Puxico, MO; Band; CncrtBnd; MrchBnd; PepBnd; FFA; PpCl; College; Agriculture.

SMITH, Rona S; Henry Ford HS; Detroit, MI; 10/500 HonRl; NatlMeritSF; OffAde; SpnCl; Michigan St Univ; Mathematics.

SMITH, Rory D; Kenwood HS; Chicago, IL; 31/450 CmntyWkr; HonRl; NatlMeritCmnd; PolWkr; PresStuCncl; StuGov; YthLg; EdYrBk; KeyCl; FrCl; IMSpt; Stanford University; Law.

SMITH, Rose; St Marys HS; Fort Yates, ND; ALAGirlsSt; HonRl; StuCncl; SchPpr; College; Social Service.

SMITH, Roy; Hampton Public HS; Hampton, NE; 1/19 ChrhWkr; HonRl; NHS; StuGov; 4-H; IMSpt; Trade School; Vocation.

SMITH, Ruth A; Pinckney HS; Pinckney, MI; 7/172 CncrtBnd; HonRl; MrchBnd; NHS; PepBnd; TchrAde; FHA; SpnCl; Trk; Clg; Appl Instrumental Music.

SMITH, Ruth A; Cuba HS; Cuba, IL; 33/68 Chrs; ChrhWkr; HonRl; Spoon River College; Secretary.

SMITH, Ruthann P; Huron HS; Ann Arbor, MI; TrsSrCls; StuGov; TchrAde; RptrYrbk; FrCl; Miami Of Oh;art Architec.

SMITH, Ruth M; Weaubleau HS; Collins, MO; 2/40 Chrs; ChrhWkr; SchPl; RptrYrbk; EdSchPpr; FHA; College; Journalism.

SMITH, Sabina J; Fargo North HS; Fargo, ND; Chr; ChrhWkr; HonRl; NHS; NatlMeritSF; Orch; RptrSchPpr; PresFFA; LatCl; VPSpnCl; DARAwd; Univ; Veterinarian.

SMITH, Sally M; Southwest HS; St Louis, MO; ChrhWkr; HonRl; HospAde; ModUN; PolWkr; SchMus; SchPl; StuGov; YthLg; Swmmng; St Louis U; Pediatric Surgery.

SMITH, Samuel; Perry Community HS; Perry, IA; 10/145 ALBoysSt; IntrClCncl; JrNHS; NatlFornLg; NatlThespSoc; SchMus; YthFlsp; SpnCl; AmLegAwd; KiwanAwd; University; Professional.

SMITH, Samuel E; Murdock HS; Ashland, NE; 2/20 PresFrshCls; HonRl; NatlMeritCmnd; StuCncl; Bsktbl; Ftbl; Trk; University.

SMITH, Sandra J; Seneca HS; Seneca, IL; 4/58 HonRl; NHS; StuCncl; TchrAde; RptrYrbk; FHA; GerCl; Illi State Univ; History Teacher.

SMITH, Sandy L; Lourdes HS; Chicago, IL; 20/299 PresJrCls; HonRl; NHS; StuGov; RptrYrbk; Bsbl; CaptFtbl; IMSpt; College.

SMITH, Sarah; Twin Valley HS; East Jordon, MI; Band; ChrhWkr; CncrtBnd; HonRl; MrchBnd; PepBnd; SchPpr; College; Art.

SMITH, Sara S; Pennfield HS; Battle Creek, MI; HonRl; JA; SpnCl; College; Commercial Art.

SMITH, Scott A; Dillsboro HS; Dillsboro, IN; 7/36 Aud/Vis; ChrhWkr; HonRl; SchPl; LetterBsbl; LetterBsktbl; LetterGlf; LetterTrk; IMSpt; CitAwd; Purdue U.

SMITH, Scott B; Parkway West Sr HS; Manchester, MO; CmntyWkr; NatlMeritSF; Univ Of Mo.

SMITH, Scott D; West Monona HS; Onawa, IA; HonRl; NatlThespSoc; PolWkr; SchPl; RptrSchPpr; GerCl; PpCl; Univ Of Denver; Mass Communications.

SMITH, Scott P; Central Cass HS; Amenia, ND; SecSrCls; ALBoysSt; Band; Chr; CncrtBnd; HonRl; NHS; SchPl; Ftbl; University.

SMITH, Sharon; Argonia HS; Argonia, KS; Chr; Chrl; Chrs; ChrhWkr; HonRl; SchPl; RptrYrbk; Vo Tech School; Lpn.

SMITH, Sharon K; Community R 6 HS; Laddonia, MO; 3/70 TrsSophCls; Band; Chrs; ChrhWkr; Mdrgl; NHS; Yrbk; EdSchPpr; 4-H; FTA; Hannibal Lagrange Clg; Elem Educ.

SMITH, Shavonne F; Heelan HS; Sioux City, IA; SecSrCls; Chrs; HonRl; JA; SchMus; SchPl; EdSchPpr; PpCl; LetterGlf; IMSpt; College.

SMITH, Sherrie K; Lidgerwood Public HS; Lidgerwood, ND; 1/49 VPSrCls; Band; ChrhWkr; HonRl; NHS; Yrbk; RptrSchPpr; FHA; GerCl; PpCl; Nd St Univ; Elem Ed.

SMITH, Sheryl L; St Thomas Apostle HS; Chicago, IL; 16/47 CmntyWkr; HonRl; HospAde; SchMus; SchPl; StuCncl; TchrAde; RptrSchPpr; PpCl; Swmmng; College.

SMITH, Sonya D; Henry Ford HS; Detroit, MI; 33/505 HonRl; JrNHS; OffAde; SchAde; TchrAde; FDA; Michigan State Univ; Physical Therapy.

SMITH, Stacy; Barry Community Unit 1 HS; Barry, IL; 7/46 Band; DrlTm; HonRl; NHS; SchPl; StuCncl; TchrAde; EdYrBk; Chrldr; Univ; Elementary Education.

SMITH, Stanley R; Bradford HS; Bradford, IL; 10/44 PresJrCls; Aud/Vis; ChrhWkr; HonRl; SchPl; RptrSchPpr; CaptFtbl; Ill State Univ; Math.

SMITH, Stephanie D; Cass Technical HS; Detroit, MI; Aud/Vis; HonRl; OffAde; SchAde; SchMus; StuGov; TchrAde; FrCl; MthCl; Michigan State University; Elec Engineer.

SMITH, Stephanie L; Sacred Heart HS; Sedalia, MO; TrsFrshCls; ChrhWkr; HonRl; OffAde; SchAde; SctActv; 4-H; FrCl; PpCl; 4-HAwd; School; Fashion Designer.

SMITH, Stephen A; Lyons Township HS; Western Spgs, IL; 31/1226 ChrhWkr; CmntyWkr; HonRl; SctActv; TchrAde; Bsbl; Bsktbl; Georgetown U; Business Admin.

SMITH, Stephen J; Homewood Flossmoor HS; Homewood, IL; 112/917 HonRl; SctActv; Univ Of Wisconsin.

SMITH, Stephen K; Riverside Brookfield HS; Riverside, IL; Band; HonRl; JA; MrchBnd; SchPl; StuCncl; RptrYrbk; Tennis; Trk; JAAwd; Duke Univ; Patent Lawyer.

SMITH, Stephen R; Luther South HS; Chicago, IL; 6/215 HonRl; Glf; College; Chemical Eng.

SMITH, Steven; Southwest HS; St Louis, MO; 26/597 ChrhWkr; CmntyWkr; HonRl; GerCl; AmLegAwd; College; Law.

SMITH, Steven C; Norwalk Comm HS; Norwalk, IA; 18/76 ALBoysSt; ChrhWkr; HonRl; MrchBnd; NatlFornLg; PepBnd; SchPl; TchrAde; Glf; Iowa State University; Engineering.

SMITH, Steven C; Centralia HS; Centralia, IL; 48/333 ChrhWkr; HonRl; SchAde; Bsbl; Bsktbl; St Louis College; Pharmacist.

SMITH, Steven F; Southwestern HS; Medora, IL; 21/180 Band; Chrs; ChrhWkr; CncrtBnd; HonRl; MrchBnd; PepBnd; SchMus; SchPl; FFA; Bsbl; Bsktbl; Southern Il Univ; Agriculture.

SMITH, Steven K; Alton Sr HS; Alton, IL; ChrhWkr; HonRl; JA; College; Law.

SMITH, Steven L; Abraham Lincoln HS; Council Bluffs, IA; AFS; Chrs; HonRl; SchMus; SciCl; Ftbl; Swmmng; IMSpt; College; Md.

SMITH, Steven L; Dowagiac Union HS; Benton Harbor, MI; 20/200 HonRl; NatlFornLg; NHS; Bsbl; Davneport Business College; Computer Prog.

SMITH, Steven M; Culver Community HS; Rochester, IN; ALBoysSt; Chr; Chrs; ChrhWkr; HonRl; NHS; SchMus; SchPl; Tennis; LetterTrk; Olivet Nazarene College; Science And Math.

SMITH, Steven S; Gale Ettrick Tremplo HS; Galesville, WI; 41/112 ChrhWkr; HonRl; SctActv; YthFlsp; PpCl; LetterBsbl; LetterBsktbl; LetterFtbl; LetterGlf; CchngActv; Trade School; Professional.

SMITH, Sue R; Burnsville HS; Burnsville, MN; Band; CncrtBnd; NHS; NatlMeritSF; PepBnd; Coll; Organic Ag.

SMITH, Susan; Elizabeth Seton HS; Chicago, IL; 54/250 HonRl; RptrYrbk; RptrSchPpr; FrCl; MthCl; SciCl; CchngActv; GAA; Coll Of Saint Teresa; Elem Ed.

SMITH, Susan; Cedar Springs HS; Cedar Springs, MI; 7/127 Band; CncrtBnd; HonRl; JrNHS; MrchBnd; NHS; PepBnd; Michigan State Univ; Medical Doctor.

SMITH, Susan; Northrop HS; Fort Wayne, IN; 10/e80 Chr; HonRl; HospAde; SchPl; YthFlsp; RptrYrbk; EdSchPpr; FrCl; IMSpt; Ind Univ; Nursing Bs.

SMITH, Susan E; Savannah HS; Savannah, MO; VPFrshCls; ChrhWkr; HonRl; SpnCl; PpCl; Chrldr; College; Teacher.

SMITH, Susan F; Carlisle HS; Carlisle, IA; Band; CncrtBnd; HonRl; NHS; SchMus; YthFlsp; 4-H; MthCl; Bsbl; Bsktbl; Coll; Nurse.

SMITH, Susan L; Bethany HS; Bethany, IL; 3/30 ALAGirlsSt; Band; Chr; CncrtBnd; HonRl; NHS; PepBnd; EdSchPpr; FHA; Ill College; Biology.

SMITH, Susan M; Greenville HS; Greenville, IL; 43/186 ChrhWkr; VPJA; 4-H; PresSpnCl; LetterTennis; Trk; JAAwd; College; Medical Technologist.

SMITH, Susan R; Burnsville Sr HS; Burnsville, MN; 26/610 Band; NHS; NatlMeritFnl; U Of Wis; Agriculture & Art.

SMITH, Tamara A; Greenfield Central HS; Greenfield, IN; HonRl; NHS; TchrAde; GerCl; Trk; GAA; PPFtbl; Coll; Translator.

SMITH, Tamara K; Lesterville HS; Black, MO; TrsFrshCls; TrsJrCls; HonRl; JrNHS; LbryAde; NHS; PpCl; Trade Sch; Secretarial.

SMITH, Tami D; Blue Valley HS; Leawood, KS; TchrAde; Coll; Pro.

SMITH, Teresa R; Union County HS; Brownsville, IN; HonRl; TchrAde; 4-H; Business School; Secretary.

SMITH, Terri L; Du Quoin HS; Du Quoin, IL; 13/143 ChrhWkr; CmntyWkr; HonRl; TchrAde; YthFlsp; FTA; SpnCl; PpCl; South Ill Univ.

SMITH, Terri M; Nauvoo Colusa HS; Nauvoo, IL; SecFrshCls; TrsSophCls; PresJrCls; HonRl; MrchBnd;.

SMITH, Terry; Marion HS; Marion, KS; PresJrCls; Chrs; CmntyWkr; NatlFornLg; StuCncl; RptrYrbk; GerCl; Bsktbl; Ftbl; Trk; Wichita State; Commercial Artist.

SMITH, Theresa A; St Clement HS; Center Line, MI; TrsJrCls; HonRl; FHA; PpCl; Bsbl; Bsktbl; Chrldr; IMSpt; College; Professional.

SMITH, Theresa A; Randolph HS; Stanton, MN; 2/42 Chr; ChrhWkr; HonRl; SecNHS; SchPl; PresSciCl; College; Biology.

SMITH, Theresa D; Jamaica HS; Sidell, IL; SecJrCls; Band; Chrs; ChrhWkr; CmntyWkr; HonRl; PpCl; Chrldr; GAA; JAAwd; Business School; Secretary.

SMITH, Thomas; Humboldt HS; St Paul, MN; HonRl; SchAde; Ftbl;.

SMITH, Thomas A; South Decatur HS; Greensburg, IN; StuCncl; VPSpnCl; SecPpCl; Bsbl; Bsktbl; CaptFtbl; Trk; CaptWrstlng; College; Electronic Tech.

SMITH, Thomas J; Lourdes HS; Rochester, MN; 6/130 PresBand; ChrhWkr; HonRl; JA; JrNHS; MrchBnd; NHS; NatlMeritSF; SchPl; SctActv; CaptBsktbl; LetterFtbl; LetterTennis; College; Biological Science.

SMITH, Thomas L; Fremont HS; Fremont, IN; 3/74 VPFrshCls; TrsJrCls; ChrhWkr; HonRl; SchPl; FFA; FrCl; MthCl; College; Agricultural Science.

SMITH, Thomas L; Plainfield HS; Plainfield, IL; PolWkr; LetterTrk; Illinois State Univ.

SMITH, Thomas L; Hayden HS; Topeka, KS; 48/201 Band; Chr; CncrtBnd; HonRl; Mdrgl; MrchBnd; NHS; PepBnd; SchMus; Trk; College; Business.

SMITH, Timothy; Brodhead HS; Brodhead, WI; HonRl;.

SMITH, Timothy; St Marys HS; Burlington, WI; HonRl; StuCncl; Bsbl; Bsktbl; Ftbl; Glf; University.

SMITH, Timothy J; Wyoming Park HS; Wyoming, MI; Band; CncrtBnd; MrchBnd; Orch; PepBnd; SchAde; SchMus; TchrAde; IMSpt; University; Forestry.

SMITH, Timothy N; Newton HS; Newton, IA; 13/320 Chrs; HonRl; YthFlsp; VP4-H; FFA; LetterBsktbl; LetterFtbl; LetterTrk; 4-HAwd; Iowa State Univ; Agriculture.

SMITH, Tina; Our Lady Of Mercy HS; Dearborn Heights, MI; 4-H; Michigan State Univ; Veterinarian.

SMITH, Tina; Washington Catholic HS; Washington, IN; 10/40 Chrs; HonRl; SchPl; SctActv; PpCl; Bsbl; Tennis; Chrldr; Secretarial School; Secretary.

SMITH, Todd; Frontier HS; Brookston, IN; SecFrshCls; ChrhWkr; CmntyWkr; SchPl; 4-H; Bsktbl; 4-HAwd;.

SMITH, Tom M; Gale Ettrick Trempealeau HS; Ettrick, WI; 29/111 VPJrCls; ChrhWkr; HonRl; TchrAde; PpCl; LetterFtbl; CaptTrk; Trade Sch; Accounting.

SMITH, Toni L; New Providence Comm HS; New Providence, IA; 1/19 Chrs; DrmMjrt; HonRl; SchMus; SchPl; 4-H; CaptBsktbl; 4-HAwd; University; Vocation.

SMITH, Tracy C; West HS; Appleton, WI; AFS; Chr; Chrs; Mdrgl; NHS; Orch; SchMus; FrCl; PpCl; AFS; Lawrence U; Lawyer.

SMITH, Trudy A; Colo Comm HS; Nevada, IA; 14/26 HonRl; OffAde; StuCncl; TchrAde; RptrYrbk; Yrbk; TreasFFA; SecFHA; FTA; SpnCl; PpCl; Trade Schl; Fashion Merchandising.

SMITH, Valerie A; Mooresville HS; Mooresville, IN; 16/246 HonRl; JrNHS; NHS; 4-H; FHA; SpnCl; GAA;.

SMITH, Valerie L; Battle Creek Central HS; Battle Creek, MI; 71/514 TrsFrshCls; Chr; ChrhWkr; CtyCnl; NHS; NatlMeritCmnd; SchPl; StuGov; PpCl; CaptChrldr; U Of Mi; Medicine.

SMITH, Valerie R; North Central HS; Indianapolis, IN; 304/1168 HonRl; JA; LbryAde; ModUN; NatlMeritSF; SchPl; Bsbl; Bsktbl; GAA; Indiana Univ; Teacher.

SMITH, Vicki J; Morrison Comm HS; Morrison, IL; 4/130 HstSophCls; SecJrCls; TrsSrCls; Band; HonRl; NHS; StuCncl; RptrSchPpr; College; Obstetrician.

SMITH, Victoria L; Oak Park River Forest HS; Oak Park, IL; 86/1012 ChrhWkr; HonRl; PpCl; College Of St Teresa; Nursing.

SMITH, Walter G; Brookfield East HS; Brookfield, WI; MthCl; LetterGlf; LetterGlf; IMSpt; College; Business Administration.

SMITH, Wendy J; Brookwood HS; Norwalk, WI; Band; Chrs; ChrhWkr; LbryAde; OffAde; RedCrAde; SchMus; SchPl; StuGov; YthFlsp; SchPpr; FHA; College; Spanish.

SMITH, Wendy L; Adelphian Academy; Holly, MI; Band; Chr; ChrhWkr; CncrtBnd; DrlTm; SchPl; RptrYrbk; RptrSchPpr; FrCl; Swmmng; Andrews Univ; Psychiatry.

SMITH, Wendy L; Arapahoe HS; Arapahoe, NE; 1/33 TrsJrCls; Band; Chr; HonRl; SchPl; StuCncl; TreasFHA; PpCl; GovHonPrgAwd; MasAwd; Univ Of Ne; Medical Technology.

SMITH, Wesley T; Univ Of Detroit HS; Detroit, MI; 42/193 HonRl; NatlMeritCmnd; TchrAde; SciCl; College; Anesthesiologist.

SMITH, William; St Paul HS; St Paul, KS; /27 PresSophCls; HonRl; StuCncl; Coll; Accounting.

SMITH, William D; St Philip Catholic Cen HS; Battle Creek, MI; HonRl; NHS; SctActv; FrCl; LatCl; Bsktbl; Univ Of Miami; Marine Biology.

SMITH, William R; Tomahawk HS; Tomahawk, WI; 2/160 ALBoysSt; CncrtBnd; HonRl; NHS; StuCncl; RptrYrbk; EdSchPpr; MthCl; AmLegAwd; Col; Engineering.

SMITH, Will R; Puxico R 8 HS; Puxico, MO; 12/47 PresSophCls; Chrs; HonRl; NHS; StuCncl; RptrYrbk; Yrbk; SchPpr; FFA; Bsktbl; Semo Univ; Agri Production.

SMITH, Yvonne C; Ithaca HS; Ithaca, MI; 1/148 Chr; ChrhWkr; CncrtBnd; ChmnDrlTm; HonRl; MrchBnd; NHS; TchrAde; SecFTA; SpnCl; Alma Coll; Elem Teacher.

SMITH, Yvonne D; Lindblom Tech HS; Chicago, IL; 91/496 ChrhWkr; CmntyWkr; HonRl; OffAde; SpnCl; College; Professional.

SMITH, Zack P; Metamora HS; East Peoria, IL; LetterEldAwd;.

SMITHBACK, Julie; Stoughton Senior HS; Stoughton, WI; 3/228 AFS; Band; HonRl; MrchBnd; NHS; SpnCl; Tennis; GAA; 4-HAwd; GovHonPrgAwd; Univ Wi Eau Claire; Nurse.

SMITHSON, Kathleen; Bellevue Comm Hs; Bellevue, IA; Band; Chrs; CncrtBnd; HonRl; MrchBnd; NHS; PepBnd; 4-H; Vocations Tech; Dental Assisting.

SMITHSON, Vincent S; St Elmo Sr HS; Loogootee, IL; 14/52 Band; Chrs; CncrtBnd; HonRl; MrchBnd; SchMus; 4-H; FFA; 4-HAwd; College; Music.

SMITHY, Cinda A; St Marys Perpetual Help; Chicago, IL; HonRl; TchrAde; RptrYrbk; FTA; Business School; Professional.

SMITLEY, Debra K; Charleston HS; Charleston, IL; SecJrCls; Chrs; HonRl; ModUN; NHS; SchPl; StuCncl; 4-H; DanFAwd; DARAwd; Eastern Illinois Univ; Speech.

SMITLEY, Lori C; Urbandale HS; Urbandale, IA; Chrs; HonRl; JA; TchrAde; Business Sch; Bookkeeper.

SMITS, Cathleen L; Depere HS; De Pere, WI; 15/204 TrsSophCls; CmntyWkr; HonRl; NHS; OffAde; SchAde; TchrAde; Yrbk; 4-H; FTA; GAA; College; Elem Ed.

SMITS, Jeffrey M; Abbot Pennings HS; De Pete, WI; HonRl; PolWkr; KeyCl; LetterFtbl; Trk; IMSpt; U Of Wi Oshkosh.

SMITTER, Mark R; Whitmore Lake HS; Whitmore Lake, MI; 11/80 Band; ChrhWkr; CncrtBnd; HonRl; MrchBnd; NHS; SctActv; Univ Of Mi; Computers.

SMITTLE, Grover C; Pacific HS; Pacific, MO; 9/190 Band; Chr; CncrtBnd; HonRl; Mdrgl; MrchBnd; NatlFornLg; NatlThespSoc; SchMus; SchPl; Yrbk; SchPpr; SpnCl; College; Professional Acting.

SMOCK, Helen M; Duchesne HS; St Charles, MO; 20/189 Chrs; ChrhWkr; CmntyWkr; HonRl; SctActv; Yrbk; 4-H; GAA; IMSpt; 4-HAwd; College; Professional.

SMOCK, Wesley A; Onsted HS; Adrian, MI; 17/117 VPSrCls; HonRl; SchPl; Yrbk; 4-H; FFA; LetterFtbl; DanFAwd; 4-HAwd; Mich St U; Agriculture.

SMOGOR, Cheryl A; St Ladislaus HS; Detroit, MI; Chrl; FBLA; FrCl; College.

SMOLA, Barbara; East Detroit HS; East Detroit, MI; HonRl; NHS; YthLg; Yrbk; PresFBLA; GAA; PPFtbl; E Mich Univ; Bus Management.

SMOLAR, Joseph; Highland HS; Highland, IN; 100/535 HonRl; TchrAde; LetterFtbl; LetterWrstlng; IMSpt; College; Accounting.

SMOLECKI, Joseph A; Brother Rice HS; Chicago, IL; 37/416 HonRl; JrNHS; NHS; NatlMeritCmnd; StuGov; Univ Of Illinois; Architecture.

SMOLEN, Vicki; Thornton HS; Posen, IL; HonRl; JrNHS; NHS; Thornton Com College; Computer Science.

SMOLENSKI, Robert C; High School; Minot, ND; 32/86 ALBoysSt; SchPl; StuCncl; KeyCl; LetterFtbl; IMSpt; Univ; Prof.

SMOLER, Robert J; Newtrier West HS; Glencoe, IL; CmntyWkr; HonRl; LitMag; NatlMeritCmnd; StuGov; FrCl; Ftbl; Wrstlng; IMSpt; U Of Ill; Medical Law.

SMOLICH, Kevin M; Plainfield HS; Joliet, IL; 13/330 Band; Chr; CncrtBnd; HonRl; NHS; NatlThespSoc; SchMus; GerCl; MthCl; Univ Of Ill; Chemistry.

SMOLINSKI, Joan M; Menasha HS; Menasha, WI; 31/311 ChrhWkr; HonRl; JA; LitMag; NHS; StuCncl; TchrAde; SchPpr; EldAwd; JAAwd; U Of Wi Fox Valley; Art.

SMOLINSKI, Patricia M; Paul Vi HS; Omaha, NE; 11/97 Bishop Clarkson Nursing Schl; Rn.

SMOLINSKI, Patrick J; Gordon Tech; Chicago, IL; HonRl; Univ Of Il; Engineering.

SMOLINSKY, Lawrence J; Buffalo Grove HS; Buffalo Grove, IL; 40/290 HonRl; NatlSciFnd; KeyCl; SciCl; LetterTrk; Univ Of Chicago; Astrophysics.

SMOLLEN, Margaret A; Wm Horlick HS; Racine, WI; 1/500 ALAGirlsSt; Band; ModUN; RptrSchPpr; CaptSwmmng; Tennis; Chrldr; PresGAA; DARAwd; RotaryAwd; OptClAwd; RotaryAwd; Stanford Univ; Biology.

SMOTHERS, Jonathan H; Concordia Academy; North St Paul, MN; 14/49 ChrhWkr; CmntyWkr; HonRl; JA; NHS; NatlMeritSchl; SancSoc; StuGov; FHA; Bsbl; CaptBsktbl; CaptFtbl; Concordia College; Teaching.

SMOTRILLA, William; Thornwood HS; Dolton, IL; 71/852 Aud/Vis; HonRl; NHS; NatlMeritCmnd; Univ Of Ill; Electrical Engineering.

SMUDA, Carol A; Manistee Catholic HS; Manistee, MI; HonRl; SchPl; TchrAde; RptrYrbk; Yrbk; PpCl; Trk; BttyCrckrAwd; Mi State Univ; Interior Design.

SMUDA, Jeffrey M; Concordia Academy; St Paul, MN; PresBand; Chr; CncrtBnd; PepBnd; SchMus; SchPl; GerCl; SciCl; LetterFtbl; CaptTrk; Concordia Col; Teaching.

SMUGALA, Karen J; Cahokia Commonfields HS; Cahokia, IL; Chr; HonRl; JA; NatlMeritCmnd; SchPl; StuGov; FBLA; LatCl; Chrldr; PPFtbl; College; Professional.

SMUKALA, Suzanne M; North Huron HS; Port Austin, MI; 3/42 Band; ChrhWkr; HonRl; MrchBnd; NHS; PepBnd; SchPl; StuCncl; TchrAde; BttyCrckrAwd; Central Mich Uni; Spec Educ Tchr.

SMUTNEY, Susan L; Libertyville HS; Libertyville, IL; Chr; Chrl; NHS; SchMus; SchPl; 4-H; Augustana Univ; Music.

SMYSER, Ginnia R; Sheridan R2 HS; Sheridan, MO; 2/10 SecJrCls; TrsJrCls; SecTrsJrCls; VPSrCls; HonRl; LbryAde; SchPl; SecStuCncl; LetterBsbl; LetterBsktbl; Chrldr; AmLegAwd;.

SMYTH, Donald C; Beloit HS; Beloit, KS; HonRl; LbryAde; SchPl; TchrAde; YthFlsp; RptrSchPpr; Bsktbl; LetterFtbl; Glf; Trk; Ksu; Agronomy.

SMYTH, Edward H; Whitefish Bay HS; Whitefish Bay, WI; 34/346 ChrhWkr; HonRl; NatlMeritCmnd; FrCl; LetterFtbl; IMSpt; Univ; Medicine.

SMYTH, Todd R; Huntington North HS; Warren, IN; ChrhWkr; LbryAde; SciCl; University.

SMYTHE, Thomas R; Kimball Co HS; Kimball, NE; 18/99 Band; CncrtBnd; HonRl; MrchBnd; NatlFornLg; SpnCl; U Of Neb; Civil Eng.

SNAPP, Jinger C; Avon HS; Danville, IN; HonRl; LbryAde; ModUN; SchAde; SchPl; GerCl; PpCl; SciCl; Purdue Univ; Health.

SNARE, Paul D; Southwest HS; Kansas City, MO; 100/525 TreasChrhWkr; HonRl; Mdrgl; NHS; OffAde; SchAde; YthFlsp; Bsktbl; CchngActv; IMSpt; Umkc/mo; Actor.

SNART, Kenneth C; Green Lake HS; Ripon, WI; 9/46 ALBoysSt; Band; Chr; ChrhWkr; HonRl; NatlFornLg; NatlThespSoc; SchPl; EdYrBk; VPSpnCl; Univ Of Wisconsin; Music.

SNAUWAERT, Lori A; United Township HS; East Moline, IL; 26/750 ALAGirlsSt; Chr; HonRl; NHS; OffAde; StuCncl; Teen; PpCl; Chrldr; Illinois St Univ; Communications.

SNAVELY, Denise M; Mt Pleasant HS; Mt Pleasant, IA; Band; CncrtBnd; HonRl; MrchBnd; SctActv; RptrSchPpr; FrCl; SpnCl; College.

SNEATHEN, Cindi A; Hays HS; Hays, KS; Chr; Chrs; DrlTm; HonRl; HospAde; TchrAde; LatCl; PpCl; IMSpt; College.

SNEDDON, Julie K; Brazil HS; Brazil, IN; 34/186 Band; CncrtBnd; HonRl; MrchBnd; NHS; NatlThespSoc; PepBnd; SchPl; SctActv; Ball St Univ; Commercial Art.

SNEED, Jill; Lyons Twp HS; Western Springs, IL; Chrs; ChrhWkr; HonRl; JrNHS; NHS; OffAde; Quill&Scroll; SchPl; StuGov; TchrAde; Yrbk; Butler Univ; Religion.

SNEED, Vicki L; Carthage HS; Carthage, MO; VPJrCls; AFS; Chr; Chrl; SchPl; YthFlsp; 4-H; LatCl; PPFtbl; 4-HAwd; College.

SNELL, Amanda A; Spring Hill HS; Spring Hill, KS; 3/60 Band; DrmMjrt; HonRl; NHS; SchMus; 4-H; FHA; AmLegAwd; 4-HAwd; College.

SNELL, Edward; Spooner HS; Spooner, WI; 63/130 LbryAde; RptrYrbk; SptEdYrbk; MthCl; PpCl; SciCl; Bsbl; Ftbl; Wrstlng; Coll Eau Claire; Educ.

SNELL, Larry G; Pekin Comm HS; Pekin, IL; 126/803 ChrhWkr; CmntyWkr; HonRl; NHS; SchAde; LetterBsbl; LetterFtbl; IMSpt; College; Biology Science.

SNELL, Laura A; Dixon HS; Dixon, IL; 29/350 Band; Chr; ChrhWkr; DrmMjrt; HonRl; Mdrgl; MrchBnd; NatlThespSoc; SchMus; College.

SNELL, Roberta R; St Croix Falls HS; St Croix Falls, WI; HonRl; NHS; RptrYrbk; RptrSchPpr; FHA; Coll Or Trade.

SNELLENBARGER, Lisa J; Clinton Prairie HS; Frankfort, IN; 5/105 TrsSrCls; HonRl; VPNHS; TreasYthFlsp; TreasSpnCl; CaptBsktbl; College; Professional.

SNELLINGS, Ruth E; Gobles HS; Gobles, MI; 4/65 CncrtBnd; HonRl; HospAde; MrchBnd; NHS; PepBnd; TchrAde; Parsons Business Schl; Secretary.

SNEPP, Karen S; Glenbard West HS; Glen Ellyn, IL; 11/508 HonRl; NatlMeritCmnd; Quill&Scroll; SptEdSchPpr; MthCl; GAA; Purdue Univ; Statistics.

SNETHEN, Debbie A; Fairfield Community HS; Fairfield, IL; 20/165 ALAGirlsSt; ChrhWkr; HonRl; NHS; Quill&Scroll; EdSchPpr; 4-H; SpnCl; GAA; 4-HAwd; Northwestern U; Journalism.

SNETSELAAR, Rebecca A; Ankeny HS; Polk City, IA; 10/225 Band; Chrs; HonRl; LitMag; NHS; NatlMeritSF; PepBnd; Bsktbl; Clge; Lit.

SNIATYNSKY, Lenora; Oak Lawn Comm HS; Oak Lawn, IL; HonRl; LbryAde; NHS; OffAde; SchAde; StuGov; TchrAde; PpCl; TrkLtg; College.

SNIDER, Jacquline D; North Polk HS; Cambrdige, IA; 7/35 Chr; Chrs; ChrhWkr; DrlTm; HonRl; SchMus; RptrSchPpr; FTA; Patricia Stevens Fashion Coll; Exec Sec.

SNIDER, Judith A; Brown Co HS; Nashville, IN; 45/207 HonRl; NHS; NatlMeritCmnd; NatlMeritSchl; OffAde; Yrbk; 4-H; PpCl; BttyCrckrAwd; MasAwd; Vocational School; Secretarial Work.

SNIDER, Linda M; North Chicago HS; Lindenhurst, IL; 19/257 ChrhWkr; HonRl; NatlFornLg; NHS; SchMus; SchPl; StuGov; PresFHA; AmLegAwd; Univ Of Iowa.

SNIDER, Robert M; Harper Creek HS; Battle Creek, MI; 1/230 ChrhWkr; HonRl; NHS; SctActv; TchrAde; YthFlsp; MthCl; Bsbl; Ftbl; Wrstlng; College; Engineering.

SNIDER, Stan C; Richland HS; Dexter, MO; PresFrshCls; ChrhWkr; HonRl; SctActv; StuCncl; PresFFA; LetterBsbl; LetterBsktbl; CchngActv; Univ Of Missouri; Agriculture.

SNIDER, Thelma M; Mulberry Grv Comm Unit 1 HS; Mulberry Grove, IL; 3/39 VPSophCls; CaptDrlTm; HonRl; NHS; SchPl; FHA; FNA; PpCl; LetterChrldr; LetterGAA; Trade School; Draftsman.

SNIEGOCKI, Deborah J; George Washington HS; Chicago, IL; HonRl; NHS; NatlMeritCmnd; SchAde; TchrAde; RptrYrbk; LatCl; GAA; Business School; Accounting.

SNITILY, Ernest J; Prague Public HS; Prague, NE; 3/18 PresSrCls; Chrs; HonRl; SchPl; StuCncl; Yrbk; FFA; LetterBsktbl; LetterFtbl; LetterTrk; U Of Ne; Bus.

SNODGRASS, David L; Mt Pleasant HS; Mt Pleasant, IA; ChrhWkr; CmntyWkr; NHS; ROTC; StuCncl; YthFlsp; Yrbk; FBLA; Bsktbl; Tennis; IMSpt; Trade Schl; Vocation.

SNODGRASS, Michael A; Carlinulle HS; Carlinville, IL; 59/126 VPSrCls; Band; CAP; CncrtBnd; Bsktbl; CaptFtbl; GodCntryAwd; Usaf Acad; Officer Air Force.

SNOOK, Sheldon L; North Platte HS; Edgerton, MO; Band; CncrtBnd; HonRl; SctActv; LetterBsbl; Bsktbl; LetterFtbl; LetterTrk; GodCntryAwd; Ci-tAwd;.

SNOOZY, Darlene; Dell Rapids Public HS; Dell Rapids, SD; 1/56 SecJrCls; PresSrCls; ALAGirlsSt; CncrtBnd; NHS; NatlThespSoc; Quill&Scroll; EdSchPpr; AmLegAwd; DARAwd; Sd St Univ;art Educ.

SNOOZY, Floyd; Dell Rapids Public HS; Colton, SD; Band; CncrtBnd; HonRl; MrchBnd; PepBnd; FFA;.

SNOW, Alice I; West Nodaway R 1 HS; Elmo, MO; 1/39 ALAGirlsSt; Band; Chrs; ChrhWkr; CncrtBnd; HonRl; MrchBnd; NHS; SchPl; RptrSchPpr; EdSchPpr; SchPpr; FrCl; Manhattan Chris Col;.

SNOW, Barbara S; Amboy HS; Amboy, IL; 3/108 HonRl; NHS; SchMus; StuCncl; YthFlsp; Yrbk; FHA; Illinois Wesleyan Univ; Nursing.

SNOW, Craig C; Webberville HS; Webberville, MI; HonRl; PolWkr; SpnCl; MthCl; Bsbl; LetterBsktbl; LetterFtbl; LetterTrk; University; Math.

SNOW, George M; Huntington North HS; Warren, IN; Chr; CmntyWkr; LetterBsbl; IMSpt; Indiana University; Optometry.

SNOW, Linda K; Roanoke Benson HS; Benson, IL; 1/100 AFS; Band; CncrtBnd; HonRl; MrchBnd; PepBnd; FHA; FTA; MthCl; IMSpt; Coll; Accounting.

SNOW, Monica L; New Franklin HS; New Franklin, MO; 5/32 TrsFrshCls; TrsJrCls; PresBand; HonRl; NHS; SecStuCncl; PresYthFlsp; EdSchPpr; PresFHA; PresPpCl; Bsbl; Bsktbl; DARAwd; Central Mo State Univ; Nursing.

SNOW, Ronald T; St Peter & Paul Area HS; Saginaw, MI; 10/126 Chrs; ChrhWkr; HonRl; NHS; SchPl; Delta College; Science.

SNOW, Stephen K; Lanphier HS; Springfield, IL; Bsbl; LetterFtbl; LetterWrstlng; IMSpt; Clg; Acct.

SNOWBANK, Laurie L; Cumberland HS; Cumberland, WI; Chr; HonRl; FHA; FNA; SpnCl; Bussiness School; Vocation.

SNOWDEN, Diane; Industry HS; Industry, IL; VPJrCls; SecSrCls; CncrtBnd; HonRl; MrchBnd; PepBnd; Yrbk; SchPpr; PpCl; Chrldr;.

SNOWDEN, James H; Quincy Sr HS; Quincy, IL; 9/803 HonRl; NHS; TchrAde; LetterTrk; Grand Rapids Baptist College; Education.

SNOWDEN, Julie A; Industry HS; Macomb, IL; 3/35 Band; CncrtBnd; MrchBnd; PepBnd; RptrYrbk; RptrSchPpr; FrCl; GAA; DARAwd; Western Ill University; Elementary Educ.

SNOWDEN, Karen C; Industry HS; Vermont, IL; Band; ChrhWkr; HonRl; StuCncl; PpCl; SciCl; Trk; Chrldr; AmLegAwd; 4-HAwd; College; Special Education.

SNOWDEN, Melanee; Cedar Lake Acad; Escanaba, MI;)16/77 ChrhWkr; HstSophCls; HstJrCls; Chr; HonRl; Mdrgl; NHS; StuCncl; StuGov; Bsktbl; Southern Missionery College; Para Legalist.

SNOWDEN, Melanee L; Cedar Lake Academy; Escanaba, MI; 16/71 SecFrshCls; HstSophCls; HstJrCls; Chr; HonRl; Mdrgl; NHS; StuCncl; Southern Missionary College; Secretary.

SNYDER, Alan L; Arkansas City HS; South Haven, KS; 33/198 Chr; Chrs; ChrhWkr; HonRl; LbryAde; Mdrgl; SchMus; YthFlsp; CivCl; LetterBsktbl; College.

SNYDER, Barbara A; Bethany HS; Bethany, IL; Band; Chrs; CncrtBnd; MrchBnd; SchMus; RptrSchPpr; FHA; FTA; Chrldr; GAA;.

SNYDER, Becky A; Parkwood HS; Joplin, MO; Chr; Chrs; ChrhWkr; HonRl; LbryAde; Orch; RedCrAde; SchMus; SctActv; Teen; PpCl; Chrldr; College; Professional.

SNYDER, Bradley D; Buhler HS; Hutchinson, KS; 86/153 Band; ChrhWkr; CncrtBnd; HonRl; MrchBnd; PepBnd; StuCncl; TchrAde; YthFlsp; Ftbl; Ft Hays Ft St Clge; Forestry.

SNYDER, Brian W; Lowell Sr HS; Lowell, IN; ALBoysSt; PresChrs; ChrhWkr; HonRl; NHS; VPNatlThespSoc; PolWkr; SchMus; SchPl; StuCncl; YthFlsp; Pres4-H; Ftbl; 4-HAwd; College; Law.

SNYDER, Carolyn H; Mary C Wheeler HS; Grosse Pointe Farm, MI; CmntyWkr; SchPl; SchPpr; 4-H; Swmmng; Tennis; University; Professional.

SNYDER, Carolyn M; North Side HS; Fort Wayne, IN; 10/438 HonRl; NHS; VPOrch; PolWkr; SchMus; YthFlsp; 4-H; EngCl; IMSpt; 4-HAwd; Manchester College.

SNYDER, David F; Fulton HS; Fulton, IL; ChrhWkr; HonRl; RptrYrbk; EdYrBk; SptEdYrbk; VPSophCls; Bsktbl; Trk; 4-HAwd; Univ; Agric Tech.

SNYDER, Doug A; Central HS; Burden, KS; PresJrCls; PresSrCls; ChrhWkr; HonRl; SchAde; StuCncl; SchPpr; 4-H; Bsbl; Bsktbl; Ftbl; Trk; CchngActv; John Brown Univ.

SNYDER, Douglas J; Goshen HS; Goshen, IN; Band; ChrhWkr; SciCl; Ftbl; Wrstlng; Goshen Coll; Doctor.

SNYDER, Gayle A; Fremont Sr HS; Fremont, NE; Band; Chr; Chrl; CncrtBnd; MrchBnd; SchMus; SchPl; Swmmng; IMSpt; Trade School; Computer Programming.

SNYDER, Gene L; Nemaha Valley HS; Talmage, NE; 7/34 ALBoysSt; Band; Chr; HonRl; PepBnd; YthFlsp; Bsbl; Bsktbl; LetterFtbl; Trk; 4-HAwd; SARAwd; CitAwd;.

SNYDER, Gerald C; Lake Forest Academy; Lake Bluff, IL; ChrhWkr; CmntyWkr; HonRl; SctActv; RptrYrbk; LetterSocr; Tennis;.

SNYDER, Jack D; Hagerstown Jr Sr HS; New Castle, IN; 14/118 PresSrCls; HonRl; NHS; EdYrBk; 4-H; FFA; Bsbl; Bsktbl; LetterFtbl; Socr; Trk; 4-HAwd; College; Farmer.

SNYDER, James J; Di Cabrini HS; Allen Park, MI; 43/167 ChrhWkr; HonRl; SchPpr; LatCl; SciCl; Clge; Mechanical Eng.

SNYDER, James R; Winnebago HS; Winnebago, IL; PresSophCls; Band; ChrhWkr; CncrtBnd; HonRl; SctActv; StuCncl; YthFlsp; SpnCl; LetterFtbl; LetterGlf; GodCntryAwd; College; Ministry.

SNYDER, Jane E; St Edmond HS; Fort Dodge, IA; HonRl; NHS; StuCncl; FrCl; LetterGlf; Iowa Central Comm Clg; Home Economics.

SNYDER, Janet R; Prairie HS; Cedar Rapids, IA; Chrs; ChrhWkr; CncrtBnd; HonRl; JA; JrNHS; MrchBnd; SecStuCncl; Twrl; EdYrBk; Mt Mercy; Nursing.

SNYDER, John W; Pawnee City Pub HS; Pawnee City, NE; 18/36 PresSophCls; Chrs; SchPl; YthFlsp; 4-H; FFA; LetterFtbl; LetterGlf; 4-HAwd; College.

SNYDER, Jonathan; Fremont HS; Fremont, MI; 56/189 ChrhWkr; CncrtBnd; HonRl; OffAde; TchrAde; 4-H; GerCl; SciCl; IMSpt; Grand Rapids Baptist Col; Teacher.

SNYDER, Joni; Chillicothe HS; Chillicothe, MO; HonRl; Quill&Scroll; StuCncl; TchrAde; RptrSchPpr; 4-H; FHA; FTA; GAA; PresAwd; St Lukes Hosp; Nursng.

SNYDER, Julie A; Bronaugh R 7 HS; Bronaugh, MO; 4/23 Band; HonRl; LbryAde; SecNHS; NatlThespSoc; StuCncl; 4-H; PpCl; Bsktbl; LetterTrk;.

SNYDER, Karen; Lakeland R Iii HS; Lowry City, MO; VPSophCls; Chrs; ChrhWkr; HonRl; HospAde; Yrbk; RptrSchPpr; PpCl; Bsbl; Bsktbl; Coll; Pro.

SNYDER, Karen S; Chandlerville HS; Chandlerville, IL; 4/28 TrsFrshCls; Band; NHS; OffAde; SchAde; StuCncl; StuGov; FHA; Chrldr; IMSpt; College; Major Study.

SNYDER, Linda A; Fort Zumwalt HS; St Peters, MO; DrlTm; HonRl; JA; LitMag; StuCncl; PpCl; JAAwd; CitAwd; Job; Secretarial.

SNYDER, Linda S; West Pike HS; Hull, IL; 3/34 PresFrshCls; PresSophCls; HstJrCls; PresBand; HonRl; NHS; NatlMeritCmnd; Trk; CaptChrldr; DARAwd; So Illinois Univ; Medicine.

SNYDER, Lori A; Columbus North HS; Columbus, IN; 60/500 ChrhWkr; HonRl; JA; SchPl; SpnCl; PpCl; Indiana Univ; Biology.

SNYDER, Mark; Sabetha HS; Sebetha, KS; SecFrshCls; TrsFrshCls; ALBoysSt; HonRl; StuCncl; KeyCl; Bsbl; Trk; Hutchinson Juco; Engineering.

SNYDER, Mark B; Dixon HS; Dixon, IL; 4/337 Band; ChrhWkr; HonRl; NHS; NatlMeritCmnd; PresPepBnd; StuGov; Yrbk; SchPpr; EldAwd; Univ Of Illinois; Metallurgical Eng.

SNYDER, Mark D; Lincoln Community HS; Lincoln, IL; 32/272 HonRl; JA; 4-H; JAAwd; College; Radiologic Technology.

SNYDER, Reed E; Wilmot Union HS; Burlington, WI; 64/225 ChrhWkr; SchMus; SchPl; SchPpr; PpCl; LetterBsbl; Bsktbl; LetterFtbl; College; Phy Ed Or Pro Baseball.

SNYDER, Rory C; Jefferson HS; Rockford, IL; 6/350 Band; CncrtBnd; HonRl; MrchBnd; PepBnd; SctActv; Bradley Univ; Accounting.

SNYDER, Roxane R; Genoa Public HS; Genoa, NE; Chrs; HonRl; SchPl; RptrSchPpr; PpCl; Platte Jr Clge; Psychology.

SNYDER, Ruth M; Humboldt HS; Humboldt, IA; Chr; Chrl; ChrhWkr; CmntyWkr; HonRl; PepBnd; SchMus; SchPl; StuGov; YthFlsp; YthLg; PpCl; Chrldr; College; Nursing.

SNYDER, Sheryl; Mason HS; Lasalle, MI; HonRl; StuCncl; TchrAde; SchPpr; FHA; PpCl; Trk; Chrldr; GAA; College; Hair Stylist.

SNYDER, Steven; Springfield Southeast HS; Springfield, IL; Chr; LbryAde; PolWkr; SchMus; StuCncl; MthCl;.

SNYDER, Susan E; Marinette HS; Marinette, WI; 17/239 AFS; Chr; CmntyWkr; NHS; SctActv; StuCncl; TchrAde; FrCl; PpCl; U Of Wis; Med Tech.

SNYDER, Tamara S; Ellendale HS; Ellendale, ND; SecFrshCls; VPSophCls; SecJrCls; ALAGirlsSt; Band; Chr; NHS; Bsktbl; Trk; Chrldr; DanFAwd; College; Professional.

SNYDER, Trina G; T C Howe HS; Indianapolis, IN; 12/447 Chr; HonRl; JA; NHS; SchMus; TchrAde; RptrYrbk; GAA; PPFtbl; JAAwd; Purdue Univ ;computer Tech.

SNYDER, Vincent L; Wahoo Public HS; Wahoo, NE; Band; CncrtBnd; HonRl; MrchBnd; PepBnd; LetterBsktbl; LetterFtbl; CchngActv; Univ Of Nebraska; Engineer.

SNYDER, William; Robinson HS; Robinson, IL; 12/194 SctActv; StuCncl; KeyCl; Southern Illinois; Forestry.

SNYDER, Zane J; Keya Paha Co HS; Springview, NE; 3/26 HonRl; SchPl; Ftbl; Trade School; Agricultural.

SNYDER, Zenda J; Western HS; Kokomo, IN; 26/163 Aud/Vis; Band; ChrhWkr; CncrtBnd; HonRl; MrchBnd; YthFlsp; VPSpnCl; Bsktbl; Trk; Utc; Phys Ed.

SNYDERMAN, Mark S; Niles East HS; Skokie, IL; 2/581 CncrtBnd; HonRl; NHS; NatlMeritFnl; StuGov; Yrbk; Medical School; Physician.

SOBAS, Cheryl L; Morton Sr HS; Hammond, IN; 1/500 HonRl; NHS; University; Math.

SOBATKA, Tina; Diagonal Comm HS; Diagonal, IA; SecSophCls; TrsJrCls; ALAGirlsSt; HonRl; MrchBnd; YthFlsp; 4-H; Bsktbl; CchngActv; AmLegAwd; Ankney College; Medical Secreatry.

SOBCZAK, James M; Bogan HS; Chicago, IL; 28/708 Aud/Vis; HonRl; NHS; TchrAde; Yrbk; LetterBsktbl; University Of Illinois; Wildlife Mgmt.

SOBCZAK, Patricia; Denfeld HS; Duluth, MN; 21/369 Chrs; HonRl; RptrYrbk; PpCl; Trk; GAA; IMSpt; St Cloud St Col; Special Ed.

SOBCZAK, Stuart A; Creighton Prep; Omaha, NE; HonRl; HospAde; JA; NatlFornLg; Sdlty; RptrYrbk; 4-H; FDA; Ftbl; Wrstlng; IMSpt; 4-HAwd; JAAwd; College; Pre Med.

SOBCZYK, Christine; Notre Dame Hs; Chicago, IL; 2/262 HonRl; SchAde; StuGov; TchrAde; FTA; MthCl; LetterBsktbl; U; Veterinary Medicine.

SOBECK, Rebecca A; Morton HS; Hammond, IN; 43/492 ALAGirlsSt; CmntyWkr; HospAde; NHS; SctActv; TchrAde; PpCl; SciCl; Purdue Univ; Business Management.

SOBEK, Susan A; Lees Summit HS; Lees Summit, MO; HonRl; TchrAde; PpCl; LetterTrk; Chrldr; GAA; PPFtbl; CitAwd; Unkc; Spanish.

SOBEL, Paul; Oconomowoc HS; Oconomowoc, WI; 6/275 Band; CncrtBnd; HonRl; JrNHS; MrchBnd; NHS; PepBnd; MthCl; Glf; U; Accounting.

SOBETSKI, Rosemaire C; Marian HS; Omaha, NE; 14/152 HonRl; JrNHS; NatlFornLg; NHS; NatlMeritCmnd; NatlThespSoc; SchMus; SchPl; Sdlty; FBLA; Univ; Cpa.

SOBOLESKI, Julie M; St Stanislaus Kostka HS; Chicago, IL; 1/70 Chrs; HonRl; PresNHS; TchrAde; RptrSchPpr; TreasFTA; Northeastern Univ; Teacher.

SOBOLIK, Rose M; Pacelli HS; Austin, MN; Chr; ChrhWkr; CmntyWkr; HonRl; OffAde; SchPl; Trk; Chrldr; Trade School; Professional.

SOBOTKA, Patty J; Cainsville R 1 HS; Cainsville, MO; 2/12 HstSophCls; TrsJrCls; SecSrCls; Band; Chr; Chrs; ChrhWkr; CncrtBnd; HonRl; MrchBnd; BttyCrckrAwd; DARAwd; Nw Missouri St University.

SOBOTTA, Darlene M; Arcadia HS; Arcadia, WI; HonRl; LbryAde; OffAde; SchAde; TchrAde; RptrSchPpr; FTA; College.

SOCH, Rosanne; Oak Forest HS; Oak Forest, IL; 4/324 HonRl; NHS; TchrAde; Yrbk; FrCl; PpCl; St Francis College; Biology.

SOCHA, David M; Phillips HS; Phillips, WI; 16/107 HonRl; Bsktbl; Ftbl; CaptTrk; CchngActv; IMSpt; AmLegAwd; Trade School; Vocation.

SOCHA, Stephen; Thornton Twp Hs; Dolton, IL; 32/727 JrNHS; NHS; Thornton Comm College; Electril Engineer.

SOCHA, Thomas J; Gordon Tech HS; Chicago, IL; 37/697 PresJrCls; ChrhWkr; CncrtBnd; HonRl; MrchBnd; NHS; StuCncl; StuGov; IMSpt; Il Univ; Lawyer.

SOCIER, Michael; Essexville Garber HS; Esseville, MI; CmntyWkr; SchMus; SchPl; Delta College; Broadcasting.

SOCKEL, Mark S; Taylorville Sr HS; Taylorville, IL; 112/271 ChrhWkr; HonRl; KeyCl; LetterBsbl; LetterFtbl; LetterTrk; U Of Il; Vet.

SODERBERG, Kevan A; St Francis HS; Isanti, MN; 19/167 Aud/Vis; Band; ChrhWkr; HonRl; SctActv; TchrAde; YthFlsp; 4-H; SciCl; Bsbl; Bsktbl; Tennis; 4-HAwd; Bible College.

SODERBERG, Thomas M; Cook HS; Cook, MN; Band; ChrhWkr; MrchBnd; YthFlsp; RptrYrbk; SptEdYrbk; SptEdSchPpr; PpCl; Bsbl; Bsktbl; Coll; Prof.

SODERHOLM, Kathryn L; Ames HS; Ames, IA; 10/393 Chr; CncrtBnd; HonRl; Mdrgl; MrchBnd; Orch; PepBnd; FrCl; Isu; Engineering Or Med.

SODERLUND, Eric J; Rhinelander HS; Rhinelander, WI; 32/365 Chrs; ChrhWkr; HonRl; LbryAde; NatlMeritSF; SchPl; LatCl; OptClAwd; RotaryAwd; U Of Wi Eau Claire; Business Adm.

SODERSTROM, Mark; Muskegon HS; Muskegon, MI; Band; ChrhWkr; CncrtBnd; HonRl; MrchBnd; NHS; PepBnd; SchPl; College; Science.

SODERSTRUM, Ann L; Geneva Comm HS; Geneva, IL; 1/224 HonRl; NHS; SchPl; FrCl; MthCl; Carleton College.

SODOWSKI, Tina M; Peoria Heights HS; Peoria Heights, IL; 11/93 VPSrCls; Chr; HonRl; SpnCl; Chrldr; College; Counselor.

SOEHNLIN, Craig A; Granite City South HS; Granite City, IL; Band; ChrhWkr; CncrtBnd; JrNHS; MrchBnd; NHS; SctActv; College; Minister.

SOELDNER, Janice K; Tri Valley HS; Ellsworth, IL; 1/45 PresSophCls; VPSrCls; Band; Chrs; HonRl; VPNHS; StuCncl; Yrbk; PresFHA; DARAwd; 4-HAwd; Ill State Univ; Business Admin.

SOELLER, Mary Lee; Stanley Boyd HS; Stanley, WI; 19/108 HonRl; NatlFornLg; SchPl; 4-H; FHA; SciCl; 4-HAwd; Air Force; Meteorology.

SOENS, Cynthia M; Resurrection HS; Chicago, IL; 40/261 Band; ChrhWkr; Mundelein College; Commercial Art.

SOGLIN, David M; Evanston Township HS; Evanston, IL; 65/1100 CmntyWkr; HonRl; NatlMeritCmnd; PolWkr; StuGov; Univ Of Ill; Physician.

SOHL, James D; St Pauls College HS; Concordia, MO; TrsSophCls; Chr; CncrtBnd; HonRl; NHS; PepBnd; SchPl; StuCncl; StuGov; SciCl; Bsktbl; LetterFtbl; Tennis; Trk; University Of Missouri; Music & Science.

SOHN, Susan L; Elk Grove HS; Elk Grove, IL; Chr; Chrs; ChrhWkr; HospAde; SchMus; College; Nursing.

SOHN, Susan R; Niles East HS; Skokie, IL; 12/550 Chr; HonRl; Mdrgl; NHS; NatlMeritCmnd; NatlThespSoc; SchMus; FrCl; University Of Michigan; Medicine.

SOHR, Lynette M; Stephenson HS; Daggett, MI; Band; ChrhWkr; CncrtBnd; HonRl; MrchBnd; PepBnd; Northern Michigan Univ; Medical Lab Techn.

SOJKA, Cindy A; Lyons Township HS; La Grange, IL; ChrhWkr; CmntyWkr; HonRl; NHS; SctActv; Mac Cormac Jr College; Court Reporter.

SOKOL, Jeffrey R; Greenfield HS; Greenfield, WI; HonRl; NHS; StuCncl; SchPpr; PpCl; Bsbl; Bsktbl; Ftbl; Glf; Univ Of Wi.

SOKOL, Stephen A; Anderson HS; Anderson, IN; Aud/Vis; HonRl; FrCl; Univ; Pharmacy.

SOKOLIK, Debra J; Winona HS; Winona, MN; HonRl; RptrSchPpr; Clge; Math.

SOKOLINSKI, Linda A; James H Bowen HS; Chicago, IL; 7/613 Aud/Vis; HonRl; NHS; OffAde; TchrAde; MthCl; GAA; Northern Ill U; Elem Ed.

SOKOLOSKI, Barbara J; Sherburn HS; Sherburn, MN; 19/63 Band; Chr; Chrs; CncrtBnd; HonRl; MrchBnd; PepBnd; SchPl; RptrSchPpr; St Cloud College; Medicine.

SOKOLOWSKI, Keith J; Thomas More HS; Milwaukee, WI; 16/155 ChrhWkr; HonRl; JrNHS; NHS; StuCncl; StuGov; Bsktbl; LetterFtbl; U Of Wi Milwaukee.

SOKOLY, Lauren M; Mayville HS; Mayville, WI; HonRl; JA; SecStuCncl; RptrYrbk; SchPpr; PpCl; Bsktbl; Glf; Swmmng; CaptChrldr; CchngActv; GAA; Marian College; Nursing.

SOLA, Sharon K; Lyle Public HS; Northwood, IA; VPFrshCls; TrsJrCls; Band; Chr; DrmMjrt; HonRl; SchPl; StuCncl; Bsktbl; Chrldr; College.

SOLARCZYK, Linda M; Maria HS; Chicago, IL; 63/301 HonRl; HospAde; NHS; NatlThespSoc; RedCrAde; SchMus; SchPl; StuCncl; Univ Of Ill; Physical Therapy.

SOLARZ, Jean M; Immaculate Heart Of Mary HS; Hillside, IL; 27/243 Lewis Univ; Legal Asst.

SOLARZ, Kevin M; Upsala HS; Swanville, MN; SecJrCls; LetterBsbl; LetterBsktbl; LetterFtbl; IMSpt; Trade School; Auto Mechanic.

SOLBERG, Becky L; Viroqua Sr HS; Viroqua, WI; 16/121 Chr; Chrs; ChrhWkr; HonRl; Mdrgl; SchMus; SchPl; 4-H; 4-HAwd; Western Wisconsin Tech Inst; Secretary.

SOLBERG, Bette J; Bristol HS; Bristol, SD; VPSrCls; ALAGirlsSt; Band; HonRl; Quill&Scroll; EdSchPpr; FHA; FNA; PresPpCl; CaptChrldr; Bus Sch; Secretary.

SOLBERG, Georgia L; T C Howe HS; Indianapolis, IN; 5/616 HonRl; NHS; TchrAde; Chrldr; Indiana Univ; Physical Educ.

SOLBERG, Joseph; Fenwick Hs; Oak Park, IL; 41 HonRl; Teen; RptrYrbk; LetterBsbl; Bsktbl; Ftbl; U Of Notre Dame;cpa And Lawyer.

SOLCHENBERGER, Vicki L; Lake Mills HS; Lake Mills, WI; AFS; Chr; HonRl; MrchBnd; BttyCrckrAwd; Madison Area Tech Clge; Fashion Merchandise.

SOLDAN, Scott O; Beecher HS; Flint, MI; Chr; ChrhWkr; HonRl; Orch; Ftbl; Coll; Music.

SOLDAN, Susan M; O Neill Public HS; Oneill, NE; 2/68 VPSophCls; SecTrsSrCls; VPBand; ChrhWkr; HonRl; SecNHS; VPStuCncl; TchrAde; RptrYrbk; Chrldr; Doane Col.

SOLDNER, Jeffrey W; Dodgeland HS; Lowell, WI; CmntyWkr; HonRl; IntrClCncl; StuCncl; SptEdYrbk; SptEdSchPpr; LetterBsbl; CaptBsktbl; CaptFtbl; LetterTrk; Coll; Architect.

SOLDNER, John; Adams Central HS; Decatur, IN; 8/121 HonRl; NHS; SchPl; StuCncl; Bsktbl; IMSpt; Purdue Univ; Chemical Engineering.

SOLEM, Natalie; Hendricks HS; Astoria, SD; Chr; Chrs; MrchBnd; SchPl; TreasStuCncl; EdSchPpr; PpCl; South Dakota State Univ; Journalism.

SOLETA, Janice M; Windom Area HS; Windom, MN; 18/148 ChrhWkr; HonRl; HospAde; OffAde; SctActv; RptrSchPpr; PpCl; LetterTrk; LetterChrldr; PresAwd; College; Nursing.

SOLI, Julie; Hallock HS; Hallock, MN; Band; Chr; Chrs; ChrhWkr; CncrtBnd; HonRl; HospAde; PepBnd; FHA; Assist Vet; Voc.

SOLIDAY, Debra A; Prophetstown HS; Prophetstown, IL; 3/98 AFS; HonRl; JrNHS; NHS; FTA; Jr College; Professional.

SOLKO, Rita M; Andes Central HS; Lake Andes, SD; 9/45 Chr; CncrtBnd; HonRl; NHS; SchPl; Yrbk; LetterBsktbl; Swmmng; Trk; CaptChrldr; IMSpt; Brookings College; Paramedics.

SOLL, Karen R; Soldan HS; St Louis, MO; 3/625 Band; CncrtBnd; HonRl; JA; JrNHS; MrchBnd; Col; Accountant.

SOLL, Kenneth A; Niles North HS; Skokie, IL; 80/641 HonRl; Northwestern University; Medicine.

SOLLBERGER, Peter R; Carbondale Comm HS; Carbondale, IL; Aud/Vis; Band; CmntyWkr; JA; FSA; SciCl; Southern Ill Univ; Audio Engineering.

SOLLIE, Linda R; Oklee Public HS; Trail, MN; SecSophCls; Chrs; ChrhWkr; HonRl; SchPl; RptrYrbk; RptrSchPpr; 4-H; FHA; College; Nurse.

SOLLMAN, Thomas P; Gibson Southern HS; Fort Branch, IN; SctActv; RptrSchPpr; KeyCl; Ftbl; Wrstlng; Oakland City Clg; Welding.

SOLLOWAY, Margaret A; Mt Assisi Acad; Oak Lawn, IL; 19/193 HonRl; Bowling Green St Univ; Mathematics.

SOLMONSON, Francie K; Estherville HS; Estherville, IA; 11/182 Band; Chrs; HonRl; 4-H; FHA; Ia St Univ.

SOLODUN, Liz; Good Counsel HS; Chicago, IL; ChrhWkr; SchMus; StuCncl; IMSpt; College; Teaching Elementary.

SOLOMON, Jerry; Addison Trail HS; Addison, IL; Trade School; Vocation.

SOLOMON, Marla J; Shorewood HS; Shorewood, WI; PresAFS; Chr; HonRl; LitMag; Mdrgl; NHS; NatlMeritCmnd; Orch; StuCncl; EldAwd; Northwestern Univ; International Service.

SOLOMON, Ximena M; St Anns HS; Chicago, IL; College; Professional.

SOLOW, Cindy; Grandville HS; Grand Rapids, MI; NatlMeritCmnd; TchrAde; Grand Valley State College; Spanish Teacher.

SOLOWAY, Bruce J; Reed City HS; Paris, MI; CmntyWkr; HonRl; TchrAde; SchPpr; Bsbl; Ftbl; Tennis; College; Mechanic.

SOLOWAY, David M; Evanston Township HS; Evanston, IL; HonRl; SctActv; CaptSocr; Univ; Biology.

SOLT, Thomas A; Wright City HS; Lake Sherwood, MO; PresFrshCls; PresSophCls; NHS; SchPpr; CitAwd; Medicine.

SOLTYS, Tina; Thomas Kelly Hs; Chicago, IL; 5/415 HonRl; PresNHS; OffAde; PepBnd; TchrAde; SpnCl; MthCl; PpCl; PresGAA; BttyCrckrAwd; Loyola U;business Accounting.

SOLTYSINSKI, Susan M; Elizabeth Seton HS; Chicago, IL; 21/265 Chrs; HonRl; Mdrgl; NHS; SchMus; Purdue Univ; Lawyer.

SOLUM, James E; Larimore HS; Larimore, ND; Chrs; ChrhWkr; FFA; College; Religion.

SOLWOLD, Alan; Oak Grove Lutheran HS; Moorhead, MN; PresSophCls; Chr; Chrl; CmntyWkr; JA; StuCncl; StuGov; Wrstlng; IMSpt;.

SOLYNJES, Mark; Wahpeton HS; Wahpeton, ND; HonRl; KeyCl; Bsktbl; Trk; Wrstlng; IMSpt; Coll; Engineering.

SOLZE, Rodney F; Nes Tre La Go HS; Shields, KS; PresFrshCls; Chr; HonRl; Yrbk; SchPpr; Bsbl; Bsktbl; Trk; 4-HAwd; PresAwd; Farmer.

SOMBERG, Peter D; Glenbrook North HS; Northbrook, IL; 91/650 HonRl; LatCl; CaptWrstlng; Coe College; Law.

SOMERO, Lynn C; Hancock Central HS; Dollar Bay, MI; 16/90 ALAGirlsSt; HonRl; SchPl; GAA; Mi Tech Univ; Liberal Arts.

SOMERS, Evelyn E; Rock Bridge HS; Columbia, MO; NatlMeritSchl; PolWkr; RptrYrbk; SchPpr; Macalester College; Foreign Language.

SOMERVILLE, Peggy L; Algonac HS; Algonac, MI; Chrs; HonRl; NHS; St Clair County Comm College; Secretary.

SOMERVILLE, Susan L; Woodruff HS; Peoria, IL; AFS; VPChr; VPOrch; SchMus; SchPl; RptrSchPpr; KeyCl; SecFrCl; PresGerCl; Ill Weslyan Univ; Music.

SOMMA, Andrew; Holy Cross HS; Elmwood Park, IL; 18/308 Clge; Illustration.

SOMMARS, Wayne; Alton Sr Hs; Godfrey, IL; HonRl; NHS; Trk; S I U E;engineering.

SOMMER, Cynthia A; Immaculate Conception HS; Elmhurst, IL; 73/166 Aud/Vis; Chrs; HonRl; SchPl; TchrAde; Yrbk; SpnCl; PpCl; CaptBsktbl; IMSpt; College; Business Management.

SOMMER, Daniel K; Brimfield HS; Brimfield, IL; 9/60 HonRl; LbryAde; StuCncl; FFA; SpnCl; LetterBsbl; Wrstlng; IMSpt; Murray St U; Bus Admin.

SOMMER, Judith A; Pekin Comm HS; Pekin, IL; 11/759 ChrhWkr; CncrtBnd; HonRl; MrchBnd; NHS; Orch; SchMus; 4-H; FrCl; GAA; Goshen College; Physical Therapy.

SOMMER, Ronda K; Mission Valley HS; Eskridge, KS; Band; Chrs; HonRl; NHS; PepBnd; TchrAde; 4-H; FHA; College; Receptionist.

SOMMER, Tracy W; Comstock Park HS; Comstock Park, MI; HonRl; JA; College; Mechcanical Engineer.

SOMMERER, John; Wauwatosa West HS; Wauwatosa, WI; 1/436 ALBoysSt; NatlMeritSchl; EdSchPpr; AmLegAwd; NCTE; PresAwd; VoiceDemAwd; Wa Univ; Research Medicine.

SOMMERER, Julie L; Murphysboro HS; Murphysboro, IL; 4/220 Chrs; ChrhWkr; Mdrgl; SchMus; RptrYrbk; RptrSchPpr; College; Music.

SOMMERER, Kendra K; Logan View HS; Craig, NE; ALAGirlsSt; Band; CncrtBnd; HonRl; MrchBnd; PpCl; SciCl; Bsktbl; Trk; Chrldr; GAA; AmLegAwd; Trade School.

SOMMERFELDT, Ann M; Msgr Hackett HS; Kalamazoo, MI; 7/144 PresCncrtBnd; HonRl; NHS; Orch; SchMus; SctActv; Univ; Librarian.

SOMMERHALDER, Elizabeth J; Lewiston Consolidated HS; Steinauer, NE; Band; Chrs; ChrhWkr; HonRl; YthFlsp; Yrbk; FHA; PpCl; College; Nurse.

SOMMERLOT, Cynthia; Tripoli Community HS; Tripoli, IA; 1/66 Chr; Chrs; HonRl; HospAde; NHS; RedCrAde; SchMus; EdSchPpr; PPFtbl; Allen Memorial Sch Of Nursing; Rn.

SOMMERS, Jeffry R; Wahlert HS; Dubuque, IA; HonRl; StuGov; PpCl; LetterFtbl; IMSpt; St Johns U; Cpa.

SOMMERS, Mary A; Andrew HS; Bellevue, IA; 5/40 SecTrsFrshCls; Band; Chrs; CncrtBnd; HonRl; NHS; StuCncl; YthFlsp; LetterBsktbl; LetterTrk; College.

SOMMERS, Mary M; Random Lake HS; Random Lake, WI; 21/98 VPAFS; HonRl; Mdrgl; NatlMeritCmnd; SchMus; Yrbk; EdSchPpr; FBLA; SecPpCl; Chrldr; GAA; University Of Wisconsin; Fashion Merch.

SOMMERS, Roxanna R; Main Street HS; Spring Grove, IL; College; Professional.

SOMMERS, Teresa J; Andrew HS; Andrew, IA; 1/33 VPSrCls; PresChrs; PresNHS; NatlThespSoc; PresStuCncl; PresGerCl; LetterBsbl; CaptBsktbl; LetterTrk; DARAwd; Marycrest College; Nursing.

SOMMERVILLE, Vivian; Parker Sr HS; Janesville, WI; 92/387 BttyCrckrAwd; CitAwd; Univ Of Wi; Home Ec.

SOMOGYI, Cynthia L; Limestone Comm HS; Bartonville, IL; 23/396 HonRl; NHS; TchrAde; College; Business Administration.

SONDAG, Joan; FormanHS; Manito, IL; 8/69 SecSrCls; Chrs; HonRl; JrNHS; Mdrgl; NHS; SchMus; SchPl; Bsktbl; GAA; College; Business.

SONDAY, Roy; Monroe HS; Monroe, MI; HonRl; College; Cpa Laywer.

SONDGEROTH, Lorraine L; Mendota HS; Mendota, IL; Chr; Chrl; Chrs; ChrhWkr; HonRl; 4-H; 4-HAwd; College.

SONDGEROTH, Michael S; Yankton Sr HS; Yankton, SD; ALBoysSt; ChrhWkr; HonRl; NatlFornLg; NatlThespSoc; SchMus; RptrSchPpr; SciCl; LetterTennis; VoiceDemAwd; College; Professional.

SONDHAUS, Elizabeth L; Clayton HS; Clayton, MO; 15/201 CmntyWkr; NatlMeritSF; RptrSchPpr; FrCl; SpnCl; PpCl; LetterBsktbl; LetterTennis; Washington Univ; Physician.

SONDHELM, Deborah B; Ida Crown Jewish Academy; Chicago, IL; 5/71 Chr; HonRl; NHS; OffAde; SchPl; StuCncl; Univ; Liberal Arts.

SONEFELD, Debra J; Freeland HS; Freeland, MI; 3/120 Chr; HonRl; NHS; NatlMeritSchl; RedCrAde; SchMus; SchPl; TchrAde; PpCl; PPFtbl; U Of Mich; Forestry.

SONG, Kit M; Mason City HS; Mason City, IA; HonRl; ModUN; NHS; NatlThespSoc; StuCncl; LatCl; SciCl; Ftbl; LetterSwmmng; AmLegAwd; Univ Of Minn; Medica Doctor.

SONGER, Matthew N; Wayland Academy; Northbrook, IL; 2/80 Aud/Vis; HonRl; LbryAde; RptrYrbk; GerCl; SciCl; Ftbl; Glf; Amherst College; Doctor.

SONKSEN, Lori L; Mallard Comm HS; Curlew, IA; 6/33 Chrs; DrlTm; HonRl; SchPl; YthFlsp; SchPpr; 4-H; Bsktbl; Chrldr; 4-HAwd; Business School; Secretary.

SONNEMAN, Jean E; Central HS; Rapid City, SD; 6/559 ALAGirlsSt; HonRl; LitMag; NHS; PolWkr; TreasYthFlsp; EdSchPpr; 4-H; SciCl; Carleton College.

SONTA, Irene Y; Notre Dame HS; Chicago, IL; 19/303 Chr; HonRl; NHS; OffAde; Bsktbl; Swmmng; Chrldr; GAA; Loyola University; Nursing.

SONTAG, Tim; Edwardsville Sr HS; Edwardsville, IL; HonRl; NHS; NatlMeritCmnd; MthCl; College; Environmental Design.

SOORHOLTZ, Joni L; West Marshall HS; Melbourne, IA; Chr; Chrs; CmntyWkr; HonRl; MrchBnd; YthFlsp; EdSchPpr; PpCl; Bsktbl; Trk; Ia U; Biology.

SOPRON, Debbie A; Lourdes HS; Chicago, IL; 26/299 ChrhWkr; HonRl; NatlFornLg; NHS; Quill&Scroll; TchrAde; EdSchPpr; College; Speech Pathology.

SORANNO, David A; Barrington HS; Barrington, IL; 27/652 HonRl; NHS; LetterBsktbl; Ftbl; Tennis; IMSpt; Univ; Science.

SOREM, Richard J; Jetmore HS; Jetmore, KS; 3/45 Band; ChrhWkr; CmntyWkr; CncrtBnd; HonRl; MrchBnd; Univ Of Kansas; Business.

SORENSEN, Ann L; Warren Tw HS; Wildwood, IL; Chr; HonRl; HospAde; LbryAde; NatlThespSoc; SchPl; StuCncl; StuGov; EdSchPpr; Elmhurst College; Journalism.

SORENSEN, Carol; Verdigre Public HS; Verdigre, NE; 22/38 Band; Chrs; ChrhWkr; CmntyWkr; SchMus; YthFlsp; 4-H; PpCl; 4-HAwd; Trade School; Vocational.

SORENSEN, Charles; Belleville HS; Belleville, MI; Band; HonRl; Socr; IMSpt; Michiga Stae Univ; Chem Major.

SORENSEN, Cliff A; South Sioux City Senior HS; South Sioux City, NE; Band; JA; SchMus; SpnCl; LetterBsktbl; IMSpt; University Of Nebraska; Pharmacy.

SORENSEN, Craig R; Wawasee HS; Milford, IN; ALBoysSt; HonRl; Bsktbl; College.

SORENSEN, Dennis R; Galva Community HS; Galvo, IA; 4/19 TrsFrshCls; Band; CncrtBnd; HonRl; MrchBnd; ModUN; YthFlsp; RptrYrbk; 4-H; FrCl; Univ; Pro.

SORENSEN, Linda K; Stapleton HS; Gandy, NE; 1/17 Band; Chrs; CncrtBnd; HonRl; MrchBnd; NHS; PepBnd; SchPl; Yrbk; PpCl; LetterTrk; Chrldr; GAA; IMSpt;.

SORENSEN, Marcia C; Elkhorn Kimballton HS; Elk Horn, IA; 1/37 PresJrCls; Band; Chrs; CncrtBnd; Mdrgl; MrchBnd; NHS; SchMus; StuCncl; ChmnChrldr; Midland Lutheran College; Nursing.

SORENSEN, Mark; Durant Community Hs; Durant, IA; 8/78 PresFrshCls; TrsJrCls; HonRl; JrNHS; ModUN; NHS; StuCncl; LetterBsbl; Bsktbl; Glf; College Or U;engineering Or Accounting.

SORENSEN, Michelle S; Ogallala HS; Ogallala, NE; Chr; Chrl; Chrs; NatlThespSoc; SchAde; SchPl; YthFlsp; PpCl; Trk; Chrldr; University; Nursing.

SORENSEN, Nelsen S; Frontier HS; Brookston, IN; PresFrshCls; VPSophCls; HonRl; NHS; YthFlsp; Bsktbl; Ftbl; Trk; Ball St Univ; Forestry.

SORENSEN, Randall C; Kenmare HS; Kenmare, ND; VPFrshCls; ALBoysSt; HonRl; NHS; StuCncl; YthFlsp; FFA; Bsbl; LetterGlf; College; Accounting.

SORENSEN, Randy H; East Grand Forks HS; East Grand Forks, MN; CmntyWkr; SctActv; Univ; Business.

SORENSEN, Rhonda L; Oak Park HS; Gladstone, MO; Chr; Chrs; HonRl; LbryAde; SchMus; TchrAde; RptrYrbk; Yrbk; RptrSchPpr; SchPpr; Maple Woods Jr College; Cpa.

SORENSEN, Robert E; Florence HS; Florence, SD; 3/14 Band; Chrl; HonRl; MrchBnd; PepBnd; SchPl; Bsktbl; LetterFtbl; LetterTrk; Trade Of Business School; Vocational.

SORENSEN, Robin A; Taft HS; Chicago, IL; 22/790 HonRl; NHS; TchrAde; SpnCl; PpCl; GAA; Univ Of Ill; Anthropology.

SORENSEN, Susan; Gretna Jr Sr HS; Gretha, NE; 4/80 ALAGirlsSt; Chrs; PresFrshCls; NHS; SchMus; SchPl; 4-H; FHA; DanFAwd; 4-HAwd; Trade School; Fashion Field.

SORENSEN, Susan K; Waukegan East HS; Waukegan, IL; 25/1050 Chr; DrmBgl; JrNHS; NHS; Twrl; RptrYrbk; LetterSwmmng; CaptChrldr; AmLegAwd; Michigan State Univ; Prof Figure Skater.

SORENSON, Dave A; Preston HS; Preston, MN; Band; Chrs; CncrtBnd; HonRl; Mdrgl; NHS; PresStuCncl; FFA; LetterBsktbl; LetterTrk; Univ Of Minnesota; Business Electronics.

SORENSON, Dean C; Oregon HS; Oregon, WI; Orch; Swmmng; Tennis; Wrstlng; Milwaukee Sch Of Eng; Elec Eng.

SORENSON, Janet G; Luck Public HS; Luck, WI; 2/53 SecTrsFrshCls; ALAGirlsSt; Band; Chr; TreasNHS; SchPpr; VPFHA; Bsktbl; CaptTrk; LetterGAA; U Of Wis Eau Claire; Accounting.

SORENSON, Jay C; Argyle Public HS; Argyle, MN; PresSophCls; PresSrCls; Aud/Vis; Chr; Chrs; HonRl; LbryAde; SchMus; SptEdSchPpr; Bsbl; LetterBsktbl; LetterFtbl; LetterGlf; Trade Schl; Vocation.

SORENSON, Jeffrey; Luck HS; Luck, WI; PresSrCls; Band; CncrtBnd; MrchBnd; YthFlsp; 4-H; Bsktbl; Trk; Coll.

SORENSON, Keith M; Park River HS; Park River, ND; FFA; SciCl; Bsktbl; Ftbl; Glf; University; Professional.

SORENSON, Lori J; Newcastle Public HS; Newcastle, NE; VPSrCls; ChrhWkr; DrlTm; HonRl; OffAde; SchPl; TchrAde; SchPpr; PpCl; Chrldr;.

SORG, Joellen C; Meridian Senior HS; Hope, MI; 4/125 Band; HonRl; NHS; NatlThespSoc; SchMus; YthFlsp; VP4-H; Bsktbl; LetterChrldr; BttyCrckrAwd; PresAwd; Michigan State University; Medicine.

SORGATZ, Julie K; Arlington HS; Arlington Hts, IL; 28/598 Band; Chrs; HonRl; MrchBnd; NHS; Orch; Northwestern Univ; Professional.

SORGENFREY, Sandra L; Durant Community HS; Stockton, IA; Band; HonRl; JrNHS; NHS; RptrYrbk; RptrSchPpr; 4-H;.

SORIC, Susan E; Parkview HS; Springfield, MO; HonRl; NatlFornLg; SchPl; StuCncl; RptrYrbk; RptrSchPpr; SecCivCl; PpCl; LetterTennis; IMSpt; Smsu And Mu; Plantoenter Law Journalism.

SORKIN, Lynne S; Niles Twp West HS; Lincolnwood, IL; 29/666 Chr; Chrs; HonRl; Twrl; FTA; Univ Of Illinois; Medical Lab Science.

SORLEY, Brian S; Ben Davis HS; Indianapolis, IN; CmntyWkr; HonRl; NHS; StuCncl; TchrAde; LetterBsbl; LetterFtbl; Tennis; IMSpt; Purdue Univ; Engineering.

SORRELL, Jeffrey A; Waldron HS; Shelbyville, IN; Band; CncrtBnd; RptrYrbk; RptrSchPpr; LetterBsbl; LetterBsktbl; LetterTrk; College; Coach.

SORRELL, Larry; Fulton HS; Hubbardston, MI; TrsSophCls; Band; HonRl; StuCncl; College; Electronics.

SORRELS, Nan; Anna Jonesboro HS; Anna, IL; 20/136 HonRl; Yrbk; FTA; FrCl; PpCl; Bsktbl; Trk; PresGAA; PresAwd; Univ Of Tn; Social Work.

SORRILL, Dennis R; Liberty HS; Quincy, IL; VPFrshCls; PresJrCls; NHS; SchPl; 4-H; VPFFA; SciCl; LetterBsbl; Trk; 4-HAwd; College; Agriculture.

SORRILL, Lise A; Triopia HS; Meredosia, IL; Chrs; HonRl; SchPl; 4-H; LetterBsbl; LetterTrk; 4-HAwd; Nursing Sch; Rn.

SORRILL, Pamela S; Liberty HS; Liberty, IL; 23/56 HonRl; VPYthFlsp; Yrbk; SchPpr; Pres4-H; PresFBLA; PpCl; Trk; SecGAA; 4-HAwd; Business School; Legal Sec.

SORSEN, Steve; Milbank HS; Milbank, SD; Band; ChrhWkr; CmntyWkr; JrNHS; NHS; PolWkr; SctActv; StuGov; IMSpt; Univ; Carpentry.

SORTOR, Robin; Phillips Exeter Academy; Hales Corner, WI; HonRl; NatlMeritSF; SchMus; SchPl; SctActv; RptrSchPpr; FrCl; College.

SORUM, Shelley F; Rushford Public HS; Rushford, MN; Chr; HonRl; LbryAde; Winona Vo Tech Univ; General Office Clerk.

SORZICKAS, Jill S; Waukegan East HS; Waukegan, IL; Band; CncrtBnd; MrchBnd; PepBnd; SchMus; LetterBsbl; LetterSwmmng; GAA; MasAwd; PresAwd; University; Elementary Education.

SOSA, Roger A; Chominade College Prep; Germantown, IL; 6/116 Band; CncrtBnd; HonRl; LitMag; VPNHS; PepBnd; SchPl; OptClAwd; Clge; Md.

SOSA, Steve; West Washington HS; Campbellsburg, IN; 1/93 CncrtBnd; HonRl; MrchBnd; NHS; PepBnd; FFA; SpnCl; SciCl; Us Air Force Acad; Aviation.

SOSINSKE, Janet G; Stewartville HS; Stewartville, MN; 1/98 Chrs; HonRl; SchPl; TchrAde; EdYrBk; FHA; TreasFTA; Rochester Comm College; Liberal Arts.

SOSKIN, Susan E; Parkway Central HS; Chesterfield, MO; 44/455 AFS; SchPpr; IMSpt; Univ Of Missouri; International Relations.

SOSNOVSKE, Kathryn A; Antigo Senior HS; Antigo, WI; 6/376 Band; CncrtBnd; MrchBnd; NatlFornLg; PepBnd; SchPl; TchrAde; RptrSchPpr; LatCl; IMSpt; Uw Madison; Biological Sciences.

SOSNOWSKI, Cynthia H; Lincoln Way HS; Frankfort, IL; HonRl; NHS; StuCncl; TchrAde; Illinois St Univ; Special Educ.

SOSNOWSKI, John S; Amos Alonzo Stagg HS; Palos Hills, IL; 26/478 HonRl; LitMag; ModUN; NHS; SchPpr; LetterTennis; GovHonPrgAwd; College; History.

SOSNOWSKI, Linda M; C S Mott Sr HS; Sterling Heights, MI; PresFrshCls; PresSophCls; PresJrCls; PresSrCls; HonRl; NHS; NatlMeritSchl; NatlThespSoc; EdYrBk; EdSchPpr; Univ Of Mich; Prof Medical Field.

SOTHMAN, Kyle M; Griswold HS; Griswold, IA; 3/78 HonRl; NHS; 4-H; SpnCl; PpCl; Bsktbl; College; Law.

SOTTER, Andrea K; Glenbrook North HS; Northbrook, IL; Chrl; Chrs; HonRl; Mdrgl; OffAde; PolWkr; SchMus; StuGov; IMSpt; Univ Of Ill; Music Education.

SOUBY, Myra C; Central HS; Grand Forks, ND; Band; ChrhWkr; CncrtBnd; HonRl; JrNHS; NHS; SchMus; SctActv; FrCl; University; Professional.

SOUCEK, Sandy J; Seward HS; Seward, NE; PresJrCls; Band; Chr; HonRl; Mdrgl; PolWkr; SchPl; StuCncl; 4-H; PpCl; Univ.

SOUCHEK, Marie A; Lawrence HS; Deweese, NE; ALAGirlsSt; Chrs; CncrtBnd; HonRl; NHS; SchPl; Yrbk; 4-H; PpCl; Trk; Coll; Spec Educ.

SOUCHERAY, Alisan M; Hill Murray HS; Mahtomedi, MN; TrsJrCls; PresSrCls; Chrs; HonRl; SchMus; StuGov; FrCl; Trk; IMSpt; College; Enviromental Sciences.

SOUDEN, Janet; Fredericktown HS; Fredericktown, MO; ChrhWkr; FHA; PpCl; Bsbl; Trk; Armed Forces; Police Officer.

SOUDEN, Karla L; St Charles HS; St Charles, MI; Chr; Chrs; HonRl; HospAde; NHS; SchPl; StuGov; Nursing School; Nurse.

SOUDER, Brenda K; Lafayette Co C I HS; Higginsville, MO; SecSophCls; AFS; Band; DrmMjrt; HonRl; MrchBnd; Twrl; SecFrCl; PpCl; SecSciCl; Business School; Curriculum Of Major Study.

SOUDERS, Sherrie K; Kapaun Mt Carmel HS; Wichita, KS; Ks St; Veterinarians Asst.

SOUFFRANT, Donald J; Hillcrest HS; Hazel Crest, IL; 58/478 Chr; ChrhWkr; CncrtBnd; Mdrgl; MrchBnd; NHS; PepBnd; SctActv; YthFlsp; LetterSwmmng; College; Business.

SOUKUP, Joan M; Marian HS; Omaha, NE; HonRl; JA; LbryAde; NatlFornLg; NHS; SctActv; Sdlty; SpnCl; MthCl; College; Medical Health.

SOUKUP, Timothy R; Regis HS; Cedar Rapids, IA; Chr; Chrl; Chrs; ChrhWkr; CmntyWkr; SchMus; SctActv; CchngActv; IMSpt; Loras Clg; Phys Ed.

SOUL, Janice C; Phillips HS; Phillips, WI; 15/106 Band; CncrtBnd; HonRl; MrchBnd; PepBnd; Bsktbl; Trk; GAA; Univ Of Wisconsin; Computer Science.

SOULE, Mark S; Hackett HS; Kalamazoo, MI; ChrhWkr; CmntyWkr; JA; PolWkr; StuCncl; StuGov; UNYO; 4-H; Bsktbl; Tennis; College; Law.

SOULEK, Barbara A; Kimball HS; Kimball, SD; Chrs; HonRl; 4-H; FHA; PpCl; Trk; 4-HAwd; Trade School;.

SOULEK, Daniel J; East Charles HS; Armour, SD; ChrhWkr; CmntyWkr; HonRl; FFA; MthCl; Bsktbl; LetterFtbl; LetterTrk; LetterWrstlng; VoiceDemAwd; Trade School; Agriculture.

SOULIGNY, Ann C; Watseka Comm HS; Watseka, IL; 26/159 LbryAde; NatlThespSoc; SchPl; TchrAde; RptrYrbk; RptrSchPpr; FTA; Indiana Univ; Stage Tech.

SOUR, Joan; Hamlin HS; Hazel, SD; 32/73 CmntyWkr; HonRl; MrchBnd; SchPl; Yrbk; FBLA; Bsktbl; Trk; GAA; IMSpt;.

SOUREK, Lynn M; Morton East HS; Cicero, IL;

Chrs; HonRl; IntrClCncl; StuGov; SpnCl; Univ Of Illinois; Political Science.

SOUSLEY, Timothy A; Allegan HS; Allegan, MI; HonRl; ModUN; NHS; LatCl; PpCl; LetterBsbl; Hope College; Secondary Education.

SOUTH, Mary; Richland HS; Essey, MO; 3/33 TrsSophCls; HonRl; Yrbk; Se Mo State.

SOUTH, Randal; Central HS; Albert Lea, MN; HonRl; Austin Comm College; Liberal Arts.

SOUTHARD, Beth A; Hamilton Heights HS; Noblesville, IN; 2/102 VPSophCls; PresJrCls; ALAGirlsSt; HonRl; VPNHS; SecStuCncl; PresMthCl; SecSciCl; LetterBsktbl; GAA; Univ; Certified Public Accountant.

SOUTHARD, Clifford V; Harrisonville HS; Harrisonville, MO; SecTrsSophCls; Band; CncrtBnd; HonRl; PepBnd; Quill&Scroll; SctActv; RptrSchPpr; SchPpr;.

SOUTHARD, Demar R; Washington HS; Cedar Rapids, IA; 40/476 Chr; PresCncrtBnd; MrchBnd; NHS; NatlThespSoc; Orch; PepBnd; SchMus; SchPl; RptrYrbk; Univ Of Iowa; Music.

SOUTHARD, Peggy; Schuyler Hs; Queen City, MO; 14/85 Band; Chrs; CncrtBnd; HonRl; MrchBnd; NHS; SctActv; YthFlsp; Pres4-H; FBLA; Business School; Secretary.

SOUTHCOMBE, Michael T; Glenbard East HS; Lombard, IL; 77/656 ChrhWkr; VPNatlFornLg; NHS; NatlMeritCmnd; Quill&Scroll; SchPpr; GerCl; University Of Illinois; Law.

SOUTHER, Sandra K; Lockport Central HS; Lockport, IL; Chrs; ChrhWkr; HonRl; NHS; Lewis University; Nursing.

SOUTHERLAN, Penny S; Beason Comm HS; Lincoln, IL; 3/13 SecFrshCls; SecSophCls; SecJrCls; Chr; Chrs; ChrhWkr; HonRl; Mdrgl; SchMus; SchPl; TchrAde; YthFlsp; FHA; GerCl; CaptChrldr; College; Nursing.

SOUTHERN, David D; New Trier East HS; Kenilworth, IL; 55/847 Band; Chr; ChrhWkr; CncrtBnd; HonRl; Orch; SchMus; Univ; Business.

SOUTHERN, Kyle D; Lake Park HS; Roselle, IL; ChrhWkr; NatlFornLg; StuCncl; TchrAde; College; Law.

SOUTHLEA, Patricia; Our Lady Star Of The Sea HS; Grosse Pte Woods, MI; PresFrshCls; PresSophCls; SecTrsJrCls; SecTrsSrCls; NatlFornLg; NHS; SchMus; SchPl; Marygrove College; Secondary Eng Teacher.

SOUTHOFF, David A; Rock Falls HS; Rock Falls, IL; 3/250 HonRl; NHS; 4-H; LetterTrk; AmLegAwd; EldAwd; Bradley University; Electronics.

SOUTHWICK, Keith L; South Shore HS; Stockholm, SD; 1/8 PresFrshCls; PresJrCls; ALBoysSt; HonRl; SptEdYrbk; Bsktbl; LetterTrk; AmLegAwd; ChmbCommrsAwd; Pres4-HAwd; CitAwd; College; Music.

SOUTOR, Mark V; Henning HS; Hennings, MN; 5/61 Chr; SchPl; PresStuCncl; CaptBsbl; CaptBsktbl; CaptFtbl; CaptTrk; United State Coast Guad Academy; Biology.

SOUZA, Martha S; Fountain Central HS; Kingman, IN; 20/124 ChrhWkr; HonRl; NHS; OffAde; YthFlsp; SpnCl; Trk; GAA; University; Missionary Nurse.

SOUZA, Matthew F; Columbus North HS; Columbus, IN; 27/513 PresFrshCls; VPAFS; ChrhWkr; LitMag; NatlFornLg; NatlMeritFnl; Quill&Scroll; SchPl; StuCncl; LetterSwmmng; University; Professional.

SOVA, Laura L; St Francis Academy; Joliet, IL; 3/176 SecFrshCls; CmntyWkr; HonRl; NHS; NatlMeritCmnd; NatlThespSoc; SchPl; StuCncl; StuGov; RptrYrbk; Physician.

SOVA, Mary C; Marian HS; Omaha, NE; 12/162 TrsSophCls; HonRl; HospAde; NHS; SctActv; FrCl; Bsbl; College; Medicine.

SOVERN, Ellen E; New Trier West HS; Wilmette, IL; 26/694 AFS; HonRl; JrNHS; NatlMeritCmnd; SecNatlThespSoc; SchMus; SchPl; StuGov; FrCl; Univ Of Virginia; Mathematics.

SOVINSKI, Candy; Suring HS; Suring, WI; Band; HonRl; SchPl; StuCncl; RptrYrbk; EdSchPpr; Chrldr; 4-HAwd; PresAwd; Univ; Writer.

SOWA, Sharon L; Bishop Noll Institute; Munster, IN; 50/360 HonRl; LitMag; MthCl; GAA; University.

SOWADA, Sandra M; Little Falls Comm HS; Little Falls, MN; HonRl; College; Accounting.

SOWDEN, Scottie L; Yale HS; Yale, MI; Chr; HonRl; SchPl; YthFlsp; Yrbk; W Michigan Unv; Medicine.

SOWDER, Debra; Charlestown HS; Charlestown, IN; 18/200 ChrhWkr; HonRl; NHS; TchrAde; RptrYrbk; FTA; FrCl; Nursing.

SOWDER, Lori L; Madrid Community HS; Madrid, IA; 47/65 Chr; Chrs; ChrhWkr; DrlTm; MrchBnd; SchMus; TchrAde; YthFlsp; Yrbk; 4-H;.

SOWERS, Cheryl A; Newton HS; Jewett, IL; 16/187 Band; Chr; ChrhWkr; CncrtBnd; MrchBnd; NHS; Trk; Chrldr; GAA; IMSpt; 4-HAwd; JCAwd; E Illinois Univ; Physical Ed.

SOWERS, Christine L; Fountain Central HS; Hillsboro, IN; 2/128 Chr; Chrs; ChrhWkr; HonRl; Mdrgl; NHS; OffAde; Business School; Exec Secretary.

SOWERS, Jo E; Fountain Central HS; Kingman, IN; 12/128 Band; Chr; ChrhWkr; HonRl; SecNHS; SchPl; TchrAde; EdYrBk; PpCl; DARAwd; In State U; Elementary Ed.

SOWERS, Kyle C; Leo HS; Grabill, IN; PresSrCls; Chr; Chrs; DrlTm; NHS; SchPl; StuGov; PresYthFlsp; PresPpCl; DARAwd; Manchester College.

SOYK, Kathy A; Parkston HS; Dimock, SD; Band; Chr; Chrs; ChrhWkr; CncrtBnd; Mdrgl; SchMus; SchPl; RptrYrbk; RptrSchPpr; College; Secondary Ed.

SPADARO, Julie A; Airport HS; Newport, MI; SecJrCls; HonRl; NHS; SchPl; StuCncl; RptrSchPpr; SptEdSchPpr; PpCl; Bsktbl; CaptTrk; IMSpt; Coll; Social Worker.

SPADONI, David G; Nevada HS; Nevada, MO; CncrtBnd; MrchBnd; ROTC; SctActv; PpCl; LetterBsbl; LetterBsktbl; LetterFtbl; LetterTrk; IMSpt; Univ Of Mo; Navy.

SPAETH, Mark J; West Bend East HS; West Bend, WI; 1/243 HonRl; NHS; NatlMeritCmnd; SchMus; SchPl; PresStuGov; LetterFtbl; Trk; RotaryAwd; University Of Wisconsin; Surgeon.

SPAGNVOLO, Achilles W; Hill Comm HS; Lansing, MI; Chr; Chrl; Chrs; ChrhWkr; HonRl; JA; NHS; SchMus; SchPl; SctActv; TchrAde; YthFlsp; 4-H; Hope College; Psychology.

SPAHN, Mary M; Immaculate Heart Of Mary HS; Westchester, IL; Sacrstn; TchrAde; SchPpr; FrCl; Bsktbl; Tennis; CaptTrk; Chrldr; CchngActv; GAA; College; Physical Ed.

SPAHR, Perry; Huntington North HS; Warren, IN; HonRl; YthFlsp; 4-H; FFA; 4-HAwd; PresAwd; Coll.

SPAINHOUR, Sara A; Cheney HS; Cheney, KS; Chr; Chrl; HonRl; Mdrgl; MrchBnd; PepBnd; SchMus; TchrAde; RptrYrbk; Friends Univ Wichita; Elem Music Educ.

SPAINHOWER, Patricia A; Princeton Comm HS; Princeton, IN; 1/190 Band; ChrhWkr; CncrtBnd; HonRl; JrNHS; NHS; TchrAde; MthCl; PpCl; Univ Of Evansville; Accounting.

SPAK, Karen E; Waterford Township HS; Pontiac, MI; HonRl; NHS; StuGov; EdYrBk; Bsktbl; CchngActv; Mi State U.

SPALDING, John; Pontiac Twp HS; Pontiac, IL; PresFrshCls; PresSophCls; ChrhWkr; CmntyWkr; HonRl; NHS; StuCncl; KeyCl; Knox Coll; Med.

SPALL, James C; Rochester Adams HS; Rochester, MI; TchrAde; LetterGlf; LetterTennis; Oakland U; Eng.

SPANBERGER, Linda S; Stephen Decatur HS; Decatur, IL; 14/368 Chr; HonRl; NHS; 4-H; KeyCl; DanFAwd; College; Designer.

SPANGELO, James K; Cavalier #6 HS; Hensel, ND; PresJrCls; Band; Chrs; CncrtBnd; HonRl; MrchBnd; PepBnd; StuCncl; Bsktbl; LetterFtbl; University; Professional.

SPANGENBERG, Ruth; Appleton HS West; Appleton, WI; ALAGirlsSt; Chr; CncrtBnd; Mdrgl; NHS; NatlThespSoc; Orch; SchMus; SchPl; RptrSchPpr; Univ Of Wi; Voice.

SPANGLER, Jeff J; Prairie HS; Ely, IA; Band; HonRl; SchMus; SpnCl; Bsktbl; Univ Of Iowa; Music.

SPANGLER, Kathryn; Oak Creek Sr HS; Oak Creek, WI; 11/342 HonRl; NHS; SpnCl; Univ Of Wi Madison; Dietitian.

SPANGLER, Lori F; Morgan Public HS; Morgan, MN; SchPl; YthFnd; 4-H; FTA; LetterTrk; GAA; PPFtbl; College; Major Study.

SPANGLER, Shirley; Worthington Jefferson HS; Worthington, IN; VPSrCls; Chrs; HonRl; NHS; 4-H; PpCl; GAA; 4-HAwd; College; German.

SPANGUS, Ursula M; Sterling Hts HS; Warren, MI; 15/600 ChrhWkr; HonRl; NHS; PresGerCl; GAA; IMSpt; N Michigan Univ; Special Ed.

SPANHAKE, Susan M; Leigh Comm HS; Leigh, NE; ALAGirlsSt; Band; ChrhWkr; HonRl; PepBnd; FHA; GerCl; Bsktbl; Trk; PPFtbl; Univ; Bus.

SPANIOL, Jane M; Charleston HS; Charleston, IL; TrsJrCls; AFS; Band; Chrs; HonRl; NHS; SecStuCncl; EdYrBk; Yrbk; Swmmng;.

SPANN, James F; Gregory HS; Gregory, SD; 5/46 Chr; Chrs; CmntyWkr; HonRl; 4-H; Trk; AmLegAwd; 4-HAwd; VFWAwd; College; Pilot.

SPANN, Katharine; Marian HS; Birmingham, MI; ChrhWkr; HonRl; ModUN; College; Math Business Major.

SPANN, Linda; Steinmetz Hs; Chicago, IL; Chr; CmntyWkr; HonRl; HospAde; NHS; StuCncl; StuGov; TchrAde; SchPpr; Trk; College; Registered Nurse.

SPANYERS, Ruth A; Dorchester Public HS; Dorchester, NE; PresBand; Chr; Chrl; Chrs; CncrtBnd; HonRl; MrchBnd; PepBnd; SchPl; TchrAde; LetterBsktbl; LetterTrk; Chrldr; Josephs College Of Beauty; Professional.

SPARKMAN, Katherine R; Wheaton Christian HS; Glen Ellyn, IL; SecJrCls; Chr; HonRl; LbryAde; SecNHS; SchMus; SecStuCncl; PpCl; AmLegAwd; Wheaton Coll; Medicine.

SPARKMAN, Starla J; Yarbrough HS; Elkhart, KS; 2/12 VPFrshCls; PresSophCls; Band; Chrs; ChrhWkr; CncrtBnd; HonRl; MrchBnd; NHS; SchPl; Bsktbl; Trk; DARAwd; Bob Jones Univ; Business.

SPARKS, Barbara A; Turner HS; Shawnee Mission, KS; Chrs; DrlTm; HonRl; JrNHS; StuCncl; SchPpr; PpCl; Baptist Bible College; Music.

SPARKS, Cheryl J; Fisher HS; Fisher, IL; 6/56 TrsFrshCls; TrsSophCls; PresJrCls; DrlTm; NHS; NatlThespSoc; Yrbk; VP4-H; GAA; VoiceDemAwd; Univ Of Virginia; Therapy.

SPARKS, Jeffrey A; Goodland HS; Goodland, KS; 8/133 ALBoysSt; Band; CncrtBnd; HonRl; MrchBnd; NHS; PepBnd; Quill&Scroll; SchMus; RptrSchPpr; Univ Of Kansas.

SPARKS, Jennifer; Kirksville Senior HS; Kirksville, MO; ChrhWkr; HonRl; MrchBnd; PepBnd; TchrAde; EdYrBk; FFA; PpCl; LetterTennis; GAA; Ne Missouri St Univ; Teach.

SPARKS, Lana M; Lexington HS; Lexington, IL; 3/58 HonRl; JrNHS; NHS; StuCncl; Yrbk; 4-H; FHA; Chrldr; GAA; 4-HAwd; U Of Il; Parks & Recreation.

SPARKS, Mary A; Jeff HS; Jeffersonville, IN; 4-H; FHA; SpnCl; PpCl;.

SPARKS, Mary L; Mount Zion HS; Mount Zion, IL; 25/198 SecAFS; CmntyWkr; HonRl; SchMus; SchPl; TchrAde; RptrYrbk; SchPpr; Illinois State University.

SPARKS, Melody D; Cedar Lake Academy; Nunica, MI; 9/72 SecSrCls; HonRl; NHS; IMSpt; Andrews Univ; Premed.

SPARKS, Teresa A; Worthington Jefferson HS; Worthington, IN; Band; DrlTm; HonRl; MrchBnd; NHS; TchrAde; 4-H; PpCl; LetterBsktbl; 4-HAwd; College.

SPARKS, Vernon; Ri North Callaway HS; Auxvasse, MO; 6/80 PresFrshCls; VPSrCls; HonRl; SchPl; StuCncl; TchrAde; 4-H; SpnCl; IMSpt; College At Westminster; Cpa.

SPARKS, Vernon K; Ri North Callaway HS; Auxvasse, MO; 7/80 VPSrCls; HonRl; StuCncl; TchrAde; 4-H; PresSpnCl; IMSpt; DARAwd; Univ Of Mo.

SPARKS, Virgil; Gideon HS; Gideon, MO; 8/40 ALBoysSt; Band; CncrtBnd; NHS; SchPl; StuCncl; Bsbl; Bsktbl; DARAwd; CitAwd; School Of The Ozarks; Law.

SPARR, Eileen M; H L Richards HS; Palos Heights, IL; 84/1035 Band; ChrhWkr; CtyCnl; HonRl; MrchBnd; TreasNHS; SchAde; TchrAde; GAA; Lewis Univ; Cpa.

SPARROW, Kim A; Warsaw HS; Warsaw, IL; VPJrCls; AFS; Band; Chr; Chrs; ChrhWkr; CncrtBnd; Mdrgl; MrchBnd; SchMus; SchPl; StuCncl; YthFlsp; Yrbk; Business School.

SPATZ, David D; Lakeland Union HS; Minocqua, WI; HonRl; StuCncl; StuGov; RptrYrbk; RptrSchPpr; SchPpr; Ftbl; LetterTrk; AmLegAwd; Technical School; Architecture.

SPAUDE, Jon C; Gibbon HS; Gibbon, MN; VPFrshCls; VPSophCls; HonRl; StuCncl; FFA; LetterBsbl; CaptFtbl; LetterTrk; CchngActv; PresAwd; Clge; Phy Ed.

SPAULDING, Diane M; Lapeer HS; Lapeer, MI; 1/426 HonRl; NHS; NatlMeritCmnd; NatlThespSoc; SchPl; EdYrBk; RptrYrbk; FrCl; PpCl; Tennis; University Of Mi ;surgeon.

SPAULDING, Lynn M; Lincoln HS; Wis Rapids, WI; NatlFornLg; Quill&Scroll; RptrSchPpr; Univ Of Wisc; Law.

SPAULDING, Paul T; Delano HS; Delano, MN; ChrhWkr; CmntyWkr; HonRl; PolWkr; StuGov; YthFlsp; Yrbk; SchPpr; Ftbl; IMSpt; U Of Mn; Business Managemane.

SPAULDING, Shawn A; Breckenridge HS; Merrill, MI; 6/100 Chr; MrchBnd; StuCncl; Twrl; 4-H; Chrldr; College; Radiologic Tech.

SPAYEV, Rodney G; De Pue HS; De Pue, IL; TrsJrCls; Chr; Chrs; ChrhWkr; SctActv; TchrAde; YthFlsp; Yrbk; SciCl; Bsktbl; College; Professional Photography.

SPEAKER, James W; Richmond Burton Community HS; Richmond, IL; 1/110 ALBoysSt; Aud/Vis; CmntyWkr; HonRl; NHS; Illinois State University; Math.

SPEAKS, Marcus L; Chicago Vocational HS; Chicago, IL; 25/997 Chr; Chrl; Chrs; ChrhWkr; HonRl; Mdrgl; NHS; OffAde; Orch; StuCncl; Ill Inst Of Technology; Engineering.

SPEAR, David G; Lawrence HS; Lawrence, KS; HonRl; NatlMeritSF; TchrAde; GerCl; College; Medicine.

SPEAR, Gail L; Jamestown Public HS; Jamestown, KS; 2/6 SecSophCls; SecJrCls; PresSrCls; Chrs; HonRl; Teen; RptrSchPpr; PpCl; Bsbl; Trk; Marriage; Professinal.

SPEAR, Paul R; North Senior HS; Eau Claire, WI; 1/390 HonRl; NHS; NatlMeritCmnd; GerCl; Univ Wi Eau Claire; Computer Science.

SPEAR, Sally L; Washington Park HS; Racine, WI; AFS; Mdrgl; SchMus; TreasGerCl; MthCl; KiwanAwd; University; Engineering.

SPEARS, Bradley R; Bell City HS; Bell City, MO; 5/27 ALBoysSt; Chrs; HonRl; NHS; SchPl; PresStuCncl; PpCl; SciCl; CaptBsktbl; VoiceDemAwd; College.

SPEARS, Lucia M; Shortridge HS; Indianapolis, IN; 8/330 Chr; HonRl; Mdrgl; NHS; NatlThespSoc; SchPl; TreasStuCncl; Purdue Univ; Pre Med.

SPEARS, Mark R; Lucas HS; Lucas, KS; Chrs; HonRl; StuCncl; LetterBsktbl; LetterFtbl; College.

SPEARS, Ronald N; Ottawa Twp HS; Marseilles, IL; 29/420 AFS; Chr; DrmBgl; HonRl; LitMag; Mdrgl; NHS; SchMus; SchPl; Ill State Univ; Music Ed.

SPEARS, Susan E; Southern HS; Stronghurst, IL; 1/56 VPSophCls; PresSrCls; Band; Chrs; CncrtBnd; DrmMjrt; HonRl; MrchBnd; NHS; PepBnd; SchPl; StuCncl; Bsktbl; Western Ill Univ; Special Ed.

SPEARS, Timothy L; Southern HS; Stronghurst, IL; 4/56 PresFrshCls; PresSrCls; TreasBand; CmntyWkr; HonRl; NHS; SchPl; StuCncl; RptrYrbk; RptrSchPpr; Univ Of Illinois; Premed.

SPECHA, Mary L; Oaklawn Community HS; Oak Lawn, IL; Chrs; TchrAde; LetterBsktbl; IMSpt; College; Physical Ed Teacher.

SPECHT, James L; Yates Center HS; Piqua, KS; 9/58 Band; HonRl; MrchBnd; NHS; PepBnd; StuCncl; VPFFA; Bsktbl; Ftbl; LetterTrk; Independence Jr Coll; Agriculture.

SPECHT, Lori D; Davenport West HS; Davenport, IA; Chrs; ChrhWkr; DrlTm; HonRl; PolWkr; RptrSchPpr; GerCl; PpCl; IMSpt; Ia State U; Special Ed.

SPECHT, Michelle M; Iola HS; Piqua, KS; 4/133 HonRl; OffAde; StuCncl; TchrAde; PpCl; LetterBsktbl; LetterTrk; IMSpt; PPFtbl; PresAwd; Ksu ;math.

SPECHT, Scott; Columbus HS; Marshfield, WI; 4/108 Band; CncrtBnd; HonRl; MrchBnd; PepBnd; RptrSchPpr; SchPpr; FrCl; MthCl; Bsktbl; College; Professional.

SPECK, Kathleen M; Denby HS; Detroit, MI; 6/625 Chr; ChrhWkr; NHS; NatlMeritSchl; ROTC; RptrYrbk; RptrSchPpr; Wayne State Univ; Journalism.

SPECKHART, Brenda L; Seymour HS; Quincy, IL; Band; ChrhWkr; HonRl; StuCncl; 4-H; FNA; PpCl; CaptChrldr; GAA; IMSpt; Western Illinois University; Nursing.

SPECKMAN, Katherine D; Metropolis HS; Metropolis, IL; ChrhWkr; HonRl; NHS; SctActv; StuCncl; CivCl; 4-H; GerCl; Southern Il Univ; Animal Science.

SPECTOR, James M; Loyola Academy; Evanston, IL; 61/442 Band; ChrhWkr; CncrtBnd; HonRl; LitMag; MrchBnd; NHS; NatlMeritCmnd; NatlMeritSF; Orch; College; Music.

SPEED, Paul S; Warsaw HS; Wausaw, IL; Band; CncrtBnd; DrmMjrt; MrchBnd; NatlMeritCmnd; PepBnd; SchMus; GerCl; VoiceDemAwd; Blackburn College; Musican.

SPEER, Bradley E; Gothenburg HS; Gothenburg, NE; Band; CncrtBnd; MrchBnd; Orch; PepBnd; SchMus; YthFlsp; Bsktbl; Ftbl; Glf; IMSpt; College.

SPEER, Doris L; Lincoln Park HS; Lincoln Park, MI; 15/580 PresBand; NHS; VPStuGov; CaptBsktbl; LetterTrk; LetterGAA; PPFtbl; JCAwd; Univ Of Detroit; Music.

SPEER, Lora L; Golden City Riii HS; Joplin, MO; Band; ChrhWkr; CncrtBnd; HonRl; MrchBnd; PepBnd; Twrl; 4-H; FHA; MthCl;.

SPEER, Scott R; Lawrence Central HS; Indianapolis, IN; VPFrshCls; VPSophCls; VPJrCls; StuCncl; Bsbl; Bsktbl; Ftbl; LetterSwmmng; LetterTrk; IMSpt; Arizona State Univ; Business.

SPEICHINGER, Michelle A; Wahoo HS; Malmo, NE; 3/80 TrsJrCls; Chrs; HonRl; TchrAde; PpCl; LetterBsktbl; College; Professional.

SPEIDEL, Mark E; Washburn HS; Minneapolis, MN; Chr; LitMag; Mdrgl; NHS; OffAde; SchMus; SchPl; SchPpr; NCTE; Univ Of Minn; Theater.

SPEIRER, Jan M; Pontiac Township HS; Pontiac, IL; 22/187 Chr; Chrs; HonRl; HospAde; SchMus; StuCncl; 4-H; SpnCl; PpCl; SciCl; Bsbl; College.

SPEISER, Serese M; Glasgow HS; Glasgow, MO; Band; CncrtBnd; MrchBnd; NHS; YthFlsp; RptrSchPpr; FHA; PpCl; LionAwd; College.

SPELDE, Edward C; Thornwood HS; South Holland, IL; 10/852 ChrhWkr; HonRl; NHS; MthCl; Valparaiso University; Law.

SPELICH, Tina M; St Francis Academy; Joliet, IL; Chr; CmntyWkr; NatlThespSoc; SchMus; SchPl; SctActv; StuCncl; SchPpr; IMSpt; College; Nurse.

SPELLMAN, Joseph J; Pecatonica HS; Mineral Point, WI; 1/60 PresFrshCls; ALBoysSt; HonRl; 4-H; FFA; MthCl; LetterBsbl; LetterBsktbl; LetterFtbl; LetterTrk; Clg; Engineering.

SPENA, Paul M; Raymore Peculiar HS; Peculiar, MO; 1/110 Band; Chr; ChrhWkr; CncrtBnd; HonRl; MrchBnd; NHS; PepBnd; SchMus; SctActv; GerCl; CaptTrk; College; Lawyer.

SPENCE, James A; Douglas Mac Arthur HS; Saginaw, MI; 6 289 HonRl; TreasJA; NHS; NatlMeritSF; StuCncl; U Of Mi; Comp Science.

SPENCE, Jerri A; Lorettoin K C HS; Kansas City, MO; ChrhWkr; CmntyWkr; JA; PolWkr; SchMus; SchPl; StuGov; RptrSchPpr; Chrldr; College; Counseling Film Production.

SPENCE, Pamela K; Baxter HS; Baxter Springs, KS; 5/65 Chrs; ChrhWkr; HonRl; SchMus; SchPl; FHA; FrCl; MthCl; PpCl; Ks St Col Pittsburg; Nurse.

SPENCE, Robert M; Lakeview HS; St Clair Shores, MI; 24/650 HonRl; NHS; PresStuCncl; YthFlsp; LetterBsbl; LetterGlf; IMSpt; NCTE; Univ Of Mi; Law.

SPENCER, Ann G; Walled Lake Western HS; Walled Lake, MI; 57/400 Chr; Chrs; ChrhWkr; HonRl; NHS; SchMus; SchPl; TchrAde; Swmmng; IMSpt; Psychological Therapist.

SPENCER, Brenda S; Jamaica HS; Fairmount, IL; Chrs; HonRl; FHA; PpCl; College; Professional Nursing.

SPENCER, Candy; St Martin De Porres HS; Detroit, MI; 15/85 HonRl; JrNHS; NatlSciFnd; FrCl; Chrldr; Wayne State Univ; Pharmacist.

SPENCER, Daniel L; Marseilles HS; Marseilles, IL; 20/60 Band; CncrtBnd; HonRl; MrchBnd; Orch; PepBnd; SchMus; SchPl; SctActv; StuCncl; Bsktbl; Ftbl; Glf; College; Dentist.

SPENCER, David A; Comstock HS; Kalamazoo, MI; 1/225 TrsFrshCls; Band; CncrtBnd; HonRl; MrchBnd; NHS; PepBnd; YthFlsp; Biochemistry.

SPENCER, David M; Kalkaska HS; Kalkaska, MI; Band; CncrtBnd; HonRl; MrchBnd; RedCrAde; YthFlsp; 4-H; Bsktbl; Glf; IMSpt; 4-HAwd; Clge; Pro.

SPENCER, Gayle M; Lawton Comm HS; Lawton, MI; 13/52 PresBand; Chr; CncrtBnd; HonRl; MrchBnd; PepBnd; SchMus; TchrAde; SchPpr; Pres4-H; CaptGAA; 4-HAwd; Michigan State Univ; Teacher.

SPENCER, Jack A; Rochelle Twp HS; Rochelle, IL; ChrhWkr; HonRl; EdSchPpr; Jr College; Professional.

SPENCER, Karin I; Marysville HS; Port Huron, MI; HonRl; NHS; Quill&Scroll; SchPl; SctActv; StuCncl; Yrbk; RptrSchPpr; SciCl; GAA; Coll; Med.

SPENCER, Katherine A; Woodlands Academy; Lake Forest, IL; 1/75 VPChrs; ModUN; PolWkr; SchMus; StuCncl; EdYrBk; RptrSchPpr; FrCl; GAA; DARAwd; College; Chemistry.

SPENCER, Lawrence P; Calument HS; Griffith, IN; Chr; LbryAde; PpCl; SciCl; Bsbl; Ftbl; IMSpt; Trade School; Merchant.

SPENCER, Lisa A; Bayfield Public HS; Bayfield, WI; SecJrCls; TrsJrCls; SecTrsJrCls; SecSrCls; Band; CncrtBnd; MrchBnd; PepBnd; StuCncl; RptrYrbk; SchPpr; 4-H; LetterBsbl; Bsktbl; College; Vocation.

SPENCER, Lowanda A; Soldan HS; St Louis, MO; 6/734 Band; HonRl; JA; NHS; SchAde; SchPl; Yrbk; College; Chemical Engineer.

SPENCER, Lynne; Switz City Central HS; Worthington, IN; 6/45 SecSophCls; SecJrCls; Band; ChrhWkr; HonRl; MrchBnd; NHS; PepBnd; 4-H; SpnCl; PpCl; College ;professional.

SPENCER, Lynne M; E Grand Rapids HS; E Grand Rapids, MI; Band; ChrhWkr; CncrtBnd; HonRl; HospAde; MrchBnd; Orch; PolWkr; RedCrAde; SchMus; YthFlsp; RptrSchPpr; Hope College; Music.

SPENCER, Martha J; El Dorado Springs R 2 HS; El Dorado Springs, MO; 7/112 SecChrhWkr; HonRl; NHS; OffAde; SctActv; RptrYrbk; RptrSchPpr; FTA; LetterBsktbl; PPFtbl; Southwest Baptist College; Phy Education.

SPENCER, Michael L; Bay City Handy HS; Bay City, MI; Band; Chr; HonRl; NHS; NatlMeritSF; SchMus; StuGov; RptrYrbk; Yrbk; RptrSchPpr; Bsbl; Bsktbl; Trk; Delta College; Journalism.

SPENCER, Rhonda J; Tri Center HS; Neola, IA; Chr; Chrs; ChrhWkr; CmntyWkr; HospAde; PresYthFlsp; 4-H; PpCl; College; Special Educ.

SPENCER, Rhonda S; Hume HS; Hume, MO; 5/18 Band; ChrhWkr; HonRl; OffAde; Yrbk; RptrSchPpr; FHA; LetterBsktbl; Chrldr; 4-HAwd; College; Secretary.

SPENCER, Richard B; Albia HS; Albia, IA; Chrs; RedCrAde; SctActv; StuCncl; YthFlsp; LetterFtbl; LetterTrk; Wm Penn College; Medicine.

SPENCER, Ronda J; Hayti HS; Hayti, MO; 12/87 Band; ChrhWkr; CncrtBnd; PresFrshCls; SecFrshCls; Twrl; FHA; FTA;.

SPENCER, Scott R; Burlington Comm HS; Burlington, IA; 31/438 Band; CncrtBnd; NHS; StuCncl; Bsbl; Bsktbl; LetterFtbl; Trk; IMSpt; Iowa State Univ; Engineergin.

SPENCER, Sharon L; Ash Grove HS; Boisdare, MO; Band; ChrhWkr; CncrtBnd; HonRl; LbryAde; MrchBnd; FHA; PpCl; Trk; Chrldr; Southwest Mo State Univ; Home Economics.

SPENCER, Sheila; Sullivan HS; Sullivan, MO; 4/17213# ALAGirlsSt; HonRl; NHS; SchMus; FHA; FTA; FrCl; Southeast Mo State Univ; Medical Technology.

SPENCER, Susan M; Plattsmouth HS; Murray, NE; Chrs; ChrhWkr; DrlTm; HonRl; LbryAde; SecYthFlsp; SpnCl; MthCl; PpCl; PPFtbl; Col; Med.

SPENCER, Tamra C; Meridian HS; Mounds, IL; 9/103 SecJrCls; SecSrCls; Band; HonRl; MrchBnd; StuGov; TchrAde; RptrYrbk; LatCl; St Louis College; Pharmacy.

SPENCER, Teresa M; Corunna HS; Durand, MI; 39/201 Band; ChrhWkr; MrchBnd; Orch; PepBnd; TchrAde; Bob Jones Univ; Music.

SPENGLER, Molly; Rochester Community HS; Rochester, IL; 22/74 Band; Chr; Chrs; CncrtBnd; Mdrgl; MrchBnd; PepBnd; SchMus; GAA; 4-HAwd; Illinois State University; Education.

SPENGLER, Sarah A; Rich South HS; Park Forest, IL; Chr; Chrs; HonRl; LitMag; NatlMeritFnl; NatlMeritSF; College.

SPENNER, Diane; Central Catholic HS; West Point, NE; /68 Chr; Chrs; HonRl; SchMus; PpCl; Busin; Prof.

SPENNER, Mary B; Central Catholic HS; Beemer, NE; 16/77 SecSrCls; ChrhWkr; CmntyWkr; HonRl; Mdrgl; NHS; StuCncl; Yrbk; SchPpr; PpCl; Benediction Coll; Spec Ed.

SPENNRATH, Wendy; Mormon Trail HS; Derby, IA; Band; ChrhWkr; HonRl; SchMus; SchPl; YthFlsp; Yrbk; PpCl; Chrldr; AmLegAwd; Mercy School Of Nursing; Nursing.

SPERAL, Paul C; Fargo North HS; Fargo, ND; 21/365 PresChrhWkr; HonRl; NHS; Bsktbl; CaptFtbl; Trk; IMSpt; Coll; Wildlife Biologist.

SPERANZA, Dominick; Munster HS; Munster, IN; 189/440 SctActv; Trk; College; Professional.

SPERL, Brian G; Andrean HS; Munster, IN; 60/310 ChrhWkr; CmntyWkr; HonRl; TchrAde; Yrbk; SciCl; Indiana Univ; Medicine.

SPERLE, Brenda A; Napoleon HS; Napoleon, ND; SecJrCls; Band; Chr; PresNHS; PepBnd; RptrYrbk; SchPpr; FHA; PpCl; Glf; College.

SPERLE, Karen M; Napoleon HS; Kintyre, ND; 1/61 TrsSophCls; TrsJrCls; TrsSrCls; ALAGirlsSt; Chrs; CncrtBnd; MrchBnd; NHS; PepBnd; RptrSchPpr; Univ; Doctor.

SPERLE, Pat A; Napoleon HS; Napoleon, ND; Chr; ChrhWkr; CmntyWkr; CncrtBnd; MrchBnd; PepBnd; RptrSchPpr; FHA; LetterBsktbl; BttyCrckrAwd; Univ; Major Study.

SPERLICH, Wanda R; Blue Earth Public HS; Blue Earth, MN; 22/106 ChrhWkr; CmntyWkr; HonRl; 4-H; FHA; PpCl; IMSpt; U Of Wi Stout; Early Childhood Education.

SPERLING, Susan K; Arlington HS; Arlington, NE; 2/57 Chr; Chrs; ChrhWkr; CmntyWkr; HonRl; NHS; StuGov; Yrbk; Trk; Chrldr; Concordia Luth Clge; Organ Music.

SPEROFF, Sally I; Taylor HS; Kokomo, IN; 80/167 FrCl; PpCl; Business College; Admin Secretary.

SPERR, Arlou; Chokio Alberta HS; Chokio, MN; SecSrCls; Band; HonRl; MrchBnd; PepBnd; SchPl; RptrYrbk; EdSchPpr; SpnCl; LetterChrldr; Secretarial.

SPERRY, Colleen R; Westwood Community HS; Smithland, IA; SecTrsSophCls; Band; Chr; ModUN; NHS; RptrSchPpr; FHA; PpCl; Chrldr; BttyCrckrAwd; College; Psychology.

SPERRY, Martha; St Elmo Community HS; Loogootee, IL; 15/52 ChrhWkr; HonRl; SchPl; 4-H; FHA; PpCl; Trade Sch;beautician.

SPERRY, Wally; Coffey HS; Pattonsburg, MO; 5/11 Northwest Mo State Univ; Aug Busi.

SPESARD, Heidi A; Shelbyville HS; Shelbyville, IL; 17/135 VPSophCls; Band; CncrtBnd; HonRl; MrchBnd; NHS; SchMus; SchPl; StuCncl; RptrYrbk; FrCl; VPPpCl; Tennis; Univ Of Illinois; Dance.

SPETH, John; Belmont HS; Mineral Point, WI; StuGov; Yrbk; 4-H; FFA; PpCl; Bsbl; IMSpt; 4-HAwd; PresAwd; Trad School; Vocation.

SPEXARTH, Daniel; Precious Blood Seminary; Colwich, KS; 1/8 PresSophCls; PresSrCls; Chr; ChrhWkr; CmntyWkr; NHS; SchPl; Bsktbl; 4-HAwd; College; Vocational.

SPEXARTH, Gregory R; Andale HS; Colwich, KS; Chr; Chrs; SchMus; TchrAde; 4-H; SpnCl; Bsbl; Bsktbl; IMSpt; Jr College; Agri Business.

SPHATT, Sally J; Larkin HS; Elgin, IL; Chrs; HonRl; RptrSchPpr; PresPpCl; LetterBsktbl; LetterTrk; Elgin Comm Clge; Physical Ed.

SPIARS, Terri A; Northwest HS; Grand Island, NE; 19/149 HonRl; NatlThespSoc; SchPl; TchrAde; RptrSchPpr; Nebraska Wesleyan University; Teaching.

SPICA, Michael C; Lake Michigan Catholic HS; St Joseph, MI; 19/96 HonRl; SchAde; SchPl; StuGov; TchrAde; TreasKeyCl; Trk; Nazareth College; Elemenatary Eduction.

SPICKARD, Sandra L; Saline HS; Saline, MI; HonRl; NatlMeritSchl; SchMus; SchPl; FrCl; SpnCl; Univ Of Mi; Languages.

SPICKARD, Valerie L; Saline HS; Saline, MI; HonRl; NHS; TchrAde; Clg; Legal Or Medical Sec.

SPICKERMAN, Frances; Fredericktown HS; Fredericktown, MO; 4/150 HonRl; College; Clinical Psychologist.

SPICUZZI, Karen L; South Lake HS; St Clair Shores, MI; 35/517 VPSrCls; HonRl; NHS; LetterBsktbl; CaptTrk; Clg; Nursing.

SPIDLE, Bruce L; Penney HS; Nettleton, MO; 8/80 HonRl; SchPl; RptrSchPpr; SptEdSchPpr; FFA; EngCl; SpnCl; LetterBsktbl; LetterFtbl; Trk; Northwest Missouri St Univ; Conservation.

SPIECKERMAN, Jill M; St Johns Cathedral HS; Milwaukee, WI; 14/95 HonRl; JrNHS; NHS; TchrAde; IMSpt; College; Nursing.

SPIEGAL, Barbara M; Carl Sandburg HS; Palos Park, IL; 27/700 HonRl; HospAde; NHS; NatlMeritFnl; Purdue Univ; Engineering.

SPIEGEL, Cris C; Lamoille Community HS; La Moille, IL; SctActv; RptrSchPpr; FrCl; PpCl; Bsktbl; Ftbl; Trade School; Diesel Mechanic.

SPIEGELBERG, Jane L; Little Wolf HS; Manawa, WI; 9/79 PresJrCls; HonRl; TchrAde; 4-H; FHA; PpCl; GAA; IMSpt; 4-HAwd; CitAwd; Nursing School; Nurse.

SPIEKER, Beverly J; Adrian Public HS; Kenneth, MN; 1/89 Chr; HonRl; ModUN; NHS; NatlMeritCmnd; RptrYrbk; FTA; Trk; BttyCrckrAwd; Sw Mn State College; Medically Oriented.

SPIEKERMAN, Rhonda S; Arthur Hill HS; Zilwaukee, MI; HonRl; JrNHS; StuCncl; CivCl; GerCl; PpCl; SciCl; Swmmng; Trk; Chrldr; College; Psychology.

SPIELER, Kurt J; Parkway West HS; Chesterfield, MO; JrNHS; LetterFtbl; LetterTrk; PPFtbl; College; Lawyer.

SPIELER, Steven J; Joliet Township West HS; Joliet, IL; VPChr; HonRl; LetterTrk; LbryAde; Mdrgl; NatlThespSoc; SchMus; SchPl; StuCncl; Univ; Elect Eng.

SPIELHAGEN, Claire; De Soto HS; Lenexa, KS; ChrhWkr; HonRl; NatlFornLg; NHS; NatlThespSoc; SchPl; StuCncl; RptrSchPpr; FBLA; PpCl; Coll; Eng.

SPIES, Vicky J; Laboure HS; St Louis, MO; 6/65 SecFrshCls; TrsSophCls; VPSrCls; HonRl; NHS; StuCncl; Bsktbl; CaptSocr; Tennis; Chrldr; University Of Mo.

SPIESE, Gail; Homewood Flossmoor Hs; Glenwood, IL; 28/917 HonRl; Indiana U; Social Service.

SPIHLMAN, Jeff J; Wesclin HS; Trenton, IL; YthFlsp; Bsktbl; College.

SPIKING, Larry; King City R I HS; King City, MO; 12/45 VPFrshCls; PresSophCls; ALBoysSt; HonRl; NHS; StuCncl; YthFlsp; Swmmng; Tennis; Vocational.

SPILGER, David L; West Liberty HS; Alalissa, IA; ALBoysSt; Chrs; ChrhWkr; CmntyWkr; SchAde; YthFlsp; FFA; College; Agricultur.

SPILGER, Steven P; Lakeshore HS; Baroda, MI; 14/239 Band; CncrtBnd; HonRl; NatlMeritCmnd; NatlMeritSF; SchAde; SchMus; KeyCl; GerCl; IMSpt; Univ Mi; Dr Pathology.

SPILKER, Jeffrey A; Tri County HS; Beatrice, NE; VPJrCls; Band; Chr; ChrhWkr; CncrtBnd; HonRl; Mdrgl; MrchBnd; Swmmng; LetterTrk; West Point Military Academy; Military Engr.

SPILLANE, Kathleen M; Our Lady Of Mercy HS; Livonia, MI; Schoolcraft Col ;acct.

SPILLER, William L; St Anne Comm HS; Hopkins Park, IL; University; Medicine.

SPILLERS, Kim E; Beardstown HS; Beardstown, IL; 1/123 VPSophCls; VPJrCls; VPSrCls; Chrs; HonRl; MrchBnd; NHS; NatlMeritCmnd; OffAde; RedCrAde; SchAde; SchMus; Trk; Univ; Medical Technology.

SPILLMAN, David; Southwestern HS; Hanover, IN; 7/109 PresJrCls; ALBoysSt; HonRl; NHS; NatlMeritCmnd; NatlThespSoc; DanFAwd; RotaryAwd; Us Coast Guard Acad; Engineering.

SPILLMAN, Mark A; Scecina Memorial HS; Indiannapolis, IN; 40/160 Band; CncrtBnd; MrchBnd; Orch; PepBnd; Mens Clothing Salesman.

SPILMAN, John D; David Co Comm HS; Bloomfield, IA; ALBoysSt; StuCncl; Wrstlng; N Ia Comm Clg; Automotive Service.

SPINA, Marijo; Trinity HS; Melrose Park, IL; 4/206 VPJrCls; PresSrCls; Chr; Chrs; ChrhWkr; HonRl; HospAde; NHS; SchMus; StuCncl; Teen; Bsktbl; IMSpt; Loyola University; Nursing.

SPINDLER, Alicia; Gibson Southern HS; Haubstadt, IN; 10/231 ALAGirlsSt; EdSchPpr; FHA; PpCl; SciCl; Trk; State Univ; Nursing.

SPINDLER, Elizabeth A; Gibson Southern HS; Ft Branch, IN; 2/225 HonRl; NHS; FHA; 4-HAwd; Indiana State U; Home Econimics.

SPINDLER, Jeanne L; Benson HS; Omaha, NE; AFS; ChrhWkr; CmntyWkr; HonRl; TreasJA; NHS; NatlSciFnd; OffAde; StuCncl; TchrAde; College; Medical Records.

SPINDLER, Jerry L; Woodlan HS; Woodburn, IN; 21/144 ChrhWkr; HonRl; NHS; LetterBsktbl; LetterFtbl; LetterTrk; College; Chemist.

SPINDLER, Rosanne; Browns Valley HS; Browns Valley, MN; 10/42 TrsSrCls; Band; CncrtBnd; HonRl; PepBnd; SchPl; Yrbk; PpCl; Chrldr; GAA; Alex Area Voc Inst; Fashion Mcd.

SPINN, Michael; Brownell Talbot HS; Omaha, NE; HonRl; PepBnd; RptrSchPpr; Bsktbl; Ftbl; Glf; Institute; Architelture.

SPINNER, Gregory A; Gull Lake HS; Battle Creek, MI; 28/250 Band; CncrtBnd; HonRl; MrchBnd; NHS; NatlMeritCmnd; PepBnd; SchMus; TchrAde; FBLA; College; Accounting.

SPINNER, Sarah; Springfield HS; Springfield, IL; AFS; NHS; Springfield College.

SPINNER, Sarah L; Springfield HS; Springfield, IL; 79/539 AFS; College.

SPIRDUSO, Wendy L; Central HS; La Crosse, WI; 1/507 ALAGirlsSt; Chr; HonRl; NHS; Quill&Scroll; EdSchPpr; SpnCl; Tennis; DARAwd; Ohio Wesleyan University; Journalism.

SPIRE, Harold W; Northeast Nodaway R V HS; Parnell, MO; 7/29 PresFrshCls; SecJrCls; ALBoysSt; HonRl; PepBnd; SchPl; SctActv; Bsbl; LetterBsktbl; Trk; College; Farming.

SPIRE, Teri L; Maryville R Ii HS; Maryville, MO; Chr; Chrs; HonRl; NHS; StuCncl; RptrYrbk; 4-H; University.

SPIRES, Candy L; Macon HS; Macon, IL; 3/57 TrsJrCls; ALAGirlsSt; Chrs; HonRl; NHS; SchMus; Yrbk; FBLA; PpCl; AmLegAwd; Work; Computer Programmer.

SPIRRA, Richard R; Berlin HS; Berlin, WI; Chrs; ChrhWkr; CmntyWkr; HonRl; NHS; NatlMeritFnl; SchPl; 4-H; KeyCl; Bsktbl; CaptTennis; IMSpt; College; Law.

SPITSNOGLE, Gary A; Odell Public HS; Odell, NE; SecFrshCls; SecJrCls; Band; Chr; Chrs; CncrtBnd; Mdrgl; MrchBnd; RptrYrbk; Yrbk; College; Vocation.

SPITZ, Otto M; Proviso East HS; Melrose Park, IL; Chr; Chrs; HonRl; Mdrgl; NHS; NatlMeritCmnd; NatlMeritSchl; LetterSwmmng; LetterTennis; Illinois Inst Tech; Electronic Engineer.

SPITZER, Brenda; Bluffs HS; Bluffs, IL; 4/29 ChrhWkr; HonRl; NHS; OffAde; SchAde; SctActv; TchrAde; Yrbk; 4-H; 4-HAwd; ;navy Radiology Techn.

SPITZER, Brenda C; Bluffs HS; Bluffs, IL; 5/35 HonRl; NHS; SchAde; TchrAde; Yrbk; 4-H; FHA; 4-HAwd; Navy Or Airforce; Radiology Technologist.

SPITZER, Ella; Eureka HS; Eureka, SD; 12/57 Band; Chr; Chrs; HonRl; SchMus; SchPl; StuGov; RptrSchPpr; PpCl; VoiceDemAwd; Coll; Nursing.

SPITZER, Jimmie A; Hebron Public HS; Hebron, ND; 3/33 PresFrshCls; Band; CncrtBnd; HonRl; MrchBnd; PepBnd; SchPpr; TreasFHA; LetterBsktbl; Chrldr; Minot St; X Ray Tech.

SPITZER, John; James B Conant Hs; Hoffman Estates, IL; 33 HonRl; NHS; Tennis; College;business Or Law.

SPITZER, Karen D; Hebron Public HS; Hebron, ND; 3/33 SecFrshCls; SecSophCls; VPJrCls; HonRl; StuCncl; FHA; LetterBsktbl; Trk; Chrldr; GAA; Coll; Dental Hygine.

SPIVACK, Laurie; Harrison HS; Farmington Hills, MI; ALAGirlsSt; CmntyWkr; HonRl; LitMag; SchPl; StuGov; TchrAde; PPFtbl; Michigan State U.

SPIVEY, Lucinda S; Galva HS; Galva, IL; 13/75 HonRl; NatlMeritCmnd; NatlThespSoc; OffAde; SchPl; EdYrBk; FHA; Northern Ill Univ; English.

SPLETTER, Gary J; Appleton HS; Appleton, WI; 7/700 Chrs; ChrhWkr; HonRl; LitMag; NHS; NatlMeritCmnd; RptrSchPpr; ChmnWrstlng; Clge; Eng.

SPLETTER, Stephen D; New Holstein Senior HS; New Holstein, WI; HonRl; NHS; IMSpt; College; Business.

SPLETTSTOESZER, Catherine A; Lutheran HS; Mayer, MN; 9/64 SchPl; Hutchinson Voc Tech Inst; Mech Drafting.

SPODEN, Jerry; Western Dubuque HS; Epworth, IA; 72/234 ALBoysSt; StuCncl; Bsktbl; LetterTrk; IMSpt;.

SPOELSTRA, Edwin G; No Mahaska HS; New Sharon, IA; HonRl; JA; ModUN; NHS; RedCrAde; ROTC; StuCncl; StuGov; 4-H; FBLA; TreasFFA; SciCl; Indian Hills Comm College; Farm Mechanics.

SPOELSTRA, Marlys G; Pella Christian HS; New Sharon, IA; 20/92 Band; CncrtBnd; HonRl; MrchBnd; PepBnd; PresYthFlsp; SptEdSchPpr; PpCl; LetterTrk; IMSpt;.

SPOENEMAN, Edith; Lewellen Rural HS; Lewellen, NE; Chr; CncrtBnd; HonRl; PepBnd; SchPl; StuGov; YthFlsp; 4-H; Univ Of Ne; Pharmicy Physicaled.

SPOERL, June M; Hempstead HS; Sherrill, IA; 18/455 Band; CncrtBnd; HonRl; MrchBnd; NHS; Orch; SchMus; SecYthFlsp; VP4-H; ChmbCommrsAwd; University Of Dubuque; Medical Technology.

SPOERL, Mary; Appleton HS; Appleton, WI; AFS; Chr; Chrl; HospAde; Mdrgl; Yrbk; 4-H; PpCl; Swmmng; Trk; Technical School; Secretarial Work.

SPOHN, Dixie; Silver Creek Public HS; Genoa, NE; 8/19 SecSophCls; Chrs; HonRl; SchPl; Yrbk; SchPpr; Platte Tech Comm Coll; Licensedpractical Nr.

SPOKELY, Michael; Climax Public HS; Climax, MN; CmntyWkr; HonRl; SchPl; FFA; SciCl; Bsbl; Trk; Mayville St Col; Teacher.

SPOLARICH, Michael J; Highland HS; Highland, IN; 87/578 Trk; Rose Hulman Inst; Mechanical.

SPOLARICH, Tina L; Thornton Fraction No HS; Calumet City, IL; HonRl; JrNHS; PresNHS; NatlMeritCmnd; OffAde; SchAde; FTA; PresSpnCl; College; Speech Pathology.

SPON, Robert S; Rockford East HS; Rockford, IL; 65/637 HonRl; NHS; LetterGlf; Col; Pre Med.

SPONG, David B; Naperville Central HS; Naperville, IL; HonRl; YthFlsp; College.

SPONSLER, Cynthia L; Mormon Trail Comm HS; Humeston, IA; 1/36 ALAGirlsSt; ChrhWkr; HonRl; StuCncl; YthFlsp; RptrYrbk; EdYrBk; 4-H; 4-HAwd; CitAwd; College; Journalism.

SPOON, Bonnie; Marquette HS; Marquette, KS; ALAGirlsSt; ChrhWkr; CmntyWkr; DrlTm; HonRl; SchMus; YthFlsp; PpCl; Trk; Chrldr; Bus School; Fashion Merchandising.

SPOON, Geneva L; Marquette HS; Marquette, KS; 4/17 HstSophCls; SecSrCls; ALAGirlsSt; Band; Chrs; CncrtBnd; HonRl; MrchBnd; PepBnd; SchPl; YthFlsp; RptrYrbk; Business School.

SPORE, Daniel L; Warsaw HS; Silver Lake, IN; ALBoysSt; Band; CncrtBnd; HonRl; MrchBnd; PepBnd; SchMus; College; Engineering.

SPORER, Sally A; Rich Central HS; Park Forest, IL; 10/400 NHS; TchrAde; YthFlsp; Swmmng; Trk; Chrldr; CchngActv; IMSpt; PresAwd; College; Psychology.

SPOTANSKI, Dave R; Loup City HS; Loup City, NE; 14/64 ChrhWkr; HonRl; LbryAde; StuGov; TchrAde; Yrbk; FFA; AmLegAwd; Univ; Professional.

SPOTTS, William A; Centerville HS; Centerville, IN; Aud/Vis; ChrhWkr; HonRl; JA; FFA; SpnCl; SciCl; LetterTennis; LetterTrk; JAAwd; Service;.

SPOUSTA, Dianne L; Wilber HS; Wilber, NE; Chrs; ChrhWkr; SchMus; FHA; Trk; Business School; Accountant.

SPRACKLEN, Denise A; Notre Dame HS; Chicago, IL; 17/298 CmntyWkr; HonRl; NHS; RedCrAde; Yrbk; SpnCl; Tennis; Ne Illinois Univ; Biology.

SPRADLIN, Ellen J; Ashland HS; Ashland, IL; PresFrshCls; VPSophCls; HonRl; StuCncl; SchPpr; PpCl; Bsbl; Trk; Chrldr; University; Professional.

SPRADLIN, Jo E; R 1 North Callaway HS; Auxvasse, MO; 7/77 SecFrshCls; HonRl; MrchBnd; OffAde; SchPl; SptEdYrbk; FHA; FrCl; Business College; Secretary.

SPRADLIN, Jo Ellen; R 1 North Callaway HS; Auxvasse, MO; 8/77 SecFrshCls; Band; HonRl; MrchBnd; SchPl; Yrbk; VP4-H; SecFHA; FrCl; CaptChrldr; DARAwd; College; Secretary.

SPRADLIN, Mary E; Jacksonville HS; Jacksonville, IL; 93/363 Chr; CncrtBnd; HospAde; MrchBnd; RedCrAde; SchMus; CaptTwrl; YthFlsp; 4-H; LetterBsktbl; DanFAwd; 4-HAwd; College; Professional.

SPRADLIN, Vicky L; Martinsville HS; Martinsville, IN; 34/364 HonRl; TchrAde; SecFTA; Butler Univ; Elementary Ed.

SPRAGUE, David; Brookfield R 3 HS; Brookfield, MO; 53/135 PresSophCls; Band; HonRl; MrchBnd; OffAde; College; Coaching Career.

SPRAGUE, Linda L; Deland Weldon HS; Weldon, IL; 2/37 HonRl; NHS; OffAde; StuCncl; YthFlsp; 4-H; PpCl; Chrldr; GAA; DARAwd; 4-HAwd; College; Nursing.

SPRAGUE, Lora M; Nort Miami HS; Peru, IN; 16/140 Chr; DrlTm; HonRl; MrchBnd; SchMus; SchPl; RptrYrbk; SciCl; LetterBsktbl; Manchester U; Medcine.

SPRAGUE, Mark H; Berlin HS; Berlin, WI; 25/175 Chrs; ChrhWkr; HonRl; SctActv; PresKeyCl; SpnCl; Bsbl; Bsktbl; Tennis; Wrstlng; CaptIMSpt;.

SPRAGUE, Pamela M; Hononegah HS; Roscoe, IL; 4/188 TrsJrCls; TrsSrCls; NHS; StuCncl; EdSchPpr; Northwestern Univ; Journalism.

SPRAGUE, Thomas B; Lakewood HS; Woodland, MI; 23/203 HonRl; NHS; TchrAde; FFA; College; Teacher.

SPRANK, Glen J; Bellevue Community HS; Bellevue, IA; ChrhWkr; HonRl; IMSpt; Farming; Farmer.

SPRATT, Thomas; St Laurence Hs; Burbank, IL; 37/372 Band; ChrhWkr; CmntyWkr; CncrtBnd; HonRl; MrchBnd; PepBnd; TchrAde; De Paul U; Accounting.

SPRAU, Scott J; Meservey Thornton HS; Meservey, IA; PresJrCls; ALBoysSt; Band; SchPl; PresStuCncl; LetterBsktbl; CaptFtbl; LetterTrk; AmLegAwd; 4-HAwd; Jr Coll; Vocation.

SPRECHER, Amy V; Sauk Prairie HS; N Freedom, WI; 17/236 AFS; ChrhWkr; HonRl; NatlFornLg; NHS; SchMus; StuCncl; LetterTrk; AmLegAwd; PresAwd; U Of La Crosse; Psychology.

SPRECHER, Joan R; Sauk Prairie HS; Prairie Du Sac, WI; HonRl; LbryAde; 4-H; FHA; SecTrsFrshCls; GerCl; PpCl; LetterTennis; CAP; OptClAwd; Col Uw Madison ;history.

SPREEN, Sandra J; Medford HS; Medford, WI; 33/254 Chr; DrlTm; Chrs; HonRl; NHS; SpnCl; Trk; U Of Minn; Vet Asst.

SPRENGER, Susan A; Cathedral HS; New Ulm, MN; Chrs; HonRl; LbryAde; SchMus; SchPl; PpCl; School; Nursing.

SPRENGER, Vicki; Marion HS; Marion, WI; Band; ChrhWkr; CncrtBnd; MrchBnd; PepBnd; Yrbk; FHA; PpCl; Chrldr;.

SPRENKLE, David C; University HS; Urbana, IL; PresFrshCls; NatlMeritSF; SctActv; StuCncl; StuGov; YthLg; LetterBsktbl; LetterTrk; IMSpt;.

SPRICK, Duane R; Ft Calhoun HS; Fort Calhoun, NE; Band; Chr; Chrl; Chrs; CncrtBnd; HonRl; Mdrgl; MrchBnd; NHS; PepBnd; Bsbl; Bsktbl; LetterFtbl; LetterTrk; College; Landscape Architect.

SPRIMONT, Thomas; Bishop Martin D Mcnamara HS; Bradley, IL; VPSrCls; HonRl; IntrClCncl; SchPl; StuCncl; StuGov; SptEdYrbk; FrCl; Trk; IMSpt; Purdue Univ; Corporate Lawyer.

SPRING, John W; Washington Community HS; Washington, IL; 76/350 VPSrCls; AFS; ALBoysSt; CmntyWkr; HonRl; SchPl; StuCncl; YthFlsp; LetterFtbl; LetterWrstlng; North Central Coll; Busi.

SPRING, Mark E; North Boone HS; Roscoe, IL; ALBoysSt; CmntyWkr; HonRl; LbryAde; NHS; SctActv; KeyCl; LetterBsbl; Ftbl; LetterTrk; Clge; Biology & Literature.

SPRINGAN, Denise K; Valley HS; Hoople, ND; 2/31 SecTrsSrCls; ALAGirlsSt; Band; Chrs; ChrhWkr; CncrtBnd; HonRl; PepBnd; RptrSchPpr; SecPpCl; Univ Of N Dakota; Nursing.

SPRINGER, Dale W; Cannon Falls HS; Cannon Falls, MN; VPSophCls; TrsSrCls; Band; Chr; NHS; SchMus; YthFlsp; Ftbl; Trk; VFWAwd; U Of Minn; Elec Eng.

SPRINGER, David S; Lake Forest HS; Lake Forest, IL; 10/443 Band; HonRl; NHS; SctActv; CaptSocr; LetterWrstlng; Dartmouth Coll; Biology.

SPRINGER, Joyce E; Metamora Twp HS; Metamora, IL; 11/171 SecJrCls; AFS; NHS; FrCl; Goshen College; Accounting.

SPRINGER, Mariann; Wayne HS; Ossian, IN; SecSrCls; HonRl; OffAde; StuCncl; Teen; Indiana Purdue Univ; Physical Therapy.

SPRINGER, Mark S; Cathedral HS; Indianapolis, IN; ChrhWkr; HonRl; JrNHS; LbryAde; NHS; PolWkr; TchrAde; RptrYrbk; EdYrBk; SpnCl; Indiana Univ; Journalism.

SPRINGER, Paula; Central High HS; Salem, WI; CncrtBnd; HonRl; StuCncl; Trk; GAA; PPFtbl; Coll; Veterinary Ass.

SPRINGER, Sherry L; Olympia HS; Minier, IL; 1/200 Chr; Chrs; ChrhWkr; HonRl; NHS; SchMus; YthFlsp; SpnCl; College; Physical Therapy.

SPRINGER, Susan L; Hanover HS; Hanover, KS; 2/38 SecSophCls; Chr; Chrs; ChrhWkr; CmntyWkr; CncrtBnd; HonRl; Mdrgl; NHS; LetterTrk; Ks Wesleyan Univ.

SPRINGER, William; Lamphere HS; Madison Heights, MI; 1/420 HonRl; JrNHS; NHS; NatlMeritCmnd; IMSpt; Mass Institute Of Technology; Engineering.

SPRINGER, William R; Virginia HS; Virginia, IL; HonRl; TchrAde; KeyCl; LetterBsktbl; ChmnFtbl; Technical; Elec Tech.

SPRINGGATE, Susan K; Msgr J R Hackett HS; Kalamazoo, MI; VPSrCls; HonRl; NHS; Yrbk; FrCl; Univ Of Michigan; Dentist.

SPRINGMEIER, Sharon L; North Decatur HS; St Paul, IN; 22/78 HonRl; OffAde; SctActv; StuCncl; TchrAde; RptrSchPpr; 4-H; Ind Univ; Nursing.

SPRINGS, Charles R; Mt Carmel HS; Mt Carmel, IL; 6/185 ChrhWkr; HonRl; NHS; YthFlsp; Wabash Valley College; Engineering.

SPROCK, Brenda K; R 1 North Callaway HS; Auxvasse, MO; 1/70 Chr; Chrs; HonRl; NHS; SchPl; StuCncl; FrCl; DARAwd; Mo; Medical Lab Tech.

SPROLL, Patricia A; Wellington HS; Wellington, IL; 2/20 Chrs; HonRl; SchMus; StuCncl; Yrbk; SchPpr; FHA; GAA; Danville Jr College; Nurses Training.

SPROULE, Susan E; University Lake HS; Nashotah, WI; CmntyWkr; SctActv; TchrAde; CivCl; SciCl; Bsbl; Bsktbl; Trk; Chrldr; PresAwd; Univ; Pro.

SPROUSE, Suzanne L; Colfax Comm HS; Colfax, IA; HonRl; LbryAde; FTA; SpnCl; LetterBsktbl; College; Accountant.

SPRUNGER, Sandra D; Fort Madison HS; Fort Madison, IA; 13/289 Band; Chr; Chrs; ChrhWkr; CmntyWkr; CncrtBnd; HonRl; IMSpt; LionAwd; OptClAwd; Ia State Univ; Chemical Eng.

SPRUTTA, Kathy A; Mother Of Sorrows HS; Chicago, IL; VPJrCls; Chr; HonRl; HospAde; FrCl; RotaryAwd; College; Lawyer.

SPRY, Beverly R; Lake Orion HS; Lake Orion, MI; Band; ChrhWkr; CmntyWkr; CncrtBnd; HonRl; MrchBnd; NHS; Orch; PepBnd; TchrAde; Mi State U; Music Therapist.

SPRYSZAK, Gregory C; Berkley HS; Berkley, MI; Band; CncrtBnd; MrchBnd; PepBnd; RptrSchPpr; SchPpr; Glf; Wayne State Univ; Journalist.

SPUDOWSKI, Judith; John J Pershing HS; Detroit, MI; HonRl; HospAde; NHS; OffAde; TchrAde; Grace Hosp Schl Nursing; Rn.

SPURGEON, Jani L; Canton R V HS; Monticello, MO; TrsSophCls; PresJrCls; HonRl; LitMag; PresNHS; TchrAde; RptrYrbk; KeyCl; PpCl; SciCl; Tennis; IMSpt; DanFAwd; University; English.

SPURGEON, Susan K; J T West HS; Joliet, IL; 40/600 NHS; GerCl; PpCl;.

SPURLOCK, Michael; Laurel HS; Laurel, IN; HstJrCls; ALBoysSt; HonRl; SctActv; StuCncl; GodCntryAwd; KiwanAwd;.

SPURLOCK, Rodney C; South Newton HS; Goodland, IN; Band; CncrtBnd; MrchBnd; PepBnd; StuCncl; RptrYrbk; FFA; FTA; SciCl; Purdue University; Professional.

SPURR, Cynthia M; La Porte HS; La Porte, IN; 38/515 Chr; Chrs; ChrhWkr; HonRl; IntrClCncl; Mdrgl; NHS; SchMus; TreasStuCncl; Pres4-H; Purdue; Fashion Retailing.

SPURR, Debra L; Wheeler HS; Crown Point, IN; 3/34 TrsSrCls; ALAGirlsSt; TreasBand; SecNHS; PepBnd; SchPpr; PpCl; Trk; Chrldr; TreasGAA; Bus School; Computer Programer.

SPURRIER, Marianne; Clinton Comm HS; Clinton, IL; PresSrCls; DrlTm; HospAde; SchPl; TreasStuGov; EdYrBk; Pres4-H; FFA; KeyCl; VPSpnCl; GAA; DanFAwd; 4-HAwd; Univ Of Wisc; Agricultural Journalism.

SPYKER, Jeffrey; Hastings HS; Hastings, MI; HonRl; ModUN; Orch; StuCncl; TchrAde; YthFlsp; RptrYrbk; RptrSchPpr; SciCl; PresAwd; Central Mich Univ; Electrical Engr.

SPYKER, Marvin L; Hastings HS; Hastings, MI; 13/297 VPSophCls; Band; MrchBnd; NHS; Orch; StuCncl; KeyCl; LetterGlf; LetterTrk; Albion College; Law & Music.

SQUIBB, Cindy J; P C HS; Polo, IL; Chr; Chrs; HonRl; SchPl; StuCncl; SpnCl; PpCl; Chrldr; GAA; IMSpt; College; Political Science.

SQUIRES, Abby; Seaholm HS; Birmingham, MI; 19/707 Chr; HonRl; HospAde; JrNHS; ModUN; NHS; SchMus; Albion College; Medicine.

SQUIRES, Jamie L; Franklin Comm HS; Franklin, IN; Chr; ChrhWkr; CncrtBnd; JrNHS; Mdrgl; MrchBnd; PepBnd; SchMus; LatCl; College; Accounting.

SQUIRES, Janet K; Ackley Geneva HS; Ackley, IA; SecTrsSrCls; Band; Chrs; NHS; OffAde; LetterGlf; CaptChrldr; Univ Of N Iowa; Elementary Ed.

SQUIRES, Norma J; R 1 North Callaway HS; Auxvasse, MO; SecJrCls; Chrs; HonRl; NHS; OffAde; EdYrBk; FHA; FrCl; Chrldr; 4-HAwd; College.

SRADER, Randy E; Doniphan Sr HS; Doniphan, MO; HonRl; PpCl; College; Business Mgmt.

SRAMEK, Michael M; Howells Public HS; Clarkson, NE; TrsJrCls; SchPl; TchrAde; RptrYrbk; College.

SRAMEK, Vanessa L; Lacrosse HS; La Crosse, KS; ChrhWkr; HonRl; SchPl; PpCl; Bsktbl; Tennis; LetterTrk; College Or Bus Schl; Business.

SRENIAWSKI, Theresa M; J F Kennedy St Paul HS; Chicago, IL; 37/610 Chrs; HonRl; JrNHS; LbryAde; NHS; OffAde; SchAde; StuCncl; TchrAde; Nursing School; Nursing.

SRNSKY, Judy K; Goodridge HS; Goodridge, MN; 12/36 Chrs; HonRl; LbryAde; Yrbk; FHA; PpCl; Bsktbl; GAA; Vo Tech Sch.

SROKA, Frank G; Lakeview HS; St Clair Shores, MI; 14/660 HonRl; JrNHS; Trk; Coll; Engineer.

SROKA, Jeffrey J; Holy Cross HS; Chicago, IL; 1/314 SecFrshCls; PresSophCls; TrsJrCls; HonRl; NHS; NatlMeritCmnd; SctActv; StuCncl; StuGov; EdYrBk; SchPpr; MthCl; LetterTrk; CaptIMSpt; University Of Chicago; Medicine.

STAAB, Alan R; Everett HS; Lansing, MI; HonRl; PresNHS; NatlMeritSF; LatCl; Bsktbl; Ftbl; West Point; Engineering Or Med.

STAAB, Dennis J; Hars HS; Catherine, KS; HonRl; Bsbl; Trade School; Vocation.

STAAB, Diane; St Marys HS; Remsen, IA; 21/60 Band; Chrs; CncrtBnd; HonRl; OffAde; PepBnd; SchMus; RptrSchPpr; 4-H; PpCl; College; Handicapped And Retarded Children.

STAAB, Doris; Hays HS; Hays, KS; 9/190 Chrs; HonRl; TchrAde; PpCl; College; Business.

STAAKE, Ronald; Meredosia Chambersburg HS; Meredosia, IL; TrsFrshCls; HonRl; MrchBnd; NHS; SchPl; StuCncl; RptrYrbk; FFA;.

STAATS, Deborah; Mediapolis HS; Burling, IA; 11/88 Chrs; ChrhWkr; CmntyWkr; DrmMjrt; MrchBnd; SchMus; Yrbk; Bsktbl; Trk; 4-HAwd; College; Special Education.

STABEN, Chuck; Waukegan HS; Joliet, IL; 41/818 HonRl; JrNHS; NatlMeritSF; Swmmng; Tennis; RotaryAwd; U Of Il; Bio Chem.

STABLES, Stanley T; Bethany HS; Bethany, IL; Lake Land College.

STABNOW, Michael; Sheldon HS; Sheldon, ND; 1/16 Band; CncrtBnd; HonRl; MrchBnd; PepBnd; SchPl; FFA; Bsktbl; University; Physics.

STACEY, Gordon J; Glenbard West HS; Glen Ellyn, IL; 40/500 Chr; Chrs; HonRl; NatlMeritFnl; NatlMeritSchl; NatlMeritSF; StuCncl; StuGov; Yrbk; SchPpr; MthCl; LetterTrk; LetterWrstlng; College; Astro Physics.

STACHEL, Evelyn; Alvernia; Chicago, IL; 5/215 LitMag; NHS; PolWkr; RptrYrbk; FrCl; Northwestern Univ; Econiomics.

STACHOWIAK, Patricia L; Lasalle Peru HS; Lasalle, IL; 36/505 Chrs; HonRl; NHS; FrCl; Illinois Vly Comm College; Veterinarian.

STACHOWIAK, Raymond C; Washington HS; South Bend, IN; PolWkr; FDA; TrsSrCls; HonRl; JA; JrNHS; NHS; SpnCl; Bsktbl; FTA; Univ ;acct.

STACHOWICZ, Karen S; Marian Catholic HS; Flossmoor, IL; 16/365 HonRl; HospAde; NHS; NatlMeritCmnd; StuGov; RptrYrbk; LatCl; Purdue U; Speech Ther.

STACHURA, Sharon A; Pulaski HS; Pulaski, WI; 55/192 HonRl; NatlFornLg; SchPl; TchrAde; FHA; PpCl; Chrldr;.

STACHURSKI, Anita; St Ladislaus HS; Detroit, MI; 11/110 CmntyWkr; HonRl; FBLA; FrCl; GerCl; LatCl; SciCl; Bsktbl; Wayne St U; Dietetics.

STACHYRA, Carol A; Hobbard HS; Chicago, IL; 6/431 TrsJrCls; TrsSrCls; HonRl; NHS; OffAde; StuCncl; SpnCl; PpCl; SciCl; Chrldr; GAA; College; Vocation.

STACK, Catherine M; Maria HS; Chicago, IL; 12/300 HonRl; NHS; NatlMeritCmnd; StuCncl; 4-H; FrCl; Northwestern Univ; Pre Medicine.

STACK, Colleen; Portage Central HS; Portage, MI; SecJrCls; Chr; ChrhWkr; HonRl; OffAde; SchAde; StuCncl; Trk; PresAwd; Western Mi Univ; Broadcasting.

STACK, Daniel A; Assumption HS; Davenport, IA; 6/225 TrsJrCls; VPSrCls; HonRl; NHS; NatlMeritSF; PolWkr; StuCncl; RptrSchPpr; FrCl; IMSpt; Univ; Physicist.

STACK, Nancy J; Leland HS; Earlville, IL; TrsJrCls; Band; Chr; CncrtBnd; HonRl; NHS; StuCncl; TchrAde; FHA; SpnCl; Junior College; Secretarial Science.

STACKHOUSE, James; Mount Michael HS; Omaha, NE; 1/24 VPFrshCls; HonRl; JA; NHS; Quill&Scroll; StuCncl; Bsktbl; Ftbl; Trk; IMSpt; Univ Of Neb; Engineering.

STACKPOOL, Mike J; Glenwood HS; Glenwood, MN; CmntyWkr; HonRl; NatlFornLg; NatlMeritCmnd; SchMus; SchPl; StuCncl; StuGov; Wrstlng; CitAwd; U Of Cgo;.

STACY, Lynn; Aurora Hoytlakes HS; Hoytlakes, MN; 12/230 Band; CncrtBnd; HonRl; MrchBnd; NHS; NatlThespSoc; PepBnd; SchPl; SctActv; Yrbk; College; Biology.

STADE, Debra A; Good Counsel HS; Chicago, IL; 108/247 Chrl; JA; NatlFornLg; NatlMeritCmnd; NatlMeritSchl; SchMus; SchPl; SctActv; RptrSchPpr; SchPpr; SpnCl; PpCl; Chrldr; College; Nursing.

STADLER, Judith E; Clio HS; Clio, MI; NHS; NatlMeritSF; OffAde; SchMus; PresTeen; YthFlsp; EdYrBk; Yrbk; SpnCl; 4-HAwd; College.

STADLER, Kevin; Cedarburg HS; Cedarburg, WI; 32,301 ALBoysSt; NatlMeritFnl; EdSchPpr; Ftbl; Trk; Wrstlng; College; Psychology.

STADLER, Marilyn; Hampshire HS; Hampshire, IL; /70 ALAGirlsSt; Band; Chrs; CncrtBnd; HonRl; PepBnd; SchMus; TchrAde; FHA; CitAwd; Bus Sch;cpa.

STADNICKI, Karen L; H L Richards HS; Worth, IL; 14/1084 Chr; HonRl; NHS; OffAde; StuCncl; TchrAde; GAA; Air Force Comm Coll; Electronics.

STADNIK, Terrie M; Good Counsel HS; Chicago, IL; 31/272 HonRl; JA; FBLA; GerCl; Business School; Court Reporting.

STADTLANDER, Sandra K; Klemme Community HS; Klemme, IA; 2/34 PresFrshCls; Chrs; ChrhWkr; HonRl; MrchBnd; NHS; Yrbk; SpnCl; Bsktbl; Bus Sch;.

STAES, Andrew T; Chicago Christian HS; Blue Island, IL; HonRl; JrNHS; Bsktbl; Glf; College; Vocation.

STAFFELD, Vicki L; Walled Lake Western HS; Novi, MI; HonRl; Oakland University; Business Mgmt.

STAFFORD, Barbara L; Downers Grove South HS; Woodridge, IL; 152/976 HonRl; Chrldr; CchngActv; College; Orthodontics.

STAFFORD, Cheryl L; Woodlawn HS; Woodlawn, IL; Chrs; HonRl; EdYrBk; RptrSchPpr; EdSchPpr; FHA; PpCl; LetterChrldr; College; Liberal Arts.

STAFFORD, Joseph D; Lumen Christi HS; Jackson, MI; 43/272 HonRl; NHS; LetterSciCl; Michigan Tech; Engineering.

STAFFORD, Kim E; Lincoln Park HS; Lincoln Park, MI; 123/576 Chrs; SchMus; SchPl; TchrAde; EdYrBk; RptrSchPpr; SchPpr; Centra Mich U; Science.

STAFFORD, Mary T; Good Counsel Acad; Richfield, MN; 3/50 SchPl; Yrbk; SchPpr; LetterBsktbl; LetterTennis; LetterTrk; PresGAA; IMSpt; College; Med Tech.

STAFFORD, Pamela; St Joseph HS; St Joseph, MI; 80/380 Band; Chr; CncrtBnd; HonRl; LitMag; MrchBnd; NatlThespSoc; PepBnd; SchMus; StuCncl; SchPpr; Coll; Music Ther.

STAFFORD, Robin M; Holton HS; Holton, MI; 7/52 CncrtBnd; HonRl; MrchBnd; NHS; PepBnd; SchPl; StuCncl; PpCl; Chrldr; Jr Col; Psychoanalist.

STAFFORD, Ronald J; J C Harmon HS; Kansas City, KS; 3/355 ALBoysSt; Band; HonRl; JrNHS; NHS; PepBnd; StuCncl; SpnCl; LetterFtbl; Trk; Univ; Percussion Major.

STAFFORD, Sallie M; Fremont HS; Fremont, IN; PresBand; TreasChr; HonRl; SchMus; SchPl; SecFHA; FrCl; LatCl; PpCl; LetterChrldr; College; Professional.

STAFFORD, Susan L; Fremd HS; Rolling Meadows, IL; 4/550 HonRl; JrNHS; NHS; SchMus; LatCl; Univ Of Notre Dame; Biological Sciences.

STAFFORD, Terry W; Douglass HS; Douglass, KS; VPSrCls; HonRl; LbryAde; SchPl; StuCncl; Bsbl; College; Psychology.

STAFL, Jan; Brookfield Central HS; Brookfield, WI; 30/480 AFS; NHS; Quill&Scroll; Yrbk; SchPpr; MthCl; Tennis; IMSpt; CitAwd; Northwestern Univ; Medine.

STAFLIN, Mary R; Adlai E Stevenson HS; Deerfield, IL; 4/231 ChrhWkr; CncrtBnd; HospAde; MrchBnd; NHS; StuGov; Yrbk; VPPpCl; Purdue Univ; Pharmacy.

STAGGS, Janet L; North Putnam HS; Greencastle, IN; 32/130 HonRl; NHS; 4-H; PresFHA; PpCl; 4-HAwd; Central Bus College; Accountant.

STAGGS, Randy D; Muncie North HS; Muncie, IN; PolWkr; SctActv; SciCl; LetterFtbl; LetterTrk; IMSpt; De Pauw University.

STAGL, Mary J; St Marys HS; New England, ND; Band; Chr; CncrtBnd; MrchBnd; PepBnd; PpCl; Bsktbl; Trk; Chrldr; Col; Professional.

STAHELI, Carol; Wahlert HS; Dubuque, IA; 38/450 HonRl; SchAde; SctActv; StuGov; SchPpr; Tennis; IMSpt; Univ Ia; Prof.

STAHL, Emma J; Central HS; Worthington, IN; Band; CncrtBnd; DrmMjrt; HonRl; MrchBnd; OffAde; PepBnd; PpCl; Bsktbl; Trade School; Business.

STAHL, Jamey L; Primghar Comm HS; Primghar, IA; Chr; CmntyWkr; HonRl; StuCncl; Bsktbl; Trk; IMSpt; PPFtbl; Junior College; Licensed Practial Nurse.

STAHL, Kathy; Hampton Comm HS; Hampton, IA; 14/111 HonRl; NHS; FBLA; American Institute Of Business; Secretary.

STAHL, Mark; Marion Adams HS; Sheridan, IN; PresJrCls; HonRl; JrNHS; NHS; StuCncl; SpnCl; IMSpt; In Univ; Doctor.

STAHL, Marsha L; Niantic Harristown HS; Niantic, IL; PresSophCls; Band; ChrhWkr; CncrtBnd; HonRl; NHS; SctActv; 4-H; SpnCl; Chrldr; GAA; College; Accounting.

STAHL, M L; Saugatuck HS; Saugatuck, MI; Chr; HonRl;.

STAHL, Rita F; Sullivan HS; Sullivan, IN; 16/154 HonRl; SchMus; SchPl; Pres4-H; FHA; LatCl; MthCl; PpCl; 4-HAwd; College; Teacher.

STAHL, Roxanne L; Galva Comm HS; Galva, IA; Band; Chrs; CncrtBnd; DrlTm; HonRl; MrchBnd; SchPl; YthFlsp; 4-H; LetterBsktbl; LetterTrk; 4-HAwd; St Lukes Hosp; Nurse.

STAHL, Steven R; Binford Public HS; Binford, ND; SecSophCls; Band; HonRl; PepBnd; SchMus; SchPl; 4-H; Bsbl; Bsktbl; 4-HAwd; Ndsu; Research In Microbiology.

STAHL, Vicki L; Freeman HS; Freeman, SD; 5/52 TrsFrshCls; SecJrCls; Band; Chrs; DrmMjrt; HonRl; SecNHS; SecStuCncl; Treas4-H; PresFHA; Freeman Jr Coll; Nurse.

STAHLEY, Steven R; East Central HS; Sunman, IN; Aud/Vis; Chrs; ChrhWkr; NatlSciFnd; SchPl; SctActv; 4-H; FSA; FrCl; College; Engineering.

STAHLHOOD, Wilson R; Coldwater HS; Coldwater, MI; 70/277 Chr; ChrhWkr; HonRl; LitMag; PolWkr; SchMus; YthFlsp; RptrSchPpr; EngCl; Bsbl; Grand Valley State Coll; Major Arts & Media.

STAHLHUTH, Mark W; Francis Howell HS; St Charles, MO; Band; CncrtBnd; HonRl; MrchBnd; NHS; NatlMeritSF; SchMus; SchPl; Univ; Jazz Musician.

STAHNKE, Bruce I; Evanston Twp HS; Evanston, IL; SchPl; Washington Univ; Fine Arts.

STAI, Michael R; Sacred Heart Public HS; Sacred Heart, MN; TrsSophCls; Chr; Chrs; ChrhWkr; SctActv; YthFlsp; Yrbk; LetterBsbl; Bsktbl; LetterFtbl; Alexandria Area Vocational Inst; Accounting.

STAIDL, Cynthia J; Oconto Sr HS; Oconto, WI; Band; ChrhWkr; HonRl; LbryAde; NHS; Quill&Scroll; SchPl; RptrSchPpr; SchPpr; 4-H; Madison Area Tech Schl; Child Care Asst.

STAINBROOK, Bonnie B; Mitchell Sr HS; Mitchell, SD; Band; ChrhWkr; CncrtBnd; HonRl; NHS; YthFlsp; FHA; SpnCl; OptClAwd; Yankton College; Social Work.

STAINBROOK, Deborah L; Mount St Benedict HS; Crookston, MN; Chrs; CmntyWkr; HonRl; SchPl; Sdlty; SchPpr; PpCl; GAA; IMSpt; College; Special Education.

STAKE, Sharon L; Lincoln HS; Wisconsin Rapids, WI; Chrs; HonRl; NHS; StuCncl; GerCl; PpCl; Chrldr; College; Doctor.

STAKER, Victoria L; Amboy HS; Harmon, IL; 6/123 PresSophCls; ChrhWkr; HonRl; NHS; StuCncl; TchrAde; AmLegAwd; DARAwd; JAAwd; Oral Roberts U; Special Ed.

STALDER, Donita E; Beaver City HS; Beaver City, NE; 7/21 Chrs; ChrhWkr; HonRl; HospAde; Business School; Secretary.

STALEY, Cheryll J; Oregon Sr HS; Oregon, WI; 39/194 Band; Chrs; ChrhWkr; CncrtBnd; HonRl; MrchBnd; SchMus; SchPl; SctActv; PresFHA; PpCl; Swmmng; Stevens Point Univ; Elementary Music.

STALEY, Cynthia K; Brimfield HS; Brimfield, IL; 3/53 HonRl; NHS; OffAde; PresStuCncl; TchrAde; YthFlsp; EdYrBk; SpnCl; PpCl; Chrldr; Ill State Univ; Elem Ed.

STALLBAUMER, Daniel J; B & B Baileyville HS; Seneca, KS; HonRl; SchPl; LetterTrk;.

STALLBAUMER, Jeanette F; B & B HS; Seneca, KS; Chrs; PresStuCncl; TchrAde; TreasFHA; PpCl; LetterBsktbl; LetterTrk; Chrldr; PresAwd; Coll; Preschool.

STALLCOP, Evelyn A; Brazil HS; Brazil, IN; Chr; HonRl; HospAde; NHS; SchMus; KiwanAwd; College; Professional.

STALLING, David; Horace Mann HS; Gary, IN; Aud/Vis; Band; Chr; ChrhWkr; CncrtBnd; HonRl; MrchBnd; StuCncl; EdSchPpr; SptEdSchPpr; Bsbl; Bsktbl; Marquette Univ; Bus Admin.

STALLINGS, Heidi A; Downers Grove Comm HS; Downers Grove, IL; 47/826 Chr; Chrl; Chrs; HonRl; Mdrgl; NatlFornLg; NHS; NatlThespSoc; SchMus; SchPl; Ill Wesleyan Univ; Theatre.

STALLINGS, John G; Memorial HS; Evansville, IN; HonRl; PolWkr; SchMus; SchPl; Swmmng; University; Law.

STALLMAN, Janice K; Prairie HS; Fairfax, IA; 4/200 Chr; DrlTm; HospAde; JrNHS; NatlMeritSF; SchPl; SecStuCncl; Pres4-H; 4-HAwd; Univ; Pharmacy.

STALLMAN, Sandra A; La Salle HS; Walford, IA; 2/95 VPJrCls; PresSrCls; Chr; HonRl; ModUN; NHS; NatlMeritSchl; PresStuCncl; StuGov; IMSpt; DARAwd; St Teresas College; Nursing.

STALLMANN, Brenda; Sheldon Public HS; Hospers, IA; Coll; Enginerring.

STALLSMITH, Karen; Southwest HS; Green Bay, WI; 162/420 Band; CncrtBnd; HospAde; JA; MrchBnd; Orch; PepBnd; SchMus; RptrYrbk; Swmmng; Univ Of Wi Ab; Music Therapy.

STALP, Alice; Central Catholic HS; West Point, NE; 12/69 HonRl; NHS; RedCrAde; MthCl; PpCl; SciCl; Trk; PPFtbl; College; Medical Tech.

STALTER, Rebecca L; Flanagan HS; Gridley, IL; Band; CncrtBnd; HonRl; MrchBnd; PepBnd; SchPl; TchrAde; GerCl; PpCl; SciCl; GAA; IMSpt; College.

STALZER, John P; St Rita HS; Chicago, IL; 41/435 Band; HonRl; NatlMeritCmnd; SctActv; StuGov; Northwestern; Science.

STALZER, Margaret; Evergreen Park C HS; Evergreen Park, IL; 78/452 TrsSrCls; HonRl; LbryAde; NHS; SchPl; StuCncl; StuGov; EdSchPpr; MthCl; CchngActv; Univ; Professional.

STALZER, Rosemary L; Semco Community HS; Haverhill, IA; Chrs; HonRl; Mdrgl; NatlThespSoc; SchMus; SchPl; TchrAde; College; Social Worker.

STALZLE, Dennis W; Marist HS; Oak Lawn, IL; 74/393 ChrhWkr; HonRl; PolWkr; SchMus; SctActv; YthFlsp; LetterFtbl; LetterTrk; GodCntryAwd; PresAwd; Northwestern; Md.

STAMAN, Paul R; Amana HS; Amana, IA; TrsJrCls; Chrs; CncrtBnd; HonRl; MrchBnd; ModUN; PolWkr; SptEdSchPpr; Bsktbl; Glf; Univ Of Iowa; Political Science.

STAMATKIN, Gary C; Crispus Attucks HS; Indianapolis, IN; 3/232 HonRl; NHS; NatlMeritCmnd; Purdue Univ; Mathematics.

STAMBAUGH, Cathy S; Astoria HS; Browning, IL; 30/50 Band; CmntyWkr; CncrtBnd; HonRl; NHS; OffAde; 4-H; SpnCl; GAA; JAAwd; Spoon River Clg; Med Tech.

STAMENKOVICH, Julie; Washington HS; Chicago, IL; ChrhWkr; CmntyWkr; HonRl; JrNHS; NHS; OffAde; LatCl; Bsktbl; Trk; PresAwd; Coll; Medical.

STAMER, Kandace A; Auburn HS; Auburn, IL; TrsSrCls; Chrs; HonRl; NHS; SchMus; Yrbk; PpCl; Chrldr; GAA; VFWAwd;.

STAMER, Theresa M; Pattonville HS; Bridgeton, MO; CmntyWkr; HonRl; NatlMeritCmnd; SchAde; StuCncl; TchrAde; PpCl; CaptChrldr; GAA; CitAwd; College; Vocation.

STAMM, Carl A; Dryden HS; Dryden, MI; HonRl; NHS; StuCncl; TchrAde; LetterBsbl; LetterGlf; IMSpt; Michigan State University; Engineering.

STAMMAN, Kay L; Gladwin Comm HS; Gladwin, MI; 14/151 Band; ChrhWkr; HonRl; NHS; TchrAde; Yrbk; SchPpr; 4-H; FHA; Spring Arbor College; Teacher.

STAMMER, Russell D; Storm Lake Sr HS; Storm Lake, IA; NatlMeritSF; StuCncl; LetterFtbl; LetterTrk; CaptWrstlng; JETSAwd; Iowa State Univ; Engineering.

STAMNESS, Cindy L; Kensington Public HS; Kensington, MN; 18/19 ALAGirlsSt; HonRl; StuCncl; EdYrBk; SchPpr; FHA; CaptBsktbl; LetterTrk; BttyCrckrAwd; Univ Of Mn; Pre Library Science.

STAMNESS, Patricia J; Kensington Public HS; Kensington, MN; ALAGirlsSt; Band; Chr; HonRl; SchPl; EdYrBk; RptrSchPpr; FHA; CaptChrldr; VPGAA; College; Elementary Education.

STAMP, Joni; Southern HS; Stronghurst, IL; Band; Chr; Chrs; HonRl; NHS; SchPl; FHA; FTA; FrCl; Coll.

STAMP, Mary A; Holstein Community HS; Holstein, IA; HonRl; Yrbk; 4-H; College; Computer Programming.

STAMPE, Scott J; Sully Superimposed HS; Pierre, SD; VPSophCls; Chrs; HonRl; SchPl; SptEdYrbk; 4-H; PpCl; LetterBsktbl; LetterTrk; College; Engineering.

STAMPFL, Burtrom L; Three Lakes HS; Monico, WI; 1/45 VPJrCls; Band; ChrhWkr; CmntyWkr; HonRl; NHS; StuCncl; StuGov; LetterWrstlng; College; Electrical Field.

STAMPLEY, Anita R; Harlan HS; Chicago, IL; 2/800 ChrhWkr; HonRl; JrNHS; NHS; TreasStuCncl; GerCl; SciCl; Tennis; GAA; IMSpt; Carleton; Physician.

STAMPLEY, Debra T; J M Harlan HS; Chicago, IL; 36/550 Chrs; ChrhWkr; CmntyWkr; HonRl; NHS; StuCncl; FHA; FTA; CchngActv; Chicago State University; Elementary Educ.

STAMPS, Douglas W; Heritage Hills HS; Richland, IN; 1/147 VPSophCls; HstSrCls; CncrtBnd; MrchBnd; PresNHS; PepBnd; SchMus; StuCncl; 4-HAwd; OptClAwd; Univ; Engineering.

STAMSCHROR, Pamela J; Morrison Community HS; Morrison, IL; Chr; HonRl; NHS; FrCl; LetterTrk; TreasGAA; Ill State Univ; Elem Ed.

STANASZEK, John D; Comstock HS; Kalamazoo, MI; HstSrCls; Chr; SchMus; SchPl; StuCncl; StuGov; GerCl; Western Mi U.

STANCLIFF, Diane; Ravenna HS; Conklin, MI; 5/108 Band; ChrhWkr; HonRl; NHS; TchrAde; Bsktbl; Trk; IMSpt; Moody Bible Institute.

STANCZAK, Janice L; St Clement HS; Centerline, MI; 52/97 LbryAde; SchPl; StuCncl; RptrYrbk; PresFHA; PpCl; Macomb County Comm Coll; Music.

STANCZAK, Stephen P; Carmel HS; Waukegan, IL; 17/166 HonRl; NHS; PolWkr; West Virginia Univ; Lawyer.

STANDAGE, Leann J; Lakewood HS; Lake Odessa, MI; 6/203 Chr; ChrhWkr; HonRl; Mdrgl; NHS; SchMus; SchPl; SctActv; TchrAde; YthFlsp; Univ; Speech.

STANDARD, M Jean; Rolla HS; Rolla, MO; HonRl; FHA; FrCl; College; Professional.

STANDEN, Charles; Edgemont HS; Edgemont, SD; 2/16 AFS; ALBoysSt; Band; Chr; HonRl; MrchBnd; NHS; NatlThespSoc; Yrbk; Ftbl; S D School Mines P Tech; Civil Engineering.

STANDEN, Gertrude; Edgemont HS; Edgemont, SD; 7/33 AFS; Band; Chrs; ChrhWkr; CncrtBnd; HonRl; MrchBnd; PepBnd; Yrbk;.

STANDER, Linda M; Marion C Early HS; Bolivar, MO; 1/40 PresFrshCls; Chrs; HonRl; ModUN; OffAde; SchPl; Yrbk; SchPpr; FHA; FrCl; PpCl; Bsktbl; College.

STANDER, Victor J; Weeping Water Public HS; Weeping Water, NE; HonRl; JrNHS; PresNHS; RptrSchPpr; SptEdSchPpr; Ftbl; Univ; Math.

STANDERFER, Sheila K; Bethany HS; Bethany, IL; 5/36 SecSrCls; Band; Chrs; ChrhWkr; HonRl; Mdrgl; MrchBnd; YthFlsp; PresFHA; LetterTrk; Eastern Univ; Physical Education.

STANDERFORD, Judy D; Humboldt Public HS; Humboldt, NE; PresJrCls; Band; Chrs; HonRl; Mdrgl; SecStuCncl; Yrbk; 4-H; PpCl; Chrldr; 4-HAwd; College; Secretary.

STANEK, Joseph P; Mc Henry Comm HS; Mc Henry, IL; Band; CncrtBnd; MrchBnd; PepBnd; LetterBsbl; Bsktbl; IMSpt; University.

STANEK, Kathleen M; Grosse Pointe North HS; Harper Woods, MI; 31/613 VPSophCls; NHS; TchrAde; Trk; Chrldr; GAA; U Of Mich; Phy Therapy.

STANFIELD, Melanie A; Oakley HS; Oakley, KS; PresJrCls; Chrl; Chrs; HonRl; SchPl; StuCncl; TchrAde; FHA; PpCl; CaptChrldr; Kansas St Univ; Office Admin.

STANFORD, Gerald J; Arthur HS; Arthur, IL; 7/45 Band; CncrtBnd; HonRl; MrchBnd; PepBnd; Eastern Illinois University; Biology.

STANFORD, Jerry A; Flora HS; Flora, IL; 15/137 CmntyWkr; HonRl; NHS; PolWkr; StuCncl; StuGov; SpnCl; MthCl; SciCl; Lincoln Trail College.

STANG, David W; Brookville HS; Brookville, IN; StuCncl; 4-H; VPFFA; OptClAwd; Farming.

STANG, Sally E; Glenwood City HS; Glenwood City, WI; 3/81 Band; Chr; ChrhWkr; NHS; NatlMeritCmnd; SchPl; SchPpr; FHA; PpCl; Chrldr; College; Music Therapy.

STANG, Susan J; Menominee HS; Menominee, MI; 13/275 TrsJrCls; Band; NHS; NatlMeritCmnd; Quill&Scroll; StuCncl; EdYrBk; PresPpCl; LetterGlf; Tennis; Alma Clge.

STANGEL, Philip D; Mishicot HS; Tisch Mills, WI; 17/97 Band; Chr; Chrs; CncrtBnd; HonRl; Mdrgl; MrchBnd; PepBnd; SchMus; SchPl; LatCl; LetterWrstlng; Univ Of Wisconsin; Music.

STANGL, Dale; Manning Comm HS; Manning, IA; HonRl; FFA; Bsktbl; IMSpt; Farming.

STANGL, Jean M; Auburndale HS; Arpin, WI; Chrs; HonRl; LbryAde; SchPl; FHA; FrCl; PpCl; Us Army.

STANGL, Thomas J; Greenway HS; Coleraine, MN; Aud/Vis; Chr; CmntyWkr; HonRl; StuGov; RptrYrbk; RptrSchPpr; FrCl; LetterFtbl; IMSpt; St Thomas Univ; Dentistry.

STANGLAND, Sherry L; Central Noble HS; Albion, IN; ChrhWkr; CmntyWkr; SchPl; StuCncl; YthFlsp; 4-H; PpCl; Business Schl; Secretary.

STANGLE, Karen A; Oxford HS; Oxford, KS; 2/39 SecFrshCls; SecJrCls; VPSrCls; Band; Chrs; HonRl; HospAde; NHS; SchPl; StuCncl; College.

STANHOPE, Bill I; Chesaning HS; Owosso, MI; ChrhWkr; HonRl; YthFlsp; 4-H; MthCl; Tennis; Trade School; Vocation.

STANHOPE, Deborah S; Chesaning HS; Chesaning, MI; Band; ChrhWkr; CncrtBnd; HonRl; MrchBnd; NHS; OffAde; YthFlsp; FHA; SpnCl; College; Elem Educ.

STANIC, Kathy S; S Milwaukee Senior HS; S Milwaukee, WI; 23/435 HonRl; NHS; FBLA; Trade School; Secretarial Field.

STANICK, Pamela J; Waterford Township HS; Pontiac, MI; 1/355 VPBand; CncrtBnd; HonRl; MrchBnd; NHS; PepBnd; Trk; BttyCrckrAwd; DanFAwd; U Of Mi; Mathematics.

STANISH, Ronald A; Arlington HS; Indianapolis, IN; 10/300 HonRl; NHS; NatlMeritCmnd; Ftbl; Trk; LetterWrstlng; GodCntryAwd; CitAwd; Indiana State University; Medical Tech.

STANISLAV, Cynthia M; Duchesne Academy; Omaha, NE; Chr; EdYrBk; CaptBsktbl; GAA; University Of Nebraska; English.

STANISLAWSKI, Barbara A; Immaculate Heart Of Mary HS; Chicago, IL; 25/260 Chrl; StuCncl; RptrYrbk; 4-H; Bsktbl; GAA; IMSpt; Mccormic Jr College; Accountant.

STANISZEWSKI, Stanley; St Clement HS; Warren, MI; Yrbk; RptrSchPpr; Wayne State Univ; Law School.

STANKEWICZ, Kevin J; Bishop Mc Namara HS; Kankakee, IL; 3/165 HonRl; LitMag; NHS; NatlMeritCmnd; NatlThespSoc; SchMus; SchPl; TchrAde; EdYrBk; SpnCl; Marquette; Commercial Law.

STANKIEWICZ, Michael F; Maine South HS; Park Ridge, IL; Aud/Vis; ChrhWkr; CmntyWkr; HonRl; PolWkr; SchPl; Univ Of Ill; Accounting.

STANKUS, Margaret M; St Joseph HS; Kenosha, WI; 1/138 Chr; HonRl; LbryAde; Mdrgl; NHS; TchrAde; KiwanAwd; Univ Of Wi; Math, Ed, Bus.

STANLAKE, Karen; North Adams HS; North Adams, MI; Band; CncrtBnd; MrchBnd; PepBnd; TchrAde; 4-H; FHA; FTA; PpCl; Bsktbl; Hillsdale Coll; Pre Med.

STANLEY, Craig; Rossville HS; Frankfort, IN; 7/62 VPSrCls; HonRl; NHS; PolWkr; SchPl; 4-H; SpnCl; PpCl; Chrldr; IMSpt; Ball State Univ; Pre Law.

STANLEY, Daniel D; Cresbard HS; Cresbard, SD; TrsJrCls; HonRl; PresYthFlsp; Bsbl; LetterBsktbl; Ftbl; Trk;.

STANLEY, Debra; North Miami HS; Macy, IN; 14/119 ChrhWkr; HonRl; LbryAde; YthFlsp; FHA; LatCl; PpCl; SciCl; Vocational; Health Occupations.

STANLEY, Gayle A; Metamore HS; E Peoria, IL; Chrs; ChrhWkr; RedCrAde; TchrAde; PresYthFlsp; GAA; Univ; Phy Therapy.

STANLEY, James; Frankton HS; Anderson, IN; Aud/Vis; SctActv; FrCl; Bsktbl; Purdue Univ; Pharmacy.

STANLEY, James L; Clay City HS; Louisville, IL; 4-H; PpCl; Bsktbl; IMSpt; Wabash College.

STANLEY, Julie K; Woodruff HS; Peoria, IL; 7/232 Chr; HonRl; HospAde; NHS; SchMus; Teen; Yrbk; PresKeyCl; FrCl; Northern Ill Univ; Nursing.

STANLEY, Karen J; High School; Marion, SD; 17/42 Band; Chr; Chrs; CncrtBnd; HonRl; MrchBnd; PepBnd; RptrYrbk; FHA; Bsktbl; Univ; Sociology Major.

STANLEY, Lester R; Delta HS; Albany, IN; CtyCnl; JA; JCC; LbryAde; PolWkr; StuCncl; StuGov; YthFlsp; RptrSchPpr; College; Professional.

STANLEY, Lynne E; Muscatine HS; Muscatine, IA; 1/373 NHS; NatlMeritSF; Quill&Scroll; YthFlsp; EdYrBk; PresFrCl; PpCl; Trk; Univ; Psychology.

STANLEY, Mary E; Owosso HS; Owosso, MI; 33/452 ModUN; NHS; NatlMeritCmnd; YthFlsp; 4-H; LatCl; Trk; GAA; IMSpt; Central Michigan Univ; Journalism.

STANLEY, Mary J; Fairfield HS; Fairfield, IA; TrsFrshCls; Chr; ChrhWkr; CncrtBnd; HonRl; MrchBnd; YthFlsp; LetterBsbl; Bsktbl; IMSpt; College; Medicine.

STANLEY, Scott L; Highland Park HS; Highland Park, MI; 21/260 HonRl; NHS; CaptTrk; IMSpt; U Of Detroit; Architecture Or Law Enforcemt.

STANLEY, Stephen; St Elmo Comm HS; St Elmo, IL; 15/56 Band; Chrs; ChrhWkr; CncrtBnd; MrchBnd; PepBnd; SchMus; SchPl; PpCl; Ftbl; College; Accountant.

STANLEY, Thomas O; Wilsonville HS; Wilsonville, NE; PresFrshCls; PresJrCls; PresSrCls; Aud/Vis; HonRl; ModUN; SchPl; StuGov; RptrYrbk; LetterFtbl; LetterTrk; Univ Of Nebraska; Elec Engineering.

STANSBERRY, Linda C; Virden HS; Virden, IL; ChrhWkr; HonRl; LbryAde; NHS; SchPl; TchrAde; YthFlsp; RptrSchPpr; FTA; College; Business.

STANSELL, Leslie A; Ernest W Seaholm HS; Birmingham, MI; 92/702 HonRl; JrNHS; ModUN; NHS; NatlMeritCmnd; SchAde; StuCncl; TreasStuGov; Oakland Univ; Social Work.

STANSFIELD, Richard; St Pius X HS; Festus, MO; /126 Band; ChrhWkr; CncrtBnd; MrchBnd; NatlThespSoc; SchAde; SctActv; StuCncl; Trk; Univ; Forestry.

STANTON, John M; Merrillville HS; Merrillville, IN; 10/545 ALBoysSt; Band; CncrtBnd; HonRl; MrchBnd; NHS; NatlMeritSF; NatlThespSoc; Orch; PepBnd; Indiana Univ; Scientific Research.

STANTON, Kathleen A; Metropolis Comm HS; Metropolis, IL; ChrhWkr; CmntyWkr; HonRl; MrchBnd; SctActv; StuCncl; SpnCl; PpCl; Glf; Tennis; College; Special Ed.

STANTON, Kevin V; West Holt HS; Lancaster, WI; Yrbk; 4-H; FFA; Bsktbl; Ftbl; Swmmng; Trk; IMSpt; 4-HAwd; Vo Tech; Farming.

STANTON, Mary; Academy Of The Visitation; Ballwin, MO; 7/42 CmntyWkr; PolWkr; RedCrAde; SchPl; StuCncl; StuGov; UNYO; CivCl; 4-H; GAA; Loyola Univ; Business Admin.

STANTON, Nancy; Wichita West HS; Wichita, KS; 19/522 HonRl; NHS; NatlMeritCmnd; OffAde; TchrAde; FrCl; Wichita St Univ;sec Educ.

STANTON, Pamela L; Harper Creek HS; Battle Creek, MI; 5/282 SecBand; ChrhWkr; SecCncrtBnd; HonRl; SecMrchBnd; NHS; SecOrch; SecPepBnd; TchrAde; SecSpnCl; Kalamazoo Col; Math.

STANTON, Robert T; Willowbrook HS; Lombard, IL; ChrhWkr; HonRl; MrchBnd; PepBnd; SctActv; TchrAde; College; Recreation.

STANTON, Sheryl L; Gull Lake HS; Battle Creek, MI; 30/228 Band; CncrtBnd; HonRl; MrchBnd; OffAde; PepBnd; SchMus; College; Math Teacher.

STANTON, Suzanne M; Maine South HS; Park Ridge, IL; HonRl; JrNHS; NatlMeritSF; PolWkr; SpnCl; Univ Of Illinois; Physician.

STANWAY, Sarah F; Richmond HS; Richmond, MO; FHA; U Of Mo; Child Development.

STAPELBROEK, Cathy; Seymour HS; Seymour, WI; Chrs; HonRl; GAA; College; Journalism.

STAPLES, Margaret M; Grayslake Comm HS; Grayslake, IL; 67/208 PolWkr; RedCrAde; StuCncl; StuGov; RptrYrbk; FDA; FSA; GerCl; LatCl; College; Vet Med.

STAPLES, Mark A; Jeffersonville HS; Jeffersonville, IN; CmntyWkr; JA; KeyCl; PpCl; Bsbl; Swmmng; Trade School; Construction.

STAPLES, Robert E; Montrose Hill Mc Cloy HS; Flushing, MI; 7/140 PresSrCls; Band; CncrtBnd; HonRl; MrchBnd; NHS; SchPl; StuGov; LetterBsktbl; IMSpt; AmLegAwd; CitAwd; College; Computer Technologist.

STAPLETON, David J; W H Taft HS; Chicago, IL; VPFrshCls; SctActv; StuCncl; RptrSchPpr; LetterFtbl; Trk; Illinois State Univ; Special Education.

STAPLETON, Diane L; Bogan HS; Chicago, IL; 15/679 HonRl; JrNHS; NHS; TchrAde; PpCl; St Xaviers Col; Education.

STAPLETON, Lawrence R; Van Far R1 HS; Vandalia, MO; 70/90 HonRl; PolWkr; StuGov; RptrSchPpr; SptEdSchPpr; Bsbl; Bsktbl; SecJrCls; AFS; CitAwd; Warrensburg Coll.

STAPLETON, Lisa K; Wilson Campus HS; Mankato, MN; Chr; LitMag; NatlThespSoc; RptrYrbk; SchPpr; 4-H; Chrldr; 4-HAwd; KiwanAwd; Coll; Prof.

STAPLETON, Michael E; Routt HS; New Berlin, IL; 10/61 TrsJrCls; HonRl; NHS; StuCncl; SpnCl; MthCl; Bsktbl; College; Professional.

STAPLETON, Patrick L; Caro HS; Caro, MI; Band; CncrtBnd; HonRl; MrchBnd; PepBnd; SchAde; RptrYrbk; SchPpr; PpCl; Swmmng; Navy; Photo Journialist.

STAPLETON, Sharon M; Mother Mc Auley HS; Chicago, IL; 75/484 ChrhWkr; HonRl; Quill&Scroll; StuCncl; RptrSchPpr; PresFrCl; Bsktbl; Ftbl; Trk; Depaul Univ; Accountant.

STAPLETON, Susan; Manchester HS; N Manchester, IN; 4 DrlTm; HonRl; NatlFornLg; OffAde; StuCncl; FrCl; GAA; Purdue Univ; Science.

STAPONSKI, Sharon E; Pierce City R 6 HS; Purdy, MO; Chr; SecLbryAde; SchPl; StuGov; RptrYrbk; RptrSchPpr; SecFHA; SecPpCl; Bsktbl; Trk; GAA; College.

STAPP, Bonnie G; Hauser HS; Hope, IN; 3/83 Chr; CaptDrlTm; HonRl; ModUN; NHS; Quill&Scroll; SchAde; SchPl; EdSchPpr; SecFFA; Sullivan Bus College; Computer Programming.

STAPP, Paul W; Charleston HS; Charleston, IL; HonRl; NHS; NatlMeritCmnd; Orch; St Olaf College; Music.

STAPP, Timothy; Tri County Area HS; Howard City, MI; 33/96 Band; Chr; HonRl; NatlMeritCmnd; PepBnd; SctActv; Bsbl; Bsktbl; Ftbl; Trk; Ferris State Col; Automotive Service.

STARAN, John D; Redford HS; Westland, MI; HonRl; U Of Mich Dearborn; Attorney.

STARASINIC, Carol J; St Francis Academy; Joliet, IL; 4/186 HonRl; VPNHS; SpnCl; Bsbl; Bsktbl; GAA; College; Accounting.

STARBUCK, John W; Sedan HS; Longton, KS; Band; CncrtBnd; HonRl; MrchBnd; Orch; PepBnd; TchrAde; FSA; IMSpt; Medical Schl; Medicine.

STARCEVICH, Theresa A; Farmington East HS; Farmington, IL; 37/145 ALAGirlsSt; Band; CncrtBnd; HonRl; MrchBnd; SchPl; 4-H; TreasFrCl; GAA; 4-HAwd; College; Art.

STARICKA, Susan K; Wilmot Union HS; Twin Lakes, WI; 1/209 Chr; DrlTm; HonRl; NHS; FHA; SpnCl; PpCl; Chrldr; GAA; Uw Madison; Music.

STARIWAT, Ricky D; Oak Park HS; Gladstone, MO; Band; ChrhWkr; CncrtBnd; HonRl; JrNHS; NHS; PepBnd; RedCrAde; SctActv; LetterTrk; Air Force Academy; Pathology.

STARK, Alice J; Neche Public HS; Neche, ND; 4/20 PresSrCls; ALAGirlsSt; HonRl; StuCncl; TchrAde; EdYrBk; FHA; Bsktbl; GAA; Univ Of North Dakota; Occupational Therapy.

STARK, Chris A; Delta HS; Muncie, IN; ChrhWkr; CmntyWkr; HonRl; RedCrAde; Sdlty; YthFlsp; RptrYrbk; Yrbk; PpCl; LetterSwmmng; College; Professional.

STARK, Connie L; Loomis Public HS; Loomis, NE; Chr; Chrs; SchAde; YthFlsp; LetterPpCl; GAA; College; Fashion Designin.

STARK, Darcy A; Spring Lake Park HS; Minneapolis, MN; 2/297 TrsSrCls; VPLitMag; NHS; NatlMeritCmnd; SchPl; StuGov; Pres4-H; LetterTennis; 4-HAwd; Gustavus Adolphus Col.

STARK, Darrie D; Loomis Public HS; Loomis, NE; ALAGirlsSt; Chrs; CmntyWkr; SchPl; StuCncl; 4-H; PpCl; GAA; AmLegAwd; Tech Schl; Secretary.

STARK, Deborah E; Jennings Senior HS; Jennings, MO; 22/242 Chrs; HonRl; NHS; SchMus; FrCl; PpCl; Tennis; GAA; IMSpt; GodCntryAwd; Univ Of Mo St Louis; Business Admin.

STARK, Diana K; Northridge HS; Goshen, IN; 20/117 Chr; HonRl; NHS; YthFlsp; 4-H; PpCl; CaptBsktbl; Chrldr; GAA; Col; Physical Education.

STARK, Donald A; Prospect HS; Arlington Hts, IL; 44/625 ChrhWkr; HonRl; Quill&Scroll; Iowa State Univ; Engineering.

STARK, Janice L; Norborne Public HS; Norborne, MO; 3/25 SecSophCls; SecJrCls; SecSrCls; ALAGirlsSt; Band; ChrhWkr; HonRl; NHS; SchPl; FHA; Missouri Western State Univ; Accounting.

STARK, Kay; Riceville Comm HS; Riceville, IA; SecSrCls; Band; DrlTm; HonRl; NHS; 4-H; IMSpt; 4-HAwd; Business School; Secrearial.

STARK, Kelly; Pleasanton Public HS; Hazard, NE; 3/28 ALAGirlsSt; HonRl; SchPl; StuCncl; RptrYrbk; EdSchPpr; Bsktbl; Trk; AmLegAwd; BttyCrckrAwd; Coll; Phschology.

STARK, Mark E; Belleville East HS; Fairview Hgts, IL; 17/70 Band; CncrtBnd; JrNHS; MrchBnd; NHS; NatlMeritFnl; Orch; SchMus; SctActv; Yrbk; Northwestern Univ; Medicine.

STARK, Mary C; Kimball HS; Royal Oak, MI; 44/705 Chr; HonRl; NHS; NatlMeritCmnd; TchrAde; College; Nursing.

STARK, Michelle R; Cousino Senior HS; Warren, MI; 1/575 Chrl; Chrs; HonRl; JrNHS; NHS; PresAwd; Central Mich U; Secondary Educ.

STARK, Theodore E; Edina East HS; Edina, MN; ChrhWkr; VPYthFlsp; LetterSocr; Monmouth College; Ministry.

STARK, Thomas M; Saint Edmond HS; Fort Dodge, IA; VPFrshCls; VPSophCls; ALBoysSt; NHS; SctActv; StuCncl; LatCl; LetterFtbl; LetterTrk; Iowa State Univ.

STARKE, Debra; Chamois HS; Chamois, MO; ALAGirlsSt; Band; HonRl; StuCncl; FHA; PpCl; Trk; IMSpt; Univ Of Mo; History.

STARKE, Phil A; Mexico HS; Mexico, MO; Yrbk; LetterFtbl; Wrstlng; Art Sch; Commercial Art.

STARKEN, Phyllis C; Horace Mann HS; Biwabik, MN; Chr; SchPl; PpCl; LetterSwmmng; LetterTrk; PresGAA; VoiceDemAwd; Clge.

STARKEY, Gregory A; West Vigo HS; New Goshen, IN; Band; ChrhWkr; YthFlsp; 4-H; FTA; Indiana State University.

STARKMAN, Robert D; Birmingham Seaholm HS; Birmingham, MI; Chr; CmntyWkr; HonRl; ModUN; NatlFornLg; NatlMeritSF; PolWkr; StuGov; Mich St Univ; Pre Med.

STARKMAN, Sandra R; Niles West HS; Lincolnwood, IL; HonRl; NHS; GAA; JCAwd; U Of Mich; Lawyer.

STARKOWSKI, John E; Maine Twp South HS; Park Ridge, IL; ChrhWkr; HonRl; OffAde; PolWkr; SchPl; SciCl; Trk; IMSpt; University.

STARKS, Carol D; Anderson HS; Anderson, IN; 37/562 Chr; Chrs; HonRl; JrNHS; NHS; SchMus; Butler Univ; Medicine.

STARKS, Louis; East HS; Waterloo, IA; TrsJrCls; ALBoysSt; ChrhWkr; HonRl; ModUN; StuCncl; AmLegAwd; University; Professional.

STARMAN, Darlene A; Petersburg Public HS; Petersburg, NE; Chr; Chrs; HonRl; SchPl; TchrAde; PpCl;.

STARMAN, Deanna K; Petersburg Public HS; Petersburg, NE; 1/25 SecJrCls; Chrs; HonRl; StuCncl; TchrAde; SchPpr; PpCl; Trk;.

STARMAN, Nancy R; Forman HS; Manito, IL; 10/90 HonRl; JrNHS; NHS; SchPl; 4-H; FFA; FHA; Bsbl; 4-HAwd; Icc Jr Coll; Business Administration.

STARNER, Carrie E; Mt Pleasant HS; Mt Pleasant, MI; 47/332 Band; Chr; HonRl; Mdrgl; NHS; NatlThespSoc; SchMus; SchPl; FrCl; PpCl; Albion Coll; Pre.

STARNES, Mary T; St Phillip Cc HS; Battle Creek, MI; Chrl; JA; RptrSchPpr; SpnCl; PpCl; PPFtbl; Kellogg Comm Clge; Journalism.

STARNICK, Michael D; Boone Grove HS; Val Paraiso, IN; Aud/Vis; Band; ChrhWkr; CncrtBnd; LbryAde; TchrAde; SciCl; Bsktbl; Trk; IMSpt; College; Vocation.

STAROSTKA, Nancy; Clarks Public HS; Clarks, NE; Band; Chrs; HonRl; PepBnd; SchPl; TchrAde; Yrbk; SchPpr; PpCl; Vocation.

STARR, Amy L; Niles West HS; Lincolnwood, IL; 21/626 CmntyWkr; HonRl; LitMag; StuGov; U Of Ill; Attonrey.

STARR, Carol D; St Marys Academy; Nauvoo, IL; 10/27 Chr; ChrhWkr; CmntyWkr; HonRl; LbryAde; OffAde; TchrAde; RptrSchPpr; 4-H; SciCl; IMSpt;.

STARR, Carolyn M; Rockwell Swaledale HS; Rockwell, IA; Band; CmntyWkr; CncrtBnd; HonRl; MrchBnd; NHS; PepBnd; RedCrAde; LetterBsktbl; LetterTrk; College; Prof.

STARR, Donna M; Andrean HS; Merrillville, IN; 68/286 HonRl; FrCl; Purdue Univ; Nursing.

STARR, Jean M; Nauvou Colusa HS; Nauvoo, IL; ALAGirlsSt; Band; ChrhWkr; HonRl; NatlThespSoc; SchPl; EdYrBk; 4-H; GAA; 4-HAwd; Clge; Pro.

STARR, Karl R; Washburn HS; Minneapolis, MN; 21/495 ALBoysSt; Chr; ChrhWkr; Mdrgl; NatlFornLg; NHS; SchMus; StuCncl; SchPpr; VoiceDemAwd; St Olaf;.

STARR, Kevin R; Martinsville HS; Martinsville, IN; PpCl; LetterFtbl; IMSpt; College; Football Coach.

STARR, Laura; Sunset Hill HS; Kansas City, MO; 5/30 TrsSrCls; Quill&Scroll; StuGov; SchPpr; Tennis; LetterTrk; Washington U; Architecture.

STARR, Margaret; Hamilton HS; Nauvoo, IL; 1/76 AFS; Chrs; ChrhWkr; HonRl; StuCncl; StuGov; YthFlsp; CivCl; FrCl; CaptChrldr; Univ; Pro.

STARR, Shane E; Dekalb HS; Auburn, IN; 8/280 TrsFrshCls; TrsSophCls; TrsJrCls; Aud/Vis; ChrhWkr; NHS; NatlMeritSF; NatlThespSoc; SchPl; StuCncl; GerCl; LetterFtbl; Dartmouth; Medicine.

STARR, Timothy; White Pigeon HS; Union, MI; 1/85 PresFrshCls; ALBoysSt; Band; HonRl; SchMus; SchPl; College; Professional.

STARR, Wanda J; Mullen HS; Mullen, NE; Band; HonRl; SchMus; SchPl; RptrSchPpr; 4-H; FHA; PpCl; LetterTrk; 4-HAwd; Wayne State College; Data Processing.

STARR, William G; Rushville Cons HS; Glenwood, IN; 2/275 CncrtBnd; HonRl; MrchBnd; NatlFornLg; PresNHS; NatlMeritSF; StuCncl; PresLatCl; MthCl; SciCl; Rose Hulman Inst Of Tech; Engineering.

STARRETT, Jane; Holdrege HS; Holdrege, NE; PresBand; Chrs; CncrtBnd; HonRl; Yrbk; PpCl; Trk; IMSpt; Ne Univer; Medicine.

STARRETT, Joanne M; Lancaster HS; Lancaster, WI; 5/159 AFS; HonRl; JrNHS; ModUN; NHS; StuCncl; EdYrBk; FHA; PpCl; 4-HAwd; Uw Of Whitewater; Ed Therapy.

STARRETT, Judy; Holdrege HS; Holdrege, NE; 20/115 Band; Chrs; CncrtBnd; HonRl; PpCl; IMSpt; Univ;.

STARRICK, Mike; Boone Grove HS; Val Pariso, IN; Band; ChrhWkr; CncrtBnd; LbryAde; TchrAde; SciCl; Bsktbl; Trk; IMSpt; BttyCrckrAwd; College; Vocation.

STARRING, George; St Philip HS; Battle Creek, MI; TchrAde; Bsbl; Bsktbl; Ftbl; College Football;public Relations.

STARZEC, Michael R; Gordon Technical; Park Ridge, IL; HonRl; StuCncl; Bsktbl; Tennis; Trk; IMSpt; College; Optometry.

STASEY, Janet L; Wm A Wirt HS; Gary, IN; 8/234 Band; Chr; HonRl; NHS; SchPl; TchrAde; SpnCl; SciCl; U Of Chicago; Lawyer.

STASIAK, Richard W; Weber HS; Chicago, IL; 16/193 HonRl; HospAde; RptrYrbk; RptrSchPpr; SciCl; Tennis; Univ; Biology.

STASIOSKI, Walter S; Lane Tech HS; Chicago, IL; 117/1240 Illinois Inst Of Tech; Elec Engineer.

STASSEN, Karen M; Walnut Grove HS; Walnut Grove, MN; 9/49 Chr; HonRl; StuGov; RptrSchPpr; SptEdSchPpr; 4-H; PpCl; Chrldr; CchngActv; 4-HAwd; Business Sch; Professional.

STASTNY, Mary J; New Lisbon HS; New Lisbon, WI; 1/63 TrsJrCls; Band; ChrhWkr; CmntyWkr; NHS; StuCncl; Yrbk; RptrSchPpr; PpCl; University; Science.

STASUKAITIS, Christine A; Maria HS; Chicago, IL; RptrSchPpr; SpnCl; College.

STASZAK, Lynn A; St Joseph Academy; Krakow, WI; ALAGirlsSt; Chrs; LitMag; LbryAde; Mdrgl; NHS; SchMus; Sdlty; TchrAde; University; Music.

STATEN, Donna M; Hackett HS; Kalamazoo, MI; ChrhWkr; SchMus; SctActv; TchrAde; CivCl; College; Professional.

STATEN, Stephen F; Griffin HS; Springfield, IL; HonRl; NHS; TchrAde; SptEdYrbk; RptrSchPpr; PpCl; LetterBsbl; Bsktbl; LetterFtbl; GovHonPrgAwd; Illinois Benedictine College; Pre Medicine.

STATES, Leslie S; Auburn HS; Auburn, IL; Chrs; HonRl; LbryAde; SchMus; YthFlsp; FHA; SpnCl; College; P E Teacher.

STATES, Monica R; West Holt HS; Atkinson, NE; Band; ChrhWkr; CncrtBnd; NHS; PepBnd; SchPl; Yrbk; Trk; CitAwd; Coll; Nurse.

STATON, Brenda S; Metropolis Comm HS; Belknap, IL; 14/158 ChrhWkr; CmntyWkr; HonRl; NHS; SchPpr; 4-H; MthCl; DanFAwd; 4-HAwd; Baptist Memorial Hosp; Nursing.

STATON, Valda D; Andrean HS; Gary, IN; ChrhWkr; HonRl; NHS; Quill&Scroll; SchPl; YthFlsp; SptEdSchPpr; MthCl; PpCl; University; Law.

STATTNER, Diana S; Cloverdale HS; Cloverdale, IN; Band; Chr; HonRl; HospAde; NHS; 4-H; SecSpnCl; Indiana Univ; Medicine.

STATZ, Joseph J; West HS; Madison, WI; NHS; NatlMeritSF; Uwm; Major In History.

STATZ, Mary; Oregon Senior HS; Oregon, WI; SecJrCls; VPSrCls; AFS; ALAGirlsSt; HonRl; NHS; SpnCl; Univ Of Wi; Accounting Math & Econ.

STATZ, Sandy T; Mc Donell HS; Chippewa Falls, WI; Band; ChrhWkr; HonRl; PepBnd; SchPl; RptrYrbk; 4-H; PpCl; College; Medical Technology.

STAUB, Marcia S; Marshall HS; Marshall, IL; 10/115 ALAGirlsSt; Band; ChrhWkr; CmntyWkr; CncrtBnd; MrchBnd; PepBnd; 4-H; SpnCl; PpCl; College; Professional.

STAUCH, James; Spencer HS; Spencer, IA; HonRl; NHS; Ia State Univ; Banker.

STAUDENMAIER, Daniel L; Troy HS; Troy, KS; VPSrCls; ALBoysSt; ChrhWkr; HonRl; NHS; SchPl; KeyCl; SpnCl; LetterTrk; Engineering.

STAUDT, Loretta A; Maine East Twp HS; Niles, IL; HonRl; NHS; NatlThespSoc; SchMus; University Of Illinois; Physical Therapy.

STAUFFACHER, Ruth A; Darlington HS; Mineral Point, WI; 6/120 AFS; Band; Chrs; CncrtBnd; DrlTm; HonRl; Mdrgl; NatlFornLg; PepBnd; SchMus; StuCncl; YthFlsp; Trk; Univ Of Wisconsin; English Teacher.

STAUFFER, Janice K; North White HS; Monon, IN; Chrs; CncrtBnd; HonRl; NHS; Orch; SchMus; TchrAde; YthFlsp; GerCl; PpCl; Vincennes Univ; Music Ed.

STAUFFER, Kim C; East Kentwood HS; Kentwood, MI; Chr; LetterBsktbl; IMSpt; Collegef Physical Education Teacher.

STAUFFER, Rebecca M; Roosevelt HS; Des Moines, IA; 170/440 ChrhWkr; CmntyWkr; PolWkr; FrCl; LetterSwmmng; LetterTennis; GAA; IMSpt; Southern Methodist Univ; Business Adm.

STAUFFER, William L; Willowbrook HS; Lombard, IL; ChrhWkr; HonRl; JA; JrNHS; NatlMeritCmnd; StuCncl; Principia College; Law.

STAUSKE, Lois A; Athens HS; Athens, WI; HonRl; LbryAde; NHS; StuCncl; Yrbk; SchPpr; FBLA; FHA; SpnCl; PpCl; Secretarial Work.

STAUSS, Randall R; Hortonville HS; Hortonville, WI; HonRl; NHS; StuCncl; College; Curr Major Study.

STAVENAU, David H; Wellcome Memorial HS; Good Thunder, MN; Band; HonRl; SchPl; FFA; Trade Sch; Mechanic.

STAVISH, Dawn; Little Falls Comm HS; Little Falls, MN; Chr; MrchBnd; SchMus; SchPl; FFA; Trk; PPFtbl; College; Agriculture.

STAVROPOULOS, Mark; St Viator HS; Mt Prospect, IL; 26/250 Ftbl; LetterTrk; Northwestern Univ; Electrical Engineering.

STAWYCHEY, Sandra; Oak Forest Hs; Oak Forest, IL; 16/325 HonRl; NHS; Twrl; FrCl; GAA; St Francis Hosp Of Nursing; Nursing.

ST CLAIR, Beth A; Colfax Community HS; Colfax, IA; Chr; Chrl; Chrs; HonRl; ModUN; NHS; SchMus; StuCncl; RptrSchPpr; FTA; Bus Schl; Bus Pro.

ST CLAIR, Bryce W; Perry HS; Perry, MI; 3/127 Band; HonRl; NHS; SchAde; TchrAde; FrCl; LetterBsbl; Bsktbl; LetterFtbl; Trk; Case Inst Of Technology; Research.

ST CLAIR, Lynda M; Attica HS; Attica, KS; 1/12 VPJrCls; Band; Chr; HonRl; NHS; PepBnd; StuCncl; StuGov; Teen; RptrSchPpr; SpnCl; PpCl; LetterTrk; PPFtbl; College; Rn.

ST CLAIR, Ran D; Rochester HS; Rochester, IN; CAP; HonRl; JrNHS; SctActv; Swmmng; College.

ST CLAIR, Rufus; Pusea Hs; Kansas City, MO; 14/290 Band; HonRl; MrchBnd; NHS; LetterFtbl; LetterTrk; Kv; Electrical Engineer.

STEAD, Joyce M; Madison HS; Madison, KS; 3/23 SecSrCls; Band; LbryAde; MrchBnd; PepBnd; SchPl; TchrAde; 4-H; PpCl; College; Data Processing.

STEADHAM, Christopher A; Roncalli HS; Indianapolis, IN; 16/189 Chr; HonRl; SchMus; SchPl; StuCncl; RptrYrbk; EdSchPpr; PpCl; Socr; VoiceDemAwd; Col; Navy Or Politic.

STEADMAN, Dale T; Woodstock HS; Woodstock, IL; PresSrCls; ALBoysSt; HonRl; 4-H; FFA; 4-HAwd; Junior College; Agriculture.

STEARLEY, Douglas E; Brazil HS; Brazil, IN; 7/180 Band; Chr; CncrtBnd; HonRl; MrchBnd; PresNHS; NatlThespSoc; PepBnd; SchMus; SecKeyCl; Rose Hulman Institute; Civil Engineer.

STEARNS, Dwight C; Murphysboro Township HS; Carbondale, IL; HonRl; NatlMeritSF; PolWkr; SchMus; SchPl; LetterBsktbl; LetterFtbl; Northwestern Univ; Police Science.

STEARNS, Laura E; South Knox HS; Monroe City, IN; 23/96 Chrs; Quill&Scroll; SchMus; SchPpr; Automated Machines Trng Ctr; Computor Prg.

STEARNS, Stephen C; New Trier East HS; Winnetka, IL; 382/847 University Of Colorado; Science.

STEARNS, Teresa D; Clarke Comm HS; Osceola, IA; 12/104 ALAGirlsSt; Quill&Scroll; SctActv; RptrYrbk; RptrSchPpr; VP4-H; FHA; LetterBsktbl; 4-HAwd; American Inst; Legal Secretary.

STEARS, Rita; Constantine Hs; Constantine, MI; HonRl; StuCncl; RptrYrbk; RptrSchPpr; 4-H; FrCl; PpCl; Bsktbl; 4-HAwd; College;registered Nurse.

STEBANE, Audrey M; Brillion Public HS; Kaukauna, WI; 1/84 PresAFS; ChrhWkr; HonRl; NHS; SchMus; SecStuCncl; PresYthFlsp; RptrSchPpr; Sec4-H; LetterBsktbl; GAA; DARAwd; 4-HAwd; Marquette Univ; Nursing.

STEBIC, Curtis R; Forest Park HS; Crystal Falls, MI; 9/89 ALBoysSt; HonRl; SchPl; SctActv; Bsktbl; AmLegAwd; LionAwd; CitAwd; Mi Tech Univ; Math.

STEBLER, Kenneth K; Calumet HS; Hubbell, MI; 16/169 Chrs; DrlTm; NHS; NatlMeritSF; ROTC; SchMus; SchPl; Trk; IMSpt; PresAwd; Dental School At Marquette; Entistry.

STECHER, Coleen M; St Marys HS; Bucyrus, ND; Band; Chr; Chrl; Chrs; CncrtBnd; HonRl; MrchBnd; PepBnd; SchPl; PresPpCl; University; Business Admin.

STECICH, Daniel K; Leo HS; Chicago, IL; 34/200 CmntyWkr; CncrtBnd; HonRl; JA; MrchBnd; RptrYrbk; RptrSchPpr; CivCl; Swmmng; College; Mechanical Engineer.

STECK, Amy R; Helias HS; Jefferson, MO; HonRl; LbryAde; PpCl; LetterBsktbl; LetterTrk; Missouri Univ; Agriculture.

STECK, Robert L; Anna Jonesboro HS; Anna, IL; Chrs; HonRl; Quill&Scroll; SchMus; SctActv; SptEdYrbk; PpCl; LetterFtbl; LetterTrk; Siu Carbondale; Pro Scouting.

STECK, Robert M; St Louis Univ HS; St Louis, MO; 29/209 HonRl; TreasNHS; TchrAde; Glf; Wrstlng; St Louis U; Political Science Froeifn Servc.

STECKER, Danny K; Harmony HS; Bonaparte, IA; CncrtBnd; HonRl; SchPl; Yrbk; Bsbl; Bsktbl; Ftbl; Glf; Trk; 4-HAwd; College; Music.

STECKER, Donald K; Unionville Sebewaing Area HS; Sebewaing, MI; 426/125 Chr; Chrs; ChrhWkr; CmntyWkr; HonRl; YthFlsp; RptrSchPpr; VP4-H; FFA; DanFAwd; 4-HAwd; Michigan State Univ; Agriculture.

STECKER, James C; Grand Island HS; Grand Island, NE; 47/467 Band; HonRl; NatlFornLg; PepBnd; CchngActv; IMSpt; Univ Of Nebraska; Agriculture.

STECKER, Lori; Hilbert HS; Potter, WI; TrsSophCls; Chrs; HonRl; JrNHS; NatlFornLg; TchrAde; YthFlsp; PpCl; Chrldr; CitAwd; Technical School; Vocation.

STECKER, Peggy S; Hilbert HS; Hilbert, WI; 2/65 TrsSophCls; Chrs; HospAde; NHS; StuGov; TchrAde; YthFlsp; RptrYrbk; LetterBsktbl; GAA; Tech Inst; Nurse.

STECKHAN, Diana; Sullivan HS; Chicago, IL; 93/276 PresSrCls; Chr; HonRl; MrchBnd; NHS; Orch; StuGov; EdYrBk; SciCl; Swmmng; Il Inst Of Tech; Surgical Nursing.

STECKLEIN, Sherri K; Hays HS; Victoria, KS; 13/188 HonRl; PresNatlFornLg; NHS; StuCncl; TchrAde; PpCl; IMSpt; CitAwd; VoiceDemAwd; Ft Hays State Col; Education.

STECKLER, Daniel J; Mt Carmel HS; Mt Carmel, IL; 17/185 ChrhWkr; NHS; 4-H; FFA; Wrstlng; Trade Sch; Voc Mech.

STECKLER, Mark T; Yankton Sr HS; Yankton, SD; 36/243 HonRl; NHS; SctActv; StuGov; LetterBsktbl; Ftbl; Glf; Trk; IMSpt; So Dakota St Univ; Oceanography.

STECKLINE, Terry J; Thomas More Prep HS; Hays, KS; 1/65 PresSrCls; CtyCnl; CmntyWkr; HonRl; NHS; PolWkr; StuCncl; StuGov; YthLg; RptrSchPpr; Univ Of Notre Dame; Math.

STECYK, Michael A; Hanover Central HS; Cedar Lake, IN; 1/135 HonRl; JrNHS; NHS; LetterBsbl; Purdue Univ; Engineering.

STECYK, Polly E; University HS; Urbana, IL; Chrs; U Of Il; Las.

STEDRONSKY, Judy C; Barrington HS; Barrington, IL; 51/682 Chrs; ChrhWkr; HonRl; JA; NHS; NatlMeritFnl; NatlMeritCmnd; StuCncl; SpnCl; Southern Ill Univ; Dental Hygenist.

STEE, Brenda J; Watertown Sr HS; Watertown, SD; 26/297 HonRl; SecNatlFornLg; NHS; NatlThespSoc; SchMus; SchPl; RptrYrbk; FHA; Augustana College; Social Work.

STEEBY, Karen M; Coldwater HS; Coldwater, MI; LbryAde; PolWkr; SchMus; TchrAde; EdSchPpr; 4-H; CchngActv; 4-HAwd; Western Mich Univ; Biology.

STEEBY, Roy C; Basehor HS; Basehor, KS; 2/44 Band; Chrs; ChrhWkr; CmntyWkr; HonRl; NHS; YthFlsp; Bsbl; Bsktbl; Ottawa Univ; Music.

STEED, Vicki S; James B Conant HS; Hoffman Ests, IL; 1/621 Chr; ChrhWkr; HonRl; NHS; Olivet Nazarene College; Medicine.

STEEG, Carl K; Northrop HS; Fort Wayne, IN; 31/568 HonRl; NHS; SchMus; SchPl; StuCncl; Tennis; Chrldr; IMSpt; GovHonPrgAwd; CitAwd; Miami Univ; Bus Adm.

STEEGE, Paul B; Naperville Central HS; Naperville, IL; 1/844 Band; HonRl; MrchBnd; NatlMeritCmnd; Orch; SchPl; GerCl; Nw Univ; Secondary Sch Teacher.

STEEL, Richard; West Lafayette HS; West Lafayette, IN; PresJrCls; ALBoysSt; Chr; JrNHS; NHS; NatlMeritFnl; PolWkr; StuCncl; Glf; Wabash College; Law.

STEELE, Carolyn S; Oakland Comm HS; Oakland, IA; 5/52 SecFrshCls; PresJrCls; HonRl; RptrYrbk; RptrSchPpr; FNA; Univ; Elem Education.

STEELE, Cathy L; La Plata HS; Kirksville, MO; 4/33 TrsFrshCls; HonRl; SchPl; FHA; PpCl; Bsktbl; Secretary.

STEELE, Cindy; Topeka HS; Topeka, KS; AFS; Chrl; DrlTm; HonRl; HospAde; ModUN; TchrAde; RptrYrbk; RptrSchPpr; FrCl; Kansas University; Sociology.

STEELE, Keith A; Scott Community HS; Scott City, KS; ALBoysSt; HonRl; MrchBnd; PepBnd; SchMus; GerCl; SciCl; LetterTrk; IMSpt; PresAwd; College.

STEELE, Laura E; Lexington HS; Lexington, MO; 13/96 TrsJrCls; PresSrCls; Band; CncrtBnd; HonRl; LbryAde; MrchBnd; NHS; PepBnd; StuCncl; RptrYrbk; Central Miss St Univ; Accounting.

STEELE, Mark P; Mattawan HS; Mattawan, MI; Band; Chr; ChrhWkr; CncrtBnd; HonRl; JrNHS; MrchBnd; NHS; NatlMeritSF; Orch; PepBnd; SchPl; SctActv; YthFlsp; College; Sciences.

STEELE, Mary P; Akron Fairgrove HS; Akron, MI; 9/80 Band; ChrhWkr; CncrtBnd; HonRl; HospAde; PresNHS; PepBnd; SctActv; FHA; Clge; Nursing.

STEELE, Patrick R; Freeport Sr HS; Freeport, IL; 135/994 HonRl; NatlMeritCmnd; NatlThespSoc; PolWkr; Quill&Scroll; SchMus; SchPl; SctActv; StuCncl; Univ Of Illinois; Pharmacology.

STEELE, Robert T; Thedford HS; Brownlee, NE; 4/23 TrsJrCls; SecTrsJrCls; Chrs; SchPl; StuGov; 4-H; Bsktbl; LetterFtbl; Trk; 4-HAwd; Univ; Agric.

STEELMAN, Jan; Osborn HS; Osborn, MO; SecFrshCls; VPSophCls; PresJrCls; Band; Chr; HonRl; MrchBnd;.

STEEN, Emily S; Luck HS; Luck, WI; 11/56 Chr; ChrhWkr; HonRl; TchrAde; RptrSchPpr; 4-H; SecPpCl; Bsktbl; Trk; PresGAA; College; Physical Ed Teacher.

STEEN, Michelle; Jasper HS; Jasper, MN; 6/51 Band; Chrl; CncrtBnd; HonRl; MrchBnd; PepBnd; SchMus; SctActv; 4-H; FHA; Vocational School; Veterinary Assistance.

STEEN, Patricia; Bradley Bourbonnais Comm HS; Bourbonnais, IL; ChrhWkr; HonRl; LbryAde; NHS; PolWkr; College.

STEEN, Robert; Bradley Bourbonnais Comm HS; Bourbennais, IL; 16/320 Aud/Vis; ChrhWkr; HonRl; NHS; PolWkr; GerCl; Trk; College; Bio Chemistry.

STEEN, Rodney G; Iberia R V HS; Iberia, MO; 10/44 Band; ChrhWkr; CncrtBnd; HonRl; MrchBnd; PepBnd; SchPl; PpCl; CaptBsktbl; University.

STEEN, Stacy L; Owensville HS; Owensville, MO; Band; ChrhWkr; CncrtBnd; HonRl; MrchBnd; NHS; OffAde; PepBnd; College; Accounting.

STEEN, Susan K; Minot HS; Minot, ND; 172/674 Band; HonRl; JrNHS; MrchBnd; SecNHS; PepBnd; SchPpr; PpCl; Minot State Col; Nursing.

STEENBOCK, Martin; Blair Jr Sr HS; Blair, NE; RptrYrbk; FrCl; Dana College; Business Adm Major.

STEENHAUSEN, John J; Warsa Comm HS; Wausau, IN; EngCl; PpCl; Glf; IMSpt; College; Science.

STEENHOVEN, Alethea F; George Comm HS; George, IA; SecJrCls; Chrs; HonRl; LbryAde; NHS; SchMus; StuCncl; RptrSchPpr; FTA; LetterChrldr; Bus Sch; Sec.

STEENSNES, Robert A; Newman Grove HS; St Edward, NE; 13/45 Band; ChrhWkr; HonRl; LbryAde; YthFlsp; Pres4-H; FFA; CaptFtbl; Trk; 4-HAwd;.

STEENSON, Michael J; Wolbach Public HS; Wolbach, NE; 1/21 Chrs; CncrtBnd; HonRl; SchPl; StuCncl; TchrAde; LetterBsktbl; LetterFtbl; LetterTrk; 4-HAwd; University; Professional.

STEENSTRA, Cherie; Holland Chr HS; Holland, MI; ChrhWkr; CmntyWkr; NHS; SchPl; RptrYrbk; SpnCl; Calvin College; Secial Education.

STEENWYK, Debra A; Holland Chr HS; Holland, MI; ChrhWkr; SchPl; StuCncl; SchPpr; SpnCl; Bsktbl; IMSpt; Hope Coll; Psych.

STEEP, Janet A; Seneca Township HS; Seneca, IL; 5/72 PresJrCls; Band; HonRl; NHS; StuCncl; StuGov; PpCl; Bsktbl; Socr; Trk; Chrldr; GAA; College; Professional.

STEEP, Jean B; Seneca HS; Seneca, IL; 1/54 VPSrCls; Band; HonRl; NHS; NatlMeritSchl; StuCncl; RptrYrbk; GerCl; Chrldr; GAA; Lutheran Gen Hospital; Nurse.

STEERMAN, David R; Wheatland HS; Gove, KS; HonRl; SchPl; SctActv; FFA; Bsktbl; Ftbl; Garden City Comm Jr College; Technology.

STEES, Timothy L; Shannon HS; Shannon, IL; 2/26 Band; ChrhWkr; CncrtBnd; HonRl; MrchBnd; VPStuCncl; PresYthFlsp; PpCl; LetterBsktbl; LetterGlf; Bob Jones Univ; Accounting.

STEFANECK, Celeste M; St Mary Cathedral; Saginaw, MI; 12/78 Chrs; CmntyWkr; DrmMjrt; HonRl; JrNHS; LbryAde; NHS; Twrl; PpCl; Aquinas College; Music Ed.

STEFANIW, Sonja M; Kewaunee HS; Kewaunee, WI; 9/141 AFS; HonRl; NHS; OffAde; RptrYrbk; SciCl; ChmnBsbl; Bsktbl; GAA; Stevens Point; Accounting.

STEFANKO, Madeleine; St Agatha HS; Detroit, MI; HonRl; NHS; U Of Mi; Public Accountant.

STEFANSKI, Janet D; Our Lady Of The Lakes HS; Ortonville, MI; Band; CncrtBnd; HonRl; SchPl; LetterBsbl; LetterBsktbl; CchngActv; IMSpt; PPFtbl; Ferris State; Printing.

STEFFA, Becky L; Pittsfield HS; Pittsfield, IL; 29/131 Band; ChrhWkr; HonRl; NHS; PolWkr; RedCrAde; SctActv; RptrSchPpr; PresFHA; PpCl; Hannibal Lagrange; Social Work.

STEFFAN, Judith C; Michigan Public HS; Michigan, ND; 1/23 SecTrsSophCls; Band; Chr; Chrs; CncrtBnd; HonRl; MrchBnd; PepBnd; Yrbk; SchPpr; College; Elementary Ed.

STEFFANI, Rudolph L; Onsted HS; Tipton, MI; ALBoysSt; Band; CncrtBnd; HonRl; PepBnd; SchPl; SctActv; LetterFtbl; CaptTrk; CaptWrstlng; Armed Services; Medical Doctor.

STEFFEN, Barbara; Rutland HS; Nunda, SD; Band; CncrtBnd; HonRl; MrchBnd; StuCncl; Yrbk; 4-H; FHA; PpCl; Bsktbl; Coll; Vocation.

STEFFEN, Barbara J; Rutland HS; Nunda, SD; SecJrCls; Band; HonRl; MrchBnd; Yrbk; Bsktbl; Chrldr; AmLegAwd; 4-HAwd; CitAwd; Trade School; Vocation.

STEFFEN, Carol L; Menominee HS; Menominee, MI; 45/275 HonRl; NHS; Quill&Scroll; RptrYrbk; FrCl; Tennis; U Of Mich; Professional.

STEFFEN, Carolyn R; Rutland Public HS; Nunda, SD; SecJrCls; Chrs; DrmMjrt; LbryAde; OffAde; SchPl; Twrl; RptrSchPpr; FHA; Chrldr;.

STEFFEN, Daniel J; West Delaware HS; Ryan, IA; Aud/Vis; HonRl; NHS; FFA; Iowa State; Ag Ed.

STEFFEN, Dawn R; White Lake HS; White Lake, SD; 1/27 PresJrCls; Chrs; ChrhWkr; HonRl; SecStuCncl; EdYrBk; Bsktbl; Ftbl; Tennis; DARAwd; College; Journalist.

STEFFEN, Denise A; Bluffton Allen HS; Bluffton, IN; Chr; JA; 4-H; SpnCl; University; Elem Education.

STEFFEN, Ed A; Adams Central HS; Decatur, IN; Band; CncrtBnd; HonRl; MrchBnd; PepBnd; SpnCl; Trk; IMSpt; College; Business Admin.

STEFFEN, Karlyne; Okabena HS; Brewster, MN; Chrs; HonRl; NHS; SchPl; YthFlsp; Yrbk; RptrSchPpr; EdSchPpr; GAA; IMSpt;.

STEFFEN, Linda K; Remsen Union HS; Remsen, IA; 1/40 HonRl; NHS; SchPl; Yrbk; SchPpr; VPFHA; FNA; VPJrCls; Coll; Med Tech.

STEFFEN, Linda L; Leo HS; New Vienna, IA; Chrs; HonRl; LbryAde; SchMus; SchPl; TchrAde; RptrYrbk; SchPpr; IMSpt; CitAwd; Clge; Pe/math.

STEFFEN, Mary C; Janesville Consolidated HS; Janesville, IA; 2/41 Band; Chr; Chrs; CncrtBnd; HonRl; MrchBnd; NHS; PepBnd; SchMus; TchrAde; PpCl; LetterBsktbl; LetterTrk; College; Professional.

STEFFEN, Melissa K; Central Community HS; W Point, IA; 24/101 VPJrCls; Band; HonRl; MrchBnd; OffAde; SchMus; RptrYrbk; RptrSchPpr; 4-H; Trk; Ia St U; Law.

STEFFEN, Timothy W; Milwaukee Lutheran HS; Milwaukee, WI; 90/265 LetterBsbl; Bsktbl; Ftbl; IMSpt; Univ; Sports.

STEFFENHAGEN, Dean; Lincoln HS; Red Wing, MN; 2/125 SecJrCls; Chr; Chrs; ChrhWkr; HonRl; NHS; SchMus; SpnCl; College.

STEFFENS, Brenda E; Litchfield Sr HS; Litchfield, IL; 18/137 HonRl; JrNHS; LbryAde; NHS; OffAde; SctActv; FrCl; GAA; Millikin Univ; Physical Therapy.

STEFFENS, Karen L; Benton Co R 1 HS; Cole Camp, MO; Chr; SchPl; StuCncl; SpnCl; PpCl; GAA; Jr College.

STEFFENS, Loren R; Sidney HS; Sidney, NE; 24/131 TrsSophCls; Band; Chrs; JrNHS; Mdrgl; SchMus; EdYrBk; 4-H; MthCl; VoiceDemAwd; College; Banker.

STEFFENS, Randell G; Benton County R 1 HS; Cole Camp, MO; 4/52 CmntyWkr; HonRl; NHS; FFA; PpCl; Bsktbl; Trade School; Vocation.

STEFFENS, Rita J; Anita Community HS; Wiota, IA; Chrs; DrlTm; HonRl; FHA; FTA; PpCl; LetterTrk; Chrldr;.

STEFFENSMEIER, David J; Marquette HS; West Point, IA; ALBoysSt; ChrhWkr; RptrYrbk; SptEdSchPpr; Bsbl; Bsktbl; Glf; AmLegAwd; Coll; Major Study.

STEFFENSMEIER, Kathy; Central Catholic HS; Dodge, NE; Chrs; HonRl; JA; SchMus; 4-H; LatCl; PpCl; 4-HAwd; Trade Sch; Sec.

STEFFENSMEIER, Loretta; Howells HS; Howells, NE; ALAGirlsSt; ChrhWkr; CmntyWkr; HonRl; JA; NHS; NatlMeritSchl; PepBnd; RedCrAde; PresAwd; Bus Sch.

STEFFENSMEIER, Penny; Marquette HS; Donnellson, IA; 2/49 VPSrCls; Chr; LbryAde; NHS; RptrYrbk; 4-H; LetterTrk; 4-HAwd; Iowa State Univ; Nutrition.

STEFFENSON, David; New Richmond HS; New Richmond, WI; 7/160 Chrs; HonRl; Mdrgl; NatlFornLg; SchMus; SchPl; JCAwd; Concordia College; Math Business Religion.

STEFFES, Mark R; Cudahy Sr HS; Cudahy, WI; 84/354 CmntyWkr; HonRl; NHS; Bsktbl; Ftbl; Trk; U Of Wi; Physical Therapy.

STEFFEY, Kimberely K; Dallas City HS; Dallas City, IL; 6/32 TrsFrshCls; Band; Chrs; CmntyWkr; HonRl; SchMus; StuCncl; EdYrBk; RptrSchPpr; Western Ill Univ; Political Science.

STEFFI, Charlene A; Belview Public HS; Belview, MN; TrsJrCls; Band; Chrs; LbryAde; StuGov; EdSchPpr; 4-H; CaptBsktbl; LetterTrk; GAA; Trade School.

STEFFL, Donna M; Wabasso Public HS; Wabasso, MN; HonRl; NHS; SchPpr; GerCl; Bsktbl; Trk; GAA; IMSpt; PPFtbl; Univ; Teaching Education.

STEFL, David E; Thomas Jefferson HS; Cedar Rapids, IA; 10/520 Band; CncrtBnd; HonRl; JrNHS; MrchBnd; NHS; NatlMeritSF; Orch; PepBnd; Quill&Scroll; SchMus; TchrAde; EngCl; MthCl; Univ Of Iowa; Pharmacy.

STEGE, Kathleen S; Buckley Loda HS; Loda, IL; 2/43 SecSophCls; HonRl; NHS; SchPl; YthFlsp; EdYrBk; FHA; SpnCl; MthCl; Bauder Fashion College; Fashion Merchandis.

STEGEMAN, Janice K; Wolsey HS; Wolsey, SD; SecSrCls; TrsSrCls; ChrhWkr; HonRl; TchrAde; RptrYrbk; EdSchPpr; FHA; SciCl; IMSpt; College; Professional.

STEGEMAN, Sharon J; Quincy Notre Dame HS; Quincy, IL; 16/83 DrlTm; HonRl; SchPl; StuCncl; SpnCl; ChmnTennis; Illinois State Univ; Special Education.

STEGER, Julie; Lomira HS; Theresa, WI; ALAGirlsSt; Band; CncrtBnd; MrchBnd; PepBnd; SchPl; TchrAde; Yrbk; FHA; Coll; Major Study.

STEGER, Theresa A; Holy Angels HS; Richfield, MN; Trk; IMSpt; PPFtbl; Col; Data Processing.

STEGMAN, Brian B; Kinsley HS; Offerle, KS; SecFrshCls; HonRl; LetterWrstlng; Dodge City Comm Clg; Agriculture.

STEGMAN, Leon; Holcomb HS; Garden City, KS; HonRl; FFA; College; Vocation.

STEGMAN, Melinda S; Sacred Heart HS; Salina, KS; Band; Chr; Chrs; CncrtBnd; HonRl; MrchBnd; PepBnd; FBLA; PpCl; Ft Hays Kansas St Col; Music Education.

STEGMAN, Wayne H; Drayton Public HS; Drayton, ND; VPFrshCls; PresJrCls; Band; Chr; Chrs; ChrhWkr; HonRl; PepBnd; SchMus; Bsbl; Bsktbl; Ftbl; Glf; Mayville St College; Physical Educ.

STEGMEYER, Susan M; St Francis HS; Winfield, IL; 5/88 HonRl; FrCl; GAA; Col ; Journalsim Sport.

STEGNER, Timothy; Williamsburg HS; Pomona, KS; Chr; Chrs; ChrhWkr; StuCncl; FFA; IMSpt; Votech School; Machinist.

STEHOUWER, Dave L; Western Mich Christian HS; Spring Lake, MI; VPFrshCls; VPSophCls; HonRl; NHS; Bsktbl; Socr; IMSpt; Clge.

STEHR, John P; Bishop Leblond HS; St Joseph, MO; 13/115 ChrhWkr; HonRl; ModUN; NHS; Quill&Scroll; RptrYrbk; Yrbk; RptrSchPpr; SchPpr; FrCl; SpnCl; MthCl; TreasSciCl; BauchLmbAwd; Univ Of Missouri; Nuclear Physist.

STEICHEN, Curtis J; Wessington Springs HS; Alpena, SD; 1/58 PresSophCls; ALBoysSt; NHS; StuCncl; PresKeyCl; Bsktbl; Ftbl; South Dakota State University; Engineer.

STEIDER, Luann; Shickley Public HS; Strang, NE; Chrs; SchPl; StuCncl; YthFlsp; RptrYrbk; PpCl; Hesston Coll; Nursing.

STEIDL, Vicki L; Lincoln HS; Wisconsin Rapids, WI; Band; Chr; Chrs; ChrhWkr; HonRl; SchAde;.

STEIER, Guy R; North Central HS; Haddam, KS; PresJrCls; Band; Chrs; CncrtBnd; HonRl; MrchBnd; PepBnd; 4-H; FFA; Univ Of Kansas; Law.

STEIG, Debra L; Whitehall Memorial HS; Osseo, WI; 16/73 Chrs; HonRl; SchPl; SchPpr; VPFBLA; FHA; SpnCl; GAA;.

STEIGER, Majeana L; Lincoln Sr HS; Red Lake Falls, MN; HonRl; NHS; RptrYrbk; SpnCl; PpCl; Northland Comm College; Medicine.

STEIGER, Monica R; Bowdle HS; Bowdle, SD; HstSrCls; Chrs; ChrhWkr; DrlTm; HonRl; RptrYrbk; RptrSchPpr; FTA; LetterTrk; CaptChrldr; College; Secondary Teaching.

STEIGERWALD, Ann; Bishop Du Bourg HS; St Louis, MO; /475 Chr; HonRl; SchMus; TchrAde; FNA; FTA; Notre Dame Coll; Childhood Ed.

STEIL, Valerie G; Beloit Memorial HS; Beloit, WI; 34/460 AFS; Band; CncrtBnd; DrmMjrt; MrchBnd; NHS; SchMus; SchPl; SpnCl; PpCl; LetterSwmmng; Univ; Professional.

STEILBERGER, Karen E; Ladywood St Agnes HS; Indianapolis, IN; LbryAde; RptrSchPpr; VoiceDemAwd; College.

STEILEN, Diane M; Hanson Ind #40 HS; Farmer, SD; DrlTm; HonRl; Quill&Scroll; SchPl; TchrAde; RptrSchPpr; FBLA; FHA; PpCl; 4-HAwd; Tech ; Nursing.

STEILEN, Sandra S; Catholic Central HS; Muskegon, MI; 3/215 TrsJrCls; ChrhWkr; CmntyWkr; HonRl; HospAde; NHS; PolWkr; SctActv; StuCncl; TchrAde; CaptBsktbl; College; Nurse.

STEIMAN, Valerie; Bethlehem Academy; Faribault, MN; 2/93 Band; Chrs; HonRl; Mdrgl; NHS; PepBnd; SchMus; SchPl; StuCncl; College Of St Benedict.

STEIMEL, Sheila M; Charles City Comm HS; Charles City, IA; 47/230 Chrs; HonRl; SchPl; 4-H; GerCl; PpCl; Bsktbl; Trk; IMSpt; PPFtbl; Creighton U; Medical.

STEIMLE, Kathleen A; Kewanee HS; Kewanee, IL; 43/213 AFS; OffAde; StuCncl; StuGov; Yrbk; RptrSchPpr; EdSchPpr;.

STEIMLE, Mary Bertha G; Kelly HS; New Hamburg, MO; 7/66 Chrs; HonRl; StuCncl; Yrbk; SchPpr; 4-H; FHA; PpCl; Chrldr; 4-HAwd; Coll Semo U; Sec.

STEIN, Annette; Bloomfield Community HS; Bloomfield, NE; 13/66 SecJrCls; Chrs; HonRl; LbryAde; Mdrgl; NHS; Yrbk; PpCl; Chrldr; CitAwd; Norfolk Nntcc; Executive Secratary.

STEIN, Becki R; Mendota HS; Mendota, IL; Band; ChrhWkr; CncrtBnd; DrlTm; HonRl; MrchBnd; StuCncl; FNA; SpnCl; Tennis; Trk; College; Med Tech.

STEIN, Cindy L; Urbana HS; Urbana, IL; 1/428 CncrtBnd; HonRl; MrchBnd; NatlMeritCmnd; PepBnd; PresSctActv; RptrSchPpr; Trk; GodCntryAwd; Univ Of Illinois; Writer.

STEIN, David M; Sullivan HS; Chicago, IL; HonRl; StuCncl; Teen; College; Professional.

STEIN, E John; Bishop Luers HS; Ft Wayne, IN; 43/225 ChrhWkr; HonRl; TreasKeyCl; Bsktbl; Ftbl; CchngActv; Coll; Priest.

STEIN, Julie A; Amery Pub HS; Amery, WI; 1/118 SecJrCls; SecAFS; Band; Chr; HonRl; NHS; SchPl; StuCncl; PpCl; Chrldr; CitAwd; Minnesota Schl Of Business; Senior Accountg.

STEIN, Lyle A; Marquette Univ HS; Elm Grove, WI; 6/280 ChrhWkr; HonRl; NHS; NatlMeritCmnd; KeyCl; LetterSocr; CchngActv; GovHonPrgAwd; Univ; Engineering.

STEIN, Paul F; Wm Fremd HS; Palatine, IL; 177/621 NatlMeritCmnd; PolWkr; Tennis; PPFtbl; Us Service Acad; Engin.

STEIN, Rhonda S; La Grove Comm HS; Loogootee, IL; SecTrsFrshCls; HstSophCls; Band; Chrs; ChrhWkr; CncrtBnd; HonRl; MrchBnd; PepBnd; LetterChrldr; Parkland Jr Col; Business.

STEINACHER, Phyllis; Carrollton HS; Carrollton, IL; 8/88 HonRl; LbryAde; NHS; OffAde; SchPl; TchrAde; SpnCl; Lewis And Clark Comm Coll; Business Admin.

STEINACHER, Phyllis A; Carrollton HS; Carrollton, IL; 8/85 HonRl; LbryAde; NHS; SchPl; TchrAde; PresFBLA; SecFTA; SpnCl; PpCl; LetterBsktbl; GAA; PPFtbl; Lewis & Clark Comm College; Business Mgmt.

STEINBACH, Albert E; Thomas Jefferson HS; Cedar Rapids, IA; 10/587 PresJrCls; ALBoysSt; NHS; SctActv; PresStuCncl; RptrSchPpr; LetterTrk; Coll; Engineering.

STEINBACH, Gary M; South Haven HS; South Haven, MI; 28/217 HonRl; IMSpt; PresAwd; Univ; Math.

STEINBACH, Rita A; Stewart HS; Stewart, MN; 18/36 AFS; CmntyWkr; HospAde; RedCrAde; YthLg; FHA; FNA; GAA; IMSpt; BttyCrckrAwd; Willmar Jr Coll; Soc Serv.

STEINBECK, David J; Independence HS; Brandon, IA; 5/186 ALBoysSt; Band; ChrhWkr; HonRl; NHS; NatlMeritCmnd; SchMus; StuCncl; YthFlsp; Wrstlng; Air Force Academy; Aeronautical Engineering.

STEINBECK, Jennifer L; Glenbrook North HS; Evanston, IL; 56/690 Univ Of Illinois; Law.

STEINBERG, Carla A; Shanley HS; Fargo, ND; 1/160 HonRl; NHS; FBLA; SpnCl; Trk; Univ; Pro.

STEINBERG, Wendi C; Thornwood HS; Lansing, IL; 10/876 Chrs; HonRl; JrNHS; NHS; OffAde; StuCncl; StuGov; SpnCl; CaptSwmmng; GAA; DARAwd; Ill State Univ; Teaching.

STEINBERGER, Mary; Carpio Public HS; Carpio, ND; 3/24 SecJrCls; ALAGirlsSt; ChrhWkr; CmntyWkr; HonRl; LbryAde; SchPl; Yrbk; PpCl; IMSpt; Mayville St Coll; Child Care.

STEINBRECHER, Gary A; Scottsbluff HS; Scottsbluff, NE; ChrhWkr; HonRl; JrNHS; LitMag; SctActv; YthFlsp; LetterBsbl; LetterTrk; CchngActv; IMSpt; College.

STEINBRENNER, Dawn R; St Joseph HS; Chicago, IL; SecSophCls; Chrs; HonRl; NHS; SchMus; SchPl; StuCncl; Yrbk; 4-H; SpnCl; MthCl; Trk; Chrldr; College.

STEINBRENNER, Susan M; York Comm HS; Elmhurst, IL; 12/876 Chrs; HonRl; JrNHS; TreasNHS; NatlMeritFnl; NatlMeritSchl; RptrYrbk; GerCl; TreasMthCl; Univ; Engineering.

STEINBRING, Larry L; Jetmore HS; Jetmore, KS; ChrhWkr; HonRl; JA; StuCncl; SciCl; LetterBsktbl; LetterFtbl; LetterGlf; Ks St U; Carpentry.

STEINBRUECK, Randy E; Boonville HS; Boonville, MO; Band; CncrtBnd; HonRl; NHS; PepBnd; RptrSchPpr; PPFtbl; LetterFtbl; LetterTrk; IMSpt; Central Mo State University; Music.

STEINEM, John R; Connersville HS; Connersville, IN; Band; HonRl; 4-H; FrCl; LetterSwmmng; 4-HAwd; College; Professional.

STEINER, Dean B; Pekin Community HS; Pekin, IL; 58/780 ChrhWkr; CmntyWkr; HonRl; NatlFornLg; NHS; StuCncl; TchrAde; EdSchPpr; GerCl; OptClAwd; College; Business.

STEINER, Janell D; Hoisington HS; Hoisington, KS; SecFrshCls; ChrhWkr; HonRl; HospAde; ModUN; St Josephs School; Nursing.

STEINER, Jeanne M; Notre Dame HS; Chicago, IL; 11/302 CmntyWkr; HonRl; PolWkr; SchPl; Northeastern Univ; Business.

STEINER, Jennifer G; H H Dow HS; Midland, MI; ChrhWkr; CmntyWkr; HonRl; LitMag; NHS; NatlMeritSF; Orch; PolWkr; StuGov; College; Psychology.

STEINER, Jennifer J; Rothsay Public HS; Rothsay, MN; 15/43 TrsSophCls; Band; Chrs; CncrtBnd; HonRl; Mdrgl; PepBnd; SchMus; SchPl; SchPpr; Trade Vocational Tech; Vocation.

STEINER, Jodi A; Perry HS; Perry, MI; CncrtBnd; MrchBnd; LatCl; Lansin Comm Coll; Court Reporter.

STEINER, Karen K; Buckley Loda HS; Onarga, IL; 3/41 HstSrCls; Band; HonRl; NHS; StuCncl; EdSchPpr; 4-H; PresFHA; 4-HAwd; Parkland College; Home Economics.

STEINER, Katharine M; Lansing HS; Leavenworth, KS; 8/82 ChrhWkr; HonRl; NHS; NatlThespSoc; SchMus; SchPl; StuCncl; Yrbk; Bsktbl; LetterTrk; PPFtbl; Kansas Comm College; Accounting.

STEINER, Kevin A; Granton HS; Granton, WI; 2/36 PresFrshCls; TrsSophCls; SecJrCls; PresSrCls; PresBand; Chr; Chrs; ChrhWkr; CmntyWkr; CncrtBnd;

HonRl; CaptBsbl; CaptBsktbl; LetterGlf; Univ Of Wisconsin; Agriculture.

STEINER, Linda C; Elmwood Public HS; Elmwood, NE; 1/11 Band; Chr; Chrs; HonRl; SchMus; SchPl; TchrAde; 4-H; PpCl; 4-HAwd; Coll; Teach.

STEINER, Lisa J; Waukesha South HS; Waukesha, WI; AFS; HonRl; NHS; SchMus; SchPl; 4-H; FrCl; PpCl; LetterGAA; Marquette U; Dentist.

STEINER, Lynn K; Norfolk Catholic Sr HS; Norfolk, NE; 2/42 CmntyWkr; HonRl; Univ Of Nebraska; Special Education.

STEINER, Marcia L; Central HS; Davenport, IA; 30/551 Chr; Chrs; HonRl; Mdrgl; SpnCl; St Ambrose College; Accountant Cpa.

STEINER, Neil B; Butler HS; Butler, MO; 9/86 VPFrshCls; VPSophCls; SecChrhWkr; HonRl; NHS; PresStuCncl; PresYthFlsp; PresFFA; CaptFtbl; CaptIMSpt; Univ Of Mo; Agriculture.

STEINER, Neil B; Butler R V HS; Butler, MO; 9/82 VPFrshCls; VPSophCls; AFS; SecChrhWkr; HonRl; NHS; PresStuCncl; PresYthFlsp; 4-H; FBLA; PresFFA; CaptFtbl; IMSpt; College; Agriculture.

STEINER, Ruth; New Holstein Sr HS; Chilton, WI; 3/197 AFS; Chrs; HonRl; LitMag; LbryAde; NatlFornLg; NHS; RptrSchPpr; 4-H; Trk; Lawrence; Social Science.

STEINER, Wesley D; Toccoa Falls HS; Marion, IN; HonRl; FrCl; LetterBsktbl; IMSpt; College; Engineering.

STEINES, Geriann M; Stratford HS; Stratford, WI; 3/89 Band; CncrtBnd; HonRl; MrchBnd; SecNHS; PepBnd; Yrbk; SecFHA; EldAwd; U Of Wisc Eau Claire; Social Work.

STEINES, Jim; Stratford HS; Stratford, WI; 16/112 VPFrshCls; Chr; Chrs; NHS; StuGov; Bsbl; Ftbl; Technical School.

STEINHAGEN, Peter; Princeton Senior HS; Princeton, MN; 1/160 PresSrCls; NHS; NatlMeritCmnd; RptrYrbk; RptrSchPpr; SpnCl; Chrldr; Mit; Engineering.

STEINHART, Barry N; University Liggett HS; Detroit, MI; 3/77 HonRl; NatlMeritSF; RptrSchPpr; Stanford; Economics.

STEINHAUER, Patricia E; Willowbrook HS; Lombard, IL; 3/746 Band; ChrhWkr; HonRl; NHS; NatlMeritFnl; NatlMeritSchl; LetterBsktbl; TreasGAA; Purdue Univ; Engineering.

STEINHAUER, Patricia E; Willowbrook Comm HS; Lombard, IL; 3/822 Band; HonRl; NHS; NatlMeritSchl; SctActv; LetterBsbl; LetterBsktbl; PresGAA; BauchLmbAwd; Purdue Univ; Engineering.

STEINHAUSER, David W; Truman HS; Independence, MO; Bsbl; Glf; Swmmng; GodCntryAwd; Warrensburg Univ; Law Enforcement.

STEINHAUSER, Mary B; Sheridan Rii HS; Parnell, MO; 1/10 PresJrCls; PresSrCls; Yrbk; Pres4-H; SecPpCl; LetterBsktbl; Chrldr; AmLegAwd; DanFAwd; 4-HAwd; CitAwd; Northwest Mo State Univ.

STEINHOFF, Bonnie L; High School; West Alton, MO; Chrs; ChrhWkr; HonRl; StuCncl; PpCl; College; Liberal Arts.

STEINHOFF, Donna K; Orchard Farm HS; Portage Des Sioux, MO; Chr; HonRl; OffAde; Teen; YthFlsp; RptrSchPpr; SchPpr; 4-H; FBLA; FHA; College; Professional.

STEINHOFF, James R; Aquinas HS; La Crosse, WI; ALBoysSt; ChrhWkr; FrCl; LetterFtbl; LetterTrk; College; Chemist.

STEINHOFF, Sharon A; West Leyden HS; Northlake, IL; 29/430 HonRl; SpnCl; Triton College; Accounting & Business.

STEINHORST, Thomas H; Baraboo HS; Baraboo, WI; RptrSchPpr; KeyCl; LetterBsbl; LetterBsktbl; LetterFtbl; College.

STEINKAMP, Betty M; Okawville HS; Venedy, IL; 6/67 Chrs; HonRl; NHS; NatlThespSoc; OffAde; SchPl; YthFlsp; GerCl; PpCl; Augustana College; Legal Assistant.

STEINKAMP, Kathleen A; Quincy Notre Dame HS; Quincy, IL; Chrs; HonRl; SchPl; StuCncl; RptrYrbk; 4-H; SpnCl; IMSpt; 4-HAwd; College.

STEINKAMP, Sara A; Reitz Memorial HS; Evansville, IN; 8/200 HonRl; SchPl; GerCl; Purdue Univ; Professional.

STEINKE, Boyce E; St Marys HS; Sleepy Eye, MN; PresFrshCls; PresSophCls; PresJrCls; PresSrCls; Quill&Scroll; SchPl; TchrAde; RptrYrbk; Swmmng; CchngActv; AmLegAwd; LionAwd; VFWAwd; St Cloud Univ; Business Mgmt.

STEINKE, Gary W; Central Comm HS; De Witt, IA; VPFrshCls; ALBoysSt; Chr; Chrs; CmntyWkr; HonRl; SchMus; RptrSchPpr; LetterWrstlng; AmLegAwd; College; Professional.

STEINKE, James H; Auburndale HS; Wisconsin Rapids, WI; HonRl; LbryAde; NatlFornLg; NHS; TchrAde; Pres4-H; FrCl; GerCl; College; Psychology.

STEINKE, Linda K; Durand HS; Davis, IL; 2/62 Chr; Chrs; ChrhWkr; DrlTm; HonRl; SchPl; Yrbk; Rock Valley College; Computer Science.

STEINKE, Lori L M; Fort Atkinson Sr HS; Fort Atkinson, WI; 30/245 Band; ChrhWkr; CncrtBnd; HonRl; MrchBnd; Orch; PepBnd; SchMus; FrCl; SpnCl; IMSpt; MasAwd; College; Language.

STEINKOPF, Anthony P; Cathedral HS; St Cloud, MN; 30/163 Chrs; Mdrgl; NHS; SctActv; Ftbl; Trk; College.

STEINKRAUS, Wendy B; Plainview HS; Plainview, NE; 6/54 PresJrCls; Band; Chrs; HonRl; NHS; RedCrAde; StuCncl; Trk; Chrldr; GodCntryAwd; PresAwd; Univ Of Ne; Physical Education.

STEINKRUEGER, Rayma; Franklin HS; Franklin, NE; 4/32 TrsJrCls; ALBoysSt; ALAGirlsSt; ChrhWkr; HonRl; NHS; SecStuCncl; Pres4-H; TreasFHA; Chrldr; Univ Of Neb; Hm Econ.

STEINKRUGER, Mark W; Franklin HS; Franklin, NE; 6/54 HonRl; NHS; 4-H; LetterFtbl; 4-HAwd; College; Education.

STEINKRUGER, Rayma L; Franklin HS; Franklin, NE; 4/32 Band; Chrs; ChrhWkr; HonRl; SchPl; StuCncl; FHA; SciCl; Chrldr; VoiceDemAwd; U Of Ne; Home Ec.

STEINLAGE, Marceil A; Centralia HS; Corning, KS; Chrs; ChrhWkr; HonRl; LbryAde; SchPl; StuCncl; PpCl; SciCl; Bsbl; Bsktbl; Washborn Univ; Physical Education.

STEINLAGE, Mary C; Turkey Valley HS; West Union, IA; Chr; HonRl; Sdlty; IMSpt; Vocational School.

STEINMAN, Dan P; Lyons Twp HS; La Grange, IL; ChrhWkr; HonRl; OffAde; TchrAde; Univ Of Ill; Accounting.

STEINMETZ, Mary J; St Ursula Academy; Lambertville, MI; ChrhWkr; LatCl; GAA; Toledo Univ; Accounting.

STEINMETZ, Nancy R; Hartford HS; Hartford, WI; Band; Chrs; ChrhWkr; HonRl; JrNHS; NHS; GAA; U Of Wi Oshkosh; Nursing.

STEINMETZ, Stephen P; Marist HS; Chicago, IL; 114/364 HonRl; Glf; Tennis; Univ; Dentist.

STEINPREIS, Julie H; Fremont HS; Fremont, NE; NHS; PolWkr; Quill&Scroll; SchPpr; FrCl; PpCl;.

STEINSLAND, Kjell T; Oak Park & River Forest HS; Oak Park, IL; Chr; Chrs; SctActv; Olivet Nazarene College; Ministry.

STEINWACHS, Doreen M; Bonner Spgs Sr HS; Bonner Springs, KS; 4/197 ChrhWkr; CncrtBnd; HonRl; HospAde; LbryAde; MrchBnd; PepBnd; TchrAde; LatCl;.

STEINWAGNER, Judy L; Columbus HS; Marshfield, WI; 22/114 Band; HonRl; HospAde; LbryAde; MrchBnd; NHS; PepBnd; SchPpr; FrCl; PpCl; Univ; Nurse.

STEINWAND, Jennifer H; Ellendale HS; Ellendale, ND; 2/45 VPFrshCls; Band; Chr; Chrs; ChrhWkr; CncrtBnd; DrlTm; Bsktbl; Trk; Chrldr; Clge.

STEINWAND, Victoria M; Ellendale Public HS; Ellendale, ND; HstSrCls; Chr; Chrs; ChrhWkr; CncrtBnd; HospAde; MrchBnd; PepBnd; SchPl; Chrldr; Univ; Prof.

STEITZ, Susan M; Syracuse HS; Syracuse, KS; SecFrshCls; SecSophCls; ALAGirlsSt; Band; Chrs; ChrhWkr; CncrtBnd; HonRl; HospAde; LetterBsktbl; LetterTrk; Univ; Professional.

STEJSKAL, Ricky L; La Crosse HS; Tinmken, KS; 3/35 Band; Chr; HonRl; JA; Mdrgl; SchMus; StuGov; FFA; LetterBsktbl; JAAwd; Kansas State University; Agri Business.

STEJSKAL, Ricky L; La Crosse HS; Timken, KS; 3/34 ChrhWkr; HonRl; JA; Mdrgl; ModUN; NHS; StuGov; TchrAde; FFA; LetterBsktbl; IMSpt; VoiceDemAwd; Kansas St Univ; Agriculture.

STELK, Colleen S; G I Northwest HS; Grand Island, NE; 15/140 HonRl; NHS; 4-H; FBLA; GerCl; PpCl; Kearny State College; Accounting.

STELLMACH, Mark L; St Patrick HS; Chicago, IL; HonRl; SctActv; MthCl; SciCl; Northwestern Univ; Doctor.

STELPFLUG, Stephen; Menomonee Falls North HS; Menomonee Falls, WI; 174/325 HonRl; IMSpt; Uw Whitewater; Professional Accountant.

STELTENPOHL, Rebecca J; Seymour HS; Seymour, IN; 1/335 HonRl; NatlMeritSF; YthFlsp; Yrbk; FTA; LatCl; PpCl; College; Professional.

STELTER, Carol M; Lakeshore HS; Baroda, MI; Band; CncrtBnd; HonRl; JA; MrchBnd; NHS; Orch; PepBnd; SchMus; College; Music.

STELTER, Dorraine I; Belview HS; Redwood Falls, MN; Band; Chr; ChrhWkr; CncrtBnd; HonRl; MrchBnd; SchPl; StuGov; RptrSchPpr; Trade School; Apparel Specialist.

STELTER, Judy A; Bloomer HS; Bloomer, WI; Chr; YthFlsp; 4-H; LetterBsktbl;.

STELTER, Richard; Lincoln Way HS; New Lenox, IL; HonRl; IMSpt; Coolege; Accountant.

STELTMAN, Robert C; St Josephs HS; Hillside, IL; 18/178 PresSophCls; HonRl; PolWkr; Quill&Scroll; SchMus; StuCncl; StuGov; RptrYrbk; LetterBsktbl; IMSpt; De Paul Univ; Special Education.

STELTMAN, Robert C; St Joseph's HS; Hillside, IL; 20/162 PresSophCls; VPJrCls; HonRl; SchMus; StuCncl; StuGov; GerCl; PpCl; LetterBsktbl; Tennis; Depaul Univ; Law.

STELTZ, Lauri; Solomon Juneau HS; Milwaukee, WI; PresSrCls; DrlTm; HonRl; NHS; PpCl; Bsbl;.

STE MARIE, Kathryn A; Lafayette HS; Red Lake Falls, MN; Band; Chrs; ChrhWkr; HonRl; HospAde; SchMus; StuCncl; 4-H; FHA; Chrldr; St Luke Sch Of Nursing.

STEMMLER, Robert W; Gillett HS; Gillett, WI; 7/80 TrsSophCls; TrsJrCls; MrchBnd; PepBnd; SctActv; StuCncl; RptrYrbk; Ftbl; Trk; ChmnWrstlng; College Uw Madison; Nuclear Engineering.

STEMPER, Joanne; Roosevelt HS; Minneapolis, MN; 5/625 ChrhWkr; HonRl; JA; LitMag; NHS; U Of Minn Col Of Liveral Arts;biology/chem.

STEMPER, Marlene M; Redfield HS; Redfield, SD; VPAFS; ALAGirlsSt; Chrs; HonRl; SchMus; PresFHA; PpCl; LetterTrk; DARAwd; Sd St Univ; Home Economics.

STEN, Sally; Horace Mann HS; Gilbert, MN; PresJrCls; Band; Chr; NatlFornLg; StuCncl; RptrSchPpr; Coll; Home Economics.

STENBERG, Christine E; Annandale HS; Maple Lk, MN; 1/120 HonRl; NHS; SchPl; StuCncl; StuGov; YthFlsp; PpCl; Bsktbl; IMSpt; PresAwd; College; Professional.

STENBERG, Robert M; Abraham Lincoln HS; Council Bluffs, IA; HonRl; TchrAde; Yrbk; College; Veterinarian.

STENCEL, Charles F; St Joseph HS; Berwyn, IL; 9/203 HonRl; PolWkr; StuCncl; StuGov; SptEdYrbk; GerCl; SciCl; Socr; Wrstlng; Usaf Academy; Mathematics.

STENDAHL, Roslyn M; William Fremd HS; Palatine, IL; 3/575 LitMag; NHS; Univ Of Missouri; English.

STENDBACK, Patrick P; Carrollton Comm HS; Carrollton, IL; HonRl; JrNHS; NHS; StuCncl; FBLA; FTA; PresSciCl; Bsbl; LetterWrstlng; College; Veterinarian.

STENDBACK, Patrick P; Carrollton Community Unit HS; Carrollton, IL; HonRl; NHS; SchPl; StuCncl; FBLA; FTA; PresSciCl; Bsbl; LetterWrstlng; University Of Illinois; Veterinarian.

STENDER, Sherry E; Blair HS; Blair, NE; Band; Chr; CncrtBnd; HonRl; MrchBnd; NHS; NatlMeritFnl; NatlMeritCmnd; RedCrAde; StuCncl; Business; Professional.

STENE, Kathryn M; Halstad HS; Shelly, MN; 2/22 ALAGirlsSt; HonRl; StuCncl; 4-H; FHA; CaptBsktbl; AmLegAwd; BttyCrckrAwd; 4-HAwd; VFWAwd; Concordia Coll; Medical.

STENE, Timothy J; Altoona HS; Altoona, WI; Band; Chrl; ChrhWkr; CncrtBnd; MrchBnd; NHS; PepBnd; StuCncl; LetterFtbl; LetterTrk; College Or Univ; Professional Football.

STENFORS, Debra L; Ewen Trout Creek HS; Bruce Crossing, MI; Chr; NHS; OffAde; RptrSchPpr; 4-H; GAA; 4-HAwd; College; Animal Husbandry Or Vet.

STENFTENAGEL, Edward J; Jasper HS; Jasper, IN; CmntyWkr; PolWkr; SpnCl; Ftbl; Univ Of Mississippi; Business.

STENGEL, Jeffrey W; Pius Xi HS; Milwaukee, WI; CaptTennis; College; Professional.

STENGEL, Kathleen A; Palmyra HS; Milwaukee, WI; 15/63 Band; HonRl; MrchBnd; PepBnd; TchrAde; SpnCl; Trk; GAA; PPFtbl; PresAwd; College; Cpa.

STENGEL, Marilyn E; Mt Morris HS; Mt Morris, IL; 4/76 AFS; Chrs; VPCncrtBnd; HonRl; MrchBnd; NHS; PepBnd; SchPl; TchrAde; RptrYrbk; College; Actress.

STENGER, Mark; Riverton HS; Baxter Springs, KS; HonRl; LbryAde; NatlMeritFnl; NatlMeritCmnd; NatlMeritSF; SchAde; TchrAde; RptrYrbk; Trk; PresAwd; Coll; Pro.

STENHOLM, Jeanne M; Wauwatosa East HS; Wauwatosa, WI; 27/430 ChrhWkr; HonRl; LitMag; NHS; OffAde; SchAde; SctActv; RptrSchPpr; MthCl; GAA; U Of Wis; Physician.

STENKLYFT, Lois; Hilbert HS; Hilbert, WI; 5/65 ChrhWkr; HonRl; HospAde; LbryAde; SchPl; TchrAde; YthFlsp; Yrbk; GerCl; GAA; Vocational School; Nursing.

STENKLYFT, Terry N; Hilbert HS; Hilbert, WI; ChrhWkr; HonRl; TchrAde; VPYthFlsp; KeyCl; Bsktbl; IMSpt; College; Professional.

STENKRUGER, Kenneth E; Porta HS; Petersburg, IL; 1/137 PresSophCls; HonRl; PresJrNHS; SchMus; PresStuCncl; KeyCl; Northwestern Univ; Pre Med.

STENMO, Thomas M; Northwood Public HS; Hatton, ND; PresSophCls; CncrtBnd; HonRl; RptrSchPpr; FFA; LetterFtbl; LetterTrk; LetterWrstlng; Nd State Univ; Aeronautical Engineering.

STENNER, Richard A; Crispus Attucks HS; Indianapolis, IN; Chr; ChrhWkr; HonRl; NHS; NatlMeritCmnd; YthFlsp; College ; Mathematics.

STENSEN, Kathy J; Harper Woods Secondary HS; Harper Woods, MI; 13/158 HonRl; NHS; NatlMeritCmnd; NatlMeritSchl; OffAde; StuCncl; TchrAde; SpnCl; LetterBsktbl; GAA; Michigan St Univ.

STENSLAND, Robert S; Ballard HS; Slater, IA; 9/71 ChrhWkr; HonRl; NHS; StuCncl; StuGov; FFA; FTA; Iowa State Univ; Agriculture Architecture.

STENSLIE, Keith L; North HS; Fargo, ND; Chr; HonRl; NHS; StuCncl; KeyCl; SpnCl; CitAwd; Univ; Professional.

STENSON, Margaret K; Calumet HS; Laurium, MI; Chr; Chrl; CncrtBnd; MrchBnd; NHS; PepBnd; SchMus; EdYrBk; FTA; College; Chemical Engineering.

STENSON, Twila F; Tolna HS; Hamar, ND; ChrhWkr; HonRl; NHS; NatlMeritCmnd; StuCncl; YthFlsp; RptrSchPpr; 4-H; VPPpCl; LetterBsktbl; Univ; Vocation.

STENSTAD, Jon L; Crosby Ironton HS; Emily, MN; 47/149 PresFrshCls; ChrhWkr; HonRl; PolWkr; StuCncl; EdYrBk; FBLA; MthCl; Ftbl; ChmbCommrsAwd; Coll; Law.

STENSTROM, Robert A; Maine East HS; Park Ridge, IL; 91/800 ChrhWkr; HonRl; JA; NatlMeritSF; SchPpr; MthCl; Swmmng; Ill Inst Of Technology; Electrical Engineer.

STEPAL, John P; Luther HS North; Chicago, IL; 12/215 HonRl; NHS; SpnCl; CaptGlf; Ne Illinois Univ; Broadcasting.

STEPANEK, Curtis E; Berkeley Sr HS; St Louis, MO; 1/290 ALBoysSt; Band; CncrtBnd; HonRl; NHS; PepBnd; SchMus; LetterBsbl; LetterBsktbl; LetterFtbl; DARAwd; Univ Of Mo; Engineering.

STEPANEK, Dennis E; Berkeley Sr HS; St Louis, MO; 1/380 ALBoysSt; Band; CncrtBnd; HonRl; MrchBnd; NHS; PepBnd; SchMus; Bsbl; Bsktbl; LetterFtbl; College; Engineering.

STEPANEK, Nancy E; Parkway Central HS; Chesterfield, MO; 70/475 Chr; CaptDrlTm; HospAde; Mdrgl; NHS; PpCl; CaptBsktbl; IMSpt; PPFtbl; GovHonPrgAwd; William Woods College; Art Therapy.

STEPANSKI, Edward J; Shrine HS; Royal Oak, MI; HonRl; NatlMeritCmnd; PolWkr; StuCncl; EdSchPpr; Univ Of Detroit; Psychology.

STEPHAN, Debra K; Leadwood HS; Bonne Terre, MO; 4/60 SecSrCls; Chrs; HonRl; LitMag; NHS; PpCl; SciCl; College; Mathematics.

STEPHAN, Margaret M; Bonner Springs HS; Bonner Springs, KS; HonRl; FBLA; FHA; PpCl; Bsbl; Bsktbl; Trk; Chrldr; CchngActv; PPFtbl; Universty; Computer Science.

STEPHAN, Robert; Hobart Sr HS; Hobart, IN; 2/400 ALBoysSt; DrlTm; HonRl; ROTC; AmLegAwd; DanFAwd; HonRl; VFWAwd; College; Engineering.

STEPHAN, Rosemary B; Fingal Public HS; Fingal, ND; 1/21 Band; Chr; Chrs; CncrtBnd; HonRl; LbryAde; MrchBnd; PepBnd; SchPl; Bsktbl; Nd State U; Computer Sci.

STEPHAN, Thomas C; Bonner Springs HS; Bonner Springs, KS; 6/200 PresFrshCls; PresSophCls; CmntyWkr; HonRl; StuCncl; YthFlsp; KeyCl; LetterBsktbl; LetterFtbl; RotaryAwd; College; Computer Analysis.

STEPHANI, John A; Pacehli HS; Austin, MN; HonRl; NHS; LetterFtbl; IMSpt; St Marys College.

STEPHANUS, Julia A; Madison Cons HS; Deputy, IN; 1/325 SecSophCls; HonRl; LitMag; NHS; NatlThespSoc; OffAde; TreasStuGov; SecSpnCl; PpCl; SecSciCl; Hanover College; Lawyer.

STEPHEN, Royce D; N Mahaska HS; New Sharon, IA; HonRl; NHS; SchPl; YthFlsp; FFA; LetterFtbl; CaptTrk; IMSpt; Trade School; Carpentry.

STEPHENS, Byron E; Exeter HS; Washburn, MO; 1/12 SecSophCls; ChrhWkr; HonRl; LbryAde; SchPl; StuCncl; MthCl; LetterBsbl; LetterBsktbl; LetterTrk; BauchLmbAwd; College; Accounting.

STEPHENS, Daniel A; Reita Memorial HS; Evansville, IN; 43/228 ChrhWkr; HonRl; SchMus; PresSciCl; Wrstlng; IMSpt; OptClAwd; Ind Univ; Business.

STEPHENS, Debra S; Cowden Herrick HS; Herrick, IL; 10/45 4-H;.

STEPHENS, Dena M; Sully Buttes HS; Onida, SD; VPSophCls; VPJrCls; TrsSrCls; Chrs; ChrhWkr; HonRl; LbryAde; TchrAde; LetterBsktbl; Chrldr; Nettleton Commercial; Fashion Merch.

STEPHENS, Dennis G; Forrest Strawn Wing HS; Forrest, IL; 6/60 HonRl; StuCncl; SchPpr; 4-H; SpnCl; Bsbl; Bsktbl; Ftbl; AmLegAwd; Univ Of Illinois; Accounting.

STEPHENS, Eileen M; Lawrence Central HS; Indianapolis, IN; ChrhWkr; HonRl; NHS; SancSoc; 4-H; 4-HAwd; University; Accounting.

STEPHENS, Fred O; Morton HS; Hammond, IN; 37/500 Band; CncrtBnd; HonRl; MrchBnd; NHS; Orch; PepBnd; SchMus; SciCl;.

STEPHENS, Jacky L; Fairbury HS; Fairburg, NE; 9/138 CmntyWkr; HonRl; SpnCl; Wrstlng; EldAwd; Trade School; Electronics.

STEPHENS, James K; Moline Sr HS; Moline, IL; 53/850 Band; ChrhWkr; CncrtBnd; HonRl; JrNHS; MrchBnd; NHS; PepBnd; SchPpr; Central College; German.

STEPHENS, James L; Naperville Central HS; Naperville, IL; ChrhWkr; CmntyWkr; HonRl; SctActv; Northwestern Univ; Medicine.

STEPHENS, Jamie M; Granite City North HS; Granite City, IL; 46/375 Chr; LitMag; NHS; OffAde; SecQuill&Scroll; SptEdYrbk; EdSchPpr; PpCl; College Il St; Special Ed.

STEPHENS, Jennifer D; Hinsdale Central HS; Hinsdale, IL; HonRl; HospAde; NatlMeritCmnd; LetterSwmmng; CchngActv; Univ Of Illinois; Medicine.

STEPHENS, Kari Lynn; Norfolk Sr HS; Norfolk, NE; Chr; Chrl; Chrs; DrmBgl; OffAde; TchrAde; 4-H; FBLA; PpCl; College; Teaching.

STEPHENS, Kyle; St Ignatius College Prep; Chicago, IL; 55/210 HonRl; NatlThespSoc; SchPl; College; Aeronautical Engineering.

STEPHENS, Lawrence W; St Rita HS; Chicago, IL; Band; HonRl; MrchBnd; Orch; PepBnd; SchMus; RptrYrbk; SciCl; IMSpt; Univ Of Ill; Vet.

STEPHENS, Marsha L; Westview HS; Kankakee, IL; 2/223 ChrhWkr; CmntyWkr; HonRl; HospAde; NHS; OffAde; SchMus; StuCncl; Chrldr; GAA; Valparaiso Univ; Social Work.

STEPHENS, Marve S; Exeter HS; Exeter, MO; VPSophCls; ALBoysSt; Chr; HonRl; SchMus; StuCncl; RptrYrbk; LetterBsbl; CaptBsktbl; LetterTrk; Univ; Professional.

STEPHENS, Michael E; North St Francois City Ri HS; Desloge, MO; VPSrCls; Band; ChrhWkr; CncrtBnd; HonRl; MrchBnd; PolWkr; StuCncl; StuGov; Tennis; Bio Busin Adm ;mortuary Scie.

STEPHENS, Monica J; Cassville HS; Cassville, MO; Band; CmntyWkr; CncrtBnd; MrchBnd; PepBnd; SchMus; YthFlsp; 4-H; Glf; Chrldr; Burge Sch; Nurse.

STEPHENS, Richard; Wm G Mather HS; Munising, MI; 32/124 ALBoysSt; ChrhWkr; CmntyWkr; HonRl; SecFrshCls; Tennis; Military; Professional.

STEPHENS, Scott D; Stillman Valley HS; Monroe Center, IL; HonRl; NHS; NatlMeritCmnd; U Of Ill; Engineering.

STEPHENS, Sharon; St Edward Public HS; St Edward, NE; VPSrCls; Chr; ChrhWkr; HonRl; NatlThespSoc; SchPl; StuCncl; FHA; PpCl; Chrldr; Col; Curriculum Of Major Study.

STEPHENS, Stephen; Oskaloosa HS; Oskaloosa, KS; VPFrshCls; VPSophCls; VPJrCls; Band; HonRl; StuCncl; 4-H; College.

STEPHENS, Terri L; Robinson HS; Robinson, IL; 22/190 HonRl; ModUN; VPFHA; SecFrCl; PpCl; SciCl; Vincennes Univ; Nursing.

STEPHENSON, Cheryl K; Whiteland HS; New Whiteland, IN; 30/183 CncrtBnd; HonRl; MrchBnd; NHS; PepBnd; FBLA; FTA; PpCl; Cumberland College.

STEPHENSON, Cynthia; Memorial HS; Joplin, MO; AFS; ChrhWkr; HonRl; StuCncl; Yrbk; RptrSchPpr; College.

STEPHENSON, Dixie A; Kearney HS; Kansas City, MO; 11/86 Band; Chr; CncrtBnd; HonRl; MrchBnd; PepBnd; PpCl; LetterTrk; Chrldr; Maple Woods College; Secretary.

STEPHENSON, James E; North Linn HS; Center Point, IA; ALBoysSt; Band; ChrhWkr; CncrtBnd; FFA; Bsktbl; Ftbl; Trk; College; Vocation.

STEPHENSON, Jerry L; Morgan Co R Ii HS; Fortuna, MO; VPSophCls; AFS; HonRl; NHS; NatlMeritCmnd; NatlMeritSF; SctActv; StuCncl; FrCl; LetterBsktbl; LetterFtbl; Univ Of Chicago; Physics.

STEPHENSON, John E; Benson HS; Omaha, NE; Band; CncrtBnd; HonRl; JA; MrchBnd; NatlCathMusEdAsoc; Orch; PepBnd; ROTC; SctActv; College; Data Systems Repair.

STEPHENSON, Julie K; Chippewa Falls HS; Chippeawa Falls, WI; 24/360 SecBand; CncrtBnd; HonRl; MrchBnd; NHS; PepBnd; SchMus; SpnCl; LetterGAA; Luther Hospital X Ray Program.

STEPHENSON, Kim A; Galena HS; Galena, IL; 11/114 PresSophCls; AFS; Band; HonRl; ModUN; SctActv; StuCncl; EdYrBk; LetterTennis;.

STEPHENSON, Lu Ann; New Haven Sr HS; New Haven, IN; Chr; ChrhWkr; GAA; IMSpt; Indiana University; Social Work.

STEPHENSON, Patrick K; Lawrenceburg HS; Lawrenceburg, IN; Aud/Vis; JA; PpCl; SciCl; Bsbl; Ftbl; Trk; IMSpt; PresAwd; Spartion Sch Of Aeronatics.

STEPHENSON, Paulette M; Romeo HS; Washington, MI; Aud/Vis; CmntyWkr; HonRl; LbryAde; NHS; FrCl; Mi State; Vet.

STEPHENSON, Richard A; Ottawa Sr HS; Ottawa, KS; ALBoysSt; HonRl; SchMus; SchPl; SctActv; TchrAde; SchPpr; PresFBLA; LionAwd; College; Business Management.

STEPHENSON, Rick; Van Buren HS; Keosauqua, IA; ;65 AFS; DrmMjrt; JA; ROTC; SctActv; 4-H; FFA; FSA; SciCl; Wrstlng; Vocational School.

STEPHENSON, Rick L; Cassopolis HS; Cassopolis, MI; .

STEPHENSON, Sharon E; Derby HS; Derby, KS; 21/400 ChrhWkr; DrlTm; HonRl; HospAde; JrNHS; NatlFornLg; NHS; ROTC; SchPl; RptrYrbk; Wichita St Univ; Medical Technology.

STEPHEY, Douglas W; Lexington HS; Lexington, IL; 15/40 College; Forestry.

STEPNAKOWSKI, Maureen M; Bedford North Lawrence HS; Bedford, IN; 40/800 ChrhWkr; HonRl; NatlCathMusEdAsoc; NHS; NatlThespSoc; PolWkr; StuCncl; YthFlsp; FDA; GerCl; GAA; Univ Of California; Medicine.

STEPP, Robert V; Tipton HS; Tipton, MO; 2/90 HonRl; LbryAde; NHS; NatlMeritSF; Univ Of Mo; Theoretical Physicist.

STEPROWSKI, Catherine A; Centerville HS; Centerville, IA; 20/125 Band; HonRl; NHS; PepBnd; SchPl; SctActv; RptrYrbk; FHA; TreasSpnCl; PpCl; Journalism.

STERBLING, John W; Lane Tech HS; Chicago, IL; 19/1165 CAP; DrlTm; HonRl; NHS; Orch; ROTC; StuCncl; EdYrBk; Trk; Northwestern Univ; Biology.

STERGAR, Paul A; Northwest HS; Indianapolis, IN; 26/450 HonRl; JrNHS; NHS; NatlMeritSF; VPStuCncl; IMSpt; General Motors Inst; Business Mgmt.

STERK, Monica L; Lasalle HS; St Ignace, MI; Band; CncrtBnd; HonRl; MrchBnd; NHS; PepBnd; TchrAde; UNYO; Northwood Inst; Business.

STERLING, Everette M; Knoxville HS; Knoxville, IA; 35/180 VPFrshCls; ALBoysSt; HonRl; ModUN; StuCncl; MthCl; PpCl; VPJrCls; LetterFtbl; Swmmng; Ia State U; Constr Engr.

STERLING, Lisabeth A; Seneca HS; Seneca, MO; Chr; HonRl; RptrSchPpr; SchPpr; 4-H;. LetterBsktbl; College;science.

STERLING, Sydney S; South Barber HS; Hardtner, KS; SecFrshCls; SecSophCls; ALAGirlsSt; ChrhWkr; CmntyWkr; HonRl; StuCncl; CivCl; 4-H; FFA; SpnCl; PpCl; IMSpt; College; Social Work.

STERMER, James E; Climax Scotts HS; Scotts, MI; HonRl; SctActv; 4-H; LetterBsbl; 4-HAwd; Coll; Voc.

STERN, Abraham J; Yeshiva HS; Chicago, IL; VPFrshCls; VPSophCls; VPJrCls; SchPl; Yrbk; College; Accounting.

STERN, Ann M; Edgewood HS; Madison, WI; 2/181 Chrs; HonRl; HospAde; NHS; RptrSchPpr; SchPpr; LetterTennis; U Of Wi; Dietetics.

STERN, Dale M; New Leipzig Public HS; New Leipzig, ND; 1/14 PresSophCls; HstJrCls; HonRl; PepBnd; StuCncl; EdYrBk; SchPpr; Bsktbl; Ftbl; Trk; College; Mathmatics.

STERN, David; Hlv Community HS; Victor, IA; PresFrshCls; VPSophCls; Band; ChrhWkr; HonRl; NHS; LetterBsktbl; LetterFtbl; LetterGlf; Trk; Coll; Business.

STERN, Deborah A; New Trier East HS; Glencoe, IL; 19/847 VPAFS; HonRl; NatlMeritFnl; Orch; SchAde; SchMus; MthCl; University Of Illinois; Linguistics.

STERN, Marian V; Proviso West HS; Bellwood, IL; 54/1086 HonRl; NHS; SpnCl; College; Nursing.

STERN, Michael J; Niles North HS; Skokie, IL; 9/641 HonRl; College; Chemistry.

STERN, Richard; Beaver Dam Sr HS; Beaver Dam, WI; 23/314 ALBoysSt; HonRl; NHS; StuCncl; RptrSchPpr; PpCl; SciCl; Trk; Carroll Col; Chemist.

STERN, Susan E; West Waterloo HS; Waterloo, IA; Chr; Chrl; ChrhWkr; HonRl; HospAde; NatlMeritSF; NatlThespSoc; PolWkr; SchPl; EdSchPpr; FrCl; College; Theatre.

STERN, Wilhelm R; Maconaquah HS; Grissom Afb, IN; 14/229 SecFrshCls; HonRl; NHS; SctActv; RptrSchPpr; FrCl; MthCl; LetterFtbl; Socr; IMSpt; Us Air Force Acad.

STERNAD, John; Boscobel HS; Boscobel, WI; ChrhWkr; HonRl; College; Professional.

STERNAL, Nancy R; St Francis Academy; Joliet, IL; 3/178 PresFrshCls; HonRl; HospAde; RedCrAde; StuCncl; RptrYrbk; FrCl; CchngActv; Univ Of Illinois; Liberal Arts.

STERNBERG, Kevin E; Forest Lake Sr HS; Forest Lake, MN; 55/353 Aud/Vis; CncrtBnd; DrmMjrt; MrchBnd; NHS; PepBnd; Quill&Scroll; SctActv; Yrbk; SchPpr; LetterBsbl; LetterBsktbl; GodCntryAwd; Vocational; Commercial Photographer.

STERNECKER, David D; Raytown HS; Kansas City, MO; ALBoysSt; CncrtBnd; HonRl; JrNHS; MrchBnd; PepBnd; StuCncl; RptrSchPpr; KeyCl; SciCl; Bsbl; College.

STERNER, Catherine M; St Agnes HS; St Paul, MN; Aud/Vis; Chr; Chrl; Chrs; HonRl; NHS; SchMus; RptrYrbk; EdYrBk; University Of Minnesota; Medical Tech.

STERNER, James F; Holy Trinity HS; Winsted, MN; HonRl; SctActv; TchrAde; Bsktbl; LetterFtbl; LetterTrk; LetterWrstlng; College; Veterinarian.

STERNER, Sherayl J; Prairie HS; Swisher, IA; Chrs; HonRl; JrNHS; SchMus; Yrbk; EdSchPpr; 4-H; FTA; SpnCl; College; Vocational.

STERNSDORFF, Susan M; Atchison County Comm HS; Effingham, KS; 3/87 TrsFrshCls; TrsSophCls; Band; Chr; Trk; Chrldr; PPFtbl; AmLegAwd; DARAwd; 4-HAwd; U Of Ks; Biochemistry.

STERNWEIS, David A; Columbus HS; Marshfield, WI; 7/114 HonRl; NHS; RptrSchPpr; SchPpr; MthCl; EldAwd; Uw Green Bay; Bus Adm.

STERNWEIS, Joan; Columbus HS; Marshfield, WI; 1/114 HonRl; NHS; NatlSciFnd; SchMus; SchPl; RptrYrbk; RptrSchPpr; GAA; EldAwd; Ripon College; Socialogy.

STERNWEIS, Joan M; Columbus HS; Marshfield, WI; 1/117 Chrs; HonRl; NHS; NatlSciFnd; SchMus; SchPl; Yrbk; SchPpr; SpnCl; PpCl; GAA; College; Science.

STERR, Jeffrey S; Joliet Catholic HS; Joliet, IL; 40/179 PresSrCls; HonRl; StuCncl; TchrAde; SptEdYrbk; GerCl; Bsbl; Wrstlng; IMSpt; University; Law Enforcement.

STERRENBERG, George B; Culver Military Academy; Beaverville, IL; Band; ChrhWkr; CAP; CncrtBnd; DrmBgl; HonRl; MrchBnd; RedCrAde; GerCl; IMSpt; Albion Clg; Pediatrics.

STERRENBERG, Margot A; Thompson Comm HS; Thompson, IA; 4/33 LetterBand; LetterChrs; CncrtBnd; HonRl; LbryAde; MrchBnd; TreasStuCncl; RptrYrbk; 4-H; Bsktbl; 4-HAwd; Stephens College; Training Horses.

STERRETT, Stephen W; Twin Lakes HS; Burnettsville, IN; 8/210 ALBoysSt; HonRl; JrNHS; NHS; LetterFtbl; Trk; LetterWrstlng; Indiana St Univ; Industrial Chemist.

STERRETT, Teresa A; Anthon Oto Community HS; Anthon, IA; 7/31 Band; Chrs; DrlTm; HonRl; NHS; SchPl; RptrYrbk; FHA; PpCl; CaptBsktbl; Schl Of Radiology; Radiologic Tech.

STERRETT, William R; Hardee Cnty HS; Cape Girardeau, MO; 13/146 Band; Chr; HonRl; IntrClCncl; MrchBnd; NHS; SchPl; TchrAde; SpnCl; Southeast Missouri State Univ; Architect.

STERUP, William L; Osceola HS; Osceola, NE; Band; CncrtBnd; HonRl; MrchBnd; Trk; U Of Ne; Electrical Engineer.

STETZEL, Caryn A; Huntington North HS; Roanoke, IN; ChrhWkr; JrNHS; VPYthFlsp; 4-H; College; Speech Therapy.

STETZER, Debra L; Melrose Mindoro HS; Mindoro, WI; VPJrCls; Band; CncrtBnd; HonRl; MrchBnd; PepBnd; SchPl; RptrYrbk; 4-H; FHA; LetterTrk; Chrldr; GAA; 4-HAwd; Western Wisconsin Tech Inst.

STETZER, Faith A; Melrose Mindoro HS; Mindoro, WI; SecSophCls; SecJrCls; Band; CncrtBnd; HonRl; MrchBnd; PepBnd; Yrbk; 4-H; FHA; SciCl; Trk; GAA;.

STEUERWALD, Donna L; Grafton HS; Grafton, WI; CncrtBnd; DrmMjrt; HonRl; MrchBnd; NHS; PepBnd; SchMus; Yrbk; SciCl; Chrldr; University; Microbioloby.

STEUVER, Douglas P; Aurora Sr HS; Aurora, IN; 31/120 Band; Chr; Chrs; ChrhWkr; CncrtBnd; DrmMjrt; HonRl; MrchBnd; Bsktbl; Ftbl; LetterGlf; Trk; CchngActv; Ball St Univ; Med Technology.

STEUVER, Linda K; Aurora Sr HS; Aurora, IN; 3/139 TrsJrCls; ALAGirlsSt; ChrhWkr; HonRl; NHS; SchPl; YthFlsp; GAA; IMSpt; AmLegAwd; Indiana Univ; Elem Education.

STEVENS, Brian; Ashwaubenon HS; Green Bay, WI; SctActv; Bsktbl; Ftbl; IMSpt; Technical School; Professional.

STEVENS, Clifford A; Mt Vernon Comm HS; Greenfield, IN; ALBoysSt; HonRl; JA; NHS; NatlMeritSF; SctActv; College; Mathematics.

STEVENS, Dann F; Primghar Community HS; Primghar, IA; 5/42 Band; Chr; Chrs; ChrhWkr; CmntyWkr; HonRl; Mdrgl; LetterBsktbl; LetterFtbl; LetterTrk; College.

STEVENS, Dean L; Uniontown HS; Uniontown, KS; HonRl; Yrbk; SptEdSchPpr; MthCl; Bsbl; LetterFtbl; Coll; Acct.

STEVENS, Debora K; South Newton HS; Kentland, IN; HospAde; SchMus; SchPl; Yrbk; RptrSchPpr; FFA; FHA; FTA; GerCl; LatCl; Bsbl; Bsktbl; Arizona State Univ; Nursing.

STEVENS, Diane K; Ballard Comm HS; Huxley, IA; CmntyWkr; HonRl; JrNHS; NHS; NatlMeritFnl; YthFnd; FBLA; GovHonPrgAwd; JAAwd; CitAwd;.

STEVENS, Garth; Wautoma HS; Wautoma, WI; VPFrshCls; Band; CncrtBnd; HonRl; MrchBnd; FrCl; IMSpt; College.

STEVENS, James C; Columbus North HS; Columbus, IN; 1/500 ALBoysSt; HonRl; ModUN; NatlMeritSF; RedCrAde; CaptTennis; CaptChrldr; DARAwd; OptClAwd; CitAwd; Univ; Pre Dentistry.

STEVENS, James R; Glenbard North HS; Carol Stream, IL; ChrhWkr; SctActv; Bsktbl; Ftbl; College; Draftsman.

STEVENS, Joan M; Houghton HS; Houghton, MI; 19/109 Chrs; ChrhWkr; DrlTm; HonRl; HospAde; LbryAde; SctActv; StuCncl; TchrAde; 4-H; FNA; PresPpCl; Bsktbl; PPFtbl; Michigan Tech Univ; Nursing.

STEVENS, Jon R; Pike HS; Indianapolis, IN; 60/258 ALBoysSt; Band; ChrhWkr; HonRl; JrNHS; Pres4-H; Bsktbl; Ftbl; Trk; 4-HAwd; Purdue University; Agriculture.

STEVENS, Karen J; South Barber HS; Kiowa, KS; 1/38 PresJrCls; Chr; HonRl; NHS; StuCncl; TchrAde; TreasPpCl; Bsktbl; PPFtbl; University; Science.

STEVENS, Laurel; Sargent Public HS; Sargent, NE; 6/43 DrmMjrt; NHS; NatlThespSoc; SchMus; SchPl; SctActv; YthFlsp; PpCl; Bsktbl; Trk; College; Interior Design.

STEVENS, Leslie J; Gaylord HS; Gaylord, MI; HonRl; NHS; TchrAde; KeyCl; FrCl; Univ Of Michigan; Intl Law.

STEVENS, Mark A; Eastern Heights HS; Phillipsburg, KS; VPFrshCls; VPSophCls; VPJrCls; Chrl; HonRl; Mdrgl; LetterBsktbl; LetterFtbl; Trk; VoiceDemAwd; Kansas St U; Veterinarian.

STEVENS, Mark C; Mc Donell Central HS; Chippewa Falls, WI; 4/95 VPFrshCls; VPSophCls; SecTrsJrCls; ALBoysSt; HonRl; StuCncl; KeyCl; LetterBsbl; LetterBsktbl; LetterFtbl; College; Medicine.

STEVENS, Mark D; Pennfield HS; Battle Creek, MI; Band; CncrtBnd; SctActv; YthFlsp; 4-H; SciCl; LetterBsbl; LetterBsktbl; LetterFtbl; 4-HAwd; University; Conservation.

STEVENS, Mark J; Rantoul Twshp HS; Rantoul, IL; JrNHS; LetterFtbl; LetterWrstlng; Univ Of Illinois; Computer Science.

STEVENS, Nancy M; Cedar Catholic HS; Hartington, NE; 10/69 SecSophCls; Band; HonRl; JrNHS; NHS; StuCncl; EdYrBk; FrCl; MthCl; Trk; U Of Nebraska; Math Business.

STEVENS, Nanette; Atherton HS; Burton, MI; 1/160 Band; HonRl; HospAde; NHS; StuGov; RptrSchPpr; FSA; SciCl; Bsbl; Ftbl; Univ Of Mich; Medicine.

STEVENS, Patricia J; Rockford East HS; Rockford, IL; Chr; HonRl; Mdrgl; SchMus; University; Music.

STEVENS, Randall R; St Edward Public HS; St Edward, NE; Band; ChrhWkr; SchMus; StuCncl; StuGov; SchPpr; SciCl; Bsbl; Bsktbl; Ftbl; New Mexico Military Inst; Military Officer.

STEVENS, Randy L; Sand Creek HS; Adrian, MI; ChrhWkr; CtyCnl; CAP; HonRl; NHS; RedCrAde; Glf; AmLegAwd; DARAwd; SARAwd; Mi State U.

STEVENS, Richard D; Lane Tech HS; Chicago, IL; 370/1213 TrsSophCls; Aud/Vis; HonRl; StuGov; Yrbk; KeyCl; College; Sociology.

STEVENS, Robert E; North Kansas City Sr HS; Kansas City, MO; Chr; Chrl; ChrhWkr; HonRl; SchMus; SctActv; TchrAde; YthFlsp; Univ Of Missouri; Chemical Engineering.

STEVENS, Robert J; Green Bay West HS; Green Bay, WI; 14/400 HonRl; StuCncl; LetterBsktbl; Ftbl; Trk; Coll; Medicine.

STEVENS, Robyn L; Croswell Lexington HS; Applegate, MI; Band; Chr; CncrtBnd; HonRl; MrchBnd; NHS; StuCncl; RptrSchPpr; Trk; Oakland University; Psychology.

STEVENS, Sally L; Ladysmith HS; Ladysmith, WI; 2/144 Band; CncrtBnd; HonRl; NHS; SctActv; StuCncl; EdYrBk; RptrSchPpr; PresFHA; BttyCrckrAwd; Univ Of Wi; Registered Nurse.

STEVENS, Scott M; West Bend Comm HS; West Bend, IA; Band; CncrtBnd; MrchBnd; PepBnd; SchPl; YthFlsp; IMSpt; Trade; Professional.

STEVENS, Shelly L; Jacksonville HS; Jacksonville, IL; 4/352 Band; HonRl; MrchBnd; NHS; StuGov; Twrl; EdSchPpr; FrCl; Tennis; Chrldr; Mac Murray Coll; Chem.

STEVENS, Susan L; Brazil Senior HS; Brazil, IN; 21/200 PresChr; HonRl; NHS; NatlThespSoc; Quill&Scroll; SchMus; TchrAde; PresYthFlsp; SecYrbk; SchPpr; PresSciCl; 4-HAwd; Univ; Dental Assisting.

STEVENS, Thomas; Thornwood HS; S Holland, IL; 21/852 HonRl; JrNHS; NHS; NatlMeritCmnd; KeyCl; MthCl; LetterTennis; LetterTrk; Purdue Univ; Elec Eng.

STEVENS, William S; Speedway HS; Speedway, IN; 1/200 CncrtBnd; HonRl; MrchBnd; NHS; NatlMeritFnl; PepBnd; SchMus; GerCl; VPJrCls; RotaryAwd; Purdue Univ; Computer Science.

STEVENSON, Cathy L; Glenburn Public HS; Maxbass, ND; 5/28 PresFrshCls; VPSophCls; SecSophCls; SecSrCls; Band; Chrs; HonRl; MrchBnd; SchPl; RptrSchPpr; 4-HAwd; Business College.

STEVENSON, Deanna K; Sault Area HS; Sault St Marie, MI; HonRl; TchrAde; Business.

STEVENSON, Debra S; St George HS; St George, KS; SecTrsFrshCls; Chr; HonRl; SchPl; TchrAde; PresFHA; Bsktbl; Trk; Chrldr; 4-HAwd; Kansas St Univ; Special Ed.

STEVENSON, Jennifer L; Franklin HS; Jacksonville, IL; Chrs; HospAde; JA; PepBnd; FFA; SpnCl; Trk; Wrstlng; GAA; 4-HAwd; Clge.

STEVENSON, Lora M; Winsor HS; Windsor, IL; 6/47 TrsJrCls; PresBand; ChrhWkr; NHS; NatlThespSoc; SchPl; StuCncl; RptrYrbk; CaptChrldr; GAA; Lakeland College; Secretary.

STEVENSON, Lou; Yorkville Comm HS; Yorkville, IL; 23/130 VPSophCls; ChrhWkr; CmntyWkr; HonRl; NHS; StuCncl; 4-H; GAA; 4-HAwd; College; Probation Officer.

STEVENSON, Michael R; Van Buren HS; Brazil, IN; 1/74 VPChr; HonRl; PresNHS; SchMus; Pres4-H; KeyCl; FrCl; SciCl; 4-HAwd; Purdue Univ; Veterinarian.

STEVENSON, Sherryl K; Lincoln Co R Ii HS; Elsberry, MO; 3/62 ALAGirlsSt; Band; Chrs; ChrhWkr; CncrtBnd; DrmMjrt; HonRl; SecNHS; SchPl; TchrAde; Hannibal La Grange College; Music.

STEWARD, Janet R; Lincoln HS; Wisc Rapids, WI; Band; Chr; ChrhWkr; CmntyWkr; HonRl; Mdrgl; MrchBnd; Orch; PepBnd; SchMus; Nurse.

STEWARD, Jeffrey G; Clintonville HS; Clintonville, WI; 6/181 PresJrCls; PresSrCls; HonRl; LetterFtbl; LetterFTA; LetterWrstlng; IMSpt; JAAwd; PresAwd; VoiceDemAwd; Carroll College.

STEWARD, John T; Mendel C HS; Riverdale, IL; 8/190 HonRl; NatlFornLg; NHS; PolWkr; StuGov; YthLg; EdSchPpr; Northwestern; Law.

STEWARD, Kenny; Lewellen Rural HS; Lewellen, NE; 6/15 ALBoysSt; Band; Chrs; CncrtBnd; HonRl; MrchBnd; SptEdYrbk; Bsktbl; Ftbl; Trk; Trade; Vocation.

STEWARD, Timothy W; Monrovia HS; Mooresville, IN; 16/104 PresJrCls; PresSrCls; ALBoysSt; MrchBnd; NHS; PolWkr; StuCncl; YthFlsp; SchPpr; SpnCl; Trk; EldAwd; Indiana St Univ; Marketing.

STEWART, Ann C; Athens HS; Fulton, MI; 2/62 PresFrshCls; TrsSophCls; VPJrCls; SecSrCls; HonRl; HospAde; NHS; OffAde; RedCrAde; SchPl; StuCncl; Bsktbl; Chrldr; GAA; Michigan State Univ; Fisheries.

STEWART, Betsy D; Corunna HS; Corunna, MI; JA; 4-H; College; Secretary.

STEWART, Brenda J; Clay City HS; Bowling Green, IN; 15/64 Band; ChrhWkr; HonRl; NHS; TchrAde; YthFlsp; Yrbk; PpCl; GAA; College; Vocation.

STEWART, Brent L; Durand HS; Durand, WI; Band; ChrhWkr; CncrtBnd; HonRl; MrchBnd; PepBnd; SchPl; YthFlsp; 4-H; Bsktbl; Tennis; Wrstlng; Univ; Draftsman.

STEWART, Cathy J; Washington HS; South Bend, IN; 47/320 HonRl; NHS; OffAde;.

STEWART, Cecilia B; St Marys Academy; Morris, MN; SecTrsFrshCls; VPSrCls; ALAGirlsSt; Band; Chrs; HonRl; LbryAde; MrchBnd; PepBnd; SchPl; Bsbl; Bsktbl; Trk; University Of Detroit; Psychology.

STEWART, Charles A; Nobles HS; Noblesville, IN; 7/156 ChrhWkr; HonRl; NHS; FrCl; IMSpt; Purdue Univ; Chemical Engineer.

STEWART, Charles R; Vandercook HS; Clarklake, MI; 6/98 TrsFrshCls; SecSophCls; ChrhWkr; HonRl; NHS; NatlMeritCmnd; PresStuCncl; Bsktbl; ChmnFtbl; Trk; College Or Univ.

STEWART, Connie S; Cassville HS; Shell Knob, MO; NHS; SctActv; StuCncl; Yrbk; SchPpr; FHA; FTA; PpCl; Trk; IMSpt; Smsu; Wildlife Conservation.

STEWART, Constance; Academy Of Our Lady; Chicago, IL; 24/160 HonRl; NHS; Univ Of Chicago; Doctor.

STEWART, Cynthia H; Eldora Consolidated HS; Eldora, IA; Band; CncrtBnd; HonRl; MrchBnd; YthFlsp; PpCl; Bsbl; Bsktbl; Trk; Univ Of Northern Iowa; Education.

STEWART, Cynthia L; Springfield HS; Springfield, IL; 10/589 ChrhWkr; CmntyWkr; JrNHS; NHS; NatlMeritFnl; NatlMeritSF; OffAde; PolWkr; SctActv; Bradley Univ; Social Worker.

STEWART, Cynthia S; Carlinville Community HS; Carinville, IL; 46/158 HonRl; OffAde; PolWkr;

SchPl; RptrSchPpr; SpnCl; PpCl; Lincoln College; Sociology.

STEWART, Deanna S; Hamilton HS; Hamilton, KS; TrsFrshCls; VPSophCls; SecJrCls; SecSrCls; SchPl; EdYrBk; Bsktbl; Trade School; Vocation.

STEWART, Deborah J; Big Rapids HS; Big Rapids, MI; TrsSophCls; HonRl; NatlFornLg; NHS; SchPpr; Univ Of Michigan.

STEWART, Deborah M; Libertyville HS; Libertyville, IL; HonRl; NHS; PolWkr; SchMus; SchPl; College; Anthropology.

STEWART, Debra L; Ladywood St Agnes HS; Indianapolis, IN; ChrhWkr; CmntyWkr; JA; PolWkr; SchPpr; LatCl; Glf; CchngActv; GAA; IMSpt; College; Archeology.

STEWART, Delbert; Durand HS; Durand, WI; RptrSchPpr; SptEdSchPpr; PpCl; Bsktbl; Ftbl; Trk; Trade; Vocation.

STEWART, Eric B; East St Louis Sr HS; E St Louis, IL; 10/691 HonRl; JA; JrNHS; NHS; MthCl; PpCl; SciCl; Southern Illinois Univf Medicine.

STEWART, Gary L; Milton Senior HS; Milton, WI; HonRl; SctActv; SciCl; Bsbl; IMSpt; CitAwd; Navy; Prof Trucker.

STEWART, Georgia E; Arthur Hill HS; Zilwaukee, MI; CtyCnl; HonRl; JA; StuGov; UNYO; YthLg; FshEdSchPpr; FDA; JCAwd; CitAwd; Medical School; Doctor.

STEWART, Jackson R; Dickinson HS; Dickinson, ND; PresFrshCls; Chrl; HonRl; SchPl; SctActv; StuGov; SchPpr; FFA; GerCl; Bsktbl; Dickinson State Coll; Psych.

STEWART, James A; Huron HS; Ann Arbor, MI; 60/700 ALBoysSt; RptrYrbk; RptrSchPpr; LetterSwmmng; AmLegAwd; Mi State Univ; Pre Med.

STEWART, James C; Sturgis HS; Sturgis, MI; Band; HonRl; MrchBnd; NHS; NatlMeritSF; Orch; SchMus; SctActv; TchrAde; Ftbl; Univ Of Michigan; Engineering.

STEWART, Jeffrey J; Waverly HS; Fagle, NE; HonRl; SctActv; TchrAde; 4-H; FFA; LetterFtbl; LetterTrk; LetterCchngActv; GodCntryAwd; Doane Coll; Bus Admin.

STEWART, Jeff W; Winchester Comm HS; Winchester, IN; 1/170 HonRl; NHS; SpnCl; BauchLmbAwd; Purdue Univ; Computer Prog.

STEWART, John A; St Joseph HS; Kenosha, WI; Aud/Vis; HonRl; LbryAde; SchMus; StuCncl; RptrYrbk; Yrbk; Clge; Law.

STEWART, Julie J; Franklin HS; Franklin, IL; Chrs; NHS; OffAde; Yrbk; SpnCl; PpCl; AmLegAwd; Trade School; Vocational.

STEWART, Kathleen C; Northrop HS; Ft Wayne, IN; 2/643 SecFrshCls; Chr; CmntyWkr; HonRl; SctActv; StuCncl; 4-H; PresLatCl; CitAwd; College; Medical Doctor.

STEWART, Kathleen M; Brunswick HS; Brunswick, MO; 9/43 ALAGirlsSt; HonRl; LbryAde; NHS; SchPl; EdYrBk; EdSchPpr; 4-H; FHA; LetterBsbl; U Of Mo; Child Development.

STEWART, Kathy J; Parkview HS; Orfordville, WI; PresFrshCls; Band; CncrtBnd; DrlTm; HonRl; MrchBnd; NHS; StuCncl; TchrAde; YthFlsp; EdSchPpr; PpCl; LetterChrldr; GAA; Univ Of Wisc; Medicine.

STEWART, Kevin C; Lanphier HS; Springfield, IL; 4/475 ChrhWkr; VPNHS; NatlMeritSF; Univ Of Il; Engineering.

STEWART, Laura L; Mt Vernon Twp HS; Mt Vernon, IL; 30/415 HonRl; LbryAde; NHS; TchrAde; RptrYrbk; Yrbk; 4-H; LatCl; DanFAwd; College.

STEWART, Lawrence C; Northwestern HS; Detroit, MI; Aud/Vis; ChrhWkr; CmntyWkr; NatlFornLg; NatlMeritCmnd; OffAde; Orch; PolWkr; SchPl; SctActv; StuGov; TchrAde; FDA; College; Political Science.

STEWART, Linda S; Pepin HS; Stockholm, WI; HonRl; LbryAde; NHS; TchrAde; Yrbk; SchPpr; FHA; LatCl; Col; Professional.

STEWART, Lisa A; Romeoville HS; Lockport, IL; 15/293 HonRl; SchPl; StuCncl; StuGov; Yrbk; RptrSchPpr; PpCl; Bsktbl; Tennis; Illinois State Univ; Stewardess.

STEWART, Lynda A; Springfield HS; Springfield, IL; 38/535 Yrbk; Ill College; Engineer.

STEWART, Marjorie E; Brown County HS; Columbus, IN; 49/206 HonRl; OffAde; Quill&Scroll; SchPpr; FHA; LatCl; Trade School.

STEWART, Mark T; Fargo North HS; Fargo, ND; HonRl; PolWkr; Wrstlng; Nd State Univ; Biology.

STEWART, Marla D; St Charles HS; St Charles, MO; CmntyWkr; HonRl; NHS; PolWkr; College; Historian.

STEWART, Matthew C; Lena Winslow HS; Lena, IL; 5/98 ALBoysSt; HonRl; PresNHS; VPStuCncl; LetterBsktbl; LetterTrk; College; English.

STEWART, Michael; William R Harper HS; Chicago, IL; 1/520 Band; Chr; Chrs; ChrhWkr; CmntyWkr; CncrtBnd; DrlTm; DrmBgl; HonRl; JrNHS; LbryAde; MrchBnd; NHS; PepBnd; RedCrAde; De Paul Univ; Chemical Eng.

STEWART, Michael T; Dixon HS; Dixon, MO; PresJrCls; Band; CmntyWkr; CncrtBnd; HonRl; NHS; SchPl; StuCncl; FTA; Bsktbl; Trk; Univ Of Mo Columbia; Broadcasting.

STEWART, Nancy J; Wahoo Public HS; Wahoo, NE; Band; Chrs; ChrhWkr; HonRl; YthFlsp; 4-H; SpnCl; PpCl; Trk; Chrldr; U Of Neb; Allied Health.

STEWART, Norine M; Chicago Vocational HS; Chicago, IL; 123/776 HonRl; SchAde; StuCncl; TchrAde; SchPpr; GAA; Harrington Univ; Interior Design.

STEWART, Rebecca L; Vienna HS; Vienna, IL; 13/102 Chr; ChrhWkr; HonRl; SchAde; TchrAde; Yrbk; FrCl; PpCl; College.

STEWART, Renae D; United Township HS; Siluis, IL; 18/529 Band; Chr; ChrhWkr; CmntyWkr; HonRl; JrNHS; Mdrgl; NHS; RedCrAde; SecFrCl; Bsktbl; Ftbl; GAA; AmLegAwd; Marycrest College; Nurse.

STEWART, Rhonda S; Chadwick HS; Chadwick, IL; 1/26 Chr; Chrs; HonRl; SchPl; StuCncl; RptrYrbk; FHA; SecGAA; BttyCrckrAwd; Augustana College.

STEWART, Ronald B; Fairbury HS; Fairbury, NE; SecTrsSophCls; Chrs; HonRl; StuCncl; StuGov; GerCl; Bsktbl; LetterFtbl; LetterTrk; Southeast Comm College; Physical Therapy.

STEWART, Ron J; Upsala Area HS; Bowlus, MN; 5/42 PresFrshCls; PresJrCls; PresSrCls; HonRl; NHS; StuCncl; FFA; LetterFtbl; CaptTrk; Brainerd Community College; Education.

STEWART, Roxanne; Tekamah Herman HS; Tekamah, NE; 3/70 Chr; Chrl; Chrs; DrlTm; HonRl; FHA; PpCl; Univ Of Ne; Secondary Education.

STEWART, Sheila J; Raymore Peculiar HS; Belton, MO; Chrs; CmntyWkr; HonRl; ROTC; SctActv; SpnCl; PpCl; College; Professional.

STEWART, Sherri L; Winfield HS; Winfield, KS; VPSrCls; ALAGirlsSt; Chr; CncrtBnd; HonRl; MrchBnd; Orch; PepBnd; SchMus; LetterBsktbl; College; Music.

STEWART, Stephen; Springville Community Hs; Springville, IA; 7/57 TrsSophCls; Band; Chr; HonRl; MrchBnd; TreasNHS; PresStuGov; FSA; LetterFtbl; LetterTrk; U Of Iowa; Professional Medicine.

STEWART, Steve J; Roanoke Benson HS; Roanoke, IL; 32/95 HonRl; PpCl; LetterBsktbl; LetterTrk;.

STEWART, Susan; Lincoln Way HS; Moken, IL; 193/566 Chrs; HonRl; SchMus; StuCncl; IMSpt; AmLegAwd; Junior Coll; Secretary.

STEWART, Susan L; North Knox HS; Oaktown, IN; 6/138 ChrhWkr; DrlTm; HonRl; NHS; SchAde; 4-H; FHA; LatCl; Special Education.

STEWART, Terri L; Dunlap HS; Peoria, IL; 25/80 Chrs; HonRl; LbryAde; SchAde; SchMus; RptrYrbk; SpnCl; PpCl; CaptChrldr; GAA; College; Professional.

STEWART, Vera L; Coulterville HS; Coulterville, IL; 4/22 SecTrsJrCls; Chr; ChrhWkr; HonRl; SchPl; RptrSchPpr; 4-H; FHA; SpnCl; PpCl; College; Bus Voc.

ST GERMAIN, Donna M; Crawford Ausable HS; Grayling, MI; 3/147 PresFrshCls; TrsSrCls; Band; CncrtBnd; HonRl; MrchBnd; NHS; PepBnd; SchMus; StuGov; Bsktbl; Central Michigan University.

ST HILLIER, Sandra J; Belleville East HS; Caseyville, IL; HonRl; JrNHS; TchrAde; LatCl; Siu Edwardsville; Accounting.

STIBAL, Denise M; Silver Lake HS; Silver Lake, MN; 2/57 Band; Chrs; Sdlty; Yrbk; RptrSchPpr; PpCl; BttyCrckrAwd; U Of Minn; Music.

STICE, Daniel L; Aquinas HS; T Madison, IA; Bsktbl; Trk; IMSpt;.

STICH, Karen L; Athens HS; Athens, IL; 3/51 TrsSophCls; Chrs; HonRl; NHS; OffAde; FHA; GAA; Univ; Comp Sci.

STICHA, Neil A; Lincoln Sr HS; Bloomington, MN; 44/562 Band; CncrtBnd; HonRl; MrchBnd; NHS; PepBnd; SctActv; StuCncl; Univ Of Minnesota; Mathematics.

STICHLER, Shawni L; Abraham Lincoln HS; Council Bluffs, IA; Chr; Chrl; Chrs; ChrhWkr; Mdrgl; SchMus; StuCncl; LetterBsktbl; Glf; LetterChrldr; College; Psychology.

STICHTER, Michelle D; Morrison HS; Morrison, IL; HonRl; NatlThespSoc; SchPl; 4-H; FTA; AmLegAwd; DARAwd; Western Illinois Univ; Sociology.

STICKEL, Cheryl A; Dominican HS; Detroit, MI; Chrl; HonRl; HospAde; SchMus; SchPl; Teen; Univ; Vet Med.

STICKELMAN, Megan J; York Sr HS; York, NE; 39/123 VPSophCls; ChrhWkr; CncrtBnd; HonRl; MrchBnd; RptrYrbk; EdSchPpr; PpCl; Bsktbl; Chrldr; Ne Wesleyan U; Dental Hygiene.

STICKLE, Joanie E; Knoxville Sr HS; Knoxville, IA; CmntyWkr; HonRl; MrchBnd; NatlThespSoc; OffAde; Twrl; SptEdSchPpr; 4-H; LetterBsktbl; LetterTrk; CchngActv; College; Nursing.

STICKLE, Pamela; Cass City HS; Cass City, MI; Band; HonRl; TchrAde; YthFlsp; 4-H; PpCl; 4-HAwd; Coll.

STICKLER, Daniel L; Cornell HS; Cornell, WI; HonRl; SpnCl; LetterBsktbl; Glf; Col;.

STICKLES, Beth A; Clay City HS; Coal City, IN; 2/64 Band; Chr; ChrhWkr; HonRl; NHS; StuCncl; PresYthFlsp; Yrbk; 4-H; MthCl; GAA; 4-HAwd; Purdue Univ; Computer Science.

STICKLING, Nancy; Elgin HS; Elgin, IL; ChrhWkr; CmntyWkr; SchAde; SctActv; TchrAde; Col; Special Ed.

STICKMAN, Elizabeth A; Griggsville Community Unit 4; Griggsville, IL; 1/24 Chrs; ChrhWkr; NHS; NatlThespSoc; YthFlsp; EdYrBk; 4-H; FHA; Bsktbl; 4-HAwd; Univ; Home Ec Education.

STICKNEY, Duane D; Mason County Eastern HS; Custer, MI; 4/45 VPSophCls; VPJrCls; PresSrCls; HonRl; NHS; SchPl; TchrAde; LetterBsbl; LetterBsktbl; LetterTrk; Ferris St Coll; Tech Drafting.

STICKROD, Kimberley A; Wheeling HS; Wheeling, IL; DrlTm; HonRl; NHS; StuCncl; Twrl; Yrbk; Purdue Univ; Foreign Languages.

STIDHAM, Jamie E; Frankfort Sr HS; Frankfort, IN; 20/242 Band; CncrtBnd; MrchBnd; TreasNHS; OffAde; TchrAde; PresFTA; FrCl; PpCl; GAA; Indiana St Univ; Elementary Ed.

STIDHAM, Jeanne M; Ing Hill HS; Spring Hill, KS; Chr; ChrhWkr; HonRl; LbryAde; TchrAde; FHA; FTA; SpnCl; PpCl; Friends Univ; Physician.

STIEBER, Cheryl A; Marathon HS; Edgar, WI; VPFrshCls; SecJrCls; Band; DrlTm; HonRl; MrchBnd; FrCl; Trk; LetterChrldr; GAA; College.

STIEFEL, Wanda; Stanton HS; Stanton, ND; 10/17 SecTrsFrshCls; Band; Chr; Chrs; CncrtBnd; HonRl; MrchBnd; StuCncl; EdYrBk; FshEdSchPpr; Wapeton College; Dental Hygeine.

STIEFVATER, Kurt M; Springfield Catholic HS; Springfield, MO; HonRl; SctActv; LatCl; Bsbl; Bsktbl; Trk; Univ; Psychology.

STIEG, Ronald N; Riverside Brookfield HS; Brookfield, IL; HonRl; LetterTrk; Western Illinois U; Optometry.

STIEGEMEIER, Craig L; Staunton HS; Staunton, IL; 2/98 PresSophCls; Chrs; Mdrgl; NHS; SchPl; U Of Il Champaign; Electrical Engr.

STIELOW, Terri S; Hiawatha HS; Hiawatha, KS; ALAGirlsSt; Chr; Chrs; HonRl; SchMus; TchrAde; PpCl; Bsktbl; Chrldr; AmLegAwd; Bus Sch; Court Reporting.

STIER, Diane M; Grand Meadow Public HS; Grand Meadow, MN; 4/45 PresFrshCls; Band; ChrhWkr; HonRl; MrchBnd; NHS; SchPl; FFA; Bsktbl; IMSpt; Mankato State Clge; Phy Ed & Special Ed.

STIERMAN, Terry; Wahlerr HS; Dubuque, IA; 7/453 NHS; StuCncl; StuGov; TchrAde; FrCl; SpnCl; SciCl; College.

STIERWALT, Sharon J; High School; Sadorus, IL; DrmMjrt; SchMus; StuCncl; 4-H; FFA; PresFHA; Swmmng; LetterTrk; GAA; 4-HAwd; Parkland Jr College; Elementary Education.

STIEVE, Carol L; South Haven HS; South Haven, MI; 1/216 HonRl; NHS; SchAde; StuGov; PpCl; Trk; Chrldr; CchngActv; AmLegAwd; KiwanAwd; Kalamazoo Valley; Physical Ed Or Business.

STIEWE, Barbara A; Harding HS; St Paul, MN; 1/725 AFS; HonRl; NHS; SpnCl; SciCl; IMSpt; U Of Mn; Foreign Languages.

STIFTER, Catherine M; Holy Trinity HS; Winsted, MN; PresFrshCls; PresSophCls; PresJrCls; ALAGirlsSt; HonRl; VPStuCncl; EdYrBk; CaptBsktbl; LetterTrk; Chrldr; BttyCrckrAwd; Macalester College.

STIGLMIRE, Billi S; Lansing HS; Lansing, KS; HstFrshCls; HstSophCls; Band; Chrs; CncrtBnd; HonRl; MrchBnd; PepBnd; StuCncl; StuGov; College; Professional.

STIKSEL, Monica E; Lourdes HS; Chicago, IL; 77/299 PresBand; CncrtBnd; HonRl; MrchBnd; SchMus; StuCncl; SecGerCl; PpCl; Business School; Vocation.

STILABOWER, Pamela L; Windsor HS; Windsor, MO; 26/51 Band; HonRl; OffAde; FNA; MthCl; Burge Sch Of Nursing; Nurse.

STILES, Douglas L; Liberal HS; Liberal, KS; 7/240 ALBoysSt; Band; ChrhWkr; CncrtBnd; HonRl; NatlFornLg; NHS; NatlMeritCmnd; PepBnd; University; Engineering.

STILES, Gregory L; Concord HS; Spring Arbor, MI; PresSophCls; Aud/Vis; HonRl; SctActv; StuGov; TchrAde; RptrSchPpr; College; Xray Technology.

STILES, Nancy J; Sycamore HS; Sycamore, IL; 3/201 Chrs; HonRl; Mdrgl; NHS; NatlMeritCmnd; StuCncl; LetterBsbl; LetterBsktbl; LetterTrk; PresGAA; DARAwd; Knox College; Medicine.

STILES, Robert E; Plainfield HS; Plainfield, IN; 12/259 Chrs; HonRl; PresNHS; SchMus; StuCncl; Glf; Swmmng; OptClAwd; RotaryAwd; Indiana Univ; Business Econ.

STILGER, Kathy; Floyd Central HS; New Albany, IN; 9/276 Chr; HonRl; NHS; SchMus; SchPl; TchrAde; FTA; PPFtbl; 4-HAwd; College Iupui; Radiology.

STILLINGS, Dan M; Ava HS; Ava, MO; 21/146 Band; HonRl; NatlMeritCmnd; PepBnd; SchPl; KeyCl; SpnCl; School Of The Ozarks; Aircraft Mech.

STILLMANK, Renee S; Parker Sr HS; Janesville, WI; 11/423 TreasAFS; NHS; NatlThespSoc; SchPl; EdYrBk; 4-H; VPGAA; 4-HAwd; CitAwd; Fashion Inst Of Tech; Patternmaking.

STILLMOCK, Richard A; Roncalli HS; Omaha, NE; HonRl; PresJA; NHS; PresSctActv; Yrbk; RptrSchPpr; 4-H; SciCl; JAAwd; Univ Ne; Cpa.

STILLS, Judy M; Martensdale St Marys HS; Matensdale, IA; Band; HonRl; PepBnd; PpCl; Bsktbl; LetterTrk; Office Work.

STILLWELL, Sondra R; Belton HS; Belton, MO; ChrhWkr; HonRl; LbryAde; NHS; SctActv; Yrbk; FBLA; FrCl;.

STILTZ, William R; Porta HS; Tallula, IL; 2/129 Band; HonRl; VPNHS; NatlThespSoc; SchMus; Pres4-H; SecKeyCl; FrCl; LetterGlf; DanFAwd; 4-HAwd; KiwanAwd; Harvard University; Law.

STILWELL, Mickey R; Lawton Bronson HS; Lawton, IA; Bsktbl; Ftbl; Trk; IMSpt; College; Accountant.

STIMAC, Anthony G; Orchard View HS; Muskegon, MI; Band; HonRl; NatlMeritSF; SchPl; TchrAde; Bsktbl; Ftbl; Trk; CchngActv; ChmbCommrsAwd; Central Mi; Teacher.

STIMAC, Joan M; Streator Twp HS; Streator, IL; 55/378 HonRl; HospAde; NatlMeritSchl; Quill&Scroll; TchrAde; RptrSchPpr; SpnCl; St Francis Hosp Schl Nursing.

STIMAC, Julie A; Streator Township HS; Streator, IL; HonRl; Junior College; Business.

STIMAC, Mary Jo; Houghton HS; Houghton, MI; 26/111 Band; Chrs; CncrtBnd; DrlTm; HonRl; MrchBnd; PepBnd; SpnCl; Mi Technological Univ; Engineering.

STIMPERT, John L; El Paso HS; El Paso, IL; Band; ChrhWkr; CncrtBnd; HonRl; MrchBnd; ModUN; NHS; PresStuCncl; RptrSchPpr; MthCl; Il Wesleyan U; Music.

STINAR, Joseph T; Lakefield HS; Lakefield, MN; HonRl; 4-H; SecFFA; Bsktbl; CaptTrk; JCAwd; Univ Of Minnesota; Agriculture.

STINCHCOMB, Wendy K; Lowell Sr HS; Lowell, MI; ChrhWkr; CncrtBnd; HonRl; LbryAde; MrchBnd; NHS; PepBnd; RptrYrbk; 4-H; Grand Rapids Jr College; Physical Therapy.

STINE, Cathy L; Bonner Sps HS; Kansas City, KS; PresSrCls; ALAGirlsSt; Chr; ChrhWkr; HonRl; NHS; StuCncl; FBLA; FHA; BauchLmbAwd; College; Missionary To Canada.

STINE, Nancy J; Brownstown Comm HS; Brownstown, IL; 2/38 PresSrCls; HonRl; LbryAde; OffAde; SchPl; TchrAde; Yrbk; PresFHA; TreasGAA; DARAwd; Work; Secretarial.

STINEBACK, Melinda; Schaumburg Hs; Schaumburg, IL; 2/537 Chr; Chrs; HonRl; Mdrgl; NHS; SchMus; YthFlsp; FrCl; Chrldr; Northern Illinois U; Elementaryeducation.

STING, Joann; Unionville Sebewaing Area HS; Sebewaing, MI; 21/125 ChrhWkr; HonRl; NHS; Yrbk; FHA; FrCl; PpCl; Concordia Lutheran Jr Coll; Hist Teacher.

STINNETT, Cynthia; Illmo Scott City HS; Scott City, MO; 15/75 ALBoysSt; ALAGirlsSt; HonRl; Quill&Scroll; StuCncl; EdYrBk; DanFAwd; PresAwd; CitAwd; Freed Hardeman Tn; Bible.

STINSON, Bill; Udall HS; Udall, KS; PresJrCls; SecSrCls; Band; Chr; Chrs; CncrtBnd; HonRl; Coll; Teach.

STINSON, Janine; Andrean HS; Gary, IN; 50/258 ChrhWkr; HonRl; HospAde; RptrYrbk; Yrbk; RptrSchPpr; Purdue Univ; Medical Field.

STINSON, Jo Ellen; Morton HS; Morton, IL; HonRl; OffAde; YthFlsp; RptrYrbk; Yrbk; 4-H; PpCl; LetterBsbl; LetterBsktbl; TreasGAA; Coll; Curriculum Of Major Study.

STINSON, Joe W; Norfolk Catholic HS; Norfolk, NE; HonRl; NatlFornLg; NatlThespSoc; SchMus; SchPl; StuCncl; Ftbl; Trk; University; Disc Jockey.

STINSON, Michael E; Bethlehem Acad; Faribault, MN; 20/83 Aud/Vis; CmntyWkr; HonRl; NatlMeritCmnd; PolWkr; SchPl; RptrSchPpr; LetterTrk; Univ; Secondary Teacher.

STINSON, Sarah E; Grand Island Sr HS; Grand Island, NE; Chr; Chrl; Chrs; CmntyWkr; HonRl; NatlThespSoc; SchMus; SchPl; StuGov; TchrAde; University; Law.

STINSON, Sharon L; Northern Heights HS; Reading, KS; SecJrCls; Band; HonRl; NHS; SchMus; SchPl; StuCncl; YthFlsp; PpCl; CaptChrldr; Kansas St Univ; Home Ec.

STINSON, Sherry L; Rolling Meadows HS; Arlington Heights, IL; 15/581 HonRl; Univ Of Illinois; Mathematics.

STIPEK, Donna; St Pius X HS; Kansas City, MO; 10/131 HonRl; SchMus; College; Law.

STIRWIMAN, John P; Minooka Community HS; Minooka, IL; 2/102 ALBoysSt; Band; CncrtBnd; HonRl; MrchBnd; NHS; Orch; SchPl; Bsktbl; LetterTrk; U Of Il; Engineering.

STISHER, Mickey D; North Putnam HS; Bainbridge, IN; 40/135 Band; Chr; ChrhWkr; CncrtBnd; MrchBnd; PepBnd; SchMus; TchrAde; YthFlsp; 4-H; Ball State U; Instrumental Music Teaching.

STITES, Jennifer E; Raytown HS; Raytown, MO; 2/650 ChrhWkr; HonRl; JrNHS; NatlFornLg; SecNHS; NatlThespSoc; SchPl; RptrYrbk; CivCl; FrCl; Univ; Special Ed Teacher.

STITES, Saundra L; Hill City HS; Wakeeney, KS; Chrs; HonRl; PepBnd; SchPl; PpCl; CaptBsktbl; LetterTrk; PPFtbl; Jr College; Business.

STITH, Debra K; Raytown HS; Raytown, MO; HonRl; SchPpr; Univ; English Teacher/writer.

STITH, Janet K; Tri County R 7 HS; Jamesport, MO; PresSrCls; Band; SchPl; StuCncl; Yrbk; SptEdSchPpr; Bsktbl; Trk; DARAwd; CitAwd; Accounting.

STITH, Leo H; Northwest HS; St Louis, MO; 45/513 Chr; HonRl; NHS; NatlMeritCmnd; MthCl; LetterBsbl; CaptSocr; IMSpt; Col; Accounting.

STITT, Doak C; Salina Central HS; Salina, KS; HonRl; CaptFtbl; Kansas St Univ; Veterinarian.

STITT, June A; Greenway HS; Bovey, MN; HonRl; HospAde; SchPpr; FrCl; PpCl; GAA; Itasca Comm Col; Acct.

STITTLEBURG, Kathryn M; Weston HS; Cazenovia, WI; SecJrCls; SecSrCls; HonRl; JrNHS; NatlFornLg; NHS; Quill&Scroll; EdYrBk; RptrSchPpr; Chrldr; Madison Tech Clge; Fashion Retailing.

STIVER, Cheryl A; Prospect HS; Mt Prospect, IL; 115/610 HonRl; HospAde; NHS; VPNatlThespSoc; SchMus; SchPl; SctActv; RusCl; PpCl; Western Illinois University.

STIVER, Dan J; Merrill HS; Merrill, WI; 26/400 ChrhWkr; HonRl; OffAde; SchAde; StuCncl; StuGov; RptrSchPpr; GerCl; LetterBsktbl; LetterFtbl; University Superior; Air Foruce.

ST JOHN, Ann; Waldron HS; Camden, MI; /50 Chrs; ChrhWkr; NHS; SchPl; YthFlsp; RptrYrbk; RptrSchPpr; FHA; Chrldr; Business; Major Study.

ST JOHN, Ann R; Waldron HS; Camden, MI; Chrs; ChrhWkr; HonRl; NHS; SchPl; RptrYrbk; RptrSchPpr; FHA; Business School.

ST JOHN, Denise C; Josephinum HS; Chicago, IL; HonRl; JA; NHS; SchPl; StuGov; College; Law Enforcement.

ST JOHN, Jody L; Lexington St Ann HS; Lexington, NE; Chrs; HonRl; HospAde; SchMus; SchPl; StuCncl; SpnCl; PpCl; Trk; Chrldr; College; Florist.

ST JOHN, Lori L; Cornell HS; Cornell, IL; Band; Chrs; Aud/Vis; HonRl; NHS; SchPl; RptrYrbk; EdSchPpr; SpnCl; LetterBsbl; Ill State U; Music.

ST JOHN, Marlene C; Bradley Bourbonnais Com HS; Bourbonnais, IL; ChrhWkr; CmntyWkr; HonRl; TchrAde; Yrbk; SchPpr; 4-HAwd; College; Home Economics.

ST JOHN, Roberta M; Cornell HS; Blackstone, IL; 12/29 SecFrshCls; SecJrCls; SecSrCls; PresBand; SecChrs; HonRl; SchPl; Yrbk; FHA; Chrldr; College; Music.

ST JOHN, Sandra K; Allegan HS; Allegan, MI; Band; ChrhWkr; CncrtBnd; HonRl; LbryAde; ModUN; NHS; SchMus; SchPl; PPFtbl; Univ Of Mi; Vetrinary Medicine.

ST JULIAN, Grant; Richwoods HS; Peoria, IL; VPSrCls; CmntyWkr; JA; NatlMeritSF; StuCncl; Bsktbl; Ftbl; Univ; Engineering.

ST LOUIS, Deidre S; Willowbrook HS; Villa Park, IL; 3/750 Chrs; HonRl; NHS; NatlMeritCmnd; SctActv; SchPpr; Univ Of Mich; Recreation.

ST LOUIS, Joann L; Rudyard HS; Rudyard, MI; 2/101 DrlTm; HonRl; NHS; SchPl; StuCncl; RptrYrbk; Chrldr; GAA; PPFtbl; BttyCrckrAwd; Univ; Home Ed.

ST MARIE, Dreux V; Appleton W HS; Appleton, WI; NatlMeritSF; LatCl; Ftbl; Univ Of Wi; Business Admin.

ST MARTIN, Edward J; Escanaba Area Public HS; Escanaba, MI; 72/383 College; Prof Artist.

STOCH, Monica A; Aurora Hoyt Lakes HS; Hoyt Lakes, MN; 22/227 Chrs; PresChrhWkr; CncrtBnd; HonRl; NHS; NatlThespSoc; SchMus; SchPl; SctActv; YthFlsp; MthCl; U Of Mn.

STOCK, Bonita J; Hoopeston East Lynn HS; Hoopeston, IL; 2/127 TrsSrCls; NHS; NatlMeritCmnd; StuCncl; EdYrBk; 4-H; KeyCl; FrCl; AmLegAwd; 4-HAwd; Mennonite Hosp School; Registered Nurse.

STOCK, Donna L; Prairie Home HS; Prairie Home, MO; TrsFrshCls; VPSophCls; PresJrCls; Chrs; DrlTm; HonRl; SchPl; StuCncl; RptrSchPpr; SptEdSchPpr; PresFHA; Bsbl; Bsktbl; College.

STOCK, Pamela S; Murdock C 7 HS; Murdock, NE; HstFrshCls; SecTrsSophCls; Chr; Chrs; ChrhWkr; DrlTm; LetterBsktbl; LetterTrk; Chrldr; 4-HAwd; College; Nursing.

STOCKDALE, Ian E; Ann Arbor Huron HS; Ann Arbor, MI; 72/570 Band; ChrhWkr; SctActv; YthFlsp; Univ Of Michigan; Physics.

STOCKDALE, Todd O; Leroy Ostrander HS; Chester, IA; CmntyWkr; HonRl; JCC; NHS; OffAde; SchPl; TchrAde; YthFlsp; RptrSchPpr; EdSchPpr; SchPpr; FFA; Bsbl; Ftbl; Business School; Agriculture.

STOCKER, Diane M; Albia Comm HS; Albia, IA; LetterBand; CncrtBnd; HonRl; MrchBnd; PepBnd; SchPl; PresFHA; SecFTA; Iowa St Univ; Child Development.

STOCKER, Yvonne S; Tipton HS; Tipton, IN; 10/195 ALAGirlsSt; HonRl; NHS; OffAde; VPStuCncl; VPYthFlsp; EdYrBk; PpCl; GAA; College; Medical.

STOCKHAM, Susan L; Bushnell Prairie City HS; Prairie City, IL; 18/100 Chr; Chrs; ChrhWkr; CmntyWkr; HonRl; PresYthFlsp; 4-H; FHA; PpCl; SciCl; GAA; 4-HAwd; Graham Hospital Schl Of Nrsg; Nurse.

STOCKLE, David A; Octavia HS; Colfax, IL; ChrhWkr; HonRl; SctActv; Bsbl; LetterBsktbl; LetterFtbl; Illinois Wesleyan University; Business.

STOCKLEY, Phyllis J; Serena Community HS; Serena, IL; 2/79 Band; CncrtBnd; HonRl; MrchBnd; NHS; SchPl; TchrAde; Yrbk; FrCl; PpCl; University; Professional.

STOCKMAN, Kay L; Waubay HS; Waubay, SD; 1/55 Band; Chr; Chrs; ChrhWkr; CncrtBnd; HonRl; HospAde; MrchBnd; PepBnd; SchPl; 4-H; FHA; FNA; GerCl; University; Electrical Engineering.

STOCKMAN, Terry A; Tippecanoe Valley HS; Claypool, IN; Aud/Vis; ChrhWkr; CmntyWkr; HonRl; SctActv; FrCl; LetterBsktbl; LetterFtbl; CchngActv; College; Retail Mgmt.

STOCKMANN, Paul T; St Marys HS; St Louis, MO; 8/180 HonRl; JrNHS; LitMag; NHS; SctActv; LetterFtbl; LetterTrk; IMSpt; OptClAwd; Univ Of Missouri; Veterinarian.

STOCKMEIER, Carole M; John Marshall HS; Milwaukee, WI; 5/711 Chrs; ChrhWkr; HonRl; LitMag; NHS; NatlMeritCmnd; SecYthFlsp; Yrbk; FHA; GerCl; U Of Wi Milwaukee; Geology.

STOCKMENT, Dianna L; Frontier HS; Chalmers, IN; 6/71 ALAGirlsSt; HonRl; NHS; NatlMeritCmnd; StuCncl; Yrbk; RptrSchPpr; 4-H; Chrldr; GAA; Coll; Nursing.

STOCKOWITZ, Joy E; Merrill Sr HS; Merrill, WI; Band; Chr; ChrhWkr; CncrtBnd; DrmMjrt; MrchBnd; SctActv; StuCncl; Trk; Chrldr; U W Marathon; Teacher Phy Ed Accounting.

STOCKS, Cheri L; Mt Zion HS; Dalton City, IL; 9/198 TrsSrCls; ChrhWkr; CncrtBnd; HonRl; NHS; StuCncl; 4-H; SciCl; CaptBsktbl; CaptChrldr; DanFAwd; 4-HAwd; Univ Of Ill; Medical Technician.

STOCKTON, Brent W; South Sioux City HS; South Sioux City, NE; 35/200 Band; CncrtBnd; HonRl; SchAde; StuCncl; SchPpr; Ftbl; Glf; Commercial Art Schl; Artist.

STOCKTON, Jerry L; West Chicago Comm HS; West Chicago, IL; 40/320 HonRl; NHS; Bsktbl; Ftbl; Baylor Univ; Dentistry.

STOCKTON, Karen S; Plainfield HS; Plainfield, IN; 9/260 Band; Chrs; CncrtBnd; HonRl; MrchBnd; NHS; Orch; PepBnd; StuCncl; In Univ; Medicine.

STODA, Francine L; Dekalb HS; Dekalb, IL; ChrhWkr; HonRl; HospAde; NHS; RptrYrbk; SpnCl; PpCl; Mesa Clg; Nursing.

STODDARD, Brian; Bath HS; Bath, MI; 4/79 PresSrCls; ALBoysSt; Band; HonRl; NHS; PepBnd; StuCncl; StuGov; TchrAde; Trk; Lansing Comm College; Pharmacy.

STODDARD, Donna; Cass Lake HS; Cass Lake, MN; 3/48 PresSophCls; PresJrCls; ChrhWkr; HonRl; SchPl; EdYrBk; SchPpr; FHA; Ftbl; Airline Stewardess.

STODDARD, Floyd; Mount Michael Benedictine HS; Mullen, NE; HonRl; NHS; Bsktbl; Trk; IMSpt; Univ; Doctor Of Veterinary Medicine.

STODDARD, Peggy; Plankinton Independant HS; Plankinton, SD; 1/26 ALAGirlsSt; Chrs; HonRl; NHS; SchPl; EdYrBk; FHA; Chrldr; College; Medical.

STODDARD, William J; Berlin HS; Berlin, WI; ALBoysSt; HonRl; JA; SctActv; SptEdSchPpr; CaptBsktbl; Ftbl; Glf; LetterTrk; JAAwd; College; Architecture.

STODGHILL, Robert S; Gibson Southern HS; Ft Branch, IN; Band; ChrhWkr; CncrtBnd; MrchBnd; PepBnd; PolWkr; SchPpr; PpCl; LetterFtbl; LetterTrk; Vincennes Univ; Funeral Director.

STOEBENER, Rose; Baldwin HS; Baldwin, KS; SecSrCls; ChrhWkr; DrlTm; HonRl; NHS; StuCncl; TchrAde; FHA; Secretary.

STOEGBAUER, Julie M; Winnebago Luth Acad; Fon Du Lac, WI; SecJrCls; Band; ChrhWkr; JA; NatlFornLg; StuCncl; Yrbk; EdSchPpr; Swmmng; Trk; College; Nursing.

STOEHR, Linda K; Seneca HS; Eastman, WI; 2/40 VPFrshCls; PresSophCls; Band; HonRl; JrNHS; NatlFornLg; SchPl; MthCl; Bsktbl; GAA; U Of Mn; Vetrinarian.

STOEHR, Peggy A; Berkeley Sr HS; Berkeley, MO; 10/294 Chr; HonRl; NHS; OffAde; SchPl;.

STOELB, Celia; North HS; Sheboygan, WI; HonRl; NHS; TchrAde; Bsktbl; Tennis; Chrldr; IMSpt;.

STOENNER, Martha; Washington Sr High; Wahsington, MO; Chr; HonRl; NHS; SchMus; TreasStuCncl; Yrbk; PresPpCl; U Mo Columbia ; Fashion Design.

STOETZEL, Barbara; Morton HS; Pekin, IL; Isu, Stewardess.

STOETZEL, Carol J; Maywood HS; North Platte, NE; 3/22 Chrs; ChrhWkr; HonRl; NHS; RptrYrbk; RptrSchPpr; 4-H; LetterTrk; 4-HAwd; Kearney St Col; Home Economics.

STOFFEL, Susan K; Leo HS; Rickardsville, IA; SecSophCls; HonRl; SchMus; RptrYrbk; RptrSchPpr; SpnCl; SciCl; LetterGlf; IMSpt; CitAwd; Area I Vocational Sch; Registered Nurse.

STOGA, Judith E; Marywood Academy; Grand Rapids, MI; Chr; HonRl; JA; JrNHS; NHS; NatlMeritCmnd; PolWkr; StuCncl; FrCl; Ftbl; Univ; Finance Mgmt.

STOGBAUER, Colleen M; Slinger HS; Hartford, WI; VPSophCls; Chrs; ChrhWkr; CmntyWkr; StuCncl; TchrAde; RptrSchPpr; SpnCl; Bsktbl; GAA; Coll; Physical Therapist.

STOGSDILL, James E; Collinsville HS; Collinsville, IL; 130/750 Aud/Vis; ChrhWkr; HonRl; Bsbl; Southern Illinois Univ; Civil Engineer.

STOGSDILL, Kathy L; Edgewood HS; Bloomington, IN; 4/167 TrsSrCls; Band; CncrtBnd; DrlTm; HonRl; MrchBnd; TreasNHS; PepBnd; FHA; PpCl; In St Univ; Nursing.

STOHLMANN, Dennis F; Louisville HS; Louisville, NE; 9/37 Band; CncrtBnd; HonRl; MrchBnd; PepBnd; SchPl; RptrYrbk; FrCl; Ftbl; Univ; Bus Admin.

STOHLMANN, Suzanne M; Murdock Consolidated HS; Murdock, NE; 2/18 SecJrCls; PresSrCls; Chrs; HonRl; SchMus; RptrYrbk; PpCl; Bsktbl; Chrldr; GAA; Univ Of Ne; Nurse.

STOHS, Luther E; Concordia Lutheran HS; Seward, NE; 5/54 HonRl; JrNHS; Orch; SctActv; Bsktbl; LetterTrk;.

STOIBER, William M; James Madison HS; Milwaukee, WI; ChrhWkr; HonRl; Bsbl; Bsktbl; Ftbl; College; Professional.

STOIKE, Nadine M; Lafayette Jefferson HS; Lafayette, IN; 67/607 ChrhWkr; HonRl; LitMag; OffAde; RptrSchPpr; 4-H; FHA; PpCl; Purdue Univ; Creative Writing.

STOIKES, Steven J; Sauk Prairie HS; Prairie Du Sac, WI; ALBoysSt; HonRl; SchPl; Ftbl; Wrstlng; College.

STOJEVICH, Anthony J; Morgan Park HS; Duluth, MN; 37/129 ChrhWkr; CmntyWkr; SctActv; RptrSchPpr; EdSchPpr; LetterFtbl; LetterTrk; Univ Mn Duluth.

STOKER, Debra J; Kirksville Sr HS; Kirksville, MO; SecTrsSophCls; ALAGirlsSt; Band; ChrhWkr; CncrtBnd; HonRl; MrchBnd; NHS; OffAde; Orch; PepBnd; Chrldr; Ne Missouri St Univ; History.

STOKER, Jill M; Murphysboro HS; Murphysboro, IL; ChrhWkr; CmntyWkr; HonRl; NHS; SctActv; StuCncl; StuGov; Twrl; YthFlsp; 4-H; SpnCl; SciCl; University; Language.

STOKES, David; Maconaguah HS; Grissom Afb, IN; ChrhWkr; NatlFornLg; SpnCl; Wrstlng; College; Ministry.

STOKES, David E; Brownstown Comm HS; Brownstown, IL; South Ill Univ; Medicine.

STOKES, Douglas L; Sunnydale Academy; Olivette, MO; 1/40 PresSophCls; Chr; HonRl; NHS; NatlMeritCmnd; Orch; EdYrBk; SchPpr; Union College; Physician.

STOKES, Gary J; Ridgefarm HS; Ridgefarm, IL; 1/32 PresFrshCls; VPSophCls; HonRl; NHS; RptrYrbk; SptEdYrbk; SchPpr; PresFFA; LetterBsktbl; CaptFtbl; LetterTrk; AmLegAwd; SARAwd; Davidson College; Law.

STOKES, John P; Holy Cross HS; Chicago, IL; HonRl; NatlMeritCmnd; Loyola Univ; Business Management.

STOKES, Keith; Kaneland Hs; Sugar Grove, IL; 5/162 Chr; HonRl; Mdrgl; NHS; NatlThespSoc; SchPl; YthFlsp; MthCl; Bsktbl; LetterFtbl; College; Commercial Airline Pilot.

STOKES, Nicholas P; Monroe Sr HS; Monroe, WI; ChrhWkr; HonRl; SctActv; Trk; Trade Sch; Diesel Mechanic.

STOKES, Tammy E; Assumption HS; Assumption, IL; Band; CncrtBnd; HonRl; MrchBnd; NHS; PepBnd; FrCl; College; Professional.

STOKES, Wanda A; Appleton City HS; Butler, MO; 1/45 AFS; Chr; Chrs; HonRl; LbryAde; NHS; SctActv; StuCncl; TchrAde; 4-H; Missouri State Coll; Med Tech.

STOKKE, Kristin M; Ellendale HS; New Richland, MN; PresSophCls; PresSrCls; HonRl; NHS; SchMus; SchPl; StuCncl; TchrAde; EdSchPpr; FTA; College; Art Therapy.

STOKKE, Sherry A; Watertown Sr HS; Watertown, SD; 3/297 ALAGirlsSt; HonRl; NatlFornLg; SecNHS; Quill&Scroll; SchMus; StuCncl; TchrAde; RptrYrbk; Swmmng; Tennis; Trk; GAA; South Dakota St Univ; Physical Educ.

STOKSTAD, Sara; Stoughton Senior HS; Stoughton, WI; ALAGirlsSt; HonRl; LitMag; NHS; SchPl; StuCncl; Univ;.

STOLARSKI, David J; St Francis De Sales HS; Chicago, IL; 1/296 JrNHS; NHS; NatlMeritSF; SchPl; StuCncl; EdYrBk; RptrSchPpr; LatCl; Tennis; Univ Of Michigan; Medicine.

STOLARZ, Jeannette J; Grand Haven HS; Grand Haven, MI; 19/388 Chr; ChrhWkr; HonRl; HospAde; JrNHS; NHS; NatlMeritFnl; SchPl; SctActv; 4-H; Mi Tech U; Computer Sci.

STOLCERS, Anita; Rockford East Hs; Rockford, IL; HonRl; NHS; SecOrch; SchMus; SchPl; Yrbk; SpnCl; U; Pharmacist.

STOLE, Morris R; Radcliffe Comm HS; Radcliffe, IA; Band; Chr; Chrs; CncrtBnd; HonRl; Mdrgl; MrchBnd; NHS; PepBnd; RptrSchPpr; Ia St U; Eleme Ed.

STOLEY, Cindy L; Aberdeen Central HS; Aberdeen, SD; AFS; Chr; Chrs; HonRl; Quill&Scroll; RptrYrbk; RptrSchPpr; PpCl; Trk; GAA; Univ; Professional Physical Therapy.

STOLFA, Ellen F; Marian Central HS; Cary, IL; 11/115 HonRl; NHS; NatlMeritSF; StuCncl; Yrbk; RptrSchPpr; College; Lawyer.

STOLINSKI, Karen M; Notre Dame HS; St Louis, MO; 13/110 Chrs; CmntyWkr; HospAde; NHS; OffAde; SchMus; TchrAde; RptrYrbk; PpCl; University; Med Tech.

STOLL, Andrew H; Chaminade HS; St Louis, MO; 47/117 CaptBsbl; CaptFtbl; IMSpt; College; Professional.

STOLL, Arletha N; Barr Reeve HS; Washington, IN; 10/75 HonRl; StuCncl; YthFlsp; FHA; LatCl; PpCl; Bsktbl; GAA; IMSpt; Coll; Nurse.

STOLL, Jean A; Unionville Sebewaing Area HS; Unionville, MI; 38/125 Chrs; HospAde; LbryAde; Yrbk; 4-H; FHA; FrCl; PpCl; GAA; 4-HAwd; College; Medicl Assistant.

STOLL, Koburn C; Brown HS; Piedmont, SD; 14/208 ALBoysSt; CmntyWkr; HonRl; PolWkr; StuGov; 4-H; GerCl; LetterFtbl; Trk; 4-HAwd; Clge; Nuclear Energy.

STOLL, Norma J; Humboldt HS; Humboldt, KS; 4/57 SecTrsJrCls; ChrhWkr; HonRl; NHS; SecStuCncl; SecFHA; Allen Co Comm College; Accounting.

STOLL, Scott B; Elwood HS; Elwood, NE; ChrhWkr; NHS; FFA; Bsbl; LetterBsktbl; LetterFtbl; University Of Nebraska; Agriculture.

STOLL, Veronica D; Barr Reeve HS; Washington, IN; ChrhWkr; HonRl; EdYrBk; SpnCl; PpCl; Bsktbl; College; Nursing.

STOLL, William; Pan American Christian Acad; Wheaton, IL; Chr; ChrhWkr; SchMus; SchPl; SciCl; Bsktbl; Swmmng; Trk; Wheaton Coll; Professional.

STOLLENWERK, Barbara L; Greendale HS; Greendale, WI; AFS; SctActv; SpnCl; PpCl; LetterBsktbl; LetterTrk; GAA; College; Phy Ed.

STOLLER, Allen S; Algoma HS; Algoma, WI; TrsFrshCls; TrsSophCls; Chrs; HonRl; Mdrgl; NHS; SchAde; SchMus; SctActv; StuGov; College; Accounting.

STOLLER, Ann M; Gridley HS; Gridley, IL; 4/40 SecSophCls; SecJrCls; AFS; Chrs; HonRl; SchMus; SctActv; StuCncl; YthFlsp; PpCl; GAA; Illinois State University.

STOLLER, Cynthia L; Kewaunee HS; Kewaunee, WI; 5/139 HonRl; LbryAde; NHS; Yrbk; FHA; GAA; Univ Of Wi; Medical.

STOLLER, Diane L; Gridley HS; Gridley, IL; Band; Chr; Chrs; HonRl; HospAde; SchMus; YthFlsp; SchPpr; FHA; GAA; Jr College; Business.

STOLS, Rita; Maria HS; Chicago, IL; 66/335 HospAde; JrNHS; NHS; KeyCl; GerCl; Loyola U; Chemistry.

STOLT, Carol M; Boyne City HS; Boyne City, MI; 7/126 HonRl; SchMus; TchrAde; 4-H; GerCl; Coll; Elem Teacher.

STOLTE, William K; Edwardsville HS; Edwardsville, IL; HonRl; StuCncl; LetterBsbl; Bsktbl; College.

STOLTENBERG, Martin A; Bergan HS; Fremont, NE; 15/50 CmntyWkr; HonRl; JA; SchPl; RptrYrbk; SchPpr; Ftbl; Trk; IMSpt; JAAwd; College; Professional.

STOLTENBERG, Mary L; North HS; Cleveland, WI; Band; Orch; Twrl; 4-H; FHA;.

STOLTENBERG, Nola; Iola Scandinavia Hs; Iola, WI; VPSophCls; Band; HonRl; MrchBnd; NHS; TreasStuCncl; EdYrBk; PresPpCl; LetterBsktbl; VPGAA; Uw La Crosse ; Recreation.

STOLTENBERG, Wendy M; Durant Comm HS; Walcott, IA; Band; Chrs; CncrtBnd; HonRl; JrNHS; MrchBnd; NHS; College; Music.

STOLTENBURG, Rodney R; Watertown Senior HS; Watertown, SD; 1/305 ALBoysSt; HonRl; NHS; FFA; College; Science.

STOLTZ, Carl R; Mt Vernon Twp HS; Mt Vernon, IL; 9/433 NHS; NatlMeritCmnd; Rend Lake Jr College; Engineering.

STOLTZ, Diane E; Reitz Memorial HS; Evansville, IN; 12/230 Chrs; ChrhWkr; CmntyWkr; HonRl; TchrAde; Indiana St Univ; Education.

STOLTZNER, Tara S; Arlington HS; Arlington Hts, IL; 32/585 HonRl; HospAde; TchrAde; Illinois State Univ; Med Technology.

STOLZ, John B; North Posey HS; Evansville, IN; 28/163 ChrhWkr; CmntyWkr; HonRl; NHS; Sacrstn; 4-H; Bsbl; Trk; Wrstlng; 4-HAwd; Trade School; Plumbing.

STOLZ, Susan J; Wauwatosa East HS; Wauwatosa, WI; 1/430 ALAGirlsSt; Chrl; HonRl; LitMag; NatlFornLg; NHS; NatlMeritSF; Orch; SchMus; MthCl; Carroll Col; Accounting.

STOLZ, Tom J; Carroll HS; Colwich, KS; ChrhWkr; HonRl; NatlMeritSchl; StuCncl; EdSchPpr; Bsbl; CchngActv; College.

STOLZE, Jeffrey A; Marion HS; Marion, IA; 26/179 ChrhWkr; CmntyWkr; HonRl; PolWkr; RedCrAde; StuCncl; StuGov; YthFlsp; RptrSchPpr; LetterBsbl; LetterBsktbl; Ftbl; LetterTrk; College; Professional.

STOMBAUGH, Steven E; South Newton Jr Sr HS; Goodland, IN; SchPl; TchrAde; RptrYrbk; EdSchPpr; FTA; PresGerCl; VPSciCl; Ftbl; Glf; In U; Business.

STOMBER, Laura A; Farmington HS; Farmington, MI; HstFrshCls; HstSophCls; HonRl; SchAde; StuCncl; RptrSchPpr; PpCl; Chrldr; IMSpt; PPFtbl; Mich State; Journ.

STOMMEL, Jennifer R; Highland HS; Highland, IN; PpCl; GAA; Business School; Professional.

STONE, Alice; New Hampton Comm HS; New Hampton, IA; Band; CncrtBnd; HonRl; MrchBnd; PepBnd; College;.

STONE, Bruce L; Marathon Consolidated HS; Marathon, IA; ChrhWkr; HonRl; NHS; SchPl; YthFlsp; Bsktbl; Ftbl; Trk; College; Engineering.

STONE, Chad H; Austin Catholic Prep; Grosse Pt Woods, MI; 24/135 HonRl; NHS; SctActv; U S Air Force Academy; Pilot.

STONE, Charles R; Marmion Military Academy; Saint Charles, IL; 3/89 Band; CncrtBnd; HonRl; NHS; ROTC; SctActv; Yrbk; SchPpr; College.

STONE, Connie R; Rosiclare HS; Rosiclare, IL; 3/46 Band; Chrs; ChrhWkr; CncrtBnd; HonRl; MrchBnd; RptrSchPpr; FHA; SpnCl; SciCl; Easter Il U; Acct.

STONE, Corliss C; Jerome Case HS; Racine, WI; TrsFrshCls; CmntyWkr; HonRl; NatlMeritSF; SchAde; SchPl; StuCncl; RptrSchPpr; Bsbl; Bsktbl; IMSpt; 4-HAwd; Mich St Univ; Law.

STONE, David; Williamsville HS; Williamsville, IL; 5/50 ChrhWkr; CmntyWkr; HonRl; Bsktbl; Trk; PresAwd; College; Engineering.

STONE, Debbie A; Risco HS; Lilbourn, MO; TrsSophCls; VPJrCls; ChrhWkr; HonRl; OffAde; SchPl; RptrYrbk; EdYrBk; FHA; Chrldr;.

STONE, Debbie M; Bucklin R 2 HS; Bucklin, MO; PresFrshCls; TrsSophCls; VPJrCls; CncrtBnd; HonRl; NHS; FHA; Bsktbl; Trk; Chrldr; Univ; Phy Therapist.

STONE, John R; Shiloh HS; Hume, IL; 11/38 ALBoysSt; ChrhWkr; HonRl; 4-H; FFA; LetterBsbl; LetterBsktbl; LetterTrk; 4-HAwd; Easter Ill Univ.

STONE, John W; Oscoda Area HS; Oscoda, MI; 17/240 ChrhWkr; NHS; StuCncl; Trk; Michigan State Univ.

STONE, Jolyn; Maine North Hs; Glenview, IL; 929 Chr; ChrhWkr; HonRl; HospAde; Orch; SchMus; VPYthFlsp; RptrSchPpr; U Of Illinois;nurse.

STONE, Kimberly; Heritage Christian HS; Indianapolis, IN; Chr; ChrhWkr; CncrtBnd; Orch; PepBnd; SchMus; TchrAde; GerCl; PpCl; Bob Jones University; Nursing.

STONE, Kimberly E; Stanton Comm HS; Stanton, IA; SecFrshCls; Band; Chr; Chrs; ChrhWkr; CmntyWkr; CncrtBnd; HonRl; Mdrgl; MrchBnd; LetterBsbl; LetterBsktbl; 4-HAwd; College; Nursing.

STONE, Leslie A; Bishop Ryan HS; Minot, ND; Band; Chr; Chrs; ChrhWkr; CncrtBnd; HonRl; MrchBnd; NHS; SchAde; SchMus; College; Prof Medicine.

STONE, Linda A; Elkhart Central HS; Elkhart, IN; Chr; HonRl; HospAde; SchMus; SchPl; StuCncl; Teen; 4-H; PpCl; Socr; Trk; Indiana Univ; Nursing.

STONE, Mark H; Ashwaubenon HS; Green Bay, WI; 44/202 HonRl; NHS; NatlMeritCmnd; PolWkr; RedCrAde; ROTC; RptrYrbk; PresKeyCl; U Of Wi; Politacal Sci.

STONE, Michael H; Flint Central HS; Flint, MI; HonRl; TchrAde; GerCl; Bsbl; IMSpt; Central Mi Univ; Broadcasting.

STONE, M R; Craig R Iii HS; Forest City, MO; PresJrCls; Band; Chrs; HonRl; StuCncl; FHA; PpCl; Bsktbl; Chrldr; College; Airline Stewardess.

STONE, Pamela A; Palestine HS; Palestine, IL; 5/50 Band; Chrs; CmntyWkr; HonRl; VPStuCncl; RptrSchPpr; EngCl; Chrldr; GAA; IMSpt; 4-HAwd; PresAwd; College; Lab Tech.

STONE, Scott; Valley HS; Des Moines, IA; 86/520 HonRl; Wrstlng; Iowa State Univ; Conservation.

STONE, Sheila; Southwestern HS; Detroit, MI; 9/150 VPSrCls; Chr; CmntyWkr; CncrtBnd; MrchBnd; SpnCl; PpCl; Bsbl; Mi St Univ; Professional.

STONE, Sherri L; Pacific HS; Pacific, MO; NatlThespSoc; SchMus; FTA; PpCl; College; History.

STONE, Shirley C; Deland Weldon HS; Weldon, IL; Band; Chrs; ChrhWkr; CncrtBnd; HonRl; MrchBnd; SchMus; SchPl; StuCncl; RptrYrbk; RptrSchPpr; 4-H; FHA; IMSpt; Cosmotology School; Cosmotologist.

STONE, Steven D; Southwestern HS; Detroit, MI; Band; CmntyWkr; Yrbk; FrCl; SciCl; Fisk Univ; Dentistry.

STONE, Terry; Northwest HS; Eureka, MO; TrsSophCls; Chr; DrlTm; LbryAde; PpCl; Chrldr; PresAwd; College; Professionakl.

STONE, Terry A; Newman Grove Public HS; Lindsay, NE; 11/42 Chr; Chrs; ChrhWkr; HonRl; LbryAde; SchPl; YthFlsp; 4-H; FFA; AmLegAwd; Trade School; Farming.

STONE, Thomas; 433 Vine Avenue Hs; Highland Park, IL; NHS; CaptSwmmng; BauchLmbAwd; University Of Rochester; Optice.

STONE, Wanda; Washington HS; Washington, KS; 4/42 ChrhWkr; CmntyWkr; HonRl; FBLA; FHA; PpCl; SciCl; AmLegAwd; CitAwd; Kansas State Univ; Home Ec.

STONE ARD, Donna F; Webber Township HS; Mt Vernon, IL; SchPl; StuCncl; RptrSchPpr; SecFBLA; GAA;.

STONEBRAKER, Cynthia C; Brown County HS; Columbus, IN; 6/201 SecSophCls; Chrs; DrlTm; HonRl; TchrAde; Twrl; 4-H; LatCl; PpCl; Indiana Univ; Medical Technology.

STONEBURG, Mary R; United Township HS; East Moline, IL; 4/570 Chr; Chrs; ChrhWkr; HonRl; JrNHS; SecNHS; NatlThespSoc; SchPl; RptrYrbk; SecFrCl; GAA; Illinois State Univ; Elementary Education.

STONECIPHER, Danna L; Parsons HS; Parsons, KS; DrlTm; NatlFornLg; NHS; SchAde; TchrAde; Yrbk; LatCl; Tennis; College; Psychology.

STONEHOCKER, Larry; Dexfield; Redfield, IA; ALBoysSt; ChrhWkr; CmntyWkr; HonRl; SctActv; Bsbl; Ftbl; Trk; College; Professional.

STONEKING, Michael S; Louisa Muscatine HS; Letts, IA; 16/51 HonRl; Wrstlng; Farming.

STONEKING, Nancy L; Dekalb HS; Corunna, IN; NatlFornLg; SchMus; SchPl; 4-H; College; Engineering.

STONER, James H; Senn HS; Chicago, IL; 13/500 DrmBgl; HonRl; NHS; SchMus; MthCl; LetterBsbl; LetterBsktbl; LetterGlf; IMSpt; CitAwd; College; Professional.

STONER, Patricia S; Kickapoo HS; Springfield, MO; SecFrshCls; CmntyWkr; HonRl; TchrAde; PresFHA; College; Home Economics.

STONER, Patrick; Pius Xi HS; Milwaukee, WI; NHS; StuGov; TchrAde; SptEdYrbk; Yrbk; FTA; Bsbl; Bsktbl; U Of Wis Eau Claire; Acct.

STONES, Kristine A; Hancock Central HS; Hancock, MI; PresChrhWkr; CmntyWkr; HonRl; SchPl; Trk; GAA; IMSpt; Brigham Young Univ; Professional Artist.

STONG, Debra A; Ankeny HS; Ankeny, IA; 11/223 Chr; Chrs; ChrhWkr; CmntyWkr; HonRl; JrNHS; LitMag; NHS; SchMus; SchPl; PresYthFlsp; Trk; 4-HAwd; College; English Teacher.

ST ONGE, Kevin L; Rudyard HS; Trout Lake, MI; 26/104 Band; Chrl; Chrs; CncrtBnd; HonRl; Mdrgl; MrchBnd; Oakland Univ; Political Science.

STONUEY, Joseph F; Gibbon HS; Gibbon, NE; TchrAde; Yrbk; SchPpr; University Of Nebraska; Fashion Design.

STOODY, Jocelyn L; Fenton HS; Holly, MI; HonRl; LitMag; NHS; SchMus; University.

STOOPS, Lenore; St Mary Acad; Indianapolis, IN; TrsSrCls; Chrs; HonRl; SchPl; Yrbk; SpnCl; BauchLmbAwd; Iupui In; Child Education.

STOOPS, Lillian; St Mary Academy; Indianapolis, IN; ALAGirlsSt; Chrs; HonRl; NHS; EdYrBk; GerCl; GAA; I S U ; Pre School Ed.

STOPPELMOOR, Cynthia; Clarksville HS; Clarksville, IA; 3/36 SchPl; StuCncl; Yrbk; DanFAwd; Ocupational Or Physical Therapy.

STORCK, Thomas J; Ste Gen Public HS; Ste Genevieve, MO; Chrs; HonRl; LbryAde; SchMus; Trk; College; Pharmacist.

STORDAHL, Mark; Moorhead Sr HS; Moorlead, MN; 10/560 Chr; ChrhWkr; LitMag; HonRl; MrchBnd; Orch; PepBnd; IMSpt; College; Ministry.

STOREY, Euea J; Glendale HS; Springfield, MO; AFS; OffAde; StuCncl; YthFlsp; RptrSchPpr; FBLA; FHA; PpCl; SciCl; Smsu; Fashion Designer.

STOREY, Gary L; Woodward Granger HS; Woodard, IA; 8/54 ALBoysSt; ChrhWkr; HonRl; PolWkr; YthFlsp; RptrYrbk; RptrSchPpr; SchPpr; LetterBsbl; Bsktbl; LetterTrk; Wrstlng; Nw Mo State; Accounting.

STOREY, Valerie D; Robert A Waller HS; Chicago, IL; 8/214 PresFrshCls; Band; Chrs; HonRl; SchMus; StuCncl; RptrYrbk; SptEdSchPpr; Macmurray; Special Education.

STORIE, Lisa; English HS; Taswell, IN; 5/36 Chr; NHS; VPSophCls; 4-H; FrCl; Chrldr; Ind Univ; Med.

STORJOHANN, Lisa D; Sturgis HS; Sturgis, SD; ALAGirlsSt; Chr; HonRl; NatlFornLg; NHS; NatlThespSoc; SchPpr; GerCl; SpnCl;.

STORK, Theresa L; Effingham HS; Effingham, IL; 47/215 LbryAde; SctActv; LatCl; Trk; College; Engineering.

STORKEL, Karen J; Evergreen Park HS; Evergreen Park, IL; 1/439 ALAGirlsSt; CncrtBnd; MrchBnd; NHS; Orch; PepBnd; PresGerCl; MthCl; PpCl; GAA; Univ Of Illinois; Business Administration.

STORM, Bradley W; Mattoon Sr HS; Mattoon, IL; TrsFrshCls; HonRl; NHS; SctActv; StuCncl; Yrbk; LetterBsbl; Swmmng; Tennis; IMSpt; University; Professional.

STORMBERG, Kim M; St Patricks HS; Sidney, NE; VPSophCls; Chrs; HonRl; NHS; SchMus; SchPl; RptrYrbk; Yrbk; RptrSchPpr; College.

STORMENT, Kim S; Salem Comm HS; Salem, IL; 1/203 Chr; Chrs; ChrhWkr; JrNHS; NHS; SchMus; SchPl; TchrAde; Graceland College; Secondary Education.

STORMO, Keith E; Watertown HS; Hayti, SD; 20/310 ALBoysSt; Chrs; PresChrhWkr; NHS; StuGov; Trk; College; Oceanography.

STORNICK, Cindy L; Chisholm HS; Chisholm, MN; Chr; HonRl; HospAde; LbryAde; OffAde; RptrSchPpr; FNA; PpCl; IMSpt; PresAwd; Coll; Nurse.

STORTZ, Susan B; Mount Assisi Acad; Chicago Ridge, IL; Chrs; HonRl; NHS; StuCncl; Teen; IMSpt; AmLegAwd; Teacher Or Stewardess.

STORY, Ann D; Normandy HS; St Louis, MO; 41/495 HonRl; JrNHS; YthFlsp; College; Interior Designer.

STORY, Dawn M; Hancock Central HS; Hancock, MI; 13/90 HstSophCls; HonRl; NatlMeritCmnd; NatlMeritSF; SchPl; YthFlsp; RptrYrbk; SpnCl;.

STORY, Vicki L; Liberty HS; Birch Tree, MO; 6/112 Band; HonRl; HospAde; MrchBnd; NHS; PepBnd; SchMus; RptrYrbk; FHA; VoiceDemAwd; Burge Sch Of Nursing; Nursing.

STOSIK, Sue A; Garber HS; Essexville, MI; 9/180 Chr; HonRl; NatlFornLg; NatlMeritCmnd; PolWkr; TchrAde; PpCl; VoiceDemAwd; Univ Of Mi; English Or Psych.

STOTLER, Mary A; Metamora HS; Metamora, IL; TrsJrCls; AFS; ALAGirlsSt; NHS; Quill&Scroll; SchMus; EdYrBk; GAA; DanFAwd; Ill St U; Teaching.

STOTLER, Tina M; Civic Memorial HS; Bethalto, IL; 10/221 SecFrshCls; SecSophCls; TrsJrCls; SecSrCls; ChrhWkr; HonRl; JrNHS; NHS; OffAde; SchPl; SctActv; Chrldr; Lewis & Clark Comm Coll; Accounting.

STOTT, Cynthia L; Dupo Community HS; Dupo, IL; 24/110 VPFrshCls; ChrhWkr; HonRl; ModUN; NHS; FTA; SciCl; Trk; GAA; AmLegAwd; Univ; Special Ed.

STOTT, Gary W; Athens Comm HS; Athens, IL; 3/54 TrsJrCls; Band; CncrtBnd; HonRl; NHS; RptrYrbk; SecKeyCl; Bsbl; Bsktbl; Glf; AmLegAwd; College; Engineering.

STOTTLEMYRE, Danny; Houston HS; Houston, MO; 16/113 Chrs; ChrhWkr; CmntyWkr; HonRl; NHS; OffAde; SchPl; School Of The Ozarks; Teaching.

STOTTLEMYRE, Denise A; Trenton HS; Spickard, MO; AFS; Band; ChrhWkr; MrchBnd; NHS; StuCncl; PpCl; LetterTrk; Chrldr; GAA; Col.

STOTTLEMYRE, Tammy C; Putnam Co Ri HS; Unionville, MO; Band; ChrhWkr; CncrtBnd; HonRl; MrchBnd; StuCncl; Twrl; Centerville; Business Manage.

STOTTS, David E; Savannah HS; Savannah, MO; Band; Chr; CncrtBnd; MrchBnd; SchMus; SctActv; Yrbk; LetterFtbl; LetterTrk; AmLegAwd; GodCntryAwd; College; Vocation.

STOTTS, Mari C; Frontenac HS; Frontenac, KS; ALAGirlsSt; HonRl; OffAde; SchPl; SctActv; PresStuCncl; Yrbk; TreasFHA; SpnCl; PpCl; Trk; CaptChrldr; DARAwd; Kansas State College; Accounting.

STOUDT, Liz M; Morrison Comm HS; Morrison, IL; 4/120 AFS; HonRl; PolWkr; SecStuCncl; AmLegAwd; College.

STOUFFER, William K; La Moille Comm HS; La Moille, IL; 12/41 PresJrCls; HonRl; SchMus; RptrYrbk; RptrSchPpr; FrCl; PpCl; Bsktbl; Ftbl; Trk; Eureka College.

STOUGH, Kevin D; Normal Comm HS; Normal, IL; 43/443 Band; CncrtBnd; HonRl; LbryAde; MrchBnd; NHS; Orch; PepBnd; SctActv; StuCncl; PresYthFlsp; FrCl; Tennis; Univ Of Ill; Liberal Arts.

STOUT, Barbara J; Lamberton HS; Lamberton, MN; Band; Chr; Chrs; ChrhWkr; CncrtBnd; DrlTm; HonRl; MrchBnd; PepBnd; PolWkr; SchPl; StuCncl; TchrAde; GAA; College; Interior Design.

STOUT, Beth J; Raytown HS; Raytown, MO; Chr; ChrhWkr; HonRl; NatlThespSoc; SchMus; SchPl; PpCl; IMSpt; University; Performing Arts.

STOUT, Bonnie S; Hoisington Senior HS; Hoisington, KS; HonRl; OffAde; SctActv; PpCl; Barton Co Comm Jr College; Secretary.

STOUT, Claire D; Hagerstown Jr Sr HS; Greens Fork, IN; 8/119 ChrhWkr; HonRl; LbryAde; NHS; TreasFHA; LetterTrk;.

STOUT, Dianne; Northridge HS; Middlebury, IN; Band; Chr; DrlTm; HonRl; NHS; PepBnd; PpCl; Coll; Sec.

STOUT, John P; Lincoln East HS; Lincoln, NE; VPJrCls; ALBoysSt; Chrs; ChrhWkr; JA; JrNHS; Orch; StuCncl; CaptFtbl; LetterTrk; IMSpt; University; Medicine.

STOUT, Kathy S; Kingsville HS; Kingsville, MO; 12/22 Band; Chrs; HonRl; NHS; PepBnd; SchPl; RptrYrbk; PpCl; LetterBsktbl; CitAwd; Central Mo State U; Agricultural Bus.

STOUT, Larry D; Winterset Comm HS; Lorimor, IA; HonRl; NatlMeritSchl; Teen; FFA; Ryder Tech Inst.

STOUT, Lisa A; Porta HS; Petersburg, IL; DrlTm; LbryAde; MrchBnd; SchMus; YthFlsp; SchPpr; Chrldr; SecGAA; IMSpt; College.

STOUT, Phillip; Hannibal HS; Hannibal, MO; 32/212 HonRl; StuCncl; LetterBsbl; Bsktbl; IMSpt; BttyCrckrAwd;.

STOUT, Sheila M; Huntington North HS; Huntington, IN; 29#33#46 MrchBnd; PepBnd; SchMus; YthFlsp; GerCl; Bsktbl; GAA; Col; Practical Nurse.

STOUT, Trena J; Crothersville HS; Crothersville, IN; 11/75 Chr; Chrs; ChrhWkr; HospAde; NHS; SchMus; SchPl; TchrAde; Yrbk; 4-H; FHA; PpCl; SciCl; College; Professional.

STOUTLAND, Linda K; Lamberton HS; Lamberton, MN; 11/47 Band; Chr; SchPl; StuCncl; RptrYrbk; RptrSchPpr; FHA; FTA; Chrldr; GAA; Willmar Comm College; Counseling.

STOVALL, Donald L; Desmet Jesuit HS; Kinloch, MO; CmntyWkr; HonRl; JA; NatlMeritSF; LetterTrk; IMSpt; College; Business.

STOVALL, Gavin D; Academy Of The Sacred Heart; Chicago, IL; 2/50 HonRl; LitMag; NHS; SchPl; SchPpr; Chrldr; Scripps College; Foreign Relations.

STOVER, Leonard G; Dowagiac Union HS; Dowagiac, MI; 70/198 AFS; SctActv; StuCncl; 4-H; LetterBsbl; LetterBsktbl; CaptFtbl; LetterTrk; IMSpt; 4-HAwd; JAAwd; Hillsdale College; Business.

STOVFFER, Charles D; Avondale HS; Auburn Heights, MI; Band; ChrhWkr; HonRl; LitMag; MrchBnd; PepBnd; SchMus; SchPl; StuGov; CaptTrk; Mich Tech Univ; Mechanical Engineer.

STOVNER, Kregg B; North Sr HS; Eau Claire, WI; 23/376 SecChr; HonRl; Mdrgl; NHS; TreasNatlThespSoc; PresOrch; SchMus; SchPl; RptrSchPpr; LetterTennis; Univ Of Wis; Violinist.

STOWELL, Joan A; Crown Point HS; Crown Point, IN; CmntyWkr; HonRl; NHS; SchPl; StuCncl; PpCl; Chrldr; GAA; IMSpt; Purdue University; Mechanical Engineer.

STOWERS, Debra L; Marion Adams HS; Sheridan, IN; 5/99 Chr; HonRl; JrNHS; YthFlsp; 4-H; FHA; LatCl; College; Nursing.

STOWERS, Jody L; Washington Twp HS; Valparaiso, IN; TrsFrshCls; HonRl; SchPl; StuCncl; TchrAde; RptrSchPpr; VP4-H; CaptBsktbl; Trk; CchngActv; GAA; IMSpt; DanFAwd; Purdue Univ; Recreational Therapy.

STOXEN, Julie M; Hampshire HS; Hampshire, IL; 8/70 PresJrCls; PresSrCls; Chrs; NHS; SchMus; StuCncl; 4-H; FHA; LetterTrk; GAA; 4-HAwd; Univ Of Illinois; Business.

STOY, Michael A; Benet Academy; Woodridge, IL; 8/239 HonRl; NHS; NatlMeritSchl; IMSpt; GovHonPrgAwd; Washinton Univ; Medicine.

STOY, Stacey; Hamilton HS; Hamilton, IN; 17/60 ChrhWkr; HonRl; MrchBnd; SchAde; StuCncl; 4-H; FHA; GAA; 4-HAwd; MasAwd; Nursing School; Nursing.

STOYANOFF, James V; West HS; Waterloo, IA; YthFlsp; LetterTrk; LetterWrstlng; Univ Of Iowa.

ST PETER, Roy J; Wabeno HS; Wabeno, WI; 14/33 HonRl; FBLA; PpCl; LetterBsktbl; Milwaukee Area Tech Col; Visual Commctns.

ST PIERRE, Denise M; Herscher HS; Herscher, IL; 1/152 Chrs; HonRl; SchPl; Meridian Jr College; Singer.

STRAATMANN, Julie F; Holdrege HS; Holdrege, NE; Band; Chrs; CncrtBnd; HonRl; MrchBnd; PepBnd; SchMus; RptrYrbk; RptrSchPpr; PpCl; Univ; Law.

STRABALA, Elizabeth J; Highland Comm HS; Riverside, IA; 1/50 Chrs; ChrhWkr; HonRl; VPNHS; SchMus; RptrYrbk; SchPpr; SpnCl; Iowa State.

STRABALA, Elizabeth; Highland HS; Riverside, IA; 1/48 Chrs; HonRl; SchMus; RptrYrbk; SpnCl; PpCl; BttyCrckrAwd; Iowa St Univ.

STRACEY, Valerie J; Alden Hebron HS; Alden, IL; 24/42 HonRl; LbryAde; SchPl; TchrAde; CchngActv; University; Geology.

STRACK, Jonathan; Cathedral HS; St Cloud, MN; RotaryAwd;.

STRADLEY, Robert E; Des Moines East HS; Des Moines, IA; VPSophCls; StuCncl; StuGov; Bsbl; LetterFtbl; Swmmng; Trk; IMSpt; College; Liberal Arts.

STRADTNER, Lori K; Wyoming Park HS; Wyoming, MI; 2/238 ChrhWkr; HonRl; NHS; SchPl; StuCncl; StuGov; FrCl; PpCl; GAA; AmLegAwd; DanFAwd; EldAwd; Central Michigan Univ; Social Work.

STRAETER, Loraine R; Mater Dei HS; Breese, IL; 17/198 Chrs; ChrhWkr; CncrtBnd; HonRl; MrchBnd; PepBnd; SchMus; SchPpr; FrCl; AmLegAwd; Clge.

STRAGAPEDE, Maria; Josephinum HS; Chicago, IL; 4/104 CmntyWkr; HonRl; Univ Of Illinois; Accounting.

STRAHANOSKI, Kimberly; Lockport Central HS; Lockport, IL; HonRl; NHS; EdYrBk; GAA; Joliet Jr Coll; Sec.

STRAHOTA, Richard L; Iowa Grant HS; Cobb, WI; VPFrshCls; VPJrCls; Band; Chr; Chrs; CncrtBnd; HonRl; MrchBnd; NatlThespSoc; Orch; Uw Platteville; Political Science.

STRAIN, John C; Edinburg Community HS; Edinburg, IN; 4/65 PresChr; ChrhWkr; CmntyWkr; HonRl; NHS; SchPl; Trk; AmLegAwd; College; Art.

STRAIN, Kathleen A; Munster HS; Munster, IN; Chr; Chrs; CmntyWkr; HonRl; YthFlsp; College; Doctor.

STRAIT, Barbara A; Cornell HS; Cornell, WI; 1/57 SecSophCls; ChrhWkr; HonRl; SchPl; SecSchPpr; PpCl; Bsktbl; Trk; Chrldr; GAA; College Or Univ; Science & Math.

STRAIT, Davena L; High School; Keosauqua, IA; Band; ChrhWkr; CncrtBnd; MrchBnd; RedCrAde; 4-H; PpCl; Chrldr; PPFtbl; Business Sch;.

STRAIT, Harold E; Owensville HS; Gerald, MO; HonRl; YthFlsp; KeyCl; PpCl; LetterFtbl; College; Professional.

STRAIT, Janese K; Battle Creek Comm HS; Danbury, IA; 4/23 SecTrsJrCls; ChrhWkr; HonRl; SchPl; YthFlsp; SptEdSchPpr; PpCl; Bsbl; Bsktbl; Chrldr; Col.

STRAIT, Richard A; Highland Park HS; St Paul, MN; 28/550 Band; CncrtBnd; NatlMeritSF; PepBnd; GerCl; Socr; IMSpt; College; Professional.

STRAKA, Gary L; No St Paul Senior HS; North St Paul, MN; JA; NatlSciFnd; TchrAde; RptrYrbk; RptrSchPpr; U Of M Institute Of Tech; Sales Engineer.

STRAKA, Mike K; Atkinson West Holt HS; Atkinson, NE; 16/80 TrsFrshCls; VPSophCls; TrsJrCls; Chr; Chrs; HonRl; NHS; SchPl; Bsktbl; Ftbl; College; Teacher.

STRAMA, Kim; Medford Senior HS; Medford, WI; 4/20 SecSrCls; ALAGirlsSt; CncrtBnd; HonRl; MrchBnd; NHS; StuCncl; SpnCl; DARAwd; CitAwd; Uw River Falls; Pre Veterinary.

STRAMEL, Jean; Hays HS; Hays, KS; 43/191 Band; CncrtBnd; HonRl; MrchBnd; SchMus; StuCncl; TchrAde; SciCl; Tennis; IMSpt; Fort Hays Ks St Coll; Bio.

STRAMEL, Karlene K; Diamond R 4 HS; Diamond, MO; 3/57 TrsJrCls; Band; HonRl; ModUN; NHS; OffAde; StuCncl; RptrYrbk; RptrSchPpr; FHA; MthCl; Business School; Vocation.

STRAMICH, Rita H; Carmel Girls HS; Mundelein, IL; 7/173 Chrs; HonRl; JrNHS; NHS; OffAde; SchMus; SchPl; SecGerCl; University; Professional.

STRANATHAN, Carol; Appelton West HS; Appleton, WI; 30/640 PpCl; Eau Claire Univ; Special Education.

STRAND, Dawn E; Washburn HS; Minneapolis, MN; Band; ChrhWkr; LbryAde; NatlFornLg; PolWkr; SchAde; SchMus; MthCl; PpCl; IMSpt; Univ; Law.

STRAND, Duane D; Richland HS; Wahpeton, ND; 3/28 ALBoysSt; Band; HonRl; RptrSchPpr; Treas4-H; LetterBsktbl; LetterFtbl; 4-HAwd; College.

STRAND, Eric J; Muskegon HS; Muskegon, MI; HonRl; FrCl; Ftbl; LetterTennis; Wrstlng; Nw Mich; Maritime Serv.

STRAND, Judy M; Halstad HS; Shelly, MN; 7/22 PresJrCls; Chrs; NatlThespSoc; StuGov; Yrbk; RptrSchPpr; FFA; FHA; Trk; Univ Of Mn; Horticulture.

STRAND, Keither A; Green Lake Public HS; Green Lake, WI; TrsSophCls; Aud/Vis; Chr; Chrs; ChrhWkr; HonRl; RedCrAde; SchPl; RptrSchPpr; Ftbl; Wrstlng; College; Math.

STRAND, Mark O; Centennial HS; Circle Pines, MN; Band; NHS; PepBnd; StuCncl; LetterTennis; College; Professional.

STRAND, Rebecca C; Central HS; Chebanse, IL; Chr; HonRl; NHS; MthCl; College; Teacher.

STRAND, Scott R; Ada Jr Sr HS; Ada, MN; 1/59 LbryAde; PresNatlFornLg; NHS; NatlMeritSF; PresNatlThespSoc; PolWkr; SchPl; PresStuCncl; ChmnRptrYrbk; RptrSchPpr; Univ Of Mn; Pre Law.

STRAND, William R; Mounds View HS; St Paul, MN; 5/673 ChrhWkr; CncrtBnd; NHS; NatlMeritSF; SctActv; StuCncl; LetterSocr; LetterTrk; 4-HAwd; VoiceDemAwd; Univ; Medicine.

STRANDE, Dianne L; Redfield Public HS; Redfield, SD; SchMus; SchPl; SctActv; TchrAde; YthFlsp; FHA; FTA; PpCl; Tennis; Trk; Sdsu; Physical Education.

STRANDEMO, Jill; Mahnomen HS; Mahnomen, MN; Band; Chr; Chrs; HonRl; MrchBnd; PepBnd; SchMus; StuCncl; PpCl; College.

STRANDLUND, Gary; Huntington North HS; Huntington, IN; 11/522 Band; LitMag; SchPpr; MthCl; SciCl; College; Literature.

STRANG, Barbara L; Richland Center HS; Richland Center, WI; 50/185 Band; ChrhWkr; CncrtBnd; HonRl; HospAde; MrchBnd; PepBnd; SchPl; GAA; BttyCrckrAwd; Uw Eau Claire; Med Tech.

STRANG, Nancy K; North Greene HS; White Hall, IL; VPFrshCls; VPSophCls; PresJrCls; HonRl; NHS; Yrbk; FFA; Trk; CaptWrstlng; IMSpt; Univ Of Il; Agriculture.

STRANG, Trinda J; Richland Center HS; Richland Center, WI; Chrs; HonRl; HospAde; LbryAde; NatlFornLg; Treas4-H; FBLA; FHA; 4-HAwd; College.

STRANGBERG, Sharon L; St Joseph HS; Kenosha, WI; 8/140 Chrs; HonRl; PpCl; Univ ; Nursing.

STRANGE, Daniel K; Salem HS; Salem, IN; Band; MrchBnd; College; Computer Tech.

STRANGE, Pamela S; West Washington HS; Salem, IN; Band; ChrhWkr; CncrtBnd; HonRl; MrchBnd; OffAde; PepBnd; SchPl; TchrAde; YthFlsp;.

STRANGE, Shelley A; Cardinal Ritter HS; Brownsburg, IN; 19/151 DrmMjrt; HonRl; MrchBnd; NHS; SchMus; SchPl; StuGov; TchrAde; PresSpnCl; Vincennes U; Secretarial.

STRANGEWAY, Robert; Rice Lake Senior HS; Rice Lake, WI; 2/265 NHS; 4-H; BauchLmbAwd; Milwarkee Sch Of Engrg; Chem.

STRANSKI, Harry S; Mt Vernon HS; Mt Vernon, IL; 27/437 TrsFrshCls; SecSophCls; SecJrCls; PresSrCls; StuCncl; LetterBsbl; CaptBsktbl; CaptFtbl; Northwestern Univ; Natural Science.

STRANSKY, Timothy J; Marian HS; Owatonna, MN; 15/55 TrsSrCls; Chrl; Chrs; ChrhWkr; CmntyWkr; HonRl; SchMus; SchPl; StuCncl; St Johns Univ.

STRANTZ, Susan E; E Peoria Comm HS; E Peoria, IL; 13/450 HospAde; NHS; SctActv; RptrYrbk; FrCl; Illinois Central College; Business Admin.

STRAS, Betty; Rothsay Public HS; Rothsay, MN; ALAGirlsSt; Chrs; CtyCnl; HonRl; NHS; YthFlsp; GAA; Vocational/technical School;vocation/profes.

STRASBURGER, Jeannette C; Adlai Stevenson HS; Sterling Hgts, MI; HonRl; NHS; GerCl; U Of Michigan; Dental Hygienist.

STRASSBURG, Steven M; Perry Community HS; Perry, IA; HonRl; NHS; Quill&Scroll; SchPl; SctActv; StuCncl; RptrSchPpr; Glf; Wrstlng; Ia State U; Architect.

STRASSER, Robert K; Forestview HS; Mt Prospect, IL; CmntyWkr; HonRl; Quill&Scroll; RptrSchPpr; KeyCl; Bsbl; Bsktbl; Ftbl; LetterTrk; St Olaf College; Medicine.

STRATE, Marilyn B; Norfolk Sr HS; Hoskins, NE; ALAGirlsSt; ChrhWkr; HonRl; HospAde; NHS; YthFlsp; 4-H; PpCl; LetterTrk; DARAwd; 4-HAwd; College.

STRATELAK, Gerard A; Grosse Pointe North HS; Grosse Pointe, MI; HonRl; NHS; IMSpt; College; Professional.

STRATEMEYER, David A; West Platte HS; Farley, MO; Band; CncrtBnd; HonRl; MrchBnd; NHS; PepBnd; LetterBsbl; LetterBsktbl; LetterFtbl; Trk; Coll; Engineering.

STRATEMEYER, Karen S; Metropolis Comm HS; Metropolis, IL; 15/148 PresChrhWkr; HonRl; HospAde; NHS; StuCncl; YthFlsp; SchPpr; Murray Univ; Nurse.

STRATHMAN, Daniel K; Norborne HS; Norborne, MO; HonRl; NHS; SchPl; FrCl; Bsktbl; LetterFtbl; IMSpt; DanFAwd; U Of Mo Columbia; Bus Mang.

STRATHMAN, Susan J; Hayden HS; Topeka, KS; 4/200 HonRl; HospAde; JrNHS; NHS; SchMus; SctActv; StuCncl; FDA; PpCl; Trk; Benedictine College; Doctor.

STRATMAN, Anne; Jasper HS; Jasper, IN; Band; CncrtBnd; HonRl; MrchBnd; PepBnd; Purdue Univ; Nursing.

STRATMAN, Charles; St Pius X HS; Kansas City, MO; ChrhWkr; JA; ModUN; ROTC; SctActv; StuGov; Yrbk; FBLA; JAAwd; RotaryAwd; College; Professional.

STRATMAN, Kenneth R; Aurora Central HS; Aurora, IL; 1/165 Band; CncrtBnd; HonRl; Orch;.

STRATMAN, Marvin S; Malden HS; Malden, MO; HonRl; SchPpr; PpCl; Three Rivers Jr Clg; Agriculture.

STRATMANN, Deborah L; Dupo HS; E Carondelet, IL; 1/110 ALAGirlsSt; HonRl; ModUN; NHS; StuCncl; TchrAde; Yrbk; MthCl; Trk; IMSpt; University; Mathematics.

STRATTON, Deborah L; Otsego HS; Otsego, MI; 28/227 Chr; Chrs; ChrhWkr; HonRl; NHS; SchMus; VPYthFlsp; 4-H; LatCl; PpCl; Northern Michigan Univ; Nursing.

STRATTON, Donald E; Hill Mccloy HS; Clio, MI; 4/140 Chr; CncrtBnd; HonRl; MrchBnd; NHS; NatlMeritCmnd; SchPl; LetterBsktbl; Rose Hulman Inst Of Techn; Professional.

STRATTON, Donald J; Ben Davis HS; Indianpolis, IN; Band; CncrtBnd; HonRl; YthFlsp; LetterBsktbl; LetterTrk; College; Professional.

STRATTON, Earleen R; Frankfort HS; Elberta, MI; Chrs; HonRl; HospAde; LbryAde; SchPl; Yrbk; Bsktbl; Trk; GAA; IMSpt; Army; Medicine.

STRATTON, Kenneth R; Truman HS; Independence, MO; Band; CncrtBnd; JA; MrchBnd; SctActv; StuCncl; Ftbl; Trk; Wrstlng; IMSpt; Clge.

STRATTON, Monty E; Weeping Water Public HS; Weeping Water, NE; ALBoysSt; Band; Chr; ChrhWkr; Mdrgl; SchMus; SchPl; StuGov; College.

STRATZ, Susan C; Minooka Comm HS; Minooka, IL; VPSophCls; HonRl; JrNHS; NHS; SchPl; Yrbk; RptrSchPpr; 4-H; LetterSocr; Trk; BttyCrckrAwd; DanFAwd; College; Art.

STRAUB, Laura A; Tinley Pk HS; Tinley Pk, IL; 38/350 Band; CncrtBnd; HonRl; JrNHS; MrchBnd; NHS; NatlMeritCmnd; College; Art.

STRAUBE, Jim; Nemaha Valley HS; Sterling, NE; 15/34 ALBoysSt; HonRl;.

STRAUBE, Lee H; Nemaha Valley HS; Sterling, NE; Chrs; HonRl; SchPl;.

STRAUBE, Ruth; Sterling HS; Sterling, NE; /22 VPSrCls; Chr; Chrs; ChrhWkr; CmntyWkr; SchPl; 4-H; PpCl; CaptBsktbl; Trk; Techn; Practical Nurse.

STRAUGHM, Michael K; G E Thompson HS; St Charles, IL; HonRl; SchPl; CivCl; SciCl; Ftbl; College; Forestry.

STRAUMANIS, Andris; Murphysboro Township HS; Murphysboro, IL; 11/250 HonRl; ModUN; RptrSchPpr; KeyCl; Southern Il Univ;.

STRAUMANN, Shelley; Cosmos HS; Cosmos, MN; ALAGirlsSt; Band; ChrhWkr; CmntyWkr; CncrtBnd; HonRl; LbryAde; MrchBnd; SchPl; RptrYrbk; College; Prof.

STRAUP, Kenneth A; La Salle HS; South Bend, IN; 10/515 HonRl; NHS; 4-H; SciCl; LetterTrk; KiwanAwd; Purdue Univ; Optometry.

STRAUS, Gary A; St Johns HS; De Witt, MI; 73/335 HonRl; NatlFornLg; NHS; NatlMeritCmnd; NatlThespSoc; SchMus; SchPl; YthFlsp; LetterFtbl; IMSpt; Central Mi Univ; Science.

STRAUSE, John E; Monticello HS; Monticello, WI; TrsSophCls; Band; HonRl; PepBnd; SchPl; SctActv; StuCncl; TchrAde; YthFlsp; RptrYrbk; 4-H; Bsbl; Bsktbl; College.

STRAUSER, Janet K; Bedford North Lawrence HS; Bedford, IN; 1/405 Band; ChrhWkr; HonRl; NHS; YthFlsp; Yrbk; 4-H; LatCl; Bsktbl; 4-HAwd; Vincennes Univ; Secretarial.

STRAUSS, Scott A; Maine East HS; Morton Grove, IL; HonRl; JrNHS; NHS; NatlMeritCmnd; MthCl; LetterSwmmng; U Il; Accntng.

STRAW, Karen L; New Bloomfield HS; New Bloomfield, MO; Band; Chrs; CncrtBnd; HonRl; MrchBnd; NHS; PepBnd; StuCncl; TchrAde; SchPpr; College; Professional.

STRAWBRIDGE, Sharon K; Cooter HS; Steele, MO; 2/24 VPJrCls; Chrs; HonRl; SchPl; Yrbk; FHA; PpCl; Arkansas State Univ; Business.

STRAWN, Rebecca J; South County Tech HS; Valley Park, MO; VPSophCls; SecJrCls; Chr; ChrhWkr; HonRl; SchPl; SchPpr; FBLA; FTA; IMSpt; College.

STRAWSER, Corydon L; Decatur Central HS; Indpls, IN; 8/350 VPFrshCls; VPJrCls; Aud/Vis; ChrhWkr; CmntyWkr; HonRl; JA; NHS; NatlThespSoc; PolWkr; Glf; LetterTennis; CchngActv; IMSpt; Earlham; Medicine.

STRAYER, Kerry A; Fairbury HS; Fairbury, NE; 56/158 Band; CncrtBnd; JCC; MrchBnd; PepBnd; SchMus; CchngActv; Doane College; Music.

STRAYER, Mark A; Monroe HS; Monroe, MI; 21/523 VPBand; CncrtBnd; HonRl; MrchBnd; NHS; PepBnd; SchMus; StuGov; LetterTrk; Mich St Univ; Physics.

STRAYER, Rodney; Lakeland HS; La Grange, IN; /149 CmntyWkr; YthFlsp; 4-H; GerCl; MthCl; SciCl; Ftbl; Trk; Wrstlng; 4-HAwd; Manchester Coll; Political Science.

STRECK, Cathy J; Ida Grove Comm HS; Ida Grove, IA; 2/70 Band; VPChrhWkr; CncrtBnd; DrlTm; HonRl; MrchBnd; PepBnd; SchPl; TchrAde; RptrYrbk; 4-H; 4-HAwd; Iowa State Univ; Accounting.

STRECKEL, Hagen; Mukwonago HS; Mukwonago, WI; HonRl; NHS; StuGov; GerCl; Ftbl; Trk; Wrstlng; IMSpt; PresAwd; Univ; Prof.

STRECKER, Elizabeth A; High School; Annandale, MN; Band; CncrtBnd; HonRl; MrchBnd; NHS; PpCl; Chrldr; PPFtbl; College.

STRECKER, Marlyce J; Lyman HS; Lyman, NE; HonRl; NHS; StuCncl; 4-H; FHA; FNA; PpCl; Trk; Chrldr; College Registered Nurse.

STREED, Karen; Waukegan East HS; Waukegan, IL; 24/502 Band; Chr; ChrhWkr; CncrtBnd; HonRl; LitMag; MrchBnd; SchMus; YthFlsp; Trk; College.

STREEPER, Patricia L; Alton Senior HS; Alton, IL; 21/858 Chrs; HonRl; JA; NHS; OffAde; TchrAde; FrCl; PpCl; SciCl; LetterTennis; GAA; Drake University; Fine Art.

STREET, Gail M; Dubois HS; Jasper, IN; Band; HonRl; MrchBnd; PepBnd; YthFlsp; 4-H; FHA; PpCl; Business School; Art Field.

STREET, Rebecca K; Grant Deuel HS; Revillo, SD; 5/40 SecFrshCls; SecSophCls; ALAGirlsSt; Chrs; ChrhWkr; HonRl; NHS; NatlThespSoc; SchMus; AmLegAwd; Clge; Navigation.

STREETER, Alan W; Sioux Valley HS; Volga, SD; 14/66 Band; Chr; CncrtBnd; HonRl; MrchBnd; PepBnd; SchPl; 4-H; IMSpt; College; Business Admin.

STREETER, Deborah; Otterville R Vi HS; Otterville, MO; 1/23 HstSophCls; Band; Chrs; ChrhWkr; HonRl; UNYO; RptrYrbk; Trk; IMSpt; Trade School; Vocation.

STREETER, Holly A; Andrew Comm HS; La Motte, IA; TrsSrCls; HonRl; GerCl; Bsktbl; Trk; Coll; Voc.

STREETER, Martin W; East HS; Des Moines, IA; 69/489 PresBand; CncrtBnd; HonRl; MrchBnd; PepBnd; SciCl; Bsktbl; Trk; Ia State U; Construction Engineering.

STREETING, Nancy; Mona Shores HS; Muskegon, MI; ChrhWkr; MrchBnd; ModUN; NatlFornLg; PepBnd; PpCl; Bsktbl; Trk; GAA; IMSpt; College Army; Phy Ed.

STREFF, Jane M; St Cecilia HS; Hastings, NE; 13/60 DrlTm; HonRl; SchMus; SchPl; StuGov; Yrbk; SchPpr; FrCl; LatCl; PpCl; U Of Ne.

STREFF, Lisa M; Plano HS; Plano, IL; 3/96 HonRl; StuCncl; SpnCl; College; Art.

STREFLING, Pamela J; River Valley HS; Three Oaks, MI; HonRl; NHS; TchrAde; FHA; Bsbl; College; Secretarial Business.

STREFLING, Shelly; Niles HS; Berrien Springs, MI; Band; CncrtBnd; HonRl; HospAde; MrchBnd; PepBnd; Twrl; 4-H; 4-HAwd; PresAwd; Memorial Hospital Nrsng Prgrm; Rn.

STREHLOW, Aaron J; Cudahy Sr HS; Cudahy, WI; 54/360 ChrhWkr; CmntyWkr; HonRl; HospAde; NHS; NatlThespSoc; SchAde; SchPl; TchrAde; LetterSwmmng; Univ Wi Milwaukee; Medical Field.

STREIBICH, F Michael; Woodruff HS; Peoria, IL; Band; CncrtBnd; HonRl; MrchBnd; Orch; PepBnd;.

STREICH, Gregory; Ortonville HS; Big Stone City, SD; ALBoysSt; Chr; Chrl; Chrs; ChrhWkr; 4-H; FFA; South Dakota State Univ; Agriculture.

STREICHER, Eric T; Hanover HS; Elizabeth, IL; 1/38 Aud/Vis; HonRl; NHS; NatlMeritCmnd; LetterFtbl; LetterTrk; Univ Of Illinois; Engineer.

STREICHER, Kathy L; Seymour Community HS; Black Creek, WI; 6/200 HonRl; NHS; EdYrBk; Sec4-H; PresFrCl; BttyCrckrAwd; 4-HAwd; Univ Wi Stevens Point; Erly Child Education.

STREIFF, Alison L; Southeast HS; Wichita, KS; 27/650 Chrs; DrlTm; HonRl; PolWkr; StuGov; Chrldr; Wichita State Univ;.

STREIGHT, Lonna B; Lincolnwood HS; Raymond, IL; 1/61 TrsSrCls; Band; PresNHS; EdYrBk; 4-H; TreasFHA; LetterTrk; DARAwd; Univ Of Ill; Engineer.

STREIT, John J; Sibley Comm HS; Ashton, IA; 1/100 PresJrCls; Chr; HonRl; NHS; SchMus; StuCncl; Bsktbl; ChmnFtbl; DARAwd; Iowa St U; Accounting.

STREIT, Robert J; Holton HS; Holton, KS; HonRl; LetterWrstlng; BauchLmbAwd; Kansas St Univ; Chemical Engineer.

STREITMATTER, Leeann M; Glen Ullin HS; Glen Ullin, ND; 4/40 VPJrCls; Band; Chrs; HospAde; ModUN; SchPl; EdYrBk; RptrSchPpr; VPFHA; LetterTrk; Nd Stte Schl Of Sci; Data Processing.

STREJC, Janice M; Maria HS; Chicago, IL; 5/335 ChrhWkr; HonRl; HospAde; NHS; LatCl; PresMthCl; KiwanAwd; College; Professional.

STRELKA, Patricia A; Greendale HS; Greendale, WI; 8/861 HonRl; LbryAde; NatlFornLg; NHS; SchAde; TchrAde; 4-H; PpCl; Mount Mary Col; Clinical Dietetics.

STREMICK, Robert; Walhalla HS; Walhalla, ND; 9/57 SecFrshCls; VPSophCls; HonRl; RusCl; Bsbl; Tennis; College; Engineering.

STREMMING, Timothy G; Stewardson Strasburg HS; Strasburg, IL; 2/49 VPFrshCls; PresJrCls; ALBoysSt; Band; HonRl; NHS; SchPl; YthFlsp; LetterBsbl; Bsktbl; AmLegAwd; Undecided; Medical Doctor.

STRENG, Debra J; John Marshall Jr Sr HS; Milwaukee, WI; 59/711 Chr; ChrhWkr; DrlTm; HonRl; LbryAde; NHS; SchPl; SctActv; StuCncl; TchrAde; University; Professional.

STRESCH, Gregory H; Ortonville HS; Big Stone City, SD; ALBoysSt; Chr; Chrs; ChrhWkr; 4-H; FFA; Bsbl; Bsktbl; S Dakota State; Gen Agriculture.

STRESE, Deanna J; Somerset HS; Somerset, WI; 1/59 ChrhWkr; HonRl; LbryAde; Pres4-H; PresFHA; BttyCrckrAwd; 4-HAwd; Stout State Univ; Dietetics.

STRETCHER, Julia; Blue Valley Senior HS; Bucyrus, KS; TrsFrshCls; Band; Chrl; Chrs; HonRl; NHS; SchMus; SchPl; YthFlsp; FTA; Johnson Cnty Comm Col; Graphic Commun.

STREULY, Carolyn A; West Allis Central HS; West Allis, WI; 1/460 ChrhWkr; HonRl; NatlFornLg; NHS; RedCrAde; YthFlsp; RptrYrbk; RptrSchPpr; SpnCl; Mt Mary Univ; Education.

STREUTER, Phillip; Murphysboro HS; Murphysboro, IL; ChrhWkr; HonRl; KeyCl; Bsktbl; LetterTennis; AmLegAwd; Univ; Bus.

STRIBRNY, Lynne M; Carl Sandburg HS; Palos Park, IL; 38/680 Band; CncrtBnd; HonRl; MrchBnd; Orch; College.

STRICKER, Jane E; Huntington North HS; Huntington, IN; TreasALAGirlsSt; Chrl; TreasChrhWkr; PpCl; SecGAA; University; Special Education.

STRICKER, Marianne; Gering HS; Gering, NE; 43/143 Chr; Chrs; ChrhWkr; HonRl; GerCl; PpCl; 4-HAwd; Nebraska Western Col; Accountant.

STRICKER, Nancy K; Wellsburg Comm HS; Grundy Center, IA; 10/33 Chrs; CncrtBnd; HonRl; MrchBnd; SchPl; Yrbk; SchPpr; LetterBsktbl; LetterGlf; LetterChrldr; American Inst; Secretary.

STRICKLAND, Duane A; David H Hickman HS; Columbia, MO; Chrs; ChrhWkr; HonRl; NHS; NatlMeritCmnd; LetterTrk; Univ; Pol Sci.

STRICKLAND, Leslie G; O Fallon Township HS; O Fallon, IL; 6/294 ChrhWkr; HonRl; HospAde; NHS; YthFlsp; FHA; Mc Kendree College; Science.

STRICKLAND, Vivian G; Rudyard HS; Kincheloe Afb, MI; TrsJrCls; PresSrCls; HonRl; SchPl; StuCncl; Yrbk; RptrSchPpr; PpCl; LetterChrldr; PPFtbl; E Carolina Univ; Psychology.

STRICKLER, Dana; Moulton Udell HS; Centerville, IA; TrsJrCls; Band; Chrs; HonRl; MrchBnd; PepBnd; SchMus; FTA; Bsktbl; 4-HAwd; Trade.

STRICKLIN, Joel; Central Riii HS; Flat River, MO; HonRl; TchrAde; SciCl; Wrstlng; PresAwd; Coll; Biol.

STRIDER, Pattie J; Hardin Central HS; Hardin, MO; PresFrshCls; SecTrsJrCls; Band; Chrs; HonRl; StuCncl; RptrYrbk; FHA; Chrldr; OptClAwd; Mo Western State Coll.

STRIEBICH, Janice S; Cheboygan Area HS; Cheboygan, MI; HonRl; Bsktbl; Tennis; Trk; CchngActv; GAA;.

STRIEGEL, Bonnie J; Logan HS; La Crosse, WI; 13/234 TrsSrCls; NatlFornLg; NHS; StuCncl; Yrbk; RptrSchPpr; TreasFBLA; TreasPpCl; LetterBsktbl; LetterTrk; College; English.

STRIEGEL, Rita A; Keota HS; Harper, IA; Chrs; HonRl; NHS; RptrYrbk; RptrSchPpr; EdSchPpr; SptEdSchPpr; PpCl; LetterBsktbl; Ottumwa Hts Coll; Medical Technology.

STRIGENZ, Michael A; Kewaskum HS; Kewaskum, WI; 20/200 PresSophCls; HonRl; NHS; SchMus; SchPl; StuCncl; StuGov; LetterBsbl; CaptFtbl; LetterWrstlng; IMSpt; Marquette Univ; Professional.

STRIGENZ, Pete S; Milwaukee Lutheran HS; Milwaukee, WI; 80/232 ChrhWkr; PepBnd; YthFlsp; LetterFtbl; Trk; Chrldr; CchngActv; IMSpt; GodCntryAwd; CitAwd; Coll; Major Study.

STRIKER, Jennifer J; Grosse Pointe S HS; Grosse Pointe, MI; 50/637 ChrhWkr; HonRl; NHS; NatlThespSoc; SchAde; SctActv; YthFlsp; PPFtbl; Univ; Math.

STRIMPLE, Connie L; South Ripley HS; Versailles, IN; 9/102 Band; ChrhWkr; HonRl; NHS; Twrl; SecYthFlsp; FTA; PpCl; GAA; BttyCrckrAwd; Northwood Inst Of Ind; Fashion Merchandsng.

STRINGER, Catherine A; Mary D Bradford HS; Kenosha, WI; HonRl; NHS; NatlMeritSF; YthFlsp; 4-H; SpnCl; Univ Of Wis; Linguistics.

STRINGER, Philip G; Rockford East HS; Rockford, IL; HonRl; JrNHS; Univ Of Arizona; Geologist.

STRINGER, Susan J; Spring Valley HS; Spring Valley, WI; 4/70 Chr; Chrs; HonRl; NatlFornLg; NHS; SchPl; StuCncl; FHA; Bsktbl; College; Professional.

STRINGFIELD, Elizabeth A; William Chrisman HS; Independence, MO; 30/420 HonRl; NHS; TchrAde; PresFTA; College; Mechanical Engineering.

STRIPLING, Cedric R; Highland HS; St Paul, MN; Band; Chr; ChrhWkr; CncrtBnd; HonRl; NatlThespSoc; Orch; SchMus; SctActv; College; Professional.

STRIPLING, Perry L; Buffalo Grove HS; Arlington Hts, IL; 56/290 Chr; HonRl; NHS; SchPpr; LetterFtbl; Harper Jr College; Computer Operator.

STRIZ, Jeanne L; Whitmore Lake HS; Whitmore Lake, MI; 1/88 SecSophCls; SecJrCls; CncrtBnd; HonRl; JrNHS; MrchBnd; NHS; SchPl; Chrldr; 4-HAwd; College; Professional.

STRIZ, Susan K; Whitmore Lake HS; Whitmore Lake, MI; 2/73 ChrhWkr; HonRl; JrNHS; LbryAde; NHS; OffAde; StuCncl; TchrAde; YthFlsp; RptrYrbk; Tennis; 4-HAwd; College; Professional.

STROBEL, Barbara J; Oak Forest HS; Oak Forest, IL; DrmBgl; StuCncl; SpnCl; MthCl; PpCl; LetterTrk; LetterChrldr; GAA; College; Medicine.

STROBEL, Cheryl M; Central HS; Aberdeen, SD; ALAGirlsSt; Chrs; ChrhWkr; HonRl; Mdrgl; NHS; StuCncl; YthFlsp; PpCl; Chrldr; Northern St Col; Special And Elem Ed.

STROBEL, Cynthia; Cedarburg HS; Cedarburg, WI; 14/305 SecSophCls; DrmBgl; HonRl; NHS; SctActv; GerCl; PpCl; GAA; Univ Of Wis Eau Claire; Pharmacy.

STROBEL, Lisa A; New Haven HS; New Haven, MO; 8/43 PresFrshCls; SecSrCls; HonRl; NHS; StuCncl; RptrSchPpr; FTA; PpCl; College; Social Work.

STROBLE, Paul E; Van Comm HS; Vandalia, IL; Band; Chr; Chrs; ChrhWkr; CncrtBnd; DrlTm; HonRl; MrchBnd; NHS; NatlThespSoc; Orch; SchPl; Greenville College; History.

STROBRIDGE, Suzzette; Grandville HS; Grandville, MI; ChrhWkr; HonRl; NatlFornLg; NHS; SchMus; StuCncl; TchrAde; YthFlsp; PpCl; IMSpt; Grand Valley State College;.

STRODE, Robin R; Joliet Township HS; Joliet, IL; 7/375 PresJrCls; Chr; ChrhWkr; HonRl; NHS; SchPl; PresStuCncl; RptrSchPpr; GAA; DARAwd; College; High School Teacher & Admin.

STRODE, Sherrie L; Rochester HS; Rochester, IL; 22/74 Band; HonRl; OffAde; SchPl; EdYrBk; FFA; PpCl; Chrldr; GAA; 4-HAwd; Lincoln Coll; Law.

STRODE, Yvonne D; Bradford HS; Bradford, IL; 4/47 Band; CncrtBnd; HonRl; MrchBnd; NHS; PepBnd; U Of Il; Physician.

STRODEL, Ross A; South Side HS; Fort Wayne, IN; 48/451 Band; CncrtBnd; VPJA; MrchBnd; PepBnd; JAAwd; In U; Dentist.

STROEDE, Terence J; Baraboo Sr HS; West Baraboo, WI; RptrSchPpr; KeyCl; Bsbl; Bsktbl; Ftbl; Florida State U; Engineering.

STROEHLEIN, Cathy L; Cobden Unit HS; Cobden, IL; Band; CncrtBnd; HonRl; MrchBnd; PepBnd; SchPl; TchrAde; FHA; PpCl;.

STROH, Keevin B; Ashley HS; Ashley, ND; HonRl; StuCncl; YthFlsp; LetterFtbl; College.

STROH, Morgan R; Midway HS; Johnstown, ND; Univ;.

STROHBEEN, Linda L; Somerset Public HS; Somerset, WI; HonRl; College; Professional.

STROHECKER, Renee; Lanark HS; Lanark, IL; 6/55 Chrs; HonRl; SpnCl; GAA; University; Journalism.

STROHL, Richard L; Roosevelt HS; East Chicago, IN; 39/217 Band; CncrtBnd; HonRl; SchPl; FTA; Wrstlng; Wabash Clg; Law.

STROHM, Bonnie; Marshall HS; West Union, IL; DrlTm; MrchBnd; SchPl; TchrAde; 4-H; FHA; FTA; LatCl; 4-HAwd; Coll; Dance.

STROHM, Sandra; Platteville HS; Platteville, WI; Chr; ChrhWkr; HonRl; Mdrgl; Orch; SchMus; SchPl; RptrYrbk; RptrSchPpr; Univ Of Wi At Platteville; Mus Ed.

STROHMAIER, Carl W; Wauwatosa East HS; Wauwatosa, WI; 29 440 HonRl; NatlMeritSF; SctActv; StuCncl; StuGov; EdSchPpr; MthCl; PpCl; U Of Wi; Acct.

STROHMAN, Joseph L; English Valley HS; N English, IA; 5/63 PresJrCls; ALBoysSt; PresBand; CncrtBnd; HonRl; MrchBnd; VPNHS; PepBnd; PresStuCncl; PpCl; Trk; College; Business.

STROHMEIER, Patricia A; Edwardsville HS; Edwardsville, IL; 40/451 Chrs; HonRl; OffAde; Siu; Cpa.

STROHMEYER, Karen L; Edwardsville HS; Edwardsville, IL; 12/465 Band; Chr; Chrs; ChrhWkr; CncrtBnd; HonRl; JrNHS; LitMag; MrchBnd; PepBnd; University.

STROHSCHEIN, Ricky A; Avondale Senior HS; Auburn Heights, MI; 41/247 ALBoysSt; HonRl; Mdrgl; NHS; SchPl; SchPl; StuGov; TchrAde; SptEdYrbk; Yrbk; Oakland Community College; Police Science.

STROKA, Cynthia A; Onemia Public HS; Onamia, MN; Band; CncrtBnd; DrlTm; HonRl; MrchBnd; PepBnd; 4-H; GAA; College; Nurse.

STROKER, Karen J; Van Far HS; Vandalia, MO; 3/89 ChrhWkr; HonRl; JrNHS; NHS; SchPl; FBLA; Nmsll; Accountant.

STROLE, Terri R; Hutsonville HS; Hutsonville, IL; 9/40 Band; ChrhWkr; HonRl; LbryAde; MrchBnd; PepBnd; SchPl; YthFlsp; FHA; PpCl; Lincoln Trail Jr Col; Vocational.

STROM, Craig; Hudson Senior HS; Hudson, WI; CmntyWkr; Ftbl; Trk; College; Conservation.

STROM, David E; H H Dow HS; Midland, MI; Band; CncrtBnd; HonRl; MrchBnd; NatlMeritSF; Orch; Univ; Professional.

STROM, Luann M; White City HS; White City, KS; 1/16 Band; Chrs; HonRl; SchPl; EdYrBk; PpCl; LetterBsktbl; Trk; PPFtbl; LionAwd; Univ; Elementary Ed.

STROM, Russell R; Southeast HS; Lincoln, NE; HonRl; Orch; SciCl; Southern Missionary Col; Math.

STROMAN, Pat A; Imlay City HS; Imlay City, MI; 28/151 HstSophCls; HstJrCls; PresSrCls; NatlMeritSF; OffAde; PolWkr; StuGov; TchrAde; SchPpr; LetterFtbl; Tennis; RotaryAwd; Univ Of Mich Flint; C P A.

STROMBERG, Larry A; Hammond Baptist HS; Hammond, IN; ChrhWkr; HonRl; NHS; EdSchPpr; SptEdSchPpr; LetterFtbl; Socr; LetterWrstlng; Hyles Anderson College; Ministry.

STROMMEN, Thomas L; Kensington HS; Kensington, MN; TrsJrCls; Band; Chr; Chrl; Chrs; ChrhWkr; CmntyWkr; SchMus; SchPl; StuCncl;.

STROMSKA, Christine A; Anstagg HS; Hickory Hills, IL; 30/518 TrsJrCls; PresSrCls; HonRl; NHS; StuCncl; RptrYrbk; SpnCl; Trk; Chrldr; GAA; Univ Of Illinois; Social Science.

STRONG, Charles S; Fremont HS; Fremont, MI; 55/200 Band; ChrhWkr; CncrtBnd; HonRl; MrchBnd; PepBnd; GerCl; Tennis; Muskegon Community College; Social Studies.

STRONG, Cindy; Merrill Hs; Merrill, MI; Band; Chr; HonRl; NHS; RedCrAde; TchrAde; VPFFA; Michigan State U; Veterinarian.

STRONG, Joyce M; Paseo HS; Kansas City, MO; 39/290 Chr; ChrhWkr; CmntyWkr; HonRl; NHS; StuCncl; PpCl; Baker Univ; Accounting.

STRONG, Julie A; Ontonagon Area HS; Greeland, MI; 18/108 Band; Chrs; HonRl; Bsktbl; Chrldr; GAA;.

STRONG, Kelly C; Logan Magnolia HS; Logan, IA; 1/60 VPJrCls; ALBoysSt; Band; Chrs; HonRl; NHS; SchPl; StuCncl; LetterBsbl; LetterBsktbl; Ia Univ; Teacher.

STRONG, Kelly C; Logan Magnolia Comm HS; Logan, IA; 1/52 VPJrCls; ALBoysSt; Chrs; CncrtBnd; HonRl; NHS; SchMus; LetterBsbl; LetterBsktbl; LetterFtbl; LetterTrk; CchngActv; Iowa State Univ; Research Scientist.

STRONG, Lee A; Hart HS; Hart, MI; Band; CncrtBnd; MrchBnd; TchrAde; RptrYrbk; 4-H; Bsktbl; IMSpt; PPFtbl; 4-HAwd; Central Mi Univ.

STRONG, Margaret A; Arkansas City HS; Arkansas City, KS; 1/200 Band; CncrtBnd; DrmMjrt; HonRl; HospAde; Orch; PepBnd; SchMus; SpnCl; OptClAwd; Wichita State Univ; Medicine.

STRONG, Sonja E; Rushville HS; Rushville, NE; 9/43 Band; Chr; CncrtBnd; HonRl; PepBnd; YthFlsp; FHA; PpCl; CaptTrk; Chrldr; College; Vocational.

STRONG, Stephen J; Union City HS; Union City, MI; VPFrshCls; PresSophCls; PresJrCls; HonRl; NHS; 4-H; FFA; Trk; College; Agriculture.

STRONG, Sue E; Lockport Central HS; Lockport, IL; 5/612 HonRl; NHS; Quill&Scroll; PresYthFlsp; RptrSchPpr; SptEdSchPpr; PpCl; Tennis; GAA; Augustana College; Journalism.

STRONG, Sue L; Hicksville HS; Auburn, IN; 3/83 Chrs; ChrhWkr; HonRl; JrNHS; NHS; Quill&Scroll; StuCncl; UNYO; YthFlsp; Yrbk; Trade School.

STRONG, Tanya L; Maconaquah HS; Grissom Afb, IN; Chr; HonRl; MrchBnd; NatlFornLg; NHS; SchMus; MthCl; Swmmng; Trk; GAA; Texas A&m Univ ;marine Biology.

STROPE, Linda Y; Atchison HS; Atchison, KS; 16/166 Chr; HonRl; ModUN; NHS; NatlThespSoc; SchMus; StuCncl; SchPpr; PpCl; Sch Of Ozarks; Med Tech.

STROPE, Mary M; Assumption HS; Wis Rapids, WI; Band; Chr; Chrl; CncrtBnd; MrchBnd; PepBnd; SchMus; StuCncl; FNA; PpCl; U Of Wi; Nurse.

STROTHEIDE, Paul J; Flanagan HS; Flanagan, IL; SecFrshCls; TrsJrCls; TrsSrCls; AFS; Chrs; ChrhWkr; Mdrgl; SchMus; YthFnd; SciCl; Univ; Professional.

STROTHER, Lisa A; Harry A Burke HS; Omaha, NE; DrlTm; HonRl; HospAde; IntrClCncl; Quill&Scroll; StuGov; TchrAde; EdYrBk; FFA; LetterSwmmng; College.

STROTHER, Ralph M; Potosi HS; Potosi, MO; HonRl; JrNHS; NHS; SciCl; Ftbl; IMSpt; College; Electrical Engineer.

STROTZ, Kimberly S; Aurora Cenral Catholic HS; Aurora, IL; HonRl; SchAde; TchrAde; PpCl; Bsktbl; Tennis; Trk; College; Psychology.

STROUD, Deborah J; Jac Cen Del HS; Osgood, IN; 2/58 Chr; HonRl; NHS; RptrSchPpr; Coll; Nurse.

STROUD, Julie A; Estherville Sr HS; Estherville, IA; 6/189 VPSophCls; Band; Chr; Chrs; ChrhWkr; DrmMjrt; HonRl; MrchBnd; SchPl; StuCncl; 4-H; FFA; LetterTrk; Chrldr; GAA; University; Medicine.

STROUD, Roy E; Murray Community;; Murray, IA; MrchBnd; SchPl; PpCl; Bsbl; Bsktbl; LetterFtbl; Junior College.

STROUD, Sue L; North Boone HS; Poplar Grove, IL; Chrs; DrlTm; HonRl; SchMus; 4-H; PpCl; LetterBsbl; Trk; LetterGAA; 4-HAwd; Trinity College; Physical Education.

STROUP, Jonathan C; Tipton HS; Tipton, IN; 1/200 Band; HonRl; TreasNHS; NatlMeritFnl; NatlMeritSF; PresStuCncl; PresSciCl; LetterFtbl; LetterGlf; IMSpt; College; Engineering.

STROUP, Patrick J; Blackford HS; Hartford City, IN; ChrhWkr; HonRl; NHS; SchPl; StuCncl; Teen; YthFlsp; SciCl; Ball State Univ; Chemistry.

STROUP, Steven F; Benkelman HS; Benkelman, NE; Band; Chrs; ChrhWkr; CncrtBnd; MrchBnd; PepBnd; SctActv; YthFlsp; SptEdSchPpr; 4-H; SciCl; Bsktbl; Ftbl; Univ Of Nebraska; Farmer.

STROUSE, Donald B; Bedford Sr HS; Lambertville, MI; 149/425 NatlMeritSchl; PolWkr; SchAde; SctActv; Glf; Adrian College; Veterinarian.

STROUSE, Douglas G; Alma HS; Alma, MI; Band; Chrl; CncrtBnd; Mdrgl; MrchBnd; PepBnd; SchMus; SchPl; YthFlsp; Adrian College; Music.

STROUSE, Lorraine M; Ashley Community HS; Ithaca, MI; 7/49 Band; HonRl; SctActv; TchrAde; FHA; LetterBsbl; Col;.

STRUB, Jerry; Duchesne HS; St Peters, MO; HonRl; SchMus; KeyCl; IMSpt; Northeast Mo State U; Pharmacist.

STRUB, Patricia S; Lancaster Sr HS; Lancaster, WI; AFS; HonRl; PepBnd; SpnCl; PpCl; Univ; Pharmacy.

STRUBE, Kim S; Claflin HS; Claflin, KS; Band; HonRl; SchPl; Twrl; FHA; PpCl; Bsbl; LetterBsktbl; LetterTennis; LetterTrk; Chrldr; CchngActv; Barton County Comm Jr College; Physical Ed.

STRUBHART, Lawrence L; Wesclin Sr HS; New Baden, IL; 4/111 PresSophCls; VPJrCls; Aud/Vis; Band; ChrhWkr; HonRl; JrNHS; NHS; SctActv; StuCncl; FFA; GerCl; Bsktbl; College.

STRUCK, Joann C; New Effington Ind #102 HS; New Effington, SD; Band; Chrs; CncrtBnd; HonRl; LbryAde; MrchBnd; PepBnd; SchMus; SchPl; RptrYrbk; College; Cirriculum.

STRUCK, Timothy J; Valley HS; W Des Moines, IA; 25/440 Chr; Chrs; ChrhWkr; HonRl; Mdrgl; NHS; NatlMeritSF; NatlThespSoc; SchMus; SchPl; SctActv; StuCncl; Nebraska Wesleyan; Psychology.

STRUKL, Thomas J; St Rita HS; Chicago, IL; 39/428 HonRl; NHS; RptrSchPpr; SptEdSchPpr; Southern Illinois University.

STRUNC, David A; Central HS; Omaha, NE; CmntyWkr; HonRl; LetterFtbl; Swmmng; Univ Of Ne At Omaha; Accounting.

STRUNK, Gayle M; Moulton HS; Moulton, IA; 5/38 Chrs; ChrhWkr; HonRl; YthFlsp; FHA;.

STRUNK, Kathy S; Eastern HS; Springville, IN; Chr; JrNHS; SctActv; PpCl; GAA; DARAwd; Trade School; Commercial Artist.

STRUNK, Linda; Tremont HS; Tremont, IL; AFS; Band; Chrs; ChrhWkr; CncrtBnd; NatlThespSoc; RptrYrbk; PpCl; GAA; College; Forestry Or Agriculture.

STRUPECK, Paula; Queen Of Peace Hs; Burbank, IL; 34/450 Chrs; NHS; SchMus; StuCncl; FrCl; Chrldr; Western Illinois U; Lawyer.

STRUPP, Steve; West Bend East HS; West Bend, WI; SctActv; Ftbl; Swmmng; Trk; IMSpt; Vocational School; Graphic Arts.

STRUSS, Julie A; United Twp HS; East Moline, IL; 20/689 Band; ChrhWkr; HonRl; JrNHS; NHS; SchMus; SchPl; StuCncl; GerCl; Bsktbl; Glf; GAA; Iowa St Univ; Veterinarian.

STRUTZ, Eric T; John Hersey HS; Arlington Heights, IL; 131/783 AFS; HonRl; NHS; NatlMeritCmnd; OffAde; Sdlty; SpnCl; Ftbl; Wrstlng; U Of Il.

STRUTZ, Karl L; Lourdes Acad; Oshkosh, WI; 43/126 StuCncl; FrCl; Bsktbl; Ftbl; Trk; Marquette U; Dentistry.

STRUTZ, Terry C; Kingsford HS; Iron Mountain, MI; CmntyWkr; JA; JrNHS; NHS; NatlMeritFnl; NatlMeritCmnd; NatlSciFnd; OffAde; TchrAde; YthFlsp; Univ; Curruculum Of Major Study.

STRUVE, Carol J; Manning Comm HS; Manning, IA; 2/66 SecSophCls; ALAGirlsSt; Band; Chrs; NHS; PolWkr; 4-H; PpCl; 4-HAwd; Clge; Animal Science.

STRUVEN, Christian P; Proviso West HS; Westchester, IL; Univ Of Miami; Medicine.

STRYCKER, David B; Zionsville Community HS; Zionsville, IN; ChrhWkr; CncrtBnd; HonRl; JrNHS; MrchBnd; YthFlsp; Bsktbl; LetterTennis; College; Predentistry.

STRYK, Lydia D; Dekalb HS; Dekalb, IL; DrlTm; HonRl; NHS; NatlThespSoc; SchPl; StuCncl; University; Theatre.

STRZALKA, Mary Alice C; Regina Dominican HS; Chicago, IL; HonRl; LitMag; NatlMeritCmnd; SchMus; SctActv; Sdlty;.

STRZYNSKI, Barbara A; St Ann HS; Chicago, IL; 1/65 VPSophCls; PresJrCls; Chr; ChrhWkr; CmntyWkr; HonRl; JA; LbryAde; OffAde; Sacrstn; University; Curriculum Of Major Study.

STUAAN, Kirk M; Limestone Community HS; Bartonville, IL; ChrhWkr; HonRl; PolWkr; StuGov; PpCl; LetterFtbl; Glf; LetterWrstlng; University; Architecture.

STUART, A; East Alton Wood River Com HS; Wood River, IL; 67/287 Band; Chr; CncrtBnd; HonRl; MrchBnd; OffAde; YthFlsp; RptrSchPpr; FHA; Col ;vocation.

STUART, Darrell W; Parkside HS; Jackson, MI; Band; CncrtBnd; MrchBnd; NatlMeritSF; PepBnd; Mi St Univ; Med.

STUART, David M; Cozad Sr HS; Cozad, NE; Band; Chrs; ChrhWkr; CncrtBnd; SctActv; Sdlty; YthFlsp; FBLA; Bsbl; Ftbl; Trk; IMSpt; Business College; Vocation.

STUART, Frederick R; Lexington St Ann HS; Lexington, NE; 1/19 PresJrCls; ALBoysSt; Chrs; CncrtBnd; HonRl; NHS; PepBnd; SctActv; EdSchPpr; Bsktbl; Univ.

STUART, Karen A; R Nelson Snider HS; Fort Wayne, IN; 28/510 PresSophCls; HonRl; MrchBnd; NatlMeritSchl; StuCncl; Chrldr; Purdue Univ; Pre Med Physician.

STUART, Karen A; R Nelson Snieder HS; Fort Wayne, IN; 28/500 PresSophCls; HonRl; NatlMeritSF; StuCncl; Chrldr; Purdue University; Medicine.

STUART, Michael; St Bede Acad; Lasalle, IL; 2/87 HonRl; SchPl; StuGov; Depaun Univ; Pre Med.

STUART, Michael J; St Bede Academy; Lasalle, IL; 3/100 ChrhWkr; HonRl; SchMus; StuGov; LetterBsbl; LetterBsktbl; LetterFtbl; College; Medicine.

STUART, Philip E; Marian HS; Mishawaka, IN; 1/118 HonRl; NHS; SctActv; RptrSchPpr; Notre Dame; Micro/biology.

STUART, Timothy W; Southeast Polk HS; Altoona, IA; ALBoysSt; Band; ChrhWkr; CncrtBnd; MrchBnd; PepBnd; SctActv; SchPpr; Wrstlng; AmLegAwd; Coll; Vet.

STUBBE, Donna M; Jackson HS; Alpha, MN; YthFlsp; Yrbk; 4-H; FHA; Bsbl; CchngActv; GAA; PPFtbl; 4-HAwd; PresAwd; College; Medical Secretary.

STUBBE, Julie; Plano HS; Plano, IL; Band; CncrtBnd; HonRl; MrchBnd; NHS; NatlThespSoc; PepBnd; SchMus; Socr; GAA; College; Professional.

STUBBENDICK, Keith A; George S Parker HS; Jamesville, WI; TrsJrCls; TrsSrCls; HonRl; NHS; StuCncl; Yrbk; RptrSchPpr; PresLatCl; LetterSwmmng; GovHonPrgAwd; Univ Of Wis La Crosse; Political Science Mj.

STUBBLEFIELD, Billie S; Mexico HS; Mexico, MO; Band; NHS; SecStuCncl; PresLatCl; PpCl; Bsktbl; CaptTrk; CaptChrldr; U Of Mo.

STUBBLEFIELD, Lori A; Odell HS; Odell, IL; 2/35 SecSophCls; Band; Chr; Chrs; ChrhWkr; HonRl; YthFlsp; RptrYrbk; 4-H; FHA; FrCl; GAA; IMSpt; Univ Of Illinois; Mathematics.

STUBBLEFIELD, Lori A; Odell Comm HS; Odell, IL; 2/35 SecSophCls; Band; Chr; Chrs; ChrhWkr; HonRl; YthFlsp; Yrbk; 4-H; FHA; FrCl; PpCl; GAA; Univ Of Illinois; Mathematics.

STUBBS, Brian L; Kearney HS; Kearney, NE; Band; CmntyWkr; HonRl; JA; SchPl; StuCncl; YthFlsp; Pres4-H; FFA; PpCl; Kearney State; Eng.

STUBBS, Delta; Coon Rapids Senior HS; Coon Rapids, MN; Chr; HonRl; JrNHS; OffAde; SchMus; SchPl; StuCncl; SpnCl; Trk; Aneka Ramsey Comm Coll; Comp Uter Engin.

STUBBS, Joni S; Green Mountain HS; Marshalltown, IA; SecFrshCls; Chrs; HonRl; SchMus; SchPl; TchrAde; FTA; LetterBsktbl; LetterTrk; Trade; Vocation.

STUBBS, Stephen W; Harlem HS; Loves Park, IL; 7/520 Band; HonRl; PresNHS; VPQuill&Scroll; SctActv; PresStuCncl; SptEdSchPpr; LetterSwmmng; CaptTrk; BauchLmbAwd; Us Air Force Acad; Officer.

STUBE, Lynn M; C S Mott HS; Warren, MI; HonRl; NHS; Trk; GAA; College; Env Science.

STUBENHOFER, Michael D; Chase County HS; Strong City, KS; PresFrshCls; PresSrCls; ALBoysSt; HonRl; StuCncl; LetterBsbl; LetterBsktbl; LetterFtbl; Cloud County Community Jr College; Engineer.

STUBER, Marilyn L; Caston HS; Logansport, IN; Chr; Chrs; HonRl; NHS; OffAde; SchMus; SchPl; FTA; FrCl; PpCl; Manchester College.

STUBER, Paul D; Howell HS; Howell, MI; ALBoysSt; Band; Chrl; MrchBnd; VPNHS; PepBnd; SchMus; GerCl; LetterTennis; LetterWrstlng; U Of Mi; Law.

STUBLER, Karen S; Belton HS; Belton, MO; 8/282 Chr; ChrhWkr; DrlTm; HospAde; NHS; StuCncl; Yrbk; FrCl; Chrldr; PPFtbl; Central Mo St U; Secondary Teaching.

STUCHEL, Dena M; Albia Comm HS; Albia, IA; Chrs; HonRl; LbryAde; RptrSchPpr; Art.

STUCKENSCHMIDT, Rilla; Wisner Pilger HS; Wisner, NE; Chrs; ChrhWkr; SptEdYrbk; Yrbk; 4-H; FHA; SpnCl; PpCl; 4-HAwd; Wayne St Coll; Bus.

STUCKER, Cathy P; Wayne HS; Fort Wayne, IN; Chr; Univ; Vet.

STUCKER, Jean A; Lyons Township HS; Western Springs, IL; Chr; Chrs; ChrhWkr; HonRl; LitMag; NHS; NatlMeritCmnd; SchMus; GerCl; College; History.

STUCKER, Susan M; Stillman Valley HS; Monroe Center, IL; HonRl; SchMus; FHA; College; Architect.

STUCKEY, Cristie L; Southwestern HS; Medora, IL; 40/173 Band; Chrs; ChrhWkr; CmntyWkr; HonRl; SchMus; 4-H; VPFHA; DanFAwd; 4-HAwd; S I U Carbondale; Music Education.

STUCKEY, Jeffery V; Alma HS; Alma, MI; 3/266 CncrtBnd; MrchBnd; NHS; PepBnd; PolWkr; SctActv; StuGov; FrCl; BauchLmbAwd; GodCntryAwd; Mi State U; Physics Law.

STUCKEY, Michael B; Gibson Southern HS; Owensville, IN; 48/224 Chr; CncrtBnd; MrchBnd; PepBnd; SctActv; SchPpr; FFA; LetterBsbl; LetterBsktbl; College; Professional.

STUCKEY, Thomas L; Gibson Southern HS; Owensville, IN; Band; CncrtBnd; MrchBnd; PepBnd; SctActv; StuCncl; FFA; PpCl; LetterBsbl; LetterBsktbl; College; Professional.

STUCKWISCH, Dennis H; Brownstown Central HS; Seymour, IN; 4/143 HonRl; PresNHS; TchrAde; FSA; TreasSciCl; Bsktbl; IMSpt; Hanover College; Math.

STUCKY, Richard S; South Adams HS; Geneva, IN; Band; ChrhWkr; HonRl; PolWkr; StuCncl; VPYthFlsp; PpCl; Bsbl; LetterTrk; College; Accountant.

STUCKY, Tamera S K; Moundridge HS; Moundridge, KS; ALAGirlsSt; HonRl; Mdrgl; NHS; SchMus; StuCncl; PresYthFlsp; SecFHA; PresPpCl; College; Music.

STUCKY, Timothy R; Berean Academy HS; Newton, KS; VPJrCls; ChrhWkr; YthFlsp; PpCl; CaptBsktbl; LetterTrk; IMSpt; Tabor College.

STUDDARD, Pamela; Sullivan Senior HS; Sullivan, MO; 2/150 ChrhWkr; CncrtBnd; HonRl; OffAde; SchPl; RptrYrbk; FrCl; MthCl; RotaryAwd; Univ Of Mo; Accounting.

STUDE, Wesley; Brewster Public HS; Brewster, MN; TrsJrCls; TrsSrCls; Chrs; ChrhWkr; HonRl; SchPl; RptrSchPpr; FFA; PpCl; Vocational School; Auto Mechanics.

STUDEBAKER, Gregory S; Haven HS; Haven, KS; TrsFrshCls; TrsSophCls; PresJrCls; HstSrCls; Chr; HonRl; NHS; StuCncl; Ftbl; Trk; Harding Col Pre Med.

STUDEBAKER, Shirley; Gull Lake HS; Richland, MI; HonRl; JrNHS; NatlMeritSF; SciCl; Trk; GAA; IMSpt; PresAwd; Mich St U; Vet.

STUDENT, Suzanne P; Edina East HS; Edina, MN; Quill&Scroll; EdYrBk; Chrldr; NCTE; Carleton College.

STUDER, Dean J; Garrigan HS; Wesley, IA; HonRl; LbryAde; MthCl; SciCl; Iowa State Univ; Horticulture.

STUDER, Jane C; Sherburn HS; Sherburn, MN; 3/62 Band; ChrhWkr; CncrtBnd; HonRl; MrchBnd; NHS; PepBnd; SchPpr; CaptTennis; St Cloud State Col; Physical Therapy.

STUDER, Terrence M; T F South HS; Lansing, IL; NHS; StuGov; RptrSchPpr; LatCl; Swmmng; University Of Illinois; Dentistry.

STUDIER, Karen M; Superior HS; Superior, NE; ALAGirlsSt; CmntyWkr; LbryAde; PolWkr; StuCncl; TchrAde; YthFlsp; YthLg; FBLA; FHA; U Of Ne; Music Performer.

STUDT, Jeff; Ritenour Sr HS; Overland, MO; HonRl; LitMag; OffAde; Quill&Scroll; RptrYrbk; SchPpr; Coll; Journ.

STUDY, Kimberley L; Warsaw Comm HS; Warsaw, IN; Chrs; HonRl; LbryAde; MrchBnd; OffAde; Modeling Fashion Designing Col; Professiona.

STUDZINSKI, Linda A; Edwin G Foreman HS; Chicago, IL; 2/354 HonRl; PolWkr; SchPl; SctActv; TchrAde; GerCl; Univ Of Il; Mathematics.

STUEBE, Suzanne M; Bedford North HS; Bedford, IN; 69/380 Chr; HonRl; NatlMeritSF; SchMus; SchPl; EdYrBk; SecGerCl; PpCl; Swmmng; GAA; College; Science.

STUEBS, Lois M; Manitowoc Lutheran HS; Kewaunee, WI; Band; Chr; Chrs; ChrhWkr; CncrtBnd; PepBnd; PpCl; Bsbl; LetterBsktbl; LetterTrk; IMSpt; College.

STUECHELI, Kenneth J; Libertyville HS; Libertyville, IL; 50/460 HonRl; JrNHS; NHS; LetterFtbl; LetterWrstlng; Univ; Ecology.

STUECKROTH, Dawn M; Solomon Juneau HS; Milwaukee, WI; ChrhWkr; HonRl; HospAde; MrchBnd; NHS; OffAde; SchAde; SctActv; GerCl; PpCl; Marquette Univ; Medical Tech.

STUEDEMANN, Sharon R; Central Comm HS; De Witt, IA; AFS; Band; Chrs; NHS; SchMus; YthFlsp; EdYrBk; SpnCl; BttyCrckrAwd; 4-HAwd; Coll; Dictitian.

STUENKEL, Barbara A; Rich South HS; Monee, IL; 10/280 ChrhWkr; HonRl; NHS; StuCncl; Teen; YthFlsp; FHA; Prairie State Jr College; Accounting.

STUERMAN, Beth A; Gary Public HS; Gary, SD; PresSophCls; PresJrCls; Band; ChrhWkr; HonRl; SchPl; StuCncl; 4-H; Bsktbl; Swmmng; College.

STUERMAN, Fay L; Gary HS; Gary, SD; 2/13 TrsSophCls; Band; Chrs; ChrhWkr; CmntyWkr; HonRl; JA; JrNHS; MrchBnd; NHS; Bsktbl; Chrldr; BttyCrckrAwd; Trade School; Office Machine Repair.

STUESSE, Suzanne K; Union HS; Leslie, MO; 22/174 Chr; ChrhWkr; HonRl; TchrAde; College; Remedial Educ.

STUESSY, Mary S; Platteville HS; Platteville, WI; Band; CncrtBnd; HonRl; HospAde; Orch; SchMus; FSA; SpnCl; SciCl; KiwanAwd; Univ Of Wi; Astronemy.

STUEVE, Sandra M; Graceville Public HS; Dumont, MN; Band; Chrs; HonRl; NHS; StuCncl; Yrbk; SchPpr; LetterFtbl; Chrldr; GAA; PPFtbl; PresAwd; Business School; Vocation.

STUEVER, Dale R; Capac HS; Capac, MI; HonRl; TchrAde; Pres4-H; PresFFA; KeyCl; 4-HAwd; Michigan State Univ; Farming.

STUEWE, Shirley; Lutheran HS; Norwood, MN; 4/65 Chr; HonRl; NHS; RptrSchPpr; PPFtbl; PresAwd; Bethany Luthern Coll; Soc Serv.

STUEWE, Shirley D; Lutheran HS; Norwood, MN; SecSophCls; Chr; HonRl; NHS; StuCncl; PresFTA; CaptBsktbl; Trk; PPFtbl; PresAwd; College; Social Work.

STUFFLEBEAM, Mark G; Lewistown Comm HS; Lewistown, IL; Aud/Vis; ChrhWkr; CtyCnl; CmntyWkr; NHS; PolWkr; RedCrAde; YthFnd;.

STUHLER, Jean C; St Peter And Paul HS; Saginaw, MI; CmntyWkr; HospAde; FDA; FrCl; SpnCl; PpCl; Michigan State; Doctor.

STUHR, Cristine B; La Salle Peru HS; Peru, IL; Chr; ChrhWkr; CmntyWkr; HonRl; PolWkr; SchMus; YthFlsp; FrCl; IMSpt; PresAwd; College; Music.

STUHR, Cynthia E; Bradshaw HS; Bradshaw, NE; 1/16 SecFrshCls; VPSophCls; PresJrCls; Band; Chr; CncrtBnd; DrmMjrt; HonRl; MrchBnd; PepBnd; Univ Of Nebraska; Interior Deisgn.

STUIBER, Sydney; Valders HS; Whitelaw, WI; 29#37#41 MrchBnd; RptrSchPpr; Ftbl; Trade School; Machinist.

STUKEY, Mary J; Northrop HS; Fort Wayne, IN; 18/643 Chr; HonRl; Orch; SchMus; YthFlsp; EdSchPpr; Univ Purdue; Mathematics.

STULL, Cheryl L; Melcher Dallas HS; Lacona, IA; DrlTm; HonRl; SchMus; StuCncl; Yrbk; 4-H; FrCl; Bsbl; Bsktbl; LetterTrk; Chrldr; 4-HAwd; Iowa State University.

STULL, Deborah L; Streator HS; Streator, IL; Band; ChrhWkr; CncrtBnd; DrmMjrt; HonRl; MrchBnd; PepBnd; SchMus; PresFTA; SecSpnCl; University; Law.

STULL, Kimberly S; Beach HS; Beach, ND; 5/42 HstFrshCls; Band; Chr; Chrs; CncrtBnd; DrlTm; HonRl; MrchBnd; NHS; PepBnd; SchPl; StuCncl; YthFlsp; LetterBsktbl; Chrldr; Univ; Teacher.

STULTS, Judy; Argos Community HS; Argos, IN; 14/73 Chrs; HonRl; LbryAde; SchMus; 4-H; 4-HAwd;.

STULTZ, Kathi A; Madison HS; Madison, NE; Band; Chr; CncrtBnd; HonRl; LbryAde; MrchBnd; PepBnd; Twrl; 4-H; PpCl; Hesston College; Social Worker.

STULTZ, Steven K; Evanston Township HS; Evanston, IL; Band; Chr; ChrhWkr; CncrtBnd; HonRl; MrchBnd; NatlMeritSF; SchAde; RptrSchPpr; EdSchPpr; Chicago Bible C; Missionary.

STULZ, Susan M; Rockridge HS; Muscatine, IA; 2/144 HonRl; NHS; SchMus; RptrYrbk; FrCl; Bsktbl; College; Science.

STUMF, Rosann M; Hemingford HS; Hemingford, NE; PresFrshCls; Band; Chrs; HonRl; PepBnd; StuCncl; RptrSchPpr; FHA; Trk; Chrldr; GAA; College; Physical Ed.

STUMFF, Allen L; Columbia HS; Columbia, IL; Trade School; Mechanic.

STUMMER, Tim M; St Josephs HS; Kenosha, WI; 3/165 Band; CncrtBnd; DrlTm; HonRl; LbryAde; MrchBnd; NHS; Orch; PepBnd; SchMus; College; Accounting.

STUMP, Judy A; Jasper HS; Jasper, MO; TrsSophCls; Chr; Chrs; ChrhWkr; StuCncl; Pres4-H; FHA; TreasFTA; PpCl; Bsbl; Business School; Secretarial.

STUMP, Paul E; La Porte City Comm HS; La Porte City, IA; 3/77 PresJrCls; ALBoysSt; Band; CncrtBnd; HonRl; MrchBnd; NatlThespSoc; PepBnd; PolWkr; SchPl; StuCncl; StuGov; College.

STUMPF, Chris; Manson Community HS; Manson, IA; SecSrCls; Band; Chr; CncrtBnd; MrchBnd; Yrbk; FNA; Swmmng; Tennis; College; Medical Assistant.

STUMPF, Ida Lee; Valmeyer HS; Valmeyer, IL; 2/39 SecFrshCls; SecSophCls; Band; Chr; Chrs; HonRl; NHS; SchMus; SchPl; StuCncl; TchrAde; Chrldr; Univ Of Illinois.

STUMPF, Jane; Rockwell City Comm HS; Rockwell City, IA; Chrs; HonRl; SchMus; FHA; Trade School; Law Enforcement.

STUMPF, Lynette A; Atwater Public HS; Atwater, MN; 3/52 SecTrsJrCls; VPSrCls; ALAGirlsSt; NHS; SecStuCncl; EdYrBk; EdSchPpr; PresFHA; Bsktbl; Chrldr; GAA; Willmar Area Vo Tech; Legal Secretary.

STUMPF, Patty A; Calhoun HS; Batchtown, IL; Chrs; HonRl; NHS; EdYrBk; SecCivCl; FTA; IMSpt; Col; Vocation.

STUMPS, Janet L; Holyrood HS; Holyrood, KS; 4/16 VPJrCls; TrsSrCls; Band; Chr; Chrs; ChrhWkr; HonRl; MrchBnd; AmLegAwd; University; Professional.

STUNDA, David G; Mt Vernon HS; Greenfield, IN; ALBoysSt; HonRl; NHS; NatlThespSoc; SchMus; RptrYrbk;.

STUNDERFORD, Kent W; Humboldt HS; Humboldt, NE; Chrs; ChrhWkr; CncrtBnd; HonRl; MrchBnd; SctActv; TchrAde; Bsbl; Wrstlng; AmLegAwd; Univ; Music.

STUNTEBECK, Laurie S; Centerville Public HS; Centerville, SD; Band; Chr; Chrs; HonRl; LbryAde; SchAde; TchrAde; FHA; PpCl; College; Professional.

STUPP, Joan E; Mehlville Sr HS; St Louis, MO; 52/500 HonRl; LitMag; NHS; Quill&Scroll; SchMus; EdYrBk; Yrbk; FrCl; SciCl; Univ Of Missouri; Writing.

STUPP, Paula J; Mehlville HS; St Louis, MO; 131/592 ChrhWkr; HonRl; HospAde; Quill&Scroll; SctActv; StuGov; EdYrBk; FrCl; PpCl; Southeast Mo State; Business Administration.

STUPPY, Robert J; Valle HS; Ste Genevieve, MO; 5/85 VPFrshCls; HonRl; NHS; IMSpt; PPFtbl; Univ Of Missouri; Medical Doctor.

STURDEVANT, Jo; Waterford Mott Hs; Pontiac, MI; Chr; ChrhWkr; HonRl; SchAde; SchPl; YthFlsp; Yrbk; JCAwd; College; Speicial Education.

STURE, Rita J; Pork Hill Sr HS; Kansas City, MO; CmntyWkr; HonRl; MrchBnd; NatlThespSoc; 4-H; LetterTrk; GAA; IMSpt; PPFtbl; PresAwd; Missouri Western Univ; Professional.

STUREK, Chris J; Industry HS; Industry, IL; PresSophCls; HonRl; SchPl; StuCncl; SciCl; LetterFtbl; LetterGlf; IMSpt; Bradley Univ; Construction.

STUREK, Michael; Industry HS; Industry, IL; 7/35 TrsSophCls; PresJrCls; HstJrCls; HonRl; Bsktbl; CaptFtbl; Glf; LetterTrk; IMSpt; DanFAwd; Augustana Coll;pe Or Bus Admin.

STUREK, Michael S; Industry HS; Industry, IL; 8/35 TrsSophCls; PresJrCls; PresSrCls; HonRl; GerCl; SciCl; Bsktbl; CaptFtbl; Glf; Augustana College; P E Teacher.

STURGEON, Cynthia J; Benton Central HS; Oxford, IN; 10/283 Band; CncrtBnd; HonRl; MrchBnd; NHS; PepBnd; PresKeyCl; Purdue U; Animal Science.

STURGILL, John E; Niantie Harristown HS; Decatur, IL; CmntyWkr; HonRl; NHS; SchPl; StuCncl; SpnCl; LetterTrk; College; Art.

STURGILL, Rod W; Grass Lake HS; Grass Lake, MI; 2/100 VPFrshCls; VPJrCls; HonRl; NHS; SchPl; StuCncl; RptrYrbk; SchPpr; CaptBsbl; CaptBsktbl; CaptFtbl; Trk; DanFAwd;.

STURGIS, Brenda; East Noble HS; Kendallville, IN; SecFrshCls; SecSophCls; SecJrCls; SecSrCls; Band; CncrtBnd; HonRl; MrchBnd; Teen; PpCl; In Univ; Comp Tech.

STURING, Stanley J; Pella Christian HS; Oskaloosa, IA; Chr; ChrhWkr; HonRl; SchPl; Bsbl; LetterTrk; IMSpt; Dordt College.

STURKEY, Vanessa; Rezin Orr HS; Chicago, IL; Chr; Chrs; HonRl; College.

STURM, Lori D; Lesterville HS; Lesterville, MO; Band; Chrs; HonRl; PepBnd; Yrbk; PpCl; University; Professional.

STURM, Mark A; Plano HS; Plano, IL; 2/97 SecSrCls; HonRl; NatlMeritCmnd; PresFFA; Wrstlng; Bemidji State College; Fisheries Biologist.

STURN, John; Bushton HS; Bushton, KS; VPSophCls; PresJrCls; ALBoysSt; HonRl; NHS; Bsbl; Bsktbl; GodCntryAwd; Univ.

STURN, Peter R; Menasha Senior HS; Menasha, WI; Bsktbl; Ftbl; CchngActv; IMSpt; College.

STUTTS, Kathy S; Wilmington HS; Wilmington, IL; 3/137 HonRl; SchPl; RptrYrbk; SpnCl; MthCl; PpCl; Socr; Chrldr; CchngActv; Northern Illinois Univ; Sciences.

STUTZ, Doris S; Alton Senior HS; Alton, IL; JrNHS; TchrAde; College; Accounting.

STUTZ, Robin; Northridge HS; Middlebury, IN; Chr; HonRl; Twrl; PpCl; Trk; Chrldr; GAA;.

STUTZMAN, Cindy; Hot Springs HS; Hot Springs, SD; Band; CncrtBnd; HonRl; MrchBnd; NHS; PepBnd; TchrAde; FrCl; PpCl; College; Elementary Education.

STUTZMAN, Cynthia S; Van Buren HS; Birmingham, IA; CtyCnl; CmntyWkr; JA; NHS; StuGov; YthFnd; YthLg; MthCl; GovHonPrgAwd; JCAwd; College.

STUTZMAN, Kathy; Halstead HS; Halstead, KS; 1/66 Band; ChrhWkr; CncrtBnd; HonRl; NHS; OffAde; YthFlsp; 4-H; 4-HAwd; CitAwd; Business School; Executive Secretary.

STUWE, Gretchen; Dundee HS; Dundee, MI; 5/126 Band; CncrtBnd; HonRl; NHS; NatlMeritCmnd; PepBnd; SchPl; FTA; GerCl; Msu; Health Profession.

STYBR, David J; Coal City HS; Coal City, IL; 9/91 Aud/Vis; Band; Chrs; ChrhWkr; CncrtBnd; HonRl; MrchBnd; NatlMeritSchl; PepBnd; Joliet Jr College; Chemical Engineer.

STYPA, James A; Manistee Catholic Central HS; Manistee, MI; ALBoysSt; Band; CmntyWkr; CncrtBnd; DrmMjrt; HonRl; MrchBnd; NatlMeritSF; PepBnd; Bsktbl; Ftbl; Michigan State Univ; Business Admin.

STYRCZULA, Sophie A; St Ann HS; Chicago, IL; TrsJrCls; Chr; HonRl; JA; RedCrAde; SchPpr; SpnCl; JAAwd; College; Doctor.

STYS, Marybeth J; Greenfield HS; Greenfield, WI; Band; CncrtBnd; HonRl; MrchBnd; NHS; NatlMeritCmnd; Col; Music.

SUAD, Mary I; Superior HS; Guide Rock, NE; Chrs; HonRl; NHS; RedCrAde; 4-H; FHA; PpCl; DARAwd; VoiceDemAwd; Univ Of Nebr; Professional.

SUAREZ, Edith A; Richmond Sr HS; Richmond, IN; Band; ChrhWkr; CncrtBnd; MrchBnd; SpnCl; Bsbl; Bsktbl; Swmmng; Tennis; GAA; College; Music Law.

SUAREZ, Suzanne; Lasalle Peru HS; La Salle, IL; ChrhWkr; CmntyWkr; HospAde; JrNHS; PolWkr; StuGov; RptrYrbk; FBLA; GAA; IMSpt; University; Secretarial.

SUBBERT, Mary; St Anne Community Hs; St Anne, IL; 11/150 CncrtBnd; HonRl; JA; MrchBnd; OffAde; YthFlsp; FNA; FTA; GAA; 4-HAwd; Kankakee Community College;forestry.

SUBER, Michael A; Southwestern HS; Flint, MI; CmntyWkr; PolWkr; Univ Of Michigan; Business.

SUCH, Albert J; Stanley Boyd HS; Stanley, WI; 10/113 ALBoysSt; HonRl; Univ; Math.

SUCHODOLSKI, Charles V; All Saints Central HS; Bay City, MI; Chrs; HonRl; SchMus; Trk; Central Mich U; Accontant.

SUCHOMEL, Jeffrey R; St Joseph HS; La Grange Park, IL; 28/175 TreasBand; ChrhWkr; CncrtBnd; HonRl; PepBnd; PolWkr; SctActv; GerCl; University; Law.

SUCHOMEL, Joanne J; Necedah HS; Necedah, WI; CncrtBnd; HonRl; MrchBnd; OffAde;.

SUCHTA, Kathleen C; Maine West HS; Des Plaines, IL; CncrtBnd; HonRl; MrchBnd; NatlMeritCmnd; Orch; PepBnd; Univ; Music.

SUCKOW, Mark; Van Meter Comm HS; Van Meter, IA; Band; HonRl; MrchBnd; PepBnd; SchPl; YthFlsp; PpCl; Washburn Univ; Accounting.

SUCKUT, Charlotte M; Sheyenne River Academy; Bowdon, ND; 4/17 VPSrCls; Chr; CncrtBnd; OffAde; StuCncl; StuGov; Yrbk; RptrSchPpr; 4-H; CaptFtbl; College; Veterinarian Science.

SUDA, Marianne; St Joseph HS; Chicago, IL; 1/123 VPFrshCls; TrsSophCls; TrsJrCls; StuCncl; Bsbl; Bsktbl; CchngActv; GAA; College; Medicine.

SUDAC, Cecelia M; Kingsford HS; Kingsford, MI; 2/163 TrsJrCls; ChrhWkr; HonRl; JrNHS; NHS; StuCncl; RptrYrbk; RptrSchPpr; EdSchPpr; SchPpr; Mi Technological.

SUDBECK, Jeanne; B B HS; Seneca, KS; Chrs; CmntyWkr; HonRl; SchPl; StuCncl; FHA; Beautician School; Beautician.

SUDBECK, Steven J; Wynot Public HS; Hartington, NE; StuCncl; Bsbl; Ftbl; Wrstlng;.

SUDBROCK, Becky L; Southeast Warren HS; Lucas, IA; HonRl; 4-H; LetterBsbl; Bsktbl; IMSpt; 4-HAwd; PresAwd; Trade Sch; Bus.

SUDDITH, Ronnie W; Tina Avalon HS; Bogard, MO; ALBoysSt; Band; CncrtBnd; HonRl; Central Missouri State Univ; Teaching.

SUDDS, Karen L; Wheaton Central HS; Wheaton, IL; SecJrCls; Chr; HonRl; HospAde; NHS; NatlMeritCmnd; SchMus; SchPl; YthFlsp; Trk; Northwestern Univ; Medicine.

SUDDUTH, Kenneth A; Fatima HS; Westphalia, MO; Chrs; HonRl; U Of Missouri.

SUDDUTH, Pamela S; Springfield Se HS; Springfield, IL; 41/450 OffAde; TchrAde; FrCl; College; Professional.

SUDERMAN, Carol D; Newton HS; Newton, KS; 16/317 Chr; Chrs; ChrhWkr; HonRl; SchPl; TchrAde; YthFlsp; 4-H; Clge; Pro.

SUDERMAN, Carole; Mt Lake HS; Mountain Lake, MN; 3/72 NHS; NatlMeritCmnd; SchMus; RptrSchPpr; Glf; Trk; GAA; IMSpt; Bethel College; Elementary Education.

SUDERMAN, Joel E; Hillsboro HS; Marin, KS; 4/66 SecTrsSophCls; Band; Chrs; ChrhWkr; HonRl; Mdrgl; ModUN; OffAde; TchrAde; PresFFA; Tabor Col; Business Administration.

SUEEN, Glenn M; St Ignatius College Prep; Chicago, IL; ChrhWkr; CmntyWkr; LitMag; Northwestern Univ; Pre Medicine.

SUEHRING, Kim E; Marion HS; Clintonville, WI; SecTrsSophCls; ALAGirlsSt; Band; CncrtBnd; HonRl; MrchBnd; NHS; PepBnd; StuCncl; TchrAde; Vocation.

SUEHS, Roger L; Little Wolf HS; Manawa, WI; ALBoysSt; Band; ChrhWkr; HonRl; MrchBnd; NHS; PepBnd; 4-H; FFA; Ftbl; Horticulture & Landscaping.

SUELMANN, Thomas R; Duchesne HS; Saint Charles, MO; 2/130 HonRl; NHS; NatlMeritFnl; NatlMeritSchl; NatlMeritSF; RptrYrbk; RptrSchPpr; FrCl; Georgetown U; Interpreter German.

SUEPER, Cathy J; St Francis HS; Humphrey, NE; PresSophCls; Chrs; HonRl; SchMus; StuCncl; TchrAde; 4-H; PpCl; College; Professional.

SUEPER, Melvin R; Holy Family HS; Lindsay, NE; 1/33 HonRl; NHS; SchPl; StuCncl; PresSophCls; 4-H; Bsbl; Ftbl; IMSpt; AmLegAwd; Bus Sch.

SUESS, Cynthia M; Comfrey Public HS; Comfrey, MN; Band; Chr; CncrtBnd; HonRl; MrchBnd; PepBnd; RptrSchPpr; FHA; SciCl; LetterChrldr; College; Medical Lab Technician.

SUESS, Jacqueline J; Elk Mound HS; Elkmound, WI; 3/45 PresJrCls; SecSrCls; ALAGirlsSt; Band; Chr; Chrs; ChrhWkr; CncrtBnd; HonRl; GAA; Univ ; Pro.

SUEVER, Michael; Northrop HS; Fort Wayne, IN; HonRl; NatlFornLg; SchPpr; SciCl; Tennis; Indiana Univ; Chemistry.

SUFFICOOL, Craig A; Crofton Public HS; Crofton, NE; PresSophCls; Chr; Chrs; ChrhWkr; ModUN; SchAde; SctActv; TchrAde; LetterFtbl; LetterTrk; Navy.

SUGA, Les J; Yankton HS; Yankton, SD; ALBoysSt; ChrhWkr; CmntyWkr; HonRl; NatlFornLg; NHS; NatlThespSoc; OffAde; SchMus; SchPl; YthLg; SpnCl; AmLegAwd; Univ Of South Dakota; Medicine.

SUGAS, William C; Richmond HS; Richmond, IN; HonRl; NHS; Quill&Scroll; SpnCl; Univ; Computer Science.

SUGG, Cathy A; Brown City HS; Melvin, MI; Band; ChrhWkr; HonRl; StuCncl; TchrAde; Yrbk; FHA; PresFTA; Bsktbl; Chrldr; College; Social Work.

SUGHROUE, Angie M; Holdrege Sr HS; Holdrege, NE; Chr; Chrs; HonRl; SchMus; FBLA; PpCl; Trk; College.

SUGHROUE, Christy M; Republican Valley HS; Stockville, NE; Band; CncrtBnd; HonRl; MrchBnd; PepBnd; SecStuCncl; RptrYrbk; RptrSchPpr; 4-H; PpCl; LetterTrk; Chrldr; PresGAA; College; Agricuture.

SUGIHARA, Joseph N; Elgin HS; Streamwood, IL; 25/868 HonRl; FrCl; LatCl; Electrical.

SUHANY, Barbara J; Dexter HS; Dexter, MO; ChrhWkr; HonRl; NHS; OffAde; TchrAde; FBLA; MthCl; PpCl; SciCl; Baptist Memorial Hosp; Rn.

SUHL, Cindy L; Sullivan HS; Sullivan, IL; SecTrsJrCls; Chrs; HonRl; NHS; OffAde; 4-H; FTA; FrCl; SciCl; GAA; Lakeland Clg; Accounting.

SUHR, Dawn; South Adams HS; Bryant, IN; 1/120 CncrtBnd; MrchBnd; NatlMeritCmnd; PepBnd; TchrAde; FrCl; Ball State Univ; Math Computerscience.

SUHRE, Steven C; Shawnee HS; Mc Clure, IL; 2/64 FBLA; FTA; FrCl; PpCl; Bsbl; Bsktbl; IMSpt; U Of Il; Accounting.

SUHRE, Steven C; Shawnee HS; Mcclure, IL; 2/64 HonRl; FBLA; FTA; FrCl; PpCl; Univ Of Ill; Accounting.

SUHUSKY, Craig A; Wayland Union HS; Wayland, MI; 1/140 VPBand; CmntyWkr; VPCncrtBnd; HonRl; MrchBnd; NHS; PepBnd; SchMus; EldAwd; Western Michigan Univ; Music.

SUHY, Paula M; St Clement HS; Warren, MI; TrsSophCls; HonRl; NHS; OffAde; Yrbk; FHA; PpCl; Chrldr; IMSpt; Coll; Bus.

SUITCA, Cathy L; Joliet Central HS; Joliet, IL; 8/491 Chr; HonRl; NHS; SchMus; RptrYrbk; GerCl; PpCl; Chrldr; Loyola Univ; Nursing.

SUITER, Janice L; Weaubleau R Iii HS; Quincy, MO; SecFrshCls; SecSophCls; Chrs; DrmMjrt; HonRl; SchPl; PresStuCncl; Yrbk; SchPpr; VPFHA; Interior Decorating.

SUJKOWSKI, Timothy J; Bay City Central HS; Bay City, MI; HonRl; College; Electronics.

SUKALSKI, Gloria L; East Chain HS; Fairmont, MN; 4/26 TrsFrshCls; Chrs; CncrtBnd; HonRl; SchMus; SchPl; StuCncl; Twrl; EdYrBk; Chrldr; College; Teaching.

SUKOVATY, Connie S; Wilber Clatonia HS; Wilber, NE; Band; CncrtBnd; HonRl; LbryAde; MrchBnd; PepBnd; SchAde; SchPl; TchrAde; FBLA; Secretary.

SUKOWATEY, Carol R; Oakfield HS; Oakfield, WI; 5/56 Band; CncrtBnd; HonRl; MrchBnd; NHS; OffAde; PepBnd; StuCncl; SptEdSchPpr; Chrldr; Tech Schl Or Col; Professional.

SUKOWATY, Stanley G; Reedsville Public HS; Cato, WI; 18/99 HonRl; NHS; FHA; Ne Wisconsin Tech Inst; Computer Data Proc.

SUKOWICZ, Mark J; Brother Rice HS; Chicago, IL; Northern Ill Univ; Accounting.

SULASKI, Susan M; Woodruff HS; Peoria, IL; 57/281 AFS; Chr; Chrl; Chrs; DrlTm; SchMus; SctActv; KeyCl; FrCl; Univ Il; French/accounting.

SULENTIC, Cathy; Lead HS; Deadwood, SD; TrsFrshCls; SecSophCls; ChrhWkr; HonRl; StuCncl; StuGov; PpCl; Swmmng; Chrldr; PPFtbl; Univ; Medical Tech.

SULKOWSKI, Richard P; Carmel HS; Libertyville, IL; 7/180 HonRl; IntrClCncl; NHS; NatlMeritSF; FrCl; PpCl; Tennis; Loyola Univ; Attorney.

SULLENS, Leslie A; Memorial HS; Joplin, MO; 4/221 AFS; HonRl; ModUN; VPNatlFornLg; SecNHS; NatlMeritCmnd; SchPl; StuCncl; EdSchPpr; Missouri Univ; Journalism.

SULLINGER, Jana C; Pittsburg HS; Pittsburg, KS; 13/283 Orch; SchMus; SchPl; LatCl; Tennis; CchngActv; GAA; IMSpt; DARAwd; KiwanAwd; College; Medical.

SULLINS, Harold; Roseville HS; Roseville, MI; 58/534 Aud/Vis; HonRl; NHS; ROTC; SchAde; Bsbl;.

SULLIVAN, Albert J; Dekalb Sr HS; Dekalb, IL; ALBoysSt; KeyCl; Univ; Professional.

SULLIVAN, Amy J; Taylorville Sr HS; Taylorville, IL; 62/300 Aud/Vis; Band; Chrs; ChrhWkr; CncrtBnd; DrlTm; LbryAde; MrchBnd; NatlThespSoc; PepBnd; SchMus; SchPl; SctActv; YthFlsp; College; Professional.

SULLIVAN, Barbara K; Logan HS; Lacrosse, WI; 27/226 Chrs; HonRl; NHS; OffAde; Yrbk; FrCl; PpCl;

Trk; Chrldr; IMSpt; Western Wi Tech Inst; Commercial Art.

SULLIVAN, Bobby G; Stoutland HS; Lebanon, MO; Chrs; SchAde; StuCncl; TchrAde; SchPpr; EngCl; PpCl; LetterBsbl; CchngActv; IMSpt; College; Teacher.

SULLIVAN, Brenda K; Jennings HS; St Louis, MO; Band; Chr; PresChrhWkr; HospAde; StuCncl; TchrAde; FHA; VPFNA; FrCl; GAA; Junior College; Medical Office Assistant.

SULLIVAN, Brian J; Notre Dame HS; Niles, IL; 26/278 VPFrshCls; PresSophCls; PresSrCls; HonRl; PolWkr; SchMus; SchPl; StuGov; RptrYrbk; PpCl; LetterFtbl; Trk; Chrldr; CchngActv; College; Broadcasting.

SULLIVAN, Carolyn A; Charles City Comm HS; Charles City, IA; ChrhWkr; HonRl; NHS; FHA; FNA; MthCl; SciCl; GovHonPrgAwd; CitAwd; U Of Iowa; Dental Hygiene.

SULLIVAN, Cheryle L; Kingsford HS; Kingsford, MI; 3/163 HonRl; JrNHS; NHS; SecStuCncl; RptrYrbk; 4-H; Coll; Pre Med.

SULLIVAN, Christine; Edgewood HS; Madison, WI; Chrs; CmntyWkr; HonRl; Swmmng; Tennis; Univ Dotre Dame.

SULLIVAN, Christine L; Notre Dame HS; Quincy, IL; Gem City Business Schl; Legal Secretary.

SULLIVAN, Colleen M; Taylor Center HS; Taylor, MI; ChrhWkr; CmntyWkr; HonRl; LitMag; LbryAde; OffAde; SchPl; TchrAde; Western Michigan Univ; Medicine.

SULLIVAN, Daniel P; Dunlap HS; Dunlap, IL; PresSophCls; ALBoysSt; HonRl; JrNHS; VPNHS; SctActv; TchrAde; Yrbk; LatCl; PpCl; LetterBsbl; LetterBsktbl; LetterGlf; University; Art.

SULLIVAN, David M; Central Catholic HS; Bloomington, IL; ChrhWkr; SctActv; FrCl; SciCl; Bsbl; Ftbl; College; Accounting.

SULLIVAN, Deborah M; North Liberty HS; North Liberty, IN; 8/100 VPBand; ChrhWkr; CncrtBnd; HonRl; MrchBnd; TreasNHS; SchMus; VPYthFlsp; FrCl; DARAwd; Ball St U; Teacher.

SULLIVAN, Debra; Appleton Public HS; Appleton, MN; HonRl; 4-H; SpnCl; Trk; 4-HAwd; PresAwd; Bookkeeper.

SULLIVAN, Debra K; Andover HS; Wichita, KS; NHS; NatlMeritFnl; RedCrAde; SchPl; StuCncl; RptrYrbk; SchPpr; SpnCl; CitAwd; VoiceDemAwd; Univ; Bio Sci.

SULLIVAN, Edwin S; Parkway West HS; St Louis, MO; Aud/Vis; CmntyWkr; JrNHS; NatlMeritSF; SctActv; Socr; GodCntryAwd; Univ; Psych.

SULLIVAN, F P; Denison HS; Denison, IA; PresJrCls; ALBoysSt; ChrhWkr; StuCncl; LetterLetterFtbl; LetterTrk; College; Professional Athelete.

SULLIVAN, Georgia K; Peoria Heights HS; Peoria Heights, IL; 1/99 Band; CncrtBnd; HonRl; MrchBnd; NHS; PepBnd; GerCl; LetterTrk; Chrldr; Illinois State University; Teaching.

SULLIVAN, Glenn; Evergreen Park HS; Evergreen Park, IL; Band; ChrhWkr; CncrtBnd; HonRl; MrchBnd; NatlThespSoc; SchPl; TchrAde; CchngActv; Southern Ill U; Ministry.

SULLIVAN, James B; Marian Catholic HS; Riverdale, IL; 23/375 CAP; HonRl; NHS; NatlMeritSF; SctActv; SciCl; LionAwd; St Josephs Coll; Civil/environmental Engin.

SULLIVAN, Jane E; Bourbon HS; Leasburg, MO; HospAde; JA; JrNHS; NHS; NatlMeritSchl; RedCrAde; ROTC; GAA; 4-HAwd; JAAwd; Busi Sch; Sec.

SULLIVAN, Jean M; Kewanee HS; Kewanee, IL; PresSrCls; HonRl; SchMus; SchPl; StuCncl; RptrYrbk; FrCl; LetterTennis; LetterTrk; CaptChrldr; College; Theatre Or Foreign Language.

SULLIVAN, Jeff M; Mormon Trail HS; Weldon, IA; PresSophCls; SecJrCls; HonRl; SchPl; YthFlsp; RptrSchPpr; 4-H; FFA; LetterBsbl; LetterFtbl; LetterTrk; LetterWrstlng; 4-HAwd; College; Vocation.

SULLIVAN, Jerald B; Sentral HS; Armstrong, IA; 9/37 PresFrshCls; PresSophCls; ChrhWkr; HonRl; NHS; StuCncl; FFA; LetterFtbl; LetterTrk; AmLegAwd; VoiceDemAwd; Iowa St Univ; Agriculture.

SULLIVAN, John K; Jeffersonville HS; Jeffersonville, IN; 39/556 Chr; HonRl; Bsktbl; IMSpt; Butler Univ; Pharmacy.

SULLIVAN, Julie; West HS; Rockford, IL; 19/324 TrsSophCls; TrsJrCls; VPSrCls; Chr; HonRl; Mdrgl; NHS; SchMus; Eastern Il Univ; History.

SULLIVAN, Katherine N; Charleston HS; Charleston, IL; 37/258 Chr; Chrs; HonRl; NatlFornLg; NatlMeritCmnd; SchMus; SchPl; GAA; Eastern Ill Univ; Theatre.

SULLIVAN, Katherine J; Anderson HS; Anderson, IN; Band; Chr; CncrtBnd; HospAde; MrchBnd; TrsSophCls; Swmmng; Ball Mem Hosp Sch Of Radiologic Tech.

SULLIVAN, Kathleen; St Francis Academy; Joliet, IL; 23/189 CmntyWkr; HonRl; SecNHS; StuCncl; TchrAde; RptrYrbk; RptrSchPpr; FrCl; College; Liberal Arts.

SULLIVAN, Kathleen M; Proviso East HS; Maywood, IL; 46/735 ALAGirlsSt; LbryAde; NHS; NatlMeritCmnd; SciCl; Bsktbl; College; Professional.

SULLIVAN, Kathleen R; Meridian HS; Daykin, NE; Band; ChrhWkr; CtyCnl; HospAde; PepBnd; SchMus; StuGov; GAA; PPFtbl; 4-HAwd; Servic; Ferrier.

SULLIVAN, Laura A; North Vigo HS; Terre Haute, IN; Aud/Vis; Chr; SecJA; LbryAde; VPTeen; Chrldr; GAA; PPFtbl; Cosmetology School.

SULLIVAN, Linda M; Academy Of Our Lady; Chicago, IL; 3/164 HonRl; Univ Of Ill; Psychology.

SULLIVAN, Marilyn J; Mother Of Sorrows HS; Chicago, IL; Chrs; CmntyWkr; HonRl; PolWkr; SchAde; Twrl; RptrYrbk; SptEdYrbk; Yrbk; MthCl; SciCl; Chrldr; GAA; College; Medicine.

SULLIVAN, Mark E; Daleville HS; Daleville, IN; 1/92 PresFrshCls; PresSrCls; ALBoysSt; Aud/Vis; HonRl; NHS; LetterBsbl; Glf; LetterTrk; Wrstlng; College; Vet Medicine.

SULLIVAN, Mary K; Antioch Comm HS; Lake Villa, IL; Aud/Vis; Chr; ChrhWkr; HonRl; SchMus; RptrYrbk; EdYrBk; Northern Illinois Univ; Business Management.

SULLIVAN, Mary Margaret; Willowbrook HS; Villa Park, IL; Chr; ChrhWkr; CmntyWkr; HonRl; SchMus; StuCncl; StuGov; RptrSchPpr; Pres4-H; 4-HAwd; College Of St Francis; Medical Tech.

SULLIVAN, Maureen A; St Elizabeth Acad; St Louis, MO; 1/116 HonRl; NHS; NatlMeritSF; OffAde; SchMus; VPStuCncl; EdSchPpr; GAA; IMSpt; PPFtbl; U Of Notre Dame; Mathematics.

SULLIVAN, Maureen A; Resurrection HS; Chicago, IL; VPCncrtBnd; HonRl; MrchBnd; SchMus; GerCl; SpnCl; MthCl; VPSciCl; GAA; IMSpt; University Of Illinois; Pharmacist.

SULLIVAN, Michael A; Desmet Jesuit HS; St Louis, MO; 33/179 ChrhWkr; HonRl; NHS; PolWkr; SchPpr; Ftbl; CchngActv; Univ; Professional.

SULLIVAN, Michael J; Clay Center HS; Clay Center, NE; 2/27 ALBoysSt; Band; CncrtBnd; HonRl; NHS; PepBnd; SchPl; SctActv; TchrAde; Ftbl; LetterTrk; LetterWrstlng; Univ Of Ne; Medical Research.

SULLIVAN, Patricia K; Bourbon HS; Leasburg, MO; Band; Chrs; HonRl; LbryAde; StuGov; YthFlsp; RptrSchPpr; FHA; FTA; EngCl; Univ; Teacher.

SULLIVAN, Patrick E; Clay Center HS; Clay Center, NE; 3/30 HonRl; NHS; StuCncl; Ftbl; Trk; Wrstlng; Univ Of Ne; Lawyer.

SULLIVAN, Philip; St Patrick; Chicago, IL; HonRl; Lewis U ; Law.

SULLIVAN, Sandra R; Sentral Comm HS; Armstrong, IA; 8/38 VPJrCls; ALAGirlsSt; HonRl; Mdrgl; NHS; SchMus; RptrSchPpr; PpCl; Trk; BttyCrckrAwd; St Joseph Mercy; Nursing.

SULLIVAN, Sarah M; J E Murphy HS; Montreal, WI; 2/120 PresSrCls; HonRl; NatlMeritSF; SchMus; StuCncl; Yrbk; SchPpr; VPFrCl; PpCl; DARAwd; College; Business.

SULLIVAN, Sue E; Viroqua HS; Viroqua, WI; 14/121 Chr; Chrs; HonRl; Orch; SchMus; SchPl; 4-H; PpCl; GAA; 4-HAwd; Army.

SULLIVAN, Susan L; Sullivan HS; Sullivan, IL; Band; ChrhWkr; CncrtBnd; PepBnd; StuCncl; RptrYrbk; 4-H; Trk; Chrldr; GAA; Coll.

SULLIVAN, Tammie; Mason Senior HS; Mason, MI; Chrs; SchPl; TchrAde; YthFlsp; Business; Bookkeeper.

SULLIVAN, Theresa M; Duchesne Acad; Dunlap, IA; CmntyWkr; Sdlty; TchrAde; 4-H; 4-HAwd; Buena Vista Col; Art.

SULLIVAN, Tim; Mason City HS; Mason City, IA; VPFrshCls; TrsSophCls; HonRl; RptrSchPpr; Glf; Trk; IMSpt; GodCntryAwd; PresAwd; College; Journalist.

SULLIVAN, William; Shiloh Hs; Brocton, IL; 5/35 PresFrshCls; ChrhWkr; HonRl; StuCncl; 4-H; PresFFA; LetterBsktbl; AmLegAwd; 4-HAwd; College;ag.

SULLIVAN, William J; University City Sr HS; Universty City, MO; 10/401 Band; HonRl; HospAde; JCC; Orch; SctActv; StuCncl; SchPpr; LetterGlf; Socr; College; Md.

SULLIVAN, William T; Depue HS; Depue, IL; SecJrCls; Band; Chrs; ChrhWkr; CncrtBnd; HonRl; LbryAde; MrchBnd; PepBnd; SchAde; SchMus; Bsbl; St Louis Univ; Pharmacy.

SULZMAN, Melanie A; Decatur Community HS; Oberlin, KS; SecFrshCls; Chrs; ChrhWkr; RedCrAde; FHA; Swmmng; LetterTrk; Chrldr; GAA; IMSpt; Col; Nursing.

SUMAN, Amy C; Galesburg HS; Henderson, IL; Chr; HonRl; Mdrgl; NHS; SchMus; SecYthFlsp; VP4-H; PpCl; SciCl; GodCntryAwd; Vocational.

SUMIDA, Colin W; Downers Grove South HS; Downers Grove, IL; 1/830 HonRl; JrNHS; NHS; Orch; SctActv; StuCncl; Bsbl; LetterFtbl; LetterTrk; LetterWrstlng; Northwestern Univ; Doctor.

SUMINSKI, Rosanne M; Geneva Comm HS; Geneva, IL; AFS; Chr; HonRl; IntrClCncl; JrNHS; OffAde; StuCncl; FrCl; PpCl; Purdue Univ; Pharmacy.

SUMMER, Carol A; Olivet Community HS; Springport, MI; 7/58 SecSrCls; Band; ChrhWkr; DrmMjrt; HonRl; NHS; NatlThespSoc; PepBnd; SchMus; Trk; GAA; Michigan State Univ; Nursing.

SUMMERFORD, Daniel M; Central HS; St Joseph, MO; CmntyWkr; SchMus; Mo West State Clg; Art.

SUMMERS, Harvey; Adair County HS; Brashear, MO; VPJrCls; Band; CncrtBnd; HonRl; MrchBnd; SchPl; Mo State Iniv;.

SUMMERS, Jamie L; Crawford HS; Crawford, NE; 3/41 ALAGirlsSt; Chrs; HonRl; SchPl; TchrAde; YthFlsp; PpCl; IMSpt; PPFtbl; EldAwd; Oral Roberts Univ; Religion.

SUMMERS, Jane A; Southwest HS; St Louis, MO; Band; ChrhWkr; CncrtBnd; HonRl; MrchBnd; TchrAde; YthFlsp; PpCl; CaptChrldr; GAA; College; Nurse.

SUMMERS, Latisha; Southwestern HS; Flint, MI; 83/587 VPSophCls; Chr; Chrl; Chrs; CmntyWkr; HonRl; HospAde; Mdrgl; NHS; NatlMeritSchl; Olivet College; Vocal Music.

SUMMERS, Leetta S; Fountain Central HS; Veedersburg, IN; 3/128 Chr; ChrhWkr; HonRl; NHS; TchrAde; PpCl; Trk; GAA; IMSpt; 4-HAwd; College; Pharmacy.

SUMMERS, Mark G; Franklin HS; Livonia, MI; 70/695 Univ Of Mi; Bus Admn.

SUMMERS, Michael W; St Viator HS; Elk Grove, IL; 16/250 Band; ChrhWkr; CncrtBnd; HonRl; MrchBnd; NatlMeritCmnd; PolWkr; SctActv; StuCncl; SpnCl; College; Psychology.

SUMMERS, Richard; Camdenton R111 HS; Camdenton, MO; 22/156 Chr; ChrhWkr; HonRl; NHS; SctActv; Ftbl; Trk; GodCntryAwd; Linn Tech Coll; Auto Mech.

SUMMERS, Ricky L; Mullen _hs; Mullen, NE; 1/36 TrsSophCls; PresJrCls; PresSrCls; ALBoysSt; HonRl; SchPl; GerCl; Univ Of Nebr; Chemical Eng.

SUMMERS, Robin S; Marengo HS; Marengo, IN; TrsFrshCls; ALAGirlsSt; TreasChrs; TreasChrhWkr; HonRl; SchPl; Treas4-H; FHA; TreasPpCl; 4-HAwd;.

SUMMERS, Shirley A; Northwest HS; House Springs, MO; Band; Chr; Chrs; HonRl; LbryAde; PepBnd; SchPl; SctActv; TchrAde; College; Professional.

SUMMERS, Timothy K; Cowden Herrick HS; Cowden, IL; PresFrshCls; HonRl; StuCncl; StuGov; Yrbk; FFA; LetterBsbl; LetterBsktbl; LetterTrk; 4-HAwd; U; Professional.

SUMMERSIDE, Paul R; Lemars Community HS; Lemars, IA; 11/185 VPFrshCls; AFS; ALBoysSt; Chr; NHS; PolWkr; Bsktbl; Glf; Trk; AmLegAwd; College; Professional.

SUMMERVILL, Gloria A; Chanute Sr HS; Chanute, KS; ChrhWkr; CncrtBnd; MrchBnd; OffAde; TchrAde; YthFlsp; 4-H; FHA; Trade Schl; Vocation.

SUMMERVILLE, Deb J; Hay Springs Public HS; Hay Springs, NE; HonRl; Yrbk; SecPpCl; Chadron St Col; Sec.

SUMMERVILLE, Yvonne; North Division HS; Milwaukee, WI; 10/200 HonRl; JA; NHS; FHA; FTA; SpnCl; Chrldr; LetterGAA; IMSpt; JAAwd; College; Physical Therpist.

SUMNER, Clark L; Watertown Sr HS; Watertown, SD; Chr; Chrs; ChrhWkr; HonRl; NatlFornLg; NatlThespSoc; PolWkr; SchMus; SchPl; YthFlsp; Univ; Poli Sci.

SUMNER, William R; Hutchinson Sr HS; Hutchinson, KS; PresSrCls; SecCncrtBnd; NatlMeritCmnd; NatlThespSoc; SchMus; SchPl; StuCncl; PresSpnCl; LetterTennis; RotaryAwd; Kansas Univ; Foreign Language.

SUMPTER, Linda J; Lutheran HS; Florissant, MO; HonRl; VPNHS; NatlMeritSF; SctActv; RptrSchPpr; SchPpr; College; Librarian.

SUMWALT, James A; Juda HS; Juda, WI; 2/44 ALBoysSt; ModUN; SchMus; SchPl; PresStuCncl; FHA; CaptFtbl; LetterTrk; LetterWrstlng; Ind Central Univ; Engineering.

SUND, Richard O; Superior HS; Guide Rock, NE; FFA; LetterWrstlng; College.

SUNDAY, David A; Thomas Jefferson HS; Cedar Rapids, IA; 2/540 TreasChr; HonRl; NHS; NatlMeritFnl; SchMus; MthCl; LetterFtbl; LetterTennis; LetterTrk; IMSpt; St Univ; Engineer.

SUNDBERG, John D; Madrid Community HS; Madrid, IA; 5/63 ALBoysSt; Band; HonRl; MrchBnd; PepBnd; SctActv; YthFlsp; FrCl; Glf; College; Ag Mech.

SUNDBERG, Vicki; Harlem HS; Rockford, IL; HonRl; GAA; College; Professional.

SUNDBY, Mary B; Turtle Lake Mercer HS; Turtle Lake, ND; 19/43 Band; HonRl; FHA; Clg; Med Secretery.

SUNDELL, Cathleen; Rochester HS; Rochester, MI; ChrhWkr; HonRl; NHS; TchrAde; SpnCl; Central Mich Uniz; Spanish.

SUNDELL, Richard C; Southeast Of Saline HS; Assaria, KS; 3/51 Band; Chrs; HonRl; NatlMeritSF; SctActv; RptrYrbk;.

SUNDERLAGE, Diane M; Woodstock HS; Woodstock, IL; 38/265 CncrtBnd; MrchBnd; NHS; College; Medicine.

SUNDERLIN, Terry C; Lewis Central Comm HS; Council Bluffs, IA; 26/176 Band; CncrtBnd; HonRl; JA; MrchBnd; PepBnd; Univ Of Iowa; Music.

SUNDERMAN, Charmaine L; South Page Community HS; Coin, IA; SecTrsJrCls; Band; HonRl; StuCncl; 4-H; FHA; Chrldr; Trade School; Vocation.

SUNDERMAN, Janell J; South Page HS; Braddyville, IA; SecFrshCls; HonRl; LbryAde; NHS; 4-H; FHA; LetterBsbl; LetterBsktbl; LetterTrk; DanFAwd; 4-HAwd;.

SUNDERMAN, Mark; Madison HS; Humphrey, NE; VPFrshCls; SecSophCls; MrchBnd; Orch; PepBnd; SchPl; StuCncl; 4-H; Trade School; Mechanic.

SUNDERMAN, Randy; Madison HS; Humphrey, NE; SecFrshCls; VPJrCls; Chr; Chrs; ChrhWkr; SchPl; CivCl; Bsktbl; Trk; Bus Sch.

SUNDERMAN, Rita; Madison HS; Humphrey, NE; VPSophCls; Chr; ChrhWkr; StuGov; CivCl; PpCl; Trk; Wrstlng; IMSpt; 4-HAwd; Coll; Voc.

SUNDERMAN, Tracy H; Waukegan East HS; Waukegan, IL; HonRl; HospAde; JA; LitMag; TreasSctActv; GerCl; GAA; College; Psychology.

SUNDERMEYER, Beverly S; New Bloomfield Riii HS; New Bloomfield, MO; ChrhWkr; CmntyWkr; HonRl; JA; StuGov; PpCl; Bsbl; LetterBsktbl; CchngActv; GAA; Vocational School; Vocation.

SUNDERMEYER, Steven W; Owen Withee HS; Withee, WI; 10/75 PresSophCls; ChrhWkr; HonRl; TchrAde; RptrSchPpr; SptEdSchPpr; FFA; Ftbl; Trk; IMSpt; Northland College; Biology.

SUNDIN, Karen J; Banner County HS; Harrisburg, NE; 1/14 TrsFrshCls; TrsSophCls; SecTrsJrCls; HonRl; NHS; W Ne Schl Of Nursing; Reg Nurse.

SUNDIN, Lee B; Fargo North HS; Fargo, ND; ALBoysSt; HonRl; NHS; ROTC; SctActv; KiwanAwd; Usma West Point.

SUNDQUIST, Gale; Holdrege Senior HS; Holdrege, NE; Band; CncrtBnd; MrchBnd; PepBnd; FBLA; FHA; Bus School;.

SUNDQUIST, Susan A; West Iron County HS; Caspian, MI; ChrhWkr; HonRl; 4-H; LatCl; Northern Michigan Univ; Elem Education.

SUNDSTROM, Gregory A; Jenison HS; Jenison, MI; HstSrCls; HonRl; NHS; NatlMeritSchl; PepBnd; SchPl; StuGov; RptrSchPpr; 4-H; Tennis; U Of Mi; Architecture.

SUNDY, Gail L; Sarcoxie HS; La Russell, MO; TrsFrshCls; Chr; Chrs; HonRl; MrchBnd; FHA; FTA; SpnCl; Trade Schl; Vocation.

SUNKEN, Nancy J; Wenona Comm Unit I HS; Wenona, IL; 4/43 Band; Chrs; ChrhWkr; HonRl; NHS; OffAde; SchMus; SchPpr; FHA; AmLegAwd; Illinois Valley Comm College; Music.

SUNSERI, Thaddeus; Don Bosco HS; Waterloo, IA; 20/57 HonRl; JrNHS; NHS; NatlThespSoc; SchMus; SchPl; RptrYrbk; RptrSchPpr; IMSpt; U Of Northern Iowa; Physics.

SUNTKEN, Catherine A; St Augustine HS; Chicago, IL; 5/90 HonRl; NHS; StuCncl; Business Sch; Professional.

SUNTKEN, Sandy; Cal Community HS; Blemond, IA; SecJrCls; SchPl; EdYrBk; 4-HAwd; Business School; Accountant.

SUNVOLD, Sandra L; Sacred Heart HS; Sacred Heart, MN; Band; CncrtBnd; HonRl; MrchBnd; PepBnd; Yrbk; 4-H; Bsktbl; Wrstlng; 4-HAwd; Coll.

SUOBODA, Roberta L; Crete HS; Crete, NE; 14/111 Band; Chr; ChrhWkr; CncrtBnd; HonRl; MrchBnd; TchrAde; FBLA; FTA; PpCl; Clg; Teacher.

SUPPLEE, Carol L; Fremont Public HS; Fremont, MI; Band; ChrhWkr; HonRl; MrchBnd; OffAde; Orch; PepBnd; Twrl; SpnCl; PpCl; College.

SUPPLITT, John T; St Ignatius College Prep HS; La Grange, IL; 23/155 CmntyWkr; HonRl; JrNHS; LitMag; NHS; StuGov; SptEdSchPpr; CaptSocr; Dartmouth; Medicine.

SUPRENANT, Bryan K; Bradley Bourbonnais Comm HS; Bradley, IL; PresJrCls; PresSrCls; Aud/Vis; HonRl; NHS; SchPl; Yrbk; LetterFtbl; LetterTrk; LetterWrstlng; Normal U; Phy Ed.

SURBAUGH, Richard B; Harrison HS; Chicago, IL; 10/408 Aud/Vis; ChrhWkr; CtyCnl; HonRl; HospAde; JrNHS; NHS; SchAde; StuCncl; Swmmng; Univ Of Ill; Phys Ed Teacher.

SURBER, Amy; Meadville Hs; Wheeling, MO; 7 Band; ChrhWkr; CncrtBnd; HonRl; MrchBnd; StuCncl; Yrbk; FHA; Bsbl; Bsktbl;.

SURBER, Erika M; Main St HS; Eureka, KS; PresChr; Chrs; HonRl; SchMus; SchPl; 4-H; FFA; FHA; LetterTrk; GAA;.

SURBER, Peggy A; Raytown HS; Kansas City, MO; 118/614 AFS; Chrs; ChrhWkr; HonRl; JrNHS; SctActv; TchrAde; PpCl; IMSpt; MasAwd; College; Accounting.

SURBER, Ronald; Sherwood Cass R Viii HS; Garden City, MO; 10/63 Chrs; ChrhWkr; HonRl; JA; SchMus; SchPl; StuCncl; Bsbl; Ftbl; Culver Stockton College; Teaching.

SURDU, Steve L; Clio HS; Clio, MI; 12/340 HonRl; VPNHS; Ftbl; LetterGlf; CaptIMSpt; Us Naval Acad; Officer In The Navy.

SURETTE, Gibb D; Primghar HS; Primghar, IA; Band; CncrtBnd; HonRl; MrchBnd; NatlMeritFnl; PepBnd; PolWkr; StuCncl; RptrSchPpr; SchPpr; Univ; Law Politics.

SURIAN, Paula K; St Mary Cathedral HS; Saginaw, MI; 1/77 VPSophCls; HonRl; LbryAde; NHS; StuCncl; StuGov; RptrYrbk; LatCl; PpCl; Clg; Nursing.

SURINAK, Linda J; Plainfield HS; Joliet, IL; TrsJrCls; HonRl; MrchBnd; PepBnd; StuCncl; 4-H; GAA; IMSpt; PPFtbl; VoiceDemAwd; Jr Clg; Professional.

SURMA, Kathleen F; Queen Of Peace HS; Chicago, IL; 41/435 Chrs; HonRl; SecNHS; StuCncl; FrCl; JAAwd;.

SURRATT, Barbara J; Triopia Jr Sr HS; Jacksonville, IL; Chrs; ChrhWkr; HonRl; SchPl; StuCncl; Chrldr;.

SURRATT, Debbie J; Lyman HS; Lyman, NE; 1/16 TrsSophCls; Chrs; DrlTm; HonRl; FHA; Colorado St Univ; Accountant.

SUSALLA, John; Meridian Senior HS; Sanford, MI; 1/125 VPJrCls; ChrhWkr; HonRl; NHS; NatlMeritSF; SchMus; StuCncl; SptEdSchPpr; FrCl; Us Air Force Academy; Officer.

SUSELAND, Jeffrey C; Cassopolis HS; Cassopolis, MI; HonRl; 4-H; FFA; Trade Sch; Voc.

SUSICK, Steven J; Southfield Lathrup HS; Lathrup Vlg, MI; Band; CncrtBnd; HonRl; LbryAde; MrchBnd; PepBnd; ROTC; SctActv; LetterTrk; Lawrence Inst Of Tech; Armied Forces.

SUSLICK, Janet; New Trier East Hs; Glenco, IL; HonRl; Trk; GAA; University; Social Sciences.

SUSMAN, Barbara; Waukegan East HS; Waukegan, IL; Chr; HonRl; JrNHS; LitMag; NHS; SpnCl; College; Foriegn Language.

SUSSENBACH, Thomas C; Bond Co Community Unit HS; Greenville, IL; 7/190 Band; Chr; HonRl; Mdrgl; NHS; NatlMeritSF; SchMus; LetterBsktbl; LetterFtbl; LetterTrk; College; Liberal Arts.

SUSZ, Paul E; Quigley South HS; Chicago, IL; 15/175 HstJrCls; Band; CncrtBnd; StuCncl; Teen; RptrSchPpr; SchPpr; Socr; Tennis; Purdue Univ; Veterinarian.

SUTER, Patricia M; Jacksonville HS; Jacksonville, IL; HonRl; SctActv; FrCl; LatCl; College; Doctor.

SUTFIN, Shirley J; Northwest HS; Jackson, MI; 18/266 VPJrCls; Band; Chr; Chrl; HonRl; MrchBnd; NHS; SchMus; StuGov; SchPpr; Central Michigan Univ; Voice.

SUTHER, Susie G; Westmoreland HS; Blaine, KS; SecTrsFrshCls; TrsJrCls; SecSrCls; ChrhWkr; HonRl; SchPl; StuCncl; Yrbk; PpCl; Chrldr; Nursing Sch; Rn.

SUTHERLAND, Alan D; Romeo HS; Romeo, MI; ALBoysSt; CncrtBnd; HonRl; NatlMeritSF; Orch; PepBnd; Bsktbl; Glf; Trk; IMSpt; Mi St Univ; Law.

SUTHERLAND, Pamela L; Fairfield Comm HS; Fairfield, IL; 11/165 TrsSophCls; SecJrCls; Band; CncrtBnd; HonRl; MrchBnd; NHS; OffAde; FTA; SpnCl; College; Dental Hygienist.

SUTHERLAND, Pamela L; Fairfield Community HS; Fairfield, IL; TrsSophCls; SecJrCls; Band; CncrtBnd; HonRl; NHS; FTA; SpnCl; College; Dental Hygiene.

SUTHERLAND, Peggy A; Farmington HS; Farmington, MI; HonRl; HospAde; JA; LbryAde; GerCl; College; Floral Designor.

SUTHERLAND, Stephen F; Huron HS; Ann Arbor, MI; ALBoysSt; SecSophCls; CmntyWkr; CncrtBnd; HonRl; Bsbl; Ftbl; Socr; Trk; IMSpt; Mi St Univ; Veterinary Medicine.

SUTHERLAND, Sue C; Tomahawk HS; Tomahawk, WI; HonRl; PpCl; U Of Wi; Forestry.

SUTHERLAND, Susan G; Proviso West HS; Westchester, IL; 126/1150 HonRl; NHS; StuCncl; LetterBsktbl; GAA; Univ Of Ill; Veterinarian.

SUTHERLAND, Yvonne M; Waterford Mott HS; Drayton Plains, MI; 37/410 Chr; HonRl; SchMus; SchPl; TchrAde; Twrl; Sch Of Nursing; Nurse.

SUTHERLIN, Janet M; Bishop O Hara HS; Independence, MO; 10/200 CmntyWkr; HonRl; NHS; StuCncl; TchrAde; RptrYrbk; PpCl; Chrldr; JCAwd; St Marys Col; Special Ed.

SUTHERLIN, Vicki L; Arlington HS; Indianapolis, IN; HonRl; JA; SchPl; FrCl; PPFtbl; In U; Nursing.

SUTKER, Marla L; Morgan Park Academy; Chicago, IL; 2/40 VPSophCls; SecSrCls; HonRl; LitMag; NHS; NatlThespSoc; Quill&Scroll; StuCncl; EdYrBk; University Of Illinois; Law.

SUTKO, Thomas J; Creightor Prep; Omaha, NE; HonRl; Bsktbl; ChmnFtbl; Socr; IMSpt; U Of Col; Business.

SUTKOWSKI, Robert J; St Laurence HS; Chicago, IL; ChrhWkr; HonRl; IMSpt; Electronics.

SUTKUS, Laura A; Bogan HS; Chicago, IL; 54/700 SecJrCls; VPSrCls; HonRl; JA; NHS; TchrAde; College; Business Administration.

SUTLEY, Kathleen A; Mount Assisi Academy; Palos Heights, IL; Chrs; HonRl; HospAde; NHS; StuCncl; RptrSchPpr; Chrldr; GAA; College; Forestry.

SUTOR JR, William; Marshall Sr HS; Marshall, MN; HonRl; SchAde; StuGov; TchrAde; SchPpr; SpnCl; Bsktbl; Trk; IMSpt; Univ Of Mn; Law.

SUTTER, Andrew J; Notre Dame HS; Burlington, IA; 1/80 PresFrshCls; ALBoysSt; HonRl; ModUN; NHS; NatlMeritFnl; NatlMeritSF; SecNatlThespSoc; SchPl; RptrSchPpr; LetterBsbl; LetterFtbl; LetterTrk; IMSpt; College.

SUTTER, Carolyn T; Bishop Gallagher HS; Harper Woods, MI; 8/300 HonRl; VPNHS; SchPl; StuGov; CaptBsktbl; CaptTrk; Us Navy.

SUTTER, Cindy L; Mt Horeb HS; Mt Horeb, WI; Band; CncrtBnd; HonRl; MrchBnd; NHS; Orch; PepBnd; SchMus; SchPl; Clge; Pro.

SUTTER, D Bruce; Octavia HS; Colfax, IL; 10/48 PresFrshCls; PresSophCls; HonRl; NHS; SchMus; SchPl; StuCncl; LetterBsbl; Bsktbl; LetterFtbl; LetterWrstlng; Il State Univ; Business Admin.

SUTTER, Mary Beth; Danville HS; Danville, IL; Chr; HonRl; JA; SchAde; SchMus; CivCl; IMSpt; Univ; Medical Field.

SUTTIE, Mark; Truman HS; Independence, MO; ChrhWkr; TchrAde; YthFlsp; Wrstlng; GodCntryAwd; Tech; Shop Related.

SUTTNER, Therese; Catholic Memorial HS; New Berlin, WI; HonRl; NHS; TchrAde; PpCl; Chrldr; IMSpt;.

SUTTON, Carol A; De Soto Sr Ii HS; De Soto, MO; SecFrshCls; Chrs; CncrtBnd; HonRl; TreasJrNHS; NHS; SchPl; StuCncl; Twrl; Yrbk; SecFBLA; PpCl; Chrldr; DARAwd; College; Speech Therapy.

SUTTON, Christine D; Northville HS; Northville, MI; HonRl; HospAde; JrNHS; NHS; U Of Mi.

SUTTON, Danny R; Mt Carmel HS; Mt Carmel, IL; 10/200 Blackburn College.

SUTTON, David P; Wauwatosa West HS; Wauwatosa, WI; 1/426 ALBoysSt; PresNHS; NatlMeritFnl; TreasSctActv; PresMthCl; LetterFtbl; LetterTrk; LetterWrstlng; BauchLmbAwd; RotaryAwd; U Of Wi; Weterinary Med.

SUTTON, Gary B; United Township HS; Silvis, IL; 23/650 HonRl; Tennis; IMSpt; RotaryAwd; Northwestern Univ; Accounting.

SUTTON, Lucretia L; Peoria HS; Peoria, IL; 68/450 Band; CncrtBnd; HonRl; HospAde; JA; JrNHS; MrchBnd; FrCl; College; Russian.

SUTTON, Mary K; El Paso HS; Gridley, IL; 11/95 SecSophCls; AFS; Chrs; HonRl; NHS; SecStuCncl; Yrbk; SpnCl; Chrldr; GAA; U Of Il; Medical.

SUTTON, Patricia I; Richwoods HS; Peoria, IL; 77/525 Chr; ChrhWkr; CmntyWkr; HonRl; HospAde; TchrAde; YthFlsp; RptrSchPpr; SpnCl; PpCl; College; Nursing.

SUTTON, Phyllis J; Sylvan Unified #299 HS; Hunter, KS; 9/22 ALAGirlsSt; CmntyWkr; HonRl; LbryAde; SchPl; TchrAde; YthFlsp; RptrSchPpr; LetterBsktbl; CchngActv; Barton Co Com College; Sec/acctwork.

SUTTON, Ronald D; Mishawaka HS; Mishawaka, IN; 8/422 ChrhWkr; VPJA; NatlMeritSF; SctActv; PresGerCl; PresMthCl; VPSciCl; CchngActv; IMSpt; JAAwd; Purdue Univ; Aerospace Engineer.

SUTTON, Shelley R; Hyannis HS; Ashby, NE; SecFrshCls; Chr; SchPl; 4-H; FHA; PpCl; Bauder Fashion Col; Interior Decorating.

SUTTON, Stanley E; Chicago Vocational HS; Chicago, IL; Chr; ChrhWkr; TchrAde; SciCl; CaptFtbl; CchngActv; University Of Ohio; Football.

SUTTON, Theresa; Tawas Area HS; East Tawas, MI; 8 HonRl; HospAde; NHS; NatlMeritCmnd; RedCrAde; TchrAde; KeyCl; University Of Michigan; Prof.

SUTULA, Noreen E; Carmel HS; Mundelein, IL; 20/200 Chrl; Chrs; HonRl; NHS; OffAde; 4-H; Swmmng; Trk; CchngActv; 4-HAwd; Coll; Business.

SUTULA, Sandra; Maria HS; Chicago, IL; 18/338 HonRl; ChrhWkr; SpnCl; Bsktbl; IMSpt; Secondary Educ.

SUYCOTT, Mark L; Northwest HS; High Ridge, MO; 9/370 ALBoysSt; Chr; PresNHS; SctActv; PresYthFlsp; Yrbk; Bsktbl; Ftbl; Univ Of Missouri At Columbia.

SUZAMA, George B; Todd County HS; Mission, SD; ALBoysSt; HonRl; NHS; NatlThespSoc; Bsbl; Bsktbl; Ftbl; Glf; Trk; College.

SVANDA, Cindy R; Trico HS; Percy, IL; TrsSrCls; Band; DrmMjrt; HonRl; MrchBnd; SchPl; SctActv; StuCncl; Yrbk; EdSchPpr; Trk; GAA; John A Logan Jr College; Business.

SVEC, Chris A; Mercy HS; St Louis, MO; 25/193 HonRl; NHS; TchrAde; RptrYrbk; Yrbk; PpCl; Chrldr; IMSpt; PPFtbl; Nursing School; Nurse.

SVEC, Jeanne M; Maria HS; Chicago, IL; 38/335 HonRl; LitMag; CivCl; Bsbl; CaptBsktbl; GAA; IMSpt; College; Phy Ed.

SVEC, Melanie; Alleman HS; Rock Island, IL; 12/220 HonRl; LbryAde; NHS; IMSpt; Drake Univ; Public Administeation.

SVEEN, Matthew; Bottineau HS; Bottineau, ND; ALBoysSt; Band; CncrtBnd; SchPl; StuCncl; SptEdYrbk; Bsktbl; Ftbl; Trk; DanFAwd; College;.

SVEHLA, David A; Friend Public HS; Friend, NE; 2/40 ALBoysSt; Chrs; HonRl; TchrAde; YthFlsp; 4-H; LetterBsktbl; LetterFtbl; LetterTrk; LetterWrstlng; Doone College; Mathematics.

SVEJDA, Steven A; Benton Community HS; Atkins, IA; ALBoysSt; Band; ChrhWkr; HonRl; SchPl; SctActv; YthFlsp; 4-H; Ftbl; Open Bible Coll; Minister.

SVENDSEN, Mark J; Washington Park HS; Racine, WI; ALBoysSt; ChrhWkr; CncrtBnd; HonRl; HospAde; SchMus; SchPl; LetterBsbl; Ftbl; CchngActv; College; Professional.

SVIHEL, Hallie J; Lake Preston HS; Lake Preston, SD; 1/37 ALAGirlsSt; SecBand; Chrs; ChrhWkr; CncrtBnd; HonRl; HospAde; Mdrgl; MrchBnd; PepBnd; RedCrAde; SchMus; SchPl; PresStuCncl; Chrldr; So Dakota State Univ; Nursing.

SVOBODA, Anne M; New Prague HS; New Prague, MN; Chrs; HonRl; LbryAde; FHA; SpnCl; IMSpt; Willmar Community College; Social Work.

SVOBODA, David A; Hill HS; Lansing, MI; LetterTennis; IMSpt; Lansing Comm College.

SVOBODA, Jo Anne; David City HS; David City, NE; 2/52 PresFrshCls; PresSophCls; PresJrCls; PresSrCls; ALAGirlsSt; HonRl; Quill&Scroll; EdYrBk; PpCl; Trk; College; Prof.

SVOBODA, John; Maine Township North Hs; Des Plaines, IL; 4/360 CncrtBnd; HonRl; JrNHS; NHS; Orch; MthCl; LetterBsbl; LetterBsktbl; Trk; DARAwd; Williams College; Political Economt.

SVOBODA, Joy E; Lincoln Comm HS; Mechanicsville, IA; 4/64 PresJrCls; CncrtBnd; HonRl; PresNHS; TreasStuCncl; YthFlsp; Yrbk; SchPpr; Bsktbl; Trk; PPFtbl; CitAwd; Mt Mercy College; Criminal Justice Admin.

SVOBODA, Linda M; Morton West HS; Berwyn, IL; Chr; ChrhWkr; HonRl; HospAde; VPJA; StuCncl; TchrAde; TreasTeen; JAAwd; Coll; Dentist.

SVOBODA, Mary M; Providence HS; Midlothian, IL; 20/121 VPChrs; CmntyWkr; HonRl; NHS; RptrSchPpr; FrCl; College; Math.

SVOBODA, Mike P; Webb HS; Reedsburg, WI; CmntyWkr; KeyCl; LetterBsktbl; U W Platteville; Meat Inspector.

SVOBODA, Nancy A; Marian HS; Omaha, NE; HonRl; HospAde; NHS; FDA; LatCl; MthCl; College; Medicine.

SVOBODA, Ronda E; Leigh Community HS; Leigh, NE; Band; Chr; Chrs; ChrhWkr; CncrtBnd; HonRl; MrchBnd; PepBnd; SchMus; SchPl; SctActv; TchrAde; 4-H; FHA; College; Counselor.

SVOBODA, Sandra R; Burwell Jr Sr HS; Burwell, NE; LetterBand; SchPl; StuCncl; Twrl; RptrYrbk; SecFHA; SpnCl; TreasPpCl; LetterBsktbl; LetterTrk; Chrldr; IMSpt; College; Teacher.

SWAFFORD, David B; Northside HS; Muncie, IN; YthFlsp; LetterBsktbl; LetterFtbl; LetterTrk; IMSpt; Univ Of N Colorado; Business.

SWAFFORD, Jeri A; Union City Sr HS; Tekonsha, MI; Band; Chr; CncrtBnd; HonRl; MrchBnd; 4-H; FHA; PpCl; EldAwd; Michigan St Univ; Floriculture.

SWAILS, John E; Cotter HS; Winona, MN; VPJrCls; ChrhWkr; HonRl; NatlFornLg; NatlMeritFnl; StuCncl; YthLg; FDA; SpnCl; Wrstlng; Winona State College.

SWAIM, Pamela S; R Nelson Snider HS; Ft Wayne, IN; 99/504 ChrhWkr; HonRl; St Francis Col; Psychology.

SWAIN, David K; Northrop HS; Fort Wayne, IN; RptrSchPpr; LetterFtbl; LetterTrk; IMSpt; Purdue; Engineer.

SWAIN, Karen J; Thomas M Cooley HS; Detroit, MI; 32/365 HstJrCls; HstSrCls; ChrhWkr; HonRl; NHS; OffAde; ROTC; SchAde; StuGov; TchrAde; Univ Of Detroit; Business Admin.

SWAIN, Richard B; West Harrison HS; Pisgah, IA; 3/49 Band; Chr; Chrs; ChrhWkr; CncrtBnd; HonRl; Mdrgl; MrchBnd; NHS; SchPl; StuCncl; Bsktbl; Ftbl; College; Communications.

SWAIN, Sandra F; Waukesha South Campus HS; Waukesha, WI; Band; HonRl; JrNHS; LitMag; NHS; NatlSciFnd; PepBnd; SchPl; YthFlsp; RptrSchPpr; Univ Wi Madison; Medical Field.

SWAIN, Sara E; Castle HS; Newburgh, IN; 3/293 Chr; NHS; NatlThespSoc; PolWkr; Quill&Scroll; SchMus; SchPl; Yrbk; FTA; Indiana Univ; Science.

SWAIN, Timothy M; Marion HS; Marion, IN; CmntyWkr; HonRl; NHS; NatlMeritSF; StuCncl; StuGov; GerCl; Bsktbl; CchngActv; IMSpt; Indiana Univ; Military.

SWALLER, Edna M; St Pius X HS; Imperial, MO; 7/101 Chrs; ChrhWkr; HonRl; HospAde; NHS; StuCncl; EngCl; SciCl; Deaconess Hosp Sch Of Nursing; Rn.

SWALLEY, Kevin J; Sanborn Comm HS; Sanborn, IA; 2/41 PresFrshCls; VPJrCls; VPSrCls; NHS; PresStuCncl; Bsbl; Bsktbl; Ftbl; Glf; CitAwd; Northwestern Col; Cpa.

SWALLOWS, Tom R; Puxico HS; Puxico, MO; VPFrshCls; Band; CncrtBnd; HonRl; MrchBnd; PepBnd; SctActv; PpCl; Bsbl; College; Engineering.

SWALWELL, Barbara; Maxwell Comm HS; Nevada, IA; Chrs; HonRl; SchMus; SchPl; YthFlsp; RptrYrbk; FHA; Mechanic.

SWAN, Esther J; Arthur County HS; Lewellen, NE; 3/12 Band; Chr; ChrhWkr; HonRl; PepBnd; SchMus; SchPl; YthFlsp; RptrYrbk; AmLegAwd; College; Accounting.

SWAN, Jerry; Ida Public HS; Temperance, MI; ChrhWkr; CmntyWkr; NatlMeritCmnd; TchrAde; FFA; Bsktbl; IMSpt; College; Vocational.

SWAN, Margo L; Hillsdale HS; Hillsdale, MI; Chr; HonRl; LitMag; NHS; PPFtbl; College; Professional.

SWAN, Mark S; Bloomington HS; Bloomington, IL; 25/391 ChrhWkr; CncrtBnd; DrmMjrt; HonRl; MrchBnd; NHS; Orch; PepBnd; StuCncl; SpnCl; MthCl; PpCl; Illinois State; Accounting.

SWAN, Marshall A; Boone Valley Community HS; Hardy, IA; Band; Chr; Chrs; ChrhWkr; CmntyWkr; LetterBsbl; CaptBsktbl; LetterFtbl; LetterGlf; CchngActv; Nort•western; Coaching.

SWAN, Rosemary; St Joseph HS; Chicago, IL; 5/128 SecFrshCls; SecSophCls; Chr; ChrhWkr; HonRl; SecNHS; StuCncl; College; Teacher.

SWAN, Scott W; Dixon HS; Dixon, IL; 41/320 HonRl; NHS; SchMus; EdSchPpr; PpCl; LetterSwmmng; IMSpt; Univ Of Illinois; Liberal Arts.

SWANBERG, Christine; Cornell HS; Cornell, IL; 2/29 DrmMjrt; NHS; OffAde; SchPl; StuCncl; SchPpr; Bsktbl; Chrldr; Parkland College; Dental Assisting.

SWANBERG, Christine M; Cornell HS; Cornell, IL; 2/29 ALAGirlsSt; HonRl; SchPl; StuCncl; Yrbk; RptrSchPpr; PresFHA; Chrldr; GAA; AmLegAwd; Parkland Jr College; Dental Hygiene.

SWANBERG, Gary D; Clarissa HS; Clarissa, MN; 15/40 Band; Chr; PolWkr; SchMus; SchPl; StuCncl; Bsbl; Ftbl; LetterTrk; Wrstlng; College; Medical Technology.

SWANHORST, Diane J; Cresbard HS; Chelsea, SD; HstSophCls; Band; Chrs; ChrhWkr; DrlTm; HonRl; SchPl; SptEdSchPpr; Trk; CitAwd; Sd State Univ; Secretarial Science.

SWANHORST, Renee J; Cresbard Public HS; Cresbard, SD; 5/30 SecSrCls; Band; CncrtBnd; HonRl; PepBnd; StuCncl; SchPpr; PpCl; LetterTrk; Chrldr; Presentation Sd; Nursing.

SWANK, Donna K; Bremen Sr HS; Bremen, IN; ChrhWkr; HonRl; OffAde; TchrAde; SecYthFlsp; 4-H; FTA; SpnCl; Michiana Coll Of Commerce; Secretary.

SWANK, Karen J; Clay City HS; Center Point, IN; 8/64 Band; Chr; PresSophCls; HonRl; MrchBnd; TreasNHS; OffAde; FBLA; PpCl; Secretary.

SWANK, Leslie E; Noblesville HS; Noblesville, IN; 40/300 VPFrshCls; PresSophCls; SpnCl; MthCl; Bsbl; Ftbl; Trk; Wrstlng; College.

SWANKE, James; Ladysmith HS; Ladysmith, WI; VPSrCls; NatlFornLg; RptrSchPpr; SpnCl; Bsktbl; Ftbl; Trk; Univ Of Wis; Lawyer.

SWANN, John P; Immaculata HS; Leavenworth, KS; 6/60 HonRl; ModUN; PolWkr; SchPl; TchrAde; FSA; Bsbl; Ftbl; IMSpt; BauchLmbAwd; Univ; Medical Science.

SWANSBRO, Robin L; Joliet West HS; Joliet, IL; 17/495 Chr; ChrhWkr; HonRl; NHS; OffAde; PolWkr; StuCncl; FrCl; Drake Univ; Pharmacy.

SWANSON, Ann E; East HS; Sioux City, IA; 53/354 Chrs; ChrhWkr; HonRl; HospAde; SchAde; SchMus; PpCl; College; Educationn.

SWANSON, Barbara A; Mooseheart HS; Mooseheart, IL; 2/22 PresFrshCls; VPSophCls; PresJrCls; PresSrCls; Chrs; CncrtBnd; HonRl; JA; NHS; StuCncl; Oregon St Univ; Business.

SWANSON, Barbara L; Muskegon HS; Muskegon, MI; HonRl; FrCl; AmLegAwd; Ferris State Col; Nuclear Medicine Techicia.

SWANSON, Carol A; Van Buren HS; Douds, IA; Band; Chr; ChrhWkr; HonRl; NatlThespSoc; SchPl; YthFlsp; 4-H; Wrstlng; Univ Of Iowa; Medical Doctor.

SWANSON, Carol E; Elk Grove HS; Elk Grove Village, IL; 2/507 Band; CncrtBnd; HonRl; LitMag; MrchBnd; NatlFornLg; PresNHS; NatlMeritCmnd; StuCncl; SecKeyCl; SpnCl; Univ Of Chicago; Corporate Law.

SWANSON, Catherine L; Thomas Jefferson HS; Council Bluffs, IA; 5/460 Chr; CmntyWkr; HonRl; HospAde; LbryAde; NHS; PolWkr; UNYO; YthLg; GerCl; Iowa State Univ; Biochemistry.

SWANSON, Cathy L; La Ville Jr/sr HS; Plymouth, IN; 21/170 ALAGirlsSt; Chr; ChrhWkr; NHS; StuCncl; FrCl; PpCl; Chrldr; AmLegAwd; Purdue U; Recreation.

SWANSON, Cinda S; Streator HS; Streator, IL; HonRl; NHS; GerCl; U Of Il; Accounting Major.

SWANSON, David L; Carrington HS; Carrington, ND; 4-H; FFA; PpCl; LetterFtbl; LetterTrk; IMSpt; 4-HAwd; Trade Schl; Vocation.

SWANSON, David L; Colo Comm HS; Colo, IA; 11/24 Band; CncrtBnd; HonRl; MrchBnd; PepBnd; StuCncl; YthFlsp; 4-H; FFA; PpCl;.

SWANSON, Deanna M; Alwood HS; Lynn Center, IL; 12/67 Chr; ChrhWkr; CmntyWkr; LbryAde; NHS; TchrAde; RptrYrbk; FTA; SpnCl; Bsktbl; Blackhawk College; Spanish & Music.

SWANSON, Debora C; Alexis HS; Aledo, IL; 1/47 CncrtBnd; DrmMjrt; HonRl; NHS; NatlMeritCmnd; SchPl; TreasStuCncl; RptrYrbk; VPGAA; DARAwd; Illinois State Univ; Business Admin.

SWANSON, Denise M; Coal City HS; Coal City, IL; HonRl; LbryAde; SchMus; SchPl; Yrbk; FHA; Loyola Univ; Physician.

SWANSON, Donald A; Balaton HS; Balaton, MN; Aud/Vis; CncrtBnd; HonRl; NHS; LetterBsbl; Bsktbl; LetterFtbl; LetterTrk; IMSpt; College; Broadcasting.

SWANSON, Eric; Oregon Senior HS; Oregon, WI; HonRl; NHS; SctActv; Bsbl; Bsktbl; Trk; PPFtbl; College Or Univ.

SWANSON, Grant E; Huntley HS; Huntley, IL; 12/54 VPFrshCls; Band; HonRl; SctActv; GerCl; LetterBsbl; LetterFtbl; Parks College; Pilot.

SWANSON, Jay I; Stevens HS; Rapid City, SD; 22/416 ALBoysSt; CtyCnl; HonRl; StuCncl; StuGov; FrCl; Trk; Wrstlng; CchngActv; AmLegAwd; Coll; Dentist.

SWANSON, Joann R; Glenbard West HS; Glen Ellyn, IL; 76/586 AFS; HonRl; HospAde; NatlMeritCmnd; Evangelical School; Nursing.

SWANSON, John S; Pekin Community HS; Ollie, IA; 13/48 VPFrshCls; ChrhWkr; HonRl; StuCncl; YthFlsp; 4-H; FFA; Bsbl; Bsktbl; Iowa State University; Vet.

SWANSON, Judy A; Dundee Comm HS; Dundee, IL; 1/412 Band; Chrs; HonRl; Orch; GerCl; Southern Ill Univ; Biologist.

SWANSON, Judy L; Pine River HS; Leroy, MI; 31/86 Chr; CncrtBnd; DrmMjrt; HonRl; MrchBnd; SchPl; YthFlsp; EdSchPpr; FHA; LetterBsktbl; Grace Bible Clge; Religion.

SWANSON, Julia A; Irving Crown HS; Algonquin, IL; 27/355 NHS; Northwestern Univ; Doctor.

SWANSON, Julie A; Tomahawk HS; Tomahawk, WI; Chr; ChrhWkr; CncrtBnd; HonRl; MrchBnd; PepBnd; RptrYrbk; RptrSchPpr; SpnCl; University Of Wisconsin; Teacher.

SWANSON, Julie K; High School; Warren, MN; SecSrCls; SecBand; Chrs; HonRl; SchMus; StuCncl; SchPpr; CaptChrldr; CaptGAA; IMSpt; Coll; Nursing.

SWANSON, Julie R; J D Darnall HS; Geneseo, IL; 12/207 HonRl; NHS; SchPl; Yrbk; 4-H; Western Ill Univ; Business Administration.

SWANSON, Kelly S; Mc Gregor HS; Mcgregor, MN; 2/54 PresJrCls; ChrhWkr; CmntyWkr; HonRl; JrNHS; PresNHS; SchPl; StuCncl; EdYrBk; Chrldr; Univ Of Mn; Cpa.

SWANSON, Kristi R; Springfield HS; Springfield, SD; 1/39 ALAGirlsSt; Chr; ChrhWkr; CncrtBnd; HonRl; MrchBnd; SctActv; EdYrBk; LetterTrk; Coll; Wildlife Specialist.

SWANSON, Larry D; Johnson Brock Public HS; Tecumseh, NE; 2/26 HstFrshCls; HstSophCls; TrsJrCls; SecSrCls; ALBoysSt; Band; CncrtBnd; HonRl; MrchBnd; PepBnd; SchPl; Yrbk; Univ Of Nebraska; Pre Pharmacy.

SWANSON, Leslie H; York Comm HS; Bensenville, IL; Northern Ill Univ; Speech Therapy.

SWANSON, Lyndon W; Watseka HS; Martinton, IL; 40/137 TrsFrshCls; HonRl; FTA; LetterBsbl; LetterBsktbl; LetterFtbl; LetterTrk; Univ; Professional.

SWANSON, Lynne J; Raymond Central HS; Wahoo, NE; Band; Chr; Chrs; ChrhWkr; CncrtBnd; MrchBnd; PepBnd; SchMus; 4-H; FHA; LetterPpCl; Bsktbl; 4-HAwd; Southeast Comm; Human Services.

SWANSON, Michael; West HS; Davenport, IA; 4/751 ALBoysSt; ChrhWkr; CmntyWkr; HonRl; Orch; Twrl; 4-H; Bsbl; Bsktbl; AmLegAwd; Iowa Univ; Agricultural.

SWANSON, Michael D; Mexico HS; Mexico, MO; ALBoysSt; Chr; Yrbk; KeyCl; Bsktbl; CaptGlf; Univ.

SWANSON, Pamela K; Willmar Sr HS; Willmar, MN; Chr; ChrhWkr; CncrtBnd; MrchBnd; NHS; SchPl; College; Social Work.

SWANSON, Patrick; Boylan Central Hs; Rockford, IL; 51/353 HonRl; Bsktbl; Ftbl; Trk; Illinois State U; Fbi.

SWANSON, Paul J; Fenwick HS; Chicago, IL; HonRl; LatCl; LetterBsbl; LetterFtbl; LetterTrk; CchngActv; AmLegAwd; Depaul Univ; Accounting.

SWANSON, Richard J; Anoka HS; Anoka, MN; 131/762 Chr; Chrs; CncrtBnd; JrNHS; MrchBnd; NHS; PepBnd; SchMus; 4-H; Wrstlng; College; Biology.

SWANSON, Scott; Hamlin HS; Lake Norden, SD; PresFrshCls; VPSophCls; HonRl; SchPl; SchPpr; 4-H; Bsktbl; Trk; IMSpt; 4-HAwd; So Dak State Univ.

SWANSON, Sherrill A; Rova HS; Oneida, IL; 1/78 PresFrshCls; Chr; Chrs; HonRl; NHS; YthFlsp; 4-H; PpCl; SciCl; VPGAA; Augustana Coll; Acct.

SWANSON, Sidney J; Leola HS; Leola, SD; HonRl; Mdrgl; MrchBnd; PepBnd; SchMus; SchPl; RptrYrbk; Bsbl; Bsktbl; Trk; Sd St U.

SWANSON, Sonja B; Tri Valley HS; Crooks, SD; 2/63 SecTrsSrCls; CncrtBnd; DrlTm; DrmMjrt; HonRl; Mdrgl; SecNHS; SchPl; EdYrBk; RptrSchPpr; College; Professional Major.

SWANSON, Steven C; Sherburn HS; Dunnell, MN; Band; CncrtBnd; HonRl; MrchBnd; PepBnd; SctActv; LetterFtbl; CaptWrstlng; PresAwd; Univ Of Minnesota; Engineering.

SWANSON, Susan A; Coon Rapids Sr HS; Fridley, MN; Chr; HonRl; College; Veterinarian.

SWANSON, Trudy J; Gibson City HS; Gibson City, IL; 28/98 Chrs; HonRl; SchPl; FHA; PpCl; Parkland Jr College; Sewing Design.

SWANSTONE, Shirley J; Laura Speed Elliott HS; Boonville, MO; Band; ChrhWkr; CncrtBnd; MrchBnd; NHS; RptrYrbk; PpCl; TreasSciCl; Chrldr; College; Nursing.

SWANTNER, Paula I; Sacred Heart HS; Dearborn Heights, MI; 17/117 HonRl; LbryAde; NHS; SctActv; GAA; Siena Heights Clg; Accounting.

SWARD, Chris A; Rockford East HS; Rockford, IL; 6/700 HonRl; Ill State Univ; Math.

SWARD, Kim M; Belview Public HS; Belview, MN; TrsFrshCls; SecSophCls; TrsJrCls; Band; HonRl; MrchBnd; SchPl; 4-H; LetterFtbl; College; Professional.

SWARM, Randy E; Northridge HS; Middlebury, IN; PresBand; PresCncrtBnd; SchMus; SchPl; PresStuCncl; Pres4-H; KeyCl; LetterBsktbl; Ftbl; IMSpt;.

SWART, Constance V; Lowell Sr HS; Lowell, IN; 28/243 College; Computer Science.

SWARTHOUT, Shelly R; Garden City West HS; Garden City, MI; Chr; Chrs; ChrhWkr; HonRl; NatlMeritSF; SchMus; PpCl;.

SWARTZ, Barbara K; Raymore Peculiar HS; Raymore, MO; 9/89 HonRl; VPNHS; VPYthFlsp; FHA; PresGerCl; SecPpCl; Chrldr; GAA; PPFtbl; University Of Missouri; Veterinarian.

SWARTZ, Brian S; Sacred Heart Public HS; Sacred Heart, MN; VPSrCls; Chr; YthFlsp; FFA; Bsbl; Bsktbl; Ftbl; Glf; Trk; PresAwd; Willmar Community College; Farm Machinery.

SWARTZ, Cheryl L; Connersville HS; Connersville, IN; 11/370 DrmMjrt; HonRl; JA; LbryAde; NHS; SctActv; 4-H; GerCl; SciCl; Indiana Univ; Optometrist.

SWARTZ, Donald E; Sunnydale Academy; Raytown, MO; Chr; ChrhWkr; HonRl; StuCncl; College; Teacher.

SWARTZ, Douglas A; Lincoln Central HS; Dolliver, IA; 1/17 TrsFrshCls; TrsJrCls; ALBoysSt; Band; Chr; Chrs; ChrhWkr; CncrtBnd; HonRl; MrchBnd; NHS; LetterBsktbl; LetterFtbl; 4-HAwd; College; Mathematics.

SWARTZ, Eric J; Brazil Sr HS; Brazil, IN; PresSophCls; CmntyWkr; HonRl; NHS; StuCncl; Trk; Trade School; Vocational.

SWARTZ, Jerry J; Moberly HS; Moberly, MO; 26/212 PresSophCls; PresJrCls; PresSrCls; ALBoysSt; HonRl; Quill&Scroll; LetterFtbl; LetterTrk; LetterWrstlng; Univ; Journalism.

SWARTZ, Karl R; Premont HS; Hesston, KS; 3/75 HonRl; NatlFornLg; NatlMeritFnl; SchPl; YthFlsp; RptrYrbk; Hesston Coll; Psych/soc.

SWARTZ, Michael E; Gaylord Community HS; Gaylord, MI; Band; CmntyWkr; CncrtBnd; HonRl; NHS; NatlSciFnd; SctActv; StuCncl; Glf; Trk; University; Chemist Phd.

SWARTZ, Michael J; Chippewa Valley HS; Utica, MI; 8/350 ChrhWkr; NHS; Mich St Univ; Acct.

SWARTZ, William R; East Pike HS; Pittsfield, IL; 4/27 ChrhWkr; CmntyWkr; HonRl; LbryAde; PolWkr; RptrYrbk; FFA; IMSpt; College; Professional.

SWARTZBERG, Joanne; Oshkosh West HS; Oshkosh, WI; 7/400 AFS; LitMag; NHS; NatlMeritSF; NatlThespSoc; SchMus; SchPl; StuCncl; RptrYrbk; PresFrCl; MthCl; College; Astro Physics.

SWARTZENDROFER, Douglas J; Iowa Mennonite HS; Wellman, IA; 3037 SchPl; StuCncl; LetterBsktbl; LetterSocr; LetterTrk;.

SWARTZENTRUBER, Barbara D; Ellendale HS; Ellendale, ND; 3/45 ChrhWkr; HonRl; LbryAde; OffAde; PresFrCl; Trinity Bible Inst; Secretary.

SWARTZMAN, Susan B; Sunset Hill HS; Shawnee Mission, KS; 3/30 AFS; Chr; LbryAde; Quill&Scroll; SchMus; RptrSchPpr; EdSchPpr; Clg; Conductress.

SWARUP, Shashi K; Orleans HS; Orleans, IN; 1/60 TrsFrshCls; Chr; HonRl; JrNHS; NHS; SchMus; PresYthFlsp; EdYrBk; 4-H; Hanover College; Pre Med.

SWARZ, Patrick J; St Ladislaus HS; Detroit, MI; 27/112 TrsFrshCls; PresJrCls; SecSrCls; ALBoysSt; HonRl; SchPl; StuCncl; FrCl; GerCl; Wayne State Univ; Psychology.

SWATTS, Susan; Bishop Noll Institute HS; Schererville, IN; Chrs; HonRl; College; Nursing.

SWEANY, Raymond; Breckenridge HS; Breckenridge, MI; 34/94 VPSrCls; Band; ChrhWkr; HonRl; Mdrgl; SchAde; SchPl; SpnCl; RotaryAwd; Spring Arbor College; Elementary Education.

SWEARENGEN, Dianne; Milan Cii HS; Milan, MO; Band; ChrhWkr; CncrtBnd; DrmMjrt; MrchBnd; SchPl; StuCncl; Twrl; Yrbk; 4-H; Bsbl; CaptBsktbl; GAA;.

SWEARINGEN, Lisa J; Olympia HS; Atlanta, IL; Band; ChrhWkr; CncrtBnd; HonRl; MrchBnd; PolWkr; SpnCl; PpCl; Col; Physical Therapist.

SWEARINGEN, Stephen P; Staunton HS; Brazil, IN; VPSophCls; NatlSciFnd; HonRl; MrchBnd; ModUN; KeyCl; Lincoln Tech Institute.

SWEARNGIN, Kevin G; High School; Warsaw, MO; Chr; ChrhWkr; CmntyWkr; HonRl; PolWkr; StuCncl; YthFlsp; 4-H; LetterBsktbl; 4-HAwd; College; Professional.

SWEATMAN, Cheryl J; Virginia HS; Virginia, IL; 3/45 Band; HonRl; SchPl; PresStuCncl; 4-H; FHA; LetterTrk; CaptChrldr; PresGAA; AmLegAwd; DanFAwd; 4-HAwd; Millikin University; Professional.

SWEAZY, John R; Eisenhower HS; Decatur, IL; Aud/Vis; Us Armed Forces; Electronics Engineering.

SWEDBERG, Katherine J; Mt Morris HS; Mt Morris, IL; ChmnAFS; PresChrs; HonRl; Mdrgl; VPNHS; SchMus; SchPl; Yrbk; PresGerCl; PpCl; Chrldr; College.

SWEDBERG, Lu Ann; Columbus HS; Marshfield, WI; 18/114 ChrhWkr; HonRl; NHS; SchMus; SchPl; RptrYrbk; SchPpr; PpCl; Uw Marshfield,wood Co; Nursing.

SWEDBERG, Rodney E; Bay City Central HS; Bay City, MI; HonRl; GerCl; LetterTrk; Mich Tech Univ.

SWEDEEN, Kendall J; Redfield HS; Redfield, SD; 5/100 VPSophCls; Band; Chrs; HonRl; PresNHS; StuCncl; EdSchPpr; PresFTA; LetterBsktbl; ChmnFtbl; College; Professional.

SWEDIN, Mary K; Central HS; Rapid City, SD; Chr; HonRl; HospAde; Mdrgl; NatlFornLg; PolWkr; RedCrAde; SchPl; StuCncl; TchrAde; Augustana College; Special Ed.

SWEDLUND, Judy; Monroe HS; Monroe, WI; 24/255 AFS; ChrhWkr; HonRl; YthFlsp; SptEdSchPpr; FFA; PPFtbl; Farmer.

SWEDLUND, Kay D; Watseka HS; Watseka, IL; 6/130 AFS; Band; Chr; ChrhWkr; HonRl; HospAde; VPNHS; Quill&Scroll; StuCncl; EdYrBk; Chrldr; SecGAA; 4-HAwd; Bradley University; Accounting.

SWEENEY, Ann M; Watertown HS; Watertown, WI; 11/310 AFS; CmntyWkr; HonRl; JA; ModUN; NHS; NatlMeritCmnd; SchMus; StuCncl; SchPpr; Uw Madison; Psychology.

SWEENEY, Brian; Edgewood HS; Madison, WI; HstFrshCls; TrsSophCls; VPJrCls; SecTrsSrCls; Chr; Chrs; CmntyWkr; SchPl; RptrSchPpr; Trk;.

SWEENEY, Brian R; Munster HS; Munster, IN; ChrhWkr; HonRl; University;.

SWEENEY, Cynthia M; Lincoln HS; Wisconsin Rapids, WI; Chr; ChrhWkr; CmntyWkr; HonRl; SchMus; TchrAde; Nursing Schl; Physician Asst.

SWEENEY, Delores D; La Salle HS; Cedar Rapids, IA; 4/88 Aud/Vis; Chr; CmntyWkr; HonRl; NHS; MthCl; PpCl; PresAwd; Mt Mercy Coll; Phys Thera.

SWEENEY, Joan E; Mercy HS; St Louis, MO; HonRl; NHS; FrCl; Trk; Cigr; Accounting.

SWEENEY, Kevin M; Watseka Comm HS; Watseka, IL; SecSrCls; Illinois Wesleyan Univ; Medicine.

SWEENEY, Lori; Lancaster Sr HS; Lancaster, WI; Chrs; ChrhWkr; CmntyWkr; HospAde; TchrAde; 4-H; SpnCl; IMSpt; Univ Of Wi Madison; Pediatrician.

SWEENEY, Margo M; Ladywood St Agnes HS; Indianapolis, IN; 3/97 HonRl; SchMus; SchPl; Yrbk; FrCl; College; Lawyer.

SWEENEY, Mary M; Hempstead HS; Dubuque, IA; 2/455 HonRl; SchMus; StuGov; FrCl; Tennis; Chrldr; University Of Iowa; Dancer.

SWEENEY, Michael S; Northeast HS; Lincoln, NE; HonRl; RptrSchPpr; EdSchPpr; SchPpr; Tennis; Univ Of Nebraska; Journalism.

SWEENEY, Nora; Addison Trail HS; Villa Park, IL; 165/500 VPJrCls; VPSrCls; Chr; Chrl; HonRl; StuCncl; StuGov; Bsktbl; Chrldr; GAA; Coll; Teach English.

SWEENEY, Patricia A; Maria HS; Chicago, IL; 23/301 HonRl; NHS; Sdlty; College; Geology.

SWEENEY, Patrick M; St Paul Cretin HS; St Paul, MN; Aud/Vis; HonRl; NHS; RptrSchPpr; LetterBsktbl; Ftbl; IMSpt; College; Television.

SWEENEY, Peter A; West Bloomfield HS; West Bloomfield, MI; AFS; HonRl; NatlMeritCmnd; NatlMeritSF; OffAde; Sacrstn; SctActv; GerCl; University Of Michigan; Cpa.

SWEENEY, Teresa M; Shanley HS; Fargo, ND; Band; Chr; Chrl; Chrs; CncrtBnd; HospAde; LitMag; SchMus; SchPl; 4-HAwd; St Catherine Coll; Theatre.

SWEENEY, Thomas E; Morgan Park HS; Chicago, IL; 112/559 Chrs; OffAde; PolWkr; SchPpr; MthCl; LetterFtbl; Swmmng; Univ Of Il; Engineering.

SWEET, Cynthia J; Emmons Public HS; Emmons, MN; PresFrshCls; SecJrCls; Chr; Chrs; ChrhWkr; HonRl; LbryAde; Orch; SchPl; StuCncl; Vo Tech.

SWEET, Debbie K; North Miami HS; Mexico, IN; Chr; HonRl; YthFlsp; PpCl; Bsbl; LetterBsktbl; Trk; GAA; IMSpt; PPFtbl; Undecided; Undecided.

SWEET, Debra; Highland HS; Labelle, MO; 30/130 Band; Chr; Chrs; HonRl; NHS; PepBnd; SchMus; FrCl; Trk; IMSpt; U Of Mo; Pre Law.

SWEET, Doreen K; Franklin Public HS; Franklin, NE; 1/32 CmntyWkr; HonRl; LbryAde; NHS; StuCncl; TchrAde; Yrbk; PpCl; PresSciCl; 4-HAwd; VoiceDemAwd; Kearny State Col; History.

SWEET, Guy L; Holt HS; Holt, MI; 43/254 HonRl; NatlFornLg; NHS; PolWkr; SctActv; LetterTrk; GodCntryAwd; CitAwd; Albion Coll; Law.

SWEET, John T; Garden County HS; Oshkosh, NE; SecFrshCls; HonRl; SchPl; StuGov; Bsktbl; LetterFtbl; College; Law Enforcement.

SWEET, Marlyn C; High School; East Jordan, MI; HonRl; MrchBnd; NHS; PepBnd; TchrAde; RptrSchPpr; 4-H; Bsktbl; Trk; 4-HAwd; College; Professional.

SWEET, Michael A; Coldwater HS; Coldwater, MI; HonRl; LetterBsktbl; Univ Of Michigan; Law.

SWEET, Robert S; Belvidere HS; Belvidere, IL; HonRl; SctActv; Univ Of Il; Art.

SWEET, Ronald J; Cretin HS; St Paul, MN; 19/217 CAP; HonRl; ROTC; SctActv; LetterWrstlng; IMSpt; Univ Mn; Pilot.

SWEET, Shelly A; Octavia HS; Colfax, IL; Band; Chr; Chrs; CncrtBnd; HonRl; SchMus; SchPl; VPYthFlsp; Trk; CaptChrldr; PPFtbl; 4-HAwd; JCAwd; College; Interior Design.

SWEET, Tommy E; Salem Community HS; Salem, IL; ChrhWkr; HonRl; SchPl; YthFnd; FFA; PpCl; LetterBsktbl; LetterFtbl; Trk; CchngActv; IMSpt; College; Electronics.

SWEETON, Rick D; Baxter Springs HS; Baxter Springs, KS; Band; ChrhWkr; CncrtBnd; MrchBnd; PepBnd; RedCrAde; SchMus; SctActv; KeyCl; Bsbl; College; Drafting.

SWEIGARD, Kenneth E; Joliet Catholic HS; Joliet, IL; 47/180 Band; CmntyWkr; CncrtBnd; DrmBgl; HonRl; MrchBnd; NatlThespSoc; Orch; PepBnd; SchMus; Glf; Trk; IMSpt; College; Education.

SWEIGART, Mary C; Linwood HS; Linwood, KS; 2/17 HonRl; LbryAde; SchPl; RptrYrbk; RptrSchPpr; SpnCl; PpCl; College; Nurse.

SWEITZER, Bobbie J; Cogden Unit HS; Cobden, IL; 1/50 PresJrCls; HonRl; SchPl; SecStuCncl; Twrl; RptrYrbk; SciCl; CaptChrldr; University; Professional.

SWEITZER, Jeffrey; Marshall Hs; Marshall, IL; 6 NHS; LetterBsbl; Ftbl;.

SWEITZER, Julie A; West HS; Madiosn, WI; Band; CmntyWkr; CncrtBnd; NHS; NatlMeritFnl; SchMus; SchPl; FrCl;.

SWEITZER, Karen M; Cobden Unit HS; Cobden, IL; SecBand; CncrtBnd; HonRl; MrchBnd; NHS; PepBnd; SchPl; EdSchPpr; PresFHA; SecPpCl; GAA; Macmurray College; Teacher.

SWEM, Lisa L; Buchanan HS; Buchanan, MI; 13/142 PresBand; HonRl; PepBnd; SchMus; PresStuGov; PresSpnCl; LetterBsktbl; LetterTrk; GAA; AmLegAwd; Centre College Of Ky; Biology Major.

SWENDENER, Theodore C; Hooker Co HS; Mullen, NE; HonRl; SchPl; LetterTrk; LetterWrstlng; Trade School; Ranch.

SWENDSEN, Kathleen S; Mc Clusky HS; Mc Clusky, ND; 2/31 ALAGirlsSt; Band; Chr; ChrhWkr; HonRl; SchMus; EdYrBk; SchPpr; FHA; PpCl; LetterBsktbl; GAA; BttyCrckrAwd; DanFAwd; North Dakota St University.

SWENHAUGEN, Michelle R; Tracy Jr Sr HS; Walnut Grove, MN; Band; CncrtBnd; MrchBnd; PepBnd; SchMus; FFA; PpCl; SciCl; LetterTrk; CaptPPFtbl; Trade Sch; Professional.

SWENSEN, Linda K; River Falls HS; River Falls, WI; 1/184 ALAGirlsSt; Chr; NHS; PresStuCncl; Yrbk; EdSchPpr; FrCl; GerCl; Trk; IMSpt;.

SWENSON, Ann L; Monroe Sr HS; New Glarus, WI; Band; Chrs; CncrtBnd; DrlTm; HonRl; HospAde; NatlFornLg; Orch; PepBnd; 4-H; College; Nursing.

SWENSON, Cynthia; Border Central HS; Calvin, ND; 3/9 VPSophCls; PresJrCls; HonRl; PepBnd; SchPl; StuCncl; EdYrBk; RptrSchPpr; PpCl; Trk; Minot State Coll; X Ray Technologist.

SWENSON, Donna; Spring Valley HS; Wilson, WI; HonRl; OffAde; SchAde; TchrAde; FHA; Bsktbl; GAA; 4-HAwd; PresAwd; Art Sch; Art.

SWENSON, Donna E; Mount Ellis Academy; Halliday, ND; VPSophCls; Band; Chrs; ChrhWkr; CncrtBnd; HonRl; PepBnd; TchrAde; Walla Walla College; Nursing.

SWENSON, Gail L; Lake Preston HS; Lake Preston, SD; 3/37 ALAGirlsSt; Band; Chr; ChrhWkr; CmntyWkr; HonRl; SchMus; SchPl; StuCncl; RptrSchPpr; So Dakota State Univ; Pharmacy.

SWENSON, Jennifer E; Moline HS; Moline, IL; 1/845 Band; Chr; Chrl; Chrs; CncrtBnd; HonRl; LitMag; Mdrgl; MrchBnd; NatlFornLg; NHS; College; Biochemestry.

SWENSON, Joanne M; Jamestown HS; Fargo, ND; SecChr; NHS; NatlMeritFnl; NatlMeritSchl; VPStuCncl; RptrYrbk; RptrSchPpr;.

SWENSON, Kimberly R; Storden Jeffers HS; Storden, MN; Chr; Chrs; HonRl; SchPl; StuCncl; RptrSchPpr; 4-H; FHA; PpCl; LetterTrk; Chrldr; GAA; PPFtbl; Mankato St Univ; Medical Tech.

SWENSON, Laurie K; Storden Jeffers HS; Storden, MN; ALAGirlsSt; Band; Chr; HonRl; NHS; SchPl; TchrAde; LetterTrk; Chrldr; IMSpt; Univ Of Missouri; Pharmacy.

SWENSON, Mary A; Glenbard West HS; Glen Ellyn, IL; 67/530 TreasChr; HonRl; NHS; NatlThespSoc; StuGov; PpCl; GAA; PPFtbl; U Of Okl; Env Sci.

SWENSON, Nancy J; Harlem Sr HS; Loves Park, IL; 9/520 Chr; ChrhWkr; HonRl; HospAde; NatlFornLg; NHS; NatlThespSoc; SchMus; SchPl; SecStuCncl; RptrYrbk; SpnCl; Mac Murray College; Theatre.

SWENSON, Robin M; Forest Lake HS; Wyoming, MN; 11/416 HonRl; SctActv; YthFlsp; RptrYrbk; LetterBsktbl; LetterTrk; PresAwd; College;.

SWENSON, Rodney A; Fargo North HS; Fargo, ND; PresFrshCls; Band; CncrtBnd; HonRl; PepBnd; SctActv; LetterBsbl; Bsktbl; LetterFtbl; AmLegAwd; U Nd; History & Music.

SWENSON, Susan M; Rolling Meadows HS; Rolling Meadows, IL; 32/546 HonRl; HospAde; NHS; SctActv; TchrAde; IMSpt; College; Agronomy.

SWENSON, Theresa L; William Horlick HS; Racine, WI; 4/600 Band; HonRl; LitMag; MrchBnd; NatlMeritCmnd; Orch; PepBnd; SchMus; TchrAde; Univ Wis Parkside; Pre Med.

SWENSON, Veron D; Council Grove HS; Dwight, KS; ChrhWkr; CmntyWkr; HonRl; NHS; SctActv; YthFlsp; RptrYrbk; RptrSchPpr; PresFBLA; PresFHA; Washburn University.

SWENSRUD, Elaine M; Palermo Public HS; Blaisdell, ND; SecFrshCls; SecTrsSophCls; VPJrCls; HonRl; SchPl; EdYrBk; RptrSchPpr; Bsktbl; Trk; Chrldr; College Or Trade Sch.

SWERBINSKY, Michael J; St Joseph HS; St Joseph, MI; 8/350 NHS; NatlMeritCmnd; SchAde; PresStuCncl; RptrSchPpr; IMSpt; NCTE; College.

SWERTZIC, Timothy E; Silver Creek Public HS; Silver Creek, NE; ALBoysSt; Band; ChrhWkr; SchPl; SctActv; Yrbk; 4-H; Bsktbl; Trk; GodCntryAwd; Kearney St Col; Communications.

SWETS, Keith A; Holland Christian HS; Holland, MI; ChrhWkr; HonRl; ModUN; NHS; NatlMeritCmnd; SchPl; Yrbk; Bsbl; CaptSwmmng; Calvin Clge; Law.

SWETT, Tim; Fairbury HS; Fairbury, NE; 56/141 FBLA; FFA; Bsktbl; Trk; Wrstlng; Trade School; Vocational Agriculture.

SWIDER, Barbara J; Good Counsel HS; Chicago, IL; 144/278 HonRl; YthFnd; GAA; IMSpt; Bus Sch; Exec Sec.

SWIDER, Lawrence E; Niles East HS; Skokie, IL; 90/588 HonRl; JrNHS; Ftbl; Ill Inst Of Tech; Patent Lawyer.

SWIDER, Susan; Proviso West Hs; Wesrchester, IL; 50 CncrtBnd; HospAde; NHS; NatlMeritCmnd; FrCl; Tennis; CchngActv; BttyCrckrAwd;.

SWIDERSKI, Ann Marie; Gabriel Richard HS; Grosse Ile, MI; CmntyWkr; HonRl; LbryAde; NHS; NatlMeritSF; SchMus; SchPl; PresSctActv; FNA; SpnCl; U Of Mi; Nursing.

SWIECICKI, Carol A; Taft HS; Chicago, IL; 25/790 Chrs; HonRl; NHS; PresFNA; KeyCl; GAA; Ne Ill Univ; Nat Sciences.

SWIER, Kevin L; Tri Valley HS; Colton, SD; PresSophCls; VPJrCls; ALBoysSt; Chr; Chrs; HonRl; Mdrgl; NHS; SchPl; SchPpr; Bsbl; LetterFtbl; LetterTrk; College; Guidance Counselor.

SWIERS, Becky S; Central Comm HS; Argyle, IA; 6/66 PresFrshCls; PresSophCls; PresJrCls; Band; Chr; HonRl; HospAde; NHS; PpCl; Chrldr; Clge.

SWIETER, John A; Maquoketa Comm HS; Maquoketa, IA; ChrhWkr; CmntyWkr; HonRl; SctActv; VPYthFlsp; EdYrBk; SptEdYrbk; FBLA; LetterBsktbl; LetterFtbl; Swmmng; LetterTrk; CchngActv; Univ Of No Iowa; Teaching.

SWIFT, Daniel J; Harrison Co R#4 HS; Gilman City, MO; 2/17 VPFrshCls; VPSophCls; ChrhWkr; HonRl; ModUN; EdSchPpr; PresFFA; PresSpnCl; Bsktbl; Trk; CitAwd; University Of Missouri; Journalism.

SWIFT, Jean E; West HS; Davenport, IA; AFS; Chr; CmntyWkr; HonRl; HospAde; NatlThespSoc; SctActv; FrCl; SpnCl; University; Professional.

SWIFT, Mary L; Bishop Miege HS; Shawnee Msn, KS; Chrl; CmntyWkr; DrlTm; HonRl; HospAde; NHS; SchMus; SchPl; TchrAde; SpnCl; College; Medicine.

SWIFT, Stephen; Mattawan HS; Kalamozoo, MI; LbryAde; NatlMeritFnl; NatlMeritSF; SchAde; SctActv; TchrAde; Trk; IMSpt; College; Marine Biologist.

SWIGART, Jan E; Eureka HS; Eureka, IL; 1/104 TrsSrCls; AFS; Band; Chr; Chrl; Chrs; HonRl;

JrNHS; Mdrgl; MrchBnd; NHS; NatlMeritCmnd; PepBnd; SchMus; CaptChrldr; Monmouth College.

SWIGER, Janice S; Adrian HS; Adrian, MI; ChrhWkr; Adrian College; Law.

SWIGER, William E; Unionville HS; Lucerne, MO; 17/76 ALBoysSt; HonRl; 4-H; LetterBsbl; Trade School.

SWIGERT, Sharon E; Tremont HS; Tremont, IL; 8/63 ALAGirlsSt; Chrs; ChrhWkr; LbryAde; NHS; YthFlsp; VP4-H; PresFHA; GerCl; Bsktbl; Banking.

SWIHART, Karen; South Side HS; Ft Wayne, IN; 36/425 AFS; HonRl; JA; PolWkr; SchMus; TchrAde; RptrYrbk; 4-H; EngCl; FrCl; College; Socialogist Psychologist.

SWILLE, Randall D; Ashwaubenon HS; Green Bay, WI; HonRl; Ftbl; St Norbert College; Business.

SWIM, Gregory; Keya Paha County HS; Springview, NE; 7/23 ChrhWkr; HonRl; SchPl; StuCncl; StuGov; 4-H; Bsktbl; Ftbl; AmLegAwd; Oklahoma Univ; Pre Vet.

SWINARSKI, Daniel J; Brownell Talbot HS; Omaha, NE; TrsJrCls; HonRl; SchPl; TchrAde; Yrbk; EdSchPpr; College; Psychology.

SWINDELL, Cynthia M; Oak Park HS; Kansas City, MO; ChrhWkr; HonRl; SchMus; FrCl; PpCl; Nw Missouri St Univ; Teacher.

SWINDLER, Sharon J; Fairfax R 3 HS; Fairfax, MO; 4/27 Band; Chr; Chrs; ChrhWkr; CmntyWkr; CncrtBnd; DrmMjrt; HonRl; HospAde; MrchBnd; PepBnd; SchMus; SchPl; Chrldr; Cntrl Missouri St Univ; Business.

SWINEHART, Deborah L; Necedah Area HS; Necedah, WI; 3/45 ALAGirlsSt; CncrtBnd; HonRl; NatlFornLg; StuCncl; EdYrBk; PresFHA; PpCl; LetterBsktbl; LetterTrk; Chrldr; GAA; Technical School; Business.

SWINEHART, Gloriann; Riverdale HS; Avoca, WI; Chr; CncrtBnd; HonRl; JA; PepBnd; SchPl; FHA; SpnCl; SciCl; 4-HAwd; JAAwd; College; Home Ec.

SWINEHART, Terry L; Antigo HS; Antigo, WI; NatlFornLg; NatlThespSoc; OffAde; SchPl; SchPpr; PpCl; Technical Inst; Optemetric Assistant.

SWINEY, Windy K; St Mary Academy; Indianapolis, IN; PresJrCls; Chr; JA; StuCncl; LatCl; GAA; Fisk University; History.

SWINFORD, Susie E; Maconaquah HS; Peru, IN; TrsFrshCls; ChrhWkr; HonRl; TchrAde; PresYthFlsp; PpCl; Bsktbl; Trk; Chrldr; GAA; PresAwd; Indiana St Univ; Physical Ed.

SWINGEL, James; Hall HS; Spring Valley, IL; 14/124 NHS; PpCl; Bsktbl; Il Valley Comm Col.

SWINGEN, Pamela S; Woden Crystal Lake HS; Woden, IA; ChrhWkr; HonRl; YthFlsp; FNA; PpCl; Bsktbl; N Ia Area Com Col; Secretary.

SWINNEY, Rhonda J; Centre HS; Herington, KS; VPSophCls; VPSrCls; Band; Chr; Chrl; Chrs; ChrhWkr; CncrtBnd; HonRl; LetterBsktbl; Glf; Trk; IMSpt; PPFtbl; Bethany College; Teacher.

SWINTON, Joan M; Arthur Hill HS; Saginaw, MI; Band; CmntyWkr; CncrtBnd; HonRl; HospAde; LbryAde; MrchBnd; NHS; Orch; PepBnd; RedCrAde; FTA; Central Michigan Univ; Secondary Educ.

SWINTON, Lisa G; Loretto HS; Kansas City, MO; SecTrsSophCls; ChrhWkr; Orch; PolWkr; SchPl; StuGov; RptrYrbk; CivCl; CchngActv; IMSpt; College; English.

SWIONTEK, Marie; St Mary Central HS; Menasha, WI; Chrs; HonRl; SchMus; SchPl; SpnCl; PpCl; Univ; Psych.

SWIP, Lesslie A; Collinsville HS; Collinsville, IL; 3/700 ChrhWkr; CmntyWkr; HonRl; NHS; SctActv; Sdlty; 4-H; SpnCl; MthCl; College; Mathematics.

SWIRTZ, Thomas L; Eden Prairie HS; Bloomington, MN; 10/144 ALBoysSt; Band; Chr; HonRl; NHS; SctActv; LetterTrk; AmLegAwd; ChmbCommrsAwd; PresAwd; St Thomas Col; Law.

SWISHER, Donald D; Stanley County HS; Fort Peirre, SD; StuCncl; LetterRptrYrbk; LetterSchPpr; PresSpnCl; PpCl; LetterBsktbl; Sd State U; Sociology.

SWISHER, Marilee M; Warsaw HS; Warsaw, IL; 1/70 ALAGirlsSt; Band; Chrs; DrlTm; HonRl; NHS; NatlMeritCmnd; SchMus; GerCl; GAA; U Of Ill; Medical.

SWISHER, Michael P; St Johns Seminary; Independence, MO; Aud/Vis; HonRl; JA; SchAde; StuGov; 4-H; LetterBsktbl; LetterTennis; LetterTrk; IMSpt; Conception Seminary; Priest.

SWISHER, Nina S; Vienna HS; Cypress, IL; 1/104 TrsFrshCls; Band; Chrs; CncrtBnd; HonRl; MrchBnd; PepBnd; TchrAde; FNA; FTA; SpnCl; MthCl; Trk; Southern Ill Univ; Biological Science.

SWITAJ, Nadine M; Resurrection HS; Chicago, IL; 8/275 HonRl; HospAde; NHS; FNA; SpnCl; MthCl; SciCl; Loyola Univ; Nursing.

SWITZER, Cynthia J; Charleston HS; Charleston, IL; 37/259 AFS; Band; Chr; Chrl; Chrs; ChrhWkr; CmntyWkr; HonRl; Mdrgl; SchMus; SchPl; East Ill Univ; Acting.

SWITZER, Penny S; Dixon HS; Dixon, IL; 25/340 Band; ChrhWkr; CmntyWkr; CncrtBnd; HonRl; MrchBnd; NHS; SchMus; FNA; Swmmng; St Francis Hosp Schl; Nursing.

SWITZER, Russell A; Hill City HS; Hill City, KS; CAP; HonRl; SctActv; TchrAde; Bsbl; Trk; IMSpt; Col; Profssional.

SWITZER, Scott D; Lovington HS; Lovington, IL; Band; Chrs; CncrtBnd; HonRl; MrchBnd; NHS; OffAde; SchMus; PresStuCncl; YthFlsp; Univ; Computer Engineer.

SWITZER, Susan E; Mid Buchanan HS; St Joseph, MO; 1/52 SecJrCls; SecTrsSrCls; Chrs; HonRl; NHS; SchPl; FHA; PpCl; LetterBsktbl; LetterTrk; PPFtbl; University Of Missouri; Medical Technology.

SWITZER, Tamara J; Loup Co Public HS; Almeria, NE; Aud/Vis; CmntyWkr; HonRl; MrchBnd; TchrAde; Teen; RptrSchPpr; Bsktbl; LionAwd; CitAwd; Plattle Tech Comm Col; Music Major.

SWOB, Gregory A; Otis Bison U D #403 HS; Albert, KS; Chrs; HonRl; SchPl; StuCncl; VoiceDemAwd; U Of Ks; History Teacher.

SWOBODA, Diane; West HS; Sioux City, IA; 25/270 VPSrCls; Band; CncrtBnd; HonRl; MrchBnd; PepBnd; StuCncl; PpCl; Morningside College; Computers.

SWOBODA, James E; Creighton Preparatory HS; Omaha, NE; SchPl; Chrldr; GAA; University; Professional.

SWOBODA, Julie; Malvern Comm HS; Malvern, IA; TrsJrCls; Band; Chrs; HonRl; NHS; SchPl; Yrbk; Bsktbl; Bus School.

SWOBODA, Thomas J; Creighton Prep; Omaha, NE; Band; Chr; CncrtBnd; MrchBnd; PepBnd; PpCl; Chrldr; CchngActv; IMSpt; Univ; Prof.

SWOFFORD, Kelly A; Derby Sr HS; Derby, KS; ChrhWkr; CncrtBnd; HonRl; JrNHS; MrchBnd; NatlFornLg; NatlThespSoc; SchMus; YthFlsp; Kansas St Univ; Liberal Arts.

SWOMLEY, Dean A; Hudson HS; Hudson, IA; Bsbl; Ftbl; Trk; Wrstlng; Vocation.

SWOPE, Brenda A; Hanover Horton HS; Hanover, MI; PresSophCls; Band; CncrtBnd; HonRl; MrchBnd; NHS; SchPl; StuCncl; ChmnBsktbl; GAA; Mich St Univ; Counseling.

SWOPE, Darla A; Greenville HS; Coldwater, MO; VPFrshCls; Chrs; HonRl; StuCncl; FHA; SpnCl; PpCl;.

SWOPES, Kathy J; Walker HS; Nevada, MO; VPFrshCls; ChrhWkr; DrlTm; HonRl; LbryAde; TchrAde; 4-H; PresPpCl; Bsbl; LetterBsktbl; Trk; 4-HAwd; JCAwd;.

SWORDEN, Kathryn; Flat Rock HS; Flat Rock, MI; Chrs; HonRl; NHS; Quill&Scroll; SchMus; Yrbk; PpCl; SciCl; Chrldr; PPFtbl; College; Science.

SWORDS, Thomas J; St Thomas Academy; St Paul, MN; 17/96 HonRl; HospAde; ROTC; College.

SYDOR, Robin M; Le Sueur HS; Lesueru, MN; Chr; Chrs; HonRl; JA; NHS; StuCncl; TchrAde; 4-H; IMSpt; PPFtbl; Univ Of Duluth; Sex Education.

SYDOW, Libby; Smithton HS; Otterville, MO; 3/40 TrsJrCls; Band; HonRl; MrchBnd; NHS; SchAde; SchPl; EdYrBk; SchPpr; FBLA; State Fair Community College; Secretary.

SYDOW, Stephanie M; Hillsdale HS; Hillsdale, MI; 21/183 NHS; Orch; RptrYrbk; 4-H; LetterBsktbl; Valparaiso U; Engr.

SYFERT, Richard; Van Buren Comm HS; Keosavqua, IA; HonRl; StuCncl; StuGov; Trk; Wrstlng; College Iowa State;professional.

SYKES, Brian L; Cameron HS; Cameron, WI; 10/51 SecFrshCls; Band; HonRl; StuCncl; RptrSchPpr; Ftbl; CaptGlf; College; Engineering.

SYKES, Cynthia K; Ogallala Senior HS; Ogallala, NE; Chr; Chrs; LbryAde; RptrYrbk; SchPpr; LetterTrk; IMSpt; MasAwd; University.

SYKES, Paul B; Mendel Catholic Prep; Chicago, IL; 5/140 Band; Chr; ChrhWkr; CncrtBnd; HonRl; MrchBnd; OffAde; PepBnd; MthCl; IMSpt; U Of Il; Medicine.

SYKES, Sheila J; Chicago Vocational HS; Chicago, IL; 42/778 HonRl; JA; TchrAde; GAA; Univ Of Illinois; Elem Education.

SYKES, Teresa M; Alma HS; Naponee, NE; 5/27 ALAGirlsSt; Band; Chrs; HonRl; MrchBnd; PepBnd; RptrYrbk; 4-H; Central Community College; Accounting.

SYKORA, Douglas J; Bloomer HS; Bloomer, WI; ChrhWkr; CmntyWkr; HonRl; StuCncl; 4-H; FFA; LetterFtbl; LetterWrstlng; CchngActv; AmLegAwd; Clge; Math Or Science.

SYKORA, Scott J; Hinsdale Central HS; Oak Brook, IL; Band; CmntyWkr; HonRl; NHS; ROTC; SctActv; RptrSchPpr; PpCl; Ftbl; LetterWrstlng; University.

SYLVARA, Debra R; Centerville HS; Centerville, IA; 15/136 VPFrshCls; VPSophCls; VPJrCls; Band; CncrtBnd; HonRl; NHS; StuCncl; YthFlsp; LetterBsktbl; LetterTrk; College; Physical Therapist.

SYLVESTER, David A; Pioneer Jr Sr HS; Logansport, IN; 9/120 Chr; Chrs; ChrhWkr; CmntyWkr; HonRl; Mdrgl; NHS; NatlThespSoc; SchMus; SchPl; College; Professional.

SYLVESTER, Maureen K; Reese HS; Reese, MI; 25/128 ChrhWkr; HonRl; LbryAde; ModUN; TchrAde; Yrbk; GerCl; Ferris State College; Medical Tech.

SYLVESTER, Michael J; Joliet West HS; Joliet, IL; 5/495 ALBoysSt; HonRl; NHS; SptEdYrbk; GerCl; MthCl; LetterFtbl; Univ Of Notre Dame; Medicine.

SYLVESTER, Peggy; Adrian HS; Adrian, MI; Bsktbl; Glf; GAA; IMSpt; College; Accountant.

SYMBER, Diane; York Community Hs; Elmhurst, IL; 20 HonRl; SecNHS; NatlMeritCmnd; MthCl; GAA; Indiana U;environmental Engineering.

SYMMONDS, Teresa M; Dallas City HS; Dallas City, IL; Band; Chrs; HonRl; HospAde; RedCrAde; StuCncl; YthFlsp; FDA; PpCl; GAA; Blessing Hosp Lab Sch; Lab Technician.

SYNDERGAARD, Brad; Sioux Valley HS; Peterson, IA; HonRl; Bsbl; Bsktbl; Ftbl; Trk;.

SYNDRAM, Tamara S; Elmhurst HS; Fort Wayne, IN; ALAGirlsSt; Chr; Chrl; ChrhWkr; CmntyWkr; HonRl; OffAde; YthFlsp; CitAwd; College; Professional.

SYNK, Robert M; Harry Hill HS; Lansing, MI; PresNHS; LetterTennis; Hope Coll; Systems Ana.

SYPAL, Mary K; Aguinas HS; Brainard, NE; Band; CncrtBnd; MrchBnd; NHS; Yrbk; 4-H; SpnCl; MthCl; PpCl; 4-HAwd; Unif Of Nebraska.

SYPERSMA, Patricia A; Lawton Bronson HS; Sioux City, IA; Chrs; DrlTm; NatlThespSoc; SchPl; College; English Ed.

SYRING, Charles A; Gretna HS; Gretna, NE; HonRl; TchrAde; SciCl; Trk; Univ Of Nebr; Archaeologist.

SYRJANEN, Merry B; Florence HS; Florence, WI; SecFrshCls; TrsSophCls; Band; CmntyWkr; CncrtBnd; DrmMjrt; HonRl; MrchBnd; NHS; PepBnd; Twrl; 4-H; Trk; Chrldr; College; Pharmacy.

SYRNYK, Irene M; Regina Dominican HS; Chicago, IL; 2/208 HonRl; NatlMeritCmnd; NatlMeritSF; PolWkr; Quill&Scroll; SchAde; StuCncl; TchrAde; EdSchPpr; Northwestern University; Law.

SYRON, John T; Catholic Central HS; Livonia, MI; HonRl; NatlMeritCmnd; FrCl; Glf; Michigan St Univ; Veterinarian.

SYROVATKA, Ruthie A; Scotland HS; Lesterville, SD; 4/45 SecSophCls; HonRl; SchPl; PpCl; LetterBsktbl; LetterTrk; Chrldr; DanFAwd; University; Secretary.

SYROWIK, Paul; Catholic Central HS; Redford, MI; PresFrshCls; NHS; RptrSchPpr; SciCl; Univ Of Mich; Law.

SYTSMA, Nancy; Timothy Christian; Wheaon, IL; 11/80 Chr; Chrs; ChrhWkr; CmntyWkr; HonRl; OffAde; Orch; SchMus; Tennis; GAA; College; Professional.

SYVERSON, Deborah W; Stewart Public HS; Stewart, MN; 27/37 PresSrCls; ChrhWkr; CmntyWkr; OffAde; StuGov; YthFlsp; YthFnd; YthLg; FBLA; Chrldr; GAA; Mankato Vo Tech Ins; Secretary.

SYVERSON, Kevin K; Warwick Public HS; Warwick, ND; AFS; CAP; CmntyWkr; DrlTm; ROTC; SchPl; TchrAde; SptEdSchPpr; FFA; CchngActv; Valley City State Clg.

SZABELA, Richard D; Lincoln Way HS; Mokena, IL; 18/498 Aud/Vis; HonRl; NHS; TchrAde; Bsbl; LetterBsktbl; Tennis; Univ Of Illinois; Civil Engineering.

SZABO, Laura; Our Lady Of The Lakes HS; Pontiac, MI; 15/51 HonRl; LbryAde; NHS; OffAde; SchPl; TchrAde; IMSpt;.

SZABO, Mary A; Divine Child HS; Dearborn, MI; Chr; Chrs; ChrhWkr; HonRl; NHS; NatlThespSoc; SchMus; SchPl; FTA; University Of Michigan; Accounting.

SZAFRANIEC, Andrea; Notre Dame Girls HS; Chicago, IL; 8/262 HonRl; SchPl; TchrAde; Univ; Medicine.

SZAFRANSKI, Vicky L; Elizabeth Seton HS; Chicago, IL; 23/252 HonRl; NHS; RptrYrbk; RptrSchPpr; FSA; FrCl; MthCl; Univ Of Illinois; Veterinarian.

SZALACHA, Laura A; St Marys Academy; Chicago, IL; 6/51 PresFrshCls; PresSophCls; PresJrCls; PresSrCls; Chr; NHS; RptrYrbk; EdSchPpr; SciCl; Bsktbl; Trk; College; Theology.

SZALEWSKI, Stephen M; Washington HS; South Bend, IN; 21/334 CmntyWkr; HonRl; JrNHS; NHS; NatlMeritSchl; SchAde; SctActv; Ftbl; Trk; IMSpt; Purdue Univ; Pharmacy.

SZALKA, Ronald W; St Clement HS; Center Line, MI; ChrhWkr; CmntyWkr; HonRl; PolWkr; IMSpt; JAAwd; College; Vocational Trade.

SZANDZIK, Edward G; Lakeview HS; St Clair Shores, MI; 46/650 ChrhWkr; HonRl; NHS; OffAde; Teen; IMSpt; Wayne State U; Pharmacist.

SZARKA, Daniel D; St Johns HS; Laingsburg, MI; Mtu; Physics.

SZATKOWSKI, Gary S; St Laurence HS; Chicago, IL; 8/385 HonRl; NatlMeritSF; Parks Coll;aeronautical Meteorology.

SZCZECH, Bernadette A; Notre Dame HS; Chicago, IL; 7/302 HonRl; NHS; NatlMeritCmnd; TchrAde; RptrSchPpr; EdSchPpr; SchPpr; SpnCl; Rosary College; Art.

SZCZEPANIK, Mark J; Columbia Central HS; Clarklake, MI; 3/180 HonRl; NHS; NatlMeritSF; SchMus; Trk; AmLegAwd; Colleg; Ecology.

SZCZEPANSKI, Adam T; Gordon Technical HS; Chicago, IL; 3/647 SecTrsSrCls; HonRl; LitMag; PresNHS; StuCncl; SchPpr; MthCl; PpCl; IMSpt; Notre Dame U; Accnt.

SZCZEPANSKI, Mary H; Lourdes HS; Chicago, IL; 45/278 Chrs; HonRl; JA; LbryAde; Quill&Scroll; SchPl; StuCncl; EdSchPpr; SchPpr; Illinois St Univ; Communications.

SZCZEPANSKI, Nadine M; Kelly HS; Chicago, IL; 27/552 Band; HonRl; HospAde; NHS; TchrAde; 4-H; PresMthCl; GAA; Loyola Univ; Veterinarian.

SZCZERBAK, Natalie A; Immaculata HS; Chicago, IL; 5/220 ChrhWkr; CmntyWkr; HonRl; NHS; NatlMeritCmnd; NatlSciFnd; FDA; GerCl; SciCl; Northwestern Univ; Medicine.

SZCZESNIAK, James R; Maine North HS; Des Plaines, IL; VPSrCls; HonRl; OffAde; Sacrstn; Bsbl; Bsktbl; Kendall College; Business Admin.

SZCZESNIAK, Judy A; St Clement HS; Center Line, MI; 13/95 PresJrCls; HonRl; HospAde; NHS; StuCncl; RptrYrbk; Bsbl; Bsktbl; GAA; PPFtbl; Mercy Cent Nursing Sch;rn.

SZCZESNIAK, Thomas F; Bay City Central HS; Bay City, MI; ALBoysSt; Chrs; HonRl; StuCncl; StuGov; Bsbl; Ferris State College; Pharmacist.

SZCZYGIEL, Ted R; St Bonaventure HS; Chicago, IL; LbryAde; SchAde; SchPl; RptrYrbk; Yrbk; SchPpr; CaptBsbl; IMSpt; College; Professional.

SZCZYPKA, Denis F; St Laurence HS; Chicago, IL; Yrbk; SchPpr; LetterTennis; IMSpt; College; Photo Journalism.

SZEBUNTSCHAK, Katharina A; Chadsey HS; Detroit, MI; HonRl; SchPl; StuCncl; TchrAde; Yrbk; Swmmng; College; Ba.

SZELC, Bernadette R; St Andrew HS; Detroit, MI; 5/84 HonRl; NHS; SchMus; RptrYrbk; RptrSchPpr; EngCl; MthCl; Chrldr; IMSpt; CitAwd; U Of Detroit Dental Center; Dental Asistant.

SZELIGA, Elizabeth A; Roncalli HS; Omaha, NE; Chr; ChrhWkr; HonRl; HospAde; JA; NHS; Bsbl; CaptSwmmng; Tennis; Trk; Univ; Prof Med.

SZESZYCKI, Mary L; Ladywood St Agnes HS; Indianapolis, IN; Chrs; CmntyWkr; SchPl; FrCl; Chrldr; College; Computer Science.

SZEWCZYK, Claudia; Good Counsel Hs; Chgo, IL; 6/247 Chrs; HonRl; NatlFornLg; NHS; Quill&Scroll; SctActv; RptrYrbk; RptrSchPpr; GerCl; GAA; U Of Illinois; Medicine.

SZILAGYI, Claudia V; Amos Alonzo Stagg HS; Palos Hills, IL; 30/470 Chr; ChrhWkr; HonRl; NHS; RptrSchPpr; GerCl; Wheaton College; Engineering.

SZILLAGYI, Beth; Springfield HS; Springfield, IL; 64/600 Chr; Bsktbl; Trk; Lincoln Land Comm College; Secretary.

SZMYD, Nancy; Thomas Kelly Hs; Chicago, IL; NHS; TchrAde; SpnCl; GAA; U Of Illinois;social Work.

SZNAJDER, Monika M; Carmel Girls HS; Zion, IL; 13/195 Chrs; HonRl; NHS; OffAde; SchPl; RptrSchPpr; University; Music.

SZOKE, Charles J; Maine Twp East HS; Park Ridge, IL; HonRl; LetterTrk; St Francis College; Physical Therapy.

SZOSTAK, Lynn M; St Thomas Aquinas HS; Florissant, MO; Chrs; ChrhWkr; CtyCnl; CmntyWkr; HonRl; HospAde; TreasJA; JrNHS; LbryAde; SecNHS; Bsbl; Bsktbl; Socr; IMSpt; College; Social Worker.

SZOSTAK, Susan M; Mt Assisi Acad; Chicago, IL; HonRl; LbryAde; NHS; StuCncl; GAA; IMSpt; Moraine Valley Col; Nursng.

SZPONDER, Diane J; Lourdes HS; Chicago, IL; Chr; Chrs; ChrhWkr; CmntyWkr; HonRl; Mdrgl; NatlMeritCmnd; PolWkr; RedCrAde; SchMus; PpCl; University; Professional.

SZUMSKI, Peter A; J F Kennedy HS; Chicago, IL; SchPl; SctActv; TchrAde; Coll; Dentistry.

SZUSTER, Lucille; Resurrection HS; Chicago, IL; 27/260 VPSophCls; HonRl; TchrAde; FrCl; Depaul U; Accounting.

SZWEDO, Susan C; Josephinum HS; Chicago, IL; SecTrsSophCls; SecTrsJrCls; HonRl; HospAde; NHS; SchMus; SchPl; StuGov; Yrbk; SchPpr; Bsktbl; GAA; Mac Cormac Jr College; Accountant.

SZYMAN, Robert M; Deerfield HS; Deerfield, IL; HonRl; SctActv; CaptSwmmng; CchngActv;.

SZYMANOWSKI, Mark D; Whitnall HS; Greenfield, WI; 6/263 HonRl; ModUN; NHS; MthCl; St Francis; Priesthood.

SZYMANSKI, Elizabeth A; Brown HS; Sturgis, SD; 5/212 Band; HonRl; HospAde; PresNHS; StuCncl; YthFlsp; RptrYrbk; VPSpnCl; AmLegAwd; CitAwd; College; Nursing.

SZYMANSKI, Jane M; Josephinum HS; Chicago, IL; HonRl; LbryAde; NHS; NatlMeritCmnd; RedCrAde; Sdlty; RptrYrbk; RptrSchPpr; FNA; Loyola University.

SZYMANSKI, Monica A; St Florian HS; Detroit, MI; Chr; Chrs; HonRl; SchMus; SchPl; StuCncl; IMSpt; CitAwd; College; Architecture.

SZYMONIAK, Edward J; Highland HS; Highland, IN; 245/543 ROTC; SctActv; KeyCl; FrCl; College; Astronomy.

SZYNKOWSKI, Kathy A; Adelphian Academy; Royal Oak, MI; TrsJrCls; ChrhWkr; CmntyWkr; DrlTm; HonRl; NHS; OffAde; StuGov; TchrAde; RptrYrbk; Andrews University; Medicine.

SZYNWELSKI, Patricia S; Huron HS; Ann Arbor, MI; PresFrshCls; CmntyWkr; IntrClCncl; StuCncl; StuGov; YthLg; Yrbk; 4-H; FrCl; SciCl; College; Teach Or Commercial Artist.

SZYWALA, Cindy A; Barrington HS; Barrington, IL; 75/680 HonRl; NHS; StuCncl; RptrYrbk; Yrbk; RptrSchPpr; RusCl; SpnCl;.

T

TAAKE, Janet S; Century 100 HS; Ullin, IL; 4/60 ChrhWkr; HonRl; SchPl; StuCncl; RptrYrbk; RptrSchPpr; 4-H; FHA; Chrldr; GAA; Univ.

TAAKE, Michael L; Century HS; Ullin, IL; 7/60 ChrhWkr; HonRl; FrCl; Univ; Electronics.

TABACHKI, Stephen; Dansville HS; Webberville, MI; 4/74 HonRl; NHS; NatlMeritCmnd; TchrAde; Michigan U; Science.

TABBERT, Donna J; Osceola HS; Osceola, WI; ChrhWkr; OffAde; FHA; FrCl; College; Professional.

TABBERT, Jennifer S; Holmen HS; Onalaska, WI; SecBand; CncrtBnd; MrchBnd; TchrAde;

RptrSchPpr; FHA; VPPpCl; Glf; Chrldr; GAA; College; Teaching.

TABER, Brenda; Atkinson HS; Atkinson, IL; Chrs; HonRl; SchPl; StuCncl; 4-H; FHA; PpCl; Bsbl; Chrldr; GAA; Black Hawk College; Day Care Worker.

TABER, Denise; Anoka Senior Hs; Anoka, MN; Chrs; HonRl; JrNHS; NHS; RptrYrbk; VPCivCl; Pres4-H; 4-HAwd; U Minnesota School Radiologic Tech; X Ray T.

TABER, Lynn R; Eldora HS; Eldora, IA; 30/66 Chrs; DrlTm; HonRl; NatlThespSoc; SchMus; SchPl; RptrYrbk; Univ Of No Iowa; English.

TABER, Mark E; Greenhills HS; Ann Arbor, MI; Chrs; HonRl; NatlFornLg; NatlMeritCmnd; PolWkr; SchMus; SchPl; YthFlsp; Yrbk; LetterSocr; Albion Coll;.

TABER, Tina M; Atkinson HS; Atkinson, IL; 10/40 TrsJrCls; HonRl; NHS; Yrbk; 4-H; FHA; SpnCl; PpCl; Bsbl; GAA; Black Hawk College; Secretary.

TABOR, Patricia A; Madison HS; Madison, SD; 2/161 PresJrCls; ALAGirlsSt; Band; SecStuCncl; PresYthFlsp; FBLA; FHA; Tennis; Chrldr; EldAwd; College; Pharmacy.

TACCOLINI, Diane; Marquette Senior HS; Marquette, MI; 27/388 TrsFrshCls; TrsJrCls; Band; HonRl; NatlMeritFnl; Orch; SchMus; SptEdSchPpr; Trk; Northern Michigan U; Elementary Education.

TACHA, Jeri A; Prairie Heights HS; Jennings, KS; TrsFrshCls; SecSophCls; VPJrCls; ALAGirlsSt; Band; HonRl; SchPl; TchrAde; YthFlsp; Yrbk; FHA; PpCl; Bsktbl; Fort Hays State College; Business.

TACHAU, Daniel P; New Trier Twp East HS; Wilmette, IL; 3/850 NatlMeritCmnd; Orch; PolWkr; SchPpr; MthCl; Yale College; Musician.

TACK, Cindy; Savanna HS; Savanna, IL; 5/85 Band; HonRl; HospAde; 4-H; Freeport Memorial School Of Nursing; Nurse.

TACK, Cindy L; Savanna HS; Savanna, IL; 5/60 Band; HonRl; HospAde; LbryAde; Freeport Nursing School; Nurse.

TACK, Joseph E; Marmian Military Academy; Aurora, IL; 35/90 LetterSwmmng; LetterTrk; University; Veternary Medicine.

TACKETT, Penny C; Wisconsin Academy; Rock Falls, IL; ChrhWkr; HonRl; HospAde; JA; NatlMeritCmnd; SctActv; StuCncl; FHA; FrCl; Bsbl; GAA; S Missionary College; Physical Therapy.

TACKMANN, Paul R; Lincoln HS; Lake City, MN; 20/140 Chrs; HonRl; NHS; SchMus; SchPl; StuCncl; LetterBsbl; College; Social Work Or Teach.

TACY, Mary E; Woodbine Comm HS; Woodbine, IA; Chrs; ChrhWkr; CmntyWkr; HonRl; HospAde; Mdrgl; SchMus; FrCl; Trade School.

TADAJEWSKI, Joan M; Alpena HS; Alpena, MI; TchrAde; Yrbk; RptrSchPpr; Saginaw Valley St Coll; English.

TADAJEWSKI, Lorelei; St Clement Hs; Detroit, MI; VPFrshCls; HonRl; OffAde; StuCncl; RptrYrbk; PpCl; Bsbl; Bsktbl; GAA; IMSpt; Eastern Michigan U ; Physical Education.

TADER, Douglas B; St Francis HS; Minneapolis, MN; 14/160 HonRl; NHS; SchPpr; Bsbl; Bethel College.

TADER, Naomi L; St Francis HS; Minneapolis, MN; Chr; ChrhWkr; HonRl; JrNHS; Bethel College; Medicine.

TADLOCK, Lynn M; Freeburg Community HS; Freeburg, IL; 26/125 Band; ChrhWkr; HonRl; LbryAde; MrchBnd; PepBnd; RedCrAde; Yrbk; FHA; GAA; Clge;.

TADLOCK, Terry R; Warren Woods HS; Warren, MI; 5/300 HonRl; Western Mi Univ.

TAEGE, Patricia J; Wisner Pilger HS; Pilger, NE; 10/80 Chrs; ChrhWkr; HonRl; HospAde; LbryAde; MrchBnd; NatlMeritCmnd; AmLegAwd; BttyCrckrAwd; 4-HAwd; Ne Methodist Hospital School Of Nursing; Rn.

TAFF, James A; Rushville Consolidated HS; Rushville, IN; 24/325 Band; Chr; CncrtBnd; HonRl; MrchBnd; SctActv; YthFlsp; FrCl; Bsktbl; LetterTennis; Indiana Univ; Dentistry.

TAFT, Ronald E; Avon Sr HS; Avon, IL; 25/45 Chrs; SchMus; SchPl; VPFFA; Bsktbl; Ftbl; Trk; PresAwd; Trade Schl; Vocation.

TAFT, Sherry L; Van Meter Comm HS; Van Meter, IA; Chrs; ChrhWkr; HonRl; MrchBnd; SchMus; SchPl; TchrAde; PpCl; Chrldr; DanFAwd; College; Nursing.

TAG, Deonne E; Marshfield HS; Marshfield, MO; AFS; Band; ChrhWkr; HonRl; JrNHS; ModUN; StuCncl; TchrAde; Twrl; FHA; Univ; Professional.

TAGGART, Cynthia M; Columbia Central HS; Brooklyn, MI; 35/150 Chr; Chrs; HonRl; Mdrgl; SchMus; StuCncl; RptrYrbk; FHA; College; Performance Singing.

TAGGART, Maureen K; Gregory Public HS; Dallas, SD; 17/57 VPSophCls; SecJrCls; Band; CmntyWkr; CncrtBnd; Bsktbl; Trk; Chrldr; GAA; IMSpt; Black Hills State;.

TAGGART, Michael W; Casey HS; Hazel Dell, IL; 13/94 CncrtBnd; HonRl; MrchBnd; NHS; StuCncl; 4-H; SpnCl; Trk; DanFAwd; 4-HAwd; Univ; Major Study.

TAGGART, Robert; Bishop Luers HS; Fort Wayne, IN; CmntyWkr; HonRl; NHS; Yrbk; KeyCl; RotaryAwd; St Josephs Coll; Law.

TAGGART, Theresa L; Benet Academy; Lisle, IL; SchPl; University; Business.

TAGGART, Todd F; Maplewood Academy; Minneapolis, MN; 3/65 Chr; Chrl; HonRl; Bsbl; Bsktbl; Ftbl; Union Clg; Md.

TAGHON, Denise E; Thomas Jefferson HS; Bloomington, MN; Band; DrmMjrt; MrchBnd; PepBnd; Twrl; College; Physical Therapy.

TAGNANI, Chandra; Northwest Sr HS; Fenton, MO; 56/384 Chr; ChrhWkr; HonRl; LitMag; NHS; RptrSchPpr; PpCl; Southwest Mo St Coll; Teacher.

TAGUE, David F; Noblesville HS; Noblesville, IN; 9/250 Band; CncrtBnd; HonRl; MrchBnd; NHS; PepBnd; SchMus; Indiana Univ; Medicine.

TAGUE, Glenda S; Paris HS; Paris, IL; 38/254 Chrs; DrlTm; DrmBgl; HonRl; MrchBnd; StuCncl; PpCl; LetterBsktbl; EldAwd; College.

TAHTINEN, Dixie; Baraga HS; Pelkie, MI; Band; HonRl; NHS; PepBnd; PpCl; Chrldr; Trade School; Vocation.

TAHTINEN, Susie J; Baraga HS; Baraga, MI; Chr; HonRl; LbryAde; NHS; SchPl; Yrbk; RptrSchPpr; EdSchPpr; PpCl; Mi State Univ;.

TAINTER, Timothy K; Port Washington HS; Port Washington, WI; AFS; Chr; SctActv; YthFlsp; LetterBsbl; LetterBsktbl; LetterTrk; University Of Wisconsin; Civil Engineering.

TAIPALE, Patricia A; South Shore HS; Iron River, WI; Chr; Chrs; HonRl; LbryAde; Yrbk; SchPpr; Bsktbl; Vocational; Vocation.

TAIT, Eugene O; Clarkston Sr HS; Pontiac, MI; 193/487 HstFrshCls; AFS; DrmBgl; NatlCathMusEdAsoc; ROTC; FshEdYrbk; FFA; Socr; IMSpt; Podunk Coll; Earthworm Breeder.

TAIT, Lorene; St Johns Sr HS; St Johns, MI; 10/333 Band; CncrtBnd; HonRl; MrchBnd; NHS; NatlMeritCmnd; PepBnd; TchrAde; YthFlsp; Michigan St Univ, Social Work.

TAIT, William C; Coldwater HS; Coldwater, MI; Chr; LbryAde; OffAde; GerCl; ChmbCommrsAwd; Univ Of Mich.

TAKACS, Diane; Riverview HS; Riverview, MI; 20/253 ChrhWkr; HonRl; JrNHS; NHS; SchMus; SchPl; Kendall School Of Design; Advertising Desig.

TAKAI, Thomas A; North Farmington HS; Farmington Hills, MI; 72/461 Band; Chrl; NatlMeritCmnd; Orch; PepBnd; SchMus; SctActv; StuCncl; LetterSwmmng; LetterTrk; Usaf Acad; Economics.

TAKAKI, Steven K; Lane Technical HS; Chicago, IL; 91/1213 HonRl; LbryAde; SchAde; TchrAde; LatCl; University Of Illinois; Law.

TAKALA, Carol J; Alexander Ramsey HS; St Paul, MN; 20/559 Band; ChrhWkr; CncrtBnd; HonRl; MrchBnd; NHS; NatlMeritSF; PepBnd; SchMus; College.

TAKAMORI, Mike H; South Adams HS; Berne, IN; Band; Chr; Chrs; ChrhWkr; CncrtBnd; Mdrgl; MrchBnd; Orch; PepBnd; SchMus; YthFlsp; LetterFtbl; LetterGlf; Wrstlng; University; Psychology.

TAKANEN, David P; Cotton HS; Eveleth, MN; CmntyWkr; HonRl; SchPl; LetterBsbl; LetterFtbl; Trade School.

TAKASAKI, Ted A; Chatsworth HS; Chatsworth, IL; 2/48 PresFrshCls; PresSophCls; VPJrCls; Band; Chr; Chrs; CncrtBnd; HonRl; MrchBnd; NatlMeritSchl; Orch; PepBnd; StuCncl; LetterBsbl; LetterFtbl; Univ; Engineering.

TALARCZYK, Gregory; Sacred Heart HS; Dearborn, MI; Univ; Mich Engr.

TALARICO, Sally A; Plainfield HS; Joliet, IL; 6/297 HonRl; Univ Of Ill; Veterinarian.

TALBOT, Paul E; Three Lakes HS; Three Lakes, WI; Aud/Vis; HonRl; JrNHS; Bsbl; LetterFtbl; Glf; IMSpt; CitAwd; U Of Wi; Professional.

TALBOT, Polly; Rushville HS; Rushville, NE; 10/43 HonRl; LbryAde; Mdrgl; StuCncl; StuGov; 4-H; PpCl; 4-HAwd; College; Vocation.

TALBOTT, Bruce F; Greencastle HS; Greencastle, IN; Band; CncrtBnd; HonRl; MrchBnd; NatlThespSoc; PepBnd; PolWkr; SchPl; 4-H; SpnCl; Purdue Univ; Preveterinary Science.

TALBOTT, Michael A; Harrison HS; Lafayette, IN; 56/273 Chr; CncrtBnd; DrmMjrt; HonRl; MrchBnd; NatlFornLg; NHS; Orch; PepBnd; SchMus; SchPl; SctActv; Yrbk; 4-H; College; Pharmacy.

TALENT, Rebecca L; Parkview HS; Springfield, MO; HonRl; College; Riding Instructor.

TALICH, Debra G; Sidney HS; Sidney, NE; Band; CncrtBnd; MrchBnd; PepBnd; PpCl; GAA; College; Business.

TALKINGTON, Jay A; Chase County HS; Matfield Green, KS; HonRl; 4-H; SpnCl; Bsbl; Bsktbl; Ftbl; 4-HAwd; Coll; Game Bio.

TALKINGTON, Mark A; Virden HS; Virden, IL; Band; MrchBnd; PpCl; SciCl; LetterFtbl; Glf; Illinois College; Science.

TALLEY, Cynthia A; Sacred Heart HS; Salina, KS; TrsFrshCls; PresJrCls; PresSrCls; ALAGirlsSt; Band; CncrtBnd; HonRl; MrchBnd; NHS; PepBnd; LetterBsktbl; PresAwd; Dodge City Comm College; Nursing.

TALLEY, Eugene J; St Vincent De Paul HS; Sussex Drive, IL; 3/9 PresSophCls; Chr; ChrhWkr; HonRl; SchMus; SchPl; StuCncl; Yrbk; RptrSchPpr; SchPpr; LatCl; SpnCl; College; Priest.

TALLEY, Gladys; East HS; Kansas City, MO; 15/186 DrlTm; HonRl; IntrClCncl; NHS; StuCncl; Yrbk; PpCl; Trk; GAA; IMSpt; College; Professional.

TALLEY, Kevin M; Litchfield Senior HS; Litchfield, IL; ALBoysSt; Chr; HonRl; StuCncl; YthFlsp; KeyCl; FrCl; PpCl; LetterBsbl; LetterBsktbl; LetterFtbl; IMSpt; Murray State Univ; Radio.

TALLEY, Marianne; Mediapolis Community HS; New London, IA; 10/90 Band; Chr; Chrs; HonRl; PepBnd; YthFlsp; RptrYrbk; SchPpr; 4-H; FHA; Bus School; Secretarial P Bus Training.

TALLMAN, Julie A; Colfax HS; Colfax, WI; SecJrCls; Chr; CncrtBnd; HonRl; Mdrgl; NHS; SchPl; Yrbk; FFA; GAA; U; Veterinarian Assist.

TALLMON, William; Mitchell HS; Mitchell, NE; TrsSophCls; TrsJrCls; CncrtBnd; HospAde; OffAde; KeyCl; Bsktbl; Ftbl; Trk; 4-HAwd; Trade School; Jeweler.

TALLYN, Kristen L; Bergan HS; Peoria Hts, IL; 25/199 CmntyWkr; HonRl; LitMag; LbryAde; TchrAde; EdYrBk; Yrbk; RptrSchPpr; Illinois State University.

TALSMA, Dale A; Mason County Central HS; Scottville, MI; 1/128 Aud/Vis; HonRl; SchMus; YthFlsp; Bsktbl; Concordia Lutheran Jr College; Mathematics.

TALTY, Marcia A; Westside HS; Omaha, NE; 70/820 HonRl; NHS; StuGov; FrCl; PpCl; Chrldr; Lawyer.

TAM, Christie A; New Trier East HS; Wilmette, IL; HonRl; Trinity College.

TAMASON, Patricia A; Dwight D Eisenhower HS; Blue Island, IL; 14/631 AFS; SecChr; Chrs; HonRl; NHS; Quill&Scroll; StuCncl; TchrAde; RptrYrbk; RptrSchPpr; Moraine Valley Comm College; Biology.

TAMERIUS, Debbie A; Savannah HS; Savannah, MO; Band; HonRl; PepBnd; SpnCl; PpCl; LetterBsktbl; Trk; PPFtbl; Nwmsu At Maryville Mo.

TAMLYN, Scheri L; La Salle HS; St Ignace, MI; ChrhWkr; HonRl; JrNHS; NHS; PolWkr; RptrYrbk; Albion College.

TAMMINEN, Gail L; Negaunee HS; Negaunee, MI; 1/147 Band; ChrhWkr; CncrtBnd; HonRl; MrchBnd; NHS; Orch; PepBnd; PpCl;.

TAMRAZ, Timberlee; Elgin HS; Streamwood, IL; 74/748 SchAde; StuCncl; TchrAde; Univ Of Illinois; Med Technology.

TAMURA, Michelle M; Hazel Park HS; Hazel Park, MI; 45/410 HonRl; NHS; StuCncl; StuGov; YthFnd; RptrSchPpr; Oakland Univ; Journalism.

TAN, Linda L; Esko HS; Esko, MN; 20/109 Band; Chr; ChrhWkr; CncrtBnd; HonRl; TreasJA; PepBnd; TchrAde; 4-H; 4-HAwd; U Of Mn; Elementary Education.

TANAKA, Katherine; Prospect HS; Mt Prospect, IL; 1/613 DrlTm; HonRl; NHS; StuCncl; PpCl; IMSpt; Univ Of Illinois; Medicine.

TANAKA, Patricia Ann Y; Southwest HS; St Louis, MO; Chr; Chrl; ChrhWkr; HonRl; Quill&Scroll; SchMus; SchPl; SchPpr; TchrAde; GAA; Univ Of Mi; Computer Science.

TANCK, Catherine A; Washington HS; Sioux Falls, SD; ALAGirlsSt; Band; CncrtBnd; HonRl; MrchBnd; NatlFornLg; NHS; PepBnd; DARAwd; College; Mathematics.

TANCULA, James E; Libertyville HS; Libertyville, IL; ChrhWkr; HonRl; NHS; PolWkr; LatCl; LetterBsktbl; Univ Of Marquette; Law.

TANDBERG, Christine M; Osceola HS; Dresser, WI; Band; Chr; ChrhWkr; HonRl; NatlFornLg; PepBnd; RptrYrbk; Yrbk; FHA; FrCl; Univ; Professional.

TANDE, Brian; Lake Preston HS; Hetland, SD; VPSophCls; SecSrCls; College; Business Management.

TANDET, Bruce D; Buffalo Grove HS; Arlington Hts, IL; 32/288 HonRl; NatlFornLg; NHS; PolWkr; KeyCl; TreasFrCl; LetterTennis; Univ Of Illinois; Medicine.

TANGEMAN, Karen J; B & B HS; Baileyville, KS; 1/39 Chr; Chrs; ChrhWkr; CmntyWkr; HonRl; SchPl; Yrbk; RptrSchPpr; 4-H; PpCl; GAA; College; Music.

TANGEMAN, William; Centralia HS; Corning, KS; ALBoysSt; HonRl; Sacrstn; SchPl; FFA; SciCl; Bsbl; Ftbl; Univ; Mechanical Engineering.

TANGEN, Pamila L; Larimore Public HS; Larimore, ND; HonRl; LbryAde; RptrYrbk; SptEdYrbk; Yrbk; FHA; MthCl; PpCl; IMSpt; College; Curriculum Of Major Study.

TANGEN, Vonnie L; Chosen Valley HS; Fountain, MN; SecFrshCls; Band; Chr; ChrhWkr; CncrtBnd; HonRl; Mdrgl; MrchBnd; PepBnd; SchPl; SctActv; StuCncl; Bsktbl; Chrldr; College; Nursing.

TANGUAY, Frances M; Marian HS; Royal Oak, MI; ChrhWkr; CmntyWkr; HonRl; JA; ModUN; SctActv; Chrldr; VFWAwd; VoiceDemAwd; University; Special Education.

TANIGAWA, Joan Y; Lane Tech HS; Chicago, IL; 276/1100 Loyola Univ; Medicine.

TANK, Bradley C; Martin Luther HS; Milwaukee, WI; HonRl; NatlMeritSF; SchPl; RptrSchPpr; Bsbl; Bsktbl; Trk; CaptWrstlng; IMSpt; PresAwd; Coll.

TANK, Joni L; Columbus Sr HS; Columbus, NE; ALAGirlsSt; Chrs; HonRl; SchMus; StuCncl; TchrAde; SchPpr; SpnCl; LetterTrk; CchngActv; Med Sch; Nurse.

TANK, Mickey L; North Bend Central HS; North Bend, NE; 2/55 ALBoysSt; CmntyWkr; HonRl; NHS; SptEdYrbk; FFA; Bsbl; Univ Of Nebraska; Animal Science.

TANKOFF, Linda M; Sisseton HS; Sisseton, SD; ChrhWkr; TchrAde; Yrbk; SchPpr; Watertown Business Univ.

TANLE, Rickey D; North Bend Central HS; North Bend, NE; 4/55 ALBoysSt; CmntyWkr; HonRl; SptEdYrbk; RptrSchPpr; FBLA; Univ Of Nebraska; History.

TANNATT, Douglas K; Southeast Polk HS; Des Moines, IA; 2/220 VPFrshCls; HonRl; NHS; SchPl; StuCncl; StuGov; TchrAde; RptrYrbk; SpnCl; CaptSwmmng; Tennis; Iowa State Univ; Architecture.

TANNEHILL, Mitchell B; Pittsford HS; Pittsford, MI; ALBoysSt; TchrAde; SptEdYrbk; Bsktbl; Ftbl; Glf; Trk; Coll; Sociologist.

TANNENBAUM, Peter S; Pioneer HS; Ann Arbor, MI; 21/600 Band; CncrtBnd; MrchBnd; Orch; SciCl;.

TANNER, Catherine E; Pope County HS; Golconda, IL; SecSophCls; PresJrCls; HonRl; LbryAde; VPStuCncl; Yrbk; FHA; VPSpnCl; PpCl;.

TANNER, David R; Thornridge HS; Harvey, IL; CncrtBnd; HonRl; MrchBnd; TreasNHS; SctActv; MthCl; College; Engineering.

TANNER, Doug; Hartley Comm HS; Hartley, IA; 1/69 ChrhWkr; HonRl; NHS; SctActv; Bsbl; Bsktbl; Ftbl; Trk; Univ N Ia; Tech.

TANNER, Gary E; East HS; Wichita, KS; ALBoysSt; Band; ChrhWkr; CncrtBnd; HonRl; MrchBnd; Orch; Chem.

TANNER, Joe E; Covington Comm HS; Covington, IN; 20/120 HonRl; SchPl; Bsbl; LetterFtbl; LetterWrstlng; Manchester College; Geologist.

TANNER, John E; Independence Community HS; Independence, IA; 4/160 HonRl; NHS; NatlMeritFnl; NatlMeritCmnd; NatlMeritSF; 4-H; Wartburg Col; Math.

TANNER, Lynette E; Marion HS; Marion, IA; 11/179 CncrtBnd; HonRl; HospAde; MrchBnd; PepBnd; SchMus; YthFlsp; 4-H; 4-HAwd; CitAwd; Nursing School; Nurse.

TANNER, Martin A; Ida Crown Jewish Academy; Chicago, IL; HonRl; NHS; NatlMeritSF; StuCncl; RptrSchPpr;.

TANNER, Mary Lisa; Acad Of The Sacred Heart; Royal Oak, MI; LbryAde; NHS; EdSchPpr; Mi St U ;.

TANNURA, Frank V; St Laurence HS; Burbank, IL; 3/385 HonRl; NHS; LetterGlf; LetterTrk; CchngActv; Loyola; Business.

TAO, Amy; Niles Township Hs; Lincolnwood, IL; 8/666 Chrs; HonRl; HospAde; NHS; NatlMeritFnl; NatlMeritSF; University; Math & Science.

TAO, Amy R; Niles West HS; Lincolnwood, IL; 1 666 Chrs; HospAde; NHS; NatlMeritSF; StuGov; GAA; Univ; Profes.

TAPHOUSE, Vanessa M; Ann Arbor Pioneer HS; Ann Arbor, MI; 4/622 CncrtBnd; HonRl; LitMag; MrchBnd; SctActv; Yrbk; FrCl; MthCl; Kalamazoo Clge; Math & Physics.

TAPIA, Celeste M; Carl Sandburg HS; Orland Park, IL; 1/700 HonRl; NatlMeritCmnd; SpnCl; MthCl; Coll;biol, Dentistry.

TAPIO, Lois S; Oak Park River Forest HS; Oak Park, IL; HonRl; HospAde; Orch; SchMus; StuCncl; RptrYrbk; Trk; CchngActv; Triton College; Nurse.

TAPKE, Dorothy J; Burlington Comm HS; Burlington, IA; 5/500 NHS; StuCncl; YthFlsp; Yrbk; ChmnPpCl; SciCl; Iowa State Univ; Textiles.

TAPLETT, Mike F; Tyndall Public HS; Tyndall, SD; VPFrshCls; VPJrCls; CmntyWkr; HonRl; YthFnd; SptEdYrbk; PpCl; Bsbl; Ftbl; Glf; Coll; Teacher.

TAPLEY, Karen A; Armada Area HS; Armada, MI; 9/93 VPChr; ChrhWkr; HonRl; Mdrgl; NHS; SchMus; TchrAde; SpnCl; John Wesley College; Social Work.

TAPLEY, Sheldon C; Parkway Central Sr HS; Chesterfield, MO; 38/470 ModUN; NHS; NatlMeritSF; SchPl; Trk; College; Medicine.

TAPLIN, Duane A; Adams Friendship HS; Hancock, WI; LetterFtbl; LetterWrstlng;.

TAPLIN, Karen; East Central HS; Green Island, IA; Band; Chrs; ChrhWkr; CncrtBnd; HonRl; MrchBnd; SchMus; SchPpr; PpCl; Chrldr; Cllege;nursing.

TAPP, Teresa L; Yorkville HS; Oswego, IL; 20/140 SecSophCls; Band; HonRl; NHS; SchPl; SecStuCncl; TchrAde; FrCl; LetterSocr; VPGAA; PresAwd; College; Business.

TAPPENBECK, Naydene; Triopia HS; Chapin, IL; SecSrCls; DrlTm; HonRl; NHS; StuCncl; StuGov; LetterBsbl; Trk; GAA; DARAwd; Il College; Accounting.

TAPPER, Cynthia R; Northeast Hamilton HS; Kamrar, IA; 13/46 SecTrsSrCls; Band; HonRl; YthFlsp; EdYrBk; 4-H; VPFTA; PresPpCl; Bsktbl; Trk; 4-HAwd; Business School; Med Secretary.

TAPPER, Scott; Ne Hamilton Hs; Webster City, IA; Chr; Chrs; CncrtBnd; HonRl; Mdrgl; MrchBnd; SchMus; StuCncl; Pres4-H; 4-HAwd; Isa Ames Ia; Farming.

TARASIEWICZ, Alyson C; St Mary Of Perpetual Help HS; Chicago, IL; VPSophCls; TrsJrCls; HonRl; SctActv; Sdlty; StuCncl; Yrbk; Tennis; GAA; Depaul Univ; Liberal Arts.

TARBUTTON, Vicki; West Point Jr Sr HS; West Point, NE; 13/59 VPJrCls; Chrs; HonRl; SchPl; EdYrBk; RptrSchPpr; FFA; PpCl; Chrldr; BttyCrckrAwd; Univ Of Nebf Horticulture.

TARCZYNSKI, Gary C; Notre Dame HS; Niles, IL; 4/276 HonRl; NatlMeritSF; TchrAde; Air Force Academy; Engineering.

TARCZYNSKI, Timothy F; St Alphonsus HS; Detroit, MI; 8/142 HonRl; SctActv; Ftbl; College; Professional.

TARDANI, Joanne M; Musk Catholic Central HS; Muskegon, MI; HonRl; FrCl; Chrldr; Central Mi; Elem Schl Teacher.

TARGOSZ, Thomas J; Lockport Central HS; Lockport, IL; HonRl; College; Dentist.

TARKOWSKI, James A; Pinconning HS; Linwood, MI; HonRl; Bsbl; Delta Coll; Lawyer.

TARMAN, Douglas C; Fairfield Jr Sr HS; New Paris, IN; VPFrshCls; TrsSophCls; TrsSrCls; Band; ChrhWkr; CncrtBnd; HonRl; MrchBnd; StuCncl; StuGov; YthFlsp; LetterBsktbl; LetterTrk; Ferris State College; Pharmacy.

TARNAWA, Michael J; York HS; Elmhurst, IL; HonRl; NatlMeritCmnd; Quill&Scroll; SptEdSchPpr; Univ Of Ill; Engineering.

TARNOW, Donna J; Arrowhead HS; Pewaukee, WI; ChrhWkr; HonRl; NHS; RptrYrbk; FHA; Technical School; Accountant.

TARPEIN, Dee L; Adair Co Rii HS; Brashear, MO; 2/24 VPSophCls; Band; Chrs; ChrhWkr; HonRl; MrchBnd; SchMus; StuCncl; FHA; LetterBsbl; LetterBsktbl; LetterTrk; 4-HAwd; College; Nursing.

TARPLEY, Aubrey V; Caruthersville HS; Caruthersville, MO; ALBoysSt; CAP; JCC; NHS; SctActv; StuCncl; YthFlsp; FBLA; FFA; FSA; U Of Missouri; Civil Engineer.

TARR, Daniel W; Flat Rock HS; Fla Rock, MI; HonRl; StuCncl; TchrAde; LetterBsbl; Bsktbl; LetterFtbl; CchngActv;.

TARRANT, Cindy L; Bath HS; Bath, MI; Band; ChrhWkr; CncrtBnd; HonRl; MrchBnd; NHS; PepBnd; SchPl; TreasStuCncl; StuGov; College; Biology.

TARSIKES, Susan K; South HS; Omaha, NE; 68/674 Band; Chr; ChrhWkr; HonRl; TreasJA; NHS; SchMus; SchPl; IMSpt; JAAwd; Univ Of Neb; Business Admin.

TARTER, Donna C; Ramsey HS; Ramsey, IL; 1/46 PresJrCls; HonRl; VPLbryAde; StuCncl; Yrbk; RptrSchPpr; Sec4-H; FTA; PresFrCl; PpCl; 4-HAwd; Ill State Univ; Biology.

TARTT, Deborah L; Holy Redeemer HS; Southfield, MI; 16/190 HonRl; JrNHS; College; Professional.

TARTT, Deirdre S; Holy Redeemer HS; Southfield, MI; 17/190 HonRl; HospAde; JA; JrNHS; NHS; SchAde; StuGov; TchrAde; RptrYrbk; SpnCl; PpCl; College; Professional.

TARVIN, Gregory L; Lapel HS; Lapel, IN; 3/81 Chr; ChrhWkr; CmntyWkr; CncrtBnd; JA; PresNHS; SchMus; Yrbk; LatCl; LetterTrk; Rose Hulman Inst Of Tech; Elect Engr.

TARWATER, Katherine; Edwardsville Sr Hs; Glen Carbon, IL; 14/443 Chrs; HonRl; NHS; NatlMeritCmnd; VPNatlThespSoc; SchMus; SchPl; Southern Illinois U; Foreign Language.

TASCHNER, Mary Lee; South Milwaukee HS; South Milwaukee, WI; HonRl; Bsbl; LetterBsktbl; LetterSwmmng; LetterTrk; IMSpt; PresAwd; Clge.

TASLER, Mike L; West Holt HS; Atkinson, NE; ChrhWkr; CmntyWkr; SchAde; SchPl; StuGov; RptrYrbk; SptEdYrbk; 4-H; FFA; Ftbl; College; Vocation.

TASLITZ, Lauren S; Highland Park HS; Highland Park, IL; Chrs; HonRl; NHS; NatlMeritFnl; NatlMeritSF; SchMus; SchPl; StuGov; EdSchPpr; College; Medicine.

TATARELLI, James; Denby HS; Detroit, MI; 40/650 NatlMeritCmnd; NatlMeritSchl; Coll; Food Science.

TATAROWICZ, Walter A; St Benedict HS; Chicago, IL; 1/180 VPFrshCls; Chrs; NHS; Orch; SchPl; SchPpr; MthCl; IMSpt; Loyola Univ; Med.

TATE, Alicia L; Hannibal Senior HS; Griggsville, IL; HonRl; LbryAde; PresNHS; NatlMeritSF; FTA; SpnCl; PpCl; GAA; IMSpt; University; Political Science.

TATE, Anna L; Floyd Central HS; New Albany, IN; 16/266 SecSophCls; ALAGirlsSt; CmntyWkr; HonRl; SecNHS; Yrbk; FTA; PpCl; Chrldr; PPFtbl; Indiana University; Business Administration.

TATE, Barbara J; Raytown HS; Raytown, MO; Chr; ChrhWkr; HonRl; NHS; SctActv; EdSchPpr; IMSpt; University; Nurse.

TATE, Emory D; Concord Comm HS; Elkhart, IN; Chr; Chrl; Chrs; HonRl; NatlMeritCmnd; SchMus; SchPl; G Washington Univ; Business Adm.

TATE, Gregory P; Austin Catholic Prep; Grosse Pt, MI; 47/135 HonRl; U S Naval Academy; Pilot.

TATE, J Susan; Burlington Comm HS; Burlington, IA; 40/501 HonRl; HospAde; ModUN; NatlFornLg; NHS; PolWkr; Quill&Scroll; StuCncl; EdSchPpr; KiwanAwd; Drake Univ; Journalism.

TATE, Randall C; Hales Franciscan HS; Chicago, IL; 9/79 Aud/Vis; ChrhWkr; CmntyWkr; HonRl; PolWkr; StuGov; GerCl; LetterBsbl; LetterBsktbl; CchngActv; Il Inst Of Tech; Mech Engr.

TATE, Sandra J; North Division HS; Milwaukee, WI; HonRl; JA; JrNHS; NHS; StuCncl; RptrYrbk; Yrbk; SchPpr; FrCl; PpCl; Chrldr; Matc; Business Data Processing.

TATE, Stephen V; Kewanee HS; Kewanee, IL; AFS; StuCncl; StuGov; PresKeyCl; Bsktbl; Glf; Tennis; LetterTrk; CchngActv; IMSpt; Univ; Professional Pre Med.

TATE, Susan G; R 1 North Callaway HS; Kingdom City, MO; 6/72 Chrs; HonRl; HospAde; SchPl; TchrAde; Yrbk; 4-H; FHA; TreasFTA; TreasSpnCl; Missouri State Univ; Special Education.

TATSUMI, Kathlene L; Sheldon HS; Sheldon, IA; Chr; ChrhWkr; DrlTm; HonRl; HospAde; Quill&Scroll; RptrSchPpr; FHA; College; Nursing.

TATUM, Terri S; Central HS; Burden, KS; Chr; ChrhWkr; HonRl; SchPl; SchPpr; 4-H; FFA; LetterBsktbl; LetterTrk; College; Forestry.

TAUBE, De Etta; Comm Unit 2 HS; Liberty, IL; Chrs; HonRl; NHS; SchPl; SpnCl; College; Interior Design.

TAUBE, Kathleen M; Jefferson City Sr HS; Jefferson City, MO; HonRl; JrNHS; NHS; OptClAwd; Univ; Vocational Art.

TAUBENHEIM, Julie; Broken Bow HS; Broken Bow, NE; PresSophCls; Band; ChrhWkr; HonRl; LbryAde; RptrYrbk; 4-H; FHA; Chrldr; 4-HAwd; College; Business.

TAUBER, Thomas W; York Comm HS; Elmhurst, IL; 112/980 HonRl; Univ Of Illinois; Architect.

TAUGHER, Bridget S; Catholic Memorial HS; Waukesha, WI; 6/140 HonRl; JrNHS; NHS; RedCrAde; RptrYrbk; MthCl; PpCl; Chrldr; GAA; IMSpt; Mt Mary Clg; Occupational Therapy.

TAUSK, Theresa N; Benet Academy; Downers Grove, IL; 68/230 HonRl; OffAde; SchAde; RptrYrbk; RptrSchPpr; EdSchPpr; FrCl; Northern Ill Univ; Journalism.

TAUSSIG, Cara J; Niles Township No HS; Skokie, IL; 28/632 HonRl; NHS; SchMus; SchPl; StuCncl; TchrAde; Trk; CaptChrldr; University.

TAYLOE, Daniel; Ballard Comm HS; Cambridge, IA; 3/81 Band; CncrtBnd; HonRl; MrchBnd; NHS; NatlThespSoc; SchMus; SchPl; FrCl; KiwanAwd; Ia St Univ; Electrical Eng.

TAYLOR, A Lavar; Collinsville HS; Collinsville, IL; 1/650 Band; CncrtBnd; HonRl; MrchBnd; NHS; NatlMeritCmnd; PepBnd; LatCl; SciCl; U Of Il; Law School.

TAYLOR, Anna J; Arsenal Technical HS; Indianapolis, IN; Chrl; Chrs; HonRl; Twrl; GerCl; LetterTrk; College; Professional.

TAYLOR, Anne M; Oregon HS; Oregon, WI; Chrs; HonRl; Mdrgl; NatlFornLg; NHS; SchPl; Univ Of Wi Madison; Lawyer.

TAYLOR, Anne M; Columbus HS; Columbus, WI; 5/120 ALAGirlsSt; Band; HospAde; MrchBnd; NHS; StuCncl; EdYrBk; SpnCl; Bsktbl; GAA; University; Medicine.

TAYLOR, Anthony L; Hales Franciscan HS; Chicago, IL; 25/73 ChrhWkr; CmntyWkr; HonRl; OffAde; SctActv; StuGov; SciCl; Trk; College; Liberal Arts.

TAYLOR, Anthony W; Riverview HS; St Louis, MO; 154/779 HonRl; OffAde; StuCncl; LetterBsbl; LetterBsktbl; Univ At Tulsa; Pro.

TAYLOR, Barbara; Carter H Harrison HS; Chicago, IL; 8/408 HonRl; NHS; Orch; Univ; Prof.

TAYLOR, Bonnie; Rochester Adams HS; Rochester, MI; 12/369 HonRl; HospAde; NHS; PolWkr; GAA; Calamazoo Coll; Gp.

TAYLOR, Brian S; Carmel HS; Mundelein, IL; 3/182 VPFrshCls; CmntyWkr; HonRl; JrNHS; LitMag; NHS; PolWkr; StuGov; TchrAde; EdSchPpr; GerCl; Ftbl; Glf; Northwestern Univ; International Affairs.

TAYLOR, Carol L; Mentor Public HS; Mentor, MN; 5/13 Chrs; ChrhWkr; HonRl; LbryAde; OffAde; SchPl; EdSchPpr; FHA; PpCl; Northland Jr College; Nurse.

TAYLOR, Carolyn M; Parsons HS; Parsons, KS; Chrs; ChrhWkr; HonRl; IntrClCncl; NHS; SchPl; StuCncl; PpCl; Chrldr; PPFtbl; College; Psychologist.

TAYLOR, Cheryl E; Frederic Remington HS; Benton, KS; Band; Chr; Chrs; ChrhWkr; CncrtBnd; DrlTm; HonRl; Mdrgl; MrchBnd; NHS; PresNatlThespSoc; College.

TAYLOR, Cynthia M; Chicago Vocational HS; Chicago, IL; 9/700 HonRl; NHS; StuCncl; StuGov; Roosevelt Univ; English Teacher.

TAYLOR, Cynthia S; Stanley County HS; Fort Pierre, SD; 4/52 PresSophCls; PresSrCls; PresBand; HonRl; NHS; PolWkr; StuCncl; TchrAde; RptrYrbk; LetterBsktbl; LetterGAA; College; Major Study.

TAYLOR, Danese B; Harper HS; Chicago, IL; Band; CncrtBnd; DrlTm; HonRl; JrNHS; OffAde; SctActv; StuCncl; SchPpr; Univ Of California; Law.

TAYLOR, Daphne A; William Chrisman HS; Independence, MO; 113/365 Band; Chrs; ChrhWkr; CmntyWkr; HospAde; NatlThespSoc; OffAde; PolWkr; SchPl; SctActv; Swmmng; PresAwd; Nursing School; Nurse.

TAYLOR, David; Hillsboro HS; Festus, MO; Chr; StuCncl; Ftbl; Trk; College; Medical Profession.

TAYLOR, David M; Galesburg Senior HS; Galesburg, IL; 12/588 PresFrshCls; HonRl; JrNHS; NHS; StuCncl; SpnCl; LetterFtbl; CaptTrk; CaptWrstlng; Univ Of Missouri; Pre Med.

TAYLOR, David R; Greensburg Comm HS; Greensburg, IN; 1/191 VPSrCls; ALBoysSt; NHS; YthFlsp; LetterBsbl; LetterFtbl; LetterTrk; KiwanAwd; OptClAwd; RotaryAwd; Coll; Engi.

TAYLOR, Debbie J; Wesclin HS; Trenton, IL; 1/110 Band; CncrtBnd; HonRl; JrNHS; MrchBnd; NHS; Orch; SchPpr; FBLA; LatCl; St Louis Col; Pharmacy.

TAYLOR, Deborah A; Chicago Vocational HS; Chicago, IL; Chr; HonRl; Univ Chicago; Acct.

TAYLOR, Deborah A; North Platte Sr HS; North Platte, NE; StuCncl; TchrAde; VP4-H; VPFFA; Tennis; Trk; GAA; IMSpt; LetterPPFtbl; 4-HAwd; College; Veterinarian.

TAYLOR, Deborah L; Saint Teresa HS; Decatur, IL; 17/117 HonRl; LbryAde; RptrYrbk; Univ Of Ill; Fine Or Applied Arts.

TAYLOR, Debra A; Washington HS; Washington, MO; 14/276 Chrs; HonRl; NHS; SchMus; SchPl; StuCncl; Yrbk; PresFrCl; TreasPpCl; Southeast Mo State Univ; Elem Ed.

TAYLOR, Debra S; Canton R V HS; Canton, MO; ChrhWkr; HonRl; LbryAde; OffAde; SchAde; SchMus; SchPl; TchrAde; FSA; SciCl; Central Mo State U; Medical Tech.

TAYLOR, Denise M; Shortridge HS; Indianapolis, IN; ChrhWkr; CmntyWkr; HonRl; JA; LatCl; SpnCl; Univ; Professional.

TAYLOR, Dirk A; Jeffersonville HS; Jeffersonville, IN; 100/700 PresFrshCls; Chr; HonRl; JrNHS; SctActv; YthFlsp; Bsbl; Bsktbl; Ftbl; CchngActv; AmLegAwd; Univ Of Louisville; Law.

TAYLOR, Donna L; So Bo Co R 1 HS; Ashland, MO; Chr; ChrhWkr; HonRl; LbryAde; OffAde; SchPl; RptrYrbk; FHA; SpnCl; University; Professional.

TAYLOR, Eartha L; West Side HS; Gary, IN; 100/840 Band; ChrhWkr; HonRl; JrNHS; PpCl; Swmmng; I U Bloomington Ind; Nursing.

TAYLOR, Eldra J; St Mark HS; St Louis, MO; 21/38 Chrs; PresJA; SchMus; SchPl; SchPpr; 4-H; MthCl; PpCl; DanFAwd; 4-HAwd; College; Home Ec Major.

TAYLOR, Elvin; Lew Wallace HS; Gary, IN; ChrhWkr; CmntyWkr; DrlTm; JA; ROTC; StuCncl; 4-H; KeyCl; ChmbCommrsAwd; Howard Univ; Lawyer.

TAYLOR, Freda K; Fairfield Comm HS; Fairfield, IL; HonRl; OffAde;.

TAYLOR, Gary S; Escanaba HS; Escanaba, MI; 21/392 Chrl; MrchBnd; NatlMeritFnl; StuGov; YthLg; VPPpCl; LetterBsktbl; LetterGlf; VPJAAwd; U Of Mi ; Dentist.

TAYLOR, Gayla R; Fairfield HS; Geff, IL; Chr; DrmMjrt; SchMus; SchPl; StuCncl; YthFlsp; 4-H; Chrldr; GAA; AmLegAwd; Wabash Jr Clg; Child Developement.

TAYLOR, Gwen; Manhattan Hs; Manhattan, KS; Chr; ChrhWkr; Orch; SchMus; YthFlsp; SpnCl; Swmmng; College ; Music.

TAYLOR, James R; Oak Park HS; Kansas City, MO; HonRl; JCC; NHS; NatlMeritFnl; NatlMeritCmnd; FDA; FFA; LetterWrstlng; JCAwd; JAAwd; MasAwd; University; Petroleum Geologist.

TAYLOR, Jill A; Trenton HS; Trenton, MI; HonRl; NHS; OffAde; SchPl; StuCncl; TchrAde; PpCl; PPFtbl; Univeristy; Health Professions.

TAYLOR, Joan E; Willowbrook HS; Villa Park, IL; HonRl; JrNHS; NHS; Orch; SchMus; Illinois St Univ; Business Admin.

TAYLOR, Joe F; Galena HS; Galena, MO; 8/35 HstSophCls; Band; ChrhWkr; CmntyWkr; CncrtBnd; HonRl; SchPl; StuCncl; Yrbk; SchPpr; PpCl; Univ; Dramatics.

TAYLOR, John; Horace Mann HS; Gary, IN; /300 ALBoysSt; Band; CncrtBnd; HonRl; JrNHS; MrchBnd; NHS; SptEdYrbk; Ftbl; Swmmng; Coll;pro.

TAYLOR, Judith A; Pennfield HS; Battle Creek, MI; Chr; Chrl; CmntyWkr; HonRl; LbryAde; TchrAde; YthFlsp; FTA; SpnCl; LetterBsktbl; Kcc ;elem Educ.

TAYLOR, Julie K; Morton Sr HS; Hammond, IN; 44/499 Band; ChrhWkr; CmntyWkr; CncrtBnd; HonRl; MrchBnd; Quill&Scroll; StuGov; TchrAde; YthFlsp; Yrbk; Univ; Accounting.

TAYLOR, Julie L; King City Ri HS; King City, MO; HstFrshCls; HstSophCls; HonRl; SchPl; StuCncl; FHA; SpnCl; PpCl; TchrAde; Trk; LetterCollege.

TAYLOR, Karen L; Gibson Southern HS; Fort Branch, IN; ALBoysSt; ALAGirlsSt; CmntyWkr; HonRl; JrNHS; MrchBnd; NHS; NatlMeritSchl; StuCncl; University; Accounting.

TAYLOR, Kathy R; Washburn Rural HS; Topeka, KS; Band; DrlTm; HonRl; OffAde; SchMus; YthFlsp; PpCl;.

TAYLOR, Kristine H; Arthur Hill HS; Saginaw, MI; Band; Chr; ChrhWkr; CncrtBnd; HonRl; Mdrgl; YthFlsp; Delta College; Dental Hygiene.

TAYLOR, Laura; Kalkaska HS; Alden, MI; CmntyWkr; HonRl; TchrAde; RptrYrbk; SpnCl; Alma College; Psychology.

TAYLOR, Lilma K; Greenfield HS; Greenfield, MO; 7/35 Band; ChrhWkr; RedCrAde; SctActv; StuCncl; YthFlsp; EdYrBk; FHA; FTA; PpCl; Housewife; Raise A Family.

TAYLOR, Linda; Lincoln County R Ii Hs; Elsberry, MO; HonRl; LbryAde; NHS; FHA; Voc School; Secretarial.

TAYLOR, Lisa; Mills Prairie HS; Mill Shoals, IL; 1/15 TrsFrshCls; SecJrCls; HonRl; LbryAde; RptrYrbk; RptrSchPpr; FHA; PpCl; SciCl; Chrldr; Siu C Carbondale; Dietician.

TAYLOR, Lois A; Craig Sr HS; Janesville, WI; 55/485 Band; ChrhWkr; CncrtBnd; HonRl; PolWkr; SchPl; TchrAde; College; Science.

TAYLOR, Margaret; Glenbrook South HS; Glenview, IL; Chr; Chrs; CmntyWkr; HonRl; NHS; SchPl; GAA; IMSpt; Moody Bible Institute; Christian Education.

TAYLOR, Mark A; Mitchell HS; Mitchell, IN; VPFrshCls; PresSophCls; PresJrCls; HonRl; NHS; OffAde; VPStuCncl; LetterBsbl; LetterBsktbl; LetterFtbl; College.

TAYLOR, Mark D; Mazon Verona Kinsman Cons HS; Mazon, IL; HonRl; Quill&Scroll; SchPl; EdSchPpr; SptEdSchPpr; MthCl; College; Novelist.

TAYLOR, Marley M; Mac Arthur HS; Decatur, IL; 15/410 Band; CmntyWkr; CncrtBnd; HonRl; HospAde; MrchBnd; NHS; Orch; SchMus; Univ Of Illinois; Physician.

TAYLOR, Marvin; Sioux County HS; Harrison, NE; Band; SchPl; Yrbk; FFA; SciCl; CitAwd; College; Curriculum.

TAYLOR, Mary; Edsel Ford HS; Dearborn, MI; HonRl; HospAde; JA; RptrYrbk; PpCl; Univ; Professional.

TAYLOR, Matthew F; St Clement HS; Center Line, MI; ChrhWkr; CmntyWkr; HonRl; JA; SpnCl; MthCl; Wayne State; Law.

TAYLOR, Michael L; Cotter HS; Winona, MN; 30/102 HonRl; SchPl; RusCl; College; Business.

TAYLOR, Michael R; West Richland HS; Noble, IL; Chrs; HonRl; 4-H; FrCl; Bsbl; 4-HAwd; Work.

TAYLOR, Michelle R; Oregon HS; Oregon, IL; 5/136 ChrhWkr; DrlTm; HonRl; NHS; Quill&Scroll; StuCncl; RptrSchPpr; SecFrCl; GAA; PPFtbl; AmLegAwd; College; Professional.

TAYLOR, Norma J; Providence St Mels HS; Chicago, IL; 6/41 CmntyWkr; JA; JrNHS; NHS; NatlMeritSchl; NatlSciFnd; StuCncl; RptrYrbk; GovHonPrgAwd; Univ Of So California; Theatre.

TAYLOR, Pamela A; El Paso HS; Elpaso, IL; AFS; CaptDrlTm; SchPl; SchPpr; PpCl; CaptChrldr; MasAwd; Secretary.

TAYLOR, Peggy S; Mater Dei HS; Beckemeyer, IL; 55/190 CmntyWkr; DrlTm; SchAde; SchMus; TchrAde; SchPpr; FBLA; SpnCl; Chrldr; College; Nursing.

TAYLOR, Phyllis R; West Side HS; Gary, IN; ChrhWkr; CncrtBnd; MrchBnd; College; Business.

TAYLOR, Rebecca S; Cardinal HS; Eldon, IA; 1/73 SecJrCls; Band; NHS; StuCncl; RptrSchPpr; 4-H; Bsktbl; Trk; BttyCrckrAwd; DARAwd; Ia Wesleya Col; Nursing.

TAYLOR, Robert; Emerson HS; Gary, IN; HonRl; Bsbl; Ftbl; College; Vocation.

TAYLOR, Robert J; Sparta HS; Sparta, MI; Chr; SchPl; TchrAde; Bsbl; Bsktbl; LetterFtbl; LetterTennis; RotaryAwd; De Pauw University; Teaching.

TAYLOR, Ronald; R 1 North Callaway HS; Auxvasse, MO; SchPl; SctActv; 4-H; FFA; SpnCl; Vocation.

TAYLOR, Sarah P; Alexis HS; Alexis, IL; 14/46 Chr; HonRl; SchPl; PresYthFlsp; Yrbk; Pres4-H; VPFHA; FrCl; 4-HAwd; College; Fashion Designing.

TAYLOR, Scott D; Northwood Kensett HS; Kensett, IA; 2/52 HonRl; NHS; NatlMeritSF; LetterBsktbl; Waldorf College; Music.

TAYLOR, Scott L; Washington Comm HS; Washington, IL; 5/345 PresSophCls; Band; Chr; Mdrgl; NHS; SchPl; StuCncl; SpnCl; LetterBsbl; LetterFtbl; Western Ill Univ; Science.

TAYLOR, Sherry L; Exeter Public HS; Exeter, NE; SecTrsFrshCls; Band; MrchBnd; PepBnd; Teen; Twrl; YthFlsp; 4-H; PpCl; College; Professional.

TAYLOR, Sondra C; Miller R 2 HS; Everton, MO; 4/43 PresFrshCls; Chr; Chrs; HonRl; NHS; OffAde; SchPl; StuCncl; FHA; FTA; Coll; Army.

TAYLOR, Sue A; Kinsley HS; Kinsley, KS; Band; Chr; ChrhWkr; HonRl; NHS; PepBnd; StuCncl; RptrYrbk; PpCl; Bsktbl; Clg; Nursing.

TAYLOR, Susan E; Alexis HS; Alexis, IL; 2/48 Chrs; NHS; StuCncl; TchrAde; PresYthFlsp; RptrYrbk; Pres4-H; LetterBsktbl; DanFAwd; LionAwd; U Of Ill; Home Ec.

TAYLOR, Susan E; Morton HS; Morton, IL; 16/287 PresSophCls; HonRl; NHS; NatlMeritSF; SchPl; StuCncl; PpCl; GAA; Coll; Psy.

TAYLOR, Susan E; Notre Dame De Sion HS; Leawood, KS; PresJrCls; Chr; Chrs; CmntyWkr; HonRl; NHS; PolWkr; SchMus; SchPl; SctActv; CaptTennis; Trk; CchngActv; IMSpt; Kansas University; Doctor.

TAYLOR, Thomas J; Bedford North Lawrence HS; Bedford, IN; 68/410 NHS; Trk; College; Professional.

TAYLOR, Tracy D; Carlyle HS; Carlyle, IL; 11/143 Band; CncrtBnd; HonRl; Mdrgl; MrchBnd; PepBnd; SchMus; SchPl; FrCl; Bsbl; Southern Il Univ; Mortuary Science.

TAYLOR, Trent E; Arlington HS; Arlington Hts, IL; 55/585 HonRl; LetterBsbl; LetterBsktbl; Univ Of Illinois; Business Admin.

TAYLOR, Victor L; Ft Calhoun HS; Omaha, NE; Band; CncrtBnd; HonRl; LitMag; MrchBnd; NHS; PepBnd; SchPl; Yrbk; SciCl; Medicine.

TAYLOR, Yvette G; Oscoda Area HS; Oscoda, MI; DrlTm; HonRl; Quill&Scroll; RptrSchPpr; SchPpr; LetterBsktbl; Trk; GAA; IMSpt; Univ; Sociolgy.

TCHIDA, Teresa M; Sisseton HS; Sisseton, SD; 101/108 PresSophCls; ALAGirlsSt; Band; HonRl; HospAde; JrNHS; NHS; SchMus; GerCl; LetterTrk; Coll; Rn.

TEACHOUT, Star B; Harper Creek HS; Battle Creek, MI; 2/235 VPSrCls; ALAGirlsSt; HonRl; VPNHS; SchPl; StuCncl; TreasFrCl; VPPpCl; LetterTennis; DARAwd; U Of Mi; Agronomy.

TEACHOUT, Walter F; Hudsonville HS; Hudsonville, MI; PresSophCls; PresJrCls; PresChr; NatlFornLg; NHS; SchMus; SchPl; PresStuCncl; EdSchPpr; Grand Rapids Baptist College; Speech.

TEAGARDIN, Sandra K; Roncalli HS; Indianapolis, IN; HospAde; TchrAde; RptrYrbk; RptrSchPpr; Bsktbl; Swmmng; Trk; GAA; IMSpt; PPFtbl;.

TEAGUE, Gale; Mt Vernon Senior HS; Mt Vernon, IN; ChrhWkr; HonRl; OffAde; SctActv; YthFlsp; RptrSchPpr; PpCl; College Or U; Special Education.

TEAL, Linda M; Tomahawk HS; Tomahawk, WI; HonRl; OffAde; TchrAde; RptrYrbk; RptrSchPpr; FBLA; SpnCl; GAA; College; Major Study.

TEAS, Susan L; Streator Twp HS; Streator, IL; 72/383 Chr; SecChrs; NatlThespSoc; SchMus; SchPl; StuCncl; YthFlsp; RptrYrbk; GerCl; College; Psychology.

TEASDALE, Betty J; Belleville HS; Belleville, MI; 106/525 Band; ChrhWkr; CncrtBnd; HonRl; MrchBnd; PepBnd; SchMus; SchPl; LatCl; SciCl; Mi State U; Foreign Languages.

TEBO, Cindy L; Carney Nadeau HS; Carney, MI; HonRl; NatlFornLg; NatlMeritSchl; SchPl; TchrAde; RptrYrbk; FHA; PpCl; Trk; GAA; College Home Ec.

TECH, David M; Brih HS; Brih, IA; VPJrCls; PresSrCls; ALBoysSt; ChrhWkr; StuCncl; LetterBsbl; LetterBsktbl; Ftbl; Glf; Trk; Col.

TEDDER, Timothy A; Waterford Township HS; Pontiac, MI; Chr; HonRl; JrNHS; NHS; NatlMeritFnl; NatlMeritCmnd; NatlMeritSchl; StuGov; Bsktbl; Swmmng; Grand Rapids Bapt Coll; Music.

TEDFORD, Claudia M; Kaneland HS; Elburn, IL; 15/160 AFS; Chr; Chrs; HonRl; NHS; NatlThespSoc; SchPl; StuCncl; SpnCl; MthCl; PpCl; Chrldr; College; Engineering.

TEDFORD, Evelyn M; Sikeston Sr HS; Sikeston, MO; 1/258 Chr; ChrhWkr; HonRl; NHS; Orch; TchrAde; PresFTA; FrCl; MthCl; SciCl; Soutwest Baptist Clg; Ed.

TEDFORD, Kim E; Guilford HS; Rockford, IL; HonRl; Iowa State University; Art.

TEDROW, Jefferson E; Three Rivers HS; Three Rivers, MI; 30/269 HonRl; Orch; SchAde; TchrAde; Teen; LatCl; MthCl; Bsktbl; Ftbl; PresAwd; Mi State U; Nuclear Physics.

TEDROW, Rebecca; New Rockford HS; New Rockford, ND; SecJrCls; ALAGirlsSt; Band; Chrs; ChrhWkr; CmntyWkr; CncrtBnd; HonRl; MrchBnd; PepBnd; College; Day Care Management.

TEEGARDEN, Linda J; Pleasant Hill HS; Pleasant Hill, MO; 16/112 Band; ChrhWkr; HonRl; MrchBnd; NHS; TchrAde; Yrbk; RptrSchPpr; Oral Roberts Univ; Math.

TEEMAN, Bonnie A; O Gorman HS; Sioux Falls, SD; ALAGirlsSt; ChrhWkr; CmntyWkr; NHS; College.

TEEPLE, Barb; Warsaw Community HS; Leesburg, IN; Band; ChrhWkr; HonRl; SctActv;.

TEESLINK, Jan M; Fairmont HS; Fairmont, MN; 187/249 ALAGirlsSt; HonRl; PolWkr; StuCncl; RptrYrbk; 4-H; LatCl; SecGAA; Mankato State College; Law.

TEETERS, Kim E; Bemidji Sr HS; Bemidji, MN; 42/350 ChrhWkr; NHS; VPNatlThespSoc; Quill&Scroll; SchMus; SchPl; 4-H; DanFAwd; 4-HAwd; KiwanAwd; VoiceDemAwd; Thief River Vo Tech; Communications.

TEGEL, Ann M; Dominican HS; Detroit, MI; Chr; JA; NHS; NatlMeritFnl; StuGov; Teen; Yrbk; Trk;.

TEGEL, Renee D; Lakeview HS; St Clair Shores, MI; 26/650 HonRl; NHS; PresOrch; SchMus; GerCl; Tennis; Univ; Violin.

TEGELER, Rebecca L; Greenwood HS; Springfield, MO; 2/30 VPJrCls; Chrs; DrmBgl; HonRl; ModUN; StuCncl; Yrbk; SchPpr; Chrldr; PresAwd;.

TE GROOTENHUIS, Kim A; Wheaton Warrenville HS; Wheaton, IL; Band; HonRl; NHS; StuCncl; Trk; Univ Of Il; Biology.

TEGTMEYER, Cindy; Lake Park HS; Bloomingdale, IL; 31/536 HonRl; StuCncl; StuGov; College; Psychology.

TEHOLIZ, Peter A; Ludington HS; Ludington, MI; HonRl; LbryAde; NHS; NatlMeritSF; VPLatCl; Univ; Law.

TEICHER, Sheri D; Maine East HS; Des Plaines, IL; HonRl; OffAde; PolWkr; SchPl; StuGov; SpnCl; Northern Illinois Univ; Business.

TEIGEN, Ross C; Scranton HS; Gascoyne, ND; 3/27 PresFrshCls; PresSrCls; ALBoysSt; HonRl; NHS; SchPl; StuCncl; Yrbk; FBLA; Coll; Pro.

TEIGLAND, Debbi A; Fargo North HS; Fargo, ND; Chr; ChrhWkr; NatlThespSoc; SchMus; SchPl; RptrYrbk; Yrbk; RptrSchPpr; FrCl; SecSpnCl; College; Social Work.

TEILH, Thomas J; Griffin HS; Springfield, IL; 14/200 HonRl; Ftbl; Swmmng; Trk; Marquette U; Liberal Arts.

TEISAN, Martha A; Decatur HS; Decatur, MI; 9/73 ChrhWkr; CncrtBnd; HonRl; MrchBnd; NHS; OffAde; PepBnd; TchrAde; RptrYrbk; Coll; Pharmacy.

TEITGEN, Marcia K; Nicolet HS; Milwaukee, WI; NHS; NatlMeritSF; SchPl; StuCncl; YthFlsp; SpnCl; Tulane Univ; Architecture.

TEITGEN, Mary E; Mosinee HS; Mosinee, WI; 1/163 Chr; ChrhWkr; HonRl; NHS; EdYrBk; MthCl; PpCl; Trk; Chrldr; GAA; Uw Stout; Comp Sci.

TELFER, Roxanne; Gull Lake HS; Richland, MI; 11/250 CmntyWkr; HonRl; JA; SchMus; StuCncl; TchrAde; SciCl; GAA; PPFtbl; MasAwd; University; Medicine.

TELFER, Valerie J; Corunna HS; Owosso, MI; Chr; ChrhWkr; HonRl; 4-H; 4-HAwd; Olivet Nazerane; Music.

TELFORD, James L; Albion Sr HS; Albion, MI; 8/227 PresJrCls; PresSrCls; ALBoysSt; HonRl; NHS; SctActv; EdSchPpr; CaptSwmmng; Tennis; EldAwd; Kalamazoo College; Engineer.

TELKER, Charlotte A; Charleston R 1 HS; Charleston, MO; 10/180 SecJrCls; ChrhWkr; HonRl; SchPl; RptrSchPpr; SptEdSchPpr; SchPpr; 4-H; Chrldr; LetterIMSpt; College; Heath Sciences.

TELKER, Patricia C; Charleston R 1 HS; Charleston, MO; 16/168 Chrs; ChrhWkr; CmntyWkr; DrlTm; HonRl; Mdrgl; SchMus; SctActv; CivCl; 4-H; Chrldr; Se Missouri St Univ; Professor.

TELL, Maria B; Divine Child HS; Pinckney, MI; 61/175 PresSrCls; ALAGirlsSt; CmntyWkr; NHS; NatlThespSoc; StuCncl; RptrYrbk; Chrldr; DARAwd; EldAwd; Coll; Fashion Merch.

TELLEKSON, David K; Freeport Sr HS; Freeport, IL; ChrhWkr; CmntyWkr; HonRl; SctActv; Glf; LetterSwmmng; Tennis; Univ Of Utah; Doctor.

TELLER, Bill J; Ladue HS; Creve Coeur, MO; 30/503 TrsFrshCls; HstSophCls; ChrhWkr; CmntyWkr; HonRl; JA; PolWkr; SchAde; StuGov; FBLA; Ks St Univ; Architecture.

TELLER, Katherine L; Hays HS; Hays, KS; Chr; ChrhWkr; DrlTm; HonRl; NatlFornLg; PpCl; Ft Hays State Col; Physical Therapy.

TELSER, Joshua A; U Of Chicago Lab HS; Chicago, IL; NatlMeritSF; RusCl; MthCl; IMSpt; U; Engineering.

TELTHORST, Karen A; Sullivan HS; Sullivan, MO; 14/159 Band; CncrtBnd; HonRl; MrchBnd; OffAde; PepBnd; FTA; FrCl; VPSpnCl; PpCl; Clge; Interpreter.

TEMME, Alan J; Petersburg Public HS; Petersburg, NE; ALBoysSt; HonRl; LetterBsktbl; LetterFtbl; LetterTrk; AmLegAwd; VoiceDemAwd;.

TEMME, Barb A; Petersburg Public HS; Petersburg, NE; 2/15 VPSrCls; Chrs; HonRl; NHS; SchPl; Yrbk; PpCl; Trk; AmLegAwd; VoiceDemAwd;.

TEMME, Robert A; Central HS; Evansville, IN; HonRl; NHS; SctActv; Indiana St U; Technologist.

TEMPEL, Judith L; Southridge HS; Huntingburg, IN; 1/140 Band; HonRl; NatlMeritSF; VPStuCncl; Yrbk; Treas4-H; PresFrCl; LetterTrk; Chrldr; DARAwd; Notre Dame Clge; Engineer.

TEMPEL, Sylvia U; Winona Sr HS; Winona, MN; 1/431 Band; CncrtBnd; HonRl; MrchBnd; NHS; Orch; PepBnd; SchMus; Yrbk;.

TEMPFER, Margaret J; Dighton HS; Dighton, KS; VPJrCls; Chrs; HonRl; NHS; StuCncl; TchrAde; Yrbk; PpCl; Chrldr; Bethany Clge Lindsborg Ks.

TEMPLAR, Leann; Gering HS; Gering, NE; 8/152 Band; CncrtBnd; DrlTm; HonRl; MrchBnd; NHS; PepBnd; Trk; Chrldr; PPFtbl; Business School; Secretary.

TEMPLE, Deborah; Elmhurst HS; Fort Wayne, IN; AFS; ChrhWkr; YthFlsp; IMSpt; School Of Nursing; Professional.

TEMPLE, Ramona; Wamego HS; Wamego, KS; 1/100 ALAGirlsSt; CncrtBnd; HonRl; MrchBnd; NHS; PepBnd; StuCncl; GerCl; Bsbl; Washburn U; Registered Nurse.

TEMPLE, Victoria M; Mc Henry HS; Mc Henry, IL; 61/449 Chrs; HonRl; Northern Illinois University.

TEMPLEMAN, Jon C; Grandview HS; Kansas City, MO; ChrhWkr; HonRl; NHS; ROTC; StuCncl; LatCl; U Of Mo Kansas City; Orthodontics.

TEMPLETON, John; Concord HS; Concord, MI; ChrhWkr; DrmBgl; HonRl; TchrAde; YthFlsp; RptrSchPpr; SptEdSchPpr; Trk; IMSpt; College; Professional.

TEMPLETON, Randall K; Jefferson City Sr HS; Jefferson City, MO; 36/478 SecTrsSrCls; ChrhWkr; HonRl; JA; StuCncl; U Of Mo; Accounting.

TEMPLETON, Robert G; Pville Comm HS; Pinckneyville, IL; 16/112 ChrhWkr; HonRl; NHS; 4-H; FFA; KeyCl; PpCl; DanFAwd; South Ill Univ; Agriculture.

TEMPLIN, Patricia E; Andover HS; Bloomfield Hills, MI; ChrhWkr; HonRl; NHS; NatlMeritSF; SchMus; TchrAde; LatCl; PpCl; SciCl; GAA; University; Med School.

TEMPLIN, Pattie A; Shawano HS; Shawano, WI; 12/239 ChrhWkr; CmntyWkr; NHS; SecStuCncl; YthFnd; YthLg; PresFHA; PresFrCl; PpCl; DARAwd; LionAwd; Univ Of Wisconsin; Sociology.

TEN BENSEL, Debra M; Arapahoe Public HS; Arapahoe, NE; 2/35 TrsJrCls; Band; CmntyWkr; PepBnd; SchPl; YthFlsp; SchPpr; FBLA; Trk; Chrldr; Kearney St Coll; Cpa.

TENBRUNSEL, John D; Bentley HS; Livonia, MI; HonRl; Univ Of Michigan; Business.

TEN EYCK, Jo A; Union HS; Union, MO; Band; CncrtBnd; HonRl; JA; MrchBnd; NatlFornLg; OffAde; SchMus; SpnCl; East Central Jr College; Sec Science.

TENEYCK, Timothy A; Proviso West HS; Berkeley, IL; 90/1200 Band; CncrtBnd; HonRl; NHS;.

TENHOLDER, James J; Adrian Riii HS; Butler, MO; 1/55 ALBoysSt; HonRl; TreasNHS; SchPl; PresFFA; LetterBsktbl; College At Cmsu; Agri Business.

TENLEY, Patricia J; Olin Consolidated HS; Olin, IA; VPJrCls; Band; Chrs; HonRl; NatlThespSoc; SchPl; JCC; RptrYrbk; Yrbk; 4-H; College.

TENNANT, Dale A; Whitko HS; Pierceton, IN; RptrSchPpr; LetterFtbl;.

TENNANT, Teresa K; Bayard HS; Bayard, NE; 2/45 Band; Chrs; DrmMjrt; HonRl; NHS; SchMus; SchPl; PpCl; Bsktbl; LetterTrk; Chrldr; GAA; IMSpt; College; Professional.

TENNELLE, Melton D; West Side HS; Gary, IN; 23/841 TreasChr; VPChrhWkr; HonRl; JrNHS; LbryAde; NHS; NatlMeritCmnd; OffAde; FrCl; Trk; Us Air Force Academy; Professional.

TENNISON, Larry R; Southwest HS; St Louis, MO; SecSrCls; Band; CncrtBnd; MrchBnd; Orch; StuGov; RptrYrbk; LetterBsbl; LetterFtbl; IMSpt; College; Military Aeropynamics.

TEN PAS, Connie J; Litchville HS; Litchville, ND; HonRl; NHS; Quill&Scroll; YthFlsp; Yrbk; EdSchPpr; FHA; Bsktbl; Chrldr; BttyCrckrAwd; Bottineau College; Florist.

TENUTA, Michael A; Reavis HS; Burbank, IL; 9/800 HonRl; JrNHS; NHS; YthLg; RptrSchPpr; LatCl; SpnCl; College; Architecture.

TEPATTI, Rebecca A; Bullock Creek HS; Midland, MI; CncrtBnd; HonRl; HospAde; StuCncl; StuGov; TchrAde; RptrSchPpr; SpnCl; GAA; IMSpt; College; Language.

TEPEN, Linda A; North Greene HS; White Hall, IL; 5/125 Band; CncrtBnd; HonRl; MrchBnd; NHS; OffAde; Orch; PepBnd; SchAde; SchMus; TchrAde; 4-H; PresFTA; 4-HAwd; Blackburn College; Accountant.

TEPLINSKY, Cheryl J; Highland Park HS; Highland Park, IL; NatlFornLg; NHS; NatlMeritFnl; Univ Of Michigan; Elementary Educ.

TEPPEN, Franklin; New Richmond Senior HS; New Richmond, WI; 3/180 Band; ChrhWkr; CncrtBnd; HonRl; MrchBnd; PepBnd; YthFlsp; RptrSchPpr; Bsktbl; Glf; Univ; Physics.

TERBORG, Kathleen M; St Martins Academy; Rapid City, SD; PresJrCls; ChrhWkr; HonRl; HospAde; ModUN; NHS; RptrYrbk; EdYrBk; RptrSchPpr; PpCl;.

TERBROCK, Linda S; Duchesne HS; St Charles, MO; Chrs; HonRl; MrchBnd; NHS; SchMus; StuCncl; SpnCl; PpCl; PPFtbl; College; Professional.

TERBUSH, Larry D; Vassar HS; Vassar, MI; 17/153 NHS; IMSpt; Saginaw Valley Clg; Computer Math.

TERCA, Jim; Lyman HS; Presho, SD; ALBoysSt; Chrs; HonRl; NHS; StuCncl; Ftbl; Sd State Univ; Farming.

TERESHINSKI, Deborah M; St Florian HS; Hamtamck, MI; 8/125 HonRl; HospAde; SchMus; FBLA; Madonna Coll; Teach.

TERESI, Michael J; York Comm HS; Bensenville, IL; HonRl; SchPl; SpnCl; Elmhurst Clg; Psychology.

TERHARK, Heidi H; Shannon HS; Shannon, IL; ChrhWkr; CmntyWkr; CncrtBnd; HonRl; Mdrgl; RptrYrbk; KeyCl; Bsbl; LetterGlf; LetterTrk; LetterGAA; DanFAwd; Univ Of Wisconsin; Medicine.

TERHERST, Josephine; Green Forest HS; Blue Eye, MO; ChrhWkr; HonRl; TchrAde; FHA; SciCl; Business School; Secretarial Sciences.

TERHUNE, Janice M; Savannah R Iii HS; Savannah, MO; TrsSophCls; TrsJrCls; CncrtBnd; MrchBnd; OffAde; 4-H; LetterBsktbl; LetterTrk; College.

TERHUNE, Timothy A; Birch Run HS; Birch Run, MI; 3/175 Aud/Vis; Chr; Chrs; ChrhWkr; HonRl; LitMag; NHS; NatlMeritSF; Orch; SchPl; LetterBsbl; LetterBsktbl; LetterSocr; College; Broadcasting.

TERLECKYJ, Roksolana D; York HS; Elmhurst, IL; 113/888 HonRl; NHS; StuGov; Illinois Inst Tech; Architecture.

TERMAN, Barbara J; Columbia City Joint HS; Columbia City, IN; Band; ChrhWkr; CncrtBnd; HonRl; MrchBnd; ModUN; NatlFornLg; NatlMeritSF; NatlThespSoc; SchMus; RptrYrbk; 4-H; Colorado Col; Journalism.

TERMANSEN, Susan M; Yankton HS; Yankton, SD; DrlTm; HonRl; NHS; Bsktbl; LetterTrk; GAA; IMSpt; College.

TERNES, Linda A; Flasher Public HS; Flasher, ND; SecTrsJrCls; Band; Chrs; CncrtBnd; DrlTm; HonRl; SchPl; SchPpr; FHA; Bsktbl; Bus School; Secretary.

TERNES, Stuart V; Flasher Public HS; Raleigh, ND; Chrs; HonRl; StuCncl; 4-H; LetterBsktbl; LetterTrk; Coll; Accountant.

TERNEUS, Rhonda K; St Teresa HS; Decatur, IL; 6/120 Chrs; HonRl; NatlThespSoc; SchMus; PpCl; Ill State University.

TERNUS, Gwen S; St Francis HS; Humphrey, NE; TrsSophCls; Chrs; HonRl; NHS; TchrAde; 4-H; PpCl; College; Professional.

TERNUS, Roger A; Humphrey HS; Humphrey, NE; PresFrshCls; PresSophCls; Chrs; HonRl; RptrYrbk; FFA; Bsktbl; Ftbl; Trade School; Mechanic.

TE RONDE, Roy W; Oostburg HS; Oostburg, WI; 11/70 Band; Chrs; CncrtBnd; HonRl; Mdrgl; MrchBnd; StuCncl; StuGov; YthFlsp; IMSpt; College; Business.

TERPENING, Timothy D; Waterford Township HS; Union Lake, MI; Chr; CncrtBnd; MrchBnd; PepBnd; TchrAde; Adrian College; Music.

TERPSTRA, Doug J; North Mahaska HS; New Sharon, IA; SecSophCls; HonRl; StuCncl; YthFlsp; SchPpr; 4-H; Wrstlng; Univ Of Ia; Acct.

TERPSTRA, Rick L; East Kentwood HS; Kentwood, MI; Bsbl; Bsktbl; Ftbl; Trk; TrsSrCls; Coll; Professional.

TERPSTRA, Ronald G; N Mahaska Community HS; New Sharon, IA; 19/63 HonRl; SchPl; Sdlty; YthFlsp; RptrSchPpr; 4-H; FFA; Bsbl; Ftbl; Wrstlng; CchngActv; Trade Sch; Farming.

TERRELL, Roxanne; Salem HS; Salem, IN; 27/171 TrsFrshCls; Band; CncrtBnd; HonRl; MrchBnd; 4-H; FHA; LatCl; PpCl; University; Accounting.

TERRELL, Sandra D; Centennial HS; Champaign, IL; TreasChr; HospAde; NatlThespSoc; SchMus; SchPl; StuGov; Bsbl; Bsktbl; GAA; Univ Of Ill; Food Science.

TERRELL, Tim D; East HS; Des Moines, IA; 31/503 Chr; HonRl; LitMag; Mdrgl; SchMus; StuGov; Yrbk; VPGerCl;.

TERRES, Thomas R; Albany Senior HS; Albany, MN; 1/129 SecSrCls; Band; Chr; Chrs; CncrtBnd; HonRl; LbryAde; MrchBnd; Orch; PepBnd; College; Accounting.

TERRICK, Stephen; Mt Vernon HS; Mt Vernon, MO; 2/93 Band; ChrhWkr; CmntyWkr; CncrtBnd; HonRl; MrchBnd; ModUN; NatlSciFnd; PepBnd; Univ Of Missouri Rolla; Research Chemist.

TERRILL, Jill D; Gallatin Rv HS; Gallatin, MO; 11/42 Band; Chr; ChrhWkr; CncrtBnd; HonRl; MrchBnd; NHS; PepBnd; RedCrAde; RptrSchPpr; FHA; PpCl; LetterGlf; Chrldr; College; Special Education.

TERRILL, Marie E; Mineral Point HS; Mineral Point, WI; Chr; HonRl; LbryAde; Mdrgl; SchMus; Treas4-H; LetterChrldr; GAA; PPFtbl; 4-HAwd; Business School; Secretary.

TERRIO, Pamela J; Martin Hughes HS; Kinney, MN; Chr; NHS; SchPl; TchrAde; RptrSchPpr; FTA; PpCl; EdYrBk; TreasFHA; Mesabi Community College.

TERRITO, Cynthia E; Waterford Mott HS; Pontiac, MI; PresJrCls; CmntyWkr; HonRl; SchAde; SchPl; StuCncl; TchrAde; 4-H; PpCl; Michigan State Univ; Professional.

TERRITO, Joseph L; Waterford Mott HS; Pontiac, MI; 1/400 VPJrCls; PresBand; CncrtBnd; HonRl; Orch; SchMus; SchPl; 4-H; Tennis; 4-HAwd; Univ; Engineering.

TERRITO, Steven M; Curie HS; Chicago, IL; 110/595 Band; Chr; Chrs; HonRl; PresNatlThespSoc; SchAde; SchMus; SchPl; SctActv; TchrAde; Blackburn College; Theatre.

TERRY, Alice M; Shortridge HS; Indianapolis, IN; CmntyWkr; HonRl; HospAde; SecJA; LbryAde; SecNHS; LetterOrch; TchrAde; SpnCl; LetterTrk; Bell St Univ; Teacher/social Service.

TERRY, Christopher D; Creighton Prep HS; Omaha, NE; CmntyWkr; PolWkr; SchPl; TchrAde; RptrSchPpr; Trk; Creighton Univ; Law.

TERRY, Melody L; Maries R1 HS; Vienna, MO; PolWkr; SchPl; YthFlsp; Yrbk; 4-H; FBLA; FHA; FTA; Chrldr; Univ; Professional.

TERRY, Moya G; Swartz Creek HS; Swartz Creek, MI; 12/390 PresBand; CncrtBnd; HonRl; MrchBnd; NHS; PepBnd; SchMus; TchrAde; LetterBsktbl; LetterTrk; Michigan State Univ; Medical Technology.

TERRY, Robert P; Grand Haven HS; Grand Haven, MI; HonRl; StuCncl; KeyCl; MthCl; Swmmng; Tennis; Michigan State Univ;.

TERRY, Robert W; Mulberry Grove HS; Mulberry Grove, IL; 6/39 TrsJrCls; HonRl; NHS; SchPl; Yrbk; SchPpr; VPSciCl; LetterBsbl; Trade School; Vocation.

TERSCHLUSE, Marilyn A; Academy Of The Visitation; St Louis, MO; Chr; HospAde; JA; RedCrAde; Yrbk; PpCl; Univ Of Missouri; Theatre.

TERTADIAN, David J; South Milwaukee Sr HS; South Milwaukee, WI; 55/435 ChrhWkr; HonRl; NHS; Bsktbl; Swmmng; Trk; Univ Of Wisconsin; Engineer.

TERVEEN, Lloyd P; Pierce City HS; Wentworth, MO; ALBoysSt; Band; Chr; HonRl; 4-H; FFA; LetterFtbl; Trk; 4-HAwd; Springfield Missouri; Vocation.

TERVEER, Kenneth R; Freeburg Community HS; Marissa, IL; 5/127 TrsFrshCls; TreasBand; HonRl; ModUN; NHS; SchMus; Treas4-H; SciCl; AmLegAwd; Coll; Ecle Eng.

TERVO, Judy; Chassell HS; Chassell, MI; 3/24 VPFrshCls; PresJrCls; NatlFornLg; SchPl; NatlMeritFnl; 4-H; Bsbl; Trk; 4-HAwd; Michigan State Univ; Vet.

TERVONEN, Janice K; Houghton HS; Houghton, MI; 9/110 Band; CncrtBnd; HospAde; MrchBnd; NatlFornLg; PepBnd; TreasStuCncl; FNA; SpnCl; Mi Tech Univ; Mathematics.

TERWILLIGER, Cindy M; Morrill HS; Morrill, NE; Chrs; ChrhWkr; HospAde; NHS; SchPl; YthFlsp; 4-H; College; Professional.

TERZE, Patricia A; Lumen Christi HS; Jackson, MI; 30/223 HonRl; NHS; NatlMeritCmnd; PolWkr; Yrbk; 4-H; PpCl; CaptBsktbl; GAA; 4-HAwd; Jackson Comm Col; Law Enforcement.

TESARIK, Brian M; Mishicot HS; Denmark, WI; Band; CncrtBnd; HonRl; MrchBnd; PepBnd; RptrYrbk; Trade Sch; Building Construction.

TESCH, Barbara; Webb HS; Reedsburg, WI; AFS; HonRl; Orch; LatCl; PpCl; Coll; Psychology.

TESCH, Jean E; Watertown HS; Bemis, SD; 49/361 Chr; Chrl; Chrs; CmntyWkr; HonRl; ModUN; NatlFornLg; NatlThespSoc; PolWkr; GerCl; College.

TESCH, Lynn; Pecatonica HS; Blanchardville, WI; SecFrshCls; Band; Chrs; CncrtBnd; HonRl; MrchBnd; Bsktbl; Chrldr; GAA; IMSpt; Uw Lacrosse.

TESCH, Robert W; Milwaukee Lutheran HS; Milwaukee, WI; 138/224 Bsktbl; LetterFtbl; Milwaukee Tech College; Draftmen.

TESDAHL, Caren A; Clarion Comm HS; Clarion, IA; 16/83 Chr; Chrs; ChrhWkr; HonRl; Mdrgl; SchMus; StuCncl; YthFlsp; RptrSchPpr; Pres4-H; FrCl; LetterBsbl; LetterBsktbl; College; History.

TESDALL, Kathleen A; Rosati Kain HS; St Louis, MO; Chr; CmntyWkr; NHS; SchMus; RptrYrbk; IMSpt; College; Benedictine Clg; Art.

TESKE, Joanne C; Walther Lutheran HS; Summit, IL; 26/87 Chr; HonRl; NHS; OffAde; SchMus;

SctActv; YthLg; LetterTrk; GAA; Concordia Teachers Clge; Elem Ed.

TESLIK, Freda J; Rockford East HS; Rockford, IL; HospAde; NHS; College; Medical Technology.

TESS, Barbara C; Cousino Sr HS; Warren, MI; TreasBand; TreasChr; SecCncrtBnd; HonRl; VPJA; StuCncl; SecMthCl; University Of Michigan; Medicine.

TESS, Daniel E; Warsaw Community HS; Warsaw, IN; CmntyWkr; LbryAde; SctActv; FrCl; College; Professional.

TESS, Nancy K; Kewaunee HS; Kewaunee, WI; 6/155 AFS; Band; CncrtBnd; HonRl; JrNHS; LbryAde; MrchBnd; NHS; RptrYrbk; GAA; Bus Sch; Nurse.

TESS, Terry J; Mishicot Comm HS; Michicot, WI; 2/130 Chrs; HonRl; NHS; Bsktbl; Ftbl; Trk; Clg; Pro.

TESSENE, Paul; East Troy HS; East Troy, WI; 4/117 Band; HonRl; NHS; NatlMeritCmnd; GovHonPrgAwd; Ripon Coll; Bio.

TESSMAN, Kae E; Ventura Comm HS; Garner, IA; CncrtBnd; MrchBnd; NHS; NatlThespSoc; YthFlsp; RptrSchPpr; 4-H; Morningside College; Nursing.

TETER, Julie C; Louisville HS; Louisville, NE; 5/41 PresFrshCls; PresJrCls; Yrbk; FHA; FrCl; PpCl; LetterTrk; Chrldr; GAA; U Of Ne; Elem Teach.

TETER, Rodney L; Wolbach Dist No 43 HS; Wolbach, NE; VPFrshCls; VPJrCls; Chr; ChrhWkr; HonRl; SchPl; Bsbl; Bsktbl; Ftbl; Trk; State College.

TETERS, Robert J; Mitchell HS; Mitchell, NE; 7/55 VPJrCls; Band; CncrtBnd; HonRl; PresNHS; SchMus; LetterFtbl; LetterTrk; LetterWrstlng; CchngActv; PPFtbl; MasAwd; College; Forestry.

TETHEROW, Cindy L; Valentine HS; Wood Lake, NE; Band; DrlTm; HonRl; NHS; SchPl; TchrAde; Twrl; YthFlsp; 4-H; FTA; PpCl; 4-HAwd; University Of Nebraska; Vet.

TETRICK, Cynthia S; Huntington North HS; Warren, IN; College.

TETRICK, Gregory S; Aitkin HS; Airkin, MN; ALBoysSt; Chr; Chrs; CncrtBnd; JrNHS; NatlFornLg; NatlMeritSF; PepBnd; SchMus; 4-H; College; Engineering.

TEUNISSEN, Helen J; Sioux Center Community HS; Sioux Center, IA; 10/81 Chr; Chrs; HonRl; GerCl; College; Nursing.

TEVEBAUGH, Mary E; Schlarman HS; Danville, IL; 7/74 PresSrCls; Chrs; ChrhWkr; HonRl; NHS; PolWkr; StuCncl; StuGov; RptrYrbk; CivCl; Millikin Univ; Physical Therapy.

TEVFEHV, James A; Ceylon Public HS; Ceylon, MN; Band; Chr; HonRl; NatlThespSoc; PepBnd; SchPl; PpCl; Ftbl; Trk; AFS; College; Professional.

TEVLIN, James L; Jennings HS; Jennings, MO; 52/250 VPSophCls; PresJrCls; ALBoysSt; HonRl; StuCncl; RptrYrbk; SptEdYrbk; LetterFtbl; LetterTrk; LetterWrstlng; Cl; Acct.

TEW, Joy R; Marshall HS; Marshall, MI; 15/237 Chr; ChrhWkr; HonRl; VP4-H; LatCl; Bible College; Medical Tech.

TEWES, Bruce A; Hartley HS; Hartley, IA; 10/63 HonRl; NHS; Bsktbl; LetterTrk; College; Accounting.

TEWKSBURY, Tracey; Wheaton Central Hs; Wheaton, IL; Chr; ChrhWkr; CncrtBnd; HonRl; MrchBnd; NHS; PepBnd; StuCncl; SecYthFlsp; College; Double Major.

TEWS, Jean M; Antigo HS; Antigo, WI; ChrhWkr; LitMag; StuCncl; IMSpt; Univ; Professional.

TEX, Jim M; Northwest HS; Grand Island, NE; 35/140 NHS; NatlThespSoc; RptrYrbk; SptEdSchPpr; PresFFA; GerCl; Bsbl; CaptFtbl; LetterTrk; CaptWrstlng; Univ Of Nebraska; Agriculture.

THACH, Gary; Burrton HS; Burrton, KS; 8/25 VPJrCls; ALBoysSt; Chr; Chrs; ChrhWkr; HonRl; NHS; StuCncl; YthFlsp; RptrSchPpr; Kansas State College; Elementary Education.

THACH, John L; San Marcas Academy; Belvidere, IL; Band; Chrs; CncrtBnd; DrlTm; HonRl; MrchBnd; PepBnd; ROTC; Bsktbl; Ftbl; College; Business Admin.

THACKER, Gabriela M; Malden HS; Malden, MO; ChrhWkr; HonRl; NHS; NatlThespSoc; OffAde; SchPl; YthFlsp; PpCl; Tennis; GAA; College.

THACKER, Glee E; La Ville HS; Lakeville, IN; NatlFornLg; Quill&Scroll; TchrAde; RptrYrbk; SptEdSchPpr; 4-H; GerCl; PpCl; LetterTrk; GAA; College; Writer.

THACKER, Kathy Jo; Logan Magnolia Comm HS; Missouri Valley, IA; 5/50 HonRl; NHS; Yrbk; Nursing School; Nurse.

THACKER, Leanne L; Titonka Consolidated HS; Titonka, IA; 13/48 Chr; Chrs; ChrhWkr; HonRl; LbryAde; NHS; NatlMeritFnl; SchMus; SctActv; StuCncl; Yrbk; RptrSchPpr; SchPpr; PpCl; Simpson College; Music.

THACKER, Susan C; Central HS; St Joseph, MO; ChrhWkr; CmntyWkr; PolWkr; RedCrAde; SchAde; YthFlsp; RptrYrbk; FBLA; Tennis; Trk; College; Business.

THACKER, Toni; Kimball County HS; Kimball, NE; Chr; Chrs; HonRl; SchMus; SchPl; FHA; SpnCl; PpCl; RotaryAwd; Doanc Coll; Social Sciences.

THACKHAM, Lori L; Adelphian Acad; Fenton, MI; Chr; ChrhWkr; HonRl; LbryAde; SchMus; SchPl; FrCl; IMSpt; Private College; Professional.

THADEN, John E; D H Hickman HS; Columbia, MO; 11/536 HonRl; NHS; NatlSciFnd; GerCl; SpnCl; ChmnSciCl; U Of Mi; Engr, Usaf Pilot.

THAKE, Debra D; Walther Lutheran HS; Melrose Park, IL; 7/96 Chr; Chrl; HonRl; HospAde; NHS; SchMus; SchPl; Southern Illinois Univ; Zoology.

THAKOR, Dennis S; St Marys Central HS; Bismarck, ND; 1/175 ALBoysSt; NatlMeritSF; StuCncl; StuGov; RptrYrbk; SciCl; Bsbl; Bsktbl; Tennis; Univ; Medicine.

THALACKER, Diane L; Edgerton Comm Sr HS; Edgerton, WI; 6/160 AFS; ChrhWkr; MrchBnd; SchPl; StuCncl; TchrAde; Yrbk; SpnCl; Concordia Teachers Clg Ne; Elementary Teach.

THALACKER, Mike A; Lead HS; Nemo, SD; 1/153 PresJrCls; ALBoysSt; HonRl; NatlMeritSF; StuCncl; StuGov; KeyCl; Swmmng; LetterWrstlng; KiwanAwd; Clge; Eng.

THALDORF, Peter D; Cochrane Fountain City HS; Cochrane, WI; 5/97 VPFrshCls; PresJrCls; ALBoysSt; Band; Chrs; MrchBnd; NHS; SchMus; StuCncl; LetterBsbl; CaptBsktbl; LetterFtbl; LetterGlf; Univ Of Wisconsin; Dentist.

THALHAMMER, Kristina; Derham Hall HS; St Paul, MN; Chr; Chrs; ChrhWkr; HospAde; NHS; SctActv; GerCl; College; Political Science.

THALHEIMER, Gary A; Evanston Twp HS; Evanston, IL; 92/1100 HonRl; SchAde; StuGov; TchrAde; LetterBsbl; LetterSocr; Univ Of Illinois; Architecture.

THALMANN, John; Henning HS; Henning, MN; 18/60 PresSophCls; ChrhWkr; HonRl; SchPl; StuCncl; SchPpr;.

THALMANN, Ruth R; Henning HS; Ottertail, MN; PresSophCls; PresJrCls; Chr; ChrhWkr; HonRl; Mdrgl; SchMus; StuCncl; EdYrBk; 4-H; PresFHA; LetterTrk; 4-HAwd; College; Teaching.

THARES, Cheryl A; Ipswich HS; Ipswich, SD; 9/50 PresSrCls; HonRl; NHS; PresPolWkr; SptEdSchPpr; FHA; LetterBsktbl; LetterTrk; BttyCrckrAwd; DARAwd; So Dak State Univ; Dietician.

THARNISH, Albert J; Junction City Sr HS; Junction City, KS; 8/303 ALBoysSt; HonRl; NHS; SctActv; CivCl; SpnCl; MthCl; SciCl; Kansas St Univ; Nuclear Engineering.

THARP, Eric; South Harrison HS; Bethany, MO; PresSophCls; ALBoysSt; CncrtBnd; ModUN; NHS; PepBnd; StuCncl; CaptFtbl; LetterTrk; LetterWrstlng; Univ Of Mo; Civil Engin.

THARP, Patty; Marion HS; Marion, IA; Chr; HonRl; PolWkr; YthFlsp; FNA; PPFtbl; OptClAwd; Univ Of Wi; Occ Therapy.

THARP, Sue K; Western Comm Unit HS; Neponset, IL; SecFrshCls; SecSophCls; CncrtBnd; HonRl; NHS; PepBnd; Yrbk; RptrSchPpr; LetterTrk; Chrldr; Coll.

THARP, Thomas E; Muncie Northside HS; Muncie, IN; 61/312 StuGov; SpnCl; PpCl; Bsktbl; Ftbl; Trk; IMSpt; College; Professional.

THATCHER, Bruce C; Twin Rivers HS; Bode, IA; ALBoysSt; Band; Chrs; CncrtBnd; HonRl; MrchBnd; PepBnd; Yrbk; Bsktbl; Iowa College.

THATCHER, Sherry D; Fremont HS; Fremont, IN; HonRl; LbryAde; SchPl; Pres4-H; FHA; LatCl; PpCl; Trk; PPFtbl; 4-HAwd; Business School; Business.

THAXTON, Patricia L; Greenfield HS; Greenfield, IL; 7/77 ALAGirlsSt; Band; ChrhWkr; HonRl; NHS; PresStuCncl; 4-H; KeyCl; Trk; DanFAwd; U Of Il; Political.

THAYER, Mostyn O; Lapeer HS; Lapeer, MI; NHS; RptrSchPpr; EdSchPpr; LetterTennis; Cen Mi U ; Disc Jockey.

THAYER, Rodney A; Wallace HS; Dickens, NE; TrsFrshCls; Chrs; HonRl; SchPl; StuCncl; Yrbk; LetterBsktbl; LetterFtbl; CaptTrk; College.

THEDE, Diane; Battle Creek Central HS; Battle Creek, MI; 50/520 HonRl; LitMag; NHS; Quill&Scroll; RedCrAde; SchMus; RptrYrbk; RptrSchPpr; SpnCl; College; Education.

THEDE, Patti A; Unionville Sebewaing HS; Sebewaing, MI; Chr; Chrs; LbryAde; StuCncl; 4-H; FHA; LatCl; PpCl; Chrldr; College; Health.

THEDEN, Emma C; Desoto HS; Desoto, KS; HonRl; NHS; EdSchPpr; PpCl; Univ Of Ks; Nursing.

THEILER, Philip F; Tomahawk HS; Tomahawk, WI; 16/156 TrsFrshCls; TrsSophCls; TrsJrCls; HonRl; StuGov; SpnCl; MthCl; Bsktbl; Ftbl; Trk; College; Forestry.

THEILGAARD, Diana L; Luther South HS; Blue Island, IL; Chr; Chrl; Chrs; ChrhWkr; HonRl; LbryAde; PolWkr; SchAde; SchMus; TchrAde; St Johns Winfield; Church Worker.

THEILIG, Melanie A; Ladysmith HS; Ladysmith, WI; Band; Chr; CncrtBnd; HonRl; Mdrgl; MrchBnd; PepBnd; SchMus; FBLA; TreasFTA; Bsktbl; Trk; GAA; Univ Of Wisc; Music.

THEIS, Linda K; Wausau West HS; Wausau, WI; Chr; PresChrhWkr; RedCrAde; TchrAde; YthFlsp; FHA; Univ Of Wis; Special Education.

THEISEN, Annette C; Slinger HS; Allenton, WI; SecJrCls; HonRl; StuCncl; RptrYrbk; EdYrBk; RptrSchPpr; GAA; IMSpt; PresAwd; RotaryAwd; Technical Sch; Occupational Therapist.

THEISEN, Joan M; Rocori HS; Cold Spring, MN; 3/164 TrsFrshCls; Chr; HonRl; NHS; NatlMeritCmnd; SchPl; StuCncl; LetterTrk; PPFtbl; St Cloud Bus Coll; Secretary.

THEISEN, Lisa A; Grand Is Senior HS; Grand Island, NE; ChrhWkr; HonRl; TchrAde; PpCl; CaptChrldr; IMSpt; PPFtbl; College; Science.

THEISEN, Richard; Bishop Luers HS; Fort Wayne, IN; Aud/Vis; Chrs; ChrhWkr; HonRl; NatlFornLg; NatlMeritCmnd; PolWkr; SchMus; Ftbl; College; Professional.

THEISEN, Roger D; New Haven HS; New Haven, IN; 38/234 HonRl; Ftbl; Purdue; Wildlife Conservation.

THEISEN, Tony; East Chain HS; Fairmont, MN; VPSophCls; TrsJrCls; HonRl; StuCncl; YthFlsp; RptrYrbk; SchPpr; Bsktbl; Trk; Mankato St Coll; Comp Sci Or Math.

THEISING, Jane H; Dubois HS; Dubois, IN; VPSophCls; Band; Chr; ChrhWkr; HonRl; PepBnd; Sdlty; RptrSchPpr; 4-H; FHA; College; Vocation.

THELEMANN, Ann M; Le Sueur HS; Le Sueur, MN; Band; CncrtBnd; JA; MrchBnd; NHS; TchrAde; SchPpr; MthCl; AmLegAwd; JAAwd; Coll; Sci.

THELEMANN, Arthur R; Benilde HS; Golden Valley, MN; Aud/Vis; Chr; HonRl; SchPl; SchPpr; LetterFtbl; LetterTrk; St Thomas College; Dentist.

THELEN, Joseph J; St Johns HS; St Johns, MI; HonRl; SchPl; 4-H; Coll.

THELEN, Tamara L; Pewamo Westphalia HS; Westphalia, MI; 5/103 TrsJrCls; TrsSrCls; HospAde; NHS; SchMus; StuCncl; EdYrBk; RptrSchPpr; PPFtbl; 4-HAwd; Michigan St Univ; Research Scientist.

THELL, Susan; Willmar Sr HS; Wilmar, MN; 4/368 CncrtBnd; HonRl; NatlFornLg; NHS; RptrSchPpr; FHA; 4-HAwd; VoiceDemAwd; College.

THENNES, Gisele A; Gladstone Area HS; Gladstone, MI; 37/180 ChrhWkr; HonRl; HospAde; StuCncl; RptrYrbk; RptrSchPpr; PpCl; Basde Noc Comm Clg; L P N.

THEOBALD, Brazilla A; Greenview HS; Greenview, IL; 5/49 PresFrshCls; PresSophCls; HonRl; NHS; SchMus; StuCncl; YthFlsp; RptrYrbk; FSA; College; Religious Field.

THEOBALD, Bruce C; Evanston Twp HS; Evanston, IL; SctActv; YthLg; Univ Of Illinois; Law.

THEOBALD, Donald M; Plainfield HS; Joliet, IL; HonRl; JrNHS; SctActv; LetterBsbl; LetterBsktbl; Joliet Jr College; Carpenter.

THEOBALD, Jaime T; Forest Lake HS; Cedar, MN; 2/416 HonRl; NatlFornLg; 4-H; FrCl; VoiceDemAwd;.

THEOBALD, Pamela; Elk Grove Hs; Elk Grove Vlg, IL; 99/504 HonRl; Quill&Scroll; SchMus; YthFlsp; RptrSchPpr; SchPpr; Chrldr; GovHonPrgAwd; Western Illinois U;mass Communications.

THEOBALD, Sara E; Lincoln HS; Vincennes, IN; HonRl; PolWkr; StuCncl; PresPpCl; LetterBsktbl; LetterTrk; GAA; Indiana Univ; Teach.

THEODORE, Constance; Maine Township Hs North; Glenview, IL; HonRl; SchMus; SchPl; StuCncl; StuGov; RptrSchPpr; EdSchPpr; PpCl; Northwestern; Journalist.

THEORET, Marilyn G; Gladstone Area HS; Gladstone, MI; 17/171 Band; CncrtBnd; HonRl; MrchBnd; NHS; PepBnd; Yrbk; LetterTrk; CchngActv; GAA; IMSpt; Bayde Noc Community College; Math.

THERING, Michael R; Sacred Heart Academy; Mt Pleasant, MI; ChrhWkr; CmntyWkr; HonRl; JrNHS; NHS; NatlMeritCmnd; SchPpr; SpnCl; LetterBsbl; IMSpt; College Aquinas.

THESSEN, Cindy; Blair Oaks HS; Jefferson City, MO; ALAGirlsSt; Band; StuCncl; EdYrBk; 4-H; PpCl; AmLegAwd; DARAwd; Univ Of Missouri Columbia; Industrial Engin.

THESSIN, Jane E; Mc Farland HS; Mc Farland, WI; 1/84 PresAFS; Band; Chrs; NatlFornLg; SecNHS; NatlMeritCmnd; SchPl; YthFlsp; EdYrBk; DARAwd; Lawrence University; Interpretor.

THETARD, Meg; University HS; Hudson, IL; StuCncl; StuGov; PpCl; Chrldr; College; Professional.

THETFORD, Linda K; Herrin Twp HS; Herrin, IL; 53/209 Band; Chr; Chrs; ChrhWkr; CmntyWkr; CncrtBnd; LitMag; MrchBnd; PepBnd; YthFlsp; FHA; John A Logan Col; Child Care.

THEURER, Sarah; Portland HS; Portland, IN; 6/18 ChrhWkr; HonRl; NHS; SchPl; StuCncl; EdSchPpr; 4-H; LatCl; AmLegAwd; Ball State Univ; Journalism.

THEUSCH, Lynn M; Kewaskum Community HS; Kewaskum, WI; SecAFS; ChrhWkr; CmntyWkr; HonRl; TreasStuGov; Yrbk; Pres4-H; SpnCl; GAA; 4-HAwd; College; Professional.

THEVENOT, Mathew; Odebolt Arthur Comm HS; Arthur, IA; 1/47 TrsFrshCls; TrsSophCls; TrsJrCls; HonRl; BauchLmbAwd; Iowa State Univ; Physics Major.

THEWES, Karen A; Dubois HS; Celestine, IN; 3/79 PresSrCls; Chrs; HonRl; RptrSchPpr; FHA;.

THIBAULT, Michael A; St Andrew HS; Detroit, MI; 45/108 RptrSchPpr; Mercy Col Of Detroit; Political Science.

THIBEAULT, Cathy J; Cheboygan Area HS; Cheboygan, MI; TrsSophCls; HonRl; HospAde; RedCrAde; TchrAde; YthFlsp; FrCl; MthCl; Trk; Chrldr; N Michigan Univ; Nursing.

THIBEAULT, Rene R; Cheboygan Area HS; Cheboygan, MI; 33/209 Chr; HonRl; TchrAde; YthFlsp; Central Michigan Univ; Business Admin.

THIBERT, Gary A; Lafayette HS; Red Lake Falls, MN; Band; SchPl; StuCncl; RptrSchPpr; SciCl; Bsktbl; LetterTrk; University; Architecture.

THIBERT, Suzy; Niagara HS; Niagara, WI; VPSophCls; ALAGirlsSt; Chrs; ChrhWkr; NHS; StuCncl; EdYrBk; 4-H; Chrldr; Marion College; Nursing.

THIBODEAU, Jamie D; Assumption HS; Wiconsin Rapids, WI; PresFrshCls; HonRl; StuCncl; RptrSchPpr; Bsktbl; Ftbl; Trk; College; Professional.

THIBODEAU, Paul M; St Agatha HS; Detroit, MI; HonRl; RptrSchPpr; Ftbl; Univ Of Mich; Biologist.

THIEBEN, Dirk; Eagle Grove HS; Eagle Grove, IA; TrsSrCls; Band; Chr; HonRl; Mdrgl; SchMus; SpnCl; Bsktbl; Drake Univ; Music.

THIEDE, Kenneth W; Riverdale HS; Muscoda, WI; 21/95 SecAFS; ALBoysSt; Band; PresChrhWkr; PresStuCncl; EdSchPpr; SpnCl; LetterBsbl; LetterBsktbl; LetterFtbl; College.

THIEL, Brent L; Central HS; Aberdeen, SD; Chr; HonRl; 4-H; 4-HAwd; Coll; Pro.

THIEL, Christine E; Morton Sr HS; Morton, IL; 2/292 HonRl; NHS; Orch; StuCncl; SciCl; Univ Of Illinois; Chemical Engineer.

THIEL, Christine E; Morton HS; Morton, IL; 2/292 HonRl; NHS; Orch; StuCncl; SciCl; U Of Il; Liberal Arts.

THIEL, Donald T; Lawrenceville HS; Lawrenceville, IL; 10/189 ALBoysSt; Chrs; HonRl; NHS; SchPl; SctActv; KeyCl; SpnCl; SciCl; Ftbl; U S Military Academy; Military.

THIEL, Jane M; Chesaning Union HS; Chesaning, MI; Chr; HonRl; TchrAde; Teen; 4-H; FrCl; GAA; Bus School; Vocation.

THIEL, Julie A; T L Handy HS; Bay City, MI; ChrhWkr; RptrYrbk; GAA; Practical Nursing School; Nursing.

THIEL, Laura; California R 1 HS; California, MO; 1/98 Band; Chr; LitMag; MrchBnd; NHS; NatlMeritCmnd; SchMus; StuCncl; Yrbk; U Of Mo; Chemistry.

THIEL, Laura R; Beaver Dam Sr HS; Beaver Dam, WI; HonRl; OffAde; SchAde; PpCl; Tennis; Chrldr; GAA; College.

THIEL, Nancy M; Hilbert Public HS; Hilbert, WI; 2/67 Band; Chr; CncrtBnd; HonRl; Mdrgl; NHS; PepBnd; LetterBsktbl; LetterTrk; GAA; Trade; Secretarial.

THIEL, Peggy A; Stockbridge HS; Stockbridge, WI; Chr; HonRl; StuCncl; RptrYrbk; PpCl; Bsktbl; Chrldr; GAA; College & Rotc; Vocation.

THIEL, Richard D; Hilbert HS; Hilbert, WI; 12/65 VPFrshCls; ALBoysSt; Chr; CmntyWkr; HonRl; NHS; SchPl; SptEdYrbk; 4-H; Ftbl; Bus Sch; Electrician.

THIEL, Rob G; Riley HS; South Bend, IN; Band; CncrtBnd; DrmBgl; HonRl; MrchBnd; NHS; PepBnd; YthFlsp; Trk; Univ Of Evansville; Music.

THIELE, Lynn E; Valparaiso HS; Valparaiso, IN; 13/419 ALAGirlsSt; HonRl; NHS; OffAde; PolWkr; VPGerCl; PpCl; Chrldr; GAA; NCTE; Indiana Univ; Physical Therapy.

THIELE, Nancy R; Alexandria Monroe HS; Alexandria, IN; 5/200 SecChrhWkr; CncrtBnd; ModUN; NHS; NatlMeritSF; SchPl; 4-H; FrCl; GerCl; 4-HAwd; Anderson College; Psychology.

THIELEKE, Janet L; Randolph HS; Randolph, WI; Band; Chr; CncrtBnd; HonRl; MrchBnd; PepBnd; RptrYrbk; Bsktbl; Lakeland Acad; Lab Tech.

THIELEN, Cheryl K; Salina Central HS; Salina, KS; 31/313 HonRl; StuCncl; RptrSchPpr; SchPpr; TreasPpCl; Tennis; Chrldr; IMSpt; Ft Hays Kansas St College; Business.

THIELEN, Donna M; Nevis HS; Nevis, MN; Band; Chr; Chrs; CncrtBnd; LbryAde; MrchBnd; OffAde; SchAde; Vocational School.

THIELEN, John; Roncalli HS; Omaha, NE; HonRl; NHS; Bsbl; U Nebraska; Business Profession.

THIELKER, Maureen; Normandy Senior HS; Northwoods, MO; HonRl; HospAde; SchAde; TchrAde; Socr; IMSpt; College; Nursing.

THIELKER, Stephen E; Normandy HS; Northwoods, MO; 1/550 Aud/Vis; HonRl; NHS; NatlMeritCmnd; Yrbk; College; Engineering.

THIEME, Julie A; Paul Harding HS; Fort Wayne, IN; Chr; Chrl; HonRl; SchMus; PpCl; Chrldr; College; Professional.

THIEME, Mark G; Greenwood HS; Springfield, MO; PresFrshCls; Chrs; HonRl; FrCl; LatCl; LetterBsktbl; LetterFtbl; OptClAwd; College; Medicine.

THIEN, Glenda K; Tipton HS; Tipton, IA; Band; Chrs; HonRl; MrchBnd; SchMus; StuCncl; YthFlsp; Yrbk; 4-H; FrCl; LetterBsktbl; LetterTrk; GAA; Iowa State Univ.

THIERRY, Albert J; Southgate Aquinas HS; Detroit, MI; 20/220 HonRl; JA; ModUN; NHS; Ftbl; Trk; IMSpt; Univ; Spec Educ.

THIES, Betty J; Glasgow R 11 HS; Glasgon, MO; 9/45 ALAGirlsSt; Chr; CmntyWkr; DrlTm; HonRl; NHS; SctActv; FHA; PpCl; Bsktbl; College; Rn.

THIES, Laurie; Trico HS; Ava, IL; Chr; ChrhWkr; HonRl; OffAde; SchMus; 4-H; FHA; PpCl; 4-HAwd; JAAwd; Office Work.

THIESS, Lori A; Crown Point HS; Crown Point, IN; Band; Chr; SctActv; TchrAde; 4-H; FrCl;.

THIESSE, Bryan K; Brainerd Sr HS; Brainerd, MN; 83/474 Chr; HonRl; NHS; RptrSchPpr; PresFFA; GerCl; Brainerd Community Coll; Agriculture.

THIESSE, Douglas; Armstrong HS; Armstrong, IA; Band; Chrs; HonRl; SchPl; StuCncl; YthFlsp; LetterBsbl; Bsktbl; LetterFtbl; Tennis; Trk; Univ; Pro.

THIESSEN, Russell E; Berean Academy; Whitewater, KS; Band; ChrhWkr; HonRl; NHS; PepBnd; SchPl; StuCncl; 4-H; Bsktbl; Junior College; Agriculture.

THILGES, Lynnette M; Garrigan HS; Bode, IA; 12/104 Chrs; DrlTm; HonRl; 4-H; PpCl; University; Physical Therapy.

THILL, Gregory J; Washington HS; Sioux Falls, SD; Band; CncrtBnd; DrlTm; HonRl; IntrClCncl;

MrchBnd; Orch; PepBnd; GerCl; PpCl; Wrstlng; College; Park Mgmt.

THILL, Ronald M; Thornton Fractional North HS; Calumet City, IL; 419/449 HonRl; JrNHS; NHS; Bsktbl; LetterFtbl; Trk; Univ Of Illinois; Industrial Engineering.

THILTGES, Kenneth S; Sacred Heart HS; Rulo, NE; 9/24 Chrs; ChrhWkr; CmntyWkr; SchMus; SchPl; StuGov; RptrYrbk; RptrSchPpr; 4-H; 4-HAwd; Coll; Voc.

THINESEN, Pamela; Dassel Cokato HS; Cokato, MN; Band; Chr; CncrtBnd; HonRl; MrchBnd; PepBnd; RptrYrbk; SchPpr; GAA; Willmar Voc; Medical Secretary.

THIRY, Teresa A; White Lake HS; White Lake, SD; Band; Chrs; CncrtBnd; MrchBnd; PepBnd; SchMus; SchPl; RptrSchPpr; PpCl; College.

THISSEN, Teresa K; Kingman HS; Kingman, KS; Band; HonRl; MrchBnd; OffAde; PepBnd; SchMus; SchPl; StuCncl; Teen; Yrbk; Emporia Kansas State Clg; Business.

THODE, Diane L; West HS; Green Bay, WI; Chrs; ChrhWkr; HonRl; NHS; Orch; SchMus; Yrbk; FTA; SpnCl; GAA; College; Music.

THODE, John S; Notre Dame HS; Niles, IL; 19/276 Band; CncrtBnd; HonRl; MrchBnd; NatlCathMusEdAsoc; NHS; PepBnd; SchMus; SchPl; TchrAde; Univ Of Ill; Engineering.

THODE, Ronald W; Rogers HS; Michigan City, IN; 134/550 ChrhWkr; YthFlsp; IMSpt; Depauw; Chemical Engineering.

THOE, Gary A; West Lafayette HS; W Lafayette, IN; ChrhWkr; HonRl; SctActv; SptEdYrbk; Bsktbl; LetterTennis; CaptIMSpt; Purdue Univ; Medicine.

THOE, Jeffrey D; Hayfield HS; Hayfield, MN; ChrhWkr; HonRl; NHS; StuCncl; 4-H; PresFFA; LetterFtbl; LetterWrstlng; PresAwd; Univ Of Wisconsin; Farming.

THOELE, Mary A; Central Heights HS; Rantoul, KS; Chrs; ChrhWkr; HonRl; NHS; SchMus; TchrAde; 4-H; FHA; PpCl; Bus Shool; Vocation.

THOENEN, Rose A; Fatima HS; Bonnots Mill, MO; 19/119 Chr; ChrhWkr; HonRl; LbryAde; FBLA; FHA; Lincoln University; Physical Educ.

THOLE, Vicky A; Mater Dei HS; Carlyle, IL; ChrhWkr; HonRl; NHS; College; Vocation.

THOM, David; Farmington HS; Farmington, MN; 13/140 ALBoysSt; CncrtBnd; HonRl; NHS; SchPl; StuCncl; RptrSchPpr; Bsbl; Bsktbl; Ftbl; CchngActv; College; Prof Athlete.

THOM, Martha J; Waconia HS; Waconia, MN; 1/140 SecJrCls; Chr; ChrhWkr; CncrtBnd; DrmBgl; Mdrgl; MrchBnd; NHS; SchMus; GAA; Gustavus Adolphus Col.

THOM, Raymond E; Centerville HS; Centerville, IA; 10/145 Band; Chrs; CncrtBnd; HonRl; VPNHS; PepBnd; SchMus; StuCncl; PresSciCl; Glf; Iowa State Univ; Engineering Science.

THOMA, Edward J; Willmar HS; Wilmar, MN; ChrhWkr; NatlFornLg; NHS; PolWkr; RptrSchPpr; SptEdSchPpr; GerCl; Willmar Community Col; Journalism.

THOMALLA, Steve L; Goth Public HS; Gothenburg, NE; 25/81 TrsFrshCls; VPJrCls; Chr; ChrhWkr; HonRl; Mdrgl; StuCncl; TchrAde; RptrYrbk; Bsbl; College; Professional.

THOMANN, Diane L; Pekin Community HS; Ollie, IA; ChrhWkr; HonRl; LbryAde; SchPl; RptrSchPpr; PresFHA; SecFNA; FTA; Indian Hills Comm College; Nursing.

THOMANN, Donna J; Highland Community HS; Riverside, IA; 1/58 PresFrshCls; Chr; Chrs; HonRl; NHS; SchMus; StuCncl; 4-H; FTA; 4-HAwd; Coll; Vocational.

THOMANN, Lyndal S; Noble HS; Noble, IL; SecTrsFrshCls; ALAGirlsSt; Band; Chr; Chrs; ChrhWkr; CmntyWkr; HonRl; PolWkr; SchMus; SchPl; SctActv; Yrbk; Chrldr; College; Nursing.

THOMAS, Alice; Van Buren HS; Brazil, IN; 10/69 PresSrCls; CncrtBnd; HonRl; MrchBnd; NHS; PepBnd; TchrAde; LatCl; PpCl; SciCl; Indiana State U; Medical Technology.

THOMAS, Althea R; Carthage Senior HS; Carthage, MO; 6/209 ALAGirlsSt; Band; ChrhWkr; HonRl; LbryAde; NHS; NatlMeritCmnd; FBLA; Oklahoma Christian College; Library Science.

THOMAS, Amy L; Union HS; Union Grove, WI; ALAGirlsSt; HonRl; NHS; OffAde; Quill&Scroll; TchrAde; EdYrBk; PpCl; Coll; Accounting.

THOMAS, Barbara A; Brown County HS; Morgantown, IN; 16/169 HonRl; LbryAde; NHS; TchrAde; FBLA; Vincennes Univ; Secondary Educ.

THOMAS, Barbara J; Eureka HS; Eureka, IL; 8/100 AFS; ALAGirlsSt; HonRl; JrNHS; LitMag; ModUN; NHS; SchPl; Eureka College; Social Sciences.

THOMAS, Becky R; Cosmos HS; Lake Lillian, MN; 1/35 VPSophCls; Chr; HonRl; SecNHS; SchPl; StuCncl; EdYrBk; SecFHA; LetterTrk; LetterChrldr; LionAwd; Mn Inst Of Med & Dent Ass; Med Assistant.

THOMAS, Brian P; West HS; Coralville, IA; 15/227 Band; Chrs; NatlMeritFnl; Univ Of Ia;.

THOMAS, Brian P; Iowa City West HS; Coralville, IA; Aud/Vis; Chrs; NatlMeritSF; Univ.

THOMAS, Carol L; Delta HS; Muncie, IN; Band; HonRl; MrchBnd; SchMus; Pres4-H; KeyCl; SecSpnCl; MthCl; SciCl; Ball State Univ; Meteorology.

THOMAS, Carolyn; Forman HS; Manito, IL; ChrhWkr; HonRl; RptrYrbk; RptrSchPpr; FHA; PpCl; GAA;.

THOMAS, Catherine E; Pittsfield HS; Pittsfield, IL; Band; Chrs; CncrtBnd; HonRl; MrchBnd; NHS; PepBnd; SchMus; StuCncl; LatCl; Robert Morris College; Medical Asst.

THOMAS, Charles R; New Trier West HS; Glencoe, IL; 394/694 HospAde; NatlMeritCmnd; StuCncl; StuGov; Bsktbl; Ftbl; Darmouth; Md.

THOMAS, Christine; Wahlert HS; Dubuque, IA; SecJrCls; Chr; Chrl; Chrs; ChrhWkr; CmntyWkr; HospAde; JA; PolWkr; StuCncl; Coll; Law Enforce.

THOMAS, Cindy J; Basehor HS; Basehor, KS; Band; Chr; Chrl; CncrtBnd; HonRl; MrchBnd; NHS; PepBnd; Yrbk; PpCl; College; Secretary.

THOMAS, David C; Carmel HS; Carmel, IN; PresSophCls; PresBand; ChrhWkr; CmntyWkr; HonRl; PresJA; PresNatlThespSoc; PolWkr; SchPl; 4-H; Taylor U; Medicine.

THOMAS, Deb M; Rushville HS; Hay Springs, NE; Chr; Chrs; ChrhWkr; HonRl; SchMus; SchPl; SchPpr;.

THOMAS, Deborah A; Carrollton HS; Carrollton, MO; PresJrCls; Band; CncrtBnd; HonRl; NHS; SchPl; StuCncl; Twrl; SpnCl; Chrldr; Coll; Major In Music.

THOMAS, Debra L; Gibbon HS; Gibbon, NE; Chr; Chrs; ChrhWkr; DrlTm; HonRl; MrchBnd; YthFlsp; PpCl; Lincoln Univ; Social Work.

THOMAS, Denise A; Lovejoy HS; St Louis, IL; Aud/Vis; ChrhWkr; HonRl; JA; StuCncl; YthFlsp; RptrSchPpr; 4-H; MthCl; 4-HAwd; College Or Univ.

THOMAS, Denise E; Fremont Sr HS; Fremont, NE; 1/413 Band; Chr; ChrhWkr; CncrtBnd; HonRl; MrchBnd; NHS; PepBnd; SchMus; SctActv; MthCl; Univ; Optometrist.

THOMAS, Denise G; Northwestern HS; K/komo, IN; ChrhWkr; HonRl; NHS; NatlMeritSF; YthFlsp; RptrYrbk; 4-H; FHA; PpCl; PPFtbl; Purdue Univ Fashion Retailer.

THOMAS, Diane K; Western HS; Taylor, MI; CmntyWkr; HonRl; NatlFornLg; OffAde; Orch; YthFlsp; GerCl; Univ;.

THOMAS, Edwina D; Lindblom Tech HS; Chicago, IL; 27/722 VPJrCls; Chr; HonRl; TreasJA; SctActv; TchrAde; SecTwrl; YthFlsp; GAA; AmLegAwd; University; Architecture.

THOMAS, Elizabeth A; Woodruff HS; Peoria, IL; 4/281 Chrs; ChrhWkr; HonRl; Orch; SchMus; SctActv; KeyCl; FrCl; Tennis; College.

THOMAS, Frank; North Side HS; Fort Wayne, IN; 8/498 ALBoysSt; HonRl; NHS; StuCncl; JAAwd; LionAwd; CitAwd; College; Medicine.

THOMAS, Gywen E; Brethren HS; Wellston, MI; Chrs; ChrhWkr; HonRl; HospAde; LbryAde; SchAde; StuCncl; TchrAde; FHA; GerCl; PpCl; Ferris State College; Registered Nurse.

THOMAS, James M; Doniphan HS; Doniphan, MO; HonRl; SchPl; KeyCl; LetterBsbl; LetterFtbl; LetterTrk; College; Pre Law.

THOMAS, Jane E; Kettle Moraine HS; Dousman, WI; Band; Chr; CncrtBnd; HonRl; MrchBnd; SchAde; Pres4-H; CaptChrldr; 4-HAwd; PresAwd; College; Professional.

THOMAS, Janet L; Carmi Community HS; Carmi, IL; VPJrCls; PresSrCls; CncrtBnd; HonRl; MrchBnd; NHS; SchPl; StuCncl; VPSciCl; Murray State Univ; Pathologist.

THOMAS, Jeffrey K; Bowdle HS; Bowdle, SD; 16/29 HonRl; LetterBsktbl; LetterTrk; University; Spacecraft Engineering.

THOMAS, Jennifer; Glen Ullin HS; Glen Ullin, ND; 8/40 SecFrshCls; SecJrCls; SecSrCls; ALAGirlsSt; Chr; Chrs; HonRl; ModUN; PpCl; Chrldr; Dickinson St Coll; Airline Hostess.

THOMAS, Jerry; Leroy HS; Leroy, IL; VPSrCls; PpCl; Ftbl; Trk; Wrstlng; College; Law Enforcement.

THOMAS, Jerry B; Edwardsville HS; Edwardsville, IL; HonRl; JrNHS; NHS; Bsbl; Univ Of Missouri; Computer Science.

THOMAS, Jill A; Wabash HS; Wabash, IN; 49/210 ALAGirlsSt; HonRl; SchPl; StuGov; FrCl; PpCl; Bsktbl; LetterChrldr; GAA; IMSpt; In U; Office Mgmt.

THOMAS, Jimmy J; Northwest HS; High Ridge, MO; HonRl; Bsbl; Bsktbl; Ftbl; Trk; PresAwd; College; Dentist.

THOMAS, Karen E; Ladywood HS; Westland, MI; Chr; Chrl; Chrs; ChrhWkr; HonRl; Orch; PolWkr; SchMus; SchPl; FHA; Craft Clg; Mass Comm.

THOMAS, Karen L; Jetmore HS; Jetmore, KS; 7/43 Band; ChrhWkr; CmntyWkr; CncrtBnd; LbryAde; MrchBnd; PepBnd; SchPl; PpCl; Hutchinson Jr College; Secretary.

THOMAS, Karen M; Clark HS; Hammond, IN; 20/260 Chrs; JA; Yrbk; College; Computer Science.

THOMAS, Karin G; Mt Vernon HS; Marionville, MO; 5/95 HstFrshCls; HonRl; NatlThespSoc; SchMus; SchPl; StuCncl; RptrSchPpr; SchPpr; MthCl; Trk; College; Certified Public Accountant.

THOMAS, Karren S; Coldwater HS; Coldwater, MI; Chrs; HonRl; OffAde; ChmbCommrsAwd; Bus Schl; Vocational.

THOMAS, Kay; Mt Pleasant HS; Mt Pleasant, IA; 1/160 Band; Chrs; CncrtBnd; HonRl; MrchBnd; NHS; NatlThespSoc; PepBnd; SciCl; AmLegAwd; Iowa Meth Coll; Nursing.

THOMAS, Ken L; Austin Cath Prep HS; Detroit, MI; College; Lawyer.

THOMAS, Kevin L; Mendel Catholic HS; Chicago, IL; 31/187 Chrs; NatlMeritCmnd; College.

THOMAS, Kimberly; Central HS; Aberdeen, SD; Chrs; HonRl; HospAde; PpCl; Trade Sch.

THOMAS, Lane L; Blackford HS; Hartford City, IN; ChrhWkr; CmntyWkr; HonRl; YthFlsp; RptrSchPpr; SchPpr; 4-H; SciCl; College; Vet Medicine.

THOMAS, Larry F; Oak Grove HS; Oak Grove, MO; 28/82 Chrs; ChrhWkr; HonRl; LbryAde; NatlFornLg; SchPl; RptrSchPpr; College; Professional.

THOMAS, Leonard O; Lindblom Technical HS; Chicago, IL; Chr; Chrs; Mdrgl; NatlMeritCmnd; SchAde; StuGov; RptrSchPpr; LetterSwmmng; IMSpt; College; Computer Science.

THOMAS, Linda A; Wm Henry Harrison HS; Evansville, IN; 65/471 ChrhWkr; NatlFornLg; NHS; NatlMeritCmnd; SchPl; University; Professional.

THOMAS, Lori L; Newcastle Public HS; Newcastle, NE; 1/24 SecFrshCls; PresSophCls; ALAGirlsSt; CncrtBnd; HonRl; MrchBnd; PepBnd; SecStuCncl; RptrYrbk; SecPpCl; Trade Schl; Technician.

THOMAS, Lori S; Mc Donald County HS; Noel, MO; Band; Chrs; CncrtBnd; DrmMjrt; HonRl; LbryAde; MrchBnd; 4-H; FFA; FTA; Northeastern Oklahoma A & M Univ; Law.

THOMAS, Lynn A; Mc Donald Co HS; Noel, MO; 11/164 Band; Chr; HonRl; NHS; SchPl; 4-H; FFA; LetterBsktbl; DanFAwd; 4-HAwd; Crowder Jr College.

THOMAS, Lynn E; West HS; Rockford, IL; 1/350 NHS; VPOrch; SchMus; SchPl; TreasStuCncl; TchrAde; Bsktbl; GAA; Univ Of Ill; Elem Education.

THOMAS, Lynne M; Farmington East HS; Farmington, IL; Band; Chr; Chrs; CncrtBnd; HonRl; MrchBnd; PepBnd; SchMus; SchPl; 4-H; Millikin Univ; Theater.

THOMAS, Madeleine A; Marian HS; Tray, MI; 16/182 ChrhWkr; HonRl; ModUN; NHS; OffAde; PolWkr; StuCncl; UNYO; YthLg; SchPpr; U Of Mi; Political Science.

THOMAS, Marilyn J; Gurdon S Hubbard HS; Chicago, IL; 31/411 Band; HonRl; VPJA; OffAde; SchAde; PresSctActv; TreasStuCncl; PpCl; GAA; PPFtbl; University Of Illinois; Lawyer.

THOMAS, Martha A; Lew Wallace HS; Gary, IN; 88/513 TrsFrshCls; ALAGirlsSt; Band; CtyCnl; HonRl; IntrClCncl; PresStuCncl; EdSchPpr; GAA; CitAwd; Iu Bloomington; Journalism.

THOMAS, Mary; Springfield HS; Springfield, SD; Chrs; HonRl; SchPl; PpCl; Bsktbl; BttyCrckrAwd; Mount Marty College; Nursing.

THOMAS, Mary A; Hill Murray HS; St Paul, MN; HonRl; NHS; StuCncl; RptrSchPpr; FrCl; IMSpt; St Catherines College; Home Economics.

THOMAS, Mary C; Colo Comm HS; Colo, IA; 7/28 VPSophCls; TrsJrCls; SecSrCls; Band; Chrs; CncrtBnd; HonRl; MrchBnd; OffAde; PepBnd; SchMus; SchPl; StuCncl; LetterBsktbl; Trk; Mankato St College; Secretarial.

THOMAS, Mary K; Lincoln Sr HS; Bloomington, MN; 17/496 HonRl; JA; NHS; LetterTennis; IMSpt; College; Anthropology.

THOMAS, Mary M; Bowdle HS; Bowdle, SD; 2/16 TrsSrCls; Band; ChrhWkr; CmntyWkr; HonRl; SchPl; StuCncl; RptrSchPpr; Bsktbl; PresAwd; Presentation Col; Social Worker.

THOMAS, Monica L; Ashland Greenwood Sr HS; Ashland, NE; 1/60 ChrhWkr; HonRl; NHS; NatlThespSoc; PolWkr; SchMus; SchPl; PresStuCncl; Bsbl; Trk; Chrldr; PPFtbl; JCAwd; University Of Nebraska; Dentistry.

THOMAS, Nancy L; Kohler Public HS; Kohler, WI; Band; CncrtBnd; HonRl; MrchBnd; NHS; SctActv; RptrYrbk; Bsktbl; Trk; Randolph Macon Womens Clg; History.

THOMAS, Nathan B; Connersville Senior HS; Connersville, IN; ChrhWkr; CtyCnl; CmntyWkr; HonRl; StuCncl; FTA; LetterBsktbl; LetterTrk; IMSpt; CitAwd; College; American History.

THOMAS, Pamela L; Inkster HS; Inkster, MI; ChrhWkr; HonRl; HospAde; JrNHS; LbryAde; NHS; OffAde; StuCncl; SciCl; LetterSwmmng; CitAwd; College; Professional.

THOMAS, Pamela S; Onarga HS; Onarga, IL; PresSophCls; HonRl; Yrbk; FHA; E Illinois Univ; Textile.

THOMAS, Patricia A; Custer HS; Milwaukee, WI; Chr; Chrs; ChrhWkr; CmntyWkr; HonRl; LbryAde; NHS; NatlMeritCmnd; OffAde; SchAde; Bsktbl; CchngActv; College; Law.

THOMAS, Patricia A; St Anns HS; Lexington, NE; Chrs; HonRl; 4-H; PpCl; LetterTrk; Kearney College; Art.

THOMAS, Patricia E; Urbandale HS; Des Moines, IA; 19/245 Band; Chr; Chrs; CncrtBnd; MrchBnd; NHS; NatlMeritSF; PepBnd; SchMus; College; Music.

THOMAS, Paul W; South Harrison HS; Bethany, MO; ALBoysSt; Band; ChrhWkr; CncrtBnd; HonRl; MrchBnd; PepBnd; SchMus; LetterBsktbl; LetterTrk; U Of Mo; Agriculture.

THOMAS, Rebecca A; Southern Boone County R 1 HS; Hartsburg, MO; 1/44 ALAGirlsSt; ChrhWkr; SecNHS; TreasQuill&Scroll; SchPl; Yrbk; RptrSchPpr; Pres4-H; FHA; SpnCl; Bsktbl; 4-HAwd; Univ Of Missouri; Occupational Therapy.

THOMAS, Rebecca A; Southern Boone Cty R 1 HS; Hartsburg, MO; 1/43 ALAGirlsSt; ChrhWkr; SecNHS; TreasQuill&Scroll; SchPl; Yrbk; RptrSchPpr; Pres4-H; FHA; SpnCl; Bsktbl; 4-HAwd; Univ Of Missouri; Occupational Therapy.

THOMAS, Reggie D; Acc HS; Holton, KS; PresSrCls; StuCncl; FHA; MthCl; Bsbl; CaptBsktbl; CaptFtbl; Trk; College.

THOMAS, Rhonda L; Salem HS; Salem, MO; 10/173 Band; CncrtBnd; HonRl; MrchBnd; NHS; SchPl; PpCl; College; Computer Science.

THOMAS, Robert; Antigo HS; Antigo, WI; 1/375 ALBoysSt; NatlFornLg; SchPl; LatCl; MthCl; CchngActv; OptClAwd; Univ Yale; Medicine.

THOMAS, Robert W; Glendale HS; Springfield, MO; Chr; Chrs; ChrhWkr; HonRl; Mdrgl; SchPl; College; Professional.

THOMAS, Robyn; Underwood HS; Underwood, IA; PresFrshCls; PresJrCls; PresSrCls; AFS; HonRl; NHS; NatlMeritCmnd; PepBnd; IMSpt; Business Office.

THOMAS, Robyn E; Brazil Sr HS; Brazil, IN; 25/163 ChrhWkr; HonRl; OffAde; PolWkr; TchrAde; YthFlsp; Yrbk; FTA; PpCl; LetterBsbl; LetterBsktbl; LetterGlf; College; Professional.

THOMAS, Rodney K; Airport HS; Carleton, MI; 1/223 Aud/Vis; ChrhWkr; HonRl; LbryAde; NHS; YthFlsp; Yrbk; SpnCl; IMSpt; College; Commercial Art.

THOMAS, Ronald J; Eisenhower HS; Saginaw, MI; 18/367 CncrtBnd; HonRl; MrchBnd; NHS; StuGov; College; Drummer.

THOMAS, Russell A; Tri County Comm HS; What Cheer, IA; 4/29 TrsFrshCls; TrsSophCls; TrsJrCls; HonRl; SchPl; LetterTrk; Business School; Business.

THOMAS, Sam R; Fair Grove HS; Springfield, MO; 7/60 HonRl; MthCl; University.

THOMAS, Sarah B; Paola HS; Paola, KS; 14/130 ChrhWkr; CmntyWkr; CncrtBnd; HonRl; PolWkr; Quill&Scroll; SchPl; RptrYrbk; EdYrBk; DARAwd; Kansas Univ; Pol Journalism.

THOMAS, Scott A; Cavalier Public HS; Cavalier, ND; 1/70 Chrs; HonRl; SchPl; YthFlsp; Yrbk; RptrSchPpr; FrCl; SciCl; LetterFtbl; Trk; Univ Of Cincinnati; Science.

THOMAS, Sharon A; Saint Joseph HS; Chicago, IL; 5/130 PresSrCls; Chrs; ChrhWkr; HonRl; LitMag; NHS; StuCncl; LatCl; Ill Inst Of Tech; Physics.

THOMAS, Sheila A; Clay Center Public HS; Clay Center, NE; 10030 Band; Chr; Chrs; ChrhWkr; CmntyWkr; MrchBnd; PresYthFlsp; Pres4-H; LetterTrk; Univf Elementary Education.

THOMAS, Sheri J; Hannibal HS; Hannibal, MO; 4/256 ChrhWkr; CncrtBnd; HonRl; LbryAde; MrchBnd; NHS; NatlMeritCmnd; FBLA; GAA; IMSpt; Hannibal La Grange Coll; Math.

THOMAS, Stephen L; Lake Shore HS; St Clair Shores, MI; AFS; Chr; ChrhWkr; CmntyWkr; HonRl; NHS; Univ Of Alaska; Computer Systems.

THOMAS, Steve B; Moline Sr HS; Moline, IL; Chr; HonRl; NHS; LatCl; Black Hawk College; Graphic Design.

THOMAS, Steven; St Pius X HS; Kansas City, MO; Chrs; PolWkr; Ftbl; Trk; Univ; Soc Wrk.

THOMAS, Steven A; Marshall HS; Marshall, MI; 2/245 Band; CncrtBnd; HonRl; MrchBnd; NHS; NatlMeritFnl; NatlMeritSF; Orch; Mi State Univ; Accountant.

THOMAS, Steven L; Lu Verne Comm HS; Lu Verne, IA; PresSophCls; HonRl; StuCncl; Bsbl; Col.

THOMAS, Susan; Charleston Hs; Charleston, IL; 26/246 AFS; Chrs; HonRl; NHS; StuCncl; 4-H; LetterTrk; GAA; 4-HAwd; University; History.

THOMAS, Susan L; Woodruff HS; Peoria, IL; 2/281 Chr; CncrtBnd; HonRl; MrchBnd; Orch; SchMus; SctActv; KeyCl; FrCl; Trk; College.

THOMAS, Teresa A; Det Lakes Sr HS; Detroit Lakes, MN; AFS; Chr; HonRl; LitMag; NatlFornLg; SchMus; StuCncl; StuGov; SchPpr; VoiceDemAwd; St Benedicts College; Marine Biology.

THOMAS, Theodore; Luther L Wright HS; Ironwood, MI; HonRl; JCC; NHS; ROTC; SctActv; PpCl; Bsktbl; IMSpt; Michigan Tech; Civil Engineer.

THOMAS, Timothy; Arlington HS; Indianapolis, IN; Aud/Vis; DrlTm; HonRl; ROTC; StuCncl; GerCl; IMSpt; VFWAwd; CitAwd; Howard U; Professional.

THOMAS, Timothy L; Lisle Sr HS; Lisle, IL; 16/210 PresJrCls; VPSrCls; HonRl; NHS; StuCncl; Bsbl; Bsktbl; Eastern Illinois Univ; Journalism.

THOMAS, Todd H; Homewood Flossmoor HS; Homewood, IL; 86/940 CncrtBnd; HonRl; NatlFornLg; VPNatlThespSoc; SchMus; SchPl; StuGov; Bsktbl; Swmmng; College; Political Science.

THOMAS, Vivian; Hayti North Hs; Hayti Heights, MO; VPFrshCls; DrlTm; HonRl; NHS; SctActv; FHA; SpnCl; PpCl; GAA;.

THOMAS, Wayne; Dunbar Vocational HS; Chicago, IL; 2/450 PresJrCls; HonRl; NHS; RptrSchPpr; MthCl; LetterBsbl; LetterTennis; College; Pre Med.

THOMAS, Wendy R; Mandan Sr HS; Mandan, ND; HonRl; OffAde; FBLA; PpCl; Business Sch; Secretary.

THOMASMA, Teresa M; Sturgis HS; Sturgis, MI; Chr; Chrl; HonRl; JA; NatlFornLg; NHS; SchMus; SchPl; FrCl; PPFtbl; Glen Oaks Comm Clg; Zoo.

THOMASON, Benjamin A; Mansfield HS; Mansfield, MO; 6/44 Chrs; HonRl; NatlMeritCmnd; SchPl; 4-H; PresFFA; LatCl; MthCl;.

THOMASON, Mona; Lilbourn HS; Lilbourn, MO; PepBnd; SchAde; SchPl; TchrAde; RptrYrbk; SchPpr; 4-H; FBLA; FrCl; PpCl; College; Vocational.

THOMASON, Yvonne; Huron HS; Belleville, MI; HonRl; SpnCl; College; Mathematics.

THOMASSON, Jeff H; Zionsville Community HS; Zionsville, IN; PresSrCls; ALBoysSt; ChrhWkr; CmntyWkr; HonRl; NHS; StuCncl; StuGov; Ball St Univ; Banking And Finacne.

THOMBLESON, Patrick J; Washington HS; Washington, IN; ChrhWkr; PresSctActv; PresYthFlsp; 4-H; SecKeyCl; PpCl; Ftbl; Trk; CchngActv; 4-HAwd; College; Police Work.

THOME, Mary A; West Catholic HS; Comstock Park, MI; 22/314 Band; HonRl; MrchBnd; NHS; StuCncl; 4-H; LatCl; Chrldr; 4-HAwd; CitAwd; Michigan State; Home Ec.

THOMECZEK, Sally M; Desoto HS; Desoto, MO; ALAGirlsSt; HonRl; JrNHS; NHS; FBLA; University; Dentist.

THOMEN, Shirley; Gardner HS; Gardner, KS; 2/90 HstJrCls; Band; CmntyWkr; HonRl; MrchBnd; NHS; NatlMeritCmnd; StuCncl; FrCl; PpCl; Kansas State Univ; Computer Science.

THOMES, Gregory; Arlington Green Isle HS; Arlington, MN; 5/91 Band; HonRl; JrNHS; NHS; Yrbk; PpCl; VoiceDemAwd; St Johns U; Pre Dental.

THOMMES, James E; Maine Township HS; Park Ridge, IL; HonRl; NHS; PolWkr; Bsbl; Loyola Univ; Dentist.

THOMPSEN, Philip H; Halstad Public HS; Halstad, MN; 3/22 VPChr; PresNatlThespSoc; OffAde; StuCncl; RptrYrbk; RptrSchPpr; TreasFFA; LetterBsbl; LetterBsktbl; LetterFtbl; College; Engineering.

THOMPSON, Alan D; Assumption HS; Wisconsin Rapids, WI; HonRl; NHS; Bsbl; LetterBsktbl; LetterFtbl; Trk; CchngActv; AmLegAwd; RotaryAwd; Brown Univ; Chemistry.

THOMPSON, Alan D; Manistee HS; Manistee, MI; Band; CncrtBnd; HonRl; MrchBnd; SchAde; Bsktbl; Ftbl; IMSpt; College Merchant.

THOMPSON, Anne L; Worthington Senior HS; Worthington, MN; Chr; ChrhWkr; JrNHS; NatlFornLg; SchMus; YthLg; FrCl; PpCl; Chrldr; Jr College; Teaching English.

THOMPSON, Audrey D; Buena Vista HS; Saginaw, MI; Band; ChrhWkr; CncrtBnd; HonRl; MrchBnd; NHS; TchrAde; Midwestern; Missionary.

THOMPSON, Bonnie S; Pontiac Twp HS; Pontiac, IL; 12/150 AFS; Chr; Chrs; HonRl; JrNHS; Mdrgl; NHS; NatlMeritSchl; NatlThespSoc; SchMus; SchPl; RptrYrbk; FrCl; College.

THOMPSON, Brian; Ubly HS; Ubly, MI; HonRl; NHS; SchPl; StuCncl; TchrAde; College; Data Processing.

THOMPSON, Brian M; Humboldt HS; Humboldt, IA; 20/141 Band; Chr; Chrs; CncrtBnd; HonRl; MrchBnd; NHS; SchMus; SctActv; LetterTrk; Iowa Central Comm College; Engineering.

THOMPSON, Bruce R; Peru HS; Peru, IN; 18/229 Chr; HonRl; NatlFornLg; NHS; SctActv; YthFlsp; FrCl; IMSpt; College; Professional.

THOMPSON, Burton D; Holdrege HS; Holdrege, NE; Band; Chr; Chrs; CncrtBnd; MrchBnd; PepBnd; SchMus; SchPl; FFA; GodCntryAwd; Trade School; Professional.

THOMPSON, Carla; Saybrook Arrowsmith HS; Colfax, IL; 2/28 ALAGirlsSt; Band; Chr; HonRl; SchMus; RptrYrbk; EdYrBk; RptrSchPpr; FHA; PpCl; Mennonite Hosp Sch Of Nursing.

THOMPSON, Carla J; Switz City Central HS; Switz City, IN; TrsJrCls; HonRl; NHS; OffAde; PresFHA; PpCl; Jincennes Univ; Accounting.

THOMPSON, Carol D; Edinburg HS; Edinburg, IL; Band; CncrtBnd; HonRl; HospAde; PepBnd; SchPl; SchPpr; FFA; LetterTrk; 4-HAwd; Natl Guard Basic Training; Nat Guard.

THOMPSON, Catherine A; Davenport Comm HS; Davenport, NE; 2/23 Chrs; CncrtBnd; HonRl; MrchBnd; PepBnd; SchPl; StuCncl; 4-H; PpCl; Univ Of Nebraska; Nursing.

THOMPSON, Cheryl D; Cathedral HS; Chicago, IL; CmntyWkr; HonRl; HospAde; JA; NatlMeritCmnd; RedCrAde; StuGov; RptrSchPpr; Chrldr; Coll; Vet.

THOMPSON, Cheryl L; Mt Zion HS; Decatur, IL; Lpn School; Nurse.

THOMPSON, Christine E; Sault Area HS; Sault Ste Marie, MI; 16/350 HonRl; LitMag; NHS; Orch; Quill&Scroll; SchMus; RptrSchPpr; Univ; Journalism.

THOMPSON, Connie V; Frazee Vergas HS; Frazee, MN; ChrhWkr; Yrbk; FHA; LetterTrk; PPFtbl; Vo Tech School; Medical Secretary.

THOMPSON, Cynthia H; Parkview HS; Springfield, MO; Chr; ChrhWkr; CmntyWkr; HonRl; LbryAde; Mdrgl; NatlFornLg; NatlThespSoc; SchMus; SchPl; Tennis; Trk; College; Foreign Language.

THOMPSON, Cynthia J; Paxton HS; Paxton, IL; 9/130 AFS; Band; CncrtBnd; HonRl; MrchBnd; NHS; PepBnd; SchPl; YthFlsp; LetterChrldr; GAA; AmLegAwd; College; Nursing.

THOMPSON, Cynthia J; Belfield HS; Belfield, ND; 1/64 Band; Chrs; ChrhWkr; NHS; RptrYrbk; SchPpr; SecFHA; PpCl; SecSciCl; PPFtbl; Concordia College.

THOMPSON, Cynthia M; Cottonwood HS; Cottonwood, MN; 6/40 SecSrCls; ALAGirlsSt; Band; HonRl; NHS; SchPl; FHA; Bsktbl; GAA; IMSpt; H Cloud Sch Of Nursing; Registered Nurse.

THOMPSON, Dale E; Pecatonica HS; Hollandale, WI; 1/58 PresFrshCls; ALBoysSt; HonRl; SchMus; StuCncl; LetterBsktbl; LetterFtbl; U Of Wis; Chem Engr.

THOMPSON, David; Long Prairie HS; Long Prairie, MN; Chr; NHS; StuCncl; TchrAde; YthFlsp; FFA; FTA; Bsbl; Tennis; VoiceDemAwd; College; Professional.

THOMPSON, Dean M; Ava HS; Sparta, MO; 25/135 ChrhWkr; HonRl; Pres4-H; FBLA; SecKeyCl; LionAwd; College; Aviation.

THOMPSON, Deanna L; Fairfax Riii HS; Fairfax, MO; Band; Chrs; CncrtBnd; HonRl; MrchBnd; PepBnd; Twrl; FHA; PpCl; Chrldr;.

THOMPSON, Debbie A; Prairie Farm HS; Prairie Farm, WI; TrsJrCls; Chr; HonRl; NHS; SchMus; SchPl; Yrbk; SchPpr; FHA; PpCl; Bus Sch; Secretarial Work.

THOMPSON, Deborah; Winchester Community HS; Winchester, IN; Band; CncrtBnd; HonRl; MrchBnd; NHS; FHA; SpnCl; Univ; Elementary School Teacher.

THOMPSON, Dennis; Bemidji HS; Bemidji, MN; Band; CncrtBnd; MrchBnd; NHS; PepBnd; SchMus; SchPl; SciCl; College; Chemical Engineering.

THOMPSON, Dennis H; Campbell HS; Campbell, MO; 6/63 SecFrshCls; TrsJrCls; HonRl; PresNHS; SchPl; PresStuCncl; StuGov; TchrAde; FFA; PpCl; IMSpt;.

THOMPSON, Diane M; Hastings Senior HS; Hastings, MN; Band; HonRl; JA; MrchBnd; NHS; TchrAde; YthFlsp; LetterBsktbl; LetterTennis; LetterTrk; College; Phy Ed.

THOMPSON, Donavan K; Fairmont HS; Fairmont, NE; SchPl; 4-H; Bsbl; Bsktbl; LetterFtbl;.

THOMPSON, Donna M; Willowbrook HS; Villa Park, IL; 2/825 HonRl; JrNHS; ModUN; SecNHS; NatlMeritCmnd; TchrAde; Illinois St Univ; Mathematics.

THOMPSON, Elaine M; Kenowa Hills HS; Grand Rapids, MI; HonRl; NHS; StuCncl; RptrSchPpr; EdSchPpr; SptEdSchPpr; TreasSchPpr; LetterBsktbl; LetterTennis; CchngActv; Grand Rapids Jr College; Journalism.

THOMPSON, Erik M; Milan Public HS; Milan, MN; 1/31 PresJrCls; SecALBoysSt; PresChrhWkr; CncrtBnd; HonRl; PresStuCncl; EdSchPpr; CaptBsktbl; Ftbl; CaptTrk; Stanford U; Statesman.

THOMPSON, Gale L; Riceville HS; Riceville, IA; Band; Chr; Chrs; ChrhWkr; CncrtBnd; MrchBnd; PepBnd; YthFlsp; 4-H; College; Professional.

THOMPSON, Gary E; Marquette HS; Ottawa, IL; 6/100 ALBoysSt; HonRl; NHS; KeyCl; Bsbl; Bsktbl; University; Professional.

THOMPSON, Gary O; Viroqua HS; Viroqua, WI; 2/121 ChrhWkr; HonRl; 4-H; FFA; 4-HAwd; Univ Of Wisconsin; Vet.

THOMPSON, Gayle M; Monroe City R 1 HS; Monroe City, MO; /100 Band; Chr; Chrs; CncrtBnd; DrmMjrt; HonRl; MrchBnd; FFA; PpCl; Chrldr; Business School; Fashion Merchandising.

THOMPSON, Gerald L; Stillwater Sr HS; Stillwater, MN; 120/616 CmntyWkr; HonRl; NHS; SctActv; Col Of St Thomas; Pre Med.

THOMPSON, Jack; North Platte Senior HS; North Platte, NE; Chr; ChrhWkr; HonRl; SchPl; StuCncl; SptEdSchPpr; Bsbl; Ftbl; Trk; College; Professional.

THOMPSON, James D; Fort Zumwalt HS; St Peters, MO; 95/353 HonRl; SctActv; LetterFtbl; LetterTrk; LetterWrstlng; Se Mo State Univ; Business.

THOMPSON, James G; Wapello Comm HS; Wapello, IA; HonRl; SctActv; SciCl; GodCntryAwd; College; Chemical Eng.

THOMPSON, James R; Charleston HS; Charleston, IL; ChrhWkr; CmntyWkr; KeyCl; Ftbl; Trk; IMSpt; Clge; Special Ed.

THOMPSON, Jan E; Peotone HS; Peotone, IL; 3/105 Band; ChrhWkr; CncrtBnd; MrchBnd; NHS; PepBnd; SchPpr; 4-H; College; Animal Science.

THOMPSON, Janice E; Astoria HS; Summum, IL; 9/50 Chrs; HonRl; NHS; TchrAde; SpnCl; SciCl; PPFtbl; College; Nurse.

THOMPSON, Jeffrey A; Thomas Jefferson HS; Crescent, IA; HonRl; SctActv; IMSpt; U Of Ia Iowa City; Astronomy.

THOMPSON, Jenille; Edmore Public HS; Edmore, ND; 8/24 ALAGirlsSt; Chrl; ChrhWkr; PresFrshCls; SecTrsFrshCls; EdSchPpr; FHA; PpCl; Trinity School Of Nursing; Rn.

THOMPSON, Jennie J; Neenah HS; Neenah, WI; ChrhWkr; NatlThespSoc; YthLg; SpnCl; Northwestern Univ; Journalism.

THOMPSON, Jerome A; St Mary HS; Cairo, IL; StuCncl; StuGov; FrCl; SciCl; IMSpt; VFWAwd; Rotc; Aeronautical.

THOMPSON, Jerry L; Westwood Heights HS; Flint, MI; Band; Chr; ChrhWkr; ROTC; StuCncl; StuGov; GerCl; Swmmng; Wrstlng; GodCntryAwd; Montcalm; Air Frame Power Plant.

THOMPSON, Joan; Dickinson Hs; Dickinson, ND; 108/200 SecTrsFrshCls; SecTrsSophCls; DrlTm; HonRl; LbryAde; FFA; GerCl; GAA; North Dakota State U;horticulture.

THOMPSON, Joanne M; Central HS; Detroit, MI; HonRl; HospAde; RedCrAde; TchrAde; RptrYrbk; EdYrBk; Yrbk; GovHonPrgAwd; College; Nursing.

THOMPSON, Jody M; Harding County HS; Buffalo, SD; 11/29 Band; Chr; Chrl; SecChrs; CncrtBnd; HonRl; LbryAde; Mdrgl; MrchBnd; PepBnd; CaptChrldr; LetterGAA; 4-HAwd; Black Hills State Col; Child Development.

THOMPSON, John F; Mt Carmel HS; Chicago, IL; 47/197 SecSophCls; HonRl; IntrClCncl; NHS; NatlMeritSF; SchPpr; PpCl; Bsktbl; University; Law.

THOMPSON, John J; St Marys HS; Kansas City, MO; Chr; CmntyWkr; GerCl; SciCl; LetterTrk; CchngActv; Long View Comm College; Law Enforcement.

THOMPSON, John L; Swea City Community HS; Swea City, IA; VPFrshCls; PresSophCls; TrsSrCls; Band; Chr; Chrs; CncrtBnd; HonRl; MrchBnd; PepBnd; SchMus; StuCncl; YthFlsp; 4-H; FFA; Iowa State University; Farming.

THOMPSON, John L; Swea City Comm HS; Swea City, IA; 6/31 Aud/Vis; HonRl; StuCncl; YthFlsp; FFA; Bsbl; Bsktbl; Ftbl; Glf; Iowa State Univ; Veterinarian.

THOMPSON, Judith; Benton Central HS; Oxford, IN; 2,260 Band; CncrtBnd; HonRl; NHS; PepBnd; RptrSchPpr; 4-H; FrCl; GAA; PPFtbl; University Purdue; Veterinary Medicine.

THOMPSON, Juli A; Willmar Sr HS; Willmar, MN; 9/367 Chr; HonRl; HospAde; JA; NatlThespSoc; SchPl; StuCncl; TchrAde; FrCl; GAA; JAAwd; College; Medicine.

THOMPSON, Julie A; Thompson Public HS; Thompson, ND; ALAGirlsSt; Band; CtyCnl; CmntyWkr; HospAde; JCC; PolWkr; SchPl; StuCncl; StuGov; AmLegAwd; Business School; Secretary.

THOMPSON, Julie E; Chase County HS; Cedar Point, KS; Chr; Chrs; ChrhWkr; HonRl; SchMus; SchPl; 4-H; SpnCl; PpCl; Emporia State Teachers College; Nursing.

THOMPSON, June; Dickinson Hs; Dickinson, ND; DrlTm; HospAde; LbryAde; StuCncl; FFA; GerCl; College;nursing.

THOMPSON, Ken; Cambridge HS; Cambridge, NE; ChrhWkr; HonRl; JA; NatlMeritFnl; SctActv; SptEdSchPpr; GodCntryAwd; GovHonPrgAwd; CitAwd; Vocation.

THOMPSON, Kevin J; Midland HS; Midland, MI; NHS; NatlMeritSF; StuCncl; StuGov; KeyCl; FrCl; SciCl; LetterTrk; IMSpt; Clge; Prof.

THOMPSON, Kimberlee S; Minot HS; Minot, ND; SecSophCls; Chrs; HonRl; NHS; StuCncl; PpCl; Clg; Professional.

THOMPSON, Kimberly A; Deubrook HS; Toronto, SD; Band; Chr; HonRl; SchAde; SchMus; SecStuCncl; RptrSchPpr; SchPpr; CaptChrldr; 4-HAwd; Sd St Univ; Child Development.

THOMPSON, Kris L; Chillicothe HS; Chillicothe, MO; 1/185 ALBoysSt; Band; ChrhWkr; CncrtBnd; HonRl; MrchBnd; SchPl; TchrAde; SciCl; Central Missouri St Univ; Music.

THOMPSON, Larry R; Bucklin HS; Bucklin, KS; HonRl; Univ; Journalism.

THOMPSON, Lea M; Oslo Public HS; Oslo, MN; 4/47 HonRl; OffAde; FHA; Vocational School; Art.

THOMPSON, Lee; Gilman HS; Thorp, WI; TrsSophCls; ALBoysSt; HonRl; 4-H; FFA;.

THOMPSON, Lee A; Hayti HS; Hayti, MO; 3/87 Band; Chr; NHS; NatlThespSoc; SchMus; SchPl; StuCncl; Yrbk; SchPpr; FTA; Murray St Coll; Law.

THOMPSON, Lila J; C V HS; Cedar Vale, KS; 1/20 Band; Chr; HonRl; NHS; StuCncl; 4-H; CaptBsktbl; LetterTrk; Chrldr; GAA; College; Prof.

THOMPSON, Linda J; Atkinson HS; Atkinson, IL; 7/30 Band; HonRl; MrchBnd; RptrYrbk; 4-H; FHA; SpnCl; PpCl; Bsbl; Chrldr;.

THOMPSON, Lisa; Waldron Area HS; Walron, MI; HonRl; LbryAde; GAA; Siena Heights College; Psychology.

THOMPSON, Lois C; Newark HS; Newark, IL; Band; CncrtBnd; HonRl; NHS; SchPl; FrCl; Wheaton College; Med Tech.

THOMPSON, Lori A; New Haven HS; New Haven, MI; 9/110 Band; CncrtBnd; HonRl; LbryAde; MrchBnd; NHS; PepBnd; Macomb County Comm College; Registered Nurs.

THOMPSON, Margaret J; St Pius X HS; Kansas City, MO; 3/137 HonRl; ModUN; NHS; SchMus; PpCl;.

THOMPSON, Marilee J; Deckerville Comm HS; Minden City, MI; Band; HonRl; JA; YthLg; RptrSchPpr; SptEdSchPpr; Bsktbl; Tennis; IMSpt; JAAwd; College; Phy Ed Instructor.

THOMPSON, Mark A; Jeffersonville HS; Jeffersonville, IN; HonRl; IntrClCncl; SciCl; Ftbl; LetterTrk; Coast Guard Academy; Marine Biologist.

THOMPSON, Mark W; Milan HS; Milan, MN; 6/31 VPSrCls; ALBoysSt; Chr; CncrtBnd; HonRl; NatlMeritSchl; Orch; SchPl; YthFlsp; YthFnd; Bsktbl; Concordia College; Research Geneticist.

THOMPSON, Mary A; Waldron Area HS; Waldron, MI; HonRl; SchAde; SchPl; TchrAde; RptrSchPpr; FHA; SecTrsSophCls; LetterTrk; LetterChrldr; GAA;.

THOMPSON, Mary A; Lasalle Peru HS; Peru, IL; 118/509 Chr; HonRl; FrCl; SpnCl; PpCl; LetterTrk; Ivcc&isu Coll.

THOMPSON, Mary Anne; Our Lady Of Mercy HS; Orchard Lake, MI; Chr; NHS; TchrAde; FrCl; CaptBsktbl; IMSpt; Mi St Univ; Biochemistry.

THOMPSON, Mary J; Prairie Farm HS; Prairie Farm, WI; Band; Chrs; ChrhWkr; CncrtBnd; HonRl; MrchBnd; NHS; PepBnd; FHA; PpCl; Art Or Music Col ;art Music.

THOMPSON, Michael; Southwest HS; St Louis, MO; 2/597 HonRl; LbryAde; ModUN; PolWkr; Univ; Professional.

THOMPSON, Michael H; Brookville HS; Brookville, IN; 50/167 Band; ChrhWkr; Quill&Scroll; TchrAde; SchPpr; FTA; SciCl; Cincinnati Bible Col; Christian Ecucation.

THOMPSON, Michelle R; Lynnville Sully HS; Taintor, IA; ChrhWkr; NatlThespSoc; SchPl; EdSchPpr; Clge; Pre Med.

THOMPSON, Nancy; Glasgow Rii HS; Glasgow, MO; 4/49 Chr; ChrhWkr; DrlTm; HonRl; NHS; TchrAde; RptrYrbk; PpCl; Mo Valley College; Special Education.

THOMPSON, Nancy A; Colby HS; Dorchester, WI; 12/135 Chrs; HonRl; NHS; RptrSchPpr; FBLA; FHA; SpnCl; PpCl; Bsktbl; Swmmng; University Of Wisconsin; Nursing.

THOMPSON, Nancy L; Raymore Peculiar HS; Peculiar, MO; Chr; HonRl; JA; Sec4-H; TreasFrCl; Trk; Chrldr; GAA; PPFtbl; JAAwd; College.

THOMPSON, Nancy P; Kensington Public HS; Kensington, MN; TrsJrCls; Band; Chrs; HonRl; SchPl; EdSchPpr; 4-H; FHA; LetterTrk; PresAwd; Nursing.

THOMPSON, Pamela B; Kenwood HS; Chicago, IL; VPFrshCls; HonRl; NHS; Bsktbl; Tennis; GAA; IMSpt; PresAwd;.

THOMPSON, Pamela R; North Knox HS; Bicknell, IN; 5/125 DrlTm; HonRl; NHS; NatlMeritCmnd; TchrAde; 4-H; FHA; LatCl; MthCl; College.

THOMPSON, Patricia E; Peoria HS; Peoria, IL; 19/450 Chr; Chrl; Chrs; ChrhWkr; HonRl; JrNHS; NHS; College; Music.

THOMPSON, Patrick T; Lees Summit Sr HS; Lees Summit, MO; 12/400 HonRl; VPJA; NHS; NatlMeritSF; SctActv; TchrAde; PresYthFlsp; SciCl; GodCntryAwd; OptClAwd; College; Physician.

THOMPSON, Philip; Boone HS; Onamia, MN; ChrhWkr; HonRl; NHS; PepBnd; StuCncl; YthFlsp; Bsbl; Bsktbl; Ftbl; IMSpt; Northwestern Coll.

THOMPSON, Philip R; Hartford Union HS; Hartford, WI; HonRl; JA; NHS; LatCl; SpnCl; Suomi College; Computer Technology.

THOMPSON, Ramona K; Milan HS; Milon, MN; HonRl; LbryAde; RedCrAde; SchPl; TchrAde; EdYrBk; 4-H; FHA; PpCl; Chrldr; College; Social Work.

THOMPSON, Randall C; Exira Comm HS; Exira, IA; Chrs; YthFlsp; Pres4-H; PresFFA; LetterFtbl; LetterGlf; LetterTrk; CaptWrstlng; Des Moines Comm College; Agra Business.

THOMPSON, Randall J; Marion Adams HS; Sheridan, IN; 2/99 VPJrCls; Aud/Vis; HonRl; JrNHS; LbryAde; SchPl; SpnCl; LetterBsktbl; IMSpt; Indiana Univ; Radio Tv.

THOMPSON, Randall R; Blair Community HS; Blair, NE; CmntyWkr; HonRl; SctActv; SpnCl; Bsbl; Bsktbl; Ftbl; Glf; CchngActv; Trade School.

THOMPSON, Rebecca S; Munster HS; Munster, IN; 127/442 Chr; CmntyWkr; HonRl; SchMus; SchPl; StuCncl; Yrbk; GAA; IMSpt; PPFtbl; College; Special Ed.

THOMPSON, Renae L; Drayton Public HS; Drayton, ND; Band; Chr; Chrs; HonRl; SchPl; FHA; PpCl; Bsktbl; Chrldr; Clge Mayville Nd; Pro Special Ed Teacher.

THOMPSON, Rhonda; Orient Macksburg HS; Orient, IA; Chrs; HonRl; SchMus; Business School.

THOMPSON, Richard; Wonewoc Center HS; Woneowoc, WI; FFA;.

THOMPSON, Robert; Holcomb HS; Holcomb, KS; ChrhWkr; HonRl; 4-H; FFA; SciCl; Bsktbl; Ftbl; 4-HAwd; Univ; Vocation.

THOMPSON, Robert A; Pecatonica HS; Hollandale, WI; 3/58 VPFrshCls; PresSophCls; ChrhWkr; HonRl; StuCncl; StuGov; LetterBsktbl; LetterFtbl; University; Health Field.

THOMPSON, Roberta J; Chamberlain HS; Chamberlain, SD; 2/100 HonRl; NHS; SchPl; RptrYrbk; VPSpnCl; SciCl; Trk; U Of Sd; General.

THOMPSON, Robin M; Geo S Parker Sr HS; Janesville, WI; Chr; Chrl; Chrs; ChrhWkr; HonRl; Mdrgl; Orch; SchMus; SchPl; College; Professional Singer.

THOMPSON, Roxanne; Waldron HS; Prattville, MI; Chrs; HonRl; RptrYrbk; RptrSchPpr; FHA;.

THOMPSON, Ruth; Dolard HS; Doland, SD; MrchBnd; NatlFornLg; PepBnd; SchMus; EdYrBk; 4-H; FHA; FNA; PpCl; 4-HAwd; So Dak St Univ; Child Dev.

THOMPSON, Sally J; Auburn HS; Auburn, IL; Chrs; HonRl; VPJA; FFA; PpCl; JAAwd; Bus Clg; Sec.

THOMPSON, San B; West Side HS; Gary, IN; Chr; HonRl; NatlMeritCmnd; SchMus; PpCl; Indiana Univ; Business Admin.

THOMPSON, Sandra J; Pellston HS; Pellston, MI; Band; CncrtBnd; MrchBnd; PepBnd; SchPl; Business Schl; Secretary.

THOMPSON, Sandra M; Martinsville HS; Martinsville, IL; 6/63 Band; HonRl; HospAde; LbryAde; NHS; OffAde; SchPl; EdYrBk; Indiana State Univ; Nurse.

THOMPSON, Sandy E; Alton HS; Alton, MO; 6/58 SecBand; CncrtBnd; HonRl; MrchBnd; PepBnd; SchPl; StuCncl; PresPpCl; SciCl; Sw Mo State; Elementary Education.

THOMPSON, Sharon; Gibbon HS; Gibbon, NE; 5/59 Chrs; HonRl; TchrAde; Yrbk; FBLA; College; Vocational.

THOMPSON, Sharon E; Newtown Harris Riii HS; Newtown, MO; ALAGirlsSt; HonRl; NHS; Quill&Scroll; RptrYrbk; EdSchPpr; 4-H; FBLA; FHA; Bsbl; Bsktbl; Trk; Nmsu Kirksville; Special Ed.

THOMPSON, Sharon S; Fort Scott HS; Ft Scott, KS; ChrhWkr; DrlTm; HonRl; NatlFornLg; SecStuCncl; RptrYrbk; PpCl; CaptChrldr; College; Teacher.

THOMPSON, Sherri L; Serena Comm HS; Sheridan, IL; 2/72 HonRl; NHS; OffAde;.

THOMPSON, Sheryl; South Hamilton Comm HS; Ellsworth, IA; 6/91 Band; Chrs; CncrtBnd; HonRl; MrchBnd; PepBnd; SchMus; MthCl; Ia State Univ; Law.

THOMPSON, Stacie; Missouri Valley HS; Missouri Valley, IA; Chrs; 4-H; FHA; FNA; PpCl; 4-HAwd; College; Nursing.

THOMPSON, Stephen E; Hirsch HS; Chicago, IL; Chrs; HonRl; OffAde; SchMus; TchrAde; University; Business.

THOMPSON, Stephen L; Clinton Community HS; Clinton, IL; 34/154 Band; ChrhWkr; CncrtBnd; MrchBnd; SchMus; SchPl; StuCncl; SpnCl; IMSpt; University Of Mo; Commercial Art.

THOMPSON, Steven B; Marquette HS; Donnellson, IA; College; Agriculture.

THOMPSON, Susan J; Platteville HS; Platteville, WI; PresFrshCls; VPJrCls; ChrhWkr; HonRl; SchMus; StuGov; EdYrBk; RptrSchPpr; FrCl; PpCl; Wisconsin State Univ; Journalism.

THOMPSON, Susan P; Cary Grove HS; Cary, IL; 18/294 Chr; ChrhWkr; HonRl; NHS; SecGerCl; GAA; University.

THOMPSON, Terrica; New Holland Middletown HS; New Holland, IL; Band; Chr; CncrtBnd; HonRl; NHS; PepBnd; FHA; SpnCl; Bsktbl; Chrldr; Bus Coll; Sec.

THOMPSON, Theresa A; Beardstown HS; Beardstown, IL; SecJrCls; CmntyWkr; CncrtBnd; HonRl; LbryAde; MrchBnd; 4-H; FTA; SciCl; Tennis; Univ; Professional.

THOMPSON, Theresa K; Quincy Sr HS; Quincy, IL; AFS; Chr; ChrhWkr; HonRl; NHS; SchMus; YthFlsp; GerCl; Isu; German Teacher.

THOMPSON, Thomas J; Central HS; Red Wing, MN; 15/312 VPSrCls; Band; NHS; StuGov; YthLg; EdSchPpr; LetterBsbl; Bsktbl; Ftbl; IMSpt; AmLegAwd; EldAwd; KiwanAwd; North Dakota State Univ; Mech Engineer.

THOMPSON, Valerie R; North Boone HS; Capron, IL; 3/80 ALAGirlsSt; NHS; SchMus; FNA; SpnCl; LetterBsktbl; GAA; North Park College; Nursing.

THOMPSON, Vicki S; Bethany HS; Macon, IL; 2/30 VPFrshCls; VPSophCls; Band; Chr; Chrs; CncrtBnd; DrmMjrt; HonRl; Mdrgl; MrchBnd; NHS; PepBnd; SchMus; StuCncl; SecFHA; College; Mathematics.

THOMPSON, William J; Newton HS; Willow Hill, IL; 17/181 HonRl; NHS; 4-H; College; Veterinarian.

THOMS, Laura G; Nehawka HS; Nehawka, NE; 5/13 SecSophCls; VPJrCls; Chr; CmntyWkr; HonRl; SchMus; SecStuCncl; EdYrBk; 4-H; FHA; PpCl; Trk; Chrldr; 4-HAwd; College Of Saint Mary; Nurse.

THOMSEN, Dana W; Isle HS; Mc Grath, MN; 1/50 PresSophCls; NHS; StuGov; RptrSchPpr; EdSchPpr; MthCl; Pratt Institute; Architecture.

THOMSEN, Katherine E; St Paul HS; St Paul, NE; ALAGirlsSt; Chr; HonRl; NHS; SchMus; SchPl; StuCncl; 4-H; PresFHA; 4-HAwd; College; Professional.

THOMSEN, Lynda; St Paul Public HS; St Paul, NE; 4/72 CncrtBnd; HonRl; MrchBnd; NHS; Orch; PepBnd; SchMus; PPFtbl; 4-HAwd; JCAwd; Ne Wesleyan Univ; Resp Theraphy Technician.

THOMSEN, Michael L; Medicine Valley HS; Curtis, NE; PresSophCls; VPJrCls; Aud/Vis; NHS; PresStuCncl; RptrYrbk; SptEdSchPpr; SchPpr; LetterFtbl; LetterTrk; Purdue Univ; Engineering.

THOMSEN, Patricia; Everly Community HS; Moneta, IA; VPJrCls; Band; CncrtBnd; HonRl; MrchBnd; OffAde; SptEdYrbk; Ellsworth Comm College, Fashion Merchandisi.

THOMSEN, Sheryl; Dow City Arion Comm HS; Dow City, IA; HonRl; LbryAde; NHS; Quill&Scroll; SchPl; TchrAde; EdSchPpr; PpCl; SciCl; College; Teacher.

THOMSEN, Timothy; North Branch HS; North Branch, MN; HonRl; SchPl; Bsktbl; IMSpt; College; Biology.

THOMSON, Bruce; Huron HS; Ann Arbor, MI; Band; CtyCnl; CmntyWkr; CncrtBnd; HonRl; MrchBnd; NatlMeritSF; PepBnd; RedCrAde; SctActv; StuCncl; Socr; Swmmng; College.

THOMSON, Frederick J; Oscoda Area HS; Mikado, MI; Band; Chr; CncrtBnd; HonRl; LbryAde; MrchBnd; PepBnd; Lake Superior State Univ; Liberal Arts.

THOMSON, Isabel T; Sunset Hill HS; Kansas City, MO; VPJrCls; Chrl; HospAde; Quill&Scroll; SchMus; RptrSchPpr; LetterBsktbl; Tennis; GAA; IMSpt;.

THOMSON, Mary B; Lincoln Way Comm HS; Manhattan, IL; 53/498 College; Philosophy.

THOMSON, Scott; Morton HS; Morton, IL; Chr; ChrhWkr; CmntyWkr; PolWkr; SctActv;.

THOMURE, Kathleen A; Oakville HS; St Louis, MO; HonRl; NHS; FHA; KeyCl; FrCl; SpnCl; LetterTennis; LetterTrk; GAA; IMSpt; College; Nursing.

THON, Stephen C; Dighton HS; Healy, KS; 5/46 ALBoysSt; HonRl; NHS; PresStuCncl; Bsktbl; Trk; AmLegAwd; CitAwd; Colby Comm Jr College; Art.

THORELL, Cindy R; Loomis Public HS; Loomis, NE; Chrs; SchPl; StuGov; SecPpCl; Trk; Chrldr; CchngActv; PresGAA;.

THOREN, Debbi L; East HS; Rockford, IL; ChrhWkr; HonRl; StuGov; PpCl; PPFtbl; Rock Valley Coll; Soc Work.

THORESON, Barbara; Shanley HS; Fargo, ND; 14/122 Chr; HonRl; HospAde; NHS; SchMus; StuCncl; SchPpr; 4-H; PpCl; Chrldr; College; Occupational Therapy.

THORESON, Eric A; Grantsburg HS; Grantsburg, WI; PresSrCls; Chr; HonRl; SchPl; SctActv; RptrSchPpr; SptEdSchPpr; Bsktbl; LetterFtbl; Glf; Col; Business.

THORESON, Wallace B; Rock Bridge HS; Columbia, MO; ChrhWkr; HonRl; LitMag; NHS; NatlMeritFnl; NatlMeritSF; SctActv; StuCncl; KeyCl; Bsktbl; Socr; Trk; College; Biochemistry.

THORESON, William; East Monona HS; Soldier, IA; Band; Chr; CncrtBnd; HonRl; MrchBnd; PepBnd; SchPl; FFA; Dana College; Busineess Admin.

THORGAARD, Gregory; West HS; Iowa City, IA; 8/284 HonRl; StuCncl; StuGov; FrCl; Trk; IMSpt; ChmbCommrsAwd; GovHonPrgAwd; Arizona St; Md.

THORMAN, Gary A; Albert Lea HS; Albert Lea, MN; Band; Chrs; ChrhWkr; CncrtBnd; MrchBnd; PepBnd; Quill&Scroll; RptrSchPpr; College; Public Service.

THORMODSON, Patricia J; Ashby Public HS; Dalton, MN; 2/24 PresSophCls; TrsJrCls; ALAGirlsSt; Band; Chr; HonRl; NHS; 4-H; FHA; Bsktbl; Alexandria Tech Sch; Computer Programming.

THORMODSON, Patti J; Ashby Public HS; Dalton, MN; 2/24 TrsJrCls; ALAGirlsSt; Band; Chr; HonRl; NHS; TchrAde; 4-H; FHA; CaptBsktbl; Alexandria Tech; Computer Prog.

THORN, Kathy; West Marshall HS; State Center, IA; 3/84 HonRl; MrchBnd; NHS; Yrbk; ChmbCommrsAwd; Trade School; Horseback Riding Instructor.

THORN, Wesley G; Carthage HS; Carthage, MO; AFS; HonRl; NHS; FFA; Univ; Vocatioanl Ag Instructor.

THORNBLOOM, Richard; Mc Gregor HS; Mc Gregor, MN; Chr; HonRl; JrNHS; SctActv; StuCncl; 4-H; Bsktbl; Glf; Trade; Vocational.

THORNBRO, Bill; Daleville HS; Daleville, IN; VPSophCls; ChrhWkr; CmntyWkr; YthFlsp; RptrYrbk; RptrSchPpr; PpCl; LetterTrk; CaptWrstlng; College.

THORNBRO, Kim A; Lakeview HS; St Clair Shores, MI; Band; ChrhWkr; CncrtBnd; HonRl; MrchBnd; OffAde; PepBnd; David Lipscomb Coll; Elem Tech.

THORNBURG, Anna I; Van Buren Comm HS; Keosauqua, IA; ChrhWkr; HonRl; SchMus; TchrAde; PresFHA; PpCl; CaptChrldr; PPFtbl; Business College; Court Reporter.

THORNBURG, Gayle N; Wapello Comm HS; Oakville, IA; HonRl; RptrSchPpr; 4-H; Bsktbl; Chrldr; IMSpt;.

THORNBURG, Larry A; Moline Senior HS; Moline, IL; HonRl; TchrAde; Ftbl; CchngActv; IMSpt; Eastern Illinois; History Teacher.

THORNBURG, Linda; Ballard R 2; Adrian, MO; 3/14 SecSophCls; PresJrCls; TrsSrCls; Chr; Chrs; SchPl; SctActv; StuCncl; Bsbl; Chrldr; College; Home Economics.

THORNBURG, Marilee; Ottawa HS; Ottawa, KS; 8/180 Band; DrlTm; HonRl; NHS; SchPl; StuCncl; TchrAde; Yrbk; FrCl; PpCl; U Of Ks.

THORNBURG, Mary E; Bronaugh R 7 HS; Bronaugh, MO; 2/23 VPJrCls; Band; ChrhWkr; DrlTm; HonRl; LbryAde; StuCncl; 4-H; PpCl; DARAwd; Clge.

THORNBURG, Mary J; Prairie Senior HS; Prairie Du Chien, WI; SecTrsFrshCls; SecTrsSophCls; VPJrCls; CncrtBnd; HonRl; Twrl; Yrbk; RptrSchPpr; SecPpCl; GAA; University Of Wi Madison; Journalism.

THORNBURG, Robert; Pleasantville HS; Pleasantville, IA; VPFrshCls; VPSophCls; VPJrCls; Band; HonRl; StuCncl; FFA; Glf; Iowa State Univ; Biology.

THORNBURGH, Debra K; Charleston HS; Charleston, IL; 3/259 Band; Chrs; HonRl; NatlMeritCmnd; Orch; StuCncl; Yrbk; 4-H; Southern Illinois Univ; Economics.

THORNE, Alan A; New Trier HS; Wilmette, IL; Band; Chrs; ChrhWkr; CmntyWkr; CncrtBnd; PepBnd; GerCl; SciCl; Luther College; History.

THORNE, Alexander D; Greenhills HS; Ann Arbor, MI; PresJrCls; TrsSrCls; Chrs; HonRl; SchMus; SchPl; EdYrBk; Yrbk; LetterBsktbl; LetterSocr; Tennis; College Of Wooster; Economics.

THORNE, Cheryl; Nehawka Hs; Nehawka, NE; SecFrshCls; MrchBnd; PepBnd; StuCncl; YthFlsp; 4-H; GerCl; PpCl; Trk; Chrldr;.

THORNE, Denise J; Everly Community HS; Moneta, IA; SecJrCls; Band; Chrs; CncrtBnd; HonRl; MrchBnd; NHS; SchPl; 4-H; LetterBsktbl; College.

THORNE, Edward R; Roncalli HS; Indianapolis, IN; HonRl; LetterBsbl; Clg Or University; Chemistry Or Math.

THORNE, Jane E; Morton Sr HS; Hammond, IN; 18/492 HonRl; JrNHS; NHS; StuGov; Indiana University.

THORNE, Jean; Brainerd Senior HS; Brainerd, MN; HonRl; Trk; Hamhne; Recreation.

THORNE, Sabrina A; Carmel HS; Indianapolis, IN; HonRl; FTA; FrCl; University; Professional.

THORNE, Susan K; Wilber Clatonia HS; Wilber, NE; Chr; ChrhWkr; HonRl; HospAde; StuCncl; TchrAde; YthFlsp; FBLA; PpCl; Trk; Chrldr; IMSpt; College.

THORNQUIST, Brian C; Stillman Valley HS; Stillman Valley, IL; ChrhWkr; HonRl; NHS; Yrbk; SchPpr; FrCl; MthCl; IMSpt; Drake Univ; Acct.

THORNS, Jennifer R; Hays HS; Hays, KS; 3/231 ALAGirlsSt; ChrhWkr; HonRl; VPNatlFornLg; SchMus; StuCncl; Yrbk; SchPpr; SpnCl; IMSpt; Colege; Psychology.

THORNSON, Michael; Northrop HS; Fort Wayne, IN; 7/568 VPSrCls; ALBoysSt; HonRl; NHS; StuCncl; StuGov; FDA; Trk; Wrstlng; Usma West Point Ny; Medicine.

THORNTON, Daniel W; Crawford HS; Crawford, NE; Aud/Vis; HonRl; SchPl; StuCncl; YthLg; 4-H; Bsbl; Bsktbl; Trk; CchngActv; DARAwd; College.

THORNTON, Dan W; Crawford HS; Crawford, NE; TrsFrshCls; HstSophCls; HonRl; SchPl; SctActv; StuCncl; Bsbl; Bsktbl; CchngActv; DARAwd; Coll; Business.

THORNTON, Debora L; Nesco Community HS; Zearing, IA; TrsFrshCls; SecSophCls; SecJrCls; Band; Chrs; CncrtBnd; HonRl; Yrbk; Sec4-H; Bsktbl; Trk; Chrldr; IMSpt; 4-HAwd; College; Special Educ.

THORNTON, Jean M; Hibbing HS; Hibbing, MN; 62/389 VPSrCls; AFS; HonRl; PresJA; NHS; PresYthFlsp; SpnCl; PpCl; PresJAAwd; College Of St Catherine; Social Work.

THORNTON, John J; St Patricks HS; Chicago, IL; 66/377 HonRl; IMSpt; Engineering.

THORNTON, Kimberly J; Savannah Riii HS; Savannah, MO; Chr; ChrhWkr; HonRl; NHS; SchMus; SecStuCncl; MthCl; PpCl; ChmnBsktbl; GAA; Mid America Nazarene College.

THORNTON, Mark; Lindblom Tech Hs; Chicago, IL; Chr; Quill&Scroll; StuCncl; RptrSchPpr; GerCl; Trk; College; Medical Doctor.

THORNTON, Phil; Superior HS; Superior, NE; ALBoysSt; Chr; ChrhWkr; SchPl; YthFlsp; FBLA; SpnCl; Bsktbl; Trk; AmLegAwd; Coll; Professional.

THORNTON, Rebecca R; Lincoln HS; Des Moines, IA; Band; Chr; Chrs; ChrhWkr; HonRl; LbryAde; NatlMeritSF; RptrSchPpr; Oral Roberts Univ; Counseling.

THORNTON, Sue A; Bullock Creek HS; Midland, MI; Band; CncrtBnd; HonRl; HospAde; JA; LbryAde; MrchBnd; SchPl; TchrAde; YthFlsp; Tennis; Chrldr; College; Business.

THORNTON, Victor R; Mendel Catholic Prep; Chicago, IL; 77/161 ChrhWkr; HonRl; NatlMeritCmnd; SctActv; Ftbl; IMSpt; Clg; Acctng.

THORP, David; Gordon HS; Gordon, NE; 1/90 SecFrshCls; ALBoysSt; CmntyWkr; HonRl; SctActv; TchrAde; RptrYrbk; EdSchPpr; College; Law.

THORP, Julia L; Milton Sr HS; Milton, WI; Band; ChrhWkr; HonRl; MrchBnd; 4-H; FHA; 4-HAwd; Stout Univ; 1st Grade Teacher.

THORP, Kevin; Wapella HS; Clinton, IL; 1/16 HonRl; NHS; StuCncl; FFA; College.

THORP, Peter J; Carpio HS; Carpio, ND; Aud/Vis; Band; ChrhWkr; SchPl; Bsktbl; Electrician.

THORPE, Carolyn I; Dearborn HS; Dearborn, MI; Chr; Mdrgl; NatlFornLg; NHS; NatlMeritCmnd; NatlThespSoc; SchMus; StuCncl; CaptChrldr; IMSpt; Coll; Teacher.

THORPE, Daniel P; D C Everest HS; Aniwa, WI; 37/337 Chr; ChrhWkr; HonRl; Mdrgl; NHS; SchMus; Ftbl; IMSpt; U Of Wisc; Math.

THORPE, Kathryn; Tri West Hendricks HS; Lizton, IN; 3/55 SecJrCls; HonRl; NHS; SchPl; YthFlsp; EdYrBk; 4-H; FrCl; PpCl; Chrldr; College; Math.

THORSE, Dave S; Wheaton North HS; Wheaton, IL; 90/400 ChrhWkr; HonRl; PolWkr; SpnCl; SciCl; IMSpt; KiwanAwd; LionAwd; RotaryAwd; Univ Of Il; Engineer.

THORSELL, Deborah L; Meade HS; Meade, KS; 1/45 ALAGirlsSt; Band; Chrs; ChrhWkr; HonRl; SchMus; SecStuCncl; PpCl; GAA; University Of Kansas; Engineering.

THORSELL, Diane L; Meade HS; Meade, KS; Chrs; HonRl; SchMus; PresSophCls; YthFlsp; PpCl; College.

THORSELL, Elaine C; Granton Public HS; Granton, WI; 1/26 TrsSophCls; Chrs; HonRl; NHS; StuCncl; TchrAde; Yrbk; SchPpr; Coll; Commercial Art.

THORSON, Jeffrey L; Custer HS; Milwaukee, WI; 11/700 ALBoysSt; NHS; BauchLmbAwd; Univ Of Wi Milwaukee; Computer Science.

THORSTAD, Michael D; West Fargo HS; West Fargo, ND; 16/130 HonRl; NHS; SchPpr; LetterFtbl; CaptIMSpt; RotaryAwd;.

THORSTEN, Susan M; Deerfield HS; Deerfield, IL; VPAFS; HonRl; HospAde; LitMag; ModUN; Yrbk; University Of Georgia; Journalism.

THORWALDSEN, Jan A; Grosse Pointe South HS; Grosse Pointe, MI; Band; ChrhWkr; HonRl; MrchBnd; NHS; Orch; SpnCl; GovHonPrgAwd; Univ Of Mi; Music.

THORWALDSEN, Jan C; Mhd HS; Moorhead, MN; Chr; HonRl; Tennis; Univ; Lawyer Or English Teacher.

THOUVENOT, Mary M; Collinsville HS; Collinsville, IL; 39/654 ChrhWkr; HonRl; JA; TchrAde; College; Nursing.

THRACKMORTON, Mark D; Platteville HS; Platteville, WI; 40/200 Aud/Vis; ChrhWkr; CncrtBnd; Mdrgl; MrchBnd; ModUN; Orch; PepBnd; SchMus; College; Psychologist.

THRAILKILL, Donna K; Emerson Hubbard HS; Emersn, NE; 16/56 Band; CncrtBnd; MrchBnd; PepBnd; YthFlsp; RptrSchPpr; 4-H; PpCl; Bsktbl; 4-HAwd; Coll; Nurse.

THRAMS, Richard L; Colon HS; Colon, MI; 3/64 PresJrCls; HonRl; NatlMeritCmnd; LetterBsbl; LetterBsktbl; LetterFtbl; Mich St Univ; Civil Engr.

THRAP, Craig A; Prairie HS; Fairfax, IA; 2/196 ChrhWkr; SchPl; SctActv; StuCncl; RptrYrbk; RptrSchPpr; EdSchPpr; 4-H; FTA; AmLegAwd; U Of Brig Young; Mech Eng.

THRASHER, Constance K; Moweaqua HS; Moweaqua, IL; 4/50 Chrs; CmntyWkr; HonRl; NHS; TchrAde; EdYrBk; EdSchPpr; FFA; FHA; BttyCrckrAwd; Surgical Tech.

THRASHER, Marianne; Bushnell Prairie City HS; Bushnell, IL; 2/88 Band; Chr; HonRl; SecNHS; PepBnd; Sec4-H; SecFHA; PpCl; PresSciCl; GAA; Eastern Ill U; English Teacher.

THROCKMORTON, Gregory; Chariton Community HS; Chariton, IA; 20/150 ALBoysSt; HonRl; StuCncl; StuGov; PpCl; Bsktbl; Ne Mo State Univ; Police Science.

THROLSON, Cindy; Bismarck HS; Bismarck, ND; 74/588 NHS; 4-H; Bismarck Jr College; Mathematics.

THRON, Shirley R; Redford Union HS; Detroit, MI; Chr; HonRl; NHS; LetterGerCl; Bsbl; Wayne State University; Nurse.

THRONEBURG, Debra; Paris HS; Paris, IL; Band; Chr; Chrs; ChrhWkr; CncrtBnd; HonRl; Mdrgl; MrchBnd; NHS; NatlThespSoc; Millikin Univ; Music Education.

THRONTVEIT, Jon C; Rich Township E Campus HS; Park Forest, IL; ChrhWkr; HonRl; Bsbl; College; Pre Dentistry.

THRUSH, Lisa; Mt Horeb HS; Madions, WI; 4/150 ALAGirlsSt; Band; Chr; CncrtBnd; HospAde; NHS; SchMus; SchPl; StuCncl; Chrldr; College; Medicine.

THUE, Dan; Muskegon Sr HS; Muskegon, MI; CmntyWkr; College; Physics.

THUEME, Diane S; St Clair HS; St Clair, MI; 15/192 TrsSophCls; HonRl; StuCncl; TchrAde; RptrYrbk; LetterChrldr; GAA; IMSpt; LionAwd; PresAwd; U Of Mi; Dental Hygiene.

THUERWACHTER, Louise M; Lincoln Comm HS; Lincoln, IL; Band; CncrtBnd; HonRl; MrchBnd; SchMus; 4-H; College; Accounting.

THUL, Julie Ann; Wellcome Memorial HS; Vernon Center, MN; 11/45 VPFrshCls; SecJrCls; Chrs; DrlTm; HonRl; OffAde; SchPl; StuCncl; EdYrBk; 4-H; Coll Or Trade Sch.

THULL, Jane L; Berlin HS; Berlin, WI; 21/175 SchPl; Pres4-H; FBLA; SecFHA; FNA; Univ Of Wisconsin; Business Admin.

THUMA, Nathan; Shortridge HS; Indianapolis, IN; 2/350 HonRl; NHS; Quill&Scroll; SchPl; RptrSchPpr; FrCl; Yale College; Economics.

THUMS, Jolene A; Lincoln HS; Park Falls, WI; HstJrCls; Band; CncrtBnd; HonRl; JrNHS; MrchBnd; PepBnd; Bsktbl; Swmmng; GAA; Major Study.

THUNMAN, Susan; Galesburg Augusta HS; Galesburg, MI; 1/115 AFS; CncrtBnd; HonRl; MrchBnd; NHS; NatlMeritCmnd; TchrAde; Bsktbl; JAAwd; Mich Univ; Mathematics.

THUNSELLE, Robert D; Senior HS; Fergus Falls, MN; CncrtBnd; MrchBnd; PepBnd; 4-H; FFA; Trade School; Vocation.

THURBER, Vicki M; Chester Hubbell HS; Hubbell, NE; 1/15 TrsSophCls; Chrs; HonRl; SchPl; YthFlsp; 4-H; PpCl; Bsktbl; Bus Sch; Management.

THURMAN, Larry H; Central HS; Esther, MO; Chr; Chrs; HonRl; Yrbk; LetterFtbl; Bsbl; LetterWrstlng; LetterTrk; Col; St Patrolmen.

THURMAN, Loretta D; Univ HS; Lone Jack, MO; 2/44 SecJrCls; Chr; HonRl; ModUN; NHS; FFA; SpnCl; Univ; Medical.

THURMAN, Michael D; North Central HS; Indianapolis, IN; HonRl; PresJA; NatlMeritSF; SctActv; StuCncl; TchrAde; GerCl; IMSpt; Indiana Univ; Law.

THURMAN, Timarie R; Potosi R 3 HS; Potosi, MO; Band; Chr; HonRl; VPNatlThespSoc; PepBnd; SchPl; StuCncl; PpCl; Chrldr; PresAwd; Univ.

THURMER, Douglas S; Bishop Du Bourg HS; St Louis, MO; Band; CncrtBnd; HonRl; JA; PepBnd; SctActv; LatCl; IMSpt; University; Zoology.

THUROW, Debra; Peshtigo Public HS; Peshtigo, WI; 3/80 TrsSrCls; HonRl; HospAde; NHS; StuCncl; Trk; Bllin Memorial Hospital; Nurse.

THUROW, Lisa A; Black River Fls Sr HS; Black River Falls, WI; TrsFrshCls; TrsSrCls; HonRl; Twrl; RptrSchPpr; SptEdSchPpr; LatCl; CaptBsktbl; Glf; LetterTrk; U Of Wi; Communication Arts.

THUROW, Lora J; Black River Falls Sr HS; Black River Falls, WI; TrsSophCls; SecSrCls; HonRl; StuCncl; Twrl; EdSchPpr; LetterBsktbl; LetterGlf; Trk; GAA; U Of Wi; Registerd Nurse.

THUROW, Roger G; Crystal Lake Comm HS; Crystal Lake, IL; 4/477 ChrhWkr; HonRl; NHS; Quill&Scroll; YthFlsp; EdSchPpr; Univ Of Iowa; Journalism.

THURSTON, Katherine L; Athens HS; Battle Creek, MI; ChrhWkr; Quill&Scroll; RedCrAde; TchrAde; EdSchPpr; FshEdSchPpr; SchPpr; 4-H; EngCl; GAA; College.

THURSTON, Pamela K; Galva HS; Galva, IL; Chr; Chrs; ChrhWkr; HonRl; YthFlsp; 4-H; FHA; 4-HAwd; Hawk East College.

THYBAULT, John; Owen Gage HS; Gagetown, MI; PresSophCls; PresJrCls; ALBoysSt; HonRl; NHS; SchPl; StuCncl; Bsktbl; Ftbl; Trk; Coll.

THYDEAN, Beverly E; Littlefork Big Falls HS; Littlefork, MN; SecTrsFrshCls; TrsSrCls; DrmMjrt; HonRl; SchPl; Yrbk; SchPpr; FHA; Chrldr; Medical Records Librarian.

THYFAULT, Cheryl S; Palco HS; Damar, KS; Band; Chr; Chrs; CncrtBnd; HonRl; MrchBnd; SchMus; SchPl; FHA; PpCl; Ks State College.

TIARKS, Karen; Underwood Comm HS; Mcclelland, IA; VPFrshCls; TrsSophCls; Band; Chrs; HonRl; NHS; IMSpt; 4-HAwd; College;.

TIARKS, William M; Underwood Comm HS; Underwood, IA; PresFrshCls; Band; Chr; Chrs; CncrtBnd; HonRl; MrchBnd; PepBnd; SchMus; YthFlsp;.

TIBBITS, Jeffrey A; Douglas Mac Arthur HS; Saginaw, MI; 3/304 HonRl; PresNHS; Bsbl; Wrstlng; Michigan State Univ; Medicine.

TIBBITTS, Karen R; Big Foot HS; Zenda, WI; Chrs; HonRl; SchMus; 4-H; SpnCl; IMSpt; 4-HAwd; Univ; Prof.

TIBBOEL, Lola K; Prairie City Comm HS; Prairie City, IA; 3/45 Chr; Chrs; HonRl; MrchBnd; SchMus; TchrAde; SecYthFlsp; LetterBsbl; PPFtbl; College; Vocation.

TIBBS, Richard J; Sandoval HS; Sandoval, IL; 26/43 Band; CncrtBnd; HonRl; MrchBnd; PepBnd; SchPl; LetterFtbl; LetterTrk; Wrstlng; Coll; Marine Biology.

TIBKE, Perry D; Valley City HS; Valley City, ND; LetterFtbl; LetterTrk; LetterWrstlng; CchngActv; Coll; Art.

TIBODEAU, Christine L; Wells Easton HS; Easton, MN; SecJrCls; VPSrCls; Chrs; HonRl; Mdrgl; MrchBnd; SchMus; SchPl; StuCncl; FFA; College; Nursing.

TIBODEAU, Janice; Delavan Public HS; Delavan, MN; 7/30 PresJrCls; Band; Chr; ChrhWkr; HonRl; NHS; PepBnd; SchPl; StuCncl; EdYrBk; St Benedicts; Nursing.

TICE, Crystal Y; Sullivan HS; Sullivan, MO; 13/150 HonRl; HospAde; NHS; StuCncl; TchrAde; SptEdSchPpr; FTA; Bsbl; Bsktbl; GAA; IMSpt; PPFtbl; Jr College; Elementary Educ.

TICE, Lori L; Northeastern HS; Richmond, IN; 6/136 ALAGirlsSt; Chr; HonRl; JA; NHS; TchrAde; Twrl; Sec4-H; SpnCl; SciCl; GAA; Ball State Univ; Teacher.

TICHENOR, Terry J; Wheaton HS; Wheaton, MO; ChrhWkr; CmntyWkr; SchPl; SctActv; YthFlsp; 4-H; Bsbl; Bsktbl; Crowder College.

TICHY, Cynthia S; Lake Park HS; Roselle, IL; 29/536 HonRl; HospAde; LbryAde; StuCncl; EdYrBk; College Of Du Page; Secretary.

TICK, David B; Macarthur HS; Decatur, IL; 24/390 CmntyWkr; CncrtBnd; HonRl; JA; MrchBnd; NHS; Orch; SchMus; SciCl; College; Doctor.

TICKEN, Mark A; Gibson Southern HS; Ft Branch, IN; Quill&Scroll; StuGov; SptEdSchPpr; LatCl; PpCl; Tennis; College.

TICKNER, Dianna; Alton Senior Hs; Alton, IL; CncrtBnd; HonRl; Orch; TchrAde; GerCl; LetterTrk; University Of Ill; Chemical Engineer.

TIDABACK, Dale R; Lasalle Peru Twp HS; Peru, IL; Band; HonRl; MrchBnd; SchMus; StuGov; Tennis; Us Naval Academy; Naval Pilot.

TIDABACK, Douglas B; La Salle Peru Township HS; La Salle, IL; Band; MrchBnd; PepBnd; SchMus; Univ Of Ill; Music Major.

TIDMARSH, Jay H; Marquette Univ HS; Milwaukee, WI; 1/247 HonRl; LitMag; ModUN; NHS; NatlMeritCmnd; SchPl; RptrYrbk; RptrSchPpr; KeyCl; MthCl; LetterBsktbl; Univ; Law.

TIDO, Anthony L; St Paul Kennedy HS; Chicago, IL; Aud/Vis; Chrs; ChrhWkr; CmntyWkr; HonRl; Orch; FrCl; MthCl; College; Data Processing.

TIEDEMAN, Raymond G; Grayslake Comm HS; Lindenhurst, IL; 15/219 CAP; HonRl; NHS; LatCl; College Of Lake County; Pilot.

TIEDEMANN, Joann R; Robert M La Follette HS; Madison, WI; AFS; Band; Chr; HonRl; LbryAde; NHS; NatlMeritSF; Orch; SchMus; College; Education.

TIEFENAUER, Dave W; North County HS; Desloge, MO; 16/170 Chrs; HonRl; JrNHS; Mdrgl; NHS; TchrAde; SptEdYrbk; Bsbl; Bsktbl; Ftbl; Clge; Psychology.

TIEFENTHAL, David; Manistee Catholic Central; Manistee, MI; Ftbl; IMSpt; VoiceDemAwd;.

TIEHEN, Ann M; Galesburg Sr HS; Galesbrug, IL; 62/629 HonRl; IntrClCncl; SchPl; Yrbk; SpnCl; U Of I; Pre Med.

TIEHES, Mike A; Pacific HS; Catawissa, MO; HonRl; SchMus; SchPl; SctActv; TchrAde; Bsbl; E C J C; Engineering.

TIELKE, Gerald A; Yankton Senior HS; Yankton, SD; Chrs; HonRl; NHS; SchMus; MthCl; SciCl; College; Math.

TIEMAN, Dawn M; Carthage HS; Carthage, MO; AFS; Chr; HonRl; FHA; PpCl; Chrldr; PPFtbl; Col.

TIEMAN, Marilyn L; Seymour HS; Liberty, IL; 11/64 TrsFrshCls; Chr; Chrs; HonRl; Mdrgl; NHS; TchrAde; FHA;.

TIEMANN, Mark A; Triopia HS; Chapin, IL; ALBoysSt; Chr; Chrs; ChrhWkr; CncrtBnd; SchPl; PresStuCncl; LetterBsktbl; LetterFtbl; LetterTrk; Il College; Business Admin Pe.

TIEMEIER, Gregory J; Notre Dame HS; Burlington, IA; 25/75 PresSrCls; Aud/Vis; HonRl; StuCncl; StuGov; RptrYrbk; SptEdSchPpr; Bsbl; IMSpt; KiwanAwd; College; Bus Adm.

TIENSVOLD, Carol J; Rushville HS; Rushville, NE; Aud/Vis; Chrs; CncrtBnd; HonRl; MrchBnd; PepBnd; SchMus; StuCncl; FHA; Trk; College; Fashion Design.

TIEPELMAN, Linda; Orchard Farm HS; Saint Charles, MO; HonRl; FBLA; PpCl; Chrldr; Trade School.

TIERNAN, Mary E; Woodlands Academy; Libertyville, IL; 1/78 NatlMeritCmnd; SchMus; SchPl; RptrYrbk; Yrbk; FrCl; CaptChrldr; Univ Of Illinois; Biochemistry.

TIERNEY, Jane E; Pleasant Hill HS; Pleasant Hill, MO; 5/112 ChrhWkr; HonRl; IntrClCncl; LbryAde; NHS; StuCncl; TchrAde; EdYrBk; EdSchPpr; FTA; PresSpnCl; SciCl; Missouri Univ; Law.

TIES, Debbie; Lewiston HS; Winona, MN; 29/87 Chr; HonRl; NHS; SchMus; SchPl; Yrbk; FHA; Trk; 4-HAwd; College; Social Worker.

TIESKOTTER, Maxine E; Turkey Valley Comm HS; Lawler, IA; 15/111 Chrs; HonRl; VPSophCls; NHS; TchrAde; FHA; SpnCl; IMSpt; Hawkeye Inst Tech; Dental Assist.

TIESZEN, Norman E; Marion Ind HS; Marion, SD; 14/42 VPSophCls; TrsSrCls; ALBoysSt; Chr; HonRl; StuCncl; SptEdYrbk; Bsbl; Bsktbl; Univ Of So Dakota; Nurse.

TIETJEN, Julie M; Marion HS; Marion, IA; 5/179 Band; Chr; ChrhWkr; CmntyWkr; HonRl; NHS; Bsktbl; LetterGlf; IMSpt; College; Vocation.

TIETSORT, Cheryl A; Laplata Rii HS; Laplata, MO; 1/41 Band; DrmMjrt; NHS; SchPl; SctActv; Twrl; FHA; PpCl; LetterBsbl; Chrldr; College; Mathematics.

TIETZ, Dale E; Wild Rose HS; Pine River, WI; Band; ChrhWkr; CncrtBnd; JA; MrchBnd; 4-H; FFA; Tech Sch; Mech.

TIFFANY, Thomas; Elmwood HS; Spring Valley, WI; ALBoysSt; HonRl; NHS; FFA; IMSpt; College.

TIFFEN, Anne L; New Trier East HS; Winnetka, IL; 1/847 Chr; NatlMeritSF; SchMus; SchPl; RptrSchPpr; Bsktbl; Swmmng; Tennis; University; Law.

TIFFIN, Patricia; St Joseph HS; Chicago, IL; 4/120 Chr; TreasChrs; HonRl; NHS; NatlMeritCmnd; SchMus; SchPl; FrCl; University Of Illinois; Pharmacist.

TIFFIN, Vicki L; Casey HS; Casey, IL; 5/100 Chr; ChrhWkr; HonRl; LbryAde; OffAde; SchMus; FTA; SpnCl; PpCl;.

TIGNER, Rochelle T; Central Webster HS; Lehigh, IA; SecSophCls; SecSrCls; Band; Chrs; HonRl; Yrbk; 4-H; SpnCl; IMSpt; 4-HAwd; Iowa State Univ; Advertizing Design.

TIGWELL, Denise S; Crystal Lake HS; Crystal Lake, IL; DrlTm; HonRl; VPNHS; NatlMeritCmnd; PolWkr; StuCncl; FrCl; Univ Of Illinois; Author.

TIJERINA, Alice; Chesaning HS; Montrose, MI; ChrhWkr; CncrtBnd; HonRl; HospAde; ModUN; NatlMeritSchl; RedCrAde; StuCncl; StuGov; FshEdYrbk; Trade Sch; Prof.

TILDEN, Diann E; Greenway HS; Grand Rapids, MN; Chr; HonRl; NHS; PpCl; SciCl; LetterBsktbl; LetterTrk; LetterGAA; IMSpt; PPFtbl; College; Medicine.

TILL, Lois J; Lourdes HS; Rochester, MN; HonRl; 4-H; 4-HAwd; College.

TILL, Randy; Catholic Boys HS; Quincy, IL; 30/75 HonRl; EngCl; PpCl; IMSpt; Illinois State U.

TILLEMANS, Tammy M; Marshall Senior HS; Marshall, MN; 8/219 Chr; ChrhWkr; CncrtBnd; HonRl; MrchBnd; Orch; SchMus; YthFlsp; College; Music.

TILLER, Lesa C; Lincoln Co R Ii; Elsberry, MO; PresFrshCls; HonRl; VPNHS; StuCncl; TchrAde; SecFHA; VPSciCl; Nursing Sch; Rn.

TILLERY, Jeffrey M; Divernon Twp HS; Divernon, IL; 2/30 PresFrshCls; PresSophCls; VPJrCls; PresBand; HonRl; SchPl; StuGov; Bsbl; LetterBsktbl; College; Science.

TILLERY, Luchina; Kenwood HS; Chicago, IL; HonRl; OffAde; TchrAde; SchPpr; JAAwd; University; Fine Arts & Writing.

TILLETT, Andrea; Maryville Rii HS; Maryville, MO; Band; Chr; Chrs; ChrhWkr; CmntyWkr; CncrtBnd; HonRl; HospAde; Mdrgl; MrchBnd; PolWkr; YthFnd; Business Sch; Professional.

TILLIE, Leoter A; Community HS; North Chicago, IL; Bsktbl; IMSpt; College; Professional.

TILLITT, Glenn S; Beardstown Sr HS; Beardstown, IL; 2/128 Band; Chr; Chrl; PresChrs; CncrtBnd; DrmMjrt; HonRl; Mdrgl; MrchBnd; VPNHS; Bsktbl; IMSpt; AmLegAwd; SARAwd; Univ Of Illinois; Musician.

TILLMAN, Carol S; Mexico HS; Mexico, MO; Band; HospAde; NHS; LatCl; College; Nursing.

TILLOU, Lynn; Mason City HS; Mason City, IA; ChrhWkr; CmntyWkr; HonRl; NHS; NatlMeritCmnd; Orch; Quill&Scroll; TchrAde; FshEdYrbk; PpCl; Univ; Pharmacy.

TILSON, Sibyl L; Barstow HS; Prairie Village, KS; 2/34 HonRl; LitMag; NatlMeritSF; StuCncl; StuGov; RptrYrbk; SchPpr; Bsktbl; Trk; DARAwd; Clge.

TILTON, Celeste L; Yorkville HS; Yorkville, IL; Band; CncrtBnd; MrchBnd; NHS; Orch; PepBnd; TchrAde; SchPpr; FHA; College; Mathematics.

TILTON, Dixie L; Circle HS; El Dorado, KS; 10/108 Aud/Vis; Band; Chrs; CncrtBnd; HonRl; LbryAde; MrchBnd; PepBnd; SciCl; IMSpt; College.

TILUS, Kenneth W; Buffalo Sr HS; Buffalo, MN; 7/219 Chrs; HonRl; StuCncl; RptrYrbk; RptrSchPpr; GerCl; PpCl; ChmnIMSpt; Oral Roberts Univ; Finance.

TIMBERLAKE, Kathi D; Central HS; Kansas City, MO; 18/375 HonRl; NHS; LatCl; Umkb; Pharacist.

TIMBS, Karen A; Polo HS; Sterling, IL; 31/93 HonRl; LbryAde; TchrAde; RptrSchPpr; SchPpr; University Of Illinois; Science.

TIMINSKY, Herbert M; North Side HS; Fort Wayne, IN; 7/467 Chr; ChrhWkr; HonRl; NHS; SctActv; IMSpt; ChmbCommrsAwd; College; Accounting.

TIMKE, Patricia L; Batesville HS; Batesville, IN; TchrAde; Business School; Secretary.

TIMKOVICH, Gertrude C; Bishop Noll Institute; Hammond, IN; 6/360 CmntyWkr; HonRl; College; Medicine.

TIMM, Claire R; Eustis Public HS; Eustis, NE; Chrs; HonRl; SchPl; YthFlsp; RptrYrbk; EdYrBk; Pres4-H; Trk; Chrldr; 4-HAwd; VoiceDemAwd;.

TIMM, David J; Brodhead HS; Brodhead, WI; VPSophCls; PresJrCls; Band; HonRl; VPYthFlsp; Ftbl; IMSpt; College; Professional.

TIMM, Donna J; Monroe HS; Monroe, WI; Aud/Vis; Band; CncrtBnd; HonRl; LbryAde; MrchBnd; 4-H; Chrldr; GAA; Business Schl; Professional.

TIMM, Gayle; East Detroit HS; Warren, MI; ChrhWkr; HonRl; TchrAde; Coll; Bus Or Music.

TIMM, Gretchen J; Butternut HS; Butternut, WI; Band; Chrs; CncrtBnd; DrmMjrt; HonRl; MrchBnd; SchPpr; SpnCl; PpCl; Chrldr; College; Communications.

TIMM, Jody R; Loup City Public HS; Loup City, NE; Band; Chr; Chrs; CmntyWkr; CncrtBnd; HonRl; MrchBnd; NHS; Orch; Concordia Clg; Pre Med.

TIMM, Julie A; Forest Lake HS; Forest Lake, MN; Band; CncrtBnd; HonRl; JA; MrchBnd; PepBnd; RptrYrbk; Bsktbl; PPFtbl; College.

TIMM, Loris L; Huron HS; Huron, SD; 45/301 OffAde; PpCl; College; Psychology.

TIMM, Martin L; Shorewood HS; Shorewood, WI; Chrs; HonRl; NatlMeritSF; SchMus; SchPl; StuCncl; RptrSchPpr; LetterSwmmng; BauchLmbAwd; Univ; Science.

TIMM, Sherri; Melrose Mindoro HS; Holmen, WI; 5/89 Band; ChrhWkr; HonRl; SchPl; StuCncl; EdSchPpr; 4-H; FHA; Chrldr; 4-HAwd; Coll; Home Economics.

TIMM, Sherri A; Melrose Mindoro HS; Holmen, WI; 5/89 Band; ChrhWkr; HonRl; SchPl; StuCncl; EdSchPpr; 4-H; FHA; Chrldr; 4-HAwd; College; Home Ec.

TIMMCKE, Glen R; Beloit Memorial HS; Beloit, WI; Band; Chr; CncrtBnd; MrchBnd; Orch; PepBnd; SchMus; SchPl; Tennis; Trk; Univ; Professional.

TIMMER, Lisa M; Warren HS; Warren, MI; LetterBand; CncrtBnd; HonRl; MrchBnd; NHS; PepBnd; LetterTennis; GAA; College.

TIMMERMAN, Barbara J; City HS; Iowa City, IA; 7/304 TrsSrCls; HonRl; NHS; NatlMeritCmnd; Quill&Scroll; University Of Iowa; Medicine.

TIMMERMAN, Brenda; Wj Bryan Senior HS; Omaha, NE; HonRl; ModUN; StuCncl; SpnCl; PpCl; Trk; Chrldr; GAA; College; Lab Tech.

TIMMERMAN, Debora A; Lourdes HS; Rochester, MN; Chrs; HonRl; HospAde; NHS; SchMus; SchPl; SctActv; Rochester Comm Col; Nursing.

TIMMERMAN, Gary B; Papillion HS; Papillion, NE; 137/360 Aud/Vis; SctActv; StuGov; 4-H; FTA; LetterFtbl; LetterTrk; LetterWrstlng; 4-HAwd; KiwanAwd; PresAwd; College; Teacher.

TIMMERMAN, Judith A; Watertown Sr HS; Watertown, SD; 15/298 ALAGirlsSt; Band; Chr; HonRl; JrNHS; SchPl; LetterBsktbl; LetterTennis; LetterTrk; Chrldr; GAA; JCAwd; S Dakota St Univ; Physical Therapy.

TIMMERMAN, Kay M; Bennett Community HS; Bennett, IA; Chr; HonRl; LbryAde; StuCncl; FshEdYrbk; VPSophCls; SecSophCls; 4-H; Bsbl; Bsktbl; Trade School; Cosmotology.

TIMMERMAN, Lorie M; Lake View Auburn HS; Auburn, IA; 6/44 VPFrshCls; Chrs; HonRl; HospAde; Mdrgl; NatlThespSoc; SchMus; SchPl; RptrYrbk; RptrSchPpr; Iowa St Univ; Child Development.

TIMMERMAN, Terri L; Dwight Township HS; Dwight, IL; 16/111 PresFrshCls; Band; HonRl; NHS; RptrYrbk; LatCl; LetterBsbl; LetterChrldr; LetterGAA; IMSpt; Univ Of Illinois; Physical Ed.

TIMMERMANN, Anne; Mater Dei HS; Breese, IL; Chrs; ChrhWkr; DrlTm; HonRl; OffAde; SchMus; TchrAde; Chrldr; AmLegAwd; Creighton Univ; Accountant.

TIMMERMANN, Suzann C; St Paul HS; Highland, IL; 5/70 SecTrsFrshCls; Band; Chr; ChrhWkr; CmntyWkr; HonRl; HospAde; LbryAde; PolWkr; RedCrAde; LetterSocr; Trk; GAA; IMSpt; College; Optometry.

TIMMERMANN, Suzy C; Saint Paul HS; Highland, IL; 5/55 SecTrsFrshCls; Band; Chrs; ChrhWkr; CmntyWkr; HonRl; HospAde; LbryAde; PolWkr; RedCrAde; Bsbl; LetterSocr; GAA; IMSpt; College; Optometry.

TIMMERMANS, Susan; Geneva Public HS; Fairmont, NE; 5/60 HonRl; NHS; YthFlsp; RptrSchPpr; 4-H; PpCl; GAA; 4-HAwd; Lincoln Sch; Accounting.

TIMMIS, Michael W; North Side HS; Fort Wayne, IN; 140/493 Band; CncrtBnd; MrchBnd; Orch; PepBnd; SchMus; Business School; Computer Programmer.

TIMMONS, Dale J; Hordville Public HS; Hardville, NE; VPSophCls; CncrtBnd; HonRl; ROTC; SctActv; YthFlsp; SptEdSchPpr; LetterBsktbl; LetterFtbl; CaptTrk; Kearney State Clg; Pilot.

TIMMONS, David; St Xaviers HS; Junction City, KS; 6;33 HonRl; TchrAde; LetterBsktbl; Trk; Business;professional.

TIMMONS, Dwight W; Prairie City Comm HS; Prairie City, IA; 15/42 Band; Chr; Chrs; CncrtBnd; DrmMjrt; HonRl; MrchBnd; PepBnd; SchMus; SchPl; SctActv; College; Prof Athlete.

TIMMONS, Jeanne L; Centralia HS; Centralia, IL; 34/356 HonRl; HospAde; SchMus; SchPl; LatCl; TreasSciCl; Bsktbl; Trk; Illinois State Univ; Physical Oceanographer.

TIMMONS, Karla J; Athens HS; Battle Creek, MI; Band; CncrtBnd; HonRl; JA; JrNHS; MrchBnd; NHS; PepBnd; YthFlsp; 4-H; LetterBsktbl; IMSpt; 4-HAwd; JCAwd; College; Accounting.

TIMMONS, Robert R; Assumption HS; Bettendorf, IA; 18/202 ALBoysSt; HonRl; LetterBsbl; CaptFtbl; LetterTrk; LetterWrstlng; IMSpt; AmLegAwd; Augustana College Sd Sioux Falls.

TIMMONS, Scott L; Marion Adams HS; Sheridan, IN; HonRl; JrNHS; NHS; SchAde; SpnCl; SciCl; Bsbl; LetterFtbl; IMSpt; Indiana U; Business.

TIMMRECK, Julie A; Alpena Sr HS; Ossineke, MI; ChrhWkr; CmntyWkr; HonRl; HospAde; TchrAde; FNA; LatCl; Alpena Comm Col; Ministry.

TIMON, Camille E; Fairfield HS; Fairfield, IA; 5/183 Chr; HonRl; NHS; OffAde; Quill&Scroll; EdYrBk; FBLA; SecSpnCl; PpCl; IMSpt; Coll; Computer Sci.

TIMP, Hope; Galena HS; Galena, IL; HonRl; TchrAde; Twrl; Yrbk; FHA; FTA; Tennis; GAA; Univ; Armed Forces.

TIMPANY, Cindy M; Parker HS; Janesville, WI; SecBand; CncrtBnd; HonRl; MrchBnd; TreasNHS; PepBnd; StuGov; Univ Of Wisconsin; Mathematics.

TIMPE, Karen E; Notre Dame HS; Quincy, IL; 2/103 TrsSophCls; PresJrCls; PresSrCls; Chrs; HospAde; NHS; NatlMeritCmnd; SchPl; RptrSchPpr; St Louis Univ; Medicine.

TIMPSON, Meredith L; Kalkaska HS; Alden, MI; 10/125 Band; CncrtBnd; HonRl; MrchBnd; NHS; PepBnd; SchPl; TchrAde; Yrbk; SchPpr; College.

TIMS, Nancy K; Worthington Sr HS; Worthington, MN; Chr; ChrhWkr; HonRl; NHS; Orch; SchMus; StuCncl; TchrAde; GerCl; IMSpt; Col; Professional.

TINBERG, Joan; Monroe Sr HS; Monroe, WI; AFS; Chr; Chrl; VPFrshCls; SecFrshCls; PresFrshCls; Mdrgl; SchMus; GerCl; College; German Or Music.

TINCHER, Clifford A; Lake Forest HS; Lake Bluff, IL; 26/417 HonRl; LitMag; NHS; NatlMeritFnl; NatlMeritSchl; Quill&Scroll; CaptBsktbl; Ftbl; IMSpt;.

TINCHER, Mark; Plattsmouth HS; Plattsmouth, NE; SctActv; StuGov; YthFlsp; 4-H; Bsbl; Swmmng; Wrstlng; 4-HAwd; College; Professional.

TINDALL, Cathy M; Emerson HS; Gary, IN; TrsSophCls; TrsJrCls; DrlTm; NHS; ROTC; Bsktbl; PresGAA; AmLegAwd; LionAwd; CitAwd; Indiana Inst Of Tech; Recreation Management.

TINDALL, Jeffrey; Benton Consolidated HS; Benton, IL; Band; CncrtBnd; MrchBnd; Orch; PepBnd; SchMus; KeyCl; IMSpt; Ne Louisiana Col; Pharmacist.

TINDALL, Jill D; Akron Community HS; Akron, IA; Band; Chrs; HonRl; NHS; VPNatlThespSoc; Orch; SchPl; PresYthFlsp; Pres4-H; 4-HAwd; College; Music.

TINDALL, Kenneth; Luverne Comm HS; Luverne, IA; PresJrCls; Band; Chrs; CncrtBnd; HonRl; Mdrgl; PepBnd; SchPl; StuCncl; Yrbk; Iowa St U; Geology.

TINDALL, Laurie J; Akron Community HS; Akron, IA; PresJrCls; Chrs; HonRl; Mdrgl; NHS; SchPl; StuCncl; YthFlsp; FHA; PpCl; College; Vocation.

TINDALL, Mike L; Chester HS; Chester, IL; VPFrshCls; VPSophCls; Band; ChrhWkr; CncrtBnd; HonRl; MrchBnd; PepBnd; RedCrAde; SchMus; SchPl; Bsbl; Bsktbl; Ftbl; College; Oceanography.

TINDALL, Peggy S; Osceola HS; Osceola, NE; Chrs; CncrtBnd; MrchBnd; PepBnd; PpCl; Chrldr; College.

TINDELL, David J; Potosi HS; Potosi, WI; 2/65 Aud/Vis; HonRl; NHS; NatlMeritCmnd; SchPl; StuCncl; TchrAde; EdSchPpr; SptEdSchPpr; Bsktbl; U Of Wisc; Radio Tv Broadcasting.

TINDER, David B; Charleston HS; Charleston, IL; ChrhWkr; HonRl; 4-H; Bsktbl; Ftbl; Trk; 4-HAwd; Univ.

TINDLE, Gwen L; Grant Comm HS; Lake Villa, IL; Chr; ChrhWkr; CncrtBnd; HonRl; MrchBnd; NHS; PepBnd; College; Mathematics.

TINEBRA, Paul R; Grafton HS; Grafton, WI; ALBoysSt; CncrtBnd; HonRl; MrchBnd; PepBnd; SctActv; MthCl; College; Professional.

TINES, Janelle R; Bergan HS; Fremont, NE; Chrs; CmntyWkr; HonRl; LbryAde; NHS; SchMus; Yrbk; PresPpCl; LetterTrk; St Marys College; Business.

TINGLE, Thomas L; Rock Island Sr HS; Rock Island, IL; ChrhWkr; JrNHS; PolWkr; VPStuCncl; StuGov; TchrAde; KeyCl; PpCl; CaptBsbl; JETSAwd; College; Engineer.

TINGLEY, Kim M; Normal Community HS; Normal, IL; 1/443 ChrhWkr; HonRl; NHS; NatlMeritCmnd; StuCncl; TchrAde; U Of Ill; Eng.

TINKER, Nancy E; Macomb Sr HS; Macomb, IL; 11/245 TrsSrCls; SecChr; HonRl; Mdrgl; NHS; PresNatlThespSoc; StuCncl; Yrbk; Chrldr; EldAwd; W Illinois Univ; Medicine.

TINKER, Sharon; West Delaware HS; Manchester, IA; 6/200 Aud/Vis; HonRl; LbryAde; NHS; Yrbk; RptrSchPpr; 4-HAwd; Univ Of Iowa; Engineering.

TINKER, Sherry A; Civic Memorial HS; Bethalto, IL; 13/250 HonRl; NHS; StuCncl; Yrbk; SchPpr; PpCl; Chrldr; GAA; IMSpt; Business School; Secretarial.

TINKEY, David M; Warsaw Community HS; Warsaw, IN; 13/380 ChrhWkr; CmntyWkr; HonRl;

LbryAde; PolWkr; YthFlsp; LetterBsbl; IMSpt; Coll; Busi.

TINKHAM, Scott A; Sargent HS; Sargent, NE; Band; Chrs; ChrhWkr; NHS; NatlThespSoc; SchMus; YthFlsp; FBLA; Bsbl; CaptBsktbl; LetterFtbl; Glf; LetterTrk; College; Professional.

TINNES, Carmel L; Oslo HS; Oslo, MN; 5/47 Band; Chrs; ChrhWkr; SchPl; StuCncl; RptrSchPpr; Pres4-H; SciCl; DARAwd; 4-HAwd; Moorhead State U; Biomedical Research.

TINNON, Brenda K; East Prairie HS; East Prairie, MO; 10/84 SecTrsSrCls; CncrtBnd; DrmMjrt; HonRl; MrchBnd; NHS; SchPl; SctActv; StuCncl; RptrSchPpr; FHA; College.

TINOCO, Josephine; St Marys HS; Chicago, IL; PresSrCls; Chr; Chrs; CmntyWkr; HonRl; StuCncl; StuGov; RptrSchPpr; LatCl; SpnCl; College; Pre Law.

TINSLEY, Katherine A; Pike HS; Indianapolis, IN; 18/238 Chr; HonRl; HospAde; JrNHS; SecNHS; NatlMeritSF; NatlThespSoc; SchMus; SchPl; TchrAde; VPYthFlsp; VPFrCl; DARAwd; Univ; Physician.

TINSLEY, Shirley A; Fredericktown HS; Fredericktown, MO; CmntyWkr; HonRl; NHS; Yrbk; SchPpr; PpCl; Mineral Area Jr Col.

TINSMAN, Paul R; Lakeview HS; St Clair Shores, MI; ChrhWkr; HonRl; SctActv; StuCncl; Bsktbl; LetterTennis; CchngActv; IMSpt; University; Oceanography.

TIPPEY, Crystal J; Canton Sr HS; Canton, IL; 1/266 Band; ChrhWkr; CmntyWkr; HonRl; NHS; SchPl; RptrSchPpr; EdSchPpr; SpnCl; SecSciCl; Univ Of Iowa; Medicine.

TIPPIN, James H; North Putnam HS; Greencastle, IN; Chr; SchMus; SchPl; SctActv; StuCncl; RptrSchPpr; LetterFtbl; Trk; LetterWrstlng; IMSpt; Indiana Univ; Mathematics Teacher.

TIPPIN, Larry D; North Putnam HS; Bainbridge, IN; HonRl; SchMus; 4-H; FFA; SpnCl; MthCl; PpCl; SciCl; LetterFtbl; LetterTrk; LetterWrstlng; IMSpt;.

TIPPIT, Stephen L; Charleston HS; Charleston, IL; 17/239 Band; ChrhWkr; CncrtBnd; HonRl; MrchBnd; NHS; PepBnd; Yrbk; VPFTA; SpnCl; University; Business.

TIPPS, Velanne C; Crystal Lk Community HS; Crystal Lake, IL; 8/475 Band; Chr; HonRl; MrchBnd; NHS; Orch; FTA; TreasFrCl; Ill St U; Music.

TIPSWARD, Joyce M; Southwestern HS; Brighton, IL; 31/173 ChrhWkr; HonRl; HospAde; VPJA; LbryAde; TchrAde; EdYrBk; SchPpr; BttyCrckrAwd; JAAwd; Lewis & Clark Clg; Banking & Finance.

TIPSWORD, Gary; United Township Hs; Silvis, IL; 47/517 Chr; Chrl; Chrs; HonRl; Mdrgl; SchAde; SchMus; College; Medical Technology.

TIPTON, Jerry R; Union County HS; Liberty, IN; ALBoysSt; HonRl;.

TIPTON, Mary A; Roosevelt HS; Gary, IN; HonRl; OffAde; SchPl; Indiana Univ; Professional.

TIPTON, Samuel E; Hobart HS; Hobart, IN; 119/380 ChrhWkr; HonRl; StuCncl; StuGov; SciCl; Perdue Univ; Engineering.

TIREY, Cindy A; Mitchell HS; Mitchell, IN; 6/120 ALAGirlsSt; DrlTm; HonRl; SecNHS; SchMus; ChrhWkr; Sec4-H; FHA; GAA; AmLegAwd; Indiana U; Elem Ed.

TIREY, Kathy J; Mitchell HS; Mitchell, IN; 28/169 Chrs; HonRl; NHS; OffAde; SchPpr; 4-H; PpCl; 4-HAwd; Trade Sch; Professional.

TISCHER, Candace A; St John Cathedral HS; Milwaukee, WI; Band; Chr; MrchBnd; SchMus; StuCncl; TchrAde; RptrSchPpr; SpnCl; Matc; Marines Accountanting.

TISCHER, June M; Lockport Central HS; Lockport, IL; 56/540 HonRl; NHS; SecTrsSophCls; LetterGAA;.

TISCHER, Linda M; Wellcome Memorial HS; Good Thunder, MN; 9/43 Chrs; CncrtBnd; DrlTm; PepBnd; SchPl; TchrAde; RptrYrbk; EdSchPpr; PresFHA; Trk; Dr Martin Luther College; Elem Education.

TISCHER, Steve G; Whitnall HS; Franklin, WI; VPJrCls; HonRl; ModUN; SctActv; StuCncl; Bsktbl; Ftbl; Glf; CchngActv; IMSpt; College; Engineering.

TISDALE, Darla; Fox Valley Hs; Milton, IA; 2/17 PresFrshCls; TrsJrCls; Band; Chrs; HonRl; NHS; Yrbk; 4-H; LetterBsktbl; 4-HAwd;.

TISDALE, Mary D; St Thomas HS; St Thomas, ND; SecSophCls; ALAGirlsSt; Chrs; HonRl; HospAde; SchPl; EdSchPpr; GAA; PPFtbl; Wahpeton St Sch Of Sci; Nursing.

TISDALE, Peggy; Saugatuck HS; Douglas, MI; SecTrsFrshCls; Band; Chrs; HonRl; MrchBnd; OffAde; StuCncl; RptrYrbk; Yrbk; Bsktbl;.

TISH, Martin H; Niles Township East HS; Skokie, IL; HonRl; NHS; NatlMeritCmnd; FrCl; Clge; Pre/law.

TISHENDORF, Janet G; Chappell HS; Chappell, NE; 1/29 TrsJrCls; Band; Chr; Chrs; ChrhWkr; CmntyWkr; CncrtBnd; HonRl; JrNHS; Mdrgl; University Of Nebr; English Teacher.

TISINGER, Thomas W; Durant Community HS; Durant, IA; 1/70 PresFrshCls; PresSrCls; HonRl; JrNHS; NHS; NatlMeritSF; SchMus; SchPl; SctActv; StuCncl; RptrSchPpr; EdSchPpr; SchPpr; Bsktbl;.

TISINGER, Thomas W; Durant Comm HS; Durant, IA; 1/68 PresFrshCls; PresSrCls; Chrs; HonRl; JrNHS; NHS; NatlMeritSF; SchMus; SchPl; SctActv; StuCncl; RptrSchPpr; EdSchPpr; SptEdSchPpr; LetterBsktbl; College; Aviation.

TISLOW, Gregory L; Sullivan HS; Carlisle, IN; 13/154 HonRl; ModUN; KeyCl; PresSpnCl; Univ; Architect.

TITEL, Lisa M; Wrightstown HS; Wrightstown, WI; SecSrCls; ALAGirlsSt; Band; DrlTm; RptrSchPpr; Bsktbl; Trk; Chrldr; GAA; College; Nursing.

TITERA, Kenneth J; Ladysmith HS; Ladysmith, WI; 13/132 VPSophCls; ALBoysSt; HonRl; NHS; RptrSchPpr; LetterBsbl;.

TITHERAGE, Steve C; Holly HS; Holly, MI; 19/250 TrsFrshCls; NHS; RptrSchPpr; FTA; SpnCl; Bsktbl; Ftbl; Wrstlng; IMSpt; JCAwd; College; Broadcasting.

TITLER, Debbie L; Morley Stonwood HS; Big Rapids, MI; Band; HonRl; SchMus; SchPl; TchrAde; SchPpr; FBLA; Trk; IMSpt; 4-HAwd; Mercy Sch Of Nursing; Nurse.

TITTEL, Colleen J; Alliance HS; Alliance, NE; 7/150 HonRl; GerCl; PpCl; College.

TITTLE, James F; Central HS; Red Wing, MN; PresSrCls; AFS; CncrtBnd; HospAde; NHS; NatlMeritCmnd; NatlThespSoc; YthLg; Yrbk; SchPpr; College; Communications.

TITUS, Jay L; Enderlin HS; Enderlin, ND; 7/44 Band; Chr; CncrtBnd; PepBnd; SchMus; KeyCl; Trade School; Computer Programming.

TITUS, Leslie A; Okabena HS; Okabena, MN; Band; Chrs; HonRl; NHS; YthFlsp; RptrYrbk; Yrbk; Pres4-H; 4-HAwd; College; Graphic Communications.

TITUS, Robert D; Midland HS; Midland, MI; 25/430 Band; ChrhWkr; CncrtBnd; HonRl; MrchBnd; Orch; Hope College; Medicine.

TITUS, Veda R; West Side HS; Gary, IN; Band; CncrtBnd; HonRl; LbryAde; MrchBnd; Orch; Trade School; Modeling.

TITZER, Demara J; North HS; Evansville, IN; 97/440 ChrhWkr; HonRl; SchMus; SchPl; PPFtbl; In Univ Bloomington; Bus Admin.

TITZER, Kimberly D; Gibson Southern HS; Fort Branch, IN; Chrs; OffAde; SchPl; EdSchPpr; FHA; PpCl; Secretary/clerical.

TIWALD, Suzanne M; Mercy HS; Omaha, NE; Chr; CmntyWkr; JA; RedCrAde; SchMus; SchPl; Sdlty; FrCl; SciCl; GAA; Creighton U; Radiologia Technology.

TJADEN, Lisa M; Roanoke Benson HS; Roanoke, IL; 7/92 Band; Chrs; CncrtBnd; HonRl; IntrClCncl; MrchBnd; NHS; Yrbk; GAA; IMSpt; Coll; Art.

TJARKS, Timothy W; Missouri Valley HS; Missouri Valley, IA; 1/100 ALBoysSt; PresBand; ChrhWkr; HonRl; NHS; PepBnd; SchMus; YthFlsp; PresFTA; SecKeyCl; Ia St Univ; Math.

TLAMKA, Ron R; Scotus Central Catholic HS; Columbus, NE; Chrs; HonRl; PolWkr; LetterFtbl; Trk; College; Professional.

TLUSTOS, Deborah K; Louisville HS; South Bend, NE; 5/38 TrsSophCls; PresJrCls; PresSrCls; HonRl; NHS; RptrYrbk; PresFHA; FrCl; PpCl; Chrldr; College; Nursing.

TOADER, Adrian; Lincoln Park HS; Lincoln Park, MI; 3/580 NHS; NatlMeritSchl; TchrAde; Wayne St University; Electrical Engineer.

TOALSON, Larry D; Hallsville HS; Hallsville, MO; SctActv; StuCncl; Bsbl; College; Professional.

TOBEN, Cynthia; Akron Community HS; Akron, IA; 1/60 SecTrsFrshCls; SecTrsSophCls; Band; HonRl; HospAde; NHS; StuCncl; 4-H; Bsktbl; Trk; College; Education.

TOBEN, Cynthia L; Akron Community HS; Akron, IA; 1/60 ALAGirlsSt; Band; Chr; Chrs; ChrhWkr; CmntyWkr; CncrtBnd; HospAde; NHS; StuCncl; Bsktbl; College; Secretary.

TOBERMAN, Terri L; Harold L Richards HS; Alsip, IL; 81/1196 CmntyWkr; HonRl; JrNHS; MrchBnd; NHS; TchrAde; SchPpr; SpnCl; GAA; College; Phsical Educ.

TOBEY, Christine E; Corunna HS; Corunna, MI; 8/209 HonRl; JA; LbryAde; OffAde; SchMus; TchrAde; PpCl; Mi State Univ; Pre Medical.

TOBEY, Kurt E; Gresham Public HS; Gresham, NE; VPFrshCls; TrsJrCls; Chrs; CmntyWkr; StuCncl; 4-H; Bsbl; Bsktbl; LetterTrk; Professional Baseball.

TOBIAS, Audrey F; Northwood HS; Nappanee, IN; 7/195 ALAGirlsSt; HonRl; LbryAde; NHS; Teen; YthFlsp; PpCl; College; Math And Science.

TOBIAS, Betsy A; William Horlick HS; Racine, WI; 9/603 HonRl; NatlMeritCmnd; NatlMeritSF; Orch; SchMus; SchPl; Chrldr; IMSpt; University.

TOBIAS, Richard L; Buena Vista HS; Saginaw, MI; ChrhWkr; HonRl; SchPl; SctActv; PpCl; Wrstlng; Delta College; Auto Service Tec.

TOBIASON, Laurie; Adrian Public HS; Magnolia, MN; Band; Chr; CncrtBnd; HonRl; LbryAde; MrchBnd; NHS; PepBnd; Pepestone Area Voc Tech; Accounting.

TOBIN, Anthony K; Maryville Rii HS; Maryville, MO; Ftbl; Wrstlng;.

TOBIN, David M; Flint Central HS; Flint, MI; 21/450 HonRl; NHS; SchAde; TchrAde; Central Michigan Univ; Teaching.

TOBIN, Elizabeth E; Rich South HS; Park Forest, IL; HonRl; NHS; LatCl; PpCl; Chrldr;.

TOBIN, Jane; Wabeno HS; Wabeno, WI; 6/36 VPJrCls; ALAGirlsSt; Chrs; HonRl; SchPl; EdYrBk; Chrldr; DARAwd; Univ; Criminal Justice.

TOBIN, John M; W Nodaway R 1 HS; Burlington Jct, MO; 1/45 PresSophCls; PresJrCls; CncrtBnd; HonRl; MrchBnd; NHS; SchPl; KeyCl; LetterBsktbl; LetterTrk; Univ Of Missouri; Science.

TOBIN, John M; West Nodaway R 1 HS; Burlington Jct, MO; 1/45 PresSophCls; PresJrCls; Band; CncrtBnd; HonRl; MrchBnd; NHS; SchPl; LetterBsktbl; LetterTrk; U Of Mo; Medicine.

TOBIN, Margaret A; Acad Of Our Lady; Chicago, IL; 1/189 NHS; SchAde; SchMus; SchPl; StuCncl; StuGov; SpnCl; MthCl; PpCl; Tennis;.

TOBIN, Michael K; Pike HS; Indianapolis, IN; 46/238 NHS; LetterBsbl; Bsktbl; IMSpt; Purdue Univ; Meteorology.

TOBIN, Terrence M; New Market Community HS; New Market, IA; 1/21 ALBoysSt; HonRl; NHS; SchPl; StuCncl; RptrSchPpr; FFA; Bsbl; CaptBsktbl; CaptFtbl; Ia State Univ; Law.

TOBIN, Thomas M; Shawnee Mission West HS; Overland Park, KS; 3/603 HonRl; NHS; NatlMeritCmnd; StuCncl; StuGov; LetterTrk; IMSpt; Stanford Univ; Electrical Engineering.

TOBLER, Jane E; Olathe HS; Olathe, KS; VPJrCls; TrsSrCls; AFS; Band; CncrtBnd; DrlTm; HonRl; JrNHS; MrchBnd; Chrldr; College.

TOBUREN, Amy E; Wausau East HS; Wausau, WI; NatlFornLg; NHS; Orch; Quill&Scroll; RptrYrbk; Yrbk; RptrSchPpr; SchPpr; MthCl; Univ Of Wisconsin; Law.

TOBUREN, Jacqueline; Clay Center Community HS; Clay Center, KS; 40/127 HonRl; OffAde; SchPl; SctActv; PpCl; LetterTrk; Coll; Phys Educ.

TOBUREN, Theodore L; Geneva HS; Geneva, IL; 32/228 HonRl; SchAde; SchPl; StuCncl; StuGov; Bsbl; Bsktbl; Colorado State Univ; Vet Medicine.

TOBYNE, Arlis E; Clifton HS; Clifton, KS; 1/25 Band; Chrl; HonRl; SchPl; StuCncl; EdYrBk; FHA; PpCl; LetterTrk; Chrldr; PPFtbl; 4-HAwd; College.

TODAHL, Kristi B; Leeds Public HS; Leeds, ND; ALAGirlsSt; Band; Chr; ChrhWkr; CmntyWkr; CncrtBnd; HonRl; MrchBnd; PepBnd; FHA; College; Professional.

TODD, Carolyn M; Holstein Community HS; Holstein, IA; 2/55 Chrs; ChrhWkr; HonRl; LbryAde; NHS; OffAde; TchrAde; Yrbk; SchPpr; Wester Iowa Tech; Medical Secretary.

TODD, Craig W; Woodward Granger HS; Woodward, IA; 4/54 VPSophCls; ALBoysSt; Band; HonRl; NHS; PepBnd; SchPl; StuGov; RptrYrbk; MthCl; Univ Of N Ia; Musician.

TODD, Daniel L; Washington HS; South Bend, IN; HonRl; JrNHS; NHS; NatlMeritCmnd; LatCl; MthCl; SciCl; ChmbCommrsAwd; GovHonPrgAwd; Indiana Univ; Computer Tech.

TODD, Donald; Golden City HS; Lamar, MO; .

TODD, Jane B; Plattsmouth HS; Union, NE; 1/138 TrsFrshCls; NatlMeritCmnd; StuCncl; EdYrBk; Pres4-H; Trk; PPFtbl; DARAwd; 4-HAwd; CitAwd; Univ Of Nebraska; Journalism.

TODD, Jonathan L; Sunshine Bible Academy; Onida, SD; 3/27 PresJrCls; ALBoysSt; IMSpt; College; Agriculture.

TODD, Mary K; Atchison HS; Atchison, KS; 3/184 PresFrshCls; AFS; ChrhWkr; HonRl; PresNHS; SchPl; EdSchPpr; SpnCl; LetterTrk; Chrldr; BttyCrckrAwd; Kansas St U; Prof Of Psychology.

TODD, Michael W; University City Sr HS; University City, MO; JA; NatlMeritCmnd; SctActv; Yrbk; Univ Mo; Nuclear Physics.

TODD, Richard A; Maple Valley HS; Vermontville, MI; 4/108 VPJrCls; ALBoysSt; ChrhWkr; HonRl; NHS; Ftbl; Trk; Mi St Univ; Electrical Engineer.

TODD, Samuel J; North Montgomery HS; Crawfordsville, IN; 26/214 Chr; ChrhWkr; HonRl; NatlFornLg; NHS; SchMus; SchPl; Pres4-H; PresFFA; PresSpnCl; Purdue University; Pre Veterinary Science.

TODD, Susan A; Civic Memorial HS; Bethalto, IL; HonRl; LbryAde; NHS; SctActv; TchrAde; RptrSchPpr; PpCl; College; Journalism.

TODEY, Lawrence M; Centerville HS; Rathbun, IA; Aud/Vis; HonRl; NHS; StuCncl; LetterFtbl; Trk; LetterWrstlng; Trade School; Electronics.

TODHUNTER, Laura; New Trier East HS; Winnetka, IL; Chr; Chrs; Orch; Indiana Univ; Singer.

TODOROFSKY, Irwin M; Homewood Flossmoor HS; Chicago Hts, IL; PresSrCls; CtyCnl; CAP; CmntyWkr; ROTC; FBLA; CchngActv; IMSpt; AmLegAwd; GovHonPrgAwd; JCAwd; Univ Of Illinois; Pilot.

TODT, Karen E; Brighton HS; Brighton, MI; 3/287 Band; Chr; HonRl; JrNHS; Mdrgl; MrchBnd; NHS; NatlThespSoc; SchMus; Univ Of Michigan; Medicine.

TOEPFER, Beverly L; Blue Hill HS; Blue Hill, NE; Band; Chr; Chrs; ChrhWkr; CncrtBnd; DrlTm; MrchBnd; PepBnd; SchPl; RptrYrbk; RptrSchPpr; 4-H; FHA; LetterTrk; Kearney State College; Teacher.

TOEVS, Richard; Remington HS; Whitewater, KS; 2/55 PresJrCls; PresSrCls; ALBoysSt; Chr; ChrhWkr; CncrtBnd; NHS; SchMus; YthFlsp; 4-H; College.

TOEWS, Bonnie G; Cumberland HS; Cumberland, WI; 1/126 ChrhWkr; HonRl; StuCncl; TreasFNA;.

TOFIL, Cynthia L; Ladywood St Agnes HS; Indianapolis, IN; Chrs; HonRl; Mdrgl; SchMus; TchrAde; Trk; Chrldr; GAA; Ball State Univ; Physical Therapy.

TOFT, Andrew M; Lyons Twp HS; Western Springs, IL; Chr; HonRl; StuGov; GerCl; Trk; Univ Of Nebraska; Business Admin.

TOGIKAWA, Jean Y; Woodruff HS; Peoria, IL; 1/281 AFS; HonRl; Orch; SchMus; SctActv; TchrAde; FrCl; GerCl; College; Scientific Research.

TOIVONEN, Karen M; Ontonagon Area HS; Mass, MI; ALAGirlsSt; ChrhWkr; HonRl; NHS; RptrSchPpr; LetterBsktbl; LetterTrk; CaptChrldr; PresGAA; 4-HAwd; College; Court Reporting.

TOKAR, Susan D; Mattoon Senior HS; Mattoon, IL; AFS; Chrs; HonRl; JA; NHS; SecStuCncl; PpCl; SciCl; CaptChrldr; Purdue Univ; Major Study.

TOKAR, Thomas F; Goshen HS; Goshen, IN; 5/263 HonRl; PresNHS; NatlMeritFnl; NatlMeritSchl; NatlMeritSF; SchPl; SecSciCl; Rose Hulman Inst; Mathematics.

TOKARZ, Cheryl A; Elgin HS; Streamwood, IL; 35/750 SecSophCls; Chr; StuCncl; StuGov; PresSpnCl; PpCl; CchngActv; GAA; IMSpt; N Illinois Univ; Nursing.

TOKUHISA, James G; Maine West HS; Des Plaines, IL; TrsJrCls; Band; HonRl; TreasJA; StuCncl; YthFlsp; SciCl; DARAwd; Univ Of Ill; Biology.

TOLAN, Juliana E; West Depere HS; De Pere, WI; ChrhWkr; CmntyWkr; HonRl; NHS; StuCncl; TchrAde; FTA; LetterTrk; LetterChrldr; IMSpt; Technical School; Lpn.

TOLAN, Mark E; Griffin HS; Springfield, IL; HonRl; StuCncl; Glf; Illinois State University.

TOLAR, John W; Homewood Flossmoor HS; Homewood, IL; 23/900 Chr; Chrs; HonRl; NHS; GerCl; Univ Of Ill; Business Admin Accounting.

TOLBERT, Carol L; Okemos HS; Okemos, MI; 22/265 Chr; ChrhWkr; Mdrgl; NHS; SchMus; Michigan State Univ.

TOLBERT, Larry B; Switz Co HS; Vevay, IN; HonRl; SchPl; SctActv; TchrAde; FFA; SpnCl; PpCl; IMSpt; Bus School.

TOLBERT, Vickie; Gideon HS; Gideon, MO; Band; CncrtBnd; HonRl; MrchBnd; PepBnd; FHA; PpCl; Chrldr; Business School.

TOLIVER, Cathy S; Marshall HS; Marshall, IL; 2/115 Band; CncrtBnd; MrchBnd; NHS; PepBnd; YthFlsp; FHA; FTA; SpnCl; In State U; Rn.

TOLL, Marvin D; Prospect HS; Mt Prospect, IL; 56/610 Chrs; ChrhWkr; CncrtBnd; HonRl; MrchBnd; NHS; PepBnd; SchAde; SchMus; Univ Of Ill; Music.

TOLL, Sheila A; Winnebago Luth Acad; Fon Du Lac, WI; SecSrCls; Band; Chr; Chrs; MrchBnd; SchPl; Yrbk; RptrSchPpr; PpCl; Bsktbl;.

TOLLAS, Michael A; Lakeshore HS; Stevensville, MI; PresChr; HonRl; NatlThespSoc; SchMus; SchPl; RptrYrbk; TreasYrbk; RptrSchPpr; TreasSchPpr; LetterTrk; Northern Mich Univ; Oceanography.

TOLLEFSON, Lori A; Columbus HS; Marshfield, WI; 35/114 Chr; Chrs; HonRl; RptrSchPpr; FrCl; PpCl; University; Nursing.

TOLLEFSON, Tamara; Eleva Strum Central HS; Eleva, WI; 22/72 SecSrCls; NatlFornLg; SchAde; SchPl; StuCncl; YthFlsp; RptrYrbk; Trk; Chrldr; GAA; Vocational; Secretarial.

TOLLETT, Melissa D; North Platte HS; North Platte, NE; Chrs; ChrhWkr; HospAde; SchPl; SctActv; TchrAde; PpCl; GAA; IMSpt; PPFtbl; College; Physical Therapist.

TOLLIVER, Kevin L; John Pershing HS; Detroit, MI; 4/140 ChrhWkr; HonRl; NHS; NatlMeritCmnd; BauchLmbAwd; Mich State U; Professional Engineer.

TOLO, Susan M; Wahpeton HS; Wahpeton, ND; AFS; Band; ChrhWkr; CncrtBnd; MrchBnd; SchPl; RptrYrbk; PpCl; GAA; Nd State Schl Of Sci.

TOLSTEDT, Brad L; Gordon HS; Gordon, NE; JA; SchAde; SctActv; StuGov; TchrAde; YthFlsp; LetterFtbl; LetterGlf; LetterWrstlng; University; Professional.

TOLTON, James R; Independent 114 HS; Midland, SD; PresFrshCls; PresSophCls; Chrs; ChrhWkr; HonRl; SchMus; SchPl; StuCncl; RptrYrbk; RptrSchPpr; 4-H; LetterBsktbl; LetterFtbl; LetterTrk; Univ.

TOMAC, Charles A; Mcintosh HS; Watauga, SD; PresSrCls; ALBoysSt; HonRl; SchPl; StuCncl; Yrbk; FHA; LetterFtbl; LetterTrk; CchngActv; Nd State Univ; Communications.

TOMAC, Randy; Carson City HS; Hubbardston, MI; HonRl; SchAde; StuCncl; TchrAde; RptrSchPpr; EdSchPpr; OptClAwd; Armed Services; Ind Const.

TOMAKA, John; Thornton Fractional North Hs; Burnham, IL; 31/435 HonRl; SctActv; Wrstlng; College; Computer Science.

TOMAN, Marshall B; St Thomas Acad; Minneapolis, MN; 10/100 DrlTm; HonRl; NatlMeritCmnd; ROTC; SctActv; EdYrBk; RptrSchPpr; LetterTennis; SciCl; IMSpt; St Thomas Coll; Law.

TOMAN, Susan L; Muskegon HS; Muskegon, MI; 16/458 Band; ChrhWkr; HonRl; MrchBnd; NHS; NatlMeritCmnd; PepBnd; StuCncl; FrCl; Univ Of Mi; Pre Medical.

TOMARO, Dianne M; St Mary Academy; Monroe, MI; HonRl; JA; NHS; NatlMeritCmnd; VPStuCncl; Bsbl; LetterBsktbl; VPGAA; IMSpt; Univ Of Michigan; Medical Technologist.

TOMARS, John R; Cretin HS; St Paul, MN; 8/208 PresSrCls; HonRl; LitMag; NatlMeritSF; PolWkr; ROTC; StuCncl; StuGov; LetterTrk; IMSpt; Coll; Social Work.

TOMASH, David R; Prairie HS; Swisher, IA; Band; CncrtBnd; HonRl; JrNHS; MrchBnd; PepBnd; RptrSchPpr; Univ; Vocation.

TOMASI, Anthony J; Norway HS; Norway, MI; 17/115 ChrhWkr; HonRl; StuGov; Bsktbl; LetterFtbl; Trk; IMSpt; College; Professional.

TOMASIK, Mark S; Maine East HS; Park Ridge, IL; HonRl; Trk; College; Professional.

TOMASINO, Cheryl L; Corunna HS; Corunna, MI; Band; ChrhWkr; CmntyWkr; CncrtBnd; HonRl; MrchBnd; TchrAde; College; Teaching.

TOMASOSKI, Robert J; West Iron County HS; Gaastra, MI; 5/178 PresJrCls; CncrtBnd; HonRl; MrchBnd; NHS; NatlMeritSF; RptrYrbk; Bsbl; Bsktbl; CaptFtbl; Mi Tech Univ; Chemestry Major.

TOMASSI, Roberto A; Fordson HS; Dearborn, MI; CncrtBnd; HonRl; MrchBnd; NHS; IMSpt; Henry Ford Comm Clge; Mech Eng.

TOMASZCZYK, Kenneth B; Bishop Borgess HS; Detroit, MI; 20/450 HonRl; NatlFornLg; NHS; SctActv; Univ Of Mi; Medicine.

TOMASZEK, Cynthia A; Marquette HS; Michigan City, IN; SecSophCls; Chr; HonRl; NHS; Quill&Scroll; SchMus; EdSchPpr; SpnCl; GAA; St Marys Clg; Social Work.

TOMASZEWSKI, Diane M; Crivitz HS; Crivitz, WI; 13/70 ALAGirlsSt; HonRl; NHS; TchrAde; CaptBsbl; Glf; Chrldr; DARAwd; Univ Of Wisconsin; Special Education.

TOMASZEWSKI, Randy L; Lasalle Peru Twp HS; Peru, IL; 17/516 Aud/Vis; ChrhWkr; CtyCnl; HonRl; LitMag; LbryAde; NHS; NatlMeritFnl; TchrAde; RptrSchPpr; LatCl; SciCl; Univ; Science.

TOMCALA, Karen A; Flushing HS; Flusing, MI; 23/445 PresChr; HonRl; VPNHS; VPNatlThespSoc; SchMus; SchPl; U Of Mi Ann Arbor.

TOMCZAK, Ellen; Lourdes HS; Chicago, IL; 12/299 HonRl; IMSpt; U Of Il Urbana; Computer Programming.

TOMCZAK, John G; York HS; Elmhurst, IL; HonRl; NHS; College; Accounting.

TOMCZAK, Patricia A; Osborn HS; Detroit, MI; 120/630 TchrAde; Wayne State U.

TOMCZYK, Marsha; Lumen Christi HS; Jackson, MI; CmntyWkr; HonRl; NHS; NatlMeritCmnd; OffAde; RedCrAde; StuCncl; StuGov; PpCl; IMSpt; Mich State Univ; Social Work.

TOMECEK, Frank; Otis Bison Senior HS; Timken, KS; ChrhWkr; HonRl; NHS; StuCncl; College; Accounting.

TOMENELLO, Maria E; Regina HS; East Detroit, MI; HonRl; NHS; SecNatlThespSoc; SchMus; SchPl; StuCncl; FHA; PresFNA; MthCl; Tennis; Mercy College Of Detroit; Nursing.

TOMER, Carol J; Maine South HS; Park Ridge, IL; Band; Chrs; CncrtBnd; HonRl; MrchBnd; NHS; NatlMeritCmnd; Orch; Quill&Scroll; TreasStuCncl; Tennis; GAA; College; Doctor.

TOMES, Kathy M; Eastern HS; Salem, IN; 12/76 ChrhWkr; HonRl; NHS; SchPl; TchrAde; RptrYrbk; Yrbk; PpCl; In Central Univ; Rn.

TOMES, Patricia A; Eastern HS; Salem, IN; Band; ChrhWkr; HonRl; HospAde; 4-H; PpCl; GAA; 4-HAwd;.

TOMETICH, John J; Muscatine HS; Muscatine, IA; 49/375 VPJrCls; VPSrCls; ALBoysSt; StuCncl; 4-H; CaptFtbl; AmLegAwd; 4-HAwd; RotaryAwd; Creighton Univ; Medicine.

TOMETICH, Timothy D; Centerville HS; Numa, IA; Band; Chrs; ChrhWkr; CncrtBnd; HonRl; MrchBnd; NHS; Ftbl; LetterTrk; Wrstlng; College; Professional.

TOMFELD, Deborah M; Grinnell Community HS; Grinnell, IA; 5/189 HonRl; ModUN; NHS; OffAde; IMSpt; Clge; Prof.

TOMINAC, Karen S; De Tour Area HS; Goetzville, MI; 1/48 TrsFrshCls; SecSophCls; Chr; HonRl; VPNHS; Yrbk; 4-H; Trk; Chrldr; 4-HAwd; Northern Mi Univ; Business.

TOMKINS, Mitchell B; Westport HS; Kansas City, MO; 13/173 ALBoysSt; HonRl; NHS; Quill&Scroll; SchPl; StuCncl; StuGov; RptrYrbk; RptrSchPpr; FTA; PresGerCl; College; Christian Counseling.

TOMKO, Kender T; Hinsdale Twp Central HS; Hinsdale, IL; ChrhWkr; CncrtBnd; HonRl; NatlMeritSF; StuCncl;.

TOMKOVICH, Edward J; North Chicago Comm HS; North Chicago, IL; 14/356 ChrhWkr; CmntyWkr; HonRl; NHS; SctActv; TchrAde; LetterBsktbl; LetterGlf; GodCntryAwd; CitAwd; Miami Univ; Business Admin.

TOMLIN, Diane J; Cambridge Public HS; Cambridge, NE; Band; CncrtBnd; MrchBnd; PepBnd; SchPl; StuCncl; YthFlsp; TreasFBLA; PpCl; Chrldr; College.

TOMLIN, Jeffrey M; Moline Sr HS; Moline, IL; 1/830 CncrtBnd; LitMag; NHS; Orch; StuCncl; StuGov; LatCl; SciCl; Bsktbl; College; Natural Science.

TOMLIN, Steven; Easton HS; Mason City, IL; 11/20 CncrtBnd; HonRl; MrchBnd; PepBnd; SchPl; StuCncl; YthFlsp; RptrSchPpr; FFA; Bsktbl; Agri.

TOMLINS, Patricia A; Churubusco HS; Churubusco, IN; TrsJrCls; VPSrCls; JrNHS; SchPl; FHA; FNA; PpCl; BttyCrckrAwd; In State U;.

TOMLINSON, Brian L; North Polk Comm HS; Bondurant, IA; 7/60 PresFrshCls; ALBoysSt; Band; CncrtBnd; HonRl; MrchBnd; PepBnd; SchMus; StuCncl; LetterFtbl; LetterTrk; LetterWrstlng; AmLegAwd; College; Engineering.

TOMLINSON, Evelyn K; Pekin Comm HS; Pekin, IL; 7/759 ChrhWkr; HonRl; NHS; Bsktbl; College.

TOMLINSON, Joy A; Academy Of The Sacred Heart; Birmingham, MI; PresJrCls; PresSrCls; ModUN; NHS; StuGov; Yrbk; Swmmng; Tennis; Univ Of Michigan; Business.

TOMLINSON, Martha E; Macon HS; Macon, IL; 6/56 VPJrCls; HonRl; HospAde; NHS; StuCncl; SptEdSchPpr; SpnCl; SecPpCl; Chrldr; GAA; Illinois Wesleyan Univ; Nursing.

TOMLINSON, Teresa E; Cowden Herrick HS; Lakewood, IL; SecFrshCls; HonRl; HospAde; SchPl; Yrbk; PpCl; LetterTrk; Chrldr; GAA; College; Vocational.

TOMLINSON, Virginia M; North Huron HS; Kinde, MI; 5/45 TrsFrshCls; PresJrCls; SecSrCls; Band; HonRl; NHS; StuCncl; Yrbk; 4-H; LetterBsktbl; LetterTrk; LetterChrldr; GAA; Mich State Univ; Animal Husbandry.

TOMLONSON, Janet R; Kalamazoo Central HS; Kalamazoo, MI; Band; ChrhWkr; CncrtBnd; MrchBnd; Orch; Quill&Scroll; SchMus; SchPpr; Manchester Clg; English.

TOMMER, Mary; Kinsley HS; Kinsley, KS; 3/73 SecJrCls; Band; CncrtBnd; HonRl; NHS; RptrSchPpr; PpCl; Chrldr; Hutchinson Comm Jr Coll; Nursing.

TOMOVICH, Nicholas; George Washington HS; Chicago, IL; 8/481 HonRl; NHS; TchrAde; PresJETSAwd; Univ Of Illinois; Elec Engineer.

TOMPKINS, Chauncey T; Midland Comm HS; Wyoming, IA; TrsFrshCls; VPJrCls; PresSrCls; HonRl; 4-H; LetterFtbl; LetterWrstlng; 4-HAwd; College; Professional.

TOMPKINS, Jacqueline A; Mullinville HS; Ford, KS; 3/13 VPSrCls; Aud/Vis; Chrs; CAP; CncrtBnd; SchMus; SchPl; Yrbk; FSA; Kansas State University; Chemical Engineer.

TOMPKINS, Mary J; Mc Cook Senior HS; Mc Cook, NE; ChrhWkr; CmntyWkr; HonRl; LbryAde; SctActv; TchrAde; YthFlsp; 4-H; FTA; University; Professional.

TOMS, Terri D; Benton HS; Benton, IL; 4/185 Chrs; ChrhWkr; HonRl; LbryAde; NHS; SchMus; SpnCl; AmLegAwd; LionAwd; Rend Lake Coll; Business.

TOMSHEPPARD, Thomas A; Pittsfield HS; Pittsfield, IL; 42/129 Band; ChrhWkr; CncrtBnd; HonRl; MrchBnd; PepBnd; 4-H; FFA; FTA; KeyCl; LatCl; Trade School; Vocation.

TOMSON, Debra J; North Miami HS; Denver, IN; 3/120 ALAGirlsSt; Band; HonRl; NHS; YthFlsp; 4-H; SpnCl; CaptChrldr; IMSpt; PPFtbl; 4-HAwd; CitAwd; Ball State; Business Teacher.

TOMSOVIC, Nancy L; Cumberland HS; Comstock, WI; 8/124 HonRl; Pres4-H; FHA; PpCl; Trk; 4-HAwd; Voc Sch; Police Work.

TONDA, Julie A; Knoxville HS; Knoxville, IA; 19/177 SecJrCls; Chr; Chrs; HonRl; ModUN; PolWkr; SchPl; Teen; DARAwd; American Inst Of Business; Court Reporting.

TONDERUM, Paul H; Maquoketa Community HS; Delmar, IA; 3/145 HonRl; ModUN; NatlMeritCmnd; SchPl; 4-H; FFA; 4-HAwd; College; Production Agriculture.

TONELLO, Darlene I; Regina HS; St Clair Shores, MI; ChrhWkr; HonRl; LitMag; SchMus; RptrSchPpr; Trk; GAA; PPFtbl; Oakland Univ; Environmental Health.

TONER, Lisa R; Dixon HS; Dixon, MO; 7/65 Band; Chr; ChrhWkr; CncrtBnd; HonRl; MrchBnd; NHS; PepBnd; SchMus; StuCncl; University; Teacher.

TONG, Andrew B; E T H S Beardsley HS; Chicago, IL; 264/1200 HonRl; IntrClCncl; SctActv; YthFnd; FDA; Univ Of Il; Science.

TONGEN, Keith O; Brownton Public HS; Brownton, MN; TrsSophCls; PresJrCls; ChrhWkr; HonRl; SchPl; SctActv; StuCncl; StuGov; FFA; LetterWrstlng; Farm.

TONIA, Linda J; Lancaster HS; Lancaster, MN; SecSrCls; HonRl; LbryAde; OffAde; SchAde; SchPl; YthFlsp; Bemidji State Univ; Community Service.

TONIES, Rose M; O Fallon Twp HS; O Fallon, IL; 25/292 ChrhWkr; HonRl; HospAde; NHS; SchPl; SchPpr; FHA; SciCl; No Illinois Univ; Nursing.

TONJES, Daniel L; Scribner HS; Scribner, NE; Band; ChrhWkr; CncrtBnd; HonRl; LetterFtbl; LetterTrk; College; Electronics Technology.

TONN, Catherine J; Elmhurst HS; Ft Wayne, IN; 8/381 AFS; Band; Chr; CncrtBnd; HonRl; HospAde; LbryAde; Orch; FTA; Nursing Sch; Nursing.

TONN, Martha L; Moorhead HS; Moorhead, MN; 13/585 SecJrCls; CmntyWkr; HonRl; NatlFornLg; NatlMeritSF; PolWkr; StuCncl; StuGov; RptrSchPpr; Macalester Col; Law.

TONNAR, Teresa A; Carrollton HS; Carrollton, MO; 15/102 Chrs; HonRl; NHS; TchrAde; SptEdYrbk; GerCl; PpCl; LetterTrk; CaptChrldr; IMSpt; Missouri U; Teaching.

TONNESON, Larry; Baltic Ind HS; Baltic, SD; 1/19 PresJrCls; ALBoysSt; Aud/Vis; CncrtBnd; HonRl; StuGov; Bsktbl; Military Acad, Officer.

TOOHEY, Maureen S; St Marys HS; Storm Lake, IA; Aud/Vis; Chr; Chrl; Chrs; HonRl; HospAde; NatlThespSoc; SchMus; SchPl; SctActv; College; Special Ed.

TOOKEY, Keith R; Richwoods HS; Peoria, IL; 33/499 Band; CncrtBnd; HonRl; JA; MrchBnd; NatlMeritCmnd; TchrAde; De Paul University.

TOOLE, Lewis M; Stanton Co HS; Manter, KS; 1/45 Band; Chr; HonRl; NHS; PresStuCncl; SpnCl; DanFAwd; University; Medical Technology.

TOOLE, Pamela S; Gideon HS; Gideon, MO; PresFrshCls; SecSophCls; Band; ChrhWkr; CncrtBnd; HonRl; MrchBnd; NHS; Yrbk; FHA; Chrldr; College.

TOOLE, Rhonda L; Monrovia HS; Monrovia, IN; 25/94 Band; ChrhWkr; CncrtBnd; MrchBnd; ModUN; TchrAde; 4-H; Ftbl; Bussiness Work.

TOOLEY, Martha L; Mt Pleasant HS; Mt Pleasant, MI; HonRl; SchMus; Bsktbl; Trk; Central Mi Univ; Dental Hygenist.

TOOLEY, Michael; Jackson County Western HS; Spring Arbor, MI; 15/150 VPSophCls; NHS; SchPl; TchrAde; SpnCl; Trk; CchngActv; DanFAwd; Albion College; Business Admin.

TOOMBS, Vicki C; Fairfield Community HS; Fairfield, IL; 12/165 CmntyWkr; HonRl; NHS; FHA; LatCl; MthCl; Southern Illinois University; Accounting.

TOOMEY, Nancy; Mother Mcavley Hs; Chicago, IL; 56/474 Chrs; HonRl; HospAde; SctActv; College;business.

TOON, Nancy J; Heyworth Comm HS; Heyworth, IL; 2/51 SecJrCls; VPSrCls; Chrs; HonRl; NHS; SchMus; SchPl; StuCncl; 4-H; College.

TOOPS, Richard J; Byron Community HS; Byron, IL; HonRl; JA; StuCncl; TchrAde; GerCl; Bsbl; Bsktbl; Ftbl; Swmmng; Trk; Augustana; Cpa.

TOPE, Kelly L; Collinsville HS; Collinsville, IL; CtyCnl; CaptDrlTm; HonRl; JrNHS; NHS; Quill&Scroll; TreasStuCncl; TchrAde; RptrYrbk; PpCl; Southern Illinois Univ; Business Admin.

TOPLIFF, Randy D; Goodland HS; Goodland, KS; Chr; Chrs; HonRl; NatlFornLg; SchMus; VPStuCncl; PresYthFlsp; 4-H; Wrstlng; 4-HAwd; Wichita St Univ; Physicians Asst.

TOPP, Dennis W; Atwater HS; Atwater, MN; 1/63 VPFrshCls; PresSophCls; PresJrCls; ALBoysSt; Band; CncrtBnd; HonRl; MrchBnd; NHS; PepBnd; Bsbl; Ftbl;.

TOPP, Susan L; West Central HS; Francesville, IN; 16/86 Band; ChrhWkr; CncrtBnd; HonRl; MrchBnd; NHS; PepBnd; SchPl; Yrbk; FHA; FTA; College; Secondary Ed.

TOPPING, Renee S; Ida Public HS; Temperance, MI; 9/175 Band; CncrtBnd; PresFrshCls; MrchBnd; NHS; PresNatlThespSoc; PepBnd; SchMus; SchPl; Col; Teaching & Journalism.

TOPPMEYER, Pamela M; Mercy HS; St Louis, MO; HonRl; JA; JrNHS; TchrAde; Bsktbl; Trk; Chrldr; IMSpt; Jr Clge; Stewardess.

TOPPMEYER, Randy J; Brussels Comm HS; Brussels, IL; 3/29 PresSophCls; SecJrCls; ChrhWkr; HonRl; SchPpr; CaptBsktbl; Trk; IMSpt; AmLegAwd; Univ; Dentist.

TORBERT, Edward E; Clinton Comm HS; Clinton, IL; Band; CncrtBnd; MrchBnd; U Of Il;.

TORBET, Steve W; Rensselaer Central HS; Rensselaer, IN; HonRl; YthFlsp;.

TORBICA, Sophia; Washington HS; East Chicago, IN; 17/313 Chrl; ChrhWkr; JrNHS; NHS; KeyCl; FrCl; RusCl; MthCl; Purdue Univ; Pharmacy.

TORCHIA, Nina L; Princeton HS; Princeton, IL; 4/163 AFS; HonRl; NHS; NatlThespSoc; SchMus; SchPl; EdYrBk; 4-H; GAA; 4-HAwd; Glen Fensterman; Counselor.

TORCZYNSKI, John R; Lyons Twp HS; Western Springs, IL; 1/1200 AFS; HonRl; NHS; NatlMeritFnl; SctActv; TchrAde; GerCl; TreasMthCl; TreasSciCl; Rice Univ; Geophysics.

TORELLO, George; Port Huron Central Hs; Port Huron, MI; Pres4-H; Farris St; Vocation.

TOREN, Carl; Illiana Christian Hs; Lansing, IL; 11/186 Chr; ChrhWkr; NatlFornLg; NHS; NatlMeritCmnd; SchMus; YthFlsp; GerCl; LetterTennis; Hope College; Math Major.

TORGUSON, Lyle; Rosemount HS; Rosemount, MN; CAP; HonRl; SctActv; Swmmng; College, Psychology.

TORNABANE, Jo M; Saint Edmond HS; Fort Dodge, IA; 4/152 SecSophCls; ChrhWkr; HonRl; ModUN; NHS; SchPl; UNYO; LatCl; Bsktbl; Trk; College.

TORNABANE, Margaret A; Saint Edmond HS; Fort Dodge, IA; 7/114 Chrs; HonRl; NHS; FrCl; College; Education Music.

TORNETEN, Carol; Underwood Comm HS; Council Bluffs, IA; 13/60 Band; Chr; HonRl; MrchBnd; NHS; PepBnd; SchMus; SchPl; FHA; IMSpt; Drake Univ; Vocal Mus Ed Teacher.

TORNQUIST, Chris W; Shenandoah Comm HS; Shenandoah, IA; 1/94 Band; CncrtBnd; HonRl; MrchBnd; NHS; Quill&Scroll; SchMus; StuCncl; EdSchPpr; MthCl; Nw Mo State U; Music Teaching.

TORPY, Betty; West Holt HS; Atkinson, NE; Chrs; 4-H; FHA; Bsbl; GAA; 4-HAwd; P F Teacher.

TORRENCE, Roberta E; Hanover Central HS; Cedar Lake, IN; ChrhWkr; CmntyWkr; HonRl; SctActv; PresStuCncl; TchrAde; PpCl; LetterBsktbl; LetterTrk; Chrldr; GAA; IMSpt; Indiana Univ; Physical Education.

TORRENCE, Susan M; Galesburg Sr HS; Galesburg, IL; 45/741 Chr; HonRl; StuCncl; College; Biology.

TORRENS, Deborah J; Harvard Comm HS; Harvard, IL; Chr; Chrs; Mdrgl; SchMus; SchPl; 4-H; College; Teaching.

TORRES, Ann L; Churchill HS; Westland, MI; Chr; IntrClCncl; College; Designer.

TORRES, Christine V; Mother Of Sorrows HS; Dolton, IL; 44/143 VPSophCls; LbryAde; StuCncl; PpCl; GAA; College; English Lit Prof Counseling.

TORRES, Enid; Bishop Noll Institute; East Chicago, IN; 51/342 CmntyWkr; HonRl; University; Med Tech.

TORRES, Ernest E; Berlin HS; Berlin, WI; 14/175 PresAFS; HonRl; Yrbk; SchPpr; SecKeyCl; SpnCl; LetterBsbl; LetterWrstlng; IMSpt; LionAwd; Univ Of Wisconsin; Architecture.

TORRES, Guy A; St George HS; Manhattan, KS; 1/32 VPSophCls; ALBoysSt; Chr; HonRl; SchPl; StuCncl; SpnCl; LetterBsktbl; LetterFtbl; Trk; College; Pre Medicine.

TORRES, Jose G; Gering HS; Gering, NE; HonRl; JrNHS; StuGov; SpnCl;.

TORRES, Paul R; Carmel Boys HS; Libertyville, IL; 2/172 HonRl; JrNHS; LitMag; NHS; LetterBsbl; Northwestern Univ; Biology.

TORRES, Socorro D; Round Lake HS; Round Lake Beach, IL; 1/282 PresFrshCls; NHS; StuCncl; Chrldr; College; Rn.

TORREY, Tammy R; Fairbury HS; Fairbury, NE; Chr; ChrhWkr; HonRl; JrNHS; OffAde; YthFlsp; FHA; DARAwd; College.

TORREZ, Yolanda M; Waukegan East HS; Waukegan, IL; HonRl; Business School; Court Recorder.

TORRIE, Scott; South Side HS; Fort Wayne, IN; 1/425 ChrhWkr; HonRl; SptEdSchPpr; LatCl; LetterBsbl; LetterFtbl; IMSpt; College; Pro.

TORRISON, Marilyn; Benson HS; Omaha, NE; 4/496 CncrtBnd; HonRl; MrchBnd; NHS; NatlSciFnd; YthLg; MthCl; SciCl; BauchLmbAwd; KiwanAwd; Northwestern Univ; Church Music.

TORRY, David A; Hutchinson HS; Hutchinson, MN; ChrhWkr; HonRl; SctActv; YthFlsp; LetterFtbl; LetterTennis; College; Vocational.

TORSKE, Roger E; Kenesaw Public HS; Heartwell, NE; TrsJrCls; Chrs; HonRl; SchMus; SchPl; StuGov; TchrAde; 4-H; CaptBsktbl; Clg; Teacher.

TORTOREA, Suzanne A; Irving Crown HS; Carpentersville, IL; SecJrCls; HonRl; MrchBnd; TchrAde; SecTrsSophCls; Bsktbl; LetterFtbl; CaptChrldr; GAA; PresAwd; College; Pe Teacher.

TORTORELLI, James P; Maine Twp West HS; Des Plaines, IL; Aud/Vis; CtyCnl; HonRl; NHS; NatlMeritCmnd; NatlThespSoc; SchMus; SchPl; SctActv; PresMthCl; PresSciCl; Ftbl; Us Naval Academy; Naval Officer.

TORWIRT, Arthur E; Malcolm HS; Malcolm, NE; 3/26 Band; Chr; Chrs; CncrtBnd; HonRl; JA; JrNHS; Mdrgl; MrchBnd; College; Army And Commercial Art.

TOSCANO, Anthony J; N Senior HS; North St Paul, MN; Band; CncrtBnd; HonRl; MrchBnd; PepBnd; IMSpt; College; Business.

TOSER, Jay R; Stevens Point Sr HS; Stevens Point, WI; 107/534 NatlMeritSF; NatlThespSoc; SchMus; University; Professional.

TOSH, Randall D; Valley Falls HS; Valley Falls, KS; 4/48 Band; Chrs; ChrhWkr; CncrtBnd; HonRl; MrchBnd; PepBnd; SchMus; 4-H; University; Professional.

TOSO, Sarah E; Stoughton HS; Stoughton, WI; ChrhWkr; CmntyWkr; HonRl; HospAde; SchMus; StuCncl; SpnCl; LetterTrk; CaptChrldr; GAA; PPFtbl; College; Nurse.

TOSTENSON, Dwight H; District 507 HS; Nicollet, MN; Band; Chrs; ChrhWkr; HonRl; NHS; SctActv; VP4-H; TreasFFA; SciCl; University; Music.

TOTEFF, Kathleen G; St Stephens HS; Saginaw, MI; HonRl; NHS; RptrYrbk; LetterBsktbl; LetterSwmmng; LetterTennis; Mi Tech U.

TOTMAN, Jo A; Edgewood Colesburg Comm HS; Edgewood, IA; LetterBand; LetterChrs; ChrhWkr; CncrtBnd; Mdrgl; MrchBnd; LetterPepBnd; Quill&Scroll; EdSchPpr; SecSpnCl; LetterGlf; Swmmng; Chrldr; College; Stewardess.

TOTOS, Bart R; John F Kennedy HS; Chicago, IL; SctActv; PresAwd; Loyola University; Dentistry.

TOTTEN, Carmen K; White Cloud HS; White Cloud, MI; 6/96 Band; HonRl; MrchBnd; NHS; OffAde; StuCncl; RptrYrbk; FrCl; PpCl; Central Michigan Univ; Social Work.

TOTTEN, David; Marysville HS; Marysville, KS; Band; ChrhWkr; CmntyWkr; CncrtBnd; MrchBnd; PepBnd; 4-H; FFA; Bsbl; Glf; Vo Tech; Agricultural.

TOURDOT, Janice L; Weston HS; Hillpoint, WI; 1/52 ChrhWkr; HonRl; NatlFornLg; NHS; Quill&Scroll; EdYrBk; EdSchPpr; PresSpnCl; Univ; Professional.

TOURTELLOTTE, Donald A; Saugatuck HS; Glenn, MI; 2/55 TrsSrCls; ALBoysSt; Band; HonRl; MrchBnd; PepBnd; 4-H; SciCl; LetterBsktbl; 4-HAwd; Hope College; Chemistry.

TOUSSAINT, Audrey; Fairfield Community HS; Fairfield, IL; 9/176 ALAGirlsSt; CncrtBnd; HonRl; MrchBnd; NHS; SchMus; RptrSchPpr; Univ Of Il; Psychology.

TOWARNICKY, Michael R; Fessenden HS; Fessenden, ND; VPJrCls; Band; Chr; Chrs; CncrtBnd; HonRl; MrchBnd; PepBnd; PolWkr; RedCrAde; LetterBsbl; CaptBsktbl; LetterFtbl; Univ Of North Dakota; Medicine.

TOWELL, Michael G; Martinsville HS; Martinsville, IN; 53/435 StuCncl; TchrAde; CaptBsbl; LetterBsktbl; College; Engineering.

TOWER, Craig W; York HS; Elmhurst, IL; Band; CncrtBnd; HonRl; MrchBnd; Orch; PepBnd; SchMus; Ill Wesleyan Univ; Liberal Arts.

TOWLE, Edward; Memorial HS; Eau Claire, WI; 50/450 CmntyWkr; HonRl; JrNHS; NHS; SchPl; Bsktbl; Ftbl; Tennis; Trk; IMSpt; Univ Of Wisc; Chemistry.

TOWLER, Brenda L; Patoka HS; Patoka, IL; 4/25 PresFrshCls; Chrs; ChrhWkr; HonRl; StuCncl; Yrbk; FHA; PpCl; Jr College; Secretary.

TOWNE, Roxanne K; Maywood HS; Curtis, NE; SecSrCls; Band; Chr; HonRl; NHS; Yrbk; 4-H; Trk; Chrldr; 4-HAwd; Univ Of Nebraska.

TOWNER, Mary L; Herman HS; Herman, MN; 2/36 Band; CncrtBnd; HonRl; NHS; PepBnd; RptrYrbk; RptrSchPpr; 4-H; 4-HAwd; PresAwd; Trade Sch; Business.

TOWNER, Steve R; Mankato East HS; Munkato, MN; NatlFornLg; NHS; PolWkr; YthLg; LetterBsktbl; LetterFtbl; LetterTennis; VoiceDemAwd; College; Medicine.

TOWNLEY, Steven T; Lawrence Central HS; Indianapolis, IN; 25/700 HonRl; StuCncl; LetterBsbl; LetterFtbl; LetterTrk; Wrstlng; IMSpt;.

TOWNS, Linda E; Waukegan HS; Waukegan, IL; 37/861 Band; HonRl; JrNHS; NHS; SchMus; SecFNA; University; Business Administration.

TOWNSEL, Darryl E; Emerson HS; Gary, IN; DrlTm; College.

TOWNSEND, Brian T; Griffin HS; Springfield, IL; 21/172 TrsSrCls; ChrhWkr; CncrtBnd; HonRl; MrchBnd; NHS; StuCncl; Yrbk; Springfield College; English.

TOWNSEND, Denise; Harlan HS; Chicago, IL; SecJrCls; SecSrCls; HonRl; JrNHS; OffAde; SchAde; StuCncl; Chrldr; GAA; IMSpt; Business School; Secreterial.

TOWNSEND, Kathleen; Coldwater HS; Coldwaer, MI; ChrhWkr; LbryAde; StuCncl; RptrYrbk; RptrSchPpr; SpnCl; Univ; Prof.

TOWNSEND, Kim D; High School; St Paul, NE; Band; ChrhWkr; HonRl; JrNHS; SchMus; Ftbl; AmLegAwd; College.

TOWNSEND, Michelle D; Chesaning Union HS; Chesaning, MI; Aud/Vis; HonRl; NHS; SctActv; StuCncl; Teen; RptrSchPpr; FrCl; Chrldr; GAA; College; Receptionist.

TOWRY, Sandra L; Dundee HS; Dundee, MI; 5/125 ChrhWkr; CncrtBnd; DrmMjrt; LbryAde; MrchBnd; NHS; SchPl; SecSpnCl; SciCl; Taylor Univ; Missionary Nursing.

TOYCEN, Brian D; Creston HS; Creston, IA; ALBoysSt; ALAGirlsSt; Band; CncrtBnd; HonRl; MrchBnd; NHS; PepBnd; SchMus; SchPl; College; Professional.

TOYNE, Lori E; Grand Comm HS; Pilot Mound, IA; 2/22 TrsJrCls; Band; Chrs; NHS; SchMus; SchPl; EdSchPpr; SciCl; LetterGlf; LetterChrldr; College; Medicine.

TOZER, Julie F; Cedarlake Acad; Nattawan, MI; 7/71 SecSophCls; Chr; HonRl; HospAde; NHS; StuGov; Andrews U; Nursing.

TOZSER, James M; Robichaud HS; Dearborn Hts, MI; 1/170 CtyCnl; HonRl; NHS; TchrAde; CitAwd; U Of Mi; Mathematics.

TRABILSY, Steven W; Hinsdale Twp HS; Hinsdale, IL; HonRl; NHS; Quill&Scroll; SptEdSchPpr; Univ Of Illinois; Electrical Engineering.

TRACEY, Kevin; Elpaso HS; Secor, IL; SchAde; TchrAde; Ftbl; Icc; Writer.

TRACEY, Thomas J; Edsel Ford HS; Dearborn, MI; HonRl; RptrSchPpr; Univ Of Michigan; Journalism.

TRACHTE, Cynthia L; Pittsville HS; Arpin, WI; 3/86 PresBand; Chr; ChrhWkr; HonRl; JrNHS; NHS; SchPl; Chrldr; GAA; AmLegAwd; EldAwd; College; Education.

TRACHTE, Mary B; East Depere HS; De Pere, WI; 3/200 HonRl; NatlFornLg; PresNHS; SchPl; StuCncl; StuGov; EdYrBk; FTA; PpCl; Glf; Butler Univ; Dance Theater.

TRACY, Barbara J; Elk Grove HS; Elk Grove Vil, IL; 66/505 HonRl; NatlMeritCmnd; NatlMeritSchl; RedCrAde; SchAde; SchMus; StuCncl; TchrAde; FrCl; Western Illinois Univ; Special Education.

TRACY, Barbara L; Rolla HS; Rolla, MO; 8/289 NatlFornLg; NHS; NatlMeritSF; NatlThespSoc; SchPl; StuCncl; PpCl; LetterBsktbl; GAA; PresAwd; Univ Of Mo; Physician.

TRACY, Bobbie; Red Hill Hs; Bridgeport, IL; 1/125 Band; Chrs; ChrhWkr; HonRl; NHS; NatlMeritCmnd; SchMus; YthFlsp; RptrYrbk; PpCl;.

TRACY, Cynthia R; Toivola Meadowlands HS; Meadowslands, MN; 1/30 DrlTm; HonRl; Coll; Psychology.

TRACY, Donald P; Melvindale HS; Allen Park, MI; 25/350 Band; HonRl; NHS; PepBnd; Bsktbl; Glf; U Of Detroit; Accountant.

TRACY, Gregory L; Clarion HS; Clarion, IA; 11/92 PresFrshCls; Band; Chrs; HonRl; Mdrgl; PepBnd; SchMus; StuCncl; RptrYrbk; Central College; Music.

TRACY, Harry R; Lexington HS; Lexington, IL; 17/63 AFS; Chr; HonRl; SchPl; StuCncl; RptrYrbk; College; Travel Agent.

TRACY, Jacqueline A; Cameron HS; Cameron, WI; SecFrshCls; SecSophCls; Band; Chrs; CncrtBnd; HonRl; TchrAde; EdSchPpr; GerCl; Chrldr; Cosmotology Sch; Beautician.

TRACY, Julia D; Ponca Public HS; Ponca, NE; 4/28 ALAGirlsSt; Chrs; HonRl; LbryAde; NHS; SchPl; YthFlsp; RptrYrbk; PpCl; Nebraska Wesleyan Univ; Biology.

TRACY, Julia M; Marquette HS; Alton, IL; 5/135 Chrs; HonRl; NatlThespSoc; SchPl; RptrSchPpr; FrCl; Physician.

TRACY, Kathleen M; Immaculate Heart Of Mary HS; Westchester, IL; 8/246 HospAde; College; Lab Technician.

TRACY, Leeann; Grand Island Sr HS; Grand Island, NE; 14/442 ChrhWkr; HonRl; NatlFornLg; NatlMeritSF; YthFlsp; FDA; FrCl; PpCl; Glf; LetterSwmmng; GAA; IMSpt; PPFtbl; Mt Holyoke College; Pathologist.

TRACY, Lillian G; Yale HS; Goodells, MI; HonRl; College; Secretarial.

TRACY, Patrick T; Marquette HS; Alton, IL; NHS; NatlMeritCmnd; RptrYrbk; LetterFtbl; LetterTrk;.

TRADER, Cynthia A; Oriska Public HS; Valley City, ND; VPSophCls; SecJrCls; ALAGirlsSt; Chr; HospAde; Yrbk; Pres4-H; LetterTrk; 4-HAwd; Waphetom Trade School; Psychology.

TRAFF, Rodney S; Mascoutah HS; Mascoutah, IL; 22/261 ChrhWkr; HonRl; NHS; RedCrAde; SchAde; YthFlsp; Yrbk; Bsktbl; Ftbl; Trk; Wrstlng; Univ Of Chicago; Engineering.

TRAFTON, Wyatt A; Christian Brother Collage; St Louis, MO; VPSrCls; ChrhWkr; HonRl; ROTC; YthFlsp; Ftbl; Socr; Trk; IMSpt; St Louis Univ; Accounting.

TRAGARZ, Dennis E; Alleman HS; Rock Island, IL; Aud/Vis; HonRl; NHS; SchPl; Yrbk; SchPpr; University Of Illinois; Engineering.

TRAGER, Linda J; Harmony Community HS; Farmington, IA; LbryAde; FHA; Bsktbl;.

TRAGER, William L; Illinois Valley Central HS; Edelstein, IL; 1/230 ChrhWkr; HonRl; VPNHS; ROTC; StuCncl; LetterTrk; Univ Of Notre Dame.

TRAHAN, Demetra E; Oak Ridge Central HS; Myrtle, MO; 2/16 HonRl; LbryAde; SchPl; SptEdSchPpr; SchPpr; CaptBsktbl; Vocational Tech School; Secretary.

TRAINOR, Colleen A; Streator Twnp HS; Blackstone, IL; 31/485 HonRl; HospAde; JrNHS; SecNHS; GerCl; PpCl; Illinois State University; Med Technologist.

TRAINOR, Colleen A; Streator Twp HS; Blackstone, IL; HonRl; HospAde; JrNHS; NHS; GerCl; PpCl; Il St Univ; Med Tech.

TRAINOR, Cynthia; Roncalli HS; Omahah, NE; HonRl; SpnCl; Univ Of Nebr; Psychology.

TRAINOR, Cynthia M; Roncalli HS; Omaha, NE; HonRl; NHS; SpnCl; Univ Of Neb; Psychology.

TRAINOR, Debora J; O Fallon HS; O Fallon, IL; ALAGirlsSt; Chrl; Chrs; LbryAde; Mdrgl; SctActv; FrCl; AmLegAwd; JCAwd; MasAwd; State Univ Of Ny Brockport; Scientist.

TRAINOR, Jolene M; Galena HS; Galena, IL; 2/107 TrsSrCls; SecAFS; Band; ChrhWkr; CncrtBnd; DrmMjrt; HonRl; HospAde; MrchBnd; NatlMeritCmnd; Glf; BttyCrckrAwd; DARAwd; Univ Of Illinois; Accounting.

TRAINOR, Neal R; Galena HS; Galena, IL; AFS; ChrhWkr; CmntyWkr; HonRl; Sacrstn; SctActv; StuGov; College; Vocation.

TRAINOR, Patrick; Milw Alexander Hamilton HS; Milwaukee, WI; 146/786 HonRl; Orch; Trk; Univ; Profession.

TRAISMAN, Edward S; Evanston Twp HS; Evanston, IL; HonRl; TchrAde; College; Medicine.

TRAMBLY, Lori R; Franklin Public HS; Franklin, NE; SecJrCls; HonRl; NHS; SchPl; Twrl; FHA; PpCl; LetterTrk; Chrldr; GAA; College.

TRAMMEL, Kevin G; Marion HS; Marion, IL; 10/277 Aud/Vis; Band; Chr; Chrs; CAP; CncrtBnd; HonRl; Mdrgl; MrchBnd; NHS; Swmmng; Trk; Mass Institute Of Tech; Aerodynamics.

TRAMP, Katherine A; O Gorman HS; Sioux Falls, SD; ChrhWkr; CtyCnl; CmntyWkr; HonRl; JA; JrNHS; NHS; OffAde; SchAde; SctActv; StuCncl; StuGov; TchrAde; DARAwd; Univ South Dakota; Foreign Language.

TRAMPEL, Allen L; Northeast Hamilton HS; Williams, IA; Band; CncrtBnd; HonRl; MrchBnd; Orch; PepBnd; SchMus; 4-H; 4-HAwd; Iccc Ft Dodge; Accounting.

TRAMPF, Mark; Ripon HS; Ripon, WI; VPJrCls; VPALBoysSt; Band; NHS; PresNatlThespSoc; SchPl; RptrYrbk; SptEdYrbk; Trk; Coll; Drama.

TRANDAHL, Mark; Winner HS; Winner, SD; ALBoysSt; HonRl; Coll; Pre Med.

TRANDEL, Paul J; Washington Park HS; Racine, WI; HonRl; ModUN; NHS; KeyCl; Trk; U Of Wi; Computer Science.

TRANTHAM, Janie; Marion C Early HS; Willard, MO; ChrhWkr; HonRl; OffAde; TchrAde; Yrbk; SchPpr; FBLA; FHA; PpCl; SciCl; Business School.

TRANTHAM, Paul D; Kelvyn Park HS; Chicago, IL; 1/299 ChrhWkr; HonRl; NHS; PresYthFlsp; BauchLmbAwd; Trinity College.

TRAPP, Steve E; Brookings HS; Brookings, SD; 38/191 ALBoysSt; NHS; PolWkr; SchMus; Sdlty; YthFlsp; Ftbl; Glf; IMSpt; Sd State Univ; Engineering.

TRAPP, Terry L; Delavan Darien HS; Delavan, WI; HonRl; SctActv; StuCncl; 4-H; LetterBsbl; LetterFtbl; IMSpt; 4-HAwd; Univ Of Wisconsin; Mathematics.

TRAROP, Elaine K; Birch Run HS; Birch Run, MI; 18/154 Chrs; HonRl; LbryAde; SchAde; TchrAde; RptrSchPpr; SchPpr; PPFtbl; College Mich State Univ; Social Work.

TRATAR, Sandra L; Beaver Dam Sr HS; Beaver Dam, WI; 40/350 AFS; NatlFornLg; StuCncl; SpnCl; PpCl; Chrldr; GAA; IMSpt; College; Professional.

TRAUB, Barbara E; Fairbury Cropsey HS; Fairbury, IL; 6/100 SecSophCls; ALAGirlsSt; Chr; HonRl; NHS; SchMus; MthCl; Univ Of Illinois.

TRAUFLER, Cindy L; Gehlen HS; Le Mars, IA; Chr; DrlTm; HonRl; SchPl; SctActv; RptrSchPpr; MthCl; LetterGlf; College; Professional.

TRAUSCH, Denise J; Roseland Public HS; Roseland, NE; VPFrshCls; PresJrCls; PresSrCls; Chrs; HonRl; StuCncl; EdYrBk; PpCl; LetterTrk; DARAwd; Vocational College.

TRAUSCH, James E; St Viator HS; Arlington Hts, IL; 35/250 HonRl; FshEdYrbk; GerCl; LetterGlf; Univ Of Notre Dame; Law.

TRAUT, Terence; Sauk Centre HS; Sauk Centre, MN; 20/158 Chr; ChrhWkr; HonRl; SchPl; SctActv; RptrSchPpr; Ftbl; Tennis; MasAwd; St Cloud State College.

TRAUTMANN, Joy R; Lawson HS; Rayville, MO; SecSophCls; SecSrCls; Chrs; HonRl; NHS; SchPl; FHA; LetterTrk; Chrldr; PresAwd; Cmsu; Nursing.

TRAUTSCH, Cynthia; Oak Lawn Community HS; Oak Lawn, IL; 90/667 HonRl; HospAde; OffAde; PolWkr; TchrAde; College; Cpa.

TRAVELUTE, Roxanne R; Hanover HS; Hanover, KS; 1/48 PresJrCls; ALAGirlsSt; Chrs; HonRl; HospAde; NHS; Twrl; 4-H; Chrldr; Ks State Univ; Pharmacist.

TRAVER, James W; Cairo HS; Madison, MO; ChrhWkr; CmntyWkr; HonRl; JA; TchrAde; YthFlsp; FBLA; CchngActv; JAAwd; Woodland Hospital; Lab Tech.

TRAVERS, Darla; Malden HS; Malden, MO; VPSophCls; HonRl; TchrAde; FHA; FrCl; PpCl; College; Vocational.

TRAVERS, Michael; Evanston Township HS; Evanston, IL; HonRl; NatlSciFnd; PolWkr; MthCl; Computor Science.

TRAVERS, Victoria A; Streator HS; Streator, IL; 35/400 CmntyWkr; HonRl; GerCl; LetterSwmmng; Trk; George Williams College; Program Director.

TRAVIS, Carrie L; Badger HS; Lake Geneva, WI; Chr; DrlTm; HonRl; NatlFornLg; SchMus; College; Music.

TRAVIS, Charles E; Hirsch HS; Chicago, IL; ALBoysSt; LatCl; Chicago Jr College; Accounting.

TRAVIS, Donna M; Platte Public HS; Academy, SD; VPSophCls; SecTrsSrCls; Chr; Chrs; ChrhWkr; CmntyWkr; HonRl; HospAde; LbryAde; Mdrgl; SchPl; LetterTrk; Chrldr; 4-HAwd; College; Professional.

TRAVIS, Elizabeth; Lucy L Flower V HS; Chicago, IL; OffAde; College; Nursing.

TRAVIS, Elizabeth; Flower Voc HS; Chicago, IL; OffAde; StuGov; Professional Modeling School Of Nursing.

TRAVIS, Randy; Atlanta C3 HS; Atlanta, MO; ChrhWkr; CmntyWkr; HonRl; SchAde; TchrAde; YthFlsp; FSA; U; Prof.

TRAVIS, Susan; Caston HS; Logansport, IN; 10/88 Chrs; JrNHS; LbryAde; NHS; SchMus; SchPl; Trk; JAAwd; Purdue Univ; M S In Engineering.

TRAVIS, Theresa A; La Grove Comm HS; St Peter, IL; 1/33 PresChrs; HonRl; SchMus; EdYrBk; EdSchPpr; PresFrCl; Trk; IMSpt; DARAwd; College; Liberal Arts.

TRAVIS, Theresa A; La Grove HS; St Peter, IL; 1/33 Chrs; ChrhWkr; HonRl; NHS; EdYrBk; EdSchPpr; FrCl; PpCl; BttyCrckrAwd; College; Liberal Arts.

TRAVNICEK, Jane A; Clarkson Public HS; Clarkson, NE; 2/39 Band; Chrs; CncrtBnd; HonRl; PepBnd; SchPl; StuCncl; VPYthFlsp; LetterTrk; GAA; U Of Nebraska; Phys Therepy.

TRAWICK, Michael; Plano HS; Plano, IL; HonRl; NatlFornLg; Bsktbl; Univ; Business Law.

TRAWICKI, Steven A; Edgar HS; Edgar, WI; 12/84 Chr; Chrs; HonRl; StuCncl; RptrSchPpr; PpCl; LetterBsbl; LetterBsktbl; LetterFtbl; LetterTrk; Vocational Sch; Vocation.

TRAWINSKI, Cindy J; Niles East HS; Skokie, IL; VPSophCls; PresJrCls; AFS; MrchBnd; NatlThespSoc; SchMus; SchPl; TchrAde; National College Of Ed; Education.

TRAXEL, Marilyn; Golden Valley Public HS; Golden Valley, ND; 5/12 TrsFrshCls; Band; Chrs; LbryAde; SchPl; Yrbk; SchPpr; 4-H; PpCl; 4-HAwd; Dickenson State College; Secretary.

TRAYINGER, Kenneth; Lee HS; Wyoming, MI; 1/100 HonRl; NHS; Bsbl; Bsktbl; Glf; College; Prof.

TRAYNOR, Timothy N; Guilford HS; Rockford, IL; 120/700 Band; CncrtBnd; HonRl; MrchBnd; NHS; SctActv; LatCl; College; Dentistry.

TRCA, Randy E; Britt Community HS; Britt, IA; ALBoysSt; HonRl; NHS; LetterBsbl; LetterFtbl; GovHonPrgAwd; RotaryAwd; Buena Vista College; Law.

TREADWAY, Daniel W; Earlham HS; Earlham, IA; Chr; Chrs; ChrhWkr; HonRl; Mdrgl; NatlMeritSF; PolWkr; SchPl; SpnCl; Bsktbl; Earlham Col; Ministry.

TREANOR, Peggy E; Adlai Stevenson HS; Kiedeer, IL; Chrs; HonRl; SchMus; College; Liberal Arts.

TREASURE, Charles B; Kennett HS; Kennett, MO; PresFrshCls; PresSophCls; PresJrCls; ALBoysSt; HonRl; NHS; StuCncl; YthFlsp; LetterFtbl; LetterTennis; Univ; Medicine.

TREASURE, Sandra J; Kirksville Sr HS; Kirksville, MO; 30/180 Chrs; HonRl; StuCncl; PpCl; Chrldr; GAA; College; Elementary Education.

TREAT, Rhonda D; Vienna HS; Ozark, IL; 21/104 VPSophCls; OffAde; TchrAde; FNA; SpnCl; PpCl; Bsktbl; Trk; College.

TREBRA, Janice L; J I Case HS; Racine, WI; CncrtBnd; HonRl; NHS; Orch; PepBnd; SchMus; TchrAde; CaptBsktbl; LetterTennis; LetterTrk; Un Of Wis; Interior Designer.

TRECARTIN, Diane E; Warren HS; Gurnee, IL; 12/343 Band; CncrtBnd; HonRl; MrchBnd; SpnCl; GAA; College; Radiologic Technology.

TREECE, Cheryl L; Jackson R 2 HS; Jackson, MO; ChrhWkr; HonRl; NHS; RptrYrbk; RptrSchPpr; FHA; PpCl; Trk; Freed Hardeman Col; Pharmacy.

TREECE, Jerry L; Shawnee HS; Wolf Lake, IL; 3/61 TrsSrCls; Aud/Vis; ChrhWkr; HonRl; FFA; PpCl; Bsbl; Bsktbl; CchngActv; Southern Illinois Univ; Education.

TREEN, Mary E; Morton Senior HS; Hammond, IN; 36/492 HonRl; HospAde; JrNHS; NHS; Quill&Scroll; StuGov; TchrAde; RptrSchPpr; SchPpr; Trade Sch; Vocation.

TREESE, William D; Lincoln HS; Vincennes, IN; ChrhWkr; HonRl; YthFlsp; FFA; Vincennes Univ; Wildlife Biology.

TREESH, Erica L; Halstead HS; Halstead, KS; SecSophCls; HonRl; NHS; Teen; RptrYrbk; BttyCrckrAwd; College.

TREFFER, Dawn; Broken Bow HS; Broken Bow, NE; Band; Chr; CncrtBnd; HonRl; LbryAde; MrchBnd; PepBnd; 4-H; FHA; 4-HAwd; Univ Of Ne.

TREFZ, Mike L; Charles City Comm HS; Charles City, IA; ALBoysSt; HonRl; NHS; LetterBsktbl; LetterFtbl; LetterTrk;.

TREFZ, Terrie L; Central HS; New Munster, WI; Chrs; HonRl; NatlFornLg; NatlThespSoc; SchMus; SchPl; 4-H; PpCl; 4-HAwd; Technical Inst.

TREFZGER, Thomas E; Woodruff HS; Peoria, IL; 1/225 Band; CncrtBnd; HonRl; MrchBnd; NHS; PepBnd; Quill&Scroll; Yrbk; RptrSchPpr; KeyCl; FrCl; LetterBsbl; DARAwd; Bradley University; Journalism.

TREGLIA, David P; Rochester HS; Rochester, IN; HonRl; NHS; SchPl; StuCncl; TchrAde; SpnCl; LetterBsbl; Bsktbl; LetterFtbl; IMSpt; College.

TREGLIA, Michael; Rochester HS; Rochester, IN; 5/150 HonRl; NHS; NatlMeritCmnd; StuCncl; SpnCl; SciCl; LetterFtbl; Univ; Ocean.

TREIBER, Anne M; Maple Valley Comm HS; Danbury, IA; ALAGirlsSt; Chr; ChrhWkr; HonRl; HospAde; JrNHS; NHS; FNA; PpCl; LetterBsktbl; LetterTrk; St Josephs School; Nursing.

TREIMER, Leanne S; Durant Comm HS; Durant, IA; 3/73 HonRl; NHS; YthFlsp; RptrYrbk; RptrSchPpr; FHA; College; Secretary.

TREINEN, Clark E; Remsen Union Comm HS; Temsen, IA; VPSrCls; Chr; Chrs; HonRl; NHS; StuCncl; Bsktbl; CaptFtbl; Tennis; Iowa State Univ; Industrial Admin.

TREINEN, David J; Roncalli HS; Omaha, NE; HonRl; NHS; StuCncl; SchPpr; MthCl; Univ Of Ne; Cpa.

TRELA, Deborah; St Ann HS; Chicago, IL; TrsFrshCls; TrsSophCls; TrsJrCls; Chrs; JA; NHS; MthCl; SciCl; Chrldr; JAAwd; Coll; Nursing.

TRELOAR, Michelle A; Little Wolf HS; Ogdensburg, WI; Chrs; CmntyWkr; HonRl; LbryAde; OffAde; Trade School; Nurse.

TREMAIN, Kini M; Brown Co HS; Nashville, IN; 63/207 Band; ChrhWkr; CncrtBnd; ModUN; Orch; StuCncl; FHA; Trk; 4-HAwd; PresAwd;.

TREMAIN, Thomas M; Columbus North HS; Columbus, IN; 20/500 ChrhWkr; CncrtBnd; HonRl; NatlMeritFnl; PolWkr; StuCncl; SciCl; Bsbl; CchngActv; Purdue Univ; Business Mgmt.

TREMBACK, Thea M; St Joseph HS; Chicago, IL; VPSophCls; Chrl; HonRl; NHS; Quill&Scroll; PresStuCncl; StuGov; SchPpr; MthCl; SciCl; Loyola Univ; Communications.

TREMBLAY, Paul L; Grand Blanc HS; Grandblanc, MI; 14/567 NHS; Yrbk; LetterSwmmng; U Of Mi ;med.

TREMBLY, Barbara S; Cardinal Community HS; Agency, IA; Band; Chr; ChrhWkr; CncrtBnd; HonRl; PresLbryAde; MrchBnd; NHS; Orch; PepBnd; College; Child Therapy.

TREML, Maureen A; East De Pere HS; Depere, WI; 18/200 HonRl; HospAde; TreasJA; LbryAde; RptrYrbk; GAA; IMSpt; JAAwd; VoiceDemAwd; Col; Pre Veterinary.

TREMMEL, Lynann M; Lincoln HS; Wisconsin Rapdis, WI; .

TRENCH, Susan E; Columbia Hts Sr HS; Columbia Heights, MN; 5/525 Chr; CncrtBnd; HonRl; NHS; OffAde; Hamline Univ; Psychologist.

TRENKLER, Karen E; Good Counsel HS; Chicago, IL; 8/245 HonRl; LbryAde; StuCncl; SpnCl; SciCl; Northwestern Univ; Biology.

TRENNEPOHL, Tammy; Lawrenceburg HS; Lawrenceburg, IN; VPFrshCls; PresSophCls; Band; CncrtBnd; JrNHS; MrchBnd; SctActv; SpnCl; PpCl; Univ; Pro.

TRENT, Danny C; Hutchinson HS; Hutchinson, KS; Band; Chr; ChrhWkr; CncrtBnd; HonRl; MrchBnd; NatlMeritCmnd; StuCncl; FrCl; SciCl; Univ Of Kansas; Political Science.

TRENT, Douglas B; Haven HS; Haven, KS; 12/92 Band; CncrtBnd; HonRl; MrchBnd; PepBnd; SchAde; SctActv; BttyCrckrAwd; GodCntryAwd;.

TRENT, Michael L; Gordon Tech HS; Chicago, IL; 36/630 PresSrCls; HonRl; VPJA; NHS; NatlThespSoc; PresStuCncl; PresPpCl; Tennis; Chrldr; IMSpt; San Diego U; Law.

TRENT, Paulanna L; Cedar Vale HS; Cedar Vale, KS; Band; Chr; Chrs; HonRl; LbryAde; NHS; RptrYrbk; 4-H; PpCl; SciCl; Bsktbl; Trk; 4-HAwd; Trade School; Stewardess.

TRENTMAN, Marlene A; St Paul Public HS; T Libory, NE; HonRl; Secretary.

TRENUM, David H; Canyonville Bible Academy; Indianapolis, IN; PresSophCls; PresJrCls; Chr; HonRl; Yrbk; LetterBsktbl; IMSpt; University; Liberal Arts.

TRESH, Perry; Bishop Bongess HS; Westland, MI; HonRl; StuGov; MthCl; SciCl; University; Vocation.

TRESKE, Michael E; Greendale HS; Greendale, WI; PresJrCls; ALBoysSt; Band; Chr; NHS; SchPl; StuGov; TchrAde; Bsktbl; Ftbl; Eau Claire; Communications.

TRETOW, Michael E; Piux Xi HS; Franklin, WI; Band; CncrtBnd; MrchBnd; NatlThespSoc; Orch; PepBnd; SchMus; SchPl; SchPpr; FTA; Univ Of Wis Milwaukee; Mechanical Engineer.

TRETTER, Ann E; Southridge HS; Huntingburg, IN; 21/142 Chr; CncrtBnd; HonRl; MrchBnd; SchMus; PpCl; LetterBsbl; Chrldr; GAA; PPFtbl; Univ Evansville; Nurse.

TRETTER, Randy P; Upsala Area HS; Upsala, MN; 31/42 CaptBsbl; CaptBsktbl; CaptFtbl; College.

TREU, Bodo W; Bryan HS; Omaha, NE; 3/400 HonRl; NatlFornLg; NHS; NatlMeritSF; StuCncl; CaptSocr; AmLegAwd; University; Physician.

TREUDE, Vaughn L; Dickinson HS; Dickinson, ND; Band; NatlMeritSF; NatlThespSoc; SchMus; SchPl; StuCncl; EdSchPpr; VPGerCl; SciCl; Trk; Lawrence U; Engineering.

TREVARROW, Virginia E; Seaholm HS; Bloomfield Hills, MI; ChrhWkr; CmntyWkr; HonRl; HospAde; ModUN; PolWkr; SctActv; StuGov; YthFlsp; FrCl; Central Mi U; Special Education.

TREVARTHEN, Donald S; Luther L Wright HS; Ironwood, MI; 35/201 NHS; NatlMeritCmnd; RptrSchPpr; Tennis; Mich St U; Elec Engin.

TREVETT, Marylee B; Milbank HS; Milbank, SD; Chrs; HonRl; Yrbk; LetterTrk; IMSpt; PPFtbl; College; Art.

TREVILLYAN, Laurie J; Harding County HS; Buffalo, SD; PresJrCls; Chrs; DrlTm; HonRl; SchPl; StuCncl; Yrbk; PpCl; LetterBsktbl; Chrldr; GAA; College; Nursing.

TREWARTHA, Carol A; Streator Twp HS; Streator, IL; 15/382 Band; HonRl; NHS; Univ Of Illinois.

TREXLER, Kevin E; Cobden Unit Dist 17 HS; Alto Pass, IL; 7/42 TrsJrCls; HonRl; RptrSchPpr; SciCl; Bsktbl; Trk; Southern Il U; Statitician.

TRI, Laurine A; Bellows Free Acad; Mazeppa, MN; 1/3 Chr; SecFrshCls; CmntyWkr; HonRl; NHS; SchMus; SchPl; StuGov; RptrYrbk; SchPpr; Makato State Col; Social Work.

TRIBBETT, David P; Frontier HS; Chalmers, IN; 5/70 TrsJrCls; ALBoysSt; Band; Chrs; CncrtBnd; HonRl; MrchBnd; NHS; PresStuCncl; Bsktbl; LetterFtbl; Glf; Trk; IMSpt; Col; Architecture.

TRIBBEY, Jerry L; Rushville HS; Rushville, IL; 19/127 HonRl; OffAde; Bsbl; Ftbl; LetterTrk; University; Accounting.

TRIBBLE, Jeffery L; Lindblom Tech HS; Chicago, IL; 3/722 VPBand; VPChr; ChrhWkr; HonRl; Mdrgl; NHS; Trk; College; Engineer.

TRIBBLE, Randy J; Cleveland HS; St Louis, MO; ChrhWkr; CmntyWkr; HonRl; SpnCl; College.

TRIBBLE, Sherman R; Lindblom Tech HS; Chicago, IL; 20/657 Chr; Chrl; Chrs; ChrhWkr; HonRl; Mdrgl; NatlMeritCmnd; SchAde; TchrAde; LatCl; Trk; Fisk Univ; Music.

TRIBBLE, Stephanie; Conway HS; Conway, MO; 2/65 Chr; CncrtBnd; HonRl; MrchBnd; PepBnd; TchrAde; Twrl; FTA; School Of The Ozarks; Teaching.

TRIBBY, James L; Kimball HS; Royal Oak, MI; 62/650 CncrtBnd; HonRl; MrchBnd; NHS; PresPepBnd; SchMus; SctActv; PresYthFlsp; SpnCl; CchngActv; Michigan St Univ; Music.

TRIBBY, Yvonne M; Kansas HS; Kansas, IL; Band; Chr; Chrs; ChrhWkr; CmntyWkr; CncrtBnd; HonRl; LbryAde; MrchBnd; NatlThespSoc; PepBnd; SchMus; SchPl; SctActv; Lake Land College; Home Economics.

TRIBE, Barbara K; Edwards County Sr HS; Albion, IL; 5/104 ChrhWkr; HonRl; LbryAde; NHS; SchMus; FHA; E Illinois Univ; Elem Teacher.

TRIBITT, Robert C; Magic City Campus HS; Minot, ND; PresBand; TreasCncrtBnd; HonRl; MrchBnd; ROTC; SchMus; StuCncl; Treas4-H; AmLegAwd; DARAwd; 4-HAwd; College; Music.

TRIEBULL, Donna; Proviso East HS; Maywood, IL; ChrhWkr; DrlTm; HonRl; OffAde; TchrAde; FHA; IMSpt; LionAwd; Junior College; Pre School Teacher.

TRIEFENBACH, Laura K; Crystal Lake Community HS; Crystal Lake, IL; 79/500 AFS; Band; Chr; DrmMjrt; HonRl; NHS; NatlMeritCmnd; Orch; YthFlsp; YthLg; University Of Illinois; Music Educator.

TRIER, John C; Keota Comm HS; Keota, IA; 5/57 HonRl; StuCncl; 4-H; LetterFtbl;.

TRIGG, Cindy A; North Miami HS; Macy, IN; Band; HonRl; YthFlsp; SchPpr; 4-H; Bsbl; Trk; PPFtbl; 4-HAwd; JCAwd; College; Art Creative Writting.

TRIGG, Michael E; Lillis HS; Kansas City, MO; 9/85 ALBoysSt; Chr; Chrl; Chrs; ChrhWkr; CmntyWkr; HonRl; JrNHS; NHS; SpnCl; Bsktbl; Univ Of Kentucky Louisville; Engineering.

TRIGGS, David A; South Clay Community HS; Dickens, IA; 1/30 VPBand; VPChrs; HonRl; SchPl; StuCncl; Sec4-H; VPFFA; LetterBsbl; CaptBsktbl; DanFAwd; Iowa State University; Agriculture.

TRIMARCHI, Julie A; Bishop Dwenger HS; Ft Wayne, IN; Chrs; HospAde; OffAde; Quill&Scroll; RptrSchPpr; College; Business Admin.

TRIMARCO, Gina M; Maine South HS; Park Ridge, IL; HonRl; NHS; Quill&Scroll; Yrbk; University; Journalism.

TRIMBERGER, Diane; Neillsville HS; Meillsville, WI; Band; CncrtBnd; HonRl; MrchBnd; PepBnd; SchPl; RptrYrbk; FTA; SpnCl; Bsktbl; College;history Of Phy Ed.

TRIMBLE, Bryan; Pleasanton HS; Amherst, NE; HonRl; SchPl; StuGov; RptrYrbk; SchPpr; Trade School; Vocation.

TRIMBLE, Eric R; Atchison HS; Atchison, KS; TrsSophCls; Chrs; HonRl; NHS; SchMus; SchPl; LetterFtbl; Ks State Univ; Architectural Drafting.

TRIMBLE, Layne; Pleasanton HS; Amherst, NE; 3/23 TrsFrshCls; Chr; ChrhWkr; HonRl; NHS; StuCncl; YthFlsp; College.

TRIMBLE, Martha J; Blackduck HS; Tenstrike, MN; Band; ChrhWkr; HonRl; SchPl; StuCncl; CivCl; VP4-H; FHA; Chrldr; 4-HAwd; Anoka Vo Tech; Fashion.

TRIMBLE, Tony R; Newton HS; Montrose, IL; 30/160 ChrhWkr; HonRl; NHS; 4-H; FFA; MthCl; LetterFtbl; University Of Illinois; Animal Science.

TRIMBY, James A; Reed Custer Township HS; Wilmington, IL; 10/60 HonRl; ROTC; RptrSchPpr; Wrstlng; Clge; Military Officer.

TRINE, Barbara A; Notre Dame HS; Quincy, IL; 26/107 CmntyWkr; SctActv; TchrAde; Bsktbl; Tennis; GAA; IMSpt; Springfield College.

TRINGALI, Susan M; Roncalli HS; Manitowoc, WI; 6/140 CncrtBnd; NHS; PepBnd; StuCncl; MthCl; LetterBsktbl; LetterTennis; GAA; KiwanAwd; Univ Of Wisconsin; Medical Technology.

TRINKLE, Jeffrey D; Albia Comm HS; Albia, IA; Band; CncrtBnd; DrmMjrt; MrchBnd; PepBnd; YthFlsp; 4-H; VPFFA; 4-HAwd; Trade School; Farming.

TRINKLEIN, Mark S; Frankenmuth HS; Vassar, MI; ChrhWkr; HonRl; Ftbl; Michigan State Univ; Computer Science.

TRINKNER, Susan; De Pere East; De Pere, WI; Chr; ChrhWkr; JA; VPFrshCls; SctActv; RptrSchPpr; SchPpr; 4-H; Northern Wi Tech Inst; Medical.

TRIPAM, Linda A; Mother Mcauley HS; Oak Lawn, IL; Chrs; HonRl; SchMus; IMSpt; Loyola Univ; Dental Hygiene.

TRIPLETT, Ann M; Brazil HS; Brazil, IN; Band; CncrtBnd; DrlTm; HonRl; LbryAde; MrchBnd; PepBnd; FHA; FTA; University; Pre School Education.

TRIPLETT, Jon W; Liberty HS; Mtn View, MO; Band; Chr; Chrs; Mdrgl; PepBnd; SchMus; StuCncl; YthFlsp; SpnCl; Ftbl; Coll; Conservation.

TRIPLETT, Pamela M; Mahomet Seymour HS; Mahomet, IL; Band; Chr; Chrs; HonRl; Mdrgl; NatlThespSoc; Orch; SchMus; SchPl; University; Music.

TRIPOLI, David J; St Patrick HS; Chicago, IL; 33/395 HonRl; SctActv; College; Optometry.

TRIPP, Christine R; Ypsilanti HS; Ypsilanti, MI; HonRl; JA; NHS; TchrAde; Yrbk; SpnCl; CchngActv; Univ Of S Florida; Business Admin.

TRIPP, Elaine; White Lake HS; White Lake, SD; 2/28 PresSrCls; Chrs; HonRl; MrchBnd; PepBnd; SchPl; EdSchPpr; FHA; Sd St Univ; Sci.

TRIPP, Frederick L; East Catholic HS; Detroit, MI; HonRl; NHS; OffAde; FrCl; PpCl; TreasSciCl; LetterBsktbl; LetterFtbl; LetterTrk; Univ Of Mich; Accountant.

TRIPP, Jeffrey A; Adrian HS; Adrian, MI; 2/450 HonRl; TreasNHS; NatlMeritSF; StuCncl; RptrSchPpr; SchPpr; PresFBLA; VPMthCl; Glf; College; Banking.

TRIPP, Karen; Tawas Area HS; East Tawas, MI; CncrtBnd; HonRl; MrchBnd; NatlFornLg; NHS; StuCncl; RptrYrbk; EdYrBk; FrCl; Univ Of Michigan.

TRIPP, Mary; Warren HS; Warren, MI; ChrhWkr; CmntyWkr; HonRl; NHS; SctActv; StuCncl;.

TRIPP, Sandra L; Newton Senior HS; Newton, IA; HonRl; LbryAde; SctActv; Bsktbl; Glf; Swmmng; IMSpt; College; Liberal Arts.

TRISLER, Stephanie; Mormon Trail HS; Humeston, IA; 3/38 HonRl; LbryAde; StuCncl; Yrbk; SchPpr; FHA; GovHonPrgAwd; Central College; Business.

TRITES, Nancy C; Atchison HS; Atchison, KS; VPFrshCls; Band; Chr; Chrl; Chrs; ChrhWkr; CncrtBnd; HonRl; MrchBnd; PepBnd; Work; Secretary.

TRITT, Bonita J; Boylan HS; Rockford, IL; 18/350 Band; CncrtBnd; HonRl; MrchBnd; NHS; SecLatCl;.

TRITTIN, Deloria; Lidgerwood HS; Lidgerwood, ND; Chrs; HonRl; SchMus; SchPl; SchPpr; FHA; PpCl;.

TRITTIPOE, Joy L; Joliet East HS; Elwood, IL; 12/407 Chr; ChrhWkr; HonRl; NatlMeritFnl; MthCl; LetterBsktbl; GAA; Letouneau; Asst Tech Design.

TRITZ, Patricia J; Pardeeville HS; Pardeeville, WI; TrsSophCls; TrsJrCls; SecSrCls; ALAGirlsSt; HonRl; NHS; SchPl; StuCncl; Yrbk; SchPpr; 4-H; GAA;.

TROCHINSKI, Deborah; Wautoma Sr HS; Neshkoro, WI; Chr; HonRl; RptrYrbk; Yrbk; RptrSchPpr; SchPpr; FHA; PpCl; IMSpt; PresAwd; Tech School; Secretarial.

TROCHUCK, Terese A; Prospect HS; Mt Prospect, IL; Chr; Chrs; ChrhWkr; CmntyWkr; HonRl; PolWkr; SchMus; StuCncl; 4-H; PpCl; GAA; Univ Of Missouri; Occup Therapy.

TROEMEL, Michael B; Thornwood HS; So Holland, IL; CncrtBnd; DrmMjrt; HonRl; JrNHS; MrchBnd; NHS; SctActv; StuCncl; Valparaiso Univ; Law.

TROENDLE, Diane M; Kee HS; Lansing, IA; 13/67 Band; Chrs; CncrtBnd; HonRl; MrchBnd; PepBnd; SchPl; 4-H; FTA; PpCl; LetterBsktbl; LetterTrk; College; Computer Programmer.

TROESTER, David J; Central HS; St Joseph, MO; Chr; Chrs; HonRl; NHS; StuGov; GerCl; LatCl; SciCl; LetterBsbl; LetterBsktbl; Univ Of Missouri; Business Admin.

TROESTER, Mary Jo; Forman Sargent Central HS; Cayuga, ND; VPFrshCls; Band; Chrl; Chrs; CncrtBnd; HonRl; MrchBnd; PepBnd; SchMus; FHA; Trade Sch.

TROESTER, Matthew; Hampton HS; Hampton, NE; PresFrshCls; TrsJrCls; Chrs; HonRl; TchrAde; SptEdYrbk; Bsbl; College; Professional.

TROFHOLZ, Mark S; Fremont Senior HS; Freemont, NE; RptrYrbk; RptrSchPpr; GerCl; MthCl; Bsktbl; LetterFtbl; Wrstlng; Univ Of Nebraska; Business Management.

TROFTGRUBEN, Melanie M; St Thomas Public HS; St Thomas, ND; Band; HonRl; SchPl; StuCncl; RptrYrbk; CaptBsktbl; LetterTrk; CaptChrldr; GAA; PPFtbl; Bemidji State Univ; Phy Ed.

TROHKIMOINEN, Alta M; Wm J Brown HS; Sturgis, SD; ALAGirlsSt; CncrtBnd; MrchBnd; PepBnd; PpCl; Bsktbl; Trk; College.

TROKEY, Daniel E; Hillsboro HS; Desoto, MO; Chr; HonRl; Mdrgl; SchPl; VPStuCncl; SptEdSchPpr; FTA; SpnCl; MthCl; Bsbl; Bsktbl; Ftbl; College; Conservation.

TROKEY, Donald; Potosi HS; Mineral Point, MO; HonRl; NatlMeritCmnd; SchPpr; Trade; Professional.

TROKEY, Judy F; Potosi HS; Mineral Point, MO; Chr; ChrhWkr; YthFlsp; College; Secretary.

TROLINGER, Mark A; Arcadia Valley HS; Ironton, MO; 8/89 Band; Chr; Chrs; CncrtBnd; MrchBnd; NHS; PepBnd; SptEdSchPpr; LetterBsbl; LetterBsktbl; IMSpt; St Louis College; Pharmacy.

TROLLA, Therese; J E Murphy HS; Hurley, WI; TrsFrshCls; Chr; HonRl; HospAde; NatlFornLg; SchMus; Yrbk; Chrldr; CitAwd; College; Airline Stewardess.

TROMANHAUSER, Tamara; Colby Public HS; Medford, WI; Chr; Chrs; ChrhWkr; CmntyWkr; NatlFornLg; OffAde; SchMus; SchPl; TchrAde; 4-HAwd; Coll; Nursing.

TROMBLEY, Janine M; Reese HS; Reese, MI; Band; CncrtBnd; HonRl; MrchBnd; NHS; OffAde; PepBnd; 4-H; FHA; Chrldr; Delta College; Medical Tech.

TROMLEY, Robert T; Lincoln HS; Vincennes, IN; 10/328 HonRl; StuCncl; TchrAde; FTA; MthCl; Rose Hulman Inst Of Tech; Teacher.

TROMPETER, Gregory M; Bergan HS; Peoria, IL; 27/210 HonRl; SchPl; RptrSchPpr; Illinois State Univ; Accounting.

TRONNIER, Joanne; Southwest HS; Green Bay, WI; 74;427 HonRl; HospAde; PresJA; NHS; SchMus; VPRptrYrbk; RptrSchPpr; VPFTA; LatCl; PpCl; University Hospital;radiology.

TROSEN, Cindy L; Larimore HS; Larimore, ND; PresSophCls; Band; HonRl; 4-H; SecFHA; PpCl; SciCl; LetterChrldr; AmLegAwd; 4-HAwd; Univ Of Minnesota; Dentist.

TROSHYNSKI, Jerry J; West Holt HS; Atkinson, NE; PresFrshCls; Band; Chr; Chrs; ChrhWkr; CncrtBnd; HonRl; MrchBnd; NHS; PepBnd; SchMus; Bsbl; LetterBsktbl; LetterFtbl; College.

TROSHYNSKI, Tom J; West Holt HS; Atkinson, NE; 7/69 VPFrshCls; ALBoysSt; Band; CncrtBnd; HonRl; MrchBnd; NHS; PepBnd; SchMus; SchPl; GerCl; Bsbl; CaptBsktbl; LetterFtbl; Kearny St College; Pharmacy.

TROSKE, Danette E; Doland Ind HS; Turton, SD; SecTrsSophCls; Band; Chrs; HonRl; VPNatlFornLg; SchPl; Pres4-H; TreasFHA; VPFNA; LetterTrk; College; English.

TROST, Jennifer L; Parkside HS; Jackson, MI; 2/415 Band; CncrtBnd; MrchBnd; PepBnd; LetterBsktbl; GAA; IMSpt; Albion Clge; Zoology.

TROST, Joanne C; Warren HS; Warren, IL; 22/58 PresJrCls; PresBand; CncrtBnd; HonRl; LbryAde; MrchBnd; PepBnd; Yrbk; 4-H; Glf; GAA; DanFAwd; 4-HAwd; Business School; Vocation.

TROST, Steven M; Taylorville HS; Taylorville, IL; 35/271 CncrtBnd; Mdrgl; NatlMeritFnl; SchMus; RptrSchPpr; Ftbl; LetterTrk; CchngActv; 4-HAwd; Univ Of Illinois.

TROST, Susan A; Grosse Pointe South HS; Grosse Pointe Farm, MI; Chrs; HonRl; StuGov; TchrAde; CaptSwmmng; GAA; U Of Vermont; Clothing And Textiles.

TROTTER, Andrea J; Coal City HS; Coal City, IL; 2/92 Band; Chrs; HonRl; MrchBnd; NHS; NatlMeritSchl; PepBnd; SchMus; SchPl; RptrYrbk; Il State Univ; Mathematics.

TROTTER, Christopher W; Lake Zurich HS; Barrington, IL; AFS; Chr; Chrl; ChrhWkr; HonRl; NHS; NatlThespSoc; PolWkr; SchMus; College; Theater.

TROTTER, James M; South Iron HS; Annapolis, MO; Band; ChrhWkr; CncrtBnd; HonRl; MrchBnd; PepBnd; StuCncl; PpCl; LetterBsbl; LetterBsktbl; Oakland City Clge; Music.

TROTTER, Jeffrey P; Maine Twp North HS; Glenview, IL; HonRl; NatlMeritCmnd; Univ Of Illinois; Medicine.

TROTTER, Jim S; Edgemont HS; Provo, SD; VPSophCls; PresJrCls; Chrs; ChrhWkr; HonRl; SchPl; SctActv; StuCncl; LetterBsktbl; LetterFtbl; LetterTrk; College; Engineer.

TROTTIER, Gail K; William Horlick HS; Racine, WI; 102/568 HonRl; NatlFornLg; SchMus; SchPl; U Of Wi; Theatre.

TROTTIER, Gail M; Laona HS; Green Bay, WI; 12/36 SecJrCls; Band; Chrs; CncrtBnd; HonRl; MrchBnd; PepBnd; RptrYrbk; EdSchPpr; PpCl; LetterBsktbl; College; Accounting.

TROUB, Elizabeth A; Mason HS; Mason, MI; 9/233 HonRl; JrNHS; NHS; SchMus; EdYrBk; 4-H; FrCl; Bsktbl; Tennis; 4-HAwd; Mi St Univ; Education.

TROUGHTON, Robert N; Fremont HS; Fremont, MI; Aud/Vis; HonRl; LbryAde; GerCl; College; Engineer.

TROUP, Brad L; Plymouth HS; Plymonth, IN; Ftbl; Trade Sch; Voc.

TROUP, Debbie M; North Daviess HS; Odon, IN; 8/114 ChrhWkr; DrlTm; HonRl; OffAde; SchPpr; PpCl; IMSpt;.

TROUT, Cathy L; Central HS; St Joseph, MO; CncrtBnd; HonRl; HospAde; SchMus; SchPl; SchPpr; GerCl; SciCl; LetterSwmmng; College; Fashion Mdse.

TROUT, Gary J; Advance HS; Advance, MO; 1/45 PresFrshCls; ALBoysSt; ChrhWkr; HonRl; StuCncl; EdSchPpr; FFA; SciCl; LetterBsbl; CaptBsktbl; Murray State U; Journalism.

TROUT, Pamela K; New Palestine HS; Greenfield, IN; 13/180 Band; CncrtBnd; HonRl; MrchBnd; NHS; PepBnd; SptEdYrbk; LatCl; LetterBsktbl; LetterTennis; College; Physical Ed.

TROUT, Robert J; South Side 'S; Ft Wayne, IN; 93/451 HonRl; College; Medicine.

TROUT, Samuel; Staunton HS; Brazil, IN; 6/60 VPFrshCls; VPSophCls; ALBoysSt; HonRl; ModUN; NHS; StuCncl; KeyCl; LatCl; MthCl; Ind St Univ;law.

TROUT, Scott E; Northside HS; Muncie, IN; 23/250 Chr; HonRl; NHS; NatlMeritSF; SchMus; SctActv; LatCl; PpCl; LetterFtbl; LetterSwmmng; Indiana Univ; Medicine.

TROUT, Sharron; Twin Rivers HS; Broseley, MO; Chr; ChrhWkr; CmntyWkr; HonRl; LbryAde; FHA; PpCl; Coll.

TROUT, William E; New Palestine HS; Greenfield, IN; 16/185 Band; CncrtBnd; MrchBnd; NHS; KeyCl; LatCl; Glf; Tennis; Purdue U; Biology.

TROUTMAN, Mark R; Bishop Luers HS; New Haven, IN; 1/225 HonRl; NHS; NatlMeritCmnd; Yrbk; KeyCl; ChmbCommrsAwd; KiwanAwd; Univ Of Michigan; Actuarial Science.

TROUTMAN, Robert A; Wichita HS; Wichita, KS; 1/600 ALBoysSt; Chr; HonRl; NHS; StuGov; GerCl; MthCl; LetterTrk; Us Military Acad;.

TROUTT, David A; Rolla HS; Rolla, MO; 60/277 Band; Chr; ChrhWkr; CncrtBnd; DrmMjrt; MrchBnd; KeyCl; LetterBsktbl; LetterFtbl; IMSpt; Col; Civil Eng.

TROUTT, Frederick P; Pope County Community HS; Golconda, IL; TrsFrshCls; Chr; Chrs; HonRl; TchrAde; YthFlsp; 4-H; PpCl; Bsktbl; LetterTrk; College; Teacher.

TROUTT, Mark W; Harrisonville HS; Harrisonville, MO; HonRl; SchMus; SchPl; StuCncl; TchrAde; LetterBsbl; LetterBsktbl; LetterTennis; LetterTrk; University; Professional.

TROVILLION, David P; Pope County Comm HS; Golconda, IL; 3/56 TrsFrshCls; PresJrCls; Band; ChrhWkr; HonRl; SchPl; 4-H; SpnCl; LetterTennis; DanFAwd; Technical School; Commercial Graphics.

TROVILLION, Jill; Vienna HS; Grantsburg, IL; LbryAde; StuCncl; TchrAde; FHA; PpCl;.

TROXEL, Carol L; Clinton HS; Clinton, IL; Chrs; HonRl; HospAde; SctActv; YthFlsp; Yrbk; SchPpr; 4-H; FNA; FrCl; PpCl; Trade School; Secretary.

TROXELL, Monte R; Chrysler HS; New Castle, IN; ChrhWkr; CmntyWkr; RptrSchPpr; Vincennes University; Law Enforcement.

TROY, Kathleen E; Elizabeth Seton HS; South Holland, IL; 60/251 HonRl; IntrClCncl; NHS; RptrYrbk; SchPpr; FSA; PresMthCl; PresSciCl; Purdue University; Science.

TROY, Patrick J; Amos Alonzo Stagg HS; Palos Hills, IL; 110/499 SpnCl; Ftbl; IMSpt; Il Institute Of Tech; Electrical Engineer.

TROYER, Clayton R; Iowa Mennonite HS; Kalona, IA; Band; HonRl; SchPl; StuCncl; YthFlsp; SchPpr; Socr; IMSpt; CitAwd; Agriculture; Farming.

TROYKE, Janet M; Lake Park HS; Roselle, IL; HonRl; Bsbl; Bsktbl; GAA; IMSpt; PPFtbl; College; Registered Nursing.

TRUDEAU, Michele A; Reese HS; Vassar, MI; 24/130 SecSophCls; HonRl; NHS; NatlMeritSchl; SchAde; SctActv; StuCncl; TchrAde; RptrSchPpr; SchPpr; GerCl; PpCl; Alma College; Social Work.

TRUDEAU, Steve W; Columbus HS; Marshfield, WI; 21/118 PresJrCls; HonRl; Trk; Trade Schl; Professional.

TRUDELL, Gerry J; Central HS; Bay City, MI; NatlMeritSF; LatCl; LetterBsktbl; College; Science.

TRUDELL, Rosemary; St Hedwig HS; Detroit, MI; HonRl; JA; NHS; StuCncl; Henry Ford Com College; Management.

TRUE, Dale; Brown County HS; Nashville, IN; ChrhWkr; HonRl; SchPl; SctActv; StuCncl; FrCl; College.

TRUEBLOOD, Brian; Griffith HS; Griffith, IN; Chr; HonRl; TchrAde; Trk; IMSpt;.

TRUEBLOOD, Maureen A; Raymond Central HS; Raymond, NE; Chrs; HonRl; StuCncl; RptrSchPpr; SecFHA; College; Professional.

TRUEBLOOD, Rebecca; Maconaquah HS; Peru, IN; LbryAde; TchrAde; College; Teacher.

TRUEBLOOD, Susan D; Central City HS; Central City, NE; PresSophCls; Band; CncrtBnd; MrchBnd; TchrAde; Yrbk; SpnCl; Chrldr; University; Social Studies.

TRUELOVE, Kevin M; East Noble HS; Laotto, IN; 18/274 HonRl; NHS; NatlMeritFnl; FFA; SciCl; GovHonPrgAwd; JETSAwd; LionAwd; Purdue U; Mechanical Engineering.

TRUELOVE, Kevin M; East Noble HS; La Otto, IN; 24/269 HonRl; NatlMeritSF; NatlSciFnd; FFA; Purdue Univ; Mech Engineer.

TRUETKEN, Robert L; Wheatland HS; Park, KS; HonRl; SchPl; StuGov; TchrAde; RptrYrbk; RptrSchPpr; LetterTrk; LetterWrstlng; IMSpt; AmLegAwd; GodCntryAwd; CitAwd;.

TRUITT, Lorraine; Murphysboro Township HS; Murphysboro, IL; Chrs; ChrhWkr; HospAde; OffAde; SchMus; SchPl; StuCncl; FshEdSchPpr; SciCl; MasAwd; Coll; Pro.

TRULSON, Robert W; Edgerton Sr HS; Edgerton, WI; AFS; Band; MrchBnd; PepBnd; SchPl; TchrAde; Wrstlng; VFWAwd; University; Professional.

TRUMBLE, Wendi S; Pecatonica Area HS; Blanchardville, WI; TrsSophCls; ALAGirlsSt; Band; ChrhWkr; CncrtBnd; HonRl; MrchBnd; NatlFornLg; PepBnd; Twrl; Sec4-H; Bsktbl; LetterTrk; GAA; Trade School; Vocation.

TRUMBULL, Rodney D; Mc Pherson County HS; Tryon, NE; 3/12 SecJrCls; ALBoysSt; HonRl; Sec4-H; SecKeyCl; Bsktbl; LetterFtbl; LetterTrk; IMSpt; 4-HAwd; Univ.

TRUMBULL, Tracy K; Norway Community HS; Norway, IA; 4/33 PresSophCls; Band; ChrhWkr; HstFrshCls; HonRl; NHS; SchPl; StuCncl; SptEdYrbk; Trk; Ia State U; Math.

TRUMM, Ann M; Aquin HS; Hopkinton, IA; 4/67 TrsJrCls; Chr; Chrs; CmntyWkr; HonRl; LbryAde; SchMus; SchPl; StuCncl; RptrYrbk; Mount Mercy College; Elementary Teacher.

TRUMP, John R; Topeka West HS; Evanton, IL; ChrhWkr; HonRl; LitMag; ModUN; NatlFornLg; PolWkr; TchrAde; RptrYrbk; FrCl; HstJrCls; College; Management Executive.

TRUMP, Karla R; Knightstown HS; Knightstown, IN; 1/135 ALAGirlsSt; ChrhWkr; HonRl; LbryAde; SecNHS; NatlMeritCmnd; FrCl; DARAwd; KiwanAwd; OptClAwd; Indiana Univ; French.

TRUMP, Michael J; Kingsford Sr HS; Kingsford, MI; 1/168 PresSophCls; PresSrCls; AFS; Band; NHS; NatlMeritFnl; Bsktbl; LetterFtbl; Tennis; KiwanAwd; Northwestern Univ; Physician.

TRUSSELL, Debra K; Mt Pleasant HS; Mt Pleasant, MI; 46/332 Band; CncrtBnd; HonRl; MrchBnd; NHS; StuCncl; Yrbk; Central Michigan Univ; Computer Programming.

TRYBON, Lori M; Regina HS; Detroit, MI; NHS; MthCl; GAA; IMSpt; College; Public Accountant.

TRYBULA, Paula A; Alvernia HS; Chicago, IL; 1/300 NatlFornLg; NHS; Knox Univ; Chemistry.

TRYBULA, Peggy J; Neillsville HS; Neillsville, WI; ChrhWkr; HonRl; Yrbk; RptrSchPpr; FBLA; FHA; PpCl; Eau Claire Tech; Secretary.

TRYNIECKI, Timothy; St Louis HS; St Louis, MO; 35/206 Chr; HonRl; NatlMeritCmnd; SctActv; Bsktbl; Socr; IMSpt; Univ Of Missouri; Professional.

TRYON, Thea A; Waterford Mott HS; Pontiac, MI; Band; Chr; ChrhWkr; MrchBnd; NatlMeritSF; PepBnd; SchMus; SchPl; StuGov; YthFlsp; Michigan State University.

TRYTTEN, Anne L; Maine South HS; Park Ridge, IL; 99/849 Chr; Chrs; HonRl; NHS; Orch; SchMus; TchrAde; YthFlsp; PpCl; Tennis; Med Tech Or Computer Science.

TSAMPIS, Mary; Andrean HS; Gary, IN; LbryAde; FrCl; Ind Univ; History Teacher.

TSAO, Pearl W; Evanston Twp HS; Evanston, IL; HonRl; Univ Of Oregon; Art.

TSCHANZ, Susan E; Monroe Sr HS; Monroe, WI; 88/255 4-H; FHA;.

TSCHARNER, Larry; Stephan Hempstead HS; Dubuque, IA; 29/509 Band; CncrtBnd; HonRl; JA; MrchBnd; NHS; PepBnd;.

TSCHIMPERLE, Mike; Chaska Sr HS; Chaska, MN; ALBoysSt; ChrhWkr; HonRl; JrNHS; NHS; StuCncl; College; Physical Ed.

TSCHIRHART, James M; Plymouth Salem HS; Plymouth, MI; ChrhWkr; NatlMeritFnl; NatlMeritSF; SctActv; LetterSwmmng; Univ; Medicine.

TSCHUOR, Teresa; Delta HS; Muncie, IN; 7/293 VPFrshCls; VPSophCls; Chr; HonRl; NHS; RedCrAde; SchMus; SciCl; CchngActv; College.

TSIANG, Judith A; Wheaton Christian HS; Wheaton, IL; VPSrCls; Chr; HonRl; SchMus; StuGov; EdYrBk; Yrbk; SchPpr; LetterTennis; LetterTrk; College; Professional.

TSIGULOFF, Laura; Homestead HS; Ft Wayne, IN; HonRl; TchrAde; Yrbk; Chrldr; PPFtbl; Ball St Univ; Business.

TSITMIS, Sophia; Emerson HS; Gary, IN; 7/224 Northwest Indiana Univ; Business Admin.

TSOU, Carole V; Pontiac Catholic HS; Bloomfield Hills, MI; 1/149 HonRl; LbryAde; ModUN; NHS; NatlMeritFnl; NatlMeritSchl; RptrYrbk; RptrSchPpr; FrCl; BauchLmbAwd; U Of Mi; Physician.

TSOUCHLOS, Gussie; Thorton Fractional North HS; Calumet City, IL; 3/433 HonRl; TreasNHS; VPStuCncl; TchrAde; Purdue University; Computer Technology.

TSUJI, Lisa L; Central HS; Omaha, NE; 29/446 HonRl; NHS; VPSpnCl; PresPpCl; Univ Of Ne At Lincoln.

TUADER, James A; New Richmond HS; New Richmond, WI; 60/175 VPFrshCls; AFS; ChrhWkr; SchMus; StuCncl; LetterBsbl; LetterBsktbl; LetterFtbl; PresAwd; Clge; Journalism.

TUASON, Theresa D; Alexander Ramsey HS; Roseville, MN; 50/557 AFS; ALAGirlsSt; HonRl; HospAde; JrNHS; NHS; NatlSciFnd; Yrbk; FrCl; LetterTrk; St Benedicts.

TUBBS, Denise; Northrop HS; Ft Wayne, IN; Band; CncrtBnd; SecJA; MrchBnd; NatlMeritSF; TchrAde; PPFtbl; Purdue Univ; Psychology.

TUBBS, Jerry D; Forest Lake HS; Forest Lake, MN; ChrhWkr; HonRl; NatlFornLg; StuCncl; SchPpr; Coll; Psychiatrist.

TUBBS, Linda G; Metropolis Community HS; Brookport, IL; HonRl; NHS; FHA; MthCl; Shawnee Jr Coll; Computer Math.

TUBBS, Mark; Lincoln Community Hs; Lincoln, IL; HonRl; NHS; NatlMeritCmnd; SptEdSchPpr; SciCl; LetterTennis; U; Professional.

TUBBS, Teri N; Appleton HS; Appleton, MN; Chrs; HonRl; SchMus; SchPl; RptrSchPpr; SptEdSchPpr; SchPpr; 4-H; FHA; 4-HAwd; Coll; Drama.

TUBBS, Terry W; Craig Riii HS; Bigelow, MO; 2/20 PresFrshCls; ALBoysSt; HonRl; PresStuCncl; FFA; LetterBsktbl; LetterFtbl; DARAwd; College.

TUCK, David P; Pennfield HS; Battle Creek, MI; 7/184 PresBand; PresCncrtBnd; PresMrchBnd; PresNHS; NatlMeritCmnd; PepBnd; StuCncl; SpnCl; PresAwd; Albion College; Engineering.

TUCKER, David C; Mediapolis Comm HS; Mediapolis, IA; 8/80 HonRl; 4-H; PresFFA; Bsbl; Bsktbl; LetterGlf; 4-HAwd; College.

TUCKER, Debra J; Warsaw Comm HS; Warsaw, IN; Chr; ChrhWkr; NatlFornLg; SchMus; SchPl; 4-H; FHA; KeyCl; PpCl; Purdue Univ; Pharmacy.

TUCKER, Elizabeth; Immaculata HS; Leavenworth, KS; HonRl; HospAde; PolWkr; RedCrAde; SchAde; StuGov; TchrAde; PpCl; SciCl; Trk; St Mary College; Biology.

TUCKER, Elizabeth S; Normal Comm HS; Normal, IL; 54/441 Band; SecCncrtBnd; HonRl; MrchBnd; NHS; NatlThespSoc; Orch; PepBnd; SchPpr; Illinois State Univ; Music.

TUCKER, James R; Riverton HS; Riverton, IL; CmntyWkr; HonRl; NHS; ROTC; StuCncl; Trk; Colorado Sch; Gunsmith.

TUCKER, Jill; Blue Valley HS; Stanley, KS; Band; Chr; CncrtBnd; HonRl; MrchBnd; Orch; PepBnd; SctActv; TchrAde; LetterTennis; Kansas Univ; Law.

TUCKER, Julie K; Escanaba Sr HS; Escanaba, MI; 27/389 Band; Chrs; ChrhWkr; CncrtBnd; HonRl; MrchBnd; NHS; Orch; PepBnd; SchMus; StuGov; CivCl; College; Elementary Ed.

TUCKER, Karen S; Valle HS; Ste Genevieve, MO; TrsFrshCls; TrsSophCls; DrlTm; HonRl; HospAde; NHS; StuCncl; SchPpr; PpCl; IMSpt; Nursing School; Rn.

TUCKER, Kathy M; New Palestine HS; Greenfield, IN; 13/128 Band; HonRl; NHS; YthFlsp; Yrbk; 4-H; Bsktbl; Tennis; GAA; Franklin Clg; Physical Ed.

TUCKER, Kelley A; University HS; Milwaukee, WI; AFS; Chr; CmntyWkr; HonRl; ModUN; NatlMeritSF; OffAde; SctActv; YthFlsp; SchPpr; PpCl; LetterTrk; Johns Hopkins Univ; Medicine.

TUCKER, Kevin L; Roxana Sr HS; South Roxana, IL; VPSophCls; Chrs; ChrhWkr; HonRl; SchMus; SchPl; SctActv; TchrAde; FFA; SciCl; Bsbl; Bsktbl; LetterTrk; College; Medicine.

TUCKER, Kimberly A; Vienna HS; Babbitt, MN; 23/140 DrmBgl; HonRl; NatlThespSoc; SchPl; YthFlsp; FNA; LatCl; SpnCl; MthCl; BttyCrckrAwd; Vermillian Comm College; Pharmacist.

TUCKER, Lyle A; Warren HS; Warren, IL; 8/60 Band; Chrs; ChrhWkr; CmntyWkr; CncrtBnd; MrchBnd; PresStuCncl; StuGov; LetterFtbl; LetterTrk; College; Engr.

TUCKER, Marland A; Carlyle HS; Huey, IL; 7/135 Chr; ChrhWkr; HonRl; NHS; SchPl; YthFlsp; PpCl; College; Teacher.

TUCKER, Mary S; Webster Groves HS; Webster Groves, MO; SecTrsSrCls; AFS; HonRl; HospAde; ModUN; NatlMeritSF; SecNatlThespSoc; SchPl; YthLg; SchPpr; Yale U; Journalism, Dramatics.

TUCKER, Nancy W; Southwest HS; Kansas City, MO; HonRl; NatlFornLg; NatlThespSoc; Quill&Scroll; SctActv; StuCncl; EdSchPpr; FrCl; University Of South; Journalism.

TUCKER, Patricia A; O Fallon Twns HS; O Fallon, IL; Chrs; HonRl; ModUN; FrCl; Bsbl; College; Professional.

TUCKER, Robert L; Notre Dame HS; Kelso, MO; HonRl; NHS; TchrAde; LetterBsktbl; Trk; Missouri State Univ; Computer Science.

TUCKER, Teresa F; Paxton HS; Paxton, IL; 16/136 HonRl; NHS; NatlThespSoc; SchPl; StuCncl; RptrSchPpr; EdSchPpr; EngCl; LatCl; Marion College; Psychology.

TUCKER, Terry R; Jasper HS; Jasper, IN; 38/286 HonRl; JrNHS; NHS; SctActv; LetterBsbl; CaptBsktbl; LetterTrk; GovHonPrgAwd; Ind State Univ; Drafting.

TUCKER, Tim D; Stevens HS; Rapid City, SD; 33/431 Chrl; Chrs; HonRl; NatlMeritFnl; NatlMeritSF; SchMus; LetterGlf; IMSpt; Law Enforcement.

TUCKER, William T; Evanston Twp HS; Evanston, IL; Band; CmntyWkr; HonRl; Orch; RedCrAde; Medical School; Medicine.

TUCKETT, Harold W; Swartz Creek HS; Flint, MI; 27/400 Band; CncrtBnd; HonRl; NatlMeritCmnd; StuCncl; TchrAde; YthFlsp; SpnCl; LetterTrk; Univ Of Michigan; Journalism.

TUDISCO, Catherine M; Taft HS; Chicago, IL; Chrs; CmntyWkr; OffAde; StuCncl; TchrAde; Teen; KeyCl; PpCl; Trade School; Beautician.

TUEGEL, Marcia L; Parkway North HS; St Louis, MO; 26/468 Chr; Chrs; ChrhWkr; NHS; NatlMeritSF; TchrAde; PpCl; University; Elem Education.

TUFTE, Greg N; Northwood Public HS; Northwood, ND; Band; ChrhWkr; HonRl; MrchBnd; PepBnd; VPYthFlsp; FFA; Ftbl; Wrstlng; University; Agriculture.

TUFTE, Gregory; Northwood Public HS; Northwood, ND; Band; ChrhWkr; CmntyWkr; CncrtBnd; HonRl; MrchBnd; PepBnd; YthFlsp; FFA; Ftbl; Wrstlng; Univ; Major Study.

TUFTE, Mark G; Northwood HS; Northwood, ND; TrsSrCls; Band; Chr; Chrs; ChrhWkr; StuCncl; SchPpr; Bsbl; LetterBsktbl; LetterFtbl; LetterTrk; Univ Of North Dakota; Chemical Engineering.

TUGGLE, Brenda G; Laurel HS; Laurel, IN; ALBoysSt; ALAGirlsSt; JA; NHS; StuCncl; FTA; GAA; JAAwd; PresAwd; CitAwd; Clge; Curr Of Major Study.

TUGGLE, Robert M; Centerville HS; Richmond, IN; HonRl; StuCncl; RptrYrbk; LetterBsbl; Tennis; IMSpt; Coll; Radio Broadcasting.

TUINSTRA, Penelope R; W Chicago Comm HS; W Chicago, IL; 3/311 HonRl; JA; NHS; NatlMeritSF; StuCncl; EdSchPpr; 4-H; GerCl; 4-HAwd; College; Veterinarian.

TUITT, Molly A; Cary Grove HS; Cary, IL; Chr; Chrs; HonRl; NatlFornLg; NHS; SchMus; SchPl; SctActv; Yrbk; University; Veterinarian.

TUKESBREY, Robert A; Deerfield HS; Deerfield, IL; HonRl; Trk; No Illinois Univ; Accountant.

TULARE, Walter; Winona Sr HS; La Moille, MN; Chr; HonRl; SctActv; Wrstlng; College; Engr.

TULEY, Michael J; Canton R V HS; Canton, MO; Band; Chr; Chrs; CncrtBnd; MrchBnd; PepBnd; SchMus; SchPl; SciCl; University.

TULEY, Millie A; Marion Co R Ii HS; Palmyra, MO; /29 VPFrshCls; PresSophCls; ChrhWkr; HonRl; SchPl; FHA; LetterBsbl; LetterBsktbl; Trk; PresAwd; Trade Or Business School; Vocational.

TULIP, Lori J; Pepin HS; Pepin, WI; SecFrshCls; HonRl; LbryAde; StuCncl; YthFlsp; RptrSchPpr; FHA; PpCl; Chrldr; GAA; College; Curriculum Of Major Studies.

TULL, Ava J; Diagonal Comm HS; Diagonal, IA; SecFrshCls; Band; Chr; Chrs; HonRl; SchPl; StuCncl; 4-H; LetterBsktbl; College; Medical Secretary.

TULLOCK, Donna J; R3 Potosi HS; Potosi, MO; 3/223 Band; CncrtBnd; HonRl; JrNHS; MrchBnd; NHS; PepBnd; FTA; SciCl; College; Speech.

TUMAVICH, James R; Morton East HS; Cicero, IL; 61/724 VPSrCls; JrNHS; NHS; NatlMeritSF; GerCl; LetterFtbl; Univ Of Ill; Engineer.

TUMBLESON, Theresa A; Western HS; Neponset, IL; 2/54 SecSrCls; Band; ChrhWkr; HonRl; NHS; NatlThespSoc; Quill&Scroll; SchPl; EdYrBk; 4-H; FTA; PpCl; SciCl; W Illinois Univ; Science.

TUMMETT, David J; Appleton West HS; Appleton, WI; 50/603 Band; PresJA; NHS; Orch; PepBnd; PolWkr; StuCncl; YthLg; Ftbl; Socr;.

TUMY, Tamara L; Boonville HS; Boonville, MO; Band; Chrl; ChrhWkr; NHS; SchPl; SecFrCl; PpCl; VPSciCl; Bsktbl; Trk; Chrldr; University; Wildlife Mgmt.

TUNBERG, Jeffrey; Lincoln HS; Thief River Falls, MN; 28/250 Band; HonRl; JrNHS; NHS; StuCncl; GerCl; Swmmng; Ftbl; Nd Univ; Business.

TUNDALL, Ron; Laverne Comm HS; Luverne, IA; 5/47 PresSophCls; HstSrCls; Aud/Vis; Band; Chrs; ChrhWkr; HonRl; JCC; OffAde; PepBnd; Agriculture.

TUNE, Barbara; Galesburg Sr Hs; Galesburg, IL; 20/588 ChrhWkr; HonRl; NHS; NatlMeritCmnd; TchrAde; FrCl; LatCl; College; Special Education Deaf.

TUNELL, Linda J; Downers Grove HS; Westmont, IL; 44/827 Chr; Chrs; ChrhWkr; DrlTm; HonRl; NHS; SchMus; SchPl; Eastern Illinois Univ; Special Education.

TUNGSETH, Joy H; Kennedy Public HS; Drayton, ND; 2/27 TrsJrCls; Band; ChrhWkr; HonRl; LbryAde; NatlMeritCmnd; Yrbk; SchPpr; SecSpnCl; College; Accounting.

TUNHEIM, Julie S; Marshall County Central; Newfolden, MN; 3/39 ALAGirlsSt; ChrhWkr; CncrtBnd; HonRl; NHS; RptrSchPpr; SchPpr; FHA; LetterBsktbl; LetterTrk; Concordia College; Teacher.

TUNINK, Anna; Guthrie Center HS; Guthrie Center, IA; Chrs; HonRl;.

TUNINK, Douglas G; Randolph Public HS; Randolph, NE; 9/60 VPJrCls; Chr; Chrs; NatlThespSoc; SchMus; SchPl; Bsbl; Bsktbl; Ftbl; Trk; College; Professional.

TUNNELL, Connie L; Mt Vernon HS; Mt Vernon, MO; 19/120 HonRl; ModUN; NatlThespSoc; SchMus; SchPl; StuCncl; EdSchPpr; 4-H; FHA; FTA; ChmbCommrsAwd; Missouri Southern St College; Business.

TUNNELL, David W; Jeffersonville HS; Jeffersonville, IN; Aud/Vis; VPChr; SchPl; Ius.

TUNNEY, Margaret M; St Augustine HS; Chicago, IL; 17/97 TrsSophCls; DrlTm; HonRl; PolWkr; SchPl; StuCncl; RptrYrbk; Yrbk; Trk; IMSpt; St Xaivers College; Nursing.

TUNNING, Rick; Guthrie Center HS; Guthrie Center, IA; Chr; Chrs; HonRl; NHS; 4-H; Bsbl; 4-HAwd; Univ.

TUPPER, Luanne K; Logan Magnolia HS; Logan, IA; SecJrCls; Band; Chrs; CncrtBnd; HonRl; MrchBnd; NHS; PepBnd; StuCncl; FHA; College; Professional.

TUPPER, Peggy J; Logan Magnolia HS; Logan, IA; Chrs; ChrhWkr; Mdrgl; SchMus; SchPl; YthFlsp; FHA; SecPpCl; CaptBsktbl; Trk; Trade School; Pro.

TURBETT, Marilyn K; Farmington East HS; Hanna City, IL; 13/133 Chrs; HonRl; NHS; StuCncl; Pres4-H; LetterTrk; GAA; CaptIMSpt; PPFtbl; 4-HAwd; College.

TURCHAN, Laura A; Ladywood St Agnes HS; Indianapolis, IN; TrsSophCls; TreasStuCncl; SpnCl; Coll; Health.

TURCOHE, Mary J; New Rockford Central HS; New Rockford, ND; Chr; Chrs; DrlTm; MrchBnd; FHA; Bsktbl; Chrldr; GAA; Nd St U; Home Ec.

TURECHEK, Thomas W; Lincoln Way HS; New Lenox, IL; 8/498 HonRl; NHS; Joliet Jr College.

TUREK, Alice M; Gibbon HS; Gibbon, NE; 7/59 ChrhWkr; HonRl; HospAde; ModUN; PresStuCncl; SecFHA; Bsbl; BttyCrckrAwd; DARAwd; EldAwd; College; Nursing.

TUREK, Donald; Big Bay De Woo HS; Rapid River, MI; Band; ChrhWkr; CncrtBnd; SchPl; SptEdSchPpr; 4-H; Bsktbl; IMSpt; College; Radio Disc Jockey.

TUREK, Elizabeth A; Geneva Public HS; Geneva, NE; Chrs; LbryAde; SchMus; SchPl; PpCl; Trk; GAA; IMSpt; MasAwd;.

TUREK, Jeffrey; Reavis Hs; Chicago, IL; 104/676 HonRl; SchAde; TchrAde; Southern Ill U; Cinematography.

TURESON, David R; Harlem HS; Loves Park, IL; 1/504 Band; ChrhWkr; HonRl; MrchBnd; NHS; PepBnd; Ftbl; Trk; College; Electrical Engineering.

TURIGLIATTO, Truci L; Joliet West HS; Joliet, IL; 51/511 VPSophCls; Chr; HonRl; Mdrgl; NHS; OffAde; SchMus; Chrldr; Southern Methodist Univ; Comm Arts.

TURK, Anna; Wisconsin Heights HS; Black Earth, WI; 3/105 OffAde; SchAde; RptrYrbk; SchPpr; FBLA; Matc; Court Reporting.

TURK, Barbara; Kaneland HS; Maple Park, IL; 3/151 SecJrCls; VPSrCls; HonRl; SchMus; StuCncl; Yrbk; PpCl; Cosmotology School; Cosmotology.

TURK, James J; Nashwauk Keewatin HS; Keewatin, MN; ALBoysSt; Band; Chrs; HonRl; MrchBnd; PepBnd; SctActv; Bsktbl; Swmmng; Coll; Law.

TURK, Matthew J; Central HS; Burlington, IL; 4/75 ALBoysSt; ChrhWkr; HonRl; NHS; NatlThespSoc; SchPl; PresStuCncl; EdYrBk; CaptBsktbl; CaptTrk; Quincy College; Priesthood.

TURKOWSKI, Linda A; Madonna HS; Chicago, IL; 8/294 HonRl; NHS; NatlMeritCmnd; SpnCl; MthCl; BauchLmbAwd; Northwestern Univ; Dr.

TURLEY, Erica J; Hobart Sr HS; Hobart, IN; 28/366 TrsSrCls; ALAGirlsSt; HonRl; SecJrNHS; NHS; StuCncl; PresGerCl; PpCl; Valparaiso Univ; Nursing.

TURLEY, Janie L; East Prairie HS; East Prairie, MO; HstSophCls; Chr; ChrhWkr; HonRl; StuCncl; FHA; PpCl; Trk; CaptChrldr; PresAwd; Cape Giradeau College; Nursing.

TURLEY, Jerri L; Kewanee HS; Kewanee, IL; 44/224 HonRl; FHA; PpCl; LetterBsktbl; CaptTrk; Chrldr; GAA; College; Major Study.

TURLEY, Pamela S; Roseville HS; Roseville, IL; 13/53 PresSophCls; VPJrCls; Chr; Chrs; HonRl; SchMus; SchPl; Business College; Secretary.

TURLINGTON, Laura M; Mayo Senior HS; Rochester, MN; 60/422 DrlTm; NHS; SpnCl; SciCl; Denison University.

TURMELL, Wayne J; Pinconning Area HS; Pinconning, MI; 10/258 NHS; TchrAde; Bsbl; Bsktbl; Ftbl; Cntrl Mi U; Teaching.

TURNAGE, Pamela S; Carthage Sr HS; Carthage, MO; HstSrCls; AFS; DrlTm; HospAde; ROTC; SctActv; PpCl; College; Nursing.

TURNBULL, Elizabeth J; Griggsville HS; Griggsville, IL; PresFrshCls; VPSophCls; TreasBand; Chrs; NHS; SchPl; StuCncl; SecSpnCl; CaptChrldr; GAA; IMSpt; AmLegAwd; College; Professional.

TURNBULL, Patricia A; Battle Creek Central HS; Battle Creek, MI; Chr; HospAde; RedCrAde; FrCl; GerCl; Mich State Univ; German Major.

TURNBULL, Paula J; John Hersey HS; Mt Prospect, IL; 1/800 SecTrsSrCls; HonRl; StuCncl; TchrAde; SptEdYrbk; PpCl; Chrldr; Millikin Univ; Physical Therapy.

TURNBULL, Theresa; Morton Senior Hs; Hammond, IN; 33 OffAde; SctActv; TchrAde; GAA; Trade School ; Nursing.

TURNER, Carolyn A; Dexfield Comm HS; Redfield, IA; 9/45 Chr; HonRl; HospAde; NHS; SchAde; SchMus; TchrAde; FNA; FTA; Bsktbl; Trade; Lab Tech.

TURNER, Cindy; Lapel HS; Lapel, IN; 6/84 SecFrshCls; SecSophCls; HonRl; NHS; RedCrAde; StuCncl; YthFlsp; 4-H; Chrldr; 4-HAwd; Ball St Univ; Journalist.

TURNER, Clifford D; Yates City HS; Yates City, IL; ALBoysSt; RptrSchPpr; SchPpr; PpCl; SciCl; LetterBsktbl; LetterTrk; Work.

TURNER, Dan; Edinburg Community HS; Edinburg, IN; ALBoysSt; Aud/Vis; HonRl; LitMag; Quill&Scroll; StuCncl; RptrSchPpr; FshEdSchPpr; SchPpr; SpnCl; Trade Sch; Disc Jockey.

TURNER, Dean F; Avon Comm School Corp HS; Plainfield, IN; HonRl; NatlCathMusEdAsoc; StuGov; YthFlsp; 4-H; Bsktbl; LetterFtbl; Purdue Agricultural Course; Animal Science.

TURNER, Debra; Wentzville HS; Wentzville, MO; 6/211 VPJrCls; CmntyWkr; NHS; SchPl; SchPpr; PPFtbl; PresAwd; Univ Of Mo; Medical.

TURNER, Denis A; Hartville HS; Hartville, MO; 11/65 ALBoysSt; HonRl; NHS; PresStuCncl; VPFFA; FrCl; CaptBsbl; DanFAwd; Bsktbl; PresFrshCls; Clg Sch Of The Ozarks; Ag Business.

TURNER, Helene J; Highland Park HS; Highland Park, IL; CmntyWkr; HonRl; NHS; OffAde; PolWkr; SchAde; SchMus; TchrAde; YthFlsp; Brandeis University; Medicine.

TURNER, Jacqueline S; Wichita Hts HS; Wichita, KS; 18/430 VPSrCls; CtyCnl; HonRl; JA; NatlFornLg; NatlMeritCmnd; NatlMeritSF; OffAde; StuCncl; StuGov; FrCl; PpCl; IMSpt; Mit; Psychiatrist.

TURNER, James D; Sullivan HS; Sullivan, IN; 6/140 Band; Chr; Chrs; ChrhWkr; CmntyWkr; CncrtBnd; HonRl; IntrClCncl; Bsktbl; ChmnGlf; Us Naval Acad.

TURNER, James J; Wheaton Central HS; Wheaton, IL; Chr; HonRl; NatlFornLg; NHS; SchMus; SchPl; TchrAde; University; Communications.

TURNER, Janice E; Anderson Senior HS; Anderson, IN; HonRl; NHS; NatlThespSoc; SchPl; TchrAde; YthFlsp; FrCl; PpCl; Chrldr; GAA; Ball State University; Pe.

TURNER, Jeanne M; Roncalli HS; Omaha, NE; Chrs; HonRl; PresSpnCl; College.

TURNER, Jeffrey K; North Vermillion HS; Danville, IL; 1/72 PresBand; Chrs; PresNHS; PresPepBnd; PresStuCncl; YthFlsp; LetterBsbl; LetterBsktbl; LetterTrk; Indiana St Univ; Mathematics.

TURNER, Joyce D; Ecorse HS; Ecorse, MI; 9/209 HonRl; LbryAde; NHS; StuCncl; FTA; PpCl; Detroit Coll Business; Legal Secretary.

TURNER, Kathleen A; Pinconning HS; Pinconning, MI; 3/255 CncrtBnd; HonRl; MrchBnd; NatlFornLg; NHS; PresYthFlsp; Yrbk; TreasFTA; PresGerCl; VoiceDemAwd; Taylor Univ; Speech And Drama.

TURNER, Kevin K; Beardstown Sr HS; Beardstown, IL; 10/150 Band; CncrtBnd; HonRl; MrchBnd; NHS; SchMus; RptrYrbk; SptEdYrbk; SciCl; LetterGlf;.

TURNER, Lonnie M; Austin HS; Austin, IN; 3/79 ALBoysSt; HonRl; NHS; SchPl; LatCl; SciCl; College; Professional.

TURNER, Lynn M; Stillman Valley HS; Davis Junction, IL; HonRl; 4-H; FHA; PpCl; Chrldr; GAA;.

TURNER, Mark D; Yates City HS; Yates City, IL; 1/35 HonRl; SchMus; EdYrBk; SchPpr; SpnCl; Bsbl; Bsktbl; College; Professional.

TURNER, Mike; Moulton Udell HS; Moulton, IA; ChrhWkr; CmntyWkr; HonRl; PolWkr; SchPl; SctActv; StuGov; UNYO; YthLg; Bsbl; College; Law.

TURNER, Nan L; Hudson Sr HS; Hudson, WI; AFS; Band; ChrhWkr; HonRl; MrchBnd; GerCl; LetterBsktbl; LetterSwmmng; LetterTrk; Chrldr; College; Professional.

TURNER, Pamela J; Waverly HS; Waverly, IL; SecSrCls; HonRl; NHS; StuCncl; Yrbk; FHA; Trk;.

TURNER, Patrice K; Sioux Valley HS; Harris, IA; 3/13 SecTrsSrCls; ALAGirlsSt; HonRl; SchPl; StuCncl; YthFlsp; RptrYrbk; RptrSchPpr; FTA; CaptBsktbl; GAA; IMSpt; AmLegAwd; Junior College; Psychology.

TURNER, Richard L; Galva HS; Galva, IL; 6/75 Band; HonRl; NHS; NatlThespSoc; SchPl; VPStuCncl; Yrbk; FTA; FrCl; Wrstlng; College.

TURNER, Russell W; Rosiclare HS; Rosiclare, IL; PresSrCls; ChrhWkr; HonRl; ROTC; SctActv; YthFlsp; SpnCl; PpCl; Bsbl; Ftbl; U Of Southern Il; Professional Art.

TURNER, Sanita A; West Side Sr HS; Gary, IN; CncrtBnd; NHS; Quill&Scroll; RptrYrbk; College.

TURNER, Seymour M; Mather HS; Chicago, IL; 60/420 CncrtBnd; JA; NatlSciFnd; StuGov; RptrSchPpr; FrCl; MthCl; PresSciCl; Swmmng; Shimer College; Bioanthropology.

TURNER, Shawn C; Springfield Se HS; Springfield, IL; 8/464 NHS; StuCncl; Illinois College; Business Admin.

TURNER, Susan G; Saline HS; Saline, MI; SecFrshCls; SecJrCls; HonRl; 4-H; FHA; GerCl; SpnCl; Trk; College; Airline Stewardess.

TURNER, Tamara L; Aurora Sr HS; Aurora, IN; 6/125 ChrhWkr; CncrtBnd; HonRl; NHS; YthFlsp; Elem Teacher.

TURNER, Teresa M; Stephen Decatur HS; Decatur, IL; 45/476 Chr; CmntyWkr; HonRl; HospAde; NHS; NatlMeritCmnd; StuGov; Yrbk; Univ Of Ill; Sociology.

TURNER, Terri D; Northern HS; Flint, MI; 12/608 PresJrCls; Band; CmntyWkr; CncrtBnd; JA; MrchBnd; NHS; NatlMeritCmnd; Orch; PepBnd; StuCncl; StuGov; RptrSchPpr; JAAwd; Notre Dame; Pre Med.

TURNER, Terry J; Divine Heart Seminary; Walkerton, IN; 1/21 PresSophCls; ChrhWkr; HonRl; NHS; RedCrAde; SctActv; LetterBsbl; CaptBsktbl; LetterFtbl; Purdue Univ; Engineering.

TURNER, Timothy H; Joliet Catholic HS; Braidwood, IL; 51/166 Band; Chrs; ChrhWkr; HonRl; LbryAde; SchAde; SchMus; SchPpr; Bsktbl; CchngActv; College; Accounting.

TURNER, Vernessa A; Lindblom Tech; Chicago, IL; 80/725 SecSrCls; IntrClCncl; OffAde; SchAde; StuCncl; StuGov; TchrAde; YthFlsp; SpnCl; GAA; Univ; Phy Therapist.

TURNER, Vicki L; Exira Comm HS; Exira, IA; 1/47 Band; Chrs; HonRl; NHS; EdYrBk; Yrbk; Pres4-H; LetterBsktbl; LetterTrk; 4-HAwd; Univ; Commercial Art.

TURNEY, Jan E; Clinton HS; Clinton, IL; Chr; Chrs; ChrhWkr; HonRl; NHS; SchMus; FNA; Swmmng; CaptChrldr; IMSpt; Univ; Physical Ed.

TURNEY, Kevin N; Mellen HS; Mellen, WI; 2/44 Band; Chr; ChrhWkr; CncrtBnd; HonRl; MrchBnd; NHS; PepBnd; SchPl; StuCncl; StuGov; 4-H; SpnCl; MthCl; College; Professional.

TURNHULL, Randall; Pittsburg HS; Pittsburg, KS; 38/238 Band; HonRl; MrchBnd; StuCncl; YthFlsp; Glf; Trk; KiwanAwd; RotaryAwd; Ks St Coll Of Pittsburg; Buss Adm.

TURNQUEST, Deborah A; Harlan HS; Chicago, IL; 5/600 SecJrCls; HonRl; NHS; NatlMeritCmnd; SchPl; Yrbk; FrCl; MthCl; Swmmng; CaptChrldr; Il Univ ;med.

TURNQUIST, Robert B; West Vigo HS; W Terre Haute, IN; ALBoysSt; Band; CncrtBnd; PresJA; ModUN; NHS; PresStuCncl; RptrSchPpr; PresKeyCl; Tennis; Purdue Univ; Lawyer.

TURNWALD, Richard S; New Lothrop HS; New Lothrop, MI; 14079 ChrhWkr; HonRl; LbryAde; NHS; NatlMeritCmnd; SchPl; RptrSchPpr; SchPpr; 4-H; PresSpnCl; Mi St Univ; Journalism.

TUROVITZ, Eden H; Niles North HS; Skokie, IL; HonRl; Quill&Scroll; SchAde; TchrAde; RptrSchPpr; EdSchPpr; SchPpr; Univ Of Il; Social Work.

TURPEN, Steve R; Bedford North Lawrence HS; Bedford, IN; 21/423 VPFrshCls; VPSophCls; HonRl; NHS; SchPl; MthCl; SciCl; Bsktbl; Trk; College; Engineering.

TURPIN, Jane A; Troy HS; Troy, KS; SecFrshCls; VPSophCls; VPJrCls; ALAGirlsSt; SchPl; RptrSchPpr; 4-H; PpCl; Highland Jr College.

TURPIN, Lisa A; Worthington Jefferson HS; Worthington, IN; Band; CncrtBnd; HonRl; JrNHS; MrchBnd; NHS; PepBnd; Bsbl; Bsktbl; GAA; Business Sch; Vocation.

TURPIN, Richard A; George Rogers Clark HS; Whiting, IN; 2/260 Chrs; VPNHS; StuCncl; TchrAde; PresSpnCl; KiwanAwd; College; Special Education.

TURPIN, Susan L; Waverly HS; Waverly, IL; 5/33 PresSophCls; VPJrCls; HonRl; NHS; NatlThespSoc; SchPl; VPStuCncl; PresSpnCl; LetterTrk; VoiceDemAwd; College; Professional.

TURTON, Scott D; Niles West HS; Morton Grove, IL; 12/690 HonRl; NHS; NatlMeritCmnd; PepBnd; PolWkr; SctActv; StuCncl; SchPpr; LetterSocr; CaptWrstlng; Loyola Univ.

TURUNEN, Denise E; Baraga Twp HS; Pelkie, MI; Band; HonRl; MrchBnd; SchPl; SctActv; StuCncl; YthLg; 4-H; PpCl; Trk; Mi Tech Univ ;med.

TURVEY, Patricia A; Wm G Mather HS; Munising, MI; 15/124 PresJrCls; ALAGirlsSt; Band; Chr; CncrtBnd; HonRl; SchPl; StuCncl; StuGov; EdYrBk; Mi Tech Univ; Pre Medicine.

TURYK, Mary E; Prospect HS; Mt Prospect, IL; 48/614 Chrs; CmntyWkr; HonRl; HospAde; NatlFornLg; Univ Of Illinois; Science.

TURZENSKI, Terese B; Lourdes Academy; Oshkosh, WI; 8/126 Band; CncrtBnd; HonRl; MrchBnd; NHS; PepBnd; Trk; Univ Of Wisconsin; Accounting.

TUSA, Edward A; Eueleth HS; Eveleth, MN; 60/170 HonRl; SctActv; StuCncl; StuGov; CivCl; LetterBsbl; CaptBsktbl; LetterFtbl; Trk; CchngActv; St Thomas Coll; Law.

TUSCHERER, Joy A; Lennox Public HS; Lennox, SD; Chrs; ChrhWkr; CmntyWkr; HonRl; RptrYrbk; Yrbk;.

TUSKIEWICZ, Suzanne; Regina HS; Detroit, MI; HonRl; NHS; FNA; SpnCl; Harper Nursing Schl; Registered Nurse.

TUTEUR, Peter Z; Evanston Township HS; Evanston, IL; 2/1100 HonRl; NatlMeritSF; PolWkr; SchPl; Univ; Technical Theater.

TUTON, Judy L; Lakeview HS; Decatur, IL; 9/184 Chr; ChrhWkr; CmntyWkr; HonRl; NHS; SctActv; RptrSchPpr; EdSchPpr; Univ; Business Admin.

TUTT, Lisa A; Marathon Cons HS; Marathon, IA; 3/19 Band; Chr; ChrhWkr; CncrtBnd; HonRl; LbryAde; MrchBnd; PepBnd; Quill&Scroll; SchPl; SecStuCncl; TchrAde; YthFlsp; EdYrBk; Bsktbl; Northwestern College; Special Education.

TUTTLE, Barbara; Greeley County HS; Tribune, KS; 10/31 Band; CncrtBnd; HonRl; MrchBnd; PepBnd; TchrAde; SptEdYrbk; Medical Technician.

TUTTLE, Beth A; Ind State Univ Laboratory; Terre Haute, IN; 3/52 PresSophCls; PresJrCls; Band; Chr; Chrs; CmntyWkr; HonRl; NHS; StuCncl; DARAwd; Univ; Teaching Art.

TUTTLE, Debra K; Breckenridge R 1 HS; Breckenridge, MO; PresSophCls; HstSrCls; Chrs; HonRl; SchPl; StuCncl; Yrbk; 4-H; MthCl; PpCl; Bsktbl; Nw Mo State Univ; P E Coach.

TUTTLE, Karen D; Allegan HS; Allegan, MI; 29/189 Chr; ChrhWkr; HonRl; LbryAde; OffAde; SctActv; YthFlsp; 4-H; SpnCl; 4-HAwd; Parson Business School; Business Adm.

TUTTLE, Kimberly K; Albia Community HS; Louilia, IA; Band; ChrhWkr; CncrtBnd; HonRl; MrchBnd; PepBnd; SchPl; Yrbk; Bsbl; LetterWrstlng; College Or Trade School; Undecided.

TUTTLE, Robert; Union City Senior HS; Sherwood, MI; CmntyWkr; HonRl; SctActv; LetterFtbl; Coll; Electronics Tech.

TUTTLE, Sandra L; Wheatland HS; Gove, KS; HonRl; SchPl; StuCncl; YthFlsp; RptrSchPpr; VP4-H; SecFHA; TreasPpCl; LetterBsktbl; 4-HAwd; Clge.

TUTTLE, Steven L; Deland Weldon HS; Deland, IL; ChrhWkr; HonRl; PepBnd; SchPl; SptEdYrbk; FFA; LetterBsbl; LetterFtbl; LetterTrk; SARAwd; Univ; Ag Research.

TUTTLE, Sue E; West Marshall Comm HS; Marshalltown, IA; 4/107 Band; Chrs; CncrtBnd; HonRl; Mdrgl; MrchBnd; PepBnd; Bsktbl; LetterTrk; PPFtbl; Univ; Indust Engr.

TUTUSH, Dusan; Morton Sr HS; Hammond, IN; 9/499 HonRl; Indiana Univ; Doctor.

TUXEN, Betty; Cochran Fountain City HS; Cochrane, WI; 14/93 Band; ChrhWkr; CncrtBnd; MrchBnd; NHS; PepBnd; SchMus; 4-HAwd; Vocational School; Business.

TUXHORN, Rocky L; Smith Center HS; Smith Center, KS; PresStuCncl; StuGov; FFA; LetterFtbl; LetterWrstlng; IMSpt;.

TUZINSKI, Patrick A; Archbishop Wm O Brady HS; W St Paul, MN; 10/140 Chrs; HonRl; NatlThespSoc; SchMus; SchPl; SecStuCncl; LetterBsbl; LetterFtbl; LetterGlf; Clg Of St Thomas; Chem Engineering.

TVEITE, Michael D; Greenway HS; Grand Rapids, MN; 2/165 Band; HonRl; NHS; NatlMeritFnl; NatlMeritSchl; PepBnd; MthCl; SciCl; Glf; Swmmng; St Olaf Clge; Math & Sci.

TWADDLE, Randy; West Nodaway Hs; Elmo, MO; 6/39 ALBoysSt; CncrtBnd; HonRl; ModUN; NHS; PresYrbk; CaptBsktbl; CaptFtbl; U Of Missouri; Journalism.

TWAIT, Susan J; Westview HS; Kankakee, IL; ChrhWkr; HonRl; NHS; NatlThespSoc; Quill&Scroll; SchMus; Yrbk; Kankakee Comm College; Art.

TWARDON, Elizabeth; Our Lady Of Mercy HS; Detroit, MI; HonRl; LbryAde; NatlFornLg; NHS; NatlMeritCmnd; NatlMeritSF; SchMus; SchPl; TchrAde; FrCl; Wayne State Univ; Journalism.

TWARDY, Christine J; Proviso West HS; Westchester, IL; 13/1086 HonRl; NHS; Business School; Fashion Mgmt.

TWAROG, Donna D; Proviso West HS; Bellwood, IL; 86/1200 HonRl; NHS; NatlMeritCmnd; FDA; FNA; RusCl; SpnCl; SciCl; University Of Illinois; Medicine.

TWEDT, John B; Ballard HS; Slater, IA; PresSrCls; Band; Chr; Chrs; HonRl; SctActv; StuGov; TchrAde; YthFlsp; FrCl; Bsktbl; Waldorf College; Telecommunicative Arts.

TWEEDIE, Kathy D; Stet HS; Norborne, MO; Band; ChrhWkr; CncrtBnd; HonRl; SchPl; StuCncl; Yrbk; SchPpr; Pres4-H; SecFHA; LetterBsbl; LetterBsktbl; CitAwd; College.

TWEEDIE, Michelle M; Sterling Hts HS; Sterling Hts, MI; 22/528 Aud/Vis; Band; CncrtBnd; HonRl; MrchBnd; NHS; PepBnd; StuCncl; StuGov; IMSpt; Clg; Music Per.

TWEEDT, Bonnie M; Racine Lutheran HS; Racine, WI; Chr; HonRl; PpCl; Business Schl; Vocation.

TWEEDY, Scott S; East Alton Woodriver Comm HS; Wood River, IL; 4 Aud/Vis; StuCncl; RptrSchPpr; Trade School; Carpenter.

TWEET, Douglas J; Harding HS; St Paul, MN; 4/755 ALBoysSt; Band; CncrtBnd; HonRl; MrchBnd; NHS; NatlMeritSF; TchrAde; GerCl; PresSciCl; LetterFtbl; AmLegAwd; OptClAwd; Univ Of Arizona; Physicist.

TWEETEN, Susan D; Lake Mills Comm HS; Joice, IA; 13/83 Band; Chrs; HonRl; Mdrgl; SchMus; SchPl; TchrAde; SciCl; Bsktbl; Waldorf College; Special Education.

TWENHAFEL, Mark A; Hlv Community HS; Victor, IA; 12/65 HonRl; Trk; IMSpt; Northwestern University; Professional.

TWENTER, Dana A; Pilot Grove HS; Pilot Grove, MO; 3/37 SecSrCls; Chrs; HonRl; SchPl; TchrAde; RptrSchPpr; FshEdSchPpr; 4-H; FHA; 4-HAwd; Bus Schl; Bus Secretary.

TWENTER, Evelyn; Morgan County HS; Stovwer, MO; 9/39 HonRl; NHS; SchPl; FHA; LionAwd; CitAwd; Homemaking.

TWENTER, Mark A; Pilot Grove HS; Pilot Grove, MO; ChrhWkr; SchPl; RptrYrbk; Yrbk; RptrSchPpr; SchPpr; 4-H; FFA; College; Agriculture.

TWETEN, Debra J; East Grand Forks Sr HS; East Grand Forks, MN; 5/157 HonRl; NatlFornLg; SpnCl; Purdue Univ; Fashion Retailing.

TWETEN, William H; Central Valley HS; Buxton, ND; PresFrshCls; HstSophCls; Chrs; CncrtBnd; HonRl; MrchBnd; StuCncl; Yrbk; FFA; College; Architecture.

TWIBELL, Cynthia J; Blackford HS; Hartford, IN; Band; ChrhWkr; DrmMjrt; HonRl; PepBnd; StuCncl; Yrbk; SchPpr; FTA; Ball St Univ; Special Educ.

TWIGG, Charles R; Brother Rice HS; Lathrup Village, MI; Band; CncrtBnd; HonRl; MrchBnd; Univ Of Michigan; Engineering.

TWIGG, Deborah L; Central HS; Aberdeen, SD; 110/420 AFS; Aud/Vis; Chr; ChrhWkr; HonRl; LitMag; SchPl; Wheaton College; Journalism.

TWIGG, Larry D; John Marshall HS; Indianapolis, IN; 58/444 Chr; ChrhWkr; DrlTm; JA; LbryAde; NHS; ROTC; YthFlsp; FTA; MthCl; Cedarville Clg; Minister.

TWILLING, John; Marshall HS; Marshall, MO; ChrhWkr; CtyCnl; CmntyWkr; HonRl; NHS; PolWkr; StuCncl; StuGov; EdYrBk; GovHonPrgAwd; College; Vocation.

TWILLING, Mark A; East Grand Rapids HS; Grand Rapids, MI; HonRl; LetterFtbl; Clge; Chemical Eng.

TWITCHELL, Cindy D; Mehlville Senior HS; St Louis, MO; College.

TWITE, Bruce; Logan Sr HS; La Crosse, WI; 75/226 HonRl; LetterBsbl; LetterBsktbl; LetterFtbl; Coll Uw Madison; Therapist.

TWITON, John H; Barneveld Public HS; Barneveld, WI; PresSophCls; Band; CncrtBnd; HonRl; MrchBnd; PolWkr; StuCncl; Ftbl; LetterGlf; Wrstlng; College.

TWYMAN, Timothy E; Orrick HS; Orrick, MO; VPJrCls; ALBoysSt; HonRl; FFA; GerCl; Bsbl; Bsktbl; LetterFtbl; LetterTrk; College.

TYAHLA, Steven J; Bogan HS; Chicago, IL; 48/704 Band; HonRl; JrNHS; NHS; NatlMeritFnl; SchAde; TchrAde; SpnCl; SciCl; LetterBsbl; College; Finance.

TYCHMAN, Judith H; St Louis Park HS; St Louis Park, MN; 33/749 AFS; ChrhWkr; CmntyWkr; HonRl; HospAde; NatlMeritSF; OffAde; SctActv; RptrYrbk; RptrSchPpr; Pacific U; Bi Linguist.

TYDEMAN, Ann C; Loy Norrix HS; Kalamazoo, MI; NHS; NatlMeritCmnd; Mi State Univ; Environmental Studies.

TYGART, Steven; Southwest HS; Seligman, MO; VPJrCls; HonRl; SchPl; SchPpr; FHA; College; Law Enforcement.

TYKWINSKI, Judy A; Cadillac Sr HS; Cadillac, MI; 49/289 SecSrCls; HonRl; NHS; OffAde; StuCncl; StuGov; YthLg; Davenport College; Secretary.

TYL, Barbara T; Immaculate Heart Of Mary HS; Westchester, IL; TrsSophCls; SecSrCls; SctActv; RptrSchPpr; PresSciCl; Bsktbl; Ftbl; GAA; Triton Jr Clge; Medicine.

TYLER, David C; Granton HS; Granton, WI; 6/24 TrsJrCls; ChrhWkr; HonRl; NatlFornLg; NHS; SchAde; TchrAde; FFA; Bsbl; Glf; Trade School ; Vocation.

TYLER, Jennie L; Lenox Community HS; Lenox, IA; 5/45 Band; HonRl; NHS; PepBnd; SchMus; StuCncl; YthFlsp; Yrbk; ChmnBsktbl; Glf; Amer Inst Busi; Voc.

TYLER, Natalie A; Lakeland Union HS; Minocqua, WI; 3/175 Band; Chr; ChrhWkr; HonRl; HospAde; NatlFornLg; NHS; SchMus; SchPl; Glf; Univ Wi Madison; Pre Med.

TYLON, Sandra L; Parker HS; Chicago, IL; 6/200 TrsSrCls; ChrhWkr; HonRl; StuCncl; CitAwd; Univ; Major Study.

TYMA, Christine E; Nazareth Academy; Hinsdale, IL; 1/154 HonRl; JrNHS; NHS; NatlMeritFnl; Univ Of Chicago; Chemistry.

TYMA, Christine E; Nazareth Acad; Hinsdale, IL; 1/167 HonRl; JrNHS; NHS; NatlMeritSF; Yrbk; U Of Chicago.

TYNAN, Margaret M; Immaculate Conception HS; Elmhurst, IL; 14/186 SecTrsSrCls; HonRl; JA; SchPl; StuGov; RptrYrbk; EdSchPpr; FHA; FTA; IMSpt; U Of Il; English.

TYNDALL, Karen L; Ashland HS; Ashland, WI; 80/215 Band; CmntyWkr; CncrtBnd; HonRl; PepBnd; RedCrAde; SchPl; Twrl; SpnCl; PpCl; Coll; Nurse.

TYNER, Angela L; Fountain Central HS; Veedersburg, IN; HonRl; NHS; Yrbk; FSA; GerCl; PresSpnCl; SciCl; DARAwd; Univ Of Indiana; Medicine.

TYO, Jeanne; Duluth Central HS; Duluth, MN; AFS; HonRl; LbryAde; NHS; FHA; Chrldr; GAA; Coll; Home Ec.

TYRA, Kenneth T; Pioneer HS; Ann Arbor, MI; Chr; NatlFornLg; NatlSciFnd; SchMus; StuCncl; StuGov; RptrSchPpr; LatCl; Univ Of Michigan; International Relations.

TYRE, Harry T; Oakes HS; Oakes, ND; 1/74 ALBoysSt; HonRl; StuCncl; LetterBsktbl; Ftbl; Coll; Biology.

TYRER, Karen A; Trenton HS; Trenton, MI; 105/571 HospAde; NHS; NatlThespSoc; SchMus; SchPl; StuCncl; TchrAde; VPSophCls; PpCl; Mercy School Of Nursing; Nurse.

TYRRELL, Margaret; English Valley HS; North English, IA; Chrs; CmntyWkr; HonRl; PolWkr; SchMus; StuCncl; RptrYrbk; RptrSchPpr; Glf; Trk; College; Profesional Art.

TYRRELL, Mary A; Harry A Burke HS; Omaha, NE; 1/650 ChrhWkr; HonRl; PresNHS; NatlMeritSF; Orch; StuGov; FrCl; MthCl; DARAwd; KiwanAwd; Univ; Professional.

TYSON, Donna K; Cambridge Public HS; Cambridge, NE; HonRl; LbryAde; RptrSchPpr; SchPpr; 4-H; PpCl; College.

TYSON, Paul H; Wichita East HS; Wichita, KS; 71/629 Band; CncrtBnd; HonRl; MrchBnd; NatlMeritSF; Orch; College.

TYSON, Walter E; Lindblom Tech HS; Chicago, IL; HonRl; NHS; NatlMeritCmnd; OffAde;

Quill&Scroll; SchAde; EdSchPpr; SpnCl; Trk; CchngActv; U Of Il; Architect.

TYSOWSKY, George W; Brady HS; St Paul, MN; 11/150 CmntyWkr; HonRl; LbryAde; NHS; PolWkr; SctActv; TchrAde; SciCl; Socr; St Thomas College; Medical Doctor.

TYSZKO, Kenneth A; Lyons Township HS; La Grange, IL; University Of Illinois; Accounting.

TYYKILA, Kenneth E; South Shore HS; Iron River, WI; HonRl; FFA; LetterFtbl; Agriculture.

U

UBBELOHDE, Kurt F; Clear Lake Comm HS; Clear Lake, IA; 6/150 AFS; Band; Chr; HonRl; PresNHS; SchPl; PresStuCncl; YthFlsp; LetterBsktbl; LetterTrk; Us Military Academy; Engr.

UBER, Norma J; Catholic Central HS; Custer, MI; 9/209 HonRl; LbryAde; SpnCl; PpCl; Coll; Dato Proc.

UBERT, Sue; Marion HS; Hays, KS; DrlTm; HonRl; SchPl; StuCncl; SpnCl; PpCl; College; Professional.

UCKERT, Margaret; Clear Lake HS; Clear Lake, SD; 9/57 ALAGirlsSt; ChrhWkr; CmntyWkr; HonRl; NatlFornLg; Orch; StuCncl; 4-H; FHA; 4-HAwd; S Dak St Univ; Clncl Lab Tech.

UDELHOVEN, Cheryl A; Lancaster Sr HS; Lancaster, WI; 18/155 AFS; Band; Chrs; HonRl; MrchBnd; RptrYrbk; RptrSchPpr; FHA; PpCl; IMSpt; U Of Wi Whitewater; Accounting.

UDELHOVEN, James R; Fennimore HS; Fennimore, WI; HonRl; PresFFA; Wrstlng; University; Dairy Farmer.

UDELHOVEN, Karen A; Bloomington HS; Bloomington, WI; 2/50 ALAGirlsSt; HonRl; NHS; StuCncl; StuGov; EdYrBk; Bsktbl; Chrldr; GAA; IMSpt; PPFtbl; DARAwd; Univ Of Wisconsin; Accounting.

UDELL, Jack W; Burwell Jr Sr HS; Burwell, NE; TrsSrCls; Chr; Chrl; Chrs; HonRl; Mdrgl; NHS; RptrYrbk; MthCl; LetterBsktbl; LetterFtbl; College; Science.

UDELL, Jeri K; New Glarus HS; New Glarus, WI; 13/60 Chr; Chrs; HonRl; NHS; SchPl; StuCncl; FBLA; FHA; FTA; PpCl; Univ Of La Crosse; Communications.

UDELL, Suzanne R; Salem HS; Salem, IN; SecFrshCls; SecSophCls; SecJrCls; SecSrCls; HonRl; NHS; NatlThespSoc; SchMus; SchPl; SctActv; RptrSchPpr; FHA; FrCl; Indiana State Univ; Commercial Art.

UDSTUEN, Kelly E; Clayton HS; Clayton, MO; 4/201 Chr; NHS; NatlMeritSF; SchMus; SchPpr; PpCl; LetterBsktbl; CitAwd; College; Physical Therapist.

UEBELHOR, Christy; Forest Park HS; Ferdinand, IN; PpCl; GAA;.

UEBINGER, Jeffrey K; R 1 North Callaway HS; Williamsburg, MO; 6/80 VPJrCls; HonRl; NHS; SchPl; SctActv; FFA; Ftbl; College; Chemical Engineer.

UECKER, Cheryl A; Gaylord Public HS; Gaylord, MN; Chr; ChrhWkr; CmntyWkr; HonRl; SchMus; YthFlsp; 4-H; FHA; LetterBsktbl; GAA; Gustavus Adolphus Clge; Social Work.

UECKER, Jan E; Lena Winslow HS; Lena, IL; 7/98 ChrhWkr; HonRl; NHS; SchPl; SctActv; StuCncl; YthFlsp; Yrbk; VPFHA; GAA; Ill State Univ; Teacher.

UERLING, Lisa A; Republican Valley HS; Indianola, NE; 5/33 PresJrCls; HonRl; StuCncl; Yrbk; PpCl; Trk; College; Business Management.

UERLING, Mark; Republican Valley HS; Indianola, NE; Chrs; CmntyWkr; MrchBnd; SchMus; Sdlty; YthFlsp; 4-H; FFA; Bsbl; Trk; College; Civil Engineering.

UFFELMAN, Sandra; Concordia Lutheran Hs; Decatur, IN; 2 Band; Chr; SecChrhWkr; CncrtBnd; HonRl; MrchBnd; Orch; PepBnd; TchrAde; GAA; College ; Music.

UFHEIL, William J; Notre Dame HS; Niles, IL; 51/256 HonRl; LetterTrk; College; Astrophysics.

UFKES, Julie M; Central HS; Golden, IL; 7/71 TreasChrs; ChrhWkr; HonRl; NHS; SchPl; RptrSchPpr; GerCl; Bsktbl; Trk; PPFtbl; West Ill; Math.

UGLOW, Dennis; Bushnell HS; Bushnell, NE; ALBoysSt; Chrs; ChrhWkr; HonRl; SctActv; StuCncl; YthFlsp; SptEdYrbk; Peru State Coll; Physical Ed.

UHEN, Jane; St Marys HS; New Munster, WI; Chrs; ChrhWkr; CmntyWkr; HonRl; SchMus; SchPl; Yrbk; PpCl; IMSpt; PPFtbl; Trade School; Business.

UHEN, Jean M; St Mary HS; Burlington, WI; 5/71 PresJrCls; Chr; HonRl; LbryAde; SchMus; SctActv; StuCncl; Yrbk; Trk; Chrldr; U Of Wis Madison.

UHEN, Judith A; St Mary HS; Burlington, WI; 12/76 Chr; Chrs; DrlTm; HonRl; SchMus; SctActv; RptrYrbk; SpnCl; SciCl; IMSpt; Wi Univ; Accntg.

UHER, Diane; Milligan Public HS; Western, NE; 1/11 VPFrshCls; VPSophCls; VPJrCls; Band; Chrs; HonRl; StuCncl; Yrbk; PpCl; Chrldr; Coll; Professional.

UHL, Kathryn M; Heelan HS; Sioux City, IA; HonRl; HospAde; MrchBnd; RedCrAde; StuCncl; CaptTwrl; SpnCl; VPPpCl; IMSpt; PPFtbl; Clg; Nursing.

UHL, Mary I; St Teresa HS; Decatur, IL; 9/118 AFS; HonRl; HospAde; PresNHS; NatlMeritCmnd; StuCncl; PpCl; GAA; Univ Of Notre Dame; American Studies.

UHL, Rick A; East Noble HS; Avilla, IN; 1/274 ChrhWkr; HonRl; NatlMeritCmnd; RptrSchPpr; LetterBsbl; LetterFtbl; Purdue Univ; Teacher.

UHLAND, Gary C; Liberty Comm HS; Liberty, IL; 17/56 PresSrCls; Band; CncrtBnd; HonRl; MrchBnd; NHS; SchPl; RptrYrbk; SptEdYrbk; SecFFA; SciCl; CaptBsbl; CaptBsktbl; University; Professional.

UHLAND, Gayla L; Liberty HS; Liberty, IL; 9/62 SecJrCls; VPBand; HonRl; NHS; SchPl; StuCncl; RptrYrbk; Yrbk; Treas4-H; PresFHA; TreasPpCl; Trk; GAA; Univ; Teacher.

UHLENHOP, Susan; Andover HS; Andover, KS; SecSophCls; SecJrCls; Band; CncrtBnd; HonRl; NHS; OffAde; TchrAde; RptrYrbk; Bsktbl; College; Teacher.

UHLIG, Mark A; Wichita Southeast HS; Wichita, KS; ALBoysSt; ChrhWkr; HonRl; NatlMeritFnl; PolWkr; Quill&Scroll; RedCrAde; PresStuCncl; StuGov; SchPpr; Harvard Coll; International Relation.

UHLIG, Mary C; Glidden Public HS; Glidden, WI; ALAGirlsSt; Band; Chr; Chrs; ChrhWkr; CncrtBnd; HonRl; JCC; MrchBnd; PepBnd; CaptBsbl; CaptBsktbl; GAA; IMSpt; State Univ; Professional.

UHLIR, Jennifer M; Harvard HS; Harvard, IL; 27/159 HonRl; NatlThespSoc; Western Illinois Univ; Medical Lab Tech.

UHLMEYER, Greg L; Ccr 1 HS; St Patrick, MO; ChrhWkr; CmntyWkr; HonRl; 4-H; FFA; PpCl; Bsbl; LetterBsktbl; IMSpt; 4-HAwd; Trade Or Business School; Vocation.

UHLRICH, Rich J; Washington HS; Washington, KS; Chrs; ChrhWkr; 4-H; LetterGAA; Flint Hills Area Vo Tech; Vocation.

UHRICH, Terry G; Regis HS; Altoona, WI; VPSophCls; Band; ChrhWkr; CncrtBnd; HonRl; MrchBnd; Orch; SchMus; LatCl; Wrstlng; Marquette Med; Gp.

UITVLUGT, Annette; Kalkaska HS; South Boardman, MI; 2/129 SecSophCls; VPJrCls; VPSrCls; ChrhWkr; HonRl; NHS; NatlMeritSF; SchPl; 4-H; 4-HAwd; Unsure; Medical Field.

UKELE, Lee F; Sabetha HS; Sabetha, KS; AFS; ALBoysSt; HonRl; StuCncl; VP4-H; FFA; LetterFtbl; LetterWrstlng; CchngActv; 4-HAwd; Trade Schl; Agriculture.

UKKESTAD, Elizabeth A; Rushford Public #234 HS; Rushford, MN; AFS; Chrs; ChrhWkr; DrlTm; HonRl; SchPl; RptrSchPpr; FHA; Rochester Schl; Nursing.

UKLEJA, Beth A; Resurrection HS; Chicago, IL; 32/294 HonRl; HospAde; SchAde; SchPl; StuCncl; SpnCl; SciCl; Ne Il Univ; Dentistry.

ULAHAKIS, Tanya L; Memorial HS; Eau Claire, WI; GAA; IMSpt; Univ; Prof.

ULANSKI, Roseann; Saint Florian HS; Hamtramck, MI; 14/126 Chrs; CmntyWkr; HonRl; SchMus; RptrSchPpr; FBLA; Madonna College; Elementary Teacher.

ULASZEK, Carl; Jf Kennedy Hs; Chicago, IL; 13/610 HonRl; TreasNHS; SecSchPl; RptrYrbk; KeyCl; SpnCl; PresMthCl; Loyola U; Dentist.

ULASZEK, Eric F; Hinsdale South HS; Darien, IL; N Central College; Horticulture.

ULASZEK, Karen; James B Conant Hs; Hoffman Estates, IL; HonRl; NHS; StuCncl; RptrYrbk; FshEdSchPpr; Tennis; GAA; University; Professional.

ULBERT, Loretta L; Good Counsel HS; Chicago, IL; Dental Hyg.

ULDRICH, Ronald P; Milligan Public HS; Milligan, NE; SecFrshCls; Band; Chrs; CncrtBnd; MrchBnd; LetterBsbl; Bsktbl; Ftbl; Trk; PresAwd;.

ULFERS, Dallas J; Jefferson HS; Cedar Rapids, IA; TchrAde; Tennis; Kirkwood Comm Clge; Pro Accountant.

ULFERS, Rebecca; Fairbury Cropsey HS; Fairbury, IL; 1/100 Chr; Mdrgl; NHS; NatlMeritFnl; Quill&Scroll; SchPl; StuCncl; RptrYrbk; EdSchPpr; MthCl; Univ; Pre Medicine.

ULFERS, Rebecca L; Fairbury Cropsey HS; Fairbury, IL; 2/113 Chr; HonRl; Mdrgl; NHS; NatlMeritSF; SchPl; StuCncl; YthFlsp; RptrYrbk; EdSchPpr; 4-H; MthCl; Univ Of Utah; Medicine.

ULLMAN, Daniel H; Pioneer HS; Ann Arbor, MI; 5/680 Chr; Mdrgl; NatlMeritSF; NatlSciFnd; Orch; SchMus; RptrSchPpr; MthCl; Yale Univ; Math.

ULLMAN, Shelley A; Hillsboro HS; Hillsboro, IL; 18/188 Chr; Chrs; ChrhWkr; HonRl; NatlMeritCmnd; SchMus; SpnCl; Univ Of Illinois; Veterinarian.

ULLMER, Joy A; Riverside Brookfield HS; Riverside, IL; 7/489 HonRl; LbryAde; NatlMeritCmnd; Univ Of Illinois; Computer Science.

ULLMER, Mary S; St Josephs Academy; Green Bay, WI; 30/155 Chrs; HospAde; LbryAde; NHS; 4-H; FrCl; Marion College; Rn Nurse.

ULLOM, Duane D; Daleville HS; Daleville, IN; ALBoysSt; Aud/Vis; ChrhWkr; HonRl; PpCl; LetterWrstlng; Clge; English.

ULLSTRUP, Mary C; Greenfield HS; Greenfield, WI; Band; ChrhWkr; CncrtBnd; HonRl; HospAde; TchrAde; Madison General School Of Nursing; Nursing.

ULLSTRUP, Michael M; Greenfield HS; Greenfield, WI; ALBoysSt; Band; ChrhWkr; CncrtBnd; HonRl; LitMag; MrchBnd; ModUN; PresNHS; OffAde; St Norbert Col; International Business.

ULM, Lori L; Southeast HS; Springfield, IL; ChrhWkr; StuCncl; YthFlsp; Memorial Medical Center; X Ray Technician.

ULMER, Jaqulin; Carl Junction Hs; Asbury, MO; AFS; ChrhWkr; HonRl; OffAde; SchAde; TchrAde; YthFlsp; TreasFFA; FHA; FTA; College;agribusiness.

ULREY, John; Mcpherson Senior HS; Mcpherson, KS; 57/212 HonRl; StuCncl; TchrAde; Teen; Bsktbl; Ftbl; Hutchinson Community Col; Pharmacist.

ULRICH, Ann E; Aberdeen Central HS; Aberdeen, SD; 1/435 ALAGirlsSt; ChrhWkr; CncrtBnd; CaptDrlTm; HonRl; MrchBnd; NatlFornLg; NHS; Orch; SchMus; PPFtbl; CitAwd; South Dakota St University.

ULRICH, Cheryl A; Stratford HS; Stratford, WI; 5/92 PresSophCls; Band; Chrs; ChrhWkr; CncrtBnd; HonRl; HospAde; Mdrgl; MrchBnd; Bsktbl; U Of Wis La Crosse; Elem Phy Ed.

ULRICH, Daniel; Muncie Burris HS; Muncle, IN; 6;50 VPFrshCls; VPSophCls; PresJrCls; ALBoysSt; PresStuCncl; EdYrBk; RptrSchPpr; LetterBsbl; CaptTrk; OptClAwd; Ball State Univ;architecture.

ULRICH, Joan M; Howards Grove HS; Howards Grove, WI; 1/75 ALAGirlsSt; Band; Chrs; HonRl; SecNatlSciFnd; SchPl; TchrAde; YthFlsp; RptrYrbk; RptrSchPpr; Lakeland College; Math Major.

ULRICH, Joan R; Eureka HS; Eureka, IL; 6/100 PresJrCls; AFS; HonRl; JrNHS; ModUN; NHS; SchPl; StuCncl; FrCl; Univ Of Ill; Psychology.

ULRICH, Lori S; Stratford HS; Stratford, WI; 1/115 Band; Chrs; ChrhWkr; HonRl; HospAde; NHS; Yrbk; FHA; Bsktbl; LetterTrk; Univ; Medical.

ULRICH, Mary Anne L; West Liberty HS; Nichols, IA; 2/100 HonRl; LbryAde; SchPl; RptrSchPpr; 4-H; SciCl; GovHonPrgAwd; Dr Martin Luther College; Teacher.

ULRICH, Rita M; Concordia Academy; Apple Valley, MN; 1/47 HonRl; RptrYrbk; RptrSchPpr; GerCl; College; Computer Science.

ULRICH, Sharon J; Pattonville HS; Bridgeton, MO; HonRl; SctActv; FrCl; PpCl; Chrldr; PPFtbl; College; Business.

ULRICH, Terry W; Ashley HS; Ashley, ND; Chr; Chrs; CncrtBnd; HonRl; PepBnd; SchPl; Trk; Ndsu; Architect.

ULTSCH, Mark K; Beloit Memorial HS; Beloit, WI; ChrhWkr; HonRl; U Of Wi Madison; Elect & Computer Engr.

ULTVLUGT, David P; Battle Creek Central HS; Battle Creek, MI; 1/550 ALBoysSt; NatlFornLg; NatlMeritSF; StuGov; LetterFtbl; Trk; Calvin Coll; Law.

ULVILDEN, Deborah J; Oak Grove HS; Russell, MN; PresFrshCls; PresSrCls; Chr; HospAde; NHS; SchPl; SecStuCncl; FHA; PpCl; Trk; Chrldr; GAA; Augustana College; Theater Arts.

UMBAUGH, Scott E; Edwardsville Sr HS; Edwardsville, IL; 32/435 Chrs; HonRl; NatlMeritCmnd; Berklee School Of Music; Musician.

UMBERGER, Barbara S; De Soto HS; Stoddard, WI; 5/75 Chrs; HonRl; RptrYrbk; PpCl; SecGAA; Viterbo College; English.

UMBERGER, Jean M; Desoto HS; Genoa, WI; 9/75 SecSrCls; HonRl; NatlFornLg; TchrAde; Yrbk; FHA; PpCl; GAA; College; Physical Therapy.

UMBERGER, Laura A; Elwood HS; Elwood, NE; 3/18 VPSophCls; HonRl; HospAde; PresNHS; NatlMeritFnl; TchrAde; YthFlsp; VPFHA; PpCl; LetterTrk; Chrldr; BttyCrckrAwd; Nursing School; Nurse.

UMDENSTOCK, Debbie K; E N Woodruff HS; Peoria, IL; ChrhWkr; CmntyWkr; OffAde; SctActv; YthFlsp; Illinois Central College; Nurse.

UMFLEET, Daniel E; Mt Zion HS; Mount Zion, IL; 14/195 Band; HonRl; NHS; SctActv; LetterTrk; Southern Illinois Univ; Engineering.

UMFLEET, Donna; Dexter Sr HS; Dexter, MO; 10/133 ChrhWkr; HonRl; FBLA; SpnCl; PpCl; Three Rivers Community College; Accounting.

UMFLEET, Jeanne L; Calumet HS; Gary, IN; 4/330 Band; CncrtBnd; HonRl; JrNHS; MrchBnd; EdYrBk; RptrSchPpr; Trk; Chrldr; GAA; Marriage; Secretarial Work.

UMLAND, James M; Bloom Township HS; Chicago Heights, IL; HonRl; OffAde; Bsktbl; IMSpt; Southern Il.

UMPHREY, William J; Bradley Bourbonnais HS; Bourbonnais, IL; HonRl; SchAde; SchPpr; Bsbl; Bsktbl; College; Engineer.

UNANGST, Ty K; Hanover HS; Hanover, IL; 11/38 CncrtBnd; HonRl; Mdrgl; MrchBnd; NatlMeritCmnd; MthCl; LetterBsktbl; LetterFtbl; CaptGlf; University Of Illinois; Business.

UNCAPHER, Jonathan; Blackford HS; Hartford City, IN; ChrhWkr; HonRl; NatlMeritSF; IMSpt; Coll; Electrical Engineering.

UNDERDAHL, Patricia A; Southland HS; Adams, MN; 12/122 VPSophCls; ChrhWkr; HonRl; NHS; RptrYrbk; GerCl;.

UNDERDOWN, Pleys R; Sullivan HS; Leslie, MO; Chr; ChrhWkr; CncrtBnd; HonRl; MrchBnd; NHS; 4-H; FFA; FTA; 4-HAwd; College; Teaching.

UNDERRINER, David J; Rockwell City HS; Rockwell City, IA; VPJrCls; Band; ChrhWkr; CncrtBnd; HonRl; MrchBnd; PepBnd; StuCncl; Glf; GodCntryAwd; Ia State U; Engineering.

UNDERWOOD, Allen R; Bradley Bourbonnais HS; Bourbonnais, IL; HonRl;.

UNDERWOOD, Jonathan A; Seymour HS; Seymour, MO; ChrhWkr; CmntyWkr; HonRl; FFA; PpCl; Bsbl; College; Professional.

UNDERWOOD, Keith A; Lane Tech HS; Chicago, IL; 108/1200 Band; CncrtBnd; MrchBnd; SchPpr; LetterTrk; University; Engineer.

UNDERWOOD, Kimberly J; Jefferson City Sr HS; Jefferson City, MO; 28/500 ChrhWkr; CmntyWkr; HonRl; JrNHS; NHS; SchPl; SpnCl; PpCl; GAA; Southwest Mo State Univ.

UNDERWOOD, Lee W; Winfield Mt Union HS; Winfield, IA; 5/41 HonRl; SctActv; LetterWrstlng; University; Engineering.

UNDERWOOD, Sheri L; Hanover Central HS; Cedar Lake, IN; 5/139 LetterBand; ChrhWkr; HonRl; MrchBnd; NatlThespSoc; Orch; PepBnd; SchPl; FrCl; CitAwd; Taylor Univ; Computer Programing.

UNDERWOOD, Theresa A; Bradley Bourbonais HS; Bourbonnais, IL; 82/334 HonRl; GerCl; University; Professional.

UNDI, Joanne K; Donald E Gavit HS; Hammond, IN; 1/350 HonRl; JrNHS; NHS; NatlMeritSF; TchrAde; GerCl; Purdue Univ; Engineering.

UNFERTH, Julie A; Lomira HS; Campbellsport, WI; PresAFS; ALAGirlsSt; VPBand; SecStuCncl; PresYthFlsp; EdSchPpr; 4-H; Chrldr; AmLegAwd; EldAwd; Eau Claire College; Business Education.

UNGER, Cynthia K; Lake Shore HS; St Clair Shores, MI; 17/700 HonRl; NHS; Yrbk; TrsSrCls; U Of Detroit ;dentist.

UNGER, Linda S; Crete HS; Crete, NE; 1/115 Band; CncrtBnd; HonRl; MrchBnd; PepBnd; RptrYrbk; RptrSchPpr; 4-H; FBLA; College; Law Enforcement.

UNGER, Margaret M; Riverside Brookfield HS; Riverside, IL; 28/488 AFS; ChrhWkr; HonRl; JrNHS; LbryAde; NHS; NatlMeritCmnd; StuCncl; FrCl; GerCl; Univ Of Illinois; Elem Education.

UNGER, Neal S; Lincoln Se HS; Lincoln, NE; 4/490 ALBoysSt; HonRl; JA; NatlFornLg; NHS; StuCncl; SchPpr; EldAwd; Univ Of Pennsylvania; Law.

UNGER, Robert E; Lutheran West HS; Detroit, MI; Chr; ChrhWkr; HonRl; PresNHS; NatlMeritCmnd; LatCl; Bsktbl; LetterTennis; IMSpt; College; Teaching.

UNGER, Stephen J; Liberty HS; Liberty, MO; PresJrCls; Band; Chr; HonRl; SctActv; StuCncl; Yrbk; KeyCl; Bsktbl; Ftbl; Trk; College; Journalism.

UNKE, Arlys E; St Thomas Public HS; St Thomas, ND; 2/21 PresSophCls; ALAGirlsSt; Aud/Vis; Band; Chrs; HonRl; EdYrBk; LetterBsktbl; LetterTrk; LetterGAA; U Of Nd; Cpa.

UNKE, Kimberly D; Fairmont HS; Fairmont, MN; ChrhWkr; CncrtBnd; HonRl; HospAde; MrchBnd; NatlMeritCmnd; 4-H; GerCl; GAA; Gustavus Adolphus College; Nursing.

UNKRAUT, Debbie J; St Anthony HS; Effingham, IL; 3/79 VPJrCls; Chrs; HonRl; NHS; SchPl; RptrSchPpr; FTA; PpCl; Chrldr; E Ill Univ; Professional Teacher.

UNKRAUT, Sue K; St Anthony HS; Effingham, IL; 4/63 Chrs; DrlTm; HonRl; NHS; SchMus; StuCncl; Yrbk; PpCl; AmLegAwd; DARAwd; Eastern Il Univ; Speech Pathologist.

UNNERSTALL, Marsha A; St Francis Borgia HS; Washington, MO; 28/95 HonRl; NHS; SchPl; TchrAde; RptrSchPpr; SchPpr; PpCl; IMSpt; E Central Jr Clg; Elementary Education.

UNREIN, Becky M; Marian HS; Hays, KS; Band; HonRl; LbryAde; MrchBnd; PepBnd; StuCncl; FBLA; SpnCl; PpCl; College; Professional.

UNREIN, Juanita M; Andale HS; Colwich, KS; 29/87 Band; CncrtBnd; HospAde; MrchBnd; NatlMeritSchl; RedCrAde; StuCncl; StuGov; RptrYrbk; RptrSchPpr; Ks Newman Clg; Nursing.

UNRUH, Barbara J; Newton HS; Newton, KS; VPFrshCls; Chr; Chrl; Chrs; HonRl; JA; LetterTrk; IMSpt; 4-HAwd; PresAwd; College; Phys Ed.

UNRUH, Dale G; Great Bend HS; Great Bend, KS; ChrhWkr; HonRl; 4-H; College; Vocation.

UNRUH, Harold E; Newton HS; Newton, KS; 29/305 Band; CncrtBnd; HonRl; MrchBnd; PepBnd; SchAde; TchrAde; MthCl; SciCl; IMSpt; Ks St U; Biology.

UNRUH, Janice D; Berean Academy; Valley Center, KS; 10/50 Chr; ChrhWkr; CmntyWkr; CncrtBnd; HonRl; NHS; TreasStuCncl; 4-H; SecPpCl; SecSciCl; Bsbl; Bsktbl; Trk; Tabor College; Medicine.

UNRUH, John M; Colby HS; Colby, KS; 12/93 AFS; HonRl; SchPl; TchrAde; Yrbk; SchPpr; University; Medicine.

UNRUH, Leon D; Macksville HS; Pawnee Rock, KS; 2/37 Band; DrmBgl; HonRl; VPNHS; NatlMeritSF; RptrYrbk; RptrSchPpr; KeyCl; Bsktbl; LetterTennis; 4-HAwd; LionAwd; Kansas Univ; Journalism.

UNRUH, Mary L; Niles East HS; Skokie, IL; 8/581 SecFrshCls; SecSophCls; HonRl; NHS; KeyCl; CaptChrldr; Univ Of Notre Dame; Medicine.

UNRUH, Susan G; Macksville HS; Pawnee Rock, KS; Band; Chr; Chrl; Chrs; CncrtBnd; MrchBnd; PepBnd; PpCl; College; Vocation.

UNTERBRUNNER, Bruce A; Carthage Public HS; Artesian, SD; ALBoysSt; Band; ChrhWkr; HonRl; SchPl; EdSchPpr; 4-H; Ftbl; Trk; IMSpt; College; Elementry Principa.

UNTERNAHRER, Debra A; Westview HS; Shipshewana, IN; 8/67 TrsSrCls; Band; ChrhWkr; CncrtBnd; HonRl; MrchBnd; NHS; PepBnd; TchrAde; YthFlsp; Trk; GAA; Ft Wayne Internl; Bookkeeping.

UNTERREINER, Anne; Irving Crown Hs; Fox River Grove, IL; Chrs; HonRl; NHS; Yrbk; FTA; College; Elementary School Teacher.

UNTERREINER, Marie A; Bishop Dubourg HS; St Louis, MO; 15/469 HonRl; LbryAde; NHS; EdYrBk; College.

UNTIEDT, Roger L; Sioux Valley Consolidated HS; Lake Park, IA; TrsFrshCls; VPJrCls; PresSrCls; ALBoysSt; HonRl; StuCncl; 4-H; FFA; LetterBsktbl; Ftbl; Trk; College.

UNVERRICHT, Heidi B; Niles West HS; Morton Grove, IL; 56/626 HonRl; YthFlsp; KeyCl; Univ Of Illinois; Home Economics.

UNVERZAGT, Jane E; Divine Savior Holy Angels HS; Hales Corners, WI; Chrs; HonRl; Georgetown University; Nursing.

UNWALA, Ashfaque; Highland Park HS; Oakpark, IL; AFS; CmntyWkr; JA; JrNHS; NHS; PolWkr; StuGov; UNYO; FSA; SciCl; College; Bs Biology.

UNZEN, Rebecca A; Madison Public HS; Madison, MN; 1/86 HonRl; JrNHS; NHS; NatlMeritCmnd; St Cloud St College; Accounting.

UNZICKER, Dottie J; Fisher HS; Fisher, IL; 4/57 ChrhWkr; SecDrlTm; HonRl; NHS; StuCncl; SecYthFlsp; EdYrBk; PresFHA; Chrldr; GAA; BttyCrckrAwd; 4-HAwd; College; Data Processing.

UPAH, David A; Rochelle Township HS; Rochelle, IL; 30/230 Band; Chr; Chrs; CncrtBnd; HonRl; Mdrgl; MrchBnd; NatlFornLg; NHS; NatlMeritCmnd; Bsktbl; Glf; LetterTennis; PresAwd; University Of Illinois; Law.

UPCHURCH, Jill A; Columbia HS; Columbia, IL; 11/126 Band; ChrhWkr; HospAde; NHS; SchPl; PresSctActv; SecStuCncl; FTA; VPFrCl; GAA; College; Medicine.

UPCHURCH, Kelly; Frankeon HS; Anderson, IN; HonRl; SpnCl; Ftbl; Trk; Wrstlng; Purdue Univ;elecerical Engineering.

UPCHURCH, Trina; Blue River Valley HS; New Castle, IN; 27/85 SecTrsSrCls; ALAGirlsSt; Chr; ChrhWkr; HonRl; HospAde; RedCrAde; SchAde; SchMus; Tennis; Ivy Tech; Medical Tech.

UPELL, Joan M; Tecumseh HS; Tecumseh, MI; 5/240 Band; LitMag; NHS; RptrSchPpr; EdSchPpr; Bsktbl; IMSpt; Mi St U ;journalism.

UPHAM, Sally R; St Charles HS; St Charles, IL; 47/435 Chr; Chrl; Chrs; ChrhWkr; HonRl; Mdrgl; SchMus; YthFlsp; RptrYrbk; Millikin University; Art.

UPMANN, Ronald A; East Dubuque HS; East Dubuque, IL; TrsSophCls;.

UPMEYER, Robert P; Solon Community HS; Solon, IA; 9/70 ALBoysSt; Band; Chr; ChrhWkr; HonRl; NatlThespSoc; FFA; Glf; AmLegAwd; DanFAwd; Univ Of Ia.

UPPERMAN, Sandra C; Anderson HS; Anderson, IN; NHS; LatCl; PpCl;.

UPPGAARD, Heidi L; Edina West HS; Edina, MN; Chr; ChrhWkr; CncrtBnd; DrmMjrt; HonRl; HospAde; MrchBnd; NatlMeritCmnd; Orch; St Olaf College; Medicine.

UPSCHULTE, Bernard L; Quincy HS; Quincy, IL; HonRl; JrNHS; NHS; FrCl; Quincy College; Math.

UPSTON, Russell E; Marshall HS; Marshall, MI; ChrhWkr; HonRl; TchrAde; SchPpr; FrCl; LatCl; LetterFtbl; IMSpt; Marine Corps.

UPTON, Alan N; Zion Benton Twsp HS; Zion, IL; 140/450 CAP; HonRl; GerCl; IMSpt; College Of Lake County; Electronics Draftin.

UPTON, Carol J; Antigo HS; Antigo, WI; Band; MrchBnd; OffAde; FHA; LatCl; Trade School.

UPTON, Debra J; Bradley Bourbonnais Comm HS; Bourbonnais, IL; 1/365 TrsSophCls; Aud/Vis; HonRl; SecNHS; PolWkr; StuCncl; GAA; Univ Of Illinois; Lawyer.

UPTON, Mary Beth; St Marys Academy; Milwaukee, WI; ChrhWkr; CmntyWkr; NHS; StuGov; UNYO; Yrbk; SchPpr; PpCl; Bsktbl; Chrldr; Denver College.

UPTON, William L; Huron HS; Ann Arbor, MI; 18/580 Band; CncrtBnd; HonRl; MrchBnd; Orch; SchPl; StuGov; CaptGlf; Univ; Professional.

URAM, Margaret; St Hedwig Hs; Detroit, MI; PresJrCls; HonRl; JA; NHS; Sdlty; StuCncl; RptrYrbk; SchPpr; PpCl; Chrldr; College ; Professional.

URASH, Laurie; Carmi Community Hs; Carmi, IL; 17/139 HonRl; NHS; OffAde; SchPl; StuCncl; RptrYrbk; RptrSchPpr; SpnCl; College; Photography.

URATA, Guy V; Francis Parker HS; Chicago, IL; Chrs; JA; LetterBsbl; LetterGlf; College; Mathematics.

URBAN, Audrey; Holy Redeemer HS; Detroit, MI; 27/190 HonRl; OffAde; RedCrAde; SchPl; StuCncl; TchrAde; Bsbl; Hospital Nursing Program; Registered Nurse.

URBAN, Brenda; Neillsville Hs; Neillsville, WI; 2 NHS; SchPl; RptrYrbk; RptrSchPpr; SchPpr; 4-H; FHA; PpCl; Trk; BttyCrckrAwd;.

URBAN, Dawn M; Neillsville HS; Neillsville, WI; Band; Chr; Chrs; ChrhWkr; PepBnd; SchPl; 4-H; FBLA; Bsktbl; Trk; Univ Stevens Point; Music.

URBAN, Diane; T L Handy HS; Bay City, MI; 1/366 HonRl; StuCncl; Mich Univ; Pre Med.

URBAN, Kathy J; Otis Bison Sr HS; Albert, KS; Chrs; HonRl;.

URBAN, Lori A; Bay City HS; Bay City, MI; LbryAde; NHS; SecGerCl; Trk; GAA; PPFtbl; Central Michigan Univ; Mathematics.

URBANCE, Mary T; Streator Twp HS; Streator, IL; HonRl; JrNHS; College; Teacher.

URBANIAK, Ann E; Regina HS; Detroit, MI; HonRl; SciCl; Mi Technological Univ; Chemistry.

URBANIAK, Bonnie J; Bedford HS; Temperance, MI; 13/410 Chr; Chrs; HonRl; NHS; Yrbk; Monroe Comm College; Accounting.

URBANIAK, David G; John Glenn HS; Westland, MI; 10/675 HonRl; U Of Mi; Medicine.

URBANIK, John; Mount Carmel Hs; Chicago, IL; 17/197 NHS; LetterSwmmng; College Ill State; Accounting.

URBANIK, Linda J; Whiting HS; Whiting, IN; ALAGirlsSt; HonRl; VPNHS; EdSchPpr; SchPpr; PpCl; Bsktbl; Tennis; Trk; PresGAA; Univ; Medical.

URBANK, Beverly A; Oak Lawn Comm HS; Hometown, IL; 28/868 Band; HonRl; MrchBnd; NatlFornLg; NHS; NatlThespSoc; OffAde; SchPl; SctActv; YthFlsp; Comm Coll; Computer Science.

URBANSKI, Constance M; Boylan Central Cath HS; Rockford, IL; Chrs; HonRl; LbryAde; SchMus; TchrAde; RptrYrbk; RptrSchPpr; PresFrCl; PpCl; St Louis College; Pharmacy.

URBAS, Andrea; Hinsdale Twp HS South; Darien, IL; 10/489 AFS; Chr; CmntyWkr; JA; LbryAde; NHS; Quill&Scroll; StuCncl; Yrbk; Univ Of Ill; Architecture.

URBATCH, Brad; North Central HS; Manly, IA; HonRl; Niacc College;.

URBAUER, John R; Evergreen Park C HS; Evergreen Park, IL; 54/445 HonRl; NHS; GerCl; College; Professional.

URBINA, James R; Franklin Public HS; Bloomington, NE; 4/53 PresSophCls; Chrs; HonRl; SchPl; StuCncl; StuGov; FFA; LetterFtbl; LetterTrk; LetterWrstlng; College; Arigculture Or Vetinary.

URDA, Mary Ann H; St Alphonsus HS; Detroit, MI; 8/145 SecBand; CncrtBnd; HonRl; MrchBnd; Orch; PepBnd; PolWkr; SchMus; SchPl; SecLatCl;.

URFER, Brian D; Lyons Township HS; Western Springs, IL; ChrhWkr; HonRl; NHS; TchrAde; Univ Of Kentucky; Engineering.

URIAN, Theresita E; Josephinum HS; Chicago, IL; 10/99 HonRl; LbryAde; NHS; OffAde; StuCncl; TchrAde; Chrldr; College; Professional.

URISH, Dave A; Green Valley HS; Green Valley, IL; 7/30 VPFrshCls; ChrhWkr; CmntyWkr; HonRl; StuCncl; 4-H; CaptBsbl; CaptBsktbl; LetterTrk; 4-HAwd; College; Professional.

URMIE, Daniel; West HS; Walcott, IA; 372/807 Chrs; LbryAde; OffAde; Ftbl; Trade School; Vocation.

URNESS, Kevin J; Leeds Public HS; Leeds, ND; PresJrCls; PresSrCls; ALBoysSt; ChrhWkr; HonRl; JCC; JrNHS; NatlMeritSF; ROTC; RptrYrbk; Ndsu; Farming.

URY, Beverly J; Shawnee HS; Jonesboor, IL; Band; CncrtBnd; HonRl; MrchBnd; RptrYrbk; RptrSchPpr; FBLA; FHA; FTA; Chrldr; College; Physical Therapy.

URYASZ, Julie A; Marian HS; Omaha, NE; ChrhWkr; HonRl; NHS; SchAde; TchrAde; CaptBsktbl; CchngActv; IMSpt; ChmbCommrsAwd; RotaryAwd; College.

USASZ, Steven J; Northwest HS; Grand Island, NE; HonRl; GerCl; Wrstlng; Trade School; Carpenter.

USBORNE, Robin; Hastings HS; Hastings, MI; Chr; HonRl; ModUN; OffAde; SchMus; RptrYrbk; FrCl; SciCl; GAA; PPFtbl; Univ; Biol Sci.

USEVICIUS, Danute M; Maria HS; Chicago, IL; 16/300 HonRl; HospAde; JrNHS; NHS; NatlMeritSchl; GerCl; BauchLmbAwd; ChmbCommrsAwd; GovHonPrgAwd; PresAwd; Univ Il Chicago Circle; Pharmacy.

USIAK, Andrea P; Normal Comm HS; Normal, IL; 1/450 Chrs; HonRl; HospAde; NHS; SchMus; TreasStuCncl; TchrAde; Yrbk; St Olaf College; Psychology.

USSERY, William C; El Dorado HS; El Dorado, KS; Aud/Vis; PresNatlFornLg; SchPl; YthLg; Tennis; Southwestern College.

UTHE, Kevin D; Chester Area HS; Chester, SD; SchPl; YthFlsp; SptEdSchPpr; 4-H; FFA; LetterFtbl; LetterWrstlng; Trade School; Auto Mechanics.

UTIC, James M; West HS; Green Bay, WI; 20/396 ALBoysSt; ChrhWkr; HonRl; JA; NHS; StuCncl; FrCl; Bsbl; Ftbl; Trk; Univ; Psychology.

UTLAUT, Ronald N; St Charles HS; St Charles, MO; NatlMeritCmnd; SctActv; YthFlsp; University Of Missouri; Chemistry.

UTLEY, Karen L; Richland Center HS; Richland Center, WI; Band; CmntyWkr; HonRl; HospAde; SctActv; 4-H; FrCl; Trk; Chrldr; Univ Of Wis Richland Ctr; Social Work.

UTLEY, Lisa G; East Detroit HS; East Detroit, MI; HonRl; NHS; NatlMeritCmnd; NatlMeritSF; NatlThespSoc; SchMus; SchPl; MthCl; PpCl; Macomb Co Comm Coll; Graphic & Comm Art.

UTSLER, Janis L; Mt Zion HS; Decatur, IL; 19/195 ChrhWkr; HonRl; NHS; Millikin Univ; Fine Arts.

UTSLER, Leisa M; Schulte HS; Terre Haute, IN; 8/88 Chr; HonRl; NHS; SchPl; Yrbk; SchPpr; St Mary Of The Woods Col; Therapist.

UTT, Valerie; Windsor HS; Windsor, MO; 14/52 Chr; ChrhWkr; DrlTm; HonRl; NHS; Quill&Scroll; Yrbk; RptrSchPpr; LatCl; PpCl; Sw Baptist College.

UTTECHT, Cathy J; Armour HS; Armour, SD; 2/42 Band; Chr; Chrs; HonRl; NHS; PepBnd; SchMus; YthFlsp; 4-H; FHA; Coll; Zoology.

UTTER, Andrea G; Dillsboro Public HS; Dillsboro, IN; 4/45 VPSophCls; Band; HonRl; MrchBnd; SchPl; Yrbk; 4-H; Chrldr; GAA; Clge; Journ.

UTTER, Karyn S; Rushville HS; Rushville, IL; Band; Chrs; ChrhWkr; HospAde; SchPl; YthFlsp; SchPpr; FrCl; Trk; Illinois Wesleyan Univ; Social Welfare.

UTTERBACK, Cinthia S; Oblong HS; Robinson, IL; 9/71 HonRl; OffAde; EdYrBk; SchPpr; FrCl; PpCl; Indiana State Univ; Medical Rec Ords Tech.

UTTERBACK, Janet L; Holton HS; Holton, KS; Band; CncrtBnd; HonRl; MrchBnd; Quill&Scroll; RptrYrbk; EdSchPpr; University; Medicine.

UTTERBACK, Lori J; Hannibal Sr HS; Hannibal, MO; Chrs; HonRl; LbryAde; NHS; TchrAde; RptrSchPpr; FBLA; PpCl; GAA; Univ Of Missouri; Accounting.

UVELLI, Debra L; William Howard Taft HS; Chicago, IL; Chrs; HonRl; NHS; NatlMeritSchl; StuCncl; TchrAde; Northern Illinois Univ; Medicine.

UYEDA, Sharon L; Hinsdale South HS; Hinsdale, IL; 62/475 HonRl; JrNHS; NHS; TchrAde; Jr Col; Criminology.

UZUBELL, Ronald J; Lake Central HS; Crown Point, IN; 39/454 Indiana Univ; Medicine.

V

VAAL, Randell J; Forest Park HS; Ferdinand, IN; PresFrshCls; TrsSophCls; PresJrCls; VPSrCls; ALBoysSt; Band; ChrhWkr; HonRl; NatlMeritCmnd; 4-HAwd; Rose Hullman Coll; Engineering.

VACCA, Carol; Liberal R 2 HS; Arcania, KS; 11/45 HonRl; MrchBnd; PepBnd; SchPl; FHA; FSA; FTA; SciCl; Trk; PPFtbl; Mo S St Col Of Joplin; High Schcounselor.

VACCARO, Paula; Mother Of Sorrows HS; Blue Island, IL; 30/116 HonRl; NHS; StuCncl; TchrAde; MthCl; SciCl; GAA; Northern Illinois U; Medical Technology.

VACEK, Betty; Wilber Clatonia HS; Western, NE; 19/44 Band; CncrtBnd; HonRl; LbryAde; NHS; SchMus; SchPl; TchrAde; EdYrBk; FBLA;.

VACEK, Jane A; Daniel Gross HS; Bellevue, NE; HonRl; NHS; SchMus; SchPl; SctActv; 4-H; PpCl; Trk; CaptChrldr; Pres4-HAwd; College; Biology.

VACEK, Susan J; Bloom Township HS; Chicago Hgts, IL; HonRl; NHS; OffAde; StuCncl; StuGov; MthCl; Swmmng; Trk; Wrstlng; Northwestern Univ; Medicine.

VACEY, Sandra L; Academy Of Our Lady; Chicago, IL; 24/160 HonRl; JrNHS; NHS; PepBnd; RedCrAde; Sdlty; FNA; SpnCl; MthCl; Ne Missouri St Univ; Med Secretary.

VACHON, Diane M; Northrop HS; Fort Wayne, IN; 26/568 HonRl; OffAde; TchrAde; In St U; Spanish.

VAGNER, Ellen; Bonner Springs HS; Bonner Springs, KS; HonRl; FrCl; LatCl; RotaryAwd;.

VAHALA, Michael E; Elkhart Memorial HS; Elkhart, IN; 1/441 VPBand; CncrtBnd; DrmMjrt; HonRl; MrchBnd; NatlFornLg; NHS; NatlMeritSF; PresOrch; SchMus; StuGov; TchrAde; RptrSchPpr; College; International Law.

VAHL, Donna J; Oak Lawn Comm HS; Oak Lawn, IL; 17/680 HonRl; LbryAde; NHS; Northern Illinois Univ; Accounting.

VAHLDICK, Margaret E; Luther South HS; Chicago, IL; 9/204 SecSrCls; Chr; Chrs; HonRl; NHS; YthLg; Yrbk; RptrSchPpr; SchPpr; GerCl; GAA; Mac Cormac Jr College; Law.

VAHLE, Sandra L; Seymour HS; Payson, IL; 1/65 Band; Chr; CncrtBnd; HonRl; MrchBnd; PepBnd; SchMus; PresYthFlsp; FHA; College; Mathematics.

VAHLKAMP, Michelle A; Horton Watkins HS; St Louis, MO; 175/435 CaptBsktbl; PresGAA; College.

VAI, Laurel R; Highland Park HS; Highland Park, IL; HonRl; PpCl; Bsbl; College; Business.

VAIL, Karen S; Mt Vernon Comm HS; Mc Cordsville, IN; 15/143 CncrtBnd; HonRl; MrchBnd; NHS; OffAde; YthFlsp; 4-H; IMSpt; Ball St Univ; Physical Therapy.

VAIL, Mary S; Central Catholic HS; Bloomington, IL; 18/81 Chrs; ChrhWkr; CmntyWkr; HonRl; NHS; SchPl; Sdlty; StuCncl; StuGov; 4-H; FrCl; PpCl; Tennis; Southern Illinois Univ; Pre Law.

VAIL, William A; Kapaun Mt Carmel HS; Wichita, KS; 50/134 Aud/Vis; NHS; NatlThespSoc; RedCrAde; SchMus; SchPl; SctActv; Yrbk; 4-H; GerCl; Ks State Univ; Vetinary Medicine.

VAILPORTER, Joy A; Connersville HS; Connersville, IN; 26/371 HonRl; SecNHS; NatlThespSoc; StuCncl; Sec4-H; VPFHA; GerCl; PpCl; SciCl; Clge; Dental Hygiene.

VAIS, Kathy S; Nazareth Acad; Chicago, IL; SctActv; Sdlty; StuCncl; StuGov; TchrAde; FNA; PpCl; Socr; Trk; Loyola U; Nursing.

VAIYA, Hamid H; Everett HS; Lansing, MI; College ;professional.

VAJDA, Lynn M; Whiting HS; Whiting, IN; 5/100 ALAGirlsSt; HonRl; HospAde; NHS; NatlThespSoc; SchMus; StuCncl; BttyCrckrAwd; DARAwd; KiwanAwd; Saint Marys College; Nursing.

VAKSDAL, Diane L; Grantsburg Intergrated HS; Grantsburg, WI; 1/82 Band; CncrtBnd; HonRl; MrchBnd; NatlFornLg; PepBnd; SchPl; FHA; PpCl; Chrldr; College; Professional Law.

VALDES, Robert; St Patrick Hs; Stone Park, IL; 81 LetterFtbl; CchngActv; U Of Ill;aerautical Engineering.

VALDETTARO, Gemma M; Lourdes HS; Rochester, MN; SecTrsSrCls; DrlTm; HonRl; HospAde; RptrSchPpr; FDA; PresFrCl; Trk; CitAwd; College; Medicine.

VALDEZ, Marie V; Gabriel Richard HS; Riverview, MI; SecSophCls; SecSrCls; ChrhWkr; HospAde; NHS; StuCncl; TchrAde; FNA; SpnCl; Chrldr; College; Professional.

VALDEZ, Michael R; St Mary Cntr For Learning; Chicago, IL; Aud/Vis; CmntyWkr; MrchBnd; OffAde; SchPl; TchrAde; SpnCl;.

VALELA, Deborah; St Barbara HS; Chicago, IL; 29/88 SecJrCls; HonRl; StuCncl; SchPpr; FTA; SpnCl; GAA; Univ Of North Ill; Special Educ Teacher.

VALENTE, Dominic; South Lake HS; E Detroit, MI; HonRl; LetterWrstlng; Univ Mi; Elec Eng.

VALENTI, Catherine J; Mehlville HS; St Louis, MO; DrlTm; HonRl; NHS; StuGov; SpnCl; Univ; Physical Therapy.

VALENTINE, Donna L; Bedford Comm HS; Gravity, IA; VPFrshCls; TrsJrCls; Band; HonRl; PepBnd; SchPl; StuCncl; PresFHA; Chrldr;.

VALENTINE, John M; Bedford Sr HS; Temperance, MI; 14/450 HonRl; NHS; University; Journalism.

VALENTINE, Joseph L; Blakesburg HS; Blakesburg, IA; 1/16 Band; ChrhWkr; CncrtBnd; HonRl; MrchBnd; PepBnd; SchPl; SctActv; StuCncl; StuGov; RptrSchPpr; LetterBsbl; LetterBsktbl; LetterTrk; University; Math.

VALENTINE, Kathleen; St Johns HS; De Witt, MI; HonRl; NHS; NatlMeritFnl; NatlMeritSF; SchPpr; 4-H; 4-HAwd; Michigan State Univ; Horticulture.

VALENTINE, Laura L; Novi HS; Novi, MI; HonRl; PresNHS; SecStuGov; EdYrBk; RptrSchPpr; PresFrCl; SecBsktbl; Trk; DARAwd; Eastern Mi Univ; Elementary Education.

VALENTINE, Lisa A; Cathedral HS; Chicago, IL; VPSophCls; PresJrCls; HonRl; ModUN; NHS; StuCncl; StuGov; UNYO; YthLg; FDA; FSA; Purdue Univ; Lab Tech.

VALENTINE, Rosita; Paseo Hs; Kansas City, MO; 19 VPJrCls; ChrhWkr; HonRl; RedCrAde; NatlMeritCmnd; FshEdYrbk; EdSchPpr; Oakwood College ; Home Economics.

VALENTINE, Sherri; Sandy Creek Jr Sr HS; Glenvil, NE; 5/53 VPJrCls; PresSrCls; ChrhWkr; DrlTm; HonRl; NHS; StuCncl; 4-H; Tennis; 4-HAwd; Kearney St Col; Bus Admin.

VALENTINE, Teresa L; Portland HS; Portland, IN; 17/185 ChrhWkr; CncrtBnd; HonRl; JrNHS; NHS; SchPl; YthFlsp; KeyCl; GAA; 4-HAwd; Taylor Univ; Phy Ed.

VALETTE, Elaine M; Christopher Community HS; Mulkeytown, IL; 1/58 TrsFrshCls; TrsSophCls; ChrhWkr; HonRl; NHS; OffAde; SchPl; RptrYrbk; FHA; AmLegAwd; College; History.

VALITCHKA, Matthew J; Ashwaubenon HS; Green Bay, WI; 25/220 Band; CncrtBnd; NHS; StuCncl; SptEdSchPpr; LetterBsktbl; LetterFtbl; LetterGlf; College; Lawyer.

VALITIS, Barbara A; Maria HS; Chicago, IL; 41/301 ChrhWkr; HonRl; JA; NHS; NatlMeritSF; PolWkr; SctActv; FBLA; FrCl; Ill State Univ; Elem Education.

VALIUNAS, Donna M; Oak Lawn Comm HS; Oak Lawn, IL; 70/666 HonRl; NatlMeritCmnd; PolWkr; YthLg; SchPpr; FrCl; PpCl; Chrldr; GAA; Marquette University; Accounting.

VALLANDINGHAM, Terry M; Niobrara HS; Niobrara, NE; Aud/Vis; ChrhWkr; HonRl; JrNHS; SchPl; FTA; Ftbl; Trk; Wrstlng; DanFAwd; MasAwd; CitAwd; Trade School; Vocation.

VALLBRACHT, Edna J; Hillsboro HS; Coffeen, IL; HonRl; RptrYrbk; SchPpr; GerCl; GAA; College.

VALLEAU, Pam L; Turner HS; Kansas City, KS; 16/350 NatlMeritFnl; NatlMeritCmnd; NatlMeritSF; SpnCl; Univ; Pro.

VALLEY, Lynn L; Wabeno HS; Wabena, WI; 5/35 ALBoysSt; HonRl; SctActv; StuCncl; StuGov; LetterBsktbl; Ftbl; Glf; CchngActv; University; Health Field.

VAMMER, Paul D; Glenham HS; Glenham, SD; 6/18 PresFrshCls; PresJrCls; ALBoysSt; Chrs; HonRl; SchPl; StuCncl; LetterBsktbl; Med Lab Tech.

VANA, David B; William Howard Taft HS; Chicago, IL; VPSophCls; VPJrCls; ChrhWkr; CmntyWkr; HonRl; LitMag; NHS; SchAde; SctActv; StuCncl; TchrAde; MthCl;.

VAN ABEL, Terry A; St Joseph Academy; De Pere, WI; VPSrCls; College; Nursing.

VANAGS, Kristine S; Jefferson HS; Rockford, IL; 19/330 Chr; ChrhWkr; HonRl; NHS; PolWkr; SchMus; SchPl; StuGov; TchrAde; SpnCl; C; Elementary Teacher.

VANAGS, Laura A; Proviso West HS; Hillside, IL; NatlSciFnd; NatlThespSoc; YthFlsp; GerCl; SciCl; Knox College; Math.

VAN AGTMAEL, Suzanne J; Fremont Public HS; Fremont, MI; Band; ChrhWkr; CncrtBnd; HonRl; Orch; ROTC; PolWkr; RptrSchPpr; FTA; GerCl;.

VANAHN, Jean E; West View HS; Lake City, IA; SecJrCls; AFS; HonRl; Quill&Scroll; StuCncl; TchrAde; PpCl; CaptBsktbl; Glf; University Of Iowa; Physical Therapy.

VAN ALLEN, Cindy L; Hayden HS; Topeka, KS; ALAGirlsSt; ChrhWkr; HonRl; NHS; PolWkr; SchMus; RptrSchPpr; FTA; PpCl; GAA; Washburn Univ; Criminology.

VAN ALLSBURG, Lynda S; Comstock Park HS; Comstock Pk, MI; Band; CncrtBnd; HonRl; LbryAde; MrchBnd; NHS; PepBnd; YthFlsp; Treas4-H; LetterBsbl; Trk; GAA; 4-HAwd; College; Science.

VAN ANTWERP, Kristin; Cheboygan Catholic HS; Cheboygan, MI; 10/30 ChrhWkr; HonRl; SchPl; TchrAde; RptrYrbk; RptrSchPpr; FrCl; SpnCl; Bsktbl; St Marys Coll Of Notre Dame.

VAN ANTWERP, Marguerite H; Lakeview HS; St Clair Shores, MI; 30/570 PresSophCls; HonRl; NHS; StuCncl; StuGov; Teen; GerCl; PpCl; Bsbl; Bsktbl;.

VAN ANTWERP, Nancy E; Big Rapids HS; Big Rapids, MI; 1/200 Chr; ChrhWkr; HonRl; Mdrgl; NHS; NatlMeritCmnd; NatlSciFnd; SchMus; TchrAde; Ferris State Coll; Science.

VAN ARKEL, Jon W; Oskaloosa HS; Oskaloosa, IA; PresSophCls; ALBoysSt; JrNHS; StuCncl; Bsktbl;.

VAN ARSDALEN, Douglas J; Hillsdale HS; Hillsdale, MI; Chr; NHS; KeyCl; CaptBsbl; CaptBsktbl; CaptFtbl; Col.

VANARSDALL, Karen; Lawrence Central HS; Indianapolis, IN; Univ; Art.

VANASSE, Bradley S; Bemidji HS; Bemidji, MN; Chr; HonRl; NHS; SchMus; SctActv; LetterSwmmng; College; Mechanical Engineering.

VAN ASSELT, Allan; Mc Pherson HS; Mc Pherson, KS; Band; CncrtBnd; HonRl; NatlFornLg; Orch; PepBnd; SctActv; SciCl; LetterFtbl; LetterTrk; Clge; Math.

VANATTA, Chris W; Garden City Senior HS; Garden City, KS; StuCncl; TchrAde; SciCl; Univ; Chemical Engineer.

VAN AUSDALL, Laura J; United Twp HS; East Moline, IL; 19/645 Chr; ChrhWkr; HonRl; JrNHS; NHS; NatlThespSoc; SchMus; SchPl; StuCncl; GerCl; Augustana College; History Teacher.

VAN BEEK, Calvin K; Central Wisc Christian HS; Randolph, WI; Band; Chr; PepBnd; Yrbk; RptrSchPpr; LetterBsktbl; LetterTrk; Trade School; Math.

VAN BEEK, Clifford W; Marion Ind HS; Marion, SD; HonRl; FFA; SciCl; Ftbl; Trade School; Diesel Mechanic.

VAN BEEK, Cynthia S; Oskaloosa Sr HS; Oskaloosa, IA; 1/195 Chr; HonRl; NHS; NatlMeritSchl; YthFlsp; Bsktbl; Tennis; Trk; IMSpt; College; Commercial Artist.

VAN BEEK, Elaine; Holland Chr HS; Zeeland, MI; 10/260 Chr; ChrhWkr; HonRl; HospAde; LitMag; LbryAde; NHS; SchPl; Bsktbl; IMSpt; Coll; Bs In Nursing.

VAN BEEK, Mary L; Rock Valley Comm HS; Rock Valley, IA; Band; Chrs; HonRl; VPStuCncl; LetterTrk; Chrldr; IMSpt; PPFtbl; PresAwd; Augustana College; Social Work.

VAN BERKUM, Bruce; Swea City Community Hs; Swea City, IA; 3/38 Chr; Chrs; ChrhWkr; HonRl; SchPl; YthFlsp; FFA; SpnCl; College;science Or Math.

VAN BLARCUM, Gary R; Warrensburg HS; Warrensburg, MO; 49/151 HonRl; SchMus; Ftbl; College; Business.

VAN BOCKERN, Diane L; Canton HS; Canton, SD; SecTrsFrshCls; SecTrsSophCls; SecTrsJrCls; ALAGirlsSt; CncrtBnd; HonRl; MrchBnd; NHS; NatlMeritSF; RptrYrbk;.

VAN BOCKERN, Julie A; Elk Point HS; Elk Point, SD; 1/39 ALAGirlsSt; Band; ChrhWkr; HonRl; SchPl; TchrAde; Yrbk; RptrSchPpr; GAA; Clge.

VAN BOGAERT, Cynthia A; Belmont HS; Belmont, WI; 2/60 Band; CncrtBnd; HonRl; MrchBnd; ModUN; PepBnd; SchPl; RptrSchPpr; SchPpr; 4-H; FHA; Univ; Chemistry.

VAN BROOKER, Laurie; Southeastern HS; Augusta, IL; 5/49 SecFrshCls; ChrhWkr; HonRl; HospAde; JA; MrchBnd; NHS; SchMus; SchPl; Trk; Blessing School Of Nursing; Rn.

VAN BROOKER, Laurie L; Southeastern HS; Augusta, IL; 5/47 SecFrshCls; HonRl; HospAde; JA; MrchBnd; NHS; SchPl; SctActv; StuCncl; StuGov; LetterTrk; SecGAA; LetterIMSpt; 4-HAwd; Blessing; Nurse.

VAN BUREN, Isabelle I; Verdigre Public HS; Verdigre, NE; CmntyWkr; SchPpr; FBLA; SpnCl; Stewart Sch Of Hairstyling; Professional.

VAN BUREN, Kurt E; St Johns HS; De Witt, MI; 19/325 NatlMeritCmnd; Tennis; Michigan State; Mech Eng.

VAN BURGEL, Nancy E; Spring Lake HS; Springlake, MI; 4/190 CncrtBnd; HonRl; NHS; StuCncl; YthFlsp; PpCl; LetterSwmmng; LetterTennis; CaptTrk; PPFtbl; Coll; Prof.

VAN BUSKIRK, Daniel J; St Johns Seminary; Kansas City, MO; HonRl; Sacrstn; SchMus; RptrYrbk; LetterTrk; IMSpt; Clinic Psychology.

VAN BUSKIRK, Dorthy A; Liberal HS; Liberal, KS; 57/212 SecFrshCls; SecSophCls; Chrl; ChrhWkr; HonRl; StuCncl; College; Business.

VAN BUSKIRK, Patricia; Acad Of Our Lady Spalding Ins; East Peoria, IL; TrsSophCls; PresJrCls; Chrs; HonRl; SchPl; StuGov; RptrSchPpr; SchPpr; C; English.

VAN BUSKIRK, Randy A; St Clair HS; St Clair, MI; 42/190 HonRl; StuGov; LetterTennis; IMSpt; Oakland Univ; Engineer.

VAN CAMP, Cheryl L; Elkhart Central HS; Elkhart, IN; 92/450 SecSrCls; CtyCnl; CmntyWkr; HonRl; SchMus; SchPl; StuCncl; StuGov; GovHonPrgAwd; Western Mich Univ; Art.

VANCE, Dale J; Sacred Heart HS; Salina, KS; PresCivCl; FBLA; Bsktbl; Ftbl; Trk; College.

VANCE, Gale S; East HS; Kansas City, MO; Chr; ChrhWkr; HonRl; HospAde; TchrAde; William Jewell Col; Nursing.

VANCE, Karen; Harmony Community HS; Farmington, IA; 5/40 CmntyWkr; HonRl; SchPl; Yrbk; Keokuk Comm Coll; Rn.

VANCE, Kevin G; Central HS; St Joseph, MO; 17/625 ALBoysSt; ChrhWkr; HonRl; SchPpr; LatCl; MthCl; SciCl; AmLegAwd; MasAwd; Medical School; Doctor.

VANCE, Kimberly C; Arlington HS; Indianapolis, IN; Chr; ChrhWkr; CmntyWkr; HonRl; NatlThespSoc; SchMus; SctActv; StuCncl; TchrAde; University; Professional.

VANCE, Lauren M; Unity HS; Chicago, IL; HonRl; JrNHS; NHS; FNA; College; Nursing.

VANCE, Norman S; Hillsdale HS; Hillsdale, MI; Band; LetterCncrtBnd; HonRl; LetterMrchBnd; NHS; Orch; PepBnd; SctActv; Ftbl; LetterTrk; College; Lawyer.

VANCE, Roy E; International Falls Sr HS; International Flls, MN; SctActv; VPYthFlsp; RptrSchPpr; EdSchPpr; SptEdSchPpr; IMSpt; Clge; Chem Engr.

VANCIL, Linda S; Du Quoin HS; Du Quoin, IL; SecSrCls; Band; Chrs; HonRl; SchMus; SpnCl; PpCl; SecGAA; Southern Illinois University.

VANCIL, Marna G; Metropolis Comm HS; Metropolis, IL; 8/150 ALAGirlsSt; ChrhWkr; HonRl; HospAde; NHS; PolWkr; StuCncl; YthFlsp; MthCl; PpCl; Clge; Mathematics.

VAN CLEAVE, Deanna D; Tippecanoe Valley HS; Silver Lake, IN; 25/145 Band; Chr; ChrhWkr; CncrtBnd; HonRl; MrchBnd; NHS; PepBnd; RedCrAde; SchMus; YthFlsp; 4-H; College; Professional.

VAN CLEAVE, Mary E; Wm Chrisman HS; Independence, MO; 77/386 Quill&Scroll; StuCncl; Yrbk; University; Special Education.

VANCO, Rosemary; Immaculate Conception HS; Elmhurst, IL; HonRl; StuCncl; RptrYrbk; PpCl; Trk; IMSpt; College; Professional.

VAN DAM, Blaine A; Lincoln HS; Sioux Falls, SD; ALBoysSt; HonRl; NatlMeritSF; SpnCl; Univ; Engineering.

VAN DAMME, Lee Ann; Atkinson HS; Atkinson, IL; 5/40 SecFrshCls; HonRl; SchPl; EdYrBk; RptrSchPpr; FHA; SpnCl; PpCl; GAA; College; Professional.

VANDEBERG, Marcia R; Neillsville HS; Neillsville, WI; TrsSophCls; HonRl; PresNHS; SchPl; SecStuCncl; YthFlsp; Yrbk; PpCl; GAA; CitAwd; College; Home Ec.

VAN DEELEN, Rose; Minneota Public HS; Minneota, MN; Band; HonRl; HospAde; MrchBnd; PpCl; Vocatonal; Lpn.

VAN DEEST, William R; Lake Central HS; Madison, SD; 13/156 ALBoysSt; HonRl; NHS; KeyCl; LetterBsktbl; LetterTrk; College; Forestry.

VAN DE GRAAF, William C; Bloomfield Hills Lahser HS; Bloomfield Hills, MI; 9/470 Band; CncrtBnd; MrchBnd; NHS; Trk; Univ Of Mi; Pre Med.

VANDEGRIFT, Lynetta; Everton R 111 HS; Everton, MO; 1/14 SecTrsSrCls; HonRl; SchPl; Yrbk; EdSchPpr; PpCl; Bsktbl; Chrldr; GAA;.

VANDE HEI, Paul M; Premontre HS; Green Bay, WI; 58/147 Chrs; ChrhWkr; HonRl; OffAde; ROTC; SctActv; Trade School; Carjpentry.

VANDE LUNE, Karla S; Pella Christian HS; Pella, IA; HonRl; LbryAde; SchPl; RptrSchPpr; PpCl; Bsbl; Bsktbl; Trk; CchngActv; IMSpt; Univ Or Hospt School; Nursing.

VAN DE MARK, Sheryl L; Culver Community HS; Culver, IN; 2/99 Band; HonRl; IntrClCncl; NHS; SchPl; StuCncl; 4-H; FTA; SpnCl; 4-HAwd; Purdue Univ; Veterinary Medicine.

VANDEMORE, Roxanne M; Hudson HS; Hudson, SD; SecSrCls; Chrs; HonRl; HospAde; SchMus; SchPl; Yrbk; RptrSchPpr; FHA; GerCl; Presentation College; Nursing.

VANDEN AKKER, Martin; Albion Senior HS; Albion, MI; 8/204 HonRl; NHS; SchPl; VPFrCl; Bsktbl; KiwanAwd; Albion Clg; Medicine.

VAN DEN BELDT, Nancy L; Zeeland HS; Zeeland, MI; Chr; Chrs; ChrhWkr; HonRl; HospAde; Mdrgl; OffAde; SctActv; LatCl; College ; Nurse.

VANDENBERG, Darwin J; Worthington Sr HS; Brewster, MN; HonRl; NHS; NatlSciFnd; TchrAde; YthFlsp; FSA; SciCl; Southwest Mn State Univ; Biology.

VANDEN BERG, Mark J; Wrightstown HS; De Pere, WI; Chr; Chrs; HonRl; NatlFornLg; SpnCl; Tech Schl; Artist Or Astronomy.

VANDENBERG, Robert W; Martin Public HS; Martin, MI; 9/67 PresSophCls; HonRl; NHS; StuCncl; SptEdYrbk; EdSchPpr; SptEdSchPpr; Bsbl; Bsktbl; College; Engineering.

VANDEN BERG, Scott B; Holland HS; Holland, MI; Aud/Vis; Band; CncrtBnd; HonRl; MrchBnd; PepBnd; SchPl; Grand Valley College; Business Mgmt.

VAN DENBOSCH, Kevin L; Zeeland HS; Zeeland, MI; 12/180 Band; CncrtBnd; HonRl; JrNHS; MrchBnd; NHS; NatlMeritSchl; SchPl; RptrSchPpr; EdSchPpr; Mi State; Social Ser.

VANDEN BOSCH, Randall J; Zeeland HS; Zeeland, MI; Band; CncrtBnd; MrchBnd; Michigan St Univ; Computer Prog.

VAN DEN BROEKE, Duane T; Marshall HS; Marshall, MN; Chr; HonRl; StuCncl; SpnCl; LetterFtbl; LetterTrk; LetterWrstlng; IMSpt; College; Mathematics.

VANDENBROUCKE, Debra S; Glenbard East HS; Lombard, IL; 18/673 Chr; HonRl; JrNHS; NatlFornLg; NHS; Yrbk; Eureka College; Business.

VANDENBROUCKE, Mary F; Crystal Lake HS; Crystal Lake, IL; 31/477 Chr; Chrs; HonRl; NHS; FTA; PresSpnCl; SecGAA; College; Nursing.

VANDENBURG, Cynthia; Flasher Public HS; Lark, ND; ALAGirlsSt; Band; Chrs; LbryAde; SchPl; Yrbk; EdSchPpr; FHA; Bsktbl; 4-HAwd; College; Music Or Math.

VANDENBURG, Sandra; Flasher Public HS; Lark, ND; 2/39 Dorott Coll; English Ed.

VANDENBURGH, Patrice L; Western HS; Parma, MI; 9/157 HonRl; NHS; TchrAde; 4-H; Lackson Comm College; Medical Assistant.

VAN DEN EEDEN, Carol D; Glenbard East HS; Lombard, IL; 35/680 Band; CncrtBnd; HonRl; JrNHS; MrchBnd; NHS; PepBnd; PpCl; Northern Ill University; Music.

VANDEN HOEK, Jillayne; Western Mich Christian HS; Fremont, MI; SecJrCls; SecSrCls; Band; ChrhWkr; HonRl; LitMag; NHS; SchPl; SchPpr; CitAwd; College.

VAN DE POL, Cynthia J; Reeths Puffer HS; Muskegan, MI; Band; ChrhWkr; CmntyWkr; CncrtBnd; HonRl; MrchBnd; NHS; TchrAde; SpnCl; LetterBsktbl; Musk Jr Col; Social Psychologist.

VANDERBEEK, Cindy; Thomas Jefferson HS; Carter Lake, IA; HonRl;.

VANDER BEEK, Paula L; No Mahaska HS; New Sharon, IA; SecJrCls; Band; HonRl; NHS; StuCncl; YthFlsp; FBLA; Bsktbl; Trk; Wrstlng; CchngActv; PPFtbl; Iowa St Univ; Physical Education.

VANDER BILT, Joyce D; Pollock HS; Kalamazoo, MI; 2/19 TrsSophCls; TrsJrCls; TrsSrCls; HonRl; OffAde; SchPl; StuCncl; EdYrBk; FHA; PpCl; Chrldr;.

VANDERBORGHT, Claudia T; Orono HS; Farmington, MN; CncrtBnd; HonRl; MrchBnd; U Of Minnesota; Vet.

VANDERBY, Christine D; Thornton Fractional South HS; Lansing, IL; 20/567 HonRl; JrNHS; LbryAde; NHS; FNA; SpnCl; Swmmng; Purdue Univ; Computer Programming.

VANDERCOOK, David; Cha B Whitnall HS; Hales Corners, WI; 60/259 Band; CncrtBnd; MrchBnd; SctActv; Yrbk; Tennis; Trk; Wrstlng; Us Air Force Acad; Engineering.

VAN DER DYKE, Michael A; Timothy Christian HS; Villa Park, IL; 20/90 HonRl; IntrClCncl; YthFlsp; SchPpr; Bsktbl; Trk; IMSpt;.

VANDERGON, Janet F; Brainerd Sr HS; Brainerd, MN; 106/440 ChrhWkr; CncrtBnd; HonRl; MrchBnd; Orch; PepBnd; SchPl; StuGov; Yrbk; Bethel College.

VAN DER HAGEN, Jon; Bird Island Public HS; Bird Island, MN; 2/60 SecSrCls; HonRl; NHS; CchngActv; IMSpt; St Johns Univ; Medicine.

VANDER HEYDEN, Kathryn M; St Marys Acad; Milwaukee, WI; PresSrCls; HonRl; NHS; Bsbl; Bsktbl; IMSpt; St Norbert Clg; Intnl Bus & Foreign Lang.

VANDERHOLM, Paul G; Stanton Comm HS; Villisca, IA; Band; CncrtBnd; HonRl; MrchBnd; PepBnd; SchAde; FFA; LetterBsbl; LetterBsktbl; LetterFtbl; Trade School; Farming.

VANDERHOOF, Darel D; Pine River HS; Luther, MI; Aud/Vis; HonRl; Ftbl; IMSpt; Ferris State Coll; Electronics Eng.

VANDERHOOF, Debbie S; Hammond Baptist HS; Gary, IN; 15/88 Chrl; ChrhWkr; HonRl; NHS; OffAde; SchMus; TchrAde; RptrSchPpr; SchPpr; Hyles Anderson Clg; Elem Teacher.

VANDERHOOF, Lovina K; Campus HS; Wichita, KS; Chr; HonRl; ModUN; NatlFornLg; Orch; SctActv; TchrAde; YthLg; SpnCl; PpCl; College; Law.

VANDER HOONING, Bob; Holland Christian HS; Holland, MI; Band; CmntyWkr; MrchBnd; NHS; PepBnd; RptrSchPpr; Bsktbl; Socr; Trk; IMSpt; Wheaton Coll; Economics.

VANDER HULST, Debra; Holland Christian HS; Holland, MI; Band; Chr; CncrtBnd; HonRl; NHS; 4-H; SpnCl; Calvin College; Elem Teacher.

VANDER HYDEN, Roberta J; Appleton HS; Appleton, WI; 37/650 SecSrCls; LitMag; NatlMeritCmnd; PresNatlThespSoc; SchMus; SchPl; StuCncl; StuGov; RptrSchPpr; FrCl; NCTE; Col; Psychologist.

VAN DER KAMP, Robert; Washington HS; Washington, MO; 12/276 Band; Chrs; CncrtBnd; HonRl; JA; MrchBnd; NHS; PepBnd; SecNavy.

VANDERKLEED, Vernon; Mccutcheon HS; Lafayette, IN; Chr; HonRl; Orch; SchPl; FFA; SpnCl; Bsktbl; Trk; Wrstlng; IMSpt; Univ; Agriculture.

VANDER KLOK, Janice A; Kalamazoo Christian HS; Kalamazoo, MI; 15/136 Chr; Chrs; HonRl; NHS; SchMus; SchPl; TchrAde; SchPpr; Calvin Col; Math Teacher.

VAN DER KROL, Alexander R; Shelbyville HS; Shelbyville, IN; TchrAde; SciCl; Landbouwhogeschool Wageningen; Chem.

VANDER LAAN, Jerry D; Lake City Area HS; Lake City, MI; Band; ChrhWkr; CmntyWkr; CncrtBnd; HonRl; LbryAde; MrchBnd; NatlMeritSchl; PepBnd; PolWkr; Bsbl; LetterBsktbl; LetterFtbl; Swmmng; Delta College; Business.

VANDER LANDEN, Marie A; Little Chute HS; Little Chute, WI; .

VANDER LEEST, Kim A; Pekin Community HS; Pekin, IL; Band; ChrhWkr; CncrtBnd; HonRl; MrchBnd; NHS; Orch; PepBnd; Bsktbl; VPGAA; College; Fashion Merchandising.

VANDER LEEST, Kim A; Pekin Comm HS; Pekin, IL; Band; ChrhWkr; CncrtBnd; HonRl; MrchBnd; NHS; Orch; TchrAde; Bsktbl; VPGAA; Stephens College; Fashion Mdse.

VANDERLIN, Kimberly K; Edison Sr HS; East Gary, IN; 21/203 TrsFrshCls; Band; Chr; CncrtBnd; HonRl; JrNHS; Mdrgl; MrchBnd; PepBnd; SchMus; SctActv; StuCncl; Chrldr; GAA; Col; Teacher.

VAN DER LINDEN, Karey; Joliet East HS; Joliet, IL; 59/381 VPSrCls; Chr; HonRl; JrNHS; Mdrgl; SchMus; SchPl; StuCncl; LetterTennis; GAA; University.

VANDER MAAZEN, Lisa B; Xavier HS; Appleton, WI; CmntyWkr; HonRl; HospAde; SctActv; FDA; SciCl; University; Medicine.

VANDERMARK, Cinda J; George A Dondero HS; Royal Oak, MI; NHS; NatlThespSoc; SchPl; EdYrBk; GerCl; PpCl; Michigan St Univ; Theater.

VANDERMEULEN, Robert M; Servite HS; Detroit, MI; Chrl; HonRl; NatlMeritCmnd; RptrSchPpr; EdSchPpr; Business School; Business Management.

VANDERMEUSE, Barb T C; Algoma HS; Forestville, WI; ChrhWkr; OffAde; TchrAde; UNYO; 4-H; FFA; Bsktbl; Wrstlng; GAA; College; Communications.

VANDER MEY, Keith E; Kal Christian HS; Portage, MI; NatlMeritCmnd; Yrbk; Wrstlng; Kvcc; Elec.

VANDER MOLEN, Marcia K; Springport HS; Springport, MI; Chr; ModUN; SchPl; StuCncl; TchrAde; RptrYrbk; PpCl; LetterChrldr; Bus Educ.

VAN DER MOLEN, Ronald E; Martin Public HS; Martin, MI; 12/70 Band; CncrtBnd; HonRl; MrchBnd; SchPl; TchrAde; MthCl; SciCl; Glf; Trk; College; Med Doctor.

VAN DE ROSTYNE, Kathleen M; Atkinson HS; Atkinson, IL; ALAGirlsSt; SchPl; StuCncl; EdYrBk; RptrSchPpr; FHA; SpnCl; PpCl; Bsktbl; University; Professional.

VANDER PLAATS, Suzanne; Verdi Public HS; Ward, SD; 1/12 Band; Chrs; HonRl; SchPl; StuCncl; RptrYrbk; RptrSchPpr; Chrldr; BttyCrcrkAwd; CitAwd; Dordt Coll; Music.

VANDER PLAS, Cynthia A; Lake Fenton HS; Fenton, MI; 16/146 HonRl; JA; NHS; SchPl; TchrAde; RptrYrbk; SchPpr; Chrldr; PPFtbl; Western Mich College; Business Education.

VANDER PLOEG, Beth C; Oostburg HS; Oostburg, WI; Band; Chr; HonRl; NHS; YthFlsp; Yrbk; SchPpr; Chrldr; College; Pro.

VANDERPLOEG, Lynn; Oostburg HS; Oostburg, WI; 2/68 Band; ChrhWkr; CncrtBnd; HonRl; MrchBnd; NHS; PepBnd; Yrbk; SchPpr; GAA; College.

VANDER PLOEG, Richard J; Zeeland HS; Zeeland, MI; Aud/Vis; ChrhWkr; Vocation.

VANDERPOOL, Roger D; Triopia Jr Sr HS; Arenzville, IL; ChrhWkr; HonRl; LitMag; TreasNHS; TreasYthFlsp; FFA; Bsbl; Bsktbl; LetterFtbl; Trk; Univ Of Ill; Computer Science.

VANDERPORT, Darcel R; Superior HS; Superior, WI; Chr; CmntyWkr; HonRl; OffAde; RedCrAde; SpnCl; PpCl; Bsktbl; GAA; IMSpt; Univ Of Wi Superior; Speech Pathology.

VANDER ROEST, William J; Kal Christian HS; Kalamazoo, MI; 5/139 Band; ChrhWkr; CncrtBnd; HonRl; JA; NHS; SchMus; YthFlsp; RptrYrbk; SptEdSchPpr; Calvin College; Engineering.

VANDER SCHAAF, Bruce E; Timothy Christian HS; Western Springs, IL; 13/87 VPFrshCls; Band; Chr; HonRl; NHS; PresStuCncl; Bsktbl; Glf; Tennis; CchngActv; Coll; Pre Med.

VANDERSNICK, Margaret L; Ewing Public HS; Ewing, NE; 8/29 VPFrshCls; TrsSophCls; Band; Chrs; HonRl; NHS; PepBnd; SchPl; TchrAde; Yrbk; Bsbl; Bsktbl; Glf; College; Nursing.

VANDER STREEK, Paul; Pella Community HS; Pella, IA; VPFrshCls; AFS; ALBoysSt; ChrhWkr; CmntyWkr; PolWkr; StuCncl; StuGov; YthFlsp; Ftbl; College; Business.

VANDERSYS, Jeffrey P; Grand Haven Senior HS; Spring Lake, MI; Band; Chr; PolWkr; SctActv; College; Art.

VANDER VEEN, Colleen R; Msgr Hackett HS; Kalamazoo, MI; Chr; HonRl; Mdrgl; NHS; NatlMeritSF; SchMus; Mi Tech Univ; Bus Admin.

VANDER VEEN, David S; Pontiac Central HS; Sylvan Lake, MI; CmntyWkr; HonRl; NHS; StuCncl; LetterGlf; LetterTennis; Olivet College; Dentist.

VANDER VEEN, Krista L; Zeeland HS; Zeeland, MI; 66/160 HonRl; RptrSchPpr; Davenport Clge Of Bus; Receptionist.

VANDER VEEN, Linda R; Chicago Christian HS; Oak Lawn, IL; Chr; ChrhWkr; HonRl; LbryAde; OffAde; SchAde; TchrAde; YthFlsp; PpCl; IMSpt; College; Social Work.

VANDER VORST, Patty E; Pollock HS; Hague, ND; 3/19 VPSophCls; VPJrCls; Chrs; HonRl; SchPl; YthFlsp; 4-H; FHA; PpCl; Bsbl; 4-HAwd; State Schl Science Wahpeton Nd; Bus.

VAN DERVORT, Michael A; Lamphere HS; Madison Heights, MI; Univ Of Mi; Law Business Adminstration.

VANDER WAAL, David J; Paxton HS; Paxton, IL; 30/125 PresSophCls; CncrtBnd; HonRl; MrchBnd; SchPl; StuCncl; StuGov; YthFlsp; LetterBsktbl; LetterTennis; Univ Of Il; General Business.

VANDER WAL, Lisa K; Pella Christian HS; New Sharon, IA; 1/89 SecJrCls; Band; Chr; ChrhWkr; CncrtBnd; HonRl; MrchBnd; NHS; LetterBsktbl; Trk; Coll.

VAN DER WEELE, Nancy; North HS; Sheboygan, WI; 41/515 Chrs; ChrhWkr; CmntyWkr; HonRl; NHS; TchrAde; GerCl; Tennis; Chrldr; CchngActv; School Of Nursing; Nursing.

VANDER WEGEN, Peter G; Altoona Public HS; Altoona, WI; TchrAde; LetterBsbl; LetterFtbl; U Of Wis; Chemistry.

VANDERWELL, Mary; Turner HS; Kansas, KS; 70/350 Chrs; ChrhWkr; CncrtBnd; HonRl; NHS; Quill&Scroll; SchAde; SchPpr; SpnCl; PpCl; Coll;nurse.

VANDERWERF, Linda J; St Croix Falls HS; Dresser, WI; ChrhWkr; HonRl; NHS; NatlMeritSchl; SchPl; Lawrence University.

VANDERWERF, Linda J; Redwood Falls HS; Redwood Falls, MN; SecBand; Chr; CtyCnl; MrchBnd; NatlFornLg; NHS; PepBnd; SchMus; EdSchPpr; SpnCl; Um Morris; Psych.

VANDERWERF, Linda J; St Croix Falls HS; Dresser, WI; ChrhWkr; HonRl; NHS; NatlMeritSF; NCTE;.

VANDERWEST, Debra J; Catholic Central HS; Muskegon, MI; 20/215 Band; Chrl; CmntyWkr; HonRl; VPJA; VPNHS; PresSctActv; StuCncl; Sec4-H; 4-HAwd; College.

VANDER ZEC, Dale L; Kenowa Hills HS; Grand Rapids, MI; Aud/Vis; HonRl; Ftbl; Trade School.

VANDER ZIEL, Rodney G; Edgerton Public HS; Kenneth, MN; 5/35 VPJrCls; PresSrCls; ChrhWkr; HonRl; NHS; TchrAde; PresYthFlsp; LetterBsktbl; LetterTrk; Sw Minn St; Certified Public Accountant.

VANDE STREEK, Mary A; St Mary Springs HS; Fond Du Lac, WI; 20/120 ChrhWkr; HospAde; SchAde; SchPl; Yrbk; FDA; FHA; FNA; PresFrCl; SciCl; Moraine Pk Tech Inst; Nursing.

VAN DEUSEN, Candi M; Hillsdale HS; Hillsdale, MI; HonRl; NHS; LatCl; LetterTrk; GAA; University; Major Study.

VAN DEUSEN, Timothy C; Waterford Township HS; Pontiac, MI; PresBand; Chr; HonRl; MrchBnd; NHS; PepBnd; SchMus; StuCncl; StuGov; TchrAde; University; Professional.

VAN DE VEN, Cynthia T; St Mary Central HS; Neenah, WI; ALAGirlsSt; Chr; Chrs; ChrhWkr; NatlFornLg; EdYrBk; Yrbk; 4-H; LetterTrk; 4-HAwd; College; Phy Ed.

VANDEVENDER, Pennie L; Trenton HS; Laredo, MO; 8/128 ChrhWkr; HonRl; LbryAde; NHS; 4-H; CaptBsktbl; CchngActv; GAA; 4-HAwd; PresAwd; Trenton Jr Coll; Tchr.

VAN DEVENTER, Darrell; United Township HS; East Moline, IL; 34/640 HonRl; Trk; AmLegAwd; PresAwd; Black Hawk Coll; Data Processing.

VAN DEVENTER, David L; Taylorville HS; Taylorville, IL; 19/350 Band; ChrhWkr; CncrtBnd; HonRl; JrNHS; MrchBnd; NHS; NatlThespSoc; Orch; PepBnd; SchMus; SctActv; YthFlsp; Bsbl; Military Academy; Engineering.

VAN DE VOORDE, Mary J; Erie HS; Erie, IL; 7/81 AFS; Chrs; HonRl; SecStuCncl; Yrbk; FHA; GAA; Moline Lutheran School; Nurse.

VAN DE VOORT, Gregory L; Phillips HS; Kennan, WI; Chrs; ChrhWkr; HonRl; LbryAde; Mdrgl; SctActv; StuGov; RptrSchPpr; Ftbl; IMSpt; Voc Sch.

VANDE VOORT, John J; Ashwaubenon HS; Green Bay, WI; 90/269 Chrs; SchPl; LetterFtbl; Trk; LetterWrstlng; Coll; Bus Admin.

VANDEVORT, Brenda L; Summersville HS; Mountain View, MO; 7/39 Chrs; ChrhWkr; HonRl; LbryAde; OffAde; StuCncl; TchrAde; YthFlsp;.

VANDE VUSSE, Laurie; Holland HS; Holland, MI; HonRl; Orch;.

VANDE VUSSE, Stacy M; Maine West HS; Des Plaines, IL; HonRl; JrNHS; NHS; StuCncl; FBLA; FrCl; SciCl; College; Business.

VAN DE WALLE, Cheryl; Millard HS; Omaha, NE; 30/315 HonRl; NHS; NatlMeritCmnd; OffAde; PpCl; Univ Ne;med.

VANDEWEERD, Debbie L; Preston HS; Preston, MN; 3/57 ALAGirlsSt; HonRl; NHS; NatlMeritCmnd; EdYrBk; RptrSchPpr; FHA; SpnCl; GAA; VoiceDemAwd; Winona State College; Math Major.

VAN DE WIELE, Bernadette A; Walnut Grove Public HS; Walnut Grove, MN; 5/49 LetterChr; HonRl; LbryAde; StuCncl; SptEdSchPpr; SchPpr; PpCl; LetterChrldr; GAA; Trade School; Cosmotology.

VAN DEWIELE, Rebecca A; Walnut Grove HS; Revere, MN; 8/49 Band; Chr; ChrhWkr; HonRl; HospAde; LbryAde; OffAde; SchPl; StuCncl; 4-H; Stewarts Sch Of Cosmetology; Professional.

VANDE ZANDE, Kenneth M; Westfield HS; Westfield, WI; ALBoysSt; Band; CncrtBnd; MrchBnd; PepBnd; SpnCl; Ftbl; College; Music.

VANDIVER, Bob D; Houston HS; Cabool, MO; ChrhWkr; CmntyWkr; HonRl; LetterFtbl; LetterTrk; CchngActv; Sw Missouri St College.

VANDIVER, Tamara A; Oregon Howell HS; Brandsville, MO; ChrhWkr; HonRl; YthFlsp; SptEdYrbk; EdSchPpr; SptEdSchPpr; Bsbl; CaptBsktbl; Chrldr; IMSpt; Coll; Coach.

VAN DIVER, Von R; St Pius X HS; Festus, MO; ALBoysSt; Univ Of Tampa; Business Admin.

VANDIVORT, Dave J; Maple Valley HS; Mapleton, IA; College; Mass Communications.

VANDLIK, Mark J; J F Kennedy HS; Chicago, IL; 65/610 PresChrhWkr; HonRl; NHS; KeyCl; LetterBsbl; LetterBsktbl; LetterTrk; Univ Of Illinois; Pre Law.

VAN DOMMELEN, John; Okemar Hs; Okeros, MI; 21 NHS; TchrAde; Mich State U ; Chemistry.

VAN DONSELAAR, Norman J; Kalamazoo Central HS; Kalamazoo, MI; 31/436 Band; ChrhWkr; CncrtBnd; HonRl; PepBnd; YthFlsp; LetterFtbl; Western Mich Univ; Pre Med.

VAN DORPE, Paula M; Ressurection HS; Chicago, IL; ChrhWkr; CmntyWkr; RedCrAde; SchPl; SctActv; SecStuCncl; FDA; SpnCl; GAA; College; Child Development.

VAN DORPE, Therese M; Taft HS; Chicago, IL; 258/861 Chrs; ChrhWkr; CmntyWkr; TreasJA; RedCrAde; SchMus; SchPl; PresSctActv; SpnCl; GAA; Univ Of Illinois; Physical Therapy.

VANDRE, Gary P; Rochelle Township HS; Rochelle, IL; 46/212 HonRl; Bsktbl; Ftbl; Southern Illinois Univ; Engineering.

VAN DRUNEN, Mary R; Pella Christian HS; Pella, IA; HonRl; LbryAde; Bsbl; IMSpt; Dordt College; Special Education.

VAN DUSEN, Susan; Sand Creek HS; Weston, MI; Band; Chr; HospAde; MrchBnd; StuCncl; StuGov; RptrYrbk; EdYrBk; SptEdYrbk; Bus School; Sec.

VAN DUYNE, Cindy S; St Francis Academy; Joliet, IL; HonRl; NHS; SchMus; SciCl; Chrldr; CchngActv; GAA; AmLegAwd; VFWAwd; College; Biology.

VAN DYKE, Aaron J; Mount Vernon HS; Mount Vernon, IA; 28/81 VPJrCls; Chr; CncrtBnd; MrchBnd; PepBnd; LetterBsbl; LetterBsktbl; CaptFtbl; LetterTrk; Cornelle Clg; Teach & Coach.

VAN DYKE, Joan A; Grant Park HS; Grant Park, IL; 1/54 SecFrshCls; ALAGirlsSt; Chr; Chrs; ChrhWkr; CmntyWkr; HonRl; LbryAde; Mdrgl; NHS; Bsktbl; Trk; GAA; Bradley Univ; Nursing.

VAN DYKE, Patty A; Appleton West HS; Appleton, WI; AFS; ChrhWkr; CmntyWkr; HonRl; JA; StuCncl; StuGov; YthFlsp; RptrSchPpr; CivCl; Bus Sch.

VAN DYKE, Steven W; Almont HS; Almont, MI; 13/87 Band; MrchBnd; NatlFornLg; NHS; NatlMeritCmnd; LetterBsktbl; LetterFtbl; LetterTrk; DanFAwd; 4-HAwd; Michigan State University; Agriculture.

VAN DYNE, Terry D; Mascoutah Comm HS; Mascoutah, IL; Band; CncrtBnd; HonRl; PepBnd; Univ Of Illinois; Architecture.

VAN EE, Robert C; Wyoming Park HS; Wyoming, MI; Band; Chr; DrmMjrt; LitMag; ModUN; VPStuCncl; Yrbk; RptrSchPpr; LetterTrk; CaptWrstlng; Olioet Clg; Humanities.

VAN EERDEN, Christine L; John Marshall HS; Milwaukee, WI; 71/711 Band; CncrtBnd; HonRl; MrchBnd; NHS; Orch; StuCncl; SchPpr; Swmmng; GAA; Univ Of Madison; Professional.

VAN EGMOND, Thomas; Austin Catholic Prep; Grosse Pointe Wood, MI; 13/193 HonRl; NHS; SchPl; SciCl; Bsbl; Coll; Dentistry.

VANEK, Carol J; Prague Public HS; Prague, NE; ALAGirlsSt; SchPl; CncrtBnd; SecNHS; SecStuCncl; Yrbk; SchPpr; PresFHA; PpCl; Chrldr; Lincoln Sch Of Comerce; Secretary.

VANEK, Margaret M; Whiting HS; Whiting, IN; 7/90 SecFrshCls; SecSophCls; SecJrCls; DrlTm; HonRl; NHS; StuCncl; RptrYrbk; AmLegAwd; KiwanAwd; College; Medical Field.

VAN ELSEN, Lynda D; Colfax Comm HS; Colfax, IA; 1/75 SecSophCls; Band; CncrtBnd; DrlTm; HonRl; MrchBnd; NHS; OffAde; PepBnd; LetterBsbl; Pella Central Clge; Journalism.

VANERIO, Cheryl A; Spalding HS; Chicago, IL; Chrs; ChrhWkr; HonRl; HospAde; JA; JCC; JrNHS; NHS; StuCncl; College; Medical.

VAN ESLER, John W; Jennings HS; Jennings, MO; 21/250 ALBoysSt; HonRl; NHS; StuCncl; EngCl; College; Accounting.

VAN ESS, Kristie; Grand Rapids Chr HS; Grand Rapids, MI; Chr; ChrhWkr; College; Professional.

VAN ESSEN, Debra; Fulton HS; Fulton, IL; SecSophCls; SecJrCls; Chrs; HonRl; NHS; FTA; SpnCl; GAA; College; Social Worker.

VANETTI, Carol S; Park Hill Sr HS; Parkville, MO; 1/400 Band; CmntyWkr; HonRl; MrchBnd; ModUN; NatlFornLg; NHS; SctActv; TchrAde; GodCntryAwd; Univ Of Missouri; Medicine.

VANEVENHOVEN, Rose A; Kaukauna HS; Kaukauna, WI; Chr; DrlTm; HonRl; HospAde; LbryAde; StuCncl; RptrSchPpr; LatCl; PpCl; Trk; Col; Medicine.

VAN EVERY, Judith M; O Neill Public HS; O Neill, NE; Chr; HonRl; 4-H; Trk; 4-HAwd; Nurse.

VAN EVERY, Mary J; O Neill Public HS; Page, NE; Chr; HonRl; RptrSchPpr; 4-H; Southeast Comm College; Art.

VAN FLEET, Jeff H; Sigourney HS; Sigourney, IA; Band; Chrs; HonRl; Mdrgl; MrchBnd; NHS; VPNatlThespSoc; PepBnd; SchMus; SchPl; Kirkwood Clg; Dental Lab Technology.

VAN FOSSON, Marion H; Southeast Polk HS; Mitchellville, IA; HonRl; NHS; SctActv; TchrAde; YthFlsp; SciCl; LetterSwmmng; Trk; GodCntryAwd; Univ Of Iowa; Medical.

VANG, Doug G; D L Central HS; Devils Lake, ND; ChrhWkr; HonRl; PolWkr; RedCrAde; SctActv; YthFlsp; LetterBsbl; LetterBsktbl; LetterFtbl; LetterGlf; University Nd; Professional.

VANGEISON, Dirk J; Pawnee HS; Pawnee, IL; Band; ChrhWkr; HonRl; StuCncl; FrCl; Bsbl; Bsktbl; Ftbl; Illinois State College; Corrections.

VAN GELDER, Loren J; Floyd Valley HS; Hosprs, IA; Chr; Chrs; ChrhWkr; CmntyWkr; SchPl; YthFlsp; CaptBsktbl; LetterTrk; Trade Or Vocational; Vocation.

VAN GENDEREN, Linda K; Corsica Public HS; Harrison, SD; TrsFrshCls; SecTrsJrCls; Band; HonRl; SchMus; YthFlsp; Yrbk; LetterBsktbl; Trk; CaptChrldr;.

VAN GENT, Elissa W; Zeeland HS; Zeeland, MI; 7/185 Band; Chr; ChrhWkr; CncrtBnd; HonRl; MrchBnd; PepBnd; SchMus; SchPl; LatCl; College.

VAN GERPEN, Nancy A; Kearney HS; Kearney, MO; 4/71 PresJrCls; PresChrs; DrlTm; HonRl; NHS; SchPl; StuCncl; RptrYrbk; TreasFrCl; Chrldr; Maryville Nw Mo State U; Child Development.

VAN GHEEM, Theresa L; West De Pere HS; De Pere, WI; HonRl; HospAde; JA; NHS; SchPl; RptrSchPpr; 4-H; FHA; FNA; LatCl; Trade School; Nursing.

VAN GINHAVEN, Janice M; River Valley HS; Sawyer, MI; SecJrCls; SecSrCls; Band; CncrtBnd; HonRl; MrchBnd; NHS; PepBnd; U Of Michigan; Accounting.

VAN GINKEL, John C; Atlantic HS; Atlantic, IA; 11/178 Chrs; HonRl; NHS; Quill&Scroll; SctActv; YthFlsp; RptrYrbk; EdYrBk; Ftbl; Trk; Clge; Science & Math.

VAN GORDER, John E; Bremen HS; Midlothian, IL; 52/430 ChrhWkr; HonRl; NHS; Bsbl; Swmmng; Work; Mechanic.

VAN GORP, John D; Pella Christian HS; Pella, IA; VPJrCls; HonRl; StuCncl; LetterBsbl; LetterBsktbl; LetterTrk;.

VAN GORP, Laura B; Pella Christian HS; Pella, IA; SecSophCls; Band; Chr; TreasHonRl; LbryAde; MrchBnd; PepBnd; SchPl; RptrSchPpr; College; Elementary Education.

VANGSNESS, Bruce E; Magic City HS; Minot, ND; 125/600 TrsSophCls; HstJrCls; ALBoysSt; Band; CncrtBnd; HonRl; JrNHS; MrchBnd; Orch; PepBnd; LetterFtbl; Glf; Wrstlng; Minot State College; Music.

VAN HAEIST, Denise M; Reed Custer HS; Wilmington, IL; TrsSophCls; VPJrCls; Band; Chrs; CncrtBnd; HonRl; NHS; PepBnd; SchMus; CaptChrldr; Univ.

VAN HAITSMA, Sherril L; Zeeland HS; Zeeland, MI; Band; CncrtBnd; HonRl; HospAde; MrchBnd; Orch; PepBnd; SchMus; PpCl; Bsktbl; Bronson Methodist School Of Nursing Nurse.

VAN HAL, Sharon G; Pella Christian HS; Leighton, IA; Chr; HonRl; LbryAde; PpCl; IMSpt;.

VAN HAMMOND, Anthony; Kimberly Senior HS; Kimberly, WI; Chrl; Chrs; ChrhWkr; HonRl; JA; SchMus; KeyCl; Wrstlng; IMSpt; PresAwd; College; Architect.

VAN HARTESVELT, Dennis L; West Ottawa HS; Holland, MI; ChrhWkr; NHS; SchPl; SctActv; YthFlsp; PresGerCl; College; Psychology.

VAN HOOK, Jeanie M; Otterville Public HS; Florence, MO; LbryAde; OffAde; StuCncl; StuGov; Yrbk; SchPpr; FHA; FrCl; BttyCrckrAwd; College; Professional.

VAN HOORNE, Doreen M; Cheboygan Area HS; Cheboygan, MI; CmntyWkr; HospAde; TchrAde; Kalamazoo College; Interior Dec.

VAN HOOSER, Buckley B; Baxter Springs HS; Baxter Springs, KS; Chr; Chrl; HonRl; NHS; PolWkr; SctActv; RptrYrbk; Yrbk; KeyCl; PresAwd; Drury Coll; Pharmacology.

VAN HOOSER, Gary L; Orrick HS; Orrick, MO; HonRl; NHS; 4-H; FFA; 4-HAwd; College; Vocation.

VAN HOOSER, Jacky W; Carl Junction HS; Joplin, MO; Band; CncrtBnd; HonRl; MrchBnd; PepBnd; ROTC; MthCl; Mssc College.

VAN HORN, Dave; Parker Senior HS; Janesville, WI; HonRl; IMSpt; College.

VAN HORN, Rodney L; Beaverton HS; Beauerton, MI; HonRl; LetterBsbl; LetterFtbl; IMSpt; College; Air Force Officer.

VAN HORN, Shelley R; Humboldt Comm Public HS; Humboldt, IA; VPFrshCls; Chr; Chrs; SctActv; StuCncl; TchrAde; RptrSchPpr; Trk; Chrldr; College; Secretary.

VAN HORN, Thomas E; St Marys Springs HS; Plymouth, WI; Aud/Vis; ChrhWkr; JA; LbryAde; NatlMeritCmnd; SchPl; StuCncl; RptrYrbk; RptrSchPpr; SptEdSchPpr; LetterFtbl; LetterTrk; IMSpt; College.

VAN HORN, Thurston; Colby HS; Colby, KS; VPSrCls; PolWkr; SctActv; RptrSchPpr; SptEdSchPpr; SpnCl; CaptFtbl; Swmmng; Trk; Wrstlng; Us Military Acad; Engineering.

VAN HOUGHTON, Janet V; St Scholastica HS; Park Ridge, IL; College; Zoology.

VAN HOUT, Brian; Premontre HS; Green Bay, WI; 10/174 VPJrCls; HonRl; RptrYrbk; EdYrBk; Yrbk; KeyCl; SpnCl; Bsktbl; Trk; IMSpt; College; Professional.

VAN HOUTAN, Raymond L; Columbus HS; Columbus, ND; 2/22 ALBoysSt; HonRl; SchAde; SchPl; LetterFtbl; LetterTrk; IMSpt; U Of North Dakota; Geological.

VAN HOUTAN, Raymond L; Columbus Public HS; Columbus, ND; HonRl; LetterFtbl; LetterTrk; Univ; Geological Engineering.

VAN HOUTEN, Sidney C; Airport Community HS; Carleton, MI; NHS; StuCncl; 4-H; LetterBsbl; LetterCollege; Electronics.

VAN HOVE, Lorri K; Brookings HS; Brookings, SD; PresSrCls; Band; Chr; Chrl; Chrs; ChrhWkr; CmntyWkr; CncrtBnd; IntrClCncl; Mdrgl; Sd State Univ; Pharmacy.

VAN HOVELN, Theresa J; Crescent Iroquois HS; Milford, IL; VPSophCls; TrsSrCls; Band; Chr; CncrtBnd; HonRl; MrchBnd; SchPpr; 4-H; FHA; Bsktbl; GAA; IMSpt; Nursing Schl; Nursing.

VAN HOWE, Robert; Chicago Christian HS; Palos Heights, IL; Chrl; CncrtBnd; HonRl; Mdrgl; NHS; SchMus; SchPl; EdYrBk; LetterFtbl; CaptIMSpt; College; Medical Dr.

VAN HUIS, Karen J; Hamilton HS; Holland, MI; 16/125 Band; ChrhWkr; HonRl; MrchBnd; TchrAde; YthFlsp; 4-H; FTA; SpnCl; Business Career In Retailing.

VAN ISEGHEM, Margaret J; Incarnate Word Academy; St Ann, MO; ChrhWkr; CmntyWkr; HonRl; JA; StuCncl; PpCl; Chrldr; PPFtbl; JAAwd; St Louis Univ; Physical Therapy.

VANKAT, Karen J; Thornridge HS; Dolton, IL; HonRl; NHS; FrCl; PpCl; Coll; Secondard Ed.

VAN KEULEN, Ralph H; New Ulm HS; New Ulm, MN; VPSrCls; Band; Chr; CncrtBnd; HonRl; StuCncl; Trk; University; Business Admin.

VAN KLOMPENBERG, Cathy J; Unity Christian HS; Hudsonville, MI; Band; Chr; ChrhWkr; CmntyWkr; CncrtBnd; MrchBnd; PepBnd; SchAde; SchMus; 4-H; FTA; PpCl; IMSpt; Calvin College; Elementary Ed.

VAN KLOMPENBURG, David W; Montevideo Senior HS; Montevideo, MN; 22/147 HonRl; MrchBnd; PresFFA; LetterFtbl; LetterWrstlng; VFWAwd; North Dakota State School; Mechanic.

VANKO, Alice M; Lyons Twp HS; La Grange, IL; ChrhWkr; HonRl; LbryAde; Business School; Court Reporting.

VAN KOOTEN, Cheryl J; Pella Christian HS; Pella, IA; Chr; ChrhWkr; HonRl; LbryAde; SchPl; RptrSchPpr; Dordt College.

VAN KOOTEN, Marva J; Pella Christian HS; Pella, IA; 8/83 HonRl; HospAde; JrNHS; LbryAde; NatlFornLg; NHS; Yrbk; PpCl; IMSpt; Cllege; Nursing.

VAN KOOTEN, Pamela J; Pella Christian HS; Pella, IA; Band; Chr; ChrhWkr; CncrtBnd; HonRl; MrchBnd; PepBnd; SchPl; RptrSchPpr; Bsktbl;.

VAN LAAN, Clare; Garber HS; Essexville, MI; 10/170 ChrhWkr; StuCncl; TchrAde; PpCl; Glf; PPFtbl; PresAwd; Univ Mi.

VAN LAAR, Debra; Unity Christian HS; Grandville, MI; Band; ChrhWkr; CmntyWkr; HonRl; MrchBnd; SchPl; 4-H; FTA; IMSpt; 4-HAwd; College; Spec Ed.

VAN LAAR, James B; Grand Rapids Christian HS; Grand Rapids, MI; PresFrshCls; Aud/Vis; Chr; ChrhWkr; JA; Bsktbl; Socr; Trk; IMSpt; JAAwd; Clg; Engineering.

VANLANINGHAM, Lori A; Belvidere HS; Belvidere, IL; 43/350 HonRl; StuCncl; FNA; GerCl; PpCl; Bsbl; Chrldr; PPFtbl; Valparaiso In; Nursing Or Doctor.

VAN LEER, Cynthia L; Union HS; Union, MO; Band; CncrtBnd; HonRl; HospAde; MrchBnd; Orch; PepBnd; SchMus; StuCncl; 4-H; SpnCl; PpCl; Trk; College.

VAN LIERE, Luann; Hamilton HS; Hamilton, MI; HonRl; SchPl; StuCncl; StuGov; GerCl; Chrldr; Michigan State Univ.

VAN LIESHOUT, Debra L; Thornwood HS; Dolton, IL; HonRl; NHS; TchrAde; LatCl; VPPpCl; Thornton Comm Clge; Physical Therapy.

VAN LIESHOUT, Mari L; Appleton West HS; Appleton, WI; Band; Chrl; ChrhWkr; HonRl; PresJA; OffAde; SctActv; Yrbk; PpCl; JAAwd; College; Cpa.

VAN L MAAS, Jean H; The Principia HS; St Louis, MO; Chrs; CmntyWkr; NatlMeritSF; StuCncl; StuGov; FrCl; SpnCl; Socr; GAA; Clg; Languages.

VAN LUE, Lila D; North Miami HS; Roann, IN; 8/122 TrsJrCls; ALAGirlsSt; Band; ChrhWkr; DrmMjrt; PresNHS; StuCncl; 4-H; SpnCl; DARAwd; Manchester Clg; Music Ed.

VAN MERSBERGEN, Sharon; Pella Community HS; Pella, IA; Chrs; HonRl; PpCl; Kirkwood Comm Coll; Dental Ass.

VAN METER, Rebecca L; Frontier HS; Monticello, IN; 5/57 PresJrCls; HonRl; StuCncl; TchrAde; PpCl; Law.

VAN METER, Roseanna; Belton HS; Belton, MO; 20/279 Chr; DrlTm; HonRl; LbryAde; NHS; StuCncl; FrCl; PpCl; Chrldr; PPFtbl; Central Mo State U; Business.

VAN METRE, David L; Keya Paha County HS; Springview, NE; 2/23 PresFrshCls; PresJrCls; HonRl; NHS; SchPl; StuCncl; SptEdYrbk; Bsbl; Bsktbl; Ftbl; Univ Of Ne; Public Relations.

VAN METRE, David L; Keya Paha Cty HS; Springview, NE; 2/22 PresFrshCls; PresJrCls; HonRl; JrNHS; NHS; SchPl; StuCncl; StuGov; YthFlsp; SptEdYrbk; Bsbl; Bsktbl; Ftbl; Norfolk Jr College; Journalism.

VAN MEURS, Douglas; Western Mich Christian HS; Muskegon, MI; Band; SchPl; Calvin College; Science.

VAN MIDDLESWORTH, Vicki L; Climax Scotts HS; Climax, MI; 11/70 TrsSophCls; Chrs; HonRl; SctActv; StuCncl; TchrAde; RptrSchPpr; 4-H; Chrldr; 4-HAwd; Coll; Home Ec.

VANN, Pamela D; Concordia Acad; St Paul, MN; 15/51 Chr; NatlMeritFnl; SchMus; TchrAde; LatCl; Bsktbl; IMSpt; Concordia College; Social Work.

VAN NADA, Gregory; Grand Blanc HS; Grand Blane, MI; 64/637 ChrhWkr; HonRl; JA; NHS; IMSpt; PresAwd; CitAwd; Alma Mi College; Education.

VAN NESS, Connie S; Delta HS; Muncie, IN; Band; ChrhWkr; CncrtBnd; HonRl; MrchBnd; PepBnd; 4-H; FrCl; Michigan State Univ; Dog Trainer & Beeder.

VAN NESS, Elaine G; Brazil Sr HS; Brazil, IN; Band; CncrtBnd; HonRl; MrchBnd; PepBnd; Yrbk; FHA; FrCl; College; Professional.

VAN NORDEN, Joann; Hlv Community HS; Victor, IA; Chr; Chrl; Chrs; HonRl; NHS; SchMus; SpnCl; Trade School; Professional.

VANNOSTER, Dennis D; Field Kindly HS; Coffeyville, KS; HonRl; StuCncl; StuGov; KeyCl; MthCl; SciCl; Tennis; CchngActv; IMSpt; Trade Sch; Machine Shop.

VAN NOY, Kathleen D; Centerville HS; Centerville, IA; 16/135 Chrs; CncrtBnd; NHS; PolWkr; Central College Of Pella; Psychology.

VANO, Linda N; Southfield Senior HS; Southfield, MI; 53/680 HonRl; OffAde; SctActv; College; Mathematics.

VAN OEVEREN, Cheryl L; Allendale Shs; Allendale, MI; 5/38 Band; ChrhWkr; CmntyWkr; CncrtBnd; HonRl; MrchBnd; Orch; PepBnd; Yrbk; EdSchPpr; Grand Valley State College.

VAN OPDORP, Cheryl A; United Township HS; East Moline, IL; 22/586 HonRl; JrNHS; NHS; StuCncl; Twrl; YthFlsp; GerCl; PpCl; GAA; College; Accounting.

VAN OPENS, Katherine M; St Catherine HS; Racine, WI; 3/260 Band; CmntyWkr; CncrtBnd; HonRl; NatlFornLg; RedCrAde; SchMus; SchPl; TchrAde; OptClAwd; College; Professional.

VAN ORDSTRAND, Stephanie A; Princeton HS; Princeton, IL; TrsSophCls; AFS; HonRl; NHS; OffAde; GerCl; GAA; Clg; Med Tech.

VAN ORMER, Linda C; Taylors Falls HS; Taylors Falls, MN; SecJrCls; Band; Chr; HonRl; RptrYrbk; GerCl; LetterTrk; Chrldr; PresAwd; College; Professional Medicine.

VAN ORSON, Jane M; Bethlehem Academy; Faribault, MN; 9/83 Chrs; HonRl; PresNHS; SchMus; SchPl; StuCncl; EdYrBk; LetterBsktbl; LetterTrk; Chrldr; St Bens College; Accounting.

VAN ORT, Steven J; Lyons Township HS; La Grange Park, IL; HonRl; NatlMeritCmnd; Western Mi Univ; Accounting.

VAN OSTRAND, Daniel K; Buffalo Lake HS; Buffalo Lake, MN; 2/50 Band; Chrs; ChrhWkr; CncrtBnd; HonRl; MrchBnd; PepBnd; 4-H; LetterBsktbl; LetterFtbl; College; Math.

VAN OSTRAND, Myra J; Buffalo Lake Sr HS; Buffalo Lake, MN; Band; Chr; Chrs; ChrhWkr; CmntyWkr; CncrtBnd; HonRl; MrchBnd; NatlFornLg; PepBnd; Bsbl; Bsktbl; College; Music.

VAN OYEN, Mary E; Southfield HS; Southfield, MI; Band; ChrhWkr; CncrtBnd; MrchBnd; SchMus; SchPl; TchrAde; Univ; Medical Tech.

VAN PARYS, Joseph M; Leavenworth Sr HS; Leavenworth, KS; .

VAN PELT, Debra L; Perry Community HS; Perry, IA; 11/118 DrmMjrt; HonRl; MrchBnd; NHS; StuCncl; Chrldr; Mercy Hosp Sch Of Nursing; Nurse.

VAN PELT, Greg D; Panora Linden HS; Panora, IA; 3/50 PresFrshCls; VPJrCls; ALBoysSt; HonRl; NHS; StuGov; LetterBsbl; LetterBsktbl; LetterFtbl; LetterTrk; College; Coaching.

VAN PELT, Kariena R; Hanson Ind #40 HS; Fulton, SD; 13/44 CmntyWkr; HonRl; Quill&Scroll; SchPl; Yrbk; RptrSchPpr; SchPpr; FHA; PpCl; IMSpt; Vocational School; Nursing.

VAN PELT, Marianne; Banner County HS; Kimball, NE; 4/25 VPSophCls; Band; Chrs; HonRl; NHS; StuCncl; LetterBsktbl; LetterTrk; Chrldr; 4-HAwd; LionAwd; PresAwd; University; Genetic Science.

VAN PELT, Sharon L; Sandwich Comm HS; Sandwich, IL; TrsFrshCls; SecSophCls; VPJrCls; Chr; ChrhWkr; Mdrgl; MrchBnd; SchPl; GerCl; GAA;.

VAN PELT, Sharon L; Sandwich HS; Sandwich, IL; 14/125 TrsFrshCls; SecSophCls; VPJrCls; Chrs; MrchBnd; NHS; SchPl; FTA; PresGerCl; PresGAA; College; Secondary Education.

VAN PETTEN, Jeffrey F; Mission Valley HS; Eskridge, KS; 20/65 Chrs; MrchBnd; SchAde; SchPl; StuCncl; StuGov; TchrAde; 4-H; FFA; Bsktbl; Ftbl; Glf; College; Veterinarian.

VAN PETTEN, Sue I; Reese Public HS; Fairgrove, MI; 56/128 HonRl; SchPl; TchrAde; Yrbk; RptrSchPpr; EdSchPpr; FHA; GerCl; PpCl; Saginaw Valley College; Nursing.

VAN RHEENEN, Bonnie S; Fulton Community HS; Fulton, IL; 22/122 AFS; Band; ChrhWkr; CncrtBnd; HonRl; MrchBnd; NHS; PepBnd; 4-H; Northwestern College; Law.

VAN RHEENEN, Randy L; Mendota HS; Mendota, IL; Band; DrlTm; MrchBnd; SctActv; Sdlty; SciCl; College; Vocation.

VAN RIPER, Michael J; Onalaska HS; Onalaska, WI; 1/129 Chr; ChrhWkr; HonRl; NHS; SchPpr; LetterBsbl; Bsktbl; LetterFtbl; Tennis; Wrstlng; University; Math.

VAN RITE, Daniel R; Ashwaubswon HS; Green Bay, WI; LetterFtbl; Trade School; Professional.

VAN ROEYEN, Eileen W; Maine West HS; Des Plaines, IL; AFS; HonRl; NHS; OffAde; Orch; SchMus; RptrSchPpr; Northwestern Univ; Law.

VAN SAMBEEK, Paul W; Milbank HS; Corona, SD; PresJrCls; HonRl; NHS; FFA; KeyCl; LetterFtbl; LetterWrstlng; College; Professional.

VAN SCHINDEL, Bonnie S; Freedom HS; Appleton, WI; 21/110 TrsJrCls; TrsSrCls; HonRl; SchAde; SchPl; TchrAde; VPFBLA; PpCl; Chrldr; GAA; Vocation.

VAN SCOTTER, Thomas; Mt Morris HS; Mt Morris, IL; 6/77 PresFrshCls; PresSophCls; PresJrCls; PresSrCls; HonRl; NHS; SchPl; Bsbl; Bsktbl; LetterFtbl; LetterTrk; IMSpt; AmLegAwd; Univ; Chemistry.

VAN SCOY, Brenda L; Dixon HS; Dixon, MO; Band; Chr; Chrs; CncrtBnd; DrmMjrt; HonRl; MrchBnd; PepBnd; Twrl; FHA; PpCl; Rolla College; Cosmetology.

VAN SICKLE, Roberta S; Dexler HS; Dexter, MI; 22/163 HonRl; NHS; NatlMeritCmnd; SchPpr; CivCl; 4-H; GerCl; USJCAwd; U Of M; Natural Res.

VAN SICKLE, Timothy D; Shelby HS; Shelby Hs, MI; 3/116 Band; CncrtBnd; HonRl; JrNHS; LitMag; MrchBnd; NHS; NatlMeritCmnd; PepBnd; Bsktbl; Michigan State Clg; Music.

VAN SICKLE, Treva J; Salem Comm HS; Iuka, IL; 1/203 HonRl; NHS; NatlMeritCmnd; SecStuCncl; TreasSpnCl; DARAwd; Kaskaskia College; Exec Secretary.

VAN SLEMBROUCK, Lauri; Cheboygan Area HS; Cheboygan, MI; Band; CncrtBnd; HonRl; MrchBnd; SchPl; 4-H;.

VAN SLOOTEN, Timothy A; Holland HS; Holland, MI; ChrhWkr; HonRl; Orch; Hope College; Biology.

VAN SOMEREN, Beverly J; Baldwin Woodville HS; Baldwin, WI; Chr; Chrs; ChrhWkr; HonRl; Mdrgl; Orch; SchMus; SchPl; TchrAde; YthFlsp; SchPpr; College; Psychology.

VAN SOMEREN, Karen M; Baldwin Woodville HS; Baldwin, WI; TrsSophCls; Chr; Chrl; Chrs; ChrhWkr; CmntyWkr; HonRl; SchMus; SchPl; LetterBsktbl; LetterTrk; GAA; College; Nursing.

VAN SOMEREN, Rebecca; Baldwin Woodville Hs; Baldwin, WI; ALAGirlsSt; Chr; ChrhWkr; HonRl; OffAde; SchPpr; College; Elementary Teacher.

VAN SOMEREN, Rebecca F; Baldwin Woodville HS; Baldwin, WI; ALAGirlsSt; ChrhWkr; CmntyWkr; HonRl; NHS; OffAde; College; Elementary Teacher.

VAN STRIKE, Troy W; West Sioux HS; Ireton, IA; PresFrshCls; PresSophCls; Chr; ChrhWkr; HonRl; NatlMeritSchl; StuCncl; FFA; Ftbl; Wrstlng; University; Professional.

VANT HOF, Cindy L; Jenison HS; Jwenison, MI; Band; Chr; HonRl; SchPpr; GerCl; CaptChrldr; IMSpt; PPFtbl; College; Professional.

VANT HUL, Randal K; Grandville HS; Grandville, MI; Band; Chr; CmntyWkr; HonRl; MrchBnd; NHS; NatlMeritFnl; SchMus; StuGov; LetterTrk; Coll; Sci.

VAN THULLENAR, Diane M; Bishop Miege HS; Shawnee Mission, KS; 9/215 Chr; Chrl; Chrs; HonRl; HospAde; NHS; NatlMeritCmnd; SchMus; SchPl; TchrAde; Rockhurst Clg; Education.

VANTREASE, Mark S; Alton Sr HS; Alton, IL; Band; HonRl; MrchBnd; NHS; Orch; PepBnd; SchMus; Siue; Computer Science.

VAN TREECK, Robert J; Lyons Township HS; La Grange, IL; ChrhWkr; HonRl; SchPl; PresSctActv; IMSpt; NCTE; Univ Of Illinois.

VAN TRESS, Robert J; Abingdon HS; Abingdon, IL; 15/90 PresBand; ChrhWkr; PresCncrtBnd; HonRl; NHS; SchPpr; Pres4-H; VPFFA; 4-HAwd; Univ Of Ill; Veterinarian.

VANTRIES, Cynthia D; Cyrus HS; Farwell, MN; HstSophCls; SecJrCls; Band; Chr; HonRl; NHS; SchPl; TchrAde; Bsktbl; LetterTrk; U Of Mn Marris; Teaching.

VANTRUMP, Mike A; Carrollton HS; Carrollton, MO; Band; CncrtBnd; HonRl; MrchBnd; NHS; TchrAde; LetterBsktbl; LetterGlf; CchngActv; Univ Of Missouri; Accounting.

VAN VLAENDEREN, Jesse R; Lidgerwood Public HS; Lidgerwood, ND; HonRl; NHS; SchPl; GerCl; PpCl; LetterTrk; Col; Pharmacy.

VAN VLECK, Randall D; Maine West HS; Des Plaines, IL; HonRl; ModUN; NHS; SchPl; StuGov; CaptSocr; CaptTrk; Washburn Univ; Law.

VANVLEET, Barbara; Wheaton North Hs; Wheaton, IL; 32/308 Chr; Chrl; ChrhWkr; CmntyWkr; JrNHS; NHS; SchMus; StuCncl; StuGov; PpCl; Secondary Education; Social Science Studies.

VAN VOROUS, Mary T; East Leyden HS; Schiller Park, IL; Chrs; HonRl; Trade School; Professional.

VAN VRANKEN, Bradley D; Meade HS; Meade, KS; ALBoysSt; Band; Chrs; HonRl; SchMus; StuCncl; RptrYrbk; Yrbk; EdSchPpr; Bsktbl; Tennis; Jr College; Professional Artist.

VAN VREEDE, Paul; Little Chute HS; Little Chute, WI; 8/110 ALBoysSt; HonRl; JrNHS; NHS; SchPl; SpnCl; Bsktbl; Ftbl; Coll; Acct.

VAN VYNCKT, Randall J; D E Gavit HS; Hammond, IN; 12/350 HonRl; LitMag; NatlFornLg; NatlMeritSF; Quill&Scroll; SchPl; PresStuCncl; Yrbk; SchPpr; EngCl; Ind Univ;journalism.

VAN WASSENHOVE, Christine M; Annawan HS; Sheffield, IL; 1/80 TrsJrCls; MrchBnd; NHS; StuCncl; Yrbk; 4-H; SpnCl; Bsbl; Bsktbl; Chrldr; GAA; AmLegAwd; College; Professional.

VAN WASSENHOVE, Douglas J; Kewanee HS; Kewanee, IL; 1/226 PresFrshCls; HonRl; NatlMeritSF; OffAde; StuCncl; YthLg; EdSchPpr; FTA; GerCl; College; Mathematics.

VAN WASSENHOVE, Mark S; Kewanee HS; Kewanee, IL; ChrhWkr; HonRl; OffAde; SchMus; RptrSchPpr; College; Business.

VAN WIEREN, Doris R; Mc Bain Public HS; Mc Bain, MI; CncrtBnd; HonRl; NHS; OffAde; PepBnd; SchPl; TchrAde; FHA; Central Michigan Univ; Business Admin.

VAN WINKLE, Gwendolyn J; Northeastern Wayne HS; Fountain City, IN; 4/150 ALAGirlsSt; Chr; ChrhWkr; HonRl; LbryAde; NHS; StuCncl; VP4-H; Chrldr; Trade School.

VAN WINKLE, Martha E; Alton R Iv HS; Alton, MO; 3/87 HonRl; LbryAde;.

VAN WORMER, Valerie H; Lincoln HS; Wisconsin Rapids, WI; HonRl; RptrYrbk; 4-H; 4-HAwd; Univ Wi Stevens Point; Zoology.

VAN WYHE, Ricky L; Ellsworth HS; Ellsworth, MN; 1/34 Band; Chr; CncrtBnd; HonRl; MrchBnd; PepBnd; SchMus; StuGov; LetterBttyCrckrAwd; RptrYrbk; Coll; Bus.

VAN WYK, Ronald D; Floyd Valley Community HS; Alton, IA; Chr; ChrhWkr; HonRl; SchPl; Yrbk; LetterBsktbl; LetterFtbl; LetterTrk; IMSpt; PresAwd;.

VANYO, Phillip J; Alvarado HS; E Grand Forks, MN; 4/23 PresSophCls; Band; Chr; HonRl; SchPl; PresStuCncl; VP4-H; CaptBsbl; LetterBsktbl; 4-HAwd; East Grand Forks; Vocation.

VANYO, Richard G; Sacred Heart HS; East Grand Forks, MN; 17/55 ChrhWkr; SchPl; RptrYrbk; Yrbk; RptrSchPpr; Bsktbl; Ftbl; Northland Jr College; Business.

VAN YUGT, Alva N; South Christian HS; Grand Rapids, MI; Chr; HonRl; NHS; GerCl; Trk; College; German.

VAN ZANDBERGEN, Kirk K; Westside HS; Omaha, NE; HonRl; SctActv; StuCncl; StuGov; Yrbk; LetterTrk; LetterWrstlng; Coll; Undecided.

VAN ZANDT, Terri L; Prospect HS; Mt Prospect, IL; 21/610 CmntyWkr; HonRl; NatlFornLg; NHS; NatlMeritCmnd; Quill&Scroll; RptrYrbk; EdYrBk; Univ Of Ill; Law.

VAN ZANTE, June E; Pella Community HS; Pella, IA; Band; CncrtBnd; MrchBnd; PepBnd; YthFlsp; 4-H; FHA; College; Rn.

VAN ZANTEN, Karen R; Pepin HS; Pepin, WI; Band; Chr; Chrs; CncrtBnd; HonRl; MrchBnd; NHS; PepBnd; SchPl; StuCncl; YthFlsp; Bsktbl; Chrldr; University; Professional.

VAN ZEE, Carma J; Pella Comm HS; Pella, IA; 20/115 ChrhWkr; CmntyWkr; HonRl; PolWkr; YthFlsp; Yrbk; FHA; PpCl; Uni At Cedar Falls; English.

VAN ZEE, Cheryl L; White Lake Ind HS; White Lake, SD; PresSophCls; Chr; Chrs; ChrhWkr; HonRl; Yrbk; FNA; PpCl; CaptChrldr; VoiceDemAwd; College; Professional.

VAN ZELST, Jean L; Marillac HS; Glenview, IL; CmntyWkr; HonRl; LitMag; Orch; SchMus; SctActv; StuCncl; StuGov; University; Education.

VANZO, Karl K; Morton HS; Hammond, IN; 2/492 HonRl; JrNHS; NatlFornLg; VPNHS; NatlMeritFnl; StuGov; Univ Of Notre Dame; Law.

VARBLE, Randall S; Rochelle Township HS; Rochelle, IL; 14/215 Band; CncrtBnd; DrmBgl; HonRl; MrchBnd; NHS; Orch; SchPpr; 4-H; Milwaukee School Of Engineering; Engineer.

VARBLE, Vickey L; United Twp HS; East Moline, IL; HonRl; OffAde; SchAde; StuCncl; Teen; RptrYrbk; College.

VARDSVEEN, Kathryn A; Magic City Campus HS; Minot, ND; Chr; ChrhWkr; HonRl; NatlFornLg; NHS; PolWkr; SchPl; StuGov; YthFlsp; RptrSchPpr; Minot State Col; Lawyer.

VARE, Karen; Col Heights Sr HS; Minneapolis, MN; HonRl; NHS; OffAde; Junior College; Nursing.

VAREL, Allan L; Central Comm HS; St Rose, IL; CmntyWkr; HonRl; SchPl; StuCncl; StuGov; PpCl; LetterFtbl; CchngActv; JAAwd; PresAwd; Trade Sch; Voc.

VARGA, Ann F; Thorton Frac South HS; Lansing, IL; Band; Purdue Univ; Botany.

VARGA, Wilma A; Monroe City R 1 HS; Monroe, MO; VPJrCls; SecChrs; HonRl; JrNHS; NHS; SchPl; StuCncl; TchrAde; PpCl; Trk; Chrldr; College; Business Secretary.

VARGO, David J; Dearborn HS; Dearborn, MI; ChrhWkr; HonRl; NHS; SctActv; IMSpt; U Of Mi; Financial Administration.

VARGO, Dianne K; Broad Ripple HS; Indianapolis, IN; Chr; ChrhWkr; HonRl; NHS; NatlThespSoc; OffAde; Orch; SchMus; SchPl; De Paul University; Nursing.

VARGO, Jeffrey R; Brebeuf Prep; Indianapolis, IN; ChrhWkr; CmntyWkr; HonRl; SpnCl; PpCl; LetterFtbl; Trk; IMSpt; General Motors Inst; Engr.

VARGO, Theresa A; Resurrection HS; Chicago, IL; 63/294 ChrhWkr; HonRl; HospAde; OffAde; PresSchAde; StuCncl; SecFBLA; FNA; SpnCl; GAA; College; Nursing.

VARGUS, Lorie J; Hannibal HS; Hannibal, MO; 11/212 ChrhWkr; Univ Of Missouri; Speech Pathology.

VARILEK, Gary W; Daniel Gross HS; Omaha, NE; 11/170 HonRl; NHS; Bsktbl; Ftbl; LetterTrk; IMSpt; Creighton Univ; Medicine.

VARKER, Ruth A; East Lansing HS; East Lansing, MI; LitMag; PolWkr; SchAde; SchMus; SchPl; TchrAde; RptrSchPpr; SchPpr; Bsbl; Tennis; W Mi Univ; Communications.

VARNER, Jacqueline M; Glenwood HS; Glenwood, MN; Band; CncrtBnd; HonRl; MrchBnd; NatlMeritCmnd; PepBnd; SchMus; TchrAde; GerCl; College; Music Or Natural Science.

VARNER, Lynn A; Buckley Loda HS; Loda, IL; ALAGirlsSt; Chrs; TchrAde; RptrSchPpr; FHA; PpCl; Parkland College; Teachers Aide.

VARNER, Vicky J; Ida Grove Comm HS; Ida Grove, IA; 7/70 Chrs; DrlTm; HonRl; NHS; NatlThespSoc; SchMus; TchrAde; SchPpr; LetterTrk; PPFtbl; Coll; Major In Theatre Arts.

VARNUM, Annette M; Colo Comm HS; Colo, IA; 1/27 Band; Chrs; CncrtBnd; HonRl; MrchBnd; SecNHS; PepBnd; SchMus; SecStuCncl; LetterBsktbl; Trk; BttyCrckrAwd; 4-HAwd; Iowa State Univ; Education.

VARSHO, Judy A; Columbus HS; Marshfield, WI; Chr; Chrs; ChrhWkr; HonRl; SchPl; Yrbk; FrCl; Business School; Bookkeeper.

VARVELL, Keith W; Malden HS; Malden, MO; ChrhWkr; HonRl; SctActv; FrCl; LetterTennis; University.

VASDEKAS, Tom J; Lane Tech HS; Chicago, IL; HonRl; SchAde; SchPl; StuCncl; University; Medicine.

VASEK, Raeann; East Grand Forks Senior HS; East Grand Forks, MN; /210 PresJrCls; HonRl; NHS; Sdlty; StuGov; RptrYrbk; EdYrBk; FHA; Swmmng; Tennis; ; Vocation Legal Sec.

VASICHEK, James A; Michigan Public HS; Michigan, ND; VPSophCls; TrsJrCls; HonRl; StuCncl; FFA; Bsbl; LetterBsktbl; CaptFtbl; Trk; ALAGirlsSt; Coll; Bus Admin.

VASICHEK, Joanne M; Lakota HS; Lakota, ND; Band; Chr; CncrtBnd; HonRl; MrchBnd; NHS; RptrSchPpr; FHA; PpCl; 4-HAwd; College; Professional Nurse.

VASILE, Betty Ann; Argo Community HS; Justice, IL; 4/500 Chr; Chrs; HonRl; Mdrgl; SecNHS; NatlMeritCmnd; OffAde; SchAde; SchMus; StuGov; Loyola Univ; Medicine.

VASILJEVICH, Thomas; Lane Technical HS; Chicago, IL; ChrhWkr; TchrAde; RusCl; College; Lawyer.

VASKE, Leroy K; Watertown Senior HS; Watertown, SD; AFS; ChrhWkr; HonRl; NatlFornLg; Orch; SchPl; RptrYrbk; EdYrBk; GerCl; University; Professional.

VASPER, Harley E; Saltillo HS; Moberly, MO; 7/54 Band; ChrhWkr; CncrtBnd; HonRl; MrchBnd; NHS; PepBnd; U Of Mo; Chemical Engin.

VASQUEZ, Kenneth R; Elk Grove HS; Elk Grove Vlg, IL; ChrhWkr; HonRl; LetterTennis; College; Physics.

VASQUEZ, Rosa; Calumet HS; Gary, IN; 8/330 HonRl; JrNHS; LbryAde; FSA; SpnCl; PpCl; Purdue Univ Cal Camp; Comp Tech.

VASS, Sally; Dallas City Comm HS; Dallas City, IL; /45 Band; Chrs; ChrhWkr; HonRl; NHS; SctActv; EdYrBk; FHA; Bsbl; Trk; Iowa Wesleyan Univ; Nursing.

VASSAR, Timothy M; Highland HS; Highland, IN; ChrhWkr; TchrAde; LetterBsktbl; LetterFtbl; Trk; IMSpt;.

VASTINE, Judy L; Durant HS; Durant, IA; 13/68 Chr; Chrs; HonRl; JrNHS; NHS; StuCncl; EdYrBk; LetterBsbl; LetterTrk; PresGAA; Clg; Cpa.

VASUMPAUR, Alison L; Glenbard South HS; Glen Ellyn, IL; DrlTm; University; Fashion Design.

VATER, Susan G; Bishop Miege HS; Leawood, KS; 45/202 CmntyWkr; DrlTm; HonRl; NHS; PolWkr; SchMus; SchPl; StuCncl; PpCl; IMSpt; Ks St Univ; Major Science.

VATTER, Robert P; Cass City HS; Cass City, MI; 15/130 NHS; PolWkr; StuCncl; StuGov; FDA; FSA; SciCl; OptClAwd; CitAwd; VoiceDemAwd; Msu; Professional Pre Med.

VATTHAUER, Edlyn E; Pershing HS; Plummer, MN; VPJrCls; VPSrCls; CncrtBnd; HonRl; Quill&Scroll; SchPl; RptrYrbk; RptrSchPpr; Bsktbl; Trk; Clge; Pro.

VAUBEL, Gretchen A; South Hamilton Comm HS; Jewell, IA; Chrs; CncrtBnd; HonRl; MrchBnd; PepBnd; SchMus; RptrYrbk; MthCl; Iowa State U; Science Humanities.

VAUGHAN, Lisa A; Mills Prairie HS; Mill Shoals, IL; 3/15 VPSophCls; VPJrCls; Chr; HonRl; SchPl; 4-H; FHA; PpCl; Chrldr; 4-HAwd; Jr College; Business.

VAUGHAN, Rebecca J; Yjb Comm HS; Yale, IA; Band; ChrhWkr; CncrtBnd; HonRl; MrchBnd; PepBnd; SchPl; YthFlsp; RptrYrbk; RptrSchPpr; Bsktbl; Trk; Chrldr; College; Physical Ed.

VAUGHN, Celeste A; Ann Arbor Huron HS; Ann Arbor, MI; Chr; LitMag; SchMus; SchPl; SctActv; StuGov; Yrbk; SptEdSchPpr; SpnCl; Bsktbl; Mount Holyoke College; Lawyer.

VAUGHN, Cynthia; Bogard HS; Bogard, MO; 2/9 VPSophCls; TrsJrCls; Band; Chr; HonRl; SchPl; RptrYrbk; RptrSchPpr; SchPpr; BttyCrckrAwd; Nemsu; Med Sec.

VAUGHN, Cynthia; Odin Hs; Odin, IL; 8/32 Band; Chr; ChrhWkr; PepBnd; SchPl; StuCncl; Yrbk; RptrSchPpr; FHA; Chrldr; Kaskaski College; Cosmetology.

VAUGHN, Daniel L; Grandview HS; Grandview, MO; HonRl; MrchBnd; NHS; SchMus; StuCncl; YthFlsp; MthCl; LetterBsbl; Bsktbl; Trk; Af Acad Of Engineering.

VAUGHN, David W; Northwest HS; House Springs, MO; ALBoysSt; LetterBsktbl; LetterFtbl; Trk; College; Law.

VAUGHN, Delia; Adrian HS; Adrian, MO; TrsJrCls; SchPl; TchrAde; RptrYrbk; FHA; FTA; Bsktbl; College; Teach Mentally Handicap.

VAUGHN, Diana R; Dallas City HS; Lomax, IL; 2/45 Chrs; ChrhWkr; CmntyWkr; HonRl; SchMus;

SchPl; FHA; PpCl; Trk; Chrldr; College; Agriculture.

VAUGHN, Dianne D; Central HS; St Joseph, MO; 72/498 Chr; ChrhWkr; CmntyWkr; HonRl; LitMag; PolWkr; SpnCl; LetterSwmmng; GodCntryAwd; University; Education.

VAUGHN, Floyd; Soldan HS; St Louis, MO; 5/734 Band; CncrtBnd; HonRl; MrchBnd; NHS; NatlMeritCmnd; IMSpt; Univ Mo At Rolla; Electrical Engineering.

VAUGHN, Gregory A; Marquette HS; Alton, IL; 16/116 PresSophCls; PresJrCls; HonRl; JrNHS; NHS; StuCncl; StuGov; LetterFtbl; LetterTrk; University.

VAUGHN, Jed P; Fairbury HS; Fairbury, NE; Chrs; CmntyWkr; Mdrgl; SchMus; 4-H; Bsktbl; Ftbl; Trk; 4-HAwd; KiwanAwd; Trade School; Vocation.

VAUGHN, Jo E; Madison HS; Madison, IN; 20/285 PresSrCls; NHS; Quill&Scroll; StuCncl; SptEdYrbk; SpnCl; PpCl; SciCl; LetterSwmmng; LetterTrk; GAA; PPFtbl; College; Professional.

VAUGHN, John E; Richland R 4 HS; Richland, MO; 15/68 Chr; Chrs; ChrhWkr; HonRl; VPFFA; LetterBsktbl; CaptBsktbl; Trk; IMSpt; Air Force Acad.

VAUGHN, Lynell; Herrin HS; Herrin, IL; 12/216 Chrs; ChrhWkr; HonRl; NHS; SchMus; SchPl; TchrAde; FHA; AmLegAwd; BauchLmbAwd; Eastern Il U; Medical Tech.

VAUGHN, Mary A; Pleasant Hill HS; Pleasant Hill, MO; Chr; Chrs; ChrhWkr; HonRl; SchMus; RptrSchPpr; SecFHA; JAAwd; Southwest Baptist College; Youth Music Dir.

VAUGHN, Pamela J; Maconaquah HS; Peru, IN; HonRl; SchMus; SchPl; YthFlsp; SpnCl; Univ Or Bus School.

VAUGHN, Paula L; Herrin HS; Herrin, IL; 12/216 Chrs; ChrhWkr; HonRl; NHS; SchMus; SchPl; TchrAde; FHA; AmLegAwd; Eastern Illinois Univ; Medical Technology.

VAUGHN, Sharon D; Academy Of Our Lady; Chicago, IL; 32/178 ChrhWkr; CmntyWkr; HonRl; NHS; NatlMeritCmnd; Univ Of Illinois; Corporate Lawyer.

VAUGHN, Tammie D; Jimtown HS; Elkhart, IN; 34/125 Chr; HonRl; SchAde; SchMus; StuGov; RptrYrbk; RptrSchPpr; EdSchPpr; FTA; SciCl; Bethel College; Social Worker Writer.

VAUGHN, Toby M; Pana Sr HS; Pana, IL; 31/139 SchPl; YthFlsp; SchPpr; Ftbl; Glf; Trk; E Illinois Univ; Psychology.

VAUGHN, William B; Pleasant Hill HS; Pleasant Hill, MO; 11/112 Band; HonRl; NHS; SchMus; VPStuCncl; YthFlsp; SpnCl; SciCl; LetterFtbl; CaptWrstlng; Univ Of Missouri; Chemical Engineer.

VAUGHN, William R; Lincoln HS; Vincennes, IN; 1/330 PresFrshCls; PresSophCls; PresJrCls; PresSrCls; ALBoysSt; Band; ChrhWkr; HonRl; YthFlsp; SptEdSchPpr; 4-H; SciCl; LetterBsktbl; LetterFtbl; Ind Univ; Physician.

VAUL, Debra L; Thornridge HS; South Holland, IL; 122/684 HonRl; LitMag; OffAde; StuCncl; TchrAde; TreasFTA; PpCl; College; Teaching.

VAVERKA, Cindy L; Crete HS; Pleasant Dale, NE; 2/115 Band; Chrs; CncrtBnd; HonRl; MrchBnd; PepBnd; SchMus; RptrSchPpr; FBLA; University; Medical Field.

VAVRIK, Cindy M; Mother Of Sorrows HS; Calumet Park, IL; HonRl; JrNHS; StuCncl; SptEdYrbk; Yrbk; FrCl; PpCl; Chrldr; GAA; VoiceDemAwd; Loyola; Dentist.

VAVRINEK, Ronald; Downers Grove Comm HS; New Lenox, IL; Chr; ChrhWkr; HonRl; NHS; NatlThespSoc; TchrAde; MthCl; Coll; Ed.

VAYO, David J; Carmel HS; Carmel, IN; 1/525 Band; HonRl; LitMag; NHS; NatlMeritSF; In U; Music.

VAZQUEZ, Lucita; St Augustine HS; Chicago, IL; College; English Teacher.

VEACH, Glenn O; Claflin HS; Claphlin, KS; HonRl; JA; SchPl; Yrbk; EdSchPpr; LetterGlf; Trk; Univ Of Ka; Civil Engineer.

VEACH, Priscilla J; Paris HS; Paris, IL; 42/226 Chr; Chrs; ChrhWkr; HonRl; RptrYrbk; 4-H; FHA; PpCl; 4-HAwd; E Il U; Accounting.

VEACH, Vickie L; North HS; Sioux City, IA; 2/316 ChrhWkr; HonRl; HospAde; NatlMeritCmnd; OffAde; YthFnd; 4-H; South Dakota St University; Pharmacy.

VEARRIER, Jolene A; Hanson Ind #40 HS; Fulton, SD; 4/44 Aud/Vis; ChrhWkr; HonRl; SchPl; SpnCl; PpCl; Co St Univ; Forestry.

VEASEY, Glenda; Ecorse HS; Ecorse, MI; 2/210 PresJrCls; CmntyWkr; HonRl; NHS; NatlMeritSF; StuCncl; EdYrBk; PpCl; AmLegAwd; OptClAwd; Univ ; Bus.

VEATCH, Gary D; Monroe City R I HS; Monroe City, MO; 20/92 VPSrCls; ALBoysSt; HonRl; NHS; StuCncl; YthFlsp; Bsktbl; LetterGlf; University Of Missouri; Business Admin.

VEATCH, Johnny L; Prescott Comm HS; Prescott, IA; ALBoysSt; Chrs; LbryAde; SctActv; Bell & Howell School; Electrical Tech.

VEBINGER, Jeffrey K; R 1 North Callaway HS; Williamsburg, MO; 6/78 VPJrCls; HonRl; NHS; FFA; LetterFtbl; LetterTrk; College; Chemistry.

VECERA, Dave R; Lincoln Way HS; Mokena, IL; 75/550 Chrs; HonRl; SchMus; StuCncl; Univ Of Illinois; Law.

VEDAS, Steven B; Pekin Community HS; Pekin, IL; 10/750 HonRl; NHS; Bradley Univ; Computer Science.

VEDRAL, Maria J; Immaculate Heart Of Mary HS; Cicero, IL; PresFrshCls; SecSrCls; StuCncl; TchrAde; Depaul Univ; Law.

VEDUEI, Alan J; Lake Preston Public HS; Hetland, SD; 3/31 ALBoysSt; ChrhWkr; CmntyWkr; HonRl; SciCl; Bsbl; Bsktbl; Ftbl; AmLegAwd; 4-HAwd; VFWAwd; College; Vocation.

VEEHOFF, Bonny M; St Marys HS; Storm Lake, IA; 3/37 PresFrshCls; TrsJrCls; Chr; HonRl; OffAde; SchMus; StuCncl; 4-H; Bsktbl; Chrldr; College; Professional.

VEEHOFF, Carolyn A; St Marys HS; Storm Lake, IA; 6/45 Chrs; HonRl; NHS; SchMus; StuCncl; EdYrBk; SchPpr; PpCl; Bsktbl; DARAwd; Univ;.

VEENHUIZEN, Michael A; Greenfield Central HS; Greenfield, IN; 3/247 VPJrCls; ALBoysSt; HonRl; NHS; StuCncl; 4-H; FFA; GerCl; MthCl; LetterSwmmng; 4-HAwd; Purdue Univ; Engineering.

VEERKAMP, Gregory W; Bishop Dwenger HS; Fort Wayne, IN; HonRl; PresFrCl; Swmmng; College; Medicine.

VEESART, John A; Clifton Rural HS; Clifton, KS; Band; ChrhWkr; CncrtBnd; DrmBgl; HonRl; HospAde; LbryAde; SchPl; StuCncl; Swmmng; College; Lab Technologist.

VEGA, Inez C; Harrison HS; Chicago, IL; 43/388 Band; CncrtBnd; HonRl; Orch; ROTC; StuCncl; TchrAde; PresSpnCl; Bsktbl; IMSpt; University Of Illinois; Engineering.

VEGEAIS, James; Taft HS; Chicago, IL; 1/850 Band; HonRl; NHS; Orch; College; Chemical Engineer.

VEGERLEHNER, Donna B; Clay City HS; Clay City, IN; 5/65 TrsJrCls; Chr; ChrhWkr; CncrtBnd; MrchBnd; NHS; YthFlsp; 4-H; FHA; Chrldr; Purdue Univ; Dietician.

VEIGELT, Denise K; Reed Custer HS; Wilmington, IL; 2/59 PresSrCls; HonRl; NHS; OffAde; SchPl; StuCncl; EdYrBk; RptrSchPpr; SpnCl; PpCl; Bsbl; GAA; AmLegAwd;.

VEIK, John A; Petersburg HS; Petersburg, NE; 8/25 Sdlty; Bsbl; Bsktbl; Swmmng; Trk; PresAwd; Trade School.

VEIL, Jeff A; Streeter Public HS; Streeter, ND; 12/18 PresJrCls; ALBoysSt; Band; Chrs; MrchBnd; PepBnd; StuCncl; YthFlsp; YthLg; LetterBsktbl; Trade School At Whapeton; Mechaics.

VEIRE, John; Lake Benton HS; Lake Benton, MN; TrsFrshCls; PresSrCls; ALBoysSt; HonRl; NHS; StuCncl; LetterBsbl; LetterBsktbl; LetterFtbl; Glf;.

VEIT, Cynthia; Wyndmere Public HS; Mooreton, ND; 6/45 Band; CncrtBnd; HonRl; MrchBnd; NHS; PepBnd; FHA; Univ; Med Tech.

VEIT, Cynthia K; Wyndmere HS; Mooreton, ND; Band; CncrtBnd; HonRl; MrchBnd; PepBnd; FHA; LetterBsktbl; College; Medical Lab Tech.

VEIT, Dairo; Atherton HS; Milington, MI; 42/160 SchPl; Glf; Trk; Cllege; Electronics.

VEIT, Janice L; St Thomas Aquinas HS; Florissant, MO; 7/324 Chr; CncrtBnd; HonRl; NHS; SchMus; RptrYrbk; EdYrBk; RptrSchPpr; Bsktbl; PPFtbl; U Of Missouri; Journalism.

VEIT, Steven; Littlefork Big Falls HS; Big Falls, MN; TrsSophCls; Chr; HonRl; SchPl; StuCncl; RptrYrbk; RptrSchPpr; Bsktbl; Ftbl; Coll Or Service; Law Or Anuclear Program.

VEITH, Anthony J; Clearwater HS; Viola, KS; 6/70 Chrs; HonRl; SchMus; SchPl; Ftbl; Kansas State University; Architecture.

VEITH, John G; Cardinal Stritch HS; Keokuk, IA; 7/33 ALBoysSt; HonRl; SchPl; SctActv; StuCncl; StuGov; LetterBsbl; LetterBsktbl; LetterGlf; Trk; College.

VELA, Leticia; Crestwood HS; Dbrn Hgts, MI; HonRl; JA; NatlMeritSchl; TchrAde; JAAwd; Eastern Mi Univ; Computer Science.

VELAND, Carla M; Maplewood Acad; St Paul, MN; Chr; Chrl; ChrhWkr; HonRl; SchPl; StuCncl; RptrYrbk; Yrbk; 4-H; FHA; Oakwood College; Social Work.

VELAND, James; Central Cass HS; Harwood, ND; ALBoysSt; ChrhWkr; HonRl; SchPl; SptEdYrbk; Wrstlng; College; Eng.

VELASCO, Claude R; Homewood Flossmoor HS; Flossmoor, IL; 6/910 HonRl; NHS; NatlMeritCmnd; StuCncl; Univ Of Virginia; Medicine.

VELASQUEZ, Teresa N; Lake Central HS; Crown Point, IN; CncrtBnd; MrchBnd; NHS; NatlThespSoc; PepBnd; SchMus; StuGov; TchrAde; VPSpnCl; LetterTennis; University.

VELDBOOM, Roy R; Cedar Grove HS; Cedar Grove, WI; Aud/Vis; NatlMeritSF; SchPl; RptrSchPpr; Bsktbl; U Of Wi;actor.

VELDE, Le Ann R; Clarkfield HS; Clarkfield, MN; Band; Chr; CncrtBnd; HonRl; MrchBnd; PepBnd; SchPl; Yrbk; EdSchPpr; St Cloud St College; Criminal Justice.

VELDER, Eileen; Newell HS; Newell, SD; 1/48 NHS; TchrAde; FHA; PpCl; Bsktbl; Trk; PresAwd; College; Major In Biology.

VELDHUIZEN, Mark G; Oskaloosa Sr HS; Oskaloosa, IA; 34/179 Aud/Vis; Band; Chr; Chrs; CncrtBnd; HonRl; YthFlsp; 4-H; IMSpt; Iowa St Univ; Physics.

VELDMAN, Geri; Holton HS; Holton, MI; 1/64 TrsSrCls; ChrhWkr; CmntyWkr; HonRl; NHS; TchrAde; YthFlsp; RptrSchPpr; DanFAwd; Muskegon Comm College; Veterinarian.

VELDT, Joel G; Little Wolf HS; Manawa, WI; Aud/Vis; Band; Chrs; ChrhWkr; HonRl; LbryAde; Mdrgl; SctActv; Yrbk; SchPpr; Coll;graphic Arts.

VELEZ, Debra A; Granite City South HS; Granite City, IL; 23/630 HonRl; JrNHS; NatlFornLg; NHS; SchPl; SctActv; Georgetown Univ; Law.

VELKY, Sharon K; St Pius X HS; Kansas City, MO; Chrs; HonRl; NHS; OffAde; SctActv; College; Teaching.

VELLA, Gerald; Holy Redeemer HS; Detroit, MI; 12/210 HonRl; JrNHS; NHS; NatlMeritSF; CitAwd; Univ; Professional.

VELLA, Terri J; Jackson HS; Jackson, MI; 1/375 Chr; HonRl; NHS; SchMus; SchPl; StuGov; Trk; PPFtbl; Eastern Mi U; Special Ed Teacer.

VELLEK, Ann M; Tyndall HS; Tabor, SD; 4/58 Band; Chr; Chrs; ChrhWkr; CmntyWkr; CncrtBnd; HonRl; LbryAde; MrchBnd; NatlMeritSchl; PepBnd; AmLegAwd; Univ Of S Dakota; Physical Therapist.

VELTEMA, Diana; Hudsonville Public HS; Hudsonville, MI; Chr; HonRl; NHS; PpCl; Grand Rapids Baptist Coll; Secretary.

VELTEMA, Donna; Hudsonville Public HS; Hudsonville, MI; Chrs; HonRl; JrNHS; NHS; Grand Valley St College; Registered Nurse.

VELTING, Janette; Cedar Lake Acad; Benton Harbor, MI; 1/72 VPFrshCls; Chr; LitMag; NHS; SchMus; TchrAde; Yrbk; FHA; IMSpt; PresAwd; Anoreus Univ; Cmmunications.

VELTING, Janette E; Cedar Lake Academy; Benton Harbor, MI; 1/72 VPFrshCls; Chr; HonRl; Mdrgl; NHS; SchMus; StuCncl; StuGov; RptrYrbk; RptrSchPpr; EngCl; Andrews Univ; Communications.

VENA, Tom; Highland Park HS; Highland Park, IL; PolWkr; RedCrAde; College; Medical.

VENABLE, Francilda A; Rolla HS; Newburg, MO; 11/280 Chr; ChrhWkr; LbryAde; NatlMeritSF; Orch; SchPl; Pres4-H; FTA; FrCl; MthCl; IMSpt; Univ Of Missouri; Ceramic Eng.

VENABLE, Susan; Rockridge HS; Reynolds, IL; 10/140 HonRl; HospAde; JrNHS; NHS; YthFlsp; YthFlsp; FTA; LatCl; Chrldr; Univ; Public Accountant.

VENABLE, Susan E; Slater HS; Slater, MO; Band; Chrs; HonRl; StuGov; 4-H; FrCl; PpCl; GAA; IMSpt; 4-HAwd; AmLegAwd; AmLegAwd;.

VENARDOS, Christine; Southwest HS; St Louis, MO; TrsSrCls; Chr; Chrldr; PPFtbl; Univ Mo Kansas City; Fine Arts Major Dance.

VENCILL, Jennifer J; Trenton HS; Trenton, MO; Chr; ChrhWkr; HonRl; JrNHS; SchMus; SctActv; StuCncl; StuGov; SpnCl; PpCl; Chrldr; Univ Of Missouri.

VENDEGNA, Vicki A; Proviso West HS; Bellwood, IL; 40/1100 Univ Of Illinois; Computer Science.

VENDITTI, Anthony D; Austin Catholic Prep; Detroit, MI; 86/115 Chr; NatlFornLg; PolWkr; SchMus; SchPl; StuGov; RptrYrbk; Bsktbl; LetterTrk; College; Professional.

VENEGAS, Marcelina C; West Side Sr HS; Gary, IN; HonRl; NHS; OffAde; SpnCl;.

VENEGONI, Angela L; Spalding Academy; Washington, IL; 15/100 TrsFrshCls; ChrhWkr; HonRl; NHS; StuGov; 4-H; FrCl; PpCl; Chrldr; PPFtbl; Univ; Nursing.

VENEMA, Bruce A; Northwest HS; Jackson, MI; 20/266 ChrhWkr; CncrtBnd; MrchBnd; NHS; College; Business.

VENEMA, Bryan J; Wheaton Christian HS; Wheaton, IL; 2/33 Chr; HonRl; NHS; SchPl; StuCncl; Bsbl; Bsktbl; Ftbl; Tennis; Trk; Col; Scientific Research.

VENEZIA, Margo K; Belvidere HS; Belvidere, IL; AFS; Chrs; HonRl; Mdrgl; NHS; SchMus; StuCncl; FrCl; Chrldr; Illinois State Univ; Accountant.

VENHUIZEN, Alvin J; Central Wis Christian HS; Burnett, WI; PresJrCls; HonRl; SchPl; TchrAde; RptrSchPpr; IMSpt; CitAwd; Vocational Sch; Farming.

VENKER, Robert A; De Smet Jesuit HS; St Louis, MO; 35/168 CmntyWkr; HonRl; SchPl; SctActv; LetterFtbl; LetterTrk; IMSpt; U Of Mo Columbia; Engineering.

VENN, Celesta; St Joseph Acad; Detroit, MI; 9/23 TrsJrCls; Chrl; HonRl; SchPl; StuCncl; FNA; Bsktbl; GAA; Michigan State Univ; Journalism.

VENNER, Elizabeth A; St Bernard HS; Breda, IA; 3/18 PresJrCls; Band; Chr; Chrs; ChrhWkr; HonRl; JrNHS; TchrAde; EdYrBk; IMSpt; Iowa St Univ; Home Ec Educ.

VENNER, Susan L; Bancroft HS; Bancroft, NE; 3/32 Band; Chrs; ChrhWkr; HonRl; SchPl; SciCl; Chrldr; 4-HAwd; College; Biology Major.

VENNERBERG, Dwayne C; Stanton Community HS; Stanton, IA; 2/35 ALBoysSt; Band; Chr; HonRl; StuCncl; Pres4-H; PresFFA; Bsktbl; LetterTrk; 4-HAwd; Coll;farming.

VENO, William G; Brighton HS; Brighton, MI; 31/287 Chr; HonRl; Mdrgl; NHS; NatlThespSoc; SchMus; LetterTennis; Trk; IMSpt; Mich St Univ; Accounting.

VENOHR, Karin V; Peck HS; Peck, MI; 2/58 HonRl; TreasNHS; TchrAde; FHA; Bsktbl; Central Mi Univ.

VENSTRA, Terri L; Pembine HS; Pembine, WI; 1/31 PresFrshCls; SecSophCls; Band; EdYrBk; SchPpr; Bsbl; Bsktbl; Chrldr; Bus Sch.

VENTEICHER, Alice L; Elkhorn Valley HS; Meadow Grove, NE; 5/42 SecFrshCls; Chr; ChrhWkr; HonRl; SchAde; SchMus; StuGov; TchrAde; 4-H; FHA; Wayne State Clg; Lawyer.

VENTERS, Brenda; Morris Community Hs; Morris, IL; Band; HonRl; SpnCl; U Of Ill; Pharmacy.

VENTERS, James D; Mills Prairie Comm HS; Mill Shoals, IL; 3/16 Chrs; HonRl; SchPl; StuCncl; RptrYrbk; FFA; Bsktbl; So Il Univ.

VENTIMIGLIA, Roseanne M; Carl Brablec HS; Roseville, MI; 1/500 VPChrl; ChrhWkr; HonRl; Mdrgl; SecNHS; NatlMeritSF; SchMus; SchPl; StuGov; SciCl; College; Professional.

VENTO, Joseph L; West Milwaukee HS; West Allis, WI; 50/177 Yrbk; SchPpr; LetterWrstlng; Univ; Business Administration.

VENTRE, Christine M; Milford HS; Highland, MI; PresSrCls; HonRl; NHS; StuCncl; StuGov; FrCl; PpCl; Bsbl; Trk; IMSpt; College; Medicine.

VENTRES, William B; Pine Crest HS; Hopkins, MN; 10/120 PresFrshCls; Chr; HonRl; Mdrgl; NatlFornLg; NatlSciFnd; SecStuCncl; StuGov; SciCl; LetterSwmmng; LetterTrk; Univ; Medicine.

VENTURI, Joan L; Toluca HS; Toluca, IL; Band; CncrtBnd; HonRl; LbryAde; MrchBnd; NHS; Orch; PepBnd; FHA; PresSpnCl; SciCl; GAA; BttyCrckrAwd; Ivcc; Police Science.

VENZKE, Deanna L; Ventura Comm HS; Clear Lake, IA; Band; Chr; Chrs; ChrhWkr; CncrtBnd; HonRl; Mdrgl; MrchBnd; LetterGlf; LetterChrldr; College; Nursing.

VERAGUTH, Kathleen L; Cochrane Fountain City HS; Fountain City, WI; 30/91 ChrhWkr; CaptDrlTm; SchPl; Pres4-H; FHA; FNA; PpCl; LetterTrk; Chrldr; LetterGAA; 4-HAwd; Winonna St College; Speech.

VERBECK, Brenda G; Holdrege HS; Funk, NE; Chrs; CncrtBnd; HonRl; HospAde; MrchBnd; PepBnd; SchMus; FBLA; PpCl; 4-HAwd; Bus Sch; Vocation.

VERBECK, Doreen C; Annawan HS; Sheffield, IL; 1/51 TrsSophCls; HonRl; JrNHS; LbryAde; SecNHS; StuCncl; TchrAde; PresFHA; SpnCl; TreasGAA; Business Sch; Vocation.

VERBECK, Julia L; Winfield HS; Winfield, KS; DrmMjrt; HonRl; MrchBnd; Orch; SchMus; Twrl; 4-H; FHA; CchngActv; 4-HAwd; College; Fashion Merchandiser.

VERBEKE, Marianne L; Servite HS; Detroit, MI; 1/90 TrsJrCls; HospAde; JA; PresNHS; NatlMeritCmnd; EdYrBk; Univ; Chemistry.

VERBETEN, Peter; Wrightstown HS; Wrightstown, WI; ALBoysSt; ChrhWkr; CmntyWkr; HonRl; StuGov; IMSpt; LionAwd; College; Engineering.

VERBOOMEN, Susan A; Wrightstown HS; Kaukauna, WI; ChrhWkr; CmntyWkr; HonRl; HospAde; RedCrAde; StuGov; YthFlsp; FHA; SpnCl; GAA; Secretarial School; Secretary.

VERDINE, Rodney; Wautoma HS; Wautoma, WI; 4/109 HonRl; TchrAde; Bsbl; Ftbl; Univ Of Wis Stevens Point; Business Admin.

VER DOUW, Rita M; Edgeley HS; Edgeley, ND; 4/45 HonRl; HospAde; OffAde; PepBnd; RptrSchPpr; SchPpr; 4-H; FHA; 4-HAwd; Ndsu Fargo; Home Ec.

VER DUGHT, Patty J; New Monroe Comm HS; Monroe, IA; 5/54 Band; Chr; ChrhWkr; HonRl; NHS; NatlThespSoc; PepBnd; StuCncl; SciCl; LetterBsktbl; LetterTrk; College; Professional.

VERDUN, Michael P; Odell Community HS; Odell, IL; PresFrshCls; VPSrCls; Sacrstn; SchPl; StuCncl; RptrYrbk; FrCl; PpCl; So Illinois University.

VERDUZCO, Michelle T; Andrean HS; Gary, IN; 55/250 ChrhWkr; HonRl; NHS; Yrbk; RptrSchPpr; SchPpr; MthCl; PpCl; GAA; PPFtbl; College; Doctor.

VEREMIS, Susan A; North Clay HS; Louisville, IL; 5/68 PresFrshCls; Band; ChrhWkr; HonRl; SchPl; StuCncl; RptrYrbk; Chrldr; GAA; AmLegAwd; University; Science.

VERGE, Karen E; Streator HS; Streator, IL; 36/396 HonRl; NHS; Univ Of Il; Veterinary Medicine.

VERGO, Steven W; Riverside Brookfield HS; Riverside, IL; 77/475 HonRl; PresJA; NatlMeritCmnd; StuCncl; LetterFtbl; JAAwd; Air Force Academy; Electronics.

VERHAGEN, Connie M; Western Mich Chr HS; Muskegon, MI; Chr; ChrhWkr; HonRl; HospAde; LbryAde; NHS; RptrSchPpr; GAA; Muskegon Comm College; Dental Assistant.

VERHOEF, Marjorie E; Pella Christian HS; Pella, IA; Chr; ChrhWkr; HonRl; SchPl; Yrbk; PpCl; IMSpt; Trade Sch; Nursing.

VER HOEVEN, Rebecca; Hudsonville HS; Hudsonville, MI; HonRl; NHS; RptrYrbk; Chrldr; Hope Col; Doctor.

VERHOFF, Susanne E; St Anthony HS; Arnold, MO; 2/72 TrsJrCls; Chrl; HonRl; NHS; SchMus; SchPl; StuCncl; TchrAde; LatCl; Bsktbl; CaptFtbl; CchngActv; IMSpt; University Of Missouri; Pharmacy.

VERHULST, Carol E; Richland Center HS; Richland Center, WI; Band; Chr; Chrs; CncrtBnd; HonRl; Mdrgl; MrchBnd; NHS; PepBnd; AmLegAwd; Uw Milwaukee; Music Ed.

VER MAAS, Vicki; Norris HS; Lincoln, NE; 7/92 NHS; NatlThespSoc; SchPl; TchrAde; YthFlsp; RptrYrbk; EdYrBk; Yrbk; FHA; FrCl; U Of Ne At Lincoln; Social Work.

VERMEER, Marianne; No Platte HS; No Platte, NE; ALAGirlsSt; HonRl; NatlFornLg; SchPl; YthFlsp; YthLg; 4-HAwd; College; Law Psychology Or Speech.

VERMEESCH, Pam M; Garber HS; Essexville, MI; HonRl; TchrAde; Trade Sch.

VERMELINE, Carol M; Wahoo HS; Waheo, NE; PresFrshCls; PresJrCls; Band; ChrhWkr; HonRl; StuCncl; YthFlsp; 4-H; Chrldr; 4-HAwd; College; Medical Field.

VERMELINE, Kristie; Prague Public HS; Malmo, NE; 1/14 TrsFrshCls; VPJrCls; ChrhWkr; HonRl; NHS; SchPl; EdYrBk; EdSchPpr; Chrldr; College Or Bus Sch; Secretary.

VER MERRIS, Patricia J; Jenison Public HS; Jenison, MI; Chr; ChrhWkr; HonRl; SchMus; StuCncl; YthFlsp; 4-H; FrCl; Chrldr; 4-HAwd; College; Professional.

VERMETTE, Glen; St Charles HS; St Charles, MO; 159/600 HonRl; SctActv; TchrAde; Ftbl; Trk; CitAwd; College; Curriculum.

VERMEULEN, Edwin A; Fremont HS; Fremont, MI; 6/193 Chr; HonRl; Mdrgl; NHS; YthFlsp; Yrbk; Univ Of Mi; Art & Psychology.

VERMEULEN, Susan A; St Josephs Acad; Depere, WI; ChrhWkr; HonRl; JA; LitMag; PolWkr; SchPl; StuCncl; SchPpr; Trade Sch; Interior Decorator.

VERNER, Carol J; Robert A Waller HS; Chicago, IL; 9/250 TrsJrCls; PresSrCls; Band; CncrtBnd; HonRl; JrNHS; NHS; Orch; SchAde; StuCncl; TchrAde; Ftbl; Tennis; GAA; Macmurray; Computer Programming.

VERNIER, Lucien; Alba HS; Evart, MI; PresJrCls; SctActv; StuCncl; YthFlsp; 4-H; Bsbl; Bsktbl; AmLegAwd; 4-HAwd; CitAwd; State Police Academy; State Police.

VERNIMMEN, Anita; Servite HS; Detroit, MI; 3/90 HonRl; HospAde; JA; NatlFornLg; NHS; Yrbk; RptrSchPpr; SchPpr; PpCl; Univ Of Detroit; Communications.

VERNON, Cathy L; Centerville Senior HS; Centerville, IN; 31/178 Chrs; DrlTm; HonRl; NatlThespSoc; PolWkr; RedCrAde; SchAde; StuCncl; StuGov; VPTeen; Stratford Womens Clg; Fashion Merch.

VEROEVEN, Mary; Walnut Grove Public HS; Walnut Grove, MN; 1/41 SecJrCls; TrsSrCls; Chrs; ChrhWkr; HonRl; SchAde; SchPl; StuGov; RptrYrbk; FHA; Granite Falls Vo Tech; Secretarial.

VERONGOS, Helen T; Mishawaka HS; Mishawaka, IN; 10/411 Chr; LitMag; NHS; NatlMeritFnl; NatlThespSoc; Quill&Scroll; TreasStuCncl; EdSchPpr; SecGerCl; NCTE; VoiceDemAwd; College; Journalism.

VER PLOEG, Scott L; Lynnville Sully HS; Sully, IA; 1/58 TrsFrshCls; TrsJrCls; PresSrCls; Band; HonRl; PresNHS; 4-H; LetterBsktbl; LetterFtbl; LetterTrk; Univ; Engr.

VERR, Steven R; Riverside Brookfield HS; Brookfield, IL; 62/500 PresJrCls; PresSrCls; PresQuill&Scroll; EdSchPpr; College; Business.

VERSCHELDEN, Timothy W; St Marys HS; St Marys, KS; PresFrshCls; PresSophCls; PresJrCls; HonRl; NHS; TchrAde; Bsktbl; Ftbl; LetterTrk; Univ; Undecided.

VERSCHOOR, Carolyn M; Barrington HS; Barrington, IL; 11/652 Chr; HonRl; HospAde; NHS; NatlMeritCmnd; StuCncl; YthFlsp; RptrYrbk; RptrSchPpr; Medical School; Medicine.

VERSTEGEN, Sarah E; Wayland Academy; Sioux City, IA; NatlMeritCmnd; PresNatlThespSoc; StuGov; Bsktbl; Trk; GAA; University.

VERTICCHIO, Jayne M; Gillespie HS; Mt Clare, IL; 1/131 ALAGirlsSt; NHS; EdYrBk; FHA; FTA; PresFrCl; Chrldr; GAA; Illinois State Univ; Special Education.

VERTIN, Mark M; Bishop Foley HS; Clawson, MI; CmntyWkr; LetterTrk; CaptWrstlng; Eng Degree.

VERTOVEC, Steven; Immaculate Conception; Elmhurst, IL; 14/132 Aud/Vis; HonRl; NHS; EdYrBk; LatCl; IMSpt; VFWAwd; VoiceDemAwd; U Of Colorado.

VERTREESE, Janice M; East HS; Kansas City, MO; 42/200 Band; Chr; ChrhWkr; CncrtBnd; NatlMeritFnl; OffAde; Orch; University; Psychology.

VERVENIOTIS, William A; Charles P Steinmetz HS; Addison, IL; 9/640 DrlTm; HonRl; NHS; ROTC; SchAde; StuCncl; StuGov; TchrAde; RptrYrbk; RptrSchPpr; AmLegAwd; DARAwd; Univ Of Illinois; Computer Science.

VERWERS, Debbie; Prairie City Comm HS; Prairie City, IA; SecTrsSophCls; ChrhWkr; CncrtBnd; HonRl; MrchBnd; PepBnd; StuCncl; Twrl; YthFlsp; College; Business Ed.

VERWOLD, Julia A; Union County HS; Liberty, IN; ChrhWkr; HonRl; OffAde; YthFlsp; RptrSchPpr; 4-H; FFA; LatCl; Bsbl; College; Liberal Arts.

VERZAL, Janet; West Holt HS; Atkinson, NE; Chrs; HonRl; SchPl; CivCl; 4-H; Bsbl; AmLegAwd;.

VESCOVI, Ellen R; Mater Dei HS; Evansville, IN; 20/200 HonRl; JrNHS; RedCrAde; SctActv; PpCl; SciCl; Swmmng; Trk; LetterChrldr; GAA; College; Engineer.

VESELAK, Steve P; Elcho HS; Elcho, WI; ALBoysSt; Band; CncrtBnd; HonRl; NHS; SchMus; TchrAde; SciCl; LetterGlf; LetterWrstlng; Univ; Anesthetist.

VESELKA, Diana M; Benedictine HS; Detroit, MI; 2/130 TrsFrshCls; HonRl; JrNHS; NHS; StuCncl; VPSophCls; Oakland Univ; Engineering.

VESELY, Patricia J; Verdigre Public HS; Verdigre, NE; Band; Chr; Chrs; HonRl; MrchBnd; PepBnd; SchPl; 4-H; SpnCl; PpCl; Trade School; Veterinarinarian.

VESKRNA, Larry D; Wahoo Public HS; Colon, NE; HonRl; StuGov; Teen; RptrYrbk; RptrSchPpr; 4-H; Bsktbl; CchngActv; Trade Sch.

VESSELS, Joey A; Gibson Southern HS; Ft Branch, IN; 2/230 ChrhWkr; RptrSchPpr; PpCl; Bsktbl; Ftbl; Trk; Indiana State; Journalism.

VEST, Monica; Anderson HS; Anderson, IN; 54;620 Band; HonRl; LitMag; NHS; Quill&Scroll; EdSchPpr; NCTE; College;laworjournalisn.

VEST, Phillip R; Blue Mound HS; Blue Mound, IL; 3/40 TrsJrCls; HonRl; NHS; Yrbk; Univ Of Illinois; Engineering.

VESTAL, Barbara L; Marshfield HS; Marshfield, MO; 5/132 SecBand; CncrtBnd; HonRl; MrchBnd; StuCncl; TchrAde; RptrYrbk; RptrSchPpr; PresFHA; FTA; Smsu; Home Economics.

VESTAL, Jennifer L; Niangua HS; Niangua, MO; Chr; Chrs; HonRl; LbryAde; NHS; SchPl; RptrYrbk; Yrbk; LetterBsbl; LetterBsktbl; Chrldr; GAA; IMSpt; College; Insurance.

VESTER, David A; Daleville HS; Muncie, IN; HonRl; Bsktbl; Trk; Anderson Voc; Tool & Dies.

VESTUTO, Paul V; Wheaton Central HS; Wheaton, IL; 43/317 HonRl; JA; LbryAde; NHS; RptrSchPpr; Ftbl; CaptTrk; Wrstlng; College; Engineering.

VETRONE, Deborah L; Neillsville HS; Neillsville, WI; SecSrCls; HonRl; NHS; OffAde; StuCncl; SecYrbk; RptrSchPpr; SchPpr; FBLA; PresFHA; PpCl; GAA;.

VETTE, Jill; Tarkio HS; Westboro, MO; TrsSophCls; VPSrCls; HonRl; HospAde; NHS; StuCncl; RptrYrbk; Trk; Nwmsu Col; Physical Ed.

VETTEL, Vicki S; Thompson Public HS; Thompson, ND; PresSophCls; Chrs; HonRl; SchPl; EdYrBk; RptrSchPpr; Chrldr; Tech Sch; Interior Design.

VETTER, Brian; West Liberty HS; West Liberty, IA; ALBoysSt; Band; Chrs; ChrhWkr; CncrtBnd; HonRl; 4-HAwd; College; Engineer.

VETTER, Dalila J; Flasher Public HS; Flasher, ND; 10/39 Chrs; HonRl; SchPl; Yrbk; Pres4-H; FHA; PpCl; LetterBsktbl; GAA; 4-HAwd; College; Professional.

VETTER, Daniel R; Sully Buttes HS; Onida, SD; 1/55 PresJrCls; PresBand; Chrs; ChrhWkr; HonRl; Mdrgl; MrchBnd; NHS; StuCncl; YthFlsp; Bsktbl; Glf; Trk; Tabor Col; Music.

VETTER, Kathleen M; Incarnate Word Academy; St Louis, MO; 11/110 Chrs; HonRl; NHS; SchMus; SchPl; SctActv; StuCncl; RptrSchPpr; GAA; University; Veterinarian.

VETTER, Kathy; West Delaware HS; Manchester, IA; 7/198 Band; Chr; Chrs; CncrtBnd; HonRl; MrchBnd; NHS; StuCncl; Yrbk; SchPpr; Univ Of Ia; Elementary Teacher.

VETTER, Michael J; Annawan HS; Prophetstown, IL; ALBoysSt; HonRl; TreasNHS; SchPl; PresYthFlsp; 4-H; SecFFA; SpnCl; LetterTrk; Univ Of Illinois; Veterinarian.

VETTER, Michael J; Mankato East HS; Kasota, MN; 1/270 Band; HonRl; NHS; NatlMeritSF; Orch; VP4-H; LetterTrk; 4-HAwd; Msu; Mathematics.

VETTER, Monica I; Aurora HS; Aurora, NE; 4/90 HonRl; NHS; Yrbk; SchPpr; Col; English.

VETTER, Nancy S; Jewell HS; Formoso, KS; SecJrCls; Band; Chr; CncrtBnd; MrchBnd; PepBnd; SchPl; Twrl; 4-H; PpCl; School Of Cosmetology; Cosmetologist.

VETTER, Steven C; Arlington HS; Arlington Hts, IL; 40/580 HonRl; PresJA; TchrAde; FTA; PresMthCl; SciCl; Univ Of Il; Computer Programming.

VEUM, Melissa; Appleton West HS; Appleton, WI; AFS; ChrhWkr; Orch; SchMus; SctActv; LatCl; St Olaf College; Physical Therapy.

VEURINK, Calvin G; Dakota Christian HS; Harrison, SD; Chr; ChrhWkr; SchPl; PpCl; Bsbl; Bsktbl; Ftbl; Trk; College; Recreational Director.

VEVEA, Eric D; Rhinelander HS; Rhinelander, WI; ALBoysSt; HonRl; NHS; NatlMeritFnl; NatlMeritCmnd; LetterBsbl; LetterFtbl; CchngActv; Um Minneapolis; Architect.

VEZAIN, Thomas L; La Salle Peru HS; Utica, IL; ChrhWkr; HonRl; NatlMeritSchl; SchAde; SpnCl; Bsktbl; Northern Il Univ; Accountant.

VIALLE, Kimberly; Lexington R V HS; Lexington, MO; 2/98 DrmMjrt; HonRl; NHS; SctActv; StuCncl; EdSchPpr; FrCl; BttyCrckrAwd; DARAwd; Univ Of Missouri Columbia.

VIBETO, Kim R; Velva Public HS; Velva, ND; 12/47 PresJrCls; HonRl; MrchBnd; NHS; StuCncl; TchrAde; Yrbk; FBLA; FHA; LetterBsktbl; Clge; Professional.

VICE, Cynthia E; Fremont HS; Fremont, IN; 8/76 TrsSophCls; Chr; HonRl; NHS; SchPl; StuCncl; YthFlsp; FHA; LatCl; Trk; College; Professional.

VICE, Marsha L; Sullivan HS; Sullivan, IL; 16/120 ALAGirlsSt; Band; Chr; DrlTm; HonRl; NHS; FTA; FrCl; SciCl; GAA; Univ;professional.

VICENT, Evangeline B; Baldwin HS; Baldwin, MI; 3/42 ChrhWkr; HonRl; LbryAde; OffAde; SchPl; StuCncl; StuGov; TchrAde; RptrSchPpr; SpnCl; EldAwd; Michigan State Univ; Special Education.

VICKERS, Barbara J; Wellsville HS; Ottawa, KS; 2/65 SecFrshCls; VPSophCls; PresJrCls; TrsSrCls; ALAGirlsSt; VPNHS; SchMus; TreasStuCncl; Chrldr; BttyCrckrAwd; 4-HAwd; Emporia Kansas State College; Sec Teaching.

VICKERS, Dennis W; Pacific HS; Pacific, MO; VPJrCls; HonRl; SchMus; StuCncl; TchrAde; YthFlsp; FTA; PresSpnCl; CaptBsktbl; LetterTrk; Chrldr; PresAwd; College.

VICKERS, Timothy C; Dollar Bay HS; Dollar Bay, MI; HonRl; NatlMeritCmnd; VPStuCncl; LetterBsktbl; LetterTrk; Michigan Tech Univ; Electrician.

VICKERS, Vicky; Dupo Comm HS; Dupo, IL; 49/117 HonRl; StuCncl; TchrAde; RptrYrbk; EdYrBk; Belleville Area Jr College; Computor Prog.

VICKERY, Ronald R; Desoto HS; Desoto, WI; CmntyWkr; HonRl; SchPpr; VPFFA; LetterTrk; IMSpt; Uw Lacrosse; Marine Biologist.

VICKSTROM, Lynda L; Marquette Sr HS; Marquette, MI; Band; ChrhWkr; HonRl; MrchBnd; PepBnd; StuCncl; RptrYrbk; SciCl; Swmmng; PPFtbl; South College; Medical Technology.

VICTOR, Lynda A; Tower HS; Warren, MI; HonRl; NatlMeritSchl; OffAde; LetterChrldr; Mich State U; Nursing.

VIDA, Karolyn M; Thurston HS; Detroit, MI; CmntyWkr; HonRl; JrNHS; Madonna College; Nursing.

VIDAKOVICH, Paul S; Waterford Township HS; Pontiac, MI; HonRl; Bsktbl; Ftbl; CaptTrk; Central Eastern Mi; Human Environment.

VIDAL, Patricia A; Andrean HS; Crown Point, IN; 40/260 ChrhWkr; HonRl; RedCrAde; SchMus; College; Biology.

VIDEEN, Susan M; Chisago Lakes HS; Chisago City, MN; CncrtBnd; HonRl; MrchBnd; PepBnd; SchMus; Bemidji State College.

VIDIMOS, Alfred S; Andrean HS; Merrillville, IN; 12/301 ChrhWkr; HonRl; NHS; SchPl; StuCncl; CaptGlf; LetterWrstlng; Miami Univ; Professional.

VIDIMOS, Allison T; Andrean HS; Merrillville, IN; 1/250 HonRl; NHS; MthCl; Bsbl; Glf; Swmmng; GAA; PPFtbl; College.

VIDITO, Robert S; Fowlerville HS; Fowlerville, MI; Band; Chr; CncrtBnd; HonRl; LbryAde; MrchBnd; PepBnd; SctActv; Coll; Civil Engr.

VIDMAR, Paul; Memorial Senior HS; Ely, MN; 6/135 TrsFrshCls; TrsSophCls; TrsJrCls; TrsSrCls; ALBoysSt; HonRl; PolWkr; StuGov; EdYrBk; Bsbl; St Cloud State; Accountant.

VIDUSEK, David A; Hinsdale Central HS; Hinsdale, IL; NHS; NatlMeritCmnd; Illinois State University; Chemistry.

VIEAUX, Peter M; Rhinelander Sr HS; Rhinelander, WI; HonRl; Ftbl; Wrstlng; College.

VIED, Nancy C; Charleston R 1 HS; Charleston, MO; 27/168 Chrs; ChrhWkr; CncrtBnd; HonRl; MrchBnd; PepBnd; SchMus; SchPl; SctActv; Southeast Missouri State Univ; Teaching.

VIEHL, Brian M; Milwaukee Luthern HS; Wauwatosa, WI; 73/231 AFS; ChrhWkr; HonRl; SctActv; YthFlsp; LetterWrstlng; University; Engineering.

VIEHWEG, Lynn A; Octavia HS; Anchor, IL; 1/50 HonRl; NHS; SchMus; StuCncl; EdSchPpr; SpnCl; LetterTrk; Chrldr; GAA; IMSpt; Ill Wesleyan Univ; Acct.

VIELBIG, Mary A; Oakfield HS; Oakfield, WI; ChrhWkr; HonRl; NHS; RptrYrbk; SchPpr; FHA; SpnCl; Chrldr;.

VIELLIEUX, Alyce M; Somerset Public HS; Somerset, WI; 3/59 Chr; HonRl; Yrbk; Trade School; Seamstress.

VIEREGGE, Katherine A; Brookwood HS; Norwalk, WI; 6/49 Band; Chrs; CncrtBnd; HonRl; LbryAde; NHS; SchPl; RptrYrbk; 4-H; FHA; Viterbo College; Nursing.

VIEREGGE, Patricia S; Mound Westonka HS; Wayzata, MN; AFS; Band; CncrtBnd; HonRl; MrchBnd; PepBnd; SctActv; 4-H; GerCl; Trk; Univ; Teach Special Ed Handicapped.

VIESTENZ, Cheryl J; Dakota HS; Arthur, ND; 1/25 Band; Chrs; HonRl; HospAde; LbryAde; NHS; SchPl; EdSchPpr; FHA; LetterBsktbl; U Of Nd; Physical Therapy.

VIET, Dennis D; Dike Community HS; Reinbeck, IA; Band; CncrtBnd; MrchBnd; StuCncl; Bsktbl; LetterFtbl; LetterTrk; Trade School.

VIETA, Patricia K; Jackson HS; Jackson, MI; Chr; HonRl; NHS; RedCrAde; Univ Of Michigan; Doctor Of Medicine.

VIETH, Charles R; Brookwood HS; Norwalk, WI; 3/56 ALBoysSt; HonRl; NHS; StuCncl; YthFlsp; 4-H; FFA; LetterBsktbl; Uw Eau Claire; Business.

VIETH, Perry J; Marinette HS; Marinette, WI; ALBoysSt; TreasChrs; PresNHS; SchMus; SctActv; VPStuCncl; Yrbk; PresLatCl; Bsktbl; Glf; IMSpt; Marquette University; Business Admin.

VIGARS, Rebecca S; Eldora Comm HS; Eldora, IA; 11/66 SecChrs; CmntyWkr; HonRl; NatlThespSoc; SchMus; SchPl; StuCncl; VP4-H; 4-HAwd; MaSAwd; U Iowa State; Vet Or Interior Design.

VIGDAL, Anna Mae C; Garrigan HS; Whittemore, IA; Aud/Vis; Chr; Chrs; ChrhWkr; Sacrstn; SchMus; SchPl; RptrYrbk; Yrbk; PpCl; Cundelien College; Religious Education.

VIGEN, Lorelle K; Mapleton HS; Mapleton, ND; 4/10 VPSophCls; PresJrCls; ALAGirlsSt; Band; Chr; Chrs; ChrhWkr; CncrtBnd; HonRl; PepBnd; SchPl; CaptBsktbl; Trk; CaptChrldr; Concordia College; Business Admin.

VIGLIATURO, Antionette R; St Marys HS; Kansas City, MO; 15/130 Chrs; HonRl; NHS; SchMus; SchPl; GerCl; PpCl; Tennis; Chrldr; OptClAwd; PresAwd; Coll; Pro Edu.

VIGNALI, Kim M; Phelps Union Free HS; Phelps, WI; 3/14 PresFrshCls; PresSophCls; PresJrCls; Chrs; HonRl; LbryAde; NHS; OffAde; SchPl; StuCncl; North Central Tech Inst; Accountant.

VIGNEAU, Denise; St Clement HS; Centerline, MI; 16/97 HonRl; OffAde; SchPl; StuCncl; RptrYrbk; SptEdYrbk; FHA; Bsbl; Bsktbl; GAA; Trade School; Cosmotology.

VIGSTOL, Maribeth R; Pershing HS; Plummer, MN; Band; Chrs; CncrtBnd; HonRl; MrchBnd; PepBnd; Yrbk; RptrSchPpr; FHA; College.

VIK, Dennis P; Central HS; Aberdeen, SD; 2/437 AFS; ALBoysSt; Band; ChrhWkr; CncrtBnd; HonRl; JrNHS; MrchBnd; NHS; NatlMeritSF; Ftbl; Wrstlng; Washington Univ; Chemistry.

VIK, Kathy A; Draper HS; Draper, SD; SecFrshCls; TrsSophCls; SecJrCls; VPSrCls; ALAGirlsSt; Band; Chrs; DrlTm; HonRl; MrchBnd; NHS; Bsktbl; Trk; Chrldr;.

VIKEN, Jeffrey K; Parkview HS; Footville, WI; 4/160 TrsFrshCls; HonRl; NHS; Bsktbl; College; Professional.

VILANDER, Richard A; Wamego HS; Wamego, KS; 2/97 Band; ChrhWkr; HonRl; MrchBnd; NHS; PepBnd; StuCncl; StuGov; YthFlsp; Kansas State Univ; Engineer.

VILES, Louise J; Hartford HS; Neosho Rapids, KS; DrlTm; HonRl; Voc Tech.

VILETA, David; Riverside Brookfield Hs; Brookfield, IL; 42/488 ChrhWkr; HonRl; NHS; Bsbl; U Of Ill; Accting.

VILHAUER, Jeff L; Stanton HS; Stanton, ND; 2/15 PresJrCls; CncrtBnd; HonRl; PepBnd; SchPl; StuCncl; LetterBsktbl; LetterFtbl; Trk; PresAwd; College; Professional.

VILLALOBOS, Patricia A; St Augustine HS; Chicago, IL; TrsFrshCls; Chrs; ChrhWkr; CmntyWkr; HonRl; JA; NHS; SchPl; RptrSchPpr; De Paul University; Medical Technology.

VILLAMARIA, Lynn A; Frontenac HS; Frontenac, KS; HstJrCls; ALAGirlsSt; Chrs; HonRl; SchMus; SchPl; StuCncl; FHA; SpnCl; MthCl; PpCl; LetterBsktbl; Trk; College; Professional.

VILLENEUVE, Anne; Marian HS; Troy, MI; 7/180 Chr; Chrl; HonRl; HospAde; ModUN; NHS; TchrAde; RptrYrbk; Univ Mich.

VILLHARD, Victor J; Bishop Du Bourg HS; St Louis, MO; 7/487 ALBoysSt; Band; ChrhWkr; CncrtBnd; HonRl; Mass Institute Of Technology; Engineering.

VILLIARD, Esther M; Libertyville HS; Libertyville, IL; 28/428 HonRl; TreasNHS; OffAde; TchrAde; PresSwmmng; CchngActv; Purdue Univ; Biology.

VILLINSKI, Mary L; Brookfield Central HS; Brookfield, WI; 14/479 NHS; NatlMeritSF; RptrSchPpr; FrCl; GAA; LionAwd; U Of Wi; Chemical Engineering.

VINARDI, Donald L; Northeast HS; Girard, KS; 9/55 ALBoysSt; HonRl; SctActv; SciCl; Bsktbl; Trk; College; Professional.

VINCE, Michele P; Geneva Comm HS; Geneva, IL; 12/236 Chr; HonRl; NHS; SchMus; StuCncl; FshEdYrbk; Yrbk; SpnCl; PpCl; Univ Of Iowa; Art.

VINCENT, Bonnie J; Sturgis HS; Sturgis, MI; Band; CncrtBnd; HonRl; MrchBnd; NHS; PepBnd; LatCl; PpCl; Ferris St Coll; Pharmacy.

VINCENT, Diana L; Smithville HS; Smithville, MO; SecSophCls; VPJrCls; ALAGirlsSt; DrlTm; HonRl; NHS; SchMus; SctActv; FHA; CaptChrldr; College; Professional.

VINCENT, Emily R; Routt HS; Jacksonville, IL; SecJrCls; Chrs; SpnCl; Bsktbl; Chrldr; College; Special Education.

VINCENT, George H; Lutheran West HS; Dearborn Heights, MI; 9 149 VPSophCls; HonRl; ModUN; NHS; NatlMeritFnl; NatlMeritSF; PolWkr; StuCncl; RptrSchPpr; Trk; Yale; Attorney.

VINCENT, Jeffery; Ankeny HS; Ankeny, IA; 4/p260 ChrhWkr; HonRl; JrNHS; NHS; StuCncl; YthFlsp; SpnCl; Bsktbl; Ftbl; Arizona St U; Professional.

VINCENT, Kathleen A; Coon Rapids HS; Blaine, MN; 130/732 Band; ChrhWkr; CncrtBnd; HonRl; JrNHS; NHS; PepBnd; SpnCl; Bimidji State Clge; Math.

VINCENT, Kent A; Pleasant Valley HS; Bettendorf, IA; 2/180 PresFrshCls; TreasBand; Chrs; PolWkr; SchMus; SctActv; StuCncl; SptEdSchPpr; LetterBsktbl; LetterTrk; University; Life Science.

VINCENT, Kristine A; Estherville Sr HS; Estherville, IA; 16/166 Chrs; HonRl; NatlFornLg; RptrYrbk; Yrbk; RptrSchPpr; LetterBsktbl; LetterTrk; IMSpt; PresAwd; Westmar College; Physical Educ.

VINCENT, Lezlie; Marconaquah HS; Amboy, IN; 4/170 ALAGirlsSt; ChrhWkr; HonRl; NHS; StuCncl; YthFlsp; SptEdYrbk; PpCl; Purdue Univ; Medical Tech.

VINCENT, Patricia L; Lutheran West HS; Dearborn Hts, MI; Chr; ChrhWkr; JrNHS; NHS; PolWkr; SecStuCncl; SecStuGov; GerCl; PresPpCl; IMSpt; Univ Of Mi.

VINCENT, Paulette; Risco HS; Risco, MO; Chr; ChrhWkr; LbryAde; SchPl; Yrbk; SchPpr; 4-H; FHA; PpCl; Bsktbl; Trk; Chrldr; College; Rn.

VINCENT, Peggy S; Clarks Public HS; Clarks, NE; Band; Chrs; HonRl; StuCncl; YthFlsp; EdYrBk; EdSchPpr; PpCl; Business Schl; Secretarial.

VINCENT, Susan L; Reed City HS; Reed City, MI; 9/157 HonRl; NatlMeritCmnd; SchAde; TchrAde; FHA; PPFtbl; Trade Sch; Data Processing.

VINCENT, Victoria; Washburn Rural HS; Topeka, KS; 9/185 Chr; DrlTm; HonRl; Mdrgl; SchMus; TchrAde; Yrbk; PpCl; Kansas Univ.

VINCENTINI, Anthony R; Bishop Borgess HS; Detroit, MI; Chrl; Chrs; ChrhWkr; HonRl; JrNHS; NHS; SchMus; TchrAde; Teen; Univ Of Michigan; Political Science.

VINE, Charles J; Pontiac Northern HS; Pontiac, MI; 1/406 HonRl; NHS; TchrAde; General Motors Inst; Engineering.

VINE, Jeff F; Neillsville HS; Franton, WI; VPFrshCls; Chr; HonRl; SchPl; StuCncl; FFA; CaptBsktbl; CaptFtbl; CaptUniv; Professional.

VINEHOUT, Kathleen A; Aurora Central HS; Aurora, IL; Chrs; HonRl; SchMus; SchPl; StuCncl; StuGov; RptrYrbk; EdSchPpr; Pres4-H; LetterBsktbl; Clg; Journalist.

VINES, Billie B; West HS; Wichita, KS; SctActv; StuCncl; TchrAde; Manhattan Christian College; Veterinarian.

VINEYARD, Ben; Central HS; St Joseph, MO; HonRl; StuGov; SciCl; Bsbl; Ftbl; Wrstlng; IMSpt; U Of Mo; Science.

VINEYARD, Teri L; Central Riii HS; Flat River, MO; HospAde; NHS; NatlThespSoc; SchPl; Yrbk; FHA; SciCl; LetterTennis; Chrldr; College; Nurse.

VINOGRADOV, Sophia; Huron HS; Ann Arbor, MI; 7/570 HonRl; LitMag; SchPl; University; Biology.

VINSON, Kenneth W; Lawrenceburg HS; Lawrenceburg, IN; 15/150 PresSophCls; Aud/Vis; HonRl; PresJA; PresJrNHS; NHS; StuCncl; PresFBLA; SpnCl; JAAwd; Hanover College; Elem Teacher Or Business.

VINSON, Rochelle A; Truman HS; Independence, MO; Chr; HonRl; HospAde; JA; SctActv; FNA; Nursing Schl; Nurse.

VINT, Kathy A; St Marys HS; Storm Lake, IA; 7/45 Chr; Chrs; ChrhWkr; DrlTm; HonRl; SchMus; SchPl; RptrYrbk; RptrSchPpr; 4-H; PpCl; Vocational Tech; Surgical Tech.

VINTON, Brian G; St Agnes Academy; Whitman, NE; 4/20 HonRl; NHS; SchPl; Sdlty; StuGov; FrCl; SciCl; Bsktbl; Ftbl; Trk; Coll.

VINTON, David A; Adrian HS; Adrian, MI; 93/390 ChrhWkr; CncrtBnd; HonRl; MrchBnd; NHS; SchMus; SchPl; StuCncl; TchrAde; LetterSwmmng; Central Mi U.

VINTON, Theresa L; Gordon HS; Eli, NE; 8/67 Band; Chrs; DrlTm; HonRl; StuCncl; TchrAde; FHA; PpCl; LetterTrk; PPFtbl; Nursing.

VINZANT, David; Hobart HS; Hobart, IN; 14/400 AFS; HonRl; JrNHS; NHS; SctActv; TchrAde; GerCl; SciCl; Swmmng; Purdue Univ; Medicine.

VIOHL, Robert B; Schaumburg HS; Schaumburg, IL; HonRl; NatlMeritSF; RptrSchPpr; Ftbl; Tennis; Northern Ill Univ; Law.

VIOL, Robert; Herbert Henry Dow HS; Midland, MI; HonRl; LbryAde; NHS; Michigan State Univ; Education.

VIOLANTE, Edward V; Tinley Park HS; Tinley Park, IL; 5/350 HonRl; JrNHS; NHS; NatlMeritFnl; NatlMeritSF; Swmmng; Trk; Wrstlng; Univ Of Illinois; Biology.

VIOX, Mark G; Valle HS; Ste Genevieve, MO; 7/81 PresSophCls; HonRl; NHS; StuCncl; Bsktbl; Ftbl; LetterTrk; CaptIMSpt; AmLegAwd; 4-HAwd; Clge; Computer.

VIRDEN, Marshall L; Falls HS; International Fall, MN; HonRl; LitMag; RptrSchPpr; CaptBsbl; LetterBsktbl; LetterFtbl; Concordia Coll; Sociology.

VIRGA, Marrian C; Edwin Denby HS; Detroit, MI; 39/637 ChrhWkr; CmntyWkr; JA; JrNHS; NHS; NatlMeritSF; NatlThespSoc; StuCncl; TchrAde; SecSciCl; Univ Of Detroit; Environmental Eng.

VIRGILIO, Denise A; Dominican HS; Mt Clemens, MI; Band; HonRl; FrCl; University; Professional.

VIRGIN, Becky J; Mt Vernon HS; Mc Cordsville, IN; 30/144 CmntyWkr; HonRl; MrchBnd; NHS; SchPpr; PresCivCl; 4-H; PpCl; GAA; 4-HAwd; OptClAwd; Indiana Purdue Univ; Radiologic Tech.

VIRGIN, Bradley K; Litchfield Comm HS; Litchfield, IL; 10/148 ALBoysSt; Band; CncrtBnd; DrlTm; HonRl; MrchBnd; NHS; Orch; PepBnd; SchMus; SchPl; KeyCl; SpnCl; Univ Of Illinois; Medicine.

VIRGIN, Michelle M; St Joseph Acad; Detroit, MI; 3/15 VPSophCls; Chrl; HonRl; JrNHS; NHS; Yrbk; SpnCl; VPPPFtbl; Detroit Coll; Acct.

VIRNIG, Jody C; Waupaca HS; Waupaca, WI; 53/153 HonRl; Quill&Scroll; SchPl; SctActv; TchrAde; SchPpr; FrCl; GerCl; SpnCl; University; Social Psychology.

VIRTA, Raymond O; Bergland Comm HS; Bergland, MI; 1/27 PresSophCls; Band; ChrhWkr; HonRl; NatlSciFnd; StuCncl; Teen; SciCl; Bsktbl; IMSpt; Univ; Professional.

VIRTS, Elizabeth L; Arlington HS; Indianapolis, IN; 3/500 HonRl; NHS; PPFtbl; Miami U; Chemistry.

VIRTUE, Daniel R; Hinckley Big Rock HS; Hinckley, IL; Chrs; HonRl; VPNHS; SchMus; SchPl; RptrYrbk; LatCl; PresSciCl; CchngActv; DanFAwd; Univ; Research Scientist.

VIS, William; Pinckney HS; Brighton, MI; 8/190 Band; CncrtBnd; HonRl; MrchBnd; NHS; PepBnd; AmLegAwd; Univ Of Michigan.

VISINTAINER, Mary M; Norway HS; Norway, MI; 30/103 HonRl; HospAde; NatlFornLg; SchPl; Teen; Yrbk; SchPpr; FBLA; FHA; Bryant Business College; Secretary.

VISKOZKI, Debra K; Whitnall HS; Greenfield, WI; 4/280 Chrs; HonRl; ModUN; NatlFornLg; NHS; NatlMeritSF; SchMus; SchPl; EdSchPpr; Univ Of Wisc; Nurse.

VISOTSKY, Robin L; Evanston Township HS; Evanston, IL; CmntyWkr; YthFlsp; JAAwd; Univ; Artist.

VISSCHER, Kristy K; Holland HS; Holland, MI; 37/317 HonRl; LetterBsktbl; Grand Valley St Coll; Elem Educ.

VISSER, Debra; Grand Rapids HS; Grand Rapids, MI; Chr; HonRl; JrNHS; NHS; Bsktbl; IMSpt; College; Veterinary.

VISSER, Grace A; Bob Jones Academy; Nashville, IN; Band; ChrhWkr; MrchBnd; PepBnd; LatCl; Bob Jones U; Music Piano.

VISSER, Nancy J; Hinsdale Central HS; Hinsdal, IL; Chrs; CmntyWkr; HonRl; EdYrBk; College; Intnl Affairs.

VISSER, Patricia A; Holland Christian HS; Holland, MI; Band; Chr; ChrhWkr; HonRl; HospAde; NatlMeritCmnd; YthFlsp; 4-H; FNA; Nursing School; Nurse.

VISTY, Mary Jo; Daniel J Gross HS; Omaha, NE; HonRl; NatlFornLg; NHS; Quill&Scroll; Yrbk; RptrSchPpr; Creighton U; Pharmacy.

VITALE, Carmela; Dominican Hs; Detroit, MI; NHS; StuCncl; Wayne State U; Engineering.

VITALE, Joseph M; St Marys HS; St Louis, MO; LetterBsbl; LetterFtbl; LetterSocr; University; Physical Education Teacher.

VITCK, Michael G; Subiaco Academy; West Chester, IL; VPSophCls; Chrs; ChrhWkr; HonRl; SchPl; StuCncl; SptEdSchPpr; SpnCl; Bsktbl; Ftbl; St Gregorys; Law.

VITKUS, Perrin J; Hinsdale HS; Darien, IL; PresJrCls; Chr; HonRl; NHS; NatlMeritSF; SchPl; StuCncl; CaptGlf; Univ Of Ill; Architecture.

VITOSH, Mark A; Odell Public HS; Odell, NE; SecJrCls; Band; Chr; Chrs; CncrtBnd; HonRl; MrchBnd; PepBnd; SchPl; StuCncl;.

VITT, Michael; St Paul HS; St Paul, KS; Chr; ChrhWkr; HonRl; OffAde; StuCncl; FFA; PpCl; Bsktbl; Farming.

VIVEROS, Esther M; Bishop Miege HS; Shawnee Mission, KS; ChrhWkr; HonRl; HospAde; LbryAde; NHS; SchMus; SchPl; TchrAde; SpnCl; PpCl; College; Accounting.

VIVIAN, Douglas L; John M Harlan HS; Chicago, IL; SecTrsFrshCls; TrsSophCls; Aud/Vis; LbryAde; OffAde; RptrSchPpr; SchPpr; Bsbl; Art Inst Of Chicago; Photographer.

VIZTHUM, Robert; Stockbridge HS; Stockbridge, MI; 9/123 HonRl; NHS; SchPl; YthFlsp; MthCl; Bsbl; Ftbl; DanFAwd; Eastern Mich Univ; Business Administration.

VLACHOS, Christ; Trenton HS; Trenton, MI; CAP; HonRl; NHS; SctActv; StuGov; SchPpr; Tennis; IMSpt; W Mich Univ; Photography.

VLADOVA, Fred M; Downers Grove North HS; Downers Grove, IL; Band; CncrtBnd; DrmMjrt; MrchBnd; NHS; NatlMeritCmnd; University Of Illinois; Music.

VLASAK, Wayne L; New Lisbon HS; New Lisbon, WI; 6/58 PresJrCls; PresSrCls; ALBoysSt; CncrtBnd; HonRl; MrchBnd; PresNHS; PepBnd; LetterTrk; BauchLmbAwd; Univ Of Wisconsin; Electrical Engineer.

VLASIC, Anica; Sts Peter And Paul HS; Saginaw, MI; 1/125 Chrs; ChrhWkr; HonRl; Mdrgl; NHS; TchrAde; EdYrBk; GAA; IMSpt; BttyCrckrAwd; Col; Professional.

VLASIN, Randy A; Hayes County HS; Hayes Center, NE; PresFrshCls; PresJrCls; Band; Chrs; CncrtBnd; MrchBnd; PepBnd; 4-H; FFA; Ftbl; Trk; Univ; Vocation.

VLNA, Ann M; Portage Northern HS; Ge, MI; TrsSrCls; ChrhWkr; CmntyWkr; HonRl; JrNHS; NHS; StuCncl; LatCl; Mi St U; Pre Vet.

VLRICH, Maragaret M; Holy Angels HS; Richfield, MN; 3/106 NHS; SchMus; SchPl; StuCncl; LetterTrk; U Of Mn.

VOBORIL, Greg K; Columbus Slotus HS; Columbus, NE; ChrhWkr; HonRl; NHS; StuCncl; StuGov; GerCl; Bsbl; Bsktbl; Ftbl; Trk; U Of Ne; Nuclear Eng.

VOCK, Donald E; Polo Comm HS; Polo, IL; 7/90 SecFrshCls; TrsSophCls; TrsJrCls; PresSrCls; ALBoysSt; HonRl; NHS; SchPl; SctActv; StuCncl; SpnCl; Bsktbl; Ftbl; College; Business Administration.

VOCK, Joy; Polo Community HS; Polo, IL; 7/100 Chr; ChrhWkr; HonRl; NHS; StuCncl; RptrSchPpr; FHA; GAA; 4-HAwd;.

VODER, Jim L; Arthur HS; Arthur, IL; VPJrCls; HonRl; SchPl; RptrYrbk; RptrSchPpr; LetterBsbl; LetterFtbl; CaptTrk; IMSpt; Col;.

VODNIK, Sandra J; Whitnall HS; Hales Corners, WI; 22/258 TrsSrCls; HonRl; NHS; SctActv; StuGov; FrCl; GAA; U Of Wi Madison; Psychology.

VOELLER, Marie F; Newport HS; Towner, ND; Band; Chr; Chrs; CncrtBnd; HonRl; MrchBnd; PepBnd; TchrAde; Trk; Clg; Park Ranger.

VOELPEL, Thomas E; Lawrence Central HS; Indianapolis, IN; ChrhWkr; YthFlsp; Purdue University; Aeronautical Engineer.

VOEPEL, Beth; Williamsville HS; Sherman, IL; TrsJrCls; ChrhWkr; CmntyWkr; HonRl; OffAde; SchPl; StuCncl; TchrAde; Yrbk; FHA; Col; Special Education Teacherfor Deaf.

VOET, Perry L; Southern HS; Wymore, NE; Band; CmntyWkr; PresSophCls; MrchBnd; PepBnd; SchAde; Bsbl; Bsktbl; Ftbl; PPFtbl; Milford Tech Coll; Electrician.

VOETBERG, Ruth H; Holland Chr HS; Zeeland, MI; ChrhWkr; CmntyWkr; HonRl; StuCncl; YthFlsp; SchPpr; 4-H; FBLA; SpnCl; Hope College; Spanish Major.

VOGEL, Cathleen C; St Charles HS; St Charles, IL; 4/400 Chr; Chrl; HonRl; NHS; SchMus; SchPl; StuCncl; Bradley Univ; Journalism.

VOGEL, Daniel J; Melrose Senior HS; Melrose, MN; Chr; ChrhWkr; CmntyWkr; HonRl; EdSchPpr; FBLA; Bsktbl; LetterTrk; College; Sales Management.

VOGEL, David G; Duluth Central HS; Duluth, MN; 90/432 ChrhWkr; HonRl; YthFlsp; University Of Minnesota; Art.

VOGEL, Dawn R; Fulton HS; Fulton, IL; TrsSophCls; Chrs; ChrhWkr; HonRl; NatlThespSoc; Chrldr; Vocation.

VOGEL, Fred; Coleman HS; Coleman, MI; 9/84 Band; CncrtBnd; HonRl; MrchBnd; PepBnd; SchPl; GerCl; Trk; Univ; Engineer.

VOGEL, Gary G; Sanborn Public HS; Sanborn, MN; Band; Chr; CncrtBnd; MrchBnd; PepBnd; FFA; Bsktbl; LetterFtbl; Wrstlng; Trade.

VOGEL, Jill E; Stewardson Strasburg HS; Strasburg, IL; PresSophCls; Band; ChrhWkr; CncrtBnd; HonRl; MrchBnd; SchPl; FHA; PpCl; IMSpt; Lake Land Jr Clg; Accounting.

VOGEL, Joyce; Brussels Comm HS; Golden Eagle, IL; PresJrCls; ChrhWkr; HonRl; SchPl; TchrAde; Yrbk; FHA; FTA; PpCl; AmLegAwd; Coll.

VOGEL, Julie A; Windsor HS; Gays, IL; 12/54 PresFrshCls; Band; HonRl; NHS; NatlThespSoc; SchPl; StuCncl; GAA; AmLegAwd; Eastern Illinois Univ; Art.

VOGEL, Julie L; Pike HS; Indianapolis, IN; 14/226 SecFrshCls; ALAGirlsSt; Aud/Vis; Chr; HonRl; NHS; OffAde; PolWkr; StuCncl; StuGov; YthFlsp; LatCl; PpCl; Chrldr; Indiana University; Law.

VOGEL, Kathy A; Roncalli HS; Manitowoc, WI; 2/141 AFS; SecBand; Chrs; HonRl; JA; SecNHS; SecStuCncl; RptrYrbk; MthCl; GAA; U Of Wis Madison; Pharmacy.

VOGEL, Kendall L; Bayard HS; Bayard, NE; 4/50 TrsFrshCls; TrsSophCls; ALBoysSt; HonRl; NHS; StuGov; YthFlsp; LetterBsbl; LetterBsktbl; LetterFtbl; College; Business Admin.

VOGEL, Kevin L; Bayard HS; Bayard, NE; 5/44 PresFrshCls; VPJrCls; PresSrCls; ALBoysSt; Band; NHS; YthFlsp; LetterFtbl; Wrstlng; SARAwd;.

VOGEL, Kim; Jefferson Senior HS; Jefferson, WI; ChrhWkr; CmntyWkr; HonRl; YthFlsp; College; Physical Therapy.

VOGEL, Lisa A; Richmond Burton HS; Richmond, IL; 2/72 Band; ChrhWkr; HonRl; NHS; SchMus; SchPl; Yrbk; FrCl; PpCl; Trk; GAA; Illinois Wesleyan Univ; Social Science.

VOGEL, Lu; Christopher Comm HS; Christopher, IL; 2/62 Band; CncrtBnd; HonRl; MrchBnd; NHS; OffAde; Twrl; Yrbk; FHA; Chrldr; College; Professional.

VOGEL, Mark; Panora Linden HS; Panora, IA; 30/60 ChrhWkr; SchAde; TchrAde; PpCl; CchngActv; College; Professional.

VOGEL, Monica A; Mankato West HS; N Mankato, MN; ALAGirlsSt; Mankato St University; Computer Programming.

VOGEL, Pamela; St Joseph HS; Saint Joseph, MI; 91/335 Band; CmntyWkr; JrNHS; NHS; Quill&Scroll; EdYrBk; Yrbk; Swmmng; GAA; DARAwd; Michigan State Univ; Human Ecology.

VOGEL, Paul J; St Marys HS; Lemay, MO; TreasNHS; NatlMeritSF; SchPl; StuCncl; IMSpt; Ma Inst Of Tech; Engineering.

VOGEL, Rick; Carlyle HS; Carlyle, IL; 2/138 PresSophCls; PresJrCls; HonRl; NHS; YthFlsp; FrCl; Bsbl; LetterBsktbl; LetterFtbl; U Of Illinois; Engineer.

VOGEL, Rosalie; Horicon HS; Horicon, WI; 130117 NHS; SchAde; SchPpr; Office Work.

VOGEL, Ruth; St Pauls College HS; Kansas City, KS; PresJrCls; Chrs; HonRl; NHS; Tennis; Chrldr; College; Teaching Handicapped Children.

VOGEL, Timothy J; All Saints Central HS; Bay City, MI; 5/180 Band; CmntyWkr; HonRl; NatlFornLg; NHS; PepBnd; SchPl; MthCl; SciCl; Trk; Naval Acad; Naval Officer.

VOGELEI, Nancy L; Southfield Lathrup HS; Lathrup Village, MI; 12/680 VPChr; HonRl; Mdrgl; NHS; NatlMeritSchl; NatlMeritSF; NatlThespSoc; SchMus; TchrAde; YthFlsp; Western Mi Univ; Music Therapy.

VOGELMAN, Marc R; Remington HS; Potwin, KS; Aud/Vis; ChrhWkr; CmntyWkr; HonRl; YthFlsp; YthFnd; Butler Co Jr College; Vocation.

VOGEN, Gary N; Newark Community HS; Newark, IL; 4/51 Chr; Chrs; ChrhWkr; HonRl; NHS; StuCncl; Bsbl; LetterSocr; Trk; IMSpt; U Of Il; Agricultural Economics.

VOGEN, Jeffrey L; Newark HS; Newark, IL; TreasBand; TreasChrhWkr; HonRl; NHS; SctActv; VPStuCncl; PresFFA; FTA; Bsktbl; Trk; College; Aviation.

VOGLER, Mark L; Colon HS; Mendon, MI; 16/65 Band; NHS; PepBnd; 4-H; 4-HAwd; Tri State Coll; Gen Engr.

VOGT, Dale; Slinger HS; Slinger, WI; FFA; LetterTrk; LetterWrstlng; School; Nursing.

VOGT, Debi K; Dow City Arion Comm HS; Dow City, IA; SecSrCls; Chrs; ChrhWkr; HonRl; LbryAde; PolWkr; SchMus; SchPl; StuCncl; StuGov;.

VOGT, Gerrianne T; Duchesne HS; St Charles, MO; 1/138 Band; Chrs; ChrhWkr; HonRl; LbryAde; MrchBnd; NatlMeritSF; SchMus; RptrYrbk; RptrSchPpr; Washington Univ; Mathematic.

VOGT, James M; Butterfield Odin HS; Butterfield, MN; PresJrCls; Band; Chr; ChrhWkr; CncrtBnd; HonRl; Mdrgl; MrchBnd; SchPl; StuCncl; LetterBsbl; LetterBsktbl; LetterFtbl; Col; Prof.

VOGT, Joann; St Marys HS; Burlington, WI; Chr; Chrs; HonRl; Yrbk; PpCl; IMSpt;.

VOGT, Kathryn J; Elmwood Public HS; Elmwood, NE; 2/11 PresFrshCls; ALAGirlsSt; Band; HonRl; SchPl; RptrYrbk; 4-H; LetterTrk; Chrldr; EldAwd; Univ Of Nebraska; Accounting.

VOGT, Kimberly J; Arlington HS; Arlington Hts, IL; 81/585 Chrs; HonRl; HospAde; Illinois St Univ; Liberal Arts.

VOGT, Laurel A; Wichita East HS; Wichita, KS; 29/625 Chrs; HonRl; NatlMeritCmnd; NatlThespSoc; SchMus; SchPl; PresTeen; Kansas Univ; Psychology.

VOGT, Le Ann M; Union HS; Union, MO; 33/165 Chrl; HonRl; JA; NHS; Yrbk; 4-H; GerCl; PpCl; 4-HAwd; JAAwd; E Central Jr Coll.

VOGT, Philip; Jeffersonville HS; Jeffersonville, IN; ALBoysSt; Band; CmntyWkr; CncrtBnd; MrchBnd; ModUN; PepBnd; PolWkr; Ind Univ; Law.

VOGT, Robert; Memorial HS; Evansville, IN; 35/228 Chr; ChrhWkr; HonRl; HospAde; NHS; OffAde; GerCl; Ftbl; Wrstlng; IMSpt; University; Orthopedic Surgeon.

VOGT, Roger L; Valley Center HS; Valley Center, KS; 16/119 Chr; HonRl; Mdrgl; NHS; SchMus; SctActv; LetterFtbl; LetterTrk; CitAwd; Butler Co Comm Clg; Dentist.

VOGT, Russell; Henry Independent HS; Henry, SD; ALBoysSt; Chrs; HonRl; SchPl; StuCncl; SptEdSchPpr; 4-H; CchngActv; 4-HAwd; College.

VOGT, Scott A; Sullivan HS; Sullivan, MO; Band; Chr; Chrs; ChrhWkr; CncrtBnd; MrchBnd; PepBnd; StuCncl; SpnCl; PpCl; Bsktbl; College; Architect.

VOGT, Susan; East Lansing HS; East Lansing, MI; 2/362 VPFrshCls; Band; Chr; Chrl; MrchBnd; NHS; NatlMeritFnl; NatlMeritSchl; Orch; TchrAde; Radcliffe College; Lawyer.

VOGT, William T; Washington HS; Vinton, IA; ALBoysSt; CncrtBnd; HonRl; MrchBnd; NHS; NatlThespSoc; Quill&Scroll; SchMus; SchPl; EdSchPpr; Iowa State Univ; Journalism.

VOGTMANN, William M; John Adams HS; South Bend, IN; 45/442 HonRl; NatlMeritSF; College; Engineering.

VOGTS, Karen S; Moundridge HS; Moundridge, KS; ALAGirlsSt; Band; ChrhWkr; CmntyWkr; CncrtBnd; HonRl; NHS; PresStuCncl; FHA; VPPpCl; Coll; Nursing.

VOGTS, Paula K; Canton Galva HS; Canton, KS; PresFrshCls; PresSophCls; ChrhWkr; HonRl; StuCncl; TchrAde; EdYrBk; LetterBsktbl; CchngActv; IMSpt; DanFAwd; St Johns College; Mathematics.

VOGTS, Steven J; Oregon HS; Madison, WI; HonRl; SctActv; YthFlsp; IMSpt; College; Electronics.

VOHLAND, Robert G; Valley HS; Canton, IL; Band; Chrs; ChrhWkr; CncrtBnd; HonRl; MrchBnd; PepBnd; SchMus; SchPl; YthFlsp; FFA; College; Farming.

VOHLAND, William H; Spoon River Valley Jr Sr HS; Canton, IL; PresSrCls; Band; Chrs; ChrhWkr; CncrtBnd; MrchBnd; Orch; PepBnd; SchPl; StuCncl; YthFlsp; SchPpr; Vocational Schl; Farming.

VOHS, Thomas; Galva Comm HS; Galva, IA; MrchBnd; PepBnd; SchPl; StuCncl; YthFlsp; Bsbl; Bsktbl; Ftbl; Trk; AmLegAwd; Dana College.

VOIE, Ellen C; Iola Scandinivia HS; Iola, WI; 6/56 HonRl; NatlFornLg; NHS; SchPl; SecStuCncl; RptrYrbk; EdSchPpr; SecPpCl; LetterBsktbl; LetterTrk; GAA;.

VOIGHT, Barbara S; Auburndale HS; Arpin, WI; Band; ChrhWkr; CmntyWkr; HonRl; YthFlsp; Treas4-H; FBLA; GerCl; LetterBsktbl; SecGAA; 4-HAwd;.

VOIGHT, Ken J; Antigo HS; Antigo, WI; SecTrsFrshCls; VPSophCls; PresJrCls; Aud/Vis; CmntyWkr; HonRl; JA; NatlSciFnd; ROTC; LetterSwmmng; College.

VOIGHT, Larry J; St Clement HS; Warren, MI; HonRl; NHS; PolWkr; StuCncl; StuGov; Bsbl; LetterBsktbl; LetterFtbl; LetterTrk; CchngActv; University; Psychology.

VOIGT, Dorothy A; Thornwood HS; Thornton, IL; 43/842 AFS; Chr; Chrl; HonRl; NHS; College; Medical Technology.

VOIGT, Kari L; Beulah HS; Zap, ND; 12/56 Chr; Chrl; Chrs; HonRl; SchPl; SchPpr; 4-H; FBLA; PresFHA; SecGerCl; PpCl; Trk; Chrldr; University; Vocation.

VOIGT, Paula K; Armstrong HS; Neenah, WI; 68/647 HospAde; NHS; NatlMeritCmnd; RedCrAde; Yrbk; EdSchPpr; FrCl; NCTE; Macalester College; Chemistry.

VOIGT, Sheryl D; Lincoln Park HS; Lincoln Park, MI; Band; DrmBgl; DrmMjrt; HonRl; StuCncl; Twrl; RptrYrbk; Yrbk; AmLegAwd; University Of Michigan; Dental Hygienist.

VOIGT, Steven P; Manitowoc Luth HS; Manitowoc, WI; 5/81 VPSrCls; Chr; Chrs; SchPl; StuCncl; Ftbl; RotaryAwd; Dr Martin Luth Col;teacher.

VOIGT, Virginia J; Wahpeton HS; Wahpeton, ND; Band; Chr; ChrhWkr; HonRl; NHS; Yrbk; FHA; TrsSophCls; Trk; IMSpt; Coll; Accounting.

VOISARD, Michael J; Marysville HS; Marysville, MI; ALBoysSt; ChrhWkr; DrmBgl; SchMus; SchPl; TchrAde; SciCl; Ftbl; Swmmng; University; Doctor.

VOLD, Rhonda L; Bottineau HS; Bottineau, ND; ALAGirlsSt; Chrs; CncrtBnd; PepBnd; SchPl; FFA; FHA; PpCl; LetterBsktbl; College; Social Work.

VOLDEN, Mark A; Paxton HS; Paxton, IL; 3/137 HonRl; NHS; NatlMeritCmnd; LetterBsktbl; CaptFtbl; AmLegAwd; CitAwd; Univ; Professional.

VOLESKY, Calvin; South Heart HS; Dickinson, ND; 6/25 TrsSophCls; ALBoysSt; Chr; ChrhWkr; HonRl; SchPl; StuGov; PpCl; Bsktbl; Trk; Trade; Vocational.

VOLESKY, Kenneth; South Heart HS; Belfield, ND; PresJrCls; HonRl; SchPl; Sdlty; StuCncl; PpCl; IMSpt; DanFAwd; PresAwd; Dickinson St Col; Bus.

VOLK, Dee A; West Richland Comm HS; Newton, IL; ChrhWkr; HonRl; LbryAde; SchPl; StuCncl; GAA; IMSpt; Business Careet.

VOLK, Joletta; St Gertrudes HS; Raleigh, ND; 3/26 Chrs; HonRl; NHS; SchMus; SchPl; SchPpr; GerCl; SpnCl; SciCl; Mary Coll; Nurse.

VOLK, Joletta; St Gertrudes Hs; Raleigh, ND; 3/27 Chrs; HonRl; NHS; SchMus; SchPl; SchPpr; GerCl; SpnCl; MthCl; SciCl; Mary College; Nursing.

VOLK, Jordan D; St Gertrudes HS; Shields, ND; Chrs; HonRl; NHS; RptrSchPpr; SpnCl; MthCl; SciCl; Bsktbl; LetterTrk; University; Professional.

VOLK, Katherine S; Fairbury Cropsey HS; Fairbury, IL; 17/99 DrlTm; SchPl; YthFlsp; SchPpr; GAA; Coll; Med Tech.

VOLK, Raymond E; Western Dubuque HS; Cascade, IA; 15/243 Band; Chrs; HonRl; MrchBnd; NHS; SctActv; StuGov; LetterBsktbl; LetterTrk; IMSpt; Univ Of Notre Dame; Engineering.

VOLK, Susan; East Richland Hs; Claremont, IL; HospAde; JrNHS; Sec4-H; LatCl; Olney Central College ; Nursing.

VOLKER, Mark A; Fort Zumwalt HS; St Peters, MO; 3/365 HonRl; TreasNHS; YthLg; EdSchPpr; Capt-Tennis; IMSpt; Univ Of Missouri; Accounting.

VOLKERT, Paul D; West Bend E HS; West Bend, WI; 3/230 HonRl; PresNHS; SchMus; SchPl; SptEdYrbk; PresKeyCl; LetterBsktbl; LetterFtbl; Glf; Trk; AmLegAwd; BauchLmbAwd; St Francis De Sales College; Psychology.

VOLKMANN, Mark; Bishop Noll Inst; Hammond, IN; 70/342 CmntyWkr; HonRl; OffAde; StuCncl; StuGov; PpCl; CchngActv; Purdue Univ; Medicine.

VOLKMER, Marilyn A; St Cecilia HS; Hastings, NE; Chrs; HonRl; LbryAde; NHS; SchMus; SchPl; TchrAde; FrCl; SpnCl; BttyCrckrAwd; Univ Of Northern Iowa; Language.

VOLKMUTH, John D; Cathedral HS; St Cloud, MN; 19/153 Band; CncrtBnd; MrchBnd; Orch; PepBnd; SchMus; LetterFtbl; LetterWrstlng; RotaryAwd; College; Math.

VOLKMUTH, Steve H; Apollo HS; St Cloud, MN; Aud/Vis; CmntyWkr; HonRl; Bsbl; Bsktbl; Ftbl; Glf; College; Anesthesia Nurse.

VOLLBRACHT, Roger D; Central HS; Clayton, IL; 3/76 TrsFrshCls; PresSophCls; HonRl; NHS; StuGov; 4-H; College.

VOLLE, Louis A; Mt Pulaski HS; Mt Pulaski, IL; Band; CncrtBnd; MrchBnd; PepBnd; 4-H; FFA; PpCl; 4-HAwd; Trade School; Mechanic.

VOLLE, Susan; Moberly Sr HS; Moberly, MO; 9/215 ChrhWkr; HonRl; LbryAde; NHS; TchrAde; FBLA; FHA; FTA; Northeast Missouri State Univ; Teacher.

VOLLMAN, Patricia J; Divine Child HS; Dearborn, MI; 3/170 Chr; HonRl; NHS; NatlThespSoc; SchMus; SchPl; StuCncl; Bsktbl; PPFtbl; Univiversity; Professional.

VOLLMER, Sharon S; Bishop Hogan HS; Kansas City, MO; 2/119 SecJrCls; HonRl; OffAde; SchMus; SchPl; StuGov; TchrAde; FrCl; PpCl; Bsktbl; Rockhurst College; Medical Technology.

VOLLMERHAUSEN, Susan L; Gabriel Richard HS; Wyandotte, MI; TrsSrCls; HonRl; LbryAde; NHS; SchAde; StuCncl; StuGov; EdSchPpr; College; Special Education.

VOLLMUTH, Rick; Bottineau HS; Bottineau, ND; SecSophCls; ALBoysSt; FFA; PpCl; SciCl; Ftbl; Trk; IMSpt; College; Medicine.

VOLMER, Michael W; Lyman HS; Presho, SD; VPJrCls; ALBoysSt; HonRl; NHS; EdSchPpr; LetterBsktbl; LetterFtbl; LetterTrk; College; Professional.

VOLNER, Enid I; Lesterville HS; Black, MO; Band; HonRl; JrNHS; NHS; PepBnd; SchMus; SchPl; RptrYrbk; EdYrBk; Trade School; Nurses Aid.

VOLOVSEK, Brenda; Superior Senior HS; Superior, WI; 20/540 HonRl; HospAde; NHS; StuCncl; SpnCl; PpCl; GAA;.

VOLP, Mary K; Benilde St Margarets HS; Robbinsdale, MN; Band; CncrtBnd; NHS; PepBnd; LetterTrk; CchngActv; GAA; PresAwd; Univ; Eningineer.

VOLTZ, Charles F; Wauwatosa East HS; Wauwatosa, WI; 7 430 ALBoysSt; HonRl; NHS; NatlMeritFnl; NatlMeritSF; SchAde; MthCl; Bsktbl; Ftbl; AmLegAwd; U Of Wi.

VOLZ, Bruce E; Norway Comm HS; Norway, IA; PresBand; Chrs; CncrtBnd; HonRl; MrchBnd; PepBnd; SchPl; RptrYrbk; LetterBsbl; LetterBsktbl; College; Agriculture.

VOLZ, Edward C; Bourbon HS; Leasburg, MO; VPJrCls; HonRl; NHS; SpnCl; MthCl; Trk; Coll; Geology.

VOLZ, Karen A; La Salle HS; Fairfax, IA; 13/139 Aud/Vis; ChrhWkr; HonRl; ModUN; NatlFornLg; NHS; SchPl; VPStuCncl; VPStuGov; RptrYrbk; U Of I; Law/political Science.

VOLZ, Pamela M; Stevens HS; Black Hawk, SD; 50/413 TrsSophCls; Band; MrchBnd; Orch; PepBnd; 4-H; GerCl; PpCl;.

VOLZKE, Marcia; Centennial HS; Waco, NE; 19/64 SecJrCls; Band; Chr; HonRl; NHS; TchrAde; CivCl; Chrldr; Univ Of Nebraska; Florist.

VOLZKE, Marcia J; Centennial HS; Waco, NE; 17/63 Chr; CncrtBnd; HonRl; NHS; StuCncl; YthFlsp; FHA; PpCl; University Of Nebraska; Horticulture.

VONADA, Damon R; Sylvan Unified HS; Sylvan Grove, KS; LetterTrk; College; Agriculture.

VON BERGEN, Lynann R; Big Foot HS; Walworth, WI; Chrs; ChrhWkr; HonRl; ModUN; SchMus; FrCl; Trk; GAA; IMSpt; 4-HAwd; Cl; Engineer Frenc.

VON BORSTEL, Robert M; George Washington HS; Chicago, IL; 6/495 HonRl; NHS; SctActv; StuGov; RptrSchPpr; SchPpr; FBLA; Illinois Inst Of Tech; Computer Science.

VONCKX, Joe A; Ashwaubenon HS; Green Bay, WI; Aud/Vis; Band; HonRl; MrchBnd; PepBnd; StuCncl; Bsbl; LetterBsktbl; LetterFtbl; IMSpt; Navy; Nuclear Power.

VONDAL, Paula K; Wahpeton HS; Wahpeton, ND; ALAGirlsSt; Band; CncrtBnd; HonRl; MrchBnd; SchPl; StuCncl; KeyCl; PpCl; Chrldr; Col; Vocation.

VON DE BUR, Joseph J; Griffin HS; Springfield, IL; SecSrCls; HonRl; StuCncl; RptrYrbk; Springfield College; Liberal Arts.

VONDERFECHT, Susan M; Holbrook HS; Holbrook, NE; 3/14 PresSrCls; Band; Chr; Chrs; ChrhWkr; HonRl; SchMus; TchrAde; FHA; College; Professional.

VONDER HAAR, Joseph F; St Louis University HS; St Louis, MO; HonRl; StuCncl; StuGov; RptrSchPpr; LetterFtbl; Wrstlng; CchngActv; College; Environmental Science.

VON DER SUMP, Susan K; Markesan HS; Dalton, WI; 2/114 Aud/Vis; Chrs; HonRl; Mdrgl; LetterTrk; Chrldr; GAA; IMSpt; 4-HAwd; College; Conservationist.

VONDRA, Jane M; Warren HS; Warren, IL; 1/63 Band; CncrtBnd; HonRl; MrchBnd; PepBnd; FHA; SecPpCl; GAA; Loras College; Medical Tech.

VONDRAS, Steven; Plattsmouth HS; Plattsmouth, NE; 31/138 PresSophCls; JA; StuGov; TchrAde; SptEdYrbk; SptEdSchPpr; 4-H; FFA; LetterFtbl; LetterTrk; U Of Nebraska; Civil Engineer.

VONDRASEK, Bobette J; Table Rock Public HS; Table Rock, NE; SecSrCls; HonRl; MrchBnd; SchPl; Twrl; PpCl; Chrldr; Dental Assistant.

VON FELDT, James L; Larned HS; Larned, KS; Band; HonRl; SctActv; TchrAde; RptrYrbk; SchPpr; GerCl; Ftbl; Wrstlng; Fort Hays State; Medicine.

VON HOLZEN, Tammy L; Lincoln HS; Wisconsin Rapids, WI; HonRl; SchPpr; SpnCl; PpCl; SciCl; University; Professional.

VON ITTER, Maureen; Warren Woods HS; Wareen, MI; 33/289 Band; CncrtBnd; HonRl; MrchBnd; NHS; Orch; PepBnd; SchMus; SctActv; Trk; GAA; General Motors Inst; Ind Adm.

VON KNOBELSDORFF, Renate; Goodhue 253 HS; Goodhue, MN; 6/76 TrsJrCls; HonRl; NHS; SchPl; StuCncl; EdYrBk; 4-H; FHA; GerCl; 4-HAwd; Army; Interpreter.

VON MINDEN, Kim D; Ponca Public HS; Ponca, NE; 1/28 PresSrCls; HonRl; NHS; PresStuCncl; PresPpCl; Bsktbl; LetterTrk; BttyCrckrAwd; 4-HAwd; Univ Of Nebraska; Accounting.

VON REIN, Joan; North Bend Central HS; North Bend, NE; HonRl; FTA; PpCl; Trk; Meth Hosp School Of Nursing; Rn.

VON RUDEN, Mary E; Mayville Portland Public HS; Hatton, ND; ALAGirlsSt; Chr; HonRl; SchPl; StuCncl; 4-H; PresFHA; LetterTrk; GAA; 4-HAwd; Art.

VON RUEDEN, Michelle M; Wahpeton HS; Wahpeton, ND; 5/139 AFS; NHS; StuCncl; EdYrBk; SchPpr; GerCl; Tennis; IMSpt; DARAwd; RotaryAwd; Nd St Sch Science; Medical Field.

VON SEGGERN, Randy E; Wisner Pilger HS; Wisner, NE; VPSophCls; HonRl; StuGov; YthFlsp; SpnCl; LetterFtbl; Trk; Wrstlng; CchngActv; University.

VON SOOSTEN, Kay A; Unified Dist #248; Girard, KS; Chr; ChrhWkr; HonRl; HospAde; NHS; PolWkr; RedCrAde; SchPpr; 4-H; FHA; College; Home Economics.

VON SOOSTEN, Kay A; Girard HS; Girard, KS; ALAGirlsSt; HonRl; HospAde; NHS; PolWkr; FHA; PpCl; Trk; 4-HAwd; CitAwd; Coll; Home Ec.

VON SPRECKELSEN, Lyle D; Clay Center Public HS; Clay Center, NE; 4/30 Band; ChrhWkr; HonRl; NHS; SchPl; StuCncl; YthFlsp; LetterBsktbl; CaptFtbl; Trk; 4-HAwd; Col; Professional.

VONSTROH, Carol E; Lockwood HS; Lockwood, MO; 17/42 PresChr; ChrhWkr; HonRl; ModUN; SchPl; StuCncl; PresFHA; PpCl; CaptChrldr; PPFtbl; Univ; Nursing.

VON TERSCH, Paul B; Denison Comm HS; Denison, IA; NHS; KeyCl; LetterFtbl; LetterTrk; ChmnWrstlng; IMSpt; College; Professional.

VOORHEIS, Philip J; Oak Hill Jr Sr HS; Swayzee, IN; 43/156 Band; Chrl; NHS; PepBnd; SchMus; SchPl; University; Accounting.

VORACEK, Kris K; Yankton Sr HS; Yankton, SD; Band; HonRl; NHS; Quill&Scroll; SctActv; StuCncl; RptrYrbk; RptrSchPpr; College; Professional.

VORBECK, John C; De Smet Jesuit HS; St Louis County, MO; HonRl; PolWkr; Yrbk; LetterSocr; LetterTrk; University; Professional.

VORDERBRUGGEN, Thomas J; Al Brook HS; Brookston, MN; 1/60 HonRl; Yrbk; 4-H; FHA; Bsktbl; CaptTrk; BauchLmbAwd; 4-HAwd; PresAwd;.

VORDERER, Mary Jo; Mt Assisi Acad; Worth, IL; 40/189 HonRl; RptrSchPpr; SchPpr; Junior College; Praiologic Technology.

VOREIS, Diane L; Hinckley Big Rock HS; Somonauk, IL; 1/75 VPBand; NatlFornLg; NHS; SchPl; YthFlsp; RptrYrbk; RptrSchPpr; 4-H; LetterTrk; 4-HAwd; University.

VORHES, Joel A; Sheldon Community HS; Sheldon, IA; Chr; HonRl; PolWkr; StuCncl; RptrSchPpr; SchPpr; SpnCl; SciCl; Bsktbl; IMSpt;.

VORHES, Mary E; Menomonie HS; Menomonie, WI; 1/228 Chr; HonRl; 4-H; LetterTrk; CchngActv; GAA; ChmbCommrsAwd; 4-HAwd; GodCntryAwd; RotaryAwd; Augustana College; Special Education.

VORISEK, Robert F; Marmion Mil Academy; Fox River Grove, IL; 19/69 SecSrCls; ALBoysSt; Chrs; HonRl; ROTC; SchAde; SchMus; SchPl; SctActv; Sdlty; Duke University; Pre Dentistryt.

VORK, Norman L; Ogilvie HS; Ogilvie, MN; 7/54 PresFrshCls; Chr; HonRl; SchMus; SchPl; RptrYrbk; RptrSchPpr; LetterFtbl; St Cloud State Coll; Art.

VORLAND, Galen; Chokio Alberta HS; Morris, MN; HonRl; StuCncl; SptEdYrbk; Yrbk; 4-H; St Cloud State College; Bus Finance.

VORLAND, Ronald D; North Central HS; Clear Lake, IA; VPFrshCls; VPSophCls; VPJrCls; VPSrCls; PolWkr; RptrSchPpr; Ftbl; College; English.

VORNHAGEN, Jeffry C; Franklin HS; Livonia, MI; LitMag; TchrAde; U Of Mi; Special Ed.

VORTHERMS, Daniel T; Spalding HS; Hospers, IA; Band; ChrhWkr; CncrtBnd; DrmMjrt; HonRl; MrchBnd; PepBnd; SctActv; College; Business.

VORWALD, Lorna J; Leo HS; Holy Cross, IA; 2/38 Chrs; CmntyWkr; HonRl; SchMus; LatCl; PpCl; Bsktbl; Chrldr; IMSpt; College; Stewardess.

VOS, David L; Edsel Ford HS; Dearborn, MI; Chrs; ChrhWkr; HonRl; NatlFornLg; NatlMeritSF; Calvin Col; Biologist.

VOS, Debie S; Pella Christian HS; Pella, IA; 20/83 Band; CncrtBnd; LbryAde; MrchBnd; PepBnd; SchPl; PpCl; IMSpt; College; Professional.

VOS, Larry D; Chander Lake Wilson HS; Slayton, MN; LbryAde; SchPl; TreasYthFlsp; 4-H; BttyCrckrAwd; Northwestern Clg; Navy Then Minister.

VOS, Stuart M; Pella Community HS; Pella, IA; 10/117 PresSrCls; NHS; NatlMeritCmnd; PresNatlThespSoc; SchMus; SchPl; PresStuCncl; Ftbl; Trk; Ia State Univ; Political Science.

VOSBURG, Cynthia E; Sedgwick HS; Sedgwick, KS; 5/30 ALAGirlsSt; HonRl; TreasStuCncl; TchrAde; Yrbk; TreasPpCl; Bsktbl; Chrldr; GAA; PPFtbl; College; Secretary.

VOSBURG, Polly A; Hudson HS; Hudson, MI; 4/125 Chrs; HonRl; NHS; SchPl; TchrAde; Chrldr; Univ;.

VOSE, Julie; Mitchell Sr HS; Mitchell, SD; 1/300 ALAGirlsSt; Band; CncrtBnd; HonRl; JrNHS; MrchBnd; NHS; SchPpr; SpnCl; IMSpt; Coll; Micro Bio.

VOSEJPKA, Lori A; Derham Hall HS; St Paul, MN; Band; Chr; Chrs; JA; NHS; SchMus; SchPl; StuCncl; RptrSchPpr; College; Professional.

VOSEN, Dennis P; La Farge Public HS; La Farge, WI; 4/34 TrsFrshCls; PresJrCls; Band; Chrs; CncrtBnd; HonRl; PolWkr; SptEdYrbk; FrCl; LetterFtbl; Col; Pro.

VOSIK, Richard J; Ryan HS; Omaha, NE; Univ; Accountant.

VOSKUIL, Joseph C; Cedar Grove HS; Cedar Grove, WI; 9/89 HstFrshCls; Band; Chrs; ChrhWkr; HonRl; SctActv; StuCncl; StuGov; YthFlsp; RptrYrbk; Yrbk; SchPpr; Bsbl; Bsktbl; Milwaukee Business Inst; Computer Programer.

VOSS, Betty J; Eddyville Comm HS; Eddyville, IA; PresSrCls; Band; CncrtBnd; HonRl; LbryAde; MrchBnd; OffAde; PepBnd; SchPl; PresPpCl; Northeast Mo St Univ; Business Ed.

VOSS, Brian; Parkersburg Comm HS; Parkersburg, IA; Chr; Chrs; ChrhWkr; CmntyWkr; HonRl; YthFlsp; Yrbk; Bsbl; Bsktbl; Glf; College; Bookeeping.

VOSS, Bruce K; Lu Verne Comm HS; Lu Verne, IA; 2/13 VPFrshCls; PresJrCls; Chrs; HonRl; StuCncl; RptrYrbk; Bsbl; Trk; Iowa State Univ; Bus Admin.

VOSS, Charlene A; Washington HS; Washington, MO; HonRl; Sdlty; StuCncl; SecFBLA; FHA; East Central Jr Coll; Acct.

VOSS, Christine M; St Mary HS; Storm Lake, IA; TrsFrshCls; Chr; Chrs; HonRl; HospAde; SchMus; RptrYrbk; RptrSchPpr; Bsktbl; Trk; Trade Sch; Nursing Profession.

VOSS, Dale R; Manual HS; Peoria, IL; 14/329 ChrhWkr; HonRl; JA; NatlMeritCmnd; Illinois State Univ; Accounting.

VOSS, David J; Auoha Community HS; Hancock, IA; NHS; Yrbk; LetterFtbl; BauchLmbAwd; Ia St U; Engineering.

VOSS, Debra E; Sullivan HS; Sullivan, MO; 53/159 HonRl; TchrAde; 4-H; FTA; SpnCl; 4-HAwd; Clge; Pro.

VOSS, Dennis; Washington Senior Hs; Washington, MO; 21/267 HonRl; JA; NHS; SciCl; JAAwd; College; Electrical Engineer.

VOSS, Diana E; Union HS; Beaufort, MO; TrsJrCls; HonRl; HospAde; LbryAde; RptrYrbk; FFA; FrCl; IMSpt; PPFtbl; University; Physical Therapy.

VOSS, Jane E; Lakota Public HS; Lakota, ND; TrsJrCls; ALAGirlsSt; Band; Chr; HonRl; NHS; StuCncl; RptrSchPpr; FHA; PpCl; Univ; Professional.

VOSS, Janice M; St Pius X HS; Arnold, MO; 10/115 HonRl; NHS; IMSpt; College; Vocation.

VOSS, Jean C; Rhinelander HS; Rhinelander, WI; 30/330 AFS; ChrhWkr; CncrtBnd; HonRl; LitMag; PolWkr; YthFlsp; GerCl; LetterSwmmng; IMSpt; U Of Wi Madison; Botanist.

VOSS, Jerry L; Grundy Center Comm HS; Grundy Center, IA; 80 Chrs; StuCncl; PpCl; LetterBsbl; CaptBsktbl; CaptFtbl; Glf; Tennis; LetterTrk; Cornell Clg; Bus Maj.

VOSS, John M; Rock Island HS; Rock Island, IL; NHS; Quill&Scroll; EdSchPpr; SpnCl; Augustana Coll; Journalism.

VOSS, Jonathan C; Northwestern Prep; Green Bay, WI; StuCncl; SchPpr; PpCl; LetterBsbl; LetterBsktbl; LetterFtbl; Northwestern College; Minister.

VOSS, Judith L; Covenant Christian HS; Jenison, MI; Chr; HonRl; HospAde; NatlMeritCmnd; NatlMeritSchl; RptrSchPpr; Calvin College; Medical Field.

VOSS, Karen J; Bishop Mc Namara HS; Saint Anne, IL; 84/173 Chr; Chrs; ChrhWkr; HonRl; SctActv; CivCl; Bsbl; GAA; IMSpt; ALAGirlsSt; Col; Social Worker.

VOSS, Kimberly A; Petoskey HS; Petoskey, MI; ChrhWkr; DrmBgl; HonRl; NHS; SchAde; SecStuCncl; TchrAde; PresYthFlsp; FrCl; PpCl; Mi St U; Elem Ed.

VOSS, Mark W; Laker HS; Pigeon, MI; 16/146 HonRl; NHS; NatlMeritSF; LetterBsbl; LetterBsktbl; LetterFtbl; LetterTennis; LetterTrk; Western Mi; Bus.

VOSS, Martin A; Worthington HS; Worthington, MN; 68/305 PresFrshCls; PresSophCls; PresSrCls; Chr; JrNHS; StuCncl; GerCl; LetterTrk; LetterWrstlng; IMSpt; Worthington Comm Coll.

VOSS, Melissa M; Villa De Chantal HS; Rock Island, IL; Chr; HonRl; SchMus; SchPl; StuCncl; StuGov; RptrYrbk; Yrbk; RptrSchPpr; FrCl; College; Professional.

VOSS, Robert J; Thornridge HS; So Holland, IL; 141/684 Aud/Vis; CmntyWkr; HonRl; NatlFornLg; Quill&Scroll; RptrSchPpr; SchPpr; Southern Ill Univ; Journalism.

VOSS, Sherri L; Hastings HS; Hastings, MI; HonRl; NatlThespSoc; StuCncl; StuGov; TchrAde; YthLg; Yrbk; Pres4-H; FrCl; SciCl; PPFtbl; Mi State Univ Lyman Briggs; Doctor.

VOSS, Terrence G; Memorial HS; Eau Claire, WI; Band; CncrtBnd; HonRl; PepBnd; SchMus; GerCl; Swmmng; Tennis; Trk; Wrstlng; Coll; Teach.

VOSSLER, Kimberly A; Wishek Public HS; Wishek, ND; 1/40 VPFrshCls; PresSophCls; ChrhWkr; HonRl; NHS; SchPl; YthFlsp; PpCl; College; Accounting.

VOTA, Martin; Taylorville HS; Taylorville, IL; 100/275 Band; Chr; CmntyWkr; HonRl; NatlThespSoc; Orch; SchMus; RptrSchPpr; 4-H; KeyCl; Ill State Univ; Tv Broadcast.

VOTAPKA, Nancy J; Decatur Community HS; Oberlin, KS; AFS; ALBoysSt; ALAGirlsSt; CmntyWkr; HonRl; FBLA; FHA; FNA; FSA; FTA; Ks St Univ; Pre School Educ.

VOTAVA, Kenneth F; Park River HS; Grafton, ND; ALBoysSt; Band; Chrs; CncrtBnd; HonRl; MrchBnd; NHS; PepBnd; FFA; LetterFtbl; Univ; Vocation.

VOTAW, Stanley J; Pennville HS; Pennville, IN; 1/40 PresFrshCls; TrsJrCls; TrsSrCls; ALBoysSt; PresBand; VPNHS; SchPl; StuCncl; LetterBsbl; AmLegAwd; Purdue Univ; Pharmacy.

VOTE, Cindy L; Lake View Auburn HS; Auburn, IA; 5/44 SecTrsSophCls; SecTrsJrCls; Chrs; HonRl; SchMus; SchPl; 4-H; Bsktbl; Trk; 4-HAwd; Ellsworth Comm College; Accountant.

VOTE, James J; Holy Redeemer HS; Detroit, MI; 74/190 PresSrCls; Aud/Vis; HonRl; NHS; StuGov; TchrAde; RptrYrbk; LetterFtbl; IMSpt; LionAwd; College; Veterinarian.

VOTIPKA, Ronald T; Exeter Public HS; Exeter, NE; SecTrsSophCls; Band; HonRl; Yrbk; 4-H; FFA; Ftbl; AmLegAwd; 4-HAwd; PresAwd; Univ; Prof.

VOTRA, Charlene K; Wabash HS; Wabash, IN; CmntyWkr; NatlFornLg; Twrl; SciCl; GAA; Manchester; Social Worker.

VOTRUBA, Colleen M; Hemingford HS; Hemingford, NE; Chrs; HonRl; NHS; SchMus; SchPl; StuCncl; Twrl; Yrbk; Trk; Chrldr; TreasGAA; AmLegAwd; Lincoln Schl Of Commerce; Secretary.

VOTSMIER, Terrie; Jacksonville HS; Jacksonville, IL; 12/352 Band; HonRl; Orch; Twrl; YthFlsp; Yrbk; LatCl; PPFtbl; Northeast Missouri State Univ; Music Teach.

VOVOLKA, Jay; Glenbard West Hs; Glen Ellyn, IL; TrsJrCls; TrsSrCls; Chr; HonRl; StuGov; Yrbk; LetterFtbl; Trk; GodCntryAwd; Illinois State U;biological Scince.

VOYLES, Delinda J; Westville HS; Westville, IL; Aud/Vis; Chrs; DrlTm; HonRl; SctActv; RptrSchPpr; SpnCl; SciCl; Tennis; GAA; Coll; Nurse.

VOYTUS, Karla K; Marissa HS; Coulterville, IL; 5/54 TrsFrshCls; Band; ChrhWkr; CmntyWkr; CncrtBnd; HonRl; PresNHS; OffAde; SchMus; StuCncl; 4-H; FFA; PpCl; Bsbl; Chrldr; Murry St College; Special Educ.

VOYVODIC, Blair J; Hinsdale Central HS; Hinsdale, IL; 52/583 VPSrCls; AFS; ChrhWkr; CmntyWkr; HonRl; NHS; NatlMeritCmnd; PolWkr; SchPl; College; Science.

VRAA, Richard G; Goodrider HS; Goodridge, MN; VPFrshCls; VPJrCls; ChrhWkr; CmntyWkr; HonRl; VPStuCncl; YthFlsp; FFA; LetterFtbl; LetterWrstlng; Trade Sch; Lawyer.

VRAB, James L; Thornton Fractional South HS; Lansing, IL; 4 Band; Chr; CncrtBnd; HonRl; MrchBnd; NatlFornLg; NHS; NatlMeritSF; PepBnd; University Of Illinois; Music.

VRABEC, Michael P; Wayland Academy; Beaver Dam, WI; 10/70 HonRl; OffAde; RedCrAde; SchPl; RptrSchPpr; SchPpr; KeyCl; Bsbl; Bsktbl; Ftbl; Tennis; Univ Of Wisconsin; Engineering.

VRANEY, Serene M; W Chicago Comm HS; West Chicago, IL; 111/340 HonRl; 4-H; Loyola Univ; Dental Hygienist.

VRATIL, James; Larned HS; Larned, KS; 3/100 PresJrCls; ALBoysSt; Band; PresNHS; StuCncl; YthFlsp; SptEdSchPpr; Bsktbl; Ftbl; Glf; Kan Univ; Engin.

VRBKA, Colleen M; East Butler HS; Brainard, NE; 6/38 ALAGirlsSt; CncrtBnd; HonRl; LbryAde; NHS; RedCrAde; RptrYrbk; 4-H; FHA; PpCl; Univ Of Ne Lincoln; Human Development.

VRBKA, Michael D; Shelby Public HS; Shelby, NE; TrsSophCls; TrsJrCls; Aud/Vis; Chrs; HonRl; Yrbk; Trk;.

VREDENBURG, Cynthia; Mandan Senior HS; Mandan, ND; HonRl; NHS; SchPl; StuCncl; Bsktbl; Glf; Trk; Chrldr; GAA; College; Professional.

VREELAND, Diana M; Hillsdale HS; Hillsdale, MI; DrmMjrt; LitMag; MrchBnd; TchrAde; Twrl; FrCl; LetterTennis; GAA; IMSpt; Central Michigan Univ; Journalism.

VREELAND, Juanita A; Burr Oak Comm HS; Burr Oak, MI; 5/34 VPFrshCls; HonRl; PepBnd; SchPl; 4-H; Bsktbl; PPFtbl; 4-HAwd; Coll; Phy Ed.

VREELAND, Sally J; Lincoln HS; Wisconsin Rapids, WI; Chrs; ChrhWkr; HonRl; Quill&Scroll; StuCncl; RptrSchPpr; SchPpr; SpnCl; SciCl; PPFtbl; Col; Primary Ed.

VREUGDENHIL, Brad W; Akron Community HS; Akron, IA; SecTrsFrshCls; SecTrsSophCls; ALBoysSt; PresChrs; TreasChrhWkr; HonRl; NHS; VPNatlThespSoc; PresStuCncl; PresFFA; Sasu; Farming.

VREUGDENHIL, Max; Dakota Christian HS; Gorsica, SD; PresSophCls; ALBoysSt; ChrhWkr; HonRl; ModUN; NHS; SchPl; StuCncl; EdSchPpr; PpCl; Calvin College; Biology.

VREUGDENHIL, Max W; Dakota Christian HS; Corsica, SD; 1/20 PresSophCls; ALBoysSt; HonRl; SchPl; StuCncl; EdSchPpr; SptEdSchPpr; Trk; IMSpt; Calvin Col; Biology Or Journalsim.

VRHEL, Janet A; Morton West HS; Lyons, IL; HonRl; SecJA; SecStuCncl; Twrl; RptrSchPpr; SpnCl; Northern Ill Univ; Political Science.

VRIEZE, Judith J; Baldwin Woodville HS; Baldwin, WI; Chr; Chrl; Chrs; Business School; Secretary.

VRIEZEN, James; Delevan Darien HS; Delevan, WI; Band; CncrtBnd; RptrSchPpr; SchPpr; LetterBsktbl; LetterFtbl; Swmmng; Trk; IMSpt; Univ; Teach.

VROMAN, Dawn M; Alleman HS; Rock Island, IL; Band; CncrtBnd; HonRl; LitMag; MrchBnd; NHS; PepBnd; SchMus; Augastana College; Psychology Major.

VROMAN, Marc R; Tri County HS; Hancock, WI; ALBoysSt; HonRl; JrNHS; NHS; Bsktbl; College; Engineering.

VROOMAN, Karen S; West Holt HS; Atkinson, NE; ALAGirlsSt; Chr; DrlTm; HonRl; LbryAde; NHS; SchPl; StuGov; CivCl; PpCl; Bus Sch.

VRTIS, Ann M; St Edward HS; St Charles, IL; HonRl; NHS; NatlSciFnd; SctActv; StuCncl; FshEdYrbk; MthCl; SciCl; Trk; Univ; Medical Engineer.

VRUGGINK, Debra; Zeeland Hs; Zeeland, MI; 3/186 Chr; ChrhWkr; CmntyWkr; HonRl; LbryAde; ModUN; SchMus; SctActv; YthFlsp; LatCl; Collge Health Pro Or Elementaryedc.

VRUNO, Nancy J; Maria HS; Chicago, IL; 43/301 HonRl; HospAde; Pres4-H; SpnCl; 4-HAwd; De Paul Univ; Law.

VRYHOF, Tom A; Calvin Chr HS; Wyoming, MI; Aud/Vis; Chr; HonRl; JrNHS; NHS; NatlMeritCmnd; SchAde; FBLA; GerCl; Bsktbl; Davenport Coll; Accounting.

VRZAK, Cindy L; Turkey Valley HS; Waucoma, IA; Chr; ChrhWkr; CmntyWkr; HonRl; 4-H; SpnCl; LetterTrk; GodCntryAwd; College; Special Educ.

VUKELIC, Jelena; George Washington HS; Chicago, IL; 15/495 HonRl; SecNHS; TchrAde; RptrYrbk; LatCl; Tennis; Trk; GAA; College; Pharmacy.

VULGAMOTT, Judith E; Savannah HS; Savannah, MO; VPFrshCls; SecSophCls; SecJrCls; Chr; HonRl; NHS; OffAde; RedCrAde; SchMus; StuCncl; TchrAde; SchPpr; FrCl; PpCl; University; Journalism.

VUYLSTEKE, Gerard G; Fitzgerald HS; Warren, MI; HonRl; NHS; NatlMeritFnl; NatlMeritSchl; TchrAde; Bsbl; Bsktbl; Glf; CaptSwmmng; College; Forestry.

VYAS, Usha; Rich East HS; Park Forest, IL; CmntyWkr; DrlTm; HonRl; Purdue Univ; Medicine.

VYHANEK, James; Oak Forest HS; Oak Forest, IL; ChrhWkr; HonRl; LitMag; NHS; StuCncl; GerCl; AmLegAwd; Concordia Teachers College; Ministry.

W

WAAGMEESTER, Susan J; Baltic HS; Baltic, SD; 1/24 ALAGirlsSt; Band; Chrs; HonRl; SecNHS; SchPl; 4-H; PresFHA; PpCl; Trk; U Of Sd; Elem Educ.

WAALEN, Mary A; Hudson HS; Hudson, WI; AFS; Band; Chrs; ChrhWkr; CncrtBnd; MrchBnd; NatlFornLg; SchMus; SchPpr; AmLegAwd; College.

WAATTI, Irene L; Hartland HS; Howell, MI; 10/157 Band; Chrs; HonRl; JrNHS; NHS; Orch; Ferris State College; Pharmacy.

WACASER, John D; Arlington Hts HS; Arlington Hts, IL; 75/600 HonRl; SctActv; GerCl; Univ Of Chicago; Law.

WACH, Michael J; Lyons Twp HS; Western Springs, IL; AFS; HonRl; NHS; Cornell Univ; Horticulture.

WACHA, Darlene; Wyndmere HS; Wyndmere, ND; Band; Chr; CncrtBnd; HonRl; MrchBnd; PepBnd; SchAde; FHA; Trk; Trade School.

WACHAL, Julia R; Prairie HS; Cedar Rapids, IA; HonRl; JrNHS; TchrAde; YthFlsp; SecFTA; GerCl; Univ Of Northern Iowa; Special Education.

WACHSMUTH, Cynthia A; Wausau East HS; Wausau, WI; 25/295 AFS; ChrhWkr; CmntyWkr; HonRl; HospAde; NHS; RedCrAde; Yrbk; Univ Of Wisconsin; Med Technologist.

WACHTEL, Howard K; Buffalo Grove HS; Buffalo Grove, IL; 9/290 VPFrshCls; HonRl; JA; NHS; NatlMeritFnl; NatlMeritSchl; SchMus; MthCl; Clge; Math.

WACHTEL, Timothy J; J D Darnall HS; Geneseo, IL; 5/215 JA; NHS; StuCncl; YthLg; SptEdYrbk; SciCl; LetterFtbl; LetterGlf; LetterWrstlng; Univ Of Illinois; Surgeon.

WACHTER, Gretchen; St Pius X HS; Kansas City, MO; 8/136 VPSophCls; DrlTm; HonRl; HospAde; NHS; OffAde; StuCncl; EdYrBk; RptrSchPpr; CivCl; U Of Mo Columbia; Business Adm.

WACHTER, Laura J; Rich Central HS; Matteson, IL; Band; CncrtBnd; HonRl; MrchBnd; PepBnd; 4-H; DanFAwd; Northern Illinois Univ; Nursing.

WACKER, Curtis; Plainview Public HS; Plainview, NE; Chr; Chrs; HonRl; NHS; Quill&Scroll; SchMus; SchPl; Bsktbl; Ftbl; Concordia Teachers Coll; Coach.

WACKER, Joanna M; Klemme Community HS; Garner, IA; SecFrshCls; TrsSophCls; SecJrCls; ChrhWkr; HonRl; HospAde; LbryAde; NHS; TchrAde; Bsktbl; Trk; Marycrest College; Nursing.

WACKER, Patrick R; Jefferson HS; Bloomington, MN; NHS; LetterBsbl; LetterBsktbl; LetterFtbl; College; Engineering.

WACKERIE, Rex B; La Ville HS; Lapaz, IN; Band; SpnCl; Glf; IMSpt; Notre Dame; Science.

WACKERLE, Cynthia D; Washington Sr HS; Sioux Falls, SD; Chr; HonRl; NatlMeritFnl; NatlThespSoc; Quill&Scroll; SchPl; EdSchPpr; GerCl; SpnCl; College; Math.

WACKERMAN, Thomas J; Brother Rice HS; Troy, MI; 12/200 TrsFrshCls; TrsSophCls; TrsJrCls; HonRl; NatlFornLg; PresNHS; SchPl; TreasStuCncl; SptEdYrbk; LetterFtbl; Univ Of Michigan; Archetecture.

WACKERNAGEL, Jane M; Montague HS; Montaque, MI; Band; CncrtBnd; HonRl; MrchBnd; NHS; PepBnd; Bsktbl; Glf; Chrldr; GAA; Cntrl Mi Univ; Nursing.

WACLAWEK, Barbara J; Whiting HS; Whiting, IN; 15/103 Band; CncrtBnd; MrchBnd; NHS; PepBnd; TchrAde; FTA; SpnCl; GAA; Univ; X Ray Tech.

WADAS, Michael A; St Marys HS; Clinton, IA; 8/50 ALBoysSt; HonRl; NatlFornLg; PresNatlMeritCmnd; VPStuCncl; SptEdYrbk; LetterFtbl; LetterTrk; U Of Ia.

WADDELL, Benita R; Healy HS; Pierz, MN; Chrs; FHA; Chrldr; St Cloud Voc; Typographer.

WADDELL, Jeanette L; Newton Comm HS; Newton, IL; Chrs; ChrhWkr; DrlTm; HonRl; MrchBnd; NHS; SctActv; YthFlsp; FBLA; SecFTA; PpCl; LetterTennis; GAA; Eastern Illinois Univ; Special Educ.

WADDELOW, Daniel R; Mt Morris HS; Mt Morris, IL; PresFrshCls; VPSophCls; HonRl; StuCncl; Bsktbl; LetterFtbl; LetterTrk; Ill State Univ; Aeronautics.

WADDINGTON, Tracy L; Assumption HS; Pana, IL; 5/40 HonRl; NHS; NatlThespSoc; SchPl; EdYrBk; FFA; Ftbl; Lakeland Jr Col; Agriculture.

WADDINGTON, Tracy L; Assumption HS; Para, IL; 7/40 Band; CncrtBnd; HonRl; NHS; PepBnd; StuCncl; EdYrBk; FFA; LetterFtbl; Lakeland Jr College; Farmer.

WADDLE, Barbara A; Waverly HS; Lincoln, NE; 19/100 HonRl; Quill&Scroll; TchrAde; RptrYrbk; PresGerCl; Business School; Secretary.

WADDLE, Sheryl M; Superior HS; Superior, NE; TrsSophCls; LetterBand; ChrhWkr; MrchBnd; VPStuCncl; RptrSchPpr; SchPpr; PresFHA; PpCl; LetterIMSpt; Col ; Nurse.

WADE, Constance; Anderson HS; Anderson, IN; HonRl; JrNHS; NHS; OffAde; SchAde; TchrAde; 4-H; FrCl; PpCl; 4-HAwd; College; Prof.

WADE, Gordon E; Shabbona HS; Malta, IL; 3/45 PresJrCls; ChrhWkr; CmntyWkr; HonRl; NHS; OffAde; SchAde; StuGov; YthFlsp; 4-H; PpCl; Bsbl; Bsktbl; College; Farm.

WADE, Gwendolyn; Covert HS; Covert, MI; SecFrshCls; SecSophCls; Chrs; ChrhWkr; HonRl; JA; SctActv; StuCncl; StuGov; TchrAde; Michigan State Univ; Business.

WADE, Jacqualine R; Clifton Central HS; Clifton, IL; 15/128 SecSophCls; ALAGirlsSt; Band; Chrs; CaptDrlTm; NHS; Pres4-H; PresFTA; GAA; 4-HAwd; Mennonite Hosp School Of Nursing; Reg Nurse.

WADE, Karen S; Weeping Water HS; Weeping Water, NE; CncrtBnd; HonRl; VPNHS; StuCncl; EdYrBk; RptrSchPpr; PpCl; LetterBsktbl; LetterTrk; PresGAA; College.

WADE, Kevin E; Perry Lecompton HS; Grantville, KS; VPJrCls; HonRl; LbryAde; NHS; SctActv; TchrAde; RptrSchPpr; 4-H; LetterBsktbl; LetterFtbl; LetterTrk; College; Professional.

WADE, Mary J; Linden HS; Linden, MI; HospAde; LbryAde; SctActv; SpnCl; Mid Michigan Jr Clg; Licensed Practical Nrs.

WADE, Michael R; Delta C7 HS; Bragg City, MO; ALBoysSt; Band; HonRl; EdYrBk; FFA; FTA; PpCl; GodCntryAwd;.

WADE, Nina S; Malta Bend R V HS; Malta Bend, MO; 3/20 ALAGirlsSt; Band; Chrs; HonRl; JrNHS; VPNHS; SchPl; SecStuCncl; EdYrBk; FHA; MthCl; PpCl; SciCl; College; Radiology.

WADE, Robbin; Williamsburg HS; Williamsburg, IA; CncrtBnd; HonRl; NHS; SchPl; StuCncl; TchrAde; Twrl; RptrYrbk; Chrldr; GAA; Coll; Professional.

WADE, Susan L; Bloomington HS; Bloomington, IL; 10/391 SecFrshCls; Chr; ChrhWkr; HonRl; SchPl; StuCncl; GerCl; MthCl; CaptChrldr; DARAwd; Coll.

WADE, Theresa A; Berkeley Sr HS; Berkeley, MO; 6/265 HonRl; NHS; Quill&Scroll; SpnCl; PpCl; LetterTennis; GAA; U Of Mo.

WADE, Theresa L; Huntington North HS; Huntington, IN; Chr; Chrl; HospAde; JrNHS; SchMus; 4-H; PpCl; Nurses School St Joseph Hospital; Nurse.

WADE, William E; St Johns Cathedral HS; Milwaukee, WI; 20/151 ChrhWkr; CmntyWkr; HonRl; StuCncl; StuGov; SciCl; Bsktbl; Ftbl; Trk; BauchLmbAwd; Univ; Lung Research.

WADEKAMPER, Debra A; Good Counsel Academy; Mankato, MN; StuCncl; RptrYrbk; RptrSchPpr; FrCl; Univ Of Wisconsin; Human Behavior.

WADERICH, Renita R; Dow City Arion HS; Dow City, IA; 2/30 Band; Chr; Chrs; CncrtBnd; HonRl; MrchBnd; NHS; StuCncl; TchrAde; Yrbk; PpCl; LetterBsbl; CaptBsktbl; IMSpt; Western Iowa Tech; Accounting.

WADHAMS, Jane M; Huron HS; Huron, SD; Band; Chr; ChrhWkr; JrNHS; SchMus; StuGov; RptrYrbk; FHA; PpCl; Trade School.

WADLE, Frank A; Southeast Warren HS; Lacona, IA; 7/54 Band; ChrhWkr; CncrtBnd; HonRl; MrchBnd; PepBnd; SchPpr; FFA; ;farming.

WADLE, Marge L; Southeast Warren HS; Lacona, IA; 6/52 Band; ChrhWkr; CncrtBnd; HonRl; MrchBnd; PepBnd; Yrbk; FshEdSchPpr; Hand Crafting.

WADLEIGH, Alan D; Madison Public HS; Madison, MN; 4/86 ALBoysSt; Chrs; HonRl; JrNHS; NHS; SptEdSchPpr; Bsktbl; Ftbl; CaptGlf; KiwanAwd; St Cloud State Univ; Business Educ.

WADMAN, Gary A; Walter P Chrysler Mem HS; New Castle, IN; 16/352 PresSophCls; PresJrCls; VPSrCls; CncrtBnd; MrchBnd; NHS; Orch; SchMus; StuCncl; Ball State University; Music.

WADMAN, Robert; Thornridge Hs; Dolton, IL; MthCl; JETSAwd; College;computers Or Engineering.

WADSWORTH, Joni D; Charlestown HS; Charlestown, IN; 36/225 ChrhWkr; HospAde; SchAde; TchrAde; FBLA; FHA; Indiana Univ Se; Nursing Profession.

WADSWORTH, Larry J; El Paso HS; El Paso, IL; 3/80 PresFrshCls; NHS; SchPl; YthFlsp; SptEdYrbk; FFA; MthCl; LetterBsbl; LetterBsktbl; LetterFtbl; Eureka Col; Conservation.

WADSWORTH, Sally J; North Scott HS; Davenport, IA; 30/200 Band; CmntyWkr; HonRl; HospAde; MrchBnd; NHS; PepBnd; SctActv; FHA; IMSpt; U Of Dubuque; Pre Med.

WAECHTER, Daryle A; Forrest Strawn Wing HS; Forrest, IL; 1/58 AFS; Band; CncrtBnd; HonRl; MrchBnd; PepBnd; TreasSpnCl; GAA; University; Medicine.

WAETZIG, Robin; Santa Fe Trail HS; Carbondale, KS; 17/83 Band; Chrs; ChrhWkr; CncrtBnd; HonRl; MrchBnd; NHS; PepBnd; SchMus; SctActv; Josephs School Of Hair Styling; Beautician.

WAGAR, Sherry L; Croswell Lexington HS; Jeddo, MI; 3/197 DrlTm; HonRl; NHS; RedCrAde; SchMus; StuCncl; TchrAde; Pres4-H; KeyCl; 4-HAwd; KiwanAwd; College; Med Tech.

WAGENBACH, Jerilyn J; Mediapolis Comm HS; Burlington, IA; 1/74 Chrs; HonRl; LbryAde; NatlMeritCmnd; OffAde; Sec4-H; PresFHA; Nursing School; Surgical Nurse.

WAGENBLAST, Pamela J; Southwestern HS; Brighton, IL; 14/180 RedCrAde; SchMus; YthFlsp; FNA; FTA; PpCl; Bsktbl; GAA; PPFtbl; DARAwd; E Il Coll Univ; Professional.

WAGENMAN, Daniel J; Bisbee HS; Bisbee, ND; 3/7 SecTrsFrshCls; SecTrsJrCls; Chrs; HonRl; PepBnd; SchPl; SctActv; StuCncl; CaptBsktbl; Trk; Trade School; Vocation.

WAGER, Pamela S; North Decatur HS; Greensburg, IN; Band; ChrhWkr; CncrtBnd; DrmMjrt; HonRl; MrchBnd; PepBnd; EdSchPpr; 4-H; GAA; Univ; Psychology Or Social Work.

WAGGONER, David W; Truman HS; Independence, MO; PresFrshCls; HonRl; JrNHS; ModUN; NHS; StuCncl; LetterFtbl; Trk; College; Law.

WAGGONER, Lisa; Montgomery County R Ii HS; Montgomery City, MO; PresJrCls; HonRl; SchPl; SptEdSchPpr; PpCl; SciCl;.

WAGGONER, Michael; Alma HS; Alma, NE; 5/30 HstSrCls; ALBoysSt; Band; Chr; Chrs; HonRl; PepBnd; 4-H; Bsbl; Swmmng; Univ; Professional.

WAGGONER, Paul R; Alma Public HS; Republican City, NE; Aud/Vis; Band; Chrs; HonRl; MrchBnd; SchMus; StuCncl; LetterBsktbl; LetterFtbl; LetterTrk; Kearney State College.

WAGGONER, Reford W; Lawrenceville HS; Lawrenceville, IL; 10/180 HonRl; LatCl; College; Mathematics.

WAGGONER, Sara J; Danville HS; Danville, IL; Chr; SchAde; SchMus; StuCncl; RptrYrbk; PpCl; Chrldr; University; Professional.

WAGNER, Anne M; Mother Mc Auley HS; Chicago, IL; 18/486 Chrs; HonRl; PresNHS; NatlMeritSF; SchMus; TchrAde; Yrbk; FrCl; IMSpt; Univ; Law.

WAGNER, Ben J; Kee HS; Lansing, IA; TrsFrshCls; Chrs; ChrhWkr; HonRl; StuCncl; 4-H; KeyCl; PpCl; LetterBsbl; LetterBsktbl; Ellsworth Coll; Coaching.

WAGNER, Beth A; Duchesne HS; St Charles, MO; Chrs; HonRl; NHS; SchMus; StuCncl; PpCl; Chrldr; IMSpt; PPFtbl; CitAwd; College; Medicine.

WAGNER, Candace; Lisbon HS; Engle Vale, ND; TrsFrshCls; AFS; Chr; CncrtBnd; HonRl; PepBnd; StuCncl; Yrbk; FHA; Trk; Ndsu; Home Economics.

WAGNER, Charles A; Kiel HS; Kiel, WI; Chrs; HonRl; JA; MthCl; PpCl; Bsktbl; Ftbl; IMSpt; JAAwd; Trade School; Professional.

WAGNER, Cheryl A; Holly HS; Holly, MI; HstJrCls; VPSrCls; HonRl; NHS; StuCncl; YthFlsp; RptrSchPpr; SchPpr; PpCl; Oakland Univ; Journalism.

WAGNER, Christine L; Divernon HS; Divernon, IL; 1/28 SecFrshCls; SecSophCls; SecJrCls; Band; CncrtBnd; DrmMjrt; HonRl; MrchBnd; PepBnd; SchPl; TchrAde; Trk; College; Teacher.

WAGNER, Cynthia C; Richardton Public HS; Richardton, ND; 4/38 PresSophCls; Chr; Chrs; ChrhWkr; CmntyWkr; HonRl; SchMus; StuCncl; FBLA; Bsktbl; Ndsu Fargo; Home Ec Dietetics.

WAGNER, Cynthia J; Yates Center HS; Yates Center, KS; 3/51 SecTrsJrCls; SecTrsSrCls; ALAGirlsSt; Band; DrlTm; HonRl; StuCncl; VP4-H; PresFHA; LetterTrk; 4-HAwd; College; Professional.

WAGNER, Danny J; Carrollton HS; Carrollton, IL; Band; CncrtBnd; HonRl; MrchBnd; PepBnd; SpnCl; SciCl; Wrstlng; Eastern Ill U; Agriculture.

WAGNER, David; Armada HS; Romeo, MI; Band; Chr; ChrhWkr; CmntyWkr; CncrtBnd; HonRl; MrchBnd; PepBnd; FrCl; Coll; Professional.

WAGNER, David; Lakeland HS; Lagrange, IN; 14/150 HonRl; TchrAde; SchPpr; LatCl; MthCl; Glf; Tennis; Coll; Pro.

WAGNER, Dean; Bloomfield Community HS; Bloomfield, NE; ChrhWkr; CmntyWkr; SchPl; SctActv; Ftbl; Glf; IMSpt; U Of Ne; Business.

WAGNER, Delmin C; Litchfield HS; Litchfield, MN; Band; Chr; ChrhWkr; HonRl; SctActv; StuCncl; TchrAde; YthFlsp; Bsbl; Bsktbl; Ftbl; Trk; CchngActv; University; Professional.

WAGNER, Denise P; Ada HS; Ada, MN; SecJrCls; SecSrCls; Band; ChrhWkr; HonRl; NHS; PepBnd; StuCncl; RptrYrbk; LatCl; N D State U; Nursing.

WAGNER, Dennis N; Johnson Brock HS; Brock, NE; 3/30 ALBoysSt; Band; Chrs; CncrtBnd; HonRl; MrchBnd; PepBnd; YthFlsp; Yrbk; LetterTrk; Coll; Pro.

WAGNER, Donald C; Marissa HS; Marissa, IL; 23/69 Chr; ChrhWkr; CncrtBnd; MrchBnd; SchMus; YthFlsp; 4-H; FFA; Trk; AmLegAwd; Belleville Area Jr College; Agriculture.

WAGNER, Elizabeth; Fennimore HS; Fennimore, WI; 6/112 Band; CncrtBnd; HonRl; MrchBnd; TrsFrshCls; PepBnd; SchPl; SecTrsFrshCls; RptrYrbk; GAA; Univ; Forestry.

WAGNER, Elizabeth A; Triton Central HS; Fairland, IN; HospAde; ModUN; PolWkr; RedCrAde; UNYO; FFA; FSA; FTA; Chrldr; IMSpt; College.

WAGNER, Eric J; Cretin HS; St Paul, MN; Chr; LbryAde; ROTC; RusCl; LetterFtbl; Univ; Professional.

WAGNER, Gerald J; Sandwich Comm HS; Sandwich, IL; 10/130 HonRl; NHS; NatlThespSoc; SchPl; StuCncl; LatCl; Bsbl; Univ Of Illinois; Political Science.

WAGNER, Harry W; Grand Blanc HS; Grand Blanc, MI; 150/600 ALBoysSt; PresBand; CncrtBnd; MrchBnd; SctActv; PresYthFlsp; AmLegAwd; GodCntryAwd; Western Michigan Univ; Business Admin.

WAGNER, Holly S; Wyaconda HS; Luray, MO; VPJrCls; ChrhWkr; HonRl; SchPl; Bsbl; Bsktbl; Trk; College; Athlete.

WAGNER, Jane; Caledonia HS; Caledonia, MN; DrlTm; HonRl; MrchBnd; SctActv; StuCncl; StuGov; EdYrBk; FHA; GAA; College; Professional.

WAGNER, Janet S; Highland HS; Highland, IN; 71/538 4-H; FTA; GAA; IMSpt; PPFtbl; 4-HAwd; Airline School; Airline Stewardess.

WAGNER, Jo Anne; Rosary HS; Florissant, MO; 7/350 Band; Chrs; NHS; NatlMeritFnl; Natl-

MeritSchl; PolWkr; SchMus; StuCncl; PpCl; Chrldr; Col; Prof.

WAGNER, Joanne T; Rosary HS; Florissant, MO; 7/350 Band; Chrs; DrlTm; HonRl; NHS; NatlMeritSF; PolWkr; SchMus; StuCncl; PpCl; University; Professional.

WAGNER, John A; Minooka HS; Joliet, IL; 8/106 HonRl; NHS; NatlMeritSchl; NatlSciFnd; FTA; MthCl; LetterTrk; LetterWrstlng; Univ; Professional.

WAGNER, John C; Blissfield HS; Blissfield, MI; PresSophCls; HonRl; NatlMeritCmnd; NatlMeritSchl; SctActv; TchrAde; FBLA; SpnCl; Glf; U S Marine Corps; Law Enforcement.

WAGNER, John F; St Ignatius Cp HS; Chicago, IL; 15/158 CmntyWkr; LitMag; NHS; NatlMeritSF; StuCncl; TchrAde; Teen; RptrSchPpr; LatCl; Bsbl; Univ Of Illinois; Biomedical Engineering.

WAGNER, John L; Mamaton Valley Usd 256 HS; Moran, KS; Band; CncrtBnd; HonRl; MrchBnd; PepBnd; 4-H; LetterFtbl; 4-HAwd; Trade Schl; Vocation.

WAGNER, Joseph R; St Pius X HS; Festus, MO; 24/101 PresFrshCls; PresJrCls; PresSrCls; ALBoysSt; SchAde; StuCncl; 4-H; LetterFtbl; LetterTrk; 4-HAwd; PresAwd; University Of Missouri; Economics.

WAGNER, Julie A; Hanson Ind #40 HS; Alexandria, SD; Chr; Chrs; CmntyWkr; HonRl; SchPl; StuGov; FHA; PpCl; 4-HAwd; JAAwd; Office Secretary.

WAGNER, Karen K; Corunna HS; Owosso, MI; Band; ChrhWkr; CncrtBnd; DrlTm; HonRl; LbryAde; MrchBnd; TchrAde; 4-H; 4-HAwd; Business Sch; Social Worker.

WAGNER, Karen S; John Hersey HS; Arlington Hts, IL; SecAFS; DrlTm; HonRl; NHS; TchrAde; SpnCl; GAA; South Methodist Univ; Biomed Engineering.

WAGNER, Kenneth M; Preble HS; Green Bay, WI; Chr; Chrs; ChrhWkr; HonRl; JA; RptrSchPpr; FrCl; Ftbl; University.

WAGNER, Kimi K; Lemmon HS; Lemmon, SD; 27/68 CAP; CmntyWkr; HonRl; OffAde; FHA; SciCl; Swmmng; Tennis; IMSpt; 4-HAwd; Northern St Clge; Special Ed.

WAGNER, Lawrence J; New Trier East HS; Wilmette, IL; Univ; Pianist.

WAGNER, Leonard K; South Pemiscot HS; Caruthersville, MO; 5/67 VPJrCls; ChrhWkr; HonRl; NHS; SchPl; StuCncl; TchrAde; RptrYrbk; EdYrBk; RptrSchPpr; EdSchPpr; FSA; FrCl; Ambassador College; Journalism.

WAGNER, Mark G; St Marys HS; St Louis, MO; Band; HonRl; JrNHS; NHS; LetterFtbl; LetterTrk; IMSpt; College; Audio Technology.

WAGNER, Marlene M; North HS; Sheboygan, WI; Chrs; HonRl; NHS; TchrAde; Univ; Architecture.

WAGNER, Mary; Watertown Senior HS; Watertown, WI; ;321 AFS; Chr; OffAde; StuCncl; GerCl; College;certified Public Accountant.

WAGNER, Michael A; Harbor Beach HS; Harbor Beach, MI; 45/136 HonRl; RptrSchPpr; LetterBsktbl; LetterFtbl; LetterTrk; Delta Clg; Broadcasting.

WAGNER, Michael J; Quigley South HS; Chicago, IL; 1/167 TrsFrshCls; PresSophCls; HonRl; NHS; StuGov; RptrYrbk; RptrSchPpr; SchPpr; LatCl; Bsktbl; Northwestern Univ; Lawyer.

WAGNER, Michael Q; Oconomowoc Sr HS; Oconomowoc, WI; Chr; Chrs; HonRl; JrNHS; SchPl; SpnCl; Ftbl; College; Dietician.

WAGNER, Micheal L; Dorchester HS; Dorchester, NE; Aud/Vis; ChrhWkr; CmntyWkr; HonRl; SchAde; SchPl; StuGov; TchrAde; 4-H; Bsbl; Wrstlng;.

WAGNER, Neil L; Howell HS; Brighton, MI; 4/380 Aud/Vis; HonRl; NHS; SctActv; TchrAde; SchPpr; Eastern Michigan Univ; Wildlife.

WAGNER, Pamela J; Naperville Central HS; Plainfield, IL; HonRl; NHS; Loyola Univ Of Dentistry; Dental Assistant.

WAGNER, Phillip; Lincoln Way HS; Mokena, IL; 220/566 HonRl; College; Entomology.

WAGNER, Randy L; Lincoln Comm HS; Stanwood, IA; HonRl; SchMus; StuCncl; FSA; SpnCl; SciCl; Bsbl;.

WAGNER, Rory K; La Crosse HS; Rush Center, KS; VPJrCls; HonRl; ModUN; NatlMeritSchl; SchPl; YthFlsp; PpCl; Bsbl; LetterBsktbl; LetterFtbl; Tennis; College; Professional.

WAGNER, Rose; Marinette Sr HS; Marinette, WI; 44/239 4-H; FHA; Lakeland Medical Dental Acad; Med Lab Tech.

WAGNER, Sara J; Waldron HS; Waldron, IN; 1/68 HonRl; LbryAde; NHS; NatlMeritCmnd; SchPl; TchrAde; RptrYrbk; RptrSchPpr; 4-H; College; Journalism.

WAGNER, Sharon E; Steinmetz HS; Chicago, IL; Chrs; ChrhWkr; HonRl; OffAde; SchMus; TchrAde; YthFnd; SecFBLA; KeyCl; Stewardess.

WAGNER, Stephen M; Thomas More Preparatory; Grandview, MO; Sacrstn; SchMus; SchPl; SctActv; RptrSchPpr; SpnCl; University; Veterinary Medicine.

WAGNER, Steven O; Northwest HS; High Ridge, MO; 48/400 Aud/Vis; HonRl; SctActv; SchPpr; SciCl; Air Force; Math.

WAGNER, Sue A; Engadine Consolidated HS; Engadine, MI; SecFrshCls; Chr; HonRl; LitMag; OffAde; SchAde; StuCncl; PpCl; Chrldr; IMSpt; College; Professional.

WAGNER, Teresa M; Logan View HS; Hooper, NE; 7/56 Band; CmntyWkr; HonRl; MrchBnd; OffAde; SchPl; Yrbk; PpCl; Trk; Chrldr; Work.

WAGNER, Thomas J; Parkston HS; Dimock, SD; ALBoysSt; ChrhWkr; HonRl; NatlMeritCmnd; LetterWrstlng; Air Force; Bus.

WAGNER, Tina M; Standish Sterling Central HS; Sterling, MI; 79/156 Chr; ChrhWkr; HonRl; SchPl; College; Theatre.

WAGNER, Tina M; Ripon HS; Pickett, WI; Chr; HonRl; NatlFornLg; NatlThespSoc; SchPl; StuCncl; StuGov; RptrYrbk; Ripon College; English Major.

WAGNER, Vicki L; Pleasant Hill HS; Pleasant Hill, MO; StuCncl; StuGov; TchrAde; RptrSchPpr; FHA; College; Physical Educ Teacher.

WAGNESS, Maren; Lakota HS; Lakota, ND; SecSophCls; ALAGirlsSt; Chrs; CncrtBnd; DrmMjrt; HonRl; NHS; RptrSchPpr; 4-H;.

WAGONER, Bradley D; Burlington C HS; Burlington, IA; 1/520 AFS; ALBoysSt; Band; Chr; ChrhWkr; CmntyWkr; HonRl; JA; ModUN; NHS; CaptTrk; IMSpt; AmLegAwd; PresAwd; University; Medicine.

WAHID, Sunita J; St Ann HS; Cicero, IL; CmntyWkr; NHS; NatlMeritSchl; StuGov; UNYO; FDA; FHA; CitAwd; VoiceDemAwd; Univ Of Il Cir Campus; Dentist.

WAHL, David S; Preston HS; Preston, MN; 5/57 Band; Chrs; ChrhWkr; CncrtBnd; PresFrshCls; NatlMeritCmnd; SchPl; RptrSchPpr; SpnCl; LetterBsbl; LetterBsktbl; St Olaf College.

WAHL, James P; Anamosa Comm HS; Anamosa, IA; 8/133 ALBoysSt; Band; Chrs; HonRl; NHS; PepBnd; SchMus; SchPl; SciCl; CaptGlf; Iowa St Univ; Vet Med.

WAHL, Jerry L; Newton Community HS; Kellogg, IA; 44/305 Band; CncrtBnd; HonRl; MrchBnd; Orch; PepBnd; SchMus; FFA; University; Music.

WAHL, Karen S; North Huron HS; Port Austin, MI; 4/45 SecBand; HospAde; NHS; OffAde; SchPl; StuCncl; TchrAde; RptrYrbk; VP4-H; CaptChrldr; Oakland Univ; Ed Field.

WAHL, Patrick J; Forest Park HS; Ferdinand, IN; HonRl; GerCl; Bsbl; Bsktbl; In U; Acct.

WAHL, Robert J; North Side HS; Fort Wayne, IN; ChrhWkr; HonRl; KeyCl; Bsbl; Bsktbl; Tennis; Trk; IMSpt; CitAwd; College.

WAHLBERG, Gwen A; Hudson Sr HS; Hudson, WI; 8/220 ALAGirlsSt; Band; Chr; ChrhWkr; CncrtBnd; HonRl; LbryAde; MrchBnd; PepBnd; SchAde; LetterSwmmng; LetterTrk; CchngActv; College; Medicine.

WAHLEN, Ann L; Hillcrest HS; Hazel Crest, IL; 64/474 RptrYrbk; FrCl; Univ Of Illinois; Political Science.

WAHLERT, David A; Anita HS; Anita, IA; HonRl; NatlFornLg; NHS; StuGov; RptrYrbk; SciCl; Bsbl; LetterFtbl; CaptWrstlng; CchngActv; Morningside.

WAHLFELDT, Kathy J; Danville HS; Danville, IL; 30#32#33 PresFrshCls; TrsFrshCls; SchMus; Yrbk; SchPpr; GerCl; SpnCl; Navy Waves.

WAHLHEIM, Debora J; J D Darnall HS; Geneseo, IL; 69/212 Chr; HonRl; NatlThespSoc; SchMus; SchPl; SctActv; StuCncl; RptrYrbk; 4-H; FNA; LetterBsktbl; LetterTrk; CaptChrldr; Nursing Sch; Nursing.

WAHLSTROM, Beverly; Sheldon Community HS; Sheldon, IA; ChrhWkr; CmntyWkr; HonRl; NHS; StuCncl; YthFlsp; FHA; PpCl; Bsbl; Bsktbl; Coll; Vacational.

WAIBEL, Brent D; Tri County HS; Remington, IN; 9/88 CncrtBnd; LitMag; MrchBnd; PepBnd; SchMus; SptEdYrbk; RptrSchPpr; 4-H; FFA; IMSpt;.

WAIBEL, Charles E; St Cloud Technical HS; Cold Spring, MN; 83/476 PresSrCls; Chr; Chrs; ChrhWkr; CAP; HonRl; Mdrgl; NatlMeritSF; StuCncl; StuGov; Bible Coll;minister.

WAIBEL, Sonia E; Tri County HS; Remington, IN; 23/77 VPFrshCls; SecSophCls; CncrtBnd; HonRl; HospAde; MrchBnd; PepBnd; YthFlsp; 4-H; PpCl; Bsbl; Trk; Trade School; Vocation.

WAID, Diane L; Prairie HS; Cedar Rapids, IA; Band; Chrs; HonRl; JrNHS; Mdrgl; SchPl; YthFlsp; PpCl; Trk; Univ Of Iowa; Home Economics.

WAIDEN, Mark A; East Detroit HS; East Detroit, MI; Aud/Vis; Chr; HonRl; SctActv; StuCncl; CaptSwmmng; Univ; Marine Biologist.

WAIDMANN, Randall C; Owensville HS; Gerald, MO; VPFrshCls; Chrs; ChrhWkr; CmntyWkr; HonRl; StuCncl; RptrSchPpr; Bsbl; CaptFtbl; CchngActv; College; Professional.

WAINSCOTT, Jennifer D; Rushville Consolidated HS; Arlington, IN; 13/263 Band; CncrtBnd; HonRl; MrchBnd; NHS; Teen; Purdue Univ; Teaching.

WAIT, Karen L; Carmel HS; Lake Bluff, IL; 26/173 Chrs; HonRl; College; Accounting.

WAIT, Linda V; Joliet Twp West HS; Joliet, IL; 12/499 HonRl; JrNHS; NHS; StuCncl; GerCl; GAA; Purdue Univ; Fashion Merchandising.

WAITE, Julie A; Wheeling Riv HS; Wheeling, MO; 1/12 ALAGirlsSt; HonRl; LbryAde; SchPl; StuCncl; EdYrBk; SchPpr; Bsbl; Bsktbl; Trk; College.

WAITE, Leroy; Orchard Farm HS; St Charles, MO; 1/119 HonRl; NHS; NatlMeritCmnd; Ftbl; Trk; CchngActv; BauchLmbAwd; BttyCrckrAwd; Culver Stockton College; Engineering.

WAITE, Marcia A; Maquoketa Comm HS; Maquoketa, IA; 10/142 Band; Chrs; CncrtBnd; HonRl; LitMag; MrchBnd; PepBnd; SchPl; RptrSchPpr; 4-H; College; Journalism.

WAITE, Terri; Lake Central HS; Dyer, IN; 11/453 Chrs; NHS; NatlMeritSF; TreasSciCl; Florida Inst Tech; Astronomy.

WAITS, Bradford E; Ainsworth HS; Ainsworth, NE; Band; HonRl; MrchBnd; NatlThespSoc; PepBnd; SchPl; RptrSchPpr; LetterBsktbl; LetterFtbl; AmLegAwd; Tech Coll; Elec Lineman.

WAKE, Brian R; Riverdale HS; Port Byron, IL; HonRl; NHS; LetterBsktbl; CaptFtbl; College; Professional.

WAKE, Cindi L; Hammond Baptist HS; Hammond, IN; SecTrsFrshCls; Chrl; ChrhWkr; HonRl; OffAde; SchMus; SchPl; RptrSchPpr; Chrldr; Hyles Anderson College; Home Economics.

WAKE, Thomas J; Lanphier HS; Springfield, IL; ChrhWkr; SchPl; Trk; College; Pilot.

WAKEEM, James D; Lamar HS; Lamar, MO; AFS; Ftbl; Col; Engineering.

WAKEFIELD, Kathy L; Beecher City HS; Shumway, IL; 1/50 SecJrCls; Band; Chrs; HonRl; PepBnd; StuCncl; Yrbk; SpnCl; Eastern Ill Univ; Teaching.

WAKELIN, James H; Illiopolis HS; Illipolis, IL; Band; Chr; Chrl; CncrtBnd; DrmMjrt; MrchBnd; NatlThespSoc; Orch; PepBnd; SchMus; Eureka Col; English Teacher Or Major.

WAKEMAN, Kaye D; Oxford HS; Oxford, KS; 6/39 SecSrCls; HonRl; HospAde; NHS; SchPl; TchrAde; Yrbk; RptrSchPpr; LetterBsktbl; Chrldr; School Of License Practical Nursing.

WAKEMAN, Lori L; Brewster HS; Brewster, MN; Aud/Vis; ChrhWkr; HonRl; LbryAde; RptrSchPpr; FHA; FTA; PpCl; College.

WAKEVAINEN, Donald D; Wakefield HS; Wakefield, MI; 3/62 HonRl; NatlMeritSF; Bsktbl; Ftbl; Mit; Electrical Engineer.

WALBERG, Jill S; Kindred HS; Walcott, ND; 16/46 SecJrCls; Chrs; HonRl; NHS; SchPl; TchrAde; 4-H; FHA; Chrldr; Bible School; Vocation.

WALBERG, Teresa; Van Buren HS; Van Buren, MO; 6/45 Band; Chrs; CncrtBnd; HonRl; MrchBnd; PpCl; College.

WALBRIDGE, Don J; Gull Lake HS; Augusta, MI; 6/245 CmntyWkr; HonRl; JrNHS; SchPl; Bsbl; LetterBsktbl; LetterFtbl; CchngActv; OptClAwd; CitAwd; College.

WALBRIDGE, Randy A; Gull Lake HS; Augusta, MI; 38/225 HonRl; LitMag; NHS; Yrbk; LetterFtbl; LetterTennis; LetterWrstlng; CchngActv; IMSpt; PPFtbl; CitAwd; College At Western Michigan Univ; Artist.

WALBURN, Mark T; Gobles Public HS; Gobles, MI; 8/70 HonRl; JrNHS; FrCl; MthCl; SciCl; Bsbl; Bsktbl; Ftbl; Kalamazoo Valley Comm Col; Math.

WALBY, Janet L; Viroqua Senio HS; Viroqua, WI; CncrtBnd; HonRl; MrchBnd; SchPl; RptrSchPpr; 4-H; FHA; SpnCl; 4-HAwd; CitAwd; Univ Wis Stout; Home Ec.

WALBY, Jayne L; Viroqua Sr HS; Viroqua, WI; CncrtBnd; HonRl; MrchBnd; Orch; SchPl; RptrSchPpr; 4-H; FHA; SpnCl; 4-HAwd; Uw Stout; Home Ec Teacher.

WALCKER, Brian D; Eisenhower HS; Hopkins, MN; Chr; HonRl; Mdrgl; SchMus; YthFlsp; LetterBsktbl; Trk; College; Engineering.

WALCKER, Terrie L; Coon Rapids HS; Coon Rapids, MN; 1/749 ALAGirlsSt; Band; ChrhWkr; HonRl; NHS; SchPl; GerCl; AmLegAwd; VFWAwd; VoiceDemAwd; Northwestern Univ; Us Foreign Service Dept.

WALCZAK, Thaddeus S; St Ignatius College Prep HS; Chicago, IL; 2/158 Band; Chr; Chrl; ChrhWkr; HonRl; NatlFornLg; NHS; NatlMeritSF; RedCrAde; StuCncl; RptrSchPpr; LatCl; College; Neurology.

WALD, Cindy; Napoleon Public HS; Kintyre, ND; Band; Chr; Chrs; CncrtBnd; LbryAde; MrchBnd; PpCl; Bus Sch; Prof Secty.

WALD, Deborah K; Trinity HS; Dickinson, ND; ChrhWkr; SchPl; College; Professional.

WALD, F. ·ces; Napoleon HS; Kintyre, ND; 22/61 Band; CncrtBnd; MrchBnd; PpCl; Bus Sch; Vocation.

WALDECKER, Clare L; Bishop Borgess HS; Detroit, MI; DrlTm; HonRl; NHS; LetterChrldr; College; Dental Hygenist.

WALDEE, Jody K; Waterman HS; Waterman, IL; VPFrshCls; Chrs; HonRl; Mdrgl; NHS; StuCncl; TreasFHA; FrCl; LetterSocr; Chrldr; College; Nursing.

WALDEN, Charles H; Hallsville R Iv HS; Hallsville, MO; Chr; CncrtBnd; HonRl; MrchBnd; RptrYrbk; SpnCl; SciCl; Bsbl; Bsktbl; IMSpt; Army Bandsman; Band Director.

WALDEN, Deborah D; Assumption HS; Assumption, IL; Chr; Chrs; HonRl; HospAde; TchrAde; 4-H; FHA; GAA; College; Teacher.

WALDEN, John L; Thomas Moore HS; Milwaukee, WI; HonRl; StuGov; CaptTrk; Univ Of Wisc; Professional Accountant.

WALDEN, Shelley K; North County HS; Desloge, MO; 32/175 Band; CncrtBnd; HonRl; MrchBnd; NHS; StuCncl; FTA; PpCl; Mineral Area College; Natural Sciences.

WALDEN, Steven W; Carrollton HS; Carrollton, MO; 19/104 Band; Chrs; HonRl; NHS; TchrAde; GerCl; Bsktbl; Ftbl; Trk; LionAwd; U Of Mo Columbia; Accountant.

WALDEN, Sue A; Harper Creek HS; Battle Creek, MI; 14/231 Band; ChrhWkr; HonRl; NHS; TchrAde; SchPpr; College; Data Processing.

WALDENMEYER, Karen T; Alpena HS; Alpena, MI; HonRl; HospAde; NatlMeritFnl; NatlMeritCmnd; NatlMeritSchl; NatlMeritSF; CivCl; SpnCl; LetterGlf; PPFtbl; Col; Occupational Therapy.

WALDER, Kay M; Hoopeston East Lynn HS; Rankin, IL; 4/133 Chr; HonRl; MrchBnd; NatlThespSoc; RptrYrbk; RptrSchPpr; Pres4-H; SecPpCl; Bsbl; Bsktbl; GAA; 4-HAwd; Univ Of Illinois; Home Economics.

WALDERZAK, Kay; Arthur Hill HS; Saginaw, MI; CmntyWkr; HonRl; HospAde; NHS; NatlSciFnd; PolWkr; UNYO; SciCl; GAA; Saginaw Valley College; Biology.

WALDHART, Lynda S; Medford Sr HS; Stetsonville, WI; 56/254 Chr; Chrs; ChrhWkr; HonRl; YthFnd; 4-H; Trk; GAA; 4-HAwd; CitAwd; Coll; Oc.

WALDIE, Joann M; Owosso HS; Owosso, MI; 32/452 HospAde; NHS; TchrAde; SpnCl; GAA; PPFtbl; Coll; Nursing.

WALDMAN, Mitchell J; Niles North HS; Skokie, IL; 119/637 HonRl; KeyCl; U Of Il; Psy.

WALDMANN, Michael J; Burwell HS; Burwell, NE; VPSrCls; Chrs; HonRl; Mdrgl; NHS; StuCncl; MthCl; Bsktbl; LetterFtbl; LetterWrstlng; College; Business Administration.

WALDO, Kathy A; Iowa Falls Sr HS; Iowa Falls, IA; 32/193 CmntyWkr; HonRl; VPHospAde; SctActv; RptrSchPpr; EdSchPpr; FFA; VPFNA; GAA; Marshalltown School Of Nursing; Nurse.

WALDO, Patricia A; Paw Paw HS; Paw Paw, MI; HonRl; OffAde; TchrAde; 4-H; FrCl; Trade School.

WALDREP, Thomas W; Greenfield Central HS; Greenfield, IN; 50/300 ALBoysSt; ChrhWkr; NHS; GerCl; LetterFtbl; CaptWrstlng; AmLegAwd; KiwanAwd; LionAwd; Purdue; Professional.

WALDRIDGE, Marlen G; Eastern HS; Springville, IN; 31/68 Band; Chr; ChrhWkr; CncrtBnd; HonRl; MrchBnd; PepBnd; SchMus; SpnCl; IMSpt; Coll; Computer Programmer.

WALDRON, Bryant L; Fairbury HS; Fairbury, NE; Band; Chr; CncrtBnd; MrchBnd; RedCrAde; SchPl; SpnCl; Bsktbl; Swmmng; LetterTrk; Coll; Prof.

WALDRON, Donna L; Sturgis HS; Sturgis, MI; CmntyWkr; HonRl; NHS; NatlMeritSchl; StuCncl; FBLA; FrCl; Chrldr; Northwestern Mi Coll; Bus Admin.

WALDRON, Julie; Mound Westonka HS; Mound, MN; HonRl; NHS; Quill&Scroll; TchrAde; YthFlsp; RptrYrbk; RptrSchPpr; EdSchPpr; SchPpr; SpnCl; College; Nursing.

WALDRON, Julie M; Edsel Ford HS; Dearborn, MI; HonRl; StuCncl; StuGov; PpCl; GAA; PPFtbl; IMSpt; Univ; Dietitian.

WALDRON, Roxann; Vestaburg Community HS; Edmore, MI; SecSophCls; Band; Chr; ChrhWkr; CncrtBnd; HonRl; MrchBnd; NHS; PepBnd; YthLg; SpnCl; Central Mich Univ; Data Processing.

WALDRUP, Stephen R; Homewood Flossmoor HS; Homewood, IL; 158/921 Chr; Chrs; HonRl; NatlThespSoc; SchMus; SchPl; SpnCl; College; Teaching.

WALDSMITH, Jean M; St Marys Academy; Washington, IL; 24/50 VPSophCls; HonRl; OffAde; SchMus; SchPl; SctActv; StuCncl; TchrAde; SchPpr; 4-H; SpnCl; Trk; College; Primary School Teacher.

WALDSMITH, Mary K; Boylan Central Catholic HS; Rockford, IL; 44/345 Chrs; CmntyWkr; HonRl; HospAde; LbryAde; NHS; SctActv; TchrAde; SpnCl; PresPpCl; Ill State Univ; Speech Therapy.

WALDVOGEL, Faye M; St Francis HS; Little Falls, MN; Chr; SchMus; SchPl; Yrbk; Staples Vo Tech; Graphic Art.

WALDVOGEL, Terry J; Antigo Sr HS; Antigo, WI; 14/375 PresSophCls; ALBoysSt; HonRl; StuCncl; GerCl; LetterBsbl; LetterFtbl; DARAwd; College; Accounting.

WALEGA, Gary E; Catholic Central HS; Detroit, MI; HonRl; IntrClCncl; StuCncl; LatCl; CaptFtbl; CaptTrk; IMSpt; College; Biology.

WALENT, Adrienne; York Community HS; Elmhurst, IL; 41/888 HonRl; NHS; Quill&Scroll; RptrSchPpr; SchPpr; GAA; U Of Illinois; Computer Science.

WALES, Nancy L; Akron Community HS; Akron, IA; Band; Chr; HonRl; HospAde; NatlThespSoc; SchPl; RptrSchPpr; 4-H; Trk; 4-HAwd; Nursing Sch; Rn.

WALEZAK, Barbara; Jennings HS; Jennings, MO; 4/250 Chr; HonRl; NHS; EngCl; IMSpt; College; Psychology.

WALGENBACH, Kay D; Tonica HS; Tonica, IL; 4/47 Band; Chrs; CncrtBnd; HonRl; LbryAde; NHS; PepBnd; SchMus; RptrYrbk; RptrSchPpr; PresFHA; GAA; College; Sec Science.

WALGREN, Joan A; Hay Springs Public HS; Hay Springs, NE; 4/40 SecJrCls; ChrhWkr; DrmMjrt; SecNHS; StuCncl; TchrAde; Yrbk; PpCl; DARAwd; 4-HAwd; U Of Neb; Elementary Education.

WALICKI, Russell J; Bishop Borgess HS; Dearborn Hts, MI; 22/400 Chrl; Chrs; HonRl; NatlFornLg; NHS; NatlMeritSF; SchMus; Bsbl; Bsktbl; LetterFtbl; Trk; IMSpt; Univ; Doctor.

WALK, Deborah J; Neoga HS; Neoga, IL; 2/85 SecFrshCls; PresJrCls; AFS; HonRl; SchPl; RptrYrbk; EdYrBk; RptrSchPpr; Tennis; Eastern Illinois Univ; Physical Education.

WALKE, Sue A; Acad Of The Immaculate Concep; Batesville, IN; 3/60 ChrhWkr; CmntyWkr; HonRl; NatlMeritSchl; SchMus; RptrYrbk; GerCl; College.

WALKENBACH, Louise K; Regina HS; Detroit, MI; HonRl; NHS; RptrSchPpr; FHA; Univ.

WALKER, Barry L; West Vigo HS; Westterre Haute, IN; 38/192 HonRl; SecNHS; PepBnd; StuGov; VPKeyCl; LetterBsbl; LetterFtbl; Trk; IMSpt; AmLegAwd; In State Univ; Pre Law.

WALKER, Beverly A; Brown City HS; Brown City, MI; 4/90 HonRl; LbryAde; NHS; NatlMeritSchl; OffAde; TchrAde; FHA; Michigan St Univ; Audiology.

WALKER, Brian; Lafayette HS; Red Lake Falls, MN; HonRl; College; Vocation.

WALKER, Carol M; Lancaster HS; Lancaster, WI; AFS; Band; HonRl; NHS; SchMus; 4-H; SpnCl; GAA; IMSpt; 4-HAwd; Lacrosse; Social Work.

WALKER, Charles F; Hays HS; Hays, KS; HonRl; ModUN; NatlFornLg; NatlMeritSF; SchPl; StuCncl; Coll; Law.

WALKER, Charlon D; Yates Center HS; Yates Center, KS; Band; NHS; OffAde; SchMus; StuCncl; Yrbk; FHA; LetterTrk; Chrldr; CitAwd; Trade School.

WALKER, Christine S; West Nodaway Ri HS; Quitman, MO; 2/37 ALAGirlsSt; Chrs; HonRl; NHS; NatlMeritSF; EdSchPpr;.

WALKER, Cindy A; Liberty HS; Liberty, IL; 7/56 Band; Chrs; ChrhWkr; HonRl; NHS; SchPl; FHA; SpnCl; PpCl; SciCl; Blessing Hosp School; Nurse.

WALKER, Colleen E; Streator Twp HS; Streator, IL; HonRl; RptrSchPpr; FTA; College; Teacher.

WALKER, Cynthia K; Oak Park HS; Kansas City, MO; 27/602 Chr; ChrhWkr; HonRl; SchMus; SchPl; YthFlsp; Oral Roberts Univ; Music.

WALKER, Daniel W; Eisenhower HS; Decatur, IL; HstFrshCls; HstSophCls; HstSrCls; HonRl; NHS; StuGov; RptrSchPpr; SptEdSchPpr; Bsbl; Millikin Univ; Journalism.

WALKER, Danny L; North Mahaska HS; New Sharon, IA; SecSophCls; CmntyWkr; SctActv; YthFlsp; RptrSchPpr; SchPpr; FFA; Bsktbl; Ftbl; Area Xv; Mechanics.

WALKER, David P; Lane Technical HS; Chicago, IL; 52/1210 NHS; RptrYrbk; Univ Of Il; Engineering.

WALKER, Dawn M; Tri Valley HS; Cotton, SD; Chrs; ChrhWkr; CmntyWkr; HonRl; LbryAde; SchPl; SctActv; TchrAde; 4-H; 4-HAwd; Trade School; Beautician.

WALKER, Dawn R; Warren Twp HS; Libertyville, IL; Band; Chrs; CmntyWkr; HonRl; StuCncl; 4-H; KeyCl; CchngActv; GAA; IMSpt; PPFtbl; DanFAwd; Lake County College; Agriculture.

WALKER, Debbie K; Lesterville HS; Black, MO; SecFrshCls; HonRl; LbryAde; RptrYrbk; PpCl; LetterChrldr; Bus Schl; Vocation.

WALKER, Deborah A; Mariner HS; White Bear Lake, MN; NHS; StuGov; 4-H; FHA; CaptChrldr; PPFtbl; 4-HAwd; Univ Of Minnesota; Nursing.

WALKER, Debra S; John F Kennedy HS; Bloomington, MN; Aud/Vis; HonRl; LbryAde; PolWkr; TchrAde; College; Photographer.

WALKER, Diane K; Neillsville HS; Neillsville, WI; SecTrsFrshCls; Chrs; HonRl; StuCncl; FBLA; FHA; PpCl; Chrldr; Trade Sch; Dental.

WALKER, Douglas R; Alma HS; Alma, NE; 4/30 Band; ChrhWkr; CncrtBnd; HonRl; MrchBnd; NHS; PepBnd; University Of Nebraska; Law.

WALKER, Gayle E; Danville Comm HS; Danville, IA; VPJrCls; Band; Chrs; ChrhWkr; CncrtBnd; MrchBnd; SchMus; YthFlsp; RptrYrbk; CaptBsktbl; College; Bible.

WALKER, George C; Mankato West HS; Mankato, MN; ALBoysSt; Chr; Chrs; ChrhWkr; HonRl; NatlThespSoc; SchMus; SchPl; VPStuCncl; StuGov; College; Prof Environmental Work.

WALKER, Gladys I; Gideon HS; Gideon, MO; MrchBnd; FHA; FrCl; PpCl; Chrldr; College.

WALKER, James A; Stillman Valley HS; Chana, IL; 5/105 VPSrCls; HonRl; VPNHS; SchMus; SchPl; VPStuCncl; TchrAde; TreasFTA; CaptFtbl; LetterTrk; Capt.

WALKER, James J; Brebeuf Prep; Indianapolis, IN; CmntyWkr; HonRl; NHS; TchrAde; PpCl; LetterBsbl; LetterFtbl; Chrldr; CchngActv; IMSpt; Wabash College; Economics.

WALKER, Jeanne A; Carroll HS; Wichita, KS; ALAGirlsSt; HonRl; JrNHS; NHS; FrCl; PpCl; Trk; Chrldr; GAA; PPFtbl; College; Nursing.

WALKER, Joan L; Hamilton HS; Hamilton, IL; 7/70 SecSophCls; SecJrCls; ALAGirlsSt; HonRl; StuCncl; TchrAde; SecFrCl; CaptChrldr; GAA; 4-HAwd; Ill Wesleyan Univ; Elem Ed.

WALKER, John K; Morton HS; Morton, IL; RptrSchPpr; SchPpr; College; Data Processing.

WALKER, John R; Tomah Sr HS; Tomah, WI; 12/268 HonRl; NHS; StuCncl; Bsktbl; Glf; College; Math Major.

WALKER, Judy L; Algona Comm HS; Algona, IA; 37/125 Band; CncrtBnd; HonRl; MrchBnd; PepBnd; SchMus; Pres4-H; SecFBLA; PpCl; 4-HAwd;.

WALKER, Kathleen; Coleman HS; Coleman, WI; HonRl; StuCncl; Yrbk; 4-H; Trk; 4-HAwd; Trade School; Vocation.

WALKER, Kathleen; Greenfield Central HS; Greenfield, IN; 20/265 HonRl; NHS; TchrAde; FTA; GerCl; SpnCl; CchngActv; GAA; Depauw Univ; Physical Educ.

WALKER, Kimberly K; Glenbard West HS; Glen Ellyn, IL; Chr; IntrClCncl; LitMag; NatlFornLg; NatlMeritCmnd; PolWkr; StuGov; TchrAde; RptrSchPpr; LatCl; Univ; Vet.

WALKER, Kimberly L; Charlestown HS; Charlestown, IN; HonRl; FHA; FrCl; Indiana Clg; Dietitian.

WALKER, Linda M; Villard Public HS; Villard, MN; PresSrCls; ALAGirlsSt; Chr; ChrhWkr; CncrtBnd; HonRl; SchPl; StuCncl; LetterBsktbl; CaptChrldr; Um Morris; Home Ec.

WALKER, Linda S; Farmington East HS; Farmington, IL; 44/131 Chrs; ChrhWkr; HonRl; SctActv; TchrAde; FrCl; Busi Sch; Sec.

WALKER, Lonnie G; New Monroe HS; Monroe, IA; HonRl; YthFlsp; RptrYrbk; FFA; College; Vocation.

WALKER, Lori; Marshall Senior HS; Marshall, MN; 2/229 AFS; Chr; ChrhWkr; HonRl; NatlFornLg; SchMus; SchPl; StuCncl; Chrldr; Moorhead St Coll; Public Relations.

WALKER, Louanne M; Highland HS; Highland, IN; 4-H; PpCl; GAA; PPFtbl; 4-HAwd; Creative Beauty Acad; Beautician.

WALKER, Lynn A; Beardstown HS; Beardstown, IL; 25/137 CmntyWkr; HonRl; LitMag; LbryAde; PolWkr; RedCrAde; StuGov; YthFlsp; FshEdSchPpr; Tennis; Trade Or Bus Sch; Nurse Or Elec Engin.

WALKER, Margo S; New Palestine HS; Greenfield, IN; 5/145 HonRl; FHA; Trade Schl; Systems Analysis.

WALKER, Mary E; John Adams HS; South Bend, IN; 8/442 Chr; Chrs; HospAde; NatlMeritSF; SchMus; 4-H; Treas4-HAwd; Indiana Univ; Medicine.

WALKER, Mary E; Imlay City HS; Imlay City, MI; 15/134 ChrhWkr; HonRl; SchAde; TchrAde; YthFlsp; 4-H; FHA; 4-HAwd; Central Mich U; Elem Teacher.

WALKER, Mary S; Orono HS; Maple Plain, MN; HonRl; OffAde; SchMus; SchPl; TchrAde; SchPpr; LetterTrk; GAA; Bus Schl; Accountant.

WALKER, Michael D; Goreville HS; Goreville, IL; 3/30 Band; CmntyWkr; PresStuCncl; Sec4-H; LetterBsbl; LetterBsktbl; LetterTrk; CchngActv; IMSpt; DanFAwd; 4-HAwd; So Illinois Univ; Veterinarian.

WALKER, Michael J; Lancaster Sr HS; Lancaster, WI; HonRl; ModUN; YthFlsp; SpnCl; CaptBsktbl; LetterFtbl; LetterTrk; IMSpt; College; Professional.

WALKER, Milo B; Moravia HS; Centerville, IA; TrsJrCls; PresSrCls; ChrhWkr; HonRl; StuCncl; FFA; CaptBsbl; LetterBsktbl; LetterFtbl; Faith Baptist Bible College; Youth Minister.

WALKER, N; Beloit HS; Beloit, KS; Chrs; ChrhWkr; HonRl; LbryAde; Orch; SchMus; 4-H; EngCl; PpCl; 4-HAwd; Bethany Coll; Vocation.

WALKER, Nancy; Glenbard East Hs; Lombard, IL; 9 HonRl; HospAde; NHS; NatlMeritCmnd; PpCl; Chrldr; U Of Iowa;nursing.

WALKER, Nancy A; Oak Park River Forest HS; Oak Park, IL; 164/1012 ChrhWkr; HonRl; OffAde; SctActv; SchPpr; University; Business Administration.

WALKER, Nancy E; Sacred Heart Academy; Springfield, IL; 2/143 HonRl; HospAde; NHS; SchMus; Sdlty; PresStuCncl; FrCl; MthCl; PpCl; TreasSciCl; DARAwd; OptClAwd; Univ Of Illinois; Physical Therapy.

WALKER, Nancy K; Aurora Hoyt Lakes HS; Hoyt Lakes, MN; Chr; ChrhWkr; HonRl; NatlMeritCmnd; FrCl; MthCl; College; English.

WALKER, Nancy L; Nesco HS; Zearing, IA; ALAGirlsSt; Band; Chr; Chrs; ChrhWkr; CmntyWkr; CncrtBnd; HonRl; CaptMrchBnd; PepBnd; College; Law Degree.

WALKER, Patricia; Humboldt HS; Humboldt, IA; Chr; HonRl; Nursing.

WALKER, Robert E; Fair Grove HS; Fairgrove, MO; Band; Chr; Chrl; Chrs; ChrhWkr; CncrtBnd; HonRl; LbryAde; MrchBnd; PepBnd; Mo St Univ; Law.

WALKER, Scott D; Kearney HS; Kearney, NE; Band; CncrtBnd; HonRl; MrchBnd; PepBnd; Glf; Tennis; IMSpt; U Of Ne; Business Finance.

WALKER, Shelley J; East Lansing HS; Okemos, MI; Chr; HospAde; OffAde; PolWkr; RedCrAde; TchrAde; Teen; 4-H; SpnCl; PpCl; PPFtbl; College; Nursing.

WALKER, Sherry J; Greenfield HS; Greenfield, IL; 10/58 SecBand; ChrhWkr; CmntyWkr; HonRl; TchrAde; FHA; LetterTrk; LetterChrldr; VPGAA; IMSpt; College.

WALKER, Steven J; Sidney HS; Sidney, NE; ChrhWkr; HonRl; JrNHS; YthFlsp; Trk; CitAwd; College; Professional.

WALKER, Susan; Lawrence Central HS, Indpls, IN; Chr; HonRl; TchrAde; YthFlsp; 4-H; PpCl; Swmmng; Trk; PPFtbl; PresAwd; College; Medical Doctor.

WALKER, Teresa; Marshall HS; Marshall, IL; TrsFrshCls; VPSophCls; Band; MrchBnd; PepBnd; SchPl; StuCncl; FHA; LatCl; GAA; Sociology Psych.

WALKER, Teresa A; Cahokia Senior HS; Cahokia, IL; 51/532 Band; CncrtBnd; HonRl; JA; MrchBnd; JAAwd; Business School; Office Work.

WALKER, Teri L; Olympia HS; Mackinaw, IL; 50/237 HonRl; YthFlsp; FNA; FrCl; Illinois St Univ; Special Ed.

WALKER, Thelma E; Lucy Flower Voc; Chicago, IL; PresSrCls; Band; Chr; ChrhWkr; LbryAde; SchMus; StuCncl; YthFlsp; GAA; Bus; Steno.

WALKER, Thomas R; West Ottawa HS; Holland, MI; HonRl; U Of Mi; Engineering.

WALKER, Tim; Northern University; Cedar Falls, IA; 34/57 SchPl; University; Professional Writer.

WALKER, Tom J; Mcdonald Co HS; Noel, MO; Chrs; HonRl; StuCncl; FFA; Bsbl; LetterBsktbl; LetterFtbl; LetterGlf; Trk; College; Biology Major.

WALKER, Wendy K; St Charles HS; St Charles, MO; ChrhWkr; HonRl; OffAde; Marriage Church Office Secretary.

WALKOWIAK, Diane K; Spalding Acad; Spalding, NE; SecFrshCls; Chrs; HonRl; NHS; SchMus; SchPl; Yrbk; SchPpr; Tennis; U Of Ne; Teaching.

WALKOWICZ, Linda A; John Hersey HS; Mt Prospect, IL; 55/783 AFS; ChrhWkr; CmntyWkr; HonRl; HospAde; JrNHS; NatlFornLg; NatlMeritCmnd; RedCrAde; Knox Bush Program; Nursing.

WALKUP, Brian K; Atwood Hammond HS; Atwood, IL; Chrs; ChrhWkr; CncrtBnd; HonRl; Mdrgl; SchMus; SchPl; RptrSchPpr; Ftbl; VoiceDemAwd; Millikin Univ; Nursing.

WALKUP, Cathy A; South Newton HS; Kentland, IN; 1/97 TrsJrCls; TrsSrCls; ALAGirlsSt; HonRl; NHS; SchMus; SchPl; StuCncl; Yrbk; RptrSchPpr; Purdue Univ; Audiology & Speechsci.

WALKUP, Rick M; Attica HS; Attica, IN; 16/85 Aud/Vis; HonRl; RptrSchPpr; PresSpnCl; SciCl; LetterBsbl; LetterBsktbl; Ftbl; LetterTennis; RotaryAwd; Bus Sch; Computer Programmer.

WALKUP, Susan P; Benson HS; Omaha, NE; 20/425 Chr; HonRl; OffAde; TchrAde; PpCl; GAA; College; Travel Agency Work.

WALL, Alan J; Fruitport HS; Nunica, MI; 9/290 ALBoysSt; CncrtBnd; MrchBnd; NHS; PepBnd; PresStuCncl; SptEdYrbk; RptrSchPpr; LetterBsbl; Mich St; Engr.

WALL, Cynthia J; Worthington Jefferson HS; Coal City, IN; SecJrCls; Band; ChrhWkr; CncrtBnd; HonRl; NHS; PepBnd; VP4-H; PpCl; GAA; College; Secretarial.

WALL, Donald C; Central Comm Argyle HS; Montrose, IA; 9/65 HstJrCls; PresSrCls; CncrtBnd; HonRl; MrchBnd; VPNHS; SchPl; Bsktbl; LetterFtbl; CaptTrk; Univ Of Ia; Bus Admin.

WALL, Janice C; Dupree HS; Dupree, SD; 2/17 Band; Chrs; CncrtBnd; HonRl; MrchBnd; OffAde; SchPl; StuCncl; RptrYrbk; RptrSchPpr; LetterBsktbl; Bartlesville Wesleyan Col; Rn.

WALL, Janice R; St Elizabeth Riv HS; Iberia, MO; Chr; ChrhWkr; HonRl; SchPl; State Fair Comm College; Vocation.

WALL, Julie; Whitnall HS; Hales Corners, WI; 14/261 SecJrCls; NHS; StuGov; FrCl; MthCl; IMSpt; DARAwd; GovHonPrgAwd; CitAwd; Univ W Eau Claire; Nursing.

WALL, Kelly; St Teresa HS; Decatur, IL; CmntyWkr; HonRl; StuCncl; TchrAde; PpCl; Chrldr;.

WALL, Patrick S; Edgewood HS; Madison, WI; 4/150 PresFrshCls; PresSophCls; PresJrCls; ALBoysSt; Chr; HonRl; NHS; NatlMeritCmnd; SctActv; IMSpt; Cl; Bus Or Bio Sci.

WALL, Russell K; Raytown HS; Independence, MO; ChrhWkr; HonRl; YthFlsp; KeyCl; GerCl; University Of Missouri; Opthamologist.

WALL, Samuel T; Ashland Greenwood HS; Greenwood, NE; Band; CncrtBnd; HonRl; MrchBnd; PepBnd; Ftbl; Glf; Wrstlng; College; Curriculum Of Major Study.

WALL, Teresa A; Bond Co Community HS; Sorento, IL; 1/183 ALAGirlsSt; ChrhWkr; MrchBnd; NHS; NatlMeritCmnd; OffAde; StuGov; LatCl; PpCl; GAA; Kaskaskia Junior College; Court Reporter.

WALLACE, Christopher B; Oakville HS; St Louis, MO; 33/350 HonRl; JA; NHS; NatlMeritCmnd; GerCl; MthCl; LetterFtbl; LetterGlf; IMSpt; Coll; Doctor.

WALLACE, Debra; Lucas Public HS; Tipton, KS; 1014 VPFrshCls; SecTrsSophCls; SecTrsJrCls; Band; Chrs; HonRl; PepBnd; SchMus; 4-H; 4-HAwd;.

WALLACE, Debra L; Lanark HS; Mt Carroll, IL; SecTrsSrCls; FHA; Illinois State University.

WALLACE, Donald W; John F Kennedy HS; Taylor, MI; 45/420 Band; CncrtBnd; HonRl; MrchBnd; NHS; LetterTennis; Business Sch; Cpa.

WALLACE, Edwin B; Central HS; St Joseph, MO; 1/525 HonRl; JrNHS; ModUN; NHS; NatlMeritSF; SchMus; RptrSchPpr; CivCl; LatCl; MthCl; Univ Of Mo; Anthropology.

WALLACE, Erin J; Norris City HS; Omaha, IL; 13/54 PresFrshCls; PresSophCls; HonRl; SchPl; TchrAde; LetterTrk; GAA; IMSpt; NCTE; VoiceDemAwd; Eastern Ill Univ; Law.

WALLACE, Glenda; Powers Lake Public HS; Powers Lake, ND; 4/25 ALAGirlsSt; Band; Chr; ChrhWkr; CncrtBnd; HonRl; LbryAde; MrchBnd; PepBnd; SchPl; College; Music.

WALLACE, Glenda I; Powers Lake Public HS; Powers Lake, ND; Band; Chr; Chrs; ChrhWkr; CncrtBnd; DrlTm; HonRl; LbryAde; MrchBnd; PepBnd; SchPl; YthFlsp; SchPpr; College; Music Teacher.

WALLACE, Hugh J; Rogers HS; Michigan City, IN; 30/550 Band; HonRl; College; Liberal Arts.

WALLACE, Jeffrey L; Chrysler HS; New Castle, IN; Aud/Vis; Band; ChrhWkr; CncrtBnd; HonRl; MrchBnd; NHS; NatlThespSoc; SchMus; Indiana Central U.

WALLACE, Jeryl A; Nebraska City HS; Nebraska City, NE; 17/127 ChrhWkr; HonRl; OffAde; Quill&Scroll; RptrSchPpr; PpCl; Peru St Coll; Bus Educ.

WALLACE, Joan; Stuart Menlo Community HS; Menlo, IA; 22/65 Band; CmntyWkr; HospAde; JA; MrchBnd; NHS; NatlSciFnd; RedCrAde; YthFlsp; 4-H; FNA; College; Professional.

WALLACE, Linda R; Chicago Vocational HS; Chicago, IL; HonRl; Bsktbl; CaptTrk; GAA; IMSpt; College; Psychology.

WALLACE, Margaret L; University HS; Chicago, IL; Band; CncrtBnd; NatlMeritSF; SchMus; SchPl; TchrAde; GAA; IMSpt; Professional.

WALLACE, Marie A; Billings HS; Billings, MO; Chrl; HonRl; SchAde; SchPl; YthFlsp; FHA; PpCl; Bsbl; Bsktbl; College; Physical Education.

WALLACE, Michael P; Marquette HS; Alton, IL; VPSrCls; ChrhWkr; CmntyWkr; HonRl; JrNHS; NHS; SchPl; StuCncl; StuGov; RptrSchPpr; EngCl; CaptTrk; Quincy College.

WALLACE, Patricia A; Burr Oak HS; Burr Oak, KS; HonRl; StuCncl; Twrl; YthFlsp; 4-H; PpCl; LetterBsktbl; Chrldr; PPFtbl; College; Vocational.

WALLACE, Renalta; Bishop Noll Institute HS; Gary, IN; 107 Chrl; HonRl; RedCrAde; SchMus; SchPl; StuCncl; TchrAde; Yrbk; FshEdSchPpr; VoiceDemAwd; Valpraiso Univ; Corparation Lawyer.

WALLACE, Richard; Arthur Hill HS; Saginaw, MI; HonRl; JA; SciCl; Tennis; College; Ecology.

WALLACE, Robert E; Clarke Comm HS; Weldon, IA; 17/104 Chrs; ChrhWkr; SchMus; SchPl; YthFlsp; 4-H; FTA; PresSpnCl; Wrstlng; 4-HAwd; Morningside College; Ministry.

WALLACE, Robert L; Dixon HS; Dixon, IL; 12/333 ALBoysSt; NHS; VPStuCncl; SptEdSchPpr; CaptGlf; Univ Of Ill; Accounting.

WALLACE, Ronald; Central HS; Aberdeen, SD; Chrs; Mdrgl; SctActv; IMSpt; College; Medicine.

WALLACE, Ruth H; Collinsville HS; Collinsville, IL; Chrs; HonRl; Quill&Scroll; RptrSchPpr; SchPpr; SpnCl; Trk; GAA;.

WALLACE, Scott A; Edwardsville HS; Edwardsville, IL; 121/451 Chr; Chrs; ChrhWkr; SctActv; YthFlsp; YthFnd; SchPpr; GerCl; University; Horticulture.

WALLACE, Sheri; Ft Atkinson Senior H; Ft Atkinson, WI; ChrhWkr; SchMus; SctActv; YthFlsp; RptrYrbk; SpnCl; PpCl; Chrldr; University.

WALLACE, Wendy E; Waterford Twp HS; Pontiac, MI; CAP; HonRl; NHS; TchrAde; Bsktbl; College; Physical Therapy.

WALLEM, Daniel B; Streator Twp HS; Streator, IL; HonRl; Wheaton College; Geology.

WALLENDAL, Andrew M; Adams Friendship HS; Grand Marsh, WI; HonRl; TchrAde; YthFlsp; FFA; Ftbl; Trk; Wrstlng; Univ Of Wis Madison; Agri Business.

WALLENDORF, Lisa R; Calhoun HS; Batchtown, IL; TrsJrCls; Band; CncrtBnd; PepBnd; TreasStuCncl; FHA; PpCl; Bsbl; Bsktbl; Chrldr; GAA; IMSpt; 4-HAwd; College; Physical Education.

WALLER, Bonita M; Clarke Community HS; Weldon, IA; 16/104 CmntyWkr; HonRl; Quill&Scroll; TchrAde; EdYrBk; SchPpr; 4-H; FHA; GAA; Nw Missouri State Univ; Home Economics.

WALLER, De Ann M; Southern HS; Raritan, IL; 21/55 SecFrshCls; Chrs; LbryAde; MrchBnd; FHA; FrCl; GAA; College; Vocation.

WALLER, Jackie L; Berkeley Sr HS; Berkeley, MO; Band; CncrtBnd; DrlTm; HonRl; MrchBnd; SchMus; RptrYrbk; Bsktbl; Swmmng; GAA; College.

WALLER, Kimberly L; Holstein Comm HS; Holstein, IA; Chrs; HonRl; NHS; RptrSchPpr; 4-H; PpCl; Bsktbl; Glf; CchngActv; College; Education.

WALLER, Richard L; Normal Community HS; Towande, IL; 166/459 Bradley Univ; Electrical Engineer.

WALLER, Shanda J; Lyons Township HS; Minong, WI; 83/1226 ChrhWkr; HonRl; Univ; Speech Pathology.

WALLER, Spencer; Francis Parker HS; Chicago, IL; TrsFrshCls; NatlMeritCmnd; PolWkr; SchPl; StuGov; FshEdSchPpr; FrCl; MthCl; Socr; Univ Of Michigan; Government.

WALLER, Thomas; Sullivan Hs; Sullivan, MO; CncrtBnd; HonRl; MrchBnd; NHS; SctActv; FFA; Bsktbl; Ftbl; Glf; GodCntryAwd; East Central Jr Coll; Law.

WALLER, Wenonah L; Chambers Public HS; Ewing, NE; 1/21 Band; Chrs; ChrhWkr; HonRl; NHS; SchPl; Twrl; 4-H; PpCl; Trk; Chrldr; AmLegAwd; College; Medicine.

WALLESER, Anne; Kee HS; Lansing, IA; Band; CncrtBnd; HonRl; LbryAde; MrchBnd; Quill&Scroll; Yrbk; RptrSchPpr; PpCl; CchngActv; Iowa State Iniv; Veterinary Medicine.

WALLESER, Elizabeth E; Kee HS; Lansing, IA; 4/66 HonRl; JrNHS; NHS; 4-H; IMSpt; 4-HAwd;.

WALLESVERD, Mari B; West Bend East HS; West Bend, WI; 4/240 ALAGirlsSt; HonRl; NatlFornLg; VPNHS; SchMus; StuGov; YthFlsp; EdYrBk; Tennis; Chrldr; DARAwd; VoiceDemAwd; Univ Of Wisconsin; Social Work.

WALLICK, Jerry B; Lewistown Comm HS; Lewistown, IL; 7/85 DrlTm; HonRl; NHS; OffAde; SchPl; Yrbk; 4-H; PpCl; GAA; College; Law.

WALLICK, Patricia A; Ellsworth Comm HS; Ellsworth, MI; Band; CncrtBnd; HonRl; NHS; SchPl; TchrAde; SchPpr; CaptBsktbl; LetterTrk; CaptChrldr; Davenport Business Clg; Bus Management.

WALLIN, David L; Newark HS; Newark, IL; 8/60 College; Manufacturing.

WALLIN, Lawrence A; St Charles HS; St Charles, IL; 17/500 AFS; Band; Chr; CncrtBnd; HonRl; MrchBnd; LatCl; College; Zoology.

WALLIN, Paul K; Chaska HS; Chanhassen, MN; Chr; HonRl; SctActv; YthFlsp; Bsktbl; Univ Of Minnesota; Dentist.

WALLIN, Richard J; Worthington Jefferson HS; Worthington, IN; 10/38 Aud/Vis; Band; HonRl; SctActv; TchrAde; Yrbk; 4-H; Bsktbl; IMSpt; 4-HAwd; College.

WALLIS, Lyle E; University HS; Warrensburg, MO; 7/45 HonRl; SchMus; SchPl; StuCncl; RptrSchPpr; Ftbl; Engineering.

WALLIS, Marilyn L; Grinnell Newburg Comm HS; Grinnell, IA; 19/186 Band; Chr; ChrhWkr; CncrtBnd; HonRl; SecLbryAde; MrchBnd; PepBnd; YthFlsp; 4-H; LetterTrk; 4-HAwd; College; Business.

WALLISCH, William J; St Louis HS; Northwoods, MO; 8/200 HonRl; StuGov; Ftbl; Chrldr; CchngActv; IMSpt; Col; Journalism.

WALLJASPER, Wayne R; Marquette School Inc HS; Salem, IA; Chrs; PpCl; IMSpt; Southeast Community College.

WALLMAN, Barry J; Assumption HS; Fairview Hts, IL; Band; HonRl; ModUN; PepBnd; SchPl; SctActv; RptrYrbk; Tennis; Trk; Univ Of Ill; Medicine.

WALLNER, David L; Girard HS; Waggoner, IL; 1/60 ChrhWkr; CmntyWkr; HonRl; JrNHS; NHS; StuGov; FrCl; SciCl; AmLegAwd; KiwanAwd; Siu Edwardsville; Physics.

WALLNER, Gary; Alexander Ramsey HS; St Paul, MN; TchrAde; Bsktbl; CchngActv; IMSpt; Univ Of Minn; Computer Prog.

WALLNER, Gregory J; Alexander Ramsey HS; St Paul, MN; PresSrCls; Band; HonRl; TchrAde; SptEdYrbk; SptEdSchPpr; MthCl; SciCl; Bsbl; Ftbl; U Of Mn; Dr Or Aeronautical Eng.

WALLS, Deborah L; South Haven HS; South Haven, MI; 21/216 Chrs; CmntyWkr; HonRl; OffAde; StuGov; TchrAde; FshEdYrbk; PpCl; IMSpt; KiwanAwd; Mich State Univ; Vet Med.

WALLS, James C; Malta HS; Malta, IL; 13/35 Band; CncrtBnd; HonRl; MrchBnd; PepBnd; Kishwaukee Col; Computer Programming.

WALLS, James L; Charlestown HS; Charlestown, IN; 22/145 ChrhWkr; CmntyWkr; HonRl; YthFlsp; FTA; SpnCl; Tennis; Purdue Univ; Engineering.

WALLS, Linda F; Westview HS; Kankakee, IL; 83/288 Chrs; ChrhWkr; HonRl; JrNHS; LbryAde; NatlThespSoc; Quill&Scroll; RptrYrbk; FHA; Trk; Illinois St Univ; Lawyer.

WALLSCHLAEGER, Douglas T; Three Lakes Public HS; Three Lakes, WI; HonRl; StuCncl; YthFlsp; YthFnd; YthLg; Bsbl; Bsktbl; Ftbl; Univ; Prof.

WALMSLEY, Carol L; Mott HS; Warren, MI; Chr; Chrl; HonRl; HospAde; LbryAde; Mdrgl; NHS; NatlMeritSchl; SchPl; SpnCl; College; Psychology.

WALNOFER, Kathy; Ewing Public HS; Ewing, NE; 15/28 TrsSrCls; Chrs; HonRl; SchPl; Yrbk; SchPpr; FFA; PpCl; Trk; IMSpt; Cent Tech Comm College; Dental Assistant.

WALPOLE, Kimberly L; Elgin Acad; West Dundee, IL; HonRl; SchMus; SchPl; RptrSchPpr; GerCl; Swmmng; Coll; Journalism.

WALSER, Donna J; Wisconsin Heights HS; Mazomanie, WI; TrsSophCls; Band; ChrhWkr; HonRl; MrchBnd; PepBnd; SchPl; EdYrBk; PpCl; GAA; College; English.

WALSH, Butch; Shelby HS; New Era, MI; CmntyWkr; HonRl; LitMag; SctActv; StuCncl; StuGov; TchrAde; IMSpt; College; Professional.

WALSH, Carol A; Midway HS; Denton, KS; VPSophCls; PresJrCls; Band; HonRl; SchPl; TchrAde; PpCl; LetterBsktbl; LetterTrk; IMSpt; College; Medicine.

WALSH, Catherine; Caston HS; Kewanna, IN; 1/85 SecFrshCls; SecJrCls; VPSrCls; ALAGirlsSt; Band; DrmMjrt; NHS; EdYrBk; Purdue; Interior Decorating.

WALSH, Cheryl L; Blue Mound HS; Blue Mound, IL; HonRl; SchPl; RptrYrbk; RptrSchPpr; 4-H; FHA; GAA; Jr College; Secretary.

WALSH, Daniel; Marshall HS; Marshall, MI; 51/273 NatlMeritCmnd; Tennis; IMSpt; RotaryAwd; Michigan State Univi; Lawyer.

WALSH, David B; Civic Memorial HS; Bethalto, IL; 11/221 HonRl; NHS; SctActv; StuCncl; FrCl; SciCl; Bsktbl; Ftbl; College; Dentistry.

WALSH, Denise E; Good Counsel HS; Chicago, IL; 21/255 HonRl; LbryAde; Depaul Univ; Accountant.

WALSH, Diane B; Watertown HS; Juneau, WI; Band; Chrs; CncrtBnd; JA; MrchBnd; SchPl; Sec4-H; FHA; Bsktbl; 4-HAwd; College; Professional.

WALSH, Geralyn A; St Joseph HS; Chicago, IL; Chrs; HonRl; NHS; Sdlty; StuCncl; FrCl; SciCl; College; Criminology.

WALSH, Jean E; St Francis Academy; Joliet, IL; StuCncl; Trk; IMSpt; College; Proiessional.

WALSH, Jo Ann; Spalding Acad; Spalding, NE; ChrhWkr; Sdlty; TchrAde; RptrSchPpr; FHA; PpCl;.

WALSH, Julia M; Derham Hall HS; St Paul, MN; Chrs; ChrhWkr; JA; SchMus; SctActv; RptrSchPpr; FrCl; College.

WALSH, Katherine E; St Joseph HS; Chicago, IL; 11/109 HonRl; NHS; SchMus; College; Curriculum Of Major Study.

WALSH, Kevin F; St Ignatius College Prep HS; Westchester, IL; 7/155 VPSrCls; CmntyWkr; JA; NHS; VPStuCncl; EdSchPpr; Trk; College; Pre Medicine.

WALSH, Kimberly K; Weston HS; Cazenovia, WI; 10/53 SecFrshCls; Band; Chr; CncrtBnd; HonRl; MrchBnd; PepBnd; Quill&Scroll; StuCncl; RptrYrbk; RptrSchPpr; Trk; Chrldr; TreasGAA; Univ Of Wisconsin; Psychology.

WALSH, Liane M; Central HS; Antioch, IL; Chrs; DrlTm; HonRl; FrCl; LetterChrldr; GAA; Northwestern Univ; Dental Hygiene.

WALSH, Mary; Kirksville Sr HS; Kirksville, MO; 101/188 ALAGirlsSt; CtyCnl; CmntyWkr; HonRl; StuCncl;.

WALSH, Michael J; Bishop Foley HS; Warren, MI; 7/183 ALBoysSt; HonRl; NHS; NatlMeritSF; PolWkr; SchPl; StuCncl; RptrYrbk; LatCl; LetterWrstlng; Politics.

WALSH, Michael W; St Joseph HS; Westchester, IL; 1/174 HonRl; ModUN; NHS; NatlMeritCmnd; Quill&Scroll; StuCncl; StuGov; RptrSchPpr; Univ Of Ill; Engineering.

WALSH, Patricia A; Maria HS; Chicago, IL; 31/335 HonRl; NHS; College; Journalism.

WALSH, Robert S; St Viator HS; Elk Grove Village, IL; 34/276 PresSophCls; PresJrCls; PresSrCls; ALBoysSt; HonRl; SchMus; StuGov; SpnCl; Bsbl; Ftbl; Naval Acad; Engineering.

WALSH, Sharon J; Nazareth Academy; Westchester, IL; 12/154 NHS; SchMus; StuCncl; TchrAde; RptrSchPpr; Drake Univ; Liberal Arts.

WALSH, Steve G; Serena HS; Serena, IL; 27/85 Chr; Chrs; PepBnd; SchMus; SchPl; StuCncl; 4-H; FFA; FrCl; PpCl; Bsbl; Bsktbl; Socr; Univ Of Illinois; Vet.

WALSH, Timothy P; Riverdale HS; Muscoda, WI; 13/96 PresSophCls; HonRl; NHS; LetterBsbl; LetterBsktbl; LetterFtbl; College; Professional.

WALSH, Valerie A; Durand Comm HS; Durand, IL; 7/62 SecSophCls; PresSrCls; ChrhWkr; NHS; SchPpr; 4-H; VPFHA; DARAwd; So Illinois Univ; Nursing.

WALSKI, Marilyn; Oslo HS; Oslo, MN; Band; Chr; CncrtBnd; HonRl; MrchBnd; SchAde; TchrAde; RptrSchPpr; FHA; Trk; Avti; Sec.

WALSMAN, Robert C; Park Tudor HS; Indianapolis, IN; Aud/Vis; ChrhWkr; HonRl; SchPl; TchrAde; RptrSchPpr; PresSciCl; Socr; Tennis; Trk; Purdue Univ; Astrophysics.

WALSTEN, Steven; Grayslake Comm HS; Grayslake, IL; 10/238 AFS; ChrhWkr; CncrtBnd; HonRl; MrchBnd; NHS; NatlThespSoc; SchPl; SciCl; Glf; College; Professional.

WALSTON, Mark P; Brown Deer HS; Brown Deer, WI; Chr; HonRl; JA; StuCncl; RptrSchPpr; LatCl; JAAwd; U Of Wi; Bus Admin.

WALSTON, Tina M; Dillsboro Public HS; Dillsboro, IN; Band; Chrs; ChrhWkr; CncrtBnd; HonRl; MrchBnd; PepBnd; Yrbk; SchPpr; In Central Col; Nursing.

WALSTON, William G; Tri County Comm HS; Barnes City, IA; Band; Chr; Chrs; CncrtBnd; HonRl; MrchBnd; PepBnd; SchPl; YthFlsp; 4-H; FFA; Trk; Col; Farmer.

WALSTROM, Cheryl K; Ramsey HS; Ramsey, IL; 4/46 PresChrs; HonRl; PresLbryAde; OffAde; SchPl; TreasStuCncl; Yrbk; Pres4-H; BttyCrckrAwd; 4-HAwd; Sparks Business College; Exec Secretary.

WALSTROM, Lori A; Cambridge Sr HS; Isanti, MN; TrsSophCls; HonRl; NHS; StuCncl; St Cloud State College.

WALT, James; Aurora Central HS; Aurora, IL; 32/124 PresFrshCls; PresSophCls; PresJrCls; PresSrCls; NHS; IMSpt; BauchLmbAwd; JETSAwd; Bradley Univ; Mechanical Engineering.

WALTER, Becky L; Melbeta HS; Melbeta, NE; Aud/Vis; Chr; Chrs; ChrhWkr; HonRl; SchPl; TchrAde; Chrldr; GAA; PresAwd; Business School; Vocation.

WALTER, David L; Pershing HS; Plummer, MN; SecSophCls; HonRl; SchPl; StuCncl; TchrAde; 4-H; Bsktbl; Ftbl; Trk; 4-HAwd; Trade Sch; Highway Patrol.

WALTER, Julia A; Pope County HS; Golconda, IL; Band; Chrs; ChrhWkr; CmntyWkr; HonRl; MrchBnd; PepBnd; StuCncl; YthFlsp; SptEdSchPpr; PpCl; GAA; College; Dentistry.

WALTER, Karen A; St Marys HS; Sleepy Eye, MN; TrsSophCls; VPSrCls; Band; Chrs; StuCncl; StuGov; TchrAde; RptrYrbk; GAA; Willmar Community Clg; Social Service.

WALTER, Linda K; Central Heights HS; Princeton, KS; PresSophCls; PresJrCls; HonRl; NHS; PepBnd; YthFlsp; 4-H; LetterBsktbl; LetterTrk; Chrldr; College.

WALTER, Lisa L; Harrisburg HS; Harrisburg, IL; 15/179 Band; ChrhWkr; HonRl; NatlThespSoc; Pres4-H; TreasFHA; LatCl; MthCl; DanFAwd; 4-HAwd; Se Ill College; Teacher.

WALTER, Melinda K; Morrisonville HS; Palmer, IL; 3/55 TrsSrCls; Band; SchPl; StuCncl; YthFlsp; RptrSchPpr; PpCl; Millikin Univ; Poli Sci.

WALTER, Peter P; John Hersey HS; Mt Prospect, IL; 24/783 Chr; HonRl; NHS; SciCl; Univ Of Illinois; Elec Engineering.

WALTER, Rebecca A; Toulon HS; Laura, IL; 2/56 AFS; Band; Chrs; ChrhWkr; HonRl; ModUN; SctActv; FHA; Midstate College; Exec Secretary.

WALTER, Richard W; Onaway HS; Millersburg, MI; PresFrshCls; VPSophCls; Band; ChrhWkr; CncrtBnd; LbryAde; StuCncl; YthFlsp; LetterBsbl; LetterBsktbl; LetterFtbl; University; Chemistry.

WALTER, Robert J; Harper Creek HS; Battle Creek, MI; HonRl; NatlMeritSF; TchrAde; FrCl; PpCl; LetterFtbl; Trk; LetterWrstlng; OptClAwd; Community Coll; Engineering.

WALTER, Susan; Max HS; Benedict, ND; 28 ChrhWkr; JrNHS; NHS; TchrAde; EdSchPpr; 4-H; BttyCrckrAwd;.

WALTER, Terri L; Orchard Farm HS; St Charles, MO; 26/132 Chr; Chrl; Chrs; HonRl; LitMag; LbryAde; OffAde; PolWkr; Quill&Scroll; SchAde; TchrAde; TreasFHA; FrCl; Lindenwood College; Psychology.

WALTER, Terry L; Manchester HS; Manchester, MI; 10/103 HonRl; RptrSchPpr; SchPpr; Glf; College; Professional.

WALTERS, Adale M; Cass Technical; Detroit, MI; Band; CmntyWkr; HonRl; JrNHS; NHS; Quill&Scroll; StuCncl; RptrYrbk; SciCl; Tennis; Univ Of Mi; Doctor.

WALTERS, Beriecia C; Bishop Ward HS; Kansas City, KS; CmntyWkr; DrlTm; HonRl; ModUN; NatlThespSoc; SchMus; SchPl; SctActv; MthCl; PpCl; Lawyer.

WALTERS, Brian F; Portage Central HS; Portage, MI; 10/341 ChrhWkr; HonRl; SciCl; LetterGlf; LetterTennis; IMSpt; Kalamazoo Col; Pro Dentistry.

WALTERS, Bruce E; Benson HS; Omaha, NE; ; HonRl; SchMus; SchPl; Ftbl; Uno; Computer Programmer.

WALTERS, Craig A; Freeman Public HS; Freeman, SD; Chr; Chrs; HonRl; SchMus; SchPl; SctActv; University Of Springfield; Marine Biologist.

WALTERS, Curt; Central HS; Young America, MN; 15/100 Aud/Vis; HonRl; IntrClCncl; NHS; SchPl; SctActv; YthFlsp; RptrSchPpr; SciCl; Bsktbl; College; Unknown.

WALTERS, Cynthia A; Lasalle Peru Twp HS; Lasalle, IL; 208/505 ChrhWkr; CmntyWkr; HonRl; OffAde; SchAde; SpnCl; PpCl; Il Valley Com Col; Dental Assistant.

WALTERS, Denise P; Marquette HS; Alton, IL; AFS; Chr; Chrs; ChrhWkr; HonRl; JA; LbryAde; NHS; NatlMeritCmnd; NatlThespSoc; Sacrstn; Augustana College; Psychology.

WALTERS, Dennis L; Vicksburg HS; Vicksburg, MI; 18/159 ALBoysSt; CAP; NHS; NatlMeritCmnd; PolWkr; FDA; RusCl; Bsbl; Bsktbl; Glf; Tcu.

WALTERS, Donna M; Hays HS; Catherine, KS; HonRl; TchrAde; SpnCl; PpCl; DARAwd; College; Professional.

WALTERS, Elaine R; Lincolon Northeast HS; Lincoln, NE; 71/555 Chr; HonRl; Orch; SchMus; PpCl; GAA; Univ. Of N.e.; Music Ed..

WALTERS, Glenda J; Kirksville Senior HS; Kirksville, MO; Chrs; DrlTm; HonRl; HospAde; FHA; SpnCl; PpCl; College; Psycology.

WALTERS, Gregory; Marinette Sr HS; Marinette, WI; Wrstlng; Trade School; Electronics.

WALTERS, Joel; West Side HS; Gary, IN; College; Business.

WALTERS, John C; Notre Dame HS; Chicago, IL; 23/289 HonRl; HospAde; NatlMeritCmnd; Sacrstn; SctActv; RptrSchPpr; SchPpr; FDA; SciCl; LetterWrstlng; Univ Of Illinois; Medicine.

WALTERS, Joyce A; Manchester HS; N Manchester, IN; 3/147 TrsSophCls; TrsJrCls; TrsSrCls; HonRl; NatlFornLg; SecStuCncl; EdYrBk; FrCl; PpCl; Ftbl; Purdue U; Medical Tech.

WALTERS, Joyce E; Brimfield HS; Brimfield, IL; 5/55 VPJrCls; Chrs; ChrhWkr; HonRl; SecNHS; NatlMeritCmnd; PresPpCl; Univ; Paramedic Or Art.

WALTERS, Julie M; Antigo HS; Antigo, WI; 92/370 OffAde; FBLA; FHA; PresAwd; Secretary.

WALTERS, Kathy S; Centerville HS; Centerville, IA; 32/135 Chrs; ChrhWkr; DrlTm; HonRl; MrchBnd; ModUN; NatlThespSoc; StuCncl; Yrbk; RptrSchPpr; Indian Hills Comm Clg; Journalism.

WALTERS, Margaret M; Howell Senior HS; Howell, MI; 102/372 HonRl; OffAde; 4-H; 4-HAwd; Nmu; Liberal Arts.

WALTERS, Paul E; University HS; Warrensburg, MO; Chr; HonRl; SctActv; StuCncl; YthFlsp; 4-H; SpnCl; Bsktbl; IMSpt; GodCntryAwd; University; Accounting.

WALTERS, Ruth E; Nemaha Valley HS; Talmage, NE; Band; Chrs; ChrhWkr; CncrtBnd; HonRl; MrchBnd; PepBnd; SchPl; GerCl; Business School; Secretarial.

WALTHER, Brian W; Hastings HS; Hastings, MN; 60/443 ChrhWkr; HonRl; NHS; RedCrAde; TchrAde; SchPpr; Trk; Bob Jones Univ; Pre Med.

WALTHER, John R; Franklin Twp HS; Lanesville, IN; ChrhWkr; HonRl; JA; NHS; SchPl; RptrSchPpr; 4-H; PpCl; SciCl; 4-HAwd; Coll; Business.

WALTKE, Duane E; Mc Pherson County HS; Tryon, NE; 2/12 PresJrCls; HonRl; SchPl; LetterBsktbl; LetterFtbl; LetterTrk; IMSpt; University Of Nebraska; Legal Profession.

WALTMAN, Bradley N; Charleston HS; Charleston, IL; 30/259 TrsJrCls; HonRl; NHS; VPStuCncl; LetterBsktbl; LetterFtbl; LetterGlf; CchngActv; JCAwd; Eastern Il Univ; Accounting.

WALTON, Alan H; Potosi HS; Potosi, MO; PresFrshCls; PresSrCls; Band; CncrtBnd; HonRl; MrchBnd; StuCncl; Bsktbl; Ftbl; Trk; CchngActv; College.

WALTON, Delores M; Parkside HS; Jackson, MI; 18/416 Chr; ChrhWkr; HonRl; NatlMeritSF; StuCncl; StuGov; YthFlsp; FrCl; PpCl; Adrian College; Medicine.

WALTON, John W; Paoli HS; Marengo, IN; 14/118 HonRl; NHS; TchrAde; LetterTrk; Trade School.

WALTON, Judith K; St Bede Academy; Peru, IL; HonRl; Trk; Chrldr;.

WALTON, Linda D; Caruthersville HS; Caruthersville, MO; HonRl; LbryAde; NatlMeritFnl; OffAde; TchrAde; FBLA; FHA; SpnCl; Chrldr; PresAwd; Univ; Curriculum Of Major Study.

WALTON, Pamela S; Greencastle HS; Greencastle, IN; 6/160 Band; CncrtBnd; HonRl; NHS; Teen; FrCl; Glf; Swmmng; GAA; DARAwd; Ball State U.

WALTON, Sheryl D; Elmore Public HS; Elmore, MN; 11/30 SecJrCls; TrsSrCls; Chr; CncrtBnd; HonRl; SchPl; EdYrBk; GerCl; HstSrCls; IMSpt; Southwest Mn State Coll; Accounting.

WALTRIP, Laurie R; Thomson HS; Thomson, IL; 3/40 Band; Chrs; ChrhWkr; HonRl; VPNHS; SchMus; SctActv; TchrAde; EdYrBk; VPFHA; GAA; Augustana College; Music Education.

WALTRIP, Rebecca S; Greenfield HS; Greenfield, IL; 1/58 Chr; Chrs; ChrhWkr; CmntyWkr; CncrtBnd; HonRl; Mdrgl; MrchBnd; NHS; PepBnd; Mo Baptist Coll; Music.

WALTZ, Ginny L; Edinburg HS; Edinburg, IN; HonRl; FrCl; PpCl; Business School.

WALTZ, John G; Bunker Hill HS; Brighton, IL; Chrs; ChrhWkr; LbryAde; SchPl; FFA; GerCl; University; Vocational.

WALTZ, Melanie L; Madison Consolidated HS; Madison, IN; Band; CncrtBnd; HonRl; MrchBnd; NHS; PepBnd; SchMus; PpCl; LetterBsktbl; GAA; Purdue; Music.

WALTZ, Samuel; Maconaquah HS; Peru, IN; HonRl; SchAde; TchrAde; Bsktbl; Trade School; Vocation.

WALTZER, Julie; Catlin HS; Catlin, IL; Band; Chr; CncrtBnd; HonRl; Mdrgl; SchPl; StuCncl; EdYrBk; FrCl; Chrldr; Johnson Bible Coll; Music Major.

WALZ, Connie K; Bowdle HS; Java, SD; Band; Chr; Chrs; ChrhWkr; CmntyWkr; DrlTm; HonRl; 4-H; FTA; Bsktbl; Sd State U.

WALZ, David K; Ainsworth HS; Ainsworth, NE; PresFrshCls; ALBoysSt; HonRl; NHS; NatlThespSoc; StuCncl; StuGov; SptEdYrbk; Bsbl; LetterBsktbl; LetterFtbl; College; Professional.

WALZ, Gregory S; St Johns Prep HS; St Joseph, MN; 5/60 Band; ChrhWkr; CmntyWkr; CncrtBnd; HonRl; MrchBnd; PresNHS; PepBnd; PolWkr; LetterBsktbl; LetterFtbl; LetterTrk; IMSpt; Univ; Science.

WALZ, Jeff; Valentine HS; Valentine, NE; 1/96 HonRl; NHS; NatlSciFnd; Quill&Scroll; StuCncl; YthFlsp; FTA; Chadron St College; Physics Ed.

WALZ, Kim M; Ashley HS; Ashley, ND; 1/41 PresSophCls; PresJrCls; PresSrCls; Band; HonRl; PepBnd; Yrbk; RptrSchPpr; FHA; Chrldr; U Of Nd; Engineering.

WALZ, Margaret J; Beach Nigh HS; Beach, ND; 8/39 TrsFrshCls; SecTrsSophCls; Chr; Chrs; CncrtBnd; HonRl; MrchBnd; PepBnd; StuCncl; FHA; Concordia; Music.

WALZ, Margie; Grass Lake Sr HS; Grass Lake, MI; 7/89 ALAGirlsSt; Band; CncrtBnd; HonRl; MrchBnd; NHS; OffAde; PepBnd; 4-H; 4-HAwd; Michigan State U; Veterinary Medicine.

WALZ, Michele G; Central HS; Aberdeen, SD; Chrs; ChrhWkr; DrlTm; HonRl; LbryAde; OffAde; PolWkr; SchAde; StuGov; RptrSchPpr; Coll; Bus Admin.

WALZ, Michele M; Quincy Sr HS; Quincy, IL; 13/850 NHS; PresGerCl; Univ Of Illinois; Biology.

WAMBACK, Betty; Arthur Hill HS; Saginaw, MI; 1/683 Band; CncrtBnd; HonRl; LbryAde; MrchBnd; NHS; PepBnd; SchMus; SchPl; SctActv; College; Electrical Engineering.

WAMBLE, Grace M; Winnetonka HS; Kansas City, MO; Chr; DrlTm; HonRl; ModUN; PolWkr; SchMus; VPStuCncl; EdSchPpr; PpCl; Chrldr; College; Math Social Sciences.

WAMHOFF, Fredrick C; Haslett HS; E Lansing, MI; 5/149 PresSrCls; Band; ChrhWkr; NatlMeritCmnd; PresStuCncl; CaptBsbl; CaptBsktbl; CaptFtbl; AmLegAwd; CitAwd; Michigan State University.

WAMHOFF, Teresa J; Centennial HS; Circle Pines, MN; Chr; ChrhWkr; DrlTm; HonRl; Mdrgl; NHS; SchMus; LetterIMSpt; PPFtbl; Business School; Vocation.

WAMPFLER, Diana M; Stockton HS; Stockton, IL; LbryAde; NHS; SctActv; VPFTA; TreasFrCl;.

WAMPLER, Desiree A; North Andrew R 6 HS; Rosendale, MO; 3/18 SecSophCls; Band; HonRl; ModUN; SchPl; CaptChrldr; IMSpt; PPFtbl; AmLegAwd; DARAwd; College; Interior Decorator.

WAMPLER, Timothy L; Center Grove HS; Greenwood, IN; 6/235 ALBoysSt; Band; CncrtBnd; HonRl; MrchBnd; NHS; PepBnd; FrCl; Coll; Teach Music.

WAMSER, Judith A; Cedarburg HS; Cedarburg, WI; ChrhWkr; HonRl; Uw Milwaukee; Elem Ed.

WAMSLEY, Gary D; Midland HS; Midland, MI; Band; LbryAde; SctActv; SptEdYrbk; RptrSchPpr; PpCl; IMSpt; Central Mich U; Dentistry.

WAMSLEY, Michael D; Centerville HS; Centerville, IN; HonRl; StuGov; Bsbl; LetterBsktbl; Ftbl; IMSpt; College; Business.

WANEK, Mary M; Marian HS; Omaha, NE; Band; Chr; Chrs; ChrhWkr; HospAde; NHS; NatlMeritSF; Quill&Scroll; SpnCl; MthCl; Georgetown Univ; Pre Law Foreign Relations.

WANEK, Theresa L; Marian HS; Omaha, NE; Band; Chr; CncrtBnd; HonRl; MrchBnd; NHS; PepBnd; SpnCl; MthCl; SciCl; LetterBsktbl; CaptGlf; IMSpt; College; Law.

WANGERIN, Judith A; Winnebago Lutheran Acad; Ripon, WI; Chrs; Trade.

WANGLER, Louis B; Metropolis Comm HS; Metropolis, IL; 17/158 HonRl; PresNHS; PresKeyCl; GerCl; LetterFtbl; DanFAwd; Paducah Comm College; Pharmacist.

WANICKI, Fred L; Highland HS; Highland, IN; 127/538 Bsbl; Bsktbl; College; Law.

WANINGER, Lorna M; Perry Central HS; Magnet, IN; 10/82 Band; HonRl; MrchBnd; NHS; PepBnd; SchPl; Twrl; 4-H; FrCl; PpCl; Owensboro Bus Coll; Executive Secaretary.

WANKEL, Phyllis S; Triopia Jr Sr HS; Concord, IL; SecSophCls; Chr; Chrs; ChrhWkr; CncrtBnd; HospAde; LbryAde; SchMus; SchPl; FHA; College; Business.

WANLESS, Ginger R; Warren HS; Warren, IL; HonRl; NHS; OffAde; SchAde; RptrSchPpr; PresFHA; GAA; IMSpt; DARAwd; 4-HAwd; Ill St Univ; Home Ec.

WANNEMACHER, Ellen M; St Mary Academy; Monroe, MI; 11/143 Chrl; ChrhWkr; CmntyWkr; HonRl; JA; NHS; TchrAde; FrCl; JAAwd; Siena Heights College; Music.

WANNER, Leon; South Adams HS; Berne, IN; IMSpt; Trade School.

WANSTRATH, James L; Batesville HS; Batesville, IN; 12/145 HonRl; JrNHS; NHS; TchrAde; Bsbl; Bsktbl; Glf; PresAwd; CitAwd; College; Business.

WANTA, Margaret M; D C Everest HS; Schofield, WI; 12/345 Aud/Vis; ChrhWkr; HonRl; NHS; Yrbk; OptClAwd; Tech Inst; Nursing.

WANTA, Marilyn J; Newman HS; Wausau, WI; ChrhWkr; HonRl; SchMus; SchPl; StuCncl; Twrl; LatCl; MthCl; PpCl; Tennis; Univ Of Wisconsin; Mathematics.

WAPP, Daniel J; Frankfort HS; Frankfort, KS; SecTrsFrshCls; SecTrsJrCls; ALBoysSt; HonRl; StuCncl; Yrbk; FFA; LetterBsktbl; LetterFtbl; LetterTrk; Highland Com Jr Coll; Business Administrato.

WAPPEL, Rosemary F; Lourdes HS; Chicago, IL; Band; ChrhWkr; CmntyWkr; HonRl; JrNHS; LitMag; LbryAde; NatlFornLg; NHS; OffAde; SchMus; Bsktbl; Ftbl; Univ Of Illinois; Psychologist.

WAPPES, Bryce; Hamilton Comm Hs; Hamilton, IN; HonRl; SchPl; FFA; Ftbl; Glf; Trk; College; Vocational.

WARAWELL, Dawn; Hamilton Hs; Hamilton, IL; 5 Chrs; HonRl; IntrClCncl; LbryAde; FHA; FrCl;.

WARBURTON, Robert J; Washington Comm HS; Washington, IL; 81/325 Band; ChrhWkr; CmntyWkr; CncrtBnd; HonRl; MrchBnd; PepBnd; SchMus; SchPl; College; Engineering.

WARCHOL, David; Ofallow Township HS; Ofallon, IL; Band; CncrtBnd; HonRl; MrchBnd; Orch; SchMus; Univ; Professional.

WARCHOL, Loretta; Muskego HS; Muskego, WI; 17/329 ChrhWkr; HonRl; SecNHS; Bsbl; Bsktbl; GAA; IMSpt; Univ Wi Oshkosh;advertising.

WARCZYNSKI, Richard C; Hanover Central HS; Cedar Lake, IN; HonRl; JrNHS; NHS; TchrAde; FrCl; SpnCl; MthCl; Bsktbl; Purdue U; Mathematics.

WARD, Brad J; Maple Lake HS; Buffalo, MN; Band; CncrtBnd; HonRl; MrchBnd; PepBnd; LetterTrk; LetterWrstlng; IMSpt; Southwest Univ; Accounting.

WARD, Bradley J; Prophetstown HS; Prophetstown, IL; 14/98 HonRl; StuCncl; CaptFtbl; Illinois State Univ; Engineering.

WARD, Cathy; Springport Public HS; Springport, MI; 8/75 HospAde; LbryAde; MrchBnd; StuCncl; Twrl; 4-H; GAA; 4-HAwd; Jackson Community College; Dataprocessing.

WARD, Cecelia G; Puxico R 8 HS; Puxico, MO; Band; Chr; Chrl; Chrs; ChrhWkr; CmntyWkr; CncrtBnd; HonRl; LbryAde; Bsbl; Bsktbl; Trk; IMSpt; College; Nursing.

WARD, Cheryl J; Laboure HS; St Louis, MO; 38/89 Chr; Chrs; CmntyWkr; JA; SchMus; SchPpr; Tennis; IMSpt; AmLegAwd; U Of Mo.

WARD, David; Maquoketa Community HS; Maquoketa, IA; Chr; LbryAde; RptrSchPpr; Bsktbl; Ftbl; Trk; College; Teacher.

WARD, Deanna G; Brewster HS; Winona, KS; SecTrsFrshCls; TrsSophCls; Band; Chrl; Chrs; HonRl; MrchBnd; PolWkr; YthFlsp; RptrSchPpr; College; Prof Law Or Special Ed.

WARD, Deborah L; Eminence HS; Monrovia, IN; TrsFrshCls; SecSophCls; SecJrCls; MrchBnd; YthFlsp; PpCl; LetterBsktbl; Chrldr; GAA; IMSpt; Brymans Pro Career Inst; Paramedical Recpt.

WARD, Denise F; Greenville HS; Greenville, MO; Band; Chr; Chrs; CncrtBnd; HonRl; MrchBnd; PepBnd; StuCncl; TchrAde; FHA; PpCl; LetterChrldr; IMSpt;.

WARD, Diane M; Minooka HS; Joliet, IL; 3/100 Chrs; HonRl; JrNHS; MthCl; University Of Illinois; Business.

WARD, Eric; Macomb HS; Macomb, IL; Aud/Vis; Chr; NatlThespSoc; SchMus; SchPl; SctActv; IMSpt; Drake Univ; Drama.

WARD, Evelyn J; Rock Island HS; Rock Island, IL; 123/654 Chrs; ChrhWkr; CmntyWkr; Ill State U; Special Education.

WARD, Gail L; Jennings HS; Clayton, KS; 1/22 PresSrCls; Band; Chr; ChrhWkr; CncrtBnd; HonRl; MrchBnd; PepBnd; SchPl; VPYthFlsp; 4-HAwd; Colby Comm College; Nursing.

WARD, Gayla Y; Lucas HS; Lucas, KS; 3/13 Band; Chrs; DrmMjrt; NHS; SchMus; StuCncl; LetterBsktbl; Trk; Chrldr; DanFAwd; Ft Hays St Coll; Business.

WARD, Georgina R; Chisago Lakes HS; Lindstrom, MN; Band; Chr; Chrs; HonRl; OffAde; SchMus; PpCl; Business School; Vocational.

WARD, Gregory T; East Buchanan HS; Masonville, IA; 10/67 PresFrshCls; TrsSrCls; ChrhWkr; HonRl; NHS; Sacrstn; StuCncl; LetterBsktbl; LetterFtbl; CitAwd; Iowa St Univ; Engineering.

WARD, Harry M; Rockhurst HS; Prairie Village, KS; Chr; HonRl; TchrAde; Florida Inst Of Tech; Oceanographer.

WARD, Hilary M; Sacred Heart Of Mary HS; Palatine, IL; HonRl; NHS; NatlMeritCmnd; SchPl; TreasStuGov; Yrbk; RptrSchPpr; Rosary College; Creative Writing.

WARD, James; Sullivan HS; Sullivan, IL; Band; HonRl; YthFlsp; FTA; Bsktbl; Ftbl; Glf; 4-HAwd; Univ; Professional.

WARD, Judy K; Northeastern HS; Williamsburg, IN; 18/120 Band; Chr; Chrl; ChrhWkr; SchMus; TchrAde; YthLg; RptrYrbk; 4-H; Ball State Univ; Music.

WARD, Kathryn G; William Fremd HS; South Barrington, IL; Band; CncrtBnd; HonRl; MrchBnd; NHS; NatlThespSoc; SchMus; StuCncl; TchrAde; PPFtbl; Harper Western Ill; Acting.

WARD, Kevin M; Maquoketa Community HS; Maquaketa, IA; Chr; Ftbl;.

WARD, Kimberley A; Fordville HS; Fordville, ND; Band; Chrs; MrchBnd; SchMus; Yrbk; RptrSchPpr; 4-H; PpCl; LetterTrk; 4-HAwd; Nd State U; Pre Vet.

WARD, Lesa D; Carrollton HS; Carrollton, MO; Band; Chr; Chrs; HonRl; HospAde; Mdrgl; SchPl; TchrAde; Twrl; William Jewell College; Voice.

WARD, Linda D; United Township HS; East Moline, IL; 44/650 Aud/Vis; HonRl; StuCncl; Teen; Tennis; Trk; GAA; College; Business Admin.

WARD, Lisa C; Reeths Puffer HS; Muskegon, MI; 6/287 Chr; HonRl; JA; NHS; SchPl; StuCncl; PpCl; LetterTrk; Central Michigan Univ; Engineer.

WARD, Lisa J; Crown Point HS; Crown Point, IN; 1/574 HonRl; NHS; SchPl; CivCl; SpnCl; Tennis; Trk; GAA; IMSpt; KiwanAwd; Purdue Univ; Engineering.

WARD, Lois R; Danville Community HS; Danville, IA; Chrs; ChrhWkr; RptrSchPpr; SpnCl; College; Nurse.

WARD, Lonnie; Reed City HS; Reed, MI; 20/157 HonRl; NHS; RptrSchPpr; FFA; Bsbl; Ftbl; Coll;bus Management.

WARD, Lynetta; Andrean HS; Gary, IN; Chr; ChrhWkr; CmntyWkr; SancSoc; YthFlsp; SpnCl; PpCl; Indiana Univ; Art.

WARD, Mary C; Academy Of Our Lady; Peoria, IL; 4/100 PresJrCls; ChrhWkr; HospAde; NHS; NatlMeritCmnd; SchMus; StuGov; Yrbk; Wellesley College; Medicine.

WARD, Mary H; Benet Academy; Glen Ellyn, IL; 18/229 HonRl; NHS; Univ Of Dallas; Biochemistry.

WARD, Mary J; North Linn HS; Coggon, IA; Chr; Chrs; DrmMjrt; HonRl; JrNHS; SchMus; SchPl; FBLA; SpnCl; College; Journalism.

WARD, Michael; Jennings HS; North Vernon, IN; HonRl; 4-H; SpnCl; Bsktbl; Ftbl; Indiana Central; Business Administration.

WARD, Michael E; J D Darnall Senior HS; Geneseo, IL; HonRl; NatlThespSoc; SchMus; SchPl; LetterGlf; Northern Ill Univ; Geology.

WARD, Michael J; Gordon Tech HS; Chicago, IL; 30/585 HonRl; SecNHS; StuCncl; StuGov; Prof;.

WARD, Michael V; Berkley HS; Huntington Woods, MI; OffAde; StuCncl; StuGov; TchrAde; SchPpr; Bsktbl; Ftbl; Trk; IMSpt; Coll; Law.

WARD, Pamela; North Boone Hs; Caledonia, IL; ChrhWkr; CncrtBnd; HonRl; MrchBnd; NatlMeritCmnd; SchMus; FHA; SpnCl; Bsktbl; GAA; Rockford College; Music.

WARD, Ray; Hayes Center Public HS; Mccook, NE; Chr; ModUN; RptrYrbk; RptrSchPpr; EdSchPpr; FFA; 4-HAwd; Business School; Computer Management.

WARD, Ray; Hayes Center Public HS; Mccode, NE; Chr; ModUN; RptrYrbk; RptrSchPpr; EdSchPpr; FFA; 4-HAwd; Business School; Computer Management.

WARD, Raymond L; Lakewood HS; Lake Odessa, MI; 68/203 Chr; PresFrshCls; Chrs; HonRl; SchPl; 4-H; VPFrshCls; TrsSophCls; SciCl; 4-HAwd; Davenport Co ;acct.

WARD, Rhonda; Platteville HS; Platteville, WI; 14/200 Chr; HonRl; LitMag; SchMus; SchPl; TchrAde; FSA; SpnCl; SciCl; College; Mathematics.

WARD, Robert L; Fountain Central HS; Hillsboro, IN; 2/129 Band; Chr; HonRl; NHS; SchPl; TchrAde; TreasYthFlsp; Yrbk; Pres4-H; SciCl; 4-HAwd; College; Speech.

WARD, Sharon; Cedar Falls HS; Cedar Falls, IA; ChrhWkr; HonRl; HospAde; SctActv; YthFlsp; PpCl; Bacone College; Nursing.

WARD, Sharon M; Harold L Richards HS; Oak Lawn, IL; 53/1035 CncrtBnd; HonRl; MrchBnd; NHS; Orch; PepBnd; TchrAde; FrCl; LetterTennis; PresGAA; No Illinois Univ; Nursing.

WARD, Susan; Nazareth Acad; Westchester, IL; RptrYrbk; EdSchPpr; GerCl; College; Biological Sciences.

WARD, Tammy L; Union HS; Mooreland, IN; TrsSophCls; Chr; Chrs; ChrhWkr; LbryAde; NHS; StuCncl; SchPpr; FHA; PpCl; LetterBsktbl; Chrldr; College; Radiologic Technologist.

WARD, Teresa A; La Moille HS; La Moille, IL; 5/40 TrsFrshCls; SecJrCls; PresChrs; DrlTm; HonRl; LbryAde; VPNHS; OffAde; SchMus; StuCncl; EdYrBk; RptrSchPpr; Chrldr; SecGAA; University Of Illinois; Nursing.

WARD, Terri S; Dexter HS; Dexter, MO; PresFrshCls; Band; HonRl; MrchBnd; Orch; SchPl; StuCncl; FTA; PpCl; CaptChrldr; College.

WARD, Thomas J; Maine West HS; Des Plaines, IL; Band; ChrhWkr; CncrtBnd; DrmMjrt; HonRl; MrchBnd; NHS; Orch; PepBnd; SchMus; College; Veterinary Medicine.

WARD, Timothy B; Woodstock HS; Woodstock, IL; 25/275 Band; Chr; ChrhWkr; CncrtBnd; HonRl; Mdrgl; MrchBnd; NHS; FTA; Bsktbl; LetterTrk; College; Accounting.

WARD, Yvonne; Fenger HS; Chicago, IL; 6/593 HonRl; LbryAde; NHS; OffAde; RptrSchPpr; GAA; Business School; Computer Programming Analy.

WARDELL, James E; Center Senior HS; Kansas City, MO; ChrhWkr; CmntyWkr; DrlTm; PolWkr; KeyCl; SpnCl; CaptBsbl; CaptBsktbl; LetterFtbl; KiwanAwd; Us Military Acad; Army Career.

WARDEN, Cynthia; Waterford Mott HS; Pontiac, MI; 58/365 ChrhWkr; Univ; Social Work.

WARDEN, Edwin D; Salem HS; Salem, MO; 26/173 Chr; ChrhWkr; HonRl; TchrAde; RptrSchPpr; 4-H; DanFAwd; 4-HAwd; Broadcasting.

WARDEN, Janet L; Memorial HS; Joplin, MO; 1/257 AFS; Chr; HonRl; JrNHS; SecStuCncl; MthCl; LetterTennis; College.

WARDEN, Martha L; Brunswick R Ii HS; Brunswick, MO; 1/46 PresSrCls; ALAGirlsSt; Chrs; CncrtBnd; MrchBnd; NHS; OffAde; SchPl; StuCncl; FHA; Ne Missouri State Univ; History.

WARDEN, Mary; Memorial HS; Joplin, MO; AFS; HonRl; JrNHS; NHS; Tennis; GAA; PPFtbl; College; Therapist.

WARDENBURG, Wilma K; Terre Haute HS; Terre Haute, IN; 55/595 Band; CmntyWkr; CncrtBnd; HonRl; MrchBnd; ModUN; NHS; Indiana State Univ; Nursing.

WARDIN, Gloria A; Hinsdale Central HS; Hinsdale, IL; 12/608 HonRl; NHS; NatlMeritSF; Northern Il Univ; Business.

WARDLOW, Craig M; Burlington Comm HS; Burlington, IA; 9/501 HonRl; JA; SchPpr; Iowa State; Engineering.

WARDRIP, Dan; Heyworth HS; Heyworth, IL; 3/52 Chrs; HonRl; SchPl; SctActv; SpnCl; Coll; Accounting.

WARDYNSKI, Mark S; All Saints Central HS; Bay City, MI; PresFrshCls; HonRl; SchPl; StuCncl; StuGov; FrCl; Glf; IMSpt; Univ Of Michigan; Pharmacy.

WARE, Christy L; Thomas Jefferson HS; Rockford, IL; 11 335 ALAGirlsSt; HonRl; JrNHS; NHS; NatlMeritSF; Orch; SchMus; TchrAde; FTA; LatCl; U Of Il; Biology.

WARE, Donna L; Puxico R 8 HS; Puxico, MO; PresSrCls; CmntyWkr; CncrtBnd; MrchBnd; PolWkr; SchPl; StuCncl; RptrYrbk; RptrSchPpr; FHA; College; Social Studies Field.

WARE, John F; Grandview HS; Grandview, MO; VPSrCls; Band; CncrtBnd; HonRl; MrchBnd; NHS; SctActv; Bsbl; Ftbl; Trk; University; Professional.

WARE, Kay L; Merrill HS; Midland, MI; 4/110 TrsSrCls; Band; ChrhWkr; CncrtBnd; HonRl; MrchBnd; NHS; SchAde; TchrAde; YthFlsp; Business School.

WAREING, Michael A; Northrop HS; Ft Wayne, IN; 175/737 ChrhWkr; HonRl; JA; PolWkr; YthFlsp; Bsktbl; Glf; Tennis; IMSpt; JAAwd; Valparaso U; Law.

WARFIELD, Leann M; Lyons Township HS; La Grange, IL; ChrhWkr; HonRl; NatlMeritCmnd; RptrYrbk; SecPpCl; Trk; Mac Cormac Jr College; Court Reporter.

WARFIELD, Paul F; Creighton Prep; Omaha, NE; Band; ChrhWkr; CmntyWkr; CncrtBnd; DrmMjrt; MrchBnd; Orch; PepBnd; SchPl; Univ; Professional.

WARGULA, Elizabeth; Notre Dame For Girls; Chicago, IL; 28/300 Chrs; HonRl; NHS; TchrAde; SchPpr; Wright Jr Coll; Business.

WARHOVER, Michell M; Hillsboro HS; Hillsboro, MO; 27/215 Chr; CmntyWkr; HonRl; PresNHS; RedCrAde; SchAde; TchrAde; 4-H; MthCl; PpCl; SciCl; Swmmng; Col; Accountant.

WARJU, Bryan D; Cass City HS; Cass City, MI; 34/170 ChrhWkr; HonRl; NHS; Ftbl; Trk; Wrstlng; Nw Mich; Computer.

WARKENTIEN, Randall L; Winnebago HS; Winnebago, IL; VPFrshCls; AFS; HonRl; StuCncl; SchPpr; SpnCl; PpCl; Ftbl; Glf; IMSpt; Trade School; Vocation.

WARMAN, Marion; Blair Jr Sr HS; Blair, NE; PolWkr; Coll; Psych.

WARMBIER, David D; Litchfield HS; Litchfield, MN; Band; ChrhWkr; CncrtBnd; HonRl; MrchBnd; PepBnd; SctActv; SchPpr; LetterFtbl; LetterTrk; College; Professional.

WARNEKE, Dell A; Elkhorn Valley HS; Tilden, NE; Chr; ChrhWkr; CaptBsktbl; Glf; Univ Of Nebraska; Business Admin.

WARNEKE, Diane L; Fremont HS; Fremont, NE; 8/430 PresChrhWkr; HonRl; NHS; GerCl; MthCl; PpCl; College; Teaching.

WARNEKE, Pamela; Osmond HS; Osmond, NE; 18/43 Chr; Chrs; HonRl; HospAde; StuCncl; TchrAde; PpCl; Airforce Or National Guard; Secretarial Nur.

WARNEMENT, Fred; Sturgis HS; Sturgis, MI; Band; CncrtBnd; MrchBnd; PepBnd; SctActv; TchrAde; KeyCl; Glenn Oaks Com Col; Bus Manage Ment.

WARNER, Barbara J; Lowell HS; Lowell, IN; 50/267 TrsJrCls; TrsSrCls; DrlTm; HonRl; TchrAde; 4-H; PresFHA; TreasFTA; 4-HAwd; Col; Teaching.

WARNER, Deanna M; Winfield Jr Sr HS; Winfield, KS; Band; ChrhWkr; CmntyWkr; HonRl; HospAde; Teen; YthFlsp; College; Nurse.

WARNER, Denise R; Valley Center HS; Valley Center, KS; 13/119 SecFrshCls; PresJrCls; Chr; HonRl; NatlFornLg; NatlThespSoc; SchMus; StuCncl; RptrSchPpr; PpCl; BttyCrckrAwd; U Of Ks; Humanities.

WARNER, Gregory; Pekin Community Hs; Pekin, IL; 131/759 Band; CncrtBnd; JA; MrchBnd; PepBnd; SchMus; SchPl; JAAwd; Apprenticeship; Pahermaker.

WARNER, Gwen A; South Side HS; Fort Wayne, IN; 10/411 Chr; ChrhWkr; HonRl; SchMus; TchrAde; Chrldr; College; Music.

WARNER, Jay R; Blue Valley HS; Stanley, KS; HonRl; SctActv; LetterBsktbl; LetterGlf; Socr; Swmmng; Tennis; LetterTrk; Clg; Prof.

WARNER, Jeffrey; Bullock Creek HS; Midland, MI; /200 Band; NatlFornLg; TchrAde; RptrYrbk; TreasSchPpr; FrCl; LetterBsbl; LetterFtbl; Wrstlng; Northwood Ins; Hot & Rest Manag.

WARNER, John J; Chippewa Falls HS; Chippewa Falls, WI; 1/375 ALBoysSt; NatlFornLg; NHS; NatlMeritSF; SchPl; VPStuCncl; LetterTennis; RotaryAwd; Univ; Research In Lit Science.

WARNER, Joni; Beaver City HS; Beaver City, NE; Band; Chr; SchMus; SchPl; StuCncl; RptrYrbk; RptrSchPpr; FHA; PpCl; Chrldr; Central Tech Comm Coll; Human Services.

WARNER, Judy; Whitko HS; Pierceton, IN; ChrhWkr; CmntyWkr; HonRl; HospAde; YthFlsp; 4-H; College; Social Work Business.

WARNER, Leslie L; Meridian Sr HS; Sanford, MI; 31/140 Chr; HonRl; NHS; NatlThespSoc; SchMus; SchPl; TreasStuCncl; Pres4-H; AmLegAwd; 4-HAwd; Delta Clg; Fine Arts.

WARNER, Patricia L; Mt Olive HS; Mount Olive, IL; 10/56 Band; Chrs; HonRl; SchPl; TchrAde; EdYrBk; FBLA; FHA; Trk; GAA; Southern Ill U; Art.

WARNER, Russell F; Burlington Comm HS; Burlington, IA; HonRl; StuCncl; LetterFtbl; U Of Iowa; Bus.

WARNER, Ruth E; East Peoria Comm HS; East Peoria, IL; Chr; Chrs; ChrhWkr; HonRl; Mdrgl; OffAde; SchMus; MthCl; PpCl; GAA; Coll; Musc.

WARNER, Stacey L; Fulton HS; Albany, IL; Band; CncrtBnd; JA; MrchBnd; PepBnd; RptrYrbk; SchPpr; SpnCl; Trade School; Curriculum Of Major Study.

WARNER, Tracie M; Badger HS; Lake Geneva, WI; 4/210 ALAGirlsSt; Chr; HonRl; SchMus; TchrAde; Tennis; Trk; Clge; Vocation.

WARNICK, Elizabeth A; Warrensburg HS; Warrensburg, MO; 15/150 HonRl; NHS; OffAde; StuCncl; Yrbk; SpnCl; IMSpt; College; Commercial Art.

WARNICK, Nancy E; Hlv Community HS; Vixtor, IA; Chrs; ChrhWkr; DrlTm; HonRl; SchMus; SchPl; FTA; SpnCl; PpCl; LetterChrldr; College; Mathmatics.

WARNICK, Stephen L; Eisenhower HS; Decatur, IL; 20/308 Band; ChrhWkr; CncrtBnd; HonRl; JA; MrchBnd; NHS; Orch; PepBnd; SchMus; YthFlsp; Eastern Ill Univ; Spanish.

WARNKE, Andrea L; Elgin HS; Elgin, IL; Band; Chr; Chrs; ChrhWkr; CmntyWkr; CncrtBnd; DrmMjrt; MrchBnd; Orch;.

WARNKE, Brenda S; Fairfax HS; Fairfax, SD; VPSophCls; PresJrCls; Band; Chrs; HonRl; SchPl; StuCncl; 4-H; Trk; Chrldr;.

WARNKE, Janice M; Butte Public HS; Butte, NE; Band; Chrs; CncrtBnd; HonRl; LbryAde; MrchBnd; PepBnd; RptrSchPpr; PpCl; LetterTrk; Tech Comm Coll; Accounting.

WARNKE, Kirk R; Sanborn Comm HS; Sanborn, IA; PresSophCls; HonRl; NHS; SchPl; SctActv; StuCncl; RptrYrbk; LetterBsbl; LetterBsktbl; LetterGlf; Coll; Banking Busines.

WARNKE, Marlene A; Tripoli Comm HS; Sumner, IA; HonRl; LbryAde; College; Archaeology.

WARNKE, Susan K; Pawnee Public HS; Pawnee City, NE; 1/32 Band; Chr; Chrs; ChrhWkr; CncrtBnd; HonRl; MrchBnd; PepBnd; RptrSchPpr; SchPpr; PpCl; Trk; Univ Of Nebraska; Nursing.

WARNOCK, Caroline C; Rich South HS; Matteson, IL; 44/268 Band; CncrtBnd; HonRl; MrchBnd; PepBnd; Univ Of Ill; Biology.

WARNS, Martin D; Madison HS; Madison, SD; ALBoysSt; ChrhWkr; CmntyWkr; HonRl; NHS; YthFlsp; SchPpr; 4-H; Bsktbl; Trk; IMSpt; College; Business.

WARPINSKI, Anthony B; Denmark HS; Denmark, WI; HonRl; FFA; Ftbl; LetterTrk; LetterWrstlng;.

WARRANT, Thomas L; Mankato East HS; Mankato, MN; 12/212 ChrhWkr; HonRl; CaptBsbl; IMSpt; Mankato St; Mathematics.

WARREN, Breit A; Cedar Rapids Kennedy HS; Cedar Rapids, IA; ALBoysSt; Band; CncrtBnd; HonRl; MrchBnd; PepBnd; PolWkr; SctActv; StuGov; Ftbl; Law.

WARREN, Cameron D; Winola HS; Viola, IL; PresSophCls; ALBoysSt; HonRl; NHS; SchMus; StuCncl; SpnCl; LetterFtbl; LetterWrstlng; Univ Of Illinois; Accounting.

WARREN, Carol; Jonesville HS; Jonesville, MI; 9/87 Chr; ChrhWkr; CmntyWkr; HonRl; OffAde; SchPl; TchrAde; RptrSchPpr; Grand Rapids Baptist Col; Writer.

WARREN, Carol D; St Charles HS; St Charles, IL; 3/460 Band; CncrtBnd; HonRl; MrchBnd; TreasNHS; Orch; PepBnd; TreasSpnCl; Purdue University.

WARREN, Cynthia; Baldwin HS; Overbrook, KS; ALAGirlsSt; HonRl; NHS; PpCl; College.

WARREN, Glenda; Hays HS; Hays, KS; HonRl; SpnCl; Fort Hays Ks State Col; Bookkeeper.

WARREN, Glenn E; Southern HS; Wymore, NE; HonRl; JrNHS; NHS; NatlMeritSchl; StuCncl; Ftbl; LetterTrk; Chrldr; AmLegAwd; 4-HAwd; College; Electronics.

WARREN, James P; Battle Creek Central HS; Battle Creek, MI; StuCncl; Wmu; Electrical Engineer.

WARREN, Joan L; Oakville Sr HS; St Louis, MO; 5/365 HonRl; PresNHS; SchMus; RptrYrbk; FDA; PresFTA; SecSciCl; LetterSwmmng; LetterTrk; GAA; PresAwd; College; Medicine.

WARREN, Marguerite; Southwest HS; St Louis, MO; SchMus; StuCncl; StuGov; GerCl; SciCl; Swmmng; GAA; IMSpt; PPFtbl; Meramec Comm Col; Technical Illustration.

WARREN, Marsha J; New Lothrop HS; Corunna, MI; 8/80 DrlTm; SchMus; MrchBnd; NHS; OffAde; TchrAde; YthFlsp; 4-H; SpnCl; 4-HAwd; U Of Michigan; Science Technology.

WARREN, Martha C; Carrollton HS; Carrollton, MO; 7/106 VPSrCls; Band; Chrs; ChrhWkr; SecNHS; SchMus; TchrAde; LetterTennis; IMSpt; VoiceDemAwd; Coll; Pro.

WARREN, Mary M; Willowbrook HS; Villa Park, IL; 17/822 Chr; University Of Illinois; Pharmacy.

WARREN, Michael J; St Agatha HS; Detroit, MI; ChrhWkr; CmntyWkr; HonRl; NHS; NatlMeritCmnd; PolWkr; Mich State Univ; Management.

WARREN, Pamela; Saybrook Arrowsmith HS; Arrowsmith, IL; Chr; HonRl; SchMus; SchPl; StuCncl; EdYrBk; RptrSchPpr; CchngActv; GAA; Eastern Il Univ; Home Ec And Music.

WARREN, Patricia A; Sand Creek HS; Lansing, MI; 1/52 SecFrshCls; SecSophCls; PresJrCls; Band; ChrhWkr; CncrtBnd; HonRl; MrchBnd; NHS; SchPl; Grand Rapids Baptist College.

WARREN, Rodney R; Bay City Western HS; Auburn, MI; 79/448 HonRl; NHS; PepBnd; SchAde; StuGov; TchrAde; LatCl; SpnCl; CchngActv; IMSpt; Oakland Univ; Law.

WARREN, Scott H; Wm Horlick HS; Racine, WI; 39/560 Band; ChrhWkr; HonRl; SchAde; SctActv; TchrAde; YthFlsp; FrCl; U W Parkside; Chemistry.

WARREN, Susan B; Grinnell HS; Kellogg, IA; 57/189 SpnCl; LetterPpCl; Tennis; Trk; LetterChrldr; University Of Iowa; Nursing.

WARREN, Susan M; Neil A Armstrong HS; Neenah, WI; 34/600 HonRl; NHS; NatlMeritSF; SchMus; SchPl; StuGov; EdYrBk; Yrbk; SchPpr; OptClAwd; College; Commercial Art.

WARREN, Terry; Bennett Community HS; Bennett, IA; 1/32 VPSophCls; VPJrCls; VPSrCls; ALBoysSt; HonRl; NHS; StuCncl; Univ; Vetenary.

WARREN, William H; Bay City Central HS; Bay City, MI; NatlMeritSchl; YthFlsp; 4-H; 4-HAwd; Delta Clg; Pharmacy.

WARREN, Zella M; Broken Bow HS; Broken Bow, NE; Band; CncrtBnd; HonRl; MrchBnd; EdYrBk; FHA; PpCl; LetterTrk; Chrldr; IMSpt; College; Zoology.

WARRENS, Debra A; North HS; Sheboygan, WI; HonRl; NHS; SchPl; SctActv; GerCl; PpCl; Univ Of Wis Madison; Math.

WARRICK, Julian E; Kenwood HS; Chicago, IL; 27/413 Aud/Vis; Chrs; HonRl; NHS; NatlMeritCmnd; SchPl; StuCncl; StuGov; RptrYrbk; FrCl; Stanford Univ; Elec Engineer.

WARRICK, Norman; River Rouge HS; River Rouge, MI; 12/213 HonRl; NHS; PolWkr; TchrAde; YthFlsp; FBLA; FSA; PpCl; SciCl; Bsktbl; Michigan State; Lawyer.

WARRINER, George; Msgr John R Hackett HS; Kalamazoo, MI; PresSrCls; HonRl; IntrClCncl; JA; PolWkr; SchAde; StuCncl; StuGov; FrCl; Ftbl; Michigan State Univ; Philosophy.

WARRINGTON, Dawn D; Campus HS; Haysville, KS; 22/265 HonRl; NatlThespSoc; SchPl; PpCl; College; Nursing.

WARSINSKI, Robert A; Southfield Lathrup HS; Southfield, MI; ChrhWkr; HonRl; NatlMeritFnl; NatlMeritCmnd; NatlMeritSchl; NatlMeritSF; Univ; Medicine.

WARTGOW, Ricky; Butternut HS; Butternut, WI; 1/21 Band; ChrhWkr; CncrtBnd; HonRl; MrchBnd; PepBnd; StuCncl; StuGov; SpnCl; Bsktbl; Univ; Professional.

WARTHA, Lynn A; Saint Josephs HS; South Bend, IN; 43/282 ALAGirlsSt; CmntyWkr; HonRl; PolWkr; StuGov; FrCl; PpCl; University; Medicine.

WARTHEN, Nowell J; Waterford Mott HS; Pontiac, MI; 3/400 Band; ChrhWkr; CncrtBnd; DrmMjrt; MrchBnd; RedCrAde; StuGov; LetterTrk; Univ Of Michigan; Medicine.

WARTMAN, Brad L; Stanton County HS; Johnson, KS; 6/42 HonRl; SpnCl; Bsktbl; Ftbl; University.

WARTON, Dale; Wm J Bogan Hs; Chicago, IL; 5/728 ChrhWkr; CncrtBnd; HonRl; NHS; OffAde; SecFrshCls; GerCl; VPMthCl; VPSciCl; GAA; Loyol U; Biological Science Premed.

WARTON, Gale E; William J Bogan HS; Chicago, IL; 4/728 ChrhWkr; HonRl; NHS; OffAde; SctActv; TchrAde; SpnCl; MthCl; SciCl; Mundelein College; Communicative Disorders.

WARTSBAUGH, Shirley; Newton HS; Newton, IL; 29#33#37 HonRl; 4-H; LatCl; GAA; IMSpt; Eastern Illinois Univ; Elementary Education.

WARWICK, Karen A; Valparaiso HS; Valparaiso, IN; 36/423 HonRl; SctActv; LetterSwmmng; Tennis; GAA; GodCntryAwd; U Of Evansville; Nursing.

WARZALA, Lillian C; South Division HS; Milwaukee, WI; ChrhWkr; NHS; Yrbk; FBLA; FTA; GerCl; Business Work; Secretarial.

WARZECHA, Thomas J; Lane Technical HS; Chicago, IL; 323/1209 LbryAde; OffAde; SchAde; SctActv; KeyCl; Clge; Medicine.

WASCHER, Cheryl L; Owosso HS; Owosso, MI; 144/452 Band; MrchBnd; TchrAde; 4-H; GAA; IMSpt; ALBoysSt; Cen Mi U ; Physical Ed Or Acct.

WASEMILLER, Paul S; Maplewood Academy; Wahpeton, ND; 3/65 PresSophCls; HonRl; TchrAde; RptrSchPpr; College; Doctor.

WASH, Hallee D; Jackson County Western HS; Spring Arbor, MI; 10/149 Mdrgl; NHS; SchPl; TreasStuCncl; LetterTrk; Chrldr; College; Professional.

WASH, Perry; Robert Lindblom Technical HS; Chicago, IL; 315/722 HonRl; NHS; Ill Inst Of Tech; Engineering.

WASHBURN, Mark D; Hoxie HS; Hoxie, KS; 2/77 PresFrshCls; PresJrCls; PresSrCls; HonRl; PresStuCncl; TchrAde; Yrbk; LetterFtbl; LetterGlf; AmLegAwd; Fort Hays State College; Cpa.

WASHBURN, Mary C; La Salle HS; Cedar Rapids, IA; Chrs; HonRl; HospAde; ModUN; NHS; SchMus; SchPl; GAA; IMSpt; College; Sociology.

WASHBURN, Steven J; Memorial HS; Eau Claire, WI; HonRl; LetterBsktbl; Work.

WASHBURNE, Eleanor P; Miss Porters HS; Birmingham, MI; Col; Pr.

WASHECHEK, Mary A; Kimball Public HS; Kimball, SD; ALAGirlsSt; Band; ChrhWkr; CncrtBnd; HonRl; MrchBnd; PepBnd; SchMus; RptrSchPpr; PresFHA; Business School; Secretary.

WASHELESKY, Andrew; Lasalle Peru Twp Hs; Peru, IL; HonRl; GerCl; Bradley U; Civil Engineering.

WASHER, Colleen J; Princeton HS; Princeton, IL; Chr; HonRl; NatlThespSoc; SchPl; College; Art.

WASHINGTON, Anita; Von Steuben HS; Chicago, IL; 33/257 Band; ChrhWkr; CncrtBnd; HonRl; HospAde; NatlMeritCmnd; OffAde; PolWkr; SchMus; SchPpr; Loyola Univ; Nurse.

WASHINGTON, Chester P; Washington HS; Indianapolis, IN; 27/350 Band; ChrhWkr; CmntyWkr; HonRl; JA; NatlMeritFnl; StuCncl; YthFlsp; RptrYrbk; RptrSchPpr; College; Professional.

WASHINGTON, Cynthia J; Romulus Sr HS; Romulus, MI; 73/294 Band; ChrhWkr; CtyCnl; CmntyWkr; CncrtBnd; HonRl; MrchBnd; SctActv; StuCncl; StuGov; FHA; PPFtbl; Michigan St Univ; Management.

WASHINGTON, Gale A; Lindblom Tech HS; Chicago, IL; 34/695 Chr; ChrhWkr; CmntyWkr; HonRl; LbryAde; OffAde; SchAde; SctActv; TchrAde; Northwestern College; Accountant.

WASHINGTON, Hurdistine; Tilden HS; Chicago, IL; 5/306 HonRl; PresNHS; StuCncl; CaptTwrl; RptrYrbk; RptrSchPpr; SecFHA; LetterBsktbl; GAA; CitAwd; Chicago State Univ.

WASHINGTON, Joe L; Chicago Vocational HS; Chicago, IL; 201/1000 OffAde; SchAde; StuCncl; StuGov; TchrAde; YthLg; Northwestern Univ; Interior Designer.

WASHINGTON, Joyce; West Side Hs; Gary, IN; Band; ChrhWkr; CncrtBnd; HonRl; JrNHS; NHS; SchMus; StuGov; YthFlsp; Yrbk; College; Professional.

WASHINGTON, Julius K; Lindblom Technical HS; Chicago, IL; 34/722 HonRl; SchAde; TchrAde; PpCl; SciCl; LetterFtbl; Univ; Law.

WASHINGTON, Julius K; Lindblom Tech HS; Chicago, IL; 34/695 PresSrCls; ChrhWkr; HonRl; SchAde; StuGov; TchrAde; YthFlsp; PpCl; SciCl; CaptFtbl; University Of Illinois; Lawyer.

WASHINGTON, Kimm; Chicago Vocational HS; Chicago, IL; 81/689 HonRl; OffAde; SchAde; TchrAde; PpCl; LetterGAA; IMSpt; JAAwd; CitAwd; Univ Of Ill; Architecture.

WASHINGTON, Maurice O; Englewood HS; Chicago, IL; 7/372 Chrs; HonRl; JrNHS; StuCncl; Iit; Electronics.

WASHINGTON, Phyllis K; St Thomas Apostle HS; Chicago, IL; 1/44 PresSophCls; Chr; HonRl; RedCrAde; SchPl; StuCncl; TchrAde; Yrbk; Chrldr; GAA; University; Professional.

WASHINGTON, Willinda K; University Of Chicago HS; Chicago, IL; SecSrCls; Chr; ChrhWkr; LbryAde; NatlMeritCmnd; OffAde; SctActv; StuCncl; YthFlsp; FrCl; Bsktbl; University; Pediatrician.

WASHNIESKI, Vanessa; Manistee Catholic Central HS; Manistee, MI; Chr; ChrhWkr; SchAde; SchPl; PpCl; Bsktbl; Coll; Home Ec Teacher.

WASIELESKI, Lynn K; Glidden Public HS; Glidden, WI; PresFrshCls; VPSophCls; ChrhWkr; HonRl; Yrbk; RptrSchPpr; 4-H; FTA; PpCl; CaptChrldr; 4-HAwd; College; Nursing.

WASIK, Richard J; St Ignatius College Prep; Chicago, IL; 40/210 ChrhWkr; CmntyWkr; HonRl; IntrClCncl; StuCncl; TchrAde; LetterBsbl; Swmmng; IMSpt; University; Medicine.

WASIKOWSKI, Paul L; Cudahy HS; Cudahy, WI; 3/350 HonRl; NHS; MthCl; LetterBsktbl; CaptFtbl; Uw Madison; Engineering.

WASILAS, Susan M; Batavia Senior HS; Batavia, IL; AFS; Chrs; SchPl; StuCncl; 4-H; FHA; KeyCl; DanFAwd; 4-HAwd; Bradley Univ; Fashion Merchandise.

WASILEWSKI, David L; Thomas Kelly HS; Chicago, IL; Chrs; ChrhWkr; HonRl; NHS; Quill&Scroll; SptEdSchPpr; Bsbl; Bsktbl; VFWAwd; CitAwd; Univ Of Il Circle Campus; Creative Writer.

WASINGER, Lavonne R; Ness City HS; Ness City, KS; Chr; DrlTm; HonRl; NatlThespSoc; SchMus; SchPl; PpCl; Bsbl; Bsktbl; Chrldr; College; Interior Decorator.

WASLASKI, Kathy L; Cavalier Public HS; Concrete, ND; HonRl; HospAde; SchPl; 4-H; FrCl; Bsbl; Chrldr; GAA; PPFtbl; 4-HAwd; Clge; Prof.

WASLEWSKI, Mark A; St Vincent De Paul Sem; Chicago, IL; 1/9 Chr; Chrs; CmntyWkr; HonRl; SchMus; StuCncl; St Marys College; Priesthood.

WASMOEN, Brian R; New Ulm Public HS; New Ulm, MN; Band; Chrs; HonRl; NatlFornLg; SchMus; SchPl; RptrSchPpr; GerCl; LetterFtbl; IMSpt; College; Math.

WASS, Duane; Bellmont HS; Monroeville, IN; HonRl; JrNHS; NHS; YthFlsp; LatCl; EldAwd; Ball St Univ; Speech Pathology.

WASS, Kathleen; Centerville Public HS; Centerville, SD; Band; Chrs; DrlTm; HonRl; SchPl; StuCncl; FHA; Chrldr; South Dak State Univ.

WASSALL, Edward; Meramec Valley R Iii HS; Pacific, MO; 85/186 Aud/Vis; Band; CncrtBnd; DrlTm; MrchBnd; Orch; PepBnd; SchPl; StuCncl; Meramec Comm College; Law Enforcement.

WASSAM, Mary A; Windsor HS; Windsor, MO; Chrs; ChrhWkr; HonRl; NHS; FHA; FNA; PpCl; Coll; Voc.

WASSEF, Samir Y; Catholic Central HS; Detroit, MI; Aud/Vis; ChrhWkr; CncrtBnd; MrchBnd; Orch; PepBnd; SctActv; MthCl; SciCl; IMSpt; Univ; Proffessional.

WASSERMAN, Ellen D; Hoxie HS; Hoxie, KS; ChrhWkr; DrlTm; HonRl; PresYthFlsp; SchPpr; Pres4-H; SecFHA; PpCl; Trk; 4-HAwd; Kansas State Univ; Home Economics.

WASSERSTROM, Bruce A; Pembroke Country Day HS; Kansas City, MO; Aud/Vis; Band; Chrl; Chrs; CmntyWkr; HonRl; NatlMeritFnl; NatlMeritSF; SchMus; SctActv; StuCncl; StuGov; RptrSchPpr; Ftbl; College; Psychology.

WASSINGER, James E; Central Catholic HS; Grand Island, NE; VPJrCls; VPBand; Chrl; Chrs; CncrtBnd; PepBnd; SchMus; TchrAde; Glf; Wrstlng; College; Music.

WASSMANN, Lori J; Waterman HS; Waterman, IL; 1/35 TrsSophCls; Band; LbryAde; NHS; StuCncl; RptrYrbk; FTA; FrCl; GAA; University; Mathematics.

WASSON, Carol L; Mark Twain HS; Center, MO; VPSophCls; Chrs; CncrtBnd; HonRl; MrchBnd; PepBnd; Yrbk; FHA; PpCl; Chrldr; College; Music.

WASSON, Kathryn K; Holcomb HS; Holcomb, KS; Band; Chrs; HonRl; SchPl; TchrAde; FHA; PpCl; LetterBsktbl; LetterTrk; PPFtbl; College; Nursing.

WASSON, Linda J; Lincoln HS; Cambridge City, IN; TrsJrCls; ChrhWkr; CncrtBnd; HonRl; MrchBnd; NHS; PepBnd; YthFlsp; Tennis; GAA; Trade; Radiology.

WASSON, Teresa L; Van Far HS; Vandalia, MO; 1/90 TrsJrCls; VPSrCls; AFS; HonRl; NHS; Quill&Scroll; SchPl; EdSchPpr; FHA; BttyCrckrAwd; U Of Mo; Journalism.

WASSON, Toni; Dixon Hs; Dixon, IL; 47/339 HonRl; NHS; Bsktbl; GAA; College; Teach Physical Ed Or Health.

WASUNG, Julie A; St Florian HS; Detroit, MI; 7/126 Chr; ChrhWkr; CmntyWkr; HonRl; SecNHS; SchMus; RptrYrbk; RptrSchPpr; VPFTA; Michigan State Univ; Accounting.

WASYLEAN, Joseph D; York HS; Elmhurst, IL; 42/912 HonRl; NHS; Quill&Scroll; SptEdSchPpr; Univ Of Illinois; Doctor.

WASYLEWSKI, Garret L; Boyne Falls Public HS; Elmira, MI; PresSophCls; HonRl; SchAde; SctActv; TchrAde; Bsbl; Bsktbl; Trk; Trade Sch; Automotive Mech.

WASYNCZUK, Andrew; Maine North HS; Glenview, IL; 5/350 HonRl; NHS; LetterSocr; Case Western Reserve Univ; Engineer.

WASZAK, Lillian; Amos Alonzo Stagg Hs; Hickory Hills, IL; ChrhWkr; HonRl; NatlMeritCmnd; RptrSchPpr; College; Accounting.

WATANABE, Shauna K; Princeton Community HS; Princeton, IN; 11/255 ALAGirlsSt; Aud/Vis; Band; Chr; HonRl; NHS; OffAde; StuCncl; PpCl; Chrldr; Indiana Univ; Major Psychology.

WATCHORN, Carolee T; Fremont Sr HS; Fremont, NE; 47/438 ALAGirlsSt; HonRl; HospAde; StuCncl; SecTeen; VP4-H; PresFHA; PpCl; Chrldr; DARAwd; 4-HAwd; College; Home Economics.

WATCHOUS, Pamela J; Desoto HS; Desoto, KS; 1/94 ChrhWkr; HonRl; Mdrgl; SecNHS; NatlMeritSF; NatlThespSoc; SchMus; Chrldr; DARAwd; 4-HAwd; Baker Univ; Christian Service.

WATERHOUSE, Charles N; Niles Senior HS; Niles, MI; ALBoysSt; HonRl; NHS; NatlMeritFnl; StuCncl; TchrAde; LetterTrk; University; Math Major.

WATERMAN, Ellen R; Dysart Geneseo HS; Rock Valley, IA; 2/55 VPFrshCls; Band; Chrs; ChrhWkr; PresLbryAde; NHS; SchPl; SecStuCncl; SecYthFlsp; Westmar College; Music.

WATERMAN, Sandra A; Grace HS; Minneapolis, MN; Chr; Chrl; LitMag; SchMus; RptrSchPpr; U Of M; Piano.

WATERMAN, Vicky L; Mt Pleasant HS; Wayland, IA; Chrs; HonRl; StuCncl; PpCl; Des Moines Area Comm College; Medical Lab.

WATERS, Fred; West Branch Comm HS; Iowa City, IA; 5/72 TrsSophCls; PresJrCls; ChrhWkr; HonRl; NHS; NatlMeritCmnd; SchPl; StuGov; SpnCl; GovHonPrgAwd; Univ Of Ia; Mathematics.

WATERS, James L; Manistique HS; Manistique, MI; 8/157 Michigan Tech Univ; Engineering.

WATERS, Jennifer; O Neill Public HS; O Neill, NE; Band; CncrtBnd; HonRl; MrchBnd; NHS; PepBnd; SchMus; SchPl; RptrYrbk; RptrSchPpr; Univ Of Nebraska; Biology Major.

WATERS, John A; Pittsfield HS; Baylis, IL; 2/129 NatlMeritCmnd; SctActv; LatCl; LetterTrk; GodCntryAwd; Quincy College; Medicine.

WATERS, John M; Lincoln HS; Vincennes, IN; 1/350 ALBoysSt; ChrhWkr; HonRl; PolWkr; RptrSchPpr; SchPpr; SciCl; Bsbl; College Of Wm&mary; Lawyer.

WATERS, Mary H; Taylorville HS; Taylorville, IL; 14/251 Chr; CmntyWkr; HonRl; NHS; NatlThespSoc; SchPl; RptrSchPpr; SchPpr; LatCl; PpCl; Southern Methodist Univ; Art.

WATERS, Matthew; Union HS; Grand Rapids, MI; Band; Mi St Univ; English.

WATERS, Robyn D; Winner Sr HS; Carter, SD; 4/140 Band; Chr; Chrl; Chrs; ChrhWkr; CncrtBnd; HonRl; Mdrgl; MrchBnd; PepBnd; SchAde; SchMus; 4-HAwd; College; Laboratory Tech.

WATERS, Steven B; Mount Clemens HS; Mt Clemens, MI; 6/416 HonRl; NHS; Swmmng; CaptTennis; Trk; Mich State; Pre Medicine.

WATERS, Tamara C; Baldwin HS; Baldwin, KS; 3/70 Band; CncrtBnd; MrchBnd; PepBnd; SchMus; SchPl; RptrYrbk; EdSchPpr; University; Fine Arts.

WATERSON, Timmie R; Davison HS; Davison, MI; 46/433 Chr; Chrl; Chrs; HonRl; NHS; SchMus; TchrAde; LetterWrstlng; CchngActv; IMSpt; Cntrl Michigan Univ; Coach.

WATERWORTH, Joel B; Marshall County Central HS; Newfolden, MN; TrsFrshCls; LetterBsbl; LetterBsktbl; LetterTrk;.

WATERWORTH, Sherry L; Wellington HS; Wellington, MO; Chrs; ChrhWkr; HonRl; OffAde; SchPl; Yrbk; SchPpr; FHA; PpCl; Evangel College; Art.

WATFORD, Don; Plattsmouth HS; Plattsmouth, NE; Chr; HonRl; LbryAde; SchPl; StuCncl; SpnCl; Lithera Farmer.

WATHIER, Marty A; Waukon HS; Waukon, IA; ChrhWkr; HonRl; College.

WATKINS, Andrew L; Fox Sr HS; Arnold, MO; 22/600 ALBoysSt; CmntyWkr; HonRl; NHS; NatlMeritCmnd; PolWkr; StuGov; LetterFtbl; IMSpt; RotaryAwd; VoiceDemAwd; College; Lawyer.

WATKINS, Anne E; Green Valley HS; Green Valley, IL; VPJrCls; DrlTm; HonRl; NHS; SchPl; RptrYrbk; RptrSchPpr; 4-H; LetterBsktbl; LetterTrk; GAA; 4-HAwd; University; Professional.

WATKINS, Brenda; Alton R 4 HS; West Plains, MO; HospAde; StuGov; UNYO; FBLA; FDA; FFA; FHA; FNA; FSA; FTA; College; Vocation.

WATKINS, Brian D; Bay View HS; Milwaukee, WI; Chr; ChrhWkr; CncrtBnd; JA; Orch; SchMus; SctActv; CaptSocr; Swmmng; JAAwd; College; Computer Science.

WATKINS, Carmen L; Castle HS; Newburgh, IN; 1/298 TrsSrCls; HonRl; NHS; OffAde; FHA; FTA; SecLatCl; PpCl; Indiana Univ; Chemical Eng.

WATKINS, Carolyn E; East Catholic HS; Detroit, MI; HonRl; NHS; OffAde; SchAde; TchrAde; RptrYrbk; SciCl; Bsbl; Bsktbl; GAA; E Mi Univ; Rn.

WATKINS, Cathi A; Anderson HS; Anderson, IN; Chr; ChrhWkr; HonRl; LbryAde; OffAde; SchAde; SctActv; TchrAde; FHA; Bible College; Spanish Teacher.

WATKINS, Christopher L; Assumption HS; Caseyville, IL; Aud/Vis; HonRl; Parks College; Aviation.

WATKINS, Dale A; Chandlerville HS; Chandlerville, IL; 1/17 PresFrshCls; Band; ChrhWkr; CncrtBnd; HonRl; MrchBnd; NHS; Orch; PepBnd; Yrbk; FFA; PpCl; Western Ill Univ; Accounting.

WATKINS, Ellie S; Hillsdale HS; Hillsdale, MI; 1/190 Chr; Chrl; HonRl; JrNHS; NHS; SchMus; StuCncl; Central Mi Univ; Vocation.

WATKINS, Gregory; Proviso West Hs; Bellwood, IL; Band; ChrhWkr; CmntyWkr; HonRl; NatlMeritCmnd; SctActv; SciCl; U Of Illinois; Chemistry.

WATKINS, Gregory A; Mt Zion HS; Decatur, IL; 16/190 Chr; Chrl; Chrs; HonRl; Mdrgl; NHS; SchAde; SchMus; SchPl; TchrAde; FrCl; SciCl; Bsktbl; Millikin Univ; Medicine.

WATKINS, Jeff E; Paxton HS; Paxton, IL; 30/136 Band; CncrtBnd; HonRl; MrchBnd; NHS; PepBnd;

SchPl; StuCncl; Glf; GodCntryAwd; U Of Ill; Computer Science.

WATKINS, Jo; Newton HS; Newton, IL; 21/187 Band; ChrhWkr; HonRl; MrchBnd; NHS; PepBnd; Business School; Business.

WATKINS, Judy L; Peoria Heights HS; Peoria Heights, IL; 20/93 SecSophCls; CmntyWkr; DrlTm; HonRl; Quill&Scroll; SchPl; StuCncl; RptrYrbk; Yrbk; PPFtbl; College; Airline Hostess.

WATKINS, Laurel; Paxton HS; Paxton, IL; 38/128 Band; CncrtBnd; HonRl; MrchBnd; NatlThespSoc; PepBnd; SchPl; StuCncl; YthFlsp; Parkland Univ; Veteranary Tech.

WATKINS, Mary; Pellston HS; Carp Lake, MI; 2/49 VPFrshCls; TrsFrshCls; Band; CncrtBnd; HonRl; MrchBnd; PepBnd; StuCncl; Trk; College; Medical Technology.

WATKINS, Michael W; Rockridge HS; Milan, IL; 1/150 PresSophCls; HonRl; NHS; StuCncl; EdYrBk; FTA; LatCl; LetterFtbl; LetterTrk; JETSAwd; Univ Of Illinois; Engineering.

WATKINS, Penny; Urbana Sr Hs; Urbana, IL; 20/428 Band; HonRl; MrchBnd; NatlThespSoc; SchMus; SchPl; SctActv; RptrSchPpr; SchPpr; GodCntryAwd; Illinois Wesleyan U; Dramatics.

WATKINS, Richard M; Chaminade HS; St Louis, MO; 49/113 Band; CmntyWkr; CncrtBnd; HonRl; JrNHS; PepBnd; SchPl; StuGov; College; Law.

WATKINS, Sally J; Woodbine HS; Woodbine, IA; 2/58 Band; Chrs; ChrhWkr; HonRl; NHS; PolWkr; EdSchPpr; 4-H; FTA; 4-HAwd; Wayne St College; Library Science.

WATKINS, Stephen N; Henry Senachwine HS; Henry, IL; 8/73 ChrhWkr; HonRl; JrNHS; NHS; StuCncl; RptrYrbk; LetterGlf; Ill Central College.

WATKINS, Thelma J; Our Lady Of Providence HS; New Albany, IN; 1/130 ALAGirlsSt; Chr; HonRl; StuCncl; TchrAde; PpCl; LetterTrk; PPFtbl; DARAwd; Purdue Univ; Engineering.

WATKINS, Wendy L; Crete Monee HS; Park Forest, IL; Band; CmntyWkr; HonRl; MrchBnd; Quill&Scroll; SctActv; UNYO; YthFlsp; RptrYrbk; FshEdYrbk; College; Elem Ed.

WATLAND, Daniel T; Sawyer HS; Sawyer, ND; 1/25 ALBoysSt; Band; Chr; HonRl; MrchBnd; Yrbk; Pres4-H; Bsktbl; 4-HAwd; Ndsu; Pharmacy.

WATROUS, Gillian K; Whitewater HS; Whitewater, WI; 16/190 Band; Chr; Mdrgl; NHS; NatlMeritSF; Quill&Scroll; SchMus; StuCncl; SchPpr; FrCl; Univ; Music.

WATROUS, Jill C; Theodore Roosevelt HS; Des Moines, IA; 13/471 ChrhWkr; HonRl; NatlMeritCmnd; SchMus; SchPl; StuCncl; Nw Missouri St Univ; Art.

WATRY, Kay; Elkhart Lake Glen Hs; Elkhart Lake, WI; AFS; SchPl; Yrbk; 4-H; FHA; U Of Wisconsin; Medical Technician.

WATRY, Larry S; Port Washington HS; Port Washington, WI; 10/235 CmntyWkr; HonRl; NHS; PresStuGov; MthCl; Ftbl; KiwanAwd; LionAwd; Uw Milwaukee; Business.

WATRY, Stephen J; Hermantown HS; Duluth, MN; AFS; Chrs; NHS; SchMus; SchPl; Pres4-H; FrCl; Devry Inst Of Tech; Electronics.

WATSON, Alan J; Fargo North HS; Fargo, ND; Band; Orch; SchMus; SchPl; SctActv; StuCncl; StuGov; RptrYrbk; KeyCl; Trk; College.

WATSON, Angela; Emerson HS; Gary, IN; 54/223 Chr; HonRl; LbryAde; SchPl; De Vry Inst Of Tech; Data Processing.

WATSON, Brenda J; Lindblom Tech HS; Chicago, IL; 84/730 Chr; Chrs; ChrhWkr; CmntyWkr; HonRl; NHS; OffAde; SchAde; TchrAde; RptrYrbk; Yrbk; FDA; SpnCl; Univ Of Illinois; Medicine.

WATSON, Brenda K; Northside HS; Ft Wayne, IN; VPSrCls; ALAGirlsSt; HonRl; SecJA; OffAde; KeyCl; EngCl; SciCl; GAA; College; Major Study.

WATSON, Brian; Snider HS; Fort Wayne, IN; 124/612 Band; HonRl; SctActv; Univ; Pharmacy.

WATSON, Brigid; Gull Lake HS; Richland, MI; Chr; ChrhWkr; HonRl; JA; NHS; SchPl; TchrAde; FTA; FrCl; Western Michigan U; Teacher.

WATSON, Carol J; Lindblom Technical HS; Chicago, IL; 55/722 Chr; Chrs; HonRl; Mdrgl; PolWkr; StuCncl; TchrAde; SchPpr; SciCl; Northwestern University; Physical Therapy.

WATSON, Claude E; Corydon Central HS; Corydon, IN; 4/147 Band; CncrtBnd; HonRl; MrchBnd; NHS; NatlMeritSF; PepBnd; StuCncl; EdSchPpr; MthCl; Ftbl; Trk; Purdue Univ; Engineering.

WATSON, Colette L; Annapolis HS; Dbn Hts, MI; Band; CncrtBnd; HonRl; MrchBnd; NatlThespSoc; SchMus; SchPl; TchrAde; YthFlsp; Concordia Lutheran Jr College; Teacher.

WATSON, Daniel L; University HS; Champaign, IL; ChrhWkr; SchPl; EdSchPpr; GerCl; LetterBsktbl; Ftbl; Art School; Artist.

WATSON, Debbie C; North Decatur HS; Greensburg, IN; 1/92 Chr; CaptDrlTm; HonRl; NHS; StuCncl; RptrSchPpr; Chrldr; GAA; College Or Univ.

WATSON, Diane L; Merrill HS; Merril, MI; 10/107 OffAde; SchMus; SchPl; TchrAde; SecFHA; GAA; BttyCrckrAwd; Delta College; Accounting.

WATSON, James A; Jeffersonville HS; Jeffersonville, IN; 157/548 ALBoysSt; ChrhWkr; HonRl; ROTC; SctActv; TchrAde; KeyCl; LetterFtbl; LetterSwmmng; Tennis; Trk; IMSpt; AmLegAwd; Ball State Univ; Law Enforcement.

WATSON, Janet L; Rockridge HS; Muscatine, IA; 31/140 VPBand; Chr; ChrhWkr; CncrtBnd; HonRl; MrchBnd; NatlThespSoc; PepBnd; Yrbk; GAA; Muscatine Comm Clg; Music/bus Educ.

WATSON, Jeronical; Malcolm Price Lab HS; Waterloo, IA; Chr; LetterTrk; Trade Sch; Pro Med Tech.

WATSON, Jerry N; Cavalier HS; Cavalier, ND; PresSophCls; PresSrCls; Band; Chr; Chrs; ChrhWkr; CncrtBnd; HonRl; Mdrgl; MrchBnd; PepBnd; LetterBsktbl; LetterFtbl; LetterTrk; Westminster College; Veterinarian.

WATSON, John R; United Township HS; East Moline, IL; Bsktbl; Ftbl; College; Professional.

WATSON, Joseph R; Lincolnwood HS; Farmersville, IL; HonRl; TchrAde; Yrbk; CivCl; 4-H; FTA; Armed Forces; Professional.

WATSON, Judith A; Wabash HS; Wabash, IN; 16/198 Chr; Chrl; HonRl; LbryAde; StuCncl; VPYthFlsp; VPSpnCl; SciCl; College; Accountant.

WATSON, Julie; Galesburg Sr HS; Galesburg, IL; 26/582 HonRl; NHS; GAA; Drake Univ.

WATSON, Julie A; Beloit Memorial HS; Beloit, WI; ChrhWkr; HonRl; SchAde; SchPl; TchrAde; YthFlsp; College; Education.

WATSON, Karen; Goodhue HS; Goodhue, MN; TrsSrCls; Chr; HonRl; SchPl; Yrbk; RptrSchPpr; 4-H; FHA; GerCl; Winona State; Undecided.

WATSON, Karen K; Sioux County HS; Harrison, NE; SecSophCls; SecJrCls; PresSrCls; HonRl; NatlFornLg; NHS; StuCncl; 4-H; FHA; Chrldr; Univ Of Nebraska; Home Ec.

WATSON, Lori G; Charleston HS; Ashmore, IL; 5/237 VPSrCls; AFS; SecBand; PresChrs; ChrhWkr; CncrtBnd; HonRl; MrchBnd; NHS; Orch; PepBnd; StuCncl; GAA; CitAwd; University; Music.

WATSON, Mark D; Bloomington HS; Bloomington, IL; PresSophCls; Chr; HonRl; PresStuCncl; TreasLatCl; MthCl; U Of Il; Engi.

WATSON, Mary C; Southwest HS; St Louis, MO; 85/587 Aud/Vis; Chr; HonRl; HospAde; Mdrgl; PresSchMus; SchPl; Univ Of Ill; Singer Or Actress.

WATSON, Myra J; Adair County Rii HS; Gibbs, MO; TrsFrshCls; PresJrCls; CmntyWkr; HonRl; MrchBnd; NHS; StuCncl; Yrbk; SchPpr; Bsktbl; College; Business.

WATSON, Nancy J; Newburg HS; Newburg, ND; Band; Chrs; CncrtBnd; HonRl; PepBnd; RedCrAde; YthFlsp; PpCl; LetterBsktbl; LetterChrldr; College.

WATSON, Raymond J; Odell Community HS; Odell, IL; 3/33 PresSrCls; HonRl; PolWkr; SchPl; PresStuCncl; FFA; PresFrCl; PpCl; LetterGlf; LetterTrk; BttyCrckrAwd; University Of Notre Dame; Lawyer.

WATSON, Raymond J; Odell Comm HS; Odell, IL; 3/33 PresSrCls; Chr; HonRl; SchPl; PresStuCncl; FFA; PresFrCl; Glf; AmLegAwd; BttyCrckrAwd; Univ Of Notre Dame; Lawyer.

WATSON, Robert J; St Bede Academy; Chicago Hgts, IL; CmntyWkr; HonRl; MrchBnd; SchPl; Bsbl; Ftbl; Illinois State University.

WATSON, Roger D; Paris HS; Paris, IL; ALBoysSt; HonRl; NHS; FFA; KeyCl; LetterBsbl; Bsktbl; CaptFtbl; Univ Of Ill; Lawyer.

WATSON, Ronald K; Lindblom Tech; Chicago, IL; 6/517 DrlTm; DrmBgl; HonRl; ROTC; TchrAde; Yrbk; SchPpr; GerCl; SciCl; Hospital Admin; Phd.

WATSON, Susan L; Vanburen Community HS; Stockport, IA; TrsJrCls; AFS; HonRl; NHS; SchPl; Yrbk; SchPpr; Bsktbl; Ftbl; LetterChrldr; College; Game Biologist.

WATSON, Taji M; Harrisonville Sr HS; Harrisonville, MO; 11/169 PresSophCls; PresJrCls; HonRl; Quill&Scroll; SchPl; StuCncl; SchPpr; FrCl; SpnCl; Chrldr; CchngActv; College; Foreign Language.

WATSON, Tenby R; R 1 North Callaway HS; Williamsburg, MO; HonRl; LbryAde; SchPl; Nursing School; Rn.

WATSON, Timothy; Hales Franciscan HS; Chicago, IL; 23/73 ChrhWkr; HonRl; JA; NHS; Teen; Yrbk; SpnCl; MthCl; Bsbl; College; Professional.

WATSON, Veatrice L; Calumet HS; Chicago, IL; 6/270 Chrs; ChrhWkr; HonRl; JrNHS; NHS; OffAde; StuGov; TchrAde; SpnCl; Univ Of Illinois; Special Educ.

WATSON, Wendy J; Ernest W Seaholm HS; Birmingham, MI; 60/709 Band; ChrhWkr; HonRl; JrNHS; MrchBnd; NatlFornLg; NatlMeritCmnd; Michigan St Univ; Doctor.

WATT, Dorian H; Gresham Public HS; Gresham, NE; LetterChr; LbryAde; SchPl; LetterBsktbl; LetterFtbl; LetterTrk;.

WATT, James; Duluth Central HS; Duluth, MN; HospAde; IntrClCncl; ModUN; SctActv; UNYO; EdYrBk; EdSchPpr; Glf; Swmmng; Chrldr; College; Professional.

WATTERS, Christine A; Breckenridge HS; Breckenridge, MI; 1/96 Band; Chr; ChrhWkr; CncrtBnd; HonRl; Mdrgl; MrchBnd; PresNHS; PepBnd; 4-H; College; Math Or Science.

WATTERS, Lee D; Buffalo HS; Buffalo, ND; 1/21 ALBoysSt; PresBand; ChrhWkr; NatlMeritCmnd; EdYrBk; LetterBsktbl; LetterFtbl; LetterTrk; BttyCrckrAwd; Trinity University; Broadcasting.

WATTERS, Sheryl A; Maquoketa Sr HS; Maquoketa, IA; 27/150 AFS; Band; Chrs; CmntyWkr; HonRl; LitMag; 4-H; LetterBsktbl; Glf; DanFAwd; 4-HAwd; Univ Of Iowa; Social Work.

WATTERSON, Brian R; Thornton Fract South HS; Lansing, IL; 147/523 Bsktbl; Ftbl; College; Liberal Arts.

WATTERSON, Lelsie D; Kingsville HS; Kingsville, MO; 6/22 SecFrshCls; TrsSophCls; Chr; Chrs; CmntyWkr; HonRl; HospAde; JrNHS; LbryAde; NHS; OffAde; SchAde; Nursing School; Registerd Nurse.

WATTERUD, Dean A; Columbus HS; Portal, ND; Band; HonRl; SchPl; SctActv; SptEdSchPpr; EngCl; Bsbl; LetterBsktbl; LetterFtbl; LetterTrk; Wrstlng; Nd State Sch Of Science; Electriacal Tech.

WATTIER, Patricia J; Bristol Independent HS; Conde, SD; PresSophCls; SecJrCls; Chrs; CncrtBnd; HospAde; StuCncl; Yrbk; EdSchPpr; FHA; FNA; College; Journalism.

WATTLES, Linda S; North Clay HS; Louisville, IL; SecSophCls; ChrhWkr; HonRl; SchPl; RptrSchPpr; Sec4-H; PpCl; Chrldr; GAA; 4-HAwd; College; Secretary.

WATTS, Cynthia R; Galena HS; Galena, MO; VPJrCls; Band; HonRl; NHS; RptrYrbk; EdSchPpr; FHA; PpCl; Trk; IMSpt; Smsu; Wildlife Conserv.

WATTS, Delores; Robert Lindbloom HS; Chicago, IL; 72/657 HonRl; OffAde; SchMus; TchrAde; MthCl; SciCl; CchngActv; College; Medicine.

WATTS, Evelyn E; Ansley Public HS; Ansley, NE; 1/31 Band; Chrs; ChrhWkr; HonRl; PepBnd; RptrYrbk; 4-H; SecPpCl; BttyCrckrAwd; EldAwd; 4-HAwd; University Of Nebraska; Professional.

WATTS, Frederica D; Soldan HS; St Louis, MO; ChrhWkr; DrlTm; HonRl; College.

WATTS, Kathleen E; Ferndale HS; Ferndale, MI; ChrhWkr; HonRl; JrNHS; NHS; NatlMeritCmnd; Ferris State College; Court Reporter.

WATTS, Lonnie; Lincoln Co Hs; Elsberry, MO; 5/60 Band; CncrtBnd; HonRl; MrchBnd; NHS; PepBnd; TchrAde; FFA; Trade School; Vocational.

WATTS, Marsha; Tuscola Community HS; Tuscola, IL; 8/124 CmntyWkr; HonRl; SctActv; YthFlsp; LatCl; AmLegAwd; RotaryAwd; Nursing.

WATTS, Mary; Pius X HS; Lincoln, NE; 13/150 SctActv; Yrbk; PpCl; Tennis; Trk; College; Professional.

WATTS, Reginald A; Everett HS; Lansing, MI; Band; HonRl; NatlMeritCmnd; StuGov; LetterTrk; Univ Of Detroit; Biology.

WATZ, Mary; Maple Valley Jr Sr HS; Charlotte, MI; 6 108 CncrtBnd; NHS; PepBnd; SchMus; StuCncl; SptEdSchPpr; FFA; LetterBsktbl; LetterTennis; GAA; Mich Tech Univ; Veterinary Medicine.

WATZKE, Janice L; Taft HS; Chicago, IL; 60/843 Chrs; HonRl; LitMag; SpnCl; PpCl; Univ Of Ill; Journalism.

WAUCHOP, Lawrence; Luther South HS; Chicago, IL; 53/192 HonRl; SchMus; SctActv; YthFlsp; SchPpr; Univ; Business.

WAUGH, Judy K; Fremont Senior HS; Valley, NE; 78/412 Chrs; ChrhWkr; LbryAde; YthFlsp; LetterTrk; College; Social Work.

WAUGH, Mary H; Anderson HS; Anderson, IN; Chrs; ChrhWkr; HonRl; OffAde; StuCncl; SchPpr; FrCl; PpCl; Swmmng; Trk; Chrldr; AmLegAwd; Univ; Pro.

WAUTHIER, Nancy K; Clifton Central HS; Clifton, IL; Band; Chrs; CncrtBnd; HonRl; HospAde; MrchBnd; VPNHS; Yrbk; FrCl; GAA; St Francis Hospital; Nursing.

WAVERING, Kenneth E; Griffin HS; Springfield, IL; 8/175 TrsJrCls; ChrhWkr; HonRl; NHS; SctActv; Sdlty; StuCncl; SpnCl; PpCl; SciCl; LetterBsbl; LetterFtbl; LetterTrk; Us Air Force Academy; Chemical Engineering.

WAWRZYNIAK, Lucyna A; Rich Central HS; Olympia Fields, IL; Chr; ChrhWkr; HonRl; HospAde; SchMus; SchPl; SctActv; YthFlsp; SchPpr; RusCl; PpCl; Northern Illinois Univ; Physical Therapy.

WAWRZYNIEC, Gary M; St Andrew HS; Detroit, MI; 4/110 HonRl; NHS; NatlMeritSF; SchPl; SctActv; CaptBsbl; CaptBsktbl; DanFAwd; Chemical Eng.

WAY, Becky A; Holly HS; Holly, MI; Chr; Chrl; Chrs; ChrhWkr; HonRl; SchMus; SchPl; Teen; Hurley Hosp; Nursing.

WAY, Walter D; Glenbard West HS; Wheaton, IL; NatlMeritCmnd; Bsbl; LetterBsktbl; LetterFtbl; Glf; LetterTennis; IMSpt; Knox College; Business.

WAYBRIGHT, Lynn M; St Mary Academy; Monroe, MI; SecJrCls; SecSrCls; HonRl; NHS; StuCncl; College; Art.

WAYDE, Susan M; Grosse Pointe North HS; Grosse Pte Shores, MI; HonRl; HospAde; NHS; SchMus; StuGov; RptrSchPpr; Bsktbl; GAA; IMSpt; PPFtbl; Univ; Nursing.

WAYLAND, Kelly R; Washington HS; Washington, KS; HonRl; MrchBnd; PepBnd; SchPl; 4-H; PpCl; Bsbl; Bsktbl; Trk; GAA; College; Commercial Art.

WAYMAN, Jerri L; Lansing HS; Lansing, KS; TchrAde; 4-H; FTA; IMSpt; PPFtbl; College; Child Education.

WAYMASTER, Charles P; Luray HS; Bunker Hill, KS; SecTrsJrCls; ChrhWkr; HonRl; StuCncl; 4-H; LetterBsbl; CaptBsktbl; LetterFtbl; CaptTrk; Fort Hays Coll; Data Processing.

WAYMIRE, Joseph; Villa Grove HS; Camargo, IL; 10/78 ChrhWkr; NHS; StuCncl; KeyCl; MthCl; Bsbl; Ftbl; Trk; SARAwd; U Of Illinois; Chemical Engineering.

WAYNE, Cheryl A; Northern Valley HS; Almena, KS; SecJrCls; Band; Chrs; MrchBnd; PepBnd; SchPl; YthFlsp; PpCl; Trk; Chrldr;.

WAYNE, Cynthia M; St Charles HS; St Charles, MO; HonRl; SecStuCncl; FNA; FrCl; IMSpt; College.

WAYNE, Mark A; Steinmetz HS; Chicago, IL; 84/541 Band; HonRl; StuCncl;.

WAYNE, Marthalyn; Bishop Noll HS; East Chicago, IN; 67/342 CncrtBnd; HonRl; HospAde; MrchBnd; PepBnd; SchMus; Univ; Psychology.

WAYT, Rhonda S; Brown County HS; Nashville, IN; Band; HonRl; MrchBnd; PepBnd; TchrAde; Twrl; FrCl; PpCl; Trk; GAA; Coll; Pro.

WAYTASHEK, Cindy M; Healy HS; Pierz, MN; 12/113 HonRl; LbryAde; IMSpt; Vocational School; Nursing.

WAZBINSKI, Susan M; T L Handy HS; Bay City, MI; HonRl; NHS; NatlMeritCmnd; StuCncl; StuGov; PpCl; Chrldr; College; Med Assistant.

WAZETEK, Francis X; Msgr John R Hackett HS; Kalamazoo, MI; 20/144 Band; CncrtBnd; HonRl; MrchBnd; NHS; SchMus; SpnCl; College; Medicine.

WEAKLAND, Jackie E; Tecumseh Public HS; Tecumseh, NE; TrsFrshCls; TrsJrCls; HonRl; StuCncl; 4-H; PpCl; Chrldr; IMSpt; Bus School; Vocation.

WEAKLEY, Kent C; Dixon HS; Dixon, IL; 26/337 Chr; ChrhWkr; CncrtBnd; HonRl; Mdrgl; NHS; NatlThespSoc; SchMus; SchPl; Millikin Univ; Music.

WEAKS, Joyce; New Haven HS; New Haven, MI; PresSrCls; TrsSrCls; Chrs; HospAde; JrNHS; NHS; NatlMeritCmnd; NatlMeritSchl; StuCncl; RptrYrbk; Macomb Comm Coll; Nurse.

WEAR, Sindy S; Mt Pleasant HS; Mt Pleasant, IA; HospAde; Chrldr; GAA; Coll; Prod.

WEARING, Doug M; W A Central HS; West Allis, WI; 134/574 HonRl; LetterTrk; IMSpt; Univ Of Stevens Point; Forestry.

WEATHERHOLT, Vera E; St Francis HS; Williamsburg, MI; HonRl; NHS; IMSpt; Northwestern Mi; Law Enforcement.

WEATHERMAN, Daniel T; Ballard Community HS; Cambridge, IA; 1/75 Band; Chr; Chrs; CncrtBnd; NHS; NatlThespSoc; SchMus; SchPl; StuCncl; EdSchPpr; Iowa State University; Architect.

WEATHERS, Lisa M; Rochester HS; Rochester, MI; HonRl; NatlThespSoc; SchPl; TchrAde; 4-H; SciCl; 4-HAwd; Oakland Univ; Communications.

WEATHERS, Scott M; Benton Consolidated HS; Benton, IL; 8/168 ChrhWkr; CAP; HonRl; NHS; Univ Of Illinois; Aeronautical Engineering.

WEATHERWAX, Mona J; Arapahoe HS; Arapahoe, NE; SecFrshCls; ChrhWkr; HonRl; SctActv; RptrYrbk; FHA; PpCl; GovHonPrgAwd; Univ Of Nebraska; Secondary Education.

WEAVER, Anna M; Virden HS; Virden, IL; Chrs; HonRl; HospAde; SchMus; StuCncl; Yrbk; SecFHA; PpCl; Colege; Registered Nurse.

WEAVER, Cynthia R; Northridge HS; Middlebury, IN; 11/145 Band; Chr; CncrtBnd; HonRl; MrchBnd; PepBnd; Twrl; YthFlsp; Yrbk; 4-H; PpCl; College.

WEAVER, Jeffery D; Ida HS; Monroe, MI; Band; ChrhWkr; CncrtBnd; HonRl; MrchBnd; NHS; PolWkr; YthFlsp; Monroe County Com Col; Draftsman.

WEAVER, Jenny L; Central HS; St Joseph, MO; Chr; Chrl; HonRl; SchMus; YthFlsp; 4-H; SpnCl; LetterSwmmng; GAA; 4-HAwd; University; Professional.

WEAVER, Joseph C; Soldan HS; St Louis, MO; CmntyWkr; HonRl; JrNHS; LitMag; NHS; StuCncl; StuGov; RptrYrbk; JAAwd; PresAwd; Coll; Writer.

WEAVER, Karen B; R Nelson Snider HS; Fort Wayne, IN; HonRl; OffAde; StuCncl; TchrAde; SpnCl; PpCl; Trk; Chrldr; Indiana Univ; Dental Hygiene.

WEAVER, Karen E; Elkhart Central HS; Elkhart, IN; 1/460 PresFrshCls; TrsSrCls; Chr; Chrl; HonRl; NHS; NatlThespSoc; Orch; SchMus; SchPl; Goshen Coll; Music.

WEAVER, Kimberly K; Northridge HS; Goshen, IN; Band; CncrtBnd; DrmMjrt; HonRl; MrchBnd; PepBnd; Indiana Univ; Business.

WEAVER, Mablene S; Colchster Jr Sr HS; Colchestr, IL; Chrl; Chrs; HonRl; NHS; SchMus; SchPl; SecSpnCl; SecMthCl; Chrldr; GAA; Business School; Secretarial.

WEAVER, Marilyn J; Northridge HS; Middlebury, IN; 10/116 Chr; ChrhWkr; HonRl; SchMus; YthFlsp; SpnCl; PpCl; Coll; Music.

WEAVER, Martha J; Harrisonville Senior HS; Harrisonville, MO; AFS; Chrs; ChrhWkr; CmntyWkr; HonRl; NatlFornLg; Quill&Scroll; SchPl; SctActv; RptrSchPpr; Chrldr; CchngActv; PPFtbl; University Of Missouri; Journalism.

WEAVER, Mary C; So Sioux City HS; South Sioux City, NE; 8/200 Band; Chr; HonRl; JrNHS; NHS; SchMus; Yrbk; SchPpr; University; Spanish.

WEAVER, Maureen C; Ravenna HS; Ravenna, MI; 57/222 HonRl; HospAde; LbryAde; Orch; TchrAde; Sec4-H; FFA; 4-HAwd; College; Registured Nurse.

WEAVER, Melanie S; Brazil HS; Brazil, IN; ChrhWkr; HonRl; LbryAde; SchAde; SchPl; TchrAde; YthFlsp; Yrbk; PpCl; 4-HAwd; Vocation.

WEAVER, Michael A; Glenbrook South HS; Glenview, IL; 66/581 HonRl; NHS; LetterBsktbl; Univ Of Illinois; Civil Engineering.

WEAVER, Michael W; Indian Creek HS; Morgantown, IN; HonRl; NHS; Quill&Scroll; EdYrBk; 4-H; FTA; FrCl; PpCl; SciCl; Bsktbl; Univ Of Tampa; Fine Arts.

WEAVER, Mitchell J; Goshen HS; Goshen, IN; Chr; HonRl; StuCncl; LatCl; PpCl; Bsbl; LetterFtbl; IMSpt; College; Law.

WEAVER, Ralph M; Heritage Christian HS; Indianapolis, IN; Band; Chr; PepBnd; SchMus; Yrbk; LetterSocr; College; Engineering.

WEAVER, Ronald; Stevens HS; Rapid City, SD; 237/413 Band; Bsbl; Trk; IMSpt; AmLegAwd; PresAwd; Univ; Areo Space Engineer.

WEAVER, Ruth C; S Sioux Sr HS; S Sioux City, NE; Band; Chr; HonRl; JrNHS; SchMus; StuCncl; RptrYrbk; SchPpr; Univ Of S Dakota; Nursing.

WEAVER, Tamelyn J; Zeeland HS; Zeeland, MI; ChrhWkr; LatCl; Bsbl; Tennis; Col; Social Work.

WEAVER, Thomas C E; Brownstown Central HS; Freetown, IN; Band; Chr; CncrtBnd; MrchBnd; PepBnd; SchMus; SchPl; SpnCl; PpCl; LetterFtbl; LetterTrk; IMSpt; Indiana Central College; Accountant.

WEAVER, William; Casey HS; Casey, IL; 8/104 Band; CncrtBnd; HonRl; JrNHS; MrchBnd; Bsbl; Bsktbl; Ftbl; Tennis;.

WEBB, Bob; Geneva HS; Geneva, NE; /65 HonRl; Ftbl; Glf; Trk; IMSpt; Univ;.

WEBB, Cheryl L; Newton Comm HS; Newton, IL; 8/187 PresFrshCls; PresSophCls; ALAGirlsSt; HonRl; MrchBnd; NHS; StuCncl; MthCl; College; Professional.

WEBB, Cynthia A; Greendale HS; Greendale, WI; 125/338 Aud/Vis; Chr; CmntyWkr; HonRl; LbryAde; SctActv; SpnCl; PpCl; Technical College; Professional.

WEBB, Debra; Benton Consolidated HS; Ewing, IL; HonRl; Glf; GAA; IMSpt; DanFAwd; 4-HAwd; Rend Lake Jr Coll; Med Lab Tech.

WEBB, Derrick; O A Carlson HS; Rockwood, MI; 12/200 HstFrshCls; SecTrsSophCls; SecJrCls; VPSrCls; HonRl; EdYrBk; FSA; Swmmng; IMSpt; DanFAwd; RotaryAwd; Mi Tech; Mechanical Engineer.

WEBB, Felicia C; River Valley HS; Three Oaks, MI; 18/141 Chr; HonRl; NHS; TchrAde; RptrYrbk; Yrbk; FHA; PpCl; Hope Col; Journalism & Photography.

WEBB, Gilbert A; St Ignatius C P HS; Chicago, IL; 34/200 ChrhWkr; CmntyWkr; HonRl; HospAde; PolWkr; SchAde; CivCl; IMSpt; College.

WEBB, James; Nauvoo Colusa HS; Nauvoo, IL; Band; ChrhWkr; CncrtBnd; MrchBnd; SchPl; 4-H; FFA; 4-HAwd; Carl Sandburg; Agriculture Resources.

WEBB, James F; Bishop Mc Namara HS; Bradley, IL; 5/161 Aud/Vis; ChrhWkr; CmntyWkr; HonRl; HospAde; NHS; SchPl; SctActv; Teen; SpnCl; Purdue Univ; Electrical Engineer.

WEBB, James M; Waterford Kettering HS; Drayton Plains, MI; 50/424 CmntyWkr; HonRl; NHS; StuCncl; StuGov; PpCl; Bsktbl; College.

WEBB, Jerome G; Western HS; Kokomo, IN; 12/202 ALBoysSt; HonRl; StuCncl; LetterBsbl; LetterBsktbl; LetterFtbl; LetterTrk; CchngActv; University; Engineer.

WEBB, Kathy; Vienna HS; Vienna, IL; 8/85 Band; ChrhWkr; HonRl; LbryAde; TchrAde; 4-H; SpnCl; PpCl; Bsktbl; Shawnee Jr Coll; Nursing.

WEBB, Larry L; Lewistown Community HS; Lewistown, IL; Band; ChrhWkr; CncrtBnd; SctActv; RptrSchPpr; FFA; FrCl; PpCl; Glf; Trk; College; Professional.

WEBB, Leah R; Williamsfield HS; Dahinda, IL; 1/32 VPFrshCls; VPJrCls; SecTrsSrCls; Chrs; HonRl; LbryAde; NHS; SchMus; YthFlsp; RptrSchPpr; SpnCl; PpCl; Chrldr; College; Liberal Arts.

WEBB, Lora A; Twin Rivers HS; Arnold, MO; 3/101 Band; Chrs; ChrhWkr; HonRl; JrNHS; NHS; SchPl; PresFHA; Coll; Lab Tech.

WEBB, Pamela M; North Chicago Comm HS; N Chicago, IL; 9/236 CncrtBnd; HonRl; MrchBnd; NHS; NatlMeritCmnd; Eastern Illinois Univ; Accounting.

WEBB, Peter M; Clinton Prairie HS; Frankfort, IN; ChrhWkr; 4-H; FFA; SciCl; Purdue Univ; Agriculture Science.

WEBB, Rebecca A; Clarke Comm HS; Osceola, IA; Chrs; ChrhWkr; CmntyWkr; HonRl; PolWkr; SctActv; YthFlsp; Pres4-H; Bsktbl; Tennis; Chrldr; 4-HAwd; College; Vocation.

WEBB, Richard L; Cape Central HS; Cape Girardeau, MO; Band; HonRl; MrchBnd; SctActv; LetterBsbl; LetterFtbl; LetterTrk; LetterWrstlng; AmLegAwd; Univ; Engineering.

WEBB, Sherrie L; West Platte Rii HS; Weston, MO; 15/53 VPJrCls; AFS; Chrs; ChrhWkr; HonRl; ModUN; StuGov; 4-H; Bsktbl; CaptChrldr; Nw Mo St Univ; Teaching.

WEBB, Tamera L; Memorial HS; Eau Claire, WI; 122/434 HonRl; MrchBnd; Orch; SchMus; College; Spanish.

WEBB, Tamra A; Goreville HS; Goreville, IL; Band; ChrhWkr; HonRl; RptrSchPpr; Pres4-H; VPFHA; Chrldr; DanFAwd; 4-HAwd; Southern Il U; Bus Adm.

WEBB, Timothy; Sacred Heart Hs; Dearborn, MI; 3/120 TrsFrshCls; HonRl; NHS; SchPl; Swmmng; LetterTrk; M U; Forestry Wildlife Management.

WEBB, Timothy W; Westview HS; Shipshewana, IN; 11/69 VPSophCls; Band; Chr; CncrtBnd; HonRl; MrchBnd; NHS; PepBnd; SchPl; StuCncl; Bsktbl; Manchester College.

WEBB, William S; St Charles HS; St Charles, IL; Chr; Chrl; HonRl; NHS; NatlMeritSF; SchMus; SctActv; LatCl; IMSpt; College; Economics.

WEBBER, Mary P; Morton HS; Morton, IL; Chrs; ChrhWkr; CncrtBnd; HonRl; MrchBnd; PolWkr; RedCrAde; SchMus; SctActv; Knox Clg; Math.

WEBBER, Michael W; Downers Grove South HS; Downers Grove, IL; NHS; Bsbl; Ftbl; University Of Illinois; Engineering.

WEBBER, Patrick; Shullsburg Public HS; Shullsburg, WI; VPFrshCls; HonRl; SchPl; StuCncl; RptrSchPpr; SptEdSchPpr; Bsbl; Trade; Data Processing.

WEBBER, Ronald D; Putnam County R 1 HS; Unionville, MO; 2/85 HonRl; NHS; LetterFtbl; Trk; Ne Missouri University.

WEBBER, Stephen W; Glendale HS; Springfield, MO; Band; ChrhWkr; HonRl; Mdrgl; NatlThespSoc; NatlFornLg; Quill&Scroll; SchMus; RptrSchPpr; SchPpr; University.

WEBEL, Vicki L; Perry HS; Chambersburg, IL; 3/16 TrsFrshCls; TrsSophCls; TrsSrCls; Band; Chrs; CncrtBnd; HonRl; Mdrgl; MrchBnd; PepBnd; SchPl; Yrbk; FHA; PpCl; Western Illinois Univ; Physical Education.

WEBER, Allen D; Oak Park Acad; Muscatine, IA; VPFrshCls; Chrl; Chrs; ChrhWkr; CncrtBnd; HonRl; StuCncl; StuGov; Yrbk; RptrSchPpr; College; Pastoral Minister.

WEBER, Ann; La Salle Peru HS; Peru, IL; AFS; SecChrs; ChrhWkr; HonRl; NHS; SchMus; VPStuCncl; SpnCl; PpCl; Chrldr; DARAwd; RotaryAwd; Illinois Vly Comm College; Elem Teacher.

WEBER, Anne M; Ann Arbor Huron HS; Ann Arbor, MI; ALAGirlsSt; Chr; ChrhWkr; CncrtBnd; HonRl; MrchBnd; SchMus; StuCncl; YthFlsp; FrCl; Univ; Nursing.

WEBER, Annette; Don Bosco HS; Jesup, IA; 10/57 Aud/Vis; Chrs; HonRl; NHS; SchPl; IMSpt;.

WEBER, Barbara J; Fatima HS; Freeburg, MO; 20/126 ChrhWkr; HonRl; MrchBnd; NHS; OffAde; SchPl; StuCncl; FHA; Univ Of Missouri; Med Technician.

WEBER, Bill F; Trinity HS; Hutchinson, KS; PresSrCls; ALBoysSt; ChrhWkr; HonRl; PresNHS; VPStuCncl; RptrYrbk; KeyCl; LetterBsktbl; LetterFtbl; LetterGlf; College; Engineering.

WEBER, Bo; Dixon HS; Dixon, IL; VPSophCls; HstJrCls; HonRl; StuCncl; SchPpr; LetterChrldr; Coll; Social Worker.

WEBER, Bruce A; Oconto Sr HS; Oconto, WI; 5/137 ALBoysSt; ChrhWkr; HonRl; SchPl; SctActv; StuCncl; Ftbl; Glf; Wv Eau Claire; Business Ad.

WEBER, Carol A; Morrisonville HS; Morrisonville, IL; 4/68 Chrs; HonRl; SchPl; StuCncl; FHA; PpCl; LetterTrk; CaptChrldr; 4-HAwd; Lincolnland Comm College; Business.

WEBER, Cheryl L; Hamilton HS; Milwaukee, WI; CmntyWkr; HonRl; OffAde; SctActv; SpnCl; Chrldr; PPFtbl; College; Private Secretary.

WEBER, Cheryl L; Don Bosco HS; Gilbertville, IA; Band; HonRl; HospAde; NHS; SchPl; SptEdYrbk; Socr; Chrldr; GAA; BttyCrckrAwd; College; Airline Work.

WEBER, Constance E; Glenwood HS; Glenwood, MN; 17/142 Band; ChrhWkr; CncrtBnd; HonRl; MrchBnd; NHS; StuCncl; RptrYrbk; RptrSchPpr; LetterBsktbl; Nursing Sch; Nurse.

WEBER, Craig D; East Charles Mix 102 HS; Wagner, SD; ChrhWkr; HonRl; NHS; NatlMeritSchl; YthFlsp; FFA; FSA; LetterBsktbl; LetterFtbl; LetterTrk; College; Professional.

WEBER, Craig E; Chaminade HS; St Charles, MO; 10/107 HonRl; JrNHS; LitMag; YthLg; University; Business.

WEBER, David R; St Laurence HS; Chicago, IL; 86/385 HonRl; LbryAde; RedCrAde; StuCncl; RptrYrbk; RptrSchPpr; Tennis; North Central College; Medicine.

WEBER, Debbie L; Friend Public HS; Lincoln, NE; TrsSophCls; SecJrCls; Band; Chr; Chrs; HonRl; MrchBnd; PepBnd; StuGov; PpCl; Secretary.

WEBER, Duane; Johnson Creek HS; Watertown, WI; 1/44 PresSrCls; ALBoysSt; HonRl; NatlMeritCmnd; SchPl; EdYrBk; EdSchPpr; LetterBsktbl; LetterFtbl; LetterTrk; Uw Whitewater;bus Admin.

WEBER, Edward; Bremen HS; Midlothian, IL; HonRl; JrNHS; NHS; SchAde; TchrAde; MthCl; Univ Of Il; Astronomy.

WEBER, Elizabeth A; Clay HS; Granger, IN; HonRl; LitMag; Quill&Scroll; EdSchPpr; SpnCl; Univ Of Notre Dame; Liberal Arts.

WEBER, Eric D; Central HS; Ashkum, IL; 34/138 ALBoysSt; Chr; Chrs; HonRl; Mdrgl; StuCncl; StuGov; FFA; LetterTrk; LetterWrstlng; College; Agriculture.

WEBER, Eugene; St Johns HS; St Louis, MO; 1/80 Chr; HonRl; SchMus; SchPl; Bsktbl; Trk; IMSpt; AmLegAwd; PresAwd; College; Physical Ed Teacher.

WEBER, Helen M; Bishop Luers HS; Ft Wayne, IN; HonRl; NatlMeritCmnd; RptrSchPpr; LetterTrk; CaptChrldr; GAA; BttyCrckrAwd; ChmbCommrsAwd; EldAwd; U Of Notre Dame; Physician.

WEBER, James J; Deerfield HS; Deerfield, IL; HonRl; NatlMeritSF; SctActv; FrCl; IMSpt; GodCntryAwd; U Of Il; Law.

WEBER, James K; Atchison HS; Atchison, KS; ALBoysSt; HonRl; ModUN; SptEdYrbk; EdSchPpr; Bsktbl; Ftbl; LetterGlf; U Of Kansas; Business.

WEBER, James L; Grundy Center Comm HS; Grundy Ctr, IA; ALBoysSt; CmntyWkr; HonRl; JrNHS; StuCncl; StuGov; YthFlsp; FBLA; Bsbl; Ftbl; Glf; Wrstlng; PPFtbl; College; Education.

WEBER, Janice A; Parkston HS; Dimock, SD; 2/98 ALAGirlsSt; ChrhWkr; DrlTm; HonRl; NHS; StuCncl; FHA; FTA; MthCl; PPFtbl; Anoka Area Voc Tech Inst; Surgical Tech.

WEBER, Jay R; Vianney HS; St Louis, MO; 64/186 HonRl; LetterGlf; IMSpt; College.

WEBER, Jeffrey; Elmwood Area HS; Elmwood, WI; ALBoysSt; ChrhWkr; HonRl;.

WEBER, Jim R; Grant Deuel HS; Revillo, SD; ALBoysSt; Chrs; ChrhWkr; HonRl; NatlThespSoc; SchAde; SchMus; SchPl; TchrAde; RptrYrbk; Trade School; Electrician.

WEBER, John F; Arlington Green Isle Pub HS; Henderson, MN; SecJrCls; ChrhWkr; HonRl; SchPl; RptrYrbk; SpnCl; LetterBsbl; LetterBsktbl; LetterFtbl; LetterTrk; Col; Professional.

WEBER, John T; Lake Benton Public HS; Lake Benton, MN; 18/49 PresFrshCls; Chr; HonRl; Chrs; StuCncl; 4-H; FFA; CaptWrstlng; S Dakota St Univ.

WEBER, Joseph J; St Johns Prep HS; St Paul, MN; SecFrshCls; PresSophCls; HonRl; RptrYrbk; GerCl; LetterTrk; LetterWrstlng; University.

WEBER, Judith A; Arlington HS; Indpls, IN; 11/428 HonRl; JrNHS; NHS; NatlThespSoc; SchPl; TchrAde; Purdue Univ; Vet.

WEBER, Judith R; William J Bogan HS; Chicago, IL; 2/704 ChrhWkr; HonRl; SecNHS; NatlMeritCmnd; SchAde; SchPl; SctActv; StuCncl; GerCl; SciCl; GAA; Univ Of Illinois; Physician.

WEBER, Julie J; Lincoln Northeast HS; Lincoln, NE; PresSophCls; Chr; HonRl; SchMus; StuCncl; Yrbk; SchPpr; PpCl; LetterSwmmng; Chrldr; Univ Of Nebraska; Nursing.

WEBER, Julie K; Pacific HS; Gray Summit, MO; 10/230 CmntyWkr; HonRl; Meramac Jr College; Psychology.

WEBER, Kae A; Beloit HS; Beloit, KS; Chrs; LbryAde; SchMus; YthFlsp; RptrYrbk; CivCl; 4-H; FNA; PpCl; 4-HAwd; Brown Mackie College ;general Business.

WEBER, Katherine A; Stratford HS; Stratford, WI; 1/89 VPSophCls; SecBand; ChrhWkr; CncrtBnd; HonRl; MrchBnd; NHS; PepBnd; Yrbk; FHA; VPFrCl; EldAwd; Univ Of Wisconsin; Psychology.

WEBER, Kathleen M; Newton Community HS; Dundas, IL; VPSophCls; ChrhWkr; HonRl; NHS; StuCncl; 4-H; FBLA; IMSpt; Beauty Sch; Beautician.

WEBER, Kim C; Rolla HS; Rolla, MO; Band; HonRl; MrchBnd; College; Art.

WEBER, Kirk; Hoover HS; Des Moines, IA; 12/360 PresFrshCls; ALBoysSt; ModUN; NatlMeritCmnd; StuCncl; UNYO; KeyCl; Bsbl; AmLegAwd; Ia St Univ;engineering.

WEBER, Lucille M; Bellevue Comm HS; Bellevue, IA; 1/44 SecNHS; RptrYrbk; EdSchPpr; Marycrest College; Nursing.

WEBER, Margaret M; Jfk Prep; Chilton, WI; Band; Chr; Chrl; Chrs; ChrhWkr; CmntyWkr; CncrtBnd; HonRl; JA; MrchBnd; Swmmng; LetterTrk; Chrldr; GAA; Univ; Bs.

WEBER, Marilyn D; Jesup Community HS; Waterloo, IA; 3/86 TrsJrCls; Chr; HonRl; NHS; RptrYrbk; 4-H; FrCl; Mt Mercy Col; Nursing.

WEBER, Mark E; Arthor Oto Comm HS; Nayleton, IA; VPJrCls; NHS; Wrstlng; DanFAwd; Agricultural School; Farming.

WEBER, Mary; Goodridge HS; Oklee, MN; HonRl; LbryAde; NHS; SchPl; Yrbk; SchPpr; FFA; SecSophCls; PpCl; GAA; Navy.

WEBER, Mary E; Custer HS; Milwaukee, WI; HonRl; JA; JrNHS; NHS; PolWkr; StuCncl; Ftbl; Trk; GAA; PPFtbl; Col; Pro.

WEBER, Maureen A; Lourdes HS; Chicago, IL; CmntyWkr; HonRl; LbryAde; NatlFornLg; NHS; SchMus; SchPl; SctActv; TchrAde; PpCl; College; Nursing.

WEBER, Michael J; Thompson Public HS; Thompson, ND; 2/19 PresJrCls; ALBoysSt; Band; Chrs; ChrhWkr; HonRl; PolWkr; SchPl; StuCncl; University Of No Dakota; Music.

WEBER, Michele A; De Forest HS; Winsdsor, WI; Chrs; HonRl; PolWkr; SchMus; SchPl; 4-H; GerCl; LetterTrk; IMSpt; 4-HAwd;.

WEBER, Nancy M; Otis Bison Sr HS; Bison, KS; Band; Chr; CncrtBnd; HonRl; Mdrgl; MrchBnd; NHS; PepBnd; SchPl; College; Vocation.

WEBER, Pamela A; Lourdes Academy; Oshkosh, WI; Chrs; Mdrgl; SchMus; LetterTennis; LetterTrk; Chrldr; IMSpt; Univ Of Oshkosh; Botany & Art Education.

WEBER, Paul E; Bedford N Lawrence HS; Bedford, IN; NHS; NatlThespSoc; SchMus; SchPl; MthCl; SciCl; Indiana U; Doctor.

WEBER, Paul R; Coon Rapids Sr HS; Coon Rapids, MN; 1/732 Chr; CncrtBnd; HonRl; NHS; PepBnd; U Of Minn; Meteorology.

WEBER, Randy J; Millington HS; Millington, MI; 8/200 ALBoysSt; Band; CncrtBnd; NHS; PepBnd; StuCncl; TchrAde; RptrYrbk; RptrSchPpr; SchPpr; Univ; Cpa.

WEBER, Richard G; Anthon Oto Comm HS; Anthon, IA; 3/35 VPFrshCls; PresSophCls; HonRl; NHS; SchPl; StuCncl; RptrYrbk; PpCl; Bsktbl; Ftbl; Trk; Wrstlng; Univ; Professional.

WEBER, Richard J; Thompson HS; Thompson, ND; Band; HonRl; PepBnd; SchPl; MthCl; LetterBsbl; LetterBsktbl; Ftbl; AmLegAwd; Trade School.

WEBER, Richard J; 523 Madison HS; Marcus, IA; 11/60 SecJrCls; ChrhWkr; HonRl; LbryAde; SchMus; SchPl; StuCncl; 4-H; Ia State Univ; Ag.

WEBER, Richard L; Carrollton HS; Carrollton, IL; 3/89 PresFrshCls; PresSophCls; PresJrCls; HonRl; NHS; SchPl; 4-H; FFA; FTA; PpCl; LetterBsktbl; LetterFtbl; LetterTrk;.

WEBER, Rick; Emery HS; Emery, SD; ALBoysSt; ChrhWkr; HonRl; SchPl; Bsbl; Ftbl;.

WEBER, Sandy M; Morgan Public HS; Morgan, MN; ALAGirlsSt; Band; Chrs; CncrtBnd; MrchBnd; PepBnd; StuCncl; RptrSchPpr; PpCl; Chrldr; Business School.

WEBER, Scott M; Fairmont HS; Fairmont, MN; Chr; HonRl; Orch; PolWkr; SchMus; SchPpr; AmLegAwd; Univ;.

WEBER, Sharon; Corunna Hs; Owosso, MI; 36/210 CncrtBnd; HonRl; JA; MrchBnd; NHS; PepBnd; Pres4-H; VPFHA; KeyCl; 4-HAwd; Delta College; Clothing Construction.

WEBER, Sharon M; Corunna HS; Owosso, MI; 36/210 Band; HonRl; JA; NHS; SctActv; 4-H; FHA; KeyCl; Delta College; Clothing Constr.

WEBER, Shelly R; West Holt HS; Stuart, NE; Chrs; HonRl; LbryAde; SchPl; EdYrBk; 4-H; GerCl; Trk; Chrldr; 4-HAwd; College.

WEBER, Stephen F; West Richland HS; Newton, IL; 3/33 PresFrshCls; VPSrCls; ALBoysSt; Band; ChrhWkr; HonRl; RptrYrbk; 4-H; FrCl; AmLegAwd; Southern Illinois Univ; Medicine.

WEBER, Steven J; Oostburg HS; Sheboygan Falls, WI; 8/80 HonRl; SchPpr; Bsktbl; Ftbl; Trk; Univ; Psychology.

WEBER, Susan A; Mt Assisi Acad; Palos Heights, IL; 1/194 CmntyWkr; HonRl; LitMag; NatlFornLg; NatlMeritSF; SchPpr; 4-H; FrCl; DanFAwd; NCTE; Drake Univ.

WEBER, Susan A; Mt Assisi Academy; Palos Hts, IL; 1/189 CtyCnl; LitMag; NatlFornLg; NatlMeritFnl; EdSchPpr; 4-H; KeyCl; GAA; AmLegAwd; DanFAwd; TIMEAwd; Drake Univ; Broadcasting.

WEBER, Susan M; Normal Comm HS; Normal, IL; HonRl; NatlMeritCmnd; Quill&Scroll; RptrYrbk; EdYrBk; 4-H; FrCl; Augustana College.

WEBER, Suzan E; Philip HS; Philip, SD; 5/40 Band; CncrtBnd; HonRl; MrchBnd; NHS; PepBnd; SchPl; PpCl; LetterBsktbl; LetterTrk; U Of Sd; Psychology.

WEBER, Tara R; Lisbon HS; Lisbon, ND; 5/75 VPJrCls; ALAGirlsSt; CncrtBnd; HonRl; JrNHS; MrchBnd; NHS; StuCncl; SecFHA; Chrldr; Univ Of Nd; Dietetics.

WEBERG, Mervin D; Oak Grove HS; Maynard, MN; Band; Chr; HonRl; Mdrgl; NHS; NatlMeritFnl; SchPl; SctActv; Yrbk; BttyCrckrAwd; Concordia College; Physics.

WEBS, Debra A; La Crosse HS; Alexander, KS; Chr; ChrhWkr; HonRl; Mdrgl; ModUN; SchMus; StuGov; FHA; LetterTennis; LetterTrk; College; Social Worker Music.

WEBSTER, Charles W; Savanna HS; Savanna, IL; 1/67 ALBoysSt; HonRl; NatlMeritSF; SciCl; LetterGlf; Univ Of Illinois; Engineering.

WEBSTER, Christopher J; Nickerson HS; Hutchinson, KS; HonRl; NatlFornLg; SchPl; StuCncl; StuGov; TchrAde; RptrYrbk; SchPpr; PpCl; Tennis; Juco At Hutch; X Ray Tech.

WEBSTER, Connie L; Jefferson City Senior HS; Jefferson City, MO; 15/500 SecAFS; Chr; ChrhWkr; HonRl; JrNHS; NHS; SpnCl; PpCl; Univ; Accountant.

WEBSTER, Cynthia M; Wm Rainey Harper HS; Chicago, IL; 81/300 ChrhWkr; HospAde; LbryAde; TchrAde; College; Professional Nurse.

WEBSTER, Daniel J; Central HS; St Joseph, MO; HonRl; NHS; SchPl; StuCncl; StuGov; LatCl; SciCl; LetterBsktbl; LetterFtbl; LetterTrk; Univ Of Ks; Architecture.

WEBSTER, Dennis F; Rushville HS; Rushville, NE; 6/40 VPFrshCls; VPJrCls; SecSrCls; Chrs; HonRl; NHS; SchPl; YthFlsp; VPGerCl; LetterBsktbl; LetterGlf; LetterTrk;.

WEBSTER, Glenn C; Ida HS; Ida, MI; 51/150 Band; ChrhWkr; CncrtBnd; MrchBnd; StuCncl; YthFlsp; Yrbk; SchPpr; 4-H; 4-HAwd; College; Biologist.

WEBSTER, Joseph A; Calhoun HS; Hamburg, IL; Chrs; HonRl; FFA; Bsktbl; LetterBsktbl; LetterFtbl; LetterTrk; IMSpt; Univ Of Mo; Mechanical Engineer.

WEBSTER, Keith D; Cashton HS; Cashton, WI; ALBoysSt; Chr; Chrs; HonRl; LbryAde; Mdrgl; SctActv; RptrYrbk; Ftbl; Wrstlng;.

WEBSTER, Randall W; Hannibal Sr HS; Hannibal, MO; Band; ChrhWkr; CncrtBnd; DrlTm; ROTC; SctActv; SciCl; Bsbl; LetterFtbl; IMSpt; University; Professional.

WEBSTER, Rick L; Riverdale Public HS; Riverdale, ND; PresFrshCls; VPSophCls; ALBoysSt; HonRl; SctActv; StuCncl; StuGov; Bsktbl; Ftbl; Trk; College; Prof.

WEBSTER, Ronald W; St Agatha HS; Detroit, MI; 4/109 Chrl; HonRl; NHS; Yrbk; RptrSchPpr; SchPpr; SpnCl; College; Law.

WEBSTER, Ruth J; Griffith HS; Griffith, IN; 74/310 ChrhWkr; HonRl;.

WEBSTER, Theresa; Sacred Heart Acad; Mt Pleasant, MI; 9/54 SecJrCls; HonRl; NHS; Yrbk; SchPpr; FrCl; PpCl; Trk; College; Special Ed Teacher.

WEBSTER, Therese M; Oregon Senior HS; Oregon, WI; AFS; Chr; NatlCathMusEdAsoc; HonRl; LbryAde; NatlFornLg; OffAde; SchMus; SctActv; TchrAde; Trade School; Professional.

WEBSTER, William; New Ulm Public HS; Newulm, MN; Aud/Vis; SctActv; Ftbl; Trk; Professional.

WECHSLER, Ben F; Mt Vernon Twp HS; Mt Vernon, IL; Band; Chr; HonRl; NHS; NatlThespSoc; Orch; SchMus; SchPl; VPYthFlsp; University Of Illinois; Music.

WECHTER, Diane J; Loy Norrix HS; Kalamazoo, MI; 32/541 HonRl; NHS; Orch; LetterTennis; U Of Mi; Lawyer.

WECK, Gary E; Hutsonville HS; Annapolis, IL; VPFFA; PpCl;.

WECK, Terry L; Hutsonville HS; Annapolis, IL; PresFrshCls; HonRl; NHS; NatlMeritSchl; StuGov; Yrbk; PresFFA; PpCl; Bsktbl; BauchLmbAwd; GovHonPrgAwd; JAAwd; Lockyears College Of Business; Accountant.

WEDDE, Sandra; Wautoma HS; Wautoma, WI; 4/93 HonRl; Yrbk; FBLA; FHA; PresAwd;.

WEDDELL, Gail L; Newton HS; Yale, IL; 33/183 Band; Chrs; HonRl; JA; MrchBnd; PepBnd; Pres4-H; 4-HAwd; JAAwd; CitAwd; Coll; Business.

WEDDELL, Jill A; Medora HS; Medora, IN; HonRl; HospAde; Yrbk;.

WEDDLE, Barry; Our Lady Of Lakes HS; Pontiac, MI; HonRl; PpCl; Ftbl; IMSpt;.

WEDE, Brian S; Larkin HS; Elgin, IL; 106/573 Bsktbl; Elgin Comm Clg; Business.

WEDE, Donna; Tri Center HS; Neola, IA; 7/71 HonRl; NHS; StuGov; RptrSchPpr; 4-H; Bsbl; IMSpt; BttyCrckrAwd; 4-HAwd; Univ North Ia; Mathmatics.

WEDE, Greg L; Clay Central HS; Peterson, IA; ChrhWkr; CmntyWkr; HonRl; SchPl; Trade School; Farmer.

WEDE, Karen; Clay Central Hs; Peterson, IA; 5/44 Chr; ChrhWkr; CmntyWkr; HonRl; SchMus; FFA; Bsktbl; Business School;accounting.

WEDEL, Karen D; Minneapolis HS; Minneapolis, KS; Band; Chrs; ChrhWkr; CncrtBnd; HonRl; MrchBnd; PolWkr; RedCrAde; SchMus; SchPl; Kansas State Univ; Court Reporter.

WEDEL, Marilee A; Central Christian HS; Buhler, KS; 2/22 Chr; Chrl; ChrhWkr; HonRl; SchMus; SchPl; TreasStuCncl; SpnCl; PresPpCl; DARAwd;.

WEDELL, Stanley R; Girard HS; Girard, KS; ALBoysSt; ChrhWkr; HonRl; NHS; StuCncl; 4-H; LetterFtbl; 4-HAwd; College; Vocation.

WEDELSTAEDT, Catherine A; Wheaton Central HS; Wheaton, IL; TrsSrCls; ALAGirlsSt; ChrhWkr; CmntyWkr; HonRl; NHS; OffAde; SchMus; SchPl; StuGov; TchrAde; Bsktbl; Trk; Purdue Univ; Chemistry.

WEDEMEIER, Herbert J; Bishop Du Baury HS; St Louis, MO; TrsFrshCls; TrsSophCls; Chrs; HonRl; NHS; SchAde; StuGov; RptrSchPpr; Ftbl; Socr; University.

WEDEMEYER, Daniel J; Mercy HS; Overland, MO; HonRl; SctActv; College; Wildlife Management.

WEDGE, Michael C; Dundee Comm HS; Carpentersville, IL; 35/35 Bsbl; College; Accounting.

WEDGEWOOD, De Ann L; Big Springs Dist 80 HS; Big Springs, NE; 2/21 CmntyWkr; HonRl; SchAde; SecStuCncl; 4-H; FHA; LetterPpCl; LetterTrk; GAA; LetterIMSpt; College; Professional.

WEDIG, Denise R; Belmont HS; Cuba City, WI; 3/46 HonRl; SchPl; RptrSchPpr; SpnCl; MthCl; PpCl; Finley Hosp Sch Of Nursing; Rn.

WEDIG, Judy A; Black Hawk HS; Gratiot, WI; TrsJrCls; ChrhWkr; DrlTm; HonRl; NHS; EdYrBk; Sec4-H; PresFHA; TreasPpCl; Chrldr; College; Home Economics.

WEDMAN, Judy A; Bluestem HS; Leon, KS; 4/42 Chrs; HonRl; SchPl; SchPpr; FHA; PpCl; LetterBsktbl; Chrldr; Trade; Vocation.

WEDMORE, David E; Stevens HS; Rapid City, SD; 32/410 ALBoysSt; Band; CncrtBnd; HonRl; JCC; MrchBnd; NatlFornLg; Orch; PepBnd; SctActv; YthLg; GerCl; South Dakota School Of Mines.

WEDRYK, Susan; Bishop Noll Inst; Chicago, IL; 16/350 ChrhWkr; HonRl; NHS; SctActv; Notre Dame; Chemistry Major.

WEEDA, Patrick O; Mount Ayr Community HS; Tingley, IA; ChrhWkr; HonRl; PresStuCncl; 4-H; FFA; LetterBsktbl; LetterFtbl; LetterTrk; DanFAwd; 4-HAwd;.

WEEDE, Tina L; Malden HS; Malden, MO; Band; CncrtBnd; MrchBnd; OffAde; PepBnd; FHA; Bus Schl; Homemaker.

WEEDEN, Roland E; Beloit Memorial HS; Beloit, WI; 1/495 HonRl; NHS; StuGov; Bsktbl; Tennis; Trk; Univ Of Wisconsin; Physical Education.

WEEDEN, Susan M; Richland Center HS; Richland Center, WI; Chr; HonRl; HospAde; LitMag; SecLbryAde; NHS; TchrAde; 4-H; FBLA; LionAwd; Madison Business Clg; Secretarial.

WEEDFALL, Lynette J; St Joseph HS; St Joseph, MI; 17/330 ChrhWkr; NHS; SchPl; StuCncl; TchrAde; PresYthFlsp; SecSpnCl; MthCl; Trk; GAA; Lake Michigan Col; Physical Therapis.

WEEDIN, Sharon K; Salem HS; Salem, MO; 7/169 Chr; HonRl; OffAde; SchMus; SchPl; RptrYrbk; RptrSchPpr; VPFrCl; VFWAwd; Mo So St Coll; Lawyer.

WEEKS, Bruce E; Rock Island HS; Rock Island, IL; HonRl; Quill&Scroll; SchMus; StuGov; EdSchPpr; FrCl; Ftbl; IMSpt; Western Illinois Univ; History.

WEEKS, Christopher; Clayton HS; Clayton, MO; Chrs; ChrhWkr; SchMus; SchPpr; SpnCl; SciCl; Univ Of Mo; Oceanography.

WEEKS, Dana S; Hoisington HS; Hoisington, KS; 17/109 CmntyWkr; DrmBgl; HonRl; LbryAde; NHS; SchPl; StuCncl; TchrAde; PresYthFlsp; Chrldr; PPFtbl; Colby Community College; Veterinarian.

WEEKS, David L; West Vigo HS; W Terre Haute, IN; 21/215 Band; HonRl; JA; EdYrBk; Yrbk; TreasFTA; LetterTennis; Trk; JAAwd; College.

WEEKS, Derald L; Irving Crown HS; Algonquin, IL; ChrhWkr; HonRl; SciCl; Ftbl; LetterWrstlng; Elgin Com College; Bookkeeping.

WEEKS, Gerald L; Irving Crown HS; Algonquin, IL; 24/500 ALBoysSt; ChrhWkr; HonRl; SciCl; Ftbl; Wrstlng; College; Professional.

WEEKS, Judith; Bishop Ryan HS; Minot, ND; 4/77 HonRl; NHS; OffAde; TchrAde; Trk; Chrldr; IMSpt; PPFtbl;.

WEEKS, Judith M; Bishop Ryan HS; Minot, ND; 3/83 HonRl; JrNHS; VPNHS; OffAde; PresSctActv; SecSdlty; TchrAde; FHA; GerCl; PpCl; Minot St; Social Work.

WEEKS, Lee Ann; Naperville Central HS; Naperville, IL; Chrs; DrlTm; HonRl; HospAde; NatlFornLg; NHS; NatlThespSoc; SchMus; College.

WEEKS, Michael S; Pittsfield HS; Hamilton, IL; 3/137 ChrhWkr; HonRl; NHS; SchPl; StuCncl; 4-H; LatCl; MthCl; Bsbl; Ftbl; College; Marine Biology.

WEEKS, Michael S; Pittsfield HS; Pittsfield, IL; 3/135 ChrhWkr; HonRl; NHS; SchPl; SctActv; StuCncl; 4-H; LatCl; MthCl; PpCl; SciCl; 4-HAwd; College; Marine Biologist.

WEEKS, Pamela D; Campbell HS; Campbell, MO; Chr; Chrs; ChrhWkr; CmntyWkr; HonRl; NHS; PolWkr; SchMus; SchPl; SctActv; Univ; Social Work.

WEEKS, Paul E; Rudyard HS; Kincheloe Afb, MI; ChrhWkr; CncrtBnd; DrmMjrt; HonRl; MrchBnd; NHS; NatlMeritSF; PepBnd; SchMus; StuCncl; Univ Of Michigan; Orthodontist.

WEEKS, Raymond R; Rosemount Sr HS; Apple Valley, MN; 4/347 HonRl; NHS; MthCl; LetterTrk; Bemidji St College; Accounting.

WEEKS, Robert; Hauser HS; Columbus, IN; 36/83 HonRl; SchPl; 4-H; FFA; MthCl; Bsbl; Tri State Coll; Computer Programming.

WEENER, Laurie A; Holland Christian HS; Holland, MI; ChrhWkr; NHS; NatlMeritSchl; 4-H; IMSpt; Calvin College; Spec Ed.

WEERTS, Keith E; Eastridge HS; St Anne, IL; 9/285 Chr; NHS; NatlMeritCmnd; SchMus; Glf; Swmmng; Anapolis Naval Academy; Ocean Engineer.

WEESE, Mike; Lenox Community HS; Lenox, IA; VPJrCls; Band; CncrtBnd; HonRl; MrchBnd; Orch; PepBnd; 4-H; Bsktbl; BauchLmbAwd;.

WEFSO, Claire D; Rushville HS; Rushville, NE; 9/40 PresJrCls; ALAGirlsSt; Band; CncrtBnd; HonRl; NHS; SchMus; PresStuCncl; GerCl; RotaryAwd; Univ; Pro.

WEGEHAUPT, Kevin B; Delmont Public HS; Delmont, SD; PresFrshCls; ALBoysSt; ChrhWkr; HonRl; Mdrgl; SchPl; StuCncl; SptEdSchPpr; Bsktbl; Ftbl; U Of Sd; Bus.

WEGENER, Linda; Bay City Western HS; Auburn, MI; 3/448 NHS; NatlMeritSchl; FrCl; IMSpt; PPFtbl; Michigan Tech Univ; Civil Engineer.

WEGENER, Renee; Louisville Public HS; Louisville, NE; 1/41 ALAGirlsSt; Chr; Chrs; HonRl; NHS; YthFlsp; 4-HAwd; College; Med Tech.

WEGER, Debra E; Paris HS; Paris, IL; 14/234 Aud/Vis; HonRl; NHS; RptrSchPpr; EdSchPpr; PpCl; Glf; Danville Jr College; Accounting.

WEGIER, Susan M; Buffalo Grove HS; Arlington Hts, IL; HonRl; HospAde; NatlFornLg; Univ Of Illinois; Accountant.

WEGMAN, Cathleen; Riceville Community HS; Riceville, IA; Band; CncrtBnd; HonRl; SchPl; 4-H; Bsktbl; GAA; 4-HAwd; College; Amimal Science.

WEGMAN, John J; Union HS; Biggsville, IL; 4/60 PresSophCls; Band; Chrs; HonRl; Mdrgl; NHS; StuCncl; LetterBsktbl; LetterFtbl; LetterTrk; Univ Of Ill; Engineering.

WEGMANN, Dawn T; Western Dubuque HS; Epworth, IA; 2/243 SecFrshCls; TrsFrshCls; SecJrCls; TrsJrCls; ModUN; PresSctActv; StuCncl; FBLA; Bsktbl; Ftbl; LetterTrk; Chrldr; GAA; Loras College; Nursing.

WEGMANN, John G; Bloomington Community HS; Bloomington, WI; ALBoysSt; Chrs; JrNHS; NHS; 4-H; FFA; Univ Of Wisconsin; Agriculture.

WEGMANN, Steven A; Geneva Community HS; Geneva, IL; 10/250 University Of Illinois; Nuclear Physics.

WEGMANN, Wayne; Notre Dame Hs; Chicago, IL; 17/266 Band; CncrtBnd; HonRl; MrchBnd; NHS; Orch; SchMus; RptrSchPpr; SciCl; GovHonPrgAwd; University; Biological Sciences.

WEGNER, Charles T; Hinsdale Central HS; Oak Brook, IL; Aud/Vis; CmntyWkr; HonRl; RedCrAde; SchPl; SctActv; SptEdYrbk; SciCl; Ftbl; University; Lawyer.

WEGNER, Diane L; Oconomowoc Sr HS; Watertown, WI; 24/800 AFS; Band; Chr; ChrhWkr; NHS; YthFlsp; 4-H; FTA; SpnCl; GAA; Univ Of Eau Claire; Child Education.

WEGNER, Donald; Armstrong Comm HS; Armstrong, IA; TchrAde; FFA; Bsktbl;.

WEGNER, John A; Evergreen Pk Comm HS; Evergreen Park, IL; 77/439 Band; CncrtBnd; HonRl; MrchBnd; PepBnd; SchAde; Loyola Univ; Biology.

WEGNER, Nancy C; Sparta HS; Sparta, WI; 25/190 PresChr; Chrs; HonRl; Mdrgl; NHS; Orch; SchMus; YthFlsp; RptrSchPpr; 4-H; U W Stevens Point; Professionalpiano.

WEGNER, Rogalyn R; Senior HS; Archer, NE; 7/75 Band; CncrtBnd; HonRl; MrchBnd; NHS; PepBnd; Teen; 4-H; FFA; PpCl; Trade School; Professional.

WEGNER, Steven G; Northwestern Military; Madison, WI; Aud/Vis; HonRl; NatlFornLg; Quill&Scroll; ROTC; SchPl; RptrYrbk; SptEdSchPpr; SchPpr; Tennis; Univ; Medicine.

WEGNER, Thomas W; Prospect HS; Arlington Heights, IL; 35/654 CncrtBnd; MrchBnd; LatCl; Bsbl; Swmmng; LetterTennis; Univ Of Illinois; Medicine.

WEGRZYN, Kenneth J; Marian Catholic HS; Chicago Hts, IL; 107/365 HonRl; YthFnd; Bsktbl; Ftbl; College; Professional.

WEHINGER, David; Black Hawk HS; South Wayne, WI; HonRl; StuGov; RptrSchPpr; FFA; Sw Wi Voc Tech Inst; Agriculture.

WEHKING, Debra A; Lutheran East HS; Warren, MI; Chr; HonRl; NHS; NatlMeritSchl; RptrYrbk; RptrSchPpr; PpCl; Concordia Junior College; Deacones.

WEHLAND, Valerie L; Holdrege HS; Holdrege, NE; HonRl; TchrAde; EdYrBk; SptEdSchPpr; PpCl; Bsktbl; U Of Ne; Biology Teacher.

WEHMAN, Mary L; Woodlands HS; Winnetka, IL; ChrhWkr; CmntyWkr; JA; PolWkr; StuCncl; StuGov; Bsktbl; GAA; IMSpt; College; Professional.

WEHMEYER, Debbie; Owensville HS; Gerald, MO; HonRl; SctActv; GAA; Business School; Secretarial.

WEHMEYER, Glenna M; Wellsville HS; Wellsville, KS; 8/65 Band; Chr; CncrtBnd; HonRl; MrchBnd; NHS; SchMus; FrCl; PpCl; LetterIMSpt; Baker U Baldwin City Ks.

WEHMEYER, Karen; Gasconade County R2 HS; Rosebud, MO; 2/122 Chrs; HonRl; NHS; YthFlsp; FHA; CitAwd; College; Accounting.

WEHMEYER, Mark L; Owensville R 2 HS; Rosebud, MO; 10/120 ALBoysSt; HonRl; JrNHS; Yrbk; LatCl; College; Pharmacy.

WEHMEYER, Mary R; Alvernia HS; Chicago, IL; JA; NHS; TchrAde; University; Medicine.

WEHMEYER, Scarlet L; Arlington HS; Arlington, NE; 5/57 Band; HonRl; NHS; Yrbk; 4-H; GerCl; PresPpCl; LetterBsktbl; LetterTrk; 4-HAwd; Concordia Teachers Coll; Elementary Educ.

WEHNER, Darryl J; Trinity HS; Dickinson, ND; Band; ChrhWkr; CncrtBnd; MrchBnd; PepBnd; RedCrAde; SchMus; SchPl; SctActv;.

WEHNES, Jeanne; Immaculate Conception; Elmhurst, IL; 10/166 ALAGirlsSt; HonRl; NHS; RptrYrbk; Yrbk; FrCl; PpCl; IMSpt; Univ; Major In Envionmental Studies.

WEHNES, Patricia R; Red Cloud HS; Red Cloud, NE; Chr; Chrl; Chrs; HonRl; SchMus; 4-H; FHA; PpCl; Chrldr; 4-HAwd; Business School; Secretary.

WEHR, Nanette E; Batesville HS; Greensburg, IN; 19/146 Band; DrlTm; HonRl; NHS; Yrbk; 4-H; SpnCl; PpCl; GAA; 4-HAwd; College; Home Economics.

WEHRBEIN, Susie G; Plattsmouth HS; Plattsmouth, NE; 1/163 VPJrCls; Band; HonRl; Mdrgl; NHS; SchMus; YthFlsp; FrCl; Chrldr; College; Biology.

WEHRENBERG, Ted P; North Side HS; Fort Wayne, IN; Bsbl; RotaryAwd; I U Bloomington.

WEHREND, Shirley J; Edwardsville HS; Worden, IL; 5/474 Chr; Chrs; HonRl; TchrAde; YthFlsp; 4-H; GAA; Deaconess Sch Nursing; R N.

WEHRI, Mary Ann B; Hebron Public HS; Hebron, ND; 10/40 Band; Chrs; CncrtBnd; HonRl; PepBnd; SchPl; TchrAde; FshEdYrbk; FshEdSchPpr; GerCl; PpCl; Bsktbl; Trk; Josefs School; Beautician.

WEHRLE, Joni J; Mulberry Grove HS; Mulberry Grove, IL; 1/26 VPSophCls; SecSrCls; Chrs; CmntyWkr; HonRl; NHS; RptrYrbk; GAA; BttyCrckrAwd; DARAwd; Kaskaskia Comm Clg; Teacher.

WEHRLE, Kathleen L; Lena Winslow HS; Lena, IL; 3/98 SecSophCls; SecTrsJrCls; HonRl; NHS; SchMus; SchPl; EdYrBk; RptrSchPpr; College; Computer Engineering.

WEHRLI, Ann K; Roanoke Benson HS; Roanoke, IL; HstSophCls; PresJrCls; ALAGirlsSt; HonRl; SchPl; SctActv; RptrSchPpr; 4-H; FHA; FTA; Eastern Ill Univ; Learning Disabilities.

WEHRMAN, Nathan; Lockwood HS; Lockwood, MO; 10/42 ALBoysSt; Band; ChrhWkr; HonRl; MrchBnd; SchPl; YthFlsp; Southwest Missouri State Univ; Ag Busines.

WEHRS, David; Plainview HS; Plainview, MN; 12/91 ChrhWkr; HonRl; NatlFornLg; SchPl; StuCncl; EdSchPpr;.

WEHRS, Rebecca; Concordia R 2 HS; Concordia, MO; 15/50 TrsFrshCls; SecSophCls; PresSrCls; ChrhWkr; CmntyWkr; MrchBnd; NHS; NatlThespSoc; TchrAde; FTA; Cen Mo St Univ;spec Ed Teach.

WEIAND, Jacquelyn S; Mundelein HS; Mundelein, IL; Band; CncrtBnd; HonRl; HospAde; LitMag; MrchBnd; NHS; College Of Lake County; Law Enforcement.

WEICHMAN, Cindy J; Benton Community HS; Atkins, IA; SecFrshCls; ALAGirlsSt; Chr; Chrl; Chrs; ChrhWkr; CmntyWkr; HonRl; HospAde; Mdrgl; SchMus; Bsktbl; LetterTrk; CchngActv; Mt Mercy College; Nursing.

WEICK, Cynthia M; Proviso West HS; Westchester, IL; 159/948 Band; Chr; ChrhWkr; HonRl; MrchBnd; PepBnd; YthFlsp; PpCl; Trk; GAA; Univ; Music Therapy.

WEIDEMANN, Dennis D; Laporte Cy HS; La Porte City, IA; 1/72 PresFrshCls; HonRl; EdSchPpr; Bsktbl; LetterTennis;.

WEIDENBACH, Jeanne M; Minooka HS; Minooka, IL; Band; ChrhWkr; HonRl; NHS; OffAde; SchPl; YthFlsp; RptrSchPpr; GAA; AmLegAwd; Bethel Coll; Psych.

WEIDENHAMER, Jeffrey D; Flat Rock HS; Flat Rock, MI; CncrtBnd; HonRl; MrchBnd; NHS; NatlMeritSF; PepBnd; SctActv; Yrbk; EdSchPpr; LetterTrk; Ashland Coll.

WEIDERHAFT, Terry L; Frontier HS; Brookston, IN; 3/59 PresSophCls; HonRl; NHS; Trk; Purdue Univ; Engineering.

WEIDLER, Catherine M; Tripoli Community HS; Tripoli, IA; SecJrCls; Band; Chr; Chrs; ChrhWkr; CncrtBnd; DrmMjrt; HonRl; Mdrgl; MrchBnd; College; Parish Worker.

WEIDLER, Tami K; Balfour Public HS; Balfour, ND; 3/12 PresFrshCls; PresJrCls; ALAGirlsSt; HonRl; SchPl; RptrYrbk; RptrSchPpr; Bsktbl; Trk; Chrldr; IMSpt; AmLegAwd; University Of No Dakota; Special Educ.

WEIDMAN, Charles P; Rich Central HS; Park Forest, IL; 40/420 HonRl; JA; YthFlsp; GerCl; College; Business.

WEIDMAN, Michael L; Laker HS; Elkton, MI; HonRl; NHS; LetterBsbl; LetterFtbl; Tennis; LetterTrk; Western Michigan U; Medical Technician HS.

WEIDMAN, Sue M; Auburndale HS; Auburndale, WI; DrlTm; HonRl; JrNHS; NHS; Yrbk; FBLA; PpCl; Bsktbl; Trk; PresAwd; Bus Sch;vocation.

WEIDNER, Wanda K; Zap Public HS; Zap, ND; VPFrshCls; VPSophCls; VPJrCls; Band; ChrhWkr; CncrtBnd; HonRl; LbryAde; MrchBnd; ModUN; PepBnd; SchMus; SchPl; TchrAde; CaptBsktbl; Dickinson State; Elem Teacher.

WEIER, May; Fairbury HS; Fairbury, NE; 16/132 HonRl; HospAde; JAAwd; PpCl; Boutheastern Comm Col; Undecided.

WEIER, Peggy; Freeman Public HS; Freeman, SD; 15/64 Band; Chr; Chrs; ChrhWkr; CmntyWkr; HonRl; NHS; SchPl; Bsktbl;.

WEIER, Sue M; Central Community HS; Breese, IL; 2/129 Band; CncrtBnd; HonRl; Quill&Scroll; SchPl; TchrAde; FHA; MthCl; College; Accounting.

WEIERKE, Sandra L; Rosemount HS; Eagan, MN; HonRl; StuCncl; GerCl; Trk; GAA; IMSpt; College; Socialwork.

WEIERS, Cheryl; New Prague HS; New Plague, MN; 34/200 HonRl; LbryAde; StuCncl; SchPpr; FHA; FTA; PpCl; Hutchinson Area Vo Tech; Accounting.

WEIGAND, Kenneth R; Deerfield HS; Deerfield, IL; HonRl; NHS; SctActv; LetterTrk; International Insurance.

WEIGAND, Terrill V; Maysville HS; Weatherby, MO; Chrs; ChrhWkr; HonRl; NHS; SchMus; Trade School; Vocation.

WEIGEL, David J; Aberdeen Central HS; Aberdeen, SD; Chr; Chrs; HonRl; LbryAde; Mdrgl; SchAde; SchMus; SchPl; StuCncl; Yrbk; Trade School; Vocation.

WEIGEL, David J; Batesville HS; Oldenburg, IN; 5/140 VPJrCls; HonRl; JA; NHS; NatlThespSoc; SchPl; StuCncl; StuGov; SpnCl; Bsbl; Ftbl; Wrstlng; University; Optometry.

WEIGEL, Donald A; Cassville Sr HS; Cassville, MO; 38/96 Chr; ChrhWkr; FFA; Bsktbl; Ftbl; College; Agriculture.

WEIGEL, Mary K; Norborne HS; Carrollton, MO; 4/24 VPSrCls; ALAGirlsSt; HonRl; NHS; StuCncl; TchrAde; EdSchPpr; FHA; PpCl; CaptBsktbl; Nwsmu; Phy Ed.

WEIGEL, Steven; Winona Sr HS; La Moille, MN; HonRl; NHS; SpnCl; Trk; Wrstlng; JETSAwd; College; Architect.

WEIGEL, Thomas J; St Josephs HS; Westchester, IL; 2/203 HonRl; SpnCl; PpCl; SciCl; Bsbl; Bsktbl; Univ; Medicine.

WEIGHTMAN, Cynthia L; Edwards County HS; Browns, IL; 10/104 TrsSrCls; ALAGirlsSt; Band; Chr; HonRl; NHS; NatlMeritCmnd; SchPl; StuCncl; RptrSchPpr; U Of Evansville; Bme.

WEIGLE, Elizabeth J; East Grand Rapids HS; E Grand Rapids, MI; Chr; CmntyWkr; HospAde; NatlMeritSF; FrCl; LetterBsktbl; GAA; Adrian College; Home Ec.

WEIHS, Larry J; William Jennings Bryan HS; Omaha, NE; Band; CncrtBnd; HonRl; MrchBnd; NHS; Orch; PepBnd; SchAde; SctActv; TchrAde; KeyCl; GerCl; LetterBsbl; LetterBsktbl; College; Science.

WEIKART, Christopher M; Ottawa Township HS; Ottawa, IL; 1/420 TrsSrCls; Chr; HonRl; NHS; NatlMeritCmnd; FrCl; LetterSwmmng; Univ Of Ill; Engineering.

WEIL, Susan; Highland Park HS; Highland Park, IL; Chrs; PresJrNHS; PresNHS; SchMus; SchPl; College.

WEILAND, Chuck; Lincoln Community HS; Stanwood, IA; 4/63 ALBoysSt; HonRl; NHS; FFA; Iowa Univ; Ag Business.

WEILAND, Chuck F; Lincoln Community HS; Stanwood, IA; 5/64 ALBoysSt; HonRl; NHS; FFA; LetterBsbl; LetterFtbl; Iowa State Univ; Agriculture.

WEILAND, Kenneth; St Alphonsus HS; Detroit, MI; HonRl; Detroit Col Of Bus; Accounting.

WEILAND, Scott; Lakeland HS; Howe, IN; CncrtBnd; HonRl; PepBnd; SchMus; SchPl; FFA; SpnCl; Glf; Wrstlng; IMSpt; In Univ; Agriculture.

WEILAND, Teresa M; Minonk Dana Rutland HS; Rutland, IL; 20/58 Chrs; HonRl; OffAde; RptrSchPpr; FHA; PpCl; Bsktbl; GAA;.

WEILAND, Wayne H; Royall HS; Kendall, WI; 2/120 VPFrshCls; PresJrCls; ALBoysSt; ChrhWkr; NHS; SchMus; StuCncl; 4-H; CaptFtbl; CaptWrstlng; U Of Wi; Veterinarian.

WEILANDICH, G R; Ritenour Sr HS; Overland, MO; 175/929 Chr; HonRl; LitMag; SchMus; SchPl; TreasStuCncl; RptrYrbk; Yrbk; RptrSchPpr; SchPpr; U Of Mo Veterinary Medicine.

WEILBAKER, Denise; West Washington HS; Fredericksburg, IN; 2/79 Band; CncrtBnd; HonRl; MrchBnd; NHS; PepBnd; StuCncl; RptrSchPpr; SpnCl; PpCl; College; Business.

WEILBAKER, Randall; West Washington HS; Fredricksburg, IN; PresSophCls; PresJrCls; PresSrCls; CncrtBnd; HonRl; PepBnd; Yrbk; LatCl; Bsktbl; Trk;.

WEILER, Cynthia M; Auburndale HS; Auburndale, WI; DrlTm; HonRl; NatlFornLg; NHS; SchPl; Pres4-H; FBLA; PpCl; Bsktbl; LetterTrk; GAA; 4-HAwd; College.

WEILER, Ghislaine O; Carmel Girls HS; Lake Forest, IL; 30/173 HonRl; LbryAde; NHS; OffAde; College; Veterinarian.

WEILER, Kim L; Burlington Community HS; Burlington, IA; Band; CncrtBnd; HonRl; HospAde; NHS; Orch; PepBnd; StuGov; EdSchPpr; IMSpt; Ia Univ; Journalism.

WEILER, Patrick J; St Marys HS; Remsen, IA; Band; Chr; Chrs; CncrtBnd; HonRl; PepBnd; SchMus; SchPl; LetterBsbl; LetterBsktbl; LetterTrk; LetterCchngActv; College; Professional.

WEILLER, Raoul N; G P South HS; Grosse Pointe, MI; Band; ChrhWkr; CmntyWkr; HonRl; MrchBnd; Orch; PepBnd; GerCl; Tennis; IMSpt; Annapolis Naval Acad; Math.

WEILLS, Michelle; East HS; Wichita, KS; ChrhWkr; CmntyWkr; LbryAde; SctActv; TchrAde; Trk; Social Work.

WEIMER, Linda K; R 1 North Callaway; Auxvasse, MO; Band; HonRl; NatlThespSoc; SchMus; SchPl; StuCncl; RptrYrbk; VPFHA; FTA; SpnCl; College; Professional.

WEIMER, Lisa A; Highland Comm HS; Riverside, IA; HonRl; PpCl; Trk; Chrldr; Southeast Comm College; Nursing Rn.

WEINBENDER, Susan; Eleva Strum Central HS; Strum, WI; 5/75 Univ; Language.

WEINBERG, Audrey J; Urbana HS; Urbana, IL; 8/428 AFS; Chr; NHS; NatlMeritCmnd; NatlThespSoc; SchMus; SchPl; Univ; Computer Science.

WEINBERG, Constance A; Kewaunee HS; Kewaunee, WI; 6/150 AFS; HonRl; JrNHS; SecNHS; SpnCl; SciCl; College; Business Admin.

WEINBERG, David; Clinton Hs; Clinton, IL; 1/160 HonRl; PresNHS; SchMus; SchPl; VPStuCncl; SpnCl; PpCl;.

WEINBERG, James R; De Soto HS; Stoddard, WI; HonRl; PolWkr; SchPl; TchrAde; EdSchPpr; SptEdSchPpr; 4-H; FFA; LetterTrk; LetterWrstlng; Military Academy; Professional.

WEINBERGER, Mary Ann; Thornridge HS; Dolton, IL; 27/684 HonRl; NHS; SctActv; StuGov; College; Medicine.

WEINBURG, Patricia E; Langdon HS; Langdon, ND; ALAGirlsSt; HonRl; NHS; NatlMeritSF; PpCl; LetterBsktbl; LetterTrk; College; Engineering.

WEINDEL, Linda M; Staunton Community HS; Staunton, IL; 12/100 Chr; HonRl; NHS; RptrYrbk; GAA; Bames Hospital School; Nursing.

WEINER, Debra L; Columbus HS; Columbus, WI; Band; CmntyWkr; CncrtBnd; HonRl; MrchBnd; NHS; PepBnd; StuCncl; 4-H; SpnCl; PPFtbl; 4-HAwd; U Of Wi; Accountant.

WEINER, James D; Clayton HS; Clayton, MO; Band; LitMag; ModUN; NatlMeritSF; PolWkr; SctActv; LatCl; PpCl; LetterGlf; LetterWrstlng; College; Professional.

WEINER, Martin J; Jersey Community HS; Jerseyville, IL; 1/300 HonRl; VPNHS; NatlMeritCmnd; FFA; LetterBsbl; Tennis; LetterWrstlng; College; Dentistry.

WEINFIELD, Debra E; Morgan Park Academy; Oak Lawn, IL; 3/41 PresSophCls; HonRl; LitMag; NHS; NatlThespSoc; Quill&Scroll; SchPl; StuCncl; EdYrBk; Newcomb College; Medicine.

WEINGARDEN, David; Yeshivah Beth Yehudah HS; Southfield, MI; PresSrCls; ChrhWkr; CmntyWkr; HonRl; NatlMeritCmnd; SchPl; StuGov; EdSchPpr; CivCl; SciCl; College; Medicine.

WEINGART, Charlene M; Mc Henry Comm HS; Mc Henry, IL; 1/441 PresSrCls; AFS; ChrhWkr; CmntyWkr; HonRl; NHS; SchMus; SchPl; StuCncl; SchPpr; 4-H; GAA; University Of Iowa; Pharmacy.

WEINGART, James H; Midway 433 HS; Denton, KS; Chrs; ChrhWkr; HonRl; NHS; Sacrstn; SchPl; TchrAde; YthFlsp; Yrbk; College; Prof.

WEINHOLD, Leanne M; St Francis Academy; Joliet, IL; 19/174 CmntyWkr; HonRl; NHS; NatlThespSoc; SchMus; SchPl; StuCncl; FrCl; College; Pre School Education.

WEINMANN, Robert A; Heritage Christian HS; Indianapolis, IN; Band; CncrtBnd; PepBnd; YthFlsp; LetterSocr; Olivet Nazarene College; Business.

WEINMEISTER, David R; Gering HS; Gering, NE; Band; Chr; Chrs; CncrtBnd; HonRl; MrchBnd; Orch; PepBnd; SchMus; GerCl; Ftbl; Glf; Trk; Colorado St Univ; Music.

WEINRICH, Steve P; Owensville HS; Rosebud, MO; 16/122 HonRl; SctActv; 4-H; Bsktbl; Ftbl; Trk; College; Computer Science.

WEINSTEIN, Cathy L; Highland Park HS; Highwood, IL; 13/643 NHS; NatlMeritSF; SpnCl; U Of Il; Ba In Commerce & Bus Admn.

WEINSTEIN, Randall S; Grandview HS; Kansas City, MO; TrsJrCls; ChrhWkr; CmntyWkr; HonRl; JrNHS; LitMag; NHS; SchPl; StuCncl; RptrYrbk; College; Professional.

WEINZAPFEL, Linda; Central HS; Evansville, IN; 13/600 ChrhWkr; HonRl; NHS; TchrAde; 4-H; SciCl; Univ; Pharmacology.

WEIR, E; Albia Community HS; Albia, IA; Band; CncrtBnd; HonRl; MrchBnd; PepBnd; SctActv; 4-H; 4-HAwd; Trade School; Cosmotology.

WEIR, Karen D; Yates City HS; Maquon, IL; 1/22 SecSrCls; Chrs; HonRl; LbryAde; SchMus; TchrAde; EdYrBk; 4-H; FHA; GAA; College; Secretary.

WEIRES, Marjorie L; White Lake Independent HS; White Lake, SD; Chrs; CmntyWkr; HonRl; LbryAde; Mdrgl; MrchBnd; TchrAde; 4-H; PpCl; 4-HAwd; Vo Tech School; Vet.

WEIRICH, James N; Westview HS; Shipshewana, IN; 1/65 Band; CncrtBnd; HonRl; MrchBnd; NHS; NatlMeritSF; PepBnd; SchPl; College; Physics.

WEIRICK, Marrilee A; Grandville Senior HS; Grandville, MI; Chr; Chrs; ChrhWkr; CmntyWkr; HonRl; IntrClCncl; StuCncl; PpCl; CchngActv; PPFtbl; Western Mi Univ; Professional.

WEIS, Ann P; St Mary Acad; Monroe, MI; 58/143 Chr; Chrl; LbryAde; SchMus; SchPl; FNA; LatCl; Montoe Cnty Comm Col; Tchr Dramatic Arts.

WEIS, John R; Paynesville Sr HS; Paynesville, MN; 1/115 ALBoysSt; Band; HonRl; NHS; NatlMeritSF; PolWkr; SchPl; PresGerCl; LetterFtbl; LetterGlf; LetterWrstlng; College.

WEIS, Kathleen S; Marian HS; Mishawaka, IN; 18/129 VPSophCls; HonRl; SchMus; SchPl; StuCncl; SchPpr; Trk; College; Psychology.

WEISBECK, Allen F; Hague Public HS; Hague, ND; 1/13 PresSrCls; Chrs; HonRl; ModUN; TchrAde; EdSchPpr; LetterBsktbl; LetterTrk; VFWAwd; VoiceDemAwd; Bus School; Accounting.

WEISE, Karen A; Rosedale HS; Rosedale, IN; 15/47 Band; CncrtBnd; HonRl; MrchBnd; Bsktbl; Trk; GAA; Indiana University; Physical Therapy.

WEISENBECK, Donna; Durand HS; Durand, WI; SecSophCls; VPJrCls; Band; HonRl; NHS; PepBnd; Sdlty; GerCl; PpCl; College; Med Lab Tech.

WEISENBECK, Joann M; New Richmond HS; New Richmond, WI; 4/176 Band; ChrhWkr; CncrtBnd; HonRl; MrchBnd; NatlMeritCmnd; Orch; SchMus; EdYrBk; GovHonPrgAwd; Univ Of Wi; Acct.

WEISENBECK, Michelle A; Durand Sr HS; Durand, WI; Band; CncrtBnd; HonRl; MrchBnd; PepBnd; SctActv; Sdlty; FHA; GAA; 4-HAwd; College; Registered Nurse.

WEISENBERG, Elliot S; N Shore Country Day HS; Waukegan, IL; TrsSophCls; PresJrCls; TrsJrCls; Chrs; SchMus; LetterFtbl; LetterGlf; Medicine Or Science.

WEISENBURGER, Cindy A; Ashley HS; Ashley, ND; Band; Chr; ChrhWkr; CncrtBnd; HonRl; MrchBnd; NatlMeritSF; PepBnd; Col; English.

WEISHAAR, Tim J; Atchison Co Comm HS; Nortonville, KS; 9/87 ALBoysSt; HonRl; LbryAde; MthCl; SciCl; LetterFtbl; LetterTrk; College; Biology.

WEISHEIT, Michael D; Dubois HS; Jasper, IN; 2/81 PresFrshCls; PresSophCls; ALBoysSt; HonRl; SchPl; RptrYrbk; SchPpr; LetterBsbl; LetterBsktbl; LetterTrk; Indiana University; Dentist.

WEISMAN, Jan R; Metro HS; Chicago, IL; ChrhWkr; CmntyWkr; JrNHS; NatlMeritSF; SchAde; SctActv; Roosevelt Univ; Child Psychology.

WEISMAN, Thomas; Pike Central HS; Otwell, IN; 53/190 VPFrshCls; VPSrCls; ALBoysSt; CmntyWkr; HonRl; SchPl; 4-H; PpCl; Bsktbl; 4-HAwd; Vincennes Univ.

WEISNICHT, Julie T; Ashwaubenon HS; Green Bay, WI; HonRl; NHS; SchPpr; PpCl; CaptChrldr; Nursing School; Rn.

WEISS, Brent; Granite City Hs; Granite City, IL; 2/375 PresChrs; PresNHS; StuCncl; GerCl; MthCl; SciCl; University Of Ill; Doctor Of Medicine.

WEISS, Edward J; Proviso West HS; Westmont, IL; Chrs; HonRl; Loras Col; Computer Science.

WEISS, Faith R; Niles Township N Division HS; Skokie, IL; 152/648 CmntyWkr; HospAde; RedCrAde; SctActv; StuCncl; TreasMthCl; Bsbl; Swmmng; GAA; Univ Az; Oceanography.

WEISS, James J; Gilbert HS; Gilbert, MN; 21/80 Band; CncrtBnd; HonRl; MrchBnd; PepBnd; Sacrstn; SchPl; SctActv; Mesabi Comm Coll; Engineering.

WEISS, Jane C; Niles West HS; Skokie, IL; HonRl; Swmmng; University; Education.

WEISS, Janet L; Green Lake HS; Green Lake, WI; 6/46 Band; HonRl; MrchBnd; NHS; PepBnd; SchPl; RptrYrbk; GAA; College; Biology.

WEISS, Janice; Holdrege HS; Holdrege, NE; Chrs; 4-H; FBLA; Univ; Lab Technician.

WEISS, Jill A; Nicolet HS; Bayside, WI; 21/530 Band; CmntyWkr; MrchBnd; NHS; Madison Univ; Handicapped Children.

WEISS, Judith A; Glenbrook No HS; Northbrook, IL; 51/650 CncrtBnd; HonRl; MrchBnd; GAA; IMSpt; University Of Illinois; Liberal Arts.

WEISS, Julie A; Madison HS; Humphrey, NE; LetterChr; Chrs; StuCncl; TchrAde; PpCl; Chrldr; Wayne State; Educational.

WEISS, Karen; St Charles HS; St Charles, MO; ChrhWkr; CmntyWkr; HonRl; NHS; SctActv; KeyCl; FrCl; IMSpt; DARAwd; College; Education.

WEISS, Kevin R; Lincoln HS; Park Falls, WI; ChrhWkr; HonRl; LetterFtbl; Trk; College.

WEISS, Lori L; Laker HS; Pigeon, MI; Chr; HonRl; SchPl; SctActv; TchrAde; YthFlsp; FFA; 4-H; FHA; FTA; West Mich Univ; Art Teacher.

WEISS, Marcy R; Ida Crown Jewish Academy; Chicago, IL; 5/70 SecJrCls; HonRl; NHS; SchPl; University.

WEISS, Mary J; Elkhart Lake HS; Glenbeulah, WI; Chr; Chrs; HonRl; LbryAde; SchPl; RptrYrbk; SecYrbk; RptrSchPpr; 4-H; PpCl;.

WEISS, Stephen N; Highland Park HS; Highland Park, IL; 42/643 NHS; EdYrBk; University Of Illinois; Architecture.

WEISS, Steven J; Glenbrook North HS; Northbrook, IL; 140/750 HonRl; Univ Of Miami; Medical.

WEISS, Susan; Stevenson HS; Livonia, MI; 28/740 Chr; HonRl; Orch; SchMus; SctActv; Wayne State Univ; Medicine.

WEISS, Susan E; Montini HS; Lombard, IL; 2/154 HonRl; PresNHS; NatlMeritCmnd; RedCrAde; RptrSchPpr; GerCl; College; Accounting.

WEISS, Theresa; Springfield Catholic HS; Springfield, MO; Chrs; ChrhWkr; CmntyWkr; CncrtBnd; HonRl; SchMus; SctActv; StuCncl; Chrldr; Southwest Missouri State Univ; Forestry.

WEISS, William P; F.j. Reitz HS; Evansville, IN; 135/500 HonRl; SchPl; VPFFA; Ftbl; Wrstlng; Purdue Of Minn Univ.; Veterinarian.

WEISSE, Martin E; Lourdes Academy; Oshkosh, WI; VPSrCls; Chrs; StuCncl; KeyCl; LetterFtbl; CaptTrk; CchngActv; KiwanAwd; University; Md.

WEISSER, Patricia A; Tripp Public HS; Tripp, SD; 6/36 SecFrshCls; VPSophCls; PresSrCls; HonRl; NHS; SchPl; YthFlsp; RptrYrbk; FHA; Swmmng; Bible Clge; S Nurse Or Cosmetology.

WEISSERT, Susan L; Good Counsel HS; Lincolnwood, IL; 12/285 HonRl; HospAde; LbryAde; VPSpnCl; Swmmng; Tennis; Loyola U; Pre Med.

WEISSEY, Peter G; Leola Independent HS; Leola, SD; ALBoysSt; Band; HonRl; StuCncl; StuGov; Ftbl; South Dakota State Univ; Engineering.

WEISSINGER, Ellen M; North HS; Omaha, NE; PresFrshCls; PresSrCls; ALAGirlsSt; CmntyWkr; HonRl; LbryAde; NHS; NatlMeritFnl; OffAde; PolWkr; SchAde; LetterGlf; LetterSwmmng; LetterTennis; Univ Of Nebraska; Biology.

WEISSMAN, Howard M; Evanston Twp HS; Skokie, IL; 160/1100 HonRl; TchrAde; Grinnell College; Journalism.

WEIST, Cindy; Columbia City Joint HS; Ft Wayne, IN; 75/290 SecChr; VPNatlFornLg; OffAde; Yrbk; Pres4-H; FrCl; PpCl; GAA; 4-HAwd; Purdue Univ; Veterinarian.

WEISZ, Barbara E; Ashley HS; Ashley, ND; 19/42 HonRl; LbryAde; YthFlsp; GerCl; Trk; Nat Coll Of Bus; Airlines.

WEITEKAMP, Debra K; Lincolnwood HS; Raymond, IL; NHS; Pres4-H; FHA; PresPpCl; SciCl; 4-HAwd; Lincolnland Comm College; Accounting.

WEITTENHILLER, Kim S; Mauston Area HS; Mauston, WI; 12/128 Band; Chr; HonRl; Mdrgl; PepBnd; SchPl; YthFlsp; RptrYrbk; LatCl; PPFtbl; Cardinal Stritch College; Special Ed.

WEITZ, Gary R; Stillwater HS; Stillwater, MN; 1/650 ModUN; NHS; NatlThespSoc; SchPl; StuGov; RptrYrbk; KeyCl; Wrstlng; U S Air Force Academy.

WEITZEL, Brenda; Tri Central HS; Kempton, IN; 20/86 HonRl; OffAde; TchrAde; PpCl; Chrldr; GAA; PPFtbl; Indiana University; Earth Science And Cheme.

WEITZEL, Denise M; Harrison HS; Harrison, MI; 1/120 VPSophCls; VPJrCls; HonRl; LitMag; NHS; SchPl; StuCncl; RptrYrbk; MthCl; PpCl; Kalamazoo Coll; Medicine.

WEITZELL, Donald W; Ldf Community HS; Le Grand, IA; 12/46 PresSrCls; HonRl; NHS; SchMus; SchPl; SptEdYrbk; Bsbl; Ftbl; Work; Printing.

WEKO, Tom E; Gibraltar HS; Sister Bay, WI; VPFrshCls; Band; Chrs; CncrtBnd; LbryAde; MrchBnd; PepBnd; SchPl; StuCncl; StuGov; College; Phy Ed Teacher.

WELAND, Brenda K; W Nodaway R 1 HS; Elmo, MO; CncrtBnd; HonRl; MrchBnd; SecNHS; SecStuCncl; YthFlsp; Bsktbl; Trk; Band; Chrs; U Of Nw M St.

WELBORN, Larry R; Mc Cook HS; Mc Cook, NE; 1/170 ALBoysSt; ChrhWkr; HonRl; VPNHS; YthFlsp; MthCl; SciCl; Bsktbl; Glf; Trk; AmLegAwd; DARAwd; University; Lawyer.

WELBOURNE, Jack F; Hinsdale South HS; Darien, IL; 60/425 HonRl; LetterTrk; Augustana College; Actuary Science.

WELCH, Colleen; Reedsville HS; Reedsville, WI; 2/97 AFS; HonRl; NHS; Orch; SchPl; FBLA; PpCl; GAA; Lakeshore Tech Inst; Medical Secretary.

WELCH, Dale; Loyola Ac HS; Skokie, IL; 16/450 HonRl; NatlMeritSchl; Bsbl; LetterBsktbl; CchngActv; IMSpt; Marquette Univ; Engin.

WELCH, Daniel; Willowbrook Hs; Lombard, IL; Chr; HonRl; ModUN; NHS; College Of Dupage;humanities Communications.

WELCH, David A; Providence Sr Jr HS; New Albany, IN; ChrhWkr; CmntyWkr; HonRl; NHS; SctActv; RptrYrbk; SptEdYrbk; Yrbk; RptrSchPpr; SptEdSchPpr; SchPpr; CivCl; PpCl; Tennis; Indiana Univ; Photo Journalism.

WELCH, Glenda M; North Central HS; Haddam, KS; 1/26 PresJrCls; Band; Chrs; HonRl; SchPl; SecYthFlsp; 4-H; FHA; VPPpCl; LetterTrk; College; Business Major.

WELCH, Gregory A; Bishop Luers HS; Fort Wayne, IN; 12/237 HonRl; In Inst Of Tech; Elect Eng.

WELCH, Joey L; Exeter HS; Exeter, MO; 9/24 VPFrshCls; VPSophCls; TrsJrCls; PresSrCls; Chr; Chrs; SchPl; PresStuCncl; 4-H; Bsbl; Bsktbl; LetterTrk; College; Law Enforcement.

WELCH, Jonathan; Pelham Memorial HS; Bloomfield Hills, MI; Chrs; ChrhWkr; HonRl; SctActv; StuGov; Bsbl; Ftbl; IMSpt; Coll.

WELCH, Joseph F; Churchill HS; Livonia, MI; ALBoysSt; HonRl; Bsktbl; LetterTennis; IMSpt; AmLegAwd; College; Professional.

WELCH, Julie A; Belvidere HS; Belvidere, IL; 4/340 AFS; ChrhWkr; HonRl; NHS; YthFlsp; FNA; GerCl; PpCl; Illinois State Univ; Psychologist.

WELCH, Mark L; Tri HS; Spiceland, IN; 28/105 VPFrshCls; VPSophCls; Aud/Vis; ChrhWkr; CncrtBnd; MrchBnd; PepBnd; SchAde; StuCncl; 4-H; SpnCl; Purdue Univ; Electronics.

WELCH, Patrick; Sac Community HS; Sac City, IA; 30/98 TrsFrshCls; PresSophCls; TrsJrCls; ChrhWkr; HonRl; IntrClCncl; Bsktbl; Ftbl; Trk; IMSpt; College; Physical Education.

WELCH, Phyllis S; Worthington Jefferson HS; Worthington, IN; SecTrsSrCls; Chrs; HonRl; OffAde; SchAde; SctActv; RptrYrbk; Yrbk; PpCl; Bsktbl; Coll; Phy Therpist.

WELCH, Robert T; Wautoma HS; Redgranite, WI; 1/115 CncrtBnd; HonRl; NatlFornLg; NatlThespSoc; SchMus; SchPl; StuCncl; StuGov; Bsbl; Bsktbl; Ftbl; College; Music.

WELCH, Scott; Polo Community HS; Polo, IL; 6/93 Band; CncrtBnd; HonRl; MrchBnd; NHS; PepBnd; YthFlsp; 4-H; Glf; Ill Wesleyan Univ; Dentistry.

WELCH, Stephen R; Baxter HS; Baxter Springs, KS; ALBoysSt; DrlTm; ROTC; Bsbl; Bsktbl; Ftbl; Wrstlng; CchngActv; IMSpt;.

WELCH, Steven L; Marshall HS; Marshall, IL; 12/120 Band; ChrhWkr; MrchBnd; SctActv; LatCl; SciCl; LetterBsbl; Bsktbl; LetterGlf; AmLegAwd; Butler U; Pharmacy.

WELCH, Timothy G; Union Grove HS; Caledonia, WI; ALBoysSt; Band; Chrs; ChrhWkr; HonRl; MrchBnd; NHS; SchMus; StuCncl; 4-H; Luther College; Music.

WELDING, Mickey J; Marquette HS; West Point, IA; 15/49 Band; Aud/Vis; ChrhWkr; SctActv; LetterBsktbl; CaptGlf; IMSpt; Southeastern Com Col; Business.

WELDISHOFER, Sandra J; Kearney HS; Kearney, MO; Chrs; PolWkr; TchrAde; 4-H; SpnCl; PpCl; LetterBsktbl; Swmmng; Trk; 4-HAwd; Univ Of Mo; Phy Ed.

WELDON, Cynthia M; Elkhart Central HS; Elkhart, IN; 15/495 CmntyWkr; HonRl; JA; NHS; SchMus; LetterGlf; University; Industrial Engineer.

WELDON, Jeffrey J; English Valley HS; North English, IA; 15/63 Chr; Chrs; ChrhWkr; HonRl; SchMus; SchPl; RptrYrbk; EdYrBk; RptrSchPpr; Drake Univ; Pharmacy.

WELDON, Joan M; Bishop Dwenger HS; Fort Wayne, IN; ChrhWkr; HonRl; OffAde; StuCncl; Yrbk; FrCl; PpCl; Tennis; College; Mass Communications.

WELDY, Allen C; Northridge HS; Goshen, IN; PresJrCls; Chr; Chrl; Chrs; ChrhWkr; HonRl; SchMus; SchPl; StuCncl; StuGov; LetterFtbl; LetterTrk; IMSpt; College; Social Worker.

WELDY, Mark J; Wauzeka Public HS; Wauzeka, WI; ALBoysSt; Band; Chrs; ChrhWkr; CncrtBnd; HonRl; MrchBnd; SecFrshCls; TrsFrshCls; PepBnd; College; Liberal Arts.

WELESKI, Barbara I; Lancaster Public HS; Lancaster, MN; 8/23 TrsSrCls; HonRl; OffAde; SchPl; Yrbk; RptrSchPpr; FHA; PpCl; Vo Tech Sch; Med Sec.

WELESKI, Kathy; Lancaster Public HS; Lancaster, MN; SecSophCls; Chr; ChrhWkr; LbryAde; OffAde; TchrAde; SchPpr; 4-H; FHA; SciCl; Coll.

WELK, Cynthia B; Wishek Public HS; Wishek, ND; 13/40 Chrs; HonRl; MrchBnd; OffAde; SchPl; StuCncl; PpCl; Trk; GAA; Nd State Univ; Accounting.

WELK, Randy L; Pardeeville HS; Cambria, WI; Band; Chrs; CncrtBnd; PepBnd; 4-H; CaptTrk; Univ Of Wisconsin; Business.

WELKER, Alan; Sargent Central HS; Cogswell, ND; HonRl; 4-H; Bsbl; Bsktbl; Ftbl; Trk; IMSpt; 4-HAwd; College.

WELKER, Virgil N; Canton Rv HS; Williamstown, MO; 3/67 PresSrCls; ALBoysSt; ChrhWkr; NHS; StuCncl; LetterBsbl; AmLegAwd; DanFAwd; KiwanAwd; CitAwd; Univ Of Mo Columbia; Accounting.

WELKO, Christine M; St Charles HS; St Charles, MO; 62/547 CmntyWkr; HonRl; NHS; PolWkr; TchrAde; PpCl; Univ Of Missouri; Child Development.

WELLBORN, Sonny; Salisbury HS; Salisbury, MO; Chr; Chrs; HonRl; JrNHS; LbryAde; NHS; SchPl; FrCl; LetterBsbl; GAA; Univ Of Missouri; Chem Engr.

WELLE, Ann; Healy HS; Pierz, MN; 1/110 SecTrsFrshCls; Aud/Vis; HonRl; FFA; FHA; Coll; Professional.

WELLENRAITER, Beth; Tremont HS; Tremont, IL; ChrhWkr; CmntyWkr; SchPl; Yrbk; PpCl; Trk; Chrldr; GAA; IMSpt; Coll; Bus Adm.

WELLER, Barrett S; Ida Crown Jewish Academy; Chicago, IL; 21/71 TrsSrCls; HonRl; NHS; Orch; SchPl; StuCncl; RptrYrbk; Yrbk; RptrSchPpr; Bsktbl; University Of Illinois; Medicine.

WELLER, Chris A; Solomon HS; Solomon, KS; ChrhWkr; CmntyWkr; HonRl; StuCncl; YthFlsp; SptEdYrbk; SptEdSchPpr; FFA; Bsktbl; LetterTrk; College.

WELLER, David W; Waukesha South HS; Waukesha, WI; NHS; Univ Of Wi; Professional Electrical Eng.

WELLER, Debra S; Palmer Public HS; Palmer, NE; SecTrsFrshCls; HstSophCls; Band; HonRl; NHS; SchPl; Twrl; RptrSchPpr; College; Liberal Arts.

WELLER, Diane M; Ar We Va Comm HS; Westside, IA; GovHonPrgAwd; Lpn.

WELLER, Donna M; Whitefish Bay HS; Whitefish Bay, WI; Aud/Vis; HonRl; NatlMeritCmnd; Trk; GAA; IMSpt; Univ; Science.

WELLER, Gerald C; Dwight Township HS; Dwight, IL; 23/110 PresSophCls; PresJrCls; AFS; Aud/Vis; HonRl; PolWkr; EdSchPpr; 4-H; PresFFA; LetterTrk; University Of Illinois; Agriculture.

WELLER, James; Littlefield Public HS; Alanson, MI; Band; CncrtBnd; HonRl; MrchBnd; PepBnd; StuCncl; TchrAde; FFA; PpCl; Bsktbl; Trade School; Vocational.

WELLER, Laurel A; Memorial HS; Joplin, MO; 1/257 HonRl; JrNHS;.

WELLER, Mona K; Beardstown HS; Beardstown, IL; 7/125 Chr; CmntyWkr; HonRl; Mdrgl; NHS; SchMus; EdYrBk; RptrSchPpr; Robert Morris College; Medical Assistant.

WELLER, Myrana L; Belle HS; Belle, MO; LetterHonRl; NHS; FHA; SpnCl; College.

WELLER, Nancy; South Harrison HS; Bethany, MO; VPFrshCls; Chr; CncrtBnd; MrchBnd; NatlFornLg; NHS; NatlThespSoc; PpCl; LetterGlf; Chrldr; College; Liberal Arts.

WELLER, Randall; Eureka HS; Eureka, SD; 2/56 PresJrCls; PresSrCls; Chr; ChrhWkr; CmntyWkr; HonRl; StuCncl; Yrbk; SchPpr; SciCl; Univ; Professional Pharmacy.

WELLER, Randy R; New Leipzig Public HS; New Leipzig, ND; 3/16 VPJrCls; HonRl; SchPl; StuCncl; LetterBsktbl; CaptFtbl; LetterTrk; Trade School; Vocation.

WELLER, Shawn R; Fullerton HS; Fullerton, NE; Band; Chr; Chrl; Chrs; ChrhWkr; CmntyWkr; CncrtBnd; HonRl; Mdrgl; MrchBnd; College; Music.

WELLES, Linda J; Prospect HS; Mt Prospect, IL; 21/600 AFS; ChrhWkr; DrlTm; HonRl; NHS; NatlMeritCmnd; NatlThespSoc; SctActv; Drake Univ; Spanish.

WELLHOEFER, Joyce A; Slinger HS; Allenton, WI; 4-H; CaptBsktbl; LetterTrk; 4-HAwd;.

WELLIK, Sandra P; Britt Comm HS; Britt, IA; 11/79 Chrs; HonRl; HospAde; LbryAde; NHS; 4-H; FHA; FNA; SecTrsSophCls; Glf; College Of St Teresa; Nursing.

WELLING, Edward J; Bishop Luers HS; Ft Wayne, IN; 27/230 PresFrshCls; PresSophCls; PresJrCls; HonRl; TreasStuCncl; SchPpr; PresKeyCl; LetterFtbl; LetterTrk; RotaryAwd; Ball St Univ; Architecture.

WELLING, Michael J; Elmhurst HS; Fort Wayne, IN; HonRl; Engineering.

WELLINGTON, Susan M; Rogers HS; Wyoming, MI; HonRl; PolWkr; SchMus; Michigan St Univ; Business.

WELLMAN, Andrea M; Randolph Public HS; Hampton, MN; 6/43 ALAGirlsSt; TreasNHS; PresStuCncl; RptrYrbk; DARAwd; Univ Of Minnesota; Child Care.

WELLMAN, David M; Dixon HS; Dixon, IL; Band; CncrtBnd; HonRl; MrchBnd; NatlMeritCmnd; SchMus; IMSpt; U Of Ill.

WELLMAN, Lynn M; Elizabeth Seton HS; Calumet City, IL; 1/252 HonRl; NHS; RptrYrbk; RptrSchPpr; FrCl; MthCl; Purdue Univ; Math.

WELLNER, Gloria M; Thorp HS; Thorp, WI; HonRl; NatlFornLg; StuCncl; Yrbk; FBLA; FHA;.

WELLNITZ, John L; Oconto Falls HS; Oconto Falls, WI; 69/151 Band; CncrtBnd; MrchBnd; YthFlsp; FFA; LetterTrk; 4-HAwd; Dairy Farmer.

WELLNITZ, Thomas R; Len Wallace HS; Gary, IN; 2/513 PresJrCls; ALBoysSt; HonRl; PresNHS; NatlMeritCmnd; SctActv; StuCncl; Yrbk; Swmmng; CaptTennis; College.

WELLS, Amy L; Owen Valley HS; Worthington, IN; Band; ChrhWkr; CncrtBnd; MrchBnd; StuCncl; YthFlsp; 4-H; FBLA; SpnCl; PpCl; Business Sch; Secretary.

WELLS, Barbara L; Fox Valley HS; Milton, IA; 2/22 PresJrCls; HonRl; MrchBnd; NHS; PepBnd; SchMus; SchPl; EdYrBk; DARAwd; University Of Missouri; Physical Therapy.

WELLS, Brenda K; Earlham Comm HS; Dexter, IA; 2/41 Chrs; HonRl; NHS; SchMus; StuCncl; Teen; YthFlsp; LetterBsktbl; LetterTrk; PPFtbl; College Or Trade School; Stewardess Or Pe T.

WELLS, Chris E; Stephen Decatur HS; Decatur, IL; Chr; NHS; OffAde; StuCncl; College; Executive Secretary.

WELLS, Connie A; Lincoln Way HS; Frankfort, IL; 100/498 ChrhWkr; HonRl; OffAde; TchrAde; YthFlsp; 4-H; Joliet Jr Col; Art.

WELLS, Donald A; Davis Co Comm HS; Pulaski, IA; 5/132 HonRl; NHS; NatlMeritCmnd; YthFlsp; FFA; LetterBsktbl; LetterFtbl; LetterTrk; Ia State U; Commerical Art.

WELLS, Edward L; Jonesville HS; Jonesville, MI; 3/86 SecSophCls; Band; Chrs; HonRl; PepBnd; StuGov; TchrAde; FTA; College; Mathematics.

WELLS, Gregory M; Elwood Comm HS; Elwood, IN; PresSrCls; HonRl; VPJA; PresNHS; PolWkr; StuCncl; FTA; LatCl; PpCl; EldAwd; JAAwd; Purdue Univ; Horticulture.

WELLS, Jason; Unionville HS; Unionville, MO; ALBoysSt; Band; CncrtBnd; HonRl; MrchBnd; NHS; PepBnd; North East Mo State Univ; Pre Veterinary.

WELLS, Jay W; Springs Valley HS; Dubois, IN; 2/80 ALBoysSt; HonRl; NHS; StuCncl; EdYrBk; FFA; FrCl; CaptFtbl; Purdue Univ; Agriculture.

WELLS, Jeffery; East HS; Rockford, IL; NatlMeritCmnd; FrCl; LetterFtbl; College; Pre Law.

WELLS, Jimmie J; Siren Consolidated HS; Siren, WI; PresFrshCls; Chrs; ChrhWkr; CncrtBnd; HonRl; CaptBsktbl; CaptFtbl; CaptTennis; CaptTrk; CaptWrstlng; Univ Wis; Music.

WELLS, John H; East HS; Waterloo, IA; 3/370 Band; CncrtBnd; HonRl; JA; MrchBnd; PepBnd; SctActv; StuCncl; RptrYrbk; MthCl; SciCl; Swmmng; Tennis; Iowa State; Electronics Eng.

WELLS, Jonathan A; Macon Jr Sr HS; Macon, MO; Chr; HonRl; SchMus; StuCncl; RptrSchPpr; SpnCl; Bsbl; LetterBsktbl; LetterFtbl; LetterTrk; College.

WELLS, Leslie A; Wheaton North HS; Wheaton, IL; 5/274 ALAGirlsSt; Chrs; HonRl; TreasNHS; PresNatlThespSoc; SchMus; SchPl; StuCncl; StuGov; PpCl; CaptChrldr; GAA; DARAwd; Univ Of Colorado; Architecture.

WELLS, Linda C; West Washington HS; Hardinsburg, IN; 3/93 TrsFrshCls; Band; NHS; NatlThespSoc; StuCncl; UNYO; Yrbk; FHA; LatCl; Indiana University.

WELLS, Lynnette J; Ankeny HS; Ankeny, IA; 98/214 Chrs; HonRl; LitMag; SchPl; YthFlsp; SchPpr; FNA; FrCl; IMSpt; MasAwd; Voc Tech; Nursing.

WELLS, Mark D; Lake Central HS; Dyer, IN; Band; CncrtBnd; HonRl; MrchBnd; NatlThespSoc; PepBnd; SchMus; Apprentice Printer; Printing.

WELLS, Nolan W; Hale HS; South Branch, MI; PresJrCls; HonRl; NHS; SchPl; StuCncl; StuGov; Bsbl; Ftbl; PresAwd; College; Lawenforcement.

WELLS, Pamela J; Buhler HS; Hutchinson, KS; 16/150 VPFrshCls; CmntyWkr; HonRl; OffAde; PolWkr; SchAde; TchrAde; RptrSchPpr; FHA; SpnCl; PpCl; Trk; Chrldr; Texas Christian University.

WELLS, Rick C; Salem HS; Salem, MO; 47/180 ALBoysSt; ChrhWkr; HonRl; SptEdSchPpr; PpCl; Bsbl; LetterBsktbl; University.

WELLS, Robert A; Farmer City Mansfield HS; Farmer City, IL; 20/80 AFS; HonRl; StuCncl; YthFlsp; 4-H; FFA; KeyCl; LetterFtbl; Trk; DanFAwd; 4-HAwd; Western Ill Univ; Agriculture.

WELLS, Roxie M; Lyman HS; Vivian, SD; ALAGirlsSt; Band; ChrhWkr; HonRl; TchrAde; Bsktbl; Trk; Chrldr; AmLegAwd; PresAwd; College; Biology Teacher.

WELLS, Scott; Sheffield Chapin HS; Sheffield, IA; ALBoysSt; Chr; Chrs; HonRl; StuCncl; RptrSchPpr; FTA; SciCl; Ftbl; AmLegAwd; U; Prof Science.

WELLS, Stacey L; Buckley Loda HS; Buckley, IL; 1/40 PresFrshCls; HstJrCls; Chr; Chrs; ChrhWkr; HonRl; NHS; SchMus; Bsktbl; Chrldr;.

WELLS, Susan K; Medford Sr HS; Medford, WI; Band; HonRl; MrchBnd; FrCl; PpCl; Univ Of Wisconsin; Genetics.

WELLS, Susan M; Earlham Community HS; Dexter, IA; 2/38 PresSrCls; Band; Chrs; CncrtBnd; HonRl; MrchBnd; PresNHS; SchMus; StuCncl; Teen; Bsktbl; Trk; PPFtbl; BttyCrckrAwd; College.

WELLS, Tami D; O Fallon Township HS; O Fallon, IL; ChrhWkr; CmntyWkr; HonRl; HospAde; OffAde; RedCrAde; SctActv; SchPpr; FNA; Coll; Nurse.

WELLS, Teri L; Gering HS; Gering, NE; 4-H; PpCl; Trk; GAA; IMSpt; DARAwd; 4-HAwd; MasAwd; Clge; Med Assistant.

WELLS, Timothy R; Monmouth HS; Monmouth, IL; JrNHS; Quill&Scroll; SchPl; StuCncl; RptrYrbk; EdSchPpr; Ftbl; LetterSwmmng; Trk; Univ Of Illinois; Engineering.

WELLS, Vernie E; Wyandotte HS; Kansas City, KS; 3/500 Band; ChrhWkr; HonRl; LbryAde; MrchBnd; ModUN; NHS; NatlMeritCmnd; Orch; PepBnd; Baker Univ; Chemical Engineering.

WELLS, William; Wilmot HS; Powers Lake, WI; 26/200 HonRl; NHS; Quill&Scroll; StuCncl; CaptWrstlng; AmLegAwd; College; Business.

WELLS, William E; Evanston Twp HS; Evanston, IL; Aud/Vis; CmntyWkr; HonRl; NatlMeritCmnd; SchPl; Univ Of Illinois; Electrical Engineering.

WELNIAK, Nancy; Ord HS; Elyria, NE; 3/106 Band; DrlTm; HonRl; NHS; 4-H; FHA; PpCl; Bsktbl; IMSpt; 4-HAwd; U Of Ne Lincoln; Medical Record Adm.

WELP, Linda D; St John HS; Bancroft, IA; 1/45 Band; Chrs; CmntyWkr; HonRl; NatlMeritCmnd; NatlMeritSchl; NatlMeritSF; SchMus; SchPl; 4-H; LetterTennis; LetterChrldr; 4-HAwd; University Of Iowa; Music.

WELP, Mary; Southridge HS; Huntingburg, IN; Band; VPChr; CncrtBnd; DrlTm; HonRl; MrchBnd; SchPl; Twrl; RptrYrbk; RptrSchPpr; FBLA; EngCl; SpnCl; PpCl; Brescia College; Speech.

WELPER, Rory D; Caledonia HS; Caledonia, MN; ALBoysSt; Aud/Vis; Band; HonRl; MrchBnd; NHS; PepBnd; Ftbl; Trk; Wrstlng; Usaf Academy; Af Pilot & Officer.

WELS, Candyce; Sacred Heart HS; Bennington, KS; HstFrshCls; SecSophCls; Band; ChrhWkr; CncrtBnd; HonRl; MrchBnd; PepBnd; SctActv; SpnCl; Brown Mackie Bus College; Business.

WELS, Pamela J; Monroe HS; Monroe, WI; 27/211 TrsJrCls; TrsSrCls; Chr; Chrl; HonRl; LbryAde; Mdrgl; SchMus; SchPl; 4-H; DARAwd; Blackhawk Tech Schl; Accounting.

WELSAND, Sonya A; Russell Public HS; Russell, MN; SecSophCls; Band; Chrs; CncrtBnd; HonRl; MrchBnd; NHS; PepBnd; FHA; PpCl; Univ; Major Study.

WELSANDT, Diane F; John F Kennedy HS; Chicago, IL; HospAde; FNA; FrCl; Nursing Schl; Physical Therapy.

WELSCH, David; Milford HS; Milford, NE; 12/59 ALBoysSt; ChrhWkr; CncrtBnd; MrchBnd; PepBnd; SctActv; YthFlsp; 4-H; Bsktbl; Trk; College; Teacher Coach.

WELSCH, Julie A; Springville Comm HS; Springville, IA; 4/60 VPSrCls; Band; HonRl; PresNHS; SciCl; Ia State U; Home Ec Dietetics.

WELSCH, Mary P; Brentwood HS; Brentwood, MO; PresJrCls; ALAGirlsSt; ChrhWkr; CmntyWkr; HonRl; NHS; StuCncl; FTA; GAA; IMSpt; Jr College; Child Care Worker.

WELSCH, Virginia A; Nerinx Hall HS; St Louis, MO; 9/84 VPJrCls; Chrl; HonRl; HospAde; NatlThespSoc; PolWkr; SchMus; SchPl; StuGov; GAA; U Of Missouri; Theatre.

WELSH, Barbara; Kee HS; Lansing, IA; 4/53 Chr; ChrhWkr; HonRl; PolWkr; Quill&Scroll; SchMus; Bsktbl; IMSpt; St Ambrose College; Sociologist.

WELSH, Cynthia L; Norwell HS; Bluffton, IN; Band; CncrtBnd; HonRl; MrchBnd; TchrAde; LatCl; University; Special Educ.

WELSH, Jerald R; Pekin Comm HS; Hedrick, IA; Aud/Vis; Band; CncrtBnd; MrchBnd; PepBnd; SchMus; SchPl; 4-H; PpCl; LetterBsktbl; LetterTrk; IMSpt; Iowa St University; Engineering.

WELSH, Karen M; Carroll HS; Flora, IN; 34/133 HonRl; OffAde; TchrAde; Sec4-H; FTA; VPSpnCl; 4-HAwd; Purdue Univ; Elementary Education.

WELSH, Kevin; Barrington Hs; Barrington, IL; 9/652 HonRl; NHS; NatlMeritCmnd; SchPpr; FrCl; Socr; College; Science And Math.

WELSH, Patricia A; Sullivan HS; Sullivan, IL; Band; Chrs; RptrYrbk; RptrSchPpr; 4-H; FTA; GerCl; 4-HAwd; E Ill Univ; Music.

WELSHER, David R; Auburn HS; Oak Park, IL; ChrhWkr; HonRl; SctActv; YthFlsp; Bsbl; LetterBsktbl; LetterFtbl; LetterTrk; CchngActv; IMSpt; Western II Univ; Lawyer.

WELTE, Cindy; Castle HS; Chandler, IN; 27/328 ChrhWkr; CmntyWkr; SchPl; StuCncl; 4-H; FBLA; FFA; Tech Sch; Drafting.

WELTE, Duane H; Richland Center HS; Richland Center, WI; ALBoysSt; Band; CncrtBnd; HonRl; MrchBnd; ModUN; NHS; PepBnd; StuCncl; KeyCl; College; Professional.

WELTER, Herb J; Midland Community HS; Onslow, IA; University; Professional.

WELTER, Vernon; Leo HS; Sherrill, IA; PresSophCls; HonRl; SchPl; RptrSchPpr; LatCl; MthCl; Socr; Wrstlng; IMSpt;.

WELTON, Brian K; Ovid Elsie HS; Elsie, MI; ALBoysSt; Band; CncrtBnd; HonRl; MrchBnd; PepBnd; SctActv; LetterBsbl; LetterBsktbl; LetterFtbl; AmLegAwd; Michigan State University.

WELTON, Charlene C; Sidney HS; Sidney, NE; Chrs; OffAde; TchrAde; GAA; PPFtbl; Vocation.

WELTON, Mark L; Seaholm HS; Birmingham, MI; 239/702 Band; Chr; ChrhWkr; CncrtBnd; HonRl; MrchBnd; NatlMeritCmnd; NatlMeritSF; Swmmng; GovHonPrgAwd; No Michigan Univ; Music.

WELTY, Amy L; Shawnee Mission West HS; Overland Park, KS; 1/650 HonRl; NHS; CaptChrldr; Univ; Math Or Engineering.

WELTY, Sandra L; Onamia HS; Garrison, MN; 23/85 Band; Chr; CncrtBnd; HonRl; PepBnd; SchAde; SchPl; TchrAde; FHA; PpCl; Bsktbl; Trk; GAA; College; Teacher.

WELTY, Seema; Evanston Twp HS; Evanston, IL; University; Medicine.

WELTZER, Timothy; Crystal Lake Comm HS; Crystal Lake, IL; 41#77#10 SecTrsFrshCls; SciCl; IMSpt; Univ Of Il; Profesional Math.

WELU, George M; Wahlert HS; Dubuque, IA; 117/441 CtyCnl; CmntyWkr; StuGov; MthCl; SciCl; LetterBsktbl; LetterFtbl; Glf; IMSpt; Ia St Univ; Physical Therapy.

WEMETTE, Julene J; Alma Area HS; Alma, WI; Band; Chr; CncrtBnd; HonRl; MrchBnd; NHS; PepBnd; SctActv; YthFlsp; FTA; Trk; LetterChrldr; College; Teaching.

WEMHOFF, Norman; St Francis HS; Humphrey, NE; HonRl; FFA; Univ Lincoln; Engineering.

WEMPLE, Rita G; Assumption HS; Assumption, IL; 3/35 VPSrCls; HospAde; LbryAde; NHS; OffAde; SchPl; StuCncl; Yrbk; FHA; Tennis; College; Vocation.

WEMPNER, Roberta A; Lincoln HS; Lake City, MN; 2/146 Aud/Vis; HonRl; LbryAde; NHS; NatlMeritFnl; NatlMeritSF; SchAde; StuCncl; TchrAde; RptrSchPpr; 4-H; 4-HAwd; Augustana College; Special Ed.

WENANDE, Donald J; Hanson Indep #40 HS; Alexandria, SD; PresFrshCls; PresSophCls; VPJrCls; SecSrCls; Band; Bsbl; Ftbl; Trk; Chrldr; IMSpt; College; Vocation.

WENDEL, Sandra A; Beaver Dam Sr HS; Beaver Dam, WI; 27/296 HonRl; HospAde; NatlMeritCmnd; StuCncl; Yrbk; RptrSchPpr; PpCl; GAA; IMSpt; ChmbCommrsAwd; College; Nursing Rn.

WENDELSCHAFER, Chad J; Milton HS; Milton Jct, WI; FrCl; Ftbl; Trk; IMSpt; University; Law Enforcement.

WENDLAND, Charles M; Traverse City HS; Traverse City, MI; CtyCnl; CmntyWkr; HonRl; JA; ModUN; NHS; PolWkr; StuGov; CivCl; Ftbl; U Of Az; Architecture.

WENDLING, Pamela M; Effingham HS; Effingham, IL; Band; DrlTm; HonRl; MrchBnd; SctActv; YthFlsp; 4-H; GAA; 4-HAwd; CitAwd;.

WENDLING, Richard A; North Clay HS; Louisville, IL; TreasChrhWkr; JA; SchPl; 4-H; PpCl; Bsktbl; Trk; Treas4-HAwd; Lake Land Jr Col; Agriculture.

WENDORF, Elizabeth S; Wayland Academy; Beaver Dam, WI; OffAde; SchPl; SctActv; SpnCl; CaptSwmmng; Tennis; CaptChrldr; IMSpt; PresAwd; College; Physical Therapy.

WENDORF, Ned E; Rolling Meadows HS; Arlington Heights, IL; 1/581 Chr; HonRl; Mdrgl; PresNHS; NatlMeritCmnd; NatlThespSoc; SchMus; College; Engineering.

WENDT, Debra A; Trumbull HS; Trumbull, NE; Band; Chr; CncrtBnd; MrchBnd; PepBnd; SchPl; PpCl; LetterTrk; Chrldr; PPFtbl;.

WENDT, Frankie; Princeton HS; Princeton, MO; Band; ChrhWkr; CncrtBnd; HonRl; MrchBnd; NHS; PepBnd; FFA; SpnCl; College; Literary Law.

WENDT, Kyle; Seaman HS; Topeka, KS; Band; ChrhWkr; HonRl; HospAde; JA; MrchBnd; PolWkr; SchMus; StuCncl; Kansas Univ; Architect.

WENDT, Randal L; Truman Public HS; Truman, MN; 7/50 ALBoysSt; HonRl; 4-H; FFA; LetterBsktbl; Ftbl; LetterTrk; AmLegAwd; 4-HAwd; College; Engineering.

WENDT, Ricky D; Leigh Comm HS; Clarkson, NE; SecTrsSophCls; ChrhWkr; CtyCnl; CmntyWkr; SchPl; StuGov; Pres4-H; SecFFA; Ftbl; Wrstlng; College.

WENDT, Sheri L; Wainwright HS; Lafayette, IN; 4/105 PresFrshCls; HonRl; NHS; YthFlsp; StuCncl; StuGov; Trk; Chrldr; GAA; PPFtbl; Univ; Vocation.

WENDT, Terry V; Leigh Comm HS; Clarkson, NE; 9/40 VPJrCls; ALBoysSt; Band; ChrhWkr; HonRl; StuGov; Pres4-H; VPFFA; Bsktbl; CaptFtbl; School Of Agriculture; Livestock Judge.

WENDT, Weylin W; Protection HS; Protection, KS; ALBoysSt; Band; Chrs; CncrtBnd; HonRl; MrchBnd; PepBnd; SchMus; 4-H; LetterFtbl; Clge; Pro Eng.

WENDTE, Dennis R; Beecher City HS; Altamont, IL; 2/39 PresSophCls; VPSrCls; Chr; HonRl; SchPl; StuCncl; YthFlsp; EdYrBk; Yrbk; 4-H; FFA; LetterTrk; IMSpt; DanFAwd; Univ Of Illinois.

WENDTE, Pamela A; Newcastle Public HS; Newcastle, NE; 2/24 VPFrshCls; SecJrCls; Band; CncrtBnd; HonRl; MrchBnd; PepBnd; RedCrAde; SchPl; EdSchPpr; PpCl;.

WENEER, Dave; Tioga HS; Tioga, ND; Chr; CncrtBnd; MrchBnd; PepBnd; SptEdYrbk; Minot State Col; Business Administration.

WENELL, Lynn E; Albert City Truesdale Com HS; Albert City, IA; Aud/Vis; ChrhWkr; YthFlsp; Yrbk; SchPpr; 4-H; FFA; LetterWrstlng; CchngActv; 4-HAwd; U Of Ia Wayne; Farm Operation.

WENELL, Stephanie K; East Peoria Comm HS; E Peoria, IL; HonRl; StuGov; GerCl; MthCl; College; Accounting.

WENGER, Deverne F; Max Public HS; Benedict, ND; 4/29 SecFrshCls; VPJrCls; Band; HonRl; StuCncl; StuGov; TchrAde; Yrbk; SchPpr; 4-H; Minot State Clg; Computer Programming.

WENGER, Donald; Elmhurst HS; Fort Wayne, IN; 2/382 Aud/Vis; CAP; DrlTm; HonRl; TchrAde; Us Air Force Acad; Nuclear Physicist.

WENGER, James W; Warsaw Comm HS; Warsaw, IN; 75/346 ALBoysSt; HonRl; NatlMeritCmnd; StuCncl; Manchester College; Medicine.

WENGER, Robert E; Versailles HS; Versailles, MO; Chr; Chrl; Chrs; ChrhWkr; Mdrgl; NHS; SchMus; FFA; FTA; IMSpt; College; Bible Study.

WENGER, Roger G; St Thomas Seminary; Louisiana, MO; 3/9 PresSophCls; HonRl; EdSchPpr; FrCl; LatCl; MthCl; PpCl; Bsktbl; LetterSocr; IMSpt; Trade School; Accounting.

WENIG, Daniel L; Burlington HS; Burlington, IA; 79/501 ChrhWkr; HonRl; ROTC; Bsktbl; Trk; Wrstlng; College; Coaching.

WENIG, Nancy R; Benton Co HS; Lincoln, MO; SecTrsFrshCls; SecTrsJrCls; Band; Chrs; HonRl; SchPl; RptrYrbk; RptrSchPpr; FHA; College.

WENK, Karen A; Arlington HS; Arlington Hts, IL; 12/595 Chr; HonRl; NHS; NatlThespSoc; Quill&Scroll; SchMus; SchPl; Univ Of Il; Communications.

WENKE, Deanna K; Central Community HS; Farmington, IA; AFS; HonRl; NHS; SchPl; FTA; Univ; Vet Sci.

WENKEL, Gary J; Assumption HS; E St Louis, IL; 26/198 SchMus; PpCl; LetterFtbl; IMSpt; JETSAwd;.

WENNDT, Jacquelyn; Clarence Lowden HS; Lowden, IA; Mdrgl; RptrSchPpr; GerCl; PpCl; Bsbl; Bsktbl; IMSpt; PPFtbl; Luther College; Biology.

WENNDT, Kristi R; Lincoln Comm HS; Stanwood, IA; 1/65 PresFrshCls; SecJrCls; Chr; Chrs; ChrhWkr; HonRl; NHS; SchMus; PresStuCncl; SecYthFlsp; EdYrBk; LetterBsbl; LetterTrk; 4-HAwd; Mercy Hospital; Radiology.

WENNEBERG, Luke R; Gordon Tech HS; Chicago, IL; 7/661 HonRl; NHS; SchAde; StuCncl; StuGov; TchrAde; Univ Of Il; Architect.

WENNEKER, Lana J; Marion Co R Ii HS; Ewing, MO; 1/26 ChrhWkr; DrmMjrt; HonRl; SchPl; StuCncl; 4-H; FHA; PpCl; SciCl; Bsktbl; Chrldr; U Of Mo; Med.

WENNING, Roger P; North Decatur HS; Greensburg, IN; 6/104 HonRl; TreasNHS; 4-H; SecFFA; LetterBsktbl; LetterFtbl; Trk; Purdue U;agriculture.

WENSING, Mary L; Quincy Notre Dame HS; Quincy, IL; DrlTm; HonRl; JA; StuCncl; College; Special Ed.

WENSTROM, Reuben M; Lincoln HS; Floodwood, MN; 6/41 Band; HonRl; NHS; SchPl; StuCncl; EdYrBk; RptrSchPpr; LetterBsbl; LetterBsktbl; Univ Of Minnesota; Business Admministration.

WENTLAND, Wyann L; Hazen HS; Hazen, ND; 18/38 ALAGirlsSt; RedCrAde; SchPl; Yrbk; PresFHA; PpCl; LetterFtbl; LetterTrk; College; Special Education.

WENTWORTH, Nancy; Mt Pleasant HS; Rosebush, MI; 12/332 Chr; HonRl; NHS; SchMus; StuCncl; StuGov; YthFlsp; RptrYrbk; Yrbk; Cent Mich Univ; Child Dev.

WENTWORTH, Robert L; Kalkaska HS; Kalkaska, MI; 43/180 JrNHS; College; Political Science.

WENTZ, Brett A; Tennings HS; Norcatur, KS; SchPl; RptrYrbk; FFA;.

WENTZ, Dwight J; Ryan HS; Minot, ND; ALBoysSt; Band; CncrtBnd; MrchBnd; PepBnd; SchPl; College; Liberal Arts.

WENTZ, Lyndon; Napoleon Public HS; Napoleon, ND; Band; Chrs; ChrhWkr; CncrtBnd; MrchBnd; PepBnd; SchMus; StuGov; RptrSchPpr; FFA; Trade School; Electrical Tech.

WENTZ, Sheila M; Shepherd HS; Shepherd, MI; 1/128 Band; ChrhWkr; CncrtBnd; HonRl; MrchBnd; NHS; OffAde; PepBnd; FrCl; PpCl; Secretarial Position.

WENTZ, Steven P; Fort Atkinson Senior HS; Fort Atkinson, WI; HonRl; SchPl; KeyCl; Tennis; Univ; Bus Management.

WENTZEL, Daniel C; Pocahontas Comm HS; Pocahontas, IA; 10/75 PresFrshCls; PresSophCls; ALBoysSt; JA; StuCncl; VPSophCls; CivCl; PpCl; SciCl; Bsbl; Univ; Pre Law.

WENTZEL, Jerold W; Fisher HS; Fisher, MN; TrsFrshCls; Band; Chr; Chrl; Chrs; ChrhWkr; HonRl; MrchBnd; PepBnd; 4-H; Nd St Univ; Horticulture.

WENTZEL, Lorelee; Weyauwega HS; Fremont, WI; 15/85 Band; HonRl; PepBnd; SchPl; YthFlsp; FHA; PpCl; GAA; Trade; Lpn.

WENTZEL, Wilford L; Harrisburg HS; Harrisburg, IL; 10/170 ALBoysSt; HonRl; NHS; KeyCl; LatCl; LetterBsktbl; LetterFtbl; LetterTrk; DARAwd; SARAwd; Se Illinois Univ; Accounting.

WENZ, Mark G; Lincoln East HS; Lincoln, NE; 10/409 HonRl; EngCl; Bsktbl; IMSpt; Nebraska Wesleyan Univ; Psychology.

WENZ, Melody A; Mid County HS; Lacon, IL; 8/60 Chrs; HonRl; LbryAde; FHA; GAA; College; Chemist.

WENZEL, Carol A; Oregon Davis HS; Walkerton, IN; 5/63 HonRl; NHS; Yrbk; 4-H; 4-HAwd; Ancilla Coll; Teacher.

WENZEL, Cathy L; William J Brown HS; Enning, SD; 33/208 HospAde; NHS; YthFlsp; Trade School; Medical Secretary.

WENZEL, Deborah R; La Moille HS; La Moille, IL; VPBand; Chrs; HonRl; SchPpr; VP4-H; VPFHA; FrCl; PpCl; GAA; 4-HAwd; Illinois St Univ; Special Educ.

WENZEL, Diane L; St Bernard HS; Wall Lake, IA; 10/34 TrsFrshCls; Chrs; HonRl; LbryAde; SchMus; SchPl; RptrYrbk; SchPpr; PpCl; IMSpt; College; Curriculum Of Major Study.

WENZEL, James J; Senior HS; Jamestown, ND; ALBoysSt; VPCncrtBnd; HonRl; MrchBnd; PresTeen; PresYthFlsp; FFA; Bsktbl; LetterTennis; IMSpt; College; Liberal Arts.

WENZEL, Janitha; Merrill Community HS; Merrill, MI; 4/105 HonRl; TchrAde; 4-H; FHA; GAA; Delta Coll; Computers.

WENZEL, John B; Elmwood HS; Elmwood, NE; VPFrshCls; PresSophCls; TrsJrCls; TrsSrCls; Band; Chr; Chrs; ChrhWkr; CncrtBnd; HonRl; MrchBnd; LetterBsbl; LetterBsktbl; LetterFtbl; College; Liberal Arts.

WENZEL, Julie A; St Catherines HS; Racine, WI; PolWkr; Quill&Scroll; SchMus; SchPl; SctActv; Yrbk; RptrSchPpr; GerCl; CchngActv; IMSpt; U Of Wi; Cpa.

WENZEL, Michael S; Sturgis HS; Sturgis, MI; VPJrCls; VPSrCls; NHS; StuGov; LetterFtbl; IMSpt; RotaryAwd; Univ Of Notre Dame; Medicine.

WENZEL, Patricia M; Madonna HS; Chicago, IL; 25/289 HonRl; JA; NHS; NatlThespSoc; SchMus; SchPl; SctActv; Yrbk; GerCl; Depaul Univ; Mathematics.

WENZEL, Robert F; St Clair HS; St Clair, MI; Aud/Vis; HonRl; LbryAde; TchrAde; SciCl; JCAwd; Msu; Vet.

WENZEL, Sheryl M; Williamsburg HS; Williamsburg, IA; 4/94 Chrs; HonRl; NHS; YthFlsp; Radiology.

WEPFER, Karen C; Wauwatosa East HS; Wauwatosa, WI; 20/480 Aud/Vis; HonRl; JA; NatlFornLg; NHS; SchPpr; MthCl; SciCl; PresJAAwd; Wellesley College; Communications.

WEPPRECHT, John B; R U C E HS; Essex, IL; PolWkr; SchPl; StuCncl; 4-H; FFA; LetterBsbl; LetterBsktbl; LetterFtbl; LetterTrk; College; Baseball.

WERBLOW, Sheri K; Dodge HS; Dodge, NE; VPJrCls; Chrs; ChrhWkr; HonRl; SchMus; SchPl; StuCncl; SpnCl; PpCl; Trk; Univ.

WERCHEY, Taffy; Lincoln Community HS; Lincoln, IL; 1/255 JA; NHS; NatlMeritCmnd; SchPl; 4-H; FrCl; PpCl; Whittier Coll.

WERDERITS, Paul S; Farmington East HS; Farmington, IL; NHS; Caterpillar Tractor Co Apprent; Mecahnical.

WERDERMAN, Cynthia J; Romeo HS; Romeo, MI; 40/322 Band; ChrhWkr; CncrtBnd; HonRl; MrchBnd; NHS; PepBnd; RptrYrbk; 4-H; Kalamazoo College; Computer Programming.

WERDIN, Beverly J; Kaneland HS; Elburn, IL; 2/160 Band; Chr; HonRl; Mdrgl; PresNHS; NatlMeritCmnd; PresYthFlsp; 4-H; SecFrCl; CaptChrldr; E Il Univ; Educ.

WERGER, Diane; Garnavillo HS; Garnavillo, IA; 9/42 Band; Chr; ChrhWkr; CncrtBnd; DrmMjrt; HonRl; LetterBsktbl; Swmmng; Tennis; Trk; Nursing Sch; Nurse.

WERGES, Joyce A; Mother Of Sorrows HS; Chicago, IL; LbryAde; StuCncl; TchrAde; RptrYrbk; RptrSchPpr; SchPpr; PresFrCl; GAA; VoiceDemAwd; Western Illinois Univ; Political Science.

WERLING, Nicholas C; Wayne HS; Ft Wayne, IN; 9/300 HonRl; NatlMeritSF; LetterBsktbl; Ftbl; Trk; Univ; Military.

WERMELING, Mary A; St Marys HS; Burlington, WI; 4/77 Chrs; CaptDrlTm; HonRl; NatlMeritSF; SchMus; Yrbk; PpCl; Univ Of Wisc; Social Welfare.

WERMERS, Deborah K; Mt Vernon Independent HS; Mt Vernon, SD; Band; Chrs; CncrtBnd; HonRl; MrchBnd; PepBnd; SchPl; Yrbk; EdSchPpr; PpCl; Mitchell Area Vo Tech; Acct.

WERMUND, Steve A; Mc Donell Central HS; Chippewa Falls, WI; 20/93 ALBoysSt; Chrs; HonRl; ModUN; SchPl; StuCncl; 4-H; PresSpnCl; PpCl; Bsbl; Bsktbl; Ftbl; Chrldr; Univ Of Wisconsin; Medical Technology.

WERNEKE, Nancy A; Marshall HS; Nelson, MO; HonRl; NHS; SecStuCncl; 4-H; GAA; 4-HAwd; Central Mo State U; Criminal Justice.

WERNER, Carl W; Austin Catholic Prep; Grosse Pt Woods, MI; 32/135 PresFrshCls; VPSophCls; VPJrCls; HonRl; NatlFornLg; NatlMeritSF; Quill&Scroll; RedCrAde; SctActv; StuGov; College; Doctor.

WERNER, Cindi; Maria HS; Chicago, IL; 18/364 Chrs; HonRl; JrNHS; LbryAde; NHS; NatlMeritSF; NatlSciFnd; LatCl; LionAwd; College.

WERNER, David; Nicolet HS; Milwake, WI; 26/495 NHS; SchAde; SciCl; Tennis; Univ Of Wisconsin; Business.

WERNER, Deborah E; Falls City HS; Salem, NE; Band; Chrs; ChrhWkr; CncrtBnd; MrchBnd; 4-H; GerCl; 4-HAwd; Univ; Nursing.

WERNER, Doris; Milnor Public HS; De Lamere, ND; 2/36 Chr; Chrs; ChrhWkr; CmntyWkr; HonRl; LbryAde; MthCl; PpCl;.

WERNER, Elizabeth H; Hinsdale Twp HS; Hinsdale, IL; 124/608 Chrs; ChrhWkr; HonRl; NHS; SchMus; FDA; Northwestern Univ; Medicine.

WERNER, Elizabeth J; Carmel HS; Mundelein, IL; 13/195 Chrs; CmntyWkr; HonRl; NHS; SchMus; StuCncl; SecGerCl; Univ Of Ill; Chemical Engineering.

WERNER, Ellen L; La Ville HS; Bremen, IN; 3/165 NHS; TchrAde; YthFlsp; GerCl; AmLegAwd; Purdure U.

WERNER, James M; Schuyler R 1 HS; Lancaster, MO; 22/71 ChrhWkr; HonRl; NHS; RptrSchPpr; FBLA; Bsbl; LetterBsktbl; University.

WERNER, Jayne E; Oregon Davis HS; Knox, IN; 3/63 ChrhWkr; HonRl; NHS; SchPl; StuCncl; RptrYrbk; RptrSchPpr; 4-H; LetterChrldr; GAA; Ball St U; Business.

WERNER, Judy T; St Francis HS; Humphrey, NE; Chrs; CncrtBnd; HonRl; MrchBnd; StuCncl; StuGov; TchrAde; Yrbk; 4-H; Trk; Univ; Pro.

WERNER, Karen S; Jasper HS; Jasper, IN; 9/291 ALAGirlsSt; HonRl; NatlMeritCmnd; Quill&Scroll; SchPl; Yrbk; College; Accounting.

WERNER, Linda A; William J Bogan HS; Chicago, IL; Chr; Chrs; HonRl; TreasNHS; OffAde; StuCncl; Treas4-H; FrCl; LetterGAA; 4-HAwd; Univ Of Ill; Accounting.

WERNER, Louise A; Peru HS; Peru, IN; 17/230 ALAGirlsSt; ChrhWkr; HonRl; NHS; OffAde; LatCl; SpnCl; Trk; Concordia Teachers College; Elem Educ.

WERNER, Mark T; Harding HS; St Paul, MN; Band; ChrhWkr; CncrtBnd; HonRl; JA; JrNHS; MrchBnd; NHS; PepBnd; StuCncl; Bsktbl; CaptSocr; Tennis; JAAwd; St Olaf College; Business.

WERNER, Mary C; Carmel Girls HS; Mundelein, IL; 29/190 Chrs; HonRl; LbryAde; NHS; SchMus; GerCl; PresMthCl; Mundelein College; Biology.

WERNER, Richard E; St Paul Kennedy HS; Chicago, IL; Chrs; HonRl; Yrbk; MthCl; University; Chemistry.

WERNER, Robert J; Carroll HS; Wichita, KS; 25/289 ChrhWkr; CmntyWkr; HonRl; PolWkr; StuCncl; StuGov; CaptFtbl; CaptTrk; Wrstlng; IMSpt; College.

WERNER, Robert J; St Thomas Aquinas HS; Florissant, MO; 7/335 ChrhWkr; CmntyWkr; HonRl; HospAde; LbryAde; VPNHS; SchMus; SchPl; RptrYrbk; 4-HAwd; Univ; Archi.

WERNER, Stephanie J; Medford Sr HS; Medford, WI; CncrtBnd; HonRl; MrchBnd; TreasStuCncl; SpnCl; PpCl; GAA; College; Nursing.

WERNER, Terry; St Pius HS; Festus, MO; VPJrCls; ALBoysSt; HonRl; Yrbk; RptrSchPpr; Bsbl; Bsktbl; CitAwd; Northeast Mo St Univ; Conservation.

WERNERSBACH, Karen A; Groves HS; Birmingham, MI; JA; Orch; Bsktbl; GAA; Michigan State Univ; Science.

WERNIMONT, Nancy A; St Bernard HS; Breda, IA; 12/18 Chr; Chrs; HonRl; LbryAde; SchPl; RptrYrbk; RptrSchPpr; LatCl; CaptBsktbl; U Of Northern Iowa; Elem Ed.

WERNING, James; Milwaukee Lutheran HS; Wauwatosa, WI; 12/231 Chr; NHS; NatlThespSoc; SchMus; SctActv; RptrYrbk; Uw Madison; Science Research.

WERNING, Katherine J; Lafayette County HS; Higginsville, MO; 17/98 Chrs; ChrhWkr; HonRl; HospAde; JrNHS; NHS; PresFHA; Trade School; Nurse.

WERNING, Michael C; Lafayette Co HS; Higginsville, MO; 15/100 ALBoysSt; Band; CncrtBnd; HonRl; MrchBnd; NHS; PepBnd; YthFlsp; RptrYrbk; EdSchPpr; FFA; SpnCl; IMSpt; University; Agri Business.

WERNKE, Edward E; Hemingford HS; Hemingford HS, NE; PresSrCls; ChrhWkr; HonRl; NHS; Quill&Scroll; StuCncl; RptrSchPpr; SchPpr; FFA; Bsktbl; Trade School.

WERNOWSKY, Mark A; Liberty HS; Quincy, IL; 18/64 HonRl; SchPl; StuCncl; FFA; PpCl; SciCl; CaptBsbl; Bsktbl; LetterTrk; University; Anaesthesiologist.

WERNSING, Sheri A; Lincolnwood HS; Harvel, IL; SecSophCls; Chr; ChrhWkr; HonRl; NHS; StuCncl; TchrAde; FHA; FTA; Chrldr; Univ; Bio Or Special Ed.

WERPY, David G; Marshall Sr HS; Marshall, MN; 23/230 Band; Chr; Chrs; ChrhWkr; HonRl; Mdrgl; YthFlsp; CaptBsktbl; Ftbl; CaptTrk; Coll; Dentistry.

WERRY, Glenn A; Farmington East HS; Farmington, IL; Band; CncrtBnd; DrmBgl; HonRl; MrchBnd; NHS; PepBnd; SctActv; StuCncl; 4-H; FFA; FrCl; Wrstlng; Univ Of Illinois; Agriculture.

WERSCHEY, Tarry; Lincoln Comm HS; Lincoln, IL; 1/255 JA; NHS; 4-H; FrCl; PpCl; Whittier College; Mathematics.

WERSTLER, Peggy A; Whitko HS; Pierceton, IN; Band; CncrtBnd; HonRl; MrchBnd; NHS; YthFlsp; PpCl; Business School; Bookkeeping.

WERT, Beth A; Atwater HS; Atwater, MN; 4/63 ChrhWkr; HonRl; LbryAde; NHS; Twrl; YthFlsp; 4-H; SpnCl; 4-HAwd; College; Elem Education.

WERT, Kathleen R; Hampton HS; Hampton, NE; Band; Chr; Chrl; Chrs; CncrtBnd; HonRl; MrchBnd; PepBnd; SchPl; StuCncl; LetterTrk; College; Vet Technician.

WERTH, Glenn A; Caro HS; Caro, MI; HonRl; FFA; Ftbl; Trade Schl; Liberal Arts.

WERTH, Janet E; Marian HS; Schoenchen, KS; /61 SecSrCls; HonRl; SpnCl; PpCl; College; Professional.

WERTH, Kurt W; Gavit HS; Hammond, IN; 39/360 Band; Chr; Chrs; CncrtBnd; HonRl; JrNHS; MrchBnd; Orch; PepBnd; StuCncl; PresGerCl; LetterFtbl; LetterSocr; Indiana Univ; Accounting.

WERTH, Ronald L; Thomas More Prep; Hays, KS; Chr; ChrhWkr; HonRl; NHS; 4-H; Ftbl; Trk; Wrstlng; College.

WERTKE, Scott; Glenbrook South Hs; Glenview, IL; IntrClCncl; NHS; NatlMeritCmnd; CaptSwmmng; Valparaiso U; Dentistry.

WERTMAN, Kenton L; Southridge HS; Holland, IN; ALBoysSt; Band; Chr; ChrhWkr; CmntyWkr; HonRl; SchMus; SctActv; StuCncl; StuGov; YthFlsp; 4-H; LetterFtbl; LetterWrstlng; Indiana Univ; Doctor.

WERTON, Julie A; St Francis HS; Wheaton, IL; 1/85 SecSophCls; ALAGirlsSt; HonRl; NatlFornLg; NHS; SchMus; SchPl; StuCncl; Trk; Univ Of Illinois; Medicine.

WERTZ, Janet L; Brkway West Sr HS; Creve Coeur, MO; CmntyWkr; HospAde; TchrAde; Univ Of Missouri; Horticulture.

WERTZ, Tamara L; Southwestern HS; Flat Rock, IN; 3/66 SecFrshCls; SecSophCls; SecJrCls; TreasBand; Chrs; ChrhWkr; HonRl; NHS; PpCl; Chrldr; Evansville Univ; Nursing.

WERTZBERGER, Ruth A; Wahlert HS; Dubuque, IA; 36/500 VPFrshCls; PresSophCls; PresJrCls; CmntyWkr; HonRl; NHS; StuCncl; StuGov; SchPpr; Chrldr; Univ.

WERTZLER, Kimberly S; Bushnell Prairie City HS; Bushnell, IL; Band; CncrtBnd; HonRl; MrchBnd; PepBnd; SchAde; SchPl; StuCncl; TreasFHA; BttyCrckrAwd; Eastern Illinois Univ; Home Economics.

WESBEY, Tim A; Morton W HS; Lyons, IL; 40/755 TrsSrCls; HonRl; JrNHS; NHS; StuCncl; Glf; Univ Of Ill; Mech Engineering.

WESBROOKS, Pamela G; Usd 462; Burden, KS; Chr; Chrs; ChrhWkr; HonRl; SchPl; StuCncl; RptrSchPpr; PpCl; Trk; Chrldr; College; Professional.

WESCHE, Julie A; Watertown Sr HS; Watertown, SD; 94/312 Band; Chr; Chrs; CncrtBnd; HonRl; MrchBnd; PepBnd; SctActv; GerCl; Bsktbl; Swmmng; LetterTrk; GAA; College; Physical Educ.

WESCOTT, Carrie A; Raymond Central HS; Raymond, NE; Band; CncrtBnd; HonRl; MrchBnd; PepBnd; SchMus; Twrl; YthFlsp; 4-H; FBLA; FHA; SecPpCl; Chrldr; 4-HAwd; University; Home Economics.

WESCOTT, Cherie W; Boyne City HS; Boyne City, MI; 2/126 Band; Chrs; HonRl; HospAde; SchMus; GerCl; Univ Of Oklahoma; Music/organ.

WESCOTT, Dean T; St Marys Central HS; Menoken, ND; PpCl; LetterBsktbl; Ftbl; Trk; Trade School; Vocation.

WESCOTT, Kay; Fruitport HS; Fruitport, MI; 44/308 Band; CmntyWkr; CncrtBnd; HonRl; MrchBnd; NHS; TchrAde; SpnCl; Central Michigan Univ; Pys Ed.

WESCOTT, Lloyd K; Sargent Public HS; Brewster, NE; PresSophCls; HonRl; JrNHS; StuCncl; YthFlsp; 4-H; FFA; LetterBsktbl; Ftbl; Trk; PresAwd; Vet College; Agriculture.

WESELOH, Harold W; Cosmos HS; Hector, MN; 4/34 PresJrCls; ALBoysSt; HonRl; NHS; SchPl; RptrSchPpr; Bsbl; Ftbl; Trk; Wrstlng; College.

WESELY, David A; Creighton Prep; Omaha, NE; 140/249 Sdlty; Bsbl; CaptBsktbl; AmLegAwd; College Of Univ; Major Study.

WESELY, Mark E; Mt Pleasant HS; Mt Pleasant, IA; ChrhWkr; CtyCnl; HonRl; SctActv; StuCncl; YthFlsp; SptEdSchPpr; Ftbl; Wrstlng; CchngActv; University; Professional.

WESEMANN, Gail D; Arlington HS; Kennard, NE; 5/57 SecFrshCls; PresJrCls; ALAGirlsSt; HonRl; SecNHS; VPTeen; RptrYrbk; GerCl; PpCl; GAA; U Of Ne; Dental Tech.

WESEMANN, Karen S; Nemaha Valley HS; Cook, NE; SecFrshCls; Chrs; ChrhWkr; HonRl; SchPl; VPYthFlsp; Sec4-H; GerCl; PpCl; 4-HAwd; Coll; Elem Ed.

WESEMANN, Wendolyn L; Southwest HS; Leawood, KS; 107/500 Chr; ChrhWkr; HonRl; NHS; SchMus; PresTeen; YthLg; PpCl; Washburn University; Accounting.

WESENER, Judith A; Gresham HS; Shawano, WI; SecTrsJrCls; Band; Chrs; HonRl; NHS; PepBnd; SchPl; TchrAde; Yrbk; SchPpr; Univ; Music.

WESENER, Karen A; Kiel HS; Newton, WI; AFS; HonRl; FHA; GerCl; Univ; Math Teacher.

WESHINSKEY, Gwenna J; Carbondale Community HS; Carbondale, IL; 3/323 HonRl; LitMag; NatlMeritSF; PolWkr; SchPl; YthLg; NCTE; Univ; Writer.

WESLE, Janet; University Hs; Normal, IL; 10/125 PresVPChrs; HonRl; Mdrgl; NHS; RptrYrbk;.

WESLEY, Francie M; Columbus HS; Marshfield, WI; Band; ChrhWkr; HonRl; MrchBnd; PepBnd; SchPl; RptrSchPpr; SchPpr; FrCl; Bsktbl; St Norberts College; Psychology.

WESLEY, James T; Weber HS; Chicago, IL; Band; CncrtBnd; HonRl; MrchBnd; NHS; NatlMeritCmnd; SciCl; Trk; University; Professional.

WESMAN, George F; Luther L Wright HS; Ironwood, MI; HonRl; NatlMeritFnl; NatlMeritSchl; NatlMeritSF; SchPl; Bsktbl; Ftbl; CaptTennis; IMSpt; College; Professional.

WESNER, Robert B; Lyons Twp HS; La Grange Pk, IL; CncrtBnd; HonRl; LitMag; MrchBnd; ModUN; NHS; Orch; PepBnd; SchMus; Univ Of Illinois; Lawyer.

WESNER, Sandy; High School; Bloomington, MN; Band; CncrtBnd; DrlTm; HonRl; MrchBnd; Orch; Colleg.

WESOL, Marlene A; Good Counsel HS; Chicago, IL; Chr; Chrs; ChrhWkr; NHS; SchMus; SchPl; SctActv; StuCncl; GAA; IMSpt; College; Professional.

WESOLIK, Clinton J; New Athens HS; New Athens, IL; 3/66 PresFrshCls; Band; ChrhWkr; PresNHS; SciCl; LetterBsbl; LetterBsktbl; BttyCrckrAwd; Ill State Univ; Political Science.

WESSA, Patricia A; Catholic Memorial HS; Waukesha, WI; CmntyWkr; NHS; TchrAde; PpCl; LetterBsktbl; LetterTrk; GAA; PresAwd; Col; Ed.

WESSEL, Alane R; Central Community HS; Elkader, IA; Band; HonRl; NHS; Quill&Scroll; YthFlsp; SptEdYrbk; LetterBsktbl; LetterGlf; GAA; College.

WESSEL, Cathy A; Holy Family HS; Lindsay, NE; 2/27 SecSophCls; Chr; Chrs; HonRl; NHS; SchPl; StuCncl; RptrSchPpr; 4-H; Chrldr; Grand Island School Of Bus; Pro Secretary.

WESSEL, Dennis P; Melrose Sr HS; Melrose, MN; ALBoysSt; ChrhWkr; HonRl; SecStuCncl; Yrbk; PpCl; LetterBsbl; LetterBsktbl; LetterFtbl; CchngActv; Dunwoody; Drafting.

WESSEL, James A; Kettle Moraine HS; Delafield, WI; 60/176 HonRl; Quill&Scroll; SctActv; FBLA; MthCl; LetterTennis; IMSpt; Col; Pro.

WESSEL, Jane; Acad Of The Immaculate Con; Batesville, IN; Chrs; ChrhWkr; CmntyWkr; HonRl; Orch; SchMus; GerCl;.

WESSEL, Lorraine; Memphis HS; Smith Creek, MI; 11/75 VPJrCls; HonRl; TchrAde; SptEdYrbk; 4-H; IMSpt; 4-HAwd; St Clair County Comm Coll; Law Enforcement.

WESSEL, Mark S; Moberly HS; Moberly, MO; CmntyWkr; HonRl; VPJA; LitMag; NHS; NatlMeritCmnd; SctActv; PresEngCl; FrCl; MthCl; IMSpt; JAAwd; Univ Of Missouri; Civil Engineering.

WESSEL, Peggy; Mitchell HS; Mitchell, SD; ALAGirlsSt; HonRl; LbryAde; NHS; SchMus; KeyCl; PpCl; GAA; IMSpt; CitAwd; College; Nurse.

WESSELDYKE, Lynda S; Holland Christian HS; Holland, MI; Band; Chr; ChrhWkr; CmntyWkr; CncrtBnd; Mdrgl; MrchBnd; Orch; Hope College; Music.

WESSELINK, Bryan D; Stephen Decatur HS; Decatur, IL; ChrhWkr; CmntyWkr; HonRl; JrNHS; NHS; RedCrAde; YthFlsp; GerCl; LetterFtbl; LetterTrk; Univ Of Illinois; Dentist.

WESSELMAN, Brenda G; Porta HS; Tallula, IL; 26/118 DrlTm; HonRl; MrchBnd; SchPpr; Pres4-H; PresFHA; GAA; College; Nursing.

WESSELMAN, Rodney A; Center Grove HS; Greenwood, IN; 17/235 Band; Chr; HonRl; MrchBnd; NHS; PepBnd; SchMus; SchPl; KeyCl; IMSpt; Franklin Coll; Acct.

WESSELS, Cynthia M; Hononegah HS; Rockton, IL; 24/188 HonRl; SpnCl; PpCl;.

WESSELS, David L; Watseka Community HS; Watseka, IL; Aud/Vis; SecFrshCls; RptrSchPpr; LetterFtbl; Col;.

WESSELS, John H; Humboldt HS; St Paul, MN; LbryAde; LetterBsktbl;.

WESSELS, Linda K; Belmond Community HS; Goodell, IA; 2/69 HonRl; NHS; RptrYrbk; LetterTrk; GovHonPrgAwd; University Of Northern Iowa; Medical Illust.

WESSELS, Patrick; Warren Township HS; Grayslake, IL; 2/372 HonRl; LbryAde; NHS; StuCncl; RptrSchPpr; EdSchPpr; SchPpr; GerCl; College; Engineer.

WESSELY, John J; Buena Vista HS; Saginaw, MI; Band; CncrtBnd; HonRl; MrchBnd; GerCl; Coll; Prof.

WESSIC, Linda E; Shelbyville HS; Shelbyville, IN; 83/318 ChrhWkr; HonRl; Indiana Univ; Nursing.

WESSLER, Susan S; Tarkio HS; Westboro, MO; 9/69 DrmMjrt; HonRl; NHS; StuCncl; TchrAde; Yrbk; LetterBsktbl; LetterTrk; 4-HAwd; GodCntryAwd; Lpn School; Nurse.

WESSLING, Connie R; Sacred Heart HS; New Cambria, KS; Band; HonRl; SecIntrClCncl; NatlMeritCmnd; NatlMeritCmnd; Orch; CivCl; Pres4-H; FBLA; PpCl; PresAwd; Marymount; Business Admn.

WESSLING, Mary L; Sacred Heart HS; New Cambria, KS; SecFrshCls; ChrhWkr; CmntyWkr; CncrtBnd; HonRl; MrchBnd; PepBnd; 4-H; FHA; PpCl; Coll; Dental Hygienist.

WESSLING, William; Benton Community HS; Atkins, IA; SecSophCls; HonRl; Yrbk; 4-H; SpnCl; SciCl; CaptBsbl; Bsktbl; Ftbl; IMSpt; College; Fish Wildlife Biologist.

WEST, Ann R; Cowden Herrick HS; Cowden, IL; PresJrCls; Band; Chr; HonRl; PepBnd; SchMus; SctActv; Yrbk; FHA; College; Music.

WEST, Barbara; Winola HS; New Windsor, IL; 1/66 SecFrshCls; ALAGirlsSt; HonRl; NHS; StuCncl; Yrbk; FTA; SpnCl; Chrldr; GAA; Univ Of Ill; Counseling Hs.

WEST, Barbara A; Ritenour Senior HS; St Louis, MO; 15/878 HospAde; JrNHS; MrchBnd; NHS; NatlMeritCmnd; Orch; StuGov; GerCl; University Of Missouri; Medicine.

WEST, Becky A; Clarkfield HS; Clarkfield, MN; Band; Chr; ChrhWkr; CncrtBnd; HonRl; MrchBnd; PepBnd; SchPl; EdYrBk; SchPpr; Trade School; Cake Decorating.

WEST, Belinda; Beaumont HS; St Louis, MO; Chr; ChrhWkr; HonRl; JA; SchAde; StuCncl; TchrAde; FBLA; JAAwd; CitAwd; College; Vocation.

WEST, Benjamin C; Allegan Sr HS; Allegan, MI; 50/196 Band; CncrtBnd; HonRl; MrchBnd; PepBnd; SchMus; LatCl; Michigan Technological Univ; Geology.

WEST, Bradley A; Wellcome Memorial HS; Garden City, MN; VPFrshCls; Chr; Chrs; ChrhWkr; HonRl; SchPl; StuCncl; FFA; LetterFtbl; LetterTrk; College.

WEST, Cassandra L; Vashon HS; St Lousi, MO; 2/317 VPSrCls; ChrhWkr; HonRl; LitMag; NHS; EdSchPpr; Trk; Mount Holyoke Clg; Lawyer.

WEST, Charles F; Westport HS; Kansas City, MO; 56/175 Band; CmntyWkr; HonRl; MrchBnd; SchMus; SctActv; StuCncl; Bsbl; Ftbl; Trk; University; Business Admin.

WEST, David G; Hillcrest HS; Country Club Hls, IL; Band; CncrtBnd; MrchBnd; PepBnd; RedCrAde; SctActv; North Central College; Radio & Tv.

WEST, David J; Effingham HS; Effingham, IL; 5/218 HonRl; PresJA; SctActv; PresKeyCl; SpnCl; LetterGlf; ChmbCommrsAwd; EldAwd; Southern Illinois Univ; Accounting.

WEST, Deanna L; Ben Davis HS; Indianapolis, IN; 49/814 Band; CmntyWkr; HonRl; SchAde; StuCncl; RptrYrbk; LetterBsktbl; LetterGlf; GAA; IMSpt; Indiana Univ Purdue; Law Enforcement.

WEST, Deborah S; Winola HS; New Windsor, IL; 1/90 HonRl; LbryAde; SchPl; StuCncl; TchrAde; FNA; FTA; SpnCl; PpCl; Chrldr; U Of Il; Med Technology.

WEST, Dennis M; Ridgway HS; Omaha, IL; 12/45 Band; Chrs; HonRl; Yrbk; SchPpr; 4-H; FBLA; FFA; 4-HAwd; College; Farming.

WEST, Gale E; Lacrosse HS; Rush Center, KS; ChrhWkr; CmntyWkr; HonRl; LbryAde; Orch; TchrAde; EdYrBk; FHA; PpCl; DARAwd; Coll; English.

WEST, James T; Wayne Comm HS; Corydon, IA; 57/120 TrsFrshCls; TrsJrCls; Chr; Chrs; CmntyWkr; StuCncl; Ftbl; Trk; Wrstlng; Central; Phy Ed.

WEST, John E; Catholic Memorial HS; Waukesha, WI; 6/147 HonRl; NHS; CaptFtbl; LetterTrk; AmLegAwd; BauchLmbAwd; GovHonPrgAwd; KiwanAwd; CitAwd; Univ Wi Milwaukee; Computer Eng.

WEST, Judy; Grass Lake HS; Grass Lake, MI; 22/94 Chrs; ChrhWkr; DrlTm; YthFlsp; RptrYrbk; RptrSchPpr; PpCl; Chrldr; GAA; IMSpt; College.

WEST, Karen M; Mount Assisi Academy; Hickory Hills, IL; 25/145 HonRl; TchrAde; Yrbk; Bsbl; CchngActv; GAA;.

WEST, Kathy S; Elkader HS; Farmersburg, IA; TreasLbryAde;.

WEST, Loraine A; Forest View HS; Mt Prospect, IL; 3/645 ChrhWkr; HonRl; NHS; PolWkr; Quill&Scroll; 4-H; SpnCl; Univ Of Arizona; Agriculture.

WEST, Marcia K; Marinette HS; Marinette, WI; Band; CncrtBnd; HospAde; MrchBnd; NHS; PepBnd; SchMus; FrCl; Columbia Schl; Nursing.

WEST, Monty E; Westwood HS; Sloan, IA; HonRl; YthFlsp; Glf; Trk; College; Curriculum Of Major Study.

WEST, Rhonda B; Southeast HS; Kansas City, MO; 1/350 SecSrCls; SecBand; CncrtBnd; DrmMjrt; NHS; NatlMeritCmnd; YthFlsp; FHA; PresSpnCl; BauchLmbAwd; PresAwd; Stanford Univ; Math.

WEST, Sheri; Irving Crown Hs; Carpentersville, IL; 15/351 HonRl; HospAde; NHS; Yrbk; University; Nursing.

WEST, Susan D; Morton Sr HS; Hammond, IN; 52/499 Purdue Univ; Nursing.

WEST, Teresa A; Shakamak HS; Jasonville, IN; 2/80 HonRl; NHS; OffAde; Quill&Scroll; RptrYrbk; EdSchPpr; Indiana State U; Elementary Education.

WEST, Timothy J; Allegan Sr HS; Allegan, MI; Band; CncrtBnd; HonRl; MrchBnd; Orch; PepBnd; SchMus; SchPl; TchrAde;.

WEST, Vicki; Pittsfield Hs; Pittsfueld, IL; 1/129 Band; Chr; ChrhWkr; CncrtBnd; HonRl; Mdrgl; NHS; NatlThespSoc; YthFlsp; LatCl; St Louis Christian College; Mathematics.

WEST, Vicki L; Wentzville HS; O Fallon, MO; CAP; CmntyWkr; HospAde; LitMag; StuGov; YthFlsp; SchPpr; 4-H; JAAwd; CitAwd; College; Journalism.

WEST, Virginia M; W Chicago Comm HS; West Chicago, IL; TrsSrCls; Chr; Chrs; ChrhWkr; HonRl; JA; SchMus; StuCncl; FrCl; GerCl; PpCl; Tennis; CchngActv; Louisiana State Univ; Oceanography.

WEST, Wallace D; Gordon Tech HS; Chicago, IL; 66/594 HonRl; LetterBsbl; LetterFtbl; IMSpt; College; Ed Math Bus.

WEST, William B; Farmington East HS; Hanna City, IL; ALBoysSt; Chrs; ChrhWkr; YthFlsp; 4-H; FFA; Bsbl; Bsktbl; DanFAwd; University; Agriculture.

WESTALL, Judith E; Breckenridge HS; Breckenridge, MI; 16/98 HonRl; LetterBsktbl; PPFtbl; Central Mi Univ; Special Educ.

WESTBERG, David A; Pepin HS; Pepin, WI; HonRl; NHS; StuCncl; FFA; LetterBsbl; ChmnBsktbl; ChmnFtbl; Voc Sch; Police.

WESTBROOK, Lynn B; Enterprise Acad; Wichita, KS; Southwestern Union; Law.

WESTBY, John D; Glenbard East HS; Lombard, IL; 71/653 HonRl; PolWkr; SchPl; Univ Of Illinois; English.

WESTBY, Timothy S; Valley City HS; Valley City, ND; 2/162 CncrtBnd; HonRl; MrchBnd; NatlMeritSF; StuCncl; YthLg; SciCl; LetterTennis; IMSpt; BauchLmbAwd; KiwanAwd; College; Engineering.

WESTEMEIER, Michael L; Central HS; Waterloo, IA; JA; CaptFtbl; LetterTrk; JAAwd; College.

WESTEMEYER, Donald D; Pekin Community HS; Pekin, IL; 246/744 Bsbl; Bsktbl; CaptFtbl; LetterWrstlng; IMSpt; Blackhawk Coll; Teacher.

WESTENBERG, Dawn L; Edgerton Public HS; Edgerton, MN; PresJrCls; NHS; PepBnd; SchPl; StuCncl; YthFlsp; Yrbk; RptrSchPpr; FHA; PpCl; College; Teaching.

WESTENBURG, Teresa A; Gretna Jr Sr HS; Gretna, NE; 11/80 ALAGirlsSt; Band; CncrtBnd; HonRl; MrchBnd; NHS; PepBnd; SchAde; TchrAde; PpCl; College Univ Of Ne;nursing Medical Technol.

WESTENDORF, Cynthia; Teutopolis Hs; Teutopolis, IL; 4/116 SecSrCls; Chrs; CncrtBnd; HonRl; Yrbk; 4-H; SpnCl; Tennis; DARAwd; 4-HAwd; Eastern Illinois U; Elementary Education.

WESTERDORP, Allen; Lakewood HS; Lake Odessa, MI; 10/203 ChrhWkr; CmntyWkr; HonRl; JrNHS; NHS; NatlMeritCmnd; StuCncl; TchrAde; 4-H; Trk; Olivet Coll; Professional.

WESTERFELD, Cynthia L; St Charles Senior HS; St Charles, MO; HonRl; NHS; GerCl; PpCl; Chrldr; University; Professional.

WESTERFELD, Debbie; Orchard Farm HS; St Charles, MO; /120 HonRl; HospAde; OffAde; 4-H; SciCl; Trk; CchngActv; IMSpt; PPFtbl; Semo; Nursing.

WESTERFIELD, John; Olympia HS; Mclean, IL; 65/264 ChrhWkr; CncrtBnd; HonRl; MrchBnd; SpnCl; MthCl; SciCl; Bsbl; Ftbl; Wrstlng; University; Professional.

WESTERFIELD, Kathleen M; Olympia HS; Mc Lean, IL; 7/192 ALAGirlsSt; HonRl; NHS; SctActv; PresStuCncl; Twrl; RptrSchPpr; PresGerCl; PresMthCl; PpCl; PresSciCl; Chrldr; Univ Of Illinois; Accounting.

WESTERFIELD, Marla; Woodruff Hs; Peoria, IL; 14/232 HonRl; JA; NHS; SctActv; TchrAde; Yrbk; RptrSchPpr; FrCl; SciCl; Chrldr; Illinois Central College; Dental Hygiene.

WESTERFIELD, Michael J; Taylor HS; Kokomo, IN; 11/191 HonRl; NatlThespSoc; FrCl; SciCl; Ftbl; IMSpt; DARAwd; Science Field.

WESTERHOLD, Craig F; Edwardsville HS; Worden, IL; ChrhWkr; HonRl; YthFlsp; 4-H; 4-HAwd; U Of Il; Math.

WESTERHOLD, Deborah A; Lutheran HS; Florissant, MO; 29/131 TrsJrCls; CmntyWkr; HospAde; NHS; PolWkr; RedCrAde; SctActv; StuCncl; StuGov; YthFlsp; Ks State U; Architectural Design.

WESTERMAN, Charles B; Nicolet HS; Glendale, WI; 60/500 Chr; NHS; PolWkr; SchMus; SchPl; YthFlsp; EdSchPpr; Ftbl; Swmmng; IMSpt; Coll; Writing.

WESTERMAN, Connie J; Metropolis Comm HS; Metropolis, IL; 1/161 ChrhWkr; HonRl; VPNHS; PolWkr; SchPl; StuCncl; RptrYrbk; SchPpr; MthCl; PpCl; Murray State Univ; Medicine.

WESTERMAN, Cynthia K; Maroa Forsyth HS; Decatur, IL; Band; Chrs; ChrhWkr; HonRl; MrchBnd; Treas4-H; TreasFHA; PpCl; Chrldr; 4-HAwd;.

WESTERMANN, David L; Snyder HS; Scribner, NE; 2/15 SecTrsSophCls; Chrs; HonRl; SchMus; SchPl; EngCl; MthCl; LetterFtbl; Se Comm Coll; Elec Service.

WESTERN, Gayla L; Rothsay Public HS; Rothsay, MN; VPSophCls; PresJrCls; CncrtBnd; HonRl; Mdrgl; RptrYrbk; EdSchPpr; LetterBsktbl; LetterTrk; PresGAA; College.

WESTERN, Mike E; Oakes HS; Oakes, ND; 54/80 ALBoysSt; HonRl; CaptBsktbl; LetterFtbl; LetterGlf; College; Accounting.

WESTERN, Susan K; Hill Murray HS; St Paul, MN; SctActv; U; Pro.

WESTERVALL, Brenda L; Hope HS; Hop, ND; 4/13 Band; Chr; Chrs; CncrtBnd; HonRl; MrchBnd; PepBnd; SchPl; RptrYrbk; SchPpr; Ndsw; Music Major.

WESTFALL, Jeffrey B; George Rogers Clark HS; Whiting, IN; Band; DrmBgl; MrchBnd; Orch; PepBnd; TchrAde; Indiana St University; Music.

WESTFALL, Linda K; Eastbrook HS; Van Buren, IN; 34/129 Band; ChrhWkr; CmntyWkr; CncrtBnd; HonRl; MrchBnd; PepBnd; YthFlsp; 4-H; LatCl; PpCl; LetterBsktbl; LetterTrk; Taylor Univ; Nursing.

WESTFALL, Marla K; O Fallon Township HS; O Fallon, IL; 41/296 Band; CncrtBnd; HonRl; HospAde; JrNHS; MrchBnd; SctActv; StuCncl; 4-H; 4-HAwd; Junior College; Business.

WESTFALL, Mary C; English Valleys HS; North English, IA; TrsSophCls; Band; Chrs; CncrtBnd; HonRl; MrchBnd; NHS; SchMus; SctActv; TchrAde; YthFlsp; Bsktbl; LetterTrk; Ne Missouri St Univ; Nursing.

WESTFALL, Tamara; Northeast R HS; Jacksonville, MO; 1/25 PresSophCls; PresJrCls; HonRl; NHS; SchPl; RptrYrbk; SchPpr; SpnCl; Univ Of Mo; Journalism.

WESTFIELD, Grishondra L; Benton Harbor HS; Benton Harbor, MI; Band; ChrhWkr; CncrtBnd; DrmBgl; HonRl; MrchBnd; College; Business Admins.

WESTFIELD, Lisa A; St Marys Acad; Monmouth, IL; 1/50 VPFrshCls; TrsJrCls; Chrs; HonRl; HospAde; NHS; Orch; RptrYrbk; RptrSchPpr; SpnCl; College; Professnl.

WESTHOUSE, Charles A; South Christian HS; Moline, MI; HonRl; NHS; NatlMeritSF; LetterBsktbl; Calvin Col; Pre Seminary.

WESTIE, Elizabeth H; Mt Pleasant HS; Mt Pleasant, MI; 14/370 Aud/Vis; Band; Chr; Chrl; CncrtBnd; HonRl; LitMag; Mdrgl; MrchBnd; NHS; U Of M; English Proffessor.

WESTMAN, Debra J; Bloom Township HS; Chicago Hts, IL; 7/932 Chr; Chrs; ChrhWkr; HonRl; LbryAde; NHS; SchMus; StuCncl; MthCl; SciCl; Evangelical Sch; Nurse.

WESTMAN, Paul W; Waseca HS; Waseca, MN; Chrs; ChrhWkr; CncrtBnd; HonRl; LbryAde; MrchBnd; StuCncl; EdSchPpr; Bsktbl; Ftbl; Trk; Wrstlng; Univ Of Minnesota.

WESTMORELAND, Douglas V; East Detroit HS; East Detroit, MI; Band; CncrtBnd; HonRl; MrchBnd; NHS; NatlMeritSF; PepBnd; YthFlsp; Michigan State University.

WESTON, Earl D; Valentine HS; Valentine, NE; SchAde; TchrAde; FFA; SciCl; Bsktbl; Glf; Ranching.

WESTON, Kathleen M; Washburn HS; Minneapolis, MN; 2/495 HonRl; LitMag; NHS; NatlMeritSF; SchMus; StuGov; Michigan State Univ; Political Science.

WESTON, Stevan W; Seneca HS; Seneca, MO; Chr; HonRl; FTA; MthCl; LetterFtbl; College; Business.

WESTON, Terri A; Fulton HS; Albany, IL; 12/124 SecJrCls; Band; HonRl; NatlThespSoc; RedCrAde; SchPl; SctActv; Twrl; SpnCl; E Illinois Univ; Law.

WESTOVER, Georgiana J; Westwood HS; Sloan, IA; 10/80 CmntyWkr; HonRl; LbryAde; ModUN; NatlMeritCmnd; NatlThespSoc; UNYO; FHA; SpnCl; PpCl; Wrstlng; Cornell Univ; Restaurant Management.

WESTOVER, Terri A; Neil A Armstrong HS; Neenah, WI; 49/600 Band; ChrhWkr; CmntyWkr; CncrtBnd; HonRl; StuCncl; StuGov; Bsktbl; Trk; PresAwd; Carthage Clg; Biology Med Tech.

WESTPHAL, Arthur T; Southwest HS; St Louis, MO; 1/465 HonRl; RedCrAde; SchAde; TchrAde; BauchLmbAwd; Washington U; M D.

WESTPHAL, Deborah S; Anita Comm HS; Anita, IA; 3/65 Chrs; HonRl; Quill&Scroll; Yrbk; 4-H; FHA; FTA; PpCl; LetterTrk; CaptChrldr; American Inst Of Bus; Court Reporter.

WESTPHAL, Jennifer M; Gull Lake HS; Augusta, MI; HonRl; NHS; Orch; SctActv; StuCncl; TchrAde; 4-H; FrCl; SciCl; 4-HAwd; Mich State U; Vet.

WESTPHAL, Kimberly L; Oak Park HS; Kansas City, MO; Junior College; Professional.

WESTPHAL, Michael J; Elgin HS; Morristown, SD; 1/35 HonRl; SchPl; FFA; College; Physics.

WESTRA, Evelyn J; Chicago Christian HS; Worth, IL; Chr; Mdrgl; StuCncl; RptrYrbk; SchPpr; GerCl; SecPpCl; Bsktbl; Chrldr; AmLegAwd; Univ; Teaching & Music.

WESTRA, Laia L; Southwestern HS; Flint, MI; Chr; ChrhWkr; HonRl; JA; LbryAde; NHS; Univ Michigan Flint; Pharmacy.

WESTRA, Lynda J; Kelloggsville HS; Kentwood, MI; HonRl; TchrAde; Bus Sch; Sec.

WESTRA, Paul W; Christian HS; Waupun, WI; Band; Chr; HonRl; NHS; SchPl; Yrbk; LetterBsktbl; CaptTrk; KiwanAwd; Coll; Math.

WESTRATE, Julie A; Kingsley Area HS; Kingsley, MI; 1/43 VPFrshCls; VPSophCls; Band; Chrs; ChrhWkr; HonRl; NHS; NatlMeritCmnd; SchPl; StuCncl; Ferris St Coll; Optometry.

WESTRICH, Brian; St Pius X HS; Arnold, MO; 5/110 VPSophCls; ALBoysSt; HonRl; NHS; StuCncl; 4-H; SciCl; Bsbl; Ftbl; Coll; Professional.

WESTRICH, Carol A; St Pius X HS; Kansas City, MO; 7/136 HonRl; LbryAde; NHS; SchMus; SchPl; St Marys College.

WESTRICH, Thomas J; Notre Dame HS; Cp Girardeau, MO; Aud/Vis; HonRl; PresNHS; StuCncl; LetterBsktbl; LetterTrk; CchngActv; College; Pharmacy.

WESTROPE, Deborah J; Holdrege HS; Holdrege, NE; 5/114 CncrtBnd; HonRl; MrchBnd; NatlThespSoc; OffAde; PepBnd; SchPl; RptrYrbk; RptrSchPpr; Univ Of Notre Dame; Engineering.

WESTVEER, Sally; Comstock HS; Kalamazoo, MI; Band; ChrhWkr; CncrtBnd; HonRl; HospAde; MrchBnd; NHS; Yrbk; IMSpt; Cmu; Biology.

WETHEKAM, Thomas J; Maine East HS; Niles, IL; ChrhWkr; HonRl; JrNHS; NHS; NatlMeritCmnd; GerCl; MthCl; Univ Of Illinois; Dentist.

WETHERBEE, Thomas C; Galesburg HS; Galesburg, IL; 3/650 AFS; Chr; Chrl; NHS; StuCncl; YthLg; SpnCl; LetterSwmmng; Tennis; DARAwd; College; Law.

WETHERELL, Robin A; Vienna Twp HS; Vienna, IL; 10/104 PresSrCls; Band; ChrhWkr; CncrtBnd; HonRl; MrchBnd; PepBnd; StuCncl; Yrbk; RptrSchPpr; 4-H; FTA; DanFAwd; Univ Of Illinois; Dentistry.

WETHERINGTON, Carol; Metropolis Community HS; Metropolis, IL; 1;161 ChrhWkr; HonRl; NHS; SchPl; StuCncl; EdYrBk; TreasSpnCl; MthCl; DanFAwd; EldAwd; Universityofillinois;microbiology.

WETHERINGTON, Carol L; Metropolis Comm HS; Metropolis, IL; 1/161 ChrhWkr; HonRl; NHS; SchPl; TreasStuCncl; PresYthFlsp; EdYrBk; TreasSpnCl; MthCl; DanFAwd; Univ Of Illinois; Microbiology.

WETNIGHT, Bonny J; Thornton Fractional North HS; Burnham, IL; 15/500 Band; CncrtBnd; HonRl; JrNHS; MrchBnd; NHS; OffAde; PepBnd; Northern Illinois University; Computer Prog.

WETNIGHT, Thomas L; Brazil HS; Brazil, IN; HonRl; NHS; KiwanAwd; Isu; Teaching Foreign Language.

WETROSKY, David A; Akron Community HS; Akron, IA; TrsJrCls; Band; ChrhWkr; CncrtBnd; HonRl; MrchBnd; NHS; PepBnd; SchPl; StuCncl; Bsktbl; Trk; College; Engineering.

WETTA, Earl; Andale HS; Andal, KS; HonRl; NatlMeritCmnd; SpnCl; Kansas State Univ; Engineering.

WETTA, Kathleen; Kearney Catholic HS; Kearney, NE; PresFrshCls; Band; RedCrAde; StuCncl; RptrYrbk; SpnCl; Chrldr; DARAwd; Univ Of Ne; Undecided.

WETTACH, Jeffrey; Mt Pleasant Sr HS; Mt Pleasant, IA; Band; CncrtBnd; HonRl; MrchBnd; NHS; PepBnd; StuCncl; YthFlsp; Ftbl; Luther College.

WETTER, Barbara A; Duchesne HS; St Charles, MO; Chrs; ChrhWkr; HonRl; VPStuCncl; RptrYrbk; PpCl; College; Journalism.

WETTER, Linda M; Cuba City HS; Cuba City, WI; Band; HonRl; MrchBnd; RptrYrbk; RptrSchPpr; FHA; PpCl; Trk; CaptChrldr; GAA; Voc School; Pro.

WETTERAU, Tad D; Stratford HS; Stratford, WI; SecJrCls; ChrhWkr; SchPl; SecJrCls; Wrstlng; IMSpt; Police Science; Law.

WETTERSTROEM, Nanette; Ladywood HS; Northville, MI; HonRl; NatlMeritCmnd; StuCncl; 4-HAwd; Sch Craft College; Veterinary Medicine.

WETTIG, Robert A; Richmond HS; Richmond, IN; HonRl; NHS; FrCl; LetterBsbl; Ftbl; Trk; Tri State College; Civil Engineer.

WETTON, Nancy J; Rolling Meadows HS; Arlington Heights, IL; 21/58 ChrhWkr; CncrtBnd; HonRl; MrchBnd; NatlFornLg; NHS; NatlMeritSF; NatlThespSoc; SchMus; SchPl; Univ; Linguistics.

WETTSTEIN, Sheila; St Marys Springs HS; Eden, WI; 2/120 Band; Chr; Chrs; ChrhWkr; CncrtBnd;

HonRl; LbryAde; MrchBnd; NHS; SpnCl; Technical; Accounting.

WETZ, James; Keokuk Sr HS; Keokuk, IA; Band; HonRl; MrchBnd; PepBnd; SchMus; Ftbl; IMSpt; KiwanAwd; Univ Of Iowa.

WETZEL, Carl M; Frankfort HS; Frankfort, IN; 9/243 NHS; SchMus; SchPl; StuCncl; TchrAde; KeyCl; FrCl; MthCl; SciCl; LetterFtbl; In Univ; Law.

WETZEL, Cindy L; Wayne HS; Fort Wayne, IN; ChrhWkr; Nursing School; Nurse.

WETZEL, Gregg S; Central Noble HS; Wolf Lake, IN; ChrhWkr; CmntyWkr; HonRl; NHS; YthFlsp; LetterBsbl; LetterBsktbl; LetterFtbl; IMSpt; Jr Clg; Law Enforcement.

WETZEL, James D; St Mary Of Redford HS; Detroit, MI; HonRl; JrNHS; NHS; NatlMeritCmnd; RptrSchPpr; SptEdSchPpr; SchPpr; Bsbl; Ftbl; LetterTrk; W Michigan Univ; Law.

WETZEL, John G; St Paul HS; Highland, IL; 2/54 TrsSophCls; Aud/Vis; Band; Chr; HonRl; ModUN; PepBnd; SchMus; StuCncl; Yrbk; Bsbl; Bsktbl; Univ; Engineering.

WETZEL, Kimberly K; Greensburg HS; Greensburg, KS; 1/43 ALAGirlsSt; HonRl; NatlFornLg; VPNHS; NatlMeritCmnd; StuCncl; RptrYrbk; Bsktbl; Tennis; Trk;.

WETZEL, Michael V; River Valley HS; Lake Side, MI; Band; CncrtBnd; HonRl; MrchBnd; PepBnd; TchrAde; Bsktbl; LetterWrstlng; CchngActv; CaptIMSpt;.

WETZEL, Perran G; Campion HS; Chicago, IL; 12/90 SctActv; StuCncl; StuGov; Swmmng; Tennis; Trk; Luther College; Elec Engineer.

WETZEL, Rick; Elgin HS; Elgin, IL; 70/720 HonRl; Glf; RotaryAwd; Ill Inst Of Tech; Achitecture.

WETZSTEIN, Vivian P; Alton Sr HS; Godfrey, IL; 33/803 Chrs; HonRl; HospAde; NHS; TchrAde; PresFBLA; Southern Ill Univ; Interior Design.

WEURDING, Dean; Lawton HS; Lawton, MI; ALBoysSt; CncrtBnd; HonRl; MrchBnd; SchPl; SctActv; YthFlsp; College; Marine Biologist.

WEVIK, Douglas D; Beresford Ind HS; Beresford, SD; 3/85 SecTrsFrshCls; Chr; ChrhWkr; HonRl; NHS; StuCncl; FFA; LetterBsktbl; LetterFtbl; LetterTrk;.

WEYER, Judith A; Forest Park HS; Ferdinand, IN; Band; CncrtBnd; MrchBnd; PepBnd; 4-H; PpCl; Indiana St Univ; Nursing.

WEYER, Kathy A; Jeffersonville HS; Jeffersonville, IN; Aud/Vis; JrNHS; 4-H; PpCl; Swmmng; PPFtbl; 4-HAwd; College; Criminology.

WEYER, Laverne T; Forest Park HS; Ferdinand, IN; 3/124 VPFrshCls; ALAGirlsSt; ChrhWkr; HonRl; NHS; SchPl; StuCncl; PpCl; LetterTrk; GAA; Clge; Nurse.

WEYERMULLER, Mary S; Acad Of The Sacred Heart; Chicago, IL; 3/38 Chrs; ChrhWkr; HospAde; SchPl; FrCl; Socr; Swmmng; GAA; IMSpt; Loretto Heights Clg; Nursing.

WEYERS, Gene D; Palmyra HS; Bennet, NE; 1/38 ALBoysSt; HonRl; NHS; Ftbl; Glf; Trade School; Electrical.

WEYERS, Linda K; Lewiston Consolidated HS; Crab Orchard, NE; 6/24 SecSophCls; PresJrCls; Band; HonRl; MrchBnd; SchPl; Yrbk; FHA; CaptTrk; Chrldr;.

WEYHER, Jeri A; Dundee HS; Dundee, MI; 3/125 Band; ChrhWkr; CncrtBnd; HonRl; JrNHS; LitMag; MrchBnd; LetterSwmmng; CchngActv; GAA; OptClAwd; Univ Of Michigan; Physical Therapy.

WEYHRICH, Jody A; Green Valley Comm HS; Green Valley, IL; 5/28 Band; Chr; Chrs; ChrhWkr; DrlTm; HonRl; JrNHS; MrchBnd; NHS; PepBnd; SchPl; SctActv; LetterBsbl; LetterBsktbl; College; Accounting.

WEYMILLER, Jean R; Waukon HS; Harpers Ferry, IA; 2/155 ALAGirlsSt; Chr; HonRl; NHS; RptrYrbk; 4-H; GerCl; LetterBsktbl; LetterTrk; GAA; Luther Col; Foods And Nutrition.

WEYRAUCH, Bob J; Ava HS; Squires, MO; Chrs; HonRl; SctActv; 4-H; FFA; Sch Of The Ozarks; Agri Bus.

WEZNER, John P; Catholic Central HS; Detroit, MI; HonRl; NHS; NatlMeritSF; SctActv; RptrYrbk; Yrbk; RptrSchPpr; SchPpr; General Motors Inst; Systems Analysis.

WHALEN, Gerald P; St Louis Univ HS; Manchester, MO; Socr; Clg; Professional.

WHALEN, Patricia A; Serena HS; Sheridan, IL; ChrhWkr; CncrtBnd; HonRl; MrchBnd; OffAde; PepBnd; SchPl; PpCl; SciCl; Swmmng; Clge; Cosmetology.

WHALEN, Timothy S; La Salle Peru HS; La Salle, IL; 95/548 ALBoysSt; Chrs; HonRl; LatCl; Tennis; Wrstlng; Univ Of Illinois; Veterinarian.

WHALEY, Carol E; Wainwright HS; Lafayette, IN; 1/105 ChrhWkr; HonRl; VPNatlFornLg; TreasNHS; PresNatlThespSoc; OffAde; SchMus; SchPl; YthFlsp; Yrbk; Pres4-H; FTA; LatCl; Purdue Univ; Home Economics.

WHALEY, Cheryl A; South Newton HS; Kentland, IN; Quill&Scroll; SchPl; YthFlsp; RptrYrbk; SchPpr; FTA; LatCl; PpCl; PPFtbl; 4-HAwd; Am Fashion Clg Of Switzerlnd; Fash Designer.

WHALEY, Judith A; La Ville HS; La Paz, IN; 52/155 Chr; CmntyWkr; TchrAde; YthFlsp; RptrSchPpr; 4-H; College; Nursing.

WHALEY, Julee A; South Newton HS; Brook, IN; 6/101 ChrhWkr; Quill&Scroll; SchMus; SctActv; StuCncl; YthFlsp; RptrSchPpr; 4-H; GerCl; LatCl; PpCl; SciCl; GAA; Ball State Univ; Landscape Architecture.

WHALEY, Randall G; La Ville HS; Lakeville, IN; Band; Chr; CncrtBnd; MrchBnd; OffAde; StuCncl; YthFlsp; Bsktbl; Indiana Univ; Accounting.

WHALEY, Sherril D; St Thomas Apostle HS; Chicago, IL; 10/52 Chr; ChrhWkr; CmntyWkr; HonRl; HospAde; SchPl; TchrAde; Chrldr; GAA; Univ; Pro.

WHALEY, Steven M; South Newton HS; Morocco, IN; ChrhWkr; SchMus; SchPl; Yrbk; 4-H; FFA; FTA; LatCl; LetterBsbl; 4-HAwd; Purdue Univ; Meteorology.

WHAM, Robert M; Springfield HS; Springfield, IL; 17/545 Band; ChrhWkr; HonRl; SctActv; TchrAde; Trk; Wrstlng; PresJETSAwd; Univ Of Illinois; Chemical Engineer.

WHAMOND, Vicki L; Barrington HS; Barrington, IL; 1/652 PresBand; HonRl; MrchBnd; NHS; Orch; PepBnd; SchPl; StuGov; PresFrCl; Rice; Engineering.

WHAN, David R; Knox County HS; Knox City, MO; ChrhWkr; HonRl; PolWkr; StuGov; TreasFFA; Bsktbl; Univ; Professional.

WHARTON, Anne E; Interlochen Arts Academy; Rockford, IL; Chr; HonRl; JrNHS; NHS; Orch; SchMus; College Of Conservation; Pro Flutist.

WHARTON, Marc D; University City HS; University City, MO; Band; JA; NatlMeritCmnd; PolWkr; SctActv; TchrAde; SpnCl; MthCl; CaptSocr; IMSpt; College; Chem Eng.

WHARTON, Mary; Academy Of Our Lady; Chicago, IL; HonRl; JA; Mdrgl; NHS; SchPl; Sdlty; RptrYrbk; Pres4-H; SpnCl; Western Illinois U; Horticulture.

WHARTON, Sandra J; Chilhowee HS; Chilhowee, MO; 1/19 HstJrCls; Chrs; HonRl; StuCncl; StuGov; RptrYrbk; RptrSchPpr; EdSchPpr; FHA; PpCl; Secretarial Practice.

WHARTON, William D; York Comm HS; Elmhurst, IL; HonRl; NHS; NatlMeritCmnd; Yrbk; College; Biology.

WHATLEY, Gregory; Lindblom HS; Chicago, IL; 59/585 ChrhWkr; CmntyWkr; HonRl; ROTC; SctActv; StuCncl; RptrYrbk; Yrbk; College; Professional.

WHATTOFF, Becky; United Community HS; Ames, IA; Band; Chr; Chrl; CncrtBnd; MrchBnd; PepBnd; SchMus; SchPl; EngCl; Bsktbl; College; Art.

WHEALY, Sela; Tri Valley HS; Ccolton, SD; Band; ChrhWkr; CncrtBnd; HonRl; HospAde; NatlFornLg; NHS; PepBnd; RedCrAde; EdSchPpr; Sd State U; Nursing.

WHEAT, James D; Fenton HS; Fenton, MI; 5/300 Band; CncrtBnd; HonRl; MrchBnd; NHS; NatlMeritFnl; NatlMeritSchl; NatlMeritSF; Orch; PepBnd; SchPl; StuGov; Swmmng; College; Politics.

WHEATLEY, Sandra L; Rich Hill HS; Rich Hill, MO; 11/45 HonRl; VPStuCncl; TreasFBLA; TreasFHA; PpCl; Chrldr; BttyCrckrAwd; Univ; Business.

WHEATLEY, Steven E; South Pemiscot HS; Steele, MO; VPFrshCls; Chr; Chrs; JrNHS; NHS; VPStuCncl; RptrYrbk; FFA; PpCl; Bsktbl; CaptFtbl; Trk; School Of The Ozarks.

WHEATON, Linda A; Lakeview HS; St Clair Shores, MI; TrsSophCls; SecChr; ChrhWkr; HonRl; Mdrgl; NHS; SchMus; StuCncl; FrCl; Bsbl; Bsktbl; Swmmng; CitAwd; College; Professional.

WHEEKER, Darlene K; Huron HS; New Boston, MI; 2/180 Chr; ChrhWkr; CmntyWkr; HonRl; NHS; SchMus; SchPl; FHA; SpnCl; Grand Rapids Baptist Col; Phy Therapy.

WHEELER, Cheryl L; Campus HS; Haysville, KS; ChrhWkr; HonRl; TchrAde; FHA; PpCl; Tennis; Accounting School; Cpa.

WHEELER, Cynthia A; Marquette Inc HS; West Point, IA; PresFrshCls; DrlTm; LbryAde; NHS; PpCl; Bsbl; IMSpt; Clge; Rn.

WHEELER, Frederick; Saginaw HS; Saginaw, MI; ChrhWkr; CmntyWkr; HonRl; JrNHS; LbryAde; NHS; FrCl; College; Medicine.

WHEELER, Jeanne; Central HS; Bristol, WI; Chr; HonRl; Mdrgl; NatlThespSoc; SchMus; SchPl; SctActv; YthFlsp; PpCl; Chrldr; Univ; Music Education And Drama.

WHEELER, Jeanne L; Marion C Early HS; Walnut Grove, MO; 1/45 CmntyWkr; HonRl; RptrSchPpr; 4-H; FBLA; FHA; PpCl; SciCl; LetterBsbl; LetterBsktbl; Univ.

WHEELER, Jeffrey B; Bloomington HS; Bloomington, IN; CncrtBnd; HonRl; NHS; NatlMeritSF; NatlThespSoc; SchPpr; FrCl; Trk; 4-HAwd;.

WHEELER, Jeffrey T; Highland Park HS; St Paul, MN; LitMag; Yrbk; Rochester Inst; Photographer.

WHEELER, Kaye E; Marquette HS; West Point, IA; 1/55 SecJrCls; Band; Chr; Chrs; ChrhWkr; CncrtBnd; DrlTm; MrchBnd; NHS; PepBnd; StuCncl; Trk; College.

WHEELER, Kim L; Alton Sr HS; Alton, IL; HonRl; MrchBnd; NHS; Orch; SchMus; LetterBsktbl; LetterTrk; GAA; College; History.

WHEELER, Nadeen E; Huron Sr HS; Huron, SD; ChrhWkr; Teen; 4-H; PpCl; 4-HAwd; LionAwd; Trade School; Interior Decoration.

WHEELER, Nancy J; Industry HS; Industry, IL; TrsFrshCls; TrsSophCls; TrsJrCls; Band; Chrs; CncrtBnd; HonRl; MrchBnd; PepBnd; RptrSchPpr; LetterBsbl; LetterBsktbl; LetterGlf; LetterTrk; Knox College; Law.

WHEELER, Peggy K; Southeast Sr HS; Kansas City, MO; 4/337 Chr; ChrhWkr; DrlTm; HonRl; JrNHS; NatlMeritCmnd; SchMus; SchPl; StuCncl; StuGov; TchrAde; Chrldr; PPFtbl; Denver Univ; Computer Engineer.

WHEELER, Rita C; Mercy HS; St Ann, MO; 15/180 HonRl; NHS; SpnCl; PpCl; College; Curriculum Of Major Study.

WHEELER, Rita J; Western HS; Sheffield, IL; Band; DrmMjrt; HonRl; HospAde; NatlThespSoc; SchPl; Twrl; FHA; TrsSophCls; GAA; College; Nursing.

WHEELER, Roy P; Avon HS; Danville, IN; Band; CncrtBnd; MrchBnd; LetterBsbl;.

WHEELER, Sarah D; Mississinewa HS; Gas City, IN; ChrhWkr; HonRl; VPJA; NHS; TchrAde; 4-H; FTA; JAAwd; Vocational Sch; Accounting.

WHEELER, Theresa; Spencer Comm HS; Spencer, IA; 2/166 HonRl; JrNHS; NHS; NatlThespSoc; Quill&Scroll; StuCncl; Yrbk; Bsktbl; Trk; IMSpt; Iowa State Univ; Zoology.

WHEELER, Theresa S; Pekin Community HS; Pekin, IL; 3/803 Chr; Chrs; ChrhWkr; HonRl; NHS; SecYthFlsp; FrCl; GAA; DARAwd; Ill Central College; Nursing.

WHEELER, Tony J; North Putnam HS; Roochdale, IN; 9/135 HonRl; NHS; SchPl; RptrYrbk; RptrSchPpr; SecFFA; LatCl; Rose Hulman; Engr.

WHEELER, Wendell A; Mt Carmel HS; Chicago, IL; 16/204 HonRl; JrNHS; NHS; NatlMeritFnl; NatlMeritCmnd; NatlMeritSF; RptrYrbk; Nothwestern Univ; Medicine.

WHEELER, Yvonne Y; Beaumont HS; St Louis, MO; HonRl; NHS; TchrAde; Twrl; St Louis University; Social Worker.

WHEELEY, Cynthia E; Clio HS; Clio, MI; 109/370 ChrhWkr; CncrtBnd; LbryAde; MrchBnd; NatlMeritSchl; Orch; PepBnd; SchMus; PresYthFlsp; LatCl; Michigan St Univ; Fashion Design.

WHEELOCK, Stephanie A; Brown County HS; Nashville, IN; 15/169 HonRl; NHS; SpnCl; Indiana Univ; Business.

WHELAN, Jeffrey G; Valley HS; Crystal, ND; 3/24 VPSophCls; SecTrsJrCls; ALBoysSt; Band; HonRl; EdYrBk; SecTrsFrshCls; LetterBsktbl; LetterTrk; 4-HAwd; Nd State U; Agriculture.

WHELAN, Maureen; Arrowhead HS; Hartland, WI; 8/303 AFS; HonRl; NHS; StuGov; Yrbk; Uw Stevens Pt; Child Psychology.

WHELCHEL, Chauncey D; Macomb Sr HS; Macomb, IL; 23/241 HonRl; NHS; NatlMeritCmnd; Western Illinois Univ; Elec Engineer.

WHELPLEY, Donald L; Potterville HS; Charlotte, MI; 1/55 PresFrshCls; ChrhWkr; HonRl; NHS; SchPl; TchrAde; GerCl; Ftbl; Spring Arbor College; English Major.

WHERLEY, Elaine J; Tolley Public HS; Tolley, ND; Chrs; HonRl; SchPl; TchrAde; 4-H; Trade School; Major Study.

WHERRY, Maryan; Orion HS; Orion, IL; 14/121 Band; NHS; YthFlsp; Wrstlng; Illinois State Univ; Art Major.

WHETSTINE, Jennifer; Maconaquah HS; Kokomo, IN; 2/220 HonRl; JrNHS; NHS; StuCncl; StuGov; Yrbk; LatCl; MthCl; DanFAwd; CitAwd;.

WHETSTINE, Richard L; Indian Creek HS; Trafalgar, IN; 14/110 ChrhWkr; HonRl; SchAde; TchrAde; Purdue Univ; Mech Engineering Tech.

WHEWELL, Calvin D; Southeastern HS; West Point, IL; 8/49 TrsFrshCls; VPJrCls; StuCncl; Quincy College; Accounting.

WHICKER, Mary E; Cloverdale HS; Spencer, IN; ALAGirlsSt; HonRl; NHS; SpnCl; GAA; IMSpt; Univ; Interior Decorating.

WHIPPLE, Betty J; Jefferson HS; Cedar Rapids, IA; Chrs; HonRl; LitMag; Orch; SchMus; Bsktbl; Glf; Tennis; Mount Mary Coll.

WHIPPLE, Cynthia L; Lawton HS; Lawton, MI; 4/53 Band; CncrtBnd; HonRl; MrchBnd; NHS; PepBnd; SchMus; RptrSchPpr; LetterBsktbl; IMSpt; Business School; Accounting.

WHIPPLE, Diane M; Caledonia HS; Caledonia, MI; Band; CncrtBnd; HonRl; NHS; SchAde; StuCncl; TchrAde; RptrSchPpr; Bsktbl; Chrldr; Grand Valley Coll; Elem Edu.

WHIPPLE, Milton L; Hanston HS; Hanston, KS; 3/15 TrsJrCls; Chrs; HonRl; SchPl; StuCncl; Yrbk; Bsktbl; CaptFtbl; Trk; Univ; Business.

WHIRLEDGE, Ben R; Fairfield Jr Sr HS; Millersburg, IN; 6/108 PresBand; ChrhWkr; CncrtBnd; MrchBnd; PepBnd; SchMus; PresYthFlsp; 4-H; VPFFA; LetterCchngActv;.

WHIRLEY, Jennifer J; Lincoln HS; Pershing, IN; 1/126 ALAGirlsSt; Chr; NHS; SecTeen; EdYrBk; FrCl; CaptChrldr; GAA; IMSpt; MasAwd; Earlham Coll; Biology.

WHISENHUNT, David E; Benkelman HS; Benkelman, NE; SecJrCls; HonRl; SciCl; Bsktbl; Ftbl; Univ Of Arkansas; Chemistry.

WHISENTON, Ethel L; Soldan HS; St Louis, MO; Band; PresChr; CmntyWkr; CncrtBnd; HonRl; MrchBnd; SchAde; PresYthFlsp; CitAwd; College; Chemistry.

WHISLER, Wayne L; Oskaloosa HS; Oskaloosa, KS; Band; ChrhWkr; CmntyWkr; CncrtBnd; MrchBnd; Orch; PepBnd; SchMus; SchPl; YthFlsp; Clg; Social Science Or Music.

WHISMAN, Michael O; Charlestown HS; Charlestown, IN; ALBoysSt; Band; ChrhWkr; CncrtBnd; JA; MrchBnd; PepBnd; 4-H; LatCl; Ftbl; LetterWrstlng; College; Electronics.

WHISNER, Michael E; Adel HS; Adel, IA; HonRl; Quill&Scroll; StuCncl; SchPpr; LetterBsbl; LetterFtbl; LetterTrk; Junior College.

WHISNEY, Ronald; Jackson HS; Jackson, MN; SchAde; TchrAde; 4-H; FFA; College; Vocation.

WHISTLE, Rebecca J; Castle HS; Newburgh, IN; HonRl; FHA; University; Medical Tech.

WHITAKER, Beth A; Mooresville HS; Mooresville, IN; 21/244 CmntyWkr; HonRl; JA; JrNHS; NHS; TchrAde; EdYrBk; SpnCl; CaptChrldr; GAA;.

WHITAKER, Dennis; Cloverdale HS; Cloverdale, IN; Aud/Vis; ChrhWkr; HonRl; NHS; 4-H; 4-HAwd; Purdue Univ; Electronics Tech.

WHITAKER, Julie; Moline Sr Hs; Moline, IL; 69 PresCncrtBnd; MrchBnd; NHS; Orch; PepBnd; Quill&Scroll; SchMus; Twrl; EdYrBk; GerCl; Augustana College ; Music Ed Biology.

WHITAKER, Orion C; Wauwatosa West HS; Wauwatosa, WI; Aud/Vis; Band; Chr; Chrs; CmntyWkr; CncrtBnd; HonRl; JA; MrchBnd; NatlFornLg; IMSpt; AmLegAwd; VFWAwd; Massachusetts Inst Of Tech; Physician.

WHITAKER, Patricia L; Clifton HS; Green, KS; TrsSrCls; CmntyWkr; HonRl; HospAde; JA; RedCrAde; TreasFHA; Trk; PresAwd; CitAwd; College; Professional.

WHITAKER, Wendy; Lasalle Peru Township HS; Lasalle, IL; VPSophCls; VPJrCls; VPSrCls; HonRl; RptrYrbk; SpnCl; College; Counselor.

WHITCHER, Rick F; North HS; West Union, IA; 24/110 PresChrs; HonRl; NatlThespSoc; SchMus; SchPl; StuCncl; SciCl; Ftbl; LetterTrk; LetterWrstlng; Univ Of Iowa; Medicine.

WHITCOMB, Allen P; Oak Park Acad; Sioux City, IA; Chr; HonRl; LbryAde; SchPl; StuGov; Trk; Trade School.

WHITE, Alan M; Lawrence HS; Lawrence, KS; Band; CncrtBnd; HonRl; ModUN; NatlFornLg; NatlMeritSF; Orch; PolWkr; StuCncl; University.

WHITE, Allen L; Macomb HS; Macomb, IL; 27/274 Aud/Vis; ChrhWkr; CmntyWkr; HonRl; SctActv; RptrYrbk; FrCl; PpCl; Western Illinois University; Psychology.

WHITE, Anna M; Liberal 'S; Iantha, MO; 13/48 HstJrCls; ALAGirlsSt; HonRl; JrNHS; StuCncl; YthFlsp; FBLA; GAA; CitAwd; VoiceDemAwd; Trade Sch; Vocation.

WHITE, Barbara; Charleviox HS; Charlevoix, MI; TrsFrshCls; TrsSophCls; HonRl; 4-H; SpnCl; Bsbl; CchngActv; 4-HAwd; College; Business.

WHITE, Beverly K; La Moille HS; La Moille, IL; Band; HonRl; NHS; EdYrBk; EdSchPpr; CchngActv; College; Journalism.

WHITE, Brent T; Pierce City HS; Sarcoxie, MO; ChrhWkr; HonRl; MrchBnd; StuCncl; YthFlsp; 4-H; Bsbl; Bsktbl; Trk; Trade Schl; Welder.

WHITE, Carlis C; Northeastern HS; Williamsburg, IN; 15/120 Aud/Vis; ChrhWkr; HonRl; PolWkr; SchPl; SctActv; TchrAde; YthLg; LatCl; Johnson Bible College; Minister.

WHITE, Carol; Paoli HS; Paoli, IN; 6/114 HonRl; NHS; SciCl; 4-HAwd; Vincennes Univ; Mental Health.

WHITE, Carol A; Ottawa HS; Ottawa, KS; Band; CncrtBnd; HonRl; SecNHS; PepBnd; SchPl; SchPpr; FrCl; PpCl; LetterTrk; U Of Ks.

WHITE, Carol R; Jersey Community HS; Jerseyville, IL; Chr; HonRl; SchMus; StuCncl; FrCl; Trk; Chrldr; University; Professional.

WHITE, Catherine A; Alton Sr HS; Godfrey, IL; 14/895 AFS; HonRl; JrNHS; NHS; TchrAde; RptrYrbk; RptrSchPpr; VPGerCl; PpCl; College; Pharmacist.

WHITE, Cathy S; Belton HS; Belton, MO; Band; Chr; DrmMjrt; HonRl; MrchBnd; NHS; SchAde; Twrl; LatCl; Jr College; Secretary.

WHITE, Charlene E; College HS; Muncie, IN; Band; Chr; ChrhWkr; CmntyWkr; CncrtBnd; HospAde; JA; MrchBnd; OffAde; SchMus; FrCl; Ball St Univ; Nursing.

WHITE, Cheryle R; Hillcrest HS; Springfield, MO; 36/306 Chr; Chrs; ChrhWkr; HonRl; NatlFornLg; SchMus; StuCncl; PpCl; Chrldr; VoiceDemAwd; Southwest Mo St Univ; Elem Ed.

WHITE, Connie; Davis County Community HS; Bloomfield, IA; HonRl; Business.

WHITE, Cynthia D; Franklin Center HS; Lee Center, IL; 2/50 SecFrshCls; Chrs; HonRl; NHS; SchMus; SchPl; SecStuCncl; Yrbk; RptrSchPpr; Pres4-H; FrCl; PpCl; Chrldr; GAA; College; Accountant.

WHITE, Daniel P; Postville HS; Postville, IA; HonRl; NatlThespSoc; SchPl; StuCncl; YthFlsp; YthFnd; Pres4-H; TreasFFA; Ftbl; LetterWrstlng; 4-HAwd; Trade School; Farming.

WHITE, Darlene E; Southside HS; Muncie, IN; 62/323 ChrhWkr; CncrtBnd; HospAde; JA; MrchBnd; Ball St Univ; Nursing.

WHITE, David; Dearborn HS; Dearborn, MI; Band; Chr; ChrhWkr; CncrtBnd; HonRl; Orch; YthFlsp; Ftbl; IMSpt; Univ; Law.

WHITE, David L; Miller HS; Bols D Arc, MO; Band; ChrhWkr; CncrtBnd; HonRl; TreasNHS; Pres4-H; FFA; SpnCl; MthCl; 4-HAwd; Coll; Ministry.

WHITE, David T; Lyons Township HS; La Grange, IL; Chr; ChrhWkr; HonRl; SchMus; SchPl; Northwestern Univ; Music.

WHITE, Dawn R; Urbana HS; Urbana, IL; 21/428 HonRl; NatlMeritSF; SctActv; Trk; Univ Il; Metallurgical Engr.

WHITE, Deanna A; Yale HS; Goodells, MI; 12/150 PresFrshCls; PresSophCls; HonRl; NatlMeritSF; StuCncl; 4-H; SpnCl; Chrldr; GAA; PPFtbl; College; Physical Thera.

WHITE, Debra; Southeast Polk Sr HS; Altoona, IA; 51/218 Chrs; ChrhWkr; HonRl; HospAde; JA; SctActv; 4-H; FNA; 4-HAwd; Marshalltown School Of Nursing; Nurse.

WHITE, Debra S; Staunton HS; Brazil, IN; 4/61 Band; DrmMjrt; HonRl; ModUN; NHS; StuCncl; Twrl; Yrbk; FHA;.

WHITE, Denise E; Ottawa Township HS; Ottawa, IL; 18/450 SecJrCls; Chr; HonRl; NHS; NatlThespSoc; PresYthFlsp; SciCl; Illinois State Univ; Biology.

WHITE, Dennis D; Ankeny HS; Ankeny, IA; 37/234 Band; CncrtBnd; HonRl; JrNHS; MrchBnd; Bsbl; LetterWrstlng; CchngActv; Trade School; Auto Body Repair.

WHITE, Donna L; Waukegan East HS; Waukegan, IL; 12/861 Band; Chr; PresJrNHS; SecNHS; NatlMeritCmnd; PresNatlThespSoc; SchMus; SchPl; SchPpr; LetterSwmmng; GAA; Northwestern Univ; Radio.

WHITE, Elaine G; Stratford Community HS; Stratford, IA; SecJrCls; Chrs; ChrhWkr; HonRl; OffAde; Twrl; RptrSchPpr; EdSchPpr; FTA; GerCl; Community Coll; Dental Asst.

WHITE, Evelyn; George Washington HS; Indianapolis, IN; Chr; ChrhWkr; HonRl; PresNHS; NatlMeritSF; OffAde; StuCncl; College; Math.

WHITE, Florence A; William J Bogan HS; Chicago, IL; 19/704 HonRl; NHS; SchPl; SctActv; TchrAde; Yrbk; FDA; SpnCl; MthCl; SciCl; St Xavier College; Physician.

WHITE, Frank X; North Shore County Day HS; Wilmette, IL; OffAde; PolWkr; SchAde; Bsbl; Bsktbl; LetterSocr; LetterTennis; CchngActv; IMSpt; College; Professional.

WHITE, Garret W; Waverly HS; Lansing, MI; Band; HonRl; MrchBnd; NHS; PepBnd; SchMus; TchrAde; GerCl; Michigan St Univ; Science Field.

WHITE, Gary L; Thornapple Kellogg HS; Middleville, MI; HonRl; NHS; StuCncl; LatCl; MthCl; PpCl; CaptBsktbl; CaptFtbl; Trk; College; Mathmatics.

WHITE, Gary R; Roncalli HS; Manitowoc, WI; PresAFS; HonRl; SchPl; StuCncl; Secondary Ed Journalism.

WHITE, Gary W; North Decatur HS; St Paul, IN; 1/83 Band; NHS; PepBnd; RptrSchPpr; 4-H; FFA; KeyCl; LetterTrk; Wrstlng; KiwanAwd; College.

WHITE, Glenn R; Roncalli HS; Manitowoc, WI; SecJrCls; ChrhWkr; HonRl; KeyCl; LetterBsktbl; LetterFtbl; EldAwd; Uw Eau Claire; Lawyer.

WHITE, Harold E; Millington HS; Millington, MI; HonRl; SchPl; SctActv; TchrAde; 4-H; LetterBsbl; Bsktbl; CaptFtbl; LetterTrk; CaptWrstlng; College; Professional.

WHITE, Janice M; North Putnam HS; Greencastle, IN; 17/140 Band; Chrs; HonRl; NatlFornLg; NHS; NatlThespSoc; SecYrbk; PresFHA; PresSpnCl; SecMthCl; Secretary.

WHITE, Jeffrey R; Lindblom Tech HS; Chicago, IL; 86/700 SchMus; TchrAde; SpnCl; Northwestern Ill Univ; Dentist.

WHITE, Joan L; Mother Mc Auley HS; Evergreen Pk, IL; 25/480 Chrs; ChrhWkr; HonRl; Univ Of Ill; Nursing.

WHITE, Jody L; East Richland HS; Olney, IL; ALBoysSt; ChrhWkr; CmntyWkr; RedCrAde; LetterBsbl; LetterBsktbl; LetterFtbl; LetterTrk; CchngActv; CitAwd; Undecided.

WHITE, Joseph M; West Plains HS; West Plains, MO; SctActv; 4-H; VPFBLA; Ftbl; Trk; IMSpt; University.

WHITE, Joy A; Santa Fe Trail HS; Overbrook, KS; Chr; HonRl; RptrYrbk; Kaw Vly Vo Tech Schl; Computer Programming.

WHITE, Joyce A; Canistota Public HS; Canistota, SD; 9/21 Band; Chrs; CncrtBnd; HonRl; LbryAde; MrchBnd; OffAde; PepBnd; SchAde; SchPl; Sd State Univ; Physical Educ.

WHITE, Karen; Jackson HS; Jackson, MI; SecSophCls; DrlTm; HonRl; StuGov; RptrYrbk; PPFtbl; JCAwd; College; Nurse.

WHITE, Kathryn M; Melvern HS; Melvern, KS; Band; DrlTm; HonRl; OffAde; SchPl; PpCl; Bsbl; Bsktbl; Trk; Emporia St College.

WHITE, Kathy M; Highland Public HS; Highland, WI; PresSophCls; Chr; Chrl; Chrs; DrmMjrt; HonRl; Mdrgl; SchMus; SchPl; UNYO; YthFlsp; FHA; Bsktbl; Trk; College.

WHITE, Keith E; Brown County HS; Morgantown, IN; 1/206 TrsJrCls; ChrhWkr; HonRl; SchMus; LatCl; SpnCl; MthCl; Ftbl; Wrstlng; Purdue Univ; Dentistry.

WHITE, Kevin L; Richmond Burton Comm HS; Richmond, IL; HonRl; Trade School; Truck Driver.

WHITE, Kimberly J; Grand Island HS; Grand Island, NE; DrlTm; HonRl; NatlThespSoc; TchrAde; YthFlsp; FrCl; PpCl; Chrldr; IMSpt; PresAwd; College; Pe.

WHITE, Laine E; Jac Cen Del HS; Osgood, IN; PresSrCls; HonRl; NHS; StuCncl; TchrAde; LetterTrk; Air Force; Finance.

WHITE, Larry; Lc Mohr HS; South Haven, MI; 49/217 Aud/Vis; Chr; Chrl; Chrs; HonRl; MrchBnd; SchMus; SchPl; StuGov; FNA; Kslsmozoo Valley College; Registered Nurse.

WHITE, Laurel A; Hastings HS; Hastings, MI; Chrl; ChrhWkr; HonRl; HospAde; NHS; NatlThespSoc; SchPl; StuCncl; Aquinas Coll; Music.

WHITE, Laurel S; Pella Communtiy; Pella, IA; 4/113 PresBand; NHS; PolWkr; Quill&Scroll; TreasYthFlsp; RptrYrbk; LetterBsktbl; CaptChrldr; College; Business.

WHITE, Linda M; St Josephs Academy; Kirkwood, MO; 3/129 Chrs; ChrhWkr; HonRl; JrNHS; NHS; StuCncl; StuGov; FrCl; MthCl; De Paul University; Professional.

WHITE, Lynn M; St Marys HS; Independence, MO; HospAde; SchMus; SchPl; PpCl; College; Dental Hygienist.

WHITE, Mary E; Trico HS; Murphysboro, IL; Chrs; HonRl; 4-H; FBLA; FHA; PpCl; 4-HAwd; J A Logan; Cpa.

WHITE, Nancy S; Sycamore HS; Sycamore, IL; 24/226 Chr; Chrs; HonRl; FrCl; LetterTrk; Chrldr; GAA; Univ; Ecducation.

WHITE, Neil P; Griffin HS; Springfield, IL; CncrtBnd; HonRl; MrchBnd; NHS; PepBnd; SchMus; SchPl; StuCncl; SchPpr; Indiana Univ; Musician.

WHITE, Noel W; Urbandale HS; Urbandale, IA; HonRl; PolWkr; Bsbl; CaptFtbl; Trk; College; General Business.

WHITE, Patricia A; Morgan Park HS; Chicago, IL; HstFrshCls; HstSophCls; HstJrCls; HstSrCls; DrlTm; MrchBnd; OffAde; SchAde; StuCncl; TchrAde; College; Physical Education.

WHITE, Patrick; Berkeley Senior Hs; Berkely, MO; PresSrCls; HonRl; NHS; NatlMeritSF; SchMus; SchPl; StuCncl; CivCl; PpCl; GovHonPrgAwd; College ; Acting Or Commercial Art.

WHITE, Rebecca; Campbell HS; Campbell, MO; 1/78 HonRl; FHA; Nursing Sch.

WHITE, Regina D; Morton HS; Hammond, IN; 8/492 ChrhWkr; HonRl; JrNHS; NHS; TchrAde; Secretarial.

WHITE, Reginald D; Beaumont HS; St Louis, MO; ChrhWkr; CmntyWkr; HonRl; SchAde; StuCncl; StuGov; Bsbl; Ftbl; Socr; Trk; St Louis U; Medical Record Admin.

WHITE, Renae M; Lindblom Tech HS; Chicago, IL; 40/600 CmntyWkr; HonRl; College; Dental Lab Tech.

WHITE, Renee C; Cass Technical HS; Detroit, MI; HonRl; NatlMeritSF; Liberal Arts.

WHITE, Rene M; Prospect HS; Mt Prospect, IL; 177/614 Chr; HonRl; Univ Of Illinois; Agricultural Science.

WHITE, Robert K; Houston HS; Houston, MO; Band; CncrtBnd; HonRl; MrchBnd; PepBnd;.

WHITE, Ronald M; Chisago Lakes HS; Stacy, MN; HonRl; Yrbk; Bsbl; Bsktbl; CaptFtbl; PresAwd; Anoka Tec; Maintenance Engineer.

WHITE, Roxanne; Knoxville HS; Knoxville, IA; 3/195 Band; CncrtBnd; HonRl; MrchBnd; PepBnd; 4-H; FHA; 4-HAwd; Coll; Home Ec.

WHITE, Sandra J; Palestine HS; Palestine, IL; TrsSrCls; Chrs; CncrtBnd; HonRl; SchMus; StuCncl; FHA; Chrldr; College; Vocation.

WHITE, Scott A; Boone Valley HS; Goldfield, IA; 3/33 Band; Chr; HonRl; RedCrAde; FDA; Bsbl; Bsktbl; Ftbl; Trk; CchngActv; IMSpt; Wartburg University; Medicine.

WHITE, Sharon L; Jersey Community HS; Jerseyville, IL; 4/277 VPSophCls; CncrtBnd; CaptDrlTm; HonRl; LitMag; NHS; StuGov; SecMthCl; Trk; GAA; College; Lawyer.

WHITE, Sheryl A; Lutheran West HS; Inkster, MI; Chr; HonRl; JA; JrNHS; LbryAde; NHS; OffAde; SchAde; Bsbl; CitAwd; Bus School; Secretary.

WHITE, Steven B; Southwest HS; St Louis, MO; Chrs; OffAde; Bsbl; Ftbl; Trk; CchngActv; IMSpt; College; Professnl.

WHITE, Steven P; Marquette Sr HS; Marquette, MI; ALBoysSt; Ftbl; Trk; Wrstlng; IMSpt; Northern Mi U; Law.

WHITE, Sue J; Senior HS; Beaver Dam, WI; SpnCl; Bsktbl; Trk; GAA; College.

WHITE, Susan L; Hillsboro HS; Irving, IL; 26/179 Band; ChrhWkr; CncrtBnd; HonRl; HospAde; MrchBnd; Pres4-H; SpnCl; SciCl; TreasGAA; 4-HAwd; Southern Il Univ; Nursing.

WHITE, Tamara L; Kenwood HS; Chicago, IL; Chr; ChrhWkr; HonRl; HospAde; StuCncl; RptrSchPpr; Chrldr; GAA; College; Professional.

WHITE, Tammy R; La Salle HS; Cedar Rapids, IA; 16/150 Chrs; HonRl; HospAde; OffAde; SctActv; SpnCl; College; Social Work.

WHITE, Tanya A; Crispus Attucks HS; Indianapolis, IN; 10/245 SecJrCls; ALAGirlsSt; ChrhWkr; HonRl; NHS; Orch; PresStuCncl; EngCl; SciCl; Trk; CaptChrldr; GAA; KiwanAwd; Univ Of Cincinnati; Chemical Engineering.

WHITE, Teresa A; Nauvoo Colusa HS; Adrian, IL; ChrhWkr; CmntyWkr; HonRl; JA; MrchBnd; SchPl; StuCncl; 4-H; PresFHA; 4-HAwd; Business School; Vocation.

WHITE, Terry L; Centerville HS; Centerville, IA; 8/117 HonRl; NHS; RptrYrbk; EdSchPpr; Bsktbl; University.

WHITE, Theresa L; North County HS; Bonne Terre, MO; ChrhWkr; HonRl; HospAde; SchPl; FBLA; FHA; FTA; University; Missionary.

WHITE, Timothy L; Garden County HS; Oshkosh, NE; VPFrshCls; SecSophCls; ChrhWkr; HonRl; LetterBsktbl; LetterFtbl; LetterTrk; College; Professional.

WHITE, Udell; Hales Franciscan; Chicago, IL; 5/100 Chr; ChrhWkr; CmntyWkr; HonRl; NatlMeritCmnd; RptrYrbk; GerCl; PpCl; Eastern I U; Business.

WHITE, Udell; Hales Franciscan HS; Chicago, IL; 6/71 ChrhWkr; CmntyWkr; HonRl; NatlMeritCmnd; RptrYrbk; PpCl; IMSpt; Quincy Coll; Sociology.

WHITE, Vicki; Rockford Senior HS; Rockford, MI; YthFlsp; PPFtbl; Grand Valley State College; Medicine.

WHITE, Walter; Peoria Heights HS; Peoria Heights, IL; Band; CncrtBnd; HonRl; MrchBnd; PepBnd; KeyCl; SpnCl; LetterBsbl; LetterBsktbl; LetterFtbl; Cllege.

WHITEAKER, Marta L; Jennings County HS; North Vernon, IN; 9/280 ChrhWkr; DrlTm; HonRl; NHS; SchPl; Michigan St Univ; Social Science.

WHITEFLEET, Todd L; Northwest HS; Jackson, MI; 32/266 Chrl; HonRl; LitMag; Mdrgl; SchMus; SchPl; StuCncl; StuGov; Yrbk; PpCl; Coll; Com Sci.

WHITEFOOT, Julie A; Sidney HS; Sidney, NE; Chrs; CmntyWkr; JrNHS; Mdrgl; SchMus; SecYthFlsp; RptrSchPpr; PpCl; Chrldr; GAA; PPFtbl; Business College; Secretary.

WHITEHEAD, Ann J; Central HS; Aberdeen, SD; SecTrsSophCls; Chr; Chrs; ChrhWkr; CncrtBnd; HonRl; MrchBnd; PepBnd; SchMus; University; Medical Tech.

WHITEHEAD, Ellen; Charles City Comm HS; Charles City, IA; 9/225 HonRl; NHS; FNA; MthCl; Univ Of Iowa; Nursing And Airforce.

WHITEHEAD, Jo; Goreville Hs; Tunnel Hill, IL; Band; Chrs; CmntyWkr; HonRl; LbryAde; RptrSchPpr; VP4-H; TreasFHA; DanFAwd; 4-HAwd;.

WHITEHEAD, Keith A; North Chicago Community HS; North Chicago, IL; 100/353 Chr; Chrs; ChrhWkr; CmntyWkr; SctActv; SpnCl; Bsbl; Ftbl; Wrstlng; IMSpt; University; Professional.

WHITEHEAD, Moira; Appleton HS West; Appleton, WI; Band; CmntyWkr; NatlMeritCmnd; SchPl; SchPpr; College; Md.

WHITEHEAD, Ron A; Cashton HS; Cashton, WI; HonRl; LetterFtbl; LetterWrstlng; Trade Sch; Voc.

WHITEHEAD, Sue E; Jefferson City HS; Jefferson City, MO; 26/533 CncrtBnd; HonRl; JrNHS; MrchBnd; NHS; Quill&Scroll; SctActv; StuCncl; Twrl; YthFlsp; U Of Mo Columbia; Journalism.

WHITEHEAD, Valarie L; High School; Maroa, IL; Chrs; HonRl; 4-H; FFA; Chrldr; DARAwd; PresAwd; Col;.

WHITEHEAD, Walton C; Edwards Sr HS; Albion, IL; ALBoysSt; NHS; StuCncl; YthFlsp; PpCl; Bsbl; Bsktbl; LetterFtbl; SARAwd; Mt Carmel Jr Col; Farming.

WHITEHILL, Dave L; Central HS; Latham, KS; 13/52 Band; ChrhWkr; HonRl; MrchBnd; StuCncl; Bsbl; Bsktbl; Ftbl; Trk; Southwestern Univ; Science.

WHITEHILL, David L; Central HS; Latham, KS; Band; CncrtBnd; HonRl; MrchBnd; PepBnd; SchPl; PresStuCncl; 4-H; FFA; LetterBsbl; CaptBsktbl; Ftbl; 4-HAwd; Kansas State Univ; Physical Ed.

WHITEIS, Diane R; Freeborn HS; Albert Lea, MN; 11/25 Chrs; HonRl; OffAde; EdYrBk; Augsburg Clg; Medicine.

WHITELEY, Julie R; Miller HS; Ash Grove, MO; HstSrCls; PresChrs; HonRl; LbryAde; OffAde; StuCncl; VPFHA; SecFTA; PpCl; SciCl; Bsbl; Smsu; Professional.

WHITEMAN, James D; Wawasee HS; Syracuse, IN; Band; Chr; CncrtBnd; HonRl; JrNHS; MrchBnd; SciCl; Bsktbl; Ftbl; Purdue; Physics.

WHITEMAN, Kelly J; Rich South HS; Matteson, IL; HonRl; NatlThespSoc; Quill&Scroll; SchPl; EdYrBk; RptrSchPpr; Indiana Univ; English.

WHITENER, Mary D; Poplar Bluff HS; Poplar Bluff, MO; 10/400 SecSophCls; SecJrCls; ChrhWkr; HonRl; Quill&Scroll; TchrAde; RptrSchPpr; EdSchPpr; MthCl; SciCl; Clge; Journalism.

WHITESELL, James R; Central HS; Elkhart, IN; SchPpr; Ftbl; College; Science.

WHITESIDE, James R; St Viator HS; Arlington Hts, IL; HonRl; PepBnd; SchPl; SptEdSchPpr; SpnCl; University; Business.

WHITESIDE, Jerry D; Aberdeen Central HS; Aberdeen, SD; PresFrshCls; Band; CmntyWkr; HonRl; SchPl; StuCncl; SchPpr; Bsktbl; Ftbl; Wrstlng; College; Law.

WHITESIDE, Patricia A; Roncalli HS; Aberdeen, SD; Band; JrNHS; NatlFornLg; NHS; NatlMeritCmnd; NatlMeritSF; Teen; Bsktbl; NCTE; College; Medicine.

WHITFIELD, Gwenda L; Rezin Orr HS; Chicago, IL; Band; Chr; CmntyWkr; CncrtBnd; Orch; RedCrAde; SchAde; SchPl; RptrYrbk; 4-H; College; Professional.

WHITFORD, Gary D; St Johns HS; St Johns, MI; Bsbl; Bsktbl; Ftbl; College; Building Trades.

WHITFORD, Merlynda; Clarissa Public HS; Clarissa, MN; HonRl; LbryAde; SchPl; SchPpr; FHA; Trade School; Vocation.

WHITING, Constance; Ritenour Sr HS; Overland, MO; HonRl; HospAde; JrNHS; NHS; StuCncl; PpCl; Chrldr; PPFtbl; Fontbonne Coll; Accountant.

WHITING, Dennis; Southwest HS; Green Bay, WI; 376/427 JA; SctActv; TchrAde; Ftbl; Trk; College; Printing.

WHITING, Eleanor B; Anna Jonesboro C HS; Anna, IL; Band; CncrtBnd; MrchBnd; PepBnd; Yrbk; SchPpr; FHA; FrCl; SecSciCl; Chrldr; College; Natural Science.

WHITING, Macauley; The Hotchkiss HS; Midland, MI; VPJrCls; VPSrCls; HonRl; NatlMeritFnl; StuGov; SciCl; LetterBsbl; IMSpt; Yale Univ; Chemistry.

WHITING, Richard; Lena HS; Oconto, WI; 5/74 ChrhWkr; HonRl; StuCncl; TchrAde; Yrbk; SchPpr; 4-H; MthCl; Tennis; Wrstlng; Tech Inst; Data Process.

WHITLATCH, Lynne M; Tower Hill HS; Tower Hill, IL; 1/32 HonRl; NHS; SecStuCncl; TreasYthFlsp; Yrbk; Pres4-H; PresFHA; PresSpnCl; Chrldr; 4-HAwd; Lincoln Christian Col; Christian Ed.

WHITLER, Jason E; Lincoln Comm HS; Lincoln, IL; 7/269 Band; Chr; CncrtBnd; HonRl; Mdrgl; MrchBnd; NatlMeritSF; PepBnd; Mich St Univ; Lawyer.

WHITLEY, Cheryl A; Hillsboro HS; Hillsboro, IL; SecJrCls; HstFrshCls; HonRl; PpCl; CaptChrldr; GAA; IMSpt; College.

WHITLEY, Sandy K; Brown County HS; Morgantown, IN; HonRl; LbryAde; NHS; SpnCl; PpCl; Broadcasting Sch; Radio.

WHITLOCK, David S; Springfield HS; Springfield, IL; Band; ChrhWkr; CmntyWkr; NatlMeritSF; PolWkr; SctActv; YthFlsp; Greenville College; Engineering.

WHITLOCK, Erin R; Holdrege Sr HS; Holdrege, NE; Chr; Chrs; ChrhWkr; HospAde; NatlThespSoc; SchMus; SchPl; YthFlsp; YthLg; RptrYrbk; University; Professional.

WHITLOCK, Kenneth W; La Salle Peru Township HS; Peru, IL; ALBoysSt; HonRl; LatCl; College; Engineer.

WHITLOW, Lee A; Our Lady Of The Lakes HS; Lake Orion, MI; 3/51 HonRl; NHS; 4-H; BauchLmbAwd; College; Veterinarian.

WHITMAN, Barbara J; Lisbon Comm HS; Lisbon, IA; Chrs; HonRl; NHS; OffAde; SchMus; SchPl; StuCncl; TchrAde; UNYO; YthFlsp; LetterBsbl; LetterTrk; CaptChrldr; College.

WHITMAN, David R; Calamus Comm HS; Grand Mound, IA; ALBoysSt; ALAGirlsSt; JCC; NHS; StuCncl; StuGov; Bsbl; LetterBsktbl; Trk; IMSpt; Trade Sch; Vocational.

WHITMAN, Theresa A; Pierce City HS; Pierce City, MO; ChrhWkr; HonRl; ModUN; PresNHS; NatlMeritSF; Pres4-H; FHA; MthCl; PpCl; PresSciCl; 4-HAwd; Univ Of Missouri; Medicine.

WHITMER, Jeffrey M; Ames Senior HS; Ames, IA; 16/396 Band; HonRl; NatlMeritSF; StuCncl; YthFlsp; Bsktbl; Ftbl; LetterTrk; Iowa State Univ; Geology.

WHITMORE, Elizabeth A; Woodlands Acad Sacred Heart; Deerfield, IL; 7/75 HospAde; NatlMeritCmnd; SchMus; SchPl; CaptChrldr; Duke Univ; Med.

WHITMORE, Elizabeth A; Woodlands Acad/sacred Heart; Deerfield, IL; 7/75 HospAde; NatlMeritCmnd; SchMus; SchPl; CaptChrldr; GAA; Duke University; Medicine.

WHITMORE, James M; Reitz Memorial HS; Evansville, IN; 80/230 SecSophCls; SecJrCls; Chrs; ChrhWkr; HonRl; PolWkr; SchMus; LetterFtbl; LetterWrstlng; U Of Il; Cpa Tax Law.

WHITMORE, Jon M; Central HS; Evansville, IN; 16/650 ChrhWkr; VPCncrtBnd; HonRl; VPMrchBnd; NHS; Orch; PepBnd; SchMus; Bsbl; CchngActv; U Of Evansville; Pharmacy.

WHITMORE, Todd; Mosinee HS; Mosinee, WI; 28/170 Band; Chrs; CncrtBnd; HonRl; Mdrgl; NHS; PepBnd; SchPl; StuCncl; Coll; English.

WHITMYRE, Lisa C; Wabash HS; Wabash, IN; Chr; HonRl; NHS; SchMus; PpCl; Chrldr; College; Music.

WHITNEY, Carol M; Irving Crown HS; Algonquin, IL; AFS; Chr; Chrs; HonRl; SchAde; SchMus; PpCl; Clge; Child Care & Development.

WHITNEY, Damon S; Sycamore Sr HS; Sycamore, IL; HonRl; SctActv; StuCncl; PpCl; Ftbl; Glf; Wrstlng; IMSpt; Trade School; Professional.

WHITNEY, Debra K; Pawnee Public HS; Pawnee City, NE; 8/35 Band; Chrs; HonRl; SchPl; StuCncl; YthFlsp; CaptBsktbl; Chrldr; VFWAwd; VoiceDemAwd; Concordia Teachers College; Speech.

WHITNEY, Karen; Kimberly Sr HS; Combined Locks, WI; 27;273 PresJrCls; ChrhWkr; HonRl; NatlFornLg; NHS; SctActv; StuCncl; StuGov; FshEdYrbk; BttyCrckrAwd; Uw Stout; Professional.

WHITNEY, Katherine A; Rudyard HS; Kincheloe Afb, MI; DrlTm; HonRl; NHS; SchAde; SctActv; StuCncl; FHA; PpCl; Chrldr; PPFtbl; Business School.

WHITNEY, Luann; Delavan HS; Delavan, MN; 3/29 SecSophCls; SecSrCls; Chr; HonRl; NHS; PepBnd; SchPl; YthFlsp; AmLegAwd; 4-HAwd; College; Teaching.

WHITNEY, Mark D; Rudyard HS; Kincheloe Afb, MI; TrsSophCls; PresJrCls; Chr; HonRl; NHS; NatlMeritCmnd; SchPl; StuCncl; FrCl; Bsktbl; U Of Mi; Medicine.

WHITNEY, Mary L; Douglass HS; Douglass, KS; VPJrCls; Band; Chr; Chrl; Chrs; ChrhWkr; RptrSchPpr; FHA; PpCl; Bsktbl; Clge; Home Ec.

WHITNEY, Melody A; Oak Park HS; Kansas City, MO; HonRl; NHS; College; Author.

WHITNEY, Michael R; Pike HS; Zinnsville, IN; Band; CncrtBnd; MrchBnd; Orch; PepBnd; SchMus; GerCl; Indiana U; Psychology.

WHITNEY, Sharon K; Draper HS; Draper, SD; VPSophCls; PresSrCls; HonRl; NHS; Orch; SchMus; SchPl; LatCl; LetterBsktbl; LetterTrk; College; Professional.

WHITNEY, Steve F; Battle Creek Central HS; Battle Creek, MI; 15/540 NHS; Coll; Mech Eng Tech.

WHITNEY, Thomas R; Grand Rapids HS; Grand Rapids, MN; AFS; Chr; CmntyWkr; HonRl; Mdrgl; Trk; CchngActv; IMSpt; Univ Of Mn; Law.

WHITNEY, Vicky L; Norton Community HS; Norton, KS; CmntyWkr; HospAde; RedCrAde; FFA; FHA; PpCl; College; Nursing.

WHITNEY, Zehavah; Harvard St George HS; Chicago, IL; 3/20 Chrs; CAP; HonRl; LbryAde; NHS; StuCncl; StuGov; TchrAde; RptrYrbk; AmLegAwd;.

WHITSELL, Judy; Maysville HS; Clarksdale, MO; 3/56 SecTrsJrCls; Band; CncrtBnd; MrchBnd; NHS; YthFlsp; PpCl; SciCl; CitAwd; Nursing.

WHITSELL, William M; Reeths Puffer HS; Muskegon, MI; 73/300 Bsbl; Trk; IMSpt; College; Business.

WHITSITT, Pamela G; Southridge HS; Huntingburg, IN; Chr; ChrhWkr; HonRl; SchMus; VPStuCncl; YthFlsp; FHA; LetterTrk; Chrldr; Univ; Phy Educ.

WHITSON, Debra A; Circle HS; Benton, KS; Band; Chr; HonRl; LbryAde; Mdrgl; PepBnd; YthFlsp; RptrYrbk; VPPpCl; IMSpt; Bus Clge.

WHITSON, Marice K; Shawnee Mission East HS; Mission, KS; Band; ChrhWkr; CmntyWkr; HonRl; HospAde; LitMag; NatlMeritSF; Orch; YthFlsp; University; Anesthesiologist.

WHITSON, Marla K; Mt Pulaski HS; Mt Pulaski, IL; 3/105 TrsJrCls; Band; CncrtBnd; HonRl; MrchBnd; NHS; Orch; Yrbk; PpCl; College; Vocation.

WHITSON, Stephan A; Coldwater HS; Coldwater, MI; SchMus; SctActv; StuGov; Bsktbl; Ftbl; LetterTennis; IMSpt; Western Michigan Univ; Business Admin.

WHITTAKER, Stanley U; Cheboygan Area HS; Cheboygan, MI; Band; CncrtBnd; HonRl; MrchBnd; PepBnd; SchAde; SctActv; TchrAde; LetterFtbl; IMSpt; Trade Schl; Professional.

WHITTAKER, Terrie L; Earlville HS; Earlville, IL; 8/45 Chrs; CncrtBnd; HonRl; Mdrgl; MrchBnd; PepBnd; SchMus; YthFlsp; Yrbk; SchPpr; Col; Music.

WHITTENBURG, James M; Harlem HS; Rockford, IL; Band; CncrtBnd; HonRl; MrchBnd; PepBnd; TchrAde; MthCl; LetterBsktbl; LetterGlf; RotaryAwd; Vocational School; Vocation.

WHITTENBURG, Nancy; Spencer HS; Spencer, IA; Aud/Vis; Band; HonRl; ModUN; NatlFornLg; NHS; Quill&Scroll; SchPl; StuCncl; Drake Univ; Broadcast Journ.

WHITTIER, Lisa M; Dakota HS; Arthur, ND; Chrs; HonRl; CtyCnl; SchPl; StuCncl; YthFlsp; FHA; CaptBsktbl; Chrldr; GAA; Univ; Biology.

WHITTLE, Jeanine; St Marys HS; St Marys, KS; PresSrCls; Chrs; ChrhWkr; CmntyWkr; HonRl; NHS; PolWkr; SctActv; YthFlsp; Browne Mackie Bus College; Admin Asst.

WHITTLE, Judy L; Shelbyville HS; Shelbyville, IN; HonRl; FTA; FrCl; GAA; PPFtbl; In Central Busi College; Secretarial.

WHITTLE, Paul O; Oak Park River Forest HS; Oak Park, IL; 32/1012 Band; CncrtBnd; HonRl; MrchBnd; NatlMeritSF; College.

WHITTON, Cheryl; Cs Mott; Warren, MI; HonRl; StuCncl; Ball State Univ; Architecy.

WHITTON, Kenneth G; Casey HS; Casey, IL; 50/98 Band; CncrtBnd; HonRl; MrchBnd; Bsbl; Ftbl; IMSpt; College; Elect Engr.

WHITWORTH, Susan V; Union HS; Beaufort, MO; 1/165 ALAGirlsSt; Chrs; ChrhWkr; HonRl; OffAde; StuCncl; EdSchPpr; FHA; FTA; MthCl; PPFtbl; BttyCrckrAwd; University; Journalism.

WHOOLEY, Mary; Regis HS; Eau Claire, WI; 17/130 Band; Chr; ChrhWkr; CncrtBnd; HonRl; OffAde; PepBnd; TchrAde; PpCl; GAA; Univ Of Wis River Falls; Elem Education.

WHORLOW, Gary L; Grand Community HS; Boxholm, IA; 3/23 PresJrCls; Band; Chrs; CncrtBnd; HonRl; MrchBnd; NHS; PepBnd; SchMus; SchPl; StuCncl; RptrYrbk; Bsbl; Bsktbl; College.

WHYBREW, Kaylene M; Switzerland County HS; Vevay, IN; 9/105 Band; ChrhWkr; HonRl; LbryAde; NHS; PolWkr; SchPl; FHA; SecFrCl; SciCl; Univ; Oral Hygiene.

WHYDE, Kimberly J; Lewistown HS; Canton, IL; 7/100 HospAde; FHA; FrCl; GAA; College.

WHYTE, Terri R; Alton Sr HS; Godfrey, IL; Chrs; ChrhWkr; NHS; NatlMeritCmnd; NatlMeritSF; OffAde; SctActv; FrCl; Harding College; English.

WIARDA, Cynthia A; Dows Community HS; Dows, IA; 8/26 PresSrCls; Chrs; HonRl; StuCncl; YthFlsp; EdSchPpr; 4-H; FHA; 4-HAwd; LionAwd; U Of Northern Ia; Jr High English.

WIATER, Michelle J; Resurrection HS; Norridge, IL; 22/265 Aud/Vis; HonRl; HospAde; LitMag; LbryAde; NHS; Quill&Scroll; RptrSchPpr; SchPpr; FNA; Rosary College; Arts.

WIBBENMEYER, David; St Vincent HS; Perryville, MO; 2/85 PresFrshCls; CncrtBnd; HonRl; NHS; SchPl; RptrYrbk; Univ Of Mo Rolla; Engineer.

WIBIRT, Jane L; Hastings HS; Hastings, MI; 13/286 ChrhWkr; HonRl; ModUN; NHS; SchPl; Central Michigan Univ; Special Ed.

WIBRIGHT, Bruce M; Round Lake Comm HS; Round Lake, IL; 1/218 VPJrCls; PresSrCls; HonRl; NHS; Quill&Scroll; EdSchPpr; SptEdSchPpr; LetterBsktbl; No Illinois Univ; Journalism.

WICHLINSKI, Lawrence J; Mendel Catholic HS; Lansing, IL; 1/171 HonRl; VPNHS; NatlMeritCmnd; StuCncl; RptrYrbk; SchPpr; IMSpt; Earlham Col; Psychology.

WICHMAN, Denise E; South Page HS; Clarinda, IA; 14/39 Band; Chr; CncrtBnd; MrchBnd; Orch; PepBnd; SchMus; FHA; PpCl; LetterBsktbl; LetterTrk; GAA; IMSpt; College; Vocation.

WICHMAN, Mary; Washington Catholic HS; Washington, IN; 1/32 VPSophCls; ALAGirlsSt; Chrs; HonRl; NHS; 4-H; PpCl;.

WICHMAN, Pamela S; Marian Cath HS; Steger, IL; 117/335 Band; CncrtBnd; HonRl; MrchBnd; PepBnd; 4-H; FrCl; PpCl; College; Medical Secretary.

WICK, Mary; St James Sr HS; St James, MN; Band; Chr; CncrtBnd; HonRl; TreasHospAde; MrchBnd; PepBnd; Quill&Scroll; TchrAde; RptrYrbk; SchPpr; FHA; GerCl; GAA; College Of St Catherine; Elementary Ed.

WICKE, Kyle K; Palisade Public HS; Palisade, NE; 4/10 Band; Chr; ChrhWkr; CncrtBnd; HonRl; MrchBnd; NHS; SchPl; StuGov; Yrbk; Univ Of Nebraska; Accountant.

WICKE, Ruth; Winnebago Luth Acad; Fond Du Lac, WI; Chr; ChrhWkr; NatlMeritFnl; NatlMeritSF; SchPpr; PpCl; Univ Of Wisconsin; Business.

WICKENHAUSER, Nancy A; Marquette HS; Godfrey, IL; 15/115 JrNHS; SecNHS; RptrYrbk; RptrSchPpr; Chrldr; Illinois State University; Medical Tech.

WICKENHEISER, Brian E; Monroe Catholic Central HS; Monroe, MI; Band; Chr; CncrtBnd; HonRl; MrchBnd; PepBnd; SchMus; SchPl; StuCncl; 4-H; Trk; IMSpt; Vandercook College; Music.

WICKER, Catherine E; Morristown HS; Shelbyville, IN; 1/76 HonRl; NHS; NatlMeritSF; SchPl; EdYrBk; LatCl; SciCl; BauchLmbAwd; Indiana Central Clge; Nursing.

WICKER, Catherine E; Morristown Jr Sr HS; Shelbyville, IN; 1/76 Chrs; ChrhWkr; HonRl; NHS; NatlMeritFnl; SchPl; EdYrBk; LatCl; SciCl; Indiana Central Univ; Nursing.

WICKER, Dawn F; Custer HS; Milwaukee, WI; RedCrAde; SchPl; GAA; CitAwd; College; Major English.

WICKERAAD, Ruth A; Willmar Sr HS; Willmar, MN; 22/368 Chr; HonRl; TchrAde; YthFlsp; 4-H; FHA; Vocational Tech School; Vocation.

WICKERSHAM, Carol A; Bradley Bourbonnais Comm HS; Bourbonnais, IL; 1/365 Chr; HonRl; Olivet Nazarene College; Music.

WICKERSHAM, John H; Madison HS; Madison Hgts, MI; 2/242 VPJrCls; HonRl; JrNHS; NHS; SctActv; RptrSchPpr; LetterFtbl; Trk; Wrstlng; IMSpt; U Of Mi; Dr.

WICKERSHEIM, Cynthia L; White Lake HS; Polar, WI; Band; Chr; Chrs; ChrhWkr; CncrtBnd; HonRl; MrchBnd; SchMus; TchrAde; 4-H;.

WICKEY, Karla J; Burr Oak HS; Burr Oak, MI; 3/35 VPSophCls; VPJrCls; VPSrCls; Band; Chrs; ChrhWkr; CncrtBnd; HonRl; JrNHS; LbryAde; GAA; College; Music Therapy.

WICKHAM, Karen; Frankfort HS; Frankfort, MI; 12/62 Band; DrmMjrt; HonRl; NHS; SchPl; StuCncl; RptrYrbk; 4-H; 4-HAwd; Michigan St Univ; Medicine Or Art.

WICKHAM, Randall C; East Richland HS; Olney, IL; 38/260 Chrs; ChrhWkr; Mdrgl; PresYthFlsp; LetterTennis; College; Mechanical Engineering.

WICKLAND, Sharon E; Lyons Twp HS; La Grange, IL; Chr; Chrs; ChrhWkr; HonRl; NatlMeritCmnd; Univ Of Ill; Art.

WICKLANDER, Suzanne M; Vine St HS; Hudson, WI; 22/220 SecTrsFrshCls; AFS; Band; Chr; ChrhWkr; HonRl; HospAde; SchMus; YthFlsp; FNA; College Of St Catherine; Music.

WICKLINE, Jack I; Hazel Park HS; Hazel Park, MI; Band; ChrhWkr; LetterCncrtBnd; HonRl; MrchBnd; SpnCl; Oakland Univ; Business Management/accountin.

WICKLUND, Kyle A; Sault Area HS; Sault Ste Marie, MI; HonRl; NHS; IMSpt; Lake Superior State Col; Computer Engineer.

WICKLUND, Thomas A; East Jackson HS; Jackson, MI; 16/119 NHS; LetterBsbl; LetterFtbl; LetterGlf; Wrstlng; Jackson Comm Clge; Draft/engr.

WICKMAN, Daniel L; West HS; Green Bay, WI; Chr; ChrhWkr; HonRl; SctActv; YthFlsp; KeyCl; Bsbl; LetterBsktbl; LetterFtbl; LetterTrk; College; Professional.

WICKMAN, Kathy A; West Delaware HS; Manchester, IA; 16/200 Band; HonRl; MrchBnd; NatlSciFnd; SchMus; SctActv; TchrAde; Yrbk; RptrSchPpr; College; Journalism.

WICKMAN, Scott A; Lyons Twp HS; Western Springs, IL; Band; CncrtBnd; HonRl; MrchBnd; Orch; Iowa State Univ; Business Admin.

WICKS, Gene E; Carman HS; Flint, MI; CncrtBnd; HonRl; MrchBnd; PepBnd; Central Michigan Univ; Medical Technology.

WICKS, Jonathan P; Montrose HS; Montrose, SD; 2/25 Band; Chrs; CncrtBnd; HonRl; MrchBnd; PepBnd; SchPl; RptrYrbk; Bsbl; Bsktbl; Sioux Falls College; Criminal Justice.

WICKS, Vonda J; Laboure HS; St Louis, MO; SecSrCls; Chrs; DrlTm; JA; SchMus; StuCncl; College; Business.

WICKSTROM, Carol I; Barrett Public HS; Barrett, MN; SecSophCls; TrsJrCls; Band; Chr; HonRl; SchPl; 4-H; FHA; Bsktbl; Ftbl; Tennis; Trk; IMSpt; Alexandria Voc & Trade; Nursing.

WICKSTROM, Cynthia J; Marquette HS; Marquette, KS; TrsJrCls; DrlTm; HonRl; NHS; SchPl; LetterTrk; Chrldr; 4-HAwd; College.

WICKSTROM, Cynthia L; Joliet Central HS; Joliet, IL; 33/590 Chr; ChrhWkr; DrlTm; HonRl; HospAde; Mdrgl; NHS; PolWkr; SchMus; SecStuCncl; GAA; DARAwd; Augustana College; Political Science.

WICKSTROM, Donna M; Harding County HS; Buffalo, SD; Chrs; CmntyWkr; HonRl; SchAde; SchPl; Yrbk; PpCl; Chrldr; College; Social Worker.

WICKSTROM, Mark S; Toivola Meadowlands HS; Meadowlands, MN; VPJrCls; HonRl; SchPl; StuCncl; StuGov; RptrYrbk; RptrSchPpr; FFA; LetterFtbl; IMSpt; PresAwd; College; Architect.

WICKUS, Scott; Central HS; La Crosse, WI; 1/507 HonRl; LitMag; NatlMeritFnl; NatlMeritSchl; SctActv; YthFlsp; SpnCl; Trk; Univ Of Wi; Electrical Engineering.

WIDDER, Edward S; Sturgeon Bay HS; Sturgeon Bay, WI; 1/126 PresJrCls; HonRl; PolWkr; StuCncl; TchrAde; SciCl; Swmmng; BauchLmbAwd; GovHonPrgAwd; U Of Wi Madison; Mechanical Engr.

WIDDIFIELD, Vicki L; Nicollet Public HS; St Peter, MN; 3/56 Chr; Chrs; HonRl; NHS; SchPl; RptrSchPpr; 4-H; FHA; 4-HAwd; Austin Comm College; Stewardess.

WIDELSKI, Blanche M; Calumet HS; Gary, IN; 31/310 TrsJrCls; ALAGirlsSt; PresDrlTm; NHS; SecStuCncl; YthFnd; TreasSciCl; VPGAA; IMSpt; PPFtbl; PresAwd; Indiana Univ Northwest; Nurse.

WIDEMAN, Charles R; Fairview HS; Fairview, MI; ChrhWkr; HonRl; NatlFornLg; LetterBsktbl; LetterTrk; College.

WIDEMAN, Deborah L; Valley Park HS; Valley Park, MO; Chr; HonRl; LbryAde; NatlThespSoc; SchPl; TchrAde; College; Social Worker.

WIDEMAN, Howard P; Fairview HS; Fairview, MI; ChrhWkr; HonRl; LetterBsktbl; LetterTrk; CchngActv; College.

WIDEMAN, Renee J; Gull Lake HS; Richland, MI; HonRl; OffAde; PolWkr; SpnCl; Trade School Or Col; Pro.

WIDGER, Sharon K; Ellington R 2 HS; Ellington, MO; 3/55 HstJrCls; Band; Chr; Chrs; ChrhWkr; CncrtBnd; HonRl; MrchBnd; SchPl; College; Vocation.

WIDHELM, Barbara S; Archbishop Bergan HS; Valley, NE; 1/4/36 Chrs; HonRl; OffAde; Yrbk; 4-H; PpCl; CaptTrk; Chrldr; DanFAwd; 4-HAwd;.

WIDI, Lawrence J; West HS; Green Bay, WI; ChrhWkr; HonRl; NHS; StuCncl; RptrSchPpr; FFA; Bsktbl; CaptGlf; CchngActv; CaptIMSpt; College; Psychology.

WIDICUS, Nancy J; Lebanon Community HS; Trenton, IL; 9/9 HonRl; SecNHS; SchPl; TchrAde; RptrSchPpr; Pres4-H; SecFSA; PpCl; SecSciCl; 4-HAwd; College; Biology.

WIDMER, Mary E; North HS; Evansville, IN; 36/440 ChrhWkr; HonRl; JA; NHS; PolWkr; Quill&Scroll; StuCncl; EdYrBk; SchPpr; GAA; Indiana Univ; Journalism.

WIDSOM, Brenda F; Atlanta C 3 HS; Macon, MO; SecSophCls; Chrs; HonRl; NHS; StuCncl; FHA; Chrldr; Ne Mo Univ; Veterinarian.

WIDSTROM, Bradley J; Guilford HS; Rockford, IL; ChrhWkr; HonRl; Trk; CchngActv; Trinity College; Christian Ed.

WIDSTROM, Denise M; Jefferson HS; Alexandria, MN; 21/340 AFS; HonRl; NHS; TchrAde; RptrSchPpr; CivCl; MthCl; Moorhead St Coll; Medical Technology.

WIEBENGA, Cheryl S; Fulton HS; Fulton, IL; 27/123 AFS; Band; CncrtBnd; HonRl; MrchBnd; NatlThespSoc; PepBnd; SchPl; Trade School; Cosmetology.

WIEBENGA, Janet L; Morrison Comm HS; Morrison, IL; 7/112 HonRl; YthFlsp; FTA; College; Elem Education.

WIEBENGA, Joel; Northern Michigan Christ HS; Mc Bain, MI; ChrhWkr; CmntyWkr; HonRl; SchPl; SctActv; RptrYrbk; RptrSchPpr; IMSpt; Electronics Technician.

WIEBER, Dean; Cathedral HS; St Cloud, MN; 23/153 CmntyWkr; NatlFornLg; NHS; RedCrAde; IMSpt; St Cloud St Coll; Economics.

WIEBERG, Dale V; Fatima HS; Westphalia, MO; 10/124 Band; CncrtBnd; HonRl; MrchBnd; FBLA; LetterBsktbl; LetterTrk; Central Missouri State; Computer Science.

WIEBERS, Amy S; Lanark HS; Lanark, IL; 8/54 PresFrshCls; CncrtBnd; HonRl; Mdrgl; VPStuCncl; Yrbk; PresSpnCl; GAA; Northern Illinois University.

WIEBKE, Gale J; Caledonia Public HS; Caledonia, MN; Band; Chrs; DrlTm; HonRl; MrchBnd; NHS; StuCncl; Chrldr; IMSpt; Coll; Major Study.

WIEBOLD, Patricia A; Hlv Comm HS; Ladora, IA; 14/66 Chrs; DrlTm; HonRl; 4-H; FTA; PpCl; IMSpt; 4-HAwd; St Lures School Of Nursing; Lpn.

WIEBOLD, Paula J; Harding HS; St Paul, MN; 3/750 AFS; Band; ChrhWkr; CncrtBnd; HonRl; NHS; NatlMeritCmnd; PepBnd; SpnCl; SciCl; University Of Minnesota; Pharmacy.

WIECHMANN, Darilyn; Lutheran HS; New Germany, MN; CmntyWkr; PolWkr; StuCncl; 4-H; FTA; PpCl; Bsktbl; PPFtbl; Bethany Lutheran College.

WIECKI, Richard; J F K Prep HS; Menasha, WI; Chr; University; Theology.

WIECZOREK, Cynthia R; Mt Vernon HS; Mt Vernon, SD; VPSrCls; Band; SecChrs; HonRl; VPNHS; StuCncl; RptrSchPpr; SpnCl; PpCl; BttyCrckrAwd; Mid America Nazarene Col; Medicine.

WIECZOREK, Joel; St Laurence HS; Chicago, IL; 38/389 HonRl; LatCl; Bsbl; Swmmng; Trk; North Central College; Dentistry.

WIECZOREK, Linda M; Pinckney HS; Whitmore Lake, MI; 23/170 Band; Chr; CncrtBnd; HonRl; HospAde; MrchBnd; NHS; TreasSchPpr; SpnCl; IMSpt; Michigan Tech Univ; Geology.

WIEDEMAN, Michelle E; East Central HS; Sunman, IN; SecFrshCls; CncrtBnd; DrlTm; MrchBnd; SchPl; StuCncl; PpCl; Chrldr; GAA; College; Dental Hygienist.

WIEDEMAN, Susie E; Bishop Miege HS; Shawnee Msn, KS; DrlTm; HonRl; StuCncl; PpCl; CchngActv; IMSpt; PPFtbl; Kansas Univ; Professional.

WIEDEMEIER, Mary A; Crivitz HS; Porterfield, WI; 5/69 SecSophCls; SecJrCls; VPSrCls; Band; HonRl; NatlFornLg; NHS; StuCncl; EdYrBk; Univ Of Wisconsin; Home Ecnomics.

WIEDER, Frank P; Washington HS; Germantown, WI; 12/239 ALAGirlsSt; NHS; MthCl; Ftbl; LetterWrstlng; Coll; Chem.

WIEDERHOLT, Barbara A; Heelan HS; Sioux City, IA; 11/247 Chr; Chrs; HonRl; HospAde; NHS; SchMus; SctActv; StuCncl; TchrAde; SpnCl; PpCl; Tennis; PPFtbl; College; Science.

WIEDMAIER, Robert F; Troy HS; Atchison, KS; ALBoysSt; HonRl; NHS; StuGov; Yrbk; GerCl; Trade School; Commercial Art.

WIEDMANN, Jeniece M; Martensdale St Marys HS; Norwald, IA; VPFrshCls; TrsSophCls; TrsJrCls; HonRl; NHS; RptrYrbk; Yrbk; PpCl; Bsktbl; Trk; Trade Sch; Vocation.

WIEDMANN, Lynn L; Gregory HS; Dixon, SD; ALAGirlsSt; Chrs; LbryAde; Quill&Scroll; RptrSchPpr; FBLA; FHA; College.

WIEDMEYER, Rachell A; Slinger HS; West Bend, WI; CmntyWkr; HonRl; HospAde; FHA; SpnCl; LetterTrk; LetterChrldr; GAA; PresAwd; Univ Of Minnesota; Commercial Art.

WIEDOW, James L; D C Everest Sr HS; Rothschild, WI; Band; DrmBgl; MrchBnd; Orch; PepBnd; LetterFtbl; CaptTrk; GAA; IMSpt; RotaryAwd; College; Mechanical Engineer.

WIEDRICH, Glenda; Stanton Public HS; Stanton, ND; 8/16 Band; Chr; ChrhWkr; CncrtBnd; HonRl; MrchBnd; PepBnd; SchPl; RptrYrbk; BttyCrckrAwd; R D Hairstyling Col; Hairstyling.

WIEDRICH, William W; Sault Area HS; Sault Ste Marie, MI; 1/360 VPSrCls; CncrtBnd; MrchBnd; Quill&Scroll; EdSchPpr; Bsktbl; IMSpt; Michigan St Univ; Journalism.

WIEDRICK, Cindie R; Aberdeen Central HS; Aberdeen, SD; Chr; DrlTm; HonRl; Mdrgl; PpCl; Prestentation Clg; Nurse.

WIEGAND, Catherine A; Woodlands Academy; Lake Forest, IL; 1/75 StuCncl; RptrSchPpr; EdSchPpr; SchPpr; College; Journalism.

WIEGAND, Lynnette M; Petersburg Public HS; Petersburg, NE; 2/25 VPJrCls; Band; Chrs; CncrtBnd; HonRl; PepBnd; SchPl; EdYrBk; SciCl; Chrldr;.

WIEGAND, Rebecca L; Bellevue Comm HS; Battle Creek, MI; Band; CncrtBnd; HonRl; MrchBnd; NHS; PepBnd; SecStuCncl; TchrAde; SchPpr;.

WIEGAND, Sheryl A; Aquinas HS; Fort Madison, IA; Band; CncrtBnd; MrchBnd; PepBnd; RptrYrbk; Tech/voc; Inhilation Therapy.

WIEGAND, Timothy F; Marquette HS; Michigan City, IN; PresJrCls; HonRl; NHS; SchMus; StuCncl; Bsktbl; LetterTrk; AmLegAwd;.

WIEGMANN, Loreen M; St Francis Academy; Joliet, IL; 33/178 Chrs; ChrhWkr; HonRl; NHS; 4-H; GerCl; College; Day Care.

WIELAGE, Jill D; Stephen Hempstead Sr HS; Dubuque, IA; 7/455 HonRl; NHS; PolWkr; StuGov; 4-H; FrCl; PpCl; Chrldr; IMSpt; BttyCrckrAwd; Univ Of No Iowa; Accounting.

WIELAND, Kathleen Ann; Central Catholic HS; Bloomington, IL; 3/100 PresFrshCls; Chrs; HonRl; NHS; SchMus; StuCncl; FrCl; PpCl; Tennis; College; Medicine.

WIELAND, Kim M; Beloit Catholic HS; Beloit, WI; VPFrshCls; Chr; DrlTm; HonRl; StuCncl; StuGov; RptrSchPpr; 4-H; SpnCl; Bsktbl; Clg; Biologist.

WIELAND, Martha; Jersey Community HS; Dow, IL; Band; ChrhWkr; CmntyWkr; CncrtBnd; HonRl; HospAde; MrchBnd; NHS; PepBnd; SpnCl; Us Army; Finance.

WIELAND, Paula K; Marshall HS; Marshall, IL; 43/115 Band; CncrtBnd; JA; MrchBnd; PepBnd; Pres4-H; FHA; FSA; SciCl; 4-HAwd; JAAwd; Business School.

WIELAND, Tamara M; Charlevoix HS; Charlevoix, MI; 25/147 MrchBnd; SchPl; StuGov; PresLatCl; GAA; 4-HAwd; CitAwd; Spring Arbor College; Biology.

WIELAND, Victor R; Luverne Public HS; Dazey, ND; 2/7 TrsSrCls; Band; Chrs; CncrtBnd; DrlTm; MrchBnd; LetterBsbl; LetterBsktbl; LetterTrk; 4-HAwd; Lake Region Jr Coll; Vocation.

WIELE, Diane S; West Liberty HS; West Liberty, IA; Band; Chr; Chrs; ChrhWkr; CncrtBnd; DrmMjrt; HonRl; MrchBnd; NHS; PepBnd; SchMus; Bsktbl; LetterTrk; Mt Mercy College; Nursing.

WIELGAT, Michael W; St Florian HS; Detroit, MI; 16/127 HonRl; JA; NHS; SchMus; SpnCl; MthCl; JAAwd; Wayne State U; Medical.

WIELT, Tammela J; Mt Vernon Twp HS; Bluford, IL; ChrhWkr; CmntyWkr; HonRl; NHS; OffAde; Quill&Scroll; TchrAde; YthFlsp; Yrbk; SchPpr; SpnCl; Siu; Journalism.

WIEMANN, Tom J; Howells Public HS; Howells, NE; TrsSophCls; SecJrCls; Band; CncrtBnd; HonRl; MrchBnd; PepBnd; RptrSchPpr;.

WIEMER, Denise A; Centennial HS; Utica, NE; Band; CncrtBnd; MrchBnd; NHS; PepBnd; SchPl; FTA; MthCl; Nebraska Wesleyan Univ; Special Education.

WIEMER, Eugene L; Centennial HS; Waco, NE; NHS; YthFlsp; PpCl; LetterWrstlng; Trade School; Vocation.

WIEMER, Sherry J; Centennial HS; Waco, NE; 11/58 Chrs; NHS; YthFlsp; Business School; Secretarial.

WIENBERG, Linda; Concordia HS; Concordia, MO; SecSrCls; Chrs; HonRl; HospAde; Quill&Scroll; SchMus; SchPl; EdYrBk; Trk; PresAwd; College; Nursing.

WIENBERG, Linda S; Concordia HS; Concordia, MO; SecSrCls; HonRl; NatlThespSoc; Quill&Scroll; SchMus; SchPl; EdYrBk; FHA; PpCl; PresAwd; College; Nursing Rn.

WIENEKE, Melinda R; Morton HS; Morton, IL; SecTrsJrCls; StuCncl; RptrYrbk; PpCl; Chrldr; GAA; IMSpt; PPFtbl; Business Sch; Court Reporting.

WIENER, Drusilla A; Rensselaer Central HS; Rensselaer, IN; 14/156 CncrtBnd; HonRl; MrchBnd; NHS; PepBnd; StuCncl; 4-H; Bsbl; Bsktbl; GAA; Ball Univ; Home Ec.

WIENER, Scott A; Shorewood HS; Shorewood, WI; VPSophCls; VPJrCls; HonRl; NatlMeritSF; SchPl; StuGov; RptrSchPpr; Bsbl; IMSpt; U Of Wisc Madison; Bioengineering.

WIENHOLTS, Rita J; Clay HS; South Bend, IN; HonRl; HospAde; NHS; FrCl; Memorial Sch; Nursing.

WIENKE, Lynn A; Warren HS; Gurnee, IL; Chrs; HonRl; OffAde; SchAde; TchrAde; College; Dental Hygienist.

WIENS, Emery F; Hillsboro HS; Hillsboro, KS; 7/70 TrsSrCls; Band; PepBnd; GerCl; Tennis; BauchLmbAwd; Tobor Coll; Math.

WIENS, Joni D; Marion HS; Marion, KS; ALAGirlsSt; SecBand; HonRl; MrchBnd; 4-H; PresFHA; GerCl; SecPpCl; Bsktbl; Trk; Butler Community College.

WIER, Steven R; Cudahy Sr HS; Cudahy, WI; HonRl; College; Chemist.

WIERDA, Kevin J; Mona Shores HS; Muskegon, MI; Coll; Accountant.

WIERENGA, Karen S; Unity Chr HS; Jenison, MI; Band; CncrtBnd; HonRl; SchPl; Socr; Trk; Clg.

WIERENGA, Terrie L; Central Decatur Comm HS; Weldon, IA; 1/58 Band; Chr; Chrs; CmntyWkr; CncrtBnd; HonRl; MrchBnd; NatlMeritCmnd; Orch; PepBnd; Bsktbl; Iowa State Univ; Vet.

WIERING, Ron J; Tyler Public HS; Tyler, MN; PresSrCls; StuCncl; VPFFA; LetterBsktbl; CaptFtbl; LetterTrk; CitAwd; College; Professional.

WIERMAN, Cheryl J; Dwight D Eisenhower HS; Blue Island, IL; 1/700 CncrtBnd; HospAde; MrchBnd; PresNHS; NatlMeritCmnd; Orch; PepBnd; PresFTA; GerCl; MthCl; Illinois Wesleyan Univ; Music.

WIERSBECK, La Vonne E; John Marshall HS; Rochester, MN; 84/562 Band; ChrhWkr; CncrtBnd; MrchBnd; NHS; Orch; PepBnd; College; Professional.

WIERSEMA, Luanne; Marseilles HS; Marseilles, IL; VPJrCls; ChrhWkr; HonRl; NHS; NatlThespSoc; SchMus; SchPl; StuGov; YthFlsp; RptrYrbk; RptrSchPpr; LetterBsktbl; LetterSocr; CaptChrldr; Loyola University; Dental Hygiene.

WIERSMA, Donna L; Armour HS; Armour, SD; Band; Chrs; CncrtBnd; HonRl; MrchBnd; PepBnd; SchMus; TchrAde; Yrbk; FHA; Marriage.

WIERSMA, Mark S; Allendale Public HS; Allendale, MI; TrsFrshCls; HonRl; SchPl; StuCncl; StuGov; GerCl; MthCl; CaptBsbl; CaptBsktbl; CaptFtbl; CitAwd; College; Science.

WIERSMA, Polly A; Harvard HS; Harvard, IL; AFS; Band; ChrhWkr; HonRl; Orch; FTA; GerCl; PpCl; Chrldr; IMSpt;.

WIERSMA, Steven E; Mitchell Sr HS; Mitchell, SD; FrCl; Dakota Weslyan Univ; English.

WIERTELAK, Eric P; Geo Washington HS; Chicago, IL; HonRl; IntrClCncl; SchAde; SchPl; StuGov; TchrAde; EdSchPpr; LatCl; University; Accounting.

WIERZBICKI, Carolyn A; New Haven HS; New Haven, MI; SecSophCls; Band; ChrhWkr; CncrtBnd; DrmMjrt; HonRl; JA; MrchBnd; PepBnd; SctActv; Yrbk; College.

WIERZBICKI, Kevin W; White Pine HS; White Pine, MI; 9/40 ALBoysSt; HonRl; Yrbk; Trade; Broadcast Prod.

WIERZBINSKI, Janet; Marian HS; Owatonna, MN; TrsJrCls; Chrs; DrlTm; HonRl; NHS; SchMus; TchrAde; RptrYrbk; RptrSchPpr; LatCl; College Of St Teresa; Music Therapy.

WIESDA, Jon; Holland Christian HS; Holland, MI; Band; HonRl; MrchBnd; SchPl; SpnCl; Tennis; IMSpt; Farris State Col; Accountant.

WIESE, Cameron; Ryan HS; Omaha, NE; ChrhWkr; CmntyWkr; Trk; IMSpt; Univ Of Nebrska; Undecided.

WIESE, Carolyn M; West Point Public HS; West Point, NE; SecJrCls; SecSrCls; Chr; HonRl; StuCncl; TchrAde; EdYrBk; RptrSchPpr; FHA; PpCl; Midland College; Nurse.

WIESE, Chris M; Bishop Du Bourg HS; St Louis, MO; 4/500 CmntyWkr; HonRl; NHS; RptrYrbk; SchPpr; Trk; PPFtbl; University; Professional Botanist.

WIESE, David S; Manning Comm HS; Manning, IA; ALBoysSt; ChrhWkr; CncrtBnd; StuCncl; TchrAde; YthFlsp; FFA; CaptFtbl; ChmbCommrsAwd; 4-HAwd; Iowa State; Agricultural Business.

WIESE, Diane M; River Falls Sr HS; River Falls, WI; 4/187 SecSophCls; ALAGirlsSt; ChrhWkr; StuCncl; RptrSchPpr; GerCl; LetterBsktbl; LetterTrk; GAA; IMSpt; University; Physical Education.

WIESE, Jayne; United Community HS; Ames, IA; CncrtBnd; HonRl; NatlMeritFnl; RptrSchPpr; Bsbl; Bsktbl; PPFtbl; BttyCrckrAwd; 4-HAwd; Utah St Univ; Political Sci.

WIESE, John; Fort Calhoun HS; Fort Calhoun, NE; VPFrshCls; ALBoysSt; HonRl; NHS; SctActv; FBLA; LetterBsktbl; LetterFtbl; AmLegAwd; College; Vocation.

WIESE, Jon D; Scribner HS; Scribner, NE; 1/46 Band; HonRl; PresNHS; SchPl; Bsbl; LetterBsktbl; LetterFtbl; LetterTrk; BauchLmbAwd; EldAwd; U Of Ne.

WIESE, Marieta R; Wilber Clatonia HS; Wilber, NE; 7/34 Chr; ChrhWkr; CmntyWkr; HonRl; OffAde; StuGov; Yrbk; 4-H; Trk; CchngActv;.

WIESE, Marty J; Central City Sr HS; Central City, NE; 19/93 ALBoysSt; HonRl; NHS; NatlThespSoc; SchPl; SctActv; StuCncl; Bsktbl; Ftbl; Trk; U Of Neb; Psych.

WIESE, Nancy A; River Falls HS; River Falls, WI; ALAGirlsSt; NHS; College; Business.

WIESE, Paul; Marquette HS; Michigan City, IN; TrsFrshCls; HonRl; NHS; SchMus; StuCncl; AmLegAwd; College; Professional.

WIESE, Terri A; Howells Public HS; Howells, NE; VPJrCls; Chr; HonRl; LbryAde; SchPl; StuCncl; StuGov; TchrAde; PpCl; LetterTrk; Trade School; Nurse.

WIESEHAN, Martin D; Metamora Twp HS; East Peoria, IL; 3/171 ALBoysSt; HonRl; NHS; Univ Of Illinois; Accounting.

WIESELER, Carol L; Wynot Public HS; Wynot, NE; 10/38 VPJrCls; SecSrCls; Chrs; HonRl; MrchBnd; PepBnd; EdYrBk; PpCl; LetterTrk; Chrldr; Trade Sch; Medical Asst.

WIESELER, Jon M; Cedar Catholic HS; Hartington, NE; 3/70 PresFrshCls; PresSrCls; ALBoysSt; HonRl; NHS; SchPl; StuCncl; LetterFtbl; LetterTrk; College; Medicine.

WIESELER, Vicki; Faulkton HS; Orient, SD; Chrs; HonRl; SchPl; StuGov; SchPpr; FHA; PpCl; Tennis; IMSpt; Univ; Major Study.

WIESEMAN, Monica; Bunker Hill HS; Bunker Hill, IL; 15/80 ALAGirlsSt; HonRl; EdYrBk; Lewis Clark Comm Coll; Child Care.

WIESER, Cheryl J; Scotus Central Catholic HS; Columbus, NE; Chr; Chrs; HonRl; JA; NHS; Yrbk; RptrSchPpr; SchPpr; PpCl; LetterTrk; IMSpt; JAAwd; Briar Cliff College.

WIESER, John P; La Crescent HS; Hokah, MN; PresChr; SchMus; SchPl; PresStuCncl; PresGerCl; LetterFtbl; CitAwd; Univ Of Minnesota; Veterinarian.

WIESER, Randy D; Scotus Central Catholic HS; Columbus, NE; VPSrCls; HonRl; Ftbl; Trk; IMSpt; Trade; Air Conditioning.

WIESLER, Carol M; Evergreen Park HS; Evergreen Park, IL; 103/442 TrsJrCls; SecSrCls; HonRl; JrNHS; NHS; FHA; GerCl; GAA; IMSpt; AmLegAwd; College; Vacation.

WIESMAN, Shirley A; Stratford HS; Stratford, WI; 9/113 Band; Chrs; HonRl; MrchBnd; NHS; PepBnd; Yrbk; SecFBLA; FHA; College; Nursing.

WIESMEYER, Catherine A; Lane Technical HS; Chicago, IL; 15/1209 Band; CncrtBnd; HonRl; NHS; OffAde; TchrAde; RptrYrbk; RptrSchPpr; GAA; U Of Il; Accounting.

WIEST, Deb E; Brule HS; Brule, NE; 2/17 PresFrshCls; SecSophCls; Band; Chr; ChrhWkr; HonRl; LbryAde; NHS; PepBnd; SchMus; SchPl; StuCncl; EdYrBk; MthCl; PresPpCl; Business School; Accounting.

WIEST, Jeanne M; Adams HS; Rochester, MI; 35/370 CncrtBnd; HonRl; HospAde; MrchBnd; NHS; Orch; GerCl; LetterBsktbl; LetterTrk; LetterGAA; Oakland U; Medical Technology.

WIETBROCK, Diana L; Hanover Central HS; Cedar Lake, IN; 10/150 SecFrshCls; SecSophCls; SecJrCls; NHS; StuCncl; LetterBsktbl; LetterTrk; Chrldr; GAA; PresAwd; Business School; Court Reporter.

WIETERS, Julie D; Downers Grove HS; Downers Grove, IL; 37/840 HonRl; NHS; OffAde; PolWkr; RptrYrbk; PpCl; Chrldr; IMSpt; George Williams College; Natural Science.

WIETGREFE, Linda L; Aberdeen Central HS; Aberdeen, SD; HonRl; HospAde; SctActv; Pres4-H; FHA; GerCl; SpnCl; Bus Sch; Accountant.

WIETHOP, Eileen M; Mehlville HS; St Louis, MO; 196/526 Chrl; Chrs; ChrhWkr; CmntyWkr; HonRl; LbryAde; PolWkr; SchAde; SctActv; TchrAde; YthFlsp; SchPpr; FHA; GerCl; College; Medicine.

WIETHORN, Lisa A; E Lansing HS; E Lansing, MI; CmntyWkr; OffAde; Tennis; Trk; Nursing School; Rn.

WIFF, James; Spring Valley HS; Spring Valley, WI; 1/78 TrsJrCls; ALBoysSt; ChrhWkr; CncrtBnd; MrchBnd; NHS; PepBnd; StuCncl; SchPpr; 4-H; College; Teacher.

WIFLER, Paul R; Thorp HS; Thorp, WI; 13/76 VPJrCls; PresSrCls; HonRl; NHS; StuCncl; FBLA; LetterBsbl; LetterBsktbl; LetterTrk; IMSpt; Stevens Point U Of Wi; Business.

WIGANO, Jeffrey; Jasper HS; Jasper, IN; 7/292 HonRl; NHS; KeyCl; Wrstlng; Rose Hulman; Computer Sci.

WIGELL, Kevin W; Bradley Bourbonnais Comm HS; Bourbonnais, IL; 7/350 HonRl; NHS; NatlMeritCmnd; StuCncl; RptrYrbk; SptEdYrbk; Yrbk; GerCl; Northwestern Univ; Astronomy.

WIGEN, Roy; Spencer HS; Spencer, IA; JrNHS; SchPl; LetterBsbl; LetterBsktbl; LetterFtbl; LetterTrk;.

WIGGERS, Timothy E; Morton HS; Morton, IL; 7/287 VPSrCls; NHS; SctActv; RptrSchPpr; Ftbl; CaptTennis; IMSpt; DanFAwd; JETSAwd; Univ Il; Engineering.

WIGGINS, Christopher; Brother Rice HS; Bloomfield Hills, MI; 29/210 HonRl; NHS; Oakland Univ;.

WIGGINS, Gloria D; Houghton Lake HS; Merritt, MI; HonRl; NHS; TchrAde; PpCl; Chrldr; Northwestern Mich Coll; Med Asst.

WIGGINS, Marilyn C; Trenton HS; Trenton, MI; ChrhWkr; HonRl; LbryAde; NHS; NatlMeritSF; FTA; GAA; Kalamazoo College; Library Workscience Math.

WIGGS, David B; South Sioux City Senior HS; South Sioux City, NE; ROTC; SctActv; SpnCl; Trk; Wrstlng; AmLegAwd; JAAwd; Border Patrol Officer.

WIGHTMAN, John C; Kohler HS; Kohler, WI; 10/37 TrsJrCls; ChrhWkr; HonRl; SctActv; StuCncl; RptrYrbk; LetterBsbl; LetterBsktbl; CaptFtbl; Trk; Air Force; Electronic Engineer.

WIGTON, Mary; Rochester HS; Rochester, MI; 72/370 VPSrCls; AFS; Chr; Mdrgl; ModUN; NHS; StuCncl; GerCl; Oakland Univ.

WIKA, Lawrence A; St Patrick HS; Chicago, IL; 12/382 Chrs; HonRl; SchAde; CaptTrk; IMSpt; Univ.

WIKA, Marcella; Webster Public HS; Webster, SD; HonRl; NatlFornLg; NHS; FHA; GerCl; GAA; U; Biology.

WIKE, Diana; Kapaun Mt Carmel HS; Wichita, KS; 7/134 HonRl; HospAde; LbryAde; NHS; NatlMeritCmnd; RptrYrbk; SchPpr; LetterBsktbl; Wichita St Univ; Math, Actuary.

WIKLUND, Jeffrey C; East HS; Duluth, MN; CmntyWkr; HonRl; SchPl; TchrAde; IMSpt; College; Lawyer.

WIKNER, Steven; Johnston HS; Des Moines, IA; 10/79 ChrhWkr; HonRl; NHS; SctActv; StuCncl; 4-H; IMSpt; 4-HAwd; Iowa State Univ; Landscape Arch.

WIKOWSKY, Karen J; Tri Valley HS; Ellsworth, IL; 7/40 ALAGirlsSt; Band; Chrs; HonRl; PepBnd; SchMus; RptrSchPpr; 4-H; Chrldr; Illinois St Univ; Art.

WIKRE, Sharon K; Grand Community HS; Boxholm, IA; 4/24 ALAGirlsSt; Chrs; HonRl; NHS; SchMus; StuCncl; Twrl; RptrSchPpr; SciCl; LetterTrk; Community Coll; Secretary.

WILBERDING, Debra C; New Hampton Comm HS; Elma, IA; 14/179 HonRl; NHS; Quill&Scroll; RptrYrbk; RptrSchPpr; U Of Ia; Journalism.

WILBON, Jennifer R; Normandy HS; St Louis, MO; 175/514 Chr; ChrhWkr; HonRl; JA; NatlThespSoc; SchPl; StuCncl; RptrSchPpr; FrCl; Ne Missouri St Univ; Special Ed.

WILBOURN, James; Hanover Central HS; Cedar Lake, IN; HonRl; TchrAde; Bsktbl; Coll; Vocation.

WILBUR, Nicolyn S; Storm Lake HS; Storm Lake, IA; Chr; Chrs; LbryAde; NHS; NatlMeritSF; TchrAde; EdYrBk; FTA; GerCl; PPFtbl; College.

WILBUR, Valorie; Ainsworth HS; Flint, MI; 35/283 Band; Chr; JA; NHS; NatlThespSoc; PolWkr; StuCncl; StuGov; LionAwd; CitAwd; Univ Mi; Physical Therapy.

WILBURN, Lawana J; Delta HS; Kennett, MO; 6/28 VPJrCls; Chrs; HonRl; StuCncl; RptrYrbk; FHA; FTA; PpCl; Chrldr;.

WILCHESKI, Paula M; Divine Child HS; Dearborn Heights, MI; Chrl; CmntyWkr; HonRl; TreasJA; NHS; TchrAde; FTA; FrCl; PpCl; Chrldr; Univ Of Michigan; Accounting.

WILCKE, Brenda; East Central Hs; Miles, IA; PresSophCls; Band; Chrs; SchMus; StuCncl; YthFlsp; RptrYrbk; 4-H; LetterBsktbl; 4-HAwd; College; Phy Ed.

WILCOX, Carol J; Prairie HS; Cedar Rapids, IA; 8/178 Band; ChrhWkr; CncrtBnd; HonRl; JrNHS; MrchBnd; PepBnd; SchMus; Trk; Ozark Bible Inst; Bible.

WILCOX, Colette A; Nauvoo Colusa HS; Niota, IL; 2/53 Chrs; ChrhWkr; HonRl; MrchBnd; NatlThespSoc; SchPl; PresStuCncl; YthFlsp; Yrbk; GAA; Sterling College; Secondary Education.

WILCOX, David E; Griffith HS; Griffith, IN; 9/320 ALBoysSt; Band; Chr; ChrhWkr; NHS; NatlMeritCmnd; SchMus; SctActv; LetterFtbl; VoiceDemAwd; Purdue University; Engineering.

WILCOX, Debra; Jenison HS; Jenison, MI; 71/254 ALAGirlsSt; Chr; ChrhWkr; HonRl; Mdrgl; StuCncl; Chrldr;.

WILCOX, Edward A; Centreville HS; Nottawa, MI; 7/55 PresSrCls; Chr; ChrhWkr; NHS; SchPl; StuCncl; YthFlsp; FFA; Bsbl; BttyCrckrAwd; Col; Engineering.

WILCOX, Julie A; Wesclin HS; Trenton, IL; PresJrCls; JrNHS; NHS; YthFlsp; RptrSchPpr; GerCl; PpCl; LetterTrk; GAA; PresAwd; Univ; Phy Ed.

WILCOX, Julie M; Marshall County Central HS; Newfolden, MN; Chrs; ChrhWkr; HonRl; NHS; FHA; LetterBsktbl; LetterTrk; LetterChrldr; PPFtbl; College; Teacher.

WILCOX, Kathleen A; Immaculata HS; Detroit, MI; 25/106 University Of Michigan; Pediatrician.

WILCOX, Matthew; Arlington HS; Indanapolis, IN; 41#73#81 SciCl; Socr; IMSpt; Indiana Univ; Research Biology.

WILCOX, Rhonda L; Summersville Rii HS; Summersville, MO; PresSophCls; HonRl; SchPl; PresStuCncl; StuGov; Yrbk; SchPpr; TreasFHA; PpCl; Chrldr; College; Major Study.

WILCOX, Rose A; Bismarck Henning HS; Alvin, IL; Chrs; HonRl; SchPl; RptrSchPpr; GerCl; College; Journalist.

WILCOX, Wendy L; Clare HS; Clare, MI; 2/148 Band; ChrhWkr; HonRl; NHS; PepBnd; Twrl; YthFlsp; VPFrCl; GAA; Central Mich U; Secondary Ed.

WILCOXON, Rebecca L; Everly HS; Everly, IA; Chrs; ChrhWkr; CmntyWkr; HonRl; HospAde; Trade School; Dental Asst.

WILCOXSON, Kimberly J; Mason City HS; Mason City, IL; 9/45 ALAGirlsSt; Chrs; HonRl; LbryAde; MrchBnd; NatlThespSoc; PolWkr; SchPl; PresFHA; GAA;.

WILCZYNSKI, Cynthia M; Mount Assisi Academy; Chicago, IL; 1/158 Chr; ChrhWkr; HonRl; LitMag; College; Medicine.

WILCZYNSKI, John M; St Patrick HS; Chicago, IL; 20/456 HonRl; NHS; NatlMeritSF; PolWkr; SchMus; SchPl; SctActv; StuGov; SpnCl; College; Chemical Engineering.

WILCZYNSKI, Kathleen F; Dominican HS; Detroit, MI; PresFrshCls; HonRl; HospAde; NHS; SchMus; SchPl; StuGov; University; Medicine.

WILCZYNSKI, Robert P; Weber HS; Chicago, IL; 50/180 VPFrshCls; PresSophCls; PresJrCls; SecSrCls; HonRl; JCC; NHS; StuCncl; StuGov; Bsktbl; Ftbl; Univ Of Illinois; Law.

WILD, Cherie A; Divine Child HS; Inkster, MI; HonRl; JA; NHS; NatlThespSoc; ChmnSchMus; SchPl; EldAwd; Univ Of M Ann Arbor; Oceanography.

WILD, Debra E; Oregon Senior HS; Oregon, WI; AFS; HonRl; HospAde; Orch; Luther College; Elem Ed.

WILD, Terry; Mayville HS; Mayville, WI; 17/122 SecFrshCls; SecSophCls; SecJrCls; SecSrCls; HonRl; NHS; SptEdYrbk; Chrldr; GAA; Colombia School Of Nursing; Nurse.

WILD, Terry M; Mayville HS; Mayville, WI; 16/126 AFS; Band; Chr; NHS; Yrbk; Swmmng; LetterTennis; LetterChrldr; IMSpt; PPFtbl; College; Nursing.

WILD, William B; Thornton Fractional So HS; Lansing, IL; HonRl; NHS; StuCncl; LatCl; LetterFtbl; Trk; Wrstlng; Univ Of Ill; Veterinarian.

WILDEISEN, Lori L; South Callaway HS; Williamsburg, MO; PresFrshCls; SecSophCls; Chrs; HonRl; SchMus; StuCncl; TchrAde; SptEdYrbk; Yrbk; FBLA; FHA; Bsbl; Chrldr; GAA; College; Professional.

WILDEMAN, Dennis; Sheldon Comm HS; Sheldon, IA; 48/148 HonRl; YthFlsp; Glf; Trk; CchngActv; IMSpt; Nitc; Electronics.

WILDEMAN, Lori L; Worthington Sr HS; Bigelow, MN; PpCl; College; Professional.

WILDER, Charles J; Kennett HS; Kennett, MO; PresJrCls; ChrhWkr; HonRl; NHS; KeyCl; LetterFtbl; Chrldr; CchngActv; KiwanAwd; PresAwd; Southeast Missouri Univ; Eng Or Accounting.

WILDER, Craig A; Summerfield HS; Petersburg, MI; HonRl; Bsbl; Ftbl; Trade School; Tv & Radio.

WILDER, Dolores M; Good Counsel HS; Chicago, IL; 50/250 HonRl; NatlMeritCmnd; FrCl; Illinois Benedictine College; Medical Tech.

WILDER, Glen A; Royal Valley HS; Mayetta, KS; TchrAde; Washburn Univ; Chemistry.

WILDEY, Debra; Dekalb HS; Dekalb, IL; HonRl; StuCncl; FNA; FrCl; IMSpt; Kishwaukee Col; History.

WILDHABER, Lisa A; Fatima HS; Argyle, MO; Chr; 4-H; 4-HAwd; College; Field Wireman.

WILDING, Timothy J; Wright City HS; Wright City, MO; 2/48 TrsSophCls; ALBoysSt; HonRl; NHS; NatlMeritCmnd; SchPl; StuCncl; EdSchPpr; LetterBsktbl; CitAwd; Univ; Medicine.

WILDMAN, Arleta M; Phillipsburg HS; Phillipsburg, KS; SecTrsJrCls; ALAGirlsSt; HonRl; NHS; StuCncl; TchrAde; Yrbk; Treas4-H; PresFHA; 4-HAwd; College; Vocation.

WILDMAN, Michael C; Mundelein HS; Mundelein, IL; HonRl; NatlMeritCmnd; College; Professional.

WILDY, Rosetta; Camelot HS; Cairo, IL; 2/16 SecFrshCls; SecSrCls; Chrs; ChrhWkr; CmntyWkr; HonRl; OffAde; Quill&Scroll; SchPl; SctActv; StuCncl; RptrSchPpr; FBLA; FrCl; Shawnee College; Business.

WILE, Jill E; Paynesville HS; Paynesville, MN; 103/111 Band; Chr; ChrhWkr; CncrtBnd; HonRl; MrchBnd; NHS; OffAde; GerCl; LetterBsktbl; GAA; Ramsey Jr College; Occupational Therapy.

WILEBSKI, Nancy M; Lancaster Public HS; Lancaster, MN; 3/23 SecFrshCls; Band; Chrs; CncrtBnd; HonRl; MrchBnd; SchAde; StuCncl; Chrldr; GAA; Univ; Social Worker.

WILEN, Yvonne M; Martin Hughs HS; Buhl, MN; Chr; HonRl; FTA; College.

WILER, Robert W; Crown Point HS; Crown Point, IN; HonRl; NHS; TchrAde; Ftbl; Purdue Univ; Dentist.

WILES, Candy L; Parkwood HS; Joplin, MO; ChrhWkr; HonRl; Glf; Tennis; College; Teacher.

WILES, Daniel L; Willmar Sr HS; Willmar, MN; Band; Chr; CncrtBnd; MrchBnd; NatlFornLg; NHS; NatlMeritSF; Orch; PepBnd; PolWkr; SchMus; SchPl; FrCl; Augustana College; Music.

WILES, David L; Leavenworth HS; Ft Leavernworth, KS; Band; HonRl; MrchBnd; PepBnd; ROTC; SctActv; KeyCl; LetterTrk; IMSpt; Univ;.

WILES, Douglas D; Milan C 2 HS; Milan, MO; 24/48 VPSophCls; PresSrCls; ChrhWkr; StuCncl; SptEdSchPpr; LetterBsktbl; CaptFtbl; LetterGlf; LetterTrk; Missouri Valley College; Physical Educ.

WILES, Truman L; Willow Springs HS; Willow Springs, MO; 2/97 VPSrCls; ALBoysSt; Band; ChrhWkr; HonRl; Yrbk; RptrSchPpr; FFA; PresSciCl; Bsktbl; Univ Of Missouri; Veterinarian.

WILEY, Jenelle L; Mehlville Sr HS; St Louis, MO; Chr; ChrhWkr; HonRl; LitMag; NHS; SchPl; YthFlsp; TreasFHA; TreasSpnCl; VPSciCl; Jr College; Medicine.

WILEY, John; Oak Park & River Forest Hs; Oak Park, IL; 97/100 College; Medicine.

WILEY, Mark E; Stockbridge HS; Gregory, MI; ALBoysSt; Band; CncrtBnd; HonRl; JrNHS; MrchBnd; NHS; PepBnd; SchPl; 4-H; LatCl; Washtenaw; Mechanics.

WILEY, Melinda J; Connersville Sr HS; Connersville, IN; VPSrCls; Band; CncrtBnd; MrchBnd; PepBnd; 4-H; FTA; GerCl; GAA; IMSpt; 4-HAwd; Ball State College; Elem Educ.

WILEY, Rebecca S; Summerfield HS; Petersburg, MI; 5/69 SecFrshCls; HstSrCls; Band; HonRl; SchPl; StuCncl; 4-H; LetterBsktbl; LetterTrk; Chrldr; Valparaiso Univ In; Doctor.

WILEY, Ruth A; Marmaton Valley HS; Moran, KS; 2/57 Band; Chrs; ChrhWkr; CncrtBnd; HonRl; MrchBnd; PepBnd; FHA; LetterBsktbl; College; English.

WILEZEWSKI, Mary Lu; Resurrection HS; Chicago, IL; 34/260 HospAde; LbryAde; StuCncl; TchrAde; MthCl;.

WILEZYNSKI, Carol A; Whiteford HS; Ottawa Lake, MI; 7/83 PresSophCls; Band; CmntyWkr; HonRl; NHS; SchMus; StuCncl; EdSchPpr; LetterBsktbl; Trk; Chrldr; CchngActv; 4-HAwd; Western Michigan Univ; Physical Ed.

WILFONG, Meredith L; Central Riii HS; Esther, MO; Band; Chrs; HonRl; NHS; SctActv; FrCl; SciCl; LetterTrk; College; Pharmacist.

WILGENBUSCH, Vickie; Leo HS; Durango, IA; TrsSophCls; Chrs; HonRl; LbryAde; SchMus; TchrAde; RptrYrbk; RptrSchPpr; SpnCl; IMSpt; Coll; Vocation.

WILHELM, Ann; Jefferson HS; Alexandria, MN; 2/330 Chr; ChrhWkr; HonRl; LbryAde; NHS; TchrAde; RptrSchPpr; FTA; College Of St Benedict; Education.

WILHELM, George W; Lake Forest HS; Lake Bluff, IL; 21/371 HonRl; NHS; NatlMeritFnl; NatlMeritSchl; NatlMeritSF; Rochester Inst Of Tech; Electrical Eng.

WILHELM, Joni L; Lu Verne Comm HS; Luverne, IA; PresFrshCls; SecJrCls; Band; Chrs; CncrtBnd; HonRl; MrchBnd; StuCncl; LetterBsktbl; Trk; College.

WILHELM, Joni L; Lu Verne Comm HS; Lu Verne, IA; 1/12 PresFrshCls; VPSophCls; SecJrCls; Band; Chrs; CncrtBnd; HonRl; Mdrgl; MrchBnd; PepBnd; SchMus; StuCncl; YthFlsp; Bsktbl; College; Vocation.

WILHELM, Kathleen M; Brighton HS; Brighton, MI; 84/290 HonRl; NatlMeritSchl; StuCncl; Trk; LetterChrldr; IMSpt; PPFtbl; E Michigan St College; Liberal Arts.

WILHELM, Keith W; Preble HS; Green Bay, WI; LetterFtbl; IMSpt; College; Professional.

WILHELM, Linda; Calamus Comm HS; Calamus, IA; TrsSophCls; Band; Chrs; CncrtBnd; HonRl; PepBnd; YthFlsp; RptrYrbk; GerCl; Jr College; Secretary.

WILHELM, Margaret E; Nazareth Acad; Lagrange Park, IL; HstJrCls; HstSrCls; StuGov; GAA; Elmhurst Col; Nursing.

WILHELM, Muriel S; East Peoria Comm HS; Creve Coeur, IL; 45/420 Chr; HonRl; NHS; StuGov; FTA; FrCl; Ill State Univ; Education.

WILHELM, Nancy J; St Paul HS; Highland, IL; 5/45 ALAGirlsSt; HonRl; SchMus; StuCncl; Yrbk; KeyCl; GAA; AmLegAwd; ChmbCommrsAwd; DanFAwd; Univ Of Illinois; Physical Ed.

WILHELM, Patricia H; Lomira HS; Lomira, WI; AFS; HonRl; SchPl; RptrYrbk; SchPpr; FHA; FrCl; College; Interior Design.

WILHELM, Roseanne M; Wisconsin Heights HS; Mazomanie, WI; Band; CncrtBnd; MrchBnd; PepBnd; SchPl; 4-H; FBLA; GerCl; Trk; GAA; College; Elementary Education.

WILHELM, Susan J; Lakeland HS; La Grange, IN; AFS; FHA; PpCl; Business School.

WILHELMI, Mark L; Morris HS; Morris, IL; 10/240 VPSrCls; HonRl; NHS; PolWkr; StuGov; GerCl; Bsktbl; LetterGlf; Notre Dame Univ; Law.

WILHELMI, Terrance D; Gettysburg HS; Gettysvurg, SD; 10/64 VPJrCls; SecSrCls; ALBoysSt; HonRl; NHS; SchMus; SchPl; StuGov; Bsktbl; Trk; College.

WILHELMS, Robin R; Shannon HS; Shannon, IL; SecFrshCls; SecJrCls; Band; Chr; Chrl; Chrs; ChrhWkr; CmntyWkr; CncrtBnd; HonRl; Trk; Chrldr; Purdue Univ; Biomedical Engineering.

WILHELMUS, Robert T; Vianney HS; Crestwood, MO; 113/691 CmntyWkr; HonRl; SchAde; RptrYrbk; PpCl; Wrstlng; IMSpt; College; Dentist.

WILHELMY, Scott F; St Thomas Acad; St Paul, MN; Chrs; DrlTm; HonRl; OffAde; ROTC; StuCncl; RptrYrbk; LetterBsbl; LetterBsktbl; LetterFtbl; Clge; Md.

WILHITE, Cathy A; Williamsville HS; Sherman, IL; 2/48 VPSophCls; HonRl; HospAde; LbryAde; NHS; OffAde; SchPl; EdYrBk; FTA; Univ Of Ill; Pharmacist.

WILHITE, Jill S; South Barber HS; Hardtner, KS; Band; Chr; ChrhWkr; CncrtBnd; HonRl; SchPl; TchrAde; EdYrBk; RptrSchPpr; PpCl; Nw Okla State Univ; Teach Music.

WILIS, David L; Marion HS; Marion, WI; HonRl; Bsktbl; Ftbl; College.

WILJAMAA, David J; Central HS; Flint, MI; NHS; SchPl; Yrbk; Mott Comm College; Liberal Arts.

WILK, Andrea; Madonna Hs; Chicago, IL; 15/273 Chrs; HonRl; MthCl; GAA; Northeastern Ill U; Mathematicsteacher.

WILK, Deborah A; West Milwaukee HS; West Allis, WI; VPJrCls; HonRl; NHS; StuCncl; PpCl; Bsktbl; College Of Lettersand Science; Medical Tech.

WILKA, Suzanne M; Ogorman HS; Sioux Falls, SD; PresSophCls; PresJrCls; ChrhWkr; College.

WILKE, Charles W; Belvidere HS; Belvidere, IL; ChrhWkr; NatlThespSoc; Quill&Scroll; SchPl; YthFlsp; EdYrBk; Illinois State Univ; Biology.

WILKE, Colin M; Columbus Lakeview HS; Richland, NE; PresJrCls; HonRl; NHS; StuCncl; TchrAde; LetterTrk; AmLegAwd; OptClAwd; College; Law Enforcement.

WILKE, Curtis; Holdrege Senior HS; Holdrge, NE; 29/115 Band; CncrtBnd; HonRl; PepBnd; SctActv; CitAwd; U Of Nebraska; Stockbroker.

WILKE, Keith J; Parkers Prairie HS; Parkers Prairie, MN; 9/74 ChrhWkr; HonRl; NHS; SchPl; SchPpr; GerCl; LetterBsktbl; Alexandria Vo Tech School; Computer Prog.

WILKEN, Billy J; Benton Co Ri HS; Mora, MO; Band; CncrtBnd; HonRl; MrchBnd; NHS; NatlThespSoc; PepBnd; SchPl; VPFFA; LetterBsktbl; University; Agriculture.

WILKEN, Vicki J; Ar We Va HS; Westside, IA; 1/42 Band; ChrhWkr; HonRl; SchPl; YthFlsp; SptEdYrbk; 4-H; LetterBsktbl; Trk; CchngActv; IMSpt; 4-HAwd; Yankton College; Med Tech.

WILKENING, Annette; Appleton Public HS; Appleton, MN; 5/75 Band; DrlTm; HonRl; SchMus; RptrYrbk; Trk; BttyCrckrAwd; Winona St Univ; Rn.

WILKENING, Julie K; Hanover Central HS; Cedar Lake, IN; SecSrCls; HonRl; JrNHS; NHS; StuCncl; TchrAde; GAA;.

WILKENS, Cheryl A; Kewaskum HS; West Bend, WI; 3/180 SecJrCls; PresSrCls; AFS; HonRl; NHS; GerCl; Trk; GAA; KiwanAwd; Dr Martin Luther Clge; Elem Ed.

WILKENS, Deb K; Ada HS; Ada, MN; 16/60 Band; Chr; HonRl; 4-H; FHA; LetterBsktbl; Trk; PresGAA; 4-HAwd; PresAwd; Moorhead State; Spec Ed.

WILKENS, Janet L; Benkelman HS; Benkelman, NE; 1/43 SecTrsJrCls; HonRl; NHS; OffAde; Quill&Scroll; StuCncl; EdYrBk; EdSchPpr; 4-H; Univ Of Nebraska; Journalism.

WILKENSON, Michael; Oakville Sr HS; St Louis, MO; 167/350 Band; CncrtBnd; HonRl; MrchBnd; PepBnd; SchPl; KeyCl; Univ Se Mo State; Law Enforcement.

WILKER, Cindy; Waseca HS; Waseca, MN; Band; HonRl; MrchBnd; PepBnd; StuGov; PresFrshCls; GAA; PresAwd; Mankato State; Phy Ed.

WILKERSON, Carla J; Miller HS; Miller, MO; SecTrsFrshCls; ChrhWkr; HonRl; NHS; RptrSchPpr; FTA; SpnCl; MthCl; PpCl; Trk; Chrldr; GAA; College; Liberal Arts.

WILKERSON, Donna M; Oak Park HS; Kansas City, MO; 126/571 HonRl; SctActv; StuCncl; Maple Woods Comm College; Business.

WILKERSON, Jana S; Braymen C 4 HS; Braymen, MO; Band; CncrtBnd; HonRl; LbryAde; SecSophCls; MrchBnd; SchPl; FHA; LetterTrk; 4-HAwd; College; Pro.

WILKERSON, Roma J; R 1 North Callaway HS; Huxvasse, MO; HonRl; SchMus; SchPl; StuCncl; FHA; FrCl; PpCl; Chrldr; PPFtbl; William Woods College; Nursing.

WILKERSON, Thomas D; Granite City N HS; Granite City, IL; 41/375 Chr; Chrs; ChrhWkr; LitMag; SecSophCls; NHS; SchMus; SchPl; SctActv; Southern Ill Univ; Business.

WILKES, Loren; Walker HS; Walker, MN; VPFrshCls; PresSrCls; ALBoysSt; HonRl; StuCncl; SpnCl; Bsktbl; Ftbl; Glf; AmLegAwd; PresAwd; College.

WILKES, Yolanda C; Short Ridge HS; Indianapolis, IN; PresFrshCls; PresSrCls; Chr; ChrhWkr; HonRl; HospAde; TreasJA; PolWkr; RedCrAde; SchMus; RptrYrbk; Indiana U; Law.

WILKEY, Catherine A; Watertown Sr HS; Watertown, SD; 17/312 Band; ChrhWkr; CncrtBnd; HonRl; NHS; PolWkr; Twrl; 4-H; GAA; 4-HAwd; Augustana Col; Pre Med.

WILKINS, Ann W; Divine Savior Holy Angels HS; Wauwatosa, WI; PpCl; University; Vet.

WILKINS, Anthony E; Mendel Cath Prep HS; Chicago, IL; 9/183 PresJrCls; PresSrCls; Aud/Vis; Band; ChrhWkr; CmntyWkr; HonRl; JrNHS; NHS; StuCncl; StuGov; Ftbl; Trk; CchngActv; Northwestern; Medicine.

WILKINS, Ken; Prairie HS; Cedarrapids, IA; SptEdSchPpr; CaptWrstlng; U Of Northern Ia; P E Teacher.

WILKINS, Larry E; Topeka HS; Topeka, KS; 20/534 Band; HonRl; SctActv; StuCncl; SchPpr; LetterSwmmng; LetterTrk; GodCntryAwd; Kansas St Univ; Chem Engineer.

WILKINS, Lois; Marion C Early Hs; Walnut Grove, MO; 6/45 VPSophCls; PresJrCls; Chr; ChrhWkr; HonRl; ModUN; StuCncl; FHA; SciCl; LetterBsktbl; J College & U; Doctor Teacher.

WILKINS, Mamie; Cambridge Sr HS; Isanti, MN; 48/246 CmntyWkr; HospAde; RedCrAde; College; Nurse.

WILKINS, Mary J; Soldan HS; St Louis, MO; 10/700 HonRl; NHS; SctActv; College; Business Admin.

WILKINS, Scott E; Pleasant Hill HS; Pleasant Hill, MO; PresFrshCls; PresSophCls; VPJrCls; TrsSrCls; Band; ChrhWkr; HonRl; NHS; PepBnd; SchMus; StuCncl; StuGov; LetterFtbl; LetterTrk; Mo Western At St Joseph.

WILKINS, Sherrie L; Webb City HS; Oronogo, MO; 47/200 Chr; ChrhWkr; LbryAde; NHS; SchAde; TchrAde; SchPpr; VPFHA; FTA; MasAwd; Dental Asst.

WILKINS, Theodore W; Calumet HS; Griffith, IN; 5/300 ALBoysSt; Band; CncrtBnd; HonRl; TreasJrNHS; MrchBnd; SecNHS; PepBnd; YthFlsp; FSA; VPFrCl; In Univ; Instru Music Teacher.

WILKINSON, Anita L; Wilber Clatonia HS; Clatonia, NE; Chrs; HonRl; SchMus; StuCncl; PpCl; College; Teaching.

WILKINSON, Becky J; Franklin Community HS; Franklin, IN; HonRl; HospAde; NHS; FBLA; FHA; LatCl; Indiana State Univ; Accountant.

WILKINSON, Daniel D; Fremont Sr HS; Fremont, NE; 1/412 Band; CncrtBnd; HonRl; MrchBnd; PepBnd; GerCl; University Of Nebraska; Mathematics.

WILKINSON, Diane L; Northville HS; Northville, MI; 1/320 NHS; NatlMeritFnl; NatlMeritSchl; NatlMeritSF; TchrAde; LetterSwmmng; Trk; GAA; BauchLmbAwd; BttyCrckrAwd; U Of Mi; Professional Md.

WILKINSON, Gregory; Central HS; Red Wing, MN; Band; CncrtBnd; HonRl; MrchBnd; NHS; Univ; Education Coaching.

WILKINSON, James M; Central HS; Evansville, IN; 88/650 HonRl; JA; NatlMeritCmnd; RptrYrbk; SchPpr; JAAwd; Ball State Univ; Architecture.

WILKINSON, Jan Y; Whitke HS; Larwill, IN; Band; HonRl; SchMus; StuCncl; TchrAde; Twrl; YthFlsp; Pres4-H; FFA; FHA; FTA; PpCl; Chrldr; GAA; College; Business.

WILKINSON, Jeffrey A; Lakeland HS; Wolcottville, IN; Band; CncrtBnd; MrchBnd; SchMus; 4-H; Trk; IMSpt; 4-HAwd;.

WILKINSON, Judy; Central City HS; Central City, IA; ChrhWkr; CncrtBnd; MrchBnd; NHS; PepBnd; Quill&Scroll; RptrYrbk; Bible College; Nursing.

WILKINSON, Shelley J; Thornridge HS; Dolton, IL; 19/670 AFS; HonRl; LitMag; NatlFornLg; NHS; NatlMeritCmnd; NatlThespSoc; VFWAwd; Mt Holyoke College; Pathology.

WILKINSON, Tina; Paw Paw HS; Paw Paw, MI; 7/170 HonRl; NHS; 4-H; Bsktbl; GAA; BttyCrckrAwd; Mich St Univ;pre Vet.

WILKS, Pam; Adams Central HS; Monroe, IN; 2/122 Band; HonRl; NHS; SchPl; TchrAde; YthFlsp; SchPpr; 4-H; Taylor Univ; Physical Therapist.

WILKS, Sandra; North Division HS; Milwaukee, WI; VPChrhWkr; TreasCncrtBnd; HonRl; NHS; SecStuCncl; PpCl; SciCl; Trk; Chrldr; SecGAA; Psyciatrist Or Psychologist.

WILKUS, Annette P; Lourdes HS; Rochester, MN; Band; CncrtBnd; MrchBnd; PepBnd; SecSctActv; SciCl; College; Medicine.

WILKUS, Stephen A; Rich South HS; Park Forest, IL; 8/267 HonRl; NHS; NatlMeritFnl; PolWkr; Quill&Scroll; SchPl; StuCncl; RptrSchPpr; Michigan State Univ; Physics.

WILL, Catherine S; Arlington HS; Arlington Hts, IL; 16/593 ChrhWkr; HonRl; SchPpr; SpnCl; LetterBsktbl; GAA; Augustana College; Education.

WILL, Catherine J; Osseo Fairchild HS; Fairchild, WI; ALAGirlsSt; CncrtBnd; HonRl; MrchBnd; NHS; GerCl; GAA; College; Business.

WILL, James A; Wayland Academy; Columbus, WI; Chr; ChrhWkr; HospAde; Mdrgl; Orch; RedCrAde; SchMus; RptrYrbk; Yrbk; FDA; EngCl; FrCl; LatCl; University; Medicine.

WILL, John; Ridgway HS; Equality, IL; 6/50 ALBoysSt; HonRl; CivCl; FFA; SpnCl; PpCl; Bsbl; Bsktbl; Goto Rets Elect Trade School Louisville.

WILL, Larry D; Kaneland HS; Sugar Grove, IL; 6/160 Chrs; NatlFornLg; NHS; NatlThespSoc; FSA; MthCl; Bsbl; Bsktbl; Ftbl; College; Engineer.

WILL, Linda I; Halstead HS; Halstead, KS; 3/65 TrsJrCls; Band; CncrtBnd; HonRl; MrchBnd; NHS; PepBnd; SchPl; RptrYrbk; EdYrBk; Bethel College Art.

WILL, Nancy E; Bishop Du Bourge HS; St Louis, MO; HonRl; PpCl; LetterChrldr; IMSpt; College; Political Science.

WILL, Thomas E; North Judson San Pierre HS; San Pierre, IN; 3/126 PresSrCls; ALBoysSt; HonRl; JrNHS; VPNHS; YthFlsp; FFA; CaptBsktbl; CaptTrk; ChmbCommrsAwd; Purdue University; Engineering.

WILLARD, Bruce; East Pike Hs; Milton, IL; TrsFrshCls; TrsSophCls; TrsJrCls; NHS; SctActv; StuCncl; FFA; LetterBsbl; LetterBsktbl; LetterTrk; College;church Work Or Deaf Worker.

WILLARD, Cindy L; Edinburg HS; Edinburg, IN; ALAGirlsSt; Band; HonRl; SpnCl; PpCl; College; Vocation.

WILLARD, Gregory D; Morristown HS; Morristown, IN; 6/77 PresSrCls; HonRl; NHS; PresStuCncl; YthFlsp; RptrYrbk; LetterBsbl; LetterBsktbl; Trk; Ball State.

WILLARD, Julie M; Aurora HS; Aurora, MO; AFS; Band; ChrhWkr; HonRl; MrchBnd; NHS; FTA; FrCl; PpCl; Chrldr; Sw Mo St Univ; Accountant.

WILLARD, Mary T; Centreville HS; Sturgis, MI; VPJrCls; ALAGirlsSt; HospAde; SchPl; SctActv; StuCncl; LatCl; VPLetterTrk; PPFtbl; Mich State U; Psychology.

WILLARD, Randall R; Stapleton HS; Stapleton, NE; ChrhWkr; StuGov; YthFlsp; 4-H; KeyCl; LetterBsktbl; LetterFtbl; 4-HAwd; Trade School; Diesel Trade.

WILLARD, Sherri L; Hagerstown HS; Cambridge City, IN; 13/128 SecSophCls; SecJrCls; ALAGirlsSt; ChrhWkr; CmntyWkr; HonRl; NHS; TchrAde; FHA; FrCl; Isu; Cpa.

WILLAREDT, Nancy L; Edwardsville HS; Edwardsville, IL; HonRl; NHS; PresYthFlsp; Pres4-H; GAA; IMSpt; 4-HAwd; College; Accounting Major.

WILLBANKS, Randy C; Ruskin HS; Kansas City, MO; Chr; ChrhWkr; HonRl; JrNHS; NHS; LetterBsbl; LetterFtbl; IMSpt; Umkc; Attorney.

WILLBORN, Pamela; Pecatonica HS; Hollandale, WI; 3/59 Band; HonRl; NatlFornLg; SchPl; 4-H; PpCl; Chrldr; GAA; 4-HAwd;.

WILLBRANDT, Carolyn I; Athens HS; Fulton, MI; HonRl; LbryAde; Business Schl; Secretary.

WILLCOCKSON, Susan J; Leeton HS; Leeton, MO; Band; Chrs; CncrtBnd; SchPl; FHA; PpCl; LetterBsbl; LetterBsktbl; Trk; Chrldr; Central Mo Univ; Theatrical Arts.

WILLCOX, Dale A; Grafton HS; Grafton, WI; 3/225 HonRl; LbryAde; NHS; SpnCl; MthCl; SciCl; Florida St Univ; Marine Chemistry.

WILLCOX, Robert D; Rosemount HS; Rosemount, MN; 6/444 VPFrshCls; ChrhWkr; HonRl; Sacrstn; StuCncl; StuGov; FrCl; Wrstlng; College; Catholic Ministry.

WILLE, Gayle L; Edwardsville Sr HS; Edwardsville, IL; Chr; HonRl; LbryAde; StuCncl; StuGov; TchrAde; RptrSchPpr; SchPpr; 4-H; Chrldr; GAA; IMSpt; Eastern Illinois Univ; Medicine.

WILLE, Jodie R; Klemme Community HS; Klemme, IA; 4/33 Band; Chr; HonRl; NHS; StuCncl; YthFlsp; 4-H; SpnCl; LetterBsktbl; LetterTrk; Niacc; Nursing.

WILLE, Luann; Ventura Community HS; Garner, IA; 6/38 TrsJrCls; Band; CncrtBnd; HonRl; MrchBnd; NatlThespSoc; PepBnd; SchPl; YthFlsp; RptrYrbk; Niacc Or Isu.

WILLE, Marianne; Moberly HS; Moberly, MO; TrsSrCls; ChrhWkr; HonRl; NHS; SchPl; StuGov; EngCl; SpnCl; Nemsu Kirksville; Teach Spanish.

WILLE, Steven L; Maine Twp HS West; Des Plaines, IL; 98/900 HonRl; JrNHS; NHS; NatlMeritCmnd; MthCl; Loyola University Of Chicago; Chemistry.

WILLEM, Stephen J; Reitz Mem HS; Evansville, IN; 2/211 Band; CncrtBnd; HonRl; MrchBnd; NatlMeritCmnd; RptrYrbk; VPGerCl; IMSpt; DARAwd; U F Evansville; Bus.

WILLEMS, Jennifer L; Huntington North HS; Huntington, IN; Chr; Chrl; Quill&Scroll; SchMus; College; Journalism.

WILLEMS, Kirby E; Winola HS; New Windsor, IL; 9/75 ALBoysSt; HonRl; JA; NHS; SctActv; SpnCl; Bsbl; Bsktbl; Ftbl; College; Engineer.

WILLEMS, Mary C; Stockbridge HS; Hilbert, WI; ChrhWkr; HonRl; OffAde; SchAde; SchPl; StuCncl; TchrAde; EdSchPpr; MthCl; PpCl; Tech Sch; Therapist.

WILLEN, Claudia; Marian Hts Academy; Affton, MO; 1/28 HonRl; NHS; NatlMeritFnl; SchPl; StuCncl; RptrYrbk; FrCl; GAA; BttyCrckrAwd; College; Biology.

WILLEN, Jean M; Hazelwood West HS; Hazelwood, MO; 103/428 HonRl; PpCl; LetterChrldr; CchngActv; PPFtbl; St Louis Univ; Physical Therapist.

WILLENBORG, Nyla R; Beckman HS; Newvienna, IA; 41/143 Chr; Chrs; CmntyWkr; HonRl; JrNHS; SchAde; SchPpr; PpCl; Trk; GAA; Francisian Sch Of Nursing; Rn.

WILLENS, Linda R; Barstow HS; Kansas City, MO; 8/33 Aud/Vis; CmntyWkr; HonRl; LbryAde; OffAde; SchAde; TchrAde; SpnCl; Tennis; College; Education.

WILLER, David B; Batesville HS; Batesville, IN; 16/150 ALBoysSt; HonRl; NHS; SchPl; SpnCl; Bsktbl; Trk; Coll; Professional.

WILLERTON, Becky J; Olympia HS; Danvers, IL; AFS; HonRl; NHS; 4-H; FNA; GerCl; PpCl; Bsktbl; Ftbl; 4-HAwd; U Of Illinois; Dentist.

WILLETT, Cindy S; Superior HS; Superior, NE; Band; Chr; CncrtBnd; MrchBnd; PepBnd; Quill&Scroll; SchPl; EdYrBk; RptrSchPpr; FBLA; Kansas State Univ; Special Educ.

WILLETT, Karen A; Marian HS; Omaha, NE; 6/162 Chrs; ChrhWkr; HonRl; NHS; Sacrstn; SctActv; StuGov; TchrAde; Bsktbl; GAA; College; Mathematics.

WILLETT, Mary Lou; T L Handy HS; Bay City, MI; 35/360 Chr; HonRl; LitMag; NatlMeritCmnd; StuCncl; Delta College; Elementary Education.

WILLETT, Rose M; Jackson HS; Jackson, MN; 35/123 University Of Minn; Asst Vet.

WILLEY, Donald L; Bishop Dubourg HS; St Louis, MO; CmntyWkr; HonRl; LetterBsktbl; LetterFtbl; LetterTrk; College; Science Or Pro Football.

WILLEY, Kyle D; Zionsville Co HS; Whitestown, IN; 29/122 Chr; Chrl; Chrs; ChrhWkr; HonRl; HospAde; LbryAde; OffAde; StuCncl; RptrSchPpr; PpCl; Butler Univ; Fashion Merchandising.

WILLEY, Lori A; H L Richards HS; Chicago Ridge, IL; 38/1100 HonRl; JrNHS; NHS; Orch; TchrAde; FTA; SpnCl; ChmbCommrsAwd; Univ Of Ill; Medicine.

WILLHELM, Karen V; Brookville HS; Cedar Grove, IN; 30/180 VPFrshCls; TrsSophCls; HonRl; StuCncl; FHA; PpCl; GAA;.

WILLHITE, Barbara; Plato R 5 HS; Plato, MO; 6/36 TrsFrshCls; Band; ChrhWkr; HonRl; MrchBnd; SchAde; TchrAde; Twrl; Yrbk; FHA; Sw Mo State Univ; Art Teaching.

WILLHITE, Colleen R; Hector HS; Hector, MN; ALAGirlsSt; HonRl; NHS; NatlMeritSF; SchPl; RptrSchPpr; LetterBsktbl; LetterTrk; GAA; Univ; Chemical Engineering.

WILLHITE, Duane A; Orangeville HS; Dakota, IL; 9/54 HonRl; NHS; YthFlsp; Yrbk; PpCl; LetterBsbl; LetterFtbl; LetterTrk; Central College.

WILLHITE, Kathy A; Algoma HS; Aloma, WI; Chrs; HonRl; SchMus; EdSchPpr; PpCl; U Of Wi Eau Claire; Journalism.

WILLHITE, Robert J; Waynesville Sr HS; Waynesville, MO; 7/255 Chr; HonRl; NHS; RptrYrbk; FDA; KeyCl; LetterBsktbl; CaptFtbl; LetterTrk; LetterWrstlng; Univ; Professional.

WILLHOITE, Kimberly A; St Charles HS; St Charles, MO; Band; CmntyWkr; CncrtBnd; HonRl; JrNHS; MrchBnd; NHS; PepBnd; IMSpt; Univ Of Mo; Veterinarian.

WILLI, Martin L; Spalding Institute; Peoria, IL; 2/125 VPJrCls; HonRl; StuGov; LetterTrk; IMSpt; Univ; Engineer.

WILLIAM, Marisa K; Hoxie HS; Hoxie, KS; HonRl; SchPl; StuCncl; TchrAde; EdYrBk; FFA; SpnCl; PresPpCl; Chrldr; AmLegAwd; Kansas Univ; Accountant.

WILLIAMS, Alice H; Lindblom HS; Chicago, IL; Chr; Chrl; Chrs; HonRl; TchrAde; Cal Tech; Engineering.

WILLIAMS, Allen J; West Branch HS; West Branch, IA; 3/78 ALBoysSt; NHS; 4-H; FFA; LetterFtbl; LetterTrk; LetterWrstlng; AmLegAwd; Iowa St Univ; Agriculture.

WILLIAMS, Barbara; Northeastern HS; Williamsburg, IN; 32/129 StuCncl; 4-H; FrCl; Indiana University; Law Social Work Pol.

WILLIAMS, Ben; Riceville HS; Riceville, IA; HonRl; NatlSciFnd; FFA; SciCl; 4-HAwd; Univ.

WILLIAMS, Beth; Rich Central Hs; Olympia Fields, IL; AFS; Band; HonRl; Mdrgl; MrchBnd; PepBnd; SctActv; FrCl; LetterTennis; GAA; College; Professional.

WILLIAMS, Brent C; C A Lindbergh HS; Minnetonka, MN; Chr; ChrhWkr; HonRl; NatlFornLg; NatlMeritSF; SchPl; SctActv; StuGov; YthLg; EdSchPpr; Tennis; College.

WILLIAMS, Bruce G; Washington Sr HS; Cedar Rapids, IA; 18/487 Chr; HonRl; LbryAde; NHS; NatlMeritSF; NatlThespSoc; SchMus; SchPl; SctActv; FrCl; GodCntryAwd; College; Forester.

WILLIAMS, Bryan J; F J Reitz HS; Evansville, IN; 1/474 PresSophCls; PresSrCls; NHS; NatlMeritCmnd; StuCncl; StuGov; LetterTrk; IMSpt; DARAwd; JAAwd; NCTE; Wabash College; Medicine.

WILLIAMS, Candice C; Pattonville HS; Bridgeton, MO; 58/817 ChrhWkr; HonRl; NHS; OffAde; StuCncl; MthCl; Swmmng; Chrldr; CchngActv; College; Pediatrician.

WILLIAMS, Cara L; Le Roy HS; Le Roy, KS; HonRl; Yrbk; PpCl;.

WILLIAMS, Charles B; Aurora Hoyt Lakes HS; Hoyt Lakes, MN; AFS; Chr; HonRl; NHS; NatlThespSoc; SchMus; StuCncl; Yrbk; EdSchPpr; LetterSwmmng; Concordia; Health.

WILLIAMS, Charles E; Carrollton HS; Carrollton, MO; 18/97 ChrhWkr; HonRl; NHS; SchPl; RptrYrbk; Yrbk; SchPpr; 4-H; SpnCl; College; Lawyer.

WILLIAMS, Charlese; West Side Hs; Gary, IN; ChrhWkr; HonRl; MrchBnd; PepBnd; StuCncl; Teen; SpnCl; PpCl; VPSwmmng;.

WILLIAMS, Cheryl L; Bethany HS; Findlay, IL; 14/32 Band; Chr; Chrs; CncrtBnd; HonRl; MrchBnd; PepBnd; 4-H; FrCl; PpCl; LetterTrk; PresAwd;.

WILLIAMS, Cindy L; Forest Lake Sr HS; Wyoming, MN; 5/353 CncrtBnd; HonRl; LitMag; NHS; PepBnd; Quill&Scroll; SchMus; SchPl; YthFlsp; SchPpr; Concordia Col; Foreign Language.

WILLIAMS, Connie M; Waldron HS; Pittsford, MI; 4/55 ALAGirlsSt; HonRl; NHS; NatlMeritCmnd; SchPl; PresStuCncl; SciCl; LetterChrldr; GAA; CitAwd; Adrtan Col ;psychology Major.

WILLIAMS, Connie M; Macarthur HS; Decatur, IL; 6/410 HonRl; HospAde; NHS; NatlMeritCmnd; TchrAde; SecFrCl; Univ Of Ill; Pharmacy.

WILLIAMS, Craig; Park Hill HS; Kansas City, MO; Band; CncrtBnd; MrchBnd; NatlMeritCmnd; Orch; PepBnd; SctActv; TchrAde; Wrstlng; Musician.

WILLIAMS, Craig D; Staples HS; Staples, MN; 1/157 Band; Chr; HonRl; MrchBnd; PepBnd; SchMus; SchPl; SctActv; JAAwd; Brainerd Vo Tec; Accountant.

WILLIAMS, Daniel; Elk Rapids HS; Elk Rapids, MI; PresFrshCls; HonRl; NHS; StuCncl; Mavitime Acad; Engineer.

WILLIAMS, Daniel B; Chelsea HS; Chelsea, MI; ChrhWkr; HonRl; NHS; TchrAde; Michigan St Univ; Chemical Engineer.

WILLIAMS, Daniel L; Dundee Community HS; Carpentersville, IL; 126/363 Central College; French.

WILLIAMS, Danny E; Du Quoin HS; Du Quoin, IL; 40/143 ChrhWkr; HonRl; SchPl; SchPpr; SpnCl; PpCl; SciCl; Bsktbl; Glf; Southern Ill Univ; Medicine.

WILLIAMS, David B; Horace Mann HS; Gary, IN; 42/262 ALBoysSt; Chr; CncrtBnd; DrlTm; Mdrgl; MrchBnd; NatlMeritCmnd; PepBnd; SchMus; TreasStuCncl; Jackson St Univ; Lawyer.

WILLIAMS, David L; Scottsbluff Sr HS; Scottsbluff, NE; HonRl; JrNHS; LetterTrk; University.

WILLIAMS, Dawnette K; Huron HS; New Boston, MI; ChrhWkr; CmntyWkr; HonRl; RedCrAde; StuCncl; YthFlsp; RptrYrbk; FNA; Nursing School; Nurse.

WILLIAMS, Debbie A; Hume HS; Stotesbury, MO; 1/18 SecFrshCls; SecSophCls; SecJrCls; Band; Chrs; ChrhWkr; CmntyWkr; CncrtBnd; HonRl; MrchBnd; PepBnd; LetterBsbl; LetterBsktbl; LetterTrk; Missouri So St College; Business.

WILLIAMS, Debbie F; Waukegan HS; Waukegan, IL; CncrtBnd; JrNHS; LbryAde; MrchBnd; NatlFornLg; NHS; N Illinois Univ; Journalism.

WILLIAMS, Debbie R; Dunseith HS; Dunseith, ND; Band; SecChr; Chrs; CncrtBnd; HonRl; MrchBnd; PepBnd; SchPl; RptrYrbk; RptrSchPpr; SchPpr; Sec4-H; FHA; PpCl; Minot State College; Special Education.

WILLIAMS, Deborah R; Evart Public HS; Evart, MI; SchPl; TchrAde; YthFlsp; TreasYthLg; RptrSchPpr; FHA; PPFtbl; Ferris St Clg; Social Serv.

WILLIAMS, Debra A; Shortridge HS; Indianapolis, IN; SpnCl; Indiana Univ; Nursing.

WILLIAMS, Debra E; Marshall HS; Marshall, IL; 3/115 StuCncl; 4-H; FBLA; FTA; LatCl; SciCl; Trk; IMSpt; 4-HAwd; Business Sch; Exec Secretary.

WILLIAMS, Denise; Streeter Public HS; Streeter, ND; 8/21 PresSophCls; ALAGirlsSt; Chrs; CncrtBnd; HonRl; StuCncl; EdYrBk; RptrSchPpr; Bsktbl; Chrldr; College; Elem. Education.

WILLIAMS, Dennis L; Seymour HS; Seymour, MO; HonRl; MthCl; Bsktbl; College; Armed Forces.

WILLIAMS, Dennis L; Exira Community HS; Exira, IA; ALBoysSt; Band; CncrtBnd; HonRl; MrchBnd; PepBnd; PresStuCncl; Yrbk; LetterFtbl; LetterTrk; Trade School; Vocation.

WILLIAMS, Desiree; John Marshall Harlan HS; Chicago, IL; 7/707 HonRl; JrNHS; NHS; Yrbk; PresMthCl; Univ Of Illinois; Lab Tech.

WILLIAMS, Diana; Greenfield HS; Greenfield, IL; TrsSophCls; TrsJrCls; Band; ChrhWkr; CncrtBnd; HonRl; HospAde; JrNHS; NHS; GAA; College; Professional.

WILLIAMS, Diane L; Maine West HS; Des Plaines, IL; HonRl; IntrClCncl; StuCncl; PpCl; CaptChrldr; GAA; Lutheran Gen School Of Nursing; Nursing.

WILLIAMS, Donna J; Hastings HS; Hastings, MN; HonRl; OffAde; SchPl; Clge; Nurse.

WILLIAMS, Donna M; Mt Vernon HS; Mt Vernon, SD; 9/29 TrsJrCls; ChrhWkr; HonRl; SchPl; Sec4-H; LetterBsktbl; LetterTrk; Chrldr; 4-HAwd; Mitchell Area Voc; Stenographic.

WILLIAMS, Donna R; L C Mohr HS; South Haven, MI; Chr; ChrhWkr; HonRl; TchrAde; IMSpt; KiwanAwd; Nsu Or Bus School; Secretray Or Business.

WILLIAMS, Douglas D; Adlai E Stevenson HS; Livonia, MI; 18/740 ALBoysSt; NatlFornLg; NatlMeritSF; SctActv; StuGov; GodCntryAwd; Coll; Physics.

WILLIAMS, Eleanor; Urbana Hs; Urbana, IL; 1/423 AFS; HonRl; NatlMeritFnl; NatlSciFnd; U Of Illinois; Engineering Mechanics.

WILLIAMS, Elizabeth E; Southside HS; Ft Wayne, IN; 13/348 Chr; DrmMjrt; OffAde; LatCl; CitAwd; Univ; Veterinary Medicine.

WILLIAMS, Elizabeth; El Paso HS; El Paso, IL; ALAGirlsSt; ChrhWkr; HonRl; NHS; SchPl; StuCncl; RptrSchPpr; SpnCl; PpCl; Swmmng; Private Col; Med Or Lab Tech.

WILLIAMS, Ellecia; Southeast Sr HS; Kansas City, MO; HonRl; SchAde; Yrbk; Socr; CitAwd; Trade School; Professional.

WILLIAMS, Elvin A; Bennett HS; Bennett, IA; Band; ChrhWkr; CncrtBnd; MrchBnd; PepBnd; SctActv; YthFlsp; 4-H; FFA; PpCl; Clge; Vocation.

WILLIAMS, Erica E; Homewood Flossmoor HS; Homewood, IL; 4/940 AFS; HonRl; NHS; NatlMeritCmnd; MthCl; Bsktbl; University Of Dallas; Biochemistry.

WILLIAMS, Eric W; Anderson HS; Anderson, IN; 19/650 ALBoysSt; ChrhWkr; HonRl; NHS; StuCncl; StuGov; TchrAde; YthFlsp; Swmmng; LetterTrk; College; Mathematics.

WILLIAMS, Ernest C; North Mahaska HS; New Sharon, IA; 5/61 SecSophCls; VPSrCls; NHS; YthFlsp; Yrbk; SchPpr; 4-H; FFA; PpCl; LetterBsbl; LetterBsktbl; LetterFtbl; Trk; Nw Missouri State Univ; Teacher.

WILLIAMS, Exie M; Murphysboro HS; Myrphysboro, IL; Chr; ChrhWkr; HonRl; SchAde; TchrAde; 4-H; FTA; MthCl; 4-HAwd; JAAwd; Clg; Elem Teacher.

WILLIAMS, Frank E; John Marshall HS; Indianapolis, IN; 44/444 Chr; HonRl; PresJA; NHS; NatlMeritCmnd; Quill&Scroll; SchPl; SchPpr; FrCl; Wrstlng; Purdue University; Physisist.

WILLIAMS, Gail; Normandy Sr HS; St Louis, MO; 145/493 TrsSrCls; DrlTm; HonRl; JA; StuCncl; FBLA; PpCl; CaptBsktbl; LetterTrk; IMSpt; College; Business.

WILLIAMS, Gary L; Rosemont Sr HS; Burnsville, MN; ALBoysSt; ChrhWkr; HonRl; NHS; StuCncl; YthFlsp; LetterBsbl; Bsktbl; CaptFtbl; Wrstlng; College.

WILLIAMS, Genevieve; Weyauwega HS; Weyauwega, WI; 27/87 Band; ChrhWkr; CncrtBnd; HonRl; JA; MrchBnd; NHS; PepBnd; Bsktbl; Trk; Work And Farm.

WILLIAMS, Gilbert D; West Side HS; Gary, IN; Band; CncrtBnd; HonRl; JA; MrchBnd; PepBnd; RptrYrbk; RptrSchPpr; FDA; FSA; Col ; Pro.

WILLIAMS, Gordon L; North Mahaska HS; New Sharon, IA; 4/63 PresJrCls; HonRl; NHS; SchPl; StuCncl; SchPpr; LetterFtbl; LetterTrk; LetterWrstlng; IMSpt; Iowa State Univ; Engineer.

WILLIAMS, Gregory A; Metropolis Comm HS; Metropolis, IL; 41/158 ChrhWkr; 4-H; FFA; DanFAwd; Paducah Area Voc Tech; Electronics.

WILLIAMS, Gregory B; Connersville Sr HS; Connersville, IN; 37/371 ALBoysSt; Aud/Vis; HonRl; JA; NHS; NatlThespSoc; SchPl; PresYthFlsp; Yrbk; GerCl; College; Television.

WILLIAMS, Gregory E; Ex Spring West HS; Excelsior Springs, MO; HonRl; NHS; YthFlsp; Bsbl; Bsktbl; Ftbl; College; Physical Ed.

WILLIAMS, Gregory J; East Richland HS; Olney, IL; Bsktbl; LetterTrk; Univ Of Illinois; Lawyer.

WILLIAMS, Gregory W; Larned HS; Larned, KS; HonRl; SchPl; Trk; Kansas State Univ; Architecture.

WILLIAMS, Harold E; Richmond HS; Richmond, MO; Band; CncrtBnd; HonRl; MrchBnd; NHS; PepBnd; SchMus; DARAwd; Univ Of Ks; Music Education.

WILLIAMS, Helen J; Central HS; Evansville, IN; 20/650 Chr; HonRl; Mdrgl; NHS; Orch; SchMus; SctActv; StuCncl; In Univ; Piano Music Major.

WILLIAMS, Ivy A; De Kalb HS; De Kalb, IL; 25/350 Chr; CmntyWkr; DrlTm; HonRl; NHS; SchMus; TchrAde; EdYrBk; EdSchPpr; University; Dance.

WILLIAMS, Jacqueline J; Riverdale HS; Muscoda, WI; PresAFS; Chr; Mdrgl; NHS; SchMus; FHA; GerCl; SpnCl; CchngActv; College; Languages.

WILLIAMS, James; Paseo Hs; Kansas City, MO; Chr; ChrhWkr; CmntyWkr; HonRl; SctActv; Yrbk; 4-H; RusCl; SpnCl; MthCl; College; Teacher.

WILLIAMS, James L; South Shelby HS; Shelbina, MO; VPJrCls; Band; ChrhWkr; CncrtBnd; HonRl; MrchBnd; NHS; Orch; Bsktbl; Trk; Univ; Journalism.

WILLIAMS, James R; North Nodaway HS; Hopkins, MO; 11/37 TrsJrCls; HonRl; ModUN; SchMus; SchPl; VPStuCncl; 4-H; PresFFA; LetterBsktbl; DanFAwd; Univ; Vet Med.

WILLIAMS, James R; Cobden HS; Cobden, IL; Band; Chrs; CncrtBnd; HonRl; MrchBnd; PepBnd; SchPl; SciCl; Univ; Bus & Finance.

WILLIAMS, James R; West Elk HS; Moline, KS; ChrhWkr; HonRl; StuCncl; StuGov; Pres4-H; VPFFA; CaptBsktbl; LetterFtbl; 4-HAwd; Kansas State College.

WILLIAMS, Jane A; Brown City HS; Brown City, MI; 4/97 SecSrCls; PresNHS; SchMus; SecStuCncl; FHA; PPFtbl; University; Music.

WILLIAMS, Janet R; St John HS; Independence, IA; 2/27 SecFrshCls; SecJrCls; PresSrCls; HonRl; HospAde; NHS; Yrbk; EdSchPpr; Bsktbl; Clarke College; Education.

WILLIAMS, Jay W; Stillman Valley HS; Davis Junction, IL; 3/105 HonRl; NHS; NatlMeritFnl; SchMus; SchPl; StuCncl; TchrAde; CaptBsbl; LetterBsktbl; LetterFtbl; IMSpt; PPFtbl; College; Lawyer.

WILLIAMS, Jean T; Glenbard So HS; Glen Ellyn, IL; 41/292 HonRl; NHS; StuGov; University; History.

WILLIAMS, Jeffrey D; Sand Creek HS; Adrian, MI; 3/53 PresFrshCls; VPSophCls; HonRl; NHS; Bsbl; Bsktbl; Ftbl; Glf; CitAwd; Mi State Univ.

WILLIAMS, Jeffrey S; Mendel Catholic HS; Chicago, IL; 50/150 HonRl; Loyola Univ; Law.

WILLIAMS, Jimmie L; Beaumont HS; St Louis, MO; JA;.

WILLIAMS, Joan; Incarnate Word Acad; St Louis, MO; PresFrshCls; Chrl; GAA; IMSpt; PPFtbl; JAAwd; Northeast Missouri State U; Juvenile Office.

WILLIAMS, Jodi R; Norfolk HS; Norfolk, NE; 22/298 Band; Chr; ChrhWkr; CncrtBnd; HonRl; MrchBnd; NHS; Orch; SchMus; SchPl; YthFlsp; FrCl; PpCl; College.

WILLIAMS, Joe R; Gideon HS; Gideon, MO; 3/40 Band; HonRl; SecNHS; StuCncl; RptrYrbk; FrCl; PpCl; College.

WILLIAMS, John; State HS; Terre Haute, IN; RptrYrbk; EdYrBk; SptEdSchPpr; FBLA; Bsktbl; IMSpt; College; Professional.

WILLIAMS, John D; St Johns Prep HS; Chicago, IL; 8/61 PresSrCls; HonRl; NHS; NatlMeritCmnd; StuCncl; StuGov; CaptBsktbl; IMSpt; KiwanAwd; CitAwd; Marquette Univ; Computer Technician.

WILLIAMS, John M; Jefferson City Sr HS; Jefferson City, MO; Aud/Vis; ChrhWkr; OffAde; College; Doctor.

WILLIAMS, Joyce; St Thomas Aquinas HS; Florissant, MO; HonRl; NHS; RptrYrbk; College; Legal Assistant.

WILLIAMS, Joyce A; Ash Grove HS; Springfield, MO; 19/59 SecTrsSrCls; Band; Chrs; CncrtBnd; HonRl; HospAde; MrchBnd; NHS; PepBnd; SchPl; Sw Mo State U; Home Ec.

WILLIAMS, J Spencer; St Viator HS; Palatine, IL; 29/250 Chr; HonRl; LitMag; Socr; Trk; Annapolis Univ; Naval Officer.

WILLIAMS, Judson E; Waterford Mott HS; Pontiac, MI; ChrhWkr; HonRl; JrNHS; SpnCl; University; Professional.

WILLIAMS, Julie A; Enfield HS; Enfield, IL; 3/33 VPFrshCls; VPJrCls; SecBand; Chrs; CncrtBnd; DrmMjrt; HonRl; MrchBnd; OffAde; PepBnd; StuCncl; TchrAde; Twrl; Yrbk; Chrldr; S Il Univ; Journalism.

WILLIAMS, Julie M; Basehor HS; Leavenworth, KS; Band; HonRl; NHS; PepBnd; RptrYrbk; RptrSchPpr; Business School; Legal Secretary.

WILLIAMS, Karen; Madison Senior HS; Madison, IL; 8/116 HonRl; NHS; PpCl; U; Urban Plan.

WILLIAMS, Karl J; Lyons Township HS; La Grange Park, IL; Chr; Chrs; ChrhWkr; HonRl; NatlMeritCmnd; YthFlsp; GerCl; LetterSocr; Univ Of Iowa; Marketing.

WILLIAMS, Keith L; Ofallon HS; Ofallon, IL; ChrhWkr; CmntyWkr; HonRl; Yrbk; RptrSchPpr; Glf; CchngActv; College; Professional.

WILLIAMS, Keith M; Greenwood HS; Springfield, MO; 6/28 VPFrshCls; VPSophCls; VPJrCls; PresSrCls; AFS; Chrs; ChrhWkr; HonRl; ModUN; RptrSchPpr; SchPpr; LetterFtbl; GodCntryAwd; Col; Physician.

WILLIAMS, Kelley A; Taylorville Sr HS; Taylorville, IL; 37/251 Chr; HonRl; Mdrgl; VPOrch; SchMus; VPYthFlsp; LatCl; PpCl; LetterTennis; GAA; Eastern Illinois University; Finance.

WILLIAMS, Kenneth T; Chester Area HS; Colton, SD; 2/32 ALBoysSt; HonRl; NHS; PolWkr; StuCncl; StuGov; EdSchPpr; LetterBsktbl; LetterFtbl; AmLegAwd; Dakota St Coll; Bus.

WILLIAMS, Kevin D; York Comm HS; Elmhurst, IL; 125/912 HonRl; NHS; LetterSocr; Trk; Univ Of Illinois; Computer Engineering.

WILLIAMS, Kevin L; Mendel Cath Prep HS; Chicago, IL; 36/191 HonRl; NatlMeritFnl; SctActv; StuCncl; StuGov; YthFnd; PpCl; CaptTrk; IMSpt; PresAwd; College; Professional.

WILLIAMS, Kim M; Watertown Sr HS; Watertown, SD; Band; Chrs; CncrtBnd; HonRl; HospAde; MrchBnd; FBLA; GerCl; College; Accounting.

WILLIAMS, Kristen M; John Marshall HS; Indianapolis, IN; 11/400 HonRl; NHS; StuCncl; SpnCl; SciCl; PPFtbl; DanFAwd; Indiana Univ.

WILLIAMS, Kristen T; Willmar Willmar HS; Willmar, MN; SecFrshCls; Chr; StuCncl; FHA; Tennis; Trk; LetterChrldr; IMSpt; DARAwd; Coll.

WILLIAMS, Laura K; Breckenridge HS; Wheeler, MI; HonRl; NHS; StuCncl; Pres4-H; SecPpCl; LetterTrk; Chrldr; PPFtbl; Central Mi University.

WILLIAMS, Laurie J; Carlisle Community HS; Carlisle, IA; 6/105 Chrs; HonRl; NHS; SchMus; SctActv; Yrbk; RptrSchPpr; FHA; MthCl; Glf; Iowa State Univ; Aerospace Engineering.

WILLIAMS, Leslie; Philip HS; Philip, SD; 7/40 VPSrCls; Chrs; ChrhWkr; NHS; SchPl; StuCncl; EdYrBk; FHA; GAA; Sd St Univ; Rn Or Phys Assis.

WILLIAMS, Linda M; Tarkio HS; Tarkio, MO; Chr; Chrs; ChrhWkr; HonRl; LbryAde; NHS; SchPl; StuCncl; TchrAde; DARAwd; Central Mo State Univ; Spe Ed Teacher.

WILLIAMS, Llena; Gchs North HS; Granite City, IL; 42/375 Chrs; ChrhWkr; JA; LbryAde; NHS; SctActv; Yrbk; PpCl; GAA; JAAwd; Nurses Training; Registered Nurse.

WILLIAMS, Lori M; Lincoln Community HS; Olin, IA; 14/64 VPFrshCls; Band; Chr; Chrl; Chrs; CncrtBnd; DrlTm; HonRl; SchPl; Chrldr; Hawkeye Inst Tech ;comm Art.

WILLIAMS, Luann A; North Branch HS; North Branch, MI; 4/140 HonRl; JA; ModUN; SecNHS; TchrAde; Yrbk; SecFrCl; PpCl; SciCl; Baker Jr College Of Business; Admin Asst.

WILLIAMS, Lynne M; O L Of Mount Carmel HS; Ecorse, MI; Chrs; HonRl; NHS; PpCl; Chrldr; IMSpt; CitAwd;.

WILLIAMS, Lynn M; Manistee Catholic HS; Manistee, MI; HonRl; SchPl; SecStuCncl; RptrYrbk; SchPpr; PpCl; Trk; IMSpt; CitAwd; VoiceDemAwd; Central Mi; Theatre Arts.

WILLIAMS, Marcia J; North Central HS; Lewis, IN; HonRl; LbryAde; OffAde; Yrbk; FBLA; PpCl; Technical Clg.

WILLIAMS, Mark D; Northern Univ HS; Cedar Falls, IA; 1/58 Chr; Mdrgl; NatlMeritSF; Orch; StuCncl; StuGov; SpnCl; LetterFtbl; LetterTennis; DARAwd; Stanford Univ; Millionaire.

WILLIAMS, Mark W; New Providence HS; New Providence, IA; PresSrCls; Band; Chrs; CmntyWkr; CncrtBnd; HonRl; MrchBnd; PepBnd; SchMus; SchPl; LetterBsbl; CaptBsktbl; LetterTrk; College; Agriculture.

WILLIAMS, Marshall D; Du Quoin HS; Du Quion, IL; Bsktbl; Ftbl; Trk; John A Logan; Electrical Engineering.

WILLIAMS, Marvin W; Carthage HS; Reeds, MO; 16/208 AFS; DrlTm; HonRl; ROTC; SecFFA; MthCl; IMSpt; AmLegAwd; DARAwd; CitAwd; Southwest Mo State U; Agricultural.

WILLIAMS, Mary; Harrison HS; Farmington Hills, MI; HonRl; JA; Orch; TchrAde; CchngActv; IMSpt; PPFtbl; Oakland Univ; Earth Sci.

WILLIAMS, Mary E; West Side HS; Gary, IN; 174/700 CmntyWkr; DrlTm; HonRl; HospAde; JrNHS; FHA; LatCl; PpCl; College; Nursing.

WILLIAMS, Mary J; Oak Park HS; Kansas City, MO; 32/545 College; Secretary.

WILLIAMS, Mary M; Fatima HS; Bonnots Mill, MO; Chr; Chrs; HonRl; LbryAde; CivCl; FBLA; FHA; SpnCl; PpCl; Chrldr; College.

WILLIAMS, Michael B; John M Harlan HS; Chicago, IL; 115/850 Aud/Vis; ChrhWkr; HonRl; JA; FrCl; Bsbl; Ftbl; Wrstlng; IMSpt; Univ; Professional.

WILLIAMS, Michael J; Lamphere HS; Madison Heights, MI; Aud/Vis; HonRl; SchPl; StuCncl; StuGov; TchrAde; LetterFtbl; IMSpt; College; Medicine.

WILLIAMS, Michael J; Fairbury HS; Fairbury, NE; ChrhWkr; CmntyWkr; SctActv; 4-H; Bsbl; Bsktbl; Ftbl; CchngActv; IMSpt; 4-HAwd; GodCntryAwd; Milford Tech College; Construction.

WILLIAMS, Michael W; Oblong HS; Oblong, IL; 29/69 HonRl; NatlMeritSchl; FrCl; Bsbl; Bsktbl; Ftbl; IMSpt; AmLegAwd; College; Professional.

WILLIAMS, Monretta; East Catholic HS; Detroit, MI; VPSophCls; Chr; ChrhWkr; CmntyWkr; HonRl; NHS; StuCncl; TchrAde; SpnCl; PpCl; SciCl; University Of Michigan; Lawyer.

WILLIAMS, Myra A; Crystal Lake Comm HS; Crystal Lake, IL; ALAGirlsSt; Chr; Chrs; ChrhWkr; PresNatlThespSoc; SchMus; SchPl; StuCncl; TchrAde; PresFrCl; Swmmng; Rockford Clg; Theatre Arts.

WILLIAMS, Neil; Morgan County HS; Vresailles, MO; AFS; Chr; ChrhWkr; CmntyWkr; SchPl; Teen; StuCncl; StuGov; Ftbl; Glf; College; Commercial Artist.

WILLIAMS, Neta L; Alton HS; Alton, MO; 16/87 ChrhWkr; CtyCnl; CmntyWkr; JA; NatlMeritSchl; StuCncl; StuGov; FBLA; PpCl; Bsbl; Trade Sch; Vocation.

WILLIAMS, Orlantha; Unity HS; Chicago, IL; CtyCnl; HonRl; NatlFornLg; NHS; NatlMeritFnl; StuCncl; StuGov; EdYrBk; RptrSchPpr; FBLA; Fisk Univ; Social Worker.

WILLIAMS, Otis L; Chicago Vocational HS; Chicago, IL; 17/775 HonRl; NHS; ROTC; StuCncl; MthCl; LetterFtbl; Trk; CitAwd; College; Liberal Arts.

WILLIAMS, Patricia; Orrick HS; Orrick, MO; 1/36 PresFrshCls; Band; CncrtBnd; DrmMjrt; HonRl; NHS; StuCncl; Twrl; FHA; AmLegAwd;.

WILLIAMS, Patricia A; Charlotte HS; Charlotte, MI; 4/267 ChrhWkr; HonRl; TreasNHS; SctActv; TchrAde; YthFlsp; SecGerCl; PpCl; Swmmng; CaptTrk; College; Veterinary Medicine.

WILLIAMS, Patricia C; Moline HS; Moline, IL; CmntyWkr; StuCncl; YthFlsp; LetterBsktbl; IMSpt; Col; Professional.

WILLIAMS, Patricia R; Thornwood HS; Markham, IL; HstJrCls; Band; CncrtBnd; HonRl; OffAde; StuGov; RptrSchPpr; SchPpr; Tennis; IMSpt; U Of Il; Journalism.

WILLIAMS, Paula A; Rantoul Township HS; Rantoul, IL; LbryAde; OffAde; Parkland Jr Clge Champaign Il; Computer Sci.

WILLIAMS, Paul D; O Fallon Twp HS; O Fallon, IL; HonRl; JrNHS; NHS; SchPl; EngCl; GerCl; College; Minister.

WILLIAMS, Pearl N; B C Central HS; Battle Creek, MI; Band; ChrhWkr; HonRl; TchrAde;.

WILLIAMS, Rachel; Geneva Comm Hs; Geneva, IL; Chr; HonRl; LbryAde; SchMus; SchPl; Yrbk; RptrSchPpr; Swmmng; GAA; Carthage Collage ; Art.

WILLIAMS, Regina A; Lindblom Tech HS; Chicago, IL; 78/657 ChrhWkr; CmntyWkr; LbryAde; NHS; SchAde; TchrAde; YthFlsp; Trk; CaptChrldr; GAA; University Of Kansas; Chemical Engineer.

WILLIAMS, Reginald; Washington Park HS; Racine, WI; LetterBsktbl; Ftbl; University; Major Study.

WILLIAMS, Richard; Leaf River HS; Egan, IL; PresFrshCls; PresSophCls; PresJrCls; ALBoysSt; Band; Chrs; SchPl; StuCncl; 4-HAwd; Trade School; Vocation.

WILLIAMS, Richard J; Jackson Lumen Christi HS; Jacksn, MI; HonRl; Yrbk; Ftbl; LetterWrstlng; Grand Valley State U; Business Administrati.

WILLIAMS, Rita E; East Catholic HS; Detroit, MI; 4/92 VPSophCls; ChrhWkr; HonRl; NHS; StuCncl; Yrbk; RptrSchPpr; 4-H; PpCl; SciCl; Michigan State Univ; Accounting.

WILLIAMS, Rita M; Fatima HS; Bonnots Mill, MO; 3/120 SecTrsSrCls; Chrs; ChrhWkr; CmntyWkr; HonRl; LbryAde; PresCivCl; PresFBLA; VPFHA; PpCl; Lincoln Univ; Elem Education.

WILLIAMS, Robert J; Morton HS; Morton, IL; CmntyWkr; JA; RptrSchPpr; LetterGlf; JAAwd; Inst Of Tech; Marine Biol.

WILLIAMS, Robin D; Redford HS; Detroit, MI; HonRl; Ambassador College; Business Admin.

WILLIAMS, Ron; Stockbridge HS; Stockbridge, MI; 5/123 Band; CncrtBnd; HonRl; JrNHS; MrchBnd; NHS; SchPpr; Bsktbl; IMSpt; AmLegAwd; Mich State Univ; C P A.

WILLIAMS, Ron; Ritenour Sr HS; Overland, MO; Chr; HonRl; JrNHS; NHS; RptrYrbk; SptEdYrbk; Yrbk;.

WILLIAMS, Rosalind R; Roosevelt HS; Gary, IN; 118/623 ChrhWkr; HonRl; NatlMeritCmnd; OffAde; VPFBLA; FTA; SciCl; Bsktbl; GAA; Illinois University; Business Admin.

WILLIAMS, Roxie M; Ipswich HS; Ipswich, SD; 18/50 Band; HonRl; NHS; SchMus; SecStuCncl; YthFlsp; RptrSchPpr; FHA; LetterBsktbl; LetterTrk; Yankton Coll.

WILLIAMS, Ruth E; Van Far HS; Farber, MO; 9/97 SecSophCls; CmntyWkr; HonRl; MrchBnd; Quill&Scroll; TchrAde; Yrbk; FBLA; GAA; Marriage.

WILLIAMS, Ryan K; Tippecanoe Valley HS; Rochester, IN; NHS; SchMus; TchrAde; Bsktbl; Ftbl; Swmmng; Trk; College; Aviation.

WILLIAMS, Sandra; Morton HS; Morton, IL; 40/301 Chr; Chrl; HonRl; Mdrgl; PolWkr; SchMus; EdYrBk; 4-H; FrCl; 4-HAwd; College; Music.

WILLIAMS, Sandra J; Grand Ledge Acad; Des Moines, IA; SecSophCls; SecJrCls; HonRl; NHS; Yrbk; Andrews Univ; Accountant.

WILLIAMS, Sandra L; Southwest HS; Saint Louis, MO; Chr; ChrhWkr; CmntyWkr; HonRl; JA; SchPl; FBLA; PpCl; Trk; Chrldr; GAA; IMSpt; University; Chemistry.

WILLIAMS, Scott L; Forest Park HS; Crystal Falls, MI; PresSophCls; VPJrCls; Band; CncrtBnd; HonRl; MrchBnd; PepBnd; LetterBsktbl; LetterTennis; CitAwd; Mi Tech U; Bus Adm & Acct.

WILLIAMS, Settoria J; Thomas M Cooley HS; Detroit, MI; 2/150 HonRl; HospAde; JrNHS; NHS; OffAde; SchAde; SctActv; TchrAde; FBLA; Detroit College Of Business; Secretary.

WILLIAMS, Sheila C; East Catholic HS; Detroit, MI; 1/92 CmntyWkr; HonRl; ModUN; NHS; TchrAde; FrCl; SecSciCl; CaptBsktbl; Univ Of Michigan; Medicine.

WILLIAMS, Sheryl; Shawnee Mission South HS; Overland Park, KS; HonRl; HospAde; SctActv; TchrAde; PpCl; Trk; Univ; Nursing.

WILLIAMS, Sheryl L; Calumet HS; Gary, IN; 11/315 Band; CncrtBnd; DrmMjrt; HonRl; JrNHS; MrchBnd; NHS; PepBnd; SctActv; Indiana Univ; Nursing.

WILLIAMS, Stanley E; University City HS; St Louis, MO; Chr; ChrhWkr; HonRl; OffAde; TchrAde; YthFlsp; Bsbl; Ftbl; LetterSocr; IMSpt; College; Professional.

WILLIAMS, Steve D; Marion HS; Marion, KS; HonRl; FFA; SpnCl; Ftbl; Trade Sch; Vocation.

WILLIAMS, Sue Ann M; Breck HS; Minneapolis, MN; 1/66 Band; ChrhWkr; CmntyWkr; College; Social Work.

WILLIAMS, Susan A; South Side HS; Fort Wayne, IN; 2/420 ALAGirlsSt; HonRl; OffAde; SptEdYrbk; Yrbk; SchPpr; SpnCl; PpCl; CaptBsktbl; Trk; GAA; IMSpt; PPFtbl; Purdue University; Vet Science.

WILLIAMS, Susan A; Hanover Central HS; Crown Point, IN; ChrhWkr; DrlTm; OffAde; SctActv; StuCncl; TchrAde; Yrbk; 4-H; PpCl; LetterBsktbl; Social Work.

WILLIAMS, Susan L; East Buchanan C 1 HS; Agency, MO; 5/68 Band; Chrs; ChrhWkr; HonRl; SchPl; Yrbk; FHA; PpCl; School Of Nursing; Rn.

WILLIAMS, Susan L; Elgin HS; Elgin, IL; 7/985 Chr; HonRl; Illinois State Univ; Music.

WILLIAMS, Tammy L; Knightstown Comm HS; New Castle, IN; 16/126 TrsFrshCls; TrsJrCls; ALAGirlsSt; ChrhWkr; HospAde; OffAde; SchPl; SctActv; Sec4-H; PpCl; Bsktbl; Trk; GAA; 4-HAwd; College; Anesthesiologist.

WILLIAMS, Ted; Warsaw HS; Warsaw, IN; ALBoysSt; College; Writer Or Bus.

WILLIAMS, Terry; Owosso HS; Owosso, MI; 52/452 JA; NHS; TchrAde; JAAwd; Business School; Secretarial.

WILLIAMS, Terry J; Murray Wright HS; Detroit, MI; 2/380 HonRl; JrNHS; NHS; NatlMeritSchl; OffAde; SchAde; SchPl; TchrAde; YthFnd; Univ Of Detroit; Business Admin.

WILLIAMS, Terry W; Bernie HS; Bernie, MO; 8/52 ChrhWkr; CmntyWkr; HonRl; StuCncl; RptrYrbk; EdSchPpr; FFA; PpCl; Bsktbl; IMSpt; School Of Ozarks; Teaching.

WILLIAMS, Theodore J; Turner HS; Kansas City, KS; PresBand; ChrhWkr; CncrtBnd; HonRl; HospAde; JrNHS; MrchBnd; Orch; SchMus; University; Medicine Pro Musician.

WILLIAMS, Theresa A; Easton Comm Unit HS; Easton, IL; 4/19 Band; Chrs; CncrtBnd; HonRl; MrchBnd; PepBnd; YthFlsp; 4-H; PresFHA; GAA; Meth Schl Of Nursing; Nursing.

WILLIAMS, Thomas S; Cadillac HS; Cadillac, MI; CtyCnl; CmntyWkr; HonRl; NHS; SchPl; StuCncl; Kalamazoo Coll; Lawyer.

WILLIAMS, Thomas W; Shortridge HS; Indianapolis, IN; 6/421 ALBoysSt; ChrhWkr; CtyCnl; CmntyWkr; HonRl; IntrClCncl; JrNHS; PresNHS; NatlMeritSF; PresNatlThespSoc; PolWkr; SchPl; PresStuCncl; NCTE; Brown Univ; Lawyer.

WILLIAMS, Tim M; Mexico HS; Mexico, MO; ALBoysSt; SecNatlFornLg; SchMus; SchPl; SctActv; RptrYrbk; SecKeyCl; TreasLatCl; Univ; Bsnss.

WILLIAMS, Tim S; Interstate 35 HS; New Virginia, IA; VPSophCls; Chrs; CmntyWkr; HonRl; PepBnd; StuCncl; LetterFtbl; Trade Area Xi; Mechanic.

WILLIAMS, Tracey D; Anna Jonesboro C HS; Anna, IL; 1/143 HonRl; RptrYrbk; RptrSchPpr; FTA; SpnCl; PpCl; SciCl; Bsktbl; GAA; AmLegAwd; College; Vocational.

WILLIAMS, Tracy A; Salem HS; Salem, IN; Band; DrlTm; HonRl; JrNHS; NHS; RptrYrbk; LatCl; PpCl; LetterChrldr; GAA; Indiana Univ.

WILLIAMS, Tracy A; Whitewater HS; Whitewater, WI; 3/186 AFS; ALAGirlsSt; Band; Chr; Chrs; ChrhWkr; CncrtBnd; HonRl; JrNHS; Mdrgl; Univ Of Madison Wis; Pre Med.

WILLIAMS, Trudy J; Huntington North HS; Huntington, IN; Band; ChrhWkr; CncrtBnd; HonRl; MrchBnd; OffAde; SchMus; College; Medicine.

WILLIAMS, Valerie S; Wayne HS; Fort Wayne, IN; HonRl; YthFlsp; RptrSchPpr; Butler Univ; Ministry.

WILLIAMS, Vernette; Lucy Flower HS; Chicago, IL; AFS; Chr; Chrs; ChrhWkr; CmntyWkr; HonRl; JA; SchMus; SchPl; StuCncl; De Paul Univ; Drama, Special Ed.

WILLIAMS, Vincel W; Raymore Peculiar HS; Peculiar, MO; Aud/Vis; HonRl; NHS; 4-H; SpnCl; Trk; 4-HAwd; College; Liberal Arts.

WILLIAMS, Wanda A; 28814 Sumpter Rd; New Boston, MI; Chrs; ChrhWkr; CmntyWkr; HonRl; OffAde; StuCncl; TchrAde; Medical Tech.

WILLIAMS, Wanda R; St Thomas Apostle HS; Chicago, IL; 4/45 VPJrCls; Chr; ChrhWkr; CmntyWkr; HonRl; HospAde; SchPl; StuCncl; College; Liberal Arts.

WILLIAMS, William; St Louis Priory; St Louis, MO; 10/34 ChrhWkr; CmntyWkr; HonRl; NatlMeritCmnd; Orch; Teen; YthFlsp; RptrYrbk; FDA; Bsktbl; Duke Univ; Pro.

WILLIAMS, Wyman L; Center Grove HS; Greenwood, IN; 5/235 ALBoysSt; HonRl; JrNHS; NHS; SchMus; SchPl; RptrSchPpr; KeyCl; College; Electrical Engineering.

WILLIAMS, Yvette M; Laboure HS; St Louis, MO; Chrs; ChrhWkr; DrlTm; HonRl; SchPl; TchrAde; YthFnd; CchngActv; Kansas U; Architecture.

WILLIAMSON, Andrea L; Winchester Community HS; Ridgeville, IN; ALAGirlsSt; HonRl; NHS; SchPl; StuCncl; RptrSchPpr; FBLA; SpnCl; PpCl; GAA; Ball State Univ; Business.

WILLIAMSON, Ann K; Peoria Central HS; Peoria, IL; 24/481 Chr; HonRl; JrNHS; NHS; SchPl; SctActv; StuGov; SpnCl; PpCl; Augustana College; Social Work.

WILLIAMSON, Christine J; Mc Henry West Campus HS; Mc Henry, IL; ChrhWkr; HonRl; Trinity College; Science.

WILLIAMSON, Cynthia A; Platteview HS; Papillion, NE; DrlTm; HonRl; HospAde; JrNHS; NHS; ROTC; SchPl; StuCncl; StuGov; RptrYrbk; SchPpr; SpnCl; PpCl; College; Lawyer.

WILLIAMSON, David B; Highland Park HS; St Paul, MN; 24/544 Band; CncrtBnd; HonRl; NatlMeritSF; SchMus; University Of Minn; Elec Engineer.

WILLIAMSON, Debra L; Deerfield HS; Deerfield, IL; HonRl; NHS; NatlMeritSF; SchAde; SchMus; SchPl; StuCncl; StuGov; RptrYrbk; FrCl; Univ; Liberal Arts.

WILLIAMSON, Dennis A; Creighton Prep; Omaha, NE; 66/249 CmntyWkr; HonRl; SchPl; Sdlty; Bsktbl; Ftbl; Glf; IMSpt; College; Prof.

WILLIAMSON, Donna M; Bogan HS; Chicago, IL; 9/704 CmntyWkr; HonRl; NHS; OffAde; TchrAde; RptrSchPpr; SpnCl; MthCl; PpCl; GAA; U Of Illinois; Teacher.

WILLIAMSON, Elyse K; Southwestern HS; Lafayette, IN; 1/130 PresJrCls; ChrhWkr; CmntyWkr; NHS; NatlMeritSF; StuGov; EdSchPpr; MthCl; SciCl; DARAwd; Purdue Univ; Pre Med Major.

WILLIAMSON, Jody; Serena HS; Marseilles, IL; 17/82 SecFrshCls; SecSophCls; Band; Chrs; HonRl; PepBnd; SchMus; SchPl; StuCncl; 4-HAwd; Business College; Business.

WILLIAMSON, Karen; Marion Independent HS; Marion, IA; 1/179 Band; Chr; CncrtBnd; NHS; Trk; Univ; Engineering.

WILLIAMSON, Kathryn J; Ray Pec HS; Peculiar, MO; 4/130 Band; CncrtBnd; MrchBnd; PepBnd; SchMus; FHA; FTA; FrCl; PpCl; LetterTrk; Chrldr; GAA; Central Missouri St University.

WILLIAMSON, Myrna Y; Glenville HS; Glenville, MN; 3/49 Band; Chrs; HonRl; SchPl; StuCncl; TchrAde; FHA; LetterBsktbl; CaptChrldr; IMSpt; Vocational School; Sales.

WILLIAMSON, Patricia D; Mukwonago HS; Mukwonago, WI; Band; ChrhWkr; CncrtBnd; HonRl; JrNHS; MrchBnd; PresNHS; PepBnd; YthFlsp; TreasPpCl; IMSpt; LionAwd; College.

WILLIAMSON, Randall L; East Kentwood HS; Grand Rapids, MI; 16/389 HonRl; NHS; StuGov; LetterBsktbl; LetterFtbl; CchngActv; Coll; Law.

WILLIAMSON, Rhonda S; Northrop HS; Fort Wayne, IN; 37/630 Chr; Chrl; ChrhWkr; HonRl; HospAde; SchMus; SchPl; StuCncl; FshEdYrbk; CitAwd; College; Professional.

WILLIAMSON, Susan L; Peoria HS; Peoria, IL; 21/481 Chr; Chrl; Chrs; CmntyWkr; HonRl; JrNHS; Mdrgl; NHS; OffAde; SctActv; Teen; YthFlsp; SpnCl; PpCl; Augustana College; Medicine.

WILLIAMSON, Timothy L; Rochester HS; Rochester, MI; 1/372 PresSrCls; Chr; LitMag; ModUN; NHS; NatlMeritSF; PolWkr; SchPl; PresGerCl; LetterTennis; Amherst College; Political Science.

WILLIAMSON, Wesley B; Dearborn HS; Dearborn, MI; CmntyWkr; HonRl; LitMag; NatlThespSoc; SchMus; SchPl; UNYO; FrCl; GerCl; Clg; Prof.

WILLICK, Kim A; Waterford Union HS; Waterford, WI; 11/189 AFS; Band; HonRl; NHS; PepBnd; RptrYrbk; RptrSchPpr; PpCl; LetterTennis; LetterGAA; Clge.

WILLIFORD, Grady H; East Prairie HS; East Prairie, MO; HonRl; StuCncl; StuGov; FFA; SpnCl; CaptBsktbl; Ftbl; Trk; IMSpt; Col; Physical Ed.

WILLIS, Anne; Chesterton HS; Chesterton, IN; SecBand; CncrtBnd; HonRl; LitMag; MrchBnd; NatlFornLg; SecNHS; SctActv; StuGov; FrCl;.

WILLIS, Carl M; Roosevelt HS; Gary, IN; NatlMeritCmnd; LetterBsbl; CitAwd; Coll; Accountant.

WILLIS, Carol A; Carrollton Sr HS; Carrollton, MO; 17/100 VPFrshCls; HonRl; HospAde; LbryAde; NHS; TchrAde; 4-H; GerCl; PpCl; SciCl; University; Nursing.

WILLIS, Catherine; Louisiana HS; Louisiana, MO; SecJrCls; Band; Chr; HonRl; NHS; NatlMeritCmnd; SchMus; SchPl; FTA; FrCl; Univ Of Missouri; Psych.

WILLIS, Cheryl L; Santa Fe HS; Concordia, MO; TrsJrCls; DrlTm; HonRl; SecNHS; SecStuCncl; FHA; SecPpCl; Central Miss St U; Home Ec.

WILLIS, Clifford L; Bowling Green HS; Bowling Green, MO; Chr; Chrs; HonRl; NatlMeritCmnd; SchMus; RptrSchPpr; Trk; IMSpt; College; English Or Journalism.

WILLIS, Debra J; Bellevue HS; Bellevue, MI; 14/120 CncrtBnd; DrmMjrt; TreasNatlFornLg; NHS; YthFlsp; EdSchPpr; LetterBsktbl; Chrldr; DARAwd; CitAwd; Mich State U; Elem Ed.

WILLIS, Dotty J; Macks Creek HS; Macks Creek, MO; SecTrsFrshCls; TrsJrCls; PresSrCls; Chr; Chrs; ChrhWkr; HonRl; OffAde; SchAde; StuCncl; LetterBsbl; LetterBsktbl; LetterChrldr; College.

WILLIS, James W; Centerville HS; Centerville, IA; HonRl; SchPl; Business School.

WILLIS, Joann; Maysville HS; Clarksdale, MO; Chr; Chrs; HonRl; NHS; OffAde; RptrYrbk; RptrSchPpr; FHA; PpCl;.

WILLIS, Michael E; Maconaquah HS; Peru, IN; CmntyWkr; StuCncl; Bsktbl; Ftbl; Trk; College; Business.

WILLIS, Nancy S; Dows Community HS; Dows, IA; 2/27 TrsJrCls; Band; Chrs; CncrtBnd; HonRl; LbryAde; MrchBnd; NHS; OffAde; PepBnd; SchPpr; 4-H; University; Home Economics.

WILLIS, Robert W; Mt Vernon Twp HS; Mt Vernon, IL; HonRl; TchrAde; Ftbl; CitAwd; Siu.

WILLIS, Rose; David Mackenzie HS; Detroit, MI; 10/348 PresJrCls; Chr; HonRl; NHS; OffAde; SchAde; StuCncl; FTA; PpCl; Mi State Univ; Bus Admin.

WILLIS, Samuel; Ic Elston Sr HS; Michigan City, IN; Aud/Vis; HonRl; NHS; TchrAde; SptEdYrbk; SpnCl; SciCl; Univ Of Notre Dame; State Dept.

WILLIS, Sherman A; Hayti HS; Hayti, MO; 40/92 Chr; ChrhWkr; CmntyWkr; LbryAde; YthFlsp; SchPpr; FrCl; Bsbl; Bsktbl; Trade School; Printing.

WILLIS, Tony J; Jeffersonville HS; Jeffersonville, IN; 32/560 VPSophCls; HonRl; NHS; PolWkr; RptrYrbk; SptEdSchPpr; GerCl; PpCl; Indiana University; Journalism.

WILLITS, Diane E; Westmer HS; New Boston, IL; 10/65 Band; Chrs; HonRl; SchMus; Yrbk; FTA; SpnCl; SciCl; GAA; PresAwd; Western Illinois Univ; Accountant.

WILLKE, Patty; Octavia HS; Anchor, IL; Band; Chrs; NHS; SchMus; SchPl; StuCncl; RptrSchPpr; Trk; 4-HAwd; Trade School; Radiological Technologist.

WILLKOMM, Mary Beth; Salem Central HS; Salem, WI; 62/214 ChrhWkr; TchrAde; 4-H; FHA; PpCl; 4-HAwd; LionAwd; Milwaukee Area Tech Col; Physical Therapy.

WILLMAN, Charles A; Westmer HS; Seaton, IL; 1/68 HonRl; StuCncl; FTA; SpnCl; SciCl; Bsbl; Bsktbl; Ftbl; Trk; College; Professional.

WILLMAN, Stephen; St Louis Priory HS; St Louis, MO; StuCncl; StuGov; Yrbk; Ftbl; Socr; Trk; Umiv.

WILLMANN, Jutta; Lisle Senior Hs; Lisle, IL; 12/200 AFS; ChrhWkr; HonRl; NHS; NatlThespSoc; StuCncl; EdSchPpr; FBLA; FrCl; LetterSocr; Ui Urbana;journalism Major.

WILLMS, Gary L; Centerville Public HS; Centerville, SD; HonRl; LbryAde; SpnCl;.

WILLMS, Lyndon G; St Elmo HS; St Elmo, IL; Band; CncrtBnd; HonRl; MrchBnd; PepBnd; SchMus; RptrYrbk; RptrSchPpr; FrCl; PpCl; SciCl; S Illinois Univ; Justice Admin.

WILLMS, Myra K; Stuart Menlo Comm HS; Casey, IA; 4/65 Chrs; DrlTm; HonRl; MrchBnd; NatlThespSoc; SchMus; SchPl; 4-H; FHA; 4-HAwd; College; Vocation.

WILLNERD, Marjean; Wolbach Public HS; Wolbach, NE; 3/17 TrsSophCls; SecJrCls; SecSrCls; ALAGirlsSt; SchPl; StuGov; TchrAde; Yrbk; 4-H; Chadron State College; Medical Technology.

WILLNS, James S; Dike Comm HS; Parkersburg, IA; SecSophCls; PresSrCls; ChrhWkr; CmntyWkr; 4-H; LetterBsbl; LetterBsktbl; LetterFtbl; LetterTrk; 4-HAwd; Iowa St Univ; Farm.

WILLOUGHBY, David M; Pendleton Heights HS; Lapel, IN; 24/290 CaptSwmmng; LetterTrk; Univ; Chemistry.

WILLOUGHBY, Debbie L; Sarcoxie HS; Reeds, MO; Chr; ChrhWkr; HonRl; Mdrgl; FHA; William Jewell College; Music.

WILLOUGHBY, Jill L; Arthur HS; Arthur, IL; Band; Chr; Chrs; CncrtBnd; HonRl; Mdrgl; MrchBnd; NHS; PepBnd; SchPl; RptrYrbk; FHA; College; Vocation.

WILLOUGHBY, John J; Midland HS; Midland, SD; Chrs; ChrhWkr; HonRl; SchMus; SchPl; StuCncl; RptrYrbk; SptEdSchPpr; 4-H; Bsbl; CaptLetterFtbl; LetterTrk; Trade School.

WILLOUGHBY, Lance M; Jefferson County North HS; Nortonville, KS; 3/48 PresFrshCls; ALBoysSt; Band; ChrhWkr; CncrtBnd; HonRl; NHS; Natl-MeritCmnd; NatlMeritSF; SctActv; StuCncl; YthFlsp; LetterBsktbl; LetterFtbl; University Of Kansas; Professional.

WILLOUGHBY, Patrick J; Argenta Oreana HS; Argenta, IL; 9/77 NHS; Bradley University; Engineering.

WILLOUGHBY, Paula J; Keokuk Senior HS; Keokuk, IA; 31/134 Band; CncrtBnd; HonRl; MrchBnd; NHS; NatlThespSoc; PepBnd; SchPl; RptrSchPpr; SchPpr; Southeastern Iowa Comm College; Rn.

WILLRETT, Linda R; Malta HS; Malta, IL; 7/35 Chr; Chrs; HonRl; NHS; OffAde; YthFlsp; RptrYrbk; FHA; University; Professional.

WILLS, Alan C; Galena HS; Galena, IL; 17/105 HonRl; ModUN; Pres4-H; PresFFA; 4-HAwd; Bus Sch; Farm.

WILLS, Bill R; Lexington HS; Lexington, IL; 14/62 HonRl; IMSpt; Western Illinois Univ.

WILLS, Jeffery; South Decatur HS; Westport, IN; CmntyWkr; HonRl; SchPl; SctActv; FrCl; PpCl; Bsbl; Bsktbl; Glf; College; Dentist.

WILLS, Karen S; Risco HS; Malden, MO; Chrs; SchAde; SchMus; SchPl; SctActv; YthFlsp; RptrSchPpr; PpCl; Bsktbl; College; Physical Education.

WILLS, Kenneth J; Sevastopol HS; Sturgeon Bay, WI; 1/73 PresFrshCls; PresSophCls; PresSrCls; Band; MrchBnd; NHS; PepBnd; SchMus; Bsktbl; IMSpt; Col; Engineering.

WILLSON, Becky L; Litchville Public HS; Litchville, ND; 11/28 Band; Chrs; HonRl; StuCncl; 4-H; Bsktbl; Trk; Chrldr; GAA; IMSpt; Business; Acctng.

WILLSON, Jeannie L; Vienna HS; Vienna, IL; 3/100 ChrhWkr; HonRl; NatlThespSoc; SchPl; Sec-StuCncl; PresFTA; PresMthCl; SecPpCl; Bsktbl; GAA; DARAwd; Shawnee Jr College; Sec Science.

WILLSON, Michael W; St Peter HS; Kasota, MN; HonRl; JrNHS; NHS; SchPl; SctActv; StuCncl; Bsbl; Ftbl; VFWAwd; College; Professional.

WILLSON, Pamela S; Glenbrook North HS; Northbrook, IL; SecJrCls; HonRl; StuCncl; StuGov; RptrYrbk; EdYrBk; PpCl; College; Philosophy.

WILLY, John P; Parkside HS; Jackson, MI; 3/415 HonRl; Trk; Univ Of Az; Astronomy.

WILLY, Kathleen E; Brookfield Academy; Elm Grove, WI; TrsFrshCls; PresSophCls; PresJrCls; HonRl; NatlThespSoc; SchPl; EdYrBk; PpCl; CaptBsktbl; Chrldr; College.

WILLYARD, Douglas C; Lebanon Comm HS; Lebanon, IL; 5/100 Band; HonRl; NHS; Natl-MeritCmnd; SchPl; StuCncl; LetterTennis; Univ Of Illinois; Medicine.

WILMER, Alyce; Warroad HS; Warroad, MN; SctActv; Trk; Chrldr; CchngActv; GAA; IMSpt; PPFtbl; 4-HAwd; PresAwd; College; Health Field.

WILMINGTON, Wray P; Plainfield HS; Joliet, IL; HonRl; NatlThespSoc; PolWkr; Quill&Scroll; SchMus; Bsbl; Bsktbl; Ftbl; IMSpt; VoiceDemAwd; College; Business Admin.

WILMOT, Dana R; Keokuk HS; Keokuk, IA; 1/200 HonRl; NatlFornLg; NHS; NatlMeritCmnd; Natl-ThespSoc; SctActv; YthFlsp; MthCl; GodCntryAwd; VoiceDemAwd; Iowa State U; Engineering.

WILMOT, Michael S; St Patrick HS; Norridge, IL; CmntyWkr; HonRl; LetterBsktbl; College.

WILMOTH, Walter; Rolla HS; Cuba, MO; 63/307 Band; CncrtBnd; HonRl; MrchBnd; NHS; SchAde; Bsktbl; Coll; Accountant.

WILMSMEYER, Maria E; Warren County R Ii HS; Wright City, MO; 2/45 TrsJrCls; TrsSrCls; Pres-Band; Chrs; HonRl; SecNHS; StuCncl; FTA; LionAwd; Univ Of Mo Rolla; Medecine.

WILSON, Angie M; Corning Comm HS; Corning, IA; 17/74 PresSrCls; HonRl; NHS; NatlThespSoc; SchPl; StuCncl; Bsbl; Bsktbl; Ftbl; CitAwd; Northwest Mo St Univ; Elem Ed Teacher.

WILSON, Anita D; Edinburg Community HS; Edinburg, IN; ChrhWkr; HonRl; HospAde; SctActv; FHA; SpnCl; PpCl; Bsktbl; Trk; Col; Nursing.

WILSON, Barbara J; Eastern HS; Owensburg, IN; 8/69 ChrhWkr; HonRl; HospAde; NHS; Business School; Secretary.

WILSON, Becky A; Glasgow R Ii HS; Glasgow, MO; ALAGirlsSt; HonRl; SchPpr; FHA; LetterBsbl; Bsktbl; Swmmng; Tennis; LetterTrk; PresAwd; College; Physical Therapist Or Nurse.

WILSON, Berneil R; High School; Birmingham, IA; Chrs; ChrhWkr; HonRl; SchPl; SpnCl; Calvary Bible College; Speech Pathologist.

WILSON, Beth Anne H; Glenbard East HS; Glen Ellyn, IL; 47/653 Chr; Chrl; Chrs; HonRl; College; Medical Technologist.

WILSON, Betty J; Hayes County HS; Culbertson, NE; 1/24 ALAGirlsSt; Chrs; HonRl; ModUN; NHS; Twrl; GAA; Mccook Community College; Accounting.

WILSON, Bruce D; Fairfield HS; Barnhill, IL; Aud/Vis; OffAde; Quill&Scroll; TchrAde; RptrSchPpr; SchPpr; 4-H; Business Sch; Accounting.

WILSON, Candi A; Alton HS; West Plains, MO; Chrs; SchPl; TchrAde; FHA; College; Mathematics.

WILSON, Carla J; Central Noble HS; Albion, IN; 23/111 Chrs; ChrhWkr; VP4-H; GAA; 4-HAwd; School Of Nursing; Registered Nurse.

WILSON, Carol A; Charlevoix HS; Charlevoix, MI; 11/147 HonRl; LatCl; TreasSpnCl; Butterworth Hosp Schl; Nursing.

WILSON, Cathy L; Cowan HS; Muncie, IN; ChrhWkr; CncrtBnd; HonRl; HospAde; MrchBnd; PepBnd; SchAde; Yrbk; Bsktbl; GAA; Cumberland Coll; Physical Ed.

WILSON, Cecilia A; South Pemiscot HS; Steele, MO; Chr; Chrs; ChrhWkr; LbryAde; OffAde; PepBnd; PpCl; Marriage.

WILSON, Cheryl A; Bunker Hill HS; Bunker Hill, IL; 2/80 Chr; Chrs; ChrhWkr; HonRl; JrNHS; NHS; NatlMeritFnl; NatlMeritSF; SctActv; YthFlsp; College; Pharmacy.

WILSON, Christine D; Arlington HS; Indianapolis, IN; Chr; HonRl; Quill&Scroll; SchMus; SchPl; StuCncl; Yrbk; RptrSchPpr; Chrldr; Indiana University.

WILSON, Curtis L; Chicago Vocational HS; Chicago, IL; 80/668 ChrhWkr; Univ Of Ill; Accounting.

WILSON, Cynthia; Central Of Argyle HS; Donnellson, IA; 7/63 VPJrCls; SecSrCls; HospAde; NHS; SctActv; RptrYrbk; FHA; CchngActv; Kirkwood Coll; Floriculture.

WILSON, Daniel L; Culbertson HS; Culbertson, NE; 3/23 VPFrshCls; SecSophCls; PresJrCls; Band; Chr; Chrs; ChrhWkr; CmntyWkr; CncrtBnd; HonRl; W Point Military Academy.

WILSON, Daniel L; Plano HS; Plano, IL; HonRl; NHS; FFA; Bsbl; LetterFtbl; LetterTrk; LetterWrstlng; CchngActv; College; Vocation.

WILSON, David E; Raymond Central HS; Ceresco, NE; SchPl; SctActv; EngCl; SciCl; LetterWrstlng; University Of Ne; Architect.

WILSON, David G; Mona Shores HS; Muskegon, MI; HonRl; NHS; LetterFtbl; Trk; Muskegon Comm College.

WILSON, David S; Zion Benton Twp HS; Zion, IL; 30/405 Band; ChrhWkr; CncrtBnd; HonRl; MrchBnd; NHS; PepBnd; SctActv; YthFlsp; College; Biology.

WILSON, David W; Fox Valley HS; Milton, IA; 2/17 ALBoysSt; Chr; HonRl; MrchBnd; NHS; PepBnd; SchMus; SchPl; PresStuCncl; Trk; Iowa State Clg; Engineering.

WILSON, Dean R; Denby HS; Detroit, MI; Aud/Vis; HonRl; SchPl; StuCncl; College; Chemist.

WILSON, Debbie K; Shelbyville HS; Shelbyville, IN; Chr; ChrhWkr; HonRl; OffAde; FHA; FTA; PpCl; Lee Coll; Bus.

WILSON, Deborah; Beecher HS; Flint, MI; OffAde; Beautician.

WILSON, Deborah S; Milan HS; Milan, MI; 13/170 Band; CncrtBnd; HonRl; HospAde; MrchBnd; SecNHS; PepBnd; TchrAde; Twrl; LetterSwmmng; CchngActv; Mercy School; Nursing.

WILSON, Del M; Seymour HS; Seymour, MO; PresFrshCls; VPJrCls; HonRl; TchrAde; PpCl; LetterBsbl; Bsktbl; Univ Of Mo Rolla; Engineering.

WILSON, Douglas A; Lawrence Central HS; Indianapolis, IN; 25/750 NHS; CaptSocr; Clge; Medicine.

WILSON, Douglas D; Larkin HS; Elgin, IL; ChrhWkr; NatlMeritCmnd; NatlMeritSF; TchrAde; LetterBsktbl; LetterTrk; College; Engineering.

WILSON, Edwin I; Crowleys Ridge Academy; Senath, MO; Chrs; ChrhWkr; HonRl; Quill&Scroll; SchPl; TchrAde; RptrYrbk; RptrSchPpr; FTA; Oklahoma Christian College; Cartoonist.

WILSON, Ellen K; Northwest HS; Grand Island, NE; Band; Chr; CncrtBnd; HonRl; NatlThespSoc; SchMus; SchPl; Kearney State Coll; Dietitian.

WILSON, Erin K; Seymour HS; Hull, IL; Band; Chrs; ChrhWkr; HonRl; HospAde; TchrAde; 4-H; FHA; PpCl; Bsktbl; GAA; College; Marketing.

WILSON, Esther K; Winfield HS; Winfield, KS; 6/173 ALAGirlsSt; ChrhWkr; HonRl; HospAde; StuCncl; TchrAde; YthFlsp; PpCl; Bsbl; LetterBsktbl; Sw College; Business.

WILSON, Gene B; Brown HS; Piedmont, SD; 6/200 ALBoysSt; Band; ChrhWkr; HonRl; NHS; YthFlsp; 4-H; Wrstlng; IMSpt; Navy; Electronics.

WILSON, Geneva J; Mc Henry Community HS; Mc Henry, IL; 47/491 Band; ChrhWkr; CncrtBnd; HonRl; HospAde; MrchBnd; NHS; SctActv; RptrYrbk; Yrbk; FBLA; Swmmng; Tennis; Business School; Accounting.

WILSON, Glenn; Vashon HS; St Louis, MO; 191/404 HonRl; LetterBsbl; CaptSocr; Wrstlng; JAAwd; CitAwd; Trade School; Vocation.

WILSON, Gregory; North Putnam HS; Roachdale, IN; 3/135 Band; CncrtBnd; HonRl; MrchBnd; NHS; Orch; SchAde; LatCl; MthCl; IMSpt; Indiana Univ;.

WILSON, James; Holt HS; Holt, MI; 28/290 VPSrCls; CncrtBnd; HonRl; MrchBnd; NHS; PepBnd; SchMus; StuGov; Michigan State Univ; Pre Med.

WILSON, James A; Hannibal HS; Hannibal, MO; ALBoysSt; NHS; StuCncl; FBLA; KeyCl; Tennis; IMSpt; ChmbCommrsAwd; JCAwd; KiwanAwd; Mo Univ; Forestry.

WILSON, James E; Benton Co R2 HS; Lincoln, MO; PresSrCls; ALBoysSt; Band; Chrs; CncrtBnd; HonRl; MrchBnd; NHS; SchPl; StuCncl; Yrbk; Central Missour State Univ; Dentistry.

WILSON, James G; Putnam Co R 1 HS; Unionville, MO; 5/88 CncrtBnd; HonRl; MrchBnd; NHS; Natl-MeritSchl; SchPl; SchPpr; Bsbl; LetterBsktbl; Trk; Northeast Missouri State Univ; Business Adm.

WILSON, James R; Bellmont HS; Decatur, IN; 33/255 ALBoysSt; ChrhWkr; HonRl; NHS; StuCncl; PpCl; SciCl; IMSpt; AmLegAwd; LionAwd; Ind Univ; Mechanical Engineering.

WILSON, Jan A; Tecumseh HS; Tecumseh, MI; 13/239 CncrtBnd; HonRl; MrchBnd; NHS; PepBnd; TchrAde; Central Mi Univ; Music.

WILSON, Jane M; Marion Co R 2 HS; Philadelphia, MO; Chrs; HonRl; HospAde; SchPl; StuCncl; 4-H; FHA; LetterBsbl; LetterBsktbl; 4-HAwd; Bus Sch; Profess.

WILSON, Janet; Holdrege HS; Holdrege, NE; Band; CncrtBnd; MrchBnd; PepBnd; StuGov; PpCl; Bsktbl; Trk; Coll; Professional.

WILSON, Jay L; De Soto HS; Dittmer, MO; HonRl; JrNHS; Sw Baptist College; Religion.

WILSON, Jeanne K; St Josephs Academy; University City, MO; 38/125 VPSophCls; CmntyWkr; HonRl; LitMag; VPStuCncl; PpCl; Tennis; CchngActv; GAA; IMSpt; Benedictine College; Education.

WILSON, Jeannie L; Lilbourn HS; Lilbourn, MO; Band; CncrtBnd; HonRl; MrchBnd; StuCncl; RptrYrbk; FBLA; FHA; TreasPpCl; BttyCrckrAwd;.

WILSON, Jeffrey A; Grandview HS; Grandview, MO; 37/487 ALBoysSt; Band; CncrtBnd; HonRl; StuCncl; YthFlsp; Ftbl; Trk; Wrstlng;.

WILSON, Jennifer L; North Mercer R Iii HS; Grain Valley, MO; SecJrCls; TrsSrCls; HonRl; OffAde; SchPl; StuCncl; TchrAde; EdYrBk; SchPpr; DARAwd;.

WILSON, Jerry; Northeast Usd Hs; Girard, KS; ChrhWkr; HonRl; RptrYrbk; RptrSchPpr;.

WILSON, Jerry L; Holcomb HS; Holcomb, MO; Chrs; HonRl; LbryAde; NHS; StuGov; RptrYrbk; SchPpr; FHA; PpCl; Chrldr; College; Professional.

WILSON, Jill S; Watertown Sr HS; Watertown, SD; DrlTm; HonRl; NatlThespSoc; SctActv; StuGov; GerCl; PpCl; SciCl; Trk; GAA; University; Professional.

WILSON, Jim B; Clarks Public HS; Clarks, NE; Band; Chrl; CncrtBnd; HonRl; MrchBnd; PepBnd; SchMus; YthFlsp; 4-H; LetterBsktbl; Ftbl; Trk; DanFAwd; 4-HAwd; Univ Of Nebr; Extension Agent.

WILSON, Jo E; Fairfield Community HS; Fairfield, IL; Band; CncrtBnd; HonRl; MrchBnd; LatCl; PpCl; GAA; Univ Of Il; Math.

WILSON, Jonathan A; Memorial HS; Joplin, MO; 1/300 ChrhWkr; HonRl; JrNHS; LitMag; SctActv; RptrSchPpr; SptEdSchPpr; SchPpr; LatCl; MthCl; LetterTrk; College.

WILSON, Joni; Palmyra HS; Bennet, NE; Chrs; HonRl; SchPl; RptrYrbk; EdSchPpr; 4-H; SpnCl; PpCl; Trk; U Ne.

WILSON, Karen; Westville HS; Westville, IL; 1/105 ChrhWkr; CtyCnl; CmntyWkr; HonRl; JrNHS; LitMag; LbryAde; CchngActv; IMSpt; PPFtbl; Eastern Il Univ; Law.

WILSON, Kathleen A; Alleman HS; Rock Island, IL; ChrhWkr; HonRl; LbryAde; NHS; FrCl; GAA; Blackhawk College; Nursing.

WILSON, Kathleen A; Civic Memorial HS; Bethalto, IL; 42/221 SecTrsJrCls; SecTrsSrCls; ChrhWkr; CmntyWkr; HonRl; SchPl; Yrbk; GerCl; Bsbl; Chrldr; GAA; College; Art.

WILSON, Kenneth; Luther South HS; Chicago, IL; 14/204 Chr; HonRl; JrNHS; LbryAde; NHS; SchPl; StuCncl; YthLg; Yrbk; Bsktbl; Ftbl; LetterTrk; PresAwd; College; Doctor.

WILSON, Kenneth J; Washington Twp HS; Valparaiso, IN; 2/30 ALBoysSt; HonRl; StuCncl; SpnCl; Bsbl; Bsktbl; Trk; JETSAwd; Notre Dame; Engineering.

WILSON, Kennith W; Oak Grove HS; Oak Grove, MO; SecFrshCls; Band; CncrtBnd; LbryAde; MrchBnd; StuCncl; Ftbl; Trk; Univ; Doctor.

WILSON, Kimball F; Caro HS; Caro, MI; 59/168 HonRl; PpCl; Bsktbl; Ftbl; Tennis; IMSpt; AmLegAwd; JCAwd; RotaryAwd; College; Professional.

WILSON, Kimberly A; Cairo HS; Cairo, IL; Chrs; ChrhWkr; SchAde; SchMus; 4-H; PpCl; LetterBsbl; CaptBsktbl; GAA; IMSpt; 4-HAwd; College; Medical Lab Tech.

WILSON, Kymberly P; North Chicago HS; North Chicao, IL; Chr; HonRl; NHS; SchMus; SchPl; StuCncl; TchrAde; San Jose State Univ; Law.

WILSON, Linda A; St Mary Central HS; Neenah, WI; Band; CncrtBnd; JA; MrchBnd; PepBnd; FrCl; PpCl; College; Professional.

WILSON, Linda K; George Washington HS; Indianapolis, IN; VPSophCls; Chr; JA; StuCncl; 4-H; PpCl; SciCl; 4-HAwd; Purdue Univ; Computor Tech.

WILSON, Lloyd C; Southwest HS; St Louis, MO; 50/491 Band; NatlMeritCmnd; College; Engineer.

WILSON, Margaret A; Kirksville HS; Kirksville, MO; 15/185 ChrhWkr; CncrtBnd; HonRl; HospAde; LbryAde; MrchBnd; SctActv; FrCl; SciCl; LetterTennis; Nmsu; Pre Osteopath.

WILSON, Marilyn E; Marshalltown Senior HS; Marshalltown, IA; Chr; Chrs; ChrhWkr; HonRl; Natl-MeritSF; SctActv; TchrAde; FTA; Univ Of Iowa; Pharmacy.

WILSON, Marion; Seaman HS; Topeka, KS; Band; ChrhWkr; HonRl; ModUN; NatlMeritCmnd; SchMus; SchPl; Chrldr; PPFtbl; VFWAwd; Univ; Elec Engr.

WILSON, Mark D; Albia Comm HS; Albia, IA; 35/149 HonRl; YthFlsp; 4-H; FFA; 4-HAwd; Indian Hills Comm College.

WILSON, Mark E; Univ Of Detroit HS; Detroit, MI; SecFrshCls; HonRl; NatlMeritCmnd; SchPl; StuGov; Yrbk; SchPpr; Ftbl; Trk; Kalamazoo Univ; Medicine.

WILSON, Mark T; U HS; Warrensburg, MO; PresSophCls; HonRl; NHS; SchPl; StuCncl; SptEdSchPpr; FFA; Bsktbl; Ftbl;.

WILSON, Marla K; Edwardsville Sr HS; Edwardsville, IL; Chrs; DrlTm; SpnCl; GAA; IMSpt; College; Teacher.

WILSON, Mary E; Grand Blanc HS; Grand Blanc, MI; PresChr; PresChrs; CmntyWkr; HonRl; Mdrgl; NatlFornLg; NatlThespSoc; SchMus; AmLegAwd; VoiceDemAwd; Oakland University; Music.

WILSON, Mary M; Central Catholic HS; Bloomington, IL; 5/85 Chrs; HonRl; JA; NHS; StuCncl; FrCl; PpCl; Bsktbl; Tennis; Univ Of Illinois.

WILSON, Mary T; St Mary Acad; Indianapolis, IN; 12/35 PresFrshCls; Chrl; Chrs; HonRl; HospAde; SchPl; StuCncl; Yrbk; SpnCl; GAA; Iupui & Marian; Secondary Ed.

WILSON, Matthew D; Plano Sr HS; Plano, IL; 3/95 ALBoysSt; HonRl; PresNHS; TreasFFA; LetterBsbl; CaptFtbl; LetterTrk; CaptWrstlng; CchngActv; Illinois State Univ; Agriculture.

WILSON, Michael; Franklin HS; Livonia, MI; ChrhWkr; Univ Of Mich; School Of Engineering.

WILSON, Michael A; Raytown HS; Kansas City, MO; 27/629 HonRl; JrNHS; LitMag; NatlFornLg; NHS; NatlMeritSF; GerCl; LetterBsktbl; IMSpt; NCTE; Univ Of Mo; Engineering.

WILSON, Michael P; Bishop Mc Namara HS; Kankakee, IL; 9/168 HonRl; NHS; NatlMeritCmnd; SchPl; StuCncl; TchrAde; EdYrBk; University Of Illinois; Accounting.

WILSON, Millicent; Sunnydale Acad; Pleasant Hill, MO; Band; Chr; HonRl; HospAde; LbryAde; OffAde; Orch; StuCncl; Yrbk; College; Nursing.

WILSON, Nancy J; Weeping Water Public HS; Weeping Water, NE; VPJrCls; ALAGirlsSt; Band; HonRl; NHS; RedCrAde; RptrYrbk; RptrSchPpr; TreasFBLA; Chrldr;.

WILSON, Pamela G; Delavan HS; Delavan, IL; HonRl; JrNHS; NHS; NatlMeritSchl; SctActv; GAA; 4-HAwd; GovHonPrgAwd; JAAwd; PresAwd;.

WILSON, Pamela J; Canton Sr HS; Canton, IL; 8/266 Chrs; ChrhWkr; HonRl; PresNHS; NatlThespSoc; SchMus; SchPl; VPFrCl; PresSciCl; CaptTennis; College; Biology.

WILSON, Pamela J; Newton HS; Dundas, IL; 30/185 Chrs; HonRl; HospAde; LbryAde; 4-H; FNA; Indiana U; Nursing.

WILSON, Pamela S; Tipton HS; Tipton, IN; Chr; HonRl; NHS; FHA; PpCl; Clg.

WILSON, Patricia; Arthur County HS; Lemoyne, NE; Band; Chrs; HonRl; PepBnd; SchPl; Yrbk; 4-H; Chrldr; PPFtbl; College; Professional.

WILSON, Peter C; Marquette Sr HS; Marquette, MI; 31/388 Aud/Vis; PresChrl; CmntyWkr; CncrtBnd; MrchBnd; NatlMeritCmnd; NatlThespSoc; Orch; PepBnd; SchMus; SchPl; EldAwd; Michigan Tech Univ; Electrical Engineering.

WILSON, Randall; Central HS; St Joseph, MO; 10/507 ChrhWkr; HonRl; IntrClCncl; StuCncl; YthLg; GerCl; SciCl; College; Science.

WILSON, Randy; Central Noble HS; Albion, IN; 28/111 HonRl; StuCncl; Bsktbl; Glf; Tennis; IMSpt; Univ; Brdcasting.

WILSON, Raymond D; Lathrop HS; Lathrop, MO; 5/57 PresSophCls; Band; ChrhWkr; CncrtBnd; HonRl; MrchBnd; PepBnd; StuCncl; RptrYrbk; Yrbk; Bsktbl; Us Naval Academy; Career Officer.

WILSON, Renee A; Greenway HS; Grand Rapids, MN; 2/176 Band; Chr; ChrhWkr; HonRl; NHS; RptrYrbk; RptrSchPpr; PpCl; Chrldr; GAA; Univ; Medicine.

WILSON, Reta F; Oskaloosa HS; Oskaloosa, KS; HonRl; NHS; SchPl; TchrAde; 4-H; FBLA; PpCl; LetterBsktbl; 4-HAwd; PresAwd;.

WILSON, Rhonda F; Wayne City HS; Keenes, IL; 4/58 Chrs; CmntyWkr; HonRl; YthFlsp; PpCl; Chrldr; GAA; College; C P A.

WILSON, Rhonda Lee; Maddock Public HS; Maddock, ND; VPFrshCls; PresJrCls; Band; HonRl; PepBnd; SchPl; EdYrBk; SchPpr; FHA; Univ Nd; Medical.

WILSON, Robert D; Beecher HS; Mt Morris, MI; Band; CncrtBnd; DrmMjrt; JA; MrchBnd; Orch; PepBnd; SchMus; Bsbl; LetterWrstlng; College; Professional.

WILSON, Robin; Central HS; St Joseph, MO; 15/505 ChrhWkr; HonRl; NHS; SchMus; TchrAde; FrCl; PpCl;.

WILSON, Rolf; Argenta HS; Argenta, IL; 1/79 Band; CncrtBnd; NatlMeritFnl; NatlMeritSchl; SchPl; SciCl; Trk; Wrstlng; DanFAwd; OptClAwd; Univ Of Ill.

WILSON, Ronald J; Hartford HS; Hartford, KS; SecTrsFrshCls; Band; ChrhWkr; HonRl; MrchBnd; StuCncl; 4-H; Ftbl; Wrstlng; 4-HAwd; Trade Sch; Vocation.

WILSON, Ronda J; Arkansas City Sr HS; Arkansas City, KS; 20/192 Band; CmntyWkr; HonRl; MrchBnd; SchPl; StuCncl; TchrAde; Yrbk; RptrSchPpr; 4-H; FFA; FTA; Swmmng; Kansas St University.

WILSON, Russell; R1 North Callaway HS; Auxvasse, MO; VPFrshCls; CmntyWkr; HonRl; SchPl; SptEdYrbk; FrCl; Bsktbl; Ftbl; Trk; CitAwd; Univ; Bilology.

WILSON, Sandra S; Dakota HS; Dakota, IL; Band; ChrhWkr; CncrtBnd; HonRl; MrchBnd; PepBnd; SchPl; YthFlsp; SchPpr; 4-H; Trk; GAA; College; Vocation.

WILSON, Seth; East Central HS; Miles, IA; Band; CncrtBnd; HonRl; MrchBnd; NHS; SchPpr; 4-H;.

WILSON, Sharon; Hesperia HS; Hesperia, MI; 65/85 Band; HonRl; TchrAde; Yrbk; Bsktbl; Trk; GAA; Ferris State College; Office Administration.

WILSON, Shelley K; Huron HS; Ann Arbor, MI; Chr; ChrhWkr; HonRl; HospAde; NatlMeritFnl; NatlMeritSchl; NatlMeritSF; Concordia Luth Jr College; Liberal Arts.

WILSON, Sheryl L; Cole R I HS; Lohman, MO; SecSophCls; HonRl; LbryAde; SchPl; FHA; PpCl; Chrldr; IMSpt; College; Social Worker.

WILSON, Sheryl L; East Richland HS; Olney, IL; 12/250 Band; Chrs; CncrtBnd; Mdrgl; MrchBnd; SchMus; SchPl; Twrl; FrCl;.

WILSON, Stanley W; Enfield HS; Enfield, IL; 2/35 VPFrshCls; VPSophCls; HstJrCls; VPSrCls; HonRl; StuCncl; EdYrBk; Bsktbl; KiwanAwd; CitAwd; Mung Univ; Eng.

WILSON, Stewart J; Monroe HS; Monroe, WI; 4/215 HonRl; LitMag; NatlMeritSF; SchMus; Univ Of Wisconsin.

WILSON, Sue D; Ionia HS; Ionia, MI; Band; HonRl; NHS; NatlMeritFnl; NatlMeritCmnd; NatlMeritSchl; NatlMeritSF; SchMus; Trk; LetterChrldr; Central Michigan Univ; Teaching.

WILSON, Susan; Goldfield Comm HS; Goldfield, IA; 3/32 HonRl; RptrYrbk; RptrSchPpr; Iccc Webster City; Physical Education.

WILSON, Susan L; Huron HS; Ann Arbor, MI; ChrhWkr; HonRl; HospAde; NatlMeritFnl; NatlMeritSchl; NatlMeritSF; FrCl; Concordia Luth Jr College; Liberal Arts.

WILSON, Susan L; Fredericktown HS; Fredericktown, MO; 11/135 Band; Chr; CncrtBnd; HonRl; MrchBnd; Twrl; College; Law.

WILSON, Terrie; South Barbor HS; Kiowa, KS; Chr; HonRl; LbryAde; Mdrgl; RptrYrbk; RptrSchPpr; EdSchPpr; Secretary.

WILSON, Tracy A; Monroe HS; Monroe, MI; ChrhWkr; HonRl; JA; StuCncl; Chrldr; GAA; University Of Michigan; Oceanography.

WILSON, Tracy L; Janesville Cons HS; Denver, IA; 3/48 SecTrsJrCls; HonRl; NHS; StuCncl; LetterBsktbl; LetterTrk; College; Med Laboratory Tech.

WILSON, Travis L; Westville HS; Westville, IL; VPFrshCls; VPSophCls; HonRl; TchrAde; Yrbk; SpnCl; LetterBsbl; Bsktbl; LetterFtbl; Glf; College.

WILSON, Tyrone; Northeastern HS; Detroit, MI; Bsktbl; Trk; Siena Heights; Acc.

WILSON, Vanessa F; Clay City Comm HS; Clay City, IL; 7/41 CncrtBnd; HonRl; EdYrBk; Sec4-H; FHA; PpCl; GAA; 4-HAwd; Lincoln Land Jr College; Medical Tech.

WILSON, Vanessa L; Chaska Sr HS; Chaska, MN; HonRl; NatlFornLg; NHS; TchrAde; Trk; College; Speech Therapy.

WILSON, Vicki S; Atchison Jr Sr HS; Atchison, KS; HonRl; ModUN; NatlFornLg; UNYO; Univ Of Arizona; Nursing.

WILSON, William; Danville HS; Danville, IL; Band; ChrhWkr; DrmBgl; HonRl; MrchBnd; PepBnd; SchMus; SctActv; TchrAde; Univ; Music Education.

WILSON, William J; Benton Community HS; Van Horne, IA; 5/108 Band; Chrs; HonRl; SchMus; SchPl; PresYthFlsp; MthCl; LetterBsbl; CaptBsktbl; Ftbl; Iowa State Univ; Professional.

WILSON, William K; Smithville HS; Smithville, MO; HonRl; JrNHS; NHS; College; Professional.

WILT, Ann R; Brookfield HS; Brookfield, MO; 7/104 Chrs; CncrtBnd; HonRl; MrchBnd; NHS; SctActv; StuCncl; FHA; PpCl; LetterGlf; GAA; IMSpt; Univ Of Missouri; Elem Education.

WILT, David A; Chaparral HS; Anthony, KS; 9/98 ALBoysSt; Band; CncrtBnd; HonRl; MrchBnd; PepBnd; KeyCl; KiwanAwd; College; Medicine.

WILT, Diane M; Chaparral HS; Anthony, KS; 10/98 Band; ChrhWkr; CncrtBnd; HonRl; HospAde; MrchBnd; TchrAde; FHA; PpCl; GodCntryAwd; Nursing School.

WILT, Leslie O; South Shelby HS; Shelbina, MO; Band; Chr; Chrs; ChrhWkr; CncrtBnd; HonRl; Mdrgl; MrchBnd; NHS; SchMus; SchPl; 4-H; FFA; SciCl; LetterFtbl; University; Agriculture.

WILTFANG, Jayne; Northwestern HS; Mansfield, SD; 3/35 ALAGirlsSt; Band; Chrs; CncrtBnd; HonRl; Mdrgl; MrchBnd; Quill&Scroll; Northern St College, Speech Therapist.

WILTSCHECK, Joyce M; Gibbon Public HS; Gibbon, MN; SchPl; VP4-H; FFA; FHA; BttyCrckrAwd; 4-HAwd; Univ Of Minnesota; Business.

WILTSIE, David S; Belleville Township HS East; Belleville, IL; 6/650 ALBoysSt; HonRl; NHS; SchMus; StuCncl; Yrbk; SchPpr; GerCl; MthCl; Tennis; Northwestern U; Physician.

WILTZ, Janice C; Sabetha Senior HS; Sabetha, KS; SecSophCls; ALAGirlsSt; CncrtBnd; HonRl; MrchBnd; SecNHS; PepBnd; FHA; VPPpCl; BttyCrckrAwd; Kansas State U; Biology.

WILWERT, Cynthia Sue; Leo HS; Sherrill, IA; Chrs; HonRl; SchMus; TchrAde; RptrYrbk; RptrSchPpr; 4-H; LatCl; PpCl; Chrldr; Trade School; Nursing.

WILZ, George J; Washington Catholic HS; Washington, IN; HonRl; SchPl; Yrbk; SchPpr; PresKeyCl; Bsbl; IMSpt; Univ; Vocation.

WILZBACHER, Paul A; Gibson Southern HS; Haubstadt, IN; Band; CncrtBnd; PepBnd; SchMus; 4-H; Ftbl; LetterTrk; IMSpt; 4-HAwd; Trade Sch; Vocation.

WIMBISCUS, Sarah A; Hall HS; Spring Valley, IL; HonRl; RptrYrbk; PpCl; SciCl; Trk; GAA; College.

WIMMER, Christopher; Charlevoix Sr HS; Charlevoix, MI; HonRl; TchrAde; CchngActv; IMSpt; Trade Sch; Vocational Draftsman.

WIMMER, Cindy E; Hale R 1 HS; Hale, MO; ALAGirlsSt; Chrs; HonRl; Mdrgl; RedCrAde; StuGov; SptEdYrbk; PpCl; LetterBsbl; LetterBsktbl; LetterTrk; 4-HAwd; School Of Nursing; Nurse.

WIMMER, Mary; Pierz Healy HS; Pierz, MN; Aud/Vis; HonRl; TchrAde; 4-H; FFA; Bsktbl; Trk; GAA; 4-HAwd; CitAwd; College; Veterinary Medicine.

WIMMER, Wanda; Shelbyville Senior HS; Shelbyville, IN; Band; Chr; Chrs; ChrhWkr; CncrtBnd; HonRl; MrchBnd; LatCl; College; Professional.

WIMPFHEIMER, Dianna L; Fisher HS; E Grand Forks, MN; Band; Chrs; CncrtBnd; HonRl; NatlThespSoc; PepBnd; SchPl; EdYrBk; FHA; Univ Nd Grand Forks; Special Education.

WINANS, Cheryl; Belvidere HS; Belvidere, IL; 70/342 Band; CncrtBnd; HonRl; MrchBnd; PolWkr; StuGov; TchrAde; SptEdSchPpr; FrCl; DARAwd; Col; Sports Writer.

WINANS, Julie A; Hartford HS; Watervliet, MI; Band; CncrtBnd; HonRl; MrchBnd; Twrl; PpCl; LetterBsbl; Bsktbl; LetterTrk; CaptChrldr; Western Mi Univ; Dance.

WINANS, Richard A; Wayne HS; Fort Wayne, IN; Chr; ChrhWkr; StuCncl; YthFlsp; Ftbl; PPFtbl; Indiana Univ Extension.

WINCHELL, Lianne E; Waukesha HS; Waukesha, WI; Chrs; PresNHS; StuCncl; RptrSchPpr; SpnCl; MthCl; PpCl; CaptGAA; Marquette U; Dentist.

WINCHESTER, Kimberly S; Edison Sr HS; East Gary, IN; Chr; ChrhWkr; JrNHS; YthFlsp; FBLA; PpCl;.

WINCHESTER, Randy K; High School; Denton, KS; HonRl; SchPl; StuCncl; StuGov; SptEdYrbk; SptEdSchPpr; PpCl; Bsktbl; Ftbl; AmLegAwd; College; Professional.

WINCHESTER, Sharon J; North Clay Comm HS; Farina, IL; 13/65 SecSophCls; TrsSrCls; HonRl; SchPl; SpnCl; PpCl;.

WINCHIP, Wade A; Anamosa Community HS; Anamosa, IA; Band; Chr; CncrtBnd; MrchBnd; SchMus; 4-H; ChmnFtbl; LetterTrk; College; Civil Engineer.

WIND, Carol D; Hill Murray HS; St Paul, MN; HonRl; HospAde; JA; NHS; SctActv; FrCl; PpCl; College; Professional.

WIND, Jeffrey R; Mehlville Sr HS; St Louis, MO; 6/502 Chrs; ChrhWkr; HonRl; NHS; Quill&Scroll; YthFlsp; RptrYrbk; SptEdSchPpr; Bsbl; NCTE; Univ Of Missouri; Business Admin.

WIND, Valoyce S; Humboldt HS; Humboldt, IA; Band; Chr; Chrs; CncrtBnd; HonRl; MrchBnd; PepBnd; SchMus; College; Nurse Rn.

WINDELS, Charles; Meadville R1v HS; Meadville, MO; 13/38 Band; CncrtBnd; HonRl; NHS; SchPl; 4-H; IMSpt; Central Missouri State Univ.

WINDERLICH, Rudolph W; Clark HS; Hammond, IN; 21/260 ALBoysSt; Chr; HonRl; NatlThespSoc; SchPl; RptrYrbk; PresGerCl; Ftbl; LetterSocr; AmLegAwd; College; Radio/tv.

WINDERS, Susan E; Roxana Comm HS; East Alton, IL; 18/310 Chrs; ChrhWkr; HonRl; HospAde; MrchBnd; TchrAde; FNA; PpCl; College; Teacher.

WINDHAM, Jarvis; Chicago Vocational HS; Chicago, IL; 27/788 CncrtBnd; HonRl; JA; NHS; SchAde; StuCncl; SpnCl; LetterBsktbl; LetterFtbl; Trk; Northwestern U; Accounting.

WINDHOLZ, Rhoda M; Victoria HS; Victoria, KS; DrlTm; HonRl; NatlFornLg; NHS; SchPl; SctActv; EdYrBk; EdSchPpr; FHA; Tennis; College; Journalism.

WINDISCH, Randall A; Butler HS; Butler, MO; HonRl; NatlMeritSF; VPStuCncl; StuGov; RptrSchPpr; SptEdSchPpr; CaptBsktbl; Ftbl; IMSpt; College; Psychology.

WINDISH, Ann M; Fingal Public HS; Fingal, ND; 3/21 Band; Chr; ChrhWkr; HonRl; MrchBnd; NHS; SchPl; EdSchPpr; PpCl; Bsktbl; Nd State U; Science & Math.

WINDLE, Dean M; Southern HS; Wymore, NE; TrsFrshCls; VPSophCls; VPJrCls; HonRl; NHS; StuCncl; Ftbl; Trk; Wrstlng; U Of Neb; Engineering.

WINDLE, Kevin M; Lawrence Central HS; Indianapolis, IN; PresSrCls; Band; SchPl; TchrAde; Wrstlng; Ball State; English Pro.

WINDMANN, Ralph L; Mexico HS; Mexico, MO; HonRl; RptrSchPpr; 4-H; FFA; KeyCl; Wrstlng; University; Agriculture.

WINDOFFER, Becky S; Seymour HS; Payson, IL; ChrhWkr; Sdlty; TchrAde; College; Vocation.

WINDSCHITL, Leo N; Stewart Public HS; Stewart, MN; PresSophCls; HonRl; SchPl; StuCncl; RptrSchPpr; CaptFtbl; CaptWrstlng; College.

WINDSCHITL, Michael H; Rocoli HS; Cold Spring, MN; ChrhWkr; HonRl; LetterSwmmng; CchngActv; Trade School; Us Navy.

WINDT, Frank C; Cudahy Sr HS; Cudahy, WI; 13/354 HonRl; NHS; SctActv; LetterSwmmng; Trk; Univ Of Milwaukee; Accounting.

WINEBRENNER, Dale; Highland HS; Highland, IN; 35/579 Durdue Univ; Physics Aerospace.

WINEBRENNER, Susan L; Portage Northern HS; Portage, MI; 3/350 CmntyWkr; HonRl; NHS; SchMus; StuCncl; FrCl; LetterTrk; Michigan St.

WINEFKA, Steven R; Bloom HS; Sauk Village, IL; 87/978 ChrhWkr; HonRl; NHS; SchAde; StuCncl; Northern Ill U; Medicine.

WINEGAR, Rebecca J; Lewistown HS; Lewistown, IL; Band; Chr; ChrhWkr; HonRl; MrchBnd; PepBnd; YthFlsp; RptrSchPpr; FHA; FrCl; Pillsbury Baptist Bible Clg; Secretarial.

WINEINGER, Dale E; Orchard Farm HS; West Alton, MO; 5/132 Aud/Vis; Band; ChrhWkr; CmntyWkr; CncrtBnd; HonRl; MrchBnd; NHS; PepBnd; SchMus; Abilene Christian Clg; Bible.

WINEINGER, Kerry K; Greeley Cnty HS; Tribune, KS; SecJrCls; Band; Chr; HonRl; NatlThespSoc; SchPl; StuCncl; SptEdSchPpr; 4-H; Steven F Austin Univ; Journalism.

WINEMAN, Alicia A; Lincoln HS; Vincennes, IN; 36/346 SecSophCls; SecJrCls; SecSrCls; YthFlsp; RptrYrbk; RptrSchPpr; 4-H; FHA; SciCl; Tennis; Indiana U; Medicine.

WINEMAN, David; Unionville Sebewaing Area HS; Sebewaing, MI; 8/125 Band; DrmMjrt; MrchBnd; PepBnd; SchPl; SctActv; StuCncl; 4-H; LatCl; 4-HAwd; Albion Coll; Physicaian.

WINEMILLER, Teresa A; Sheridan R Ii HS; Sheridan, MO; HonRl; StuCncl; 4-H; PpCl; Bsbl; CaptBsktbl; Trk; AmLegAwd; 4-HAwd; College; Professional.

WINES, William M; Au Gres Sims HS; Au Gres, MI; 5/60 HonRl; LitMag; LbryAde; RptrSchPpr; Bsktbl; Glf; College; Law.

WINFREY, Edwin E; Fort Osage HS; Sibley, MO; HonRl; ModUN; PresNatlFornLg; SctActv; TchrAde; MthCl; SciCl; Coll; Agriculture.

WING, Karen M; Montini HS; Downers Grove, IL; HonRl; NHS; GerCl; SecGAA; IMSpt; Eastern Illinois Univ.

WING, Loren D; Colfax HS; Colfax, IA; 9/66 Band; ChrhWkr; CncrtBnd; HonRl; MrchBnd; YthFlsp; 4-H; LetterFtbl; LetterTrk; LetterWrstlng; Iowa St Univ; Dairy Farmer.

WING, Rose; Laingsburg HS; Laingsburg, MI; HonRl; HospAde; LbryAde; StuGov; TchrAde; FHA; Chrldr; College; Practical Nurse.

WINGARD, Marianne; Elwood Community HS; Elwood, IN; 41/198 HonRl; NHS; PolWkr; PresYthFlsp; FBLA; FrCl; PpCl; Tri State College; Accounting.

WINGATE, Keith A; Crystal Lake Comm HS; Crystal Lake, IL; 36/477 ChrhWkr; HonRl; Univ; Professional.

WINGEN, Jon; Wellcome Memorial HS; Good Thunder, MN; 8/45 PresFrshCls; VPJrCls; Band; Chr; Chrs; ChrhWkr; HonRl; Bsktbl; 4-HAwd; College; Agriculture Engineer.

WINGER, Ross J; Jefferson Senior HS; Alexandria, MN; 62/312 PresBand; CncrtBnd; HonRl; MrchBnd; PepBnd; IMSpt; Moorhead St Univ; Business.

WINGERT, Ann; Ogorman HS; Sioux Falls, SD; Chr; Chrs; 4-H; Trade School.

WINGERT, Kimberly C; Elk Grove HS; Elk Grove, IL; 10/505 HonRl; NHS; PolWkr; GerCl; Chrldr; Il Univ; Lawyer.

WINGFIELD, Darlene E; Westside Senior HS; Gary, IN; HonRl; NHS; PresFHA; SciCl; University Of Indiana; Nursing.

WINGROVE, Kendall J; Algonac HS; Algonac, MI; 6/208 Band; CncrtBnd; HonRl; MrchBnd; PepBnd; SchPl; SctActv; EdSchPpr; LatCl; VoiceDemAwd; St Clair Co Comm Clg; Journalism.

WINIGER, Gilbert J; Mater Del HS; Evansville, IN; HonRl; JrNHS; VPNHS; StuGov; LetterBsbl; LetterFtbl; LetterTrk; AmLegAwd; ChmbCommrsAwd; VoiceDemAwd; Colege; Engineering.

WININGER, Cindy L; Barr Reeve HS; Montgomery, IN; ALAGirlsSt; Band; Chrs; ChrhWkr; CncrtBnd; HonRl; JrNHS; MrchBnd; NHS; PepBnd; Yrbk; CivCl; FHA; SpnCl; Indiana Univ; Music.

WININGER, Dwight E; Dubois HS; Dubois, IN; 1/85 ALBoysSt; Band; ChrhWkr; CmntyWkr; CncrtBnd; HonRl; MrchBnd; NHS; Orch; PepBnd; SchMus; SchPl; YthFlsp; Bsktbl; Indiana University; Science.

WINKA, Sandra M; Wheeling HS; Wheeling, IL; ChrhWkr; HonRl; NHS; Northern Illinois Clg; Nursing.

WINKEL, Brian S; Toluca HS; Toluca, IL; 10/39 Band; Chrs; HonRl; MrchBnd; PepBnd; PpCl; Bsbl; Bsktbl; Glf; Trk; Illinois Valley Com Clg; Architectural.

WINKEL, Phyllis; Waconda East HS; Cawker City, KS; 1/25 Chrs; ChrhWkr; HonRl; SchPl; StuCncl; Teen; Yrbk; SchPpr; PpCl; Coll; Data Process.

WINKELHORST, Loren J; Edgerton Public HS; Leota, MN; Band; Chr; Chrl; Chrs; CncrtBnd; HonRl; MrchBnd; NHS; PepBnd; GerCl; Bsbl; Bsktbl; Ftbl; College; Professional.

WINKELMAN, L Dianne; Triopia Jr Sr HS; Arenzville, IL; 5/50 ALAGirlsSt; Chrs; ChrhWkr; HonRl; LbryAde; NHS; PepBnd; SchMus; SchPpr; Pres4-H; PresFHA; College; Medical Lab.

WINKELMAN, Lorie R; Mead HS; Fremont, NE; 2/27 SecSrCls; Chrs; TreasChrhWkr; HonRl; NHS; NatlThespSoc; TchrAde; MthCl; PpCl; Sch Of Nursing; Nurse.

WINKELMAN, Lorie R; Mead Jr Sr HS; Fremont, NE; SecSrCls; Chrs; ChrhWkr; HonRl; NHS; NatlThespSoc; SchMus; SchPl; TchrAde; MthCl; Methodist School; Nursing.

WINKELMAN, Stephen E; Sacred Heart HS; Salina, KS; VPSophCls; ALBoysSt; Chrs; CmntyWkr; HonRl; JA; JCC; StuCncl; SptEdSchPpr; FBLA; KeyCl; Bsbl; Bsktbl; College; Accountant.

WINKELMAN, Theresa; Fatima Hs; Meta, MO; 7 Band; ChrhWkr; CmntyWkr; HonRl; LbryAde; Sdlty; PresPpCl; Bsbl; Chrldr; CchngActv; Southwest Mo State U;biology Or Math.

WINKELMAN, Wendy J; Summerfield HS; Dundee, MI; ChrhWkr; HonRl; NHS; 4-H; CaptBsbl; Chrldr; GAA; IMSpt; JAAwd; PresAwd; Bus Coll; Pro.

WINKER, Gregory J; O Gorman HS; Sioux Falls, SD; ALBoysSt; Band; CncrtBnd; MrchBnd; Orch; PepBnd; SchMus; College; Physical Science.

WINKER, Jeffrey P; O Gorman HS; Sious Falls, SD; ALBoysSt; Band; Chrs; CncrtBnd; JrNHS; MrchBnd; NatlFornLg; NHS; NatlMeritSF; StuCncl; College; Physics.

WINKLE, Curtis R; I S U Laboratory HS; Terre Haute, IN; 12/50 ALBoysSt; ModUN; StuCncl; RptrYrbk; RptrSchPpr; EdSchPpr; In St Univ; Urban Planer.

WINKLE, Kerry; Ashton Hs; Ashton, IL; Band; HonRl; NatlThespSoc; StuCncl; SchPpr; SciCl; Ftbl; Glf; Trk; Wrstlng; Parks College; Transportation.

WINKLER, Brian K; Kimball HS; Royla Oak, MI; HonRl; NatlMeritFnl; NatlMeritCmnd; Lawrence Inst Of Tech; Architect.

WINKLER, Cynthia R; Cheney HS; Wichita, KS; Chr; HonRl; LbryAde; SchMus; EdYrBk; RptrSchPpr; LatCl; PpCl; Marriage; Secretarial Work.

WINKLER, Deborah; Desoto Hs; Desoto, WI; 1/72 Band; Chr; ChrhWkr; CncrtBnd; HonRl; MrchBnd; PepBnd; 4-H;.

WINKLER, Gary; Bishop Dwenger HS; Ft Wane, IN; Aud/Vis; HonRl; IMSpt; College; Professional.

WINKLER, Jane; St Francis HS; Traverse City, MI; HonRl; JrNHS; NHS; SchPl; StuCncl; TchrAde; 4-H; PpCl; IMSpt; College.

WINKLER, Marilyn S; Yutan Public HS; Yutan, NE; 7/25 Chr; Chrs; HonRl; LbryAde; SchPl; LetterPpCl; LetterTrk; Metropolitan Tech Comm College; Dentist.

WINKLER, Mary E; Hays HS; Hays, KS; ChrhWkr; HonRl; MrchBnd; SchAde; SctActv; StuGov; TchrAde; PpCl; SciCl; Trk; Ks State U.

WINKLER, Scott R; Loomis HS; Loomis, NE; PresJrCls; HstSrCls; ALBoysSt; Band; HonRl; SctActv; EdYrBk; LetterFtbl; IMSpt; EldAwd; 4-HAwd; Univ Of Nebraska.

WINKLER, Stacey L; Alexis HS; Alexis, IL; 1/50 PresJrCls; Band; HonRl; NHS; StuCncl; 4-H; FrCl; Chrldr; GAA; DARAwd; College; Nursing.

WINKLER, Thomas W; Riverside Brookfield HS; Lagrange Pk, IL; 40/490 Band; CncrtBnd; MrchBnd; NHS; Univ Of Illinois; Accounting.

WINKLER, Vickie; Franklin Comm HS; Franklin, IN; Chr; ChrhWkr; HonRl; SchPl; FHA; GerCl; PpCl; GAA; Northwood Inst; Fashion Merchandising.

WINKLER, William A; Harrisonville HS; Harrisonville, MO; HonRl; SchPl; StuCncl; YthFlsp; FrCl; Bsbl; LetterBsktbl; LetterFtbl; LetterTrk; PPFtbl; Coll; Forester Or Small Businessman.

WINKLEY, Cynthia S; Proviso West HS; Westchester, IL; 90/1100 HonRl; NHS; SchAde; StuCncl; PpCl; CaptChrldr; Univ Of Illinois; Biology.

WINN, Frank L; Scollard Hall HS; Edina, MN; Chr; JA; NatlMeritSF; StuCncl; TchrAde; YthFlsp; RptrSchPpr; LatCl; College; Architecture.

WINN, James K; Mt Vernon HS; Mt Vernon, MO; ChrhWkr; HonRl; YthFlsp; FTA; Bsktbl; Ftbl; LetterTrk; Ne A & M College; Mech Engineer.

WINN, Mary E; Laura Speed Elliott HS; Boonville, MO; Band; ChrhWkr; CncrtBnd; MrchBnd; NHS; PepBnd; SchPl; PpCl; Chrldr; IMSpt; Univ Of Mo Columbia; Nursing.

WINN, Patricia K; Pana HS; Pana, IL; 5/139 Band; CmntyWkr; CncrtBnd; HonRl; MrchBnd; NHS; YthFlsp; RptrYrbk; LetterTennis; LetterTrk; GAA; Univ Of Ill; Business Admin.

WINN, Pete; Danville HS; Danville, IL; 1/613 PresFrshCls; ChrhWkr; CmntyWkr; HonRl; PolWkr; StuCncl; StuGov; TchrAde; YthLg; RptrSchPpr; PresSpnCl; PresSciCl; GovHonPrgAwd; Ripon College; Law.

WINNER, Tamera R; Coldwater HS; Bronson, MI; Chr; HonRl; OffAde; TchrAde; 4-H; FTA; Chrldr; GAA; 4-HAwd; PresAwd; Trade School; Prof Lpn.

WINNETT, Kristine A; Bayard Comm HS; Bayard, IA; Chrs; ChrhWkr; HonRl; NHS; RptrYrbk; SchPpr; Bsktbl; Chrldr; BttyCrckrAwd; LionAwd; Des Moines Comm Clg; Assc Degree Nursing.

WINNETT, Stephanie L; Roxana HS; East Alton, IL; 14/295 Chrs; HonRl; NatlThespSoc; OffAde; SchPl; FHA; FNA; PpCl; Southern Illinois Univ; Psychology.

WINSEMAN, Albert L; Milford HS; Milford, NE; 3/60 Band; Chrs; NHS; SchMus; SchPl; StuCncl; EdSchPpr; LetterBsktbl; LetterFtbl; LetterTrk; College; Music Or Drama.

WINSHALL, Jay J; Wylie E Groves HS; Birmingham, MI; 51/690 JrNHS; NatlMeritSF; SchMus; SchPpr; Coll And Grad Sch;architect.

WINSHIP, Harold L; Henry Senachwine HS; Putnam, IL; ALBoysSt; ChrhWkr; SchMus; StuCncl; YthFlsp; College; Agriculture.

WINSLOW, Hugh T; Central HS; Evansville, IN; 60/617 HonRl; NHS; SctActv; StuGov; SciCl; Trk; Rose Hulman Inst;.

WINSLOW, Linda; Adelphian Acad; Lapeer, MI; HonRl; TchrAde; Yrbk; RptrSchPpr; College; Secondary Education.

WINSLOW, Martha M; Spalding Academy; Washington, IL; 5/95 Chrs; ChrhWkr; HonRl; NatlMeritSF; RptrYrbk; 4-H; TreasFNA; FrCl; College; Nurse.

WINSON, Terry J; Havana HS; Havana, IL; 1/90 PresFrshCls; TrsJrCls; Band; ChrhWkr; CncrtBnd; HonRl; IntrClCncl; Mdrgl; MrchBnd; NHS; NatlThespSoc; PepBnd; PolWkr; SchMus; SchPl; StuCncl; College; Professional.

WINSTON, Beverly; Paseo Hs; Kansas City, MO; 17/290 HonRl; JA; NHS; SctActv; RptrYrbk;.

WINSTON, David; Osborn R O Hs; Osborn, MO; CmntyWkr; CncrtBnd; HonRl; MrchBnd; SchPl; YthFlsp; PpCl; CaptBsktbl; LetterTrk; 4-HAwd; College; Business.

WINSTON, Patricia; Paseo Hs; Kansas City, MO; HonRl; PpCl; Umkc; Law.

WINSTON, Paula J; Morton Sr HS; Hammond, IN; 43/492 Chr; HonRl; Mdrgl; NHS; OffAde; TchrAde; Yrbk; FrCl; CchngActv; College; Physical Education.

WINSTON, Veronica L; Chicago Vocational HS; Chicago, IL; HonRl; Tennis; College; Law.

WINTER, Barbara A; North Loup Scotia HS; Scotia, NE; SecJrCls; Band; Chrs; CncrtBnd; MrchBnd; PepBnd; StuGov; 4-H; PpCl; 4-HAwd;.

WINTER, Bruce K; Nicolet HS; Milwaukee, WI; 89/520 CmntyWkr; OffAde; PolWkr; SchPpr; FrCl; IMSpt; College; Professional.

WINTER, Deborah J; Oskaloosa HS; Oskaloosa, KS; Chr; Chrs; ChrhWkr; HonRl; NHS; SctActv; YthFlsp; 4-H; FBLA; FHA; Univ Of Ks; Piano.

WINTER, Edwin R; Woodruff HS; Peoria, IL; 55/257 Chr; SchMus; SchPl; Trade School; Machinist.

WINTER, Gretchen A; Luther South HS; Chicago, IL; SecJrCls; Chr; ChrhWkr; HonRl; NatlFornLg; NHS; NatlMeritCmnd; StuCncl; SchPpr; Chrldr; Coll; Journalism.

WINTER, James R; Morton West HS; Berwyn, IL; JrNHS; TchrAde; LetterBsktbl; Ftbl; Us Coast Guard; Electronics.

WINTER, Larry A; Goodland HS; Kenorado, KS; 17/132 VPFrshCls; CmntyWkr; HonRl; NHS; StuCncl; 4-H; Ftbl; EldAwd; Kansas State Univ; Veterinarian.

WINTER, Marcia C; Elkhorn Jr Sr HS; Elkhorn, NE; AFS; Chr; ChrhWkr; HonRl; LbryAde; SchPl; EdYrBk; EdSchPpr; FHA; College; Theatre.

WINTER, Mar Jo E; Belle Plaine HS; Belle Plaine, KS; PresJrCls; Chrs; HonRl; SchMus; StuCncl; TchrAde; SpnCl; Bsktbl; College; Occupational Therapy.

WINTER, Mary; Perry Lecompton HS; Lecompton, KS; Band; Chr; HonRl; NHS; PepBnd; SchMus; Yrbk; 4-H; PpCl; 4-HAwd; Trade Sch; Med Assist.

WINTER, Michael; Rhinelander HS; Harshaw, WI; 30/331 ALBoysSt; Band; CncrtBnd; HonRl; MrchBnd; PepBnd; SchMus;.

WINTER, Richard A; New Trier East HS; Glencoe, IL; 64/900 CmntyWkr; HonRl; LetterTrk; Grinnell College; Law.

WINTER, Robb M; Halliday Public HS; Marshall, ND; ALBoysSt; HonRl; LbryAde; StuCncl; TchrAde; RptrYrbk; SptEdSchPpr; 4-H; FFA; SciCl; Trk; Col; Chemistry.

WINTER, Sam S; Andale HS; Mt Hope, KS; 5/89 PresSophCls; HonRl; StuCncl; RptrSchPpr; SpnCl; IMSpt; Ks St Univ ;mech Enginer.

WINTER, Terri M; West Sr HS; Iowa City, IA; 37/277 SecSrCls; HonRl; Orch; RptrYrbk; FrCl; PpCl; Chrldr; U Of Ia; Engineering.

WINTERBAUER, Lori S; St Marys Acad; Springfield, IL; HonRl; SchPl; 4-H; SpnCl; PpCl; Chrldr; 4-HAwd; College; Social Studys.

WINTERBERG, Sheila K; Trico HS; Percy, IL; Aud/Vis; ChrhWkr; HonRl; SchPpr; FBLA; FHA; PpCl; Trk; GAA; Bible Teacher.

WINTERBOTTOM, Linda K; H H Dow HS; Midland, MI; 31/461 HonRl; NatlMeritSF; PolWkr; SchPl; YthFlsp; RptrYrbk; RptrSchPpr; GerCl; Univ Of Mi; Law.

WINTERFELD, Lori; West Sioux Community HS; Ireton, IA; /76 Chrs; VPChrhWkr; HonRl; HospAde; LbryAde; SchMus; SchPl; Pres4-H; GAA; 4-HAwd; Trade; Therapists Aide.

WINTERFELD, Michael; West Sioux Comm HS; Ireton, IA; ALBoysSt; HonRl; SchPl; StuCncl; FFA; Bsbl; Iowa State Univ; Agricultural Business.

WINTERNHEIMER, Christina M; Mt Vernon HS; Evansville, IN; 5/225 AFS; Chr; ChrhWkr; HonRl; NHS; StuCncl; YthFlsp; LatCl; U Of Evansville; Medical Technology.

WINTERS, Brenda I; Carlinville HS; Carlinville, IL; 17/154 HonRl; JrNHS; NHS; OffAde; SchPl; FrCl; PpCl; College; Business.

WINTERS, Cheryl A; Grass Lake HS; Grass Lake, MI; 6/89 Band; CncrtBnd; HonRl; HospAde; MrchBnd; NHS; PepBnd; FHA; Jackson Coll; Med Tech.

WINTERS, David E; Charles P Steinmetz HS; Chicago, IL; 2/700 PresFrshCls; Band; ChrhWkr; CncrtBnd; HonRl; MrchBnd; NHS; NatlMeritCmnd; SchMus; StuCncl; Univ Of Chicago; Medicine.

WINTERS, Gary M; Rosedale HS; Terre Haute, IN; PresFrshCls; PresJrCls; NHS; Bsktbl; Trk; Indiana State Univ; Dentistry.

WINTERS, Jay P; Routt HS; Jacksonville, IL; Band; HonRl; MrchBnd; NHS; SpnCl; Illinois College; Sociology.

WINTERS, Julie M; Annandale HS; Annandale, MN; 11/115 SecJrCls; Band; CncrtBnd; HonRl; HospAde; JrNHS; MrchBnd; NHS; OffAde; Orch; College.

WINTERS, Linda A; Lyons Township HS; La Grange, IL; Chr; CmntyWkr; HonRl; NHS; OffAde; SchAde; SctActv; Teen; Twrl; College; Accounting.

WINTERS, Martin A; Vandercook Lake HS; Jackson, MI; 1/115 TrsFrshCls; PresSophCls; VPJrCls; HonRl; TchrAde; Jackson Comm College; Applied Arts Or Math.

WINTERS, Mary K; Oak Park River Forest HS; Oak Park, IL; 37/1056 TrsSophCls; ChrhWkr; HonRl; OffAde; StuCncl;.

WINTERS, Nancy; St Teresa Hs; Decatur, IL; 10/120 SecHonRl; OffAde; Yrbk; SpnCl; PpCl; Swmmng; U Of No Colorado; Special Education.

WINTERS, Patricia L; Mt Lake HS; Bingham Lake, MN; Band; ChrhWkr; CncrtBnd; HonRl; MrchBnd; PepBnd; StuCncl; Twrl; EdSchPpr; 4-H; College; Law.

WINTERS, Sandra J; St Francis De Sales HS; Chicago, IL; 13/290 Chrs; HonRl; NHS; TchrAde; RptrYrbk; RptrSchPpr; Trk; Chrldr; GAA;.

WINTERS, Scot L; Morton HS; Morton, IL; 2/310 HonRl; NHS; SciCl; LetterTrk; LetterWrstlng; College; Medicine.

WINTERS, Tracy M; Greensburg Comm HS; Greensburg, IN; 39/205 Chr; HonRl; Mdrgl; SchMus; FrCl; PpCl; SciCl; Bsktbl; Ftbl; LetterTrk; Indiana Univ; Business Admin.

WINTERS, Vickie S; Lanphier HS; Springfield, IL; 32/476 TrsFrshCls; TrsSophCls; TrsJrCls; TrsSrCls; Chr; NHS; PolWkr; StuGov; RptrYrbk; North Central College; Political Science.

WINTERSCHEIDT, Daniel L; Immaculata HS; Leavenworth, KS; Chrs; HonRl; SchMus; SctActv; Bsktbl; LetterFtbl; LetterTrk; College; Engineer.

WINTERTON, Darrell M; Garretson HS; Sherman, SD; 14/50 Band; Chrs; HonRl; SchMus; SchPl; 4-H; FFA; Ftbl; LetterWrstlng; Air Force; Computer Electronics.

WINTHEISER, Alice; Morgan Public HS; Morgan, MN; Chrs; HonRl; SchPl; TchrAde; RptrSchPpr; FTA; Trade School; Vocation.

WINTHEISER, Ricky D; St Marys HS; Sleepy Eye, MN; 13/71 PresJrCls; Aud/Vis; Band; CncrtBnd; MrchBnd; Orch; PepBnd; TchrAde; Yrbk; SchPpr; PpCl; Ftbl; College; Photographer.

WINTHER, Marlene M; Hubbard Comm HS; Hubbard, IA; Band; Chr; Chrs; ChrhWkr; CmntyWkr; CncrtBnd; HonRl; LbryAde; MrchBnd; Orch; PepBnd; LetterBsbl; LetterBsktbl; CaptTrk; Iowa Weslayn Col; Teaching.

WINTON, Michael; Terre Haute North Vigo HS; Terre Haute, IN; NatlMeritSF; U Of Mi; Econ.

WINZENRIED, Bret L; Monticello HS; Monticello, WI; NatlFornLg; TchrAde; SpnCl; Bsktbl; Trade School; Vocation.

WINZER, Karen J; Circle HS; Towanda, KS; Band; CncrtBnd; MrchBnd; Twrl; EdSchPpr; PpCl; Business School; Professional.

WIORA, John M; Benet Academy; Naperville, IL; 41/243 HonRl; Bsbl; Bsktbl; Ftbl; Dayton University; Business.

WIORA, Sandra L; Benet Academy; Naperville, IL; 100/273 CmntyWkr; HonRl; HospAde; SchMus; SchPl; SctActv; TchrAde; Bsbl; Bsktbl; Ill Benedictine; Dancer.

WIPF, Jane; Freeman HS; Freeman, SD; 1/63 VPSophCls; HstJrCls; ALAGirlsSt; Chrs; CncrtBnd; NHS; Orch; StuCncl; YthFlsp; College; Social Work.

WIPF, Rowen; Iroquois HS; Iroquois, SD; 1/25 VPJrCls; PresSrCls; ALBoysSt; HonRl; PepBnd; StuCncl; YthFlsp; Bethany Fellowship; Missionary.

WIPFLI, Jay M; Assumption HS; Vesper, WI; ChrhWkr; HonRl; NHS; SchMus; SchPl; StuCncl; SpnCl; MthCl; Bsktbl; IMSpt; Univ; Pro.

WIPPMAN, Robert A; New Trier East HS; Glencoe, IL; 154/847 Band; CncrtBnd; HonRl; NHS; Orch; SchMus; TchrAde; University Of Illinois; Liberal Arts.

WIRE, Kenneth L; North Boone HS; Capron, IL; 2/80 ALBoysSt; HonRl; NHS; SchMus; SchPl; Yrbk; EdSchPpr; SptEdSchPpr; GerCl; Southern Ill; Law.

WIRGAU, Lu Ann; Alpena HS; Posen, MI; HonRl; Clg; Engineering.

WIRGES, Charlotte; Petersburg Public HS; Petersburg, NE; Band; Chr; Chrs; HonRl; MrchBnd; PepBnd; SchPl; Yrbk; RptrSchPpr; PpCl; College; Professional.

WIRT, Gregory T; Parkway North Sr HS; St Louis, MO; ChrhWkr; CmntyWkr; HonRl; SctActv; StuCncl; TchrAde; LatCl; Washington Univ; Medicine.

WIRTH, Barbara M; South HS; Omaha, NE; 12/611 HonRl; PresLbryAde; NHS; OffAde; Pres4-H; VPFTA; EngCl; TreasSpnCl; TreasMthCl; 4-HAwd; U Of Ne Omaha; Elementary Education.

WIRTH, Christopher; Middleton HS; Cross Plains, WI; Chr; SchMus; Bsktbl; College; Art.

WIRTH, Jodie; Stewardson Strasburg HS; Strasburg, IL; SecJrCls; Chr; Chrs; HonRl; LbryAde; Yrbk; 4-H; Chrldr; NCTE; CitAwd; Lakeland Junior College; Undecided.

WIRTH, Mary; Lockwood R 1 HS; Lockwood, MO; VPJrCls; ChrhWkr; CmntyWkr; CncrtBnd; HonRl; SptEdYrbk; 4-H; FHA; 4-HAwd; JAAwd; Coll; Professional.

WIRTH, Richard D; Proviso West HS; Bellwood, IL; 57/1086 HonRl; Triton Jr College; Accountant.

WIRTH, Roderick; Mt Horeb HS; Mt Horeb, WI; 44/137 Band; Chr; CncrtBnd; MrchBnd; PepBnd; TchrAde; Bsktbl; Ftbl; Glf; IMSpt; Univ; Electronics.

WIRTH, Terry L; Prairie Farm HS; Ridgeland, WI; VPFrshCls; VPJrCls; HonRl; NHS; StuCncl; FFA; Bsbl;.

WIRTHELE, Debra; Douglas Community HS; Burr, NE; VPSophCls; HonRl; SchPl; StuGov; YthFlsp; Yrbk; PpCl; Chrldr;.

WIRTHELE, Patricia; Douglas Community HS; Burr, NE; SecJrCls; HonRl; SchPl; StuGov; YthFlsp; Yrbk; PpCl; Chrldr;.

WIRTJES, Rodney A; Independent #219 HS; Elmore, MN; 14/27 SecFrshCls; ChrhWkr; StuCncl; SchPpr; Bsktbl; CaptFtbl; LetterGlf; LetterTrk; College.

WIRTZ, Anne L; St Pius X HS; Gladstone, MO; 4/129 Chrs; HonRl; NHS; RedCrAde; SchMus; PpCl; Trk; GAA; Coll; Vocation.

WIRTZ, Carrie; Divine Savior Holy Angels HS; West Allis, WI; 19/118 VPSophCls; Band; Chr; Chrs; DrmBgl; DrmMjrt; NHS; Sacrstn; SchMus; Alverno College; Theory.

WIRTZ, Joseph G; Central HS; West Allis, WI; Chr; Chrs; ChrhWkr; CmntyWkr; Mdrgl; Bsbl; Ftbl; CchngActv; IMSpt; College; Architecture.

WIRTZ, Julie A; Argyle HS; Argyle, WI; PresSophCls; Band; Chrs; HonRl; PepBnd; YthFlsp; Yrbk; SchPpr; FHA; PpCl; Business School; Office Work.

WIRTZ, Julie A; Webster HS; Webster, SD; HonRl; NatlThespSoc; SchPl; StuCncl; RptrYrbk; Yrbk; VPFHA; SpnCl; Patricia Stevens School.

WIRTZ, Karen R; Freeland HS; Freeland, MI; Band; CncrtBnd; HonRl; LbryAde; MrchBnd; TchrAde; PPFtbl; College; Elementary Education.

WIRTZ, Mark P; Woden Crystal Lake HS; Crystal Lake, IA; ALBoysSt; Band; ChrhWkr; CmntyWkr; CncrtBnd; HonRl; MrchBnd; PepBnd; Bsktbl; Trade Sch; Voc.

WIRTZ, Mary; Bishop Hogan HS; Kansas City, MO; 3/118 Chrs; HonRl; SchAde; SchMus; SchPl; StuCncl; RptrYrbk; EdYrBk; PpCl; GAA; Rockhurst Coll; Elementary Education.

WIRZFELD, Diana L; Santa Fe Trail HS; Carbondale, KS; 1/86 DrlTm; HonRl; VPNHS; OffAde; TchrAde; RptrYrbk; PpCl; IMSpt; BttyCrckrAwd; DARAwd; Stormont Vail Hosp; X Ray Tech.

WISBER, Jean C; Roosevelt HS; Marenisco, MI; 3/10 SecTrsFrshCls; SecTrsSophCls; ChrhWkr; HonRl; MrchBnd; StuCncl; Yrbk; SchPpr; LetterBsktbl; 4-HAwd; College.

WISBROCK, Lynne M; Immaculate Conception HS; Elmhurst, IL; 21/175 Chrs; ChrhWkr; HonRl; NHS; FrCl; PpCl; IMSpt;.

WISBY, Janelle E; Gen Wm Mitchell HS; Lincoln, NE; 14/820 ChrhWkr; HonRl; JrNHS; NHS; NatlMeritFnl; StuCncl; ChmnYthFlsp; SpnCl; Ne Wesleyan Univ; Elem/spec Ed.

WISCH, Mark W; Arlington Green Isle HS; Arlington, MN; ChrhWkr; CmntyWkr; HonRl; NHS; NatlMeritCmnd; SchPl; YthFlsp; RptrSchPpr; SchPpr; Voc Tech School; Auto Mechanic.

WISCHOW, Kathy M; Beach HS; Beach, ND; 4/42 VPSophCls; HstJrCls; ALAGirlsSt; Band; Chr; Chrs; ChrhWkr; CncrtBnd; HonRl; NHS; LetterBsktbl; Trk; LetterChrldr; BttyCrckrAwd; Univ Of North Dakota; Special Educ.

WISDOM, Randy D; Salem HS; Salem, MO; 52/164 ALBoysSt; CmntyWkr; HonRl; PolWkr; SchAde; TchrAde; SchPpr; FFA; PpCl; Bsktbl; College; Vocation.

WISE, Anita L; Franklin Central HS; Indianapolis, IN; 67/221 ChrhWkr; CmntyWkr; SchPl; 4-H; SpnCl; Tennis; GAA; IMSpt; 4-HAwd; College; Secretarial.

WISE, Donita D; Assumption HS; Assumption, IL; PresSophCls; HonRl; NHS; NatlThespSoc; VPStuCncl; PresFrCl; LetterTrk; GAA;.

WISE, Douglas L; Whitko HS; Warsaw, IN; 30/169 Chr; ChrhWkr; CmntyWkr; HonRl; SchMus; YthFlsp; 4-H; FFA; HstSophCls; 4-HAwd; Wyoming Tech; Diesel Mechanic.

WISE, Fletcher E; Farmer City Mansfield HS; Farmer City, IL; 13/88 VPJrCls; AFS; CncrtBnd; HonRl; SchMus; StuCncl; YthFlsp; LetterBsbl; LetterFtbl; LetterGlf; Ill Wesleyan U; Pre Med.

WISE, John W; Trenton R 9 HS; Trenton, MO; 15/171 AFS; Aud/Vis; HonRl; NHS; SctActv; TchrAde; FFA; LetterFtbl; Trk; College; Forestry.

WISE, Laurie J; Milbank HS; Milbank, SD; 21/120 Chr; HonRl; PpCl; Northern St Col; Elem Ed.

WISELY, Debora; Oblong Hs; Oblong, IL; 1/72 TrsJrCls; Band; Chrs; HonRl; NHS; Yrbk; FTA; LatCl; SciCl; Lincoln Trail Jr College; Medical Technlogy.

WISEMAN, Betty J; Porta HS; Petersburg, IL; ChrhWkr; MrchBnd; NHS; Yrbk; RptrSchPpr; GAA; College.

WISEMAN, Brian E; Elston Sr HS; Michigan City, IN; ChrhWkr; CmntyWkr; HonRl; SctActv; YthFlsp; PpCl; LetterFtbl; AmLegAwd; College; Engineering.

WISEMAN, Cathy D; Athens HS; Athens, IL; 1/51 TrsFrshCls; Band; HonRl; HospAde; RptrYrbk; FHA; College; Airlines.

WISEMAN, Rita E; Edwards Sr HS; Albion, IL; 1/98 Band; Chrs; ChrhWkr; HonRl; NatlMeritCmnd; SchMus; Univ Of Evansville; Music.

WISEMAN, Rita E; Edwards County HS; Albion, IL; 1/99 Band; Chrs; HonRl; HospAde; NHS; SchMus; RptrSchPpr; 4-H; FNA; FTA; GAA; University Of Evansville; Business.

WISEMEN, Louis; White Pine HS; Ontonagon, MI; ALBoysSt; Chrs; ChrhWkr; NatlFornLg; RptrYrbk; Univ Of Wis; Speech Broadcasting.

WISHMEYER, Karen; Taft HS; Chicago, IL; 17/876 Chrs; HonRl; JrNHS; NatlMeritFnl; NatlSciFnd; Orch; IMSpt; AmLegAwd; JETSAwd; Univ; Biochemistry.

WISKERCHEN, Connie J; Auburndale HS; Auburndale, WI; SecFrshCls; ChrhWkr; HonRl; MrchBnd; NHS; SchPl; TreasEdYrBk; 4-H; PresFBLA; Uw Eau Claire; Accounting.

WISNASKY, Susan L; O Fallon Township HS; Belleville, IL; 67/304 Chrs; HonRl; ModUN; SchMus; FHA; SpnCl; LetterBsktbl; IMSpt; Southern Ill U; Phy Ed Teacher.

WISNER, Kyle L; Guilford HS; Rockford, IL; HonRl; Orch; SchMus; LetterSwmmng; Trk; CchngActv; Jr College; Christian Counseling.

WISNER, Timothy D; T L Grace HS; Minneapolis, MN; Chr; Chrs; SchMus; SchPl; TchrAde; CivCl; 4-H; Univ Of Mn; Major In Biology.

WISNESKI, Martin E; Walled Lake Western HS; Walled Lake, MI; 4/400 HonRl; NHS; CaptTrk; RotaryAwd; Western Mi Univ; Librarianship.

WISNEWSKI, Richard A; Cardinal Muench Seminary; Geneseo, ND; PresFrshCls; Chrs; SchPl; StuCncl; SchPpr; PpCl; LetterBsktbl; IMSpt; PPFtbl; 4-HAwd; College; Phy Ed.

WISNIEWSKI, Bridget; Saints Peter And Paul HS; Saginaw, MI; 5/104 Chrs; HonRl; JrNHS; NatlFornLg; NHS; FDA; FrCl; PpCl; College; Professional.

WISNIEWSKI, Bryan; Alpena Senior HS; Alpena, MI; NatlFornLg; NatlThespSoc; SchPl; StuCncl; LatCl; Work Wayne State Univ; Criminal Lawyer.

WISNIEWSKI, Gayle A; St Augustine HS; Chicago, IL; PresSophCls; Chrs; ChrhWkr; CmntyWkr; HonRl; NHS; StuCncl; TchrAde; RptrYrbk; VoiceDemAwd;.

WISNIEWSKI, Janet M; All Saints Central HS; Bay City, MI; 1/138 VPSophCls; PresJrCls; PresSrCls; ALAGirlsSt; HonRl; NHS; StuGov; CaptBsktbl; Chrldr; CchngActv; Univ Of Michigan; Physical Therapy.

WISNIEWSKI, Jodle L; Ernest W Seaholm HS; Birmingham, MI; 23/709 HonRl; JrNHS; ModUN; NatlFornLg; NHS; StuCncl; StuGov; Glf; Tennis; IMSpt; Mounte Holyoke Clg; Law.

WISNIEWSKI, Laura L; Hanover Central HS; Cedar Lake, IN; 7/140 ALAGirlsSt; HonRl; JrNHS; NHS; NatlThespSoc; OffAde; SchPl; RptrSchPpr; SchPpr; College; Special Ed.

WISOWATY, Harry R; Gordon Technical HS; Chicago, IL; 88/618 DrmMjrt; HonRl; Orch; PepBnd; StuCncl; RptrSchPpr; PpCl; IMSpt; St Marys Col ;psychology.

WISSEL, Darrel A; Illini Bluffs HS; Glasford, IL; 8/75 HonRl; AmLegAwd; College; Math.

WISSEL, Roseann M; Acad Of The Immaculate Concep; Batesville, IN; 8/60 VPJrCls; PresSrCls; Chr; Chrs; HonRl; NHS; SchPl; StuCncl; Col; Drama.

WISSIAK, Jay A; Sheldon Community HS; Sheldon, IA; 15/146 HonRl; SchMus; LetterFtbl; IMSpt; Univ Of Northern Ia; Bus Profession.

WISSING, Marcia L; Oregon HS; Oregon, IL; 3/104 Band; CncrtBnd; HonRl; MrchBnd; NHS; NatlThespSoc; Quill&Scroll; SchMus; SchPl; EdSchPpr; Rockford Mem School Of Nursing; Nurse.

WISSINK, Stephen E; Harper Creek HS; Battle Creek, MI; Band; CncrtBnd; HonRl; MrchBnd; PolWkr; SchPl; TchrAde; FrCl; College; Music.

WISSMANN, Rodney W; Washington HS; Defiance, MO; 27/276 Band; CncrtBnd; HonRl; MrchBnd; PepBnd; YthFlsp; 4-H; FFA;.

WISSNER, Wendy S; Usa HS; Sebewaing, MI; 12/104 ALAGirlsSt; Band; HonRl; PepBnd; StuCncl; FHA; LatCl; PpCl; LetterTrk; CaptChrldr; Ferris; Dental Hygiene.

WISTHUFF, Scott D; Lyons Twp HS; La Grange, IL; 4/1214 SecBand; Chr; HonRl; NatlMeritFnl; Orch; SctActv; PresYthFlsp; MthCl; University; Engineering.

WISWASSER, Cynthia L; Bath HS; E Lansing, MI; 4/86 Band; CncrtBnd; HonRl; MrchBnd; NHS; PepBnd; TchrAde; Lansing Comm Coll; Nursing.

WITALEC, Karen M; Yale HS; Avoca, MI; 8/150 TrsSophCls; HonRl; NatlMeritFnl; NatlMeritCmnd; NatlMeritSF; StuCncl; FHA; Chrldr; PPFtbl; BttyCrckrAwd; Ferris State; Radiologic Tech.

WITBERLER, Donna M; Marathon HS; Marathon, WI; 5/98 Chrs; HonRl; SchMus; SchPl; StuCncl; EdYrBk; Yrbk; RptrSchPpr; MthCl; GAA; Coll; Nursing.

WITCOFF, David L; New Trier East HS; Glencoe, IL; 47/850 Chrs; HonRl; SptEdYrbk; MthCl; Stanford University; Lawyer.

WITECK, Carol A; Appleton W HS; Appleton, WI; 60/640 AFS; HospAde; PolWkr; RptrYrbk; Yrbk; SpnCl; PpCl; CaptChrldr; U Of Wi; Accounting.

WITEK, Laura L; William J Bogan HS; Chicago, IL; 3/756 Chrs; HonRl; JrNHS; LbryAde; OffAde;

SchAde; SchPl; SctActv; TchrAde; VPFrCl; SciCl; GAA; University; Biology.

WITHAM, Novelene E; Tippecanoe Valley HS; Mentone, IN; HonRl; SptEdYrbk; SchPpr; FHA; SpnCl; College; Sociological Study.

WITHBROE, Patty; East De Pere HS; De Pere, WI; 54/200 RptrYrbk; SptEdYrbk; RptrSchPpr; EdSchPpr; SptEdSchPpr; Bsktbl; GAA; IMSpt; Univ Of Green Bay; Phy Ed.

WITHEM, Matthew J; Roncalli HS; Indianapolis, IN; CmntyWkr; HonRl; SctActv; FBLA; FTA; Bsktbl; Ftbl; Trk; GodCntryAwd; CitAwd; In Univ; Actg.

WITHERBY, Toni L; Madison Consolidated HS; Madison, IN; Chr; CAP; MrchBnd; NatlThespSoc; SchMus; SchPl; TchrAde; LatCl; PpCl; Swmmng; Col; Teacher.

WITHERS, Cathy; Van Buren HS; Brazil, IN; 9/65 Band; CncrtBnd; HonRl; MrchBnd; NHS; PepBnd; EdYrBk; FTA; PpCl;.

WITHERS, Gregory; Carbondale Community Hs; Carbondale, IL; 11/289 Chr; HonRl; NHS; NatlMeritCmnd; Orch; PepBnd; GerCl; Bsktbl; Ftbl; LetterTrk; U Of Illinois; Engineering.

WITHERSPOON, Sherri; Shawneetown HS; Shawneetown, IL; Chr; Chrs; HonRl; MrchBnd; RptrYrbk; Yrbk; RptrSchPpr; SchPpr; PpCl; Bsktbl; College; Secretary.

WITHROW, Catherine A; Springfield HS; Springfield, IL; Chr; OffAde; SchPl; SctActv; RptrSchPpr; EdSchPpr; SchPpr; SpnCl; Eastern Il Univ; Journalism.

WITHROW, Kimberly A; West Holt HS; Atkinson, NE; ChrhWkr; DrlTm; DrmMjrt; HospAde; LbryAde; YthFlsp; Yrbk; FrCl; College; Vocation.

WITHROW, Randall M; De Soto HS; Stoddard, WI; 2/78 PresFrshCls; HonRl; SchPl; SctActv; StuCncl; StuGov; TchrAde; Bsktbl; LetterTrk; Univ Of Wis; Corporate Law.

WITKOP, Paul W; Springfield HS; Springfield, IL; 7/600 Band; JrNHS; NHS; TchrAde; SpnCl; MthCl; SciCl; Augustana College.

WITSCHER, Douglas R; Harvard HS; Harvard, IL; 26/159 HonRl; GerCl; Ftbl;.

WITSMAN, Lavonda M; Covington HS; Covington, IN; Band; CncrtBnd; HonRl; MrchBnd; PepBnd; SchPl; SchPpr; 4-H; FHA; 4-HAwd; Lakeview Sch Of Radiology; Xray Technician.

WITT, Alfreda; Henryville HS; Henryville, IN; HonRl; LbryAde; RptrYrbk;.

WITT, Brenda S; Adelphian Academy; Flint, MI; Band; ChrhWkr; CncrtBnd; HonRl; HospAde; Ftbl; Collge; Professional.

WITT, Carol A; Glidden HS; Glidden, WI; TrsJrCls; Band; Chr; ChrhWkr; CncrtBnd; HonRl; MrchBnd; NatlFornLg; PepBnd; 4-H; PpCl; College; Professional.

WITT, Cindy L; Sheboygan Falls HS; Sheboygan Falls, WI; Chrs; ChrhWkr; HonRl; NHS; SchPl; RptrYrbk; PpCl; LetterChrldr; GAA; Business School; Vocation.

WITT, Darlene; Ava HS; Ava, MO; Chr; Chrs; HonRl; SpnCl; LetterTrk; IMSpt; PresAwd; St Lukes Sch Of Nursing; Rn.

WITT, Diane; Ava HS; Ava, MO; 7/134 HonRl; Quill&Scroll; SchPl; RptrSchPpr; SchPpr; FBLA; PpCl; CaptBsktbl; LetterTrk; IMSpt; St Lukes Hosp Sch Of Nursing; Rn.

WITT, Elaine M; West Fargo HS; West Fargo, ND; Chr; HonRl; SecFBLA; GAA; College; General Secretary.

WITT, Gene G; Scotus Central Catholic HS; Columbus, NE; HonRl; Trk; IMSpt;.

WITT, George H; Unity HS; Mendon, IL; ALBoysSt; ChrhWkr; HonRl; NHS; PresYthFlsp; Treas4-H; TreasFFA; MthCl; SciCl; Bsbl; College.

WITT, Greg A; Starden Jeffers HS; Storden, MN; 4/50 VPSrCls; ALBoysSt; ChrhWkr; CmntyWkr; NHS; SchPl; SctActv; StuGov; Teen; Trk; Jackson Vo Sch; Electro Mechanical Drafting.

WITT, Janice M; Abbotsford HS; Abbotsford, WI; AFS; HonRl; HospAde; LbryAde; NHS; RptrYrbk; RptrSchPpr; PresFHA; PpCl; GAA; St Joseph Sch Of Nursing; Registered Nurse.

WITT, Jeanne M; Alvernia HS; Chicago, IL; HonRl; NHS; StuCncl; De Paul Univ; Accounting.

WITT, Jeffrey A; Mt Vernon Sr HS; Mt Vernon, IN; 70/260 VPFrshCls; ChrhWkr; HonRl; IntrClCncl; StuCncl; YthFlsp; KeyCl; LetterBsbl; LetterBsktbl; LetterFtbl; College; Industrial Arts.

WITT, Kevin B; Milford Township HS; Milford, IL; 8/78 PresSophCls; Band; Chr; CncrtBnd; HonRl; JrNHS; MrchBnd; NHS; NatlMeritCmnd; PepBnd; StuCncl; LetterBsktbl; Illinois Wesleyan; Music.

WITT, Larry; Blackford HS; Hartford City, IN; HonRl; Quill&Scroll; RptrYrbk; SptEdYrbk; SchPpr; PpCl; Glf; Swmmng; Trk; IMSpt; Indiana Univ; Publications.

WITT, Lois M; Lutheran West HS; Livonia, MI; Chr; ChrhWkr; CmntyWkr; HonRl; OffAde; RptrYrbk; PpCl; BttyCrckrAwd; Grand Valley St Coll; Nursing.

WITT, Mary; Warsaw Hs; Warsaw, IL; 2/66 PresAFS; CncrtBnd; PresNHS; NatlMeritCmnd; SchMus; StuCncl; EdYrBk; GerCl; TreasGAA; DARAwd; U Of Illinois; Lawyer.

WITT, Michael H; Dundee Community HS; West Dundee, IL; AFS; MrchBnd; NatlFornLg; SchMus; SctActv; StuCncl; EdYrBk; GerCl; Bsktbl; Southern Illinois University; Broadcasting.

WITT, Richard B; Omaha Benson HS; Omaha, NE; PresJrCls; HonRl; LbryAde; NatlMeritSF; OffAde; SctActv; LetterWrstlng; NCTE; Us Air Force Academy; Engineering.

WITT, Tamara S; Maysville HS; Amity, MO; 7/57 Chr; Chrs; HonRl; PepBnd; 4-H; FFA; SciCl; Trk; College; English.

WITT, Tammy A; Avondale Sr HS; Pontiac, MI; Chr; ChrhWkr; CmntyWkr; HonRl; LbryAde; OffAde; SchPl; RptrSchPpr; SchPpr; SpnCl; College; Business.

WITT, Thomas F; Champaign Central HS; Champaign, IL; 1/411 Band; CncrtBnd; HonRl; JrNHS; NHS; NatlMeritSF; StuCncl; GerCl; Ftbl; Tennis; IMSpt; Univ Of Ill; Lawyer.

WITT, Thomas W; Rich South HS; Matteson, IL; 32/290 Band; CncrtBnd; HonRl; MrchBnd; PolWkr; Quill&Scroll; StuCncl; EdSchPpr; Bsbl; Bsktbl; U Of Ill; English.

WITTBRODT, Deborah A; Blissfield Sr HS; Riga, MI; 8/150 CncrtBnd; HonRl; MrchBnd; NHS; SchPl; YthFlsp; VPFHA; VPSpnCl; Univ Of Michigan; Literature.

WITTCHOW, Jeffrey; Lakeside Luth HS; Watertown, WI; TrsFrshCls; Chr; Ftbl; IMSpt; 4-HAwd; Trade School; Voc.

WITTE, Elaine M; Richmond Senior HS; Richmond, IN; 1/582 VPFrshCls; HonRl; JrNHS; TchrAde; FrCl; SecPpCl; Swmmng; GAA; IMSpt; KiwanAwd; Purdue Univ; Pharmacy.

WITTE, James C; Naperville Central HS; Naperville, IL; 30/864 Band; CncrtBnd; HonRl; MrchBnd; NatlMeritFnl; LetterFtbl; Beloit Coll; Law.

WITTE, James R; East Lansing HS; East Lansing, MI; Band; MrchBnd; NHS; Mi St U; Architecture.

WITTE, Joyce E; Louisville HS; Louisville, NE; Chr; Chrs; HonRl; NHS; SchMus; YthFlsp; 4-H; PpCl; LetterBsktbl; 4-HAwd; School; Beauticiation.

WITTE, Keith J; Louisville HS; Louisville, NE; 2/40 Chr; HonRl; YthFlsp; 4-H; FrCl; Bsktbl; 4-HAwd; College; Agriculture.

WITTE, Linda; Fremont HS; Fremont, MI; 5/189 ChrhWkr; HonRl; NHS; SpnCl; BttyCrckrAwd; Michigan State Univ;.

WITTE, Scott; Schalles HS; Schaller, IA; 6/30 Chr; Chrs; Mdrgl; SchPl; PresStuCncl; EdYrBk; CaptBsbl; CaptBsktbl; CaptFtbl; LetterTrk; Northwestern Coll; Bus Admin.

WITTE, Steven L; L C Mohr HS; South Haven, MI; ChrhWkr; HonRl; StuGov; TchrAde; TreasYthFlsp; Yrbk; Bsktbl; Ftbl; Trk; Northwestern College; Ministry.

WITTE, Tammy L; Brookfield R Iii HS; Brookfield, MO; Band; Chrs; CncrtBnd; HonRl; MrchBnd; NHS; SchMus; TchrAde; FHA; FTA; College; Secretarial.

WITTENBERG, Eugena A; Windsor HS; Windsor, IL; 13/56 Chr; HonRl; SchPl; 4-H; FHA; PpCl;.

WITTENBORN, Jan L; Rushville Consolidated HS; Rushville, IN; 4/270 Chr; CncrtBnd; HonRl; NatlFornLg; SecNHS; RedCrAde; FrCl; MthCl; PresPpCl; Chrldr; PPFtbl; Indiana Univ; Mathematics.

WITTER, Teresa A; Randolph Southern HS; Lynn, IN; 4/61 Band; Chr; ChrhWkr; HonRl; MrchBnd; SecNHS; RptrYrbk; PpCl; Trk; GAA; Olivet Nazarene Coll; Probation Officers.

WITTEVEEN, Debra L; West Ottawa HS; Holland, MI; HonRl; ModUN; NatlFornLg; NHS; NatlThespSoc; SchPl; TchrAde; GerCl; Bsbl; IMSpt; Art Sch; Commercial Art.

WITTGEN, Donald; Reitz Memorial HS; Evansville, IN; 3/214 HonRl; MrchBnd; NHS; NatlMeritFnl; RptrYrbk; Glf; RotaryAwd; Notre Dame; Pre Med.

WITTHOEFT, Elida S; Arlington HS; Arlington Hts, IL; 7/586 HonRl; LitMag; NHS; Quill&Scroll; TchrAde; RptrSchPpr; EdSchPpr; SchPpr; PresGerCl; GAA; Northwestern Univ; Journalism.

WITTHOFT, Wayne H; Cobden Unit HS; Cobden, IL; 3/55 VPFrshCls; HonRl; OffAde; StuCncl; SchPpr; LetterBsktbl; LetterTrk; Eastern Ill Univ; Foreign Ser.

WITTHUHN, Sue; Southwest HS; Greenbay, WI; Band; Chr; Chrs; CncrtBnd; HonRl; MrchBnd; Bsbl; Swmmng; Business School; Secretary.

WITTIG, Jackie A; Appleton West HS; Appleton, WI; Band; CncrtBnd; HonRl; MrchBnd; Twrl; FTA; FrCl; Coll; Nurse.

WITTIG, Leslie A; Granite City South HS; Granite City, IL; IntrClCncl; OffAde; Quill&Scroll; SchAde; SctActv; YthFlsp; RptrSchPpr; Trk; GAA; IMSpt; Clge; Mass Communications.

WITTLAND, Gregory A; Seymour HS; Marblehead, IL; 5/65 VPFrshCls; PresJrCls; HonRl; NHS; StuCncl; 4-H; Bsbl; LetterBsktbl; Bradley Univ; Elec Engineering.

WITTLAND, Michael F; Seymour HS; Marblehead, IL; 29/67 Band; CncrtBnd; MrchBnd; SctActv; 4-H; LetterBsbl; LetterBsktbl;.

WITTMAACK, Maryann; Northwest HS; House Springs, MO; RptrSchPpr; Univ; Journalism.

WITTMAN, Cynthia K; Alton Sr HS; Godfrey, IL; 58/803 HonRl; NHS; StuCncl; TchrAde; RptrSchPpr; SchPpr; Lewis & Clark Comm College; Artist.

WITTMANN, Thomas G; Brillion Public HS; Brillion, WI; 1/91 ALBoysSt; Band; ChrhWkr; HonRl; NHS; StuCncl; Yrbk; TreasSpnCl; SciCl; Trk; Marquette Univ; Medicine.

WITTMER, Coleen J; Barr Reeve HS; Montgomery, IN; 3/67 HstFrshCls; PresSophCls; TrsJrCls; VPSrCls; ALAGirlsSt; ChrhWkr; HonRl; HospAde; NHS; StuCncl; TchrAde; GAA; IMSpt; AmLegAwd; Univ Of Evansville; Nursing.

WITTORFF, Dorothy C; Ava HS; Ava, MO; Band; Chr; Chrs; ChrhWkr; CmntyWkr; CncrtBnd; HonRl; JA; MrchBnd; PepBnd; 4-H; FFA; Bsbl; 4-HAwd; Univ Of Arkansas; Veterinary Med.

WITTROCK, Debbie A; South HS; Sheboygan, WI; CmntyWkr; PresRedCrAde; SctActv; PpCl; GAA; IMSpt; PresAwd; College; Dental Hygiene.

WITTROCK, Mary Jo; B I L L HS; Bird Island, MN; Chr; ChrhWkr; HonRl; NatlFornLg; NHS; StuCncl; RptrYrbk; PpCl; LetterChrldr; GAA; PPFtbl; Moorhead St College; Special Educ.

WITTROCK, Paul B; Colfax HS; Colfax, WI; VPSophCls; ChrhWkr; HonRl; LbryAde; SchPl; 4-H; Bsbl; Bsktbl; Ftbl; University; Professional.

WITTRY, Barbara K; St Bernard HS; Breda, IA; 1/18 VPSrCls; HonRl; NHS; RptrYrbk; RptrSchPpr; 4-H; LatCl; BttyCrckrAwd; EldAwd; 4-HAwd; U Of Iowa; Professional.

WITTRY, David; St Bernard HS; Breda, IA; 3/34 ALBoysSt; Chrs; ChrhWkr; HonRl; JA; NHS; SchPl; Univ; Professional.

WITTSTRUCK, Brad L; Crete HS; Martell, NE; 39/110 PresSrCls; ALBoysSt; HonRl; StuCncl; LetterBsktbl; LetterFtbl; ChmbCommrsAwd; College.

WITTWER, Dan C; Dawson Verdon HS; Dawson, NE; ChrhWkr; SchPl; StuGov; YthFlsp; Bsktbl; Trade School; Vocation.

WITTWER, Deborah; Appleton West HS; Appleton, WI; /630 AFS; Chrs; ChrhWkr; LbryAde; Orch; GerCl; PpCl; Minn Insti Of Med; Veterinary Technology.

WITTWER, Karen J; Mccook HS; Mccook, NE; AFS; HonRl; LitMag; NHS; Quill&Scroll; SecStuCncl; EdSchPpr; PpCl; Mccook Comm Coll; Journalism.

WITZIG, Jacqueline A; Benilde St Margarets HS; Golden Valley, MN; Band; CncrtBnd; HonRl; NHS; PepBnd; RedCrAde; SchMus; SchPl; StuCncl; Swmmng; College; Art.

WITZKE, Gary K; Oshkosh North HS; Oshkosh, WI; 199/429 Band; Chrs; Mdrgl; PepBnd; Bsbl; LetterFtbl; Coll; Auto Mech.

WITZKE, Kathryn L; Tri County HS; Hancock, WI; 11/50 HonRl; NHS; TchrAde; SpnCl; GAA; Coll; Social Work.

WITZMAN, Barbara; Senior HS; Sparta, WI; 13/195 Chrs; CncrtBnd; HonRl; Mdrgl; MrchBnd; NHS; Orch; PepBnd; SchMus; SpnCl; La Crosse Univ; Business Adm.

WIWCZAROSKI, Cynthia K; Oakville HS; St Louis, MO; ChrhWkr; CmntyWkr; HonRl; LbryAde; NatlCathMusEdAsoc; SchMus; FDA; LatCl; MthCl; SciCl; Medical School; Physician.

WIXCEY, Carla; Hutchinson Jr Sr HS; Hutchinson, MN; AFS; Chr; NHS; OffAde; SchMus; StuCncl; Chrldr; St Clouds Beauty Coll; Beautician.

WIXSON, Sally; Brandon HS; Ortonville, MI; Band; HonRl; MrchBnd; PepBnd; SctActv; SpnCl; Ferris State College, Rn.

WIZNER, Anne J; Freeland HS; Freeland, MI; 14/115 ChrhWkr; CmntyWkr; HonRl; NHS; NatlMeritSchl; TchrAde; RptrYrbk; EdYrBk; SptEdYrbk; College.

WNUK, Dennis R; Cahokia Sr HS; Cahokia, IL; HonRl; NHS; College; Business.

WOBBE, Barbara M; Mater Dei HS; Trenton, IL; 2/182 VPJrCls; Chrs; HonRl; JrNHS; NHS; SchMus;.

WOCHNIK, Michael M; Mercy HS; St Louis, MO; NHS; University; Psychology.

WODEK, Edward J; Petoskey HS; Petoskey, MI; 1/4/276 VPJrCls; VPSrCls; Band; CncrtBnd; MrchBnd; NatlMeritSchl; NatlMeritSF; StuCncl; TchrAde; Glf; Univ; Optometrist.

WODILL, Sheryl J; Beaver Dam Sr HS; Beaver Dam, WI; 5/314 SecSophCls; SecJrCls; SecSrCls; HonRl; StuCncl; RptrSchPpr; PpCl; GAA; College; Industrial Engineer.

WODLINGER, Rhonda S; Roger Sullivan HS; Chicago, IL; SecSrCls; Chr; Chrs; HonRl; NHS; SchAde; StuGov; TchrAde; FrCl; Univ Of Il; Special Ed.

WODTKE, Sharon M; Chippewa Valley HS; Mt Clemens, MI; Band; CncrtBnd; HonRl; MrchBnd; NHS; OffAde; PepBnd; College; Writer.

WOEBBEKING, Doug A; Gladbrook Comm HS; Gladbrook, IA; VPSrCls; AFS; Band; Chr; ChrhWkr; HonRl; ModUN; StuCncl; EdYrBk; 4-H; Bsktbl; Iowa State Univ; Agricultural Business.

WOEHL, Timothy T; Ashley HS; Ashley, ND; VPSophCls; SecSrCls; Chr; Chrs; SptEdSchPpr; Bsktbl; Glf; Univ; Pro.

WOEHLER, Wendy J; Downers Grove Comm HS; Woodridge, IL; Chrs; HonRl; LbryAde; NHS; SchMus; Illinois Benedictine College.

WOEHRMANN, Jan L; Sullivan HS; Sullivan, MO; 59/159 Chrs; ChrhWkr; HonRl; NHS; OffAde; SctActv; TchrAde; RptrYrbk; FshEdSchPpr; FNA; College; Vocation.

WOELFEL, Donna M; Calhoun HS; Hardin, IL; Band; HonRl; NHS; PepBnd; Lewis & Clark Comm Coll; Med Lab Tech.

WOELFEL, Sandy; Hilbert HS; Hilbert, WI; 41/69 PresSrCls; HonRl; OffAde; StuCncl; TchrAde; SchPpr; Bsbl;.

WOESSNER, Kristina F; Proviso East HS; Forest Park, IL; 72/1001 Chrs; Triton College; Behavioral Science.

WOESTE, Karen L; Edgewood Colesburg HS; Edgewood, IA; Band; Chr; NHS; SchMus; RptrSchPpr; Univ; Pro.

WOFFORD, Beverly J; Valley Falls HS; Valley Falls, KS; 2/38 PresJrCls; HonRl; NHS; OffAde; TchrAde; LetterBsktbl; LetterTrk; College; Physical Education.

WOFFORD, Linda K; Normandy Sr HS; Uplands Park, MO; Chr; Chrl; Chrs; ChrhWkr; HonRl; JA; SchPl; FrCl; PpCl; Bsbl; Bsktbl; IMSpt; St Louis Univ; Professional.

WOFFORD, Michael R; Arlington HS; Bennington, NE; PresSophCls; HonRl; NHS; SchPl; StuGov; LetterBsktbl; LetterTrk; LetterWrstlng;.

WOFFORD, Susan K; Granite South HS; Granite City, IL; 20/700 JA; NHS; OffAde; SctActv; PpCl; GAA; College; Accounting Or Law.

WOGSLAND, Laurie A; Tomahawk HS; Tomahawk, WI; 1/164 ALAGirlsSt; ChrhWkr; CmntyWkr; HonRl; RedCrAde; TchrAde; RptrSchPpr; FBLA; Bsktbl; GAA; College; Teaching.

WOHEAD, Elizabeth T; Naperville Central HS; Naperville, IL; 65/844 Chrs; CmntyWkr; HonRl; NHS; Univ Of Illinois.

WOHLER, Judith A; Fairfield Comm HS; Fairfield, IL; 6/165 HonRl; NHS; 4-H; VPSpnCl; TreasMthCl; PresSciCl; LetterBsktbl; LetterTennis; LetterTrk; GAA; 4-HAwd; E Illinois Univ; Law.

WOHLERS, Lynn D; Underwood Community HS; Underwood, IA; Band; Chrs; CncrtBnd; MrchBnd; PepBnd; LetterBsbl; LetterFtbl; LetterWrstlng; Ames Coll; Farming.

WOHLERS, Renae E; Lincoln HS; Lake City, MN; AFS; Chr; Chrs; ChrhWkr; HonRl; NHS; PolWkr; SchMus; SchPl; StuCncl; College; Music Therapist.

WOHLERS, Terry T; St Paul Public HS; St Paul, NE; Band; Chr; CncrtBnd; HonRl; MrchBnd; NHS; PepBnd; StuGov; LetterFtbl; LetterTrk; Col; Pro.

WOHLFERT, David A; South Haven HS; South Haven, MI; 54/213 Band; Chr; HonRl; PepBnd; SchPl; StuGov; TchrAde; EdYrBk; Trk; LetterWrstlng; Sw Mich Clg; Auto Mechanics.

WOHLGEMUTH, David L; Holdrege HS; Holdrege, NE; Chrs; SchMus; SchPl; StuGov; FFA; Bsbl; Bsktbl; Ftbl; 4-HAwd; CitAwd; Trade; Vocation.

WOHLGEMUTH, Jane S; Atchison HS; Atchison, KS; SecSophCls; Band; ChrhWkr; HonRl; NHS; OffAde; SchPl; StuCncl; PpCl; GAA; Washburn U; Medical.

WOHLRAB, Jean A; Bogan HS; Chicago, IL; 3/737 Chr; ChrhWkr; CncrtBnd; HonRl; JrNHS; OffAde; SchMus; YthFlsp; SchPpr; GerCl; College;math.

WOHLRABE, David C; Springfield Public HS; Springfield, MN; Chr; Chrs; ChrhWkr; CmntyWkr; HonRl; Yrbk; LetterBsktbl; LetterFtbl; LetterGlf; LetterTrk; Univ Of Morris Minn; Pre Detistry.

WOIRHAYE, Paula S; Lamar R1 School District HS; Lamar, MO; 14/84 Band; Chrs; ChrhWkr; CncrtBnd; HonRl; Mdrgl; MrchBnd; NatlFornLg; NHS; SchPl; Southwest Baptist College; Music.

WOITASZEWSKI, Anastasia; Loup City HS; Loup City, NE; VPFrshCls; PresSophCls; VPJrCls; PresSrCls; Chrs; HonRl; HospAde; LbryAde; NHS; StuGov; College; Nursing.

WOITTE, Linda D; Balfour Public HS; Balfour, ND; TrsFrshCls; Chrs; ChrhWkr; HonRl; LbryAde; SchPl; YthFlsp; RptrYrbk; EdSchPpr; LetterBsktbl; Coll; Professional.

WOJAHN, Beth S; Sleepy Eye Public HS; Comfrey, MN; 7/75 ChrhWkr; HonRl; JrNHS; NatlThespSoc; SchMus; SchPl; TchrAde; YthFlsp; RptrYrbk; TreasFHA; Sw Mn State Clg; Accounting.

WOJAK, Richard P; Campion Jesuit HS; Des Plaines, IL; LitMag; Glf; Chrldr; Marquette Univ; Marketing.

WOJCHIK, Jane M; Cochrane Fountain City HS; Cochrane, WI; SecJrCls; SchPpr; FBLA; FHA; PpCl; LetterChrldr;.

WOJCHIK, Phyllis J; Arcadia Public HS; Independence, WI; 13/102 HonRl; NHS; StuCncl; SchPpr; PresCivCl; Pres4-H; FHA; GAA; IMSpt; 4-HAwd; U Of Wisc Stout; Rehabilitation.

WOJCIECHOWSKI, Lynne M; All Saints Central HS; Bay City, MI; CmntyWkr; LbryAde; SpnCl; Bsktbl; College; Physical Therapy.

WOJCIECHOWSKI, Patty A; St Marys Cathedral HS; Gaylord, MI; 10/49 HonRl; NHS; SchPl; TchrAde; LatCl; SecPpCl; PPFtbl; OptClAwd; Business Col; Executive Sec.

WOJCIECHOWSKI, Scott; La Salle Peru Twp HS; La Salle, IL; Chrs; HonRl; Sacrstn; SchAde; SchMus; SctActv; StuCncl; GerCl; IMSpt; College; Law.

WOJCIECHOWSKI, Theresa A; St Francis Academy; Joliet, IL; 20/178 HonRl; NHS; University Of Illinois.

WOJCIEHOWSKI, Jeannette L; George Rogers Clark HS; Hammond, IN; 98/260 SecSophCls; Band; HonRl; RedCrAde; SchPl; FNA; Univ; X Ray Tech.

WOJCIK, Candace D; John Hersey HS; Mount Prospect, IL; 18/783 CmntyWkr; CncrtBnd; HonRl; JrNHS; MrchBnd; NHS; NatlMeritFnl; PepBnd; SptEdYrbk; LetterTrk; Univ Of Iowa; Medicine.

WOJCIK, Margaret M; Lake View HS; Chicago, IL; 3/310 Chrs; HonRl; HospAde; NHS; TchrAde; PresMthCl; GAA; BauchLmbAwd; Mundelein College; Special Educ Teacher.

WOJCIK, Nancy J; St Ladislaus HS; Hanmtramck, MI; 8/112 CmntyWkr; HonRl; SchPl; StuGov; FNA; FrCl; PpCl; Chrldr; GAA; Univ; Medical Technologist.

WOJCIK, Therese M; Lane Tech HS; Chicago, IL; 28/1413 HonRl; NHS; NatlMeritCmnd; TchrAde; Yrbk; LatCl; LetterTrk; LetterChrldr; GAA; College; Medicine.

WOJNAROWSKI, Carol; St Marys HS; Burlington, WI; 1/71 PresSophCls; Chrs; HonRl; StuCncl; Yrbk; PpCl; SciCl; Univ Of Wis; Computer Science.

WOJNICKI, Michael S; St Joseph HS; Cicero, IL; 12/175 HonRl; NHS; StuCncl; StuGov; SchPpr; GerCl; MthCl; PpCl; CaptTennis; IMSpt; College; Medicine.

WOJOY, Douglas; St Benedictine HS; Detroit, MI; HonRl; SchAde; Bsktbl; IMSpt; Univ Mich; Professional.

WOJTA, Francis H; Kewaunee HS; Two Rivers, WI; 36/140 AFS; Band; CncrtBnd; HonRl; MrchBnd; NHS; PepBnd; Sacrstn; FFA; LetterFtbl; IMSpt; Madison Trade School; Agri Business.

WOJTACNA, Donna M; St Ladislaus HS; Detroit, MI; 1/112 HonRl; NHS; RedCrAde; SctActv; TchrAde; RptrYrbk; Yrbk; FNA; PresMthCl; LetterTrk; Henry Ford Hospital; Nursing.

WOJTAK, Mary F; St Francis Academy; Joliet, IL; 18/178 HonRl; NHS; PolWkr; Northern Illinois Univ; Political Science.

WOJTALA, Gerald T; Trenton HS; Trenton, MI; 83/580 VPSrCls; HonRl; LitMag; NHS; SchMus; CaptTrk; Eastern Mich Univ.

WOJTALEWICZ, Barbara M; Pacelli HS; Stevens Point, WI; Chr; Chrs; ChrhWkr; CmntyWkr; HonRl; Sdlty; TchrAde; FHA; Trk; Univ Of Stevens Pt; Home Ec Ed.

WOJTALIK, Louann; Hamtramck HS; Hamtramck, MI; 1/144 HonRl; JrNHS; NHS; NatlMeritCmnd; RptrSchPpr; EdSchPpr; FrCl; BauchLmbAwd; Mi St Univ; Vet Med.

WOJTAN, Mary E; Ladywood HS; Livonia, MI; 2 97 HonRl; NHS; NatlMeritSF; Orch; SchMus; SctActv; StuCncl; RptrSchPpr; OptClAwd; VoiceDemAwd; Clg; Math.

WOJTASIK, Bonnie Lynn; Immaculate Heart Of Mary HS; Summit, IL; Chr; Chrs; ChrhWkr; CncrtBnd; Orch; SchMus; SchPl; FSA; SpnCl; SciCl; Il Benedictine Col; Vet.

WOKASCH, Thomas J; Highland Park HS; St Paul, MN; VPFrshCls; Chrs; SchMus; StuCncl; FrCl; Bsbl; Socr; CaptWrstlng; Univ Of Minnesota; Math.

WOKER, Cynthia S; Carlyle HS; Centralia, IL; 15/137 HonRl; HospAde; 4-H; PresFBLA; FTA; SpnCl; PpCl; GAA; Jr College; Business.

WOLAN, Daniel F; West Bloomfield HS; W Bloomfield, MI; IMSpt; Central Mich Univ; Radio & Tv Broadcasting.

WOLBAUM, Robert; Trinity HS; Dickinson, ND; StuCncl; Yrbk; IMSpt; U Of North Dakota; Broadcasting.

WOLBAUM, Sharon A; South Heart HS; Dicinson, ND; 5/25 SecSophCls; SecJrCls; Chr; HonRl; SchPl; TchrAde; RptrYrbk; EdYrBk; FHA; Bismarck Hosp Sch Of Nursing; Nurse.

WOLBER, David M; Rock Falls Twp HS; Rock Falls, IL; 1/250 ALBoysSt; ChrhWkr; CmntyWkr; HonRl; TreasNHS; PolWkr; TchrAde; FrCl; AmLegAwd; College; Accounting.

WOLBER, Kathy J; Hammond Baptist HS; Highland, IN; 2/88 SecTrsSophCls; Chr; ChrhWkr; HonRl; NHS; OffAde; RptrYrbk; RptrSchPpr; Chrldr; College.

WOLBER, Kent R; Warren HS; Warren, IL; PresSrCls; ALBoysSt; Band; ChrhWkr; HonRl; IntrClCncl; SchMus; SchPl; SctActv; Bsktbl; Ftbl; LetterTrk; EldAwd; Western Illinois Univ; Optometry.

WOLBER, Loni A; Chadwick HS; Chadwick, IL; SecFrshCls; SecSophCls; Band; Chrs; YthFlsp; 4-H; Glf; Chrldr; GAA; IMSpt; Coll.

WOLCOTT, Becki J; West Holt HS; Atkinson, NE; 25/70 SecJrCls; Chr; SchPl; StuGov; FFA; FHA; EngCl; LetterBsktbl; LetterTrk; Chrldr; College; Ranch Management.

WOLCOTT, Kim L; Waunota HS; Palisade, NE; Band; CmntyWkr; CncrtBnd; HonRl; NHS; PresFrshCls; RptrSchPpr; 4-H; FFA; 4-HAwd; Tech Col ;mech.

WOLD, Jeffrey M; Bottineau HS; Bottineau, ND; ALBoysSt; Chr; ChrhWkr; CncrtBnd; HonRl; SchPl; PpCl; SciCl; Ftbl; Glf; College; Civil Engineer.

WOLD, Lynette E; Richland #44 HS; Wahpeton, ND; TrsFrshCls; ALAGirlsSt; Chrs; CncrtBnd; MrchBnd; YthFlsp; Yrbk; FHA; PpCl; College.

WOLD, Marc S; Alexander Ramsey HS; St Paul, MN; 12/550 CncrtBnd; MrchBnd; NHS; NatlMeritFnl; NatlMeritSF; SchMus; StuCncl; GerCl; SciCl; LetterFtbl; College; Chemistry.

WOLD, Richard; Memorial HS; Eau Claire, WI; Band; HonRl; ModUN; PolWkr; SchAde; SchPl; RptrSchPpr; Univ Of Wi; Journalism And Bus Admin.

WOLDANSKI, Sharon A; Notre Dame HS; Milwaukee, WI; 12/117 Chrs; ChrhWkr; HonRl; SchMus; SchPl; StuCncl; Yrbk; SchPpr; SpnCl; PpCl; Chrldr; Bryant College; Med Secretary.

WOLDEN, Roger L; Philip Independent HS; Philip, SD; 18/44 Band; Chr; Chrs; ChrhWkr; CncrtBnd; HonRl; MrchBnd; PepBnd; SchPl; YthFlsp; College; Farmer.

WOLDT, Lori L; Michigan Lutheran Seminary; Milwaukee, WI; 1/81 SecFrshCls; Band; Chr; CncrtBnd; HonRl; Mdrgl; RptrSchPpr; SchPpr; IMSpt; Dr Martin Luther College; Teacher.

WOLDTVEDT, Allen H; Ashby Public HS; Ashby, MN; SecSophCls; Band; Chr; ChrhWkr; CncrtBnd; HonRl; MrchBnd; NHS; Orch; PepBnd; SchPl; LetterFtbl; Wrstlng; Trade; Marine Engineer.

WOLF, Annette B; Rochelle Twp HS; Rochelle, IL; 4/223 Chrs; HonRl; Univ Of Illinois; Accounting.

WOLF, Christine M; Slinger HS; Allenton, WI; Chr; HonRl; SchPl; RptrYrbk; SecFBLA; FHA; SecGAA; PresAwd; CitAwd; Coll; Educ.

WOLF, Colleen M; Odell Community HS; Odell, IL; 1/33 Chr; HonRl; SchPl; Yrbk; FHA; SpnCl; PpCl; Bsbl; Chrldr; GAA; Joliet Jr College; Computer Science.

WOLF, Cynthia E; Whitnall HS; Greenfield, WI; HonRl; HospAde; JA; JrNHS; LbryAde; SchPpr; FNA; FrCl; GAA; BttyCrckrAwd; Uw Eau Chaire; Nursing.

WOLF, Cynthia L; Wishek HS; Wishek, ND; 7/40 SecSrCls; Band; Chrs; CncrtBnd; HonRl; MrchBnd; OffAde; SchPpr; Bsbl; GAA; Bismarck Jr College; Secretarial Work.

WOLF, Darlene A; Winola HS; Aledo, IL; 22/65 DrlTm; HonRl; LbryAde; 4-H; FHA; FNA; 4-HAwd; KiwanAwd;.

WOLF, David C; Lakeland HS; La Grange, IN; 30/141 TrsSophCls; Band; ChrhWkr; NHS; PepBnd; 4-H; MthCl; VPSciCl; Bsktbl; Ftbl; 4-HAwd; Tri State College; Mechanical Engineering.

WOLF, Deborah M; Mc Henry Comm HS; Mc Henry, IL; 13/550 SecAFS; Chrs; HonRl; NHS; SchPl; RptrSchPpr; SchPpr; PpCl; GAA; Univ; Social Welfare.

WOLF, Elizabeth C; Mercy HS; Omaha, NE; PresSrCls; HonRl; NatlFornLg; SecRedCrAde; SchMus; SctActv; FrCl; Swmmng; Trk; 4-HAwd; University; Professional.

WOLF, Eydie M; Hazen HS; Hazen, ND; TrsJrCls; ALAGirlsSt; Chrs; HonRl; RptrSchPpr; Nd St Univ.

WOLF, Gene T; Hazen Public HS; Hazen, ND; DrmMjrt; 4-H; FFA; Ftbl; Trk; Trade Sch; Voc.

WOLF, Jamie A; Niles West HS; Morton Grove, IL; Chrs; HonRl; HospAde; NHS; TchrAde; Bsbl; Chrldr; GAA; University Of Illinois; Dietician.

WOLF, Janet C; Miller HS; Sarcoxie, MO; 1/43 ALAGirlsSt; Band; ChrhWkr; CmntyWkr; CncrtBnd; HonRl; VPNHS; SchMus; TchrAde; Pres4-H; FHA; KeyCl; PpCl; DanFAwd; University; Home Economics.

WOLF, Janet F; Mater Dei HS; Evansville, IN; 16/160 HonRl; JrNHS; NHS; StuCncl; SpnCl; PpCl; Trk; Chrldr; IMSpt; University; Major Study.

WOLF, Jo A; Dixon HS; Dixon, MO; 5/89 HonRl; StuCncl; TchrAde; FHA; FTA; PpCl; Chrldr;.

WOLF, John W; Newton Comm HS; Wheeler, IL; 52/215 ChrhWkr; HonRl; NHS; YthFlsp; LetterBsbl; LetterBsktbl; CaptFtbl; LetterGlf; College; Forestry.

WOLF, Judith; Wheatland HS; Grainfield, KS; HonRl; LbryAde; EdSchPpr; FHA; IMSpt;.

WOLF, Judy D; Sullivan HS; Chicago, IL; 13/276 TrsJrCls; TrsSrCls; Chr; CmntyWkr; NHS; RedCrAde; StuGov; Yrbk; SchPpr; Eastern Illinois Univ; Health Science.

WOLF, Kevin D; Brownstown Comm HS; Brownstown, IL; 1/38 HonRl; SchPl; Yrbk; 4-H; Eastern Illinois Univ; Accountant.

WOLF, Kim; Hanson Indp 40 HS; Alexandria, SD; 2/44 ALAGirlsSt; HonRl; PepBnd; Quill&Scroll; SchPl; RptrYrbk; RptrSchPpr; Bsbl; Trk; Univ; Interior Design.

WOLF, Kristine H; Carl Brablec HS; Roseville, MI; 4/451 HonRl; SecJrNHS; NHS; SecStuCncl; LatCl; SciCl; CaptLetterBsktbl; Univ Of Mi; Sci.

WOLF, Larry D; Napoleon Public HS; Kintyre, ND; 15/62 Chrs; Trade School.

WOLF, Leland; Hudson Area HS; Hudson, MI; 3/126 ALBoysSt; HonRl; NHS; TchrAde; Ftbl; IMSpt; Adrian College; Pre Med.

WOLF, Loren D; Comm Unit Dist 5 HS; Sterling, IL;

WOLF, Lori J; Mehlville Sr HS; St Louis, MO; ChrhWkr; HospAde; JA; LitMag; SchMus; SchPl; StuCncl; SecLatCl; SecPpCl; MasAwd; Nursing School; Anestitist.

WOLF, Mary L; Pacelli HS; Austin, MN; HonRl; NHS; NatlMeritFnl; NatlMeritSchl; EdYrBk; MthCl; Winona St Clge; Journalism.

WOLF, Mary L; Sacred Heart Public HS; Sacred Heart, MN; ALAGirlsSt; Band; Chr; ChrhWkr; HonRl; NHS; SctActv; EdYrBk; FHA; Bsktbl; Jr College; Elementary Education.

WOLF, Merry A; Valders HS; Oc, WI; 1/112 TreasAFS; Chr; Chrs; Mdrgl; NHS; SchPl; StuCncl; SecYthFlsp; RptrSchPpr; 4-H; Univ Of Wi; Elec Engi.

WOLF, Pamela K; Mobridge HS; Mobridge, SD; Band; Chr; CncrtBnd; HonRl; NatlMeritFnl; NatlMeritCmnd; SchMus; SchPl; StuGov; PpCl; College; Elementary Education.

WOLF, Ricka P; Sacred Heart Acad; Bloomfield Hills, MI; 1/32 LitMag; NHS; NatlMeritSF; SchPl; StuGov; RptrYrbk; FrCl; Georgetown Univ; French Major.

WOLF, Ronni D; Matthews HS; Sikeston, MO; SecJrCls; TrsSrCls; SchPl; StuCncl; EdYrBk; FHA; Harding College.

WOLF, Rory A; Hartford Union HS; Richfield, WI; /362 HonRl; IMSpt; College West Bend; Business Management.

WOLF, Roslea A; Doland HS; Doland, SD; Band; CncrtBnd; HonRl; HospAde; Orch; RedCrAde; ROTC; SchPl; StuCncl; YthFlsp; VPSchPpr; Trk; 4-HAwd; College; Nursing.

WOLF, Ruthann; Cedar Valley Comm HS; Farnhamville, IA; 4/27 PresFrshCls; SecJrCls; HonRl; MrchBnd; PepBnd; SchMus; SchPl; EdYrBk; Kirkwood Comm College; Respiratory Therapy.

WOLF, Sally D; Gaylord HS; Gaylord, MI; TrsFrshCls; Band; HonRl; NHS; OffAde; SchPl; StuCncl; Chrldr; IMSpt; PPFtbl; Coll; Elem Ed.

WOLF, Scott W; Cozad HS; Cozad, NE; CncrtBnd; MrchBnd; PepBnd; SchPl; Pres4-H; Bsktbl; LetterFtbl; IMSpt; 4-HAwd; National College Of Business; Farming.

WOLF, Sharon; South Milwaukee Sr HS; South Milwaukee, WI; 5/491 HonRl; NHS; Wi Univ Milw; Nurse.

WOLF, Steven E; Mexico HS; Mexico, MO; 39/256 TrsFrshCls; ALBoysSt; CncrtBnd; HonRl; TreasStuCncl; TreasStuGov; TreasKeyCl; Ftbl; LetterTrk; Wrstlng; Applied Us Naval Acad; Civil Engineer.

WOLF, Susan L; Durant Community HS; New Liberty, IA; 31/68 TrsJrCls; TreasBand; MrchBnd; StuCncl; TchrAde; RptrSchPpr; 4-H; PresFTA; LetterTrk; BttyCrckrAwd; Univ Of Northeast Mo; Special Ed.

WOLF, Thomas G; Granton Public HS; Chili, WI; 3/37 PresSophCls; TrsJrCls; HonRl; LbryAde; StuCncl; TreasFFA; Univ Of Wisconsin; Mechanics.

WOLF, Thomas P; South HS; Sheboygan, WI; 1/495 HonRl; NatlMeritSF; StuCncl; Yrbk; RotaryAwd; Ba At U Of Wi; Acctg.

WOLF, Wendy; Adlai E Stevenson HS; Prairie View, IL; Chr; ChrhWkr; CncrtBnd; HonRl; HospAde; MrchBnd; NHS; SchMus; FNA; SpnCl; College; Pharmacy.

WOLF, Wendy L; Adlai E Stevenson HS; Prairie View, IL; 24/240 Chr; ChrhWkr; CncrtBnd; HonRl; MrchBnd; NHS; RedCrAde; SchMus; FNA; Purdue Univ; Professional.

WOLFE, Alice D; Grain Valley HS; Oak Grove, MO; 5/42 TrsFrshCls; TrsSophCls; Band; Chrs; HonRl; VPNHS; SchPl; EdYrBk; SchPpr; DARAwd; Central Methodist Col; Drama.

WOLFE, Bradley P; Allendale HS; Allendale, IL; 1 21 PresJrCls; Chrs; HonRl; YthFlsp; FFA; PpCl; LetterBsktbl; Clg; Profes.

WOLFE, Carl D; La Salle Peru HS; Peru, IL; 41/491 HonRl; College; Elec Engineer.

WOLFE, Catherine A; Creston Sr HS; Creston, IA; Chrs; HonRl; MrchBnd; TchrAde; PpCl; Chrldr; College; Dental Hygienist.

WOLFE, David J; Cochrane Fountain City HS; Fountain City, WI; Aud/Vis; LetterBsbl; LetterWrstlng; Vocational; Elect.

WOLFE, David L; Northern Valley HS; Almena, KS; PresSophCls; PresSrCls; Chrs; ChrhWkr; CmntyWkr; SchPl; StuCncl; SptEdYrbk; EdSchPpr; FFA; LetterBsbl; CaptBsktbl; LetterFtbl; College; Physical Ed.

WOLFE, Dawn C; South Side HS; Fort Wayne, IN; CmntyWkr; PolWkr; RedCrAde; SctActv; Bsktbl; GAA; PresAwd; College; Environmental Science.

WOLFE, Deana S; Wichita HS; Wichita, KS; Chr; CaptDrlTm; HonRl; SchMus; StuCncl; Yrbk; FrCl; LetterSwmmng; Chrldr; PPFtbl; Col.

WOLFE, James L; Oakwood Twp HS; Oakwood, IL; VPSrCls; HonRl; NHS; SecNatlThespSoc; OffAde; SchMus; SchPl; StuCncl; RptrYrbk; PpCl; College;.

WOLFE, Jean M; Arcadia HS; Arcadia, WI; 16/95 Band; MrchBnd; NHS; Orch; PepBnd; Yrbk; FHA; FTA; LetterBsktbl; GAA; Clg; Bus Admin.

WOLFE, Julia; Dixon HS; Dixon, IL; 38/346 HonRl; StuCncl; FHA; Chrldr; Univ; Undecided.

WOLFE, Kathy; Bishop Carroll HS; Colwich, KS; HonRl; NHS; SchPpr; College; Professional.

WOLFE, Kevin W; James Whitcomb Riley HS; South Bend, IN; 1/256 HonRl; NatlFornLg; NHS; ChmnGlf; SARAwd; KiwanAwd; CitAwd; Manchester College; Pre Med.

WOLFE, Kim M; Bergland Comm HS; Bergland, MI; VPFrshCls; SecSophCls; SecJrCls; CncrtBnd; HonRl; PepBnd; Trk; Chrldr; GAA; 4-HAwd; College; Vocation.

WOLFE, Kim M; Auburn Senior HS; Rockford, IL; 7/350 Chr; ChrhWkr; HonRl; NHS; SchMus; Lincoln Christian Col; Sacred Music.

WOLFE, Kim R; Ord HS; Shelton, NE; 14/109 HonRl; HospAde; Mdrgl; SchMus; StuCncl; RptrYrbk; 4-H; Chrldr; Wesleyan College; Nursing.

WOLFE, Luann E; Bridgeport HS; Saginaw, MI; 32/340 VPJrCls; VPSrCls; Chr; PresChrhWkr; HonRl; LbryAde; NatlFornLg; NHS; NatlMeritSF; SchMus; SchPl; TchrAde; DARAwd; 4-HAwd; Central Michigan College; Teaching.

WOLFE, Lucinda S; H H Dow HS; Midland, MI; HonRl; 4-H; PresFrCl; Swmmng; 4-HAwd; College; Nursing.

WOLFE, Margaret E; Cody HS; Detroit, MI; HospAde; LbryAde; PolWkr; StuCncl; TchrAde; LetterSwmmng; GAA; College; Nursing Or Forestry.

WOLFE, Martin E; Cisne HS; Cisne, IL; 3/60 PresFrshCls; Band; NHS; PresStuCncl; LatCl; VPMthCl; PpCl; Trk; SARAwd; Univ Of Tenn; Law.

WOLFE, Mary L; Roanoke Benson HS; Roanoke, IL; 3/98 ChrhWkr; HonRl; NHS; PresYthFlsp; Sec4-H; FHA; SecFNA; LatCl; IMSpt; BttyCrckrAwd; PresAwd; Illinois Central College; Dental Hygiene.

WOLFE, Michael M; Odessa R Vii HS; Bates City, MO; 15/119 Chr; Chrl; Chrs; HonRl; NHS; FTA; MthCl; Missouri Western; Cpa.

WOLFE, Nancy; Pioneer HS; Ann Arbor, MI; 39/649 Chr; CmntyWkr; HonRl; LitMag; NatlFornLg; Orch; PolWkr; SchMus; SchPl; Oberlin Coll; Medical Doctor And Chinese.

WOLFE, Patricia E; St Marys HS; Oneill, NE; /30 Chrs; LbryAde; Mdrgl; SchMus; StuCncl; EdYrBk; LetterTrk; Chrldr; IMSpt; PPFtbl; University; Professional.

WOLFE, Patti J; Whitko HS; South Whitley, IN; ChrhWkr; HonRl; NHS; NatlThespSoc; StuCncl; TchrAde; Yrbk; SchPpr; FHA; GAA; Business Sch; Secretary.

WOLFE, Rita; Milford Jr Sr HS; Milford, NE; Chrs; ChrhWkr; HospAde; RedCrAde; YthFlsp; RptrSchPpr; 4-H; GerCl; Trk; College; Secretarial Work.

WOLFE, Robert A; Brodhead HS; Brodhead, WI; Chrs; ChrhWkr; HonRl; SchPl; YthFlsp; YthFnd; SchPpr; 4-H; FFA; LetterBsbl; CaptFtbl; LetterWrstlng; Uw Platteville; Animal Science.

WOLFE, Susan; Tech HS; St Cloud, MN; ChrhWkr; CncrtBnd; HonRl; PepBnd; Tennis; Trk; CchngActv; GAA; PPFtbl; Coll; Phys Ed.

WOLFE, Susan K; Hill Community HS; Lansing, MI; 25/315 HonRl; NHS; SchMus; SctActv; TchrAde; PpCl; Chrldr; Coll.

WOLFE, Susanne; Central Sr HS; Chebause, IL; 16/147 Chrs; Mdrgl; NatlFornLg; NHS; RptrYrbk; MthCl; GAA; Illinois State Univ; Music.

WOLFE, Susanne K; Central Sr HS; Chebanse, IL; 16/146 Chrs; Mdrgl; NatlFornLg; NHS; NatlThespSoc; SchMus; Yrbk; 4-H; FrCl; MthCl; Il St U; Music.

WOLFE, Terri; Sandy Creek HS; Faifield, NE; 8/54 ALAGirlsSt; Chrs; CncrtBnd; LbryAde; MrchBnd; NHS; PepBnd; SchMus; SctActv; Twrl; PpCl; Trk; Lincoln Sch Of Commerce; Legal Assistant.

WOLFE, Theresa M; La Salle Peru HS; Lasalle, IL; 30#31#32 CmntyWkr; HonRl; Mdrgl; OffAde; SchMus; PpCl; Navy Choir; Singer.

WOLFER, Mark S; Sparta HS; Sparta, IL; 70/165 StuCncl; LetterBsbl; LetterBsktbl; LetterFtbl; LetterGlf; LetterTrk; Millikin University; Physical Therapy.

WOLFER, Terry; Seward Senior HS; Utica, NE; 1/150 ChrhWkr; HonRl; StuCncl; YthFlsp; RptrYrbk; FFA;.

WOLFF, Candice M; Glenbard East HS; Lombard, IL; 109/653 ChrhWkr; HonRl; StuCncl; Teen; YthFlsp; Yrbk; GAA; Tri State College; Transportation/traffic.

WOLFF, Carol J; Monango Public HS; Monango, ND; 1/12 Chr; Chrs; HonRl; SchPl; YthFlsp; SchPpr; LetterBsktbl; LetterTrk; Us Air Force; Accounting.

WOLFF, Daniel H; Wausaukee HS; Amberg, WI; 6/48 HonRl; Fox Valley Tech Inst; Conservation Tech.

WOLFF, Darlene K; Neenah HS; Neenah, WI; 43/604 HonRl; JA; NatlMeritSF; RptrSchPpr; Univ Of Wisc; Journalism.

WOLFF, Daryl H; Elgin Public HS; Elgin, ND; HonRl; SchPl; YthFlsp; Yrbk; SciCl; LetterBsbl; LetterBsktbl; LetterFtbl; LetterTrk; Ncb Rapid City Sd; Accounting.

WOLFF, Debra K; Howells Public HS; Clarkson, NE; 7/42 Chrs; PresLbryAde; SchAde; SchMus; SchPl; StuCncl; 4-H; PresFHA; PpCl; 4-HAwd; Platte Tech College; Clerical Secretary.

WOLFF, Dennis; Tigerton Hs; Tigerton, WI; 4 VPFrshCls; Chrs; ChrhWkr; HonRl; NHS; SchPl; RptrSchPpr; FFA; LetterFtbl; LetterWrstlng; U Wisconsin River Falls ; Agriculture Teach.

WOLFF, Gail A; York HS; Elmhurst, IL; HonRl; NHS; SctActv; MthCl; Tennis; College; Nursing.

WOLFF, James A; Nashua HS; Charles City, IA; SecSophCls; Band; CncrtBnd; HonRl; MrchBnd; NatlThespSoc; PepBnd; SchPl; StuCncl; Ftbl; Wartburg College; Education.

WOLFF, Jill N; Frederick HS; Frederick, SD; HonRl; LbryAde; Yrbk; College; Elem Ed.

WOLFF, Joseph; Muskegon Catholic HS; Muskegon Hts, MI; 71/191 VPSrCls; ChrhWkr; HonRl; NatlMeritCmnd; SchPl; SctActv; StuGov; Ftbl; Trk; College; Management.

WOLFF, Michael R; Northrop HS; Fort Wayne, IN; 33/610 HonRl; NatlMeritCmnd; NatlMeritSchl; StuCncl; RptrYrbk; RptrSchPpr; EdSchPpr; FSA; ChmbCommrsAwd; College; Professional.

WOLFF, Sharon A; Golden Valley HS; Golden Valley, ND; 1/11 PresFrshCls; TrsSophCls; Band; Chrs; HonRl; PresStuCncl; RptrYrbk; EdSchPpr; Bsktbl; Chrldr; Dickinson State Coll.

WOLFF, Stephen F; St Joseph Seminary HS; Downers Grove, IL; Chr; NatlMeritCmnd; Yrbk; RptrSchPpr; College; Environemental Engineering.

WOLFF, Stephen P; Gurley Public HS; Gurley, NE; PresJrCls; Chr; SchPl; Bsktbl; LetterFtbl; LetterTrk; College; Vocational.

WOLFF, Thomas C; Murphysboro Twp HS; Murphysboro, IL; Aud/Vis; PresChrs; Mdrgl; SchMus; SchPl; VPStuCncl; SecKeyCl; SpnCl; LetterGlf; LetterTennis; College; Education.

WOLFF, William G; Ankeny Comm HS; Ankeny, IA; 6/252 ChrhWkr; CmntyWkr; HonRl; JrNHS; NHS; SctActv; GodCntryAwd; Univ; Pro.

WOLFGRAM, Dave J; White Bear HS; White Bear Lake, MN; 31/360 LetterFtbl; LetterTrk; CchngActv; Lakewood Jr Clge; Pro.

WOLFORD, Delores J; Lewellen Rural HS; Lewellen, NE; 1/14 PresJrCls; Band; Chr; Chrs; CncrtBnd; HonRl; MrchBnd; PepBnd; YthFlsp; PpCl; University Of Nebraska; Professional.

WOLFORD, Doris J; Lewellen Rural HS; Lewellen, NE; 2/14 SecFrshCls; VPJrCls; Band; Chrs; HonRl; LbryAde; StuCncl; PpCl; Univ Of Ne; Wildlife Mgmt.

WOLFORD, Randy J; Newton HS; Newton, IL; 6/187 HonRl; NHS; StuCncl; MthCl; Pharmacy Sch; Pharmacist.

WOLFORD, Rodney; Muncie South HS; Muncie, IN; NHS; SptEdSchPpr; FrCl; Bsbl; Bsktbl; Ball State; Chemistry.

WOLGAN, Terry L; Manual HS; Peoria, IL; 10/329 Chr; Chrs; DrlTm; HonRl; FTA; Illinois Central College.

WOLGAST, Janet A; East Leyden HS; Franklin Park, IL; 3/650 Band; Chr; HonRl; HospAde; NHS; NatlMeritSchl; SchMus; SchPl; SciCl; Northern Illinois Univ; Nursing.

WOLITARSKY, Barbara J; Turtle Lake Mercer HS; Turtle Lake, ND; 4/42 Band; ChrhWkr; SchAde; VPYthFlsp; TreasSciCl; LetterTrk; Chrldr; PresGAA; BttyCrckrAwd; MasAwd; Nd State U; Vet Med.

WOLKOFF, Richard S; St Louis Pk HS; St Louis Pk, MN; Brandeis Univ; Law Field.

WOLLAR, Philip C; Barrington HS; Barrington, IL; 20/652 CmntyWkr; HonRl; NHS; NatlMeritSF; GerCl; Glf; IMSpt; Coll; Mathematics.

WOLLARD, Alan D; Marion Sr HS; Marion, IL; HonRl; YthFlsp; Southern Ill Univ; Radio.

WOLLENBURG, Lorraine; Tri County HS; Beatrice, NE; HonRl; OffAde; TchrAde; Yrbk; Trk; 4-HAwd; Central Nebraska Tech Coll; Horticulture.

WOLLIN, David K; Waconia HS; Waconia, MN; 10/165 Chrl; Chrs; ChrhWkr; HonRl; JrNHS; NHS; NatlThespSoc; SchMus; SchPl; YthFlsp; RptrYrbk; Bsbl; Bsktbl; Mankato St College; Journalism.

WOLLING, Susan C; Kirkwood HS; Kirkwood, MO; SecChr; DrmBgl; ROTC; Twrl; SchPpr; Swmmng; GAA; SARAwd; South County Tech Sch; Nuclear Physicist.

WOLLMAN, Dick P; Central HS; Aberdeen, SD; CncrtBnd; HonRl; MrchBnd; NHS; PolWkr; StuCncl; StuGov; YthFlsp; LetterTrk; CitAwd; College; Professional.

WOLLMANN, George J; Lane Tech HS; Chicago, IL; JA; LbryAde; TchrAde; Univ Of Illinois; Optometry.

WOLNER, Paul F; Cloquet HS; Cloquet, MN; 2/241 HonRl; JrNHS; Orch; LetterTrk; IMSpt; College; Chem Eng.

WOLOHAN, Michael J; St Stephen Area HS; Saginaw, MI; Band; CncrtBnd; HonRl; NHS; StuCncl; RptrSchPpr; CaptTennis; College; Business.

WOLOSHUN, Jean; Ursuline Academy; Springfield, IL; SecFrshCls; SctActv; StuCncl; RptrSchPpr; Lincoln Land Comm College; Radio Broadcaste.

WOLOVER, Lucinda M; Onalaska Public HS; Onalaska, WI; 13/144 Band; Chr; CncrtBnd; HonRl; MrchBnd; NHS; PepBnd; TreasYthFlsp; Yrbk; Univ Of La Crosse; Interior Decorator.

WOLOWSKI, Bruce A; Yorktown HS; Muncie, IN; Aud/Vis; Quill&Scroll; RptrSchPpr; SchPpr; SciCl; Bsktbl; Ftbl; LetterTrk; College; Photography.

WOLPER, Judith A; Mather HS; Chicago, IL; 6/445 HonRl; LitMag; Columbia College; Tv Producer.

WOLSCHLAGER, Mary A; Regina HS; Detroit, MI; 3/170 HonRl; NHS; StuCncl; FHA; FNA; SpnCl; PpCl; IMSpt; PPFtbl; Nursing School; Nursing.

WOLSKI, Ann P; Elizabeth Seton HS; Dolton, IL; Chr; Chrl; Chrs; ChrhWkr; HonRl; Mdrgl; NatlFornLg; NHS; SchMus; SchPl; College; Theatre.

WOLTER, Cheryl; Oak Creek Senior Hs; Oak Creek, WI; 18/361 Band; ChrhWkr; CncrtBnd; DrlTm; HonRl; JrNHS; NHS; SchPl; 4-H; GerCl; University; Speech.

WOLTER, Debbie; Holcombe HS; Halcombe, WI; Band; CncrtBnd; HonRl; MrchBnd; OffAde; PepBnd; Teen; FHA; GerCl; Vocational.

WOLTER, Dennis A; Garnavillo HS; Guttenberg, IA; VPFrshCls; PresSophCls; NHS; StuCncl; PresFFA; BttyCrckrAwd;.

WOLTER, Michael A; Antigo Sr HS; Antigo, WI; 4-H; FFA; VPKeyCl; Ftbl; Wrstlng; CchngActv; IMSpt; 4-HAwd; College; Vocation.

WOLTERING, Denise M; Mater Dei HS; Breese, IL; 1/185 Chrs; ChrhWkr; CncrtBnd; HonRl; MrchBnd; NHS; PepBnd; SchMus; SchPl; Univ Of Ill; Music.

WOLTERING, Donna S; Mater Dei HS; Breese, IL; 7/185 Band; Chrs; CncrtBnd; HonRl; NHS; SchPl; 4-H; SciCl; Trk; 4-HAwd; U Of Ill Urbana; Veterinary Medicine.

WOLTERS, Debra; Steeleville Community HS; Percy, IL; Chrs; ChrhWkr; MrchBnd; YthFlsp; 4-H; FBLA; FHA; PpCl; 4-HAwd; College; Secretarial.

WOLTERS, Karen S; Mssa HS; Atchison, KS; TrsJrCls; Band; Chrs; HonRl; MrchBnd; PepBnd; SctActv; Sdlty; PpCl; GAA;.

WOLTERS, Lauri; Timothy Christian Hs; Des Plaines, IL; 5/80 Chr; Chrs; ChrhWkr; HonRl; SchMus; SchPl; TchrAde; Yrbk; Calvin College; Teacher.

WOLTERS, Richard; South Christian HS; Grand Rapids, MI; HonRl; NHS; Grand Rapids Jr College; Engineer.

WOLTERSTORFF, Kevin; Central Christian HS; Renville, MN; PresFrshCls; Band; Chr; CncrtBnd; HonRl; PepBnd; SchMus; IMSpt; Calvin College.

WOLVERT, David J; St Thomas Military Acad; Brooklyn Park, MN; ChrhWkr; CmntyWkr; HonRl; ROTC; SchAde; SctActv; Yrbk; MthCl; LetterFtbl; CaptIMSpt; Univ Of Mn; Math.

WOLVERTON, Richard H; Richfield HS; Richfield, MN; HonRl; NHS; LetterSocr; IMSpt; Normandale Community College; Business.

WOMACK, Crystal D; Lindblom HS; Chicago, IL; 88/722 LbryAde; OffAde; SchAde; SctActv; TchrAde; YthLg; Yrbk; RptrSchPpr; Univ Of Ill; Medicine.

WOMBACHER, Mary L; Bergan HS; Peoria, IL; 9/208 DrlTm; HonRl; Univ Of Notre Dame; Business.

WOMBACHER, Steven G; Shelby Public HS; Shelby, NE; VPSophCls; TrsSrCls; Aud/Vis; HonRl; SchPl; StuGov; Bsbl; Bsktbl; LetterFtbl; Trk; Univ; Teacher.

WOMBLE, Vicki A; Weaubleau HS; Collins, MO; HstSrCls; Chrs; DrlTm; HonRl; SchMus; SchPl; FHA; PpCl; Bus Sch;legal Sec.

WOMMACK, Cindi A; Reeds Spring HS; Kimberling City, MO; SecSophCls; VPJrCls; ChrhWkr; HonRl; SchPl; Yrbk; FHA; SciCl; LetterTrk; CaptChrldr; Clge; Curr In Phy Ed.

WONDERLICH, Rhonda J; Centerville HS; Centerville, IA; 33/147 SecFrshCls; SecSophCls; SecJrCls; HonRl; NHS; StuCncl; FrCl; PpCl; Trk; Business School; Secretary.

WONDERS, Robert G; Lourdes Acad; Oshkosh, WI; 42/126 KeyCl; LetterFtbl; Tennis; Trk; IMSpt; KiwanAwd; College; Professional.

WONDRASEK, Gale M; Bottineau HS; Bottineaw, ND; Band; Chr; ChrhWkr; HospAde; PepBnd; RedCrAde; FHA; PpCl; LetterBsktbl; LetterTrk; Coll; Food.

WONG, Betty; Catholic Memorial HS; Brookfield, WI; 20/148 Univ Of Wi Madison; Undecided.

WONG, Darlene; St Mary Of Perpetual Help HS; Chicago, IL; 8/100 Chr; HonRl; JA; JrNHS; PepBnd; SchAde; YthFlsp; SpnCl; Northwestern Univ; Medicine.

WONG, Elizabeth; Catholic Memorial HS; Brookfield, WI; 20/148 Univ.

WONG, Ella H; Niles Township HS; Skokie, IL; HonRl; NHS; NatlMeritSF; NatlSciFnd; BauchLmbAwd; College; Science.

WONG, Jane; Benedictine HS; Detroit, MI; HonRl; Col; Pro.

WONG, Kalane J; Wauwatosa West HS; Wauwatosa, WI; 7/436 HonRl; VPNatlSciFnd; SchAde; StuCncl; SecMthCl; Tennis; Chrldr; GAA; Harvard Radcliffe.

WONG, Kenneth K; Lincoln Park HS; Lincoln Park, MI; 13/585 HonRl; NHS; Orch; SchPl; Univ Of Michigan; Pre Medical.

WONG, Peter; U City HS; Saint Louis, MO; Socr; St Louis University.

WONKA, Diane K; Blue Hill Comm HS; Blue Hill, NE; 2/40 SecTrsJrCls; ALAGirlsSt; Chr; HonRl; Mdrgl; MrchBnd; SchPl; StuCncl; EdYrBk; Chrldr; Univ; Journalism.

WONSER, Timothy P; St Marys Central HS; Menasha, WI; ChrhWkr; JA; SctActv; Teen; SptEdSchPpr; SpnCl; Bsktbl; LetterFtbl; LetterTrk; IMSpt; OptClAwd; Trade School.

WONTA, Denise; St Mary Central HS; Menasha, WI; HonRl; SchPpr; FrCl; Fox Valley Tech Inst; Social Worker.

WOOCK, Shirley L; Reeths Puffer HS; Muskegon, MI; 1/280 SecTrsSophCls; ChrhWkr; HonRl; NHS; NatlMeritCmnd; Tennis; Trk; Hope College; Medical Tech.

WOOD, Beth A; Moline Sr HS; Moline, IL; Chr; HonRl; Mdrgl; NHS; NatlThespSoc; SchMus; SchPl; St Ambrose College; Broadcasting.

WOOD, Bradley D; Pana Sr HS; Pana, IL; PresSophCls; PresJrCls; PresSrCls; HonRl; NHS; Yrbk; AmLegAwd; Univ; Pre Med.

WOOD, Bruce D; Tuscola Comm HS; Tuscola, IL; VPBand; CncrtBnd; HonRl; MrchBnd; NatlThespSoc; PepBnd; SchPl; RptrYrbk; RptrSchPpr; PresLatCl; St Louis Col; Pharmacy.

WOOD, Carolyn A; Cotton HS; Culver, MN; PresSophCls; SecTrsJrCls; ChrhWkr; NHS; SchAde; StuCncl; EdSchPpr; FHA; Chrldr; Nursing School; Rn.

WOOD, Christine; Sacred Heart Acad; Pesotum, IL; 35/145 Chrs; HonRl; Sacrstn; SchMus; RptrSchPpr; IMSpt; 4-HAwd; Sec.

WOOD, Cindy R; Atwood Hammond HS; Atwood, IL; Chrs; HonRl; NHS; NatlThespSoc; SchPl; StuCncl; Yrbk; 4-H; LatCl; PpCl; Tennis; Univ Of Ill; Psychology.

WOOD, Connie L; Adrian R 3 HS; Adrian, MO; 3/55 TchrAde; FHA; Jr College.

WOOD, Corliss D; North Division Sr HS; Milwaukee, WI; ChrhWkr; TreasDrlTm; HonRl; VPJA; SchPl; YthFlsp; RptrYrbk; EdYrBk; TreasFBLA; Trk; VPGAA; SecJAAwd; Knoxville Univ; Special Educ.

WOOD, Dennis L; Grinnell Senior HS; Grinnell, IA; ALBoysSt; HonRl; NHS; PepBnd; SctActv; PresSciCl; DARAwd; College; Medicine.

WOOD, Donna K; Gallatin R V HS; Gallatin, MO; 8/52 Band; ChrhWkr; CmntyWkr; HonRl; ModUN; NHS; RedCrAde; YthFlsp; FHA; LetterTrk; Chrldr; 4-HAwd; Univ Of Missouri; Accounting.

WOOD, Douglas; Otsego HS; Otsego, MI; 1/227 Band; HonRl; NatlMeritCmnd; SchMus; SciCl; Tennis; EldAwd; College; Pre Medicine.

WOOD, Douglas S; Mt Vernon Township HS; Mt Vernon, IL; 30/450 HonRl; PolWkr; Univ Of Illinois; Political Science.

WOOD, Gregory; West Catholic HS; Gd Rapids, MI; HonRl; RptrSchPpr; SchPpr; SpnCl; College; Veterianarian.

WOOD, James H; Orchard View HS; Muskegon, MI; 15/250 Band; HonRl; NHS; NatlMeritCmnd; PepBnd; PresFrCl; Bsktbl; CaptTennis; IMSpt; Michigan State Univ; Law School.

WOOD, Jean E; Pembine HS; Pembine, WI; Band; ChrhWkr; CncrtBnd; HonRl; LbryAde; MrchBnd; PepBnd; SchPl; RptrYrbk; Yrbk; RptrSchPpr; Col; Professional.

WOOD, Jeannine M; St Johns HS; De Witt, MI; 6/333 Band; CncrtBnd; HonRl; JrNHS; NHS; Orch; TchrAde; 4-H; Mich St Univ; Comp Prog.

WOOD, John M; Charleston HS; Charleston, IL; 6/254 CmntyWkr; HonRl; NHS; PolWkr; Univ Of Illinois; Liberal Arts.

WOOD, Joseph W; Red Oak HS; Emerson, IA; HonRl; SctActv; YthFlsp; Bsbl; Bsktbl; Ftbl; Tennis; EldAwd; College; Professional.

WOOD, Kathy A; Rich Central HS; Country Club Hills, IL; HonRl; SchMus; PpCl; Bsbl; GAA; Northern Il Univ; Bus Educ.

WOOD, Kenneth E; Lane Tech HS; Chicago, IL; 46/1209 CmntyWkr; LbryAde; NHS; NatlSciFnd; SctActv; StuGov; GerCl; College; Fire Protection.

WOOD, Leslie J; Cabool HS; Mtn Grove, MO; VPFrshCls; SecTrsSophCls; LetterChrs; ChrhWkr; HonRl; Mdrgl; NHS; SchPl; SctActv; StuCncl; College.

WOOD, Linda M; North Nodaway R 6 HS; Hopkins, MO; Chr; Chrs; HonRl; SchPl; TchrAde; EdYrBk; SchPpr; PpCl; College; Art.

WOOD, Lisa R; Southeastern HS; West Point, IL; ALAGirlsSt; VPNHS; TreasStuCncl; TchrAde; VPFTA; PresGAA; Blessing School; Nursing.

WOOD, Lorna M; Platte HS; Platte, SD; Chr; Chrs; HonRl; LbryAde; OffAde; 4-H; SpnCl; Trk; Trade Sch.

WOOD, Lynnel; Chase County Hs; Benkelman, NE; ChrhWkr; HonRl; MrchBnd; SchPl; RptrYrbk; Yrbk; 4-H; PpCl; DanFAwd; 4-HAwd; College; Area Home Agent.

WOOD, Lynnel G; Chase County HS; Benkelman, NE; Band; PepBnd; TchrAde; 4-H; DanFAwd; Kearney State Col; Industrial Arts.

WOOD, Margo A; Limestone HS; Bartonville, IL; 1/326 TrsJrCls; ChrhWkr; HonRl; LbryAde; Mdrgl; SchPl; StuCncl; FrCl; Trk; College.

WOOD, Mark D; David H Hickman HS; Columbia, MO; Chr; ChrhWkr; CmntyWkr; HonRl; LitMag; LbryAde; OffAde; Orch; SctActv; FFA; Auburn Univ; Veterinary Medicine.

WOOD, Mark H; Avon HS; Danville, IN; 9/165 HonRl; NatlMeritSF; TchrAde; GerCl; TreasLatCl; PresSciCl; Univ; Computer Technology.

WOOD, Mark N; Parkway West HS; Ballwin, MO; 208/749 JrNHS; YthFnd; FrCl; LetterSocr; CchngActv; IMSpt; DanFAwd; College; Science.

WOOD, Martin L; Dekalb HS; Dekalb, IL; Band; Chr; Chrs; CncrtBnd; NHS; SchMus; TreasStuCncl; FrCl; LetterSwmmng; LetterTennis; Clg; Medecine.

WOOD, Mary A; East Dubuque HS; East Dubuque, IL; PresSophCls; Chrs; HonRl; JA; SchPl; StuCncl; FHA; Glf; JAAwd; Clge; Teach Art.

WOOD, Mary J; Deerfield HS; Deerfield, IL; AFS; HonRl; ModUN; NHS; YthFlsp; FrCl; PpCl; LetterGlf; Swmmng; Tennis; Chrldr; GAA; IMSpt; Indiana Univ; Business.

WOOD, Michael C; Lanphier HS; Springfield, IL; 11/473 NHS; LetterFtbl; Univ Of Illinois; Business Admin.

WOOD, Michael D; Bartley HS; Stockville, NE; VPSophCls; VPJrCls; SchPl; LetterBsktbl; LetterFtbl; LetterTrk; Farming.

WOOD, Michael J; Lyons Township HS; La Grange Park, IL; 37/1214 HonRl; NHS; NatlMeritCmnd; LetterSocr; Texas Christian Univ; Med School.

WOOD, Patricia L; St Anthony HS; St Louis, MO; 3/72 Chrs; HonRl; NHS; NatlMeritCmnd; SchMus; SchPl; LatCl; Lutheran Hosp Sch; Rn.

WOOD, Patrick H; Jefferson HS; Lafayette, IN; Band; HonRl; NHS; GerCl; Purdue Univ; Engineer.

WOOD, Paul A; Chelsea HS; Chelsea, MI; 10/200 VPFrshCls; HonRl; NHS; SptEdSchPpr; KeyCl; Bsbl; Bsktbl; Ftbl; CchngActv; CitAwd; Mi State U; Television & Radio.

WOOD, Renee A; Truman HS; Independence, MO; Chrs; HonRl; NatlFornLg; OffAde; PolWkr; SecQuill&Scroll; StuCncl; SchPpr; FTA; FrCl; PpCl; Bsktbl; College.

WOOD, Richard; Hammond Baptist Hs; Hobart, IN; Band; ChrhWkr; HonRl; TchrAde; RptrYrbk; SpnCl; LetterBsbl; LetterBsktbl; CaptSocr; College; Ministry.

WOOD, Richard P; Lake Central HS; St John, IN; 23/465 ChrhWkr; HonRl; StuCncl; StuGov; GerCl; SciCl; Rose Hulman Univ; Electrical Engineer.

WOOD, Sheila M; Thomas Jefferson HS; Council Bluffs, IA; 18/460 SecBand; VPChrs; CncrtBnd; HonRl; Mdrgl; MrchBnd; NHS; Orch; PepBnd; Coe Coll; Music Education.

WOOD, Sheri L; Pewamo Westphalia HS; Hubbardston, MI; Band; HonRl; NHS; PepBnd; SchPl; SctActv; StuCncl; TchrAde; RptrYrbk; FHA; Montcalm Comm Clg; Cpa.

WOOD, Stephanie M; Tinley Park HS; Tinley Park, IL; 41/289 CmntyWkr; HonRl; NHS; NatlSciFnd; StuGov; University Of Illinois; Veterinary Medicine.

WOOD, Stephen K; Shawneetown HS; Shawneetown, IL; TrsFrshCls; VPSophCls; PresJrCls; HonRl; StuCncl; FFA; PresAwd; Coll; Pro.

WOOD, Stephen R; Republican Valley HS; Indianola, NE; VPSophCls; Chrs; SchMus; Ftbl; Trk; Wrstlng; Clg; Major Study.

WOOD, Teresa A; Schuyler Central HS; Schuyler, NE; 2/83 VPSophCls; Chr; Chrs; ChrhWkr; HonRl; Mdrgl; NHS; OffAde; StuCncl; TchrAde; YthFlsp; Trk; Chrldr; Univ Of Nebraska.

WOOD, Teresa A; Bloomington HS; Bloomington, IL; CmntyWkr; HonRl; TchrAde; GerCl; PpCl; SciCl; Univ Of Illinois; Veterinary Medicine.

WOOD, Terry A; Wabash HS; West Branch, MI; 25/200 Band; Chr; CncrtBnd; HonRl; MrchBnd; PepBnd; SchMus; StuCncl; YthFlsp; University; Music.

WOOD, Therese; Arlington HS; Indianapolis, IN; HonRl; LbryAde; StuCncl; Business School; Accountant.

WOOD, Timothy P; Horton HS; Horton, KS; Band; Chr; Chrs; CncrtBnd; HonRl; MrchBnd; NatlMeritSF; SchPl; Yrbk; Baker Univ; Law.

WOOD, Trudy J; Anna Jonesboro C HS; Anna, IL; 1/139 Band; CncrtBnd; HonRl; MrchBnd; PepBnd; RptrYrbk; RptrSchPpr; FTA; SecFrCl; PpCl; Univ; Writer.

WOOD, Vicky L; La Plata R Ii HS; La Plata, MO; HstFrshCls; HonRl; LbryAde; OffAde; SchPl; FHA; PpCl; LetterBsktbl; Trade School; Nursing.

WOOD, William; Bismarck Henning HS; Danville, IL; Chr; Chrs; ChrhWkr; HonRl; Bob Jones U; Veterinary Medicine.

WOOD, William E; Shawneetown HS; Junction, IL; 7/33 VPFrshCls; PresSophCls; PresStuCncl; EdYrBk; SchPpr; Bsbl; Bsktbl; Sic; Law.

WOOD, William M; Bismarck Henning HS; Danville, IL; Chrs; ChrhWkr; Bob Jones Univ; Veterinary Surgeon.

WOODALL, Richard A; Blue Valley HS; Leawood, KS; HonRl; JrNHS; KeyCl; LetterTrk; Baylor Univ; Lawyer.

WOODARD, Cynthia A; Albia Community HS; Albia, IA; 3/150 Chrs; HonRl; RptrSchPpr; FHA; FTA; SpnCl; Bsbl; Bsktbl; CchngActv; Iowa State Univ; Child Care & Development.

WOODARD, Cynthia L; Bentley HS; Livonia, MI; SecSrCls; TrsSrCls; CmntyWkr; HonRl; RedCrAde; StuCncl; StuGov; Yrbk; Chrldr; Madonna Clg; Special Educ.

WOODARD, Debra S; Chorobusco HS; Columbia City, IN; 15/105 HonRl; LbryAde; Univ; Factory Work.

WOODARD, Michael E; Marshall HS; Dennison, IL; TrsSophCls; TrsJrCls; TrsSrCls; ALBoysSt; Band; StuGov; EdSchPpr; PresSciCl; AmLegAwd; 4-HAwd; Indiana State Univ; Health Educ.

WOODARD, Pamela E; Dongola HS; Dongola, IL; 1/30 SecTrsJrCls; Band; HonRl; 4-H; FHA; FTA; PresSciCl; GAA; AmLegAwd; DanFAwd; 4-HAwd; Univ Of Illinois; History.

WOODBRIDGE, Donald A; Wellington HS; Wellington, KS; 17/160 LetterBand; LetterChr; HonRl; LbryAde; PepBnd; TchrAde; FrCl; LetterTennis; CaptWrstlng; AmLegAwd; Coll; Music/law.

WOODBURN, Cynthia A; East Peoria Comm HS; East Peoria, IL; 2/467 AFS; PresChrhWkr; NHS; NatlMeritCmnd; StuCncl; SchPpr; PresFrCl; MthCl; SciCl; AmLegAwd; Bradley Univ; Accounting.

WOODBURN, Thomas J; Riverdale Sr HS; Port Byron, IL; 1/109 Band; ChrhWkr; CncrtBnd; HonRl; MrchBnd; PresNHS; NatlMeritCmnd; PepBnd; SchMus; StuGov; Treas4-H; LetterFtbl; 4-HAwd; College; Medicine.

WOODBURY, Philip; Pendleton Heights HS; Anderson, IN; 1/337 PresSophCls; PresJrCls; PresSrCls; CmntyWkr; HonRl; NHS; StuGov; LatCl; SciCl; Coll; Med.

WOODBURY, Traci L; Central HS; St Joseph, MO; Chr; ChrhWkr; HonRl; SchMus; SchPl; SctActv; FrCl; PpCl; SciCl; College.

WOODEN, Cindy L; Jonesville HS; Jonesville, MI; 14/80 Band; CncrtBnd; HonRl; LbryAde; MrchBnd; PepBnd; StuCncl; TchrAde; SchPpr; 4-H; College; Music.

WOODEN, Evelyn; Norborne HS; Norborne, MO; 6/30 TrsSophCls; CncrtBnd; HonRl; JrNHS; NHS; SchPl; StuCncl; FHA; Chrldr; 4-HAwd; College;lit Teacher Or Social Worker.

WOODEN, Martin C; Shawneetown HS; Shawneetown, IL; 1/35 PresFrshCls; PresSophCls; TrsJrCls; Band; HonRl; MrchBnd; StuCncl; AmLegAwd; Coll; Law.

WOODERSON, Charles R; Waterford Mott HS; Drayton Plains, MI; SchAde; StuCncl; StuGov; TchrAde; LetterFtbl; LetterTrk; College.

WOODFORD, Mark M; Springfield Southeast HS; Springfield, IL; 10/450 AFS; Band; NHS; StuCncl; Yrbk; KeyCl; LetterTennis; University Of Virginia.

WOODHAM, Danis L; Dighton HS; Dighton, KS; ALAGirlsSt; Band; Chrl; HonRl; NHS; StuCncl; EdYrBk; PpCl; GAA; IMSpt; PPFtbl; Fort Hays Kansas St College; Accounting.

WOODHEAD, Kent D; North Platte HS; North Platte, NE; StuCncl; LetterFtbl; IMSpt; U Of Nebraska; Architect.

WOODHOUSE, Jeffrey T; Peoria HS; Peoria, IL; 39/450 JrNHS; NHS; Quill&Scroll; SptEdYrbk; University Of Illinois; Engineering.

WOODIN, Leola J; Chadwick HS; Mt Carroll, IL; 4/33 VPJrCls; Band; Chrs; HonRl; SctActv; StuCncl; EdYrBk; FHA; IMSpt; College; Rec Dir.

WOODIN, Linda L; Chadwick HS; Mt Carroll, IL; Band; Chrs; CncrtBnd; HonRl; YthFlsp; EdYrBk; FHA; Trk; College.

WOODLAND, Laura A; Sullivan HS; Sullivan, MO; Chrs; HonRl; OffAde; TchrAde; FTA; SpnCl; PpCl; College; Teacher.

WOODMAN, Claudia C; Jerseyville Comm HS; Jerseyville, IL; 28/280 Chr; ChrhWkr; CmntyWkr; HonRl; NHS; SchMus; StuCncl; 4-H; LetterChrldr; VoiceDemAwd; College; Teaching.

WOODMAN, Denis; Shelton Public HS; Kenesaw, NE; 10/32 ChrhWkr; HonRl; Mdrgl; SchPl; 4-H; Bsbl; Glf; Ftbl; Trk; 4-HAwd; U Of Ne Lincoln; Agriculture.

WOODRICH, Barbara J; Paul Vi HS; Omaha, NE; 10/90 HonRl; JrNHS; NHS; TchrAde; RptrSchPpr; MthCl; Bank Employment.

WOODROME, Kathleen; Mc Cluer HS; Ferfuson, MO; Chr; CmntyWkr; HospAde; SchAde; TchrAde; GerCl; GAA; IMSpt;.

WOODROW, Jeffery L; Covington HS; Covington, IN; 9/91 PresJrCls; PresSrCls; Chrs; HonRl; NHS; Quill&Scroll; SchPl; StuCncl; LetterFtbl; CaptTrk; Purdue University; Veterinary Science.

WOODROW, Ronald; Fairfield Comm HS; Barnhill, IL; HonRl; 4-H; FFA; EngCl; Bsbl; Bsktbl; Trk; Siu Carbondale; Petroleum Engineer.

WOODRUFF, Christopher A; Hillboro HS; Hillsboro, MO; ALBoysSt; Band; CncrtBnd; HonRl; LitMag; MrchBnd; SctActv; LetterFtbl; LetterTrk; IMSpt; College; Professional.

WOODRUFF, David L; Fort Dodge Sr HS; Fort Dodge, IA; ModUN; NatlFornLg; NHS; NatlMeritFnl; StuGov; GerCl; LetterSwmmng;.

WOODRUFF, David P; George Washington HS; Cedar Rapids, IA; NHS; StuGov; Beloit College.

WOODRUFF, Deborah A; Salem Community HS; Salem, IL; 24/213 PresBand; Chrs; HonRl; MrchBnd; NHS; NatlMeritCmnd; SchMus; SchPl; RptrSchPpr; SpnCl; PpCl; CaptChrldr; GAA; Univ Of Illinois; Lawyer.

WOODRUFF, Gregory; Bosse HS; Evansville, IN; Chr; Chrs; PolWkr; SchMus; SchPl; FrCl; PpCl; Wrstlng; IMSpt; College; Police Officer.

WOODRUFF, John A; Central Catholic HS; Grand Island, NE; PresFrshCls; PresSophCls; PresSrCls; Band; Chr; StuCncl; Yrbk; SptEdSchPpr; LetterBsktbl; LetterGlf; Bus.

WOODRUFF, Sharon K; Northeastern HS; Richmond, IN; 1/120 ChrhWkr; HonRl; NHS; NatlMeritSchl; FHA; BttyCrckrAwd; Indiana U East; Bus.

WOODRUM, Cindy L; Waynesville HS; Richland, MO; Band; Chr; Chrs; ChrhWkr; HonRl; MrchBnd; 4-H; DanFAwd; St Johns College; Nursing.

WOODRUM, Sterling T; Golden City R 3 HS; Golden City, MO; 3/19 VPJrCls; PressSrCls; ALBoysSt; Band; ChrhWkr; CmntyWkr; CncrtBnd; HonRl; MrchBnd; NatlSciFnd; PepBnd; Ftbl; University Of Missouri; Professional.

WOODS, Anthony E; Edsel Ford HS; Dearborn, MI; TrsFrshCls; ChrhWkr; HonRl; LitMag; NatlFornLg; NatlMeritCmnd; SchPl; IMSpt; College; Law.

WOODS, Barbara A; North Side HS; Fort Wayne, IN; ALAGirlsSt; HospAde; SecNHS; StuCncl; YthFlsp; SecEngCl; SecLatCl; Chrldr; CitAwd; College; Pharm Or Med Tech.

WOODS, Barbara L; Academy Of Our Lady; Chicago, IL; HonRl; NatlMeritCmnd; SchPl; College; Physician.

WOODS, Carla; Glenville HS; Glenville, MN; Band; Chr; Chrs; CncrtBnd; DrmMjrt; HonRl; MrchBnd; SchPl; SctActv; IMSpt; Austin Area Voc Tech School;cosmotology.

WOODS, Cheryl D; Proviso East HS; Maywood, IL; 139/1001 PresFrshCls; TrsJrCls; Chr; ChrhWkr; HonRl; SchPl; StuCncl; TchrAde; PpCl; Univ; Psychology.

WOODS, Claudia; Paseo Hs; Kansas City, MO; 5/402 Chr; HonRl; Trk; College; Nursing.

WOODS, Darla J; Brown County HS; Nashville, IN; 10/169 HonRl; NHS; 4-H; SpnCl;.

WOODS, Deborah L; Winona HS; Winona, MO; Aud/Vis; HonRl; JrNHS; LbryAde; SchPl; SchPpr; FBLA; FHA; SpnCl;.

WOODS, Donna M; Divine Savior Holy Angels HS; Milwaukee, WI; NHS; MthCl; Mt Mary Col; Biology.

WOODS, Harry; Mattoon Senior HS; Mattoon, IL; 40/400 HonRl; NHS; College, Literature.

WOODS, Ilene A; Newton HS; Newton, IL; 8/200 PresSophCls; Chrs; HonRl; NHS; OffAde; StuCncl; StuGov; EdSchPpr; CivCl; 4-H; MthCl; Chrldr; EldAwd; Olney Central College; Mathematic.

WOODS, Jackie L; Wood River Rural HS; Alda, NE; 3/55 Band; DrlTm; VPNHS; StuCncl; Yrbk; 4-H; SecFHA; PpCl; Trk; BttyCrckrAwd; 4-HAwd; Univ Of Nebraska; Teaching.

WOODS, Karen D; Maria HS; Oaklawn, IL; 41/335 HonRl; HospAde; NHS; TchrAde; FrCl; GAA; IMSpt; PresAwd; Business School; Professional.

WOODS, Kevin R; Eddyville HS; Cedor, IA; ChrhWkr; Quill&Scroll; Yrbk; Trade Schl; Photographer.

WOODS, Kimberly L; Park Rapids HS; Park Rapids, MN; VPJrCls; Band; CncrtBnd; MrchBnd; NHS; PepBnd; StuCncl; CaptBsktbl; LetterTrk; CaptChrldr; IMSpt; Moorhead St College; Biology.

WOODS, Linda S; Murray Comm HS; Murray, IA; SecFrshCls; TrsSophCls; HonRl; FHA; FNA; Coll; Therapy.

WOODS, Loraine M; Perry HS; Perry, IL; 1/16 PresChrs; PresCncrtBnd; StuCncl; EdYrBk; Sec4-H; PresFHA; KeyCl; Bsktbl; BttyCrckrAwd; DanFAwd; 4-HAwd; Western Illinois Univ; Music.

WOODS, Melfred C; Richland Center HS; Gillingham, WI; ChrhWkr; HonRl; YthFlsp; Vocational School; Auto Mechanic.

WOODS, Robin W; Ritenour Sr HS; St Johns, MO; ChrhWkr; CncrtBnd; HonRl; JA; NatlMeritCmnd; OffAde; PolWkr; SchAde; YthFlsp; Yrbk; EdSchPpr; SchPpr; FBLA; IMSpt; College; Liberal Arts.

WOODS, Sheryl A; Sullivan HS; Sullivan, IN; 46/139 HonRl; OffAde; SchMus; SchPl; TchrAde; 4-H; FHA; SecSpnCl; PpCl; 4-HAwd; Indiana St Univ; Teacher.

WOODS, Susan E; Riverdale HS; Blue River, WI; AFS; Chrs; CncrtBnd; Mdrgl; NHS; SchMus; Yrbk; FHA; SpnCl; Business School.

WOODS, Twila J; Winona R Iii HS; Winona, MO; SecJrNHS; OffAde; SchPl; RptrYrbk; SecYrbk; SchPpr; SchPpr; FHA; VPSpnCl; Bsbl; Bsktbl; Sw Mo St; Busi.

WOODS, Twila J; Winona R 111 HS; Winona, MO; CmntyWkr; HonRl; OffAde; SecYrbk; SchPpr; FBLA; PresFHA; VPSpnCl; Bsbl; Bsktbl; Sms; Busi Computering.

WOODS, Valerie C; Lindblom Tech HS; Chicago, IL; PresSophCls; IntrClCncl; NatlMeritCmnd; NatlThespSoc; OffAde; SchAde; SchPl; StuCncl; StuGov; TchrAde; RptrSchPpr; LetterBsktbl; Trk; GAA; Univ Of South Calif; Theater Arts.

WOODSIDE, Steven L; Cozad HS; Cozad, NE; 16/102 Band; ChrhWkr; CncrtBnd; HonRl; MrchBnd; NHS; StuCncl; YthFlsp; LetterBsktbl; LetterFtbl; Glf; Trk; Univ Of Nebraska; Criminal Justice.

WOOD SMITH, Steven; Vianney HS; St Louis, MO; 9/170 HonRl; NHS; StuGov; Wrstlng; OptClAwd; Wash Univ; Pre Med.

WOODSON, Cynthia J; Crispus Attucks HS; Indianapolis, IN; HonRl; NHS; StuCncl; RptrYrbk; College.

WOODSON, Dale R; Southwest HS; St Louis, MO; HonRl; JA; JrNHS; NHS; NatlMeritSchl; EdSchPpr; FBLA; AmLegAwd; GovHonPrgAwd; College; History.

WOODSON, Marilynn B; Waukegan HS; Waukegan, IL; 41/861 AFS; ChrhWkr; HonRl; HospAde; JrNHS; NHS; OffAde; SchPl; StuCncl; YthFlsp; RptrYrbk; Ill Wesleyan Univ; Business Admin.

WOODSON, Mark W; Saint Francis Borgia HS; Union, MO; ChrhWkr; HonRl; Sacrstn; SchAde; SchMus; FrCl; LetterBsktbl; Ftbl; LetterSocr; IMSpt; College; Science.

WOODWARD, David M; Taylor HS; Kokomo, IN; Band; HonRl; Bsktbl; Glf; Wrstlng; College.

WOODWARD, Dennis E; Beaman Conrad Liscomb HS; Conrad, IA; 10/37 Chr; ChrhWkr; HonRl; LetterFtbl; LetterTrk; IMSpt; Bartlesville Wesleyan College; Technology.

WOODWARD, Emily F; Sunset Hill HS; Shawnee Mission, KS; Chr; Chrs; ChrhWkr; CmntyWkr; HospAde; OffAde; SchMus; YthFlsp; IMSpt; College.

WOODWARD, Grant A; Millington Community HS; Millington, MI; ChrhWkr; HonRl; SctActv; StuCncl; College; Forestry & Agriculture.

WOODWARD, Paul L; Southwest HS; St Louis, MO; 160/600 Band; ChrhWkr; CmntyWkr; CncrtBnd; MrchBnd; Quill&Scroll; StuCncl; YthFlsp; FBLA; LetterWrstlng; Northeast St Univ; Business.

WOODWARD, Timothy J; Rockwell City Comm HS; Rockwell City, IA; ChrhWkr; CmntyWkr; PolWkr; YthFlsp; IMSpt; Air Force; Pro.

WOODWARD, Vicki; Pingree HS; Pingree, ND; 2/7 ALAGirlsSt; Band; Chrs; HonRl; Yrbk; EdSchPpr; BttyCrckrAwd; VoiceDemAwd; Bismarck Jr College; Legal Secretary.

WOODWORTH, Mark G; Jacksonville HS; Jacksonville, IL; 46/352 HonRl; SctActv; StuGov; RptrSchPpr; LatCl; Ftbl; Wrstlng; GodCntryAwd; Valparaiso Univ; Law.

WOODWORTH, Melissa E; Cedar Springs HS; Cedar Springs, MI; Band; ChrhWkr; HonRl; NHS; SchPl; TchrAde; YthFlsp; Yrbk; 4-H; IMSpt; Central Mich U; Psychology.

WOODWORTH, Michael J; Sparta HS; Sparta, WI; 1/198 Chrs; HonRl; NHS; NatlMeritSF;.

WOODWORTH, Nada; Reading HS; Reading, KS; Band; Chrs; HonRl; MrchBnd; PepBnd; 4-H; PpCl; Trk; 4-HAwd; Emporia State Univ; Veterinarian.

WOODWORTH, Ronald A; Paxton HS; Paxton, IL; Band; CncrtBnd; HonRl; MrchBnd; YthFlsp; Bsktbl; Ftbl; Trk; IMSpt; Univ Of Il; Engineering.

WOODWORTH, Stanley F; Shullsburg HS; Shullsburg, WI; 5/65 ALBoysSt; Aud/Vis; Band; CncrtBnd; HonRl; MrchBnd; ModUN; NHS; RedCrAde; SchPl; Univ Of Wisc Madison; Medical Doctor.

WOODWORTH, Steven F; Shullsburg HS; Shullsburg, WI; 7/61 Band; ChrhWkr; HonRl; ModUN; SchPl; RptrYrbk; RptrSchPpr; SchPpr; 4-H; KeyCl; PpCl; Bsktbl; Ftbl; Univ Of Wisconsin; Medicine.

WOODY, Michael C; Heelan HS; Sioux City, IA; SecFrshCls; HonRl; SctActv; StuCncl; StuGov; FrCl; Trk; College; Doctor.

WOODY, Suzette L; Waynesville HS; Waynesville, MO; Band; ChrhWkr; CncrtBnd; HonRl; JrNHS; MrchBnd; NHS; Orch; PepBnd; Clge; Tchr.

WOODY, Theresa L; New Monroe Community HS; Beasnor, IA; 6/48 Band; HonRl; NHS; NatlMeritCmnd; SchPl; RptrSchPpr; FHA; LetterGlf; LetterChrldr; AmLegAwd; Iowa Methodist Sch Of Nursing; Nursing.

WOODYARD, Leslie A; Chrisman HS; Chrisman, IL; 2/41 PresSrCls; Band; CncrtBnd; HonRl; MrchBnd; NHS; OffAde; PepBnd; StuCncl; Purdue Univ; Pharmacy.

WOOLDRIDGE, Claudia L; Springfield HS; Springfield, IL; Band; Chr; IMSpt; College; Liberal Arts.

WOOLDRIDGE, Daniel E; Winterset Comm HS; Winterset, IA; ALBoysSt; Chr; Chrs; HonRl; 4-H; LetterBsbl; LetterGlf; 4-HAwd; College.

WOOLERY, Darrell J; Pleasant Hill HS; Pleasant Hill, MO; 14/112 ALBoysSt; HonRl; PresNHS; SpnCl; Univ Of Missouri; Computer Programming.

WOOLEY, Carol E; Union County HS; Liberty, IN; ChrhWkr; HonRl; NHS; NatlThespSoc; SchMus; SctActv; SchPpr; SpnCl; SciCl; LetterBsktbl; Ball St Univ; Social Work.

WOOLF, La Fonda; Clay City HS; Bowling Green, IN; Band; CncrtBnd; DrlTm; MrchBnd; TchrAde; LetterBsbl; Trk; Chrldr; GAA; 4-HAwd; University; Physical Education.

WOOLFOLK, Mary N; Boone County R Vi HS; Centralia, MO; ChrhWkr; CmntyWkr; HonRl; HospAde; Mdrgl; NHS; SchMus; SchPl; SecYthFlsp; 4-H; Univ Of Missouri; Home Ec Educ.

WOOLFREY, Ann E; Mounds View HS; St Paul, MN; CncrtBnd; HonRl; NHS; NatlMeritCmnd; NatlThespSoc; StuCncl; YthFlsp; Yrbk; LetterTrk; VoiceDemAwd; St Olaf Coll; Doctor.

WOOLLEY, Michele L; Walled Lake Western HS; Walled Lake, MI; ChrhWkr; HonRl; NHS; SchPl; YthFlsp; PpCl; Bsbl; LetterBsktbl; Swmmng; IMSpt; Mercy College; Nursing.

WOOLLIS, Janet L; Wayne Comm HS; Corydon, IA; Band; CncrtBnd; HonRl; NHS; PresTeen; VPYthFlsp; Pres4-H; TreasFTA; 4-HAwd; Business School; Secretary.

WOOLRIDGE, Virgil W; Salisbury R #4 HS; Salisbury, MO; 20/86 HonRl; NHS; StuCncl; PpCl; CaptBsktbl; Univ Of Missouri; Elec Engineering.

WOOLWINE, Latauna B; Fountain Central HS; Kingman, IN; 1/130 PresChrs; ChrhWkr; HonRl; HospAde; LbryAde; VPNHS; TchrAde; YthFlsp; VPLatCl; Chrldr; DARAwd; St Elizabeth Hospital; Nursing.

WOOSTER, Brenda L; Alba Public HS; Mancelona, MI; Chrs; HonRl; SchPl; StuCncl; TchrAde; Chrldr; College; Special Ed.

WOOSTER, Terry L; Prairie Heights HS; Orland, IN; 21/107 Band; PepBnd; SchMus; LetterTrk; Tri State Col; Engineer.

WOOTERS, Brenda; Moweaqua HS; Moweaqua, IL; 15/50 VPJrCls; HonRl; LbryAde; OffAde; SchMus; EdYrBk; Chrldr; AmLegAwd; Richland Jr College.

WOOTERS, Brenda A; Moweaqua HS; Moweaqua, IL; 16/54 VPJrCls; Chrs; ChrhWkr; HonRl; LbryAde; OffAde; SchMus; SchPl; EdYrBk; PresFHA; Chrldr; AmLegAwd; College.

WORBY, Marsha L; Bishop Mc Namara HS; Kankakee, IL; 5/161 HonRl; NHS; NatlMeritCmnd; SchPl; TchrAde; Yrbk; SpnCl; Illinois State Univ; Accounting.

WORCESTER, Joyce; Heritage HS; Monroeville, IN; 1/165 Chr; ChrhWkr; CncrtBnd; MrchBnd; NHS; TchrAde; Yrbk; FTA; VoiceDemAwd; Col; Nrsng.

WORDEKEMPER, James L; Central Catholic HS; West Point, NE; ChrhWkr; CmntyWkr; OffAde; SchAde; 4-H; IMSpt; Trade Sch; Mechanic.

WORDEKEMPER, Joel; Central Catholic HS; West Point, NE; Chr; Chrs; ChrhWkr; HonRl; NHS; SchMus; SchPl; SciCl; College; Music Teacher.

WORDEN, Kimberly S; Rosiclare HS; Golconda, IL; Band; ChrhWkr; SchPl; RptrSchPpr; 4-H; 4-HAwd; College; Professional.

WORDEN, Michelle M; Stevens HS; Rapid City, SD; 71/418 HonRl; SchMus; SchPl; FrCl; SciCl; Trk; Coll; Pharmacology.

WORDEN, Mike L; Dysart Geneseo HS; Dysart, IA; Band; CncrtBnd; MrchBnd; SchPl; SctActv; Ftbl; University; Professional.

WORDEN, Scott R; Dowagiac Union HS; Dawagioc, MI; Bible Sch; Student Of The Holy Spirit.

WORDEN, Susan K; Brighton HS; Brighton, MI; Chr; HonRl; JrNHS; NatlThespSoc; SchAde; SchMus; SchPl; TchrAde; College; Computer Field.

WORDEN, Tom M; Iowa Falls HS; Iowa Falls, IA; HonRl; RptrSchPpr; FTA; Univ Of Iowa; Professional.

WORF, Karol D; Garden City HS; Garden City, KS; TchrAde; 4-H; Ft Hays Kans St Coll; Accounting.

WORKING, Susan E; West Ottawa HS; Holland, MI; 8/271 Chr; HonRl; NHS; SchMus; SchPl; Western Mich U; Math.

WORKMAN, Allen A; Elk Point HS; Elk Point, SD; PresFrshCls; PresSophCls; Chrs; HonRl; Bsbl; LetterBsktbl; LetterFtbl; Trk; Clge; Farming.

WORKMAN, Dale W; Lake Park HS; Roselle, IL; HonRl; LbryAde; SchAde; TchrAde; Elmhurst College; Business Admin.

WORKMAN, Marna K; Deland Weldon HS; Weldon, IL; 1/50 SecFrshCls; PresSophCls; AFS; Band; Chr; HonRl; NHS; SchMus; EdYrBk; GAA;.

WORKMAN, Paul; Parsons HS; Parsons, KS; Chrl; HonRl; PolWkr; SchPl; SctActv; FDA; RusCl; JCAwd; OptClAwd;.

WORKMAN, Sylvia K; Concordia HS; Concordia, KS; 3/160 VPChr; ChrhWkr; CmntyWkr; HonRl; Mdrgl; NatlFornLg; SchPl; FTA; SciCl; Kansas Univ; Broadcast Journalism.

WORKUN, Terry L; Murphysboro HS; Murphysboro, IL; SecChrs; ChrhWkr; CmntyWkr; DrlTm; NHS; SchMus; SchPl; SctActv; PresStuCncl; SecYthFlsp; College; Convention Director.

WORL, Debra S; Shenandoah Comm HS; Shenandoah, IA; 13/95 AFS; Band; Chrs; HospAde; NHS; SchMus; SchPl; StuCncl; PresFNA; PpCl; Chrldr; Univ Of Iowa; Nursing.

WORL, Julie A; West Nodaway Ri HS; Burlington Jct, MO; VPFrshCls; PresSrCls; ALAGirlsSt; Band; HonRl; MrchBnd; SchPl; EdYrBk; 4-H; Trk; Univ; Elem Educ.

WORLEY, Ellen; Senior HS; Sturgeon Bay, WI; Band; Chr; CncrtBnd; HonRl; MrchBnd; PepBnd; SchMus; PpCl; Trk; GAA; College; Business Teacher.

WORLEY, James L; University HS; Urbana, IL; PresSrCls; SctActv; StuCncl; Bsktbl; Univ Of Illinois.

WORLEY, Judith A; Linden Sr HS; Swartz Creek, MI; Band; CncrtBnd; HonRl; HospAde; MrchBnd; NHS; PepBnd; SctActv; StuCncl; SpnCl; Mid Michigan; Health.

WORLEY, Mary C; Wayland Academy; South Bend, IN; Chr; Chrl; Chrs; HonRl; NatlThespSoc; SchMus; SchPl; StuCncl; StuGov; Yrbk; SchPpr; FrCl; Tennis; W Michigan Univ; Voice.

WORLEY, Mary C; Wayland Academy; Bridgman, MI; Chr; HonRl; NatlThespSoc; SchPl; StuGov; Yrbk; SchPpr; Tennis; Chrldr; GAA; IMSpt; W Michigan Univ; Music.

WORLEY, Patrick H; Warren Central HS; Indianapolis, IN; 1/750 ChrhWkr; HonRl; JrNHS; NHS; NatlMeritSchl; NatlMeritSF; TreasYthFlsp; VPMthCl; SciCl; JETSAwd; KiwanAwd; Deep Springs College; Physics.

WORLEY, Peggy J; Centerville HS; Centerville, IA; 12/139 HonRl; ModUN; NHS; VPSchPl; StuCncl; RptrYrbk; RptrSchPpr; VPFrCl; PpCl; CaptChrldr; College; History.

WORLEY, Teresa A; Fairfield Comm HS; Fairfield, IL; Chrs; ChrhWkr; CmntyWkr; OffAde; StuCncl; RptrYrbk; 4-H; FHA; KeyCl; MthCl; SciCl; DanFAwd; Jr College; Medicine.

WORLEY, Thomas R; University HS; Urbana, IL; SctActv; Univ Of Illinois.

WORMAN, Carol D; Westran HS; Huntsville, MO; SecSophCls; TrsSophCls; Chrs; DrlTm; HonRl; Mdrgl; OffAde; SchPl; Twrl; RptrYrbk; College; Business Or Phy Ed.

WORMAN, Karen I; Desoto HS; De Soto, WI; 7/70 HonRl; LbryAde; OffAde; SchPl; StuCncl; TchrAde; PpCl; Trk; College; Spec Education.

WORMAN, Krisanne E; Crete Monee HS; Park Forest, IL; 58/382 HonRl; Orch; SchMus; Ill Inst Of Tech; Psychology.

WORMLEY, Steven G; Keith HS; Rockford, IL; JrNHS; NatlMeritCmnd; SchPl; RptrYrbk; LetterBsktbl; CaptSocr; Tennis; University; Accounting.

WORMMEESTER, Randy B; Rogers HS; Wyoming, MI; HonRl; SctActv; Hope Coll; Engr.

WORMS, Jan S; Mascoutah HS; Mascoutah, IL; 60/221 Band; Chrs; ChrhWkr; CncrtBnd; HonRl; Mdrgl; MrchBnd; SchMus; YthFlsp; RptrYrbk; Belleville Area College; Medical Tech.

WORNER, Donald K; Aledo HS; Aledo, IL; ALBoysSt; HonRl; StuCncl; YthFlsp; SpnCl; Bsktbl; Ftbl; LetterGlf; Eastern Ill Univ; Accounting.

WORNER, Timothy C; Metamora HS; Metamora, IL; ChrhWkr; CmntyWkr; SchMus; SchPl; YthFlsp; 4-H; FFA; PpCl; Trk; CchngActv; IMSpt; Illinois Cntrl College; Agriculture.

WORONIEC, Diana S; St Clement HS; Center Line, MI; HonRl; SpnCl; PpCl; SciCl; PPFtbl; Marygrove Col; Math.

WORONOWICZ, Mandi E; Morton West HS; Lyons, IL; 71/742 HonRl; LitMag; ModUN; NHS; Hope College; Hematologist.

WORREL, Alan L; La Moure HS; La Moure, ND; ALBoysSt; HonRl; FFA; LetterBsbl; LetterBsktbl; LetterFtbl; LetterTrk;.

WORRELL, Cynthia L; Hudson HS; Hudson, WI; 20/220 HonRl; FHA; Wyoming Univ; Agric.

WORRELL, Edward O; West Richland HS; Noble, IL; 89#105#1 PresJrCls; Bsktbl; Wabash Valley Jr Col.

WORST, Mary A; Muskegon Catholic Central HS; Muskegon, MI; 3/215 ChrhWkr; CmntyWkr; HonRl; JA; LbryAde; NHS; Ferris State College; Research Pharmacist.

WORSTER, Kevin S; Granite City HS; Granite City, IL; HonRl; NHS; LetterGlf; LetterTennis; College; Forestry.

WORT, Mark E; Scott Comm HS; Scott City, KS; 46/103 Band; Chr; Chrl; Chrs; HonRl; PepBnd; SchMus; SchPl; 4-H; IMSpt; College; Music.

WORTH, Cynthia M; Capac HS; Capac, MI; Band; Chr; Chrs; CmntyWkr; HonRl; RedCrAde; StuCncl; RptrSchPpr; Chrldr; GAA; St Cccc; Professional.

WORTH, Doug E; Alliance HS; Alliance, NE; 8/160 HonRl; NatlMeritCmnd; LatCl; Ftbl; Kearney St Coll; Archi.

WORTH, Kathleen D; Eagle Union HS; Zionsville, IN; CmntyWkr; HonRl; LbryAde; TchrAde; Bsbl; Business College; Vocational.

WORTH, Marc R; N Chicago Comm HS; North Chicago, IL; 7/300 ALBoysSt; Band; Chr; HonRl; NHS; SchAde; SchPl; Univ Of Ill; Engineering.

WORTHINGTON, Tina L; Pioneer HS; Logansport, IN; 10/109 Chr; Chrs; HonRl; Mdrgl; SchMus; University; Professional.

WORTHY, Brian D; Monte Comm HS; Montezuma, IA; SecTrsJrCls; VPSrCls; TreasAFS; PresNatlThespSoc; SchPl; VPStuCncl; RptrYrbk; Yrbk; RptrSchPpr; PresFTA; Bil; Philosophy.

WORTLEY, Karen M; East Lansing HS; East Lansing, MI; ChrhWkr; NHS; OffAde; TchrAde; Teen; PPFtbl; College; Music Therapy.

WORTLEY, Linda M; Pennfield HS; Battle Creek, MI; 5/172 HonRl; NHS; TchrAde; VoiceDemAwd; Western Michigan Univ; Chemistry.

WORTMAN, Carolyn A; Ruskin HS; Ruskin, NE; 3/9 SecSrCls; HonRl; OffAde; SchPl; TchrAde; PresPpCl; CaptBsktbl; LetterTrk; 4-HAwd; Univ Of N Colorado; Physical Ed.

WORTMAN, Lori K; Stillman Valley HS; Stillman Valley, IL; Band; ChrhWkr; CncrtBnd; HonRl; MrchBnd; PepBnd; SchPl; Yrbk; 4-H; FHA; SecSpnCl; PpCl; GAA; PPFtbl; College.

WORTMAN, Robin J; Highland HS; Highland, IN; 108/565 SpnCl; Bsktbl; College; Professional.

WORTSMANN, Diane J; Roger C Sullivan HS; Chicago, IL; 32/276 CmntyWkr; HonRl; CaptTennis;.

WOS, George; Winona Senior HS; Minnesota City, MN; HonRl; MthCl; U Of Mn; Physics.

WOSEPKA, Joanne R; Golva Public HS; Golva, ND; Band; Chrs; ChrhWkr; CncrtBnd; HonRl; HospAde; PepBnd; SchPpr; LetterBsktbl; Chrldr; Coll; Nursing.

WOSIK, John; Campion HS; Henry, IL; .

WOSLAGER, Barbara S; Ewing Public HS; Ewing, NE; SecFrshCls; SecTrsJrCls; Chr; HonRl; NHS; SchAde; TchrAde; Yrbk; Trk; Chrldr; Ne Nebraska Tech Coll; Medical Secy.

WOTTA, Paul R; Pius Xi HS; Milwaukee, WI; 20/380 LbryAde; NHS; OffAde; TchrAde; FTA; LetterBsktbl; CaptTennis; St Johns Univ Mn; Accounting.

WOULF, Robert J; Catholic Central HS; Peshtigo, WI; SchPl; Bsbl; Bsktbl; Ftbl; Glf; University; Athletics.

WOULFE, Margaret F; Queen Of Peace HS; Oak Lawn, IL; 12/417 VPJrCls; PresSrCls; HonRl; NHS; SctActv; Pres4-H; FrCl; GAA; 4-HAwd; CitAwd; Ill State University.

WOUTERS, Beth C; St Clement HS; Warren, MI; 18/98 TrsFrshCls; HonRl; NatlMeritCmnd; OffAde; TchrAde; EdYrBk; PpCl; Bsbl; Bsktbl; CchngActv; GAA; Ferris State Col; Journalism.

WOUTERS, Chris M; St Clement HS; Warren, MI; HonRl; NatlMeritCmnd; Bsbl; Bsktbl; Ftbl; CchngActv; Macomb County Cc HS.

WOUTERS, Christopher; St Clement HS; Warren, MI; HonRl; NHS; NatlMeritCmnd; TchrAde; PpCl; Bsbl; Bsktbl; Ftbl; IMSpt; College; Law Enforcement.

WOVCHA, Laurie J; Roosevelt HS; Virginia, MN; 18/290 HonRl; LbryAde; NatlFornLg; NatlMeritSF; SecSctActv; StuGov; Community College; Language.

WOYCHEK, Andrew J; Lancaster Sr HS; Lancaster, WI; 22/155 AFS; HonRl; EngCl; SpnCl; LetterFtbl; College; Professional Mecidine.

WOYTOWICZ, Karen; Niles West Hs; Niles, IL; 10/495 TreasChr; Chrs; ChrhWkr; HonRl; SchMus; TchrAde; GAA; Northern Illinois U; Registered-nurse.

WOZNIAK, Brian; Stanley Boyd HS; Stanley, WI; PresSrCls; ChrhWkr; CtyCnl; HonRl; PolWkr; StuCncl; FFA; LetterFtbl; LetterWrstlng; Vocational School; Mechanic Arts.

WOZNIAK, John A; John Hersey HS; Mt Prospect, IL; 34/776 CncrtBnd; HonRl; VPMrchBnd; NHS; NatlMeritCmnd; NatlMeritSF; SctActv; PresSciCl; Bsktbl; Trk; College; Engineering.

WOZNIAK, Kathleen A; Bishop Noll Institute HS; Hammond, IN; 9/342 HonRl; NHS; Quill&Scroll; Yrbk; Purdue Univ Calumet Campus; Chemistry.

WOZNIAK, Mario F; Hempstead HS; Dubuque, IA; ALBoysSt; HonRl; NHS; Orch; Tennis; Us Military Academy.

WOZNIAK, Marjorie C; Hempstead HS; Dubuque, IA; HonRl; NHS; Univ Of Iowa; Engineer.

WOZNIAK, Mary S; Alleman HS; Rock Island, IL; HonRl; JA; NHS; RptrYrbk; Coll; Med Tech.

WOZNICKI, Jane A; Appleton West HS; Appleton, WI; AFS; Chrl; CmntyWkr; NHS; SchPl; RptrYrbk; Yrbk; FrCl; VPPpCl; Uw Madison; Teacher.

WRAGE, Cynthia; Gladbrook Community HS; Gladbrook, IA; 25#36#41 JA; ModUN; NHS; NatlMeritSchl; StuCncl; SecYthFlsp; 4-H; College; Professional.

WRAGE, Marty; Hudson Comm HS; Hudson, IA; ChrhWkr; JA; YthFlsp;.

WRAGGE, Connie L; Pierce Public HS; Pierce, NE; 1/62 Band; Chr; HonRl; NHS; FHA; College; Physical Science.

WRAGGE, Douglas J; Pierce Public HS; Pierce, NE; 3/63 VPJrCls; PresSrCls; ChrhWkr; HonRl; HospAde; NHS; SchAde; SchPl; StuCncl; TchrAde; Wayne State; Elem Ed.

WRANESCHETZ, Patrick J; Grace HS; Minneapolis, MN; SciCl; Ftbl; Univ Of Minn; Electrical Engr.

WRATE, Wendy J; Delton Kellogg HS; Delton, MI; 27/117 OffAde; SchPl; SpnCl; PPFtbl; College; Secretarial.

WRAY, Lisa J; Livingston HS; Livingston, IL; SecTrsJrCls; SecTrsSrCls; Chrs; ChrhWkr; HonRl; LbryAde; OffAde; YthFlsp; EdSchPpr; 4-H; FHA; PpCl; College.

WRAY, Max R; Warsaw Community HS; Warsaw, IN; Chr; ChrhWkr; SchMus; SctActv; 4-H; CmntyWkr; CncrtBnd; MrchBnd; PepBnd; StuCncl;.

WRAY, Russell C; Wayne Community HS; Corydon, IA; 13/72 ALBoysSt; Band; Chr; CncrtBnd; HonRl; MrchBnd; NHS; SchMus; LetterFtbl; CaptGlf; Northeast Missouri State Univ; Business Adm.

WREGGELSWORTH, Fred A; Buchanan HS; Buchanan, MI; FFA; LetterWrstlng;.

WREGGLESWORTH, Scott M; Buchanan HS; Buchanan, MI; HonRl; SchPl; TchrAde; SpnCl; Hope Coll; Poli Sci.

WREN, Jenny A; Elizabeth Seton HS; Homewood, IL; 7/252 HonRl; IntrClCncl; NHS; StuCncl; FrCl; SciCl; Butler Univ; Pharmacy.

WREN, Stephen; Ritenour Sr HS; St Louis, MO; 80/796 Aud/Vis; HonRl; SpnCl; Ftbl; CchngActv; Washington Univ; Art Arch.

WRENN, Douglas; Bettendorf HS; Bettendorf, IA; 56/425 HonRl; NHS; Ftbl; Trk; Univ Of Ia; Dentistry.

WRIGHT, Alice M; Monticello HS; Cisco, IL; 3/136 ALAGirlsSt; ChrhWkr; HonRl; NHS; PresYthFlsp; AmLegAwd; Patricia Stevens Clg; Legal Secretary.

WRIGHT, Ann E; Memorial HS; Joplin, MO; 1/226 HonRl; JrNHS; NHS; StuCncl; EdYrBk; Tennis; CaptChrldr; College; Journalism.

WRIGHT, Anthony L; W P Chrysler HS; New Castle, IN; 23/390 Aud/Vis; ChrhWkr; HonRl; LbryAde; NHS; Pres4-H; LatCl; Bsktbl; Trk; 4-HAwd; Purdue Univ; Soil Conservation.

WRIGHT, Brent D; Grandview HS; Grandview, MO; 82/432 Chr; HonRl; NHS; SchMus; SctActv; YthFlsp; Bsktbl; LetterFtbl; Trk; LetterWrstlng; Central Ms St.

WRIGHT, Brent E; Farmer City Mansfield HS; Mansfield, IL; ALBoysSt; Band; CncrtBnd; HonRl; MrchBnd; SctActv; Bsbl; Bsktbl; IMSpt; Parkland College; Farming.

WRIGHT, Candy S; Pennville HS; Portland, IN; 1/40 ChrhWkr; HonRl; LbryAde; NHS; TchrAde; YthFlsp; RptrSchPpr; SchPpr; PpCl; Coll; Secondary Education.

WRIGHT, Cecilia M; Bishop Borgess HS; Detroit, MI; 2/362 PresChr; HonRl; NHS; Quill&Scroll; SchMus; StuGov; EdYrBk; FrCl; Swmmng; DARAwd; Eastern Mi Univ; Occupational Therapy.

WRIGHT, Cheri; Savanna HS; Savanna, IL; 19/83 Aud/Vis; ChrhWkr; HonRl; SchPl; Yrbk; 4-H; FHA; SciCl; Trk; Coll; Med.

WRIGHT, Curtis; Carrollton HS; Carrollton, MO; HonRl; RptrSchPpr; SptEdSchPpr; SpnCl; MthCl; Bsktbl; Ftbl; CchngActv; IMSpt; Univ; Prof.

WRIGHT, Cynthia; New Providence Comm HS; New Providence, IA; SecTrsFrshCls; PresJrCls; Chrs; HonRl; SchMus; SchPl; StuCncl; YthFlsp; Chrldr; PPFtbl; College.

WRIGHT, Cynthia L; Brazil HS; Brazil, IN; Chr; HonRl; 4-H; FHA;.

WRIGHT, Cynthia L; Turkey Run HS; Marshall, IN; Band; HonRl; YthFlsp; SchPpr; 4-H; FHA; College; Home Economics.

WRIGHT, Cynthia M; Howell Senior HS; Howell, MI; 21/362 ChrhWkr; CmntyWkr; HonRl; NHS; NatlMeritFnl; NatlMeritSchl; PolWkr; TchrAde; SecYthFlsp; RptrYrbk; TreasGAA; IMSpt; PPFtbl; 4-HAwd; Grand Valley State College; Liberal Arts.

WRIGHT, Cynthia S; New London HS; New London, IA; 13/39 Band; Chrs; CncrtBnd; HonRl; MrchBnd; SchMus; StuCncl; 4-H; LetterBsktbl; Swmmng; LetterTrk; Chrldr; 4-HAwd; Mount Mercy College; Registered Nurse.

WRIGHT, David; Mohammad Univ Of Islam HS; Chicago, IL; 1/20 DrmMjrt; OffAde; Medicine.

WRIGHT, David A; Griffith HS; Griffith, IN; HonRl; SpnCl; SciCl; Ftbl; Indiana Univ; Business.

WRIGHT, Deborah R; Mt Vernon HS; Fortville, IN; 5/167 PresJrCls; Chr; ChrhWkr; DrlTm; HonRl; MrchBnd; SchMus; StuCncl; TchrAde; PpCl; College; Music.

WRIGHT, Donald V; Swartz Creek HS; Swartz Creek, MI; HonRl; SctActv; StuGov; TchrAde; PresFrCl; LetterFtbl; Wrstlng; W Michigan Univ; History.

WRIGHT, Edwin G; Loy Norrix HS; Kalamazoo, MI; 25/436 HonRl; NHS; SchPl; SctActv; TchrAde; PpCl; Bsbl; LetterTrk; Us Air Force; Pro.

WRIGHT, Gary J; Bon Homme #96 HS; Tyndall, SD; VPSophCls; Band; ChrhWkr; CmntyWkr; CncrtBnd; HonRl; PepBnd; SctActv; Bsktbl; Ftbl; College ;pro.

WRIGHT, Gerald R; Beech Grove HS; Beech Grove, IN; Band; CmntyWkr; HonRl; PolWkr; TchrAde; YthFlsp; PresCivCl; Trk; IMSpt; Ball State Univ; Law.

WRIGHT, Glenn A; Waverly Shell Rock HS; Waverly, IA; 38/196 College; Dentistry.

WRIGHT, Gregory R; Kapaun Mount Carmel HS; Wichita, KS; HonRl; ModUN; NHS; StuCncl; SchPpr; GerCl; University; Education.

WRIGHT, Heather; Hannibal Senior HS; Hannibal, MO; 23/210 ChrhWkr; HonRl; NHS; FTA; SpnCl; GAA; College; Social Science.

WRIGHT, James R; Cahokia HS; Cahokia, IL; 16/559 Chr; CncrtBnd; NHS; NatlMeritCmnd; Quill&Scroll; SchPl; TchrAde; Yrbk; FTA; Murray State Univ; Choral Conducting.

WRIGHT, Jerry D; Borden HS; Border, IN; 4/65 ALBoysSt; HonRl; NHS; Yrbk; Bsktbl; AmLegAwd; In Univ Se & Purdue; Engin.

WRIGHT, Johnny G; Gallatin HS; Gallatin, MO; 12/52 CncrtBnd; HonRl; LbryAde; MrchBnd; PresNHS; SchPl; VPFFA; LetterBsktbl; LetterFtbl; LetterTrk; College; Machine Tool And Die.

WRIGHT, Joseph E; Huntington HS; Hunting, IN; HonRl; CaptBsktbl; LetterGlf; CchngActv; Bus Sch; Prof Golf.

WRIGHT, Karen K; Waterloo Public HS; Columbia, IL; 11/140 Band; HonRl; JrNHS; MrchBnd; NHS; SchMus; StuCncl; TchrAde; GerCl; Chrldr; College; Med Assistant.

WRIGHT, Karren; Triad HS; Collinsville, IL; 7/176 HonRl; NHS; Southern Ill Univ.

WRIGHT, Kathryn E; Stillman Valley HS; Monroe Center, IL; Band; ChrhWkr; HonRl; LbryAde; SecNHS; SchMus; SchPl; FHA; College; Education.

WRIGHT, Kenneth G; Arthur Hill HS; Saginaw, MI; 23/734 PresSophCls; PresJrCls; PresSrCls; HonRl; NHS; SchPl; StuCncl; StuGov; RptrSchPpr; PpCl; SciCl; IMSpt; Michigan St Univ; Medicine.

WRIGHT, Kevin D; So Sioux HS; So Sioux City, NE; 2/168 AFS; LitMag; NHS; TreasNatlThespSoc; PresSpnCl; Ftbl; AmLegAwd; ChmbCommrsAwd; GodCntryAwd; KiwanAwd; CitAwd; Univ Of Minnesota; International Relations.

WRIGHT, Lois; Wheaton Christian Hs; Wheaton, IL; 2/32 Chr; Chrl; ChrhWkr; HonRl; NHS; NatlMeritCmnd; Yrbk; SchPpr; Wheaton College; Musician.

WRIGHT, Lon A; Cowan HS; Muncie, IN; 1/57 PresJrCls; ALBoysSt; ChrhWkr; HonRl; NHS; StuCncl; Yrbk; 4-H; LetterBsktbl; Trk; Purdue; Med.

WRIGHT, Lori A; Flasher Public HS; New Salem, ND; 3/40 Band; Chrs; ChrhWkr; CncrtBnd; HonRl; MrchBnd; PepBnd; SchPl; SchPpr; 4-H; FHA; Bsktbl; College; Professional.

WRIGHT, Lyle; Gage Park Hs; Chicago, IL; 37/462 Aud/Vis; CncrtBnd; ModUN; OffAde; Quill&Scroll; EdSchPpr; SptEdSchPpr; Swmmng; Tennis; CchngActv; University; Engineer.

WRIGHT, Margaret L; Elm Creek HS; Elmcreek, NE; 1/30 SecSrCls; Band; Chrs; CncrtBnd; HonRl; MrchBnd; NHS; PepBnd; RptrYrbk; Univ Of Nebraska; Nursing.

WRIGHT, Mark A; Benedict HS; Benedict, NE; Band; CmntyWkr; StuCncl; YthFlsp; 4-H; Bsbl; LetterBsktbl; Ftbl;.

WRIGHT, Mary; Coldwater HS; Coldwater, MI; ALAGirlsSt; CmntyWkr; HonRl; FDA; FSA; Chrldr; DARAwd; GovHonPrgAwd; RotaryAwd; CitAwd; College; Professional.

WRIGHT, Megan; Caruthersville HS; Caruthersville, MO; 3/105 Stephens Coll; Pediatrician.

WRIGHT, Michael R; Baxter HS; Baxter Springs, KS; 27/67 VPSophCls; PresJrCls; ALAGirlsSt; Chr; Chrs; ChrhWkr; CmntyWkr; DrlTm; HonRl; NatlThespSoc; Wichita State Univ; Hospital Administrator.

WRIGHT, Myra S; Wm W Borden HS; Borden, IN; 7/75 TreasBand; ChrhWkr; HonRl; JrNHS; NHS; OffAde; StuCncl; TchrAde; PresFHA; FTA; LetterTrk; GAA; IMSpt; Indiana Univ; Teaching.

WRIGHT, Paula L; Park River HS; Park River, ND; ChrhWkr; HonRl; NHS; SchPl; Bsktbl; Swmmng; LetterTrk; Chrldr; GAA; Harding College; Physical Ther.

WRIGHT, Renee C; Manchester HS; N Manchester, IN; 2/142 HonRl; LitMag; NatlFornLg; NHS; SchPl; TchrAde; Yrbk; EdSchPpr; 4-H; Indiana University.

WRIGHT, Rita M; Lowell HS; Schneider, IN; 8/232 Chr; HonRl; NHS; NatlThespSoc; SchMus; EdSchPpr; 4-H; MthCl; PpCl; Purdue University.

WRIGHT, Robert E; Joliet Catholic HS; Joliet, IL; Aud/Vis; HonRl; JA; LbryAde; SchAde; SctActv; StuCncl; TchrAde; SchPpr; FrCl; Notre Dame Univ; Law.

WRIGHT, Robin L; Pacific HS; Catawissa, MO; 22/186 Chr; Chrs; HonRl; NatlFornLg; NatlThespSoc; SchMus; SchPl; TchrAde; FTA; Southwest Baptist College; Teacher Acctg.

WRIGHT, Ronald U; Chicago Vocational HS; Chicago, IL; HonRl; Quill&Scroll; SchPl; SctActv; StuCncl; StuGov; TchrAde; University; Political Science.

WRIGHT, Stephen W; Edgewood HS; Bloomington, IN; Band; Chrs; ChrhWkr; CncrtBnd; MrchBnd; PepBnd; SchPl; SctActv; GerCl; LetterGlf; IMSpt; Ind Univ; Medical Doctor.

WRIGHT, Steven C; Galesburg HS; Galesburg, IL; 13/588 Band; ChrhWkr; CncrtBnd; HonRl; MrchBnd; NHS; PepBnd; SchMus; Bsktbl; Univ Of Illinois; Computer Science.

WRIGHT, Steven M; Morton HS; Pekin, IL; 7/254 HonRl; NHS; NatlMeritSF; SciCl; Socr; U Of Il; Electrical Engineer.

WRIGHT, Sue A; Valle HS; Ste Genevieve, MO; 5/82 Chrs; DrlTm; HonRl; NHS; StuCncl; RptrYrbk; SchPpr; PpCl; LetterTrk; IMSpt; University; Psychology.

WRIGHT, Susan M; Collinsville HS; Collinsville, IL; 121/645 TrsFrshCls; TrsSophCls; TrsJrCls; HonRl; PolWkr; StuCncl; PpCl; Chrldr; Univ Of Ill; Pre Law.

WRIGHT, Susan R; Farmington East HS; Hanna City, IL; 6/140 ALAGirlsSt; HonRl; SecNHS; SctActv; FHA; SecFrCl; PPFtbl; Nursing School; Nurse.

WRIGHT, Terry L; Union HS; Modoc, IN; ChrhWkr; HonRl; LbryAde; OffAde; TchrAde; 4-H; FHA; Chrldr; Business School; Computer Science.

WRIGHT, Thomas; Yankton Senior HS; Yankton, SD; PresFrshCls; PresSophCls; TrsJrCls; ALBoysSt; ChrhWkr; HonRl; LitMag; NatlFornLg; StuCncl; RptrSchPpr; College; Professional.

WRIGHT, Thomas R; Lebanon Comm HS; Lebanon, IL; HonRl; JrNHS; NHS; EdSchPpr; Bsbl; Technical School.

WRIGHT, Wendy L; Labette County HS; Parsons, KS; 2/150 TrsFrshCls; Chr; ChrhWkr; HonRl; NHS; NatlMeritCmnd; SchMus; SchPl; SecSpnCl; TreasSciCl; Wichita State Univ; Music Education.

WRIGHT, Zena R; Vienna HS; Simpson, IL; 4/104 HonRl; StuCncl; YthFlsp; FHA; FNA;.

WRISTON, Theresa A; St Patricks HS; Sidney, NE; TrsFrshCls; TrsSophCls; TrsJrCls; Chr; HonRl; NHS; SchPl; SptEdSchPpr; SchPpr; PpCl; Chrldr; College; Social Work Or Lawyer.

WRNER, James D; Fremont HS; Fremont, MI; 41/198 HonRl; GerCl; Ferris State College; Accounting.

WROBEL, Denise; Muskego HS; Wind Lake, WI; HonRl; StuCncl; RptrYrbk; RptrSchPpr; PpCl; Univ Of Whitewater; Journalism.

WROBEL, Roberta A; St Augustine HS; Chicago, IL; 14/75 TrsFrshCls; SecSophCls; Band; Chr; Chrs; ChrhWkr; CmntyWkr; HonRl; SchMus; SchPl; Bsbl; Ftbl; Swmmng; Chrldr;.

WROBLEWSKI, Daniel J; Pittsville HS; Marshfield, WI; HonRl; LbryAde; RptrSchPpr; FTA; FrCl; SciCl; Coll; Psychology.

WROBLEWSKI, Mary T; St Joseph HS; Chicago, IL; PresFrshCls; PresJrCls; OffAde; SchAde; SchPl; StuCncl; 4-H; Chrldr; GAA; College; Art.

WRONKIEWICZ, David J; Proviso East HS; Melrose Park, IL; 130/984 Ftbl; KiwanAwd; U Of Il; Veterinary.

WRONSKI, William T; J S Morton West HS; Berwyn, IL; 77/755 CncrtBnd; HonRl; JrNHS; MrchBnd; NatlThespSoc; Orch; SchMus; SchPl; Tennis; Northwestern Univ; Actor.

WRUBLIK, Joanna M; Elk Grove HS; Elk Grove Vlg, IL; 28/540 VPChr; Chrs; HonRl; Mdrgl; NHS; TreasNatlThespSoc; PolWkr; SchMus; SchPl; JCAwd; Il St U.

WRUCK, Marc F; Crystal Lake HS; Crystal Lake, IL; 33/473 ChrhWkr; HonRl; NHS; SpnCl; Bsbl; Notre Dame Univ; Bio Engineering.

WRUCKE, Wendy; Horicon HS; Horicon, WI; 2/88 PresSophCls; ALAGirlsSt; Chr; NHS; Quill&Scroll; EdYrBk; SchPpr; GerCl; Trk; GAA; Uw Madison.

WRYE, Richard W; Mt Carmel HS; Mt Carmel, IL; 61/183 Band; ChrhWkr; CncrtBnd; MrchBnd; SchMus; SchPl; YthFlsp; Ftbl; Univ; Electronic Tech.

WRZENSKI, Lavon M; North Loup Scotia HS; Cotesfield, NE; TrsSophCls; TrsJrCls; Band; Chr; Chrl; Chrs; CncrtBnd; DrmMjrt; HonRl; MrchBnd; PepBnd; Kearney State College; Nursing.

WUBBELS, Barbara J; Norris HS; Hickman, NE; 6/90 Band; ChrhWkr; HonRl; NHS; YthFlsp; 4-H; FNA; LetterBsktbl; LetterTrk; LetterWrstlng; Southeast Comm Coll; Nursing Prof.

WUBBEN, James; Central Minn Christian HS; Clara City, MN; 1/29 Chr; HonRl; NHS; NatlMeritCmnd; SchMus; Bsktbl; IMSpt; BauchLmbAwd; Dordt College; Teaching.

WUBBEN, Sharon J; Central Minn Christian HS; Clara City, MN; Chr; TchrAde; RptrSchPpr; FTA; SecPpCl; Coll; Science.

WUDTKE, Mark; Toluca Community HS; Rutland, IL; Band; Chrs; CmntyWkr; CncrtBnd; HonRl; MrchBnd; PepBnd; SchPl; FSA; Bsktbl; College; Aeronautics.

WUEBBELS, Gary J; Wesclin HS; Trenton, IL; 14/111 Aud/Vis; ChrhWkr; CncrtBnd; HonRl; JrNHS; MrchBnd; NHS; PepBnd; GerCl; PpCl; Coll; Electronics.

WUEBKER, Janean A; Ayrshire Consolidated HS; Ayrshire, IA; 2/20 Chr; Chrs; ChrhWkr; DrlTm; HonRl; SchMus; SchPl; StuCncl; FHA; LetterBsktbl; IMSpt; PresAwd; College; Home Econ.

WUEBKER, Leon J; Rockwell City HS; Rockwell City, IA; PresFrshCls; ChrhWkr; HonRl; VPStuCncl; RptrSchPpr; FFA; PpCl; LetterFtbl; LetterWrstlng; Iowa State Univ; Agriculture.

WUEBKER, Wayne J; Ayrshire Cons HS; Ayrshire, IA; 3/16 Chr; Chrs; ChrhWkr; HonRl; SchMus; SchPl; StuCncl; LetterBsbl; LetterBsktbl; LetterTrk; IMSpt; PresAwd; Loras College; Mathematics.

WUELLNER, Andrew V; Chaminade College Prep; Alton, IL; CmntyWkr; CncrtBnd; HonRl; SchPl; LetterBsbl; LetterFtbl; IMSpt; Univ; Engineer.

WUERTZ, Mark E; Courtland HS; Courtland, KS; 8/22 PresJrCls; PresSrCls; Chrs; HonRl; NatlMeritSchl; SchPl; SctActv; RptrYrbk; FFA; LetterTrk; Ks St Univ; Dr Of Veterinarian Medicine.

WUJCIAK, Kathryn A; Grand Blanc HS; Grand Blanc, MI; 80/560 PresSophCls; CmntyWkr; HonRl; NHS; PolWkr; SchAde; TchrAde; PpCl; IMSpt; PPFtbl; Univ Of Mi; Politica Science.

WULF, Cindy K; West Sioux HS; Hawarden, IA; Chrs; HonRl; NatlMeritSchl; YthFlsp; PpCl; College; Home Economics.

WULF, Debbie A; Bloomfield HS; Bloomsfield, NE; 12/47 SecTrsFrshCls; Band; DrlTm; LbryAde; MrchBnd; 4-H; Chrldr; 4-HAwd; PresAwd; CitAwd; College; Professional.

WULF, Gary L; Guide Rock Public HS; Guide Rock, NE; 1/11 PresFrshCls; VPSophCls; SecJrCls; ALBoysSt; Chr; Chrs; StuCncl; RptrSchPpr; SchPpr; Bsktbl; Ftbl; LetterFtbl; LetterGlf; AmLegAwd; College; Broadcaster.

WULF, Kelby K; Holstein Comm HS; Holstein, IA; VPSophCls; VPJrCls; ALBoysSt; HonRl; 4-H; Clg; Farm Operation.

WULF, Linda A; Blair HS; Blair, NE; HonRl; LbryAde; FBLA; FrCl; Dana College; Teacher.

WULF, Verlon L; Chenev HS; Cheney, KS; PresSrCls; HonRl; Mdrgl; SchMus; StuCncl; RptrYrbk; EdSchPpr; PresFFA; LetterFtbl; LetterTrk; Dodge City Com Col; Agriculture Engineer.

WULFEKUHLE, Edward A; West Delaware HS; Manchester, IA; College; Agriculture.

WULFF, Doris J; Sacred Heart HS; Sedalia, MO; 7/28 TrsSrCls; HonRl; NHS; SchPl; PpCl; State Fair Comm College; Accountant.

WULFF, Elizabeth A; Hinsdale Central HS; Hinsdale, IL; 10/583 ChrhWkr; VPHospAde; NHS; SchPl; PpCl; Louisiana St University.

WULFF, Joanne; Lakeland Union HS; Woodruff, WI; ChrhWkr; HonRl; Univ Of Wi; Home Ec.

WULKOW, Barbara L; Lytton Community HS; Sac City, IA; 1/29 ALAGirlsSt; DrlTm; HonRl; NHS; NatlMeritCmnd; StuCncl; VPFHA; Iowa State Univ; Medical Technology.

WUNDER, Maria K; Valley Falls HS; Valley Falls, KS; Band; Chrs; DrlTm; HonRl; SecNHS; PepBnd; RptrYrbk; RptrSchPpr; FHA; PpCl; K State University.

WUNDER, Sharon; Harlan Community HS; Harlan, IA; 26/256 Band; CmntyWkr; HonRl; MrchBnd; PepBnd; SctActv; StuCncl; YthFlsp; Uni; Recreation.

WUNDERLIN, John E; Bishop Dwenger HS; Ft Wayne, IN; SctActv; KeyCl; Ftbl; Socr; Trk; CaptWrstlng; IMSpt; College; Professional.

WUNSCH, Randall; Greene Community HS; Greene, IA; Band; ChrhWkr; CmntyWkr; CncrtBnd; HonRl; MrchBnd; NHS; PepBnd; Hamilton Business College; Adm Accounting.

WUORI, Cathy M; Rolla Public HS; Hansboro, ND; ALAGirlsSt; Band; CncrtBnd; HonRl; MrchBnd; PepBnd; SchPl; FHA; PpCl; Chrldr; Univ; Professional.

WUORI, Glen; Baraga Twp HS; Pelkie, MI; 16/42 SecFrshCls; Chrs; HonRl; NHS; OffAde; SchMus; SchPl; SchPpr; Univ; Major Study.

WUORI, Lisa M; Marshall HS; Marshall, MI; 5/255 ChrhWkr; HonRl; JrNHS; NHS; NatlMeritCmnd; OffAde; SctActv; FrCl; SpnCl; Swmmng; Coll;.

WURGLER, Eris E; Leeds Public HS; York, ND; SecFrshCls; SecJrCls; ALAGirlsSt; ChrhWkr; HonRl; SchPl; TchrAde;.

WURGLITZ, Glen M; Gordon Tech HS; Chicago, IL; 32/697 HonRl; NHS; SchAde; StuCncl; StuGov; TchrAde; PpCl; Northeastern Univ; Mathematics.

WURL, Amy J; Illiopolis HS; Illiopolis, IL; VPFrshCls; PresJrCls; Chrs; NHS; NatlThespSoc; TchrAde; Yrbk; Chrldr; GAA; Eastern Ill U; Vet.

WURSCHMIDT, Leif B; John Glenn HS; Westland, MI; PresFrshCls; ChrhWkr; HonRl; SctActv; YthFlsp; LatCl; PresAwd; College; Mortician.

WURST, Charlene K; Osceola HS; Osceola, WI; SecSophCls; ALAGirlsSt; Band; MrchBnd; PepBnd; Yrbk; 4-H; FHA; LetterTrk; 4-HAwd; College; Nursing.

WURSTER, Brenda S; Elizabeth HS; Elizabeth, IL; 7/28 VPSrCls; ChrhWkr; HonRl; LbryAde; SchMus; StuCncl; RptrSchPpr; SptEdSchPpr; Chrldr; IMSpt; Nursing Home.

WURSTER, Susan K; Lenox Community HS; Lenox, IA; 6/33 SecFrshCls; VPSophCls; Chrs; ChrhWkr; HonRl; MrchBnd; SchPl; StuCncl; Bsktbl; LetterGlf; College; Vocational.

WUSSOW, Bryan D; Bonduel HS; Bonduel, WI; 4/122 ALBoysSt; Band; Chr; CncrtBnd; HonRl; SchPl; StuCncl; EdYrBk; PresSciCl; LetterTrk; General Motors Inst; Eng.

WUSTHOFF, Mary J; Ypsilanti HS; Ypsilanti, MI; Chr; HonRl; LbryAde;.

WUTHRICH, Richard E; Wawasee HS; Milford, IN; 25/218 HonRl; NHS; 4-H; FrCl; Ftbl; LetterTrk; IMSpt; College; Engineer.

WUTHRICH, Scott A; York Community HS; Menomonee Falls, WI; 18/850 Chr; Chrl; HonRl; NHS; NatlMeritSchl; SctActv; MthCl; IMSpt; PresAwd; CitAwd; Bradley University; Elec Engineering.

WUTHRICH, Scott A; York Community HS; Elmhurst, IL; 18/920 Chr; ChrhWkr; HonRl; NHS; NatlMeritFnl; NatlMeritSchl; MthCl; IMSpt; PresAwd; Bradley Univ; Electrical Engineering.

WUTTKE, Karen L; Luther HS; La Crosse, WI; Band; Chrs; HonRl; MrchBnd; SchPl; StuCncl; RptrSchPpr; LetterBsbl; LetterTrk; IMSpt; College; Phy Ed Teacher Coach.

WYANT, Bruce B; Andrews Academy; Sodus, MI; Chr; JA; Andrews U; Civil Engineer.

WYANT, Lila L; Richland HS; Richland, MO; Chrs; HonRl;.

WYATT, Bruce W; Harlem HS; Loves Park, IL; Chr; Chrs; DrlTm; LbryAde; ROTC; SchMus; RptrSchPpr; SchPpr; LetterBsktbl; Ftbl; University; Architect.

WYATT, Linda J; Dallas City HS; Lomax, IL; 4/47 SchMus; SchPl; StuCncl; TchrAde; Twrl; 4-H; FHA; PpCl; Bsktbl; Trk; Se Comm Jr C; Psychologist.

WYATT, Neil G; Harlem HS; Loves Park, IL; HonRl; HospAde; NHS; SctActv; College; Physical Therapy.

WYATT, Peggy S; Superior HS; Superior, NE; HonRl; LbryAde; FBLA; PpCl; Col; Major Study.

WYCKSTANDT, Phillip G; Imlay City HS; Imlay City, MI; 29/128 HonRl; LetterFtbl; LetterTennis; Western Mi Univ; Aviation Eng Tech.

WYCOFF, Brenda K; Macksville HS; Seward, KS; 3/34 Band; CncrtBnd; HonRl; HospAde; MrchBnd; NHS; PepBnd; StuCncl; Kansas State University; Medical Lab Tech.

WYCOFF, Debra J; Bryan Senior HS; Omaha, NE; 39/389 Band; CncrtBnd; HonRl; MrchBnd; PepBnd; TchrAde; PpCl; College; Professional.

WYCOFF, Henry R; Ford Central Unit 8 HS; Piper City, IL; 8/61 PresSrCls; HonRl; Mdrgl; NHS; SchPl; YthFlsp; Ftbl;.

WYCOFF, Kathleen L; Robichaud HS; Inkster, MI; College; Nursing.

WYCZAWSKI, Paul J; New Ulm HS; New Ulm, MN; 72/302 TrsJrCls; HonRl; StuCncl; StuGov; YthFlsp; RptrSchPpr; SptEdSchPpr; Bsbl; Bsktbl; University.

WYGLE, Carol L; Clarksville Comm HS; Greene, IA; PresFrshCls; Band; Chr; Chrs; ChrhWkr; CncrtBnd; HonRl; LbryAde; MrchBnd; NHS; PepBnd; SchPl; Twrl; YthFlsp; SptEdYrbk; College; Professional.

WYLAM, Mark E; Highland HS; Anderson, IN; 6/243 VPJrCls; ALBoysSt; VPJA; NHS; YthFnd; LatCl; LetterGlf; AmLegAwd; 4-HAwd; GovHonPrgAwd; JAAwd; CitAwd; Univ Of Notre Dame; Medicine.

WYLAND, Lugene D; Oak Grove Lutheran HS; Hawley, MN; Chr; ChrhWkr; CmntyWkr; HonRl; SchPl; StuCncl; TchrAde; EdYrBk; SchPpr; FHA; PpCl; Trk; College; Special Educ.

WYLES, Cathy A; Riverton Comm HS; Riverton, IL; 18/60 Chrs; HonRl; SchMus; RptrYrbk; RptrSchPpr; PpCl; Bsktbl; Ftbl; IMSpt; Blackburn College; Sociology.

WYMAN, Blair; Rapid City Central HS; Rapid City, SD; CncrtBnd; HonRl; MrchBnd; NatlMeritFnl; NatlMeritSF; SchMus; Univ Of Wy; Theatre.

WYMAN, Jamie A; Dexter HS; Pinckney, MI; 36/161 HonRl; TchrAde; Cleary College; Legal Secretarial.

WYMAN, Mark J; Silver Creek Public HS; Silver Creek, NE; 5/30 Band; Chrl; Chrs; HonRl; SchPl; YthFlsp; Bsbl; Bsktbl; Ftbl; Trk; College; Math Teacher.

WYMAN, Martha E; Williamsburg Community HS; Williamsburg, IA; Band; CncrtBnd; HonRl; JrNHS; LitMag; LbryAde; MrchBnd; NHS; Orch; SctActv; KiwanAwd; College; Legal Secretary.

WYMAN, Patricia L; Wrenshall HS; Wrenshall, MN; 6/30 PresFrshCls; PresSrCls; Aud/Vis; HonRl; NHS; OffAde; SchPl; PresStuCncl; StuGov; TchrAde; Southwest Minn State Clg.

WYMAN, Robin R; Saginaw HS; Saginaw, MI; 8/435 TrsSrCls; Chr; Chrs; HonRl; JA; JrNHS; NHS; StuGov; College; Office Occupations.

WYMAN, Susie M; Osceola HS; Osceola, NE; VPSophCls; Band; Chrs; CncrtBnd; MrchBnd; PepBnd; SchMus; 4-H; PpCl; Chrldr; College.

WYMER, Joyce; Protection HS; Protection, KS; 1/20 TrsFrshCls; TrsSrCls; Chrs; ChrhWkr; HonRl; SchMus; YthFlsp; PpCl; Tennis; Coll; Registered Nurse.

WYMORE, Ann B; Liberty Senior HS; Liberty, MO; AFS; ChrhWkr; CmntyWkr; HonRl; JrNHS; NHS; OffAde; SctActv; PpCl; IMSpt; William Jewell College; Business Admin.

WYMORE, Ronald D; Cambridge HS; Cambridge, NE; PresFrshCls; TrsSophCls; PresJrCls; ChrhWkr; CmntyWkr; HonRl; SchPl; StuCncl; Bsbl; Bsktbl; LetterFtbl; LetterTrk; College; Professional.

WYMORE, Teresa; North Chicago Community HS; Great Lakes, IL; 36/275 AFS; CmntyWkr; HospAde; NHS; OffAde; SctActv; GerCl; IMSpt; PresAwd; Jr College; Secretary.

WYNIA, Mark J; Rock Valley Comm HS; Rock Valley, IA; 18/62 Chr; Chrs; ChrhWkr; HonRl; SchMus; StuCncl; YthFlsp; Bsbl; Bsktbl; Ftbl;.

WYNN, Barbara J; Whitmore Lk HS; Whitmore Lk, MI; 4/67 ALAGirlsSt; ChrhWkr; HonRl; HospAde; JrNHS; SchAde; StuCncl; UNYO; YthLg; RptrYrbk; Concordia Lutheran Jr College; Special Ed.

WYNN, Eric D; Riley HS; South Bend, IN; 6/271 HonRl; NHS; NatlMeritCmnd; SchPl; SpnCl; Glf; Wrstlng; Univ; Accnt.

WYNN, Thomas P; South Milwaukee HS; S Milwaukee, WI; 28/465 HonRl; SchPl; College; Journalist.

WYNN, Yvonne; Winnetonka HS; Kansas City, MO; Chr; HospAde; SchMus; Trk; GAA; IMSpt;.

WYNNS, Zonia K; John Adams HS; South Bend, IN; 146/434 Band; Chrs; CncrtBnd; HonRl; MrchBnd; NatlMeritCmnd; PepBnd; RedCrAde; 4-H; PpCl; Purdue University; Pre Vet.

WYNSTRA, Jean R; Racine Lutheran HS; Racine, WI; Band; Chr; ChrhWkr; HonRl; TreasNHS; OffAde; PepBnd; TchrAde; SchPpr; PpCl; Coll; Music.

WYPYSZYNSKI, Ken R; West De Pere HS; West De Pere, WI; HonRl; NHS; StuCncl; Bsbl; Bsktbl; Ftbl; IMSpt; CitAwd; College.

WYSOCKI, David J; Almond HS; Almond, WI; PresSrCls; HonRl; NHS; LetterBsbl; LetterBsktbl; LetterFtbl; IMSpt; AmLegAwd; DanFAwd; 4-HAwd; Mid State Tech Sch Wi Rapids; Electronics.

WYSONG, Lyn E; Fairfield HS; New Paris, IN; Chr; Chrs; HonRl; SchPl; YthFlsp; RptrYrbk; Yrbk; 4-H; PpCl; Tri State College; Business Admin.

WYSOPAL, Joseph F; John F Kennedy HS; Chicago, IL; 43/600 CncrtBnd; HonRl; MrchBnd; Orch; University Of Illinois; Engineering.

WYSS, Heidi S; South Side HS; Fort Wayne, IN; 8/402 Band; ChrhWkr; CncrtBnd; HonRl; SecJA; MrchBnd; PresYthFlsp; Pres4-H; KeyCl; PresFrCl; Trk; 4-HAwd; Indiana Univ; Physician.

WYSS, Kimberly J; Donoran HS; Watseka, IL; 3/50 TrsJrCls; TrsSrCls; Band; HonRl; NHS; Quill&Scroll; SchMus; EdSchPpr; Univ Of Illinois; Psychology.

WYSS, Roxanne D; Truman HS; Independence, MO; 36/598 HonRl; Quill&Scroll; StuCncl; Yrbk; TreasFHA; FrCl; PpCl; College; Home Economics.

WYSZYNSKI, Wayne V; South Haven HS; South Haven, MI; HonRl; TchrAde; CaptSwmmng; Kalamazoo Valley Comm Clg; Accounting.

WYZGOSKI, Paul M; Pontiac Catholic HS; Pontiac, MI; HonRl; NHS; NatlMeritCmnd; NatlMeritSF; StuCncl; CaptBsktbl; CaptFtbl; Trk; OptClAwd; CitAwd; Univ Of Detroit; Accounting.

Y

YABLONSKI, Michael A; Maconaquah HS; Bunker Hill, IN; 45/220 HonRl; Bsbl; Bsktbl; Ftbl; Tennis; Trk; College.

YACK, Susan D; Woodruff HS; Peoria, IL; 23/268 SecFrshCls; SecSophCls; VPSrCls; AFS; Band; CncrtBnd; HonRl; JA; MrchBnd; PepBnd; SctActv; StuCncl; StuGov; RptrSchPpr; Univ Of Illinois; Social Work.

YACKLEY, Georgieanna; Atkinson HS; Atkinson, IL; 16/41 SecSrCls; HonRl; HospAde; LbryAde; SchPl; SctActv; SchPpr; FHA; GAA; Univ Of Ia; Nurse.

YACKLEY, Katherine A; Notre Dame HS; Taylor, MO; Chrs; HonRl; NHS; EdSchPpr; BttyCrckrAwd; Col Of Pharmacy; Pharmacist.

YAEGER, Bridget A; Brookfield HS; Brookfield, MO; Band; Chrs; HonRl; SctActv; CaptTrk; IMSpt; College; Physical Education.

YAEGER, James K; Columbus HS; Marshfield, WI; 30/110 ALBoysSt; HonRl; LetterBsbl; LetterBsktbl; LetterFtbl; LetterTrk; College.

YAGER, Janelle M; Mackinaw City P HS; Mackinaw City, MI; 1/22 SecSophCls; Band; Chrs; HonRl; PpCl; Bsktbl; Alpena Com Clg; Social Contact Or Bus.

YAGER, Janet M; North Decatur HS; Rushville, IN; 15/92 TrsFrshCls; SecJrCls; Band; VPNHS; VPQuill&Scroll; SchPl; Yrbk; 4-H; PpCl; Chrldr; Iupui; Medicine.

YAGER, Jerry E; North Decatur HS; Rushville, IN; TrsFrshCls; TrsSophCls; HstJrCls; TrsSrCls; ALBoysSt; HonRl; SchPl; StuCncl; SptEdSchPpr; 4-H; Bsktbl; Ftbl; Trk; Purdue Univ; Meteorology.

YAGOW, Maxine A; North Sargent HS; Milnor, ND; 6/15 PresJrCls; ChrhWkr; HonRl; LbryAde; EdSchPpr; Pres4-H; TreasFHA; SecPpCl; LetterBsktbl; 4-HAwd; North Dakota St Univ; Home Economics.

YAGYU, Sachi; Fridley Senior HS; Fridley, MN; SecFrshCls; CncrtBnd; HonRl; NHS; StuCncl;.

YAHNKE, Rita R; Plainfield HS; Plainfield, IL; 44/300 SecFrshCls; HonRl; HospAde; NHS; OffAde; Quill&Scroll; SecStuCncl; StuGov; TchrAde; RptrYrbk; FNA; SpnCl; PpCl; Wrstlng; College; Nursing.

YAHR, Kathryn; Muskego HS; Muskego, WI; 19/324 Chr; Chrs; ChrhWkr; HonRl; Mdrgl; NHS; SchAde; SchMus; Casper College;.

YAKAS, Ann M; Plymouth HS; Plymouth, IN; HonRl; Yrbk; IMSpt; Univ S Bend; Criminal Jstce.

YAKEL, Randy R; Klemme Community HS; Klemme, IA; 12/32 ChrhWkr; HonRl; StuCncl; YthFlsp; FFA; SpnCl; SciCl; Bsbl; Trk; Des Moines Area Cmm Clg; Med Tech.

YAKEL, Terri L; Scottsbluff Sr HS; Scottsbluff, NE; 13/325 Band; ChrhWkr; CmntyWkr; HonRl; Mdrgl; NHS; SchMus; TreasYthFlsp; PpCl; Chrldr; IMSpt; 4-HAwd; University; Social Work.

YAKIMOW, Elaine; Good Counsel Hs; Chicago, IL; HonRl; JA; SchPl; StuCncl; RptrSchPpr; FNA; SpnCl; PpCl; Chrldr; GAA; College; Nursing.

YAMAGUCHI, Julie; Francis W Parker HS; Chicago, IL; SecSophCls; SecJrCls; SecSrCls; Chr; Chrs; Mdrgl; NatlMeritCmnd; SchMus; SchPl; StuGov; Yale Univ; Biology.

YAMAMOTO, Cynthia; Minatare HS; Minatare, NE; 1/32 TrsSrCls; Band; HonRl; Yrbk; PpCl; BauchLmbAwd; EldAwd; Univ Of Nebraska; Pre Medical Technology.

YAMASHITA, Marcia S; Irving Crown HS; Algonquin, IL; Band; ChrhWkr; CncrtBnd; MrchBnd; Orch; PepBnd; StuCncl; YthFlsp; SpnCl; College.

YAMMINE, Cynthia J; Casey Senior HS; Casey, IL; 13/94 Chr; Chrs; ChrhWkr; HonRl; OffAde; SchMus; RptrYrbk; FrCl; PpCl; PPFtbl; University; Economics.

YANA, Jim; Sheldon HS; Sheldon, IL; VPJrCls; HonRl; SchPl; Yrbk; 4-H; PpCl; Bsbl; CchngActv; Junior Coll; Farming.

YANCEY, Alan J; Attica HS; Attica, KS; 2/16 PresFrshCls; PresSophCls; SecJrCls; HonRl; JA; JrNHS; NHS; SpnCl; Bsbl; Bsktbl; Clge; Forestry.

YANCEY, Antronette K; Washington HS; Kansas City, KS; 1/564 ChrhWkr; CmntyWkr; HonRl; NHS; NatlMeritCmnd; RptrYrbk; GerCl; SpnCl; CaptBsktbl; GAA; IMSpt; Northwestern Univ; Medicine.

YANCEY, Robert B; Buckley Loda HS; Buckley, IL; 8/41 PresSrCls; HonRl; NHS; StuCncl; RptrSchPpr; SpnCl; MthCl; PpCl; Bsktbl; Glf; Parkland Jr College; Mechanics.

YANCEY, Stephanie D; Immaculata HS; Chicago, IL; 12/201 HonRl; HospAde; NHS; NatlMeritSF; NatlThespSoc; SchMus; SchPl; FrCl; PpCl; Illinois State Univ; Research.

YANDA, Diane M; Merrill HS; Merrill, WI; 8/360 Chrl; ChrhWkr; HonRl; NatlMeritCmnd; SctActv; GerCl; Bsbl; Trk; PresAwd; U W Eau Claire; Vet.

YANDA, Randy; Marquette Comm HS; Maquoketa, IA; ALBoysSt; Band; Chrl; Chrs; NHS; Bsbl; Bsktbl; Ftbl; Iowa Univ; Midicine.

YANDELL, Dee A; South Pemiscot HS; Steele, MO; 9/48 Band; CmntyWkr; LbryAde; NHS; SchPl; SctActv; RptrYrbk; FHA; PpCl; PPFtbl; Coll; Inhalation Therapist.

YANDURA, Debra L; Joliet East HS; Joliet, IL; HonRl; SchMus; StuCncl; StuGov; RptrYrbk; FrCl; Chrldr; IMSpt; Western Il U; Med Tech.

YANISH, Jeanine M; Oriska HS; Oriska, ND; 2/41 HonRl; SchPl; SchPpr; Col;d Art.

YANKALA, Donna J; East Troy HS; East Troy, WI; Chr; HonRl; Mdrgl; FTA; FrCl; PpCl; University Of Wisconsin; Elem Education.

YANKE, Debbie R; St Bede Acad; Peru, IL; HonRl; Trk; Chrldr; GAA; College; Medicine.

YANKOVIC, Mary C; Notre Dame HS; Chicago, IL; 2/302 HonRl; HospAde; NHS; University Of Illinois; Nursing.

YANKOWIAK, Thomas W; Bishop Dwenger HS; Fort Wayne, IN; PolWkr; StuCncl; StuGov; Purdue Univ; Computer Science.

YANKOWIAK, William; Bishop Dwenger HS; Fort Wayne, IN; 8/245 Aud/Vis; ChrhWkr; HonRl; JA; SchMus; StuGov; Yrbk; SchPpr; GerCl; JAAwd; College; Engineering.

YANSKA, Randy; Kingsley Area HS; Buckley, MI; ChrhWkr; CmntyWkr; HonRl; 4-H; Coll; Prof.

YANSKE, Marsha R; Kickapoo HS; Yuba, WI; 5/53 TrsSrCls; ChrhWkr; HonRl; MrchBnd; SchPl; YthFlsp; Yrbk; FHA; AmLegAwd; BttyCrckrAwd; Univ Of Wi; Medical Technology.

YANT, Jennifer; Warsaw Community HS; Claypool, IN; 19/423 ChrhWkr; SchPl; YthFlsp; GAA; PresAwd; Business; Vocation.

YANTORNI, James J; Norway HS; Norway, MI; 7/101 VPJrCls; ChrhWkr; CmntyWkr; HonRl; JrNHS; NHS; NatlMeritCmnd; LetterBsktbl; LetterFtbl; LetterGlf; Mi State Univ; Veterinary.

YANTZ, Lori L; Fairbury HS; Fairbury, NE; 54/148 MrchBnd; TchrAde; Twrl; FBLA; IMSpt; College; Vocation.

YANUCK, Kathryn A; Central HS; St Joseph, MO; TrsFrshCls; TrsSophCls; HonRl; NHS; OffAde; StuCncl; StuGov; SchPpr; SpnCl; Chrldr; College; Journalism.

YAPLE, Edward G; Gull Lake HS; Augusta, MI; HonRl; JA; TchrAde; RptrYrbk; FrCl; Ftbl; JAAwd; Georgetown Univ; Languages.

YAPP, Robert J; Redford Union HS; Detroit, MI; PresSrCls; CtyCnl; CmntyWkr; HonRl; NHS; ROTC; StuCncl; UNYO; LetterBsbl; LetterFtbl; LetterWrstlng; College.

YARBER, Kathleen; Freeburg Comm HS; Smithton, IL; HonRl; Chrldr; College; Nursing.

YARBER, Linda K; Jeffersonville HS; Jeffersonville, IN; Aud/Vis; JrNHS; OffAde; GerCl; PpCl; Trk; GAA; IMSpt; Indiana University; Psychology.

YARBORO, Kimball F; Smith Cotton HS; Sedalia, MO; 33/358 HonRl; SctActv; StuCncl; FrCl; Socr; U Of Missouri; Engineering.

YARBROUGH, Kathryn A; Lincoln Way HS; Mokena, IL; 64/498 Band; CncrtBnd; HonRl; MrchBnd; NHS; College; English.

YARBROUGH, Lee M; Champaign Central HS; Champaign, IL; 1/450 ChrhWkr; HonRl; JrNHS; NHS; PolWkr; RptrSchPpr; LetterSwmmng; Univ Ol Il; Accountancy.

YARBROUGH, Robin L; Central Of Burden HS; Atlanta, KS; SecJrCls; VPSrCls; Chrs; ChrhWkr; HonRl; OffAde; SchPl; StuCncl; TchrAde; Yrbk; 4-H; Chrldr; PPFtbl; College.

YARDLEY, Wayne L; Golden City HS; Golden, MO; ChrhWkr; SctActv; College; Electrician.

YARGER, David P; Morgan Co R Ii HS; Versailles, MO; 1/75 ALBoysSt; VPBand; MrchBnd; VPNHS; PepBnd; SchPl; YthFlsp; Bsktbl; Ftbl; LionAwd; Univ Of Missouri, Columbia; Engineering.

YARGER, Nyla D; Flat Rock HS; Rockwood, MI; Chr; HonRl; OffAde; RptrYrbk; PpCl; SciCl; College; English.

YARGUS, Mina J; Hannibal Sr HS; Hannibal, MO; ChrhWkr; HonRl; Missouri Univ.

YARIAN, Luther W; Metropolis HS; Metropolis, IL; 8/158 Chr; Chrs; HonRl; NHS; YthFlsp; KeyCl; GerCl; MthCl; SciCl; Univ Of Ill; Mathematics.

YARKE, Marlene A; Sauk Centre HS; Sauk Centre, MN; Band; Chr; CncrtBnd; HonRl; PepBnd; SchPl; StuCncl; Twrl; SchPpr; Chrldr; College; Math.

YARMOSKI, Sandra A; Nazareth Academy; Chicago, IL; 14/167 HonRl; JrNHS; NHS; SchMus; StuCncl; EdYrBk; Yrbk; SpnCl; Univ Of Denver; Biology.

YARNELL, Tamara; Lucas HS; Lucas, KS; PresSophCls; Band; Chrs; HonRl; PepBnd; SchPl; PpCl; Trk; 4-HAwd; LionAwd; Accountant.

YAROCH, Pamela A; John Hersey HS; Mount Prospect, IL; HonRl; JrNHS; NHS; StuCncl; SptEdYrbk; PpCl; Chrldr; Millikin Univ; Physical Therapy.

YARTZ, Kenneth R; Northeast HS; Arma, KS; ChrhWkr; JCC; NHS; Quill&Scroll; StuGov; Yrbk; SptEdSchPpr; Bsbl; Bsktbl; Ftbl; Kscp Voc School; Electronics.

YASECKO, Susan P; Amos Alonzo Stagg HS; Palos Hills, IL; Band; HonRl; Quill&Scroll; SchPpr; Western Illinois University; Journalist.

YATES, Barbara J; Rich Central HS; Park Forest, IL; 10/400 SecAFS; Chr; NatlFornLg; NHS; Orch; StuCncl; VPSpnCl; MthCl; PresSciCl; Northwestern Univ; Biology.

YATES, Debby B; East Union HS; Thayer, IA; 2/51 Chrs; HonRl; LbryAde; SchMus; Des Moines Area Coll; Lawyer.

YATES, Pamela K; Auburn HS; Peru, NE; 8/86 HonRl; NHS; SpnCl; VPPpCl; LetterBsktbl; GAA; KiwanAwd; College; Professional.

YATES, Thomas D; Holstein Comm HS; Holstein, IA; ALBoysSt; Chr; HonRl; NHS; StuCncl; Bsktbl; LetterFtbl; Swmmng; Trk; GodCntryAwd; Univ; Law.

YAUSSI, Kevin E; Marysville HS; Marysville, KS; 26#29#31 CncrtBnd; HonRl; MrchBnd; StuCncl; Univ; Business Math.

YBARRA, Bernadette; Chase County HS; Cottonwood Falls, KS; Chrs; HonRl; StuCncl; Teen; SpnCl; PpCl; Vocational School; Commercial Art.

YBARRA, Cynthia A; Elmhurst HS; Fort Wayne, IN; ChrhWkr; HonRl; JA; FNA; SpnCl; Bsbl; Bsktbl; Ftbl; Tennis; LetterGAA; IMSpt; PPFtbl; Nursing School; Nurse.

YEADON, Timothy S; Rock HS; Rock, MI; Band; ChrhWkr; CncrtBnd; MrchBnd; NatlFornLg; SchPl; YthFlsp; RptrYrbk; RptrSchPpr; Bsktbl; College; Major Study.

YEAGER, Cheryl L; John F Kennedy HS; Bloomington, MN; Band; CmntyWkr; HonRl; LbryAde; OffAde; SchAde; StuCncl; Teen; CchngActv; Business School; Professional.

YEAGER, Joyce L; Monroe HS; Monroe, MI; 24/523 HonRl; JA; NHS; TchrAde; FNA; KeyCl; LatCl; JAAwd; Michigan State Univ; Vet.

YEAGER, Susan K; Marquette HS; Bellevue, IA; Chrs; HonRl; SchMus; SchPl; StuCncl; SpnCl; PpCl; LetterGlf; Chrldr; IMSpt; Trade School; Veterinarian Asst.

YEAGER, Terry; Washington HS; Sioux Falls, SD; HonRl; NHS; Iowa State University.

YEARGANS, Randy D; Lincoln HS; Kansas City, MO; 5/230 ALBoysSt; HonRl; JrNHS; NHS; NatlMeritSF; PresSciCl; Coll; Bio Chemical Res.

YEAROUT, Kim M; South Haven HS; South Haven, KS; PresSrCls; NHS; Yrbk; CaptBsktbl; LetterTrk; Chrldr; DARAwd; College; Science.

YEATES, Connie E; Raytown HS; Kansas City, MO; 10/600 ChrhWkr; HonRl; JrNHS; NHS; NatlMeritSF; OffAde; RptrSchPpr; SpnCl;.

YEAZEL, Sharon; Rockwell City HS; Rockwell City, IA; 11/72 VPFrshCls; SecSophCls; Band; CncrtBnd; DrmMjrt; HonRl; MrchBnd; PepBnd; FHA; Bsktbl; Military Career.

YECK, Susan D; Woodruff HS; Peoria, IL; 22/265 SecFrshCls; SecSophCls; VPSrCls; AFS; Band; CncrtBnd; HonRl; NHS; StuCncl; RptrSchPpr; SpnCl; Univ Of Illinois; Social Work.

YEE, Bowman A; Jared W Finney HS; Detroit, MI; 1/175 TrsSrCls; PresLbryAde; TreasNHS; PresStuCncl; FrCl; Wayne State U; Elect Engr.

YEE, Harvey G; St Charles HS; St Charles, IL; 36/450 AFS; Univ Of Illinois; Medicine.

YEE, Jim; Southfield Lathrup HS; Soughfield, MI; 250/683 TchrAde; Univ Of Mich, Engr.

YEGERLEHNER, Debra A; Clay City HS; Clay City, IN; Chr; ChrhWkr; CncrtBnd; HonRl; MrchBnd; NHS; OffAde; SecYthFlsp; 4-H; 4-HAwd; Indiana State U; Business Ed.

YEHL, Janice M; Garber HS; Essexville, MI; 7/180 PresSrCls; HonRl; OffAde; StuCncl; TchrAde; Yrbk; Ftbl; Northwood Institute; Retailing Merchandisin.

YEHLING, Gregory A; Carbondale Community HS; Carbondale, IL; 99/323 Aud/Vis; SctActv; YthFlsp; SciCl; U Of Il; Electronic Engineering.

YEITER, Cheryl A; Huntington North HS; Huntington, IN; ChrhWkr; CmntyWkr; NHS; PpCl; Business School; Business.

YELICK, Steven E; Washington HS; Sioux Falls, SD; ALBoysSt; Band; CncrtBnd; HonRl; MrchBnd; NHS; NatlMeritSF; Orch; StuCncl; MthCl;.

YELK, Rita; Sun Prairie Senior HS; Sun Prairie, WI; 16/325 Chr; Chrs; HonRl; HospAde; NHS; SctActv; YthFlsp; FBLA; MthCl; GAA; Madison Area Tech Coll; Data Processing.

YELKEN, Kevin S; Franklin Public HS; Franklin, NE; ALBoysSt; ChrhWkr; DrmMjrt; MrchBnd; SchPl; VPStuCncl; PpCl; Bsbl; LetterBsktbl; LetterFtbl; LetterTrk; Chrldr; Business School; Computer Science.

YELLOW HAIR, Thomas D; Hemingford Public HS; Hemingford, NE; HonRl; NHS; StuCncl; TchrAde; RptrSchPpr; SchPpr; LetterBsktbl; Ftbl; LetterTrk; University; Coach Or Pe Teacher.

YELLOW ROBE, Luther P; Stevens HS; Rapid City, SD; LetterBsktbl; LetterTrk; Black Hills State Clg; Pre Law.

YELM, Kenneth E; Galva HS; Galva, IL; 2/75 PresJrCls; PresSrCls; ALBoysSt; HonRl; NHS; NatlMeritCmnd; NatlThespSoc; RptrYrbk; LetterBsktbl; LetterFtbl; Trk; Western Illinois Univ; Chemistry.

YEN, Robert L; University HS; Urbana, IL; 9/42 Univ Of Illinois; Elec Engineer.

YENCHESKY, Faye E; Marion HS; Marion, WI; 24/84 CmntyWkr; LbryAde; OffAde; PolWkr; RedCrAde; SchAde; TchrAde; Gateway Tech Inst; General Sales Hotel/mote.

YENGER, James; Red Bird HS; Stratford, IA; 3/25 VPSrCls; Band; Chrs; HonRl; NatlFornLg; NHS; YthFlsp; Yrbk; RptrSchPpr; 4-H; College; Professional.

YENGLIN, Larry D; Davison Sr HS; Davison, MI; 63/460 HonRl; NatlThespSoc; SchPl; Michigan St Univ; Forestry.

YENSER, Vicki; Watertown Sr HS; Watertown, WI; 17/312 ChrhWkr; HonRl; JA; NHS; SchAde; TchrAde; YthFlsp; Bsbl; Trk; GAA; Carthage Coll; Math Major.

YEOMAN, Shirley M; Bishop Mcnamara HS; St Anne, IL; 11/161 SecSrCls; HonRl; NHS; StuCncl; StuGov; GAA; Ill State Univ; Elem Ed.

YEPSEN, Raymond S; La Salle Peru Twp HS; Utica, IL; 64/645 VPCmntyWkr; HonRl; JrNHS; VPSctActv; StuCncl; RptrSchPpr; SchPpr; VPFDA; SciCl; LetterFtbl; Wrstlng; Univ Of Illinois; Physician.

YERBY, Tobey L; Morton HS; Morton, IL; 15/350 VPFrshCls; Chrs; HonRl; NHS; GAA; College; Biological Sciences Or Medical Tec.

YERGLER, Rodney E; Watseka Community HS; Watseka, IL; 5/125 ChrhWkr; CmntyWkr; HonRl; JrNHS; NHS; SctActv; StuCncl; Yrbk; SpnCl; LetterBsktbl; CaptFtbl; Coll; Professional.

YERINGTON, Jeffrey A; West HS; Blue Grass, IA; 50/655 ALBoysSt; HonRl; SctActv; SpnCl; IMSpt; Iowa State University.

YERKES, Kathy; Fountain Central Hs; Kingman, IN; HonRl; TchrAde; SciCl; CaptBsbl; CaptBsktbl; LetterGlf; Trk; GAA; Purdue U;professional.

YESKEY, David J; Bishop Gallagher HS; Detroit, MI; 80/310 TrsFrshCls; HonRl; Bsbl; IMSpt; Wayne St U; Busi Management.

YESSAK, Keban M; Grand Rapids Senior HS; Grand Rapids, MN; 112/377 Band; ChrhWkr; PepBnd; YthFlsp; 4-H; CaptTennis; LetterWrstlng; IMSpt; College; Professional.

YI, Theodore I; Niles Twp West HS; Morton Grove, IL; 16/666 HonRl; NHS; NatlMeritCmnd; Univ Of Illinois; Medicine.

YING, Rodney; Plymouth Salem HS; Plymouth, MI; HonRl; IMSpt; Mich St Univ; Medicine.

YINGER, Paul R; Hillsdale HS; Hillsdale, MI; 40/200 HstFrshCls; HstSophCls; PresJrCls; PresSrCls; ALBoysSt; Chr; ChrhWkr; CmntyWkr; HonRl; HospAde; NHS; RedCrAde; Ftbl; CaptSwmmng; GodCntryAwd; Northern Michigan University; Medicine.

YKEMA, Sharon; Muskegon Christian HS; Grand Haven, MI; /135 ChrhWkr; HonRl; LbryAde; SchPl; StuCncl; LetterBsktbl; IMSpt; Davenport Coll Of Bus;sec.

YLINEN, Susie M; St Peter HS; St Peter, MN; HonRl; NatlFornLg; NHS; 4-H; LatCl; AmLegAwd; 4-HAwd; VFWAwd; College; Anthropology.

YLITALO, Cindy L; Hancock Central HS; Hancock, MI; 10/90 Chr; CncrtBnd; HonRl; MrchBnd; OffAde; PepBnd; SchMus; SchPl; FTA; College.

YOAS, Karl M; Airport HS; Newport, MI; 13/224 PresSrCls; Band; CncrtBnd; HonRl; MrchBnd; NHS; Orch; PepBnd; StuGov; IMSpt; U Of Mi; Electronics Engr.

YOAS, Krystal A; Jefferson HS; Monroe, MI; 5/152 Band; CncrtBnd; HonRl; JA; MrchBnd; TreasNHS; PepBnd; LetterTrk; CchngActv; PresGAA; Marquette Univ; Law Enforcement.

YOCH, Diane P; West Bend Community HS; West Bend, IA; 1/48 Band; Chr; CncrtBnd; HonRl; MrchBnd; SchPl; RptrYrbk; RptrSchPpr; 4-H; Chrldr; Mt Mercy College; Med Tech.

YOCHUM, Jennifer J; Peoria Manual HS; Peoria, IL; 7/329 TrsSrCls; Chrs; HonRl; JA; StuCncl; Western Ill Univ; Sociology.

YOCIUS, Dominick P; St Laurence HS; Chicago, IL; 29/380 HonRl; SchPl; Yrbk; SchPpr; IMSpt; College; Accounting.

YOCKEY, Danial D; Gibbon HS; Gibbon, NE; HonRl; SctActv; SpnCl; Bsktbl; Glf; College; Major Study.

YOCKEY, Rosemary; Laville HS; Bremen, IN; 25/125 ChrhWkr; CmntyWkr; HonRl; NHS; YthFlsp; 4-H; GAA; Business School.

YOCOM, Joel A; Spring Hill HS; Spring Hill, KS; 1/60 Chr; HonRl; JA; Mdrgl; SchMus; TchrAde; LetterBsktbl; University; Professional.

YODE, Juliana; Iowa Mennonite HS; Kalona, IA; SecSophCls; HonRl; NHS; SchPl; StuCncl; PpCl; Chrldr; GAA; Hesston College; Child Care.

YODER, Brenda L; Burrton HS; Burrton, KS; SecSrCls; ChrhWkr; CncrtBnd; HonRl; MrchBnd; NHS; PepBnd; SchPl; StuCncl; TchrAde; Bus Sch; Legal Sec.

YODER, Darrell E; Iowa Mennonite HS; Kalona, IA; PresJrCls; Chr; HonRl; NHS; StuCncl; SptEdSchPpr; Bsktbl; Trk; Coll; Pro.

YODER, Dru L; Northridge HS; Middlebury, IN; Band; ChrhWkr; CncrtBnd; HonRl; MrchBnd; PepBnd; SctActv; 4-H; FHA; PpCl; Bsktbl; Trk; College; Physical Educ.

YODER, Heidi B; Wolford Public HS; Wolford, ND; SecFrshCls; TrsJrCls; Band; Chr; Chrs; ChrhWkr; CncrtBnd; HonRl; OffAde; PepBnd; Bsktbl; Trk; College.

YODER, Jack S; Wolford HS; Wolford, ND; 2/7 TrsJrCls; PresBand; Chr; CncrtBnd; HonRl; PepBnd; SchPl; StuCncl; Yrbk; SptEdSchPpr; PresSophCls; HonRl; StuCncl; VPSophCls; Jamestown Coll.

YODER, Janell D; Northridge HS; Bristol, IN; VPBand; ChrhWkr; CncrtBnd; HonRl; MrchBnd; PepBnd; YthFlsp; FHA; PpCl; LetterGAA; College; Architecture.

YODER, Kimberly D; Penn HS; Mishawaka, IN; 68/470 Band; Chr; Chrs; ChrhWkr; MrchBnd; NHS; OffAde; PepBnd; SchPl; TchrAde; Ball St U; Interior Design.

YODER, Kimberly L; Falls City HS; Falls City, NE; Band; Chrs; CtyCnl; CaptDrlTm; MrchBnd; PepBnd; SchMus; TchrAde; Yrbk; PpCl; University; Medical Field.

YODER, Lloyd R; Northridge HS; Middlebury, IN; HonRl; PpCl; Trade Sch; Carpenter.

YODER, Raymond E; Millington HS; Vassar, MI; 10/175 ALBoysSt; HonRl; NHS; TchrAde; Bsbl; CchngActv; Col; Chemistry Research.

YODER, Regina K; Bethany Christian HS; Shipshewana, IN; HonRl; Yrbk; Trk; GAA;.

YODER, Roger A; Westview HS; Shipshewana, IN; PresFrshCls; VPSophCls; PresJrCls; PresSrCls; Chr; Chrs; ChrhWkr; CmntyWkr; HonRl; NHS; YthFlsp; Bsbl; Bsktbl; CchngActv;.

YODER, Sherry E; Northridge HS; Goshen, IN; 4/116 Chr; HonRl; HospAde; 4-H; FHA; SpnCl;.

YOGT, Richard L; Tri County HS; Plymouth, NE; Chrs; HonRl; SchPl; RptrYrbk; Yrbk; RptrSchPpr; SchPpr; LetterGlf; College; Journalism.

YOHE, Christopher M; Harrisonville HS; Harrisonville, MO; Band; Longview Comm College; Pharmacist.

YOHNKE, Mary; Wall Lake Community HS; Wall Lake, IA; 7/31 Chrs; DrlTm; HonRl; SchPl; RptrYrbk; RptrSchPpr; EdSchPpr; FrCl; Bsktbl; Trk; Ia Central College; Nurse.

YOHO, Kathy J; Eastern HS; Solsberry, IN; VPJrCls; Band; ChrhWkr; DrlTm; HonRl; NHS; Quill&Scroll; SchMus; Yrbk; GAA; College; Professional.

YOKLEY, Christine A; Bronaugh HS; Moundville, MO; Band; Chr; MrchBnd; TreasNatlThespSoc; SchPl; Yrbk; SchPpr; FHA; LetterTrk; CaptChrldr; College; Dental Hygienist.

YOKLEY, Sharon; Lindblom HS; Chicago, IL; 30/695 ChrhWkr; HonRl; VPNHS; Quill&Scroll; RptrYrbk; FshEdSchPpr; SecLatCl; MthCl; SciCl; PresGAA; Nw ; Md Or Sur.

YOKOM, Sharon R; Mapleton HS; Mapleton, ND; 2/10 PresFrshCls; ALAGirlsSt; HonRl; SchPl; YthFlsp; RptrYrbk; 4-H; PpCl; LetterTrk; CaptChrldr; BttyCrckrAwd; 4-HAwd; Concordia College; Elementary Educ.

YOMAN, Bonnie J; Summerfield HS; Petersburg, MI; 2/65 CncrtBnd; HonRl; LbryAde; MrchBnd; NHS; SchPl; SctActv; EdSchPpr; SchPpr; CaptBsbl; E M U; Professional.

YOMAN, Jerome; Grand Rapids HS; Grand Rapids, MN; 15/359 Chr; HonRl; Mdrgl; NatlFornLg; SchMus; SchPl; IMSpt; College; Psychology.

YONASH, Linda M; Riverdale Sr HS; Boscobel, WI; 7/79 Band; Chrs; HonRl; Mdrgl; SecNHS; EdYrBk; SciCl; LetterBsktbl; VPGAA; Univ Of Wisconsin; Medical Tech.

YONKE, Marcella L; Almond Public HS; Almond, WI; VPJrCls; Band; Chr; Chrs; HonRl; SchAde; TchrAde; YthFlsp; 4-H; FHA; Accounting.

YONKE, Martha L; Milford Township HS; Milford, IL; 1/70 CncrtBnd; HonRl; NHS; NatlMeritCmnd; StuCncl; Yrbk; MthCl; VPSciCl; Bsktbl; LetterTrk; GAA; University Of Illinois; Chemical Engineer.

YONKER, Jeffrey T; St Willibrord HS; Chicago, IL; 16/72 VPSrCls; HonRl; VPNHS; SecStuCncl; RptrSchPpr; SpnCl; SecMthCl; SciCl; Univ Of Ill; Engineering.

YONTS, James J; Rushford Public HS; Rushford, MN; ChrhWkr; CmntyWkr; HonRl; NHS; YthFnd; 4-H; Bsktbl; LetterTrk; AmLegAwd; LionAwd; CitAwd; Trade Sch; Machinist.

YONTZ, Cynthia J; Tipton HS; Tipton, MO; Chrs; HonRl; SchMus; SchPl; TreasFHA; FrCl; TreasPpCl; Jefferson Pub Sch; Nursing.

YOON, Joo Hong; Glenbrook South HS; Glenview, IL; 8/581 Chr; HonRl; NHS; RptrSchPpr; KeyCl; College; Physics.

YOOS, Norma J; Bronaugh R 7 HS; Arcadia, KS; 3/26 HstSrCls; HonRl; LbryAde; NHS; TreasNatlThespSoc; SchPl; 4-H; PpCl; BttyCrckrAwd; 4-HAwd; Sw Missouri State U; Biology.

YOPST, Thomas B; Dekalb HS; Dekalb, IL; 29/350 HonRl; StuCncl; Bsbl; College; Business Adm.

YORDING, Christopher; Routt HS; Jacksonville, IL; HonRl; SchPl; StuCncl; RptrSchPpr; SpnCl; MthCl; SciCl; Bsbl; Bsktbl; Ftbl; Trk; Univ Of Missouri; Journalism.

YORDY, Michael E; Morton HS; Morton, IL; 8/345 Chr; ChrhWkr; HonRl; JrNHS; YthFlsp; Pres4-H; PresFFA; KeyCl; LetterFtbl; DanFAwd; 4-HAwd; CitAwd; Univ Of Il; Agriculture.

YORK, Anita A; Forest Lake HS; Forest Lake, MN; 2/460 Band; CncrtBnd; HonRl; MrchBnd; PepBnd; GAA; College; Horsemanship.

YORK, Cynthia; Murphysboro HS; Murphysboro, IL; Band; Chr; Chrl; ChrhWkr; HonRl; PepBnd; YthFlsp; 4-H; SpnCl; PPFtbl; Siu; Pharmacy.

YORK, Kenneth L; Marion HS; Marion, IA; SecChrhWkr; CncrtBnd; HonRl; MrchBnd; ModUN; NHS; Orch; PepBnd; StuCncl; College; Math.

YORK, Patricia L; Elmhurst HS; Ft Wayne, IN; 28/482 Chr; Chrl; Chrs; ChrhWkr; HonRl; 4-H; IMSpt; PPFtbl; 4-HAwd; College; Veterinary Study.

YORK, Patrick B; Shawneetown HS; Shawneetown, IL; 1/35 PresFrshCls; Band; HonRl; StuCncl; Jr College; Veterinarian.

YORK, Ronnie W; Enfield HS; Enfield, IL; 8/33 SecFrshCls; TrsSophCls; TrsSrCls; ChrhWkr; CmntyWkr; HonRl; StuCncl; FFA; SpnCl; Rendlake; Agriculture.

YORK, Sandra L; Neodesha HS; Meodesha, KS; VPFrshCls; VPSophCls; SecJrCls; SecSrCls; Band; ChrhWkr; HonRl; MrchBnd; PepBnd; SctActv; Teen; FHA; PpCl; Chrldr; PPFtbl; College; Vocation.

YORK, Shirley; Stanton Co HS; Johnson, KS; 4/48 Chr; ChrhWkr; CncrtBnd; HonRl; NHS; OffAde; SchPl; Dodge City Juco; Nrsng.

YORK, Steven W; Mt Zion HS; Decatur, IL; 20/190 Band; HonRl; NHS; FrCl; LetterBsbl; LetterBsktbl; LetterTrk; College; Journalism.

YORK, William M; Grosse Ile HS; Grosse Ile, MI; Aud/Vis; Band; Chr; Chrl; CncrtBnd; DrmBgl; Mdrgl; MrchBnd; NatlMeritSF; NatlThespSoc; SchMus; SchPl; Yrbk; SchPpr; University.

YOSAN, Christine; Thornridge HS; Dolton, IL; 57/680 HonRl; JrNHS; NHS; OffAde; StuCncl; StuGov; TchrAde; MthCl; Northwestern Univ; Math.

YOST, Michael E; Beardstown Senior HS; Beardstown, IL; 13/126 Aud/Vis; HonRl; JrNHS; NHS; SchMus; Bsbl; Bsktbl; Ftbl; Trk; IMSpt; University; Commercial Art.

YOST, Sally J; Kalkaska HS; Kaikaska, MI; Chr; HonRl; HospAde; NHS; SchPl; TchrAde; GAA; College; Nursing.

YOST, Stephen W; Savannah HS; St Joseph, MO; PresJrCls; ALBoysSt; HonRl; NHS; PolWkr; StuCncl; VPSpnCl; Trk; CaptWrstlng; LionAwd; College; Professional.

YOST, Steven K; Mahnomen HS; Mahnomen, MN; HonRl; TchrAde; LetterBsbl; LetterBsktbl; CaptGlf; Alexandria Tech; Law Enforcement.

YOTKO, Kathleen S; Waukegan East HS; Waukegan, IL; TrsFrshCls; TrsSophCls; AFS; HonRl; JrNHS; NHS; OffAde; StuCncl; LetterSwmmng; Chrldr; College; Science.

YOTTY, Douglas A; Mid Prairie HS; Kalona, IA; 4/74 TrsJrCls; ALBoysSt; HonRl; NHS; StuCncl; FrCl; LetterBsktbl; LetterFtbl; LetterTrk; DanFAwd; Iowa St Univ; Math.

YOUDES, Jeffrey L; High School; Jackson, MI; HonRl; NHS; GerCl; LetterFtbl; Michigan State Univ; Accounting.

YOUELL, Mary L; Manson HS; Manson, IA; 6/83 Band; Chr; CncrtBnd; HonRl; MrchBnd; NHS; NatlMeritCmnd; PepBnd; SchMus; SchPl; Wheaton College; Liberal Arts.

YOUKEY, Paul A; Luther South HS; Chicago, IL; 9/197 ChrhWkr; HonRl; LbryAde; NHS; SchAde; LetterCchngActv; Illinois Inst Tech; Computer Sys Analyst.

YOUMANS, Michael J; Waynesville HS; Waynesville, MO; Aud/Vis; CAP; ModUN; TreasNatlFornLg; TreasNatlThespSoc; SchMus; SchPl; SctActv; Tennis; IMSpt; Military Service; Computers.

YOUMANS, Richard L; Douglas Mac Arthur HS; Saginaw, MI; Band; CncrtBnd; HonRl; MrchBnd; PepBnd; SchPl; SctActv; TchrAde; LetterFtbl; Socr; U Of Mich; Cpa.

YOUNCE, Richard C; Waterford Township HS; Pontiac, MI; TreasBand; ChrhWkr; CncrtBnd; HonRl; MrchBnd; NHS; PepBnd; TchrAde; Tennis; DanFAwd; Univ; Engr.

YOUND, Cindy; Exeter Public HS; Exeter, NE; ALAGirlsSt; Chr; CncrtBnd; HonRl; MrchBnd; PepBnd; Teen; Yrbk; MthCl; PpCl; College; Nurse.

YOUND, Sandra L; Exeter Public HS; Exeter, NE; Band; CncrtBnd; HonRl; MrchBnd; PepBnd; RptrYrbk; PpCl; BttyCrckrAwd; Southeast Comm College; Veterinarian.

YOUNG, Alicia J; Sunset Hill HS; Kansas City, MO; VPJrCls; Chrs; CmntyWkr; Mdrgl; SchMus; PresYthFlsp; Yrbk; PpCl; SciCl; IMSpt; Clge; Biology.

YOUNG, Ann; Preble Hs; Green Bay, WI; 62/451 Chr; Chrs; CmntyWkr; HonRl; NHS; OffAde; StuCncl; RptrSchPpr; 4-H; Trk; U Of Wi; Elementary Education.

YOUNG, Annette L; Garner Hayfield Comm HS; Garner, IA; 2/68 CncrtBnd; HonRl; Mdrgl; MrchBnd; NHS; SctActv; StuCncl; Bsbl; Bsktbl; Trk; Mercy; X Ray Tech.

YOUNG, Bobbi S; Bedford No Lawrence HS; Heltonville, IN; 19/397 VPJrCls; CmntyWkr; HonRl; NHS; PolWkr; SctActv; Twrl; Indiana Univ; Biology.

YOUNG, Bruce D; Decatur Central HS; Indianapolis, IN; 1/336 PresFrshCls; PresJrCls; HonRl; PresNHS; PolWkr; StuCncl; LatCl; SciCl; Swmmng; AmLegAwd; GodCntryAwd; Univ; Law.

YOUNG, Bryan G; Salem Comm HS; Odin, IL; Band; MrchBnd; Kaskaskia College; Engineering.

YOUNG, Carla J; Wabash HS; Wabash, IN; 11/202 ChrhWkr; HonRl; NHS; OffAde; PolWkr; StuCncl; StuGov; YthFlsp; GerCl; PpCl; College.

YOUNG, Carol A; Eben HS; Chatham, MI; 3/35 LitMag; StuCncl; RptrSchPpr; 4-H; PpCl; LetterBsktbl; LetterTrk; LetterChrldr; HstSrCls; 4-HAwd; U Of Mi ;physical Threapy.

YOUNG, Cheryl; Winamac Comm HS; Winamac, IN; Chr; Chrs; DrlTm; HonRl; MrchBnd; PolWkr; FHA; PpCl; Univ; Teach History.

YOUNG, Cindy S; Blair HS; Blair, NE; 5/140 Band; CncrtBnd; HonRl; MrchBnd; PepBnd; FHA; FNA; FrCl; SciCl; Ne Methodist; Rn.

YOUNG, Clyde A; Mount Carmel HS; Chicago, IL; 56/203 Chr; HonRl; HospAde; NatlFornLg; NatlMeritCmnd; SchAde; SctActv; StuCncl; SciCl; College; Corporate Law.

YOUNG, Cynthia R; Central HS; Evansville, IN; 1/665 ChrhWkr; HonRl; StuCncl; PresYthFlsp; SecSpnCl; SciCl; GAA; PPFtbl; ChmbCommrsAwd; U Of Evansville; Pharmacy.

YOUNG, Dale J; Menasha HS; Appleton, WI; Technical Institute; Mechanical Design.

YOUNG, Daniel J; Stockbridge HS; Chilton, WI; Chr; HonRl; StuCncl; GerCl; Bsbl; Bsktbl; Ftbl; Trk; Clge; Pro.

YOUNG, David A; Shelbyville HS; Shelbyville, IL; Band; CncrtBnd; HonRl; MrchBnd; PepBnd; SchMus; SchPl; PpCl; Bsktbl; Ftbl; LetterGlf; St Francis Schl; Nursing.

YOUNG, Debra L; Dansville Agricultural Sch; Stockbridge, MI; 3/75 VPFrshCls; TrsSophCls; PresJrCls; PresSrCls; Chr; ChrhWkr; CmntyWkr; HonRl; NHS; 4-H; Michigan State Univ; Scientific Research.

YOUNG, Dorris K; Sandwich Comm; Sandwich, IL; VPSrCls; VPAFS; NHS; NatlThespSoc; StuCncl; SptEdYrbk; LatCl; LetterSocr; Trk; GAA; Coll.

YOUNG, Edward A; Lenox Community HS; Lenox, IA; 1/45 PresFrshCls; HonRl; NHS; ChrhWkr; SchPl; StuCncl; YthFlsp; Wrstlng; BauchLmbAwd; GovHonPrgAwd;.

YOUNG, Edward A; Lenox Comm HS; Lenox, IA; 1/45 PresFrshCls; Chr; ChrhWkr; HonRl; NHS; SchPl; StuCncl; YthFlsp; Ftbl; Wrstlng; BauchLmbAwd; Trade School; Vocation.

YOUNG, Elaine; Chesaning Union HS; Chesaning, MI; HonRl; NHS; TchrAde; EdYrBk; Michigan State Univ; Zoology.

YOUNG, Elizabeth M; Ladywood St Agnes HS; Indianapolis, IN; Chr; Chrs; ChrhWkr; CmntyWkr; Sacrstn; SchMus; SctActv; Sdlty; 4-H; SpnCl; CchngActv; IMSpt; College; Physical Therapy.

YOUNG, Elizabeth A; Prospect HS; Mt Prospect, IL; University Of Illinois; Art.

YOUNG, Eric A; Highland Park HS; Highland Park, IL; NatlMeritCmnd; Orch; PolWkr; SchPl; SctActv; StuGov; LetterSwmmng; Univ; Dealing In Securities.

YOUNG, Erma M; Pope County HS; Herod, IL; Aud/Vis; ChrhWkr; HonRl; FTA; MthCl; LetterBsktbl; CchngActv; GAA; S Illinois Univ; Psychology.

YOUNG, Gregory A; Medford HS; Medford, MN; HonRl; SchPl; 4-H; LetterBsbl; LetterBsktbl; LetterFtbl; LetterTrk; CchngActv; 4-HAwd; University; Professional.

YOUNG, Gwen L; South Iron HS; Annapolis, MO; VPSophCls; PresJrCls; HonRl; LbryAde; StuCncl; Yrbk; FHA; PpCl; Chrldr;.

YOUNG, Jacquelyn A; Republic HS; Republic, MO; HonRl; NHS; PpCl; Univ; Cpa.

YOUNG, Janet L; Whiting HS; Whiting, IN; Band; CmntyWkr; CncrtBnd; JA; MrchBnd; PepBnd; SchMus; Business School; Professional.

YOUNG, Joni; Hillsboro Hs; Irving, IL; SecCncrtBnd; SecMrchBnd; SecStuCncl; RptrSchPpr; TreasSpnCl; GAA; U Of Ill; General Studies.

YOUNG, Julie A; Wakonda Public HS; Wakonda, SD; Band; Chr; Chrs; CncrtBnd; HonRl; MrchBnd; PepBnd; TchrAde; FHA; PpCl; Bsbl; Chrldr; U Of Sd; Music.

YOUNG, Karla S; Carroll HS; Cutler, IN; Chrs; DrlTm; Twrl; RptrSchPpr; FHA; FrCl; GAA;.

YOUNG, Katherine; Josephinum HS; Chicago, IL; 34/98 Chr; ChrhWkr; CtyCnl; HonRl; HospAde; LbryAde; OffAde; StuCncl; StuGov; TchrAde; YthLg; SpnCl; Bsktbl; Lewis University; Nursing.

YOUNG, Kathleen A; Bishop Gallagher HS; Detroit, MI; 7/300 Band; HonRl; MrchBnd; NHS; SchPl; StuGov; Yrbk; FrCl; PPFtbl; Wayne State Univ; Foreign Languags.

YOUNG, Kathleen A; Duluth Central HS; Duluth, MN; 152/500 Aud/Vis; HonRl; HospAde; Orch; SchAde; TchrAde; LetterTrk; GAA; IMSpt;.

YOUNG, Kathy M; Heritage Christian HS; Indianapolis, IN; TrsSophCls; SecJrCls; Chr; HonRl; NHS; Pensacola Christian College; Nursing.

YOUNG, Kevin E; Glenwood HS; Pacific Jct, IA; HonRl; SctActv; LetterFtbl; LetterWrstlng; IMSpt; Trade; Professional.

YOUNG, Kevin E; Astoria HS; Astoria, IL; 10/48 TrsSrCls; Band; CncrtBnd; HonRl; LbryAde; MrchBnd; NHS; Orch; PepBnd; SchPl; SctActv; Southern Ill Univ; Zoology.

YOUNG, Kevin L; Roxana HS; Wood River, IL; HonRl; NHS; SctActv; So Il Univ; Geologist.

YOUNG, Kristine L; Huntington North HS; Huntington, IN; Chr; ChrhWkr; Quill&Scroll; SchMus; StuCncl; StuGov; RptrSchPpr; Huntington College; Journalism.

YOUNG, Laura; Southeast Polk HS; Altoona, IA; 22/218 Chr; HonRl; NHS; SchMus; StuCncl; UNYO; 4-H; Tennis; Chrldr; Ia St Univ;elem Educ.

YOUNG, Laurie; Lanark HS; Lanark, IL; 5/54 YthFlsp; SpnCl; Trk; GAA; IMSpt; University; Commercial Art.

YOUNG, Linda D; Northwestern R 1 HS; Mendon, MO; SecSophCls; Band; CncrtBnd; HonRl; MrchBnd; NHS; StuCncl; LetterBsktbl; GAA; CitAwd;.

YOUNG, Linda S; Carman HS; Flint, MI; Chr; HonRl; PPFtbl; College; Social Work.

YOUNG, Lonnie; Perry HS; Shaftsburg, MI; 6/123 Band; CncrtBnd; HonRl; MrchBnd; NHS; Bsktbl; Mi St Univ, Fisheries Biologist.

YOUNG, Marcy A; Normal Comm HS; Normal, IL; PresAFS; HonRl; HospAde; NHS; StuCncl; TchrAde; FNA; FrCl; MthCl; PpCl; Illinois State Univ; Nurse.

YOUNG, Margaret; Solomon Junea HS; Milwaukee, WI; DrmMjrt; MrchBnd; StuCncl; SchPpr; GerCl; Wi Univ Milwaukee; Bi Lingual Ed.

YOUNG, Mark D; St Johns Seminary; Kansas City, MO; Chr; ChrhWkr; OffAde; SchMus; SchPl; TchrAde; Yrbk; RptrSchPpr; Bsktbl; College; Public Relations.

YOUNG, Mark T; Decatur Community HS; Selden, KS; ALBoysSt; Chr; Chrl; Chrs; HonRl; NHS; SchMus; StuCncl; LetterFtbl; LetterTrk; LetterWrstlng; University.

YOUNG, Miriam R; Central HS; St Louis, MO; Band; CncrtBnd; HonRl; LbryAde; MrchBnd; NHS; PepBnd; SchPl; TchrAde; PpCl; Clge; Nurse.

YOUNG, Nancy P; Rock Island HS; Rock Island, IL; ChrhWkr; VPHospAde; SchAde; SctActv; TchrAde; RptrYrbk; 4-H; GerCl; SciCl; Ill St Univ; Jr High Educ.

YOUNG, Patricia; Midland HS; Midland, MI; 29/433 Chr; ChrhWkr; HonRl; Orch; SctActv; YthFlsp; Albion Coll; Chemistry.

YOUNG, Patty A; Plattsmouth HS; Plattsmouth, NE; TchrAde; TreasLetterBsktbl; LetterTrk; GAA; Army; Law Enforcement.

YOUNG, Perry; West HS; Kansas City, MO; HonRl; LetterBsktbl; LetterTrk; Coll.

YOUNG, Ralph V; Lanphier HS; Springfield, IL; Aud/Vis; CmntyWkr; NHS; OffAde; PresQuill&Scroll; SchPl; Yrbk; SchPpr; Bsbl; Ftbl; Bradley University; Radio Broadcasting.

YOUNG, Randall; Lincoln East HS; Lincoln, NE; 11/409 HonRl; MrchBnd; NHS; StuCncl; Ftbl; Univ Of Neb; Vet.

YOUNG, Regina L; Sidney HS; Sidney, NE; HonRl; JrNHS; OffAde; FHA; MthCl; PpCl; GAA; Univ Of Nebraska; Teaching.

YOUNG, Reginald R; William Chrisman HS; Independence, MO; PresFrshCls; Chr; ChrhWkr; CmntyWkr; HonRl; JrNHS; StuGov; Bsktbl; Ftbl; Trk; College; Accounting.

YOUNG, Renee E; Rich Central HS; Olympia Fields, IL; ChrhWkr; HonRl; 4-H; KeyCl; FrCl; Swmmng; 4-HAwd; Univ; Bus Admin.

YOUNG, Rick; Clear Lake HS; Clear Lake, IA; AFS; HonRl; SchMus; SchPl; SctActv; Morningside College; Engineering.

YOUNG, Rita A; Laura Speed Elliot HS; Boonville, MO; ChrhWkr; NHS; OffAde; SchPl; PpCl; IMSpt; University; Math.

YOUNG, Robert; Stratford HS; Auburndale, WI; HonRl; StuCncl; StuGov; FFA; Trk; Wisc Univ River Falls.

YOUNG, Robert C; Glenbrook So HS; Glenview, IL; 130/500 HonRl; Northland College; Natural Science.

YOUNG, Robert L; Otterville R Vi HS; Otterville, MO; 8/22 VPJrCls; Band; Chr; ChrhWkr; SctActv; StuCncl; Bsbl; CaptBsktbl; LetterTrk; College.

YOUNG, Roger; Almond Public HS; Almond, WI; VPSrCls; Aud/Vis; HonRl; NHS; Yrbk; SptEdSchPpr; Bsbl; Bsktbl; Ftbl; AmLegAwd; U W Of La Crosse; Physical Education.

YOUNG, Sarah J; Marion Adams HS; Sheridan, IN; SecJrCls; DrlTm; TchrAde; 4-H; FFA; FHA; SpnCl; PpCl; Chrldr; 4-HAwd; College; Elementary Ed.

YOUNG, Sharon A; Hinsdale So HS; Darien, IL; 38/426 SecFrshCls; VPSophCls; Band; ChrhWkr; HonRl; NHS; Orch; StuCncl; Chrldr; College; Elem Education.

YOUNG, Sharon K; Moundsview HS; St Paul, MN; JrNHS; NHS; NatlMeritSF;.

YOUNG, Sherri; Elcho HS; Pickerel, WI; 5/49 SecSrCls; Chrs; HonRl; NHS; OffAde; SchPl; EdYrBk; SpnCl; SciCl; College.

YOUNG, Sherry A; Grayville HS; Grayville, IL; PresJrCls; Band; Chrs; HonRl; Sec4-H; FHA; FrCl; TreasGAA; DanFAwd; 4-HAwd; Univ.

YOUNG, Susan; 500 N Fourth; Hayti, MO; 2/8 Band; Chr; ChrhWkr; HonRl; PresNHS; NatlMeritCmnd; SecStuCncl; PresFHA; VPFTA; DARAwd; Vanderhilt University; Medicine.

YOUNG, Terrie L; Lincoln Comm HS; Lincoln, IL; 20/250 Chr; Chrs; CncrtBnd; Mdrgl; MrchBnd; NatlThespSoc; SchMus; SchPl; LatCl; Illinois St Univ; Home Economics.

YOUNG, Thomas E; Elmhurst HS; Fort Wayne, IN; Band; Chr; CncrtBnd; HonRl; MrchBnd; NatlFornLg; PepBnd; SchPl; StuCncl; 4-H; College; Physician.

YOUNG, Thomas E 3; Deandries HS; Saint Louis, MO; 6/83 Chr; ChrhWkr; CmntyWkr; HonRl; NatlMeritCmnd; SchPl; RptrSchPpr; FDA; SciCl; University; Professional.

YOUNG, Thomas H; Lakeview HS; Decatur, IL; 8/180 HonRl; Millikin Univ; Business.

YOUNG, Timothy E; Blair HS; Blair, NE; PresFrshCls; TchrAde; YthFlsp; LetterBsbl; LetterBsktbl; LetterTrk; College; History.

YOUNG, Vicki L; Alburnett Community HS; Central City, IA; 2/44 RptrSchPpr; Chr; MrchBnd; VPNHS; RptrYrbk; RptrSchPpr; 4-H; PresFTA; Bsktbl; Trk; Ia State Univ.

YOUNG, Vincent R; Memorial HS; Joplin, MO; 15/225 HonRl; LbryAde; NHS; MthCl; College; Engineering.

YOUNG, Wendy; Crete Monee Hs; Crete, IL; PresBand; HonRl; MrchBnd; NHS; Orch; GerCl; MthCl; University; Science.

YOUNG, Wendy E; Effingham HS; Effingham, IL; 15/222 Chr; HonRl; LbryAde; NatlMeritSF; SchMus; SctActv; StuGov; TchrAde; YthFlsp; College; Journalism.

YOUNG, William A; Liberty HS; Mountain View, MO; 13/120 TrsSophCls; ALBoysSt; Band; HonRl; MrchBnd; PepBnd; SctActv; Ftbl; Trk; College; Aeronautical Engineering.

YOUNG, William R; Senath Hornersville HS; Senath, MO; ALBoysSt; MrchBnd; SchMus; SchPl; SctActv; U Of Mo; Forestry.

YOUNG, Wilson A; Turkey Valley HS; Waucoma, IA; 12/110 ALBoysSt; Chr; NatlFornLg; NHS; SchMus; 4-H; SpnCl; LetterGlf; 4-HAwd; Iowa State Univ; Chemical Engineering.

YOUNGBAUER, Sonya J; Alma HS; Alma, WI; VPSophCls; Chrs; HonRl; SchPl; Pres4-H; FBLA; FTA; Trk; CaptChrldr; GAA; 4-HAwd; Eau Claire Tech Inst; Legal Sec.

YOUNGBERG, Annette M; Wm Kelley HS; Silver Bay, MN; Chr; HonRl; SchMus; SctActv; RptrSchPpr; PpCl; Swmmng; Academy Of Hair Dressing ; Beautician.

YOUNGBERG, Bryan J; Ankeny HS; Ankeny, IA; College; Drafting Architecture.

YOUNGBLOOD, Janet D; Monrovia HS; Monrovia, IN; 1/111 ChrhWkr; HonRl; NHS; OffAde; StuCncl; Yrbk; 4-H; SpnCl; Trk; College; Home Ec.

YOUNGBLOOD, Samuel M; Kirksville Sr HS; Kirksville, MO; Band; CncrtBnd; HonRl; MrchBnd; PepBnd; College.

YOUNGBLUT, James J; Don Bosco HS; Waterloo, IA; Band; CncrtBnd; HonRl; NatlThespSoc; PepBnd; SchMus; SchPl; TchrAde; RptrYrbk; Yrbk; EdSchPpr; Creighton University; Journalism.

YOUNGBLUTH, Renee R; East Charles Mix HS; Wagner, SD; 2/66 SecJrCls; ALAGirlsSt; Band; Chrs; HonRl; NHS; SecStuCncl; Pres4-H; 4-HAwd; VoiceDemAwd; College; Vet.

YOUNGER, Danny J; Effingham HS; Effingham, IL; 6/220 HonRl; JA; NHS; PresKeyCl; College; Medicine.

YOUNGS, Burton E; North Shore HS; Roseglen, ND; ALBoysSt; Chr; Chrs; ChrhWkr; HonRl; YthFlsp; Trade School; Draftsman.

YOUNKER, Dale; Hays HS; Hays, KS; CmntyWkr; HonRl; JA; SchPpr; 4-H; TreasFFA; 4-HAwd; Ft Hays St Univ; Agriculture.

YOUNKIN, Kim E; Northside HS; Red Key, IN; ALBoysSt; Band; SchMus; SchPl; StuCncl; SciCl; LetterBsbl; LetterBsktbl; LetterTrk; EldAwd; Abilene Christian College; Physical Educ.

YOUNT, David J; Fox HS; Arnold, MO; 51/472 Band; CncrtBnd; HonRl; MrchBnd; NHS; SctActv; Bsbl; Bsktbl; Ftbl; College.

YOUNT, Debbie S; Southeast Polk HS; Altoona, IA; Chrs; HonRl; JA; JrNHS; SctActv; StuGov; TchrAde; LetterBsktbl; LetterTrk; Swmmng; Clge; Educ.

YOUNT, Jo; Grinnell Newburg Comm HS; Grinnell, IA; 6/190 HonRl; NHS; Quill&Scroll; SchPl; RptrYrbk; Yrbk; 4-H; Cornell College; Prof.

YOUNT, Kevin; Berkeley Senior HS; Berkeley, MO; 9/352 Band; ChrhWkr; CncrtBnd; HonRl; MrchBnd; SchMus; SctActv; StuCncl; LetterBsktbl; U Of Missouri; Veterinary Medicine.

YOURICK, Jeffrey J; Pioneer HS; Ann Arbor, MI; ChrhWkr; HonRl; HospAde; SctActv; YthFlsp; GerCl; LetterFtbl; IMSpt; Kalamazoo Coll; Biology.

YOXALL, Patricia A; New Trier West HS; Wilmette, IL; 53/693 AFS; HonRl; HospAde; NHS; NatlMeritCmnd; PolWkr; Duke Univ; English.

YTSMA, Theodore; Grandville HS; Grandville, MI; 12/320 CncrtBnd; JA; JrNHS; MrchBnd; NHS; NatlMeritCmnd; PepBnd; SchMus; JAAwd; Michigan Technological U; Nuclear Physics.

YTTERBOE, Steven N; St James Senior HS; St James, MN; Band; CncrtBnd; HonRl; MrchBnd; PepBnd; SchPl; 4-H; FFA; SciCl; Wrstlng; College; Professional.

YUAN, Amy S; Southeast HS; Wichita, KS; VPFrshCls; CmntyWkr; HonRl; SchAde; SchMus; SchPl; SctActv; TchrAde; CaptBsktbl; CaptSwmmng; University; Professional.

YUEN, Alice M; William Fremd HS; Palatine, IL; HonRl; William R Harper College; Business.

YUHAS, Julia; Van Horn HS; Sugar Creek, MO; TrsFrshCls; HonRl; JrNHS; NHS; StuCncl; Yrbk; CivCl; KeyCl; Univ; Professional.

YUKEL, Judy A; Silver Lake Public HS; Silver Lake, MN; 1/57 PresSrCls; Chrs; HonRl; NHS; SchPl; Yrbk; FFA; FHA; PpCl; Bsktbl; Univ Mn; Rn.

YUN, Youngil; Truman HS; Independence, MO; 6/600 HonRl; JrNHS; NHS; StuCncl; FTA; College.

YUNG, Charlene M; Alexis HS; Alexis, IL; 4/4 VPFrshCls; VPSophCls; Chr; ChrhWkr; CmntyWkr HonRl; HospAde; NHS; SchPl; 4-H; FHA; FrC PpCl; GAA; Black Hawk College; Registere Nurse.

YUNG, Michael R; Springfield Southeast HS; Springfield, IL; 53/464 PresJA; PolWkr; StuCncl; StuGov JAAwd; Illinois State Univ; Medicine.

YUNG, Peter; Lindblom Tech; Chicago, IL; 55/72 HonRl; Yrbk; Il Institute Of Tech; Architecture.

YUNG, Susan K; Lindblom Tech HS; Chicago, IL 15/635 HonRl; ROTC; TchrAde; YthFlsp; Yrbk MthCl; College; Elec Engineer.

YUNGCK, Debra E; Marquette HS; Alton, IL; 28/120 ChrhWkr; HonRl; NHS; Quill&Scroll; FDA FNA; Chrldr; AmLegAwd; DARAwd; TIMEAwd GodCntryAwd; Univ; Art.

YUNGCLAS, Ted; Webster City HS; Webster City, IA; Band; Chrs; ChrhWkr; HonRl; MrchBnd; SchMus; RptrYrbk; 4-H; FrCl; 4-HAwd; Iowa State University; Elementary Educ.

YUNKER, Andy L; Toluca HS; Toluca, IL; 25/42 TrsJrCls; FBLA; LetterBsktbl; Trade School.

YURATOVAC, John M; George Washington HS; Chicago, IL; 27/495 SctActv; LatCl; LetterWrstlng; Bradley Univ; Elec Engineering.

YURDIN, Bruce J; Springfield HS; Springfield, IL; 28/585 JrNHS; NHS; LetterFtbl; LetterSwmmng; IMSpt; U Of Southern Cal; Med.

YURKOVICH, Therese M; Queen Of Peace HS; Chicago, IL; HospAde; SctActv; StuCncl; PresSpnCl; North Ill Univ; Child Development.

YUSTEN, Mary B; South Sioux City Senior HS; Dakota City, NE; Chrs; ChrhWkr; CncrtBnd; MrchBnd; NatlThespSoc; SchMus; SctActv; Yrbk; SchPpr; SpnCl; Medical.

Z

ZAAGSMA, Mary K; Regina HS; Detroit, MI; HonRl; LitMag; LbryAde; NHS; SctActv; RptrSchPpr; FHA; College; Journalism.

ZABACK, Terry; Hastings Sr HS; Hastings, NE; HonRl; StuCncl; Bsktbl; Ftbl; IMSpt; ChmbCommrsAwd; College; Major In Business.

ZABAWA, Michael J; Roncalli HS; Omaha, NE; HonRl; NHS; StuCncl; LetterBsbl; Ftbl; CchngActv; Univ; Engi.

ZABAWA, Richard N; Assumption HS; Wis Rapids, WI; 2/110 PresSophCls; Band; CncrtBnd; HonRl; MrchBnd; PepBnd; StuCncl; StuGov; FrCl; MthCl; Tennis; Univ; Engineering.

ZABEL, Cynthia L; Lincoln HS; Wisconsin Rapids, WI; ChrhWkr; CmntyWkr; HonRl; NHS; TchrAde; GerCl; PpCl; GAA; Concordia College; Lutheran Elementary Tchr.

ZABEL, Joyce; North Scott HS; Davenport, IA; 4/205 CncrtBnd; HonRl; MrchBnd; NHS; PepBnd; TchrAde; FHA; Bsbl; Office Job.

ZABEL, Mark A; Central HS; Young America, MN; 14/109 VPSrCls; HonRl; NHS; SchPl; YthFlsp; RptrYrbk; Yrbk; SciCl; LetterFtbl; IMSpt; College; Physics Or Engr.

ZABEL, Michael J; Downers Grove North HS; Boling Brook, IL; 50/500 ChrhWkr; HonRl; NHS; Syracuse Univ; Business Mgmt.

ZABEL, Richard R; Greenway HS; Grand Rapids, MN; 9/165 Band; ChrhWkr; HonRl; NHS; SctActv; YthFlsp; GerCl; LetterBsktbl; LetterFtbl; LetterTrk; Cancandia Col; Chemistry.

ZABINSKI, Gary M; Marist HS; Orland Park, IL; 16/393 Band; Chr; ChrhWkr; HonRl; VPNHS; SchMus; SchPl; SpnCl; AmLegAwd; CitAwd; Clge; Medicine Or Theatre.

ZABINSKI, Lawrence E; Marist HS; Orland Pk, IL; 5/370 Chr; ChrhWkr; HonRl; JA; NHS; NatlMeritFnl; SctActv; LatCl; Bsbl; Bradley University; Law.

ZABINSKI, Michael A; Glenbrook North HS; Northbrook, IL; Aud/Vis; ChrhWkr; HonRl; SchPl; SchPpr; Glf; Trk; Wrstlng; GovHonPrgAwd;.

ZABLOCKI, Edward G; St Ladislaus HS; Hamtramck, MI; TrsJrCls; HonRl; StuCncl; SptEdSchPpr; MthCl; SciCl; Bsktbl; IMSpt; OptClAwd; Degree In Mathematics.

ZABOLOTNEY, Lynn R; Sheyenne River Acad; Bismarck, ND; Band; Chrs; ChrhWkr; CncrtBnd; HonRl; HospAde; MrchBnd; RptrSchPpr; SchPpr; BauchLmbAwd; Nebraska Lincoln Sch; L P N.

ZABORAC, David A; Saint Viator HS; Prairie Village, KS; 4/247 ChrhWkr; CmntyWkr; HonRl; JrNHS; NHS; SctActv; Bsbl; Creighton University; Dentist.

ZABOROWSKI, Duane; Rosholt HS; Amherst Junction, WI; 3/58 TrsSrCls; HonRl; NHS; FFA; IMSpt; Univ Of Wi River Falls; Agriculture Ed.

ZABUKOVEC, Judy J; Carmel HS; Waukegan, IL; 3/173 PresSophCls; NHS; NatlMeritCmnd; StuCncl; SecGerCl; TreasMthCl; CaptChrldr; GAA; College; Mathematics.

ZACH, Janice M; St Francis HS; Humphrey, NE; 3/35 PresFrshCls; Chrs; HonRl; LbryAde; NHS; PresStuCncl; EdYrBk; 4-H; PpCl; DanFAwd; College Of St Mary; Early Childhood Educatn.

ZACH, John; St Francis HS; Humphrey, NE; HonRl; StuCncl; RptrSchPpr;.

ZACH, Marie; St Francis HS; Humphrey, NE; Chrs; HonRl; LbryAde; OffAde; Yrbk; PpCl; IMSpt; College.

ZACH, Rita A; St Francis HS; Humphrey, NE; 1/35 SecJrCls; Chrs; HonRl; LbryAde; NHS; NatlMeritCmnd; StuCncl; RptrYrbk; Trk; BttyCrckrAwd; Coll; Acct.

ZACH, Steven C; Oregon HS; Oregon, WI; ALBoysSt; Chrs; HonRl; Mdrgl; PresNHS; SchMus; SchPl; StuCncl; LetterBsbl; Bsktbl; Coll; Law.

ZACHARIAS, Yvonne M; Bishop Borgess HS; Detroit, MI; Aud/Vis; ChrhWkr; HospAde; NHS; NatlMeritSchl; NatlMeritSF; RptrYrbk; LatCl; Trk; GAA; Univ; Dental Hyg.

ZACHARIASH, Orah; Beth Jacob HS; Southfield, MI; 1/18 TrsFrshCls; TrsJrCls; ChrhWkr; CmntyWkr; HonRl; StuCncl; Yrbk; SchPpr; Swmmng; 4-HAwd; GovHonPrgAwd; Teachers Seminary; Teacher.

ZACHARY, Dan K; Warsaw Community HS; Warsaw, IN; ALBoysSt; HonRl; Glf; GodCntryAwd; PresAwd; College; Business Law.

ZACHARY, Kimma L; Northwestern HS; Palmyra, IL; 2/53 PresSophCls; Band; Chrs; HonRl; NHS; PepBnd; SchPl; YthFlsp; Yrbk; 4-H; FHA; SpnCl; Trk; GAA; Eastern Illinois Univ; Physical Education.

ZACHMANN, Ron; Golva HS; Sentinel Butle, ND; SecSophCls; PresJrCls; ALBoysSt; HonRl; StuCncl; 4-H; GerCl; MthCl; Trk; College; Vocation.

ZACHMANN, Ronald; Golva HS; Sentinal Butte, ND; SecSophCls; PresJrCls; ALBoysSt; HonRl; StuCncl; StuGov; LetterBsktbl; Trk; IMSpt; 4-HAwd; College; Vocation.

ZACHMEIER, Michael W; Mandan HS; Mandan, ND; 1/294 Band; JA; NHS; NatlMeritSF; SctActv; PresGerCl; PresLatCl; PresSciCl; EldAwd; Uofnd&mit;nuclear Eng.

ZADE, Rhonda A; Dominican HS; Detroit, MI; HospAde; SecNatlMeritCmnd; SchMus; U Of Detroit; Dentist.

ZADINA, Kim L; Superior HS; Superior, NE; Band; Quill&Scroll; SchMus; SchPl; StuCncl; Teen; RptrYrbk; SchPpr; Swmmng; Southeast Community College; Nursing.

ZADROZNY, Mary A; Proviso West HS; Bellwood, IL; 13/1086 Chr; HonRl; NHS; PresFrCl; Tennis; GAA; Univ Of Illinois; Computer Programming.

ZAFIRATOS, Carol A; Oak Park And River Forest HS; River Forest, IL; 157/973 Aud/Vis; HonRl; LbryAde; SchAde; University Of Illinois; Vet.

ZAGAR, William P; Joliet West HS; Joliet, IL; 52/495 HonRl; NHS; PpCl; CaptBsktbl; Trk; University; Pharmacy.

ZAGOTTA, Nicholas C; Mendel Catholic HS; Chicago, IL; 4/173 HonRl; StuCncl; KeyCl; MthCl; LetterBsbl; IMSpt; Notre Dame; Law.

ZAGRODNY, Susan H; Hill Mc Cloy HS; Montrose, MI; 17/138 Chr; HonRl; NHS; SchPl; YthFlsp; RptrYrbk; RptrSchPpr; FTA; PresSpnCl; PPFtbl; Alma Clg; Spanish Teacher.

ZAGURSKY, Denise; St Pius X HS; Kansas City, MO; 22/129 Chrs; CmntyWkr; HonRl; StuCncl; YthFlsp; SpnCl; PpCl; Bsktbl; Business; Prof.

ZAGYVA, Cynthia L; Quincy HS; Coldwater, MI; 30/116 Band; ChrhWkr; HonRl; TchrAde; YthFlsp; 4-H; FFA; KeyCl; 4-HAwd; JAAwd; Cliff Manns Floral Design Sch; Floral Dsn.

ZAHER, Deborah J; Morton Sr HS; Hammond, IN; 6/529 Band; CncrtBnd; HonRl; JrNHS; MrchBnd; Orch; PepBnd; SchPl; StuGov; TchrAde; FTA; FrCl; Tennis; College; Professional.

ZAHLER, Joan B; Kimball Area HS; Kimball, MN; 1/79 CncrtBnd; HonRl; JrNHS; NHS; Orch; SchAde; TchrAde; FrCl; Trk; GAA; St Cloud College; Environmental Biology.

ZAHM, Thomas P; Huntington North HS; Huntington, IN; 1/512 PresFrshCls; HonRl; NatlMeritFnl; StuCncl; MthCl; SciCl; BauchLmbAwd; Mathematics.

ZAHN, Donna M; Bishop Ryan HS; Minot, ND; PresJrCls; Chrs; HonRl; PresJrNHS; NHS; Sdlty; StuCncl; TreasGerCl; PpCl; Chrldr; GAA; Univ Of N Dakota; Medicine.

ZAHN, Jay R; Sevastopol HS; Sturgeon Bay, WI; 1/90 Band; Chr; ChrhWkr; NHS; PepBnd; Quill&Scroll; SchMus; SchPl; EdSchPpr; 4-H; Ftbl; Wrstlng; 4-HAwd; University Of Wisconsin; Broadcasting.

ZAHN, Lisa M; Shawnee Mission S HS; Overland Park, KS; SecJrCls; SecSrCls; ALAGirlsSt; ChrhWkr; HonRl; StuCncl; TchrAde; RptrYrbk; RptrSchPpr; PresPpCl; University.

ZAHNER, Thomas J; West Harrison HS; Modale, IA; Band; Chr; Chrs; CncrtBnd; HonRl; Mdrgl; MrchBnd; NHS; NatlMeritSchl; SchMus; SchPl; Bsktbl; Ftbl; Iowa State Univ; Forestry.

ZAHODNIC, Richard J; Dela Salle HS; Detroit, MI; CmntyWkr; HonRl; JA; SchPl; StuCncl; SchPpr; Chrldr; IMSpt; JAAwd; Wayne State Univ; Doctor.

ZAHORA, Julie; Lourdes Hs; Chicago, IL; 3/277 HonRl; NHS; TchrAde; Loyola; Teach Physically Handicapped.

ZAHRNDT, James; Munster HS; Munster, IN; HonRl; SchAde; SctActv; TchrAde; RptrYrbk; SchPpr; Wrstlng; Col; Electrical Engineer.

ZAINER, Christine M; St Joan Antida HS; Milwaukee, WI; HonRl; NHS; SctActv; StuCncl; RptrSchPpr; SpnCl; IMSpt; VFWAwd; Marquette U; Science.

ZAJAC, Janet K; Saint Ann HS; Chicago, IL; TrsSophCls; VPJrCls; Chr; HonRl; NHS; GAA; IMSpt; KiwanAwd; LionAwd;.

ZAJAC, Mary; St Barbara HS; Chicago, IL; 2/90 HonRl; College; Professional.

ZAJAKALA, Christine M; Marian Catholic HS; Chicago Heights, IL; 79/325 Band; CncrtBnd; HonRl; MrchBnd; PepBnd; SchMus; SctActv; RptrYrbk; Western Illinois Univ; Music Director.

ZAK, Richard D; St Viator HS; Elk Grove, IL; HonRl; NHS; GerCl; MthCl; Glf; Loyola University; Doctor.

ZAKARIASEN, Kristi R; St Charles HS; St Charles, MO; Chrs; DrlTm; HonRl; MrchBnd; NHS; SchPl; StuCncl; Univ Of Colorado; Modeling.

ZAKIBE, Michael G; Bishop Dubourg HS; St Louis, MO; 1/500 HonRl; JA; LbryAde; PresNHS; OffAde; SchAde; SchMus; RptrYrbk; RptrSchPpr; BauchLmbAwd; U Of Wa; Business.

ZAKOWSKI, Paul G; Green Bay Southwest HS; Green Bay, WI; HonRl; StuCncl; FrCl; Bsktbl; LetterTrk; College; Business Management.

ZAKRZEWSKI, Cynthia L; St Benedict HS; Chicago, IL; 7/186 Chr; Chrs; HonRl; JrNHS; NHS; SchAde; SchPl; TchrAde; SpnCl; PpCl; Northeastern College; Performing Arts.

ZAKRZEWSKI, David; St Marys HS; O Neill, NE; PresSrCls; ALBoysSt; NHS; NatlMeritFnl; EdYrBk; AmLegAwd; JCAwd; USJCAwd; PresAwd; CitAwd; Trade School; Prof Cameraman.

ZAKULA, David T; Marist HS; Chicago, IL; 74/374 NatlMeritCmnd; SchPpr; LetterBsktbl; LetterFtbl; Glf; Illinois State Univ; Criminology.

ZAKULA, Mark; Lowell HS; Lowell, IN; 1/330 HonRl; NHS; CaptTrk; Wrstlng; University; Liberal Arts.

ZALA, Christina; South Side HS; Fort Wayne, IN; 29/425 AFS; HonRl; NatlFornLg; PolWkr; SchMus; SctActv; FrCl; Coll; Theatre Arts.

ZALAN, Stephen E; Harold L Richards HS; Palos Heights, IL; 18/1035 HonRl; NHS; MthCl; LetterTrk; Univ Of Chicago; Geophysical Science.

ZALANS, Margaret V; West Aurora HS; North Aurora, IL; HonRl; NHS; Univ Of Wisconsin; Horticulture.

ZALESKI, Dean R; Granton Public HS; Granton, WI; ChrhWkr; HonRl; StuCncl; TchrAde; FFA; Bsbl; Bsktbl; Glf; DanFAwd;.

ZALESKI, Diane L; Granton Public HS; Granton, WI; Band; HonRl; LbryAde; SchPl; 4-H; RptrYrbk; FHA; Bsktbl; Chrldr; GAA; Receptionist.

ZALESKY, Jo A; Prairie HS; Cedar Rapids, IA; SecChrhWkr; HonRl; JrNHS; NHS; SchPl; PresChrldr; PPFtbl; 4-HAwd; Brigham Young Univ; Home Economics.

ZALEWSKI, Cheryl A; Maria HS; Chicago, IL; HonRl; HospAde; NHS; TreasSctActv; KiwanAwd; LionAwd; Loyola U Chicago; Psychology.

ZALUD, Nancy B; Lourdes HS; Chicago, IL; 87/299 SecTrsFrshCls; DrlTm; HonRl; LitMag; RptrSchPpr; SpnCl; PpCl; College; Accounting.

ZALUPSKI, Mark M; Aquinas HS; Lincoln Park, MI; 3/218 HonRl; NHS; NatlMeritCmnd; Quill&Scroll; TchrAde; SptEdYrbk; SptEdSchPpr; LetterGlf; LetterTrk; Univ Of Mi;med.

ZAMBO, Maryanne C; Hanover Central HS; Cedar Lake, IN; 7/144 HonRl; JrNHS; SctActv; SpnCl; MthCl; Indiana Univ; Medicine.

ZAMMIT, Edward V; Holy Redeemer HS; Detroit, MI; 66/190 IMSpt; Clg; Electrician.

ZAMOLEWICZ, Mary D; Mount Assis Academy; Chicago, IL; 15/129 HonRl; NHS; SctActv; Glf; Univ; Oceanographer.

ZAMOR, Deborah M; St Clare Academy; New Brighton, MN; 4/11 PresSophCls; SecTrsSrCls; Chrs; HonRl; SchPl; StuCncl; TchrAde; RptrSchPpr; FrCl; University; Medicine.

ZAMOYSKI, Jan A; St Marys HS; Gaylord, MI; 4/50 TrsSophCls; HospAde; JrNHS; 4-H; PpCl; Bsktbl; Col; Fashion Merchandiser.

ZANDSTRA, James S; Leola HS; Leola, SD; ChrhWkr; DrlTm; HonRl; 4-H; Bsktbl; Trk; Nat College Of Bus; Accounting.

ZANETTI, Leona; Carmel Hs For Girls; Barrington, IL; 41 HonRl; NHS; PolWkr; StuCncl; FTA; College;political Science.

ZANETTI, Loretta M; Carmel Girls HS; Barrington, IL; 50/173 HonRl; NHS; PolWkr; RptrSchPpr; George Washington Univ; Public Relations.

ZANON, Cheryl E; Norway HS; Vulcan, MI; DrmMjrt; HonRl; Sdlty; Twrl; RptrYrbk; RptrSchPpr; 4-H; FBLA; LetterTrk; IMSpt; Bay De Noc College; Business.

ZANON, Robert T; St Ignatius College Prep; Chicago, IL; 8/156 HonRl; NHS; NatlMeritSF; College; Paleontologist.

ZANONI, Theresa A; Norway HS; Norway, MI; HonRl; NatlMeritFnl; NatlMeritCmnd; SchMus; TchrAde; College; Forestry.

ZANTER, Patricia; Alpena Senior HS; Alpena, MI; Chr; ChrhWkr; Orch; SchMus; SchPl; RptrSchPpr; Olivet College; Music Major.

ZANTOW, Scott; Baraboo Senior HS; Baraboo, WI; PresSrCls; Chr; ChrhWkr; CmntyWkr; HonRl; Quill&Scroll; StuCncl; KeyCl; Bsktbl; Trk;.

ZANZOLA, Joan M; Saint Francis Acad; Joliet, IL; 33/172 HonRl; PresLbryAde; Northern Illinois U; Lawyer.

ZAPCHENK, Jeffery S; Thornridge HS; Harvey, IL; 98/637 HonRl; JrNHS; Eastern Il Univ; History.

ZAPF, Michaele M; St Stephen Area HS; Saginaw, MI; HospAde; NHS; RptrSchPpr; PpCl; College; Professional.

ZAPP, Cindy A; Okawville Community HS; Okawville, IL; TrsFrshCls; PresJrCls; ChrhWkr; CmntyWkr; SchPl; StuCncl; YthFlsp; RptrYrbk; SchPpr; FHA; PpCl; Patricia Stevens College; Stewardess.

ZAPUTIL, John A; Davis County Comm HS; Bloomfield, IA; ALBoysSt; ChrhWkr; HonRl; SpnCl; College; Pharmacist.

ZARACKI, Sherry; Louisville HS; Cedar Creek, NE; SecJrCls; Chr; Twrl; Yrbk; FHA; PpCl; GAA; Business School; Secretarial.

ZARAGOZA, Oliver J; Mars Hall U HS; Minneapolis, MN; Aud/Vis; Chr; StuGov; TchrAde; RptrSchPpr; SpnCl; LetterBsbl; LetterFtbl; LetterWrstlng; IMSpt; JCAwd; Univ Of Minnesota.

ZARATE, Cary J; West Chicago Comm HS; West Chicago, IL; 44/315 HonRl; JETSAwd; Bradley U; Engineering.

ZARICOR, Cynthia S; Dupo HS; Dupo, IL; 1/117 ALAGirlsSt; Band; Chr; ChrhWkr; HonRl; MrchBnd; NHS; StuCncl; FNA; LionAwd; College; Physical Therapist.

ZARICOR, Tad J; Lincoln HS; Manitowoc, WI; Chrs; ChrhWkr; Mdrgl; SchMus; Bsktbl; Ftbl; IMSpt; College; Conservation.

ZARINS, Edgar A; Livonia Franklin HS; Westland, MI; 42/750 Band; CncrtBnd; HonRl; SctActv; IMSpt; Univ Of Michigan; Computer Systems.

ZARR, Edward; Madison Sr HS; Madison, IL; Bsktbl; College.

ZARSE, Joan M; Frontier HS; Brookston, IN; 3/70 NHS; PpCl; Inter Jr Clge; Accntg.

ZARTMAN, Kimberly; Warsaw Senior HS; Leesburg, IN; Band; CmntyWkr; CncrtBnd; College; Professional.

ZARYBNICKY, James L; Hanover HS; Odell, NE; HonRl; NHS; SchPl; StuCncl; FFA; SciCl; LetterBsktbl; CaptFtbl; LetterTrk; Kearney State College; Business.

ZARZECKI, Charles; St Rita HS; Evergreen Park, IL; HonRl; SpnCl; LetterBsbl; LetterBsktbl; LetterFtbl; Lewis University.

ZASTOUPIL, Rockford G; Dickinson HS; Dickinson, ND; HonRl; GerCl; LetterTrk; IMSpt; College; Bus Admin.

ZASTROW, Carol J; Gillett Public HS; Pulcifer, WI; 17/78 PresChrhWkr; LbryAde; OffAde; RedCrAde; TchrAde; YthFlsp; Yrbk; TreasFBLA; SecFFA; FHA; Uw River Falls; Agricultural Ed.

ZASTROW, Gary M; Lakeside Lutheran HS; Helenville, WI; HstFrshCls; HstSophCls; HstSrCls; CncrtBnd; MrchBnd; PepBnd; YthFlsp; SptEdYrbk; LetterBsbl; Navy; Conservation.

ZASTROW, Michael L; West De Pere HS; De Pere, WI; 31/210 HonRl; JA; NHS; SchPl; StuCncl; Yrbk; FrCl; Bsbl; Ftbl; IMSpt; College; Paper Engineering.

ZASTROW, Steve T; Friend HS; Friend, NE; ChrhWkr; HonRl; LbryAde; RptrYrbk; 4-H; LetterFtbl; Trk; Univ Of Nebraska; Farmer.

ZAUNER, Katherine; Wauwatosa East HS; Wauwatosa, WI; HonRl; IntrClCncl; JA; LitMag; NatlMeritSF; SchMus; SchPl; SctActv; MthCl; Trk; College; Zoologist.

ZAVADIL, Mary; Crofton Public HS; Crofton, NE; TrsSrCls; Chrs; DrlTm; HonRl; SchPl; StuGov; TchrAde; PpCl; Nebraska U; Medicine.

ZAWA, Paul E; Roger C Sullivan Shs; Chicago, IL; 2/276 HonRl; NHS; PepBnd; SchPl; TchrAde; RptrYrbk; RptrSchPpr; KeyCl; Tennis; Biochemistry.

ZAWISLAK, Judith M; Holy Redeemer HS; Detroit, MI; PresFrshCls; HonRl; NHS; Trk; College; Medicine.

ZAWOJSKI, Linnae A; Sevastopol HS; Egg Harbor, WI; HonRl; NatlFornLg; TchrAde; SpnCl; Univ; Language Lit.

ZAYIA, Mary R; Regina Dominican HS; Chicago, IL; 38/208 HonRl; LitMag; PolWkr; Sdlty; StuCncl; RptrSchPpr; FNA; Loyola Univ; Medicine.

ZBIKOWSKI, Joseph; Northview HS; Grand Rapids, MI; HonRl; JrNHS; LbryAde; NHS; IMSpt; College; Accounting.

ZBUKA, David M; Lacrosse HS; Wanatah, IN; Band; CncrtBnd; HonRl; Trade School; Culinary.

ZEAL, Joanne R; Niles Township North HS; Skokie, IL; 52/632 Chrs; HonRl; NHS; NatlMeritCmnd; PresNatlThespSoc; SchMus; SchPl; GAA; College; Nursing.

ZEBELL, Mary E; St Francis Academy; Lockport, IL; 8/174 HonRl; NHS; StuCncl; SpnCl; LetterTrk; Northwestern Univ; Physician.

ZEBROSKI, Rita M; Sully Buttes HS; Onida, SD; VPSrCls; Chrl; Chrs; ChrhWkr; HonRl; NHS; Quill&Scroll; SchPl; Yrbk; Trk; Chrldr; Trade Sch; Secretarial.

ZEBROSKI, Tawana; Sully Buttes HS; Onida, SD; 15/55 HstSrCls; HonRl; Quill&Scroll; SchAde; SchPl; PpCl; Chrldr; CchngActv; Black Hills State Coll; Journalism.

ZEDIALIS, John B; Mark Twain HS; New London, MO; 3/69 PresJrCls; Band; ChrhWkr; CncrtBnd; HonRl; MrchBnd; PepBnd; StuCncl; Us Naval Academy; Business Admin.

ZEDNIK, Jan M; Richmond Burton Comm HS; Richmond, IL; 3/70 TrsSrCls; ALAGirlsSt; HonRl; TreasLbryAde; NHS; SchPl; SctActv; RptrYrbk; Yrbk; FrCl; PpCl; Trk; GAA; North Ill Univ; Elem Teacher.

ZEEFF, Barbara D; Grand Haven Sr HS; Spring Lake, MI; ALAGirlsSt; ChrhWkr; HonRl; JrNHS; NHS; NatlMeritSF; SchPl; RptrYrbk; Yrbk; RptrSchPpr;.

ZEEMAN, Timothy J; Swartz Creek HS; Flint, MI; 27/400 HonRl; NHS; Bsbl; CaptBsktbl; College; Forestry.

ZEHNDER, Martha; Frankenmuth HS; Frankenmuth, MI; ALAGirlsSt; NatlFornLg; SchPl; StuCncl; TchrAde; IMSpt; Valparasio Univ; Business.

ZEHR, Judy A; Flanagan HS; Flanagan, IL; Band; Chrs; CncrtBnd; HonRl; MrchBnd; PepBnd; SchMus; Sec4-H; PresGerCl; Chrldr; Icc; Dental Assistant.

ZEIDER, Julie E; South Newton HS; Goodland, IN; 15/105 Band; HonRl; MrchBnd; SchMus; FBLA; FTA; PpCl; Bsktbl; GAA; Ball State Univ; Teaching.

ZEIEN, Teresa K; New Hampton HS; New Hampton, IA; 15/170 HonRl; College; Nursing.

ZEIER, Dennis L; Queen Of Apostles HS; Madison, WI; SctActv; Ftbl; Univ; Engr.

ZEIGLER, Barb A; Estherville HS; Estherville, IA; 17/182 SecFrshCls; SecJrCls; Band; CncrtBnd; HonRl; MrchBnd; SchMus; SchPl; Teen; 4-H; SpnCl; LetterTrk; Business School; Vocation.

ZEIGLER, Dennis L; Kanawha Comm HS; Kanawha, IA; 5/18 VPFrshCls; TrsSophCls; HonRl; SctActv; StuCncl; FFA; Bsbl; LetterBsktbl; CaptFtbl; CaptTrk; College; Vocation.

ZEIGLER, Douglas L; Kanawha Comm HS; Kanawha, IA; 7/19 SecSophCls; Band; Chr; Chrs; ChrhWkr; HonRl; Mdrgl; MrchBnd; StuCncl; FFA; Ftbl; College.

ZEIGLER, Nancy; Columbus East HS; Columbus, IN; 23/323 Band; CncrtBnd; DrlTm; MrchBnd; PepBnd; TchrAde; Twrl; 4-H; Swmmng; Coll; Major Study.

ZEIGLER, Pamela D; Churubusco HS; Churubusco, IN; SecSrCls; TrsSrCls; HonRl; OffAde; StuCncl; YthFlsp; 4-H; FHA; KeyCl; PpCl; GAA; Indiana Univ; Accounting.

ZEIGLER, Rick D; Cc HS; Clinton, IL; NHS; StuCncl; 4-H; FFA; FrCl; LetterBsbl; LetterBsktbl; LetterFtbl;.

ZEIHEN, Michael B; Central HS; Bristol, WI; CmntyWkr; HonRl; JrNHS; Mdrgl; NatlFornLg; NatlThespSoc; SchPl; StuCncl; RptrYrbk; Yrbk; 4-H; College.

ZEILINGER, Jean; David City HS; David City, NE; 1/51 HonRl; Quill&Scroll; Yrbk; PpCl; BttyCrckrAwd; Platte Coll; Buss.

ZEIMENS, Mary G; Rushville HS; Rushville, NE; 5/39 Band; DrmMjrt; HonRl; NHS; FTA; GerCl; Bsktbl; Trk; Chrldr; VoiceDemAwd; Kearney State; Elem Education.

ZEIS, Jeff P; Kirkwood HS; Frontenac, MO; NatlMeritSF; Univ Of Mo.

ZEIT, Diane; Midway HS; Bendena, KS; SecJrCls; Chrs; HonRl; StuCncl; RptrSchPpr; PpCl; Chrldr; Coll; Office Worker.

ZEITINGER, Rob C; Kirkwood Senior HS; Kirkwood, MO; 7/650 HonRl; NatlMeritSF; SctActv; YthFlsp; YthLg; GerCl; College; Engineering.

ZEITLER, John H; Algoma HS; Algoma, WI; Band; ChrhWkr; CncrtBnd; HonRl; MrchBnd; NHS; PepBnd; SchMus; PresFFA; IMSpt;.

ZEKICH, Deborah L; Thornton Frac North HS; Calumet City, IL; PresSophCls; Band; CncrtBnd; HonRl; JrNHS; MrchBnd; NHS; OffAde; PepBnd; PpCl; Loyola Univ; Medicine.

ZELASKO, Cheryl R; Centralia HS; Centralia, IL; 9/360 HonRl; NHS; OffAde; Yrbk; VPLatCl; SecSciCl; LionAwd; RotaryAwd; St Louis Univ; Accounting.

ZELAZO, Kenneth L; St Laurence HS; Chicago, IL; 14/385 CmntyWkr; HonRl; NHS; StuCncl; StuGov; RptrSchPpr; FrCl; MthCl; SciCl; Univ Notre Dame; Science.

ZELDENRUST, Lauree J; Goshen HS; Goshen, IN; Chr; HospAde; RedCrAde; YthFlsp; EngCl; SpnCl; LetterTrk; Univ; Phy Therapy.

ZELE, Lisa; Detroit Lutheran West HS; Huntingyton Woods, MI; Aud/Vis; ChrhWkr; HonRl; RptrSchPpr; Col; Indust Educa.

ZELEK, Daryl L; Schafer HS; Southgate, MI; HonRl; TchrAde; SchPpr; LetterTrk; Western Michigan Univ; Teaching.

ZELEK, Karen L; Proviso East HS; Melrose Park, IL; 7/1000 Band; HonRl; Mdrgl; MrchBnd; NHS; Orch; PepBnd; Quill&Scroll; RptrSchPpr; Wheaton College; Music Or Education.

ZELENACK, George E; G R Clark HS; Whiting, IN; 51/260 NHS; StuCncl; StuGov; GerCl; SciCl; Bsbl; LetterFtbl; Tennis; Trk; CaptWrstlng; Univ; Phd.

ZELENKA, Susan J; Milligan HS; Exeter, NE; SecTrsFrshCls; SecTrsSophCls; SecJrCls; SecSrCls; Band; Yrbk; SchPpr; PpCl; Trk; Chrldr; College; Professional.

ZELENSKI, Julie A; East Troy HS; Burlington, WI; 1/126 ALAGirlsSt; HonRl; VPNHS; NatlMeritSF; SchPl; SecStuCncl; EdYrBk; SchPpr; IMSpt; DARAwd; VoiceDemAwd; Univ; Business.

ZELENY, Carol L; Milligan Public HS; Milligan, NE; 3/11 TrsFrshCls; TrsSophCls; TrsJrCls; Band; Chr; Chrs; ChrhWkr; CmntyWkr; CncrtBnd; HonRl; Wesleyon Univ Of Ne; Music Education.

ZELL, Karen A; Dearborn HS; Dearborn, MI; Band; CncrtBnd; HonRl; JA; MrchBnd; NHS; RptrSchPpr; College; Vocation.

ZELL, Lillian I; Mosinee Sr HS; Mosinee, WI; Band; Chr; Chrs; CncrtBnd; HonRl; MrchBnd; NatlFornLg; NHS; Orch; PepBnd; North Central Tech Inst; Radiologic Techn.

ZELLAR, Doyle M; Lakefield Public HS; Lakefield, MN; 4/68 Band; Chrs; CncrtBnd; HonRl; JrNHS; Mdrgl; MrchBnd; NHS; PepBnd; SchPl; LetterBsbl; LetterBsktbl; AmLegAwd; 4-HAwd; University; Professional.

ZELLAR, Paul; Reed City HS; Reed City, MI; 31/168 HonRl; NHS; RptrSchPpr; RotaryAwd; VoiceDemAwd; Michigan Tech Univ; Civil Engn.

ZELLE, Nathan D; East HS; Waterloo, IA; 2/340 Band; Chr; HonRl; JA; JrNHS; ModUN; Orch; PepBnd; Yrbk; SchPpr; LetterFtbl; Wartburg College; Math.

ZELLER, Don R; St Pius X HS; Kansas City, MO; ALBoysSt; ChrhWkr; HonRl; NHS; RedCrAde; SchMus; SctActv; Tennis; Trk; GodCntryAwd; College.

ZELLER, Francis J; Richland Center HS; Richland Center, WI; 14/185 PresSophCls; PresJrCls; PresSrCls; Chr; CmntyWkr; HonRl; Mdrgl; NHS; SchPl; StuCncl; FFA; KeyCl; LetterFtbl; LetterWrstlng; Us Air Force Academy; Officer.

ZELLER, John M; Harper Creek HS; Battle Creek, MI; YthFlsp; RptrYrbk; LetterFtbl; Trk; College; Coach.

ZELLERS, Elizabeth A; Lake Central HS; St John, IN; 121/436 HospAde; SchPl; TchrAde; Teen; YthFlsp; SchPpr; FrCl; PpCl; PPFtbl; Purdue Univ Calumet; Journalist.

ZELLERS, Laura A; Ozark HS; Ozark, MO; 5/100 SecTrsFrshCls; SecTrsSrCls; Band; Chr; ChrhWkr; CncrtBnd; HonRl; MrchBnd; Orch; PepBnd; SchPl; SctActv; StuCncl; YthFlsp; Col; Music.

ZELLERS, Nancy J; Rochester HS; Rochester, IN; Chr; Chrs; HonRl; SchMus; SchPl; StuCncl; RptrSchPpr; PpCl; College; Elementary Educ.

ZELLMER, Pamela K; Butler HS; Butler, MO; 3/90 AFS; HonRl; NHS; SchPl; SecStuCncl; FBLA; FHA; SecPpCl; CaptChrldr; IMSpt; College; Business Education.

ZELLNER, Sally A; Wayland Academy; Beaver Dam, WI; 1/80 HonRl; NHS; NatlMeritSF; SchPl; TchrAde; College; Medicine.

ZELMER, Becky L; Downers Grove North HS; Downers Grove, IL; 9/509 Chr; Chrs; HonRl; JrNHS; NHS; NatlMeritCmnd; OffAde; FNA; College Of William & Mary; Law.

ZELONY, Gail L; Madison Consolidated HS; Madison, IN; TrsJrCls; TrsSrCls; ALAGirlsSt; HonRl; NHS; PresNatlThespSoc; Quill&Scroll; SchMus; SchPl; Yrbk; PpCl; SciCl; Swmmng; GAA; College.

ZEMAITIS, Michael E; Maine West HS; Des Plaines, IL; ChrhWkr; Teen; MthCl; SciCl; Univ Of Ill; Biology.

ZEMAITIS, Nancy K; North HS; Eau Claire, WI; NHS; SchPl; PpCl; Chrldr; Univ Of Wi Stout; Vocational Rehabilitation.

ZEMAN, Dwana L; Trego Comm HS; Wakeeney, KS; HonRl; 4-H; FHA; SciCl; Kansas State Univ; Veterinarian.

ZEMAN, Kathy; Marian Hs; Owatonna, MN; 1/42 VPFrshCls; PresSophCls; ChrhWkr; HonRl; NHS; LatCl; MthCl; LetterBsktbl; LetterTrk; 4-HAwd; Um;dairy Farming.

ZEMICKI, Edward J; Aquinas HS; Lincoln Park, MI; 56/249 HonRl; NHS; Col; Computer Operator.

ZEMLICKA, Kari L; Iowa Grant HS; Cobb, WI; Band; CncrtBnd; HonRl; MrchBnd; PepBnd; YthFlsp; TreasFHA; Bus Sch; Secretary.

ZEMLIN, Therese Y; Centennial HS; Champaign, IL; ChrhWkr; University; Art.

ZEMON, Arthur J; Valparaiso HS; Valparaiso, IN; CAP; HonRl; Quill&Scroll; SctActv; YthLg; RptrYrbk; Law School; Lawyer.

ZEMPLINSKI, Steven J; Cudahy Sr HS; Cudahy, WI; HonRl; NHS; Bsbl; CaptBsktbl; LetterFtbl; Univ Of Wi Whitewater; Accounting.

ZEMTSEFF, Paul B; Loyola Academy; Skokie, IL; 61/442 Aud/Vis; HonRl; Univ Of Illinois; Engineering.

ZENDER, Julie R; Sr James HS; Butterfield, MN; Chr; Chrs; ChrhWkr; HonRl; SchPl; TchrAde; RptrYrbk; RptrSchPpr; FHA; PPFtbl; College; Veterinarian.

ZENDER, Karen M; Lockport Central HS; Lockport, IL; 20/630 HonRl; JA; JrNHS; NHS; EdYrBk; FNA; FTA; Joliet Jr College; Accounting.

ZENKER, Sharlene; Gackle Public HS; Gackle, ND; 1/22 Chr; ChrhWkr; HonRl; Mdrgl; SchPl; EdYrBk; FFA; Chrldr; BttyCrckrAwd; College; Nursing.

ZENNER, Daniel R; Kingsley Area HS; Kingsley, MI; 11/43 PresFrshCls; PresSophCls; Band; HonRl; NHS; TchrAde; Muskegon Business College; Business Admin.

ZENNER, Kevin J; Little Falls Community HS; Little Falls, MN; 35/272 ALBoysSt; SchMus; TchrAde; LetterBsktbl; LetterFtbl; CaptTennis; West Point Military Acad; Prof.

ZENNER, Laurie A; Apollo HS; St Cloud, MN; 5/595 AFS; Band; CncrtBnd; HospAde; MrchBnd; NatlFornLg; NatlMeritSF; Chrldr; PPFtbl; College; Journalism.

ZENOR, Cynthia A; North Putnam HS; Bainbridge, IN; 4/135 Band; Chr; ChrhWkr; HonRl; NHS; TchrAde; YthFlsp; SpnCl; Ball State Univ; Music.

ZENOR, Jo Ann; Madrid Comm HS; Madrid, IA; ChrhWkr; HonRl; YthFlsp; Yrbk; FrCl; Bsktbl;.

ZENTGRAF, Monica; Wheaton HS; Fairmount, ND; 7/88 TrsSrCls; Band; Chr; HospAde; RptrYrbk; FHA; FNA; GAA; 4-HAwd; JCAwd; Nd State Univ; Nursing.

ZENTNER, Debra S; Oshkosh West HS; Oshkoh, WI; 13/402 AFS; Chr; HonRl; JrNHS; NHS; SchMus; VPGerCl; MthCl; PpCl; IMSpt; Uw Oshkosh; Accounting.

ZENTZ, Dean R; Argos HS; Argos, IN; 23/75 PresFrshCls; ALBoysSt; SchPl; PresStuCncl; PresYthFlsp; FTA; CaptBsbl; CaptBsktbl; CaptSocr; LetterTrk; AmLegAwd; Grace College; Education.

ZENTZ, Don J; Bremen HS; Bremen, IN; 10/123 PresChr; CmntyWkr; HonRl; Mdrgl; PresNHS; SchMus; FrCl; LetterBsbl; LetterFtbl; LetterTrk; Indiana Univ; Science.

ZENTZ, Ronald; Bremen HS; Bremen, IN; 6/123 HonRl; NHS; FrCl; Butler Univ; Pharmacy.

ZEPEDA, Carla M; Mother Mc Auley HS; Oak Lawn, IL; 28/484 Chr; Chrl; HonRl; HospAde; TreasJA; JrNHS; NHS; TchrAde; RptrSchPpr; FTA; IMSpt; JAAwd; Moraine Valley Jr College; Medical Tech.

ZEPS, Ausma A; Central HS; Grand Rapids, MI; ChrhWkr; NHS; OffAde; StuCncl; GerCl; Bsktbl; Univ; Medical Sec.

ZERAFA, Janice; Holy Redeemer HS; Detroit, MI; 15/186 NHS; SpnCl;.

ZERBS, Charlotte; Carl Sandburg HS; Orland Park, IL; ChrhWkr; HonRl; NHS; NatlThespSoc; Orch; Quill&Scroll; StuCncl; SchPpr; College; Law.

ZERGER, Timothy J; Marion HS; Marion, KS; VPFrshCls; VPSophCls; VPJrCls; Chrs; JrNHS; SctActv; StuCncl; YthFlsp; GerCl; Bsktbl; Ftbl; College; Medicine.

ZERKEL, Carolyn L; Collinsville HS; Collinsville, IL; 50/700 Chr; Chrs; ChrhWkr; CmntyWkr; HonRl; HospAde; NHS; OffAde; SchMus; SchPl; Southern Il Univ; Nursing.

ZERR, Mark A; Shelbyville Sr HS; Shelbyville, IN; 134/318 ChrhWkr; CmntyWkr; HonRl; SctActv; TchrAde; SchPpr; LatCl; SciCl; Bsbl; Ftbl; CchngActv; IMSpt; Purdue Univ; Business.

ZERR, Randal; Karlsruhe Public HS; Karlsruhe, ND; 5/20 TrsJrCls; ALBoysSt; ChrhWkr; HonRl; SchPl; StuGov; RptrYrbk; Bsbl; Bsktbl; Trk; Nd State Univ; Mechanical Engineering.

ZERTH, Lugene M; North White HS; Monticello, IN; 17/89 PresSrCls; ALAGirlsSt; ChrhWkr; CmntyWkr; HonRl; RptrYrbk; 4-H; GAA; IMSpt; Univ; Nursing.

ZERWAS, Lisa M; Joliet West Twp HS; Joliet, IL; 49/495 HonRl; NHS; OffAde; StuGov; University; Nursing.

ZERWIG, Neil F; St Genevieve Sr HS; St Genevieve, MO; 17/168 HonRl; SctActv; StuCncl; FrCl; LetterFtbl; LetterWrstlng; Mineral Area Col; Electronics.

ZESCH, Christina E; L D F Community HS; Gilman, IA; Band; Chr; Chrs; CncrtBnd; HonRl; MrchBnd; Orch; PepBnd; 4-H; Bsktbl; Marshalltown Comm Clg; Cerifeid Public Acct.

ZESSIN, Patti; South Page HS; Clarinda, IA; TrsFrshCls; SecSophCls; PresJrCls; HonRl; NHS; Yrbk; PpCl; College.

ZETAH, Roger A; Motley Public HS; Motley, MN; 3/35 VPSrCls; Aud/Vis; Band; HonRl; MrchBnd; SchPl; RptrYrbk; LetterFtbl; Trk; Vo Tech; Vocation.

ZETTEL, Hubert A; Southern Door HS; Sturgeon Bay, WI; ALBoysSt; HonRl; NHS; RptrYrbk; University; Computer Science.

ZEULI, John A; Hudson Sr HS; Hudson, WI; 2/190 ModUN; SchPpr; GerCl; Bsbl; Ftbl; Tennis; Trk; LetterWrstlng; College; Business Admin.

ZEUSKE, Debra L; Gresham HS; Gresham, WI; Band; Chr; CncrtBnd; HonRl; NHS; SchPl; Yrbk; Trk; GAA; PresAwd; Tech Schl; Court Reporting.

ZIAH, Suellen; Glenbrook South HS; Northbrook, IL; ChrhWkr; CmntyWkr; HonRl; IntrClCncl; NHS; Quill&Scroll; StuGov; RptrYrbk; EdYrBk; GAA; Wheaton Coll; Communications.

ZIBER, Thomas; Antigo HS; Antigo, WI; RptrSchPpr; Us Navy; Operator Specialist.

ZICH, Margaret M; Galesburg HS; Galesburg, IL; 57/588 HonRl; HospAde; TchrAde; Univ Of Il; Zoology.

ZICHTERMAN, Julie A; Carl Sandburg HS; Palos Heights, IL; 6/836 VPFrshCls; HonRl; NHS; GerCl; PpCl; Chrldr; Univ; Psychology.

ZICK, Kim K; South Campus HS; Waukesha, WI; 6/550 CncrtBnd; JrNHS; MrchBnd; NHS; Orch; PepBnd; TchrAde; Yrbk; SchPpr; GAA; Carroll Clge; Music.

ZICK, Victoria J; Pardeeville HS; Pardeeville, WI; Chrs; HonRl; LbryAde; FHA; Trk; GAA; Data Processing.

ZICKERT, Matthew P; Winnebago HS; Rockford, IL; HonRl; NHS; LetterFtbl; LetterTrk; LetterWrstlng; College.

ZICKUHR, Tom D; East HS; Waterloo, IA; Band; CncrtBnd; HonRl; JrNHS; MrchBnd; PepBnd; SchMus; CaptSwmmng; LetterTennis; Iowa State Univ; Aerospace Engineer.

ZIDON, Dennis; Cardinal Muench Seminary; Pisek, ND; /13 Cardinal Muench Seminary; Musical.

ZIEBART, Harold O; Westview HS; Kankakee, IL; 40/223 ChrhWkr; HonRl; LitMag; NHS; PolWkr; PresQuill&Scroll; EdYrBk; SchPpr; LetterBsbl; Eastern Ill Univ; Commercial Artist.

ZIEBARTH, Vicki M; Chisago Lakes HS; Chisago City, MN; Band; Chr; Chrs; ChrhWkr; CncrtBnd; HonRl; LbryAde; MrchBnd; PepBnd; SptEdYrbk; PpCl; LetterBsktbl; LetterTrk; GAA; University; Nursing.

ZIEBELL, Mary C; Trinity HS; Forest Park, IL; 31/203 HonRl; Loyola University; Medicine.

ZIEBKA, Jeanne M; East Leyden HS; Schiller Park, IL; Chrs; ChrhWkr; HonRl; JrNHS; NHS; TchrAde; SciCl; Clge; Med Tech.

ZIEDONIS, Arvids; Arlington HS; Indianapolis, IN; 17/478 HonRl; NHS; StuCncl; College.

ZIEGELBAUER, Sandra; Kiel HS; Kiel, WI; Chr; Chrs; Quill&Scroll; SchPl; TchrAde; 4-H; GerCl; Swmmng; 4-HAwd; Technical School; Interior Decorator.

ZIEGENFUSS, Teresa M; Cardinal Stritch HS; Keokuk, IA; 4/30 VPSrCls; HonRl; PolWkr; Sdlty; StuCncl; TchrAde; Yrbk; PpCl; Bsbl; KiwanAwd; Ia St Univ; Sociology.

ZIEGENHAGEN, Pamela K; Morgan HS; Sleepy Eye, MN; Band; Chr; Chrs; ChrhWkr; CncrtBnd; HonRl; LbryAde; MrchBnd; PepBnd; SchPl; College; Ecology.

ZIEGLE, Janet S; Rich East HS; Park Forest, IL; HonRl; Bsktbl; Tennis; Eastern Illinois Univ; Zoology.

ZIEGLER, Barbara A; York Comm HS; Elmhurst, IL; 144/986 PresSrCls; Band; HonRl; MrchBnd; PepBnd; StuCncl; Purdue U; Pharmacy.

ZIEGLER, David R; Hancock Central HS; Hancock, MI; 8/95 PresSophCls; PresJrCls; VPSrCls; HonRl; SchPl; LetterFtbl; LetterTrk; Mi Tech Univ; Electrical Engineering.

ZIEGLER, David W; Hays HS; Hays, KS; Aud/Vis; Band; CncrtBnd; HonRl; MrchBnd; SctActv; LetterBsktbl; IMSpt; Ft Hays State Clg; Business.

ZIEGLER, Julie K; Kennedy Public HS; Kennedy, MN; Chrs; DrmMjrt; RptrYrbk; FHA; SpnCl; PpCl; Chrldr; GAA; Univ; Social Work.

ZIEGLER, Kathy M; Poynette HS; Arlington, WI; 2/94 HonRl; JA; JrNHS; Mdrgl; MrchBnd; NHS; PepBnd; FHA; PpCl; Secretary.

ZIEGLER, Kimberly S; Fenton HS; Fenton, MI; Chrs; HonRl; JA; NHS; YthFlsp; 4-H; Trk; Mott Comm Clg; Accountant.

ZIEGLER, Kim K; North Platte Senior HS; North Platte, NE; HonRl; SchPl; YthFlsp; SchPpr; 4-H; PpCl; Trk; Chrldr; GAA; IMSpt; PPFtbl; DARAwd; College.

ZIEGLER, Louise A; Academy Of Our Lady; Peoria, IL; 1/250 HonRl; SchMus; SchPl; SctActv; StuCncl; RptrSchPpr; College.

ZIEGLER, Michael A; Middleton HS; Middleton, WI; 11/265 AFS; HonRl; ROTC; SchPl; FrCl; GerCl; Univ Of Wisconsin; Nuclear Engineer.

ZIEGLER, Michael E; Lutheran HS; Chaska, MN; PresFrshCls; PresSophCls; Band; Chrs; ChrhWkr; HonRl; NHS; PresStuCncl; SciCl; CaptBsktbl; LetterFtbl; LetterTrk; Univ Of Mn; Dentistry.

ZIEGLER, Milissa J; Trego Community HS; Collyer, KS; PresSophCls; Chr; HonRl; LbryAde; SchPl; StuCncl; FHA; Vocational Schl; Nursing.

ZIEGLER, Rodney L; Circle HS; Towanda, KS; Band; CncrtBnd; HonRl; MrchBnd; PepBnd; SciCl; Trade Sch.

ZIEGLER, Susan; Franklin; Riverton, NE; 27#29#30 HonRl; MrchBnd; NHS; PepBnd; SchPl; StuCncl; 4-H; Univ;.

ZIEGLER, William J; Oelwein Comm HS; Oelwein, IA; PresSophCls; Band; CncrtBnd; MrchBnd; PepBnd; SchPl; StuCncl; SciCl; Ftbl; LetterWrstlng; Iowa St Univ; Marine Biology.

ZIEHER, Pamela J; Auburndale HS; Arpin, WI; TrsJrCls; Band; Chr; HonRl; SchPl; SctActv; StuCncl; FBLA; PpCl; Trk; Trade Schl; Fashion Merchandizing.

ZIEHLI, Andy P; Belleville HS; Belleville, WI; Aud/Vis; ChrhWkr; CncrtBnd; MrchBnd; ModUN; PepBnd; SctActv; FFA; LetterFtbl; LetterWrstlng;.

ZIEHLSDORF, Paula J; Martin Luther HS; Milwaukee, WI; 1/87 SecFrshCls; Chr; ChrhWkr; HonRl; JrNHS; Mdrgl; NHS; OffAde; PresAwd; RotaryAwd; Concordia River Forest Clge; Math.

ZIEL, Eric R; United Community HS; Boone, IA; 2/40 TrsJrCls; Band; MrchBnd; NHS; StuCncl; RptrSchPpr; FFA; BauchLmbAwd; DanFAwd; 4-HAwd; Ia State University; Veterinarian.

ZIELAZINSKI, Mark; Morton West Hs; Berwyn, IL; CtyCnl; CmntyWkr; HonRl; ModUN; PolWkr; TchrAde; UNYO; YthFnd; MthCl; Ftbl; Illinois State U; Political Science.

ZIELINSKI, James; Gordon Tech; Chicago, IL; Chrs; CncrtBnd; HonRl; MrchBnd; NHS; PolWkr; StuCncl; KeyCl; U Chgo Circle ; Major Study Biology.

ZIELINSKI, Loraine M; Manistee Catholic Central HS; Manistee, MI; 8/69 HonRl; NHS; EdYrBk; EdSchPpr; LetterBsktbl; DARAwd; Northwestern Michigan College; Comm Art.

ZIELINSKI, Patricia C; Manistee Catholic Central HS; Manistee, MI; 18/67 HonRl; HospAde; West Shore Community College; Nurse.

ZIELSKI, Clark D; Eldora HS; Eldora, IA; Chr; Chrl; Chrs; HonRl; NatlThespSoc; SchMus; StuCncl; FrCl; CaptBsbl; Ftbl; Univ; Teacher.

ZIEMAN, Dwight; Oakes HS; Oakes, ND; 24/69 ALBoysSt; ChrhWkr; HonRl; SchPl; StuCncl; Construction Management.

ZIEMBA, Kathleen; Saint Ladislaus HS; Hamtramck, MI; HonRl; JA; FrCl; PpCl; College.

ZIEMEK, Pamela M; Mauston Area HS; Lyndon Station, WI; ChrhWkr; HonRl; FrCl; PpCl; Chrldr; Coll; Medica Technology.

ZIEMER, Cynthia A; Bullock Creek HS; Midland, MI; CncrtBnd; HonRl; HospAde; MrchBnd; NHS; PepBnd; Yrbk; 4-H; FrCl; GAA; University; Medicine.

ZIEMER, Kevin W; St Thomas Acad; S St Paul, MN; 7#41#55# ROTC; SchPl; StuCncl; RptrYrbk; SchPpr; SciCl; CaptSocr;.

ZIEMER, Wayne H; Luther HS; Chicago, IL; 7/208 ChrhWkr; HonRl; LbryAde; NHS; SctActv; StuCncl; Glf; Illinois Institute Of Tech; Architecture.

ZIEMKE, Deb L; Tracy HS; Garvin, MN; LbryAde; RptrSchPpr; FHA; Chrldr; CchngActv; GAA; IMSpt; PPFtbl; PresAwd; Bus School; Accounting Or Math.

ZIENTAK, David W; St Clement HS; Warren, MI; HonRl; SciCl; Bsbl; Bsktbl; CitAwd; Coll; Pro.

ZIEPIELA, Kristine A; Lumen Christi HS; Jackson, MI; 1/225 ChrhWkr; CmntyWkr; HonRl; LitMag; NHS; NatlMeritSF; SchPpr; PpCl; IMSpt; Mi St Univ; Education.

ZIER, Cynthia A; Bayard HS; Bayard, NE; ChrhWkr; HonRl; OffAde; Yrbk; FHA; SpnCl; Secretary.

ZIEREN, Julia A; Mater Dei HS; Carlyle, IL; 30/200 Chrs; HonRl; SchMus; SchPl; RptrSchPpr; EdSchPpr; FrCl; Univ Of Illinois; Psychology.

ZIERKE, David L; Belvidere HS; Belvidere, IL; 35/350 ChrhWkr; HonRl; VPStuCncl; GerCl; PpCl; LetterBsbl; College; Lawyer.

ZIEROLD, Juanita M; Amana HS; South Amana, IA; 1/40 HonRl; RptrYrbk; Yrbk; Swmmng; CchngActv; Univ Of Iowa; Medicine.

ZIESEMER, Gary; Brooten HS; Brooten, MN; 2/45 HonRl; NHS; NatlThespSoc; SchPl; SchPpr; BauchLmbAwd; LionAwd; Alexandria Tech; Appliance Rep.

ZIESER, Jane E; St Johns HS; Independence, IA; 1/24 SecJrCls; Chr; Chrl; Chrs; ChrhWkr; CmntyWkr; HonRl; NHS; SchMus; SchPl; SctActv; RptrYrbk; RptrSchPpr; Bsktbl; College; Secretarial.

ZIESERL, Teresa L; Loy Norrix HS; Kalamazoo, MI; ChrhWkr; NHS; NatlMeritCmnd; TchrAde; CaptBsktbl; Trk; Nazareth College; Nursing Rn.

ZIESMAN, Beth; Eldora HS; Eldora, IA; Chr; HonRl; SchMus; 4-H; FHA; SpnCl; IMSpt; 4-HAwd; College.

ZIESMAN, Craig A; Algona HS; Luverne, IA; 3/125 HonRl; NatlMeritSF; PolWkr; PresStuGov; TchrAde; RptrSchPpr; 4-H; PpCl; Bsktbl; KiwanAwd; Macalester College; Biophysics.

ZIESNER, David J; Ventura Community HS; Ventura, IA; VPFrshCls; VPJrCls; CncrtBnd; HonRl; MrchBnd; PepBnd; TchrAde; LetterBsktbl; LetterFtbl; LetterTrk; College; Professional.

ZIETLOW, Duane A; Edgar HS; Edgar, WI; 10/82 TrsJrCls; ALBoysSt; Band; Chrs; HonRl; SchPl; PresFFA; LetterFtbl; Trk; CitAwd; N Central Tech Inst; Ag Mechanics.

ZIGTERMAN, Paul K; Illiana Christian HS; Lansing, IL; Band; ChrhWkr; CncrtBnd; MrchBnd; NatlFornLg; NHS; SchPl; StuCncl; Yrbk; College; Architecture.

ZILCH, Cheryl A; Central Montcalm HS; Stanton, MI; 7/130 VPSophCls; VPSrCls; Band; HonRl; HospAde; VPNHS; StuCncl; 4-H; LetterChrldr; VoiceDemAwd; Mi State Univ; Registered Nurse.

ZILINSKAS, Susette A; Alpena HS; Ossineke, MI; Band; CncrtBnd; LbryAde; MrchBnd; PepBnd; LatCl; Coll; Librarian.

ZILKA, Jullene E; Academy Of Holy Angels; Richfield, MN; Chrs; CaptBsktbl; CaptTrk; IMSpt; PPFtbl;.

ZILLI, Karen S; East Central HS; Guilford, IN; 17/200 Chrs; HonRl; NHS; NatlMeritFnl; NatlMeritCmnd; NatlMeritSchl; NatlMeritSF; SpnCl; IMSpt; Purdue; Data Processing.

ZILLINGER, Jeffrey J; Phillipsburg HS; Phillipsburg, KS; 10/81 VPFrshCls; Chrl; LbryAde; Mdrgl; NHS; NatlThespSoc; SchMus; SchPl; TchrAde; FFA; Kansas State University; Vet.

ZILLIOX, Maureen E; Dundee Comm HS; Dundee, IL; HonRl; NatlFornLg; NatlThespSoc; Orch; SchMus; SchPl; PresGerCl; University; Lawyer.

ZILLMANN, Eric R; Northwestern Military Acad; Evanston, IL; 3/33 DrlTm; HonRl; Quill&Scroll; ROTC; TchrAde; Yrbk; LetterBsbl; LetterTennis; LetterWrstlng; Univ; Professional.

ZILLMER, Ricky D; Litchfield HS; Watkins, MN; Band; Chr; ChrhWkr; SchPl; GerCl; LetterBsbl; Bsktbl; Ftbl; MasAwd; Univ Of Wisconsin; History.

ZILM, Marla; Toluca HS; Toluca, IL; SecFrshCls; SecSrCls; Band; Chrs; CncrtBnd; HonRl; MrchBnd; NHS; PepBnd; FHA; PpCl; GAA; AmLegAwd; Col; Professional.

ZIMDARS, Jeanette M; Dieterich HS; Dieterich, IL; SecFrshCls; Band; Chr; Chrs; ChrhWkr; CncrtBnd; HonRl; MrchBnd; YthFlsp; 4-H; FHA; SpnCl; PpCl; Chrldr; Trade School.

ZIMMER, Dennis J; O Gorman HS; Sioux Falls, SD; ChrhWkr; CAP; CmntyWkr; DrlTm; SchPl; TchrAde; IMSpt; College; Electrochemistry.

ZIMMER, Diana; Brown County HS; Morgantown, IN; 14/175 Band; CncrtBnd; HonRl; MrchBnd; Orch; PepBnd; SchMus; SchPl; PpCl; GAA; College; Major Study.

ZIMMER, Dorlene; Cornell Hs; Cornell, IL; 2 VPSophCls; PresJrCls; PresSrCls; HonRl; OffAde; SchPl; StuCncl; YthFlsp; RptrYrbk; SptEdSchPpr; Iowa Wesleyan College ; Nursing.

ZIMMER, Joel A; Hackett HS; Kalamazoo, MI; 15/142 Band; CncrtBnd; HonRl; MrchBnd; Orch;

PepBnd; LetterBsktbl; LetterFtbl; LetterTrk; IMSpt; Kalamazoo Valley; Criminal Justice.

ZIMMER, Juliann M; Creston Sr HS; Grand Rapids, MI; PresFrshCls; PresSophCls; PresJrCls; PresSrCls; CmntyWkr; HospAde; StuGov; LetterTrk; IMSpt; TIMEAwd; VoiceDemAwd; Davenport College; Legal Secretary.

ZIMMER, Mark S; West Ottawa HS; Holland, MI; 1/265 HonRl; NHS; StuCncl; YthLg; SchPpr; GerCl; LetterBsbl; IMSpt; BauchLmbAwd; Hope College; Chemist.

ZIMMER, Michael J; Thornapple Kellogg HS; Caledonia, MI; 10/130 ChrhWkr; JrNHS; NHS; SchMus; SchPl; RptrYrbk; EdYrBk; RptrSchPpr; SptEdSchPpr; Ftbl; College Msu; Journalism.

ZIMMER, Susan M; Messmer HS; Milwaukee, WI; 16/209 HonRl; LbryAde; NHS; StuGov; TchrAde; RptrSchPpr; FTA; PpCl; LetterBsbl; Swmmng; Univ; Biology.

ZIMMER, Thomas R; Steeleville HS; Steeleville, IL; 6/56 TrsJrCls; HonRl; NHS; SctActv; Yrbk; TreasSpnCl; PpCl; Bsktbl; U Of Il; Engineering.

ZIMMERER, Jacquline J; Holy Family HS; Madison, NE; HonRl; PepBnd; SchPl; SchPpr; 4-H; PpCl; Trk; IMSpt; Coll; Voc.

ZIMMERLINE, Debbie A; Bridgewater Fontanelle HS; Fontanelle, IA; Band; ChrhWkr; CncrtBnd; HonRl; MrchBnd; NHS; PepBnd; SchPl; RptrYrbk; Southwestern Community College; Teaching.

ZIMMERMAN, Alan R; Glenbard West HS; Glen Ellyn, IL; HonRl; NatlMeritCmnd; SchMus; SchPl; RptrYrbk; SchPpr; SciCl; College; Electrical Engineer.

ZIMMERMAN, Amy L; Algoma HS; Alogma, WI; PresSophCls; ALAGirlsSt; Chrs; Mdrgl; NHS; SchAde; SchMus; SchPl; EdYrBk; RptrSchPpr; Bellin Mem Hosp; Nursing.

ZIMMERMAN, Ann M; Salina HS; Salina, KS; 2/350 PresSophCls; HonRl; NatlMeritCmnd; SchMus; Pres4-H; VPFTA; LetterTennis; LetterTrk; DanFAwd; CitAwd; Univ Ks State; Elementary Education.

ZIMMERMAN, Beth; Monticello HS; Monticello, WI; 2/27 PresSophCls; Band; HonRl; SchPl; StuCncl; EdYrBk; 4-H; SpnCl; DanFAwd; DARAwd; Univ Of Wi Eau Claire; Nursing.

ZIMMERMAN, Betty; Mccune HS; Mccune, KS; SecSophCls; VPSrCls; Band; Chrs; CmntyWkr; HonRl; RptrYrbk; RptrSchPpr; Kscp Of Pittsburg.

ZIMMERMAN, Carla G; Ottawa HS; Ottawa, KS; Chr; ChrhWkr; HonRl; NHS; SchMus; SchPl; RptrSchPpr; SpnCl; PpCl; LetterTrk; College; Psychology.

ZIMMERMAN, Cathie S; Noblesville HS; Noblesville, IN; 25/249 Band; CncrtBnd; HonRl; MrchBnd; PepBnd; YthFlsp; Yrbk; FrCl; MthCl; PpCl; Purdue U; Computor Science.

ZIMMERMAN, Cindy D; Taylor Public HS; Taylor, ND; 1/19 PresFrshCls; SecTrsJrCls; ALAGirlsSt; Band; ChrhWkr; CmntyWkr; HonRl; ModUN; SchPl; StuCncl; StuGov; RptrSchPpr; FHA; LetterBsktbl; LetterTrk; Mayville State College; Child Specialist.

ZIMMERMAN, Edward P; Lew Wallace HS; Gary, IN; 5/513 ALBoysSt; CmntyWkr; HonRl; JrNHS; LbryAde; NHS; Quill&Scroll; StuCncl; EdYrBk; CitAwd; Coll; Lawyer.

ZIMMERMAN, Gary M; St Viator HS; Mt Prospect, IL; 39/245 SecSophCls; PresBand; CncrtBnd; DrmMjrt; MrchBnd; SchMus; EdYrBk; College.

ZIMMERMAN, Joe; Chaparral Hs; Harper, KS; ChrhWkr; HonRl; SchPl; PresYthFlsp; KeyCl; College;agriculture.

ZIMMERMAN, Julie A; Northwest HS; Grand Island, NE; 15/130 Chr; Chrs; ChrhWkr; HonRl; SchMus; YthFlsp; Kearney State College.

ZIMMERMAN, Kathleen A; El Paso HS; El Paso, IL; 3/90 AFS; HonRl; IntrClCncl; NHS; SchPl; YthFlsp; EdYrBk; FHA; SpnCl; MthCl; Icc; Vocation.

ZIMMERMAN, Ken; New Glarus HS; New Glarus, WI; 20/65 TrsSrCls; Orch; PepBnd; SchPl; YthFlsp; RptrYrbk; SptEdSchPpr; PpCl; Bsbl; Bsktbl; Univ Of Lacrosse; Accounting.

ZIMMERMAN, Kenneth M; Trico HS; Percy, IL; HonRl; FrCl; PpCl; SciCl; Univ.

ZIMMERMAN, Kent E; Leo HS; Grabill, IN; 1/96 PresFrshCls; VPSophCls; HstJrCls; TrsSrCls; Band; ChrhWkr; CncrtBnd; HonRl; JA; JCC; JrNHS; MrchBnd; CaptBsbl; LetterFtbl; Indiana University; Business.

ZIMMERMAN, Loren P; Graceville Public HS; Johnson, MN; 12/50 Band; Chr; Chrs; ChrhWkr; CmntyWkr; CncrtBnd; Bsbl; Bsktbl; Ftbl; 4-HAwd; U Of Minnesota; Law.

ZIMMERMAN, Mark A; Eisenhower HS; Saginow, MI; Band; CncrtBnd; HonRl; GerCl; Michigan Univ; Mech Eng.

ZIMMERMAN, Pamela G; Bloom Township HS; Chicago Heights, IL; 83/1000 Band; CncrtBnd; HonRl; MrchBnd; NHS; Orch; SchMus; SchPl; YthFlsp; No Illinois Univ; Nursing.

ZIMMERMAN, Patrick G; St Mary Springs HS; Lomira, WI; 45/139 Aud/Vis; ChrhWkr; CmntyWkr; LbryAde; Sacrstn; SchPl; EdSchPpr; FSA; SpnCl; SciCl; IMSpt; Marquette Univ; Medicine.

ZIMMERMAN, Paul K; Ottawa Township HS; Ottawa, IL; 40/426 HonRl; NHS; StuCncl; GerCl; LetterBsbl; LetterBsktbl; LetterFtbl; Univ Of Illinois; Economics.

ZIMMERMAN, Robert E; St Agatha HS; Detroit, MI; PresSophCls; ChrhWkr; HonRl; NatlMeritCmnd; StuCncl; Yrbk; SchPpr; LetterTrk; University; Business.

ZIMMERMAN, Ronald J; Bethany Christian HS; Goshen, IN; PresJrCls; Chr; NatlMeritSF; StuCncl; FshEdYrbk; SptEdYrbk; GerCl; LetterSocr; Goshen College; Biology.

ZIMMERMAN, Scott A; Darlington HS; Darlington, WI; 7/130 HonRl; Teen; YthLg; 4-H; FFA; SpnCl; MthCl; SciCl; LetterBsbl; LetterBsktbl; LetterFtbl; CchngActv; College; Dairy Science.

ZIMMERMAN, Steven G; Tomah Sr HS; Tomah, WI; 2/283 HonRl; PresNHS; SpnCl; Bsktbl; LetterTennis; University; Engineering.

ZIMMERMAN, Thomas E; Snider HS; Fort Wayne, IN; 38/525 Band; CncrtBnd; HonRl; MrchBnd; PepBnd; TchrAde; LatCl; In Univ; Law Field.

ZIMMERMAN, Vickie; Juda HS; Juda, WI; PresJrCls; Band; DrmMjrt; HonRl; StuCncl; EdYrBk; RptrSchPpr; Chrldr; GAA; DARAwd; Business.

ZIMMERMAN, Wayne R; Quincy HS; Quincy, IL; 205/644 AFS; ChrhWkr; StuCncl; Quincy College; Business.

ZIMMERMANN, Deborah A; Albany HS; Avon, MN; 21/129 ChrhWkr; HonRl; JrNHS; SchPl; LetterChrldr; Voc School; Dental Asst.

ZIMMERMANN, Denise R; Lamberton Public HS; Lamberton, MN; 18/44 Band; ChrhWkr; CncrtBnd; MrchBnd; SchPpr; SchMus; SchPl; TchrAde; RptrYrbk; SecFHA; Voc School; Dental Assistant.

ZIMMERMANN, Joseph E; Br Rice HS; Oaklawn, IL; 53/431 Aud/Vis; HonRl; NHS; NatlMeritSF; IMSpt; U Of Notre Dame; Engineering.

ZIMMERMANN, Joseph E; Brother Rice HS; Oaklawn, IL; 51/416 Aud/Vis; NHS; Univ Of Notre Dame; Engineering.

ZIMMERMANN, Phyllis E; Hampton Public HS; Hampton, NE; 2/18 Chr; Chrs; ChrhWkr; DrlTm; HonRl; HospAde; LbryAde; SchAde; SchMus; SchPl; YthFlsp; School Of Nursing; Nurse.

ZIMMERMANN, Stephanie J; Mt Pleasant HS; Mt Pleasant, MI; 6/348 HonRl; TreasJA; NatlMeritSF; TchrAde; RptrYrbk; FrCl; JAAwd; Kalamazoo College; Psychologist.

ZIMPRICH, Gloria A; Hamlin HS; Hazel, SD; 3/66 Band; HonRl; LbryAde; SchPl; Yrbk; RptrSchPpr; FHA; LetterBsktbl; Trk; IMSpt; Dakota St Coll; Acct.

ZIMPRICH, Virginia M; Binford Public HS; Binford, ND; 3/22 ALAGirlsSt; Aud/Vis; HonRl; LbryAde; NHS; OffAde; SchPl; PpCl; IMSpt; College; Professional.

ZINDA, Vicki L; Danube Public HS; Danube, MN; 11/44 VPSophCls; SecSrCls; LbryAde; Chrldr; Willmar Vo Tech; Nurse.

ZINGSHEIM, Michael J; Muskego HS; Muskego, WI; HonRl; NHS; MthCl; CaptSwmmng; Trk; Purdue University; Engineer.

ZINIEL, Lawrence W; Evanston Twp HS; Evanston, IL; 8/040 ChrhWkr; HonRl; Purdure Univ; Engineering.

ZINK, Ann; Carrington HS; Edmunds, ND; Band; CncrtBnd; HonRl; JrNHS; NHS; PepBnd; PpCl; GAA; College; Med Tech.

ZINK, Gary D; Meridian Sr HS; Sanford, MI; 19/128 ALBoysSt; CncrtBnd; HonRl; MrchBnd; NHS; SchPl; StuCncl; LetterBsbl; LetterBsktbl; CaptFtbl; Central Mi U; Bus.

ZINK, Greg J; High School; St Louis, MO; Band; HonRl; JA; LbryAde; SctActv; Trk; Wrstlng; AmLegAwd; College; Journalism.

ZINK, Janet; North Clay Community HS; Louisville, IL; Band; HonRl; PepBnd; StuCncl; SpnCl; PpCl; Trk; GAA; Lincoln Christian Col.

ZINK, Kathleen B; Logan HS; Logan, KS; VPFrshCls; TrsJrCls; ALAGirlsSt; HonRl; RptrYrbk; PpCl; LetterTrk; CaptChrldr; Cl; Pro.

ZINK, Margaret M; Nazareth Acad; Mc Cook, IL; HonRl; JrNHS; NHS; StuCncl; StuGov; TchrAde; Yrbk; SpnCl; GAA; U Of Il; Science.

ZINKE, Jill D; Wonewoc Center HS; Wonewoc, WI; 4/43 Band; CncrtBnd; HonRl; NHS; Yrbk; FHA; Bsktbl; Trk; IMSpt; DanFAwd;.

ZINN, Karl; South Harrison HS; Bethany, MO; 4/93 ChrhWkr; CmntyWkr; HonRl; NHS; PolWkr; RedCrAde; SctActv; Ftbl; Trk; Wrstlng; College;engineering.

ZINN, Kenneth S; Shawnee Mission South HS; Prairie Village, KS; StuGov; Univ; Political Science.

ZINN, Pamela J; Yorkville HS; Bristol, IL; DrmBgl; LbryAde; MrchBnd; PepBnd; SchAde; SctActv; TchrAde; Teen; YthFlsp; SptEdSchPpr; Illinois Inst Tech; System Analysis.

ZINN, Patty; Falls City HS; Falls City, NE; Chrs; Mdrgl; NatlThespSoc; SchMus; SchPl; YthFlsp; PresFrshCls; Glf; /.peru State College; Music.

ZINN, Phyllis; B C Central HS; Battle Creek, MI; Bus College; Professional.

ZINNEL, Dorian F; Reed Custer HS; Braidwood, IL; HonRl; NHS; StuCncl; SpnCl; Bsbl; Bsktbl; IMSpt; University; Professional.

ZINS, Dorothy M; St Gertrudes HS; Raleigh, ND; 6/27 Chr; Chrs; HonRl; SchMus; StuCncl; LetterTrk;.

ZINTHER, Timothy E; Peshtigo HS; Peshtigo, WI; Chr; Chrs; ChrhWkr; HonRl; LbryAde; SchPl; RptrYrbk; 4-H; 4-HAwd; College; Professional.

ZINTSMASTER, Sheila; North Miami HS; Roann, IN; 4/120 SecJrCls; ALAGirlsSt; Chr; ChrhWkr; HonRl; Mdrgl; NHS; Trk; PPFtbl; St Paul Bible College.

ZIPPERER, Nancy R; Lincoln HS; Park Falls, WI; VPJrCls; Band; DrmBgl; HonRl; MrchBnd; Trk; Chrldr; GAA; University.

ZIPPERIAN, Nancy J; Peru HS; Peru, IN; 16/231 TrsFrshCls; ALAGirlsSt; CncrtBnd; DrlTm; HonRl; SecNHS; StuCncl; RptrYrbk; FrCl; Purdue Univ; Computer Science.

ZIRALDO, John F; Catholic Central HS; Detroit, MI; ChrhWkr; IntrClCncl; StuGov; RptrYrbk; Yrbk; LatCl; Tennis; Seminary College; Roman Catholic Priesthood.

ZIRFAS, Janice T; Bishop Miege HS; Prairie Village, KS; Chr; Chrl; Chrs; HonRl; HospAde; SecNHS; SchMus; FNA; PpCl; Avila College; Nursing.

ZISKA, Cheryl; West Holt HS; Stuart, NE; 10/80 Chrs; DrlTm; HonRl; NHS; SchPl; 4-H; FHA; PpCl; Trk; College; Music Or Fashion.

ZISKA, Luanne; West Holt HS; Atkinson, NE; Chr; Chrs; DrlTm; MrchBnd; SchPl; Yrbk; LetterGAA; TreasAmLegAwd; Police Academy.

ZISOOK, Lisa A; Stephen Tyng Mather HS; Chicago, IL; 1/425 TreasChr; HonRl; LitMag; LbryAde; NHS; NatlMeritCmnd; OffAde; SchAde; EdSchPpr; University; Lawyer.

ZITELLA, Joanne C; Ridgewood HS; Norridge, IL; 3/369 HonRl; SecNHS; PolWkr; SchPl; SecStuCncl; SecStuGov; SchPpr; PpCl; GAA; Loyola Univ; Business.

ZITNICK, Kathleen M; Glenbard West HS; Glen Ellyn, IL; 77/545 Chrs; HonRl; HospAde; NatlThespSoc; RedCrAde; SchMus; SchPl; SctActv; TchrAde; RptrSchPpr; Ill State Univ; Home Economics.

ZITNIK, Frank J; Cathedral HS; Omaha, NE; CmntyWkr; LetterFtbl; LetterTrk; LetterWrstlng; CchngActv; GovHonPrgAwd; College.

ZITTERKOPF, Jeffory D; Morrill HS; Morrill, NE; Band; Chr; Chrs; CncrtBnd; HonRl; MrchBnd; NHS; NatlThespSoc; PepBnd; SchAde; SchMus; SchPl; StuGov; TchrAde; College; Science.

ZITTLOW, Raymond J; Northland HS; Ball Club, MN; PresJrCls; HonRl; NHS; SchPl; StuCncl; 4-H; LetterBsbl; LetterBsktbl; IMSpt; U Of Minn Duluth; Medicine.

ZITUR, Mary A; Armstrong HS; Minneapolis, MN; 6/595 HonRl; NHS; PolWkr; RptrYrbk; EdYrBk; FrCl; College Of St Benedict; Medicine.

ZIZZO, Celeste G; Queen Of Peace HS; Chicago, IL; CmntyWkr; HonRl; SchAde; GAA; IMSpt; St Xavier College; Teacher.

ZLOTOPOLSKI, Nancy J; Buchanan HS; Hawk Point, MO; 2/154 CmntyWkr; HonRl; LbryAde; NHS; OffAde; RedCrAde; 4-H; FNA; PresMthCl; PresSciCl; College; Nursing.

ZLUTICKY, Ronald W; Breckenridge HS; Breckenridge, MN; ChrhWkr; CmntyWkr; HonRl; SctActv; StuGov; SptEdYrbk; 4-H; Bsbl; Bsktbl; CaptFtbl; Tennis; 4-HAwd;.

ZMEK, Randy W; Central City HS; Archer, NE; Band; HonRl; MrchBnd; NHS; PepBnd; YthFlsp; PresFFA; Wrstlng; IMSpt; Coll; Voc.

ZMIERSKI, Patricia; East Gary Edison HS; East Gary, IN; ChrhWkr; HonRl; SpnCl; College; Dentistry.

ZMIJA, Robert J; Thornton Fractional So HS; Lansing, IL; 8/522 Band; CncrtBnd; HonRl; JrNHS; NHS; SchMus; LetterWrstlng; Indiana University; Medicine.

ZMOLEK, Janie M; Cedar Catholic HS; Hartington, NE; 2/67 Chr; Chrs; ChrhWkr; CmntyWkr; HonRl; NHS; OffAde; StuCncl; TchrAde; RptrYrbk; Trk; Chrldr; GAA; Ne Nebraska Tech Col; Secretarial.

ZMUDA, Cheryl L; Thornwood HS; Calumet City, IL; 64/852 HonRl; NHS; StuCncl; StuGov; Chrldr; De Paul Univ; Law.

ZMUDA, Debbie V; Wheeling HS; Wheeling, IL; DrlTm; HonRl; Trade School; Vocation.

ZNAMENACEK, Denise S; Wilber Clatonia HS; Wilber, NE; 3/32 Band; HonRl; SchPl; TchrAde; Yrbk; SchPpr; FBLA; FHA; PpCl; BttyCrckrAwd; Southeast Community College; Comercial Art.

ZNAVOR, Nancy J; Washington HS; Chicago, IL; 12/491 ChrhWkr; HonRl; JrNHS; NHS; NatlMeritSF; SchPl; StuCncl; TchrAde; SpnCl; GAA; English Educ.

ZOBEL, Ann M; Chippewa Valley HS; Mt Clemens, MI; ChrhWkr; CmntyWkr; HonRl; JA; PolWkr; SchPl; SctActv; GAA; U Of Mich; Law.

ZOCHER, Naomi; Flat Rock HS; Flat Rock, MI; Chr; Chrs; ChrhWkr; CmntyWkr; HonRl; HospAde; JrNHS; NHS; PolWkr; SchPl; College; Professional.

ZODROW, John A; Cudahy HS; Cudahy, WI; 21/354 HonRl; NHS; NatlMeritSF; FrCl; College.

ZOELLICK, Steven; Crystal Lake Comm Hs; Crystal Lake, IL; 8/453 Chr; HonRl; Mdrgl; NHS; SchMus; PresLatCl; CaptBsktbl; LetterTennis; CchngActv; College; Pre Med.

ZOET, Bonnie J; Sheldon Sr HS; Sheldon, IA; HonRl; SecYrbk; RptrSchPpr; FTA; PpCl; Bsktbl; LetterTrk; IMSpt; College.

ZOGG, Carol S; Central HS; Grand Forks, ND; 2/316 ALAGirlsSt; Band; ChrhWkr; NatlFornLg; VPNHS; SecNatlThespSoc; StuCncl; RptrSchPpr; PresFrCl; LetterTrk; Univ Of Nd; Elem Ed.

ZOLFO, Bryan M; Marist HS; Calumet Park, IL; 86/365 HonRl; SpnCl; LetterBsktbl; Glf; AmLegAwd; College; General Business.

ZOLLARS, Marilyn L; Van Buren Comm HS; Keosauqua, IA; VPJrCls; HonRl; NHS; SchPl; YthFlsp; 4-H; LetterBsktbl; LetterTrk; PPFtbl; 4-HAwd; College.

ZOLLIN, Susan A; Taylor HS; Kokomo, IN; 3/179 HonRl; NHS; TchrAde; FrCl; Gmi; Computer Analyst.

ZOLLINGER, Wayne; South Side HS; Fort Wayne, IN; 76/438 Aud/Vis; HonRl; SchAde; Ftbl; IMSpt; PresAwd; College; Professional.

ZOLLMAN, Carla J; Phillipsburg HS; Prairie View, KS; Band; Chr; ChrhWkr; CmntyWkr; HonRl; PepBnd; TchrAde; FHA; PpCl; Chrldr; College; Businss.

ZOLMAN, Pamela A; Waldron HS; Waldron, MI; Band; Chrs; CncrtBnd; DrmMjrt; HonRl; MrchBnd; NHS; SchPl; YthFlsp; Lansing Business Univ; Secretary.

ZOLMAN, Pamela A; Waldron Area HS; Waldron, MI; 4/50 TrsFrshCls; Band; Chrs; CncrtBnd; DrmMjrt; HonRl; NHS; SchPl; SchPpr; CitAwd; Bus Schl; Bus Admin.

ZOLTANI, Annette C; Bradley Bourbonnais HS; Bourbonnais, IL; SecJrCls; HonRl; NHS; StuCncl; PpCl; Chrldr; GAA; Business School; Secretarial.

ZOLTEK, Margaret A; Rudyard HS; Trout Lake, MI; Aud/Vis; CmntyWkr; HonRl; NHS; NatlMeritFnl; SchPl; StuGov; Yrbk; Chrldr; Northern Mi Univ; Psuchology.

ZOMA, Susan T; Marian HS; Bloomfield Hills, MI; CmntyWkr; HonRl; NHS; PolWkr; TchrAde; Univ Of Michigan; Psychology Sociology.

ZONIA, Laura E; Mehlville HS; St Louis, MO; 89/526 Chr; LbryAde; GAA; Univ; Professional.

ZONSIUS, Edward J; Notre Dame HS; Niles, IL; 50/286 Chrs; HonRl; SchPl; Bsbl; CaptSwmmng; Notre Dame; Business Admn.

ZOOK, James R; Metamora Twp HS; Metamora, IL; 1/183 AFS; Band; CncrtBnd; HonRl; MrchBnd; NHS; Orch; PepBnd; SchMus; PresSciCl; AmLegAwd; College; Engineer.

ZOOK, Kathryn M; Braymer C 4 HS; Cowgill, MO; 14/36 ChrhWkr; LbryAde; SctActv; TchrAde; 4-H; FFA; PpCl; Bsbl; LetterBsktbl; Trk; U Of Missouri; Veterinarian.

ZOOK, Lauren L; Beach HS; Beach, ND; 9/39 ALAGirlsSt; Chr; Chrs; ChrhWkr; HonRl; SchPl; 4-H; FHA; GerCl; North Dakota St Univ; Dietetics.

ZOOK, Lois; Morgan Co R Ii HS; Versailles, MO; Chrs; ChrhWkr; HonRl; SchMus; StuCncl; TchrAde; YthFlsp; Bsktbl; Eastern Mennonite College; Physical Ed Maj.

ZOOK, Patricia L; Sigourney Comm HS; Sigourney, IA; 45/76 Chrs; NatlThespSoc; SchMus; SchPl; Yrbk; RptrSchPpr; Univ Of Iowa; Humanities.

ZOOK, Ruth A; Woodland R Iv HS; Glen Allen, MO; ChrhWkr; HonRl; YthFlsp; FHA; PpCl;.

ZOOK, Velma K; Sherwood Cass HS; Garden City, MO; Band; ChrhWkr; HonRl; NHS; YthFlsp; CaptBsktbl; LetterTrk; PresAwd; College; Nursing.

ZORGER, Kelle; Wichita East HS; Wichita, KS; 1/57830# HonRl; Mdrgl; FrCl; PpCl; Coll Of Wichita.

ZORICH, Diane; Maria HS; Chicago, IL; 29/335 CmntyWkr; HonRl; HospAde; LitMag; NHS; SchPl; GAA; IMSpt; College; Sociology Anthropology.

ZORICH, Donna M; Bishop Dubourg HS; St Louis, MO; HonRl; JrNHS; NHS; OffAde; GAA; IMSpt; PPFtbl; College; Elementart Teacher.

ZORN, David L; Claflin HS; Claflin, KS; PresJrCls; Aud/Vis; Band; Chrs; HonRl; MrchBnd; SchPl; StuCncl; Wichita State Univ; Administration Of Justi.

ZORN, Michael A; Claflin HS; Claflin, KS; Band; CncrtBnd; HonRl; MrchBnd; PepBnd; SchPl; StuCncl; StuGov; RptrYrbk; Tennis; Kansas St Univ; Engineering.

ZORN, Michael D; Cavalier HS; Cavaliet, ND; Chr; Chrl; Chrs; ChrhWkr; 4-H; Trade School; Carpenter.

ZORN, Zoe E; Sacred Heart Academy; Springfield, IL; 18/148 Band; Chrs; CmntyWkr; DrmBgl; HonRl; NatlMeritSF; StuCncl; MthCl; PpCl; Western Ill Univ; Pre Law Degree.

ZORTMAN, Philip G; West Monona HS; Onawa, IA; ALBoysSt; Band; Chrs; CncrtBnd; HonRl; MrchBnd; PepBnd; SchMus; Wrstlng; Iowa State Univ; Business.

ZORZIN, Eugene; West Iron County HS; Caspian, MI; 38/170 Mi Tech Univ; Chemistry.

ZOSCHKE, Annettia C; Markoma Bible Acad; Coffeyville, KS; PresFrshCls; PresSophCls; Chr; Chrl; ChrhWkr; HonRl; StuGov; Bsktbl;.

ZOUCHA, Janice M; Senior HS; Central City, NE; 3 Chrs; HonRl; SchMus; RptrYrbk; IMSpt; PresAwd; U Of Ne Lincoln; Business.

ZSCHAU, Susan L; Marshall HS; Marshall, IL; Band; CncrtBnd; MrchBnd; PepBnd; SchPl; SchPpr; 4-H; FHA; SpnCl; PpCl; College.

ZSOHAR, Susan; Waukesha North HS; Waukesha, WI; 8/326 Chr; HonRl; JrNHS; NHS; SpnCl; MthCl; Trk; College; Math Computers.

ZUB, Suzanne F; Mehlville Sr HS; St Louis, MO; 5/505 Chrs; HonRl; JrNHS; NHS; SchPl; SctActv; RptrSchPpr; VPFHA; FrCl; Swmmng; OptClAwd; College; Home Economics.

ZUBA, Lori J; Nicolet HS; Milwaukee, WI; DrlTm; HonRl; NHS; SchPl; RptrYrbk; RptrSchPpr; PpCl; Chrldr; GAA; IMSpt; Business Sch; Legal Secty.

ZUBER, Lawrence; East Richland HS; Olney, IL; NHS; NatlMeritCmnd; Quill&Scroll; SchPl; StuCncl; RptrYrbk; RptrSchPpr; SchPpr; 4-H; FrCl; College; Broadcasting.

ZUBROD, Carlene R; Riceville Comm HS; Elma, IA; Chr; Chrs; HonRl; SchPl; 4-HAwd; Iowa State U; Optometrics.

ZUCHELSKI, Debra A; Franklin HS; Westland, MI; HonRl; SctActv; Coll; Dental Tech.

ZUCK, Kimberlee A; Lanark HS; Chadwick, IL; Chr; Chrs; SchMus; SecYthFlsp; Sec4-H; FHA; GAA; 4-HAwd; Rock Valley College; Dental Asst.

ZUCKERMAN, Alan I; Dub Sr HS; Dubuque, IA; 101/527 SchPpr; FrCl; CaptFtbl; CaptWrstlng; PresAwd; Univ Of Iowa; Education.

ZUCKSWORTH, Brenda S; Mulberry Grove HS; Smithboro, IL; Band; CncrtBnd; HonRl; NHS; SchPl; Yrbk; RptrSchPpr; SchPpr; FHA; Trade School; Secretary.

ZUEGE, Lori J; Haigler Public HS; Haigler, NE; 2/9 SecTrsJrCls; SecTrsSrCls; ALAGirlsSt; Band; Chr; Chrl; Chrs; ChrhWkr; HonRl; SchMus; SchPl; Trk; BttyCrckrAwd; Kearney St Univ; Business Admin.

ZUEHLKE, Judith A; Oconomowoc Sr HS; Oconomowoc, WI; AFS; Band; Chr; ChrhWkr; CncrtBnd; HonRl; JrNHS; MrchBnd; NHS; PepBnd; TchrAde; Teen; 4-H; GerCl; Waukeshau County Tech Institute; Child Care.

ZUELCH, Bruce; Le Center Public HS; Le Center, MN; 7/63 HonRl; NHS; ROTC; RptrSchPpr; University Of Mn; Electrical Engineering.

ZUELKE, Debra K; Stratford HS; Stratford, WI; HonRl; FHA; LetterBsktbl; LetterTrk; PPFtbl; U Of Wisconsin; Secondary Education.

ZUELKE, Mary E; Stratford Public HS; Stratford, WI; Chrs; ChrhWkr; StuCncl; 4-H; FHA; Bsktbl; Trk; GAA; PPFtbl; Univ; Professional.

ZUELSDORF, James D; Husfisford HS; Hustisford, WI; 2/30 VPSrCls; Band; ChrhWkr; CncrtBnd; HonRl; MrchBnd; ModUN; NHS; PepBnd; SchMus; Univ Milwaukee; Criminal Justice.

ZUFALL, Frank J; Elmore Public HS; Elmore, MN; 18/30 HonRl; Bsktbl; Ftbl; Trk; Mankato State.

ZUHL, Dena M; West HS; Battle Creek, MI; Band; Chr; ChrhWkr; CmntyWkr; CncrtBnd; HonRl; HospAde; MrchBnd; OffAde; SpnCl; Clg In Indiana; Social Work.

ZUHONE, Michael H; Mattoon Sr HS; Charleston, IL; SecAFS; College; Law Enforcement.

ZUK, Denise M; Trenton HS; Trenton, MI; 53/571 HonRl; Washtenaw Comm College; Radiologic Tech.

ZUKOSKY, John C; Collinsville HS; Collinsville, IL; 36/654 Univ Of Ill; Psychology.

ZUKOWSKI, Janet M; Marillac Hs; Glenview, IL; 3/250 Chrs; NHS; SchPl; Sdlty; TchrAde; EdYrBk; SpnCl; Drake U; Law.

ZUKOWSKI, Julia; St Bede Academy; Peru, IL; 5/125 Chrs; ChrhWkr; HonRl; SchMus; StuGov; FrCl; Chrldr;.

ZUKOWSKI, Perry; Columbus HS; Marshfield, WI; HonRl; StuCncl; LetterFtbl; Trk; IMSpt; College; Dentist.

ZULSKI, David J; Pellston HS; Pellston, MI; 6/50 StuCncl; TchrAde; EdYrBk; PresFFA; LetterBsbl; LetterBsktbl; CaptFtbl; Trk; College; Business Admin.

ZUMBRUNN, Kathy D; Fullerton Public HS; Belgrade, NE; 2/59 ALAGirlsSt; ChrhWkr; HonRl; PresJA; YthFlsp; Yrbk; Pres4-H; PresFHA; LetterPpCl; 4-HAwd; Midland Lutheran Coll; Rn.

ZUMBRUNN, Stephen L; Hartford HS; Hartford, KS; VPJrCls; ALBoysSt; Chrs; HonRl; SchMus; SchPl; KeyCl; LetterFtbl; LetterTrk; LetterWrstlng; College; Engineering Major.

ZUMDAHL, Lyle L; Forreston HS; Baileyville, IL; 11/70 TrsFrshCls; HonRl; NHS; YthFlsp; 4-H; FFA; LetterBsktbl; Highland Comm College; Agriculture.

ZUMSTEIN, Barbara J; Wm Borden HS; Floyds Knobs, IN; 3/65 PresFrshCls; PresChr; HonRl; PresNHS; StuCncl; FHA; Indiana Univ Se; Medicine.

ZUMWALT, James R; Sheldon HS; Sheldon, IL; PresFrshCls; PresSophCls; PresSrCls; Band; SchPl; StuCncl; RptrYrbk; EdYrBk; SchPpr; PpCl; Bsbl; Bsktbl; Univ Of Illinois; Liberal Arts.

ZUMWALT, Janis V; Southeast HS; Wichita, KS; 26/679 ALAGirlsSt; HonRl; LitMag; NatlMeritFnl; NatlMeritSF; Orch; PolWkr; SchMus; SecGerCl; Univ Of Kansas; Nursing.

ZUNAMON, Alan M; Niles West HS; Lincolnwood, IL; 1/666 Chr; CncrtBnd; HonRl; MrchBnd; NHS; NatlMeritSF; Orch; SchMus; StuGov; GerCl; Socr; Harvard Univ; Medicine.

ZUNDEL, Sharon; Forest View HS; Mt Prospect, IL; 150/645 Band; ChrhWkr; CncrtBnd; HonRl; HospAde; MrchBnd; NHS; Orch; PepBnd; SchMus; Luther College; Maor In Music.

ZUNIGA, Linda R; Riverview Gardens HS; St Louis, MO; HonRl; HospAde; NHS; OffAde; StuCncl; StuGov; TchrAde; College; Lawyer.

ZUPTICH, Mary L; Bishop Leblond HS; St Joseph, MO; 1/116 HonRl; NatlFornLg; NHS; Quill&Scroll; SctActv; RptrYrbk; EdYrBk; BttyCrckrAwd; OptClAwd; College; Special Elem Ed.

ZURAWSKI, Ann Marie; Resurrection HS; Chicago, IL; HospAde; SchPl; TchrAde; GAA; St Norbert Clg; Travel Tourism.

ZURCHER, Lori; Elkhorn Valley HS; Meadow Grove, NE; TrsFrshCls; PresSophCls; Chr; Chrs; HonRl; SchMus; StuCncl; TchrAde; PpCl; Trk; University; Teacher And Rec Leader.

ZURCHER, Robert; Huntington North HS; Huntington, IN; Chr; Teen; YthFlsp; IMSpt; Olivet Nazarene College; Business Admin.

ZURLIENE, Diana; Fairfield Comm HS; Fairfield, IL; ChrhWkr; HonRl; 4-H; LatCl; SciCl; DanFAwd; 4-HAwd; Med Technician.

ZURN, Lois A; Moorhead Sr HS; Moorhead, MN; 22/560 Chrs; HonRl; HospAde; NatlMeritCmnd; SpnCl; Univ; Nurse.

ZUZGA, Mary Ann; St Ladislaus HS; Deltoit, MI; 4/112 HonRl; HospAde; StuCncl; FNA; FTA; MthCl; Bsbl; Bsktbl; PPFtbl; Oakland U; Medical Technology.

ZWEBER, Ron J; New Prague HS; Elko, MN; PresSrCls; HonRl; NHS; SchPl; VPStuCncl; EdSchPpr; PpCl; LetterTrk; U Of Mn; Business Admin.

ZWEIFEL, Sheila J; Luray Public HS; Waldo, KS; 2/19 HstFrshCls; SecTrsSophCls; Band; Chrs; HonRl; TchrAde; Twrl; Yrbk; SchPpr; LetterBsktbl; Coll; Voc.

ZWEIG, Jacalyn J; Morton HS; Hammond, IN; 46/500 Band; CncrtBnd; CaptDrlTm; HonRl; JrNHS; MrchBnd; PepBnd; StuGov; SecFTA; SciCl; GAA; Univ Of Denver; Forestry.

ZWEYGARDT, Cathy L; St Francis Comm HS; St Francis, KS; PresSophCls; TrsJrCls; HonRl; StuCncl; VPFHA; PpCl; IMSpt; PPFtbl; Kansas St Univ; Interior Decorator.

ZWICK, Brenda K; Nickerson HS; Sterling, KS; Band; Chr; ChrhWkr; CmntyWkr; CncrtBnd; HonRl; NHS; YthFlsp; 4-H; IMSpt; Kansas St Univ; Rn.

ZWIEFEL, Eugene D; Titanka HS; Wesley, IA; ALBoysSt; HonRl; TchrAde; FFA; Bsbl; Bsktbl; Ftbl; Trk; CchngActv; College&teaching.

ZWIEG, David L; Waupun HS; Fox Lake, WI; AFS; Chr; MthCl; Ftbl; Trk; Wrstlng; AmLegAwd; U W Madison; Physical Therapist.

ZWIENER, John J; District 55 HS; Spalding, NE; TrsJrCls; ChrhWkr; CncrtBnd; HonRl; StuCncl; RptrYrbk; 4-H; FFA; Bsktbl; LetterFtbl; 4-HAwd; Trade School; Vocation.

ZWIENER, Kimberly A; Sycamore HS; Sycamore, IL; 36/226 ChrhWkr; HonRl; TchrAde; FHA; SpnCl; PpCl; Coll; Elem Tchr.

ZWIESELBAUER, Sharon M; Oakville Sr HS; St Louis, MO; 58/336 Chrs; HonRl; NHS; SctActv; KeyCl; GerCl; PpCl; SecGAA; BttyCrckrAwd; U Of Southeast Mo; Home Economist.

ZWILLER, Rosemarie; Our Lady Of Mercy HS; Detroit, MI; 7/290 LbryAde; NHS; StuCncl; StuGov; TchrAde; LatCl; Swmmng; Univ Of Michigan.

ZWILLING, Alvin D; East Richland HS; Claremont, IL; 26/242 ChrhWkr; CmntyWkr; 4-H; FFA; Olney Central College; Agri Instructor.

ZWILLING, Marilynn; Laboure HS; Saint Louis, MO; SecJrCls; Chrs; SchAde; SchMus; SchPl; StuCncl; GAA; IMSpt; Public Relations.

ZWILLING, Norma L; E Richland HS; Claremont, IL; 1/260 ALAGirlsSt; NHS; 4-H; LatCl; College; Accounting.

ZWOLINSKI, David L; Maine So HS; Park Ridge, IL; HonRl; Univ Of Ill; Business Administration.

ZWOLINSKI, Michael R; Lyons Twp HS; La Grange, IL; SchAde; Washington Univ; Physician.

ZYCHOWSKI, Mark R; Norway HS; Vulcan, MI; ChrhWkr; HonRl; 4-H; LetterFtbl; LetterTrk; IMSpt; 4-HAwd; College; Agricultural Ext.

ZYGARLICKE, Sheree D; Columbus HS; Marshfield, WI; 12/117 HonRl; NHS; SchMus; SchPl; RptrYrbk; PpCl; IMSpt; Col; Registered Nurse.

ZYK, Linda D; Notre Dame HS; Chicago, IL; 4/262 HonRl; NHS; SchPl; TchrAde; FTA; FrCl; PresMthCl; GAA; College; Computer Science.

ZYK, Stephen N; Weber HS; Chicago, IL; Band; CncrtBnd; HonRl; SctActv; TreasStuCncl; Swmmng;.

ZYLSTRA, Nyla H; Dakota Christian HS; Geddes, SD; TrsJrCls; ALAGirlsSt; Chr; HonRl; HospAde; StuCncl; EdSchPpr; FNA; FTA; Bsktbl; University; Professional.

ZYLSTRA, Phyllis A; Chosen Valley HS; Chatfield, MN; 5/86 Band; Chr; ChrhWkr; CncrtBnd; HonRl; Mdrgl; MrchBnd; NHS; SchMus; YthFlsp; Luther Clge Decorah Ia; Chemistry.

ZYLSTRA, Rodney D; Pella Christian HS; Pella, IA; HonRl; LetterBsktbl; LetterTrk; IMSpt; Trade School; Professional.

ZYSKOWSKI, Phillip; Madison HS; Madison Heights, MI; /243 ChrhWkr; HonRl; NHS; NatlMeritFnl; FrCl; SciCl; Ftbl; Univ Of Mich;bio Chem.

ZYWCZYK, Teresa B; Downers Grove South HS; Westmont, IL; 163/752 HonRl; NHS; PpCl; GAA; IMSpt; PPFtbl; Northern Il U; Business Manage.

ZYWICIEL, Celeste M; Madonna HS; Chicago, IL; 5/265 TrsFrshCls; HonRl; NatlFornLg; NHS; StuCncl; EdSchPpr; SpnCl; MthCl; VPSciCl; GAA; IMSpt; VFWAwd; VoiceDemAwd; Univ Of Ill; Librarian.

ADDITIONAL BIOGRAPHIES

A

ACKERMAN, Mary A; Reese HS; Reese, MI; 29/127 ChrhWkr; NHS; NatlMeritFnl; NatlMeritCmnd; NatlMeritSchl; SchAde; SchPl; SctActv; StuCncl; TchrAde; GerCl; PpCl; Chrldr; W Michigan Univ; Social Work.

ADAIR, James G; Morton HS; Morton, IL; HstJrCls; HstSrCls; HonRl; StuCncl; StuGov; RptrSchPpr; PpCl; LetterFtbl; LetterWrstlng; IMSpt; W Illinois Univ; Psychology.

ADKIN, April K; South Haven HS; South Haven, MI; PresFrshCls; Band; HonRl; MrchBnd; NHS; PepBnd; TchrAde; RptrYrbk; College; Teacher.

AESOPH, Christopher N; Milbank HS; Milbank, SD; PresFrshCls; Chrs; ChrhWkr; CmntyWkr; HonRl; Mdrgl; NHS; StuCncl; KeyCl; Ftbl; LetterTrk; Wrstlng; IMSpt; PPFtbl;.

ALLEN, Leslie S; Adel HS; Adel, IA; TrsJrCls; Chrs; CmntyWkr; CncrtBnd; HonRl; NHS; NatlThespSoc; SchMus; StuGov; PresYthFlsp; IMSpt; College; Music.

ALTMAN, Rhonda M; Auburndale HS; Milladore, WI; Chr; FBLA; PpCl; LetterBsktbl; Trk; GAA; JAAwd;.

ANDERSON, Anthony J; Univ Of Detroit HS; Detroit, MI; Band; CncrtBnd; HospAde; TreasJA; MrchBnd; NatlMeritCmnd; PepBnd; StuCncl; IMSpt; Dartmouth Schlship; State Of Mich Schlship; Stud Govnmt; Skiing Tutor; Treas Jr Achieve; Attend Dartmouth; State Of Mi Scholarship; Stud Govt; Sci Tutoring; Jr Achieve; College; Medicine.

ANDERSON, Ava J; Wyaconda C 1 HS; Wyaconda, MO; 2/20 SecFrshCls; SecSophCls; Chr; Chrs; ChrhWkr; HonRl; NHS; VPStuCncl; SciCl; Bsbl; Bsktbl; IMSpt; University Of Missouri; Nursing.

ANDERSON, Crystal R; East Chas Mix #102 HS; Wagner, SD; PresSrCls; Chrs; DrlTm; HonRl; NHS; FHA; PpCl; Lake Area Vo Tech; Social Worker.

ANDERSON, Donna J; Holmen HS; Holmen, WI; 23/97 Chr; Chrs; ChrhWkr; HonRl; LbryAde; FHA; W Wisconsin Tech Inst; Ward Clerk.

ANDERSON, Eric J; Maine South HS; Park Ridge, IL; HonRl; LitMag; SchPpr; LetterFtbl; LetterTrk; GovHonPrgAwd; Honor Soc; Univ Of Ill; Advertising.

ANDERSON, Lee Ann; Harrisonville Sr HS; Harrisonville, MO; 3/165 Chrs; HonRl; SchPl; RptrYrbk; SpnCl; Bsktbl; CaptChrldr; PPFtbl; PresAwd; Stephens College; Social Work.

ANDES, Garrett M; Effingham HS; Effingham, IL; 10/239 ChrhWkr; HonRl; StuCncl; Bsbl; CaptBsktbl; Ftbl; LetterGlf; LetterTrk; AmLegAwd; Univ Of Illinois; Pharmacy.

ANDREW, Elizabeth R; Hagerstown Jr Sr HS; Hagerstown, IN; VPJrCls; VPBand; VPChr; Chrl; VPCncrtBnd; HonRl; VPMrchBnd; OffAde; Pres4-H; PresFHA; GAA; 4-HAwd;.

ARMSTRONG, George L; Mt Carmel HS; Mt Carmel, IL; 16/185 Band; CncrtBnd; MrchBnd; SchPl; RptrYrbk; Natl Honor Soc; Univ Of Ill; Engineering.

ARMSTRONG, Joseph H; Fremont HS; Fremont, MI; 15/191 Aud/Vis; CmntyWkr; HonRl; SchPl; StuCncl; Yrbk; SchPpr; PresGerCl; LetterBsbl; Natl Honor Soc; Lewis Univ; Law.

ARMSTRONG, Peggy S; North Winneshiek HS; Canton, MN; 1/34 Chrs; HonRl; JrNHS; NHS; SchPl; StuCncl; FFA; FHA; CaptBsktbl; LetterTrk; BauchLmbAwd; PresAwd; Iowa St Univ; Veterinarian.

ARNOLD, Tony D; Mitchell HS; Mitchell, IN; Band; CncrtBnd; MrchBnd; PepBnd; SciCl; LetterBsbl; LetterFtbl; CchngActv; IMSpt; College; Microbiology.

ARNTZEN, Martha L; Macomb Sr HS; Macomb, IL; Chr; SecChrhWkr; CmntyWkr; HonRl; SchMus; RptrYrbk; Pres4-H; SpnCl; DanFAwd; 4-HAwd; Natl Honor Soc; College.

ARTHUR, Cathy L; Clarion Community HS; Clarion, IA; PresBand; PresChrs; HonRl; Mdrgl; NHS; SchMus; Bsktbl; Trk; Chrldr; CitAwd; Central College; Music.

ASMUSSEN, Dane N; Pender HS; Pender, NE; TrsFrshCls; HonRl; StuCncl; TchrAde; FrCl; LetterBsktbl; LetterTennis; College; History.

ATKINS, Joleen M; Pomeroy HS; Pomeroy, IA; 4/32 VPSrCls; NHS; StuCncl; SptEdSchPpr; Bsktbl; LetterTrk; Chrldr; Jr College.

AUGUSTINE, Ann M; Forest Park HS; Crystal Falls, MI; 29/89 Chrs; NatlMeritSchl; TchrAde; Yrbk; FNA; Michigan Tech Univ; Geology.

AUNE, John F; Westview HS; Braham, MN; TrsSrCls; Band; Chr; HonRl; NHS; SchPl; Yrbk; LetterBsktbl; Ftbl; LetterTrk; Augsburg College.

AUSTIN, David J; St Marys HS; Independence, MO; GerCl; Bsktbl; College; Professional.

B

BABL, Jeanette L; West Holt HS; Atkinson, NE; Chrs; DrlTm; LbryAde; SchPl; SctActv; RptrYrbk; 4-H; PpCl; College; Teacher.

BACKLUND, Mickey L; J E Murphy HS; Hurley, WI; ALBoysSt; JA; NatlMeritSchl;.

BAHR, James W; West Salem HS; La Crosse, WI; HonRl; 4-H; FFA; PpCl; LetterBsbl; LetterFtbl; IMSpt; 4-HAwd; Trade Schl; Vocation.

BAHRKE, Barbara S; Kingsley Pierson HS; Pierson, IA; 3/61 Chr; DrmMjrt; HonRl; NHS; StuCncl; EdYrBk; VPFTA; SecSpnCl; LetterBsbl; LetterBsktbl; LetterTrk; Chrldr; Girls State; College; Education.

BAHRKE, Beverly A; Kingsley Pierson HS; Pierson, IA; Band; Chrs; CmntyWkr; HonRl; NHS; Yrbk; 4-H; LetterBsbl; LetterBsktbl; LetterTrk; PPFtbl; 4-HAwd; Girls State;.

BAKER, David C; Northridge HS; Middlebury, IN; Chr; Chrl; Chrs; ChrhWkr; CncrtBnd; Mdrgl; SchMus; SchPl; Bsbl; Bsktbl; LetterFtbl; LetterTrk; IMSpt; College; Elementary Ed.

BAKER, Rick T; Morrill HS; Morrill, NE; NHS; SchPl; YthFlsp; Bsktbl; Jr College.

BAKER, Virginia L; Marshall Jr Sr HS; Marshall, MO; SecJrCls; ChrhWkr; HonRl; StuCncl; PpCl; Bsktbl; Trk; CaptChrldr; GAA; IMSpt; College; Education.

BALASZ, Jody J; Adrian HS; Adrian, MI; 10/390 NHS; NatlMeritSchl; StuCncl; SpnCl; PpCl; Western Michigan Univ; Business Admin.

BALLARD, Imogene; Rezin Orr HS; Chicago, IL; Chr; HonRl; LbryAde; TchrAde; Northeastern Univ; Computer Science.

BANIA, Beth A; Fitzgerald HS; Warren, MI; 1/420 HonRl; NatlFornLg; PresNHS; NatlMeritFnl; NatlMeritSchl; NatlSciFnd; TchrAde; BauchLmbAwd; CitAwd; Michigan St Univ; Chemistry.

BANKHEAD, Kathleen A; Thornton Twp HS; Harvey, IL; NatlFornLg; NatlThespSoc; OffAde; PolWkr; PpCl; LetterBsktbl; GAA; JETSAwd; University; Professional.

BANUCHIE, Mary L; Ontonagon Area HS; Ontonagon, MI; 5/106 TrsSophCls; TrsJrCls; TrsSrCls; DrlTm; HonRl; NHS; LetterBsktbl; CaptTrk; Chrldr; GAA; Michigan Tech Univ; Medical Tech.

BARD, Loryn I; Deerfield HS; Deerfield, IL; 91/561 Chr; ChrhWkr; HonRl; ModUN; NatlMeritCmnd; SchMus; RptrYrbk; RptrSchPpr; Il State Scholar; Univ Of Illinois; Business Administration.

BARDIS, Judith A; Madam Curie HS; Chicago, IL; 53/800 Chrs; CaptDrlTm; HonRl; JrNHS; LbryAde; NHS; NatlThespSoc; OffAde; SchMus; StuCncl; TchrAde; Chrldr; JAAwd; KiwanAwd; Skidmore College; Ballerina.

BARKER, Lisa D; High School; Covington, IN; 3/110 HonRl; Purdue Univ; Veterinarian.

BARKS, Steve L; Puxico HS; Puxico, MO; Chr; ChrhWkr; HonRl; PepBnd; SchAde; SchPl; YthFlsp; FFA; College; Vocation.

BARTELL, Monica M; Beaver Dam Sr HS; Beaver Dam, WI; 1/320 ALAGirlsSt; Chrs; Mdrgl; NatlFornLg; NatlMeritCmnd; SchMus; SchPpr; SpnCl; PpCl; GAA; Univ Of Wisconsin; Business.

BARTELSMEYER, Bobby L; Mt Vernon HS; Mt Vernon, MO; 26/95 ChrhWkr; CmntyWkr; NatlThespSoc; PolWkr; StuGov; TchrAde; YthFlsp; YthLg; Bsktbl; Tennis; Trk; GodCntryAwd; Oral Roberts Univ; History.

BARTH, Lisa A; Shanley HS; Fargo, ND; HonRl; HospAde; PpCl; Bsktbl; LetterSwmmng; Chrldr; St Catherines College; Nurse.

BARTON, Michelle M; Oslo HS; Manvel, ND; PresJrCls; Aud/Vis; HonRl; SchPl; StuCncl; EdYrBk; RptrSchPpr; Trk; Chrldr; Wahpeton Col; Nursing.

BASHFORD, Tim R; Holdrege HS; Holdrege, NE; 36/115 Univ Of Nebraska; Engineering.

BASS, Beth A; Wabash HS; Wabash, IN; 20/198 Chr; HonRl; LbryAde; SpnCl; PpCl; Purdue Univ; Pharmacy.

BASTIAN, James H; Hannibal Sr HS; Hannibal, MO; 39/261 HonRl; StuCncl; College; Printing Mgmt.

BASTONE, Peter F; Chicago Latin HS; Chicago, IL; PresSrCls; ChrhWkr; CmntyWkr; HospAde; PolWkr; PresStuCncl; PresStuGov; Bsbl; Ftbl; Socr; Swmmng; Trk; CchngActv; Harvard Univ; Medicine.

BAUMUNK, Rodney D; Big Rapids HS; Big Rapids, MI; SchPl; TchrAde; Trade Schl; Acting.

BAUSTERT, James R; St Edward Public HS; St Edward, NE; CmntyWkr; HonRl; NatlThespSoc; Quill&Scroll; SchPl; SctActv; FFA; SciCl; LetterFtbl; LetterTrk; Trade School.

BEALLER, Sharon E; Orchard Farm HS; St Charles, MO; Band; CncrtBnd; HonRl; HospAde; Trk; Chrldr; IMSpt; PPFtbl; 4-HAwd; St Marys College; Nursing.

BEAN, Jo Ann; Le Roy HS; Le Roy, IL; 2/70 Chrs; HonRl; JrNHS; LbryAde; SecNHS; OffAde; SchMus; UNYO; Yrbk; PpCl; GAA; College; Mathematics.

BEAR, Carl A; Huntington North HS; Roanoke, IN; 1/600 PresFrshCls; PresJrCls; PresSrCls; JrNHS; StuCncl; YthFlsp; Pres4-H; LetterSwmmng; Trk; 4-HAwd; Ball St Univ; Architecture.

BEARMAN, Norman J; Hillsdale HS; Hillsdale, MI; ALBoysSt; ChrhWkr; HonRl; Bsktbl;.

BEAVERS, Harvey; Dundee Comm HS; Maybee, MI; CmntyWkr; HonRl; SchAde; LetterBsktbl; LetterFtbl; E Michigan Univ; Broadcasting.

BECKMAN, Mary R; Junction City Sr HS; Junction City, KS; HonRl; NatlFornLg; NHS; SchPl;.

BEDAR, Ross A; Elverado HS; Du Quoin, IL; 12/42 TrsSrCls; HonRl; StuCncl; SecFFA; TreasPpCl; IMSpt; Umpire School; National League.

BEEDLE, Richard L; Oakland Comm HS; Mcclelland, IA; VPSophCls; VPJrCls; StuCncl; YthFlsp; 4-H; FFA; Ftbl; IMSpt; 4-HAwd; Iowa State College; Agriculture.

BEEMAN, Robert K; Harrisonville Sr HS; Harrisonville, MO; 33/153 AFS; HonRl; NatlFornLg; Quill&Scroll; SchPl; StuCncl; Yrbk; SchPpr; Tennis; Ne Missouri State University.

BEHRENDS, Kristy E; Hartsburg Emden HS; Emden, IL; 11/37 SecJrCls; VPBand; Chr; HonRl; NatlThespSoc; PepBnd; SchPl; StuCncl; SchPpr; Bsktbl; SecGAA; 4-HAwd; 3rd Scholas Key For Honor Roll 3/4 Weeks; 1st Place Solo With Bass Clarinet; College; English Teacher.

BEHRENS, Mary J; Everly Comm HS; Everly, IA; Chrs; ChrhWkr; HonRl; LbryAde; NHS; SchPl; College; Liberal Arts.

BELL, Debra K; Regis HS; Eau Claire, WI; Chrs; HonRl; OffAde; SchMus; SchPl; GerCl; SpnCl; PpCl; Chrldr; College; Foreign Languages.

BELL, Hattie M; St Martin De Porres HS; Detroit, MI; Chr; ChrhWkr; CmntyWkr; HonRl; PepBnd; SchPl; PpCl; Univ Of Detroit; Medicine.

BENDALL, Jo Ellen M; Rochester HS; Rochester, IN; 15/162 Band; ChrhWkr; HonRl; NatlFornLg; NHS; RptrYrbk; EdSchPpr; 4-H; FrCl; PpCl; University; Journalism.

BENJAMIN, Andre A; East Catholic HS; Detroit, MI; PresSophCls; Chr; HonRl; JA; SchAde; SchMus; SchPl; SctActv; StuCncl; LetterBsbl; LetterBsktbl; LetterFtbl; Chrldr; Mccomb College; Law.

BENJAMIN, Regina A; Edwin Denby HS; Detroit, MI; SecChr; DrmMjrt; HonRl; Mdrgl; NatlMeritCmnd; NatlThespSoc; PolWkr; SchMus; SchPl; StuGov; Univ Of Michigan; Law.

BENNETT, Cassandra J; Adrian Sr HS; Adrian, MI; Chr; ChrhWkr; YthFlsp; YthLg; College; Nurse.

BENTIVENGA, Michael G; Homewood Flossmoor HS; Homewood, IL; 61/940 Band; CmntyWkr; CncrtBnd; DrmMjrt; HonRl; MrchBnd; NHS; OffAde; Orch; PepBnd; SchMus; Chrldr; IMSpt; Univ Of Illinois; Architecture.

BERGLUND, Jay L; Willmar Sr HS; Willmar, MN; KeyCl; LetterWrstlng; College.

BERKHOLTZ, Karin R; Breck HS; Minneapolis, MN; AFS; Chr; ChrhWkr; HonRl; SctActv; Yrbk; College; Professional.

BERRY, Benjamin W; Elmhurst HS; Fort Wayne, IN; Band; ChrhWkr; CncrtBnd; HonRl; MrchBnd; Fort Wayne Bible College; Music.

BEY, Sayonara A; Jones HS; Chicago, IL; HospAde; JrNHS; NHS; NatlMeritFnl; NatlMeritSchl; NatlMeritSF; RedCrAde; FshEdYrbk; FBLA; FDA; College; Data Processing.

BEYERS, John S; Wheaton Christian HS; Wheaton, IL; Aud/Vis; Band; Chr; Chrl; Chrs; ChrhWkr; CncrtBnd; LbryAde; Orch; PepBnd; SchMus; SchPl; YthFlsp; College; Music.

BEZY, Mariann; East Detroit HS; Warren, MI; HonRl; NHS; NatlMeritCmnd; NatlMeritSF; OffAde; StuCncl; FNA; College; Nursing.

BIEL, Kimberly S; Hays HS; Hays, KS; HonRl; Orch; TchrAde; LetterPpCl; LetterBsktbl; LetterTrk; IMSpt; PPFtbl; JAAwd; PresAwd; Kansas St Univ; Physical Ed.

BIERSTEDT, Roxann J; Sentral Comm HS; Lone Rock, IA; Band; Chr; Chrs; ChrhWkr; CncrtBnd; HonRl; NHS; SchMus; SchPl; Yrbk; VPFTA; PresPpCl; Univ Of N Iowa; Music.

BIRKHOLZ, Gordon W; Lester Prairie Public HS; Lester Prairie, MN; 3/35 Chr; HonRl; TreasNHS; StuCncl; LetterBsbl; LetterBsktbl; LetterFtbl; LetterTrk; IMSpt; AmLegAwd; College; Professional.

BISANZ, Dennis E; Belding Central HS; Belding, MI; Band; Chr; ChrhWkr; HonRl; MrchBnd; NHS; PepBnd; PpCl; University; Professional.

BIXLER, Dorinda S; Hayes Center Public HS; Hayes Center, NE; 1/24 DrmMjrt; NHS; 4-H; PpCl; Trk; Chrldr; DanFAwd; DARAwd; College.

BLACK, Barbara L; Akron Community HS; Merrill, IA; 11/59 Band; Chrs; CncrtBnd; HonRl; HospAde; MrchBnd; NHS; PepBnd; SchPl; YthFlsp; FHA; PpCl; Bsktbl; CaptChrldr; Univ Of Iowa; Nursing.

BLACK, Jennifer A; Huntington North HS; Huntington, IN; JrNHS; OffAde; Indiana St Univ; Elementary Ed.

BLAUWKAMP, Susan B; Holland Christian HS; Zeeland, MI; TrsFrshCls; Band; DrmMjrt; Orch; SchPl; StuCncl; SpnCl; Calvin College.

BLOETHE, Cheryl A; Hlu Community HS; Victor, IA; Band; Chr; CncrtBnd; DrmMjrt; HonRl; MrchBnd; NatlThespSoc; PolWkr; SchPl; College; Professional.

BODEAU, Terri L; Case HS; Racine, WI; 27/650 PresSrCls; ChrhWkr; HonRl; SctActv; PresStuCncl; PresStuGov; FBLA; FrCl; LetterSwmmng; DARAwd; OptClAwd; Marquette Univ; Med Engineer.

BOEHME, Lori J; Concordia Academy; St Paul, MN; Band; Chr; ChrhWkr; DrlTm; HonRl; HospAde; SchMus; SpnCl; Natl Honor Soc; Concordia College; Social Work.

BOENSCH, Sally; St Peter & Paul Area HS; Saginaw, MI; Band; Chrs; CncrtBnd; HonRl; OffAde; StuGov; RptrSchPpr; GerCl; Chrldr; Trade School.

BOGDEN, Thomas J; Taylor Center HS; Taylor, MI; HonRl; NHS; College; Engineer.

BOOKER, Marilyn E; Benton Harbor HS; Benton Harbor, MI; HonRl; LbryAde; Bsbl; Secretarial Schl; Legal Secretary.

BORGARD, Le Ann R; Rutland HS; Nunda, SD; Band; ChrhWkr; HonRl; MrchBnd; StuCncl; 4-H; FHA; PpCl; LetterBsktbl; Chrldr; PPFtbl; 4-HAwd; College.

BORNETT, Stephen A; Adrian Sr HS; Adrian, MI; HonRl; NatlFornLg; StuCncl; LatCl; Tennis; Army; Electronics.

BOSCHULT, Mark T; Fremont Sr HS; Fremont, NE; 40/425 Chr; HonRl; JrNHS; StuCncl; Treas4-H; MthCl; LetterFtbl; CaptSwmmng; IMSpt; Iowa State Univ; Engineer.

BOWAR, Connie M; O Gorman HS; Sioux Falls, SD; Band; CncrtBnd; DrlTm; MrchBnd; PepBnd; SchMus; TchrAde; FDA; LetterGAA; IMSpt; College; Medicine.

BOWMAN, Jean A; Morton Memorial HS; Knightstown, IN; 6/24 Chr; HonRl; SchMus; PpCl; SciCl; Trk; College; Law.

BOYER, Kelvin D; Potosi HS; Potosi, WI; Chrs; HonRl; RptrSchPpr; LetterBsbl; LetterBsktbl; LetterFtbl; LetterTrk; College; Professional.

BRANDT, Mary K; Columbus HS; Marshfield, WI; 5/106 Chrs; HonRl; HospAde; NHS; RptrSchPpr; FrCl; College; Nursing.

BRANDT, Paul M; Antigo Sr HS; Antigo, WI; ChrhWkr; CmntyWkr; HonRl; SchAde; KeyCl; MthCl; Bsbl; LetterFtbl; LetterTrk; Wrstlng; CchngActv; IMSpt; College; Science.

BRANDYBERRY, Darla D; Hill City HS; Edmond, KS; Band; Chrs; CmntyWkr; HospAde; PepBnd; RedCrAde; SchPl; YthFlsp; 4-H; PpCl; Trk; Trade School; Vocation.

BRATTON, Susan E; Blue Valley HS; Leawood, KS; VPJrCls; VPSrCls; Band; CncrtBnd; HonRl; MrchBnd; NatlFornLg; OffAde; PepBnd; Univ Of Missouri; Journalist.

BREHM, Douglas J; Chapman HS; Hope, KS; 5/150 PresFrshCls; HstSrCls; Band; Chr; ChrhWkr; CncrtBnd; HonRl; MrchBnd; NatlFornLg; SchPl; StuCncl; Bsktbl; LetterTennis; LetterTrk; College.

BRINTON, Bambi L; West Elk HS; Howard, KS; Chrs; ChrhWkr; HonRl; Mdrgl; NHS; Quill&Scroll; SchPl; RptrSchPpr; 4-H; FHA; SpnCl; PpCl; LetterTrk; Chrldr; College.

BRIZGYS, Victor A; St Thomas Aquinas HS; Southgate, MI; Aud/Vis; HonRl; SchPpr; University; Professional.

BRODEN, Lu Ann; Norway Vulcan Area HS; Norway, MI; 30/115 HonRl; HospAde; Yrbk; RptrSchPpr; 4-H; FBLA; FHA; FNA; GAA; College; Nursing.

BROWN, Anthony; Cairo HS; Cairo, IL; HstJrCls; Band; SchMus; StuCncl; StuGov; LetterFtbl; LetterTrk; PresAwd; College.

BROWN, Betty W; R I North Callaway HS; Kingdom City, MO; Chr; Chrs; ChrhWkr; CmntyWkr; HonRl; PolWkr; RedCrAde; UNYO; FBLA; Trade Schl; Professional.

BROWN, David L; Coldwater HS; Coldwater, MI; 16/270 ALBoysSt; Aud/Vis; Band; ChrhWkr; CncrtBnd; HonRl; MrchBnd; NHS; OffAde; PepBnd; TchrAde; Michigan St Univ; Engineer.

BROWN, Debra A; Bishop Noll Institute; Gary, IN; Band; CncrtBnd; JA; MrchBnd; StuCncl; TchrAde; Twrl; RptrSchPpr; PpCl; Swmmng; CchngActv; College; Journalism.

BROWSKE, Richard M; Rochester Adams HS; Rochester, MI; HonRl; SctActv; SchPpr; Glf; Oakland Univ; Dentist.

BRUEGGEMANN, Cheryl A; Harry A Burke HS; Omaha, NE; ChrhWkr; HonRl; NHS; StuCncl; StuGov; LatCl; PpCl; IMSpt; University; Psychology.

BRUEN, Patrick T; Sacred Heart HS; Dearborn, MI; HstFrshCls; TrsSophCls; VPSrCls; OffAde; SchPl; StuGov; LetterBsktbl; Ftbl; IMSpt; RotaryAwd; Henry Ford Comm College; Hotel Mgmt.

BRUNER, Mary K; Sullivan HS; Sullivan, IL; ChrhWkr; CmntyWkr; SctActv; YthFlsp; 4-H; FHA; GAA; ChmbCommrsAwd; 4-HAwd;.

BRUNKHORST, Timothy D; O Neill HS; O Neill, NE; Band; CncrtBnd; HonRl; MrchBnd; Orch; PepBnd; YthFlsp; RptrYrbk; SptEdYrbk; LetterBsbl; LetterFtbl; LetterGlf; LetterWrstlng; Kearney St College; Business Admin.

BRUNS, James K; Watseka HS; Watseka, IL; PresFrshCls; TrsJrCls; Chr; HonRl; StuCncl; Yrbk; SpnCl; Ftbl; University; Math.

BRUNS, Michael W; Adair Casey Comm HS; Adair, IA; 3/48 VPFrshCls; PresJrCls; HonRl; VPJrNHS; PresNHS; SctActv; LetterBsbl; LetterBsktbl; LetterFtbl; CaptTrk; AmLegAwd; Simpson College; Business.

BUCHMANN, Connie S; Pleasanton Public HS; Pleasanton, NE; PresFrshCls; LbryAde; SchPl; Yrbk; PpCl; Hastings Business Schl; Secretary.

BUGBEE, Sheryl L; Tecumseh HS; Tecumseh, MI; SecSrCls; ChrhWkr; LitMag; NHS; NatlMeritSF; StuGov; 4-H; FrCl; 4-HAwd; Natl Merit Finalist; Tri Valedictorian; Adrian College; Secondary Educ.

BULLOCK, Sharon L; Buffalo HS; Buffalo, MN; ChrhWkr; CmntyWkr; HonRl; LitMag; SchPl; StuCncl; RptrYrbk; EdSchPpr; 4-H; FrCl; IMSpt; Benedict College.

BULTMAN, Brian C; St John Cathedral HS; Milwaukee, WI; College.

BURDEN, Cathy R; Carl Sandburg HS; Palos Heights, IL; HonRl; NHS; StuCncl; RptrSchPpr; GerCl; SciCl; University; Medicine.

BURGER, Yolanda M; Flat Rock HS; Flat Rock, MI; 15/129 HonRl; NHS; SchPl; FDA; SpnCl; PpCl; SciCl; College; Medicine.

BURKHART, Deborah A; Avon Jr Sr HS; Indianapolis, IN; 3/158 ALAGirlsSt; Chr; HonRl; LbryAde; NHS; SctActv; GerCl; GAA; Ball St Univ; Architect.

BURKLEY, Pamela R; Duchesne Academy; Omaha, NE; 9/45 HonRl; Univ Of Minnesota; Sociology.

BUSH, Samuel D; Franklin Comm HS; Franklin, IN; 17/254 HonRl; JrNHS; NHS; Pres4-H; PpCl; LetterTennis; IMSpt; 4-HAwd; RotaryAwd; Indiana Cntrl College; Business Admin.

BUSKE, Keith P; Johnson Creek HS; Watertown, WI; ALAGirlsSt; CmntyWkr; HonRl; LbryAde; 4-H; VPFFA; Ftbl; IMSpt; 4-HAwd; College; Liberal Arts.

BUYS, Cindy L; Union City Sr HS; Burlington, MI; ChrhWkr; HonRl; SpnCl; PpCl; Trk; Chrldr; College.

C

CAIN, Ann M; Spalding HS; Sheldon, IA; DrlTm; SchPl; RptrYrbk; LetterTrk; IMSpt; College.

CAIN, Kathryn M; Thompson Public HS; Grand Forks, ND; HonRl; SchPl; PresStuCncl; RptrYrbk; PpCl; CaptChrldr; BttyCrckrAwd; Trade School; Medicine.

CALDERONE, Donald F; Lincoln Park HS; Lincoln Park, MI; 51/580 HonRl; NHS; NatlMeritSchl; College; Science.

CAMBRON, Angela G; West Washington HS; Fredericksburg, IN; Chrs; ChrhWkr; CmntyWkr; HonRl; OffAde; PolWkr; TchrAde; YthFlsp; Yrbk; EdSchPpr; LatCl; Vincennes Univ; Journalism.

CAMPBELL, Pamela J; Bloomington HS; Bloomington, IL; 34/391 HonRl; HospAde; SchPl; PpCl; Natl Honor Soc; Il St Univ; Art.

CAMPBELL, Sabrina S; Macon County R 1 HS; Macon, MO; 27/103 PresSrCls; CtyCnl; HonRl; NHS; NatlMeritSchl; RedCrAde; StuCncl; UNYO; DanFAwd; PresAwd; Sw Missouri St Univ; Interior Design.

CANTRELL, Glenda F; Niangua HS; Niangua, MO; Band; Chr; Chrs; ChrhWkr; HonRl; LbryAde; MrchBnd; SchPl; 4-H; FHA; PpCl; College; Vocation.

CARAKER, Teresa L; Fort Zumwalt HS; O Fallon, MO; ChrhWkr; HonRl; NHS; 4-H; FNA; PpCl; Bsbl; Chrldr; GAA; College; Nursing.

CARLSON, Jean A; Glenwood HS; Chatham, IL; 21/159 AFS; Chrs; HonRl; FHA; FrCl; PpCl; LetterTrk; LetterChrldr; GAA; Western Ill Univ; Secretary.

CARLSON, Kevin W; Taylors Falls HS; Shafer, MN; Band; Chr; CncrtBnd; HonRl; MrchBnd; PepBnd; SchPl; SciCl; LetterBsbl; LetterBsktbl; LetterFtbl; IMSpt; College; Vocation.

CARMAN, Elizabeth A; Lake Forest HS; Lake Forest, IL; 85/445 HonRl; NHS; TchrAde; RptrSchPpr; PpCl; PresGAA; IMSpt; Illinois St Univ; Accounting.

CARNAHAN, David M; Hartland HS; Hartland, MI; ChrhWkr; SctActv; LetterFtbl; LetterTennis;.

CARPENTER, Virginia A; Lakeville HS; Otisville, MI; ChrhWkr; CncrtBnd; HonRl; MrchBnd; PepBnd; SchPl; RptrYrbk; LetterBsktbl; GAA; IMSpt; College; Business.

CARR, Michelle; Mc Cook Sr HS; Mc Cook, NE; AFS; Band; CncrtBnd; HonRl; MrchBnd; NHS; PepBnd; Quill&Scroll; RptrSchPpr; University; Journalism.

CARTER, Ralph A; Adelphian Academy; Detroit, MI; College.

CARTER, Suzette I; Bradley Bourbonnais HS; Bradley, IL; SchPl; RptrYrbk; EdYrBk; Yrbk; PpCl; Community College; Nurse.

CARTWRIGHT, Chris T; Battle Creek Central HS; Battle Creek, MI; 32/503 Chr; Chrs; LitMag; NatlFornLg; NHS; NatlMeritCmnd; NatlMeritSF; Quill&Scroll; SchMus; SchPl; StuCncl; RptrYrbk; Yrbk; Univ Of Michigan; Lawyer.

CAWLY, Cheryl D; Madison HS; Madison, IL; 32/120 CmntyWkr; HonRl; College; Professional.

CENTER, Randolph S; Hillsdale HS; Hillsdale, MI; Chr; SctActv; TchrAde; College; Law Enforcement.

CESELSKI, Marie T; Memorial HS; Joplin, MO; LitMag; SchPl; Univ Of Missouri; Journalism.

CHANEY, Donald D; Gwinn HS; Ki Sawyer Afb, MI; 13/162 HonRl; NHS; CaptBsktbl; Univ Of Michigan; Computer Engineering.

CHATMAN, Andre L; Normandy HS; Northwoods, MO; TrsSrCls; ALBoysSt; CmntyWkr; JA; StuCncl; CaptBsktbl; College; Lawyer.

CHISM, Pamela R; Clarkton HS; Gideon, MO; Band; CncrtBnd; DrmMjrt; HonRl; LbryAde; MrchBnd; PepBnd; SchPl; SctActv; StuCncl; EdYrBk; RptrSchPpr; FHA; PpCl; Arkansas St Univ; Education.

CHORPENING, Jennifer L; Desoto Sr HS; Olathe, KS; 11/98 Chr; HonRl; NHS; SchMus; SchPl; StuCncl; PpCl; Johnson County Comm College; Fashion Design.

CLARDY, Terrie L; Macon Jr Sr HS; Macon, MO; SecSophCls; ALAGirlsSt; CncrtBnd; MrchBnd; RedCrAde; SchPl; YthFlsp; FBLA; SpnCl; AmLegAwd; Trade School.

CLARK, Barbara J; Riverview Comm HS; Riverview, MI; 2/249 CmntyWkr; HonRl; NHS; Quill&Scroll; SchPl; TchrAde; SchPpr; PresKeyCl; PresSpnCl; Michigan Tech Univ; Business Admin.

CLARK, Mark A; Northeastern HS; Detroit, MI; VPFrshCls; Aud/Vis; DrmBgl; LbryAde; OffAde; ROTC; TchrAde; SciCl; College; Liberal Arts.

CLARK, Terry E; Bedford HS; Lambertville, MI; 9/430 PresJrCls; HonRl; NHS; NatlMeritCmnd; StuCncl; Ftbl; Michigan St Univ; Mech Engineering.

CLARKE, Henry B; Loy Norrix HS; Kalamazoo, MI; 35/441 CmntyWkr; NHS; NatlMeritCmnd; SctActv; StuCncl; GerCl; CaptTennis; CchngActv; GodCntryAwd; Univ Of Michigan; Medicine.

CLEMENS, Diane L; Yorkville HS; Yorkville, IL; Band; CncrtBnd; MrchBnd; PepBnd; 4-H; FNA; PpCl; GAA; 4-HAwd; Univ Of N Colorado; Nursing.

CLERKIN, Kristine M; Edgewood HS; Madison, WI; ALAGirlsSt; ChrhWkr; SecNatlFornLg; PresNHS; SecSctActv; TchrAde; SptEdSchPpr; SchPpr; LetterBsktbl; CchngActv; College; Law.

CLEVEN, Gary A; Goodridge HS; Grygla, MN; Chrs; HonRl; SchPl; YthFlsp; RptrYrbk; PpCl; LetterBsktbl; LetterFtbl; LetterWrstlng;.

CLIFFORD, Kathleen A; St Anthony HS; St Louis, MO; 4/72 Chrl; Chrs; HonRl; LbryAde; NHS; SchMus; St Louis Univ; Accountant.

CLINE, Steven D; Cloverdale HS; Cloverdale, IN; VPSophCls; HonRl; StuCncl; Bsbl; University; Math.

COLE, Lauretta I; Tulare HS; Redfield, SD; Chrs; HonRl; SchPl; RptrYrbk; CaptRptrSchPpr; FHA; Trk; 4-HAwd; Dakota Wesleyan University.

COLEMAN, Charles L; Lindblom Tech HS; Chicago, IL; 26/650 HonRl; NatlMeritCmnd; SchAde; VPStuCncl; TchrAde; LatCl; MthCl; Trk; IMSpt; University; Physics.

COMBS, La Vonda R; Charlestown HS; Charlestown, IN; 10/146 CncrtBnd; CaptDrlTm; MrchBnd; NHS; StuCncl; FshEdSchPpr; FHA; LatCl; PresSciCl; GAA; Indiana Univ; Archaeology.

COMBS, Regina; Waldron HS; St Paul, IN; Band; LbryAde; MrchBnd; Yrbk; SchPpr; FHA; PpCl; Trk; GAA; Trade School; Secretary.

COMSTOCK, Wanita J; Belton HS; Belton, MO; CmntyWkr; TchrAde; FHA; PpCl; Culver Stockton Coll; Business.

CONROY, Jacqueline A; Andrean HS; Merrillville, IN; CmntyWkr; HonRl; TchrAde; Yrbk; FHA; Business School; Accounting.

CONVELSE, Diane E; Larned HS; Garfield, KS; SecTrsFrshCls; Band; Chrs; CncrtBnd; HonRl; Orch; PepBnd; RptrSchPpr; Trk; College; Music.

COOK, Keith L; North County R 1 HS; Desloge, MO; 2/180 Band; CncrtBnd; HonRl; JrNHS; MrchBnd; NHS; PepBnd; SchPl; StuCncl; FrCl; PresSciCl; Trk; Central Methodist College; Biology.

COOPER, Beth A; Reese HS; Reese, MI; 9/128 ALAGirlsSt; ChrhWkr; NHS; NatlSciFnd; StuCncl; YthFlsp; FSA; Chrldr; Ferris State College; Medical Tech.

COOPER, Catherine J; Deerfield HS; Deerfield, IL; ChrhWkr; CmntyWkr; HonRl; HospAde; NatlMeritSF; SchMus; SctActv; FrCl; IMSpt; GodCntryAwd; Natl Merit Finalist; Coll; Physician.

CORACI, Michael A; Bishop Gallagher HS; Harper Woods, MI; 131/303 Band; CncrtBnd; HonRl; Orch; SchPl; StuGov; RptrSchPpr; Trk; College; Wildlife Mgmt.

CORDS, Mark G; Sacred Heart HS; Detroit, MI; 13/127 ChrhWkr; NHS; StuCncl; PpCl; Ftbl; Univ Of Michigan; Banking.

CORLEY, John D; Newman HS; Mason City, IA; PresFrshCls; PresSophCls; PresJrCls; PresSrCls; Chrs; HonRl; StuCncl; TchrAde; VPFBLA; SpnCl; PpCl; Bsbl; Bsktbl; Ftbl; College Of St Thomas.

CORONADO, Theresa; Hazel Park HS; Hazel Park, MI; 20/410 CmntyWkr; HonRl; NHS; OffAde; StuCncl; StuGov; LetterTennis; GAA; VFWAwd; College; Marketing.

CORTNER, Deborah L; Winchester Comm HS; Winchester, IN; Band; NHS; PresYthFlsp; FHA; TreasFrCl; LetterGAA; College.

COUSIN, Peter E; Marshall U HS; Minneapolis, MN; PresJrCls; Aud/Vis; StuGov; TchrAde;.

COUTTEAU, Charles G; United Township HS; East Moline, IL; 18/642 ALBoysSt; ChrhWkr; CmntyWkr; HonRl; NHS; NatlMeritCmnd; PolWkr; YthFlsp; LetterTrk; AmLegAwd; ChmbCommrsAwd; Military Academy; Aerospace Prog.

COUTURE, Jon D; Cheboygan Area HS; Cheboygan, MI; 20/208 Band; CncrtBnd; HonRl; MrchBnd; PepBnd; TreasFrCl; LetterFtbl; LetterTrk; RotaryAwd; Central Michigan Univ; Business Admin.

COVEY, Kelley M; Princeton R 5 HS; Princeton, MO; Chr; ChrhWkr; HonRl; SchPl; SctActv; FFA; LetterFtbl; LetterTrk; GodCntryAwd; College; Professional.

COX, Christine T; Centralia Rvi HS; Centralia, MO; 25/88 CmntyWkr; HonRl; LbryAde; OffAde; SchAde; SchPl; StuCncl; StuGov; EdYrBk; Trk; Moberly Jr College; Elementary Ed.

COX, Jennifer L; Wawasee HS; Syracuse, IN; SecJrCls; Chr; HonRl; NHS; SctActv; StuCncl; Yrbk; PpCl; Chrldr; CchngActv; GAA; PPFtbl; College; Medicine.

COX, Shelly A; Benton HS; St Joseph, MO; 10/200 PresJrCls; PresSrCls; CtyCnl; CmntyWkr; JrNHS; NHS; SchMus; RptrSchPpr; PpCl; IMSpt; PPFtbl; Benedictine College; Public Relations.

COX, Susan M; Baxter Comm HS; Baxter, IA; Band; CncrtBnd; DrlTm; HonRl; MrchBnd; NatlThespSoc; PepBnd; SchPl; StuCncl; PpCl; Bsktbl; LetterTrk; CaptChrldr; Trade School; Keypunch Operator.

CRAIG, Cynthia E; Trenton HS; Trenton, MI; 74/571 HonRl; LbryAde; NHS; NatlThespSoc; OffAde; SchAde; StuCncl; StuGov; TchrAde; Adrain College; Home Econ.

CRAMOND, Judy A; Waukegan East HS; Waukegan, IL; 75/856 HonRl; JrNHS; NHS; OffAde; StuCncl; StuGov; LetterSwmmng; GAA; IMSpt; University.

CRIDER, Stanley E; Greenfield Central HS; Greenfield, IN; 25/295 NHS; RedCrAde; SctActv; StuCncl; TchrAde; 4-H; VPMthCl; SciCl; Wrstlng; 4-HAwd; Purdue Univ; Engineer.

CRIPPEN, Cindy L; Huron Sr HS; Huron, SD; Band; CncrtBnd; OffAde; Orch; PpCl; Dakota Wesleyan Univ; Nurse.

CROSBY, Sharon L; Lindblom HS; Chicago, IL; CncrtBnd; HonRl; MrchBnd; OffAde; Orch; SchAde; MthCl; Natl Honor Soc; Sr Girls Council Treas; Drama Club Sec; Student Aide; Nv Univ; Law.

CROSS, Charles R; Brewster HS; Brewster, MN; 1/25 ALBoysSt; Band; ChrhWkr; HonRl; NHS; SchPl; StuCncl; EdYrBk; AmLegAwd; Univ Of Minnesota.

CROWLEY, James K; Central HS; Evansville, IN; HonRl; NHS; Quill&Scroll; SchMus; RptrYrbk; RptrSchPpr; Ftbl; Indiana Univ; Journalism.

CULLEN, James W; Onalaska HS; Onalaska, WI; 5/144 TrsSrCls; HonRl; JrNHS; NatlFornLg; NHS; SptEdYrbk; RptrSchPpr; LetterBsktbl; Univ Of Wisconsin; Communications.

CULLOM, Philip H; Homewood Flossmoor HS; Flossmoor, IL; 2/940 Chr; HonRl; LitMag; NHS; NatlSciFnd; Quill&Scroll; SpnCl; VPMthCl; SciCl; IMSpt; Us Naval Academy; Engineering.

CUMMISKEY, Joan M; Festus Senior HS; Festus, MO; HonRl; Miss Hickeys Secretarial School; Secretary.

CURRY, Gary D; Brooklyn Guernsey Malcom HS; Guernsey, IA; 8/48 HonRl; NHS; LetterBsktbl; LetterFtbl; LetterTrk; U S Air Force Academy; Officer.

D

DAHL, Sue E; Tipton HS; Tipton, MO; 10/84 Band; Chrs; HonRl; Mdrgl; NHS; SchMus; StuCncl; PresYthFlsp; PpCl; CaptChrldr; Univ Of Missouri; Secretary.

DAILY, Susan E; Columbus East HS; Columbus, IN; 2/336 SecSophCls; SecJrCls; SecSrCls; AFS; NatlMeritSchl; StuGov; 4-H; BttyCrckrAwd; DARAwd; 4-HAwd; JAAwd; Hanover College; Psychology.

DANCER, William C; Manual HS; Kansas City, MO; ChrhWkr; CmntyWkr; HonRl; HospAde; JA; OffAde; PolWkr; ROTC; SchPl; TchrAde; Bsbl; Bsktbl; LetterFtbl; LetterTrk; College; Professional.

DARROW, Brian D; Anamosa Comm HS; Anamosa, IA; ALBoysSt; Band; ChrhWkr; CncrtBnd; StuCncl; 4-H; LetterBsbl; LetterBsktbl; LetterFtbl; LetterTrk; Iowa St Univ; Veterinarian.

DARVEAU, Kenneth G; Hemingford HS; Hemingford, NE; VPFrshCls; VPSophCls; SecJrCls; Band; Chr; CncrtBnd; MrchBnd; PepBnd; TchrAde; 4-H; FFA; Bsktbl; Trade School; Auto Body.

DAVIS, Diana S; Braymer C 4 HS; Braymer, MO; 5/31 ALAGirlsSt; Band; ChrhWkr; CncrtBnd; HonRl; MrchBnd; OffAde; PepBnd; SchPl; TchrAde; CaptBsktbl; LetterTrk; 4-HAwd; University; Secretary.

DAVIS, Maria C; Henryville HS; Henryville, IN; 10/65 HonRl; NHS; OffAde; TchrAde; Yrbk; SchPpr; FHA; Univ Of Indiana; Medicine.

DEAL, Beth A; Milton Sr HS; Milton Jct, WI; ALAGirlsSt; HonRl; HospAde; NHS; PresStuCncl; EdYrBk; Sec4-H; PresLatCl; GAA; DARAwd; 4-HAwd; KiwanAwd; Eau Claire Univ; Psychology.

DEAN, Harry E; Aurora Sr HS; Aurora, IN; 2/135 PresSophCls; PresJrCls; ALBoysSt; ChrhWkr; CncrtBnd; HonRl; NHS; SptEdYrbk; LetterBsbl; Bsktbl; Chrldr; IMSpt; AmLegAwd; College; Architect.

DE BARR, Kathy A; Litchfield Sr HS; Litchfield, IL; Chrs; HonRl; NHS; TchrAde; E Illinois Univ; Medicine.

DECKER, Thomas D; Chester HS; Chester, IL; 25/125 ALBoysSt; SciCl; AmLegAwd; Univ Of Illinois; Engineering.

DEFFENBAUGH, Penny L; Blackford HS; Hartford City, IN; .

DEGNAN, Marie E; Central Catholic HS; Bloomington, IL; CmntyWkr; HonRl; TchrAde; EdSchPpr; 4-H; FHA; FrCl; PpCl; Chrldr; Illinois St Univ; Fashion Mdse.

DE MILLE, Debra M; Stephenson HS; Stephenson, MI; 8/100 Chrs; TreasNHS; Trk; Bay De Noc Comm College; Nursing.

DENNINGTON, Gary D; Washburn Rural HS; Topeka, KS; CncrtBnd; HonRl; MrchBnd; ModUN; PepBnd; PolWkr; SchMus; SchPl; StuCncl; Baylor Univ; Law.

DESWIK, Nancy; Maine Township South HS; Park Ridge, IL; HonRl; JrNHS; NatlMeritFnl; PolWkr; Quill&Scroll; StuCncl; RptrSchPpr; CivCl; PpCl; Michigan St Univ 4 Yr Merit Schlship; Purdue Univ; Bio Chemistry.

DE TIENNE, Michelle R; Maize HS; Wichita, KS; 8/60 Band; Chrs; HonRl; NHS; PepBnd; SchPl; Yrbk; PpCl; College; Medical Tech.

DEUROY, Sue L; Peshtigo HS; Peshtigo, WI; Chr; Chrs; ChrhWkr; HonRl; SchAde; SchPl; Yrbk; Bsktbl; Univ Of Wisconsin; Data Processing.

DE VRIES, Conda L; Armour HS; Armour, SD; 1/31 Chrs; HonRl; NHS; SchMus; RptrYrbk; Dakota Wesleyan Univ; Medical Lab Tech.

DE VRIES, Cynthia K; Pearl City HS; Pearl City, IL; PresBand; NHS; StuCncl; TchrAde; FTA; PpCl; Bsbl; Bsktbl; Trk; CaptChrldr; PresGAA; IMSpt; College; Physical Educ.

DIEFENBACH, Beth A; Herscher HS; Kankakee, IL; 5/179 TrsFrshCls; Band; Chr; Chrs; ChrhWkr; CncrtBnd; HonRl; Mdrgl; MrchBnd; PepBnd; Bsbl; Bsktbl; Trk; Natl Honor Soc; University; Physical Educ.

DIEFENDORF, Christine A; Yates City HS; Elmwood, IL; 8/30 SecSophCls; SecJrCls; Band; HonRl; PepBnd; SchMus; SchPl; RptrSchPpr; 4-H; FHA; SpnCl; PpCl; CaptChrldr; GAA; Illinois Central College; Business.

DIERMEIER, Donna M; Appleton East HS; Appleton, WI; Chr; PolWkr; RedCrAde; SctActv; TchrAde; RptrYrbk; RptrSchPpr; PresPpCl; Swmmng; GAA; Santa Barbara Univ; Journalism.

DILLARD, James K; Madison Consolidated HS; Madison, IN; 65/300 Band; ChrhWkr; CncrtBnd; HonRl; MrchBnd; NatlMeritSchl; PepBnd; FrCl; SciCl; Ftbl; Trk; College; Mathematics.

DIONNE, Mary F; Southern Door HS; Forestville, WI; 45/130 Chrs; HonRl; SchMus; RptrSchPpr; EdSchPpr; SchPpr; Attend NWTI Green Bay; College; Receptionist.

DISCHLER, Brian T; River Valley HS; Loganville, WI; Chrs; ChrhWkr; RedCrAde; SptEdSchPpr; Bsktbl; Ftbl; CaptTrk; IMSpt;.

DITZLER, James R; Huntington Catholic HS; Huntington, IN; HonRl; NHS; Sacrstn; SchPl; SctActv; VPStuCncl; Yrbk; LetterBsbl; LetterBsktbl; LetterTrk; CchngActv; Business School; Business Admin.

DIVIS, Linda; Lawrenceville HS; Lawrenceville, IL; 11/175 HonRl; HospAde; NHS; SchPl; StuCncl; YthFlsp; RptrYrbk; KeyCl; SpnCl; PpCl; SciCl; Glf; CaptChrldr; Univ Of Illinois; Liberal Arts.

DOERR, Rick E; Cass City HS; Cass City, MI; HonRl; Bsbl; Central Michigan University.

DOODY, Steven J; St Rita HS; Chicago, IL; 8/450 SecFrshCls; Chrs; HonRl; NHS; SchAde; TchrAde; SchPpr; Gold Medal In Bus Ed; 4 Yr Golden Honor Roll; Notre Dame; Finance.

DORITY, Clifford L; Martin Luther King HS; Detroit, MI; 3/200 HonRl; NHS; NatlMeritSchl; Quill&Scroll; RptrSchPpr; Howard Univ; Film Director.

DORTON, Keith C; Northern Heights HS; Admire, KS; PresJrCls; HonRl; NHS; StuCncl; LetterBsbl; LetterBsktbl; CaptFtbl; LetterTrk; University; Professional.

DOSE, Doris A; Glencoe Sr HS; Glencoe, MN; 25/143 Pres4-H; Bsktbl; LetterTrk; LetterChrldr; GAA; IMSpt; PPFtbl; AmLegAwd; 4-HAwd; PresAwd; CitAwd; North Dakota St Schl; Dental Hygiene.

DOTY, David R; Lourdes HS; Rochester, MN; ChrhWkr; College; Marine Biology.

DOTZENROD, Diane L; Wyndmere HS; Wyndmere, ND; SecSrCls; Band; Chr; CncrtBnd; HonRl; MrchBnd; PepBnd; SchPl; RptrYrbk; RptrSchPpr; FHA; College; Professional.

DOUGLAS, Robert W; Hillsboro R 3 HS; Hillsboro, MO; Band; Chrs; PpCl; LetterBsbl; LetterFtbl; IMSpt; PPFtbl; PresAwd;.

DOWLING, Kimberly A; Hanover Central HS; Cedar Lake, IN; DrlTm; HonRl; Quill&Scroll; RptrSchPpr; SchPpr; LetterBsktbl; LetterTrk; GAA; IMSpt; PPFtbl;.

DOZZI, Mary J; Gwinn HS; Gwinn, MI; 10/157 Band; CncrtBnd; HonRl; LbryAde; MrchBnd; NHS; PepBnd; SchPl; StuCncl; Michigan St Univ; Librarian.

DRAEGER, Pamela S; Wausau West HS; Wausau, WI; 7/442 Chr; Mdrgl; NHS; StuGov; TchrAde; RptrYrbk; EdSchPpr; GerCl; MthCl; LetterChrldr; BttyCrckrAwd; Univ Of Wisconsin.

DREBES, Linda M; Monroe City R 1 HS; Palmyra, MO; Chr; HonRl; NatlThespSoc; Yrbk; 4-H; FHA; PpCl; Trk; DanFAwd; 4-HAwd; St Pauls College; Elem Education.

DRINNIN, Judy L; Lakeview HS; Columbus, NE; Band; Chr; ChrhWkr; CncrtBnd; MrchBnd; PepBnd; RptrSchPpr; 4-H; PpCl; CaptBsktbl; Trk; 4-HAwd; Platte Jr College; Nursing.

DROBAC, Stanley H; Okemos HS; Okemos, MI; 8/

280 NHS; NatlMeritSF; Bsbl; LetterBsktbl; Ftbl; Glf; LetterTennis; College; Engineering.

DROGE, Ronald D; Pawnee City Public HS; Dubois, NE; 3/37 HonRl; StuCncl; StuGov; FFA; Attend Boys State; Univ; Professional.

DROPP, Mark A; Waterford HS; Franksville, WI; HonRl; Bsbl; Univ Of Wisconsin; Mathematics.

DUDA, Carmen H; T F South HS; Lansing, IL; AFS; HonRl; NHS; Sdlty; GerCl; Spanish Natl Honor Soc; De Paul Univ; Medicine.

DUNAWAY, Tracy L; Fort Calhoun HS; Omaha, NE; 3/35 Chr; HonRl; TchrAde; FBLA; FrCl; LetterPpCl; Bsbl; Trk; MasAwd; VFWAwd; Dana College; Secretary.

DUNN, Stephen R; Falls City HS; Falls City, NE; 3/100 Band; ChrhWkr; CncrtBnd; HonRl; MrchBnd; NHS; PepBnd; SchMus; Yrbk; VPSpnCl; Trk; Nebraska Wesleyan; Science.

DURBIN, Carolyn L; Paris R Ii HS; Paris, MO; ChrhWkr; HonRl; LbryAde; SchPl; SctActv; FHA; PpCl; LetterTrk; IMSpt; PPFtbl; Ne Missouri St Univ; Fashion Mdse.

DURHAM, Donald G; Lesterville HS; Lesterville, MO; Chrs; HonRl; JA; Socr;.

DUVALL, Roger E; Owosso HS; Owosso, MI; Band; Chr; ChrhWkr; CncrtBnd; HospAde; MrchBnd; PepBnd; SchMus; SchPl; TchrAde; YthFlsp; College Seminary; Law.

DYER, Steve G; Baxter Springs HS; Baxter Springs, KS; 4/86 ChrhWkr; HonRl; NHS; SchPl; 4-H; Bsktbl; College; Veterinarian.

E

EASLEY, Carolyn C; Meridian HS; Pulaski, IL; PresFrshCls; Band; ChrhWkr; HonRl; TreasStuCncl; Twrl; SptEdYrbk; Chrldr; IMSpt; University; Broadcasting.

EDGCOMB, Susan J; Saugatuck HS; Saugatuck, MI; 1/55 CncrtBnd; MrchBnd; PepBnd; StuCncl; SptEdSchPpr; PpCl; SciCl; LetterBsktbl; LetterTrk; DARAwd; College; Medical Tech.

EDNEY, Geoffrey A; Arlington HS; Indianapolis, IN; 52/463 HonRl; PolWkr; Quill&Scroll; StuCncl; SptEdSchPpr; LetterBsktbl; Glf; IMSpt; College; Medicine.

EDWARDS, Linda S; Wellsville Middletown Ri HS; New Hartford, MO; 9/50 TrsFrshCls; SecJrCls; HonRl; NHS; StuCncl; TchrAde; EdYrBk; RptrSchPpr; 4-H; PresFHA; GAA; Univ Of Missouri; Accounting.

EHNI, Mark G; Richwoods HS; Peoria, IL; 30/449 HonRl; NHS; Sterling Merit Scholar; Natl Honor Soc; Appted To US Air Force Acad; Air Force Academy.

EIBS, Thomas E; Marshal University HS; Minneapolis, MN; NatlFornLg; NatlMeritCmnd; PolWkr; StuGov; Institute Of Tech; Design Engineer.

EISEN, Cynthia K; Coopersville HS; Coopersville, MI; Chr; HonRl; JA; LbryAde; SchMus; FNA; College; Nursing.

ELAM, Renee; Carter H Harrison HS; Chicago, IL; 44/488 Chr; HonRl; JA; StuCncl; Univ Of Illinois; Business.

ELLIOTT, Cynthia L; Oak Forest HS; Oak Forest, IL; 6/346 HonRl; VPNHS; NatlMeritCmnd; VPStuCncl; FrCl; PpCl; LetterBsktbl; Trk; GAA; Univ Of Illinois; Medicine.

ELLIOTT, Ricky L; Rochelle Twp HS; Rochelle, IL; HonRl; VPStuCncl; PresKeyCl; E Illinois University.

ELLIOTT, Robert J; St Louis U HS; St Louis, MO; 29/206 Chr; HonRl; SchPl; SctActv; UNYO; RptrSchPpr; EdSchPpr; Univ Of Notre Dame.

ELMES, Alexander J; Indian Creek HS; Nineveh, IN; 35/125 Aud/Vis; ChrhWkr; CmntyWkr; HonRl; Sacrstn; SchPl; LetterFtbl; CaptSocr; Trk; Wrstlng; CchngActv; College; Business Mgmt.

ELSNER, Lynn M; Freeland HS; Freeland, MI; ChrhWkr; CmntyWkr; LbryAde; NHS; RedCrAde; 4-H; Delta College; Wildlife Mgmt.

ENGELHARD, Curtis A; Carpio Public HS; Foxholm, ND; TrsFrshCls; VPJrCls; NHS; StuCncl; Bsktbl; Ftbl; Trk; Wrstlng; DanFAwd;.

ENGLER, Lawrence W; Dwight David Eisenhower HS; Saginaw, MI; 34/365 Band; CncrtBnd; HonRl; MrchBnd; NHS; SctActv; StuCncl; TchrAde; RptrSchPpr; LetterTrk;.

ENOS, Andrew D; Adrian R 3 HS; Adrian, MO; HonRl; SchPl; YthFlsp; FFA; Ftbl; GodCntryAwd;.

EPPLIN, Loretta E; Pinckneyville Comm HS; Cutler, IL; 11/118 HonRl; NHS; FHA; FrCl; Illinois St University.

ERICKSON, Becky J; Kohler HS; Kohler, WI; AFS; Band; Chrs; HonRl; NatlFornLg; NatlThespSoc; PresStuCncl; TchrAde; Yrbk; Trk; Chrldr; Univ Of Wisconsin; Nursing.

ERICKSON, Constance L; Gibraltar HS; Sister Bay, WI; 7/69 Band; Chr; Chrs; CncrtBnd; HonRl; Mdrgl; MrchBnd; PepBnd; SchPl; RptrYrbk; College; Music Therapy.

ERICKSON, David A; Jths East Campus HS; Joliet, IL; 62/381 Band; CncrtBnd; HonRl; MrchBnd; OffAde; PepBnd; LetterGlf; LetterTrk; Montana St Univ; Elec Engineer.

EVANS, Mary M; Shenandoah HS; Shenandoah, IA; 9/100 TrsSophCls; AFS; Band; CncrtBnd; HonRl; MrchBnd; NHS; PepBnd; StuGov; SchPpr; Univ Of Iowa; Medicine.

EVANS, Sheryl A; Winfield HS; Winfield, KS; SecTrsJrCls; Chrs; ChrhWkr; HonRl; Orch; SchMus; FHA; PpCl; Swmmng; LetterTennis; Washburn Univ; Liberal Arts.

EVON, Christine A; Oak Park River Forest HS; Oak Park, IL; CmntyWkr; NatlMeritSchl; TchrAde; Bsbl; Gum Laude Soc; Female Athlete Of The Year; Southern Ill Univ; Physical Therapy.

EWALD, Jacqueline K; Durant HS; Durant, IA; 7/70 Band; Chrs; CncrtBnd; HonRl; JrNHS; MrchBnd; NHS; PepBnd; SchMus; SchPl; College; Special Education.

F

FACINELLI, Dave A; Joliet Catholic HS; Joliet, IL; 26/185 VPFrshCls; VPSophCls; PresSrCls; HonRl; NHS; StuCncl; RptrSchPpr; FrCl; SpnCl; Bsbl; College.

FARBER, Jeffrey P; Arlington HS; Indianapolis, IN; CmntyWkr; HonRl; JA; LbryAde; StuGov; TchrAde; SchPpr; Bsbl; IMSpt; JAAwd; PresAwd; College; Professional.

FEDELER, Annette K; Sumner HS; Hawkeye, IA; 9/84 ChrhWkr; HonRl; NHS; FHA; PpCl; CaptBsktbl; GAA; Univ Of N Iowa; Physical Education.

FENNESSY, James R; Watervliet HS; Watervliet, MI; DrmBgl; SctActv; College; Automotive Tech.

FERGUSON, Kerry R; Ames HS; Ames, IA; 150/394 HonRl; StuCncl; RptrSchPpr; LetterBsktbl; LetterFtbl; Trk; CchngActv; University; Business.

FINKLE, Lyle A; Roeper City Country HS; Pontiac, MI; Natl Merit Finalist; College; Engineering.

FINN, Pamela A; Roncalli HS; Omaha, NE; SecFrshCls; Aud/Vis; Band; Chrs; HonRl; NHS; SchPl; Yrbk; Bsktbl; Chrldr; College; Professional.

FINNEY, Charles R; Washington HS; Sioux Falls, SD; VPSrCls; ALBoysSt; CAP; HonRl; NatlMeritCmnd; Sdlty; RptrSchPpr; GerCl; Trk; EldAwd; MasAwd; Univ Of South Dakota; Business.

FIRKUS, Tamra I; Humboldt HS; St Paul, MN; TrsJrCls; Chr; ChrhWkr; CncrtBnd; HonRl; SchMus; StuCncl; YthFlsp; FrCl; Trk; Chrldr; Business Schl; Vocation.

FISCHBACH, Robert J; Duchesne HS; St Charles, MO; 30/200 Band; Chrs; HonRl; TreasJrNHS; PresNHS; SchMus; StuCncl; EdYrBk; FrCl; Ftbl; University; Professional.

FISCHER, Bradley C; Chusen Valley HS; Chatfield, MN; AFS; Chr; SchMus; SchPl; Ftbl; College; Professional.

FISCHER, Catherine M; Humboldt Comm HS; Humboldt, IA; Chr; Chrs; ChrhWkr; HonRl; HospAde; SchMus; SchPl; SctActv; RptrSchPpr; Iowa St Univ; Art.

FISCHER, Warren L; Sevastopol HS; Egg Harbor, WI; 1/80 CncrtBnd; MrchBnd; NHS; PresStuCncl; StuGov; Ftbl; Trk; IMSpt; Univ Of Wisconsin; Law.

FISHER, David L; Washington Catholic HS; Washington, IN; 4/31 PresFrshCls; TrsSophCls; SchPl; StuCncl; RptrSchPpr; SchPpr; KeyCl; IMSpt; Pres Of Soph Class; Univ; Prof.

FITZWATER, Joe L; Villisca HS; Nodaway, IA; 3/40 PresJrCls; ALBoysSt; ChrhWkr; HonRl; StuCncl; 4-H; FFA; Bsktbl; Ftbl; Trk; College; Business.

FLAK, Frank; Schulte HS; Terre Haute, IN; 14/86 ChrhWkr; HonRl; KeyCl; LetterBsbl; Bsktbl; LetterFtbl; College; Engineering.

FLATEN, Janelle H; Park River HS; Park River, ND; Chr; Chrl; Chrs; ChrhWkr; HonRl; LbryAde; SchMus; YthFlsp; RptrYrbk; RptrSchPpr; 4-H; FHA; Univ Of North Dakota; Social Work.

FLEEMAN, Michael E; Kingsville R 1 HS; Kingsville, MO; Chr; Chrs; ChrhWkr; HonRl; SchPl; RptrYrbk; RptrSchPpr; 4-H; PpCl; LetterBsbl; CaptBsktbl; University.

FOLEY, Diane L; Blair HS; Blair, NE; TchrAde; 4-H; FNA; PpCl; Bsktbl; CchngActv; GAA; IMSpt; 4-HAwd;.

FOOTE, Jeffrey D; Bullock Creek HS; Midland, MI; Band; HonRl; StuCncl; LetterFtbl; LetterTrk; LetterWrstlng; College; Minister.

FORBES, Jennifer L; Cabool HS; Cabool, MO; TrsSrCls; HonRl; NHS; OffAde; SchPl; FBLA; FHA; FrCl; Draughon Business College; Business.

FORD, Jodi D; Climax Scotts HS; Scotts, MI; HonRl; SchPl; TchrAde; RptrYrbk; Yrbk; RptrSchPpr; SchPpr; 4-H; College; Professional.

FORD, Mari C; Janesville Parker Sr HS; Janesville, WI; 90/1700 CmntyWkr; DrlTm; HonRl; HospAde; SchAde; TchrAde; Univ Of Wisconsin; Nursing.

FORESTER, John B; South Barber HS; Hazelton, KS; Chr; Chrs; HonRl; StuCncl; FFA; Bsktbl; Ftbl; Tennis; Trk; College; Agriculture.

FOTH, Lisa L; St Mary Central HS; Neenah, WI; TrsSophCls; HonRl; JA; OffAde; StuCncl; RptrSchPpr; SchPpr; FrCl; PpCl; LetterTennis; JAAwd; College; Journalism.

FOWLER, Cathy J; Newtown Harris HS; Newtown, MO; TrsFrshCls; ALAGirlsSt; Band; DrmMjrt; HonRl; NHS; SchPl; StuCncl; Twrl; RptrSchPpr; 4-H; FBLA; FHA; LetterBsbl; College; Music.

FOWLER, Joyce E; Western HS; Russiaville, IN; 20/154 HstSrCls; ALAGirlsSt; Band; Chr; DrlTm; HonRl; NHS; StuCncl; FHA; Bsktbl; Trk; Chrldr; GAA; Trade Schl; X Ray Tech.

FOX, Steven P; Darlington HS; Darlington, WI; HonRl; 4-H; Bsbl; LetterFtbl; LetterWrstlng; Business Schl; Accounting.

FRANK, Terri S; Tri City HS; Mechanicsburg, IL; Band; Chr; ChrhWkr; CncrtBnd; HonRl; LbryAde; PepBnd; SchMus; SctActv; TchrAde; Trk; Chrldr; LetterIMSpt; 4-HAwd;.

FRANZ, Steve E; Leland HS; Leland, IL; AFS; Band; ChrhWkr; TchrAde; FFA; Bsbl; Bsktbl; Ftbl; Socr; Joliet Jr College; Mechanic.

FREEMAN, Stephen D; Anderson Sr HS; Anderson, IN; HonRl; SpnCl; Bsbl; College; Professional.

FREIER, Merritt T; Flora HS; Flora, IL; 26/150 Band; HonRl; Quill&Scroll; SchPl; SptEdSchPpr; GerCl; MthCl; LetterFtbl; LetterTrk; University; Engineer.

FRISBEY, Sallie A; Littlefield HS; Alanson, MI; 1/40 TrsSophCls; SecJrCls; RedCrAde; SchAde; SchPl; StuCncl; TchrAde; RptrYrbk; SptEdYrbk; RptrSchPpr; SptEdSchPpr; Bsktbl; College; Nursing.

FROST, Richard A; Brighton HS; Brighton, MI; HonRl; NHS; Kalamazoo College; Engineering.

FULLER, Douglas A; Tri Central HS; Sharpsville, IN; 3/125 HonRl; SctActv; LetterFtbl; Purdue Univ; Elec Engineer.

FULTON, Peggy A; Odin Public HS; Odin, IL; 6/24 Band; Chrs; DrlTm; DrmMjrt; HonRl; LbryAde; MrchBnd; StuCncl; TchrAde;.

FURLOW, Barbara L; Iron Mountain HS; Iron Mountain, MI; 6/167 Band; Chrs; CncrtBnd; HonRl; MrchBnd; StuCncl; RptrYrbk; FrCl; Western Michigan Univ; Medicine.

FURTAK, Roberta L; Irving Crown HS; Carpentersville, IL; SchAde; StuCncl; TchrAde; FTA; PpCl; College; Education.

G

GALLAGHER, John T; Milton Sr HS; Milton, WI; PresAFS; ALBoysSt; PresBand; Chr; HonRl; PepBnd; SchMus; StuCncl; Ftbl; Tennis; Univ Of Wisconsin; Music.

GALVAN, Daniel; Marion HS; Marion, IN; ChrhWkr; CmntyWkr; LetterFtbl; LetterWrstlng; Trade School; Mechanics.

GAMBLIN, David E; Tipton HS; Tipton, IN; Band; Chr; CncrtBnd; HonRl; MrchBnd; PepBnd; SctActv; 4-H; SciCl; Tennis; Purdue Univ; Physics.

GARDNER, Judith M; St Martin De Porres HS; Detroit, MI; 7/84 VPSophCls; ChrhWkr; CmntyWkr; NHS; OffAde; PepBnd; SchAde; SchMus; StuCncl; PpCl; Western Michigan Univ; Psychology.

GARNER, Angela; Sumner HS; St Louis, MO; 38/447 Band; ChrhWkr; CncrtBnd; HonRl; MrchBnd; Orch; StuCncl; Univ Of Missouri; Professional.

GAVIN, Clay G; Aquin HS; Worthington, IA; PresSrCls; ALBoysSt; Chrs; SchMus; StuCncl; RptrSchPpr; Bsktbl; College; Law.

GAVIN, Debra A; Unity HS; Chicago, IL; Chrs; NHS; RptrYrbk; FHA; Illinois St Univ; Special Ed.

GAY, William R; Dexfield Comm HS; Redfield, IA; 7/43 HstJrCls; TrsSrCls; Band; Chr; Chrs; CncrtBnd; HonRl; MrchBnd; NHS; PepBnd; LetterBsbl; LetterBsktbl; LetterFtbl; Iowa St Univ; Agriculture.

GAYLORD, Laurie A; Vandercook Lake HS; Jackson, MI; CaptDrlTm; HonRl; JA; LbryAde; NHS; SchPl; TreasStuCncl; TchrAde; RptrSchPpr; EdSchPpr; Trk; BttyCrckrAwd; Univ Of Michigan.

GENG, Cindy S; Lincoln HS; Park Falls, WI; Band; CncrtBnd; DrmBgl; MrchBnd; PepBnd; 4-H; PpCl; LetterTrk; Chrldr; GAA; College.

GENIK, Michael D C; Saline HS; Saline, MI; TchrAde; Univ Of Michigan; Oceanography.

GERTH, Joan M; Ladywood St Agnes HS; Greenwood, IN; CmntyWkr; HospAde; JA; RedCrAde; StuCncl; Yrbk; College; Nursing.

GESKE, Susan J; Milton Sr HS; Milton, WI; SecJrCls; Band; CncrtBnd; HonRl; MrchBnd; FHA; College; Vocation.

GIDDAY, Jeffrey M; Milford HS; Milford, MI; 3/575 CmntyWkr; HonRl; NHS; NatlMeritCmnd; SchPl; StuCncl; SpnCl; PpCl; Tennis; Univ Of Michigan; Medicine.

GIER, William D; Bloomfield HS; Bloomfield, NE; 18/50 Band; Chrs; ChrhWkr; HonRl; SchAde; SctActv; YthFlsp; Bsktbl; Ftbl; College; Engineering.

GIFFORD, Mary C; Farnsworth HS; Sheboygan, WI; Chrs; HonRl; College; Liberal Arts.

GINDER, Carl E; Triopia HS; Arenzville, IL; 6/56 Band; Chr; ChrhWkr; HonRl; MrchBnd; NHS; SchPl; Yrbk; LetterFtbl; LetterTrk; AmLegAwd; Western Illinois Univ; Agriculture.

GISH, Alexander R; Crandon HS; Crandon, WI; HonRl; RedCrAde; SpnCl; Trade Schl; Vocation.

GLANOPULOS, Robin I; Baxter HS; Lawrence, KS; 12/75 Chr; ChrhWkr; HonRl; LbryAde; SchMus; RptrYrbk; SchPpr; FHA; Evangel College; Sociology.

GLEASURE, Donna M; Brown City Comm HS; Brown City, MI; 26/95 Band; Chr; Chrs; ChrhWkr; CmntyWkr; HonRl; NHS; NatlMeritSchl; TchrAde; YthFlsp; 4-H; EngCl; FrCl; Faithway Baptist College; Christian Educ.

GLYNN, James F; Marist HS; South Holland, IL; HonRl; NHS; LetterFtbl; IMSpt; University; Professional.

GOCHENOUR, Anita F; La Ma HS; Logan, IA; 2/50 MrchBnd; NHS; PepBnd; SchMus; SchPl; TchrAde; 4-H; MthCl; LetterTrk; 4-HAwd; College; Nursing.

GOEMAN, Stephen D; Michigan Ctr HS; Michigan Ctr, MI; 3/150 HonRl; NHS; SctActv; TchrAde; RptrYrbk; Univ Of Michigan; Biochemist.

GOETTING, Mary P; Norborne Public HS; Norborne, MO; 1/25 ChrhWkr; HonRl; NHS; VPStuCncl; RptrYrbk; Pres4-H; SecFHA; PresFrCl; Bsktbl; Trk; 4-HAwd; Benedictine College; Medicine.

GOODMAN, Charles L; Berkeley Sr HS; Berkeley, MO; Socr; CaptTennis; Trk; Chrldr; IMSpt; JAAwd; PresAwd; CitAwd; College; Medicine.

GOODWIN, Lauri A; Frankenmuth HS; Frankenmuth, MI; Band; CncrtBnd; HonRl; MrchBnd; NHS; PepBnd; SchPl; TchrAde; 4-H; FrCl; LetterTrk; Chrldr; GAA; 4-HAwd; College; Medicine.

GORDON, Kelvin K; Bloomingdale HS; Bloomington, MI; OffAde; PolWkr; Teen; Bsktbl; Ftbl; Trk; IMSpt; GodCntryAwd; College; Social Work.

GOSTISHA, Michael D; Goodman HS; Goodman, WI; 4/36 ALBoysSt; Band; HonRl; NHS; StuCncl; EdYrBk; CaptBsktbl; LetterBsktbl; CaptFtbl; College; Liberal Arts.

GOWDY, Thomas F; Northeast Hamilton HS; Williams, IA; ALBoysSt; ChrhWkr; SchPl; FBLA; Ellsworth College; Agriculture.

GOWER, Bonita L; Lovejoy HS; Lovejoy, IL; SecSophCls; Band; ChrhWkr; CtyCnl; CmntyWkr; CncrtBnd; HonRl; PresStuCncl; TchrAde; SpnCl; E Illinois Univ; Computer Programming.

GRAF, Michael P; De Smet Jesuit HS; St Louis, MO; 1/188 Band; CmntyWkr; CncrtBnd; HonRl; NHS; NatlMeritFnl; NatlMeritSF; PepBnd; RptrSchPpr; CaptTennis; LionAwd; Cornell Univ; Elec Engineer.

GRAHAM, Kimberly A; Appleton West HS; Appleton, WI; 1/633 TrsSophCls; Chrs; HonRl; Teen; Yrbk; PresFrCl; PpCl; LetterTennis; VPGAA; College; Business.

GRAHAM, Robert A; Poplar Bluff Sr HS; Poplar Bluff, MO; 32/470 HonRl; NHS; SctActv; StuCncl; KeyCl; LetterFtbl; LetterTrk; IMSpt; College; Professional.

GRAMS, Cynthia; Morrison HS; Morrison, IL; 32/117 Chr; ChrhWkr; HonRl; SchMus; YthFlsp; RptrSchPpr; Chrldr; Awarded Il State Schlship; Western Il Univ; Elem Educ.

GRAY, Sharon K; Center HS; Kansas City, MO; 5/425 Band; CncrtBnd; HonRl; MrchBnd; NatlFornLg; NHS; PepBnd; StuCncl; GerCl; LetterTrk; College; Physical Therapy.

GREENE, Charlene M; Manistique HS; Manistique, MI; 1/157 Chrs; CncrtBnd; HonRl; HospAde; MrchBnd; PepBnd; Lake Superior St College; Medicine.

GREENE, Patricia D; Sarcoxie HS; Avilla, MO; SecChrhWkr; CmntyWkr; SecTeen; FHA; PpCl; Chrldr; Trade School; Beautician.

GRIMES, Michele R; Sandusky HS; Sandusky, MI; 41/114 Band; CncrtBnd; MrchBnd; PepBnd; SchMus; 4-H; GerCl; Michigan St University.

GRIMM, Mary L; Carl Sandburg HS; Palos Park, IL; 24/815 PresFrshCls; HonRl; SecNHS; TchrAde; TreasFrCl; PpCl; CaptChrldr; GAA; University; Professional.

GRONN, Marie R; Alvernia HS; Chicago, IL; SecTrsJrCls; NHS; EdSchPpr; University; Science.

GROSS, Le Ann E; St Marys Central HS; Bismarck, ND; Chr; SctActv; 4-H; LetterBsktbl; GAA; PPFtbl; 4-HAwd; Business College; Business Mgmt.

GROSSENBURG, Jolenne K; Winner Sr HS; Winner, SD; 12/140 Band; CncrtBnd; DrlTm; HonRl; MrchBnd; StuCncl; PpCl; Bsktbl; LetterTrk; Chrldr; IMSpt; College; Med Tech.

GROVES, Thomas K; Mankato East HS; Mankato, MN; Aud/Vis; SchPl; YthFlsp; College; Christian Educ.

GRZANICH, Deanna L; Lewistown Comm HS; Dunferm Line, IL; 25/130 ChrhWkr; CmntyWkr; HonRl; HospAde; RedCrAde; FHA; FrCl; PpCl; Spoon River College; Nursing.

GSCHWENDTNER, Susan M; Pontiac Township HS; Pontiac, IL; 1/211 SecFrshCls; SecSophCls; TrsJrCls; HonRl; Mdrgl; NHS; Treas4-H; PresFrCl; VPPpCl; GAA; DanFAwd; 4-HAwd; Amer Leg Girls State Annual Yearbook Editor In Chief; College; Lawyer.

GULBRAND, Blake A; L P Goodrich HS; Fond Du Lac, WI; .

GULLIXSON, Randy M; St Croix Central HS; Hammond, WI; College; Athletics.

GUNSTONE, Ellen F; Hermon HS; Omaha, NE; 10/88 ChrhWkr; HonRl; HospAde; JrNHS; NHS; SchAde; SchMus; SchPl; YthFlsp; SchPpr; Bsktbl; Tennis; Trk; St Marys College; Nursing.

GUTIERREZ, Ruby; Holy Redeemer HS; Detroit, MI; TrsFrshCls; TrsSophCls; TrsJrCls; CmntyWkr; HonRl; LbryAde; SchAde; College; Liberal Arts.

GUTZEIT, Michael F; Marist HS; Palos Heights, IL; 9/385 HonRl; NHS; NatlMeritCmnd; StuCncl; Bsktbl; Trk; Loyola Univ; Pre Medical.

H

HABEGER, Kent D; Burt Community HS; Burt, IA; Band; Chrs; CncrtBnd; HonRl; MrchBnd; PepBnd; SchPl; 4-H; Glf; College; Agriculture.

HACKMAN, Connie K; New Franklin HS; Fayette, MO; 3/50 SecSophCls; Chrl; ChrhWkr; HonRl; JrNHS; NHS; YthFlsp; 4-H; FHA; SpnCl; Bsbl; Bsktbl; Trk; College.

HAGAN, Jeffrey M; North Miami HS; Denver, IN; 52/124 GerCl; SciCl; Bsbl; Bsktbl; Ftbl; CaptGlf; IMSpt; Ball State Univ; Business.

HAGEN, Christopher E; Glenwood City HS; Glenwood City, WI; 4/85 SecJrCls; Chrs; ChrhWkr; CncrtBnd; HonRl; NatlSciFnd; SchPl; SctActv; TchrAde; Bsbl; Bsktbl; Ftbl; College; Medicine.

HAHN, David H; Mt Zion HS; Mt Zion, IL; 12/190 AFS; ChrhWkr; HonRl; NHS; LetterBsktbl; Ftbl; LetterTrk; Bethany College; Chemistry.

HALL, Christopher J; Bishop Dwenger HS; Fort Wayne, IN; NatlMeritSF; StuCncl; Finalists Natl Merit Schlships; Purdue Univ; Elec Engineering.

HALL, Donna G; Lincoln HS; Wisconsin Rapids, WI; Band; Chr; Chrs; CmntyWkr; CncrtBnd; DrmBgl; HonRl; Mdrgl; Orch; PolWkr; SchMus; RptrSchPpr; FrCl; GerCl; Univ Of Wisconsin; Linguistics.

HALL, Rodd L; Yorkwood HS; Little York, IL; 1/55 PresSrCls; Band; ChrhWkr; CncrtBnd; HonRl; MrchBnd; RptrYrbk; Bsktbl; LetterTrk; EldAwd; Natl Honor Soc; College; Chemistry.

HALVERSON, James G; Garner Hayfield HS; Garner, IA; 20/84 ChrhWkr; Waldorf College; Archaeology.

HAMBIDGE, Brian J; Arapahoe Public HS; Arapahoe, NE; TrsSophCls; Chrs; SchPl; StuCncl; YthFlsp; SptEdSchPpr; Ftbl; Trk; CaptWrstlng; College; Professional.

HAMMEL, Mark A; Whitnall HS; Greenfield, WI; 7/270 Band; CncrtBnd; HonRl; NHS; PepBnd; SchMus; GerCl; College.

HANKS, Krisna L; Quincy Sr HS; Quincy, IL; HonRl; JrNHS; NHS; PpCl; CaptChrldr; Univ Of Indiana; Dance.

HANSEN, Jana S; Willard HS; Springfield, MO; 4-H; FHA; Chrldr; College.

HANSEN, Judy R; Seward Sr HS; Seward, NE; 16/142 Band; DrmMjrt; HonRl; PepBnd; StuCncl; 4-H; FHA; Univ Of Nebraska; Medical Tech.

HANSEN, Linda L; Glenwood HS; Springfield, IL; AFS; Chr; HonRl; SchMus; College; Photography.

HAREM, Tina J; Ldf Community HS; Marshalltown, IA; 13/44 ChrhWkr; TreasYthFlsp; LetterPpCl; Bsktbl; LetterTrk; PPFtbl; BttyCrckrAwd; Marshalltown Comm College; Marketing.

HARMON, James E; Gage Park HS; Chicago, IL; 1/611 HonRl; TchrAde; College; Science.

HARPER, Wyvetta L; Unity HS; Chicago, IL; 20/221 Chr; CmntyWkr; DrmBgl; HonRl; HospAde; JA; NatlFornLg; NatlMeritCmnd; SchPl; SctActv; StuGov; Bsbl; Bsktbl; Transcribes Into Braile For Blind; Univ Of Chicago; Political Science.

HARRIS, Jill Anne; Dubois HS; Dubois, IN; Band; CncrtBnd; DrmMjrt; HonRl; MrchBnd; College; Teaching.

HARTLEROAD, Wanda L; Hutsonville HS; West York, IL; 6/45 SecSrCls; ChrhWkr; HonRl; StuCncl; Yrbk; FHA; College; Teacher.

HARVEY, Kristy C; Laboure HS; St Louis, MO; Chr; Chrs; NatlCathMusEdAsoc; SctActv; StuCncl; FrCl; PpCl; IMSpt; College; Nursing.

HASKINS, David S; East Noble HS; Kendallville, IN; Band; CncrtBnd; HonRl; MrchBnd; NatlThespSoc; PepBnd; SchMus; SchPl; SciCl; Indiana Univ; Law Enforcement.

HAUKE, Michael J; New Haven HS; New Haven, IN; 19/237 ALBoysSt; Chr; DrlTm; HonRl; NHS; ROTC; GerCl; SciCl; LetterFtbl; LetterTrk; LetterWrstlng; RotaryAwd; College; Medicine.

HAYES, Robert L; Lockwood Ri HS; Lockwood, MO; VPFrshCls; TrsJrCls; ALBoysSt; ChrhWkr; SchPl; Ftbl; College.

HAYS, Michael J; Mount Clemens HS; Selfridge, MI; 8/450 ChrhWkr; CmntyWkr; HonRl; NHS; KeyCl; SpnCl; LetterGlf; Socr; KiwanAwd; CitAwd; Univ Of Michigan; Civil Engineer.

HAYS, Susan K; Woodland HS; Streator, IL; 26/79 Chrs; HonRl; LbryAde; StuCncl; RptrSchPpr; EdSchPpr; SchPpr; FHA; GerCl; Trade Schl; Veterinarian.

HEATH, Steven D; King City R 1 HS; King City, MO; 13/39 ALBoysSt; PresBand; HonRl; NHS; SchPl; StuCncl; FFA; Bsbl; LetterBsktbl; LetterFtbl; Glf; College; Liberal Arts.

HEIMERL, Joann M; Forest Park HS; Amasa, MI; CtyCnl; CmntyWkr; HonRl; JrNHS; NHS; StuCncl; StuGov; RptrYrbk; FBLA; FNA; Chrldr; College; Vocation.

HEIMES, Patricia J; Heelan HS; Sioux City, IA; 13/250 HonRl; StuCncl; RptrYrbk; Yrbk; RptrSchPpr; FrCl; PpCl; LetterChrldr; College; Liberal Arts.

HEITMAN, Leslie R; Williamsburg Comm HS; Williamsburg, IA; Band; CncrtBnd; MrchBnd; PresNHS; PepBnd; YthFlsp; Yrbk; 4-H; LetterTrk; Chrldr; IMSpt; PPFtbl; DanFAwd; Iowa St Univ; Interior Design.

HELLERMAN, Daniel K; Winnetonka HS; Kansas City, MO; 87/515 HonRl; Orch; SchMus; FrCl; Maple Woods Comm College; Computer Programm.

HENDERSON, Gina L; Jacksonville HS; Jacksonville, IL; SecSophCls; Band; StuGov; TchrAde; 4-H; FTA; FrCl; S Illinois Univ; Special Educ.

HENDRICH, Becky J; Smith Center HS; Portis, KS; SecSophCls; SecJrCls; Chrs; HonRl; JrNHS; FHA; College.

HENDRICKSON, Katherine M; Pecatonica HS; Blanchardville, WI; Band; CncrtBnd; HonRl; MrchBnd; NatlFornLg; PepBnd; SchMus; SchPl; FHA; Beauty Academy; Beautician.

HERMAN, John C; Columbus HS; Marshfield, WI; Band; CncrtBnd; DrlTm; MrchBnd; Orch; PepBnd; SchMus; Trade School; Vocational.

HERNANDEZ, Josefina I; Mason City Sr HS; Mason City, IA; ALAGirlsSt; DrlTm; HonRl; PpCl; LetterBsktbl; GAA; IMSpt; College; Science.

HERNANDEZ, Ray A; Westmoreland HS; Blaine, KS; Band; HonRl; MrchBnd; PepBnd; StuCncl; 4-H; SciCl; Ftbl; West Point; Army Surgeon.

HIBBARD, John W; Jeffersonville HS; Jeffersonville, IN; PresJrCls; PresSrCls; VPStuCncl; StuGov; KeyCl; LatCl; PpCl; Bsbl; Bsktbl; IMSpt; PresAwd; Indiana Univ Se; Business.

HIGGINS, Richard M; Prairie Home HS; Prairie Home, MO; VPJrCls; PresSrCls; Chrs; HonRl; SchPl; Yrbk; SptEdSchPpr; Bsbl; Central Missouri St Univ; Industrial Arts.

HIGHFIELD, Mark C; Oscoda HS; Oscoda, MI; Band; ChrhWkr; MrchBnd; PepBnd; StuGov; KeyCl; LetterBsbl; Bsktbl; LetterGlf; LetterSwmmng; University; Dentist.

HILGEDICK, Barbara A; Salem HS; Salem, MO; 19/173 Band; CncrtBnd; HonRl; MrchBnd; PepBnd; SchPl; TchrAde; Sw Missouri St Univ; Business Admin.

HILL, J L; Raymore Peculiar HS; Raymore, MO; VPSrCls; PresChr; Chrs; ChrhWkr; CmntyWkr; HonRl; SchMus; SchPl; StuCncl; TchrAde; TreasFTA; Sw Missouri St Univ; Music.

HILLGER, David H; Fitzgerald HS; Warren, MI; Ftbl; Trk; Michigan St Univ; Respiratory Therapy.

HILLRING, Larry M; St Joseph HS; So Bend, IN; 102/260 PresSrCls; CmntyWkr; DrlTm; ROTC; StuGov; 4-H; Ftbl; Trk; IMSpt; 4-HAwd; KiwanAwd; College; Liberal Arts.

HILLS, April M; South Haven HS; South Haven, MI; 8/220 ChrhWkr; HonRl; YthFlsp; Michigan St Univ; Medicine.

HILLSON, Dory J; Norfolk Sr HS; Norfolk, NE; Band; CncrtBnd; HonRl; JrNHS; MrchBnd; NHS; Orch; PepBnd; FHA; University; Music.

HINKLE, Kim D; Circle HS; Valley Cent, KS; Band; MrchBnd; Twrl; PpCl; College; Stewardess.

HITSELBERGER, James F; Choate HS; Fond Du Lac, WI; RptrSchPpr; SchPpr; Georgetown Univ; Language.

HITTLE, Michael R; High School; Fruitport, MI; College; Elec Engineering.

HOCHSTETLER, Angela K; Iowa Mennonite HS; Oxford, IA; 3/37 VPFrshCls; Chr; Chrl; PresChrs; HonRl; Mdrgl; NHS; StuCncl; RptrYrbk; EdYrBk; E Mennonite College; English.

HODGES, Ronald F; Westport HS; Kansas City, MO; HonRl; NHS; OffAde; StuCncl; PpCl; SciCl; Bsktbl; Most Valuable Player; Distinguished Serv Award; Most Rebounds Award; Best Personality; Nicest Person; William Jewell College; Professional.

HOELTING, Jill D; Taylorville Sr HS; Taylorville, IL; 11/254 ChrhWkr; HonRl; RedCrAde; StuCncl; FrCl; PpCl; Tennis; Trk; So Illinois Univ; Eastern Illinois Univ; Recreation.

HOFFMAN, Robert G; Lincoln HS; Park Falls, WI; Band; ChrhWkr; CncrtBnd; HonRl; MrchBnd; PepBnd; College; Broadcasting.

HOFTIEZER, Scott A; Libertyville HS; Lake Bluff, IL; HonRl; NatlFornLg; NHS; NatlMeritFnl; SchPl; Univ; Medicine.

HOLMEN, Gary D; Theodore Roosevelt HS; Minneapolis, MN; Chr; HonRl; NatlMeritSF; Finalist In Natl Merit Schlship Prog; Normandale Comm Col; Accounting.

HOLTMAN, Rhonda L; Gull Lake HS; Augusta, MI; Band; Chr; HonRl; JA; MrchBnd; Orch; YthFlsp; 4-H; PPFtbl; College; Science.

HONER, Ronald J; Atchison HS; Atchison, KS; 25/167 ALBoysSt; HonRl; ModUN; RptrSchPpr; SptEdSchPpr; Bsktbl; Ftbl; Tennis; University.

HONES, Agnes T; Albion Sr HS; Albion, MI; CmntyWkr; HonRl; NatlFornLg; NHS; SchMus; StuGov; FrCl; SpnCl; Kalamazoo College; Journalism.

HORNIG, James F; Iroquois HS; Huron, SD; VPSophCls; VPJrCls; PresSrCls; Chrs; ChrhWkr; CmntyWkr; HonRl; NatlMeritFnl; NatlMeritCmnd; OffAde; SchAde; Bsbl; LetterBsktbl; LetterFtbl; Huron College; Law.

HORTON, Arlee A; West Pike HS; New Canton, IL; JrNHS; NHS; FHA; LetterBsbl; LetterBsktbl; LetterTrk; CaptChrldr; GAA; IMSpt; AmLegAwd; 4-HAwd; College; Liberal Arts.

HOSS, Anita M; Ness HS; Ness, KS; ALAGirlsSt; Chr; HonRl; NatlThespSoc; SchMus; SchPl; 4-H; FHA; 4-HAwd; College; Home Economics.

HOUGH, Stephen J; East Richland HS; Olney, IL; RptrSchPpr; LetterFtbl; LetterTrk; CchngActv; Olney Central College; Law.

HOUGHTALING, Dale E; Liberty HS; Mountain View, MO; SchMus; SctActv; PpCl; LetterBsbl; LetterFtbl; GodCntryAwd; College.

HOUSE, James H; Greenville HS; Cedar Springs, MI; LetterWrstlng; Grand Rapids Jr College; Sports Writer.

HOUSTON, Lesa M; South Barber HS; Hardtner, KS; ALAGirlsSt; Chr; HonRl; LbryAde; TchrAde; PpCl; Bsktbl; Swmmng; Trk; Chrldr; IMSpt; College; Professional.

HOUSTON, Randall J; Terre Haute North Vigo HS; Seelyville, IN; Aud/Vis; HonRl; NatlFornLg; NHS; NatlMeritCmnd; Orch; Quill&Scroll; SchMus; SchPl; RptrSchPpr; Indiana St Univ; Geology.

HOWLETT, Donald R; Richland R 4 Public HS; Richland, MO; Chr; Chrs; ChrhWkr; LetterBsktbl; LetterTrk; Trade School; Mechanic.

HOYT, Tedd J; North Sr HS; Eau Claire, WI; 1/450 HonRl; NHS; ROTC; TchrAde; GerCl; Ftbl; LetterTrk; IMSpt; Air Force Acad; Pilot.

HUBERS, Kathy K; Maurice Orange City Comm HS; Maurice, IA; SecJrCls; Chrs; HonRl; JrNHS; LbryAde; NHS; SchPl; 4-H; FTA; Bsktbl; Vocational School; Secretary.

HUDSON, Cathy M; Willow Run HS; Ypsilanti, MI; Univ Of Michigan; Fashion Design.

HUGELEN, Heidi A; Velva Public HS; Velva, ND; Band; Chrs; ChrhWkr; HonRl; MrchBnd; NHS; PepBnd; StuCncl; PresYthFlsp; FHA; LetterTrk; Chrldr; GAA; PPFtbl; College; Music.

HUGHBANKS, Julia A; Hay Springs HS; Hay Springs, NE; TrsSrCls; Band; Chrs; HonRl; NHS; SchPl; Yrbk; 4-H; VPPpCl; Trk; PPFtbl; BttyCrckrAwd; 4-HAwd; Kearney St College.

HUGHES, Nancy L; Salem Sr HS; Salem, IN; .

HUGHES, Terri J; Lake Crystal Public HS; Lake Crystal, MN; SecTrsSrCls; Band; ChrhWkr; CmntyWkr; CncrtBnd; HonRl; MrchBnd; PepBnd; SchPl; 4-H; Trk; Chrldr; GAA; Mankato Univ; Juvenile Counseling.

HUMPHREY, Steven M; Hale HS; Hale, MI; 5/65 PresFrshCls; Band; ChrhWkr; CncrtBnd; HonRl; MrchBnd; NHS; PepBnd; StuCncl; RptrSchPpr; 4-H; Bsbl; Bsktbl; Ftbl; College; Business Admin.

HUNT, Mary V; Madison Cons HS; Madison, IN; 7/340 Band; CncrtBnd; DrmMjrt; HonRl; MrchBnd; NHS; PepBnd; LatCl; University; Botany.

HUNT, Susan B; Waterman HS; Waterman, IL; PresJrCls; HonRl; Mdrgl; SchMus; StuCncl; FrCl; LetterSocr; LetterTrk; Chrldr; GAA; AmLegAwd; College; Professional.

HUNTLEY, Jeffrey L; Sycamore HS; Sycamore, IL; 49/201 Aud/Vis; CAP; HonRl; LbryAde; Bsbl; Bsktbl; Ftbl; Illinois St Scholar; Honr Mention All Confer In Football 1974; Univ Of Ill; Sciences.

HURD, Mike T; Turkey Valley Comm HS; Lawler, IA; 15/111 TrsSophCls; ALBoysSt; HonRl; NHS; SctActv; FFA; LetterBsktbl; LetterFtbl; Trade School; Agriculture.

HURSELL, Clarence E; East Gary Edison Sr HS; East Gary, IN; 9/130 ALBoysSt; HonRl; NHS; LetterSecTrsSophCls; SecFrshCls; BauchLmbAwd; College.

HUSEMAN, Jodi L; Fort Dodge Sr HS; Fort Dodge, IA; 1/425 DrlTm; HonRl; ModUN; PresNHS; FTA; VPPpCl; Glf; EldAwd; CitAwd; University; Business.

I

INVEISS, Anita I; Waukesha South HS; Waukesha, WI; ChrhWkr; SecTrsFrshCls; SctActv; SpnCl; MthCl; Bsktbl; GAA; PresAwd; University; Veterinarian.

ISENSEE, Loren L; Chosen Valley HS; Chatfield, MN; HonRl; SchMus; SchPl; TchrAde; Bsktbl; Rochester Comm College; Engineering.

J

JACKSON, Patricia A; Murray Wright HS; Detroit, MI; CmntyWkr; OffAde; SctActv; StuGov; PresAwd; Detroit Inst Of Tech; Computer Tech.

JACOBSON, Jeffrey D; Hibbing HS; Hibbing, MN; Chr; CmntyWkr; HonRl; OffAde; SpnCl; PpCl; Bsktbl; Ftbl; Trk; College; Biology.

JACOBSON, La Mont; Public HS; Sacred Heart, MN; TrsFrshCls; CmntyWkr; HonRl; FFA; Bsbl; Bsktbl; Ftbl; Trk; Corn Detasseling Forman; Vo Tech; Farming Dairy.

JACOBSON, Virginia S; Leeds Public HS; Leeds, ND; ALAGirlsSt; Band; Chrs; ChrhWkr; HonRl; PolWkr; StuCncl; 4-H; FHA; SciCl; Trk; Chrldr; CchngActv; College; Professional.

JAMES, Alton M; Notre Dame HS; Detroit, MI; VPSophCls; VPJrCls; Band; Chr; ChrhWkr; CncrtBnd; MrchBnd; NatlMeritCmnd; Orch; PepBnd; SchMus; SchPl; Chrldr; Wayne St Univ; Medicine.

JAMES, Joni M; Roosevelt HS; Gary, IN; ChrhWkr; CmntyWkr; HonRl; OffAde; PolWkr; TchrAde; YthFlsp; Yrbk; FNA; College; Nurse.

JAMES, Tami R; Wolbach Public HS; Wolbach, NE; TrsJrCls; ALAGirlsSt; SchPl; StuCncl; Twrl; SecGerCl; PpCl; Bsktbl; LetterTrk; Chrldr; PPFtbl; 4-HAwd; College; Fashion Mdse.

JANEGO, Dianne M; Corunna HS; Durand, MI; HonRl; MrchBnd; NHS; SctActv; StuGov; TchrAde; 4-H; FHA; Trk; GAA; N Michigan Univ; Dietician.

JANKOWSKI, Elyn M; Pius Xi HS; Milwaukee, WI; LitMag; PolWkr; Brigham Young Univ; Agriculture.

JARBOE, Tammy R; Caruthersville HS; Caruthersville, MO; TrsSophCls; LetterBand; CncrtBnd; HonRl; MrchBnd; NHS; NatlThespSoc; PepBnd; Twrl; FHA; IMSpt; College; Broadcasting.

JENNINGS, Kevin J; Winfield Mt Union HS; Winfield, IA; SecFrshCls; ALBoysSt; Chr; Chrl; Chrs; HonRl; Mdrgl; SchPl; StuCncl; RptrYrbk; RptrSchPpr; Bsktbl; Ftbl; Tennis; University; Journalism.

JENSEN, Sherri A; West Branch HS; West Liberty, IA; 1/72 ALAGirlsSt; PresBand; Chrs; CncrtBnd; MrchBnd; NHS; TreasStuCncl; Twrl; MthCl; Glf; Trk; Univ Of Iowa; Engineer.

JERKOVICH, George S; Lawrence HS; Lawrence, KS; 12/555 HonRl; Tennis; College; Medicine.

JETER, Debra R; Cass Technical HS; Detroit, MI; CmntyWkr; HonRl; OffAde; PepBnd; SchAde; StuCncl; StuGov; TchrAde; SchPpr; Trade School; Commercial Art.

JOHNSON, Carleen M; Chisholm Sr HS; Chisholm, MN; Band; CncrtBnd; HonRl; OffAde; Orch; PepBnd; TchrAde; LetterSwmmng; University; Professional.

JOHNSON, Darlene A; Madison Public HS; Madison, MN; VPSrCls; Band; Chr; Chrs; ChrhWkr; HonRl; MrchBnd; 4-H; FHA; GAA; IMSpt; PPFtbl; College; Mathematics.

JOHNSON, David E; Liberal HS; Liberal, KS; StuCncl; StuGov; College; Art.

JOHNSON, Fayrene; Josephinum HS; Chicago, IL; 17/101 ChrhWkr; CmntyWkr; HonRl; HospAde; NatlMeritSF; RedCrAde; SchPl; StuGov; GAA; University; Professional.

JOHNSON, James H; Harvard HS; Harvard, IL; 8/157 Band; Chr; Chrs; HonRl; TreasNHS; TchrAde; FrCl; SpnCl; MthCl;.

JOHNSON, Jeffrey L; Marshall Sr HS; Marshall, MN; Band; Chrs; CncrtBnd; HonRl; MrchBnd; PepBnd; SchMus; 4-H; Ftbl; Swmmng; College; Science.

JOHNSON, John G; Ida Grove Comm HS; Ida Grove, IA; 10/50 PresJrCls; HonRl; NHS; 4-H; FFA; CaptFtbl; Wrstlng; 4-HAwd; Amer Leg Boys State; Boys State Sec Of Agri; Iowa State Univ; Agriculture.

JOHNSON, Julie M; Hackett HS; Kalamazoo, MI; Band; Chr; CncrtBnd; HonRl; MrchBnd; SctActv; College; Child Psychology.

JOHNSON, Kristi L; Benson Sr HS; Benson, MN; 3/170 SecTrsFrshCls; ALAGirlsSt; Band; Chrl; Chrs; ChrhWkr; CmntyWkr; CncrtBnd; HonRl; HospAde; MrchBnd; Trk; Chrldr; GAA; Augsburg College; Occup Therapy.

JOHNSON, Lorraine C; Kenwood HS; Chicago, IL; Chr; CmntyWkr; IntrClCncl; SchAde; StuCncl; Twrl; RptrSchPpr; GAA; IMSpt; University; Professional.

JOHNSON, Scott C; Webster City HS; Webster City, IA; ALBoysSt; Chrs; Quill&Scroll; StuCncl; YthFlsp; RptrSchPpr; SciCl; Bsktbl; Ftbl; College.

JOHNSON, Terry B; Boone County R Vi HS; Centralia, MO; 10/80 ALBoysSt; HonRl; NHS; RedCrAde; PresStuGov; SciCl; Bsktbl; LetterFtbl; Glf; LetterTrk; RotaryAwd; CitAwd; Univ Of Missouri; Engineering.

JONES, Dianna M; Hannibal Sr HS; Hannibal, MO; 39/266 VPSophCls; Chr; Chrs; HospAde; StuCncl; RptrSchPpr; SpnCl; PpCl; Bsktbl; Trk; Chrldr; GAA;.

JONES, Joy L; La Monte R Iv HS; La Monte, MO; 2/26 ChrhWkr; HonRl; OffAde; SchPl; StuCncl; Yrbk; Pres4-H; LetterBsbl; LetterBsktbl; Chrldr; Central Missouri St Univ; Physical Educ.

JONES, Larry D; Luther South HS; Chicago, IL; CncrtBnd; SctActv;.

JORDAN, Dana L; Circle HS; El Dorado, KS; 6/90 VPSrCls; Chrs; HonRl; NHS; StuCncl; PpCl; CaptBsktbl; Trk; IMSpt; CitAwd; College; Physical Educ.

K

KACKMAN, Julie V; Lidgerwood Public HS; Lidgerwood, ND; ALAGirlsSt; Band; ChrhWkr; CncrtBnd; HonRl; MrchBnd; PepBnd; SchPl; RptrYrbk; Yrbk; SchPpr; FHA; PpCl; North Dakota St Univ; Nursing.

KACZMAREK, Steven D; Quigley South HS; Chicago, IL; 4/167 ChrhWkr; HonRl; HospAde; NatlMeritCmnd; Natl Honor Soc; Rep Quigley So In Statewide Latin Contest; Niles College; Priest.

KADRICH, Christopher C; Catholic Memorial HS; Waukesha, WI; ChrhWkr; Bsbl; Ftbl; College; Pilot.

KAISER, Kim M; Marshfield HS; Marshfield, WI; 16/325 HonRl; NHS; NatlMeritCmnd; NatlMeritSF; MthCl; Tennis; Univ Of Wisconsin; Chemistry.

KALIN, Jeffrey B; Warren HS; Warren, MI; NatlMeritCmnd; NatlMeritSchl; Bsktbl; Ftbl; College; Law.

KAMIN, Natalie V; Clark HS; Whiting, IN; 47/260 ChrhWkr; HonRl; JA; JrNHS; NHS; Quill&Scroll; StuCncl; TchrAde; Yrbk; SchPpr; Trk; Chrldr; GAA; Business School; Secretary.

KANT, Susan C; Chaska Sr HS; Chanhassen, MN; 48/215 PresSrCls; CncrtBnd; MrchBnd; NHS; StuCncl; PpCl; Trk; Chrldr; Univ Of Wisconsin; Fashion Mdse.

KARNAFEL, Pamela J; Sycamore HS; Genoa, IL; Band; CncrtBnd; HonRl; MrchBnd; OffAde; Orch; PepBnd; SchMus; SchPl; College; Vocation.

KASDAN, Deborah S; Rich South HS; Park Forest, IL; Band; CncrtBnd; HonRl; MrchBnd; PepBnd; Quill&Scroll; SchPl; SctActv; TreasStuCncl; TchrAde; SchPpr; PpCl; Thespian; University; Psychology.

KATSULIS, Demetra; Amundsen HS; Chicago, IL; .

KATT, Peter W; Aurora HS; Aurora, NE; PresSophCls; ALBoysSt; NHS; SchMus; SchPl; StuCncl; Yrbk; RptrSchPpr; LetterTrk; College; Law.

KAUFENBERG, Ray E; Lakeville HS; Lakeville, MN; Band; ChrhWkr; CncrtBnd; HonRl; MrchBnd; NHS; PepBnd; LetterFtbl; College; Professional.

KELLEY, Catherine T; Central Catholic HS; Merna, IL; 6/84 VPSophCls; HonRl; NHS; StuCncl; TchrAde; 4-H; FrCl; PpCl; Bsktbl; Trk; Univ Of Illinois; Law.

KEMNETZ, Steven A; Chatsworth HS; Chatsworth, IL; 7/47 AFS; Band; HonRl; SpnCl; MthCl; Bsktbl; LetterFtbl; Lettered In Basketball; College; Engineering.

KENWORTHY, April M; High School; Grand Rapids, MI; 1/167 YthFlsp; Tennis; University; Medicine.

KENYON, Elizabeth L; Garrigan HS; Whittemore, IA; SecSophCls; PresSrCls; Chrs; DrlTm; HonRl; OffAde; StuCncl; 4-H; LatCl; St Josephs Schl Of Nursing; Nursing.

KERCHER, Karla A; Mater Dei HS; Evansville, IN; PresChr; ChrhWkr; HonRl; NHS; OffAde; SchMus; StuCncl; StuGov; Univ Of Evansville; Nursing.

KIEH, Scott A; Thornapple Kellogg HS; Middleville, MI; 7/123 Band; ChrhWkr; CncrtBnd; HonRl; MrchBnd; NHS; NatlMeritCmnd; PepBnd; SctActv; SptEdSchPpr; LetterBsbl; LetterBsktbl; LetterTrk; Hope College.

KIENAST, Tim L; Manning HS; Manning, IA; VPFrshCls; PresJrCls; PresSrCls; ALBoysSt; Band; Chr; Chrs; CncrtBnd; HonRl; Bsbl; Bsktbl; CaptFtbl; LetterTrk; College; Vocation.

KIESEWETTER, Dale O; Cornell HS; Pontiac, IL; 1/29 TrsFrshCls; PresSophCls; ALBoysSt; Band; HonRl; SchPl; StuCncl; 4-H; LetterBsbl; LetterBsktbl; DanFAwd; 4-HAwd; Eureka College; Mathematics.

KILBURG, Donna S; Andrew Community HS; Maquoketa, IA; 1/33 HonRl; NHS; TchrAde; GerCl; LetterTrk; LetterChrldr; Community College; Accounting.

KILLION, Mark; Glenbard South HS; Glen Ellyn, IL; HonRl; LetterBsbl; Ftbl; Trk; Natl Honor Soc;.

KILMARTIN, Peggy A; Mother Of Sorrows HS; Chicago, IL; 35/143 HonRl; StuCncl; FrCl; PpCl; Bsktbl; GAA; College; Professional.

KINAS, Katie A; Greenlake Public HS; Green Lake, WI; SecFrshCls; Band; Chrs; PepBnd; PpCl; Bsktbl; College; Nursing.

KING, Elizabeth M; Durand HS; Durand, WI; 27/147 AFS; Chr; Chrs; ChrhWkr; HonRl; NatlFornLg; SchPl; SctActv; Sdlty; FrCl; Trade School.

KING, Troy S; Millard HS; Omaha, NE; Band; HonRl; NHS; SpnCl; MthCl; SciCl; Bsbl; Bsktbl; Ftbl; AmLegAwd; PresAwd; College; Professional.

KINNELL, Denise M; Trenton HS; Trenton, MI; 99/571 ChrhWkr; HonRl; JrNHS; NHS; StuCncl; PpCl; Cleary College; Secretary.

KIRKEBY, Marlys C; Drayton Public HS; Drayton, ND; 1/42 ALAGirlsSt; PresChrhWkr; SchPl; SpnCl; Univ Of North Dakota; Counselor.

KLATKIEWICZ, Arlene M; So Milwaukee Sr HS; South Milwaukee, WI; 16/442 ChrhWkr; HonRl; LitMag; LbryAde; NHS; OffAde; SchMus; Sdlty; Yrbk; FBLA; FNA; Business School; Accountant.

KLEMETT, James M; Hancock Central HS; Hancock, MI; 5/90 Band; HonRl; SchPl; YthFlsp; Yrbk; FrCl; Jr & Sr Class Play Cast; Western Michigan Univ; Business Admin.

KLIGAR, David A; Chesaning HS; Chesaning, MI; HonRl; Bsbl; Bsktbl; Ftbl; Glf; Tennis; CchngActv; IMSpt; College; Pharmacy.

KLINE, Kathryn A; Central HS; St Joseph, MO; 14/535 ChrhWkr; HospAde; LitMag; NHS; OffAde; CivCl; LatCl; College; Physician.

KLOCKE, Rita K; Rockwell City Community HS; Rockwell City, IA; 1/64 VPSophCls; Band; HonRl; NHS; NatlMeritSF; Yrbk; 4-H; FHA; DanFAwd; 4-HAwd; Ia St U; Med Technology.

KLUESNER, Deb A; Western Dubuque HS; Farley, IA; 5/243 PresSophCls; Chrs; HonRl; StuCncl; LatCl; PpCl; Chrldr; Ne Area Voc Tech Schl; Nursing.

KLUK, Diane P; Marie Sklodowska Curie HS; Chicago, IL; Chrs; HonRl; NHS; OffAde; StuCncl; Yrbk; RptrSchPpr; Maccormac Jr College; Law.

KMIECIAK, Laura R; La Salle Peru Twp HS; La Salle, IL; ChrhWkr; CmntyWkr; OffAde; SchAde; SpnCl; College; Fashion Buyer.

KNAPP, Robert C; Knoxville HS; Knoxville, IL; Aud/Vis; Band; HonRl; NHS; Orch; StuCncl; LatCl; Bsktbl; Ftbl; College; Chemistry.

KNESS, Barry G; Thomson HS; Thomson, IL; 11/42 Band; Chrs; HonRl; Mdrgl; SchMus; TchrAde; 4-H; PresFTA; PresFrCl; CaptBsktbl; CaptTrk; College; Liberal Arts.

KNOLL, Jane A; New Hampton Comm HS; New Hampton, IA; ChrhWkr; HonRl;.

KOENIG, Gregory M; Mobridge HS; Mobridge, SD; 20/75 ChrhWkr; HonRl; RptrSchPpr; SptEdSchPpr; Northern State College.

KONEMANN, Michael G; Mauston HS; Lyndon Station, WI; 1/160 ALBoysSt; LetterChr; HonRl; Mdrgl; PresNHS; SchMus; SchPl; LatCl; LetterBsbl; KiwanAwd; College; Dentistry.

KORMAN, Therese M; George Rogers Clark HS; Whiting, IN; 79/260 Chrs; HospAde; JA; SchMus; SpnCl; PpCl; Trk; GAA; Indiana Univ; Business.

KORST, Susan M; Bishop Dwenger HS; Ft Wayne, IN; ALAGirlsSt; HonRl; TreasJA; NatlMeritSF; SchPl; RptrSchPpr; GerCl; Natl Merit Finalist; Natl Honor Soc; College; Journalism.

KOTAS, Beth E; Tripp HS; Tripp, SD; ChrhWkr; HonRl; LbryAde; NatlFornLg; SchPl; TchrAde; FHA; National College Of Business; Secretary.

KOZLOWSKI, Zbigniew A; Lane Tech HS; Chicago, IL; 88/1200 VPAud/Vis; Chr; TchrAde; RptrSchPpr; SchPpr; AmLegAwd; Depaul Univ; Lawyer.

KRAGNESS, Debra K; Memorial HS; Eau Claire, WI; Univ Of Wisconsin; Marketing.

KRAUSE, Dale A; Wyndmere Public HS; Wyndmere, ND; ALBoysSt; Band; ChrhWkr; CncrtBnd; HonRl; MrchBnd; NHS; PepBnd; SchPpr; FFA; University; Veterinarian.

KRAUSE, Jody J; Echo Public HS; Echo, MN; Band; Chr; ChrhWkr; DrlTm; ModUN; SchPl; Trk; Alexandria Tech; X Ray Tech.

KRAUSNICK, Karen J; Wauneta HS; Wauneta, NE; 5/29 HstFrshCls; SecSophCls; SecJrCls; ALAGirlsSt; HonRl; NHS; 4-H; PpCl; No Platte Coll; Medical Tech.

KRENGEL, Beth F; Homewood Flossmoor HS; Flossmoor, IL; 294/900 HonRl; SchMus; College; Music.

KRIEK, Lloyd B; St Pius X HS; Kansas City, MO; 37/142 SecJrCls; HonRl; SchMus; StuCncl; LetterFtbl; LetterGlf; LetterWrstlng; Rockhurst College; Law.

KRUSE, Ken D; Central Lake Public HS; East Port, MI; Band; CncrtBnd; HonRl; Jr College; Liberal Arts.

KUDRNA, Cynthia J; Nerinx Hall HS; Des Peres, MO; 29/99 Band; Chrl; ChrhWkr; CmntyWkr; CncrtBnd; HonRl; OffAde; PolWkr; SchMus; SchPl; Univ Of Arizona; Professional.

KUHLENGEL, Keith R; Wesclin Sr HS; Trenton, IL; 1/100 Band; Chrs; HonRl; NHS; NatlMeritSF; EdYrBk; RptrSchPpr; GerCl; VPLatCl; Bsktbl; Natl Merit Finalist; Washington Univ; Physician.

KUIPERS, Ray N; Dakota Christian HS; Platte, SD; 2/35 VPJrCls; ALBoysSt; Chr; HonRl; ModUN; NHS; SchPl; StuCncl; RptrSchPpr; PpCl; LetterTrk; IMSpt; College.

KURTZ, Matt J; St Laurence HS; Chicago, IL; HonRl; RedCrAde; Univ Of Chicago; Medicine.

L

LADINE, Kevin R; Gurley Public HS; Gurley, NE; 1/10 PresFrshCls; VPSrCls; ALBoysSt; Chrs; HonRl; Mdrgl; 4-H; LetterBsktbl; LetterFtbl; LetterTrk; College.

LAFEVER, Lori L; Hagerstown Jr Sr HS; Hagerstown, IN; ALAGirlsSt; HonRl; NHS; PolWkr; SchPpr; 4-H; FrCl; PpCl; Tennis; College; Science.

LA FORTUNA, Terry L; Highmore HS; Highmore, SD; ChrhWkr; CmntyWkr; HonRl; NatlFornLg; SchPl; StuGov; RptrSchPpr; FBLA; MthCl; SciCl; LetterBsktbl; LetterFtbl; Trk; College; Civil Engineering.

LAGEMAN, Wendy R; St Joseph Academy; De Pere, WI; Chrs; Mdrgl; SchMus; SchPl; YthFlsp; RptrSchPpr; SchPpr; 4-H; Swmmng; Pres4-HAwd; College; Nuclear Medicine.

LAGENOUR, Penelope C; Marian Heights Academy; Dubois, IN; Chrs; HonRl; HospAde; NHS; Sdlty; FrCl; GAA; Northwood Univ; Special Educ.

LAMBERT, John C; Assumption HS; Bettendorf, IA; 52/207 Aud/Vis; ChrhWkr; CncrtBnd; HonRl; NatlThespSoc; Orch; SchMus; SchPl; St Louis Univ; Medicine.

LANGE, David A; Evansville HS; Evansville, WI; HonRl; YthFlsp; Technical School; Agriculture.

LANNING, David L; Rogers HS; Wyoming, MI; 10/266 HonRl; NatlMeritSF; TchrAde; Yrbk; LetterFtbl; VPSrCls; LetterWrstlng;.

LAROY, Angela M; Whiteford HS; Riga, MI; 4/87 SecSophCls; VPJrCls; SecSrCls; ChrhWkr; HonRl; NHS; OffAde; StuCncl; TchrAde; RptrYrbk; 4-H; LetterBsktbl; GAA; 4-HAwd; College; Commercial Art.

LARSON, Jeffrey B; River Falls HS; River Falls, WI; 5/186 ALBoysSt; ModUN; NatlFornLg; NHS; NatlMeritCmnd; SchPl; StuCncl; EdSchPpr; AmLegAwd; Macalester College; Economics.

LASSEN, Sally J; Grand Island Sr HS; Grand Island, NE; Band; Chr; OffAde; Twrl; YthFlsp; SpnCl; Trk; Chrldr; CchngActv; University; Professional.

LAWRENCE, John T; Alleman HS; Rock Island, IL; Band; CmntyWkr; CncrtBnd; JrNHS; MrchBnd; NHS; PepBnd; SchPl; FrCl; LetterBsbl; Bsktbl; Trk; LetterWrstlng; Drake Univ; Accounting.

LAWSON, Gilbert L; Silex R#1 HS; Silex, MO; HstSophCls; SchPl; FFA; PpCl; LetterBsbl; LetterBsktbl; PresAwd; Technical School; Mechanic.

LEAHY, Cindy M; Notre Dame HS; Quincy, IL; 46/107 HonRl; Bsktbl; Jr College; Computer Science.

LEDFORD, Sandra J; Northwest Webster HS; Barnum, IA; 4/28 SecSophCls; PresJrCls; Chrs; ChrhWkr; HonRl; NHS; SchPl; TchrAde; RptrSchPpr; 4-H; Trk; College; Nursing.

LEE, Rosalyn R; Bishop Noll Inst HS; Gary, IN; Chrl; SchMus; College; Professional.

LEEHY, John J; Blair HS; Blair, NE; PresFrshCls; Chr; ChrhWkr; HonRl; SchMus; SctActv; StuCncl; StuGov; FBLA; FFA; Bsbl; Bsktbl; LetterFtbl; LetterTrk; College; Business Mgmt.

LENTZ, Donieta Jo; Jefferson County North HS; Winchester, KS; 14/48 Band; Chrs; ChrhWkr; CncrtBnd; HospAde; MrchBnd; PepBnd; SchMus; RptrYrbk; Kansas St Univ; Nurse.

LENZ, Marcia K; Marshall Sr HS; Marshall, MN; 7/229 Chrs; ChrhWkr; CncrtBnd; HonRl; HospAde; MrchBnd; YthFlsp; SpnCl; Trk; South Dakota St Univ; Nurse.

LEONARD, Mark L; Logan Magnolia HS; Logan, IA; 4/53 PresFrshCls; PresSophCls; ALBoysSt; PresNHS; SptEdYrbk; LetterBsbl; CaptFtbl; CaptTrk; KiwanAwd; MasAwd; PresAwd; CitAwd; College; Accounting.

LESSMAN, Debra L; Willmar Sr HS; Willmar, MN; PresJrCls; ChrhWkr; OffAde; StuCncl; TchrAde; YthFnd; PPFtbl; Trade School; Vocation.

LEWIS, Cynthia A; Caro HS; Caro, MI; ChrhWkr; CmntyWkr; HonRl; JrNHS; NHS; SchAde; SchPpr; Olivet Nazarene College; Social Work.

LEWIS, David C; Marshall HS; Marshall, MO; Band; CncrtBnd; MrchBnd; FFA; LetterTrk; College.

LEWIS, Karen; Beaumont HS; St Louis, MO; 28/502 ChrhWkr; HonRl; JrNHS; NHS; NatlMeritSF; Quill&Scroll; SchPl; StuCncl; StuGov; YthFlsp; RptrSchPpr; SchPpr; SpnCl; Tennis; Drake Univ; Journalism.

LEWIS, Melissa E; Hiawatha HS; Hiawatha, KS; CmntyWkr; HonRl; SctActv; FHA; PpCl; Bsbl; Bsktbl; Socr; Swmmng; Tennis; Trk; Chrldr; College; Professional.

LIENEMANN, Dwight D; Winside HS; Norfolk, NE; HonRl; SchPl; RptrYrbk; SptEdYrbk; RptrSchPpr; 4-H; Ftbl; Trk; Wayne State College; Civil Engineer.

LIES, Michael D; Haysville Campus HS; Wichita, KS; ChrhWkr; HonRl; TchrAde; YthFlsp; LetterBsbl; LetterFtbl; IMSpt; Arizona St Univ; Professional.

LILLARD, David A; West Side HS; Gary, IN; 128/720 ChrhWkr; HonRl; JrNHS; NHS; StuCncl; FrCl; MthCl; LetterBsbl; LetterBsktbl; CitAwd;.

LINCH, Brian W; Central HS; St Joseph, MO; Chr; HonRl; GerCl; MthCl; College; Business Admin.

LINT, Bonnie F; Newton Sr HS; Newton, IA; Chrs; HonRl; OffAde; Trade School.

LITT, Deidre L; Maria HS; Chicago, IL; Chrs; CmntyWkr; HonRl; RedCrAde; Trk; Chrldr; GAA; Natl Merit Letter Of Commend; Red Cross Aid; School Play; Intra Sports; Pres Award; Ill State Scholar; Miss Il Teenager; 3rd Runner Up Miss Amer Teenager 74 75; 14th Ward Comm Serv Award; Former Campaign Singer Dancer For Mayor & Alderman; St Xavier Coll; Medical Doctor.

LOCKWOOD, Michael D; Swea City Community HS; Swea City, IA; PresFrshCls; VPJrCls; AFS; Chrs; ChrhWkr; HonRl; SchPl; SctActv; FFA; LetterBsbl; LetterBsktbl; LetterFtbl; Natl Honor Soc; College; Medicine.

LOH, Gary; Andrean HS; Gary, IN; 4/326 Band; HonRl; NHS; NatlMeritSF; Trk; IMSpt; AmLegAwd; College; Physician.

LONEY, Janice I; Sumner HS; Kansas, KS; Chr; ChrhWkr; CmntyWkr; CncrtBnd; HonRl; HospAde; JA; JCC; JrNHS; MrchBnd; NHS; Orch; PepBnd; JAAwd; University Of Kansas.

LONG, Douglas J; Alma Public HS; Alma, NE; 9/27 PresFrshCls; VPSophCls; Band; Chrs; CncrtBnd; HonRl; MrchBnd; Bsbl; Bsktbl; CaptFtbl; Trk; Univ; Profession.

LONGANBACH, Terry A; Portland Public HS; Portland, MI; 1/120 SecTrsJrCls; SecTrsSrCls; Band; HonRl; StuCncl; Chrldr; PPFtbl; DanFAwd; Michigan St Univ; Medicine.

LONOWSKI, Diane K; Marian HS; Omaha, NE; HonRl; NatlFornLg; NHS; PolWkr; Quill&Scroll; RptrSchPpr; FrCl; PresLatCl; Univ Of Nebr At Omaha; Lawyer.

LOVELL, Richard C; Castle HS; Newburgh, IN; Chrs; JrNHS; NHS; SctActv; LatCl; LetterFtbl; LetterWrstlng; IMSpt; Indiana Univ; Law.

LUECKENHOFF, Jim P; Blair Oaks HS; St Thomas, MO; PresFrshCls; VPSophCls; PresJrCls; ALBoysSt; HonRl; NHS; 4-H; MthCl; CaptBsbl; LetterBsktbl; IMSpt; VFWAwd; College; Elec Engineering.

LUNDBERG, Kurt L; Benedict Consolidated HS; Benedict, NE; SecJrCls; Band; CncrtBnd; HonRl; MrchBnd; PepBnd; YthFlsp; RptrSchPpr; GerCl; SciCl; LetterBsktbl; Ftbl; Trk; Bethel College.

LUNDE, Julie D; Taylor HS; Taylor, WI; PresFrshCls; Chrs; CncrtBnd; HonRl; LbryAde; PepBnd; EdYrBk; EdSchPpr; FHA; Chrldr; Vocational Schl; Accounting.

LYNCH, Patricia A; Benilde St Margaret HS; Edina, MN; Band; ChrhWkr; CmntyWkr; CncrtBnd; HonRl; HospAde; MrchBnd; Orch; PepBnd; SchMus; FrCl; Swmmng; Trk; College; Medicine.

Mc

MC BRAW, Molly A; Pontiac Central HS; Bloomfield Hills, MI; HonRl; NHS; TchrAde; YthLg; SpnCl; Swmmng; Wrstlng;.

MC CARTHY, Maureen K; Saint Edmond HS; Fort Dodge, IA; 1/133 ChrhWkr; NHS; RptrYrbk; PpCl; Tennis; Chrldr; College; Agriculture.

MC CARTY, Warren D; Champaign Central HS; Champaign, IL; 1/411 Band; HonRl; JrNHS; NHS; NatlMeritSF; KeyCl; SpnCl; Natl Merit Finalist; Bausch & Lomb Sci Award; Univ Of Il; Veterinary Medicine.

MC CLUSKY, Cathy D; Avon HS; Avon, IL; Band; Chrs; CncrtBnd; DrmMjrt; HospAde; MrchBnd; PepBnd; SchMus; SchPl; RptrSchPpr; College; Vocation.

MC CUTCHAN, Michael D; Canton R V HS; Canton, MO; 2/67 Band; HonRl; NHS; NatlMeritCmnd; SctActv; FSA; Bsktbl; Swmmng; Trk; Univ Of Missouri; Chemical Engineer.

MC DANIEL, Harry J; Blue Springs Sr HS; Blue Springs, MO; ALBoysSt; Chr; Chrl; ChrhWkr; HonRl; NatlFornLg; NatlThespSoc; OffAde; SchPl; SctActv; Sw Missouri St Univ; Professional.

MC DANIEL, Robert E; Avon HS; Indianapolis, IN; 9/160 Band; HonRl; TchrAde; Yrbk; MthCl; PresSciCl; LetterTennis; IMSpt; Indiana St Univ; Accounting.

MC DERMOTT, John C; Carbondale Comm HS; Carbondale, IL; 23/323 ChrhWkr; HonRl; ModUN; PolWkr; SchPl; YthLg; FrCl; Natl Honor Soc; University; Law.

MC DONALD, Kelly A; Joliet East HS; New Lenox, IL; 83/381 Chrs; HonRl; NHS; OffAde; TchrAde; PpCl; Swmmng; GAA; Lewis Univ; Professional.

MC DONNELL, Patricia A; St Willibrord HS; Calumet Park, IL; 2/72 SecSrCls; Chrs; HonRl; NHS; SchPl; StuCncl; EdSchPpr; SchPpr; LatCl; VPSciCl; Danforth I Dare You Award; Mac Cormac Jr College; Court Reporter.

MC FALL, Thomas K; Paris HS; Paris, IL; HonRl; JA; 4-H; Bsktbl; IMSpt; College; Architecture.

MC FARLAND, Vance; St Joseph HS; Urbana, IL; SpnCl; LetterWrstlng; Univ Of Illinois.

MC GAULEY, Brian T; Devils Lake Central HS; Devils Lake, ND; ALBoysSt; Band; Chr; ChrhWkr; CmntyWkr; HonRl; MrchBnd; Orch; PepBnd; StuCncl; RptrYrbk; Ftbl; Trk; University; Veterinarian.

MC KENZIE, Raymond R; Marcellus HS; Marcellus, MI; 6/84 VPFrshCls; PresSophCls; HonRl; NHS; StuCncl; TchrAde; Bsktbl; Ftbl; Michigan St Univ; Agriculture.

MC LAREN, Debra S; Knoxville HS; Knoxville, IL; 2/95 ALAGirlsSt; Band; CncrtBnd; HonRl; MrchBnd; SecNHS; FTA; LatCl; GAA; Bradley Univ; Mathematics.

MC NAUGHTON, Karen S; Durand HS; Eau Galle, WI; Band; ChrhWkr; HonRl; JA; NatlFornLg; StuCncl; YthFlsp; RptrYrbk; 4-H; Chrldr; GAA; College; Nursing.

MC PIKE, Jeffrey B; Farmington HS; Farmington, MI; 1/500 ALBoysSt; HonRl; NHS; StuCncl; MthCl; Bsktbl; LetterFtbl; LetterTrk; IMSpt; Yale Univ; Engineering.

MC QUEEN, Victoria A; Eastern HS; Solsberry, IN; 16/70 CmntyWkr; JrNHS; TchrAde; RptrSchPpr; Business Schl; Office Work.

MC SPADDEN, Rebecca; Bloomingdale HS; Pullman, MI; PresSophCls; OffAde; TchrAde; YthFlsp; Yrbk; RptrSchPpr; CivCl; Spring Arbor College.

M

MACIAK, Marianne; Fitzgerald HS; Warren, MI; Chrs; CmntyWkr; HonRl; NHS; OffAde; RedCrAde; SchMus; SchPl; SciCl; College; Respiratory Therapy.

MACISAAC, Michael J; Waukegan HS; Waukegan, IL; ALBoysSt; HonRl; JA; JrNHS; SctActv; SpnCl; Bsbl; Bsktbl; College; Science.

MAHLER, Kaye E; Culver Comm HS; Culver, IN; VPJrCls; MrchBnd; NHS; Twrl; VP4-H; PresFFA; CaptBsktbl; LetterTrk; VPGAA; 4-HAwd; Business Schl; Accounting.

MAHON, Joyce E; South Sioux City HS; South Sioux City, NE; 1/190 TrsFrshCls; VPAFS; Band; HonRl; VPJrNHS; SecNatlThespSoc; StuCncl; Pres4-H; Chrldr; 4-HAwd; Betty Crocker Award; Natl Merit Schlship; 4 Yr Univ Of Ne Lincoln Regents Schlship; U Of Ne; Pre Med, Music.

MALONE, Tom G; Liberal HS; Liberal, MO; ChrhWkr; CmntyWkr; HonRl; SchPl; Yrbk; SchPpr; College.

MALZHAN, Nancy L; Ripon Sr HS; Ripon, WI; Band; ChrhWkr; HonRl; OffAde; SchPpr; FBLA; Trade School; Law Enforcement.

MANN, Charlene K; Lakeland HS; La Grange, IN; 23/146 ChrhWkr; HonRl; YthFlsp; FHA; Anderson College; Special Educ.

MANN, Denise E; Pomeroy Comm HS; Pomeroy, IA; 1/25 Band; ChrhWkr; CncrtBnd; MrchBnd; NHS; Orch; PepBnd; StuCncl; RptrYrbk; RptrSchPpr; PpCl; Bsktbl; Trk;.

MAPPIN, Douglas C; Tippecanoe Valley HS; Akron, IN; 65/127 PresAud/Vis; Chr; Chrs; HonRl; SchMus; SchPl; Yrbk; RptrSchPpr; 4-H; FTA; LetterBsbl; LetterBsktbl; LetterTrk; College; Architecture.

MARCKESE, Rodney C; Rock Island HS; Rock Island, IL; 160/600 StuGov; SpnCl; LetterFtbl; Western Illinois Univ; Veterinarian.

MARKO, Timothy M; Chippewa Sr HS; Chippewa Fls, WI; 85/351 Aud/Vis; Band; CncrtBnd; MrchBnd; NatlThespSoc; SchMus; SchPl; SctActv; LetterTennis; IMSpt; Attend Univ Of Wis;.

MARSH, James R; Rhinelander HS; Rhinelander, WI; 33/329 ALBoysSt; ChrhWkr; DrmBgl; SchAde; Bsbl; Ftbl; Wrstlng; College; Accounting.

MARSHALL, Susan; Marian HS; Birmingham, MI; Chrs; HonRl; ModUN; FrCl; GerCl; Bsktbl; Swmmng; Tennis; Trk; University.

MARTIN, Steve M; Sandy Creek HS; Glenvil, NE; Chr; CmntyWkr; FBLA; Bsktbl; Ftbl; Trk; College; Professional.

MARTIN, Susan J; Triton Central HS; Fairland, IN; 1/143 SecFrshCls; TrsSophCls; ALAGirlsSt; Chrs; ChrhWkr; CmntyWkr; SecNHS; Yrbk; VPSpnCl; Chrldr; GAA; IMSpt; University.

MASBAUM, Gordon C; Three Lakes HS; Rhinelaunder, WI; Aud/Vis; HonRl; SctActv; TchrAde; Bsktbl; LetterFtbl; Socr; IMSpt; College.

MASON, Gregg H; Adlai E Stevenson HS; Long Grove, IL; HonRl; NatlMeritCmnd; SpnCl; Nat Honor Soc; Beloit Coll; Medicine.

MASTERS, Randy E; Woodland R Iv HS; Lutesville, MO; 4/65 PresJrCls; PresSrCls; Band; ChrhWkr; CncrtBnd; HonRl; MrchBnd; PepBnd; PresStuCncl; FFA; PpCl; Bsktbl; College; Minister.

MAYER, David A; Kiel HS; Kiel, WI; ChrhWkr; HonRl; SchPl; College; Accounting.

MAYS, Raymina Y; Benton Harbor HS; Benton Harbor, MI; 123/417 HonRl; HospAde; JA; StuGov; RptrSchPpr; SchPpr; LetterBsktbl; GAA; Speiman College; Political Science.

MEIXNER, Marcia M; Owatonna HS; Owatonna, MN; PresChrhWkr; CncrtBnd; HonRl; NHS; Pres4-H; SecFFA; FHA; SpnCl; TreasSciCl; Pres4-HAwd; Upper Midwest Exchange Club; Natl Ayrshire Girls Award; Steele Cty Dairy Princess; Natl Honor Soc; Univ Of Minnesota; Agriculture.

MELCHER, Cynthia L; Pipestone HS; Pipestone, MN; 2/135 Band; Chrs; HonRl; LbryAde; NatlMeritSF; NatlThespSoc; SchPl; 4-H; SecSpnCl; GAA; IMSpt; 4-HAwd; Hamline Univ; Biology.

MELLAND, Rebecca L; Forbes Public HS; Forbes, ND; SecSrCls; Chr; HonRl; SchPl; YthFlsp; Yrbk; SchPpr; Chrldr; National College; Business.

MELTON, Joanie A; Dadeville R Ii HS; Dadeville, MO; Chrs; ChrhWkr; HonRl; PolWkr; SchPl; TchrAde; FHA; PpCl; Burde School; Nursing.

MERRIMAN, Deana L; Mendota HS; Compton, IL; ALAGirlsSt; ChrhWkr; CmntyWkr; HonRl; LbryAde; OffAde; SchPl; TchrAde; RptrSchPpr; SchPpr; College; Interpreter.

MERSHON, Deborah S; Central Noble HS; Wolf Lake, IN; 5/100 VPSrCls; ChrhWkr; VPNHS; SchPl; EdYrBk; Yrbk; FTA; SpnCl; SecPpCl; IMSpt; DARAwd; Tennessee Temple; Journalism.

MEYER, April D; West Point Jr Sr HS; West Point, NE; HonRl; LbryAde; StuGov; TchrAde; 4-H; FHA; PpCl; Austin College; Psychology.

MEYER, Bryan H; Northwest HS; Eureka, MO; HonRl; LetterBsbl; PresAwd;.

MEYER, Cindy K; Appleton West HS; Appleton, WI; 78/633 Band; ChrhWkr; LbryAde; PepBnd; SctActv; StuCncl; YthFlsp; SpnCl; College.

MEYER, Janice I; Farmington East HS; Hanna City, IL; 4/130 HonRl; JCC; 4-H; FHA; GAA; AmLegAwd; DanFAwd;.

MEYER, Tamara L; Lake Benton HS; Lake Benton, MN; HonRl;.

MICKE, Steven J; Cloquet Sr HS; Cloquet, MN; 60/273 HonRl; FBLA; Bsbl; Bsktbl; CaptFtbl; Glf; Tennis; Trk; CchngActv; IMSpt; PresAwd; College; Accounting.

MILLER, Charles A; Hillsdale HS; Hillsdale, MI; PresJrCls; Chr; NHS; PolWkr; StuCncl; StuGov; FrCl; LatCl; Glf; Ohio St Univ; Education.

MILLER, Duane R; Hector Comm HS; Hector, MN; Band; CncrtBnd; HonRl; MrchBnd; College; Law Enforcement.

MILLER, Janet K; Morton HS; Pekin, IL; HonRl; 4-H; PresFBLA; GAA; 4-HAwd; Jr College; Computer Science.

MILLIK, Barbara A; Pawnee HS; Pawnee, IL; Band; Chr; CncrtBnd; DrlTm; HonRl; JrNHS; LbryAde; MrchBnd; NHS; TchrAde; YthFlsp; Bsktbl; SecGAA; College; French.

MILLIREN, Patricia M; Arkansaw HS; Arkansaw, WI; 1/30 SecFrshCls; TrsJrCls; Band; Chr; ChrhWkr; CncrtBnd; HonRl; PepBnd; StuCncl; Yrbk; LetterBsbl; LetterFtbl; Chrldr; GAA;.

MILLS, Daniel T; Wahlert HS; Dubuque, IA; StuCncl; StuGov; PpCl; Bsbl; Bsktbl; Ftbl; Trk; CchngActv; College; Psychologist.

MILLS, Stan; Tri HS; Straughn, IN; 2/93 ALBoysSt; Band; HonRl; MrchBnd; PresNHS; Yrbk; 4-H; SciCl; LetterWrstlng; Indiana Central Univ; Mathematics.

MITCHELL, Willie L; Harper HS; Chicago, IL; 13/300 HonRl; Univ Of Illinois; Medicine.

MOEN, John A; Fargo North HS; Fargo, ND; Aud/Vis; Chr; NHS; Orch; SchMus; SchPl; SctActv; North Dakota St Univ; Engineer.

MOHAMMED, Sam H; Pioneer HS; Ann Arbor, MI; CncrtBnd; DrmMjrt; HospAde; Teen; RptrYrbk; CaptSocr; Tennis; JAAwd; CitAwd; E Univ Of Michigan; Biology.

MOHR, Cindy L; Blair HS; Omaha, NE; ChrhWkr; CmntyWkr; HonRl; SchPl; YthFlsp; 4-H; FBLA; PpCl; 4-HAwd;.

MOLSKNESS, Robert L; Rutland HS; Wentworth, SD; ALBoysSt; Band; Chrs; ChrhWkr; CncrtBnd; HonRl; MrchBnd; NHS; StuCncl; Yrbk; RptrSchPpr; College; Music.

MONFORT, Nancy S; Iola Sr HS; Iola, KS; 8/133 Band; CncrtBnd; HonRl; JA; MrchBnd; Orch; PepBnd; TchrAde; Twrl; 4-H; PpCl; Kansas St Univ; Home Economics.

MOORE, David D; New Market Comm HS; New Market, IA; 10/24 SecFrshCls; TrsJrCls; VPSrCls; HonRl; SchPl; SctActv; StuCncl; 4-H; FFA; PpCl; LetterBsbl; LetterBsktbl; LetterFtbl; College; Engineering.

MORRIS, Cassandra T; Siena HS; Gary, IN; SecSophCls; Chr; HonRl; JA; SchPl; RptrSchPpr; SchPpr; Univ Of Mississippi; Journalism.

MORRIS, Dennis E; Stuart Menlo HS; Casey, IA; ALBoysSt; CncrtBnd; NatlThespSoc; PepBnd; SchPl; LetterBsbl; LetterBsktbl; LetterFtbl; IMSpt; AmLegAwd; CitAwd; Coe College; Pilot.

MORRIS, Mary Y; Du Quoin HS; Du Quoin, IL; DrlTm; HonRl; FHA; FTA; SpnCl; Beauty College; Beautician.

MORRIS, Michael H; Lincoln HS; Sioux Falls, SD; HstSophCls; Band; Chr; CncrtBnd; HonRl; MrchBnd; OffAde; TchrAde; SchPpr; Univ Of Utah; Business Admin.

MORRIS, Sheila Y; James Whitcomb Riley HS; South Bend, IN; 17/250 ALAGirlsSt; Chr; DrlTm; HonRl; NHS; SchMus; SctActv; University; Medicine.

MORROW, Beverly A; Simeon HS; Chicago, IL; 95/378 Band; HonRl; LbryAde; NatlMeritCmnd; SchPl; TchrAde; SchPpr; PpCl; Bsbl; College; Court Reporter.

MOWBRAY, Robert E; La Crosse HS; Wanatah, IN; 4/43 PresSrCls; Chr; Chrs; HonRl; NHS; Yrbk; GerCl; PpCl; LetterTrk; IMSpt; Purdue Univ; Computer Programming.

MOYE, Evette; Soldan HS; University City, MO; Chr; JA; TchrAde; IMSpt; Washington Univ; Nursing.

MULAVEY, Kathleen A; Grosse Pointe North HS; Grosse Pt Wds, MI; 16/625 HonRl; Univ Of Michigan; Journalism.

MULLER, Joseph T; St Marys HS; St Marys, KS; 10/70 ALBoysSt; ChrhWkr; HonRl; NatlFornLg; SchPl; VPStuCncl; RptrYrbk; SptEdSchPpr; Bsbl; Bsktbl; CchngActv; College; Business Mgmt.

MULLER, Robert E; Sheffield Chapin Comm HS; Sheffield, IA; ChrhWkr; HonRl; YthFlsp; 4-H; Iowa St Univ; Botany.

MULLIGAN, Anne S; Rosati Kain HS; University City, MO; Aud/Vis; NHS; NatlMeritSF; PepBnd; SchPl; SctActv; EdSchPpr; SpnCl; MthCl; GAA; St Louis Univ; Art.

MUNDELL, Gregory L; Tri Central HS; Sharpsville, IN; 15/89 ALBoysSt; NHS; StuCncl; Ftbl; Ball St Univ; Architecture.

MUNDINGER, Timothy P; Warsaw Comm HS; Warsaw, IN; ChrhWkr; JA; MrchBnd; NatlFornLg; College; Missionary.

MUNRO, Julie A; Rolla HS; Rolla, ND; Band; Chrs; ChrhWkr; CmntyWkr; CncrtBnd; HonRl; MrchBnd; PepBnd; SchMus; SchPl; LetterTrk; GAA; KiwanAwd; Mary College; Music.

MURDOCK, Carol J; Colfax Comm HS; Colfax, IA; Band; CncrtBnd; MrchBnd; RedCrAde; FTA; PpCl; Bsktbl; College; Nursing.

MURPHY, Harlan F; Lincolnwood HS; Farmersville, IL; ChrhWkr; StuCncl; Yrbk; RptrSchPpr; CivCl; 4-H; FFA; Bsktbl; DanFAwd; 4-HAwd; College.

MURRAY, Robert N; Kirksville HS; Kirksville, MO; VPFrshCls; ALBoysSt; Chr; ChrhWkr; CmntyWkr; HonRl; NatlMeritSF; ROTC; SctActv; 4-H; SciCl; Bsbl; Bsktbl; University; Professional.

MYERS, Margaret R; Rich Central HS; Matteson, IL; 130/410 SecSrCls; HonRl; StuCncl; PpCl; Chrldr; University; International Relations.

N

NACY, Philip K; Helias HS; Jefferson City, MO; 84/196 PresSrCls; ALBoysSt; SchMus; SchPl; StuCncl; Bsktbl; Ftbl; Tennis; OptClAwd; Southwest Missouri St Univ; Medicine.

NAHF, Debbie L; Waukegan HS; Waukegan, IL; 94/1004 AFS; CmntyWkr; Nat Honor Soc; College; Accounting.

NASH, Ronald G; Salem Sr HS; Salem, MO; 27/180 Band; CncrtBnd; HonRl; PepBnd; PpCl; LetterBsbl; CaptFtbl; LetterTrk; College; Geology.

NELSON, Keeda S; Worthington Sr HS; Wilmont, MN; ChrhWkr; LbryAde; FHA; Business School; Vocation.

NEMBARD, Diane V; Northern HS; Detroit, MI; HonRl; OffAde; PpCl; Detroit Inst Of Tech; Data Processing.

NERAT, Diane M; Stephenson HS; Wallace, MI; TrsJrCls; ChrhWkr; HonRl; NHS; PpCl; College; Dental Hygiene.

NEUMANN, Leslie A; Ferndale HS; Ferndale, MI; ModUN; NatlMeritFnl; TchrAde; LetterGAA; College; Forestry.

NEVELS, Ray D; Marion HS; Marion, IN; Band; ChrhWkr; CmntyWkr; CncrtBnd; HonRl; MrchBnd; Orch; LetterBsbl; LetterFtbl; IMSpt; AmLegAwd; Indiana St Univ; Engineering.

NEWTON, Terry D; Dora R Iii HS; Zanoni, MO; 4/28 PresJrCls; CmntyWkr; HonRl; IntrClCncl; SchPl; SctActv; RptrYrbk; RptrSchPpr; 4-H; FFA; Bsbl; Bsktbl; Outstanding Jr 1974 1975; Swine Proficiency & Star Chap Farmer Awards In FFA; Univ Of Missouri; Agriculture.

NICHOLS, Kris C; Mount Ayr Comm HS; Mount Ayr, IA; PresJrCls; ALBoysSt; ChrhWkr; CmntyWkr; SchPl; SctActv; Yrbk; SchPpr; Oklahoma St Univ; Aeronautics.

NICHTING, Joseph J; Marquette HS; Pilot Grove, IA; PresSophCls; ALBoysSt; NHS; Sdlty; StuCncl; SchPpr; PpCl; Creighton Univ; Law.

NIED, Joseph A; Thorp HS; Thorp, WI; Band; HonRl; PolWkr; SchPl; StuCncl; SchPpr; 4-H; Bsbl; Bsktbl; College; Vocation.

NIEMAN, Brian H; Mt Ayr Comm HS; Mount Ayr, IA; CmntyWkr; HonRl; Bsbl; Bsktbl; Ftbl; Glf; Crestons Sw Comm College; Carpentry.

NIKUNEN, Randy J; Horace Mann HS; Gilbert, MN; Chr; HonRl; LetterBsbl; CaptFtbl; College.

NOFS, Randall L; Harper Creek HS; Battle Creek, MI; ChrhWkr; NHS; Ftbl; CaptTennis; Michigan St University.

NOGA, Darrell G; Fenwick HS; Cicero, IL; HonRl; NatlFornLg; SchMus; StuCncl; RptrYrbk; RptrSchPpr; SchPpr; Honr Schlship By Loyola Univ Chicago; Merit Schlship By De Paul Univ; Univ; Surgeon.

NORMAN, Julie A; Estelline HS; Castlewood, SD; 3/39 Band; HonRl; HospAde; NHS; RptrYrbk; EdSchPpr; PresFHA; VPFNA; PresPpCl; Bsktbl; IMSpt; Nursing School; Nurse.

NORNES, Julie R; Climax Public HS; Climax, MN; 4/26 SecSophCls; Chrs; CncrtBnd; HonRl; NHS; SchPl; StuCncl; YthFlsp; FHA; Bsktbl; Trk; CaptChrldr; GAA; IMSpt; College; Fashion Mdse.

NORTHERN, Sheila P; South Pemiscot HS; Steele, MO; Band; Chr; Chrs; CncrtBnd; MrchBnd; NHS; OffAde; PepBnd; SchPl; SctActv; RptrSchPpr; Se Missouri St University.

NORUM, Caryn A; Harvard HS; Harvard, IL; 60/166 Band; Chr; Chrs; CncrtBnd; HonRl; MrchBnd; SchMus; Twrl; 4-H; GerCl; PpCl; Chrldr; PPFtbl; College; X Ray Technician.

NOVY, Gloria; Morton East Hs; Cicero, IL; 10/771 Chr; HonRl; JrNHS; Orch; SctActv; FrCl; Natl Honor Soc;.

O

O BERSKI, Mark D; Olgrosse Pointe North HS; Grosse Pointe Farm, MI; HonRl; NatlFornLg; NHS; SchPl; StuCncl; FBLA; Swmmng; KiwanAwd; VFWAwd; Michigan St Univ; Communications.

O BRIEN, John S; E Grand Rapids HS; Grand Rapids, MI; 35/326 HstSophCls; HstJrCls; PresSrCls; Chr; ChrhWkr; HonRl; JA; NHS; PolWkr; SchMus; SchPl; Bsktbl; Tennis; Kalamazoo College; Law.

O BRIEN, Julia A; Port Huron HS; Port Huron, MI; Chr; Chrl; ChrhWkr; HonRl; Mdrgl; OffAde; SchPl; StuGov; GAA; College; Education.

O DONNELL, Patricia A; Saint Mary Academy; Indianapolis, IN; TrsSophCls; TrsJrCls; VPSrCls; Chr; HonRl; StuCncl; SpnCl; Bsktbl; PresGAA; Arizona St Univ; Nursing.

ODRY, Karen L; Hamilton HS; Milwaukee, WI; ChrhWkr; CmntyWkr; HonRl; HospAde; LbryAde; NatlFornLg; NatlMeritCmnd; PolWkr; SchPl; RptrYrbk; University; Law.

OEHLERT, Donald J; Sycamore HS; Clare, IL; HonRl; JrNHS; Mdrgl; NatlThespSoc; SchMus; SchPl; StuCncl; TchrAde; Ftbl; N Illinois Univ; Industrial Arts.

OETTING, Nancy E; Jefferson HS; Monroe, MI; 19/155 TrsFrshCls; TrsSophCls; TrsJrCls; TrsSrCls; Band; CncrtBnd; HonRl; JrNHS; MrchBnd; NHS; PepBnd; LetterBsbl; CaptChrldr; 4-HAwd; Adrian College; Business Admin.

OFE, Thomas G; Plattsmouth HS; Plattsmouth, NE; 31/163 PresFrshCls; PresSophCls; Band; CncrtBnd; HonRl; MrchBnd; NHS; SctActv; StuCncl; StuGov; Bsbl; Bsktbl; Ftbl; Swmmng; Univ Of Nebraska; Business.

OISTAD, Marlo J; Halsted HS; Shelly, MN; SecTrsSophCls; Chr; Chrs; StuCncl; TchrAde; SptEdYrbk; Yrbk; 4-H; FFA; PpCl; LetterBsbl; LetterBsktbl; LetterFtbl; College; Vocation.

OLIVER, David A; Belleville East HS; Fairview Heights, IL; 28/677 HonRl; JrNHS; NHS; Bsbl; Selectd By St Louis Post Dispatch As 1975 Scholar; Athlete Of Belleville Twp HS E; Appointed To West Point; St Louis Cardinals 18th Round Select 1975 Free Agent Draft; Tribune Outstnd Youth Award; News Demo 1975; All Basebl Team; Metro E Journal 1975 Prep All Star Baseball Team; Sw Confer HS Coaches 1975 All Star Baseball Team; Ill HS Assoc St Tourn All Star Team;.

OLIVO, Diana A; Holy Name Cathedral HS; Chicago, IL; CmntyWkr; HonRl; HospAde; PolWkr; SchAde; Univ Of Chicago; Psychology.

OLNEY, Joan A; Marathon Consolidated HS; Marathon, IA; Band; Chrs; CncrtBnd; HonRl; MrchBnd; PepBnd; SchMus; SchPl; Yrbk; SchPpr; 4-H; LetterBsktbl; 4-HAwd; College; Health.

OLSON, Annette M; Hill City HS; Hill City, SD; SecFrshCls; Chrs; SchPl; StuCncl; Yrbk; Treas4-H; SecPpCl; Bsktbl; Trk; Chrldr; GAA; IMSpt; Black Hills State College; Counseling.

OLSON, Denise J; Lamberton Public HS; Lamberton, MN; 6/45 CncrtBnd; HonRl; VPQuill&Scroll; TchrAde; RptrYrbk; Yrbk; RptrSchPpr; FTA; PresPpCl; GAA; DARAwd; College; Mathematics.

OLSON, Janet L; Rock Island HS; Rock Island, IL; 24/680 Chr; ChrhWkr; NHS; North Park College; Psychology.

OLSON, Mark B; Sentral Community HS; Estherville, IA; VPSrCls; Chrs; CmntyWkr; Mdrgl; SchMus; SchPl; Yrbk; SchPpr; Bsktbl; LetterTrk; Trade School; Vocation.

OSGOOD, Stephen P; Naperville Central HS; Naperville, IL; 66/826 Chr; HonRl; SchMus; YthFlsp; FrCl; Natl Honor Soc; Univ Of Iowa; Pharmacy.

OSNES, Thomas P; Forest City HS; Forest City, IA; ALBoysSt; Band; Chr; CncrtBnd; HonRl; KeyCl; SpnCl; Ftbl; College; Pilot.

OSWALT, Kris S; Jefferson HS; Lafayette, IN; 2/693 ALBoysSt; Chr; ChrhWkr; HonRl; NHS; NatlMeritCmnd; SchMus; StuCncl; YthFlsp; College.

OTT, David J; St Marys HS; Reeder, ND; ALBoysSt; Band; ChrhWkr; CncrtBnd; HonRl; MrchBnd; PepBnd; TchrAde; SptEdSchPpr; Air Force Academy; Pilot.

P

PAAR, Kevin C; Hempstead HS; Dubuque, IA; 5/455 Chr; Chrs; HonRl; JrNHS; Mdrgl; NHS; NatlThespSoc; ROTC; SchMus; SchPl; LetterBsbl; LetterFtbl; IMSpt; ChmbCommrsAwd; Iowa St Univ; Engineer.

PAGE, Diana K; Jersey Comm HS; Jerseyville, IL; 1/2 Chrs; HonRl; LitMag; NHS; OffAde; FrCl; MthCl; PpCl; Tennis; Child Of Korean Vet Schol Univ Of Il; Valedictorian; Univ Of Ill; Pharmacist.

PALMER, Timothy L; Mount St Benedict HS; Crookston, MN; Chrs; OffAde; Sacrstn; Ftbl; Wrstlng; College.

PANKONIN, Philip L; Louisville HS; Louisville, NE; 8/40 PresSrCls; ALBoysSt; Band; Chr; Chrs; PepBnd; SchPl; RptrSchPpr; LetterBsktbl; LetterFtbl; LetterTrk; Univ Of Nebraska; Business.

PANKRATZ, Linda C; Waukegan East HS; Waukegan, IL; Band; Chr; HonRl; LitMag; Mdrgl; MrchBnd; PepBnd;.

PAPE, Jeffrey B; East HS; Sioux City, IA; ChrhWkr; HonRl; Tennis; Trk; CaptWrstlng; IMSpt; RotaryAwd; Morningside College; Bio Engineering.

PAPER, Pamela A; Bennett Comm HS; Stockton, IA; 7/28 PresJrCls; Band; Chrs; CncrtBnd; HonRl; NHS; PepBnd; SchPl; StuCncl; RptrYrbk; RptrSchPpr; 4-H; DARAwd; Trade School; Cosmetologist.

PAPP, Louis G; Cass City HS; Cass City, MI; 40/150 ChrhWkr; CmntyWkr; HonRl; PolWkr; FSA; GerCl; SciCl; LetterFtbl; Ohio Inst Of Tech; Technician.

PARKS, Gay; Valentine HS; Valentine, NE; Band; CncrtBnd; MrchBnd; PepBnd; StuGov; TchrAde; PpCl; Bsbl; Trk; Business School; Professional.

PARRETTE, Jeffery A; Menominee HS; Menominee, MI; ChrhWkr; CmntyWkr; SctActv; StuCncl; TchrAde; 4-H; Bsktbl; LetterFtbl; LetterTrk; IMSpt;.

PATTERSON, Yvonne; Junction City HS; Junction, KS; SchPl; SctActv; Twrl; FrCl; PpCl; College.

PATTIE, Julie A; Hays HS; Hays, KS; ChrhWkr; CmntyWkr; HonRl; NatlFornLg; PolWkr; SchMus; SchPl; SpnCl; PpCl; IMSpt; University; Professional.

PAWELSKI, Geralyn M; Good Counsel HS; Chicago, IL; Chrs; HonRl; HospAde; JA; NHS; SchAde; SchMus; SchPl; SciCl; Illinois Benedictine College; Science.

PAZDERNIK, Larry E; Pleasanton HS; Riverdale, NE; .

PEARSON, Debra L; Central HS; Glenwood, MN; VPSophCls; Band; Chr; CncrtBnd; HonRl; PepBnd; TchrAde; FHA; College; Music.

PEDERSEN, Pamela S; Sunflower HS; Mitchell, NE; HstFrshCls; Chr; Chrs; ChrhWkr; JA; SchPl; YthFlsp; 4-H; PpCl; Chrldr; PPFtbl; College; Nursing.

PENTECOST, Mark B; Holt HS; Holt, MI; 62/238 HonRl; NHS; KeyCl; LetterBsktbl; LetterTennis; Grand Valley College; Mathematics.

PERSING, Robert L; Slayton HS; Slayton, MN; ChrhWkr; CmntyWkr; HonRl; ROTC; GerCl; Conley Voc School; Business Accountant.

PETERMAN, Carol G; Onaway Area HS; Onaway, MI; ChrhWkr; CmntyWkr; CncrtBnd; HonRl; MrchBnd; NHS; NatlMeritFnl; OffAde; CaptChrldr; GAA; University; Counselor.

PETERS, Edwin C; Mahtomedi HS; Mahtomedi, MN; 1/180 HonRl; NHS; StuCncl; StuGov; GerCl; CaptTennis; College.

PETERS, Lenny J; Maconaquah HS; Bunker Hill, IN; 92/259 CmntyWkr; DrlTm; HonRl; StuCncl; RptrSchPpr; SptEdSchPpr; SchPpr; LetterBsbl; LetterBsktbl; LetterFtbl; CaptTrk; IMSpt; Trade School.

PETERS, V Carolyn; Carrollton HS; Waverly, MO; 15/101 Band; ChrhWkr; CmntyWkr; CncrtBnd; HonRl; MrchBnd; NHS; TchrAde; PresGerCl; IMSpt; College; Business.

PETERS, Victoria S; Quincy Notre Dame HS; Quincy, IL; Chrs; CmntyWkr; HonRl; HospAde;

SchMus; SctActv; StuCncl; FNA; SpnCl; Nursing School; Nurse.

PETERSEN, Ann R; Osmond Community HS; Osmond, NE; 3/42 Band; Chrs; ChrhWkr; CncrtBnd; HonRl; MrchBnd; SchPl; StuCncl; 4-H; University.

PETERSON, Daniel C; Elk Rapids Sr HS; Kewadih, MI; 1/76 TrsFrshCls; TrsSophCls; TrsJrCls; TrsSrCls; ChrhWkr; HonRl; NHS; College.

PETERSON, Daniel D; Ada HS; Ada, MN; HonRl; RptrYrbk; 4-H; FFA; LetterBsbl; LetterBsktbl; LetterFtbl; LetterTrk; LetterWrstlng; North Dakota St Univ; Professional.

PETERSON, James R; Eastwood Comm HS; Correctionville, IA; 12/44 PresSophCls; StuCncl; StuGov; SchPpr; 4-H; FFA; LetterBsbl; LetterBsktbl; LetterFtbl; LetterGlf; South Dakota St Univ; Veterinarian.

PETERSON, Lisa A; Churchill HS; Livonia, MI; 2/1000 HonRl; NatlSciFnd; Orch; TchrAde; Chrldr; Kalamazoo College; Art.

PETERSON, Parnell M; Iron Mountain HS; Iron Mountain, MI; Band; CncrtBnd; HonRl; MrchBnd; NatlMeritSchl; NatlMeritSF; PepBnd; SchPl; 4-H; KeyCl; LetterBsktbl; LetterFtbl; LetterTennis; Michigan St Univ; Architecture.

PETERSON, Ronald E; Burris HS; Muncie, IN; 8/50 HstJrCls; ChrhWkr; PolWkr; SctActv; SchPpr; LetterBsbl; LetterBsktbl; LetterSwmmng; CchngActv; IMSpt; Tennessee Temple College; Business.

PETRANOFF, Marianne; Northwest HS; Indianapolis, IN; 47/438 ALAGirlsSt; TreasBand; CncrtBnd; HonRl; JA; TreasMrchBnd; TreasNHS; Orch; SchMus; StuCncl; CaptChrldr; College.

PETRISIN, John; Alpena HS; Ossineke, MI; HonRl; TchrAde; 4-H; SpnCl; College; Pilot.

PFAFF, Eric R; Green Lake HS; Green Lake, WI; VPJrCls; HonRl; NHS; YthFlsp; RptrSchPpr; Cornell Univ; Hotel Admin.

PHILLIPS, Dawn R; Tri County HS; Sand Lake, MI; 6/9 Band; ChrhWkr; CmntyWkr; CncrtBnd; HonRl; MrchBnd; NHS; PepBnd; RedCrAde; StuCncl; Chrldr; GAA; IMSpt; Michigan St Univ; Pharmacy.

PIEPER, Jolene E; Benton Community HS; Van Horne, IA; 7/108 TrsJrCls; ChrhWkr; HonRl; SecNHS; YthFlsp; LetterBsbl; LetterBsktbl; CaptTrk; PresGAA; 2nd In Discuss Throw At Ia Girls State Track Meet; U Of Ia; Phy Ed & Biology Majors.

PIERCE, Jeffrey M; Arlington Public HS; Arlington, SD; Band; MrchBnd; PepBnd; Pres4-H; FFA; Bsktbl; LetterTrk; University; Lawyer.

PIFER, Netta F; Flora HS; Flora, IL; 27/138 ChrhWkr; HonRl; PolWkr; SchMus; SchPl; Yrbk; VPFHA; MthCl; SecSciCl; Olney Central College; Nursing.

PINER, Melissa J; Plattsmouth HS; Murray, NE; 44/150 Band; Chrs; ChrhWkr; CncrtBnd; HonRl; MrchBnd; SchAde; SctActv; TchrAde; YthFlsp; 4-H; PpCl; Chrldr; College; Dentist.

PIOJDA, Karen M; Whitnall HS; Hales Corner, WI; Band; Chrs; CmntyWkr; CncrtBnd; DrlTm; HonRl; HospAde; NHS; PepBnd; SctActv; Univ Of Wisconsin; Nursing.

PLACE, Andrew A; Boyne City HS; Boyne City, MI; TrsJrCls; SecSrCls; SchMus; FrCl; LetterBsktbl; LetterFtbl; LetterTrk; College; Business Mgmt.

PLANTE, Edward O; Paxton HS; Paxton, IL; CmntyWkr; HonRl; SctActv; YthFlsp; SpnCl; Bsktbl; Glf; College; Manager.

PLECHASH, Steven; Oak Park River Forest HS; Oak Park, IL; 14/1107 ALBoysSt; HonRl; NatlMeritSF; Orch; SchAde; Yale Univ; Law.

PLONA, Christopher D; Oak Park & River Forest HS; Oak Park, IL; 26/1012 HonRl; NatlFornLg; NatlMeritFnl; SchPl; StuCncl; RptrSchPpr; LatCl; SciCl; Univ Of Chicago; Government Administration.

PLOUCH, Susan M; Haven HS; Mt Hope, KS; Chr; ChrhWkr; HonRl; OffAde; SchPl; YthFlsp; RptrYrbk; RptrSchPpr; 4-H; PpCl; College; Special Ed.

POINTER, Sandy J; Plattsmouth HS; Plattsmouth, NE; Chr; ChrhWkr; CmntyWkr; HonRl; SctActv; TchrAde; YthFlsp; CivCl; FHA; College; Teacher.

POLSKY, Wendy R; Central HS; St Joseph, MO; 32/499 Chr; HonRl; SchMus; StuGov; TchrAde; SpnCl; SciCl; Swmmng; University; Psychology.

PORE, Kim A; Kingston HS; Silverwood, MI; 5/70 SecSrCls; DrlTm; HonRl; NHS; OffAde; TchrAde; RptrSchPpr; SpnCl; Bsktbl; Chrldr; Ferris St College; Lab Technician.

PORTER, Perry L; Owensville HS; Owensville, MO; Quill&Scroll; SctActv; SptEdYrbk; FDA; MthCl; SciCl; College; Biology.

POSTLEWAIT, Stanley E; Houston HS; Bucyrus, MO; AFS; ALBoysSt; ALAGirlsSt; ChrhWkr; CmntyWkr; JrNHS; NatlCathMusEdAsoc; RedCrAde; ROTC; SancSoc; Bsbl; Bsktbl; College; Vocation.

POWALKA, Donald S; Goodman Armstrong HS; Goodman, WI; PresJrCls; Band; HonRl; NHS; Bell & Howell Schl; Electronics Tech.

POWELL, Sandra A; Marshall HS; Marshall, WI; VPJrCls; HonRl; LbryAde; SchPl; StuCncl; FHA; PpCl; Trk; LetterChrldr; PPFtbl; Vocational Schl; Drama.

PRATHER, Teresa K; Catlin HS; Catlin, IL; Chr; HonRl; TchrAde; YthFlsp; SecFHA; PpCl; Bsbl; Bsktbl; Trk; GAA; College; Physical Education.

PRICE, Walter J; Engadine Cons HS; Engadine, MI; 4/35 HonRl; RptrYrbk; Ftbl; Trk; College; Electronics.

PROBST, Richard P; Sturgis HS; Sturgis, MI; Band; CncrtBnd; HonRl; NHS; SchPl; SctActv; LatCl; Tennis; Ferris St College; Optometry.

PROCK, Tammara L; Rolla Sr HS; Rolla, MO; Band; CncrtBnd; DrlTm; HonRl; MrchBnd; PepBnd; SchMus; SchPl; SctActv; TchrAde; FHA; FrCl; Chrldr; College.

PROCTOR, Gary D; Davis County Comm HS; Bloomfield, IA; 22/134 AFS; ALBoysSt; Band; ChrhWkr; CtyCnl; CmntyWkr; HonRl; StuCncl; YthFlsp; FBLA; Bsktbl; Ftbl; Tennis;.

PROKOPP, Terry L; Sacred Heart HS; Dearborn, MI; HonRl; JA; NatlMeritCmnd; Yrbk; FNA; FrCl; Univ Of Michigan.

PROUTY, Thomas J; O Neill Public HS; O Neill, NE; Chr; Chrs; HonRl; Mdrgl; LetterFtbl; Trade School; Vocation.

PRYDE, James P; Pekin Comm HS; Marquette Hts, IL; 5/900 ALBoysSt; Band; CmntyWkr; CncrtBnd; HonRl; MrchBnd; NatlFornLg; NHS; Orch; Ftbl; University; Law.

PRZYBYLA, James R; Midland HS; Midland, MI; 48/415 HonRl; JA; SctActv; University; Engineer.

PURDY, Caro L; Caro HS; Caro, MI; VPSophCls; Band; HonRl; MrchBnd; TreasNHS; PepBnd; TreasStuCncl; Yrbk; PpCl; Chrldr; College; Medicine.

PURVIS, Michael J; Burke HS; Burke, SD; 11/37 PresFrshCls; VPSophCls; PresSrCls; ChrhWkr; HonRl; RptrYrbk; CaptFtbl; Univ Of Nebraska; Flight Training.

PUZ, Renee M; Cabrini HS; Allen Park, MI; 45/186 Chrs; CmntyWkr; HonRl; NatlMeritCmnd; SchAde; SchPl; Yrbk; FTA; FrCl; IMSpt; PPFtbl; PresAwd; College; History.

R

RADFORD, David R; Waterford Twp HS; Pontiac, MI; HonRl; NatlFornLg; NHS; SchMus; Central Michigan University.

RAFERT, Susan; Mt Vernon HS; Fortville, IN; 22/138 Band; ChrhWkr; CncrtBnd; DrmMjrt; HonRl; MrchBnd; NHS; PepBnd; SchMus; StuCncl; Yrbk; 4-H; PpCl; Trk; Methodist Hosp; Radiology.

RAML, Steven J; O Gorman HS; Watertown, SD; Chrs; ChrhWkr; LbryAde; St Marys; Priest.

RANABARGAR, Randy P; Hannibal HS; Hannibal, MO; 55/275 DrlTm; Kemper Military Schl; Army.

RANSFORD, Ules P; Gibson Southern HS; Fort Branch, IN; HonRl; Rose Hulman Inst Of Tech; Computer Sci.

RAY, B Dianne; Parkwood HS; Joplin, MO; Chr; ChrhWkr; CmntyWkr; HonRl; HospAde; Orch; SchMus; SchPl; YthFlsp; PpCl; Bsktbl; Ftbl; Chrldr; Fayetteville Univ; Gymnastics.

RAY, Suzanne M; Bullock Creek HS; Midland, MI; 7/170 SecSrCls; ChrhWkr; HonRl; JrNHS; LbryAde; NHS; TchrAde; RptrYrbk; RptrSchPpr; Grand Valley St College; Nursing.

REDFIELD, Kristi A; Stratton Public HS; Stratton, NE; Band; Chr; ChrhWkr; CncrtBnd; MrchBnd; YthFlsp; 4-H; SciCl; LetterTrk; Chrldr; 4-HAwd; College.

REIN, Andrew R; Stoughton HS; Stoughton, WI; PpCl; CaptWrstlng; PresAwd;.

REINHOLD, Anthony V; Winamac HS; Winamac, IN; 22/105 Aud/Vis; Band; Chrs; CmntyWkr; CncrtBnd; MrchBnd; PepBnd; Quill&Scroll; SchAde; SchPl; SctActv; Bsktbl; DanFAwd; College; Medicine.

REITER, Joann M; Aquin HS; Cascade, IA; 1/66 SecTrsSrCls; Chrl; SchMus; SchPl; SecStuCncl; EdSchPpr; Bsktbl; BauchLmbAwd; Loras College; Chem Engineer.

REYNOLDS, Cindy A; Waukegan East HS; Waukegan, IL; Chr; NatlFornLg; NHS; NatlThespSoc; SchMus; University; Theater.

RHOADES, Diana M; Edinburg HS; Edinburg, IN; HstFrshCls; HstSophCls; HstJrCls; Chr; Chrl; HonRl; Art School; Professional.

RHOADS, Angela L; South Newton HS; Goodland, IN; 7/96 Band; CncrtBnd; HonRl; MrchBnd; NHS; PepBnd; SctActv; LatCl; PresSciCl; PPFtbl; Purdue U; Vet.

RHODES, Loretha; Cooley HS; Chicago, IL; .

RICE, Rebecca S; Sisseton HS; Sisseton, SD; 3/106 Band; Chrs; HonRl; HospAde; NHS; NatlMeritSF; StuCncl; TchrAde; RptrYrbk; GAA; Col; Teaching.

RICHARD, Frank E; Rolling Meadows HS; Arlington Hts, IL; ChrhWkr; HonRl; NatlFornLg; Ftbl; Natl Honor Soc; College; Engineer Or Doctor.

RICHARDSON, Lance; Martinsville HS; Martinsville, IN; 70/483 Bsktbl; LetterFtbl; LetterTrk; IMSpt; PresAwd;.

RIGGS, Vicki L; Scott Comm HS; Scott City, KS; 31/102 Band; ChrhWkr; CncrtBnd; HonRl; MrchBnd; Fort Hays St College; Medicine.

RILEY, Henrietta; Lovejoy HS; Lovejoy, IL; SecFrshCls; SecSophCls; TrsJrCls; Chr; ChrhWkr; HonRl; SchPl; TchrAde; College; Liberal Arts.

RINGER, James E; Virden HS; Virden, IL; 5/80 ALBoysSt; HonRl; PresNHS; 4-H; FFA; PpCl; SciCl; LetterBsktbl; IMSpt; 4-HAwd;.

RIPLEY, Glen S; Howell HS; Howell, MI; 91/362 Band; CncrtBnd; MrchBnd; PepBnd; SchMus; Trade School; Mechanics.

RITTERSKAMP, Tamara L; Anderson HS; Anderson, IN; 95/660 ChrhWkr; HonRl; HospAde; LbryAde; OffAde; SchAde; YthFlsp; SpnCl; Ball St Univ; Secretary.

ROBBINS, Zane S; Evanstown Twp HS; Evanston, IL; HonRl; PolWkr; SctActv; University; Wildlife Mgmt.

ROBERTS, Casey J; New Underwood HS; Owanka, SD; 1/25 SecFrshCls; ALBoysSt; HonRl; JrNHS; NHS; SchPl; Bsktbl; Ftbl; Trk; College.

ROBERTS, Paul D; Eastside HS; St Joe, IN; PresFrshCls; Band; ChrhWkr; CncrtBnd; DrmBgl; MrchBnd; Orch; PepBnd; SpnCl; Bsbl; Bsktbl; Ftbl; College; Professional.

ROBINSON, Carol A; Highland HS; Highland, IN; 59/538 CaptBsktbl; Indiana Univ; Nurse.

ROBLE, Richard R; Green Bay Preble HS; Green Bay, WI; 85/487 ALBoysSt; HonRl; JA; JrNHS; NHS; TreasKeyCl; SpnCl; Trk; IMSpt; Univ Of Wisconsin; Communications.

ROME, Alean M; Union City HS; Union City, MI; ChrhWkr; HonRl; ModUN; SctActv; StuCncl; RptrYrbk; RptrSchPpr; 4-H; FTA; Trk; Chrldr; PPFtbl; Michigan St Univ; Youth Council.

ROMMANN, Lila M; Washington Sr HS; Sioux Falls, SD; ChrhWkr; HonRl; NHS; YthFlsp; South Dakota St Univ; Pharmacy.

RONEY, Jane E; Heritage Christian HS; Anderson, IN; HonRl; HospAde; LbryAde; NHS; SchMus; TchrAde; 4-H; FNA; PpCl; College; Nursing.

ROSS, Diane M; Luther South HS; Chicago, IL; Chrs; ChrhWkr; CmntyWkr; HonRl; NHS; RptrSchPpr; SchPpr; Tuskegee Inst; Veterinarian.

ROTH, Kimberlee S; Central Cass HS; Casselton, ND; ALAGirlsSt; Band; Chr; Chrs; ChrhWkr; CncrtBnd; HonRl; HospAde; NHS; PepBnd; SchPl; Yrbk; Bsktbl; Chrldr; University; Professional.

ROUDEBUSH, Cheryl L; Sullivan HS; Sullivan, IN; DrlTm; HonRl; ModUN; RptrSchPpr; EdSchPpr; SchPpr; SpnCl; Tennis; GAA; Natl Honor Soc; Editor Of Schl Newspaper; College.

ROUGAS, Catherine; Luther North HS; Chicago, IL; Chr; ChrhWkr; CmntyWkr; HospAde; NatlThespSoc; SchMus; SchPl; Twrl; YthFlsp; Nursing School; Nurse.

ROUSE, Elaine A; Liberal R 2 HS; Liberal, MO; 11/48 ALAGirlsSt; Chrs; ChrhWkr; HonRl; StuCncl; RptrYrbk; RptrSchPpr; FHA; SpnCl; PpCl; IMSpt; Kansas St College Of Pittsburg; Hotel Admin.

ROUSSEAU, Julie M; Central HS; Glenwood, MN; Chr; Chrs; ChrhWkr; HonRl; HospAde; LbryAde; Mdrgl; SchAde; FNA; College; Medicine.

ROWLAND, Donna M; Dundee HS; Dundee, MI; 35/120 Band; Chrs; PresCncrtBnd; HonRl; MrchBnd; PepBnd; SchPl; Pres4-H; LetterSwmmng; Tennis; GAA; Central Michigan Univ; Music.

ROWLAND, Vance E; Arthur HS; Arthur, IL; 10/46 SecFrshCls; CncrtBnd; HonRl; SchPl; VPFFA; Univ Of So Illinois; Aviation.

ROZEBOOM, Ted S; W Mt Christian HS; Muskegon, MI; Band; CmntyWkr; CncrtBnd; HonRl; PepBnd; SchMus; SchPl; RptrSchPpr; College; Law.

RUBECK, Wendy J; Belvidere HS; Poplar Grove, IL; 8/430 College; Accounting.

RUBLE, Pamela K; Salem HS; Salem, MO; VPSophCls; VPJrCls; ChrhWkr; HonRl; SchPl; StuCncl; TchrAde; PpCl; LetterChrldr; PPFtbl; College.

RUCKER, Willie J; Thornton HS; Harvey, IL; PresFrshCls; TrsSophCls; VPJrCls; ChrhWkr; CmntyWkr; HonRl; OffAde; SchPl; StuGov; SpnCl; LetterFtbl; LetterWrstlng; CchngActv; IMSpt; Augustana College; Dentist.

RUFENER, Joann K; Monroe HS; Monroe, WI; 84/255 PresFrshCls; SecSophCls; SecJrCls; HonRl; PolWkr; 4-H; FHA; LetterTrk; CaptChrldr; 4-HAwd; JAAwd;.

RUFFIN, Dan C; Peoria HS; Peoria, IL; LetterBsktbl; LetterFtbl; College; Law.

RUFFNER, Marcella L; Mac Arthur HS; Decatur, IL; 43/400 SecJrCls; SecAFS; Chr; HonRl; VPJA; SctActv; TreasStuCncl; YthFlsp; SchPpr; LetterChrldr; Natl Honor Soc; Univ Of Illinois; Business Administration.

RUGGIO, Jill A; Hartford HS; Hartford, MI; SecFrshCls; SecJrCls; SecSrCls; HonRl; LitMag; SchPl; TchrAde; SptEdSchPpr; PpCl; Business School; Business.

RUNYAN, Marvin P; Corunna HS; Corunna, MI; 59/218 Central Michigan Univ; Psychiatrist.

RUSHFORD, Sheree A; Olin HS; Olin, IA; Chrs; CncrtBnd; HonRl; MrchBnd; NatlThespSoc; StuCncl; Twrl; RptrSchPpr; Bsktbl; LetterTrk; 4-HAwd; Patricia Stevens Car College; Model.

RUSK, Terry L; Cedar Lake Academy; Berrien Springs, MI; ChrhWkr; HonRl; JrNHS; NHS; NatlMeritSF; SchPl; StuCncl; StuGov; FrCl; Ftbl; LetterWrstlng; IMSpt; Andrews Univ; Teacher.

S

SABINS, Mary M; Kalkaska HS; Kalkaska, MI; Aud/Vis; ChrhWkr; HonRl; LbryAde; OffAde; SchAde; SctActv; TchrAde; FHA; Bsbl; Bsktbl; GAA; Nw Beauty Academy; Beautician.

SALARANO, John M; Vianney HS; Glendale, MO; 65/200 HonRl; PolWkr; College; Business.

SALERNO, John P; Ryan HS; Omaha, NE; Univ Of Nebraska; Business Admin.

SAMUEL, Wendell; Paseo HS; Kansas City, MO; ChrhWkr; HonRl; JA; SchPl; College; Liberal Arts.

SAMUELSON, Earl D; Adams Public HS; Adams, ND; ALBoysSt; Chrs; ChrhWkr; HonRl; SchPl; Yrbk; SchPpr; 4-H; PpCl; LetterBsktbl; IMSpt; 4-HAwd; Trade School; Mechanic.

SANDS, Lynn L; Maria HS; Chicago, IL; 40/960 HonRl; NatlMeritCmnd; NatlThespSoc; SchAde; SchPl; Sdlty; TchrAde; SpnCl; VPMthCl; LionAwd; College; Special Ed.

SAPPINGTON, Thomas W; Warrensburg HS; Warrensburg, MO; 3/149 ALBoysSt; Chr; Chrs; HonRl; JrNHS; Mdrgl; NHS; NatlMeritCmnd; SchMus; SchPl; LetterBsktbl; LetterTrk; University; Wildlife Conservation.

SASH, Carol A; Western Comm Univ HS; Buda, IL; Band; CncrtBnd; HonRl; HospAde; MrchBnd; PepBnd; RptrYrbk; College; Professional.

SAUE, Kevin E; Montevideo Sr HS; Montevideo, MN; .

SAUNDERS, Jerold A; Adelphian Academy; Detroit, MI; HonRl; JrNHS; Bsktbl; Ftbl; College; Music.

SAVARYN, Yolanda L; Waconia HS; Waconia, MN; SecSophCls; TrsJrCls; Band; Chr; Chrs; ChrhWkr; CtyCnl; CmntyWkr; CncrtBnd; HonRl; HospAde; Bsktbl; Trk; Chrldr; College; Nutritionist.

SCHAEFER, Cheryl D; Newaygo HS; Newaygo, MI; 8/90 SecFrshCls; SecSophCls; VPSrCls; Band; HonRl; ModUN; NHS; SchPl; StuCncl; Trk; College; Liberal Arts.

SCHANER, Victoria L; Wyoming Park HS; Wyoming, MI; 49/252 TrsSrCls; CmntyWkr; HonRl; HospAde; NHS; RedCrAde; RptrSchPpr; FNA; GerCl; N Michigan Univ; Nursing.

SCHAPP, Robert L; Parkway North HS; Creve Coeur, MO; PresSophCls; PresJrCls; PresAud/Vis; ChrhWkr; JrNHS; PresNHS; NatlMeritSF; Quill&Scroll; StuGov; EdSchPpr; Merit Scholarship; College; Computer Science & Systems.

SCHARFF, Kim D; Nevada HS; Nevada, IA; 13/125 Band; Chr; Chrs; CncrtBnd; HonRl; JrNHS; MrchBnd; NHS; RptrSchPpr; SchPpr; PpCl; Bsktbl; Swmmng; Univ Of Evansville; Social Work.

SCHEER, John R; La Follette HS; Madison, WI; Aud/Vis; SchPl; RptrYrbk; RptrSchPpr; SchPpr; EngCl; Ftbl; Socr; Trk; College; Psychology.

SCHIMON, Rudolf F; Adams HS; Rochester, MI; 17/386 ALBoysSt; Band; CncrtBnd; HonRl; MrchBnd; NHS; TchrAde; YthFlsp; Bsktbl; Ftbl; Trk; CchngActv; Brown Univ; Dentist.

SCHINDLER, Ilene E; Newcastle Public HS; Newcastle, NE; Chrs; HonRl; LbryAde; SchPl; TchrAde; Yrbk; PpCl; Top Math & Top Sci Awards; College; Mathematics.

SCHLAUPITZ, Ronald S; Paul K Cousino Sr HS; Warren, MI; CncrtBnd; HonRl; MrchBnd; PepBnd; MthCl; LetterFtbl; Michigan St Univ; Elec Engineer.

SCHMICK, Sheila R; Forman Comm HS; Manito, IL; Band; Chr; ChrhWkr; CmntyWkr; HonRl; HospAde; LbryAde; RedCrAde; YthFlsp; 4-H; FDA; FNA; College; Physical Therapist.

SCHMIDT, D Mark; Pike HS; Indianapolis, IN; Chr; Chrl; Chrs; ChrhWkr; HonRl; SchMus; SchPl; YthFlsp; Bsbl; Bsktbl; IMSpt; College; Professional.

SCHMIDT, Dolores L; Newton HS; Newton, IL; CmntyWkr; HonRl; PolWkr; StuCncl; StuGov; YthLg; CivCl; Pres4-H; PresSpnCl; GAA; IMSpt; Pres4-HAwd; Olney Central College; Special Educ.

SCHMITZ, Naomi J; Tolley Public HS; Tolley, ND; 1/11 HonRl; SchPl; Yrbk; LetterBsktbl; LetterTrk; Chrldr; CchngActv; BttyCrckrAwd; 4-HAwd; PresAwd; College; Nursing.

SCHMITZ, Steven R; Central HS; Waterloo, IA; 105/360 ChrhWkr; HonRl; SctActv; StuCncl; MthCl; Bsbl; LetterFtbl; University; Professional.

SCHNEEMAN, Mark A; Red Bud HS; Baldwin, IL; HonRl; YthFlsp; 4-H; Univ Of Illinois; Veterinarian.

SCHNEIDER, Barbara A; St Marys Springs HS; Fond Du Lac, WI; Band; CncrtBnd; HonRl; HospAde; MrchBnd; NHS; PepBnd; StuCncl; 4-H; FrCl; PpCl; SciCl; Chrldr;.

SCHNEIDER, Carol A; Wapello Comm HS; Wapello, IA; Band; ChrhWkr; CncrtBnd; HonRl; HospAde; MrchBnd; YthFlsp; FFA; Bsktbl; College; Social Worker.

SCHOEN, Bruce H; Oak Ridge HS; Oak Ridge, MO; PresFrshCls; Band; ChrhWkr; CmntyWkr; CncrtBnd; MrchBnd; PepBnd; SchPl; 4-H; PpCl; College; Agriculture.

SCHOON, Debra C; Sebeka Public HS; Wadena, MN; 14/68 Chr; HonRl; OffAde; YthFlsp; RptrYrbk; RptrSchPpr; FHA; PpCl; Trk; Chrldr; GAA; IMSpt; College; Nursing.

SCHOPMEYER, George M; Winchester Comm HS; Winchester, IN; Band; HonRl; MrchBnd; SctActv; StuCncl; YthFlsp; SpnCl; LetterTrk; University; Professional.

SCHRAMM, Jill M; Cathay Public HS; Cathay, ND; 1/8 PresFrshCls; PresJrCls; Chrs; ChrhWkr; HonRl; SchPl; 4-H; LetterBsktbl; 4-HAwd; CitAwd;.

SCHROEDER, Cindy L; Bishop Dwenger HS; Ft Wayne, IN; JA; 4-H; GAA; Ball St Univ; Nursing.

SCHROEDER, Mary C; Onalaska HS; Onalaska, WI; Band; CncrtBnd; HonRl; MrchBnd; PepBnd; SptEdSchPpr; CaptTrk; PresAwd; Univ Of Wisconsin; Nursing.

SCHROEDER, Valorie D; Mayo HS; Rochester, MN; 6/467 PresAFS; Band; JrNHS; MrchBnd; NHS; PepBnd; SchMus; EdSchPpr; SciCl; Swmmng; Univ Of Minnesota; Journalism.

SCHUETTE, Douglas W; Brownton Public HS; Brownton, MN; VPSrCls; ALBoysSt; Band;

CncrtBnd; HonRl; FFA; LetterBsbl; LetterBsktbl; LetterFtbl; College; Agriculture.

SCHWEITZER, Delora J; Halliday Public HS; Dodge, ND; 2/30 PresFrshCls; ALAGirlsSt; MrchBnd; NHS; StuCncl; Yrbk; PresFHA; Bsktbl; GAA; BttyCrckrAwd; Mary College; Medical Tech.

SCHWEITZER, Rod R; Poplar Bluff Sr HS; Poplar Bluff, MO; Band; CmntyWkr; CncrtBnd; HonRl; PepBnd; Ftbl; Trk; Wrstlng; College.

SCHWERY, Laura M; Harlan Comm HS; Panama, IA; 60/270 Chr; Chrs; ChrhWkr; HonRl; 4-H; FNA; College; Professional.

SCOFIELD, Kristi A; Muskegon Sr HS; Muskegon, MI; TrsFrshCls; TrsSrCls; HonRl; NHS; NatlMeritCmnd; NatlMeritSF; StuCncl; TchrAde; RptrYrbk; Chrldr; Michigan St Univ; Medicine.

SEEGER, Barbara J; Gilman HS; Sheldon, WI; 34/80 Band; ChrhWkr; CmntyWkr; CncrtBnd; HonRl; MrchBnd; OffAde; PepBnd; YthFlsp; RptrYrbk; Yrbk; PpCl; CaptTrk; GAA;.

SEEKLANDER, Linda G; Northwestern Lutheran Academy; Hazelton, ND; 3/24 PresSophCls; Chrl; CncrtBnd; MrchBnd; SchPl; StuCncl; EdSchPpr; Bsktbl; IMSpt; BttyCrckrAwd; Dr Martin Luther College; Special Educ.

SEGAL, Myra J; Niles West HS; Lincolnwood, IL; AFS; Band; CmntyWkr; HonRl; LitMag; MrchBnd; PolWkr; SchMus; SchPl; SctActv; GerCl; SciCl; Grinnel College; Law.

SELLERS, Diane M; Barr Reeve HS; Montgomery, IN; NHS; OffAde; RptrYrbk; Yrbk; FHA; LatCl; Deaconess Hospital; Nurse.

SELLERS, Shane D; Central HS; Waterloo, IA; 34/360 ALBoysSt; Band; NatlFornLg; NHS; SchMus; SchPl; SctActv; StuGov; PresTchrAde; SptEdSchPpr; Bsbl; IMSpt; OptClAwd; CitAwd; Univ Of No Iowa; Education.

SELLERS, Thomas G; Chariton Comm HS; Chariton, IA; ALBoysSt; HonRl; NHS; StuCncl; RptrSchPpr; 4-H; Iowa St Univ; Zoology.

SELLS, Kathy E; Warsaw HS; Silver Lake, IN; ALAGirlsSt; PresChr; HonRl; SchMus; SchPl; StuCncl; YthFlsp; CaptChrldr; Anderson College.

SEVCIK, Kevin E; Northfield Sr HS; Northfield, MN; 13/255 TrsFrshCls; HonRl; NHS; StuCncl; Bsbl; Bsktbl; St Olaf College; Business.

SHAKE, Deena K; Cowan HS; Muncie, IN; ALAGirlsSt; HonRl; MrchBnd; NHS; RptrYrbk; 4-H; PresFHA; LetterBsktbl; LetterTrk; GAA; College; Pharmacy.

SHEETS, Michael D; Pocahontas Comm HS; Pocahontas, IA; TrsJrCls; VPSrCls; HonRl; PpCl; LetterFtbl;.

SHERIDAN, Kelly C; Hanover HS; Hanover, IL; 12/40 VPFrshCls; VPSophCls; PresJrCls; PresSrCls; Aud/Vis; ChrhWkr; StuCncl; StuGov; MthCl; LetterBsktbl; CaptFtbl; LetterTrk; IMSpt; University; Professional.

SHOEMAKER, Brenda L; Edison HS; East Gary, IN; 10/140 HonRl; JrNHS; SctActv; TchrAde; YthFlsp; SpnCl; PpCl; Bsktbl; Trk; Chrldr; GAA; Natl Honor Soc; Business Schl; Secretary.

SHOEMAKER, Cynthia R; Pennville HS; Bryant, IN; 8/40 SecFrshCls; SecSophCls; PresSrCls; ChrhWkr; HonRl; NHS; SchPl; StuCncl; Yrbk; GAA; DAR Good Citizen Award; Internatl Jr Bus Col; Secretarial.

SHUPE, Elizabeth A; Northrop HS; Fort Wayne, IN; Chr; HonRl; NatlFornLg; NatlThespSoc; SchMus; SchPl; StuGov; Teen; Tennis; College; Speech Pathology.

SHURTZ, Richard L; Waltonville HS; Waltonville, IL; 9/40 PresSophCls; PresJrCls; HonRl; PpCl; Bsbl; Bsktbl; Trk; College; Teacher.

SIEFERT, Janet Y; Heritage Christian HS; Brownsburg, IN; SecSophCls; Chr; ChrhWkr; HonRl; JrNHS; NHS; SchMus; College; Nursing.

SIENKIEWICZ, Meta E; Minot HS; Minot Afb, ND; Chr; HonRl; JrNHS; NatlMeritSF; SctActv; StuGov; RptrSchPpr; GerCl; MthCl; Texas A & M Univ; Meteorology.

SIMKO, Hilda M; Holy Redeemer HS; Detroit, MI; Chr; ChrhWkr; DrmMjrt; LbryAde; Carnegie Institute; Med Receptionist.

SIMMONS, David W; Lilbourn HS; Catron, MO; LbryAde; StuCncl;.

SIMON, Diane L; Calhoun HS; Hardin, IL; 8/76 Chrs; ChrhWkr; HonRl; NHS; OffAde; FHA; FTA; LetterTrk; GAA; DanFAwd; 4-HAwd; JAAwd; Trade School; Nurse.

SIMON, Leslee J; St Marys HS; Eagle Butte, SD; VPJrCls; ALAGirlsSt; Chrs; ChrhWkr; HonRl; PepBnd; 4-H; Trk; BttyCrckrAwd; Univ Of South Dakota; Medical Tech.

SIMONSON, Mark A; Black River Falls Sr HS; Black River Falls, WI; Band; ChrhWkr; HonRl; SctActv; RptrYrbk; 4-H; FFA; PresLatCl; Bsktbl; Ftbl; GodCntryAwd; Purdue Univ; Medicine.

SINCHAK, Michael E; Joliet Central HS; Joliet, IL; HonRl; LetterBsktbl; Ftbl; Swmmng; LetterTrk;.

SINEK, James J; Pomeroy Comm HS; Pomeroy, IA; 5/25 SecTrsFrshCls; VPSophCls; PresJrCls; HstSrCls; Band; ChrhWkr; CncrtBnd; HonRl; MrchBnd; PepBnd; StuCncl; RptrYrbk; LetterBsbl; LetterBsktbl; College.

SINOTTE, Brian J; Catholic Memorial HS; Waukesha, WI; ALBoysSt; Chr; Chrs; HonRl; Mdrgl; SchMus; SchPl; StuCncl;.

SITES, Terry J; Sullivan HS; Sullivan, MO; 1/185 HonRl; JrNHS; NHS; StuCncl; FrCl; PpCl; Bsktbl; Ftbl; Trk; University; Medicine.

SIZER, Brent B; Pacelli HS; Austin, MN; HonRl; College; Professional.

SJOSTRAND, Barry L; Lancaster HS; Hallock, MN; TrsJrCls; VPSrCls; ALBoysSt; Band; ChrhWkr; HonRl; SchPl; StuCncl; CaptBsktbl; CaptFtbl; Bible Institute; Religion.

SKELLY, Patrick T; De La Salle HS; Minneapolis, MN; 9/127 NHS; StuCncl; EdSchPpr; LetterBsktbl; LetterFtbl; St Thomas College.

SKELTON, John M; Rockville HS; Rockville, IN; Band; Chr; ChrhWkr; CmntyWkr; CncrtBnd; HonRl; MrchBnd; PepBnd; SctActv; YthFlsp; LatCl; SciCl; Bsbl; University; Lab Technician.

SKOMSKI, Sara E; Lutheran West HS; Detroit, MI; 12/184 Chr; NHS; SchPl; StuCncl; RptrYrbk; RptrSchPpr; PpCl; University; Latin.

SLAUTER, Thomas A; Muncie Northside HS; Muncie, IN; ChrhWkr; RptrSchPpr; LetterBsbl; Wrstlng; IMSpt; University; Business Admin.

SLAY, Calvin; Chadsey HS; Detroit, MI; SchPl; StuCncl; SchPpr; CaptTrk; College; Professional.

SLAYMAKER, Edward O; West Holt HS; Atkinson, NE; Chrs; SchMus; SchPl; SctActv; StuGov; RptrYrbk; EdSchPpr; FFA; Ftbl; Wrstlng; Trade School; Vocation.

SMARTT, Joann M; Roosevelt HS; Gary, IN; 8/608 ChrhWkr; HonRl; HospAde; NHS; RedCrAde; SctActv; EdSchPpr; FSA; FTA; College; Medicine.

SMIDT, Reggie R; Belmond Comm HS; Belmond, IA; VPSophCls; PresJrCls; Band; Chr; Chrs; ChrhWkr; CncrtBnd; HonRl; Mdrgl; MrchBnd; Bsbl; CaptBsktbl; Glf; Trk; Northwestern College; Education.

SMILEY, Donald V; George Washington Sr HS; Cedar Rapids, IA; 47/486 ALBoysSt; Aud/Vis; HonRl; JrNHS; NHS; NatlThespSoc; Quill&Scroll; SchMus; SchPl; StuGov; SpnCl; Socr; Trk; Goddard College; English.

SMITH, Arla M; Cadillac Sr HS; Cadillac, MI; HonRl; NHS; StuCncl; Davenport College Of Business; Accounting.

SMITH, Bonnie L; Unity HS; Mendon, IL; ALAGirlsSt; Chrs; MrchBnd; SchMus; Twrl; SpnCl; PpCl; Bsktbl; Trk; Trade School.

SMITH, Diana S; Jamaica HS; Sidell, IL; 10/48 HstJrCls; PresSrCls; CmntyWkr; HonRl; NHS; StuCncl; FHA; SpnCl; PpCl; Bsktbl; Trk;.

SMITH, Douglas B; Clinton Community HS; Clinton, IL; ChrhWkr; SchPl; SpnCl; PpCl; LetterFtbl; Trk; Wrstlng; College; Professional.

SMITH, Jackie J; Onrick R Xi HS; Orrick, MO; 10/40 Trade School; Agriculture.

SMITH, Mabla J; Trenton Sr HS; Trenton, MO; CncrtBnd; HonRl; HospAde; LbryAde; MrchBnd; NHS; University; Professional.

SMITH, Otho L; R 1 North Callaway HS; Kingdom City, MO; 16/77 PresJrCls; PresSrCls; HonRl; NHS; SchPl; StuCncl; PresFFA; CaptFtbl; Trk; CitAwd; Missouri Univ; Professional.

SMITH, Randy; Anderson Sr HS; Anderson, IN; 50/600 ALBoysSt; CtyCnl; CmntyWkr; HonRl; NHS; StuCncl; StuGov; FrCl; IMSpt; Ball St Univ; Architecture.

SMITH, Steven A; Waukegan E Campus HS; Waukegan, IL; 10/500 Band; CmntyWkr; JrNHS; NatlFornLg; NHS; PolWkr; TreasStuCncl; PresStuGov; LetterGlf; AmLegAwd; CitAwd; University; Law.

SMITH, Suzanne M; Barr Reeve HS; Loogootee, IN; PresJrCls; JrNHS; LbryAde; TreasNHS; OffAde; TreasLatCl; PpCl; University; Medicine.

SMITH, Thomas C; Niles Sr HS; Niles, MI; Band; CncrtBnd; HonRl; JA; MrchBnd; NHS; NatlThespSoc; PepBnd; SchMus; SchPl; SctActv; StuGov; Kalamazoo College; Foreign Service.

SNYDER, Perry R; South Knox HS; Wheatland, IN; ALBoysSt; HonRl; SctActv; MthCl; Bsbl; IMSpt; Indiana Univ; Medicine.

SOBOTKA, Thomas L; Scotus Central Catholic HS; Columbus, NE; 23/78 TrsSophCls; PresSrCls; HonRl; JrNHS; NHS; LetterBsktbl; LetterTrk; Univ Of Nebraska; Professional.

SOLIS, Eusebio; Albion Sr HS; Albion, MI; HonRl; Albion College; Law.

SOLOMON, Cynthia L; Fraser HS; Fraser, MI; CmntyWkr; StuCncl; FrCl; Macomb County Comm College; Secretary.

SOPKO, Michele M; Grant Comm HS; Ingleside, IL; 11/209 TrsSrCls; ALAGirlsSt; Chrs; ChrhWkr; CncrtBnd; NHS; SchMus; PresStuCncl; TchrAde; Chrldr; GAA; IMSpt; Daughters Of Amer Revolution; Natl Col Of Ed; Teacher.

SOUMIS, Paula K; Chassell HS; Chassell, MI; PresFrshCls; TrsSophCls; TrsJrCls; HonRl; SchAde; SchPl; TchrAde; FHA; PpCl; Business School; Secretary.

SPAIN, Jeffrey L; Oskaloosa Comm HS; Oskaloosa, IA; 14/200 College; Professional.

SPARKS, Nancy K; New Holland Middletown HS; Middletown, IL; 7/28 VPFrshCls; VPSophCls; VPJrCls; SecSrCls; Chrs; ChrhWkr; CmntyWkr; HonRl; SchMus; SchPl; StuCncl; Bsktbl; Tennis; GAA; E Illinois Univ; Medical Tech.

SPENCER, Cynthia G; Orchard Farm HS; St Charles, MO; Band; Chr; CncrtBnd; HonRl; MrchBnd; SchMus; Twrl; 4-H; MthCl; SciCl; Trade Schl; Professional.

SPIRK, Irmgard E; Red Bud Community Unit HS; Red Bud, IL; 1/119 Band; HonRl; NHS; StuCncl; RptrSchPpr; 4-H; Chrldr; AmLegAwd; 4-HAwd; University; Music.

SPOEDE, Micheal R; Warren County R 3 HS; Warrenton, MO; CaptTrk; College; Industrial Art.

SPRYSZAK, Gregory C; Berkley HS; Berkley, MI; Band; CncrtBnd; MrchBnd; PepBnd; RptrSchPpr; SchPpr; Glf; Wayne St Univ; Journalism.

STAFFORD, Michael S; High School; Iron River, MI; College; Professional.

STANGL, William M; Beaver Dam Sr HS; Beaver Dam, WI; 137/306 Chrs; CncrtBnd; Mdrgl; MrchBnd; PepBnd; SchMus; StuCncl; RptrSchPpr; Ftbl; Univ Of Wisconsin; Music.

STANTON, Joy L; Chaska Sr HS; Excelsior, MN; ChrhWkr; HonRl; NatlFornLg; NHS; SchPl; SchPpr; College; Medicine.

STARK, Bonnie K; Kimberly Sr HS; Kimberly, WI; 11/293 DrlTm; HonRl; NHS; RptrYrbk; PpCl; LetterGlf; Univ Of Wisconsin; Medicine.

STASTNY, Diane E; Boscobel HS; Fennimore, WI; HonRl; SchPpr; FrCl; Technical College; Respiratory Tech.

STEIL, Paul D; Scribner HS; Scribner, NE; 13/46 PresFrshCls; PresSophCls; PresJrCls; PresSrCls; ChrhWkr; NHS; SchPl; KeyCl; LetterBsktbl; CaptFtbl; LetterTrk; College; Professional.

STEINBRECHER, Margaret A; Notre Dame HS; Quincy, IL; Aud/Vis; Chrs; DrlTm; HospAde; LbryAde; StuCncl; University; Professional.

STE MARIE, Kathryn A; Lafayette HS; Red Lake Falls, MN; Band; Chrs; ChrhWkr; HonRl; HospAde; SchMus; StuCncl; 4-H; FHA; St Lukes Schl; Nursing.

STEWART, Cynthia C; Greenwood Comm HS; Greenwood, WI; VPFrshCls; TrsJrCls; ALAGirlsSt; Chrs; HonRl; Orch; SchMus; Twrl; YthFlsp; CaptChrldr; Miss Greenwood Festivals; Eau Claire Tech Inst; Data Processing.

STEWART, Robert A; Haven HS; Hutchinson, KS; CmntyWkr; HonRl; NHS; NatlMeritSchl; StuGov; TchrAde; RptrYrbk; MthCl; SciCl; Bsktbl; Swmmng; JAAwd; University; Veterinarian.

STICKLER, Gary W; Centerville HS; Centerville, IA; 21/150 HonRl; NHS; 4-H; FFA; CaptFtbl; 4-HAwd; CitAwd; College; Agriculture.

STIKLEY, Wendall S; Clarkston Sr HS; Clarkston, MI; 15/500 ALBoysSt; Band; CAP; HonRl; NHS; PepBnd; LatCl; MthCl; Glf;.

STOLLE, Barbara J; Silver Lake HS; Silver Lake, KS; Chrs; HonRl; HospAde; StuCncl; TchrAde; YthFlsp; RptrYrbk; SchPpr; 4-H; College; Medicine.

STONE, Bruce R; Illiopolis HS; Illiopolis, IL; 5/42 PresFrshCls; HonRl; NHS; TchrAde; FTA; LetterBsbl; CaptBsktbl; CaptFtbl; LetterTrk;.

STRALEY, Valerie J; Alden Hebron HS; Alden, IL; 24/42 HonRl; LbryAde; SchPl; TchrAde; CchngActv; University; Geology.

STRAVERS, Kyle J; Southeast Polk Jr Sr HS; Mitchellville, IA; ChrhWkr; CncrtBnd; HonRl; MrchBnd; NHS; PepBnd; SctActv; Tennis; Boys State; Pres Of Natl Honor Soc; Col; Professional.

STRIETER, Cheryl K; Brown City HS; Brown City, MI; TrsSophCls; SecJrCls; Band; HonRl; Twrl; FshEdYrbk; RptrSchPpr; FHA; FTA; Trade School; Vocation.

STUBBLEFIELD, Debra J; Odell Comm HS; Odell, IL; 2/33 SecJrCls; Band; Chr; Chrs; ChrhWkr; HonRl; YthFlsp; RptrYrbk; 4-H; FHA; FrCl; PpCl; CaptChrldr; GAA; High Honor Roll; Cheerleader Soph Jr Sr Yrs; Sec Jr Class; Yrbk Staff; French Club; Pep Club; Library Club; FHA; Math Award; Sci Award; Band; Chorus; Illinois St Univ; Home Economics.

STUDENY, Priscilla S; Valentine HS; Valentine, NE; Chrs; DrlTm; PpCl; College; Law.

STUDIE, Freddie L; Malden HS; Portageville, MO; 17/118 HonRl; So Baptist College; Education.

STUTESMAN, Benny A; Casey HS; Casey, IL; Trade School; Mechanic.

SUITER, Shawn P; Mccook Sr HS; Mccook, NE; CmntyWkr; TchrAde; RptrYrbk;.

SWANSON, Fredric A; Manual HS; Peoria, IL; 5/329 JA; NatlMeritCmnd; Bausch & Lombs Honor Sci Medal; Honor Student Award; CILCO Sci & Math Cert Of Achievement 1st Place Ribbon In Oral Competition On Limits At Isu; Invitational Math Contest; Math Assoc Of Amer Award 2nd Year; University; Biology.

SWART, Linda D; Grinnell HS; Oakley, KS; Band; PresChrs; ChrhWkr; HonRl; MrchBnd; PepBnd; TchrAde; Yrbk; PpCl; Chrldr; 2nd Place In Voice Democ Contest; Pres Of Chorus; Vice Pres Of Home Ec Club;.

SWARTZ, Cheryl A; Douglas Mac Arthur HS; Saginaw, MI; 22/275 HonRl; MrchBnd; NHS; NatlMeritCmnd; NatlThespSoc; SchPl; LetterBsbl; LetterBsktbl; Vol In Read; College; Veterinary.

SWITANEK, Monica A; St Mary Academy; Newport, MI; 3/150 Chr; Chrl; HonRl; ModUN; NHS; NatlMeritSF; SchMus; SciCl; University; Professional.

SYLVESTER, Joseph J; Premontre HS; Green Bay, WI; 5/123 HonRl; StuCncl; RptrSchPpr; LetterFtbl; Trk; IMSpt; College; Engineering.

SZUMLAS, Timothy J; Bishop Noll Inst HS; Chicago, IL; HonRl; RptrSchPpr; LetterTennis; Trk; College; Veterinarian.

SZYMIALIS, Richard A; Proctor HS; Duluth, MN; VPSrCls; Chrs; HonRl; SchPl; LetterBsbl; Bsktbl; CaptFtbl; IMSpt; RotaryAwd; St Johns Univ; Pharmacist.

T

TAKEHARA, Joann M; Maine Twp South HS; Park Ridge, IL; Chr; HonRl; JrNHS; NHS; NatlMeritSF; SecNatlThespSoc; SchPl; StuCncl; TchrAde; GAA; IMSpt; Natl Merit Finalist; Purdue Univ; Engineering.

TALIAFERRO, Mary H; Neillsville HS; Neillsville, WI; Chr; HonRl; LbryAde; Yrbk; 4-H; FBLA; SpnCl; PpCl; College; Nurse.

TANEY, Joseph W; Washington HS; St Paul, MN; 15/275 ALBoysSt; Chrs; HonRl; NatlMeritCmnd; Yrbk; CaptBsbl; Ftbl; IMSpt; Univ Of Minnesota; Dentist.

TAYLOR, Daniel B; Climax Scotts HS; Climax, MI; PresSophCls; PresBand; ChrhWkr; CncrtBnd; HonRl; MrchBnd; PepBnd; PresStuCncl; TchrAde; LetterBsbl; LetterBsktbl; LetterFtbl; LetterGlf; College; Indust Arts.

TAYLOR, Debra K; Calumet HS; Gary, IN; 2/305 Chr; ChrhWkr; HonRl; JrNHS; NHS; Purdue Univ; Business.

TAYLOR, Thomas J; Northern HS; Pontiac, MI; Bsktbl; College.

TAYNOR, Earl L; Civic Memorial HS; Bethalto, IL; 51/350 HstFrshCls; StuCncl; TchrAde; PpCl; Bsktbl; Ftbl; College.

THIELE, Eric W; Hinsdale Twp HS; Darien, IL; 1/463 AFS; HonRl; NHS; NatlMeritSF; SctActv; StuCncl; TchrAde; GerCl; Socr; Natl Merit Finalist; Usafa; Science.

THOMAS, Mary C; Colo Community HS; Colo, IA; VPFrshCls; TrsJrCls; SecSrCls; Band; Chrs; CncrtBnd; HonRl; MrchBnd; OffAde; SchMus; RptrYrbk; 4-H; FHA; PpCl; Mankato St Univ; Secretary.

THOMAS, Natalie J; Connersville HS; Connersville, IN; ChrhWkr; OffAde; Quill&Scroll; StuCncl; Yrbk; SptEdSchPpr; SpnCl; PresPpCl; LetterBsktbl; LetterTrk; GAA; IMSpt; College; Journalism.

THOMPSON, Brent W; Eagle Grove HS; Eagle Grove, IA; PresSophCls; PresJrCls; PresSrCls; ALBoysSt; Band; NHS; SctActv; Bsktbl; Glf; College.

THOMPSON, Jerrel A; Southwest HS; Saint Louis, MO; Aud/Vis; Chr; Chrl; Chrs; ChrhWkr; CmntyWkr; RedCrAde; SchAde; SchMus; SchPl; SctActv; TchrAde; FBLA; LetterBsktbl; College; Business Admin.

THOMPSON, Johnny W; Dixon HS; Dixon, MO; 8/65 Band; CncrtBnd; HonRl; MrchBnd; PepBnd; StuCncl; TchrAde; EdSchPpr; FTA; LetterBsbl; LetterBsktbl; AmLegAwd; DanFAwd; College; Physical Education.

THOMPSON, Richard D; Sumner HS; Kansas City, KS; Band; CAP; HonRl; MrchBnd; FDA; Bsktbl; Ftbl; Univ Of Arkansas; Medicine.

THORSTENSON, Anne E; Two Harbors HS; Two Harbors, MN; AFS; CmntyWkr; LitMag; NatlFornLg; SchPl; RptrYrbk; PpCl; College; Envir Biology.

THROCKMORTON, Mark D; Platteville HS; Platteville, WI; Aud/Vis; ChrhWkr; CncrtBnd; Mdrgl; MrchBnd; ModUN; Orch; PepBnd; SchMus; College; Psychology.

TIPPIN, Larry D; North Putnam HS; Bainbridge, IN; HonRl; SchMus; Pres4-H; FFA; SpnCl; MthCl; PpCl; LetterFtbl; LetterTrk; LetterWrstlng; IMSpt;.

TIPPIN, Rick A; Shelbyville HS; Shelbyville, IN; Band; CncrtBnd; MrchBnd; PepBnd; YthFlsp; CivCl; Bsbl;.

TORBERT, Garry L; Farmer City Mansfield HS; Farmer City, IL; AFS; CmntyWkr; HonRl; Yrbk; Bsbl; LetterBsktbl; Ftbl; Tennis; University; Engineering.

TRACY, Cindy S; Racine Lutheran HS; Racine, WI; HospAde; RptrYrbk; Yrbk; SchPpr; PpCl; University; Professional.

TRAFTON, Melody R; Richmond HS; Richmond, MO; .

TRAPHAGAN, Jan M; Little Falls Comm HS; Little Falls, MN; AFS; TchrAde; RptrYrbk; Yrbk; FHA; FrCl; College.

TRECARTIN, Candace L; Kingsford HS; Kingsford, MI; Chrs; ChrhWkr; CmntyWkr; HonRl; NatlFornLg; NHS; NatlMeritCmnd; NatlMeritSchl; SchAde; SchPl; TchrAde; YthFnd; No Michigan University.

TROYER, Pamela J; Bronson HS; Bronson, MI; 8/141 TreasBand; CncrtBnd; HonRl; MrchBnd; NHS; PepBnd; StuCncl; 4-H; CaptBsktbl; Trk; TreasGAA; Michigan St Univ; Medical Tech.

TRUCKLE, Gail A; Gladwin HS; Gladwin, MI; Chr; ChrhWkr; HonRl; LbryAde; TchrAde; SecFHA;.

TUFTE, Mark G; Northwood HS; Northwood, ND; TrsSrCls; Band; Chr; Chrs; ChrhWkr; CncrtBnd; HonRl; MrchBnd; PepBnd; SchPl; StuCncl; Bsbl; LetterBsktbl; LetterFtbl; Univ Of No Dakota; Engineering.

TURNEK, Edward H; Moberly Sr HS; Moberly, MO; Band; CncrtBnd; MrchBnd; PepBnd; KeyCl; College; Music.

TURZA, Carl S; Rantoul Twp HS; Gifford, IL; Band; ChrhWkr; CmntyWkr; CncrtBnd; DrlTm; MrchBnd; Sacrstn; LatCl; Ftbl; Chicago Med College; Medicine.

TWOMEY, Suellen K; Northwest HS; Grand Island, NE; 5/140 Chr; ChrhWkr; CmntyWkr; HonRl; LbryAde; NHS; NatlThespSoc; SchMus; SchPl; Brigham Young Univ; Drama.

TYJESKI, Cynthia L; Lincoln HS; Wisconsin Rapids, WI; Band; ChrhWkr; CncrtBnd; HonRl; MrchBnd; PepBnd; YthFlsp; FBLA; PpCl; Bsktbl; Trk; Chrldr; College; Business.

TYLER, Marlene C; Taylor HS; Kokomo, IN; 12/162 DrlTm; HonRl; NHS; PresStuCncl; TreasYthFlsp; EdYrBk; SptEdYrbk; SpnCl; PpCl; Trk; Chrldr; GAA; LionAwd; Indiana University; Nursing.

U

UNRUH, Brad J; Berean Academy; Valley Center, KS; Band; Chr; Chrs; CncrtBnd; SchPl; Yrbk; 4-H; SciCl; Bsbl; Bsktbl; Ftbl; Socr; LetterTrk; College; Professional.

UNZICKER, Theresa E; El Paso HS; El Paso, IL; AFS; ChrhWkr; CmntyWkr; HonRl; SctActv; FHA; SpnCl; College; Nursing.

V

VAN BEEK, Edward P; St Johns Premonic HS; Green Bay, WI; HstJrCls; VPSrCls; Chr; CtyCnl; HonRl; StuGov; KeyCl; St Thomas College.

VANDAL, Brenda L; Rolla Public HS; Rolla, ND; 2/35 PresJrCls; VPSrCls; ALAGirlsSt; PresBand; SchPl; SecStuCncl; EdYrBk; VPFHA; LetterBsktbl; LetterTrk; GAA; BttyCrckrAwd; North Dakota St Univ; Mathematics.

VANDIVER, Juliuse W; Phillipsburg HS; Glade, KS; PolWkr; Bsktbl; Ftbl; Vocational Tech Schl; Mechanic.

VAN OTEGHEM, Teresa M; Three Lakes HS; Eagle River, WI; 3/44 TrsSophCls; Chr; Chrl; Chrs; ChrhWkr; CmntyWkr; HonRl; NatlMeritFnl; NatlMeritCmnd; NatlMeritSchl; NatlMeritSF; Trk; IMSpt; Technical Inst; Secretary.

VAN SITTERT, Jeanne M; De Soto HS; De Soto, KS; PresSophCls; Band; DrmBgl; HonRl; NHS; OffAde; TreasStuCncl; Yrbk; SchPpr; FBLA; PpCl; Bsktbl; Glf; LetterTrk; Emporia St Teachers College; Photography.

VAN ZUIDEN, Paula K; Fulton HS; Fulton, IL; Chrs; ChrhWkr; HonRl; HospAde; Mdrgl; NatlThespSoc; StuCncl; FTA; SciCl; Wrstlng; College; Nursing.

VENTRESS, Doreen; Benton Harbor HS; Benton Harbor, MI; ChrhWkr; HonRl; LbryAde; CaptChrldr;.

VIECK, Thomas G; Lincoln HS; Vincennes, IN; 61/328 ChrhWkr; YthFnd; Bsbl; Bsktbl; Vincennes Univ; Electronics.

VINCENT, Louzetta; Crothersville HS; Crothersville, IN; 19/75 DrlTm; HonRl; OffAde; Beauty College.

VITALE, Joseph M; St Marys HS; St Louis, MO; LetterBsbl; LetterFtbl; LetterSocr; University; Physical Educ.

VOJCIHOSKI, Kathleen A; Menominee HS; Menominee, MI; Band; Chr; Chrs; CncrtBnd; DrmBgl; HonRl; MrchBnd; PepBnd; SchMus; College; Professional.

VOLTZ, Roger H; Wauwatosa East HS; Wauwatosa, WI; TrsFrshCls; ALBoysSt; HonRl; JrNHS; NHS; SchMus; StuCncl; SchPpr; Wrstlng; AmLegAwd; College.

VON FELDT, Paige A; Derham Hall HS; St Paul, MN; 50/148 Chrs; SchMus; StuCncl; StuGov; SpnCl; LetterFtbl; CaptSwmmng; CaptChrldr; CchngActv; GAA; CaptIMSpt; PPFtbl; College; Physical Educ.

VRIELING, Burton J; West Ottawa HS; Holland, MI; 85/276 Band; Chr; CncrtBnd; HonRl; Mdrgl; MrchBnd; 4-H; SecFrCl; PpCl; Davenport College; Business.

W

WAGGONER, Robin L; Montgomery Rii HS; New Florence, MO; Band; Chr; ChrhWkr; CmntyWkr; CncrtBnd; HonRl; HospAde; MrchBnd; PolWkr; StuCncl; Bsbl; Bsktbl; IMSpt; William Jewell College; Nursing.

WAGNER, Jo Ann; Mendota HS; Mendota, IL; 2/200 SecTrsSrCls; Band; Chr; CncrtBnd; DrmMjrt; HonRl; MrchBnd; NHS; PepBnd; StuCncl; Twrl; FNA; SpnCl; Jr College; Data Processing.

WAGNER, Lyle D; Turtle Lake Mercer HS; Turtle Lake, ND; 3/40 ChrhWkr; CmntyWkr; HonRl; StuCncl; College; Vocation.

WAGONER, Steven D; Porta HS; Petersburg, IL; 11/131 VPFrshCls; Band; Chrs; ChrhWkr; CmntyWkr; CncrtBnd; HonRl; JA; JrNHS; LbryAde; MrchBnd; Ftbl; IMSpt; Kansas St Univ; Agriculture.

WAGONER, Timothy R; Rochester Comm HS; Rochester, IN; PresJrCls; HonRl; 4-H; CaptBsbl; Bsktbl; Ftbl;.

WAHL, Bruce E; Marshall Sr HS; Marshall, MN; 27/240 HonRl; SpnCl; MthCl; SciCl; Bsktbl; LetterFtbl; LetterTrk; IMSpt; Moorhead St College; Veterinarian.

WAITE, William T; Berkley HS; Huntington Woods, MI; IntrClCncl; SciCl; Univ Of Michigan; Psychology.

WALDROP, Terry A; Caruthersville HS; Caruthersville, MO; Band; CncrtBnd; DrlTm; HonRl; MrchBnd; PepBnd; PolWkr; SchMus; SctActv; TchrAde; FTA; CchngActv; IMSpt;.

WALKER, Barbara L; Wellsville HS; Wellsville, KS; 7/65 PresSophCls; Band; Chrs; HonRl; NHS; SptEdSchPpr; PpCl; LetterTrk; Chrldr; Ottawa University.

WALKER, Christina E; Gasconade Co HS; Owensville, MO; 19/119 HonRl; NHS; StuCncl; VPYthFlsp; EdSchPpr; LetterBsktbl; VPGAA; IMSpt; Deaconess Hospital Schl; Nursing.

WALKER, Gale D; Warren Twp HS; Libertyville, IL; Chrs; DrlTm; HonRl; SchMus; StuCncl; 4-H; GAA; IMSpt; PPFtbl; DanFAwd; 4-HAwd; Jr College; Agriculture.

WALKER, Tanya L; Arthur HS; Arthur, IL; 12/50 ALAGirlsSt; DrlTm; HonRl; HospAde; SchPl; StuCncl; Yrbk; FHA; FNA; College; Nursing.

WALLERSTEIN, Daniel E; Central HS; Bay City, MI; 10/518 Chr; HonRl; PresNHS; Orch; StuCncl; TchrAde; VPGerCl; Ftbl; College; Medicine.

WALTER, Gary T; United Comm HS; Luther, IA; ALBoysSt; SchPl; SctActv; StuCncl; TchrAde; YthFlsp; PpCl; LetterBsktbl; LetterFtbl; LetterTrk; CchngActv; Iowa Central Jr College; Tele Communication.

WANGEN, Pamela J; Mankato East HS; Mankato, MN; 36/224 Band; CncrtBnd; DrlTm; HonRl; College; Veterinarian.

WANZO, Warren D; Milwaukee Custer HS; Milwaukee, WI; Chr; CmntyWkr; HonRl; JrNHS; NatlMeritFnl; NatlMeritCmnd; SchAde; Bsktbl; Socr; Trk; College; Professional.

WARNE, Robert E; North Newton HS; Roselawn, IN; Band; CmntyWkr; CncrtBnd; MrchBnd; 4-H; Bsktbl; LetterTrk; College; Professional.

WARREN, Cynthia G; Granite City South HS; Granite City, IL; Chr; Chrs; HonRl; JrNHS; NHS; SctActv; StuCncl; FBLA; PpCl; SciCl; Bsktbl; GAA; College; Law.

WATERS, John A; Pittsfield HS; Baylis, IL; 2/130 HonRl; NatlMeritCmnd; PolWkr; SctActv; LatCl; MthCl; SciCl; Swmmng; LetterTrk; GodCntryAwd; Quincy College; Medicine.

WATSON, Michael J; Macomb Sr HS; Macomb, IL; Band; Chr; HonRl; NHS; SpnCl; Western Illinois Univ; Conservatory.

WEAVER, Denise A; Oconomowoc HS; Oconomowoc, WI; AFS; HonRl; JrNHS; NHS; NatlMeritSF; RptrSchPpr; SchPpr; Natl Merit Finalist; Wheaton College; Writing.

WEAVER, Martha J; Harrisonville Sr HS; Harrisonville, MO; AFS; Chrs; ChrhWkr; CmntyWkr; HonRl; NatlFornLg; Quill&Scroll; SchPl; SctActv; RptrSchPpr; Chrldr; CchngActv; PPFtbl; Univ Of Missouri; Journalism.

WEBB, Gisele L; Ladywood St Agnes HS; Indianapolis, IN; Chrs; ChrhWkr; DrmBgl; JA; SchPl; GAA; Taylor Univ; Law.

WEBBER, Debra S; Highland HS; Highland, KS; Band; Chr; DrmMjrt; MrchBnd; SchMus; SchPl; StuCncl; Twrl; SchPpr; Highland Comm Jr College; Business.

WEDGE, June A; Port Huron Central HS; Goodells, MI; 14/218 HonRl; NHS; Quill&Scroll; StuCncl; SchPpr; St Clair County Comm College; Accounting.

WEHR, Brenda J; Jasper HS; Jasper, IN; ChrhWkr; LbryAde; SctActv; Treas4-H; CchngActv; 4-HAwd; Trade Schl; Interior Design.

WEIGEL, Catherine L; Carmel HS; Carmel, IN; 8/523 TrsSrCls; SecCncrtBnd; HonRl; MrchBnd; NHS; NatlMeritSF; StuGov; YthFlsp; GerCl; GAA; Natl Merit Schlship Finalist; Purdue Univ; Engineering.

WELDEN, Dale R; Lane Tech HS; Chicago, IL; 420/1150 ChrhWkr; OffAde; SchMus; SchPl; Yrbk; Concordia Teachers College; Liberal Arts.

WELSH, Cynthia L; Barrington HS; Barrington, IL; HonRl; StuCncl; StuGov; SpnCl; CaptChrldr; GAA; College.

WESLEY, Sarah R; Waynesville Sr HS; Waynesville, MO; 13/255 Chr; HonRl; JrNHS; NHS; StuCncl; StuGov; EdYrBk; RptrSchPpr; FHA; PpCl; Chrldr; GAA; IMSpt; Univ Of Missouri; Journalism.

WESSNER, Daniel W; Glenbrook South HS; Glenview, IL; 1/589 PresSophCls; HonRl; PresNHS; Quill&Scroll; StuCncl; StuGov; RptrSchPpr; SchPpr; PresKeyCl; PpCl; Trk; CchngActv; ChmbCommrsAwd; Glenview Youth Award; Princeton Univ; Law.

WESTMAAS, Robin S; No Michigan Christian HS; Marion, MI; 1/40 Chr; ChrhWkr; HonRl; NatlMeritCmnd; PresStuCncl; YthFlsp; 4-H; LetterBsktbl; Trk; IMSpt; College; Education.

WEYHRICH, Dennis G; Delavan HS; Delavan, IL; HonRl; SchPl; StuCncl; Pres4-H; PresFFA; Wrstlng; IMSpt; 4-HAwd; Illinois Central College; Mechanic.

WHALEN, Catherine C; Routt HS; Waverly, IL; SecFrshCls; Chrs; StuCncl; FNA; TreasSpnCl; Chrldr; Honor Roll; Member Missions Club; St Marys Of Notre Dame; Paramedic Field.

WHEELER, Daniel D; Elwood Public HS; Elwood, NE; Band; ChrhWkr; HonRl; NHS; SctActv; YthFlsp; LetterBsktbl; LetterFtbl; LetterTrk; GodCntryAwd; Univ Of Nebraska; Pilot.

WHITELEY, Douglas A; Geneva HS; Geneva, NE; Chr; Chrs; HonRl; LbryAde; Mdrgl; SchMus; SchPl; YthFlsp; RptrYrbk; 4-H; GerCl; Bsktbl; LetterFtbl; LetterGlf; Univ Of Nebraska; Dentist.

WHITELEY, Julie R; Miller HS; Ash Grove, MO; HstJrCls; HstSrCls; PresChr; Chrs; ChrhWkr; HonRl; OffAde; SchPl; StuCncl; RptrSchPpr; Bsbl; Bsktbl; Glf; Trk; College; Singing.

WHITTAKER, Rhonda L; Charlestown HS; Charlestown, IN; HonRl; TchrAde; RptrSchPpr; SchPpr; TreasFTA; LatCl; PpCl; SciCl; Se Indiana Univ; Journalism.

WHITWORTH, Anne K; Kenwood HS; Chicago, IL; 28/420 Band; CncrtBnd; HonRl; NatlMeritCmnd; Orch; SchMus; Illinois St Univ; Music Therapy.

WICKE, Cynthia J; Wauneta Public HS; Wauneta, NE; ALAGirlsSt; Band; Chr; DrmMjrt; HonRl; TrsFrshCls; VPStuCncl; RptrYrbk; RptrSchPpr; 4-H; 4-HAwd; Gold Medal Band Award; Outstanding Sr Athlete; Kearney State College.

WICKER, Brent E; Lake View Auburn HS; Lake View, IA; 12/44 HonRl; SchPl; Bsktbl; Ftbl; Glf; College; Professional.

WIELER, Jilaine F; Butterfield Odin HS; Mountain Lake, MN; 6/28 SecSrCls; Band; Chr; ChrhWkr; CncrtBnd; HonRl; Mdrgl; MrchBnd; SchPl; VPStuCncl; EdYrBk; RptrSchPpr; FHA; BttyCrckrAwd; Trade School; X Ray Tech.

WIENS, Glenn A; Mt Lake Public HS; Mt Lake, MN; Aud/Vis; Chr; HonRl; NHS; StuCncl; Bsktbl; Ftbl; Trk; College; Elec Tech.

WIERZ, John K; Rolling Meadows HS; Arlington Hts, IL; 68/546 Band; CncrtBnd; DrmMjrt; MrchBnd; NHS; PepBnd; SchMus; LetterFtbl; Milikin Univ; Microbiology.

WIGGERS, Timothy E; Morton HS; Morton, IL; 9/287 VPSrCls; HonRl; NHS; StuCncl; RptrSchPpr; Ftbl; CaptTennis; JETSAwd; University Of Illinois; Engineering.

WIGGINS, James H; Argenta Oreana HS; Oreana, IL; Band; CncrtBnd; HonRl; MrchBnd; SchMus; SchPl; StuCncl; YthFlsp; RptrYrbk; FrCl; Trade Schl; Railroad.

WILDERMUTH, Ann R; J D Darnall Sr HS; Geneseo, IL; Band; ChrhWkr; CncrtBnd; HonRl; HospAde; JA; MrchBnd; NHS; PepBnd; 4-H; FNA; GAA; Augustana College; Business.

WILIE, David L; Marion HS; Marion, WI; HonRl; Bsktbl; Ftbl; College.

WILKERSON, James W; Anderson HS; Anderson, IN; HonRl; StuCncl; LatCl; College.

WILLEY, Rick E; Fulton HS; Albany, IL; Band; ChrhWkr; CncrtBnd; HonRl; PepBnd; LetterBsktbl; College; Professional.

WILLIAMS, Deborah A; Laboure HS; St Louis, MO; Chr; Chrs; ChrhWkr; CmntyWkr; HonRl; HospAde; SchMus; SchPl; Columbia College; Nursing.

WILLIAMS, Frank E; John Marshall HS; Indianapolis, IN; 44/444 Chr; HonRl; PresJA; NHS; NatlMeritCmnd; Quill&Scroll; SchPl; SchPpr; FrCl; Wrstlng; Indiana Univ; Physicist.

WILLIAMS, Robert L; Sumner HS; St Louis, MO; Chr; Chrs; ChrhWkr; JA; SchMus; SchPl; TchrAde; Teen; YthFlsp; College; Music.

WILLIAMS, Wilma S; Visitation HS; Chicago, IL; Band; Chr; HonRl; OffAde; SchMus; SchPl; StuCncl; StuGov; TchrAde; RptrSchPpr; 4-H; FrCl; De Paul Univ; Nursing.

WILLIAMSON, Annette; Merrillville; Merrillville, IN; HonRl; Pres4-H; 4-HAwd; Natl Honor Soc; College; Veterinarian.

WILSON, Julie M; Central HS; Aberdeen, SD; AFS; DrlTm; HonRl; LbryAde; TchrAde; PpCl; Trk; College; Professional.

WILSON, Mildred A; Santa Fe HS; Waverly, MO; 6/42 SecJrCls; ALAGirlsSt; CmntyWkr; HonRl; SchPl; StuGov; FHA; SpnCl; PpCl; VPSciCl; University; Law.

WILSTERMANN, Steven G; Mayo HS; Rochester, MN; 53/465 ChrhWkr; HonRl; NHS; YthFlsp; LetterBsktbl; Glf; IMSpt; College; Mechan Engineering.

WILT, Leslie O; South Shelby HS; Shelbina, MO; Band; Chr; Chrs; ChrhWkr; CncrtBnd; HonRl; Mdrgl; MrchBnd; NHS; SchMus; LetterFtbl; IMSpt; DanFAwd; 4-HAwd; University; Agriculture.

WINEBRENNER, Melvin E; East Des Moines HS; Des Moines, IA; Aud/Vis; SchPpr; Iowa St Univ; Forestry.

WINKELMAN, Stephen E; Sacred Heart HS; Salina, KS; VPSophCls; ALBoysSt; Chrs; CmntyWkr; HonRl; JA; JCC; StuCncl; SptEdSchPpr; FBLA; KeyCl; SpnCl; Bsbl; College; Accounting.

WIRTZ, Charles E; Lake City HS; Lake City, IA; 4/64 ALBoysSt; HonRl; NHS; EdSchPpr; Bsktbl; Ftbl; Trk; Univ Of Iowa; Biology.

WITT, Richard B; Omaha Benson HS; Omaha, NE; PresJrCls; HonRl; LbryAde; NatlMeritSF; OffAde; SctActv; LetterWrstlng; NCTE; Us Air Force Academy; Engineering.

WITTER, Michael D; Wausau East HS; Wausau, WI; LetterFtbl; LetterSwmmng; LetterTennis; College; Teacher.

WOLCOTT, Jeri A; New Monroe Comm HS; Monroe, IA; TrsSrCls; Chr; HonRl; HospAde; StuCncl; PresYthFlsp; SecFHA; Trk; Chrldr; VP4-HAwd; Uni; Elementary Ed.

WOLL, Linda R; Columbia City Joint HS; Columbia City, IN; Chr; HonRl; NHS; PresYthFlsp; Pres4-H; PresFHA; Trk; 4-HAwd; Business Schl; Secretary.

WOLVERTON, Jeffrey D; Clarksville HS; Clarksville, IN; 3/150 ALBoysSt; Band; JrNHS; NHS; NatlMeritCmnd; StuCncl; LetterBsbl; Bsktbl; CaptFtbl; IMSpt; Hanover College; Medicine.

WOMACK, Thomas L; Warsaw HS; Warsaw, IN; 91/358 Chr; JA; RptrSchPpr; FDA; Ftbl; Trk; College; Medicine.

WOODS, Patti G; J F Kennedy HS; Babbitt, MN; 28/144 Chr; Chrl; ChrhWkr; HonRl; NHS; OffAde; SchMus; CaptSwmmng; GAA; College; Legal Admin.

WOODWARD, Mary E; St Joseph Academy; Green Bay, WI; Chrs; ChrhWkr; HospAde; SchAde; StuCncl; StuGov; TchrAde; RptrSchPpr; FrCl; Bsktbl; Swmmng; Tennis; PPFtbl; College.

WOOLSEY, David; Cabrini HS; Allen Park, MI; 34/140 Aud/Vis; HonRl; NatlMeritSchl; Quill&Scroll; RptrYrbk; SptEdYrbk; RptrSchPpr; EdSchPpr; SptEdSchPpr; Bsbl; CaptGlf; LetterTrk;.

WORDEN, Marty D; Union HS; Dowagiac, MI; Band; ChrhWkr; HonRl; SchPl; SpnCl; Bsbl; LetterWrstlng; College; Art.

WORF, Mark E; Soctt Comm HS; Scott City, KS; 46/103 Band; Chr; Chrl; Chrs; HonRl; PepBnd; SchMus; SchPl; 4-H; IMSpt; College; Music.

WRIGHT, Bradley D; Cobden Unit HS; Cobden, IL; 8/48 PresFrshCls; ChrhWkr; SchPl; VPStuCncl; RptrSchPpr; EdSchPpr; SptEdSchPpr; LatCl; PresSciCl; Bsbl; Bsktbl; CchngActv; So Illinois University.

Y

YAX, Marie L; Cass City HS; Deford, MI; Chr; ChrhWkr; LbryAde; SctActv; TchrAde; YthFlsp; 4-H; FTA; College.

YOCUM, Rebecca S; Memorial HS; Joplin, MO; AFS; ChrhWkr; JrNHS; NHS; SctActv; YthFlsp; Yrbk; Glf; Chrldr; GAA; PPFtbl; College.

YOST, Steven M; Holdrege HS; Holdrege, NE; PresFrshCls; VPJrCls; Band; Chrs; ChrhWkr; SchMus; StuCncl; Bsktbl; Ftbl; Trk; College; Liberal Arts.

YOUNG, Clarence B; Parker HS; Chicago, IL; ChrhWkr; CtyCnl; HonRl; ModUN; OffAde; StuCncl; RptrYrbk; EdSchPpr; SptEdSchPpr; Univ Of Illinois; Medicine.

YOUNG, Daniel L; Marshall HS; Chicago, IL; Trade School.

YOUNT, Sandra J; Frankfort HS; Elberta, MI; SecTrsFrshCls; VPSophCls; Band; Chr; HonRl; HospAde; LbryAde; MrchBnd; YthFlsp; FHA; Northwestern Michigan College; Nursing.

Z

ZAREMBA, Julie A; Lincoln HS; Centerline, MI; HonRl; JrNHS; NHS; StuCncl; PpCl; LetterChrldr; PPFtbl; College; Professional.

ZELNIS, Charles R; Marist HS; Evergreen Park, IL; 15/393 ChrhWkr; HonRl; JrNHS; NHS; SchPl; RptrSchPpr; SpnCl; TreasPpCl; IMSpt; Air Force Academy; Intl Affairs.

ZILA, Rose M; Marquette HS; Michigan City, IN; DrmBgl; HonRl; JA; OffAde; SchMus; SchPl; RptrSchPpr; Swmmng; DARAwd; JAAwd; College; Accounting.

ZITNIK, Charles L; Liberal HS; Liberal, KS; Chrl; CmntyWkr; HospAde; OffAde; RedCrAde; TchrAde; FTA; College; Professional.

ZOMER, Annette F; George Community HS; Doon, IA; Chrs; HonRl; LbryAde; SchMus; StuCncl; SchPpr;.

ZOROMSKI, Paula A; Thorp HS; Thorp, WI; Band; Chr; HonRl; Mdrgl; SchMus; SchPl; 4-H; LetterBsktbl; Trk; LetterChrldr; GAA; IMSpt; 4-HAwd; Univ Of Wisconsin; Music.

ZUCK, Kimberlee A; Lanark HS; Chadwick, IL; 14/55 Chr; Chrs; HonRl; SchMus; VPYthFlsp; 4-H; FHA; GAA; 4-HAwd; Rock Valley College; Dental Asst.

ZWIEFELHOFER, Danita R; Bloomer HS; Bloomer, WI; Band; CncrtBnd; HonRl; MrchBnd; PepBnd; SchPl; 4-H; FBLA; FHA; SciCl; Trade Schl; Secretary.

ZYGARLICKE, Wayne P; Columbus HS; Marshfield, WI; Chr; Chrs; HonRl; SchPl; LetterFtbl; LetterTrk; IMSpt; Trade School.

A

Aadland Lorne A
Veblen Public HS
Veblen SD

Aaron Robert J
Niles North HS
Skokie IL

Abaravicius Alice A
St Augustine HS
Chicago IL

Abascal Bryan K
Bishop Noll HS
E Chicago IN

Abbey Barbara L
Corning Community; Hs
Bridgewater IA

Abbey Gentra L
Dodge City Sr HS
Dodge City KS

Abbott Donna
St Agnes Acad
Alliance NE

Abbott Mark R
John F Kennedy HS
Bloomington MN

Abbott Marta L
Hoopeston East Lynn HS
Hoopeston IL

Abbott Thomas R
Hammond HS
Hammond IN

Abel Bette J
Maries R Ii HS
Belle MO

Abel Susan L
Maries County Rii HS
Belle MO

Abele Mary K
Dearborn HS
Dearborn MI

Abell Carol A
Chester HS
Chester IL

Abell William R
South Hamilton Comm HS
Ellsworth IA

Abella Michael J
Girard HS
Girard KS

Aberle Jeanette S
Troy HS
Troy KS

Abernathy Nancy C
Buhler HS
Hutchinson KS

Ableman Gail K
Craig Sr HS
Jonesville WI

Ables John E
E G Edison HS
East Gary IN

Abourezk Susan R
Stevens HS
Rapid City SD

Aboussie Joyce A
St Josephs Academy
St Louis MO

Abramovich Connie L
Manitowoc Lutheran HS
Manitowoc WI

Abramson David P
New Trier West HS
Wilmette IL

Absil Robert P
Arlington HS
Arlington Heights IL

Acevedo Anita M
Central HS
Omaha NE

Acey Sherry J
Chaffee HS
Chaffee MO

Achman Beverly M
Mt Iron HS
Iron MN

Acker Barbara T
Rib Lake HS
Rib Lake WI

Ackerman Linda G
Willowbrook HS
Villa Park IL

Ackerman Paula J
Lincoln HS
Lincoln KS

Ackerson Steven E
Ionia HS
Ionia MI

Ackerson Tanya L
Bowdle Public HS
Bowdle SD

Acord Robert E
Marion HS
Marion IN

Acri Robert C
New Trier East HS
Wilmette IL

Acton Larry A
Turner HS
Kansas City KS

Adair Carolyn R
Platte Co R 3 HS
Platte City MO

Adair Chanda L
Laura Speed Elliot HS
Boonville MO

Adamczyk Mary Kay M
Streator Twp HS
Streator IL

Adams Ann E
Bishop Dwenger HS
Fort Wayne IN

Adams Brenda J
Hallsville HS
Columbia MO

Adams Cathy
Polo HS
Polo MO

Adams Charles E
South Knox HS
Wheatland IN

Adams Charles V
Spring Hill HS
Spring Hill KS

Adams Cindy L
Pontiac HS
Pontiac IL

Adams Curtis R
Carl Sandburg HS
Palos Park IL

Adams Cynthia L
Hume HS
Hume MO

Adams Daniel R
Watertown Senior HS
Watertown SD

Adams Daryl S
Harlan HS
Chicago IL

Adams David E
Metz HS
Rich Hill MO

Adams Doug D
Vandalia Comm HS
Vandalia IL

Adams Douglas M
Waukesha So HS
Waukesha WI

Adams Gail B
Erskine HS
Erskine MN

Adams Gregory M
Newton HS
Newton IA

Adams Janice J
Greenwood HS
Greenwood IN

Adams Jerry R
Nishna Valley HS
Emerson IA

STUDENTS PHOTOGRAPH SCHEDULED FOR PUBLICATION HERE COULD NOT BE REPRODUCED

Adams Karla B
Concordia Academy
St Paul MN

Adams Patricia A
E Peoria Community HS
Morton IL

Adams Patricia A
Oskaloosa HS
Oskaloosa KS

Adams Roger G
Wausau West HS
Wausau WI

Adams Sandy K
Shawnee HS
Mc Clure IL

Adams Sarah J
Norwell HS
Markle IN

Adams Scott R
Robinson HS
Robinson IL

Adams Teresa A
New Palestine HS
New Palestine IN

Adamson Randy G
Geneseo HS
Geneseo KS

Addington Philip J
Marias Des Cygnes HS
Seneca MO

Addy Robert D
Farragut Comm School;
Imogene IA

Aden Donald L
Neillsville HS
Neillsville WI

Aden Julie B
Illinois Valley Central HS
Chillicothe IL

Adix Paul K
Ogden Community Sch
Ogden IA

Adkins Susan D
Savannah HS
Savannah MO

Adkisson Timothy A
East Prairie HS
East Prairie MO

Adlam Bobbi J
Unionville Sebewaing Area HS
Unionville MI

Adolph Randy L
Farmington Sr HS
Farmington MO

Adolphson Karen D
Galesburg Sr HS
Galesburg IL

Adreon Gary F
Eddyville Comm HS
Eddyville IA

Aeikens Norine A
Raymond HS
Raymond MN

Aerts Pam A
East De Pere HS
De Pere WI

Aeschliman Rick J
Perry Lecompton HS
Topeka KS

Afable Mark V
Clifton Central HS
Clifton IL

Agar Timothy G
Browns Valley Public HS
Browns Valley MN

Aglinskas Peter R
St Laurence HS
Chicago IL

Agnew Candace A
University City Sr HS
University City MO

Agostinelli Maria
South Lake HS
East Detroit MI

Agosto Cheryle A
Neodesha HS
Altoona KS

Agran Raymond D
New Trier West HS
Wilmette IL

Ahern Craig L
Truman Public HS
Lewisville MN

Ahl Joanne M
J F K Prep HS
Green Bay WI

Ahlborn Scott E
Bloom Township HS
Chicago Hts IL

Ahlgrim Scott A
York Comm HS
Elmhurst IL

Ahlgrimm John R
Mineral Point HS
Mineral Point WI

Ahrens Rhonda L
Paynesville HS
Paynesville MN

Airgood Kristopher C
Manchester HS
N Manchester IN

Aitchison Neil J
Western Dubuque HS
Cascade IA

Aitken Lyle W
Sparta HS
Sparta IL

Akeman Susan B
Slater HS
Slater MO

Aker Sharon K
Slinger HS
Slinger WI

Akers Michael W
Crispus Attucks HS
Indianapolis IN

Akers Steve C
Paris HS
Holliday MO

Akers Toni C
North Central HS
Shelburn IN

Alander Dirk H
Plainfield HS
Plainfield IL

Alarie Peggy S
Kearsley HS
Flint MI

Albaugh Kevin L
Hillsdale HS
Hillsdale MI

Alberson Sharon K
Valley Center HS
Valley Center KS

Albertson Kerry T
Humboldt HS
Humboldt IA

Albin Rosanne A
Caro Comm HS
Caro MI

Albrecht Kenneth J
Messmer HS
Milwaukee WI

Albregts Christine L
Frontier HS
Brookston IN

Albright Mike A
Monroe Sr HS
Monroe WI

Albright Richard J
St Edmond HS
Fort Dodge IA

Alby Toni M
St Marys HS
Burlington WI

Alcorn Kathy L
Beardstown HS
Beardstown IL

Alden Belinda G
Central City Comm HS
Central City IA

Alden Johnie D
Penney HS
Hamilton MO

Alderfer Terri R
Tippecanoe Valley HS
Mentone IN

Aldred Jama L
Switzerland Co HS
Vevay IN

Aldrich Lori L
Chesaning HS
Oakley MI

Aldrich Winifred M
Harper Creek HS
Battle Creek MI

Aldridge Dawn V
Rantool Township HS
Rantoul IL

Alea Peter M
Proviso West HS
Northlake IL

Alexander Merle G
Blue Hill Community HS
Blue Hill NE

Alexander Norman C
Freeport Sr HS
Freeport IL

Alfredson Carl I
Norway HS
Norway MI

Alger Michael D
Spencer HS
Spencer IA

Aljets Dawn R
Edwardsville HS
Dorsey IL

Allaben Elizabeth A
North Farmington HS
Farmington Hills MI

Allard Lesley
Bennett County HS
Martin SD

Allee Douglas L
Sheridan Rii HS
Sheridan MO

Allegar Steve C
Maine South HS
Park Ridge IL

Alleger Richard P
Northrop HS
Fort Wayne IN

Alleman Janeen R
Putnam County HS
Magnola IL

Allen Barbara A
Pardeeville HS
Pardeeville WI

Allen Betty L
Paxton Cons HS
Paxton NE

Allen Daniel P
Lewis Central HS
Council Bluffs IA

Allen Debra J
Plainfield HS
Mooresville IN

Allen Elizabeth A
Central Catholic HS
Grand Island NE

Allen Garold R
St Rita HS
Oak Park IL

Allen Howard L
Powhattan HS
Horton KS

Allen James L
Eldorado HS
Eldorado IL

Allen Janel M
Rudyard HS
Kincheloe Afb MI

Allen Janet K
Lutheran North HS
St Louis MO

Allen Jeffrey W
Sts Peter & Paul Seminary
Port Huron MI

Allen Jennifer L
Purdy R Ii HS
Purdy MO

Allen Kelly A
Appleton HS
Appleton WI

Allen Kim R
Bishop Mc Namara HS
St Anne IL

Allen Larry D
Wawasee HS
Syracuse IN

Allen Mary J
South Page HS
Bedford IA

Allen Nellie L
Meridian HS
Pulaski IL

Allen Paul S
Sparland Unit #3 HS
Speer IL

Allen Randall R
Oregon Davis HS
Walkerton IN

Allen Sandra E
Dowagiac Union HS
Dowagiac MI

Allen Sheila M
Eastern School District HS
Koleen IN

Allen Sherry L
Lindblom HS
Chicago IL

Allen Walter V
Southwest HS
St Louis MO

Allenstein Paul A
Marquette Sr HS
Marquette MI

Allers Robin K
Red Bud C U HS
Red Bud IL

Alles Gail E
Proviso West HS
Westchester IL

Alley Pamela J
Chase County HS
Imperial NE

Alley Terry L
Chase County HS
Champion NE

Allis William H
North Central HS
Indianapolis IN

Allison Brian R
Phillipsburg HS
Phillipsburg KS

Allison Mark T
North Callawy HS
Kingdom City MO

Allman Cheryl
Central HS
Bay City MI

Allori Raymond M
St Ignatius College Prep HS
Chicago IL

Allsop Gregory L
Bethany HS
Moweaqua IL

Allsopp Lloyd R
Benton HS
Whittington IL

Allsup Nancy L
Rushville HS
Rushville IL

Almeras Mary J
North Knox HS
Bicknell IN

Alms Kent A
Steeleville Comm Unit HS
Steeleville IL

Alms Scot W
Steeleville HS
Steeleville IL

Alongi Barbara J
St Marys Acad
Rochelle IL

Aloot Darlene M
Bishop Foley HS
Madison Hts MI

Alrick John J
Hutchinson HS
Hutchinson MN

Alsman Pamela J
No Knox HS
Sandborn IN

Alt Brian L
Robert S Tower HS
Warren MI

Alter Karen S
Hale HS
Hale MO

Altier Mary C
St Mary Of P H HS
Chicago IL

Alto Nanette D
Nevis HS
Nevis MN

Alvarez Flor S
Kirksville HS
Kirksville MO

Alwin Steven L
Parker Senior HS
Janesville WI

Amann Diane M
Carmel Girls HS
Libertyville IL

Amati Susan E
Rich East HS
Park Forest IL

Amayo Anna M
Turner HS
Kansas City KS

Ambler Donna L
Highland HS
Highland IN

Ambroselli Dominic
St John Cathedral HS
Milwaukee WI

Ambroz Ann M
New Prague HS
New Prague MN

Ameduri Gina M
St Joseph HS
South Bend IN

Ames Anthony I
Clarke Community HS
Weldon IA

Ames Jeanette L
Minot HS
Minot ND

Ames Kerry L
South Putnam HS
Fillmore IN

Amman Beth M
Wahoo HS
Ithaca NE

Amos Linda M
East Union HS
Afton IA

Amos Rosalee
Sargent Public HS
Sargent NE

Anawis Mark A
Loyola Academy
Skokie IL

Ancog Consuelo
Marian HS
Birmingham MI

Anderhous Susan J
Homewood Flossmoor HS
Homewood IL

Anders Lynn L
Wm L Brown HS
Union Center SD

Anders Robyn S
Boone Jr Sr HS
Boone IA

Andersan Crystal R
East Chas HS
Wagner SD

Andersen Cynthia K
St Anthony HS
Effingham IL

Andersen Donalyn M
Aurora HS
Aurora NE

Anderson Angela J
Roosevelt HS
Gary IN

Anderson Barbara H
Grosse Pointe South HS
Grosse Point Park MI

Anderson Betsy L
Echo Public HS
Echo MN

Anderson Carol A
Horace Mann HS
N Fond Du Lac WI

Anderson Charles L
Blissfield HS
Blissfield MI

Anderson Charles R
Braymer C 4 HS
Braymer MO

Anderson Cheryl A
Monrovia HS
Mooresville IN

Anderson Claude A
Highland Pk Sr HS
St Paul MN

Anderson Cloette D
Potter Public HS
Potter NE

Anderson Cynthia J
Papillion HS
Papillion NE

Anderson Dale L
Goodland HS
Goodland KS

Anderson David B
Alpena HS
Alpena MI

Anderson David G
Ogemaw Hts HS
West Branch MI

Anderson David P
Falls HS
International Fls MN

Anderson Dawn
Laurens Community HS
Laurens IA

Anderson Debbie K
Sisseton HS
Sisseton SD

Anderson Deborah J
Prairie Farm HS
Prairie Farm WI

Anderson Debra J
Fremont HS
Fremont NE

Anderson Diana M
Starkweather Public HS
Starkweather ND

Anderson Dinah L
Marion HS
Marion IL

Anderson Edna M
Deland Weldon HS
Weldon IL

Anderson Edward A
Mooseheart HS
Mooseheart IL

Anderson Edwina D
Cambridge Senior HS
Cambridge MN

Anderson Ellen M
Plattsmouth HS
Plattsmouth NE

Anderson Eric A
Bradley Bourbonnais HS
Bourbonnais IL

Anderson Eric B
Roosevelt HS
Britt MN

Anderson Eugene L
Smithton Rvi HS
Smithton MO

Anderson Harlyn E
White Bear Sr HS
White Bear Lake MN

Anderson Irene L
Jefferson Sr HS
Alexandria MN

Anderson Ivy I
Northwestern HS
Flint MI

Anderson James A
Shabbona HS
Shabbona IL

Anderson James F
Platte City HS
Ferrelview MO

Anderson Janice L
Thornton Fractional N HS
Calumet City IL

Anderson Jill S
Maine Twp East HS
Park Ridge IL

Anderson Joel C
Hector HS
Hector MN

Anderson Julie A
J D Darnall HS
Geneseo IL

Anderson Julie N
Bethlehem Academy
Faribault MN

Anderson Karl C
Horton Watkins HS
St Louis MO

Anderson Kathy A
Lasalle Peru Twp HS
Utica IL

Anderson Kathy Jo
Pekin Community HS
Pekin IL

Anderson Kathy M
Edgemont HS
Edgemont SD

Anderson Kent J
Southwest HS
Green Bay WI

Anderson Kent M
Hanson HS
Alexandria SD

Anderson Kerry G
Stratford Community HS
Stratford IA

Anderson Laura M
Salina HS
Salina KS

Anderson Laura M
Brandon HS
Ortonville MI

Anderson Leah J
Manual HS
Peoria IL

Anderson Leeann
Harrisonville Sr HS
Harrisonville MO

Anderson Lenae C
Willmar Sr HS
Blomkest MN

Anderson Linda M
Western HS
Bay City MI

Anderson Linda S
Central HS
Hartland MN

Anderson Lisa S
Schuyler R I HS
Queen City MO

Anderson Lynn K
Cooley HS
Detroit MI

Anderson Marcie E
Belfield HS
Belfield ND

Anderson Mark D
New Hampton HS
New Hampton IA

Anderson Mark L
West Central HS
Hartford SD

Anderson Mark W
Fisher HS
Fisher MN

Anderson Nancy F
Lidgerwood Public HS
Geneseo ND

Anderson Patsi E
Wisconsin Academy
Sturgeon MO

Anderson Paul B
St Croix Falls HS
Dresser WI

Anderson Peggy R
Sargent Central HS
Forman ND

Anderson Rebecca L
Carter H Harrison HS
Chicago IL

Anderson Rebecca L
John Marshall HS
Indianapolis IN

Anderson Rhonda M
Avon HS
Avon IL

Anderson Richard C
Chaminade HS
St Charles MO

Anderson Robert P
Forest View HS
Mt Prospect IL

Anderson Roy L
Hinsdale Central HS
Hinsdale IL

Anderson Sandra K
Milaca Sr HS
Foreston MN

Anderson Sandra L
T F South HS
Lansing IL

Anderson Steven K
Pike HS
Indianapolis IN

Anderson Steven S
Burlington HS
Burlington IA

Anderson Teresa J
Cottonwood Public HS
Cottonwood MN

Anderson Terry J
Oskaloosa HS
Oskaloosa IA

Anderson Timothy C
Laurel Public HS
Laurel NE

Anderson Timothy M
Canton HS
Canton SD

Anderson Valerie K
Forest Lake Sr HS
Marine On St Croix MN

Andreas Paul A
Mitchell HS
Mitchell NE

Andreasen Jim D
Superior HS
Hardy NE

Andreini Jay P
Jeffers HS
South Range MI

Andres Stacy R
Union HS
Grand Rapids MI

Andress Howard J
Waterford Kettering HS
Drayton Plains MI

Andrew Kerin K
Lincoln Comm HS
Mechanicsville IA

Andrews Diana L
Union County HS
Liberty IN

Andrews Lynette M
Harold L Richards HS
Oak Lawn IL

Andrews Mark W
Union Star R 2 HS
Union Star MO

Andrews Pamela K
Graceville Public HS
Johnson MN

Andrews Peggy L
Pepin Public HS
Pepin WI

Andrews Wesley C
Kirksville Sr HS
Novinger MO

Andries Kristine M
Lynd Public HS
Marshall MN

Andrijauskas Loretta R
Maria HS
Chicago IL

Andvick Judith M
Bloomington HS
Bloomington IL

Anest Paula M
Bayard HS
Bridgeport NE

Angel Cathy S
Memphis HS
Goodells MI

Angel Michele A
Saint Mary Academy
Newport MI

Angeli Penny M
West Iron County HS
Iron River MI

Angeloff Veronica
West Iron County HS
Iron River MI

Angilello Peter M
Parker Sr HS
Janesville WI

Angle Theresa L
Woodland R 4 HS
Marble Hill MO

Anglen Jeff O
Rockbridge Sr HS
Columbia MO

Anglim Van M
Gladstone HS
Gladstone MI

Anglin Ann J
Tippycanoe Valley HS
Warsaw IN

Anglin Kevin D
Western HS
Sheffield IL

Angotti Nora D
El Paso HS
El Paso IL

Ankrom Jeffrey S
W P Chrysler Memorial HS
New Castle IN

Annegers Andy J
Southern HS
Stronghurst IL

Annerino Maureen F
St Mary Of Perpetual Help HS
Chicago IL

Annis Lynn F
Spencer HS
Spencer IA

Anstrom Nanette K
Bradley Bourbonnais HS
Bradley IL

Anthony James E
North Sr HS
Eau Claire WI

Anticoli Tracy L
Bellevue HS
Bellevue NE

Antolik John G
Fort Dodge Sr HS
Ft Dodge IA

Anton Nancy J
Centennial Sr HS
Lexington MN

Anton William G
South Field Lathrup HS
South Field MI

Anzalone Angela M
Joliet West HS
Joliet IL

Appelbaum Steven
Evanston Township HS
Evanston IL

Appell Dennis A
R O V A Sr HS
Altona IL

Apple Stephen M
New Buffalo HS
New Buffalo MI

Applegate Mark W
Springfield Se HS
Springfield IL

Applegate Susan R
Newton HS
Willow Hill IL

Aquilani Laureen K
Ogden HS
Ogden IA

Arango Ivette M
St Pius X HS
Kansas City MO

Arbaugh Scott J
Chaminade HS
St Louis MO

Arceri Donald L
Chaminade College Prep
Lake St Louis MO

Archer Jan G
Roosevelt HS
Des Moines IA

Archer Ronnie D
Davis Co Comm HS
Moulton IA

Arends Mary K
Oak Park River Forest HS
River Forest IL

Arens Debbie K
Sacred Heart HS
Sedalia MO

Arens Keith A
St Marys HS
Remsen IA

Arensdorf Gerald D
Mc Pherson County HS
Tryon NE

Arent Cynthia M
Coloma HS
Coloma MI

Arhart Randal D
Masn City HS
Mason City IA

Arias Teresa L
St Augustine HS
Chicago IL

Arkin Andrew J
Oak Park & River Forest HS
River Forest IL

Armagost Lesa A
North Andrew HS
Rea MO

Armbruster Barbara J
Unionville Sebewaing Sr HS
Sebewaing MI

Armitage Terry J
Smith Center HS
Smith Center KS

Arm Knecht Bonnie A
Nemaha Valley HS
Talmage NE

Armovit Jackie Z
Onsted Community HS
Onsted MI

Arms Juanita
Martin Public HS
Shelbyville MI

Armstrong Alfonzo
Soldan HS
St Louis MO

Armstrong Brent D
Creighton Preparatory HS
Omaha NE

Armstrong David S
Lyons Township HS
Lagrange Park IL

Armstrong Dianne K
Big Springs HS
Brule NE

Armstrong Donna R
Wichita S HS
Wichita KS

Armstrong Jennifer H
St Marys Academy
Chicago IL

Armstrong Robert N
Ecorse HS
Ecorse MI

Arndt Robin L
Carson HS
Carson ND

Arnold Christine K
Turner HS
Kansas City KS

Arnold Ginger R
Mark Twain HS
New London MO

Arnold Mary I
Rushford HS
Rushford MN

Arnold Mary L
Mayo HS
Rochester MN

Arnold Nathan G
Alton R 4 HS
Alton MO

Arnold Sheri S
Milton Senior HS
Milton Jct WI

Arnold Walter T
Alpena Sr HS
Alpena MI

Arnold William C
Edina East HS
Edina MN

Arp Brent W
Blair HS
Blair NE

Arquilla Carmela
Charles P Steinmetz HS
Chicago IL

Arszman Magdalene M
Our Lady Of Grace Academy
Indianapolis IN

Arteman Nancy M
Wapella HS
Wapella IL

Artis Tamara C
Lindblom Tech HS
Chicago IL

Artz Carol A
Alma HS
Alma NE

Arundel William J
St Ritas HS
Chicago IL

Asay Susan L
Bayard HS
Bayard NE

Aschenbrenner Joan L
Auburndale HS
Milladore WI

Ash Linda F
California HS
California MO

Ashbeck Richard T
Gordon Technical HS
Chicago IL

Ashelin Cynthia A
Cotter HS
Winona MN

Ashenbrenner Susan G
Bishop Borgess HS
Detroit MI

Asher Dennis A
Winona HS
Winona MO

Ashfort Cathy S
Bloom Township HS
Chicago Hts IL

Ashley David W
Velva Public HS
Velva ND

Ashley Julie A
Casey HS
Casey IL

Ashmore Bonita J
Bloomingdale HS
Grand Junction MI

Ashton Annette M
Neligh HS
Neligh NE

Ashton Timothy G
Neligh Public HS
Neligh NE

Askew David J
Harry S Truman HS
Taylor MI

Asmus Robert E
Clarke Comm HS
Osceola IA

Asmus Ronald D
Homestead HS
Mequon WI

Aspenson Jeffrey T
Seneca HS
Ferryville WI

Asperheim Scott M
Shawnee Mission Nw HS
Shawnee KS

Assmann Michael G
Dunlap Community HS
Dunlap IA

Atchison Dave A
Gibson Southern HS
Fort Branch IN

Aten Cindy J
Newton HS
Hidalgo IL

Athen Michael D
Farragut HS
Riverton IA

Athens Laura A
Trenton HS
Trenton MI

Athey Cynthia L
Casey Jr Sr HS
Casey IL

Atkins Janice E
Pomeroy Community HS
Pomeroy IA

Atkinson Charlene C
Turner HS
Kansas City KS

Atkinson Dana L
Fairfield Comm HS
Geff IL

Atkinson Melinda A
North Callaway HS
Kingdom City MO

Ator Bona J
Pittsfield HS
Pittsfield IL

Atteberry John B
Guthrie Center HS
Guthrie Center IA

Atteberry Rebecca A
Colome HS
Colome SD

Attie Desiree M
Fordson HS
Dearborn MI

Atwood Julie A
Springfield HS
Springfield IL

Aubry Kenton P
Lincoln HS
Manitowoc WI

Aubuchon Frank G
Sullivan HS
Sullivan MO

Auch Noreen J
Dickinson HS
Dickinson ND

Aufderhar Kenneth G
Wisconsin Academy
Mcfarland WI

Aughenbaugh Vince J
Watertown Sr HS
Watertown SD

Aul Diana L
Sabetha HS
Sabetha KS

Auld Jeffrey M
Oskaloosa Senior HS
Oskaloosa IA

Ault Brian J
Northrop HS
Ft Wayne IN

Aune James E
Holy Trinity HS
Winsted MN

Ausborn Kris M
Lake City HS
Lake City IA

Austin Beth A
Douglas Mac Arthur HS
Saginaw MI

Austin Debbi J
Cobden Unit HS
Cobden IL

Austin Elizabeth A
Blue Mound HS
Blue Mound IL

Austin Mark W
Frankton HS
Anderson IN

Austin Patty K
Rushford Public HS
Rushford MN

Auvinen Laura M
Freeport HS
Freeport IL

Avants Connie S
Sarcoxie HS
Sarcoxie MO

Avers Victoria A
Notre Dame HS
Chicago IL

Avery Dean R
Gresham Public HS
Gresham NE

Avery Kevin B
Grand Rapids HS
Bovey MN

Avgerinos Nickolas
George Rogers Clark HS
Hammond IN

Avila John
St Francis De Sales HS
Lansing IL

Avila Thomas D
Northside HS
Muncie IN

Aviza Anna V
Carmel Girls HS
Downey IL

Ayers Kristy L
Green City Ri HS
Green City MO

Ayers Rodney D
Green City R 1 HS
Green Castle MO

Ayotte Janice C
Walled Lake Central HS
Union Lake MI

Azeltine Leroy E
Smith Center HS
Smith Center KS

B

Baade Ryan D
Titonka HS
Titonka IA

Baatz Deborah K
Edwardsburg HS
Edwardsburg MI

Baatz Eric C
Edwardsburg HS
Edwardsburg MI

Babb Timothy J
Pioneer HS
Lucerne IN

Babcock Del M
Hammond Baptist HS
Hammond IN

Babcock Glen A
Kimball HS
Royal Oak MI

Babcock Patricia M
Chaparral HS
Attica KS

Babecki Susan E
The Immaculata HS
Chicago IL

Baber James J
Barrington HS
Barrington IL

Babi Jeanette L
West Holt HS
Atkinson NE

Babicki Raymond J
Joliet Central HS
Joliet IL

Babler Bryan C
Monticello HS
Monticello WI

Bacheller Cheryl D
Armada HS
Allenton MI

Bachenberg Phillip S
Bryan HS
Omaha NE

Bachler Kevin L
Zion Benton Township HS
Zion IL

Bachman Debbi J
Bowdle HS
Bowdle SD

Bachman Lucinda E
Salem Comm HS
Salem IL

Bachtell Paula J
Starmont HS
Wadena IA

Back Patricia E
Immaculate Conception Academy
Brookville IN

Backlin William W
Mason City Sr HS
Mason City IA

Backstrom Orn U
Highland Park HS
Highland Park IL

Bacon Chris N
Marshalltown HS
Marshalltown IA

Bacon James R
North Miami HS
Mexico IN

Badanek Katherine E
Godwin Heights HS
Wyoming MI

Bade Ladonna R
Fair Grove HS
Fair Grove MO

Badeau Terri L
Case HS
Racine WI

Bader John L
Lemars Comm HS
Lemars IA

Baehr Peter H
Thorp HS
Withee WI

Baertschi Steven W
Illinois Valley Cntrl HS
Chillicothe IL

Bagby Barbara A
Southwest HS
Kansas City MO

Bagienski Richard D
Anderson HS
Anderson IN

Bagley Janice A
Niles West HS
Morton Grove IL

Bahler Elizabeth R
Monroe Senior HS
Monroe WI

Bahr John A
Otis Bison HS
Olmitz KS

Baier Mark J
La Crosse HS
La Crosse KS

Baier Timothy L
West Liberty HS
W Liberty IA

Bailar Rodney B
North Platte HS
North Platte NE

Bailey Anita Y
Purdy HS
Purdy MO

Bailey Cindy K
N Clay HS
Louisville IL

Bailey Daryl W
Coloma HS
Coloma MI

Bailey Debra K
Sumner HS
Kansas City KS

Bailey Dennis C
Oak Park Academy
Sioux City IA

Bailey Judith A
Triton HS
Argos IN

Bailey Lloyd M
N Decatur HS
St Paul IN

Bailey Ralph E
Shenandoah HS
New Castle IN

Bailey Raymond L
Central City Comm HS
Central City IA

Bailey Renee M
Hannibal HS
Hannibal MO

Bailey Walter D
Mills Prairie HS
Mill Shoals IL

Bainbridge Jay M
Avon HS
St Augustine IL

Bainter Bradley L
Northwestern HS
Sciota IL

Baird Joy A
Bayard HS
Bayard NE

Bajt Mary Lynn S
St Francis Academy
Lockport IL

Bakenhus Spring M
Lakeview HS
Columbus NE

Baker Alania M
Laingsburg HS
Laingsburg MI

Baker Barbara S
Warren Township HS
Gurnee IL

Baker Brenda I
Lawson HS
Lawson MO

Baker Carla R
Redford Union HS
Detroit MI

Baker Cheryl L
Reitz Memorial HS
Newburgh IN

Baker Cynthia A
O Fallon Township HS
O Fallon IL

Baker Cynthia A
Laona HS
Laona WI

Baker Diana L
Baldwin HS
Wellsville KS

Baker Donna M
St Charles HS
St Charles MO

Baker Elizabeth S
Fulton HS
Fulton MO

Baker Ivan L H
Hays HS
Hays KS

Baker Jack R
Augusta HS
Augusta KS

Baker James F
Switzerland Cnty HS
Vevay IN

Baker Joan M
Eddyville Comm HS
Eddyville IA

Baker John M
West Washington HS
Salem IN

Baker Judith L
Neoga HS
Sigel IL

Baker Marie E
Winnebago HS
Winnebago IL

Baker Michael F
Rushford HS
Rushford MN

Baker Paula J
Swan Valley HS
Saginaw MI

Baker Paul D
Andes Central HS
Pickstown SD

Baker Randal L
La Plata Rii HS
La Plata MO

Baker Randy E
Sycamore HS
Sycamore IL

Baker Sam M
Knoxville HS
Knoxville IA

Baker Tracy A
Frankfort Sr HS
Frankfort IN

Baker William R
Grand Rapids Sr HS
Grand Rapids MN

Bakke Larry J
Binford HS
Binford ND

Bakke Randall W
Midway Jr Sr HS
Inkster ND

Bakos Sharon J
Morton Sr HS
Hammond IN

Balas Thomas L
Hazen HS
Hazen ND

Balasa Cindy A
Naperville Central HS
Naperville IL

Balcer Carolyn S
Millington HS
Millington MI

Balcer Debb E
Olivia Public HS
Olivia MN

Balchik Mark A
Lumen Christi HS
Jackson MI

Balciunas Regina K
Maria HS
Chicago IL

Baldauf Roseann
St Louise De Marillac HS
Morton Grove IL

Baldwin Cathy L
Norris City Omaha HS
Broughton IL

Baldwin Donald E
Roncalli HS
Omaha NE

Baldwin Gregory A
Norris City Omaha HS
Broughton IL

Baldwin Mark F
Glenbrook South HS
Glenview IL

Baldwin Starleen G
West Harrison HS
Little Sioux IA

Baldy Brian R
Hartford HS
Hartford WI

Balistreri Carol A
Pewaukee HS
Pewaukee WI

Balk Nancy A
Sr HS
Charles City IA

Balk Timothy T
Centreville HS
Centreville MI

Balke Gary D
Benton County HS
Cole Camp MO

Ball Carolyn J
West Pike HS
New Canton IL

Ball David L
Koshkonong HS
Koshkonong MO

Ball Douglas J
Saints Peter & Paul HS
Saginaw MI

Ball Lee Anna
Central HS
Switz City IN

Ball Roger D
Centralia HS
Centralia MO

Ball Steven C
Blair HS
Blair NE

Ball Timothy S
West Lafayette Sr HS
W Lafayette IN

Ballance Anya R
Bishop Ward HS
Kansas City KS

Ballinger Virginia A
Fairfield HS
Sylvia KS

Balls Leisa J
Sarcoxie HS
Sarcoxie MO

Balmer Joseph W
Bishop Du Bourg HS
St Louis MO

Baluanz Patricia A
Tripoli Comm HS
Waverly IA

Bamesberger Joanne K
Bartley HS
Indianola NE

Banas Sharon K
George Rogers Clark HS
Whiting IN

Bandrowsky Timothy
St Laurence HS
Hickory Hills IL

Bandurski Jeffrey J
Homestead HS
Mequon WI

Bane Connie M
Oakland Comm HS
Oakland IA

Banker Tracy C
North Greene HS
Roodhouse IL

Banks Cathie I
Monett HS
Monett MO

Banks David M
Lanphier HS
Springfield IL

Banks Fred
Lindblom Tech HS
Chicago IL

Banks Gregory A
St Francis HS
Glen Ellyn IL

Banks Michael A
Princeton HS
Princeton MO

Bann Jennifer M
Fridley Sr HS
Fridley MN

Banner Margaret H
Hackett HS
Kalamazoo MI

Bannick Randy L
Lake Benton Public #404 HS
Lake Benton MN

Banning Robert D
Smith Cotton HS
Sedalia MO

Bannon Laura M
Pattonville HS
Bridgeton MO

Bannon Lisa K
Pattonville Sr HS
Bridgeton MO

Bannos Thomas S
Proviso West HS
Westchester IL

Banse Perry R
Benton Community HS
Van Horne IA

Bantle Wendy M
Marinette Sr HS
Marinette WI

Banwart Sandra K
West Bend Community HS
West Bend IA

Banyard Richard A
West HS
Minneapolis MN

Baptist Michael R
Andrews Academy
Berrien Springs MI

Baran Nancy L
T F South HS
Lansing IL

Baranouski Marc L
Quincy HS
Quincy MI

Baranowski John M
Lake Central HS
Dyer IN

Barbee John S
Mt Vernon Township HS
Mt Vernon IL

Barber Glen R
Pana Sr HS
Pana IL

Barber Marvin S
West Side HS
Gary IN

Barber Troy D
Holcomb HS
Garden City KS

Barberra Michael G
Iowa Falls HS
Iowa Falls IA

Barbour Koelle G
Senior HS
Jefferson City MO

Barclay Steven C
Olympia HS
Mclean IL

Bardole Mary A
East Greene Comm HS
Rippey IA

Barent Debra J
Lewellen HS
Lewellen NE

Barenthsen Roger S
Powers Lake HS
Powers Lake ND

Bares Carol A
Tyndall HS
Tyndall SD

Barfknecht Andrew T
Ofallon Township HS
Ofallon IL

Bargen Cheryl D
Superior HS
Superior NE

Barger Floyd E
Crothersville HS
Crothersville IN

Barger Regina L
Scottsburg HS
Lexington IN

Barger Tony A
Springfield HS
Battle Creek MI

Bargstadt Julie J
Randolph Public HS
Randolph NE

Barham Joyce M
R U C E HS
Reddick IL

Bark Dale R
Desoto HS
Desoto WI

Barker Charlotte A
Pecatonica HS
Pecatonia IL

Barker Gary N
Salem Community HS
Salem IL

Barker Lauren M
Oak Park HS
Kansas City MO

Barkhaus Rodney L
Bonduel HS
Bonduel WI

Barley Angela E
Lindbloom HS
Chicago IL

Barmore Angela K
Orangeville HS
Freeport IL

Barna Debra J
Ralston HS
Omaha NE

Barnack Mark J
Lew Wallace HS
Gary IN

Barnard Gregory L
Wayne City HS
Wayne City IL

Barnard Vicki A
Crete HS
Pleasant Dale NE

Barnes Barbara J
Sandusky HS
Sandusky MI

Barnes Billy J
Walker R Iv HS
Walker MO

Barnes Cynthia L
Northridge HS
Middlebury IN

Barnes Daniel B
St Pius X HS
Arnold MO

Barnes Ginger M
Lawrence HS
Lawrence MI

Barnes Mary C
Hinsdale Central HS
Oak Brook IL

Barnes Mary E
Niantic Harristown HS
Decatur IL

Barnes Patrick W
Lourdes HS
Rochester MN

Barnes Roxie A
Smith Center HS
Smith Center KS

Barnes Teresa A
E Lansing HS
E Lansing MI

Barnes Terrance D
East Detroit HS
Warren MI

Barnes Terry S
Eaton Rapids HS
Eaton Rapids MI

Barnes Tony N
S Sioux HS
S Sioux City NE

Barnes William J
St Viator HS
Arlington Hts IL

Barnett Jeffrey M
Warsaw Comm HS
Warsaw IN

Barnett Regina K
Seneca HS
Seneca MO

Barnett Richard L
Baxter Springs HS
Baxter Springs KS

Barnett Sherry K
Arlington HS
Indianapolis IN

Barnett Steve L
Lake Crystal Public HS
Lake Crystal MN

Barnett Terry L
Atwood Hammond HS
Hammond IL

Barney Paul M
Michigan Public HS
Michigan ND

Barnhart Terri L
Oak Park HS
Kansas City MO

Barnhill Jessie M
Matthews HS
Matthews MO

Barnhouse Ricky D
Nixa HS
Nixa MO

Barr Terri J
Rushford HS
Lewiston MN

Barrand Linda M
Cadillac HS
Cadillac MI

Barrentine Sarah G
Calumet HS
Gary IN

Barrett Holly A
Essex Comm HS
Essex IA

Barrett James D
Kirksville HS
Kirksville MO

Barrett Kathleen M
Slayton HS
Avoca MN

Barrett Kim K
North Platte HS
North Platte NE

Barrett Mary Beth
Forest View HS
Mt Prospect IL

Barrett Tammara D
W Aurora HS
Aurora IL

Barrett Tammy J
Mauston Area HS
Mauston WI

Barrett Tammy K
Baraga HS
Baraga MI

Barrick Scott D
Northeast Hamilton HS
Blairsburg IA

Barron Martin R
Beardstown HS
Beardstown IL

Barrow Michelle R
Lutheran West HS
Detroit MI

Barrows Cindy E
Inland Lakes HS
Indian River MI

Barrus Janet M
Lake Forest HS
Lake Forest IL

Barry Anthony L
Lapeer HS
North Branch MI

Barry Thomas J
Adams Central HS
Hastings NE

Barsema Arthur R
Glenbard West HS
Wheaton IL

Barski Ramona M
Good Counsel HS
Chicago IL

Barta Millie C
Ellsworth HS
Ellsworth KS

Barta Thomas D
New Prague HS
Jordan MN

Barta Wayne A
Premontre HS
Green Bay WI

Bartel Gary A
Omro Senior HS
Omro WI

Bartelds Dawn R
New Prague HS
Elko MN

Bartels Cynthia K
Washington Sr HS
Sioux Falls SD

Bartels David G
Lead HS
Lead SD

Bartels Melanie L
Newell HS
Nisland SD

Bartels Teresa M
Meridian HS
Tobias NE

Bartels Thomas G
Meridian Public HS
Tobias NE

Bartels William O
Interlochen Arts Academy
Stevensville MI

Bartelt Susan J
Lyons Township HS
Western Springs IL

Barthel Weston W
Nebraska Christian HS
Amelia NE

Barthell Edward N
Armstrong Sr HS
Neenah WI

Barthuly Jane L
St Marys HS
St Marys KS

Bartlett Brian R
Frankenmuth HS
Frankenmuth MI

Bartlett Bruce A
Cozad HS
Cozad NE

Bartley David W
West Bend East HS
West Bend WI

Bartley Valerie A
Mc Donald County HS
Anderson MO

Bartman Laura B
New Holland Middletown HS
New Holland IL

Bartman Susan K
Clio Area HS
Clio MI

Bartok Patty J
Eldorado HS
Eldorado IL

Bartolomei Frederick J
De La Salle HS
Roseville MI

Barton John E
Morton HS
Morton IL

Barton Lisa A
North Newton HS
Fair Oaks IN

Barton Raymond J
Grosse Pointe North HS
Grosse Pointe MI

Barton Russell
South Beloit HS
So Beloit IL

Bartosch Michael
Ridgewood Hs
Norridge IL

Bartow Gary J
Tekonsha HS
Homer MI

Bartuska Holly A
Midway HS
Forest River ND

Barwick James F
G S Parker Sr HS
Janesville WI

Barz Danny A
Meservey Thornton HS
Thornton IA

Barzano Lorie J
Amos Alonzo Stagg HS
Hickory Hills IL

Baschult Mark T
Fremont Sr HS
Fremont NE

Basgoz Nesli O
Bloomington North HS
Bloomington IN

Bashaw John R
Lake Linden Hubbell HS
Lake Linden MI

Bashore Tanya L
F C HS
Fairfield IL

Basinger Monte R
Van Far HS
Farber MO

Bass Denise K
Branson HS
Branson MO

Bass John W
Salem Sr HS
Salem MO

Bass Lori J
University HS
Normal IL

Bass Maurice L
Anna Jonesboro Comm HS
Anna IL

Bassett Brian M
Lakeshore HS
Stevensville MI

Bassett Roberta R
Mullen Public HS
Mullen NE

Bassing Roberta L
Sycamore HS
Sycamore IL

Bastian Sue E
R Nelson Snider HS
Fort Wayne IN

Bastin Dale L
Golden Plains HS
Selden KS

Batchelder Irene M
Fort Zumwalt HS
St Peters MO

Batchman Richard K
Otis Bison Sr HS
Great Bend KS

Batdorf Tyler M
Pawhuska HS
Sedan KS

Bateman Carol S
Washington Cath HS
Washington IN

Bateman Joseph D
Atwood Hammond HS
Hammond IL

Bateman Mark D
Manual HS
Indianapolis IN

Bateman Nancy A
Farmer City Mansfield HS
Mansfield IL

Bates Elizabeth A
Oneill Public HS
Emmet NE

Bates James E
Pennfield HS
Battle Creek MI

Bates Julie A
Twin Valley HS
Boyne City MI

Bates Sharon J
Winchester Comm HS
Winchester IN

Bateson Cindy L
North Clay Comm HS
Louisville IL

Batey Diane R
Swartz Creek HS
Swartz Creek MI

Bathe David A
Lincoln HS
Vincennes IN

Batterson Timothy J
St Louis Univ HS
Granite City IL

Batterton Debra J
Astoria HS
Astoria IL

Battiato Patricia A
Driscoll HS
Addison IL

Battles Kathleen M
Waukesha North HS
Waukesha WI

Batty Cheryl A
Arthur HS
Arthur IL

Bauch Richard E
Max Public HS
Benedict ND

Bauch Thomas C
Aquin Central Catholic HS
Freeport IL

Baudler Joan M
Bridgewater Fontanelle HS
Fontanelle IA

Baudoin Kathleen M
Grand Meadow Public HS
Grand Meadow MN

Bauer Angela M
Lincoln HS
Vincennes IN

Bauer Carol A
Jeffersonville HS
Jeffersonville IN

Bauer Nancy A
Center Sr HS
Kansas City MO

Bauer Rhonda E
Bryant HS
Appleton City MO

Bauerle Rhonda L
Chase Co HS
Imperial NE

Bauernfeind Mary J
Hudson HS
Hudson WI

Baughman Jeffery M
Davis County Comm HS
Pulaski IA

Baum Karen Y
Hastings HS
Hastings MI

Bauman Ann M
Reese HS
Reese MI

Bauman Cynthia L
Mukwonago HS
Big Bend WI

Bauman Kim L
Rock Valley Comm HS
Rock Valley IA

Baumann Mark D
Riverton HS
Galena KS

Baumann Patrick J
Newman HS
Wausau WI

Baumeister Carol A
River Valley HS
Sawyer MI

Baumert Brian A
Howells Public HS
Howells NE

Baumert Michael L
Howells Public HS
Howells NE

Baumgarten Marsha L
Arthur Hill HS
Saginaw MI

Baumhover David J
Fonda Comm HS
Fonda IA

Baumle Steve R
Forest View HS
Mt Prospect IL

Baumstark Mary L
Harry A Burke HS
Omaha NE

Bautista Steven J
Mendel Catholic Prep HS
Chicago Ridge IL

Bauwens Jonathan E
Marian HS
South Bend IN

Baxley Alice G
Whiting HS
Whiting IN

Baxter Darrel L
St Louis HS
St Louis MI

Baxter Dawn M
Ralston HS
Omaha NE

Baxter Janice A
Rudyard Area HS
Rudyard MI

Baxter William J
Gordon Tech HS
Chicago IL

Bay Janet L
Salem Sr HS
Salem MO

Bay Russell D
Wayne Comm HS
Corydon IA

Bayer Janet C
Horton Watkins HS
St Louis MO

Baylom Blaire V
Kenwood HS
Chicago IL

Bays Sharon E
Wheaton North HS
Wheaton IL

Beach Cheryl D
Howell HS
Howell MI

Beach Joan M
Floyd Central HS
Pekin IN

Beach Robert L
Homewood Flossmoor HS
Homewood IL

Beachy Jill M
Laker HS
Pigeon MI

Beacom Connie J
O Gorman HS
Sioux Falls SD

Beadle Jolleen K
Swea City Comm HS
Swea City IA

Beal Ron D
Sedgwick HS
Sedgwick KS

Beal Vicki A
Zalma HS
Arab MO

Beal Vicki L
Blackford HS
Hartford City IN

Beall Cheryl L
Crown Point HS
Crown Point IN

Beals Cynthia L
Brown City HS
Brown City MI

Beals Susan L
Fairfax Independent HS
Fairfax SD

Beam Michael K
La Ville HS
Plymouth IN

Beams Valerie L
Fremont HS
Fremont IN

Bean Telitha F
Waco Comm HS
Wayland IA

Beard Cheryl R
Salem Comm HS
Salem IL

Beard Daniel L
Holden Sr HS
Holden MO

Beard Jill E
Greenview HS
Greenview IL

Beard Karen D
Centerville HS
Moulton IA

Beard Mary A
Ozark HS
Ozark MO

Beard Sheila A
Centralia HS
Centralia KS

Beard William J
South Decatur HS
Greensburg IN

Bearden Lisa A
George Rogers Clark HS
Whiting IN

Bearrows Thomas R
Rochelle Twp HS
Rochelle IL

Beary Patrick A
Knoxville HS
Knoxville IA

Beason Susan K
Lakefield HS
Lakefield MN

Beattie Jayne M
So Nodaway HS
Barnard MO

Beattie Susan K
Minden HS
Minden NE

Beatty Dawn H
Marshal HS
Marshall MI

Beatty Leslie A
Kirksville R Iii HS
Kirksville MO

Beaty Elizabeth A
Benton Consolidated HS
Ewing IL

Beauchamp Gail S
Iron Mountain HS
Iron Mountain MI

Beauchine Michael D
William G Mather HS
Munising MI

Beausoleil Laurie L
Waukegan East HS
Waukegan IL

Beauvais Bernard J
Somerset HS
Somerset WI

Beauvais Judith A
Mundelein HS
Mundelein IL

Beavers Dennis G
Covington HS
Covington IN

Bebb Leslie A
Herbert Henry Dow HS
Midland MI

Bechard Richard B
Grinnell HS
Grinnell KS

Bechmann Mary C
University HS
Milwaukee WI

Beck Brenda J
Lennox HS
Worthing SD

Beck Donna J
Cochrane Fountain City HS
Fountain City WI

Beck George A
Natoma HS
Natoma KS

Beck Leslie M
Bremen HS
Midlothian IL

Beck Scottie R
Avon HS
Danville IN

Beck Sherree J
Copeland HS
Copeland KS

Beck Sylvia
Menomonee Falls East S
Menomonee Falls WI

Beckenbach Lerae A
Hyannis HS
Hyannis NE

Becker Chris S
Parkside HS
Jackson MI

Becker Daniel P
Hinsdale Central HS
Oakbrook IL

Becker David P
Montini HS
Lombard IL

Becker Debra K
Hillsboro HS
Hillsboro IL

Becker Karl R
Greenview HS
Greenview IL

Becker Kevin A
Bishop Luers HS
Ft Wayne IN

Becker Mark E
Mendota Township HS
Sublette IL

Becker Mark H
Bishop Luers HS
Fort Wayne IN

Becker Ronald A
Aurora HS
Phillips NE

Becker Susan E
Garden City Sr HS
Garden City KS

Becker Todd A
Holmen HS
Holmen WI

Beckler Cindy M
Faulkton HS
Seneca SD

Beckman Elaine K
Newton HS
Wheeler IL

Beckman Gregory B
Huntington North HS
Huntington IN

Beckmeier Carolyn S
Patoka Comm Unit 100 HS
Vernon IL

Beckner Linda S
Rossville Alvin HS
Rossville IL

Beckner Richard R
Neosho HS
Goodman MO

STUDENTS PHOTOGRAPH SCHEDULED FOR PUBLICATION HERE COULD NOT BE REPRODUCED

Bedell Roberta J
Corunna HS
Durand MI

Bedient Brian L
Polk Public HS
Bradshaw NE

Bedman Connie K
E J Cooper Sr HS
Crystal MN

Bednar Mark F
St Edmond HS
Fort Dodge IA

Bednarczyk Diane D
Morton West HS
Berwyn IL

Bednarz Robin E
Richmond HS
Richmond MI

Bedore Gary M
Benet Academy
Lisle IL

Bee Debra L
Josephinum HS
Chicago IL

Beebe Bruce D
Glenbrook So HS
Glenview IL

Beebe Robin R
Lincoln Sr HS
Bloomington MN

Beebe Teri L
Ellsworth Sr HS
Ellsworth WI

Beed Vaughn K
West Point HS
West Point NE

Beenes David A
Marist HS
Chicago IL

Beeninga Barry L
Washington Sr HS
Sioux Falls SD

Beenken Debra D
Grundy Center Comm H
Grundy Center IA

Beer Michael S
University HS
Normal IL

Beese Rudolf H
Beloit Memorial HS
Beloit WI

Beesley Joan E
Taylor Center HS
Taylor MI

Begle Doris A
Marian Hts HS
Ferdinand IN

Beguhn Steven G
Oconomowoc Sr HS
Oconomowoc WI

Beguin Roxane C
Rushville HS
Rushville NE

Beguin Theresa L
Rushville HS
Rushville NE

Behm Randolph P
Joseph A Craig HS
Janesville WI

Behme Sharon L
Carlinville HS
Carlinville IL

Behrends Scott C
Mountain Lake HS
Mountain Lake MN

Behrens Barbara J
Brookfield East HS
Brookfield WI

Behringer Randall L
Winneconne HS
Oshkosh WI

Behrns Nancy K
Dieterich HS
Dieterich IL

Beicos Rose S
Rich South HS
Park Forest IL

Beidle Kim
South Shore HS
Cornucopia WI

Beine Beth A L
Slinger HS
Slinger WI

Beissel Tammy J
Brown County HS
Nineveh IN

Bell Claire M
Lincoln Senior HS
Rudolph WI

Bell Jeff P
Plattsmouth HS
Plattsmouth NE

Bell Kerry A
Watseka HS
Watseka IL

Bell Lawrence W
Smithton HS
Sedalia MO

Bell Steven A
North Mahaska HS
New Sharon IA

Belligan Brenda J
Oak Creek HS
Oak Creek WI

Bellinger Cathy A
Clio HS
Clio MI

Bellinger Karen
Lakeshore HS
Stevensville MI

Bellinger Kathy A
Kalkasva HS
Kalkaska MI

Bellott Barry J
Streator HS
Streator IL

Bellows Cindy J
Cameron HS
Cameron WI

Bellville Arlen T
Whittemore Prescott Area HS
Prescott MI

Bellville Dennis J
Southgate HS
Southgate MI

Beloy Mary Jo
Aurora Hoyt Lakes HS
Aurora MN

Beltz Dwight K
Haven HS
Haven KS

Benavidez Jackie L
La Moille Comm HS
Ohio IL

Benczik Stephen J
Plymouth HS
Plymouth IN

Benda David C
Bath HS
Bath MI

Bendall Joellen M
Rochester HS
Rochester IN

Bender Allen K
Northwood HS
Minong WI

Bender Janet L
Belleville East HS
Belleville IL

Bender Judy M
Appleton HS West
Appleton WI

Bender Sherieda K
Tomah Sr HS
Tomah WI

Benecki Jean M
Ladywood HS
Livonia MI

Beneda Philip J
St Vincent De Paul Sem HS
Chicago IL

Benedetto Lisa B
Metamara Township HS
E Peoria IL

Benedict Kimberly M
Frontenac HS
Frontenac KS

Benge La Donna
Flaxton HS
Flaxton ND

Bengtson Peter S
E Rockford HS
Rockford IL

Bengtson Sheldon J
Westview Sr HS
Braham MN

Benham Gary A
Galena HS
Galena MO

Beninato Gloria L
Carl Sandburg HS
Orland Park IL

Benincosa Kelly R
Galena HS
Galena IL

Benjamin George R
Tri Valley HS
Ellsworth IL

Benke Michael G
Thornton Fractional HS
Lansing IL

Benke Patti R
Oak Park HS
Kansas City MO

Benkert David E
Monroe HS
Monroe WI

Benko Edward A
Granite City HS
Granit City IL

Benner Kenneth E
Shabbona HS
Lee IL

Benner Steven L
Milford Township HS
Milford IL

Bennett Cassanra J
Adrian Sr HS
Adrian MI

Bennett Christopher M
Evanston Township HS
Evanston IL

Bennett Debbie S
West Vigo HS
West Terre Haute IN

Bennett Debra J
Benton Cons HS
Thompsonville IL

Bennett Judi A
Calhoun HS
Kampsville IL

Bennett Judith A
Lockport Central HS
Lockport IL

Bennett Lou Ann
Decatur Central HS
Indianapolis IN

Bennett Rick E
Oregon Davis HS
Grovertown IN

Bennett Sandra A
Luke M Powers HS
Flint MI

Bennett Sarah L
Pennfield HS
Battle Creek MI

Bennett Stephen D
Larkin HS
Elgin IL

Bennett Terry L
Chesaning Union HS
Chesaning MI

Benoist Terence J
Arcadia Valley HS
Ironton MO

Benson Bonnie L
Westfield HS
Noblesville IN

Benson Ellsworth J
Sheyenne Public HS
Sheyenne ND

Benson Marc S
Worthington Senior HS
Worthington MN

Benson Nancy L
Sterling HS
Sterling IL

Benson Sheryl A
West Richland HS
Noble IL

Benson Susan E
Burlington Comm HS
Burlington IA

Benson Susan M
Rutland HS
Rutland SD

Benstead Steven E
Kimball County HS
Kimball NE

Bentele Steven G
Truman Public HS
Truman MN

Benters Kim A
Lanphier HS
Springfield IL

Bentley Mary D
Broad Ripple HS
Indianapolis IN

Bentley Melodie D
Alden Hebron HS
Hebron IL

Bentley Thomas J
Notre Dame HS
St Clair Shores MI

Bentling John R
Kelloggsville HS
Kentwood MI

Benton Kimberly J
Guthrie Center Comn. HS
Guthrie Center IA

Benware Ricky E
Pleasant Hill HS
Pleasant Hill MO

Beranek Linda J
Rice Lake HS
Rice Lake WI

Beranek William M
Aquinas HS
Lacrosse WI

Berberich Connie L
Oklee Public HS
Oklee MN

Berchild Daniel P
Superior HS
Superior WI

Berendt Karol A
Bishop Gallagher HS
Harper Woods MI

Berens Karl A
Victoria HS
Victoria KS

Berg Dennis D
Sterling Public HS
Sterling NE

Berg Donald A
Frederic Remington HS
Valley Center KS

Berg Kenneth E
Oskaloosa Sr HS
Oskaloosa IA

Berg Kevin L
Dassel Cokato HS
Howard Lk MN

Berg Marsha L
Duluth Central HS
Duluth MN

Berg Thomas A
St Thomas Academy
Saint Paul MN

Bergan David L
Lake Mills Community HS
Lake Mills IA

Berge Michael J
Prospect HS
Arlington Hts IL

Bergeman Tim L
Madelia HS
Madelia MN

Berger Christine M
Mount Assisi Acad
Hickory Hills IL

Berger Cindy S
Lansing HS
Leavenworth KS

Berger Jan E
New Trier West HS
Winnetka IL

Berget Crystal J
Black Hawk HS
South Wayne WI

Berget Kyle W
Hancock Public HS
Hancock MN

Bergfield Donald D
Arcola Community HS
Arcola IL

Bergin Mary M
Elizabeth Seton HS
Harvey IL

Bergin Sharon M
Mother Mcauley HS
Oak Forest IL

Bergley Fay P
Bismarck HS
Bismarck ND

Bergman Jack C
Baxter Comm HS
Newton IA

Bergman Leah R
Marshall HS
Marshall MO

Bergmann Glenn L
Pleasant Hill HS
Pleasant Hill MO

Bergmann William G
Pleasant HS
Pleasant Hill MO

Bergmeier Jay M
Tri County HS
De Witt NE

Bergquist Brian J
Abraham Lincoln HS
Council Bluffs IA

Bergquist Christiann
Maine South HS
Park Ridge IL

Bergren Joni L
South Barber HS
Kiowa KS

Bergschneider Beverly A
Franklin HS
Franklin IL

Bergstrom Carl P
Taft HS
Chicago IL

Bergstrom Lita L
Oregon Davis HS
Grovertown IN

Bergthold Tammy L
Paris Rii HS
Perry MO

Bergwin Greg G
South Milwaukee HS
South Milwaukee WI

Berkel Susan C
Woodruff HS
Peoria IL

Berlage James S
Charlevoix HS
Charlevoix MI

Berlin Margaret A
Bonner Springs HS
Bonner Springs KS

Berlin Robert T
Millington HS
Millington MI

Berman Christopher M
Crown Point HS
Crown Point IN

Bermele Beth M
Saint Barbara HS
Chicago IL

Bernard Rebecca J
F J Reitz HS
Evansville IN

Bernard Suzetta R
Lakeland Union HS
Minocqua WI

Bernardi Rose M
Pawnee HS
Pawnee IL

Bernardo Domingo M
Proviso West HS
North Lake IL

Berndt Beth E
Brookfield East HS
Brookfield WI

Berndt Jody L
Blue Earth HS
Blue Earth MN

Berney Susan D
Griswold HS
Griswold IA

Bernhardson Pamela L
Halstad Public HS
Lockhart MN

Bernica Robert G
Hayden HS
Topeka KS

Berning Mark D
Shenandoah Community HS
Shenandoah IA

Berning Sandy K
J C N HS
Nortonville KS

Berns Lucy A
Nokomis HS
Nokomis IL

Berns Maralee R
Clay City HS
Clay City IL

Berreckman Claude E
Cozad HS
Cozad NE

Berry Brenda L
Neelyville HS
Neelyville MO

Berry Calene S
Akron Fairgrove HS
Akron MI

Berry David W
Sidney Comm HS
Percival IA

Berry Doug
Rockville HS
Rockville IN

Berry Dwayne
Rockville HS
Rockville IN

Berry Karin D
University City Sr HS
University City MO

Berry Kim A
Holdrege HS
Holdrege NE

Berry Loni S
Everett HS
Lansing MI

Berry Mark S
Washington HS
Cedar Rapids IA

Berry Michael W
Turner HS
Kansas City KS

Berry Vera L
Chicago Vocational HS
Chicago IL

Bertha Marla P
Academy Of Our Lady
Chicago IL

Bertrand Joseph G
Campion Jesuit HS
Chicago IL

Bertrang Edward P
Oswego Sr HS
Oswego IL

Bertschinger Terese L
St Martins Academy
Hill City SD

Bertucci Mary T
Ishpeming HS
Rapid River MI

Besch Greta J
Superior HS
Superior WI

Besing Jan L
Tecumseh HS
Elberfeld IN

Beson Denise A
Freeland HS
Freeland MI

Bess Juliette M
Peru HS
Peru IN

Bessac Kimberley A
Pardeeville Sr HS
Portage WI

Bessette Paul A
Marist HS
Chicago IL

Bessolo Lori A
Negaunee HS
Negaunee MI

Best Sharon K
Mc Cook HS
Mccook NE

Beswick Ralph W
Rock Island Sr HS
Rock Island IL

Bethel Courtney A
Luther South HS
Chicago IL

Bettenhausen Kathryn A
Peotone HS
Frankfort IL

Bettesworth Daniel G
Dwight D Eisenhower HS
Saginaw MI

Betting Michael R
Ellendale HS
Ellendale ND

Bettis Tammy L
Franklin HS
Franklin IL

Betts Jane E
Southwest HS
Green Bay WI

Betz Cheryl M
Larkin HS
Elgin IL

Bever Dennis W
Sedan HS
Sedan KS

Bey Claudette
Chicago Vocational HS
Chicago IL

Beyer Betty L
Hitchcock Public HS
Wolsey SD

Beyer Elizabeth K
Evanston Twp HS
Evanston IL

Beyer Wanda L
Oconto Falls HS
Oconto Falls WI

Beyers Annette M
Pana HS
Oconee IL

Beyers Kent G
Pana Sr HS
Pana IL

Bialek Richard W
Reavis HS
Burbank IL

Bianco Frederick J
Macon County Ri HS
Macon MO

Bibb Julia A
Jeffersonville HS
Jeffersonville IN

Bibbs Ricky G
Senath Hornersviller HS
Hornersville MO

Bicek Diane P
Bogan HS
Chicago IL

Bicket Chris R
Benton Consolidated HS
Benton IL

Bickford Cecilia L
Decatur Community HS
Oberlin KS

Bicsok Sheryl A
Bentley HS
Burton MI

Biddix Steven C
Adrian HS
Adrian MI

Biddlecom Charles A
Waukegan East HS
Waukegan IL

Biegert Diane J
Lyons Twp HS
La Grange IL

Biehn Julie A
Cleveland Public HS
Madison Lake MN

Bielawa Donna M
Mc Henry HS
Mchenry IL

Bienek Paul F
Harvey HS
Harvey ND

Bierlein Louann A
Reese HS
Vassar MI

Bierma Mike R
Maurice Orange City HS
Orange City IA

Bierman Laura L
Holy Family HS
Lindsay NE

Biernot Marilyn S
Port Huron Northern HS
Port Huron MI

Biesterfeld Janelle
Russell HS
Russell KS

Bievenue Diane L
Red Bud HS
Pr Du Rocher IL

Biga Mary A
Daniel J Gross HS
Omaha NE

Bigby John W
Carrollton HS
Carrollton MO

Bigelow Clifford E
Engadine HS
Epoufette MI

Biggs Amy J
Murphysboro Twp HS
Murphysboro IL

Bigham Larry D
Pinckneyville HS
Pinckneyville IL

Bigham Rodney B
Perry Lecompton HS
Grantville KS

Bigler Mary J
Anna Jonesboro HS
Anna IL

Bigley Denise A
Eldora Comm HS
Eldora IA

Bigley Teresa D
Culver Comm HS
Culver IN

Biglow Jennifer A
St Louis Park HS
St Louis Park MN

Bilderback Michael R
Southridge HS
Huntingburg IN

Bill David C
Normal Community HS
Normal IL

Billings Dave G
Northrop HS
Fort Wayne IN

Billings Larry G
Clear Lake Community HS
Clear Lake IA

Billings Leslie A
Blue Valley HS
Olathe KS

Billington Jayne M
Benkelman HS
Benkelman NE

Bills Luann R
Polk Public HS
Polk NE

Biltz Timothy G
Whitko HS
Pierceton IN

Binde Cherlyn K
Ray HS
Ray ND

Bindschatel Brenda J
Clio HS
Clio MI

Bingham Cynthia L
Mexico Sr HS
Mexico MO

Bingham Tammy S
Mulberry Grove HS
Greenville IL

Binney Lora L
Gallatin R V HS
Gallatin MO

Bird Patricia A
Vienna HS
Vienna IL

Birk Ramona J
Jasper HS
Jasper IN

STUDENTS PHOTOGRAPH SCHEDULED FOR PUBLICATION HERE COULD NOT BE REPRODUCED

Birkner Michele D
Morton HS
Morton IL

Birman Judith L
Gull Lake HS
Battle Creek MI

Biros Patricia R
Evergreen Pk Comm HS
Evergreen Pk IL

Birukoff Kristy S
Omro HS
Omro WI

Bisaillon David W
Bradley Bourbonnais HS
Bourbnnais IL

Bischoff Gloria J
Beaver Dam Sr HS
Beaver Dam WI

Bishop John F
Our Lady Of The Lakes HS
Pontiac MI

Bishop Larry J
North Decatur HS
Greensburg IN

Bishop Libby E
Ogallala Sr HS
Ogallala NE

Bishop Linda S
Rock Island HS
Rock Island IL

Bishop Mark A
Indianola HS
Indianola IA

Bishop Nancy A
Cheney HS
Cheney KS

Bishop Timothy C
Chesaning Union HS
Oakley MI

Bishopp James A
Sheldon HS
Sheldon IL

Biss Douglas D
Bridgeport HS
Bridgeport NE

Bissell Theodore R
Boyceville HS
Boyceville WI

Bitney Cheryl A
Bloomer HS
Bloomer WI

Bitting Robin D
Whitko HS
South Whitley IN

Bittner Debra K
Hoisington HS
Hoisington KS

Bivens Leslee D
Holdrege Sr HS
Holdrege NE

Bixler Dorinda S
Hayes Center Public HS
Hayes Center NE

Bjorgaard Lori L
Marshall County Central HS
Newfolden MN

Bjorneberg Timothy K
Canton HS
Canton SD

Bjornson Pat A
Central HS
New Rockford ND

Black Anita D
Madison Sr HS
Madison IL

Black David J
Downers Grove North HS
Downers Grove IL

Black Kerry L
Maine Twp Hs N HS
Des Plaines IL

Blackaby Patricia L
New Bloomfield R Iii HS
New Bloomfield MO

Blackburn Linda C
Taylorville HS
Taylorville IL

Blackburn Peggy
Prairie Hgts HS
Hudson IN

Blackford Bill H
Triton HS
Tippecanoe IN

Blacklaw Susan L
Hubbard HS
Chicago IL

Blackman Mark P
Marion Sr HS
Marion IL

Blackmore Max L
North Putnam HS
Coatesville IN

Blackmore Michael D
North Putnam HS
Coatesville IN

Blackwell Linda K
Excelsior Springs W HS
Excelsior Springs MO

Blackwell Regina M
Neenah HS
Neenah WI

Blain Amy L
Walkerville HS
Walkerville MI

Blaine Diane K
Swan Valley HS
Saginaw MI

Blair Janet L
Benkelman HS
Benkelman NE

Blair Kenneth L
Ashland HS
Ashland IL

Blair Terence C
Wrightstown HS
Kaukauna WI

Blaisdell Debbie L
Kalkaska HS
Kalkaska MI

Blake Andrea L
Ottawa Hills HS
Grand Rapids MI

Blake Charles D
Liberty Sr HS
Liberty MO

Blakely Helen R
Ovid Elsie HS
Elsie MI

Blakely Joan L
Elkton Pigeon Bay Port HS
Bay Port MI

Blakely Linda K
Winfield HS
Winfield KS

Blakey David L
Toulon HS
Toulon IL

Blakley Kathleen A
Moline HS
Moline IL

Blakley Krista L
West Platte R Ii HS
Weston MO

Blakley Linda C
Mt Vernon HS
Mt Vernon IN

Blanchard Kim Y
Charlevoix HS
Charlevoix MI

Blanco Orlando L
Monsignor Hackett HS
Kalamazoo MI

Bland Barbara J
Bethany HS
Bethany IL

Blane Joy D
Woodruff HS
Peoria IL

Blankenburg Rita K
Greenfield R 4 HS
Greenfield MO

Blankenship Debra G
Limestone Comm HS
Peoria IL

Blankenship Marcia R
Columbus Unified HS
Columbus KS

Blankenship Robert J
Salina S HS
Salina KS

Blankenship Shari A
Carrollton HS
Carrollton MO

Blase Jim G
St Louis Univ HS
St Louis MO

Blaser Kelly L
Norfolk HS
Norfolk NE

Blaser Melvin A
Rockridge HS
Milan IL

Blasius James F
Proviso West HS
Berkeley IL

Blasko Kimberly A
St Peter & Paul HS
Saginaw MI

Blastic Sharon L
Lakeland Union HS
Woodruff WI

Blatchford Timothy P
Parchment HS
Parchment MI

Blattner Joan E
St Charles HS
S Tcharles MO

Blazek Cynthia J
Prescott Comm HS
Prescott IA

Blazek Don E
Bennington HS
Omaha NE

Blazek Thomas J
Morton East HS
Cicero IL

Bleazard George R
Marshall HS
Marshall MO

Bledsoe Bradford S
Springs Valley HS
West Baden IN

Bledsoe Bryan A
Springs Valley HS
West Baden IN

Bleeke Richard R
Wayne HS
Ft Wayne IN

Blehm Mark A
Russell HS
Russell KS

Blehm Sharon K
Gering HS
Gering NE

Blesi Betsy
Sullivan HS
Sullivan MO

Blesi Joycelyn K
Sullivan HS
Sullivan MO

Bless Michael C
Lanphier HS
Springfield IL

Blessing Deidra A
South Harrison HS
Bethany MO

Blessing Martin G
Warsaw Comm HS
Warsaw IN

Blevins Vanetta J
Highland HS
Highland KS

Blickensderfer Michael D
Cerro Gordo HS
Cerro Gordo IL

Blickensderfer Peggy S
Cerro Gordo HS
Cerro Gordo IL

Blickhan William P
Bement HS
Ivesdale IL

Blink Jeffrey A
Antigo HS
Antigo WI

Blinsky Terry L
Wishek Public HS
Wishek ND

Bliss Leslie J
Norfolk Sr HS
Norfolk NE

Blobaum Dawn A
Ft Dodge Sr HS
Ft Dodge IA

Bloch William F
St Clair HS
St Clair MI

Block Joseph E
Romeoville HS
Romeoville IL

Blocker Bruce W
West HS
Davenport IA

Blodgett Le Ann C
Ontonagon Area HS
Ontonagon MI

Bloebaum Heidi J
Waynesville HS
Ft Leonard Wood MO

Bloechl Timothy D
Oshkosh No HS
Oshkosh WI

Blom Joel W
Pella Comm HS
Pella IA

Blom Shirley A
Pella Christian HS
Pella IA

Blomquist William A
Rockford Guilford HS
Rockford IL

Blood Terry R
Sacred Heart HS
Salina KS

Bloodworth Darlyne K
Hamilton J Robichaud HS
Inkster MI

Bloomburg Lynda L
Kingsford HS
Iron Mountain MI

Bloomfield Patricia A
Ashland HS
Ashland IL

Blow Michael A
Hamtramck HS
Hamtramck MI

Blue Donna J
Eagle Grove HS
Eagle Grove IA

Blue Larry A
Glenbrook South HS
Glenview IL

Blum David J
Millard HS
Omaha NE

Blum Randy L
Jefferson HS
Monroe MI

Blume Curtis L
Clarinda Comm HS
Clarinda IA

Blumenstock Cheryl A
Crab Orchard HS
Marion IL

Blumer Bruce L
Aberdeen Central HS
Aberdeen SD

Blumer Robert L
Monroe HS
Monroe WI

Blumreich Karen E
Waterford Mott HS
Pontiac MI

Blunk Joseph W
Providence HS
New Albany IN

Blunk Scott D
Elm Creek HS
Elm Creek NE

Blunk William E
Brunswick Jr&sr HS
Brunswick MO

Bly Brenda J
Drayton Public HS
Drayton ND

Blythe Benda R
Andover HS
Wichita KS

Board Rosemary L
Harlem HS
Loves Park IL

Boatright Dana D
Remington HS
Newton KS

Boatright Leslie S
Brookfield Riii HS
Brookfield MO

Bobbe Laurie E
Ellendale HS
Forbes ND

Bobick Cheryl L
Rochester Adams HS
Rochester MI

Bobka Thomas E
Maine South HS
Norridge IL

Bobolz Rita K
Hartley HS
Hartley IA

Bobowski John M
Fordson HS
Dearborn MI

Bobula Thomas G
Gordon Tech HS
Chicago IL

Bocchiardi Mariann
Mt Vernon Township HS
Mt Vernon IL

Bochtler James F
St Bede HS
Dalzell IL

Bock Carrie M
Carpio Public HS
Foxholm ND

Bockus Freddie J
North Platte Sr HS
North Platte NE

Bode Alan J
Aplington Community HS
Austinville IA

Bode Sharon E
Helias HS
Jefferson City MO

Boden Cindy E
Bloomington HS
Bloomington IL

Bodenbender Beverly E
Boscobel HS
Boscobel WI

Bodine Randy L
Mt Zion HS
Decatur IL

Bodner Steven C
Park Tudor HS
Indianapolis IN

Bodtke Dennis R
Beatrice HS
Beatrice NE

Bodtke Jean M
Bloom Twp HS
Chicago Hgts IL

Boeck Brian C
Shelby Tennant HS
Portsmouth IA

Boedecker Sandra K
Rockwell City Comm HS
Rockwell City IA

Boeder Don E
Gibbon Public HS
Gibbon MN

Boeder Terry K
Cosmos HS
Cosmos MN

Boehnke Rebecca S
Ventura HS
Garner IA

Boehs Kenneth P
Triopia HS
Bluffs IL

Boekhout Barbara A
Laboure HS
St Louis MO

Boelman Dara J
Boone Jr Sr HS
Boone IA

Boerman Twyla R
Byron Center HS
Byron Center MI

Boersma Eugene J
Central HS
Pipestone MN

Boesdorfer Marcia L
Pleasant Plains HS
Pleasant Plains IL

Boetel Rodney L
Hartley Comm HS
Hartley IA

Boetsma Debra L
Culver Comm HS
Culver IN

Boettcher Carl S
Bonduel HS
Bonduel WI

Boge Michael D
Bloomington HS
Bloomington IL

Bogenrief Bonnie B
Rockford West Sr HS
Rockford IL

Boggs Debra D
River Rouge HS
River Rouge MI

Boggs Janilee K
Mormon Trail HS
Weldon IA

Boggs Jean M
Divernon HS
Divernon IL

Boggs Jo E
Tippecanoe Valley HS
Warsaw IN

Boggs William J
Tippecanoe Valley HS
Mentone IN

Bogi John P
Dundee HS
Monroe MI

Bogle Marian D
Norwich HS
Norwich KS

Bogolin Josephine M
Lourdes HS
Chicago IL

Bogue Elizabeth A
Gull Lake HS
Augusta MI

Bogue Russell G
Hays HS
Hays KS

Boguszewski Michael J
Bradley Bourbonnais HS
Bradley IL

Bohan Jack A
St Joseph HS
Chicago IL

Bohland Michelle L
De Soto HS
De Soto WI

Bohlen Earl D
Milbank HS
Milbank SD

Bohlen Pamela J
Armstrong Township HS
Fithian IL

Bohler William J
Batavia Sr HS
Batavia IL

Bohlin Cynthia A
Hector Community HS
Hector MN

Bohling Grace K
St Pauls College HS
Concordia MO

Bohling Veronica J
Les Cheneaux HS
Cedarville MI

Bohlmann Gretchen A
Watseka Comm HS
Watseka IL

Bohls Roger A
Castlewood Independent HS
Castlewood SD

Bohm Raymond A
Seymour HS
Seymour IN

Bohn Robert F
Maconaquah HS
No Manchester IN

Bohner Sara L
Hillsdale HS
Osseo MI

Boho Bonnie A
Elizabeth Seton HS
South Holland IL

Boike Candice A
Nazareth Academy
Brookfield IL

Bojanowski Maryellen B
Argo Community HS
Summit IL

Bokhart Judith E
Lake Michigan Catholic HS
Benton Harbor MI

Bokhoven Nancy B
Pella Christian HS
New Sharon IA

Bolam Leslie J
Pekin Community HS
Pekin IL

Bolan Robin K
Norway HS
Norway MI

Bole Christy L
Athens HS
Battle Creek MI

Boles Charles L
Savannah R 3 HS
Savannah MO

Bolin Paul K
Carmel HS
Carmel IN

Bolinger Donald J
Haworth HS
Kokomo IN

Bollard Paul W
Pocahontas Community HS
Pocahontas IA

Bollier Philip A
Leo HS
Grabill IN

Bollinger Kim R
Astoria HS
Browning IL

Bollinger Rebecca G
St Charles HS
St Charles MO

Bollinger Sheri L
Bremen Public HS
Bremen IN

Bollivar Johnna L
Prophetstown HS
Prophetstown IL

Bolton Bradley J
Lauton HS
Lauton MI

Boltz James K
Big Springs HS
Big Springs NE

Bombach Daniel B
Bourbon HS
Cuba MO

Bomberger Mary L
Lincoln Southeast HS
Lincoln NE

Bommerscheim Judith A
Plainwell HS
Kalamazoo MI

Bonack Jeannette M
Three Lakes HS
Three Lakes WI

Bonar Kim E
Garrett HS
Auburn IN

Bonardi Gregory A
Harper Creek HS
Ceresco MI

Bond Penny S
Milford Twp HS
Milford IL

Bonde Kevin
Kiel HS
Kiel WI

Bone Donna L
Mc Donald County R 1 HS
Pineville MO

Bonicatto David J
Hibbing HS
Hibbing MN

Bonifield Von L
Hannibal HS
Hull IL

Bonini Bruce E
Lake Linden HS
Lake Linden MI

Bonisa Robin M
Heritage Christian HS
New Palestine IN

Bonkowski Jerome L
St Willibrord HS
Chicago IL

Bonnema Craig L
Storm Lake Sr HS
Storm Lake IA

Bonney Bret C
Fredericktown HS
Fredericktown MO

Bonney Robert A
St Charles HS
St Charles MO

Bonte Janette A
Washburn Rural HS
Wakarusa KS

Bontekoe Jane E
Linden HS
Linden MI

Booe Cindy L
Parkwood HS
Joplin MO

Booher Frandora
Bluffton HS
Bluffton IN

Booker Karen S
North Salem HS
North Salem IN

Books Cathy L
Hillsdale HS
Hillsdale MI

Bookwalter Dwayne R
Grayslake Community HS
Grayslake IL

Boomgaarden Mark L
West Sioux HS
Hawanden IA

Boorsma Roxann P
Mona Shores HS
Muskegon MI

Boose Diane C
Niles HS
Niles MI

Booth Carrin V
Concordia Acad
St Paul MN

Booth Cynthia L
Washington HS
Brighton IA

Booth Sandy A
Oak Park Academy
Cedar Rapids IA

Booth Teddie L
Beach HS
Beach ND

Bootter Ronald A
Evart HS
Evart MI

Borchert Eddy C
West Vigo HS
West Terre Haute IN

Bordwell Richard E
Pocahontas Comm HS
Pocahontas IA

Borer Nancy S
Pleasant Hill HS
Pleasant Hill MO

Borgard Leann R
Rutland HS
Nunda SD

Borges Jerome F
Glasgow R Ii HS
Glasgow MO

Borgmeyer Ellen J
Duchesne HS
St Charles MO

Borino Sheryl A
St Cecilia HS
Hastings NE

Borio Diane
St Francis Academy
Joliet IL

Bork Wayne A
Ford Central HS
Piper City IL

Borkovich Sandra D
Bogan HS
Chicago IL

Borland Michael A
Humboldt HS
Humboldt IA

Born Tammara D
Cerro Gordo HS
Hammond IL

Borrello Joseph A
Fordson HS
Dearborn MI

Borrowman Steven W
Monroe City HS
Monroe City MO

Borst Denise L
Durand Area HS
Lennon MI

Bortell Russell D
Jonesville HS
Jonesville MI

Borton Allen L
Interlochen Arts Academy
Manitou Beach MI

Borton Loretta K
Nesco HS
Zearing IA

Bos Timothy
Zeeland Public HS
Zeeland MI

Bosch Janet S
Mayville HS
Mayville WI

Bosch Kathryn S
Ogden HS
Ogden IA

Boschert Julie R
Duchesne HS
St Charles MO

Boschert Victoria C
Duchesne HS
St Charles MO

Bose Theresa M
Estherville HS
Estherville IA

Bosio John P
Houghton HS
Chassell MI

Boss Kellen L
Monroe Senior HS
Monroe WI

Boss Michael S
Shelby Public HS
Shelby NE

Bossarte Cheryl L
Seymour HS
Payson IL

Bossert Peter T
Hartford Union HS
Hartford WI

Bost Kevin W
Murphysboro Township
HS
Murphysboro IL

Bostick David A
Joliet Central HS
Joliet IL

Boston Gary E
Lanphier HS
Springfield IL

Boston Rory R
Alma Public HS
Alma NE

Boston Sandra A
Elizabeth Seton HS
Calumet City IL

Boswell Debra S
Jennings Co HS
Nebraska IN

Boswell Kaye L
Wethersfield HS
Kewanee IL

Both Benjamin A
Watseka Comm HS
Watseka IL

Bothwell Brent S
Parkview HS
Springfield MO

Bottolfson Bill E
Hastings Senior HS
Hastings NE

Bottomley Bruce J
B Carroll HS
Wichita KS

Botwinski Christopher M
Herrin HS
Herrin IL

Boudreau Marc A
Bradley Bourbonnais HS
Bourbonnais IL

Boudreau Patricia M
Bradley Bourbonnais
Comm HS
Bourbonnais IL

Boughan Patricia A
Three Rivers HS
Three Rivers MI

Boulware William T
South Shelby HS
Shelbina MO

Boundy David E
Holland HS
Holland MI

Bourisaw Michael M
Blue Mound HS
Blue Mound IL

Bourn Cindy L
Gorin R Iii HS
Gorin MO

Bousho David L
Chippewa Valley HS
Mt Clemens MI

Boven Cindy L
Mattawan HS
Mattawan MI

Bowden Diana L
Terre Haute North Vigo HS
Brazil IN

Bowen Carla J
Highland HS
Troy KS

Bowen Cary J
Riverdale HS
Riverdale ND

Bowen Cheryl R
Durand Unified HS
Durand WI

Bowen Donald D
Henry Senachwine HS
Henry IL

Bowen Eric L
Clinton Prairie HS
Colfax IN

Bowen Karen A
Durand Unified HS
Durand WI

Bowen Mark K
Hillsboro HS
Hillsboro IL

Bowen Pamela R
Nevada HS
Nevada MO

Bower Laurie A
Ottawa Twp HS
Ottawa IL

Bowerman Richard A
Trico HS
Willisville IL

Bowers Catherine A
Gaylord HS
Gaylord MI

Bowers David B
Oregon Davis HS
Hamlet IN

Bowers Frankie L
Greenwood HS
Springfield MO

Bowers Phillip C
Hordville HS
Hordville NE

Bowlds Thomas R
Tinley Park HS
Tinley Park IL

Bowling Chris E
Covington Community HS
Covington IN

Bowling Kent A
Madison Cons HS
Madison IN

Bowling Shelbie K
Delta C 7 HS
Deering MO

Bowman James R
Lakeland Union HS
Minocqua WI

Bowman Kathy S
Kewanee HS
Kewanee IL

Bowman Lea C
Hamilton Hts HS
Cicero IN

Bowman Merry T
Deland Weldon HS
Weldon IL

Bowman Patricia A
Northwest HS
House Springs MO

Bowman Rodney L
Polo Comm HS
Polo IL

Bown Kim M
Sully Buttes HS
Onida SD

Boxberger Harold G
Hoisington HS
Hoisington KS

Boyce Jeffrey W
Durand HS
Durand MI

Boyce Warren E
Hope HS
Hope KS

Boyd Brenda K
Streator Twp HS
Streator IL

Boyd Craig A
Memorial HS
Joplin MO

Boyd Debbie A
Charleston HS
Westfield IL

Boyd Debra S
Reading HS
Reading MI

Boyd Inman W
South HS
Wichita KS

Boyd Jeffrey T
Charleston HS
Charleston IL

Boyd Jim R
Avon HS
Avon IL

Boyd Kent A
Mora HS
Mora MN

Boyd Mark L
Forest Lake Sr HS
Forest Lake MN

Boyd Teresa S
Tri Jr Sr HS
Cambridge City IN

Boyd Thomas C
Riverside Brookfield HS
Brookfield IL

Boyer Judy A
Sutherland Public HS
Sutherland NE

Boyer Rick
Moravia Community HS
Unionville IA

Boyken Janine B
Titonka Cons HS
Titonka IA

Boyle Doloros C
So Sioux City HS
So Sioux City NE

Boyle Julie J
Sycamore Sr HS
Sycamore IL

Boyle Patricia L
Dexter HS
Whitmore Lake MI

Boyles Dawne Marie T
Kapaun Mt Carmel HS
Wichita KS

Boyles Gayla M
Burr Oak HS
Burr Oak KS

Boysen Donna M
Bowdle HS
Bowdle SD

Boyts Jerry D
Central HS
Springfield MO

Bozich Mark P
Hillcrest HS
Country Club Hills IL

Braasch Paula J
Carl Sandburg HS
Orland Park IL

Braaten Colleen R
Naperville Central HS
Naperville IL

Braaten David A
Oslo HS
Manvel ND

Brabec Bruce E
Braham HS
Braham MN

Brabec Cindy S
Howells Public HS
Howells NE

Brachear Dan E
Rochester HS
Rochester IL

Brachear Deborah K
Rochester HS
Rochester IL

Bracher Jeffrey L
Carmel For Boys HS
Mundelein IL

Brachle Danny R
Petersburg HS
Albion NE

Brackey Alan C
Lake Mills Community HS
Lake Mills IA

Braden James R
Marysville HS
Marysville MI

Bradford Marcia M
Schoolcraft HS
Schoolcraft MI

Bradley Barbara L
Addison Trail HS
Addison IL

Bradley Debra A
Western Dubuque HS
Epworth IA

Bradley Janice M
Streator Twp HS
Streator IL

Bradley Patricia L
Dodge City Sr HS
Dodge City KS

Bradley Shelley D
Ulysses HS
Ulysses KS

Bradley Stephanie O
Immaculata HS
Detroit MI

Bradney William E
Elgin HS
Hanover Park IL

Bradshaw Robert B
Boonville HS
Boonville MO

Brady Gerald L
Galena R2 HS
Galena MO

Brady Mary P
Central Catholic HS
Bloomington IL

Brady Rosanne K
Park Hill HS
Kansas City MO

Brady Sharon A
Gladstone Area HS
Gladstone MI

Bragg Larry M
Northwestern HS
Sumner MO

Bragg Stephen W
W Nodaway R1 HS
Burlington Jct MO

Brainard David A
Bishop Noll Institute
Highland IN

Brake Linda J
Glendale HS
Springfield MO

Braley Karma J
Northwestern HS
Modesto IL

Bralick Andrew E
Sargent Public HS
Sargent NE

Braman Corrie E
Tomahawk HS
Tomahawk WI

Braman Dave E
Tomahawk HS
Tomahawk WI

Braman Kerry A
Fulton HS
Ashley MI

Bramlet John S
Naperville Central HS
Naperville IL

Branam Brent
Finney HS
Detroit MI

Branch Pamela D
Meridian HS
Edenville MI

Branch Roxanne J
Pine River HS
Leroy MI

Branch Stephen C
Harlem HS
Loves Park IL

Brancheau Anne M
St Mary Academy
Monroe MI

Brand Jennifer A
Brown County HS
Nashville IN

Brand John D
Batavia HS
Batavia IL

Brandibur Karen A
Kingston HS
Kingston MI

Brandley Kim S
Northeastern HS
Foutain City IN

Brandt Calvin V
New Haven HS
New Haven MO

Brandt Donna G
Sweet Springs R 7 HS
La Monte MO

Brandt Samuel J
Garretson HS
Sherman SD

Braneky Donna K
Okawville HS
Okawville IL

Branham Kerry I
Northland Pines HS
Eagle River WI

Branine Shirley A
Winfield HS
Winfield KS

Branlund Ruby J
South Shore HS
Iron River WI

Brannaman Marie L
Lincoln Comm HS
Mechanicsville IA

Brannick Kathy M
Minooka HS
Minooka IL

Branson Suzanne M
Sullivan HS
Sullivan MO

Branting Darryl L
North Platte Senior HS
North Platte NE

Branting Tina M
North Platte HS
North Platte NE

Brantley Denise M
Chicago Vocational HS
Chicago IL

Brantner Becky S
Mendota Township HS
Mendota IL

Brasch Kathleen A
Mooseheart HS
Mooseheart IL

Braschler Cheryl L
South Haven HS
South Haven MI

Brasel Marilyn J
Anna Jonesboro Comm HS
Anna IL

Brashaw Paul W
Bridgeport HS
Saginaw MI

Brashear Janice F
Southern Boone County R 1 HS
Hartsburg MO

Brask Diane M
Grantsburg HS
Frederic WI

Braswell Ruth M
Cvs HS
Chicago IL

Bratland Bruce L
Twin Rivers HS
Bade IA

Bratten Steven J
Senior HS
Jefferson City MO

Bratton Ronald R
North Davitss HS
Plainville IN

Brattstrom Candice M
Tinley Park HS
Tinley Park IL

Brauer Martin J
Concordia Academy
St Paul MN

Brauher Sheree L
Waterford Twnshp HS
Pontiac MI

Braun Edward A
Princeton HS
Princeton MN

Braun Joseph A
Hibbing HS
Hibbing MN

Braun Stanley D
Baldwin HS
Baldwin City KS

Braun Stephen G
Athens HS
Athens WI

Braunagel Darwin D
Harvey HS
Harvey ND

Brauner Brenda R
Highland HS
Anderson IN

Braunscheidel Jeffrey J
Plymouth Salem HS
Plymouth MI

Braunschweig Gail D
Pocahontas Community HS
Pocahontas IA

Braunschweig Kay M
Beaver Dam Sr HS
Beaver Dam WI

Braverman Sheleen C
Brainerd HS
Brainerd MN

Brawner James S
Kirksville Senior HS
Kirksville MO

Brawner Jeff M
Kirksville Sr HS
Kirksville MO

Bray Arthur C
Bellflower Township HS
Bellflower IL

Bray Debbie S
Saybrook Arrowsmith HS
Arrowsmith IL

Bray Dennis D
Clinton HS
Clinton MO

Bray George W
Ogemaw Heights HS
West Branch MI

Bray Paula D
Lakeland R Iii HS
Lowry City MO

Bray Roger A
Blair HS
Ft Calhoun NE

Bray Russell D
Elkhorn HS
Elkhorn WI

Braye Pamela G
Nokomis HS
Nokomis IL

Brazelton Lynn
Lathrop HS
Lathrop MO

Brazinski Jeanne E
Marissa HS
Coulterville IL

Breault Rick A
Evergreen Park Comm HS
Evergreen Park IL

Brechin Monica A
Addison Trail HS
Addison IL

Brecht Ann M
Pt Austin Public HS
Port Austin MI

Bredeweg Deborah J
L And M HS
Lyons IN

Bredeweg Reita J
Central HS
Worthington IN

Breed Pat A
Nathan Hale HS
West Allis WI

Breeden David M
Norris City Omaha HS
Broughton IL

Breeden Sandra L
Chillicothe Rii HS
Chillicothe MO

Breeding Lyle A
Plymouth HS
Plymouth IN

Breedlove Frances L
Maconaquah HS
Amboy IN

Breedlove John D
Forman HS
Manito IL

Brehmer Betty J
Grant Deuel HS
Revillo SD

Brehmer Danny W
Litchfield Sr HS
Litchfield MN

Brehmer Kenneth A
Wausau East HS
Wausau WI

Brehmer William G
Hoven HS
Hoven SD

Breinig Dennis J
Acapahoe HS
Arapahoe NE

Breitenstein Colleen C
St Charles HS
St Charles MO

Breitung Terry L
Cochrane Fountain City HS
Fountain City WI

Breitweiser Karen J
Homestead HS
Mequon WI

Bremer Jill A
Abbotsford HS
Abbotsford WI

Bremmer Martin L
Lockport Central HS
Lockport IL

Brennan Glenn A
Morton Sr HS
Hammond IN

Brennan Mark E
Columbia City Joint HS
Columbia City IN

Brennan Mary K
James Whitcomb Riley HS
South Bend IN

Brennan Terri A
Cary Grove HS
Cary IL

Brennan Veronica R
Naperville Central HS
Naperville IL

Brenneke Mary C
Jefferson City Sr HS
Jefferson City MO

Brenneman John T
Warsaw Comm HS
Winona Lake IN

Brent George M
Heyworth HS
Heyworth IL

Brenton Wyndy G
Hersey HS
Wheeling IL

Bresette Edward A
Papillion HS
La Vista NE

Bresina Lynn M
St Croix HS
Solon Springs WI

Breslin Debra
Dansville Agricultural HS
Dansville MI

Bretz Michelle D
Morris Sr HS
Morris MN

Breuer Theresa L
Sheldon Community HS
Sheldon IA

Breunig Carla J
Sandwich Comm HS
Sandwich IL

Brewer Gregory M
Naperville Central HS
Naperville IL

Brewer Jennifer A
Mona Shores HS
Muskegon MI

Brewer Joyce E
Bethany HS
Moweaqua IL

Brewer Scot E
Tuscola HS
Tuscola IL

Brewner Sherri D
Carlyle HS
Shattuc IL

Brewster Bradley W
Sanborn Public HS
Sanborn MN

Brewster Pat E
Silver Lake HS
Silver Lake KS

Brickner Joetta J
Garrison HS
Douglas ND

Bridenstine Colleen H
St Charles HS
St Charles IL

Bridge Janey A
Norfolk SeniorHS
Norfolk NE

Bridge Jody L
Neligh Public HS
Neligh NE

Bridge Loretta S
Frontier HS
Monticello IN

Bridges Cindy E
Windsor HS
Windsor IL

Bridges Debra J
Hammond Baptist HS
Flossmoor IL

Bridges Donna S
Woodland R 4 HS
Lutesville MO

Bridges Larry W
Harrisonville Sr HS
Harrisonville MO

Bridges Stephen J
Coldwater HS
Coldwater MI

Bridson Theresa L
Keith Country Day HS
Belvidere IL

Briel Bonnie L
West HS
Green Bay WI

Brierley Heather C
Oak Park River Forest HS
Oak Park IL

Briggs Abraham
St Ignatius College Prep
Chicago IL

Briggs Hazen S
Oakland Christian HS
Pontiac MI

Briggs Tracy G
Bucklin Rii HS
Bucklin MO

Bright Julie R
Sully Buttes HS
Onida SD

Bright Lois A
O Neill Public HS
O Neill NE

Brill Janet A
New Holstein Sr HS
Malone WI

Brilley Donald E
St Teresa HS
Decatur IL

Brin Glen A
Niles North HS
Skokie IL

Brincks Donna L
Kuemper HS
Carroll IA

Bringgold Rhonda L
Harvey HS
Harvey ND

Brink Edward E
Plattsmouth HS
Plattsmouth NE

Brink Mary A
Graceville Public HS
Dumont MN

Brink William A
Deer River HS
Deer River MN

Brinker John P
Axtell HS
Axtell KS

Brinkley Jerry L
East Richland HS
Olney IL

Brinkman Laurel L
Garner Hayfield Comm HS
Garner IA

Brinson Margie E
Springs Valley HS
French Lick IN

Briscoe James L
Canton R U HS
Williamstown MO

Briscoe Kelly A
South Beloit HS
South Beloit IL

Brisson Debbie L
Forest Lake HS
Forest Lake MN

Brisson Marlene E
Larimore HS
Larimore ND

Bristol Kevin C
Lutheran North HS
Bridgeton MO

Britt Anne M
O Fallon Township HS
O Fallon IL

Britt Sandra J
Patoka Comm Unit 100
HS
Vernon IL

Britten Jolene M
Weyerhaeuser HS
New Auburn WI

Britten Linda M
Orient Macksburg HS
Creston IA

Brittingham Mary A
Plainfield Jr Sr HS
Plainfield IN

Britton Steven R
Wauwatosa West HS
Wauwatosa WI

Broadfoot John C
St Charles HS
St Charles MO

Broberg Loren D
Elkhorn Valley HS
Newman Grove NE

Brock Bryan C
Wichita North HS
Wichita KS

Brock Tammy S
Eastridge HS
Kankakee IL

Brockemeier Grant J
Wisner Pilger HS
Wisner NE

Brocker Richard A
Winnebago HS
Pecatonica IL

Brockgreitens Michael J
Duchesne HS
St Charles MO

Brockman Barbara L
Marinette HS
Marinette WI

Brockman Steven M
Lake Central HS
Schereville IN

Brockmeyer Tracy L
Lincolnwood HS
Harvel IL

Brockstein Sharon F
Maine Twp East HS
Des Plaines IL

Brockus Burl F
Moulton Udell HS
Moulton IA

Brodberg Cheryl M
Mason HS
Mason MI

Brodecky Ernie F
Howells HS
Howells NE

Broderick William R
George Rogers Clark HS
Whiting IN

Brodersen Jacob K
Wm G Mather HS
Munising MI

Broeder Connie S
Maywood HS
North Platte NE

Brokaw Patricia A
Gchs South HS
Granite City IL

Bromer Susan J
Lemont Township HS
Lemont IL

Brondyke Diane K
Fulton HS
Fulton IL

Bronson Eric E
Union City HS
Sherwood MI

Brooker Annette L
Pittsburg Sr HS
Pittsburg KS

Brookhouser Gregory J
Plattsmouth HS
Plattsmouth NE

Brookins Deborah A
George S Parker HS
Janesville WI

Brooks Deania R
Newton Comm HS
Newton IL

Brooks Janet W
North Clay HS
Louisville IL

Brooks Joseph D
Carthage Comm HS
Carthage IL

Brooks Kemarie
South Haven HS
South Haven MI

Brooks Lisa G
Ann Arbor Huron HS
Ann Arbor MI

Brooks Lorraine K
John Marshall HS
Indianapolis IN

Brooks Margie L
Stephen Decatur HS
Decatur IL

Brooks Sandra L
Hastings HS
Hastings MI

Brooks Steven E
Heritage Christian HS
Anderson IN

Brooks Sue K
Coldwater HS
Coldwater MI

Brooks William R
Winfield HS
Winfield KS

Brosseau Johnny K
Crane HS
Crane MO

Broten Peggy A
Roseau HS
Roseau MN

Broughton Clifford M
Lincoln Park HS
Lincoln Park MI

Broughton La Danta S
El Dorado Spgs R 2 HS
El Dorado Springs MO

Brouhard Robert E
Greenfield Central HS
Greenfield IN

Brouse Mark A
Lakeshore HS
Stevensville MI

Brower David R
Hamilton HS
Hamilton IL

Brower Leah C
Zeeland Public HS
Zeeland MI

Browers Marcia A
Marquette Sr HS
Marquette MI

Brown Beverly D
Great Bend Sr HS
Great Bend KS

Brown Bill G
Beaman Conrad Liscomb HS
Conrad IA

Brown Brenda L
Columbus North HS
Columbus IN

Brown Brenda S
Butler HS
Butler MO

Brown Brent L
Huntington North HS
Warren IN

Brown Brian K
North Side HS
Fort Wayne IN

Brown Candice C
Warren HS
Warren IL

Brown Carolyn F
St Thomas Apostle HS
Chicago IL

Brown Clifford W
Manual HS
Kansas MO

Brown Cynthia B
North Callaway HS
Auxvasse MO

Brown Daryl L
Hillsdale HS
Hillsdale MI

Brown Dawn E
Mattawan HS
Mattawan MI

Brown Deborah K
Albion HS
Albion MI

Brown Debra S
Twin Lakes HS
Burnettsville IN

Brown Denola M
Thomas Carr Howe HS
Indianapolis IN

Brown Diana S
Diamond Riv HS
Joplin MO

Brown Diane E
Dexter Sr HS
Dexter MO

Brown Donald R
Plato HS
Falcon MO

STUDENTS PHOTOGRAPH SCHEDULED FOR PUBLICATION HERE COULD NOT BE REPRODUCED

Brown Edwin T
Rockhurst HS
Kansas City MO

Brown Ernest J
Shawnee Mission South HS
Overland Park KS

Brown Eugene R
Athens HS
Athens WI

Brown Gayle A
Ocon Sr HS
Oconomowoc WI

Brown Jacqueline T
Anchor Bay HS
New Baltimore MI

Brown James A
Forreston HS
Forreston IL

Brown Janice R
Caro HS
Caro MI

Brown Jeff A
Scranton HS
Gascoyne ND

Brown Jeffrey A
Dundee HS
Dundee MI

Brown Jeffrey W
Evanston Twp HS
Evanston IL

Brown Jerry L
North White HS
Monticello IN

Brown Jerry L
Southeastern HS
Augusta IL

Brown Joe D
Griggsville HS
Girggisville IL

Brown John D
Logansport HS
Logansport IN

Brown Joy A
Aledo HS
Aledo IL

Brown Joyce A
Brazil Sr HS
Brazil IN

Brown Kathryn E
Brazil Senior HS
Brazil IN

Brown Kathy J
Brownstown HS
Brownstown IL

Brown Kenneth E
Soldan HS
St Louis MO

Brown Kevin A
Rochester HS
Rochester IN

STUDENTS PHOTOGRAPH SCHEDULED FOR PUBLICATION HERE COULD NOT BE REPRODUCED

Brown Kimberly L
Memorial HS
Joplin MO

Brown Laurie A
Lewistown HS
Lewistown IL

Brown Leland D
Oldhem HS
Oldham SD

Brown Leslie C
Pierce City HS
Pierce City MO

Brown Linda A
Churubusco HS
Churubusco IN

Brown Lynn D
J C Harmon HS
Kansas City KS

Brown Mark E
Sullivan HS
Sullivan MO

Brown Mary A
Murphysboro HS
Murphysboro IL

Brown Mary J
Grand Blanc HS
Grand Blanc MI

Brown Mary L
St Thomas Apostle HS
Chicago IL

Brown Myrna L
Ancille Domini HS
Plymouth IN

Brown Nancy J
Holden HS
Centerview MO

Brown Nola
St Mary HS
Highland Park MI

Brown Oliver E
Central HS
Minneapolis MN

Brown Patrick D
Anna Jonesboro Comm HS
Anna IL

Brown Paul E
Clarkston HS
Clarkston MI

Brown Penny L
Gallatin HS
Gallatin MO

Brown Phillip L
Nebraska Cty Sr HS
Nebraska City NE

Brown Randy A
Oshkosh West HS
Oshkosh WI

Brown Rebecca A
John Glenn HS
Westland MI

Brown Richard R
Harlan Comm HS
Harlan IA

Brown Ronice J
Batavia Sr HS
Batavia IL

Brown Scott M
Hammond Baptist HS
Alsip IL

Brown Shelby R
Bernie HS
Bernie MO

Brown Steve A
Orrick Public HS
Camden MO

Brown Steve K
Abingdon HS
Abingdon IL

Brown Teresa D
Blue Mound HS
Macon IL

Brown Thomas D
Forest Hills Central HS
Grand Rapids MI

Brown Thomas G
Fenwick HS
Oak Park IL

Brown Tresa M
Bluffs HS
Winchester IL

Brown Valerie J
Gordon HS
Porcupine SD

Brown Valerie K
Lawton HS
Lawton MI

Brown Vern A
Jonesville HS
Jonesville MI

Brown Ward W
Decatur Comm HS
Seldon KS

Browne Alicia M
Elgin Acad
Elgin IL

Browne Sue C
Brookfield East HS
Brookfield WI

Brownfield Kenneth J
South Vigo HS
Terre Haute IN

Browning Lesa A
Meredosia Chambersburg HS
Chambersburg IL

Browning Ron W
Butler HS
Butler MO

Brownlee Kathy L
Rockwell City Comm HS
Rockwell City IA

Brownlee Marcia A
Sabetha Sr HS
Sabetha KS

Broyles Deborah A
Streator HS
Streator IL

Brtko Carolyn A
Bishop Noll Institute HS
Whiting IN

Bruce Camilla L
West Side HS
Gary IN

Bruce Jeanne A
Putnam Co HS
Lucerne MO

Bruce Lesley E
Glenbrook South HS
Glenview IL

Bruce T Jeffery
Andrean HS
Merrillville IN

Bruckner John J
St Johns Mil Academy
Thiensville WI

Bruehlman Laurel J
Argyle HS
Argyle WI

Bruehlman Loren J
Arayle HS
Argyle WI

Brueland Barry L
Walker HS
Ah Gwah Ching MN

Bruggeman Clair J
O Gorman HS
Sioux Falls SD

Brugman Karla K
South Clay Community HS
Webb IA

Bruhn Charles A
River Valley HS
Spring Green WI

Bruketta Stephen P
Farmington East HS
Farmington IL

Brule Mary P
Lafayette HS
Red Lake Falls MN

Brumbaugh Curtis A
Pittsburg HS
Pittsburg KS

Brumley Patricia F
Union HS
Losantville IN

Brumley Rhonda L
Carson Macedonia HS
Carson IA

Brummett Kathy A
Diamond R 4 HS
Diamond MO

Brummett Mark L
Frontier HS
Brookston IN

Brune Kellie A
Richmond Senior HS
Richmond IN

Bruner Gary C
Uniontown HS
Uniontown KS

Bruner Janet M
Ladysmith HS
Ladysmith WI

Brunett Jeffrey L
Paul Harding HS
Fort Wayne IN

Brunette Lisa A
West Bend West HS
West Bend WI

Brungardt David J
Ellis HS
Ellis KS

Bruni Susan C
Port Huron Northern HS
Port Huron MI

Brunik Paul H
Paynesville HS
Paynesville MN

Bruning Donna F
Ellsworth HS
Ellsworth KS

Brunk Lars E
Badger HS
Lake Geneva WI

Brunken Karen J
Clarks Public HS
Clarks NE

Brunken Rodney D
Oak Park Academy
Burlington IA

Brunko Anne Marie S
Independence HS
Brandon IA

Brunmeier Kila M
Sully Buttes HS
Onida SD

Brunner Karen S
Mason Co Eastern HS
Custer MI

Brunner Roni Marie
Cook HS
Angora MN

Brunnert Gerald G
Central Catholic HS
West Point NE

Bruns Debra L
Greenway HS
Grand Rapids MN

Brusuen Myron K
Mahnomen HS
Mahnomen MN

Brutcher Brian E
Princeton HS
Princeton IL

Bryan Candy K
Morton Sr HS
Hammond IN

Bryan Daniel S
Frederic Senior HS
Frederic WI

Bryant Barbara L
Pepin HS
Pepin WI

Bryant Belinda A
Josephinum HS
Chicago IL

Bryant Donald E
Central HS
Omaha NE

Bryant Jeffrey M
Amos Alonzo Stagg HS
Hickory Hills IL

Bryant Jody A
Medicine Valley HS
Curtis NE

Bryant Kevan L
Morgan Park HS
Chicago IL

Bryant Nancy C
Warren Central HS
Indianapolis IN

Bryant Vania L
Southeast HS
Kansas City MO

Bryceson Deborah D
West Harrison HS
Mondamin IA

Bryson Debra K
Thomas Jefferson HS
Council Bluffs IA

Bryson Stephen T
Lane Technical HS
Chicago IL

Bryson Vickie R
New Franklin HS
New Franklin MO

Bsstone Peter F
Latin Sch Of Chicago
Chicago IL

Bubak Mark W
Sisseton HS
Sisseton SD

Bucaro Mary A
Maine Township HS
Park Ridge IL

Buchanan Dennis D
Osmond Comm HS
Osmond NE

Buchanan Gary R
Kingman HS
Kingman KS

Buchanan Kelly P
Craig HS
Janesville WI

Buchanan Patti L
Leland HS
Leland IL

Buchanan Richard E
Jacksonville HS
Jacksonville IL

Buchanan Stanley R
Marquette Manor Christi
HS
Chicago IL

Buchanan Tony D
Fair Grove HS
Elkland MO

Buchberger Laurie L
North HS
Eau Claire WI

Buchholz C Jeanne
Hartford HS
Hartford MI

Buchholz Kathryn A
Lutheran HS
Kenosha WI

Buchko Paul O
Ironwood Catholic HS
Ironwood MI

Buchl Elizabeth A
Rock Lake Public HS
Rock Lake ND

Buchl Mary C
Rock Lake HS
Rock Lake ND

Buchler Karen L
Lake Central HS
Dyer IN

Buchsbaum Andrew P
Oak Park River Forest HS
Oak Park IL

Buck Kenneth A
Forman HS
Manito IL

Buck Patricia D
Academy Of Mount St
Scholasti
Atchison KS

Buck Randall A
North HS
Fargo ND

Buckley Edward R
Centennial HS
Champaign IL

Buckley John J
Allegan HS
Allegan MI

Buckley Peggy L
North Side HS
Fort Wayne IN

Buckley Terrance M
Reddick HS
Buckingham IL

Bucko Robert J
Culver Military Academy
Merrillville IN

Budd Zoe Ann
Thornton Twp HS
Riverdale IL

Budde Melody L
Minonk Dana Rutland HS
Flanagan IL

Budding Wayne F
Wilton Community HS
Wilton IA

Buddy Ellen M
Dodge City Sr HS
Dodge KS

Budke Michelle L
Sacred Heart HS
Salina KS

Budlong Audrey M
De Tour Area HS
De Tour Village MI

Budweil Barbara M
Dominican HS
Hamtramck MI

Budzyn Martha H
Burlington HS
Burlington IA

Buechler William F
Colver Military Academy
Elwood IN

Buehner Marvin E
Tripp Independent HS
Tripp SD

Buell Peggy
Stephen Hempstead HS
Dubuque IA

Bueltel Alan C
Creighton Prep HS
Omaha NE

Buening Gerry E
Kirksville Sr HS
Kirksville MO

Buening Sandra E
Prairie Sr HS
Prairie Du Chien WI

Buenzli Nancy R
Central HS
Elkhart IN

Buerkett William T
Griffin HS
Springfield IL

Buesing Joni A
Lees Summit HS
Lees Summit MO

Buffington Jean M
Titonka Consolidated HS
Titonka IA

Bugan Rhonda T
Evergreen Park Comm HS
Evergreen Park IL

Bugarin John R
Tomahawk HS
Tomahawk WI

Bugbee Ernest E
Phillipsburg HS
Republican City NE

Buikema Nancy K
Fulton HS
Fulton IL

Buja Timothy K
Sycamore HS
Genoa IL

Bujel Elizabeth
St Marys Of Redford HS
Detroit MI

Bulemore Kathryn E
Corunna HS
Corunna MI

Bulgarelli Valerie A
Lakeview HS
St Clair Shores MI

Bulin Jeanette L
Meridian HS
Alexandria NE

Bulkema June E
Grand Rapids Christian HS
Grand Rapids MI

Bulko Joseph J
Vassar HS
Vassar MI

Bullock Marion E
Smithville R Ii HS
Smithville MO

Bulmer Shari L
D C Everest Sr HS
Schofield WI

Bulson Paul C
Forest Hills Northern HS
Grand Rapids MI

Buman James L
Harlan Comm HS
Portsmouth IA

Bumann Brian L
Maple Valley HS
Castana IA

Bumgardner Leigh A
Rosedale HS
Rosedale IN

Bumrungchit Naowarat Y
Louisiana HS
Louisiana MO

Bunce Polly
St Johns HS
St Johns MI

Bunch Cheryl K
Adair County Rii HS
Hurdland MO

Bunch Debra L
Dixon HS
Dixon IL

Bunch Ray C
Northwestern HS
Blandinsville IL

Bundy Debra K
Taylorville HS
Taylorville IL

Bungart Pete W
Deckerville HS
Deckerville MI

Bunge Barbara A
Central HS
Davenport IA

Bunge Kathy G
Du Quoin HS
Du Quoin IL

Bungert Terri L
Academy Of The Holy
Angels
Bloomington MN

Bunker Cheryl D
Century HS
Karnak IL

Bunting Carolyn L
New Trier East HS
Wilmette IL

Bunting Della M
South Callaway Rii HS
Tebbetts MO

Bunton Irving
Lindblom Tech HS
Chicago IL

Buoy Kimberly A
Concordia HS
Jamestown KS

Burages John M
St Charles HS
Saginaw MI

Burages William M
St Charles HS
Saginaw MI

Burau Shannon R
Columbus HS
Larson ND

Burbee Steven C
Lees Summit Senior HS
Lees Summit MO

Burch Paul J
Barr Reeve HS
Loogootee IN

Burcham Robert K
Bismarck HS
Bismarck ND

Burchett Patricia L
No Vermillion HS
Cayuga IN

Burchfiel Cherie D
Maize HS
Wichita KS

Burchfield Elizabeth M
Tekonsha HS
Tekonsha MI

Burden Thomas A
Carl Sandburg HS
Palos Heights IL

Burdette Tracy D
Bishop Ward HS
Kansas City KS

Buresh Diane K
Prairie Sr HS
Cedar Rapids IA

Buresh Douglas J
Central Public HS
Valparaiso NE

Burg Beth A
Lawton Bronson HS
Lawton IA

Burgar Laurie A
Springfield Southeast HS
Springfield IL

Burgardt Michael A
Wheatland HS
Park KS

Burge Alan J
Stewart Public HS
Brownton MN

Burge Melia L
Howell HS
Howell MI

Burger David H
Kapaun Mt Carmel HS
Wichita KS

Burger Edith A
Newman HS
Wausau WI

Burger Elizabeth M
Burris Laboratory HS
Muncie IN

Burgeson Keith J
Park River HS
Park River ND

Burgess Connie C
O Fallen Twp HS
Caseyville IL

Burgess Karla A
Wesclin HS
New Baden IL

Burgess Paula L
Croswell Lexington HS
Croswell MI

Burgess Ronald L
Batavia Sr HS
Aurora IL

Burgess Timothy L
Bloomer HS
Bloomer WI

Burk Joyce A
Perry Meridian HS
Indianapolis IN

Burkart John D
Premontre HS
Green Bay WI

Burke Denise J
Center Sr HS
Kansas City MO

Burke Diane M
Mendota Twp HS
Mendota IL

Burke Kathleen E
Cahokia Senior HS
Cahokia IL

Burke Lauren B
Zeeland HS
West Olive MI

Burke Michael A
North Side HS
Fort Wayne IN

Burke Ross D
California HS
California MO

Burkey Paul S
Zion Benton Township HS
Zion IL

Burkhardt Debra L
Northridge HS
Middlebury IN

Burki Marlan M
Gordon HS
Gordon NE

Burks Michael G
Forman HS
Manito IL

Burlet Chad R
Mound Westonka
Mound MN

Burlingame Beth M
North HS
Eau Claire WI

Burman Janel N
Badger HS
Lake Geneva WI

Burnett Diane R
Webber Twp HS
Obdyke IL

Burnett Nancy L
Casey HS
Casey IL

Burney Glenda D
C 4 HS
Viburnum MO

Burnham Charleen M
Avondale Senior HS
Rochester MI

Burnham Shari L
Walnut Grove Public HS
Walnut Grove MN

Burnison Charles S
Reese Public HS
Reese MI

Burns Cindi L
Macon HS
Macon IL

Burns Deanna L
Gibson Southern HS
Ft Branch IN

Burns James L
Hartford Union HS
Hartford WI

Burns James W
Richland Center HS
Richland Center WI

Burns Julie L
East Dubuque HS
East Dubuque IL

Burns Karen J
Millington HS
Millington MI

Burns Karen S
Alpena Senior HS
Alpena MI

Burns Kathleen P
Waterville Elysian HS
Waterville MN

Burns Michele K
Moline Sr HS
Moline IL

Burns Nancy R
Nauvoo Colusa HS
Nauvoo IL

Burns Pamela
Moline HS
Rock Island IL

Burns Rita G
Chaffee HS
Chaffee MO

Burns Sandra A
Bradley Bourbonnais
Comm HS
Bourbonnais IL

Burns Sherry L
Sparta HS
Coulterville IL

Burns Timothy E
Richland R 1 HS
Essex MO

Burrell Donna Y
Liberty Sr HS
Liberty MO

Burrell Nancy J
Lake Central HS
Crown Point IN

Burrer Douglas A
Harrold HS
Harrold SD

Burrow James L
Fort Atkinson Sr HS
Fort Atkinson WI

Burrow Robert B
Wichita North HS
Wichita KS

Burrus Tami R
Brookport HS
Brookport IL

Burson Bobbi J
Casey Jr Sr HS
Casey IL

Bursott Douglas E
West Richland HS
Noble IL

Burtch Janie M
Medicine Valley HS
Curtis NE

Burther Donald D
Southwestern HS
Hanover IN

Burtle Nancy H
Auburn HS
Auburn IL

Burtner Orval R
Noblesville HS
Noblesville IN

Burton Courtney A
St Marys Acad
Gary IN

Burton Debbie L
Woodland R 4 HS
Marble Hill MO

Burton Jocelyn P
Academy Of Our Lady
Chicago IL

Burton Martha M
Brookfield E HS
Brookfield WI

Burton Penny A
Unity HS
Tolono IL

Burton Rowly D
Irwin Kirkman Comm HS
Irwin IA

Burton Sally J
Rolla HS
Rolla MO

Busch Darcy L
Forest View HS
Mt Prospect IL

Busch Debby L
Forest View HS
Mt Prospect IL

Busch William T
East Gary Edison HS
Garg IN

Busche Roger O
Woodlan HS
Spencerville IN

Busching Carol S
Plainfield HS
Joliet IL

Buser Diana L
Arlington HS
Indianapolis IN

Bush Charles E
Oscoda Area HS
Oscoda MI

Bush Gary R
Elwood Comm HS
Elwood IN

Bush Jeffery G
Davis County Comm HS
Keota IA

Bush John M
Portage Northern HS
Portage MI

Bush Karen L
Effingham HS
Effingham IL

Bush Loretta L
Hononegah HS
Roscoe IL

Bush Peggy L
Taylor HS
Taylor WI

Bush Stephanie L
Jefferson W HS
Meriden KS

Bush Wayne M
Grant Comm HS
Ingleside IL

Bushee Dixie K
Fennville HS
Fennville MI

Bushko Jon N
Rhinelander HS
Rhinelander WI

Bushmaker Stacey A
Lincoln HS
Rudolph WI

Bushno Rose M
Annawan HS
Prophetstown IL

Bushong Pamela K
Handy HS
Bay City MI

Busjahn Sandra R
Orangeville HS
Orangeville IL

Buskirk William D
Bayard HS
Bayard NE

Buss James G
Luther North HS
Chicago IL

Bussan Kathy A
Pardeeville HS
Pardeville WI

Bussell Paul H
Grand Meadow HS
Grand Meadow MN

Bussen Patrick J
St Thomas Academy
Minneapolis MN

Bussen Thomas J
Wallace County HS
Wallace KS

Bussert Luther W
Kewanna HS
Kewanna IN

Bussert Victoria M
Munster HS
Munster IN

Bussing Stephen A
Brazil HS
Brazil IN

Bussman Denise M
Warren HS
Warren IL

Bustamante Monica D
Turner HS
Kansas KS

Buswell Roxanne S
Holcombe Public HS
Holcombe WI

Butcher Craig E
Monona Grove HS
Cottage Grove WI

Butcher Lisa M
Virden Comm HS
Virden IL

Butcher Nancy J
Lincoln Way HS
New Lenox IL

Buteau Diane L
John Hersey HS
Mount Prospect IL

Buter Gregory W
W Michigan Christian HS
Muskegon MI

Butler Betsy A
Crothersville HS
Crothersville IN

Butler Di Anne E
Lawrence Central HS
Indianapolis IN

Butler Drynda K
Milan C 2 HS
Milan MO

Butler James K
Columbus North HS
Columbus IN

Butler Jerry L
Eastern Heights HS
Agra KS

Butler Lucinda M
Marysville HS
Marysville KS

Butler Rebecca J
Central HS
Burden KS

Butler Reginald F
De Andreis HS
St Louis MO

Butler Susan R
Paris HS
Paris IL

Buttler Pamela S
Guthrie Center HS
Guthrie Center IA

Buttler Patricia A
Guthrie Center HS
Guthrie Center IA

Button Roger D
Dodge City Sr HS
Dodge City KS

Butts Michael D
Rogers HS
Michigan City IN

Buxa Stanley J
Anamoose Public HS
Anamoose ND

Buxton Phil L
Glendale HS
Springfield MO

Buyarski Daniel G
Menominee HS
Menominee MI

Buyer John J
North White HS
Monticello IN

Buzalsky Pamela J
St Gertrudes HS
Amidon ND

Bybee Carolyn L
Humboldt HS
Humboldt IA

Bybee Jonathan K
Cannelton HS
Cannelton IN

Byer Christie L
Northrop HS
Ft Wayne IN

Byers Shari L
Southridge HS
Huntingburg IN

Byers Tracy A
Marion HS
Marion WI

Byers Wendy A
Amos Alonzo Stagg HS
Worth IL

Byrd Benjamin H
Walter P Chrysler HS
New Castle IN

Byrd Debra L
Laurel HS
Rushville IN

Byrd John D
Wyoming Park HS
Wyoming MI

Byrd Julius G
Osborn HS
Detroit MI

Byrd Mary A
Iowa Falls HS
Iowa IA

Byrd Sharon D
Chicago Vocational HS
Chicago IL

Byrer Ann L
Triton HS
Bourbon IN

Byrnes Colleen D
Lourdes HS
Chicago IL

Byrnes Sylvia K
Fort Scott HS
Fort Scott KS

Bytnar Rita M
Tamaroa HS
Tamaroa IL

Bywater Carmen D
Tarkio HS
Tarkio MO

C

Cacic Donna J
Montello HS
Montello WI

Cadwallader Diana L
Stuart Public HS
Stuart NE

Cady Kati A
Brookfield Central HS
Brookfield WI

Cagle Philip V
Plainfield HS
Plainfield IN

Cagney Colleen M
Portage Central HS
Scotts MI

Cahalan James L
Moline Sr HS
Moline IL

Cahill Debbie S
Civic Memorial HS
Bethalto IL

Cahoon Timothy G
Saranac HS
Clarksville MI

Cain Lyle J
U S D #440 HS
Halstead KS

Cain Margaret M
Edgewood HS
Madison WI

Cain Patricia L
Marysville HS
Beattie KS

Cain Tim J
Prairie Heights HS
Orland IN

Caine Candace A
Hickman HS
Columbia MO

Caine Kerry L
Heritage Christian HS
Indianapolis IN

Calabrese Rose M
D D Eisenhower HS
Calumet Park IL

Calamari Arthur A
T Roosevelt HS
Chicago IL

Calbert Robert H
Greenwood HS
Springfield MO

Calder James S
Neil Armstrong HS
Minneapolis MN

Caldwell Becky K
Osborne HS
Portis KS

Caldwell Kenneth R
Lake Forest HS
Lake Bluff IL

Caldwell Michael L
Waynesville HS
Waynesville MO

Caldwell Robin L
Woodland R 4 HS
Lutesville MO

Caldwell Twyla D
Egyptian HS
Thebes IL

Calhoon Karen M
Winner Sr HS
Winner SD

Calhoun James M
Bowen HS
Chicago IL

Calich Victoria A
Bremen HS
Posen IL

Calise Christopher P
Kirksville R Iii Sr HS
Kirksville MO

Callahan Thomas W
Brother Rice HS
Chicago IL

Callen Tammie J
Grundy Co R V HS
Galt MO

Callon Catherine A
Whiteland Comm HS
Whiteland IN

Calvert Ronda A
Savannah HS
Savannah MO

Calvin Cindy J
Hillsdale HS
Hillsdale MI

Calzavara Carolyn M
Amos Alonzo Stagg HS
Palos Hills IL

Cameron Charles D
Paw Paw HS
Paw Paw MI

Cameron Kathy L
Chambers Public HS
Chambers NE

Cameron Robert B
Magic City Campus HS
Minot ND

Camp Melvin D
Bedford North Lawrence HS
Bedford IN

Camp Tracy L
Immaculata HS
Leavenworth KS

Camp Wanda K
Thornton Fractional No HS
Burnham IL

Campbell Amy M
Holy Angels HS
Edina MN

Campbell Christie K
Garden County HS
Oshkosh NE

Campbell Cynthia S
Lincoln Community HS
Lincoln IL

Campbell Dana J
Sarcoxie HS
La Russell MO

Campbell Frank
Highland HS
Anderson IN

Campbell Gerald G
Burrton HS
Burrton KS

Campbell Gregory P
Dixon R 1 HS
Dixon MO

Campbell James K
Bennington HS
Salina KS

Campbell Jodie B
Lyons Township HS
Western Springs IL

Campbell Julie R
Noblesville HS
Noblesville IN

Campbell Kimberly D
Central HS
Red Wing MN

Campbell Leslie C
Chenoa HS
Chenoa IL

Campbell Lisa K
Corunna HS
Corunna MI

Campbell Michael D
Irving Crown HS
Carpentersville IL

Campbell Myrna
Roosevelt HS
Minneapolis MN

Campbell Ralph W
Lake Crystal HS
Lake Crystal MN

Campbell Susan M
Clio HS
Clio MI

Camren Carla J
De Forest Area HS
De Forest WI

Canard Dwight W
Oklee Public HS
Trail MN

Canard Marcia L
Bedford HS
Temperance MI

Canary Mary R
Washington Catholic HS
Washington IN

Canchola Carolina
Robert A Waller HS
Chicago IL

Cannon Philip J
Southfield Sr HS
Southfield MI

STUDENTS PHOTOGRAPH SCHEDULED FOR PUBLICATION HERE COULD NOT BE REPRODUCED

Cantin Daniel M
Southwestern HS
Flint MI

Cantrell Donald A
Carmi Comm HS
Carmi IL

Cantrell Rita D
Flora HS
Xenia IL

Canty Elizabeth A
Thornwood HS
So Holland IL

Canute Mark A
East Richland HS
Olney IL

Capek Deborah E
Maine Twp HS
Niles IL

Capel Kim D
Anna Jonesboro C HS
Anna IL

Capitani Randy L
Putnam County HS
Granville IL

Capodice Christina M
Central Catholic HS
Bloomington IL

Caponi Robert E
Proviso West HS
Hillside IL

Capouch Kevin E
Central HS
Grafton ND

Capozzoli Terry M
Prospect HS
Mt Prospect IL

Cappello Ronald A
Daniel J Gross HS
Omaha NE

Capper Kristie S
Central Community HS
Dewitt IA

Cappetta Thomas J
St Ignatius College Prep
Chicago IL

Capps Russell A
Pekin Comm HS
Packwood IA

Caprio Thomas G
Taft HS
Chicago IL

Caragher Keith E
Christian Brothrs Col HS
Manchester MO

Caraker John C
Benton Consolidated HS
Benton IL

Caraway Sherri L
Gallatin Rv HS
Gallatin MO

Carbonara Richard M
Loyola Academy
Chicago IL

Card Steven J
Arthur Hill HS
Saginaw MI

Cardiff Patrick J
Badger HS
Lake Geneva WI

Carey Joseph K
New Trier West HS
Northfield IL

Carey Rebecca S
West Liberty HS
West Liberty IA

Caringer Douglas O
Litchfield Sr HS
Litchfield IL

Carlaw Clinton L
Shell Lake HS
Shell Lake WI

Carlin Joan M
Mitchell Sr HS
Mitchell SD

Carlin Robin H
Mc Donald County HS
Anderson MO

Carlisle Kimberly A
Douglas Mac Arthur HS
Saginaw MI

Carlson Bonnie E
Batavia Sr HS
Batavia IL

Carlson Christina L
J D Darnall Sr HS
Geneseo IL

Carlson Cindy D
Central Webster HS
Gowrie IA

Carlson Cindy M
Deer River HS
Spring Lake MN

Carlson Collette M
Bowdie HS
Bowdie SD

Carlson Connie E
Pecatonica Area HS
Hollandale WI

Carlson Crystal K
Higbee HS
Higbee MO

Carlson David B
Minot HS
Minot ND

Carlson Deborah K
Central Comm HS
Argyle IA

Carlson Debra L
Hiawatha HS
Kirkland IL

Carlson Dianne M
Mitchell Sr HS
Mitchell SD

Carlson Elaine M
Decatur Jr/sr HS
Dowagiac MI

Carlson Gerald J
Waynesville HS
Ft Leonardwood MO

Carlson Grant E
Laurens Comm HS
Laurens IA

Carlson Jill A
Cassville HS
Shell Knob MO

Carlson Kathryn L
Greenway HS
Coleraine MN

Carlson Kent
Twin Valley HS
Twin Valley MN

Carlson Lori A
Central Community HS
Camanche IA

Carlson Lyle F
Benson HS
Omaha NE

Carlson Lynette J
South Clay HS
Dickens IA

Carlson Lynnette M
Madrid Community HS
Madrid IA

Carlson Matthew C
Homewood Flossmoor HS
Homewood IL

Carlson Pamela J
South Hamilton HS
Stanhope IA

Carlson Patrick R
Beloit Memorial HS
Beloit WI

Carlson Randall K
Salina HS
Salina KS

Carlson Randy E
Belle Plaine HS
Belle Plaine MN

Carlson Randy S
L L Wright HS
Ironwood MI

Carlson Rick G
Chisago Lakes HS
Lindstrom MN

Carlson Rick J
Pecatonica Area HS
Hollandale WI

Carlson Steven M
Abingdon HS
Abingdon IL

Carlson Tim P
Forest Lake H S
Forest Lake MN

Carlson Wade A
Rock HS
Rock MI

Carlson Wanda L
Forest Park HS
Crystal Falls MI

Carlstrom Jane E
Grantsburg Integrated HS
Grantsburg WI

Carlue Andrea L
Southport HS
Indianapolis IN

Carman Cindy K
North Platte HS
North Platte NE

Carman Philip A
Mason City HS
Mason City IA

Carmichael Carol L
Rochelle Twp HS
Rochelle IL

Carmichael Kevin L
Harrisonville HS
Harrisonville MO

Carmody Teresa L
Calhoun HS
Hardin IL

Carnahan David M
Hartland HS
Hartland MI

Carnegie Josephine M
Edison Sr HS
East Gary IN

Carney Donna J
Rockford HS
Marble Rock IA

Carney Iva L
Craig Riii HS
Bigelow MO

Carney Lucinda A
Lakeland HS
Lagrange IN

Carney Mark D
Logansport HS
Logansport IN

Carney Robert M
Immaculate Conception HS
Elmhurst IL

Carol Albert F
St Agatha HS
Detroit MI

Carpenter David D
Dwight HS
Dwight IL

Carpenter Debbie L
John Glenn HS
Bay City MI

Carpenter Nyla J
Tri HS
Straughn IN

Carper Diane G
Mahomet Seymour HS
Seymour IL

Carper Susan K
Highland HS
La Belle MO

Carr Audrey L
Maywood HS
Maywood NE

Carr Diana M
Medicine Valley HS
Wellfleet NE

Carr Lori K
Durand Area HS
Durand MI

Carr Marsha L
Sullivan HS
Sullivan MO

Carr Robin H
Adelphian Academy
Holly MI

Carrel James A
Rogers HS
Wyoming MI

Carrick Christie L
Gurdon S Hubbard HS
Chicago IL

Carrier Nancy J
Addison Trail HS
Addison IL

Carroll David W
Warsaw HS
Warsaw MO

Carroll Gregory L
St Charles HS
St Charles MO

Carroll James A
Fenton HS
Wood Dale IL

Carroll James G
St Marys HS
St Louis MO

Carroll Laura S
Duchesne HS
St Charles MO

Carroll Ned J
Spencer HS
Spencer IA

Carroll Shawn W
Greenfield HS
Greenfield WI

Carruthers Janetta L
Vandalia Comm HS
Vandalia IL

Carry Carl D
Pekin Comm HS
Pekin IL

Carson Gay L
Osceola HS
Osceola MO

Carson Greg L
Orion HS
Coal Valley IL

Carson Stephanie A
Laboure HS
St Louis MO

Carson William S
Big Rapids HS
Big Rapids MI

Carter Annette
Kettering HS
Detroit MI

Carter Charles M
Campus HS
Haysville KS

Carter Cheryl A
Springfield HS
Springfield IL

Carter Christine A
Rushville Consolidated HS
Milroy IN

Carter Deborah S
North Clay Comm HS
Louisville IL

Carter Elizabeth L
Roxana Sr HS
East Alton IL

Carter H Randall
North Greene HS
Roodhouse IL

Carter Janice M
Franklin HS
Livonia MI

Carter Jeff A
Neosho HS
Neosho MO

Carter Joye M
Shortridge HS
Indianapolis IN

Carter Judyth A
Stes Peter & Paul Area HS
Saginaw MI

Carter Kerry D
Mazon Verona Kinsman HS
Mazon IL

Carter Kim L
Charlevoix HS
Charlevoix MI

Carter Kristine
Langdon HS
Langdon ND

Carter Mary L
Yale HS
Yale MI

Carter Michael L
Oak Park Sr HS
Kansas City MO

Carter Nancy L
Huntington North HS
Huntington IN

Carter Pamela R
Norborne Public HS
Norborne MO

Carter Patricia G
Mitchell HS
Mitchell IN

Carter Randy P
St Clair HS
St Clair MO

Carter Robert K
East HS
Rockford IL

Carter Sandra L
Western Dubuque HS
Peosta IA

Carter Terry E
Jersey Comm HS
Jerseyville IL

Carter Tina D
Rolla Senior HS
Rolla MO

Carter Victoria L
Lockport Cntrl HS
Lockport IL

Cartmill Candy J
Wheatland HS
Gove KS

Cartmill John T
Elk Mound HS
Elk Mound WI

Cartwright Linda L
Northfield HS
Andrews IN

Caruso Frank J
Wm A Wirt HS
Gary IN

Caruthers John S
R Nelson Snider HS
Ft Wayne IN

Carver Mary L
Rockwell City Comm HS
Rockwell City IA

Carver Penny K
Oak Park HS
Kansas City MO

Carver Tara L
Valentine HS
Crookston NE

Carviou Howard H
Marinette Sr HS
Marinette WI

Casady Danny J
Chillicothe HS
Chillicothe MO

Casarez Jorge A
Gabriel Richard HS
Detroit MI

Case Colin J
Plattsmouth HS
Plattsmouth NE

Case Deborah L
Marshall HS
Marshall MO

Case James R
Capital City Christian HS
Okemos MI

Case Janice L
Durand Area HS
Durand MI

Case Kathleen M
Plattsmouth HS
Plattsmouth NE

Case Steven P
Plattsmouth HS
Plattsmouth NE

Caselman Teresa J
Tri County R 7 HS
Jamesport MO

Caselton Darrel J
Calhoun HS
Hardin IL

Casey Jay H
Schulte HS
Terre Haute IN

Casey Patricia A
Hillsboro HS
Hillsboro IL

Casey Robin M
Robert Lindblom Tech HS
Chicago IL

Casey Thomas C
Marquette Jr HS
Brookfield WI

Casper Deborah S
Anna Jonesboro Comm HS
Anna IL

Cass Janice P
Kirksville Sr HS
Kirksville MO

Cassell Patrick E
Anita HS
Anita IA

Cassidy Mary L
Jeffersonville HS
Jeffersonville IN

Cassidy Thomas M
Monroe HS
Monroe MI

Casson Karen J
Pontiac Twp HS
Pontiac IL

Castaneda Cynthia A
Escanaba Area Public HS
Escanaba MI

Castegnaro Anthony M
Seymour HS
Plainville IL

Castellarin Peter F
Mount Carmel HS
Burnham IL

Castelli Bartolomeo J
Chaminade College Prep
Crestwood MO

Castle Linda K
Chase County HS
Imperial NE

Castleberry Roxlynn
Kimball County HS
Kimball NE

Castro Rito
Kewaunee HS
Kewaunee WI

Castrogiovanni Gary J
Marmion Military Academy
Chicago IL

Castrogiovanni Ronald R
Marmion Military Academy
Chicago IL

Catenacci Donald L
Pardeeville HS
Wyocena WI

Cates Sandra D
East Prairie HS
East Prairie MO

Cathcart Patty A
R 1 North Callaway HS
Auxvasse MO

Cathey Cameron H
Fairfield HS
Fairfield IA

Cathey Spencer O
Monticello HS
Monticello IL

Catholos Jo Ellen
Northwest HS
Grand Island NE

Catlin Rick J
Gibbon HS
Gibbon NE

Cato Charlotte A
Zalma HS
Zalma MO

Catron Tim D
Clinton Central HS
Russiaville IN

Cattledge Antionette
Southeast HS
Springfield IL

Causey Steven L
Cass Technical HS
Detroit MI

Cavallaro Diane B
Resurrection HS
Chicago IL

Cavanaugh Kathleen M
Ottawa HS
Ottawa IL

Cavanaugh Kevin M
S County Tech HS
Affton MO

Cavaness Terry L
Shawnee HS
Mcclure IL

Cavenaugh Timothy R
Loyola Academy
Deerfield IL

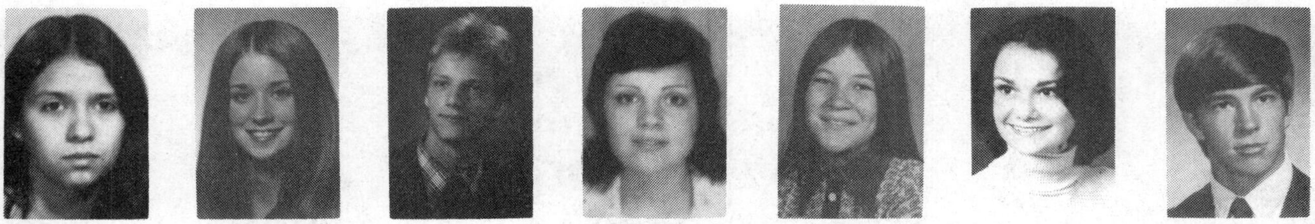

Cazares Mary
Jones Commercial HS
Chicago IL

Cazzell Cindy L
Ex Springs West HS
Excelsior Springs MO

Cebar Paul R
Pius Xi HS
Milwaukee WI

Cecere Mary R
Resurrection HS
Norridge IL

Cech Gail A
Saginaw HS
Saginaw MI

Cecich Diane R
Lourdes HS
Chicago IL

Cecil Carl P
Greenwood Community HS
Greenwood IN

Cejda Cindy L
Wamego HS
Wamego KS

Cejka Darrell G
Dorchester HS
Dorchester NE

Celeschi Rebecca M
Glenbard West HS
Glen Ellyn IL

Celis Jorge
Oak Park & River Forest HS
River Forest IL

Cenek Kurt J
Cedarburg HS
Cedarburg WI

Centella Celeste V
St Edward HS
Carpentersville IL

Cerny Danette K
Scotus Central Catholic HS
Columbus NE

Cerny Stephen R
Cobden Unit HS
Cobden IL

Cervantes Susan M
Calumet HS
Gary IN

Cevigney Connie D
Republic Michigamme HS
Michigamme MI

Chadwick Robert L
Galesburg Sr HS
Galesburg IL

Chalender Robert A
Manhattan Sr HS
Manhattan KS

Chalkey Denise E
Streator Twp HS
Streator IL

Chall Mark E
Frankenmuth HS
Frankenmuth MI

Chaloner Carole A
New Trier East HS
Wilmette IL

Chaloupka Patricia J
Stevens HS
Rapid City SD

Chamberland Michael A
O Fallon Township HS
O Fallon IL

Chamberlin Rick
Olin Consolidated HS
Olin IA

Chambers Carol A
North Huron HS
Filion MI

Chambers Clark A
Bemidji HS
Bemidji MN

Chambers Craig M
Mayo HS
Rochester MN

Chambers Deborah L
Parker HS
Chicago IL

Chambers Elden G
Turner HS
Kansas City KS

Chambers Peggy S
Maires R I HS
Vienna MO

Chambers Robert S
Lesterville R 4 HS
Lesterville MO

Chambers Steven L
Hammond Baptist HS
Lansing IL

Chambers Theresa
Cahokia HS
Centerville IL

Chamblee Marquita T
St Josephs HS
South Bend IN

Chamness Marsha L
Herrin HS
Herrin IL

Chamness Melinda S
Trico HS
Ava IL

Chamness Ricky L
Anna Jonesboro Comm HS
Jonesboro IL

Champ Timothy E
Woodlawn Community HS
Woodlawn IL

Champagne Mitchell P
Duchesne HS
St Charles MO

Champine Laurie A
Beaver Dam Sr HS
Beaver Dam WI

Champion Leesa M
Carmel HS
Carmel IN

Champlin Michael E
High School
Cedar Vale KS

Chance Jerry L
Stuart Menlo HS
Menlo IA

Chandler Charles H
Metropolis Comm HS
Metropolis IL

Chandler Karen S
Garnett HS
Richmond KS

Chandler Sherry L
Metropolis Comm HS
Metropolis IL

Chaney Andrew J
St Mary Of P H HS
Chicago IL

Chaney Gregory A
Cathedral HS
Indianapolis IN

Chang Paul J
Shawnee Mission East HS
Mission Hills KS

Chapa Deborah J
Lake Zurich Sr HS
Lake Zurich IL

Chapin Norman A
Millington HS
Millington MI

Chapinski Mary P
Newman Central Catholic HS
Rock Falls IL

Chapla Robin L
West Iron County HS
Gaastra MI

Chaplow Beata
Dominican HS
Grosse Point Park MI

Chapman Jacquilan L
Concordia Academy
St Paul MN

Chapman James M
Chippewa Hills HS
Remus MI

Chapman John S
Comstock Park HS
Comstock Park MI

Chapman Kirby J
Fairmount Public HS
Fairmount ND

Chapman Michael D
Rosedale HS
Carbon IN

Chapman Olif B
St Johns Military HS
Liberty MO

Charboneau Richard G
Rosemount HS
Rosemount MN

Charging Anita F
White Shield HS
Roseglen ND

Charging Clarice M
White Shield HS
Roseglen ND

Charles Cecilia A
Labette County HS
Altamont KS

Charles Lonnie W
Zionsville Comm HS
Zionsville IN

Charles Randal D
Marenisco HS
Marenisco MI

Charles Susan J
Stockton HS
Mt Carroll IL

Charles Susan M
Unity HS
Chicago IL

Charles Tia B
Kirksville Senior HS
Kirksville MO

Charlton Katherine L
Primghar Community HS
Primghar IA

Chartrand Gregg R
Chisago Lakes HS
Lindstrom MN

Chase Jacqueline M
Tecumseh HS
Tecumseh MI

Chase Thomas R
Sisseton HS
Sisseton SD

Chaska Lorraine C
Beach HS
Beach ND

Chastain Rhonda J
West Washington HS
Campbellsburg IN

Chatelain Jeanne M
Shawnee Mission W HS
Prairie Vlg KS

Chatham Pamela J
Brazil Senior HS
Brazil IN

Chatters Rachel C
West Side HS
Gary IN

Cheatham Lisa R
Pike HS
Indianapolis IN

Cheek Cathy E
Sheldon HS
Sheldon IL

Cheek Kathleen D
Eminence HS
Quincy IN

Chelgren Donnette F
Wahpeton HS
Wahpeton ND

Chelsvig Deborah K
South Hamilton HS
Jewell IA

Chenevert Renee M
Granite City Sr HS
Granite City IL

Cheney Pamela R
Sylvan Unified #299 HS
Sylvan Grove KS

Chenoweth Kimberley J
East Alton Wood Rvr
Comm HS
Wood River IL

Cheolas Gregory W
Brown City HS
Melvin MI

Cherf Susan M
Central HS
Lacrosse WI

Chern Lydia A
Appleton HS
Appleton WI

Cherry Gilda D
Chicago Vocational HS
Chicago IL

Cherry Zoe E
Loup City HS
Loup City NE

Chesnik Carrie A
Redfield HS
Redfield SD

Chester Mary E
New Haven HS
New Haven IN

Chevalia Timothy C
Marseilles HS
Marseilles IL

Chevremont Jacque M
Milwaukee Trade & Tech
HS
Milwaukee WI

Chicantek Thomas P
Greenfield HS
Greenfield WI

Chidester Christine L
Mormon Trail HS
Weldon IA

Childers Kevin J
Marion Senior HS
Marion IL

Childress Cynthia A
Tremont HS
Tremont IL

Childress Deanna D
Oakland HS
Oakland IL

Childress Mary J
Brown County HS
Morgantown IN

Chiles Jennifer P
Smithville Rii HS
Smithville MO

Ching Kenneth D
Nw Military & Naval Academy
Wheeling IL

Chism Denise D
West Platte HS
Rushville MO

Chism Shelly K
Senath Hornersville HS
Hornersville MO

Chitty Regina A
Butler HS
Butler MO

Chitwood Kathleen A
Limestone HS
Bartonville IL

Chivington Carol R
Gavit HS
Hammond IN

Chlapik John J
J Sterling Morton East HS
Cicero IL

Chmielewski Chester S
N Decatur HS
Greensburg IN

Chmielewski Karen S
Jackson HS
Jackson MI

Chmielik Joseph S
St Patrick HS
Chicago IL

Choat Ralph F
Lockport Central HS
Lockport IL

Chobanian Patricia R
West Allis Central HS
West Allis WI

Chocholousek Julie A
Gregory HS
Dixon SD

Chock Mark T
New Trier HS
Glenview IL

Chojnicki John A
West Sr HS
Rockford IL

Cholly Thomas A
Brother Rice HS
Chicago IL

Choponis Richard J
Pine River HS
Luther MI

Chopp Brian S
Frank Cody HS
Detroit MI

Choutka Carol A
Riverside Brookfield HS
Riverside IL

Chrisman Cindy G
Onaga HS
Onaga KS

Christel Mary T
Maria HS
Chicago IL

Christen Neil L
Jersey Comm HS
Jerseyville IL

Christensen Carla A
Loup County HS
Taylor NE

Christensen Craig E
Loganview HS
Fremont NE

Christensen Dean C
New Town HS
New Town ND

Christensen Gary L
Elk Horn Kimballton Comm HS
Eok Horn IA

Christensen Janene K
Underwood Comm HS
Honey Creek IA

Christensen Janice M
Verona Public HS
Verona ND

Christensen Ken
Centura HS
Dannebrog NE

Christensen Madonna J
St Louise De Marillac HS
Northbrook IL

Christensen Mary B
Bridgewater Fontanelle HS
Fontanelle IA

Christensen Pamela G
Eastwood HS
Correctionville IA

Christensen Troy E
Sr HS
Fremont NE

Christenson John L
Clark HS
Clark SD

Christenson Judith J
Oak Park Academy
Dodge Center MN

Christenson Mark A
Chippewa Falls HS
Chippewa Falls WI

Christenson Saundra R
De Soto HS
Dittmer MO

Christiansen Richard G
Harlan Comm HS
Harlan IA

Christie Jeanne M
Bemidji HS
Bemidji MN

Christie Karen S
Central HS
St Joseph MO

Christmon Sarita R
Tri City HS
Buffalo IL

Christoffel Cindy J
Prairie Hts HS
Angola IN

Christopher Susan
North Winneshiek HS
Decorah IA

Christopherson Donna J
Ballard Comm HS
Cambridge IA

Chubb Jo Ann
Notre Dame HS
W Burlington IA

Church Colleen A
Ithaca HS
Ithaca MI

Church Marsha K
Lutheran West HS
Detroit MI

Chye Dorothy A
Mason County Eastern HS
Custer MI

Ciers Jeanelle R
Whiting HS
Whiting IN

Cieslak Joseph G
Brother Rice HS
Chicago IL

Cieslak Mark E
Lane Tech HS
Chicago IL

Cieslinski Steven D
Hazel Park HS
Hazel Park MI

Cimino John J
Creighton Prep HS
Omaha NE

Cincotta Toni M
South Adams HS
Geneva IN

Cinnamon William M
Brimfield HS
Brimfield IL

Cinquepalmi Bruno P
Wayne Mem HS
Westland MI

Ciocan Jane
Dearborn HS
Dearborn MI

Ciochetto Donna M
West Iron County HS
Stambaugh MI

Cira Roseanne M
A A Stagg HS
Hickory Hills IL

Claassen Daniel L
Rose Hill HS
Rose Hill KS

Claassen David A
Chase County HS
Imperial NE

Claeys Chris M
United Township HS
East Moline IL

Clancy Maribeth
St Paul HS
Highland IL

Clapper Jo A
Ainsworth HS
Ainsworth NE

Clare Kathryn J
Ida HS
Temperance MI

Clark Carla A
Concordia HS
Ft Wayne IN

Clark Chipper W B
North Linn HS
Central City IA

Clark Cindy J
Centralia HS
Centralia IL

Clark Cindy K
R Nelson Snider HS
Ft Wayne IN

Clark Dale D
North White HS
Monon IN

Clark David L
Rushville Con HS
Rushville IN

Clark David M
Bentley Sr HS
Burton MI

Clark Diana
Lindblom Tech HS
Chicago IL

Clark Gaynell G
Chicago Voc HS
Chicago IL

Clark Gwen S
Raymond Central HS
Ceresco NE

Clark Jane M
Delwein Comm HS
Delwein IA

Clark Karen L
Thornton Fractional So HS
Lansing IL

Clark Leslie R
Alton Senior HS
Alton IL

Clark Louise H
Johannesbg Lewiston Area HS
Johannesburg MI

Clark Mariann E
Quincy Senior HS
Quincy IL

Clark Michael A
Chandler Lake Wilson HS
Chandler MN

Clark Nancy J
St Teresa HS
Decatur IL

Clark Niles
Westfield
Westfield IN

Clark Pamela K
West Harrison HS
Pisgah IA

Clark Patricia K
Lees Summit HS
Lees Summit MO

Clark Richard D
Mills Prairie HS
Mill Shoals IL

Clark Steve A
Alton Sr HS
Godfrey IL

Clark Tom G
Big Springs HS
Big Springs NE

Clark William R
Hinsdale Twp HS
Hinsdale IL

Clarke Charles P
Gwinn HS
K I Sawyer Afb MI

Clarke Stewart M
Roger C Sullivan HS
Chicago IL

Clary Aaron R
St Johns Military HS
Herington KS

Classen Bruce D
Adams Central HS
Glenvil NE

Clatts Michael C
St Alberts Jr Seminary
Scottarb IL

Claunch Larry O
Osceola Public HS
Osceola MO

Claus Diana J
East Pike HS
Milton IL

Clausen Kirk A
Winnebago HS
Rockford IL

Claussen Cheryl K
Porta HS
Petersburg IL

Claussen David P
Schleswig Comm HS
Ricketts IA

Claussen Kimberly S
Fremont Senior HS
Fremont NE

Clavel Nanette
Grosse Pointe South HS
Grosse Pointe Cy MI

Clavon Kimberly A
Immaculata HS
Detroit MI

Clawson Lary D
Annapolis HS
Dearborn Heights MI

Claxton Delbert L
Finney HS
Detroit MI

Clay Cynthia A
Taft HS
Chicago IL

Clay Susan A
Hannibal HS
Hannibal MO

Clay Wanda C
Rosati Kain HS
St Louis MO

Claybaugh Janet L
Hillsdale HS
Hillsdale MI

Clayton Cheryl L
Glenwood HS
Pawnee IL

Clayton Kevin D
Newton Community HS
Newton IA

Clayton Randy W
Bond County Comm Unit #2 HS
Pocahontas IL

Claywell Howard J
Union HS
Losantville IN

Cleaver John
Mark Twain HS
Perry MO

Cleaver Max B
Yorktown HS
Muncie IN

Cleeter Joyce A
Dillsboro HS
Dillsboro IN

Clemen Mary S
Leo HS
Holy Cross IA

Clemens Gale R
Excelsior Springs HS
Excelsior Springs MO

Clemens Polly R
Luther L Wright HS
Ironwood MI

Clement David R
Miller Co Riii HS
Tuscumbia MO

Clement Mary C
Jacksonville HS
Jacksonville IL

Clement Nora E
Cassopolis HS
Cassopolis MI

Clement Ruth M
Mc Bain Rural Agric HS
Mc Bain MI

Clement Sheila D
Sault Area HS
Sault Ste Marie MI

Clements Maria A
Western Dubuque HS
Epworth IA

Clemon Lonnie L
South Sioux City HS
So Sioux City NE

Clemons Bradley W
North Miami HS
Macy IN

Clemons Kirby R
Arthur HS
Arthur IL

Clennan Eileen K
Harrison HS
Harrison MI

Cleppe Ruth M
Hlv Comm HS
Victor IA

Cleveland Douglas B
Brookfield HS
Brookfield MO

Cleveland Jean D
Central HS
Detroit MI

Clevenger Robin L
John Marshall HS
Indianapolis IN

Clifford Cynthia A
North Knox HS
Edwardsport IN

Clifford Nancy R
St Mary Central HS
Neenah WI

Clifford Sherri L
Hayes Co HS
Hayes Center NE

Clinansmith Cindy M
Bronson HS
Burr Oak MI

Cline Kimberly J
Mexico Senior HS
Mexico MO

Cline Linda R
Franklin HS
Franklin NE

Cline Michael A
Clinton Central HS
Sheridan IN

Cline Roberta B
Trenton HS
Inkster MI

Clinnin David D
Wells Easton HS
Easton MN

Close James M
Edwardsville HS
Edwardsville IL

Close Stephen G
Glencoe HS
Glencoe MN

Clouse Stanley A
Brady Public HS
Brady NE

Cloutier Diane M
Escanaba Area HS
Escanaba MI

Cloyd Chuck H
Platteview Jr Sr HS
Springfield NE

Clubb Duane L
Van Buren Comm HS
Keosauqua IA

Cluts Patricia E
Tremont Unit Dist 702 HS
Tremont IL

Clutts Carey M
Pontiac Township HS
Pontiac IL

Coates Richard
Lapeer Senior HS
Lapeer MI

Coatney Billy E
Monett HS
Monett MO

Cobb Larry K
Ritenour HS
St Louis County MO

Cobb Mary E
Montgomery County R Ii HS
New Florence MO

Cobb Richard K
Meadville HS
Wheeling MO

Cobie Rick A
Ackley Geneva HS
Ackley IA

Coburn Susan A
West Holt HS
O Neill NE

Cochran John M
Griswold Comm HS
Griswold IA

Cochran Karen S
Grand Blanc HS
Grand Blanc MI

Cochran Marc A
Anita HS
Anita IA

Cockerill Julie A
Rock Island HS
Rock Island IL

Cockram Michael R
University HS
Centerview MO

Cockrum Larry R
Waltonville HS
Waltonville IL

Cocquyt Donald A
Niagara Public HS
Niagara WI

Cody Mac A
El Dorado HS
El Dorado KS

Coe Robert W
Newton HS
Newton KS

Coenen Judith M
Menasha HS
Menasha WI

Cofer Donna S
Wheeling HS
Buffalo Grove IL

Coffey Elva M
Lincoln Way HS
Mokena IL

Coffin Harley S
South Putnam HS
Fillmore IN

Coffman Pamela S
English Valleys HS
South English IA

Coffman Rebecca L
Riverton HS
Galena KS

Cofoid Lisa J
Tonica HS
Tonica IL

Cofrin Tom M
Southern Door HS
Sturgeon Bay WI

Cogdal Pamela A
La Salle Peru HS
Utica IL

Cohen Randi S
New Trier West HS
Wilmette IL

Cohn Allan L
Maine Twp HS East
Niles IL

Cohrs Nancy J
Vicksburg Community HS
Vicksburg MI

Coil Jon C
Petersburg Porta HS
Petersburg IL

Coin David L
Kirksville Sr HS
Kirksville MO

Colasinski William D
Allen Park HS
Allen Park MI

Colberg Linda M
George Rogers Clark HS
Whiting IN

Colbert Charles W
Tri County HS
Delta IA

Cole Alice M
Alliance HS
Alliance NE

Cole Debra K
Jefferson HS
Jefferson SD

Cole Jackie W
Paxton HS
Paxton IL

Cole Joyce L
Diamond HS
Neosho MO

Cole Judy M
Medicine Valley HS
Curtis NE

Cole Mary A
Anselmo Merna HS
Merna NE

Cole Rhonda A
Southwest HS
St Louis MO

Cole Rhonda D
Assumption HS
Assumption IL

Cole Robin M
Cardinal Ritter HS
Indianapolis IN

Cole Terry R
Memorial HS
Joplin MO

Coleman Barbara K
Bloom Twp HS
Crete IL

Coleman Charles L 9
Lindblom Technical HS
Chicago IL

Coleman David W
St Edmond HS
Fort Dodge IA

Coleman Gary D
Valentine HS
Valentine NE

Coleman Kim
Valentine HS
Valentine NE

Colestock Helen A
Normandy HS
Northwoods MO

Coletti Mary E
Grand Blanc HS
Grand Blanc MI

Colglazier John T
Salem HS
Salem IN

Colglazier Patrick D
Lewistown Comm HS
Lewistown IL

Colgrove Kip D
West Pike HS
Kinderhook IL

Colht Judy A
St Barbara HS
Chicago IL

Collard Linda M
Douglas Mac Arthur HS
Saginaw MI

Collatz Pamela D
Roosevelt HS
River Forest IL

Colle Joni D
Waltonville Comm HS
Nason IL

Collier Jerome A
Effingham HS
Effingham IL

Collier Robert J
Luther South HS
Chicago IL

Collins Fred R
Fort Dodge Sr HS
Fort Dodge IA

Collins Gerald R
Dwight D Eisenhower HS
Decatur IL

Collins Gregory A
Dekalb HS
Auburn IN

Collins Howard S
Hillsdale HS
Hillsdale MI

Collins Jody R
Lewellen Rural HS
Lewellen NE

Collins Joseph A
Marist HS
Chicago IL

Collins Julie L
St Francis Academy
Joliet IL

Collins Keith M
Harry S Truman HS
Taylor MI

Collins Marsha L
Riii Central HS
Flat River MO

Collins Marva K
Liberty HS
Liberty MO

Collins Nina F
Traverse City Sr HS
Traverse City MI

Collins Noreen M
Immaculate Heart Of Mary HS
Broadview IL

Collins Robert W
Rockford East HS
Rockford IL

Collins Robin S
Cass Tech HS
Detroit MI

Collins Teresa K
Gallatin Rv HS
Gallatin MO

Collman Janice L
Forreston HS
Freeport IL

Colvin Kevin W
Divernon HS
Divernon IL

Colza Carol A
Andrean HS
Gary IN

Combs Cherylyn A
Rantoul Township HS
Rantoul IL

Combs Donna G
Newton Community HS
Newton IL

Combs Kathy A
Northrop HS
Ft Wayne IN

Combs Lavonda R
Charlestown HS
Charlestown IN

Combs Linda S
Valley Center HS
Wichita KS

Combs Terri L
Joplin Memorial HS
Webb City MO

Comer Cindy G
Seeger Memorial HS
Attica IN

Comfort Keith C
Mt Pleasant HS
Mt Pleasant IA

Commons Daniel L
Salina HS
Salina KS

Compton Laura L
Lindbergh Sr HS
St Louis MO

Comstock Diane D
St Louis HS
St Louis MI

Comstock Kathy M
Blair HS
Blair NE

Comstock Timothy J
Unionville HS
Unionville MO

Conaway Louise A
Highland Sr HS
Highland IN

Cone Jacqueline S
Hermitage Public HS
Hermitage MO

Congious Tammy L
Lindblom Tech HS
Chicago IL

Conklin Kimberly K
Durand Area HS
Durand MI

Conley Donal T
Waterford Union HS
Waterford WI

Conley Susan J
Stockbridge HS
Munith MI

Conlin James D
Olympia HS
Mc Lean IL

Conn Warren A
St Johns Mil Academy
Chicago IL

Connaughton Steven R
Washington HS
Washington IN

Connelly Charlotte L
Casey HS
Casey IL

Connelly Kimberly J
Glenwood HS
Chatham IL

Connelly Patricia A
Laboure HS
St Louis MO

Connelly Richard J
Carl Sandburg HS
Orland Park IL

Conner Elizabeth L
Heritage Christian HS
Indianapolis IN

Conner Karen E
Richland HS
Parma MO

Conner Mark V
Parker HS
Chicago IL

Conner Meredith A
Red Bud HS
Prairie Du Rocher IL

Conners Annette J
Jefferson West HS
Grantville KS

Connolly Brian J
New Trier West HS
Northfield IL

Connolly Daniel G
Mason Sr HS
Erie MI

Connolly Kevin G
St Viator HS
Palatine IL

Connolly Sheila M
Bishop Luers HS
Fort Wayne IN

Connor Julie A
Jennings Sr HS
St Louis MO

Connor Scott A
Lanse HS
L Anse MI

Connors Carla J
Vermillion HS
Vermillion SD

Connors Margaret M
Snider HS
Fort Wayne IN

Conraads Yvonne E
Milbank HS
Twin Brooks SD

Conrad Bob
Hoisington Rural HS
Hoisington KS

Conrad Randolph F
Tri County Comm HS
Rose Hill IA

Conrad Thomas M
Osawatomie HS
Osawatomie KS

Conrad Walter R
Glenwood Community HS
Glenwood IA

Conrad Winona
Hoisington HS
Hoisington KS

Conrady Janet S
Northwestern HS
Hettick IL

Conroy William F
Brother Rice HS
Oak Lawn IL

Considine Timothy P
Joliet Catholic HS
Romeoville IL

Consolino Julia F
Wateruliet HS
Wateruliet MI

Constant Steven M
Godwin Heights HS
Wyoming MI

Constantz Elizabeth G
Northwest HS
House Springs MO

Contreras Magda D
Rosarian Academy
Addison IL

Conveise Diane E
Larned HS
Garfield KS

Convis Margaret J
Fairbury Cropsey HS
Fairbury IL

Conway Debra J
Mallard Community HS
Mallard IA

Conway Jill M
Elizabeth Seton HS
Tinley Park IL

Conway Mary T
Parker Senior HS
Janesville WI

Conway Patrick W
Leo HS
Chicago IL

Conway Richard A
North West HS
House Springs MO

Cook Brian R
Dupo HS
Dupo IL

Cook Christopher C
Quincy HS
Quincy IL

Cook Debra R
Beal City HS
Mt Pleasant MI

Cook Donald D
Du Quoin HS
Du Quoin IL

Cook Eugene D
East Side HS
Butler IN

Cook James P
Carrington HS
Carrington ND

Cook Jeffrey A
Sidney HS
Sidney NE

Cook Linda D
New Providence Comm HS
New Providence IA

Cook Roger A
Lincoln Way HS
Manhattan IL

Cook Susan V
Hillsdale HS
Hillsdale MI

Cook Thomas
Ionia HS
Ionia MI

Cook Tommy J
Holbomc HS
Holcomb MO

Cook William L
Gladstone Area HS
Gladstone MI

Cook William R
Northwest HS
Cedar Hills MO

Cooke Virginia T
Queen Of Peace HS
Chicago IL

Cooke William D
Haven 'S
Haven KS

Cooley Christine Z
Morrill HS
Morrill NE

Cooley Debra E
Hillsboro HS
Hillsboro IL

Cooley Holland S
Litchfield HS
Litchfield MI

Cooley Sheryl A
Mahomet Seymour HS
Seymour IL

Coolidge Kevin L
Rantoul Township HS
Rantoul IL

Coombs Carol M
Bolingbrook HS
Bolingbrook IL

Coon Gary J
Charleston HS
Charleston MO

Coon Robin J
Hillsdale HS
Hillsdale MI

Coonley Colleen A
Belvidere HS
Belvidere IL

Coonrod Doris L
Greenfield HS
Greenfield IL

Cooper Brian K
Buchanan HS
Buchanan MI

Cooper Connie L
Bladen Public HS
Bladen NE

Cooper Cynthia A
Lewistown HS
Lewistown IL

Cooper David R
Doniphan HS
Doniphan MO

Cooper Debra L
East Kentwood HS
Kentwood MI

Cooper Jeffery L
Staunton HS
Brazil IN

Cooper Karyl J
Jefferson City HS
Jefferson City MO

Cooper Lisa J
East Troy HS
East Troy WI

Cooper Lynnae L
Wilmot Union HS
Twin Lakes WI

Cooper Martha M
Liberal R 2 HS
Liberal MO

Cooper Mary A
Lincoln HS
Vincennes IN

Cooper Michael R
Anderson HS
Anderson IN

Cooper Peggy J
Beardstown Senior HS
Beardstown IL

Cooper Randy D
Mc Donald Cty HS
Rocky Comfort MO

Cooper Reba V
Glasgow HS
Glasgow MO

Cooper Rita F
Heritage Hills HS
Dale IN

Cooper Scott E
Octavia HS
Colfax IL

Coopwood Janet A
Calumet HS
Gary IN

Coots Dennas R
La Porte City HS
Mt Auburn IA

Copek Stephanie J
Fort Zumwalt HS
St Peters MO

Copeland Nancy R
Logan Rogersville HS
Rogersville MO

Copeland Randal R
North Central HS
Wilson MI

Coplan Marcia
Colchester HS
Colchester IL

Coplan Margaret M
Watertown HS
Hazel SD

Coplea Cynthia L
Fairfield Comm HS
Fairfield IL

Copley Craig W
Little Falls Community HS
Randall MN

Copley Ruth E
Clarence M Kimball HS
Royal Oak MI

Copley Shirley A
Gwinn HS
Gwinn MI

Copley Tamberly M
Cooter HS
Cooter MO

Coplin Michelle E
Academy Of Our Lady
Chicago IL

Copp Karen A
Nazareth Academy
Lyons IL

Coppess Frank R
Adams Central HS
Monroe IN

Coppinger Thomas R
St Edmond HS
Barnum IA

Copple Jamie L
Lawrenceburg HS
Lawrence Burg IN

Copple Vivian A
Charlestown HS
Charlestown IN

Corbin Rhonda J
Webster Public HS
Webster SD

Corby John T
Union HS
Grand Rapids MI

Cord David J
Shelby Sr HS
Shelbyville IN

Corder Rhoda J
Marion HS
Marion IL

Cordio Carol J
La Follete Sr HS
Madison WI

Coren Linda R
Highland Park HS
Highland Pk IL

Corey Mary L
Benton HS
Whittington IL

Corley Cathy J
William Chrisman HS
Independence MO

Corman Marilyn D
Ruskin HS
Ruskin NE

Corn Melinda K
Warsaw Community HS
Warsaw IN

Cornejo Nicholas
Saint Francis De Sales HS
Chicago IL

Cornell Cynthia L
Vandercook Lake HS
Jackson MI

Cornell Kevin A
Parkwood HS
Joplin MO

Cornell Michael C
Memorial HS
Joplin MO

Cornell Patty L
S Sioux HS
S Sioux City NE

Cornett Galen L
El Paso HS
El Paso IL

Corno Edward C
Kirkwood HS
Kirkwood MO

Cornwell Mary M
Clio Area HS
Clio MI

Corrao Pamela A
St John Cathedral
Milwaukee WI

Corrick Beth A
Mccook Sr HS
Mccook NE

Corrin Jane L
Tri Center HS
Neola IA

Corrington Bonnie M
Mitchell Sr HS
Mitchell SD

Corso Roger L
Frank Cody HS
Detroit MI

Corvino Robert F
Fenwick HS
Westchester IL

Corzine Steven A
Roxana Sr HS
East Alton IL

Corzine Suzanne
Dongola HS
Dongola ''.

Cosby Lillie K
Paseo HS
Kansas City MO

Cosentino Patricia L
Elizabeth Seton HS
Chicago IL

Cosgray Mark D
Twin Lakes HS
Idaville IN

Cosgrove Sarah A
St Bede Academy
Spring Valley IL

Cosgrove Thomas C
Hempstead HS
Dubuque IA

Costa George S
Lane Technical HS
Chicago IL

Costantino Peter D
Macomb HS
Macomb IL

Costello Anthony L
Mendota HS
Mendota IL

Costello Gene A
New Hampton Comm HS
Elma IA

Costello Melissa K
Immaculata HS
Chicago IL

Cottingham Lora A
Forman HS
Manito IL

Cotton Brian F
Harper Creek HS
E Leroy MI

Cottrell Ronda L
Marysville HS
Marysville KS

Couch Janice G
Meadville R 4 HS
Linneus MO

Coudron Tanya K
Adrion HS
Adrion MI

Coughlin Mary L
Wethersfield HS
Kewanee IL

Cougill Mary C
Central HS
Evansville IN

Coulis Louie
Bishop Noll Institute
East Chicago IN

Coulman Roseanne M
Flint Northern HS
Clio MI

Coulter Cynthia A
Marian HS
Hays KS

Coulter Timothy G
Glenbrook North HS
Northbrook IL

Counterman Karen S
Martin Public HS
Otsego MI

Countryman Lyn L
215 North 11th HS
Adel IA

Course Jeannine V
Lakeview HS
St Clair Shores MI

Courtney John L
Mt Vernon Township HS
Mt Vernon IL

Couse Debra A
Assumption HS
Wisconsin Rapids WI

Cover Christianne
Northfield Sr HS
Northfield MN

Covert Karen J
Inland Lakes HS
Alanson MI

Coville Mark P
O Fallon Township HS
O Fallon IL

Covington Andre E
Fenger HS
Chicago IL

Cowan Dawn M
Climax Scotts HS
Climax MI

Cowden Valerie S
Viroqua HS
Viroqua WI

Cowell Margie E
Lewistown HS
Lewistown IL

Cowie Islay J
Springfield HS
Springfield IL

Cowles Denise A
Belding HS
Belding MI

Cowley Nina S
Rolla HS
Rolla MO

Cox David E
Metawora HS
East Peoria IL

Cox Emily M
Pecatonica HS
Winnebago IL

Cox Heidi L
East HS
Des Moines IA

Cox Joann M
Wellcome Memorial HS
Garden City MN

Cox Kathleen A
Fort Atkinson Sr HS
Fort Atkinson WI

Cox Lawrence M
Cass Tech HS
Detroit MI

Cox Lois K
Nevada HS
Nevada MO

Cox Mark A
Frankton Sr HS
Frankton IN

Cox Marla F
Jayhawk Linn HS
Prescott KS

Cox Michael D
South Decatur HS
Greensburg IN

Cox Rebecca M
Lake Central HS
St John IN

Cox Rick M
Brownstown HS
Brownstown IL

Cox Roberta M
Central Heights HS
Princeton KS

Cox Robert J
Pennville HS
Dunkirk IN

Cox Sandra L
Flora HS
Flora IL

Cox Sara J
Beardstown Jr Sr HS
Beardstown IL

Cox Toni M
Mattoon HS
Mattoon IL

Cox William H
Wabeno HS
Wabeno WI

Coyne David J
Gordon Tech HS
Chicago IL

Coyne Denise A
Bluffton HS
Bluffton IN

Coyne Raymond M
Hinsdale So HS
Westmont IL

Cozad David C
Bay City Central HS
Bay City MI

Crabtree Elayne L
Hancock Public HS
Hancock MN

Crabtree Pamela K
Central HS
St Jospeh MO

Crabtree Susan R
Moravia HS
Blakesburg IA

Crackel Michael D
Serena HS
Earlville IL

Crackel Philip R
Miller HS
Miller SD

Craddock Richard D
Brookings HS
Brookings SD

Crader Bernard V
Woodland R Iv HS
Glen Allen MO

Craft Cary L
Argyle HS
Gratiot WI

Craft David L
Auburn HS
Rockford IL

Craft Le Ann
Argyle HS
Gratiot WI

Crago Carrie D
Belleville Twp East HS
Fairview Hts IL

Crahan Kevin F
High School
Dubuque IA

Craig Brenda C
Kirksville Sr HS
Kirksville MO

Craig Catheryn E
Central HS
Flint MI

Craig Johnetta M
Mary Inst HS
St Louis MO

Craig Joy L
Regina Dominican HS
Highland Park IL

Craig Sharon L
Baldwin HS
Baldwin City KS

Crain Karla F
Jackson HS
Jackson MO

Crain Michael M
Alexander Hamilton HS
Milwaukee WI

Crall Catherine M
Albia Community HS
Albia IA

Cramer Pamela S
Greenview HS
Greenview IL

Crane Linda K
Savannah HS
Savannah MO

Crane William M
Salem Community HS
Salem IL

Crapp Debra
Potosi HS
Potosi WI

Crase Michael W
Belmont HS
Mineral Point WI

Crates April A
Cassville HS
Shell Knob MO

Cravens Roy E
Fairfield Comm HS
Fairfield IL

Craw Lori C
Stratton Public HS
Stratton NE

Crawford Carol A
Woodruff HS
Peoria IL

Crawford Cheryl A
Antigo HS
Antigo WI

Crawford Jayne M
Columbus North Senior HS
Columbus IN

Crawford John R
Savannah Riii HS
Savannah MO

Crawford Mary A
TriHS
Lewisville IN

Cray Nicholas K
St Laurence HS
Oak Lawn IL

Craycraft Robert H
Culver HS
Culver IN

Crayton Rebecca S
Washington Comm HS
Washington IL

Creasman Craig N
Lincoln Park HS
Lincoln Pk MI

Creed Rick L
Walnut Grove HS
Walnut Grove MO

Creighton Rhonda L
Laville Jr Sr HS
Lakeville IN

Creyts David M
Everett HS
Lansing MI

Crifase Steve A
Maine East HS
Park Ridge IL

Crim Robert A
Greenhills HS
Saline MI

Cripe Debra J
Goshen HS
Goshen IN

Cripe Robert M
Sterling HS
Sterling IL

Crippen Karen L
Elmhurst HS
Fort Wayne IN

Crippen Terri E
Faith Baptist Academy
Kalamazoo MI

Criscuolo Mark A
Marmion Military Acad
Elgin IL

Crispin William K
Chrisman HS
Chrisman IL

Crist Deborah J
Harry A Burke HS
Omaha NE

Crist Marlys L
Chariton Comm HS
Chariton IA

Critten Deborah J
Gallatin HS
Gallatin MO

Crittenden John H
Community HS
West Chicago IL

Croci Carl L
St Thomas Aquinas HS
Hazelwood MO

Crockett Cathy M
West Vigo HS
West Terre Haute IN

Croegaert Richard R
Annawan HS
Mineral IL

Cromley Carolyn L
Carrollton HS
Carrollton MO

Cronkright Sally A
Vale HS
Goodells MI

Crook Barbara A
Archie HS
Archie MO

Crook Rodney E
Rising City Public HS
Rising City NE

Crosby Dale
Jefferson HS
Cedar Rapids IA

Cross Colette P
Jefferson City Sr HS
Jefferson City MO

Cross Eddie W
Kennett Sr HS
Kennett MO

Cross Francine M
Armada HS
Allenton MI

Cross Joel L
Hartsburg Emden HS
Emden IL

Cross Margaret C
Hayti HS
Hayti MO

Cross Martha C
Murphysboro Township
HS
Murphrsboro IL

Crosser Diane R
L D F Comm HS
Marshalltown IA

Crossland Karen E
Shortridge HS
Indianapolis IN

Crosthwait Camela
Crown Point HS
Crown Point IN

Crotwell Vicki E
Edison HS
Morrisville MO

Crouch Merry J
Bettendorf HS
Bettendorf IA

Crouch Samuel D
Monett Sr HS
Verona MO

Croudy Doug P
Estherville HS
Estherville IA

Crouse Gordon J
Lincoln HS
Wisconsin Rapids WI

Crow Christine A
Dexter HS
Dexter KS

Crow Connie L
North Platte HS
North Platte NE

Crowder Leona J
West HS
Aurora IL

Crowder Wayne T
Whitko HS
South Whitley IN

Crowe Alison A
Lanphier HS
Springfield IL

Crowe Greg A
Plainfield Jr Sr HS
Plainfield IN

Crowe Stacy L
John Marshall HS
Indianapolis IN

Crowl Randy D
Hamilton HS
Pleasant Lake IN

Crowley David S
Shenandoah Community HS
Shenandoah IA

Crowser Tami L
W J Brown HS
Sturgis SD

Crozier Terry L
Hoopeston East Lynn HS
Hoopeston IL

Crull Brenda D
Wabash HS
Wabash IN

Crum James A
Virginia HS
Virginia IL

Crum Melanie D
Flat River Central R3 HS
Flat River MO

Csicsko David L
Morton Sr HS
Hammond IN

Csikos Mindy C
Lake Central HS
Dyer IN

Csont Donald W
Lincoln Park HS
Lincoln Park MI

Cuckie Nancy
Northwest Webster HS
Clare IA

Culich Jean M
George Washington HS
Chicago IL

Cullen Joanne
Menomonee Falls HS
Menomonee Falls WI

Culligan Patrick E
Benet Academy
Naperville IL

Culligan Sheila A
Derham Hall HS
St Paul MN

Culp Kathy L
R Iv HS
St Joseph MO

Culver Jean A
Lake Central HS
Griffith IN

Culver Robert E
Crawford County HS
Bourbon MO

Cumby Brenda E
Carrollton HS
Carrollton IL

Cummings Eileen M
Mount Assisi Academy
Chicago Ridge IL

Cummins Douglas W
Assumption HS
Tower Hill IL

Cummins Jennifer
Carrier Mills HS
Carrier Mills IL

Cummins Kathy I
Carthage Sr HS
Carthage MO

Cundall Brad L
Louisville HS
Cedar Creek NE

Cundiff Charles A
Maconaquah HS
Grissom Air Base IN

Cundiff Rita M
Lathrop HS
Lathrop MO

Cunning Scott A
Terre Haute North Vigo HS
Terre Haute IN

Cunningham Beverly G
Montgomery County R Ii HS
New Florence MO

Cunningham Brian R
Delavan Comm HS
Delvan IL

Cunningham Carol A
Hudson HS
Hudson WI

Cunningham Dick P
North Muskegon HS
North Muskegon MI

Cunningham Kathleen M
Mother Guerin HS
River Grove IL

Cunningham Lisa K
Roseville HS
Roseville IL

Cunningham Mary K
Rosati Kain HS
St Louis MO

Cuny Cari L
East Catholic HS
Detroit MI

Cupido Cathy A
James Madison HS
Milwaukee WI

Cupples William T
Hoxie HS
Hoxie KS

Curatolo Thomas A
Thornton Twp HS
Dolton IL

Curda Carol E
Lyons Twp HS
La Grange IL

Curphy Cary E
Topeka West HS
Topeka KS

STUDENTS PHOTOGRAPH SCHEDULED FOR PUBLICATION HERE COULD NOT BE REPRODUCED

Current Thomas R
Maquoketa Comm HS
Maquoketa IA

Currie James A
High School
Powhattan KS

Currin Archie L
Luther South HS
Chicago IL

Curry Denis R
Morton HS
Pekin IL

Curry Dwight H
Nebraska Christian HS
Ponca NE

Curry Kenneth B
Morton HS
Pekin IL

Curry Lucia A
Bucklin Rii HS
Bucklin MO

Curry Mark A
Wichita North HS
Wichita KS

Curry Phyllis L
St James HS
St James MN

Curry Tamara S
Octavia HS
Colfax IL

Curtin Mark T
Logansport HS
Logansport IN

Curtis Connie J
Fremont Mills HS
Tabor IA

Curtis Danny R
Central Comm HS
De Witt IA

Curtis Joan M
Arthur Hill HS
Sagninaw MI

Curtis Sherry L
Macomb HS
Macomb IL

Cushing Melisa A
Lawrence Central HS
Indianapolis IN

Cushman Donna J
Fountain Central HS
Attica IN

Cusson Jody M
George Washington HS
Indianapolis IN

Custer Robert A
Summerfield HS
Petersburg MI

Cutler Pamela E
Christopher HS
Christopher IL

Cutler Sharon L
Auburndale HS
Arpin WI

Cutright Jennifer J
Casey HS
Casey IL

Cuva Susan K
North HS
Omaha NE

Cwach Nancy L
Yankton Sr HS
Yankton SD

Cwiakala Debra A
Grand Blanc HS
Grand Blanc MI

Cyphers Robert L
Litchfield HS
Litchfield IL

Cyr Ann M
Oconto Falls HS
Oconto Falls WI

Czaplewski Kellen K
Loup City Public HS
Loup City NE

Czech Julie A
Collinsville HS
Collinsville IL

Czech Melanie S
Thornridge HS
Harvey IL

Czerwonka Frederick W
Newton HS
Newton IL

D

Czuprynski James S
St Rita HS
Chicago IL

D Andrea Kathleen E
W L Western HS
Walled Lake MI

D Aquila Margaret M
Hibbing HS
Hibbing MN

D Arcy Jean M
Munster HS
Munster IN

D Arpini Harold A
Jefferson HS
Monroe MI

D Souza Anita M
Kirksville Sr HS
Kirksville MO

Dabbs Regina M
Union HS
Sturtevant WI

Dabrowski Edward J
Morton West HS
Stickney IL

Dado Claudia M
Maria HS
Chicago IL

Dage Sharon K
Montabella HS
Edmore MI

Dager Debra A
Fenton Senior HS
Fenton MI

Dahlberg David F
C A Lindbergh HS
Minnetonka MN

Dahle Jodi L
Harlem HS
Rockford IL

Dahle Nancy L
Milbank HS
Milbank SD

Dahlstrom Eric L
Ridgewood HS
Norridge IL

Dahmer Mary Ann
Crab Orchard HS
Marion IL

Dahmke Mark C
David City Public HS
David City NE

Dahms Cheryll A
West Concord HS
West Concord MN

Dahn Linda M
South Broward HS
Columbus IN

Daidone Robert E
Hamilton HS
Hamilton IL

Daigh Toni L
Parsons Sr HS
Parsons KS

Dailey Cathy A
Academy Of Our Lady
Washington IL

Dailey Edward G
Jonesville HS
Jonesville MI

Dailey John A
Glenbard East HS
Lombard IL

Daily Dan M
Goodland HS
Kanorado KS

Daily Susan E
Columbus East HS
Columbus IN

Dalbom William E
East Newton HS
Stella MO

Dale Jeffrey M
Clare HS
Clare MI

Daley Robert J
Quigley South HS
Chicago IL

Dalle Ave Margaret A
Lincoln HS
Vincennes IN

Dallinger Barbara L
Morton HS
Morton IL

Dallman David F
Markesan HS
Markesan WI

Dal Pian Margaret P
Verdigre HS
Verdigre NE

Dalrymple Linda K
Shawnee Mission South HS
Overland Park KS

Daluga Daniel J
Pontiac Twp HS
Pontiac IL

Daly Charles E
Thedford HS
Stapleton NE

Daly Sheryl L
Sutherland HS
Sutherland NE

Daly Thomas J
Loyola Academy
Lake Forest IL

Dameron Julie M
Virden HS
Virden IL

Dancy James N
Slater HS
Slater MO

Danczak Karen E
Mother Of Sorrows HS
Alsip IL

Danczyk Gary M
Hayward Comm HS
Hayward WI

Dangremond Debra J
Oak Lawn Comm HS
Oak Lawn IL

Danhof Brenda G
Montague HS
Rothbury MI

Daniel Dana A
Mundelein HS
Mundelein IL

Daniel James R
Elmwood Park HS
Elmwood Park IL

Daniel Jennie S
East Peoria Comm HS
Creve Coeur IL

Daniel Ronald E
Mitchell HS
Mitchell IN

Daniels Ceandra L
Lindblom Tech HS
Chicago IL

Daniels Curtis D
Seneca HS
Seneca MO

Daniels James M
Griffin HS
Springfield IL

Daniels Jean A
Carrier Mills HS
Carrier Mills IL

Daniels Koleen K
Northwest HS
Jackson MI

Daniels Robert M
Mona Shores HS
Muskegon MI

Daniels Scott A
Fayette Comm HS
Fayette IA

Daniels Scott M
Bluffton HS
Bluffton IN

Daniels Sharon G
South Pemiscot HS
Steele MO

Daniels Thomas G
Pacelli HS
Stevens Point WI

Danielson Janice M
Woodstock HS
Woodstock IL

Danielson Penny G
Grantsburg HS
Grantsburg WI

Danner Elaine
Elkhart Memorial HS
Elkhart IN

Danner Susan E
South Newton Jr Sr HS
Kentland IN

Dapper Joan M
Resurrection HS
Chicago IL

Da Pra David P
A D Johnston HS
Bessemer MI

Da Pra Deborah A
A D Johnston HS
Bessemer MI

Darbo Doug D
Aurora Hoyt Lakes HS
Hoyt Lakes MN

Darfler Jill L
Chicago Christian HS
Blue Island IL

Dargan Crystal L
Rantoul Township HS
Paxton IL

Da Rif James F
Ottawa Twp HS
Ottawa IL

Darling Jane J
Burwell Jr Sr HS
Burwell NE

Darlington Lloyd R
Normandy HS
St Louis MO

Darnell Frances V
Hanover Central HS
Cedar Lake IN

Darnell Jeffrey L
Lynch Public HS
Lynch NE

Darrah John
Union HS
Monmouth IL

Dart Michael L
Oblong HS
Oblong IL

Daschner Karen J
Watseka Community HS
Watseka IL

Dasen Joanne M
Corunna HS
Corunna MI

Dassinger Laverne D
Dickinson HS
Gladstone ND

Dassinger Loraine
Dickinson HS
Gladstone ND

Daub Bruce K
Winnebago HS
Pecatonica IL

Daugherty Arlene K
Terre Haute North Vigo HS
Terre Haute IN

Daugherty Candice D
Pana Senior HS
Pana IL

Daugherty Sharon A
St Teresas Academy
Kansas City MO

Daugherty Tammy J
St Teresa HS
Decatur IL

Daugs Douglas W
Buchanan HS
Buchanan ND

Daun Judy
New Holstein HS
St Cloud WI

Dauphin Susan M
Mt Carroll HS
Savanna IL

Dautenhahn David P
Marshall HS
Marshall MO

Davenport Nancy E
Northwest HS
House Springs MO

Davenport Terri L
Terre Haute North Vigo HS
Terre Haute IN

Davey Russell L
Rocwell City Com HS
Rockwell City IA

David Kimberly J
Alma HS
Alma NE

David Lynn A
Univ Of Chicago Lab HS
Chicago IL

Davidson Brett M
Haworth HS
Kokomo IN

Davidson Cheryl L
North Platte R I HS
Edgerton MO

Davidson Debra K
Zionsville Comm HS
Zionsville IN

Davidson Holly A
Loretto HS
Kansas City MO

Davidson Janell S
L And M HS
Bloomfield IN

Davidson Maurice A
Greenwood Comm HS
Greenwood IN

Davinroy Benjamin
Assumption Hs
Fairview Heights IL

Davis Amy J
Delta HS
Braggadocio MO

Davis Barbara L
David City HS
David City NE

Davis Benjamin L
Park Tudor HS
Indianapolis IN

Davis Blake E
Casey HS
Casey IL

Davis Brian J
Lake Shore HS
St Clair Shores MI

Davis Bryan C
East Prairie HS
East Prairie MO

Davis Carol S
Harrisonville Sr HS
Harrisonville MO

Davis Cecile A
Neutown Harris HS
Lucerne MO

Davis Cheryl R
Greenville Senior HS
Greenville MI

Davis Darlene S
Walter P Chrysler Mem HS
New Castle IN

Davis Daryl N
De La Salle HS
Chicago IL

STUDENTS PHOTOGRAPH SCHEDULED FOR PUBLICATION HERE COULD NOT BE REPRODUCED

Davis Debra D
Maple Valley HS
Castana IA

Davis Elizabeth A
East Prairie HS
E Prairie MO

Davis Ivan S
Clare HS
Clare MI

Davis Jacqueline A
Climax Scotts HS
Climax MI

Davis James E
St Joseph HS
St Joseph MI

Davis Jeff E
Cloverdale HS
Cloverdale IN

Davis Jeffery B
Casey HS
Casey IL

Davis Jeffery D
Cambridge HS
Cambridge NE

Davis Joan E
Zion Benton Township HS
Zion IL

Davis Julie M
Monett HS
Monett MO

Davis Keith R
Coloma HS
Coloma MI

Davis Kevin M
Heelan HS
Sioux City IA

Davis Kimberly L
William Fremd HS
Palatine IL

Davis Kimberly S
Nebraska City Sr HS
Nebraska City NE

Davis Kip D
Oblong HS
Oblong IL

Davis Kristi L
Atlantic HS
Atlantic IA

Davis Mark E
Fairfield Community HS
Fairfield IL

Davis Mark H
Lowell Sr HS
Hebron IN

Davis Martha A
Butler HS
Butler MO

Davis Martha E
Parkview HS
Springfield MO

Davis Martha G
Waterford Mott HS
Pontiac MI

Davis Marvin R
Limestone Comm HS
Bartonville IL

Davis Mary A
Central Montcalm HS
Stanton MI

Davis Mary L
Mancelona HS
Mancelona MI

Davis Michael D
Crown Point HS
Crown Point IN

Davis Milan S
Meade HS
Meade KS

Davis Patrick O
Pine River HS
St Cloud MN

Davis Peggy S
Beardstown HS
Beardstown IL

Davis Rickey E
Parkside HS
Jackson MI

Davis Sandra K
Emmerich Manual HS
Inidanapolis IN

Davis Sandra K
Roxana Sr HS
Wood River IL

Davis Timothy J
East Brook HS
Upland IN

Davis Wendy L
Oscoda Area HS
Oscoda MI

Davison Carol L
Sedgwick HS
Sedgwick KS

Davison Nancy L
Highland HS
Highland IN

Davy Melvin A
Caledonia HS
Hokah MN

Dawes Suzanne G
Carman HS
Flint MI

Dawson Cheryl A
St Charles HS
St Charles MO

Dawson Jody A
Concord HS
Hanover MI

Dawson Kandace E R
Pardeeville HS
Cambria WI

Dawson Kelly O
Roosevelt HS
Almont ND

Day Cynthia J
Lincoln HS
Lincoln KS

Day Dennis A
Keokuk Sr HS
Keokuk IA

Day John C
Rantoul Township HS
Rantoul IL

Day Julia L
Marshall HS
Marshall MI

Day Julie A
Prairie Du Chien Sr HS
Prairie Du Chien WI

Day Wanda B
Beaumont HS
St Louis MO

De Adam Suann M
St Benedict HS
Chicago IL

Deal James E
Brazil HS
Knightsville IN

Dean Connie
Southeast Sr HS
Kansas City MO

Dean Monica R
Mt Pleasant Comm HS
Mt Pleasant IA

Dean Patricia A
Kenowa Hills HS
Marne MI

Dearborn John D
Davis Co Comm HS
Bloomfield IA

Dearmont David D
Burwell Jr Sr HS
Burwell NE

Deasy James A
Bishop Noll Institute HS
Hammond IN

Deaton Dundri L
Bedford North Lawrence HS
Bedford IN

Deatrick Shelley M
Andrews HS
Harbor Beach MI

Debano Dee A
South Barber HS
Hazelton KS

Debertin Mollie A
Magic City Campus HS
Minot ND

De Broux James M
Hastings HS
Hastings MI

De Bruin Darlene S
Lee HS
Wyoming MI

De Bruler Philip W
George Washington HS
Indianapolis IN

Deckard Belinda L
Mitchell HS
Bedford IN

Decker Carol L
E Noble HS
Avilla IN

Decker Cyndee G
Oak Park Acad
Sioux City IA

Decker Diane L
Liberty Comm Unit 2 HS
Clayton IL

Decker Mary G
Southwest HS
St Louis MO

Deckert Richard W
Otis Bison Sr HS
Bison KS

De Cook Cheryl L
Gull Lake HS
Richland MI

De Corte Mark L
Bay City Central HS
Bay City MI

De Courcy James F
Granite City HS South
Granite City IL

Dee Mary A
Lourdes HS
Rochester MN

Deeds William C
North Miami HS
Macy IN

Deeke Von C
Mascoutah HS
Mascoutah IL

Deemer Suzette L
Platte Valley Academy
Papillion NE

De Foe Michael J
Pembina Public HS
Pembina ND

De Forest Deborah M
Battle Creek Academy
Battle Creek MI

De Forest Kathleen D
Galien HS
Galien MI

De Gayner Tarianne
Fenton HS
Linden MI

Degeberg Kim R
Edina East HS
Edina MN

Degnitz Thomas R
Kewaskum Community HS
Kewaskum WI

De Goey Gary W
North Mohaska HS
New Sharon IA

Degonia Pamela A
Arcadia Valley HS
Arcadia MO

De Good Nancy J
Peoria HS
Peoria IL

Degraeve Bill J
Raytown HS
Kansas City MO

De Grote Darla D
Edgerton Public HS
Edgerton MN

De Haan Dan R
Grand Rapids Christian HS
Grand Rapids MI

Dehring Terrence R
Alpena Sr HS
Alpena MI

Deibert Myren A
Ipswich HS
Ipswich SD

Deignan Michael J
So Sioux City HS
So Sioux City NE

Deines Brian L
Trego Community HS
Wakeeney KS

Deines Dana C
Cedar Falls HS
Cedar Falls IA

Deines Ranita S
Trego Comm HS
Ogallah KS

Deitchman Robert P
Chatard HS
Indianapolis IN

De Jonge Penny A
Zeeland HS
Zeeland MI

De Laet Dwight D
Lewellen Rural HS
Lewellen NE

De Lama George
Gordon Tech HS
Chicago IL

Delaney Dennis P
Wilmington HS
Wilmington IL

Delaney Kathy A
Duchesne HS
St Charles MO

Delaney Margaret E
Knox County HS
Baring MO

De Lany Mark P
Jefferson HS
Cedar Rapids IA

Delaplane Mary Beth
Mother Mcauley Lib Arts HS
Chicago IL

Delay Deborah J
Mckinley HS
St Louis MO

Delger Paul T
Kanawha Comm HS
Kanawha IA

Delk David L
Fulton Comm HS
Albany IL

Delk Richard A
Fulton HS
Albany IL

Dell Valerie J
Watervliet HS
Watervliet MI

De Long Patty A
Randolph Public HS
Randolph NE

Del Toro Eva M
Morton Senior HS
Hammond IN

De Luca Jolene M
Big Rapids HS
Stanwood MI

Delvecchio Francis X
St Thomas Aquinas HS
Hazelwood MO

Delvo Sandy K
Canton HS
Canton SD

Demaree Rhonda L
Nevada HS
Nevada MO

Demaretti Joseph D
Frankfort Comm HS
West Frankfort IL

De Marr Rick W
Coldwater HS
Coldwater MI

De Martino Nancy A
John F Kennedy HS
Chicago IL

De Maso Gregg T
Springfield HS
Springfield MI

Dembiec Stephen J
Custer HS
Milwaukee WI

Dement Robert A
Malden HS
Malden MO

Demich Raymond T
Morgan Park HS
Chicago IL

Demmer David A
Foley HS
Foley MN

Demorest Mark S
Centennial HS
Champaign IL

Dempski Donald A
Mexico HS
Mexico MO

Denault Orville J
Herscher HS
Kankakee IL

Denby Dennis D
Roxana Sr HS
East Alton IL

Den Hartog Sherri L
Sheldon Community HS
Sheldon IA

Denney Michael R
North Mabaska HS
Rose Hill IA

Denning Raymond B
Staples HS
Stapls MN

Dennington Bill L
Collinsville Sr HS
Collinsville IL

Dennis Debra A
Brookfield R Iii HS
Brookfield MO

Dennis Douglas E
Edwardsville Senior HS
Edwardsville IL

Dennis Jay D
Joliet West HS
Joliet IL

Dennis Scott A
Ann Arbor Huron HS
Ann Arbor MI

Dennison Sheldon L
South Central HS
Laconia IN

Denny Leslie J
Lamar R 1 HS
Lamar MO

Denomy Mary Ellen G
Dominican HS
Detroit MI

De Nooyer Rebecca L
Gull Lake HS
Richland MI

Densmore Robert G
West Richland HS
Noble IL

Denson Dorothy A
Spalding Academy
Spalding NE

Denstedt Debra K
Pinconning Area HS
Linwood MI

Denton Cynthia A
Ramsey HS
Ramsey IL

Denton Ronda G
Chillicothe HS
Chillicothe MO

Denys Scott O
Reavis HS
Burbank IL

Denzer Gary S
Normal Community HS
Bloomington IL

Depa Cynthia A
Reavis HS
Burbank IL

De Paepe Richard C
Riley Senior HS
South Bend IN

Deplanty Richard E
Rockville HS
Rockville IN

Depoy James L
Danville Community HS
Danville IN

Deppe Michael W
Creighton Prep
Omaha NE

Deppert David D
Pekin Community HS
Pekin IL

Deppish Julie H
St Xaviers HS
Junction City KS

De Preste Nancy A
Glendale HS
Springfield MO

Derbas Peggysue M
St Joseph HS
Chicago IL

Derman Betty M
Arlington HS
Nickerson NE

Dernule Monica M
Bishop Noll Institute
Highland IN

Derocher Dan N
Bark River HS
Bark River MI

Derocher David L
Menominee HS
Menominee MI

De Rosier Joseph M
Saints Peter & Paul HS
Saginaw MI

Derrick Oma J
Clarke Comm HS
Weldon IA

Derry Catherine K
Greenview HS
Greenview IL

Derse Robert F
Lake Mills Public HS
Lake Mills WI

De Rue Brian A
Saint Joseph HS
South Bend IN

De Ruiter Randall A
Lincolnway HS
Frankfort IL

Derwin Andrew P
Marist HS
Chicago IL

Desch John A
Houston HS
Houston MO

De Selm Stephen P
Bishop Mc Namara HS
Kankakee IL

De Shasier Marcia L
Paxton HS
Paxton IL

De Simone Gerald F
Arlington HS
Arlington Heights IL

Dessalet Sharon L
Wilson Campus HS
Mankato MN

Destree Steven G
Southern Door HS
Sturgeon Bay WI

Detamore Susan L
Plymouth HS
Plymouth IN

Detherage Shirley J
Macksville HS
Radium KS

Detherow Donald E
Seymour HS
Seymour MO

Detmers Peggy A
Canton HS
Canton SD

Dettlinger Butch A
New Palestine HS
New Palestine IN

Detweiler Mark P
Richwoods HS
Peoria IL

Detwiler Sara J
Tiskilwa HS
Tiskilwa IL

Deubler Jane A
Camdenton R 3 HS
Camdenton MO

Deuel Janet L
Superior HS
Superior NE

Deutsch Cynthia L
R Nelson Snider HS
Fort Wayne IN

Deutsch Kim S
Hoisington HS
Hoisington KS

Devane Colleen M
St Xaviers HS
Junction City KS

Devena Diana L
Buhler HS
Hutchinson KS

De Veranez Denise C
Lindblom Tech HS
Chicago IL

Devereaux Scott J
Kouts HS
Kouts IN

Devine Judy K
Emmerich Manual HS
Indianapolis IN

Devine Randy A
St Louis HS
St Louis MI

Devine Robert J
Kewaskum HS
Adell WI

De Viney Linda M
Bolingbrook HS
Bolingbrook IL

De Vito Susan E
Rolling Meadows HS
Arlington Hts IL

Devlin Christopher P
Benet Academy
Bolingbrook IL

De Vore Timothy G
Alma HS
Alma MI

De Vos Doreen K
Marshall HS
Marshall MN

De Vries Donna F
Rapid City Central HS
Rapid City SD

De Waay Byron O
Sheldon Comm HS
Sanborn IA

De Wald Robert M
Meridian HS
Alexandria NE

De Wall Debra D
Pocahontas Comm HS
Pocahontas IA

De Wall Jane A
Pocahontas Comm HS
Pocahontas IA

De Walt Michael L
Kewanee HS
Kewanee IL

De Walt Ronda L
Charlotte HS
Charlotte MI

De Weese Penny J
Goodhue HS
Goodhue MN

Dewell Kevin W
Fowler HS
Fowler KS

Dewhirst Curt V
Newton HS
Newton IL

De Witt David J
North Mahaska HS
New Sharon IA

Dey Justin A
Douglas Mac Arthur HS
Saginaw MI

Dey Sheryl A
Douglas Mac Arthur HS
Saginaw MI

Deyo Mike D
Martin Hughes HS
Britt MN

De Young Cheryl D
Thornwood HS
S Holland IL

De Young Merrilee D
Pella Christian HS
Pella IA

De Zeeuw Vera C
Orfordville Parkview HS
Evansville WI

Dibbern Joseph A
Yankton Senior HS
Yankton SD

Di Caro Daneil P
Holy Cross HS
Chicago IL

Dick Gerry A
Clinton HS
Clinton IN

Dicke Martin P
Concordia Academy
St Paul MN

Dickens David A
Central HS
St Joseph MO

Dickens Robert J
St John Cathedral HS
Milwaukee WI

Dickenson Clifton R
Hermitage HS
Hermitage MO

Dickerson Chris M
Newton Community HS
Newton IL

Dickes Suzanne M
Lawton Bronson HS
Sioux City IA

Dickey Kevin L
Kenwood HS
Chicago IL

Dickey Terri L
Rosedale HS
Montezuma IN

Dickinson Matthew G
Carthage Comm HS
Carthage IL

Dickman Jay W
Jacksonville HS
Jacksonville IL

Dickman Kathy A
Sac Community HS
Sac City IA

Dickman Susan M
Grinnell HS
Grinnell KS

Dicks Ramona L
Brown Deer HS
Brown Deer WI

Dickson Christopher W
Maine East HS
Niles IL

Dickson David P
Hinckley Big Rock HS
Big Rock IL

Diderich James M
Hononegah HS
Roscoe IL

Diebel Thomas W
Glenbrook South HS
Glenview IL

Diebolt Lynn D
Corunna HS
Corunna MI

Diedrichsen Sharon E
Blair HS
Blair NE

Diefendorf Ellen C
Otterville Public HS
Otterville MO

Diehl Debra J
Wheatland HS
Elsie NE

Diehl Holly L
Little Wolf HS
Manawa WI

Diekemper Lisa K
Dupo Community HS
Dupo IL

Diel Bruce A
Newton HS
Newton IL

Dielman Annette L
Petoskey Senior HS
Petoskey MI

Dierker Diane K
Forman HS
Manito IL

Dierking Keith A
Nemaha Valley HS
Talmage NE

Dierschow Duane L
Smithville HS
Smithville MO

Dietmeyer Cheryl L
Warren Township HS
Gurnee IL

Dietrich Becky L
Edison Senior HS
East Gary IN

Dietrich Catherine M
Edison Senior HS
East Gary IN

Dietrich Jane M
Seymour HS
Plainville IL

Difani James E
Perryville HS
Perryville MO

Di Giulio Thomas A
Joliet Township HS
Joliet IL

Digman Tamara L
Monroe Sr HS
Monroe WI

Dikoff Lonell G
Medina Public HS
Medina ND

Dilger Carol V
Heritage Hills HS
Ferdinand IN

Dill Joann M
Shepherd Public HS
Shepherd MI

Dillard Carolyn J
Green City HS
Green Castle MO

Dillard Dennis J
Aero Mechanics HS
Detroit MI

Dillard Valerie G
Lindblom Tech HS
Chicago IL

Diller Jayne R
Nashua Community HS
Nashua IA

Dilley Rhonda S
High School
Sedan KS

Dillman Robert C
Campion Jesuit HS
Prairie Du Chien WI

Dillon Corrinne T
Mercy HS
Omaha NE

Dills Kathryn D
Alton HS
Alton MO

Dils Michael D
Union County HS
Richmond IN

Dilsaver John S
Nixa HS
Nixa MO

Dilthey Carol J
La Monte R Iv HS
Knob Noster MO

Dilworth Janice L
St Marys Center For Learning
Chicago IL

Di Martino Angelo
St Patrick HS
Chicago IL

Di Martino Dana M
Monroe Sr HS
St Paul MN

Di Menna Cathy A
Rosemount Senior HS
Apple Valley MN

Dimmitt Kim M
Monroe City R I Public HS
Monroe City MO

Dinehart Richard L
Alexandria Monroe HS
Alexandria IN

Dinger Charles J
Marist HS
Chicago IL

Dingledein Michel J
Rock Island HS
Rock Island IL

Dinkel Brenda K
Oakley HS
Oakley KS

Dinkel Susan K
Hill City HS
Hill City KS

Dinkins Stephen W
Du Quoin HS
Du Quoin IL

Dion Marc J
Parchment HS
Parchment MI

Dionise Tony R
Farwell HS
Farwell MI

Dirks Jerry A
Omaha North HS
Omaha NE

Dishman Vonda L
W Washington HS
Campbellsburg IN

Distelrath Christine M
St Marys Of Redford HS
Detroit MI

Dittmer Christine T
Southeast Warren HS
Lacona IA

Dittmer Debra A
Southeast Warren HS
Lacona IA

Dittmer Dixie L
Eastwood HS
Cushing IA

Dittmer Jerald K
Wheatland Comm HS
Wheatland IA

Dittmer Suzanne M
Southeast Warren HS
Lacona IA

Divine Patty L
Kingsford HS
Iron Mountain MI

Divis Dianne S
Watervliet HS
Watervliet MI

Dix Stewart W
Lincoln HS
Wisconsing Rapids WI

Dixon Carol C
Bellevue HS
Bellevue MI

Dixon David A
Cowan HS
Muncie IN

Dixon Duane B
Alleman HS
Rock Island IL

Dixon Galen W
Hartville HS
Hartville MO

Dixon Jan D
Macomb Sr HS
Macomb IL

Dixon Paula L
Ann Arbor Huron HS
Ann Arbor MI

Dixon Rebecca R
Greenfield HS
Greenfield IL

Dixon Robert F
Warren County R Iii HS
Warrenton MO

Dixon Robert W
Newton Sr HS
Newton IA

Dixon Susan J
New Haven HS
New Haven IN

Dixon Terri S
Ar We Va Comm HS
Westside IA

Dixson Joycelyn Y
Arlington HS
Indianapolis IN

Djokich Joann
T F South HS
Lansing IL

Dlugosz Stephen A
St Josephs HS
South Bend IN

Doak Richard L
Hedrick Comm HS
Hedrick IA

Doane Mary L
Kent City HS
Casnovia MI

Dobben Richard L
Thornwood HS
South Holland IL

Dobbs Brenda L
Kirksville HS
Kriksville MO

Dobelmann Mark J
Lincoln Co HS
Old Monroe MO

Dobereiner Aimee M
United Township HS
East Moline IL

Dobrenski Dona M
Community Sr HS
Detroit Lakes MN

Dobrinich Tina L
Mt Olive HS
Mt Olive IL

Dobrinsky Mary H
Illiopolis HS
Springfield IL

Doby Kenneth R
Red Bud Public HS
Red Bud IL

Dockery Ray F
Engadine Consolidated HS
Gould City MI

Dockery Sandra J
Southwestern HS
Detroit MI

Dockham Patricia A
Crawford HS
Crawford NE

Dodd Brenda L
Campus HS
Haysville KS

Dodds James S
Algona HS
Lone Rock IA

Dodson Erin C
North Platte Senior HS
North Platte NE

Dodson Lisa D
Mt Vernon Township HS
Mt Vernon IL

Doe Janice E
New Ulm Sr HS
Hanska MN

Doeden Michael L
Forreston HS
Forreston IL

Doelling Bruce H
Anderson HS
Anderson IN

Doellman Maria A
Quincy Sr HS
Quincy IL

Doerffel Kathryn J
Sunnydale Academy
Kansas City MO

Doerflein Kenneth D
Brookville HS
Metamora IN

Doerfler Ronald W
Griffin HS
Springfield IL

Doering Bonnie L
Plankinton Independent HS
Wessington Springs SD

Doering Cliff G
Akron Fairgrove HS
Caro MI

Doherty John J
Motley HS
Motley MN

Doherty Patrice E
New Prague HS
New Prague MN

Dohm Della S
Grinnell HS
Grinnell KS

Dohnalek Cindy M
Prairie HS
Cedar Rapids IA

Dohr Kathi S
Round Lake Sr HS
Round Lake IL

Dohrmann James A
Reese HS
Reese MI

Dohrmann Janice A
Reese HS
Reese MI

Doke Debra A
Memorial HS
Joplin MO

Dolan Robert P
Homewood Flossmoor HS
Flossmoor IL

Dolce Sharon K
Niles West HS
Niles IL

Dole Catherine L
Warren Township HS
Gurnee IL

Dolin Sheena L
Ypsilanti HS
Ypsilanti MI

Doll Michael J
Bishop Du Bourg HS
St Louis MO

Dollar Julia A
Farmington East HS
Farmington IL

Dollen Jonette J
Tri Center HS
Shelby IA

Domeier Terry L
Geneva Public HS
Geneva NE

Domenoski Brian K
Washington HS
Two Rivers WI

Domzalski Kevin R
Carl Sandburg HS
Tinley Park IL

Donahoe Kerry R
Lamphere HS
Madison Heights MI

Donahoe Vincent A
Chosen Valley HS
Chatfield MN

Donahue Patrick M
Wahlert HS
Dubuque IA

Donajkowski Ray W
Port Washington HS
Pt Washington WI

Donaldson L Tanya E
West Side HS
Gary IN

Donham Richard G
Mason Sr HS
Erie MI

Donley Marty A
Bishop Noll Institute
East Chicago IN

Donley Michael L
Chaminade HS
Ballwin MO

Donley Pamela S
Harrisburg HS
Harrisburg IL

Donley Reba
John Marshall Harlan HS
Chicago IL

Donnelly Andrew J
Freeport Senior HS
Freeport IL

Donnelly Edward B
Freeport Senior HS
Freeport IL

Donner Brian F
Columbus HS
Columbus WI

Donner Perry P
Lincoln HS
Park Falls WI

Donohue Steven T
Mendel Catholic Prep HS
Calumet Park IL

Donovan Leslie S
Evanston Township HS
Evanston IL

Donovan Mary S
Odell Comm HS
Odell IL

Dood Steven P
W Michigan Christian HS
Ferrysburg MI

Dooley Angela A
West Excelsior Springs HS
Excelsior Springs MO

Dooley Janet L
Mount St Scholastica HS
Atchison KS

Dooley Mary Carol A
Montini HS
Lombard IL

Doolin James M
Routt HS
Jacksonville IL

Dooling Melodi A
Blue Valley HS
Stilwell KS

Dooling Timothy R
Alleman HS
Rock Island IL

Doolittle Mary A
Hillsdale HS
Hillsdale MI

Doolittle Ross A
Clio HS
Clio MI

Doppel Timothy J
Sterling Heights HS
Sterling Hts MI

Doppler Kathy J
Clark HS
Whiting IN

Doren Maryann P
Mt Pleasant Senior HS
Rosebush MI

Dorgan Roberta F
Regina HS
Harper Woods MI

Dorland Rick L
Palco HS
Palco KS

Dorn Brenda J
Belvidere HS
Rockford IL

Dorn Mark S
Brookfield Central HS
Brookfield WI

Dorociak James V
Lane Tech HS
Chicago IL

Dorr David B
St Joseph HS
Stevensville MI

Dorsch William C
Roseville HS
Roseville MI

Dorsey Debra K
E Alton Wood River Comm HS
Wood River IL

Dorsey Doug L
Winchester HS
Winchester IL

Dortmund Donald J
Weber HS
Chicago IL

Dorvil Claude M
St Thomas Apostle HS
Chicago IL

Dotson Mark A
Central HS
Flint MI

Dotson Randy C
Terril Comm HS
Langdon IA

Doubleday Lynne M
S Beloit HS
S Beloit IL

Doucet Michelle M
St George HS
St George KS

Doud Denny E
Hedrick Community HS
Hedrick IA

Doudna Dawn L
Richland Center HS
Richland Center WI

Dougherty Anne M
O Gorman HS
Sioux Falls SD

Dougherty Henry R
New Trier East HS
Wilmette IL

Dougherty Richard W
Trenton Sr HS
Laredo MO

Doughty Denice
Lindblom Technical HS
Chicago IL

Douglas David W
Joliet Catholic HS
Joliet IL

Douglas Jesse L
Potosi HS
Potosi MO

Douglas Judy K
Urbana Community HS
Vinton IA

Douglas Lori L
Marshall HS
Marshall IL

Douglas Susan E
North County R Iii HS
Bonne Terre MO

Dounis Kiki S
Fitzgerald HS
Warren MI

Douthitt Douglas A
Grandville HS
Grandville MI

Dove Robert M
Dekalb HS
Waterloo IN

Dovel Theresa C
Hamburg HS
Hamburg IA

Dow Craig M
Lakewood HS
Mulliken MI

Dowd Evon L
North Boone HS
Poplar Rove IL

Dowd Randall
Layrel HS
Layrel IN

Dowell Janie D
Tower Hill HS
Tower Hill IL

Downer Delia M
Saint Pius X HS
Kansas City MO

Downing David A
Maple Valley HS
Nashville MI

Downing Jeffrey G
Union HS
Hagerstown IN

Downs Charles E
Langdon HS
Langdon ND

Downs Stephen G
Carmel HS
Carmel IN

Downton Galen E
Twin Lakes HS
Monticello IN

Doyen Kathy M
Lansing Catholic Central HS
Lansing MI

Doyle Cathy M
Oak Forest HS
Oak Forest IL

Doyle Emily A
Mother Mc Auley HS
Palos Park IL

Doyle John J
St Thomas Academy
Burnsville MN

Doyle Maryteresa
Topeka West HS
Topeka KS

Draack Barbara J
Frazee HS
Frazee MN

Drafke Allen D
Lockport Township HS
Lockport IL

Drake Margaret A
Elwood Community HS
Elwood IN

Drane Walter K
Indian Creek HS
Trafalgar IN

Drangsholt Lois K
Sherwood Public HS
Mohall ND

Draper Dennis D
Atchison HS
Atchison KS

Draper Melissa J
Civic Memorial HS
Cottage Hills IL

Draper Steven J
Gurley Public HS
Dalton NE

Draus Richelle M
Elizabeth Seton HS
South Holland IL

Draves Melody A
Cumberland HS
Comstock WI

Drebenstedt Joni M
Marion Co Rii HS
Philadelphia MO

Drechsel Suzanne R
Dwight HS
Dwight IL

Drees Faye A
Meridian HS
Daykin NE

Drehobl Keith A
Lane Tech HS
Chicago IL

Dreiling Sandra M
Marian HS
Hays KS

Drennan Mark A
Mt Vernon Township HS
Ina IL

Drescher James H
Quincy Sr HS
Quincy IL

Dressler Nancy J
Kingman HS
Kingman KS

Drews Deborah A
Central HS
Red Wing MN

Drexel Joan D
Mercy HS
Omaha NE

Dries Mary T
St Marys Acad
Chillicothe IL

Drinka Rosemary J
Waukegan Comm HS
Waukegan IL

Drinkwine Sharon Z
Westhope HS
Westhope ND

Driscoll Kenneth J
Reavis HS
Burbank IL

Driver Lori A
Danville HS
Danville IL

Drobney Denise D
Pocahontas Comm HS
Pocahontas IA

Drochner Diane M
Triton HS
Tippecanoe IN

Droesch Kevin T
Rosary HS
St Louis MO

Drone Christopher P
Harrisburg HS
Harrisburg IL

Droste Charles V
Mt Olive Comm HS
Mt Olive IL

Droste Nanette M
Oelwein Community HS
Oelwein IA

Drozd Julie A
Allegan HS
Allegan MI

Drozdz Thomas M
Main East HS
Niles IL

Druehl Denise R
Bettendorf HS
Bettendorf IA

Drummond William T
Derby Sr HS
Derby KS

Drury Tom J
Rockwell Swaledale HS
Swaledale IA

Drutys Terese L
Maria HS
Chicago IL

Dubach Margaret M
Marseilles HS
Marseilles IL

Dubas Catherine A
Niles Township West HS
Niles IL

Du Bay Floyd D
L Anse Crewe HS
Mt Clemens MI

Dubes Cameron C
Aurelia HS
Aurelia IA

Dubke Janet E
Mankato West HS
N Mankato MN

Du Bravec Jean M
Christopher Comm HS
Christopher IL

Du Charme David P
Seneca HS
La Crosse WI

Duck Pamela S
United Township HS
Silvis IL

Duckwall Gary A
Whitnall 'S
Hales Corners WI

Duckworth Timothy A
Griffin HS
Springfield IL

Du Clos Carol J
H L Richards HS
Palos Heights IL

Dudek David B
Chosen Valley HS
Chatfield MN

Dudek Terese C
Oak Forest HS
Oak Forest IL

Duderstadt Mack H
Carrollton Senior HS
Carrollton MO

Dudley Bevely T
Holy Cross HS
Chicago IL

Dudley Diana K
Cassville HS
Shell Knob MO

Dueball Kathy L
Maine West HS
Des Plaines IL

Duer Joy L
Vienna HS
Tunnel Hill IL

Duer Patti J
Vienna HS
Tunnel Hill IL

Duerksen Jolynn K
Marion Ind HS
Marion SD

Duerst Susan R
Whitewater HS
Elkhorn WI

Duez Teresa A
Westville HS
Danville IL

Duff Charlotte V
Mansfield HS
Macomb MO

Duff Dannae M
Scranton Consolidated HS
Scranton IA

Duff Linda K
Ozark HS
Ozark MO

Duff Marsha J
David H Hickman HS
Columbia MO

Duff Philip N
Central HS
Red Wing MN

Duff Sharan P
Saint Alberts HS
Council Bluffs IA

Duffle Alan A
Pomona HS
Pomona KS

Duffy Deborah J
Humboldt HS
Humboldt IA

Duffy Lora M
Schaumburg HS
Roselle IL

Dufort Julie A
Mason HS
Leslie MI

Dugan Brenda K
Cadillac Sr HS
Cadillac MI

Dugan David A
Oak Park HS
Kansas City MO

Dugan Tom M
St Marys HS
Oneill NE

Duggan Paula S
Lake Orion HS
Lake Orion MI

Dugger Douglas A
Flora HS
Flora IL

Duke Kimberly K
Marion HS
Marion KS

Duley Sarah J
Metropolis Community HS
Metropolis IL

Dulin Joseph W
Quincy Sr HS
Quincy IL

Dumas Frederick J
Holly Sr HS
Holly MI

Dumond Leeann M
Greenville HS
Greenville MI

Dunbar Tim M
Clarke Comm HS
Osceola IA

Duncan Cindy S
Dixon R 1 HS
Dixon MO

Duncan Dianna S
Cassville HS
Cassville MO

Duncan James R
Santa Fe Trail HS
Overbrook KS

Duncan Robin D
Adel HS
Adel IA

Duncan Ronald J
Anna Jonesboro Comm
Anna IL

Duncan Scott P
Newton Community HS
Newton IL

Duncan Susan E
Southridge HS
Huntingburg IN

Dunford Bradley J
Langdon Public HS
Langdon ND

Dungey Paula S
Eisenhower HS
Saginaw MI

Dunham Thomas S
Valley City HS
Valley City ND

Dunkel Norbert W
Ashton HS
Ashton IL

Dunker Sandra M
Schuyler Central HS
Schuyler NE

Dunkin Robert D
Kimball County HS
Kimball NE

Dunlap Charlotte E
Community HS
Marengo IL

Dunlap Cheryl L
Hutsonville HS
Hutsonville IL

Dunlap Diane L
Urbandale HS
Urbandale IA

Dunlap Terry J
Maquoketa Valley HS
Hopkinton IA

Dunlavy Katherine E
Davis County Comm HS
Bloomfield IA

Dunn Alice M
Mattoon Sr HS
Mattoon IL

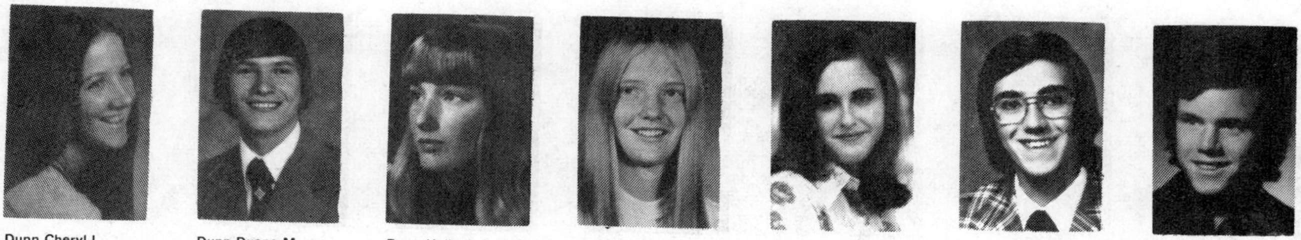

Dunn Cheryl L
Civic Memorial HS
Bethalto IL

Dunn Duane M
Rolla HS
Richfield KS

Dunn Holly J
Northern Heights HS
Emporia KS

Dunn Sandra J
Sioux County HS
Harrison NE

Dunn Sara A
Lincoln HS
Vincennes IN

Dunn Thomas B
Deep River Millersburg HS
Millersburg IA

Dunne Timothy N
Brookfield East HS
Brookfield WI

Dunnette Jan
Kenowa Hills HS
Grand Rapids MI

Dunning Douglas K
Blair HS
Blair NE

Dunning Robin J
Northridge HS
Middlebury IN

Dunscombe Laura A
Humboldt HS
Humboldt IA

Dunsmoor Debra Y
Markesan HS
Fairwater WI

Duran Andrew C
Montabella HS
Edmore MI

Du Rand Carole M
Oakes Public HS
Oakes ND

Durant Joanne M
Central HS
Detroit MI

Durant Lynn A
Hamady HS
Flint MI

Durbin David S
Springfield HS
Springfield IL

Durbin Edward M
North HS
Sioux City IA

Durbin Terry R
Shelbyville HS
Shelbyville IL

Durborow Angie D
Fort Zumwalt HS
St Peters MO

Durham Albert L
Peoria HS
Peoria IL

Durham Patty G
Dixon HS
Dixon MO

Durham Ralph E
Round Lake Sr HS
Round Lake IL

Durkee David S
Fork Union Military
Academy
Grand Rapids MI

Durocher Joanne E
Harry S Truman HS
Taylor MI

Durst David F
Northville HS
Northville MI

Duryea Dana K
Lee M Thurston HS
Redford Twsp MI

Durzinsky Dennis S
Alexandria Monroe HS
Alexandria IN

Dustman Leslie
North Central HS
Indianapolis IN

Dutcher Karen L
Truman HS
Independence MO

Dutkowski Michele R
Steinmetz HS
Chicago IL

Dutoit Kurt E
Dighton HS
Dighton KS

Duval Edward G
River Valley HS
Lakeside MI

Duvendack Tamra J
Meredosia Chambersburg
HS
Meredosia IL

Dvorak David A
Stoughton Senior HS
Stoughton WI

Dvorak Doug F
Dysart Geneseo HS
Clutier IA

Dwenger Wendy L
Columbus East HS
Columbus IN

Dwiggins Jayne E
Bevier Public HS
Bevier MO

Dworak Dale J
Mendel Catholic Prep
Chicago IL

Dwornick Robert F
Bishop Le Blond HS
St Joseph MO

Dwyer Mark S
Brother Rice HS
Birmingham MI

Dyball Kevin D
Maine East HS
Park Ridge IL

Dye Carol L
Quincy Senior HS
Quincy IL

Dye Craig D
Onawat Area Comm HS
Millersburg MI

Dye Kevin R
Maries Co Rii HS
Vichy MO

Dye Susan K
Davison HS
Burton MI

Dyer Dennis P
Tell City HS
Tell City IN

Dyer Kathleen M
Dickinson HS
Dickinson ND

Dyer Marilyn S
Edinburg HS
Edinburg IN

Dyer Rick D
Adel Community HS
Adel IA

Dyko Debra J
Fowlerville HS
Fowlerville MI

Dykstra Dale A
Fulton HS
Fulton IL

Dykstra Ronald L
Unity Christian HS
Jenison MI

Dymond Susan C
Birch Run HS
Birch Run MI

Dyschkant Roman P
Fenton HS
Wood Dale IL

Dyse Cassandra L
Chicago Voc HS
Chicago IL

Dzieglowicz Carol M
T Roosevelt HS
East Chicago IN

Dzienkowski Roxi M
Cadott Public HS
Boyd WI

Dziewior Janice M
Mauston Area HS
Mauston WI

Dziewit Renee F
Benzie Central HS
Copennish MI

E

Eades Linda S
Madison Consolidated HS
Madison IN

Eads Gregory I
Mc Donald Co HS
Anderson MO

Eads Margerie R
Shiloh HS
Hume IL

Eads Mark D
Poplar Bluff HS
Poplar Bluff MO

Eads Mark E
Charleston HS
Charleston IL

Eagleson Ronda M
Concordia HS
Concordia KS

Eakins Clayton W
Davis Co Community HS
Bloomfield IA

Eakle Mary J
Elkhart Central HS
Elkhart IN

Eakman Larry A
Dunlap HS
Dunlap IL

Eales Christopher J
Excelsior Springs West HS
Excelsior Springs MO

Ealy Maurice L
Medicine Valley HS
Moorefield NE

Ealy Wanda R
Henry Ford HS
Detroit MI

Eannarino Joyce M
Jesse Spalding HS
Chicago IL

Earhart Kathy A
Edwards County Sr HS
Albion IL

Earl Denise L
Albion Sr HS
Albion MI

Earll Michael D
Sibley Comm HS
Bigelow MN

Earls Nancy S
Rolla HS
Rolla MO

Early Marion J
John Hersey HS
Arlington Hts IL

Early Theresa S
Knox County HS
Baring MO

Eash Sheryl E
Washington HS
Washington IA

Easley Kevin L
Macon County R 1 HS
Macon MO

Easter Barbara J
Princeton R 5 HS
Princeton MO

Easter David A
Tremont HS
Tremont IL

Eastern Cynthia R
Wisconsin Lutheran HS
Milwaukee WI

Easto William D
Crown Point HS
Crown Point IN

Easton Pamela R
Hanson Ind #40 HS
Fulton SD

Eaton Albert J
Calumet HS
Gary IN

Eaton Beverly G
Monrovia HS
Monrovia IN

Eaton Donald L
Campbell HS
Campbell MO

Eaton Donald L
North County HS
Desloge MO

Eaton Ralph A
Westview HS
La Grange IN

Ebach Rebecca S
Arthur Hill HS
Saginaw MI

Ebaugh Kristel K
South Sioux City HS
South Sioux City NE

Ebbersten Darrell L
Mt Pulaski HS
Elkhart IL

Ebenhoeh Margo A
New Lothrop HS
Chesaning MI

Ebenhoeh Richard L
New Lothrop HS
New Lothrop MI

Eberle Mark A
Brookfield East HS
Brookfield WI

Eberly Rick J
Clarinda Comm HS
Clarinda IA

Ebers Sharon S
Steeleville HS
Chester IL

Ebert Steven L
John Marshall HS
Indianapolis IN

Ebstein David H
Highland Park HS
Highland Park IL

Eby Joseph H
Streator Twp HS
Streator IL

Eccles Eloise A
Kalamazoo Loy Norrix HS
Kalamazoo MI

Echer Kristy L
Luray HS
Lucas KS

Echtenkamp Lee E
Wakefield HS
Wakefield NE

Eck Tami L
Venice HS
Venice IL

Eck William B
York Comm HS
Elmhurst IL

Eckel Christopher W
Bethany HS
Sullivan IL

Eckerle Beverly A
Jasper HS
Jasper IN

Eckerle Duane J
Jasper HS
Jasper IN

Eckerle Russell A
Otterville HS
Otterville MO

Eckert Charles S
Hutsonville HS
Palestine IL

Eckert Karen L
New Athens Community HS
Lenzburg IL

Eckert Paula D
Hoopeston East Lynn HS
Hoopeston IL

Eckhoff Cindy M
Rock Bridge HS
Columbia MO

Eckles William F
Ida HS
Monroe MI

Ecklun Patti A
Holdrege Sr HS
Holdrege NE

Ecklund Robert S
Falls Sr HS
International Fls MN

Eckstein Jeff S
Dubois HS
Jasper IN

Eddleman Judith A
Dongola Unit HS
Dongola IL

Eddy Randall C
Centerville HS
Centerville IA

Eddy Raymond H
Newark Comm HS
Newark IL

Eddy Roger L
Newark HS
Newark IL

Eddy Stanley M
Parker HS
Beloit WI

Eddy Steven A
United Township HS
Silvis IL

Eddy Vivian A
Onaga HS
Onaga KS

Edel Susan S
Bad Axe HS
Bad Axe MI

Edema Ruth A
Wheaton Christian HS
Wheaton IL

Eder Margaret T
Waterford Union HS
Waterford WI

Eder Margaret T
Waterford HS
Waterford WI

Edgerly Curtis L
Alburnett Comm HS
Central City IA

Edgren Lucinda J
Oskaloosa Sr HS
Oskaloosa IA

Edington Sharon A
West Vigo HS
West Terre Haute IN

Edler Jo Jean
Pearl City HS
Pearl City IL

Edmonds Dale S
Oshkosh West HS
Oshkosh WI

Edmonds Kenneth K
Mc Louth HS
Mc Louth KS

Edmonds R Michael
Wauwatosa West HS
Wauwatosa WI

Edney Geoffrey A
Arlington HS
Indianapolis IN

Edson David V
Nashua HS
Ionia IA

Edson Rodney M
Gothenburg HS
Gothenburg NE

Edwards Barbara D
Rantoul Township HS
Rantoul IL

Edwards Charles H
Putnam County HS
Mc Nabb IL

Edwards Daniel G
Lewistown Community HS
Lewistown IL

Edwards Danny L
Ashland Greenwood HS
Ashland NE

Edwards Dennis G
Fulton HS
Fulton IL

Edwards Frances R
Greenview HS
Greenview IL

Edwards Jeffrey N
Hardy HS
Hardy NE

Edwards Joann
Walter P Chrysler HS
New Castle IN

Edwards Joni K
Meridian HS
Villa Ridge IL

Edwards Judith A
Benton Consolidated HS
Macedonia IL

Edwards Julie A
Meridian HS
Villa Ridge IL

Edwards Kimberly J
Norfolk Sr HS
Norfolk NE

Edwards Linda M
Fairbury HS
Fairbury NE

Edwards Mary A
Luray Public HS
Luray KS

Edwards Raymond M
Rich Central HS
Matteson IL

Edwards Ronald D
Pittsburg HS
Pittsburg KS

Edwards Sally A
Lawrence HS
Lawrence MI

Edwards William G
Wayne Memorial HS
Wayne MI

Edwardson Lora L
Sioux Rapids Community HS
Sioux Rapids IA

Eeten Rochelle J
Green Valley HS
Green Valley IL

Effland Claudia L
Lincoln HS
Lincoln KS

Effland Kimberly K
Lincoln HS
Lincoln KS

Egan Marlene R
Cuba City HS
Cuba City WI

Egan Michael D
Springfield HS
Battle Creek MI

Eger Kyla J
Tell City HS
Tell City IN

Eggeman Cindy L
Valley R 6 HS
Potosi MO

Eggemeyer Cathy D
Steeleville HS
Steeleville IL

Eggers Carol A
Rock Bridge Sr HS
Columbia MO

Eggers Mark D
Philip HS
Philip SD

Egland Lois J
New London Sr HS
New London WI

Egley Judy D
Crestview HS
Decatur IN

Ehlen Ann M
Salem Central HS
Salem WI

Ehlers Ginger R
Deshler HS
Deshler NE

Ehlers Leigh A
Gordon HS
Gordon NE

Ehlert Jilleen A
Geo S Parker HS
Janesville WI

Ehni Mark G
Richwoods HS
Peoria IL

Ehrhardt Danielle K
St Pauls College HS
Lohman MO

Ehrhardt John M
Putnam County HS
Mcnabb IL

Ehrnthaller Judith C
Toluca HS
Toluca IL

Eichelberger Cynthia R
Shickley Public HS
Shickley NE

Eichelman Julie A
Prospect HS
Arlington Heights IL

Eichler Edward J
St Thomas Academy
Minneapolis MN

Eichler Kelly J
Duchesne Academy
Omaha NE

Eichstedt Bonnie L
Ripon Sr HS
Ripon WI

Eickert Patricia A
Byron HS
Oregon IL

Eiffert Kenton L
Harrisonville Sr HS
Harrisonville MO

Eifler Mark A
Castle HS
Chandler IN

Eikmeier Tami M
Rocori HS
St Cloud MN

Eilderts Lisa M
Parkersburg Comm HS
Parkersburg IA

Eiler Mark V
Markesan Sr HS
Markesan WI

Eilers David G
Central HS
Waterloo IA

Einspahr Kevin D
Hildreth HS
Hildreth NE

Einsweiler Dirk A
Galena HS
Galena IL

Eis Victoria L
Perry Lecompton HS
Perry KS

Eischeid Marian C
Pope John Central HS
Elgin NE

Eisele Hermann H
Christian Brothers Col HS
St Louis MO

Eisenbeis Julie M
St Pius X HS
Festus MO

Eisenhuth Lori H
West Aurora HS
Aurora IL

Eisenreich Jami L
Downers Grove S HS
Woodridge IL

Eisfeller James D
Chadwick HS
Chadwick IL

Eissinger Paul M
Medina HS
Medina ND

Eissler Holly K
Willowbrook HS
Lombard IL

Ekberg Christine L
St Pius X HS
Kansas City MO

Ekblad Karen A
Evergreen Park
Community HS
Evergreen Park IL

Ekdahl Clayton C
White Pine HS
Ontonagon MI

Elam Arnold L
Harrisburg HS
Harrisburg IL

Elarde Karen A
Good Counsel HS
Chicago IL

Elbert Charles M
Pierce City HS
Pierce City MO

Elbert Karen M
Metamora Township HS
Metamora IL

Elbs Thomas E
Marshall University HS
Minneapolis MN

Elder Brian L
Thomas Jefferson HS
Council Bluff IA

Elder E A
Columbus HS
Columbus WI

Eldred Sheri L
Homer HS
Homer MI

Eldridge Eugene J
Sturgis HS
Sturgis MI

Eldridge Melody H
Morrice HS
Morrice MI

Elfering Douglas A
Central HS
Kenosha WI

Elfrank Betty J
Festus HS
Festus MO

Elfrink Roy J
Jennings Sr HS
Jennings MO

Elgass James A
Ann Arbor Huron HS
Ann Arbor MI

Elias Kimberly M
Camelot HS
Cairo IL

Eliason Becky J
Superior Sr HS
Superior WI

Eliker Margaret M
Overton Public HS
Overton NE

Elkins Peggy L
Campus HS
Wichita KS

Ellefson Valerie L
Lafayette HS
Red Lake Falls MN

Ellena John T
Virden HS
Virden IL

Ellens Debra K
Rutland Inde HS
Wentworth SD

Ellenwood Terry L
Chelsea HS
Chelsea MI

Ellinger Paul N
Saunemin Unit #6 HS
Pontiac IL

Ellingson Greg A
Evansville HS
Ashby MN

Ellingson Luann J
Brainerd Sr HS
Brainerd MN

Ellingson Mark J
Orangeville HS
Orangeville IL

Ellingson Rynae E
Richland #44 HS
Christine ND

Ellingsworth David P
Van Horn HS
Independence MO

Ellington Paula L
Union Corporation HS
Modoc IN

Elliott Brenda K
Carmi Comm HS
Carmi IL

Elliott Bruce L
Granite City South HS
Granite City IL

Elliott Diana L
Warrensburg Latham HS
Warrensburg IL

Elliott Donna S
Usd 237 HS
Gaylord KS

Elliott Gary L
Shawnee HS
Grand Tower IL

Elliott Jon C
Brother Rice HS
Birmingham MI

Elliott Julie A
Sullivan HS
Sullivan IL

Elliott Lois A
Waterford Township HS
Pontiac MI

Elliott Rita J
Fairfield Comm HS
Golden Gate IL

Elliott Susanne J
Fenton Sr HS
Fenton MI

Ellis Amanda M
Chicago Voc HS
Chicago IL

Ellis Cynthia L
Croswell Lexington HS
Lexington MI

Ellis Frederick P
Assumption HS
Wisconsin Rapids WI

Ellis Gregory K
Lincoln HS
Vincennes IN

Ellis James E
Ness City HS
Ness City KS

Ellis Jane E
Pittsfield HS
Pittsfield IL

Ellis Jerry R
Southwest R 5 HS
Seligman MO

Ellis John C
Lincoln Co HS
Silex MO

Ellis Karen L
Brighton Area HS
Brighton MI

Ellis Kelly J
Holdrege Sr HS
Holdrege NE

Ellis Leslie R
Central HS
Albert Lea MN

Ellis Michael S
Mendel College Prep HS
Chicago IL

Ellison Daniel J
Oakes HS
Oakes ND

Ellison Luanne
Senn HS
Chicago IL

Elliston Cheryl L
Maple Valley HS
Nashville MI

Ellsworth Lorna K
Memence HS
Momence IL

Ellwood Victoria
New Trier East HS
Winnetka IL

Elmer Barbara A
Chippewa Falls HS
Chippewa Falls WI

Elmore Catherine A
Heelan HS
Sioux City IA

Elonich Diane M
York Comm HS
Elmhurst IL

Eloph Susan K
Elmhurst HS
Ft Wayne IN

Elrod Jane M
Clinton HS
Clinton MO

Elshoff Martha K
Southridge HS
Huntingburg IN

Elsner Kenneth S
Ewen Trout Creek HS
Ewen MI

Elsner Steve J
Jennings Co HS
North Vernon IN

Elster John M
Riverside HS
Dearborn Hts MI

Elston John B
Deerfield HS
Deerfield IL

Elston Kathleen A
Brown City HS
Brown City MI

Eltz Kimberly C
Sherwood HS
Sherwood ND

Elverud Dale E
Leeds HS
Leeds ND

Elwood Steven E
Riceville Comm HS
Mc Intire IA

Ely Cynthia A
Normandy HS
St Louis MO

Elzea Donna M
Erskine Public HS
Erskine MN

Elzy Lisa D
Beecher HS
Flint MI

Eman Todd B
Bishop Ryan HS
Minot ND

Embry Janice M
Ft Scott Sr HS
Ft Scott KS

Emch Fred
Lakeland HS
Lagrange IN

Emerson Mark S
Minnehaha Academy
Edina MN

Emerson Paul H
Riverview Comm HS
Riverview MI

Emery Joy L
Turner HS
Kansas City KS

Emery Robin K
Shawnee Heights HS
Berryton KS

Emery Sue A
William Freund HS
Palatine IL

Emhoff Guy E
Subiaco Academy
Aurora MO

Emigh Kim L
Brookville HS
Brookville IN

Emily Regina T
Notre Dame De Sion HS
Kansas City MO

Emken Michele L
Yates City HS
Ma Quon IL

Emler Charles L
Valley Center HS
Valley Center KS

Emly Alison R
Herbert Hoover HS
Des Moines IA

Emmendorfer Albert C
Durand HS
Durand MI

Emmert David G
Gage Park HS
Chicago IL

Emmert Michael A
Bolingbrook HS
Bolingbrook IL

Emmons Daniel L
Monsignor Hackett HS
Galesburg MI

Emond Susan A
Divine Savior Holy Angels HS
Milwaukee WI

Emrich Terri L
Northwestern R 1 HS
Mendon MO

Emrick Brenda D
Griggsville HS
Griggsville IL

Emrick Stephan
Bishop Noll Institute
E Chicago IN

Endean Debra J
Deerfield HS
Highland Park IL

Endeman Debra D
Ash Grove Public R Iv HS
Bois D Arc MO

Endres Kathleen M
Chamberlain HS
Chamberlain SD

Engeland Sandra K
Alma HS
Alma MI

Engelbart Carol A
Newton HS
Montrose IL

Engelbright Lori J
Auburndale HS
Auburndale WI

Engelhardt Linda C
Barrington HS
Barrington IL

Engelman Harley D
St Marys Central HS
Bismarck ND

Engels Christine D
Alleman HS
East Moline IL

Engelstad Maureen G
Carrington Public HS
Carrington ND

England Steve S
East HS
Wausau WI

England Tracy E
Cassville HS
Cassville MO

Engle Brenda K
W Burlington Arnold HS
W Burlington IA

Engle Michael R
Elmhurst HS
Ft Wayne IN

Engle Rene J
Blue Springs HS
Blue Springs MO

Englehardt Jaye E
Central HS
Kansasville WI

Engleman Connie J
Stapleton HS
Stapleton NE

Engler Debra J
Odin HS
Odin IL

English Charles L
Southeast HS
Springfield IL

Englund Kay L
Grant Deuel HS
La Bolt SD

Engstrom Barbara L
St Xaviers HS
Junction City KS

Engstrom Mary K
Dist 17 HS
St Edward NE

Enke Deborah K
Parker Sr HS
Janesville WI

Enriquez Ricardo F
Loyola Academy
Park Ridge IL

Ensley Holly A
Kewanee HS
Kewanee IL

Ensminger Lindi A
Marmaton Valley HS
Moran KS

Enszer Mark R
Douglas Macarthur HS
Saginaw MI

Enszer Richard A
Midland HS
Midland MI

Enyard Richard K
Glasgow Rii HS
Glasgow MO

Epperly Dianne C
Wayne Memorial HS
Wayne MI

Epperson Gayla C
Marion C Early HS
Walnut Grv MO

Epperson John A
Orchard Farm HS
St Charles MO

Epperson Lori B
Carthage Sr HS
Carthage MO

Epple Debra L
Hermitage HS
Hermitage MO

Erb Cindy
Marissa HS
Marissa IL

Erchul William P
Xavier HS
Appleton WI

Erdenberger Brenda A
Mason City HS
Mason City IA

Erhardt Dorla
Mehlville Sr HS
St Louis MO

Ericksen Dawn M
Joliet West HS
Joliet IL

Ericksen George E
Maine West Twp HS
Des Plaines IL

Erickson Alan K
Essex Community HS
Essex IA

Erickson Betty J
Anoka Sr HS
Andover MN

Erickson Bonnie J
Sacred Heart Public HS
Sacred Heart MN

Erickson Bruce A
Pipestone HS
Pipestone MN

Erickson David A
Joliet Township HS
Joliet IL

Erickson Marie J
Galesburg Sr HS
Galesburg IL

Erickson Melody A
Superior HS
Superior NE

Erickson Nancy A
Sacred Heart HS
Sacred Heart MN

Erickson Randal V
Gobles HS
Gobles MI

Erickson Thomas W
East Greene HS
Grand Jct IA

Erickson Wanda J
Wittenberg Birnamwood HS
Tigerton WI

Erikson Barbara A
Canova Public HS
Canova SD

Erkfitz John W
Alpena HS
Alpena MI

Erlenbush Bertha M
Portage Northern HS
Portage MI

Ermer Michael G
Chaminade College Prep
St Louis MO

Ernst Betty L
Schleswig Comm HS
Danbury IA

Ernst Monica L
Warren HS
Apple River IL

Ernst Robert J
Norfolk Sr HS
Norfolk NE

Ernst Sandra R
Gering HS
Gering NE

Ernst Steven K
Univ Of Detroit HS
Detroit MI

Ernst Thomas G
Richland Center HS
Richland Center WI

Erpelding Sandi J
Garrigan HS
Bode IA

Ervin Lissa A
Pike HS
Indianapolis IN

Ervin Ronald
St Louis Priory HS
St Louis MO

Erwin Luduska L
Little Falls Comm HS
Little Falls MN

Erxleben Janice M
Bellmont HS
Decatur IN

Esarey Neal B
Heritage Hills HS
Evanston IN

Eshelman Dennis K
Rochester Comm HS
Rochester IN

Eshleman Marietta S
Carrollton HS
Carrollton MO

Esker Alan E
St Anthony HS
Effingham IL

Esler John A
Goldfield Community HS
Goldfield IA

Eslinger Lillie D
Sullivan HS
Merom IN

Espenschied Cindy K
Fremont Sr HS
Fremont NE

Esper Thomas J
Romeo HS
Romeo MI

Esposito Constance
North Shore Country Day HS
Northbrook IL

Esselstrom Adrian R
Carl Sandburg HS
Palos Heights IL

Essmann Debra J
East HS
Waterloo IA

Essmyer Tom M
Vianney HS
St Louis MO

Estela Raul R
Roberto Clemente HS
Chicago IL

Esters Crystal E
Soldan HS
St Louis MO

Estes Steven R
Pontiac Twp HS
Graymont IL

Esther Julie L
Memorial HS
Joplin MO

Estridge Paul
Carmel HS
Carmel IN

Estridge Peggy S
Carmel HS
Carmel IN

Etchison Marta L
Papillion Sr HS
Papillion NE

Etheridge Michael D
Mendota Township HS
Mendota IL

Etling Vicky J
Freeburg Community HS
Freeburg IL

Ettel Rebecca S
Hazelwood Central HS
Florissant MO

Etzel Kathleen A
Hayden HS
Topeka KS

Eubanks Bobby S
West Liberty Comm HS
West Liberty IA

Eubanks Rhonda L
Benton HS
Benton IL

Evans Becky J
Clarke Comm HS
Weldon IA

Evans Betty J
Lowell Sr HS
Hebron IN

Evans Bryan L
Sioux Valley HS
Lake Park IA

Evans Carolyn A
Chicago Vocational HS
Chicago IL

Evans Connie D
Griffith HS
Griffith IN

Evans Curtis R
Hayfield Secondary HS
Fort Riley KS

Evans Daniel J
Johnston HS
Des Moines IA

Evans David W
Moline Sr HS
Moline IL

Evans Debra J
Monticello HS
Monticello IL

Evans Denise M
Monticello HS
Monticello IL

Evans Diane M
Homer Comm HS
Homer MI

Evans Diane M
Chase County HS
Cottonwood Falls KS

Evans Eric G
South Lake HS
St Clair Shores MI

Evans Joseph A
Morristown HS
Morristown IN

Evans M Scott
Fennville HS
South Haven MI

Evans Pamela R
Claflin HS
Claflin KS

Evans Paul M
Salem Community HS
Salem IL

Evans Ron E
Hyannis HS
Ashby NE

Evans Sandra M
North Division HS
Milwaukee WI

Evanson David D
Wildrose Public HS
Wildrose ND

Eve Sue E
New Albany Sr HS
New Albany IN

Evenson Michele A
Oak Park HS
Kansas City MO

Evenstad Jane M
Northwood Public HS
Northwood ND

Everett Carl J
Mendel Prep HS
Chicago IL

Everett G Stephen
Benilde St Margarets HS
Minneapolis MN

Everhart Clark L
Harlem HS
Loves Park IL

Evers Janie A
Riverside HS
Dearborn Hts MI

Evers Jeffrey J
Guttenberg Co HS
Guttenberg IA

Evers Sandy A
Schleswig Comm HS
Schleswig IA

Eversole Bradley K
Tower Hill HS
Tower Hill IL

Evey Connie L
Alma HS
Alma MI

Evins Bretta A
Willow Springs HS
Willow Springs MO

Ewald Cindy B
Unionville Sebewaing Area HS
Unionville MI

Ewald Jacqualine K
Durant HS
Durant IA

Ewald Lynn A
Medicine Valley HS
Curtis NE

Ewald Lynne E
Marquette HS
Ottawa IL

Ewing Gary L
Centerville HS
Cincinnati IA

Ewing John R
Sycamore HS
Sycamore IL

Ewing Lynn M
Nevada HS
Nevada MO

Ewing Simeon E
St Johns HS
St Johns MI

STUDENTS PHOTOGRAPH SCHEDULED FOR PUBLICATION HERE COULD NOT BE REPRODUCED

Eyerly Donald R
Winterset Community HS
Winterset IA

Ezzell Janie L
Charleston HS
Bertrand MO

F

Fabrizi Michael A
Southwest HS
St Louis MO

Fabry M Kym
Wausau E HS
Wausau WI

Fadden Thomas P
St Bonaventure Prep HS
South Holland IL

Fahy Patricia K
Bismarck HS
Bismarck ND

Failing Douglas R
Grayling HS
Grayling MI

Fair Nancy L
Fowlerville HS
Fowlerville MI

Fairbanks Kathy E
Hudson Sr HS
Hudson WI

Fairburn Nancy E
Guilford HS
Rockford IL

Fairchild Mark J
Boylan Catholic HS
Rockford IL

Fairless Kevin M
Southwestern HS
Medora IL

Fairley Tim J
Fairbury HS
Fairbury NE

Fait Gary P
St Marys HS
Burlington WI

Falch Bonnie M
Regis HS
Chippewa Falls WI

Falcone Debera A
Downers Grove Comm HS
Downers Grove IL

Falen Julie D
Hinsdale Central HS
Hinsdale IL

Fall Lon R
Lake Orion HS
Oxford MI

Fallesen Jan L
Viburnum C 4 HS
Viburnum MO

Falloon Dawn G
Sullivan HS
Bourbon MO

Falls Patricia K
Slater HS
Slater MO

Falta Patricia A
Garden City E HS
Garden City MI

Faltis Joyce A
Prairie HS
Fairfax IA

Fanko Andrew P
Perry HS
Perry MI

Fantaski Mike F
Papillion Lavista HS
Papillion NE

Faragher David C
O Gorman HS
Sioux Falls SD

Farah Michael C
Brother Rice HS
Bloomfield Hills MI

Faraone Theresann
Coloma HS
Coloma MI

Faris Michael W
East Richland HS
Olney IL

Farless Carl R
Valley Comm HS
Arlington IA

Farmer Julie A
St Charles HS
St Charles MI

Farmer Kathryn J
Jackson Hts HS
Circleville KS

Farmer Kristy A
West Vigo HS
West Terre Haute IN

Farmer Pamela M
Marseilles HS
Marseilles IL

Farmer Rhonda L
Metropolis Comm HS
Metropolis IL

Farmer Sarah T
North Pemiscot HS
Wardell MO

Farnham Cynthia M
North HS
Fargo ND

Farnham Dale E
Prairie Community HS
Gowrie IA

Farquhar Patricia J
Harrisburg HS
Harrisburg IL

Farr Daniel T
Northern HS
Pontiac MI

Farr Jack K
West Holt HS
Atkinson NE

Farrar Kathleen J
Brookfield R Iii HS
Brookfield MO

Farrar Toya A
North Senior HS
St Paul MN

Farrell Janice M
Wamego HS
Wamego KS

Farrell Kathleen A
Burlington Comm HS
Burlington IA

Farrell Kathleen D
Jefferson HS
Rockford IL

Farrell Mary Jane
Wamego HS
Wamego KS

Farrell Thomas A
Downers Grove North HS
Downers Grove IL

Farren Mark S
Colo Comm HS
Colo IA

Farris Julie M
Galena HS
Galena KS

Farris Kay A
Southridge HS
Huntingburg IN

Farris Phillip A
Langdon HS
Langdon ND

Farriss Janice M
Elmhurst HS
Fort Wayne IN

Farritor Rodney I
St Agnes Academy
Alliance NE

Farro Carol Y
Port Huron HS
Port Huron MI

Farrow Timothy O
Lakeshore HS
St Joseph MI

Fashacht Jaclynne M
Loyola HS
Mankato MN

Fasiang Linda M
Thornwood HS
Calumet IL

Fast Kim L
Winner HS
Winner SD

Fateley Sharon D
Dixon HS
Dixon MO

Faucett Cande L
Frankfort Sr HS
Frankfort IN

Faught Mary M
Oblong HS
Oblong IL

Faulds Patrick G
Abbot Pennings HS
De Pere WI

Faulkner Gloria L
Downers Grove Comm HS
Downers Grove IL

Faulkner Lee A
Warren Township HS
Gurnee IL

Faulkner William M
Vienna HS
Vienna IL

Faust Douglas A
Wilson HS
Mankato MN

Faust Karen L
Nazareth Academy
Riverside IL

Faust Linda M
Healy HS
Pierz MN

Favero Brian V
Omaha Central HS
Omaha NE

Favish Pamela E
Niles East HS
Skokie IL

Fawcett Candice K
Miller HS
Ree Heights SD

Fay Daniel B
Anita Community HS
Anita IA

Fay Steven R
Herbert Henry Dow HS
Midland MI

Fazzari Michael F
St Paul & Kennedy HS
Chicago IL

Feak Glen A
Addison Trail HS
Addison IL

Fearnow Mark A
Wabash HS
Wabash IN

Feathers Tambra D
Crispus Attucks HS
Indianapolis IN

Fecher Diana L
Hamilton Hts HS
Atlanta IN

Fechtelkotter Gregg L
Northwestern HS
Poplar WI

Federiuk John R
North HS
Eau Claire WI

Fedolak Doris O
Frank Cody HS
Detroit MI

Fedor David W
Virden HS
Thayer IL

Fedro Randall C
Wheeling HS
Wheeling IL

Feekes Gary A
Sheldon Comm HS
Sheldon IA

Feeney Daniel J
Joliet West HS
Joliet IL

Fehler Sheri E
Harlem North Campus HS
Loves Park IL

Fehrenbacher Susan E
Newton HS
Ingraham IL

Feige Kim C
John Hersey HS
Mount Prospect IL

Feighner Jon L
Turner HS
Kansas City KS

Feild Marla K
Traverse City Sr HS
Traverse City MI

Feist Jeffrey A
Downs HS
Downs KS

Feland Debbie D
Coon Rapids Senior HS
Coon Rapids MN

Feldhake David J
St Anthony HS
Effingham IL

Feldman Julie
James Madison Mem HS
Madison WI

Feldman Randy M
Hibbing HS
Hibbing MN

Feldman Ronald E
Tomah Sr HS
Tomah WI

Feldmann Lori J
Boone HS
Boone IA

Feldt Scott W
Monticello Public HS
Monticello WI

Felker David E
Hayes County HS
Hayes Center NE

Felker Vicki L
Campbell HS
Campbell MO

Fell Bert H
Bloomington South HS
Bloomington IN

Fellows Lori J
Western HS
Buda IL

Fellwock Peter E
St Joseph HS
St Joseph MI

Felts Danny G
Hillcrest HS
Springfield MO

Felzke Harvey L
Pleasant Ridge HS
Leavenworth KS

Fender Gregory T
Salem Community HS
Salem IL

Fenner Louise J
Martin HS
Plainwell MI

Fensel Frederick A
Madison Consolidated HS
Madison IN

Fenske Mike M
New London HS
New London WI

Fensler Ruth A
Warsaw Community HS
Winona Lake IN

Fenton Linda J
Centerville HS
Centerville IA

Fenton Ricky L
Litchfield Comm HS
Litchfield IL

Ferber Leonard A
Highland Park HS
Highland Park IL

Ferguson Ann L
Minot HS
Minot ND

Ferguson Catherine T
Tipton HS
Tipton IN

Ferguson Desiree M
Cass Technical HS
Detroit MI

Ferguson John
Maconaquah HS
Bunker Hill IN

Ferguson Joleen R
Grafton HS
Grafton ND

Ferguson Josline K
Forestburg HS
Forestburg SD

Ferguson Lee E
Hyannis HS
Hyannis NE

Ferguson Leonard R
Highland HS
Highland IN

Ferguson Linda P
Mt Vernon Sr HS
Aurora MO

Fernandes Donald L
Jacksonville HS
Jacksonville IL

Ferneau Ronald G
Ldf Community HS
Marshalltown IA

Ferrante Mark V
Saint Patricks HS
Chicago IL

Ferrari Gary J
La Salle Peru HS
Oglesby IL

Ferrell Lawrence R
Lillis HS
Kansas City MO

Ferrell Paul K
Huntington North HS
Andrews IN

Ferrick Joseph T
Brother Rice HS
Chicago IL

Ferro Christi L
Lewistown Comm HS
St David IL

Fesenmaier Kathryn A
North HS
Eau Claire WI

Fessler Rodney M
Hartford HS
Neosho Rapids KS

Fetters James S
Indianaola HS
Indianola IA

Fetters Theresa L
Mt St Scholastica Academy
Excelsior Springs MO

Fetty Craig B
Woodstock HS
Woodstock IL

Fetzer Laura E
Whiteford HS
Ottawa Lake MI

Feuerborn Sandra A
Council Grove HS
Eskridge KS

Fey Dennis A
Richwoods HS
Peoria IL

Fiala Joseph L
North Linn Comm HS
Walker IA

Fiala Richard J
St John Vianney HS
Crestwood MO

Fiala Steven R
David City Public HS
David City NE

Fiala Timothy J
Riverside Brookfield HS
No Riverside IL

Fichtenmayer Patricia L
Southwest HS
St Louis MO

Fichtner Beth L
Hayes Cnty HS
Maywood NE

Fidder Timothy W
Belvidere HS
Belvidere IL

Fidler Dianne
Arthur HS
Arthur IL

Fieber Audrey L
Grayville Community HS
Grayville IL

Fiebiger John F
Montpelier Public HS
Montpelier ND

Fiedler James M
Putnam County HS
Hennepin IL

Fiedler Jill C
Calhoun HS
Batchtown IL

Field Janine M
Brighton HS
Brighton MI

Fielder Nancy L
Manchester HS
Manchester MI

Fields Bobby L
Cave In Rock HS
Cave In Rock IL

Fields Dennis W
Hinckley Big Rock HS
Hinckley IL

Fields Leslie D
Deerfield HS
Deerfield IL

Fields Pamela D
St Thomas Apostle HS
Chicago IL

Fielstra Sally A
Traverse City HS
Traverse City MI

Fienhold Mildred R
Lincoln Way HS
Mokena IL

Fierro Pedro
William A Wirt HS
Gary IN

Fiesterman Jody L
Lewellen Rural HS
Lewellen NE

Fifer Greg
Marist HS
Oak Lawn IL

Fifer Theodore D
Campion Jesuit HS
Saginaw MI

Fifi Dominique G
Assumption HS
Wis Rapids WI

Figg Janet L
North Shore Country Day HS
Palatine IL

Fike Lisa J
Caruthersville HS
Caruthersville MO

File Teresa M
La Moille HS
La Moille IL

Filemyr Ann E
Jfk Prep
Adell WI

Filipiak Michael E
Sheboygan South HS
Sheboygan WI

Filipowicz Stephen J
Bryn HS
Omaha NE

Fillbrandt Susan M
Windom Area HS
Windom MN

Finch Cheryl R
Tomah Sr HS
Camp Douglas WI

Findley Diana L
Worth Co HS
Grant City MO

Findley Tara S
Oak Park HS
Gladstone MO

Fine Jack D
Quenemo HS
Quenemo KS

Fine Jennifer M
Deerfield HS
Highland Park IL

Finger Terry E
Powhattan HS
Powhattan KS

Fink Brian B
Bolingbrook HS
Bolingbrook IL

Fink Judy L
Cal Comm HS
Latimer IA

Fink Linda G
Pekin Community HS
Pekin IL

Fink Robin T
John Hersey HS
Mt Prospect IL

Fink Tim L
Darlington HS
Darlington WI

Finkelstein Mark D
George Rogers Clark HS
Whiting IN

Finkle Rodney L
Buhler HS
Hutchinson KS

Finlayson James W
Marshall HS
Marshall MI

Finn Linda S
Good Counsel HS
Chicago IL

Finn Rory F
Alton Sr HS
Alton IL

Finnegan James K
Holy Cross HS
Elmwood Park IL

Finnie Kim L
Soldan HS
St Louis MO

Finnigan Michael D
East HS
Rockford IL

Finucane Hallie A
Lawrence HS
Lawrence KS

Firchow Cheryl L
Muskego HS
Hales Corners WI

Firestone John D
Fenwick HS
Lagrange Park IL

Firkins Lawrence D
Sycamore HS
Sycamore IL

Firkus Marcia A
Pacelli HS
Stevens Point WI

Firle Ronald K
Festus Sr HS
Festus MO

Fischer Barbara J
Maine East HS
Niles IL

Fischer Carolyn J
Wall Lake Community HS
Carnarvon IA

Fischer Grace R
Jefferson City Sr HS
Jefferson City MO

Fischer James A
St Benedicts HS
Chicago IL

Fischer Paul F
Marmon Military Academy
Westchester IL

Fischer Sheri M
Rice Lake HS
Rice Lake WI

Fischer William K
Mendota HS
Mendota IL

Fiser Marty J
North Central HS
Narka KS

Fish Diane M
Remington HS
Whitewater KS

Fish Jon K
Milton HS
Milton WI

Fish Roger J
Rockford Sr HS
Marble Rock IA

Fishbach Robert J
Duchesne HS
St Charles MO

Fishburn Susan K
Moweaqua HS
Moweaqua IL

Fishel Jo Ann
Edwards County Sr HS
West Salem IL

Fishell Kathryn A
Roscommon HS
Roscommon MI

Fisher Charles A
West HS
Wichita KS

Fisher Darrell E
Arapahoe HS
Arapahoe NE

Fisher Edwin T
Madison Consolidated HS
Madison IN

Fisher James H
Thornton Township Fractnl HS
Calumet City IL

Fisher Jean M
Dexter HS
Dexter MI

Fisher Kay E
Heyworth HS
Heyworth IL

Fisher Laura S
Lew Wallace HS
Gary IN

Fisher Rhonda D
Mehlville HS
St Louis MO

Fisher Richard J
Lake Mich Cath HS
Benton Harbor MI

Fisher Ruth E
Tawas Area HS
Tawas City MI

Fisher Stephen R
South Hamilton HS
Story City IA

Fishman Bradley J
Watertown HS
Watertown SD

Fisk Laura J
Sunnydale Academy
Rolla MO

Fitz Debra A
Cal Community HS
Alexander IA

Fitzgerald Daniel L
Blue Mound HS
Decatur IL

Fitzgerald Julia L
Rosati Kain HS
St Louis MO

Fitzgerald Kathleen M
Lourdes Academy
Oshkosh WI

Fitzgerald Marie L
St Elizabeth Academy
St Louis MO

Fitzhugh Walter D
Western HS
Bay City MI

Fitzpatrick James W
Oak Forest HS
Oak Forest IL

Fitzpatrick Kathleen A
St Barbara HS
Chicago IL

Fitzpatrick Kevin R
North Miami HS
Macy IN

Fitzpatrick William J
Oak Park River Forest HS
Oak Park IL

Fitzwater Debra A
Moulton Community HS
Moulton IA

Fitzwater Melody J
Van Buren Community HS
Birmingham IA

Fixell Daniel R
Camb Sr HS
Cambridge MN

Flaagan Rita R
Tolna HS
Pekin ND

Flack Cynthia G
Civic Memorial HS
Bethalto IL

Flacksbarth Richard R
Tartan HS
Maplewood MN

Flaherty Kevin J
Sioux County HS
Hemingford NE

Flak Michael W
Paul Schulte HS
Terre Haute IN

Flake Harvey
Romulus Sr HS
Romulus MI

Flanders Dorian
Batavia HS
Batavia IL

Flanigan Carol A
Holly HS
Holly MI

Flatt Brenda S
Salem Sr HS
Salem MO

Fleagle Sharon K
Abilene HS
Abilene KS

Fleagle Timothy J
Triton HS
Etna Green IN

Fleenor Gordon L
Lyman HS
Lyman NE

Fleer Monica E
Highland HS
Lewistown MO

Fleischman Teresa A
Antigo HS
Antigo WI

Fleming Jamie L
Ewin Trout Creek HS
Ewen MI

Fleming Judith M
Duchesne HS
St Charles MO

Fleming Laura E
Evanston Township HS
Evanston IL

Fleming Mark M
Lawrenceville HS
Lawrenceville IL

Fleming Robert E
Duchesne HS
St Charles MO

Fleming Teri L
Pinckneyville HS
Pinckneyville IL

Fleming William R
Milton HS
Milton WI

Flemmer Darcy M
Hazen HS
Beulah ND

Flemming Dave G
Bird City HS
Bird City KS

Flemming Therese A
Mother Mc Auley HS
Chicago IL

Flessner Susan J
Chatsworth HS
Chatsworth IL

Fletcher Daniel H
Swanville HS
Swanville MN

Fletcher Frank T
St Johns HS
St Louis MO

Fletcher Mary K
St Johns HS
St Louis MO

Fletcher Sallie A
Moores Hill HS
Moores Hill IN

Flick Gary A
West Milwaukee HS
West Allis WI

Flick Louise A
Wauwatosa East HS
Wauwatosa WI

Flinn Donald R
De Smet Jesuit HS
Creve Coeur MO

Flinn Shirleen M
Ellis HS
Ellis KS

Flint Colleen D
Cambridge HS
Cambridge NE

Flint Roger D
Schell City HS
Harwood MO

Flohr Douglas G
Byron HS
Byron IL

Flohr Pamela J
Dickinson HS
Dickinson ND

Flood Kim D
Clever HS
Clever MO

Flood Roger J
Albany HS
Brooklyn WI

Flora Benjamin L
Hauser HS
Hope IN

Florek Gregory J
Quigley South HS
Chicago IL

Florence Martha E
Dowling HS
Des Moines IA

Flores Elizabeth C
Roosevelt HS
East Chicago IN

Flowers Carol J
Centerville Community HS
Centerville IA

Flowers Gregory D
Houston HS
Houston MO

Flowers Mary A
St Elmo HS
St Elma IL

Floyd Malcolm V
Port Huron HS
Port Huron MI

Fluegel Mary J
Thomas Jefferson HS
Rockford IL

Flynn Daniel A
Hillsdale HS
Hillsdale MI

Flynn Kelly E
Lake Fenton HS
Fenton MI

Fodness Grace A
Canton HS
Lennox SD

Foe Darryl V
Aosiclare HS
Golconda IL

Foerster Jeffery S
Woodstock HS
Woodstock IL

Foertsch Daniel J
Leo HS
Chicago IL

Fog Susan G
Homewood Flossmoor HS
Homewood IL

Fogarty Anne E
Lidgerwood Public HS
Lidgerwood ND

Foglesong Betty S
Kirksville Sr HS
Kirksville MO

Foglesong William S
Toulon La Fayette HS
Toulon IL

Fohs Maria L
Wateruliet HS
Wateruliet MI

Foley Bruce L
Hemingford HS
Hemingford NE

Foley Kerry J
Jasper HS
Jasper IN

Foley Patti A
Le Sueur HS
Le Sueur MN

Foley Steven A
Monroe HS
La Salle MI

Folk Cathy J
Warsaw Senior HS
Warsaw IN

Folkers Rick J
B R F HS
Blackriver Falls WI

Folkerts Debra S
Steamboat Rock Comm HS
Steamboat Rock IA

Folstad Carolyn D
Mabel Canton HS
Mabel MN

Foltz Lois E
Hoxie HS
Hoxie KS

Fombelle Lisa L
Warrensburg Latham HS
Decatur IL

Foo Barbara C
Niles West HS
Skokie IL

Forbes Patricia A
Mother Of Sorrows HS
Chicago IL

Forbes Scotty R
Riverton HS
Galena KS

Forbis Bryan L
Jeff City Senior HS
Jefferson City MO

Forby Daniel P
Benilde St Margarets HS
Bloomington MN

Ford Anna Marie
Oak Creek Sr HS
Oak Creek WI

Ford Donald A
Frankfort Sr HS
Frankfort IN

Ford Jeffery L
Southern HS
Stronghurst IL

Ford Lawrence R
Marion HS
Marion KS

Ford Martin L
Harper Creek HS
Battle Creek MI

Ford Richard C
Liberty HS
Mountain View MO

Ford Ronald D
Milw Lutheran HS
Milwaukee WI

Ford Ronald P
Swartz Creek HS
Swartz Creek MI

Fordham Debra L
Coopersville HS
Nunica MI

Foree Valerie A
Van Far HS
Farber MO

Foreman Carolyn D
Crown Point HS
Crown Point IN

Forfang Kelly D
Hallock HS
Hallock MN

Forge Mary J
St Marys HS
Independence MO

Fornengo John D
Farmington East HS
Farmington IL

Forrester Kevin L
Saline HS
Saline MI

Forret Deb D
Van Meter Comm HS
Booneville IA

Forristall Susan M
Malden HS
Malden IL

Fors Hans G
Warren T HS
Grayslake IL

Forsberg Diane M
Kingsford HS
Iron Mountain MI

Forsberg Randi B
Minot HS
Minot ND

Forst Kenneth E
Swartz Creek HS
Swartz Creek MI

Forsythe Kathlene L
Raymore Peculiar HS
Peculiar MO

Forsythe Sheryllynn K
Corunna HS
Corunna MI

Fort Timothy L
Southern HS
Stronghurst IL

Forte Theodore
John Marshall HS
Indianapolis IN

Fortner Karen A
Central HS
La Crosse WI

Fosha Patsy L
Junction City Sr HS
Junction City KS

Foss Wade O
Humboldt HS
St Paul MN

Fossedal Leselie A
Hinsdale South HS
Westmont IL

Fossoy Karla K
Rapid City Cntrl HS
Rapid City SD

Fossum Brenda S
Lennox HS
Worthing SD

Fossum Burdell E
Magic City HS
Minot ND

Foster Barbara S
New Town Harris HS
New Town MO

Foster Charles L
Kirksville Sr HS
Kirksville MO

Foster Dana W
Shawnee Mission East HS
Prairie Village KS

Foster Daniel G
York Comm HS
Elmhurst IL

Foster Debra J
Northwest HS
House Springs MO

Foster Kevin L
Zionsville Community HS
Zionsville IN

Foster Larry G
School Of The Osage HS
Osage Beach MO

Foster Rodney A
Waynesville Sr HS
Ft Leonard Wd MO

Foster Russell W
Dadeville HS
Dadeville MO

Foth Brent D
Twin Rivers HS
Livermore IA

Fougerousse Mark J
Our Lady Of Providence HS
New Albany IN

Fountain Karen J
Immaculata HS
Detroit MI

Fournier Cynthia J
Bay City Western HS
Auburn MI

Foust Delbert W
North Adams HS
Hillsdale MI

Fowler Christopher G
St Joseph HS
St Joseph MI

Fowler Linda L
Kirksville Sr HS
Kirksville MO

Fowler Mary A
Morton Sr HS
Hammond IN

Fox Alice M
Edwardsville Sr HS
Edwardsville IL

Fox Carl E
Frankfort HS
Frankfort IN

Fox Carol E
Canton HS
Canton SD

Fox Darryl H
Anderson HS
Anderson IN

Fox Don W
Culver Military Acad
Greensburg IN

Fox James M
Virginia HS
Virginia IL

Fox Jay J
Elmhurst HS
Fort Wayne IN

Fox Jeffrey E
Hinckley Big Rock HS
Big Rock IL

Fox Judith R
Carl Sandburg HS
Palos Heights IL

Fox Malinda K
Norton Community HS
Norton KS

Foy Sheila J
West HS
Davenport IA

Fraker Steven R
D C HS
Oberlin KS

Frakes Sandra K
Dekalb HS
Rushville MO

Fraley Stanley L
Carroll HS
Flora IN

Frana Joel A
Northfield Sr HS
Northfield MN

Frana Joseph C
Ottumwa HS
Ottumwa IA

Francis Alan L
Palmer HS
Pocahontas IA

Francis Jill
North County HS
Desloge MO

Francis Sharon A
Woodland R 4 HS
Glen Allen MO

Francke Bradley J
Garber HS
Essexville MI

Francoeur Dorothy A
Southeast HS
Wichita KS

Francour David R
Marinette Sr HS
Marinette WI

Frangenberg Colleen K
Primghar Community HS
Primghar IA

Frank Cletus J
Morton Public HS
Morton MN

Frank Duane J
Flasher Public HS
Freda ND

Frank Joseph C
Lake Shore HS
St Clair Shores MI

Frank Kevin C
Lidgerwood Public HS
Lidgerwood ND

Frank Russell M
Hammond Baptist HS
Valparaiso IN

Franke Carolyn J
New Hampton Community HS
New Hampton IA

Franke Judy A
Dupo Comm HS
East Carondelet IL

Franklin Arlene A
Midway Usd #433 HS
Denton KS

Franklin Cheryl M
Hazelwood West Sr HS
Hazelwood MO

Franklin Doris K
Adams Central HS
Ayr NE

Franklin Susan J
Franklin Central HS
Indianapolis IN

Franklin Susan K
Lincoln Community HS
Lincoln IL

Franklin Terry L
George Rogers Clark HS
Whiting IN

Franko Marjorie K
Herbert Henry Dow HS
Midland MI

Fransen Jane A
Argyle HS
Argyle WI

Frantz Suzanne M
La Salle HS
St Ignace MI

Frantzen Susan A
Marquette HS
Bellevue IA

Franz Robert G
Leland Community HS
Leland IL

Franzen Barry R
Crivitz HS
Crivitz WI

Franzke Beth E
Appleton East HS
Appleton WI

Fraser Barbara L
Cedar Lake Academy
St Charles MI

Frazee Mark A
Lake Michigan Catholic HS
St Joseph MI

Frazer Larry D
Anderson HS
Anderson IN

Frazho Renee E
Regina HS
St Clair Shores MI

Frazier Bradley J
Belleville Twp W HS
Belleville IL

Frazier Bret M
Bradley Bour HS
Bourbonnais IL

Frazier Deborah J
Sarcoxie HS
Sarcoxie MO

Frazier Marjorie J
Hannibal Senior HS
Hannibal MO

Frazier Mary J
English Valleys HS
South English IA

Frazier Steven K
Merrillville HS
Merrillville IN

Freas Betsy M
Fountain Central HS
Veedersburg IN

Freberg Leland L
Cambridge HS
Cambridge IL

Fredde Kari B
Winterset Community HS
Winterset IA

Frederick Kathy M
Watertown Sr HS
Watertown SD

Frederick Ruth E
Prairie Home HS
Boonville MO

Fredericksen Shelley K
Frontenac HS
Frontenac KS

Frederickson Karl D
Malvern Comm HS
Malvern IA

Fredrickson Dana S
Hastings Sr HS
Hastings MN

Freeburg Teresa A
Plattsmouth HS
Plattsmouth NE

Freeburg Theodore A
Plattsmouth HS
Plattsmouth NE

Freeby Sharyl M
St Marys HS
St Marys KS

Freeland John L
Marquette HS
Michigan City IN

Freeman Brenda B
Mansfield HS
Mansfield MO

Freeman Chris D
Gideon HS
Gideon MO

Freeman Daniel J
Spring Valley HS
Spring Valley MN

Freeman Debra A
East Noble HS
Kendallville IN

Freeman Michael S
Hillsboro HS
Irving IL

Freeman Walter D
Baldwin HS
Overbrook KS

Freese Julie M
Streator Township HS
Streator IL

Freeseman De Laine H
Greene Community HS
Greene IA

Freesemann Lois J
Allison Bristow Comm HS
Allison IA

Freiberg Phyllis M
Wausau East HS
Wausau WI

Freimuth Sandra J
Columbus HS
Columbus WI

Freise Pamela S
Dundee Comm HS
Dundee IL

Freitag Julia L
Olympia HS
Minier IL

Freivogel Vicky L
Riverview Gardens HS
St Louis MO

French Colin V
Roosevelt HS
Des Moines IA

French Marie E
Rosemount HS
Apple Valley MN

French Michael R
North Greene HS
White Hall IL

Frerichs Mark L
Superior HS
Superior NE

Fresch Joseph A
Brother Rice HS
Birmingham MI

Freude Jeffrey L
Erie HS
Erie IL

Freudenburg Debra L
Madison HS
Madison NE

Freudenburg Diane L
Madison HS
Madison NE

Frey Debbie S
Brookville HS
Cedar Grove IN

Freymiller Deanna D
Boscobel HS
Woodman WI

Frick Dennis B
Kearney HS
Kansas City MO

Frick Janice A
Proviso West HS
Westchester IL

Frick Paula M
Luther HS
Hokah MN

Fricke Craig E
Prairie Community HS
Harcourt IA

Friday Karl
New Richmond HS
New Richmond WI

Friede Roger A
Webb HS
Reedsburg WI

Friedl Elizabeth C
Brookfield East HS
Elm Grove WI

Friedlein Christopher E
Leroy HS
Leroy IL

Friedman David L
Central HS
La Crosse WI

Friedrich Lu A
Harrisonville Sr HS
Harrisonville MO

Friedrich Paula S
Sceciha Memorial HS
Indianapolis IN

Friel Lori E
Maine North HS
Glenview IL

Fries Martha K
Greenville HS
Greenville MI

Frieze Vonda J
Reeds Spring HS
Galena MO

Friskey Meri De Lee
Comstock Park HS
Comstock Park MI

Fritz Brenda L
Monett HS
Monett MO

Fritz Jayne L
Delton Kellogg HS
Plainwell MI

Fritz Jeffrey H
Kouts HS
Kouts IN

Fritzsche Sue A
Marian Catholic HS
Chicago Hts IL

Froehlich James A
Crystal Lake Community HS
Crystal Lake IL

Froelich Charlene L
Oak Creek Sr HS
Oak Creek WI

Frohling Richard H
Forman HS
Forest City IL

Frost Ronald A
Overton Public HS
Overton NE

Frost Rosemary J
Hibbing HS
Hibbing MN

Fruchtl Jeffrey B
Effingham HS
Effingham IL

Fruland Di Ann M
Morris Community HS
Morris IL

Frustere Nancy J
Milwaukee Lutheran HS
Wauwatosa WI

Fry Diana L
Lead HS
Terraville SD

Fry Kevin W
Ewing Public HS
Ewing NE

Fry Lawrence A
West Chicago Comm HS
West Chicago IL

Fry Mary Lou
Winnebago HS
Seward IL

Fry Randy M
Iowa Valley Community HS
Marengo IA

Frybarger Saundra L
Moline Sr HS
Moline IL

Frye Dorene K
Donald S Gauit HS
Hammond IN

Frye John J
Pontiac Catholic HS
Pontiac MI

Frye Lorene G
Donald E Gavit HS
Hammond IN

Fryza Jeffrey A
Gilman HS
Lublin WI

Fugate Cheryl D
Oak Park HS
Gladstone MO

Fuhr Pamela F
Leigh Comm HS
Clarkson NE

Fuhrer Catherine M
O Neill Public HS
O Neill NE

Fuhrhop Linda D
Steeleville C HS
Steeleville IL

Fuhrman Clark E
Nodaway Holt HS
Mound City MO

Fuhrman Jeffrey A
Graceville HS
Graceville MN

Fukuya Penny S
Forest View HS
Des Plaines IL

Fulford Steven B
Marshall HS
Marshall IL

Fulk Steve W
West Platte HS
Platte City MO

Fulk Tia L
Morrill HS
Morrill NE

Fulker Kristi L
Aberdeen Central HS
Aberdeen SD

Fulker Ronald A
Central HS
Aberdeen SD

Fulkerson Diana L
Charleston HS
Otisco IN

Fullenworth Betty J
Storm Lake Sr HS
Storm Lake IA

Fuller Beverly J
Liberal HS
Liberal KS

Fuller Esther R
Lincoln Sr HS
E St Louis IL

Fuller Randy D
De Forest HS
De Forest WI

Fulling Eric V
Palestine HS
Palestine IL

Fullington Loretta G
Irving Crown HS
Lake In The Hills IL

Fulton Dwight D
Kearney R 1 HS
Kearney MO

Fulton Jay A
Pittsburg HS
Pittsburg KS

Fulton Sandra F
Faulkner HS
Chicago IL

Fultz Yvonne L
Bedford Sr HS
Temperance MI

Fumo David E
Forest View HS
Mt Prospect IL

Funesti Deborah A
Duchesne HS
St Charles MO

Funfsinn Cynthia A
Lasalle Peru Twp HS
Peru IL

Funk Brian T
Paxton HS
Paxton IL

Funk Christi G
Luther South HS
Chicago IL

Funk Elizabeth K
Monrovia HS
Mooresville IN

Funk Gregory G
James Madison HS
Milwaukee WI

Funk Norma J
Lawrenceville HS
Lawrenceville IL

Funk Teresa A
Sibley Community HS
Sibley IA

Funke James F
Edgewood Colesburg HS
Edgewood IA

Funkenbush Paul D
Houghton HS
Houghton MI

Funkhouser Betty J
Peru HS
Peru IN

Furfaro Tina M
Triad HS
Troy IL

Furnal Kevin D
Pleasantville Comm HS
Ackworth IA

Furness Terri S
Hillsboro HS
Nokomis IL

Furnival Ronald A
Buffalo HS
Montrose MN

Furrer Diane L
Darlington HS
Darlington WI

Furry Brian L
Charleston HS
Charleston IL

Fus Julie M
Thorton Fractional HS
Lansing IL

Fustin John M
Norris City HS
Omaha IL

Fylling Arlin J
Turtle Lake Public HS
Ruso ND

Fynewever Susan J
Holland Christian HS
Holland MI

G

Gabel Penny A
Ness City HS
Ness KS

Gabriel Donna L
Lyons Township HS
La Grange IL

Gabrielson James G
Hoven HS
Hoven SD

Gade Susan K
Webb HS
Rock Springs WI

Gaertner Patricia A
Hill Murray HS
St Paul MN

Gaffney Cary B
L C HS
Lincoln IL

Gaffney John F
Central HS
Davenport IA

Gafford Meredith L
Anderson HS
Anderson IN

Gage Gregory T
Border Central HS
Calvin ND

Gage Kenneth L
Mc Cook Sr HS
Mc Cook NE

Gage Ronald R
St Laurence HS
Willow Springs IL

Gagnon Charles L
Springfield Southeast HS
Springfield IL

Gahnz Kathy J
Newman HS
Wausau WI

Gaines Karen J
Southport HS
Indianapolis IN

Gaither Renoir W
Emmerich Manual HS
Indianapolis IN

Galbraith Cynthia A
Iron Mountain Sr HS
Iron Mountain MI

Galbraith William A
Roxana Sr HS
Wood River IL

Galbreath Robert E
St Ignatius HS
Chicago IL

Gale Mark R
Decatur HS
Decatur MI

Gale Teresa A
Summersville HS
Eunice MO

Galegher Charlotte A
Thompson Public HS
Thompson ND

Galer Anne L
Hillsboro HS
Hillsboro IL

Gales Robert H
Proctor HS
Duluth MN

Galinis Karen R
Coldwater HS
Quincy MI

Gall David W
Humboldt HS
St Paul MN

Gall Debra A
Bucklin HS
New Boston MO

Gall Diane P
Morton West HS
Berwyn IL

Gall Lynnette D
Humboldt HS
St Paul MN

Gall Mary M
Derham Hall HS
St Paul MN

Gallagher Kerry A
Papillion HS
Papillion NE

Gallap Clayton H
Union City HS
Coldwater MI

Gallas Pattijo
Lake Central HS
Schererville IN

Galleher Mary A
Three Rivers HS
Three Rivers MI

Gallemore Kimberly A
Seneca HS
Seneca MO

Gallenberg Dennis J
Antigo HS
Bryant WI

Galletti Beverly A
Algonac HS
Fair Haven MI

Gallick Randy G
Streator Twp HS
Streator IL

Galloway Bruce E
H H Dow HS
Midland MI

Gallucci Glory A
Maine West HS
Des Plaines IL

Gallup Laura D
Mason City Senior HS
Mason City IA

Gallus Robert J
Maysville R 1 HS
Maysville MO

Galluzzio Elizabeth A
Hannibal HS
Hannibal MO

Galuska Lynn A
Mt Assisi Academy
Oak Lawn IL

Galvin Leo E
Holstein Community HS
Ida Grove IA

Gambill Donald W
Rosedale HS
Rosedale IN

Gambill Donna R
Sandoval HS
Sandoval IL

Gambini Marianna
Whiting HS
Whiting IN

Gambino Valerie C
Thornton Fractional North HS
Calumet City IL

Gamble Karyn R
Hutsonville HS
Marshall IL

Gamble Richard W
Columbus North HS
Columbus IN

Gammill Cheri R
Glendale HS
Springfield MO

Gammon Michael D
Marshall HS
Marshall MI

Gammon Patrick C
Marshall HS
Marshall MI

Ganaway Robert L
Emerson HS
Gary IN

Ganey Heather E
Taylorville Sr HS
Taylorville IL

Gann Catherine S
Lafayette HS
St Joseph MO

Gann Victor E
Marshfield HS
Marshfield MO

Gannon Dorothy I
Beloit Catholic HS
Beloit WI

Gapski Leann
Lasalle Peru Twp HS
Oglesby IL

Garberson Cheryl L
Bedford HS
Lambertville MI

Garcia Sofia A
Ladywood St Agnes HS
Indianapolis IN

Gard Dan M
Maryville R Ii HS
Maryville MO

Gardner Craig M
St Ignatius College Prep HS
Chicago IL

Gardner Julie E
Eddyville HS
Ottumun IA

Gardner Nancy K
Heritage Christian HS
Indianapolis IN

Gardner Patricia A
Waukegan HS
Waukegan IL

Gardner Rodney J
Dighton HS
Dighton KS

Gardner Rose M
Morgan Park HS
Chicago IL

Gardner Theresa A
Boscobel HS
Boscobel WI

Gardner Vickie L
Wall Lake Comm HS
Wall Lake IA

Gardocki Theresa A
Port Huron Northern HS
Port Huron MI

Garigan Qullian M
Immaculata HS
Highland Park MI

Garkey Janet R
Polo Community HS
Polo IL

Garlick Sara D
Guilford HS
Rockford IL

Garman Steve
Eureka Hs
Eureka IL

Garner Deniesa A
Tri HS
New Castle IN

Garner Donald R
Viola HS
Bakersfield MO

Garner Leta J
South Barber HS
Kiowa KS

Garner Michael D
Lindbergh HS
St Louis MO

Garnett Timothy A
Neosho Sr HS
Neosho MO

Garnette Sandra K
Papillion Sr HS
Gibbon NE

Garretson Stacy L
Lanphier HS
Springfield IL

Garrett Billie D
Fairfield Comm HS
Fairfield IL

Garrett Bobbi K
Murphysboro Township HS
Murphysburo IL

Garrett Jeffery E
Rockkridge HS
Milan IL

Garrett Karen L
Central HS
Evansville IN

Garrett Linda L
Wentzville HS
Foristell MO

Garrett Marjorie J
Bullock Creek HS
Midland MI

Garrett Roy L
North Greene HS
Roodhouse IL

Garrett Susan M
Owosso HS
Owosso MI

Garrett Theresa A
Gillespie HS
Gillespie IL

Garrett Timothy F
Southeast HS
Kansas City MO

Garringer Marianne
Ansley HS
Ansley NE

Garrison Frances E
Trenton HS
Trenton MO

Garrison James M
Mid County Jr Sr HS
Varna IL

Garrison Michael H
Ozark HS
Ozark MO

Garrison Wendy A
Cambridge HS
Cambridge IL

Garry Patricia A
Wm Fremd HS
Palatine IL

Garson David F
Parkway West Sr HS
St Louis MO

Gartner Bill E
Clay Center HS
Clay Center NE

Garton Bradford G
Columbus North HS
Columbus IN

Garvey Martin C
Waterloo West HS
Waterloo IA

Garwood Thomas J
St Charles HS
St Charles MO

Gary Elizabeth A
Holly HS
Davisburg MI

Gary Joleen M
Graceville Public HS
Graceville MN

Gasbarra Shane S
Guilford HS
Rockford IL

Gascho Marlys W
Fairview HS
Fairview MI

Gaspar David L
Waterford Union HS
Waterford WI

Gaspar James M
Waterford HS
Waterford WI

Gasper Denise L
Andes Central HS
Lake Andes SD

Gass Marvin D
Montezuma Comm HS
Montezuma IA

Gasswint Danny R
Pratt HS
Pratt KS

Gastineau Wanda J
Polo HS
Polo MO

Gaston Arlene A
Potter Public HS
Potter NE

Gaston Dianne K
Lexington Public HS
Lexington NE

Gates Robin L
East Detroit HS
East Detroit MI

Gates Ronald L
Anderson HS
Anderson IN

Gatheman James G
Southwest HS
St Louis MO

Gatlin Janet M
Duluth East HS
Duluth MN

Gatmaitan Ann W
Knightstown HS
Knightstown IN

Gatrel Lester L
Indianaola Comm HS
Indianola IA

Gatzke Stephen L
Culver Military Academy
Muscatine IA

Gau William J
Newman HS
Wausau WI

Gauda Estelle B
Normandy HS
St Louis MO

Gauf Mark A
Peoria Heights HS
Peoria Heights IL

Gauger David K
Geneva HS
Geneva IL

Gautney Pamela L
John Marshall HS
Chicago IL

Gauvreau Edmond G
De Lasalle Collegiate HS
Mt Clemens MI

Gawaluck Cynthia M
Mother Theodore Guerin HS
Chicago IL

Gay James O
Benilde St Margarets HS
Hopkins MN

Gay Teresa M
Morton HS
Pekin IL

Gaydos Carol M
Rockford East HS
Rockford IL

Gaylord Tammy M
Malden Community HS
Malden IL

Gear Gary R
West Lafayette HS
West Lafayette IN

Geary Margaret A
South Central HS
Elizabeth IN

Gebers Gary W
Holstein Comm HS
Holstein IA

Gebert Sherri A
Wausau West HS
Wausau WI

Gebhard Henry D
Northern Valley HS
Long Island KS

Gebhard Rose M
Lakeshore HS
Stevensville MI

Gebhardt Sherrie L
Maine South HS
Norridge IL

Geddes Howard H
O Fallon Township HS
O Fallon IL

Gee Kimberly K
Wichita Southeast HS
Wichita KS

Geeding Curtis T
Menasha HS
Menasha WI

Geene Susan L
Eastern HS
Bloomfield IN

Geffe Kent L
Nashua Comm HS
Nashua IA

Geffre Cynthia L
Lead HS
Lead SD

Gehl Thomas W
George S Parker Sr HS
Janesville WI

Gehlbach Dan L
Shawnee Mission Nw HS
Shawnee KS

Gehlbach Michael W
Lincoln Comm HS
Lincoln IL

Gehlen Margaret E
New Prague HS
New Prague MN

Gehring Peggy J
Moundridge HS
Moundridge KS

Gehringer John D
Durand Area HS
Durand MI

Gehrke John R
Walther Lutheran HS
Melrose Park IL

Geiger Janice M
La Moille Community HS
La Moille IL

Geiger Raymond H
Quigley Prep North HS
Morton Grove IL

Geisenhof Beverly J
Long Prairie HS
Long Prairie MN

Geiser Robert D
North Platte HS
North Platte NE

Geisler Dorothy M
Ladywood St Agnes HS
Indianapolis IN

Geisler Sally A
Lawrenceburg HS
Lawrenceburg IN

Geissert Joyce A
Central Comm HS
Breese IL

Gekas Canella
Luther North HS
Chicago IL

Gekiere Michael A
Denby HS
Detroit MI

Gelbmann John W
St Bernards HS
St Paul MN

Geldner Peter D
Campion Jesuit HS
Neenah WI

Geleske Cynthia J
Goshen HS
Goshen IN

Gellerman Wendell L
Lincoln Sr HS
Wisconsin Rapids WI

Gellings Lynn M
Waterford HS
Franksville WI

Gempeler Reyne C
Monticello Public HS
Monticello WI

Gengenbach Linda M
Murphysboro Twp HS
Murphysboro IL

Gengler Kara L
Carroll HS
Derby KS

Gengler Nancy A
St Marys HS
Le Mars IA

Gennara Thomas S
Waterford HS
Franksville WI

Genovese Gasper
Osborn HS
Detroit MI

Genrich Terri L
North Boone HS
Poplar Grove IL

Gentis Rick D
Southern Wells HS
Bluffton IN

Gentleman Sylvia B
Silver Creek Public HS
Silver Creek NE

Gentry Tina E
Hallsville Riv HS
Hallsville MO

Geoghegan Patrick G
Baraboo HS
Baraboo WI

George Christopher A
Northeastern Wayne HS
Williamsburg IN

George Judy L
Lesterville R 4 HS
Lesterville MO

George Kenny E
Penney HS
Kingston MO

George Louis E
Hardin Central HS
Hardin MO

George Rita R
Fairfield Comm HS
Fairfield IL

George Rodney L
Chaparral HS
Anthony KS

George Sheila
Glendale HS
Springfield MO

Geraughty Jim
Santa Fe HS
Waverly MO

Gerber Darryl G
Adams Central HS
Decatur IN

Gerber David L
Drake HS
Drake ND

Gerbers Shirley J
Concordia Lutheran HS
Fort Wayne IN

Gerdes Julie A
Roanoke Benson HS
Benson IL

Gerdow George R
Gordon Technical HS
Chicago IL

Gerecke Melissa A
Calhoun HS
Kampsville IL

Gergely Lisa R
Highlands Sr HS
Highland IN

Gergen Joan M
Shickley Public HS
Shickley NE

Gerger Daniel J
Birch Run HS
Birch Run MI

Gerik Michael D
Saline HS
Saline MI

Gering Carol L
Prospect HS
Mt Prospect IL

Gerkins Dal R
Randolph HS
Randolph NE

Gerlach Elaine B
Lincolnwood HS
Waggoner IL

Gerlach Stephanie D
Sparta HS
Sparta IL

Gerleman Thomas G
Brookfield Academy
Waukesha WI

Gerleve Russell J
Glenbard West HS
Carol Stream IL

Germain Suzanne C
Somerset Public HS
Somerset WI

German Erling S
Chase County HS
Imperial NE

Germann Roger L
Belleville Township West HS
Belleville IL

Germic Dan R
Kingsford HS
Kingsford MI

Gero Margaret A
Columbus HS
Columbus WI

Gerth Debra Y
Dieterich HS
Dieterich IL

Gerth Paul K
Avon Community HS
Indianapolis IN

Gertsch Melva R
Monroe Public HS
Monroe NE

Gessel Michael H
Northwest HS
House Spgs MO

Gessert Robert J
Cape Central HS
Cape Girardeau MO

Gessford Julie M
Lincoln Northeast HS
Lincoln NE

Gessler Gary C
Johannesburg HS
Lewiston MI

Getchel Jon M
Farwell Area HS
Farwell MI

Gettelman Barbara
Brookfield Central HS
Brookfield WI

Getz Carol J
Morton HS
Morton IL

Geurink Sandra K
Hamilton HS
Holland MI

Geurkink Linda J
Hinsdale Central Township HS
Hinsdale IL

Geyer Audrey L
Clear Creek Comm HS
Oxford IA

Geyer Estelle A
St Scholastica HS
Chicago IL

Ghidina Michael S
Richwoods HS
Peoria IL

Gibbens Beth M
Lowpoint Washburn HS
Washburn IL

Gibbons Jane A
Johnston HS
Des Moines IA

Gibbs David E
Henry Senachwine HS
Henry IL

Gibbs Jacquelyn J
Il Valley Central HS
Chillicothe IL

Gibbs Ray E
Oscoda HS
Wortsmith Afb MI

Gibbs Robert J
Burlington Comm HS
Burlington IA

Gibbs Sandra K
Warren HS
Gurnee IL

Gibbs Susan C
Kenmare HS
Kenmare ND

Giblin Michael W
St Viator HS
Mt Prospect IL

Gibney Bart W
Prairie HS
Fairfax IA

Gibson Charles C
Goshen HS
Goshen IN

Gibson Glenn E
Flint Central HS
Flint MI

Gibson Julie A
Tremont HS
Tremont IL

Gibson Kathryn M
Springfield Catholic HS
Springfield MO

Gibson Kenneth S
Hammond HS
Hammond IN

Gibson Mark D
Bradley Bourbonnois Co HS
Bourbonnais IL

Gibson Philip A
Washington Comm HS
Washington IL

Gibson Rosalie
Dundee Community HS
Dundee MI

Gibson Susan O
Tuscola HS
Tuscola IL

Gideon Jack
Wayne HS
Fort Wayne IN

Gideon Karen S
Ozark HS
Ozark MO

Gieber Debra E
Centreville HS
Centreville MI

Giedd Susan E
Henry HS
Henry SD

Gielniak Cary F
Lake Central HS
Crn Pt IN

Gienger Tonya M
St Francis Comm HS
St Francis KS

Giertych Theresa L
Thornwood HS
South Holland IL

Gierymski Ivone I
George Rogers Clark HS
Hammond IN

Gieseman Timothy W
Rockridge HS
Milan IL

Giesen Andrea S
New Prague HS
New Prague MN

Giesen Doris E
Barrington HS
Barrington IL

Gietzen Debra L
Chippewa Hills HS
Remus MI

Giffhorn Linda S
Tremont HS
Tremont IL

Gigac Arlene D
Whiting HS
Whiting IN

Giger Roger B
Guide Rock HS
Guide Rock NE

Gigliotti Anthony J
Paul Vi HS
Omaha NE

Gilbert Charlotte M
Lincoln County R Ii HS
Elsberry MO

Gilbert Cheryl A
Antigo HS
Antigo WI

Gilbert Denise J
Prairie City Comm HS
Prairie City IA

Gilbert Gayla S
Paris HS
Paris IL

Gilbert Kathy J
Kent City HS
Kent City MI

Gilbert Kila A
Kewaunee HS
Kewaunee WI

Gilbert Lisa C
Granite City South HS
Granite City IL

Gilbert Pamela A
Waltonville HS
Waltonville IL

Gilbert Raymond B
Franklin HS
Livonia MI

Gilbert Thomas A
Hershey HS
Hershey NE

Gilbertson Kathleen R
Sterling HS
Sterling IL

Gilbertson Linda M
Albert Lea Sr HS
Albert Lea MN

Gilbertson Mark W
Amery HS
Amery WI

Gildersleeve Rhonda R
Fennimore HS
Fennimore WI

Gile Michelle D
Scandia HS
Scandia KS

Giles Craig S
Downers Grove North HS
Downers Grove IL

Giles Franklin D
New Palestine HS
New Palestine IN

Gill Toni S
La Monte HS
La Monte MO

Gillan Brian P
Central HS
Omaha NE

Gillard J Dean
Edwards Co Sr HS
Albion IL

Gillespie Gloria G
Rich East Twp HS
Park Forest IL

Gillespie Jan L
Canton Ind HS
Hudson SD

Gillespie Lawrence G
De Smet Jesuit HS
Crystal Lake Pk MO

Gillet Nicole M
Edina East HS
Edina MN

Gillett Margo L
Esbon Rural HS
Red Cloud NE

Gilley Debra A
Burke HS
Omaha NE

Gilliam Gregg E
United Township HS
East Moline IL

Gilligan Kevin L
Allegan HS
Allegan MI

Gilliland Michael V
Okemos HS
Okemos MI

Gillis Anne T
Grosse Pointe No HS
Harper Woods MI

Gillispie Aaron D
Moberly HS
Moberly MO

Gillogly Kathleen A
Sacred Heart Of Mary HS
Mt Prospect IL

Gillum Debra K
Unionville HS
Green Castle MO

Gilmore Pammy K
Emerson HS
Gary IN

Gilmore Steven J
Limestone HS
Bartonville IL

Gilmore Tracy L
North Greene HS
Roodhouse IL

Gilpin Steven N
Southern Boone County R
1 HS
Ashland MO

Gilson Craig
Havana HS
Havana IL

Ginder Joseph R
Anderson HS
Anderson IN

Gingerich Kaye M
John Glenn HS
Bay City MI

Gingerich Phillip W
Wawasee HS
Milford IN

Gingrey Kathy J
West Fargo HS
Harwood ND

Ginther Laura J
Highland HS
Highland IN

Girard Lori E
Northeast HS
Arma KS

Girbach Juanita J
Saline HS
Saline MI

Girman Karen L
George Rogers Clark HS
Whiting IN

Girman Marisa L
Lake Central HS
St John IN

Giroux Pamela M
Marian HS
Omaha NE

Gish Teresa A
Jacksonville HS
Jacksonville IL

Gist Roger B
Raymore Peculiar HS
Raymore MO

Giudici Doreen M
Farmington HS
Northville MI

Giugler Mary Ellen
Lockport Township HS
Lockport IL

Gius Richard J
St Patrick HS
River Forest IL

Giusti Lorraine M
Bradley Bourbonnais HS
Bradley IL

Gjelsvik David B
Vienna Township HS
Simpson IL

Gjernes Marvin J
Cresbard HS
Chelsea SD

Glaser Diane M
Spalding Public HS
Spalding NE

Glasgow Mark J
Roseville HS
Roseville IL

Glass Kathryn K
Remington HS
Benton KS

Glassburn Earl K
Maconaquah HS
Kokomo IN

Glatz Nancy E
Schaumburg HS
Hanover Park IL

Glaze Robert D
Plattsmouth HS
Plattsmouth NE

Gleason Marilou E
Nazareth Academy
Brookfield IL

Gleason Shannon L
New Haven HS
New Haven MI

Gleckler Mary L
Griggsville HS
New Salem IL

Gleisner Robert A
Harper HS
Chicago IL

Glenn Richard A
Olin Cons HS
Olin IA

Glenn Thomas L
Collinsville HS
Edwardsville IL

Glesener Peggy J
Bird Island Public HS
Bird Island MN

Glidewell Robert W
Casey HS
Casey IL

Glos Donna J
H L Richards HS
Oak Lawn IL

Glotzbach Susan E
Hayden HS
Topeka KS

Glover Betty A
Serena HS
Sheridan IL

Glover James S
Superior HS
Superior WI

Glover Jeffrey A
Hamilton Southeastern HS
Noblesville IN

Glover Richard E
South Side HS
Ft Wayne IN

Glowiak Pamela L
Marquette Manor Christian HS
Chicago IL

Gloyd Sheryl J
Guilford HS
Rockford IL

Glynn Devin L
Summerfield HS
Summerfield KS

Glynn John A
Millington HS
Millington MI

Glynn Rebecca J
St Charles HS
St Charles MI

Gnat Barbara L
West Allis Central HS
West Allis WI

Goacher Brenda S
Waverly HS
Waverly IL

Goade Courtney A
Baxter Springs HS
Baxter Springs KS

Goar Ann E
United Township HS
East Moline IL

Goben Sally J
Balyki HS
Kilbourne IL

Goblirsch Gregory J
Wabasso Public HS
Tyler MN

Gocken Beverly A
Stillman Valley HS
Stillman Valley IL

Gocken Jeffrey L
Stillman Valley HS
Davis Junction IL

Godbout Vickie S
Phillipsburg HS
Seward NE

Godby Michael D
Moravia Comm HS
Moravia IA

Goddard Mary B
Washington Community HS
Washington IL

Godinez Belle M
St Mary Of Perpetual Help HS
Chicago IL

Godlewski Edward A
Bishop Noll Institute
Calumet City IL

Godwin Richard A
Rosary HS
St Louis MO

Goeden Michael J
Bloomfield Community HS
Wausa NE

Goehring Duane A
Marion Independent HS
Marion IA

Goehring Ruth A
Burwell Jr Sr HS
Burwell NE

Goeke Sally A
Dakota HS
Davis IL

Goen Terri E
Sidney HS
Sidney NE

Goering Kevin J
Moundridge HS
Moundridge KS

Goering Robert A
South Luther HS
Lagrange IL

Goethe Dennis L
Rolla Senior HS
Rolla MO

Goetten Edward E
Jersey Comm HS
Jerseyville IL

Goettl Leonard J
Jefferson Sr HS
Jefferson WI

Goetz Catherine L
Hays HS
Hays KS

Goff Gregory T
Ogemaw Hts HS
West Branch MI

Goff Margaret M
Marland HS
Marland KS

Goforth Glenn A
Sparta HS
Tilden IL

Gohl Dewayne F
Hayes Center HS
Palisade NE

Gold Carl G
Parkwood HS
Joplin MO

Goldbach Cynthia M
Marathon HS
Marathon WI

Goldberg Edward J
Niles North HS
Skokie IL

Golden Douglas C
White Pine HS
White Pine MI

Golden Gary D
Wethersfield HS
Kewanee IL

Goldner Terry A
Corunna HS
Corunna MI

Golevicz Suzanne E
Maine Twp HS South
Park Ridge IL

Golightly Bradley D
Van Meter Comm HS
Booneville IA

Golliher Patricia A
Murphysboro Twp HS
Murphysboro IL

Gollonik Debra M
Stevens Point Area Senior HS
Stevens Point WI

Gomez Alfred
St John Cathedral HS
Milwaukee WI

Gondek Valerie A
Menominee HS
Menominee MI

Gonderinger Robert M
St Marys HS
Oneill NE

Gongaware Maria T A
Reeds Spring HS
Reeds Spring MO

Gongwer Geoffrey S
Bloomington HS
Bloomington IL

Gonner Jeffrey L
Marquette HS
Bellevue IA

Gonsholt Bruce O
Bergan HS
Peroria IL

Gonto Steve
Ferndale HS
Oak Park MI

Good Catherine A
Glenbard East HS
Lombard IL

Good Makayla M
St Johns HS
St Johns MI

Goodaker David M
Calumet HS
Gary IN

Goodes Pamela A
Lew Wallace HS
Gary IN

Gooding Denise S
Corunna HS
Corunna MI

Gooding Kimberly L
Fountain Central HS
Wallace IN

Goodman Walter K
Roseville HS
Roseville MI

Goodrich Barry F
Pioneer HS
Royal Center IN

Goodson Kathleen S
Central R Iii HS
Flat River MO

Goodwick Sherri L
Leland HS
Leland IL

Goodwin Carolynn L
Lincoln HS
Lincoln NE

Goodwin Peggy L
Langdon HS
Langdon ND

Goodwin Robert L
West Catholic HS
Marne MI

Goracke Cynthia A
Weeping Water HS
Weeping Water NE

Gorak Georjean M
Oak Forest HS
Oak Forest IL

Gorden Daniel W
Hawley HS
Hawley MN

Gordon Brenda C
Eastern HS
Lansing MI

Gordon Bruce B
Cass Technical HS
Detroit MI

Gordon Douglas L
Marquette HS
Michigan City IN

Gordon Jack D
Galena HS
Galena MO

Gordon Valerie D
Paseo HS
Kansas City MO

Gorecki Audrey L
Evergreen Park Comm HS
Evergreen Park IL

Gorecki Mark C
Douglas Macarthur HS
Decatur IL

Gorentz Anthony J
Northeast HS
Arma KS

Gorham Karen M
Paul Iii HS
Omaha NE

Gorham Vaughn R
Excelsior Spring HS
Excelsior Spring MO

Gorman James G
Chaminade College
St Louis MO

Gorman Richard A
Appleton West HS
Appleton WI

Gorman Thomas P
Brother Rice HS
Birmingham MI

Gorney Kevin G
All Saints Central HS
Bay City MI

Gorski Gregory F
Benet Academy
Clarendon Hills IL

Gorski John G
Glenbard East HS
Lombard IL

Gorski Michael E
Thornridge HS
S Holland IL

Gorsuch Jill A
Pattonville Sr HS
Bridgeton MO

Gorzen Kim M
St Clair HS
St Clair MI

Goschke Lori J
Langdon HS
Munich ND

Gosney David B
Monroe City R 1 HS
Monroe City MO

Goss William F
Marian Catholic HS
Chicago Hts IL

Gossage Teresa L
Oak Park HS
Kansas City MO

Goswick Randolph J
Seneca HS
Racine MO

Gotham Deborah M
Buena Vista HS
Saginaw MI

Gott Jack L
Wichita HS
Wichita KS

Gottbreht William M
Bishop Ryan HS
Minot ND

Gottschalk Sharon K
Octavia HS
Anchor IL

Gotz Robert R
Waterford Mott HS
Pontiac MI

Goudy Teresa L
Macksville HS
Macksville KS

Gould David W
North Clay HS
Louisville IL

Goulet Mary Jo R
Rosemount Sr HS
Rosemount MN

Gourd Jody C
Chanute Senior HS
Chanute KS

Gourley Dennis J
Lenox Community HS
Lenox IA

Govaker David A
Pittsburg HS
Pittsburg KS

Goven Ione R
Turtle Lake Mercer HS
Turtle Lake ND

Gowan Mary J
Oslo Public HS
Oslo MN

Gower Jeffrey R
Quincy Senior HS
Quincy IL

Gowings Bruce A
Burris HS
Muncie IN

Goysich Michael J
Morton Sr HS
Hammond IN

Grabau Teresa A
Wykoff Public HS
Wykoff MN

Graber Jacelyn N
Mt Pleasant HS
Wayland IA

Graber Jann G
Haven HS
Burrton KS

Graber Nancy L
Southern Door HS
Sturgeon Bay WI

Graber Teresa A
Freeman HS
Freeman SD

Grable Karen S
Caston HS
Twelve Mile IN

Grable Pamela D
Warsaw HS
Warsaw MO

Grabouski Jody M
North Platte Sr HS
North Platte NE

Grace Anthony R
Michigan Ctr HS
Michigan Ctr MI

Grace Jerilyn J
Valentine HS
Valentine NE

Grace Melanie L
Lake Forest Academy
Lake Bluff IL

Gracey Karen M
Dominican HS
Detroit MI

Graddy Richard L
Bourbon R 1 HS
Bourbon MO

Graf Michael P
De Smet Jesuit HS
St Louis MO

Graffeo Rosemarie
Evergreen Park Comm HS
Evergreen Pk IL

Grafford Deborah A
Lovington HS
Lovington IL

Graft Gary L
Northrop HS
Fort Wayne IN

Grager Joan M
Slinger HS
West Bend WI

Graham Cheryl L
Mark Twain HS
New London MO

Graham Cindy L
Sullivan HS
Sullivan IN

Graham Diann L
Ida Grove HS
Ida Grove IA

Graham Jeanne P
A D Johnston HS
Bessemer MI

Graham Kathryn A
Darlington HS
Darlington WI

Graham Kristine B
Unity HS
Ursa IL

Graham Larry R
Arthur Hill HS
Saginaw MI

Graham Marilyn S
Lincolnwood HS
Raymond IL

Graham Mary B
Arthur HS
Arthur IL

Graham Robert L
Glenwood HS
Glenwood IA

Graham Sandra L
H H Dow HS
Midland MI

Graham Starr K
Academy Of Our Lady
Chicago IL

Graham Tim A
Kewanna HS
Kewanna IN

Grahlman Mary A
Jefferson Sr HS
Jefferson WI

Grahn Ronald D
Carmel HS
Carmel IN

Gralak Glenn R
Hinsdale Central HS
Hinsdale IL

Gralheer Brad D
Wisner Pilger HS
Wisner NE

Gramstad Mark G
Worthington HS
Worthington MN

Grandy Ann M
Spalding HS
Chicago IL

Grandys Elizabeth F
Badger HS
Lake Geneva WI

Graner Anne M
Mandan Sr HS
Huff ND

Granger Schawnn M
Larimore HS
Emerado ND

Grannemann Laura K
Girard HS
Hepler KS

Grant Matthew R
Wheaton North HS
Wheaton IL

Grant Michael D
Johnston City HS
Johnston City IL

Grant Patrick A
Aquin Central Catholic HS
Freeport IL

Grant Robert T
Bishop Dwenger HS
Fort Wayne IN

Grant Steven M
Penney HS
Hamilton MO

Graube Davids V
Union HS
Grand Rapids MI

Grauerholz Melinda A
West Smith County HS
Kensington KS

Graupera Rosa E
Ames Senior HS
Ames IA

Gravely Karen A
Southwestern HS
Shelbyville IN

Graven Rhonda D
Moweaqua HS
Moweaqua IL

Graven Timothy G
Normandy HS
St Louis MO

Graves David J
Bonner Springs HS
Bonner Spgs KS

Graves Michael P
Carmel HS
Carmel IN

Graves Paul A
Edwardsville Sr HS
Edwardsville IL

Graves Sheila M
Vienna Township HS
Vienna IL

Graves William D
Greensburg HS
Greensburg KS

Grawcock Peggy K
Churubusco HS
Columbia City IN

Gray Carmen
High School
Bloomington IL

Gray Donna M
Lawson HS
Lawson MO

Gray Karen F
Diamond R 4 HS
Diamond MO

Gray Karen M
Polo Comm HS
Polo IL

Gray Leanna J
Du Quoin HS
Du Quoin IL

Gray Robert E
Carlisle Comm HS
Carlisle IA

Gray Ronald D
Parderville HS
Pardeeville WI

Gray Stephen K
Alexandria Monroe HS
Alexandria IN

Gray Thomas G
Bayless HS
St Louis MO

Gray Vanna L
Sweet Springs R 7 HS
Sweet Springs MO

Grayson Charles R
Lathrop HS
Lathrop MO

Grechus Maribeth A
Butler R 5 HS
Butler MO

Greco Adele E
Spalding HS
Chicago IL

Grecula Marie L
Harlem HS
Rockford IL

Green Amy S
Wausau East HS
Wausau WI

Green Beth E
Lapeer Senior HS
Metamora MI

Green Brian S
Rantool Township HS
Rantoul IL

Green Charles A
Alton Senior HS
Alton IL

Green Danny L
West Washington HS
Salem IN

STUDENTS PHOTOGRAPH SCHEDULED FOR PUBLICATION HERE COULD NOT BE REPRODUCED

Green Deborah S
Richmond Sr HS
Richmond IN

Green Henzy
Crispus Attucks HS
Indianapolis IN

Green Leslie K
Norris City HS
Norris City IL

Green Martin R
Bismarck HS
Bismarck ND

Green Michelle E
Mother Mc Auley HS
Chicago IL

Green Nancy L
Greenville HS
Greenville MI

Green Ola L
Thayer R 2 HS
Thayer MO

Green Pamela A
Christian Fenger HS
Chicago IL

Green Rhonda S
Dwight D Eisenhower HS
Saginaw MI

Green Russell W
L C Mohr HS
South Haven MI

Green Theresa J
Pontiac Central HS
W Bloomfield MI

Green Todd C
Evergreen Park Comm HS
Evergreen Park IL

Green Troxel D
Chambers Public HS
Ewing NE

Greenamyer Diann L
Reading HS
Montgomery MI

Greene Shepard J
Mt Vernon Township HS
Mt Vernon IL

Greene Sylvia K
Chase County HS
Imperial NE

Greenfield Cathleen A
Forreston HS
Forreston IL

Greenleaf Roger
Warrensburg Latham HS
Decatur IL

Greenlee Herbert B
Oak Park River Forest HS
River Forest IL

Greenlee William M
Oak Park River Forest HS
River Forest IL

Greenslaugh Bradley W
Hamilton HS
Hamilton IL

Greer Betty J
University Of Chicago HS
Chicago IL

Greer Debbie A
St Charles HS
St Charles MO

Greer Joanna
Franklin Comm HS
Franklin IN

Greer Keith G
Lutheran West HS
Detroit MI

Gregg Alisa J
Mark Twain HS
New London MO

Gregg John R
Manistee HS
Manistee MI

Gregg Michael W
Hamburg HS
Hamburg IA

Gregoire Paul J
Marshall Sr HS
Marshall MN

Gregoire Todd K
Northland Pines HS
Eagle River WI

Gregory Connie L
Bloom Township HS
Chicago Heights IL

Gregory Henry T
Central Sr HS
Kansas City MO

Gregory Joan M
Midland HS
Midland MI

Gregory Michael L
Parkway West HS
Manchester MO

Gregory Rosemary A
Pine River Public HS
Pine River MN

Greif Joyce A
Osborne HS
Osborne KS

Greim James R
R Nelson Snider HS
Fort Wayne IN

Greiner Barbara A
Saint Joseph Sr HS
Saint Joseph MI

Greiner Lisa
Woodruff HS
Peoria IL

Greiner Sandra L
Harrison HS
Harrison MI

Greminger Keith G
Valle HS
St Genevieve MO

Gremmels Stephen K
Du Quoin HS
Du Quoin IL

Grenell Virginia L
Manistee HS
Manistee MI

Grenier David P
East Grand Forks Senior HS
E Grand Forks MN

Grenisen Margie M
Aquinas HS
La Crosse WI

Grennan Martin J
Concordia HS
Jamestown KS

Grentz Renee R
Sunflower HS
Mitchell NE

Gress Mike N
Jasper HS
Jasper IN

Greve Jeffrey A
Wisner Pilger HS
Wisner NE

Grey Carole G
Earlville HS
Earlville IL

Gridley Bobbie J
Carrollton Comm Unit HS
Carrollton IL

Grieger Marvin C
Morgan Twp HS
Valparaiso IN

Griepenstroh Mark S
Heritage Hills HS
Lamar IN

Griffin Boyd E
Richwoods HS
Peoria IL

Griffin Darrick C
Harvard St George HS
Chicago IL

Griffin Debra A
Twin Rivers HS
Broseley MO

Griffin Pat W
Carlisle Commuinty HS
Carlisle IA

Griffin Rachel L
Lane HS
Chicago IL

Griffin Robin E
Noblesville HS
Noblesville IN

Griffin Steven B
Fairfield Comm HS
Fairfield IL

Griffin Teena M
Octavia HS
Saybrook IL

Griffin Timothy P
Lake Linden Hubbell HS
Lake Linden MI

Griffith Christy E
John Hersey HS
Arlington Hts IL

Griffith Ellis E
East Richland HS
Olney IL

Griffith Kean D
Frankfort Community HS
West Frankfort IL

Griffith Susan H
Roycemore HS
Evanston IL

Griffith Twyla L
Benton County HS
Lincoln MO

Griffith William B
Fairfield Community HS
Fairfield IL

Griggs Debra L
Newton Senior HS
Newton IA

Griggs Gregory W
Cass Tech HS
Detroit MI

Griggs Richard
Cowan HS
Muncie IN

Grigsby Deborah J
Westfield HS
Neshkoro WI

Grill Raymond A
Fenwick HS
Westchester IL

Grimes Daniel W
Logan Rogersville HS
Rogersville MO

Grimes John A
Balaton HS
Balaton MN

Grimes Randy L
Huntley HS
Huntley IL

Grimes Sharon K
Northrop HS
Fort Wayne IN

Grimm Lora J
Sabetha HS
Sabetha KS

Grimm Sheila S
Craig Riii HS
Craig MO

Grimmell Derek W
Elk River Sr HS
Elk River MN

Grimshaw Jerry A
Tomah HS
Camp Douglas WI

Grimske Karen M
Lakeview HS
St Clair Shores MI

Grimstad Gregory G
Stephen Decatur HS
Decatur IL

Grindatti Catherine A
West Iron County HS
Stambaugh MI

Grinolds Kim G
Palermo HS
Palermo ND

Grinstead Cody L
Davis County HS
Floris IA

Grint Jerald E
Sargent Public HS
Sargent NE

Gripka Regina L
Aurora HS
Aurora MO

Grisham Deborah K
Morton HS
Morton IL

Grismer Mary J
Burnsville Sr HS
Burnsville MN

Grissett Mary L
Portage Central HS
Portage MI

Grist Jennifer T
Blue Springs HS
Independence MO

Griswold David L
Greenfield Comm HS
Rockbridge IL

Griswold Michael R
Wichita West HS
Wichita KS

Griswold Patti J
Benson HS
Omaha NE

Griswold Rodney L
Grand Haven Sr HS
Grand Haven MI

Griswold Stan R
Fremont HS
Fremont MI

Gritten Bruce E
Covington HS
Kingman IN

Gritti Nick E
Mattoon Sr HS
Mattoon IL

Groat Marta J
Maconaquah HS
Peru IN

Groce Michele T
Dupo Comm HS
Dupo IL

Grochowsky Janet L
Carroll HS
Wichita KS

Groen Kathy A
Polo Comm HS
Polo IL

Groenendyk Kathy L
Oskaloosa Sr HS
Oskaloosa IA

Groeneveld Lorri J
Oshkosh West HS
Oshkosh WI

Groepper Peter S
Evanston Township HS
Evanston IL

Grogan Laurie J
Ogorman HS
Sioux Falls SD

Grohler Kent B
Sullivan HS
Sullivan IL

Grohs Jeffrey M
Pinckney HS
Pinckney MI

Gronewold Nancy L
Unity HS
Quincy IL

Groothuis Lisa M
Granite City N HS
Granite City IL

Gross Marti E
Elmhurst HS
Ft Wayne IN

Gross Mary E
Peotone HS
Monee IL

Gross Patty L
Alma HS
Alma WI

Gross Stacey L
Marian HS
Hays KS

Grossenburg Jolenne K
Winner Sr HS
Winner SD

Grote Mark D
De Soto HS
Shawnee KS

Grotjan Lori D
Brunswick Rii HS
Brunswick MO

Grott Deborah K
Chester HS
Chester IL

Grove Mary E
Grand Ledge HS
Grand Ledge MI

Grovenburg Douglas A
Milbank HS
Milbank SD

Grover Marsha I
Gordon HS
Gordon NE

Grover Timothy G
Independence HS
Rowley IA

Grow Lewis E
Washington Catholic HS
Washington IN

Grubb Brian T
Homer HS
Homer IL

Grubb Thomas R
El Paso HS
El Paso IL

Grubbs Karla J
Wes Del HS
Muncie IN

Gruber Susan A
Healy HS
Genola MN

Grudzien Robert A
Notre Dame HS
Chicago IL

Grudzinski Timothy L
Aurora Sr HS
Phillips NE

Gruebmeyer Lisa A
Richwoods HS
Peoria IL

Gruenloh Mary A
R 1 North Callaway HS
Williamsburg MO

Grugel Cynthia L
Waukesha South HS
Waukesha WI

Gruhlke Richard E
Hillcrest HS
Markham IL

Gruis Bradford D
Meservey Thornton HS
Thornton IA

Grulke Darlyn K
Ballard Community HS
Kelley IA

Grumish Nancy J
Bishop Mc Namara HS
Kankakee IL

Grunden David W
Reading HS
Reading MI

Grundhauser Deborah A
Lefor Public HS
Lefor ND

Grundmeier Scott M
Kelliher HS
Kelliher MN

Gruner Colleen M
Coldwater HS
Coldwater MI

Grunewald Alan G
Warsaw HS
Warsaw IL

Grunwell Howard R
Saginaw Douglas
Macarthur HS
Saginaw MI

Gudenkauf Jamie S
Nemaha Valley HS
Seneca KS

Guebert Stephen C
Red Bud Comm Unit HS
Red Bud IL

Guenette Francis J
Escanaba Area Public HS
Escanaba MI

Guengerich Gene A
Pekin Community HS
Manito IL

Guenther David J
Waubun Public HS
Waubun MN

Guerin James B
Menasha HS
Menasha WI

Guerra Donald J
Lyons Township HS
La Grange Park IL

Guerrera Gloria
Oak Forest HS
Oak Forest IL

Guerrero Eugene J
Niles East HS
Skokie IL

Guertler Bruce D
Simley Sr HS
Inver Grove Hts MN

Guest Rosemarie
Bogan HS
Chicago IL

Guggemos Patricia L
Schlarman HS
Danville IL

Guhl Steven W
Huntington North HS
Huntington IN

Guice Karen N
Englewood HS
Chicago IL

Guichard Gary G
Mendel HS
Chicago IL

Guichard Peggy J
Normal Community HS
Normal IL

Guida Cathie J
Lewiston Consolidated HS
Burchard NE

Guier Kathryn L
Sweet Springs HS R 7
Sweet Springs MO

Guigar Marilyn R
Peck Community HS
Peck MI

Guihea William E
Brother Rice HS
Chicago IL

Guill Dawn R
Sunnydale Academy
Centralia MO

Guillory Kathleen T
Rosarian Acad
Ft Wayne IN

Guinan Dan F
Missouri Valley HS
Missouri Valley IA

Guise Vicky L
Hayti HS
Hayti MO

Guiter Steven M
Comstock HS
Kalamazoo MI

Guitord Roberta
Bishop Dwenger HS
Ft Wayne IN

Guldan Debbie L
Columbus HS
Marshfield WI

Guler Gregory T
New Rockford Central HS
New Rockford ND

Guler Jeanne M
New Rockford Central HS
New Rockford ND

Gulick Craig L
Wm Chrisman HS
Independence MO

Gulik Janet M
Proviso West HS
Bellwood IL

Gulley Marilyn S
Paxton HS
Paxton IL

Gullickson Lynne J
Lanesboro HS
Whalan MN

Gullikson Vonnie J
White Shield HS
Roseglen ND

Gullion Kathy L
Marshall HS
Marshall IL

Gumm Ed L
Maryville R Ii HS
Maryville MO

Gunder Colleen D
Northrop HS
Fort Wayne IN

Gundlach Kurt E
Iowa Grant HS
Montfort WI

Gundrum Robert R
Kewaskum HS
Kewaskum WI

Gunn Mary J
Union HS
Union MO

Gunn Robert C
Waukegan East HS
Waukegan IL

Gunter Diane J
Josephinum HS
Chicago IL

Gunter Marcia K
Sacred Heart Public HS
Sacred Heart MN

Gunty Mary C
Romeoville HS
Romeoville IL

Guokas Charles R
St Francis HS
St Francis WI

Gupta Ratnamala
Westport HS
Kansas City MO

Guse Roy J
Brookfield East HS
Brookfield WI

Gusich Margaret M
Naperville Central HS
Naperville IL

Gust Cynthia A
Central HS
Grand Forks ND

Gust Loretta L
L L Wright HS
Ironwood MI

Gustafson Jeffrey S
Wayne Comm HS
Corydon IA

Gustafson Paula A
Hibbing HS
Hibbing MN

Gustafson Sherry L
Magic City Campus HS
Minot ND

Gustafson William T
Hallock HS
Hallock MN

Gut George M
Weber HS
Chicago IL

Guth John C
Washington Comm HS
Eureka IL

Guthier Martha R
St Elizabeths Academy
St Louis MO

Guthrie Timothy F
Vienna HS
Vienna IL

Guthrie Walker L
Marlette HS
Marlette MI

Gutmann Donald J
Griffin HS
Springfield IL

Gutowski Karen A
Bishop Foley HS
Madison Heights MI

Gutstein Howard B
Interlochen Arts Acad
Kalamazoo MI

Gutt Raymond T
St Mary Of Ph HS
Chicago IL

Guy Jeffrey O
Grinnell HS
Grinnell IA

Guy Johanna L
Washington Catholic HS
Washington IN

Guyer Dawson D
North Miami HS
Denver IN

Guyer John F
Lake Central HS
Schererville IN

Guyerson Michael J
Thornton Frac South HS
Lansing IL

Guziak Joyce A
Chesaning Union HS
Oakley MI

Gwinn Daniel A
Waterford Mott HS
Pontiac MI

Gysin Kathy L
Peru HS
Peru IN

H

Haag Judy R
Orient Macksburg HS
Orient IA

Haak Lee
Moberly HS
Moberly MO

Haakenson Jane L
Clifford-Galesburg HS
Galesburg ND

Haapalainen Vicki L
Newberry HS
New Berry MI

Haas Cindy L
Markesan HS
Kingston WI

Haas Jeffrey L
Jefferson Sr HS
Jefferson WI

Haas Michael G
Sparta HS
Casnovia MI

Haase Charles E
Beaver City HS
Beaver City NE

Haberland Mary E
Middleton HS
Middletown WI

Haberman David J
Parkview HS
Janesville WI

Habermehl Cathy L
O Fallon Township HS
O Fallon IL

Hack Bonnie J
Mosinee Sr HS
Mosinee WI

Hackbart Dana R
Seward HS
Seward NE

Hackbarth Cheryl A
Merrill Sr HS
Merrill WI

Hackenburg Karen S
Marshall HS
Marshall MI

Hackett Cheryl L
Charleston HS
Charleston IL

Hackett David W
Willow Springs HS
Willow Springs MO

Hackett Joel A
Catholic Central HS
Detroit MI

Hacki Lynn M
Darlington HS
Darlington WI

Hackman Thomas J
Prospect HS
Arlington Hts IL

Hackwith Randeen L
Plattsmouth HS
Plattsmouth NE

Hadland Erik M
Eisenhower HS
Hopkins MN

Hadley Joyce A
Manlius HS
Sheffield IL

Hadley Stuart D
Audubon HS
Audubon IA

Hadlock Michael R
Custer HS
Pringle SD

Haduch Cynthia M
Kennedy/st Paul HS
Chicago IL

Haefner Jane M
St Pius HS
Imperial MO

Haeger Kimberly A
Rolling Meadows HS
Arlington Heights IL

Hafenstein Norma Lu
Wabaunsee HS
Alma KS

Haferbier Julie E
East Central HS
Green Island IA

Haff Cinda K
Frontier HS
Brookston IN

Haff William A
Milan HS
Watson MN

Haga Karen S
Covington Community HS
Covington IN

Hagan Michael J
Fruitport HS
Muskegon MI

Hage Sandra F
New Ulm Sr HS
Hanska MN

Hagedorn John J
Spencer Community HS
Spencer IA

Hageman Pamela J
Wahoo Public HS
Ithaca NE

Hageman Steve J
South Newton HS
Brook IN

Hagemeier Martha L
Lincoln HS
Elsberry MO

Hagen Gary A
Ingalls HS
Ingalls KS

Hagen Jeffrey W
Northwood Public HS
Aneta ND

Hagen Mark J
Kiester HS
Kiester MN

Hagen Pamela S
Clinton HS
Clinton IL

Hagenbush Elizabeth A
North Miami HS
Peru IN

Hager Michele R
Kalkaska HS
Kalkaska MI

Hagerman Ralph K
Bronaygh HS
Moundville MO

Hagerty James D
Fraser HS
Fraser MI

Haguewood James H
Ash Grove HS
Bois D Arc MO

Hahn Carol M
Lewis Central HS
Council Bluffs IA

Hahn Clifford W
Mt Pulaski HS
Elkhart IL

Hahn Cynthia M
E Richland HS
Olney IL

Hahn Jane E
North County HS
Desloge MO

Hahn Rhoda K
Millard Sr HS
Omaha NE

Hahn Virginia L
North County HS
Desloge MO

Haidler John W
Fairborn Baker HS
Ann Arbor MI

Haight Scott C
Aurelia Comm HS
Aurelia IA

Haile Karen L
Lewistown HS
Lewistown IL

Haines Elizabeth A
Arthur Hill HS
Saginaw MI

Hains Diana E
Rockridge HS
Taylor Ridge IL

Haire Diane R
Anna Jonesboro HS
Anna IL

Hairston Norman E
West Side HS
Gary IN

Haist Leesa M
Galesburg Augusta HS
Galesburg MI

Halberg Catherine L
High School
Princeton IL

Halberg Constance A
Harvard Community HS
Harvard IL

Halbersma Connie J
Pipestone HS
Pipestone MN

Halcin April M
Benilde HS
Hopkins MN

Hald Randy K
Watertown HS
Watertown SD

Halderman Brent L
Northern Valley HS
Long Island KS

Hale Floyd B
Mitchell HS
Mitchell NE

Hale Justina M
Woodstock HS
Woodstock IL

Hale Lloyd E
Spokane R 7 HS
Ozark MO

Hale Rosemarie A
Burrton HS
Burrton KS

Hale Shelley E
East HS
Kansas City MO

Hales Kandi K
Penney HS
Hamilton MO

Hales Norma N
Arthur Hill HS
Saginaw MI

Haley Anne L
Schulte HS
Terre Haute IN

Haley James F
Lincoln Way HS
Manhattan IL

Haley Patricia M
Ritenour HS
St Ann MO

Halfacre Vickie L
Bluford HS
Kell IL

Hall Bruce W
Thornridge HS
Dolton IL

Hall Cheryl L
Lincoln East HS
Lincoln NE

Hall Cynthia L
Dixon HS
Dixon IL

Hall Debra A
University HS
Cape Girardeau MO

Hall Debra K
Spring Valley HS
Spring Valley MN

Hall Douglas R
Lawrence Central HS
Indianapolis IN

Hall Eldon C
Oxford HS
Oxford KS

Hall Holly G
Huron HS
Ann Arbor MI

Hall Jacqueline I
Merrill HS
Merrill MI

Hall James W
Holden HS
Holden MO

Hall Karen S
Galatia HS
Galatia IL

Hall Kimberly A
Granite City HS
Granite City IL

Hall Lori A
Stet HS
Richmond MO

Hall Lori J
Roland Story HS
Roland IA

Hall Lori L
Central Community HS
Low Moor IA

Hall Mary B
Norris City Omaha HS
Norris City IL

Hall Nanette L
Limestone Community HS
Hanna City IL

Hall Phillip L
Central HS
Bristol WI

Hall Rex A
Wellington Sr HS
Wellington KS

Hall William E
Troy HS
Troy MI

Halla Dennis J
Clinton HS
Clinton WI

Haller Robert W
Notre Dame HS
Morton Grove IL

Hallett Ann E
Marinette Sr HS
Marinette WI

Hallgren Janet D
Medford Senior HS
Medford WI

Hallman Bruce A
Waverly Shell Rock HS
Waverly IA

Hallo Elizabeth R
Cass Technical HS
Detroit MI

Halloran Edward H
Brodhead HS
Brodhead WI

Halloran Sheila E
New Prague HS
Belle Plaine MN

Halpin Patrick R
Fenwick HS
Oak Park IL

Halt Jane A
Central HS
Worthington IN

Haluzak Roger M
Wilton Public HS
Wilton ND

Halverson Debra L
Sycamore HS
Sycamore IL

Halverson Jill M
Springfield HS
Springfield IL

Halverson Katherine B
Lansing HS
Lansing KS

Halverson Mark A
Eagle Grove HS
Eagle Grove IA

Halvorson Daryl D
Northwestern
Mellette SD

Halvorson Martin N
Wilton HS
Regan ND

Halvorson Tracey D
M F L Comm HS
Monona IA

Ham Floyd R
F L Schlagle HS
Kansas City KS

Hamann John M
Campbell Tintah HS
Tintah MN

Hamann Melissa L
Mendota Township HS
Mendota IL

Hambek Steven L
Burke Public HS
Herrick SD

Hamblen Elaine Y
Lanesville HS
Lanesville IN

Hamblin Pamela K
Litchfield HS
Litchfield IL

Hambly Jane E
Industry HS
Macomb IL

Hambrick Patricia A
Lindblom Tech
Chicago IL

Hamel Elizabeth E
Carlinville HS
Carlinville IL

Hamel Larry R
Concordia HS
Concordia KS

Hamelink Mark C
Lincoln Sr HS
Wis Rapids WI

Hamer Dawn A
Mt Clemens HS
Mt Clemens MI

Hamers Brian O
Palermo HS
Palermo ND

Hamilton Bina J
Princeton HS
Princeton MO

Hamilton Connie L
Pine River Jr Sr HS
Luther MI

Hamilton Debra A
Morton HS
Morton IL

Hamilton Debra K
Danville HS
Danville IL

Hamilton George R
Franklin HS
Franklin IL

Hamilton Jeana R
Mark Twain HS
New London MO

Hamilton Karen L
Decatur Jr Sr HS
Stevens Point WI

Hamilton Luann M
Resurrection HS
Chicago IL

Hamilton Minnetta L
Gilman HS
Lafayette IN

Hamilton Penny L
Lafayette County C 1 HS
Higginsville MO

Hamilton Roger D
Fenton HS
Fenton MI

Hamlin Michelle L
Plymouth Salem HS
Plymouth MI

Hamm Cecilia S
South Sioux HS
South Sioux NE

Hamm Douglas C
Kingsley Pierson HS
Kingsley IA

Hamm John E
Wisconsin Dells HS
Wisconsin Dells WI

Hamm Thomas D
W P Chrysler Memorial HS
New Castle IN

Hammack Barbara J
Morrill HS
Morrill NE

Hammel Karen A
Champaign Central HS
Champaign IL

Hammer Jamie R
Elgin HS
Elgin IL

Hammer Julie A
Stockton HS
Stockton IL

Hammer Mary T
St Mary Academy
Monroe MI

Hammerle Cynthia M
Hart HS
Hart MI

Hammerschmidt Dale L
Satanta HS
Satanta KS

Hammerstrom Leroy P
Omaha Benson HS
Omaha NE

Hammond Debra J
Clay Center Public HS
Clay Center NE

Hammond Delores L
Stanton County HS
Johnson KS

Hammond Fred W
Westfield HS
Westfield IL

Hammond Kathleen A
Williamston HS
Williamston MI

Hammond Noral W
Springs Valley HS
West Baden IN

Hammond Shari D
Fremont Sr HS
Fremont NE

Hammond Susan K
Tremont HS
Tremont IL

Hammonds Thomas L
Beaumont HS
St Louis MO

Hammons Betty J
Jennings County HS
Holton IN

Hamood John A
Fordson HS
Dearborn MI

Hampel Scott E
Kapaun Mt Carmel HS
Wichita KS

Hampton Debra K
Gering HS
Gering NE

Hampton Jerry L
Mt Vernon Township HS
Mount Vernon IL

Hampton Kevin L
Eastern HS
Salem IN

Hampton Mark J
Warsaw Community HS
Warsaw IN

Hampton Melanie J
Colchester HS
Colchester IL

Hampton Theresa A
Edison HS
East Gary IN

Hampton Tina M
Christopher Comm HS
Christopher IL

Hamre Timothy L
Kelly Walsh HS
Rapid City SD

Hams Pierre F
Divine Heart Seminary HS
Kansas City MO

Han Dennis P
Ishpeming HS
Ishpeming MI

Han Kwang K
Ypsilanti HS
Ypsilanti MI

Hanacik Linda J
Waukesha North HS
Waukesha WI

Hancock Jeanne M
Collinsville HS
Edwardsville IL

Hancock Peggy A
Oak Park HS
Gladstone MO

Handly Steven E
Perry Meridian HS
Indianapolis IN

Handrich Lynn R
Fairview HS
Fairview MI

Handy Karen S
Waverly HS
Waverly IL

Handzik Leslie A
Maria HS
Chicago IL

Haneke Shirley A
Polo HS
Orient SD

Hanel Judith A
Howells HS
Howells NE

Haney Jerri L
North Vigo HS
Terre Haute IN

Haney Kenneth C
Seymour HS
Seymour MO

Haney Stuart A
Topeka West HS
Topeka KS

Hanford Kathryn J
J D Darnall HS
Geneseo IL

Hanisko Carolyn M
St Stephen HS
Saginaw MI

Hankins Andrea L
Waverly HS
Waverly IL

Hankins David J
Webb HS
Reedsburg WI

Hankins Ronald W
Twin Rivers HS
Bode IA

Hanley John E
Cathedral HS
Indianapolis IN

Hanlon Pamela J
Harmony HS
Harmony MN

Hanna Cynthia K
Liberal HS
Liberal KS

Hanna James D
Monroe HS
Monroe WI

Hanna Lisa J
Shenandoah HS
Middletown IN

Hanna Michael D
Wichita North HS
Wichita KS

Hanna Myron A
Kinmundy Alma HS
Kinmundy IL

Hanna Pam
Alexis HS
Alexis IL

Hanna Sheryl J
Burke HS
Omaha NE

Hannah Victoria L
Lincoln HS
Vincennes IN

Hanneman Russell E
Madison HS
Madison SD

Hansa Kathleen J
Proviso West HS
Westchester IL

Hansel Pamela I
Ridgeway R V HS
Ridgeway MO

Hansen Beth E
Albert Lea Sr HS
Albert Lea MN

Hansen Catherine M
Brookwood HS
Norwalk WI

Hansen David W
Maine Township North HS
Des Plaines IL

Hansen Diane M
Sterling Public HS
Sterling NE

Hansen Donald N
Rockwell Swaledale HS
Rockwell IA

Hansen Ellen J
West HS
Madison WI

Hansen Faye A
Storden Jeffers HS
Jeffers MN

Hansen Glee A
Elk Grove HS
Elk Grove Village IL

Hansen James J
Milwaukee Lutheran HS
Milwaukee WI

Hansen Jay D
Walnut Community HS
Walnut IA

Hansen Jeanne M
Boone HS
Boone IA

Hansen Lyla K
Gettysburg HS
Gettysburg SD

Hansen Nicholas G
Sutton HS
Edgar NE

Hansen Norma L
Medicine Valley HS
Curtis NE

Hansen Sharon K
Lewis Central HS
Council Bluffs IA

Hansen Sheryl A
North Bend Central HS
Ames NE

Hansen Sybel M
Litchfield Sr HS
Litchfield MN

Hansford Scott J
Premontre HS
Green Bay WI

Hanskala Sandra J
Orr HS
Orr MN

Hansmire Julie A
Fairbury HS
Fairbury NE

Hanson Barbara E
Belmond Comm HS
Belmond IA

Hanson Carol M
Superior Sr HS
Superior WI

Hanson Carolyn A
Shawnee Mission Nw HS
Lenexa KS

Hanson Cynthia E
Mormon Trail HS
Humeston IA

Hanson David M
North HS
Eau Claire WI

Hanson Denise I
Moline Sr HS
Moline IL

Hanson Edward D
North Liberty HS
North Liberty IN

Hanson Henry A
Sparta HS
Sparta WI

Hanson Keith G
Magic City Campus HS
Minot ND

Hanson Lorri K
Reeder Public HS
Reeder ND

Hanson Lualan J
Minot Sr HS
Minot ND

Hanson Marsha L
Belvidere HS
Belvidere IL

Hanson Martha K
Brandon Valley HS
Valley Springs SD

Hanson Paul K
Hope Public HS
Hope ND

Hanson Perry W
Neodesha HS
Neodesha KS

Hanson Robert D
Edw Tilden HS
Chicago IL

Hanson Stephen M
Lockport Central HS
Lockport IL

Hanson Steven W
Glidden Ralston Comm HS
Glidden IA

Hanson Timothy S
Henry Sibley HS
W St Paul MN

Hanson Wyanita A
Rushford HS
Rushford MN

Hanus Kathleen M
South HS
Omaha NE

Happ Eunice H
Mendota Twp HS
Mendota IL

Happel Dennis H
Starmont HS
Strawberry Pt IA

Harangody David J
Whiting HS
Whiting IN

Harber Kim L
Toluca HS
Toluca IL

Harber Renay A
Toluca HS
Toluca IL

Harbers Cheryl K
Roanoke Benson HS
Benson IL

Harbin Kathleen M
L C Mohr HS
South Haven MI

Harbin Terri L
South Haven HS
South Haven MI

Harbison Resa L
Robinson HS
Robinson IL

Harcourt Tracy J
Oshkosh North HS
Oshkosh WI

Hardaway Michelle Y
Cass Tech HS
Detroit MI

Hardee Jayne E
Bedford HS
Gravity IA

Harden Jennifer L
Loup County Public HS
Almeria NE

Harden Vicky L
Marseilles HS
Marseilles IL

Harder John W
Dekalb HS
Dekalb IL

Harder Patricia J
Centura HS
Cairo NE

Hardesty Sheila L
Clifton HS
Clifton KS

Hardin Carl R
Cass Technical HS
Detroit MI

Hardin Deborah L
Leavenworth HS
Milltown IN

Hardin Mary L
N Clay Community HS
Louisville IL

Harding Cindy J
Onarga HS
Onarga IL

Hardman Elaine E
Brazil HS
Brazil IN

Hardman Mary E
Brazil HS
Brazil IN

Hardwick Roger D
Fox HS
Imperial MO

Hardy Ann L
West Chicago Comm HS
West Chicago IL

Hardy Mary M
Kalkaska HS
Kalkaska MI

Hardy Rachelle
Lindblom Technical HS
Chicago IL

Hardy Tad N
Scott Comm HS
Scott City KS

Hare Gwen D
Spring Valley HS
Spring Valley MN

Hare Wilbert L
Washington Comm HS
Washington IL

Harger Kendall W
Belding HS
Orleans MI

Harker Ann D
Jasper HS
Jasper IN

Harkins Tracey L
Willowbrook HS
Lombard IL

Harkless Thomas N
Pontiac Central HS
Pontiac MI

Harkness Kevin M
Fenton HS
Bensenville IL

Harlamert David J
High School
Boggstown IN

Harlamert Edward A
Park Tudor HS
Boggstown IN

Harlan Lamon D
Holy Trinity HS
Chicago IL

Harland Elaine K
Perry Community HS
Perry IA

Harlass Adrian E
Shelbyville HS
Shelbyville IL

Harley Bruce D
Grand Blanc HS
Grand Blanc MI

Harling Christopher
Elgin HS
Wayne IL

Harmacek Susan M
Gregory Public HS
Dallas SD

Harman Kenneth L
Northeastern HS
Richmond IN

Harmeier Ann L
Lincoln HS
Cambridge City IN

Harmison Darcy W
Rova Sr HS
Oneida IL

Harmon Carl R
Hugoton HS
Hugoton KS

Harmon Darlene C
Pardeeville HS
Pardeeville WI

Harmon David A
Limestone Comm HS
Bartonville IL

Harmon Glenda J
Frank Cody HS
Detroit MI

Harmon James D
Harrisonville HS
Latour MO

Harmon Pamela M
Southern Boone HS
Ashland MO

Harmon Sue E
Turner HS
Kansas City KS

Harmon Teressa J
Rolla HS
Rolla MO

Harmon William G
Lyons HS
Lyons KS

Harmoney Marilyn S
Amherst HS
Amherst NE

Harms Janice L
Hobart HS
Hobart IN

Harmsen Ronald A
Hartsburg Emden HS
Emden IL

Harner David R
Dubois HS
French Lick IN

Harness Carl S
Hales Franciscan HS
Chicago IL

Harness Debra A
Webster Groves HS
Webster Groves MO

Harness Donita
Oregon Davis HS
Hamlet IN

Harney Patrick J
St Ignatius Cp HS
Chicago IL

Haroff Woodrow H
Harper Creek Sr HS
Battle Creek MI

Harper Arlene M
Yankton Senior HS
Yankton SD

Harper Christopher L
Newton HS
Yale IL

Harper Debra S
Morristown HS
Fountaintown IN

Harper Linda D
Colo Comm HS
Colo IA

Harper Patricia A
Muskegon Sr HS
Muskegon MI

Harpold Laura K
Rosedale HS
Rosedale IN

Harpster David L
East Grand Forks Sr HS
E Grand Forks MN

Harral Kaia L
Fairgrove HS
Fairgrove MO

Harral Loretta M
South Sioux City HS
Dakota City NE

Harrel Jon M
Pratt HS
Pratt KS

Harrell Anthony D
East Richland HS
Olney IL

Harrell Wendell K
Farmington East HS
Hanna City IL

Harrelson Robert E
Circle HS
Towanda KS

Harrer James L
Marian Central HS
Mc Henry IL

Harris Carmelita
Lew Wallace HS
Gary IN

Harris Cheryl R
Central Ymca HS
Chicago IL

Harris Cynthia
Waterford Mott HS
Drayton Plains MI

Harris Doris
Naylor HS
Nyalor MO

Harris Frances M
Sumner HS
St Louis MO

Harris Idajane
Homer Comm HS
Homer NE

Harris Jamie K
Herrin HS
Herrin IL

Harris Jean M
Stoughton Sr HS
Stoughton WI

Harris Jodi L
Cassville HS
Cassville WI

Harris Judith L
Williamsville HS
Williamsville IL

Harris Julie A
Anita HS
Anita IA

Harris Karen K
Kirksville Sr HS
Kirksville MO

Harris Kenneth D
Lillis HS
Kansas City MO

Harris Linda L
Galesburg Senior HS
Galesburg IL

Harris Lois M
Oak Park HS
Kansas City MO

Harris Mary M
Anchor Bay HS
New Baltimore MI

Harris Michael V
Mendel HS
Chicago IL

Harris Rebecca A
Crete Public HS
Hallam NE

Harris Richard E
Hermantown HS
Duluth MN

Harris Rita J
Galatia HS
Galatia IL

Harris Robin E
Red Cloud HS
Red Cloud NE

Harris Rochelle L
Lane Tech HS
Chicago IL

Harris Scott D
Rossville Alvin HS
Rossville IL

Harrison Blaine W
East Richland HS
Olney IL

Harrison D Arcy A
Mercy HS
University City MO

Harrison Gloria J
Calumet HS
Chicago IL

Harrison Karen L
Paris R 2 HS
Holliday MO

Harrison Kathy S
North Decatur HS
Milroy IN

Harrison Mary B
Fountain Central HS
Kingman IN

Harrison Montgomery A
Memorial HS
Joplin MO

Harrison Tresa A
Zeeland HS
Zeeland MI

Harrold Karen S
Hagerstown Jr Sr HS
Hagerstown IN

Harry Jeanine R
Clinton Comm HS
Clinton IL

Harshbarger Paula H
Centralia HS
Centralia MO

Harshman Ronda D
Malcolm HS
Malcolm NE

Harsin Sharon K
Twin Cedars HS
Tracy IA

Harstad Barbara J
Southeast HS
Kansas City MO

Hart Douglas E
Richmond HS
Richmond IN

Hart Garry W
Cuba HS
Cuba IL

Hart Kerry M
East Peoria Comm HS
E Peoria IL

Hart Rick D
Clarke Comm HS
Osceola IA

Hart Roxann E
North Bend Central HS
Ames NE

Hart Steve W
Slinger HS
Allenton WI

Hartenberger Brenda K
Chester HS
Chester IL

Harter Marcia L
Winner Sr HS
Winner SD

Harter Noel P
Hagerstown Jr Sr HS
Hagerstown IN

Harter Patti R
West Harrison HS
Mondamin IA

Hartford Janet L
F L Schlagle HS
Kansas City KS

Hartgers Debbie J
Pella Comm HS
Pella IA

Harthan Patricia L
Casey Sr Jr HS
Casey IL

Harting Randall C
Laporte City HS
Laporte City IA

Hartley Charles
Ernest W Seaholm HS
Troy MI

Hartley Karen L
Oak Park HS
Gladstone MO

Hartley Kimberly E
Mount Academy
Atchison KS

Hartman Beverly A
Milbank HS
Milbank SD

Hartman Laurie L
Sheldon HS
Sheldon IL

Hartman Marlin J
Mazon Verona Kinsman HS
Mazon IL

Hartnett John A
Shelbyville HS
Shelbyville IN

Hartnett Timothy P
Sidney Comm HS
Percival IA

Hartsburg Darlene L
Lebanon HS
Trenton IL

Hartwig David J
Johnson Creek HS
Johnson Creek WI

Hartwig Randy A
Galena HS
Galena IL

Hartwig Ruth A
Roseville HS
Roseville MI

Hartz Brenton M
Mapleton HS
Mapleton ND

Hartzler Cheryl A
Yates Center HS
Yates Center KS

Harvey David A
Millard Senior HS
Omaha NE

Harvey Hal D
Greenwood HS
Springfield MO

Harvey Jack L
Virden Comm HS
Virden IL

Harvey Janet L
Greenwood HS
Springfield MO

Harvey Richard R
Coloma HS
Coloma MI

Harvey Susan M
East HS
Waterloo IA

Harwood Brian K
Lake Central HS
Dyer IN

Harwood Charles R
Allegan HS
Allegan MI

Harwood Gregg S
Pawnee HS
Pawnee IL

Hash Daniel E
Olympia HS
Hopedale IL

Haskett Sally D
Eastern Heights HS
Naponee NE

Haskins Forrest P
Quincy HS
Quincy IL

Hasledalen Lee A
St Louis Park HS
St Louis Park MN

Hasler Michael G
Northwestern HS
Kokomo IN

Haslinger Richard P
Pontiac Catholic Central HS
Pontiac MI

Hass Denise L
La Salle Peru HS
La Salle IL

Hassebrook Dean R
Lakeview HS
Platte Center NE

Hassel Kathi J
South Sioux City HS
Dakota City NE

Hassemer Kathryn M
Bloomer Sr HS
Bloomer WI

Hassien Barbara L
Van Far HS
Vandalia MO

Hassing Barbara J
Blue Earth HS
Blue Earth MN

Hassing Cheryl G
Mankato East HS
Mankato MN

Hassing Jeffrey C
Kennedy Sr HS
Bloomington MN

Hastings Jeanette S
Pine River HS
Luther MI

Hatcher April J
Goodland HS
Goodland KS

Hatfield Jane R
Newton Senior HS
Newton IA

Hatfield Jay P
Fairbury HS
Fairbury NE

Hathcock Bryce L
West Plains HS
West Plains MO

Hatley Sherry M
Fenton HS
Fenton MI

Hatling Colleen A
Comfrey HS
Comfrey MN

Hatteberg Gregory A
Newark Comm HS
Newark IL

Hauge Stacy D
Oregon Sr HS
Madison WI

Haugen Glenn A
Verona Public HS
Verona ND

Haugen Katherine M
Williston HS
Williston ND

Haugen Martha B
Strandquist HS
Strandquist MN

Haugen Rita M
Altoona HS
Altoona WI

Haugen Timothy A
Sturgeon Bay HS
Sturgeon Bay WI

Haugen Vance J
Oklee Public HS
Oklee MN

Haugh Terri L
Phillipsburg HS
Phillipsburg KS

Haugrud Kevin J
Pelican Rapids HS
Pelican Rapids MN

Hauk Paul L
Coranna HS
Corunna MI

Haunsperger Blair A
Newton Sr HS
Kellogg IA

Haupt Mary J
La Salle Peru HS
Peru IL

Hauser Laureen A
St Marys HS
Sleepy Eye MN

Hausheer Jean R
Truman HS
Independence MO

Hausken Monta A
Central HS
Glenwood MN

Havalda Renee M
Corunna HS
Owosso MI

Havel Debra A
Milligan Public HS
Milligan NE

Havel George E
Riverside Brookfield HS
Brookfield IL

Havelhorst Mary E
Jenison HS
Jenison MI

Haven Renee M
Swan Valley HS
Saginaw MI

Havens Roberta J
Yale HS
Yale MI

Haverkamp Tim J
Grundy Center Community HS
Holland IA

Havice Ronald P
Niantic Harristown HS
Decatur IL

Havlik Joseph A
Campion Jesuit HS
La Crosse WI

Havlin Brenda K
North Greene HS
Roodhouse IL

Hawes Gary R
Coon Rapids Sr HS
Coon Rapids MN

Hawken James M
School Of The Osage HS
Lane Ozark MO

Hawkes James E
Potosi Sr HS
Cadet MO

Hawkins Brenda G
Fairfax R Iii HS
Skidmore MO

Hawkins Carole L
Walker R 4 HS
Walker MO

Hawkins Douglas E
Rosedale HS
Carbon IN

Hawkins Kelly J
Vienna HS
Creal Springs IL

Hawkins Linda M
Collinsville HS
Collinsville IL

Hawkins Michelle V
Lincoln Sr HS
E St Louis IL

Hawkins Pamela R
Kenwood HS
Chicago IL

Hawkins Peggy A
Glenwood Comm HS
Glenwood IA

Hawkins Phyllis A
Riverside Brookfield HS
La Grange Park IL

Hawkins Regina L
Lafayette HS
St Joseph MO

Hawkins Susan C
Willow Run HS
Upsilanti MI

Hawks Bradley E
Sidney HS
Sidney NE

Hawks Kelly M
Ft Zumwalt HS
St Peters MO

Hawn Terrie A
Hannibal HS
Hannibal MO

Hawrysh Stephen P
Fridley HS
Burnsville MN

Haws Matthew J
Dela Salle HS
Minneapolis MN

Hay Patricia L
Granite City South HS
Granite City IL

Hay Richard C
William Horlick HS
Racine WI

Hay Scott D
Milbank HS
Big Stone City SD

Hayashi John E
Maplewood Richmond Hts HS
Maplewood MO

Hayden Andrea R
Emil G Hirsch HS
Chicago IL

Hayden Karen M
Henry Senachwine HS
Putnam IL

Hayden Kevin P
Wentzville HS
Lake St Louis MO

Hayenga Dawn M
Rochelle Twp HS
Kings IL

Hayes Angela R
Enierson HS
Gary IN

Hayes Mark A
Palco HS
Palco KS

Hayes Michael J
Benton Harbor HS
Benton Harbor MI

Hayes Michael J
Waldron HS
Shelbyville IN

Hayes Roger A
Yates City HS
Yates City IL

Hayes Stephen K
Draper HS
Draper SD

Hayes Tonya R
Concordia Lutheran HS
Ft Wayne IN

Haynes Cynthia K
Yorkville HS
Yorkville IL

Haynes Dorothy A
Kewanee HS
Kewanee IL

Haynes Julianne
Highland HS
Highland IN

Haynes Ricky D
Central HS
St Joseph MO

Haynie Gregory D
Thomas Jefferson HS
Rockford IL

Hays Charles R
Braymer HS
Braymer MO

Hays Cynthia S
North County HS
Desloge MO

Hays Dennis G
Monroe City R 1 HS
Monroe City MO

Hays Steven W
Ritenour HS
Overland MO

Hayward Sandra M
Mt Pleasant HS
Mt Pleasant MI

Hayworth Linda D
Anthon Oto Comm HS
Anthon IA

Hazelett Jeannine M
Hartford HS
Hartford MI

Hazelwood Kanda S
Brainerd Sr HS
Brainerd MN

Hazlett Joyce A
Norton Comm HS
Norton KS

Head Mary K
Edwardsville Sr HS
Edwardsville IL

Head Melissa G
Gaylord HS
Gaylord MI

Heady Karen L
Nauvoo Colusa HS
Nauvoo IL

Heady Kathy D
Oakville Senior HS
St Louis MO

Healey David A
Superior Public HS
Hardy NE

Healy Daniel P
Thomas More HS
Milwaukee WI

Heard Jonathan S
St Ignatius HS
Chicago IL

Hearn Jacquelyn K
Paris HS
Paris IL

Hearne Richard A
S Siux City HS
S Sioux City NE

Heath Cheryl L
New Palestine HS
New Palestine IN

Heath Chuck V
Lafollette HS
Madison WI

Heath Debbie A
Kimball HS
Kimball SD

Heaverlo Linda J
Thomas Jefferson HS
Council Bluffs IA

Heavin Jeffrey K
Seymour HS
Seymour IN

Heazlit Cindy K
Clarkston Senior HS
Clarkston MI

Hebel Laurie A
La Salle Peru HS
Peru IL

Hecht Catherine A
Jackson HS
Altenburg MO

Hecht Marilyn E
Waseca HS
Waseca MN

Hechtner Arlan R
Sac Community HS
Sac City IA

Heck Bryan W
Senior HS
Shelbyville IN

Heck Catherine A
Ypsilanti HS
Ypsilanti MI

Heck Jeffrey L
Waltonville HS
Bonnie IL

Heckaman Kathy D
Plymouth HS
Plymouth IN

Heckman Janet S
Northwest HS
Cedar Hill MO

Hector Mary A
Cambria Friesland HS
Friesland WI

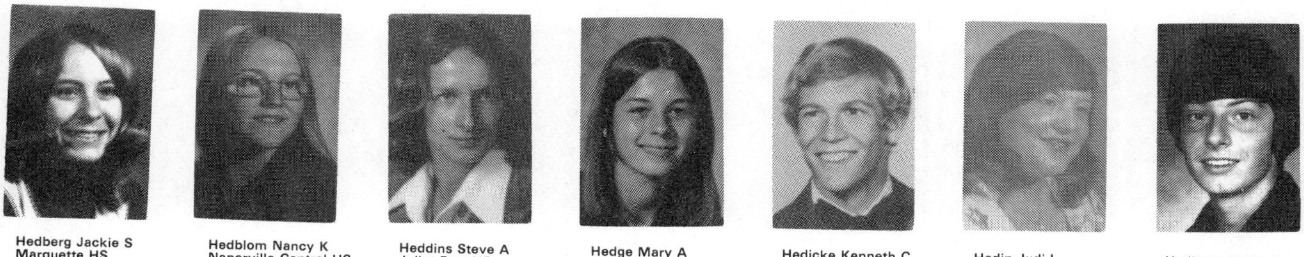

Hedberg Jackie S
Marquette HS
Marquette KS

Hedblom Nancy K
Naperville Central HS
Naperville IL

Heddins Steve A
Joliet East HS
Elwood IL

Hedge Mary A
East Prairie HS
East Prairie MO

Hedicke Kenneth C
St Charles HS
St Charles MO

Hedin Judi L
Willowbrook HS
Lombard IL

Hedinger Keith G
Jasper HS
Jasper IN

Hedley Ronald K
Salem Sr HS
Salem MO

Hedlund Debra L
St Cecilia HS
Hastings NE

Hedman Calvin D
Scranton Public HS
Scranton ND

Hedman Glenn E
Gordon Technical HS
Chicago IL

Hedrick Helen K
Hesston HS
Newton KS

Heeg Marie D
Perry HS
Perry MI

Heehn Kenneth C
Morgan Park HS
Duluth MN

Heeke Verlyn C
Jasper HS
Jasper IN

Heepke Beth E
Edwardsville HS
Edwardsville IL

Heer Ann M
Doland HS
Doland SD

Heeren Dennis R
West Sioux Comm HS
Hawarden IA

Heffelmire Daniel L
Portland HS
Bryant IN

Heffernan Steven T
Doland HS
Doland SD

Hefty Glenda K
Lu Verne Comm HS
Lu Verne IA

Hegedus Maria B
George Rogers Clark HS
Whiting IN

Hegenbarth Mary A
West Bloomfield HS
Orchard Lake MI

Hegg Kathleen L
Covington Comm HS
Covington IN

Hegge Dawn R
Oklee Public HS
Goodridge MN

Heiberger Cheryl M
Montrose HS
Montrose SD

Heiden Dana C
Greenfield Central HS
Greenfield IN

Heiden David C
Marshalltown HS
Marshalltown IA

Heidenreich Diana C
Harlem HS
Loves Park IL

Heider Barbara A
Humboldt Sr HS
Humboldt IA

Heier Linda K
Wheatland HS
Park KS

Heikens Janet C
Wellsburg HS
Wellsburg IA

Heilig Scott A
Chicago Lakes Sr HS
Lindstrom MN

Heimann Michael H
Millard Sr HS
Omaha NE

Heimberger Julie A
Earlham Community HS
Dexter IA

Heimerman Kenneth J
Oconto Sr HS
Oconto WI

Hein David A
Inswich HS
Ipswich SD

Heinemann James K
Parkway West Sr HS
Ballwin MO

Heinen John J
Marquette HS
Wauwatosa WI

Heinen Michelle R
Concordia HS
Concordia KS

Heinrichs Kristinn I
Watertown Senior HS
Watertown SD

Heins Brenda K
Wichita North HS
Wichita KS

Heintzman Terri J
Rapid City Central HS
Rapid City SD

Heinz Jenny R
High School
Vincennes IN

Heise Nancy A
Kewanee HS
Kewanee IL

Heiser Kathleen J
Lowell HS
Lowell IN

Heiser Sharon A
O Neill Public HS
Oneill NE

Heiter Michael L
Boone Valley HS
Goldfield IA

Heitman Carol J
Osceola HS
Osceola WI

Heitzman Laura J
J D Darnall HS
Geneseo IL

Hejlik Cynthia L
Garner Hayfield HS
Garner IA

Hejna William J
Riverside Brookfield HS
Riverside IL

Hekking Carol J
Morton West HS
Berwyn IL

Helberg Jeffrey H
Harlem HS
Loves Park IL

Held Richard J
Hartford Union HS
Colgate WI

Helder Norma J
Zeeland HS
Holland MI

Helenbolt Sherry R
Stuart HS
Stuart NE

Helfer Cheryl D
Richwoods HS
Peoria IL

Helis Karen S
Lyons Township HS
Western Springs IL

Helland Carolyn S
Park Center Senior HS
Brooklyn Park MN

Hellendrung Darlene J
Prairie Farm HS
Ridgeland WI

Heller Stan E
Stockton HS
Stockton IL

Hellman Brent
Hartsburg Emden HS
Emden IL

Hellman Michael A
Jackson HS
Jackson MI

Hellman Sharon K
Hancock Central HS
Hancock MI

Hellwig Donald M
Custer HS
Milwaukee WI

Helm Douglas W
Drayton Public HS
Drayton ND

Helma Kathryn T
Riverdale HS
Blue Springs MO

Helmick Robert N
Roosevelt HS
Des Moines IA

Helmick Wilbert C
Farmington HS
Hanna City IL

Helmig Steve R
Lone Jack C 6 HS
Lone Jack MO

Helming Mark T
Tomah Sr HS
Tomah WI

Helmink Sharon K
Newton Community HS
Montrose IL

Helms Jace R
South Decatur HS
Westport IN

Helmuth Robin A
Bethany Christian HS
Middlebury IN

Helsing Lori J
Randolph Public HS
Randolph NE

Helstedt Marilee P
Radcliffe Comm HS
Radcliffe IA

Helton Brent M
Bishop Dwenger HS
Ft Wayne IN

Heltsley Paula J
Charlestown HS
Charlestown IN

Helvaty Kathleen A
Our Lady Of Grace Academy
Indianapolis IN

Hemerson Cartha L
Sheldon Community HS
Sheldon IA

Hemingway Drexel
Lindblom Technical HS
Chicago IL

Hemming Carla V
Pontiac Catholic HS
Pontiac MI

Hemming Patti M
Ewen Trout Creek HS
Bruce Crossing MI

Hemmingsen Barbara L
Marion HS
Marion IA

Hemmingson Carla K
Roseau HS
Warroad MN

Hempstead Charles A
Griffin HS
Springfield IL

Henchen Cheryl A
Neillsville HS
Neillsville WI

Hendershott Paul W
Riverton HS
Baxter Springs KS

Henderson Bill A
Scottsbluff Sr HS
Scottsbluff NE

Henderson Gregory C
Sedan HS
Niotaze KS

Henderson James M
Elgin HS
Streamwood IL

Henderson Robert K
Glenbard So HS
Glen Ellyn IL

Henderson Therena L
Flint Southwestern HS
Flint MI

Henderson Vicki C
Kokomo HS
Kokomo IN

Hendrick Teresa F
Raymore Peculiar HS
Peculiar MO

Hendricker Rebecca J
Beardstown HS
Arenzville IL

Hendricks Avila D
Immaculata HS
Detroit MI

Hendricks Deborah F
West Side Sr HS
Gary IN

Hendricks Robyn E
Ofallon Township HS
Ofallon IL

Hendrickson Bruce A
Belle Fourche HS
Belle Fourche SD

Hendrickson David E
Rochester HS
Rochester IL

Hendrickson Diann M
Richland #44 HS
Colfax ND

Hendrickson Joni L
Richland 44 HS
Christine ND

Hendrickson Lyle W
Argyle HS
Argyle WI

Hendrickson Marcia L
Danville HS
Danville IL

Hendrickson Nan M
Cornell HS
Cornell WI

Hendrickson Robert H
Armstrong HS
Plymouth MN

Hendrix Leon
Lindblom Tech HS
Chicago IL

Hendrix Sandra E
North Platte HS
Dearborn MO

Hendron Sally R
Bishop Mc Namara HS
Kankakee IL

Hengy Susan M 8
Lakers HS
Pigeon MI

Heninger Ralph W
Bettendorf HS
Bettendorf IA

Henke Brenda J
Keypunch W/o
Markesan WI

Henke Jamie P
Edgewood HS
Ellettsville IN

Henke Richard L
Menasha HS
Menasha WI

Henley Betty L
Richland HS
Richland MO

Henley Philip A
Turkey Run HS
Marshall IN

Henneberry Scott M
Central Catholic HS
Bloomington IL

Hennessy Delwyn J
Minot HS
Minot ND

Hennessy Jill N
Mother Mc Auley HS
Oak Lawn IL

Henning Christine M
Plattsmouth HS
Plattsmouth NE

Henning Mary E
Grinnell Newburg HS
Grinnell IA

Henningfield Debra A
Union Grove HS
Sturtevant WI

Henrikson Angela C
Academy Of Our Lady
Peoria IL

Henry Cheryl J
Ida Public HS
Ida MI

Henry David M
Southern Reynolds R2 HS
Ellington MO

Henry John D
Big Rapids HS
Big Rapids MI

Henry John M
James B Conant HS
Hoffman Estates IL

Henry Karen L
Marshall HS
Marshall MN

Henry Leslie J
South Vigo HS
Terre Haute IN

Henry Michael R
Battle Creek Central HS
Battle Creek MI

Henry Scott D
Larimore HS
Northwood ND

Henry Sherry L
Ellington HS
Ellington MO

Henry William R
Badger HS
Lake Geneva WI

Henschke Denise C
Buffalo Lake Public HS
Hector MN

Hensel Geannie M
Carmel HS
Carmel IN

Hensel Karen A
George S Parker Sr HS
Janesville WI

Hensley Randy D
Charlestown HS
Charlestown IN

Henson Donald F
Fairfield Comm HS
Fairfield IL

Henson James B
Norris City Omaha HS
Norris City IL

Henson Kim M
Galesburg Augusta HS
Galesburg MI

Hentschell Mark S
Chaminade HS
Chesterfield MO

Henze Charles R
West Marshall HS
State Center IA

Hepner Blake A
Ottawa HS
Ottawa IL

Hepola Pamela S
Lutheran West HS
Detroit MI

Hepp Sheryl A
Trico HS
Cutler IL

Heppner Glen G
Batesville HS
Oldenburg IN

Herauf William A
Dickinson HS
Dickinson ND

Herbert Beverly A
Verdigre Public HS
Winnetoon NE

Herbert Janine M
Glenwood HS
Glenarm IL

Herbert Randy J
Greensburg HS
Greensburg IN

Herbst Jeannie M
Washington Comm HS
Washington IL

Herget Lisa L
Toulon Lafayette HS
Toulon IL

Herhager Alice M
St Mary Academy
New Boston MI

Herl Faye T
Academy Of Mt St
Scholastica
Quinter KS

Herman Diane B
Laker HS
Elkton MI

Herman Elizabeth M
Maconaquah HS
Grissom Afb IN

Herman Joe
N C HS
Norton KS

Herman Mary C
Roncalli HS
Indianapolis IN

Herman Paul C
Maconaquah HS
Grissom Afb IN

Hermann Brock G
West Delaware HS
Manchester IA

Hermes Julie E
Adrian Sr HS
Adrian MI

Herms Pamela A
Green Lake HS
Green Lake WI

Hermsen Michael L
Escanaba Area HS
Escanaba MI

Herndon Mark E
Central HS
Springfield MO

Hernley Cynthia A
Goshen HS
Goshen IN

Hernly Nancy J
Shortridge HS
Indianapolis IN

Herold Debra A
Aquinas HS
Fort Madison IA

Herr Michael E
Clinton Prairie HS
Frankfort IN

Herran Steven M
Huntington North HS
Huntington IN

Herren Kimberly A
Sioux County HS
Harrison NE

Herrick Melodee R
Kewanee HS
Kewanee IL

Herrick Timothy L
Princeton HS
Princeton IL

Herricks Ronald T
Cashton HS
Cashton WI

Herriford Anita M
Lewistown Comm HS
Lewistown IL

Herriford David V
St Louis U HS
St Louis MO

Herring Daniel W
Chariton Comm HS
Chariton IA

Herring Donald G
Meadville R Iv HS
Linneus MO

Herrmann Michele R
Columbia Central HS
Brooklyn MI

Herro Bernard L
Messmer HS
Milwaukee WI

Herro Melissa A
Mather HS
Wetmore MI

Herschberger Tammy K
Northridge HS
Middlebury IN

Herschthal Mark A
Stephen Tyng Mather HS
Chicago IL

Hertel Catherine A
Marian HS
Hays KS

Hertel Maxine M
Victoria HS
Victoria KS

Hertz Nick J
Harvey HS
Harvey ND

Hertzler Julia D
Elkhart Central HS
Elkhart IN

Herzog Carl E
Fairbury Cropsey HS
Fairbury IL

Herzog Carl R
Barrington HS
Barrington IL

Herzog Joseph P
Lake Michigan Catholic HS
Benton Harbor MI

Hesler Denise A
Charleston HS
Charleston IL

Hess Mark L
Herscher HS
Kankakee IL

Hess Teri K
North Central HS
Mahaska KS

Hesseltine Christine G
Washington Community HS
Brighton IA

Hester Patricia L
Winchester HS
Winchester IL

Hetrick Cary L
Seeger HS
Williamsport IN

Hetzel James R
Tri County Area HS
Almond WI

Hetzel Keith L
Lincoln HS
Wisconsin Rapids WI

Heuber Robin L
Hammond Baptist HS
Munster IN

Heuchert Joan C
St Thomas Public HS
St Thomas ND

Heuer Jeffrey T
Northwestern Military Academy
Des Plaines IL

Heusinkuelt Judy M
Crete HS
Hallam NE

Heuvelman John M
Marquette HS
Godfrey IL

Hewes Cheryl B
Maplewood Academy
Pierre SD

Hewitt David L
Catlin HS
Catlin IL

Hewitt Silcox Cherie L
El Dorado Springs R Ii HS
El Dorado Springs MO

Hewlett Donald R
Richland Public HS
Richland MO

Hewlett Linda G
Plainfield HS
Plainfield IL

Hewlett Roderic
Carson Long Military Inst
Troy MI

Heyrman Cynthia J
Menomonee Falls East HS
Menomonee Falls WI

Heyroth Jean R
Lodi HS
Dane WI

Hiatt Linda M
Crystal Lake HS
Crystal Lake IL

Hickam Robin L
Corunna HS
Corunna MI

Hickerson William J
Bowling Green Ri HS
Bowling Green MO

Hickey Doreen M
Carl Sandburg HS
Orland Park IL

Hickman Randy D
Lakeview HS
Columbus NE

Hickmott Suzanne T
Davison HS
Davison MI

Hicks Anthony W
Curie HS
Chicago IL

Hicks Carmen J
Harris HS
Chicago IL

Hicks David C
Willow Springs HS
Willow Springs MO

Hicks Donald E
Scranton HS
Scranton IA

Hicks Franklin D
Bishop Noll Inst
Hammond IN

Hicks Glen W
Bennington HS
Bennington KS

Hicks Heidi A
Davison HS
Davison MI

Hicks Maureen K
St Francis Academy
Joliet IL

Hicks Thomas L
Oakwood Twp HS
Oakwood IL

Hideg Laszlo M
Divine Child HS
Dearborn Hts MI

Hielscher Nancy J
Alliance HS
Alliance NE

Hieronymus Donna K
Farmer City Mansfield HS
Farmer City IL

Higdon Ray D
Pontiac Central HS
Pontiac MI

Higgins Gregory L
Tuscola HS
Tuscola IL

Higgins Maryanne P
St Charles HS
St Charles MO

Higgins Marybeth
Streator Twp HS
Streator IL

Higgins Raymond W
Homewood Flossmoor HS
Homewood IL

High Kandy L
North White HS
Reynolds IN

Higley Michael B
Oswego HS
Oswego IL

Hiland George K
Rosedale HS
Bridgeton IN

Hilbert Laneal E
Hagerstown Jr Sr HS
Hagerstown IN

Hilbrenner Kevin L
Santa Fe HS
Waverly MO

Hildenbrand Marsha D
Sullivan HS
Carlisle IN

Hileman David L
Conway HS
Niangua MO

Hileman Debbie K
Conway HS
Niangua MO

Hiley Chretta A
Gallatin HS
Altamont MO

Hilf James C
Vianney HS
St Louis MO

Hilgenberg Jim M
Artesian HS
Artesian SD

Hilgers Gary E
Moorhead HS
Moorhead MN

Hill Betty G
Winfield R Iv HS
Foley MO

Hill Cheryl R
Reynolds County R Ii HS
Redford MO

Hill Darrel L
Medicine Valley HS
Curtis NE

Hill Debra L
Fairfield HS
Plevna KS

Hill Gayleen D
Ainsworth HS
Ainsworth NE

Hill Gregory J
Glenbard East HS
Lombard IL

Hill Janet L
Valley Park HS
Valley Park MO

Hill Julie A
Everly HS
Everly IA

Hill Kevin N
Wyandotte Roosevelt HS
Wyandotte MI

Hill Mark S
Montague HS
Montague MI

Hill Nancy J
North Central HS
Indianapolis IN

Hill Randall L
Merrill Sr HS
Merrill WI

Hill Randy S
Forest City Comm HS
Leland IA

Hill Richard W
Zionsville HS
Zionsville IN

Hill Robert M
Cousino Sr HS
Warren MI

Hill Rosa M
Villa Duchesne HS
St Louis MO

Hill Susan D
Gibson City HS
Gibson City IL

Hill Thomas J
Estherville HS
Estherville IA

Hill Vanessa D
Lindblom Tech HS
Chicago IL

Hillal Michelle B
Normandy HS
St Louis MO

Hillan Janet L
Rock Island Sr HS
Rock Island IL

Hillard Ann M
Galena HS
Galena IL

Hillard Nancy K
Pine River HS
Cadillac MI

Hille Kim E
Streator Twp HS
Streator IL

Hille William L
Dakota HS
Freeport IL

Hillen Terry W
Ofallon Twp HS
Ofallon IL

Hillenbrand Teresa L
Dollar Bay HS
Dollar Bay MI

Hillhouse Lisa A
Charleston HS
Charleston MO

Hilliard James W
Luther South HS
Chicago IL

Hills Thomas G
Minonk Dana Rutland HS
Minonk IL

Hilmes Thomas F
Mater Dei HS
Breese IL

Hilt James D
Wisconsin Academy
Racine WI

Hilton Beverly A
Richwoods HS
Peoria IL

Hilton Michael J
Wilton Comm HS
Moscow IA

Hilton Ramona D
East Prairie HS
East Prairie MO

Hiltz Gail
Lincoln HS
Park Falls WI

Hilz Carey J
Beulah HS
Beulah ND

Himmelberg Michael M
Glasgow HS
Glasgow MO

Himmelrick Harold W
Havana HS
Havana IL

Hindman Geri L
Glenwood HS
Glenwood IA

Hinebaugh Paula J
Tri HS
Lewisville IN

Hiner Sharon L
Coldwater HS
Coldwater MI

Hines Brenda L
Chippewa Hills HS
Barryton MI

Hines Michael T
Assumption HS
Davenport IA

Hines William E
Watseka Comm HS
Watseka IL

Hingtgen James J
Wahlert HS
Dickeyville WI

Hink Randy R
Jefferson Senior HS
Alexandria MN

Hinkelman Carlyn R
Watervliet HS
Benton Harbor MI

Hinkelman Debbie A
Ottawa Township HS
Grand Ridge IL

Hinkle Charles L
Advance HS
Advance MO

Hinkle Gerald G
S Haven HS
South Haven MI

Hinkle Katherine L
Pacific HS
Robertsville MO

Hinkson Brian W
Centura HS
Wood River NE

Hinman Cheryl D
Mitchell HS
Mitchell NE

Hinnefeld Jon D
Seymour HS
Seymour IN

Hinnen Larry D
Balboa HS
Edwardsville IL

Hinrich Randy D
Pender Public HS
Pender NE

Hinrichs Dianne Y
Dist 2r HS
Giltner NE

Hinrichs Randall D
Riceville Comm HS
Riceville IA

Hinson Kirk A
Effingham HS
Effingham IL

Hinton Alice L
Rockford HS
Rockford MI

Hinton Gregory D
Central HS
Cape Girardeau MO

Hinton Rhonda L
Tower Hill HS
Tower Hill IL

Hintz David E
Lawton HS
Lawton IA

Hintz Kimberly R
Harrison HS
Gladwin MI

Hintz Michael A
Oak Creek HS
Franklin WI

Hintz Suzanne M
Carl Sandburg HS
Tinley Park IL

Hintzman Nancy A
Twin Lakes HS
Monticelo IN

Hipke Earl M
Oneill Public HS
Oneill NE

Hippard John M
Shelbyville HS
Shelbyville IL

Hirchent Brian D
Allen Consolidated HS
Dixon NE

Hirsch Cynthia L
Benton Consolidated HS
Benton IL

Hirschel Anthony G
Southfield Lathrup HS
Southfield MI

Hirshey Sherrill L
Carl Junction HS
Asbury MO

Hish Evelyn K
Virginia HS
Virginia IL

Hishaw Chiquita R
Southeast HS
Kansas City MO

Hislop Christine L
Hazelwood Central Sr HS
Florissant MO

Hiss Sally J
Columbia City Joint HS
Columbia City IN

Histed Denise M
Reese HS
Munger MI

Hite Linda K
Holden HS
Holden MO

Hitt Patricia K
Granite City HS
Granite City IL

Hitzemann Renee J
Akron Comm HS
Akron IA

Hixson Catherin A
Mc Cook Sr HS
Mc Cook NE

Hlad Cynthia C
J S Morton West HS
Berwyn IL

Hladky Sue G
Oak Park HS
Kansas City MO

Hlavac Mary A
Louisville HS
Louisville NE

Hloucha Sheryl M
Chamberlain HS
Chamberlain SD

Hoag Barbara A
D D Eisenhower HS
Saginaw MI

Hoagland Gary J
Gordon HS
Gordon NE

Hoan Mary P
Elizabeth Seton HS
So Holland IL

Hoard Tamara A
South Decatur HS
Westport IN

Hoback Norman A
Clinton HS
Clinton IL

Hobaugh Connie L
Braman HS
South Haven KS

Hobbs Karen S
Wellington HS
Wellington KS

Hobbs Lisa M
Madison Consolidated HS
Madison IN

Hobbs Margaret S
Bowling Green HS
Bowling Green MO

Hobson Danny A
Black Hawk HS
Browntown WI

Hobson Donald D
Birch Run HS
Birch Run MI

Hobson Eric P
Griggsville HS
Griggsville IL

Hobson Keith L
Nevada HS
Nevada IA

Hobson Venita M
Unity HS
Chicago IL

Hochnadel Sharon M
Argo HS
Burr Ridge IL

Hochstatter Susan E
Nevada HS
Nevada MO

Hock Terri S
Casey Jr Sr HS
Casey IL

Hocking Mary D
Hancock Central HS
Hancock MI

Hodapp Terry J
Collinsville Sr HS
Collinsville IL

Hodel Mark W
Roanoke Benson HS
Roanoke IL

Hodge Cindy J
Mt Vernon Twp HS
Mt Vernon IL

Hodge Linda D
South Page HS
Coin IA

Hodges Diane L
Auburn Sr HS
Julian NE

Hodges Nyla R
Mullen HS
Mullen NE

Hodous Linda L
Edmore Public HS
Edmore ND

Hodson Matthew S
Triton Central HS
Fairland IN

Hodson Pamela L
Galena HS
Galena MO

Hoeberling Thomas C
Lee M Thurston HS
Milford MI

Hoeckelberg Amy T
Hanover Central HS
Cedar Lake IN

Hoef Theodore F
Assumption HS
E St Louis IL

Hoefer Mitchell R
Lafayette Ct District C1
HS
Higginsville MO

Hoeflinger James H
St Rita HS
Chicago IL

Hoefs Brad D
Wisner Pilger HS
Wisner NE

Hoefs Danny L
Gaylord Public HS
Gaylord MN

Hoegger Elaine M
Odell Community HS
Odell IL

Hoelscher Carol J
Blair Oaks HS
Jefferson City MO

Hoerauf Sharon R
Marian HS
Birmingham MI

Hoesly David L
St Pius X HS
Kansas City MO

Hoeven John H
Bishop Ryan
Minot ND

Hofer Jeffery L
Cocrane Fountain City HS
Cochrane WI

Hofer Vernon L
Rankin HS
Rankin IL

Hoff Deborah A
Franklin Central HS
Indianapolis IN

Hoffa Sandra K
Urbandale HS
Urbandale IA

Hoffelt Nancy E
Willard HS
Spring Field MO

Hoffer Heidi R
Taft HS
Chicago IL

Hoffman Frank A
Andrean HS
Hobart IN

Hoffman Jean L
Laona HS
Laona WI

Hoffman Marcia R
Stuart HS
Stuart NE

Hoffman Melissa A
Tri Jr Sr HS
Lewisville IN

Hoffman Michael G
Homewood Flossmoor HS
Chicago Heights IL

Hoffman Rhonda D
Valentine HS
Valentine NE

Hoffman William P
Bedford HS
Temperance MI

Hoffmann Curtis H
Washington HS
St Paul MN

Hoffmeyer Mark A
Joliet Catholic HS
Joliet IL

Hoffmeyer Rodney A
Devils Lake Central HS
Devils Lake ND

Hofmann Kenneth F
Medina Public HS
Medina ND

Hofmeister Karen J
J D Darnall HS
Prophetstown IL

Hofsess Diane M
Farmington HS
Farmington Hills MI

Hogan Dan R
Abraham Lincoln HS
Council Bluffs IA

Hogan Donald A
Nauvoo Colusa HS
Nauvoo IL

Hogg Barbara C
Chippewa Hills HS
Remus MI

Hoggins George W
Milford HS
Milford NE

Hogie Bradley S
Hendricks Public HS
Astoria SD

Hoglan Cheryl L
Independence HS
Independence IA

Hograbe John R
Dows Community HS
Dows IA

Hogue Mark K
Harlan Community HS
Harlan IA

Hogue Robert D
Mission Valley HS
Eskridge KS

Hogue William E
Enfield HS
Enfield IL

Hohl Patricia A
Wentzville Riv HS
Wentzville MO

Hohlfeld Mark R
Adams Central HS
Roseland NE

Hohman David F
T L Handy HS
Bay City MI

Hoins Patricia A
Guide Rock Public HS
Guide Rock NE

Hoisington Lisa M
University HS
Warrensburg MO

Hoit Neal G
Red Cloud HS
Guide Rock NE

Hokanson Stan
River Valley HS
Three Oaks MI

Hoksbergen Michael G
Lynnville Sully Comm HS
Lynnville IA

Hol Marlene A
Pella Christian HS
Cedar IA

Holan Danny J
Madison Public HS
Madison MN

Holanda Scott B
Anderson Senior HS
Anderson IN

Holcomb Brenda L
Springfield HS
Springfield MI

Holcomb Brian J
Springfield HS
Springfield MI

Holcomb Robert A
North Muskegon HS
North Muskegon MI

Holden Connie S
Caruthersville HS
Caruthersville MO

Holden Jeffery R
Lapeer Senior HS
Metamora MI

Holden Patricia L
Northwestern HS
Iron River WI

Holden Paul C
John Marshall HS
Indianapolis IN

Holder Renee A
North Central HS
Indianapolis IN

Holding Brenda R
Auburn Sr HS
Auburn NE

Holdt Cindy R
Kearney HS
Kearney NE

Hole Eric B
Creighton Prep HS
Omaha NE

Holeman Ann E
Centerville HS
Centerville IA

Holeman Jeff L
Frontier HS
Chalmers IN

Holeman Robin D
Hanover Central HS
Cedar Lake IN

Holen Gina A
La Moure HS
La Moure ND

Holesinger Kent B
Thomson Comm HS
Mt Carroll IL

Holeton Rhonda R
Ogemaw Heights HS
West Branch MI

Holland Brenda K
Blue River HS
Springport IN

Holland Kimberly A
Sycamore HS
Sycamore IL

Holland Lane A
Norris City Omaha HS
Norris City IL

Holland Paul E
Diamond HS
Joplin MO

Hollander Dennis C
Markesan HS
Markesan WI

Hollatz Cathy A
Ridgewood HS
Norridge IL

Hollick Maryann
St Benedict HS
Chicago IL

Hollingshead Carolyn D
Princeton R 5 HS
Cainsville MO

Hollingsworth Mary A
Princeton HS
Princeton IL

Hollister Jeri S
Portage Northern HS
Portage MI

Hollon Vickie L
Sullivan HS
Sullivan IN

Holloway Nathaniel O
Cass Technical HS
Detroit MI

Holloway Robert W
Sparta HS
Sparta IL

Hollstein Kristen L
Rushville HS
Rushville NE

Holman Leah S
Danville HS
Danville IL

Holmes Kevin D
Holy Name Seminary
Janesville WI

Holmes Kim B
Thornwood HS
Markham IL

Holmes Michael R
Berkeley Sr HS
Berkeley MO

Holmes Peggy A
Miller HS
S Greenfield MO

Holmes Rodney W
Platteville HS
Platteville WI

Holmes Terri S
Jennings County HS
Butlerville IN

Holmgren Laura A
Manistee HS
Manistee MI

Holmquist Ann L
West Bend East HS
West Bend WI

Holmstrom Susan G
Gladstone Area HS
Gladstone MI

Holscher Kathy J
Noblesville HS
Noblesville IN

Holscher Vicky L
Nemaha Valley HS
Cook NE

Holsinger Terry D
Prairie Heights HS
Howe IN

Holstine Karen S
Fremont HS
Fremont NE

Holt Colette
Francis W Parker HS
Chicago IL

Holt Dona J
Cobden HS
Alto Pass IL

STUDENTS PHOTOGRAPH SCHEDULED FOR PUBLICATION HERE COULD NOT BE REPRODUCED

Holt Jeff T
Brookport HS
Brookport IL

Holt Teresa D
Zalma HS
Zalma MO

Holtman Richard H
Limestone HS
Bartonville IL

Holtmeyer Lynn M
Quincy Sr HS
Quincy IL

Holtz Elizabeth A
Dundee Community HS
Carpentersville IL

Holtz Jeffrey A
West Central HS
Westgate IA

Holtz Keith M
Hutch Jr Sr HS
Hutchinson MN

Holtz Michael C
Auo Ha Comm HS
Auoca IA

Holub David W
River Valley HS
Three Oaks MI

Holvey Renita A
Janesville Parker HS
Janesville WI

Holweger Camilla J
Midway HS
Inkster ND

Holwerda Larry D
Danube HS
Blomkest MN

Holz Darrell V
Winona Sr HS
Winona MN

Holz David C
Toluca HS
Toluca IL

Holzberger Wilda C
Gordon HS
Gordon NE

Homberg Steven L
Westview HS
Kankakee IL

Homes Laurie S
Blair HS
Blair NE

Homoki Albert A
Portage Northern HS
Portage MI

Homsey Terri A
Superior HS
Superior WI

Homstad Laurel S
Lancaster Public HS
Lancaster MN

Hon Jeanette L
North Platte HS
Camben Point MO

Honaman John M
St Charles HS
St Charles MI

Honek Eddie F
Alvarado HS
Angus MN

Hong Pamela K
Osseo Fairchild HS
Osseo WI

Honiotes James P
Joliet Twp West HS
Joliet IL

Honkomp Dennis J
St Thomas Aquinas HS
Bridgeton MO

Honzlik Frank A
Niobrara Public HS
Verdel NE

Hoobler Vernon J
Washburn Rural HS
Topeka KS

Hood Georgea L
Wood River Rural HS
Wood River NE

Hood Teresa I
Estherville HS
Estherville IA

Hoogestraat Fran M
Lennox HS
Chancellor SD

Hook Carl C
Carlinville Community HS
Carlinville IL

Hook Debra E
Northeast R Iv HS
Cairo MO

Hook Donn R
Stockton HS
Stockton IL

Hook Rick D
Wayne Comm HS
Allerton IA

Hooker Brenda J
Sand Creek HS
Adrian MI

Hooker Larry E
Spalding Public HS
Primrose NE

Hooks Melissa A
Lyons Public HS
Lyons NE

Hooley Beverly A
Westview HS
Shipshewana IN

Hooper Kathy L
North HS
Omaha NE

Hooper Vanessa
Rushville HS
Rushville NE

Hoopingarner Michael R
Bellmont HS
Decatur IN

Hoopman Nancy L
Des Lacs HS
Burlington ND

Hoos Christine K
Lakeview HS
Battle Creek MI

Hootman Craig J
Davis Co Comm HS
Floris IA

Hoover Bridget A
Falls City HS
Falls City NE

Hopen Edward P
Walker Public HS
Walker MN

Hopfner Danielle M
St Xaviers HS
Junction City KS

Hopkins Sharon K
La Monte R 4 HS
La Monte MO

Hopkins Tammy L
Marshall HS
Marshall MI

Hopkins Tony C
Southmont HS
Waveland IN

Hopp Kimberlie L
Louisville HS
Louisville NE

Hoppe Bradley J
Primghar Comm HS
Primghar IA

Hoppe Louise A
Oconto Senior HS
Oconto WI

Hopwood Rhonda E
Charlestown HS
Memphis IN

Hord Steven R
Kingsford HS
Iron Mountain MI

Hordos Doug L
Bad Axe HS
Bad Axe MI

Horkan Debra A
Webb HS
Reedsburg WI

Horkan Diane L
Webb HS
Reedsburg WI

Horky Mark M
Sargent HS
Sargent NE

Horn Brian H
Creighton Prep
Council Bluffs IA

Horn Jo A
Centerville HS
Richmond IN

Horn Roy A
Newton HS
Newton KS

Hornbacher Valerie J
Gibert Comm HS
Story City IA

Horner Joseph W
Grosse Pointe South HS
Grosse Pointe Park MI

Horner Paulette A
Napoleon HS
Burnstad ND

Horner Shirley A
Esmond HS
Esmond ND

Hornsby Michael E
Chillicothe HS
Chillicothe MO

Hornung Scott A
Walhalla Public HS
Walhalla ND

Horsic Lori A
Benton Harbor HS
Benton Harbor MI

Horstman Patricia A
Sacred Heart Academy
Springfield IL

Horton David J
Lodi Sr HS
Lodi WI

Horton Gary L
Northwest HS
Cedar Hill MO

Horton Laurisa M
Burlington HS
Burlington IA

Horvath Jean E
Stephenson HS
Stephenson MI

Horyna Jonea
Otis Bison Sr HS
Bison KS

Hosea Thomas J
Rich Central HS
Matteson IL

Hoskin Cynthia S
Davis County Comm HS
Bloomfield IA

Hoskins Ernie R
Brown County HS
Trafalgar IN

Hoskins Patricia A
Chicago Vocational HS
Chicago IL

Hoskinson Donna A
Haven HS
Burrton KS

Hosmon Tracy K
Crab Orchard HS
Marion IL

Hoss David A
Gehlen HS
Lemars IA

Hostetler Gerald D
Glendale HS
Springfield MO

Hotle Tom G
Panora Linden HS
Panora IA

Houchen Nancy L
Bogan HS
Chicago IL

Houchin Kelli A
M V K Comm HS
Mazon IL

Houck Gregory P
Highland HS
Highland IN

Houck Jean G
Princeton R V HS
Princeton MO

Houge Linda S
Albert Lea Central HS
Albert Lea MN

Houghtaling Robin A
Battle Creek Academy
Battle Creek MI

Houghton Cheryl T
Mt Morris HS
Mt Morris IL

Houghton Marsha L
Manistique HS
Manistique MI

Hougland Mary A
Santa Fe Trail HS
Topeka KS

Houin Mark A
Plymouth HS
Plymouth IN

Houlihan Mary Jane
Elizabeth Seton HS
Dolton IL

Houmes Angela D
Sheldon HS
Watseka IL

House Barry P
Lanphier HS
Springfield IL

House Harold V
Brazil HS
Brazil IN

House Linda D
Northwest HS
St Louis MO

House Sam W
Gresham HS
Gresham WI

Houser Jamie L
Streator Twp HS
Streator IL

Houser Michael A
Glenwood Community HS
Glenwood IA

Houser Rick W
Centerville HS
Centerville IA

Houser Tania M
Homewood Flossmoor HS
Homewood IL

Houser Terri J
Centerville HS
Centerville IA

Houseworth Debra L
Unity HS
Chicago IL

Houseworth Rebecca S
Carrollton HS
Carrollton MO

Houston Karen K
Truman HS
Independence MO

Houston Scott R
Rock Falls Twp HS
Rock Falls IL

Houston Velina A
Junction City HS
Junction City KS

Hove Lerri R
North Shore HS
Ryder ND

Hovermale Connie S
Anderson HS
Anderson IN

Hovis Norman E
Lapeer HS
Metamora MI

Hovland Kevin C
Northwood HS
Northwood ND

Howar Kathleen A
Tri County HS
Deep River IA

Howard Christopher R
Regis HS
Eau Claire WI

Howard David J
Waterford Twp HS
Pontiac MI

Howard Deborah M
Mulvane HS
Mulvane KS

Howard John M
Jennings County HS
North Vernon IN

Howard Larry F
Sargent Public HS
Sargent NE

Howard Mary L
Delavan Comm HS
Delavan IL

Howard Sally A
Warsaw Community HS
Winona Lake IN

Howard Sylvia A
Worth Central HS
Indianapolis IN

Howard Terry H
Milan Jr Sr HS
Milan IN

Howarter Deanna M
Princeton HS
Princeton IL

Howarter Teresa L
Lewistown Comm HS
Lewistown IL

Howe Darcy A
Kirkwood HS
Kirkwood MO

Howe Debbora M
Velva Public HS
Velva ND

Howe Holly J
Central City Comm HS
Central City IA

Howe Susan J
Farmer City Mansfield HS
Farmer City IL

Howell James R
Seymour HS
Plainville IL

Howell Robert G
Crocker HS
Crocker MO

Howell Shelly L
Truman HS
Independence MO

Howery Patricia A
Tipton HS
Tipton IN

Howey Deborah J
Watertown Sr HS
Watertown SD

Howk John M
Burr Oak HS
Burr Oak MI

Howlett Ronald D
Flat River Central HS
Flat River MO

Hoxworth Tamara L
O Fallon Twp HS
O Fallon IL

Hoyum Edward M
Jefferson HS
Cedar Rapids IA

Hozman Robert A
New Trier East HS
Glencoe IL

Hozzian Rosemary
St Ann HS
Chicago IL

Hruskocy Michael J
Whiting HS
Whiting IN

Hruza Suzanne L
North Bend Central HS
Morse Bluff NE

Hryhorysak Jo Ann
Pana Sr HS
Pana IL

Hubbard Bruce W
Fox Sr HS
Imperial MO

Hubbard Elizabeth A
Aurora Central Catholic HS
Aurora IL

Hubbard Jeff G
Elm Creek HS
Elm Creek NE

Hubbard Judith C
Powers Lake HS
Powers Lake ND

Hubbard William A
Matthews HS
Matthews MO

Hubble Melanie J
Academy Of Our Lady
Peoria IL

Huber Brian R
Melrose Mindoro HS
Melrose WI

Huber Cindy R
Andes Central HS
Lake Andes SD

Huber Paul D
Fatima HS
Jefferson City MO

Huber Raymond S
Clintonville Sr HS
Clintonville WI

Huber Robyn J
Harrison Comm HS
Harrison MI

Huber Susan M
Alton Sr HS
Alton IL

Huber T Liisa
Brown Cty HS
Columbus IN

Hubert Steven D
Charles City HS
Ionia IA

Hubert Terry D
Mauston Area HS
Mauston WI

Hubin Kendall R
Jetmore HS
Jetmore KS

Huckey Kirk A
Clark County R 1 HS
Kahoka MO

Huckins Gregory S
E A Johnson Mem HS
Mt Morris MI

Huddle Michael L
Woodruff HS
Peoria IL

Huddleston Shirley L
Paseo HS
K C MO

Huddlestun Susan L
Casey HS
Casey IL

Hudson Barbara
Oscoda Area HS
Oscoda MI

Hudson Linda B
Farmington East HS
Hanna City IL

Hudson Linda M
Wyoming Pk HS
Wyoming MI

Hudson Pamela G
Chicago Vocational HS
Chicago IL

Hudson Patricia C
Wahpeton HS
Wahpeton ND

Hudspeth Mary L
Northern HS
Flint MI

Huebner Candace L
Alma HS
Alma WI

Huebner Catherine A
Puxico HS
Puxico MO

Huedepohl Ann L
Williamsburg HS
Williamsburg IA

Huelsbeck Michael J
St Marys HS
Menasha WI

Huenergardt Gwen M
Ness City HS
Ness City KS

Hueser Mary L
Hubbard Community HS
Hubbard IA

Huff Cathy L
Wilmot HS
Twin Lakes WI

Huff Charles B
South Iron HS
Annaplois MO

Huff Daniel R
Tipton HS
Clarksburg MO

Huff Jay L
Glendale HS
Springfield MO

Huff Mark A
Anita Comm HS
Anita IA

Huff Randall P
Fremont Mills Jr Sr HS
Tabor IA

Huffman Carol L
Shawnee HS
Mcclure IL

Huffman Joe A
Southern HS
Stronghurst IL

Huffman John D
Clark County Ri HS
Kahoka MO

Huffman Zane N
Madison Consolidated HS
Madison IN

Huffstutler William D
Nashville Comm Conso HS
Nashville IL

Hugener Doreen E
Lake Mills HS
Lake Mills WI

Hughes Barry K
Campus HS
Haysville KS

Hughes Jerry A
Frankton HS
Elwood IN

Hughes Kimberly S
Winamac Comm HS
Star City IN

Hughes Lawrence R
Spencer Community HS
Spencer IA

Hughes Lori J
Central HS
St Joseph MO

Hughes Mary B
Rock Falls Twp HS
Rock Falls IL

Hughes Mary E
Okawville HS
Okawville IL

Hughes Melanie G
Benton HS
Thompsonville IL

Hughes Michele M
Godwin Heights HS
Wyoming MI

Hughes Richard P
Adlai E Stevenson HS
Livonia MI

Hughes Susan M
Stapleton Public HS
Stapleton NE

Huigens Kevin J
Rapid City Central HS
Rapid City SD

Huisenga Kevin M
Gildden Ralsten HS
Glidden IA

Huisinga Henry J
Clarion HS
Clarion IA

Huisman James D
Wellsburg Comm HS
Grundy Center IA

Huisman Lisa M
Ellsworth Public HS
Ellsworth MN

Huiting Tara J
Downs HS
Downs KS

Hull Deborah A
Chetopa HS
Chetopa KS

Hull Diane L
High School
Hill City KS

Hull Treva E
Remington HS
Whitewater KS

Hullinger Cheri L
Wayne Community HS
Corydon IA

Hulme Patricia K
Seymour HS
Seymour MO

Hulshof Helen M
West Sioux Comm HS
Ireton IA

Hultz Karen K
Marion Co HS
Philadelphia MO

Humble Douglas P
Van Buren Comm HS
Cantril IA

Humble Willard A
Meridian Dist 101 HS
Pulaski IL

Hume Melodee
Urbandale Senior Hs
Urbandale IA

Hume Starr A
Houghton HS
Houghton MI

Humerickhouse Gina R
Heritage Christian Academy
Anderson IN

Hummel Robert E
Bloom Township HS
Steger IL

Humphreville Roger G
Holy Cross HS
Chicago IL

Humphrey Douglas L
Mt Pleasant HS
Mt Pleasant IA

Humphrey Tim J
Beatrice HS
Beatrice NE

Hunnel Daniel P
Leavenworth Sr HS
Leavenworth KS

Hunsaker Karen E
Southeast HS
Springfield IL

Hunt Douglas J
Carbondale Comm HS
Carbondale IL

Hunt John D
Chesaning Union HS
Oakley MI

Hunt Lorrie K
Osky Sr HS
Oskaloosa IA

Hunt Nancy K
Charleston HS
Charleston IL

Hunt Stephen L
Churchill HS
Livonia MI

Hunter David C
Centennial HS
Champaign IL

Hunter David W
Platte Co R Iii HS
Kansas City MO

Hunter Jill A
Manhattan HS
Ogden KS

Hunter John J
Chadsey HS
Detroit MI

Huntington Jayne E
Darlington HS
Darlington WI

Huntley Kristi E
Decatur Community HS
Oberlin KS

Huntzinger Joseph K
Pendleton Hts HS
Pendleton IN

Hunzeker Judy K
Pawnee Public HS
Pawnee City NE

Hupach Linda D
Plainfield HS
Joliet IL

Hupp Nancy K
Orrick HS
Orrick MO

Hurd Margaret A
New Hampton Comm HS
New Hampton IA

Hurlburt Candyce J
Sentnal HS
Lone Rock IA

Hurley Mary A
Ladywood St Agnes HS
Indianapolis IN

Huron Susan C
St Peter & Paul Area HS
Saginaw MI

Hursell Clarence E
Edison Sr HS
East Gary IN

Hurst Daniel E
Belleville East HS
Fairview Hts IL

Hurst Diane L
Chester HS
St Marys MO

Hurst Robert M
Griggsville HS
Griggsville IL

Husband Janet S
Tri County Comm HS
What Cheer IA

Huseby Reta J
Halstad Public HS
Halstad MN

Hushour Loretta L
Centerville HS
Centerville IA

Huskey Robert C
Brownell Talbot HS
Omaha NE

Husmann H Henry
Greenville HS
Greenville IL

Huss Vicki R
Sykeston HS
Sykeston ND

Huston James D
Axtell Community HS
Axtell NE

Huston Shelly K
Lake Forest Academy
Dawson IL

Hutchcraft Douglas W
Union Star R 2 HS
Union Star MO

Hutchcroft Ann L
Knoxville HS
Knoxville IL

Hutchings Susie L
Holden R 3 HS
Latour MO

Huvaere Gregory G
Grosse Pointe South HS
Grosse Point Park MI

Huxhold David M
Shortridge HS
Indpls IN

Huxman Leigh A
Morland HS
Morland KS

Hyde Eric A
Loy Norrix HS
Kalamazoo MI

Hyde Pamela J
Culver Girls Academy
Fort Wayne IN

Hyland Eileen E
Immaculate Heart Of Mary HS
Cicero IL

Hyland Karen A
York Community HS
Elmhurst IL

Hyland Kimberly K
Gering HS
Gering NE

Hyland Norma L
Guilford HS
Rockford IL

Hynek Emil J
Wheeling HS
Wheeling IL

Hystad Susan K
Velva Public HS
Velva ND

Hyvarinen Carol B
Brimley HS
Brimley MI

I

Iafrate Joanne M
Regina HS
East Detroit MI

Iatesta Valerie
Maine Township HS South
Park Ridge IL

Ibbotson Debra J
Pekin Comm HS
Pekin IL

Ickstadt William M
Memorial HS
Eau Claire WI

Ideus Wayne L
Beatrice HS
Beatrice NE

Ignacek Michael M
Quigley South HS
Chicago IL

Ignaszewski Nina H
Badger HS
Badger MN

Ihde Lee W
Menominee HS
Menominee MI

Ihde Theresa A
Washington HS
Germantown WI

Iliff Terry G
Portland HS
Portland IN

Illias Mark R
Virginia HS
Virginia IL

Illias Marsha R
Virginia HS
Virginia IL

Iman James M
Owensville Public HS
Owensville MO

Imel Lorraine C
George Washington HS
Indianapolis IN

Imhoff Randy R
Laura Speed Elliot HS
Boonville MO

Imm Ann M
Toluca HS
Toluca IL

Immonen Kenneth L
Ontonagon HS
Greenland MI

Inbody Diane E
Buhler HS
Hutchinson KS

Indrebo Kay L
Altoona Public HS
Altoona WI

Ingebretson Mark
Meseruey Thornton HS
Thornton IA

Ingebrigtsen Nita A
Kennedy HS
Bloomington MN

Ingemansen Lynnae C
Brainerd HS
Brainerd MN

Inghram Terry H
Danville HS
Danville IA

Inglebret Vicki L
Greenway HS
Grand Rapids MN

Ingold Kathy J
Lowpoint Washburn HS
Washburn IL

Ingram Beverly J
Mackenzie HS
Detroit MI

Ingram Beverly R
Daleville HS
Daleville IN

Ingram Deborah J
Hurley HS
Crane MO

Ingvalson Michael J
Caledonia HS
Caledonia MN

Inman David R
Fenwick HS
Chicago IL

Inman Laroy D
Lindblom Tech HS
Chicago IL

Inman Tammy J
F L Schlagle HS
Kansas City KS

Innis Brian L
Virden Com HS
Thayer IL

Inskeep Susan K
Harlem HS
Loves Park IL

Iocco Gary J
Gordon Tech HS
Chicago IL

Irby Pamela S
Florence HS
Iron Mountain MI

Ireland Frank A
Doniphan HS
Doniphan MO

Irey Glenda D
Tipton HS
Latham MO

Irvin Douglas W
Goodland HS
Goodland KS

Irvin Joel G
Mcleansboro HS
Mcleansboro IL

Irvine Barbara S
Quincy Sr HS
Quincy IL

Irvine Nancy J
Holden HS
Holden MO

Irvine Vicki D
Pittsfield HS
Rockport IL

Irwin Debra L
Sterling HS
Sterling IL

Irwin Susan M
Ludington HS
Ludington MI

Isaacson Julie A
Hancock Central HS
Hancock MI

Isaacson Raeann K
West HS
Sioux City IA

Isaak Wayne D
Eureka Public HS
Eureka SD

Isely Mary M
St Marys Springs HS
Fond Du Lac WI

Isenhart Renee R
Lake Park HS
Medinah IL

Isenhower Sandra K
Fremont HS
Fremont IN

Israel Donna S
Cardinal Ritter HS
Indianapolis IN

Itrich Steven J
New Salem HS
New Salem ND

Iverson Daniel D
Canton HS
Canton SD

Iverson Ingrid
East Troy HS
East Troy WI

Iverson Kristin L
Oak Park HS
Kansas City MO

Iverson Roger W
Montezuma Comm HS
Malcom IA

Iverson Teresa J
Vandercook Lake HS
Jackson MI

Iveson Sharon R
Ionia HS
Ionia MI

Ivy Stephen C
Chicago Vocational HS
Chicago IL

Iwen Rachel J
Dakota HS
Arthur ND

Izzo John M
York Community HS
Elmhurst IL

J

Jablonski Robin A
Saint Marys Academy
New Buffalo MI

Jackson Brett M
Campion Jesuit HS
Crete IL

Jackson Emma L
Bedford Comm HS
Hopkins MO

Jackson Gerilyn S
Avon HS
Avon IL

Jackson Gwendolyn
Spalding HS
Chicago IL

Jackson Janet D
Le Roy HS
Le Roy IL

Jackson Janice L
Granite City South HS
Granite City IL

Jackson Javel
Wichita North HS
Wichita KS

Jackson John A
Centralia HS
Centralia IL

Jackson John E
East HS
Kansas City MO

Jackson Larry R
Peru HS
Peru IN

Jackson Linda F
North Division HS
Milwaukee WI

Jackson Mary L
Lindblom Tech HS
Chicago IL

Jackson Pamela G
Superior HS
Superior NE

Jackson Rhonda K
Southern Reynolds R2 HS
Ellington MO

Jackson Thomas R
Assumption HS
Assumption IL

Jackson Walter B
Mchenry West HS
Mchenry IL

Jacobs Ben H
Mc Henry HS
Wonder Lake IL

Jacobs Debra E
Rockford Sr HS
Rudd IA

Jacobs Gordon J
South Decatur HS
Mallhousen IN

Jacobs Gordon M
Gale Ettrick Trempealeau HS
Ettrick WI

Jacobs Joel M
Garber HS
Essexville MI

Jacobs John M
La Salle HS
Cedar Rapids IA

Jacobs Joy E
Ainsworth HS
Flint MI

Jacobs Linda M
Quinter HS
Gove KS

Jacobs Patrick C
Springfield Catholic HS
Springfield MO

Jacobsen Joanna L
New Trier East HS
Winnetka IL

Jacobsen Myra J
Atlantic Comm HS
Atlantic IA

Jacobson Barbara S
Estherville HS
Estherville IA

Jacobson Douglas L
Crocker HS
Richland MO

Jacobson Eric W
Riverside Brookfield HS
Riverside IL

Jacobson Howard M
Rushford HS
Rushford MN

Jacobson Joann G
Alvarado Public HS
Alvarado MN

Jacobson Kathryn K
Oak Park HS
Kansas City MO

Jacobson Margo E
West HS
Waterloo IA

Jacobson Robert S
New Glarus HS
Mt Horeb WI

Jacobson Scott A
Drake HS
Drake ND

Jacobus Craig H
Amos Alonzo Stagg HS
Hickory Hills IL

Jacques Jeffrey L
Southern Reynolds R Ii HS
Ellington MO

Jacques Saprenia M
Lincoln HS
Warren MI

Jaecques Tamyra L
Northeast Riv HS
Cairo MO

Jaffe Robert T
Maine North HS
Niles IL

Jager Donald A
Hanson HS
Fulton SD

Jager Scott L
Buffalo HS
Buffalo ND

Jaggers Larry D
Westville HS
Westville IL

Jaggi Franz M
Belleville HS
Belleville WI

Jagodka Paul J
St Patrick HS
Chicago IL

Jagodzinski Linda L
Tonica HS
Oglesby IL

Jagos Donald J
Chesaning Union HS
Owosso MI

Jahn Linda S
Dubois HS
Jasper IN

Jahnke Mark S
Appleton West HS
Appleton WI

Jajowka Anita M
Thornton Fractional So HS
Lansing IL

Jakubowicz Anne M
St Joseph HS
Chicago IL

Jakubs Bonnie J
Woodlands Academy
Lake Forest IL

Jalowiec Donna M
Nazareth Academy
Chicago IL

James Constance S
St Mary Cathedral HS
Saginaw MI

James Edward C
Dwight D Eisenhower HS
Blue Island IL

James Felicia R
Chicago Vocational HS
Chicago IL

James Michael K
Pittsburg HS
Pittsburg KS

James Randy W
William Chrisman HS
Independence MO

James Roland E
Southern Wells HS
Warren IN

James Sue E
Warrensburg HS
Warrensburg MO

James Teresa K
Central Dallas Comm HS
Polk City IA

James Thomas D
Lake Central HS
Dyer IN

Jameson David L
Serena HS
Earlville IL

Jamieson Ramona M
Lincoln County R 1 HS
Cyrene MO

Jamison Harry L
Capac Comm HS
Capac MI

Jamison Michael L
Sycamore HS
Sycamore IL

Jamison Pamela S
North Branch HS
North Branch MI

Jammer Bonnie M
Bay City Western HS
Auburn MI

Janavs Anita
Milbank HS
Milbank SD

Jandt Margaret A
The Barstow HS
Prairie Village KS

Janecke Mary A
Mount Assisi HS
Palos Park IL

Janiak James M
Paul Vi HS
Omaha NE

Janik Chester
Glen Lake HS
Cedar MI

Jankovich Lucia M
St Clement HS
Center Line MI

Jankowski Christine R
Willow Brook HS
Villa Park IL

Janney Julia M
York Community HS
Elmhurst IL

Janoski Theresa L
Downers Grove South HS
Downers Grove IL

Janovsky Molly B
South Newton HS
Kentland IN

Janowsky Susan M
Martin Public HS
Otsego MI

Jansen Bernard J
Highland Park Sr HS
St Paul MN

Jansen Jolene K
West HS
Wichita KS

Jansen Roberta P
Leopold R 3 HS
Leopold MO

Janson Galen M
Healy HS
Pierz MN

Janssen Deborah A
Adams Central HS
Hastings NE

Janssen Jana S
Porta HS
Petersburg IL

Janssen Steven M
Southeastern HS
Augusta IL

Janssens Alice L
William H Taft HS
Chicago IL

Janulevicius Rima J
Maria HS
Chicago IL

Janulis Eugene P
Argo Community HS
Justice IL

Jarboe Paul J
South Shelby HS
Clarence MO

Jarman Timothy K
Excelsior Springs HS
Excelsior Springs MO

Jarmin Michael J
Thedford HS
Thedford NE

Jarrard Debra K
Maple Valley HS
Nashville MI

Jarrett Kelly J
Mahomet Seymour HS
Mahomet IL

Jarvis Kelly F
Forest Park HS
Crystal Falls MI

Jary Mark L
Whiting Community HS
Whiting IA

Jaryszak Rick W
Campion HS
Phelps WI

Jaskey David G
Fenwick HS
No Riverside IL

Jaskiewicz Roslyn I
East Troy HS
East Troy WI

Jasper Debra L
Holden R Iii HS
Holden MO

Jasper Henry A
Carney Nadeau HS
Carney MI

Jassak Timothy E
Campion Jesuit HS
West Chicago IL

Jastrzebski Alexandra M
Marillac HS
Chicago IL

Jawor Shirley A
St Ann HS
Chicago IL

Jayne Kathleen I
Thornton Fractional So HS
Lansing IL

Jaynes Jeanne K
Bunker Hill HS
Bunker Hill IL

Jazdzyk Dianne L
Fruitport HS
Muskegon MI

Jefferson Diane M
Columbus North Sr HS
Columbus IN

Jeffreys David L
Monett HS
Monett MO

Jeffries Anne T
West Washington HS
Fredericksburg IN

Jeglum Judy A
Pecatonica Area HS
Mt Horeb WI

Jelin Diane M
St Clement HS
Center Line MI

Jelm Karen S
Serena HS
Serena IL

Jenk Lisa A
Beckman HS
Dyersville IA

Jenkins Cheryl L
Thornwood HS
Markham IL

Jenkins Debra K
Liberty HS
Quincy IL

Jenkins Jeffrica J
Auburn Sr HS
Rockford IL

Jenkins Kathleen A
Warren Township HS
Gurnee IL

Jenkins Rodney L
Broken Bow HS
Broken Bow NE

Jenkot George O
Bronson HS
Bronson MI

Jenne Deborah L
Civic Memorial HS
Carlyle IL

Jenneman Tamara A
Bloomer Sr HS
Bloomer WI

Jenner Joyce A
Notre Dame HS
Chicago IL

Jenniges Bruce D
Walnut Grove Public HS
Walnut Grove MN

Jennings Constance A
Washburn HS
Minneapolis MN

Jennings Mark S
Prairie City Comm HS
Prairie City IA

Jennison Cynthia A
Salina Central HS
Salina KS

Jensen Bruce D
Tri Center HS
Minden IA

Jensen Carol R
Gettysburg HS
Gettysburg SD

Jensen Cheryl L
Northeast Sr HS
Kansas City MO

Jensen Dale R
New Richland Hartland HS
New Richland MN

Jensen David J
Kindred Public HS
Kindred ND

Jensen David R
Oak Park Sr HS
Gladstone MO

Jensen Duane M
Abraham Lincoln HS
Council Bluffs IA

Jensen Glenn T
Fitzgerald HS
Warren MI

Jensen Joan M
Ringsted Comm HS
Ringsted IA

Jensen Jolynne
Osborn HS
Detroit MI

Jensen Kimberly K
O Neill Public HS
O Neill NE

Jensen Kim L
Chamberlain HS
Chamberlain SD

Jensen Marilyn M
Cooperstown HS
Cooperstown ND

Jensen Mark A
Clarence Lowden HS
Lowden IA

Jensen Mary K
Ashby HS
Ashby MN

Jensen Melodi K
Elk Horn Kimballton HS
Kimballton IA

Jensen Patricia S
Detroit Country Day HS
Detroit MI

Jensen Paul A
Montabella HS
Edmore MI

Jensen Robert M
Arnold HS
Arnold NE

Jensen Suzanne F
Warsaw HS
Warsaw MO

Jensen Wendy J
Kennedy HS
Dayton ND

Jenson Daniel D
Newman Grove HS
Newman Grove NE

Jeppesen Ronald R
Blair HS
Fort Calhoun NE

Jepson Paul C
West Monona HS
Little Sioux IA

Jergensen Jeff M
Valders HS
Kiel WI

Jerger Greg E
Bayard HS
Bayard NE

Jerkins Mark L
Knoxville Comm HS
Knoxville IA

Jerome Marlin L
Walhalla Public HS
Walhalla ND

Jersild Julie A
Craig Sr HS
Janesville WI

Jerzak James T
Newman HS
Wausau WI

Jesberg Christine A
Notre Dame HS
Quincy IL

Jeschke Rebecca A
Highland HS
Severance KS

Jesiolowski Maryann
La Salle Peru Township HS
La Salle IL

Jeske Norbert A
Central HS
Seymour WI

Jeskewich Sally A
Bedford North Lawrence HS
Bedford IN

Jesop Bradley D
Fairfield Community HS
Fairfield IL

Jesse Janet M
Crandon HS
Argonne WI

Jessee Brent A
South Spencer HS
Richland IN

Jessup Garry K
Marion Adams HS
Sheridan IN

Jeter Jerry J
Du Quoin HS
Du Quoin IL

Jett Marsha E
Washington HS
Elmora IN

Jetter Peggy E
Pipestone HS
Pipestone MN

Jewell Daniel A
Calumet HS
Gary IN

Jewell James M
Pembine HS
Pembine WI

Jiles Lauren
Kenwood HS
Chicago IL

Jinright Bonnie J
B C Central HS
Battle Creek MI

Jobb David W
Lyons Twp HS
Western Springs IL

Jochim Jo L
Rock Port Rii HS
Rock Port MO

Joedeman Lucinda A
Stapleton Public HS
Gandy NE

Joelson Andrew J
Rich Twp E Campus HS
Park Forest IL

Joelson Peter M S
Rich Twp E Campus HS
Park Forest IL

Joestgen Joe W
Mineral Point HS
Mineral Point WI

Johannes Carol A
Morrill HS
Morrill NE

Johannesen Debra L
Sentral Community HS
Bancroft IA

Johanningmeier Jill A
Riverview Gardens HS
St Louis MO

Johannsen Bruce J
Bayard HS
Bayard NE

Johannsen Wanda L
Lake Central HS
Winfred SD

John Ann
Dundee Comm HS
Carpentersville IL

Johnmeyer Tina M
Fayette HS
Fayette MO

Johns Harry M
Centralia HS
Centralia IL

Johns Margaret A
Charleston HS
Charleston IL

Johns Ricky R
Dixon HS
Dixon MO

Johnson Annie R
Saginaw HS
Saginaw MI

Johnson Arnold A
E St Louis Sr HS
E St Louis IL

Johnson Barbara J
Routt HS
Franklin IL

Johnson Barbara L
Sully Buttes HS
Blunt SD

Johnson Barry A
Lincoln Sr HS
Bloomington MN

Johnson Bradley A
Dassei Cokato HS
Cokato MN

Johnson Bradley C
Waverly Shell Rock Sr HS
Waverly IA

Johnson Brady N
Interlochen Arts Academy
Kalamazoo MI

Johnson Brenda A
Jefferson West HS
Meriden KS

Johnson Brent D
Columbia City Joint HS
Columbia City IN

Johnson Brian A
Hamburg Community HS
Hamburg IA

Johnson Carol A
Fessenden HS
Fessenden ND

Johnson Charles M
Winnetonka HS
Liberty MO

Johnson Cheryl A
Circle HS
Benton KS

Johnson Cheryl L
New Haven HS
New Baltimore MI

Johnson Cindy A
Dexter HS
Dexter KS

Johnson Claudia F
Elmhurst HS
Ft Wayne IN

Johnson Colleen R
Milan HS
Montevideo MN

Johnson Cynthia A
W C HS
Webster City IA

Johnson Dale K
Montevideo Senior HS
Montevideo MN

Johnson Dale M
Wahpeton HS
Wahpeton ND

Johnson Daniel J
Morris Sr HS
Donnelly MN

Johnson Daniel S
Morton HS
Morton IL

Johnson David A
Marion Adams HS
Sheridan IN

Johnson David M
Washington Park HS
Racine WI

Johnson David P
Hancock Central HS
Hancock MI

Johnson David R
Red Wing Central HS
Red Wing MN

Johnson David W
Thornridge HS
Burnham IL

Johnson Dean A
New Hampton Comm HS
Alta Vista IA

Johnson Debbie L
Kearney HS
Kearney NE

Johnson Debbi L
Kapaun Mt Carmel HS
Wichita KS

Johnson Deborah J
Faulkner HS
Chicago IL

Johnson Deborah L
Crown Point HS
Crown Point IN

Johnson Deborah R
Beaver Dam Sr HS
Beaver Dam WI

Johnson Debra S
Cambridge HS
Cambridge IL

Johnson Debra S
Carterville HS
Carterville IL

Johnson Dennis A
Beresford HS
Beresford SD

Johnson Desiree S
North Boone HS
Capron IL

Johnson Donald L
Roseville Unit HS
Roseville IL

Johnson Donald L
Broken Bow HS
Broken Bow NE

Johnson Doris R
Luther HS
Onalaska WI

Johnson Douglas A
Illiopolis HS
Illiopolis IL

Johnson Douglas A
Rockford East HS
Rockford IL

Johnson Douglas B
Russell Community HS
Charitian IA

Johnson Douglas D
Atlanta Ciii HS
Atlanta MO

Johnson Eileen M
Mother Of Sorrows HS
Chicago IL

Johnson Eric D
Eleva Strum Central HS
Eleva WI

Johnson Gail S
Richland HS
Richland MO

Johnson Gene H
Wautoma HS
Redgranite WI

Johnson Gerald A
Mendel Catholic Prep
Chicago IL

Johnson Gregory D
Greenview HS
Greenview IL

Johnson Gregory T
Northville HS
Northville MI

Johnson Gwendolyn F
Towner HS
Towner ND

Johnson Heidi A
Mc Gregor HS
Mc Gregor MN

Johnson James E
Hinckley Big Rock HS
Hinckley IL

Johnson James J
Mitchell HS
Mitchell NE

Johnson James P
Menomonee Falls East HS
Menomonee Falls WI

Johnson Jane A
Grayville Comm HS
Grayville IL

Johnson Janell M
Buena Vista HS
Saginaw MI

Johnson Jane R
Wauneta HS
Wauneta NE

Johnson Jane R
Mandovi HS
Eleva WI

Johnson Jane S
Bark River Harris HS
Bark River MI

Johnson Janet L
Davis County Comm HS
Bloomfield IA

Johnson Janis R
Paxton Comm HS
Paxton IL

Johnson Jeanine M
Louisville Public HS
Louisville NE

Johnson Jeffrey T
Centennial Sr HS
Circle Pines MN

Johnson Jennifer J
Coloma HS
Coloma MI

Johnson Joy Beth
Pine River Area HS
Luther MI

Johnson Judy A
Henry HS
Henry SD

Johnson Julianne M
Algona HS
Algona IA

Johnson Julie A
Audubon Public HS
Audubon MN

Johnson Julie K
Warren HS
Gerlaw IL

Johnson Karen J
Lancaster Public HS
Lake Bronson MN

Johnson Karen M
Gothenburg Public HS
Gothenburg NE

Johnson Karin R
Glenburn HS
Lansford ND

Johnson Kathleen S
Tomahawk HS
Tomahawk WI

Johnson Kathy M
Adlai E Stevenson HS
Buffalo Grove IL

Johnson Krisselle L
Milnor HS
Milnor ND

Johnson Kristy K
Kennedy HS
Bloomington MN

Johnson Larry D
Fairbury HS
Fairbury NE

Johnson Leona J
Plano HS
Plano IL

Johnson Lewis L
Armstrong HS
Armstrong IA

Johnson Linda J
Morris Sr HS
Morris MN

Johnson Linda S
Waverly Senior HS
Waverly NE

Johnson Lonnial D
Murray Wright HS
Detroit MI

Johnson Louise E
Brewster Public HS
Brewster MN

Johnson Lynett M
Emerson HS
Gary IN

Johnson Lynn R
Crystal Lake HS
Crystal Lake IL

Johnson Mabel P
Roosevelt HS
Gary IN

Johnson Max N
Cooter HS
Steele MO

Johnson Melanie L
Sparta HS
Sparta IL

Johnson Michael A
Soutwestern HS
Kane IL

Johnson Michael L
Lake Orion HS
Lake Orion MI

Johnson Michael O
Senior HS
Jefferson City MO

Johnson Otis L
Roosevelt HS
St Louis MO

Johnson Pamela E
Putnam County R 1 HS
Unionville MO

Johnson Patricia A
Plano HS
Plano IL

Johnson Patti J
Milnor Public HS
Milnor ND

Johnson Randal B
Chase County HS
Imperial NE

Johnson Randy J
West HS
Waterloo IA

Johnson Randy R
Bird City HS
Bird City KS

Johnson R E
Liberty Senior HS
Liberty MO

Johnson Richard E
Harlem HS
Loves Park IL

Johnson Rick D
Lyons Township HS
La Grange Park IL

Johnson Robert S
James H Bowen HS
Chicago IL

Johnson Roger W
Union HS
Union Grove WI

Johnson Roxanne L
Rockwell City Community
HS
Jolley IA

Johnson Roy E
Lincoln Way HS
Frankfort IL

Johnson Scott C
Oxford HS
Leonard MI

Johnson Sharon M
Mora HS
Mora MN

Johnson Sheila E
Marietta HS
Marietta MN

Johnson Shelia M
Belvidere HS
Belvidere IL

Johnson Sherrie A
Delton Kellogg HS
Delton MI

Johnson Stacey A
Tolley Public HS
Tolley ND

Johnson Stephen R
Parkhill Sr HS
Kansas City MO

Johnson Steven L
H H Dow HS
Midland MI

Johnson Stuart W
West Fargo HS
Harwood ND

Johnson Susie I
Stanberry Rii HS
Stanberry MO

Johnson Teresa A
Pine River HS
Tustin MI

Johnson Terri L
Pioneer HS
Ann Arbor MI

Johnson Thomas G
Lakewood HS
Lake Odessa MI

Johnson Valarie G
Sherrard HS
Aledo IL

Johnson Valerie A
Central HS
La Crosse WI

Johnson Verlyn M
Wykoff Public HS
Wykoff MN

Johnson Vicky L
Roseville HS
Roseville IL

Johnson Victoria A
Northrop HS
Fort Wayne IN

Johnsrud Judy L
Starbuck HS
Starbuck MN

Johnsrud Kevin J
Albert Lea Sr HS
Albert Lea MN

Johnston Annette L
Watervliet HS
Watervliet MI

Johnston Deborah C
Good Counsel HS
Chicago IL

Johnston Elsie L
Doniphan Ri HS
Fairdeating MO

Johnston Kathy M
Effingham HS
Mason IL

Johnston Paula L
Lawrence HS
Lawrence KS

Johnston Ron K
Mission Valley HS
Eskridge KS

Johnston Timothy W
Rapid City Central HS
Rapid City SD

Johnston Vickie L
Warren HS
Anous MN

Johring Craig L
Oneill Public HS
Oneill NE

Joiner Cherie L
Catlin HS
Catlin IL

Joines David L
United Township HS
East Moline IL

Jolley Susan D
Monroe HS
Monroe MI

Jolly Connie J
Laurel HS
Laurel IN

Jones Andrew H
Jesup Community HSS
Jesup IA

Jones Brenda S
Southwestern HS
Brighton IL

Jones Bruce E
Deckerville HS
Deckerville MI

Jones Cathy S
Murphysboro Twp HS
Murphysboro IL

Jones Christopher A
Carlson HS
Woodhaven MI

Jones Cindy S
J D Darnall HS
Geneseo IL

Jones Craig E
Lakeview HS
Battle Creek MI

Jones Cynthia D
English HS
English IN

Jones Cynthia F
Golden Plains HS
Gem KS

Jones Dana K
Benkelman HS
Benkelman NE

Jones David R
Princeton HS
Cainsville MO

Jones David V
Richmond Burton HS
Ringwood IL

Jones Deanna L
Holden Senior HS
Kingsville MO

Jones Debbie S
Earlham Comm HS
Earlham IA

Jones Debora A
Lillis HS
Kansas City MO

Jones Debra A
West Side Sr HS
Gary IN

Jones Edward C
Mexico HS
Mexico MO

Jones Edward J
Romeoville HS
Romeoville IL

Jones Geri L
Reavis HS
Burbank IL

Jones James C
Central HS
Springfield MO

Jones Jane R
Elk Valley HS
Longton KS

Jones Janice M
St Teresa Academy
Kansas City MO

Jones Janis S
Oak Park HS
Kansas City MO

Jones Jerry A
Centerville Senior HS
Centerville IN

Jones Jerry L
Dike Comm HS
Reinbeck IA

Jones John A
Harding County HS
Buffalo SD

Jones John A
Carmel Boys HS
Gurnee IL

Jones John R
Galatia HS
Galatia IL

Jones Kathleen R
Yale HS
Yale MI

Jones Kenneth S
Pratt Sr HS
Pratt KS

Jones Kim M
Normandy HS
St Louis MO

Jones Kim M
Tuscola HS
Tuscola IL

Jones Kirk S
Carman HS
Flint MI

Jones Linnea M
Harvard HS
Harvard IL

Jones Lori M
Northeastern HS
Richmond IN

Jones Marilyn J
High School
Rolla MO

Jones Marla L
Hammond Baptist HS
Hammond IN

Jones Michael A
Wesclin Jr Sr HS
Trenton IL

Jones Michael D
Riverton 404 HS
Roverton KS

Jones Michael G
Rudyard HS
Rudyard MI

Jones Nancy K
Woodruff HS
Peoria IL

Jones Pamela S
Lake Park HS
Roselle IL

Jones Patricia J
Eastridge HS
Kankakee IL

Jones Rachel B
Lindblom Technical HS
Chicago IL

Jones Rhys A
Salina Central HS
Salina KS

Jones Richard C
O Fallon HS
O Fallon IL

Jones Richard C
East Troy HS
Elkhorn WI

Jones Ricky D
Kennett HS
Kennett MO

Jones Robert A
Lincolnwood HS
Raymond IL

Jones Robin D
Arcadia Valley HS
Ironton MO

Jones Steven D
Orion HS
Orion IL

Jones Tanya S
Litchfield HS
Litchfield MI

Jones Teresa C
Highland HS
Alexandria IN

Jones Terry A
Walnut Grovers HS
Walnut Grove MO

Jones Thomas
Highland HS
Highland IN

Jones Valencia M
Kenwood HS
Chicago IL

Jones William B
Wheaton Central HS
Wheaton IL

Jones William J
New Trier West HS
Winnetka IL

Jones Yvonne C
St Thomas Apostle HS
Chicago IL

Jonkouski Jill E
John F Kennedy HS
Chicago IL

Joonas Steven R
Lebo HS
Lebo KS

Jordan Brenda M
Bentley HS
Burton MI

Jordan Linda C
Northwestern HS
Flint MI

Jordan Robert M
Duchesne HS
St Charles MO

Jordan Steven C
Orangeville HS
Orangeville IL

Jordan Steve P
Richland HS
Essex MO

Jordan Syrlilars M
Roosevelt HS
Gary IN

Jordan William L
Crab Orchard HS
Stonefort IL

Jordheim Pamela F
Kindred Public HS
Walcott ND

Jorgensen Brian K
Lakeview HS
Lakeview MI

Jorgensen Danette K
Mitchell Sr HS
Loomis SD

Jorgensen Daniel M
Eagle Grove Sr HS
Eagle Grove IA

Jorgensen Harold S
Bridgewater Fontanelle HS
Bridgewater IA

Jorgensen Jeffrey A
Minden HS
Minden NE

Jorgensen Lynne M
Manual HS
Peoria IL

Jorgensen Marcia A
Manual HS
Peoria IL

Jorgensen Wanda G
Lake Central HS
Dyer IN

Jorgensen William P
Medicine Valley HS
Curtis NE

Jorgenson Donald L
Argyle HS
Argyle MN

Jorns Kathleen B
Oconomowoc Senior HS
Oconomowoc WI

Joseph Dana L
Shawnee Mission S HS
Overland Park KS

Josephson Amy E
St Charles HS
St Charles MO

Josephson James K
Edgewood HS
Madison WI

Josi Susan A
Ladysmith HS
Ladysmith WI

Jostock Norma J
Lapeer Sr HS
Lapeer MI

Jowers Cynthia O
Soldan HS
St Louis MO

Joyal Joyce M
Naperville Central HS
Naperville IL

Joyce Barbara L
Reddick HS
Gardner IL

Joyce Jeffrey D
Woodruff HS
Peoria IL

Joyce John R
St Laurence HS
Burbank IL

Jozefiak Stanley W
St Rita HS
Chicago IL

Juckett Robert S
Maine Twp South HS
Park Ridge IL

Judd Constance J
Troy HS
Troy MI

Judd Cynthia D
Fairbury HS
Fairbury NE

Jude Maureen L
Holy Trinity HS
Maple Lake MN

Judge Anne M
Shawnee Mission N HS
Shawnee Mission KS

Judy Julia K
West Richland HS
Noble IL

Jueong Lisa L
Maconaquah HS
Peru IN

Juncer Bartholomew J
Quigley North HS
Waukegan IL

Jung Peter A
Maine West HS
Des Plaines IL

Jungles David G
Aurora Central Catholic HS
Aurora IL

Junk Joseph M
Hudson Comm HS
Waterloo IA

Junker Charlotte R
Mount Lake Public HS
Mountain Lake MN

Junker Debra L
Cass Lake HS
Cass Lake MN

Junker Lorinda L
Fairbury HS
Fairbury NE

Juntunen Gwen A
Hamlin HS
Vienna SD

Juntunen Robert D
Central HS
Grand Forks ND

Jurkowski Robert J
Lasalle Peru Twp HS
Peru IL

Jurman Ronald
Lockport HS
Lockport IL

Jurrens Karen F
Little Rock Community HS
Ellsworth MN

Jursch Kris L
Raymore Peculiar HS
Raymore MO

Jussel Julie K
Wagner HS
Wagner SD

Justice James W
Irwin Community HS
Irwin IA

Justice Kemberlee
Willow Run HS
Ypsilanti MI

Justice Michael B
West Chicago Dist 94 HS
Winfield IL

K

Kabat Carol S
Waltonville Comm #1 HS
Waltonville IL

Kabat Donald R
Traverse City HS
Traverse City MI

Kabat Sharon M
Thornton Township HS
Dolton IL

Kabisch David E
Walnut Community HS
Walnut IA

Kachelein Catherine M
Anderson HS
Anderson IN

Kachin Sharon M
Sacred Heart HS
Dearborn Heights MI

Kackley Kevin W
Maryville R Ii HS
Maryville MO

Kaczmarek Patricia A
Mother Of Sorrows HS
Blue Island IL

Kaczmarek Robert B
Greenfield HS
Greenfield WI

Kaczor Alan B
Neillsville HS
Neillsville WI

Kaddatz Sheri K
Lincoln HS
Wisconsin Rapids WI

Kadrich Bryan K
Lincoln HS
Warren MI

Kadrmas Jan
Dickinson HS
Dickinson ND

Kaeding Christopher C
Eisenhower HS
Decatur IL

Kaeser Diane R
Marion HS
Marion IL

Kagay Anita R
John Hersey HS
Arlington Hts IL

Kahl Sandra K
Clarence Lowden HS
Lowden IA

Kahle Claralee A
Owensville HS
Owensville MO

Kahle Darla A
Tomahawk HS
Tomahawk WI

Kahle Donald W
James B Conant HS
Hoffman Estates IL

Kahle John H
Southridge HS
Huntingburg IN

Kahle Karen A
Lexington HS
Lexington IL

Kahle Keri K
Hoxie HS
Hoxie KS

Kahler Lisa A
Morton HS
Morton IL

Kahre Raymond M
Maconaquah HS
Peru IN

Kahrs Julie A
Franklin HS
Bloomington NE

Kaigler Joseph M
Univ Of Detroit HS
Detroit MI

Kaiser Alan D
Chase County HS
Imperial NE

Kaiser Lisa K
Immaculate Conception Acad
Batesville IN

Kaleta David T
Lake Park HS
Itasca IL

Kalinowski Linda L
Wm Howard Taft HS
Chicago IL

Kalish Ronna S
Niles East HS
Skokie IL

Kalk Sandra A
Mc Donell Central HS
Chippewa Falls WI

Kalkwarf Michael L
Belmond Community HS
Belmond IA

Kallembach Rex H
Monticello HS
Monticello IL

Kallenbach Cynthia L
Eldorado HS
Eldorado IL

Kallhoff Bruce A
Dawson Boyd HS
Dawson MN

Kallin Dennis R
Lourdes Academy
Oshkosh WI

Kalloway Kim D
Dubuque Sr HS
Dubuque IA

Kalnes David M
Palmyra HS
Eagle WI

Kalous Karen S
Greenville HS
Pocahontas IL

Kalskett Jeanne M
East Monona Comm HS
Moorhead IA

Kalsow Daniel J
Wis Heights HS
Mazomanie WI

Kalthoff Kenneth R
Niles West HS
Lincolnwood IL

Kaluza Diane B
South Lake HS
St Clair Shores MI

Kalwasinski Kathy E
Ewen Trout Creek HS
Troutcreek MI

Kamada Mika M
St Charles HS
St Charles MO

Kamidoi Steve I
Capac HS
Capac MI

Kaminky Scott L
Earlville Comm Unit #9 HS
Earlville IL

Kaminskas Robert A
Luther So HS
Chicago IL

Kaminski Jolaine A
Schuyler Central HS
Schuyler NE

Kammandel Richard J
Creighton Prep
Omaha NE

Kammeraad Connie S
Grand Haven Sr HS
Grand Haven MI

Kammerich Gary L
Pilot Grove HS
Pilot Grove MO

Kammerman Tom A
Sherrard HS
Milan IL

Kammeyer Kathryn L
Warsaw R 9 HS
Warsaw MO

Kammeyer Ronald F
Woodlan HS
Woodburn IN

Kamp Beth A
Irving Crown HS
Carpentersville IL

Kampe Kim R
Quincy Sr HS
Quincy IL

Kampfe Steven J
Gothenburg HS
Gothenburg NE

Kamphausen Caroline K
Luther North HS
Chicago IL

Kampman Pamela R
Kearney HS
Holt MO

Kampschroeder Judith A
Washington HS
Washington MO

Kane Kelly A
Whitewater HS
Whitewater WI

Kane Rita M
Benet Academy
Naperville IL

Kannappan Maryann P
New Trier West HS
Winnetka IL

Kansanback Cynthia K
Storden Jeffers Cons HS
Sanborn MN

Kantz Diane C
Penn HS
South Bend IN

Kaperzinski Mary L
Our Lady Of Mercy HS
Royal Oak MI

Kapolnek Donald S
St Benedicts HS
Chicago IL

Karafiat Gary G
Benet Academy
Westmont IL

Karapas Eleftheria T
H L Richards HS
Oak Lawn IL

Karas Elaine S
Osborn HS
Detroit MI

Karch Kim B
Murphysboro Twp HS
Murphysboro IL

Karg Susan M
Litchfield Sr HS
Litchfield MN

Karg Susan M
North Vermillion HS
Perrysville IN

Karloski Peggy A
Stephen Decatur HS
Decatur IL

Karn Regeana L
Eau Claire HS
Eau Claire MI

Karnes Janelle S
Hoxie HS
Hoxie KS

Karnes William L
Laingsburg HS
Laingsburg MI

Karp Gregory P
White Bear HS
White Bear Lake MN

Karpawicz Cheryl A
Nauvoo Colusa HS
Nauvoo IL

Karpel Richard J
Plainfield HS
Plainfield IL

Karpinski Sharleen J
Gabriel Richard HS
Wyandotte MI

Karpus Thomas J
Batavia HS
Batavia IL

Karvonen John H
New York Mills HS
New York Mills MN

Kaseff Fred E
North Central HS
Indianapolis IN

Kasi Sandra L
Dorchester HS
Dorchester NE

Kasik Rebecca A
La Salle Peru HS
Peru IL

Kasinger Susie J
Bloomingdale HS
Pullman MI

Kasischke Daniel K
Tawas Area HS
Tawas City MI

Kasowski Collette M
Buffalo HS
Absaraka ND

Kaspar Alan J
St Edward Public HS
St Edward NE

Kaspari Danny K
Lisbon HS
Lisbon ND

Kasper Karen L
Hilbert HS
Hilbert WI

Kasper Nina M
Niles West HS
Niles IL

Kassing Stephen W
Central HS
Clayton IL

Kast Virginia L
Adrian Sr HS
Drian MI

Kastberg Judith L
Homewood Flossmoor HS
Homewood IL

Kastelic Gia C
Kenwood HS
Chicago IL

Kasten Donna K
Spring Valley HS
Spring Valley MN

Kasten Edward L
Kirkwood HS
Kirkwood MO

Kastner Teri L
Pattonville Sr HS
Maryland Hgts MO

Kasubjak Charles H
Clinton HS
Clinton IN

Kasztelan Michael J
Cody HS
Detroit MI

Katsias Stella
Finney HS
Detroit MI

Katsis Peter
Oak Park & River Forest HS
Oak Park IL

Katz Cindi R
Lakeview HS
Battle Creek MI

Katz Steven B
Downers Grove South HS
Woodridge IL

Katzenberger Diane M
Mother Mc Auley HS
Orland Park IL

Katzioris Nancy J
Oak Lawn Comm HS
Oak Lawn IL

Katzner Dennis G
Albany Area HS
Albany MN

Kauer Pamela J
Rudyard HS
Kinross MI

Kaufman Denise L
Northeast HS
Lincoln NE

Kaufman Michael J
Highland Pk HS
Highland Park IL

Kaufman Tamera L
Gering HS
Gering NE

Kaufman Tina M
Ripon Senior HS
Ripon WI

Kaufmann Michael E
Carmel Boys HS
Mundelein IL

Kaufmann Thomas C
St Laurence HS
Burbank IL

Kaup Denise A
Stuart HS
Stuart NE

Kaup Ron E
Bishop Dubourg HS
St Louis MO

Kaup Thomas J
Stuart Public HS
Stuart NE

Kaup Vencille M
Stuart Public HS
Stuart NE

Kaut Tim E
Center Point Consolidated HS
Center Point IA

Kayfish Antonette S
Plainfield HS
Joliet IL

Kaylor Kim L
Coldwater HS
Coldwater MI

Kazimour Kimberly K
Washington Sr HS
Cedar Rapids IA

Kazuk Jane
Maine Twp South HS
Park Ridge IL

Keal Sandra M
Fargo North HS
Frago ND

Kealey Paula J
Holdrege Sr HS
Holdrege NE

Kear Gina M
Golden Plains HS
Menlo KS

Kearney Darrell L
St Edmond HS
Fort Dodge IA

Kearney Jeanne L
Tomah Senior HS
Tomah WI

Kearns Michelle M
Assumption HS
Davenport IA

Keas Carolyn J
Pekin Comm HS
Pekin IL

Keating Jeffrey V
Pacelli HS
Austin MN

Keating Paula M
Marian Catholic HS
Chicago Heights IL

Kebe Frank L
Cathedral HS
Indianapolis IN

Keck Angela K
Oak Grove Senior HS
Oak Grove MO

Keck Brenda E
Lone Jack C 6 HS
Lone Jack MO

Kedzior Stanley F
Quigley South HS
Chicago IL

Keefer Kenneth K
Glenbrook South HS
Northbrook IL

Keefner Joseph E
Thornridge HS
Harvey IL

Keehnen Sara S
Dakota HS
Dakota IL

Keel John W
Shellsburg HS
Shellsburg IA

Keel Mary K
Farmington East HS
Elmwood IL

Keeler Billie W
Waynesville HS
Ft Leonardwood MO

Keeley Matthew T
Downers Grove HS
Downers Grove IL

Keen Daniel D
Oak Grove HS
Horace ND

Keen Michael R
Armstrong HS
Neenah WI

Keesling Tamra K
Fairfield HS
Sylvia KS

Keeton Anthony D
Elsberry HS
Elsberry MO

Keever Kirk A
Southern HS
Stronghurst IL

Keffer Paul N
Osseo Fairchild HS
Osseo WI

Kegler Deborah J
Pardeeville Sr HS
Pardeeville WI

Kehr Ralph W
Meadville HS
Meadville MO

Kehr Richard R
Sotuheast Nebr Cons HS
Shubert NE

Keifer Michael S
Superior HS
Guide Rock NE

Keil David W
Hoisington HS
Russell KS

Keil Peggy A
Red Bud HS
Red Bud IL

Keim Debbie S
North Miami HS
Roann IN

Keinath Howard J
Deerfield HS
Blissfield MI

Keiser Richard L
Wauneta Public HS
Enders NE

Keith Michael E
West Vigo HS
W Terre Haute IN

Kelleher Alan R
Ogden Community HS
Perry IA

Kellen Karen S
Amboy HS
Sublette IL

Kellenberger Vickie L
Sabetha HS
Sabetha KS

Keller Craig F
Hamilton HS
Sussex WI

Keller Debbie K
Harvey HS
Selz ND

Keller Debra L
Joliet East HS
Elwood IL

Keller Deena K
Dongola HS
Dongola IL

Keller Edward E
Murray Community HS
Murray IA

Keller Gerald D
Beulah HS
Beulah ND

Keller Jo Ann
Nokomis HS
Nokomis IL

Keller Larry S
Maine West HS
Des Plaines IL

Keller Michelle L
Roncalli HS
Omaha NE

Keller Sharon S
Palco HS
Zurich KS

Keller Vicki J
Edgewood HS
Bloomington IN

Kelley Bruce G
Elk Grove HS
Elk Grove Village IL

Kelley Clark M
Tyndall HS
Tyndall SD

Kelley Diane E
El Dorado HS
El Dorado KS

Kelley Ina E
Tecumseh HS
Adrian MI

Kelley James H
Walnut Grove HS
Walnut Grove MO

Kelley Kathy J
Fredericktown Sr HS
Fredericktown MO

Kelley Sandra L
Carl Sandburg HS
Tinley Park IL

Kellor Eileen M
Oregon Sr HS
Oregon WI

Kelly Andrea L
Robbinsdale Sr HS
Robbinsdale MN

Kelly Annette E
Orleans HS
Orleans IN

Kelly Ann M
Kirksville HS
Kirksville MO

Kelly Barbara A
Octavia HS
Colfax IL

Kelly Brian V
Marian Catholic HS
Park Forest S IL

Kelly Catherine S
Muncie Southside HS
Muncie IN

Kelly Cole D
St Thomas Academy
St Paul MN

Kelly Dawn
Mid County HS
Lacon IL

Kelly Diane E
Belvidere HS
Belvidere IL

Kelly Georgia A
River Valley HS
Sawyer MI

Kelly Jeffrey P
Loyola Academy
Deerfield IL

Kelly Kathleen A
Brookfield E HS
Brookfield WI

Kelly Laurie E
Maine Twp South HS
Park Ridge IL

Kelly Mary E
Regina Dominican HS
Evanston IL

Kelly Pamela D
Lindblom Technical HS
Chicago IL

Kelly Sheri L
Pembine HS
Pembine WI

Kelly Stephen A
Marion Institute HS
Portageville MO

Kelly Terry G
Virden Comm HS
Thayer IL

Kelm Louis J
Providence HS
Lockport IL

Kelner Katherine R
Velva Public HS
Velva ND

Kelnhofer Cheryl L
Lincoln HS
Park Falls WI

Kelpe Ronald M
Burke HS
Omaha NE

Kelsaw Lore
Northrop HS
Ft Wayne IN

Kemble Les L
Shelbyville Sr HS
Shelbyville IN

Kemmerer Philip B
North Clay HS
Louisville IL

Kemner Rita F
Manchester HS
Manchester MI

Kemnitz Randal S
George S Parker HS
Janesville WI

Kemp Carol L
Southwestern HS
Brighton IL

Kemp Jan M
R O V A HS
Oneida IL

Kemp Kevin L
Southridge HS
Huntingburg IN

Kemper Philip T
Wahpeton Sr HS
Wahpeton ND

Kemple Judy L
Culver Community HS
Culver IN

Kenbeek Deborah J
Parchment HS
Parchment MI

Kendall Ronald D
Jefferson West HS
N Topeka KS

Kendall Susan L
Reese HS
Reese MI

Kendrick Dennis P
Aurora Central Catholic HS
Aurora IL

Kenefick Patsy A
Highland Park HS
St Paul MN

Kenley Susan G
West Washington HS
Salem IN

Kennedy Betty A
Byron Area HS
Byron MI

Kennedy Christopher L
Bennett HS
Marion IN

Kennedy Denise K
Broken Bow HS
Broken Bow NE

Kennedy Jay I
Lafollette HS
Madison WI

Kennedy John G
Chandlerville HS
Chandlerville IL

Kennedy John W
Fairfield HS
Fairfield IA

Kennedy Joseph A
Wawasee HS
Syracuse IN

Kennedy Lawrence R
Sts Peter & Paul HS
Saginaw MI

Kennedy Linda S
Holden HS
Holden MO

Kennedy Lynn C
Lebanon HS
Lebanon KS

Kennedy Mark E
Galesburg Sr HS
Galesburg IL

Kennedy Pamela J
Delta HS
Muncie IN

Kennedy Patricia A
St Charles HS
Elburn IL

Kennedy Patricia A
Aurora Central Catholic HS
Aurora IL

Kennedy Paula J
Carmel HS
Downey IL

Kennedy Richard M
Marysville HS
Marysville MI

Kennedy Roberta A
Josephinum HS
Chicago IL

Kennedy Scott A
Nevada HS
Deerfield MO

Kennedy Sheila J
St Scholastica HS
Chicago IL

Kenney Karyn J
Inman HS
Inman KS

Kenning Dennis L
Fairbury HS
Endicott NE

Kennison Dora M
Monroe City R 1 HS
Hunnewell MO

Kensil Brian E
Tower Hill HS
Tower Hill IL

Kent Carol A
Maine Twp West HS
Des Plaines IL

Kent John G
Marist HS
Oak Lawn IL

Kent Kevin L
Southern HS
Stronghurst IL

Kent Roger L
N Senior HS
Eau Claire WI

Kenyon Colleen M
Mallard Community HS
Mallard IA

Kenyon Timothy R
Creston HS
Creston IA

Keough Colleen M
Monticello HS
Monticello WI

Keough Gary R
Holy Name Seminary
Monticello WI

Keough Michael J
Almond HS
Bancroft WI

Kephart Robyn E
Holden R Iii HS
Kingsville MO

Keppen Rose M
Rogers HS
Michigan City IN

Keranen Cheryl A
Ontonagon Area HS
Ontonagon MI

Keranen Debra K
Ontonagon Area HS
Mass MI

Kerestes Gloria L
Streator Twp HS
Streator IL

Kerff Robert E
R 1 North Callaway HS
Fulton MO

Kerkman Michelle G
Central HS
Powers Lake WI

Kerksiek Jo Ellen
Oak Park HS
Gladstone MO

Kerley La Donna T
Vienna HS
Vienna IL

Kerley Ruth E
Brown Cnty HS
Timewell IL

Kermicle John S
East Richland HS
Dundas IL

Kern Bernard J
Beckman HS
Dyersville IA

Kern Michael P
Hibbing HS
Hibbing MN

Kern Ricky J
La Harpe HS
La Harpe IL

Kern Robert J
O Fallon Township HS
O Fallon IL

Kerr Richard E
Coleman HS
Coleman WI

Kerr Susan D
Cimarron HS
Cimarron KS

Kersey Linda D
Adel HS
Adel IA

Kersten Cheryl M
Murdock HS
Ashland NE

Kersten Mark E
Howells HS
Howells NE

Keskitalo Jean E
Batavia HS
Batavia IL

Kessinger Jackie L
Mendota Twp HS
Compton IL

Kessler Jeanne A
Gresham HS
Gresham NE

Kessler Julie D
Kinmundy Alma HS
Kinmundy IL

Kestner Linda L
Central HS
Clayton IL

Ketterer Molly A
St Elizabeths Academy
Charleston MO

Kettrey Teresa A
Eastern HS
Pekin IN

Keur Michael H
Fruitport HS
Fruitport MI

Kewin Jennie A
Griswold Comm HS
Griswold IA

Keyes Richard J
Beloit Memorial HS
Beloit WI

Kezelis Robert A
Wheeling HS
Buffalo Grove IL

Khourie Tammie A
Hayti HS
Hayti MO

Khoury Holly M
Kingsford HS
Iron Mountain MI

Kibbe Barbara J
California R 1 HS
California MO

Kibler Thomas G
Spring Lake Park HS
Minneapolis MN

Kidd Kelly J
Advance HS
Advance MO

Kidd Lisa M
Washington Catholic HS
Washington IN

Kidd Teri D
Morton HS
Morton IL

Kiebel Michael F
New Haven HS
New Haven IN

Kieckhefer Linda M
So Milwaukee Sr HS
So Milwaukee WI

Kieffer Darlene M
Mt Carmel HS
Mt Carmel IL

Kies Lora L
Nashua HS
Charles City IA

Kiesetter Dale O
Cornell HS
Pontiac IL

Kiesig Debbie D
Ottawa Twp HS
Ottawa IL

Kiesow Linda M
Waupun Sr HS
Brandon WI

Kiesow Lori K
Waupun HS
Brandon WI

Kihle Tim L
Bottineau HS
Bottineau ND

Kiiskila Gail J
Hancock Central HS
Hancock MI

Kilbride Madonna L
Wakonda Public HS
Vermillion SD

Kilbury Deborah L
Rushford HS
Rushford MN

Kilcher Mary Jo
Dominican HS
Detroit MI

Kile Christie L
Rushville HS
Rushville IN

Kile Steven A
Washington HS
Red Cloud NE

Kilgore Dewitt D
St Louis Univ HS
St Louis MO

Kilgore Kimberly J
Marquette HS
Michigan City IN

Kilgore Rebecca J
Lakeland Union HS
Woodruff WI

Killian Charles R
Waukegan HS
Waukegan IL

Killian Jane M
Streator Twp HS
Streator IL

Kim Jae Hu
Lane Tech HS
Chicago IL

Kimball Laurel E
Boone Co R Vi HS
Centralia MO

Kimber Myron E
Paseo HS
Kansas City MO

Kimberling Denise M
Highland HS
Highland IN

Kimbler Deborah L
Franklin Community HS
Franklin IN

Kimes William L
Caledonia Valley HS
Potosi MO

Kimmell Bryan D
Columbus North HS
Columbus IN

Kimovec Irene B
Regina Dominican HS
Wilmette IL

Kimsey Melinda K
Prairie Home HS
Prairie Home MO

Kinast John A
Luther HS
Chicago IL

Kinasz Thomas J
Quigley South HS
Chicago IL

Kincaid Nancy E
Stet HS
Richmond MO

Kincart Jeffrey E
Davis County Comm HS
Bloomfield IA

Kinder Deborah L
Logansport HS
Logansport IN

Kinderknecht Lavern F
Grinnell HS
Grinnell KS

Kindernay Joseph A
Hillsboro HS
Panama IL

Kindred Dionne S
Bedford North Lawrence HS
Springville IN

Kindschuh Kevin K
Wisner Pilger HS
Wisner NE

King Audrey D
Thornridge HS
Phoenix IL

King Deidre A
Laboure HS
St Louis MO

King James A
Parker HS
Janesville WI

King Jane E
Reddick HS
Reddick IL

King Jeffery E
New Trier East HS
Glencoe IL

King Joseph B
Connersville HS
Connersville IN

King J Steven
Bishop Mac Namara HS
Kankakee IL

King Katherine R
Clarkston Sr HS
Clarkston MI

King Keith R
Dansville HS
Dansville MI

King Kevin D
Riverview Gardens HS
St Louis MO

King Kyle R
Univer Of Detroit HS
Detroit MI

King Mary J
Pacelli HS
Stevens Point WI

King Maureen F
Walhalla Public HS
Walhalla ND

King Michael J
St Joseph HS
Westchester IL

King Pamela L
Unity HS
Chicago IL

King Pamela S
Clever HS
Clever MO

King Ray H
Parkside HS
Jackson MI

King Thomas R
Winner HS
Winner SD

King William N
Potosi Riii HS
Flat River MO

Kingma Claudia S
Warsaw HS
Warsaw MO

Kingma Melody R
Kalamazoo Christian HS
Middleville MI

Kingsbury Matthew P
Neillsville HS
Neilsville WI

Kingsley Kathryn A
Nordonia HS
Wheatland ND

Kingsley Toni S
Elk Rapids Sr HS
Kewadin MI

Kinkade Edward E
Eddyville HS
Eddyville IA

Kinkor Roger D
S Winneshiek HS
Calmar IA

Kinlund Kurt K
Logan View HS
Hooper NE

Kinney David R
La Ville HS
Plymouth IN

Kinney Edward V
J E Murphy HS
Hurley WI

Kinnison Jennifer K
Zalma HS
Arab MO

Kinser Michael J
Greenfield HS
Greenfield IL

Kinsey Daniel B
Garrett HS
Garrett IN

Kintz Christina M
St Josephs HS
South Bend IN

Kinzey Becky S
Sweet Springs HS
Sweet Springs MO

Kinzinger Randall D
New Athens Unit Dist #60 HS
New Athens IL

Kiraly Thomas E
Edison Sr HS
East Gary IN

Kirby Michael J
Herrin HS
Herrin IL

Kirby Sara L
Mac Arthur HS
Decatur IL

Kirby Susan M
Herrin HS
Herrin IL

Kircher Sherry L
Harrisonville Sr HS
Harrisonville MO

Kirchner Cynthia M
Coon Rapids HS
Blaine MN

Kirchner Lisa A
Chandlerville HS
Virginia IL

Kirchner Randal F
St Edmond HS
Fort Dodge IA

Kirchoff Victoria A
Granite City So HS
Granite City IL

Kirick George R
Oklee Public HS
Trail MN

Kirk Franklin R
Sauk Prairie HS
Prairie Du Sac WI

Kirk Nancy V
Rockford East HS
Rockford IL

Kirkes Bryan B
Green Way HS
Bovey MN

Kirkland Eric L
Cass Tech HS
Detroit MI

Kirkpatrick Donna M
Palco HS
Palco KS

Kirn Dean F
Cape Central 'S
Cape Girardeau MO

Kirsch James D
Dickinson HS
Gladstone ND

Kirschman Cindy M
Glenham HS
Glenham SD

Kirwin Wayne C
Walkerville HS
Walkerville MI

Kish Barbara A
George Rogers Clark HS
Whiting IN

Kish Bernadette
Schulte HS
Terre Haute IN

Kissane Barbara E
Barrington HS
Barrington IL

Kissee Tom W
Greenwood HS
Springfield MO

Kissinger Cindy L
Hiawatha HS
Hiawatha KS

Kisslinger Kristi R
Larned Senior HS
Larned KS

Kitch Gayland D
Buhler HS
Hutchinson KS

Kitchen Stephen A
Roosevelt HS
Des Moines IA

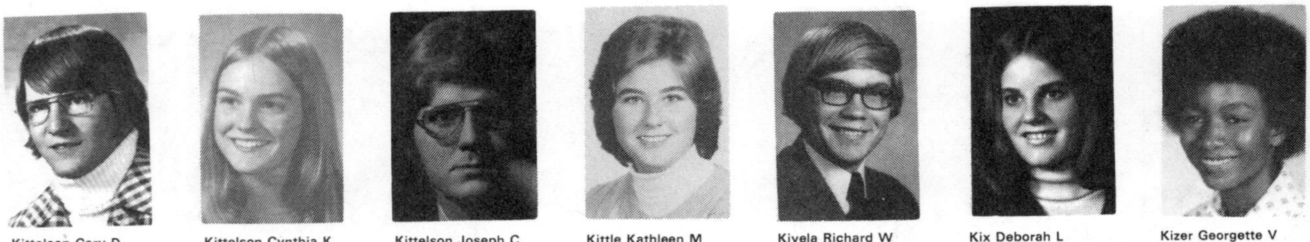

Kittelson Cary D
Veiva Public HS
Veiva ND

Kittelson Cynthia K
Watertown HS
Watertown SD

Kittelson Joseph C
Mcintosh HS
Mcintosh SD

Kittle Kathleen M
Dominican HS
Grosse Pte Pk MI

Kivela Richard W
L Anse HS
Covington MI

Kix Deborah L
Hubbard Community HS
Hubbard IA

Kizer Georgette V
Hyde Park HS
Chicago IL

Kjeldahl Joy K
Cyrus Public HS
Cyrus MN

Klabunde Jane F
White Shield HS
Emmet ND

Klaffer Johnny L
Brookport HS
Brookport IL

Klainsek Karen L
North Greene HS
White Hall IL

Klamer John M
Kirkwood HS
Frontenac MO

Klapotz Nancy R
Hutchinson HS
Hutchinson MN

Klas Paul T
Ozaukee HS
Fredonia WI

Klassen Kathy M
Burke Central HS
Lignite ND

Klaus Brenda S
Marian HS
Hays KS

Klaus Cindy M
Marian HS
Hays KS

Klaver Lenny R
Northeast Hamilton HS
Kamrar IA

Klavins Sandra
East Kentwood HS
Kentwood MI

Klawes Jeffrey N
Rio HS
Rio WI

Klebba John P
Holly HS
Holly MI

Klebe Kristy J
Beardstown HS
Beardstown IL

Kleen Christy J
Franklin Public HS
Franklin NE

Klein Cindy L
Hoisington HS
Hoisington KS

Klein Jeffrey G
Hazen Public HS
Hazen ND

Klein Jelena M
Hazen Public HS
Hazen ND

Klein Julie A
Bentley HS
Livonia MI

Klein Karen E
Hazelwood East Sr HS
St Louis MO

Klein Kathleen A
Port Huron Northern HS
Port Huron MI

Klein Michael J
Lakeshore HS
St Clair Shores MI

Klein Paul J
Loyola Academy
Chicago IL

Klein Perry G
Pella Comm HS
Pella IA

Klein Robert M
New Trier West HS
Wilmette IL

Klein Sharon M
Leo HS
Durango IA

Klein Terry W
Thomas More Prep HS
Ellinwood KS

Klein Zane L
Milan C Ii HS
Harris MO

Kleine Donna R
Aurora HS
Aurora IN

Kleinhuizer David W
Danube HS
Blomkest MN

Kleinschmidt Jodi K
Iron Mountain HS
Iron Mountain MI

Kleis John E
Burlington HS
Burlington IA

Kleist Gary A
Altoona Public HS
Altoona WI

Kleist Janice R
Janesville Craig Sr HS
Janesville WI

Klem Jackie A
Forest Park HS
Huntingburg IN

Klemek Buddy C
Mound Westonka HS
Maple Plain MN

Klemett Katherine L
Hancock Central HS
Hancock MI

Klemm Christine P
Kaneland Sr HS
Maple Park IL

Klemm David M
Waterford Mott HS
Pontiac MI

Klemm Steven R
Ludington HS
Ludington MI

Klepsteen Claudia G
Pennfield HS
Battle Creek MI

Klich Michele M
Andrean HS
Gary IN

Klickstein Lloyd B
Mt Pleasant HS
Mt Pleasant MI

Klika Cynthia A
Wrightstown HS
Greenleaf WI

Klika Mark S
Oconto HS
Oconto WI

Klimek Kristine T
Merrill Sr HS
Merrill WI

Kline David H
Seymoor HS
Barry IL

Kline Dennis L
Three Rivers HS
Three Rivers MI

Kline Rex B
Kalkaska HS
Alden MI

Kling Mark P
Carl Sandburg HS
Palos Heights IL

Klingbail Kathleen A
Saint John Cathedral HS
Milwaukee WI

Klinger Paul C
Fingal Public HS
Oriska ND

Klingler Debbie A
Clay City HS
Noble IL

Klingspon Mary J
Lakeshore HS
Baroda MI

Klinkel Douglas D
Charles City Community HS
Charles City IA

Klisares Steve C
Stephen Decatur HS
Decatur IL

Klitgaard Barbara A
Harlan Community HS
Harlan IA

Klitzke David A
Oakland Craig HS
Oakland NE

Klitzke Tom W
Cambridge Senior HS
Cambridge MN

Klobe Deborah A
Southwest HS
St Louis MO

Klobuchar Louis A
Rich Central HS
Country Club Hills IL

Kloepper Gary L
Red Bud HS
Red Bud IL

Kloepper Janell L
Neligh HS
Tilden NE

Kloker Marsha J
Beardstown Sr HS
Beardstown IL

Klont Jeffrey E
Charlotte HS
Charlotte MI

Klootwyk Kent W
Knoxville HS
Knoxville IA

Klopf Gary J
Madison HS
Madison SD

Kloppenborg Joyce S
O Neill Public HS
O Neill NE

Klopping Jeffrey L
Central HS
Omaha NE

Klose Carl O
Southwest HS
St Louis MO

Kloss Brian K
Switzerland County HS
Vevay IN

Klosterman Debra A
Platte Community HS
Platte SD

Klosterman Susan M
Wyndmere Public HS
Wyndmere ND

Klosterman Victor J
Wahpoton Senior HS
Mooreton ND

Kloth Larry W
Cahokia HS
Cahokia IL

Klotter Jenine D
Resurrection HS
Chicago IL

Kluk Diane P
Marie S HS
Chicago IL

Klump Carol A
Whiteford HS
Ottawa Lake MI

Klungseth Mary A
Hamlin Ind Dist #1 HS
Bryant SD

Klusendorf Byran J
Mount Horeb HS
Mount Horeb WI

Klyn Sharon K
Mt Pleasant HS
Mt Pleasant IA

Kmiatek Kim M
Morton Sr HS
Hammond IN

Kmucha Steven T
Galena HS
Galena IL

Knabusch Robert W
Ida HS
Monroe MI

Knack Connie J
S S Peter & Paul HS
Saginaw MI

Knapp Patricia A
Galesburg Sr HS
Wataga IL

Knapp Russell L
Western Comm HS
Sheffield IL

Kneifl Dennis G
West Salem HS
Coon Valley WI

Kness Sheree J
Fairmont HS
Grafton NE

Knezevich Mike P
Morton Sr HS
Hammond IN

Knickerbocker Kevin B
Winfield HS
Winfield KS

Knight Dianne M
Monroe HS
Monroe MI

Knight Kenneth G
Frankenmuth HS
Frankenmuth MI

Knight Pamela K
Brazil Sr HS
Brazil IN

Knipfer Sherry M
Tomahawk HS
Tomahawk WI

Knipmeyer Susan L
Pittsfield HS
Pittsfield IL

Knipp Sylvia T
Tipton HS
Tipton MO

Knobeloch Bruce N
Granite City South HS
Granite City IL

Knock David D
Williamsburg HS
Williamsburg IA

Knodel Kerry L
Velva Public HS
Velva ND

Knoll Allen J
Turner HS
Kansas City KS

Knollman Brenda J
United Township HS
East Moline IL

Knoop Shelby J
Neillsville HS
Neillsville WI

Knowlan Mary S
Jackson HS
Jackson MO

Knox Barbara S
Sand Creek HS
Sand Creek MI

Knox Robert D
Edwardsburg HS
Edwardsburg MI

Knox Twyla J
Monango Public HS
Monango ND

Knox William B
Butler HS
Butler MO

Knuckey Todd A
Rochester Comm HS
Rochester IL

Knudsen Elizabeth A
Watertown Sr HS
Watertown SD

Knudsen Kathleen A
Wheaton Christian HS
Wheaton IL

Knupp Linda J
Southern HS
Lomay IL

Knute Kristina M
Alvarado Public HS
Warren MN

Knuth Richard H
Elmhurst HS
Ft Wayne IN

Knutson Donovan L
Warren HS
Radium MN

Knutson Kathy S
St Martins Academy
Rapid City SD

Kobe Anne M
Lake Orion HS
Lake Orion MI

Kobylarczyk Roger A
Thorp HS
Thorp WI

Koca Jane
Whitnall HS
Hales Corners WI

Kocevar Gail L
Benzie Central HS
Interlochen MI

Koch Mary C
Potosi R 3 HS
Cadet MO

Koch Robert A
Forest View HS
Mt Prospect IL

Koch Russell L
Mora HS
Brook Park MN

Kochanny William F
Hubbard HS
Chicago IL

Kochka Jane C
Hinsdale Twnshp Central HS
Oak Brook IL

Kocian Stephen T
New Richmond Senior HS
New Richmond WI

Kocik Deborah S
Elk Grove HS
Des Plaines IL

Kocourek Bruce W
Tyndall HS
Tyndall SD

Koehler Cindy S
Van Buren HS
Center Point IN

Koehler Daniel E
South Adams HS
Berne IN

Koehler Elizabeth A
Oconomowoc HS
Oconomowoc WI

Koehler Gerald L
Clay Center HS
Clay Center NE

Koehler Mindy L
Van Buren HS
Center Point IN

Koehn Genette E
Larimore HS
Larimore ND

Koel Dianna L
Lenora HS
Lenora KS

Koel Janet L
Norton Co HS
Norton KS

Koelliker Gregg E
Highland HS
Highland KS

Koelling Kimberly A
Lincoln Way HS
Manhattan IL

Koelsch Nancy L A
Wyatt Rd HS
Standish MI

Koenigsfeld Ronald L
Charles City HS
Charles City IA

Koeppen Carrie J
Lytton Comm HS
Jolley IA

Koester Wayne T
Northwestern Dist #63
HS
Mansfield SD

Koestler Catherine A
Stewartville HS
Stewartville MN

Kohanek Mary L
Steinmetz HS
Chicago IL

Kohl Maureen A
Bradley Bourbonnais HS
Bourbonnais IL

Kohlbrecher Kimberly D
Wesclin Jr Sr HS
Trenton IL

Kohler Jeffrey V
Wheeling HS
Wheeling IL

Kohler Suzanne
St Marys Central HS
Biomarck ND

Kohlhase Mark E
Golden Valley HS
Golden Valley MN

Kohlmeyer Thomas L
Central HS
Evansville IN

Kohout Michael J
Brother Rice HS
Oak Lawn IL

Koif Valerie J
Buffalo Grove HS
Arlington Hts IL

Kokesh David J
Eas Chas Mix #102 HS
Wagner SD

Kokkeler Susan J
Garrison HS
Garrison ND

Kokko Joanne F
Jeffers HS
South Range MI

Kolar Mary Anne L
Center Line HS
Warren MI

Kolb Kathy J
Onalaska HS
Onalaska WI

Kolb Mark P
Rich Central HS
Matteson IL

Kolbet Alan E
New Hampton Comm HS
Alta Vista IA

Kolbusz Robert V
Saint Patrick HS
Chicago IL

Kole Cheryl A
Holland Christian HS
Holland MI

Kolean David L
West Ottawa HS
Holland MI

Kolean Warren L
West Ottawa HS
Holland MI

Kolinski Patricia G
Our Lady Of Mercy HS
Detroit MI

Koller Craig P
Iron Mountain HS
Iron Mountain MI

Kolodziej John P
St Bede Academy
La Salle IL

Kolosowski Andrew E
Prosser Vocational HS
Chicago IL

Kolschefsky Debra K
Drake Public HS
Drake ND

Kolstad Kimberly S
Gaylord Public HS
Gaylord MN

Kolves Kimberly A
Balyki Community HS
Bath IL

Komarek Cheryl L
Bethlehem Academy
Lonsdale MN

Komasa John S
Stevens Point Area Sr HS
Stevens Point WI

Kommer Michael W
Metropolis Comm HS
Metropolis IL

Komperda Joseph J
Maine Township East HS
Park Ridge IL

Kondelis Nicholas P
New Trier West HS
Wilmette IL

Konecki Mark L
Luke M Powers HS
Flint MI

Konen Deborah L
Lake Orion HS
Lake Orion MI

Konen Jeanne M
Roseland Public HS
Roseland NE

Konrad Dieder
Thornton Twp HS
South Holland IL

Koopman Cheryl M
Martin Public HS
Martin MI

Koopman Douglas L
Hamilton HS
Holland MI

Kooser Kimberly I
Perry Lecompten HS
Perry KS

Kopchik John C
Andrean HS
Merrillville IN

Kopetz Kristine L
Mac Arthur HS
Decatur IL

Kopfman Roxanne R
Lakin HS
Lakin KS

Kopish Penny E
Marinette Sr HS
Marinette WI

Kopp James O
Anderson Sr HS
Anderson IN

Koppa Susan
Wausau East HS
Wausau WI

Korb Annette J
Georgetown HS
Georgetown IL

Korb Heather C
Burr Oak HS
Burr Oak KS

Kordonowy Gerard A
Belfield HS
Belfield ND

Koressel Lynn A
Reitz Memorial HS
Evansville IN

Korf Gina M
Forest Lake HS
Forest Lake MN

Korf Therese M
Forest Lake Sr HS
Forest Lake MN

Korican Donald R
Britton Macon HS
Britton MI

Korman David L
Glenbrook North HS
Northbrook IL

Korn Tim A
Elston Sr HS
Michigan City IN

Kornelis Daniel W
Langdon HS
Langdon ND

Kornely Debra J
Mishicot Community HS
Two Rivers WI

Korol Anthony M
Marquette HS
Michigan City IN

Koronkiewicz Frank O
Thornridge HS
Dolton IL

Korpela Michael W
A D Johnston HS
Ramsay MI

Korpi Wayne I
Ishpeming HS
Ishpeming MI

Korsmeyer Vicky M
Blair Oaks HS
Jefferson MO

Korsmo Jeffrey O
Lourdes HS
Rochester MN

Kortenhoven Donald L
Thornton Fractional S HS
Lansing IL

Korthauer Cathy S
Fenton HS
Bensenville IL

Korver Karen R
Maurice Orangecity Comm HS
Maurice IA

Korzan Cheryl L
Kimball Public HS
Kimball SD

Korzeniowski Matthew C
St Laurence HS
Chicago IL

Koschmeder Kent C
Riceville HS
Riceville IA

Kosinski Timothy F
St Agatha HS
Southfield MI

Koskamp Mark A
North Linn HS
Coggon IA

Koski Julianne E
John F Kennedy HS
Babbitt MN

Koslowski Eric A
High School
North Branch MN

Kosman Joseph J
Mendel HS
Calumet Park IL

Kosmatka Mary E
Minto Public HS
Minto ND

Kosogof John
Taft HS
Chicago IL

Kosse Ronda K
Bladen Public HS
Bladen NE

Koszyk Philip M
Loyola Academy
Chicago IL

Kotecki Judith A
Thorp HS
Thorp WI

Koth James R
Ralston HS
Ralston NE

Kotinek David J
Superior HS
Superior NE

Kotowski Karen L
La Salle Peru Twp HS
La Salle IL

Koubek Catherine A
Arnold HS
Arnold NE

Kouns Cheryl A
Zionsville Comm HS
Zionsville IN

Kouns Marjorie K
West Leyden HS
Melrose Park IL

Kouros Joan
Bishop Noll HS
East Chicago IN

Koutek Robert J
Riverside Brookfield HS
La Grange Pk IL

Kovach Eugene D
Oakridge Senior HS
Muskegon MI

Kovacin Kenneth L
Thornton Twp HS
Riverdale IL

Kovack Michael J
Taylorville Sr HS
Taylorville IL

Kovacs James
Elgin HS
Hanover Park IL

Kovarik Janet S
Burwell Jr Sr HS
Burwell NE

Kovelle Debbie M
Divine Child HS
Detroit MI

Kowalczyk Katherine A
Resurrection HS
Niles IL

Kowalczyk Michael J
Evergreen Park Comm HS
Evergreen Pk IL

Kowalski Edward J
Thornton Fractional So HS
Lansing IL

Kowalski Jody A
St Joseph HS
Chicago IL

Kowalski Thomas J
Bedford HS
Temperance MI

Kowles Douglas R
Winona Sr HS
Winona MN

Kozak Trena L
St Teresa HS
Decatur IL

Kozel Donna R
E Grand Forks Sr HS
E Grand Forks MN

Koziel Ruth M
Oak Lawn Comm HS
Oak Lawn IL

Koziol Kristina E
Centerville HS
Centerville IA

Koziol Patrick J
Holy Cross HS
Chicago IL

Kozisek Joan M
David City Public HS
Bruno NE

Kozlowski Zbigniew A
Lane Tech HS
Chicago IL

Kozojed John F
Quigley South HS
Chicago IL

Krab Rodney G
Paxton Consolidated HS
Paxton NE

Kracher Beverly J
Platteview Jr Sr HS
Papillion NE

Kraemer Beverly A
Hutsonville HS
Hutsonville IL

Kraemer John C
Paris HS
Paris IL

Kraenzler Erik J
Greendale HS
Greendale WI

Kragenbring Kendall A
Atwater Public HS
Atwater MN

Krahnke Keith C
Detour HS
Drummond Island MI

Kraklow David A
Rockridge HS
Illinois City IL

Kraklow Michael P
Muscatine HS
Muscatine IA

Kralik Scott D
Marshalltown HS
Marshalltown IA

Kramer Alan D
Stapleton HS
Gandy NE

Kramer Ann D
Garrigan HS
Bode IA

Kramer James A
Stephen Decatur HS
Decatur IL

Kramer Kellee R
S F C HS
St Francis KS

Kramer Kerri J
Stapleton HS
Stapleton NE

Kramer Mary A
Luckey HS
Ogden KS

Kramer Polly A
Arthur County HS
Hyannis Rr NE

Kramer Rodney M
Winnebago HS
Rockford IL

Kramme Mark P
Plattsmouth HS
Plattsmouth NE

Kramschuster Brenda L
Bloomer HS
Bloomer WI

Krancic Karen J
La Salle Peru HS
Oglesby IL

Krane Margy L
Castlewood HS
Bemis SD

Krapu Benita R
East Grand Forks Sr HS
East Grand Forks MN

Kratcha Lynn C
Lidgerwood HS
Cayuga ND

Kratzenberg Susan A
New Glarus HS
Monticello WI

Kraus Allan
Homewood Flossmoor HS
Homewood IL

Kraus Karen
Shullsburg HS
Shullsburg WI

Kraus Kathy L
Mission Valley HS
Eskridge KS

Kraus Laurie A
Gwinn HS
Little Lake MI

Krause Debra L
Crivitz HS
Crivitz WI

Krause Ruth A
Amos Alonzo Stagg HS
Palos Hills IL

Krause Sharon F
Elkhart Memorial HS
Elkhart IN

Krause Stephen P
Roosevelt HS
Minneapolis MN

Krause Steven W
Alden Community HS
Alden IA

Krause Thomas A
John Marshall HS
Rochester MN

Krausert Kathryn E
West HS
Green Bay WI

Krcmarik Laurie A
Corunna HS
Corunna MI

Krebill Rhonda B
Central HS
Donnellson IA

Krebsbach Laure S
Lomira HS
Brownsville WI

Krebsbach Sharon M
Flint Holy Rosary HS
Flint MI

Krecsmar M Christine
Marian HS
Elkhart IN

Kreeger Robert A
Richwoods HS
Peoria IL

Kreftmeyer Linda L
High School
Owensville MO

Kreider Steven P
Kingsford HS
Kingsford MI

Kreidlkamp Karen R
Fingal Public HS
Valley City ND

Kreilein Michael A
Jasper HS
Jasper IN

Kreisel Kathleen T
Mother Theodore Guerin
HS
Chicago IL

Kreisel Maureen L
Mother Theodore Guerin
HS
Chicago IL

Krekow Roger D
Sutherland HS
Sutherland IA

Kremer Joy A
Ashley Community HS
Bannister MI

Kremin Denise J
Central HS
Glenwood MN

Kremitzki Janet M
Sacred Heart Academy
Springfield IL

Krempasky Rebecca S
Metropolis Community HS
Metropolis IL

Krenger Teresa A
Abilene HS
Abilene KS

Krenik John W
Montgomery HS
Lonsdale MN

Krenz Jay E
Wheaton HS
Wheaton MN

Kretschman Allyson K
Lakeland HS
La Grange IN

Kreutzfeldt Michael L
Spencer Independent HS
Spencer SD

Kreycik Ann
Valentine HS
Valentine NE

Kreye Debra R
Wabasha Kellogg HS
Wabasha MN

Kribs Kathleen B
Corunna HS
Corunna MI

Krich Karen M
St Charles HS
St Charles MO

Krichau Cindy L
Bladen Public HS
Bladen NE

Krick John R
Reese HS
Reese MI

Krieger Karen I
Bemidji HS
Bemidji MN

Krienke Donald H
Lester Prairie Public HS
Lester Prairie MN

Krier Bonnie M
Pocahontas Community
HS
Laurens IA

Krier Roy P
Columbus HS
Marshfield WI

Kriesche Joyce A
Holmen HS
Holmen WI

Kripowicz John P
Trenton HS
Trenton MI

Krist Robert J
Creighton Prep
Omaha NE

Kritzman Marilyn S
Deckerville HS
Deckerville MI

Krivsky Karen J
Argo Comm HS
Bridgeview IL

Kroeger Craig A
Freeport Sr HS
Freeport IL

Kroening Thomas J
Premontre HS
Green Bay WI

Krogman Terry P
St Marys HS
O Neill NE

Kroh John S
Wawasee HS
Syracuse IN

Krohn Carol A
Laker HS
Elkton MI

Krohn Kelly D
Harvey HS
Harvey ND

Krohse Mark A
Luther South HS
Chicago IL

Krone John J
Fatima HS
Westphalia MO

Krone Kayla L
Tri City HS
Riverton IL

Kronz Elizabeth K
Virden HS
Virden IL

Kroupa David L
Kimball HS
Kimball SD

Krouse Joe R
Crocker HS
Crocker MO

Krpan Thomas J
Taft HS
Chicago IL

Kruckeberg Michael G
Edwardsville Sr HS
Worden IL

Krueger Brian D
Washington HS
Richfield WI

Krueger Catherine A
Bunker Hill HS
Bunker Hill IL

Krueger Donald K
Washington Comm HS
Washington IL

Krueger Gregory W
Jefferson HS
Bloomington MN

Krueger John L
Ottawa Township HS
Ottawa IL

Krueger John M
Clarence Lowden HS
Lowden IA

Krueger Kenneth M
Breckenridge Sr HS
Wheeler MI

Krueger Linda C
Sherrard HS
Milan IL

Krug Patrick M
Hettinger HS
Bucyrus ND

Krugel Jo Ann V
Carl Schurz HS
Chicago IL

Kruger Gretchen A
Hallock HS
Hallock MN

Kruger Kevin L
Campbell Tintah HS
Wheaton MN

Kruger Sherilynn E
Pinconning Area HS
Rhodes MI

Krumm Tim D
So Hamilton HS
Stanhope IA

Krupa Steven J
St Gregorys HS
Chicago IL

Krupowicz James J
Plainfield HS
Plainfield IL

Kruse Ila M
Bradley Bourbonnais HS
Bourbonnais IL

Kruse Karen J
Brunswick Rii HS
Brunswick MO

Kruse Kathy J
Brunswick Rii HS
Brunswick MO

Kruse Lisa F
Johnson Brock HS
Tecumseh NE

Kruse Michael E
Flora HS
Flora IL

Kruse Vernamae F
Turkey Valley Comm HS
Waucoma IA

Krusenoski Gary R
Marist HS
Calumet Park IL

Krusenstjerna Christine A
Spencer HS
Spencer IA

Krusiewicz Michael R
Ferndale HS
Ferndale MI

Krusniak Jean M
Catholic Central HS
Manistee MI

Krych Nancy M
St Alphonsus HS
Detroit MI

Krysl Donald R
West Holt HS
Stuart NE

Kryston David J
Catholic Central HS
Monroe MI

Krzyewski Nancy M
Catholic Memorial HS
Hales Corners WI

Krzyston John J
Chadsey HS
Detroit MI

Kubacki Sheri
Onaway Area HS
Onaway MI

Kubalak Sharon M
Green Bay Preble HS
Green Bay WI

Kubasch Kent K
Holy Trinity HS
Winsted MN

Kubat Christopher K
Ryan HS
Omaha NE

Kubes Scott K
Niles West HS
Niles IL

Kubik Keith K
Central Public HS
Valparaiso NE

Kubik Kimberly A
Martansdale St Marys HS
St Marys IA

Kubik Pamela L
Riverside Brookfield HS
Riverside IL

Kubischta Diane M
Dickinson HS
Dickinson ND

Kubitschek Sylvia U
Proviso East HS
Maywood IL

Kucera Kevin C
Creighton Prep
Omaha NE

Kucera Ronald L
Howells HS
Howells NE

Kucharz Karen A
Lockport Township HS
Lockport IL

Kucharzyk Donald W
Riverside Brookfield HS
La Grange Park IL

Kudanowicz Miron
De La Salle HS
Minneapolis MN

Kuebler William R
Fargo North HS
Fargo ND

Kuechler Michael G
Lomira HS
Lomira WI

Kuehl Linda L
Kewaunee HS
Kewaunee WI

Kuehn Ellen M
New Hampton Comm HS
Iowa City IA

Kuehn Ronald L
Northeast HS
Lincoln NE

Kueneman Richard R
Highland Comm HS
Ainsworth IA

Kuenning Bruce H
Wahoo Public HS
Wahoo NE

Kuensting Donna M
Jefferson City Sr HS
Jefferson City MO

Kuenzli Linda A
Alton HS
Alton IL

Kuester Kerry A
Hutchinson HS
Hutchinson MN

Kugler Gary R
Stet R Xv HS
Norborne MO

Kuhl Lorri M
O Gorman HS
Sioux Falls SD

Kuhl Marsha L
Usa HS
Sebewaing MI

Kuhle Kimberly A
Assumption HS
Assumption IL

Kuhn Deborah L
Hinsdale Central HS
Hinsdale IL

Kuhn Rebecca A
Turkey Valley HS
Fort Atkinson IA

Kuhn Robert A
Victoria HS
Victoria KS

Kuhn Susan D
Oregon HS
Oregon IL

Kuhn Teri L
Parkway Central Sr HS
Chesterfield MO

Kuhns Sandra L
Archbishop Wm O Brady HS
South St Paul MN

Kuiper Jeanne E
Central Wisc Christian HS
Waupun WI

Kuipers Ray N
Dakota Christian HS
Platte SD

Kujath Jeffery J
Meridian HS
Daykin NE

Kula Gary M
Lane Tech HS
Chicago IL

Kulbaba Terry J
Farmington HS
Farmington MI

Kuldanek Gregory A
Gobles Public HS
Gobles MI

Kulinski Christine A
Divine Savior Holy Angels HS
Milwaukee WI

Kulosa Faye M
Resurrection HS
Chicago IL

Kummer Carol L
Helias HS
Jefferson City MO

Kummer Kay J
Hastngs Senior HS
Hampton MN

Kundinger Diana R
Arthur Hill HS
Saginaw MI

Kunin William E
Washburn HS
Minneapolis MN

Kunnemann Myron K
Chase County HS
Imperial NE

Kuntz Sara J
Gridley HS
Gridley IL

Kuntz Terry E
Dodgeland HS
Juneau WI

Kunz Danny L
Attica HS
Attica KS

Kunz Nancy
Lakeview HS
Decatur IL

Kupper John D
Nicolet HS
Milwaukee WI

Kurczewski Cheryl A
Hillcrest HS
Hazel Crest IL

Kurgan Mary K
Wells Easton HS
Wells MN

Kurrelmeier Kathryn S
Interlochen Arts Academy
Paris IL

Kurt Paul
Monticello Comm HS
Monticello IA

Kurtyka Kathleen A
Frankfort HS
Frankfort MI

Kurz Kathryn D
Oak Park HS
Gladstone MO

Kurzdorfer Richard S
Edison HS
East Gary IN

Kurzeja Robert M
Griffith HS
Griffith IN

Kusay Denise M
Hillcrest HS
Hazel Crest IL

Kuschel Gareth E
Ashwaubenon HS
Green Bay WI

Kuske David E
Downers Grove South HS
Downers Grove IL

Kusler Janae E
Central HS
Aberdeen SD

Kussman Keith D
Lincoln HS
Wisconsin Rapids WI

Kusyk Borys I
Wheeling HS
Prospect Heights IL

Kuykendall Patricia M
Highland HS
Highland IN

Kuyper Arend P
Corsica Comm Dist 22 HS
Corsica SD

Kvisgaard Cynthia B
Mother Guerin HS
Chicago IL

Kyes Kristi M
Farmington East HS
Farmington IL

Kyger Ronald K
Southmont HS
Crawfordsville IN

Kyker Wynell M
Polo Comm HS
Polo IL

Kyko Mary B
Huron HS
New Boston MI

Kyle Lois J
Ballard HS
Kelley IA

Kyle Shirley A
Beaumont HS
St Louis MO

Kyler Diane S
Columbia City Joint HS
Columbia City IN

L

Laabs Janet S
Sentral HS
Lone Rock IA

La Barge Jane A
Concordia HS
Concordia KS

Labedz Carol J
Bryan Sr HS
Omaha NE

Labella Peter M
Ann Arbor Pioneer HS
Ann Arbor MI

La Bine Bonnie B
Ontonagon Area HS
Ontonagon MI

La Bov Allen D
Snider HS
Ft Wayne IN

Lacey Terry L
Holton HS
Holton KS

La Chance Charles P
Saint Laurence HS
Chicago Ridge IL

La Chance Roy P
Potosi HS
Potosi MO

Lacher Julie M
St Martys Central HS
Bismarck ND

Lackens Gregory D
Academy Of Holy Angels
Minneapolis MN

Lackey Brian C
Lapel HS
Lapel IN

La Croix Cheryl A
Valders HS
Newton WI

La Croix Cheryl A
Bethlehem Academy
Faribault MN

Ladage Brent A
Auburn HS
Auburn IL

Ladd Merry M
Hanover Horton HS
Harton MI

Ladd Merry M
Hanover Horton HS
Horton MI

Ladenburger Jay T
Wheatland HS
Grainfield KS

Ladenburger Mary C
Wheatland HS
Grainfield KS

Ladman Brenda J
Crete Sr HS
Crete NE

La Fave Roberta K
Oseoda HS
Oseoda MI

Lafayette Jack N
Southern HS
Stronghurst IL

Lafever Joni L
Burlington Comm HS
Burlington IA

Lafew Valerie S
Jefferson HS
Rockford IL

Lafferty Mark E
Crestwood HS
Dearborn Heights MI

Laffoon Renee
Chicago Vocational HS
Chicago IL

Lagemann David P
Elsberry HS
Elsberry MO

Lagemann John D
Concordia HS
Concordia KS

Lager Benadict W
Scottsbluff HS
Scottsbluff NE

La Haie Linda S
Cheboygan Area Public HS
Cheboygan MI

Lahner Larry
Harvard Community HS
Harvard IL

Lahr Patricia D
Monrovia HS
Martinsville IN

Lahr Terry L
Gibson City HS
Foosland IL

Lahti Cathy L
Marquette Sr HS
Marquette MI

Laible Alan J
Lowpoint Washburn HS
Washburn IL

Laindenberger Debra K
Underwood Public HS
Underwood ND

Laing Lynda L
Harper Creek HS
Battle Creek MI

Laird Mickal E
Du Quoin HS
Du Quoin IL

Laken Michael R
Gwinn Area Community HS
Gwinn MI

Lakes Marsha K
P A Allen HS
Bluffton IN

Lakowski David E
Gordon Tech HS
Chicago IL

Lakowski Judith A
St Scholastica HS
Chicago IL

Lall Al V
Duchesne HS
St Charles MO

La Mantia Gary M
William Howard Taft HS
Chicago IL

La Mar James N
Centerville HS
Richmond IN

Lamb Beverley J
Charlestown HS
Charlestown IN

Lamb Kathleen C
Terre Haute North Vigo HS
Terre Haute IN

Lambers Beth D
Holland Christian HS
Holland MI

Lamberson Brent A
Oakland Christian HS
Pontiac MI

Lamberson Linda D
Kimball County HS
Kimball NE

Lambert Ada A
Franklin Public HS
Riverton NE

Lambert Debbie L
Pleasant Ridge HS
Leavenworth KS

Lambert Kimberly E
George Washington HS
Chicago IL

Lambert Ronda S
U D #237 HS
Smith Center KS

Lamborne Brett A
Highland HS
Alexandria IN

Lambright Richard W
Litchfield HS
Litchfield MI

Lamer Cheryl A
Elk Horn Kimballton HS
Walnut IA

Lamers Sharon A
Appleton West HS
Appleton WI

Lamkin Angi C
Lincoln HS
Willis MI

Lamm Darla J
Mt Pleasant HS
Mt Pleasant IA

Lamm Pamela J
Norris HS
Hickman NE

Lammers Tracy L
Everly Community HS
Everly IA

Lammers Vivian L
Sandoval Community HS
Sandoval IL

Lamon Margaret J
Floyd Central HS
Lanesville IN

La Montagne Rochelle A
Marian HS
Southfield MI

Lamore Karen A
River Valley HS
New Buffalo MI

Lampe Mary M
Campbell HS
Campbell MO

Lampe Roger L
Falls City HS
Falls City NE

Lampinen Karen L
Chassell HS
Chassell MI

Lamping William P
Wilmington HS
Wilmington IL

Lampros George L
Hinsdale Central HS
Oak Brook IL

Lance Dennis W
Manchester HS
N Manchester IN

Lanctot Chet D
Wylie E Groves HS
Southfield MI

Lanctot Jay J
Hancock Central HS
Hancock MI

Land Julie M
Litchfield Sr HS
Litchfield IL

Landem Carol M
Taft HS
Chicago IL

Landers Craig C
Scottsbluff Sr HS
Scottsbluff NE

Landers Karen A
Mendota HS
Earlville IL

Landers Sharlene K
Tri County Comm HS
What Cheer IA

Landers Steven W
Risco HS
Lilbourn MO

Landis Diane R
William Henry Harrison HS
West Lafayette IN

Landis James H
Byron HS
Oregon IL

Landis Pamela J
Goshen HS
Goshen IN

Landoll Joyce M
Pierce City HS
Pierce City MO

Landon John A
Carrington Sr HS
Carrington ND

Landry Donald A
East HS
Kansas City MO

Landry Margaret E
Florence HS
Florence WI

Landstrom David E
Mitchell HS
Mitchell NE

Landstrum Mike J
No Mahaska HS
Barnes City IA

Lane Bonnie M
Lincolnway HS
Manhattan IL

Lane Burel H
St Thomas Public HS
St Thomas ND

Lane David A
Rensselaer Central HS
Rensselaer IN

Lane Dwight D
South Page HS
Blanchard IA

Lane Gregory L
Wm Chrisman HS
Independence MO

Lane Laurie E
Williamston HS
Williamston MI

Lane Madalyn A
William Howard Taft HS
Chicago IL

Lane Tony L
Westmer HS
New Boston IL

Lang Christine M
Lake Central HS
Madison SD

Lang Diane M
Naperville Central HS
Naperville IL

Lang Rodney A
Custer HS
Custer SD

Lang Susan F
New Ulm Sr HS
Lafayette MN

Lang Timothy D
Thomas More Prep HS
Hays KS

Langdalen Elvina E
Wildrose Public HS
Wildrose ND

Lange Larry W
Benton HS
Benton WI

Lange Linda L
Notre Dame HS
Cudahy WI

Lange Mary E
Lasalle Peru Twp HS
Lasalle IL

Lange Susan
Winnebago HS
Rockford IL

Lange Vernon J
Seymour HS
Black Creek WI

Langel Janet M
West Delaware HS
Manchester IA

Langen David W
Kennedy Public HS
Kennedy MN

Langenberg Keith A
Platt Valley Academy
Hoskins NE

Langendonk David P
Niles Sr HS
Niles MI

Langenfeld Forrest A
Centralia HS
Irvington IL

Langenfeld Marita A
Marian Catholic HS
Chicago Hts IL

Langenfeld Phillip M
Harlan Community HS
Harlan IA

Langer Joan P
Guide Rock HS
Guide Rock NE

Langer Lawrence P
Northfield Sr HS
Northfield MN

Langford James B
Lanphier HS
Springfield IL

Langford Jon A
Beaumont HS
St Louis MO

Langland Rebecca A
North Senior HS
Eau Claire WI

Langness Terry L
Minot Magic City Campus HS
Minot ND

Langston Ava R
Maplewood HS
Richmond Hgts MO

Lanham Mary K
Monroe City R 1 HS
Monroe City MO

Lanigan Nancy M
Philippine Duchesne HS
St Charles MO

Lanning Linda D
Paul Harding HS
New Haven IN

Lannoo Michael J
Moline HS
Moline IL

Lanser Richard L
Benet Academy
Lisle IL

Lansing Lorrie M
Grafton Central HS
Grafton ND

Lanter Randolph L
Maroa Forsyth HS
Maroa IL

Lanz Michael R
Pender HS
Pender NE

La Orange Desiree L
Pope County HS
Golconda IL

Lapak Cheryl L
Birch Run HS
Birch Run MI

La Parche Marla S
Westwood HS
Champion MI

La Parl Danny R
Algonac Community HS
Algonac MI

Lape Ken B
Matthews HS
Sikeston MO

La Peer Randy L
Cass City HS
Cass City MI

Lapham Deborah L
Harbor Beach HS
Harbor Beach MI

La Piana Janet G
Thornton Fractional North HS
Burnham IL

Lapine David
Crocker HS
Crocker MO

La Pine Mary M
Gladstone HS
Gladstone MI

Lapish Martha J
Port Huron Northern HS
Port Huron MI

La Porte Jacqueline B
Saginaw HS
Saginaw MI

Lappin John A
Clinton Comm HS
Clinton IL

Large Kevin E
Chase County HS
Wauneta NE

Large Leslie A
Beardstown Senior HS
Beardstown IL

Larimore Carmen B
Tipton HS
Tipton MO

Larsen Arnold P
Norway HS
Vulcan MI

Larsen Leslie J
Keya Paha County HS
Springview NE

Larsen Leslie J
Keya Paha Co HS
Springview NE

Larsen Marguerite E
Batavia Sr HS
Batavia IL

Larsen Victoria C
Hancock HS
Hancock MN

Larson Bruce E
Spring Valley HS
Spring Valley MN

Larson Candyce J
Jamestown HS
Jamestown KS

Larson Cindy K
Bisbee HS
Bisbee ND

Larson Deanna L
Warren HS
Warren MN

Larson Diana K
Marian HS
Omaha NE

Larson Diane D
Pecatonica HS
Blanchardville WI

Larson Doris A
Chamberlain HS
Pukwana SD

Larson Douglas W
New Rockford Central HS
New Rockford ND

Larson James A
Oklee Public HS
Oklee MN

Larson Janet L
Fargo South HS
Fargo ND

Larson Joel S
Waseca HS
Waseca MN

Larson Judy M
Clear Lake HS
Clear Lake IA

Larson Kathleen E
Durand HS
Durand WI

Larson Keith R
Hinsdale Central HS
Hinsdale IL

Larson Kenneth J
Glaesburg Sr HS
Galesburg IL

Larson Laurie J
Gibbon Public HS
Winthrop MN

Larson Pamela S
Kewanee HS
Kewanee IL

Larson Randal R
Auburndale HS
Auburndale WI

Larson Robert D
Hillcrest HS
Country Club Hills IL

Larson Robert W
Bertha Hewitt HS
Bertha MN

Larson Scott D
River Falls Sr HS
River Falls WI

Larson Shirley J
Prairie HS
Swisher IA

Larson Susan K
Iron Mountain HS
Iron Mountain MI

Larson Terry H
Winnebago HS
Winnebago MN

Larson William C
Orion HS
Andover IL

Lartz John A
Niles Township HS
Lincolnwood IL

La Rue Cheryl A
Whitko Comm HS
Pierceton IN

La Rue Donald L
Churubusco HS
Churubusco IN

Lasater Tom J
Dodge City HS
Dodge City KS

La Schum Paul H
Monona Grove HS
Wild Rose WI

Lash Edward G
Mattoon Sr HS
Mattoon IL

Lasko Keith A
Oak Park River Forest HS
Willow Springs IL

Laskowski Thomas M
Pacific HS
Villa Ridge MO

Lasky Phillip L
Notre Dame Boys HS
Chicago IL

Lasky Robin L
Stephen Tyng Mather HS
Chicago IL

Lasseter Gwenda M
Blue Eye HS
Blue Eye MO

Lasswell Robert A
Lakeland R 3 HS
Deepwater MO

Latch Doris I
Stewardson Strasburg HS
Stewardson IL

Lathrop Stephen W
Granite South HS
Granite City IL

Latino Dennis J
Streator Twp HS
Streator IL

Lattin Lisa J
Smith Center HS
Smith Center KS

Lauber Ron L
West Holt HS
Atkinson NE

Laubner Randal L
Hershey HS
Hershey NE

Lauby Mark G
Wausau East HS
Wausau WI

Lauderdale Allison L
Junction City Senior HS
Junction City KS

Laue Dale A
Wethersfield HS
Kewanee IL

Laue Rolanda J
Washington HS
Greenleaf KS

Lauer Irene M
Madonna HS
Chicago IL

Lauerdiere Janet M
Macomb Sr HS
Macomb IL

Laufer William P
Christian Brothers HS
St Louis MO

Laufman James D
New Trier West HS
Glencoe IL

Laughlin Kelley L
East Alton Wood River HS
Wood River IL

Laughter David F
Parkway North Sr HS
Creve Coeur MO

Lauke Theodore M
Adlai E Stevenson HS
Lincolnshire IL

Launer Sheila F
Warsaw HS
Warsaw IL

Lautenschlager Heidi M
Milford Twp HS
Milford IL

Lauteri Theresa L
Marian Catholic HS
Chicago Hgts IL

Laux Debra A
Appleton West HS
Appleton WI

Lavastida Lisa
Whitmore Lake HS
South Lyon MI

Lavell Kym A
Hamady HS
Flint MI

Lavelle Larry W
Hordville Public HS
Clarks NE

Lavelock Tammie L
Carrollton HS
Carrollton MO

La Vergne Debra K
Lake Linden Hubbell HS
Laurium MI

Lavery Donald L
Tri County Area HS
Sand Lake MI

Lavra Albert C
St Johns HS
St Johns MI

Lavrinovich Lee A
Crown Point HS
Crown Point IN

Law Martha D
Central HS
St Joseph MO

Lawhead Nanci J
Minden HS
Kearney NE

Lawler Barbara A
Washington HS
Two Rivers WI

Lawler Kirk S
Glenbard East HS
Lombard IL

Lawless Gayle J
North Farmington HS
Farmington Hills MI

Lawrence John M
Dwight David Eisenhower HS
Saginaw MI

Lawrence Julia K
A Jchs HS
Anna IL

Lawrence Lynette T
Owosso HS
Owosso MI

Lawrence Sharon B
Wisconsin Academy
Westchester IL

Lawrenz Robert W
Baldwin HS
Baldwin City KS

Lawshe Jan M
Bishop Noll Institute
Gary IN

Lawson John C
Crestland Community HS
Early IA

Lawson Kathryn L
Central Noble HS
Albion IN

Lawson Lonnie L
Hayes County HS
Hayes Center NE

Lawson Mary M
Hayes County HS
Hayes Center NE

Lawson Theresa L
Mattoon HS
Mattoon IL

Lawton Kathleen M
Our Lady Of Mercy HS
Livonia MI

Lawton Kent C
Richland Center HS
Richland Center WI

Lawyer Jan M
Yankton Sr HS
Yankton SD

Laydon James R
Iron Mountain HS
Iron Mountain MI

Layman Lisa M
Lawrence Central HS
Indianapolis IN

Layne Kathy S
R Iii Central HS
Elvins MO

Layton Laura L
Wellsville HS
Wellsville KS

Lazar Vickie R
Ladysmith Hawkins HS
Hawkins WI

Lazaroff Pete L
Pennfield HS
Battle Creek MI

Leach Kenneth J
Fox Of Arnold HS
House Springs MO

Leach La Donna F
Mc Cluer HS
Florissant MO

Leach Linda L
Onaway HS
Onaway MI

Leach Mark A
Waukesha North HS
Waukesha WI

Leach Michele R
Immaculata HS
Detroit MI

Leach Theresa L
Waconia HS
Waconia MN

Leachman Robert E
Platte County HS
Platte City MO

Leaf Curtis D
Ogden Comm HS
Boone IA

Leannah James M
Lincoln HS
Manitowoc WI

Leannah Michael F
Marinette Catholic Centrl HS
Marinette WI

Lear Mark D
Rockville HS
Rockville IN

Leasure Janice K
Cambridge Sr HS
Cambridge MN

Leath James L
Warren HS
Cameron IL

Leatherman Cynthia L
Pardeeville HS
Pardeeville WI

Leatherman Daniel T
Central Noble HS
Albion IN

Leavell Mary S
Mt Vernon HS
Indianapolis IN

Leaver Thomas A
Juda HS
Juda WI

Le Blanc Brian J
Luke M Powers HS
Flint MI

Lebner Matthew E
Quincy HS
Quincy IL

Lechtenberg Roger E
Butte HS
Butte NE

Leckie Frederick J
Buffalo Grove HS
Buffalo Grove IL

Ledoux Judy N
Bishop Lillis HS
Kansas MO

Lee Alan L
Bishop Noll HS
Gary IN

Lee Christy E
Scottsbluff Sr HS
Scottsbluff NE

Lee Clayton R
Lafayette HS
Red Lake Falls MN

Lee Daneen R
East Monona HS
Soldier IA

Lee David R
Kirksville HS
Kirksville MO

Lee David W
Central HS
Aberdeen SD

Lee Dinah F
Westhope Public HS
Westhope ND

Lee Greg R
St Charles HS
St Charles IL

Lee Jovita D
Chicago Vocational HS
Chicago IL

Lee Larry D
Doniphan HS
Doniphan MO

Lee Michael F
Marion HS
Marion MI

Lee Robert E
Maine South HS
Park Ridge IL

Lee Sandra A
Puxico R 8 HS
Puxico MO

Lee Sheree T
St Charles HS
St Charles IL

Lee Shirley J
Southeast HS
Kansas City MO

Lee Tak K
Cass Technical HS
Detroit MI

Lee Wanda J
Grantsburg HS
Grantsburg WI

Leeman Sandra K
Ritenour HS
Overland MO

Leeper Gary D
Bremen HS
Bremen IN

Leeseberg Rodney W
Nevis HS
Nevis MN

Leet Gregory S
Riii Central HS
Flat River MO

Leet Sandra S
North HS
Eau Claire WI

Leever Steven P
Bayard HS
Bayard NE

Le Faive Jane A
Michigan Center HS
Jackson MI

Leffler Marlene M
Kadoka HS
Kadoka SD

Lefor Gregory A
Trinity HS
Dickinson ND

Le Fort Peggy J
Sunnydale Academy
Overland MO

Le Gault Mary B
Gladstone Area HS
Gladstone MI

Legg Billy G
Hammond Tech Voc HS
Hammond IN

Leggitt Danny L
Palestine HS
Palestine IL

Leguey Feilleux Michele
Incarnate Word Academy
St Louis MO

Leh Kathryn
Pontiac Catholic HS
Pontiac MI

Lehman Dexter K
Westview HS
Topeka IN

Lehman John J
Versailles HS
Versailles MO

Lehman Terese S
Grand Ledge HS
Lansing MI

Lehmann Thomas R
Falls Sr HS
Intl Falls MN

Lehner Maureen A
Mother Mc Auley HS
Chicago IL

Leib Mary R
Lourdes HS
Chicago IL

Leibfried Robert T
Chisholm Sr HS
Chisholm MN

Leible Michael R
Charleston R 1 HS
Charleston MO

Leibrand Larry A
Park Hill Sr HS
Kansas City MO

Leidig Kristen M
Plano HS
Plano IL

Leigh Tami J
Callaway Public HS
Oconto NE

Leighty Wade M
Lawrenceville HS
Lawrenceville IL

Leiker Diane M
Mc Pherson HS
Mc Pherson KS

Leininger Kathy L
O Fallon Township HS
Belleville IL

Leisinger Julie A
New Bloomfield Riii HS
Holt Summit MO

Leiter Jo L
Homestead HS
Ft Wayne IN

Leitner Wayne H
Cathay HS
Cathay ND

Leitz Frederick W
Eau Claire HS
Sodus MI

Leitzinger Jean M
Monroe HS
Monroe WI

Leksen Laurel E
Greenway HS
Coleraine MN

Le Masters Pat J
Verdigre Public HS
Orchard NE

Lemasters Sharon K
Marion HS
Marion IL

Lemberger Lynn K
Valders HS
Whitelaw WI

Lemenager Jann E
Central HS
Clifton IL

Le Mieur Steven T
L F Community HS
Little Falls MN

Le Mieux Jerome A
Sheboygan South HS
Sheboygan WI

Lemke Beth E
Lester Prairie Public HS
Lester Prairie MN

Lemke David M
North HS
Eau Claire WI

Lemmert Rocky E
Pontiac Northern HS
Pontiac MI

Lemmons Keith M
Pittsburg Senior HS
Pittsburg KS

Lemon Margie D
Hayes County HS
Palisade NE

Lems Susan K
Canton HS
Canton SD

Lenfestey Jeffery D
Marion HS
Marion IN

Lenges Linda M
West Vigo HS
West Terre Haute IN

Lenhart Pamela R
Watseka Comm HS
Watseka IL

Lenkey James J
Perry Meridian HS
Indianapolis IN

Lenox Guy R
Pleasant Hill HS
Pleasant Hill MO

Lent Penny L
Van Far R I HS
Vandalia MO

Lents Terry A
Rolling Meadows HS
Arlington Hts IL

Lentz Amy M
South HS
Westport IN

Lentz Danieta J
Jefferson Cnty North HS
Winchester KS

Lentz Linford L
Neosho Sr HS
Neosho MO

Lenz Daniel M
St Michael Albertville HS
St Michael MN

Lenz Martina E
Waterford Mott HS
Pontiac MI

Lenz Patricia A
Ellsworth HS
Adrian MN

Lenz Stephen D
Pendleton Heights HS
Middletown IN

Leonard Brian K
Peotone HS
Peotone IL

Leonard Charles H
Wakefield HS
Wakefield NE

Leonard Emily L
Jefferson City Sr HS
Jefferson City MO

Leonard Gillis C
Harrisonville Cass R9 HS
Harrisonville MO

Leonard Helen K
Pioneer HS
Ann Arbor MI

Leonard Lori J
Dekalb Sr HS
Dekalb IL

Leonard Lynn A
Dekalb Sr HS
Dekalb IL

Leonetti John P
Wheeling HS
Buffalo Grove IL

Leong Mildred K
Carter H Harrison HS
Chicago IL

Leong Yim F
Kickapoo HS
Springfield MO

Lepant Dora F
Central Catholic HS
Grand Island NE

Lepper Kevin M
Houghton Lake HS
Houghton Lake MI

Leppert Hollace D
Columbia Central HS
Brooklyn MI

Leppert Josey R
Kee HS
Lansing IA

Lerner Marla S
Maria HS
Chicago IL

Le Sac Nancy C
Oconomowoc Sr HS
Oconomowoc WI

Lesher Linda S
Clarion HS
Clarion IA

Leshley Greg S
Newton HS
Newton IL

Leslie Colleen M
Cass City HS
Decker MI

Leslie Deanna S
South Clay HS
Gillett Grove IA

Lesmeister Jerome P
New Rockford Central HS
New Rockford ND

Lesmeister Lynne A
Plymouth Canton HS
Plymouth MI

Lesniewski Robert F
St Laurence HS
Chicago IL

Lester Donald L
Colfax HS
Colfax IA

Lester Kimberley S
Moline Sr HS
Moline IL

Lester Polly J
Sullivan HS
Sullivan IN

Leszczynski Susan M
La Salle Peru Twp HS
Lasalle IL

Letizia Michelle E
Homestead Jr Sr HS
Fort Wayne IN

Letner Paula J
Eisenhower HS
Decatur IL

Leto Kathleen G
East HS
Des Moines IA

Le Tourneau David
Batavia HS
Batavia IL

Letson Larry D
Mauston Area HS
Mauston WI

Lett Ann E
New Berlin HS
New Berlin IL

Lettiere John T
Hubbard HS
Chicago IL

Letvin Craig A
Butte Public HS
Kief ND

Le Vasseur Mary Ann
All Saints Central HS
Bay City MI

Leverette Wanda Y
Cass Tech HS
Detroit MI

Levin Jeffrey H
Evanston Twp HS
Skokie IL

Levin Marci L
Smith Center HS
Smith Center KS

Le Vine Trudy J
Isaac C Elston HS
Michigan City IN

Levinsky Cheryl A
Plainfield HS
Plainfield IL

Levsch Robert A
Red Wing Central HS
Red Wing MN

Levy Lisa A
Avon Jr Sr HS
Plainfield IN

Levy Steven M
Niles Township East HS
Skokie IL

Lewallen Jeffery M
Wild Rose Public HS
Wautoma WI

Lewellen Sharon A
Sycamore HS
Sycamore IL

Lewis Audrey
John Marshall Harlan HS
Chicago IL

Lewis Brenda S
Salem Sr HS
Salem MO

Lewis Diane M
Thomas Jefferson HS
Rockford IL

Lewis Edward W
South Clay HS
Dickens IA

Lewis Florence E
Lindblom Technical HS
Chicago IL

Lewis Jacqueline J
Morgan Park HS
Chicago IL

Lewis James A
Emmerich Manual HS
Indianapolis IN

Lewis James B
Avon HS
Danville IN

Lewis James P
Salem HS
Salem IN

Lewis Kenneth V
Truman Public HS
Lewisville MN

Lewis Kimberly D
Elkhart Central HS
Bristol IN

Lewis Lori A
Genoa Public HS
Monroe NE

Lewis Mary L
North Clay HS
Louisville IL

Lewis Melanie G
Mendota Twp HS
Mendota IL

Lewis Norma M
Red Bud HS
Red Bud IL

Lewis Pamela S
Hancock Central HS
Hancock MI

Lewis Pamela S
Pomeroy Comm HS
Pomeroy IA

Lewis Rex D
Genoa Public HS
Monroe NE

Lewis Steven D
Mendel Prep HS
Chicago IL

Lewis Susan E
Marshall HS
Marshall MO

Lewis Teresa A
Chelsea HS
Grass Lake MI

Lewis Thomas L
Mendel Prep
Chicago IL

Lewis Valerie D
Northern HS
Flint MI

Lewis William D
South Iron HS
Annapolis MO

Lewitzke Timothy L
Wausau East HS
Wausau WI

Lezovich Annemarie
Corunna HS
Vernon MI

Li Lorinda M
New Haven HS
New Haven IN

Liakos Peggy A
Bayard HS
Bayard NE

Liang Jean N
Rich Central HS
Olympia Fields IL

Libberton Larry D
Mt Carroll HS
Mt Carroll IL

Liberato Leilani M
Harding Sr HS
St Paul MN

Liberty Lynn M
Wayne Memorial HS
Westland MI

Libes Valerie A
Delta HS
Muncie IN

Libsack Jamy B
Lyman HS
Lyman NE

Libsack Sandy K
Lyman HS
Lyman NE

Lichamer Joseph C
Luther South HS
Chicago IL

Lichte Susan K
Webb HS
Reedsburg WI

Lichtenberger M Ann
Richwoods HS
Peoria IL

Lichtenberger Robert B
Fairfield Community HS
Fairfield IL

Lichtenstein Carol A
Blue Valley HS
Stilwell KS

Lichter Timothy J
Mitchell HS
Mitchell SD

Lichti Timothy C
Shickley Public HS
Shickley NE

Lickey Kaiya L
Hamilton Se HS
Noblesville IN

Liddle Cheryl A
Park River HS
Park River ND

Liebenstein Brian C
Port Washington HS
Port Washington WI

Lieberman Joshua M
Homestead HS
Mequon WI

Liegl Joseph G
Medford Sr HS
Stetsonville WI

Lien James A
William Jennings Bryan HS
Omaha NE

Lien Kristi J
Border Central HS
Sarles ND

Lienemann Johnny H
Hildreth HS
Hildreth NE

Lietz Charles M
Tomahawk HS
Tomahawk WI

Lietz Thomas R
Thomas More Prep
Hays KS

Lietzau Laura A
Wheaton Warrenville HS
Wheaton IL

Lievers Elizabeth A
Pope County Community HS
Golconda IL

Liggett Jeffrey K
Catlin HS
Catlin IL

Light Gail L
Anamoose Public HS
Anamoose ND

Light Joan M
Yankton HS
Yankton SD

Lightner Monte J
Huntington North HS
Huntington IN

Liike Mary E
Avondale HS
Troy MI

Likes Rhonda L
Bunker Hill HS
Bunker Hill IL

Liles Anita M
Metz R 2 HS
Horton MO

Lilienthal Kim S
Glencoe Sr HS
Plato MN

Lillard Steven V
Collins Community HS
Collins IA

Limberg Debra S
Streator Twp HS
Streator IL

Limpert John W
Winona Sr HS
Winona MN

Lin Della M
University HS
Champaign IL

Lince Martha A
Crispus Attucks HS
Indianapolis IN

Lincoln Robin L
Madrid Community HS
Madrid IA

Lind Donna L
Huron Sr HS
Huron SD

Lind Kimberly K
Bertha Hewitt HS
Bertha MN

Lindahl Kimberly S
Elgin HS
Streamwood IL

Lindauer Pamela L
Iowa Grant HS
Cobb WI

Lindberg Jeff R
Galesburg Sr HS
Galesburg IL

Lindberg Theresa L
Holy Angels HS
Minneapolis MN

Lindell Kirk A
New Richmond Senior HS
New Richmond WI

Linden Jane E
William Horlick HS
Racine WI

Linderman De Wayne M
Hartford HS
Hartford MI

Lindfors Connie G
Eben HS
Chatham MI

Lindley Hank
Diamond HS
Diamond MO

Lindow Edgar J
Marengo Community HS
Marengo IL

Lindquist Nancy L
De Pue Public HS
De Pue IL

Lindsey Eva K
Springs Valley HS
French Lick IN

Lindsey Michael D
Rantoul Township HS
Rantoul IL

Lindsey Myra
Lindblom Tech HS
Chicago IL

Lindstrom Heather A
Harry A Burke HS
Omaha NE

Lindstrom Rebekka K
Manson HS
Manson IA

Lingenfelter Mary J
Hartford HS
Emporia KS

Link Patricia A
Brimley HS
Brimley MI

Link William H
Maine West HS
Des Plaines IL

Linn Kenny J
So Haven HS
South Haven MI

Linnell Donald A
Bluestem HS
Leon KS

Linneman Larry W
Moberly Sr HS
Moberly MO

Linoski Allen R
St Clement HS
Center Line MI

Linsmeyer Patricia J
Pembine HS
Pembine WI

Lintner Morris R
Madison HS
Madison NE

Linton Alan C
Marseilles HS
Marseilles IL

Linton Hans M
Harlan Comm HS
Harlan IA

Linz Bruce W
Forest Lake HS
Forest Lake MN

Lipcaman Lisa M
Huron HS
Ann Arbor MI

Lipe Glenda F
Egyptian HS
Olive Branch IL

Lipka Bertha E
Bishop Noll Institute HS
East Chicago IN

Lippert Daniel J
Danube Public HS
Blomkest MN

Lipski Wayne E
St Laurence HS
Chicago IL

Lisiecki John A
St Andrew HS
Detroit MI

Liska Raymond B
Hillsboro HS
Hillsboro WI

Liske Jolee G
Medford Sr HS
Medford WI

List Laurie A
Frankenmuth HS
Birch Run MI

Lister Jane M
Ottawa HS
Williamsburg KS

Listro Anita K
Morton Sr HS
Hammond IN

Litak Theodore R
Dwight D Eisenhower HS
Chicago IL

Littel Laura J
St Louise De Marillac HS
Glenview IL

Littig Christine E
Bluffs HS
Bluffs IL

Little Linda L
Riggs HS
Pierre SD

Little Richard L
Santa Fe Trail HS
Carbondale KS

Little Roger L
Tri County Community HS
What Cheer IA

Littlejohn Doris E
Oskaloosa HS
Oskaloosa IA

Littler Cheryl A
John F Kennedy HS
Babbitt MN

Littrel Patty J
English Valleys HS
N English IA

Littrell Donald R
Jennings County HS
Commiskey IN

Litwiller Christina M
Olympia HS
Delavan IL

Lively Cinda M
Shawneetown HS
Junction IL

Livermore Jean A
Southern HS
Raritan IL

Livesay Deborah J
Holly Hill HS
Holly Hill IL

Livesay Tracy D
Anna Jonesboro Comm HS
Anna IL

Livingston Eric T
Boys Town HS
Minneapolis MN

Lizarowski Noel M
Drayton HS
Drayton ND

Lloyd Donald F
Plymouth Canton HS
Plymouth MI

Lloyd Karen A
Ladywood St Agnes HS
Indianapolis IN

Loboschefski Nancy L
Sand Creek HS
Jasper MI

Locascio Lawrence J
Brother Rice HS
Chicago IL

Loch Pamela S
Fairbury HS
Fairbury NE

Lock Jane A
Carrollton HS
Carrollton MO

Lock Richard D
Avon HS
Avon IL

Lockard Mark W
West HS
Excelsior Springs MO

Lockett Dean E
Sidney Comm HS
Sidney IA

Lockhart Tom D
Humboldt HS
St Paul MN

Lockridge Judith A
Tri County HS
Jamesport MO

Lockwitz Todd A
St Joseph HS
St Joseph MI

Lockwood Denise D
Galien HS
Galien MI

Lockwood Scott A
Elmhurst HS
Fort Wayne IN

Lockyear Lisa A
Central HS
Evansville IN

Lodge Debra K
Trico HS
Willisville IL

Lodmell Ricki L
Dell Rapids Public HS
Dell Rapids SD

Loe Janette C
Welcome Comm HS
Welcome MN

Loeb Geralyn M
St Gertrudes HS
Raleigh ND

Loeffler Marnee M
Central HS
La Crosse WI

Loeffler Richard A
Green Lake HS
Green Lake WI

Loeschen Jeff L
Titonka Consolidated HS
Woden IA

Loewe Llewellyn E
Freeport Sr HS
Freeport IL

Lofgren Daniel K
Princeton HS
Princeton MN

Loftsgard Debora D
Park River HS
Park River ND

Logan Margaret A
Washington HS
Washington IA

Logsdon Thomas R
Galesburg Sr HS
Galesburg IL

Lohmeyer Luke C
Woodstock HS
Woodstock IL

Lohr Barbara C
Marian HS
Omaha NE

Lohr Ed O
Lohrville HS
Lohrville IA

Lohrbach Jan E
Cal Community HS
Latimer IA

Lohse Lori A
Marysville HS
Marysville KS

Loiacono Christina R
Du Quoin HS
Du Quoin IL

Loisel Catherine L
Brussels Community HS
Golden Eagle IL

Lokanc Mark A
Marist HS
Alsip IL

Loken Richard B
Velva Public HS
Velva ND

Loker Louise A
Highland HS
Highland IN

Lokos Sylvia A
Evergreen Park HS
Evergreen Park IL

Lomax Michael J
Jos A Craig HS
Janesville WI

Lomelind Renee
Deer Creek Mackinaw HS
Mackinaw IL

Lomen Allyn F
Bemidji HS
Solway MN

London Regina A
Madison Sr HS
Madison IL

Lonesome Sheila K
Rosati Kain HS
Northwoods MO

Loney Virginia L
Traverse City HS
Grawn MI

Long Ann R
Newman Catholic HS
Dixon IL

Long Barbara A
Holdrege HS
Holdrege NE

Long Buddy R
Dadeville HS
Aldrich MO

Long Cyril S
Dixon HS
Dixon IL

Long Darla J
Centerville HS
Centerville IA

Long Darryl R
New Berlin HS
Loami IL

Long Eva L
Mt Vernon HS
Mc Cordsville IN

Long Janice A
Cassville R 4 HS
Cassville MO

Long Mary J
Manteno HS
Manteno IL

Long Phillip J
Washington Senior HS
Washington IA

Long Randy A
Bell City HS
Bloomfield MO

Long Richard B
L R HS
Lewellen NE

Long Roger A
Wichita Hts HS
Wichita KS

Long Sherryn J
Garden County HS
Oshkosh NE

Long Stephen D
Warsaw Comm HS
Winona Lake IN

Long Stephen M
Beardstown HS
Beardstown IL

Long Teresa L
Milan Cii HS
Milan MO

Long Teri L
Mt Pleasant Comm HS
Mt Pleasant IA

Long Wanda D
St Francis Academy
Joliet IL

Long William E
Elwood HS
Elwood KS

Long William S
Central HS
St Joseph MO

Longar James K
Wentzville HS
Wentzville MO

Longbotham Steven M
Cretin HS
St Paul MN

Longenecker Jennifer C
Wawasee HS
N Webster IN

Longoria Mario R
Clark HS
Hammond IN

Longsdorf Larry D
H H Dow HS
Midland MI

Lonowski Diane K
Marian HS
Omaha NE

Loock Douglas R
Fremont Sr HS
Fremont NE

Loomis Donald E
Millington HS
Millington MI

Loomis Donna J
Earlham Community HS
Earlham IA

Loomis Rebecca J
Anna Jonesboro C HS
Anna IL

Loop Lee W
Diamond R 4 HS
Carthage MO

Looper Veronica L
Calhoun HS
Kampsville IL

Loos Keith A
Unit Dist 312 HS
Milledgeville IL

Loos Mary E
Chillicothe HS
Chillicothe MO

Lopeman Linda L
Yates City HS
Elmwood IL

Lopez Gloria M
St Procopius HS
Chicago IL

Lopez Kent V
Valentine HS
Valentine NE

Lopez Marguerite M
Morgan Park Academy
Chicago IL

Lopez Rosemarie
Andrean HS
Crown Point IN

Lord Melinda M
Washington HS
Washington IA

Lore Mary J
Dearborn HS
Dearborn MI

Lorenger Bradley P
East HS
Sioux City IA

Lorenger Jeannine M
Immaculata HS
Detroit MI

Lorenz Rose M
Grant Park HS
Grant Park IL

Lorenzen Lowell L
Jasper HS
Sherman SD

Loresch John D
Sturgeon Bay Sr HS
Sturgeon Bay WI

Loret De Mola Karen
Bishop Mc Namara HS
Kankakee IL

Lorine Thomas M
Parkers Prairie HS
Parkers Prairie MN

Lorsbach Charles W
Calhoun HS
Batchtown IL

Lorton Cindy J
Calhoun HS
Hardin IL

Lose John C
St Edmond HS
Fort Dodge IA

Loshaw Kim L
Vanderbilt Area HS
Vanderbilt MI

Losin Eric R
Greencatle HS
Greencastle IN

Lotterer James B
Warsaw HS
Warsaw MO

Lotz Kathy S
La Grove Comm HS
St Peter IL

Louden Raymond S
Harlem HS
Rockford IL

Lough Jane M
Lakeshore HS
Saint Joseph MI

Lough Mark V
Salem Sr HS
Salem MO

Louie Kenneth T
Lane Tech HS
Chicago IL

Loupee Rhonda L
Williamsburg HS
Williamsburg IA

Loushin Gerald P
Memorial HS
Ely MN

Love Brett M
Winfield HS
Winfield KS

Love Debra K
Goshen HS
Goshen IN

Love Floresia
Dunbar Voc HS
Chicago IL

Love Jonathan M
Lake Forest Academy
Glencoe IL

Love Steven M
Adrian HS
Adrian MI

Lovekamp Susan D
Triopia HS
Arenzville IL

Loveland Jane A
Canton HS
Canton SD

Lovell David L
Southern Wells HS
Marion IN

Lovell Nancy E
Forman HS
Manito IL

Lovellette Greg D
West HS
N Aurora IL

Lovely Kirk J
Mendel Catholic Prep
Chicago IL

Loven Keith H
Valley City HS
Valley City ND

Lovewell Rhonda S
Courtland HS
Courtland KS

Lovitt Max A
Stapleton Public HS
Stapleton NE

Lovitt Sue J
Ida HS
Temperance MI

Lowe Andy M
Crocker HS
Crocker MO

Lowe Kathleen M
Jefferson HS
Rockford IL

Lowe Kimberlyn J
Normandy HS
St Louis MO

Lowell Kirk G
Concordia HS
Concordia KS

Lower Debra L
Rich Central HS
C C Hills IL

Lowrance June L
Assumption Jr Sr HS
Assumption IL

Lowry Karen
Brighton HS
Brighton MI

Lowry Ladona L
Maysville HS
Maysville MO

Loy Jan M
Valley Falls HS
Valley Falls KS

Loy Steven E
Bloomington HS
Bloomington IL

Loy Timothy S
Kinmundy Alma HS
Kinmundy IL

Loyd Karen L
Southern Boone R 1 HS
Ashland MO

Loyd Rebecca J
Brazil HS
Brazil IN

Loza Christopher L
Northwestern Military Academy
Chicago IL

Lozier Cheryl A
Farmington East HS
Farmington IL

Lozier James R
Maconaquah HS
Peru IN

Lozier Jay N
North Central HS
Indianapolis IN

Lubbers Patricia J
Hamilton HS
Hamilton MI

Lubbert Richard G
Port Huron HS
Port Huron MI

Lubienski Mark B
Catholic Central HS
Dearborn Hgts MI

Lucas Kenneth R
Hobart Senior HS
Hobart IN

Lucas Marijane A
Wanwatosa West HS
Wanwatosa WI

Lucas Mark E
Plainfield HS
Joliet IL

Lucas Michael D
Macomb HS
Macomb IL

Lucas Stephen G
Roosevelt HS
Gary IN

Luchsinger Lori J
New Glarus HS
New Glarus WI

Lucht Janet K
Lake View Auburn Comm HS
Lake View IA

Luck Julie D
Hill City HS
Hill City KS

Lucker Robin A
West Aurora HS
Aurora IL

Luckew Catherine A
Taft HS
Chicago IL

Lucus Beverly J
Dwight Twp HS
Dwight IL

Ludek Kathryn A
Auburn HS
Auburn IL

Luder Kay E
Ulysses HS
Ulysses KS

Ludowese Ann C
Stewart Public HS
Stewart MN

Ludvik Elizabeth A
Mead HS
Ithaca NE

Ludwig Ronald D
Southwest HS
St Louis MO

Ludwigson Randy L
Cornell HS
Cornell WI

Lueckenhoff Edith A
Blair Oaks HS
Jefferson City MO

Luedtke Diane M
W Liberty HS
W Liberty IA

Luempert Arthur F
Columbia Central HS
Clark Lake MI

Luerding Jeffrey
St Charles HS
St Charles MO

Luetkenhaus Susan M
Duchesne HS
St Charles MO

Luke Jo B
Moweaqua HS
Moweaqua IL

Luke Keith W
Malden HS
Malden MO

Luke Larry M
Coldwater HS
Coldwater MI

Luke Margaret C
Kirkwood HS
Glendale MO

Luker Brent D
Uniontown HS
Uniontown KS

Luksan Linda M
Armstrong HS
Golden Valley MN

Lullo Geraldine J
Oak Lawn Comm HS
Oak Lawn IL

Luna Gregory M
Ritenour HS
St Louis MO

Lund Alicia A
Greenville Sr HS
Greenville MI

Lund Bruce A
Lyons Township HS
Western Springs IL

Lund Craig R
Pecatonica HS
Pecatonica IL

Lund Donna E
St Clair HS
Janesville MN

Lund Karen K
La Porte City HS
Brandon IA

Lunday Marga C
Sheyenne River Academy
Bismarck ND

Lundberg Sue K
Grant Deuel HS
Strandburg SD

Lundeen Sandra K
Arlington HS
Arlington Heights IL

Lundell Janelle M
Kennedy Public HS
Kennedy MN

Lundquist Wayne L
Beresford HS
Beresford SD

Lundstrom Carol A
Elizabeth Seton HS
Calumet Park IL

Lungren Kevin B
Frankfort Sr HS
Frankfort IN

Luning Karen A
Rosati Kain HS
St Louis MO

Lunkenheimer Julie K
Mc Henry Comm HS
Mc Henry IL

Lunn Rose M
Lillis HS
Kansas City MO

Lunoe Joan E
Homewood Flossmoor HS
Homewood IL

Lunsford Sherry A
Richmond Sr HS
Richmond IN

Luper Craig D
Augusta HS
Augusta KS

Lupton Christine Y
Northwestern HS
Blandinsville IL

Lurquin Jerome T
Harold L Richards HS
Oak Lawn IL

Lusa Deborah M
Thornwood HS
Calumet City IL

Luscomb Steve L
Belleville Township East HS
Fairview Heights IL

Luster Freddie J
Mendel HS
Chicago IL

Lusuardi Anthony A
St Bede Academy
Oglesby IL

Luther Julie A
Prescott Comm HS
Prescott IA

Lutters Marie J
Ransom HS
Ransom KS

Lutz Emily E
Benkelman HS
Benkelman NE

Lutz John J
Wenona HS
Wenona IL

Lutz Michael E
Bronson HS
Bronson MI

Lutz Scott A
Benkelman HS
Parks NE

Lutzke Thomas E
Merrill Sr HS
Irma WI

Lutzow James H
Rockford East Sr HS
Rockford IL

Luzecky Mark A
Bishop Dubourg HS
St Louis MO

Lybarger Louise A
Clay City HS
Noble IL

Lycan Connie M
Niosho HS
Joplin MO

Lychuk Paul S
Lake Orion HS
Lake Orion MI

Lyle Donna L
Edgewood HS
Bloomington IN

Lyles Fragelia D
Roosevelt HS
Gary IN

Lyman Luba D
Elwood Community HS
Elwood IN

Lynch James L
E Richland HS
Claremont IL

Lynch Janet K
Edwardsville HS
Edwardsville IL

Lynch Lindley J
West Noble HS
Kimmell IN

Lynch Nancy L
Hillsboro HS
Hillsboro IL

Lynch Randall G
Lutheran West HS
Detroit MI

Lynch Terry F
Fonda Comm HS
Varina IA

Lynn Michael R
Maine Twp East HS
Park Ridge IL

Lynn Robert S
Morton HS
Morton IL

Lyon David L
Elmore HS
Elmore MN

Lyon Delilah M
Calhoun HS
Windsor MO

Lyon Denice M
Coldwater HS
Coldwater MI

Lyon Gary R
Homer Community HS
Homer NE

Lyon Lili R
Estherville Sr HS
Estherville IA

Lyon Sara E
Bogard R4 HS
Bogard MO

Lyon Twyla P
Calhoun HS
Windsor MO

Lyons Connie L
Oak Park Sr HS
Kansas City MO

Lyons Mary T
Cathedral HS
Omaha NE

Lyons Terry L
Virginia Comm Unit #64
HS
Virginia IL

Lyons Theresa S
Cornell HS
Odell IL

Lyste Maribeth L
Sharon Public HS
Sharon ND

M

Lyter Edward A
Valley City HS
Sanborn ND

Lyttle Daniel W
Aurora HS
Aurora IN

Lyttle Heather J
Fort Zumwalt HS
Ofallon MO

Mc Adams Steven J
Walter B Hammer HS
Estherville IA

Mc Afee Louise R
Soldan HS
St Louis MO

Mc Afee Paul G
Fullerton HS
Fullerton NE

Mc Alexander Earl D
Mt Ayr Comm HS
Beaconsfield IA

Mc Alister David L
Sedan HS
Sedan KS

Mc Alister Teresa D
Lafayette HS
St Joseph MO

Mc Alister Terri D
Central HS
Omaha NE

Mc Allister Amazair
Rockhurst HS
Kansas City MO

Mc Allister Peggy L
Paul Harding HS
Ft Wayne IN

Mc Auliffe Kevin P
Forest View HS
Des Plaines IL

Mc Avoy Brian R
Owosso HS
Owosso MI

Mc Avoy Jane E
Burlington Comm HS
Burlington IA

Mc Bride Dave A
West Ottawa HS
Holland MI

Mc Bride Garry L
Coldwater HS
Coldwater MI

Mc Bride George E
Waupun HS
Waupun WI

Mc Bride Julia K
Providence HS
Clarksville IN

Mc Bride Shelly K
Joppa Community HS
Metropolis IL

Mc Bride Sherry L
Fulton HS
Fulton MO

Mc Broom Kathryn J
Hillsboro HS
Butler IL

Mc Burney Vinona M
Humboldt HS
Humboldt IA

Mc Cabe Carol J
Marillac HS
Niles IL

Mc Cabe Kathleen
Kirksville HS
Kirksville MO

Mc Cabe Toni A
Aurelia Comm HS
Alta IA

Mc Cafferty Kathleen A
Rochester HS
Rochester IL

Mc Cain Caren J
Bedford HS
Bedford IA

Mc Cain Carol J
Bedford HS
Bedford IA

Mc Cairns Sharon E
Elkton Pigeon Bay Port HS
Caseville MI

Mc Call Allen D
East Richland HS
Olney IL

Mc Call Jon K
Mediapolis Community HS
Mediapolis IA

Mc Callie Machelle
Kimball Consolidated HS
Kimball SD

Mc Callum George R
Carl Junction HS
Joplin MO

Mc Cammon John M
Whitko HS
So Whitley IN

Mc Cance Steve S
Gregory HS
Dallas SD

Mc Candless Lillian I
Highland HS
Highland IN

Mc Cann Janet M
Mother Of Sorrows HS
Chicago IL

Mc Cann Robert A
East Pike HS
Milton IL

Mc Carrell Clark G
Hales Franciscan HS
Chicago IL

Mc Carroll Leigh A
Excelsior Springs HS
Excelsior Springs MO

Mc Carthy Garry P
Manhattan HS
Manhattan KS

Mc Carthy John D
Nashua HS
Nashua IA

Mc Carthy Kerry K
Mt St Scholastica
Academy
Atchison KS

Mc Cartin Joseph G
Marist HS
Palos Heights IL

Mc Cartney Dawn M
Kelvyn Park HS
Chicago IL

Mc Cartney James E
Toman Sr HS
Toman WI

Mc Carty Branna L
Noblesville HS
Noblesville IN

Mc Carty Danny J
Hastings HS
Hastings NE

Mc Carty Debra L
Shawnee HS
Shawneetown IL

Mc Carty Kendra S
Lincoln Way HS
Mokena IL

Mc Carty Linda J
Bucklin Rii HS
Bucklin MO

Mc Carty Patrick K
Southwestern HS
Lafayette IN

Mc Carty Sandra E
South Newton HS
Kentland IN

Mc Carty Timothy J
Farmer City Mansfield HS
Farmer City IL

Mc Carver Michael J
Central HS
Flat River MO

Mc Caslin Howard S
Hillsboro HS
Hillsboro IL

Mc Causlin Kimberly G
Cheboygan Public HS
Cheboygan MI

Mc Chane Richard H
Roncalli HS
Omaha NE

Mc Clain Carol A
Anna Jonesboro Comm HS
Anna IL

Mc Clain Karen D
Southeastern HS
Detroit MI

Mc Clain Mary J
Holden R 111 HS
Holden MO

Mc Clarey Donald R
Paris HS
Paris IL

Mc Clasky Gregory J
Grayslake Comm HS
Grayslake IL

Mc Clean Alicia J
Valparaiso HS
Valparaiso IN

Mc Clellan Manulita G
Mother Mcauley Lib Arts
HS
Chicago IL

Mc Clelland Connie J
Troy HS
Troy KS

Mc Clelland Phyllis G
Harvard HS
Harvard IL

Mc Clendon Terri D
John Marshall HS
Chicago IL

Mc Clerren Robert L
Thompsonville HS
Thompsonville IL

Mc Clintick Donna L
Hammond Baptist HS
Griffith IN

Mc Clintock Daniel L
Joliet Central HS
Joliet IL

Mc Cloud Natalie Y
Kingsville HS
Kingsville MO

Mc Clun Barbara A
Louisville Public HS
Louisville NE

Mc Clure Douglas J
Mason County Central HS
Scottville MI

Mc Clure Jane E
Klemme Community HS
Klemme IA

Mc Clure Lori S
Huntington North HS
Roanoke IN

Mc Clure Michael M
Effingham HS
Effingham IL

Mc Clure William D
O Fallon Twp HS
O Fallon IL

Mc Cluskey Larry W
Virden HS
Virden IL

Mc Coach Angela C
Glenwood HS
Chatham IL

Mc Collough David D
La Ville HS
Lapaz IN

Mc Collum Madeline M
Clinton HS
Tipton MI

Mc Collum Marcia K
North Clay Comm HS
Louisville IL

Mc Collum Mike L
Vandalia HS
Vandalia IL

Mc Collum Pamela S
Palisade HS
Palisade NE

Mc Collum Terry R
Trenton HS
Trenton MO

Mc Comb Kathie L
Harvard HS
Harvard IL

Mc Conkey Elizabeth A
Collinsville HS
Collinsville IL

Mc Connell Bradley L
Vestaburg HS
Edmore MI

Mc Connell Charlene J
Sidney Public HS
Sidney NE

Mc Connell Cheryl A
West HS
Davenport IA

Mc Connell Geraldine E
North Scott HS
Davenport IA

Mc Connell Lynn E
Davis County HS
Bloomfield IA

Mc Connell Mary M
Harvard HS
Harvard IL

Mc Connell Mary R
Clinton Comm HS
Clinton IL

Mc Cord Rebecca L
Harrisonville Sr HS
Harrisonville MO

Mc Cormack Brian J
Yankton HS
Yankton SD

Mc Cormack Karen A
St Francis Academy
Joliet IL

Mc Cormack Mark A
Joliet West HS
Joliet IL

Mc Cormick Cindy L
Allegan HS
Allegan MI

Mc Cormick Edward T
Montini HS
Lombard IL

Mc Cormick James P
West HS
Green Bay WI

Mc Cormick Michael J
Caledonia HS
Caledonia MN

Mc Cormick Philip A
Airport HS
Carleton MI

Mc Coy Catherine M
Jersey Comm HS
Jerseyville IL

Mc Coy David R
Mehlville Sr HS
St Louis MO

Mc Coy Margaret T
Bloomington HS
Bloomington IL

Mc Crary William T
Greenwood HS
Springfield MO

Mc Cray Cindy L
St Charles HS
St Charles MO

Mc Crea Dee A
King City Ri HS
King City MO

Mc Crea Douglas G
Maysville HS
Maysville MO

Mc Cree Frank K
Crab Orchard HS
Marion IL

Mc Cullagh James P
Cowan HS
Muncie IN

Mc Cully David C
Toluca HS
Toluca IL

Mc Cumbers Allen E
Loomis Public HS
Atlanta NE

Mc Cune M S
Dubois HS
French Lick IN

Mc Cutcheon Aubrey V
Cass Technical HS
Detroit MI

Mc Cutcheon Brian J
Arthur Hill HS
Saginaw MI

Mc Cutcheon Patrick C
Arthur Hill HS
Sagniaw MI

Mc Cutcheon Peggy R
Diamond R4 HS
Joplin MO

Mc Dade Joseph E
Burlington HS
Burlington IA

Mc Daniel Anita J
Bloomington HS
Bloomington IL

Mc Daniel Marilyn L
Belle HS
Belle MO

Mc Dermott Patrick E
Pacelli HS
Austin MN

Mc Donagh Mary B
Queen Of Peace HS
Oak Lawn IL

Mc Donald Angela M
Chicago Vocational HS
Chicago IL

Mc Donald Mary E
St Marys HS
Independence MO

Mc Donald Michael A
Premontre HS
Green Bay WI

Mc Donald Richard S
Mitchell HS
Mitchell NE

Mc Donald Terry L
West Liberty HS
W Liberty IA

Mc Donald Timothy B
Cathedral HS
Indianapolis IN

Mc Donald Valarie R
Diagonal HS
Diagonal IA

Mc Donnell Bridget A
Nazareth Academy
La Grange IL

Mc Dougall Kenneth G
Redford Union HS
Redford Twp MI

Mc Dougan Charles M
Marceline HS
Marceline MO

Mc Duffie Mark E
West Side HS
Gary IN

Mc Eachern Anne G
Hannibal HS
Hannibal MO

Mc Elligott Timothy R
Wauwatosa East HS
Wauwatosa WI

Mc Elyea Charles S
Southwestern HS
Flint MI

Mc Ewan Dorothy M
Melvindale HS
Melvindale MI

Mc Ewan Laura A
Sts Peter & Paul Area HS
Saginaw MI

Mc Ewen Diana J
Carlinville HS
Carlinville IL

Mc Fadden Beth I
Mullinville HS
Mullinville KS

Mc Fall Treveda K
Heights HS
Wichita KS

Mc Fann Tanya R
Wellington HS
Milford IL

Mc Farland Barbara J
Hartford HS
Hartford MI

Mc Farland Leslie L
Wayne HS
Fort Wayne IN

Mc Farland Vicki G
Rolla HS
Rolla MO

Mc Feeters Debra J
Clinton Comm HS
Clinton IL

Mc Gannon Patrick J
Hinsdale Central Township HS
Hinsdale IL

Mc Gaugh Annamaria P
Central HS
St Joseph MO

Mc Gee Barbara A
Sacred Heart Academy
Springfield IL

Mc Gee Joanna M
Sumner HS
Kansas City KS

Mc Geehan Marie L
Parkway West Sr HS
Manchester MO

Mc Gehee Sharon L
Fair Grove HS
Fair Grove MO

Mc Ghee Laura J
Dexter Sr HS
Dexter MO

Mc Ginness Daniel L
Shiloh HS
Brocton IL

Mc Ginnis Michael R
Algona Comm HS
Algona IA

Mc Girr Craig L
Hinckley Big Rock HS
Hinckley IL

Mc Gonagle Mary C
Mother Guerin HS
Chicago IL

Mc Gowan Bridget A
Mauston HS
Lyndon Sta WI

Mc Gowan James K
Leo HS
Chicago IL

Mc Gowan Kendall
Beaumont HS
Saint Louis MO

Mc Gowen Mary K
Emerson Hubbard HS
Hubbard NE

Mc Grath Eileen M
Mother Mcauley HS
Oak Lawn IL

Mc Grath Vicki A
Edinburg HS
Edinburg IL

Mc Graw Kathleen M
Sts Peter & Paul HS
Saginaw MI

Mc Gregor Joseph A
Duchesne HS
St Peters MO

Mc Grew Gordon N
Richwoods HS
Peoria IL

Mc Groarty Susan M
St Josephs Academy
Crestwood MO

Mc Guinness James P
Bishop Foley HS
Clawson MI

Mc Guire Cathleen J
Ovid Elsie HS
Elsie MI

Mc Guire Corinne D
Perham Public HS
Perham MN

Mc Guire Gregory R
Springfield HS
Springfield IL

Mc Guire Monica T
Crystal Lake HS
Crystal Lake IL

Mc Guire Susan E
Morton HS
Morton IL

Mc Gurn Anita M
Bishop Ward HS
Kansas KS

Mc Gurran Ann M
Hoople HS
Hoople ND

Mc Henry Brenda L
Hays HS
Hays KS

Mc Hone Steven J
Clarion HS
Clarion IA

Mc Ilhargie Gloria J
Laker HS
Kinde MI

Mc Ilvenna Mary J
Ogorman HS
Sioux Falls SD

Mc Inerney Sally J
All Saints Central HS
Bay City MI

Mc Innes Kim K
Marion HS
Marion ND

Mc Innis Deborah L
Tri County HS
Howard City MI

Mc Intee John D
Bettendorf HS
Bettendorf IA

Mc Intee Rae A
Williston Sr HS
Williston ND

Mc Intire Evelyn R
Nevada HS
Milo MO

Mc Intyre Diane K
Dowling HS
Grimes IA

Mc Intyre Glen A
Bridgeport HS
Bridgeport MI

Mc Intyre James R
Holden HS
Holden MO

Mc Intyre Kathy S
Rogers HS
Michigan City IN

Mc Intyre Lorri S
Triton HS
Tippecanoe IN

Mc Intyre Walter W
East Alton Wood River HS
Wood River IL

Mc Kay Kimberly A
Joliet East HS
Joliet IL

Mc Keag James W
Shelby Public HS
Shelby NE

Mc Kean Lise D
Immaculate Conception HS
Elmhurst IL

Mc Kee Cathy M
Maquoketa Valley HS
Earlville IA

Mc Kee Jim E
South Side HS
Fort Wayne IN

Mc Kee Kathleen
Wabash HS
Wabash IN

Mc Kee Mary J
St Josephs Academy
St Louis MO

Mc Kee Richard A
Manhattan HS
Manhattan KS

Mc Keever Janice A
Odell Public HS
Wymore NE

Mc Kenna Donna M
Gladwin HS
Harrison MI

Mc Kenrick Gary D
Central Comm HS
Low Moor IA

Mc Kenzie Kay A
Park River HS
Park River ND

Mc Kenzie Mary J
Bradford HS
Bradford IL

Mc Kenzie Susan E
Meadville Riv HS
Meadville MO

Mc Kenzie Teresa S
Immaculate Heart Of Mary HS
Forest Park IL

Mc Keon Kimberley M
Lincoln Sr HS
Sioux Falls SD

Mc Keown James T
Columbus HS
Marshfield WI

Mc Kibben Debra J
Phillips HS
Phillips WI

Mc Kim Debra A
New Bloomfield HS
New Bloomfield MO

Mc Kim Sandra K
Daniel J Gross HS
Omaha NE

Mc Kim Wanda K
Kirksville Senior HS
Kirksville MO

Mc Kinney Charles R
Eastalton Wood River HS
Wood River IL

Mc Kinney Darlene D
Potter Public HS
Potter NE

Mc Kinney Janet G
Field Kindley HS
Coffeyville KS

Mc Kinney Joanne M
Luther S HS
Chicago IL

Mc Kinney Marcia R
Belton HS
Belton MO

Mc Kinney Michael C
Tipton HS
Kempton IN

Mc Kinney Myra J
Lytton Comm HS
Lytton IA

Mc Kinzie Rikki R
Huntington North HS
Huntington IN

Mc Kittrick Dawna E
Mayer Lutheran HS
Watertown MN

Mc Knight Jane A
Rockford Lutheran HS
Belvidere IL

Mc Knight Paul W
Cleveland HS
St Louis MO

Mc Knight Thomas M
Bedford N Lawrence HS
Bedford IN

Mc Knight William P
Gladstone HS
Gladstone MI

Mc Kowen Jane D
Highland HS
Alexandria IN

Mc Lario Lori L
Menomonee Falls East HS
Menomonee Falls WI

Mc Laughlan Bruce L
Howell HS
Howell MI

Mc Laughlin Cynthia L
Mt Vernon Community HS
Greenfield IN

Mc Laughlin Dave W
Leo HS
Palos Heights IL

Mc Laury Pamela R
Sheldon Community HS
Sheldon IA

Mc Lawhon Ronald W
Amos Alonzo Stagg HS
Palos Hills IL

Mc Lean John L
Sandwich HS
Sandwich IL

Mc Lean Mark P
De Kalb HS
De Kalb IL

Mc Lemore Joyce L
Osceola Public HS
Osceola MO

Mc Mahel Jon K
Rushville Consolidated HS
Rushville IN

Mc Mahon Anne L
Hudson HS
Hudson WI

Mc Mains Michael B
North White HS
Monon IN

Mc Manus Connie M
Savannah HS
Clarksdale MO

Mc Master Joan E
South Sioux City HS
Suth Sioux City NE

Mc Millan Lori K
Grundy R V HS
Galt MO

Mc Millen Mary A
Southeastern HS
West Point IL

Mc Mullen Diane M
Greenway HS
Bovey MN

Mc Mullen Ginny L
Sterling HS
Sterling IL

Mc Mullen Jerrilyn K
Rockville HS
Rockville IN

Mc Mullen Sharon K
Geneva HS
Geneva NE

Mc Mullin Cynthia M
St Charles HS
St Charles IL

Mc Murdie Judith A
Macomb HS
Macomb IL

Mc Murray Dru A
Alton HS
Alton IL

Mc Murray Kristin M
Belton HS
Richard Gebaur Afb MO

Mc Nabb Jean S
Calhoun HS
Hardin IL

Mc Nail Carol L
Southern R 2 HS
Centerville MO

Mc Namara Cathy A
Dwight HS
Dwight IL

Mc Natt Gwen E
Wheaton Warrenville HS
Wheaton IL

Mc Nea Debra L
Bottineau HS
Bottineau ND

Mc Neeley Patricia D
Dexter HS
Dexter MO

Mc Neely Jeffrey K
Anna Jonesboro Chs
Anna IL

Mc Neely Kathy A
Cary Grove HS
Cary IL

Mc Neely Peggy A
Lexington HS
Lexington IL

Mc Neely Steven M
Marion HS
Marion IN

Mc Neil John J
Richland HS
Richland MO

Mc Neil Teresa A
Richland HS
Richland MO

Mc Pherron Caroline J
Southridge HS
Holland IN

Mc Pherron Michael J
Southridge HS
Holland IN

Mc Pherson Timothy W
Willow Springs HS
Willow Springs MO

Mc Ray David W
O Fallon Twp HS
O Fallon IL

Mc Reynolds Lori L
Central Comm HS
De Witt IA

Mc Reynolds Myron C
Bremen HS
Markham IL

Mc Shea John J
St Viator HS
Palatine IL

Mc Sherry James T
Belleville W HS
Millstadt IL

Mc Sorley Brian P
Nathan Hale HS
West Allis WI

Mc Sweeney John T
Fenwick HS
Berwyn IL

Mc Vane Randy
St Ignatius College Prep
Chicago IL

Mc Veigh Crystal R
Elk Grove HS
Elk Grove Vlg IL

Mc Watt Kevin A
East Detroit HS
East Detroit MI

Mc Wethy Mark E
Milford Sr HS
Highland MI

Mc Williams Karen M
Oakhawn Comm HS
Oakhawn IL

Maaske Leslie L
Cozad HS
Cozad NE

Maberry Steven G
Tina Avalon HS
Dawn MO

Mabie Jamie F
Quincy HS
Quincy IL

Macaulay Lorna A
Maria HS
Chicago IL

Mac Donald Gregory G
John Glenn HS
Westland MI

Mac Donald Michael A
St Catherine HS
Sturtevant WI

Mac Girr Scott K
Spring Lake Jr Sr HS
Spring Lake MI

Mach Linda M
Manitowoc Lutheran HS
Kewaunee WI

Machkovitz Cheryl L
Beaver Dam Sr HS
Beaver Dam WI

Maciaszkiewicz John F
Gordon Tech HS
Chicago IL

Maciejauskas Ramune R
Maria HS
Chicago IL

Macik Dale D
Cosmos HS
Lake Lillian MN

Mack Brenda K
Mounds View HS
New Brighton MN

Mack John E
Beatrice Sr HS
Beatrice NE

Mack Julie M
Harvey HS
Harvey ND

Mackenzie Gerald
Onekama HS
Kaleva MI

Mackey Barbara A
Memorial HS
Elkhart IN

Mackland Thomas W
Thomas Jefferson HS
Crescent IA

Mac Laren Roger A
Belding HS
Belding MI

Macomber Scott A
Troy HS
Troy MI

Macon Gwendolyn S
Junction City Sr HS
Junction City KS

Maday David R
Standish Sterling Central HS
Sterling MI

Madden Elizabeth J
Junior Sentral HS
Armstrong IA

Madden Katherine T
Freeport Sr HS
Freeport IL

Maddock Linda J
Grant Community HS
Ingleside IL

Maddox Dee E
Washington Comm HS
Washington IL

Madeja David E
Oak Lawn Comm HS
Oak Lawn IL

Madigan Denise R
Wausau West HS
Wausau WI

Madill Karen R
Delta HS
Muncie IN

Madsen Daven L
Lincoln Northeast HS
Lincoln NE

Madsen Robert B
Charles City Sr HS
Charles City IA

Madson Arthur L
Lk Orion HS
Lk Orion MI

Magby Carol L
Skyline HS
Urbana MO

Maggard Jennifer L
Benton HS
Benton IL

Magill Robert M
Holdrege HS
Holdrege NE

Maginot Thomas J
Munster HS
Munster IN

Magnuson Douglas K
Mounds View HS
New Brighton MN

Magnusson Carol I
Luther South HS
Chicago IL

Magnusson Marilyn S
Udall HS
Udall KS

Magnusson Mary C
David H Hickman HS
Columbia MO

Magnusson Ronald M
Argyle HS
Argyle MN

Mahaffey Gaila A
University HS
Warrensburg MO

Mahan Charlotte E
Ofallon HS
Ofallon IL

Mahan Michael M
Heelan HS
Sioux City IA

Mahar Lisa M
Oscoda Area HS
Oscoda MI

Maher Douglas E
Stanton Comm HS
Stanton IA

Maher Jeffrey A
West Vigo HS
W Terre Haute IN

Maher Mary E
Brimfield HS
Brimfield IL

Maher William M
St Pius X HS
Imperial MO

Mahlandt Louise A
Union Star Rii HS
Helena MO

Mahnken Garold W
Perkins County HS
Ogallala NE

Mahoney Michael P
Northwest HS
High Ridge MO

Mahoney Patrick J
Niles HS
Niles MI

Mahoney Susan K
Chesaning Union HS
St Charles MI

Mahr Jon R
Spoon River Valley HS
Ellisville IL

Mahynski Theresa M
Fruitport HS
Nunica MI

Mai Carolyn M
Troge Community HS
Wakeeney KS

Maibenco Douglas C
Wheaton Christian HS
Wheaton IL

Maier Laurie L
Joliet Central HS
Joliet IL

Maier Sue Ann D
Glidden Public HS
Glidden WI

Mailhot Charles J
Union HS
Grand Rapids MI

Main Kristy K
Springfield HS
Springfield IL

Maine Joseph E
Dixon HS
Dixon IL

Maines Traci L
Randolph Southern HS
Lynn IN

Mainprize Susan L
Houghton Lake HS
Houghton Lk MI

Majcina Dale G
Marseilles HS
Marseilles IL

Major Terry D
West Nodaway HS
Burlington Jct MO

Majors Terri L
Auburn HS
Auburn NE

Maki Jay H
Forest Park HS
Crystal Falls MI

Maki Lee D
Wakefield HS
Wakefield MI

Makovicka Ron T
York HS
York NE

Makowski Robert J
Thomas More HS
Milwaukee WI

Malane Marsha L
Port Huron HS
Port Huron MI

Malavolti Timothy N
Blue Mound HS
Boody IL

Malcheff Susan A
Homewood Flossmoor HS
Homewood IL

Malcolm Rick D
Chase County HS
Imperial NE

Malcom Kathy A
Griswold Community HS
Griswold IA

Malecki Elizabeth A
John Hersey HS
Arlington Hts IL

Malinowski Stephanie L
Yorkville HS
Yorkville IL

Malkiewicz Robert S
St Alphonsus HS
Detroit MI

Mallak Kenneth G
Rantoul Township HS
Rantoul IL

Mallen Martin J
St Patrick HS
Chicago IL

Mallers Elaine M
Paul Harding HS
Fort Wayne IN

Mally Barbara G
Carl Sandburg HS
Palos Park IL

Malnor Kirk A
West HS
Green Bay WI

Malone Kevin M
Clarinda Comm HS
Clarinda IA

Malone Leann
Henry Senachwine HS
Henry IL

Maloney Ann M
Sunnydale Academy
Lees Summit MO

Maloney Janice L
Mc Leansboro HS
Dahlgren IL

Maloney Kathleen M
Marian Cath HS
Dolton IL

Maloney Kevin A
Ridgway HS
Ridgway IL

Maloney Philip A
York Comm HS
Elmhurst IL

Maloy Annette E
La Moille Comm HS
La Moille IL

Maly Joyce C
Marshall Public HS
Marshall WI

Maly Mary F
Marshall HS
Marshall WI

Mammel James B
Wylie E Groves HS
Birmingham MI

Mammen David L
Limestone Comm HS
Bartonville IL

Mamroth Merritt D
Parkway Central HS
Creve Coeur MO

Mance Stuart M
Broad Ripple HS
Indianapolis IN

Manchester Bret E
Central Heights HS
Lane KS

Mandernack Barbara J
Yorkville HS
Newark IL

Mandrell Sherry L
Mt Vernon HS
Waltonville IL

Manes Sharon A
Jefferson City Sr HS
Jefferson City MO

Manford Maryann L
Holden HS
Holden MO

Mani Kathy L
Mt Horeb HS
Mt Horeb WI

Manis Beverly D
Cowan HS
Muncie IN

Manis Elizabeth A
Hoopeston HS
Hoopeston IL

Manis Rick L
Cowan HS
Muncie IN

Manke Leslie A
Poynette Sr HS
Arlington WI

Manley Marlan M
Gaylord HS
Gaylord MI

Mann Cheryl L
Turner HS
Kansas City KS

Mann Francie A
Warsaw Comm HS
Warsaw IN

Mann George R
Pittsburg HS
Pittsburg KS

Mann James E
Robinson HS
Robinson IL

Mann John F
Nebr City Sr HS
Nebraska City NE

Mann Kimberly C
Reitz Memorial HS
Evansville IN

Mann Kirk D
Gibson Southern HS
Haubstadt IN

Mann Michael D
Alsen Public HS
Alsen ND

Mann Nancy R
Montezuma Comm HS
Malcom IA

Mann Roy V
Northern Heights HS
Allen KS

Manning David M
North Central HS
Indianapolis IN

Manning Duane R
Heritage Christian HS
Anderson IN

Manning Edward B
Chadwick HS
Chadwick IL

Manning Paula G
Pipestone HS
Pipestone MN

Manning William R
Kapaun Mt Carmel HS
Wichita KS

Mannix Teri L
Mitchell Jr Sr HS
Mitchell IN

Manor Diane M
Gabriel Richard HS
Wyandotte MI

Manthey Candace R
Colome HS
Colome SD

Mantz Steve L
Slinger HS
Richfield WI

Manuel Jeffrey K
Argenta Oreana HS
Oreana IL

Manus Brandon E
Delavan Community HS
Delavan IL

Manzer Cindy A
Pierce Public HS
Pierce NE

Manzer Susan K
Pierce Public HS
Pierce NE

Mapes Daniel P
Muskegon Catholic Central HS
Muskegon MI

Mapili Nina E
Owatonna HS
Owatonna MN

Marazita Dominic
Waverly HS
Lansing MI

Marbury Cheryl P
Immaculata HS
Detroit MI

Marcadis David B
Terre Haute So Vigo HS
Terre Haute IN

Marceau Daniel J
Walled Lake Western HS
Walled Lake MI

March Gary A
United Township HS
East Moline IL

Marchello Sandra M
Amos Alonzo Stagg HS
Hickory Hills IL

Marchino Linda M
South Knox HS
Vincennes IN

Marck Lori L
Beaver Dam Sr HS
Beaver Dam WI

Marco Philip L
St Joseph HS
Westchester IL

Marcotte Janet L
Westwood HS
Ishpeming MI

Marcum Jean M
Bishop Dubourg HS
St Louis MO

Margarian Melanie A
Collinsville HS
Collinsville IL

Marget Don A
Fairmont Public HS
Fairmont NE

Margolis Merle I
Community HS
West Chicago IL

Marguart Leann
Portland HS
Portland MI

Mari Jeff L
Bottineau HS
Bottineau ND

Mariani Randy R
Toluca HS
Toluca IL

Marinangel Jeffrey A
Fenton HS
Bensenville IL

Marinello Michele A
Douglas Mac Arthur HS
Saginaw MI

Marion Scott R
Brentwood HS
Brentwood MO

Maris Roxy L
Wauneta HS
Hamlet NE

Mark Gregory A
Truman HS
Independence MO

Markee Mary K
Columbus HS
Marshfield WI

Markelis Daiva M
Morton East HS
Cicero IL

Markgraf Cheryl L
Concordia Academy
St Paul MN

Markgraf Janet L
Joliet East HS
Joliet IL

Markl Cynthia A
Barstow HS
Overland Park KS

Marklein Robert A
Janesville Craig Sr HS
Janesville WI

Markley Bernard A
Donovan HS
Iroquois IL

Markley Dagmar M
West Noble HS
Cromwell IN

Markley Lance J
West Elk HS
Howard KS

Markley Mary J
Centerville HS
Richmond IN

Markley Merl A
Spoon River Valley HS
Ellisville IL

Markman Thomas I
Highland Pk HS
Highland Park IL

Marks Mari L
Waupun HS
Oakfield WI

Marks Marvin E
L L Wright HS
Ironwood MI

Markward Lisa K
Indian Creek HS
Franklin IN

Markway Theresa L
Pattonville Sr HS
St Ann MO

Marlett Bonita L
Keokuk Senior HS
Keokuk IA

Marlin Owen M
Derby HS
Derby KS

Marlow Annetta K
North Platte Senior HS
North Platte NE

Marlow Catherine J
Tamaroa HS
Tamaroa IL

Marlow Julie K
Morton Sr HS
Hammond IN

Marmion Marleen W
Granite City South HS
Granite City IL

Marmul Lawrence J
St Andrew HS
Detroit MI

Maro Michael P
Kewanee HS
Kewanee IL

Marolt Ray A
Notre Dame HS
W Milwaukee WI

Marotzke Gail A
Fulda HS
Fulda MN

Marquardt Glenna J
Lacrosse HS
Wanatah IN

Marquardt Joyce L
Schleswig Comm HS
Schleswig IA

Marquardt Rita F
Van Meter Community HS
Booneville IA

Marquardt Rock D
Bryant HS
Rich Hill MO

Marquart Barbara J
Lakota HS
Lakota ND

Marquart Patti L
Lakota Public HS
Lakota ND

Marquart Scott E
Whitewater HS
Delavan WI

Marquette Kristy L
Sterling Public HS
Sterling NE

Marquis Janice K
David City HS
Rising City NE

Marquis Jocelyn
Randolph Southern HS
Lynn IN

Marr Joe K
Superior HS
Superior NE

Marr Nils K
Papillion HS
Papillion NE

Marren Daniel G
Griffith HS
Griffith IN

Marriott Melinda K
Clinton HS
Clinton MO

Marrison Randy L
Mason County Central HS
Scottville MI

Marrs Richard L
Reed Custer HS
Braceville IL

Marsh Cindy S
Southeast Warren HS
Milo IA

Marsh James E
Reading HS
Reading MI

Marsh Joy L
St Louis HS
St Louis MI

Marsh Richard J
Atlanta HS
La Plata MO

Marsh Thomas R
Webster City HS
Webster City IA

Marshall Brenda J
Newton HS
Newton IL

Marshall Chrystal K
Kenwood HS
Chicago IL

Marshall Diane M
Calamus Comm HS
Calamus IA

Marshall Judy A
Southern Boone Co HS
Hartsburg MO

Marshall Mark H
St John Vianney HS
St Louis MO

Marshall Marsha R
West Washington HS
Campbellsburg IN

Marshall Peter C
Maine Twp East HS
Park Ridge IL

Marshall Richard S
Zionsville Comm HS
Zionsville IN

Martel Vicki L
Wishek Public HS
Wishek ND

Martell Angelo J
St Patrick HS
Chicago IL

Martens Sara A
Fremont Sr HS
Fremont NE

Martenson Karla A
Shabbona HS
Shabbona IL

Marti Edwin A
Adams Friendship HS
Friendship WI

Martin Annette E
Logansport HS
Logansport IN

Martin Benjamin J
Pender Public HS
Pender NE

Martin Betsy F
Edgewood HS
Madison WI

Martin Brenda J
Joliet Central HS
Joliet IL

Martin Brenda L
Oregon Davis HS
Walkerton IN

Martin Carrie L
Hamilton HS
Warsaw IL

Martin David N
Chenoa HS
Chenoa IL

Martin David W
Waukegan East HS
Waukegan IL

Martin Deborah A
Spring Hill HS
Spring Hill KS

Martin Dennis E
Boone Valley HS
Renwick IA

Martin Elizabeth J
Greenfield Central HS
Greenfield IN

Martin Faye M
Mt Clemens HS
Mt Clemens MI

Martin Gary L
Greenfield Central HS
Greenfield IN

Martin Glenda M
Lakeview HS
Gowen MI

Martin Gregory L
Memorial HS
Evansville IN

Martin Gregory P
Douglas Macarthur HS
Decatur IL

Martin James L
Sigourney Community HS
Sigourney IA

Martin John K
Southwest HS
Kansas City MO

Martin Kelly J
Buckley Loda HS
Buckley IL

Martin Kevin R
Schafer HS
Allen Park MI

Martin Linda F
Aurora Senior HS
Aurora IN

Martin Linda J
Salem HS
Salem IN

Martin Mary J
Duquoin HS
Du Quoin IL

Martin Melissa I
North Greene HS
White Hall IL

Martin Monty K
Perry HS
Baylis IL

Martin Pamela A
Lake Fenton HS
Fenton MI

Martin Pamela R
Immaculata HS
Detroit MI

Martin Patricia A
Taft HS
Chicago IL

Martin Rhonda M
Gibson Southern HS
Ft Branch IN

Martin Scott D
Marinette Sr HS
Marinette WI

Martin Shirley A
Benton Harbor HS
Benton Harbor MI

Martin Susan E
Ashland HS
Alexander IL

Martin Terrilyn E
Lakeland HS
Wolcottville IN

Martin Terry E
Roseville HS
Roseville IL

Martin Thomas A
Boone Valley HS
Renwick IA

Martin Vicki L
Lake Fenton HS
Fenton MI

Martine John J
St Thomas Aquinas HS
Florissant MO

Martinek Joanne H
New Effington HS
New Effington SD

Martinez Alice
Saginaw HS
Saginaw MI

Martinez Dolores P
St Francis De Sales HS
Chicago IL

Martinez Eloy
Elgin HS
Streamwood IL

Martinez Paul T
Romeoville HS
Romeoville IL

Martsching Gregory A
Cardinal HS
Agency IA

Marunczak Elizabeth R
New Haven HS
Mt Clemens MI

Marvin Michael A
Chrisman HS
Chrisman IL

Marx Laura M
Fulton HS
Fulton IL

Mascher Jane E
Eastridge HS
Kankakee IL

Masek Mark A
Odell Public HS
O Dell NE

Masek Mark J
Joliet West HS
Joliet IL

Maser Debra K
Limestone Comm HS
Bartonville IL

Masinick Betsy A
East Detroit HS
Warren MI

Mason Barbara M
Douglas Mac Arthur HS
Decatur IL

Mason Deval M
Elwood HS
Elwood KS

Mason Dwayne L
Tech HS
Indianapolis IN

Mason Joanne L
Stet HS
Norborne MO

Mason John H
Pekin Comm HS
Pekin IL

Mason Judy A
Eastern HS
Greentown IN

Mason Keith C
Soldan HS
St Louis MO

Mason Kenneth A
Wayne Community HS
Russell IA

Mason Martin D
Sullivan HS
Sullivan IN

Mason Rita U
Hall HS
Spring Valley IL

Mason Shelby J
Noble Community HS
Noble IL

Mason Stanley W
Edwards HS
Albion IL

Massaro Adrea L
Maria HS
Chicago IL

Massat Laura J
Luther South HS
Posen IL

Massee Karen R
Sioux Rapids Comm HS
Sioux Rapids IA

Massey Dorothy M
Arlington HS
Arlington Hts IL

Massey Edward H
Sycamore HS
Sycamore IL

Massiala Christina A
Ann Arbor Huron HS
Ann Arbor MI

Massie Anita G
Southern R Ii HS
Ellington MO

Massie Michael K
Palestine HS
Palestine IL

Massignan Dale T
Kingsford HS
Kingsford MI

Massman Brant L
Centerville HS
Centerville IA

Mast Alan L
Hart HS
Hart MI

Mastbergen Brian K
George Comm HS
George IA

Masters Deborah A
Chillicothe HS
Chillicothe MO

Masters Gayla J
Oak Park HS
Gladstone MO

Masters Sally M
Excelsior Springs HS
Excelsior Springs MO

Mastny Brian J
Howells Public HS
Clarkson NE

Masyga Patricia A
Cumberland HS
Cumberland WI

Matejcak Robert
Joliet Catholic HS
Joliet IL

Mathews John H
Fairfield Comm HS
Fairfield IL

Mathews Kirby A
Richmond Sr HS
Richmond IN

Mathews Michael R
Brown HS
Sturgis SD

Mathews Richard D
O Fallon Township HS
O Fallon IL

Mathias Christine
Waukegan East HS
Waukegan IL

Mathieu Mark A
Houghton HS
Chassell MI

Mathis Daniel M
De La Salle HS
Minneapolis MN

Mathis Deena G
Walker R Iv HS
Walker MO

Mathis Larry A
Pennfield HS
Battle Creek MI

Mathis Patricia A
Mount Vernon HS
Letcher SD

Mathis Steven E
Samuel C Mumford HS
Detroit MI

Mathison Diane M
Stanley Boyd HS
Thorp WI

Matkin Lori
Liberal HS
Liberal KS

Matlick Kyle E
Rockridge HS
Reynolds IL

Matlock Dianna L
Sullivan HS
Sullivan MO

Matney Clarence R
Oak Park HS
Kansas City MO

Matney Constance M
Turner HS
Kansas City KS

Matousek John M
Solomon Juneau HS
Wood WI

Matsey Madeline M
Hobart Sr HS
Hobart IN

Matsumura Alan A
Joliet Catholic HS
Joliet IL

Matsutani Carolyn M
Hershey Public HS
North Platte NE

Matt Marshall W
Marshalltown HS
Marshalltown IA

Mattas Kathleen A
Wilson HS
Wilson KS

Matteson Elizabeth A
Lincoln Way HS
Manhattan IL

Matteson Kathleen A
Orono Sr HS
Long Lake MN

Matteson Nan E
Culver Girls Academy
Brookston IN

Matthews Colette A
Carl Sandburg HS
Oak Forest IL

Matthews Kirk C
Parkway West Senior HS
Ballwin MO

Matthews Lori L
Oak Park HS
Kansas City MO

Matthews Mary A
Boyne City HS
Boyne City MI

Matthews Mary E
Liberty Sr HS
Birch Tree MO

Matthews Pauline R
St Benedict HS
Chicago IL

Matthies Timothy J
Gothenburg HS
Gothenburg NE

Mattingly Daniel L
Freeport Sr HS
Freeport IL

Mattingly Linda J
Jefferson HS
Lafayette IN

Mattingly Patricia A
Washington Catholic HS
Washington IN

Mattingly Rebecca S
Mt Vernon Twp HS
Mt Vernon IL

Mattley Phyllis J
Burwell Jr Sr HS
Burwell NE

Mattmiller Rick W
Antigo HS
Mattoon WI

Mattox Debra A
Staunton HS
Braxil IN

Mattox Sherry A
Archie HS
Archie MO

Mattson Gayle L
Luther L Wright HS
Ironwood MI

Mattson Kenneth F
Batavia Sr HS
Batavia IL

Mattson Nathan C
Muskegon HS
Muskegon MI

Mattson Raymond C
Republic Michigamme HS
Republic MI

Matulka Joe F
Aquinas HS
David City NE

Matulka Mary J
Raymond Central HS
Valparaiso NE

Matzke Tim J
El Paso HS
El Paso IL

Mauch Scott D
Lake Central HS
St John IN

Maul Terry L
St Johns Military HS
Hastings NE

Maule Dave A
Shawnee Mission South HS
Libertyville IL

Maule Michael
Leola Ind HS
Leola SD

Maule Michael R
Leola Ind Dist 2 HS
Leola SD

Maupin Michael L
South Shelby HS
Clarence MO

Maurer Mary J
Parsons Sr HS
Parsons KS

Maves Kathleen R
Lyman HS
Presho SD

Maxa Lorri A
Bethlehem Academy
Lakeville MN

Maxwell Deborah A
Meridian HS
Hope MI

May Annette J
Norris HS
Hickman NE

May Debbie A
Adrian HS
Adrian MI

May James R
Milan C Ii HS
Milan MO

May Jeffrey A
Mauston Area HS
Mauston WI

May Mary M
Holy Child HS
Waukegan IL

Mayall Marla J
Astoria HS
Astoria IL

Mayber Kenneth P
Niles West HS
Morton Grove IL

Mayer James B
Memorial HS
Beloit WI

Mayer Jerry E
Southern Wells HS
Keystone IN

Mayer Sally A
Willowbrook HS
Lombard IL

Mayer Steven A
Campion Jesuit HS
Prairie Du Chien WI

Mayes Ricky L
Ellis HS
Ellis KS

Mayes Thomas E
Winner Senior HS
Ideal SD

Mayfield John E
Bishop Ward HS
Kansas KS

Mayfield Patricia A
Granite City Sr HS
Granite City IL

Mayhew Monte N
Marysville HS
Marysville KS

Mayhoe Kathalene
West Side Sr HS
Gary IN

Maymon Douglas D
Charlestown HS
Charlestown IN

Mayo Marla G
Bradley Bourbonnais Comm HS
Bradley IL

Mayo Steven A
Bryan Sr HS
Omaha NE

Mayson Heather K
Cass Tech HS
Detroit MI

Mazanek Richard C
Loyola HS
Lincolnwood IL

Mazanowicz Catherine A
Jefferson HS
Rockford IL

Mazes Barbara J
Wakefield HS
Wakefield MI

Mazik Christine A
Bedford Sr HS
Temperance MI

Mazouch Marion A
Otis Bison HS
Timken KS

Mazur Cynthia K
Carmel HS
Mundelein IL

Mazurek Lucy M
Madonna HS
Chicago IL

Mazzone Sally A
St Stanislaus HS
Chicago IL

Mead Jan M
Weston HS
Cazenovia WI

Mead Larry W
Alton Sr HS
Alton IL

Mead Mark D
Tri Valley HS
Downs IL

Meader Craig A
Waverly HS
Waverly KS

Meaders Ellen J
Okemos HS
Okemos MI

Meadows Cindy R
Watertown HS
Watertown SD

Meakin Thomas E
Bishop Borgess HS
Detroit MI

Means Karen K
Newkirk HS
Arkansas City KS

Means Mark A
Spring Valley HS
Spring Valley MN

Meartz Nancy L
Fox Valley Lutheran HS
Neenah WI

Mecey Donald G
North County R1 HS
Desloge MO

Mechler Brian D
Titonka Cons HS
Titonka IA

Mechler Dean E
Titonka HS
Titonka IA

Mecklin Kathleen A
George Rogers Clark HS
Whiting IN

Medberry M Scott
Beaman Conrad HS
Beaman IA

Medders Dee A
Houston HS
Houston MO

Medema Jeffrey M
River Bend Comm HS
Fulton IL

Medema William L
Yankton HS
Kankton SD

Meder Cynthia L
Thornwood HS
S Holland IL

Meder Paul F
Lincoln HS
Manitowoc WI

Mederich David J
Sandwich HS
Sandwich IL

Medor Douglas H
Milan HS
Ypsilanti MI

Meduna Mary A
Bishop Neuman Central HS
Wahoo NE

Meece Candy L
Mt Vernon HS
Mccordsville IN

Meeder Lee D
Thornridge HS
So Holland IL

Meeder Patricia J
Shawnee Mission East HS
Prairie Village KS

Meehan John H
Marshall HS
Marshall IL

Meehan Theresa A
Thornwood HS
Thornton IL

Meek Esther G
North Platte HS
Edgerton MO

Meeker Anne M
Southwest HS
Kansas City MO

Meese Scott L
Oblong HS
Oblong IL

Mehling Annette L
Morrill HS
Morrill NE

Mehltretter Louis D
Wautoma HS
Wautoma WI

Meicenheimer Kim W
Litchfield Sr HS
Litchfield IL

Meidl Julie A
Valders HS
Whitelaw WI

Meier Rochne E
Aquinas HS
Niota IL

Meilaender Natalie R
Hobart Sr HS
Hobart IN

Meincke Lynn A
Durant Comm HS
Durant IA

Meindertsma R Duane
Knoxville Comm HS
Knoxville IA

Meinecke Becky J
Burwell Jr Sr HS
Burwell NE

Meiners Beth M
Caledonia HS
Caledonia MN

Meinert Dori L
Metamora Twp HS
East Peoria IL

Meinhart Paul C
Newton Comm HS
Wheeler IL

Meirick Donna M
New Hampton HS
Alta Vista IA

Meiser Glenn E
Frontier HS
Brookston IN

Meisinger Philip R
Peoria HS
Peoria IL

Meisinger Roger L
Plattsmouth HS
Louisville NE

Meisinger Terry D
Metropolis HS
Metropolis IL

Meissner Cynthia S
Sidney HS
Sidney NE

Meister Coralyn G
Hammond Baptist HS
Lowell IN

Meitl Kenneth G
Hoxie HS
Dresden KS

Mejicano Maria E
Mt Assisi Academy
Palos Park IL

Melancon Artie T
College View Academy
Lincoln NE

Melby Rolf B
Klemme HS
Klemme IA

Melcher Karla K
Fairbury HS
Fairbury NE

Melfi Sheryl A
Lakeview HS
St Clair Shores MI

Melhorn Sara J
Herrin HS
Herrin IL

Melinn Sharon K
East Kentwood HS
Kentwood MI

Melius Michael M
Faulkton HS
Faulkton SD

Melko Joseph
Thornton Fractional South HS
Lansing IL

Melnik Marianne K
Lourdes Academy
Oshkosh WI

Melody Karen M
Ottawa Twp HS
Ottawa IL

Melvin Diana R
Garden County HS
Oshkosh NE

Melvin Joseph A
Murphysboro Township HS
Murphysboro IL

Menard Raymond J
Wayland Academy
Juneau WI

Mendenhall Jerry R
Mt Pleasant HS
Mt Pleasant IA

Mendey Jean C
Trinity HS
Chicago IL

Mendicino Nancy R
Mother Theodore Guerin HS
Chicago IL

Mendoza Marcus
Kelly HS
Chicago IL

Mengel Alison M
Proviso East HS
Maywood IL

Mengwasser Helen C
Fatima HS
Jefferson City MO

Menigoz Deborah L
Bradley/bourbonnais Comm HS
Bradley IL

Menown Jean A
Kirkwood HS
St Louis MO

Menzl Judith A
Bishop Noll Institute HS
Hammond IN

Merchant Gordon C
Onaway Area Community HS
Ocqueoc MI

Mercil Mary E
Mt St Benedict HS
Crookstown MN

Meredith Vicky L
Grand Ledge HS
Grand Ledge MI

Mergel Kathleen M
Ursuline Academy
St Louis MO

Merideth Barbara W
Caruthersville HS
Caruthersville MO

Mering Kenneth D
Jamestown HS
Jamestown ND

Merkel Carl J
Northwestern Military Academy
Neenah WI

Merkel Marilyn L
Southridge HS
Huntingburg IN

Merklein Mary K
Phillipsburg HS
Phillipsburg KS

Merlau Virgil
Hoisington HS
Hoisington KS

Merrell Duane R
Harrison HS
Farmington Hills MI

Merriman David M
Coldwater HS
Coldwater MI

Merriman Kathy S
Coldwater HS
Coldwater MI

Merritt Cheryl A
North Platte Sr HS
Wellfleet NE

Merritt Karla E
Rich East HS
Park Forest IL

Merritt Kevin N
Duchesne HS
St Charles MO

Merry Margaret J
Effingham HS
Effingham IL

Merryfield Phoebe A
Newton HS
Newton KS

Merryman Brenda K
Wamego HS
Wamego KS

Mertens Steven R
Carl Junction HS
Carl Junction MO

Mertz John W
Stevenson HS
Livonia MI

Merz Jay A
Elmhurst HS
Fort Wayne IN

Mescher Marvonda J
Oak Park HS
Kansas City MO

Messer Neal C
Richardton Public HS
Richardton ND

Messer Tammy L
Moscow HS
Moscow KS

Messier Cynthia A
Escanaba HS
Escanaba MI

Messimer Donn G
Memorial HS
Joplin MO

Messmer Joann M
Lead HS
Deadwood SD

Messmer Mark J
Connersville HS
Connersville IN

Messner Connie J
Sheyenne Public HS
Sheyenne ND

Messner Jill R
Lake Linden Hubbell HS
Hubbell MI

Metcalf Lisa A
Robbinsdale Senior HS
Robbinsdale MN

Metros Craig M
Mendel Catholic Prep HS
Calumet Park IL

Mettler Linda D
Wessington Spgs HS
Wessington Sprgs SD

Metz Linda J
Yankton HS
Yankton SD

Metz Mark T
Wichita Southeast HS
Wichita KS

Metz Raymond P
St Pius X HS
Kansas City MO

Metzger Judy K
Cambridge HS
Cambridge NE

Metzger Mark G
North Boone HS
Capron IL

Metzger Marshall S
Stoutland Rii HS
Stoutland MO

Metzler Annette M
Oconto Falls HS
Oconto Falls WI

Metzler Kenneth D
Goshen HS
Goshen IN

Mewes David M
Edwards County HS
W Salem IL

Meyer Bonnie K
Weston HS
Loganville WI

Meyer Cathy L
Rochester HS
Springfield IL

Meyer Debra K
Dodge HS
Dodge NE

Meyer Diane M
Liberty HS
Liberty IL

Meyer Don G
Davenport Comm HS
Davenport NE

Meyer Douglas R
Oelwein Community HS
Oelwein IA

Meyer Gene W
Pollock HS
Pollock SD

Meyer James M
Grand Island HS
Grand Island NE

Meyer Joseph D
Aurora Senior HS
Aurora IN

Meyer Karen S
Coldwater HS
Coldwater MI

Meyer Kathy M
Macksville HS
Macksville KS

Meyer Kenneth I
Morgan Park Academy
Chicago IL

Meyer Laura A
Watseka Comm HS
Watseka IL

Meyer Lisa J
New London Sr HS
New London WI

Meyer Lynn C
Louisville HS
Louisville NE

Meyer Matt L
Forman HS
Manito IL

Meyer Phillip D
Paxton HS
Paxton IL

Meyer Robert
Alden Hebron Hs
Hebron IL

Meyer Ron D
Davenport Community HS
Davenport NE

Meyer Steve M
North HS
Sheboygan WI

Meyer Susan G
Jefferson City Sr HS
Jefferson City MO

Meyeraan Cynthia L
Worthington Sr HS
Worthington MN

Meyers Chaundra J
Veblen Public HS
Veblen SD

Meyers Cynthia J
Coloma HS
Coloma MI

Meyers Diane M
Quincy Senior HS
Quincy IL

Meyers John I
St Clair HS
St Clair MI

Meyers Sandy L
Pardeeville HS
Rio WI

Meyers Sharon K
Winnebago HS
Winnebago IL

Meylor Colleen B
Oconomowoc Sr HS
Okauchee WI

Micek Rebecca J
Platte Valley Academy
Omaha NE

Michael Gary A
Cleveland HS
St Louis MO

Michael Laurie L
Valders HS
St Nazianz WI

Michael Neil A
Fremont HS
Fremont IN

Michal Julie
Bayard HS
Bayard NE

Miche Leland I
Pearl City HS
Pearl City IL

Michealson Kirk A
Plano HS
Plano IL

Michel Joann E
Smith Center HS
Smith Center KS

Michell Timothy J
Marion HS
Marion MI

Michels Ann D
Horace Mann HS
N Fond Du Lac WI

Michels Thomas V
Anamosa HS
Anamosa IA

Michels Timothy L
Anamosa HS
Anamosa IA

Miciunas Perry P
Elgin HS
West Chicago IL

Mickelson Barb M
Mobridge Sr HS
Mobridge SD

Mickle Lawrence E
Lapeer Sr HS
Lapeer MI

Micklich Bradley J
Joliet Catholic HS
Joliet IL

Micoff David L
Marine City HS
Marine City MI

Micolichek Margie A
St Josephs Academy
De Pere WI

Mida Deborah L
Saline HS
Saline MI

Middaugh Mitzi D
Wabash HS
Wabash IN

Middaugh Randall S
Benson HS
Omaha NE

Middleton Charles H
J F Kennedy HS
Taylor MI

Middleton Jane E
Kinmundy Alma HS
Kinmundy IL

Middleton Scott A
Twin Lakes HS
Monticello IN

Midtgard Dianne L
Jonesville HS
Jonesville MI

Midtlyng David J
Thornridge HS
Dolton IL

Miedema Jane E
St Anne Community HS
St Anne IL

Mielenhausen Thomas C
Assumption HS
Davenport IA

Mielke Mark D
Lutheran HS
Racine WI

Miers Judith L
Enterprise Academy
Wichita KS

Migliorino Marc J
Homewood Flossmoor HS
Chicago Hts IL

Migon Robert C
Notre Dame HS
Harwood Hts IL

Mih Alex D
Chanute Sr HS
Chanute KS

Mih Cathy A
Chanute Sr HS
Chanute KS

Mihelich Karen A
St Francis Academy
Crest Hill IL

Mihm Randolph J
Turkey Valley HS
Waucoma IA

Mika Barbara A
Kimball Public HS
Academy SD

Mikel Elaine M
Grinnell Community Sr HS
Grinnell IA

Mikich Susan M
Edsel Ford HS
Dearborn MI

Miklas Adrianne C
Regina HS
Detroit MI

Miklas Ralph M
Southwest HS
St Louis MO

Mikolajczak David J
Thornridge HS
Dolton IL

Milakovic Nick
Marie Sklodowska Curie HS
Chicago IL

Miles Bart A
Nebraska Christian HS
Chambers NE

Miles Bernard A
Ne Christian HS
Chambers NE

Miles Christopher K
Reitz Mem HS
Evansville IN

Miles Randy H
Juda HS
Juda WI

Mileur Deborah K
Murphyboro Township HS
Murphysboro IL

Mileur Edmond C
Du Quoin HS
Du Quoin IL

Milewski Rita C
Taylorville HS
Taylorville IL

Milkint Denise T
Evergreen Park Comm HS
Evergreen Park IL

Millard Amy L
Lakeview HS
Trufant MI

Miller Alan J
Granite City South HS
Granite City IL

Miller Annette
John Marshall Harlan HS
Chicago IL

Miller Ann M
Thornton Frac South HS
Lansing IL

Miller Arden D
Jefferson Sr HS
Alexandria MN

Miller Bobbi S
Kickapoo HS
Springfield MO

Miller Brian K
Batesville HS
Batesville IN

Miller Carol J
Leland HS
Leland IL

Miller Carol J
Coal City HS
Coal City IL

Miller C Gail
Virden Comm HS
Virden IL

Miller Cheri L
Raytown HS
Kansas City MO

Miller Cindy A
New London Sr HS
Hortonville WI

Miller Clarence J
Johnson Creek HS
Rio WI

Miller Craig L
Bentley HS
Burton MI

Miller Danny L
Wawasee HS
Warsaw IN

Miller Debra J
Harrisonville Sr HS
Harrisonville MO

Miller Dennis R
Burlington HS
Burlington IA

Miller Diane G
St Edward Public HS
St Edward NE

Miller Eileen M
St Anns HS
Lexington NE

Miller Gary L
Wheaton Warrenville HS
Wheaton IL

Miller Gregg L
Westview HS
Topeka IN

Miller Gregory A
Maconaquah HS
Peru IN

Miller Hazel M
La Moille HS
Arlington IL

Miller James M
Coon Rapids Sr HS
Coon Rapids MN

Miller Jeffrey C
Le Center Public HS
Le Center MN

Miller Joan M
Joliet Central HS
Joliet IL

Miller John L
Royall HS
Elroy WI

Miller John M
Dundee HS
Dundee MI

Miller John V
Beaman Conrad Liscomb HS
Albion IA

Miller Jordan R
Morgan Park Academy
Chicago IL

Miller Julie A
Delavan Unit Dist #703 HS
Delavan IL

Miller Karen J
Harvard HS
Harvard IL

Miller Kathy A
Centreville HS
Sturgis MI

Miller Kay A
Otis Bison Sr HS
Bison KS

Miller Kevin B
Hoover HS
Des Moines IA

Miller Kevin J
Harvard HS
Harvard IL

Miller Larry E
Bellevue Comm HS
Bellevue MI

Miller Margaret M
Mancelona HS
Mancelona MI

Miller Mark A
St Louis Univ HS
Florissant MO

Miller Mark C
South Central HS
Elizabeth IN

Miller Mark L
Raymond Central HS
Ceresco NE

Miller Mary E
Fall River HS
Fall River WI

Miller Melinda D
Christopher HS
Christopher IL

Miller Melledy E
Redfield HS
Redfield SD

Miller Michael D
Marian Central HS
Mc Henry IL

Miller Mildred L
Beaumont HS
St Louis MO

Miller Natalie J
Sac Community HS
Sac City IA

Miller Pamela R
Battle Creek Central HS
Battle Creek MI

Miller Patricia L
Columbus HS
Columbus NE

Miller Paul K
Douglas Macarthur HS
Decatur IL

Miller Rebekah L
Indian Creek Sr HS
Trafalgar IN

Miller Richard D
Midway U S D HS
Denton KS

Miller Rita M
Iowa Mennonite HS
Wellman IA

Miller Robert D
Naperville Central HS
Naperville IL

Miller Robert L
Benton Cons HS
Benton IL

Miller Rue A
Tina Avalon HS
Tina MO

Miller Sandra S
Jefferson City Sr HS
Jefferson City MO

Miller Scott J
Lincoln HS
Manitowoc WI

Miller Stephen S
Parkside HS
Jackson MI

Miller Steven D
Tinley Park HS
Tinley Park IL

Miller Steven D
Dalton Public HS
Dalton NE

Miller Susan A
Sparta Senior HS
Sparta WI

Miller Susan E
Lawrenceburg HS
Lawrenceburg IN

Miller Tamela M
Lincolnwood HS
Raymond IL

Miller Terri L
Bonner Springs HS
Bonner Springs KS

Miller Terry L
Chrisman HS
Chrisman IL

Miller Terry L
Wayne HS
Ft Wayne IN

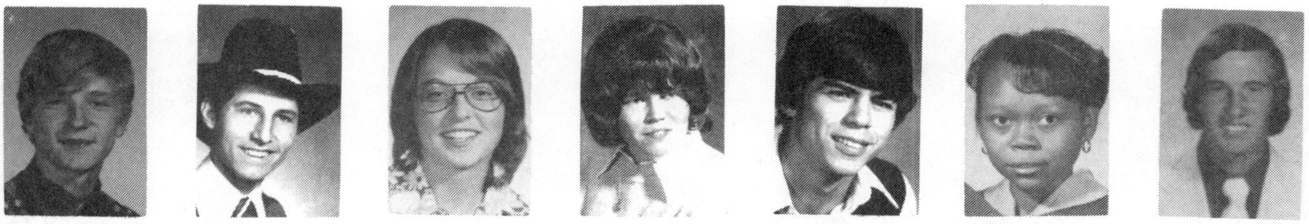

Miller Thomas W
Marist HS
Chicago IL

Miller Tommy J
Welch HS
Chetopa KS

Miller Trisha L
Cambridge HS
Cambridge NE

Miller Virginia A
Round Lake HS
Round Lake IL

Miller Walter B
Daleville HS
Daleville IN

Millhouse Phyllis
Chicago Vocational HS
Chicago IL

Millikan Keith W
St Laurence HS
Bridgeview IL

Million Donald L
Millard Sr HS
Omaha NE

Millman Myron M
Kewanee HS
Kewanee IL

Mills Barry R
Newton Senior HS
Newton IA

Mills Curtis L
North Miami HS
Macy IN

Mills Daniel P
Marlette HS
Brown City MI

Mills Kandis L
Cornell HS
Cornell IL

Mills Laurie L
St Francis Comm HS
St Francis KS

Mills Marla M
White Bear Sr HS
White Bear Lake MN

Mills Rita A
Bc HS
Denton IL

Mills Toni L
Lansing HS
Leavenworth KS

Milner Donna L
Downers Grove South HS
Downers Grov) IL

Milroy Greg M
Toulon HS
Toulon IL

Miltenberger Mark A
West Marshall Comm HS
Marshalltown IA

Minchow Mark K
Arlington HS
Arlington NE

Miner Audrey M
Gregory HS
Gregory SD

Miner Mary K
Gregory Public HS
Gregory SD

Miner Tina M
Midway HS
Denton KS

Minich Virginia L
Alton HS
Alton MO

Minker Carol J
Oregon Davis HS
Hamlet IN

Minker Catherine A
Oregon Davis HS
Hamlet IN

Minta James J
Naperville Central HS
Naperville IL

Miodus Paul A
Willowbrook HS
Lombard IL

Mioni Helen T
Ironwood Catholic HS
Ironwood MI

Mirga Tomas F
St Andrew HS
Detroit MI

Mirick Don G
Clopton HS
Clarksville MO

Mirt Sheryl F
Usd #509
South Haven KS

Misak James E
Joliet Catholic HS
Joliet IL

Mish Barbara J
George Rogers Clark HS
Hammond IN

Mishler Jerold A
Westview HS
Shipshewana IN

Misichko Emil W
Plainfield HS
Joliet IL

Misina Diane M
Lakeland HS
Lac Du Flambeau WI

Miskell Sheryl A
North Linn HS
Coggon IA

Mistiatis Robert C
Jefferson HS
Monroe MI

Mistler Patti J
Carrollton HS
Carrollton MO

Mitchell Brian L
Hartford HS
Hartford KS

Mitchell Carol L
Bgm Community HS
Grinnell IA

Mitchell Cindi L
Paris R 2 HS
Holliday MO

Mitchell David L
Battle Creek Central HS
Battle Creek MI

Mitchell Donna M
Enfield HS
Enfield IL

Mitchell Doris L
East HS
Wichita KS

Mitchell Gina M
Orchard Farm Sr HS
West Alton MO

Mitchell Hillman S
Hartford HS
Hartford KS

Mitchell James W
Proviso East HS
Maywood IL

Mitchell Joellen
Montezuma Comm HS
Malcom IA

Mitchell Judy A
Rich South HS
Matteson IL

Mitchell Karen L
Mc Leansboro HS
Mc Leansboro IL

Mitchell Kathleen A
Mother Mc Auley HS
Chicago IL

Mitchell Katie A
Central HS
Springfield MO

Mitchell Kitty B
Mc Donald County R 1 HS
Noel MO

Mitchell Margaret M
St Alphonsus HS
Dearborn MI

Mitchell Mary A
Salina Central HS
Salina KS

Mitchell Mary A
Greenfield HS
Greenfield WI

Mitchell Michele A
Valders HS
Valders WI

Mitchell Roger R
La Plata R Ii HS
La Plata MO

Mitchell Shirley A
Kewanee HS
Kewanee IL

Mitchell Timothy A
Frankfort Community HS
West Frankfort IL

Mitchell William C
Francis W Parker HS
Chicago IL

Mitchell William D
Murphysboro HS
Murphysboro IL

Mitchell Zander
Chicago Vocational HS
Chicago IL

Mitchum Charles J
Mendel Catholic Prep HS
Chicago IL

Miterko Lisa A
George Rogers Clark HS
Whiting IN

Mitrisin Jeff W
Eddyville Comm HS
Eddyville IA

Mittler Max B
Wright City HS
Wright City MO

Mitzelfelt Jeffrey D
Tremont HS
Pekin IL

Miziniak Zofia
Bloom Township HS
Chicago Heights IL

Mlinek Wendi E
St Francis Comm HS
St Francis KS

Mlynek Deborah J
James B Conant HS
Hoffman Estates IL

Moake Trina I
Vienna HS
Cypress IL

Moats Geri L
Marseilles HS
Marseilles IL

Moberg Marla R
Powers Lake HS
Battle View ND

Moburg John G
Yorkwood HS
Kirkwood IL

Modahl Debra R
Badger HS
Badger MN

Modert Ted A
Bronson HS
Bronson MI

Modin Gaylord L
Magic City Campus HS
Minot ND

Moe Patricia K
Hanson Ind #40 HS
Alexandria SD

Moeckel Debra K
Grass Lake Jr Sr HS
Grass Lake MI

Moeder Michael D
Central HS
Cape Girardeau MO

Moeller Debra A
Badger HS
Lake Geneva WI

Moeller William J
Joliet Catholic HS
Romeoville IL

Moen Janelle R
Richland #44 HS
Colfax ND

Moen Jeri L
Watertown Sr HS
Watertown SD

Moen Luann K
Hendricks HS
Astoria SD

Moffatt Keith E
Marinette Catholic Centrl HS
Marinette WI

Mohan David J
Springfield HS
Springfield IL

Mohit Julie R
Hays HS
Hays KS

Mohler John A
Yorktown HS
Yorktown IN

Mohni Lanette M
Hartley Comm HS
Hartley IA

Mohr Annetta J
Laharpe Comm HS
Lomax IL

Mohrhauser Luann R
Fremont Sr HS
Fremont NE

Mohs Roberta K
Wahpeton Sr HS
Wahpeton ND

Moklestad Larry L
Thompson Comm HS
Thompson IA

Molacek Ardene R
Howells Public HS
Howells NE

Molcyk Kathryn A
Kearney HS
Kearney NE

Molden Barbara A
Fairbury HS
Fairbury NE

Molina Paul L
Brown Deer HS
Brown Deer WI

Molinaro Anthony T
Morton West HS
Berwyn IL

Moline Deborah L
Durand Area HS
Durand MI

Moll Randall R
Lane Technical HS
Chicago IL

Moll Shelley A
Shannon HS
Shannon IL

Molloy Joseph M
Marquette HS
Alton IL

Molloy Kevin L
St Rita HS
Chicago IL

Molloy Sheryl L
Trenton HS
Trenton MO

Molo Steven F
A A Stagg HS
Palos Hills IL

Moma Alicia A
Blue Mound HS
Blue Mound IL

Monaco Helen C
John F Kennedy HS
Chicago IL

Monaghan Brian E
Homewood Flossmoor HS
Flossmoor IL

Monaghan Nancy K
Superior Sr HS
Superior WI

Monahan Joan M
Le Sueur HS
Le Sueur MN

Monday June E
Woodruff HS
Peoria IL

Mondul Mark M
Guilford HS
Rockford IL

Moniak Mary L
Saint Augustine HS
Chicago IL

Monkman James A
Brainerd HS
Brainerd MN

Monnier Donna L
Raymond Central HS
Raymond NE

Monnier Nancy J
Carthage Comm HS
Basco IL

Monroe Brian J
Central Community HS
De Witt IA

Monroe Carol A
Shenandoah HS
Shenandoah IA

Monroe Leanna M
Franklin HS
Waverly IL

Monroe Mark J
Niagara HS
Niagara WI

Monser Robert L
Richwoods HS
Peoria IL

Monshau Monique
St Francis Academy
Joliet IL

Monson Carolyn S
Lane Technical HS
Chicago IL

Monson Connie M
Merrill HS
Midland MI

Monson Echo J
New Town HS
New Town ND

Monson Raymond E
Evanston Twp HS
Evanston IL

Montague Elisabeth
Grosse Pointe South HS
Grosse Pointe MI

Monter Douglas L
Arapahoe HS
Arapahoe NE

Montgomery April
Harvard St George HS
Chicago IL

Montgomery Audrey J
Immaculata HS
Detroit MI

Montgomery Christie D
Baxter Community HS
Baxter IA

Montgomery Dennis L
Woodland HS
Hiram MO

Montgomery Donna J
Greenview HS
Greenview IL

Montgomery Joyce K
Porta HS
Petersburg IL

Montgomery Kim C
Faulkner HS
Chicago IL

Montgomery Laura L
Glenwood HS
Chatham IL

Montgomery Robert M
Benton Consolidated HS
Benton IL

Montgomery Susan K
Sabetha HS
Sabetha KS

Montgomery Valarie D
No Chicago Comm HS
North Chicago IL

Montgomery William A
Jerseyville HS
Jerseyville IL

Monyek Marcia E
Interlochen Arts Acad
Lake Forest IL

Monzu Deborah A
Paul Vi HS
Omaha NE

Mooberry Melody D
Woodruff HS
Peoria IL

Moody Anita S
North Vigo HS
Terre Haute IN

Moody Barbara F
Mehlville Sr HS
St Louis MO

Moody Carol
Millington HS
Millington MI

Moody Cheryl L
Bogan HS
Chicago IL

Moody Lawrence S
St Laurence HS
Chicago IL

Moody Nancy E
O Fallon Township HS
O Fallon IL

Moody Thomas O
Central HS
Waterloo IA

Moon Carol J
Wykoff Public HS
Wykoff MN

Moon Timothy D
Naperville Central HS
Naperville IL

Moor James D
Steinmetz HS
Chicago IL

Moore Anita L
Kent City HS
Casnovia MI

Moore Ann P
Battle Creek Central HS
Battle Creek MI

Moore Barbara L
North Chicago HS
Great Lakes IL

Moore Brian J
Lincolnway HS
Frankfort IL

Moore Carol J
U S D #462
Burden KS

Moore Christine M
Turner HS
Kansas KS

Moore Danette S
Columbia Central HS
Brooklyn MI

Moore Della M
Lyman HS
Vivian SD

Moore Janet L
Civic Memorial HS
Bethalto IL

Moore Janet L
F L Schlagle HS
Kansas City KS

Moore John K
Chippewa Valley HS
Mt Clemens MI

Moore John R
Richmond Sr HS
Richmond MO

Moore John R
Gordon Tech HS
Chicago IL

Moore Joni L
Bazine HS
Bazine KS

Moore Karen S
Greenview HS
Greenview IL

Moore Kevin D
Southwest HS
Saint Louis MO

Moore Mark F
Illiopolis HS
Illiopolis IL

Moore Martha M
Eastern HS
Lansing MI

Moore Michael D
Cisne Comm HS
Cisne IL

Moore Michael G
Mason City HS
Mason City IA

Moore Michael L
Rose Hill HS
Augusta KS

Moore Mike L
Princeton HS
Princeton MO

Moore Nancy L
Maine South HS
Park Ridge IL

Moore Patricia S
Oak Park & River Forest HS
River Forest IL

Moore Rebecca M
Shawnee HS
Mc Clure IL

Moore Renette S
Abraham Lincoln HS
Council Bluffs IA

Moore Roberta A
Carmel HS
Algonquin IL

Moore Ronnie C
Dallas City HS
Dallas Cty IL

Moore Scott L
East Richland HS
Olhey IL

Moore Shawn A
Brookfield R Iii HS
Brookfield MO

Moore Steve R
Randolph S HS
Lynn IN

Moore Terence D
Northwest HS
Indianapolis IN

Moore Teresa M
Bishop Du Bourg HS
St Louis MO

Moorehead John M
Highland HS
Highland IN

Moore Noller Tamara E
Marshall HS
Marshall IL

Moorkamp William B
Chaminade HS
Ballwin MO

Moos Jeffrey W
Greenfield HS
Greenfield WI

Moran Lisa A
Rantoul HS
Thomasboro IL

Moran Michael E
Bradley Bourbonnais HS
Bradley IL

Moran Michael G
Holy Cross HS
Chicago IL

Morden Natalie J
Arthur Hill HS
Saginaw MI

Moreau Cheryl A
Edison Sr HS
East Gary IN

Morefield Judy L
Reavis HS
Burbank IL

Morel Dayleen K
Wheatland HS
Girainfield KS

Moreland Gary L
Normal Community HS
Bloomington IL

Moreland Lamar D
Chadsey HS
Detroit MI

Moreland Mary A
El Dorado HS
El Dorado KS

Morello Merrie T
Forest Lake HS
Forest Lake MN

Morey Ruby I
Avon HS
Avon IL

Morgan Cynthia E
Benton Central HS
Fowler IN

Morgan Denise R
Oak Park And River Forest HS
Oak Park IL

Morgan Judith A
George Rogers Clark HS
Hammond IN

Morgan Karen J
Walthill Public HS
Walthill NE

Morgan Michael R
Turner HS
Kansas City KS

Morgan Pamela C
Edwardsburg HS
Niles MI

Morgan Robert E
Knightstown HS
Knightstown IN

Morgan Russell A
Maine East HS
Niles IL

Morgan Sherry G
Senath Hornersville HS
Senath MO

Morgan William P
North Central HS
Indianapolis IN

Morganelli Cynthia L
Thornwood HS
South Holland IL

Morganti Lyneen T
Rich East HS
Park Forest IL

Morgheim Curtis A
Lyman HS
Lyman NE

Moriello Karen A
William Howard Taft HS
Chicago IL

Morin Sandra K
Brainerd Sr HS
Brainerd MN

Moritz Debra S
Spring Valley Public HS
Spring Valley WI

Moritz Julianna M
St Scholastica HS
Chicago IL

Mork Shirley J
Central HS
Aberdeen SD

Morlan Karen K
Green City HS
Green Castle MO

Morlang Travis E
Ainsworth HS
Ainsworth NE

Morlen Rick A
Granite City HS
Granite City IL

Morr Garry E
Central Noble HS
Albion IN

Morrical Gregory W
Lincoln HS
Beverly KS

Morrill Myra J
Morrill HS
Morrill NE

Morris Bradley K
Mc Leansboro HS
Mc Leansboro IL

Morris Cynthia A
Marshall HS
Marshall MI

Morris Deann R
Sublette HS
Sublette KS

Morris Debra L
Pekin Comm HS
Pekin IL

Morris John M
North Side HS
Ft Wayne IN

Morris Karla K
Ash Grove R 4 HS
Ash Grove MO

Morris Kris L
Williamsfield HS
Dahinda IL

Morris Lori D
Newark Comm HS
Newark IL

Morris Mary Y
Du Quoin HS
Du Quoin IL

Morris Michael A
Flushing HS
Flushing MI

Morris Monica A
Whiteland Comm HS
Franklin IN

Morris Rhonda J
Warsaw HS
Warsaw IN

Morris William E
Eldorado HS
Eldorado IL

Morris William S
North HS
Des Moines IA

Morrison David R
St Joe Senior HS
Saint Joseph MI

Morrison Donna M
Spalding HS
Chicago IL

Morrison Martha M
Oscoda HS
Glennie MI

Morrison Ray E
Gregory HS
Gregory SD

Morrison Scott B
Stillman Valley HS
Stillman Valley IL

Morrison Tony E
Southmont HS
Ladoga IN

Morrone Kyle L
Clawson HS
Clawson MI

Morrow Bruce D
Greenway HS
Marble MN

Morrow Richard P
Lincoln Comm HS
Lincoln IL

Morsching Lynn M
Waterville Elysian HS
Waterville MN

Morse Kathlene M
Tecumseh HS
Tecumseh MI

Morse Lee J
Hill Mc Cloy HS
Montrose MI

Morse Lisa M
West HS
Davenport IA

Morse Peggy R
Central Cass HS
Wheatland ND

Mortensen Diane M
Alta Community HS
Alta IA

Morton Caroline E
Dupo Community HS
E Carondelet IL

Morton Jonathan S
Freeport HS
Freeport IL

Mosby Judith A
Litchville Public HS
Litchville ND

Moser Connie M
Medina Public HS
Medina ND

Moser Gregg M
Milbank HS
Milbank SD

Moser Mary L
North Central Area HS
Wilson MI

Moser Mike R
South Adams HS
Berne IN

Moses Mathew R
Berkley HS
Oak Park MI

Moses Richard L
Port Huron Northern HS
Port Huron MI

Mosher Michael J
Loyola Academy
Northbrook IL

Mosher Stacy A
Webberville HS
Webberville MI

Moskal John T
Clayton HS
Clayton WI

Moskalick Mariann T
Morton Sr HS
Hammond IN

Mosner Mary B
Yates City HS
Maquon IL

Moss Caron D
Westport HS
Kansas City MO

Moss Jill A
Wethersfield HS
Kewanee IL

Moss Jo A
Whitmore Lake HS
Whitmore Lake MI

Moss Kevin M
Northwest HS
High Ridge MO

Moss Tami J
Rvi Tipton HS
Tipton MO

Mossyge James D
Leroy Ostrander HS
Leroy MN

Moteberg Ladawna A
Lake Of The Woods HS
Baudette MN

Mothershead Russ A
Kelly HS
Benton MO

Motiff Nancy A
West HS
Green Bay WI

Mottet Diane M
Oskaloosa Sr HS
Oskaloosa IA

Mottet Mary A
Fairfield HS
Richland IA

Moulliet Michele A
Fenton HS
Fenton MI

Moulton Sandra M
Sycamore HS
Genoa IL

Mountin Lois A
Lincoln HS
Lake City MN

Mouradian Daniel S
Lyons Township HS
La Grange IL

Mousel Mary J
Heelan HS
Sioux City IA

Mouser Sheryl A
Woodland R Iv HS
Lutesville MO

Mowat Suzanne R
Bellevue Comm HS
Bellevue IA

Mowery John W
Dongola HS
Dongola IL

Mowery Kevin M
Southwest HS
St Louis MO

Mowery Penny S
Hillsdale HS
Hillsdale MI

Mowris Kathryn E
George S Parker HS
Janesville WI

Mowry Bonnie K
Mcpherson County HS
Scottsbluff NE

Mox Scott W
Glenbrook South HS
Glenview IL

Moyer Paul K
Alvarado HS
Alvarado MN

Moyer Peggy F
Clearwater R 1 HS
Piedmont MO

Moyers Randal E
Hays HS
Hays KS

Moyle Laura M
Nerinx Hall HS
Webster Groves MO

Mrazek Stephen J
Alleman HS
Rock Island IL

Mrkva Kip J
Dearborn HS
Dearborn MI

Mroczkowski Daniel J
Highland HS
Highland IN

Mrozinski Geri L
Ss Peter & Paul HS
Freeland MI

Mrzlack Robert B
Twin Lakes HS
Monticello IN

Mucci Michael L
North Greene HS
White Hall IL

Mucha Richard J
Benet Academy
Westchester IL

Muck Kaye M
Bonduel Comm HS
Cecil WI

Mudd Kathleen M
Grand Blanc HS
Flint MI

Mudd Steven W
Lincoln Co HS
Silex MO

Mudgett Kent J
Moorhead Sr HS
Moorhead MN

Muehlenkamp Jayne E
Sparta Senior HS
Norwalk WI

Muehling Brian K
Ofallon Township HS
Ofallon IL

Mueller Dave L
Morton HS
Morton IL

Mueller David J
Chippewa Falls Sr HS
Chippewa Falls WI

Mueller Heidi J
Greendale HS
Greendale WI

Mueller James A
Clarion Community HS
Clarion IA

Mueller Jeffery S
South HS
Shebygan WI

Mueller Julie E
United Township HS
East Moline IL

Mueller Karen K
Milwaukee Lutheran HS
Brookfield WI

Mueller Karl F
Roncalli HS
Indianapolis IN

Mueller Kim
Grinnell Comm HS
Grinnell IA

Mueller Mark M
West HS
Minneapolis MN

Mueller Mary K
Madison Sr HS
E St Louis IL

Muenzenberger Randy M
Cashton HS
Coon Valley WI

Muetzel Douglas W
Ogeman Heights HS
West Branch MI

Muhlenbruck Cynthia S
Greene Community HS
Greene IA

Muhr Timothy D
Bayard HS
Bayard NE

Muhs Vicky K
Calamus Community HS
Ccalamus IA

Muir Dana M
Brown City HS
Brown City MI

Muir Jim E
Midway HS
Inkster ND

Muir Rick B
West Bloomfield HS
W Bloomfield MI

Mukai William T
Maine Township HS
Des Plaines IL

Mulder Cheryl A
Zeeland HS
Zeeland MI

Mulder Donn M
Maurice Orange City
Comm HS
Maurice IA

Mull Dave C
Brown County HS
Versailles IL

Mullan Dianna L
Harvard HS
Harvard IL

Mullaney Mary C
Our Lady Star Of The Sea
HS
Gross Pte Shores MI

Muller Debra J
Washington Comm HS
Washington IL

Muller Keith L
Fairbury Sr HS
Fairbury NE

Muller Terry L
Howells Public HS
Howells NE

Mullice Anthony L
Huron HS
Ann Arbor MI

Mulligan Anne S
Rosati Kain HS
University City MO

Mullins Gayla S
Virden HS
Virden IL

Mullins Judi A
Ypsilanti HS
Ypsilanti MI

Mullins Martha J
Central Heights HS
Lane KS

Mullins Mary E
Unionville HS
Livonia MO

Mullins Mary J
Benton Consolidated HS
Benton IL

Mullins Rita K
Clay City HS
Ingraham IL

Mulrine Patrick G
Onalaska HS
Onalaska WI

Mulroe Stephen M
St Patrick HS
Chicago IL

Mulroe Thomas P
St Patrick HS
Chicago IL

Muma Gregory P
St Philip Cc HS
Battle Creek MI

Mumm Cheryl L
Unity HS
Philo IL

Mummert John R
Johnston City HS
Thompsonville IL

Munar Ellen M
Andrews Univ Academy
Berrien Springs MI

Mundy Marylee
Belvidere HS
Belvidere IL

Muniz Michael J
Turner HS
Kansas City KS

Munsell Debra A
Oskaloosa Senior HS
Oskaloosa IA

Munson Scott R
Dundee Comm HS
Carpentersville IL

Munster Kent A
Ogallala HS
Ogallala NE

Murdy David C
Rock Island HS
Rock Island IL

Murff Terrill N
Chicago Vocational HS
Chicago IL

Murkowski David M
Marquette Univ HS
Milwaukee WI

Murphy Doug
Notre Dame HS
Cresco IA

Murphy Frederick J
Wyandotte HS
Kansas City KS

Murphy Jill E
Holton HS
Twin Lake MI

Murphy John D
Stuart Menlo Comm HS
Stuart IA

Murphy John G
Marist HS
Oak Lawn IL

Murphy Kevin M
George S Parker HS
Janesville WI

Murphy Lisa A
Lincolnwood HS
Farmersville IL

Murphy Patricia A
Des Lacs HS
Burlington ND

Murphy Patrick E
Owosso HS
Owosso MI

Murphy Patrick G
Creighton Prep
Omaha NE

Murphy Ron E
New Bloomfield HS
Holts Summit MO

Murphy Sheryl A
Carroll HS
Flora IN

Murphy Teri L
Peoria HS
Peoria IL

Murphy William R
Parkston HS
Parkston SD

Murray Karen C
Bishop Ward HS
Kansas City KS

Murray Richard A
North Central Area HS
Spalding MI

Murray Ronald J
Monroe City HS
Monroe City MO

Murrell Lizabeth L
North Fayette County
Comm HS
West Union IA

Murry Timothy J
Delavan Public HS
Delavan MN

Murto Susan F
Wauwatosa East HS
Wauwatosa WI

Murzyn Patrick J
Thornton Fractional S HS
Lansing IL

Muscat Daniel J
Our Lady Of The Lakes HS
Clarkston MI

Musch Deborah D
St Joseph HS
Chicago IL

Mussman Michael L
Central Community HS
De Witt IA

Mustoe Mark M
Elk Valley HS
Elk City KS

Muszar Michelle A
Heritage Christian HS
Indianapolis IN

Muszynski Barbara H
N Chicago Comm HS
Great Lakes IL

Mutchler Melody A
Lake Central HS
Crown Point IN

Muth David J
Rockwell Swaledale Comm
HS
Mason City IA

Muth Sheryl M
Hartford Union HS
Hubertus WI

Mutschler Sally L
Saranac HS
Saranac MI

Muyleart Diane G
Mt Olive Community HS
Staunton IL

Myer Robert S
Harrison HS
Evansville IN

Myers Carla J
E Richland HS
Olney IL

Myers Denise L
Arcadia Valley HS
Arcadia MO

Myers Gregory A
Brazil Sr HS
Brazil IN

Myers James M
State HS
Terre Haute IN

Myers James R
Taylorville HS
Taylorville IL

Myers Jolene P
Winona HS
La Moille MN

Myers Jolynne
Perry Lecompton HS
Perry KS

Myers Kathleen J
Colchester HS
Colchester IL

Myers Linda K
Bellmont HS
Decatur IN

Myers Lisa K
Maroa Forsyth HS
Maroa IL

Myers Michael B
Barneveld HS
Barneveld WI

Myers Michael S
North Wood HS
Nappanee IN

Myers Richard J
Faulkton HS
Faulkton SD

Myers Robert L
Warsaw Comm HS
Warsaw IN

Myers Thomas J
Oconomowoc Sr HS
Oconomowoc WI

Myklebust Anna M
Wis Dells HS
Baraboo WI

Myrant Rog A
Ft Zumwalt HS
O Fallon MO

Myren Terry J
Holmen HS
Holmen WI

Myrom Kathryn G
Glenwood Central HS
Glenwood MN

Myrvold Lynne T
Glenbrook No HS
Northbrook IL

Myszka Charles J
Holy Redeemer HS
Detroit MI

Myszkowski Susan L
Wenona Comm HS
Wenona IL

N

Nabb Kevin L
O Fallon Twsp HS
O Fallon IL

Nace Vaughn M
Portageville HS
Portageville MO

Nachazel Ann M
Our Lady Of The Sea HS
Grosse Pointe MI

Nachbar Mark L
Highland Park HS
Highland Park IL

Nading Jeff L
Boone HS
Boone IA

Nadolski Connie
Bishop Noll HS
East Chicago IN

Nadolski Cynthia A
Waltonville HS
Scheller IL

Naffziger Terri L
Deer Creek Mackinaw HS
Mackinaw IL

Nagel Tim J
Dike Community HS
Dike IA

Nagle Betsy J
Lake Forest HS
Lake Bluff IL

Nagorzanski Steven M
Gordon Tech HS
Chicago IL

Nahitchevansky George H
Loyola Academy
Chicago IL

Nakamura Grant Y
Maplewood Academy
New Brighton MN

Nakutis Aldona M
Maria HS
Chicago IL

Namanny Scott L
Wentworth Military
Academy
Denison IA

Namyniuk Lorraine L
Belfield HS
Belfield ND

Nance Kathy A
Nevada Sr HS
Nevada MO

Nance Paul A
Crispus Attucks HS
Indianapolis IN

Nannetti Sheryl M
Libertyville HS
Libertyville IL

Napier Juliet B
Mexico HS
Mexico MO

Napiorkowski Walter C
Little Falls Community HS
Pierz MN

Naples Lynn
Kennedy St Paul Hs
Chicago IL

Naretto Mark M
Gardner So Wilmington HS
Gardner IL

Narhi Rae M
Baraga HS
Baraga MI

Narlock Roger M
Midway HS
Inkster ND

Narup Susan J
Union HS
Union MO

Nash Deborah Y
High School
Mineral Point MO

Nash Donald K
Holcomb HS
Kennett MO

Nash Grant E
St Joseph HS
St Joseph MI

Nash Laura N
Richwoods HS
Peoria IL

Nash Preston J
Southwestern HS
Flint MI

Nash Vickie L
Wykoff HS
Wykoff MN

Nasman Kathryn S
Taylors Falls HS
Shafer MN

Nass James P
Ralston HS
Ralston NE

Nassen Kent D
Iowa Falls Senior HS
Iowa Falls IA

Nasser Leslie E
Speedway HS
Speedway IN

Nattier Dina M
Patoka Community #100 HS
Patoka IL

Nault Linda E
Marshall HS
Marshall IL

Nault Renee R
Ishpeming HS
Ishpeming MI

Navine Marc L
Armstrong HS
Neenah WI

Nawara Bruce G
St Laurence HS
Chicago IL

Neahring John M
Sterling HS
Sterling IL

Neal Brenda M
Westville HS
Danville IL

Neal D A
Raymore Peculiar HS
Peculiar MO

Neal Jacki L
Grandview HS
Grandview MO

Neal Joe M
North Knox HS
Oaktown IN

Neal Randi A
Valley Park HS
Valley Park MO

Nearing Cherie A
Douglas Mac Arthur HS
Saginaw MI

Nease Franklin E
Slater HS
Slater MO

Nechanicky Susan M
Ellendale Geneva HS
Ellendale MN

Nechiporenko Rick J
Velva Public HS
Velva ND

Nederhoff Bruce D
Wellsburg Comm HS
Wellsburg IA

Nedrelo Randy L
Seneca HS
Seneca WI

Nedved David L
Garner Hayfield HS
Garner IA

Nedved Patricia A
East Charles Mix HS
Wagner SD

Neeb Pamela A
Freeland HS
Freeland MI

Needles Carrie L
Catholic Memorial HS
Waukesha WI

Neeld Lisa A
Lawrence Central HS
Indianapolis IN

Neemann Steven R
Nemaha Valley HS
Cook NE

Neer David L
North Knox HS
Oaktown IN

Nees Kolleen K
De Soto HS
De Soto MO

Neet Deborah Y
Effingham HS
Effingham IL

Neff David B
Goshen HS
Goshen IN

Neff Michael W
Custer HS
Custer SD

Negroni Christina
Emerson HS
Gary IN

Neice Thomas E
Oshkosh W HS
Oshkosh WI

Neidhardt Sandy D
Hebron Public HS
Hebron ND

Neier Robert I
Usd 424 HS
Mullinville KS

Neilsen Kitty A
Waupaca HS
Waupaca WI

Neise Regina M
Bloomington HS
Bloomington IL

Neiswanger Yvonne C
North Daviess HS
Odon IN

Neiteke Michael A
Detroit Lakes Sr HS
Detroit Lakes MN

Neitzel Debra R
Bird City HS
St Francis KS

Neitzke Brenda L
Winona Sr HS
Winona MN

Nelle James M
North Farmington Sr HS
Farmington Hills MI

Nelms Casey R
Hayes Center Public HS
Hayes Center NE

Nelms Sharon M
Republican Valley HS
Indianola NE

Nelsen Roxanne M
Wild Rose HS
Poy Sippi WI

Nelsin Jay N
Petoskey HS
Petoskey MI

Nelson Althea E
Balaton HS
Balaton MN

Nelson Beth L
Downers Grove North HS
Downers Grove IL

Nelson Bradley J
Hastings HS
Hastings NE

Nelson Carol J
Benson HS
Omaha NE

Nelson Carolyn S
J A Craig HS
Janesville WI

Nelson Cynthia L
Shickley Public HS
Shickley NE

Nelson Denise L
Richmond Burton Comm HS
Richmond IL

Nelson Diann E
Woodland HS
Streator IL

Nelson Dick A
Fergus Falls HS
Fergus Falls MN

Nelson Elizabeth A
Lake Central HS
Schererville IN

Nelson Gail L
Richmond Burton HS
Richmond IL

Nelson Gail L
Newton Community HS
Hidalgo IL

Nelson Glenn E
Calumet HS
Gary IN

Nelson Jane L
Fairfield HS
Turon KS

Nelson Jeffrey A
Center HS
Kansas City MO

Nelson Julie R
United Township HS
East Moline IL

Nelson Kathy K
Barron Area HS
Barron WI

Nelson Kris K
Watertown HS
Watertown SD

Nelson Kristi S
Emerson Hubbard HS
Emerson NE

Nelson Marcalene M
Alwood HS
Woodhull IL

STUDENTS PHOTOGRAPH SCHEDULED FOR PUBLICATION HERE COULD NOT BE REPRODUCED

Nelson Mark A
Staunton Military Academy
Kankakee IL

Nelson Marnette A
Cedar Valley HS
Rockwell City IA

Nelson Michele R
Litchfield Public HS
Litchfield NE

Nelson Nikita L
Douglass HS
Douglass KS

Nelson Paul E
High School
Truro IA

Nelson Peggy I
Wild Rose HS
Pine River WI

Nelson Scott M
Pembroke Country Day HS
Leawood KS

Nelson Terrea R
Bryant HS
Rich Hill MO

Nelson Thomas C
Lincoln Sr HS
Thief River Falls MN

Nemeth Joseph R
Pine River Jr Sr HS
Tustin MI

Nemgar Susan T
Eveleth HS
Eveleth MN

Nemmers Mary P
St John HS
Bancroft IA

Nenzel Sharon A
Stanley Boyd HS
Stanley WI

Neprud Dean A
Halstad HS
Shelly MN

Nerat John R
Stephenson HS
Wallace MI

Nere Russell G
Danube HS
Danube MN

Nerem Ronald G
Roland Story HS
Roland IA

Nesbitt Randy J
Sturgeon Bay HS
Sturgeon Bay WI

Nesler Dean E
Elgin HS
Hanover Park IL

Nespor James G
Fairbury HS
Fairbury NE

Ness Julie M
North HS
Eau Claire WI

Ness Lori J
Newark Co HS
Morris IL

Ness Paul A
Oak Lawn HS
Oak Lawn IL

Nesseler Molly J
Rock Island HS
Rock Island IL

Nestorovski Zvonko
Southwestern HS
Dearborn Hgts MI

Neth Steven D
Broken Bow HS
Broken Bow NE

Netter Jeffrey S
Glenbrook North HS
Northbrook IL

Nettleton Colleen M
Pickford HS
Pickford MI

Neufeld Jolene S
Newton HS
N Newton KS

Neukam Terry L
Dubois HS
Dubois IN

Neuman Lealor P
Lindblom Tech HS
Chicago IL

Neumann Dean W
Beaver Dam Sr HS
Beaver Dam WI

Neumann Michael K
St Johns Seminary
Atchison KS

Neumeyer Brenda S
Western HS
Bay City MI

Neupert Mary B
St Charles HS
St Charles MO

Nevells Janet A
Pontiac Catholic HS
Pontiac MI

Neville Carolyn S
Beaverton HS
Beaverton MI

Newby William E
Parkwood HS
Joplin MO

Newell Cynthia S
Hill City HS
Hill City KS

Newell Douglas G
Ogden HS
Ogden IA

Newell Janell G
Neche Public HS
Neche ND

Newell Robert D
Rolling Meadows HS
Rolling Meadows IL

Newhouse Patricia M
Charleston Sr HS
Charleston IL

Newlin John
Douglas Macarthur Hs
Decatur IL

Newlin Julie A
Mattoon Sr HS
Mattoon IL

Newlin Mark E
Plainfield HS
Plainfield IN

Newman Clarence G
Walker R 4 HS
Walker MO

Newman Cynthia L
Rankin Twp HS
Rankin IL

Newman Glinda L
Grandview Senior HS
Grandview MO

Newman Jean L
Toulon HS
Toulon IL

Newman Lee A
Harrisburg HS
Harrisburg IL

Newman Mike L
Walker HS
Walker MO

Newman Pamela R
Truman HS
Independence MO

Newman Peggy G
Albia Community HS
Lorilia IA

Newman Richard L
Cary Grove HS
Fox River Grove IL

Newmarch Daniel H
Kingsley Area HS
Kingsley MI

Newnam Elsie M
Fairbury Cropsgy HS
Fairbury IL

Newnum Ronald L
Turkey Run HS
Bloomingdale IN

Newport Machell R
Perry Lecompton HS
Perry KS

Newsome Allen L
Emerson HS
Gary IN

Newsome Kendall C
Lebanon HS
Lebanon IL

Newsum Danny T
Peoria HS
Peoria IL

Newton Beverly A
Dickinson HS
Dickinson ND

Newton Dennis W
South Knox HS
Decker IN

Newton Dwight
J C Harmon Sr HS
Kansas City KS

Newton James D
Kirksville Sr HS
Kirksville MO

Newton Jeffery A
Kokomo HS
Kokomo IN

Newton Pamela J
Marian Catholic HS
Chicago Hts IL

Newton Randy L
Vienna HS
Vienna IL

Nibel Pamela E
Belton HS
Belton MO

Nice Suzanne A
Leroy HS
Leroy IL

Nichelson Cathleen S
Blair HS
Blair NE

Nichol Ross L
Pittsfield HS
Pittsfield IL

Nicholas Georgina M
York HS
Elmhurst IL

Nicholas Jandallee
Walled Lake Central HS
West Bloomfield MI

Nicholls Emily A
Houghton HS
Houghton MI

Nichols Catherine A
Knoxville HS
Gilson IL

Nichols Gary W
Franklin Central HS
Indianapolis IN

Nichols Janis E
Otsego HS
Otsego MI

Nichols Karl C
Cretin HS
Minneapolis MN

Nichols Ken N
Mesick HS
Mesick MI

Nichols Linda L
Osborn HS
Osborn MO

Nichols Michael E
Cumberland HS
Toledo IL

Nichols Paula S
Willard HS
Springfield MO

Nichols Pennie A
Waynesville Sr HS
Waynesville MO

Nichols Tommy G
Dixon HS
Dixon MO

Nicholson Scott G
Concordia HS
Concordia KS

Nicholson Tammy L
Potosi R 3 HS
Potosi MO

Nickel Alfred J
Pardeeville HS
Wyocena WI

Nickele Christopher J
Notre Dame For Boys HS
Chicago IL

Nickels Darrol S
Henryville HS
Henryville IN

Nickels Dianna N
Stanley County HS
Fort Pierre SD

Nickens Gary E
Tamaroa HS
Tamoroa IL

Nickerson Elaine C
Yale HS
Yale MI

Nickman Barbara S
Northwest HS
Grand Island NE

Nickodemus Mary A
Reese HS
Richville MI

Nickrent Kathleen M
St Josephs Academy
Florissant MO

Nicks Darryl R
Gasconade Co R 2 HS
Owensville MO

Nicol David B
No Farmington HS
Farmington Hills MI

Nicolai Paul M
Milnor HS
Milnor ND

Nicoletti Patti L
Columbus Unified HS
Columbus KS

Nicolini Mary B
Marian HS
Mishawaka IN

Nicoson Chere M
Waterman HS
Waterman IL

Niebuhr Kurt W
Lutheran HS
Norwood MN

Niebur Paula S
Granite HS
Granite IL

Niece Paul A
Green City R I HS
Green Castle MO

Niedert Debra K
Sumner HS
Sumner IA

Niedfeldt Cynthia J
Lakeview HS
Columbus NE

Niedzwiecki Judith K
East Detroit HS
East Detroit MI

Nieland James K
Sisseton HS
Sisseton SD

Nielsen James W
Roosevelt Theodore HS
Des Moines IA

Nielsen Judith D
New England Public HS
New England ND

Nielsen Julie A
Unity HS
Balsam Lake WI

Nielsen Vicki A
Western Comm HS
Buda IL

Niemann Amy C
Lincoln HS
Wisconsin Rapids WI

Niemann James J
St Anthony HS
Effingham IL

Niemi Margaret R
John F Kennedy HS
Taylor MI

Niemi Marlene S
Owen Withee HS
Withee WI

Niemuth Douglas J
Oakville Sr HS
St Louis MO

Niemzyk Ronald C
Hartford Union HS
Hubertus WI

Nierodzik Henry E
Lincoln Northeast HS
Lincoln NE

Nies Douglas E
Downers Grove Comm HS
Woodridge IL

Niestvchowski Valerie A
Mason Sr HS
Erie MI

Nieters Douglas J
St Louis Univ HS
St Louis MO

Nievinski Peggy S
Muskego HS
Hales Corners WI

Niewald Gail L
Maries County R Ii HS
Belle MO

Niewoehner Roland E
Willow City HS
Willow City ND

Niewold Douglas W
Paxton HS
Loda IL

Nigg Joey M
Dubois HS
Jasper IN

Niggeman Charlene J
Adrian HS
Adrian MI

Nighswonger Kim D
Hill City HS
Hill City KS

Nighswonger Ronald N
Torrington HS
Morrill NE

Nightengale Carol L
Chase County HS
Cedar Point KS

Nightengale Janet L
Chase County HS
Cedar Point KS

Nikurs Andrejs R
Stephen T Mather HS
Chicago IL

Nila Brett E
Marmion Military Academy
Bristol IL

Nilson Nancy J
Blair Jr/sr HS
Blair NE

Ninham Paul K
West Depere HS
Depere WI

Nisonger William R
Cranbrook HS
Bloomfield Hills MI

Nissen Robert B
Oneill Public HS
Page NE

Nitka Doris A
Pacelli HS
Stevens Point WI

Nitz Cathy L
Lakeshore HS
Baroda MI

Nixon Elaine L
Southwestern HS
Medora IL

Nixon Gregory L
Oxford HS
Oxford KS

Nixon Julie A
Glenwood Community HS
Glenwood IA

Noack Carol L
Coloma HS
Coloma MI

Noah Cheryl L
James B Conant HS
Hoffman Ests IL

Noasconi Doreen A
Stephenson HS
Stephenson MI

Noble Alice M
Woodstock HS
Wonder Lake IL

Noble Deloris R
Woodstock Community HS
Woodstock IL

Noble James R
Harlan Comm HS
Harlan IA

Noble Kathleen E
Hillcrest HS
Springfield MO

Noble Laura E
Springfield HS
Springfield MI

Nobles Denise
Thornwood HS
Markham IL

Nockels Patrick J
St Patrick HS
Chicago IL

Noehrenberg Lisa L
Luther HS
Oak Lawn IL

Noel Gayle J
Mason Senior HS
Erie MI

Noel Jill M
Laplata R 2 HS
Laplata MO

Noel Margaret A
York Community HS
Elmhurst IL

Noell Scott J
Plattsmouth HS
Murray NE

Noffsinger Robin
Marian HS
Elkhart IN

Noftsger Amy R
Grand Valley HS
Kellerton IA

Nokes Deborah S
Highland HS
Highland IN

Nolan Brenda K
Van Far HS
Vandalia MO

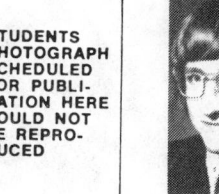

STUDENTS PHOTOGRAPH SCHEDULED FOR PUBLICATION HERE COULD NOT BE REPRODUCED

Nolan Denise L
Omaha Central HS
Omaha NE

Nolan Karen S
Belvidere HS
Belvidere IL

Nolan Linda M
Harvard HS
Harvard IL

Noll Jerald K
North Putnam HS
Coatsville IN

Nolte Diana L
Santa Fe HS
Blackburn MO

Nolte Marilyn K
Incarnate Academy
Olivette MO

Nolte Mary E
Mac Arthur HS
Decatur IL

Nommay Daniel E
Elkhart Central HS
Elkhart IN

Nook Mark A
Holstein Comm HS
Holstein IA

Noonan Mary E
Central City Comm HS
Anamosa IA

Noonan Patricia A
St Mary Of Perpetual Help HS
Chicago IL

Noramczyk James V
St Bede HS
Spring Valley IL

Nordberg Clark D
Cambridge HS
Cambridge MN

Nordberg Jackie M
Roosevelt HS
Marenisco MI

Nordby Daniel V
Menahga Public HS
Menahga MN

Nordhues Steven J
Norfolk Catholic HS
Norfolk NE

Nordyke Judy L
Pekin Community HS
Richland IA

Noreen Jennifer A
Lincoln Sr HS
Bloomington MN

Norfleet Douglas W
Franklin HS
Alexander IL

Norgard Linda B
La Follette HS
Madison WI

Norman Carl A
Pembine HS
Dunbar WI

Norman Carol A
Pembine HS
Dunbar WI

Norman Donald K
Rich Hill HS
El Dorado MO

Norman Edward M
Schuyler R 1 HS
Lancaster MO

Norman Gregg S
Pekin Comm HS
Pekin IL

Norman Mary S
Erie HS
Erie IL

Norman Sherry L
Franklin Central HS
Indianapolis IN

Normandin Becki J
Quincy HS
Quincy MI

Noroby Anna L
Powers Lake HS
White Earth ND

Norris James D
Highland HS
Highland IN

Norris Karen
New Palestine HS
New Palestine IN

Norris Mark J
Carter County R I HS
Van Buren MO

Norris Susan L
Newton Community HS
Newton IL

North Sheryl L
Center HS
Kansas City MO

Northcutt Richard E
Bridgeport Senior HS
Saginaw MI

Norton Bruce C
Winona Sr HS
Winona MN

Norton Cynthia M
Casey HS
Casey IL

Norton Kimberly J
Deckerville Comm HS
Deckerville MI

Norton Mark D
Neponset HS
Neponset IL

Norton Tom E
Central Sr HS
Clifton IL

Norton Toni L
Berkley HS
Berkley MI

Norwood Robert E
Minonk Dana Rutland HS
Rutland IL

Notbohm Thomas N
Oconomowoc HS
Oconomowoc WI

Novak Anita M
Pershing HS
Brooks MN

Novak Diane L
Chesaning HS
Chesaning MI

Novak Pamela K
Harlem North HS
Loves Park IL

Novak Phillip E
East Richland HS
Olney IL

Novich Susanna M
Plattsmouth HS
Plattsmouth NE

Novotny Bradlee N
Pender Public HS
Pender NE

Novotny Joanne G
Divine Savior Holy Angels HS
Milwaukee WI

Nowak Susan M
Thornton Twp HS
Posen IL

Nowakowski Jill A
Rochester Adams HS
Rochester MI

Nowakowski Mary L
Highland HS
Highland IN

Noward Clinton B
Pinckneyville Comm HS
Pinckneyville IL

Nowling Linda J
Turkey Run HS
Marshall IN

Nuernberger Jerry L
Hinsdale Central HS
Hinsdale IL

Null Steven R
Centerville Public HS
Centerville SD

Nulsen David J
Cahokia Sr HS
Cahokia IL

Nulton Mike T
Hoisington HS
Hoisington KS

Nunez Thomas A
Edsel Ford HS
Dearborn MI

Nunnelly Paul D
University HS
Cape Girardeau MO

Nurczyk Donna R
Joliet Twp Central HS
Joliet IL

Nurhadi Haryanto H
Northwestern HS
Good Hope IL

Nurrenbern James D
Gibson Southern HS
Ft Branch IN

Nush Charles S
East Gary Edison HS
East Gary IN

Nussbaum Frederic J
C S Mott Sr HS
Warren MI

Nussel John R
Staunton HS
Brazil IN

Nutt Sherrie
Bad Axe Hs
Bad Ate MI

Nutter Linda K
Morton HS
Morton IL

Nuyen Joseph G
Comstock HS
Kalamazoo MI

Nuzzo Frank
Lew Wallace HS
Gary IN

Nyberg Cynthia J
Gridley HS
Gridley IL

Nydegger Gregg A
Clinton Prairie HS
Colfax IN

Nygard Cindy L
Garrison HS
Roseglen ND

Nygard Shane D
Grafton Central HS
Grafton ND

Nykamp Thomas L
Holland Christian HS
Zeeland MI

Nylund Jeaneen A
Menominee HS
Menominee MI

Nylund Kim E
Menominee HS
Menominee MI

Nyquist Janice L
Northville HS
Northville MI

Nyquist Larry K
Bemidji HS
Bemidji MN

O

O Bannon Allen R
Pillager HS
Pillager MN

O Brien Bridget M
Academy Of Sacred Heart
Birmingham MI

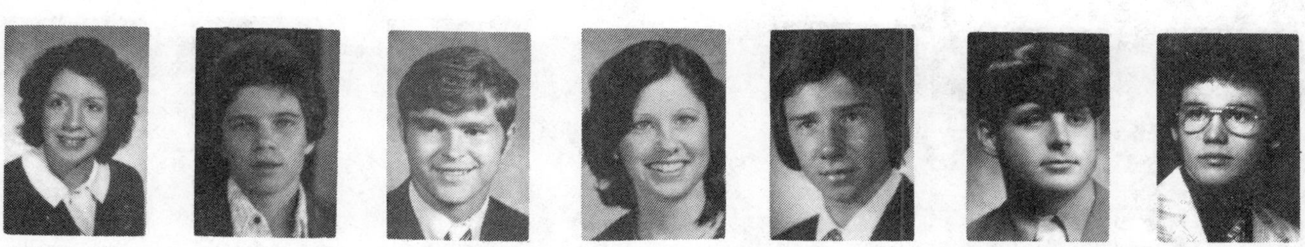

O Brien Denise
St Francis Academy
Joliet IL

O Brien James B
Big Foot HS
Fontana WI

O Brien Larry W
East Richland HS
Olney IL

O Brien Mary C
Duchesne HS
St Charles MO

O Brien Michael G
St Marys Springs HS
Fond Du Lac WI

O Brien Ronald C
Ontonagon Area HS
Ontonayon MI

O Brien Timothy J
Schleswig Comm HS
Schleswig IA

O Bryant Renee L
Delta HS
Albany IN

O Callaghan Terese M
Alcona HS
Lincoln MI

O Clair Joel A
Clay Central HS
Royal IA

O Connell Diane K
Senn HS
Chicago IL

O Connell Tim L
Anthon Oto HS
Smithland IA

O Connor Beth A
Laker HS
Elkton MI

O Connor James T
Marian Catholic HS
Lansing IL

O Connor Linda M
John F Kennedy HS
Chicago IL

O Connor Mary M
Heelan HS
Sioux City IA

O Daniel James T
Normandy Sr HS
St Louis MO

O Day Kelly B
Merrill Sr HS
Merrill WI

O Dea James A
Bridgeport HS
Bridgeport NE

O Dell Kimberly L
North Clay Comm HS
Louisville IL

O Doherty Terry M
Creighton Prep HS
Omaha NE

O Donnell Cheryl M
Mercy HS
Omaha NE

O Donnell Helen M
Woodstock Community HS
Wonder Lake IL

O Donnell James L
St Laurence HS
Chicago IL

O Donnell Linda C
St Thomas Aquinas HS
Ferguson MO

O Donnell William M
Loyola Academy
Chicago IL

O Driscoll Richard J
Mehlville Sr HS
St Louis MO

O Farrell Richard R
Bay City Central HS
Bay City MI

O Flaherty Bridget V
Queen Of Peace HS
Hickory Hills IL

O Grady Mary T
Holy Child HS
Waukegan IL

O Hanlon John A
Potosi HS
Potosi MO

O Keefe Dan T
Hudson Sr HS
Hudson WI

O Keefe Dianne C
Newton HS
Newton KS

O Keeffe Marian C
Catholic Memorial HS
Wauwatosa WI

O Malley Patrick M
Brown City HS
Brown City MI

O Mara James E
Lakewood HS
Lake Odessa MI

O Neal Mark S
Downers Grove No HS
Woodridge IL

O Neal Shirley J
Civic Memorial HS
Cottage Hills IL

O Neal Todd S
Angola HS
Angola IN

O Neil Keith C
S Newton HS
Goodland IN

O Neill James J
Creighton Prep HS
Omaha NE

O Reilly Colleen M
Irving Crown HS
Lake In The Hills IL

O Shea Kathleen A
Elizabeth Seton HS
Chicago IL

Oakes David C
Beloit Memorial HS
Beloit WI

Oakes David W
Cairo HS
Cairo IL

Oakes Thomas J
Tri County HS
Pierson MI

Oakley Cheri L
Heyworth HS
Heyworth IL

Oakley Robert C
Waterford Mott HS
Pontiac MI

Oakley Thomas J
Rogers HS
Michigan City IN

Oard Pamela S
Abilene HS
Abilene KS

Obejas Mario J
Michigan City Rogers HS
Michigan City IN

Oberg Debra J
Rock Falls Twp HS
Rock Falls IL

Oberheide Heide L
Harrison HS
Evansville IN

Oberlies James J
Carthage Community HS
Carthage IL

Oberman Mike C
Mediapolis Comm HS
Yarmouth IA

Obermeier Sondra L
Aurora Sr HS
Aurora NE

Obermiller Karen
J C Senior HS
Jefferson City MO

Obermoller Gary H
Brewster HS
Brewster MN

Obritsch Jerry M
South Heart HS
Dickinson ND

Ocha Rhonda A
Osborn HS
Detroit MI

Ochocki Kevin J
Canby HS
Canby MN

Ochs Carol R
Newton HS
West Liberty IL

Odden Mark G
Lake Preston HS
Lake Preston SD

Odeen Linda R
Lincoln Comm HS
Stanwood IA

Odegard Lynn M
Waukon Sr HS
Waukon IA

Oden Cheryl J
Centerville HS
Exline IA

Oden Vickie J
Centerville HS
Exline IA

Odle Julaine K
Chase County HS
Cedar Point KS

Odom Frances C
Caruthersville HS
Caruthersville MO

Oelke Ronald P
East Chain Cons HS
Blue Earth MN

Oeltjen Ora Mae L
Freeburg Comm HS
Freeburg IL

Oestreich Debra L
Neillsville HS
Neillsville WI

Oestreich Gretchen L
Hudson Sr HS
Hudson WI

Oeth Ronald
Fairfield HS
Fairfield IL

Oetting Rose M
Concordia HS
Concordia MO

Ogar Barbara A
Henry Ford Ii HS
Sterling Hts MI

Ogden Christopher W
Herrin HS
Herrin IL

Ogden Kevin C
Monroe Sr HS
Monroe WI

Ogle Amy E
Litchfield HS
Litchfield IL

Ogle Michael J
Kirksville Sr HS
Kirksville MO

Oglesby Anthony R
Charlestown HS
Charlestown IN

Ohaver Mary M
Farmington East HS
Farmington IL

Ohl Lori L
Oelwein Community HS
Oelwein IA

Ohl Mary D
Assumption HS
Tower Hill IL

Ohlson Loretta C
St Francis HS
Joliet IL

Ohm Karen S
Oconomowoc Sr HS
Oconomowoc WI

Ojstersek Joann
La Salle Peru HS
Oglesby IL

Olberding Leanne M
Stuart HS
Stuart NE

Olbina Mark R
Pike HS
Indianapolis IN

Oldham Jannifer D
Lincoln Community HS
Lincoln IL

Olerich June M
Wall Lake Comm HS
Breda IA

Oleszkiewicz Vincent S De La Salle HS Chicago IL	Olienyk Deborah L Belfield HS Belfield ND	Oliger Jon A Mt Vernon Twp HS Belle Rive IL	Oligschlaeger Clyde L Mexico HS Mexico MO	Olivas Johnnie J Sioux County HS Crawford NE	Oliveira Cynthia M J D Darnall HS Geneseo IL	Oliver Ella R Campbell HS Campbell MO

Oliver Larry W Louisiana HS Louisiana MO	Oliver Lisa J Lutheran HS Dearborn MI	Olivero Lisa M Lasalle Peru HS Peru IL	Ollhoff Mary L Bethlehem Acad Fairbault MN	Olmstead Danita M Fort Dodge Sr HS Fort Dodge IA	Olmstead Wiletta A Alburnett HS Toddville IA	Olsen David A Falls Sr HS International Fall MN

Olsen Sheryl A Forest Lake Sr HS Scandia MN	Olson Blaine A Almont HS Almont ND	Olson Bradley D South Hamilton HS Story City IA	Olson Christine A Garden County HS Oshkosh NE	Olson Cindy L Parkview HS Footville WI	Olson Craig L Holdrege HS Holdrege NE	Olson Cyndi A West Lyon Comm HS Inwood IA

Olson Dave Esterville HS Esterville IA	Olson David J Calamus Comm HS Grand Mound IA	Olson David P Hiawatha HS Kirkland IL	Olson Duane A Amery HS Amery WI	Olson Forrest B Detroit Lakes Sr HS Detroit Lakes MN	Olson Glendon A Wildrose HS Wildrose ND	Olson John B Shabbona HS Shabbona IL

Olson Julie A Black River Falls Sr HS Black River Falls WI	Olson Kurt A South Milwaukee HS South Milwaukee WI	Olson Margaret A Pocahontas Comm HS Pocahontas IA	Olson Pamela R Kensington Public HS Farwell MN	Olson Ricky C Southern HS Stronghurst IL	Olson Sara B Viroqua HS Viroqua WI	Olson Shelley R Wildrose Public HS Wildrose ND

Olson Susan M Kadoka HS Kadoka SD	Olson Timothy W Coon Rapids Sr HS Coon Rapids MN	Oltmanns Merri K Lockport Central HS Lockport IL	Onak Lynette M Thornridge HS Harvey IL	Ondracek Brian D J S Morton HS Berwyn IL	Onion David D Industry HS Table Grove IL	Onion Melanie S Abingdon HS Abingdon IL

Onopa Susan B
Wausau East HS
Wausau WI

Onorato Michael J
Coal City HS
Coal City IL

Onwiler Helen K
Franklin Public HS
Franklin NE

Openshaw Karen L
Chippewa Valley HS
Mt Clemens MI

Opperman Jimmy S
Springfield HS
Springfield IL

Opperman Jon E
Senior HS
Dubeuque IA

Orchard Lauren W
Magic City Campus HS
Minot ND

Ordaz Steven P
Oak Forest HS
Oak Forest IL

Orebaugh Allan K
Daleville HS
Daleville IN

Oren Dan A
Nicolet HS
Glendale WI

Orillion John S
Glenbard North HS
Bloomingdale IL

Orlando Annette R
Mason Sr HS
Mason MI

Orlowski Anthony A
Marquette HS
Michigan City IN

Orlowski Mark R
Menomonee Falls N HS
Menomonee Falls WI

Orner Cheryl L
Twin Valley HS
Bennington KS

Orns Veronica L
Gull Lake HS
Hickory Corners MI

Oros Cheryl M
Divine Child HS
Dearborn MI

Orosz Joel J
Portage No HS
Portage MI

Orr Jacquelyn M
Ritenour Sr HS
St Louis MO

Orsborn Lyle D
O Meill Public HS
O Meill NE

Orsinger Jack A
Benet Academy
Naperville IL

Ortbals Joann D
Fatima HS
Argyle MO

Orth Daniel A
Central HS
Evansville IN

Ortique Althea L
Emil G Hirsch HS
Chicago IL

Ortman Paula A
Brookville HS
Brookville IN

Ortmeier Timothy M
Luther North HS
Chicago IL

Orton Lisa R
West HS
Green Bay WI

Orton Lynn D
West Sioux HS
Hawarden IA

Osafort Joyce A
Edgerton Public HS
Woodstock MN

Osborn Jeffrey S
Winnetonka Sr HS
Kansas City MO

Osborn Julie L
Quincy Comm HS
Coldwater MI

Osborn Morris E
Thomas A Edison Sr HS
East Gary IN

Osborn Robert W
Alton Senior HS
Godfrey IL

Osborn Timothy E
Culver Comm HS
Culver IN

Osborn Vicky S
Prairie City Comm HS
Prairie City IA

Osborne Jo E
Central HS
Linton IN

Osborne Kimberly
Chaparral HS
Danville KS

Osburn Randall D
Centura HS
Cairo NE

Oscarson Renee A
Richland HS
Wahpeton ND

Ose Susan I
Coon Rapids HS
Coon Rapids MN

Oskandy Maureen E
Oswego HS
Oswego IL

Osowski Theodore E
Flushing HS
Flushing MI

Ossefoort James N
Edgerton Public HS
Woodstock MN

Ossian Michael S
Novi HS
Novi MI

Ost Linda C
Beulah HS
Beulah ND

Ostby Michael L
New Glarus HS
Monticello WI

Oster Catherine A
Brookfield Academy
Wauwatosa WI

Osterman Joy L
Pekin Comm HS
Pekin IL

Ostgard Daniel J
Paxton HS
Paxton IL

Ostoich Thomas A
Morton Sr HS
Hammond IN

Ostrand Deborah J
Gibraltar HS
Egg Harbor WI

Ostrander James W
Adlai E Stevenson HS
Deerfield IL

Ostrem Philip M
Eldora HS
Eldora IA

Ostrom Randy D
Patoka HS
Patoka IL

Ostrowski Donald J
Oak Lawn HS
Oak Lawn IL

Ostruszka Ellen S
Coloma HS
Coloma MI

Oswald Kay J
Gary HS
Gary SD

Oswald Mark E
Gary HS
Gary SD

Ott Don A
Deerfield HS
Deerfield IL

Ott John C
Toulon HS
La Fayette IL

Ott Kathy A
New Glarus HS
New Glarus WI

Ott Robert E
Avon HS
Avon IL

Ott Susan E
Quincy Sen HS
Quincy IL

Ott Timothy M
Madison HS
Lamont KS

Otte Daniel R
Oostburg HS
Oostburg WI

Otte Teresa L
South Page HS
Clarinda IA

Otterness Craig A
Spring Grove HS
Spring Grove MN

Otterson David J
Caledonia HS
Caledonia MN

Otterson Keith E
Benton HS
Benton IL

Otto Kristina E
Herbert Henry Dow HS
Midland MI

Otto Mark A
Heyworth HS
Heyworth IL

Ottoson Rebecca J
Monroe Sr HS
Monroe WI

Overbey Jackie D
E St Louis Sr HS
E St Louis IL

Overgaard Kaj K
Austin Central HS
Austin MN

Overgaard Steven R
Central HS
Albert Lea MN

Overholt Debra K
Pellston HS
Levering MI

Overholtzer Bretton C
Lewis Central HS
Council Bluffs IA

Overman Robert E
St Rita HS
Chicago IL

Overmyer Linda S
Culver Comm HS
Monterey IN

Overpeck Eddie R
Van Buren HS
Centerpoint IN

Overson Bruce R
Mound Westonka HS
Mound MN

Overton Judith L
Gibson Southern HS
Fort Branch IN

Overton Ronald E
Stevens HS
Rapid City SD

Overton Samuel E
Shiloh HS
Hume IL

Overton Sheila M
Stevens HS
Rapid City SD

Overvig Brian J
Rosemount Sr HS
Inver Grove Hts MN

Owen Karen A
Britton HS
Britton SD

Owen Laurel A
Proviso West HS
Westchester IL

Owens Billy J
Tipton HS
Tipton IN

Owens Dale K
Crab Orchard HS
Marion IL

Owens Diane J
Roosevelt HS
Minneapolis MN

Owens Douglas W
Mitchell HS
Mitchell IN

Owens Joellen
Springfield HS
Springfield IL

Owens Kent A
Elgin HS
Elgin IL

Owens Teri L
Manhattan HS
Manhattan KS

Owens Thomas E
Wamego HS
Wamego KS

Owers Linda J
Huron HS
Ann Arbor MI

Ownbey James M
Maconaquah HS
Grissom Afb IN

Owsen David P
Chippewa Valley HS
Mt Clemens MI

Owsley Stephen K
Marquette HS
Michigan City IN

Oxford Jaricia L
John Glenn HS
Westland MI

Oxman Lisa A
Hibbing HS
Hibbing MN

Oyster Michael C
Cass Midway HS
Freeman MO

Ozurisin Jean A
Streator Twp HS
Streator IL

P

Pabich Maureen A
All Saints Central HS
Bay City MI

Pabich Paul J
Owen Withee Sr HS
Owen WI

Pace Lawrence A
St Pius X HS
Kansas City MO

Pace Penny A
St Mary Academy
Indianapolis IN

Pachay Amy
Decatur Jr Sr HS
Decatur MI

Packard Julie K
Huron Sr HS
Huron SD

Packard Stanley A
Dundee Comm HS
Carpentersville IL

Padgett Jill L
New Harmony HS
New Harmony IN

Page Benita L
Lindblom Technical HS
Chicago IL

Page Jeanne E
Holden R Iii HS
La Tour MO

Page Leslie J
Emil Hirsch HS
Chicago IL

Page Robert K
Elgin HS
Elgin IL

Pagel Patricia A
Rockwell City HS
Rockwell City IA

Pahl Allan J
Aguinas HS
Lacrosse WI

Pahl Douglas J
Crandon HS
Crandon WI

Pahlman Lynn D
Warren Twp HS
Wildwood IL

Pahlmann Cheri E
Jacksonville HS
Murrayville IL

Painter Jeannie L
Davison Sr HS
Davison MI

Paladin Leslie S
Nerinx Hall HS
St Louis MO

Palermo Diane M
State Univ Campus HS
Cape Girardeau MO

Palermo Susan J
Andrean HS
Schererville IN

Palma Julianne
Washburn Rural HS
Topeka KS

Palmatier Julie A
Coopersville Public HS
Coopersville MI

Palmer Debra L
Ubly HS
Ubly MI

Palmer Lynn S
New Trier East HS
Winnetka IL

Palmer Sheryl A
Mormon Trail Community HS
Garden Grove IA

Palmquist Jonathan R
Glenwood Comm HS
Glenwood IA

Palombo Carmella G
De Land Weldon HS
De Land IL

Paloposki Seija S
Centralia HS
Centralia MO

Paly Oleh S
Grant Comm HS
Ingleside IL

Panasky Mary Rose
Maria HS
Chicago IL

Panek Timothy J
Carman HS
Flint MI

Panke Cynthia G
Frankfort Sr HS
Frankfort IN

Pan Kop Robert A
Churubusco HS
Churubusco IN

Pannebecker Elizabeth D
De Soto Sr HS
De Soto MO

Panosh Nancy R
Kewaunee HS
Kewaunee WI

Paoletti Ann M
Iron Mountain HS
Iron Mountain MI

Papendick Michael S
Warren Township HS
Gurnee IL

Papenhause Susan M
Tremont HS
Tremont IL

Papier Paul A
R N Snider HS
Ft Wayne IN

Papier Paul A
R Nelson Snider HS
Fort Wayne IN

Papineau Clement J
Ontonagon Area HS
Ontonagon MI

Papini Dennis R
Orion HS
Orion IL

Pappageorge Vicki G
Maine South HS
Park Ridge IL

Parish Robert M
Hinsdale South HS
Darien IL

Parish Ronda L
Riverdale HS
Muscoda WI

Park Claudia G
Mt Morris HS
Mt Morris IL

Parke Jacquelyn D
Perry Meridian HS
Indianapolis IN

Parker Christopher R
Plainfield HS
Plainfield IL

Parker Cinda K
Steelville R 3 HS
Steelville MO

Parker James D
Lockwood HS
Lockwood MO

Parker Kathleen D
Centralia HS
Centralia KS

Parker Mike R
Waynesville HS
Waynesville MO

Parker Philip L
Nebraska Christian HS
Chambers NE

Parker Thomas A
Niles HS
Niles MI

Parkey Bruce E
Highland HS
Highland IN

Parkin Joy C
Forman HS
Manito IL

Parkins Kenneth R
Chanute HS
Chanute KS

Parkinson Craig L
Oakville Sr HS
St Louis MO

Parkinson Randal L
Calhoun HS
Hardin IL

Parks John H
Beatrice HS
Beatrice NE

Parks Linda S
Ldf Comm HS
Le Grand IA

Parli Joe D
Sabetha HS
Sabetha KS

Parn Joseph B
Monroe R I HS
Monroe City MO

Paron Nicholas G
Douglas Mac Arthur HS
Saginaw MI

Parr Keith D
Hillsboro HS
Donnellson IL

Parrish Becky S
Carbondale Comm HS
Carbondale IL

Parrish Michael L
Moberly HS
Moberly MO

Parro Kathleen M
Eliz Seton HS
Dolton IL

Parrott Mark A
Northwest HS
House Springs MO

Parry Linda R
Genoa Public HS
Monroe NE

Parsons Carla J
Jasper HS
Jasper MO

Parsons Gayle A
Magic City Campus HS
Minot Air Force B ND

Parsons Richard J
Auburndale HS
Auburndale WI

Partipilo Petronilla L
Josephinum HS
Chicago IL

Partridge Dane M
Clio HS
Clio MI

Partyka Cindy M
Thornton Fractional No HS
Calumet City IL

Paschen John N
Milton HS
Milton WI

Paschen Marie
Oregon Davis HS
Walkerton IN

Pasisinic Jeanie
Lakeview HS
Decatur IL

Pasley Charles D
Richland HS
Richland MO

Pasley Marilyn R
Rock Bridge HS
Columbia MO

Pastucha Linda L
Mona Shores HS
Muskegon MI

Pasyk Rodney M
Bishop Noll Inst HS
Hammond IN

Patapack Albert J
Harlem HS
Rockford IL

Patch Randy L
South Adams HS
Geneva IN

Pate Cynthia S
Madison Consolidated HS
Madison IN

Patric Leslie A
Galien HS
Galien MI

Patrick Jocelyn D
St Francis De Sales HS
Chicago IL

Patrick Ronald L
Pratt HS
Pratt KS

Patrick Ron J
High School
Milwaukee WI

Patricoski Ann T
Mt Assisi Academy
Palos Park IL

Pattee Kim A
Evart HS
Evart MI

Pattenaude Celeste G
Mother Of Sorrows HS
Blue Island IL

Patterson Alan D
Adelphian Academy
Holly MI

Patterson Angela C
Concordia Lutheran HS
Fort Wayne IN

Patterson Bruce D
St Johns Military HS
Topeka KS

Patterson Connie S
Barr Reeve HS
Cannelburg IN

Patterson Donald A
Remington HS
Whitewater KS

Patterson Karen S
El Dorado Sr HS
El Dorado KS

Patterson Katherine F
Adelphian Academy
Holly MI

Patterson Mark E
Parkside HS
Jackson MI

Patterson Martha J
East Noble HS
Kendallville IN

Patterson Nikki A
Copeland HS
Copeland KS

Patterson Ramona G
Palestine HS
Palestine IL

Patterson Sharon K
North Winneshiek HS
Decorah IA

Patterson Steven L
Hillsdale HS
Hillsdale MI

Patterson Ted D
Cozad Sr HS
Cozad NE

Patterson Teresa L
East Jackson HS
Jackson MI

Pattinson Catherine E
Pt Huron Central HS
Port Huron MI

Patton Kevin T
Bishop Dubourg HS
Saint Louis MO

Patton Luther C
Lindblom Tech HS
Chicago IL

Patton Valerie E
Normandy Sr HS
Northwoods MO

Paucak Denise M
Whiting HS
Whiting IN

Paul John D
Swea City Comm HS
Swea City IA

Paul Rebecca E
Oregon Davis HS
Grovertown IN

Paul Robert S
Malden HS
Malden MO

Paul Steven J
Limestone Comm HS
Bartonville IL

Paul Thomas A
Hope HS
Hope ND

Pauley Craig E
Norwalk HS
Norwalk IA

Paulman Roric R
Hershey HS
Hershey NE

Pauls Linda J
Riverdale HS
Muscoda WI

Paulsen Jeffrey F
Brother Rice HS
Birmingham MI

Paulsen Mark A
Exira Comm HS
Exira IA

Paulson Martin P
Campion Jesuit HS
Waukegan IL

Pauly Mary J
Jordan HS
Jordan MN

Pauly Robert C
Premontre HS
Green Bay WI

Pavek Christine E
Steinmetz HS
Chicago IL

Pavel Sharon K
Bishop Miege HS
Prairie Village KS

Pavel Suzette L
Rochester Adams HS
Rochester MI

Pavelka Jim C
Hobart Sr 'S
Hobart IN

Pavinato Eugene A
St Bede Academy
Oglesby IL

Pavlick Gary A
West Lafayette HS
West Lafayette IN

Pavlik David M
Bloomington HS
Bloomington IL

Pavlinac Cindy A
Pontiac Northern HS
Pontiac MI

Pavlovich Mark
Geo Rogers Clark HS
Whiting IN

Pavlovich Mark G
Ironwood Catholic HS
Ironwood MI

Pavolko David T
Nokomis HS
Nokomis IL

Pavon Ricardo M
St Rita HS
Chicago IL

Pawl Michelle M
Regina HS
Roseville MI

Pawlak Mary A
All Saints Central HS
Bay City MI

Pawling Kathy S
Logan View HS
Hooper NE

Pawlowski Renee A
Wm H Taft HS
Chicago IL

Pawlus James M
Gavit Jr Sr HS
Hammond IN

Pax Robert J
Belvidere HS
Belvidere IL

Paxson John
Bluffton HS
Bluffton IN

Payne Cheryl L
Walled Lake Western HS
Union Lake MI

Payne Cornelia W
Marquette Sr HS
Marquette MI

Payne Debbie L
Pontiac Northern HS
Pontiac MI

Payne Edward C
Swea City Comm HS
Ledyard IA

Payne Joellen I
Cardinal HS
Batavia IA

Payne Kelly R
St Pius X HS
Gladstone MO

Payne Kimberly
Maroa Forsyth HS
Maroa IL

Payne Linda K
Huntley HS
Lyman NE

Payne Regina K
La Porte City HS
La Porte City IA

Payonk James J
Lake Central HS
St John IN

Peach Anthony W
Gibson Southern HS
Owensville IN

Peacock Annette M
Fulton HS
Fulton IL

Peak Mark S
Girard HS
Girard KS

Pearce Debra G
Clay City HS
Clay City IL

Pearce Laura A
Ofallon Township HS
Ofallon IL

Pearce Timothy H
Flora HS
Flora IL

Pearl Walter M
Fordson HS
Dearborn MI

Pearman Vicki K
Blue Valley HS
Stilwell KS

Pearre Cynthia N
New Bloomfield Riii HS
New Bloomfield MO

Pearson Brenda S
Marion Adams HS
Sheridan IN

Pearson Debbie L
Forest Park HS
Crystal Falls MI

Pearson Jeffrey D
George Washington HS
Chicago IL

Pearson Jeffrey E
Plainfield HS
Plainfield IL

Pearson Kris K
Lancaster HS
Lancaster MN

Pearson Susan
Clinton Comm HS
Clinton IL

Pearson Therese J
Pawnee HS
Pawnee IL

Pech Thomas R
Lincoln Comm HS
Lincoln IL

Peck Douglas L
Saline HS
Ann Arbor MI

Peck John E
Parkwood HS
Joplin MO

Peck Julie A
Tekamah Herman HS
Tekamah NE

Peck Steven D
Glenburn Public HS
Glenburn ND

Pecord Angela K
Anna Jonesboro C HS
Mill Creek IL

Pedelty Ronald R
Newaygo HS
Newaygo MI

Pedelty Sharon M
Streator Town HS
Ransom IL

Pederson Ronda J
Hatton Public HS
Hatton ND

Pedrick Kathleen L
Van Buren Comm HS
Douds IA

Peecher Mary L
Louisiana HS
Louisiana MO

Peel Julie L
Plainfield HS
Joliet IL

Pefley Albert H
Centerville HS
Centerville IA

Pelc Philip P
Howells HS
Dodge NE

Pelech Mark H
Marist HS
Palos Heights IL

Pelissero Paul D
A D Johnston HS
Bessemer MI

Pell Mary A
Van Buren HS
Brazil IN

Pelleymounter Charles R
Osage Comm HS
Osage IA

Peltz Vernon R
Glen Ullin HS
New Salem ND

Peluso Michele F
Greenway HS
Coleraine MN

Pelzer Patricia A
Plattsmouth HS
Plattsmouth NE

Pember Janice J
Hale HS
Hale MI

Pembrook Richard W
Greenfield HS
Greenfield IL

Pencak Carol M
Genoa Public HS
Genoa NE

Pendziszewski Thomas J
St Charles Borromeo
Seminary
Lockport IL

Penelton Lesley N
Crispus Attucks HS
Indianapolis IN

Pengelley Rodney A
Mt Vernon Twp HS
Belle Rive IL

Penn Cynthia L
Coldwater HS
Coldwater MI

Pennamon Rodney E
Bremen HS
Markham IL

Pennell Kathleen A
Wesclin Jr Sr HS
Trenton IL

Penner Kimberly J
Fremont HS
Fremont IN

Pennington Mary J
Silver Creek HS
Sellersburg IN

Penniston Greg K
Raytown HS
Kansas City MO

Pennock Melinda L
Jennings Sr HS
Jennings MO

Penny Linda S
Oak Ridge HS
Oak Ridge MO

Penpraze Cheryl A
Coldwater HS
Coldwater MI

Penquite Ruth E
Canton Galva Sr HS
Canton KS

Penwarden Julia A
Hononegah HS
Rockton IL

Peoni Charles A
Roncalli HS
Indianapolis IN

Peoples Nujya A
St Anne HS
Momence IL

Pepin Donna D
Hillsdale HS
Hillsdale MI

Pepin Michael K
Gladstone Area Public HS
Gladstone MI

Pepple Diane
Ccr 1 HS
Revere MO

Pepple Karen J
Cathay HS
Cathay ND

Perabeau Vicki V
Jacksonville HS
Jacksonville IL

Peradotti Donna R
Morris Comm HS
Morris IL

Perekrestenko Myrna F
Magic City Campus HS
Minot ND

Perez Barbara J
Lakeview HS
Battle Creek MI

Perez Carmen M
Josephinum HS
Chicago IL

Perez Felix
Lakeview HS
Lakeview MI

Perez Marvin
Harrison HS
Chicago IL

Perez Paulino
Harrison HS
Chicago IL

Pergams Oliver R
Albert G Lane Tech HS
Chicago IL

Periard Amy J
Birch Run HS
Burt MI

Periaswamy Cecilia N
St Stanislaus Kostka HS
Des Plaines IL

Perkins Calvin L
Stamford Public HS
Stamford NE

Perkins Cotriece
Eisenhower HS
Decatur IL

Perkins Cynthia J
Dallas Comm HS
Dallas Center IA

Perkins Daniel B
Anderson HS
Anderson IN

Perkins Daniel L
Estherville HS
Estherville IA

Perlinger Douglas W
Paxton HS
Paxton NE

Pernot Diane M
Girard HS
Mulberry KS

Perrigo David A
Arrowhead HS
Pewaukee WI

Perrine Debra J
Saline HS
Stevensville MI

Perrine Rita M
Welcome Comm HS
Fairmont MN

Perry Belinda S
Brown County HS
Timewell IL

Perry Christopher R
Watseka Community HS
Watseka IL

Perry David A
Nevada HS
Nevada MO

Perry Debra A
West Iron County HS
Iron River MI

Perry James R
Marine City Ward Cottrell HS
Marine City MI

Perry Jonathan T
Schulte HS
Terre Haute IN

Perry Mary Ann
Roncalli HS
Indianapolis IN

Perry Patti J
Saline Area HS
Saline MI

Perry Reid A
Barron HS
Barron WI

Perry Roy
Cooley HS
Detroit MI

Perry Susan L
St Francis Academy
Joliet IL

Pers Bill F
George Rogers Clark HS
Hammond IN

Perschnick Mary E
J D Darnall HS
Geneseo IL

Persin Cathy A
Morton West HS
Berwyn IL

Person Brian L
Glenburn HS
Minot ND

Persons Laura J
Kelliher HS
Waskish MN

Perzynski Elizabeth M
Riceville Comm HS
Riceville IA

Pesko Kevin M
Hillsboro HS
Taylor Springs IL

Petek Paula
Nazareth Academy
Riverside IL

Petelle Stephanie A
Proviso East HS
Maywood IL

Peter Douglas A
Garner Hayfield Comm HS
Garner IA

Peterek Heidi P
River Valley HS
Harbert MI

Peterman Mary M
Cedarbury HS
Cedarburg WI

Peterman Melinda K
Cobden Unit HS
Cobden IL

Peterman Raymond W
Ruskin HS
Kansas City MO

Peterman Sheila R
Bowdle HS
Bowdle SD

Peters Bradley D
Taylorville HS
Taylorville IL

Peters Calvin J
Alleman HS
Orion IL

Peters Craig H
Pierce HS
Pierce NE

Peters Cynthia L
Carrollton HS
Carrollton MO

Peters David A
Warsaw Senior HS
Warsaw IN

Peters David L
Big Foot HS
Walworth WI

Peters Debra M
Hastings HS
Hastings MN

Peters Francine L
Harvard Community HS
Harvard IL

Peters Glen T
Tipton HS
Tipton IA

Peters Jeffrey A
York HS
Elmhurst IL

Peters Julie N
West Pike HS
Hull IL

Peters Kent V
Avo Ha HS
Avocal IA

Peters Marjo A
Streator Township HS
Streator IL

Peters Roberta L
Dixon HS
Dixon MO

Peters Sharon M
Marian HS
Troy MI

Peters Tracy L
Stephen Decatur HS
Decatur IL

Peters V
Carrollton HS
Waverly MO

Petersen Donna J
Southridge HS
Holland IN

Petersen Gary L
Mc Cool Junction Public HS
Mc Cool Junction NE

Petersen Joel W
Schleswig HS
Schleswig IA

Petersen John W
Forest Lake Sr HS
Forest Lake MN

Petersen Kenneth L
Pella Christian HS
Pella IA

Petersen Kevin L
Pine City HS
Rock Creek MN

Petersen Kim R
Rockwell Swaledale HS
Rockwell IA

Petersen L Chris
Graettinger Comm HS
Graettinger IA

Petersen Marlene K
Medicine Valley Jr/sr HS
Curtis NE

Petersen Marty R
North Clay County HS
Louisville IL

Petersilie Kathy L
Ness HS
Ness City KS

Peterson Ann R
Osmond Community HS
Osmond NE

Peterson Bradley E
Guthrie Center Community HS
Guthrie Center IA

Peterson Connie L
Forest Lake Sr HS
Forest Lake MN

Peterson Cynthia L
Rushford HS
Rushford MN

Peterson Daryl M
Danville HS
Danville IL

Peterson David B
William A Wirt HS
Gary IN

Peterson David J
Guilford HS
Rockford IL

Peterson Deborah A
Glenbrook North HS
Northbrook IL

Peterson Debra J
Cooper Senior HS
Brooklyn Park MN

Peterson Donna S
North Winneshiek HS
Decorah IA

Peterson Eric J
Wausau East HS
Wausau WI

Peterson Gail R
Northwestern HS
Poplar WI

Peterson Jeff A
Bristol HS
Bristol SD

Peterson Joe D
Lanesboro HS
Lanesboro MN

Peterson Kelly R
Burke Central HS
Flaxton ND

Peterson Kimberly R
Wheeling HS
Wheeling IL

Peterson Kristine M
Danville HS
Danville IL

Peterson Larry L
Kearney HS
Kearney NE

Peterson Linda M
Eden Prairie HS
Eden Prairie MN

Peterson Mark L
Catholic Memorial HS
Waukesha WI

Peterson Mary E
Glenville HS
Glenville MN

Peterson Mary J
Morris Sr HS
Morris MN

Peterson Mary M
West Chicago Comm HS
West Chicago IL

Peterson Maureen L
Lincoln Way HS
Joliet IL

Peterson Michael D
Finley HS
Finley ND

Peterson Michael R
Pembroke Country Day HS
Kansas City MO

Peterson Patrick N
Watersmeet Twp HS
Watersmeet MI

Peterson Richard L
Woodstock HS
Woodstock IL

Peterson Robert G
Lake Mills Comm HS
Lake Mills IA

Peterson Steve L
Paynesville HS
Paynesville MN

Peterson Sue Ellen
River Valley HS
Three Oakes MI

Peterson Thomas J
Valders HS
Valders WI

Peterson Timothy S
Northwest HS
Fenton MO

Peterson Valerie A
Huron HS
Huron SD

Petito Guy T
Macon Sr HS
Luna Pier MI

Petonke Arthur R
Danville HS
Danville IL

Petrak Richard A
Brother Rice HS
Evergreen Pk IL

Petrakis Mary D
Freeport HS
Freeport IL

Petro Beth A
Grand Blanc HS
Grand Blanc MI

Petrone Lucille M
Notre Dame HS
Chicago IL

Petrovish Debra E
Summerfield HS
Petersburg MI

Petry Rebecca S
O Fallon Township HS
O Fallon IL

Petterson Wayne C
Beloit HS
Beloit KS

Pettis James L
Charlevoix HS
Charlevoix MI

Pettis Kevin G
Maple Wood Academy
Long Lake MN

Pettit Marcia K
Fairfield HS
Fairfield IA

Pettitt Pamela E
Spring Hill HS
Spring Hill KS

Pettus Timothy W
North County HS
Bonne Terre MO

Pettys Harlan F
Minot HS
Minot ND

Peuster Pamela S
Slater HS
Slater MO

Peuterbaugh Randy L
Calhoun HS
Hamburg IL

Pew Kathy A
Tri HS
Spiceland IN

Pew Thomas H
Le Mars Gehlen HS
Le Mars IA

Peyton Cynthia O
Highland Park Sr HS
St Paul MN

Pfander Michael B
Nixa HS
Nixa MO

Pfannenstiel Mark J
Ness City HS
Ness City KS

Pfanner Janet D
Monroe City R I HS
Monroe City MO

Pfeffer Carol L
Union Grove HS
Union Grv WI

Pfeifer Donna M
Hays HS
Hays KS

Pfeiff Doreen F
North Central Area HS
Wilson MI

Pfeiffer Robin L
Hammond Baptist HS
Hammond IN

Pfister Carmon J
Bluffton Allen HS
Bluffton IN

Pfister Joseph D
Jasper HS
Jasper IN

Pfliger Douglas A
Azen HS
Hazen ND

Pflueger Laurie A
Salem Central HS
Salem WI

Pfotenhauer David L
Sgt Bluff Luton Comm HS
Sgt Bluff IA

Pfrimmer John L
Mormon Trail HS
Derby IA

Phalen Kathleen L
Shawano HS
Shawano WI

Phebus Charles E
Plano HS
Plano IL

Phebus Dan E
Rossville HS
Frankfort IN

Phegley Richard B
Arcadia Valley HS
Ironton MO

Phelan Myra B
Tracy HS
Currie MN

Phelps Jay C
Shortridge HS
Indianapolis IN

Phelps Ruth A
Marlette Comm HS
Marlette MI

Phend Rebecca A
Whitko HS
South Whitley IN

Pherigo Nancy J
Waverly HS
Waverly KS

Philgreen Daniel I
Downers Grove Comm HS
Downers Grove IL

Phillips Andrea M
Tecumseh Senior HS
Tecumseh MI

Phillips Belinda K
Vienna HS
Vienna IL

Phillips Elizabeth A
Pana Senior HS
Pana IL

Phillips Jeanie B
Mundelein HS
Mundelein IL

Phillips Joanne M
Owosso HS
Owosso MI

Phillips John F
East Pike HS
Pittsfield IL

Phillips Kathy S
Clinton Prairie HS
Frankfort IN

Phillips Kim M
Mazon Verona Kinsman HS
Morris IL

Phillips Mark A
Dearborn HS
Dearborn MI

Phillips Penny S
Rossville HS
Rossville IN

Phillips Robert J
Milan C 2 HS
Green City MO

Phillis James W
E Peoria Comm HS
E Peoria IL

Phinney Scot A
Paris HS
Paris IL

Piasecki Paula
Maine Township South HS
Park Ridge IL

Pic Anita R
Michigan Public HS
Whitman ND

Piccolo Joann E
Hill Murray HS
St Paul MN

Picek Linda R
Kimball Independent HS
Pukwana SD

Pichea Beth D
Hillsdale HS
Hillsdale MI

Pickart Andrew P
Norway Community HS
Norway IA

Pickens Arthus C
Newton HS
Wheeler IL

Pickering Mary E
South Callaway Rii HS
Mokone MO

Pickering Patricia L
Frankton HS
Anderson IN

Pickering Suzanne
Morton Sr HS
Hammond IN

Pickett Jay A
Anna Jonesboro Comm H
Anna IL

Pickett Kathy J
Battle Creek Central HS
Battle Creek MI

Pickett Kay E
Mehlville HS
St Louis MO

Pickett Marcia A
Incarnate Word Acad
Florissant MO

Pickup Michael A
Hazelwood W Sr HS
Hazelwood MO

Piekielniak Doris E
Rolla HS
Rolla MO

Piel Cindy L
Winfield HS
Winfield KS

Pieper Pamela J
Hallock HS
Hallock MN

Pieper Patricia A
Glenwood HS
Springfield IL

Pieper Steven M
Stewardson Strasburg HS
Strasburg IL

Pier Peggy S
Venice HS
Venice IL

Pierce Jan E
Sparta HS
Sparta IL

Pierce Janice B
St Alphonsus HS
Dearborn MI

Pierce Jo Ann L
Indianola Sr HS
Indianola IA

Pierce Larry R
Bayard HS
Bayard NE

Pierce Mark A
Webber Township HS
Bluford IL

Pierce Randall W
Iron Mountain HS
Iron Mountain MI

Pierce Sherri J
Tri County HS
Keswick IA

STUDENTS PHOTOGRAPH SCHEDULED FOR PUBLICATION HERE COULD NOT BE REPRODUCED

Pierick Patty A
Maple Valley Comm HS
Danbury IA

Piermarini Charles N
Elk Grove HS
Elk Grove Village IL

Pieters Kimberly A
George Rogers Clark HS
Whiting IN

Pietruszka Jolanta I
Goodrich HS
Grand Blanc MI

Pietrzak Dorothy A
St Florian HS
Hamtramck MI

Pietrzak Jacqueline A
Donald E Gavit HS
Hammond IN

Pifer Peter A
Larimore HS
Arvilla ND

Pigula Mary Ann V
Cass Technical HS
Detroit MI

Pike Warren A
Girard Usd 248 HS
Girard KS

Pikka Mary E
Wakefield HS
Wakefield MI

Pilarski Karen S
Wethersfield HS
Kewanee IL

Pilcher Cheryl D
Civic Memorial HS
Bethalto IL

Pile Kathryn E
Morton HS
Morton IL

Pillion Mary E
Marquette HS
Ottawa IL

Pillsbury Rhoda E
Lanark HS
Lanark IL

Pine Regina L
Marshall HS
Marshall IL

Pinkerman Revona F
Bevier HS
Bevier MO

Pinkston Christine L
Pc HS
Pekin IL

Pinney Jack T
H H Dow HS
Midland MI

Pinnick Trudi A
North Knox HS
Bicknell IN

Pinter Mark A
La Moille Comm HS
Arlington IL

Pinter Michael R
La Moille Unit HS
Arlington IL

Piorkowski Donna M
St Thomas Aquinas HS
Florissant MO

Piotrowski Mary M
Little Falls Comm HS
Little Falls MN

Piotrowski Philip J
Flushing Sr HS
Mt Morris MI

Piper Mary K
Davis County Comm HS
Bloomfield IA

Piper Rex S
Cedarburg HS
Cedarburg WI

Pirc Pamela J
St Francis Academy
Joliet IL

Pirochta Tamara L
Chesaning Union HS
Chesaning MI

Pirok Cheryl A
Roxana Sr HS
E Alton IL

Pirotte Patrick J
Carroll HS
Wichita KS

Pirsig Susan C
Elmore Public HS
Elmore MN

Pirtle Charles E
Brebeuf Prep HS
Carmel IN

Piscator Kevin K
Worthington Sr HS
Worthington MN

Piske Theresa M
Albion Sr HS
Albion MI

Pistone Julie R
Palatine HS
Palatine IL

Pitcher Shannon J
Newton HS
Montrose IL

Pitchford Deborah D
Lincolnwood HS
Raymond IL

Pitney Jennifer M
Kirksville HS
Kirksville MO

Pittman Becky S
Chase County HS
Cottonwood Falls KS

Pitts Diane M
St Alphonsus HS
Detroit MI

Pitts Donna R
Emil G Hirsch HS
Chicago IL

Pitts Douglas J
Olympia HS
Mc Lean IL

Pitts Joseph L
Toluca HS
Toluca IL

Pitts Sally T
Winona Sr HS
Winona MN

Pitts Teresa L
Chippewa Hills HS
Sears MI

Pitts Trinette D
University HS
Milwaukee WI

Pivonka Myra A
Hoisington HS
Hoisington KS

Pizarek Beth A
Taylor HS
Kokomo IN

Pizarek Cherie R
Marquette HS
Laporte IN

Pizzato Michael S
Bloom Township HS
Glenwood IL

Place Carolyn S
Bladen Public HS
Bladen NE

Placek Christine S
Loup City HS
Rockville NE

Plachetka Catherine F
Lumen Christi HS
Jackson MI

Plager Kenneth W
Ballard HS
Cambridge IA

Plamann Amy S
Appleton West HS
Appleton WI

Plank Becky J
Buena Vista HS
Saginaw MI

Plantenga Paul E
Bentley Senior HS
Bunton MI

Plassmeyer John H
Fatima HS
Loose Creek MO

Plasterer Richard W
Bishop Dwenger HS
Fort Wayne IN

Plato Danny A
Eastwood HS
Correctionville IA

Platske Christine M
Ewen Trout Creek HS
Ewen MI

Platter Michael A
Hancock HS
Lemay MO

Plesha Julie A
J Sterling Morton West HS
Lyons IL

Ploen Kris Ann
Columbus HS
Marshfield WI

Ploetz Jennifer E
Hanover Central HS
Cedar Lake IN

Plotkin Debra A
Niles Township East HS
Skokie IL

Plotner Eric G
St Joseph Ogden HS
Ogden IL

Plotner Greg A
Lincoln HS
Lincoln IL

Plouche Cynthia R
Clinton HS
Clinton IA

Plugge Ramona L
Arlington HS
Arlington NE

Pluke Jean M
Lincoln HS
Wisconsin Rapids WI

Plumlee Anita M
Clinton HS
Brownington MO

Plummer Ceresa K
Circle HS
Eldorado KS

Plummer Dorothy M
Wamego HS
Wamego KS

Plummer John L
Pittsfield HS
Baylis IL

Plunger Mark A
North Central HS
Hermansville MI

Pluym Donna K
Wahlert HS
E Dubuque IL

Plymale Jon E
Lebanon HS
Lebanon IL

Pobanz Jill M
Sturgis HS
Sturgis MI

Pobanz Michelle L
Galva HS
Cambridge IL

Pochyla Karen M
Shelby HS
Shelby MI

Podey Karen M
Perry Community HS
Perry IA

Podkowski Richard J
Brother Rice HS
Chicago IL

Podvoyski Karen A
Cabrini HS
Allen Park MI

Poe Candace A
Dexter HS
Dexter MO

Poese Bruce A
Lutheran N HS
Ferguson MO

Pohlmann Lorraine
William Howard Taft HS
Chicago IL

Poi Kevin M
Lake Central HS
St John IN

Poineau Theodore
Saginaw HS
Saginaw MI

Pokojowczyk Jean C
Holy Family Academy
Chicago IL

Pokral Lorelei R
Lake Forest HS
Lake Forest IL

Polak Gary E
Proviso West HS
Berkeley IL

Polak Margaret M
Cardinal Ritter HS
Indianapolis IN

Poland Carol J
Nauvoo Colusa HS
Nauvoo IL

Polanski Steven J
Allen Park HS
Allen Park MI

Polcyn Gregory J
John Hersey HS
Mt Prospect IL

Polhemus Karen D
Oscoda Area HS
Wurtsmith Afb MI

Policandriotes Mary V
Joliet West Twp HS
Joliet IL

Polites George E
Lane Tech HS
Northbrook IL

Politte Preston R
Bismarck R 5 HS
Bismarck MO

Pollan Alan R
Holdrege HS
Holdrege NE

Pollan Jim L
Holdrege HS
Holdrege NE

Pollard Linda E
Danville HS
Danville IL

Pollard Pamela S
Galesburg HS
Galesburg IL

Polley Melinda L
Northrop HS
Ft Wayne IN

Pollick Patricia A
Chesaning HS
Oakley MI

Pollitt J Douglas
Danville HS
Danville IL

Pollock Cindy S
Oakwood HS
Oakwood IL

Pollock Kathy S
Northridge HS
Goshen IN

Pollock Nan A
St Louise De Marillac HS
Park Ridge IL

Polman Sheryl A
Sebeka Public HS
Sebeka MN

Polnaszek Jane M
Abbotsford Sr HS
Abbotsford WI

Polowski Patricia M
Port Austin HS
Port Austin MI

Polries Peggy L
Sykeston HS
Sykeston ND

Polsgrove Vicky G
Campbell HS
Campbell MO

Polson Paula E
Nevada HS
Nevada MO

Pomerantz Ruth E
Harbor Beach Comm HS
Port Hope MI

Pomeroy Deborah L
Plainfield HS
Plainfield IL

Ponce Christine
Westview HS
Middleburg IN

Pond Jean A
New Haven HS
New Haven IN

Ponder Julia C
Fountain Central HS
Veedersburg IN

Pontier Anthony L
Clarke Community HS
Osceola IA

Pontious Linda A
Lasalle Peru Township HS
Peru IL

Pool Cindy D
Meredosia Chambersburg HS
Chambersburg IL

Pool Mark G
Quincy Sr HS
Quincy IL

Poole Dale R
Vienna HS
Vienna IL

Poorman Kevin L
Terre Haute North Vigo HS
Terre Haute IN

Poorman Richard D
Hutsonville HS
West Union IL

Pope Julie M
De Soto Sr HS
Desoto MO

Popp Nancy
Lincoln Park HS
Lincoln Park MI

Popp Phyllis I
Ionia HS
Ionia MI

Poppen Richard P
Milbank HS
Milbank SD

Popson Lyle L
Holly HS
Holly MI

Poreda Joyce A
Madonna HS
Chicago IL

Portell Donald J
N St Francois County HS
Desloge MO

Porter Bruce J
Central HS
Bloomfield IN

Porter Carol L
Edgewood HS
Madison WI

Porter Christina L
North Salem HS
North Salem IN

Porter Debra L
La Salle Peru Twp HS
Oglesby IL

Porter John H
New Trier East HS
Wilmette IL

Porter Karen N
Duquoin HS
Duquoin IL

Porter Melissa J
Knightstown HS
Kennard IN

Porter Terry R
Plattsmouth HS
Plattsmouth NE

Portice Linda E
Pickford Public HS
Pickford MI

Portwood Debra D
Bowling Green R 1 HS
Bowling Green MO

Porzel Cathleen A
Richmond Burton HS
Spring Grove IL

Posey Roger D
Ava HS
Ava MO

Poshard Katherine E
Octavia HS
Colfax IL

Posluszny Mark D
De La Salle Institute
Chicago IL

Poss Janet A
Angola HS
Angola IN

Posso William M
Spooner HS
Spooner WI

Post Becky J
West HS
Sioux City IA

Post Kevin B
Chandler Lake Wilson HS
Pipestone MN

Post Paul W
Box 430 Bridgeport HS
Bridgeport NE

Post Richard A
Parkway West HS
Ballwin MO

Postel Christine A
Grayville Comm HS
Grayville IL

Postlewaite Barbara L
Palestine HS
Palestine IL

Potrament Lois A
Lancaster HS
Lancaster MN

Potter David B
Douglas Mac Arthur HS
Saginaw MI

Potter Penny M
Princeton HS
Princeton IL

Potter Ronald L
Routt HS
Jacksonville IL

Potter Steven L
Armada HS
Armada MI

Potter Tonjia D
Golden City R Iii HS
Golden City MO

Potthoff Jeffrey D
Patoka Unit 100 HS
Patoka IL

Potts Cathy L
Lake Central HS
Dyer IN

Potts Janice L
Jefferson HS
Independence IA

Potts Rhonda G
Chandlerville HS
Chandlerville IL

Potts Sheryl D
Holland Christian HS
Holland MI

Potts William H
Brown HS
Sturgis SD

Pousson James M
Duchesne HS
Saint Charles MO

Povlich James J
S Milwaukee HS
South Milwaukee WI

Powe Kenneth A
Assumption HS
Fairview Heights IL

Powell Cheryl E
Lincoln HS
Kansas City MO

Powell Daniel
Kirksville Sr HS
Kirksville MO

Powell Gregory D
Big Fork HS
Big Fork MN

Powell Jayleen R
Parkway Central HS
Chesterfield MO

Powell Jolene M
Marcus HS
Pierson IA

Powell Linda L
Elston HS
Michigan City IN

Powell Lisa G
St Francis HS
St Francis KS

Powell Pamela S
Manual HS
Peoria IL

Powers Coleen D
Monroe Sr HS
Monroe MI

Powers Diane M
Maryville Rii HS
Maryville MO

Powers Donna J
Northwest Webster HS
Fort Dodge IA

Powers Jill L
Beardsley HS
Beardsley MN

Powers Kit K
Ames Community HS
Ames IA

Powers Rod R
United Community HS
Boone IA

Powers Vickie J
North Platte HS
North Platte NE

Poynor Sally A
New Madrid HS
Kewanee MO

Poynter Gary L
North Salem HS
Lizton IN

Poynter Michael J
Avon HS
Danville IN

Pozarniuk Ann
Queen Of Peace HS
Burbank IL

Pozega Debra A
Grand Ledge HS
Lansing MI

Poznich Charles R
Southeast HS
Weir KS

Prahl Bob R
Brillion HS
Brillion WI

Praisa Nancy E
Immaculate Heart Of Mary
HS
Westchester IL

Pranke Susan A
De Pere HS
De Pere WI

Prater Brenda C
Tippecanoe Valley HS
Akron IN

Prather Charles R
Catlin HS
Atlin IL

Prather Jeffrey A
Wheatland HS
Gore KS

Prather Todd M
Glenwood Sr HS
Glenwood IA

Pratt Diana J
Harmony Comm HS
Keosauqua IA

Pratt Michael R
Greensburg HS
Greensburg IN

Pravecek Debra M
Mitchell HS
Mitchell SD

Prediger Christine A
Collinsville HS
Collinsville IL

Preedy Nancy K
Satanta HS
Satanta KS

Prehn James E
Mc Bain Public HS
Mc Bain MI

Prell Renae D
Catholic Memorial HS
Elm Grove WI

Prentler Stacey A
Leslie HS
Mason MI

Prescott Ralph A
Hononegah HS
Rockton IL

Prescott William J
Broken Bow HS
Broken Bow NE

Presidio Derrick R
Beaverton HS
Beaverton MI

Presler Kenda L
Humboldt HS
Thor IA

Presperin Jessica J
Prospect HS
Mt Prospect IL

Presswood Randall L
Wentz HS
Wentzville MO

Prestay Helen C
North Central Area HS
Powers MI

Preston Amy L
Elk Grove HS
Elk Grove Vlg IL

Preston Kristi L
Rosalie Public HS
Rosalie NE

Preston Robin P
Unity HS
Chicago IL

Preston Tomie A
Lenox Community HS
Lenox IA

Pretnar Alan A
Nokomis HS
Nokomis IL

Prettyman Glenn C
Central HS
Omaha NE

Pretzer Sherie J
Velva Public HS
Velva ND

Preusch Connie M
Marian Catholic HS
Chicago Hts IL

Prewett Jennie R
Marshall HS
Marshall IL

Prewitt Regina C
St John Cathedral HS
Milwaukee WI

Preyer Herbert M
Malden HS
Malden MO

Pribbeno Michael S
Chase County HS
Imperial NE

Pribbenow Mark D
Denver Community HS
Denver IA

Pribble Holly A
Mt Assisi Academy
Summit IL

Price Bradley E
Benton Cone HS
Benton IL

Price Charles E
Malden HS
Malden MO

Price Cheryl L
Paseo HS
Kansas City MO

Price Cindy J
Mt Pleasant Sr HS
Mt Pleasant MI

Price Jennifer L
Edwardsville Senior HS
Edwardsville IL

Price Kathryn L
Onarga HS
Onarga IL

Price Ki A
Springfield HS
Springfield IL

Price Lawrence T
Lake Forest HS
Lake Forest IL

Price Melinda A
Valley Park HS
Valley Park MO

Price Thomas M
Milbank HS
Milbank SD

Prichard Dennis L
Meramec Valley R Iii HS
Pacific MO

Pride Vernon R
Oak Park Academy HS
Nevada IA

Pridie Jeanne R
Akron Comm HS
Akron IA

Prien Cheryl A
Monroe HS
Monroe WI

Priest Jolene R
Wauneta HS
Hamlet NE

Priestley Beth A
Libertyville HS
Libertyville IL

Pringle Joseph B
Hinsdale Central HS
Hinsdale IL

Prior Cynthia K
Dupo Comm HS
Dupo IL

Pristo Lori A
Hinsdale Central HS
Oakbrook IL

Pritchard Wayne D
Bloomer HS
Bloomer WI

Privette Steve A
Willow Springs HS
Willow Springs MO

Probst John S
St Mary Central HS
Menasha WI

Probst Lucinda K
Northwestern HS
Palmyra IL

Probst Pamela J
Our Lady Of Peace HS
St Paul MN

Prochazka Dudley M
Hemingford HS
Hemingford NE

Proctor Brian D
Washington Senior HS
Washington IA

Profilet Suzanne M
Bloomington HS
Bloomington IL

Prokash Jackie M
Assumption HS
Wis Rapids WI

Proost Jean L
Duchesne HS
St Charles MO

Proszowski Richard S
St Patrick HS
Chicago IL

Prothe Darryl E
Paola HS
Paola KS

Prothe Melissa M
Wabash HS
Wabash IN

Proud Lynette J
Hanover Central HS
Cedar Lake IN

Provance Keith R
E Alton Woodriver HS
Hartford IL

Provence Timothy D
Noblesville HS
Noblesville IN

Provencher Judith A
Dassel Cokato HS
Dassel MN

Pruitt Joy L
Carrollton HS
Eldred IL

Pruitt Laura G
Chillicothe HS
Chillicothe MO

Prusa Kenneth J
Claflin Rural HS
Claflin KS

Pryor Wendy
Maria HS
Chicago IL

Przedwojewski James L
Armada HS
Armada MI

Przepiora Denise M
All Saints Central HS
Bay City MI

Przytulski Denise A
St Clare Academy
Detroit MI

Pucci Anne H
Kingsford HS
Kingsford MI

Puckett Jo Ann L
Waldron HS
Waldron IN

Puckett Pamela S
Franklin Central HS
Indianapolis IN

Puetz Janet A
Resurrection HS
Chicago IL

Puetz Rosemary J
Streator HS
Streator IL

Pufall Kevin E
Minot Sr HS
Minot ND

Pugh Ralph A
Alpena Senior HS
Alpena MI

Pugh Timothy C
Stonington HS
Stonington IL

Pulaski Sue E
Grant Park HS
Grant Park IL

Pulkownik Lawrence J
Plymouth Salem HS
Plymouth MI

Pulliam Debbie S
Carrier Mills HS
Stonefort IL

Pulter Kim M
Harry S Truman HS
Taylor MI

Pump Sharon J
Venango Consolidated HS
Venango NE

Punt Terry L
Maurice Orange City Comm HS
Orange City IA

Purcell Mark A
Washington HS
Washington IL

Purcell Teresa R
Holdrege HS
Holdrege NE

Purcell Timothi A
Lakeland HS
La Grange IN

Purdy Eric P
Porta HS
Petersburg IL

Purkapile Krista M
George S Parker HS
Janesville WI

Purkhiser Marvin L
West Washington HS
Salem IN

Purkhiser Ralph E
Springs Valley HS
W Baden Springs IN

Purol Patrick J
Round Lake Comm HS
Round Lake IL

Purpura Gregory M
Plymouth Canton HS
Plymouth MI

Pursifull Debbie J
Community R 6 HS
Martinsburg MO

Pursley David E
St Clair HS
St Clair MO

Pursley Michael J
Benkelman HS
Benkelman NE

Putnam Brett J
Sycamore HS
Sycamore IL

Putnam Gayle L
Carthage Comm HS
Carthage IL

Putnam Patrick J
Fraser HS
Fraser MI

Pyle Kathy L
Nevada Sr HS
Nevada MO

Pyle Kent C
Huntington Catholic HS
Huntington IN

Pyle Randall S
Marshall Co Central HS
Newfolden MN

Pyrzewski William J
Morley Stanwood HS
Morley MI

Pysh Thomas W
Edison Sr HS
East Gary IN

Q

Quackenbush Jeffrey L
Tri County HS
De Witt NE

Quaite Michael R
Pekin Comm HS
Pekin IL

Quale Jeffery W
Summit HS
Summit SD

Quale Jo Ann C
New Town Public HS
New Town ND

Quale Joann C
New Town HS
New Town ND

Quandt Linda J
Warren Central HS
Indianapolis IN

Quarberg Timothy D
Lancaster Sr HS
Lancaster WI

Quattrocki Anthony J
Brother Rice HS
Oak Lawn IL

Quenoy Diann M
Frontenac HS
Frontenac KS

Quick Melody C
Taylorville HS
Taylorville IL

Quiggle Julie G
New Ulm Sr HS
New Ulm MN

Quiggle Julie G
New Ulm HS
New Ulm MN

Quigley John B
Griffin HS
Springfield IL

Quiller Jill A
Calhoun HS
Hamburg IL

Quince Carlotta A
Pontiac Central HS
Pontiac MI

Quinn Alice J
Humboldt HS
St Paul MN

Quinn Rebecca J
Litchfield Sr HS
Litchfield IL

Quinn Sally A
Jacksonville HS
Jacksonville IL

Quinn Steven J
St Pius HS
Kansas City MO

Quinnell Steven E
Spring Grove Public HS
Spring Grove MN

Quint Frank R
Lake Central HS
Crown Point IN

Quint Roger L
Hill City HS
Hill City KS

Quintanilla Monica
Center Grove HS
Greenwood IN

Quiroz Luis A
Divine Heart Seminary
Chicago IL

R

Raap Denise L
Tolley Public HS
Tolley ND

Raasch James P
Oconomowoc Sr HS
Okauchee WI

Raasch Patricia E
Harlem HS
Rockford IL

Rabbers Jodi L
Lake Shore HS
Stevensville MI

Rabe Bruce K
Seymour HS
Payson IL

Rabe Daniel J
Oconomowoc HS
Oconomowoc WI

Rabelhofer Alice E
Richmond Burton HS
Spring Grove IL

Raber Kristin M
Goshen HS
Goshen IN

Raboin Carilyn A
Niagara HS
Niagara WI

Racey C Karen M
Trenton HS
Trenton MI

Racicot Larry D
Bark River Harris HS
Bark River MI

Racine Thomas L
Naperville Central HS
Naperville IL

Rackers Charles L
Senior HS
Holt Summit MO

Racop Carol E
Lawrenceville HS
Flat Rock IL

Rademacher Bruce E
Central HS
Evansville IN

Rademacher Janet K
Southridge HS
Holland IN

Rader Carolyn A
Carroll HS
Burlington IN

Raders Dean A
West HS
Sioux City IA

Radford Joyce M
Dupo HS
Dupo IL

Radice Venise L
Proviso East HS
Elmhurst IL

Radmer Ronnie C
Lafayette HS
St Joseph MO

Rads Debra A
Immaculate Heart Of Mary HS
Lyons IL

Raes Bart E
Lawrence HS
Lawrence NE

Rafalski Robert H
Ottawa HS
Ottawa IL

Ragan Tamara L
Seymour HS
Payson IL

Ragias Theodore S
Pekin Comm HS
Pekin IL

Ragsdell Philip B
Farmington HS
Farmington MO

Raham Roger M
Saline HS
Saline MI

Raihala William K
Aurora Hoyt Lakes HS
Makinen MN

Raile Brenda A
Goodland HS
Edson KS

Raile Cynthia M
Wishek HS
Wishek ND

Raimondi Josephine A
Our Lady Of Grace Academy
Indianapolis IN

Raines Cheryl A
Roxana Sr HS
Wood River IL

Rainey Lee A
Metropolis Comm HS
Joppa IL

Rainforth Jon D
New Market Comm HS
Gravity IA

Rajala Neil S
Marquette HS
Marquette MI

Rakov Elizabeth R
Verdigre HS
Verdigre NE

Ralph Joan R
Girard HS
Farlington KS

Ramaekers Roxane R
Genoa Public HS
Genoa NE

Ramage Patti J
Dupo Comm HS
Dupo IL

Rambow Brenda L
Willmar Sr HS
Willmar MN

Ramey Cheryl A
Jackson HS
Jackson MI

Ramig Paul N
Gering HS
Gering NE

Ramilo Carlos E
Maine Twp West HS
Des Plaines IL

Ramirez Mark D
Loyola Academy
Northfield IL

Ramirez Michael J
Bay City Central HS
Bay City MI

Ramsay Ann R
East Gary Edison HS
East Gary IN

Ramsour Stephen E
Memorial HS
Joplin MO

Ramstein Richard R
Crawford County Ri HS
Bourbon MO

Ramthun Randy R
Rockwell City Comm HS
Rockwell City IA

Rand Craig A
Greendale HS
Greendale WI

Randall Jason L
Springfield HS
Springfield IL

Randall Leah L
Willmar Sr HS
Willmar MN

Randall Mary F
Wisconsin Heights HS
Mazomanie WI

Randall Ronald L
Rolla Sr HS
Rolla MO

Randall Terry L
Chamberlain Public HS
Chamberlain SD

Randolph Roxanne F
Valley HS
W Des Moines IA

Raney Linda L
Barr Reeve HS
Loogootee IN

Rang Morris E
Southeastern HS
Augusta IL

Rangen Kristin K
Maddock Public HS
Maddock ND

Rank Gail A
Jefferson Sr HS
Cedar Rapids IA

Rankin Marcia J
St Joseph HS
St Joseph MI

Rankin Therese R
Alexis HS
Alexis IL

Ranshaw Maeila S
Lapeer HS
Metamora MI

Rantala Caroline M
Greenway HS
Nashwauk MN

Rantala Lori K
Proctor HS
Proctor MN

Rantz Peter R
Whitko HS
Pierceten IN

Raper Ralph W
Inter City Christian HS
Allen Park MI

Rasche Mary A
Dubois HS
Dubois IN

Rask Cindy A
Alliance HS
Alliance NE

Rask Kim P
Pekin Comm HS
Pekin IL

Raska Jerome A
Armada HS
Armada MI

Rasmussen Carol J
Chetek HS
Chetek WI

Rasmussen Cathy L
Polo Community HS
Polo IL

Rasmussen Deborah C
Salem Central HS
Bristol WI

Rasmussen Randy L
Osmond Community HS
Osmond NE

Rasmussen Robert H
Herbert Hoover HS
Des Moines IA

Rasner Dennis P
Stephenson HS
Wallace MI

Rassi Dennis D
Morton HS
Morton IL

Rasure Nora B
Auburn HS
Auburn IL

Rath Patricia A
Dundee HS
Dundee IL

Rathje Connie J
Arthur Hill HS
Saginaw MI

Rathke Rick A
Northern HS
Flint MI

Raths Martin G
Eden Prairie HS
Eden Prairie MN

Ratliff Susan R
Rock County HS
Bassett NE

Ratter Michael L
Maplewood Acad
Hutchinson MN

Rauch Lois E
Healy HS
Pierz MN

Rauk John N
Caledonia HS
Caledonia MN

Rauman Mark A
Lockport Central HS
Lockport IL

Raupp Douglas R
Harvard HS
Harvard IL

Ravenberg Debbie M
Ramona HS
Winfred SD

Ravenberg Sharrie L
Ramona Public HS
Winfred SD

Rawhouser Kent J
La Crosse Central HS
Lacrosse WI

Rawley Paula J
Clay City HS
Clay City IN

Rawlings Richard S
Northern Valley HS
Almena KS

Rawlings Tamie K
Kingsley Area HS
Kingsley MI

Rawlins Eric C
Eminence HS
Monrovia IN

Rawlins Thomas E
Henry Ind HS
Henry SD

Ray Jeffery W
Homestead HS
Fort Wayne IN

Ray John H
Avon HS
Avon IL

Ray Kevin D
West Plains HS
West Plains MO

Ray Mary A
Billings HS
Billings MO

Ray Melissa A
Bunker Hill HS
Bunker Hill IL

Ray Ola J
Northrop HS
Fort Wayne IN

Ray Paul C
Van Tar HS
Vandalia MO

Ray Rita J
Preston HS
Preston MN

Raycroft Patrick M
George Rogers Clark HS
Whiting IN

Raymer Debra J
Atkinson West Holt HS
Stuart NE

Raymond Helena B
Herscher HS
Kankakee IL

Raymond Janet L
Gurdon S Hubbard HS
Chicago IL

Raymond Jeffrey C
Spoon River Valley HS
Ellisville IL

Raymond Julia L
Harper Creek HS
Ceresco MI

Rayner Robert A
Beloit Memorial HS
Beloit WI

Razzano Dana L
Watseka Comm HS
Watseka IL

Read Kelly J
Aurora HS
Aurora NE

Read Rita M
Chambers HS
Chambers NE

Readus Mache
Lindblom Tech HS
Chicago IL

Ready Myra J
Giltner Public HS
Giltner NE

Reagan Lawrence P
Belvidere HS
Belvidere IL

Reagan Nancy L
Maine Twp South HS
Park Ridge IL

Ream Gregory L
Hamilton HS
Hamilton IN

Reamer Michelle R
Marshall Sr HS
Marshall WI

Reames Carolyn N
Pinckneyville Community HS
Pinckneyville IL

Rear Rebecca A
Valley Comm HS
Clermont IA

Rearden Timothy P
N County R I HS
Desloge MO

Reardon Charles E
Oak Lawn Comm HS
Oak Lawn IL

Reason Beverly D
Spencer HS
Spencer IA

Reau Phyllis L
Blissfield HS
Blissfield MI

Reaves Blake
Northwestern HS
Flint MI

Reba Peter J
Andrean HS
Crown Point IN

Reberger Cheryl L
Van Buren HS
Brazil IN

Reberger Lisa R
Van Buren HS
Brazil IN

Rebich Robert P
Lutheran North HS
Florissant MO

Rebsch Charles L
Northwood HS
Thompson ND

Reck Janet L
Mendota Township HS
Mendota IL

Rector Daniel J
Highland HS
Anderson IN

Rector Douglas A
Warren Township HS
Waukegan IL

Rector Karen L
Truman HS
Independence MO

Rector Lynn M
Waverly HS
Waverly IL

Reczek Michael J
Thornton Fractional No HS
Calumet City IL

Redding Debbie A
Millington HS
Millington MI

Redford Douglas S
Macarthur HS
Decatur IL

Redick Edward L
Shawneetown HS
Shawneetown IL

Rediger Lynn M
Crown Point HS
Crown Point IN

Rediker Karen K
Council Grove HS
Council Grove KS

Redington Patty J
Clayton HS
Clayton MO

Redmon Debra K
Monroe Senior HS
Monroe MI

Redwine Charles P
Vienna HS
New Burnside IL

Redwine Lisa P
Dillsboro HS
Dillsboro IN

Reed Carl A
Flora HS
Flora IL

Reed Cathy L
St Elmo HS
St Elmo IL

Reed Darrel R
Doniphan HS
Doniphan MO

Reed Deborah L
Normal Comm HS
Normal IL

Reed Debra K
West Delaware Senior HS
Manchester IA

Reed Denise K
Highland HS
Highland IN

Reed Denise L
Greenfield Central HS
Greenfield IN

Reed Dolores A
Waverly Consolidated HS
Lincoln NE

Reed Douglas E
Centreville HS
Constantine MI

Reed Grace M
Soldan HS
St Louis MO

Reed Joy A
South Knox HS
Monroe City IN

Reed Laura L
Fremont Sr HS
Fremont MI

Reed Marianne
Copeland HS
Copeland KS

Reed Mary K
Escanaba Area HS
Escanaba MI

Reed Mary K
Joseph A Craig Sr HS
Janesville WI

Reed Michael I
Centralia HS
Centralia IL

Reed Michael J
Crane HS
Crane MO

Reed Mitch M
Cannelton HS
Cannelton IN

Reed Patricia K
Highland HS
Highland IN

Reed Peter M
Mendel C HS
Chicago IL

Reed Sally R
Parkwood HS
Joplin MO

Reed Sherrill L
Fruitport HS
Muskegon MI

Reed Susan K
Macksville HS
Seward KS

Reed Zebbie S
Marseilles HS
Marseilles IL

Reeder Brian D
Ottawa HS
Ottawa IL

Reeder Dale W
Carterville HS
Cambria IL

Reeder Sam R
Washington Community HS
Washington IL

Reehm Mary A
Mc Donald HS
Pineville MO

Reel Phillip H
Tri County HS
Remington IN

Reeling Patrick J
Waterford Twp HS
Drayton MI

Reeners Scott R
Green Bay Sw HS
Green Bay WI

Rees David S
Du Quoin HS
Du Quoin IL

Rees Roger A
Golden City R 3 HS
Jasper MO

Reese Joann
Rosati Kain HS
St Louis MO

Reese Jody M
Lodi HS
Lodi WI

Reese John W
Estherville HS
Estherville IA

Reese Laura A
Dearborn HS
Dearborn MI

Reese Paul C
Perry HS
Griggsville IL

Reese Tom A
Ledyard Community HS
Ledyard IA

Reetz Randall S
Oak Park River Forest HS
Oak Park IL

Reeve Kent V
Walker HS
Walker MN

Reeves Daniel L
St Clair HS
St Clair MI

Reeves David R
Clinton HS
Clinton IL

Reeves Herbert A
Wichita HS
Wichita KS

Reeves Kristy A
Riverdale HS
Muscoda WI

Reevis Monte A
Southeast HS
Springfield IL

Refner Ken R
Oak Lawn Community HS
Oak Lawn IL

Refner Michael K
Dekalb HS
Waterloo IN

Regan Barb
Crete Monee HS
Crete IL

Regenscheid Ronald E
Le Sueur HS
St Peter MN

Reger Kevin M
Sun Prairie Sr HS
Sun Prairie WI

Regier Myron T
Frederic Remington HS
Newton KS

Reh Karen R
Rockford Sr HS
Rockford MI

Rehbein Robyn L
Forest Lake Sr HS
Lino Lakes MN

Rehberg Jeanmarie
Burlington HS
Burlington WI

Rehmert Richard L
Frederic Remington HS
Whitewater KS

Reibert Gary D
Streator Twp HS
Streator IL

Reich Barbara J
Proviso East HS
Melrose Park IL

Reichard Dale E
Williamsburg HS
Williamsburg KS

Reichart Gerald A
Plattsmouth HS
Plattsmouth NE

Reichen Debra R
Henry Senschwine HS
Henry IL

Reichert Brent L
Central HS
Crookston MN

Reichert Scott B
Thomas More HS
Milwaukee WI

Reichmuth Julie R
Leigh Comm HS
Leigh NE

Reichter Lynn C
Tremont Comm HS
Tremont IL

Reicks Mary J
New Hampton Comm HS
Alta Vista IA

Reid Debora S
Shabbona HS
Shabbona IL

Reid Linda C
Holly HS
Holly MI

Reid Ricky S
Washington HS
Germantown WI

Reid Susan K
Norway HS
Vulcan MI

Reidt Jena L
Pacific HS
Pacific MO

Reif Susan K
Hoisington HS
Claflin KS

Reiff Gary W
Twin Lakes HS
Burnettsville IN

Reifsteck Charles R
Unity HS
Tolono IL

Reigle Julie K
Madison HS
Madison NE

Reihle Jeffrey G
New Hampton Comm HS
New Hampton IA

Reilley Dawn R
Carlinville HS
Carlinville IL

Reilly Charles H
Marist HS
Palos Hts IL

Reilly Charles O
Thornton Fractional N HS
Calumet City IL

Reilly Nancy M
Mother Mcauley HS
Chicago IL

Reimer Barbara J
Jetmore HS
Spearville KS

Reimer Cindy K
Wallace County HS
Sharon Spgs KS

Reimers Thomas K
Ogallala HS
Ogallala NE

Reinarts Mary S
Winona Sr HS
Winona MN

Reinbold Rita K
Heelan HS
Sioux City IA

Reinders Mark A
Mallard Community HS
Curlew IA

Reinebach Kathy J
Seymour HS
Payson IL

Reineke Lawrence G
Browns Valley HS
Beardsley MN

Reiners Lori R
Hartsburg Emden HS
Hartsburg IL

Reinhardt Mark E
Central HS
Evansville IN

Reinhardt Melody A
Ansley Public HS
Ansley NE

Reinker Donna J
Lincoln County R 2 HS
Elsberry MO

Reinsch Linda S
Oak Park Sr HS
Kansas City MO

Reischel Joan M
Morton HS
Hammond IN

Reiser Judith E
St Marys Academy
Milwaukee WI

STUDENTS PHOTOGRAPH SCHEDULED FOR PUBLICATION HERE COULD NOT BE REPRODUCED

Reiser Michael W
Kirksville HS
Kirksville MO

Reiser Susan K
Valentine HS
Valentine NE

Reiter Deborah A
Ankeny HS
Ankeny IA

Reitsma Robert S
Bird Island Lk Lillian HS
Lake Lillian MN

Reltmeyer John D
Heyworth HS
Mc Lean IL

Remer Janice G
Winnebago HS
Winnebago IL

Remington Scott I
Barrington Community HS
Barrington IL

Remke Jean A
Forest Park HS
Ferdinand IN

Remus Rhonda K
Maywood HS
North Platte NE

Renaker Deborah E
Brookville HS
Brookville IN

Renchof Sharon A
St Francis Acad
Joliet IL

Rendina Elizabeth L
Andrean HS
Merrillville IN

Rendleman Shelba K
Wesclin HS
Trenton IL

Renfro Brent A
Taylor HS
Kokomo IN

Renfrow Carol L
Olympia HS
Atlanta IL

Rengstorf Di Anne P
South Division HS
Milwaukee WI

Renkes Jason J
Morrison Comm HS
Morrison IL

Renner Douglas H
Adams Frienship HS
Adams WI

Renner Kathy L
Dickinson HS
Dickinson ND

Renner Mary Kay
Mardan Sr HS
Mardan ND

Reno Daniel C
Muncie Northside HS
Muncie IN

Rensink Gary M
Sioux Center Comm HS
Sioux Center IA

Rentner Joann M
O Fallon Twp HS
O Fallon IL

Rentz Laurie A
Ferndale HS
Ferndale MI

Repking Cathy L
St Anthony HS
Effingham IL

Reseigh Philip M
Redford Union HS
Redford Twp MI

Ressegieu Matthew V
St Agnes HS
Alliance NE

Retzlaff Kathy L
Waverly HS
Lincoln NE

Reuss John L
Pope John Xxiii HS
Elgin NE

Reuter Barbara J
Riverside HS
Dearborn Heights MI

Reuter John T
Centerville HS
Richmond IN

Revelle George S
Poplar Bluff HS
Poplar Bluff MO

Revling Lester D
Auburndale HS
Auburndale WI

Revord Mary E
Marillac HS
Glenview IL

Rewerts Debra L
Guilford HS
Rockford IL

Rexroat Barbara J
Downs HS
Downs KS

Reyer Janet M
Highland HS
Highland KS

Reyes Michael F
Gordon Technical HS
Chicago IL

Reyes Rebbecca S
Summerfield HS
Riga MI

Reynebeau Stephen J
Little Chute HS
Little Chute WI

Reynolds Deborah R
Mounds View Senior HS
St Paul MN

Reynolds Edward J
Richwoods HS
Peoria IL

Reynolds Jona L
Farmer City Mansfield HS
Farmer City IL

Reynolds Joseph R
Battle Creek Central HS
Battle Creek MI

Reynolds Leonard D
Rochelle Twp HS
Rochelle IL

Reynolds Martin R
Kingsville HS
Pleasant Hill MO

Reynolds Rebecca A
Bedford HS
Lambertville MI

Reynolds Ricky L
Dexfield HS
Redfield IA

Reynolds Ruth A
Tri Central HS
Sharpsville IN

Reynolds Susan K
Hays HS
Hays KS

Reynolds Teri L
Morton HS
Morton IL

Reynolds Vivian M
Galena HS
Galena MO

Reyzlik Randy F
Tekamah Herman HS
Herman NE

Rezelman Ann M
Lapeer Sr HS
Lapeer MI

Reznicek Susan E
Ottawa HS
Ottawa KS

Rhee Hyun A
St Mary Academy
Monroe MI

Rhoades Dawn C
Okemos HS
Mason MI

Rhoades Denise A
Guthrie Center HS
Guthrie Center IA

Rhoades Lori L
Lincoln County HS
Elsberry MO

Rhoades Mark L
Lincoln County R Ii HS
Elsberry MO

Rhoads Russell C
Rockford West Jr HS
Rockford IL

Rhoads Samuel K
Carlinville Comm HS
Carlinville IL

Rhode Ann M
Roncalli HS
Mankowoc WI

Rhoden Don B
Plattsmouth HS
Plattsmouth NE

Rhodes Doug K
Wichita East HS
Wichita KS

Rhodes Sharon K
St Elmo Comm HS
St Elmo IL

Rhoten Don C
Brown Deer HS
Brown Deer WI

Rhoton Karen J
Santa Fe HS
Waverly MO

Rhue Deborah J
Eisenhower HS
Decatur IL

Rian Cathy M
Niles East HS
Skokie IL

Ricard Betty J
Thornwood HS
South Holland IL

Ricard Gary R
Stevens HS
Rapid City SD

Ricca Steven T
Limestone Comm HS
Bartonville IL

Rice Brenda C
Winston Churchill HS
Livonia MI

Rice Catherine E
Joliet Twp West Campus HS
Joliet IL

Rice Cathy D
Borden HS
Borden IN

Rice Daniel L
Montague Sr HS
Montague MI

Rice Gary R
N Central HS
Indianapolis IN

Rice Karen M
Plainfield HS
Joliet IL

Rice L David
Winneconne Comm HS
Winneconne WI

Rice Pamela J
Casey Jr Sr HS
Casey IL

Rice Rick L
Chillicothe HS
Chillicothe MO

Rice William T
Gordon Technical HS
Chicago IL

Rich Dixon M
Park Tudor HS
Indianapolis IN

Rich Janis A
Oblong HS
Robinson IL

Rich Leta R
Anna Jonesboro HS
Cobden IL

Richard Betty M
South Spencer HS
Rockport IN

Richard Lysette C
John Marshall Harlan HS
Chicago IL

Richard Raymond P
Crestwood HS
Dearborn Hts MI

Richards Barry F
Hayes Center HS
Hayes Center NE

Richards Betty L
Prescott Comm HS
Corning IA

Richards Bonita M
Naperville Central HS
Wheaton IL

Richards David A
New Madrid County HS
Matthews MO

Richards Debbie J
Center HS
Center ND

Richards Deborah A
Whitehall HS
Whitehall MI

Richards Lynae D
Sac Community HS
Sac City IA

Richards Mark A
North Montgomery HS
Crawfordsville IN

Richards Mindy L
Bath HS
Dewitt MI

Richards Monica
Taylor HS
Kokomo IN

Richards Pamela J
Nashville Comm HS
Nashville IL

Richards Robert P
Fenwick HS
Berwyn IL

Richards Scott T
Big Fork HS
Effie MN

Richardson Benita J
West Side Sr HS
Gary IN

Richardson Cornel C
Union Star Rii HS
Union Star MO

Richardson Denise C
Reavis HS
Burbank IL

Richardson Diana L
Davis Co Comm HS
Bloomfield IA

Richardson Dorothy B
Ann Arbor Huron HS
Ypsilanti MI

Richardson Ginger K
Orrick HS
Orrick MO

Richardson Kimberly D
Rochester HS
Rochester IN

Richardson Mareta M
Bishop Dwenger HS
Fort Wayne IN

Richardson Robert H
Fonda Comm HS
Fonda IA

Richardson Ruben H
Emerson HS
Gary IN

Richardson Sara J
Monrovia HS
Monrovia IN

Richardson Terry L
Maysville HS
Pattonsburg MO

Richardson Thomas J
Galena HS
Galena IL

Richer Stacy L
Triton HS
Bourbon IN

Riches John C
Humboldt HS
Humboldt IA

Richey David A
Southeast HS
West Mineral KS

Richey Janelle K
N Platte Senior HS
North Platte NE

Richey Robert S
Grayville Community HS
Grayville IL

Richey Rodney P
Madison Hts HS
Anderson IN

Richey Thomas D
Crab Orchard ;hs
Pittsburg IL

Richmond Anne M
East Gary Edison Sr HS
East Gary IN

Richstein Nancy L
Garden County HS
Oshkosh NE

Richt Richard P
Wm J Bryan HS
Omaha NE

Richter Kevin L
Bishop Mc Namara HS
Kankakee IL

Richter Kristine L
Oswego Sr HS
Aurora IL

Richter Randy C
Hayes County HS
Hayes Center NE

Richter Wayne D
Ash Grove HS
Ash Grove MO

Richwalski Daniel C
Lake Central HS
St John IN

Rick Brian N
Hutchinson HS
Hutchinson MN

Ricke Cheryl M
Sharon HS
Sharon KS

Ricke Steven C
Ramsey HS
Bingham IL

Ricke Tom C
Greensburg HS
Greensburg IN

Rickers Lorri J
Fairbury HS
Fairbury NE

Rickert Paul W
Elmwood Park HS
Elmwood Park IL

Rickey Thomas L
James W Riley HS
South Bend IN

Rickman Brenda A
Mackenzie HS
Detroit MI

Rickman Dan S
D C Everest Sr HS
Hatley WI

Ricks Lisa J
High School
Holliday MO

Riddle Terry J
Kearney HS
Kearney NE

Ridenour Janet F
Harrisburg HS
Harrisburg IL

Rider Shelly A
Henry HS
Hazel SD

Ridgell Tramell G
Northern HS
Flint MI

Ridgway June M
Southwestern HS
Flint MI

Ridlen Randy W
Eisenhower HS
Decatur IL

Ridley Randy R
Washington HS
Washington IA

Rieb Cynthia M
Washington Sr HS
Sioux Falls SD

Riedeman John M
Scecina Memorial HS
Indianpolis IN

Rieder Jill M
Griffith HS
Griffith IN

Riedl Margaret A
Divine Savior Holy Angels HS
Wauwatosa WI

Rief Lynn M
Waconia HS
Waconia MN

Rieger Holly A
Carmel HS
Barrington IL

Rieger Robert A
Wesclin HS
Trenton IL

Rieger Timothy
Eureka Public HS
Eureka SD

Riegle Candace D
Wapahani HS
Muncie IN

Rieke Susan A
Langdon HS
Langdon ND

Riekena Teresa L
Illini Bluffs HS
Mapleton IL

Rieker Joyce L
Eustis Public HS
Eustis NE

Riemersma Darlene L
Zeeland HS
Zeeland MI

Rienks Julie A
Verona HS
Verona WI

Riensche Barbara L
Nemaha Valley HS
Tecumseh NE

Ries Edward B
High School
Mobridge SD

Riesland Denise K
Danville HS
Danville IL

Rife Daniel J
Stratton Public HS
Stratton NE

Riffle Barbara L
Auburn HS
Rockford IL

Rigdon Ronald E
Griffin HS
Springfield IL

Riggins Ruth L
Wichita HS
Wichita KS

Riggio Joseph
Du Quoin HS
Du Quoin IL

Riggle Karen J
Sullivan HS
Sullivan IL

Riggs Beth A
Danville Comm HS
Danville IN

Riggs Leigh A
Bennett County HS
Allen SD

Riggs Robert A
Westport HS
Kansas City MO

Riggs Roger C
Newtown Harris HS
Newtown MO

Rigoni Mary A
Decatur Jr Sr HS
Decatur MI

Rigoni Steven D
Decatur Jr Sr HS
Decatur MI

Rilett Richard B
Clare HS
Clare MI

Riley Bradley A
Poplar Bluff Sr HS
Poplar Bluff MO

Riley Carol A
Nevada HS
Nevada MO

Riley Eva K
Santa Fe Trail HS
Carbondale KS

Riley Jeffrey K
Pratt Sr HS
Pratt KS

Riley Jim B
Mt Carmel HS
Evergreen Park IL

Riley Kathleen J
Waterford Kettering HS
Drayton Plains MI

Riley Kathleen O
Onsted Comm HS
Onsted MI

Riley Maritha J
Roosevelt HS
Gary IN

Riley Mary F
Oak Park River Forest HS
Oak Park IL

Riley Patrick D
Madison HS
Madison Hts MI

Riley Rita E
Cowden Herrick HS
Cowden IL

Riley Rita J
Mother Of Sorrows HS
Alsip IL

Rilinger Don J
B & B HS
Seneca KS

Rimas Audra Ann H
Comfrey Public HS
Comfrey MN

Rindfusz Karen P
Pontiac Catholic HS
Pontiac MI

Rinehart Cynthia R
Centerville HS
Mystic IA

Rinehart Jimmy D
Moravia Comm HS
Moravia IA

Rinesmith Randy A
Paris HS
Vermillion IL

Ring Daniel W
Emmons HS
Twin Lakes MN

Ring David M
Emmons HS
Twin Lakes MN

Ring Margaret R
Carmel Girls HS
Mundelein IL

Ring Randy J
Lincoln HS
Sioux Falls SD

Ring Suzanne K
Winnebago Lutheran Academy
Oshkosh WI

Ringle Shelley R
Marathon HS
Edgar WI

Ringlein Sharon M
Luke M Powers HS
Flint MI

Rinker Colleen J
Streator Township HS
Streator IL

Riopelle Tim M
Mount Cathedral HS
Crookston MN

Riordan Michael K
Rapid City Stevens HS
Rapid City SD

Riordan Michael L
Wichita East HS
Wichita KS

Riordan Susan A
Elizabeth Seton HS
Calumet Park IL

Ripberger Richard C
Tri Central HS
Sharpsville IN

Rippa Cindy M
Proviso East HS
Forest Park IL

Ripslinger Jane F
West HS
Davenport IA

Riquelme Brenda M
George Rogers Clark HS
Whiting IN

Risler Kevin P
Gilmanton HS
Alma WI

Risley Clifford R
Riverside Brookfield HS
Brookfield IL

Risner Daniel W
Penn HS
Mishawaka IN

Riss Beverly J
Dwight HS
Ransom IL

Risse Joseph W
Frankfort HS
Frankfort IN

Risselman Mary J
Connersville HS
Connersville IN

Rist Becky J
Papillion HS
Papillion NE

Ristich Samuel M
Thornton Fractional So HS
Lansing IL

Ritscher Kevin N
Alma HS
Alma WI

Rittenhouse Karin M
Kingsford HS
Kingsford MI

Ritter Bonnie L
Leigh Community HS
Creston NE

Ritter Brenda J
Avon HS
Plainfield IN

Ritter Kevin L
Kinmundy Alma HS
Kinmundy IL

Ritter Laura M
Reading Community HS
Reading MI

Ritter Marie G
Decatur Community HS
Oberlin KS

Rittgers Brian R
Prairie Comm HS
Gowrie IA

Ritzman Jeff N
Hempstead HS
Dubuque IA

Ritzwoller Robert M
Carmel HS
Waukegan IL

Rivara Kathy M
Forest View HS
Mt Prospect IL

Rivaro Raymond T
Glenwood City HS
Glenwood City WI

Rivers Randy G
Central HS
Grenola KS

Rivers Rocky D
Centralia HS
Hannibal MO

Rizer Barbara A
Atchison HS
Atchison KS

Rizzo Regina M
Carl Brablec HS
Roseville MI

Rizzuto John F
Marist HS
Blue Island IL

Roach Brian D
Central Cass HS
Wheatland ND

Roach Joseph J
Regis HS
Eau Claire WI

Roach Phil C
Northrop HS
Ft Wayne IN

Roam Karen A
Lincoln Cnty Rii HS
Elsberry MO

Robarge Lynn M
Gobles HS
Gobles MI

Robb Brenda K
Big Springs HS
Big Springs NE

Robb Dan L
Guide Rock Public HS
Guide Rock NE

Robbins Amy J
Winchester Comm HS
Winchester IN

Robbins Bonnie S
Bennett County HS
Martin SD

Robbins Dena L
Elk Point Public HS
Elk Point SD

Robbins Gary A
Kewanee HS
Kewanee IL

Robbins Kenneth E
Parsons Sr HS
Parsons KS

Robel Rick W
St Marys HS
Storm Lake IA

Roberson Vicki M
Ritenour HS
St Louis MO

Roberts Becky A
East Charles Mix HS
Wagner SD

Roberts Brion A
Tampico HS
Tampico IL

Roberts Bruce G
Burlington Comm HS
Burlington IA

Roberts Debra L
Tri Central HS
Tipton IN

Roberts Johnnie C
Central HS
St Joseph MO

Roberts Kathleen L
Sullivan HS
Sullivan MO

Roberts Kathleen L
Oak Park HS
Kansas City MO

Roberts Kelly D
Gilbert Community HS
Ames IA

Roberts Linda F
Harrisburg HS
Clark MO

Roberts Linda S
West Washington HS
Campbellsburg IN

Roberts Paul M
Hauser HS
Hope IN

Roberts Peggy J
St Martins Academy
Rapid City SD

Roberts Rhonda L
Armstrong HS
Penfield IL

Roberts Robin L
Tri Valley HS
Downs IL

Roberts Sheryl A
Bonner Springs HS
Bonner Springs KS

Roberts Susan L
Grosse Pointe South HS
Grosse Pointe MI

Roberts Susan R
Crandon HS
Hiles WI

Roberts Timothy D
Highland HS
Ainsworth IA

Roberts Toni R
Ida HS
Ida MI

Robertson Amy M
Central HS
St Joseph MO

Robertson Daniel M
Desoto Sr HS
Olathe KS

Robertson Kenneth E
Central HS
Linton IN

Robertson Lisa S
Monroe HS
Monroe MI

Robertson Merrill L
Glenwood HS
Springfield IL

Robertson Shelby G
Malden HS
Malden MO

Robertson Suzanne M
Sauk Prairie HS
Prairie Du Sac WI

Robertus Carole A
Irondale HS
New Brighton MN

Robinette Pamela K
South Sioux City HS
South Sioux City NE

Robins Kathy S
Woodruff HS
Peoria IL

Robinson Charles G
Ravenna HS
Ravenna MI

Robinson Diane M
Norfolk Senior HS
Norfolk NE

Robinson Donna M
Aquinas Dominican HS
Chicago IL

Robinson Eric V
Platteville HS
Platteville WI

Robinson Frederick D
Mendel Catholic Prep HS
Chicago IL

Robinson Henry W
Cass Tech HS
Detroit MI

Robinson Janice L
Thedford HS
Thedford NE

Robinson Lawrence B
De La Salle HS
Chicago IL

Robinson Linda J
Belleville East HS
Belleville IL

Robinson Lynnette E
United Township HS
Moline IL

Robinson Marcia G
Pinckney HS
Lakeland MI

Robinson Mary A
Gering HS
Gering NE

Robinson Mary K
Garden County HS
Oshkosh NE

Robinson Nicholas F
Holcomb HS
Holcomb MO

Robinson Nyle D
Knoxville Comm HS
Knoxville IA

Robinson Patricia F
Warrensburg HS
Decatur IL

Robinson Ron D
U Of Detroit HS
Detroit MI

Robison Meg D
Tilihandy HS
Bay City MI

Robnett George W
Webster Groves HS
Rock Hill MO

Robnett Glenn W
Christian Bros Col Mil Inst
St Louis MO

Robnett Sherolyn A
Rantoul Twp HS
Rantoul IL

Roby Cassandra M
St Elizabeth Academy
St Louis MO

Roby Elise R
Kenwood HS
Chicago IL

Roch Katrina A
Northside HS
Muncie IN

Rochnowski Donna L
La Salle Peru Township HS
Peru IL

Rock Linda M
Kadoka HS
Kadoka SD

Rock Randall W
Hope HS
Hope KS

Rock Rhonda Y
Farmington East HS
Farmington IL

Rockel Craig A
Senn HS
Chicago IL

Rockers Christopher J
Garnett HS
Garnett KS

Rockwood Gina M
Algonac HS
Algonac MI

Rod Joe J
St Rita HS
Argo IL

Rodahl Marcia A
Minot HS
Minot ND

Rodarte Dede
Southwest HS
Kansas City MO

Rodda Mary E
West Iron County HS
Iron River MI

Roderick Blake E
Lanphier HS
Springfield IL

Rodgers Cynthia J
Oak Park HS
Kansas City MO

Rodgers Jennifer R
West Vigo HS
West Terre Haute IN

Rodgers Lavonda B
Caledonia HS
Alto MI

Rodgers Pamela K
Clarke Comm HS
Woodburn IA

Rodgers Theodis
Lindblom Tech HS
Chicago IL

Rodibaugh Margaret A
Goshen HS
Goshen IN

Rodriguez Cristela
Ashton HS
Ashton IL

Rodriguez Mario A
Gordon Technical HS
Chicago IL

Rodriquez Sharon L
Southeast HS
Weir KS

Roe Kathe L
Macon Co HS
Macon MO

Roe Kirk W
Superior HS
Superior NE

Roe Sherrie L
Kirksville HS
Kirksville MO

Roebbeke Daniel M
Ceylon Public HS
Dunnell MN

Roeder Cindy L
Andrew Comm HS
Andrew IA

Roehl Lynne C
Nevis HS
Nevis MN

Roelofs Nicolas H
Morgan Park Academy
Worth IL

Roenfeld Tami D
Glenwood Comm HS
Mineola IA

Roepke Shelly L
Valley Heights HS
Waterville KS

Roesch Michael T
Fox HS
Arnold MO

Roetheli Janice K
St Francis Borgia HS
Washington MO

Roethig Larry A
Marshall HS
Marshall MO

Roewert Joy R
Elkhorn Valley HS
Tilden NE

Rogalski Anita M
Thornton Fractional N HS
Calumet City IL

Rogers Albert D
John Marshall HS
Indianapolis IN

Rogers Ann M
Harrison HS
Farmington Hills MI

Rogers Debra S
Richwoods HS
Peoria IL

Rogers Leesa L
Clinton Sr HS
Clinton IL

Rogers Marieta J
Nixa HS
Nixa MO

Rogers Marilyn D
Annapolis HS
Dearborn Hts MI

Rogers Norman H
Southmont HS
New Ross IN

Rogers Pamela S
H H Dow HS
Midland MI

Rogers Philo A
Knox Co R 1 HS
La Belle MO

Rogers Randall J
Chapman HS
Junction City KS

Rogers Shirley I
Nevada HS
Richards MO

Rogers Vicki F
Harrison HS
Chicago IL

Rogstad Mark R
Belvidere HS
Belvidere IL

Rohder James T
Lapeer HS
Metamora MI

Rohe Mary L
Manning Comm HS
Manning IA

Rohlik Patrick J
Sterling HS
Sterling IL

Rohloff Julie A
Rhinelander HS
Rhinelander WI

Rohrbacher Jody L
Waverly HS
Lansing MI

Rohrscheib Annilee
Eisenhower HS
Decatur IL

Rojas Karen K
Collinsville HS
Collinsville IL

Rojo Cynthia A
Maria HS
Bridgeview IL

Rojohn Claire E
Denver HS
Denver IA

Rokke Eunice I
Strandquist HS
Strandquist MN

Rokosz Susan M
St Joseph HS
Chicago IL

Roland Deborah J
Sycamore HS
Sycamore IL

Rolling Ann M
Dubuque Senior HS
Dubuque IA

Rollins Laura J
Morton Sr HS
Hammond IN

Roman Christopher D
Benet Academy
Woodridge IL

Roman Richard J
Carmel Boys HS
Buffalo Grove IL

STUDENTS PHOTOGRAPH SCHEDULED FOR PUBLICATION HERE COULD NOT BE REPRODUCED

Rominsky Keith A
Walled Lake Western HS
Union Lake MI

Rominsky Kenneth G
Walled Lake Western HS
Union Lake MI

Romme Fran C
Liberal HS
Liberal KS

Rommelmann Douglas W
Carlyle HS
Carlyle IL

Romohr Julia
Gresham Public HS
Gresham NE

Romsos Lisa R
Bottineau HS
Bottineau ND

Ronat William J
Jacksonville HS
Jacksonville IL

Rondot Judith M
Bishop Luers HS
Ft Wayne IN

Ronning Barbara F
Raymond HS
Raymond MN

Ronvik Tracy
Evanston Township HS
Evanston IL

Rood Scott A
Muskegon Catholic Central HS
Muskegon MI

Rook Sharon L
Elk Grove HS
Elk Grove Vlg IL

Rooney Ardith R
Satanta HS
Satanta KS

Rooney James J
Kaneland HS
Maple Park IL

Rooney Robin T
Alpena HS
Alpena MI

Root Bradford G
Saginaw HS
Saginaw MI

Root Karen S
Maple Valley HS
Nashville MI

Root Thomas A
Collinsville HS
Collinsville IL

Roper Cynthia L
Hobart HS
Hobart IN

Roper John E
Civic Memorial HS
Bethalto IL

Ropp Stephen A
Nevada HS
Nevada IA

Rose Donna M
Calhoun HS
Hardin IL

Rose Sheila M
Calhoun HS
Hardin IL

Rosebrough Linda S
Ft Scott HS
Ft Scott KS

Rosema Debra K
Oakridge HS
Muskegon MI

Rosemeyer Rick E
Webster Groves HS
Rock Hill MO

Rosenak Lynn A
Wayland Academy
Eagle River WI

Rosenbalm Larry D
Eminence HS
Martinsville IN

Rosenberg Marc A
Sullivan HS
Chicago IL

Rosenthal William N
Central HS
St Joseph MO

Rosevear Terry J
Barrington HS
Barrington IL

Rosiek Margaret M
Maria HS
Chicago IL

Rosin Robert L
Decatur Comm HS
Oberlin KS

Rosinsky Samuel J
Harry A Burke HS
Omaha NE

Ross Cindi D
Warsaw Comm HS
Warsaw IN

Ross Cynthia A
Evanston Township HS
Evanston IL

Ross Laureen G
Chesaning Sr HS
Montrose MI

Ross Linda S
Twin Lakes HS
Monticello IN

Ross Nancy K
Colby HS
Colby KS

Ross Robert J
Marist HS
Palos Hts IL

Ross Stanley H
Monroe Township HS
Muncie IN

Ross Steven C
Sullivan HS
Sullivan MO

Ross Theresa H
Dexter Sr HS
Dexter MO

Ross Vicki M
West Vigo HS
West Terre Haute IN

Rossberg Cheryl L
Rolling Meadows HS
Rolling Meadows IL

Rossetti Paula J
Marian Central HS
Mc Henry IL

Rossi Armano J
Thornton Frac S HS
Lansing IL

Rossi Douglas J
Kingsford HS
Kingsford MI

Rossi Joseph P
Crete Monee HS
Crete IL

Rossi Tina L
Lasalle Peru Twp HS
Oglesby IL

Rossman Larry W
Hammond Baptist HS
Lansing IL

Rossmiller David W
Okemos HS
Okemos MI

Rossmiller Gwen E
Wildrose HS
Wildrose ND

Rossmiller Mary K
Liberty HS
Liberty IL

Rossmiller Patty H
Liberty HS
Liberty IL

Rosso Mark A
Holy Cross HS
Chicago IL

Rossow Charles A
Ind #75 HS
Florence SD

Rost Mary E
J S Morton West HS
Lyons IL

Rostollan Daniel J
Waukesha South HS
Waukesha WI

Rostron Bruce W
Gibson Southern HS
Haubstadt IN

Roth Brian E
Mt Pleasant Community HS
Mt Pleasant IA

Rothe Dianne
Virden HS
Virden IL

Rothe Doug
Girard HS
Girard IL

Rothengass Cheryl A
Mother Of Sorrows HS
Chicago IL

Rother Gregory D
Craig Riii HS
Craig MO

Rotramel Ronald L
Jay HS
Southwest City MO

Rottmann Larry D
Metropolis HS
Metropolis IL

Roubal Susan J
North Bend Central HS
North Bend NE

Roudebush Phillip R
Central HS
Worthington IN

Rouintree Kevin P
Anderson HS
Anderson IN

Roundy Dina G
Woodbine Comm HS
Woodbine IA

Rountree Connie J
Ri North Callaway HS
Auxvasse MO

Rouse Brian D
Plattsmouth HS
Murray NE

Rouse Eric V
Mendel Cath Prep
Chicago IL

Roush Edward W
Truman HS
Independence MO

Routh Dale A
Macks Creek HS
Climax Springs MO

Routhier John B
Stephenson HS
Stephenson MI

Rovin Brad H
Maine Twp North HS
Glenview IL

Row Rita M
Desoto Sr HS
De Soto KS

Rowan Carol A
College Springs HS
Coin IA

Rowan Cedric L
Southeast HS
Kansas City MO

Rowan Michael L
Gurley Public HS
Gurley NE

Rowan Steven R
Ingalls HS
Ingalls KS

Rowden Anne K
Granite City HS
Granite City IL

Rowe Gregory G
Sturgis HS
Sturgis MI

Rowe Lynn R
Watertown HS
Watertown SD

Rowe Sue A
Rova HS
Oneida IL

Rowe Tonya L
La Ville Jr Sr HS
Lakeville IN

Rowell Bill J
Ft Dodge Sr HS
Ft Dodge IA

Rowland David L
Riverside Brookfield HS
Brookfield IL

Rowland Terry J
Fitzgerald HS
Warren MI

Roy Robert J
Adams Friendship HS
Friendship WI

Royalty Stanley P
Montague HS
Montague MI

Royce Nancy G
Eastbrook HS
Upland IN

Royer Kurt D
Otis Bison HS
Otis KS

Royle Michael J
Truman HS
Independence MO

Roys Ronald A
Coopersville HS
Grand Rapids MI

Royse Janice E
Noble HS
Noble IL

Royse Martin J
W Washington HS
Fredericksburg IN

Rozanski Thomas A
St Patrick HS
Chicago IL

Rozman Zvonka A
St Ann HS
Chicago IL

Ruark Robin A
Mitchell Sr HS
Pierre SD

Rubel Larry S
Bloomfield Hills HS
Bloomfield Hills MI

Rubendall Richard A
Hyde Co HS
Highmore SD

Rubin Glenn R
Marist HS
Palos Hts IL

Rubin Michael P
Beach Public HS
Beach ND

Rubingh Glenn A
Ellsworth Community HS
Ellsworth MI

Ruby Randy J
North Mahaska HS
New Sharon IA

Ruch Kathleen M
Eastridge HS
Kankakee IL

Rud Joni A
Sheyenne Public HS
Sheyenne ND

Rudd Peggy S
Seneca HS
Seneca MO

Rude Nancy A
Redfield Independent HS
Redfield SD

Ruden Joyce M
Western Dubuque HS
Bernard IA

Rudie Pauline R
Wahpeton Sr HS
Wahpeton ND

Rudin Thomas W
Lincoln Way HS
New Lenox IL

Rudolph Mary K
Morton HS
Morton IL

Rudy Susan K
Goshen HS
Goshen IN

Ruebling Mark R
West HS
Davenport IA

Ruedebusch Mary J
St Marys HS
Burlington WI

Ruehr Beth S
South HS
Sheboygan WI

Ruesch Fay A
Medford Sr HS
Medford WI

Ruf Cynthia A
Wilsonville HS
Wilsonville NE

Rufeder Joann K
Monroe HS
Monroe WI

Ruff Bradley R
Academy Of The Holy Angels
Richfield MN

Ruff Catherine M
Bloomer HS
Bloomer WI

Ruff Darcy D
Lehr HS
Lehr ND

Ruff Judy K
Greendale HS
Greendale WI

Ruggiero Janice A
St Marys Of Perpetual HelpHS
Chicago IL

Rugh Linda M
Highland HS
Highland IN

Ruhl Sharon A
Grayling HS
Grayling MI

Ruhlman Joseph A
North Branch HS
North Branch MI

Ruhr Kay M
Castlewood HS
Castlewood SD

Ruigh Karen E
Pine River HS
Pine River MN

Ruiz Daniel J
Gordon Tech HS
Chicago IL

Rule Mary C
Springfield HS
Springfield IL

Ruman Mary B
Marquette Sr HS
Marquette MI

Rumble Ann M
Princeton Comm HS
Princeton IN

Rummel Kim D
Holdrege Sr HS
Holdrege NE

Rummel Tammie L
Glendale HS
Springfield MO

Rumschlag Paul A
Bellmont HS
Decatur IN

Runbom Dennis E
Rockridge HS
Reynolds IL

Rundle Kimberly A
Smith Center HS
Smith Center KS

Runge Dale A
Milbank HS
Twin Brooks SD

Runyon Norman K
Chatsworth HS
Chatsworth IL

Ruotsalainen Jodi J
Rosemount Sr HS
St Paul MN

Rupp Robert L
Medicine Valley HS
Curtis NE

Rusch Thomas D
Wauwatosa West HS
Wauwatosa WI

Rush Marc
Niles East HS
Skokie IL

Rush Michael S
Shawnee Mission North HS
Mission KS

Rushton Steven A
Carlinville Comm HS
Carlinville IL

Ruskusky Rita A
Peoria Heights HS
Peoria Heights IL

Russell Kristy L
Sterling HS
Sterling IL

Russell Pamela S
Pacific HS
Robertsville MO

Russell Philip P
Beatrice HS
Beatrice NE

Russell Susan E
Edgewood HS
Spencer IN

Russell Toby L
Galatia HS
Galatia IL

Russell Todd S
Lansing HS
Lansing KS

Rust Gary D
Goodland HS
Goodland KS

Rustan Jean E
Oklee Public HS
Oklee MN

Ruth Donna J
Normandy Sr HS
St Louis MO

Rutherford Jim D
Pacific HS
Villa Ridge MO

Rutherford Katherine A
Hudson Sr HS
Hudson WI

Rutledge Joseph L
North Greene HS
White Hall IL

Rutledge Pamela
Excelsior Springs West HS
Kansas City MO

Rutt Leslea C
Metropolis Comm HS
Metropolis IL

Ruyle Enid G
Berkeley Sr HS
Berkeley MO

Ruzevich Donna J
J S Morton East HS
Cicero IL

Ruzic David N
Rogers HS
Beverly Shores IN

Ruzich Cynthia G
Pittsfield HS
Pittsfield IL

Ruzicka Douglas J
Silver Lake HS
Silver Lake MN

Ryan David J
Plattsmouth HS
Murray NE

Ryan Diane G
Pontiac HS
Pontiac IL

Ryan Douglas R
Lawton Bronson Comm HS
Bronson IA

Ryan Michael C
Kingsford HS
Kingsford MI

Ryan Myrtle K
Soldan HS
St Louis MO

Ryan Paula R
East Chanas Mix HS
Wagner SD

Ryan Randy L
Casey Junior Senior HS
Casey IL

Ryan Robert C
West Chicago Comm HS
Winfield IL

Ryan Susan A
Fonda Comm HS
Fonda IA

Ryan Susan M
Marquette Sr HS
Marquette MI

Ryckman Debra K
Laurel HS
Laurel IN

Ryden Beth J
Kennedy Public HS
Kennedy MN

Ryder Frank W
Libertyville HS
Libertyville IL

Rye Timothy W
Stephenson HS
Wallace MI

Ryherd Sandra K
Sullivan HS
Sullivan IL

Rykal Douglas A
Cadott HS
Cadott WI

Rylander Debora K
Onarga HS
Onarga IL

Rynazewski Joyce M
Daniel J Gross HS
Omaha NE

Rynish Karen P
Carmel For Girls HS
Round Lake IL

Rystrom Nancy A
Anoka Sr HS
Anoka MN

Rzepinski Jeffrey J
St John Cathedral HS
Milwaukee WI

Rzepka Cynthia M
Lourdes HS
Chicago IL

Rzepka Michael M
St Patrick HS
Chicago IL

Rzyhak Suzanne G
Port Austin Public HS
Port Austin MI

S

Saager Laura L
Bloomington HS
Bloomington IL

Saale Thomas C
Marquette HS
Alton IL

Saathoff Daniel L
Amherst Public HS
Miller NE

Sabanski Brenda K
Eastbrook HS
Fairmount IN

Sabel Mark H
Ripon 'S
Ripon WI

Sabel Michael A
Ripon Senior HS
Ripon WI

Sabin Kenneth
Armstrong Comm HS
Armstrong IA

Sabin Tammy L
Malden HS
Princeton IL

Sachs Edward A
Plattsmouth HS
Plattsmouth NE

Sachs Jean L
Plattsmouth HS
Plattsmouth NE

Sacia Denise K
Holmen HS
Holmen WI

Sadek Paul C
Stillwater HS
Stillwater MN

Sadler Jack W
Valley HS
Belgrade MO

Sadler Marla M
Maysville HS
Amity MO

Sadowy Carol A
Sandusky HS
Applegate MI

Saethre David H
Maine East HS
Niles IL

Sagataw Connee A
Bark River Harris HS
Harris MI

Sage Laura K
Waukegan HS
Park City IL

Sager Brian D
High School
New Richmond WI

Sager Lora L
Paris HS
Paris IL

Sager Paul K
Deerfield HS
Highland Park IL

Sahnow Kenneth A
Hudson HS
Hudson WI

Sailor Connie J
Frankfort Sr HS
Frankfort IN

Sajdak Margaret M
John F Kennedy HS
Chicago IL

Sakowsky Valerie M
Fitzgerald Sr HS
Warren MI

Salak Sheldon E
Rock Island HS
Rock Island IL

Salas Sharlene J
Freeland HS
Freeland MI

Salava Julie A
Grant Comm HS
Ingleside IL

Salerno Martha A
Chippewa Valley HS
Mt Clemens MI

Saliklis Dana M
Maria HS
Chicago IL

Salinas Marie L
Bishop Noll Institute
East Chicago IN

Salisbury Dean A
Pawnee HS
Pawnee IL

Salisbury Devin H
Gordon HS
Gordon NE

Salkowski Thomas M
Premontre HS
Kewaunee WI

Salla Nancy L
Benton Central HS
Earl Park IN

Salladay Sandy L
Jamaica HS
Fairmount IL

Sallans Larry
Fitzgerald HS
Warren MI

Sallee Kenneth S
Troy HS
Troy KS

Sallee Robin A
Troy HS
Troy KS

Sallie Pamela S
Hammond Baptist HS
Merrillville IN

Sallman Terrie K
Concordia HS
Aurora KS

Salsberry Bobby G
Novinger R 1 HS
Novinger MO

Salter Steven J
Slinger HS
Slinger WI

Saltzman Alisa E
Sullivan Public HS
Sullivan MO

Saltzman Kevin W
Marshall HS
Marshall MI

Salyer Richard L
Sarcoxie R2 HS
Sarcoxie MO

Salyers Sherry G
Bluffton HS
Bluffton IN

Salz William A
Streator HS
Streator IL

Salzmann Nancy B
Auburndale HS
Milladore WI

Sammarco Anthony
St Ignatius Prep HS
Chicago IL

Sammet Cheryl E
Princeville HS
Princeville IL

Sammons Mark W
West Holt HS
Atkinson NE

Sampson Gregg O
Estherville HS
Estherville IA

Sampson Michael J
Chippewa Valley HS
Mt Clemens MI

Sampson Steven J
University Milwaukee HS
Milwaukee WI

Sampson Toni R
Oakland HS
Oakland IL

Sampy Teresa L
Ansley Public HS
Ansley NE

Sams Patricia C
Kirksville Sr HS
Kirksville MO

Samson Julie A
Marian HS
Omaha NE

Samuelson Kathy R
Adams Public HS
Adams ND

Samuelson Michael L
Ottawa Township HS
Ottawa IL

Sanchez John P
St Xaviers HS
Junction City KS

Sanchez Patricia D
Lourdes HS
Chicago IL

Sanda Jayne M
Velva Public HS
Velva ND

Sandage Jeffrey A
Jefferson Comm HS
Scranton IA

Sandborn Nancy A
Saranac HS
Saranac MI

Sander Pamela A
Catholic Central HS
Muskegon MI

Sanders Charlene L
Mitchell HS
Mitchell IN

Sanders Charles W
Elhurst & Leo HS
Fort Wayne IN

Sanders Dean E
Glenwood City HS
Downing WI

Sanders Harvey B
Bishop Noll Institute
East Chicago IN

Sanders Janice A
Josephinum HS
Chicago IL

Sanders Kristin G
Delavan HS
Delavan IL

Sanders Lauri M
Aquinas Dominican HS
Chicago IL

Sanders Monte M
Taylor HS
Kokomo IN

Sanders Norma J
North Knox HS
Sandborn IN

Sanders Robin M
Albert Lea HS
Albert Lea MN

Sanders Sandra K
Venice HS
Madison IL

Sandersfeld Paul K
Cal Community HS
Latimer IA

Sanderson Susan F
Canton HS
Canton SD

Sandman Edward L
Bishop Dwenger HS
Ft Wayne IN

Sandona Cheryl
St Francis De Sales HS
Valparaiso IN

Sandquist Kevin J
Adel HS
Adel IA

Sands Jo Deen M
West Aurora Sr HS
North Aurora IL

Sandy Bradley J
Indianola HS
Indianola IA

San Filippo Jill G
Greenfield HS
Greenfield WI

Sanford Diana L
Abraham Lincoln Senior HS
Bloomington MN

Sangregario John W
Notre Dame HS
Sterling Hgts MI

Sangren Judy A
Willow River HS
Willow River MN

Sankowski Kathryn S
Clark HS
Hammond IN

Sanneman Arlyn L
Clifton HS
Palmer KS

Santala Jeanne M
Waterford Mott HS
Pontiac MI

Santman Dawn A
Dysart Geneseo HS
Dysart IA

Santoro Kathryn A
O Fallon Twnshp HS
Ofallon IL

Santoro William D
Fraser HS
Fraser MI

Sanzone Rosemarie A
Evergreen Park HS
Evergreen Park IL

Sapp Lee A
Burke HS
Omaha NE

Sapp Paul J
Sioux Valley HS
Bruce SD

Saputo Mary F
St Marys HS
Kansas City MO

Sarafa Haithem K
Brother Rice HS
Southfield MI

Sarafiny Cindy A
West Iron County HS
Caspian MI

Sarang Kathy M
Morton Sr HS
Hammond IN

Sarbacker Thomas A
Belleville HS
Belleville WI

Sargent Barbara A
Tuscola HS
Tuscola IL

Sargent Patricia A
Ransom HS
Ransom KS

Sargent Patrick C
Kapaun Mt Carmel HS
Wichita KS

Sarno Angela M
Proviso East HS
Melrose Park IL

Saroch Emil E
Rolla HS
Rolla MO

Sarokin Steven
Pontiac Central HS
Pontiac MI

Sartore Linda S
Marian Heights Academy
Evansville IN

Sarussi Julianne V
Argo Comm HS
Bridgeview IL

Sarver Janice E
Griggsville HS
Griggsville IL

Sash Bette J
Maplewood Academy
Brownsdale MN

Sass Mary B
Woodland HS
Ancona IL

Sass Michael A
Downers Grove Comm HS
Downers Grove IL

Sassen Ruth E
Grand Island Sr HS
Grand Island NE

Sather Kent P
Madison HS
Madison MN

Satinoff Abbey L
Highland Park HS
Highland Park IL

Satko Cynthia R
Prospect HS
Arlington Hts IL

Satterfield Kevin K
Olympia HS
Mc Lean IL

Sattler Gail A
Menasha HS
Menasha WI

Saucedo Anita C
Holland Senior HS
Holland MI

Sauer Bruce W
Fulda Jr Sr HS
Fulda MN

Saukstelis Laura L
Maria HS
Chicago IL

Saunders Gwendolyn J
Edgerton Sr HS
Edgerton WI

Saunders Kathy J
St Xaviers HS
Junction City KS

Saunders Philip G
South Shelby HS
Shelbina MO

Saure Brad S
Amery HS
Amery WI

Savage Brenda R
Le Sueur HS
Le Sueur MN

Savage Kent W
Carrollton Comm Unit HS
Eldred IL

Savage Robert J
Bishop Owenger HS
Ft Wayne IN

Saville Janelle L
Braddock Public HS
Moffit ND

Sawer Deanna J
Owosso HS
Henderson MI

Sawin Scott M
Washington HS
Washington KS

Sawyer Charles G
Desoto HS
Shawnee KS

Sawyer Michael L
St Laurence HS
Chicago IL

Sawyer Michael W
Clarkston HS
Clarkston MI

Saxe Kenneth D
Edwards Co HS
Albion IL

Sayers Rhonda C
Coleman HS
Coleman MI

Sayler Jeanice A
Tripp Public HS
Tripp SD

Sayler Todd P
Beulah HS
Beulah ND

Sayre Christie A
Durand Area HS
Durand MI

Scaborn Cynthia D
Ottawa Township HS
Ottawa IL

Scaffidi Anthony P
St Johns Cathedral HS
Milwaukee WI

Scaletta Marilee
Prospect Hs
Mt Prospect IL

Scalf Linda J
Lewistown Community HS
Lewistown IL

Scalise Catherine A
Queen Of Peace HS
Chicago IL

Scamahorn Ellen B
South Spencer HS
Rockport IN

Scanlan Joli F
Williston HS
Epping ND

Scanlan Mark K
Abilene HS
Abilene KS

Scanlon Bruce A
Cheasning HS
Allan Rd MI

Scarborough Shayla S
Valley HS
West Des Moines IA

Scates Geron D
Civic Memorial HS
Bethalto IL

Scering Julee D
Covington HS
Covington IN

Schaack Bonnie V
Grace City HS
Grace City ND

Schaack Laura
Sykeston HS
Sykeston ND

Schaaf Keith A
Mc Bain Public HS
Mc Bain MI

Schaaf Mark H
Sidney Comm HS
Randolph IA

Schaben Larry J
Harlan Comm HS
Panama IA

Schacher Thomas E
Brandon HS
Ortonville MI

Schacht Vivian L
Kewaskum HS
West Bend WI

Schadewalt Heidi K
Darlington HS
Argyle WI

Schaefer Cynthia A
Mater Dei HS
Albers IL

Schaefer Gregory L
Arcadia HS
Arcadia WI

Schaefer Randy J
Ann A Jonesboro C HS
Jonesboro IL

Schaefer Richard N
Milbank HS
Twin Brooks SD

Schaefer Rick R
Anna Jonesboro HS
Jonesboro IL

Schaefer Susan L
Holly Senior HS
Fenton MI

Schaefer Virginia G
Newberry HS
Mcmillan MI

Schaetz Naomi A
Brookfield Central HS
Brookfield WI

Schafer Diane M
Bath HS
Dewitt MI

Schafer Lisa S
Lutheran HS
Mayer MN

Schafer Nickie A
Dickinson HS
Dickinson ND

Schafer Veronica S
Gothenburg HS
Gothenburg NE

Schaffer Jacqueline A
Homewood Flossmoor HS
Flossmoor IL

Schaffer Karen M
Heron Lake Public HS
Heron Lake MN

Schaller James R
Logan Sr HS
La Crosse WI

Schamber Joanne M
Kent City HS
Casnovia MI

Schamens David W
O Fallon Twp HS
O Fallon IL

Scharf Antoinette L
Gregory Sr HS
Gregory SD.

Scharf Gary E
Medicine Valley HS
Curtis NE

Scharlau Vicky L
Arcadia HS
Independence WI

Scharnowske Jeffery D
River Valley HS
Sawyer MI

Scharnowske Lyle J
Highland HS
Anderson IN

Scharp Dennis L
Shenandoah HS
Shenandoah IA

Scharrer Alan J
Slinger HS
Allenton WI

Schartz Jan M
Larned Sr HS
Larned KS

Schatz Dinah L
Marian Heights Acad
St Meinrad IN

Schaubert Penney L
Rowdon Public HS
Rowdon ND

Scheen Delynn J
Alpena HS
Lachine MI

Scheeres David E
G P South HS
Grosse Pte Farms MI

Schefdore Lynn M
Oconto Falls HS
Stiles WI

Scheffler Kenneth J
Gabriel Richard HS
Trenton MI

Scheid Douglas K
Frankfort HS
Frankfort IN

Scheid Kenneth J
Belding Central HS
Belding MI

Scheidler Mary Ann R
Academy Of The
Immaculate Con
Greensburg IN

Schelhaas Marsha J
Edgerton Public HS
Edgerton MN

Schell Jayne M
Blair Oaks HS
Jefferson City MO

Schell Linda L
Lewiston HS
Minneiska MN

Schellhas Julie A
Frankenmuth HS
Vassar MI

Schenck Gordon L
Algona HS
Algona IA

Schenk Diane R
Windom Area HS
Windom MN

Schenk Mark G
Thomas More Prep HS
Olmitz KS

Scheppler Jill I
Ankeny Senior HS
Ankeny IA

Scherer Gary W
University HS
Centerview MO

Scherer Pamela S
Holly Senior HS
Holly MI

Scherer Peter A
Lakeview Sr HS
Battle Creek MI

Scheri Susan M
La Salle Peru Twn HS
Oglesby IL

Scherr David A
Cardinal Muench Seminary
Napoleon ND

Scherrer Donald H
Salem Central HS
New Munster WI

Scherrer Maureen L
Highland Comm HS
Riverside IA

Scherschel Sharon L
Mitchell HS
Mitchell IN

Schertz Nancy L
Wheaton Warrenville HS
Wheaton IL

Schettler Robert N
Iron Mountain HS
Iron Mountain MI

Scheuern Mark G
Clarkston HS
Clarkston MI

Schewe Kevin L
Riverview Gardens HS
St Louis MO

Schieber Judith A
Eureka HS
Eureka IL

Schieber Paul W
Maryville HS
Maryville MO

Schieberl Jeffrey S
Bettendorf HS
Bettendorf IA

Schield Gregory R
Merrill Sr HS
Merrill WI

Schierenbeck Paul R
Fox Valley Lutheran HS
New London WI

Schiess Janis A
Stockton HS
Stockton IL

Schiess Sandra K
Hickman HS
Columbia MO

Schiffelbein Eric A
Lakin HS
Lakin KS

Schild Becky K
Quincy Sr Ii HS
Quincy IL

Schiley Debora J
Holdredge Sr HS
Holdrege NE

Schill Linda G
Crothersville HS
Crothersville IN

Schilleman Mark D
East Troy HS
Waterford WI

Schilz Michael T
Muskego HS
Hales Corners WI

Schilz Robert J
Oconomowoc HS
Oconomowoc WI

Schimweg Mark
Duchesne HS
St Charles MO

Schipull Larry D
Boone Valley Comm HS
Renwick IA

Schlanger Joseph W
Maine North HS
Glenview IL

Schlatt Debra A
Mexico HS
Mexico MO

Schlatten Tim W
Waco HS
Wayland IA

Schleicher Allen A
Plattsmouth HS
Plattsmouth NE

Schleicher Carol J
Central HS
St Joseph MO

Schleiermacher Kathy L
Marion County R 2 HS
Ewing MO

Schlemmer Michael J
West Noble HS
Ligonier IN

Schlenker Kathryn G
Forbes Public HS
Forbes ND

Schlensker Christine
Central HS
Evansville IN

Schlesinger Keith R
Cranbrook Boys HS
Bloomfield Hls MI

Schley Jacqueline A
Brainerd HS
Brainerd MN

Schlichter George J
Bremen HS
Midlothian IL

Schlichting Deborah A
Sauk Centre Sr HS
Sauk Centre MN

Schlientz Debbie R
Stapleton Public HS
Stapleton NE

Schliewe Darlene H
Lakeside Lutheran HS
Beaver Dam WI

Schlosser Francine L
Braddock Public HS
Braddock ND

Schluter Kathy A
Dongola Unit HS
Dongola IL

Schluttenhofer Linda L
Benton Central HS
Earl Park IN

Schmadeke Rochelle J
Prairie Community HS
Callender IA

Schmalfeldt Joseph G
Center HS
Center ND

Schmaling Joyce E
Delavan Darien HS
Delavan WI

Schmalz Kathy A
Immaculate Heart Of Mary HS
Cicero IL

Schmalz Michael J
John Marshall Jr Sr H
Milwaukee WI

Schmeichel Joan M
Freeman Public HS
Freeman SD

Schmelter Philip A
Lowell Sr HS
Lowell IN

Schmid Joyce A
Fairbury Cropsey HS
Chenoa IL

Schmid Roland D
St James HS
St James MN

Schmidgall Dawn E
Hancock Public HS
Hancock MN

Schmidt Cheryl L
South Sioux HS
South Sioux City NE

Schmidt Clynt R
Jr Reedsville HS
Buckley IL

Schmidt Connie L
Willow Lake Public HS
Willow Lake SD

Schmidt Curtis C
Rosemount HS
Apple Valley MN

Schmidt Danna K
Memorial HS
Joplin MO

Schmidt David A
Wausau East HS
Wausau WI

Schmidt Dennis J
Northwestern HS
Bennett WI

Schmidt Edward L
Evart HS
Evart MI

Schmidt James A
Thorp HS
Thorp WI

Schmidt Jeff P
Sleepy Eye Public HS
Sleepy Eye MN

Schmidt Jennifer L
Garner Hayfield HS
Garner IA

Schmidt Joann M
Columbus HS
Marshfield WI

Schmidt Joyce R
Buffalo Sr HS
Buffalo MN

Schmidt Julia L
Cardinal Ritter HS
Indianapolis IN

Schmidt Julie M
Forest Lake HS
Wyoming MN

Schmidt Lynden D
Farmington East HS
Elmwood IL

Schmidt Margaret K
A Hamilton HS
Milwaukee WI

Schmidt Mark E
Rapid City Central HS
Rapid City SD

Schmidt Marlene A
Gaylord Public HS
Gaylord MN

Schmidt Michael A
Pinckneyville Comm HS
Pinckneyville IL

Schmidt Nancy E
New Holstein HS
New Holstein WI

Schmidt Paula F
Sullivan HS
Sullivan MO

Schmidt Robert A
Cosmos Public HS
Cosmos MN

Schmidt Russell L
Chester Area HS
Chester SD

Schmidt Sandra D
New England Public HS
New England ND

Schmidt Sheryl I
Bennington HS
Bennington KS

Schmidt Shirley J
Dominican HS
Detroit MI

Schmidt Tammy L
Reese HS
Fairgrove MI

Schmidt Thomas A
Proviso East HS
Maywood IL

Schmidtberger John F
Victoria HS
Victoria KS

Schmieder Tom L
Albany HS
Brooklyn WI

Schmierbach Renee B
Belleville Twp West HS
Millstadt IL

Schmit Joanne R
Randolph Public HS
Randolph NE

Schmitke Kevin E
Chelsea HS
Chelsea MI

Schmitt David L
St Francis Borgia HS
Washington MO

Schmitt Kathy J
Mabel Canton HS
Mabel MN

Schmitt Mary J
Saydel HS
Des Moines IA

Schmitt Paula A
Chaffee HS
Chaffee MO

Schmittgens Eugene P
Rich East HS
Park Forest IL

Schmitz Dee A
F J Reitz HS
Evansville IN

Schmitz Lori A
New Holstein Sr HS
St Cloud WI

Schmitz Sandy G
Lake Central HS
Dyer IN

Schmoker David P
Mullen HS
Mullen NE

Schmolze Karen E
Glenbrook So HS
Glenview IL

Schmuck Craig A
Pipestone HS
Pipestone MN

Schmuhl Kathryn L
Coloma HS
Coloma MI

Schmutte Mary E
Cardinal Ritter HS
Indianapolis IN

Schmutzler Jane L
Watertown HS
Watertown WI

Schnarre Thomas D
Nakomis HS
Nakomis IL

Schneider Debora S
Jefferson City Sr HS
Jefferson City MO

Schneider Doug P
Southland HS
Taopi MN

Schneider Heidi A
Windom Area HS
Windom MN

Schneider John A
Cape Central HS
Cape Girardeau MO

Schneider Karen M
St Teresa HS
Decatur IL

Schneider Nancy A
Red Wing Central HS
Red Wing MN

Schneider Nicholas M
Appleton East HS
Appleton WI

Schneider Paul E
Bayard HS
Bayard NE

Schneider Raymond M
St Johns HS
St Johns MI

Schnirring Carolyn B
Springfield HS
Springfield IL

Schnur David C
Reitz Memorial HS
Evansville IN

Schnurpel Charles C
Brazil HS
Brazil IN

Schob Christine M
St Thomas Aquinas HS
Florissant MO

Schoeberl Anthony R
Rush City HS
Rush City MN

Schoeder Teresa E
St Marys HS
Reeper ND

Schoen Mary L
Derham Hall HS
St Paul MN

Schoenbein Gregory D
Abingdon Comm HS
Maquon IL

Schoendienst Eileen
St Joseph Academy
St Louis MO

Schoenholz Kim R
Bruning Public HS
Bruning NE

Schoenkin Marsha J
North HS
Sheboygan WI

Schoenknecht Alison L
Lincoln Sr HS
Wisconsin Rapids WI

Schoenthal Nadine L
Lake View Auburn HS
Lake View IA

Schoenwetter Alan R
Klemme Comm HS
Garner IA

Schoffmann Albert B
West Vigo HS
W Terre Haute IN

Schofield Annette
Wichita East HS
Wichita KS

Schol Nancy L
Northwood Public HS
Northwood ND

Scholl Mary Y
Healy HS
Pierz MN

Scholten Alan L
Armour HS
Armour SD

Scholten Debra M
East Kentwood HS
Kentwood MI

Scholtes Charles E
Ains HS
Ainsworth NE

Schomaker John B
Wesclin Sr HS
New Baden IL

Schone Brenda K
Bluffs HS
Bluffs IL

Schone Craig W
Triopia HS
Chapin IL

Schoneboom Bruce A
Ash Grove HS
Bois D Are MO

Schonhorst Roger D
North Polk HS
Slater IA

Schoob Kathleen L
Joliet Central HS
Joliet IL

Schooley Teresa L
Bluffton HS
Bluffton IN

Schoon Kelvin K
Pocahontas Comm HS
Pocahontas IA

Schoonover Jeffrey D
Wood Memorial HS
Oakland City IN

Schoop Christine L
Taft HS
Chicago IL

Schoop Lori J
Rockwell City Community HS
Rockwell City IA

Schorr Teresa A
Raytown HS
Kansas City MO

Schorzman Danny D
Haigler Public Dist 7 A HS
Haigler NE

Schott Robert J
Gull Lake HS
Richland MI

Schotthofer Stephen M
Illinois Valley Central HS
Chillicothe IL

Schrader George E
Centreville HS
Centreville MI

Schraeder Renee R
Jetmore HS
Jetmore KS

Schrag Connie F
Moundridge HS
Moundridge KS

Schrage John L
St Laurence HS
Chicago IL

Schrank Michael J
Brookville HS
Brookville IN

Schrank Randy D
Webb HS
Loganville WI

Schrank William A
Naperville Central HS
Naperville IL

Schranz Thomas J
Northside HS
Muncie IN

Schreffler Rita M
Ravanna R 4 Public HS
Mercer MO

Schreiber Karen
Campbell Tintah HS
Campbell MN

Schreiman Nancy A
Santa Fe HS
Waverly MO

Schreiner Laura E
Larned Senior HS
Larned KS

Schreiner Susannah J
Shelbyville HS
Shelbyville IN

Schritter Neil H
Goodland HS
Kanorado KS

Schrock Deirdre A
Central Cass HS
Casselton ND

Schrock Lu Ann K
Metamora Township HS
Metamora IL

Schrock Rhonda R
Lakeland HS
Wolcottville IN

Schroder Nathaniel L
Moorhead HS
Moorhead MN

Schroder Phyllis A
Marshall HS
Marshall MI

Schroder Susan K
Warsaw HS
Warsaw MO

Schrodt Joseph K
St Thomas Aquinas HS
Berkeley MO

Schroeckenthaler Todd A
Wisconsin Academy
Sussex WI

Schroeder Debra E
Alma HS
Alma WI

Schroeder James W
Bellflower Twp HS
Bellflower IL

Schroeder Jane D
Harlan Comm HS
Harlan IA

Schroeder Janice K
Effingham HS
Effingham IL

Schroeder Jeffrey C
Bridgeport HS
Saginaw MI

Schroeder Linda L
Leo HS
Holy Cross IA

Schroeder Michael R
Altoona Public HS
Altoona WI

Schroeder Rusty W
Tipton HS
Tipton IA

Schroeder Shari J
Valley Center HS
Valley Center KS

Schroepfer Beth A
St Marys HS
Sleepy Eye MN

Schroer Michael S
Pattonville HS
Bridgeton MO

Schroff Karen J
Glendale HS
Springfield MO

Schrowang Brian L
Putnam Co HS
Granville IL

Schuch Arlene K
Tyndall HS
Tyndall SD

Schuch Debra A
Southridge HS
Huntingburg IN

Schuchard Bruce G
Naperville Central HS
Naperville IL

Schuele Cathy A
Mount Acad
Atchison KS

Schuelke Susan L
Murdock Cons HS
Alvo NE

Schuette Alice J
Civic Memorial HS
Bethalto IL

Schuette David T
St Anthony HS
Effingham IL

Schuette Jeffrey S
Central HS
Flint MI

Schuetz Evelyne G
Duchesne HS
St Charles MO

Schuetz Lois C
Hays HS
Catherine KS

Schuh Mervin K
Edwards County Sr HS
Albion IL

Schuld Diane M
Ursuline Academy
St Louis MO

Schuldt James T
Dundee Comm HS
Carpentersville IL

Schulist Diana L
Whitefish Bay HS
Whitefish Bay WI

Schult Cynthia J
Iowa Grant HS
Montfort WI

Schulta Linda S
Grundy Center Comm HS
Grundy Center IA

Schulte Charles J
Mc Cluer North HS
Florissant MO

Schulte Claudia A
Notre Dame HS
Quincy IL

Schulte Paul R
So Spencer HS
Rockport IN

Schulte Robert J
Creighton Preparatory HS
Omaha NE

Schultheis Angela M
Reitz Memorial HS
Evansville IN

Schultz Audrey M
Wonewoc Center HS
Wonewoc WI

Schultz Becky L
Williston HS
Williston ND

Schultz Cathy S
Pekin Comm HS
Ollie IA

Schultz Cynthia A
Sioux Rapids Comm HS
Sioux Rapids IA

Schultz Deborah A
Watervliet HS
Watervliet MI

Schultz Diane V
Wadena Sr HS
Wadena MN

Schultz Donald F
Joliet Catholic HS
Lockport IL

Schultz James R
Dundee HS
Carpentersville IL

Schultz Karen B
Thornwood HS
So Holland IL

Schultz Keith L
Mendota HS
Compton IL

Schultz Kenneth E
Burligton HS
Burlington KS

Schultz Linda C
Sts Peter & Paul Area HS
Saginaw MI

Schultz Margaret A
Macksville HS
Haviland KS

Schultz Neil T
Harvard Unit Dist 50 HS
Harvard IL

Schultz Roger R
St Croix Central HS
Roberts WI

Schultz Russell R
Northland HS
Remer MN

Schultz Scott A
Fenwick HS
Melrose Park IL

Schultze June K
Ceylon Public HS
Fairmont MN

Schulz Christine R
New Buffalo HS
New Buffalo MI

Schulz Geralyn M
Alvernia HS
Chicago IL

Schulz Joann L
Muskego HS
Muskego WI

Schulz Steven A
West Point Public HS
Beemer NE

Schulz William C
Loyola Academy
Niles IL

Schum Patricia L
Heritage Hills HS
Dale IN

Schumacher Cindy K
Arthur Hill HS
Saginaw MI

Schumacher Debora R
Garrigan HS
Whittemore IA

Schumacher Julia A
Elk Mound HS
Elk Mound WI

Schumacher Kathleen M
Beresford Independent HS
Beresford SD

Schumacher Kent J
Hempstead HS
Dubuque IA

Schumacher Pamela R
Lacrescent Jr Sr HS
Lacrescent MN

Schumacher Robert G
Downers Grove S HS
Downers Grove IL

Schumacher William G
Wautoma HS
Wautoma WI

Schumaker Lisa A
West Catholic HS
Grand Rapids MI

Schumaker Susan E
Lakeview HS
Decatur IL

Schuman Johanna D
Tinley Park HS
Tinley Park IL

Schumann Jennie M
Wisconsin Heights HS
Mazomanie WI

Schumann Kevin P
Merrill HS
Brainerd MN

Schumann Lori J
Fonda Comm HS
Albert City IA

Schuneman Mary C
Bradford HS
Bradford IL

Schunter Nancy J
Central Community HS
Dewitt IA

Schureman Jean A
Morton HS
Morton IL

Schurtter Joyce A
Edgewood HS
Bloomington IN

Schussler Craig A
Libertyville HS
Mundelein IL

Schussler Kay F
Deepwater HS
Deepwater MO

Schuster James N
Willow City Public HS
Willow City ND

Schuster Janet F
Immaculate Heart Of Mary HS
Westchester IL

Schutte Michelle M
Onsted Community HS
Adrian MI

Schwab Christine A
Potosi HS
Potosi WI

Schwab Connie J
Vassar HS
Vassar MI

Schwab Debra A
Rockford HS
Rudd IA

Schwab Elaine M
Ionia HS
Lyons MI

Schwab Eliazbeth
Holy Redeemer HS
Detroit MI

Schwab Gregory M
Mandan Sr HS
Mandan ND

Schwab Joseph J
Potosi HS
Potosi WI

STUDENTS PHOTOGRAPH SCHEDULED FOR PUBLICATION HERE COULD NOT BE REPRODUCED

Schwalb Laurie K
Marissa HS
Marissa IL

Schwarm Russell S
Brownstown Comm HS
Loogootee IL

Schwartz Constance M
Blue Valley HS
Bucyrus KS

Schwartz Kara L
Kenmare Public HS
Kenmare ND

Schwartz Lori J
Willmar Sr HS
Willmar MN

Schwartz Mary K
St Joseph Academy
Green Bay WI

Schwartz Nancy J
Marion HS
Marion SD

Schwartz Todd E
Pringhar Comm HS
Pringhar IA

Schwartzkopf Lee A
Ness City HS
Ness City KS

Schwarz Karen E
Mother Of Sorrows HS
Blue Island IL

Schwarz Katherine M
Ford Central HS
Roberts IL

Schwarz Kevin H
Woodbury HS
Moville IA

Schwehr Michael J
North Central Of Barnes HS
Sanborn ND

Schweikart Joan M
Homewood Flossmoor HS
Homewood IL

Schweikl Jay J
Columbus HS
Marshfield WI

Schweikl Scott M
Columbus HS
Marshfield WI

Schweinebart Teresa I
Baxter Community HS
Baxter IA

Schweitzer Rod R
Poplar Bluff HS
Poplar Bluff MO

Schwenke Roy A
Cumberland & Massena Comm HS
Massena IA

Schwerha Kristin D
Elkhart Central HS
Elkhart IN

Schwindt Cynthia E
Salina Central HS
Salina KS

Schwoch Terri L
Merrill HS
Merrill WI

Schymanski John J
Washington HS
South Bend IN

Sciacero Mark L
Clark HS
Hammond IN

Sciortino Rosellen
Villa Duchesne HS
St Louis MO

Scoggin Tamara R
Highland HS
Labelle MO

Scoggins Helen D
Greenfield HS
Greenfield IL

Scott Barbara J
Kirksville HS
Greentop MO

Scott Becky J
Three Rivers HS
Three Rivers MI

Scott Bradley L
Chaska HS
Exc MN

Scott Brian A
Appleton West HS
Appleton WI

Scott Brian D
Streator Twp HS
Streator IL

Scott Brian K
Mt Vernon HS
Mt Vernon MO

Scott Colby N
Hillsboro Sr HS
De Soto MO

Scott Denise K
U S D 399 Natoma HS
Waldo KS

Scott Eugene F
Lakeshore HS
Stevensville MI

Scott Gary W
Muscatine HS
Muscatine IA

Scott Gregg E
Brownstown Central HS
Brownstown IN

Scott Henry A
Collinsville HS
Collinsville IL

Scott Jean L
Lake View Auburn HS
Lake View IA

Scott John D
Pioneer HS
Logansport IN

Scott Judson R
Brebeuf Prep HS
Indianapolis IN

Scott Michael D
Carrollton HS
Carrollton MO

Scott Michael R
Plainfield HS
Joliet IL

Scott Pamela S
East Charles Mix #102 HS
Wagner SD

Scott Peggy S
Batavia HS
Batavia IL

Scott Quintin D
East Richland HS
Olney IL

Scott Rebecca K
Pleasant Hill HS
Pleasant Hill IL

Scott Steven M
Lindblom Tech HS
Chicago IL

Scott Vernon L
East Prairie HS
East Prairie MO

Scovel Susan E
Derby Sr HS
Wichita KS

Scranton Eula G
J D Darnall HS
Geneseo IL

Scripsick Mark A
Burlington HS
Kiowa KS

Scroggin Doreen K
Rockwell City HS
Rockwell City IA

Sculley Vida R
Badger HS
Lake Geneva WI

Seabaugh Kimberly A
Woodland HS
Lutesville MO

Seaburg David L
Dilworth Public HS
Dilworth MN

Seal James F
Clearwater R 1 HS
Piedmont MO

Seal John D
Anderson HS
Anderson IN

Seal Kenneth H
Barr Reeve HS
Cannelburg IN

Searcy Esther D
Kirksville Sr HS
Kirksville MO

Searles Mark N
Avon HS
Indianapolis IN

Sears Becky L
Garden County HS
Lisco NE

Sears Penny L
Southwest Ri HS
Utica MO

Sears Trudy A
Atkinson HS
Atkinson IL

Seaton Nancy R
La Salle Peru Twp HS
La Salle IL

Seaverson Wanda L
Chicago Vocational HS
Chicago IL

Seay George A
Excelsior Springs HS
Excelsior Springs MO

Seay John W
Community R 6 HS
Benton City MO

Sebacher Susan L
Duchesne HS
St Charles MO

Sebby Steven D
Sandwich HS
Sandwich IL

Seddon Judy A
Hartford HS
Hartford MI

Sedlacek Jerry J
Hanover HS
Hanover KS

See Charlotte M
Our Lady Of Lourdes HS
Chicago IL

See William C
Knox County HS
Rutledge MO

Seeba Kris L
Nemaha Valley HS
Cook NE

Seeger Joyce A
Hill City HS
Hill City KS

Seehafer Julie J
Columbus HS
Marshfield WI

Seehausen Dirk V
W Rockford HS
Rockford IL

Seelman Richard L
North Clay Comm HS
Louisville IL

Seelye Margaret S
Pekin Comm HS
Pekin IL

Seever Linda L
Oak Park HS
Gladstone MO

Seevers Boyd V
Oneill Public HS
Oneill NE

Segebart Steve E
Northwest Webster HS
Clare IA

Seger John M
Lakeview Auburn HS
Lakeview IA

Segert Sandra L
Crete Monee HS
Crete IL

Segovia Jimmy
Saginaw HS
Saginaw MI

Segoviano Fernando
Holy Cross HS
Chicago IL

Segriff James D
Washington HS
Cedar Rapids IA

Seib Larry R
Gibson Southern HS
Fort Branch IN

Seib Ronald W
Metamora Twp HS
East Peoria IL

Seibert Julie A
Clinton Comm HS
Clinton IL

Seibert Melanie K
Mt Vernon Senior HS
Mt Vernon IN

Seidel Cheryl P
Jefferson City Sr HS
Lohman MO

Seidel Karen A
John F Kennedy HS
Chicago IL

Seifert Cheryl L
Amos Alonzo Stagg HS
Hickory Hills IL

Seijas Laura M
Southwestern HS
Flint MI

Seils Cynthia A
Hanover Central HS
Dyer IN

Seistrup Chris T
Mendota Township HS
Mendota IL

Seitz Michael E
Bellmont HS
Decatur IN

Seiwald Clair L
Tonganoxie HS
Lawrence KS

Self Charles H
Alexander Ramsey HS
Roseville MN

Sell Michelle K
Burlington HS
Middletown IA

Sell Sandra L
Weeping Water HS
Weeping Water NE

Sell Walter E
Pioneer HS
Royal Center IN

Selland Mark A
Magic City Campus HS
Minot ND

Sellars Renee D
Cobden Community HS
Cobden IL

Sellhorn Mary D
Tecumseh Public HS
Tecumseh NE

Sellin Kathleen A
Waupaca HS
Waupaca WI

Sellman James C
Metamora Township HS
Metamora IL

Seltzer Ann M
Goodrich HS
Grand Blanc MI

Selves Sharon K
Granton Public HS
Granton WI

Selzer Jerry D
Schuyler Central HS
Schuyler NE

Semeniuk Camille G
Homewood Flossmoor HS
Flossmoor IL

Sempert Bekki S
St Joseph Sr HS
St Joseph MI

Semple Paul E
Newton HS
West Liberty IL

Semrau Barbara A
Marinette Sr HS
Marinette WI

Senart Michael E
Romulus HS
Romulus MI

Seng Daniel P
South Milwaukee HS
South Milwaukee WI

Senger Bonita I
Anamoose HS
Orrin ND

Sengstock Paul W
Bloom Township HS
Steger IL

Seniuta Orest S
Gordon Tech HS
Chicago IL

Senka Elizabeth A
Kennedy St Paul HS
Chicago IL

Senn Teresa M
Valley Falls HS
Valley Falls KS

Senneff Rosemary E
Thomson HS
Mt Carroll IL

Sensenbaugh Sue E
Kingsley HS
Kingsley MI

Sension Mark S
Elmwood HS
Elmwood WI

Senter Denise A
Crispus Attucks HS
Indianapolis IN

Seppala Bryan R
Stewartville HS
Stewartsville MN

Seprodi John A
Schulte HS
Terre Haute IN

Seprodi Mary K
Schulte HS
Terre Haute IN

Sera Arleen K
Lake View HS
Chicago IL

Serban Daniel E
St Josephs HS
S Bend IN

Serrano Joaquin P
La Crosse HS
La Crosse KS

Sersch Randall F
Black Hawk HS
Apple River IL

Sershen Daniel J
North HS
Fargo ND

Serva Raylene M
Lourdes HS
Chicago IL

Servais Stephen B
Union HS
Franksville WI

Servent Kim
Three Lakes HS
Rhinelander WI

Servine Beverly D
Emerson Hubbard HS
Waterbury NE

Sessions Charles E
Farmer City Mansfield HS
Farmer City IL

Sesterhenn Steven E
Libertyville HS
Libertyville IL

Sesvold Ann L
Central HS
La Crosse WI

Sesvold Karen E
Central HS
La Crosse WI

Seten Kelli J
Mahomet Seymour HS
Mahomet IL

Setina Sally S
Joliet West HS
Joliet IL

Seufert Sheila M
Forest Park HS
Ferdinand IN

Seufferlein Paul W
West View HS
Lake City IA

Sevart Carol M
Kapaun Mt Carmel HS
Wichita KS

Sevcik James J
Fullerton HS
Fullerton NE

Sever Sheryl R
Lasalle Peru Twp HS
Peru IL

Severe Kurt A
West Chicago Comm HS
W Chicago IL

Severson Douglas J
East Monona HS
Soldier IA

Severson Tanna K
Argyle HS
Argyle WI

Seward Gregory S
Hillsboro HS
Butler IL

Sewell Cynthia F
Corunna HS
Vernon MI

Sexton Michael F
Rochester HS
Rochester IL

Seyller Michael C
Kewanee HS
Kewanee IL

Seymour Cheryl L
John Glenn HS
Westland MI

Seymour Julie A
Clinton HS
Clinton IL

Seymour Linda S
Athens HS
East Leroy MI

Seymour Terri L
Northwestern HS
Mellette SD

Shackelford James L
Castle HS
Newburgh IN

Shafer Daniel L
North Greene HS
Hillview IL

Shafer Frank E
Saint Edmond HS
Fort Dodge IA

Shafer Melissa A
Fairfield HS
Fairfield IA

Shafer Vivian C
Chippewa Falls Sr HS
Jim Falls WI

Shaffer Carol J
Shelbyville HS
Shelbyville IL

Shaffer George F
West Washington HS
Milltown IN

Shaffer Rebecca J
Nevada HS
Nevada MO

Shaffer Richard S
Camden Frontier HS
Hillsdale MI

Shaffer Terina K
Junction City Sr HS
Junction City KS

Shaffer William E
Central Of Burden HS
Atlanta KS

Shafranski Nancy A
Whitefish Bay HS
Milwaukee WI

Shagene Beth A
Cass City HS
Cass City MI

Shahin Ric P
Midland HS
Midland MI

Shalda Ann M
Glen Lake HS
Empire MI

Shallow Laura
Mother Mc Auley HS
Chicago IL

Shambaugh Clarenda S
Cerro Gordo HS
Cerro Gordo IL

Shank Robin L
Carthage Sr HS
Carthage MO

Shanks Linda G
Wisconsin Dells HS
Lake Delton WI

Shanks Marcia J
Villa Grove HS
Villa Grove IL

Shanks Phillip J
Brazil Senior HS
Brazil IN

Shanle Jean E
Lincoln Community HS
Lincoln IL

Shannon Mary Jo
West Ottawa HS
Holland MI

Shannon Pamela
Englewood HS
Chicago IL

Shannon Sean J
Mauston Area HS
Mauston WI

Shannon Sherry M
Freeburg Comm HS
Freeburg IL

Shapland Janice M
Dighton HS
Shields KS

Shappell Kim E
Wabash HS
Wabash IN

Sharkey Robert R
Westhope HS
Westhope ND

Sharman Gary W
Sidney HS
Sidney NE

Sharp Mary A
Lasalle Peru HS
La Salle IL

Sharp Mary J
Troy HS
Troy MO

Sharp Samuel R
Dixon HS
Dixon MO

Sharp Susan E
Nebraska City Sr HS
Nebraska City NE

Sharpe Kathleen M
La Salle Peru HS
Oglesby IL

Sharpe Margaret D
Columbus North HS
Taylorsville IN

Shatek Ann B
Turkey Valley HS
Fort Atkinson IA

Shatzer Dale M
Jesup Comm HS
Jesup IA

Shaughnessy Rita A
Lumen Christi HS
Jackson MI

Shaul Kevin W
Ainsworth HS
Ainsworth NE

Shaw Joel L
Oskaloosa Sr HS
Oskaloosa IA

Shaw Jon R
Abraham Lincoln HS
Council Bluffs IA

Shaw Karla J
Johnston City HS
Johnston City IL

Shaw Kevin J
St Marys Springs HS
Fond Du Lac WI

Shaw Kim L
Guide Rock HS
Guide Rock NE

Shaw Larry R
Roseland Public HS
Roseland NE

Shaw Penny E
Ashley HS
Ashley MI

Shay Clifton
St Bede Academy
Chicago IL

Shay Denise E
Winfield HS
Winfield KS

Shay Joy R
New Ulm Senior HS
New Ulm MN

Shea Patricia A
Knoxville HS
Knoxville IL

Shea William J
Sacred Heart HS
Salina KS

Shear John K
Columbia Central HS
Brooklyn MI

Shearer Arnold D
Macon Co R 1 HS
Excello MO

Shearrer Susan C
Normandy HS
St Louis MO

Shedelbower Patricia
Washington Catholic HS
Washington IN

Sheets Carol A
Lewistown Comm HS
Lewistown IL

Sheets Karen C
Illiopolis Com HS
Illiopolis IL

Shefcik Barbara S
St Paul John F Kennedy HS
Chicago IL

Shehi Darlene R
Luckey HS
Manhattan KS

Shekleton Maureen
Richwoods HS
Peoria IL

Shelburne Mark R
Zionsville Comm HS
Zionsville IN

Shelby Melissa K
Edwards County Sr HS
West Salem IL

Sheldon Kevin A
Lane Tech HS
Chicago IL

Shelley Kenneth W
Breckenridge Jr Sr HS
Breckenridge MI

Shelquist Marilyn L
Moravia Community HS
Moravia IA

Shelton Deborah R
Anna Jonesboro C HS
Anna IL

Shelton John B
New Bloomfield HS
New Bloomfield MO

Shelton John C
Huron HS
Ann Arbor MI

Shelton Kris A
Richland Center HS
Richland Center WI

Sheneman Nancy J
North Liberty HS
North Liberty IN

Shepanik Robert L
D C Everest HS
Schofield WI

Shepherd Douglas A
Harrisburg HS
Harrisburg IL

Shepherd James D
Hillcrest HS
Country Club Hills IL

Shepherd Judith L
West Chicago Community HS
West Chicago IL

Shepherd Nancy S
Central Catholic HS
Bloomington IL

Sherburn Cynthia J
Berrien Springs HS
Berrien Center MI

Sheridan Patricia A
Joliet West HS
Joliet IL

Sheridan Philip E
Merrill HS
Merrill MI

Sheridan Teresa A
Jayhawk Linn HS
Mound KS

Sherlock Dennis E
Hemingford HS
Hemingford NE

Sherlock E Todd
St Francis Comm HS
St Francis KS

Sherman Kathy C
Boone Grove HS
Valparaiso IN

Sherman Mark J
Carthage HS
Carthage IL

Sherman Timothy V
Mt Carmel HS
Mt Carmel IL

Sherrell Carla J
Crispus Attucks HS
Indianapolis IN

Sherrill Donald A
Poplar Bluff Sr HS
Poplar Bluff MO

Sherrod Carmen L
Arlington HS
Indianapolis IN

Sherwin Rhonda J
Ness City HS
Beeler KS

Sherwood Carol A
Shelbyville HS
Shelbyville IL

Sherwood Leslie M
Mobridge HS
Mc Laughlin SD

Shetley Kevin L
Riverton HS
Galena KS

Shewan Eleanore J
Valparaiso HS
Valparaiso IN

Shide Georgiann
South Newton HS
Brook IN

Shields Sally J
Springs Valley HS
West Baden IN

Shields Shonda W
Cathedral HS
Chicago IL

Shields Susan M
Wahlert HS
Dubuque IA

Shiever Alan R
Coloma HS
Coloma MI

Shilling Robert W
Thornton Township HS
Riverdale IL

Shillington Thomas P
Clarion Community HS
Clarion IA

Shilt Anne D
Appleton West HS
Appleton WI

Shilt Jean M
Plymouth HS
Plymouth IN

Shimon Alan J
Pocahontas Community HS
Pocahontas IA

Shippen Larry J
Friend Public HS
Friend NE

Shirley Mark D
Maywood HS
Maywood NE

Shirley Michael H
Evanston Township HS
Evanston IL

Shirley Nancy J
South Side HS
Fort Wayne IN

Shirley Valoree L
Perry Community HS
Perry IA

Shivers Douglas R
Richland HS
Richland MO

Shives Aaron B
Milbank HS
Milbank SD

Shobe Alan W
Brainerd HS
Brainerd MN

Shobe Georgia A
Hannibal Sr HS
Hannibal MO

Shoberg David J
Kenyon HS
Kenyon MN

Shoemaker Anne L
Dakota HS
Dakota IL

Shoemaker Deborah K
Carroll HS
Bringhurst IN

Shoemaker Kimberly A
Vienna HS
Vienna IL

Shoemaker Robert J
Winner Sr HS
Winner SD

Shoenhair Karla A
Martensdale St Marys HS
Prole IA

Shofroth Robert C
Hammond Baptist HS
St John IN

Shoger Gordon L
Princeton HS
Princeton MO

Shonkwiler Cindy K
Arcola HS
Arcola IL

Shook Sara L
Lake Orion HS
Lake Orion MI

Shope John C
Barrington HS
Barrington IL

Shorb Dava L
Enfield HS
Enfield IL

Shorey Ken A
Rosemount Senior HS
Apple Valley MN

Short Jay M
Randolph Southern HS
Lynn IN

Short Kenneth L
Crispus Attucks HS
Indianapolis IN

Short Kevin L
Crispus Attucks HS
Indianapolis IN

Short Peggy S
Goodland HS
Goodland KS

Short Rick A
Farmer Cy Mansfield HS
Farmer City IL

Shotton Vicki L
Franklin HS
Livonia MI

Shoukletovich Susan D
Marion HS
Marion IL

Shouse Mary A
North Vigo HS
Terre Haute IN

Showalter Anthony R
Barr Reeve HS
Montgomery IN

Showalter Buster C
Sherman Comm HS
Goodland KS

Showalter Lisa M
Barr Reeve HS
Montgomery IN

Shroba Louis L
Joliet Twp East HS
Joliet IL

Shrout Jeffrey L
Maysville HS
Maysville MO

Shroyer Douglas L
Twin Lakes HS
Monticello IN

Shue Terry W
Chaparral HS
Harper KS

Shufeldt Barbara A
Arlington HS
Arlington Hts IL

Shuk Barbara C
Stanley Boyd HS
Stanley WI

Shulaw Thomas D
Robinson HS
Robinson IL

Shull Tamara L
Effingham HS
Effingham IL

Shultz Mary A
Warsaw Sr HS
Warsaw IN

Shumard Jo A
Lumen Christi HS
Jackson MI

Shumski David J
East Chain HS
Fairmont MN

Shuster Robert E
Rensselaer Central HS
Brook IN

Shuya George B
Hammond HS
Hammond IN

Shymanski Henry J
Sacred Heart HS
Dearborn MI

Sibert Larry J
Superior HS
Superior NE

Sibery Douglas E
Wheaton Warrenville HS
Wheaton IL

Sichko Paul M
Senior HS
Albert Lea MN

Sickel Glenda L
Dist #56 Falls City HS
Falls City NE

Sickels David L
Grand Valley Community HS
Kellerton IA

Siddons Virginia E
St Mary Academy
Indianapolis IN

Sidney Paul J
De La Salle Institute
Chicago IL

Sidwell Bill
Tri HS
Straughn IN

Siebecker Steven L
Superior HS
Superior NE

Siebel Kerri L
Bennett Community HS
Bennett IA

Siebert Laura L
Lake Central HS
Schereville IN

Sieck Tony R
Goodland HS
Goodland KS

Siedhoff Janet L
Crete HS
Milford NE

Siefert Charles S
Du Quoin HS
Du Quoin IL

Siefert Lynn L
Oconto Falls HS
Oconto Falls WI

Sieg Jeff R
Larimore HS
Emerado ND

Siegert Lisa K
Grayville HS
Grayville IL

Siegler Mary L
Assumption HS
Wisconsin Rapids WI

Sieja Joanne
Weyerhaeuser Public HS
Weyerhaeuser WI

Siemaszke Konstanty B
St Ignatius College Prep HS
Chicago IL

Siemonsma Anna M
Baltic HS
Sioux Falls SD

Siemsen Linda G
Peotone HS
Peotone IL

STUDENTS PHOTOGRAPH SCHEDULED FOR PUBLICATION HERE COULD NOT BE REPRODUCED

Sieren Anita J
Tri County Comm HS
Keswick IA

Sietsema Jacqueline K
Danube Public HS
Danube MN

Sietsema Jeffrey M
Northwood Kensett HS
Northwood IA

Sievers Kurt W
Gridley Comm Unit 10 HS
Gridley IL

Sievers Lisa A
Avoha Community HS
Avoca IA

Sievert Kathleen L
Lakeside Lutheran HS
Fort Atkinson WI

Siewert Kari L
Gaylord HS
Gaylord MN

Siewert Kim M
Lake Michigan Catholic HS
Coloma MI

Siffermann Patricia M
Harillac HS
Des Plaines IL

Sifner Thomas A
Kennedy St Paul HS
Chicago IL

Sigg Julie L
Mona Shores HS
Muskegon MI

Sigler Andrew H
Barstow HS
Kansas City MO

Sigler John M
Lincoln HS
Cambridge City IN

Sigmon Larry A
Rock Island HS
Rock Island IL

Sigmund Michael A
Plainfield HS
Indianapolis IN

Signor David B
East Kentwood HS
Kentwood MI

Sigrist Jodi L
Brookfield East HS
Elm Grove WI

Sikora Corinne A
Dominican HS
Detroit MI

Silhavy Mark M
Alma HS
Alma MI

Silkman Karman J
Hettinger HS
Reeder ND

Sillars Tina M
D C Everest HS
Schofield WI

Silva Nanette M
Queen Of Peace HS
Chicago IL

Silverstein Rachel A
Niles West HS
Lincolnwood IL

Silverstrini Dino F
West Iron County HS
Iron River MI

Simanek Joseph M
St Catherines HS
Racine WI

Simenson Robert C
Chisago Lakes HS
Lindstrom MN

Simmelink Scott D
Lebanon HS
Lebanon KS

Simmerman Keri D
Elm Creek Public HS
Elm Creek NE

Simmert Robert L
Downers Grove So HS
Downers Grove IL

Simmet Mark A
Cathedral HS
New Ulm MN

Simmons Bradley M
Brother Rice HS
Birmingham MI

Simmons James J
Creston HS
Grand Rapids MI

Simmons Jan E
Maconaquah HS
Grissom Afb IN

Simmons Joan M
Highland HS
Highland IN

Simmons Kathy J
Mt Vernon Township HS
Mt Vernon IL

Simmons Linda A
Ben Davis HS
Indianapolis IN

Simmons Marilynn N
Sumner HS
St Louis MO

Simmons Mark E
Centerville HS
Centerville IA

Simmons Renald A
Saranac Comm HS
Saranac MI

Simmons Samuel G
Roosevelt HS
Gary IN

Simmons Sandra K
Duchesne HS
St Charles MO

Simmons Sheila J
Clarion Community HS
Clarion IA

Simmons Stacy S
Madison Heights HS
Anderson IN

Simms Jayne L
Plano HS
Plano IL

Simon Debra K
Cassville HS
Shell Knob MO

Simon John J
Precious Blood Seminary
Sedalia MO

Simon Joyce M
Calhoun HS
Hardin IL

Simon Linda M
Tecumseh Sr HS
Adrian MI

Simon Paul J
Creighton Prep HS
Omaha NE

Simon Philip F
Carbondale Comm HS
Carbondale IL

Simons Marjorie A
Bellevue HS
Bellevue NE

Simonson Glenda D
Tuttle Public HS
Arena ND

Simonson Sarah E
Hillsboro HS
Hillsboro KS

Simonson Steven D
Parkview HS
Orfordville WI

Simonson Wanda M
Taylor HS
Taylor WI

Simpson Annette E
O Fallon Township HS
O Fallon IL

Simpson Dari C
C U HS
Columbus KS

Simpson Dorice F
John Marshall Harlan HS
Chicago IL

Simpson Harold D
Mitchell HS
Mitchell NE

Simpson Mari L
Edsel Ford HS
Dearborn MI

Simpson Mark R
North HS
Evansville IN

Simpson Mary J
Columbus North HS
Columbus IN

Simpson Norma N
Marshall HS
Marshall IL

Simpson Steven Q
Hesston HS
Hesston KS

Simpson Terri L
South Spencer HS
Rockport IN

Sims Carol J
Cloverdale Comm HS
Cloverdale IN

Sims Debra J
Girard HS
Girard KS

Sims Demar
Lindblom Tech HS
Chicago IL

Sims Fred D
Whitfield HS
St Louis MO

Sims Gary R
Oak Park HS
Kansas City MO

Sims Rueben A
John Marshall Harlan HS
Chicago IL

Sims Sondra W
St Thomas Apostle HS
Chicago IL

Sinclair Brad W
Jersey Comm HS
Jerseyville IL

Sinclair Renee T
Clarkston Sr HS
Clarkston MI

Sindelar Scott S
Richfield HS
Richfield MN

Sinden Sharon M
Eisenhower HS
Blue Island IL

Sindicich Ed J
Bishop Noll HS
East Chicago IN

Sinding Pamela M
Siren Consld HS
Siren WI

Sinecki Gary W
Duchesne HS
St Charles MO

Siner Mark S
Schulte HS
Terre Haute IN

Singco Judy A
Greenfield Central HS
Greenfield IN

Singiser Robert T
Warren Township HS
Gurnee IL

Singley Aylesa D
Broad Ripple HS
Indianapolis IN

Sinkey Debra J
Sheldon Comm HS
Ashton IA

Sinkfield Cecil G
Haworth HS
Kokomo IN

Sinn Jeanie K
Olympia HS
Delavan IL

Sinness Marilyn J
Minnewaukn Public HS
Minnewaukan ND

Sinnott Daniel J
St Francis Prep
Ann Arbor MI

Sinnott Jamie A
Belview Public HS
Redwood Falls MN

Sip James A
Bow Homme #96 HS
Tyndall SD

Sipple Margaret A
West Senior HS
Garden City MI

Sitasz John S
St Rita HS
Chicago IL

Sitlington James R
St Thomas HS
Ann Arbor MI

Siuba Kenneth E
St Francis De Sales HS
Chicago IL

Siuniak Louis G
Waterford Kettering HS
Drayton Plains MI

Sivils Cotton C
Bryant HS
Rich Hill MO

Sjostrand Faith R
E Grand Forks Sr HS
E Grand Forks MN

Skaar Cherry S
Central HS
Hayward MN

Skaggs Cydney R
Fredericktown Ri HS
Fredericktown MO

Skaggs Dennis F
Seneca HS
Seneca MO

Skaggs Jeffrey L
Crocker R Ii HS
Crocker MO

Skaggs Robert N
Franklin Central HS
Indianapolis IN

Skalitzky Elecia I
Platte County R Iii HS
Platte City MO

Skalka Karen L
Morton Sr HS
Hammond IN

Skalsky Rita
Beulah HS
Beulah ND

Skandera Margaret C
Glenbard West HS
Glen Ellyn IL

Skarie Mark K
Cardinal Muench Seminary HS
Balfour ND

Skau Chris T
Bishop Ward HS
Kansas City KS

Skeels Mark E
Hampshire HS
Hampshire IL

Skellenger Debra J
Orient Macksburg HS
Greenfield IA

Skelly Susan S
Beloit Catholic HS
Beloit WI

Skelton Pamela R
Eastern HS
Salem IN

Skertic Robert P
Morton HS
Hammond IN

Skibo Karen A
Forest Park HS
Alpha MI

Skibo Rebecca J
Benton Consolidated HS
Benton IL

Skiles Deidra D
Wellsville HS
Wellsville KS

Skillman Jeanne A
Morristown HS
Shelbyville IN

Skinner Joe R
Plano HS
Plano IL

Skinner Kim A
Bronson HS
Bronson MI

Skinner Patrick L
Hale HS
Hale MI

Skinner Russell D
Nokomis HS
Nokomis IL

STUDENTS PHOTOGRAPH SCHEDULED FOR PUBLICATION HERE COULD NOT BE REPRODUCED

Skinner Wendi L
West Harrison HS
Little Sioux IA

Skittone Serena M
Elk Grove HS
Elk Grove Village IL

Skjervheim Jack L
Nekoma Public HS
Alsen ND

Skocypec Russell D
Homewood Flossmoor HS
Homewood IL

Skoog Melinda R
Johnson Sr HS
St Paul MN

Skorheim Rita R
Adams Public HS
Adams ND

Skornia Mark D
Owensville HS
Gerald MO

Skrip Sharon J
Resurrection HS
Des Plaines IL

Skubiszewski Paul C
St Laurence HS
Chicago IL

Slabach Dorrine M
Adelphian Academy
Pontiac MI

Slabaugh Daniel N
Goshen HS
Goshen IN

Slaby Chad A
Gibraltar HS
Fish Creek WI

Slaga Marylou A
Elizabeth Seton HS
Chicago IL

Slager Laura L
Chicago Christian HS
Tinley Park IL

Slagle Tim K
Sargent Public HS
Sargent NE

Slama Mary E
Milton Public HS
Osnabrock ND

Slater Karen S
Norton Comm HS
Norton KS

Slaven Pamela J
North Daviess HS
Odon IN

Slavik Daniel J
Boys Town HS
Boys Town NE

Slawinski Elaine A
Lake View HS
Chicago IL

Slay Gregory D
Cooley HS
Detroi MI

Slaybaugh Janet A
Lakeland R Iii HS
Lowry City MO

Slaybaugh Keith A
Murphysboro Twp HS
Murphysboro IL

Slaymaker Kathy L
Erie HS
Erie IL

Slayton William M
Northwestern Community HS
Blandinsville IL

Sleeth Scott A
Chautauqua Co Comm HS
Peru KS

Slenzak Mary G
Regina HS
Warren MI

Sletten Linda S
Pershing HS
Plummer MN

Slikkers George T
Holland HS
Holland MI

Slind Darla K
Plaza HS
Plaza ND

Sliwa Thomas M
Morton Sr HS
Hammond IN

Sloan David W
North Adams HS
North Adams MI

Sloan William D
Superior Senior HS
Superior WI

Sloboda Joyce M
Reavis HS
Burbank IL

Sloggett Steven W
Broken Bow HS
Broken Bow NE

Sloman Dawn I
Morrisonville HS
Pawnee IL

Slovinec Joseph G
Marist HS
Riverdale IL

Slowey David E
Crete Monee HS
Park Forest IL

Slowinski Karen M
Evergreen Pk C HS
Evergreen Park IL

Slusarski Robert M
Alleman HS
E Moline IL

Small Brian
Galatia Hs
Galatia IL

Small Gregory N
Warrensburg HS
Warrensburg MO

Small Marcia L
Unity HS
Chicago IL

Smart Dale L
Forest View HS
Mt Prospect IL

Smart Kimberly K
Cameron Ri HS
Cameron MO

Smarz Jean S
Beloit Memorial HS
Beloit WI

Smedshammer Duane D
Litchville HS
Litchville ND

Smedshammer Marlin P
Litchville HS
Litchville ND

Smith Amy J
Okemos HS
Okemos MI

Smith Anita L
Marine City HS
Marine City MI

Smith Barbara H
Lumen Christi HS
Jackson MI

Smith Barbara J
La Salle Peru Twp HS
Peru IL

Smith Barbara S
Melbeta HS
Minatare NE

Smith Betsy A
Hays HS
Hays KS

Smith Bonita R
Goshen HS
Goshen IN

Smith Brenda L
Tri County R 7 HS
Jamesport MO

Smith Brian J
Mcbain Public HS
Mc Bain MI

Smith Brian J
Altoona HS
Eau Claire WI

Smith Brian K
Oak Park River Forest HS
River Forest IL

Smith Carl L
Ovid Elsie HS
Owosso MI

Smith Charlotte E
Delta C 7 HS
Steele MO

Smith Charlotte R
Andrews Laboratory HS
Berrien Springs MI

Smith Cindy L
Lake Forest Academy
Onalaska WI

Smith Cindy L
Hutchinson Senior HS
Hutchinson MN

Smith Cindy L
North Clay Comm HS
Louisville IL

Smith Connie
East HS
Wichita KS

Smith Craig L
Argo Community HS
Argo IL

Smith Craig L
Northwestern HS
Northville SD

Smith Craig R
West Catholic HS
Grand Rapids MI

Smith Cynthia J
Clarkton HS
Clarkton MO

Smith Cynthia M
Lakeland Union HS
Minocgua WI

Smith Cynthia R
Plainview HS
Coolidge KS

Smith Dan D
Prophetstown HS
Prophetstown IL

Smith Daniel D
Farmer City Mansfield HS
Farmer City IL

Smith Darla J
Manhattan HS
Manhattan KS

Smith Darrell E
Highland HS
Chesterfield IN

Smith David I
G R Clark HS
Hammond IN

Smith David L
Eureka HS
Allenton MO

Smith David S
Ontonagon Area HS
Ontonagon MI

Smith Dawn S
Effingham HS
Effingham IL

Smith Dean M
Epping Public HS
Epping ND

Smith Debbie A
Morgan Co R Ii HS
Sunrise Beach MO

Smith Deborah E
Osawatomie HS
Osawatomie KS

Smith Deborah J
Hanover Central HS
Cedar Lake IN

Smith Deborah L
Cass City HS
Decker MI

Smith Debra A
Morton HS
Hammond IN

Smith Debra A
Mankato East HS
Mankato MN

Smith Debra A
King HS
Detroit MI

Smith Debra J
Adrian HS
Adrian MI

Smith Debra L
Paseo HS
Kansas City MO

Smith Debra L
North Boone HS
Poplar Grove IL

Smith Dena L
Addison Trail HS
Lombard IL

Smith Dianne M
Parkwood HS
Joplin MO

Smith Dianne M
Mehlville Sr HS
St Louis MO

Smith Donna M
Taylorville HS
Taylorville IL

Smith Donny T
North Winnesheik HS
Decorah IA

Smith Dorene J
Bird Island Public HS
Bird Island MN

Smith Galen L
David City Public HS
David City NE

Smith Gary R
Harrisburg HS
Harrisburg IL

Smith Geneva G
Galena HS
Galena MO

Smith Gordon K
Woodstock HS
Woodstock IL

Smith Gregory
Munster HS
Munster IN

Smith Harold R
Morton East HS
Cicero IL

Smith Harry A
Midland HS
Midland MI

Smith Jacqueline L
Dundee HS
Milan MI

Smith James M
Holland Christian HS
Holland MI

Smith Janice R
Lincoln Comm HS
Lincoln IL

Smith Janie F
St Mary HS
Cairo IL

Smith Jeffrey L
Pardeeville HS
Pardeeville WI

Smith Jennifer S
Lake Forest Academy
Chillicothe IL

Smith Joann K
Lovington Jr Sr HS
Lovington IL

Smith John P
Comm HS
Pinckneyville IL

Smith Joyce A
Sommerfield HS
Petersburg MI

Smith Judith A
Southwest Sr HS
Minneapolis MN

Smith Judy K
Charleston HS
Charleston MO

Smith Julia A
Meredosia Chamersburg HS
Meredosia IL

Smith Julie Ann J
Mexico HS
Mexico MO

Smith Julie D
Pittsboro HS
Pittsboro IN

Smith Julie M
Tiskilwa HS
Tiskilwa IL

Smith Karen D
St Joseph HS
Shawnee KS

Smith Katherine E
Schell City R 1 HS
Harwood MO

Smith Kathleen D
Bunker Hill HS
Bunker Hill IL

Smith Kathleen J
Streator Twp HS
Streator IL

Smith Kathy A
Sacred Heart Of Mary HS
Prospect Hts IL

Smith Kelley C
Winner Sr HS
Winner SD

Smith Kevin L
Jackson HS
Jackson MI

Smith Kevin W
West Plains HS
West Plains MO

Smith Kimberly A
Ernest W Seaholm HS
Birmingham MI

Smith Laurie A
Pardeeville HS
Pardeeville WI

Smith Leslie D
Wheaton North HS
Wheaton IL

Smith Linda G
Columbus North HS
Edinburg IN

Smith Linda L
Portage Central HS
Portage MI

Smith Lise A
Warren Central HS
Indianapolis IN

Smith Lorraine L
Carlinville HS
Carlinville IL

Smith Mabla J
Trenton Sr HS
Trenton MO

Smith Mareta J
Frontenac HS
Pittsburg KS

Smith Marianne
Pittsfield HS
Pittsfield IL

Smith Marianne I
J W Sexton HS
Lansing MI

Smith Marianne I
Lone Tree Comm HS
Lone Tree IA

Smith Mary A
Corydon Central HS
Corydon IN

Smith Mary C
Maine Twnp HS
Park Ridge IL

Smith Mary J
Onaga HS
Onaga KS

Smith Mary L
Lourdes HS
Rochester MN

Smith Mary Lou
Brookfield HS
Brookfield MO

Smith Maureen
Pontiac Twp HS
Pontiac IL

Smith Maxine I
New Glarus HS
New Glarus WI

Smith Naomi R
Berkeley Sr HS
St Louis MO

Smith Norman P
Lane Tech HS
Chicago IL

Smith Pamela A
Bishop Lillis HS
Kansas City MO

Smith Pamela S
Ottawa HS
Ottawa IL

Smith Pamela S
Lincoln HS
Thief River Fls MN

Smith Patsy J
Sharon HS
Sharon KS

Smith Paul A
Chippewa Falls Sr HS
Chippewa Falls WI

Smith Paula J
Campbell HS
Campbell MO

Smith Phillip L
Carterville HS
Carterville IL

Smith Rebecca R
Excelsior Springs HS
Excelsior Spgs MO

Smith Rebecca S
Three Rivers HS
Three Rivers MI

Smith Renee K
Josephinum HS
Chicago IL

Smith Rhonda E
Rushville HS
Rushville NE

Smith Richelle J
Adrian R 3 HS
Adrian MO

Smith Ricky L
Paris HS
Paris IL

Smith Robyn V
Duchesne HS
St Charles MO

Smith Roger C
Cavalier HS
Cavalier ND

Smith Roger L
Puxico R 8 HS
Puxico MO

Smith Rory D
Kenwood HS
Chicago IL

Smith Ruth A
Cuba HS
Cuba IL

Smith Scott A
Dillsboro HS
Dillsboro IN

Smith Scott D
West Monona HS
Onawa IA

Smith Sheryl L
St Thomas Apostle HS
Chicago IL

Smith Sonya D
Henry Ford HS
Detroit MI

Smith Stanley R
Bradford HS
Bradford IL

Smith Stephanie D
Cass Technical HS
Detroit MI

Smith Stephen A
Lyons Township HS
Western Spgs IL

Smith Steven C
Norwalk Comm HS
Norwalk IA

Smith Steven F
Southwestern HS
Medora IL

Smith Steven K
Alton Sr HS
Alton IL

Smith Steven L
Dowagiac Union HS
Benton Harbor MI

Smith Susan M
Greenville HS
Greenville IL

Smith Teresa R
Union County HS
Brownsville IN

Smith Terri L
Du Quoin HS
Du Quoin IL

Smith Terri M
Nauvoo Colusa HS
Nauvoo IL

Smith Theresa D
Jamaica HS
Sidell IL

Smith Thomas A
South Decatur HS
Greensburg IN

Smith Thomas J
Lourdes HS
Rochester MN

Smith Thomas L
Fremont HS
Fremont IN

Smith Thomas L
Hayden HS
Topeka KS

Smith Timothy N
Newton HS
Newton IA

Smith Trudy A
Colo Comm HS
Nevada IA

Smith Valerie R
North Central HS
Indianapolis IN

Smith Vicki J
Morrison Comm HS
Morrison IL

Smith Victoria L
Oak Park River Forest HS
Oak Park IL

Smith Wesley T
Univ Of Detroit HS
Detroit MI

Smith William D
St Philip Catholic Cen HS
Battle Creek MI

Smith William R
Tomahawk HS
Tomahawk WI

Smitley Debra K
Charleston HS
Charleston IL

Smitley Lori C
Urbandale HS
Urbandale IA

Smits Jeffrey M
Abbot Pennings HS
De Pete WI

Smitter Mark R
Whitmore Lake HS
Whitmore Lake MI

Smittle Grover C
Pacific HS
Pacific MO

Smock Wesley A
Onsted HS
Adrian MI

Smolar Joseph
Highland HS
Highland IN

Smolich Kevin M
Plainfield HS
Joliet IL

Smotrilla William
Thornwood HS
Dolton IL

Smugala Karen J
Cahokia Commonfields HS
Cahokia IL

Smukala Suzanne M
North Huron HS
Port Austin MI

Snapp Jinger C
Avon HS
Danville IN

Snart Kenneth C
Green Lake HS
Ripon WI

Snauwaert Lori A
United Township HS
East Moline IL

Sneddon Julie K
Brazil HS
Brazil IN

Snell Larry G
Pekin Comm HS
Pekin IL

Snellenbarger Lisa J
Clinton Prairie HS
Frankfort IN

Snider Linda M
North Chicago HS
Lindenhurst IL

Snider Stan C
Richland HS
Dexter MO

Snodgrass David L
Mt Pleasant HS
Mt Pleasant IA

Snow Barbara S
Amboy HS
Amboy IL

Snow Craig C
Webberville HS
Webberville MI

Snow George M
Huntington North HS
Warren IN

Snow Ronald T
St Peter & Paul Area HS
Saginaw MI

Snow Stephen K
Lanphier HS
Springfield IL

Snyder Becky A
Parkwood HS
Joplin MO

Snyder Doug A
Central HS
Burden KS

Snyder Gayle A
Fremont Sr HS
Fremont NE

Snyder Gene L
Nemaha Valley HS
Talmage NE

Snyder Julie A
Bronaugh R 7 HS
Bronaugh MO

Snyder Karen S
Chandlerville HS
Chandlerville IL

Snyder Reed E
Wilmot Union HS
Burlington WI

Snyder Susan E
Marinette HS
Marinette WI

Snyder Vincent L
Wahoo Public HS
Wahoo NE

Sobas Cheryl L
Morton Sr HS
Hammond IN

Sobczak Stuart A
Creighton Prep
Omaha NE

Soboleski Julie M
St Stanislaus Kostka HS
Chicago IL

Socha David M
Phillips HS
Phillips WI

Socha Thomas J
Gordon Tech HS
Chicago IL

Sockel Mark S
Taylorville Sr HS
Taylorville IL

Soderberg Kevan A
St Francis HS
Isanti MN

Sohn Susan L
Elk Grove HS
Elk Grove IL

Sojka Cindy A
Lyons Township HS
La Grange IL

Sokoloski Barbara J
Sherburn HS
Sherburn MN

Sola Sharon K
Lyle Public HS
Northwood IA

Solarczyk Linda M
Maria HS
Chicago IL

Solberg Becky L
Viroqua Sr HS
Viroqua WI

Solberg Georgia L
T C Howe HS
Indianapolis IN

Soldan Susan M
O Neill Public HS
Oneill NE

Solem Natalie
Hendricks HS
Astoria SD

Solko Rita M
Andes Central HS
Lake Andes SD

Sollie Linda R
Oklee Public HS
Trail MN

Sollman Thomas P
Gibson Southern HS
Fort Branch IN

Solloway Margaret A
Mt Assisi Acad
Oak Lawn IL

Solum James E
Larimore HS
Larimore ND

Somerville Peggy L
Algonac HS
Algonac MI

Sommerer Kendra K
Logan View HS
Craig NE

Sommerhalder Elizabeth J
Lewiston Consolidated HS
Steinauer NE

Sommers Mary M
Random Lake HS
Random Lake WI

Sommers Teresa J
Andrew HS
Andrew IA

Somogyi Cynthia L
Limestone Comm HS
Bartonville IL

Sonday Roy
Monroe HS
Monroe MI

Sonefeld Debra J
Freeland HS
Freeland MI

Sonksen Lori L
Mallard Comm HS
Curlew IA

Sonta Irene Y
Notre Dame HS
Chicago IL

Sopron Debbie A
Lourdes HS
Chicago IL

Soranno David A
Barrington HS
Barrington IL

Sorensen Linda K
Stapleton HS
Gandy NE

Sorensen Nelsen S
Frontier HS
Brookston IN

Sorensen Susan K
Waukegan East HS
Waukegan IL

Sorenson Dave A
Preston HS
Preston MN

Sorenson Jay C
Argyle Public HS
Argyle MN

Sorg Joellen C
Meridian Senior HS
Hope MI

Sorrels Nan
Anna Jonesboro HS
Anna IL

Sorrill Lise A
Triopia HS
Meredosia IL

Sorum Shelley F
Rushford Public HS
Rushford MN

Sosa Roger A
Chominade College Prep
Germantown IL

Soskin Susan E
Parkway Central HS
Chesterfield MO

Sosnovske Kathryn A
Antigo Senior HS
Antigo WI

Sosnowski Cynthia H
Lincoln Way HS
Frankfort IL

Sosnowski John S
Amos Alonzo Stagg HS
Palos Hills IL

Soucek Sandy J
Seward HS
Seward NE

Souffrant Donald J
Hillcrest HS
Hazel Crest IL

Soul Janice C
Phillips HS
Phillips WI

Southard Beth A
Hamilton Heights HS
Noblesville IN

Southard Demar R
Washington HS
Cedar Rapids IA

Souther Sandra K
Lockport Central HS
Lockport IL

Southerlan Penny S
Beason Comm HS
Lincoln IL

Southern David D
New Trier East HS
Kenilworth IL

Sova Laura L
St Francis Academy
Joliet IL

Sowa Sharon L
Bishop Noll Institute
Munster IN

Sowada Sandra M
Little Falls Comm HS
Little Falls MN

Sowder Lori L
Madrid Community HS
Madrid IA

Sowers Cheryl A
Newton HS
Jewett IL

Sowers Christine L
Fountain Central HS
Hillsboro IN

Sowers Kyle C
Leo HS
Grabill IN

Spaeth Mark J
West Bend East HS
West Bend WI

Spagnvolo Achilles W
Hill Comm HS
Lansing MI

Spainhour Sara A
Cheney HS
Cheney KS

Spainhower Patricia A
Princeton Comm HS
Princeton IN

Spangus Ursula M
Sterling Hts HS
Warren MI

Spann James F
Gregory HS
Gregory SD

Spanyers Ruth A
Dorchester Public HS
Dorchester NE

Sparkman Starla J
Yarbrough HS
Elkhart KS

Sparks Teresa A
Worthington Jefferson HS
Worthington IN

Spatz David D
Lakeland Union HS
Minocqua WI

Spayev Rodney G
De Pue HS
De Pue IL

Spears Bradley R
Bell City HS
Bell City MO

Spears Ronald N
Ottawa Twp HS
Marseilles IL

Spears Susan E
Southern HS
Stronghurst IL

Specht James L
Yates Center HS
Piqua KS

Specht Lori D
Davenport West HS
Davenport IA

Speckhart Brenda L
Seymour HS
Quincy IL

Speckman Katherine D
Metropolis HS
Metropolis IL

Spector James M
Loyola Academy
Evanston IL

Speer Doris L
Lincoln Park HS
Lincoln Park MI

Speer Scott R
Lawrence Central HS
Indianapolis IN

Speirer Jan M
Pontiac Township HS
Pontiac IL

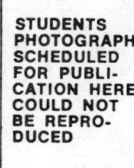

STUDENTS PHOTOGRAPH SCHEDULED FOR PUBLICATION HERE COULD NOT BE REPRODUCED

Spelich Tina M
St Francis Academy
Joliet IL

Spence Jerri A
Lorettoin K C HS
Kansas City MO

Spencer Daniel L
Marseilles HS
Marseilles IL

Spencer Gayle M
Lawton Comm HS
Lawton MI

Spencer Lynne M
E Grand Rapids HS
E Grand Rapids MI

Spencer Martha J
El Dorado Springs R 2 HS
El Dorado Springs MO

Spencer Michael L
Bay City Handy HS
Bay City MI

Spencer Richard B
Albia HS
Albia IA

Spencer Tamra C
Meridian HS
Mounds IL

Sperl Brian G
Andrean HS
Munster IN

Spexarth Gregory R
Andale HS
Colwich KS

Spidle Bruce L
Penney HS
Nettleton MO

Spiekerman Rhonda S
Arthur Hill HS
Zilwaukee MI

Spieler Kurt J
Parkway West HS
Chesterfield MO

Spilger David L
West Liberty HS
Alalissa IA

Spiller William L
St Anne Comm HS
Hopkins Park IL

Spilman John D
David Co Comm HS
Bloomfield IA

Spindler Jeanne L
Benson HS
Omaha NE

Spindler Jerry L
Woodlan HS
Woodburn IN

Spirduso Wendy L
Central HS
La Crosse WI

Spires Candy L
Macon HS
Macon IL

Spitsnogle Gary A
Odell Public HS
Odell NE

Spivey Lucinda S
Galva HS
Galva IL

Spoelstra Marlys G
Pella Christian HS
New Sharon IA

Spoerl June M
Hempstead HS
Sherrill IA

Spoon Bonnie
Marquette HS
Marquette KS

Spradlin Ellen J
Ashland HS
Ashland IL

Spradlin Mary E
Jacksonville HS
Jacksonville IL

Spradlin Vicky L
Martinsville HS
Martinsville IN

Sprague Linda L
Deland Weldon HS
Weldon IL

Spreen Sandra J
Medford HS
Medford WI

Spring John W
Washington Community HS
Washington IL

Springer Mark S
Cathedral HS
Indianapolis IN

Springs Charles R
Mt Carmel HS
Mt Carmel IL

Sprutta Kathy A
Mother Of Sorrows HS
Chicago IL

Spryszak Gregory C
Berkley HS
Berkley MI

Spurgeon Jani L
Canton R V HS
Monticello MO

Spurrier Marianne
Clinton Comm HS
Clinton IL

Squires Abby
Seaholm HS
Birmingham MI

Srader Randy E
Doniphan Sr HS
Doniphan MO

Sramek Michael M
Howells Public HS
Clarkson NE

Sramek Vanessa L
Lacrosse HS
La Crosse KS

Sroka Jeffrey J
Holy Cross HS
Chicago IL

Stables Stanley T
Bethany HS
Bethany IL

Stachyra Carol A
Hobbard HS
Chicago IL

Stack Nancy J
Leland HS
Earlville IL

Stade Debra A
Good Counsel HS
Chicago IL

Stafford Cheryl L
Woodlawn HS
Woodlawn IL

Stafford Ronald J
J C Harmon HS
Kansas City KS

Stafford Sallie M
Fremont HS
Fremont IN

Stafford Terry W
Douglass HS
Douglass KS

Staggs Randy D
Muncie North HS
Muncie IN

Stahl Emma J
Central HS
Worthington IN

Stahl Jamey L
Primghar Comm HS
Primghar IA

Stahlhood Wilson R
Coldwater HS
Coldwater MI

Stahnke Bruce I
Evanston Twp HS
Evanston IL

Stai Michael R
Sacred Heart Public HS
Sacred Heart MN

Staidl Cynthia J
Oconto Sr HS
Oconto WI

Stalder Donita E
Beaver City HS
Beaver City NE

Staley Cheryll J
Oregon Sr HS
Oregon WI

Stallings Heidi A
Downers Grove Comm HS
Downers Grove IL

Stallsmith Karen
Southwest HS
Green Bay WI

Stalzer John P
St Rita HS
Chicago IL

Stalzer Rosemary L
Semco Community HS
Haverhill IA

Stamm Carl A
Dryden HS
Dryden MI

Stamman Kay L
Gladwin Comm HS
Gladwin MI

Stamp Mary A
Holstein Community HS
Holstein IA

Stampe Scott J
Sully Superimposed HS
Pierre SD

Stampfl Burtrom L
Three Lakes HS
Monico WI

Stampley Debra T
J M Harlan HS
Chicago IL

Stamps Douglas W
Heritage Hills HS
Richland IN

Stanaszek John D
Comstock HS
Kalamazoo MI

Standard M Jean
Rolla HS
Rolla MO

Stander Victor J
Weeping Water Public HS
Weeping Water NE

Standerfer Sheila K
Bethany HS
Bethany IL

Standerford Judy D
Humboldt Public HS
Humboldt NE

Stanek Joseph P
Mc Henry Comm HS
Mc Henry IL

Stanfield Melanie A
Oakley HS
Oakley KS

Stanford Gerald J
Arthur HS
Arthur IL

Stanford Jerry A
Flora HS
Flora IL

Stangland Sherry L
Central Noble HS
Albion IN

Stanislav Cynthia M
Duchesne Academy
Omaha NE

Stanley Lester R
Delta HS
Albany IN

Stanley Mary E
Owosso HS
Owosso MI

Stanley Mary J
Fairfield HS
Fairfield IA

Stansberry Linda C
Virden HS
Virden IL

Stansell Leslie A
Ernest W Seaholm HS
Birmingham MI

Stanton Kathleen A
Metropolis Comm HS
Metropolis IL

Staples Margaret M
Grayslake Comm HS
Grayslake IL

Staples Robert E
Montrose Hill Mc Cloy HS
Flushing MI

Stapleton Diane L
Bogan HS
Chicago IL

Stapleton Lisa K
Wilson Campus HS
Mankato MN

Stapleton Sharon M
Mother Mc Auley HS
Chicago IL

Staponski Sharon E
Pierce City R 6 HS
Purdy MO

Stapp Paul W
Charleston HS
Charleston IL

Starbuck John W
Sedan HS
Longton KS

Stark Alice J
Neche Public HS
Neche ND

Stark Chris A
Delta HS
Muncie IN

Stark Darcy A
Spring Lake Park HS
Minneapolis MN

Stark Darrie D
Loomis Public HS
Loomis NE

Stark Janice L
Norborne Public HS
Norborne MO

Stark Theodore E
Edina East HS
Edina MN

Stark Thomas M
Saint Edmond HS
Fort Dodge IA

Starke Phil A
Mexico HS
Mexico MO

Starkman Robert D
Birmingham Seaholm HS
Birmingham MI

Starks Carol D
Anderson HS
Anderson IN

Starks Louis
East HS
Waterloo IA

Starr Carol D
St Marys Academy
Nauvoo IL

Starr Carolyn M
Rockwell Swaledale HS
Rockwell IA

Starr Kevin R
Martinsville HS
Martinsville IN

Staszak Lynn A
St Joseph Academy
Krakow WI

Staton Brenda S
Metropolis Comm HS
Belknap IL

Stattner Diana S
Cloverdale HS
Cloverdale IN

Stavropoulos Mark
St Viator HS
Mt Prospect IL

Stead Joyce M
Madison HS
Madison KS

Stearley Douglas E
Brazil HS
Brazil IN

Stearns Teresa D
Clarke Comm HS
Osceola IA

Stebane Audrey M
Brillion Public HS
Kaukauna WI

Steck Robert L
Anna Jonesboro HS
Anna IL

Stecker Donald K
Unionville Sebewaing Area HS
Sebewaing MI

Stecker James C
Grand Island HS
Grand Island NE

Steckler Mark T
Yankton Sr HS
Yankton SD

Steckline Terry J
Thomas More Prep HS
Hays KS

Stedronsky Judy C
Barrington HS
Barrington IL

Stee Brenda J
Watertown Sr HS
Watertown SD

Steeby Karen M
Coldwater HS
Coldwater MI

Steeby Roy C
Basehor HS
Basehor KS

Steele Mark P
Mattawan HS
Mattawan MI

Steele Robert T
Thedford HS
Brownlee NE

Steen Stacy L
Owensville HS
Owensville MO

Steen Susan K
Minot HS
Minot ND

Steensnes Robert A
Newman Grove HS
St Edward NE

Steerman David R
Wheatland HS
Gove KS

Stees Timothy L
Shannon HS
Shannon IL

Steffa Becky L
Pittsfield HS
Pittsfield IL

Steffen Carol L
Menominee HS
Menominee MI

Steffen Denise A
Bluffton Allen HS
Bluffton IN

Steffen Ed A
Adams Central HS
Decatur IN

Steffen Mary C
Janesville Consolidated HS
Janesville IA

Steffens Brenda E
Litchfield Sr HS
Litchfield IL

Steffens Randell G
Benton County R 1 HS
Cole Camp MO

Stefl David E
Thomas Jefferson HS
Cedar Rapids IA

Stegman Brian B
Kinsley HS
Offerle KS

Stegman Wayne H
Drayton Public HS
Drayton ND

Stehr John P
Bishop Leblond HS
St Joseph MO

Steidl Vicki L
Lincoln HS
Wisconsin Rapids WI

Steiger Majeana L
Lincoln Sr HS
Red Lake Falls MN

Steimle Mary Bertha G
Kelly HS
New Hamburg MO

Stein Cindy L
Urbana HS
Urbana IL

Stein E John
Bishop Luers HS
Ft Wayne IN

Stein Julie A
Amery Pub HS
Amery WI

Steinbach Gary M
South Haven HS
South Haven MI

Steinberg Wendi C
Thornwood HS
Lansing IL

Steinbrenner Dawn R
St Joseph HS
Chicago IL

Steinbrenner Susan M
York Comm HS
Elmhurst IL

Steinbrueck Randy E
Boonville HS
Boonville MO

Steiner Dean B
Pekin Community HS
Pekin IL

Steiner Janell D
Hoisington HS
Hoisington KS

Steiner Jennifer G
H H Dow HS
Midland MI

Steiner Lisa J
Waukesha South HS
Waukesha WI

Steiner Lynn K
Norfolk Catholic Sr HS
Norfolk NE

Steiner Neil B
Butler HS
Butler MO

Steiner Neil B
Butler R V HS
Butler MO

Steinhauser David W
Truman HS
Independence MO

Steinkamp Sara A
Reitz Memorial HS
Evansville IN

Steinke Boyce E
St Marys HS
Sleepy Eye MN

Steinke Gary W
Central Comm HS
De Witt IA

Steinke Lori L M
Fort Atkinson Sr HS
Fort Atkinson WI

Steinkopf Anthony P
Cathedral HS
St Cloud MN

Steinman Dan P
Lyons Twp HS
La Grange IL

Steinmetz Nancy R
Hartford HS
Hartford WI

Steinsland Kjell T
Oak Park & River Forest HS
Oak Park IL

Steinwachs Doreen M
Bonner Spgs Sr HS
Bonner Springs KS

Stelter Carol M
Lakeshore HS
Baroda MI

Stelter Dorraine I
Belview HS
Redwood Falls MN

Stendahl Roslyn M
William Fremd HS
Palatine IL

Stene Kathryn M
Halstad HS
Shelly MN

Stenfors Debra L
Ewen Trout Creek HS
Bruce Crossing MI

Stengel Marilyn E
Mt Morris HS
Mt Morris IL

Stenmo Thomas M
Northwood Public HS
Hatton ND

Stensland Robert S
Ballard HS
Slater IA

Stenson Margaret K
Calumet HS
Laurium MI

Stepanek Curtis E
Berkeley Sr HS
St Louis MO

Stepanek Dennis E
Berkeley Sr HS
St Louis MO

Stephen Royce D
N Mahaska HS
New Sharon IA

Stephens Byron E
Exeter HS
Washburn MO

Stephens Daniel A
Reita Memorial HS
Evansville IN

Stephens Fred O
Morton HS
Hammond IN

Stephens James L
Naperville Central HS
Naperville IL

Stephens Jamie M
Granite City North HS
Granite City IL

Stephens Jennifer D
Hinsdale Central HS
Hinsdale IL

Stephens Terri L
Robinson HS
Robinson IL

Stephenson Dixie A
Kearney HS
Kansas City MO

Stephenson Jerry L
Morgan Co R Ii HS
Fortuna MO

Stephenson Kim A
Galena HS
Galena IL

Stephenson Richard A
Ottawa Sr HS
Ottawa KS

Stepnakowski Maureen M
Bedford North Lawrence HS
Bedford IN

Steprowski Catherine A
Centerville HS
Centerville IA

Sterbling John W
Lane Tech HS
Chicago IL

Stergar Paul A
Northwest HS
Indianapolis IN

Stern Susan E
West Waterloo HS
Waterloo IA

Sternberg Kevin E
Forest Lake Sr HS
Forest Lake MN

Sternecker David D
Raytown HS
Kansas City MO

Sterner Catherine M
St Agnes HS
St Paul MN

Sterner James F
Holy Trinity HS
Winsted MN

Sterrenberg George B
Culver Military Academy
Beaverville IL

Sterrenberg Margot A
Thompson Comm HS
Thompson IA

Sterrett William R
Hardee Cnty HS
Cape Girardeau MO

Stetzel Caryn A
Huntington North HS
Roanoke IN

Steuver Douglas P
Aurora Sr HS
Aurora IN

Steuver Linda K
Aurora Sr HS
Aurora IN

Stevens Clifford A
Mt Vernon Comm HS
Greenfield IN

Stevens Dann F
Primghar Community HS
Primghar IA

Stevens Joan M
Houghton HS
Houghton MI

Stevens Jon R
Pike HS
Indianapolis IN

Stevens Mark D
Pennfield HS
Battle Creek MI

Stevens Mark J
Rantoul Twshp HS
Rantoul IL

Stevens Patricia J
Rockford East HS
Rockford IL

Stevens Randall R
St Edward Public HS
St Edward NE

Stevens Robert E
North Kansas City Sr HS
Kansas City MO

Stevens William S
Speedway HS
Speedway IN

Stevenson Debra S
St George HS
St George KS

Stevenson Jennifer L
Franklin HS
Jacksonville IL

Stevenson Michael R
Van Buren HS
Brazil IN

Steward Janet R
Lincoln HS
Wisc Rapids WI

Steward Timothy W
Monrovia HS
Mooresville IN

Stewart Betsy D
Corunna HS
Corunna MI

Stewart Brenda J
Clay City HS
Bowling Green IN

Stewart Brent L
Durand HS
Durand WI

Stewart Cathy J
Washington HS
South Bend IN

Stewart Cecilia B
St Marys Academy
Morris MN

Stewart Charles A
Nobles HS
Noblesville IN

Stewart Constance
Academy Of Our Lady
Chicago IL

Stewart Cynthia H
Eldora Consolidated HS
Eldora IA

Stewart Cynthia L
Springfield HS
Springfield IL

Stewart Deborah J
Big Rapids HS
Big Rapids MI

Stewart Debra L
Ladywood St Agnes HS
Indianapolis IN

Stewart Georgia E
Arthur Hill HS
Zilwaukee MI

Stewart James A
Huron HS
Ann Arbor MI

Stewart James C
Sturgis HS
Sturgis MI

Stewart Kathleen C
Northrop HS
Ft Wayne IN

Stewart Linda S
Pepin HS
Stockholm WI

Stewart Lynda A
Springfield HS
Springfield IL

Stewart Marjorie E
Brown County HS
Columbus IN

Stewart Michael T
Dixon HS
Dixon MO

Stewart Rhonda S
Chadwick HS
Chadwick IL

Stewart Ronald B
Fairbury HS
Fairbury NE

Stewart Ron J
Upsala Area HS
Bowlus MN

Stewart Steve J
Roanoke Benson HS
Roanoke IL

Stewart Terri L
Dunlap HS
Peoria IL

St Germain Donna M
Crawford Ausable HS
Grayling MI

Sticha Neil A
Lincoln Sr HS
Bloomington MN

Stickelman Megan J
York Sr HS
York NE

Stickle Joanie E
Knoxville Sr HS
Knoxville IA

Stickman Elizabeth A
Griggsville Community
Unit 4
Griggsville IL

Stidham Jamie E
Frankfort Sr HS
Frankfort IN

Stieber Cheryl A
Marathon HS
Edgar WI

Stiegemeier Craig L
Staunton HS
Staunton IL

Stiglmire Billi S
Lansing HS
Lansing KS

Stiksel Monica E
Lourdes HS
Chicago IL

Stilabower Pamela L
Windsor HS
Windsor MO

Stillwell Sondra R
Belton HS
Belton MO

Stilwell Mickey R
Lawton Bronson HS
Lawton IA

Stinchcomb Wendy K
Lowell Sr HS
Lowell MI

Stinson Sarah E
Grand Island Sr HS
Grand Island NE

Stith Debra K
Raytown HS
Raytown MO

Stith Leo H
Northwest HS
St Louis MO

Stitt Doak C
Salina Central HS
Salina KS

St John Denise C
Josephinum HS
Chicago IL

St John Roberta M
Cornell HS
Blackstone IL

St Julian Grant
Richwoods HS
Peoria IL

St Marie Dreux V
Appleton W HS
Appleton WI

St Martin Edward J
Escanaba Area Public HS
Escanaba MI

Stock Donna L
Prairie Home HS
Prairie Home MO

Stockdale Ian E
Ann Arbor Huron HS
Ann Arbor MI

Stocker Yvonne S
Tipton HS
Tipton IN

Stockle David A
Octavia HS
Colfax IL

Stockman Terry A
Tippecanoe Valley HS
Claypool IN

Stockmann Paul T
St Marys HS
St Louis MO

Stocks Cheri L
Mt Zion HS
Dalton City IL

Stockton Brent W
South Sioux City HS
South Sioux City NE

Stockton Jerry L
West Chicago Comm HS
West Chicago IL

Stockton Karen S
Plainfield HS
Plainfield IN

Stoddard William J
Berlin HS
Berlin WI

Stodghill Robert S
Gibson Southern HS
Ft Branch IN

Stoehr Peggy A
Berkeley Sr HS
Berkeley MO

Stoetzel Carol J
Maywood HS
North Platte NE

Stohlmann Dennis F
Louisville HS
Louisville NE

Stoiber William M
James Madison HS
Milwaukee WI

Stoike Nadine M
Lafayette Jefferson HS
Lafayette IN

Stoker Debra J
Kirksville Sr HS
Kirksville MO

Stokes Douglas L
Sunnydale Academy
Olivette MO

Stokes Gary J
Ridgefarm HS
Ridgefarm IL

Stokes Tammy E
Assumption HS
Assumption IL

Stokke Sherry A
Watertown Sr HS
Watertown SD

Stoll Andrew H
Chaminade HS
St Louis MO

Stoll Arletha N
Barr Reeve HS
Washington IN

Stoll Scott B
Elwood HS
Elwood NE

Stoll Veronica D
Barr Reeve HS
Washington IN

Stoltenburg Rodney R
Watertown Senior HS
Watertown SD

Stolz Susan J
Wauwatosa East HS
Wauwatosa WI

Stolze Jeffrey A
Marion HS
Marion IA

Stone Corliss C
Jerome Case HS
Racine WI

Stone John W
Oscoda Area HS
Oscoda MI

Stone Kimberly E
Stanton Comm HS
Stanton IA

Stone Leslie A
Bishop Ryan HS
Minot ND

Stone M R
Craig R Iii HS
Forest City MO

Stone Pamela A
Palestine HS
Palestine IL

Stone Shirley C
Deland Weldon HS
Weldon IL

Stone Terry A
Newman Grove Public HS
Lindsay NE

Stonebraker Cynthia C
Brown County HS
Columbus IN

Stonecipher Danna L
Parsons HS
Parsons KS

Stoner James H
Senn HS
Chicago IL

Stoner Patricia S
Kickapoo HS
Springfield MO

St Onge Kevin L
Rudyard HS
Trout Lake MI

Storey Euea J
Glendale HS
Springfield MO

Stork Theresa L
Effingham HS
Effingham IL

Storkel Karen J
Evergreen Park HS
Evergreen Park IL

Storment Kim S
Salem Comm HS
Salem IL

Story Ann D
Normandy HS
St Louis MO

Stotler Tina M
Civic Memorial HS
Bethalto IL

Stotts David E
Savannah HS
Savannah MO

Stotts Mari C
Frontenac HS
Frontenac KS

Stouffer William K
La Moille Comm HS
La Moille IL

Stough Kevin D
Normal Comm HS
Normal IL

Stout Bonnie S
Hoisington Senior HS
Hoisington KS

Stout Lisa A
Porta HS
Petersburg IL

Stout Trena J
Crothersville HS
Crothersville IN

Stover Leonard G
Dowagiac Union HS
Dowagiac MI

Stovner Kregg B
North Sr HS
Eau Claire WI

Stowers Jody L
Washington Twp HS
Valparaiso IN

St Pierre Denise M
Herscher HS
Herscher IL

Straatmann Julie F
Holdrege HS
Holdrege NE

Stracey Valerie J
Alden Hebron HS
Alden IL

Stradtner Lori K
Wyoming Park HS
Wyoming MI

Strahota Richard L
Iowa Grant HS
Cobb WI

Strait Davena L
High School
Keosauqua IA

Straka Gary L
No St Paul Senior HS
North St Paul MN

Stramel Karlene K
Diamond R 4 HS
Diamond MO

Strand Dawn E
Washburn HS
Minneapolis MN

Strand Duane D
Richland HS
Wahpeton ND

Strand Judy M
Halstad HS
Shelly MN

Strand Mark O
Centennial HS
Circle Pines MN

Strand William R
Mounds View HS
St Paul MN

Strange Daniel K
Salem HS
Salem IN

Strasburger Jeannette C
Adlai Stevenson HS
Sterling Hgts MI

Strasser Robert K
Forestview HS
Mt Prospect IL

Strate Marilyn B
Norfolk Sr HS
Hoskins NE

Stratemeyer David A
West Platte HS
Farley MO

Strathman Susan J
Hayden HS
Topeka KS

Stratton Deborah L
Otsego HS
Otsego MI

Stratton Donald E
Hill Mccloy HS
Clio MI

Stratton Monty E
Weeping Water Public HS
Weeping Water NE

Straus Gary A
St Johns HS
De Witt MI

Straw Karen L
New Bloomfield HS
New Bloomfield MO

Strawser Corydon L
Decatur Central HS
Indpls IN

Strayer Kerry A
Fairbury HS
Fairbury NE

Streeper Patricia L
Alton Senior HS
Alton IL

Street Gail M
Dubois HS
Jasper IN

Streeter Alan W
Sioux Valley HS
Volga SD

Streff Lisa M
Plano HS
Plano IL

Strefling Pamela J
River Valley HS
Three Oaks MI

Streibich F Michael
Woodruft HS
Peoria IL

Streit Robert J
Holton HS
Holton KS

Strejc Janice M
Maria HS
Chicago IL

Stremming Timothy G
Stewardson Strasburg HS
Strasburg IL

Streng Debra J
John Marshall Jr Sr HS
Milwaukee WI

Strese Deanna J
Somerset HS
Somerset WI

Streuly Carolyn A
West Allis Central HS
West Allis WI

Stricker Jane E
Huntington North HS
Huntington IN

Stricker Nancy K
Wellsburg Comm HS
Grundy Center IA

Strickland Leslie G
O Fallon Township HS
O Fallon IL

Striebich Janice S
Cheboygan Area HS
Cheboygan MI

Striegel Bonnie J
Logan HS
La Crosse WI

Strigenz Michael A
Kewaskum HS
Kewaskum WI

Strimple Connie L
South Ripley HS
Versailles IN

Stringer Catherine A
Mary D Bradford HS
Kenosha WI

Strodel Ross A
South Side HS
Fort Wayne IN

Stroh Morgan R
Midway HS
Johnstown ND

Strohman Joseph L
English Valley HS
N English IA

Strohmeyer Karen L
Edwardsville HS
Edwardsville IL

Strohschein Ricky A
Avondale Senior HS
Auburn Heights MI

Strom Luann M
White City HS
White City KS

Stroman Pat A
Imlay City HS
Imlay City MI

Stromberg Larry A
Hammond Baptist HS
Hammond IN

Strong Joyce M
Paseo HS
Kansas City MO

Strong Stephen J
Union City HS
Union City MI

Strother Ralph M
Potosi HS
Potosi MO

Stroud Julie A
Estherville Sr HS
Estherville IA

Stroud Sue L
North Boone HS
Poplar Grove IL

Stroup Steven F
Benkelman HS
Benkelman NE

Strouse Donald B
Bedford Sr HS
Lambertville MI

Strouse Douglas G
Alma HS
Alma MI

Strube Kim S
Claflin HS
Claflin KS

Strunk Kathy S
Eastern HS
Springville IN

Strycker David B
Zionsville Community HS
Zionsville IN

Stuaan Kirk M
Limestone Community HS
Bartonville IL

Stuart David M
Cozad Sr HS
Cozad NE

Stuart Philip E
Marian HS
Mishawaka IN

Stubbendick Keith A
George S Parker HS
Jamesville WI

Stubblefield Lori A
Odell Comm HS
Odell IL

Stubbs Stephen W
Harlem HS
Loves Park IL

Stubenhofer Michael D
Chase County HS
Strong City KS

Stuber Marilyn L
Caston HS
Logansport IN

Stucker Cathy P
Wayne HS
Fort Wayne IN

Stuckey Michael B
Gibson Southern HS
Owensville IN

Stuckey Thomas L
Gibson Southern HS
Owensville IN

Stucky Tamera S K
Moundridge HS
Moundridge KS

Student Suzanne P
Edina East HS
Edina MN

Study Kimberley L
Warsaw Comm HS
Warsaw IN

Studzinski Linda A
Edwin G Foreman HS
Chicago IL

Stuebs Lois M
Manitowoc Lutheran HS
Kewaunee WI

Stuenkel Barbara A
Rich South HS
Monee IL

Stuesse Suzanne K
Union HS
Leslie MO

Stueve Sandra M
Graceville Public HS
Dumont MN

Stufflebeam Mark G
Lewistown Comm HS
Lewistown IL

Stuhr Cynthia E
Bradshaw HS
Bradshaw NE

Stull Cheryl L
Melcher Dallas HS
Lacona IA

Stull Deborah L
Streator HS
Streator IL

Stults Judy
Argos Community HS
Argos IN

Stultz Steven K
Evanston Township HS
Evanston IL

Stulz Susan M
Rockridge HS
Muscatine IA

Stumf Rosann M
Hemingford HS
Hemingford NE

Stump Paul E
La Porte City Comm HS
La Porte City IA

Stunda David G
Mt Vernon HS
Greenfield IN

Stuntebeck Laurie S
Centerville Public HS
Centerville SD

Stupp Joan E
Mehlville Sr HS
St Louis MO

Stupp Paula J
Mehlville HS
St Louis MO

Sturek Chris J
Industry HS
Industry IL

Sturgill John E
Niantie Harristown HS
Decatur IL

Sturing Stanley J
Pella Christian HS
Oskaloosa IA

Sturm Lori D
Lesterville HS
Lesterville MO

Sturm Mark A
Plano HS
Plano IL

Stutz Doris S
Alton Senior HS
Alton IL

Stypa James A
Manistee Catholic Central HS
Manistee MI

Suchomel Jeffrey R
St Joseph HS
La Grange Park IL

Suddith Ronnie W
Tina Avalon HS
Bogard MO

Sueen Glenn M
St Ignatius College Prep
Chicago IL

Suess Cynthia M
Comfrey Public HS
Comfrey MN

Sughroue Christy M
Republican Valley HS
Stockville NE

Sugihara Joseph N
Elgin HS
Streamwood IL

Suhl Cindy L
Sullivan HS
Sullivan IL

Suhusky Craig A
Wayland Union HS
Wayland MI

Sujkowski Timothy J
Bay City Central HS
Bay City MI

Sukowaty Stanley G
Reedsville Public HS
Cato WI

Sullivan Barbara K
Logan HS
Lacrosse WI

Sullivan Christine L
Notre Dame HS
Quincy IL

Sullivan Colleen M
Taylor Center HS
Taylor MI

Sullivan Daniel P
Dunlap HS
Dunlap IL

Sullivan F P
Denison HS
Denison IA

Sullivan Georgia K
Peoria Heights HS
Peoria Heights IL

Sullivan Jeff M
Mormon Trail HS
Weldon IA

Sullivan Laura A
North Vigo HS
Terre Haute IN

Sullivan Marilyn J
Mother Of Sorrows HS
Chicago IL

Sullivan Michael J
Clay Center HS
Clay Center NE

Sullivan Patrick E
Clay Center HS
Clay Center NE

Sullivan Sarah M
J E Murphy HS
Montreal WI

Sullivan William J
University City Sr HS
Universty City MO

Sullivan William T
Depue HS
Depue IL

Sumida Colin W
Downers Grove South HS
Downers Grove IL

Summer Carol A
Olivet Community HS
Springport MI

Summers Leetta S
Fountain Central HS
Veedersburg IN

Summers Shirley A
Northwest HS
House Springs MO

Summervill Gloria A
Chanute Sr HS
Chanute KS

Sumner William R
Hutchinson Sr HS
Hutchinson KS

Sundby Mary B
Turtle Lake Mercer HS
Turtle Lake ND

Sunderman Charmaine L
South Page Community HS
Coin IA

Sunderman Janell J
South Page HS
Braddyville IA

Sundermeyer Steven W
Owen Withee HS
Withee WI

Sundquist Susan A
West Iron County HS
Caspian MI

Suntken Catherine A
St Augustine HS
Chicago IL

Suoboda Roberta L
Crete HS
Crete NE

Surber Erika M
Main St HS
Eureka KS

Surber Peggy A
Raytown HS
Kansas City MO

Surma Kathleen F
Queen Of Peace HS
Chicago IL

Susz Paul E
Quigley South HS
Chicago IL

Sutherland Pamela L
Fairfield Comm HS
Fairfield IL

Sutherland Susan G
Proviso West HS
Westchester IL

Sutter D Bruce
Octavia HS
Colfax IL

Sutton Carol A
De Soto Sr Ii HS
De Soto MO

Sutton Shelley R
Hyannis HS
Ashby NE

Svanda Cindy R
Trico HS
Percy IL

Svihel Hallie J
Lake Preston HS
Lake Preston SD

Svoboda Mary M
Providence HS
Midlothian IL

Svoboda Mike P
Webb HS
Reedsburg WI

Svoboda Ronda E
Leigh Community HS
Leigh NE

Svoboda Sandra R
Burwell Jr Sr HS
Burwell NE

Swafford David B
Northside HS
Muncie IN

Swafford Jeri A
Union City Sr HS
Tekonsha MI

Swain Sara E
Castle HS
Newburgh IN

Swalley Kevin J
Sanborn Comm HS
Sanborn IA

Swan Mark S
Bloomington HS
Bloomington IL

Swanberg Christine M
Cornell HS
Cornell IL

Swanberg Gary D
Clarissa HS
Clarissa MN

Swanson Barbara L
Muskegon HS
Muskegon MI

Swanson Carol A
Van Buren HS
Douds IA

Swanson Catherine L
Thomas Jefferson HS
Council Bluffs IA

Swanson David L
Colo Comm HS
Colo IA

Swanson Debora C
Alexis HS
Aledo IL

Swanson Denise M
Coal City HS
Coal City IL

Swanson Jay I
Stevens HS
Rapid City SD

Swanson John S
Pekin Community HS
Ollie IA

Swanson Larry D
Johnson Brock Public HS
Tecumseh NE

Swanson Lyndon W
Watseka HS
Martinton IL

Swanson Steven C
Sherburn HS
Dunnell MN

Sward Chris A
Rockford East HS
Rockford IL

Sward Kim M
Belview Public HS
Belview MN

Swart Constance V
Lowell Sr HS
Lowell IN

Swartz Jerry J
Moberly HS
Moberly MO

Swartz William R
East Pike HS
Pittsfield IL

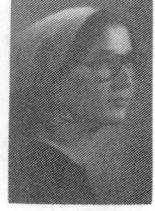

Swartzberg Joanne
Oshkosh West HS
Oshkosh WI

Swartzentruber Barbara D
Ellendale HS
Ellendale ND

Swarup Shashi K
Orleans HS
Orleans IN

Swarz Patrick J
St Ladislaus HS
Detroit MI

Swatts Susan
Bishop Noll Institute HS
Schererville IN

Swearengen Dianne
Milan Cii HS
Milan MO

Sweatman Cheryl J
Virginia HS
Virginia IL

Sweazy John R
Eisenhower HS
Decatur IL

Swedberg Rodney E
Bay City Central HS
Bay City MI

Swedin Mary K
Central HS
Rapid City SD

Sweeney Michael S
Northeast HS
Lincoln NE

Sweeney Patricia A
Maria HS
Chicago IL

Sweeney Peter A
West Bloomfield HS
West Bloomfield MI

Sweet Cynthia J
Emmons Public HS
Emmons MN

Sweet Doreen K
Franklin Public HS
Franklin NE

STUDENTS PHOTOGRAPH SCHEDULED FOR PUBLICATION HERE COULD NOT BE REPRODUCED

Sweet Tommy E
Salem Community HS
Salem IL

Sweigart Mary C
Linwood HS
Linwood KS

Swenson Ann L
Monroe Sr HS
New Glarus WI

Swenson Donna E
Mount Ellis Academy
Halliday ND

Swenson Gail L
Lake Preston HS
Lake Preston SD

Swenson Kimberly R
Storden Jeffers HS
Storden MN

Swenson Laurie K
Storden Jeffers HS
Storden MN

Swieter John A
Maquoketa Comm HS
Maquoketa IA

Swigart Jan E
Eureka HS
Eureka IL

Swiger Janice S
Adrian HS
Adrian MI

Swiger William E
Unionville HS
Lucerne MO

Swille Randall D
Ashwaubenon HS
Green Bay WI

Swindell Cynthia M
Oak Park HS
Kansas City MO

Swiney Windy K
St Mary Academy
Indianapolis IN

Swinford Susie E
Maconaquah HS
Peru IN

Swinney Rhonda J
Centre HS
Herington KS

Swinton Joan M
Arthur Hill HS
Saginaw MI

Swinton Lisa G
Loretto HS
Kansas City MO

Swirtz Thomas L
Eden Prairie HS
Bloomington MN

Swisher Donald D
Stanley County HS
Fort Peirre SD

Switzer Cynthia J
Charleston HS
Charleston IL

Switzer Penny S
Dixon HS
Dixon IL

Swoboda James E
Creighton Preparatory HS
Omaha NE

Swoboda Thomas J
Creighton Prep
Omaha NE

Swomley Dean A
Hudson HS
Hudson IA

Swope Darla A
Greenville HS
Coldwater MO

Swopes Kathy J
Walker HS
Nevada MO

Swords Thomas J
St Thomas Academy
St Paul MN

Sykes Brian L
Cameron HS
Cameron WI

Sykes Cynthia K
Ogallala Senior HS
Ogallala NE

Sykes Teresa M
Alma HS
Naponee NE

Sylvester David A
Pioneer Jr Sr HS
Logansport IN

Syndram Tamara S
Elmhurst HS
Fort Wayne IN

Sypal Mary K
Aguinas HS
Brainard NE

Syron John T
Catholic Central HS
Livonia MI

Syrovatka Ruthie A
Scotland HS
Lesterville SD

Syverson Deborah W
Stewart Public HS
Stewart MN

Syverson Kevin K
Warwick Public HS
Warwick ND

Szabo Mary A
Divine Child HS
Dearborn MI

Szalacha Laura A
St Marys Academy
Chicago IL

Szalewski Stephen M
Washington HS
South Bend IN

Szczesniak Thomas F
Bay City Central HS
Bay City MI

Szczygiel Ted R
St Bonaventure HS
Chicago IL

Szczypka Denis F
St Laurence HS
Chicago IL

Szeszycki Mary L
Ladywood St Agnes HS
Indianapolis IN

Szilagyi Claudia V
Amos Alonzo Stagg HS
Palos Hills IL

Szponder Diane J
Lourdes HS
Chicago IL

Szymanowski Mark D
Whitnall HS
Greenfield WI

Szymoniak Edward J
Highland HS
Highland IN

Szynkowski Kathy A
Adelphian Academy
Royal Oak MI

T

Tabbert Jennifer S
Holmen HS
Onalaska WI

Taber Lynn R
Eldora HS
Eldora IA

Tackett Penny C
Wisconsin Academy
Rock Falls IL

Tader Douglas B
St Francis HS
Minneapolis MN

Tader Naomi L
St Francis HS
Minneapolis MN

Taft Ronald E
Avon Sr HS
Avon IL

Taggart Cynthia M
Columbia Central HS
Brooklyn MI

Taggart Michael W
Casey HS
Hazel Dell IL

Taghon Denise E
Thomas Jefferson HS
Bloomington MN

Tague David F
Noblesville HS
Noblesville IN

Tainter Timothy K
Port Washington HS
Port Washington WI

Takai Thomas A
North Farmington HS
Farmington Hills MI

Takamori Mike H
South Adams HS
Berne IN

Takasaki Ted A
Chatsworth HS
Chatsworth IL

Talarico Sally A
Plainfield HS
Joliet IL

Talbott Bruce F
Greencastle HS
Greencastle IN

Talbott Michael A
Harrison HS
Lafayette IN

Talent Rebecca L
Parkview HS
Springfield MO

Talich Debra G
Sidney HS
Sidney NE

Talkington Mark A
Virden HS
Virden IL

Talsma Dale A
Mason County Central HS
Scottville MI

Tam Christie A
New Trier East HS
Wilmette IL

Tamason Patricia A
Dwight D Eisenhower HS
Blue Island IL

Tamerius Debbie A
Savannah HS
Savannah MO

Tamlyn Scheri L
La Salle HS
St Ignace MI

Tamura Michelle M
Hazel Park HS
Hazel Park MI

Tan Linda L
Esko HS
Esko MN

Tanigawa Joan Y
Lane Tech HS
Chicago IL

Tank Mickey L
North Bend Central HS
North Bend NE

Tankoff Linda M
Sisseton HS
Sisseton SD

Tanle Rickey D
North Bend Central HS
North Bend NE

Tannehill Mitchell B
Pittsford HS
Pittsford MI

Tanner David R
Thornridge HS
Harvey IL

Tapio Lois S
Oak Park River Forest HS
Oak Park IL

Tapley Sheldon C
Parkway Central Sr HS
Chesterfield MO

Taplin Duane A
Adams Friendship HS
Hancock WI

Tapp Teresa L
Yorkville HS
Oswego IL

Tapper Cynthia R
Northeast Hamilton HS
Kamrar IA

Tarman Douglas C
Fairfield Jr Sr HS
New Paris IN

Tarnawa Michael J
York HS
Elmhurst IL

Tarpein Dee L
Adair Co Rii HS
Brashear MO

Tarpley Aubrey V
Caruthersville HS
Caruthersville MO

Tate Alicia L
Hannibal Senior HS
Griggsville IL

Tate Anna L
Floyd Central HS
New Albany IN

Tate Emory D
Concord Comm HS
Elkhart IN

Tate Sandra J
North Division HS
Milwaukee WI

Tate Susan G
R 1 North Callaway HS
Kingdom City MO

Taube Kathleen M
Jefferson City Sr HS
Jefferson City MO

Taussig Cara J
Niles Township No HS
Skokie IL

Taylor Anthony L
Hales Franciscan HS
Chicago IL

Taylor Carol L
Mentor Public HS
Mentor MN

Taylor Carolyn M
Parsons HS
Parsons KS

Taylor Cheryl E
Frederic Remington HS
Benton KS

Taylor Daphne A
William Chrisman HS
Independence MO

Taylor David
Hillsboro HS
Festus MO

Taylor David R
Greensburg Comm HS
Greensburg IN

Taylor Debbie J
Wesclin HS
Trenton IL

Taylor Deborah A
North Platte Sr HS
North Platte NE

Taylor Denise M
Shortridge HS
Indianapolis IN

Taylor Dirk A
Jeffersonville HS
Jeffersonville IN

Taylor Eartha L
West Side HS
Gary IN

Taylor Eldra J
St Mark HS
St Louis MO

Taylor Gayla R
Fairfield HS
Geff IL

Taylor James R
Oak Park HS
Kansas City MO

Taylor Joan E
Willowbrook HS
Villa Park IL

Taylor Joe F
Galena HS
Galena MO

Taylor Julie K
Morton Sr HS
Hammond IN

Taylor Karen L
Gibson Southern HS
Fort Branch IN

Taylor Kristine H
Arthur Hill HS
Saginaw MI

Taylor Lois A
Craig Sr HS
Janesville WI

Taylor Mark A
Mitchell HS
Mitchell IN

Taylor Mark D
Mazon Verona Kinsman
Cons HS
Mazon IL

Taylor Michelle R
Oregon HS
Oregon IL

Taylor Norma J
Providence St Mels HS
Chicago IL

Taylor Peggy S
Mater Dei HS
Beckemeyer IL

Taylor Phyllis R
West Side HS
Gary IN

Taylor Robert J
Sparta HS
Sparta MI

Taylor Scott L
Washington Comm HS
Washington IL

Taylor Susan E
Notre Dame De Sion HS
Leawood KS

Taylor Trent E
Arlington HS
Arlington Hts IL

Teachout Walter F
Hudsonville HS
Hudsonville MI

Tech David M
Brih HS
Brih IA

Teeslink Jan M
Fairmont HS
Fairmont MN

Teeters Kim E
Bemidji Sr HS
Bemidji MN

Te Grootenhuis Kim A
Wheaton Warrenville HS
Wheaton IL

Teigen Ross C
Scranton HS
Gascoyne ND

Telfer Valerie J
Corunna HS
Owosso MI

Telker Patricia C
Charleston R 1 HS
Charleston MO

Tempel Sylvia U
Winona Sr HS
Winona MN

Temple Victoria M
Mc Henry HS
Mc Henry IL

Templeton Randall K
Jefferson City Sr HS
Jefferson City MO

Templin Pattie A
Shawano HS
Shawano WI

Tennant Teresa K
Bayard HS
Bayard NE

Tennelle Melton D
West Side HS
Gary IN

Tepatti Rebecca A
Bullock Creek HS
Midland MI

Terbrock Linda S
Duchesne HS
St Charles MO

Terbush Larry D
Vassar HS
Vassar MI

Teresi Michael J
York Comm HS
Bensenville IL

Terhark Heidi H
Shannon HS
Shannon IL

Terhune Janice M
Savannah R Iii HS
Savannah MO

Terneus Rhonda K
St Teresa HS
Decatur IL

Terpening Timothy D
Waterford Township HS
Union Lake MI

Terpstra Ronald G
N Mahaska Community HS
New Sharon IA

Terrell Roxanne
Salem HS
Salem IN

Terrell Sandra D
Centennial HS
Champaign IL

Terrill Jill D
Gallatin Rv HS
Gallatin MO

Territo Cynthia E
Waterford Mott HS
Pontiac MI

Territo Joseph L
Waterford Mott HS
Pontiac MI

Territo Steven M
Curie HS
Chicago IL

Terry Melody L
Maries R1 HS
Vienna MO

Terveen Lloyd P
Pierce City HS
Wentworth MO

Terwilliger Cindy M
Morrill HS
Morrill NE

Tesdahl Caren A
Clarion Comm HS
Clarion IA

Teters Robert J
Mitchell HS
Mitchell NE

Tetrick Cynthia S
Huntington North HS
Warren IN

Tew Joy R
Marshall HS
Marshall MI

Tex Jim M
Northwest HS
Grand Island NE

Thacker Leanne L
Titonka Consolidated HS
Titonka IA

Thacker Susan C
Central HS
St Joseph MO

Thakor Dennis S
St Marys Central HS
Bismarck ND

Thaldorf Peter D
Cochrane Fountain City HS
Cochrane WI

Thalmann John
Henning HS
Henning MN

Tharnish Albert J
Junction City Sr HS
Junction City KS

Tharp Thomas E
Muncie Northside HS
Muncie IN

Thatcher Bruce C
Twin Rivers HS
Bode IA

Thede Patti A
Unionville Sebewaing HS
Sebewaing MI

Theilgaard Diana L
Luther South HS
Blue Island IL

Theis Linda K
Wausau West HS
Wausau WI

Theisen Annette C
Slinger HS
Allenton WI

Theisen Roger D
New Haven HS
New Haven IN

Thelemann Arthur R
Benilde HS
Golden Valley MN

Theobald Brazilla A
Greenview HS
Greenview IL

Theobald Bruce C
Evanston Twp HS
Evanston IL

Theobald Donald M
Plainfield HS
Joliet IL

Theoret Marilyn G
Gladstone Area HS
Gladstone MI

Thessin Jane E
Mc Farland HS
Mc Farland WI

Thetford Linda K
Herrin Twp HS
Herrin IL

Thibeault Cathy J
Cheboygan Area HS
Cheboygan MI

Thibeault Rene R
Cheboygan Area HS
Cheboygan MI

Thiede Kenneth W
Riverdale HS
Muscoda WI

Thiel Brent L
Central HS
Aberdeen SD

Thiel Donald T
Lawrenceville HS
Lawrenceville IL

Thiel Jane M
Chesaning Union HS
Chesaning MI

Thiel Rob G
Riley HS
South Bend IN

Thiele Lynn E
Valparaiso HS
Valparaiso IN

Thielen Cheryl K
Salina Central HS
Salina KS

Thiess Lori A
Crown Point HS
Crown Point IN

Thiesse Bryan K
Brainerd Sr HS
Brainerd MN

Thill Gregory J
Washington HS
Sioux Falls SD

Thill Ronald M
Thornton Fractional North HS
Calumet City IL

Thode John S
Notre Dame HS
Niles IL

Thoe Gary A
West Lafayette HS
W Lafayette IN

Thoele Mary A
Central Heights HS
Rantoul KS

Thoenen Rose A
Fatima HS
Bonnots Mill MO

Thomann Diane L
Pekin Community HS
Ollie IA

Thomas Althea R
Carthage Senior HS
Carthage MO

Thomas Barbara J
Eureka HS
Eureka IL

Thomas Catherine E
Pittsfield HS
Pittsfield IL

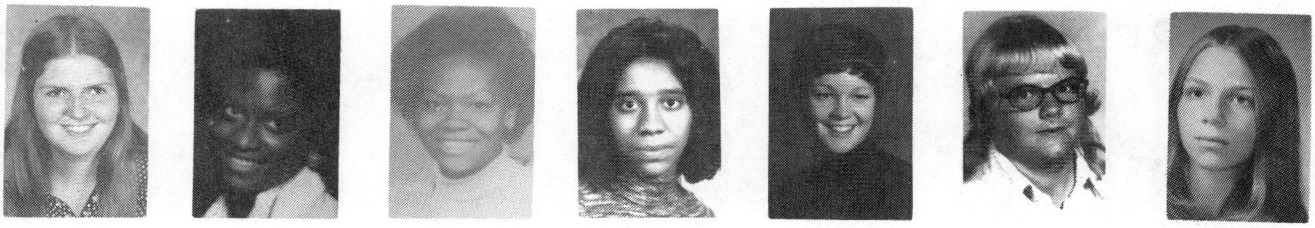

Thomas Cindy J
Basehor HS
Basehor KS

Thomas Denise A
Lovejoy HS
St Louis IL

Thomas Edwina D
Lindblom Tech HS
Chicago IL

Thomas Gywen E
Brethren HS
Wellston MI

Thomas Janet L
Carmi Community HS
Carmi IL

Thomas Karen L
Jetmore HS
Jetmore KS

Thomas Karen M
Clark HS
Hammond IN

Thomas Lane L
Blackford HS
Hartford City IN

Thomas Larry F
Oak Grove HS
Oak Grove MO

Thomas Leonard O
Lindblom Technical HS
Chicago IL

Thomas Lynne M
Farmington East HS
Farmington IL

Thomas Martha A
Lew Wallace HS
Gary IN

Thomas Monica L
Ashland Greenwood Sr HS
Ashland NE

Thomas Nathan B
Connersville Senior HS
Connersville IN

Thomas Pamela L
Inkster HS
Inkster MI

Thomas Pamela S
Onarga HS
Onarga IL

Thomas Patricia A
Custer HS
Milwaukee WI

Thomas Patricia E
Urbandale HS
Des Moines IA

Thomas Reggie D
Acc HS
Holton KS

Thomas Robert W
Glendale HS
Springfield MO

Thomas Robyn E
Brazil Sr HS
Brazil IN

Thomas Ronald J
Eisenhower HS
Saginaw MI

Thomas Russell A
Tri County Comm HS
What Cheer IA

Thomas Sam R
Fair Grove HS
Springfield MO

Thomas Stephen L
Lake Shore HS
St Clair Shores MI

Thomas Steve B
Moline Sr HS
Moline IL

Thompsen Philip H
Halstad Public HS
Halstad MN

Thompson Bonnie S
Pontiac Twp HS
Pontiac IL

Thompson Brian M
Humboldt HS
Humboldt IA

Thompson Carla J
Switz City Central HS
Switz City IN

Thompson Carol D
Edinburg HS
Edinburg IL

Thompson Dale E
Pecatonica HS
Hollandale WI

Thompson Dennis H
Campbell HS
Campbell MO

Thompson Gary O
Viroqua HS
Viroqua WI

Thompson Gerald L
Stillwater Sr HS
Stillwater MN

Thompson James D
Fort Zumwalt HS
St Peters MO

Thompson Joanne M
Central HS
Detroit MI

Thompson Jody M
Harding County HS
Buffalo SD

Thompson John J
St Marys HS
Kansas City MO

Thompson John L
Swea City Comm HS
Swea City IA

Thompson Juli A
Willmar Sr HS
Willmar MN

Thompson Julie E
Chase County HS
Cedar Point KS

Thompson Kimberlee S
Minot HS
Minot ND

Thompson Kris L
Chillicothe HS
Chillicothe MO

Thompson Lea M
Oslo Public HS
Oslo MN

Thompson Lori A
New Haven HS
New Haven MI

Thompson Mark W
Milan HS
Milan MN

Thompson Mary A
Lasalle Peru HS
Peru IL

Thompson Nancy A
Colby HS
Dorchester WI

Thompson Pamela B
Kenwood HS
Chicago IL

Thompson Pamela R
North Knox HS
Bicknell IN

Thompson Philip R
Hartford Union HS
Hartford WI

Thompson Robin M
Geo S Parker Sr HS
Janesville WI

Thompson San B
West Side HS
Gary IN

Thompson Sharon E
Newtown Harris Riii HS
Newtown MO

Thompson Theresa K
Quincy Sr HS
Quincy IL

Thompson Thomas J
Central HS
Red Wing MN

Thompson William J
Newton HS
Willow Hill IL

Thoms Laura G
Nehawka HS
Nehawka NE

Thomson Frederick J
Oscoda Area HS
Mikado MI

Thomure Kathleen A
Oakville HS
St Louis MO

Thon Stephen C
Dighton HS
Healy KS

Thorell Cindy R
Loomis Public HS
Loomis NE

Thornbro Bill
Daleville HS
Daleville IN

Thornburg Anna I
Van Buren Comm HS
Keosauqua IA

Thornburg Gayle N
Wapello Comm HS
Oakville IA

Thorne Alan A
New Trier HS
Wilmette IL

Thorne Alexander D
Greenhills HS
Ann Arbor MI

Thorne Edward R
Roncalli HS
Indianapolis IN

Thornton Debora L
Nesco Community HS
Zearing IA

Thornton Jean M
Hibbing HS
Hibbing MN

Thornton Rebecca R
Lincoln HS
Des Moines IA

Thornton Sue A
Bullock Creek HS
Midland MI

Thorp Julia L
Milton Sr HS
Milton WI

Thorpe Carolyn I
Dearborn HS
Dearborn MI

Thouvenot Mary M
Collinsville HS
Collinsville IL

Throlson Cindy
Bismarck HS
Bismarck ND

Throneburg Debra
Paris HS
Paris IL

Throntveit Jon C
Rich Township E Campus HS
Park Forest IL

Thull Jane L
Berlin HS
Berlin WI

Thurman Michael D
North Central HS
Indianapolis IN

Thurmer Douglas S
Bishop Du Bourg HS
St Louis MO

Thurston Pamela K
Galva HS
Galva IL

Tibboel Lola K
Prairie City Comm HS
Prairie City IA

Tibbs Richard J
Sandoval HS
Sandoval IL

Tibodeau Christine L
Wells Easton HS
Easton MN

Tice Crystal Y
Sullivan HS
Sullivan MO

Tichenor Terry J
Wheaton HS
Wheaton MO

Tidaback Douglas B
La Salle Peru Township HS
La Salle IL

Tiedeman Raymond G
Grayslake Comm HS
Lindenhurst IL

Tiehes Mike A
Pacific HS
Catawissa MO

Tiensvold Carol J
Rushville HS
Rushville NE

Tierney Jane E
Pleasant Hill HS
Pleasant Hill MO

Tieszen Norman E
Marion Ind HS
Marion SD

Tietsort Cheryl A
Laplata Rii HS
Laplata MO

Tiffin Vicki L
Casey HS
Casey IL

Tilden Diann E
Greenway HS
Grand Rapids MN

Tillemans Tammy M
Marshall Senior HS
Marshall MN

Tillery Jeffrey M
Divernon Twp HS
Divernon IL

Tillitt Glenn S
Beardstown Sr HS
Beardstown IL

Tillman Carol S
Mexico HS
Mexico MO

Timbs Karen A
Polo HS
Sterling IL

Timinsky Herbert M
North Side HS
Fort Wayne IN

Timm Claire R
Eustis Public HS
Eustis NE

Timm Donna J
Monroe HS
Monroe WI

Timmerman Gary B
Papillion HS
Papillion NE

Timmerman Judith A
Watertown Sr HS
Watertown SD

Timmerman Terri L
Dwight Township HS
Dwight IL

Timmis Michael W
North Side HS
Fort Wayne IN

Timmreck Julie A
Alpena Sr HS
Ossineke MI

Timpany Cindy M
Parker HS
Janesville WI

Tindall Cathy M
Emerson HS
Gary IN

Tindall Mike L
Chester HS
Chester IL

Tinebra Paul R
Grafton HS
Grafton WI

Tinker Nancy E
Macomb Sr HS
Macomb IL

Tinker Sherry A
Civic Memorial HS
Bethalto IL

Tinkey David M
Warsaw Community HS
Warsaw IN

Tinkham Scott A
Sargent HS
Sargent NE

Tippin James H
North Putnam HS
Greencastle IN

Tippit Stephen L
Charleston HS
Charleston IL

Tipton Jerry R
Union County HS
Liberty IN

Tipton Mary A
Roosevelt HS
Gary IN

Tischer Linda M
Wellcome Memorial HS
Good Thunder MN

Tislow Gregory L
Sullivan HS
Carlisle IN

Titel Lisa M
Wrightstown HS
Wrightstown WI

Titherage Steve C
Holly HS
Holly MI

Titus Leslie A
Okabena HS
Okabena MN

Titus Veda R
West Side HS
Gary IN

Titzer Demara J
North HS
Evansville IN

Toader Adrian
Lincoln Park HS
Lincoln Park MI

Toberman Terri L
Harold L Richards HS
Alsip IL

Tobey Christine E
Corunna HS
Corunna MI

Tobin Anthony K
Maryville Rii HS
Maryville MO

Tobin David M
Flint Central HS
Flint MI

Tobin Thomas M
Shawnee Mission West HS
Overland Park KS

Toburen Amy E
Wausau East HS
Wausau WI

Toburen Theodore L
Geneva HS
Geneva IL

Tobyne Arlis E
Clifton HS
Clifton KS

Todd Jonathan L
Sunshine Bible Academy
Onida SD

Todd Michael W
University City Sr HS
University City MO

Todd Susan A
Civic Memorial HS
Bethalto IL

Todorofsky Irwin M
Homewood Flossmoor HS
Chicago Hts IL

Todt Karen E
Brighton HS
Brighton MI

Tokar Susan D
Mattoon Senior HS
Mattoon IL

Tokar Thomas F
Goshen HS
Goshen IN

Toliver Cathy S
Marshall HS
Marshall IL

Tollas Michael A
Lakeshore HS
Stevensville MI

Tolliver Kevin L
John Pershing HS
Detroit MI

Tolstedt Brad L
Gordon HS
Gordon NE

Tomaszewski Diane M
Crivitz HS
Crivitz WI

Tomaszewski Randy L
Lasalle Peru Twp HS
Peru IL

Tomes Kathy M
Eastern HS
Salem IN

Tometich John J
Muscatine HS
Muscatine IA

Tominac Karen S
De Tour Area HS
Goetzville MI

STUDENTS PHOTOGRAPH SCHEDULED FOR PUBLICATION HERE COULD NOT BE REPRODUCED

Tomko Kender T
Hinsdale Twp Central HS
Hinsdale IL

Tomkovich Edward J
North Chicago Comm HS
North Chicago IL

Tomlinson Joy A
Academy Of The Sacred Heart
Birmingham MI

Tomlinson Martha E
Macon HS
Macon IL

Tomlinson Teresa E
Cowden Herrick HS
Lakewood IL

Tomlinson Virginia M
North Huron HS
Kinde MI

Tompkins Chauncey T
Midland Comm HS
Wyoming IA

Tompkins Jacqueline A
Mullinville HS
Ford KS

Toms Terri D
Benton HS
Benton IL

Tomson Debra J
North Miami HS
Denver IN

Tonies Rose M
O Fallon Twp HS
O Fallon IL

Tonn Catherine J
Elmhurst HS
Ft Wayne IN

Tonn Martha L
Moorhead HS
Moorhead MN

Toole Lewis M
Stanton Co HS
Manter KS

Toole Pamela S
Gideon HS
Gideon MO

Toombs Vicki C
Fairfield Community HS
Fairfield IL

Tope Kelly L
Collinsville HS
Collinsville IL

Topp Susan L
West Central HS
Francesville IN

Torbica Sophia
Washington HS
East Chicago IN

Torrence Roberta E
Hanover Central HS
Cedar Lake IN

Torres Christine V
Mother Of Sorrows HS
Dolton IL

Torres Enid
Bishop Noll Institute
East Chicago IN

Torres Ernest E
Berlin HS
Berlin WI

Torres Guy A
St George HS
Manhattan KS

Torres Jose G
Gering HS
Gering NE

Torrey Tammy R
Fairbury HS
Fairbury NE

Torry David A
Hutchinson HS
Hutchinson MN

Tortorea Suzanne A
Irving Crown HS
Carpentersville IL

Tortorelli James P
Maine Twp West HS
Des Plaines IL

Tosh Randall D
Valley Falls HS
Valley Falls KS

Toso Sarah E
Stoughton HS
Stoughton WI

Totman Jo A
Edgewood Colesburg Comm HS
Edgewood IA

Totten Carmen K
White Cloud HS
White Cloud MI

Tourtellotte Donald A
Saugatuck HS
Glenn MI

Towarnicky Michael R
Fessenden HS
Fessenden ND

Towell Michael G
Martinsville HS
Martinsville IN

Tower Craig W
York HS
Elmhurst IL

Townsend Brian T
Griffin HS
Springfield IL

Trachte Cynthia L
Pittsville HS
Arpin WI

Tracy Gregory L
Clarion HS
Clarion IA

Tracy Lillian G
Yale HS
Goodells MI

Trafton Wyatt A
Christian Brother Collage
St Louis MO

Tragarz Dennis E
Alleman HS
Rock Island IL

Trainor Colleen A
Streator Twp HS
Blackstone IL

Trainor Neal R
Galena HS
Galena IL

Trambly Lori R
Franklin Public HS
Franklin NE

Trammel Kevin G
Marion HS
Marion IL

Trapp Terry L
Delavan Darien HS
Delavan WI

Trautsch Cynthia
Oak Lawn Community HS
Oak Lawn IL

Travis Donna M
Platte Public HS
Academy SD

Treasure Sandra J
Kirksville Sr HS
Kirksville MO

Trebra Janice L
J I Case HS
Racine WI

Trecartin Diane E
Warren HS
Gurnee IL

Tremain Thomas M
Columbus North HS
Columbus IN

Trembly Barbara S
Cardinal Community HS
Agency IA

Trent Danny C
Hutchinson HS
Hutchinson KS

Trent Paulanna L
Cedar Vale HS
Cedar Vale KS

Trenum David H
Canyonville Bible Academy
Indianapolis IN

Trevett Marylee B
Milbank HS
Milbank SD

Trewartha Carol A
Streator Twp HS
Streator IL

Tribble Sherman R
Lindblom Tech HS
Chicago IL

Tribby Yvonne M
Kansas HS
Kansas IL

Tribitt Robert C
Magic City Campus HS
Minot ND

Triefenbach Laura K
Crystal Lake Community HS
Crystal Lake IL

Trigg Cindy A
North Miami HS
Macy IN

Trigg Michael E
Lillis HS
Kansas City MO

Triggs David A
South Clay Community HS
Dickens IA

Trimarchi Julie A
Bishop Dwenger HS
Ft Wayne IN

Trinkle Jeffrey D
Albia Comm HS
Albia IA

Tripam Linda A
Mother Mcauley HS
Oak Lawn IL

Triplett Ann M
Brazil HS
Brazil IN

Tripp Jeffrey A
Adrian HS
Adrian MI

Tripp Sandra L
Newton Senior HS
Newton IA

Troemel Michael B
Thornwood HS
So Holland IL

Troester Mary Jo
Forman Sargent Central HS
Cayuga ND

Trokey Judy F
Potosi HS
Mineral Point MO

Trolinger Mark A
Arcadia Valley HS
Ironton MO

Trombley Janine M
Reese HS
Reese MI

Tromley Robert T
Lincoln HS
Vincennes IN

Trosen Cindy L
Larimore HS
Larimore ND

Troshynski Jerry J
West Holt HS
Atkinson NE

Troshynski Tom J
West Holt HS
Atkinson NE

Trost Joanne C
Warren HS
Warren IL

Trost Steven M
Taylorville HS
Taylorville IL

Trotter Andrea J
Coal City HS
Coal City IL

Trotter Jim S
Edgemont HS
Provo SD

Trout Pamela K
New Palestine HS
Greenfield IN

Trout Scott E
Northside HS
Muncie IN

Trout William E
New Palestine HS
Greenfield IN

Troutman Mark R
Bishop Luers HS
New Haven IN

Trovillion David P
Pope County Comm HS
Golconda IL

Troxel Carol L
Clinton HS
Clinton IL

Troxell Monte R
Chrysler HS
New Castle IN

Trudeau Michele A
Reese HS
Vassar MI

Truelove Kevin M
East Noble HS
La Otto IN

Truetken Robert L
Wheatland HS
Park KS

Trump John R
Topeka West HS
Evanton IL

Trussell Debra K
Mt Pleasant HS
Mt Pleasant MI

Tryon Thea A
Waterford Mott HS
Pontiac MI

Tschanz Susan E
Monroe Sr HS
Monroe WI

Tscharner Larry
Stephan Hempstead HS
Dubuque IA

Tsouchlos Gussie
Thorton Fractional North HS
Calumet City IL

Tubbs Denise
Northrop HS
Ft Wayne IN

Tubbs Terry W
Craig Riii HS
Bigelow MO

Tucker Debra J
Warsaw Comm HS
Warsaw IN

Tucker Julie K
Escanaba Sr HS
Escanaba MI

Tucker Kelley A
University HS
Milwaukee WI

Tucker Kevin L
Roxana Sr HS
South Roxana IL

Tucker Patricia A
O Fallon Twns HS
O Fallon IL

Tucker William T
Evanston Twp HS
Evanston IL

Tuckett Harold W
Swartz Creek HS
Flint MI

Tudisco Catherine M
Taft HS
Chicago IL

Tufte Mark G
Northwood HS
Northwood ND

Tuggle Robert M
Centerville HS
Richmond IN

Tukesbrey Robert A
Deerfield HS
Deerfield IL

Tumavich James R
Morton East HS
Cicero IL

Tummett David J
Appleton West HS
Appleton WI

Tumy Tamara L
Boonville HS
Boonville MO

Tunnell David W
Jeffersonville HS
Jeffersonville IN

Turbett Marilyn K
Farmington East HS
Hanna City IL

Tureson David R
Harlem HS
Loves Park IL

Turley Erica J
Hobart Sr HS
Hobart IN

Turley Janie L
East Prairie HS
East Prairie MO

Turley Jerri L
Kewanee HS
Kewanee IL

Turley Pamela S
Roseville HS
Roseville IL

Turnage Pamela S
Carthage Sr HS
Carthage MO

Turner Dean F
Avon Comm School Corp HS
Plainfield IN

Turner Denis A
Hartville HS
Hartville MO

Turner Jeffrey K
North Vermillion HS
Danville IL

Turner Lonnie M
Austin HS
Austin IN

Turner Lynn M
Stillman Valley HS
Davis Junction IL

Turner Mark D
Yates City HS
Yates City IL

Turner Nan L
Hudson Sr HS
Hudson WI

Turner Patrice K
Sioux Valley HS
Harris IA

Turner Sanita A
West Side Sr HS
Gary IN

Turner Shawn C
Springfield Se HS
Springfield IL

Turner Teresa M
Stephen Decatur HS
Decatur IL

Turner Terri D
Northern HS
Flint MI

Turner Timothy H
Joliet Catholic HS
Braidwood IL

Turney Kevin N
Mellen HS
Mellen WI

Turpin Jane A
Troy HS
Troy KS

Turzenski Terese B
Lourdes Academy
Oshkosh WI

Tusa Edward A
Eueleth HS
Eveleth MN

Tuscherer Joy A
Lennox Public HS
Lennox SD

Tuttle Debra K
Breckenridge R 1 HS
Breckenridge MO

Tuttle Karen D
Allegan HS
Allegan MI

Tutush Dusan
Morton Sr HS
Hammond IN

Twedt John B
Ballard HS
Slater IA

Twibell Cynthia J
Blackford HS
Hartford IN

Twyman Timothy E
Orrick HS
Orrick MO

Tyner Angela L
Fountain Central HS
Veedersburg IN

Tyra Kenneth T
Pioneer HS
Ann Arbor MI

Tyson Donna K
Cambridge Public HS
Cambridge NE

Tysowsky George W
Brady HS
St Paul MN

U

Uber Norma J
Catholic Central HS
Custer MI

Udelhoven Karen A
Bloomington HS
Bloomington WI

Udell Jack W
Burwell Jr Sr HS
Burwell NE

Udell Jeri K
New Glarus HS
New Glarus WI

Udell Suzanne R
Salem HS
Salem IN

Uecker Jan E
Lena Winslow HS
Lena IL

Uerling Lisa A
Republican Valley HS
Indianola NE

Ukkestad Elizabeth A
Rushford Public #234 HS
Rushford MN

Uldrich Ronald P
Milligan Public HS
Milligan NE

Ulfers Dallas J
Jefferson HS
Cedar Rapids IA

Ulfers Rebecca L
Fairbury Cropsey HS
Fairbury IL

Ullstrup Mary C
Greenfield HS
Greenfield WI

Ullstrup Michael M
Greenfield HS
Greenfield WI

Ulm Lori L
Southeast HS
Springfield IL

Ulrich Joan R
Eureka HS
Eureka IL

Ulrich Mary Anne L
West Liberty HS
Nichols IA

Ulrich Rita M
Concordia Academy
Apple Valley MN

Ulrich Terry W
Ashley HS
Ashley ND

Umberger Barbara S
De Soto HS
Stoddard WI

Umberger Jean M
Desoto HS
Genoa WI

Umfleet Daniel E
Mt Zion HS
Mount Zion IL

Umphrey William J
Bradley Bourbonnais HS
Bourbonnais IL

Underwood Jonathan A
Seymour HS
Seymour MO

Underwood Kimberly J
Jefferson City Sr HS
Jefferson City MO

Underwood Sheri L
Hanover Central HS
Cedar Lake IN

Underwood Theresa A
Bradley Bourbonnais HS
Bourbonnais IL

Undi Joanne K
Donald E Gavit HS
Hammond IN

Unger Neal S
Lincoln Se HS
Lincoln NE

Unke Kimberly D
Fairmont HS
Fairmont MN

Unkraut Sue K
St Anthony HS
Effingham IL

Unruh Dale G
Great Bend HS
Great Bend KS

Unruh Janice D
Berean Academy
Valley Center KS

Unruh John M
Colby HS
Colby KS

Unruh Leon D
Macksville HS
Pawnee Rock KS

Unruh Mary L
Niles East HS
Skokie IL

Unruh Susan G
Macksville HS
Pawnee Rock KS

Unzen Rebecca A
Madison Public HS
Madison MN

Upham Sally R
St Charles HS
St Charles IL

Upschulte Bernard L
Quincy HS
Quincy IL

Upston Russell E
Marshall HS
Marshall MI

Urata Guy V
Francis Parker HS
Chicago IL

Urban Kathy J
Otis Bison Sr HS
Albert KS

Urbance Mary T
Streator Twp HS
Streator IL

Urbanski Constance M
Boylan Central Cath HS
Rockford IL

Urbas Andrea
Hinsdale Twp HS South
Darien IL

Urbauer John R
Evergreen Park C HS
Evergreen Park IL

Urbina James R
Franklin Public HS
Bloomington NE

Urfer Brian D
Lyons Township HS
Western Springs IL

Urish Dave A
Green Valley HS
Green Valley IL

Ussery William C
El Dorado HS
El Dorado KS

Utlaut Ronald N
St Charles HS
St Charles MO

Utley Lisa G
East Detroit HS
East Detroit MI

Utsler Janis L
Mt Zion HS
Decatur IL

Utterback Lori J
Hannibal Sr HS
Hannibal MO

Uzubell Ronald J
Lake Central HS
Crown Point IN

V

Vacek Susan J
Bloom Township HS
Chicago Hgts IL

Vagner Ellen
Bonner Springs HS
Bonner Springs KS

Vahala Michael E
Elkhart Memorial HS
Elkhart IN

Vai Laurel R
Highland Park HS
Highland Park IL

Vail Karen S
Mt Vernon Comm HS
Mc Cordsville IN

Vail Mary S
Central Catholic HS
Bloomington IL

Valdez Marie V
Gabriel Richard HS
Riverview MI

Valenti Catherine J
Mehlville HS
St Louis MO

Valentine Joseph L
Blakesburg HS
Blakesburg IA

Valette Elaine M
Christopher Community HS
Mulkeytown IL

Valitis Barbara A
Maria HS
Chicago IL

Vallandingham Terry M
Niobrara HS
Niobrara NE

Valley Lynn L
Wabeno HS
Wabena WI

Vammer Paul D
Glenham HS
Glenham SD

Vana David B
William Howard Taft HS
Chicago IL

Vanags Laura A
Proviso West HS
Hillside IL

Vanasse Bradley S
Bemidji HS
Bemidji MN

Van Beek Calvin K
Central Wisc Christian HS
Randolph WI

Van Beek Clifford W
Marion Ind HS
Marion SD

Van Beek Mary L
Rock Valley Comm HS
Rock Valley IA

Van Brooker Laurie L
Southeastern HS
Augusta IL

Van Buskirk Dorthy A
Liberal HS
Liberal KS

Van Buskirk Randy A
St Clair HS
St Clair MI

Vance Kevin G
Central HS
St Joseph MO

Vance Kimberly C
Arlington HS
Indianapolis IN

Vance Lauren M
Unity HS
Chicago IL

Vance Roy E
International Falls Sr HS
International Flls MN

Vancil Linda S
Du Quoin HS
Du Quoin IL

Van Cleave Deanna D
Tippecanoe Valley HS
Silver Lake IN

Van Dam Blaine A
Lincoln HS
Sioux Falls SD

Vandeberg Marcia R
Neillsville HS
Neillsville WI

Van De Graaf William C
Bloomfield Hills Lahser HS
Bloomfield Hills MI

Van De Mark Sheryl L
Culver Community HS
Culver IN

Vandemore Roxanne M
Hudson HS
Hudson SD

Vanden Akker Martin
Albion Senior HS
Albion MI

Vandenberg Darwin J
Worthington Sr HS
Brewster MN

Vandenberg Robert W
Martin Public HS
Martin MI

Vanden Berg Scott B
Holland HS
Holland MI

Vanden Bosch Randall J
Zeeland HS
Zeeland MI

Van Den Broeke Duane
Marshall HS
Marshall MN

Vander Beek Paula L
No Mahaska HS
New Sharon IA

Vanderby Christine D
Thornton Fractional South HS
Lansing IL

Vanderhoof Lovina K
Campus HS
Wichita KS

Vander Laan Jerry D
Lake City Area HS
Lake City MI

Van Der Linden Karey
Joliet East HS
Joliet IL

Vander Maazen Lisa B
Xavier HS
Appleton WI

Vandermark Cinda J
George A Dondero HS
Royal Oak MI

Vander Plas Cynthia A
Lake Fenton HS
Fenton MI

Vanderpool Roger D
Triopia Jr Sr HS
Arenzville IL

Vandersnick Margaret L
Ewing Public HS
Ewing NE

Vander Veen David S
Pontiac Central HS
Sylvan Lake MI

Vander Veen Linda R
Chicago Christian HS
Oak Lawn IL

Vande Streek Mary A
St Mary Springs HS
Fond Du Lac WI

Van Deusen Timothy C
Waterford Township HS
Pontiac MI

Van Deventer David L
Taylorville HS
Taylorville IL

Van De Voorde Mary J
Erie HS
Erie IL

Van De Voort Gregory L
Phillips HS
Kennan WI

Vande Voort John J
Ashwaubenon HS
Green Bay WI

Vandiver Bob D
Houston HS
Cabool MO

Vandivort Dave J
Maple Valley HS
Mapleton IA

Van Dyke Steven W
Almont HS
Almont MI

Vanetti Carol S
Park Hill Sr HS
Parkville MO

Van Hartesvelt Dennis L
West Ottawa HS
Holland MI

Van Hook Jeanie M
Otterville Public HS
Florence MO

Van Hooser Jacky W
Carl Junction HS
Joplin MO

Van Horn Shelley R
Humboldt Comm Public HS
Humboldt IA

Van Horn Thomas E
St Marys Springs HS
Plymouth WI

Van Houtan Raymond L
Columbus Public HS
Columbus ND

Van Houten Sidney C
Airport Community HS
Carleton MI

Van Hove Lorri K
Brookings HS
Brookings SD

Van Hoveln Theresa J
Crescent Iroquois HS
Milford IL

Van Iseghem Margaret J
Incarnate Word Academy
St Ann MO

Van Klompenburg David W
Montevideo Senior HS
Montevideo MN

Van Kooten Cheryl J
Pella Christian HS
Pella IA

Vann Pamela D
Concordia Acad
St Paul MN

Van Ness Elaine G
Brazil Sr HS
Brazil IN

Van Noy Kathleen D
Centerville HS
Centerville IA

Van Ostrand Myra J
Buffalo Lake Sr HS
Buffalo Lake MN

Van Pelt Marianne
Banner County HS
Kimball NE

Van Petten Jeffrey F
Mission Valley HS
Eskridge KS

Van Rheenen Randy L
Mendota HS
Mendota IL

Van Riper Michael J
Onalaska HS
Onalaska WI

Van Scoy Brenda L
Dixon HS
Dixon MO

Van Slooten Timothy A
Holland HS
Holland MI

Vant Hof Cindy L
Jenison HS
Jwenison MI

Vantrease Mark S
Alton Sr HS
Alton IL

Van Treeck Robert J
Lyons Township HS
La Grange IL

Vantrump Mike A
Carrollton HS
Carrollton MO

Van Vranken Bradley D
Meade HS
Meade KS

Van Wassenhove Christine M
Annawan HS
Sheffield IL

Van Wassenhove Douglas J
Kewanee HS
Kewanee IL

Van Winkle Gwendolyn J
Northeastern Wayne HS
Fountain City IN

Vanyo Phillip J
Alvarado HS
E Grand Forks MN

Vanyo Richard G
Sacred Heart HS
East Grand Forks MN

Van Zee Cheryl L
White Lake Ind HS
White Lake SD

Varble Randall S
Rochelle Township HS
Rochelle IL

Varble Vickey L
United Twp HS
East Moline IL

Vardsveen Kathryn A
Magic City Campus HS
Minot ND

Varga Wilma A
Monroe City R 1 HS
Monroe MO

Vargo Theresa A
Resurrection HS
Chicago IL

Vargus Lorie J
Hannibal HS
Hannibal MO

Varnum Annette M
Colo Comm HS
Colo IA

Varvell Keith W
Malden HS
Malden MO

Vasdekas Tom J
Lane Tech HS
Chicago IL

Vasile Betty Ann
Argo Community HS
Justice IL

Vaske Leroy K
Watertown Senior HS
Watertown SD

Vasper Harley E
Saltillo HS
Moberly MO

Vasquez Kenneth R
Elk Grove HS
Elk Grove Vlg IL

Vassar Timothy M
Highland HS
Highland IN

Vaughn Celeste A
Ann Arbor Huron HS
Ann Arbor MI

Vaughn Daniel L
Grandview HS
Grandview MO

Vaughn Gregory A
Marquette HS
Alton IL

Vaughn Pamela J
Maconaquah HS
Peru IN

Vaughn Sharon D
Academy Of Our Lady
Chicago IL

Vaughn Toby M
Pana Sr HS
Pana IL

Vaughn William R
Lincoln HS
Vincennes IN

Veach Glenn O
Claflin HS
Claphlin KS

Veach Priscilla J
Paris HS
Paris IL

Veatch Gary D
Monroe City R I HS
Monroe City MO

Vedas Steven B
Pekin Community HS
Pekin IL

Vedral Maria J
Immaculate Heart Of Mary HS
Cicero IL

Veduei Alan J
Lake Preston Public HS
Hetland SD

Veerkamp Gregory W
Bishop Dwenger HS
Fort Wayne IN

Veesart John A
Clifton Rural HS
Clifton KS

Vega Inez C
Harrison HS
Chicago IL

Veith Anthony J
Clearwater HS
Viola KS

Veith John G
Cardinal Stritch HS
Keokuk IA

Velasquez Teresa N
Lake Central HS
Crown Point IN

Veldhuizen Mark G
Oskaloosa Sr HS
Oskaloosa IA

Velez Debra A
Granite City South HS
Granite City IL

Venable Francilda A
Rolla HS
Newburg MO

Venable Susan E
Slater HS
Slater MO

Venardos Christine
Southwest HS
St Louis MO

Vencill Jennifer J
Trenton HS
Trenton MO

Venegas Marcelina C
West Side Sr HS
Gary IN

Ventimiglia Roseanne M
Carl Brablec HS
Roseville MI

Ventre Christine M
Milford HS
Highland MI

Ventres William B
Pine Crest HS
Hopkins MN

Venturi Joan L
Toluca HS
Toluca IL

Venzke Deanna L
Ventura Comm HS
Clear Lake IA

Verbeck Brenda G
Holdrege HS
Funk NE

Verbeck Julia L
Winfield HS
Winfield KS

Verboomen Susan A
Wrightstown HS
Kaukauna WI

Verduzco Michelle T
Andrean HS
Gary IN

Verge Karen E
Streator HS
Streator IL

Vermeesch Pam M
Garber HS
Essexville MI

Ver Ploeg Scott L
Lynnville Sully HS
Sully IA

Verwold Julia A
Union County HS
Liberty IN

Vessels Joey A
Gibson Southern HS
Ft Branch IN

Vestal Barbara L
Marshfield HS
Marshfield MO

Vestal Jennifer L
Niangua HS
Niangua MO

Vestuto Paul V
Wheaton Central HS
Wheaton IL

Vetrone Deborah L
Neillsville HS
Neillsville WI

Vetter Daniel R
Sully Buttes HS
Onida SD

Vetter Kathleen M
Incarnate Word Academy
St Louis MO

Vetter Michael J
Mankato East HS
Kasota MN

Veurink Calvin G
Dakota Christian HS
Harrison SD

Vezain Thomas L
La Salle Peru HS
Utica IL

Vickers Barbara J
Wellsville HS
Ottawa KS

Vickers Dennis W
Pacific HS
Pacific MO

Vickers Timothy C
Dollar Bay HS
Dollar Bay MI

Vidal Patricia A
Andrean HS
Crown Point IN

Videen Susan M
Chisago Lakes HS
Chisago City MN

Vidimos Alfred S
Andrean HS
Merrillville IN

Vidimos Allison T
Andrean HS
Merrillville IN

Vidito Robert S
Fowlerville HS
Fowlerville MI

Vieaux Peter M
Rhinelander Sr HS
Rhinelander WI

Vied Nancy C
Charleston R 1 HS
Charleston MO

Viet Dennis D
Dike Community HS
Reinbeck IA

Vieta Patricia K
Jackson HS
Jackson MI

Vieth Perry J
Marinette HS
Marinette WI

Vigliaturo Antionette R
St Marys HS
Kansas City MO

Vilander Richard A
Wamego HS
Wamego KS

Villalobos Patricia A
St Augustine HS
Chicago IL

Villhard Victor J
Bishop Du Bourg HS
St Louis MO

Vincent Kent A
Pleasant Valley HS
Bettendorf IA

Vincent Peggy S
Clarks Public HS
Clarks NE

Vincentini Anthony R
Bishop Borgess HS
Detroit MI

Vine Charles J
Pontiac Northern HS
Pontiac MI

Vint Kathy A
St Marys HS
Storm Lake IA

Virgin Becky J
Mt Vernon HS
Mc Cordsville IN

Visintainer Mary M
Norway HS
Norway MI

Visser Nancy J
Hinsdale Central HS
Hinsdal IL

Visser Patricia A
Holland Christian HS
Holland MI

Vitck Michael G
Subiaco Academy
West Chester IL

Vlasic Anica
Sts Peter And Paul HS
Saginaw MI

Vlasin Randy A
Hayes County HS
Hayes Center NE

Vock Donald E
Polo Comm HS
Polo IL

Vodnik Sandra J
Whitnall HS
Hales Corners WI

Voelpel Thomas E
Lawrence Central HS
Indianapolis IN

Vogel David G
Duluth Central HS
Duluth MN

Vogel Dawn R
Fulton HS
Fulton IL

Vogel Gary G
Sanborn Public HS
Sanborn MN

Vogel Julie L
Pike HS
Indianapolis IN

Vogel Kendall L
Bayard HS
Bayard NE

Vogel Kevin L
Bayard HS
Bayard NE

Vogel Lisa A
Richmond Burton HS
Richmond IL

Vogel Monica A
Mankato West HS
N Mankato MN

Vogel Paul J
St Marys HS
Lemay MO

Vogelman Marc R
Remington HS
Potwin KS

Vogen Jeffrey L
Newark HS
Newark IL

Vogt Dale
Slinger HS
Slinger WI

Vogts Paula K
Canton Galva HS
Canton KS

Vohland Robert G
Valley HS
Canton IL

Vohland William H
Spoon River Valley Jr Sr HS
Canton IL

Voie Ellen C
Iola Scandinivia HS
Iola WI

Voight Barbara S
Auburndale HS
Arpin WI

Voigt Dorothy A
Thornwood HS
Thornton IL

Voigt Kari L
Beulah HS
Zap ND

Voisard Michael J
Marysville HS
Marysville MI

Volk Raymond E
Western Dubuque HS
Cascade IA

Volkert Paul D
West Bend E HS
West Bend WI

Volkmuth Steve H
Apollo HS
St Cloud MN

Vollbracht Roger D
Central HS
Clayton IL

Vollmerhausen Susan L
Gabriel Richard HS
Wyandotte MI

Volmer Michael W
Lyman HS
Presho SD

Volner Enid I
Lesterville HS
Black MO

Volz Bruce E
Norway Comm HS
Norway IA

Vonada Damon R
Sylvan Unified HS
Sylvan Grove KS

Vonderfecht Susan M
Holbrook HS
Holbrook NE

Von Seggern Randy E
Wisner Pilger HS
Wisner NE

Von Spreckelsen Lyle D
Clay Center Public HS
Clay Center NE

Voorheis Philip J
Oak Hill Jr Sr HS
Swayzee IN

Voracek Kris K
Yankton Sr HS
Yankton SD

Voreis Diane L
Hinckley Big Rock HS
Somonauk IL

Vorisek Robert F
Marmion Mil Academy
Fox River Grove IL

Vorland Ronald D
North Central HS
Clear Lake IA

Vortherms Daniel T
Spalding HS
Hospers IA

Vos Larry D
Chander Lake Wilson HS
Slayton MN

Voskuil Joseph C
Cedar Grove HS
Cedar Grove WI

Voss Betty J
Eddyville Comm HS
Eddyville IA

Voss Karen J
Bishop Mc Namara HS
Saint Anne IL

Voss Robert J
Thornridge HS
So Holland IL

Voss Sherri L
Hastings HS
Hastings MI

Vossler Kimberly A
Wishek Public HS
Wishek ND

Votruba Colleen M
Hemingford HS
Hemingford NE

Voyles Delinda J
Westville HS
Westville IL

Vrab James L
Thornton Fractional South HS
Lansing IL

Vraney Serene M
W Chicago Comm HS
West Chicago IL

Vrhel Janet A
Morton West HS
Lyons IL

Vroman Marc R
Tri County HS
Hancock WI

Vrtis Ann M
St Edward HS
St Charles IL

Vruno Nancy J
Maria HS
Chicago IL

Vrzak Cindy L
Turkey Valley HS
Waucoma IA

Vyas Usha
Rich East HS
Park Forest IL

W

Waatti Irene L
Hartland HS
Howell MI

Wacaser John D
Arlington Hts HS
Arlington Hts IL

Wackerie Rex B
La Ville HS
Lapaz IN

Waddell Jeanette L
Newton Comm HS
Newton IL

Wade Gordon E
Shabbona HS
Malta IL

Wade Michael R
Delta C7 HS
Bragg City MO

Wade Nina S
Malta Bend R V HS
Malta Bend MO

Wade William E
St Johns Cathedral HS
Milwaukee WI

Wadekamper Debra A
Good Counsel Academy
Mankato MN

Waderich Renita R
Dow City Arion HS
Dow City IA

Wadhams Jane M
Huron HS
Huron SD

Wadleigh Alan D
Madison Public HS
Madison MN

Wadman Gary A
Walter P Chrysler Mem HS
New Castle IN

Wadsworth Joni D
Charlestown HS
Charlestown IN

Wadsworth Larry J
El Paso HS
El Paso IL

Wadsworth Sally J
North Scott HS
Davenport IA

Waechter Daryle A
Forrest Strawn Wing HS
Forrest IL

Wagar Sherry L
Croswell Lexington HS
Jeddo MI

Wager Pamela S
North Decatur HS
Greensburg IN

Waggoner David W
Truman HS
Independence MO

Waggoner Paul R
Alma Public HS
Republican City NE

Waggoner Reford W
Lawrenceville HS
Lawrenceville IL

Waggoner Sara J
Danville HS
Danville IL

Wagner Ben J
Kee HS
Lansing IA

Wagner Beth A
Duchesne HS
St Charles MO

Wagner Charles A
Kiel HS
Kiel WI

Wagner Christine L
Divernon HS
Divernon IL

Wagner Cynthia J
Yates Center HS
Yates Center KS

Wagner Delmin C
Litchfield HS
Litchfield MN

Wagner Harry W
Grand Blanc HS
Grand Blanc MI

Wagner Holly S
Wyaconda HS
Luray MO

Wagner Janet S
Highland HS
Highland IN

Wagner Karen K
Corunna HS
Owosso MI

Wagner Mark G
St Marys HS
St Louis MO

Wagner Michael J
Quigley South HS
Chicago IL

Wagner Michael Q
Oconomowoc Sr HS
Oconomowoc WI

Wagner Micheal L
Dorchester HS
Dorchester NE

Wagner Neil L
Howell HS
Brighton MI

Wagner Rory K
La Crosse HS
Rush Center KS

Wagner Teresa M
Logan View HS
Hooper NE

Wagner Tina M
Standish Sterling Central HS
Sterling MI

Wagner Vicki L
Pleasant Hill HS
Pleasant Hill MO

Wahid Sunita J
St Ann HS
Cicero IL

Wahlberg Gwen A
Hudson Sr HS
Hudson WI

Wahlheim Debora J
J D Darnall HS
Geneseo IL

Waidmann Randall C
Owensville HS
Gerald MO

Wainscott Jennifer D
Rushville Consolidated HS
Arlington IN

Waite Marcia A
Maquoketa Comm HS
Maquoketa IA

Waite Terri
Lake Central HS
Dyer IN

Wake Cindi L
Hammond Baptist HS
Hammond IN

Wake Thomas J
Lanphier HS
Springfield IL

Wakeem James D
Lamar HS
Lamar MO

Wakefield Kathy L
Beecher City HS
Shumway IL

Wakevainen Donald D
Wakefield HS
Wakefield MI

Walberg Jill S
Kindred HS
Walcott ND

Walbridge Don J
Gull Lake HS
Augusta MI

Walbridge Randy A
Gull Lake HS
Augusta MI

Wald Deborah K
Trinity HS
Dickinson ND

Walden Deborah D
Assumption HS
Assumption IL

Walden John L
Thomas Moore HS
Milwaukee WI

Waldsmith Mary K
Boylan Central Catholic HS
Rockford IL

Walker Barry L
West Vigo HS
Westterre Haute IN

Walker Beverly A
Brown City HS
Brown City MI

Walker Charlon D
Yates Center HS
Yates Center KS

Walker Colleen E
Streator Twp HS
Streator IL

Walker Cynthia K
Oak Park HS
Kansas City MO

Walker Danny L
North Mahaska HS
New Sharon IA

Walker David P
Lane Technical HS
Chicago IL

Walker Dawn M
Tri Valley HS
Cotton SD

Walker Dawn R
Warren Twp HS
Libertyville IL

Walker Deborah A
Mariner HS
White Bear Lake MN

Walker Douglas R
Alma HS
Alma NE

Walker James J
Brebeuf Prep
Indianapolis IN

Walker Joan L
Hamilton HS
Hamilton IL

Walker Linda S
Farmington East HS
Farmington IL

Walker Louanne M
Highland HS
Highland IN

Walker Margo S
New Palestine HS
Greenfield IN

Walker Nancy A
Oak Park River Forest HS
Oak Park IL

Walker Nancy E
Sacred Heart Academy
Springfield IL

Walker Nancy L
Nesco HS
Zearing IA

Walker Teri L
Olympia HS
Mackinaw IL

Walker Tom J
Mcdonald Co HS
Noel MO

Walker Wendy K
St Charles HS
St Charles MO

Walkowicz Linda A
John Hersey HS
Mt Prospect IL

Walkup Brian K
Atwood Hammond HS
Atwood IL

Walkup Susan P
Benson HS
Omaha NE

Wall Janice R
St Elizabeth Riv HS
Iberia MO

Wall Russell K
Raytown HS
Independence MO

Wall Samuel T
Ashland Greenwood HS
Greenwood NE

Wallace Christopher B
Oakville HS
St Louis MO

Wallace Donald W
John F Kennedy HS
Taylor MI

Wallace Erin J
Norris City HS
Omaha IL

Wallace Hugh J
Rogers HS
Michigan City IN

Wallace Marie A
Billings HS
Billings MO

Wallace Michael P
Marquette HS
Alton IL

Wallace Robert E
Clarke Comm HS
Weldon IA

Wallace Wendy E
Waterford Twp HS
Pontiac MI

Wallendorf Lisa R
Calhoun HS
Batchtown IL

Waller Bonita M
Clarke Community HS
Weldon IA

Waller Wenonah L
Chambers Public HS
Ewing NE

Wallesverd Mari B
West Bend East HS
West Bend WI

Wallick Jerry B
Lewistown Comm HS
Lewistown IL

Wallin Paul K
Chaska HS
Chanhassen MN

Wallin Richard J
Worthington Jefferson HS
Worthington IN

Wallis Marilyn L
Grinnell Newburg Comm HS
Grinnell IA

Walljasper Wayne R
Marquette School Inc HS
Salem IA

Wallman Barry J
Assumption HS
Fairview Hts IL

Walls James C
Malta HS
Malta IL

Walls James L
Charlestown HS
Charlestown IN

Walmsley Carol L
Mott HS
Warren MI

Walsh Cheryl L
Blue Mound HS
Blue Mound IL

Walsh Denise E
Good Counsel HS
Chicago IL

Walsh Diane B
Watertown HS
Juneau WI

Walsh Jean E
St Francis Academy
Joliet IL

Walsh Julia M
Derham Hall HS
St Paul MN

Walsh Kimberly K
Weston HS
Cazenovia WI

Walsh Liane M
Central HS
Antioch IL

Walsh Steve G
Serena HS
Serena IL

Walsman Robert C
Park Tudor HS
Indianapolis IN

Walston Tina M
Dillsboro Public HS
Dillsboro IN

Walston William G
Tri County Comm HS
Barnes City IA

Walstrom Lori A
Cambridge Sr HS
Isanti MN

Walter Julia A
Pope County HS
Golconda IL

Walter Lisa L
Harrisburg HS
Harrisburg IL

Walter Melinda K
Morrisonville HS
Palmer IL

Walter Terri L
Orchard Farm HS
St Charles MO

Walters Beriecia C
Bishop Ward HS
Kansas City KS

Walters Cynthia A
Lasalle Peru Twp HS
Lasalle IL

Waltke Duane E
Mc Pherson County HS
Tryon NE

Waltman Bradley N
Charleston HS
Charleston IL

Walton Alan H
Potosi HS
Potosi MO

Waltz John G
Bunker Hill HS
Brighton IL

Wamble Grace M
Winnetonka HS
Kansas City MO

Wamhoff Fredrick C
Haslett HS
E Lansing MI

Wanicki Fred L
Highland HS
Highland IN

Wankel Phyllis S
Triopia Jr Sr HS
Concord IL

Wanta Marilyn J
Newman HS
Wausau WI

Warburton Robert J
Washington Comm HS
Washington IL

Ward Brad J
Maple Lake HS
Buffalo MN

Ward Cecelia G
Puxico R 8 HS
Puxico MO

Ward Denise F
Greenville HS
Greenville MO

Ward Georgina R
Chisago Lakes HS
Lindstrom MN

Ward Gregory T
East Buchanan HS
Masonville IA

Ward Judy K
Northeastern HS
Williamsburg IN

Ward Lesa D
Carrollton HS
Carrollton MO

Ward Lisa J
Crown Point HS
Crown Point IN

Ward Mary C
Academy Of Our Lady
Peoria IL

Ward Mary H
Benet Academy
Glen Ellyn IL

Ward Mary J
North Linn HS
Coggon IA

Ward Michael E
J D Darnall Senior HS
Geneseo IL

Ward Robert L
Fountain Central HS
Hillsboro IN

Ward Tammy L
Union HS
Mooreland IN

Ward Timothy B
Woodstock HS
Woodstock IL

Warden Martha L
Brunswick R Ii HS
Brunswick MO

Wardenburg Wilma K
Terre Haute HS
Terre Haute IN

Wardin Gloria A
Hinsdale Central HS
Hinsdale IL

Wardlow Craig M
Burlington Comm HS
Burlington IA

Ware John F
Grandview HS
Grandview MO

Warfield Leann M
Lyons Township HS
La Grange IL

Warfield Paul F
Creighton Prep
Omaha NE

Warju Bryan D
Cass City HS
Cass City MI

Warneke Dell A
Elkhorn Valley HS
Tilden NE

Warner Denise R
Valley Center HS
Valley Center KS

Warnick Stephen L
Eisenhower HS
Decatur IL

Warnke Marlene A
Tripoli Comm HS
Sumner IA

Warnock Caroline C
Rich South HS
Matteson IL

Warren Carol D
St Charles HS
St Charles IL

Warren Glenn E
Southern HS
Wymore NE

Warren Marguerite
Southwest HS
St Louis MO

Warren Scott H
Wm Horlick HS
Racine WI

Warren Susan B
Grinnell HS
Kellogg IA

Warrick Julian E
Kenwood HS
Chicago IL

Warthen Nowell J
Waterford Mott HS
Pontiac MI

Wartman Brad L
Stanton County HS
Johnson KS

Wasemiller Paul S
Maplewood Academy
Wahpeton ND

Washington Anita
Von Steuben HS
Chicago IL

Washington Chester P
Washington HS
Indianapolis IN

Washington Cynthia J
Romulus Sr HS
Romulus MI

Washington Gale A
Lindblom Tech HS
Chicago IL

Washington Hurdistine
Tilden HS
Chicago IL

Washington Phyllis K
St Thomas Apostle HS
Chicago IL

Washington Willinda K
University Of Chicago HS
Chicago IL

Wasieleski Lynn K
Glidden Public HS
Glidden WI

Wasilewski David L
Thomas Kelly HS
Chicago IL

Wasson Kathryn K
Holcomb HS
Holcomb KS

Wasynczuk Andrew
Maine North HS
Glenview IL

Watchorn Carolee T
Fremont Sr HS
Fremont NE

Waterman Vicky L
Mt Pleasant HS
Wayland IA

Waters James L
Manistique HS
Manistique MI

Waters John A
Pittsfield HS
Baylis IL

Waters John M
Lincoln HS
Vincennes IN

Waters Robyn D
Winner Sr HS
Carter SD

Waterson Timmie R
Davison HS
Davison MI

Waterworth Sherry L
Wellington HS
Wellington MO

Watkins Andrew L
Fox Sr HS
Arnold MO

Watkins Brian D
Bay View HS
Milwaukee WI

Watkins Carmen L
Castle HS
Newburgh IN

Watkins Christopher L
Assumption HS
Caseyville IL

Watkins Gregory A
Mt Zion HS
Decatur IL

Watkins Jo
Newton HS
Newton IL

Watkins Richard M
Chaminade HS
St Louis MO

Watrous Gillian K
Whitewater HS
Whitewater WI

Watry Larry S
Port Washington HS
Port Washington WI

Watson Brenda J
Lindblom Tech HS
Chicago IL

Watson Brenda K
Northside HS
Ft Wayne IN

Watson Carol J
Lindblom Technical HS
Chicago IL

Watson Colette L
Annapolis HS
Dbn Hts MI

Watson James A
Jeffersonville HS
Jeffersonville IN

Watson Jerry N
Cavalier HS
Cavalier ND

Watson John R
United Township HS
East Moline IL

Watson Joseph R
Lincolnwood HS
Farmersville IL

Watson Judith A
Wabash HS
Wabash IN

Watson Raymond J
Odell Comm HS
Odell IL

Watson Robert J
St Bede Academy
Chicago Hgts IL

Watson Taji M
Harrisonville Sr HS
Harrisonville MO

Watson Timothy
Hales Franciscan HS
Chicago IL

Watson Wendy J
Ernest W Seaholm HS
Birmingham MI

Watt Dorian H
Gresham Public HS
Gresham NE

Watters Lee D
Buffalo HS
Buffalo ND

Watterson Lelsie D
Kingsville HS
Kingsville MO

Watterud Dean A
Columbus HS
Portal ND

Wattles Linda S
North Clay HS
Louisville IL

Watts Delores
Robert Lindbloom HS
Chicago IL

Watts Evelyn E
Ansley Public HS
Ansley NE

Watts Kathleen E
Ferndale HS
Ferndale MI

Watts Reginald A
Everett HS
Lansing MI

Watzke Janice L
Taft HS
Chicago IL

Waugh Judy K
Fremont Senior HS
Valley NE

Wavering Kenneth E
Griffin HS
Springfield IL

Wawrzyniak Lucyna A
Rich Central HS
Olympia Fields IL

Way Becky A
Holly HS
Holly MI

Waybright Lynn M
St Mary Academy
Monroe MI

Wayland Kelly R
Washington HS
Washington KS

Wayman Jerri L
Lansing HS
Lansing KS

Waymaster Charles P
Luray HS
Bunker Hill KS

Wayt Rhonda S
Brown County HS
Nashville IN

Wazbinski Susan M
T L Handy HS
Bay City MI

Weakley Kent C
Dixon HS
Dixon IL

Weathers Lisa M
Rochester HS
Rochester MI

Weaver Anna M
Virden HS
Virden IL

Weaver Cynthia R
Northridge HS
Middlebury IN

Weaver Jeffery D
Ida HS
Monroe MI

Weaver Joseph C
Soldan HS
St Louis MO

Weaver Karen B
R Nelson Snider HS
Fort Wayne IN

Weaver Mablene S
Colchster Jr Sr HS
Colchestr IL

Weaver Mary C
So Sioux City HS
South Sioux City NE

Weaver Michael W
Indian Creek HS
Morgantown IN

Weaver Ruth C
S Sioux Sr HS
S Sioux City NE

Weaver Thomas C E
Brownstown Central HS
Freetown IN

Webb Felicia C
River Valley HS
Three Oaks MI

Webb James M
Waterford Kettering HS
Drayton Plains MI

Webb Jerome G
Western HS
Kokomo IN

Webb Larry L
Lewistown Community HS
Lewistown IL

Webb Leah R
Williamsfield HS
Dahinda IL

Webb Peter M
Clinton Prairie HS
Frankfort IN

Webb Rebecca A
Clarke Comm HS
Osceola IA

Webb Richard L
Cape Central HS
Cape Girardeau MO

Webb Tamera L
Memorial HS
Eau Claire WI

Webb Timothy W
Westview HS
Shipshewana IN

Webber Ronald D
Putnam County R 1 HS
Unionville MO

Webber Stephen W
Glendale HS
Springfield MO

Weber Barbara J
Fatima HS
Freeburg MO

Weber Bruce A
Oconto Sr HS
Oconto WI

Weber Carol A
Morrisonville HS
Morrisonville IL

Weber Craig E
Chaminade HS
St Charles MO

Weber Jim R
Grant Deuel HS
Revillo SD

Weber John F
Arlington Green Isle Pub HS
Henderson MN

Weber Lucille M
Bellevue Comm HS
Bellevue IA

Weber Michael J
Thompson Public HS
Thompson ND

Weber Pamela A
Lourdes Academy
Oshkosh WI

Weber Richard J
Thompson HS
Thompson ND

Weber Scott M
Fairmont HS
Fairmont MN

Webster Cynthia M
Wm Rainey Harper HS
Chicago IL

Webster Randall W
Hannibal Sr HS
Hannibal MO

Webster Therese M
Oregon Senior HS
Oregon WI

Wechsler Ben F
Mt Vernon Twp HS
Mt Vernon IL

Wechter Diane J
Loy Norrix HS
Kalamazoo MI

Weck Gary E
Hutsonville HS
Annapolis IL

Weck Terry L
Hutsonville HS
Annapolis IL

Weddell Gail L
Newton HS
Yale IL

Wedel Karen D
Minneapolis HS
Minneapolis KS

Wedel Marilee A
Central Christian HS
Buhler KS

Weeda Patrick O
Mount Ayr Community HS
Tingley IA

Weeden Roland E
Beloit Memorial HS
Beloit WI

Weeks Dana S
Hoisington HS
Hoisington KS

Weeks David L
West Vigo HS
W Terre Haute IN

Weeks Lee Ann
Naperville Central HS
Naperville IL

Weeks Pamela D
Campbell HS
Campbell MO

Weeks Paul E
Rudyard HS
Kincheloe Afb MI

Weeks Raymond R
Rosemount Sr HS
Apple Valley MN

Wegman John J
Union HS
Biggsville IL

Wegmann Dawn T
Western Dubuque HS
Epworth IA

Wegmann John G
Bloomington Community HS
Bloomington WI

Wegner Charles T
Hinsdale Central HS
Oak Brook IL

Wegner Nancy C
Sparta HS
Sparta WI

Wegner Steven G
Northwestern Military
Madison WI

Wegner Thomas W
Prospect HS
Arlington Heights IL

Wehmeyer Mark L
Owensville R 2 HS
Rosebud MO

Wehner Darryl J
Trinity HS
Dickinson ND

Wehri Mary Ann B
Hebron Public HS
Hebron ND

Weiand Jacquelyn S
Mundelein HS
Mundelein IL

Weichman Cindy J
Benton Community HS
Atkins IA

Weidler Tami K
Balfour Public HS
Balfour ND

Weigand Terrill V
Maysville HS
Weatherby MO

Weigel Donald A
Cassville Sr HS
Cassville MO

Weilandich G R
Ritenour Sr HS
Overland MO

Weiler Cynthia M
Auburndale HS
Auburndale WI

Weiler Ghislaine O
Carmel Girls HS
Lake Forest IL

Weills Michelle
East HS
Wichita KS

Weinberg Audrey J
Urbana HS
Urbana IL

Weinberg Constance A
Kewaunee HS
Kewaunee WI

Weinberger Mary Ann
Thornridge HS
Dolton IL

Weiner Martin J
Jersey Community HS
Jerseyville IL

Weinhold Leanne M
St Francis Academy
Joliet IL

Weinstein Randall S
Grandview HS
Kansas City MO

Weirick Marrilee A
Grandville Senior HS
Grandville MI

Weis John R
Paynesville Sr HS
Paynesville MN

Weis Kathleen S
Marian HS
Mishawaka IN

Weisbeck Allen F
Hague Public HS
Hague ND

Weise Karen A
Rosedale HS
Rosedale IN

Weisman Jan R
Metro HS
Chicago IL

Weiss Lori L
Laker HS
Pigeon MI

Weiss Stephen N
Highland Park HS
Highland Park IL

Weist Cindy
Columbia City Joint HS
Ft Wayne IN

Weittenhiller Kim S
Mauston Area HS
Mauston WI

Weitz Gary R
Stillwater HS
Stillwater MN

Weitzell Donald W
Ldf Community HS
Le Grand IA

Welborn Larry R
Mc Cook HS
Mc Cook NE

Welbourne Jack F
Hinsdale South HS
Darien IL

Welch Joey L
Exeter HS
Exeter MO

Welch Timothy G
Union Grove HS
Caledonia WI

Weldon Jeffrey J
English Valley HS
North English IA

Welk Randy L
Pardeeville HS
Cambria WI

Welker Virgil N
Canton Rv HS
Williamstown MO

Wellborn Sonny
Salisbury HS
Salisbury MO

Weller Debra S
Palmer Public HS
Palmer NE

Weller Gerald C
Dwight Township HS
Dwight IL

Weller Laurel A
Memorial HS
Joplin MO

Weller Myrana L
Belle HS
Belle MO

Weller Nancy
South Harrison HS
Bethany MO

Wellik Sandra P
Britt Comm HS
Britt IA

Welling Edward J
Bishop Luers HS
Ft Wayne IN

Wellington Susan M
Rogers HS
Wyoming MI

Wellner Gloria M
Thorp HS
Thorp WI

Wells Edward L
Jonesville HS
Jonesville MI

Wells Gregory M
Elwood Comm HS
Elwood IN

Wells Jason
Unionville HS
Unionville MO

Wells Jay W
Springs Valley HS
Dubois IN

Wells Jimmie J
Siren Consolidated HS
Siren WI

Wells John H
East HS
Waterloo IA

Wells Linda C
West Washington HS
Hardinsburg IN

Wells Mark D
Lake Central HS
Dyer IN

Wells Robert A
Farmer City Mansfield HS
Farmer City IL

Wells Roxie M
Lyman HS
Vivian SD

Wells Susan K
Medford Sr HS
Medford WI

Wells Tami D
O Fallon Township HS
O Fallon IL

Wells Teri L
Gering HS
Gering NE

Wells Vernie E
Wyandotte HS
Kansas City KS

Welp Mary
Southridge HS
Huntingburg IN

Wels Pamela J
Monroe HS
Monroe WI

Welsh Cynthia L
Norwell HS
Bluffton IN

Welsh Jerald R
Pekin Comm HS
Hedrick IA

Welsh Karen M
Carroll HS
Flora IN

Welsh Patricia A
Sullivan HS
Sullivan IL

Welter Herb J
Midland Community HS
Onslow IA

Welton Brian K
Ovid Elsie HS
Elsie MI

Welton Mark L
Seaholm HS
Birmingham MI

Wendelschafer Chad J
Milton HS
Milton Jct WI

Wendland Charles M
Traverse City HS
Traverse City MI

Wendling Richard A
North Clay HS
Louisville IL

Wendorf Elizabeth S
Wayland Academy
Beaver Dam WI

Wendt Debra A
Trumbull HS
Trumbull NE

Wendt Kyle
Seaman HS
Topeka KS

Wendt Randal L
Truman Public HS
Truman MN

Wendt Ricky D
Leigh Comm HS
Clarkson NE

Wendt Terry V
Leigh Comm HS
Clarkson NE

Wenger James W
Warsaw Comm HS
Warsaw IN

Wenger Robert E
Versailles HS
Versailles MO

Wenger Roger G
St Thomas Seminary
Louisiana MO

Wenig Nancy R
Benton Co HS
Lincoln MO

Wenk Karen A
Arlington HS
Arlington Hts IL

Wenneberg Luke R
Gordon Tech HS
Chicago IL

Wentland Wyann L
Hazen HS
Hazen ND

Wentz Brett A
Tennings HS
Norcatur KS

Wentz Dwight J
Ryan HS
Minot ND

Wentzel Wilford L
Harrisburg HS
Harrisburg IL

Wenz Mark G
Lincoln East HS
Lincoln NE

Wenzel James J
Senior HS
Jamestown ND

Wenzel John B
Elmwood HS
Elmwood NE

Wenzel Michael S
Sturgis HS
Sturgis MI

Wenzel Robert F
St Clair HS
St Clair MI

Wepfer Karen C
Wauwatosa East HS
Wauwatosa WI

Wepprecht John B
R U C E HS
Essex IL

Werderits Paul S
Farmington East HS
Farmington IL

Werderman Cynthia J
Romeo HS
Romeo MI

Werges Joyce A
Mother Of Sorrows HS
Chicago IL

Werling Nicholas C
Wayne HS
Ft Wayne IN

Werner Elizabeth H
Hinsdale Twp HS
Hinsdale IL

Werner James M
Schuyler R 1 HS
Lancaster MO

Werner Louise A
Peru HS
Peru IN

Werner Mark T
Harding HS
St Paul MN

Werner Stephanie J
Medford Sr HS
Medford WI

Werning Katherine J
Lafayette County HS
Higginsville MO

Werning Michael C
Lafayette Co HS
Higginsville MO

Werpy David G
Marshall Sr HS
Marshall MN

Werry Glenn A
Farmington East HS
Farmington IL

Werth Glenn A
Caro HS
Caro MI

Werth Ronald L
Thomas More Prep
Hays KS

Wertz Janet L
Brkway West Sr HS
Creve Coeur MO

Wertz Tamara L
Southwestern HS
Flat Rock IN

Wesbey Tim A
Morton W HS
Lyons IL

Wescott Dean T
St Marys Central HS
Menoken ND

Wescott Lloyd K
Sargent Public HS
Brewster NE

Weseloh Harold W
Cosmos HS
Hector MN

Wesemann Wendolyn L
Southwest HS
Leawood KS

Wesner Robert B
Lyons Twp HS
La Grange Pk IL

Wesol Marlene A
Good Counsel HS
Chicago IL

Wessel Mark S
Moberly HS
Moberly MO

Wesseldyke Lynda S
Holland Christian HS
Holland MI

Wesselman Brenda G
Porta HS
Tallula IL

Wessels John H
Humboldt HS
St Paul MN

Wessic Linda E
Shelbyville HS
Shelbyville IN

West Ann R
Cowden Herrick HS
Cowden IL

West Barbara A
Ritenour Senior HS
St Louis MO

West Becky A
Clarkfield HS
Clarkfield MN

West Cassandra L
Vashon HS
St Lousi MO

West Charles F
Westport HS
Kansas City MO

West David G
Hillcrest HS
Country Club Hls IL

West James T
Wayne Comm HS
Corydon IA

West Marcia K
Marinette HS
Marinette WI

West Rhonda B
Southeast HS
Kansas City MO

West Susan D
Morton Sr HS
Hammond IN

West Vicki L
Wentzville HS
O Fallon MO

West Virginia M
W Chicago Comm HS
West Chicago IL

West Wallace D
Gordon Tech HS
Chicago IL

Westby Timothy S
Valley City HS
Valley City ND

Westemeyer Donald D
Pekin Community HS
Pekin IL

Western Gayla L
Rothsay Public HS
Rothsay MN

Westfall Jeffrey B
George Rogers Clark HS
Whiting IN

Westfall Linda K
Eastbrook HS
Van Buren IN

Westfield Lisa A
St Marys Acad
Monmouth IL

Westmoreland Douglas V
East Detroit HS
East Detroit MI

Weston Earl D
Valentine HS
Valentine NE

Weston Kathleen M
Washburn HS
Minneapolis MN

Weston Terri A
Fulton HS
Albany IL

Westover Georgiana J
Westwood HS
Sloan IA

Westphal Arthur T
Southwest HS
St Louis MO

Westphal Michael J
Elgin HS
Morristown SD

Wetrosky David A
Akron Community HS
Akron IA

Wetter Barbara A
Duchesne HS
St Charles MO

Wettig Robert A
Richmond HS
Richmond IN

Wetzel James D
St Mary Of Redford HS
Detroit MI

Wetzel Perran G
Campion HS
Chicago IL

Weyer Judith A
Forest Park HS
Ferdinand IN

Weyher Jeri A
Dundee HS
Dundee MI

Whaley Cheryl A
South Newton HS
Kentland IN

Whaley Judith A
La Ville HS
La Paz IN

Whaley Sherril D
St Thomas Apostle HS
Chicago IL

Whaley Steven M
South Newton HS
Morocco IN

Wham Robert M
Springfield HS
Springfield IL

Whan David R
Knox County HS
Knox City MO

Wheat James D
Fenton HS
Fenton MI

Wheeler Jeffrey B
Bloomington HS
Bloomington IN

Wheeler Theresa S
Pekin Community HS
Pekin IL

Wheeler Tony J
North Putnam HS
Roochdale IN

Wheeley Cynthia E
Clio HS
Clio MI

Whewell Calvin D
Southeastern HS
West Point IL

Whipple Betty J
Jefferson HS
Cedar Rapids IA

Whirledge Ben R
Fairfield Jr Sr HS
Millersburg IN

Whirley Jennifer J
Lincoln HS
Pershing IN

Whisenhunt David E
Benkelman HS
Benkelman NE

Whisenton Ethel L
Soldan HS
St Louis MO

Whisman Michael O
Charlestown HS
Charlestown IN

Whisner Michael E
Adel HS
Adel IA

Whitaker Orion C
Wauwatosa West HS
Wauwatosa WI

Whitcher Rick F
North HS
West Union IA

Whitcomb Allen P
Oak Park Acad
Sioux City IA

White Allen L
Macomb HS
Macomb IL

White Brent T
Pierce City HS
Sarcoxie MO

White Carlis C
Northeastern HS
Williamsburg IN

White Cathy S
Belton HS
Belton MO

White Charlene E
College HS
Muncie IN

White Daniel P
Postville HS
Postville IA

White Darlene E
Southside HS
Muncie IN

White David T
Lyons Township HS
La Grange IL

White Debra S
Staunton HS
Brazil IN

White Denise E
Ottawa Township HS
Ottawa IL

White Elaine G
Stratford Community HS
Stratford IA

White Florence A
William J Bogan HS
Chicago IL

White Gary W
North Decatur HS
St Paul IN

White Harold E
Millington HS
Millington MI

White Jeffrey R
Lindblom Tech HS
Chicago IL

White Jody L
East Richland HS
Olney IL

White Joseph M
West Plains HS
West Plains MO

White Joy A
Santa Fe Trail HS
Overbrook KS

White Joyce A
Canistota Public HS
Canistota SD

White Kathryn M
Melvern HS
Melvern KS

White Kathy M
Highland Public HS
Highland WI

White Kimberly J
Grand Island HS
Grand Island NE

White Neil P
Griffin HS
Springfield IL

White Robert K
Houston HS
Houston MO

White Ronald M
Chisago Lakes HS
Stacy MN

White Sandra J
Palestine HS
Palestine IL

White Scott A
Boone Valley HS
Goldfield IA

White Steven P
Marquette Sr HS
Marquette MI

White Susan L
Hillsboro HS
Irving IL

White Tammy R
La Salle HS
Cedar Rapids IA

White Tanya A
Crispus Attucks HS
Indianapolis IN

White Teresa A
Nauvoo Colusa HS
Adrian IL

White Theresa L
North County HS
Bonne Terre MO

White Timothy L
Garden County HS
Oshkosh NE

Whitefoot Julie A
Sidney HS
Sidney NE

Whitehead Ann J
Central HS
Aberdeen SD

Whitehead Valarie L
High School
Maroa IL

Whiteman Kelly J
Rich South HS
Matteson IL

Whitener Mary D
Poplar Bluff HS
Poplar Bluff MO

Whiteside Patricia A
Roncalli HS
Aberdeen SD

Whitfield Gwenda L
Rezin Orr HS
Chicago IL

Whitford Gary D
St Johns HS
St Johns MI

Whiting Dennis
Southwest HS
Green Bay WI

Whiting Eleanor B
Anna Jonesboro C HS
Anna IL

Whitlatch Lynne M
Tower Hill HS
Tower Hill IL

Whitler Jason E
Lincoln Comm HS
Lincoln IL

Whitlock Kenneth W
La Salle Peru Township HS
Peru IL

Whitman Theresa A
Pierce City HS
Pierce City MO

Whitmore James M
Reitz Memorial HS
Evansville IN

Whitmore Jon M
Central HS
Evansville IN

Whitney Vicky L
Norton Community HS
Norton KS

Whitson Marice K
Shawnee Mission East HS
Mission KS

Whitson Stephan A
Coldwater HS
Coldwater MI

Whittenburg James M
Harlem HS
Rockford IL

Whittle Judy L
Shelbyville HS
Shelbyville IN

Wiarda Cynthia A
Dows Community HS
Dows IA

Wibirt Jane L
Hastings HS
Hastings MI

Wick Mary
St James Sr HS
St James MN

Wicke Kyle K
Palisade Public HS
Palisade NE

Wickenheiser Brian E
Monroe Catholic Central HS
Monroe MI

Wicker Catherine E
Morristown Jr Sr HS
Shelbyville IN

Wickeraad Ruth A
Willmar Sr HS
Willmar MN

Wickersham Carol A
Bradley Bourbonnais Comm HS
Bourbonnais IL

Wickey Karla J
Burr Oak HS
Burr Oak MI

Wickham Randall C
East Richland HS
Olney IL

Wicklander Suzanne M
Vine St HS
Hudson WI

Wickline Jack I
Hazel Park HS
Hazel Park MI

Wicklund Kyle A
Sault Area HS
Sault Ste Marie MI

Wickman Kathy A
West Delaware HS
Manchester IA

Wicks Gene E
Carman HS
Flint MI

Wicks Vonda J
Laboure HS
St Louis MO

Wickstrom Cynthia J
Marquette HS
Marquette KS

Wickstrom Cynthia L
Joliet Central HS
Joliet IL

Wickstrom Mark S
Toivola Meadowlands HS
Meadowlands MN

Wideman Charles R
Fairview HS
Fairview MI

Widicus Nancy J
Lebanon Community HS
Trenton IL

Widmer Mary E
North HS
Evansville IN

Wiebenga Cheryl S
Fulton HS
Fulton IL

Wiebenga Janet L
Morrison Comm HS
Morrison IL

Wieczorek Linda M
Pinckney HS
Whitmore Lake MI

Wiedeman Michelle E
East Central HS
Sunman IN

Wiedeman Susie E
Bishop Miege HS
Shawnee Msn KS

Wiedemeier Mary A
Crivitz HS
Porterfield WI

Wieder Frank P
Washington HS
Germantown WI

Wiedmeyer Rachell A
Slinger HS
West Bend WI

Wiedow James L
D C Everest Sr HS
Rothschild WI

Wiedrich William W
Sault Area HS
Sault Ste Marie MI

Wiegand Timothy F
Marquette HS
Michigan City IN

Wielage Jill D
Stephen Hempstead Sr HS
Dubuque IA

Wieland Kim M
Beloit Catholic HS
Beloit WI

Wieland Paula K
Marshall HS
Marshall IL

Wieland Tamara M
Charlevoix HS
Charlevoix MI

Wielgat Michael W
St Florian HS
Detroit MI

Wielt Tammela J
Mt Vernon Twp HS
Bluford IL

Wier Steven R
Cudahy Sr HS
Cudahy WI

STUDENTS PHOTOGRAPH SCHEDULED FOR PUBLICATION HERE COULD NOT BE REPRODUCED

Wiering Ron J
Tyler Public HS
Tyler MN

Wiersema Luanne
Marseilles HS
Marseilles IL

Wiersma Steven E
Mitchell Sr HS
Mitchell SD

Wierzbicki Carolyn A
New Haven HS
New Haven MI

Wieser Cheryl J
Scotus Central Catholic HS
Columbus NE

Wiest Jeanne M
Adams HS
Rochester MI

Wietbrock Diana L
Hanover Central HS
Cedar Lake IN

Wieters Julie D
Downers Grove HS
Downers Grove IL

Wilbon Jennifer R
Normandy HS
St Louis MO

Wilcheski Paula M
Divine Child HS
Dearborn Heights MI

Wilcox David E
Griffith HS
Griffith IN

Wilcox Julie M
Marshall County Central HS
Newfolden MN

Wilcox Kathleen A
Immaculata HS
Detroit MI

Wilcox Wendy L
Clare HS
Clare MI

Wilcoxon Rebecca L
Everly HS
Everly IA

Wilczynski John M
St Patrick HS
Chicago IL

Wilczynski Robert P
Weber HS
Chicago IL

Wild Debra E
Oregon Senior HS
Oregon WI

Wild William B
Thornton Fractional So HS
Lansing IL

Wildeisen Lori L
South Callaway HS
Williamsburg MO

Wilder Glen A
Royal Valley HS
Mayetta KS

Wildhaber Lisa A
Fatima HS
Argyle MO

Wildy Rosetta
Camelot HS
Cairo IL

Wile Jill E
Paynesville HS
Paynesville MN

Wiler Robert W
Crown Point HS
Crown Point IN

Wiles Candy L
Parkwood HS
Joplin MO

Wiles Douglas D
Milan C 2 HS
Milan MO

Wiles Truman L
Willow Springs HS
Willow Springs MO

Wiley Mark E
Stockbridge HS
Gregory MI

Wiley Ruth A
Marmaton Valley HS
Moran KS

Wilhelm George W
Lake Forest HS
Lake Bluff IL

Wilhelm Kathleen M
Brighton HS
Brighton MI

Wilhelm Nancy J
St Paul HS
Highland IL

Wilhelm Patricia H
Lomira HS
Lomira WI

Wilhelm Susan J
Lakeland HS
La Grange IN

Wilhelmi Mark L
Morris HS
Morris IL

Wilhelmi Terrance D
Gettysburg HS
Gettysvurg SD

Wilis David L
Marion HS
Marion WI

Wiljamaa David J
Central HS
Flint MI

Wilken Vicki J
Ar We Va HS
Westside IA

Wilkerson Carla J
Miller HS
Miller MO

Wilkerson Donna M
Oak Park HS
Kansas City MO

Wilkerson Roma J
R 1 North Callaway HS
Huxvasse MO

Wilkes Yolanda C
Short Ridge HS
Indianapolis IN

Wilkey Catherine A
Watertown Sr HS
Watertown SD

Wilkinson Anita L
Wilber Clatonia HS
Clatonia NE

Wilkinson Becky J
Franklin Community HS
Franklin IN

Wilkinson Daniel D
Fremont Sr HS
Fremont NE

Wilkinson James M
Central HS
Evansville IN

Wilkinson Jan Y
Whitke HS
Larwill IN

Wilkus Annette P
Lourdes HS
Rochester MN

Will Larry D
Kaneland HS
Sugar Grove IL

Will Nancy E
Bishop Du Bourge HS
St Louis MO

Willard Randall R
Stapleton HS
Stapleton NE

Willbanks Randy C
Ruskin HS
Kansas City MO

Wille Gayle L
Edwardsville Sr HS
Edwardsville IL

Willems Jennifer L
Huntington North HS
Huntington IN

Willen Claudia
Marian Hts Academy
Affton MO

Willett Cindy S
Superior HS
Superior NE

Willett Rose M
Jackson HS
Jackson MN

Willey Kyle D
Zionsville Co HS
Whitestown IN

Willhite Robert J
Waynesville Sr HS
Waynesville MO

Williams Allen J
West Branch HS
West Branch IA

Williams Brent C
C A Lindbergh HS
Minnetonka MN

Williams Bruce G
Washington Sr HS
Cedar Rapids IA

Williams Bryan J
F J Reitz HS
Evansville IN

Williams Candice C
Pattonville HS
Bridgeton MO

Williams Connie M
Macarthur HS
Decatur IL

Williams Daniel B
Chelsea HS
Chelsea MI

Williams Danny E
Du Quoin HS
Du Quoin IL

Williams David B
Horace Mann HS
Gary IN

Williams Debbie A
Hume HS
Stotesbury MO

Williams Debbie F
Waukegan HS
Waukegan IL

Williams Debra E
Marshall HS
Marshall IL

Williams Eric W
Anderson HS
Anderson IN

Williams Gregory E
Ex Spring West HS
Excelsior Springs MO

Williams Harold E
Richmond HS
Richmond MO

Williams Jacqueline J
Riverdale HS
Muscoda WI

Williams James R
Cobden HS
Cobden IL

Williams Janet R
St John HS
Independence IA

Williams Jay W
Stillman Valley HS
Davis Junction IL

Williams Jeffrey S
Mendel Catholic HS
Chicago IL

Williams Jodi R
Norfolk HS
Norfolk NE

Williams John M
Jefferson City Sr HS
Jefferson City MO

Williams Judson E
Waterford Mott HS
Pontiac MI

Williams Julie A
Enfield HS
Enfield IL

Williams Karl J
Lyons Township HS
La Grange Park IL

Williams Kevin L
Mendel Cath Prep HS
Chicago IL

Williams Kim M
Watertown Sr HS
Watertown SD

Williams Laurie J
Carlisle Community HS
Carlisle IA

Williams Marshall D
Du Quoin HS
Du Quion IL

Williams Mary E
West Side HS
Gary IN

Williams Michael J
Fairbury HS
Fairbury NE

Williams Otis L
Chicago Vocational HS
Chicago IL

Williams Patricia R
Thornwood HS
Markham IL

Williams Paul D
O Fallon Twp HS
O Fallon IL

Williams Reginald
Washington Park HS
Racine WI

Williams Richard J
Jackson Lumen Christi HS
Jacksn MI

Williams Robin D
Redford HS
Detroit MI

Williams Sandra
Morton HS
Morton IL

Williams Sandra L
Southwest HS
Saint Louis MO

Williams Sheryl L
Calumet HS
Gary IN

Williams Steve D
Marion HS
Marion KS

Williams Sue Ann M
Breck HS
Minneapolis MN

Williams Susan A
South Side HS
Fort Wayne IN

Williams Susan L
Elgin HS
Elgin IL

Williams Tammy L
Knightstown Comm HS
New Castle IN

Williams Terry J
Murray Wright HS
Detroit MI

Williams Theodore J
Turner HS
Kansas City KS

Williams Tracey D
Anna Jonesboro C HS
Anna IL

Williams Trudy J
Huntington North HS
Huntington IN

Williams Vincel W
Raymore Peculiar HS
Peculiar MO

Williams Wyman L
Center Grove HS
Greenwood IN

Williamson Andrea L
Winchester Community HS
Ridgeville IN

Williamson Christine J
Mc Henry West Campus HS
Mc Henry IL

Williamson Cynthia A
Platteview HS
Papillion NE

Williamson Kathryn J
Ray Pec HS
Peculiar MO

Williford Grady H
East Prairie HS
East Prairie MO

Willis Carol A
Carrollton Sr HS
Carrollton MO

Willis James W
Centerville HS
Centerville IA

Willis Michael E
Maconaquah HS
Peru IN

Willms Lyndon G
St Elmo HS
St Elmo IL

Willoughby Debbie L
Sarcoxie HS
Reeds MO

Willoughby Lance M
Jefferson County North H
Nortonville KS

Willoughby Patrick J
Argenta Oreana HS
Argenta IL

Willoughby Paula J
Keokuk Senior HS
Keokuk IA

Wills Kenneth J
Sevastopol HS
Sturgeon Bay WI

Willyard Douglas C
Lebanon Comm HS
Lebanon IL

Wilson Barbara J
Eastern HS
Owensburg IN

Wilson Beth Anne H
Glenbard East HS
Glen Ellyn IL

Wilson Betty J
Hayes County HS
Culbertson NE

Wilson Bruce D
Fairfield HS
Barnhill IL

Wilson Candi A
Alton HS
West Plains MO

Wilson Cathy L
Cowan HS
Muncie IN

Wilson Christine D
Arlington HS
Indianapolis IN

Wilson Daniel L
Culbertson HS
Culbertson NE

Wilson David E
Raymond Central HS
Ceresco NE

Wilson David G
Mona Shores HS
Muskegon MI

Wilson David S
Zion Benton Twp HS
Zion IL

Wilson Deborah S
Milan HS
Milan MI

Wilson Del M
Seymour HS
Seymour MO

Wilson Douglas D
Larkin HS
Elgin IL

Wilson Edwin I
Crowleys Ridge Academy
Senath MO

Wilson Erin K
Seymour HS
Hull IL

Wilson Gene B
Brown HS
Piedmont SD

Wilson Geneva J
Mc Henry Community HS
Mc Henry IL

Wilson James R
Bellmont HS
Decatur IN

Wilson Jan A
Tecumseh HS
Tecumseh MI

Wilson Jay L
De Soto HS
Dittmer MO

Wilson Jeanne K
St Josephs Academy
University City MO

Wilson Jeffrey A
Grandview HS
Grandview MO

Wilson Jim B
Clarks Public HS
Clarks NE

Wilson Kathleen A
Civic Memorial HS
Bethalto IL

Wilson Kenneth
Luther South HS
Chicago IL

Wilson Kennith W
Oak Grove HS
Oak Grove MO

Wilson Kimberly A
Cairo HS
Cairo IL

Wilson Kymberly P
North Chicago HS
North Chicao IL

Wilson Linda K
George Washington HS
Indianapolis IN

Wilson Marilyn E
Marshalltown Senior HS
Marshalltown IA

Wilson Mark E
Univ Of Detroit HS
Detroit MI

Wilson Marla K
Edwardsville Sr HS
Edwardsville IL

Wilson Mary E
Grand Blanc HS
Grand Blanc MI

Wilson Michael A
Raytown HS
Kansas City MO

Wilson Peter C
Marquette Sr HS
Marquette MI

Wilson Rhonda F
Wayne City HS
Keenes IL

Wilson Robert D
Beecher HS
Mt Morris MI

Wilson Ronda J
Arkansas City Sr HS
Arkansas City KS

Wilson Sandra S
Dakota HS
Dakota IL

Wilson Shelley K
Huron HS
Ann Arbor MI

Wilson Sue D
Ionia HS
Ionia MI

Wilson Susan L
Huron HS
Ann Arbor MI

Wilson Susan L
Fredericktown HS
Fredericktown MO

Wilson Tracy A
Monroe HS
Monroe MI

Wilson Tracy L
Janesville Cons HS
Denver IA

Wilson Vanessa L
Chaska Sr HS
Chaska MN

Wilson Vicki S
Atchison Jr Sr HS
Atchison KS

Wilson William J
Benton Community HS
Van Horne IA

Wilt David A
Chaparral HS
Anthony KS

Wilt Diane M
Chaparral HS
Anthony KS

Wilt Leslie O
South Shelby HS
Shelbina MO

Wiltscheck Joyce M
Gibbon Public HS
Gibbon MN

Wimmer Cindy E
Hale R 1 HS
Hale MO

Winans Julie A
Hartford HS
Watervliet MI

Winans Richard A
Wayne HS
Fort Wayne IN

Wind Jeffrey R
Mehlville Sr HS
St Louis MO

Windholz Rhoda M
Victoria HS
Victoria KS

Windisch Randall A
Butler HS
Butler MO

Windt Frank C
Cudahy Sr HS
Cudahy WI

Wineinger Kerry K
Greeley Cnty HS
Tribune KS

Winemiller Teresa A
Sheridan R Ii HS
Sheridan MO

Wing Loren D
Colfax HS
Colfax IA

Wingard Marianne
Elwood Community HS
Elwood IN

Wininger Cindy L
Barr Reeve HS
Montgomery IN

Winkel Brian S
Toluca HS
Toluca IL

Winkelhorst Loren J
Edgerton Public HS
Leota MN

Winkler Cynthia R
Cheney HS
Wichita KS

Winkler Stacey L
Alexis HS
Alexis IL

Winn Frank L
Scollard Hall HS
Edina MN

Winn James K
Mt Vernon HS
Mt Vernon MO

Winn Patricia K
Pana HS
Pana IL

Winn Pete
Danville HS
Danville IL

Winseman Albert L
Milford HS
Milford NE

Winslow Martha M
Spalding Academy
Washington IL

Winston Paula J
Morton Sr HS
Hammond IN

Winter Larry A
Goodland HS
Kenorado KS

Winter Mar Jo E
Belle Plaine HS
Belle Plaine KS

Winter Terri M
West Sr HS
Iowa City IA

Winternheimer Christina M
Mt Vernon HS
Evansville IN

Winters Brenda I
Carlinville HS
Carlinville IL

Winters Tracy M
Greensburg Comm HS
Greensburg IN

Winters Vickie S
Lanphier HS
Springfield IL

Winther Marlene M
Hubbard Comm HS
Hubbard IA

Wirt Gregory T
Parkway North Sr HS
St Louis MO

Wirth Barbara M
South HS
Omaha NE

Wirth Terry L
Prairie Farm HS
Ridgeland WI

Wirtz Julie A
Argyle HS
Argyle WI

Wirtz Mark P
Woden Crystal Lake HS
Crystal Lake IA

Wirzfeld Diana L
Santa Fe Trail HS
Carbondale KS

Wisch Mark W
Arlington Green Isle HS
Arlington MN

Wise Donita D
Assumption HS
Assumption IL

Wise Douglas L
Whitko HS
Warsaw IN

Wise Fletcher E
Farmer City Mansfield HS
Farmer City IL

Wiseman Brian E
Elston Sr HS
Michigan City IN

Wiseman Cathy D
Athens HS
Athens IL

Wisniewski Janet M
All Saints Central HS
Bay City MI

Wissing Marcia L
Oregon HS
Oregon IL

Wissink Stephen E
Harper Creek HS
Battle Creek MI

Witek Laura L
William J Bogan HS
Chicago IL

Witham Novelene E
Tippecanoe Valley HS
Mentone IN

Witherspoon Sherri
Shawneetown HS
Shawneetown IL

Withrow Randall M
De Soto HS
Stoddard WI

Witt Michael H
Dundee Community HS
West Dundee IL

Witt Tammy A
Avondale Sr HS
Pontiac MI

Witt Thomas F
Champaign Central HS
Champaign IL

Wittbrodt Deborah A
Blissfield Sr HS
Riga MI

Wittenberg Eugena A
Windsor HS
Windsor IL

Wittenborn Jan L
Rushville Consolidated HS
Rushville IN

Wittman Cynthia K
Alton Sr HS
Godfrey IL

Wittmer Coleen J
Barr Reeve HS
Montgomery IN

Wittrock Mary Jo
B I L L HS
Bird Island MN

Wittrock Paul B
Colfax HS
Colfax WI

Wittstruck Brad L
Crete HS
Martell NE

Wittwer Dan C
Dawson Verdon HS
Dawson NE

Witzig Jacqueline A
Benilde St Margarets HS
Golden Valley MN

Wixson Sally
Brandon HS
Ortonville MI

Wizner Anne J
Freeland HS
Freeland MI

Wodill Sheryl J
Beaver Dam Sr HS
Beaver Dam WI

Wodtke Sharon M
Chippewa Valley HS
Mt Clemens MI

Woebbeking Doug A
Gladbrook Comm HS
Gladbrook IA

Woehl Timothy T
Ashley HS
Ashley ND

Woelfel Donna M
Calhoun HS
Hardin IL

Woessner Kristina F
Proviso East HS
Forest Park IL

Wofford Beverly J
Valley Falls HS
Valley Falls KS

Wofford Linda K
Normandy Sr HS
Uplands Park MO

Wogsland Laurie A
Tomahawk HS
Tomahawk WI

Wohead Elizabeth T
Naperville Central HS
Naperville IL

Wohlers Renae E
Lincoln HS
Lake City MN

Wohlgemuth David L
Holdrege HS
Holdrege NE

Wojcik Candace D
John Hersey HS
Mount Prospect IL

Wojcik Margaret M
Lake View HS
Chicago IL

Wojcik Therese M
Lane Tech HS
Chicago IL

Wojtalewicz Barbara M
Pacelli HS
Stevens Point WI

Wolber David M
Rock Falls Twp HS
Rock Falls IL

Wold Lynette E
Richland #44 HS
Wahpeton ND

Wolden Roger L
Philip Independent HS
Philip SD

Wolf Darlene A
Winola HS
Aledo IL

Wolf David C
Lakeland HS
La Grange IN

Wolf Janet F
Mater Dei HS
Evansville IN

Wolf Lori J
Mehlville Sr HS
St Louis MO

Wolf Pamela K
Mobridge HS
Mobridge SD

Wolf Ronni D
Matthews HS
Sikeston MO

Wolf Roslea A
Doland HS
Doland SD

Wolf Scott W
Cozad HS
Cozad NE

Wolfe Carl D
La Salle Peru HS
Peru IL

Wolfe David L
Northern Valley HS
Almena KS

Wolfe Kim R
Ord HS
Shelton NE

Wolfe Luann E
Bridgeport HS
Saginaw MI

Wolfe Lucinda S
H H Dow HS
Midland MI

Wolfe Mary L
Roanoke Benson HS
Roanoke IL

Wolfe Theresa M
La Salle Peru HS
Lasalle IL

Wolfer Mark S
Sparta HS
Sparta IL

Wolff Carol J
Monango Public HS
Monango ND

Wolff Daniel H
Wausaukee HS
Amberg WI

Wolff Debra K
Howells Public HS
Clarkson NE

Wolff James A
Nashua HS
Charles City IA

Wolff Thomas C
Murphysboro Twp HS
Murphysboro IL

Wolford Delores J
Lewellen Rural HS
Lewellen NE

Wolford Doris J
Lewellen Rural HS
Lewellen NE

Wolgan Terry L
Manual HS
Peoria IL

Wollard Alan D
Marion Sr HS
Marion IL

Wollin David K
Waconia HS
Waconia MN

Wolper Judith A
Mather HS
Chicago IL

Wolski Ann P
Elizabeth Seton HS
Dolton IL

Wolters Debra
Steeleville Community HS
Percy IL

Wolvert David J
St Thomas Military Acad
Brooklyn Park MN

Wonderlich Rhonda J
Centerville HS
Centerville IA

Wong Darlene
St Mary Of Perpetual Help HS
Chicago IL

Wonser Timothy P
St Marys Central HS
Menasha WI

Wood Bradley D
Pana Sr HS
Pana IL

Wood Bruce D
Tuscola Comm HS
Tuscola IL

Wood Carolyn A
Cotton HS
Culver MN

Wood Cindy R
Atwood Hammond HS
Atwood IL

Wood Corliss D
North Division Sr HS
Milwaukee WI

Wood Dennis L
Grinnell Senior HS
Grinnell IA

Wood Donna K
Gallatin R V HS
Gallatin MO

Wood Douglas S
Mt Vernon Township HS
Mt Vernon IL

Wood Joseph W
Red Oak HS
Emerson IA

Wood Lynnel G
Chase County HS
Benkelman NE

Wood Mark D
David H Hickman HS
Columbia MO

Wood Mark N
Parkway West HS
Ballwin MO

Wood Renee A
Truman HS
Independence MO

Wood Richard P
Lake Central HS
St John IN

Wood Stephanie M
Tinley Park HS
Tinley Park IL

Wood Teresa A
Bloomington HS
Bloomington IL

Wood Terry A
Wabash HS
West Branch MI

Wood Trudy J
Anna Jonesboro C HS
Anna IL

Wood William M
Bismarck Henning HS
Danville IL

Woodard Cynthia L
Bentley HS
Livonia MI

Woodard Debra S
Chorobusco HS
Columbia City IN

Woodard Michael E
Marshall HS
Dennison IL

Woodburn Cynthia A
East Peoria Comm HS
East Peoria IL

Woodbury Traci L
Central HS
St Joseph MO

Wooden Cindy L
Jonesville HS
Jonesville MI

Woodrum Cindy L
Waynesville HS
Richland MO

Woodrum Sterling T
Golden City R 3 HS
Golden City MO

Woods Ilene A
Newton HS
Newton IL

Woods Karen D
Maria HS
Oaklawn IL

Woods Kevin R
Eddyville HS
Cedor IA

Woods Kimberly L
Park Rapids HS
Park Rapids MN

Woods Robin W
Ritenour Sr HS
St Johns MO

Woods Susan E
Riverdale HS
Blue River WI

Woodside Steven L
Cozad HS
Cozad NE

Woodson Marilynn B
Waukegan HS
Waukegan IL

Woodward Dennis E
Beaman Conrad Liscomb HS
Conrad IA

Woodward Paul L
Southwest HS
St Louis MO

Woodworth Steven F
Shullsburg HS
Shullsburg WI

Woody Suzette L
Waynesville HS
Waynesville MO

Woodyard Leslie A
Chrisman HS
Chrisman IL

Wooldridge Claudia L
Springfield HS
Springfield IL

Wooldridge Daniel E
Winterset Comm HS
Winterset IA

Woolery Darrell J
Pleasant Hill HS
Pleasant Hill MO

Wooley Carol E
Union County HS
Liberty IN

Woolf La Fonda
Clay City HS
Bowling Green IN

Woolley Michele L
Walled Lake Western HS
Walled Lake MI

Woolwine Latauna B
Fountain Central HS
Kingman IN

Wooster Terry L
Prairie Heights HS
Orland IN

Worden Michelle M
Stevens HS
Rapid City SD

Workman Dale W
Lake Park HS
Roselle IL

Workun Terry L
Murphysboro HS
Murphysboro IL

Worley Mary C
Wayland Academy
South Bend IN

Worley Mary C
Wayland Academy
Bridgman MI

Worley Peggy J
Centerville HS
Centerville IA

Wormley Steven G
Keith HS
Rockford IL

Worner Donald K
Aledo HS
Aledo IL

Worner Timothy C
Metamora HS
Metamora IL

Woronowicz Mandi E
Morton West HS
Lyons IL

Wort Mark E
Scott Comm HS
Scott City KS

Wortman Carolyn A
Ruskin HS
Ruskin NE

Wortman Robin J
Highland HS
Highland IN

Woulf Robert J
Catholic Central HS
Peshtigo WI

Woulfe Margaret F
Queen Of Peace HS
Oak Lawn IL

Wovcha Laurie J
Roosevelt HS
Virginia MN

Wozniak John A
John Hersey HS
Mt Prospect IL

Wozniak Mario F
Hempstead HS
Dubuque IA

Wozniak Marjorie C
Hempstead HS
Dubuque IA

Wozniak Mary S
Alleman HS
Rock Island IL

Wrate Wendy J
Delton Kellogg HS
Delton MI

Wray Max R
Warsaw Community HS
Warsaw IN

Wright Ann E
Memorial HS
Joplin MO

Wright Anthony L
W P Chrysler HS
New Castle IN

Wright Brent E
Farmer City Mansfield HS
Mansfield IL

Wright Cynthia L
Turkey Run HS
Marshall IN

Wright Cynthia S
New London HS
New London IA

Wright Donald V
Swartz Creek HS
Swartz Creek MI

Wright Gerald R
Beech Grove HS
Beech Grove IN

Wright James R
Cahokia HS
Cahokia IL

Wright Johnny G
Gallatin HS
Gallatin MO

Wright Michael R
Baxter HS
Baxter Springs KS

Wright Myra S
Wm W Borden HS
Borden IN

Wright Paula L
Park River HS
Park River ND

Wright Robert E
Joliet Catholic HS
Joliet IL

Wright Ronald U
Chicago Vocational HS
Chicago IL

Wright Stephen W
Edgewood HS
Bloomington IN

Wright Steven C
Galesburg HS
Galesburg IL

Wright Susan R
Farmington East HS
Hanna City IL

Wright Terry L
Union HS
Modoc IN

Wright Zena R
Vienna HS
Simpson IL

Wroblewski Daniel J
Pittsville HS
Marshfield WI

Wrye Richard W
Mt Carmel HS
Mt Carmel IL

Wuebker Janean A
Ayrshire Consolidated HS
Ayrshire IA

Wuebker Leon J
Rockwell City HS
Rockwell City IA

Wuebker Wayne J
Ayrshire Cons HS
Ayrshire IA

Wuertz Mark E
Courtland HS
Courtland KS

Wujciak Kathryn A
Grand Blanc HS
Grand Blanc MI

Wulf Gary L
Guide Rock Public HS
Guide Rock NE

Wulf Linda A
Blair HS
Blair NE

Wulff Elizabeth A
Hinsdale Central HS
Hinsdale IL

Wurglitz Glen M
Gordon Tech HS
Chicago IL

Wurl Amy J
Illiopolis HS
Illiopolis IL

Wurschmidt Leif B
John Glenn HS
Westland MI

Wusthoff Mary J
Ypsilanti HS
Ypsilanti MI

Wuthrich Richard E
Wawasee HS
Milford IN

Wyant Lila L
Richland HS
Richland MO

Wyatt Neil G
Harlem HS
Loves Park IL

Wycoff Brenda K
Macksville HS
Seward KS

Wycoff Debra J
Bryan Senior HS
Omaha NE

Wyczawski Paul J
New Ulm HS
New Ulm MN

Wyman Blair
Rapid City Central HS
Rapid City SD

Wyman Jamie A
Dexter HS
Pinckney MI

Wyman Robin R
Saginaw HS
Saginaw MI

Wymore Ann B
Liberty Senior HS
Liberty MO

Wymore Ronald D
Cambridge HS
Cambridge NE

Wynia Mark J
Rock Valley Comm HS
Rock Valley IA

Wysong Lyn E
Fairfield HS
New Paris IN

Wyss Kimberly J
Donoran HS
Watseka IL

Wyszynski Wayne V
South Haven HS
South Haven MI

Wyzgoski Paul M
Pontiac Catholic HS
Pontiac MI

Y

Yaeger Bridget A
Brookfield HS
Brookfield MO

Yagow Maxine A
North Sargent HS
Milnor ND

Yakel Terri L
Scottsbluff Sr HS
Scottsbluff NE

Yammine Cynthia J
Casey Senior HS
Casey IL

Yancey Antronette K
Washington HS
Kansas City KS

Yandura Debra L
Joliet East HS
Joliet IL

Yankala Donna J
East Troy HS
East Troy WI

Yankowiak Thomas W
Bishop Dwenger HS
Fort Wayne IN

Yanuck Kathryn A
Central HS
St Joseph MO

Yaple Edward G
Gull Lake HS
Augusta MI

Yarber Kathleen
Freeburg Comm HS
Smithton IL

Yarbrough Robin L
Central Of Burden HS
Atlanta KS

Yarger David P
Morgan Co R Ii HS
Versailles MO

Yarger Nyla D
Flat Rock HS
Rockwood MI

Yargus Mina J
Hannibal Sr HS
Hannibal MO

Yarmoski Sandra A
Nazareth Academy
Chicago IL

Yaroch Pamela A
John Hersey HS
Mount Prospect IL

Yates Barbara J
Rich Central HS
Park Forest IL

Yates Debby B
East Union HS
Thayer IA

Yates Pamela K
Auburn HS
Peru NE

Ybarra Cynthia A
Elmhurst HS
Fort Wayne IN

Yeager Cheryl L
John F Kennedy HS
Bloomington MN

Yearout Kim M
South Haven HS
South Haven KS

Yegerlehner Debra A
Clay City HS
Clay City IN

Yelken Kevin S
Franklin Public HS
Franklin NE

Yellow Robe Luther P
Stevens HS
Rapid City SD

Yen Robert L
University HS
Urbana IL

Yenglin Larry D
Davison Sr HS
Davison MI

Yinger Paul R
Hillsdale HS
Hillsdale MI

Ylinen Susie M
St Peter HS
St Peter MN

Ylitalo Cindy L
Hancock Central HS
Hancock MI

Yoas Karl M
Airport HS
Newport MI

Yoas Krystal A
Jefferson HS
Monroe MI

Yochum Jennifer J
Peoria Manual HS
Peoria IL

Yoder Kimberly D
Penn HS
Mishawaka IN

Yoder Lloyd R
Northridge HS
Middlebury IN

Yoder Regina K
Bethany Christian HS
Shipshewana IN

Yoder Roger A
Westview HS
Shipshewana IN

Yohe Christopher M
Harrisonville HS
Harrisonville MO

Yokley Christine A
Bronaugh HS
Moundville MO

Yokom Sharon R
Mapleton HS
Mapleton ND

Yonash Linda M
Riverdale Sr HS
Boscobel WI

Yonts James J
Rushford Public HS
Rushford MN

Yopst Thomas B
Dekalb HS
Dekalb IL

Yordy Michael E
Morton HS
Morton IL

York Patricia L
Elmhurst HS
Ft Wayne IN

York William M
Grosse Ile HS
Grosse Ile MI

Yost Sally J
Kalkaska HS
Kaikaska MI

Yost Stephen W
Savannah HS
St Joseph MO

Yotko Kathleen S
Waukegan East HS
Waukegan IL

Yotty Douglas A
Mid Prairie HS
Kalona IA

Youmans Richard L
Douglas Mac Arthur HS
Saginaw MI

Younce Richard C
Waterford Township HS
Pontiac MI

Young Bobbi S
Bedford No Lawrence HS
Heltonville IN

Young Cindy S
Blair HS
Blair NE

Young Cynthia R
Central HS
Evansville IN

Young Dale J
Menasha HS
Appleton WI

Young David A
Shelbyville HS
Shelbyville IL

Young Elizabeth M
Ladywood St Agnes HS
Indianapolis IN

Young Erma M
Pope County HS
Herod IL

Young Janet L
Whiting HS
Whiting IN

Young Katherine
Josephinum HS
Chicago IL

Young Kathleen A
Duluth Central HS
Duluth MN

Young Kathy M
Heritage Christian HS
Indianapolis IN

Young Kevin E
Glenwood HS
Pacific Jct IA

Young Kevin L
Roxana HS
Wood River IL

Young Kristine L
Huntington North HS
Huntington IN

Young Linda D
Northwestern R 1 HS
Mendon MO

Young Miriam R
Central HS
St Louis MO

Young Ralph V
Lanphier HS
Springfield IL

Young Reginald R
William Chrisman HS
Independence MO

Young Robert L
Otterville R Vi HS
Otterville MO

Young Sharon A
Hinsdale So HS
Darien IL

Young Terrie L
Lincoln Comm HS
Lincoln IL

Young Thomas E 3
Deandries HS
Saint Louis MO

Young William A
Liberty HS
Mountain View MO

Youngbauer Sonya J
Alma HS
Alma WI

Youngberg Annette M
Wm Kelley HS
Silver Bay MN

Youngblood Janet D
Monrovia HS
Monrovia IN

Youngbluth Renee R
East Charles Mix HS
Wagner SD

Younker Dale
Hays HS
Hays KS

Younkin Kim E
Northside HS
Red Key IN

Yourick Jeffrey J
Pioneer HS
Ann Arbor MI

Yung Charlene M
Alexis HS
Alexis IL

Yung Susan K
Lindblom Tech HS
Chicago IL

Yungclas Ted
Webster City HS
Webster City IA

Yurkovich Therese M
Queen Of Peace HS
Chicago IL

Z

Zabawa Richard N
Assumption HS
Wis Rapids WI

Zabel Richard R
Greenway HS
Grand Rapids MN

Zabukovec Judy J
Carmel HS
Waukegan IL

Zadina Kim L
Superior HS
Superior NE

Zafiratos Carol A
Oak Park And River Forest HS
River Forest IL

Zagar William P
Joliet West HS
Joliet IL

Zagyva Cynthia L
Quincy HS
Coldwater MI

Zahn Donna M
Bishop Ryan HS
Minot ND

Zahn Jay R
Sevastopol HS
Sturgeon Bay WI

Zahn Lisa M
Shawnee Mission S HS
Overland Park KS

Zakibe Michael G
Bishop Dubourg HS
St Louis MO

Zakula Mark
Lowell HS
Lowell IN

Zalan Stephen E
Harold L Richards HS
Palos Heights IL

Zambo Maryanne C
Hanover Central HS
Cedar Lake IN

Zamor Deborah M
St Clare Academy
New Brighton MN

Zanon Cheryl E
Norway HS
Vulcan MI

Zanzola Joan M
Saint Francis Acad
Joliet IL

Zapchenk Jeffery S
Thornridge HS
Harvey IL

Zapf Michaele M
St Stephen Area HS
Saginaw MI

Zapp Cindy A
Okawville Community HS
Okawville IL

Zaragoza Oliver J
Mars Hall U HS
Minneapolis MN

Zarzecki Charles
St Rita HS
Evergreen Park IL

Zastrow Steve T
Friend HS
Friend NE

Zayia Mary R
Regina Dominican HS
Chicago IL

Zednik Jan M
Richmond Burton Comm HS
Richmond IL

Zeigler Rick D
Cc HS
Clinton IL

Zeis Jeff P
Kirkwood HS
Frontenac MO

Zekich Deborah L
Thornton Frac North HS
Calumet City IL

Zelasko Cheyrl R
Centralia HS
Centralia IL

Zelenski Julie A
East Troy HS
Burlington WI

Zeleny Carol L
Milligan Public HS
Milligan NE

Zeller Francis J
Richland Center HS
Richland Center WI

Zellers Elizabeth A
Lake Central HS
St John IN

Zeman Dwana L
Trego Comm HS
Wakeeney KS

Zenner Daniel R
Kingsley Area HS
Kingsley MI

Zenor Cynthia A
North Putnam HS
Bainbridge IN

Zentner Debra S
Oshkosh West HS
Oshkoh WI

Zentz Dean R
Argos HS
Argos IN

Zeps Ausma A
Central HS
Grand Rapids MI

Zerger Timothy J
Marion HS
Marion KS

Zerkel Carolyn L
Collinsville HS
Collinsville IL

Zerr Mark A
Shelbyville Sr HS
Shelbyville IN

Zerwig Neil F
St Genevieve Sr HS
St Genevieve MO

Zetah Roger A
Motley Public HS
Motley MN

Zich Margaret M
Galesburg HS
Galesburg IL

Ziegler Kathy M
Poynette HS
Arlington WI

Ziegler Kimberly S
Fenton HS
Fenton MI

Ziegler Kim K
North Platte Senior HS
North Platte NE

Ziegler Michael A
Middleton HS
Middleton WI

Ziegler Michael E
Lutheran HS
Chaska MN

Ziegler Milissa J
Trego Community HS
Collyer KS

Zielski Clark D
Eldora HS
Eldora IA

Zierke David L
Belvidere HS
Belvidere IL

Ziesner David J
Ventura Community HS
Ventura IA

Zilch Cheryl A
Central Montcalm HS
Stanton MI

Zilliox Maureen E
Dundee Comm HS
Dundee IL

Zillmer Ricky D
Litchfield HS
Watkins MN

Zilm Marla
Toluca HS
Toluca IL

Zimdars Jeanette M
Dieterich HS
Dieterich IL

Zimmer Joel A
Hackett HS
Kalamazoo MI

Zimmer Juliann M
Creston Sr HS
Grand Rapids MI

Zimmerman Cathie S
Noblesville HS
Noblesville IN

Zimmerman Cindy D
Taylor Public HS
Taylor ND

Zimmerman Gary M
St Viator HS
Mt Prospect IL

Zimmerman Joe
Chaparral Hs
Harper KS

Zimmerman Kent E
Leo HS
Grabill IN

Zimmerman Patrick G
St Mary Springs HS
Lomira WI

Zimmerman Paul K
Ottawa Township HS
Ottawa IL

Zimmerman Steven G
Tomah Sr HS
Tomah WI

Zimmerman Thomas E
Snider HS
Fort Wayne IN

Zimmerman Wayne R
Quincy HS
Quincy IL

Zimmermann Deborah A
Albany HS
Avon MN

Zipperian Nancy J
Peru HS
Peru IN

Zitnick Kathleen M
Glenbard West HS
Glen Ellyn IL

Zizzo Celeste G
Queen Of Peace HS
Chicago IL

Zluticky Ronald W
Breckenridge HS
Breckenridge MN

Zmija Robert J
Thornton Fractional So HS
Lansing IL

Zmuda Cheryl L
Thornwood HS
Calumet City IL

Zocher Naomi
Flat Rock HS
Flat Rock MI

Zolfo Bryan M
Marist HS
Calumet Park IL

Zoma Susan T
Marian HS
Bloomfield Hills MI

Zook Lauren L
Beach HS
Beach ND

Zook Patricia L
Sigourney Comm HS
Sigourney IA

Zorn David L
Claflin HS
Claflin KS

Zorn Zoe E
Sacred Heart Academy
Springfield IL

Zschau Susan L
Marshall HS
Marshall IL

Zuchelski Debra A
Franklin HS
Westland MI

Zucksworth Brenda S
Mulberry Grove HS
Smithboro IL

Zuege Lori J
Haigler Public HS
Haigler NE

Zuehlke Judith A
Oconomowoc Sr HS
Oconomowoc WI

Zuelsdorf James D
Husfisford HS
Hustisford WI

Zuhl Dena M
West HS
Battle Creek MI

Zuk Denise M
Trenton HS
Trenton MI

Zulski David J
Pellston HS
Pellston MI

Zumstein Barbara J
Wm Borden HS
Floyds Knobs IN

Zweig Jacalyn J
Morton HS
Hammond IN

Zweygardt Cathy L
St Francis Comm HS
St Francis KS

Zwiener John J
District 55 HS
Spalding NE

Zwilling Norma L
E Richland HS
Claremont IL

Zwolinski David L
Maine So HS
Park Ridge IL

Zyk Linda D
Notre Dame HS
Chicago IL

Zyk Stephen N
Weber HS
Chicago IL

Zywczyk Teresa B
Downers Grove South HS
Westmont IL

A

Ackerman Mary A
Reese HS
Reese MI

Aesoph Christopher N
Milbank HS
Milbank SD

Allen Leslie S
Adel HS
Adel IA

Anderson Anthony J
Univ Of Detroit HS
Detroit MI

Anderson Ava J
Wyaconda C 1 HS
Wyaconda MO

Anderson Crystal R
East Chas Mix #102 HS
Wagner SD

Anderson Eric J
Maine South HS
Park Ridge IL

Anderson Lee Ann
Harrisonville Sr HS
Harrisonville MO

Armstrong George L
Mt Carmel HS
Mt Carmel IL

Armstrong Joseph H
Fremont HS
Fremont MI

Arntzen Martha L
Macomb Sr HS
Macomb IL

Atkins Joleen M
Pomeroy HS
Pomeroy IA

Augustine Ann M
Forest Park HS
Crystal Falls MI

B

Babl Jeanette L
West Holt HS
Atkinson NE

Balasz Jody J
Adrian HS
Adrian MI

Bard Loryn I
Deerfield HS
Deerfield IL

Bardis Judith A
Madam Curie HS
Chicago IL

Bartell Monica M
Beaver Dam Sr HS
Beaver Dam WI

Bashford Tim R
Holdrege HS
Holdrege NE

Bastone Peter F
Chicago Latin HS
Chicago IL

Bear Carl A
Huntington North HS
Roanoke IN

Bendall Jo Ellen M
Rochester HS
Rochester IN

Bennett Cassandra J
Adrian Sr HS
Adrian MI

Bentivenga Michael G
Homewood Flossmoor HS
Homewood IL

Bey Sayonara A
Jones HS
Chicago IL

Bixler Dorinda S
Hayes Center Public HS
Hayes Center NE

Bodeau Terri L
Case HS
Racine WI

Boehme Lori J
Concordia Academy
St Paul MN

Boschult Mark T
Fremont Sr HS
Fremont NE

Brinton Bambi L
West Elk HS
Howard KS

Brizgys Victor A
St Thomas Aquinas HS
Southgate MI

Brown Debra A
Bishop Noll Institute
Gary IN

Browske Richard M
Rochester Adams HS
Rochester MI

Bruner Mary K
Sullivan HS
Sullivan IL

Bugbee Sheryl L
Tecumseh HS
Tecumseh MI

Bush Samuel D
Franklin Comm HS
Franklin IN

C

Cain Ann M
Spalding HS
Sheldon IA

Cantrell Glenda F
Niangua HS
Niangua MO

Carlson Kevin W
Taylors Falls HS
Shafer MN

Carnahan David M
Hartland HS
Hartland MI

Carter Suzette I
Bradley Bourbonnais HS
Bradley IL

Cartwright Chris T
Battle Creek Central HS
Battle Creek MI

Center Randolph S
Hillsdale HS
Hillsdale MI

Clark Terry E
Bedford HS
Lambertville MI

Clarke Henry B
Loy Norrix HS
Kalamazoo MI

Clifford Kathleen A
St Anthony HS
St Louis MO

Coleman Charles L
Lindblom Tech HS
Chicago IL

Combs La Vonda R
Charlestown HS
Charlestown IN

Comstock Wanita J
Belton HS
Belton MO

Convelse Diane E
Larned HS
Garfield KS

Coronado Theresa
Hazel Park HS
Hazel Park MI

Cortner Deborah L
Winchester Comm HS
Winchester IN

Couture Jon D
Cheboygan Area HS
Cheboygan MI

Cox Jennifer L
Wawasee HS
Syracuse IN

Crippen Cindy L
Huron Sr HS
Huron SD

Crosby Sharon L
Lindblom HS
Chicago IL

Cross Charles R
Brewster HS
Brewster MN

D

Daily Susan E
Columbus East HS
Columbus IN

Dancer William C
Manual HS
Kansas City MO

Darveau Kenneth G
Hemingford HS
Hemingford NE

Davis Diana S
Braymer C 4 HS
Braymer MO

De Mille Debra M
Stephenson HS
Stephenson MI

Diefendorf Christine A
Yates City HS
Elmwood IL

Dionne Mary F
Southern Door HS
Forestville WI

Dischler Brian T
River Valley HS
Loganville WI

Doody Steven J
St Rita HS
Chicago IL

Dowling Kimberly A
Hanover Central HS
Cedar Lake IN

Drobac Stanley H
Okemos HS
Okemos MI

Duda Carmen H
T F South HS
Lansing IL

Durham Donald G
Lesterville HS
Lesterville MO

E

Edgcomb Susan J
Saugatuck HS
Saugatuck MI

Edney Geoffrey A
Arlington HS
Indianapolis IN

Eibs Thomas E
Marshal University HS
Minneapolis MN

Elliott Cynthia L
Oak Forest HS
Oak Forest IL

Elliott Robert J
St Louis U HS
St Louis MO

Engler Lawrence W
Dwight David Eisenhower
HS
Saginaw MI

Evans Mary M
Shenandoah HS
Shenandoah IA

Evans Sheryl A
Winfield HS
Winfield KS

Evon Christine A
Oak Park River Forest HS
Oak Park IL

Ewald Jacqueline K
Durant HS
Durant IA

F

Finkle Lyle A
Roeper City Country HS
Pontiac MI

Fischbach Robert J
Duchesne HS
St Charles MO

Fischer Catherine M
Humboldt Comm HS
Humboldt IA

Fischer Warren L
Sevastopol HS
Egg Harbor WI

Foth Lisa L
St Mary Central HS
Neenah WI

Fox Steven P
Darlington HS
Darlington WI

Frank Terri S
Tri City HS
Mechanicsburg IL

Freeman Stephen D
Anderson Sr HS
Anderson IN

Fuller Douglas A
Tri Central HS
Sharpsville IN

G

Genik Michael D C
Saline HS
Saline MI

Geske Susan J
Milton Sr HS
Milton WI

Glynn James F
Marist HS
South Holland IL

Goetting Mary P
Norborne Public HS
Norborne MO

Graf Michael P
De Smet Jesuit HS
St Louis MO

Graham Kimberly A
Appleton West HS
Appleton WI

Graham Robert A
Poplar Bluff Sr HS
Poplar Bluff MO

Grossenburg Jolenne K
Winner Sr HS
Winner SD

Groves Thomas K
Mankato East HS
Mankato MN

Gschwendtner Susan M
Pontiac Township HS
Pontiac IL

Gutzeit Michael F
Marist HS
Palos Heights IL

H

Hackman Connie K
New Franklin HS
Fayette MO

Hahn David H
Mt Zion HS
Mt Zion IL

Hall Christopher J
Bishop Dwenger HS
Fort Wayne IN

Hanks Krisna L
Quincy Sr HS
Quincy IL

Hansen Jana S
Willard HS
Springfield MO

Hansen Judy R
Seward Sr HS
Seward NE

Harper Wyvetta L
Unity HS
Chicago IL

Hayes Robert L
Lockwood Ri HS
Lockwood MO

Hays Susan K
Woodland HS
Streator IL

Hendrich Becky J
Smith Center HS
Portis KS

Higgins Richard M
Prairie Home HS
Prairie Home MO

Hilgedick Barbara A
Salem HS
Salem MO

Hittle Michael R
High School
Fruitport MI

Hodges Ronald F
Westport HS
Kansas City MO

Hoelting Jill D
Taylorville Sr HS
Taylorville IL

Hoftiezer Scott A
Libertyville HS
Lake Bluff IL

Holmen Gary D
Theodore Roosevelt HS
Minneapolis MN

STUDENTS PHOTOGRAPH SCHEDULED FOR PUBLICATION HERE COULD NOT BE REPRODUCED

Houston Lesa M
South Barber HS
Hardtner KS

Howlett Donald R
Richland R 4 Public HS
Richland MO

Hoyt Tedd J
North Sr HS
Eau Claire WI

Hughes Terri J
Lake Crystal Public HS
Lake Crystal MN

Hunt Mary V
Madison Cons HS
Madison IN

Huntley Jeffrey L
Sycamore HS
Sycamore IL

Huseman Jodi L
Fort Dodge Sr HS
Fort Dodge IA

I

J

Jacobson Jeffrey D
Hibbing HS
Hibbing MN

Jacobson Virginia S
Leeds Public HS
Leeds ND

James Tami R
Wolbach Public HS
Wolbach NE

Jeter Debra R
Cass Technical HS
Detroit MI

Johnson Darlene A
Madison Public HS
Madison MN

Johnson Fayrene
Josephinum HS
Chicago IL

Johnson John G
Ida Grove Comm HS
Ida Grove IA

Johnson Kristi L
Benson Sr HS
Benson MN

Jones Joy L
La Monte R Iv HS
La Monte MO

Jordan Dana L
Circle HS
El Dorado KS

K

Kaczmarek Steven D
Quigley South HS
Chicago IL

Kamin Natalie V
Clark HS
Whiting IN

Kasdan Deborah S
Rich South HS
Park Forest IL

Katsulis Demetra
Amundsen HS
Chicago IL

Kelley Catherine T
Central Catholic HS
Merna IL

Kemnetz Steven A
Chatsworth HS
Chatsworth IL

Kiesewetter Dale O
Cornell HS
Pontiac IL

Killion Mark
Glenbard South Hs
Glen Ellyn IL

King Elizabeth M
Durand HS
Durand WI

King Troy S
Millard HS
Omaha NE

Klemett James M
Hancock Central HS
Hancock MI

Klocke Rita K
Rockwell City Community HS
Rockwell City IA

Kluesner Deb A
Western Dubuque HS
Farley IA

Korst Susan M
Bishop Dwenger HS
Ft Wayne IN

Kotas Beth E
Tripp HS
Tripp SD

Kozlowski Zbigniew A
Lane Tech HS
Chicago IL

Kuhlengel Keith R
Wesclin Sr HS
Trenton IL

Kuipers Ray N
Dakota Christian HS
Platte SD

Kurtz Matt J
St Laurence HS
Chicago IL

L

Ladine Kevin R
Gurley Public HS
Gurley NE

Lafever Lori L
Hagerstown Jr Sr HS
Hagerstown IN

Lange David A
Evansville HS
Evansville WI

Lentz Donieta Jo
Jefferson County North HS
Winchester KS

Lenz Marcia K
Marshall Sr HS
Marshall MN

Leonard Mark L
Logan Magnolia HS
Logan IA

Lewis David C
Marshall HS
Marshall MO

Lillard David A
West Side HS
Gary IN

Lockwood Michael D
Swea City Community HS
Swea City IA

Loh Gary
Andrean HS
Gary IN

Long Douglas J
Alma Public HS
Alma NE

STUDENTS PHOTOGRAPH SCHEDULED FOR PUBLICATION HERE COULD NOT BE REPRODUCED

Lovell Richard C
Castle HS
Newburgh IN

Lueckenhoff Jim P
Blair Oaks HS
St Thomas MO

M

Mc Carty Warren D
Champaign Central HS
Champaign IL

Mc Dermott John C
Carbondale Comm HS
Carbondale IL

Mc Donald Kelly A
Joliet East HS
New Lenox IL

Mc Kenzie Raymond R
Marcellus HS
Marcellus MI

Mc Laren Debra S
Knoxville HS
Knoxville IL

Mc Queen Victoria A
Eastern HS
Solsberry IN

Mahler Kaye E
Culver Comm HS
Culver IN

Mann Charlene K
Lakeland HS
La Grange IN

Marko Timothy M
Chippewa Sr HS
Chippewa Fls WI

Mason Gregg H
Adlai E Stevenson HS
Long Grove IL

Meixner Marcia M
Owatonna HS
Owatonna MN

Melton Joanie A
Dadeville R Ii HS
Dadeville MO

Meyer Cindy K
Appleton West HS
Appleton WI

Micke Steven J
Cloquet Sr HS
Cloquet MN

Miller Janet K
Morton HS
Pekin IL

Millik Barbara A
Pawnee HS
Pawnee IL

Mills Stan
Tri HS
Straughn IN

Moen John A
Fargo North HS
Fargo ND

Moore David D
New Market Comm HS
New Market IA

Morris Dennis E
Stuart Menlo HS
Casey IA

Morris Mary Y
Du Quoin HS
Du Quoin IL

Mulavey Kathleen A
Grosse Pointe North HS
Grosse Pt Wds MI

Muller Robert E
Sheffield Chapin Comm HS
Sheffield IA

Mulligan Anne S
Rosati Kain HS
University City MO

N

Nerat Diane M
Stephenson HS
Wallace MI

Newton Terry D
Dora R Iii HS
Zanoni MO

Nichols Kris C
Mount Ayr Comm HS
Mount Ayr IA

Nieman Brian H
Mt Ayr Comm HS
Mount Ayr IA

Noga Darrell G
Fenwick HS
Cicero IL

Nornes Julie R
Climax Public HS
Climax MN

Northern Sheila P
South Pemiscot HS
Steele MO

O

Oetting Nancy E
Jefferson HS
Monroe MI

Oliver David A
Belleville East HS
Fairview Heights IL

Osgood Stephen P
Naperville Central HS
Naperville IL

Osnes Thomas P
Forest City HS
Forest City IA

P

Page Diana K
Jersey Comm HS
Jerseyville IL

Pedersen Pamela S
Sunflower HS
Mitchell NE

Peterman Carol G
Onaway Area HS
Onaway MI

Peterson Lisa A
Churchill HS
Livonia MI

Pfaff Eric R
Green Lake HS
Green Lake WI

Pifer Netta F
Flora HS
Flora IL

Piner Melissa J
Plattsmouth HS
Murray NE

Plechash Steven
Oak Park River Forest HS
Oak Park IL

Plona Christopher D
Oak Park & River Forest HS
Oak Park IL

Postlewait Stanley E
Houston HS
Bucyrus MO

Powell Sandra A
Marshall HS
Marshall WI

Price Walter J
Engadine Cons HS
Engadine MI

R

Ray B Dianne
Parkwood HS
Joplin MO

Redfield Kristi A
Stratton Public HS
Stratton NE

Reinhold Anthony V
Winamac HS
Winamac IN

Rhoads Angela L
South Newton HS
Goodland IN

Rice Rebecca S
Sisseton HS
Sisseton SD

Richardson Lance
Martinsville HS
Martinsville IN

Roberts Paul D
Eastside HS
St Joe IN

Rome Alean M
Union City HS
Union City MI

Rommann Lila M
Washington Sr HS
Sioux Falls SD

Roney Jane E
Heritage Christian HS
Anderson IN

Ross Diane M
Luther South HS
Chicago IL

Roudebush Cheryl L
Sullivan HS
Sullivan IN

Rousseau Julie M
Central HS
Glenwood MN

Rufener Joann K
Monroe HS
Monroe WI

Ruffner Marcella L
Mac Arthur HS
Decatur IL

S

Samuel Wendell
Paseo HS
Kansas City MO

Sappington Thomas W
Warrensburg HS
Warrensburg MO

Schaefer Cheryl D
Newaygo HS
Newaygo MI

Schaner Victoria L
Wyoming Park HS
Wyoming MI

Schapp Robert L
Parkway North HS
Creve Coeur MO

Schmitz Naomi J
Tolley Public HS
Tolley ND

Schneider Barbara A
St Marys Springs HS
Fond Du Lac WI

Schoon Debra C
Sebeka Public HS
Wadena MN

Schweitzer Rod R
Poplar Bluff Sr HS
Poplar Bluff MO

Seeger Barbara J
Gilman HS
Sheldon WI

Segal Myra J
Niles West HS
Lincolnwood IL

Sells Kathy E
Warsaw HS
Silver Lake IN

Sheets Michael D
Pocahontas Comm HS
Pocahontas IA

Shoemaker Brenda L
Edison HS
East Gary IN

Shoemaker Cynthia R
Pennville HS
Bryant IN

Shupe Elizabeth A
Northrop HS
Fort Wayne IN

Sites Terry J
Sullivan HS
Sullivan MO

Sjostrand Barry L
Lancaster HS
Hallock MN

Skelly Patrick T
De La Salle HS
Minneapolis MN

Slauter Thomas A
Muncie Northside HS
Muncie IN

Smith Mabla J
Trenton Sr HS
Trenton MO

Smith Otho L
R 1 North Callaway HS
Kingdom City MO

Smith Randy
Anderson Sr HS
Anderson IN

Smith Steven A
Waukegan E Campus HS
Waukegan IL

Snyder Perry R
South Knox HS
Wheatland IN

Sopko Michele M
Grant Comm HS
Ingleside IL

Sparks Nancy K
New Holland Middletown HS
Middletown IL

Spryszak Gregory C
Berkley HS
Berkley MI

Stanton Joy L
Chaska Sr HS
Excelsior MN

Stastny Diane E
Boscobel HS
Fennimore WI

Stewart Cynthia C
Greenwood Comm HS
Greenwood WI

Stolle Barbara J
Silver Lake HS
Silver Lake KS

Straley Valerie J
Alden Hebron HS
Alden IL

Stravers Kyle J
Southeast Polk Jr Sr HS
Mitchellville IA

Strieter Cheryl K
Brown City HS
Brown City MI

Stubblefield Debra J
Odell Comm HS
Odell IL

Studeny Priscilla S
Valentine HS
Valentine NE

Swanson Fredric A
Manual HS
Peoria IL

Swart Linda D
Grinnell HS
Oakley KS

Swartz Cheryl A
Douglas Mac Arthur HS
Saginaw MI

T

Takehara Joann M
Maine Twp South HS
Park Ridge IL

Thiele Eric W
Hinsdale Twp HS
Darien IL

Thomas Natalie J
Connersville HS
Connersville IN

Tracy Cindy S
Racine Lutheran HS
Racine WI

Trafton Melody R
Richmond HS
Richmond MO

Traphagan Jan M
Little Falls Comm HS
Little Falls MN

Tufte Mark G
Northwood HS
Northwood ND

Twomey Suellen K
Northwest HS
Grand Island NE

U

V

Van Sittert Jeanne M
De Soto HS
De Soto KS

W

Wahl Bruce E
Marshall Sr HS
Marshall MN

Walker Christina E
Gasconade Co HS
Owensville MO

Walker Gale D
Warren Twp HS
Libertyville IL

Walker Tanya L
Arthur HS
Arthur IL

Waters John A
Pittsfield HS
Baylis IL

Weaver Martha J
Harrisonville Sr HS
Harrisonville MO

Webber Debra S
Highland HS
Highland KS

Wedge June A
Port Huron Central HS
Goodells MI

Weigel Catherine L
Carmel HS
Carmel IN

Welden Dale R
Lane Tech HS
Chicago IL

Westmaas Robin S
No Michigan Christian HS
Marion MI

Whalen Catherine C
Routt HS
Waverly IL

Whiteley Julie R
Miller HS
Ash Grove MO

Wicke Cynthia J
Wauneta Public HS
Wauneta NE

Wiggers Timothy E
Morton HS
Morton IL

Wilie David L
Marion HS
Marion WI

Williams Deborah A
Laboure HS
St Louis MO

Williams Frank E
John Marshall HS
Indianapolis IN

Wilson Mildred A
Santa Fe HS
Waverly MO

Wilt Leslie O
South Shelby HS
Shelbina MO

Winkelman Stephen E
Sacred Heart HS
Salina KS

Witt Richard B
Omaha Benson HS
Omaha NE

Worf Mark E
Soctt Comm HS
Scott City KS

Y

Z

Zaremba Julie A
Lincoln HS
Centerline MI

Zuck Kimberlee A
Lanark HS
Chadwick IL